2012

Advertising Red Books™

[RB] REDBOOKS

Content Operations:
General Manager: Peter Valli
Operations Manager: Patricia M. Phillips
Content Analysts: Himanshu P. Goodluck, Kieran O'Brien Kern

2012

Advertising Red Books™

Advertisers
Business Classifications

QUESTIONS ABOUT THIS PUBLICATION?

For CONTENT questions concerning this publication, please call:
The Content Operations Department at 800-908-5395, press 3

For CUSTOMER SERVICE ASSISTANCE concerning shipments, billing or other matters, please call:
The Customer Service Department at 800-908-5395, press 2

For SALES ASSISTANCE, please call:
The Sales Department at 800-908-5395, press 1

ISBN Number:
Vol. 1: 978-1-9376-0600-8 (Business Classifications volume)

Red Books LLC has used its best efforts in collecting and preparing material for inclusion in *The Advertising Red Books™* but does not assume, and hereby disclaims, any liability to any person for any loss or damage caused by errors or omissions in *The Advertising Red Books* whether such errors or omissions result from negligence, accident or any other cause.

9 781937 606008

Red Books LLC
Content Operations
475 Springfield Avenue, Suite 401
Summit, NJ 07901

www.redbooks.com

CONTENTS

CONTENTS

INDEX TO PRODUCT CATEGORIES

INDEX TO PRODUCT CATEGORIES

C

D

INDEX TO PRODUCT CATEGORIES

INDEX TO PRODUCT CATEGORIES

INDEX TO PRODUCT CATEGORIES

INDEX TO PRODUCT CATEGORIES

INDEX TO PRODUCT CATEGORIES

U

V

W

Y

Z

PREFACE

For over 100 years, *The Advertising Red Books™* have been the most comprehensive source of information on the advertising practices of companies located in the United States and Canada. *The Advertising Red Books* provide a detailed profile of the advertising industry—whether you are seeking information on advertisers and their products or agencies and their clients.

We encourage you to refer to the section titled "*How to Use The Advertising Red Books*" for a detailed summary of entry content and examples of how the various indexes function.

CONTENT AND COVERAGE

The 2012 edition of *The Advertising Red Books* features data on over 17,500 companies that spend a minimum of $50,000 on national and regional advertising. Available in two volumes, you can access data by business categories or by geographic location. The Business Classifications volume sorts companies into one of 55 general areas (Appliances, Government & State Agencies, Lighting, Sporting Goods, etc.) according to their primary product or service. In the Geographic volume, companies are listed by state and city in the United States and by province and city in Canada.

Entry listings include such general items as company name, address and telecommunication data, S.I.C. codes, N.A.I.C.S. codes, business description, statistics and personnel. Listings also include such advertising data as the approximate advertising expenditures, media used, and the advertising agency or agencies employed by the firm. In many cases, the agency data also includes a breakdown of the products or brands handled by the agency and the account executive responsible for that company's account.

INDUSTRY DATA

In the front of this volume, we present a list of companies new to the 2012 edition. The Business Classifications volume contains a breakdown of the total number of companies by business classification. The Geographic volume includes a breakdown of the total number of companies by state, as well as totals for Canada. These tables are designed to provide users with an overview of the advertising industry and the data contained in this directory.

INDEXING

The *Indexes* volume of this advertiser set contains four indexes: Product Categories by State, Brands & Products, S.I.C. Codes and Personnel. The Product Categories by State index allows users to find advertisers in each classification by the state in which they are located. The Brands & Products index contains over 121,000 trademarks or brand names associated with the companies featured in the book. An S.I.C. index allows easy and highly specific reference to companies based on their Standard Industrial Classification codes. The Personnel index features over 20,500 individuals involved in the marketing, sales, or advertising functions of their companies.

In addition to these indexes, volume one of each edition contains an alphabetical index by company name. There is also an index of companies that use in-house advertising agencies.

COMPILATION

The Advertising Red Books™ is compiled and updated from information supplied by the companies themselves, from annual reports and from business publications. Every effort is made to provide dependable data. However, the publisher cannot guarantee complete accuracy nor assume responsibility for any advertiser company listed in or omitted from this directory.

The Advertising Red Books is updated year-round. New listings and other updates such as personnel changes can be tracked in the supplement, published in April, July and October.

RELATED SERVICES

For information on the redbooks.com web site, please call (800) 908-5395.

Mailing lists compiled from information contained in The Advertising Red Books may be ordered from:

Maria Bartell, Sr. Client Services Manager
Mardevdm2
2000 Clearwater Drive, Oak Brook, IL
Tel: (630) 288-8310
E-mail: info@mardevdm2.com

Electronic database tapes of the directory in raw data format are available for licensing. For electronic database tapes or alliance opportunities, please contact:

Peter Valli, General Manager
Red Books LLC
475 Springfield Avenue, Suite 401, Summit, NJ 07901
Tel: (646) 710-4454
E-mail: peter.valli@redbooks.com

Companies who wish to add or update their listings can send information to:

Patricia Phillips, Operations Manager
Red Books LLC
475 Springfield Avenue, Suite 401, Summit, NJ 07901
Tel: (646) 710-4465
E-mail: patricia.phillips@redbooks.com

In addition to keeping the information in our directories as up to date as possible, we are constantly trying to improve their design and add useful new features. Any comments or suggestions in this regard can be directed to the General Manager at the above address.

ACKNOWLEDGMENTS

We would like to thank the personnel in thousands of companies throughout the United States and Canada who took the time to provide us with the information necessary to compile an accurate and comprehensive The Advertising Red Books.

HOW TO USE THE *ADVERTISERS EDITION*

The Advertising Red Books™ - Advertisers edition provides a comprehensive overview of over 17,500 companies in the United States and Canada that spend at least $50,000 on national or regional advertising campaigns. (For the purpose of this book, a regional campaign is one in which a company uses media that broadcasts its message in two or more states.) Arranged in an easy to use two volume format, this directory provides several different ways for the user to locate detailed information on companies that advertise. The following guidelines are intended to help you find the data you need in the most logical way, and to make that information work to your maximum benefit.

USING THE BUSINESS CLASSIFICATIONS VOLUME

Finding Groups of Companies That Produce Particular Products or Services The Business Classifications volume features 55 separate categories. A complete list of these classifications and their page references can be found in the table of contents. This breakdown of classifications makes it easy for users to locate companies that provide a particular product or service. For instance, if you are interested in gathering information on the advertising practices of companies that manufacture and service office equipment, turn to the section on Computers & Office Equipment, Supplies & Services.

If the category names are not specific enough for the information you are seeking, be sure to consult the Index to Product Categories; this provides page references to almost 750 product and service groups that are covered in the 55 classifications. As an example, if you need data only on Academies, the Index to Product Categories will lead you to the listings you want under the letter **A**.

A

Academics 2000
Accessories 1
Acids 1213
Adding Machines 357
Addressing Machines 357
Adhesive Plasters 1690
Adhesive Tapes 1651
Advertising 1531
Advertising Novelties 1531

Finding Individual Companies If there is a particular company you need data about and you know the classification in which it is listed, you can turn directly to that section. On the other hand, if you are not sure of its product category, you can consult the Index of Companies.

THOMAS INDUSTRIES, CONSUMER LIGHTING DIVISION, pg. 1038
THOMAS INDUSTRIES INC., pg. 1038
THOMAS JAY, INC., pg. 1038
THOMAS LIGHTING, pg. 1038
THOMAS LIGHTING-COMMERCIAL & INDUSTRIAL DIVISION, pg. 1038

BASIC COMPONENTS OF A LISTING

Sample Listing	Component
TRANS UNITED CORPORATION	**Company Name**
1111 US Lane Detroit, MI 48234 **Mailing Address:** PO Box 1234 Detroit, MI 48234	**Company Address**
Tel.: (313) 321-4282 **Fax**: (313) 321-4080	**Telecommunications Data**
E-Mail: mbream@trans.com **Web Site**: www.trans.com	**Electronic Address**
E-Mail For Key Personnel: **Public Relations:** mdougherty@trans.com **Sales:** swest@trans.com	
Approx. Sls.: $207,000,000 Approx. Number Employees: 6,257 Year Founded: 1928	**Company Data**
Business Description: Aluminum, Brass & Iron Castings Mfr	**Business Description**
S.I.C.: 3321, 3365, 3366	**Standard Industrial Classification Codes**
N.A.I.C.S.: 331511, 331524, 331525	**North American Industry Classification System Codes**
Import Export	**Indicates Import and/or Export of Products**
Advertising Expenditures: $11,000,000; Consumer Mags. $2,500,000; Publ. $1,500,000; D.M. to Bus. Estab. $1,500,000; Catalogs & Directories $500,000; Network T.V. $3,000,000; Exhibits (Show, Indus. Films) $500,000; Internet Adv. $500,000; Co-op Adv. $1,000,000	**Total Advertising Expenditures, Including Business Breakdown by Type of Media**
Media: 4-7-8-10-14-15-16-18-21-23-24	**Advertising Media Used (see Key to Media at bottom of each listings page)**
Distr.: Natl.; Intl.	**Distribution of Company's Products**
Budget Set: May	**Month in Which Advertising Budget Is Set**
Personnel: Marvin Bream(Chm) Thomas Sanborn (Pres & CEO) Ellen Wendall (CFO & Sr VP) Glen Lowell (Exec VP-Ops) James Bennett (VP-Engrg) Mary Ann Dougherty (VP-Comm) Gary Favio (VP, Sec & Treas) Stephen V. West (VP-Sls)	**Key Personnel**
Tradenames: ALUMINATION IRONATION	**Tradenames**

Advertising Agencies: ---------------------- **Ad Agencies Used by the Company**
Granger Advertising
4212 Cameron St
Detroit, MI 48233
Tel.: (313) 222-5151
(Iron Castings) ------------------------------ **Products Advertised**
—Stu Granger (Acct Exec)

Silver & Associates Advertising
222 Elm St
Santa Rosa, CA 95404
Tel.: (707) 432-1111
(Industrial Machines, Electronic Products,
Recreational Products)
—H.H. Silver (Acct Exec) --------------------- **Account Executive Responsible for Client**

OTHER WAYS TO FIND USEFUL INFORMATION

<u>Finding Companies That Have House Agencies</u> If you wish to isolate those companies that use house or proprietary agencies to create and place their ads, turn to **Companies That Have House Agencies** for a complete list of Advertiser companies that have organized their own in-house advertising agencies. Both indexes provide the page reference where you can find detailed information on the company.

<u>Locating Entries Geographically Within Each Classification</u> If you are interested in companies featured in a particular classification but you only want to find those within a specific geographic area, consult the **Product Categories by State** index in volume two. This index arranges the companies found in each of the 55 classifications alphabetically by state and by city within each state. Canadian companies can be found at the end of each classification section. You can find valuable data such as the company's street address, zip code, and the page reference to its entry in volume one.

<u>Locating a Company If You Know the Brand Name</u> If you know the name of a product, but cannot identify its manufacturer, the **Brands & Products Index** in the Indexes volume will be particularly helpful. This index presents over 121,000 major tradenames in common use by national advertisers. Each listing includes a brief description of the product, the manufacturer's name, and the page number referring to the company's listing in volume one.

<u>Searching for Companies in a Given Line of Business</u> If you need to identify companies that manufacture a certain type of product, the **S.I.C. Index** in the Indexes volume will simplify your search. This index groups all the companies in the book by areas of business. The index itself is arranged numerically by S.I.C. code, and then alphabetically by company. Page numbers refer you to the company's listing in volume one. The S.I.C. Index is preceded by alphabetical and numerical compendiums. If you know the S.I.C. code of a company and need to know what the code represents, use the numerical compendium. On the other hand, if you know the product or service and do not know its corresponding S.I.C. code, start with the alphabetical compendium. (NEC in a category heading stands for "Not Elsewhere Classified.")

<u>Locating Executive Personnel</u> If you are looking for a certain executive involved in a company's advertising or marketing operations, the **Personnel Index** is a useful reference tool. From the over 126,000 corporate personnel featured in the volume one listings, the Personnel index compiles over 20,500 advertising/ marketing decision makers into one handy location. In addition to the individual's name, the index also provides their title, the name of their company along with its city and state, and the page number referring to the company's listing in volume one.

MERGERS, ACQUISITIONS AND NAME CHANGES - 2011

3

3com Corporation; Palo Alto, CA - Acquired & Absorbed by Hewlett-Packard Company

A

A.D.A.M., Inc.; Atlanta, GA - Acquired by Ebix Inc.

Abraxas Corporation; San Diego, CA - Acquired by Cubic Corporation

Abri Health Plan, Inc.; Long Beach, CA - Acquired by Molina Healthcare, Inc.

Accordent Technologies, Inc.; Pleasanton, CA - Acquired by Polycom, Inc.

Accuri Cytometers, Inc.; Franklin Lakes, NJ - Acquired by Becton, Dickinson & Company

Actel Corporation; Irvine, CA - Acquired & Absorbed by Microsemi Corporation

Adenyo Inc.; Bellevue, WA - Acquired by Motricity, Inc.

Administaff, Inc.; Kingwood, TX - Name Changed to Insperity, Inc.

Admob; Mountain View, CA - Acquired & Absorbed by Google Inc.

Adviceamerica, Inc.; Brookfield, WI - Acquired by Fiserv, Inc.

Aegon Direct Marketing Services, Inc.; Baltimore, MD - Name Changed to TransAmerica Life & Protection

AFP Imaging Corporation; Elmsford, NY - Name Changed to ImageWorks

Airtran Holdings, Inc.; Dallas, TX - Acquired by Southwest Airlines Co.

Ajax-United Patterns & Molds, Inc.; Union City, CA - Name Changed to Ajax Custom Manufacturing

Akeena Solar Inc.; Campbell, CA - Name Changed to Westinghouse Solar

Alexander Utility Engineering, Inc.; Lowell, MA - Acquired by TRC Companies, Inc.

Allegheny Energy, Inc.; Akron, OH - Acquired by FirstEnergy Corp.

Allison Transmission, Inc.; Speedway, IN - Name Changed to Allison Transmission Holdings, Inc.

Allscripts-Misys Healthcare Solutions, Inc.; Chicago, IL - Name Changed to Allscripts Healthcare Solutions, Inc.

Allyn & Bacon; Boston, MA - Name Changed to Pearson Education

Alpha Scientific Medical, Inc.; Melville, NY - Acquired by Henry Schein, Inc.

American Antiquities, Inc.; Delray Beach, FL - Name Changed to Pet Airways, Inc.

American Bank Note Holographics, Inc.; Trenton, NJ - Name Changed to JDSU

American Italian Pasta Company; Saint Louis, MO - Acquired by Ralcorp Holdings, Inc.

American Life Insurance Company; New York, NY - Acquired by MetLife, Inc.

American Oil and Gas, Inc.; New York, NY - Acquired by Hess Corporation & Name Changed to Hess Bakken Investments I Corporation

American Physicians Capital Incorporated; Napa, CA - Acquired by The Doctors Company

American Physicians Service Group, Inc.; Birmingham, AL - Acquired by ProAssurance Corporation

American Pie, LLC; Omaha, NE - Acquired by ConAgra Foods, Inc.

American Sporting Goods Corporation; Saint Louis, MO - Acquired by Brown Shoe Company, Inc.

American Technology Corporation; San Diego, CA - Name Changed to LRAD Corporation

Americredit Corp; Detroit, MI - Acquired by General Motors Company

AMS Services, Inc.; Windsor, CT - Name Changed to Vertafore Inc.

Anhydro Inc.; Olympia Fields, IL - Name Changed to Dedert Corporation

API Software, Inc.; Hartford, WI - Name Changed to API Healthcare Corp.

Applied Signal Technology, Inc.; Waltham, MA - Acquired by Raytheon Company

Aprimo, Incorporated; Dayton, OH - Acquired by Teradata Corporation

Arbinet Corporation; McLean, VA - Acquired by Primus Telecommunications Group, Incorporated

Arbor Networks Inc.; Washington, DC - Acquired by Danaher Corporation

Arch Rock Corporation; San Jose, CA - Acquired & Absorbed by Cisco Systems, Inc.

Arcot Systems Inc.; Islandia, NY - Acquired by CA, Inc.

Arcsight, Inc.; Palo Alto, CA - Acquired by Hewlett-Packard Company

Ardian, Inc.; Minneapolis, MN - Acquired by Medtronic, Inc.

Argon ST, Inc.; Chicago, IL - Acquired by The Boeing Company

Arkson Nutraceuticals Corp.; Bellaire, TX - Name Changed to First Surgical Partners Inc.

Art Technology Group, Inc.; Redwood City, CA - Acquired by Oracle Corporation

Arvinmeritor, Inc.; Troy, MI - Name Changed to Meritor, Inc.

ASML MaskTools, Inc.; Santa Clara, CA - Name Changed to Brion Technologies Inc.

Aster Data Systems Inc.; Dayton, OH - Acquired by Teradata Corporation

Asthmatx, Inc.; Natick, MA - Acquired by Boston Scientific Corporation

Asynchrony Solutions, Inc.; New York, NY - Acquired by Citigroup Inc.

Atlantic Bancgroup Inc.; Jacksonville, FL - Acquired & Absorbed by Jacksonville Bancorp, Inc.

Atlas Energy, Inc.; San Ramon, CA - Acquired by Chevron Corporation

Atritech, Inc.; Natick, MA - Acquired by Boston Scientific Corporation

ATS Medical, Inc.; Minneapolis, MN - Acquired by Medtronic, Inc.

Auex Ventures, Inc.; Vancouver, Canada - Acquired & Absorbed by Fronteer Gold Inc.

Avatech Solutions, Inc.; Framingham, MA - Name Changed to Rand Worldwide, Inc.

Avicenna Technology, Inc.; Paoli, PA - Acquired by Ametek, Inc.

Azalea Networks, Inc.; Sunnyvale, CA - Acquired & Absorbed by Aruba Networks, Inc.

MERGERS, ACQUISITIONS AND NAME CHANGES

B

B & M Construction Company, Inc.; West Palm Beach, FL - Acquired by SSGI, INC.
Baggallini Inc.; Columbus, OH - Acquired by R.G. Barry Corporation
Baggallini Inc.; Pickerington, OH - Acquired by R.G. Barry Corporation
Bakbone Software, Inc.; Aliso Viejo, CA - Acquired by Quest Software, Inc.
Bari Importing Corp.; Orlando, FL - Name Changed to Bari Beef International
Barton Beers, Ltd.; Chicago, IL - Name Changed to Crown Imports
Base Technologies Inc.; Islandia, NY - Acquired by CA, Inc.
Bass & Co. Management Consultants LLC; Falls Church, VA - Acquired & Absorbed by Computer Sciences Corporation
Beceem Communications Inc.; Irvine, CA - Acquired by Broadcom Corporation
Becton Dickinson Medical; Sandy, UT - Name Changed to BD Medical
Bell Microproducts Inc.; Phoenix, AZ - Acquired & Absorbed by Avnet, Inc.
Bentek Energy LLC; New York, NY - Acquired by The McGraw-Hill Companies Inc.
Bernhardt Furniture Company; Lenoir, NC - Name Changed to Bernhardt Design
Bigfix, Inc.; Armonk, NY - Acquired by International Business Machines Corporation
Bioform Medical, Inc.; San Mateo, CA - Name Changed to Merz Aesthetics
Bioms Medical Corp.; Edmonton, Canada - Name Changed to Medwell Capital Corp.
Biotel Inc.; Conshohocken, PA - Acquired by CardioNet, Inc.
Biovail Corporation; Mississauga, Canada - Name Changed to Valeant Pharmaceuticals International, Inc.
Biovex Group, Inc.; Thousand Oaks, CA - Acquired by Amgen Inc.
Birds Eye-Berlin; Berlin, PA - Name Changed to Snyder - Berlin
Blade Network Technologies, Inc.; Armonk, NY - Acquired by International Business Machines Corporation
Blockbuster Inc.; Englewood, CO - Acquired by DISH Network Corporation
Bloodhound, Inc.; Jersey City, NJ - Acquired by Verisk Analytics
Blue Ridge Numerics, Inc.; San Rafael, CA - Acquired by Autodesk Inc.
Bluebay Asset Management PLC; Toronto, Canada - Acquired by Royal Bank of Canada
Boca Developers, Inc.; Deerfield Beach, FL - Name Changed to Stratus Asset Management, LLC
Bollam, Sheedy, Torani & Co.; Albany, NY - Name Changed to BST
Bookette Software Company; New York, NY - Acquired by The McGraw-Hill Companies Inc.
Boots & Coots, Inc.; Houston, TX - Acquired by Halliburton Company & Name Changed to Halliburton's Boots & Coots
Bowne & Co., Inc.; Chicago, IL - Acquired by R.R. Donnelley & Sons Company
Bowne & Co., Inc.; New York, NY - Name Changed to R.R. Donnelley
Bravo Health, Inc.; Franklin, TN - Acquired & Absorbed by HealthSpring, Inc.
Breach Security, Inc.; Chicago, IL - Acquired by Trustwave Holdings, Inc.
Bridgeline Software, Inc.; Woburn, MA - Name Changed to Bridgeline Digital, Inc.
Bubba Gump Shrimp Company Restaurant & Market; Houston, TX - Acquired by Landry's Restaurants Inc.
Buckman Laboratories Inc.; Memphis, TN - Name Changed to Buckman
Burntsand Inc.; Waterloo, Canada - Acquired by Open Text Corporation
Bus-Tech Inc.; Hopkinton, MA - Acquired by EMC Corporation
Byers Peak, Inc.; Schaumburg, IL - Acquired by Sparton Corporation

C

Cadbury Plc; Northfield, IL - Acquired by Kraft Foods Inc.
California Churros Corp.; Pennsauken, NJ - Acquired by J&J Snack Foods Corporation
CanWest Media Group; Toronto, Canada - Name Changed to Shaw Media Inc.
Capital Crossing Preferred Corporation; New York, NY - Name Changed to EOS Preferred Corporation
Capital Fulfillment Group Inc.; Kansas City, MO - Acquired by DST Systems, Inc.
Caprock Communications, Inc.; Melbourne, FL - Acquired by Harris Corporation
Carefx Corporation; Melbourne, FL - Acquired by Harris Corporation
Carlton Forge Works; Portland, OR - Acquired by Precision Castparts Corp.
Cast Iron Systems, Inc.; Armonk, NY - Acquired by International Business Machines Corporation
Cbaysystems Holdings Limited; Franklin, TN - Name Changed to Medquist Holdings Inc.
CC Technology; Charlotte, NC - Acquired by EnPro Industries, Inc. & Name Changed to CPI Lubrication - CC Technology
Cedar Point Communications, Inc.; Plano, TX - Acquired by Genband, Inc.
Cellmania, Inc.; Waterloo, Canada - Acquired by Research In Motion Ltd.
Celmet Company, Inc.; Newark, NY - Acquired by IEC Electronics Corp.
Central Illinois Company; Peoria, IL - Name Changed to Ameren Illinois Company
Central Jersey Bancorp; Fairfield, NJ - Acquired by Kearny Financial Corp.
Centurytel, Inc.; Monroe, LA - Name Changed to CenturyLink, Inc.
Ception Therapeutics, Inc.; Frazer, PA - Acquired by Cephalon, Inc.
Cerilliant Corp.; Saint Louis, MO - Acquired by Sigma-Aldrich Corporation
Cerniglia Products, Inc.; New York, NY - Acquired by KKR & Co. L.P. & Clayton, Dubilier & Rice, LLC
Checkfree Corporation; Norcross, GA - Name Changed to Fiserv, Inc.
Chloride Group Plc; Saint Louis, MO - Acquired by Emerson Electric Co.
Choice Environmental Services, Inc.; Charlotte, NC - Acquired by Swisher Hygiene Inc.
Chordiant Software, Inc.; Cupertino, CA - Name Changed to

Pegasystems Inc.
Clarient, Inc.; Fairfield, CT - Acquired by General Electric Company
Clarity Systems Ltd.; Armonk, NY - Acquired by International Business Machines Corporation
Clark Security Products, Inc.; Glenview, IL - Acquired by Anixter International Inc.
Clarus Corporation; Salt Lake City, UT - Name Changed to Black Diamond, Inc.
Clickability, Inc.; Tempe, AZ - Acquired by Limelight Networks, Inc.
Climate Exchange Plc; Atlanta, GA - Acquired by Intercontinental Exchange Inc.
Clinical Data, Inc.; New York, NY - Acquired by Forest Laboratories, Inc.
Clipper Windpower Plc; Hartford, CT - Acquired & Absorbed by United Technologies Corporation
Cloudshield Technologies Inc.; McLean, VA - Acquired by SAIC, Inc.
Coca-Cola Enterprises Inc.; Atlanta, GA - Name Changed to Coca-Cola Refreshments USA, Inc.
CoCreate Software, Inc.; Fort Collins, CO - Name Changed to Parametric Technology Corp.
Codesourcery, Inc.; Wilsonville, OR - Acquired by Mentor Graphics Corporation
Cogent Inc.; Saint Paul, MN - Acquired by 3M Company
Cole Hersee Company; Chicago, IL - Acquired by Littelfuse, Inc.
Comaplex Minerals Corp.; Toronto, Canada - Acquired by Agnico-Eagle Mines Limited & Name Changed to Geomark Exploration Ltd.
Comm Bancorp, Inc.; Hermitage, PA - Acquired & Absorbed by F.N.B. Corporation
Compellent Technologies, Inc.; Round Rock, TX - Acquired by Dell Inc.
Confirm Monitoring Systems, Inc.; Little Falls, NJ - Acquired by Cantel Medical Corp.
Connexus Corp.; New York, NY - Name Changed to Epic Media Group Inc.
Conseco, Inc.; Carmel, IN - Name Changed to CNO Financial Group, Inc.
Constantia Packaging AG; New York, NY - Acquired by JPMorgan Chase & Co.
Continental Airlines Inc.; Chicago, IL - Acquired by United Continental Holdings, Inc.
Conwood Company LLC; Memphis, TN - Name Changed to American Snuff Company
Coradiant, Inc.; Houston, TX - Acquired by BMC Software, Inc.
Coremetrics, Inc.; Armonk, NY - Acquired by International Business Machines Corporation
Cowlitz Bank; Olympia, WA - Acquired & Absorbed by Heritage Financial Corporation
CPEX Pharmaceuticals, Inc.; Mahwah, NJ - Acquired by Footstar, Inc.
Craig Drake Manufacturing Inc.; Philadelphia, PA - Name Changed to Craiger Drake Designs
Crescent Bank; Jasper, GA - Name Changed to Rensant Bank
Critical Path Software Inc.; San Jose, CA - Acquired by eBay Inc.
Cross Telecom Corporation; Melville, NY - Acquired by Arrow Electronics, Inc.
Crucell N.V.; Langhorne, PA - Acquired by Johnson & Johnson
Crucell N.V.; New Brunswick, NJ - Acquired by Johnson & Johnson
CSC Holdings, Inc.; Bethpage, NY - Name Changed to CSC Holdings, LLC
Curamik Electronics Gmbh; Rogers, CT - Acquired by Rogers Corporation
Curtco/Gulfshore Media LLC; Naples, FL - Spun Off From Curtco Media Labs LLC to Form Gulfshore Media LLC
Cybersource Corporation; San Francisco, CA - Acquired by Visa, Inc.
CyberTrader, Inc.; Austin, TX - Name Changed to Charles Schwab
Cydex Pharmaceuticals, Inc.; La Jolla, CA - Acquired by Ligand Pharmaceuticals Incorporated
Cypress Bioscience, Inc.; New York, NY - Acquired by Cowen Group, Inc.

D

D.S. Brown Company; Buffalo, NY - Acquired by Gibraltar Industries, Inc.
Dan Dee Display Fixtures; Brooklyn Park, MN - Acquired & Absorbed by Carlson JPM Store Fixtures
Daros Piston Rings AB; Southfield, MI - Acquired by Federal-Mogul Corporation
Datacap, Inc.; Armonk, NY - Acquired by International Business Machines Corporation
Day Software Holding Ag; San Jose, CA - Acquired by Adobe Systems Incorporated
Dayton Supply & Tool Co.; Atlanta, GA - Acquired by Genuine Parts Company
Del Monte Foods Company; New York, NY - Acquired by KKR & Co. LLP, Vestar Capital Partners, Inc. & Centerview Partners LLC
Delta & Pine Land Company; Scott, MS - Name Changed to Monsanto
Delta Plc; Omaha, NE - Acquired by Valmont Industries, Inc.
Denali Software, Inc.; San Jose, CA - Acquired by Cadence Design Systems, Inc.
Denman Tire Corporation; Quincy, IL - Acquired & Absorbed by Titan International, Inc.
Designers Edge, Inc.; Waukegan, IL - Acquired by Coleman Cable, Inc.
Detroit Newspaper Partnership, L.P.; Detroit, MI - Name Changed to Detroit Media Partnership
DiaMed USA LLC; Mundelein, IL - Acquired by Medline Industries, Inc. & Name Changed to Medline DiaMed, LLC
Diamond Management & Technology Consultants, Inc.; New York, NY - Acquired by PricewaterhouseCoopers LLP - USA & Name Changed to Diamond Advisory Services
Diamond Wireless LLC; Burnaby, Canada - Acquired by Glentel Inc.
Divx, Inc.; Novato, CA - Acquired by Sonic Solutions
Doskocil Manufacturing Company, Inc.; Chicago, IL - Acquired by Wind Point Partners
DP Brown of Detroit, Inc.; Atlanta, GA - Acquired by Genuine Parts Company
Dunkin' Brands, Inc.; Canton, MA - Name Changed to Dunkin' Brands Group, Inc.
Dunkin' Brands, Inc.; Randolph, MA - Name Changed to Dunkin' Brands Group, Inc.
Dyadem International Limited; Englewood, CO - Acquired by IHS Inc.

E

Ebook Technologies, Inc.; Mountain View, CA - Acquired by Google Inc.
Echo Metrix, Inc.; Syosset, NY - Name Changed to Protext Mobility Inc.
Eclipse Electronic Systems, Inc.; Bellevue, WA - Acquired by Esterline Technologies Corporation
Educational Television Association; Cleveland, OH - Name Changed to ideastream
Electro-Optical Sciences, Inc.; Irvington, NY - Name Changed to Mela Sciences, Inc.
Ellora Energy Inc.; Irving, TX - Acquired & Absorbed by Exxon Mobil Corporation
Emsar Inc.; Stratford, CT - Name Changed to Aptar of Stratford
Encore Productions, Inc.; Dallas, TX - Acquired by Freeman Decorating Co.
Encryptx Corp.; Oakdale, MN - Acquired by Imation Corp.
Enerplus Resources Fund; Calgary, Canada - Name Changed to Enerplus Corporation
Enodis Corporation; New Port Richey, FL - Name Changed to Manitowoc Foodservice USA
Enwisen, Inc.; Saint Paul, MN - Acquired by Lawson Software, Inc.
Evans Rule Co., Inc.; North Charleston, SC - Name Changed to Starrett
eWork Healthcare; San Francisco, CA - Name Changed to eWork
Excel Global, Inc.; New York, NY - Name Changed to The Empire Sports & Entertainment Holdings Co.
Expressjet Holdings Inc.; Saint George, UT - Acquired by Skywest Inc.

F

F.E. Myers; Ashland, OH - Name Changed to Applied Wastewater Systems
Fairbanks International Inc.; Fargo, ND - Acquired by Titan Machinery Inc.
Fairfield Resorts, Inc.; Orlando, FL - Name Changed to Wyndham Vacation Ownership
Fancy Publications Inc.; Los Angeles, CA - Name Changed to Bowtie Inc.
Fastener Innovation Technology Inc.; New Britain, CT - Acquired by Stanley Black & Decker, Inc.
Fat Spaniel Technologies, Inc.; Camarillo, CA - Acquired & Absorbed by Power-One Inc.
Ferraz Shawmut; Newburyport, MA - Name Changed to Mersen
FiberNet Telecom Group, Inc.; New York, NY - Name Changed to zColo
Fibre Glass-Evercoat; Cincinnati, OH - Name Changed to ITW - Evercoat
Firearms Training Systems, Inc.; Suwanee, GA - Name Changed to Meggitt Training Systems
First American Corporation; Santa Ana, CA - Name Changed to CoreLogic, Inc.
First Bancshares Inc.; San Luis Obispo, CA - Name Changed to Santa Barbara Bank & Trust
First Chester County Corporation; Harrisburg, PA - Acquired by Tower Bancorp, Inc.
First Colony Life Insurance Company; Lynchburg, VA - Name Changed to Genworth Financial
First Keystone Financial Inc.; Bryn Mawr, PA - Acquired & Absorbed by Bryn Mawr Bank Corporation
FisherCast Ltd.; Peterborough, Canada - Name Changed to Dynacast Ltd.
Florida Power Corporation; Saint Petersburg, FL - Name Changed to Progress Energy Florida
Flowguard Ltd.; Golden, CO - Acquired by CoorsTek, Inc.
Flying J Inc.; Ogden, UT - Name Changed to FJ Management, Inc.
Foamex Innovations, Inc.; Media, PA - Name Changed to FXI
Foot Petals, Inc.; Columbus, OH - Acquired by R.G. Barry Corporation
Foot Petals, Inc.; Pickerington, OH - Acquired by R.G. Barry Corporation
Football Fanatics Inc.; King of Prussia, PA - Acquired by GSI Commerce, Inc.
Fortify Software, Inc.; Palo Alto, CA - Acquired by Hewlett-Packard Company
Foster's Wine Estates; Napa, CA - Name Changed to Treasury Wine Estates
Frederick Fiber Optics Inc.; Edgewood, NY - Acquired by TII Network Technologies, Inc.
Freeman Metal Products Inc.; Pittsburgh, PA - Acquired by Matthews International Corporation
Fremont General Corporation; Sherman Oaks, CA - Name Changed to Signature Group Holdings, Inc.
Fuddruckers, Inc.; Houston, TX - Acquired by Luby's, Inc. and Name Changed to Luby's Fuddrucker's Restaurants, LLC
Fusionone, Inc.; Bridgewater, NJ - Acquired by Synchronoss Technologies, Inc.

G

Galaxy Technologies, Inc.; Kingwood, TX - Acquired by Insperity, Inc.
Gateway Proclean, Inc.; Charlotte, NC - Acquired by Swisher Hygiene Inc.
Gemstone Systems, Inc.; Hopkinton, MA - Acquired by EMC Corporation
General Monitors Inc.; Cranberry, PA - Acquired by Mine Safety Appliances Company
Genesis Fluid Solutions Holdings, Inc.; Henderson, NV - Name Changed to Blue Earth Inc.
Georgia Department of Industry, Trade & Tourism; Atlanta, GA - Name Changed to Georgia Department of Economic Development
Geospiza, Inc.; Waltham, MA - Acquired by PerkinElmer, Inc.
Gifts Software, Inc.; Jacksonville, FL - Acquired by Fidelity National Information Services, Inc.
Global Software Services, Inc.; Indianapolis, IN - Acquired by Interactive Intelligence, Inc.
Godwin Pumps of America, Inc.; White Plains, NY - Acquired by ITT Corporation
Golden Drapery Supply, Inc.; Middleton, WI - Acquired & Absorbed by Springs Window Fashions LLC
Goldsmith, Agio, Helms & Lynner; Minneapolis, MN - Name Changed to Lazard Middle Market LLC
Greater Louisville Convention & Visitors Bureau; Louisville, KY - Name Changed to Louisville Convention & Visitors Bureau
Green Mountain Energy Company; Princeton, NJ - Acquired by NRG Energy, Inc.
Gridapp Systems, Inc.; Houston, TX - Acquired by BMC Software,

Inc.

Griffin Industries, Inc.; Irving, TX - Acquired by Darling International, Inc.

Group DCA, Inc.; Parsippany, NJ - Acquired by PDI, Inc.

Gtronix, Inc.; Santa Clara, CA - Acquired by National Semiconductor Corporation

Gulf Coast Bearing & Supply Co., Inc.; Cleveland, OH - Acquired by Applied Industrial Technologies, Inc.

Gwaltney of Smithfield, Ltd.; Smithfield, VA - Name Changed to Smithfield Packing

H

Hammond Associates, Inc.; New York, NY - Acquired by Marsh & McLennan Companies Inc.

Harleysville National Corporation; Buffalo, NY - Acquired & Absorbed by First Niagara Financial Group Inc.

Harrah's Entertainment, Inc.; Las Vegas, NV - Name Changed to Caesar's Entertainment Corporation

Harry Pepper & Associates, Inc.; Norwalk, CT - Acquired by Emcor Group, Inc.

Hautelook, Inc.; Seattle, WA - Acquired by Nordstrom, Inc.

HCA Inc.; Nashville, TN - Name Changed to HCA Holdings Inc.

Headsprout Inc.; Atlanta, GA - Acquired by Newell Rubbermaid Inc.

Health Benefits Direct Corporation; Radnor, PA - Name Changed to Inspro Technologies Corporation

Healthtronics, Inc.; Chadds Ford, PA - Acquired by Endo Pharmaceuticals Holdings, Inc.

Healthy Fast Food, Inc.; Henderson, NV - Name Changed to U-Swirl, Inc.

Heartland Information Services, Inc.; Atlanta, GA - Acquired by Transcend Services, Inc.

Hepalife Technologies, Inc.; New York, NY - Name Changed to Alliqua, Inc.

Heroku, Inc.; San Francisco, CA - Acquired by Salesforce.com, Inc.

Hewitt Associates, Inc.; Chicago, IL - Acquired by Aon Corporation & Name Changed to Aon Hewitt

Hewitt Associates, Inc.; Lincolnshire, IL - Name Changed to Aon Hewitt

Hexion Specialty Chemicals Inc.; Columbus, OH - Name Changed to Momentive Specialty Chemicals Inc.

Hitachi Telecom (USA), Inc.; Norcross, GA - Name Changed to Hitachi Communications America Inc.

Hodyon LP; San Diego, CA - Acquired by Fallbrook Technologies Inc.

Homenet Automotive LLC; Atlanta, GA - Acquired by Cox Enterprises, Inc.

Honest Tea; Atlanta, GA - Acquired by The Coca-Cola Company

The Honolulu Advertiser; Honolulu, HI - Name Changed to The Honolulu Star-Advertiser

HR Textron Inc.; Santa Clarita, CA - Name Changed to Woodward HRT

Thehuffingtonpost.Com, Inc.; New York, NY - Acquired by AOL Inc.

Hythiam, Inc.; Los Angeles, CA - Name Changed to Catasys Inc.

I

Icrossing, Inc.; New York, NY - Acquired by The Hearst Corporation

ICX Technologies, Inc.; Wilsonville, OR - Acquired by FLIR Systems, Inc.

Image Solutions, Inc.; Falls Church, VA - Acquired by Computer Sciences Corporation

Imperial Holdings, LLC; Boca Raton, FL - Name Changed to Imperial Holdings, Inc.

Impromed, Inc.; Melville, NY - Acquired by Henry Schein, Inc.

IMW Industries Ltd.; Seal Beach, CA - Acquired by Clean Energy Fuels Corp.

Incentra LLC; Broomfield, CO - Name Changed to Presilient, LLC

Infor Global Solutions, Inc.; Alpharetta, GA - Name Changed to Infor

Inlet Technologies Inc.; San Jose, CA - Acquired by Cisco Systems, Inc.

Insight Technology Incorporated; New York, NY - Acquired by L-3 Communications Holdings Inc.

Integrated Metering Systems, Inc.; Melville, NY - Acquired by Leviton Manufacturing Company, Inc.

Interstate Seed Company; West Fargo, ND - Name Changed to Monsanto

Intuit Real Estate Solutions Inc.; Cleveland, OH - Name Changed to MRI Software, LLC

Inverness Medical Innovations Inc.; Waltham, MA - Name Changed to Alere Inc.

Isilon Systems, Inc.; Hopkinton, MA - Acquired by EMC Corporation

iskoot Inc.; San Diego, CA - Acquired by Qualcomm Incorporated & Name Changed to iSkoot Technologies, Inc.

ITA Software, Inc.; Mountain View, CA - Acquired by Google Inc.

ITC Deltacom, Inc.; Atlanta, GA - Acquired by EarthLink, Inc.

ITX Group Ltd.; Phoenix, AZ - Acquired by Avnet, Inc.

Iveda Corporation; Mesa, AZ - Name Changed to Iveda Solutions, Inc.

J

Jambool, Inc.; Mountain View, CA - Acquired by Google Inc.

Jardinier Alternative Irrigation Systems; Santa Ana, CA - Name Changed to Garden Art International

Javelin Pharmaceuticals, Inc.; Lake Forest, IL - Acquired by Hospira, Inc.

Jingle Networks; Seattle, WA - Acquired & Absorbed by Marchex, Inc.

John Sterling Corporation; Chicago, IL - Acquired & Absorbed by Wind Point Partners

Jones Apparel Group Inc.; New York, NY - Name Changed to The Jones Group, Inc.

Journey Education Marketing, Inc.; Eden Prairie, MN - Acquired by Digital River, Inc.

K

Kadient, Inc.; Lowell, MA - Merged with Sant Corp to Form Qvidian

Kayak.Com; Norwalk, CT - Name Changed to Kayak Software

Corporation
Kaz, Inc.; El Paso, TX - Acquired by Helen of Troy Limited
Keithley Instruments, Inc.; Washington, DC - Acquired by Danaher Corporation
King Pharmaceuticals, Inc.; New York, NY - Acquired by Pfizer Inc.
Klipsch Group, Inc.; Hauppauge, NY - Acquired by Audiovox Corporation
Krillion, Inc.; Irvine, CA - Acquired by Local.com Corporation
K-Tron International, Inc.; Batesville, IN - Acquired by Hillenbrand, Inc.

L

Lanier Worldwide, Inc.; Atlanta, GA - Name Changed to Ricoh Americas Corp.
Lasco Bathware; Anaheim, CA - Merged with Aquatic Whirlpools to form Aquatic
Lehman Communications Corporation; Denver, CO - Acquired by MediaNews Group, Inc. & The E.W. Scripps Company
Lighting Sciences Inc.; Northbrook, IL - Acquired by Underwriters Laboratories Inc.
Liquid Blaino Designs, Inc.; Los Angeles, CA - Name Changed to Junk Food Clothing Company
LNX Corp.; Chelmsford, MA - Acquired by Mercury Computer Systems, Inc.
Logos Communications, Inc.; Lawrence, PA - Acquired by Black Box Corporation
Louisiana Roofing Supply, LLC; Peabody, MA - Acquired by Beacon Roofing Supply, Inc. & Name Changed to West End Lumber
Love Box Company, Inc.; Wichita, KS - Name Changed to Pratt Industries

M

M.L. Stern & Co., LLC; Beverly Hills, CA - Name Changed to Southwest Securities, Inc.
Mag-Con Engineering, Inc.; Lino Lakes, MN - Name Changed to Badger Magnetics Inc.
Mallinckrodt Baker Inc.; Phillipsburg, NJ - Name Changed to Avantor Performance Materials, Inc.
Mariner Energy Inc.; Houston, TX - Acquired & Absorbed by Apache Corporation
Matrikon Inc.; Morristown, NJ - Acquired by Honeywell International Inc.
McAfee Inc.; Santa Clara, CA - Acquired by Intel Corporation
MDS Inc.; Ottawa, Canada - Name Changed to Nordion Inc.
Mechtronic Solutions, Inc.; Calabasas, CA - Acquired by National Technical Systems Inc.
Medicity, Inc.; Hartford, CT - Acquired by Aetna Inc.
Melodeo, Inc.; Palo Alto, CA - Acquired by Hewlett-Packard Company
Mepha AG; Frazer, PA - Acquired by Cephalon, Inc.
Mercer Insurance Group, Inc.; Cedar Rapids, IA - Acquired by United Fire & Casualty Company
Messageway Solutions, Inc.; Lexington, MA - Acquired & Absorbed by Ipswitch, Inc.
Metastorm, Inc.; Waterloo, Canada - Acquired by Open Text Corporation
M-Factor Inc.; San Mateo, CA - Acquired by DemandTec, Inc.
Michrom Bioresources, Inc.; Billerica, MA - Acquired by Bruker Corporation
Micro Therapeutics, Inc.; Irvine, CA - Name Changed to ev3 Inc.
Microfluidics International Corporation; Lake Forest, IL - Acquired by IDEX Corporation
Micromedex, Inc.; Greenwood Village, CO - Name Changed to Thomson Reuters
Micromedics, Inc.; Westlake, OH - Acquired by Nordson Corporation
Microtune, Inc.; Sunnyvale, CA - Acquired by Zoran Corporation
Micrus Endovascular Corporation; Langhorne, PA - Acquired by Johnson & Johnson
Micrus Endovascular Corporation; New Brunswick, NJ - Acquired by Johnson & Johnson
Millenworks; Providence, RI - Acquired by Textron Inc.
Mirant Corporation; Houston, TX - Merged with RRI Energy, Inc. to Form GenOn Energy, Inc.
Money4gold Holdings, Inc.; Fort Lauderdale, FL - Name Changed to Upstream Worldwide, Inc.
Monitronics International, Inc.; Englewood, CO - Acquired by Ascent Media Corporation
Monroe Bancorp; Evansville, IN - Acquired & Absorbed by Old National Bancorp
Morristown Grain Company Inc.; White Plains, NY - Acquired by Bunge Limited
Motorola, Inc.; Schaumburg, IL - Name Changed to Motorola Solutions, Inc.
Mount Engineering PLC; Houston, TX - Acquired by Cooper Industries PLC

N

NATCO Group Inc.; Houston, TX - Name Changed to Cameron International
Naverus Inc.; Fairfield, CT - Acquired by General Electric Company
Navisite, Inc.; New York, NY - Acquired by Time Warner Cable Inc.
Nebraska Orthotic & Prosthetic Services, Inc.; Austin, TX - Acquired by Hanger Orthopedic Group, Inc.
Nelson Laboratories LP; Meridian, ID - Acquired by MWI Veterinary Supply, Inc.
Netezza Corporation; Armonk, NY - Acquired by International Business Machines Corporation
Netviewer AG; Fort Lauderdale, FL - Acquired by Citrix Systems, Inc.
Netwitness Corporation; Hopkinton, MA - Acquired by EMC Corporation
Network International Inc.; Washington, DC - Acquired by Liquidity Services, Inc.
New Alliance Bancshares, Inc.; New Haven, CT - Name Changed to First Niagara Bank
New Alliance Bancshares, Inc.; Buffalo, NY - Acquired by First Niagara Financial Group Inc.
Newfound Communications, Inc.; Bedford, MA - Acquired by Acme Packet Inc.
Newkirk Products, Inc.; Kansas City, MO - Acquired by DST Systems, Inc.
Newscale, Inc.; San Jose, CA - Acquired by Cisco Systems, Inc.
Nexmed, Inc.; San Diego, CA - Name Changed to Apricus Biosciences Inc.
Nichols Wire Incorporated; Foothill Ranch, CA - Acquired by

Kaiser Aluminum Corporation

Nies Insurance Agency, Inc.; Daytona Beach, FL - Acquired by Brown & Brown, Inc.

North American Technologies Group, Inc.; Dallas, TX - Name Changed to TieTek

North Star Imaging, Inc.; Glenview, IL - Acquired by Illinois Tool Works Inc.

Novartis Nutrition Corporation; Minneapolis, MN - Name Changed to Nestle Healthcare Nutrition

Nu Horizons Electronics Corporation; Melville, NY - Acquired by Arrow Electronics, Inc.

O

O.I. Corporation; White Plains, NY - Acquired by ITT Corporation

Odyssey Healthcare, Inc.; Atlanta, GA - Acquired by Gentiva Health Services, Inc.

Omneon, Inc.; San Jose, CA - Acquired by Harmonic, Inc.

OmniReliant Holdings, Inc.; Clearwater, FL - Name Changed to Infusion Brands International, Inc.

One Communications Corp.; Atlanta, GA - Acquired by EarthLink, Inc.

Opal Software; Fairfield, CT - Acquired by General Electric Company

Openspirit, Corp.; Palo Alto, CA - Acquired by Tibco Software Inc.

Optical Research Associates; Mountain View, CA - Acquired by Synopsys, Inc.

Orthologic Corp.; Tempe, AZ - Name Changed to Capstone Therapeutics Corp.

Osteotech, Inc.; Eatontown, NJ - Name Changed to Medtronic

Osteotech, Inc.; Minneapolis, MN - Acquired by Medtronic, Inc.

OTCI Acquisition, LLC; Fort Myers, FL - Name Changed to BB&T - Oswald Trippe & Co.

Outcome Concept Systems, Inc.; Lincoln, NE - Acquired by National Research Corporation

P

Pacira, Inc.; Parsippany, NJ - Name Changed to Pacira Pharmaceuticals, Inc.

Pac-Kit Safety Equipment Co.; Fairfield, CT - Acquired by Acme United Corporation

Palm, Inc.; Palo Alto, CA - Acquired by Hewlett-Packard Company

Paragon Aquatics; Lagrangeville, NY - Name Changed to Pentair Water Pool and Spa, Inc.

Pari Networks Inc.; San Jose, CA - Acquired by Cisco Systems, Inc.

Patco Electronics Inc.; Clearwater, FL - Acquired by Technology Research Corporation

Patni Computer Systems Limited; Fremont, CA - Acquired by iGATE Corporation

Pengrowth Energy Trust; Calgary, Canada - Name Changed to Pengrowth Energy Corp.

Pennzoil-Quaker State Canada, Inc.; Burlington, Canada - Name Changed to Shell Lubricants - Canada

Penwest Pharmaceuticals Company; Chadds Ford, PA - Acquired & Absorbed by Endo Pharmaceuticals Holdings, Inc.

The Peoples Banctrust Company, Inc.; Selma, AL - Name Changed to BancTrust

The Pepsi Bottling Group, Inc.; Somers, NY - Name Changed to Pepsi Beverages Company

PGP Corporation; Mountain View, CA - Acquired & Absorbed by Symantec Corporation

Phase Forward Incorporated; Redwood City, CA - Acquired by Oracle Corporation

Physicians Insurance Company of Wisconsin Inc.; Madison, WI - Name Changed to ProAssurance Wisconsin Insurance Company

Phyworks Ltd.; Sunnyvale, CA - Acquired by Maxim Integrated Products, Inc.

Pink OTC Markets Inc.; New York, NY - Name Changed to OTC Markets Group Inc.

Pipeline Seal & Insulator, Inc.; Charlotte, NC - Acquired by EnPro Industries, Inc.

The Planet; Houston, TX - Name Changed to Softlayer Technologies Inc.

Platinum Solution, Inc.; Fairfax, VA - Acquired by SRA International, Inc.

Playspan, Inc.; San Francisco, CA - Acquired by Visa, Inc.

PMC Wire & Cable; Manchester, NH - Name Changed to RSCC Aerospace & Defense

Portec Rail Products Inc.; Pittsburgh, PA - Acquired by L.B. Foster Company

Portrait Software Plc; Stamford, CT - Acquired by Pitney Bowes Inc.

Premier Lubrication Systems, Inc.; Charlotte, NC - Acquired by EnPro Industries, Inc. & Name Changed to CPI Lubrication-Premier Lubrication Systems

Presidium Inc.; Washington, DC - Acquired by Blackboard Inc.

Product Partners LLC; Santa Monica, CA - Name Changed to Beachbody, LLC

Proginet Corporation; Palo Alto, CA - Acquired by TIBCO Software Inc.

Progressive Equipment, Inc.; Charlotte, NC - Acquired by EnPro Industries, Inc.

Progressive Technologies, Inc.; Carrollton, TX - Acquired by Universal Power Group, Inc.

Protus IP Solutions Inc.; Los Angeles, CA - Acquired by J2 Global Communications, Inc.

Provet Holdings Limited; Melville, NY - Acquired by Henry Schein, Inc.

Proxymed, Inc.; New Albany, IN - Name Changed to Anx E-Business Corp.

PSS Systems, Inc.; Armonk, NY - Acquired by International Business Machines Corporation

Psychiatric Solutions, Inc.; King of Prussia, PA - Acquired by Universal Health Services Inc.

Pulaski Furniture Corporation; High Point, NC - Name Changed to Home Meridian International, Inc.

Q

Q-Comm Corporation; Little Rock, AR - Acquired & Absorbed by Windstream Corporation

Quest Capital Corp.; Vancouver, Canada - Name Changed to Sprott Resource Lending Corp.

Quickparts.Com, Inc.; Rock Hill, SC - Acquired by 3D Systems Corporation

MERGERS, ACQUISITIONS AND NAME CHANGES

The Quigley Corporation; Doylestown, PA - Name Changed to ProPhase Labs, Inc.
Qwest Communications International Inc.; Monroe, LA - Acquired by CenturyLink, Inc.

R

Radian6 Technologies Inc.; San Francisco, CA - Acquired by Salesforce.com, Inc.
Raymarine Plc; Wilsonville, OR - Acquired by FLIR Systems, Inc.
Real Branding LLC; Des Plaines, IL - Acquired by Schawk, Inc.
Reco LLC; Pittsburgh, PA - Acquired by Wesco International Inc.
Recon/Optical, Inc.; Barrington, IL - Name Changed to Goodrich ISR Barrington
Reliable Knitting Works, Inc.; Milwaukee, WI - Name Changed to Reliable of Milwaukee
Rental Store Inc.; Plano, TX - Acquired by Rent-A-Center, Inc.
Reveal Imaging Technologies Inc.; McLean, VA - Acquired by SAIC, Inc.
Rewards Network, Inc.; Chicago, IL - Acquired by Equity Group Investments, LLC
Rex Stores Corporation; Dayton, OH - Name Changed to Rex American Resources Corporation
Rigzone; New York, NY - Acquired by Dice Holdings, Inc.
Rising Pharmaceuticals, Inc.; Lake Success, NY - Acquired by Aceto Corporation
RITA Medical Systems, Inc.; Fremont, CA - Name Changed to AngioDynamics
Rogers & Norman, Inc.; Daytona Beach, FL - Acquired by Brown & Brown, Inc.
Rome Bancorp, Inc.; Rome, NY - Name Changed to Berkshire Bank
Royal Style Design, Inc.; Orlando, FL - Name Changed to Diversified Global Holdings Group, Inc.
RP Data Limited; Santa Ana, CA - Acquired by CoreLogic, Inc.
RRI Energy Inc.; Houston, TX - Name Changed to GenOn Energy, Inc.

S

Sadra Medical, Inc.; Natick, MA - Acquired by Boston Scientific Corporation
Salary.Com, Inc.; Wayne, PA - Acquired by Kenexa Corporation
San Francisco Convention & Visitors Bureau; San Francisco, CA - Name Changed to San Francisco Travel Association
Saturn Telecommunication Services, Inc.; Atlanta, GA - Acquired by EarthLink, Inc.
Scaleform Corporation; San Rafael, CA - Acquired by Autodesk Inc.
Schoffman's Inc.; Fargo, ND - Acquired by Titan Machinery Inc.
Scott Wilson Group Plc; San Francisco, CA - Acquired by URS Corporation & Name Changed to URS/Scott Wilson
SeaBright Insurance Holdings, Inc.; Seattle, WA - Name Changed to SeaBright Holdings, Inc.
Seamless Corporation; Orlando, FL - Name Changed to GDT Tek, Inc.
Secure Data, Inc.; Springfield, NJ - Acquired by Emtec, Inc.
Secureworks, Inc.; Round Rock, TX - Acquired by Dell Inc.
Semitool, Inc.; Kalispell, MT - Name Changed to Applied Materials, Inc.
SenoRx, Inc.; Irvine, CA - Name Changed to C.R. Bard
SenoRx, Inc.; New Providence, NJ - Acquired by C.R. Bard, Inc.
Sepp's Gourmet Foods Ltd.; Saint Louis, MO - Acquired by Ralcorp Holdings, Inc.
Sepracor, Inc.; Marlborough, MA - Name Changed to Sunovion Pharmaceuticals Inc.
Sequal Technologies, Inc.; Garfield Heights, OH - Acquired by Chart Industries, Inc. & Name Changed to Chart Sequal Technologies, Inc.
Serverengines LLC; Costa Mesa, CA - Acquired & Absorbed by Emulex Corporation
Service1st Bank Of Nevada; Las Vegas, NV - Acquired by Western Liberty Bancorp
Shed Media Plc; New York, NY - Acquired by Time Warner Inc.
Shimmer Gold, Inc.; New York, NY - Name Changed to Absolute Life Solutions, Inc.
Shine Limited; New York, NY - Acquired by News Corporation
Siemens Energy & Automation Inc.; Alpharetta, GA - Name Changed to Siemens Industry
Siemens Energy & Automation; Nashua, NH - Name Changed to Microscan Systems Inc.
Sierra Pacific Power Company; Reno, NV - Name Changed to NV Energy
Simpson Dura-Vent Company, Inc.; Vacaville, CA - Name Changed to M&G Dura-Vent, Inc.
Slide, Inc.; Mountain View, CA - Acquired by Google Inc.
Smith International, Inc.; Houston, TX - Acquired by Schlumberger Limited
Snyder's of Hanover Inc.; Charlotte, NC - Acquired by Snyder's-Lance, Inc.
Society of Automotive Engineers, Inc.; Warrendale, PA - Name Changed to SAE International
Solidscape, Inc.; Eden Prairie, MN - Acquired by Stratasys, Inc.
South Texas Bolt & Fitting, Inc.; Bloomfield Hills, MI - Acquired by Trimas Corporation
The South Financial Group, Inc.; Toronto, Canada - Acquired & Absorbed by The Toronto-Dominion Bank
Southern California Braiding Co., Inc.; Newark, NY - Acquired by IEC Electronics Corp.
Southern Foods, Inc.; Greensboro, NC - Acquired by & Name Changed to Meat & Seafood Solutions LLC
Southwest Water Company; New York, NY - Acquired by JPMorgan Chase & Co.
Spadac Inc.; Dulles, VA - Acquired by GeoEye, Inc.
SpectraLink Corporation; Boulder, CO - Name Changed to Polycom, Inc.
Spectrum Human Resource Systems Corp.; Irvine, CA - Acquired by Epicor Software Corporation
Speedway Superamerica LLC; Enon, OH - Name Changed to Speedway LLC
Sperian Protection SA; Morristown, NJ - Acquired by Honeywell International Inc.
Sphinx CST Limited; Melville, NY - Acquired by Arrow Electronics, Inc.
SSCO Manufacturing, Inc.; Cleveland, OH - Acquired by Lincoln Electric Holdings, Inc.
Stanley, Inc.; Montreal, Canada - Acquired & Absorbed by CGI Group Inc.
STL Enterprises, Inc.; Burlington, MA - Acquired by & Name Changed To Circor Aerospace
STL Enterprises, Inc.; Sylmar, CA - Name Changed to Circor Aerospace
The Stacole Company, Inc.; Pittsburgh, PA - Acquired by The PNC Financial Services Group, Inc.
Stratavia Corp.; Palo Alto, CA - Acquired by Hewlett-Packard Company
Streamline Development LLC; Foster City, CA - Acquired by

Electronics for Imaging, Inc.
Streamserve AB; Waterloo, Canada - Acquired by Open Text Corporation
The Student Loan Corporation; Stamford, CT - Name Changed to Discover Student Loans
Sugartown Worldwide, Inc.; Atlanta, GA - Acquired by Oxford Industries, Inc.
Summit Instruments, Inc.; Fairview, PA - Acquired by Spectrum Control, Inc.
Sun Microsystems, Inc.; Santa Clara, CA - Name Changed to Oracle America, Inc.
Sun Microsystems, Inc.; Redwood City, CA - Acquired by Oracle Corporation and Named Changed to Oracle America, Inc.
Surepayroll, Inc.; Rochester, NY - Acquired by Paychex, Inc.
Surgical Information Systems LLC; San Francisco, CA - Acquired by Wells Fargo & Company
Surgient, Inc.; Aliso Viejo, CA - Acquired by Quest Software, Inc.
Swift & Company, E.A. Miller Inc.; Hyrum, UT - Name Changed to JBS
Swiger Coil Systems, LLC; Wilmerding, PA - Acquired by Westinghouse Air Brake Technologies Corporation
The Swiss Colony, Inc.; Monroe, WI - Name Changed to Colony Brands Inc.
Symyx Technologies, Inc.; San Diego, CA - Acquired & Absorbed by Accelrys, Inc.
Synbiotics Corporation; New York, NY - Acquired by Pfizer Inc.
Syntex Management Systems, Inc.; Englewood, CO - Acquired by IHS Inc.
System C Healthcare PLC; San Francisco, CA - Acquired by McKesson Corporation

T

T-3 Energy Services, Inc.; Dayton, OH - Acquired by Robbins & Myers, Inc.
Target Stamped Products Corporation; Kinsman, OH - Name Changed to Bayloff Stamped Products
Technigraphics, Inc.; Arlington, VA - Acquired by CACI International Inc.
Technitrol, Inc.; Trevose, PA - Name Changed to Pulse Electronics Corporation
TechTeam Global, Inc.; Southfield, MI - Name Changed to Stefanini TechTeam Global, Inc.
Tegrity, Inc.; New York, NY - Acquired by The McGraw-Hill Companies Inc.
Telex Communications, Inc.; Burnsville, MN - Name Changed to Bosch Communications Inc.
Termnet Merchant Services Inc.; Columbus, GA - Acquired by Total System Services, Inc.
Terra Nova Financial Group, Inc.; Dallas, TX - Name Changed to TNFG Corporation
Terra Telecom LLC; Scottsdale, AZ - Acquired by EGPI Firecreek, Inc.
Terral Seed, Inc.; Wilmington, DE - Acquired by E.I. du Pont de Nemours & Company
Terremark Worldwide, Inc.; New York, NY - Acquired by Verizon Communications Inc.
Texas Rangers Inc.; Arlington, TX - Name Changed to Rangers Baseball LLC
The Thumb Blanket; Bad Axe, MI - Name Changed to Huron County View
Thermo Electron Corporation Process Instruments; Sugar Land, TX - Name Changed to Thermo Fischer Scientific
Ticketmaster Entertainment, Inc.; Beverly Hills, CA - Acquired by Live Nation Entertainment, Inc.
Title Starts Online Inc.; Blue Ash, OH - Name Changed to AMP Holding Inc.
Tower Automotive, LLC; Livonia, MI - Name Changed to Tower International, Inc.
Trading Places International; Miami, FL - Acquired by Interval Leisure Group, Inc.
Traffic Marketplace, Inc.; San Francisco, CA - Name Changed to Epic Marketplace, Inc.
Tri State Implement, Inc.; Fargo, ND - Acquired by Titan Machinery Inc.
Tri-Mark Mfg, Inc.; Santa Monica, CA - Name Changed to 5to1 Holding Corp.
Tririga, Inc.; Armonk, NY - Acquired by International Business Machines Corporation
Tropicana Casinos & Resorts, Inc.; Las Vegas, NV - Name Changed to Tropicana Entertainment Inc.
Tyco Electronics Corporation; Berwyn, PA - Name Changed to TE Connectivity Ltd.

U

Unica Corporation; Armonk, NY - Acquired by International Business Machines Corporation
Unico Inc.; Beloit, WI - Acquired by Regal Beloit Corporation
Union Switch & Signal Inc.; Pittsburgh, PA - Name Changed to Ansaldo STS
United Biosource Corporation; Franklin Lakes, NJ - Acquired by Medco Health Solutions, Inc.
Upstate Agency, Inc.; Glens Falls, NY - Acquired by Arrow Financial Corporation
Urban Financial Group, Inc.; Jersey City, NJ - Acquired by Knight Capital Group, Inc.
USB Corporation; Cleveland, OH - Name Changed to Affymetrix

V

Valeant Pharmaceuticals International, Inc.; Mississauga, Canada - Acquired by Valeant Pharmaceuticals International, Inc.
Valley National Gases LLC; Independence, OH - Name Changed to Matheson Valley
Valuecentric Marketing Group, Inc.; Jacksonville, FL - Acquired by Fidelity National Information Services, Inc.
Vauto, Inc.; Atlanta, GA - Acquired by Cox Enterprises, Inc.
Venali, Inc.; Los Angeles, CA - Acquired by J2 Global Communications, Inc.
Veraz Networks, Inc.; San Jose, CA - Name Changed to Dialogic Inc.
VeriFone Holdings, Inc.; San Jose, CA - Name Changed to VeriFone Systems, Inc.
Veripack.Com, Inc.; Groton, MA - Name Changed to Bags & Bows
Vermont Pure Holdings, Ltd.; Watertown, CT - Name Changed to Crystal Rock Holdings Inc.
Vertica Systems, Inc.; Palo Alto, CA - Acquired by Hewlett-Packard Company
Virage Logic Corporation; Mountain View, CA - Acquired & Absorbed by Synopsys, Inc.
Vocollect, Inc.; Everett, WA - Acquired by Intermec Inc.
Voyager Learning Company; Dallas, TX - Merged with Cambium Learning, Inc. to form Cambium Learning Group, Inc.

MERGERS, ACQUISITIONS AND NAME CHANGES

Learning, Inc. to form Cambium Learning Group, Inc.

W

The Wackenhut Corporation; Jupiter, FL - Name Changed to G4S Secure Solutions USA
Wainwright Bank & Trust Company; Boston, MA - Acquired by Eastern Bank Corporation
Walt Disney Internet Group; North Hollywood, CA - Name Changed to Disney Interactive Media Group
Wareforce; Chicago, IL - Name Changed to Sarcom
Waste Services, Inc.; Vaughan, Canada - Acquired & Absorbed by IESI-BFC Ltd.
Water Services of America, Inc.; Milwaukee, WI - Name Changed to WSA Engineered Systems Inc.
WaterCare Corporation; Appleton, WI - Name Changed to Water-Right Inc.
Wattyl Limited; Minneapolis, MN - Acquired by The Valspar Corporation
Wayport, Inc.; Austin, TX - Name Changed to AT&T Wireless Services
Web Merchants, Inc.; Atlanta, GA - Acquired by WES Consulting, Inc.
Wells Rural Electric Company Inc.; Omaha, NE - Acquired by KeyOn Communications Holdings Inc.
Western Coal Corp.; Tampa, FL - Acquired by Walter Energy, Inc.
White-Rodgers; Saint Louis, MO - Name Changed to Emerson White-Rodgers
WHX Corporation; White Plains, NY - Name Changed to Handy & Harman Ltd.
WiderThan Americas, Inc.; Reston, VA - Name Changed to RealNetworks, Inc.
Wilber Corporation; De Witt, NY - Acquired by Community Bank System, Inc.
Williams Advanced Materials Inc.; Buffalo, NY - Name Changed to Materion Microelectronics & Services
Wimm Bill Dann Foods OJSC; Purchase, NY - Acquired by PepsiCo Inc.
WNOU-FM; Indianapolis, IN - Name Changed to Radio One
World Color Press, Inc.; Sussex, WI - Acquired by & Name Changed to Quad/Graphics, Inc.
World Warehouse & Distribution, Inc.; Vineland, NJ - Acquired by NFI Industries Inc.
WQN; Dallas, TX - Name Changed to Quamtel, Inc.
Wyeth LLC; New York, NY - Acquired & Absorbed by Pfizer Inc.

X

Xanboo, Inc.; Dallas, TX - Acquired by AT&T Inc.
Xelr8 Holdings, Inc.; Denver, CO - Name Changed to Bazi International Inc.
XTO Energy Inc.; Irving, TX - Acquired by Exxon Mobil Corporation

Y

York Process Systems - Frick; Waynesboro, PA - Name Changed to Johnson Controls - Frick
Youbet.Com Inc.; Louisville, KY - Acquired by Churchill Downs, Inc.
Your Man Tours, Inc.; El Segundo, CA - Name Changed to YMT Vacations
YRC Logistics, Inc.; Overland Park, KS - Name Changed to MIQ Logistics, LLC

Z

Zantaz Inc.; Pleasanton, CA - Name Changed to Autonomy Pleasanton
Zymogenetics, Inc.; New York, NY - Acquired by Bristol-Myers Squibb Company

NEW LISTINGS
2011

A

A&D Exteriors; Bartlett, IL
Abita Brewing Company; Abita Springs, LA
Absolute Life Solutions, Inc.; New York, NY
Accelerated Acquisitions V, Inc.; Dallas, TX
Accenture, Inc.; New York, NY
Aderant Holdings, Inc.; Atlanta, GA
AdvancePierre Foods, Inc.; Cincinnati, OH
The Adventure Project; Brooklyn, NY
Alexion Pharmaceuticals, Inc.; Cheshire, CT
All Market, Inc.; New York, NY
Alliqua, Inc.; New York, NY
Amerityre Corporation; Boulder City, NV
Amscan Holdings, Inc.; Elmsford, NY
Amylin Pharmaceuticals, Inc.; San Diego, CA
Angie's List Inc.; Indianapolis, IN
Aon Hewitt; Lincolnshire, IL
Apextalk Holdings, Inc.; San Francisco, CA
appssavvy; New York, NY
Arbor Masters Tree Service; Shawnee, KS
Arcadia All-Florida Championship Rodeo; Arcadia, FL
Arctic Freeze Discount Auto & Truck Repair; Largo, FL
Arena Pharmaceuticals, Inc.; San Diego, CA
The Armed Forces Military Museum; Largo, FL
Armored AutoGroup Inc.; Danbury, CT
AS America, Inc.; Piscataway, NJ

B

Bank of Commerce Holdings; Redding, CA
BDP International Inc.; Philadelphia, PA
Bio-Path Holdings, Inc.; Ogden, UT
BizBash Media Inc.; New York, NY
Black Diamond, Inc.; Salt Lake City, UT
Blue Cross & Blue Shield of Florida, Inc.; Jacksonville, FL
Blue Cross & Blue Shield of Michigan; Detroit, MI
Blue Earth, Inc.; Henderson, NV
Boingo Wireless, Inc.; Los Angeles, CA
Bradenton Motorsports Park; Bradenton, FL
Broadview University; West Jordan, UT
Butte Humane Society; Chico, CA

C

Cambium Learning Group, Inc.; Dallas, TX
Cameron Hughes Wine; San Francisco, CA
Capstone Therapeutics Corp.; Tempe, AZ
Care One Management, LLC; Fort Lee, NJ
Catchwind; Des Moines, IA
CBOE Holdings, Inc.; Chicago, IL
CBS Corporation; New York, NY
Central DuPage Health, Inc.; Winfield, IL
Chicopee Inc.; Charlotte, NC
Children's Hospital Los Angeles; Los Angeles, CA
Cimetrix Incorporated; Salt Lake City, UT
Cincinnati Hills Christian Academy; Cincinnati, OH
CitiFinancial Credit Company; Baltimore, MD
Citizens Community Bancorp, Inc.; Eau Claire, WI
The Civic Garden Center of Greater Cincinnati; Cincinnati, OH
Cleveland Clinic; Cleveland, OH
Clyde Companies Inc.; Orem, UT
The Coca-Cola Bottling Co. of New York, Inc.; Hawthorne, NY
Coca-Cola Enterprises Lakeshore Division; Niles, IL
Compass Group Diversified Holdings LLC; Westport, CT
Continuity Control; New Haven, CT
Core Blood America Inc.; Las Vegas, NV
The Corporate Executive Board Company; Arlington, VA
Crystal Cleaning by Lavina, Inc.; Largo, FL
Custom Culinary, Inc.; Oak Brook, IL

D

Dialogic Inc.; San Jose, CA
Digital Development Partners, Inc.; City of Industry, CA
Dragonfly Garden; Dunedin, FL
DynaVox Inc.; Pittsburgh, PA

E

Eagle Bancorp Montana, Inc.; Helena, MT
Eastside Powersports; Batavia, OH
EasyTurf; Escondido, CA
Ecotality, Inc.; San Francisco, CA
Eddie Bauer, Inc.; Bellevue, WA
EmblemHealth Inc.; New York, NY
The Empire Sports & Entertainment Holdings Co.; New York, NY
Encore Capital Group, Inc.; San Diego, CA
Energy Services of America Corporation; Huntington, WV
Epic Marketplace; New York, NY
Equinix, Inc.; Redwood City, CA
EverBank Financial Corp.; Jacksonville, FL
Exit Realty Central; Norfolk, VA
Express, Inc.; Columbus, OH
EZ Lube Inc.; Santa Ana, CA

F

Faces without Places; Cincinnati, OH
Family Sports Concepts, Inc.; Tampa, FL
Farrey's Wholesale Hardware Co., Inc.; Miami, FL
Federal Express Corporation; Memphis, TN
First Guaranty Bancshares, Inc.; Hammond, LA
First Surgical Partners Inc.; Bellaire, TX
Florida Crystal Corporation; West Palm Beach, FL
Flowers Today, Inc.; Haymarket, VA
FourSquare Labs, Inc.; New York, NY
Freedom Rings Document Preparation Services; Sarasota, FL
FreightGuru; Charlotte, NC
Fresh & Easy Neighborhood Market Inc.; El Segundo, CA

G

GE Capital; Norwalk, CT
General Cannabis, Inc.; Costa Mesa, CA
General Finance Corporation; Pasadena, CA
Gerber Products Company; Florham Park, NJ
Gila River Gaming Enterprises, Inc.; Chandler, AZ
Global Condiments, Inc.; State College, PA
Global Wireless Data, LLC; Norcross, GA
Great American Group, Inc.; Woodland Hills, CA

NEW LISTINGS

Green Endeavors, Inc.; Salt Lake City, UT
Greene County Bancorp, Inc.; Catskill, NY
Greenhouse Holdings, Inc.; San Diego, CA
Groupon Inc.; Chicago, IL

H

HBG Books, Inc.; New York, NY
Health Management Associates, Inc.; Naples, FL
HealthSpring, Inc.; Franklin, TN
Hewitt Associates; Chicago, IL
Hire Heroes USA; Alpharetta, GA
Home Care Industries Inc.; Clifton, NJ
Homeland Security Capital Corporation; Arlington, VA

I

i2SMS; Atlanta, GA
IGA Worldwide; New York, NY
iLoop Mobile, Inc.; San Jose, CA
Imobilis, Inc.; Beverly Hills, CA
Imperial Holdings, Inc.; Boca Raton, FL
Internet Media Services, Inc.; Santa Monica, CA
ITC Holdings Corp.; Novi, MI
Iveda Solutions, Inc.; Mesa, AZ
IVT Software, Inc.; Pittsburgh, PA

J

J.R. Simplot Company; Boise, ID
JAN Wireless LLC; Largo, FL
Jessup's Appliances; Venice, FL
John Agnelli Construction; Holmes Beach, FL
The Joy FM; Sarasota, FL
justflowers.com; Los Angeles, CA

K

Klout, Inc.; San Francisco, CA
Kon Tiki at Tahitian Inn; Tampa, FL
Kraft Foods Gevalia; Dover, DE

L

Lancaster Fine Foods, Inc.; Lancaster, PA
Laura Damiano Designs; White Plains, NY
Lavi Industries Inc.; Valencia, CA
LegalZoom.com, Inc.; Los Angeles, CA
Lenco Mobile Inc.; Santa Barbara, CA
Lenovo Group Ltd.; Morrisville, NC
Lighting Science Group Corporation; Satellite Beach, FL
Limoneira Company; Santa Paula, CA
LipoScience, Inc.; Raleigh, NC
LivingSocial, Inc.; Washington, DC
Lock-Man Locksmiths; Pinellas Park, FL
Long Grove Business & Community Partners; Long Grove, IL
LRAD Corporation; San Diego, CA
Lucasfilm, Ltd.; San Francisco, CA
Luminex Corporation; Austin, TX
LYFE Communications, Inc.; South Jordan, UT

M

Magid Glove Safety Manufacturing Co. LLC; Chicago, IL
MainStreet BankShares, Inc.; Martinsville, VA
Master Silicon Carbide Industries, Inc.; Lakeville, CT
mBlox Inc.; Sunnyvale, CA
McClatchy Interactive; Valley, NC
Mediacom LLC; Middletown, NY
Medio Systems Inc.; Seattle, WA
Medquist Holdings Inc.; Franklin, TN
Mike Kashtan's Superior Auto Sales; Pinellas Park, FL
Minden Bancorp, Inc.; Minden, LA
Minnesota Power; Duluth, MN
MK Automotive, Inc.; Las Vegas, NV
MMRGlobal, Inc.; Los Angeles, CA
Mobile Content Networks Inc.; San Mateo, CA
Morris Publishing Group, LLC; Augusta, GA
Motor Trend Auto Shows, LLC; Harrisburg, PA
Motorola Mobility Holdings, Inc.; Libertyville, IL
Mountain National Bancshares, Inc.; Sevierville, TN
MSB Financial Corp.; Millington, NJ

N

National Penn Bank; Boyertown, PA
NBTY, Inc.; Ronkonkoma, NY
Nektar Therapeutics; San Francisco, CA
Netspend Holdings, Inc.; Austin, TX
NeurogesX, Inc.; San Carlos, CA
The Nielsen Company B.V.; New York, NY
North American Breweries, Inc.; Rochester, NY
NYDJ Apparel, LLC; Vernon, CA

O

Ocean State Heating & Air; Neptune Beach, FL
OceanFirst Bank; Toms River, NJ
OpenX Technologies, Inc.; Pasadena, CA
Options Media Group Holdings, Inc.; Boca Raton, FL
Oragenics, Inc.; Tampa, FL
Orion Marine Group, Inc.; Houston, TX
Orthovita, Inc.; Malvern, PA
OtterBox Products LLC; Fort Collins, CO

P

P&F USA; Atlanta, GA
Pacira Pharmaceuticals, Inc.; Parsippany, NJ
Pamlico Packing Company Incorporated; Grantsboro, NC
Pandora Media Inc.; Oakland, CA
Papa Murphy's International, LLC; Vancouver, WA
The Pasta House Co.; Saint Louis, MO
Peak Resorts, Inc.; Wildwood, MO
Pearson Education; Upper Saddle River, NJ
People's Federal Bancshares, Inc.; Brighton, MA
Pet Airways, Inc.; Delray Beach, FL
The Pictsweet Company; Bells, TN
Pinnacle Financial Partners, Inc.; Nashville, TN
Piper Jaffray Companies; Minneapolis, MN
Polymer Group, Inc.; Charlotte, NC

Premiere Global Services, Inc.; Atlanta, GA
Protext Mobility, Inc.; Syosset, NY
Puritan's Pride, Inc.; Bohemia, NY

Q

Q Lotus Holdings, Inc.; Miami, FL
Quality Services for the Autism Community; New York, NY
Quicken Loans, Inc.; Detroit, MI
Quidsi, Inc.; Jersey City, NJ
QuinStreet, Inc.; Foster City, CA

R

Regeneron Pharmaceuticals, Inc.; Tarrytown, NY
Relativity Media, LLC; West Hollywood, CA
Rexall Sundown, Inc.; Boca Raton, FL
Rise n' Shine; Seattle, WA
RM&L Lucky Enterprises Inc.; Bastrop, LA
Rue La La; Boston, MA
Russell Hobbs, Inc.; Miramar, FL
Ruud Lighting, Inc.; Racine, WI
Rydex Distributors, LLC; Rockville, MD

S

Safelite Solutions LLC; Columbus, OH
Safeway Insurance Company; Westmont, IL
Sagent Holding Co.; Schaumburg, IL
Salamander Innisbrook, LLC; Palm Harbor, FL
Salary.com, Inc.; Needham, MA
Sandella's Flatbread Cafe; West Redding, CT
Sanders Morris Harris Group, Inc.; Houston, TX
San's Pizzeria; Palm Harbor, FL
Sarasota County Health Department; Sarasota, FL
Seacor Holdings Inc.; Fort Lauderdale, FL
Security National Financial Corporation; Salt Lake City, UT
Server Products Inc.; Richfield, WI
Shoreline Image Works LLC; Tarpon Springs, FL
Simulations Plus, Inc.; Lancaster, CA
Smaato Inc.; Redwood Shores, CA
Smart Online, Inc.; Durham, NC
Smart USA Distributor LLC; Bloomfield Hills, MI
Smashburger Master LLC; Denver, CO
Snap-on Tools; Kenosha, WI
So Act Network, Inc.; Houston, TX
Solutions Office Interiors, Inc.; San Jose, CA
Sonic Industries, Inc.; Oklahoma City, OK
Sono-Tek Corporation; Milton, NY
Southern Missouri Bancorp, Inc.; Poplar Bluff, MO
Southside Bancshares Inc.; Tyler, TX
Specialty Screen & Glass LLC; Cincinnati, OH
Spectrum Brands Holdings, Inc.; Madison, WI
Spencer Reed Group Inc.; Shawnee Mission, KS
SPS Commerce, Inc.; Minneapolis, MN
Standard Financial Corp.; Monroeville, PA
Strategic Tax Solutions; Fargo, ND
Sun Communities, Inc.; Southfield, MI
Sunvalley Solar, Inc.; Walnut, CA
Supportsave Solutions, Inc.; Studio City, CA
Swisher Hygiene Inc.; Charlotte, NC

T

Tampa Mitsubishi; Tampa, FL
Tesla Motors, Inc.; Palo Alto, CA
TH Foods Inc.; Loves Park, IL
TMX Finance LLC; Savannah, GA
Tops Holding Corporation; Williamsville, NY
Trustwave Holdings, Inc.; Chicago, IL
Twitter Inc.; San Francisco, CA

U

Ultimate Jetcharters, Inc.; Canton, OH
Unilife Corporation; Lewisberry, PA
United Dominion Realty L.P.; Highlands Ranch, CO
United States Oil & Gas Corporation; Austin, TX
United Through Reading; San Diego, CA

V

Valiance Partners, Inc.; Bernardsville, NJ
Valley Business Machines; West Valley City, UT
Veterans In Packaging, Inc.; Springfield, MA
View Systems, Inc.; Baltimore, MD
Vitamin World, Inc.; Holbrook, NY
Vitatech International, Inc.; Tustin, CA

W

Watauga Medical Center; Boone, NC
Webair Internet Development, Inc.; Garden City, NY
Webdigs, Inc.; Minneapolis, MN
Wegener Corporation; Duluth, GA
Welch's International; Concord, MA
Wellmark, Inc.; Des Moines, IA
WES Consulting, Inc.; Atlanta, GA
Western Liberty Bancorp; Las Vegas, NV
WQXR FM; New York, NY

X

XOMA Ltd.; Berkeley, CA
Xzeres Wind Corp.; Wilsonville, OR

Y

Yahoo! Mobile; Sunnyvale, CA
YaSheng Group; Redwood City, CA
YottaMark; Redwood City, CA

Z

Zevotek, Inc.; Stuart, FL
Zoo Entertainment, Inc.; Cincinnati, OH

NUMBER OF COMPANIES BY BUSINESS CLASSIFICATION

Accessories, Jewelry & Watches 233
Apparel I—Women's, Children's & Infants' Wear 232
Apparel II—Men's & Boys' Wear 135
Appliances 141
Architecture, Engineering & Construction 738
Associations, Institutions, Unions, Etc 415
Automobiles & Trucks 286
Automotive Parts & Accessories 303
Aviation & Aerospace 129
Beer, Ale & Soft Drinks 139
Broadcasting, Cable, Film & Video 545
Cleaning Agents 120
Computers & Office Equipment,
Supplies & Services 1483
Cosmetics & Toiletries 257
Cultural & Recreational Entertainment 761
Department Stores & Mail Order Houses 290
Electronics, Radio & Television 746
Fabrics, Yarns & Sewing Notions 104
Farm Equipment & Supplies 107
Financial Services 1225
Flour & Cereals 31
Food Processing & Manufacturing 681
Food Retailers 287
Furniture, Floor Coverings &Decorations 355
Games, Toys, Etc 171
Gasoline & Lubricants 186
Government & State Agencies 231
Hardware 288
Heating & Air Conditioning 148
Hotels, Resorts & Real Estate 453
Housewares 139
Industrial Chemicals 414
Insurance 309
Internet/Online 733
Lighting 101
Machinery & Supplies 1063
Miscellaneous 80
Optical, Photo & Scientific Instruments 427
Paints, Varnishes & Enamels 99
Paper, Packaging & Containers 195
Pet Food, Livestock & Poultry Feed 65
Pharmaceuticals & Health Care Prods 1154
Public Utilities 264
Publishers, Printers, Engravers, Etc 1085
Recreational Vehicles 86
Restaurants 308
Schools & Colleges 105
Seeds, Plants & Fertilizers 105
Shoes 106
Sporting Goods 226
Sweets 116
Tires, Tubes, Rubber Molded Products &
Plastics 202
Tobacco Products & Supplies 37
Travel & Transportation 375
Wines & Liquors 136

INDEX OF ASSOCIATIONS

ADVERTISERS

ADVERTISING CLUB, 989 Ave. of the Americas, 7th Fl., New York, NY 10018, Tel.: 212-533-8080, Fax: 646-792-5081, E-mail: gina@theadvertisingclub.org, Web Site: www.theadvertising club.org, Founded: 1896, Pres. & CEO: Gina Grillo, Dir-Comm: Gayle Taryn, Dir-Programs: Cathryn Weber-Gonyo, Dir-Membership: Joan Reilly, Dir-Bus Devel: Kris Earley, Mgr-Intl Andy Awards: Lucy Truglio, Coord-Intl Andy Awards & Foundation: Patricia Alonzo, Coord-Membership & Programs: Jackie Bessey, Comptroller: Apri Vitale, Membership: 3,800. Mission Statement: To be the catalyst for bringing together and inspiring the advertising, marketing and media communities in New York. Publications: Online Membership Directory (Members Only); The International ANDY Awards Creative DVD (Annually)

ADVERTISING WOMEN OF NEW YORK, 25 W. 45th St., Ste. 403 New York, NY 10036, Tel.: 212-221-7969, Fax: 212-221-8296, Web Site: www.awny.org, E-mail: awny@awny.org, Founded: 1912, Exec. Dir.: Liz Schroeder, Mgr-Membership: Lynn Zaloka, Mgr-Events: Lisa Deutsch, Membership: 1,300. Mission Statement: To provide a forum for personal and professional growth; to serve as a catalyst for the advancement of women in the communications field; to promote and support philanthropic endeavors through the AWNY Foundation. Publications: AWNY Matters Online Edition.

ASSOCIATION OF NATIONAL ADVERTISERS, 708 3rd Ave., 33 Fl., New York, NY 10017-4270, Tel.: 212-697-5950, Fax: 212-687-7310, Web Site: www.ana.net, Pres.& CEO: Bob Liodice, Membership: 400 major corporations that advertise on a national or regional basis. Mission Statement: The ANA is dedicated to helping its members - marketers and advertisers - build their businesses by building their brands. Inherent in this mission is our commitment to be an authoritative, timely resource on brand building issues, promote and preserve a positive business climate for marketers, offering marketing accountability in ROI and exhibit leadership on issues, trends and emerging ideas that are critical to the marketing and advertising industry.

BUSINESS MARKETING ASSOCIATION, 1833 Centre Point Cir., Ste. 123, Naperville, IL 60563, Tel.: 630-544-5054, Fax: 630-544-5055, Web Site: www.marketing.org, E-mail: info@marketing.org, Year Founded: 1922, Exec. Dir.: Patrick Farrey, VP-Membership: Meg Goodman, Membership: 4,000. Mission Statement: BMA helps members improve their ability to manage business-to-business marketing and communications for greater productivity and profitability by providing unique access to information, ideas and the experience of peers. Publications: The Business 2 Business Marketer (Semi-monthly), B2BDirect (Monthly), both online.

CONSUMER HEALTHCARE PRODUCTS ASSOCIATION, 900 19th St., NW, Ste. 700, Washington, D.C. 20006, Tel.: 202-429-9260, Fax: 202-223-6835, Web Site: www.chpa-info.org, Chm.: Paul L. Sturman, Pres. & CEO: Scott Melville, VP-Fin & Ops: Roman Blazauskas Membership: 200. Manufacturers of over-the-counter medicines. Mission Statement: CHPA is committed to promoting the increasingly vital role of over-the-counter medicines and nutritional supplements in America's healthcare system through science, education, and advocacy. The association provides leadership and guidance on regulatory and scientific issues to Congress; state legislatures; and federal, state, and international government agencies. CHPA shares tools and information with partners across the globe to ensure the safe and responsible use of OTC medicines.

AGENCIES

AMERICAN ASSOCIATION OF ADVERTISING AGENCIES, 1065 Ave. of the Americas, 16th Fl., New York, NY 10018, Tel.: 212-682-2500, Fax: 212-682-8391, E-mail: info@aaaa.org, Web Site: www.aaaa.org, Pres. & CEO: Nancy Hill, COO & CFO: Laura J. Bartlett, Exec. V.P.: Michael D. Donahue, 1,120 member offices. Mission Statement: To improve and strengthen the advertising agency business in the U.S.; to work with federal, state and local governments to resist unwise or unfair legislation and regulation; and to be the principal source of information and advice about advertising; to be an advocate of advertising contributions to the economy and society; to represent the agency point of view to advertisers and the media; and to serve our members' needs for information, agency management counsel, professional development and employee benefit programs. Publications: Best practice booklets, industry surveys and bulletins, white papers and position papers, 4A's SmartBrief (daily e-mail newsletter)

THINKLA, 4223 Glencoe Ave., Ste. C-100, Marina del Ray, CA 90292, Tel.: 310-823-7320, Fax: 310-823-7325, Web Site: www.thinkla.org, E-mail: info@thinkla.org, Year Founded: 2006, Exec. Dir.: Susan Franceschini, Membership: 57 corporate, 550 individual. Mission Statement: The goal of thinkLA is to promote and support world class collaboration, innovation and creativity among the marketing, media, entertainment and advertising industries of Los Angeles. As the preeminent nonprofit marketing association, thinkLA serves its constituents through initiatives that leverage members' combined resources to accomplish objectives greater than each could reasonably expect to accomplish on their own.

TRANSWORLD ADVERTISING AGENCY NETWORK, 814 Watertown St., Newton, MA, 02465, Tel.: 617-795-1706, Fax: 419-730-1706, Web Site: www.taan.org, E-mail: peterg@taan.org, Year Founded: 1936, Pres.: Peter Gerritsen, Membership: 52. Mission Statement: TANN adds strength, breadth and reach to the owners and managers of independent marketing communication companies. Strength, through the sharing of management information, systems, and technologies. Breadth, through cooperative utilization of the broad range of talents, skills, and expertise of each member. Reach, through affiliations with local independent agencies around the world. TAAN members gain assistance from one another in all areas of agency operations, growth and development. Publications: Newsletter (Semi-Annually), Agency Expertise Directory (Annually), Comparative Financial Analysis (Annually), Billing & Production Cost Survey (Annually), Employee Benefits Survey (Annually).

WORLDWIDE PARTNERS INC., 100 Spruce St., Ste. 203 Denver, CO 80230, Tel.: 303-577-9760, Fax: 303-577-9766, Web Site: www.worldwidepartners.com, Pres. & CEO: Al Moffatt, Membership: 87 agencies. Mission Statement: Advertising network for independently owned advertising agencies.

MEDIA

AMERICAN BUSINESS MEDIA, 675 3rd Ave., New York, NY 10017, Tel.: 212-661-6360, Fax: 212-370-0736, Web Site: www.americanbusinessmedia.com, E-mail: info@abmmail.com, Pres. & CEO: Gordon T. Hughes II, Membership: 271 member companies. Mission Statement: To enhance the knowledge and best practices of leading media companies that provide quality information for business and professional markets worldwide.

ASSOCIATION FOR RETAIL ENVIRONMENTS (A.R.E.), 4651 Sheridan St., Ste. 470, Hollywood, FL 33021, Tel.: 954-893-7300, Fax: 954-893-7500, Web Site: www.retailenvironments.org, E-mail: are@retailenvironments.org, Pres.: Bob Riley, Membership: 600 manufacturers, jobbers and distributors. Mission Statement: Advance the retail environments industry and the success of our member companies. Publications: Retail Environments magazine (bimonthly).

AUDIT BUREAU OF CIRCULATIONS, 48 W. Seegers Rd., Arlington Heights, IL 60005, Tel.: 224-366-6939, Fax: 224-366-6949, E-mail: service@accessabc.com, Year Founded: 1914, Pres. & Mng. Dir.: Michael J. Lavery, Exec. V.P.-Auditing Svcs.: Michael K. Moran, Sr. V.P.-Mktg. & Sls.: Mark A. Wachowicz, Exec. V.P.-Strategic Plng & Commun. & Gen Mgr.: Neal Lulofs. Membership: 4,000. Mission Statement: ABC is dedicated to being the world's pre-eminent self-regulatory auditing organization, responsible to advertisers, advertising agencies, and the media they use, for the independent verification and dissemination of our members' circulation, readership, and audience information. ABC will conduct audits that represent the industry standard for integrity, objectivity, and accuracy, and will use state-of-the-art techniques to produce and disseminate ABC-audited information. ABC is committed to its tripartite member organization, to anticipating and exceeding the needs of our members, and to providing the audited data that enable them to plan, purchase, and sell media advertising with confidence. Publications: NewsBulletin (Online Monthly). Offices in New York and Toronto.

BPA WORLDWIDE, 100 Beard Sawmill Rd., 6th Fl., Shelton, CT 06484, Tel.: 203-447-2800, Fax: 203-477-2900, E-mail: info@bpaww.com, Web Site: www.bpaww.com, Year Founded: 1931, Membership: 5,000. Mission Statement: A not-for-profit organization since 1931 and founding member of the International Federation of Audit Bureau of Circulations (IFABC), BPA Worldwide is governed by a tripartite board comprised of media owners, advertising agencies and advertisers. Headquartered in Shelton, Connecticut, USA, BPA has the largest membership of any media-auditing organization in the world, spanning more than 30 countries. Worldwide, BPA serves more than 2,600 media properties-including B-to-B publications, consumer magazines, newspapers, web sites, events, e-newsletters, databases, wireless and other advertiser-supported media-as well as more than 2,600 advertiser and agency members. Visit bpaww.com for free access to the latest audit reports, membership information and publishing and advertising industry news. Publications: Online Circulation Reports Library, Business TRAC, Consumer TRAC, Magazine Titles with Digital Distribution.

CABLETELEVISION ADVERTISING BUREAU, 830 Third Ave., 2nd Fl., New York, NY 10022, Tel.: 212-508-1200, Fax: 212-832-3268, Web Site: www.thecab.tv, E-mail: danielled@cabletvadbureau.com Year Founded: 1980, Pres & CEO: Sean Cunningham, Membership: 250. Mission Statement: To assist members in maximizing advertising revenues and promoting the use of cable as an advertising medium nationally, regionally and locally by: Educating and informing advertisers and ad agencies of the value of cable; Being a sales and management resource for MSO headquarters, local systems, interconnects, cable networks, spot representatives and industry suppliers. Maintain a positive profile for cable in consumer, business and advertising press. Publications: Cable TV Facts (Annually), Cable Network Profiles (Annually), Cable Network Promotion Calendar (Semi-Annually), Hispanic Cable Facts (Annually), Cultural Connections (Annually), Race, Relevance & Revenue (Annually).

CATHOLIC PRESS ASSOCIATION, 205 W. Monroe St., Ste. 470, Chicago, IL 60606, Tel.: 312-380-6789, Fax: 312-361-0256, Web Site: www.catholicpress.org , E-mail: twalter@catholicpress.org, Exec. Dir.: Timothy Walter, Membership: 800 Catholic newspapers, magazines and general (book and pamphlet) publishers in the U.S. and Canada. Mission Statement: To provide media data andother information about Catholic national and local newspapers, consumer and business magazines, and book and pamphlet publishers; to improve Catholic publications' content, format and circulation; to provide services to member publishers.

DIRECT MARKETING ASSOCIATION, 1120 Ave. of the Americas, New York, NY 10036-6700, Tel.: 212-768-7277, Fax: 212-302-6714, Web Site: www.the-dma.org, E-mail: membership@the-dma.org, CEO: Lawrence Kimmel, Membership: 4,700 Companies. Mission Statement: The Direct Marketing Association (www.the-dma.org) is the leading global trade association of businesses and nonprofit organizations using and supporting multichannel direct marketing tools and techniques. DMA advocates standards for responsible marketing, promotes relevance as the key to reaching consumers with desirable offers, and provides cutting-edge research, education, and networking opportunities to improve results throughout the end-to-end direct marketing process. Founded in 1917, DMA today represents more than 3,100 companies from dozens of vertical industries in the US and 48 other nations, including half of the Fortune 100 companies, as well as nonprofit organizations.

EXHIBIT DESIGNERS AND PRODUCERS ASSOCIATION, 10 Norden Pl., Norwalk, CT 06855, Tel.: 203-852-5698, Web Site: www.edpa.com, Exec. Dir.: Jeff Provost, Membership: 350. Mission Statement: To provide education, leadership and networking for the advancement of its members and the exhibition industry.

INLAND PRESS ASSOCIATION, 701 Lee St., Ste. 925, Des

Plaines, IL 60018, Tel.: 847-795-0380, Fax: 847-795-0385, Web Site: www.inlandpress.org, E-mail: tslaughter@inlandpress.org, Exec. Dir.: Tom Slaughter, Membership: 1,200 newspapers. Mission Statement: To promote the general interests of newspapers through training, financial, research and other programs and services which assist business and editorial performance.

Publications: Inlander (Monthly).

INTERNATIONAL ASSOCIATION OF BUSINESS COMMUNICATORS, 601 Montgomery St., Ste. 1900, San Francisco, CA 94111, Tel.: 415-544-4700, Web Site: www.iabc.com, Pres.: Julie Freeman, Membership: Over 15,000 worldwide. Mission Statement: To provide links for communicators in a global network that inspires, establishes and supports the highest professional standards of quality and innovation in organizational communication. Publications: Communication World.

INTERNATIONAL RADIO AND TELEVISION SOCIETY FOUNDATION, 420 Lexington Ave., Ste. 1601, New York, NY 10170, Tel.: 212-867-6650, Fax: 212-867-6653, Web Site: www.irts.org, Pres. & CEO: Joyce M. Tudryn, Membership: 900. Mission Statement: To provide an assembly for persons engaged in communication through radio, television and cable, where they can exchange ideas and information affecting their common interest and welfare.

MAILING & FULFILLMENT SERVICE ASSOCIATION, 1421 Prince St., Ste. 410, Alexandria, VA 22314-2806, Tel.: 703-836-9200, Fax: 703-548-8204, Web Site: www.mfsanet.org, E-mail: kloveridge@mfsanet.org, Year Founded: 1920, Pres. & CEO: Ken Garner, Mgr-Commun.: Kimberly Kight, Membership: 700 companies. Mission Statement: MFSA is the national trade association for the mailing and fulfillment services industry. The MFSA is comprised of over 700 mailhouses, lettershops, fulfillment businesses, and direct mail agencies across the United States and in five foreign countries. Publications: Who's Who – The MFSA Blue Ribbon Buyer's Guide to Mailing and Fulfillment Companies, PostScripts Newsletter (Monthly), Postal Points (18 times per year), The Business Owner (Bi-monthly).

NATIONAL ASSOCIATION OF BROADCASTERS, 1771 N St. N.W., Washington, D.C. 20036, Tel.: 202-429-5300, 202-775-3517, Web Site: www.nab.org, E-mail: nab@nab.org, CEO: Gordon Smith, Mission Statement: The National Association of Broadcasters is a trade association for America's broadcasters. NAB advances radio and television interests in legislative, regulatory and public affairs. Through advocacy, education and innovation, NAB enables broadcasters to best serve their communities, strengthen their businesses and seize new opportunities in the digital age. Publications: The NAB Pulse (Weekly), Radio TechCheck (Weekly), TV TechCheck (Weekly)

NATIONAL ASSOCIATION OF FARM BROADCASTERS, P.O. Box 500, Platte City, MO 64079, Tel.: 816-431-4032, Web Site: www.nafb.com, Exec. Dir.: Tom Brand, Operations Mgr.: Susan Tally, Mgr-Member Services: Jennifer Saylor, Membership: 150 voting; 450 associates. Mission Statement: To encourage better relations and understanding between Commercial radio, television and network farm broadcasting entities, farm organizations and governmental agencies working in the field of agriculture, advertising agencies, clients and groups interested in reaching farm people through radio and television; to advance the welfare of those engaged in farm broadcasting through professional improvement, sharing of ideas and techniques and encouraging commercial use of the broadcast media by advertisers.

NATIONAL ASSOCIATION OF PUBLISHERS' REPRESENTATIVES, INC., (NAPR) 1901 N. Roselle Rd., Ste. 920, Schaumburg, IL 60195 , Tel.: 847-885-2410, Fax: 847-885-8393, Web Site: www.napronline.org, E-mail: napr@napronline.com, Contact: Matthew Burnett, Account Manager, Membership: 172. Mission Statement: To support, advise and counsel member publishers' representative companies on working with publishers. To assist publishers in finding a publishers' representative company for their specific advertising needs. Publications: Member Newsletter (Monthly)

NATIONAL CABLE & TELECOMMUNICATIONS ASSOCIATION, 25 Massachusetts Ave., N.W., Ste. 100, Washington, DC 20001, Tel.: 202-222-2300, Web Site: www.ncta.com, Pres. & CEO: Michael Powell, Membership: NCTA member companies serve over 90 percent of cable television subscribers in the United States. Mission Statement: National trade association to provide its members with a strong national presence by providing a single, unified voice on issues affecting the cable and telecommunications industry.

NEWSPAPER ASSOCIATION OF AMERICA, 4401 Wilson Blvd., Ste. 900, Arlington, VA 22203-1867, Tel.: 571-366-1000, Toll-Free: 877-263-9640, Fax: 571-366-1195, E-mail: info@napronline.org, Web Site: www.naa.org, Sr. V.P.-Bus. Dev.: Randy Bennett, Membership: 122, Publications: Presstime; Digital Edge; Big Ideas for Smaller Markets; Foundation Update; Labor & Employment Law Letter; Fusion; Advertising Sales.

OUTDOOR ADVERTISING ASSOCIATION OF AMERICA, INC., 1850 M St., NW, Ste. 1040, Washington, DC 20036, Tel.: 202-833-5566, Fax: 202-833-1522, Web Site: www.oaaa.org, E-mail: info@oaaa.org, Year Founded: 1891, Pres & CEO.: Nancy J. Fletcher, Membership: Over 800, Mission Statement: OAAA is the trade association for the more than 800 outdoor advertising companies that make up more than 90 percent of the industry's revenue. For 120 years, the association has been dedicated to leading and uniting a responsible outdoor advertising industry that is committed to serving the needs of advertisers, consumers, and communities. Outdoor advertising companies generate $6.1 billion annually in ad revenues and donate space to charitable organizations in excess of $400 million each year. For more information, please visit www.oaaa.org.

THE POINT-OF-PURCHASE ADVERTISING INTERNATIONAL, 440 N. Wells St., Ste. 740, Chicago, IL 60654, Tel.: 312-863-2900, Web Site: www.popai.com, Pres: Richard Winter, Membership: 1,700. Mission Statement: POPAI is the global trade association for the marketing at-retail Industry. We are dedicated to serving its more than 1,700 members internationally by promoting, protecting and advancing the broader interests marketing at-retail through research, education, trade forums and legislative efforts on behalf of retailers, brand marketers, ad agencies and those producing marketing at-retail programs.

MPA, THE ASSOCIATION OF MAGAZINE MEDIA, 810 7th Ave., 24th Fl., New York, NY 10019, Tel.: 212-872-3700, Web Site: www.magazine.org, E-mail: mpa@magazine.org, Pres. & CEO: Nina Link, Exec V.P. & Gen. Mgr.: Frank Costello, Membership: 240 publishers of 850 periodicals. Mission Statement: To support and promote the editorial and economic vitality and integrity of MPA member publications; to advocate and litigate on behalf of the industry; to defend the freedom to write and publish under the First Amendment; to be the marketing force to increase the share that magazines capture of advertising dollars and of reader time and money; to be the primary source of information and expertise about the publishing industry for both its members and the community at large.

PROMAX/BDA, 1522E Cloverfield Blvd., Santa Monica, CA 90404, Tel.: 310-788-7600, Fax: 310-788-7616, Web Site: www.promaxbda.org, Gen Mgr: Jill Lindeman, Membership: 5,000 companies & individuals in over 70 countries. Mission Statement: PromaxBDA is the leading resource for education, community, creative inspiration and career development for marketing, promotion and design professionals within the entertainment/information industry. It's the PromaxBDA mission to lead the conversation about the role that marketing, promotion and design play in the monetization of media across content platforms. Publications: PROMAX BDA (Annually), directory (Annually) and PromoOnline (Weekly).

PROMOTION MARKETING ASSOCIATION INC., 650 First Avenue, Ste. 2SW, New York, NY 10016, Tel.: 212-420-1100, Fax: 212-533-7622, Web Site: www.pmalink.org, E-mail: pma@pmalink.org, Pres.: Bonnie J. Carlson, Chief Legal Officer: Ed Kabak, Chief Fin. Officer: Lana Mavreshko, V.P.-Membership: Dave Wallace, V.P.-Mktg: Kathleen Mulcahy, Membership: 400. Established in 1911, the Promotion Marketing Association, Inc. (PMA) is the premier not-for-profit organization and resource for research, education and collaboration for marketing professionals. Representing the $1 trillion promotion and integrated marketing industry, the organization is comprised of a majority of Fortune 500 companies, top marketing agencies, law firms, retailers, service suppliers and academia, representing thousands of brands worldwide. Championing the highest standards of excellence and recognition in the promotion and integrated marketing industry globally, PMA's objective is to foster a better understanding of promotion and integrated marketing and its role in the overall marketing process. The PMA and its affiliate the PMA Educational Foundation are headquartered in New York City. Publications: Newsletters, Law Bulletins, Reggie Video, Books, White Papers, Research Reports.

RADIO ADVERTISING BUREAU, INC., 125 W 55 St, Fl. 21, New York, NY 10019, Tel.: 212-681-7200, 800-252-7234 (Member Services); Fax: 212-681-7223, Web Site: www.rab.com, Pres & CEO.: Jeff Haley, Sr. V.P-Mktg & Commun.: Leah Kamon, Membership: 7,000. Mission Statement: The Radio Advertising Bureau is the sales and marketing arm of the radio industry, providing advertisers and agencies with research, information, and outreach programs that support their ability to best utilize radio in the media mix. With more than 6,000 member radio stations in the U.S, and over 1,000 additional members in networks, representative firms, sales, and international organizations, RAB is dedicated to designing, developing and implementing solutions-based programs, research, tools, and activities for its radio members, advertisers and agencies. Publications: Radio Marketing Guide & Fact Book for Advertisers (Online), RAB Co-op Directory (Online), RAB Instant Backgrounds (Online).

SOUTHERN NEWSPAPER PUBLISHERS ASSOCIATION, 3680 N. Peachtree Rd., Ste. 300, Atlanta, GA 30341, Tel.: 404-256-0444, Web Site: www.snpa.org, Exec. Dir.: Edward VanHorn, Membership: More than 400 daily & non-daily newspapers. Mission Statement: A trade association that serves as a clearing house for information and educational programming related to news publishing - in print and in electronic mediums.

TELEVISION BUREAU OF ADVERTISING, INC., 3 E. 54th St., 10th Fl., New York, NY 10022, Tel.: 212-486-1111, Web Site: www.tvb.org, Pres.: Steve Lanzano, Membership: 500 local television broadcast stations, broadcast groups, rep firms and broadcast syndicators. Associate Memberships are available to organizations that service regular members. Mission Statement: TVB represents local television broadcast stations to the advertising community. Its goal is to maintain and/or increase dollars to U.S. spot television.

YELLOW PAGES ASSOCIATION, (d/b/a Local Search Association) 400 Connell Drive, Ste. 1100, Berkeley Heights, NJ 07922-2747, Tel.: 908-286-2381, Fax: 908-286-0620, Web Site: www.ypassociation.org, Pres.: Negley Norton, Membership: 400. Mission Statement: Originally founded in 1975 as the National Yellow Pages Service Association (NYPSA), the Yellow Pages Association (SM) is the trade organization of a print and electronic media industry valued at more than $25 billion worldwide ($14 billion U.S.). Association members include Yellow Pages publishers, who produce leading-edge electronic products and deliver Yellow Pages directories to 100 percent of U.S. homes with telephones - and who account for almost 95 percent of Yellow Pages revenue generated in the U.S. and Canada. Members also include the industry's international, national and local sales forces, certified marketing representatives (CMRs) and associate members, a group of industry stakeholders such as Yellow Pages advertisers, vendors and suppliers to the industry. The Association has members in more than 21 countries. Publications: ELINC Newsletter.

PUBLIC RELATIONS

PUBLIC RELATIONS SOCIETY OF AMERICA, INC., 33 Maiden Ln., 11th Fl, New York, NY 10038-5150, Tel.: 212-460-1400, Fax: 212-995-0757, Web Site: www.prsa.org, E-mail: info@prsa.org, Year Founded: 1947, Pres. & COO: William Murray, Chair & CEO: Michael Cherenson, Membership: 32,000 professional and student members. Mission Statement: PRSA is the largest professional organization serving the U.S. public relations community. With a mission to "advance the profession and the professional," PRSA provides news and information, thought leadership, continuing education and networking opportunities; sets standards of professional excellence and ethical conduct; and advocates for the business value of public relations and greater diversity among public relations professionals. Based in New York, PRSA comprises 112 local Chapters; 14 Professional Interest Sections that focus on specific industries and practice areas; and the Public Relations Student Society of America (PRSSA), which is active at more than 320 colleges and universities. Publications: Public Relations Tactics newspaper (monthly); The Public Relations Strategist (quarterly); Issues & Trends eNewsletter (daily); PRSSA FORUM (monthly); Public Relations Journal (quarterly); PRSAY and ComPRehension blogs.

RESEARCH

ADVERTISING RESEARCH FOUNDATION, 432 Park Ave. S., New York, NY 10022, Tel.: 212-751-5656, Fax: 212-319-5265, Web Site: www.thearf.org, E-mail: info@thearf.org, Year Founded: 1936, Employees: 25, Pres. & CEO: Robert Barocci, Chief Strategy Officer: Taddy Hall. Mission Statement: The ARF is the preeminent professional organization in the field of advertising, market and media research. Our combined membership represents more than 400 advertisers, advertising agencies, research firms, media companies, educational institutions and international organizations. Dedicated to a role of industry leadership, ARF advocates the importance of cooperation and communication within the industry by joining forces with other associations, both nationally and internationally, to launch important new initiatives. Because the hundreds of member-company volunteers who are regularly active in ARF represent some of the industry's foremost research professionals, ARF is able to undertake research projects of a size and scope that no single company could initiate because of financial and/or technical limitations. In the past decade alone, ARF has completed key research achievements which represent more than $4 million worth of primary research. Publications: Journal of Advertising Research, ARF Webcasts. Events: Think Annual Convention & Expo, Ogilvy Awards, Audience Measurement Conference.

TRADE ASSOCIATIONS

THE ADVERTISING COUNCIL, INC., 815 2nd Ave., 9th Fl., New York, NY 10017, Tel.: 212-922-1500, Fax: 212-922-1676, Web Site: www.adcouncil.org, E-mail: info@adcouncil.org, Year Founded: 1942, Pres. & CEO: Peggy Conlon, CFO & Exec. V.P.: Jon Fish, V.P.-PR & Social Media: Ellyn Fisher, Mission Statement: To identify a select number of significant public issues and stimulate action on those issues through communications programs that make a measurable difference in our society. Publications: The Public Service Advertising Catalog (Quarterly).

AMERICAN ADVERTISING FEDERATION, 1101 Vermont Ave. N.W., Ste. 500, Washington, D.C. 20005, Tel.: 202-898-0089, Fax: 202-898-0159, Web Site: www.aaf.org, E-mail: aaf@aaf.org, Year Founded: 1967, Pres. & CEO: James E. Datri, COO: Constance Frazier, Exec V.P.: Joanne Schecter, Membership: 40,000. Mission Statement: The AAF is the unifying voice for advertising. We are advocates for the rights of advertisers. We educate policy makers, the news media and the general public on the value that advertising brings to the well-being of the nation, and develop the industry's present and future leaders. We accomplish this through a unique, nationally coordinated grassroots network of advertisers, advertising agencies, media companies, local advertising associations and college chapters. Headquartered in Washington, DC, the AAF serves 40,000 members nationwide in 130 corporations, 200 local professional advertising federations and 225 college chapters.

AMERICAN MARKETING ASSOCIATION/CHICAGO, 311 S. Wacker Dr., Ste. 5800, Chicago, IL 60606-2266, Tel.: 312-542-9000 & 800-AMA-1150, Fax: 312-542-9001, Web Site: www.marketingpower.com, E-mail: info@ama.org, Year Founded: 1937 CEO: Dennis L. Dunlap, CMO: Nancy Costopulos, CFO: Beth Taylor, CTO: Bob Panger, Membership: Over 20,000 Professional members and 10,000 Collegiate members. Mission Statement: The American Marketing Association is the largest marketing association in North America. It is a professional association for individuals involved in the practice, teaching and study of marketing worldwide. Through relevant information, comprehensive education and targeted networking, the AMA assists marketers in deepening their marketing expertise, elevating their careers and ultimately, achieving better results. The American Marketing Association's website, MarketingPower.com, is the everyday connection to marketing data, articles, case studies, best practices and a robust job bank. Additionally, the American Marketing Association is the source of the field's top magazines and journals, including Marketing News, the AMA's flagship publication. Through local and collegiate chapters, American Marketing Association members are connected with the best people and the best practices. For more information on the American Marketing Association please visit www.marketingpower.com. Publications: Marketing News (16 issues); Marketing Management (6 issues); Marketing Research (quarterly); Marketing Health Services (quarterly); The Journal of Marketing (6 issues); Journal of Marketing Research (6 issues); Journal of International Marketing (quarterly); Journal of Public Policy & Marketing (semi-annual)

BETTER BUSINESS BUREAU OF METRO WASHINGTON D.C., 1411 K St., N.W., Ste. 1000, Washington, DC 20005-3404, Tel.: 202-393-8000, Fax: 202-393-1198, E-mail: info@mybbb.org, Web Site: www.mybbb.org, Pres. & CEO: Edward J. Johnson III, Membership: 11,000. Mission Statement: To promote and foster the highest ethical relationship between business and the public through voluntary self-regulation, consumer and business education, and service excellence. Programs include: consumer information-education, company rating reports, complaint filing, philanthropic advisory service, governmental affairs, media relations, advertising review, arbitration, company accreditation.

INTERNATIONAL ADVERTISING ASSOCIATION, 275 Madison Ave., Ste. 2102, New York, NY 10016, Tel.: 212-557-1133, Fax: 212-983-0455, Web Site: www.iaaglobal.org, E-mail: iaa@iaaglobal.org, Year Founded: 1938, Chm. & World Pres: Alan

Rutherford, World Treas: Sanford J. Kornberg, Membership: 4,000. Mission Statement: The International Advertising Association is the one global organization committed to fight unwarranted regulation on behalf of all enterprises engaged in responsible commercial communications and to act as an advocate for freedom of choice across all consumer and business markets. This requires rigorous and continuing programs. Should the freedoms be curtailed, it could create economic hardship by: depriving individuals of information useful in deciding how to live; inhibiting competition among companies, thus slowing innovation; eliminating jobs in a variety of industries; reducing the absolute size of investment in marketing communications, thus restricting marketplace growth. The IAA's actions take on added significance when advertising revenues are factored in as the financial source of an independent, pluralistic, affordable media, where competing channels of information ensure that individuals have choices, the kinetic energy of a free market society.

NATIONAL RETAIL FEDERATION, 325 7th St., N.W., Ste. 1100, Washington, D.C. 20004, Tel.: 202-783-7971, Web Site: www.nrf.com, Pres. & CEO: Matthew Shay, Membership: NRF's global membership includes retailers of all sizes, formats and channels of distribution as well as chain restaurants and industry partners from the United States and more than 45 countries abroad. Mission Statement: NRF's mission is to advance the interests of the retail industry through advocacy, communications and education. NRF represents an industry that includes more than 3.6 million establishments and which directly and indirectly accounts for 42 million jobs – one in four U.S. jobs. The total U.S. GDP impact of retail is $2.5 trillion annually, and retail is a daily barometer of the health of the nation's economy. Publications: STORES Magazine, NRF SmartBrief, Shop.org SmartBrief, and NRF Global SmartBrief

PROMOTIONAL PRODUCTS ASSOCIATION INTERNATIONAL, 3125 Skyway Circle N., Irving, TX 75038-3526, Tel.: 972-252-0404 Web Site: www.ppai.org, Pres. & CEO: Paul Bellantone, Membership: Specialty advertising, distributors and suppliers. Mission Statement: PPAI is a member-driven organization devoted to meeting the needs of its members and the market. The Association is committed to leading the industry, expanding the market, establishing standards and guidelines, and enhancing professionalism and our customers' success. Publications: Promotional Products Business.

RETAIL CONFECTIONERS INTERNATIONAL, 2053 S. Waverly, Ste. C, Springfield, MO 65804, Tel.: 417-883-2775, Fax: 417-883-1108, Web Site: www.retailconfectioners.org, Exec. Dir: Kelly Brinkmann, Membership: 550. Representing manufacturing retail confectioners who make and sell their own boxed chocolates through directly owned retail shops. Mission Statement: To advance the art and science of retail candy-making through a continuing educational program; to organize and present annually in conjunction with the association convention an educational exposition of products and services; to exchange ideas in merchandising, packaging, production and advertising; to keep members informed on supply of all raw material ingredients and to guard against discriminatory federal, state and city legislation. Publications: Kettle Talk (Quarterly). Also publishes annually in June, in conjunction with the annual convention, a Convention Program and Buyer's Guide Book, which accepts display advertising.

SALES & MARKETING EXECUTIVES-INTERNATIONAL, P.O. Box 1390, Sumas, WA 98295-1390, Tel.: 312-893-0751, Web Site: www.smei.org, Chm.: Jeff Fawcett, Pres.& CEO: Willis Turner, Membership: 10,000 in 96 sales executive clubs throughout the world. Mission Statement: The organization supports the improvement of standards for professional selling, sales management and marketing, in order to establish sales and marketing as a recognized profession.

ABBREVIATIONS

GENERAL TERMS

Acct	Account	Matl	Material
Acctg	Accounting	Matls	Materials
Accts	Accounts	Mdse	Merchandise
Acq	Acquisition(s)	Mdsg	Merchandising
Admin	Administration/Administrative	Mfg	Manufacturing
Adv	Advertising	Mfr	Manufacturer
Assoc	Associate	Mgmt	Management
Asst	Assistant	Mgr	Manager
Brdcst	Broadcast	Mktg	Marketing
Bus	Business	Mng	Managing
CEO	Chief Executive Officer	Natl	National
CFO	Chief Financial Officer	Ops	Operations
Chm	Chairman of the Board	Org	Organization
CIO	Chief Information Officer	Pkg	Packaging
CMO	Chief Marketing Officer	Plng	Planning
Comm	Communication(s)	PR	Public Relations
Comml	Commercial	Pres	President
COO	Chief Operating Officer	Pro	Professional
Coord	Coordinator	Promo	Promotion
Corp	Corporate/Corporation	Promos	Promotions
CTO	Chief Technology Officer	Pub	Public
Dept	Department	Publ	Publishing
Dev	Development	Publr	Publisher
Dir	Director	Pur	Purchasing
Distr	Distribution	R&D	Research & Development
Div	Division	Reg	Regional
DP	Data Processing	Rep	Representative
Engr	Engineer	Res	Research
Engrg	Engineering	Sec	Secretary
Environ	Environmental	Sls	Sales
Exec	Executive	Sr	Senior
Fin	Finance/Financial	Supvr	Supervisor
Gen	General	Svc	Service
Govt	Government	Svcs	Services
Grp	Group	Sys	Systems
HR	Human Resources	Tech	Technology
Indus	Industry/Industrial	Telecom	Telecommunication(s)
Info	Information	Treas	Treasurer
Intl	International	Trng	Training
IR	Investor Relations	Vice Chm	Vice Chairman
IT	Information Technology	VP	Vice President
Jr	Junior		

INDEX OF COMPANIES

C

D

E

F

G

H

I

J

K

M

N

O

P

Power Creative
11701 Commonwealth Dr
Louisville, KY 40299-2358
Tel.: (502) 267-0772
Fax: (502) 267-1727

S

T

U

V

W

X

Y

Z

COMPANIES THAT HAVE HOUSE AGENCIES

A

ALAN GORDON ENTERPRISES, INC., pg. 1587
ALIMED, INC., pg. 1695
ALLETE, INC., pg. 1836
AMERICAN SCHOOL OF CORRESPONDENCE, pg. 2027
AMERICAN SLIDE-CHART CORPORATION, pg. 375
ANDIS COMPANY, pg. 553
ANGELS BASEBALL, L.P., pg. 584
ANHEUSER-BUSCH COMPANIES, INC., pg. 272
A.O. SMITH CORPORATION, pg. 1469
ARIZONA DIAMONDBACKS, pg. 585
ATLANTA CONVENTION & VISITORS BUREAU, pg. 1149
ATLANTA NATIONAL LEAGUE BASEBALL CLUB, INC., pg. 586

B

BALTIMORE ORIOLES, L.P., pg. 588
BANFI VINTNERS, pg. 2178
THE BASEBALL CLUB OF SEATTLE, L.P., pg. 588
BEHLEN MFG. CO., pg. 798
BIG O TIRES, INC., pg. 227
BINSWANGER CORPORATION, pg. 1230
BOSTON RED SOX BASEBALL CLUB LIMITED PARTNERSHIP, pg. 590
BOYD GAMING CORPORATION, pg. 1230
THE BRADFORD GROUP, pg. 663
BROWN-FORMAN BEVERAGES, pg. 2179
BROWN-FORMAN CORPORATION, pg. 2179
BWHC LLC, pg. 1980

C

CALVIN KLEIN, INC., pg. 24
CAMERON DRILLING & PRODUCTION SYSTEMS, pg. 1480
CARROLS CORPORATION, pg. 1996
CAVENDER'S, pg. 45
CHICAGO NATIONAL LEAGUE BALL CLUB, LLC, pg. 595
CHICAGO WHITE SOX LTD., pg. 596
CHRISTIANSON SYSTEMS, INC., pg. 1483
CINCINNATI SYMPHONY ORCHESTRA, pg. 597
CLEVELAND INDIANS BASEBALL COMPANY, INC., pg. 597
COLLECTOR'S ARMOURY LTD., pg. 1105
COLORADO ROCKIES BASEBALL CLUB, LTD., pg. 598
COLUMBIA UNIVERSITY PRESS, pg. 1890
COMBE INCORPORATED, pg. 1724
COPPER-BRITE, INC., pg. 349
CORNELL UNIVERSITY PRESS, pg. 1892

D

DANBURY MINT, pg. 667
DELTA FOREMOST CHEMICAL CORPORATION, pg. 1303
DETROIT TIGERS BASEBALL CLUB, INC., pg. 602
DOREL JUVENILE GROUP, INC., pg. 1069

E

EDELBROCK CORPORATION, pg. 233
EL PASO CORPORATION, pg. 1847

F

F. KORBEL BROS. INC., pg. 2182
FLORIDA MARLINS, L.P., pg. 606
FREDERICK FELL PUBLISHERS, INC., pg. 1907
FREIXENET U.S.A., pg. 2182

G

GAME SHOW PLACEMENTS LTD., pg. 607
GLOUCESTER ENGINEERING, CO., pg. 1507

H

HABAND COMPANY, INC., pg. 672
HAIR CLUB FOR MEN, LTD., INC., pg. 565
HARRIS HOLDINGS INC., pg. 1511
HASSELBLAD USA, INC., pg. 1608
HILCO INDUSTRIAL, LLC, pg. 874
HOUSE OF WESLEY, INC., pg. 674
HOUSTON ASTROS BASEBALL CLUB, pg. 610
HUNTER ENGINEERING COMPANY, pg. 238

I

INDUSTRIAL ACOUSTICS COMPANY, INC., pg. 106
INFOGROUP INC., pg. 1918
INTER-STATE NURSERIES, INC., pg. 2042
INVENTHELP, pg. 453

J

JAZZ BASKETBALL INVESTORS, INC., pg. 613
JERVIS B. WEBB COMPANY, pg. 1520
J.L. TODD AUCTION CO., pg. 675
JOHNSON SMITH COMPANY, pg. 675
JOLEN CREME BLEACH CORP., pg. 568
JOMIRA/ADVANCE, pg. 1921
JORDACHE ENTERPRISES, INC., pg. 32
JOSEPH ENTERPRISES, INC., pg. 1114

K

KANSAS CITY ROYALS BASEBALL CORPORATION, pg. 614
KRACO ENTERPRISES, LLC, pg. 241
KRAFT FOODS INC., pg. 986
KREMENTZ & COMPANY, pg. 10

L

LARRY H. MILLER GROUP OF COMPANIES, pg. 209
LAWN DOCTOR INC., pg. 2043
LEANIN' TREE, INC., pg. 1924
LEE PHARMACEUTICALS, pg. 1769
LEGGETT & PLATT, INCORPORATED, pg. 1082
LITTLE, BROWN & COMPANY, pg. 1926
LOS ANGELES DODGERS INC., pg. 617

M

MAACO FRANCHISING, INC., pg. 242
MAYER/BERKSHIRE CORPORATION, pg. 35
MAYFRAN INTERNATIONAL, INC., pg. 1530
MBI INC., pg. 678
MGM RESORTS INTERNATIONAL, pg. 1254
MILLER-STEPHENSON CHEMICAL COMPANY, INC., pg. 1322
MILWAUKEE BREWERS BASEBALL CLUB, INC., pg. 621
MINNESOTA POWER, pg. 1854
MINNESOTA TWINS, LLC, pg. 622
MUELLER SPORTS MEDICINE, INC., pg. 1786

N

NATIONAL BULK EQUIPMENT, INC., pg. 1684
NATIONAL HOT ROD ASSOCIATION, pg. 180
NEIMAN MARCUS STORES, pg. 679
NEW YORK YANKEES, pg. 629

O

OAKLAND ATHLETICS LIMITED PARTNERSHIP, pg. 630
OLD FASHION FOODS, INC., pg. 1042
OLD NAVY, pg. 52
OMAHA STEAKS INTERNATIONAL, INC., pg. 680

P

PACIFIC HANDY CUTTER, INC., pg. 125
PADRES L.P., pg. 632
PEAVEY ELECTRONICS CORPORATION, pg. 752
PENN FOSTER EDUCATION GROUP, INC., pg. 2034
THE PHILLIES, L.P., pg. 635
PITTSBURGH BASEBALL, INC., pg. 636
POGGENPOHL U.S., INC., pg. 128
PRINCETON UNIVERSITY PRESS, pg. 1948

R

RANGERS BASEBALL LLC, pg. 638
RAYMOND JAMES FINANCIAL, INC., pg. 910
REDS BASEBALL PARTNERS, LLC, pg. 638
REPLACEMENTS, LTD., pg. 1284
THE ROTARIAN MAGAZINE, pg. 1952
ROTARY INTERNATIONAL, pg. 186

S

SAINT LOUIS CARDINALS, L.P., pg. 640
SAN FRANCISCO GIANTS BASEBALL CLUB, pg. 641
SCHLUMBERGER LIMITED, pg. 915
SERFILCO, LTD., pg. 1554
SERVICE CORPORATION INTERNATIONAL, pg. 1583
SHOPSMITH, INC., pg. 1555
SMITH-MIDLAND CORPORATION, pg. 137
SOUTHWESTERN INDUSTRIES, INC., pg. 1628
STARBRITE CORP., pg. 361
STAR BUILDING SYSTEMS, pg. 139
STEAMATIC INC., pg. 69
STERLING METS, L.P., pg. 647
SYMS CORPORATION, pg. 55

T

TAMPA BAY RAYS BASEBALL, LTD., pg. 648
TORONTO BLUE JAYS BASEBALL CLUB, pg. 650
TRIBUNE COMPANY, pg. 1970
TUFFY ASSOCIATES CORPORATION, pg. 253
THE TURNER & SEYMOUR MANUFACTURING COMPANY, pg. 1206

U

ULTRA ELECTRONICS OCEAN SYSTEMS INC., pg. 1631
UNIFIED GROCERS, INC., pg. 1051
UNITED STATES ENVIRONMENTAL PROTECTION AGENCY, pg. 1172
UNIVERSAL MOTOWN RECORDS, pg. 336
UNIVERSITY OF PENNSYLVANIA, pg. 2037
U.S. PUMICE COMPANY, pg. 1337

V

VALUE LINE, INC., pg. 1972
VERMONT SKI AREAS ASSOCIATION, INC., pg. 190
VOICE OF PROPHECY, INC., pg. 338

W

WASHINGTON NATIONALS, L.P., pg. 653
WEST END DIVING & SALVAGE, INC., pg. 2099
WHITE'S ELECTRONICS, pg. 780

Y

Accessories, Jewelry & Watches

Belts — Costume Jewelry — Fine Jewelry — Hats — Hosiery — Luggage — Socks — Wallets — Watches

5TO1 HOLDING CORP.
(Formerly TRI-MARK MFG, INC.)
1453 3rd St
Santa Monica, CA 90401
Toll Free: (800) 521-8770
Approx. Sls.: $989,275
Approx. Number Employees: 19
Year Founded: 2006
Business Description:
Jewelry Mfr, Designer & Marketer
S.I.C.: 3911; 5094
N.A.I.C.S.: 339911; 423940
Media: 2-4-5-7-10
Personnel:
James C. Heckman, Jr. *(CEO)*
Mitchell Chun *(CFO)*

AAA UMBRELLA/SATCHEL CO.
230 Pegasus Ave
Northvale, NJ 07647-1904
Tel.: (201) 784-3244
Fax: (201) 784-3242
Toll Free: (800) 426-7446
E-mail: sales@aaaumbrella.com
Web Site: www.aaaumbrella.com
E-Mail For Key Personnel:
Sales Director: sales@aaaumbrella.com
Approx. Number Employees: 80
Year Founded: 1950
Business Description:
Satchel & Umbrella Mfr
S.I.C.: 3999
N.A.I.C.S.: 339999
Import Export
Media: 2-3-4-8-10-11-13-26
Distr.: Natl.
Budget Set: Apr.
Personnel:
Jeffrey Nanus *(Pres)*

AAC GROUP HOLDING CORP.
(Holding of Fenway Partners, Inc.)
(d/b/a American Achievement)
7211 Circle S Rd
Austin, TX 78745
Tel.: (512) 444-0571
Fax: (512) 443-5213
Approx. Sls.: $289,660,000
Approx. Number Employees: 1,507
Business Description:
Holding Company; High School Jewelry & Yearbooks
S.I.C.: 3961; 3911; 6719
N.A.I.C.S.: 339914; 339911; 551112
Advertising Expenditures: $3,900,000
Personnel:
Donald J. Percenti *(Chm)*
Steven Parr *(Pres & CEO)*
Kris G. Radhakrishnan *(CFO & Treas)*
Brands & Products:
ARTCARVED
BALFOUR
COMMEMORATIVE BRANDS
KEEPSAKE
WHO'S WHO AMONG AMERICAN HIGH SCHOOL STUDENTS

AARON BASHA CORP.
680 Madison Ave
New York, NY 10065
Tel.: (212) 935-1960
Fax: (212) 935-9309
E-mail: info@aaronbasha.com
Web Site: www.aaronbasha.com
Approx. Number Employees: 20
Business Description:
Jewelry Retailer & Designer
S.I.C.: 5944
N.A.I.C.S.: 448310
Media: 4-6-8-10-13
Personnel:
Aaron Basha *(Founder)*
Sasson Basha *(Pres)*
Brands & Products:
AARON BASHA
AB
EVIL EYES
LADYBUGS

ALTAMA FOOTWEAR
1200 Lk Hearn Dr
Atlanta, GA 30319
Tel.: (404) 260-2888
Fax: (404) 260-2889
E-mail: sales@altama.com
Web Site: www.altama.com
E-Mail For Key Personnel:
Sales Director: sales@altama.com
Approx. Sls.: $20,000,000
Approx. Number Employees: 220
Year Founded: 1967
Business Description:
Mfr. of Combat Boots
S.I.C.: 3143; 3144
N.A.I.C.S.: 316213; 316214
Personnel:
Jack McAliner *(Pres)*
Brands & Products:
ALTAMA
BASICS
DESERTS
INFANTRY COMBAT
JUNGLES
RIPPLE SOLE
RIPPLES
SIERRAS
TACTICALS
Advertising Agency:
EJW Associates, Inc.
Crabapple Village Office Park 1602 Abbey Ct
Alpharetta, GA 30004
Tel.: (770) 664-9322
Fax: (770) 664-9324

AMINCO INTERNATIONAL (USA) INC.
20571 Crescent Bay Dr
Lake Forest, CA 92630-8825
Tel.: (949) 457-3261
Fax: (949) 598-2864
Web Site: www.amincousa.com
Approx. Number Employees: 60
Year Founded: 1978
Business Description:
Brass Goods & Logo Pins Mfr
S.I.C.: 5099; 3961
N.A.I.C.S.: 423990; 339914
Media: 4-10-13
Personnel:
William Wu *(Pres)*
Brands & Products:
AMINCO
THE CROWN OF EXCELLENCE

ARENA BRANDS INC.
(Holding of HM Capital Partners LLC)
601 Marion Dr
Garland, TX 75042-7930
Tel.: (972) 494-0511
Fax: (972) 494-2369
Web Site: www.stetsonhat.com
Approx. Number Employees: 400
Business Description:
Mfr. of Western Hats
S.I.C.: 2353
N.A.I.C.S.: 315991
Brands & Products:
CHARLIE ONE HORSE
RESISTOL
STETSON
Advertising Agency:
Firehouse, Inc.
14860 Landmark Blvd No 247
Dallas, TX 75254
Tel.: (972) 692-0911
Fax: (972) 692-0912
Stetson
Resistol
Luccese

ARMITRON WATCH DIVISION
(Div. of E. Gluck Corp.)
2910 Thomson Ave
Long Island City, NY 11101-2929
Tel.: (718) 784-0700
Fax: (718) 786-4153
Toll Free: (800) 937-0050
Approx. Number Employees: 425
Year Founded: 1960
Business Description:
Watch Mfr
S.I.C.: 3873; 5094
N.A.I.C.S.: 334518; 423940
Advertising Expenditures: $200,000
Media: 4-5-8-10-15-16-18-19-22-23-24
Distr.: Intl.; Natl.
Personnel:
Eugene Gluck *(Pres)*
Jerry Dikowitz *(VP-Mktg & Adv)*
Ron Summers *(Dir-Premiums)*
Brands & Products:
ARMITRON

ASCH/GROSSBARDT, INC.
580 5th Ave Ste 918
New York, NY 10036
Tel.: (212) 302-3942
Fax: (212) 398-8421
Toll Free: (800) 543-2724
E-mail: information@aschgrossbardt.com
Web Site: www.aschgrossbardt.com
Approx. Number Employees: 7
Year Founded: 1987
Business Description:
Fine Inlaid Gold Jewelry Mfr
S.I.C.: 5094
N.A.I.C.S.: 423940
Media: 4-5-6
Personnel:
Eric Grossbardt *(Owner)*
Brands & Products:
ERIC GROSSBARDT COLLECTION

Key to Media (For complete agency information see *The Advertising Red Books-Agencies* edition):
1. Bus. Publs. 2. Cable T.V. 3. Catalogs & Directories. 4. Co-op Adv. 5. Consumer Mags. 6. D.M. to Bus. Estab.7. D.M. to Consumers
8. Daily Newsp. 9. Exhibits/Trade Shows 10. Foreign 11. Infomercial 12. Internet Adv.13. Multimedia 14. Network Radio
15. Network T.V. 16. Newsp. Distr. Mags. 17. Other 18. Outdoor (Posters, Transit) 19. Point of Purchase20. Premiums, Novelties
21. Product Samples 22. Special Events Mktg. 23. Spot Radio 24. Spot T.V. 25. Weekly Newsp. 26. Yellow Page Adv.

ATLANTIC LUGGAGE COMPANY

(Holding of Cerberus Capital Management, L.P.)
700 Bannon Trail
Boca Raton, FL 33431
Tel.: (724) 752-0012
Fax: (561) 998-8487
Toll Free: (800) 245-1750
E-mail: info@atlanticluggage.com
Web Site: www.atlanticluggage.com
Approx. Number Employees: 100
Business Description:
Mfr. of Airway Luggage, Business Cases & Travel Accessories
S.I.C.: 5948
N.A.I.C.S.: 448320
Media: 2-4-5-6-7-9-10-13-18-19-20-21-22-23-24-25-26
Distr.: Intl.; Natl.
Budget Set: Oct.
Personnel:
Scott Human *(Director)*
Brands & Products:
ATLANTIC

AUDEMARS PIGUET (NORTH AMERICA)

(Sub. of Audemars Piguet & Cie)
40 E 57th St
New York, NY 10022
Tel.: (212) 758-8400
Fax: (212) 980-0482
Approx. Number Employees: 25
Business Description:
Jewelry & Watches
S.I.C.: 3911; 3873; 5944
N.A.I.C.S.: 339911; 334518; 448310
Media: 6-10
Personnel:
Francois Vennahmias *(Pres)*
Anne-Cecile Theveny *(Mgr-Mktg)*

AURAFIN LLC

(Div. of Richline Group, Inc.)
6701 Nob Hill Rd
Tamarac, FL 33321
Tel.: (954) 718-3200
Fax: (954) 718-3208
Toll Free: (800) 327-1808
E-mail: consumerinfo@aurafin.com
Web Site: www.aurafin.com
Sales Range: $50-74.9 Million
Approx. Number Employees: 300
Year Founded: 1982
Business Description:
Mfr. of Gold Jewelry
S.I.C.: 3911; 5094
N.A.I.C.S.: 339911; 423940
Media: 4-6
Personnel:
David Meleski *(Pres & CEO)*
Michael Schwartz *(Sr VP-Sls)*
Brooke Myer *(Mgr-HR)*
Brands & Products:
AURAFIN
AURAFIN ORO-AMERICA
AURAGEM
BOLERO
GARNER
LEACH
LEACH & GARNER
OROAMERICA

BAGMASTERS

(Div. of CTA Manufacturing, Inc.)
1160 California Ave
Corona, CA 92881-3324
Tel.: (951) 280-2400
Fax: (951) 280-2410
Toll Free: (800) 843-2247
Web Site: www.bagmasters.com
Approx. Number Employees: 52
Year Founded: 1920
Business Description:
Custom Nylon Products; Bank & Mail Bags, Promotional Bags, Briefcases, Totes & Duffles Mfr
S.I.C.: 2393; 3993
N.A.I.C.S.: 314911; 339950
Advertising Expenditures: $100,000
Media: 4-10
Distr.: Natl.
Personnel:
Rick Whittier *(Pres)*

BAILEY HATS COMPANY

(Sub. of Bollman Hat Co.)
3800 Sandshell Dr
Fort Worth, TX 76137-2429
Tel.: (817) 232-9707
Fax: (817) 232-3480
E-mail: info@baileyhats.com
Web Site: www.baileyhats.com
Approx. Number Employees: 4
Year Founded: 1922
Business Description:
Hats Mfr
S.I.C.: 2353
N.A.I.C.S.: 315991
Export
Media: 6-22
Distr.: Intl.; Natl.
Budget Set: Sept.
Personnel:
Jerry Miller *(VP-Sls)*

BARRINGTON GROUP LTD.

2300 N Hasko Ave
Dallas, TX 75204
Tel.: (214) 528-6990
Fax: (214) 528-9449
Toll Free: (800) 360-3346
E-mail: dgowdy@barrington-ltd.com
Web Site: www.barringtongifts.com
Sales Range: $10-24.9 Million
Approx. Number Employees: 30
Year Founded: 1991
Business Description:
Executive Writing Instruments, Leather Goods & Accessories for Corporate Environments
S.I.C.: 3951; 3172
N.A.I.C.S.: 339941; 316993
Media: 4-6-7-10
Distr.: Natl.
Personnel:
J. Gil Sheehan *(Pres)*
David C. Gowdy *(Partner)*

BAUME & MERCIER, INC.

645 5th Ave Fl 6
New York, NY 10022-5346
Tel.: (212) 593-0444
Fax: (212) 755-3138
Web Site: www.baume-and-mercier.com
Sales Range: $50-74.9 Million
Approx. Number Employees: 90
Year Founded: 1830
Business Description:
Watches Whslr
S.I.C.: 5944; 3873
N.A.I.C.S.: 448310; 334518
Media: 2-3-4-6-7-8-9-10-13-16-18-19-20-22-23-24-25
Distr.: Natl.
Budget Set: Jan.
Personnel:
Alain Zimmerman *(CEO)*
Ruby Chavez *(Pres-North America)*
Brands & Products:
BAUME & MERCIER
CAPELAND
CLASSIMA
HAMPTON
LINNEA
RIVIERA

BENAY-HAT CO.

4710 Roanoke Ave
Newport News, VA 23607-2339
Tel.: (757) 244-0807
Fax: (757) 380-5728
Toll Free: (800) 333-8632
E-mail: benayhat@earthlink.net
Web Site: www.benayhat.com
Approx. Number Employees: 21
Year Founded: 1992
Business Description:
Hats Mfr
S.I.C.: 2353; 3993
N.A.I.C.S.: 315991; 339950
Import
Media: 2-4-6-7-8-13-20-26
Distr.: Intl.; Natl.
Budget Set: Sept.
Personnel:
Jeff Jacobs *(Pres)*
Stanley Molin *(Gen Mgr)*
Lawrence Molin *(Dir-Mfg & Pur)*
Brands & Products:
BENAY-HAT

BERGIO INTERNATIONAL, INC.

12 Daniel Rd E
Fairfield, NJ 07004
Tel.: (973) 227-3230
E-mail: info@bergio.com
Web Site: www.bergio.com
Approx. Sls.: $1,445,570
Approx. Number Employees: 3
Year Founded: 2007
Business Description:
Jewelry Designer & Mfr
S.I.C.: 3911
N.A.I.C.S.: 339911
Advertising Expenditures: $168,000
Media: 17
Personnel:
Berge Abajian *(Owner)*
Brands & Products:
BERGIO

BIJOUX TERNER, INC.

6950 NW 77th Ct
Miami, FL 33166
Tel.: (305) 500-7500
Fax: (305) 262-9286
E-mail: customerservice@bijouxterner.com
Web Site: www.bijouxterner.com
Approx. Rev.: $1,900,000
Approx. Number Employees: 39
Year Founded: 1974
Business Description:
Holding Companies
S.I.C.: 6719
N.A.I.C.S.: 551112
Personnel:
Gabriel Bottazzi *(Pres & CEO)*
Advertising Agency:
rbb Public Relations
355 Alhambra Cir Ste 800
Miami, FL 33134
Tel.: (305) 448-7450
Fax: (305) 448-5027

BIRKS & MAYORS INC.

1240 Phillips Sq
Montreal, QC H3B 3H4, Canada
Tel.: (514) 397-2511
Fax: (514) 397-2455
Web Site: www.birksandmayors.com
Approx. Sls.: $270,948,000
Approx. Number Employees: 831
Year Founded: 1879
Business Description:
Silverware & Jewelry Retailer & Mfr
S.I.C.: 3911; 3914
N.A.I.C.S.: 339911; 339912
Import Export
Advertising Expenditures: $8,379,000
Media: 4-6-9-19-22-25
Distr.: Intl.; Natl.
Personnel:
Lorenzo Rossi di Montelera *(Chm)*
Thomas A. Andruskevich *(Pres & CEO)*
Michael Rabinovitch *(CFO & Sr VP)*
Joseph A. Keifer, III *(COO & Exec VP)*
Milt Thacker *(CIO & Grp VP)*
John C. Orrico *(Chief Supply Chain Officer & Sr VP)*
Marco Pasteris *(Treas & Grp VP-Fin)*
Miranda Melfi *(Crop Sec & Grp VP-Legal Affairs)*
Aida Alvarez *(Sr VP-Mdsg)*
Helene Messier *(Sr VP-HR)*
Albert J. Rahm, II *(Sr VP-Retail Store Ops)*
Jeff Morris *(Grp VP-Acctg & Controller)*
Carlo Coda-Nunziante *(Grp VP-Strategy & Bus Dev)*
Brands & Products:
BIRKS
BIRKS&MAYORS
BRINKHAUS
MAYORS
ROLEX

BIRKS & MAYORS INC.

(Sub. of Birks & Mayors Inc.)
5870 N Hiatus Rd
Tamarac, FL 33321
Tel.: (954) 590-9000
Toll Free: (800) 462-9677
Web Site: www.birksandmayors.com
Sales Range: $125-149.9 Million
Approx. Number Employees: 384
Year Founded: 1983
Business Description:
Fine Jewelry, Watches & Gift Items Retailer
S.I.C.: 3873; 3911; 5094
N.A.I.C.S.: 334518; 339911; 423940
Import Export
Advertising Expenditures: $5,200,000
Media: 4-8-10-13
Personnel:
Michael Rabinovitch *(CFO & Sr VP)*
Aida Alvarez *(Sr VP-Mdsg)*
Carlo Coda-Nunziante *(Grp VP-Strategy & Bus Dev)*
Brands & Products:
MAYORS

BLUE NILE, INC.

705 5th Ave S Ste 900
Seattle, WA 98104
Tel.: (206) 336-6700
Fax: (206) 336-6750
Toll Free: (800) 242-2728

Key to Media (For complete agency information see *The Advertising Red Books-Agencies* edition):
1. Bus. Publs. 2. Cable T.V. 3. Catalogs & Directories. 4. Co-op Adv. 5. Consumer Mags. 6. D.M. to Bus. Estab.7. D.M. to Consumers
8. Daily Newsp. 9. Exhibits/Trade Shows 10. Foreign 11. Infomercial 12. Internet Adv.13. Multimedia 14. Network Radio
15. Network T.V. 16. Newsp. Distr. Mags. 17. Other 18. Outdoor (Posters, Transit) 19. Point of Purchase20. Premiums, Novelties
21. Product Samples 22. Special Events Mktg. 23. Spot Radio 24. Spot T.V. 25. Weekly Newsp. 26. Yellow Page Adv.

E-mail: service@bluenile.com
Web Site: www.bluenile.com
E-Mail For Key Personnel:
Public Relations: publicrelations@bluenile.com
Approx. Sls.: $332,889,000
Approx. Number Employees: 191
Year Founded: 1999
Business Description:
Diamonds & Fine Jewelry Retailer
S.I.C.: 5094; 5944; 5961
N.A.I.C.S.: 423940; 448310; 454111; 454113
Advertising Expenditures: $7,600,000
Media: 13
Personnel:
Mark C. Vadon *(Chm)*
Diane M. Irvine *(Pres & CEO)*
Vijay Talwar *(Interim CFO, Sr VP & Gen Mgr-Intl)*
Susan Bell *(Sr VP)*
Dwight Gaston *(Sr VP)*
Terri Maupin *(Controller & VP-Fin)*
Steven Gire *(VP-Tech)*
Brands & Products:
BLUE NILE
DIAMOND PENDANT
FIVE-STONE RING
THREE-STONE PENDANT
THREE-STONE RING

BORSHEIM JEWELRY COMPANY, INC.

(Holding of Berkshire Hathaway Inc.)
120 Regency Pkwy
Omaha, NE 68114
Tel.: (402) 391-0400
Fax: (402) 391-6694
Toll Free: (800) 642-4438
E-mail: mail@borsheims.com
Web Site: www.borsheims.com
Approx. Rev.: $33,100,000
Approx. Number Employees: 500
Business Description:
Jewelry Retailer
S.I.C.: 5944; 5947
N.A.I.C.S.: 448310; 453220
Media: 4-13
Personnel:
Susan Jacques *(Pres & CEO)*

BRAUNSCHWEIGER JEWELERS

33 S St
Morristown, NJ 07960-4137
Tel.: (973) 538-2189
Fax: (973) 539-5414
Toll Free: (877) 538-6551
E-mail: info@braunschweiger.com
Web Site: www.braunschweiger.com
Sales Range: $1-9.9 Million
Year Founded: 1947
Business Description:
Jewelry Retailer
S.I.C.: 5944; 7699
N.A.I.C.S.: 448310; 811490
Advertising Expenditures: $300,000
Media: 6-10-13-23-26
Personnel:
Bill Braunschweiger, Jr. *(Pres)*
Steve Connell *(Mgr-Svc)*
Greg Kettle *(Mgr)*

BRIGGS & RILEY TRAVELWARE

(Sub. of SOLO)
400 Wireless Blvd
Hauppauge, NY 11788-3934
Tel.: (631) 434-7722
Fax: (631) 434-7326
Web Site: www.briggsriley.com
Business Description:
Luggage Importer & Distr
S.I.C.: 5948
N.A.I.C.S.: 448320
Media: 3-8-23
Personnel:
Laura Ballereau *(Brand Mgr)*
Advertising Agency:
The Communicators Group
Marlboro Tech Ctr 28 Vernon St Ste 503
Brattleboro, VT 03501
Tel.: (802) 257-4321

BROOKVILLE GLOVE MANUFACTURING COMPANY, INC.

(Sub. of BSI Diversified LLC)
5-15 Western Ave
Brookville, PA 15825
Tel.: (814) 849-7324
Fax: (814) 849-6874
Toll Free: (800) 322-7324
E-mail: info@brookvilleglove.com
Web Site: www.brookvilleglove.com
Approx. Number Employees: 30
Year Founded: 1888
Business Description:
Mfr of Work & Garden Gloves, Rainwear, Safety Items & Personal Protective Equipment
S.I.C.: 3151; 3021
N.A.I.C.S.: 315992; 316211
Import
Advertising Expenditures: $425,000
Media: 2-4-6-7-8-13
Distr.: Natl.
Personnel:
Charles E. Breene *(Owner)*
Brands & Products:
BLACK BEAR
BOXCARS
BROOKVILLE GLOVE
BURLY BEAR
COPPER CLAD
FLAME MASTER
GREEN BRIAR
HEAT GARD
HEFTEE
KEYSTONE
LUCKY STEER
SILVER FLEECE
WHITE BUCK

BROWNLEE JEWELERS OF THE CAROLINAS

4147 Pk Rd
Charlotte, NC 28209
Tel.: (704) 527-1717
Fax: (704) 529-1935
Toll Free: (888) 276-9653
E-mail: customerservice@brownleejewelers.com
Web Site: www.brownleejewelers.com
Approx. Number Employees: 60
Year Founded: 1974
Business Description:
Jewelry, Precious Stones & Precious Metals
S.I.C.: 5944
N.A.I.C.S.: 448310
Personnel:
Harold W. Rousso *(Owner)*
Advertising Agency:
Specialized Media Services, Inc.
741 Kenilworth Ave Ste 204
Charlotte, NC 28204
Tel.: (704) 333-3111
Fax: (704) 332-7466

BULGARI CORPORATION OF AMERICA

(Sub. of Bulgari S.p.A.)
625 Madison Ave
New York, NY 10022
Tel.: (212) 315-9700
Toll Free: (800) BULGARI
Web Site: www.bulgari.com
Approx. Number Employees: 75
Year Founded: 1970
Business Description:
Import of Fine Jewelry & Watches
S.I.C.: 5944
N.A.I.C.S.: 448310
Import
Media: 4-5-6-7-8-9-10-17-18-22-30
Distr.: Natl.
Personnel:
Nicola Bulgari *(Vice Chm)*
Paolo Piantella *(Exec Dir-Corp External Rels)*
Rory Hermelee *(Dir-Comm & PR)*

BULOVA CORPORATION

(Sub. of Citizen Watch Co., Ltd.)
One Bulova Ave
Woodside, NY 11377-7826
Tel.: (718) 204-3300
Fax: (718) 204-3546
Toll Free: (800) 228-5682
E-mail: info@bulova.com
Web Site: www.bulova.com
Sales Range: $150-199.9 Million
Approx. Number Employees: 210
Year Founded: 1875
Business Description:
Mfr. & Retailer of Watches & Clocks
S.I.C.: 3873; 5094
N.A.I.C.S.: 334518; 423940
Import Export
Advertising Expenditures: $7,730,000
Media: 2-3-4-5-6-9-18-24-30
Distr.: Intl.; Natl.
Budget Set: Nov.
Personnel:
Dennis W. Perry *(Pres)*
Francie Abraham *(CMO & Sr VP)*
Warren J. Neitzel *(Gen Counsel & Sec)*
Gary Simon *(Exec VP-Sls)*
James Chan *(Sr VP)*
Tom Fosorile *(Sr VP-U.S. Retail Sls)*
Fae Druiz *(VP-Creative)*
Brands & Products:
ACCUTRON
BULOVA
CARAVELLE
DURA-CRYSTAL
WITTNAUER
Advertising Agencies:
EMG - Ethnic Marketing Group, Inc.
26074 Ave Hall Ste 20
Valencia, CA 91355
Tel.: (661) 295-5704
Fax: (661) 295-5771

Ted Barkus Company, Inc.
8017 Anderson St
Philadelphia, PA 19118
Tel.: (215) 545-0616

BULOVA WATCH COMPANY LIMITED

(Sub. of Bulova Corporation)
39 Casebridge Ct
Toronto, ON M1B 5N4, Canada
Tel.: (416) 751-7151
Fax: (416) 751-4763
Toll Free: (800) 268-6562
E-mail: jcameron@wittnaur.ca
Web Site: www.Bulova.com
Approx. Number Employees: 70
Year Founded: 1875
Business Description:
Watch & Clocks Distr
S.I.C.: 5094; 3873
N.A.I.C.S.: 423940; 334518
Media: 2-5-7-14-20-23-25-30
Distr.: Natl.
Budget Set: Jan.
Personnel:
William C. Stoner *(Pres)*
Jay Cameron *(VP-Sls)*

BUXTON ACQUISITION CO., LLC

(d/b/a Buxton Dopp)
45 Plainfield St
Chicopee, MA 01013
Mailing Address:
PO Box 1650
Springfield, MA 01102-1650
Tel.: (413) 734-5900
Fax: (413) 785-1367
Web Site:
www.buxtonaccessories.com/
E-Mail For Key Personnel:
Sales Director: sales@buxtondopp.com
Approx. Number Employees: 30
Year Founded: 1898
Business Description:
Mfr. of Billfolds, Leather Goods & Travel Accessories
S.I.C.: 5199; 4226
N.A.I.C.S.: 424990; 493190
Import Export
Media: 10-17
Distr.: Natl.
Budget Set: Apr.
Personnel:
Kendall Walsh *(CFO & Sr VP)*
Eric Lund *(VP-Sls)*
Michele Cahill *(Mgr-Design-Women?s Accessories)*
Brands & Products:
BB DESIGN
BILL-TAINERS
BUXTON
BUXTON BANKER
CAL-Q & DESIGN
CAL-Q-CLUTCH
CAL-Q-SECRETARY
CARD-TAINER
CARDEX
CARMEL
CONTINENTAL SLIMS
CONTOUR
CONVERTIBLE
CRAFTMARK
DOPP
DOPP & EAGLE DESIGN
DOPP KIT
EASY-TRAK
ELITE
ENSEMBLE CLUTCH
FLORENTINO
GAITOR-BAITOR

Key to Media (For complete agency information see *The Advertising Red Books-Agencies* edition):
1. Bus. Publs. 2. Cable T.V. 3. Catalogs & Directories. 4. Co-op Adv. 5. Consumer Mags. 6. D.M. to Bus. Estab.7. D.M. to Consumers 8. Daily Newsp. 9. Exhibits/Trade Shows 10. Foreign 11. Infomercial 12. Internet Adv.13. Multimedia 14. Network Radio 15. Network T.V. 16. Newsp. Distr. Mags. 17. Other 18. Outdoor (Posters, Transit) 19. Point of Purchase20. Premiums, Novelties 21. Product Samples 22. Special Events Mktg. 23. Spot Radio 24. Spot T.V. 25. Weekly Newsp. 26. Yellow Page Adv.

Buxton Acquisition Co., LLC — (Continued)

HEIRESS
KEY-TAINER
LADY BUXTON
LIFEBOOK-THE COMPLETE FAMILY
LORD BUXTON
MUCH CLUTCH
NATURALE
ORGANIZER
PIERSON & POST
PIK-ME-UPS
ROYAL DANSK
SPEC-TAINER
STATESMAN
THINFOLD
WEXFORD COLLECTION

CARELLE LTD.

2 W 46th St Ste 709
New York, NY 10036
Tel.: (212) 997-1156
Fax: (212) 827-0042
Toll Free: (800) 225-7782
E-mail: contact@carelle.com
Web Site: www.carelle.com
E-Mail For Key Personnel:
Sales Director: sales@carelle.com
Approx. Number Employees: 15
Business Description:
Jewelry Retailer
S.I.C.: 5094; 5944
N.A.I.C.S.: 423940; 448310
Media: 5-6
Personnel:
Chana Regev *(Pres)*

CENTURY 21 PROMOTIONS, INC.

2601 W Commodore Way
Seattle, WA 98199-1231
Tel.: (206) 282-8200
Fax: (206) 282-8832
Toll Free: (800) 935-2100
E-mail: sales@century21promotions.com
Web Site: www.century21promotions.com
E-Mail For Key Personnel:
Sales Director: sales@century21promotions.com
Approx. Sls.: $6,000,000
Approx. Number Employees: 28
Year Founded: 1980
Business Description:
Importer of Hats, Caps & Jackets
S.I.C.: 5136; 5137
N.A.I.C.S.: 424320; 424330
Media: 2-4-7-10-14-18-20-22
Distr.: Natl.
Budget Set: Apr.
Personnel:
Jeffery H. Hoch *(Pres)*
Brands & Products:
CENTURY 21
CENTURY 23
FAHRENHEIT

CHARISMA BRANDS, LLC

23482 Peralta Dr Ste A
Laguna Hills, CA 92653
Tel.: (949) 587-9400
Fax: (949) 587-9300
Toll Free: (800) 775-9272
E-mail: info@charismabrands.com
Web Site: www.charismabrands.com
Approx. Number Employees: 20
Year Founded: 1985
Business Description:
Designer, Developer & Marketer Doll & Jewelry Products
S.I.C.: 5961
N.A.I.C.S.: 454113
Media: 3-4-6-8-13-20
Distr.: Natl.
Personnel:
Anthony P. Shutts *(Pres & CEO)*
Peggy Vicioso *(VP-Mktg & Product Dev)*
Tracy Stobaugh *(Dir-Sls)*
Brands & Products:
ARTISTA
CANDY FASHION
CHARISMA
KEWPIE
MARIE OSMOND
MARIE OSMOND COLLECTION
PENNY BRITE
WHISPERING WLLOW FAIRIES

CHARLES & COLVARD LTD

300 Perimeter Park Ste A
Morrisville, NC 27560
Tel.: (919) 468-0399
Fax: (919) 468-0486
Toll Free: (800) 210-4367
E-mail: sales@moissanite.com
Web Site: www.moissanite.com
E-Mail For Key Personnel:
Sales Director: sales@moissanite.com
Approx. Sls.: $12,686,771
Approx. Number Employees: 25
Year Founded: 1995
Business Description:
Mfr., Marketer & Distributor of Moissanite Jewels
S.I.C.: 3911; 3172; 3545
N.A.I.C.S.: 339911; 316993; 333515
Advertising Expenditures: $757,000
Media: 10
Personnel:
George R. Cattermole *(Chm)*
Randy N. McCullough *(CEO)*
Timothy L. Krist *(CFO)*
Robert Curry *(VP-Mdse, Production & Distr)*
Thomas G. Pautz *(VP-Sls & Mktg)*
Kevin Raulston *(Gen Mgr-Charles & Colvard Direct, LLC)*
Cheri Lindholm *(Mgr-Visual Mktg)*
Brands & Products:
CHARLES & COLVARD
IT ALL STARTS WITH A SPARKLE
MOISSANITE
PERFECT FOR EVERY OCCASION
Advertising Agency:
Kerwin Communications
1120 Bloomfield Ave Ste 107
West Caldwell, NJ 07006
Tel.: (973) 244-0301
Fax: (973) 244-0990

CHASE-DURER LTD.

9601 Wilshire Dr Ste 1118
Beverly Hills, CA 90210
Tel.: (310) 550-7280
Fax: (310) 550-0830
Toll Free: (800) 544-4365
Web Site: www.chase-durer.com
Approx. Sls.: $3,500,000
Approx. Number Employees: 15
Business Description:
Watch Designer & Mfr
S.I.C.: 5094; 3873
N.A.I.C.S.: 423940; 334518
Media: 4-6-10-11-13
Personnel:
Brandon Chase *(Founder)*

CHELSEA CLOCK CO., INC.

284 Everett Ave
Chelsea, MA 02150-1515
Tel.: (617) 884-0250
Fax: (617) 884-3608
E-mail: sales@chelseaclock.com
Web Site: www.chelseaclock.com
E-Mail For Key Personnel:
Sales Director: sales@chelseaclock.com
Sales Range: $10-24.9 Million
Approx. Number Employees: 30
Year Founded: 1897
Business Description:
Clocks Mfr
S.I.C.: 3873
N.A.I.C.S.: 334518
Import
Advertising Expenditures: $150,000
Media: 2-6-7-8-13
Distr.: Natl.
Budget Set: Nov. -Dec.
Personnel:
J. K. Nicholas *(CEO)*
Douglas B. Mauch *(VP-Supply Chain & Mgr-Matls)*
Terry Kubarsky *(Dir-Corp Sls)*

CHRISTOPHER DESIGNS, INC.

42 W 48th St 4th Fl
New York, NY 10036
Tel.: (212) 382-1013
Fax: (212) 768-8978
Toll Free: (800) 955-0970
E-mail: info@christopnerdesigns.com
Web Site: www.christopherdesigns.com
Approx. Number Employees: 25
Business Description:
Jewelry Designer & Mfr
S.I.C.: 3911; 3915
N.A.I.C.S.: 339911; 339913
Media: 4-6
Personnel:
Christopher Slowinski *(Pres)*
Brands & Products:
CHRISTOPHER DESIGNS
CRISSCUT

CITIZEN WATCH CO. OF AMERICA, INC.

(Sub. of Citizen Watch Co., Ltd.)
1200 Wall St W
Lyndhurst, NJ 07071-3680
Tel.: (201) 438-8150
Fax: (201) 438-4161
Web Site: www.citizenwatch.com
Year Founded: 1975
Business Description:
Watch Retailer
S.I.C.: 5094
N.A.I.C.S.: 423940
Media: 4-5-6-9-13-15
Personnel:
Jeffrey Cohen *(Pres)*
James Shada *(Sr VP-Natl Accts)*
Michael Springer *(Sr VP)*
Alyson Gottlieb *(VP-Adv & PR)*

CLEOPATRA'S BARGE FINE JEWELRY

1197 3rd St S
Naples, FL 34102
Tel.: (239) 261-7952
Fax: (239) 261-7923
Toll Free: (800) 678-7934
E-mail: info@cleopatrasbarge.com
Web Site: www.cleopatrasbarge.com
Approx. Number Employees: 4
Year Founded: 1966
Business Description:
Jewelry Designer & Retailer
S.I.C.: 5944
N.A.I.C.S.: 448310
Media: 4-6-8-13
Personnel:
Marilynn Jannss *(Owner)*
Brands & Products:
CLEOPATRA'S BARGE
THE NAPLES MEDALLION
SANIBEL MEDALLION

COACH, INC.

516 W 34th St
New York, NY 10001-1311
Tel.: (212) 594-1850
Fax: (212) 594-1682
Toll Free: (800) 444-3611
E-mail: comments@coach.com
Web Site: www.coach.com
Approx. Sls.: $4,158,507,000
Approx. Number Employees: 5,200
Year Founded: 1941
Business Description:
Leather Handbags & Accessories Mfr; Retail Stores
S.I.C.: 3171; 3172
N.A.I.C.S.: 316992; 316993
Advertising Expenditures: $50,078,000
Media: 2-4-6-7-8-9-11-13-18
Distr.: Intl.; Natl.
Personnel:
Lew Frankfort *(Chm & CEO)*
Jerry Stritzke *(Co-Pres & COO)*
Reed Krakoff *(Co-Pres & Exec Dir-Creative)*
Jane Nielsen *(CFO & Exec VP)*
Andre Cohen *(Pres/CEO-Coach Asia)*
Victor Luis *(Pres-Retail Intl)*
Michael Tucci *(Pres-Retail Div-North America)*
Todd Kahn *(Gen Counsel, Sec & Sr VP)*
Sarah Dunn *(Sr VP-HR)*
Nicolas Villeger *(VP & Gen Manager-Singapore & Malaysia)*
Lee Ann Devine *(Dir-Media)*
Brands & Products:
ADDISON
AIDAN
ALBERT
ALLEGRA
AMANDA
AUBREY
AUSTIN
BACKPACK
BEEKMAN
BLEECKER
BRAIDED
BRIDGIT
CARLY
COACH
COACH HERITAGE STRIPE
CONNOR
CORSICA
CRICKET
DEACON
DELANEY
DEVYN

Key to Media (For complete agency information see *The Advertising Red Books-Agencies* edition):
1. Bus. Publs. 2. Cable T.V. 3. Catalogs & Directories. 4. Co-op Adv. 5. Consumer Mags. 6. D.M. to Bus. Estab.7. D.M. to Consumers
8. Daily Newsp. 9. Exhibits/Trade Shows 10. Foreign 11. Infomercial 12. Internet Adv.13. Multimedia 14. Network Radio
15. Network T.V. 16. Newsp. Distr. Mags. 17. Other 18. Outdoor (Posters, Transit) 19. Point of Purchase20. Premiums, Novelties
21. Product Samples 22. Special Events Mktg. 23. Spot Radio 24. Spot T.V. 25. Weekly Newsp. 26. Yellow Page Adv.

DROP
EMBASSY
ERICK
GAVIN
HAMPTONS
HARRISON
JACKSON
JANICE'S
LEANNE
LEGACY
LESBETH
LEXINGTON
LOGAN
MADISON
MAGAZINE
MARTHA
MERCER
MINISIGNATURE
NURLED
ODESSA
OPTIC SIGNATURE
PARKER
PATENT
PENELOPE
RAMBLER'S
RETRO
SIGNATURE
SOHO TWILL
SPECTATOR
STEWARDESS
TASHA
TATTOO
TEXTURED MONEY
TRANSATLANTIC
VARICK
WATER BUFFALO
WESTON
WILL SNEAKER
WILLIS
ZOE

Advertising Agencies:
Pluzynski/Associates, Inc.
26 W 17th St 10th Fl
New York, NY 10011
Tel.: (212) 645-1414
Fax: (212) 645-2013
Catalog Production
— Lori Lee *(Acct Exec)*

Roadway Solutions, Inc.
(Private-Parent-Single Location)
2524 N Ih 35
Carrollton, TX 75006
Tel.: (972) 245-2244

ZenithOptimedia
Room 1403-05 14/F 1063 Kings Road
Quarry Bay, China (Hong Kong)
Tel.: (852) 2236 9000
Fax: (852) 2250 9333
(Media)

ZenithOptimedia
1-4/F900 Huai Hai Zhong Road
Shanghai, China
Tel.: (86) 21 6133 8399
Fax: (86) 21 6133 8398
Interactive Media)

CORUM USA LLC
(Sub. of Corum Watches S.A.R.L.)
12 H Mauchly
Irvine, CA 92618
Tel.: (949) 788-6200
Fax: (949) 453-9345
E-mail: info@corum.ch
Web Site: www.corumtimepieces.com
Sales Range: $10-24.9 Million
Approx. Number Employees: 15
Year Founded: 1956
Business Description:
Watches & Parts Distr
S.I.C.: 5094
N.A.I.C.S.: 423940
Media: 6

CRAIG DRAKE MANUFACTURING INC.
(Name Changed to Craiger Drake Designs)

CRAIGER DRAKE DESIGNS
(Formerly Craig Drake Manufacturing, Inc.)
1616 Walnut St
Philadelphia, PA 19103
Tel.: (215) 253-6507
E-mail: info@craigerdrake.com
Web Site: www.craigerdrake.com
Approx. Number Employees: 12
Year Founded: 1961
Business Description:
Mfr of Jewelry
S.I.C.: 3911
N.A.I.C.S.: 339911
Media: 4-6-7-8
Personnel:
Craig Drake, Sr. *(Owner)*
Craig Drake, Jr. *(Pres)*
Brands & Products:
CRAIG DRAKE
DISTINCTIVELY DIFFERENT
Advertising Agency:
Brownstein Group
215 S Broad St 9th Fl
Philadelphia, PA 19107-5325
Tel.: (215) 735-3470
Fax: (215) 735-6298
Public Relations

CRESCENT JEWELERS INC.
1101 Marina Vlg Pkwy Ste 101
Alameda, CA 94501
Tel.: (510) 874-7600
Fax: (510) 865-2560
Toll Free: (800) 588-4367
E-mail: support@crescentonline.com
Web Site: www.crescentonline.com
Approx. Number Employees: 1,100
Year Founded: 1935
Business Description:
Jewelry Retailer
S.I.C.: 5944; 6141
N.A.I.C.S.: 448310; 522291
Import Export
Media: 4-8

CROTON WATCH COMPANY & NATIONWIDE TIME
195 Anderson Ave
Moonachie, NJ 07074
Tel.: (201) 939-5100
Fax: (201) 939-5222
Toll Free: (800) 443-7639
E-mail: customerservice@crotonwatch.com
Web Site: www.crotonwatch.com
Approx. Number Employees: 17
Year Founded: 1878
Business Description:
Mfr. of Watches
S.I.C.: 3873; 5094
N.A.I.C.S.: 334518; 423940
Import Export
Media: 2-4-6-7-9-23
Distr.: Natl.
Budget Set: Jan.
Personnel:
David Mermelstein *(Pres)*
Ron Nolan *(Gen Mgr-Sls)*
Brands & Products:
CROTON
MANHATTAN WATCHES

CRYSTAL WORLD, INC.
89 Leuning St Unit A 2
South Hackensack, NJ 07606
Tel.: (201) 488-0909
Fax: (201) 488-7447
Toll Free: (800) 445-4251
E-mail: gift@crystalworld.com
Web Site: www.crystalworld.com
Approx. Number Employees: 20
Year Founded: 1983
Business Description:
Mfr of Faceted Crystal Collectibles & Award Items
S.I.C.: 3229; 5947
N.A.I.C.S.: 327212; 453220
Import Export
Media: 4-10
Distr.: Natl.
Budget Set: Jan. -Feb.
Personnel:
Rudy Nakai *(Founder & Lead Designer)*
Nicholas Mulargia *(VP-Sls & Mktg)*
Trina Wright *(Mgr-Cust Svcs)*
Brands & Products:
CRYSTAL WORLD
ORIGINAL RAINBOW CASTLE COLLECTION
THE WORLD'S FINEST CRYSTAL

DANECRAFT INC.
1 Baker St
Providence, RI 02905-4417
Tel.: (401) 941-7700
Fax: (401) 461-8715
E-mail: dancrftri@aol.com
Web Site: www.danecraft.com
E-Mail For Key Personnel:
Sales Director: jsestric@aol.com
Approx. Number Employees: 250
Year Founded: 1934
Business Description:
Sterling Silver & Fashion Jewelry Mfr
S.I.C.: 3911; 5944
N.A.I.C.S.: 339911; 448310
Import Export
Media: 2-6-9-19-25
Distr.: Intl.; Natl.
Budget Set: Various
Personnel:
Robert Soltys *(Pres)*
Victor Primavera, III *(CEO)*
Brands & Products:
DANECRAFT
LIFE.YOURS

DANIEL K INC.
555 Madison Ave
New York, NY 10022
Tel.: (212) 759-7604
Fax: (212) 759-7606
Toll Free: (888) 841-7676
E-mail: info@danielk.net
Web Site: www.danielk.net
Sales Range: $1-9.9 Million
Approx. Number Employees: 15
Year Founded: 1999
Business Description:
Jewelry Whslr
S.I.C.: 5094
N.A.I.C.S.: 423940
Media: 5-6-10-19
Brands & Products:
DANIEL K
DIMPLE PAVE
EMPRESS
RED BY DANIEL K
REGAL
ROSEBUD
SPLIT CROWN
UTERNITY
Advertising Agency:
Outhouse PR
111 Broadway 11 Fl Ste 1104
New York, NY 10006
Tel.: (212) 349-8543
Fax: (212) 964-4934
Pub Rels

DAVID BIRNBAUM/RARE 1 CORPORATION
589 5th Ave Ste 710
New York, NY 10017
Tel.: (212) 575-0266
Fax: (212) 398-9438
E-mail: supergems@aol.com
Web Site: www.davidbirnbaum.com
Sales Range: $125-149.9 Million
Approx. Number Employees: 6
Year Founded: 2001
Business Description:
Jeweler in Precious & Rare Gems
S.I.C.: 5944
N.A.I.C.S.: 448310
Media: 8-16
Personnel:
David Birnbaum *(Pres)*
Brands & Products:
DBR1
THE RARE AND THE EXTRAORDINARY

DE HAGO, INC.
38 W 48th St Ste 600
New York, NY 10036
Tel.: (212) 869-7477
Fax: (212) 869-3895
Toll Free: (877) 771-4246
E-mail: sales@dehago.com
Web Site: www.dehago.com
Business Description:
Jewelry Designer & Mfr
S.I.C.: 3911
N.A.I.C.S.: 339911
Media: 6
Personnel:
Barkev Hagopian *(Owner)*
Brands & Products:
BANDS OF LOVE
DE HAGO
THE POWER OF COLOR

DGSE COMPANIES, INC.
11311 Reeder Rd
Dallas, TX 75229
Tel.: (972) 484-3662
Fax: (972) 241-0646
Toll Free: (800) 527-5307
Web Site: www.dgse.com
Approx. Rev.: $82,567,921
Approx. Number Employees: 66
Business Description:
Jewelry, Bullion Products, & Rare Coins
S.I.C.: 5094
N.A.I.C.S.: 423940

Key to Media (For complete agency information see *The Advertising Red Books-Agencies* edition):
1. Bus. Publs. 2. Cable T.V. 3. Catalogs & Directories. 4. Co-op Adv. 5. Consumer Mags. 6. D.M. to Bus. Estab.7. D.M. to Consumers
8. Daily Newsp. 9. Exhibits/Trade Shows 10. Foreign 11. Infomercial 12. Internet Adv.13. Multimedia 14. Network Radio
15. Network T.V. 16. Newsp. Distr. Mags. 17. Other 18. Outdoor (Posters, Transit) 19. Point of Purchase20. Premiums, Novelties
21. Product Samples 22. Special Events Mktg. 23. Spot Radio 24. Spot T.V. 25. Weekly Newsp. 26. Yellow Page Adv.

DGSE Companies, Inc. — (Continued)

Advertising Expenditures: $1,803,806
Media: 2-4-6-9-23-24-25
Personnel:
L. S. Smith *(Chm, CEO & Sec)*
William H. Oyster *(Pres)*
John Benson *(CFO)*

DIAMOND EXCHANGE INC.
(d/b/a Madison Jewelers)
2261 Black Rock Tpke
Fairfield, CT 06825
Tel.: (203) 334-4250
Fax: (203) 330-8657
Toll Free: (800) 300-GEMS
E-mail: madisonjlr@aol.com
Web Site: www.madisonjewelers.com
Approx. Number Employees: 7
Year Founded: 1939
Business Description:
Jewelry Retailer
S.I.C.: 5944
N.A.I.C.S.: 448310
Media: 4-5-6-10-22
Personnel:
Tom Losonic *(Pres)*
Advertising Agency:
S.R. Video Pictures, Ltd.
23 S Route 9W
Haverstraw, NY 10927
Tel.: (845) 429-1116
Fax: (845) 429-1117

DONALD J PLINER OF FLORIDA, INC.
(Sub. of Castanea Partners, Inc.)
745 5th Ave 25 Fl
New York, NY 10151
Tel.: (212) 688-6900
Fax: (212) 421-2900
Toll Free: (888) 307-1630
E-mail: customerservice@donaldjpliner.com
Web Site: www.donaldjpliner.com
Approx. Number Employees: 35
Business Description:
Apparel & Accessories Mfr
S.I.C.: 2389
N.A.I.C.S.: 315999
Media: 4-6
Personnel:
Donald J. Pliner *(Owner)*
Brands & Products:
DONALD J PLINER
FRIENDS OF BABYDOLL

DONNA SAYLERS' FABULOUS-FURS
25 W Robinson St
Covington, KY 41011
Tel.: (859) 291-3300
Fax: (859) 291-9687
E-mail: custserv@fabulousfurs.com
Web Site: www.fabulousfurs.com
Approx. Number Employees: 40
Business Description:
Fake Fur Clothing & Accessories Retailer
S.I.C.: 5961; 0271
N.A.I.C.S.: 454113; 112930
Media: 4-6-9-13-24-25
Personnel:
Donna Saylers *(Pres)*

THE ECHO DESIGN GROUP, INC.
10 E 40th St 16th Fl
New York, NY 10016
Tel.: (212) 686-8771
Fax: (212) 686-5017
Toll Free: (800) 331ECHO
E-mail: info@echodesign.com
Web Site: www.echodesign.com
Sales Range: $50-74.9 Million
Approx. Number Employees: 200
Year Founded: 1923
Business Description:
Scarfs, Fashion Accessories, Handbags & Home Products Designer & Distr
S.I.C.: 5137; 5136
N.A.I.C.S.: 424330; 424320
Media: 2-6
Distr.: Natl.
Personnel:
Dorothy H. Roberts *(Chm)*
Steven D. Roberts *(Pres & CEO)*
Geri Riordan *(Mng Dir)*
Susan Farrell *(CFO)*
Lynn T. Roberts *(VP-Publicity & Adv)*
Brands & Products:
ECHO
ECHO DESIGN LAB
MONSAC

ELECTRIC TIME CO., INC.
97 W St
Medfield, MA 02052
Tel.: (508) 359-4396
Fax: (508) 359-4482
Web Site: www.electrictime.com
E-Mail For Key Personnel:
Sales Director: sales@electrictime.com
Sales Range: $10-24.9 Million
Approx. Number Employees: 35
Year Founded: 1928
Business Description:
Custom Clock Mfr
S.I.C.: 3873
N.A.I.C.S.: 334518
Media: 10
Personnel:
Thomas Erb *(Pres)*

ELISA ILANA CUSTOM DESIGNS
13132 Deven Port St
Omaha, NE 68154
Tel.: (402) 926-3479
Fax: (413) 328-6111
E-mail: laurie@elisailana.com
Web Site: www.elisailana.com
Approx. Number Employees: 40
Year Founded: 1996
Business Description:
Jewelry
S.I.C.: 5944
N.A.I.C.S.: 448310
Media: 6-10
Personnel:
Laurie Langdon-Gerber *(Pres & CEO)*
Brands & Products:
ELISA ILANA

EMPIRE DIAMOND CORPORATION
350 5th Ave
New York, NY 10118
Tel.: (212) 564-4777
Fax: (212) 564-4960
Toll Free: (800) 728-3425
E-mail: info@dialadiamond.com
Web Site: www.dialadiamond.com
Approx. Number Employees: 100
Year Founded: 1931
Business Description:
Wholesaler of Diamonds & Jewelry
S.I.C.: 5094; 5944
N.A.I.C.S.: 423940; 448310
Import Export
Advertising Expenditures: $720,000
Consumer Mags.: $20,000; Daily Newsp.: $200,000; Spot Radio: $400,000; Spot T.V.: $100,000
Distr.: Direct to Consumer; Natl.
Personnel:
Gregory Herdemian *(CEO & COO)*
Ann Akers *(Dir-Adv)*
Brands & Products:
DIAL A DIAMOND
EMPIRE
EMPIRE DIAMOND

ENGER-KRESS COMPANY
6510 Aurora Rd Ste C
West Bend, WI 53090-9330
Tel.: (262) 629-1553
Fax: (262) 629-1814
Toll Free: (800) 367-7547
E-mail: info@engerkress.com
Web Site: www.engerkress.com
Approx. Number Employees: 50
Year Founded: 1885
Business Description:
Leather Goods Importer & Mfr
S.I.C.: 3172
N.A.I.C.S.: 316993
Export
Advertising Expenditures: $200,000
Media: 4-10
Distr.: Natl.
Budget Set: Mar.
Brands & Products:
BRIGHTON BAY
CHAPPARAL
CROSSROADS
ENGER-KRESS
HERITAGE
HERITAGE LEATHERS
RAWBONE

ERFFMEYER AND SON CO., INC.
(d/b/a ESCO, Inc.)
PO Box 240047
Milwaukee, WI 53224-9002
Tel.: (414) 354-7800
Fax: (414) 362-7287
Toll Free: (800) 852-4266
E-mail: info@escoinc.com
Web Site: www.escoinc.com
Approx. Sls.: $4,000,000
Approx. Number Employees: 45
Year Founded: 1934
Business Description:
Precious Emblematic Jewelry Mfr
S.I.C.: 3911; 3993
N.A.I.C.S.: 339911; 339950
Media: 17
Personnel:
Wendy Braatz *(VP-Mktg)*
Brands & Products:
AWARDS OF DISTINCTION
ESCO

EUGENE BIRO CORP.
581 5th Ave 3rd Fl
New York, NY 10017
Tel.: (212) 997-0146
Fax: (212) 764-4506
Toll Free: (800) 422-9161
E-mail: info@eugenebiro.com
Web Site: www.eugenebiro.com
Approx. Number Employees: 45
Year Founded: 1974
Business Description:
Diamond & Jewelry Mfr
S.I.C.: 5094; 3915
N.A.I.C.S.: 423940; 339913
Media: 6
Personnel:
Eugene Biro *(CEO)*

FGX INTERNATIONAL, INC.
(Sub. of Essilor International, S.A.)
500 George Washington Hwy
Smithfield, RI 02917
Tel.: (401) 231-3800
Fax: (401) 231-7235
Toll Free: (800) 283-3090
E-mail: crinfo@fgxi.com
Web Site: www.fgxi.com
Approx. Sls.: $256,100,000
Approx. Number Employees: 500
Year Founded: 2004
Business Description:
Non-Prescription Reading Glasses, Sunglasses & Costume Jewelry Designer & Marketer
S.I.C.: 3842; 3827; 3961; 6719
N.A.I.C.S.: 339113; 333314; 339914; 551112
Import Export
Advertising Expenditures: $6,600,000
Personnel:
Alec Taylor *(Chm & CEO)*
John H. Flynn, Jr. *(Pres)*
Anthony Di Paola *(CFO)*
Jeffrey J. Giguere *(Gen Counsel, Sec & Exec VP)*
Steven Crellin *(Exec VP-North America)*
Robert Grow *(Exec VP-Product Dev)*
Gerald Kitchen *(Exec VP-Ops)*
Sal Siano *(Dir-Mktg-Foster Grant)*
Brands & Products:
ADVANCED UV PROTECTION DR RECOMMENDED
ANARCHY
ANGEL
BODY GLOVE
BODY GLOVE OPTICAL
C9 BY CHAMPION
CELEBRATION OF STYLE
EYEWEAR FOR THE OUTDOORS
FGX INTERNATIONAL
FIELD & STREAM
FIND YOUR SIGNATURE FIT
FITS OVER
FOR THE ANARCHIST IN ALL OF US
FOSTER GRANT
GARGOYLES
GO THE DISTANCE
IRON MAN
JEFF BANKS
LOOK LIKE AN ATHELETE PERFORM LIKE AN ATHELETE
MAGNIVISION
ORIGINAL OUTFITTER
POLAR EYES
PREMIUM POLARIZED SUNWEAR
PRIVATE EYES
PROTECT THE CORE
SEE IT LIKE THE PROS
SIGNATURE
SOLAR SHIELD

FORWARD INDUSTRIES, INC.
1801 Green Rd Ste E
Pompano Beach, FL 33064-1052

Key to Media (For complete agency information see *The Advertising Red Books-Agencies* edition):
1. Bus. Publs. 2. Cable T.V. 3. Catalogs & Directories. 4. Co-op Adv. 5. Consumer Mags. 6. D.M. to Bus. Estab.7. D.M. to Consumers
8. Daily Newsp. 9. Exhibits/Trade Shows 10. Foreign 11. Infomercial 12. Internet Adv.13. Multimedia 14. Network Radio
15. Network T.V. 16. Newsp. Distr. Mags. 17. Other 18. Outdoor (Posters, Transit) 19. Point of Purchase20. Premiums, Novelties
21. Product Samples 22. Special Events Mktg. 23. Spot Radio 24. Spot T.V. 25. Weekly Newsp. 26. Yellow Page Adv.

Tel.: (954) 419-9544
Fax: (954) 419-9735
E-mail: info@forwardindustries.com
Web Site: www.forwardindustries.com
Approx. Sls.: $18,996,827
Approx. Number Employees: 32
Year Founded: 1961
Business Description:
Custom Leather, Nylon & Vinyl Carrying Cases Mfr & Designer for Portable Products
S.I.C.: 3171; 2782; 3082; 3084; 3161
N.A.I.C.S.: 316992; 316991; 323118; 326121; 326122
Advertising Expenditures: $111,000
Media: 4-7-8-21
Personnel:
Frank LaGrange Johnson *(Chm)*
Brett M. Johnson *(CEO)*
James O. McKenna *(CFO)*
Brands & Products:
TERRAPIN

FOSSIL, INC.

2280 N Greenville Ave
Richardson, TX 75082
Tel.: (972) 234-2525
Fax: (972) 234-4669
E-mail: ir@fossil.com
Web Site: www.fossil.com
Approx. Sls.: $2,030,690,000
Approx. Number Employees: 10,500
Year Founded: 1984
Business Description:
Watches, Sunglasses, Handbags & Fashion Accessories Marketer & Mfr
S.I.C.: 3873; 2389; 3172; 5944
N.A.I.C.S.: 334518; 315999; 316993; 448310
Advertising Expenditures: $85,600,000
Media: 4-5-6-8-9-13-16-18-25
Distr.: Intl.
Budget Set: Oct.
Personnel:
Tom Kartsotis *(Chm)*
Mark D. Quick *(Vice Chm)*
Kosta N. Kartsotis *(CEO)*
Michael L. Kovar *(CFO & Exec VP)*
Jennifer Pritchard *(Pres-Retail)*
Randy S. Hyne *(Gen Counsel & VP-Legal)*
Livio Galanti *(Exec VP-Lux, Sports & Tech)*
Audra Belger Parker *(Sr Dir-HR)*
Merk Harbour *(Dir-Integrated Mktg & Promo)*
Brands & Products:
ARKITEKT
BIG TIC
BLUE TEQ
F2
FIFTY-FOUR
FOREVER
FOSSIL
FUEL
KALEIDO
MOBILEWEAR
MW
MW MICHELE
RELIC
SPEEDWAY
ZODIAC
Advertising Agency:
Brierley & Partners
5700 Wilshire Blvd Ste 650
Los Angeles, CA 90036-3654
Tel.: (323) 932-7272
Fax: (323) 965-4100

FOWNES BROTHERS & CO., INC.

16 E 34th St 5th Fl
New York, NY 10016-2203
Tel.: (212) 683-0150
Fax: (212) 683-2832
Toll Free: (800) 345-6837
E-mail: fownes@fownesbro.com
Approx. Number Employees: 250
Year Founded: 1777
Business Description:
Gloves, Scarves & Hats Mfr
S.I.C.: 5136; 5137
N.A.I.C.S.: 424320; 424330
Import Export
Advertising Expenditures: $200,000
Media: 2-7
Distr.: Intl.; Natl.
Personnel:
Andrew Gluckman *(Pres)*
Tom Faivre *(CFO)*
Chris Giattino *(Exec VP-Sls)*

FRIEDMAN'S INC.

4550 Excel Pkwy Ste 100
Addison, TX 75001
Tel.: (972) 892-9200
Fax: (972) 892-9612
Toll Free: (800) 545-9033
E-mail: support@friedmans.com
Web Site: www.friedmans.com
Sales Range: $400-449.9 Million
Approx. Number Employees: 3,967
Year Founded: 1920
Business Description:
Specialty Retailer of Fine Jewelry
S.I.C.: 5944
N.A.I.C.S.: 448310
Advertising Expenditures: $23,529,000
Media: 4-19-22
Brands & Products:
AAFCO
FRIEDMAN'S JEWELERS
FRIEDMAN'S
REGENCY JEWELERS
THE VALUE LEADER SINCE 1920

GENEVA WATCH GROUP

47-14 32nd St
Long Island City, NY 11101
Tel.: (718) 729-8600
Fax: (718) 729-8761
Toll Free: (800) 874-0907
Web Site: www.genevawatchgroup.com
Approx. Number Employees: 200
Year Founded: 1974
Business Description:
Watches, Clocks, Watchcases & Parts Marketer
S.I.C.: 3873; 5112
N.A.I.C.S.: 334518; 424120
Import Export
Media: 10-13
Personnel:
Jeff Gregg *(CEO)*
Dena Rucker *(Sr VP-Product Dev)*
Wilson Troche *(Dir-Brand Mgmt)*
Brands & Products:
GENEVA

GEORGE GLOVE CO., INC.

301 Greenwood Ave
Midland Park, NJ 07432-1446
Tel.: (201) 251-1200
Fax: (201) 251-8431
Toll Free: (800) 631-4292
E-mail: roy@georgeglove.com
Web Site: www.georgeglove.com
Approx. Sls.: $2,500,000
Approx. Number Employees: 8
Year Founded: 1932
Business Description:
Gloves Mfr & Distr
S.I.C.: 3151
N.A.I.C.S.: 315992
Import Export
Media: 2-4-5-6-7-8-10-21
Distr.: Natl.
Budget Set: Sept.
Personnel:
Andy Wilson *(Pres)*
Clark Bullock *(CEO)*
Brands & Products:
DERMAL GLOVES
GEORGE GLOVE COMPANY
Advertising Agency:
Design 24
Rm. 08 1001 Avenue of the Americas, 12th Fl.
New York, NY 10018
Tel.: (212) 221-8140

GEVRIL USA

9 Pine Crest Rd
Valley Cottage, NY 10989
Tel.: (845) 425-9882
Fax: (845) 425-9897
E-mail: info@gevril.com
Web Site: www.gevril.com
Approx. Number Employees: 10
Business Description:
Watches
S.I.C.: 3873
N.A.I.C.S.: 334518
Media: 6-9-10-16-23-24-25
Personnel:
Samuel Friedmann *(Pres)*
Debbie Leeder *(Mgr-Mktg)*
Brands & Products:
AVENUE OF AMERICAS
CHELSEA
GEVRIL
GLAMOUR
GRAMERCY
LAFAYETTE
MADISON
MINI
SEA CLOUD
SERENADE
SOHO DELUXE

GORDON INDUSTRIES LTD.

(d/b/a Gordon Sinclair)
1500 Plz Ave
New Hyde Park, NY 11040
Tel.: (516) 354-8888
Fax: (516) 354-4440
Toll Free: (800) 226-0808
E-mail: customerservice@gordonsinclair.com
Web Site: www.gordonsinclair.com
Approx. Sls.: $3,000,000
Approx. Number Employees: 30
Year Founded: 1989
Business Description:
Calculators, Clocks, Gifts, Writing Instruments, Cameras, Tools, Drinkware & Various Other Implements & Accessories Designer & Mfr
S.I.C.: 5023
N.A.I.C.S.: 423220
Import Export
Advertising Expenditures: $200,000
Media: 2-4-7-10
Distr.: Natl.
Personnel:
Rachel Halpern *(Owner)*
Sunanda Karode *(Dir-Art)*
Brands & Products:
BRUSKI GIFT SET
GORDON SINCLAIR
QUALITY NEVER LOOKED SO GOOD
SHAKER MAKER GIFT SET
STAR PACK GIFT SET

THE GRANDOE CORPORATION

74 Bleecker St
Gloversville, NY 12078-2919
Tel.: (518) 725-8641
Fax: (518) 725-9088
Toll Free: (800) GRANDOE
E-mail: customerservice@grandoe.com
Web Site: www.grandoe.com
Approx. Number Employees: 2,000
Year Founded: 1898
Business Description:
Men's & Ladies' Dress, Ski, Bicycle & Snowboarding Gloves Retailer
S.I.C.: 3151; 3949
N.A.I.C.S.: 315992; 339920
Import Export
Advertising Expenditures: $500,000
Media: 2-3-4-5-6-7-9-10-19-25
Distr.: Intl.; Natl.
Budget Set: Oct.
Personnel:
Eric Friedman *(Pres & CEO)*
Brands & Products:
APRES SKI
CITY SLICKER
COMFORT SLICKER
COPPER
GCS
GRANDOE
ICE BREAKERS
MACRO CAP TECHNOLOGY
NAPLES
ONE UP
PATROL
PERFECTSOLE
PICASSO
POWER RIDER
PUFF
RUSTY NAIL
SIENA
SILKY WARMER
SPITFIRE
STICK IT
STORM
VAN GOGH
WATER BLOCK

GUCCI AMERICA INC.

(Sub. of Gucci Group N.V.)
685 5th Ave
New York, NY 10022-4204
Tel.: (212) 750-5220
Fax: (212) 230-0894
Web Site: www.gucci.com
Approx. Number Employees: 325
Business Description:
Luxury Shoes & Accessories Marketer & Distr
S.I.C.: 5621; 5948
N.A.I.C.S.: 448120; 448320
Media: 4-5-6-9-10-18-22-25-30

Key to Media (For complete agency information see *The Advertising Red Books-Agencies* edition):
1. Bus. Publs. 2. Cable T.V. 3. Catalogs & Directories. 4. Co-op Adv. 5. Consumer Mags. 6. D.M. to Bus. Estab.7. D.M. to Consumers
8. Daily Newsp. 9. Exhibits/Trade Shows 10. Foreign 11. Infomercial 12. Internet Adv.13. Multimedia 14. Network Radio
15. Network T.V. 16. Newsp. Distr. Mags. 17. Other 18. Outdoor (Posters, Transit) 19. Point of Purchase20. Premiums, Novelties
21. Product Samples 22. Special Events Mktg. 23. Spot Radio 24. Spot T.V. 25. Weekly Newsp. 26. Yellow Page Adv.

Gucci America Inc. — (Continued)

Distr.: Natl.
Budget Set: Feb. -July
Personnel:
Susan Chokachi *(Sr VP-Mktg & Comm)*
Annalisa Dimonte *(Dir-Mktg)*
Brands & Products:
GUCCI

GUNTHER MELE LIMITED
30 Craig St
Brantford, ON N3R 7J1, Canada
Tel.: (519) 756-4330
Fax: (519) 756-4335
Toll Free: (888) 486-8437
E-mail: packaging@gunthermele.com
Web Site: www.gunthermele.com
E-Mail For Key Personnel:
President: dking@gunthermele.com
Approx. Number Employees: 100
Year Founded: 1857
Business Description:
Mfr. & Importer of Jewelry Packaging, Jewelry Boxes & Store Supplies
S.I.C.: 2657
N.A.I.C.S.: 322212
Import Export
Advertising Expenditures: $200,000
Media: 4-19
Distr.: Natl.
Budget Set: Jan. -Feb.
Personnel:
Darrell King *(Pres)*
Douglas M. King *(CEO)*
Terry C.M. Coombs *(Mgr-Info Svcs)*
Ron Kerr *(Mgr-Pur)*
Peter Strait *(Mgr-Ops)*

H. STERN JEWELERS, INC.
(Affil. of H. Stern Com & Ind., S.A.)
645 5th Ave
New York, NY 10022-5910
Tel.: (212) 688-0300
Fax: (212) 888-5137
Toll Free: (800) 221-4768
E-mail: usamkt@hstern.net
Web Site: www.hstern.net
Sales Range: $75-99.9 Million
Approx. Number Employees: 50
Business Description:
Retail Jewelry
S.I.C.: 5944; 5094
N.A.I.C.S.: 448310; 423940
Advertising Expenditures: $850,000
Media: 4-5-8-9-10-17-20-23-25
Distr.: Natl.
Personnel:
Roberto Stern *(Pres)*
Paula Gartenkraut *(Mgr-Mktg)*
Brands & Products:
H. STERN JEWELERS
Advertising Agency:
OMD-USA
195 Broadway
New York, NY 10007
Tel.: (212) 590-7100

HARRY KOTLAR & CO., INC.
607 S Hill St Ste 710
Los Angeles, CA 90014
Tel.: (213) 626-0428
Fax: (213) 626-6425
Toll Free: (800) 675-0479
E-mail: info@harrykotlar.com
Web Site: www.harrykotlar.com
Approx. Number Employees: 5
Year Founded: 1948
Business Description:
Diamond Sales, Mfr & Importer
S.I.C.: 5944; 3911
N.A.I.C.S.: 448310; 339911
Media: 6
Personnel:
Louis Wiener *(Pres)*
David Wiener *(VP & Mgr-Sls)*
Brands & Products:
ARTISAN PAVE
DIAMONDS THAT MAKE A DIFFERENCE
HARRY KOTLAR
KOTLAR CUSHION

HARRY WINSTON, INC.
(Sub. of Harry Winston Diamond Corporation)
718 5th Ave
New York, NY 10019
Tel.: (212) 245-2000
Fax: (212) 765-8809
Toll Free: (800) 988-4110
E-mail: contact@harrywinston.com
Web Site: www.harrywinston.com
Sales Range: $10-24.9 Million
Approx. Number Employees: 250
Year Founded: 1932
Business Description:
Precious Jewelry Sales
S.I.C.: 3911; 5944
N.A.I.C.S.: 339911; 448310
Media: 6-10-30
Distr.: Intl.; Natl.
Personnel:
Frederic de Narp *(Pres & CEO)*
Cyrille Baudet *(CFO)*
Raymond N. Simpson *(COO)*
Anthony Ledru *(VP-Global Sls)*
Federica Boido *(Dir-Mktg)*
Laura Kiernan *(Dir-IR)*
Brands & Products:
HARRY WINSTON
HOPE DIAMOND
JONKER DIAMOND
STAR OF INDEPENDENCE
STAR OF SIERRA LEONE
TAYLOR-BURTON DIAMOND

HARTGERS DIAMONDS, LTD.
699 Wyckoff Ave
Wyckoff, NJ 07841
Tel.: (201) 891-0044
Fax: (201) 891-3031
Web Site: www.hartgersjewelers.com
Approx. Number Employees: 9
Year Founded: 1898
Business Description:
Mfr., Retailer, Repairer & Appraiser of Watches & Custom Jewelry
S.I.C.: 5944; 5947
N.A.I.C.S.: 448310; 453220
Media: 6-18
Personnel:
John Hartgers *(Pres)*

HARTMANN, INC.
(Holding of Clarion Capital Partners, LLC)
200 Hartmann Dr
Lebanon, TN 37087
Tel.: (615) 444-5000
Fax: (883) 443-5409
Toll Free: (800) 331-0613
Web Site: www.hartmann.com
Sales Range: $25-49.9 Million
Approx. Number Employees: 75
Year Founded: 1877
Business Description:
Luggage & Leather Accessories Mfr
S.I.C.: 3161; 3172
N.A.I.C.S.: 316991; 316993
Export
Media: 3-4-5-6-10-13-19-22
Personnel:
Frank Johnston *(COO)*
John Baker *(VP-Fin)*
Dick Kunkle *(VP-Sls & Mktg)*
Brands & Products:
HARTMANN
WHERE THE JOURNEY BEGINS

HATCO, INC.
(Sub. of Arena Brands Inc.)
601 Marion Dr
Garland, TX 75042-7930
Tel.: (972) 494-0511
Fax: (972) 494-2369
Web Site: www.stetsonhat.com
Sales Range: $250-299.9 Million
Approx. Number Employees: 600
Year Founded: 1927
Business Description:
Hats Mfr
S.I.C.: 2353
N.A.I.C.S.: 315991
Media: 2-4-6-19
Distr.: Natl.
Budget Set: June
Personnel:
Matthew Range *(Mktg Mgr)*
Jay Winborn *(Mgr-Mktg)*
Brands & Products:
CHARLEY 1 HORSE
DOBBS

HEARTS ON FIRE COMPANY
99 Summer St
Boston, MA 02110
Tel.: (617) 523-5588
Fax: (617) 523-1437
Toll Free: (877) 737-3328
E-mail: customerservice@heartsonfire.com
Web Site: www.heartsonfire.com
Approx. Number Employees: 35
Business Description:
Diamond Jewelry
S.I.C.: 3911; 5944
N.A.I.C.S.: 339911; 448310
Media: 6-10-18-19-23-24
Personnel:
Susan Rothman *(Co-Founder & CEO)*
Mark Israel *(Pres & COO)*
Caryl Capeci *(VP-Mktg)*
Brands & Products:
HEARTS ON FIRE
THE WORLD'S MOST PERFECTLY CUT DIAMOND

HELZBERG'S DIAMOND SHOPS, INC.
(Holding of Berkshire Hathaway Inc.)
(d/b/a Helzberg Diamonds)
1825 Swift Ave
Kansas City, MO 64116-3644
Tel.: (816) 842-7780
Fax: (816) 627-1294
Web Site: www.helzberg.com
Sales Range: $450-499.9 Million
Approx. Number Employees: 2,500
Year Founded: 1915
Business Description:
Retail Jewelry Stores
S.I.C.: 5944
N.A.I.C.S.: 448310
Import
Media: 3-4-5-8-9-13-18-19-22-23-24-25-26
Distr.: Reg.
Budget Set: Feb.
Personnel:
Bryan Kennedy *(Pres)*
Lonnie Lawton *(CFO & Sr VP)*
Kevin Fitzpatrick *(Exec VP-HR)*
Mitch Maggart *(Sr VP-Store Ops-Learning & Performance)*
Laura Baker *(Dir-Mktg)*
Brands & Products:
CERTIFIED PERFECT
CIRCLE O' LOVE
CONFIDENCE COMES IN A BURGUNDY BOX
THE CONTINENTAL DIAMOND COLLECTION
THE DESIGNER DIAMOND COLLECTION
HELZBERG
HELZBERG DIAMOND MASTERPIECE
HELZBERG LIMITED EDITION
I AM LOVED
MINI DIAMOND
RADIANT STAR
Advertising Agency:
Barkley
1740 Main St
Kansas City, MO 64108
Tel.: (816) 842-1500

HERFF JONES, INC.
4501 W 62nd St
Indianapolis, IN 46268-2587
Mailing Address:
PO Box 68501
Indianapolis, IN 46268-0501
Tel.: (317) 297-3740
Fax: (317) 329-3308
E-mail: mission@herff-jones.com
Web Site: www.herff-jones.com
Sales Range: $450-499.9 Million
Approx. Number Employees: 4,200
Year Founded: 1920
Business Description:
School Graduation Products, Recognition & Motivational Awards, Photography & Multi-Media Instructional Programs
S.I.C.: 3961; 2741
N.A.I.C.S.: 339914; 511199
Media: 2-4-5-7-8-10-21-26
Distr.: Direct to Consumer; Intl.; Natl.
Personnel:
Joe Slaughter *(Pres)*
Brands & Products:
ACTIVE CHEMISTRY
FRESHMAN RECORD
HERFF JONES
HJ
IMAGE PAK
IMAGEMASTER
IMAGINE
NEW STUDENT RECORD
NYSTROM
PAGEMASTER
THE RECORD PROGRAMS
REUNION RECORD

Key to Media (For complete agency information see *The Advertising Red Books-Agencies* edition):
1. Bus. Publs. 2. Cable T.V. 3. Catalogs & Directories. 4. Co-op Adv. 5. Consumer Mags. 6. D.M. to Bus. Estab.7. D.M. to Consumers 8. Daily Newsp. 9. Exhibits/Trade Shows 10. Foreign 11. Infomercial 12. Internet Adv.13. Multimedia 14. Network Radio 15. Network T.V. 16. Newsp. Distr. Mags. 17. Other 18. Outdoor (Posters, Transit) 19. Point of Purchase20. Premiums, Novelties 21. Product Samples 22. Special Events Mktg. 23. Spot Radio 24. Spot T.V. 25. Weekly Newsp. 26. Yellow Page Adv.

HIDALGO JEWELRY CORPORATION
14 NE 1st Ave Ste 1009
Miami, FL 33132
Tel.: (305) 379-0110
Fax: (305) 379-0021
E-mail: owner@hidalgojewelry.com
Web Site: www.hidalgojewelry.com
Approx. Number Employees: 12
Business Description:
Jewelry Designer & Retailer
S.I.C.: 5944; 3911
N.A.I.C.S.: 448310; 339911
Media: 4-6-10
Personnel:
Silvio Hidalgo *(Pres)*

HOWARD MILLER COMPANY
860 E Main Ave
Zeeland, MI 49464-1300
Tel.: (616) 772-7277
Fax: (616) 772-1670
E-mail: international@howardmiller.com
Web Site: www.howardmiller.com
Approx. Number Employees: 1,500
Year Founded: 1926
Business Description:
Holding Company; Furniture & Clock Mfr
S.I.C.: 6719; 2511; 3873
N.A.I.C.S.: 551112; 334518; 337122
Import Export
Media: 2-4-6-7-11-13-18-19
Distr.: Natl.
Budget Set: Oct. -Nov.
Personnel:
Howard J. Miller *(Pres)*
Robert LeHocky *(Exec VP)*
Dennis Palasek *(VP-Fin)*
Mark Siciliano *(Dir-Mktg)*
Brands & Products:
ACCUWAVE
ACCUWAVE DS
CAROLS OF CHRISTMAS II
HEKMAN
HOWARD MILLER
KIENINGER
TRAVEL LITE
WOODMARK

HUGO BOSCA COMPANY, INC.
(d/b/a Bosca Accessories & Leather)
1905 W Jefferson St
Springfield, OH 45506
Tel.: (937) 323-5523
Fax: (937) 323-7063
Toll Free: (866) 890-5696
Toll Free: (800) 732-6722
E-mail: info@boscaonline.com
Web Site: www.boscaonline.com
Approx. Number Employees: 35
Year Founded: 1911
Business Description:
Mfr. Small Leather Goods
S.I.C.: 3172; 3171
N.A.I.C.S.: 316993; 316992
Media: 4-5-6-7-8-13
Distr.: Intl.; Natl.
Budget Set: Apr.
Personnel:
Christopher Bosca *(Pres & CEO)*
Dick Rabe *(CFO)*
Brands & Products:
AMERICAN BELTING LEATHER
BOSCA
BOSCA CORRESPONDENT
BOSCA MESSENGER
KINGS CREEK
NAPPA VITELLO
OLD LEATHER
TRIBECA

IAMGOLD
(Sub. of IAMGOLD Corporation)
1111 Saint Charles W
Longueuil, QC J4K 5G4, Canada
Tel.: (450) 677-0040
Fax: (450) 677-3382
E-mail: info@iamgold.com
Web Site: www.iamgold.com
Sales Range: $300-349.9 Million
Approx. Number Employees: 2,700
Year Founded: 1986
Business Description:
Gold Producer
S.I.C.: 1041
N.A.I.C.S.: 212221
Export
Media: 10

ICETEK WATCH CO.
590 5th Ave Ste 501
New York, NY 10036
Tel.: (212) 354-4140
Fax: (212) 354-2520
Toll Free: (888) 7-ICETEK
E-mail: info@icetekwatch.com
Web Site: www.icetekwatch.com
Approx. Sls.: $10,000,000
Business Description:
Watch Distr
S.I.C.: 5094
N.A.I.C.S.: 423940
Media: 6-22
Personnel:
Daniel Pasternek *(Pres)*

IMAGE WATCHES, INC.
2501 Davidson Dr Ste 100
Monterey Park, CA 91754
Tel.: (626) 433-0311
Fax: (323) 264-3636
Toll Free: (888) 664-6243
E-mail: service@imagewatch.com
Web Site: www.imagewatch.com
Sales Range: Less than $1 Million
Approx. Number Employees: 12
Year Founded: 1989
Business Description:
Promotional Watches Mfr
S.I.C.: 3873
N.A.I.C.S.: 334518
Import
Media: 4-7-10-13
Distr.: Natl.
Personnel:
William Chien *(Pres)*
Brands & Products:
IMAGE WATCHES
OUR WATCHES, YOUR IMAGINATION.

IMPERIAL-DELTAH, INC.
795 Waterman Ave
East Providence, RI 02914-1713
Tel.: (401) 434-2597
Fax: (401) 434-0814
Toll Free: (800) 556-7738
E-mail: imperial@pearls.com
Web Site: www.pearls.com
Approx. Number Employees: 200
Year Founded: 1899
Business Description:
Mfr. of Gold Filled, 14K Gold, Pearl & Sterling Silver Jewelry
S.I.C.: 3911
N.A.I.C.S.: 339911
Import Export
Advertising Expenditures: $1,500,000
Media: 2-4-6-7-8-10-13-19
Distr.: Distr.; Natl.
Personnel:
Banice C. Bazar *(Owner)*
Kathy Grenier *(Mgr-Mktg)*
Brands & Products:
IMPERIAL
WE ARE PEARLS.

JABEL, INC.
365 Coit St
Irvington, NJ 07111
Tel.: (973) 374-6000
Fax: (973) 374-3141
Toll Free: (800) 526-4597
E-mail: info@jabel.com
Web Site: www.jabel.com/
Approx. Number Employees: 100
Year Founded: 1916
Business Description:
Mfr. & Distributor of Jewelry
S.I.C.: 3911
N.A.I.C.S.: 339911
Advertising Expenditures: $250,000
Media: 2-4-5-7-13-18
Personnel:
David Conley *(Pres)*

JACK KELEGE & CO., INC.
13946 Ventura Blvd
Sherman Oaks, CA 91423
Tel.: (213) 622-1290
Fax: (213) 622-0363
Toll Free: (877) 6KELEGE
E-mail: contact@jackkelege.com
Web Site: www.jackkelege.com
Approx. Number Employees: 12
Year Founded: 1972
Business Description:
Jewelry Mfr & Distr
S.I.C.: 5944
N.A.I.C.S.: 448310
Media: 6
Personnel:
Jack Kelege *(Pres)*

J.B. ROBINSON JEWELERS, INC.
(Sub. of Sterling Jewelers Inc.)
375 Ghent Rd
Akron, OH 44333
Tel.: (330) 668-5000
Fax: (330) 668-5184
Web Site: www.jbrobinson.com
Approx. Number Employees: 700
Business Description:
Retail Jewelers
S.I.C.: 5944
N.A.I.C.S.: 448310
Advertising Expenditures: $750,000
Media: 4-9-16-19-23-25-26
Distr.: Natl.
Budget Set: Feb.
Personnel:
Terry Burman *(Pres & CEO)*
George Murray *(Sr VP-Mktg)*
Brands & Products:
J.B. ROBINSON
JBR.COM
Advertising Agency:
Stern Advertising, Inc.
29125 Chagrin Blvd
Cleveland, OH 44122-4622
Tel.: (216) 464-4850
Fax: (216) 464-7859
(Jewelry)

JEEP COLLINS JEWELRYMAKER, INC.
648 Post Oak Rd
Fredericksburg, TX 78624
Tel.: (830) 997-3135
Fax: (830) 997-0007
Toll Free: (800) 343-9757
E-mail: info@jeepcollins.com
Web Site: www.jeepcollins.com
Approx. Number Employees: 7
Business Description:
Hand Made Jewelry Mfr & Retailer
S.I.C.: 3911; 5944
N.A.I.C.S.: 339911; 448310
Media: 4
Personnel:
Jeep Collins *(Pres)*
Brands & Products:
JEEP COLLINS
SYMBOLS OF OUR LIFE

JENSEN JEWELERS OF IDAHO LLC
(d/b/a Jensen Management)
130 2nd Ave N
Twin Falls, ID 83301
Tel.: (208) 734-7920
Fax: (208) 734-9574
E-mail: info@jensen-jewelers.com
Web Site: www.jensen-jewelers.com
Approx. Number Employees: 125
Business Description:
Jewelry Stores
S.I.C.: 5944
N.A.I.C.S.: 448310
Personnel:
Tony Pranter *(CEO)*
Advertising Agency:
Drake Cooper Inc.
416 S 8th 3rd Fl
Boise, ID 83702-5471
Tel.: (208) 342-0925
Fax: (208) 342-0635

JK JEWELRY INC.
1500 Brighton Henrietta Town Line Rd
Rochester, NY 14623
Tel.: (585) 292-0770
Fax: (585) 292-0774
E-mail: info@jkjewelry.com
Web Site: www.jkjewelry.com
Approx. Number Employees: 45
Year Founded: 1975
Business Description:
Mfr., Whslr & Importer of Jewelry & Precious Metals
S.I.C.: 5094
N.A.I.C.S.: 423940
Media: 2-10-13
Personnel:
John S. Kaupp *(Pres)*

JOHN ATENCIO GOLDSMITH, LTD.
PO Box 44189
Denver, CO 80201
Tel.: (303) 830-7733
Fax: (303) 230-0891
Toll Free: (877) 802-3501
E-mail: info@johnatencio.com
Web Site: www.johnatencio.com
Approx. Sls.: $11,322,230
Approx. Number Employees: 35
Year Founded: 1976

John Atencio Goldsmith, LTD. — (Continued)

Business Description:
Designer Jewelry Mfr & Distr
S.I.C.: 3911; 5944
N.A.I.C.S.: 339911; 448310
Media: 4-6-8-9-13-18-19-22-25

Brands & Products:
JOHN ATENCIO

JOHN HARDY USA, INC.

601 W 26th St 19th Fl
New York, NY 10001
Tel.: (212) 219-4288
Tel.: (646) 486-8329
Fax: (212) 202-6191
Web Site: www.johnhardy.com
Sales Range: $50-74.9 Million
Approx. Number Employees: 70

Business Description:
Fine Jewelry Distr
S.I.C.: 5094
N.A.I.C.S.: 423940
Media: 6-10

Personnel:
Mindy Grimes *(Pres)*
Jennifer Lavorante *(Sr Mktg Mgr)*

JOSTENS, INC.

(Joint Venture of KKR & CO. L.P. & Credit Suisse Group AG)
5501 American Blvd W
Minneapolis, MN 55437
Tel.: (952) 830-3300
Fax: (952) 830-3293
E-mail: info@jostens.com
Web Site: www.jostens.com
Sales Range: $1-9.9 Million
Approx. Number Employees: 6,300
Year Founded: 1897

Business Description:
School-Related Affinity Products & Marketing & Photography Services
S.I.C.: 7335; 8742
N.A.I.C.S.: 541922; 541613
Import Export
Media: 1-4-7-8-10-17
Distr.: Natl.

Personnel:
Timothy M. Larson *(Pres & CEO)*
Val Williams *(COO)*
Scott M. Henkel *(CIO)*
Marjorie J. Brown *(Sr VP-Fin)*
Keith Kugler *(VP-Fin)*
Gary Nelson *(VP-R&D Engrg)*
Cynthia Newsom *(VP-HR)*
Kimberly Noonan *(VP-Mktg & Emerging Markets)*
Rich Stoebe *(Dir-Comm)*

Brands & Products:
GOLD LANCE
JOSTENS

J.R. GOLD DESIGNS

555 5th Ave
New York, NY 10017
Tel.: (212) 922-9292
Fax: (212) 922-9456
Toll Free: (800) 999-0583
E-mail: info@jrgold.com
Web Site: www.jrgold.com
Approx. Number Employees: 15
Year Founded: 1965

Business Description:
Mfr of Jewelry
S.I.C.: 3911; 5094
N.A.I.C.S.: 339911; 423940
Media: 6-8-10-11

Brands & Products:
FOR THOSE WHO WANT MORE
RINA LIMOR

JUDITH RIPKA COMPANIES INC.

200 Madison Ave
New York, NY 10016-3902
Tel.: (212) 391-2340
Fax: (212) 244-4560
E-mail: info@judithripka.com
Web Site: www.judithripka.com
Approx. Number Employees: 125
Year Founded: 1973

Business Description:
Jewelry Designer, Retailer & Wholesaler
S.I.C.: 5944
N.A.I.C.S.: 448310
Media: 6-10-13

Personnel:
David Ripka *(Owner)*
Judith Ripka *(CEO)*
Erinn Einhauser *(Coord-Mktg)*

Brands & Products:
JUDITH RIPKA

KARAT PLATINUM LLC

(Sub. of Karat Platinum Inc.)
15 Hoover St
Inwood, NY 11096
Tel.: (516) 592-5600
Tel.: (516) 592-5699
Fax: (516) 592-5675
E-mail: bneuberg@karatplatinum.com
Web Site: www.karatplatinum.com
Sales Range: $250-299.9 Million
Year Founded: 2003

Business Description:
Jewelry Mfr & Distr
S.I.C.: 3911
N.A.I.C.S.: 339911
Advertising Expenditures: $91,261
Media: 10

Personnel:
David Nueberg *(Pres & CEO)*
Gary M. Jacobs *(CFO & COO)*
Howard Slochowsky *(Sr VP-Ops)*

Brands & Products:
14 KARAT PLATINUM
14KT.PT
KARAT PLATINUM

KRAIKO DIAMONDS, INC.

550 S Hill St Ste 1220
Los Angeles, CA 90013
Tel.: (213) 622-4767
Fax: (213) 622-8379
Toll Free: (800) 860-9136
E-mail: info@kraiko.com
Web Site: www.kraiko.com
Approx. Number Employees: 12

Business Description:
Mfr & Distr of Diamonds
S.I.C.: 5094
N.A.I.C.S.: 423940
Import
Media: 4-6-8

Personnel:
Comil Kohanarieh *(Co-Founder & Chm)*
Dan Kohanarieh *(Pres)*

Brands & Products:
KRAIKO

Advertising Agency:
JS2 Communications
661 N Harper Ave Ste 208
Los Angeles, CA 90048
Tel.: (323) 866-0880
Fax: (323) 866-0882
Public Relations

KREMENTZ & COMPANY

51 Commerce St
Springfield, NJ 07081
Tel.: (973) 621-8300
Fax: (973) 218-0800
Web Site: www.rkg1866.com
Sales Range: $10-24.9 Million
Approx. Number Employees: 50
Year Founded: 1866

Business Description:
Jewelry Mfr & Retailer
S.I.C.: 3911
N.A.I.C.S.: 339911
Export
Media: 2-4-6-7-9
Distr.: Natl.
Budget Set: Oct.

Advertising Agency:
Krementz Advertising
51 Thomas St
Springfield, NJ 07081
Tel.: (973) 621-8300
Fax: (973) 218-1265

KWIAT INC.

579 5th Ave
New York, NY 10017
Tel.: (212) 223-1111
Fax: (212) 223-2796
Toll Free: (800) 927-4367
E-mail: help@kwiat.com
Web Site: www.kwiat.com
Sales Range: $10-24.9 Million
Approx. Number Employees: 21
Year Founded: 1907

Business Description:
Jewelry Mfr
S.I.C.: 5094; 3915
N.A.I.C.S.: 423940; 339913
Media: 4-5-6-9-10-13-18-20-23-25-26

Personnel:
David S. Kwiat *(Owner)*
Lowell Kwiat *(Co-Pres)*
Bill Gould *(Dir-Mktg)*

Brands & Products:
KWAIT
KWAIT BLOOMS
KWAIT STAR
KWAIT TIARA
SIMPLY BRILLIANT

Advertising Agency:
Kerwin Communications
1120 Bloomfield Ave Ste 107
West Caldwell, NJ 07006
Tel.: (973) 244-0301
Fax: (973) 244-0990
— Sheila Macken *(Acct Exec)*

L. LAWRENCE PRODUCTS, INC.

445 Veit Rd
Huntingdon Valley, PA 19006-1617
Tel.: (215) 355-1021
Fax: (215) 355-0037
E-mail: info@earringaccessories.com
Web Site: www.comfees.com
Approx. Number Employees: 5
Year Founded: 1998

Business Description:
Eyeglass & Jewelry Accessories
S.I.C.: 3911; 3851
N.A.I.C.S.: 339911; 339115
Media: 4-13

Personnel:
Robert A. Kogen *(Pres)*

Brands & Products:
COMFEES

LAGOS INC.

Rittenhouse Sq 1735 Walnut St
Philadelphia, PA 19103
Tel.: (215) 925-1693
Tel.: (215) 567-0770
E-mail: info@lagos.com
Web Site: www.lagos.com
Approx. Sls.: $10,000,000
Approx. Number Employees: 100
Year Founded: 1917

Business Description:
Jewel Settings & Mountings, Precious Metal
S.I.C.: 3911
N.A.I.C.S.: 339911
Advertising Expenditures: $2,000,000
Media: 4-5-6-8-10

Personnel:
Steven Lagos *(Founder)*
Tebbie Linderman *(COO)*

Brands & Products:
ASTRAL
CAVIAR
CLASSIC KNOT
COLUMBUS CIRCLE
GLACIER
THE HEART COLLECTION
LAGOS
SIGNATURE
SUPER NOVA
WASHINGTON SQUARE

LANA UNLIMITED COMPANY

736 Northwestern Ave Ste 308
Lake Forest, IL 60045
Tel.: (312) 226-5262
Fax: (312) 492-6516
E-mail: customerservice@lanaunlimited.com
Web Site: www.lanaunlimited.com
Sales Range: $50-74.9 Million
Approx. Number Employees: 100
Year Founded: 2003

Business Description:
Jewelry Designer & Mfr
S.I.C.: 3911
N.A.I.C.S.: 339911
Media: 4-6-10

Personnel:
Lana Fertelmeister *(CEO)*

Brands & Products:
JUST ADD SKIN
LANA JEWELRY

LAURA MUNDER INC.

(d/b/a Laura Munder Fine Jewelry)
209 A Worth Ave
Palm Beach, FL 33480
Tel.: (561) 805-7008
Fax: (561) 296-5605
E-mail: info@lauramunder.com
Web Site: www.lauramunder.com
Approx. Number Employees: 7
Year Founded: 1998

Business Description:
Jewelry Mfr & Distr
S.I.C.: 5944
N.A.I.C.S.: 448310
Media: 6

Personnel:
Laura Munder *(Pres)*

Brands & Products:
LAURA M

Key to Media (For complete agency information see *The Advertising Red Books-Agencies* edition):
1. Bus. Publs. 2. Cable T.V. 3. Catalogs & Directories. 4. Co-op Adv. 5. Consumer Mags. 6. D.M. to Bus. Estab.7. D.M. to Consumers 8. Daily Newsp. 9. Exhibits/Trade Shows 10. Foreign 11. Infomercial 12. Internet Adv.13. Multimedia 14. Network Radio 15. Network T.V. 16. Newsp. Distr. Mags. 17. Other 18. Outdoor (Posters, Transit) 19. Point of Purchase20. Premiums, Novelties 21. Product Samples 22. Special Events Mktg. 23. Spot Radio 24. Spot T.V. 25. Weekly Newsp. 26. Yellow Page Adv.

LAURA MUNDER

LAURA PEARCE, LTD.
2300 Peachtree Rd NW Ste A103
Atlanta, GA 30309
Tel.: (404) 350-9207
Fax: (404) 350-9298
Toll Free: (800) 383-5007
E-mail: info@laurapearce.com
Web Site: www.laurapearce.com
Sales Range: $25-49.9 Million
Approx. Number Employees: 15
Year Founded: 1989
Business Description:
Jewelry Designer
S.I.C.: 5944; 5094
N.A.I.C.S.: 448310; 423940
Media: 6
Personnel:
Laura Pearce *(Owner)*

LAZARE KAPLAN INTERNATIONAL, INC.
19 W 44th St
New York, NY 10036
Tel.: (212) 972-9700
Fax: (212) 857-7660
Web Site: www.lazarediamonds.com
Sales Range: $350-399.9 Million
Approx. Number Employees: 148
Year Founded: 1903
Business Description:
Diamond Cutter, Polisher & Distr
S.I.C.: 5094; 3915
N.A.I.C.S.: 423940; 339913
Import Export
Advertising Expenditures: $2,200,000
Media: 5-6-11-19
Personnel:
Maurice Tempelsman *(Chm)*
Marcee M. Feinberg *(VP-Mktg)*
Brands & Products:
THE LAZARE DIAMOND
LK BEAUTY IS IN THE CUTTING
MY LAZARE DIAMOND
SETTING THE STANDARD FOR BRILLIANCE
SIMPLY LAZARE
TRELLIS
THE WORLD'S MOST BEAUTIFUL DIAMOND

LITTLE SWITZERLAND, INC.
(Sub. of NXP Corp.)
354 Indusco Ct
Troy, MI 48083
Tel.: (248) 556-2910
Fax: (248) 585-8643
Toll Free: (800) 524-2010
E-mail: gmathew@nxpco.com
Web Site: www.littleswitzerland.com
Approx. Rev.: $38,300,000
Approx. Number Employees: 450
Year Founded: 1954
Business Description:
Duty-Free Luxury Product Retailer
S.I.C.: 5944; 5122; 5719; 5947
N.A.I.C.S.: 448310; 442299; 446120; 453220
Advertising Expenditures: $2,500,000
Media: 1-2-4-5-6-7-8-9-10-11-12-13-17-18-22-23-24-25-26
Distr.: Intl.; Reg.
Budget Set: June
Personnel:
Hal Taylor *(Pres & CEO)*

LONG'S JEWELERS LTD.
60A S Ave
Burlington, MA 01803
Tel.: (781) 273-2400
Fax: (781) 273-5440
Toll Free: (877) 845-6647
E-mail: info@longsjewelers.com
Web Site: www.longsjewelers.com
Approx. Number Employees: 100
Year Founded: 1878
Business Description:
Jewelry Retailer
S.I.C.: 5944
N.A.I.C.S.: 448310
Media: 4-6-9-13-18-22-23-24-25
Distr.: Direct to Consumer; Reg.
Personnel:
Robert Rottenberg *(CEO)*

LOU MADDALONI JEWELERS INC.
1870 E Jericho Tpke
Huntington, NY 11743
Tel.: (631) 499-8800
Fax: (631) 499-2732
Web Site: www.maddaloni.net
Approx. Number Employees: 18
Business Description:
Mfr., Designer, Repairer & Retailer of Jewelry
S.I.C.: 5094; 5944
N.A.I.C.S.: 423940; 448310
Media: 6-10
Personnel:
Louis Maddaloni *(Pres)*

LOUIS GLICK & COMPANY
1271 Avenue of the Americas
New York, NY 10020
Tel.: (212) 259-0300
Fax: (212) 489-8178
Toll Free: (800) 77GLICK
E-mail: jewelry@louisglick.com
Web Site: www.louisglick.com
Approx. Number Employees: 35
Year Founded: 1945
Business Description:
Diamond Jeweler
S.I.C.: 5944; 3911
N.A.I.C.S.: 448310; 339911
Media: 6
Personnel:
Louis Glick *(Pres & CEO)*
Brands & Products:
BLONDE DIAMONDS
LOUIS GLICK
STARBURST

LUXOTTICA GROUP
(Sub. of Luxottica Group S.p.A.)
44 Harbor Park Dr
Port Washington, NY 11050-4625
Tel.: (516) 484-3800
Fax: (800) 451-4839
E-mail: info@luxottica.com
Web Site: www.luxottica.com/english/index.html
Approx. Number Employees: 25
Business Description:
Prescription Frames & Sunglasses Distr
S.I.C.: 5048; 3851
N.A.I.C.S.: 423460; 339115
Media: 30
Personnel:
Andrea Dorigo *(Pres-Wholesale-North America)*
Holly Rush *(Sr VP-Sls)*
Milena Cavicchioli *(VP-Mktg-North America)*
Jan Cory *(VP-Sls-Optical Independents & Sun Specialty Stores)*
Andrea Guaraldo *(VP-HR & Org)*
Nicolas Tesoriero *(VP-Fin & Ops)*
Brian Rowe *(Assoc VP-Sls)*
Advertising Agencies:
Brashe Advertising, Inc.
420 Jericho Tpke
Jericho, NY 11753-1344
Tel.: (516) 935-5544
Fax: (516) 931-1722

DDB Chicago
200 E Randolph St
Chicago, IL 60601
Tel.: (312) 552-6000
Fax: (312) 552-2370

Ketchum Directory Advertising/Kansas City
7015 College Blvd Ste 700
Overland Park, KS 66211-1524
Tel.: (913) 344-1900
Fax: (913) 344-1960
Toll Free: (800) 922-6977

Publicis Groupe S.A.
133 Ave des Champs-Elysee
75008
Paris, France
Tel.: (33) 1 44 43 70 00
Fax: (33) 1 44 43 75 25
Global Marketing & Advertising

R/GA
350 W 39th St
New York, NY 10018-1402
Tel.: (212) 946-4000
Fax: (212) 946-4010
Sunglass Hut

LUXOTTICA RETAIL
(Sub. of Luxottica Group)
4000 Luxottica Pl
Mason, OH 45040
Tel.: (513) 765-6000
Toll Free: (800) 767-0990
E-mail: customerservice@sunglasshut.com
Web Site: www.sunglasshut.com
Approx. Number Employees: 3,500
Year Founded: 1971
Business Description:
Eyeglass Sales
S.I.C.: 5995
N.A.I.C.S.: 446130
Media: 4-25-30
Personnel:
Pamela J. Garrett *(VP-Merchandising)*
Amy Connor *(Dir-Mktg-Sears Optical)*
Kristen McCabe *(Dir & Product Curator-Ilori)*
B.J. Schmidt *(Sr Mgr-Ecommerce)*
Rob Sarasua *(Mgr-Mktg Procurement)*
Brands & Products:
PEARLE VISION
WATCH STATION
Advertising Agencies:
J. Walter Thompson Company (d/b/a JWT)
466 Lexington Ave
New York, NY 10017-3140
Tel.: (212) 210-7000
Fax: (212) 210-7299

Ogilvy Public Relations Worldwide
636 11th Ave
New York, NY 10036
Tel.: (212) 880-5200
Fax: (212) 370-4636

LVMH INC.
(Sub. of Sofidiv S.A)
19 E 57th St 5th Fl
New York, NY 10022-2508
Tel.: (212) 931-2700
Fax: (212) 931-2737
E-mail: info@lvmh.com
Web Site: www.lvmh.com
Approx. Number Employees: 750
Year Founded: 1980
Business Description:
Holding Company
S.I.C.: 5948; 5099
N.A.I.C.S.: 448320; 423990
Personnel:
Renaud Dutreil *(Chm-NY Ops)*
Bruce G. Ingram *(Exec VP)*
Linda Maiocco *(Sr VP-Mktg & PR)*
Advertising Agencies:
Morpheus Media
127 W 26th St 7th Fl
New York, NY 10003
Tel.: (212) 253-1588
Fax: (212) 353-8793
(Interactive)

MPG
(Div. of HAVAS)
195 Broadway 12th Fl
New York, NY 10007
Tel.: (646) 587-5000
Fax: (646) 587-5005

M. FABRIKANT & SONS, INC.
1 Rockefeller Plz 28th Fl
New York, NY 10020-2102
Tel.: (212) 757-0790
Fax: (212) 581-3061
Toll Free: (800) 432-8895
Web Site: www.fabrikant.com
Sales Range: $900-999.9 Million
Approx. Number Employees: 1,000
Year Founded: 1895
Business Description:
Wholesale Distr. of Diamonds & Jewelry
S.I.C.: 3911
N.A.I.C.S.: 339911
Import Export
Media: 6-13
Personnel:
Charles Fabrikant Fortgang *(Chm)*
Brands & Products:
FABRIKANT

MAJOR WORLD WIDE LTD.
19706 53rd Ave
Fresh Meadows, NY 11365
Tel.: (718) 224-7023
Fax: (718) 279-0059
Toll Free: (800) 989-3546
E-mail: majorwwltd@aol.com
Web Site: www.majorworldwidejewelry.com
Approx. Number Employees: 32
Year Founded: 1982
Business Description:
Distributor of 14K Gold, Sterling Silver, Cubic Zirconias, Costume Jewelry & Cultured Pearls
S.I.C.: 5094; 5199
N.A.I.C.S.: 423940; 424990

Key to Media (For complete agency information see *The Advertising Red Books-Agencies* edition):
1. Bus. Publs. 2. Cable T.V. 3. Catalogs & Directories. 4. Co-op Adv. 5. Consumer Mags. 6. D.M. to Bus. Estab.7. D.M. to Consumers 8. Daily Newsp. 9. Exhibits/Trade Shows 10. Foreign 11. Infomercial 12. Internet Adv.13. Multimedia 14. Network Radio 15. Network T.V. 16. Newsp. Distr. Mags. 17. Other 18. Outdoor (Posters, Transit) 19. Point of Purchase20. Premiums, Novelties 21. Product Samples 22. Special Events Mktg. 23. Spot Radio 24. Spot T.V. 25. Weekly Newsp. 26. Yellow Page Adv.

Major World Wide Ltd. — (Continued)

Media: 2-4-20
Distr.: Natl.
Personnel:
Arthur Rosenberg *(Pres)*

MAJORICA JEWELRY, LTD.

(Sub. of Majorica, S.A.)
366 5th Ave Rm 507
New York, NY 10001
Tel.: (212) 695-1756
Fax: (212) 967-4248
Toll Free: (800) 223-7560
E-mail: majoricajewelry@majoricausa.com
Web Site: www.majorica.com
Approx. Number Employees: 31
Year Founded: 1890
Business Description:
Organic Man-Made Pearl Grower; Jewelry & Watch Mfr
S.I.C.: 5094
N.A.I.C.S.: 423940
Media: 6-10
Distr.: Natl.

MARTIN FLYER INC.

48 W 48th St
New York, NY 10036
Tel.: (212) 840-8899
Fax: (212) 768-0124
Web Site: www.martinflyer.com
Approx. Number Employees: 25
Business Description:
Mfr. of Jewelry
S.I.C.: 3911
N.A.I.C.S.: 339911
Media: 6-8-10-13
Personnel:
Gary Flyer *(Pres)*
Brands & Products:
FLYERFIT
MARTIN FLYER

MCCUBBIN HOSIERY, INC.

815 Robert S Kerr Ave
Oklahoma City, OK 73106
Mailing Address:
PO Box 2358
Oklahoma City, OK 73101-2358
Tel.: (405) 236-8351
Fax: (405) 236-8389
Toll Free: (800) 654-3201
E-mail: customerservice@mccubbin.com
Web Site: www.mccubbin.com
E-Mail For Key Personnel:
President: dmccubbin@mccubbin.com
Sales Range: Less than $1 Million
Approx. Number Employees: 30
Year Founded: 1952
Business Description:
Men's, Women's & Children's Hosiery Mfr, Retailer & Distr
S.I.C.: 5137; 5136
N.A.I.C.S.: 424330; 424320
Media: 2-4-7-8-10-13-19-21-26
Distr.: Natl.
Budget Set: Nov.
Personnel:
Mark H. McCubbin *(Owner)*
David McCubbin *(Pres)*
Brands & Products:
MCCUBBIN

MEDALLIC ART COMPANY, LTD.

80 Airpark Vista Blvd
Dayton, NV 89403
Tel.: (775) 246-6000
Fax: (775) 246-6006
Toll Free: (800) 843-9854
E-mail: minted@medallic.com
Web Site: www.medallic.com
Approx. Number Employees: 40
Year Founded: 1903
Business Description:
Mfr of Medallions, Plaques, Jewelry & Belt Buckles
S.I.C.: 3911
N.A.I.C.S.: 339911
Export
Media: 4-6-7-8-10-16-21
Distr.: Direct to Consumer; Natl.
Personnel:
Ross Henson *(Pres)*

MELE COMPANIES, INC.

2007 Beechgrove Pl
Utica, NY 13501
Tel.: (315) 733-4600
Fax: (315) 733-3183
Toll Free: (800) 635-6353
E-mail: sales@melejewelrybox.com
Web Site: www.melejewelrybox.com
E-Mail For Key Personnel:
Sales Director: sales@melejewelrybox.com
Approx. Number Employees: 30
Year Founded: 1912
Business Description:
Mfr. of Musical & Non-Musical Jewelry Boxes
S.I.C.: 2631; 2434
N.A.I.C.S.: 322130; 337110
Import Export
Media: 2-4-7-8-10
Distr.: Natl.
Brands & Products:
BLUE STAR LEATHER
MELE

MERCURY LUGGAGE/ SEWARD TRUNK

4843 Victor St
Jacksonville, FL 32207-7963
Tel.: (904) 733-9595
Fax: (904) 733-9671
E-mail: info@mercuryluggage.com
Web Site: www.mercuryluggage.com
Approx. Number Employees: 100
Year Founded: 1946
Business Description:
Luggage Mfr
S.I.C.: 3161; 5099
N.A.I.C.S.: 316991; 423990
Import Export
Media: 4
Personnel:
Andrew Pradella *(Owner)*
Randy Schilson *(CFO & VP-Fin)*
Michael Laska *(COO)*
Brands & Products:
GOING TO GRANDMA'S
MERCURY LUGGAGE

MICHAEL ANTHONY JEWELERS, INC.

(Sub. of Bel-Oro International, Inc.)
115 S MacQuesten Pkwy
Mount Vernon, NY 10550-1724
Fax: (914) 699-2335
Toll Free: (800) 966-8800
Web Site: www.richlinegroup.com
Sales Range: $100-124.9 Million
Approx. Number Employees: 730
Year Founded: 1977
Business Description:
Handcrafted Jewelry Mfr & Retailer
S.I.C.: 3911; 5944
N.A.I.C.S.: 339911; 448310
Import Export
Advertising Expenditures: $5,473,000
Media: 2-4-5-6-7-10-15-17
Distr.: Natl.
Budget Set: Jan.
Personnel:
Betty Sou *(CFO & Sr VP)*
Michael A. Paolercio *(Treas & Sr VP)*
Anthony Paolercio Jr. *(VP-Sls-HSN)*

MIKIMOTO (AMERICA) CO. LTD.

(Sub. of K. Mikimoto & Co., Ltd.)
730 5th Ave
New York, NY 10019-5429
Tel.: (212) 457-4600
Fax: (212) 457-4605
Toll Free: (888) 701-2323
E-mail: contact@mikimotoamerica.com
Web Site: www.mikimotoamerica.com
Approx. Number Employees: 120
Business Description:
Cultured Pearls & Pearl Jewelry Mfr
S.I.C.: 5944
N.A.I.C.S.: 448310
Import
Advertising Expenditures: $3,000,000
Media: 4-5-6-8-9-10-11-19
Distr.: Natl.

MONARCH DESIGNS INC.

8388 E Hartford Dr Ste 102
Scottsdale, AZ 85255
Tel.: (480) 281-2100
Fax: (480) 281-2101
Approx. Number Employees: 100
Year Founded: 1946
Business Description:
Luggage Mfr
S.I.C.: 3161
N.A.I.C.S.: 316991
Import Export
Advertising Expenditures: $400,000
Media: 2-4-6-7-19-20
Distr.: Natl.
Personnel:
John Cristiano *(Gen Mgr)*
Brands & Products:
HOLIDAY
LUCAS
MONARCH
SASSON

MONEX DEPOSIT COMPANY

4910 Birch St
Newport Beach, CA 92660-8100
Tel.: (949) 752-1400
Fax: (949) 752-7214
Toll Free: (800) 949-4653
E-mail: monex@monex.com
Web Site: www.monex.com
Approx. Number Employees: 200
Year Founded: 1967
Business Description:
Precious Metals Trading
S.I.C.: 5944; 6722
N.A.I.C.S.: 448310; 525910
Advertising Expenditures: $4,000,000
Media: 1-2-3-5-7-8-9-10-13-14-15-23-24-25
Distr.: Intl.; Natl.
Personnel:
Louis E. Carabini *(Pres)*
Geoffrey Hodes *(Dir-Adv)*
Brands & Products:
ATLAS ACCOUNT
GOLD COINS OF THE WORLD
MONEX

MOVADO GROUP, INC.

650 From Rd Ste 375
Paramus, NJ 07652-3556
Tel.: (201) 267-8000
Fax: (201) 267-8070
E-mail: e-comments@movadogroup.com
Web Site: www.movadogroup.com
Approx. Sls.: $382,190,000
Approx. Number Employees: 1,000
Year Founded: 1967
Business Description:
Holding Company; Watch & Other Personal Accessories Designer, Mfr, Whslr, Distr & Retailer
S.I.C.: 6719; 3873; 5094; 5944; 7629
N.A.I.C.S.: 551112; 334518; 423940; 448310; 811219
Import Export
Advertising Expenditures: $79,400,000
Media: 2-3-4-6-7-8-9-10-23-24
Distr.: Intl.
Budget Set: Nov.
Personnel:
Efraim Grinberg *(Chm & CEO)*
Eugene J. Karpovich *(CFO)*
Richard J. Cote *(COO)*
Mary Leach *(CMO)*
Timothy F. Michno *(Gen Counsel & Sec)*
Joseph A. Faranda *(Sr VP-Strategy & Consumer Insights)*
Alexander Grinberg *(Sr VP-Consumer/ Customer Centric Initiatives)*
Joe Zanone *(Sr VP-Special Markets)*
Brands & Products:
CELESTINA
COACH
CONCORD
EBEL
ESPERANZA
ESQ SWISS
M
MOVADO
Advertising Agency:
Lloyd & Co.
180 Varick St Ste 1018
New York, NY 10014
Tel.: (212) 414-3100
Fax: (212) 414-3113

M.Z. BERGER & CO., INC.

29 76 Northern Blvd 4th Fl
Long Island City, NY 11101
Tel.: (718) 472-7500
Fax: (718) 472-7691
E-mail: customer-service@mzb.com
Web Site: www.mzb.com
Approx. Number Employees: 100
Year Founded: 1950
Business Description:
Watches, Clocks & HBA Designer & Distr
S.I.C.: 5094; 3873
N.A.I.C.S.: 423940; 334518
Import

Key to Media (For complete agency information see *The Advertising Red Books-Agencies* edition):
1. Bus. Publs. 2. Cable T.V. 3. Catalogs & Directories. 4. Co-op Adv. 5. Consumer Mags. 6. D.M. to Bus. Estab.7. D.M. to Consumers
8. Daily Newsp. 9. Exhibits/Trade Shows 10. Foreign 11. Infomercial 12. Internet Adv.13. Multimedia 14. Network Radio
15. Network T.V. 16. Newsp. Distr. Mags. 17. Other 18. Outdoor (Posters, Transit) 19. Point of Purchase20. Premiums, Novelties
21. Product Samples 22. Special Events Mktg. 23. Spot Radio 24. Spot T.V. 25. Weekly Newsp. 26. Yellow Page Adv.

Media: 2-6-9
Distr.: Natl.
Personnel:
Joseph Mermelstein *(Pres)*
Bernard Mermelstein *(CEO)*
Marci Gordon *(CMO)*
Brands & Products:
ELGIN
GRUEN
MZB
SHARP
WALTHAM

NIKAIA, INC.
7962 Old Georgetown Rd 3C
Bethesda, MD 20814
Tel.: (301) 530-8170
Fax: (301) 530-8171
Toll Free: (888) 767-7354
E-mail: info@nikaia.com
Web Site: www.nikaia.com
Sales Range: Less than $1 Million
Approx. Number Employees: 2
Year Founded: 1998
Business Description:
Importer & Distr of European Fashion Accessories for Women
S.I.C.: 5199; 5094
N.A.I.C.S.: 424990; 423940
Import
Media: 4-8-10-13-22
Personnel:
Nathalie Duncan *(Pres)*
Brands & Products:
CLASSIC TASTE WITH AN ATTITUDE
NIKAIA

O.C. TANNER COMPANY INC.
1930 S State St
Salt Lake City, UT 84115-2311
Tel.: (801) 486-2430
Fax: (801) 493-3013
Web Site: www.octanner.com
Approx. Number Employees: 1,600
Year Founded: 1927
Business Description:
Producer of Jewelry & Precious Metal
S.I.C.: 3911; 5944
N.A.I.C.S.: 339911; 448310
Import Export
Personnel:
David A. Petersen *(CEO)*
Harold Simons *(Exec VP-Mfg)*
David Sturt *(Exec VP-Mktg & Bus Dev)*
Tim Treu *(Exec VP-Sls)*
Adrian Gostick *(Dir-Corp Comm)*
Steve Gough *(Mgr-IS Project)*
Brands & Products:
O.C. TANNER
THE RECOGNITION EXPERIENCE
Advertising Agency:
Muller Bressler Brown
4739 Belleview Ave Ste 100
Kansas City, MO 64112-1316
Tel.: (816) 531-1992
Fax: (816) 531-6692

OMEGA WATCH COMPANY
(Div. of The Swatch Group)
1200 Harbor Blvd
Weehawken, NJ 07086
Tel.: (201) 271-1400
Fax: (201) 271-5042
Toll Free: (800) 766-6342
Approx. Number Employees: 30
Business Description:
Distributor of Watches
S.I.C.: 5094; 5063
N.A.I.C.S.: 423940; 423610
Advertising Expenditures: $200,000
Media: 2-4-5-6-7-9-10-14-15-16-19-23-24-25-30
Distr.: Natl.
Personnel:
Theresa Kuiken *(Dir-Mktg)*
Steve Volcar *(Dir-IT)*
Bernadette Odoms *(Mgr-Comm)*
Advertising Agency:
KD&E
129 W 27th St 11th Fl
New York, NY 10001
Tel.: (212) 686-0006
Fax: (212) 686-6991

ORBITA CORPORATION
1205 Culbreth Dr
Wilmington, NC 28405
Tel.: (910) 256-5300
Fax: (910) 256-5356
Toll Free: (800) 800-4436
E-mail: info@orbita.net
Web Site: www.orbita.net
Approx. Number Employees: 30
Business Description:
Watchwinders Mfr
S.I.C.: 3873
N.A.I.C.S.: 334518
Media: 4-6-7-8
Brands & Products:
LUGANO
ORBITA
SPARTA
VERONA
ZURIGO

OSCAR HEYMAN & BROTHERS, INC.
501 Madison Ave 15th Fl
New York, NY 10022
Tel.: (212) 593-0400
Fax: (212) 759-8612
Toll Free: (800) 642-1912
E-mail: info@oscarheyman.com
Web Site: www.oscarheyman.com
Approx. Sls.: $9,000,000
Approx. Number Employees: 100
Year Founded: 1912
Business Description:
Jewelry Mfr
S.I.C.: 3911
N.A.I.C.S.: 339911
Media: 4-6-8-10-13
Personnel:
Marvin Heyman *(Pres)*
Brands & Products:
OHB
OSCAR HEYMAN
SIMPLY THE FINEST
Advertising Agency:
Clare Adams Kittle Co., Inc.
1921 33rd Ave S
Seattle, WA 98144-4912
Tel.: (206) 683-3882
Toll Free: (800) 346-7582

OVERLAND SHEEPSKIN CO. INC
2096 Nutmeg Ave
Fairfield, IA 52556
Tel.: (641) 472-8484
Fax: (641) 472-8474
Toll Free: (800) OVERLAND
E-mail: info@overland.com
Web Site: www.overland.com
Sales Range: $10-24.9 Million
Approx. Number Employees: 75
Year Founded: 1973
Business Description:
Leather Garments Retailer
S.I.C.: 5699; 5013; 5611; 5621; 5641; 5651; 5661; 5948
N.A.I.C.S.: 448190; 441310; 448110; 448120; 448130; 448140; 448210; 448320
Media: 4-13
Personnel:
Roger Leahy *(Pres)*
Brands & Products:
OVERLAND
OVERLAND OUTFITTERS
OVERLAND.COM

PARIS ACCESSORIES, INC.
1385 Broadway 21st Fl
New York, NY 10018
Tel.: (212) 868-0500
Fax: (212) 967-4936
Toll Free: (800) 223-7557
Approx. Number Employees: 560
Year Founded: 1910
Business Description:
Women's & Men's Scarves, Belts, Hats & Gloves Mfr
S.I.C.: 2253; 2389
N.A.I.C.S.: 315191; 315999
Media: 5-10
Personnel:
Peter Markson *(Chm)*
Patrick Falco *(CFO)*

PATEK PHILIPPE
(Sub. of Patek Philippe Geneva)
1 Rockefeller Plz Ste 930
New York, NY 10020
Tel.: (212) 218-1240
Fax: (212) 218-1255
E-mail: info@patek.com
Web Site: www.patekusa.com
Approx. Number Employees: 49
Year Founded: 1839
Business Description:
Watch Distr
S.I.C.: 5094
N.A.I.C.S.: 423940
Media: 2-5-6-9
Distr.: Natl.
Budget Set: Sept.
Personnel:
Henry Edelman *(Chm)*
Larry Pettinelli *(Pres)*
Brands & Products:
PATEK PHILIPPE
Advertising Agency:
Leagas Delaney Group Limited
1 Alfred Place
London, WC1E 7EB, United Kingdom
Tel.: (44) 207 758 1758
Fax: (44) 207 758 1760
Creative

THE PENN COMPANIES
10909 Dutton Rd
Philadelphia, PA 19154-3203
Tel.: (215) 632-7800
Fax: (215) 632-0769
Fax: (215) 632-6166
Toll Free: (800) 793-7366
Web Site: www.pennemblem.com
Approx. Number Employees: 500
Year Founded: 1945
Business Description:
Mfr & Distr of Personalization & Identification Products
S.I.C.: 2261; 2299
N.A.I.C.S.: 313311; 314999
Import Export
Advertising Expenditures: $250,000
Media: 2-3-4-7-19-20
Distr.: Natl.
Budget Set: Feb.
Personnel:
Randall Blumenthal *(Pres)*
Steve O'Grady *(CEO)*
Jon Joseph *(Sr VP-Sls & Bus Dev)*
David Braun *(Dir-Div Sls & Svc)*
Keane Hoffman *(Dir-Div Sls & Svc)*
Brands & Products:
COLOR PRINT
EXPRESSPRINT
PENN
PENN BOND
PENN SEAL
PENN SPORT
PENN TEXT
PENNBROIDERY
PENNEMBLEM

PIERCING PAGODA
(Sub. of Zale Delaware, Inc.)
901 W Walnut Hill Ln
Irving, TX 75038
Tel.: (972) 580-4000
Toll Free: (800) 866-9700
Web Site: www.pagoda.com
E-Mail For Key Personnel:
Public Relations: customerservice@pagoda.com
Sales Range: $1-4.9 Billion
Approx. Number Employees: 4,000
Business Description:
Retailer of Gold Jewelry
S.I.C.: 5944
N.A.I.C.S.: 448310
Import
Media: 7-8-17

PLATINUM GUILD INTERNATIONAL (USA) JEWELRY, INC.
Ste 220 4 Hutton Centre Dr
Santa Ana, CA 92707-5764
Tel.: (949) 760-8279
Fax: (949) 760-8780
Toll Free: (800) 208-PLAT
Web Site: www.preciousplatinum.com
Approx. Number Employees: 11
Business Description:
Platinum & Platinum Jewelry Products Promotion
S.I.C.: 5094
N.A.I.C.S.: 423940
Media: 1-4-6-10-11-13-22
Advertising Agency:
The Shand Group
1482 E Valley Rd Ste 474
Santa Barbara, CA 93108
Tel.: (805) 969-1068
Fax: (805) 969-0046

POLLACK CORPORATION
(d/b/a G.M. Pollack & Sons Jewelers)
600 Roundwood Dr
Scarborough, ME 04074-8247
Tel.: (207) 883-8455
Fax: (207) 883-1012
E-mail: info@gmpollock.com
Web Site: www.gmpollack.com

Key to Media (For complete agency information see *The Advertising Red Books-Agencies* edition):
1. Bus. Publs. 2. Cable T.V. 3. Catalogs & Directories. 4. Co-op Adv. 5. Consumer Mags. 6. D.M. to Bus. Estab.7. D.M. to Consumers
8. Daily Newsp. 9. Exhibits/Trade Shows 10. Foreign 11. Infomercial 12. Internet Adv.13. Multimedia 14. Network Radio
15. Network T.V. 16. Newsp. Distr. Mags. 17. Other 18. Outdoor (Posters, Transit) 19. Point of Purchase20. Premiums, Novelties
21. Product Samples 22. Special Events Mktg. 23. Spot Radio 24. Spot T.V. 25. Weekly Newsp. 26. Yellow Page Adv.

Pollack Corporation — (Continued)

Sales Range: $50-74.9 Million
Approx. Number Employees: 130
Year Founded: 1954
Business Description:
Jewelry, Watches & Giftware Retailer
S.I.C.: 5944
N.A.I.C.S.: 448310
Import
Advertising Expenditures: $850,000
Media: 6-8-9-19-22
Distr.: Direct to Consumer; Reg.
Personnel:
Moira O'Regan *(Dir-Adv & Mktg)*

THE PORT CANVAS COMPANY
39 Limerick Rd
Kennebunkport, ME 04046
Mailing Address:
PO Box H
Kennebunkport, ME 04046
Tel.: (207) 985-9767
Fax: (207) 985-9768
Web Site: www.portcanvas.com
Approx. Number Employees: 13
Year Founded: 1968
Business Description:
Tote Bags, Duffel Bags, Handbags, Laundry Bags, Sports Bags, Luggage, Belts & Key Chains Retailer
S.I.C.: 2211; 3161
N.A.I.C.S.: 313210; 316991
Media: 4-13
Personnel:
Margot L. Thompson *(Owner & Pres)*

PUPPYPAWS, INC.
314 Pinevalley Dr
Bridgeville, PA 15017
Tel.: (412) 221-7076
Fax: (440) 446-9978
Toll Free: (866) 807-7297
E-mail: info@puppypaws.com
Web Site: www.puppypaws.com
Approx. Number Employees: 3
Business Description:
Pet-Themed Jewelry Mfr & Whslr
S.I.C.: 5199
N.A.I.C.S.: 424990
Media: 2-6-19-20-21-22-23
Personnel:
Pamela Meltzer *(Pres)*
James Meltzer *(CFO)*
Brands & Products:
PHOTOART
PUPPYPAWS

RANJIT CORPORATION
2401 Timber Oaks Rd
Edison, NJ 08820
Tel.: (973) 267-8008
Fax: (908) 462-3881
Toll Free: (888) 807-4007
E-mail: info@diamond-essence.com
Web Site: www.diamond-essence.com
Approx. Number Employees: 35
Year Founded: 1978
Business Description:
Mfr. & Marketer of Simulated Diamonds; Retail Jewelry
S.I.C.: 5961; 3911
N.A.I.C.S.: 454113; 339911
Export
Advertising Expenditures: $1,800,000
Bus. Publs.: $450,000; Consumer Mags.: $450,000; Daily Newsp.: $450,000; Other: $450,000
Distr.: Intl.; Natl.
Personnel:
Ranjit Singh *(Owner)*
Brands & Products:
DIAMOND ESSENCE

REEDS JEWELERS, INC.
2525 S 17th St
Wilmington, NC 28401-7705
Tel.: (910) 350-3100
Fax: (910) 350-3353
E-mail: contactus@reeds.com
Web Site: www.reeds.com
Sales Range: $100-124.9 Million
Approx. Number Employees: 685
Year Founded: 1946
Business Description:
Retailer of Jewelry
S.I.C.: 5944
N.A.I.C.S.: 448310
Import
Advertising Expenditures: $2,250,000
Media: 5-8-9-16-19-23-24-26
Distr.: Direct to Consumer; Reg.
Personnel:
James R. Rouse *(CFO)*
Allan E. Metzner *(COO)*
Alan Zimmer *(Exec VP)*
Brands & Products:
SIMPLY BEAUTIFUL

ROGERS & HOLLANDS ENTERPRISES INC.
20821 Cicero Ave
Matteson, IL 60443-1201
Tel.: (708) 748-6400
Fax: (708) 679-0590
Web Site: www.rogersandhollands.com
Approx. Sls.: $45,000,000
Approx. Number Employees: 450
Year Founded: 1945
Business Description:
Jewelry Stores
S.I.C.: 5944
N.A.I.C.S.: 448310
Import Export
Personnel:
Craig Stern *(Pres)*
Advertising Agency:
Cellit
213 W Institute Pl Ste 603
Chicago, IL 60610
Tel.: (312) 492-4128
Fax: (866) 856-3936
Toll Free: (800) 790-6597

ROGERS, LUNT & BOWLEN CO.
(d/b/a Lunt Silversmiths)
298 Federal St
Greenfield, MA 01301-1932
Tel.: (413) 774-2774
Fax: (413) 774-4393
Toll Free: (800) 242-2774
E-mail: webquestions@luntsilver.com
Web Site: www.luntsilver.com
Approx. Number Employees: 223
Year Founded: 1902
Business Description:
Mfr. of Sterling Silver, Silverplated & Pewter Tableware & Cutlery
S.I.C.: 3914; 3421
N.A.I.C.S.: 339912; 332211
Media: 2-4-6-8-9-13-19
Distr.: Natl.
Budget Set: Apr. -Nov.
Personnel:
Denham Lunt *(Chm)*
James H. Lunt *(Pres & CEO)*
Paul Morton *(VP-Sls)*
Brands & Products:
COUZON
CUNILL
HERITAGE
LUNT
Advertising Agency:
Right Angle, Inc.
135 Main St
Northampton, MA 01060
Tel.: (413) 586-4694

ROLEX WATCH U.S.A., INC.
(Sub. of Rolex S.A.)
665 5th Ave
New York, NY 10022
Tel.: (212) 758-7700
Fax: (212) 583-1147
E-mail: info@rolex.com
Web Site: www.rolex.com
Approx. Number Employees: 500
Year Founded: 1948
Business Description:
Mfr. of Watches
S.I.C.: 5094
N.A.I.C.S.: 423940
Media: 2-3-6-9-13-15-30
Personnel:
Allen Brill *(Pres & CEO)*
Michael Elms *(CFO & Sr VP)*
Colette C. Bennett *(Mgr Sports Mktg)*
Brands & Products:
OYSTER COLLECTION
Advertising Agency:
J. Walter Thompson U.S.A., Inc. (Part of JWT)
466 Lexington Ave
New York, NY 10017-3140
Tel.: (212) 210-7000
Fax: (212) 210-7299

ROMAN RESEARCH, INC.
800 Franklin St
Hanson, MA 02341-1002
Tel.: (800) 225-8652
Fax: (781) 447-0995
Web Site: www.romanresearch.com
Approx. Sls.: $20,000,000
Approx. Number Employees: 110
Year Founded: 1970
Business Description:
Mfr, Retailer & Mail Order of Costume Stainless Steel Hypo-Allergenic Pierced Earrings & Nickel-Free Jewelry & Watches
S.I.C.: 5961; 3961
N.A.I.C.S.: 454113; 339914
Media: 4-8-13
Personnel:
Dale Southworth *(Pres)*
Brands & Products:
EAR REPLACEABLES
MISTY
PERFECTIONS
SIMPLY SINGLES
SIMPLY WHISPERS
ULTRA WHISPERS

ROSY BLUE INC.
529 5th Ave Fl 15
New York, NY 10017-4608
Tel.: (212) 687-8838
Fax: (212) 856-9835
Web Site: www.rosyblue.com
Sales Range: $150-199.9 Million
Approx. Number Employees: 75
Year Founded: 1990
Business Description:
Jewelry & Precious Stones
S.I.C.: 5094; 3911
N.A.I.C.S.: 423940; 339911
Import Export
Media: 10
Personnel:
Dipu Mehta *(Pres)*

ROYAL GOLD, INC.
1660 Wynkoop St Ste 1000
Denver, CO 80202-1115
Tel.: (303) 573-1660
Fax: (303) 595-9385
E-mail: info@royalgold.com
Web Site: www.royalgold.com
Approx. Rev.: $216,469,000
Approx. Number Employees: 21
Year Founded: 1981
Business Description:
Precious Metals Royalty Company
S.I.C.: 1041; 1044; 1099; 6289; 6794
N.A.I.C.S.: 212221; 212222; 212299; 523999; 533110
Media: 2
Personnel:
Stanley Dempsey *(Chm)*
Tony Jensen *(Pres & CEO)*
Stefan L. Wenger *(CFO)*
Bruce Kirchhoff *(Gen Counsel & VP)*

SAFILO USA INC.
(Div. of Safilo Group S.p.A.)
801 Jefferson Rd
Parsippany, NJ 07054
Tel.: (973) 952-2800
Fax: (973) 560-1591
Approx. Number Employees: 120
Year Founded: 1962
Business Description:
Mfr. of Ski Glasses & Sunglasses
S.I.C.: 3851
N.A.I.C.S.: 339115
Import Export
Media: 5-6
Personnel:
Ross Brownlee *(Pres & COO)*
Kristen Maloney *(Brand Dir-Mktg)*
Kim Chaveco *(Brand Mgr)*
Brands & Products:
CLAIBORNE
I SKI
ION SPORT
LIZ CLAIBORNE
LIZ CLAIBORNE COLLECTION
SUNCLOUD
Advertising Agency:
S3
718 Main St
Boonton, NJ 07005
Tel.: (973) 257-5533
Fax: (973) 257-5543

SAMSONITE CORPORATION
(Holding of CVC Capital Partners (U.S.), Inc.)
575 W St Ste 110
Mansfield, MA 02048
Tel.: (508) 851-1400
Fax: (508) 851-8715
E-mail: fredpeirce@samsonite.com
Web Site: www.samsonite.com
Approx. Sls.: $1,070,393,024
Approx. Number Employees: 5,000
Year Founded: 1910

Key to Media (For complete agency information see *The Advertising Red Books-Agencies* edition):
1. Bus. Publs. 2. Cable T.V. 3. Catalogs & Directories. 4. Co-op Adv. 5. Consumer Mags. 6. D.M. to Bus. Estab.7. D.M. to Consumers 8. Daily Newsp. 9. Exhibits/Trade Shows 10. Foreign 11. Infomercial 12. Internet Adv.13. Multimedia 14. Network Radio 15. Network T.V. 16. Newsp. Distr. Mags. 17. Other 18. Outdoor (Posters, Transit) 19. Point of Purchase20. Premiums, Novelties 21. Product Samples 22. Special Events Mktg. 23. Spot Radio 24. Spot T.V. 25. Weekly Newsp. 26. Yellow Page Adv.

Business Description:
Luggage, Business Case & Other Bag Mfr
S.I.C.: 3161
N.A.I.C.S.: 316991
Import Export
Advertising Expenditures: $77,500,000
Media: 5-6-13-18-19-20
Distr.: Intl.; Natl.
Personnel:
Kyle Gendreau *(CFO)*
Thomas Korbas *(Pres-Americas)*
Lynne Berard *(VP-Sls & Mktg)*
Dawn Sicco *(Dir-Mktg)*
Fred Peirce *(Mgr-Ops)*
Brands & Products:
AMERICAN TOURISTER
ASPIRE
BUSINESS ONE
COOL-FLOW
CRUISAIR
EXPLORATION
FOCUS
FREEFLO
FUNNYFACE
GENESIS
HEDGREN
HISIZE
HOMMAGE
LACOSTE
LARK
OYSTER
PORTSIDE
QUANTUM
SAHORA
SAMSONITE
SAMSONITE BLACK LABEL
SARANO
SIDEROLLER
SIGNATURE
SILHOUETTE
SMALL CHIROPAK
SMART POCKET
SMART SLEEVE
SPARK
STREAMLINE
SURF
T-BONE
TRUNK & CO.
ULTIMA
ULTRA
WETPAK
WIDETRACKER
X-CALIBUR
X-PANDER
ZIP-TIGHT
Advertising Agencies:
Connelly Partners
46 Waltham St Fl 4
Boston, MA 02118
Tel.: (617) 956-5050
Fax: (617) 956-5054
Brand Positioning
Web Site Design

Initiative Worldwide
(Part of The Interpublic Group of Companies, Inc.)
1 Dag Hammerskjold Plz 5th Fl
New York, NY 10017
Tel.: (212) 605-7000
Fax: (212) 605-7200
Media Planning & Buying

Ketchum
(Part of Omnicom)
1285 Ave of the Americas
New York, NY 10019
Tel.: (646) 935-3900
Fax: (646) 935-4482
Pub Rels
— Stephanie Camargo *(Acct Exec)*

SAMUELS JEWELERS, INC.
(Sub. of Gitanjali Gems Ltd.)
2914 Montopolis Dr Ste 200
Austin, TX 78741
Tel.: (512) 369-1400
Fax: (512) 369-1527
Toll Free: (877) 726-8357
E-mail: customerservice@samuelsjewelers.com
Web Site: www.samuelsjewelers.com
Approx. Number Employees: 860
Year Founded: 1891
Business Description:
Jewelry Retailer
S.I.C.: 5944
N.A.I.C.S.: 448310
Advertising Expenditures: $10,000,000
Media: 1-4-5-8-9-13-19-22-23-24-26
Distr.: Direct to Consumer; Reg.
Budget Set: Jan.

SANTA FE LEATHER CORPORATION
(d/b/a Clava)
223 S Van Brunt St
Englewood, NJ 07631-4010
Tel.: (201) 503-0225
Fax: (201) 503-0226
Toll Free: (888) 45-CLAVA
E-mail: info@clava.com
Web Site: www.clava.com
Approx. Number Employees: 17
Year Founded: 1988
Business Description:
Mfr. of Leather Handgoods & Accessories & Provider of Private Labeling of Italian & Domestic Goods
S.I.C.: 7319
N.A.I.C.S.: 541890
Advertising Expenditures: $45,000
Media: 4-6-10
Distr.: Natl. Intl.
Personnel:
Claudio Vazquez *(Pres)*
Kirsten Logan *(VP-Sls & Mktg)*
Brands & Products:
BOMBER
BUSINESS CLASS CONTROLLER
CLAVA
CLAVA AMERICAN
COMPUROLLER
THE COURIER
CUSTORM RACING
EXECUTIVE FLAP
EXECUTIVE LAPTOP
EXECUTIVE PORTHOLE FLAP
EXPANDABLE
EXPANDABLE X-TREME
EXTREME LAPTOP
LAPTOP MAILBAG
LARGE LAPTOP BACKPACK
LEGAL
PORTHOLE FLAP
PROFESSIONAL LAPTOP
PROMO
SLIM TOP HANDLE
STILETTO SLIM
TOP HANDLE
TURN LOCK
UPRIGHT VERTICAL BRIEF
WARD
XL LAPTOP

THE SARUT GROUP
780 Humbolted St
Brooklyn, NY 11222
Tel.: (718) 387-7484
Fax: (718) 387-7467
Toll Free: (800) 345-6404
E-mail: nyc@sarut.com
Web Site: www.sarut.com
Approx. Sls.: $5,000,000
Approx. Number Employees: 30
Year Founded: 1979
Business Description:
Giftware Whslr
S.I.C.: 5199
N.A.I.C.S.: 424990
Media: 6
Personnel:
Frederic Rambaud *(Owner)*
Mark Szlendak *(CFO)*
Alan Ceppos *(Principal)*

SCREAMER INC.
(d/b/a Screamer Hats)
4314 S 104th Pl
Seattle, WA 98178
Mailing Address:
PO Box 24764
Seattle, WA 98124-0764
Tel.: (206) 667-9000
Fax: (206) 624-7567
E-mail: custserv@screamerhats.com
Web Site: www.screamerhats.com
Approx. Number Employees: 4
Year Founded: 1989
Business Description:
Clothing Mfr
S.I.C.: 5699
N.A.I.C.S.: 448150
Media: 1-4-13
Personnel:
Steve Burkholder *(CEO)*
Brands & Products:
SCREAMER

SEFA INC.
(d/b/a AvantGold Jewelers)
10330 Dale Mabry Hwy N Ste 110
Tampa, FL 33618
Tel.: (813) 961-0097
Fax: (813) 961-4582
E-mail: info@avantgold.com
Web Site: www.avantgold.com
Approx. Number Employees: 12
Business Description:
Custom Jewelry Design, Repair & Sales, Appraisals, Diamond Sales & Insurance Replacement Services
S.I.C.: 5944
N.A.I.C.S.: 448310
Media: 6
Personnel:
Suanne Abeles *(Co-Owner)*

SEIKO CORPORATION OF AMERICA
(Sub. of Seiko Holdings Corporation)
1111 McArthur Blvd
Mahwah, NJ 07430-2038
Tel.: (201) 529-5730
Toll Free: (800) 782-2510
E-mail: info@seikousa.com
Web Site: www.seikousa.com
E-Mail For Key Personnel:
Marketing Director: BSwanson@scamahwah.com
Approx. Number Employees: 245
Year Founded: 1970
Business Description:
Distributors of Watches & Clocks
S.I.C.: 5094
N.A.I.C.S.: 423940
Import
Media: 1-2-3-4-5-6-7-8-9-10-13-15-18-23-24-25
Distr.: Natl.
Budget Set: Jan. -Mar.
Personnel:
Les Perry *(Exec VP)*
Daniel W. Miller *(Sr VP-Fin)*
Bob Swanson *(VP-Mktg)*
Brands & Products:
LASSALE
SPOON

SKYWAY LUGGAGE COMPANY
30 Wall St
Seattle, WA 98121-1320
Tel.: (206) 441-5300
Tel.: (206) 256-1601
Fax: (206) 441-5306
E-mail: info@skywayluggage.com
Web Site: www.skywayluggage.com
Approx. Number Employees: 30
Year Founded: 1910
Business Description:
Luggage Wholesale Distr
S.I.C.: 3161
N.A.I.C.S.: 316991
Import Export
Media: 2-5-6-7-9-10-15-19-20-23-24
Distr.: Intl.; Natl.
Budget Set: Nov.-Dec.
Personnel:
Henry L. Kotkins, Jr. *(Pres & CEO)*
Jennifer Carmichael *(Exec VP)*
Brands & Products:
CELEBRITY
CONTEMPO
FLAIR 7
MONTAGE
NORTHWEST TRAILS WESTPORT
SIGMA 2
SKYWAY
SMOOTH-ZIP
VISION 2
ZERO GRAVITY

SOLO
400 Wireless Blvd
Hauppauge, NY 11788-3934
Tel.: (631) 434-7070
Fax: (631) 434-7326
E-mail: contactus@solocases.com
Web Site: www.solocases.com
Approx. Number Employees: 40
Business Description:
Importer of Leather Attaches, Luggage & Portfolios
S.I.C.: 3161; 5948
N.A.I.C.S.: 316991; 448320
Import
Media: 2-4-5-6-7-10-13-18-19-20-26
Distr.: Natl.
Budget Set: Dec.
Personnel:
Richard Krulik *(CEO)*
Lew Levy *(Sr VP)*
Leticia Vargas *(Mgr-Media Rels)*
Brands & Products:
CHECKFAST
CLASSIC
PULSE
SMART-STRAP

Key to Media (For complete agency information see *The Advertising Red Books-Agencies* edition):
1. Bus. Publs. 2. Cable T.V. 3. Catalogs & Directories. 4. Co-op Adv. 5. Consumer Mags. 6. D.M. to Bus. Estab.7. D.M. to Consumers 8. Daily Newsp. 9. Exhibits/Trade Shows 10. Foreign 11. Infomercial 12. Internet Adv.13. Multimedia 14. Network Radio 15. Network T.V. 16. Newsp. Distr. Mags. 17. Other 18. Outdoor (Posters, Transit) 19. Point of Purchase20. Premiums, Novelties 21. Product Samples 22. Special Events Mktg. 23. Spot Radio 24. Spot T.V. 25. Weekly Newsp. 26. Yellow Page Adv.

SOLO — (Continued)

SOLO
TECH
URBAN
VINTAGE

SPARK CREATIONS, INC.
10 W 46th St 9th Fl
New York, NY 10036
Tel.: (212) 575-8385
Fax: (212) 575-8545
Web Site: www.sparkcreations.com
Approx. Number Employees: 17
Year Founded: 1973
Business Description:
Jewelry Mfr & Retailer
S.I.C.: 3911
N.A.I.C.S.: 339911
Media: 5-6
Personnel:
Eli Aviram *(Pres)*

STERLING JEWELERS INC.
(Sub. of Signet Jewelers Limited)
375 Ghent Rd
Akron, OH 44333-4601
Tel.: (330) 668-5000
Fax: (330) 668-5188
E-mail: webmaster@jewels.com
Web Site: www.kay.com
Approx. Number Employees: 1,800
Year Founded: 1932
Business Description:
Retail Fine Jewelry Stores
S.I.C.: 5944
N.A.I.C.S.: 448310
Import
Media: 6
Personnel:
Mark Light *(Pres & CEO)*
George Frankovich *(Gen Counsel & Sec)*
Lynn Dennison *(Sr VP-Legal, Compliance & Risk Mgmt)*
Robert Knapp *(Sr VP-Supply Chain Mgmt)*
George Murray *(Sr VP-Mktg)*
Stephen Martz *(Reg VP-Ops)*
Michael Molanare *(Reg VP-Ops)*
Bruce Carter *(VP)*
David Bouffard *(VP-PR)*
Dawn McGuire *(VP-Mdsg-Mall Grp)*
Anne Clark *(Media Dir)*
Kimberly Kanary *(Dir-PR)*
Brands & Products:
MARKS & MORGAN
Advertising Agency:
Stern Advertising, Inc.
29125 Chagrin Blvd
Cleveland, OH 44122-4622
Tel.: (216) 464-4850
Fax: (216) 464-7859

STULLER, INC.
302 Rue Louis XIV
Lafayette, LA 70508
Mailing Address:
PO Box 87777
Lafayette, LA 70508-7777
Tel.: (337) 262-7700
Fax: (337) 981-1655
E-mail: sales@stuller.com
Web Site: www.stuller.com
E-Mail For Key Personnel:
Sales Director: sales@stuller.com
Sales Range: $50-74.9 Million
Approx. Number Employees: 1,600
Year Founded: 1970
Business Description:
Mfr. & Distr. of Fine Jewelry & Jewelry-Related Products
S.I.C.: 3911; 5094
N.A.I.C.S.: 339911; 423940
Media: 2-7-10
Personnel:
Matthew Stuller *(Founder & Owner)*
Jay Jackson *(Pres & CEO)*
Coby Blanchard *(Chief Supply Chain Officer)*
Danny Clark *(Chief Mdsg Officer)*
Harold Dupley *(VP-Strategic Analysis)*
Stanley Zale *(VP-Diamonds & Gemstones Mdse)*
Grady Quebedeaux *(Exec Dir-IT)*
Brands & Products:
ALTERNATIVE ROCKS
AMERICAN SHIELD OF HONOR
THE BEAUTY OF IT ALL
BIRTH OF A CHILD
BUTTERFLY BALLET
CHASTITY RINGS
COCOON
DIAMOND MOMENTS
EARLUSION
ECHELON
EST
EZ-CHANGE
GIFT WRAPPED HEART
IN THE NAME OF JESUS
LASERED TITAN GOLD
MAGICAL METAL
THE MISSING PEACE
THE MOTHER'S DIAMOND
MOTHER'S EMBRACE
OCTET
PANACHE
PROTEKTOR
RUGGED CROSS
THE RUGGED CROSS
SCROLL SETTING
SOLSTICE SOLITAIRE
SS
STULLER
STULLER SETTINGS
STULLER STUDIO
TULIPSET
UNBLOSSOMED ROSE

SUPERIOR GALLERIES, INC.
(Sub. of DGSE Companies, Inc.)
20011 Ventura Blvd
Woodland Hills, CA 91364
Tel.: (818) 444-8699
Fax: (310) 203-0496
Toll Free: (800) 421-0754
Toll Free: (800) 545-1001
E-mail: info@sgbh.com
Web Site: www.sgbh.com
Approx. Rev.: $46,317,000
Approx. Number Employees: 32
Year Founded: 1930
Business Description:
Rare Coins & Retail Jewelry Retailer & Whslr
S.I.C.: 5094
N.A.I.C.S.: 423940
Advertising Expenditures: $633,000
Media: 2-8-10-13-18
Personnel:
Don Ketterling *(Pres & CEO)*
Jane Fernicola *(Exec VP)*

SWANK, INC.
90 Park Ave
New York, NY 10016
Tel.: (212) 867-2600
Fax: (212) 370-1039
E-mail: info@swankinc.com
Web Site: www.swankinc.com
Approx. Sls.: $132,702,000
Approx. Number Employees: 256
Year Founded: 1936
Business Description:
Mfr. of Jewelry, Leather Goods, Accessories & Toiletries
S.I.C.: 3161; 2295; 2389; 3172
N.A.I.C.S.: 316991; 313320; 315999; 316993
Import Export
Advertising Expenditures: $3,228,000
Media: 2-5-6-9-10-15-16-18-19-23-24-25
Personnel:
John A. Tulin *(Chm & CEO)*
Eric P. Luft *(Pres)*
Jerold R. Kassner *(CFO, Treas, Sec & Exec VP)*
Paul Duckett *(Sr VP-Distr)*
Melvin Goldfeder *(Sr VP-Special Markets)*
William F. Rubin *(Sr VP-Reg Sls)*
James E. Tulin *(Sr VP-Mdsg)*
Brands & Products:
SWANK

SWAROVSKI NORTH AMERICA LIMITED INC.
(Sub. of Swarovski & Co.)
1 Kenney Dr
Cranston, RI 02920-4468
Tel.: (401) 463-3000
Fax: (401) 463-5257
Toll Free: (800) 426-3088
Web Site: www.swarovski.com
Approx. Number Employees: 785
Year Founded: 1988
Business Description:
Glass Products & Jewelry
S.I.C.: 3961; 5023
N.A.I.C.S.: 339914; 423220
Media: 6-30
Personnel:
Richard Pacheco *(VP-HR & Organizational Dev)*
Stephan Toljan *(VP-Mktg)*
Brands & Products:
SWAROVISKI
Advertising Agencies:
Duffy & Shanley, Inc.
10 Charles St
Providence, RI 02904
Tel.: (401) 274-0001
Fax: (401) 274-3535

MPG
(Div. of HAVAS)
195 Broadway 12th Fl
New York, NY 10007
Tel.: (646) 587-5000
Fax: (646) 587-5005
(North America & Southeast Asia)

SWATCH WATCH U.S.A.
(Div. of The Swatch Group)
1200 Harbor Blvd
Weehawken, NJ 07086
Tel.: (201) 271-1400
Fax: (201) 271-4633
Toll Free: (800) 8SWATCH
E-mail: info@swatch.com
Web Site: www.swatch.com
Approx. Number Employees: 100
Business Description:
Distributor of Cosmetic Watches
S.I.C.: 5944
N.A.I.C.S.: 448310
Advertising Expenditures: $10,000,000
Media: 4-6-9-11-19-23-24-25
Distr.: Intl.; Natl.
Budget Set: May
Personnel:
John Kelly *(CFO)*
Daphney Erginor *(Dir-Mktg & Adv)*

T. ANTHONY LTD.
445 Park Ave
New York, NY 10022
Tel.: (212) 750-9797
Fax: (212) 750-7043
Toll Free: (800) 722-2406
E-mail: info@tanthony.com
Web Site: www.tanthony.com
Approx. Number Employees: 35
Business Description:
Mfr & Retailer of Luggage & Leather Goods
S.I.C.: 5948
N.A.I.C.S.: 448320
Media: 6-7-8-13-21
Personnel:
Karen Fee *(Mgr-Corp Accts)*
Brands & Products:
T. ANTHONY

TACORI ENTERPRISES
1736 Gardena Ave
Glendale, CA 91204
Tel.: (818) 863-1536
Fax: (818) 863-1520
E-mail: info@tacori.com
Web Site: www.tacori.com
Approx. Number Employees: 20
Business Description:
Fine Jewelry Mfr
S.I.C.: 5094; 5944
N.A.I.C.S.: 423940; 448310
Media: 6-8-10-13
Personnel:
Haig Tacorian *(Pres)*
Paul Tacorian *(Sr VP-Sls & Mktg)*
Brands & Products:
TACORI

TANDY BRANDS ACCESSORIES, INC.
3631 W Davis St Ste A
Dallas, TX 75211
Tel.: (214) 519-5200
E-mail: tandy_brands@tandybrands.com
Web Site: www.tandybrands.com
Approx. Sls.: $123,767,000
Approx. Number Employees: 516
Year Founded: 1990
Business Description:
Men's, Women's & Children's Fashion Accessories Mfr & Marketer
S.I.C.: 2389; 3172; 5137
N.A.I.C.S.: 315999; 316993; 424330
Import
Advertising Expenditures: $1,400,000
Distr.: Intl.; Natl.
Budget Set: Apr. -Oct.
Personnel:
N. Roderick McGeachy, III *(Chm, Pres & CEO)*
Robert D. Martin *(Interim CFO)*
Chuck Talley *(Chief Acctg Officer & VP)*

Key to Media (For complete agency information see *The Advertising Red Books-Agencies* edition):
1. Bus. Publs. 2. Cable T.V. 3. Catalogs & Directories. 4. Co-op Adv. 5. Consumer Mags. 6. D.M. to Bus. Estab.7. D.M. to Consumers
8. Daily Newsp. 9. Exhibits/Trade Shows 10. Foreign 11. Infomercial 12. Internet Adv.13. Multimedia 14. Network Radio
15. Network T.V. 16. Newsp. Distr. Mags. 17. Other 18. Outdoor (Posters, Transit) 19. Point of Purchase20. Premiums, Novelties
21. Product Samples 22. Special Events Mktg. 23. Spot Radio 24. Spot T.V. 25. Weekly Newsp. 26. Yellow Page Adv.

Sue Elliott *(Chief Performance Officer)*
Hilda McDuff *(Chief Mdsg Officer)*
Robert J. McCarten *(Sr VP-Sls-Natl)*
Missy Lukens *(VP & Gen Mgr-Small Leather Goods)*
Dan Pearson *(VP & Gen Mgr-Gifts & Outdoor)*
Jennifer Snellgrove *(VP & Gen Mgr-Belts)*
Noel Phillips *(VP-Sls-Walmart)*
David Crabtree *(Dir-IT)*
Franklin Dominguez *(Dir-Ops-California)*

Brands & Products:
ABSOLUTELY FRESH
AMITY
CANTERBURY
CHAMBERS BELTS
EDDIE BAUER
ETON
HAGGAR
PRINCE GARDNER
PRINCESS GARDNER
ROLFS
SURPLUS
TANDY BRANDS ACCESSORIES, INC.
TIGER
TOTES
WOLVERINE

Advertising Agency:
GCG Advertising
1612 Summit Ave Ste 410
Fort Worth, TX 76102-5916
Tel.: (817) 332-4600
Fax: (817) 877-4616

TANO, INC.
350 Lexington Ave
Mount Kisco, NY 10549-2725
Tel.: (914) 241-0628
Fax: (914) 241-0730
E-mail: service@tanobag.com
Web Site: www.tanobag.com
Approx. Number Employees: 30
Year Founded: 1947
Business Description:
Handbag Mfr & Wholesaler
S.I.C.: 3171; 5137
N.A.I.C.S.: 316992; 424330
Media: 6-9-17-25
Distr.: Natl.
Budget Set: Dec.
Personnel:
Steven Giner *(Owner)*
Sebastian E. Giner *(Chm)*

TIFFANY & CO.
727 5th Ave
New York, NY 10022
Tel.: (212) 755-8000
Fax: (212) 230-6633
Toll Free: (800) 526-0649
Web Site: www.tiffany.com
Approx. Sls.: $3,085,290,000
Approx. Number Employees: 9,200
Year Founded: 1837
Business Description:
Fine Jewelry, China, Crystal, Sterling Silver, Timepieces, Clocks, Stationery, Leather, Scarves & Fragrance Retailer
S.I.C.: 3873; 5094; 5944
N.A.I.C.S.: 334518; 423940; 448310
Import Export
Advertising Expenditures: $197,597,000
Media: 2-3-4-5-6-7-8-9-11-13-18-22-25-30
Distr.: Intl.; Natl.
Personnel:
Michael J. Kowalski *(Chm & CEO)*
James E. Quinn *(Pres)*
James N. Fernandez *(CFO & Exec VP)*
Caroline D. Naggiar *(CMO & Sr VP)*
Patrick B. Dorsey *(Gen Counsel, Sec & Sr VP)*
Beth O. Canavan *(Exec VP)*
Frederic Cumenal *(Exec VP)*
Jon M. King *(Exec VP)*
Victoria Berger-Gross *(Sr VP-HR-Global)*
Pamela H. Cloud *(Sr VP-Mdsg)*
Patrick F. McGuiness *(Sr VP-Fin)*
John S. Petterson *(Sr VP-Ops)*
Carson Glover *(Dir-Media Rels)*
Jacqueline Liu *(Mgr-Product Dev)*

Brands & Products:
1837
1837 COLLECTION
AMERICAN GARDEN
FIREWORKS
LITTLE SWITZERLAND
LUCIDA
PURE TIFFANY
TIFFANY-SCHLUMBERGER
SELECTIONS
TIFFANY & CO
TIFFANY & CO.
TIFFANY ATLAS
TIFFANY BLUE
TIFFANY BLUE BOX
TIFFANY CELEBRATION
TIFFANY FOR MEN
TIFFANY MARK
TIFFANY NATURE
TIFFANY SIGNATURE

Advertising Agencies:
Job Expo International
276 5th Ave Ste 906
New York, NY 10001
Tel.: (212) 655-4505
Fax: (212) 655-4501

McCann Erickson/New York
622 3rd Ave
New York, NY 10017
Tel.: (646) 865-2000
Fax: (646) 487-9610

TIFFANY & CO. INTERNATIONAL
(Sub. of Tiffany & Co.)
600 Madison
New York, NY 10022
Tel.: (212) 755-8000
Fax: (212) 755-5903
Web Site: www.tiffan
Sales Range: $50-74.9 Million
Approx. Number Employees: 100
Year Founded: 1984
Business Description:
Holding Company
S.I.C.: 6719
N.A.I.C.S.: 551112
Media: 30
Personnel:
John S. Peterson *(Sr VP-Ops)*
Advertising Agency:
BBDO China
42/F 1 Grand Gateway Plaza
Shanghai, 200030, China
Tel.: (86) 21 2401 8000
Fax: (86) 21 6448 4699
(Creative)

TILLEY OF CANADA LIMITED
864 Hurontario St
Collingwood, ON Canada
Tel.: (705) 445-4666
Fax: (705) 445-6560
Toll Free: (800) 668-6066
E-mail: info@tilley.cc
Web Site: www.tilley.cc/contact_us.htm
Approx. Number Employees: 10
Year Founded: 1938
Business Description:
Leather Accessories Mfr & Distr
S.I.C.: 3172; 3161; 3171; 3199
N.A.I.C.S.: 316993; 316991; 316992; 316999
Import Export
Media: 4-8-22-26
Distr.: Intl.; Natl.
Personnel:
Frank Tilley *(Pres & CEO)*
Jane Tilley *(VP-Mktg)*
Brands & Products:
TILLEY

TIMEX CORPORATION
555 Christian Rd
Middlebury, CT 06762
Tel.: (203) 346-5000
Fax: (203) 346-5139
Toll Free: (800) 367-8463
Web Site: www.timex.com
Sales Range: $600-649.9 Million
Approx. Number Employees: 7,500
Year Founded: 1857
Business Description:
Watches & Clocks Mfr
S.I.C.: 3873
N.A.I.C.S.: 334518
Advertising Expenditures: $10,000,000
Media: 3-6-15-17-20-22-24
Distr.: Natl.
Budget Set: Nov. -Dec.
Brands & Products:
ACQUA
CARRIAGE
EXPEDITION
I-CONTROL
INDIGLO
INTERNET MESSENGER
IRONMAN ICONTROL
IRONMAN TRIATHLON
LIFE IS TICKING
RUSH
TIMEX
TIMEXPO
TMX
Advertising Agency:
PHD New York
220 E 42nd St 7th Fl
New York, NY 10017-5806
Tel.: (212) 894-6600
Fax: (212) 894-4100
Media Buying

TOTES ISOTONER CORPORATION
(Holding of Bruckmann, Rosser, Sherrill & Co., LLC)
9655 International Blvd
Cincinnati, OH 45246
Tel.: (513) 682-8200
Fax: (513) 682-8600
Web Site: www.totes.com
Approx. Number Employees: 1,000
Year Founded: 1923
Business Description:
Weather-Resistant Products Mfr & Distr
S.I.C.: 3151
N.A.I.C.S.: 315992
Import Export
Media: 3-5-6-10-19-20-24
Distr.: Intl.; Natl.
Budget Set: Jan.
Personnel:
Douglas P. Gernert *(Pres & CEO)*
Donna Deye *(CFO & Sr VP)*
Michael Katz *(Sr VP-Wholesale Div-US)*
Linda G. Schmidt *(VP-HR)*
Kristin Stary *(Dir-Category)*
Kelly Falkenstein *(Sr Mgr-Mktg)*
Brands & Products:
IMPRESSIONS FROM ISOTONER
ISOTONER
SENSATIONS FROM ISOTONER
SPLASHFLASH
SUNGUARD
THIS IS PINK
TOTES
WE'VE GOT YOU COVERED

TOURNEAU INC.
(Holding of Leonard Green & Partners, L.P.)
3 E 54th St 3rd Fl
New York, NY 10022-3108
Tel.: (212) 758-3265
Fax: (212) 308-9145
Toll Free: (800) 348-3332
Toll Free: (800) 424-3113
Web Site: www.tourneau.com
Sales Range: $250-299.9 Million
Approx. Number Employees: 45
Year Founded: 1900
Business Description:
Watches, Clocks & Jewelry Mfr & Retailer
S.I.C.: 5944; 3873
N.A.I.C.S.: 448310; 334518
Media: 4-6-8-9-10-13-19-24-25
Distr.: Natl.; Reg.
Budget Set: Nov. -Dec.
Personnel:
Richard Caniglia *(Exec VP)*
Richard Gellman *(VP-Adv & Mktg)*
Brands & Products:
TOURNEAU
WATCH GEAR
WORLD TIMER
Advertising Agency:
Harvard Marketing, Inc.
(House Agency)
488 Madison Ave., 2nd Fl.
New York, NY 10022
Tel.: (212) 758-6346
(Ad Campaigns)

TRI-MARK MFG, INC.
(Name Changed to 5to1 Holding Corp.)

TRIMFIT, INC.
1900 Frost Rd Ste 111
Bristol, PA 19007-1519
Tel.: (215) 781-0600
Fax: (215) 781-1803
Toll Free: (800) 347-7697
E-mail: mail@trimfit.com
Web Site: www.trimfit.com
Approx. Number Employees: 300
Year Founded: 1924

Key to Media (For complete agency information see *The Advertising Red Books-Agencies* edition):
1. Bus. Publs. 2. Cable T.V. 3. Catalogs & Directories. 4. Co-op Adv. 5. Consumer Mags. 6. D.M. to Bus. Estab.7. D.M. to Consumers 8. Daily Newsp. 9. Exhibits/Trade Shows 10. Foreign 11. Infomercial 12. Internet Adv.13. Multimedia 14. Network Radio 15. Network T.V. 16. Newsp. Distr. Mags. 17. Other 18. Outdoor (Posters, Transit) 19. Point of Purchase20. Premiums, Novelties 21. Product Samples 22. Special Events Mktg. 23. Spot Radio 24. Spot T.V. 25. Weekly Newsp. 26. Yellow Page Adv.

Trimfit, Inc. — (Continued)

Business Description:
Socks, Hosiery, Tights & Stretch Wear Mfr
S.I.C.: 2252; 2251
N.A.I.C.S.: 315119; 315111
Advertising Expenditures: $300,000
Media: 2-4-6-7-19-20
Distr.: Intl.; Natl.
Budget Set: Apr. -Oct.
Personnel:
Arnold A. Kramer *(Pres)*
Brands & Products:
COMFORTOE
TRIMFIT

TROPAR MFG. CO., INC.

5 Vreeland Rd
Florham Park, NJ 07932-1505
Mailing Address:
PO Box 215
Florham Park, NJ 07932-0215
Tel.: (973) 822-2400
Fax: (973) 822-2891
Web Site: www.airflyte.com
Approx. Number Employees: 90
Year Founded: 1959
Business Description:
Trophies, Plaques & Gift Awards & Clocks Mfr
S.I.C.: 3961
N.A.I.C.S.: 339914
Import Export
Media: 7-17-21
Distr.: Intl.; Natl.
Budget Set: Nov.
Personnel:
Peter V. Ilaria *(Chm & Pres)*
Peter E. Ilaria *(Dir-Mktg, Adv & Sls)*
Brands & Products:
AIRFLYTE
CAM
TROPAR

TUMI, INC.

(Sub. of Doughty Hanson & Co. Ltd.)
1001 Durham Ave
South Plainfield, NJ 07080
Tel.: (908) 756-4400
Fax: (908) 756-5878
Toll Free: (800) 299-TUMI
E-mail: gopero@tumi.com
Web Site: www.tumi.com
Approx. Number Employees: 600
Year Founded: 1975
Business Description:
Luggage, Handbags, Wallets & Accessories Designer & Mfr
S.I.C.: 3161; 3171; 3172; 5948
N.A.I.C.S.: 316991; 316992; 316993; 448320
Media: 4-5-6-10-11-25
Personnel:
Mike Mardy *(CFO & Exec VP)*
Michelle Cutter *(VP-Mktg & Ecommerce)*

UNCAS MANUFACTURING COMPANY

150 Niantic Ave
Providence, RI 02907-3118
Tel.: (401) 944-4700
Fax: (401) 943-2951
Approx. Number Employees: 150
Year Founded: 1911
Business Description:
Mfr. of Costume Jewelry
S.I.C.: 3961
N.A.I.C.S.: 339914
Import Export
Advertising Expenditures: $500,000
Media: 4
Distr.: Natl.
Personnel:
John Corsini *(Owner)*
Michael Britto *(VP-Fin)*
Brands & Products:
CORONADO
CORSINI
CURTIS
CURTMAN
KIDDIGEM
LOIS
SORRENTO
VINCENZO

UNIVERSAL WATCH CO., INC.

5016 Schuster St
Las Vegas, NV 89118
Tel.: (702) 736-6006
Fax: (702) 736-6007
Toll Free: (800) 360-2586
E-mail: info@silverprince.com
Web Site: www.silverprince.com
Approx. Number Employees: 6
Year Founded: 1994
Business Description:
Watch Distr
S.I.C.: 5094
N.A.I.C.S.: 423940
Media: 6-10
Personnel:
Raphael Cohen *(Pres)*
Nadine Cohen *(VP-Mktg & Adv)*

VAN CLEEF & ARPELS, INC.

(Sub. of Richemont International Ltd.)
12 W 57th St
New York, NY 10019
Tel.: (212) 644-9500
Fax: (212) 265-0800
Web Site: www.vancleef.com
Approx. Number Employees: 75
Business Description:
Jewelry Stores
S.I.C.: 5944; 3911
N.A.I.C.S.: 448310; 339911
Import
Media: 4-6-8-9-25-30
Distr.: Natl.
Budget Set: Apr. -Mar.
Brands & Products:
VAN CLEEF & ARPELS

VERA BRADLEY, INC.

2208 Production Rd
Fort Wayne, IN 46808
Tel.: (260) 482-4673
Fax: (260) 484-2278
Toll Free: (877) 708-8372
Web Site: www.verabradley.com
Approx. Rev.: $366,057,000
Approx. Number Employees: 1,427
Business Description:
Handbags, Accessories, Duffel Bags, Garment Bags & Travel Accessories Designer, Producer, Marketer & Retailer
S.I.C.: 3171; 2389; 3161; 5621; 5699; 5948
N.A.I.C.S.: 316992; 315999; 316991; 448120; 448150; 448320
Advertising Expenditures: $20,149,000
Media: 4-6-19-31
Personnel:
Barbara Bradley Baekgaard *(Co-Founder & Chief Creative Officer)*
Michael C. Ray *(CEO)*
Jeffrey A. Blade *(CFO, Chief Admin Officer, Sec & Exec VP)*
Kimberly F. Colby *(Exec VP-Design)*
C. Roddy Mann *(Exec VP-Strategy & Bus Dev)*
Jill A. Nichols *(Exec VP-Philanthrophy & Community Rels)*
Matthew C. Wojewuczki *(Exec VP-Ops)*
James Shimizu *(VP-Mktg)*
Brands & Products:
EXPANDABLE WHEELABOARD
VERA BRADLEY
Advertising Agency:
InnerWorkings Inc.
600 W Chicago Ave Ste 850
Chicago, IL 60610
Tel.: (312) 642-3700
Fax: (312) 642-3704

WARREN DIAMOND POWDER COMPANY, INC.

(Sub. of Norton Company)
1401 E Lackawanna St Mid Valley Industrial Pk
Olyphant, PA 18447-2152
Tel.: (570) 383-3261
Fax: (570) 383-3218
Toll Free: (800) 368-5155
E-mail: info@warrendiamond.com
Web Site: www.warrendiamond.com
Sales Range: $1-9.9 Million
Approx. Number Employees: 50
Year Founded: 1953
Business Description:
Diamond Wheels & Diamond Electroplated Products Mfr
S.I.C.: 3291
N.A.I.C.S.: 327910
Import Export
Media: 2-4-7-10-17
Distr.: Natl.
Personnel:
Phillipe Cruzet *(Pres)*

WELLS LAMONT CORPORATION

(Sub. of Marmon Industrial Companies LLC)
6640 W Touhy Ave
Niles, IL 60714-4516
Tel.: (847) 647-8200
Fax: (847) 647-6943
Toll Free: (800) 323-2830
Web Site: www.wellslamont.com
Sales Range: $200-249.9 Million
Approx. Number Employees: 450
Year Founded: 1907
Business Description:
Glove & Hand Protection Product Mfr
S.I.C.: 3151
N.A.I.C.S.: 315992
Import Export
Media: 2-4-6-8-10-13-18
Distr.: Intl.; Natl.
Budget Set: Oct.
Personnel:
Keith Swain *(Pres)*
Wally Beckman *(CFO)*
Bill Trainer *(VP-Sls & Mktg)*
Brands & Products:
AIRDEX
DIMENSION 3
FEELTITE
FIT, FEEL & APPEAL.
GARDEN PARTY
GARDENER'S CHOICE
GLOWZONE
HARD-WORKING GLOVES FOR SERIOUS CONDITIONS.
JOMAC
KWIKPULL
OVERWRAP
SLIMFIT
STORM ZONE
SUG
WEDGY
WELLS LAMONT
XTRASTRETCH

WIGWAM MILLS, INC.

3402 Crocker Ave
Sheboygan, WI 53081-6402
Tel.: (920) 457-5551
Fax: (920) 457-0311
Toll Free: (800) 558-7760
E-mail: socks@wigwam.com
Web Site: www.wigwam.com
Approx. Number Employees: 300
Year Founded: 1905
Business Description:
Sports & Athletic Socks; Knit Headwear
S.I.C.: 2252; 2253
N.A.I.C.S.: 315119; 315191
Export
Media: 2-4-5-6-10-19-22
Distr.: Natl.
Personnel:
Robert Chesebro, Jr. *(Chm & CEO)*
Gerald Vogel *(Pres & COO)*
James G. Einhauser *(Exec VP)*
Brands & Products:
7-FOOTER
747
ANYTHING ELSE IS A SUBSTITUTE
DRY FOOT
FOOTER
INGENIUS
INNSBRUCK
LO-KUT
SIROCCO
SOF-T
SUPER 60
SUPER 60 JR.
SUPER TUBE
TEPEE
THERMOLITE
ULTIMAX
WIGWAM
WMI
WONDER-WICK
YOUTH OUTLAST
Advertising Agency:
Periscope
921 Washington Ave S
Minneapolis, MN 55415
Tel.: (612) 399-0500
Fax: (612) 399-0600
Toll Free: (800) 339-2103

W.R. COBB COMPANY

800 Waterman Ave
East Providence, RI 02914
Tel.: (401) 467-7400
Fax: (401) 434-5022
Fax: (800) 428-0041
Toll Free: (800) 428-0040
E-mail: info@wrcobb.com
Web Site: www.wrcobb.com
Approx. Number Employees: 100

Key to Media (For complete agency information see *The Advertising Red Books-Agencies* edition):
1. Bus. Publs. 2. Cable T.V. 3. Catalogs & Directories. 4. Co-op Adv. 5. Consumer Mags. 6. D.M. to Bus. Estab.7. D.M. to Consumers 8. Daily Newsp. 9. Exhibits/Trade Shows 10. Foreign 11. Infomercial 12. Internet Adv.13. Multimedia 14. Network Radio 15. Network T.V. 16. Newsp. Distr. Mags. 17. Other 18. Outdoor (Posters, Transit) 19. Point of Purchase20. Premiums, Novelties 21. Product Samples 22. Special Events Mktg. 23. Spot Radio 24. Spot T.V. 25. Weekly Newsp. 26. Yellow Page Adv.

Year Founded: 1877
Business Description:
Mfr. of Jewelers' Findings, Master Alloy, Casting Grain, Wire & Flat Stock
S.I.C.: 3915; 5944
N.A.I.C.S.: 339913; 448310
Import Export
Media: 2-4-10
Distr.: Natl.
Budget Set: Sept.
Personnel:
Theodore H. Lichtenfels *(Chm)*
Roderick H. Lichtenfels *(CEO)*
Brands & Products:
COBB

YURMAN DESIGN, INC.

(d/b/a David Yurman)
24 Vestry St
New York, NY 10013
Tel.: (212) 896-1550
Fax: (212) 593-1597
E-mail: customerservice@davidyurman.com
Web Site: www.davidyurman.com
Approx. Number Employees: 200
Year Founded: 1979
Business Description:
Mfr. of Jewelry & Watches
S.I.C.: 3911
N.A.I.C.S.: 339911
Media: 6-10-30
Personnel:
Sybil Yurman *(Pres & CMO)*
Scott Vogel *(CFO)*
Carol Penneli *(VP-Sls)*
Brands & Products:
ALBION
CABLE CAGE
CABLE KIDS
COLLECTION
DAVID YURMAN
DECO
LANTANA
MADISON CABLE
MERCER
MIXED QUATREFOIL
SILVER ICE
TAHITIAN

ZALE CORPORATION

901 W Walnut Hill Ln
Irving, TX 75038-1003
Tel.: (972) 580-4000
Fax: (972) 580-5523
Toll Free: (800) 311-5393
E-mail: in@zalecorp.com
Web Site: www.zalecorp.com
Approx. Rev.: $1,742,563,000
Approx. Number Employees: 12,600
Year Founded: 1924
Business Description:
Holding Company; Jewelry Stores
S.I.C.: 5944; 6719
N.A.I.C.S.: 448310; 551112
Import
Advertising Expenditures: $75,800,000
Media: 3-6-10-14-15-18-23-24-25
Distr.: Natl.
Personnel:
John B. Lowe, Jr. *(Chm)*
Theo Killion *(CEO)*
Thomas A. Haubenstricker *(CFO & Sr VP)*
Brad Furry *(CIO & Sr VP)*
Richard A. Lennox *(CMO & Exec VP)*
Matthew W. Appel *(Chief Admin Officer)*
James E. Sullivan *(Chief Acctg Officer, VP & Controller)*
Gilbert P. Hollander *(Chief Mdsg Officer, Chief Sourcing Officer & Exec VP)*
Becky Mick *(Chief Stores Officer & Sr VP)*
Nancy O. Skinner *(Pres-Zales Outlet & Sr VP)*
Hilary Molay *(Gen Counsel, Corp Sec & Sr VP)*
Jeannie Barsam *(Sr VP-Mdse Plng & Allocation)*
John Legg *(Sr VP-Supply Chain)*
Toyin Ogun *(Sr VP-HR & Customer Svc)*
Brands & Products:
BAILEY BANKS & BIDDLE
BAILEYBANKSANDBIDDLE.COM
BRILLANT BUY
DIAMOND
GORDON'S JEWELERS
MAPPINS JEWELERS
PEOPLES JEWELERS
PIERCING PAGODA
PLUMB GOLD
SILVER & GOLD CONNECTION
ZALE CORPORATION
ZALES
ZALES DIRECT
ZALES JEWELERS
ZALES OUTLET
ZALES.COM
ZLC DIRECT
Advertising Agency:
G&G Advertising
2804 3rd Ave N
Billings, MT 59101
Tel.: (406) 294-8113
Fax: (406) 294-8120
Toll Free: (800) 390-2892

ZUMIEZ INCORPORATED

6300 Merrill Creek Pkwy Ste B
Everett, WA 98203-6248
Tel.: (425) 551-1500
Fax: (425) 551-1555
Toll Free: (877) 828-6929
E-mail: help@zumiez.com
Web Site: www.zumiez.com
Approx. Sls.: $478,849,000
Approx. Number Employees: 1,380
Year Founded: 1978
Business Description:
Apparel, Footwear & Accessories Retailer
S.I.C.: 5611; 5621; 5699
N.A.I.C.S.: 448190; 448110; 448120; 448150
Advertising Expenditures: $1,300,000
Media: 6-22
Personnel:
Thomas D. Campion *(Chm)*
Lynn K. Kilbourne *(Pres)*
Richard M. Brooks *(CEO)*
Marc Stolzman *(CFO)*
Ford K. Wright *(Exec VP-Stores)*
Stuart Martin *(Dir-Mktg)*

Key to Media (For complete agency information see *The Advertising Red Books-Agencies* edition):
1. Bus. Publs. 2. Cable T.V. 3. Catalogs & Directories. 4. Co-op Adv. 5. Consumer Mags. 6. D.M. to Bus. Estab.7. D.M. to Consumers 8. Daily Newsp. 9. Exhibits/Trade Shows 10. Foreign 11. Infomercial 12. Internet Adv.13. Multimedia 14. Network Radio 15. Network T.V. 16. Newsp. Distr. Mags. 17. Other 18. Outdoor (Posters, Transit) 19. Point of Purchase20. Premiums, Novelties 21. Product Samples 22. Special Events Mktg. 23. Spot Radio 24. Spot T.V. 25. Weekly Newsp. 26. Yellow Page Adv.

Apparel I-Women's, Children's & Infants' Wear

A&E STORES, INC.
1000 Huyler St
Teterboro, NJ 07608-1142
Tel.: (201) 393-0600
Fax: (201) 393-0233
E-mail: info@aestores.com
Web Site: www.aestores.com
Sales Range: $150-199.9 Million
Approx. Number Employees: 1,800
Year Founded: 1973
Business Description:
Retailer of Women's Apparel
S.I.C.: 5621; 7389
N.A.I.C.S.: 448120; 561499
Import
Advertising Expenditures: $1,400,000
Media: 2-8-9
Distr.: Direct to Consumer
Budget Set: Jan.
Personnel:
Alan Ades *(CFO, Co-Founder, Principal, Owner, Chm & Pres)*
Murry Setton *(COO)*
Dennis Erani *(Exec VP & Gen Mgr)*
Philip Harrison *(VP-Fin)*
Bruce Kleiman *(VP)*
Susan Leventhal *(Dir-Mktg)*
Brands & Products:
ARCADE AMERICA
BOLTONS
J. CHUCKLES
LOCO BLUE
PAYHALF
STRAWBERRY
VELOCE 500

AEROPOSTALE, INC.
112 W 34th St 22nd Fl
New York, NY 10120
Tel.: (646) 485-5410
Fax: (646) 485-5430
E-mail: contactus@aeropostale.com
Web Site: www.aeropostale.com
Approx. Sls.: $2,400,434,000
Approx. Number Employees: 4,160
Business Description:
Clothing Designer, Marketer & Sales
S.I.C.: 5699; 5611; 5621
N.A.I.C.S.: 448150; 448110; 448120; 448190
Import Export
Advertising Expenditures: $6,800,000
Media: 13-19-22-23
Personnel:
Julian R. Geiger *(Chm)*
Michael J. Cunningham *(Pres)*
Thomas P. Johnson *(CEO)*
Marc D. Miller *(CFO)*
Ann E. Joyce *(CIO & Sr VP)*
Edward M. Slezak *(Gen Counsel, Sec & Sr VP)*
Mary Jo Pile *(Exec VP-Customer Engagement)*
Olivera Lazic Zangas *(Sr VP & Dir-Design)*
Marc A. Babins *(Sr VP)*
Scott K. Birnbaum *(Sr VP-Mktg)*
Mark A. Dorwart *(Sr VP-Construction & Logistics)*
Barbara Pindar *(Sr VP-Plng & Allocation)*
Joseph R. Licata *(Product Mgr)*
Brands & Products:
AERO ATHLETICS
AEROPOSTALE

A.H. SCHREIBER CO., INC.
460 W 34th St
New York, NY 10001-2320
Tel.: (212) 564-2700
Fax: (212) 594-7234
Web Site: www.ahschreiber.com
Approx. Number Employees: 500
Year Founded: 1920
Business Description:
Mfr. of Women's & Girl's Swimwear
S.I.C.: 2339; 2329
N.A.I.C.S.: 315239; 315228
Media: 4-5-6-7-9-10-19-20
Distr.: Natl.
Personnel:
Joel Schreiber *(Pres)*
Michael Gross *(CFO)*
Ira Greene *(VP & Mgr-Sls)*
Brands & Products:
BEACH NATIVE
DELTA BURKE
LONGITUDE
REVEL BEACH
ROBBIE LEN
SIRENA

AIDAN INDUSTRIES, INC.
(d/b/a Catherine Malandrino)
275 W 39th St
New York, NY 10018
Tel.: (212) 840-0106
Fax: (212) 840-3630
E-mail: info@catherinemalandrino.com
Web Site: www.catherinemalandrino.com
Approx. Number Employees: 30
Business Description:
Designer & Whslr of Women's Apparel
S.I.C.: 5137
N.A.I.C.S.: 424330
Exhibits/Trade Shows: 100%
Personnel:
Bernard Aidan *(CEO)*
Brands & Products:
CATHERINE MALANDRINO COLLECTION

ALFRED ANGELO, INC.
1301 Virginia Dr Ste 110
Fort Washington, PA 19034
Tel.: (215) 659-5300
Fax: (215) 659-1532
E-mail: info@alfredangelo.com
Web Site: www.alfredangelo.com
Approx. Number Employees: 476
Business Description:
Mfr. of Bridal, Bridesmaids, Flowergirl & Mother-of-the-Bride Gowns; Bridal Headpieces & Accessories
S.I.C.: 2335
N.A.I.C.S.: 315233
Import Export
Media: 2-3-4-6-8-10-14-18-19-23-24-26
Distr.: Intl.; Natl.
Personnel:
Michele Piccione *(Co-Owner & Chief Creative Officer)*
Vincent A. Piccione *(Pres & CEO)*
Denise Wash *(VP-Mktg)*
Barbara Pfaumer *(Mgr-Adv)*
Brands & Products:
ALFRED ANGELO
COLOR MIX
DESTINY
DREAM IN COLOR
IRIDESCENT TAFFETA
LITTLE WHITE DRESS
PICCIONE
SAPPHIRE
SOCIAL OCCASION
Advertising Agency:
Neiman Group
614 N Frnt St
Harrisburg, PA 17101-1057
Tel.: (717) 232-5554
Fax: (717) 232-7998

ALGY TRIMMING COMPANY
440 NE First Ave
Hallandale, FL 33008
Mailing Address:
PO Box 090490
Hallandale, FL 33008
Tel.: (954) 457-8100
Fax: (888) 928-2282
Fax: (954) 454-7370
Toll Free: (800) 458-ALGY
Web Site: www.algyperforms.com
Approx. Number Employees: 60
Year Founded: 1937
Business Description:
Dance Costumes Designer
S.I.C.: 2389; 2329; 2339; 2341
N.A.I.C.S.: 315999; 315211; 315212; 315231
Media: 4-6
Personnel:
Sue Gordon *(Pres)*

ALLSTAR PRODUCTS GROUP LLC
2 Skyline Dr
Hawthorne, NY 10532
Tel.: (914) 347-7827
Fax: (914) 347-7826
Web Site: www.allstarmg.com
Sales Range: $500-549.9 Million
Approx. Number Employees: 35
Business Description:
Household Products Sales
S.I.C.: 5199; 5099
N.A.I.C.S.: 424990; 423990
Personnel:
Scott Boilen *(Pres)*
Anne Flynn *(VP-Mktg)*
Howard Boilen *(Dir)*
Brands & Products:
ALLSTAR
SNUGGIE
Advertising Agency:
360 Public Relations LLC
140 Clareedon St Ste 401
Boston, MA 02116
Tel.: (617) 585-5770
Fax: (617) 585-5789
Public Relations Agency of Record
Snuggie Blanket Fashion Show

Key to Media (For complete agency information see *The Advertising Red Books-Agencies* edition):
1. Bus. Publs. 2. Cable T.V. 3. Catalogs & Directories. 4. Co-op Adv. 5. Consumer Mags. 6. D.M. to Bus. Estab.7. D.M. to Consumers
8. Daily Newsp. 9. Exhibits/Trade Shows 10. Foreign 11. Infomercial 12. Internet Adv.13. Multimedia 14. Network Radio
15. Network T.V. 16. Newsp. Distr. Mags. 17. Other 18. Outdoor (Posters, Transit) 19. Point of Purchase20. Premiums, Novelties
21. Product Samples 22. Special Events Mktg. 23. Spot Radio 24. Spot T.V. 25. Weekly Newsp. 26. Yellow Page Adv.

ALPHA MILLS CORP.
122 S Margaretta St
Schuylkill Haven, PA 17972-1694
Tel.: (570) 385-0511
Fax: (570) 385-0467
E-mail: alpham@alphamills.com
Web Site: www.alphamills.com
Approx. Number Employees: 174
Year Founded: 1936
Business Description:
Knitwear, Underwear & Sportswear Mfr
S.I.C.: 2254; 2253
N.A.I.C.S.: 315192; 315191
Media: 2-4-6-25
Distr.: Natl.
Personnel:
Richard D. Biever *(Pres)*

ALWAYS FOR ME INC.
740 Veterans Memorial Hwy Ste 303
Hauppauge, NY 11788
Tel.: (631) 237-4881
Fax: (631) 237-4883
E-mail: sales@alwaysforme.com
Web Site: www.alwaysforme.com
E-Mail For Key Personnel:
Sales Director: sales@alwaysforme.com
Approx. Sls.: $10,000,000
Approx. Number Employees: 15
Business Description:
Women's Plus Size Clothing Retailer
S.I.C.: 5621
N.A.I.C.S.: 448120
Media: 4-8-13
Personnel:
Susan K. Barone *(Pres & CEO)*
Greg Barone *(Exec VP)*
Brands & Products:
ALWAYS FOR ME
FOR THE CURVY YOU
PLUS SIZE LIVING
UNIQUELY ME

ALYCE DESIGNS INC.
7901 Caldwell Ave
Morton Grove, IL 60053
Tel.: (847) 966-9200
Fax: (847) 966-9207
Web Site: www.alycedesigns.com
Approx. Number Employees: 150
Business Description:
Dresses & Gowns for Proms, Special Occasions, Pageants & Weddings
S.I.C.: 2335; 2389
N.A.I.C.S.: 315233; 315299
Media: 4-8-10
Personnel:
Jean Paul Hamm *(Owner)*
Brands & Products:
ALYCE

AMERICAN APPAREL, INC.
747 Warehouse St
Los Angeles, CA 90021
Tel.: (213) 488-0226
Fax: (213) 488-0334
E-mail: investors@americanapparel.net
Web Site: www.americanapparel.net
Approx. Sls.: $532,989,000
Approx. Number Employees: 11,300
Year Founded: 2005
Business Description:
Apparel Mfr, Distr & Retailer
S.I.C.: 2389; 5699
N.A.I.C.S.: 315999; 448150
Advertising Expenditures: $243,000
Media: 4-6-7-8-9-13-18-19-25
Personnel:
Dov Charney *(Chm & CEO)*
Thomas M. Casey *(Acting Pres)*
John Luttrell *(CFO)*
Marty Bailey *(Chief Mfg Officer)*
Glenn A. Weinman *(Gen Counsel, Sec & Sr VP)*
Joyce Crucillo *(Gen Counsel)*
Nicolle Gabbay *(Dir-Retail Mktg)*

AMERICAN LEGEND COOPERATIVE
PO Box 58308
Seattle, WA 98138
Tel.: (425) 251-3200
Fax: (425) 251-3222
E-mail: info@americanlegend.com
Web Site: www.americanlegend.com
Approx. Sls.: $80,000,000
Approx. Number Employees: 40
Business Description:
Mink Producer & Mink Products Mfr
S.I.C.: 0271
N.A.I.C.S.: 112930
Media: 6-10
Brands & Products:
AMERICAN LEGEND
BLACKGLAMA
LEGEND

ANN TAYLOR STORES CORPORATION
7 Times Sq 15th Fl
New York, NY 10036
Tel.: (212) 541-3300
Fax: (212) 541-3379
Toll Free: (800) 677-6788
E-mail: clientservices@anntaylor.com
Web Site: www.anntaylor.com
Approx. Sls.: $1,828,523,000
Approx. Number Employees: 4,200
Year Founded: 1954
Business Description:
Women's Apparel, Shoes & Accessories
S.I.C.: 5621; 5699
N.A.I.C.S.: 448120; 448150
Import
Advertising Expenditures: $63,400,000
Media: 4-6-8-18-25
Personnel:
Kay Krill *(Pres & CEO)*
Michael J. Nicholson *(CFO, Chief Acctg Officer, Treas & Exec VP)*
Michael Kingston *(CIO)*
Christine M. Beauchamp *(Pres-Ann Taylor Div)*
Brian Lynch *(Pres-Corp Ops)*
Gary Muto *(Pres-LOFT)*
Barbara K. Eisenberg *(Gen Counsel, Sec & Exec VP)*
Mark Morrison *(Exec VP-HR)*
George R. Sappenfield *(Sr VP-Real Estate & Construction)*
Catherine Fisher *(VP-Corp Comm)*
Sonya Lee *(Gen Mgr-Mdse)*
Beth Feldman *(Dir-Mktg)*
Jill Harnick *(Dir-Corp Comm)*
Andrew Taylor *(Dir-PR)*
Brands & Products:
ANN
ANN TAYLOR
ANN TAYLOR LOFT
DESTINATION
MARGO
Advertising Agencies:
1508, Inc.
4048 Sonoma Hwy #4
Napa, CA 94559
Tel.: (415) 876-1508

Furman, Feiner Advertising
560 Sylvan Ave
Englewood Cliffs, NJ 07632
Tel.: (201) 568-1634
Fax: (201) 568-6262

New Media Strategies
1100 Wilson Blvd Ste 1400
Arlington, VA 22209
Tel.: (703) 253-0050
Fax: (703) 253-0065

Ultra 16
36 Cooper Sq 4F
New York, NY 10003
Tel.: (212) 260-6454
Fax: (212) 260-6552

ANTHROPOLOGIE, INC.
(Sub. of Urban Outfitters, Inc.)
5000 S Broad St Bldg 10
Philadelphia, PA 19112
Tel.: (215) 564-2313
Fax: (215) 557-4702
E-mail: service@anthropologie.com
Web Site: www.urbanoutfittersinc.com
Sales Range: $200-249.9 Million
Approx. Number Employees: 205
Year Founded: 1992
Business Description:
Women's Clothing Stores
S.I.C.: 5621
N.A.I.C.S.: 448120
Media: 4-13
Personnel:
Richard A. Hayne *(Chm)*
Wendy Wurtzberger *(Global Co-Pres)*
Glen T. Senk *(CEO)*
Wendy Brown *(COO)*
Glen A. Bodzy *(Gen Counsel & Sec)*
Amy Choyne *(Exec Dir-Mktg)*

ANVIL HOLDINGS, INC.
228 E 45th St 4th Fl
New York, NY 10017-3303
Tel.: (212) 476-0300
Fax: (212) 808-4790
Toll Free: (800) 223-0332
E-mail: info@anvilknitwear.com
Web Site: www.anvilknitwear.com
Sales Range: $150-199.9 Million
Approx. Number Employees: 4,200
Year Founded: 1994
Business Description:
Activewear Designer, Mfr & Marketer
S.I.C.: 3949; 5137
N.A.I.C.S.: 339920; 424330
Import Export
Advertising Expenditures: $1,000,000
Media: 4-7-10-13
Personnel:
Anthony Corsano *(Pres & CEO-Anvil Knitwear)*
William H. Turner *(Pres & CEO-Anvil Mining Ltd)*
Frank Ferramosca *(CFO & Exec VP-Anvil Knitwear)*
Caterina Conti *(Chief Admin Officer, Gen Counsel & Exec VP-Anvil Knitwear)*
Frank D. Keeney *(Exec VP-Sls)*
Christopher Levesque *(VP-Mktg & Mdsg-Anvil Knitwear)*
Brands & Products:
ACTIVE WEAR
ANVIL
PANS
SHIRT

ATHLETA
(Div. of The Gap, Inc.)
1622 Corporate Cir
Petaluma, CA 94954
Tel.: (707) 769-2600
Toll Free: (877) 328-4538
E-mail: custserv@athleta.com
Web Site: www.athleta.gap.com
Sales Range: $10-24.9 Million
Approx. Number Employees: 120
Year Founded: 1997
Business Description:
Women's Sportswear Mfr & Retailer
S.I.C.: 2339
N.A.I.C.S.: 315239
Media: 4-8-13
Personnel:
Joseph E. Teno, Jr. *(Pres & CEO)*
Jed Smith *(VP-Mktg & Creative)*

ATTITUDES IN DRESSING INC.
107 Trumbull St Bldg B8
Elizabeth, NJ 07206
Tel.: (908) 354-7218
Fax: (908) 354-4023
Web Site: www.bodywrappers.com
E-Mail For Key Personnel:
Sales Director: sales@bodywrappers.com
Approx. Sls.: $18,795,888
Approx. Number Employees: 50
Year Founded: 1980
Business Description:
Athletic Clothing: Women's, Misses' & Juniors' Mfr
S.I.C.: 2339; 5137
N.A.I.C.S.: 315239; 424330
Media: 6-10
Personnel:
Marie West *(Pres)*
Michael Rubin *(CEO & Partner)*
Brands & Products:
BODY WRAPPERS
PREMIERE COLLECTION
SOFT SUPPLEX
TACTEL
TOTALSTRETCH
VALUE SUPPLEX
WRAPTURE

B.A. BALLOU & CO. INC.
800 Waterman Ave
East Providence, RI 02914-1728
Tel.: (401) 438-7000
Fax: (401) 434-5022
Toll Free: (800) 755-7099
E-mail: sballou@ballou.com
Web Site: www.ballou.com
Approx. Number Employees: 155
Year Founded: 1868
Business Description:
Jewelry Findings; Jewelry
S.I.C.: 3915; 3911
N.A.I.C.S.: 339913; 339911
Advertising Expenditures: $200,000
Media: 4-8
Distr.: Natl.

Key to Media (For complete agency information see *The Advertising Red Books-Agencies* edition):
1. Bus. Publs. 2. Cable T.V. 3. Catalogs & Directories. 4. Co-op Adv. 5. Consumer Mags. 6. D.M. to Bus. Estab.7. D.M. to Consumers
8. Daily Newsp. 9. Exhibits/Trade Shows 10. Foreign 11. Infomercial 12. Internet Adv.13. Multimedia 14. Network Radio
15. Network T.V. 16. Newsp. Distr. Mags. 17. Other 18. Outdoor (Posters, Transit) 19. Point of Purchase20. Premiums, Novelties
21. Product Samples 22. Special Events Mktg. 23. Spot Radio 24. Spot T.V. 25. Weekly Newsp. 26. Yellow Page Adv.

B.A. Ballou & Co. Inc. — (Continued)

Personnel:
Graham Kidson *(Dir-Sls & Mktg-Worldwide)*
Chris Powrie *(Dir-Ops)*
Debra Seaton *(Acct Mgr)*

BABY TOGS, INC.
100 W 33rd St Ste 1400
New York, NY 10001
Tel.: (212) 868-2100
Fax: (212) 967-5433
E-mail: info@babytogs.net
Web Site: www.babytogs.com
Approx. Number Employees: 100
Year Founded: 1942
Business Description:
Infant & Toddler Apparel Mfr
S.I.C.: 2331; 2339
N.A.I.C.S.: 315232; 315212
Export
Media: 5-6-10-11-19-21-22
Personnel:
Eddie Sitt *(Chm)*
Brands & Products:
BABY TOGS
BT KIDS

BAKERS FOOTWEAR GROUP, INC.
2815 Scott Ave
Saint Louis, MO 63103-3032
Tel.: (314) 621-0699
Fax: (314) 641-0390
Toll Free: (866) 922-5377
E-mail: info@bakershoes.com
Web Site: www.bakersshoes.com
Approx. Sls.: $185,625,844
Approx. Number Employees: 545
Year Founded: 1927
Business Description:
Retailer of Women's Shoes & Accessories
S.I.C.: 5661; 5699
N.A.I.C.S.: 448210; 448150
Advertising Expenditures: $664,475
Personnel:
Peter A. Edison *(Chm, Pres & CEO)*
Charles R. Daniel, III *(CFO, Treas, Sec, Exec VP & Controller)*
Joseph R. Vander Pluym *(COO & Exec VP-Stores)*
Stanley K. Tusman *(Chief Plng Officer & Exec VP)*
Mark D. Ianni *(Chief Mdsg Officer)*
Chris Spohr *(Info Security Officer)*
Brands & Products:
BAKERS

BARCO UNIFORMS, INC.
350 W Rosecrans Ave
Gardena, CA 90248-1728
Tel.: (310) 323-7315
Fax: (310) 719-2199
Toll Free: (800) 421-1932
Web Site: www.barcouniforms.com
Approx. Number Employees: 160
Year Founded: 1929
Business Description:
Mfr. & Sales of Professional Apparel
S.I.C.: 2389; 2326
N.A.I.C.S.: 315299; 315225
Import Export
Media: 2-4-6-7-10-18-20-22
Distr.: Natl.
Budget Set: June
Personnel:
Michael Donner *(Chm & CEO)*
Danny Robertson *(Pres & COO)*
Andrew Akiyoshi *(Sr VP-Supply Chain & Ops)*
David Murphy *(Sr VP-Mktg & Sls)*
John W. Cable *(Dir-Production)*
Toni S. Lee *(Sr Mgr-Product Dev)*
Brands & Products:
BARCO
BARCO'S BEST
CAMBRIDGE
FLEXX
MULTIPLES
PRESTIGE POPLIN
RIVERWASHED
SMART POCKET
WHITES

BARE NECESSITIES, INC.
17 Mileed Way
Avenel, NJ 07001
Tel.: (973) 621-6211
Fax: (973) 643-3539
Toll Free: (877) 728-9272
E-mail: info@barenecessities.com
Web Site: www.barenecessities.com
Business Description:
Women's Clothing
S.I.C.: 5621
N.A.I.C.S.: 448120
Media: 6-13
Personnel:
William Richardson *(Pres & COO)*
Jay Dunn *(CMO)*
Jessica Jackson *(VP-Ecommerce)*
Dan Sackrowitz *(VP-Mktg & Bus Dev)*
Brands & Products:
BARE NECESSITIES
BARENECESSITIES.COM
BAREWEB LP
BAREWEB.COM
LARGE BRA SAVER
SMALL BRA SAVER
YOU FIT. YOUR STYLE. YOUR NECESSITIES

BCBG MAX AZRIA
2761 Fruitland Ave
Vernon, CA 90058
Tel.: (323) 589-2224
Tel.: (213) 624-2224
Fax: (323) 277-5454
Toll Free: (888) 636BCBG
Web Site: www.bcbg.com
Approx. Sls.: $236,224,027
Approx. Number Employees: 600
Business Description:
Women's Clothing Stores
S.I.C.: 5621; 3144
N.A.I.C.S.: 448120; 316214
Media: 6-10
Personnel:
Max Azria *(Chm & CEO)*
Jayson Kim *(Div VP-Consumer Mktg)*
Brands & Products:
BCBGMAXAZRIA
BCBGMAXAZRIA RUNWAY
HERVE LEGER
MAX AZRIA

BEACH PATROL INC.
Apt 2 3771 Lockland Dr
Los Angeles, CA 90008-3538
Tel.: (310) 522-2700
Fax: (310) 952-8444
E-mail: info@beachpatrolinc.com
Web Site: www.beachpatrolinc.com
Approx. Number Employees: 167
Year Founded: 1987
Business Description:
Women's Swimwear & Beachwear
S.I.C.: 5137
N.A.I.C.S.: 424330
Import Export
Media: 7-10
Brands & Products:
BAJA BLUE
DAFFY WATERWEAR
JAG
L.E.I.
REBEL BEACH
SILVER SWIM
SUMMER GIRL
SUN BLUSH
SWIM SYSTEMS

BEBE STORES, INC.
400 Valley Dr
Brisbane, CA 94005-1210
Tel.: (415) 715-3900
Fax: (415) 715-3939
Toll Free: (877) BEBE-777
E-mail: askus@bebe.com
Web Site: www.bebe.com
Approx. Sls.: $493,274,000
Approx. Number Employees: 1,242
Year Founded: 1976
Business Description:
Retail Clothing Stores Owner & Operator
S.I.C.: 5621; 2339
N.A.I.C.S.: 448120; 315239
Advertising Expenditures: $23,900,000
Media: 4-6-8-13-15-18-19-24
Personnel:
Manny Mashouf *(Chm & CEO)*
Emilia Fabricant *(Pres)*
Walter Parks *(CFO & COO)*
Lawrence Smith *(Gen Counsel & Sr VP)*
Renee Bell *(Exec VP-Mdsg)*
Susan Powers *(Sr VP-Stores)*
Sandra Alvarenga *(Dir-Mktg)*
Brands & Products:
2B BEBE
2BE
APHRODITE
BAMBI
BAROQUE
BBSP
BEBE
BEBE O
BEBE SPORT
BEBE.COM
BELLA
CARMEN
COLLECTION BEBE
GRECIAN
KAYLA
NAOMI
NEDA
NEDA BY BEBE
OMBRE
VICKY
WISH
Advertising Agency:
iCrossing, Inc.
15169 N Scottsdale Rd Ste C400
Scottsdale, AZ 85254
Tel.: (480) 505-5800
Fax: (480) 505-5801
Toll Free: (866) 620-3780

BEN KAHN FURS CORPORATION
424 5th Ave
New York, NY 10016
Tel.: (212) 279-0633
Fax: (212) 857-0014
Approx. Sls.: $5,000,000
Approx. Number Employees: 20
Year Founded: 1913
Business Description:
Fur Retailer
S.I.C.: 5699; 5137
N.A.I.C.S.: 448190; 424330
Import Export
Advertising Expenditures: $100,000
Media: 4-6-9-10-25
Distr.: Natl.
Personnel:
Edward Graf *(Pres & CEO)*

BEN SHERMAN USA
(Sub. of Ben Sherman Ltd)
1071 Ave of the Americas 10th Fl
New York, NY 10018
Tel.: (212) 840-8000
Fax: (646) 375-7590
E-mail: info@bensherman.com
Web Site: www.bensherman.com
Sales Range: $50-74.9 Million
Approx. Number Employees: 25
Business Description:
Apparel & Accessories Distr
S.I.C.: 5136
N.A.I.C.S.: 424320
Media: 6-22
Personnel:
Joseph Cook *(Sr VP-Sls & Mktg)*

BENDON USA
(Sub. of Bendon Limited)
180 Madison Ave Ste 2305
New York, NY 10016
Tel.: (212) 696-4570
Fax: (212) 616-4571
Web Site: www.bendongroup.com
Business Description:
Clothing Distr
S.I.C.: 5621
N.A.I.C.S.: 448120
Media: 4-8

BENETTON U.S.A. CORPORATION
(Sub. of Benetton Group S.p.A.)
601 Fifth Ave
New York, NY 10017-8260
Tel.: (212) 593-0290
Toll Free: (800) 535-4491
Approx. Number Employees: 60
Year Founded: 1965
Business Description:
Retail Sportswear Stores
S.I.C.: 2329; 2339
N.A.I.C.S.: 315228; 315239
Advertising Expenditures: $2,000,000
Bus. Publs.: $600,000; Catalogs & Directories: $400,000; Consumer Mags.: $200,000; Daily Newsp.: $600,000; Premiums, Novelties: $200,000
Distr.: Intl.; Natl.
Personnel:
Carlo Tunioli *(Pres)*
You Nguyen *(Chief Mdsg Officer)*
Brands & Products:
O12
ZEROTONDO

Key to Media (For complete agency information see *The Advertising Red Books-Agencies* edition):
1. Bus. Publs. 2. Cable T.V. 3. Catalogs & Directories. 4. Co-op Adv. 5. Consumer Mags. 6. D.M. to Bus. Estab.7. D.M. to Consumers
8. Daily Newsp. 9. Exhibits/Trade Shows 10. Foreign 11. Infomercial 12. Internet Adv.13. Multimedia 14. Network Radio
15. Network T.V. 16. Newsp. Distr. Mags. 17. Other 18. Outdoor (Posters, Transit) 19. Point of Purchase20. Premiums, Novelties
21. Product Samples 22. Special Events Mktg. 23. Spot Radio 24. Spot T.V. 25. Weekly Newsp. 26. Yellow Page Adv.

BERMO ENTERPRISES INC.
12033 US 131
Schoolcraft, MI 49087-0426
Tel.: (269) 679-2580
Fax: (269) 679-2611
E-mail: help@bermoenterprises.com
Web Site: www.bermoenterprises.com
Approx. Number Employees: 245
Year Founded: 1973
Business Description:
Family Clothing Stores
S.I.C.: 5651; 5136
N.A.I.C.S.: 448140; 424320
Import Export
Media: 4-10
Personnel:
Edward Bernard *(Pres)*
Evan Litvak *(CFO)*
Tony Peters *(VP-Sls)*

BERNARD CHAUS, INC.
530 7th Ave
New York, NY 10018
Tel.: (212) 354-1280
Fax: (646) 562-4848
E-mail: info@bernardchaus.com
Web Site: www.bernardchaus.com
Sales Range: $100-124.9 Million
Approx. Number Employees: 124
Year Founded: 1976
Business Description:
Women's Apparel Mfr & Marketer
S.I.C.: 2337; 2331; 2339
N.A.I.C.S.: 315234; 315212; 315232; 315239
Advertising Expenditures: $1,600,000
Media: 6-10
Personnel:
Josephine Chaus *(Chm & CEO)*
Jackie Muldowney *(VP-Mdsg)*
Brands & Products:
CHAUS
CHAUS & CO.
CYNTHIA STEFFE
FRANCES & RITA
JC
JOSEPHINE
JOSEPHINE CHAUS

BLAUER MANUFACTURING COMPANY, INC.
20 Aberdeen St
Boston, MA 02215
Tel.: (617) 536-6606
Fax: (617) 536-6948
Toll Free: (800) 225-6715
E-mail: info@blauer.com
Web Site: www.blauer.com
E-Mail For Key Personnel:
President: cblauer@blauer.com
Sales Range: $25-49.9 Million
Approx. Number Employees: 550
Year Founded: 1936
Business Description:
Men's & Women's Uniform Outerwear
S.I.C.: 2326; 2339
N.A.I.C.S.: 315225; 315239
Import Export
Advertising Expenditures: $200,000
Media: 4-17
Distr.: Natl.
Personnel:
Charles L. Blauer *(Chm, Pres & CEO)*
Bill Blauer *(VP-Sls & Principal)*
Michael J. Blauer *(Sr VP-Mfg)*
Stephen J. Blauer *(Sr VP)*
Tom Ames *(Dir-Mktg)*
Ryan Reynolds *(Mgr-Western Reg)*
Brands & Products:
BLAUER
CLASSACT
COMMANDO
CROSSTECH
DEFENDER
EXCEL
GTX
HI-VISIBILITY
KERMEL
LONESTAR
STANDARD
STREETGEAR
SUPERSHELL
TNT

BLUE CANOE BODYWEAR
390 A Lk Benbow Dr
Garberville, CA 95542
Tel.: (707) 923-1373
Tel.: (707) 923-4111
Fax: (707) 923-1374
Toll Free: (888) 923-1373
E-mail: info@bluecanoe.com
Web Site: www.bluecanoe.com
Sales Range: $25-49.9 Million
Approx. Number Employees: 20
Year Founded: 1991
Business Description:
Women's Bodywear Mfr
S.I.C.: 5137; 5621
N.A.I.C.S.: 424330; 448120
Media: 4-8-13
Personnel:
Laurie Dunlap *(Pres)*
Brands & Products:
BLUE CANOE
BLUE CANOE BODYWEAR
COTTON CASHMERE
JUST COTTON
SHEER ORGANICS

BON JOUR INTERNATIONAL LTD.
1400 Broadway Fl 22
New York, NY 10018-5222
Tel.: (212) 398-1000
Fax: (212) 827-9914
Approx. Number Employees: 65
Year Founded: 1973
Business Description:
Licensing Group for Sportswear, Jeans, Pants, Active Wear Shirts & Accessories
S.I.C.: 5621
N.A.I.C.S.: 448120
Advertising Expenditures: $9,000,000
Media: 2-6-7-8-10-18
Distr.: Natl.
Personnel:
Charles Dayan *(Pres)*
Zev Friedman *(CFO)*
Brands & Products:
FADED GLORY
ROUTE 66

THE BOPPY COMPANY
560 Golden Rdg Rd Ste 150
Golden, CO 80401
Tel.: (720) 746-3820
Fax: (720) 746-3838
Toll Free: (888) 77-BOPPY
E-mail: info@boppy.com
Web Site: www.boppy.com
Approx. Number Employees: 20
Year Founded: 1990
Business Description:
Mfr. & Sales of Baby Products & Clothing
S.I.C.: 5137
N.A.I.C.S.: 424330
Media: 6-10
Personnel:
Susan M. Brown *(Pres)*
Nancy Bartley *(CEO)*
Meg Heitlinger *(Mgr-Mktg)*
Brands & Products:
BOBBY
BOBBYHOOD
BOPPY
CARRY IN COMFORT
CRADLE IN COMFORT
HAPPY PLACE
NOGGIN NEST
PROTECTME
ROCK IN COMFORT
THE SLEEP EASY
SUPPORT IN STYLE

BOSCARALE OPERATING, LLC
(d/b/a Rumble Tumble)
112 W 34th St Ste 1618
New York, NY 10120-1201
Tel.: (212) 279-6542
Fax: (212) 967-6446
Web Site: www.rumbletumble.com
Approx. Number Employees: 10
Year Founded: 1986
Business Description:
Wholesale Children's Knitwear
S.I.C.: 5621; 5611
N.A.I.C.S.: 448120; 448110
Media: 2-9-21-25
Distr.: Natl.
Budget Set: Oct.
Brands & Products:
RUMBLE TUMBLE

BOSTON PROPER, INC.
6500 Park of Commerce Blvd
Boca Raton, FL 33487-8217
Tel.: (561) 241-1700
Fax: (561) 241-1055
E-mail: customerservice@bostonproper.com
Web Site: www.bostonproper.com
Approx. Number Employees: 250
Year Founded: 1951
Business Description:
Multibrand, Multichannel Direct to Consumer Retailer
S.I.C.: 5621; 5699
N.A.I.C.S.: 448120; 448150
Import Export
Media: 4-8-13
Personnel:
Michael W. Tiernan *(Chm)*
Sheryl Clark *(CEO)*
Ken Fischer *(COO)*
Amielle Duzzeppa *(Mgr-Mktg)*
Brands & Products:
BOSTON PROPER
THE MARK GROUP
WEAR IT LIKE NO ONE ELSE

BOUTIQUE DANIELLE NAULT
33 Principal N
Sawyerville, QC Canada
Tel.: (819) 889-1086
Toll Free: (888) 899-0688
E-mail: info@daniellenault.com
Web Site: www.daniellenault.com
Approx. Number Employees: 1
Business Description:
Coat, Sweater & Jacket Designer
S.I.C.: 2339; 2329; 2337; 2341; 2389
N.A.I.C.S.: 315212; 315211; 315231; 315234; 315999
Media: 10
Personnel:
Danielle Nault *(CEO)*
Brands & Products:
DANIELLE NAULT

BRA SMYTH OF CALIFORNIA, INC.
100 N Winchester Blvd
Santa Clara, CA 95050
Tel.: (408) 261-9560
Fax: (408) 261-9564
Toll Free: (800) BRA-9466
E-mail: info@brasmyth.com
Web Site: www.brasmyth.com
Sales Range: $75-99.9 Million
Approx. Number Employees: 5
Year Founded: 1991
Business Description:
Women's Intimate Apparel Retailer & Mail Order
S.I.C.: 5961
N.A.I.C.S.: 454113
Media: 4-8-13-24
Personnel:
Rebecca Simon *(Pres)*
Sandi Simon *(Principal)*

BURBERRY LIMITED
(Sub. of Burberry Group plc)
444 Maddison Ave
New York, NY 10022
Tel.: (212) 707-6500
Fax: (212) 246-9440
E-mail: info@burberry.com
Web Site: www.burberry.com
Approx. Number Employees: 4,131
Year Founded: 1970
Business Description:
Apparel for Men & Women Mfr
S.I.C.: 5621; 5611
N.A.I.C.S.: 448120; 448110
Media: 6-30
Personnel:
John Pearce *(Chm)*
Euginia Ulasewicz *(Pres & COO)*
Sarah Manley *(CMO)*
Carl Martin *(Mgr-Mobile Mktg-Global)*
Advertising Agencies:
Range Online Media
171 Madison Ave
New York, NY 10016
Tel.: (212) 981-6799
Fax: (817) 665-1327

Universal McCann
100 33rd St 8th Fl
New York, NY 10001
Tel.: (212) 883-4700

BUYSEASONS, INC.
(Sub. of Liberty Media LLC)
5915 S Moorland Rd
New Berlin, WI 53151
Tel.: (262) 901-2000
Fax: (262) 901-3333
E-mail: Davidk@buyseasons.com
Web Site: www.buyseasons.com
Sales Range: $1-9.9 Million
Approx. Number Employees: 60
Year Founded: 1999

Key to Media (For complete agency information see *The Advertising Red Books-Agencies* edition):
1. Bus. Publs. 2. Cable T.V. 3. Catalogs & Directories. 4. Co-op Adv. 5. Consumer Mags. 6. D.M. to Bus. Estab.7. D.M. to Consumers
8. Daily Newsp. 9. Exhibits/Trade Shows 10. Foreign 11. Infomercial 12. Internet Adv.13. Multimedia 14. Network Radio
15. Network T.V. 16. Newsp. Distr. Mags. 17. Other 18. Outdoor (Posters, Transit) 19. Point of Purchase20. Premiums, Novelties
21. Product Samples 22. Special Events Mktg. 23. Spot Radio 24. Spot T.V. 25. Weekly Newsp. 26. Yellow Page Adv.

BUYSEASONS, Inc. — (Continued)

Business Description:
Internet Costume, Apparel & Wig Retailer
S.I.C.: 5947; 2389
N.A.I.C.S.: 453220; 315999
Media: 7-10-13
Personnel:
Daniel Haight *(Pres & CEO)*
Terry Rowinski *(COO)*
David Karst *(VP-HR)*

CACHE INC.
1440 Broadway 5th Fl
New York, NY 10018
Tel.: (212) 575-3200
Fax: (212) 944-2842
Toll Free: (800) 788-2224
E-mail: custserv@cache.com
Web Site: www.cache.com
Approx. Sls.: $206,519,000
Approx. Number Employees: 1,026
Year Founded: 1975
Business Description:
Women's Apparel Specialty Stores Owner & Operator
S.I.C.: 5621; 5699
N.A.I.C.S.: 448120; 448150
Import
Advertising Expenditures: $8,200,000
Media: 4-6-8-18-19-22
Personnel:
Thomas Reinckens *(Chm, Pres & CEO)*
Margaret J. Feeney *(CFO & Exec VP)*
Rabia Farhang *(Exec VP & Gen Mgr-Mdse)*
Lusia Moskvicheva *(Sr VP-Concept, Trend & Design)*
Donna James *(VP & Dir-Stores)*
Amy Kerber-Brancati *(VP & Reg Mgr-Sls)*
Lisa Decker *(VP-Mktg)*
Tongyan Wang *(VP-IT)*
Margarita Croasdaile *(Mgr-HR)*

CALVIN KLEIN, INC.
(Sub. of Phillips Van Heusen Corporation)
205 W 39th St
New York, NY 10018-3102
Tel.: (212) 719-2600
Fax: (212) 768-8922
Web Site: www.calvinklein.com
Sales Range: $150-199.9 Million
Approx. Number Employees: 700
Year Founded: 1968
Business Description:
Mfr., Distributor, Licensor & Retailer of Men's & Women's Fashions
S.I.C.: 5137; 5136
N.A.I.C.S.: 424330; 424320
Import Export
Advertising Expenditures: $220,000,000
Media: 1-2-4-5-6-8-9-11-15-18-19-22-23-24-25
Distr.: Intl.; Natl.
Budget Set: July
Personnel:
Paul T. Murry *(Pres & CEO)*
Steve Shiffman *(Pres/COO-Retail Brands)*
Robert Vignola *(Pres-Collection)*
Molly Yearick *(Pres-Mens Sportswear)*
Malcolm Carfrae *(Sr VP-Global Comm)*
Regina Szeto *(Sr VP-Global Adv)*
Jennifer Crawford *(VP-Corp Comm)*
Kevin Carrigan *(Dir-Creative)*
Trisha Szeli *(Dir-Print Production)*
Brands & Products:
CALVIN KLEIN SPORT
CALVIN KLEIN UNDERWEAR
CK IN2U
OBSESSION
Advertising Agencies:
CRK Advertising
205 W 39th St 4th Fl
New York, NY 10018
Tel.: (212) 719-2600
Fax: (212) 292-9247
(All Calvin Klein Products)

One Source Visual Marketing Solution
108 W 39th St 2nd Fl
New York, NY 10018
Tel.: (212) 398-0444
Toll Free: (877) 398-0444

CARTER'S, INC.
1170 Peachtree St NE Ste 900
Atlanta, GA 30309-7674
Tel.: (404) 745-2700
Fax: (404) 892-0968
Toll Free: (888) 782-9548
E-mail: contactus@carters.com
Web Site: www.carters.com
E-Mail For Key Personnel:
Sales Director: sales@caters.com
Approx. Sls.: $1,749,256,000
Approx. Number Employees: 2,486
Year Founded: 1865
Business Description:
Children's Apparel Mfr
S.I.C.: 2339; 2241; 2253; 2254; 2361; 2389
N.A.I.C.S.: 315212; 313221; 315191; 315192; 315291; 315999
Import Export
Advertising Expenditures: $3,300,000
Media: 4-6-9-15-18-19-23-25
Distr.: Natl.
Budget Set: Jan. -Aug.
Personnel:
Michael D. Casey *(Chm & CEO)*
Richard F. Westenberger *(CFO & Exec VP)*
Charles E. Whetzel, Jr. *(Chief Supply Chain Officer & Exec VP)*
James C. Petty *(Pres-Retail Store)*
Brendan M. Gibbons *(Gen Counsel, Sec, Sr VP-Legal & Corp Affairs)*
Brian J. Lynch *(Exec VP & Brand Leader)*
Christopher W. Rork *(Exec VP-Supply Chain)*
Jill A. Wilson *(Sr VP-HR & Talent Dev)*
Brands & Products:
CARTER'S
CARTER'S CLASSIC COLLECTION
CARTERS STARTERS
CELEBRATING CHILDHOOD
CHILD OF MINE
CUDDLE-ME
DRIBBLEHAPPY
EASY- EXIT CREEPER
GENUINE KIDS
JUST ONE YEAR
KEEP-ME-DRY
SIDE-SNAP
SLEEP 'N PLAY
SLEEPLIKELY
SNUGGLE- ME
WIGGLE- IN
Advertising Agency:
Horizon Marketing Group, Inc.
1197 Neipsic Rd
Glastonbury, CT 06033
Tel.: (860) 430-1180
Fax: (860) 430-1181

CASCO BAY WOOL WORKS LLC
34 Danforth St Box 5
Portland, ME 04101-4596
Tel.: (207) 772-8170
Fax: (207) 879-0453
Toll Free: (888) 222WOOL
E-mail: customerservice@cascobaywoolworks.com
Web Site:
www.cascobaywoolworks.com
Approx. Number Employees: 10
Business Description:
Woolen & Cashmere Capes & Shawls Mfr
S.I.C.: 2253; 2392
N.A.I.C.S.: 315191; 314129
Media: 4-6-10-13
Personnel:
Persis Strong *(Owner & Mng Partner)*

THE CATO CORPORATION
8100 Denmark Rd
Charlotte, NC 28273-5975
Tel.: (704) 554-8510
Fax: (704) 551-7594
Web Site: www.catocorp.com
Approx. Rev.: $925,528,000
Approx. Number Employees: 9,600
Year Founded: 1946
Business Description:
Women's Clothing Retailer
S.I.C.: 5621
N.A.I.C.S.: 448120
Import
Advertising Expenditures: $6,663,000
Media: 6-8-9-18-19-20-23-25
Distr.: Direct to Consumer; Natl.
Budget Set: Sept.
Personnel:
John R. Howe *(CFO)*
Howard A. Severson *(Exec VP, Chief Real Estate/Store Dev Officer & Asst Sec)*
Sally Almason *(Exec VP & Gen Mgr-Mdsg)*
Michael T. Greer *(Exec VP & Dir-Stores)*
Jeff Shock *(Sr VP & Controller)*
Robert C. Brummer *(Sr VP-HR)*
Joel Hankins *(VP-Adv & Mktg)*
Brands & Products:
A NEW STATEMENT OF STYLE
CATO
CATO FASHIONS
CATO PLUS
IT'S FASHION
Advertising Agency:
Barber Martin Agency
7400 Beaufont Springs Dr Ste 201
Richmond, VA 23225-5519
Tel.: (804) 320-3232
Fax: (804) 320-1729

CHARLOTTE RUSSE HOLDING, INC.
(Holding of Advent International Corporation)
4645 Morena Blvd
San Diego, CA 92117-3650
Tel.: (858) 587-1500
Fax: (858) 587-0902
Toll Free: (877) 266-9327
E-mail: investorrelations@charlotterusse.com
Web Site: www.charlotterusse.com
Approx. Sls.: $823,252,213
Approx. Number Employees: 2,271
Year Founded: 1996
Business Description:
Women's Clothing Stores
S.I.C.: 5621; 5699
N.A.I.C.S.: 448120; 448150
Import Export
Advertising Expenditures: $497,486
Media: 8-10-11
Personnel:
Jenny Ming *(Pres, CEO & Chief Mdsg Officer)*
Dawn Dobras *(Sr VP-Strategy & Bus Dev)*
Pam O'Connor *(Sr VP-HR)*
Advertising Agency:
Red Door Interactive, Inc.
350 10th Ave Set 1100
San Diego, CA 92101
Tel.: (619) 398-2670
Fax: (619) 398-2671

CHARMING SHOPPES, INC.
3750 State Rd
Bensalem, PA 19020
Tel.: (215) 245-9100
Fax: (215) 633-4640
E-mail: ir@charming.com
Web Site:
www.charmingshoppes.com
Approx. Sls.: $2,061,819,000
Approx. Number Employees: 6,000
Year Founded: 1969
Business Description:
Retail Specialty Stores Selling Women's & Plus-Sized Women's Sportswear, Dresses, Coats, Lingerie, Accessories & Footwear
S.I.C.: 5621; 2389
N.A.I.C.S.: 448120; 315999
Advertising Expenditures: $68,100,000
Media: 1-4-6-8-9-19-20-23-24-25
Distr.: Direct to Consumer
Personnel:
Michael Goldstein *(Chm)*
Anthony M. Romano *(Pres & CEO)*
Eric M. Specter *(CFO & Exec VP)*
Joseph Long *(Fin Dir-Outlets Div)*
Denis F. Gingue *(CIO & Sr VP)*
John Lee *(Chief Acctg Officer & VP)*
William Bass *(Pres-Charming Direct)*
Jeffrey A. Elliott *(Pres-Charming Outlets Div)*
Carol L. Williams *(Pres-Catherines & Operated)*
Brian P. Woolf *(Pres-Lane Bryant)*
Jeffrey Liss *(COO-Charming Direct & Sr VP)*
Colin D. Stern *(Gen Counsel, Sec & Exec VP)*
James G. Bloise *(Exec VP)*
Anthony A. Desabato *(Exec VP)*
Fredrick Lamster *(Exec VP-HR)*
John J. Sullivan *(Sr VP & Controller)*
Kady Dalrymple *(Sr VP-Design & Product Dev)*
Jonathon Graub *(Sr VP-Real Estate)*
Joan Munnelly *(Sr VP-Mdsg)*

Key to Media (For complete agency information see *The Advertising Red Books-Agencies* edition):
1. Bus. Publs. 2. Cable T.V. 3. Catalogs & Directories. 4. Co-op Adv. 5. Consumer Mags. 6. D.M. to Bus. Estab.7. D.M. to Consumers
8. Daily Newsp. 9. Exhibits/Trade Shows 10. Foreign 11. Infomercial 12. Internet Adv.13. Multimedia 14. Network Radio
15. Network T.V. 16. Newsp. Distr. Mags. 17. Other 18. Outdoor (Posters, Transit) 19. Point of Purchase20. Premiums, Novelties
21. Product Samples 22. Special Events Mktg. 23. Spot Radio 24. Spot T.V. 25. Weekly Newsp. 26. Yellow Page Adv.

Denise C. Davis *(VP-Mdse & Sourcing Ops)*
Andrew D. Galasso *(VP-Real Estate Fin)*
Lesley M. Rindosh *(VP-Quality Control & Quality Assurance)*
James Gilmer *(Dir-Mktg)*
Stacy Shaw *(Mgr-Interactive Mktg)*
Brands & Products:
BROWNSTONE STUDIO
CACIQUE
CATHERINES
CATHERINES PLUS SIZES
CHARMING SHOPPES
COWARD SHOE
FASHION BUG
FASHION BUG PLUS
FIGI
INTIMATE APPEAL
L.A. BLUES
LANE BRYANT
LANE BRYANT OUTLET
LEW MAGRAM
LIZ & ME
MONTEREY BAY CLOTHING COMPANY
OLD PUEBLO TRADERS
PETITE SOPHISTICATE OUTLET
REGALIA
VENEZIA
WILLOW RIDGE
Advertising Agencies:
Neff + Associates, Inc.
The Novelty Bldg 15 S Third St 4th Fl
Philadelphia, PA 19106
Tel.: (215) 627-4747
Fax: (215) 923-6333

NetPlus Marketing, Inc.
625 Ridge Pike Bldg E Ste 200
Conshohocken, PA 19428
Tel.: (610) 897-2380
Fax: (610) 897-2381

CHEROKEE INC.

6835 Valjean Ave
Van Nuys, CA 91406-4713
Tel.: (818) 908-9868
Fax: (818) 908-9191
E-mail: the_cherokee_group@cherokeeusa.com
Web Site: www.cherokeegroup.com
E-Mail For Key Personnel:
President: howards@cherokeeusa.com
Public Relations: carolg@cherokeeusa.com
Approx. Rev.: $30,777,000
Approx. Number Employees: 21
Year Founded: 1973
Business Description:
Licenser of Branded Apparel, Shoes & Accessories to Retailers & Wholesalers
S.I.C.: 6794; 2253
N.A.I.C.S.: 533110; 315191
Media: 2-4-6-9-11-18-19-20-22
Distr.: Intl.
Personnel:
Howard Siegel *(Pres & COO)*
Henry Stupp *(CEO)*
Mark DiSiena *(CFO)*
Sally Mueller *(Chief Brand Officer-Minneapolis)*
Larry Sass *(Sr VP)*
Jamie Curtis *(VP-Mktg-Minneapolis)*
Brands & Products:
ALL THAT JAZZ
BETHENNY
CAROLE LITTLE
CHEROKEE
CHORUS LINE
CLII
DAVID RODRIGUEZ
KELLY HOPPEN
LAILA ALI
MOLLY MALLOY
REFRESH
SAINT TROPEZ WEST
SIDEOUT
SIDEOUT SPORT

CHICO'S FAS, INC.

11215 Metro Pkwy
Fort Myers, FL 33912-1206
Tel.: (239) 277-6200
Fax: (239) 277-5237
Toll Free: (888) 855-4986
E-mail: investor.relations@chicos.com
Web Site: www.chicos.com
Approx. Sls.: $1,904,954,000
Approx. Number Employees: 18,900
Year Founded: 1983
Business Description:
Retailer of Women's Apparel
S.I.C.: 5621
N.A.I.C.S.: 448120
Import
Advertising Expenditures: $86,800,000
Media: 4-5-8-13-18-20
Distr.: Reg.
Personnel:
Ross E. Roeder *(Chm)*
David F. Dyer *(Pres & CEO)*
Pamela K. Knous *(CFO, Chief Acctg Officer & Exec VP)*
Kent A. Kleeberger *(COO & Exec VP)*
Gary A. King *(CIO & Exec VP)*
Lee Eisenberg *(Chief Creative Officer & Exec VP)*
Mori C. Mackenzie *(Chief Stores Officer & Exec VP)*
Cynthia Murray *(Pres-Chico's Brand)*
Laurie van Brunt *(Pres-Brand-Soma Intimates)*
Rochelle Udell *(Sr VP & Dir-Creative)*
Sher Canada *(Sr VP-Chico's Stores)*
Linda Costello *(Sr VP-Trend & Design)*
Terri Meichner *(Sr VP-GMM-Soma Intimates)*
Celia Rao Visconti *(Sr VP-Mktg-Chico's)*
George M. Reider *(Sr VP-White House Black Market Stores)*
Lori Shaffer *(Sr VP-Mdse Ops)*
Ronald Shulman *(Sr VP)*
J. Brian Bitzer *(VP & Controller-Tax & Fin)*
Steven A. Ross *(VP-Tech)*
Gregory Schlegel *(Sr Dir-Design & Plng)*
Mathew W. Deziak *(Mgr-Sls Reg)*
Advertising Agency:
KD&E
129 W 27th St 11th Fl
New York, NY 10001
Tel.: (212) 686-0006
Fax: (212) 686-6991

THE CHILDREN'S PLACE RETAIL STORES, INC.

500 Plaza Dr
Secaucus, NJ 07094
Tel.: (201) 558-2400
Fax: (201) 558-2841
Toll Free: (877) PLACEUSA
E-mail: investor_relations@childrensplace.com
Web Site: www.childrensplace.com
Approx. Sls.: $1,673,999,000
Approx. Number Employees: 3,200
Year Founded: 1969
Business Description:
Children's Clothing & Accessories Retailer
S.I.C.: 5651; 5641
N.A.I.C.S.: 448140; 448130
Import
Advertising Expenditures: $46,000,000
Media: 2-4-5-6-7-8-9-11-13-16-18-19-20-22-25
Distr.: Reg.
Personnel:
Norman S. Matthews *(Chm)*
Jane T. Elfers *(Pres & CEO)*
John Taylor *(Interim CFO & VP-Fin)*
Eric Bauer *(COO)*
Kimberley Grayson *(CMO)*
Bernard McCracken *(Interim Chief Acctg Officer, VP & Controller)*
Mark L. Rose *(Chief Supply Chain Officer & Sr VP)*
Natalie Levy *(Exec VP-Mdsg & Design)*
James Bruce Marshall *(Sr VP & Mng Dir-Intl Bus Dev)*
Kevin Mead *(Sr VP & Dir-The Childrens Place Stores)*
Melissa Boughton *(Sr VP-Real Estate)*
Michael Giannelli *(Sr VP-Design)*
Larry McClure *(Sr VP-HR)*
Barrie Scardina *(Sr VP-Plng & Allocation)*
Dina Sweeney *(Sr VP-Mdsg)*
Peter Warner *(Sr VP-Global Sourcing)*
Renee Zuckerman *(Sr Dir-Media, Pub Rels & Store Programs)*
Brands & Products:
BABYPLACE
THE CHILDREN'S OUTLET
THE CHILDREN'S PLACE
THE PLACE
Advertising Agency:
Media Partnership Corporation
800 Connecticut Ave 3rd Fl N Wing
Norwalk, CT 06854
Tel.: (203) 855-6711
Fax: (203) 855-6705

CHILDREN'S WEAR CENTER

550 Getty Ave
Clifton, NJ 07011
Tel.: (973) 340-1200
Fax: (973) 340-1433
E-mail: webmanager@cliftonchildrenswear.com
Web Site: www.cliftonchildrenswear.com
Approx. Sls.: $14,747,306
Approx. Number Employees: 38
Business Description:
Children's Wear
S.I.C.: 5641; 5945
N.A.I.C.S.: 448130; 451120
Media: 4-8-16
Personnel:
Charles Tawil *(Pres)*

CHILDREN'S WEAR DIGEST INC.

3607 Mayland Ct
Richmond, VA 23233
Tel.: (804) 270-7401
Fax: (840) 270-4405
Toll Free: (800) 242-KIDS
Web Site: www.cwdkids.com
Sales Range: $25-49.9 Million
Approx. Number Employees: 20
Year Founded: 1911
Business Description:
Children's Clothing Retailer
S.I.C.: 5961
N.A.I.C.S.: 454113
Advertising Expenditures: $50,000
Media: 4-6-9-13-17-25
Personnel:
Philip W. Klaus, Jr. *(Founder & CEO)*
James Klaus *(Pres)*

CHRISTINE FOLEY INC.

430 9th St
San Francisco, CA 94103
Tel.: (415) 621-8126
Toll Free: (800) 318-8898
Web Site: www.christinefoleysf.com
Approx. Number Employees: 12
Business Description:
Sweaters, Lounge Wear, Cushions & Slippers
S.I.C.: 5641; 2261; 5611; 5621; 5699
N.A.I.C.S.: 448130; 313311; 448110; 448120; 448190
Media: 4-6-8-13
Brands & Products:
BILLIE
CHRISTINE FOLEY

CHRISTOPHER & BANKS CORPORATION

2400 Xenium Ln N
Plymouth, MN 55441
Mailing Address:
PO Box 9361
Minneapolis, MN 55440-9361
Tel.: (763) 551-5000
Fax: (763) 551-5198
E-mail: info@christopherandbanks.com
Web Site: www.christopherandbanks.com
Approx. Sls.: $448,130,000
Approx. Number Employees: 1,700
Year Founded: 1956
Business Description:
Women's Specialty Apparel Retailer
S.I.C.: 5621
N.A.I.C.S.: 448120
Import
Advertising Expenditures: $5,300,000
Media: 8-9-13-16-19
Personnel:
Larry C. Barenbaum *(Pres & CEO)*
Michael J. Lyftogt *(CFO & Sr VP)*
Luke R. Komarek *(Gen Counsel, Sec & Sr VP)*
Jules M. Rouse *(Sr VP & Gen Mgr-Mdsg)*
Monica L. Dahl *(Sr VP-ECommerce, Plng, Allocation & Strategy)*
Kim A. Decker *(Sr VP-Stores)*
Lisa M. Klein *(VP-IT)*
Cindy J. Stemper *(VP-HR)*

Key to Media (For complete agency information see *The Advertising Red Books-Agencies* edition):
1. Bus. Publs. 2. Cable T.V. 3. Catalogs & Directories. 4. Co-op Adv. 5. Consumer Mags. 6. D.M. to Bus. Estab.7. D.M. to Consumers 8. Daily Newsp. 9. Exhibits/Trade Shows 10. Foreign 11. Infomercial 12. Internet Adv.13. Multimedia 14. Network Radio 15. Network T.V. 16. Newsp. Distr. Mags. 17. Other 18. Outdoor (Posters, Transit) 19. Point of Purchase20. Premiums, Novelties 21. Product Samples 22. Special Events Mktg. 23. Spot Radio 24. Spot T.V. 25. Weekly Newsp. 26. Yellow Page Adv.

Christopher & Banks Corporation — (Continued)

Brands & Products:
CHRISTOPHER & BANKS
C.J. BANKS

CITI TRENDS INC.
104 Coleman Blvd
Savannah, GA 31408
Mailing Address:
PO Box 2075
Savannah, GA 31401
Tel.: (912) 236-1561
Fax: (912) 443-3674
Toll Free: (866) 547-5326
E-mail: goberg@cititrends.com
Web Site: www.cititrends.com
Approx. Sls.: $622,528,000
Approx. Number Employees: 2,300
Year Founded: 1946
Business Description:
Family Apparel & Accessories Retailer
S.I.C.: 5651; 5611; 5621; 5699
N.A.I.C.S.: 448140; 448110; 448120; 448150
Advertising Expenditures: $2,700,000
Personnel:
R. David Alexander, Jr. *(CEO)*
Bruce D. Smith *(CFO & Sr VP)*
Elizabeth R. Feher *(Chief Mdsg Officer & Exec VP)*
Ivy D. Council *(Sr VP-HR)*
James A. Dunn *(Sr VP-Store Ops)*

CROWN FOUNDATIONS, INC.
480 Barnum Ave Bldg 4 Fl 3
Bridgeport, CT 06608
Tel.: (203) 333-4114
Fax: (203) 333-5665
Approx. Number Employees: 20
Year Founded: 1898
Business Description:
Bras, Girdles, Panties & Corselets Mfr
S.I.C.: 2341
N.A.I.C.S.: 315231
Media: 4
Distr.: Natl.
Budget Set: Jan. -June
Personnel:
Howard Walker *(Chm & Pres)*
Harvey Gaberman *(VP & Gen Mgr)*
Brands & Products:
CROWN-ETTES
FULL FREEDOM
RENGO

CUPID FOUNDATIONS, INC.
475 Park Ave S
New York, NY 10016-3903
Tel.: (212) 686-6224
Fax: (212) 481-9357
Web Site: www.cupidintimate.com
Approx. Number Employees: 35
Business Description:
Mfr of Brassieres, Girdles & Undergarments
S.I.C.: 2341
N.A.I.C.S.: 315231
Advertising Expenditures: $400,000
Media: 2-6-7-9-14
Distr.: Natl.
Personnel:
David Welsch *(Pres)*
Mike Leary *(VP-Mdsg)*
Tom Richardson *(VP-Mktg & Sls)*
Jim McCormick *(Dir-Mktg)*
Brands & Products:
CUPID

DA-RUE OF CALIFORNIA, INC.
14102 S Broadway St
Los Angeles, CA 90061
Tel.: (310) 323-1350
Fax: (310) 323-8133
Toll Free: (877) MY-DARUE
E-mail: customerservice@darue.com
Web Site: www.darue.com
Approx. Number Employees: 40
Year Founded: 1945
Business Description:
Women's Clothing Designer, Mfr & Retailer
S.I.C.: 2339
N.A.I.C.S.: 315239
Media: 7-8-22
Personnel:
Richard McElrath *(Pres & CEO)*
Jeffrey A. Stelter *(CFO & Treas)*
Brands & Products:
DESERT VISTA COLLECTION
EARLY EDITION COLLECTION
MONTEGO BAY COLLECTION

DAFFY'S INC.
1 Daffys Way
Secaucus, NJ 07094
Tel.: (201) 902-0800
Fax: (201) 902-9016
E-mail: info@daffys.com
Web Site: www.daffys.com
Approx. Number Employees: 1,100
Year Founded: 1997
Business Description:
Sales of Family Clothing
S.I.C.: 5651
N.A.I.C.S.: 448140
Personnel:
Marsha Wilson *(Owner)*
Caryn Lerner *(CEO)*
Vanessa LeFebvre *(Chief Mdsg Officer & VP)*
Will Bracker *(Dir-Mktg)*
Advertising Agencies:
DeVito/Verdi
100 5th Ave 16th Fl
New York, NY 10011
Tel.: (212) 431-4694
Fax: (212) 431-4940
Clothing
Fall Fashion Line

Johannes Leonardo
41 East 11th St 6th Fl
New York, NY 10003
Tel.: (212) 462-8111
Fax: (212) 645-0861

DANIER LEATHER, INC.
2650 St Clair Ave W
Toronto, ON M6N 1M2, Canada
Tel.: (416) 762-8175
Fax: (416) 762-4570
E-mail: leather@danier.com
Web Site: www.danier.com
Approx. Rev.: $160,715,894
Year Founded: 1972
Business Description:
Leather & Suede Garment Designer, Retailer & Mfr
S.I.C.: 2371
N.A.I.C.S.: 315292
Import Export
Media: 4-6-8-9-13-18-19-25
Personnel:
Irving Wortsman *(Founder)*
Edwin F. Hawken *(Chm)*
Jeffrey Wortsman *(Pres & CEO)*
Bryan Tatoff *(CFO, Sec & Sr VP)*
Philip J. Cutter *(CIO & VP-IT)*
Olga E. Koel *(Chief Mdsg Officer & Exec VP)*
Guia Lopez *(Chief Sourcing Officer & VP)*
Cheryl Sproul *(VP-HR)*
Brands & Products:
DANIER
Advertising Agency:
Media Experts
495 Wellington St W Ste 250
Toronto, ON M5V 1E9, Canada
Tel.: (416) 597-0707
Fax: (416) 597-9927

DANSKIN, INC.
(Sub. of Iconix Brand Group, Inc.)
530 7th Ave Ste M1
New York, NY 10018
Tel.: (877) 443-2121
Fax: (212) 930-9138
Toll Free: (800) 288-6749
Toll Free: (800) 28-DANSKIN
E-mail: danskinpr@danskin.com
Web Site: www.danskin.com
Sales Range: $300-349.9 Million
Approx. Number Employees: 825
Year Founded: 1882
Business Description:
Fitness, Dance & Yoga Apparel Mfr
S.I.C.: 2339
N.A.I.C.S.: 315239
Advertising Expenditures: $2,561,000
Media: 4-5-6-22
Personnel:
Ralph Harary *(Chm)*
Mark Lopiparo *(CFO & Exec VP)*
Mary Beth Cook *(VP-HR)*
Elliot Beyda *(Mgr-Mktg)*
Brands & Products:
COOLMAX
DANSKIN
DANSKIN GIRL
FREESTYLE
LIGHTWEIGHT DRY ZONE
ROUND-THE-CLOCK
SUPPLEX
TELE TONE
ZEN SPORT
Advertising Agencies:
Beanstalk
220 E 42nd St 15th Fl
New York, NY 10017
Tel.: (212) 421-6060
Fax: (212) 421-6388

The Donaldson Group
88 Hopmeadow St
Weatogue, CT 06089-9602
Tel.: (860) 658-9777
Fax: (860) 658-0533

DAVID'S BRIDAL, INC.
(Holding of Leonard Green & Partners, L.P.)
1001 Washington St
Conshohocken, PA 19428-2356
Tel.: (610) 943-5000
Fax: (610) 943-5048
Toll Free: (888) 480-2743
Web Site: www.davidsbridal.com
Approx. Number Employees: 2,900
Year Founded: 1950
Business Description:
Bridal Gowns & Related Apparel & Accessories Whslr
S.I.C.: 5621
N.A.I.C.S.: 448120
Import Export
Media: 4-6-8-10-13-15-22
Personnel:
Robert Huth *(Pres & CEO)*
Brian Beitler *(CMO & Exec VP)*
Fred A. Postelle *(Sr VP-HR)*
Nathan Ricther *(VP-Internet Mktg)*
Tom Cassidy *(Dir-Media)*
Evan Goldstein *(Dir-Online Mktg)*
David Connelly *(Mgr-Strategic Sourcing)*
Advertising Agency:
PointRoll Inc.
951 E Hector St
Conshohocken, PA 19428
Tel.: (267) 558-1300
Fax: (267) 285-1141
Toll Free: (800) 203-6956

DEB SHOPS, INC.
(Holding of Lee Equity Partners LLC)
9401 Blue Grass Rd
Philadelphia, PA 19114-2305
Tel.: (215) 676-6000
Fax: (215) 698-7151
E-mail: customer@debshops.com
Web Site: www.debshops.com
E-Mail For Key Personnel:
Marketing Director: dinak@dynanet.com
Approx. Number Employees: 3,500
Year Founded: 1932
Business Description:
Women's Apparel Retailer
S.I.C.: 5621; 5651
N.A.I.C.S.: 448120; 448140
Media: 8-9-19-23-25
Distr.: Natl.
Personnel:
Diane M. Paccione *(Pres & CEO)*
Gary Thompson *(Sr VP-Retail & Ops)*
Stephen Smith *(VP-Info Sys)*
Brands & Products:
DEB PLUS

DELIA'S, INC.
50 W 23rd St 10th Fl
New York, NY 10014-3941
Tel.: (212) 807-9060
Fax: (212) 590-6300
E-mail: custserv@delias.com
Web Site: www.delias.com
Approx. Rev.: $220,697,000
Approx. Number Employees: 573
Year Founded: 1993
Business Description:
Retail Store Owner/Operator & Direct Marketer of Ladies Casual Apparel & Related Accessories
S.I.C.: 2339; 5621; 5961
N.A.I.C.S.: 315212; 448120; 454111; 454113
Media: 4-13
Personnel:
Carter S. Evans *(Chm)*
Walter Killough *(CEO)*
David Dick *(CFO & Treas)*
Dyan Jozwick *(Pres-Brand)*
Mark Schuback *(Gen Counsel, Sec & Sr VP)*

Key to Media (For complete agency information see *The Advertising Red Books-Agencies* edition):
1. Bus. Publs. 2. Cable T.V. 3. Catalogs & Directories. 4. Co-op Adv. 5. Consumer Mags. 6. D.M. to Bus. Estab.7. D.M. to Consumers 8. Daily Newsp. 9. Exhibits/Trade Shows 10. Foreign 11. Infomercial 12. Internet Adv.13. Multimedia 14. Network Radio 15. Network T.V. 16. Newsp. Distr. Mags. 17. Other 18. Outdoor (Posters, Transit) 19. Point of Purchase20. Premiums, Novelties 21. Product Samples 22. Special Events Mktg. 23. Spot Radio 24. Spot T.V. 25. Weekly Newsp. 26. Yellow Page Adv.

Edward Brennan *(VP-Fin)*
David Diamond *(VP-HR)*
Jennifer Wasik *(Dir-CRM)*
Advertising Agency:
AMP Agency (Alloy Marketing & Promotion)
77 N Washington St
Boston, MA 02114
Tel.: (617) 723-8929
Fax: (617) 723-2188

DESTINATION MATERNITY CORPORATION
456 N 5th St
Philadelphia, PA 19123-4007
Tel.: (215) 873-2200
Fax: (215) 873-0869
Web Site: www.motherswork.com
Approx. Sls.: $531,192,000
Approx. Number Employees: 1,989
Year Founded: 1982
Business Description:
Maternity Apparel Designer & Retailer
S.I.C.: 2339; 5621
N.A.I.C.S.: 315212; 315239; 448120
Import Export
Advertising Expenditures: $12,147,000
Media: 4-6-8-13
Personnel:
Dan W. Matthias *(Chm)*
Christopher F. Daniel *(Pres)*
Edward M. Krell *(CEO)*
Judd P. Tirnauer *(CFO & Sr VP)*
Rebecca C. Matthias *(Chief Creative Officer)*
Lisa Hendrickson *(Chief Mdsg Officer)*
Judie Ashworth *(Sr Mgr-PR)*
Stefanie Weiner *(Mgr-PR)*
Brands & Products:
A PEA IN THE POD
DESTINATION MATERNITY
EDAMAME
EXPECT LOW PRICES EVERY DAY
FUTURETRUST
IMATERNITY.COM
MATERNITYMALL.COM
MIMI MATERNITY
MOTHERHOOD
MOTHERHOOD MATERNITY
MOTHERHOOD NURSINGWEAR
MOTHERS WORK
OH BABY! BY MOTHERHOOD
SECRET FIT BELLY
TRENDTRACK
TWO HEARTS

DOLCE & GABBANA USA, INC.
(Sub. of Dolce & Gabbana S.R.L.)
148 Lafayette St
New York, NY 10013
Tel.: (212) 750-0055
Fax: (212) 750-2750
E-mail: info@dolcegabbana.it
Web Site: www.dolcegabbana.it/
Approx. Number Employees: 100
Business Description:
Distr of Men's & Women's Apparel
S.I.C.: 5136; 5137
N.A.I.C.S.: 424320; 424330
Import
Media: 6-8-10-11-13-30
Brands & Products:
DOLCE & GABBANA

DOLFIN INTERNATIONAL CORPORATION
4 Front St Plz
Mohnton, PA 19540-2007
Tel.: (610) 775-5500
Fax: (610) 775-5521
Toll Free: (800) 441-0818
E-mail: info@dolfinswimwear.com
Web Site: www.dolfinswimwear.com
Approx. Sls.: $2,500,000
Approx. Number Employees: 100
Year Founded: 1941
Business Description:
Swim Suits, Warm-Ups & Track Wear Mfr
S.I.C.: 2329; 2339
N.A.I.C.S.: 315228; 315239
Advertising Expenditures: $300,000
Media: 6-7-14-16-19
Distr.: Direct To Retailers; Intl.; Natl.
Budget Set: Apr.
Personnel:
James Korth *(Pres & CEO)*
Brian P. McElroy *(VP-Sls & Mktg)*
Brands & Products:
DOLFIN
DOLFIN SWIM WEAR
OCEAN
UGLIES
Advertising Agency:
Siquis, Ltd.
1340 Smith Ave Ste 300
Baltimore, MD 21209-3797
Tel.: (410) 323-4800
Fax: (410) 323-4113

DONNA KARAN INTERNATIONAL INC.
(Sub. of LVMH Moet Hennessy Louis Vuitton SA)
550 7th Ave
New York, NY 10018-3203
Tel.: (212) 789-1500
Web Site: www.donnakaran.com
Sales Range: $650-699.9 Million
Approx. Number Employees: 2,100
Business Description:
Fashion Apparel Designer Mfr
S.I.C.: 2335
N.A.I.C.S.: 315233
Media: 1-2-3-6-8-9-11-14-15-16-17-18-19-23-24-25
Personnel:
Mark Weber *(Chm & CEO)*
Patti Cohen *(Exec VP-Global Mktg & Comm)*
Cathy Volker *(Exec VP-Licensing Grp)*
Brands & Products:
DKNY
DONNA KARAN
Advertising Agency:
Laird+Partners
475 10th Ave 7th Fl
New York, NY 10018
Tel.: (212) 478-8181
Fax: (212) 478-8210

DOONEY & BOURKE, INC.
1 Regent St
Norwalk, CT 06855
Tel.: (203) 853-7515
Fax: (203) 838-7754
Toll Free: (800) 347-5000
E-mail: cservice@dooney.com
Web Site: www.dooney.com
Sales Range: $400-449.9 Million
Approx. Number Employees: 500
Year Founded: 1975
Business Description:
Handbags & Accessories Retailer & Mfr
S.I.C.: 3171; 3172
N.A.I.C.S.: 316992; 316993
Media: 4-6-10-13
Personnel:
Peter Dooney *(Pres)*
David Burbine *(Dir-ECommerce)*
Liz Kane *(Dir-Media)*
Brands & Products:
ALL-WEATHER LEATHER
DOONEY & BOURKE
Advertising Agency:
D&B In-House Advertising Agency
One Regent St.
Norwalk, CT 06855
Tel.: (203) 853-9194
Fax: (203) 853-9194
(Handbags, Belts, Suspenders & Leather Accessories)

DOROTHY GRANT LTD.
138 W 6th Ave Unit 1B
Vancouver, BC Canada
Tel.: (604) 681-0201
E-mail: info@dorothygrant.com
Web Site: www.dorothygrant.com
Approx. Number Employees: 10
Year Founded: 1994
Business Description:
Men's & Women's Clothing Designer
S.I.C.: 2329; 5621; 5641; 5699
N.A.I.C.S.: 315211; 315228; 448120; 448130; 448190
Media: 10
Personnel:
Dorothy Grant *(Owner)*

DRAPER'S & DAMON'S, INC.
(Holding of Orchard Brands Corporation)
9 Pasteur Ste 200
Irvine, CA 92618-3804
Tel.: (949) 784-3000
Fax: (949) 784-3300
Toll Free: (800) 843-1174
E-mail: service@drapers.com
Web Site: www.drapers.com
Sales Range: $125-149.9 Million
Approx. Number Employees: 98
Year Founded: 1928
Business Description:
Women's Clothing Retailer; Catalog & Mail-Order Services
S.I.C.: 5621; 5961
N.A.I.C.S.: 454113; 448120; 454111
Media: 4-8-22
Brands & Products:
DRAPER'S & DAMON'S INC.

ECOBABY ORGANICS INC.
9541 Ridgeheaven Ct
San Diego, CA 92123
Tel.: (858) 693-3112
Fax: (858) 693-3957
Toll Free: (800) 596-7450
Web Site: www.purerest.com
Approx. Number Employees: 9
Year Founded: 1992
Business Description:
Baby Clothes & Furniture Retailer
S.I.C.: 5641; 5712
N.A.I.C.S.: 448130; 442110
Advertising Expenditures: $100,000
Media: 6-13
Personnel:
Ginny Turner *(Pres)*

EILEEN FISHER, INC.
2 Bridge St
Irvington, NY 10533-1527
Tel.: (914) 591-5700
Fax: (914) 591-8900
Web Site: www.eileenfisher.com
Approx. Number Employees: 800
Year Founded: 1982
Business Description:
Women's & Misses' Outerwear Mfr
S.I.C.: 2339
N.A.I.C.S.: 315239
Import Export
Media: 4-10-22
Personnel:
Eileen Fisher *(Owner)*
Lauren Croke *(Dir-Web and eCommerce)*
Ann Gilligan *(Dir-Mktg Planning)*

EISEMAN CO., LLC
342 N Water St Fl 6
Milwaukee, WI 53202-5715
Tel.: (414) 272-3222
Fax: (414) 272-4274
Toll Free: (800) 558-9013
E-mail: info@florenceeiseman.com
Web Site: www.florenceeiseman.com
Approx. Number Employees: 18
Year Founded: 1945
Business Description:
Children's Clothing Designer & Mfr
S.I.C.: 5137
N.A.I.C.S.: 424330
Import Export
Media: 2-5-6
Distr.: Natl.
Budget Set: Apr.
Personnel:
Lawrence Eiseman *(Chm)*
Frank Botto *(Pres)*
Terri Shapiro *(VP-Design)*
Brands & Products:
FLORENCE EISEMAN

ELIZABETH LANGE, LLC
(Sub. of Bluestar Alliance, LLC)
463 7th Ave Ste 1402
New York, NY 10018
Tel.: (212) 244-1322
Fax: (212) 244-1372
Web Site: www.lizlange.com
Approx. Number Employees: 30
Business Description:
Maternity & Baby Clothing Retailer
S.I.C.: 5621
N.A.I.C.S.: 448120
Media: 6-10-13
Personnel:
Elizabeth Lange *(Owner)*
Brands & Products:
LIZ LANGE
LIZ LANGE MATERNITY

ELLEN TRACY LLC
(Joint Venture of Windsong Allegiance Group, LLC, Hilco Trading, LLC & Radius Partners, LLC)
575 7th Ave
New York, NY 10018-1805
Tel.: (212) 753-4000
Fax: (212) 398-1678
Toll Free: (800) 925-7979
E-mail: info@ellentracy.com

Key to Media (For complete agency information see *The Advertising Red Books-Agencies* edition):
1. Bus. Publs. 2. Cable T.V. 3. Catalogs & Directories. 4. Co-op Adv. 5. Consumer Mags. 6. D.M. to Bus. Estab.7. D.M. to Consumers
8. Daily Newsp. 9. Exhibits/Trade Shows 10. Foreign 11. Infomercial 12. Internet Adv.13. Multimedia 14. Network Radio
15. Network T.V. 16. Newsp. Distr. Mags. 17. Other 18. Outdoor (Posters, Transit) 19. Point of Purchase20. Premiums, Novelties
21. Product Samples 22. Special Events Mktg. 23. Spot Radio 24. Spot T.V. 25. Weekly Newsp. 26. Yellow Page Adv.

Ellen Tracy LLC — (Continued)

Web Site: www.ellentracy.com
Sales Range: $250-299.9 Million
Approx. Number Employees: 400
Year Founded: 1949
Business Description:
Women's Clothing Mfr
S.I.C.: 2339; 2337
N.A.I.C.S.: 315239; 315234
Import Export
Media: 4-5-6-8-13-22
Personnel:
Marvin S. Traub *(Chm)*
Mark Mendelson *(Pres)*
Brands & Products:
COMPANY BY ELLEN TRACY
ELLEN TRACY

ERICA TANOV INC.

1627 San Pablo Ave
Berkeley, CA 94702
Tel.: (510) 524-1762
Fax: (510) 524-5904
E-mail: info@ericatanov.com
Web Site: www.ericatanov.com
Sales Range: Less than $1 Million
Approx. Number Employees: 10
Business Description:
Women's & Children's Clothing Designer
S.I.C.: 5651
N.A.I.C.S.: 448140
Media: 10
Personnel:
Erica Tanov *(CEO)*

EVEDEN, INC.

(Div. of Eveden Ltd.)
65 Sprague St
Hyde Park, MA 02136
Tel.: (617) 361-7559
Fax: (617) 361-7527
Toll Free: (800) 733-8964
Toll Free: (800) 467-1269
Web Site: www.goddess.com
Approx. Number Employees: 80
Year Founded: 1945
Business Description:
Bra Mfr
S.I.C.: 2341
N.A.I.C.S.: 315231
Import Export
Advertising Expenditures: $1,000,000
Media: 3-4-5-6-7-8-9-10-11-13-16-19-21-23-25
Distr.: Intl.
Personnel:
Tracy Lewis *(CEO)*
Brands & Products:
FANTASY
FREYA
GODDESS
Advertising Agency:
Weber Shandwick
(Sub. of The Interpublic Group of Companies)
919 3rd Ave
New York, NY 10022
Tel.: (212) 445-8000
Fax: (212) 445-8001
(US Public Relations)

EXPRESS, INC.

(Holding of Golden Gate Capital)
1 Express Dr
Columbus, OH 43230
Tel.: (614) 415-4001
Fax: (614) 415-4340
Web Site: www.express.com
Approx. Rev.: $1,905,814,000
Approx. Number Employees: 16,000
Year Founded: 1993
Business Description:
Clothing Stores Owner & Operator
S.I.C.: 5621; 5611
N.A.I.C.S.: 448120; 448110
Advertising Expenditures: $72,600,000
Personnel:
Stefan L. Kaluzny *(Chm)*
Michael A. Weiss *(Pres & CEO)*
D. Paul Dascoli *(CFO)*
Matthew C. Moellering *(COO)*
Lisa A. Gavales *(CMO & Exec VP)*
Fran Horowitz-Bonadies *(Exec VP-Women's Mdsg & Design)*
David G. Kornberg *(Exec VP-Men's Mdsg & Design)*
Colin Campbell *(Exec VP-Sourcing & Production)*
John J. Rafferty *(Exec VP-Plng & Allocation)*
Jeanne L. St. Pierre *(Exec VP-Stores)*
Douglas H. Tilson *(Exec VP-Real Estate)*
Elliott R. Tobias *(Exec VP-HR)*
E. Keith Pickens *(Sr VP-IT)*

FASHION BUG INC.

(Sub. of CHARMING SHOPPES, INC.)
450 Winks Ln
Bensalem, PA 19020-5919
Tel.: (215) 245-9100
Fax: (215) 633-4640
Web Site: www.fashionbug.com
Sales Range: $150-199.9 Million
Approx. Number Employees: 200
Business Description:
Retailer of Women's Clothing
S.I.C.: 5621
N.A.I.C.S.: 448120
Media: 9-13-23-24
Distr.: Direct to Consumer; Natl.
Personnel:
MaryEllen MacDowell *(Pres)*
Michele B. Pascoe *(CFO)*
John Lee *(Chief Acctg Officer & VP)*
James Fogerty *(Pres-Mdsg)*
Colin D. Stern *(Gen Counsel & Sec & Exec VP)*
Laura Johnson *(Exec VP-Mdsg & Product Dev)*
Frederick Lamster *(Exec VP-HR)*
Larry Burak *(Sr VP-Sourcing)*
James A. Ferree *(Sr VP-Gen Mdsg)*
Rachel A. Ungaro *(Sr VP & Gen Mdsg Mgr)*
Tim M. White *(Sr VP-Mktg)*
Lisa J. Batra *(Dir-E-Commerce)*

FOR THE BRIDE BY DEMETRIOS

222 W 37th St
New York, NY 10018-6606
Tel.: (212) 967-5222
Fax: (212) 967-1682
E-mail: info@demetriosbride.com
Web Site: www.demetriosbride.com
Approx. Number Employees: 100
Year Founded: 1980
Business Description:
Bridal Gown Designer & Bridal Magazine Publisher
S.I.C.: 2335; 2721
N.A.I.C.S.: 315233; 511120
Advertising Expenditures: $3,000,000
Media: 3-6-10-11-14-15-23-24
Distr.: Intl.
Brands & Products:
COUTURE
DEMETRIOS
ILISSA
THE PRINCESS COLLECTION
SPOSABELLA

FOREVER 21, INC.

2001 S Alameda St
Los Angeles, CA 90058
Tel.: (213) 741-5100
Fax: (213) 741-5199
Fax: (213) 741-5161
E-mail: customerservices@forever21.com
Web Site: www.forever21.com
Sales Range: $600-649.9 Million
Approx. Number Employees: 6,000
Year Founded: 1984
Business Description:
Women's Apparel & Accessories
S.I.C.: 5621
N.A.I.C.S.: 448120
Media: 31
Personnel:
Don W. Chang *(Founder, Pres & CEO)*
Lawrence Meyer *(Sr VP)*
Jin Sook Chang *(Head-Pur)*
Linda Chang *(Dir-Mktg)*
Kirstin Nagle *(Mgr-Mktg)*
Brands & Products:
FOREVER 21
XXI FOREVER
Advertising Agency:
space150
212 3rd Ave N Ste 150
Minneapolis, MN 55401
Tel.: (612) 332-6458
Agency of Record
Digital Billboard

FREDERICK'S OF HOLLYWOOD GROUP INC.

(Sub. of Frederick's of Hollywood, Inc.)
180 Madison Ave Ste 1403
New York, NY 10016
Tel.: (212) 779-8300
Web Site: www.fohgroup.com
Approx. Sls.: $133,855,000
Approx. Number Employees: 582
Year Founded: 2008
Business Description:
Women's Lingerie, Daywear, Loungewear & Sleepwear
S.I.C.: 2341; 2254; 5137; 5621
N.A.I.C.S.: 315231; 315192; 424330; 448120
Import Export
Advertising Expenditures: $4,473,000
Media: 4-7-10-19-20-21
Distr.: Natl.
Budget Set: Sept.
Personnel:
Thomas Jerome Lynch *(Chm & CEO)*
Thomas Rende *(CFO)*
Saul Pomerantz *(COO, Sec & Exec VP)*
Brands & Products:
CINEMA ETOILE
CLAXTON
ESPECIALLY YOU
MEANT TO BE
MOVIE STAR
SEDUCTIVE WEAR
SIDNEY BERNSTEIN & SON LINGERIE
STAR DUST LINGERIE
Advertising Agency:
WHITTMANHART
4500 Wilshire Blvd 2nd Fl
Los Angeles, CA 90010
Tel.: (310) 788-1900
Fax: (310) 788-2718

GARAN, INCORPORATED

(Holding of Berkshire Hathaway Inc.)
350 5th Ave
New York, NY 10118
Tel.: (212) 563-2000
Fax: (212) 971-2250
Toll Free: (800) 759-4219
Web Site: www.garanimals.com
Sales Range: $750-799.9 Million
Approx. Number Employees: 5,100
Year Founded: 1972
Business Description:
Children's Clothing Mfr
S.I.C.: 2361; 2389
N.A.I.C.S.: 315291; 315299
Export
Media: 15-24
Distr.: Natl.
Personnel:
Jerald Kamiel *(Pres & COO)*
Seymour Lichtenstein *(CEO)*
Brands & Products:
GARANIMALS
Advertising Agency:
CooperKatz & Company
205 Lexington Ave 5th Fl
New York, NY 10016
Tel.: (917) 595-3030
Fax: (917) 326-8997
Garanimals Children's Clothing, Shoes & Toys
Public Relations Agency of Record

GILT GROUPE INC.

2 Park Ave 4th Fl
New York, NY 10016
Toll Free: (877) -445-8692
Web Site: www.gilt.com
Sales Range: $150-199.9 Million
Approx. Number Employees: 380
Business Description:
Women's Fashion Designer & Distr
S.I.C.: 5621
N.A.I.C.S.: 448120
Media: 10-22
Personnel:
Kevin Ryan *(Founder & CEO)*
Drew Patterson *(Founder & CEO-Jetsetter)*
Alexandra Wilson *(Founder & Chief Merchandising Officer)*
Susan M. Lyne *(Chm)*
Andrew Page *(Pres)*
Peter Glusker *(CEO-Gilt Groupe Japan & Gilt City Japan)*
Jennifer Miller *(VP-Corp Comm)*
Chris Ventry *(Gen Mgr-Gilt Man)*
Josh Peskowitz *(Dir-Mens Style)*
Jessica Mann *(Specialist-Social Media)*

GIORGIO ARMANI CORPORATION

(Sub. of Giorgio Armani S.p.A.)
114 5th Ave
New York, NY 10011-5604

Key to Media (For complete agency information see *The Advertising Red Books-Agencies* edition):
1. Bus. Publs. 2. Cable T.V. 3. Catalogs & Directories. 4. Co-op Adv. 5. Consumer Mags. 6. D.M. to Bus. Estab.7. D.M. to Consumers
8. Daily Newsp. 9. Exhibits/Trade Shows 10. Foreign 11. Infomercial 12. Internet Adv.13. Multimedia 14. Network Radio
15. Network T.V. 16. Newsp. Distr. Mags. 17. Other 18. Outdoor (Posters, Transit) 19. Point of Purchase20. Premiums, Novelties
21. Product Samples 22. Special Events Mktg. 23. Spot Radio 24. Spot T.V. 25. Weekly Newsp. 26. Yellow Page Adv.

Tel.: (212) 366-9720
Tel.: (212) 366-6625
Fax: (212) 366-9719
Fax: (212) 366-1685
Web Site: www.giorgioarmani.com
Approx. Number Employees: 200
Business Description:
Clothing Designer & Mfr
S.I.C.: 5136; 5137
N.A.I.C.S.: 424320; 424330
Media: 4-6-9-16-18-25-30
Distr.: Natl.
Personnel:
Giorgio Armani *(Chm & CEO)*
Bridget Bruno Laguardia *(CEO)*
Beth McFadden *(VP-Mktg & Events)*
Shawn Noble *(Mgr-Media)*
Brands & Products:
ARMANI CASA
ARMANI COLLEZIONI
ARMANI EXCHANGE
ARMANI JEANS
ARMANI JUNIOR
EMPORIO ARMANI
EMPORIO ARMANI DIAMONDS
Advertising Agency:
R/GA
350 W 39th St
New York, NY 10018-1402
Tel.: (212) 946-4000
Fax: (212) 946-4010

GLAMORISE FOUNDATIONS, INC.
135 Madison Ave
New York, NY 10016-6712
Tel.: (212) 684-5025
Fax: (212) 689-7793
E-mail: info@glamorise.com
Web Site: www.glamorise.com
Approx. Number Employees: 200
Year Founded: 1921
Business Description:
Mfr. of Intimate Apparel for Full-figured Women
S.I.C.: 2341
N.A.I.C.S.: 315231
Export
Advertising Expenditures: $350,000
Media: 2-6-9-10-19
Distr.: Intl.; Natl.
Personnel:
Bernard Pundyk *(CEO)*
Jon R. Pundyk *(CEO)*
Martin Gresack *(Sr VP)*
Brands & Products:
THE ART OF FIT
COMFORT LIFT
COMPLETELY COMFORT
ELEGANCE
EXCLUSIVELY A&B
GLAMORISE
GLAMORISE SPORT
MAGICLIFT
SOFT SHOULDERS
WONDERWIRE

GROUPE BIKINI VILLAGE INC.
21018 Rue Nobel St Julie
J3E1Z8
Boucherville, QC Canada
Tel.: (450) 449-1313
Fax: (450) 449-1317
E-mail: cgirarg@bikinivillage.com
Web Site: www.bikinivillage.com
Approx. Rev.: $40,147,411
Approx. Number Employees: 220
Year Founded: 1978
Business Description:
Beachwear Mfr & Retailer
S.I.C.: 5621; 5699
N.A.I.C.S.: 448120; 448150
Media: 6-8-9-13-14-15-18-22-23-24-25
Personnel:
Yves Simard *(Pres & CEO)*
Lise Lahaise *(Dir-Ops-Stores)*
Brands & Products:
BIKINI VILLAGE
OCEAN BIKINI VILLAGE

GUESS?, INC.
1444 S Alameda St
Los Angeles, CA 90021-2433
Tel.: (213) 765-3100
Fax: (213) 744-7838
Toll Free: (800) 22-GUESS
E-mail: ir@guess.com
Web Site: www.guessinc.com/
Approx. Rev.: $2,487,294,000
Approx. Number Employees: 15,000
Year Founded: 1981
Business Description:
Men's, Women's & Children's Clothing Mfr & Distr
S.I.C.: 2253; 2325; 2339
N.A.I.C.S.: 315191; 315212; 315224; 315239
Advertising Expenditures: $31,700,000
Media: 2-4-6-9-10-11-15-18-19-24-31
Distr.: Natl.
Budget Set: Oct. -Nov.
Personnel:
Maurice Marciano *(Chm)*
Paul Marciano *(Vice Chm & CEO)*
Dennis R. Secor *(CFO)*
J. Michael Prince *(COO)*
Michael Relich *(CIO)*
Nancy Shachtman *(Pres-North America)*
Tina Kearns *(Mktg Mgr-ECommece)*
Brands & Products:
BABY GUESS
BRAND G
G BY GUESS
GUESS?
GUESS BY MARCIANO
GUESS COLLECTION
GUESS JEANS
GUESS KIDS
GUESS U.S.A.
Advertising Agencies:
Access 360 Media Inc
2951 28th St Ste 2060
Santa Monica, CA 90405
Tel.: (310) 309-3788
Fax: (310) 309-3789

Hunter
204 Julie Dr
Parkesburg, PA 19365
Tel.: (610) 857-2977
Fax: (610) 857-2984
Toll Free: (877) 363-0606

Reprise Media
55 5th Ave 16th Fl
New York, NY 10003
Tel.: (212) 444-7474

Spero Media
295 Madison Ste 1808
New York, NY 10017
Tel.: (212) 688-8999

GULBENKIAN SWIM INC.
16 Beaver Brook Rd
Danbury, CT 06810
Tel.: (203) 790-0800
Fax: (203) 791-1449
Toll Free: (800) 431-2586
E-mail: barbarapilnick@gulbenkianswim.com
Web Site: www.gulbenkianswim.com
Approx. Number Employees: 15
Year Founded: 1957
Business Description:
Swimwear, Lifeguard Uniforms & First Aid Equipment Mfr
S.I.C.: 5961
N.A.I.C.S.: 454113
Import Export
Media: 2-4-10-20-22-23-26
Distr.: Natl.
Budget Set: Sept.
Personnel:
Barbara Pilnick *(Office Mgr)*
Brands & Products:
THE AMAZING SWIM DIAPER
GULBENKIAN

THE GYMBOREE CORPORATION
(Holding of Bain Capital, LLC)
500 Howard St
San Francisco, CA 94105
Tel.: (415) 278-7000
Fax: (415) 278-7100
Toll Free: (877) 449-6932
E-mail: media_relations@gymboree.com
Web Site: www.gymboree.com
Approx. Sls.: $1,014,911,000
Approx. Number Employees: 4,900
Year Founded: 1976
Business Description:
Children's Apparel & Accessories Retailer
S.I.C.: 5641
N.A.I.C.S.: 448130
Advertising Expenditures: $16,700,000
Media: 8-13-17
Personnel:
Matthew K. McCauley *(Chm & CEO)*
Kip M. Garcia *(Pres)*
Jeffrey P. Harris *(CFO)*
Kimberly Holtz MacMillan *(Gen Counsel & VP)*
Marina Armstrong *(Sec, Sr VP & HR-Play & Music)*
Michael E. Mayo *(Sr VP-Production)*
Audrey Ardale *(Brand Mgr)*
Brands & Products:
CRAZY 8
GYMBOREE
GYMBOREE OUTLET
GYMBOREE PLAY & MUSIC
JANIE & JACK
Advertising Agency:
The Hive Advertising
Fl 1 639 Front St
San Francisco, CA 94111-1970
Tel.: (415) 255-3000
Fax: (415) 255-3005

HAMPSHIRE DESIGNERS, INC. NY
(Sub. of Hampshire Group Limited)
114 W 41st St
New York, NY 10036
Tel.: (212) 840-5666
Fax: (212) 512-0302
E-mail: info@hamp.com
Web Site: www.hamp.com
Sales Range: $50-74.9 Million
Approx. Number Employees: 100
Business Description:
Sweaters, Skirts & Slacks Mfr
S.I.C.: 5136; 5137
N.A.I.C.S.: 424320; 424330
Media: 4-5-8-10-25
Distr.: Natl.

HAMPSHIRE DESIGNERS, INC. SC
(Sub. of Hampshire Group Limited)
1924 Pearman Dairy Rd
Anderson, SC 29625
Mailing Address:
PO Box 2667
Anderson, SC 29622
Tel.: (864) 225-6232
Fax: (864) 225-4421
E-mail: info@hamp.com
Web Site: www.hamp.com
Sales Range: $50-74.9 Million
Approx. Number Employees: 65
Business Description:
Mfr. of Sweaters & Knit Apparel
S.I.C.: 5136; 5137
N.A.I.C.S.: 424320; 424330
Import Export
Media: 5-6-8-13-19-21
Distr.: Natl.
Personnel:
Jonathan Norwood *(CFO & Treas)*

HAMPSHIRE GROUP LIMITED
114 W 41st St
New York, NY 10036
Tel.: (212) 840-5666
Fax: (646) 216-2906
E-mail: info@hamp.com
Web Site: www.hamp.com
Approx. Sls.: $134,482,000
Approx. Number Employees: 158
Year Founded: 1956
Business Description:
Holding Company; Sweaters & Hosiery Mfr & Retailer
S.I.C.: 2299; 2252; 2253
N.A.I.C.S.: 313312; 315119; 315191
Import Export
Advertising Expenditures: $1,000,000
Media: 4-5-6-8-19
Distr.: Natl.
Personnel:
Richard A. Mandell *(Chm)*
Heath L. Golden *(Pres & CEO)*
Maura Langley *(CFO)*
H. Edward Hurley *(COO & Exec VP)*
Eric Prengel *(Pres-Mens Div)*
Howard L. Zwilling *(Pres-Womens Div)*
Laura Lopez *(Sr VP-Sls & Mktg)*
Patrick Groenendaal *(VP & Dir-Creative)*
Brands & Products:
DESIGNERS ORIGINALS
HAMPSHIRE GROUP
NOUVEAUX
REQUIREMENTS
SPRING AND MERCER

Key to Media (For complete agency information see *The Advertising Red Books-Agencies* edition):
1. Bus. Publs. 2. Cable T.V. 3. Catalogs & Directories. 4. Co-op Adv. 5. Consumer Mags. 6. D.M. to Bus. Estab.7. D.M. to Consumers
8. Daily Newsp. 9. Exhibits/Trade Shows 10. Foreign 11. Infomercial 12. Internet Adv.13. Multimedia 14. Network Radio
15. Network T.V. 16. Newsp. Distr. Mags. 17. Other 18. Outdoor (Posters, Transit) 19. Point of Purchase20. Premiums, Novelties
21. Product Samples 22. Special Events Mktg. 23. Spot Radio 24. Spot T.V. 25. Weekly Newsp. 26. Yellow Page Adv.

HANESBRANDS INC.
1000 E Hanes Mill Rd
Winston Salem, NC 27105
Tel.: (336) 519-8080
Fax: (312) 726-3712
Toll Free: (800) 254-1545
Web Site: www.hanesbrands.com
Approx. Sls.: $4,326,713,000
Approx. Number Employees: 55,500
Business Description:
Underwear, Legwear & Activewear Mfr
S.I.C.: 2341; 2299; 2322; 2389
N.A.I.C.S.: 315231; 314999; 315221; 315999
Advertising Expenditures: $185,488,000
Personnel:
Richard A. Noll *(Chm & CEO)*
Richard Moss *(CFO)*
Gerald W. Evans, Jr. *(Co-COO)*
William J. Nictakis *(Co-COO)*
Dale W. Boyles *(Chief Acctg Officer, VP & Controller)*
Joia M. Johnson *(Gen Counsel, Sec & Exec VP)*
Kevin D. Hall *(Exec VP & Gen Mgr-Outerwear Strategic Bus Unit)*
W. Howard Upchurch, Jr. *(Exec VP & Gen Mgr-Domestic Innerwear)*
Joan P. Mcreynolds *(Exec VP & Chief Customer Officer)*
Kevin W. Oliver *(Exec VP-HR)*
John Marsh *(Sr VP & Gen Mgr)*
Sidney Falken *(Sr VP-Hanes Brand)*
Lauri Bauer *(Dir-Media)*
Claire Edgar *(Dir-Brand Mktg-Champion)*
Hilton Graham *(Sr Brand Mgr-Hanes)*
Kim K. McMillon *(Sr Category Mgr-Mktg)*
Brands & Products:
AIRE
BALI
BARELY THERE
BEEFY-T
C9
CACHAREL
CELEBRITY
CHAMPION
COMFORTSOFT
DAISYFRESH
DUOFOLD
HANES
HANES HOSIERY
HANESBRANDS INC.
J.E.MORGAN
JUST MY SIZE
L'EGGS
ONE HANES PLACE
OUTER BANKS
PLAYTEX
RINBROS
RITMO
SHEER ENERGY
SILK REFLECTIONS
SOL
SOL Y ORO
STEDMAN BY HANES
TAGLESS
WONDERBRA
ZORBA
Advertising Agencies:
Erwin-Penland
(Owned by Hill, Holliday, Connors, Cosmopulos, Inc., Member of the Interpublic Group)
125 E Broad St
Greenville, SC 29601
Tel.: (864) 271-0500
Fax: (864) 235-5941

The Kaplan Thaler Group
825 8th Ave 34th Fl
New York, NY 10019
Tel.: (212) 474-5000
Fax: (212) 474-5702
Champion

The Martin Agency
One Shockoe Plz
Richmond, VA 23219-4132
Tel.: (804) 698-8000
Fax: (804) 698-8001
Barely There

HELLY-HANSEN (US), INC.
(Div. of Helly-Hansen ASA)
3703 I ST NW - #100
Auburn, WA 98001
Tel.: (425) 378-8700
Fax: (253) 333-8356
Toll Free: (800) 435-5901
Telex: 152555 HELLY US
Web Site: www.hellyhansen.com
Approx. Number Employees: 50
Year Founded: 1877
Business Description:
Rainwear, Polypropylene Underwear, Outerwear, Skiwear & Sailing Gear Mfr
S.I.C.: 2339; 2329
N.A.I.C.S.: 315239; 315228
Advertising Expenditures: $800,000
Media: 2-4-6-7-8-9-17-19-21
Distr.: Intl.; Natl.
Personnel:
Gary Davis *(Gen Mgr)*
Brian Leslie *(Dir-Sls Ops)*
Scott Sutherland *(Dir-Fin)*
Christine Westermark *(Dir-Product)*
Marshall Rutman *(Mgr-Mktg-North America)*
Brands & Products:
HELLY-HANSEN
HELLY-TECH
LIFA
PROPILE

HERITAGE SPORTSWEAR, LLC
PO Box 760
Hebron, OH 43025
Tel.: (740) 928-7771
Fax: (740) 928-3223
Toll Free: (800) 537-2222
Web Site:
www.heritagesportswear.com
Approx. Number Employees: 300
Year Founded: 1983
Business Description:
Knit Women's Apparel, Knit Sweaters & Skirts Mfr & Marketer
S.I.C.: 2253; 5137
N.A.I.C.S.: 315191; 424330
Media: 10
Personnel:
Mike Jurden *(Pres)*
Tami Miller *(Dir-Mktg)*
Angie Schmidt *(Dir-Fin & Acctg)*
Jon Hays *(Mgr-Ops)*

H.K. INTERNATIONAL, INC.
2721 Illinois Rd
Northbrook, IL 60062-5248
Tel.: (847) 509-7600
Fax: (847) 509-7600
Toll Free: (800) 621-1337
Approx. Number Employees: 4
Year Founded: 1976
Business Description:
Apparel Bags, Embroidery, Rain Gear, Silk Screening, Sunglasses, Team Uniforms & Sports Apparel Mfr
S.I.C.: 5136; 5099
N.A.I.C.S.: 424320; 423990
Media: 4-7
Distr.: Intl.; Natl.
Personnel:
Jay Sul *(Gen Mgr)*
Brands & Products:
KAMPUS KOLORS

HOUSE OF Z LLC
(d/b/a Zac Posen)
13 17 Laight St
New York, NY 10013
Tel.: (212) 925-1263
Fax: (212) 925-1264
E-mail: info@zacposen.com
Web Site: www.zacposen.com
Approx. Number Employees: 40
Business Description:
Women's Clothing Designer
S.I.C.: 5137
N.A.I.C.S.: 424330
Media: 10
Personnel:
Susan Posen *(Chm)*

I.C. ISAACS & COMPANY, INC.
6610 B Tributary St Ste 205
Baltimore, MD 21224-2522
Tel.: (410) 649-4500
Fax: (410) 563-1510
E-mail: ir@icisaacs.com
Web Site: www.icisaacs.com
Sales Range: $25-49.9 Million
Approx. Number Employees: 69
Year Founded: 1913
Business Description:
Jeanswear & Sportswear Designer & Marketer
S.I.C.: 2299; 2325; 2329; 2337; 2339
N.A.I.C.S.: 313312; 315224; 315228; 315234; 315239
Advertising Expenditures: $559,966
Media: 2-6-10-11-18-22-23
Personnel:
Robert Stephen Stec *(CEO)*
Liviu Goldenberg *(VP-Production & Ops)*
Brands & Products:
AIX LES BAINS
ALBATRE
AMIENS
ANNECY
ARRAN
ARRAS
AUBUSSON
AUTOR
AUXERRE
AZZARO
BANDO
BESANCON
BLADE
BORDEAUX
BOSS
BOURG EN BRESSE
BOURGES
BRAND X
BUSTER
CAIN
CECILE
CHALON
CHALON EN CHAMPAGNE
CHARTRES
CHERIE
CHLOE
CLUG
COGNAC
COLMAR
DECOY
DELLE
DIJON
EDGE X
EKTA
ELOIS
ENYA
EPINAL
ERBAG
ESMEE
ETHO
EVREUX
GEOCENTRIC
GIRBAUD
GLIDER
GRACE
GRAM
GREEK
GRENOBLE
GYROJEAN
I.C. ISAACS
I.G. DESIGN
LA ROCHE/YON
LANDSLIDER
LE HAVRE
LE PUY
LILLE
LORD ISAACS
LYON
MARITHE AND FRANCOIS GIRBAUD
MONTPELLIER
NANTES
ORLEANS
PARIS
PARIS FOOTWEAR
PELEAS
PERPIGNAN
PICABIA
PIZZAZZ
POITIERS
POLIGNY
REARGUARD
REVERTER
ROANNE
SHUTTLE
SOISSONS
ST GERMAIN EN LAYE
STRASBOURG
TAG
TEPEE
THEA
TINONA
TITANE
TOSCA
TOULON
TRASE
TRIBAL
TUBEES
TURNOVER
VALENCE
VANNES
VERDUN
VERSAILLES
VICHY
WING
WINNY
WOLOO
WORK SKIRT

Key to Media (For complete agency information see *The Advertising Red Books-Agencies* edition):
1. Bus. Publs. 2. Cable T.V. 3. Catalogs & Directories. 4. Co-op Adv. 5. Consumer Mags. 6. D.M. to Bus. Estab.7. D.M. to Consumers 8. Daily Newsp. 9. Exhibits/Trade Shows 10. Foreign 11. Infomercial 12. Internet Adv.13. Multimedia 14. Network Radio 15. Network T.V. 16. Newsp. Distr. Mags. 17. Other 18. Outdoor (Posters, Transit) 19. Point of Purchase20. Premiums, Novelties 21. Product Samples 22. Special Events Mktg. 23. Spot Radio 24. Spot T.V. 25. Weekly Newsp. 26. Yellow Page Adv.

WOXE
XPAX
XROCK
YACA
YAM
YES
ZENOBIE
ZOLTAN
ZYRTEC

ICONIX BRAND GROUP, INC.

1450 Broadway 4th Fl
New York, NY 10018-2204
Tel.: (212) 730-0030
Fax: (212) 391-2057
E-mail: info@iconixbrand.com
Web Site: www.iconixbrand.com
Approx. Rev.: $332,559,000
Approx. Number Employees: 133
Business Description:
Women's & Girls' Casual & Fashion Footwear, Handbags, Clothing & Outerwear; Men's Underwear & Women's Intimates
S.I.C.: 5139; 2326; 2339; 3021; 3144
N.A.I.C.S.: 424340; 315225; 315239; 316211; 316214
Advertising Expenditures: $25,800,000
Media: 1-2-3-4-5-6-7-8-9-10-11-13-14-15-18-19-20-21-22-23-24-25
Personnel:
Warren Clamen *(CFO & Exec VP)*
Yehuda Shmidman *(COO)*
Dari Marder *(CMO)*
Lanie List *(Chief Mdsg Officer)*
Andrew Tarshis *(Gen Counsel & Exec VP)*
Carolyn D'Angelo *(Sr VP-Brand Mgmt-Home Div)*
Lanie Pilnock *(Sr VP-Brand Mgmt)*
Kenneth Richard *(VP-Mktg)*
Gary Klein *(Dir-Fin)*
Maria Dolgetta *(Sr Mgr-Pub Affairs)*
Brands & Products:
BADGLEY MISCHKA
BONGO
CANDIE'S
CANNON
CHARISMA
DANSKIN
FIELDCREST
ICONIX
JOE BOXER
LONDON FOG
MOSSIMO
MUDD
OP
RAMPAGE
ROCAWEAR
ROYAL VELVET
STARTER
WAVERLY

INDERA MILLS COMPANY

350 W Maple St
Yadkinville, NC 27055
Mailing Address:
PO Box 309
Yadkinville, NC 27055
Tel.: (336) 679-4440
Fax: (336) 679-4475
Toll Free: (800) 334-8605
E-mail: sales@inderamills.com
Web Site: www.inderamills.com
E-Mail For Key Personnel:
Sales Director: sales@inderamills.com
Approx. Number Employees: 88
Year Founded: 1914
Business Description:
Knitted & Thermal Garments Mfr
S.I.C.: 2341; 2322
N.A.I.C.S.: 315231; 315221
Media: 8
Distr.: Natl.
Personnel:
John Willingham *(Pres)*
Patricia Cantor *(Mgr-Acctg)*
Brands & Products:
COLDPRUF
FIGURFIT
INDERA
MR. JOHNS-ON
SLEEPING BEAUTY
TOPSTYLE
WARMTH THROUGH INNOVATION

ITA LTD.

84 Wingold Ave
Toronto, ON M6B 1P5, Canada
Tel.: (416) 780-9000
Fax: (416) 780-9010
Toll Free: (800) 265-4363
E-mail: mailbox@shearlings.com
Web Site: www.shearlings.com
Approx. Number Employees: 4
Business Description:
Leather Clothing
S.I.C.: 2371; 2329; 2339; 3199
N.A.I.C.S.: 315292; 315211; 315212; 316999
Media: 4-6
Personnel:
Paul Lindzon *(CEO)*

JACQUES MORET, INC.

1411 Broadway
New York, NY 10018
Tel.: (212) 354-2400
Fax: (212) 354-1052
Toll Free: (800) 441-1999
E-mail: info@moret.com
Web Site: www.moret.com
Sales Range: $10-24.9 Million
Approx. Number Employees: 100
Year Founded: 1975
Business Description:
Marketer Bodywear & Activewear for Women & Children
S.I.C.: 5137; 2339
N.A.I.C.S.: 424330; 315239
Import Export
Advertising Expenditures: $2,880,000
Bus. Publs.: $450,000; Co-op Adv.: $850,000; Consumer Mags.: $900,000; D.M. to Bus. Estab.: $40,000; Exhibits/Trade Shows: $40,000; Other: $50,000; Outdoor (Posters, Transit): $150,000; Point of Purchase: $250,000; Premiums, Novelties: $50,000; Spot T.V.: $100,000
Distr.: Natl.
Budget Set: Oct.
Personnel:
Joey Harary *(Pres)*
Irwin Luxemberg *(Controller)*
Brands & Products:
EVERY WOMAN EVERY DAY
JACQUES MORET KIDS
MORET ULTRA

JANTZEN APPAREL, LLC

(Sub. of Perry Ellis International, Inc.)
411 NE 19th Ave
Portland, OR 97232
Tel.: (503) 238-5000
Fax: (503) 238-5020
Toll Free: (800) 238-SWIM
E-mail: talkline@jantzen.com
Web Site: www.jantzen.com
Sales Range: $75-99.9 Million
Approx. Number Employees: 75
Year Founded: 1910
Business Description:
Women's Casual Clothing & Swimwear Mfr
S.I.C.: 2331; 2341
N.A.I.C.S.: 315232; 315231
Import Export
Media: 4-6-15
Distr.: Intl.; Natl.
Budget Set: Oct.

JAPANESE WEEKEND INC.

222 Dore St
San Francisco, CA 94103
Tel.: (415) 621-0555
Fax: (415) 621-1198
Toll Free: (800) 808-0555
Web Site: www.japaneseweekend.com
Approx. Number Employees: 65
Business Description:
Maternity Clothes Mfr & Retailer
S.I.C.: 2339; 5621
N.A.I.C.S.: 315239; 448120
Media: 4-6
Brands & Products:
DURING AND AFTER
HUG
HUG A BOO
INVISIBLE OK
JW
MAMACOAT
OK
ORIGINAL OK

JEM SPORTSWEAR

459 Park Ave
San Fernando, CA 91340
Tel.: (818) 365-9361
Fax: (818) 365-7141
Business Description:
Mfr. & Sales of Women's Apparel
S.I.C.: 2331
N.A.I.C.S.: 315232
Media: 6-13

JERZEES

(Div. of Russell Corporation)
3330 Cumberland Blvd Ste 800
Atlanta, GA 30339
Tel.: (678) 742-8000
Fax: (678) 742-8300
Toll Free: (800) 321-1138
Web Site: www.jerzees.com
Sales Range: $100-124.9 Million
Approx. Number Employees: 200
Year Founded: 1999
Business Description:
Activewear Mfr
S.I.C.: 2253; 2211
N.A.I.C.S.: 315191; 313210
Import Export
Media: 4-6-9-16-18-22-23
Distr.: Intl.; Natl.
Personnel:
Bob Keller *(Pres)*
Brands & Products:
SPOTSHIELD

JESSICA MCCLINTOCK INC.

1400 16th St
San Francisco, CA 94103-5110
Tel.: (415) 553-8200
Fax: (415) 553-8337
E-mail: advertising@jessicamcclintock.com
Web Site: www.jessicamcclintock.com
Approx. Number Employees: 100
Year Founded: 1970
Business Description:
Mfr of Women's Dresses, Bridal Wear, Fragrances, Bed & Bath Accessories, Furniture, Eyewear, China, Linens, Hosiery & Jewelry
S.I.C.: 2335; 2331
N.A.I.C.S.: 315233; 315232
Export
Media: 4-6-8-10-16-18
Distr.: Direct to Consumer; Intl.; Natl.
Personnel:
Jessica G. McClintock *(Pres)*
Dilip Parekh *(CFO)*
Brands & Products:
GUNNE SAX
JESS BY JESSICA MCCLINTOCK
JESSICA MCCLINTOCK
JESSICA MCCLINTOCK FOR GIRLS
JESSICA MCCLINTOCK NUMBER 3
SCOTT MCCLINTOCK

JLM COUTURE, INC.

225 W 37th St 5th Fl
New York, NY 10018
Tel.: (212) 921-7058
Fax: (212) 921-7608
Web Site: www.jlmcouture.com
Approx. Sls.: $19,760,973
Approx. Number Employees: 70
Year Founded: 1986
Business Description:
Bridalwear & Bridesmaid Gown Designer, Mfr & Distr
S.I.C.: 2335
N.A.I.C.S.: 315233
Media: 4-6-10-13
Personnel:
Joseph L. Murphy *(Founder, Pres & CEO)*
Daniel M. Sullivan *(Chm)*
Jerrold Walkenfeld *(CFO & Principal Acctg Officer)*
Katie Thornton-Kilbride *(Dir-Sls)*
Brands & Products:
ALVINA VALENTA
JIM HJELM COUTURE
JIM HJELM OCCASIONS
JIM HJELM VISIONS
J.L.M.COUTURE
LAZARO
LAZARO BRIDESMAID
TARA KEELY

JOCKEY INTERNATIONAL, INC.

2300 60th St
Kenosha, WI 53140
Tel.: (262) 658-8111
Fax: (262) 658-1812
Toll Free: (866) 256-2539
E-mail: ed.gill@jockey.com
Web Site: www.jockey.com
Approx. Number Employees: 5,000
Year Founded: 1876
Business Description:
Underwear Mfr
S.I.C.: 2254; 2341
N.A.I.C.S.: 315192; 315231

Key to Media (For complete agency information see *The Advertising Red Books-Agencies* edition):
1. Bus. Publs. 2. Cable T.V. 3. Catalogs & Directories. 4. Co-op Adv. 5. Consumer Mags. 6. D.M. to Bus. Estab.7. D.M. to Consumers
8. Daily Newsp. 9. Exhibits/Trade Shows 10. Foreign 11. Infomercial 12. Internet Adv.13. Multimedia 14. Network Radio
15. Network T.V. 16. Newsp. Distr. Mags. 17. Other 18. Outdoor (Posters, Transit) 19. Point of Purchase20. Premiums, Novelties
21. Product Samples 22. Special Events Mktg. 23. Spot Radio 24. Spot T.V. 25. Weekly Newsp. 26. Yellow Page Adv.

Jockey International, Inc. — (Continued)

Export
Media: 2-3-5-6-9-14-15-16-19-23-24-25
Distr.: Natl.
Budget Set: Oct.
Personnel:
Debra S. Waller *(Chm & CEO)*
Dustin Cohn *(CMO & Sr VP)*
James E. Althaus *(VP-Sls)*
Linder Stann *(Dir-Mktg Svcs)*
Tim McCue *(Dir-eCommerce & Interactive)*
Brands & Products:
BEING MAGAZINE
BIG MAN ELANCE
BIG MAN MIDWAY
BODY
CLASSIC MIDWAY
COMFIES
COOLMAX
DRI-Y
ELANCE
GO COLLECTIONS
JOCKEY
JOCKEY FOR HER
JOCKEY-SILKS
NEXT TO NOTHING
NO PANTY LINE PROMISE
POCO
POUCH
QUEEN ELANCE
RIBBED ELANCE
SIMPLE COMFORT
STRETCH LACE
STRETCH RIB
Advertising Agencies:
Periscope
921 Washington Ave S
Minneapolis, MN 55415
Tel.: (612) 399-0500
Fax: (612) 399-0600
Toll Free: (800) 339-2103

TPN Inc.
9400 N Central Expwy Ste 1500
Dallas, TX 75231-5044
Tel.: (214) 692-1522
Fax: (214) 692-8316
Brand Strategy
Digital
Marketing
Social Media
US Agency of Record

JOE'S JEANS INC.
2340 S Eastern Ave
Commerce, CA 90040
Tel.: (323) 837-3700
Fax: (323) 837-3790
E-mail: info@joesjeans.com
Web Site: www.joesjeans.com
Approx. Sls.: $98,176,000
Approx. Number Employees: 154
Year Founded: 1987
Business Description:
Denim Products Mfr & Distr
S.I.C.: 2325; 2339
N.A.I.C.S.: 315224; 315239
Advertising Expenditures: $2,368,000
Media: 4-10-18
Personnel:
Samuel J. Furrow *(Chm)*
Marc B. Crossman *(Pres & CEO)*
Hamish Sandhu *(CFO)*
Joseph M. Dahan *(Dir-Creative)*
Alejandra Dibos *(Dir-Mktg & PR)*
Brands & Products:
INDIE
JOE'S
JOES JEANS

JONES APPAREL GROUP INC.
(Name Changed to The Jones Group, Inc.)

THE JONES GROUP, INC.
(Formerly Jones Apparel Group, Inc.)
1411 Broadway
New York, NY 10018
Tel.: (212) 642-3860
Web Site: www.jny.com
Approx. Rev.: $3,642,700,000
Approx. Number Employees: 6,370
Year Founded: 1975
Business Description:
Branded Apparel, Footwear & Accessories Designer, Marketer & Whslr
S.I.C.: 2337; 3144; 5136; 5621
N.A.I.C.S.: 315234; 316214; 424320; 448120
Import Export
Advertising Expenditures: $45,300,000
Media: 4-5-6-9-18-19-22-30
Distr.: Natl.
Personnel:
Sidney Kimmel *(Chm)*
Wesley R. Card *(CEO)*
John T. McClain *(CFO)*
Stacy Lastrina *(CMO)*
Christopher R. Cade *(Chief Acctg Officer, Exec VP & Controller)*
Richard Dickson *(Pres/CEO-Branded Bus)*
Dina Battipaglia *(Pres-Handbags Grp)*
Ronald Offir *(Pres-Direct Grp)*
Jack Gross *(CEO-Jeanswear Div)*
Ira M. Dansky *(Gen Counsel, Sec & Exec VP)*
Joseph T. Donnalley *(Treas & Sr VP-Corp Taxation & Risk Mgmt)*
Rafe Totengco *(Dir-Creative & Handbags)*
Brands & Products:
AK ANNE KLEIN
ALBERT NIPON
ANNE KLEIN NEW YORK
BANDOLINO
BANDOLINOBLU
CIRCA JOAN & DAVID
DOCKERS
EASY SPIRIT
ENERGIE
ENZO ANGIOLINI
ERIKA
EVAN-PICONE
GIVENCHY JEWELRY
GLO JEANS
GLORIA VANDERBILT
JEANSTAR
J.G.HOOK
JOAN & DAVID
JONES JEANS
JONES NEW YORK
JONES NEW YORK COLLECTION
JONES NEW YORK DRESS
JONES NEW YORK SIGNATURE
JONES NEW YORK SPORT
JONES WEAR
JUDITH JACK
KASPER
LE SUIT
L.E.I.
MOOTSIES TOOTSIES
NAPIER
NINE & COMPANY
NINE WEST
NORTON MCNAUGHTON
PAPPAGALLO
RENA ROWAN
SAM & LIBBY
WESTIES
Advertising Agencies:
MPG
(Div. of HAVAS)
195 Broadway 12th Fl
New York, NY 10007
Tel.: (646) 587-5000
Fax: (646) 587-5005

Night Agency
307 Canal St Fl 2
New York, NY 10013
Tel.: (212) 431-1945
Fax: (917) 677-8327
Nine West
Jones New York

JORDACHE ENTERPRISES, INC.
1400 Broadway 15th Fl
New York, NY 10018
Tel.: (212) 944-1330
Fax: (212) 269-0063
Fax: (212) 239-0063
Approx. Sls.: $500,000,000
Approx. Number Employees: 125
Year Founded: 1977
Business Description:
Jeans, Athletic Wear & Sportswear Mfr & Distr
S.I.C.: 2339; 2325
N.A.I.C.S.: 315239; 315224
Import
Advertising Expenditures: $4,000,000
Media: 4-6-9-10-13-16-18-19-25
Distr.: Intl.; Natl.
Personnel:
Joseph Nakash *(Chm & CEO)*
Liz Berlinger *(Pres)*
Joe Taylor *(CFO)*
Shaul Nakash *(CMO)*
Robert Spiegelman *(Gen Counsel)*
Emzon Shung *(Exec VP-Real Estate & Aviation)*
Charles Flores *(Sr VP & Dir-Creative)*
Mona Laffoon *(Mgr-HR)*
Advertising Agency:
Jordache Enterprises
1400 Broadway 15th Fl
New York, NY 10018
Tel.: (212) 643-8400
Fax: (212) 269-0063

JUICY COUTURE, INC.
(Sub. of Liz Claiborne, Inc.)
12723 Wentworth St
Arleta, CA 91331
Tel.: (818) 767-0849
Fax: (818) 767-1587
Web Site: www.juicycouture.com
Sales Range: $100-124.9 Million
Approx. Number Employees: 180
Business Description:
Women's T-Shirt & Other Casual Clothing Mfr
S.I.C.: 2331
N.A.I.C.S.: 315232
Personnel:
Pamela Skaist-Levy *(Co-Founder)*
LeAnn Nealz *(Pres & Chief Creative Officer)*
John DeFalco *(CFO & COO)*
Laura Mays *(Sr VP-US Wholesale)*
Ellen Rodriguez *(Sr VP-Intl & Licensing)*
Leslie Ternes Smith *(Sr Dir-Mktg)*
Advertising Agency:
PGR Media, LLC.
34 Farnsworth St 2nd Fl
Boston, MA 02210
Tel.: (617) 502-8400
Fax: (617) 451-0451

JUNONIA LTD.
2950 Lexington Ave
Eagan, MN 55121
Tel.: (651) 365-1830
Fax: (651) 365-1855
Web Site: www.junonia.com
Approx. Number Employees: 20
Business Description:
Women's Clothing Retailer
S.I.C.: 5961; 2339
N.A.I.C.S.: 454113; 315239
Media: 4-8-13
Personnel:
Anne Kelly *(Founder & Chm)*
Brands & Products:
JUNONIA
POOLPRUF
QUIKSHAPE
QUIKWIK
SEASHELL

KASPER, LTD.
(Sub. of The Jones Group, Inc.)
1411 Broadway
New York, NY 10018
Tel.: (212) 642-3860
Web Site: www.kasper.com
Sales Range: $300-349.9 Million
Approx. Number Employees: 722
Business Description:
Women's Apparel & Accessories Retailer & Mfr
S.I.C.: 2337; 5137
N.A.I.C.S.: 315234; 424330
Advertising Expenditures: $5,100,000
Personnel:
Joseph B. Parsons *(Pres & COO)*
Wendy Chivian *(Pres-Anne Klein)*
Steven M. Kramer *(Pres-Retail Opers)*
Myron Melnyk *(VP-MIS)*
Eileen McMaster *(Sr Dir-Anne Klein Mktg)*
Vera Yuan *(Dir-Anne Klein Creative Svcs)*

KATE SPADE LLC
(Sub. of Liz Claiborne, Inc.)
48 W 25th St
New York, NY 10010
Tel.: (212) 739-6550
Fax: (212) 739-6544
E-mail: info@katespade.com
Web Site: www.katespade.com
Approx. Sls.: $70,000,000
Approx. Number Employees: 80
Business Description:
Handbags
S.I.C.: 5137; 5699
N.A.I.C.S.: 424330; 448150
Media: 4-8-10-22
Personnel:
Craig Leavitt *(Co-Pres & COO)*

Key to Media (For complete agency information see *The Advertising Red Books-Agencies* edition):
1. Bus. Publs. 2. Cable T.V. 3. Catalogs & Directories. 4. Co-op Adv. 5. Consumer Mags. 6. D.M. to Bus. Estab.7. D.M. to Consumers 8. Daily Newsp. 9. Exhibits/Trade Shows 10. Foreign 11. Infomercial 12. Internet Adv.13. Multimedia 14. Network Radio 15. Network T.V. 16. Newsp. Distr. Mags. 17. Other 18. Outdoor (Posters, Transit) 19. Point of Purchase20. Premiums, Novelties 21. Product Samples 22. Special Events Mktg. 23. Spot Radio 24. Spot T.V. 25. Weekly Newsp. 26. Yellow Page Adv.

Deborah Lloyd *(Pres & Dir-Creative)*
Suzanne Norris *(VP-eCommerce)*
Cecilia Liu *(Mktg Mgr Digital)*
Advertising Agencies:
Blue Moon Works, Inc.
304 Park Ave S 11th Fl
New York, NY 10010
Tel.: (212) 590-2507
Fax: (303) 565-1104
Digital Marketing

PGR Media, LLC.
34 Farnsworth St 2nd Fl
Boston, MA 02210
Tel.: (617) 502-8400
Fax: (617) 451-0451

KAYSER-ROTH CORPORATION
(Sub. of Golden Lady S.p.A.)
102 Corporate Ctr Blvd
Greensboro, NC 27408
Mailing Address:
PO Box 26535
Greensboro, NC 27415-6535
Tel.: (336) 852-2030
Fax: (336) 852-2011
Toll Free: (800) 575-3497
E-mail: customerservice@kayser-roth.com
Web Site: www.kayser-roth.com
Approx. Number Employees: 1,600
Year Founded: 1880
Business Description:
Legwear & Apparel Mfr & Distr
S.I.C.: 2252; 2251
N.A.I.C.S.: 315119; 315111
Media: 2-4-6-7-8-9-10
Distr.: Intl.; Natl.
Personnel:
Kevin Toomey *(Pres & CEO)*
Todd Howard *(CFO & Sr VP)*
Brands & Products:
ALMOST BARE
GREAT SHAPES
HUE
NO NONSENSE
NONSTOP
PRIMA SPORT
SHEER ENDURANCE
TRANSPARENT CONTROL
Advertising Agency:
Garage Branding
410 W 4th St Ste 100
Winston Salem, NC 27101
Tel.: (336) 721-1610
Fax: (336) 721-1984
No Nonsense

KELLWOOD COMPANY
(Holding of Sun Capital Partners, Inc.)
600 Kellwood Pkwy
Chesterfield, MO 63017-5800
Mailing Address:
PO Box 14374
Saint Louis, MO 63178-4374
Tel.: (314) 576-3100
Fax: (314) 576-3460
E-mail: corp_communications@kellwood.com
Web Site: www.kellwood.com
Approx. Sls.: $1,961,750,000
Approx. Number Employees: 1,400
Year Founded: 1961
Business Description:
Men's & Women's Apparel, Intimate Apparel, Soft Goods & Recreation Products Mfr & Marketer
S.I.C.: 2325; 2253; 2321; 2331; 2341
N.A.I.C.S.: 315224; 315191; 315223; 315231; 315232
Import Export
Advertising Expenditures: $26,701,000
Media: 2-3-4-5-6-9-22-24
Distr.: Intl.; Natl.
Personnel:
Michael W. Kramer *(Pres & CEO)*
Adrian Kowalewski *(CFO & Sr VP)*
Michael M. Saunders *(COO & Sr VP)*
Keith A. Grypp *(Gen Counsel, Sec & VP)*
J. David LaRocca, Jr. *(Corp VP-HR)*
Douglas Zarkin *(VP-Mktg)*
Timothy D. Seifert *(Dir-HR)*
John E. Bruenger *(Asst Treas)*
Luther J. Rollins, Jr. *(Asst Gen Counsel)*
Brands & Products:
THE AMERICAN COLLECTION
ARMOR-TOUGH
BICE
BILL BURNS SIGNATURE
BLAKE & MANLEY
BRIGGS NEW YORK
BURNS
CALIFORNIA INFLUENCE
CAPE COD SPORTSWEAR
CASCADE BLUES
CRICKET LANE COLLECTION
DAVID BROOKS
DAVID DART
DAVID MEISTER
DBY
DBYII
DEMOCRACY
DENVER JEANS
DORBY
DOTTI
DUE DATE
EASE SPORT
EMME
EVEREST ELITE
HARBOR NITES BY SAG HARBOR
HERBCRAFT
HERBCRAFT II
IVY
JAX
JAX COUNTRY
KATHIE LEE
KORET
L.A. INTIMATES
LADY DORBY
LOST RIVER
MELROSE STUDIO
M.H.M.
MISS DORBY
MORE INTIMATE
MY MICHELLE
NORTHERN ISLES
PANGAEA
PLAZA SOUTH
PORTRAITS BY NORTHERN ISLES
PROPHECY
RADCLIFFE
RIDGEWAY
SAG HARBOR
SIGNATURE II BY STAN HERMAN
SLATES
STAN HERMAN
STUDIO EASE
STUDIO JAX
TRAVASAK
TREKK
VINTAGE BLUE
VINTAGE STUDIO

Advertising Agency:
Integrated Corporate Relations, Inc.
761 Main Ave
Norwalk, CT 06851
Tel.: (203) 682-8200
Fax: (203) 682-8201
Media Contact
— Allison C. Malkin *(Sr Mng Dir)*

KIDS STUFF, INC.
7090 Whipple Rd NW
Canton, OH 44720
Tel.: (330) 649-5700
Fax: (330) 244-9518
Toll Free: (800) 722-5282
E-mail: kidsstuff@kidsstuff.net
Web Site: www.kidsstuff.com
Sales Range: $10-24.9 Million
Approx. Number Employees: 20
Year Founded: 1977
Business Description:
Mfr. of Child Safety Products, Natural & Organic Infant & Children's Clothing, Wooden Toys, Cotton & Organic Diapers & Diaper Covers
S.I.C.: 5961
N.A.I.C.S.: 454113
Import Export
Advertising Expenditures: $10,200,000
Consumer Mags.: $200,000; D.M. to Consumers: $10,000,000
Distr.: Natl.
Budget Set: Nov.
Personnel:
William Miller *(Pres)*
Jennifer Thames *(Gen Mgr)*
Brands & Products:
JEANNIE'S KIDS CLUB
KIDS STUFF
NATURAL BABY
PERFECTLY SAFE
VEGGIETALES

KIYONNA CLOTHING, INC.
1440 S State College Blvd Units 5F & 5G
Anaheim, CA 92806
Tel.: (714) 956-5588
Fax: (714) 956-5586
Toll Free: (888) 549-6662
E-mail: customerservice@kiyonna.com
Web Site: www.kiyonna.com
Approx. Number Employees: 12
Year Founded: 1996
Business Description:
Plus Size Women's Clothing
S.I.C.: 2331; 2335; 2337; 2339; 2341
N.A.I.C.S.: 315232; 315231; 315233; 315234; 315239
Media: 6-13
Personnel:
Kim Khanbeigi *(Founder & Pres)*
Brands & Products:
KIYONNA

KOBRA INTERNATIONAL LTD.
(d/b/a Nicole Miller)
525 7th Ave 20th Fl
New York, NY 10018-4901
Tel.: (212) 719-9200
Tel.: (212) 655-7756 (Pub Rels)
Fax: (212) 391-4327
E-mail: info@nicolemiller.com
Web Site: www.nicolemiller.com
Approx. Number Employees: 120
Year Founded: 1982
Business Description:
Dresses, Blouses, Shirts, Slacks & Accessories Mfr
S.I.C.: 2331; 2335
N.A.I.C.S.: 315232; 315233
Import Export
Advertising Expenditures: $1,000,000
Media: 6-10
Personnel:
Jeff Chiola *(Coord-Mktg & Adv)*
Brands & Products:
A LA MODE
ADORNED
ALANA JAKARTA SATCHEL
ART DECO
AVIATOR
BALTHAZAR
BARRETT FRAME
BLITZ
BRIANA MARYJANE
CAROLYN
CHANDELIER
CORSICA
DE LUXE
EVA JAVA TOTE
LUXE
LYLA
MADELLA
MIA JAKARTA CLUTCH
NAIMA WEDGES
NICOLE MILLER
PERSPECTIVE
RAFELLA
RAVEN
SATIN CLUTCH
SLINKY
STARBURST
STRAPPY PLATFORM
VOILA

LADY ESTER LINGERIE CORP.
33 E 33th St 8th Fl
New York, NY 10016-4328
Tel.: (212) 684-4446
Fax: (212) 889-7235
E-mail: sales@ladyester.com
Web Site: www.ladyester.com
E-Mail For Key Personnel:
Marketing Director: donas@ladyester.com
Sales Director: sales@ladyester.com
Approx. Number Employees: 225
Year Founded: 1935
Business Description:
Lingerie Mfr
S.I.C.: 2341
N.A.I.C.S.: 315231
Advertising Expenditures: $350,000
Media: 4-5-6-20
Distr.: Intl.; Natl.
Brands & Products:
A CURRENT EVENT
BODY CHIC
ESCAPADES
FOR REAL
JE T'ADORE
LADY ESTER
LUCIE ANN
PERFECTFORM
VAL MODE
WONDERMAID

LADY GRACE STORES INC.
5 Commonwealth Ave Unit 1
Woburn, MA 01801
Tel.: (781) 322-1721
Toll Free: (800) 922-0504
E-mail: info@ladygrace.com

Key to Media (For complete agency information see *The Advertising Red Books-Agencies* edition):
1. Bus. Publs. 2. Cable T.V. 3. Catalogs & Directories. 4. Co-op Adv. 5. Consumer Mags. 6. D.M. to Bus. Estab.7. D.M. to Consumers
8. Daily Newsp. 9. Exhibits/Trade Shows 10. Foreign 11. Infomercial 12. Internet Adv.13. Multimedia 14. Network Radio
15. Network T.V. 16. Newsp. Distr. Mags. 17. Other 18. Outdoor (Posters, Transit) 19. Point of Purchase20. Premiums, Novelties
21. Product Samples 22. Special Events Mktg. 23. Spot Radio 24. Spot T.V. 25. Weekly Newsp. 26. Yellow Page Adv.

Lady Grace Stores Inc. — (Continued)
Web Site: www.ladygrace.com
Approx. Number Employees: 200
Year Founded: 1937
Business Description:
Women's Intimate Clothing Retailer & Mail Order
S.I.C.: 5699; 5961
N.A.I.C.S.: 448150; 454111; 454113
Media: 4-8-13
Personnel:
Stephen E. Berson *(Pres)*
Bruce Green *(CFO)*

LANDAU UNIFORMS INCORPORATED
8410 W Sandidge Rd
Olive Branch, MS 38654
Tel.: (662) 895-7200
Fax: (662) 895-5099
Toll Free: (800) 238-7513
E-mail: info@landau.com
Web Site: www.landau.com
E-Mail For Key Personnel:
Sales Director: sales@landau.com
Approx. Number Employees: 1,200
Year Founded: 1959
Business Description:
Uniform Mfr & Retailer
S.I.C.: 2389
N.A.I.C.S.: 315299
Import Export
Media: 4-7-13
Personnel:
Daryl Williams *(VP-Sls & Mktg)*
Brands & Products:
FX
LANDAU
LANDAU E
LANDAU FOR HER
THE LOOK OF A PROFESSIONAL
PLATINUM
SCRUBZONE
TRENDS
WEAR. LOVE. REPEAT.

LAURA ASHLEY, INC.
(Sub. of Laura Ashley Holdings plc)
7000 Regent Pkwy
Fort Mill, SC 29715-8313
Tel.: (803) 396-7700
Fax: (803) 396-7790
E-mail: customerservice@lauraashley-usa.com
Web Site: www.lauraashley-usa.com
Approx. Number Employees: 7
Year Founded: 1953
Business Description:
Retailer of Ladies' & Children's Clothing & Home Furnishings
S.I.C.: 5699
N.A.I.C.S.: 448150
Import
Advertising Expenditures: $800,000
Media: 4-8-10-13-22
Distr.: Intl.; Natl.

L'EGGS PRODUCTS, INC.
(Div. of Hanesbrands Inc.)
1000 E Hanes Mill Rd
Winston Salem, NC 27105
Tel.: (336) 519-8080
Fax: (312) 726-3712
Toll Free: (800) 925-3447
E-mail: info@leggs.com
Sales Range: $500-549.9 Million
Approx. Number Employees: 1,800
Business Description:
Women's Hosiery Mfr
S.I.C.: 2252
N.A.I.C.S.: 315119
Media: 6-8-9-10-13-14-15-16-18-19-20-23-24
Distr.: Natl.
Personnel:
Debbie Erdman *(Brand Mgr)*
Brands & Products:
BARE L'EGGS
BODY BEAUTIFUL
BROWN SUGAR
SHEER ELEGANCE
SILKEN MIST
Advertising Agency:
Ink & Co.
446 Broadway 4th Fl
New York, NY 10013
Tel.: (212) 334-3168
Fax: (212) 334-3167

LEO'S DANCEWEAR INC.
1900 N Narragansett Ave
Chicago, IL 60639
Tel.: (773) 889-7700
Fax: (773) 889-7593
Fax: (800) 736-5330
Toll Free: (800) 736-5367
E-mail: info@leosdancewear.com
Web Site: www.leosdancewear.com
Approx. Number Employees: 75
Year Founded: 1924
Business Description:
Dancewear Mfr
S.I.C.: 5699; 3021; 5621; 5641; 5661
N.A.I.C.S.: 448190; 316211; 448120; 448130; 448210
Advertising Expenditures: $500,000
Media: 4-6-8-10-13-26
Personnel:
Glenn Baruck *(Pres)*
Sherri Giacone *(Mgr-Mktg & Comm)*
Brands & Products:
THE FIRST NAME IN DANCE
LEO'S DANCEWEAR

LIFE UNIFORM COMPANY
(Joint Venture of Reinet Investments SCA & Trilantic Capital Management LLC)
2132 Kratky Rd
Saint Louis, MO 63114
Tel.: (314) 824-2900
Fax: (314) 824-2919
Web Site: www.lifeuniform.com
Approx. Sls.: $90,550,000
Approx. Number Employees: 850
Business Description:
Retail Vocational Attire & Accessories
S.I.C.: 5699; 5661
N.A.I.C.S.: 448190; 448150; 448210
Media: 4-8
Personnel:
Jim Rudd *(Pres & CEO)*
Bryan Graiff *(CFO & VP)*
Debra Anderson *(VP-Mdsg)*
Rick Hall *(VP-IT & Fulfillment Ops)*

LINGERIE BY SUSAN, INC.
9 Lincoln Hwy
Edison, NJ 08820
Tel.: (732) 549-4343
Fax: (732) 549-4994
Toll Free: (877) 782-8062
E-mail: customer_service@lingeriebysusan.com
Web Site: www.lingeriebysusan.com
Approx. Number Employees: 4
Year Founded: 1988
Business Description:
Lingerie Retail & Mail Order
S.I.C.: 5699
N.A.I.C.S.: 448150
Media: 4-8-13
Personnel:
Susan Cohen *(Pres)*

LIZ CLAIBORNE, INC.
1441 Broadway
New York, NY 10018-1805
Tel.: (212) 354-4900
Fax: (212) 626-3416
Toll Free: (866) 549-7467
Web Site: www.lizclaiborne.com
Approx. Sls.: $2,500,072,000
Approx. Number Employees: 11,300
Year Founded: 1976
Business Description:
Branded Women's & Men's Apparel, Accessories & Fragrance Products Designer & Marketer
S.I.C.: 2389; 2331; 2335; 2339
N.A.I.C.S.: 315999; 315232; 315233; 315239
Import Export
Advertising Expenditures: $65,300,000
Media: 1-4-5-6-8-11-14-18-19-25
Distr.: Intl.; Natl.
Personnel:
Kay Koplovitz *(Chm)*
William L. McComb *(CEO)*
Andrew Warren *(CFO & Exec VP)*
Evon Jones *(CIO & Sr VP)*
Nick Rubino *(Chief Legal Officer, Gen Counsel, Corp Sec & Sr VP)*
Tim Gunn *(Chief Creative Officer)*
Elaine H. Goodell *(Chief Acctg Officer, VP & Corp Controller)*
Lisa Piovano-Machacek *(Chief HR Officer & Sr VP)*
Craig Leavitt *(Co-Pres/COO-Kate Spade)*
Deborah Lloyd *(Co-Pres/Dir-Creative-Kate Spade)*
Susan Davidson *(Grp Pres-Womenswear Bus/DKNY Enterprise-Denim)*
Sharyn Segal *(Pres-Mid-Tier Accessories)*
Robert Vill *(Treas & VP-Fin)*
Patrick Wade *(Exec VP & Dir-Creative)*
Dave Mctague *(Exec VP-Partnered Brands)*
Lawrence D. McClure *(Sr VP-HR)*
Jane Randel *(Sr VP-Corp Comm & Brand Svcs)*
Robert Zane *(Sr VP)*
Anne Cashill *(Corp VP-Design)*
Isaac Mizrahi *(Dir-Creative-Liz Claiborne Brand)*
Brands & Products:
CLAIBORNE
CRAZY HORSE
CURVE
DANA BUCHMAN
ELISABETH
EMMA JAMES
ENYCE
FIRST ISSUE
JH COLLECTIBLES
JUICY COUTURE
KATE SPADE
LAUNDRY BY SHELLI SEGAL
LIZ
LIZ CLAIBORNE
LIZCLAIBORNE INC
LIZSPORT
LIZWEAR
LUCKY
MEXX
MONET
MONET II
REALITIES
SIGRID OLSEN
TRIFARI
VILLAGER
Advertising Agencies:
Gotham Incorporated
150 E 42nd St 12th Fl
New York, NY 10017
Tel.: (212) 414-7000
Fax: (212) 414-7095

PGR Media, LLC.
34 Farnsworth St 2nd Fl
Boston, MA 02210
Tel.: (617) 502-8400
Fax: (617) 451-0451

Walrus
18 E 17th St Fl 3
New York, NY 10003
Tel.: (212) 645-2646
Fax: (212) 645-2759

LOEHMANN'S HOLDINGS INC.
(Holding of Istithmar PJSC)
(Filed Ch 11 Bankruptcy on 11/15/10 in U.S. Bankruptcy Ct, Dist of NY, Manhattan)
2500 Halsey St
Bronx, NY 10461
Tel.: (718) 409-2000
E-mail: insider@loehmanns.com
Web Site: www.loehmanns.com
Sales Range: $350-399.9 Million
Approx. Number Employees: 1,900
Year Founded: 2000
Business Description:
Holding Company; Women's & Men's Discount Branded Apparel & Accessories Stores Owner & Operator
S.I.C.: 6719; 5311; 5611; 5621; 5661; 5699
N.A.I.C.S.: 551112; 448110; 448120; 448150; 448210; 452112
Advertising Expenditures: $12,200,000
Media: 4-6-8-13-18-22-23-24-25
Personnel:
Arthur E. Reiner *(Chm)*
Gerald Politz *(Pres)*
Joe Melvin *(Interim CEO & COO)*
Joan Durkin *(CFO & Sr VP-Fin)*
Frank Lamolino *(CIO & Sr VP)*
Nancy Straface *(Sr VP-HR)*
Brands & Products:
LOEHMANN'S
Advertising Agency:
Farago+Partners
71 Broadway
New York, NY 10006
Tel.: (212) 344-9472
Fax: (212) 243-1682

LOLLYTOGS, LTD.
100 W 33rd St Ste 1012
New York, NY 10001-2914
Tel.: (212) 502-6000
Fax: (212) 268-5160
E-mail: information@lollynet.com

Key to Media (For complete agency information see *The Advertising Red Books-Agencies* edition):
1. Bus. Publs. 2. Cable T.V. 3. Catalogs & Directories. 4. Co-op Adv. 5. Consumer Mags. 6. D.M. to Bus. Estab.7. D.M. to Consumers 8. Daily Newsp. 9. Exhibits/Trade Shows 10. Foreign 11. Infomercial 12. Internet Adv.13. Multimedia 14. Network Radio 15. Network T.V. 16. Newsp. Distr. Mags. 17. Other 18. Outdoor (Posters, Transit) 19. Point of Purchase20. Premiums, Novelties 21. Product Samples 22. Special Events Mktg. 23. Spot Radio 24. Spot T.V. 25. Weekly Newsp. 26. Yellow Page Adv.

Web Site: www.lollytogs.com
Approx. Number Employees: 200
Year Founded: 1958
Business Description:
Children's & Infants' Clothing
S.I.C.: 5137; 2339
N.A.I.C.S.: 424330; 315239
Import Export
Media: 2-4-7-8-10-13-18-23
Personnel:
Sam Gindi *(Co-Owner)*
Morris Sutton *(Co-Owner)*
Richard Sutton *(CEO & Exec VP)*
Joseph Sutton *(Exec VP)*
Charlene Alpay *(Dir-Mktg)*
Brands & Products:
BABY HEALTHTEX
COTLER
FRENCH TOAST
FRENCH TOAST OFFICIAL SCHOOL WEAR
HEALTHTEX
LEE SCHOOL
LOLLYTOGS
OUR GIRL BY HEALTHTEX
RIM ROCKA
UNIVERSITY CLUB

LUCKY BRAND DUNGAREES, INC.

(Sub. of Liz Claiborne, Inc.)
5233 Alcoa Ave
Vernon, CA 90085
Tel.: (323) 282-4100
Fax: (323) 585-7771
Toll Free: (800) 964-5777
Web Site: www.luckybrandjeans.com
Sales Range: $25-49.9 Million
Approx. Number Employees: 160
Year Founded: 1990
Business Description:
Apparel & Accessories Mfr & Distr
S.I.C.: 2389
N.A.I.C.S.: 315999
Personnel:
David DeMattei *(CEO)*
Trent Merrill *(Exec VP)*
Charlie Cole *(VP-Online Mktg)*
Brands & Products:
HOT PINK
LUCKY BABY
LUCKY BRAND
LUCKY DREAMS
LUCKY GIRLS
LUCKY YOU
OLD AMERICAN DUNGAREES
TRIPLE XXX DUNGAREES
Advertising Agencies:
Lime Public Relations & Promotion
160 Varick St 4th Fl
New York, NY 10013
Tel.: (212) 633-0080
Fax: (212) 633-1711

Night Agency
307 Canal St Fl 2
New York, NY 10013
Tel.: (212) 431-1945
Fax: (917) 677-8327
Jeans

LUCY ACTIVEWEAR, INC.

(Sub. of VF Corporation)
222 SW Columbia St Ste 300
Portland, OR 97201
Tel.: (503) 228-2142
Fax: (503) 961-6530
Toll Free: (877) 999-5829
E-mail: customerservice@lucy.com
Web Site: www.lucy.com
Sales Range: $50-74.9 Million
Approx. Number Employees: 65
Year Founded: 1999
Business Description:
Women's Activewear Retailer
S.I.C.: 5621
N.A.I.C.S.: 448120
Media: 6-8-13
Personnel:
Shaz Kahng *(Pres)*
Christa Lindberg *(Dir-Mktg)*
Advertising Agencies:
Edelman Public Relations Worldwide
888 SW 5th Ave Ste 1050
Portland, OR 97204
Tel.: (503) 227-5767
Public Relations

The Felt Hat
1231 NW Hoyt St
Portland, OR 97209
Tel.: (503) 222-0068

KD&E
129 W 27th St 11th Fl
New York, NY 10001
Tel.: (212) 686-0006
Fax: (212) 686-6991

MAIDENFORM BRANDS, INC.

485F US Hwy 1 S
Iselin, NJ 08830
Tel.: (732) 621-2500
E-mail: orders@maidenform.com
Web Site: www.maidenform.com
Approx. Sls.: $556,709,000
Approx. Number Employees: 1,175
Year Founded: 1921
Business Description:
Intimate Women's Apparel Mfr
S.I.C.: 2341
N.A.I.C.S.: 315231
Advertising Expenditures: $9,944,000
Media: 2-4-5-6-8-18-19-20
Distr.: Intl.; Natl.
Budget Set: Nov.
Personnel:
Karen Rose *(Chm)*
Maurice S. Reznik *(CEO)*
Christopher W. Vieth *(CFO, COO & Exec VP)*
John A. Nelson *(Chief Acctg Officer & VP)*
Nanci Prado *(Gen Counsel, Sec & Exec VP)*
Gayle Weibley Wolman *(Exec VP)*
Patricia J. Royak *(Sr VP & Mng Dir-Intl)*
Steven Castellano *(Sr VP-Mdsg & Design Ops)*
Mitch Kauffman *(Sr VP-Sls)*
Steve Nelson *(Sr VP-Ops)*
Jamie Leskanic *(Dir-Mktg)*
Brands & Products:
ACTIVEMOTION
CONTROL IT!
DREAM BRA
FLEXEES
GENTLEMOTION
LILYETTE
MAIDENFORM
POWERMOTION
RENDEZVOUS
SELF EXPRESSIONS
SUBTRACT
SWEET NOTHINGS
THIS FEELS RIGHT

MAYER/BERKSHIRE CORPORATION

25 Edison Dr
Wayne, NJ 07470-4712
Tel.: (973) 696-6200
Fax: (973) 696-6203
Web Site: www.eberkshire.com
Approx. Number Employees: 80
Year Founded: 1945
Business Description:
Hosiery; Panty Hose; Underwear & Related Apparel; Retail Apparel
S.I.C.: 5137; 5699
N.A.I.C.S.: 424330; 448150
Import Export
Media: 6-9
Brands & Products:
BERKSHIRE
BERKSHIRE INTIMATES
BETTER THAN BARE
BRITE LEGS
EBERKSHIRE
EBONY RICH
EBONY SUPREME
EYECATCHERS
FOOTNOTES
IN CONTROL
IT FITS, IT FITS!
JUST FOR YOU
KICKS
LADY SUPREME
MAYER
PERFORMANCE
SHIMMERS
SILKY
Advertising Agency:
Michester Advertising
c/o Mayer Berkshire Corp PO Box 244
Wayne, NJ 07474
Tel.: (973) 696-6200
Fax: (973) 696-6203

MCNAUGHTON APPAREL GROUP INC.

(Sub. of The Jones Group, Inc.)
498 7th Ave 9th Fl
New York, NY 10018-7604
Tel.: (215) 826-8701
Tel.: (215) 785-4000
Fax: (215) 785-4000
Toll Free: (800) 214-0552
E-mail: cservice@mcnaughtonapparel.com
Web Site:
www.mcnaughtonapparel.com
Sales Range: $150-199.9 Million
Approx. Number Employees: 350
Year Founded: 1981
Business Description:
Junior & Women's Apparel Mfr
S.I.C.: 2339; 5137
N.A.I.C.S.: 315239; 424330
Media: 6
Brands & Products:
CURRANTS
ENERGIE
JAMIE SCOTT
NORTON MCNAUGHTON

METROPARK USA, INC.

5750 Grace Pl
Los Angeles, CA 90022
Tel.: (323) 622-3600
Fax: (323) 389-1599
Web Site: www.metroparkusa.com
Sales Range: $50-74.9 Million
Approx. Number Employees: 764
Year Founded: 2003
Business Description:
Young Adult Clothing, Apparel Retailer
S.I.C.: 5699
N.A.I.C.S.: 448150; 448190
Advertising Expenditures: $314,000
Personnel:
Orval Madden *(Chm)*
Cynthia Hariss *(CFO)*
Lance Hutchison *(COO, Sec & Exec VP-Store Ops)*

METROPOLITAN ASSOCIATION FOR RETARDED CITIZENS, INC.

(d/b/a ARC Thrift Stores)
7721 W 6th Ave
Lakewood, CO 80215
Tel.: (303) 231-9222
Fax: (303) 231-9011
Web Site: www.arcthrift.com
Sales Range: $25-49.9 Million
Approx. Number Employees: 600
Year Founded: 1963
Business Description:
Sales of Used Clothing
S.I.C.: 5932
N.A.I.C.S.: 453310
Personnel:
Loyd Lewis *(Pres & CEO)*
Advertising Agency:
Avocet Communications
1501 S Sunset St Ste A
Longmont, CO 80501-6757
Tel.: (303) 678-7102
Fax: (303) 678-7109

MICHAEL KORS, LLC

11 W 42nd St
New York, NY 10036
Tel.: (212) 201-8100
E-mail: inquiries@michaelkors.com
Web Site: www.michaelkors.com
Approx. Sls.: $30,600,000
Approx. Number Employees: 160
Business Description:
Women's & Men's Clothing & Accessories Designer
S.I.C.: 2339; 2329; 2331; 2335; 2337; 2389; 5136; 5621; 5699
N.A.I.C.S.: 315212; 315211; 315232; 315233; 315234; 315999; 424320; 448120; 448190
Media: 6-10
Personnel:
Silas K.F. Chou *(Co-Chm)*
Lawrence S. Stroll *(Co-Chm)*
John D. Idol *(CEO)*
Lee S. Sporn *(Gen Counsel, Sec & Sr VP-Bus Affairs)*
Anne Waterman *(Sr VP-Global Image)*
Donna Hernan *(VP-Special Mkts)*
Michael Kors *(Mgr-Design)*

MICHAEL STARS, INC.

12955 Chadron Ave
Hawthorne, CA 90250
Tel.: (310) 263-7375
Fax: (310) 263-7395
Toll Free: (877) STAR-TEE
E-mail: customerservice@michaelstars.com
Web Site: www.michaelstars.com

Key to Media (For complete agency information see *The Advertising Red Books-Agencies* edition):
1. Bus. Publs. 2. Cable T.V. 3. Catalogs & Directories. 4. Co-op Adv. 5. Consumer Mags. 6. D.M. to Bus. Estab.7. D.M. to Consumers
8. Daily Newsp. 9. Exhibits/Trade Shows 10. Foreign 11. Infomercial 12. Internet Adv.13. Multimedia 14. Network Radio
15. Network T.V. 16. Newsp. Distr. Mags. 17. Other 18. Outdoor (Posters, Transit) 19. Point of Purchase20. Premiums, Novelties
21. Product Samples 22. Special Events Mktg. 23. Spot Radio 24. Spot T.V. 25. Weekly Newsp. 26. Yellow Page Adv.

Michael Stars, Inc. — (Continued)

Approx. Number Employees: 100
Year Founded: 1986
Business Description:
Women's Clothing
S.I.C.: 5137
N.A.I.C.S.: 424330
Media: 6-8-10-13-20-21-22
Personnel:
Michael Cohen *(Founder)*
Brands & Products:
MICHAEL STARS
MIKEY STARS
ORIGINAL SCENT
THE ORIGINAL TEE

MILANO LTD.

525 7th Ave Ste 806
New York, NY 10018
Tel.: (212) 398-4444
Fax: (212) 398-0032
E-mail: info@milanoltd.com
Web Site: www.milanoltd.com
Approx. Number Employees: 17
Business Description:
Women's Clothing
S.I.C.: 5137; 2335
N.A.I.C.S.: 424330; 315233
Media: 4-8-10
Personnel:
Payman Yadidi *(Pres)*
Garry Benett *(Mgr-Sls & Mktg)*

MUDD, LLC

1407 Broadway Fl 29
New York, NY 10018
Tel.: (212) 730-0404
Fax: (212) 730-2289
Web Site: www.mymuddworld.com
Approx. Number Employees: 30
Year Founded: 1995
Business Description:
Mfr & Distr Girls' Jeans
S.I.C.: 5137
N.A.I.C.S.: 424330
Advertising Expenditures: $3,000,000
Media: 3-4-5-13-15-23
Distr.: Natl.
Budget Set: Sept.
Personnel:
Conrad Long *(Pres)*
Brands & Products:
MUDD

NATIONAL WHOLESALE COMPANY INC.

400 National Blvd
Lexington, NC 27292
Tel.: (336) 248-5904
Fax: (336) 249-9326
Toll Free: (800) 433-0580
Web Site: www.shopnational.com
Approx. Number Employees: 140
Business Description:
Women's Apparel, Mail Order
S.I.C.: 5961; 5137
N.A.I.C.S.: 454113; 424330
Media: 4-8-13
Personnel:
Lynda Smith Swann *(Pres)*

NEIMAN MARCUS, INC.

(Joint Venture of Leonard Green & Partners, L.P., Warburg Pincus LLC & TPG Capital, L.P.)
(d/b/a Neiman Marcus Group)
1618 Main St
Dallas, TX 75201
Tel.: (214) 743-7600
E-mail: investor_relations@neimanmarcus.com
Web Site: www.neimanmarcus.com
Approx. Rev.: $3,692,768,000
Approx. Number Employees: 14,400
Year Founded: 1907
Business Description:
Specialty Retailer, Mail-Order Catalogs & E-Commerce; Owned by TPG, Leonard Green & Partners L.P. & Warburg Pincus, LLC
S.I.C.: 5311; 5961
N.A.I.C.S.: 452111; 454111; 454113
Advertising Expenditures: $77,400,000
Media: 4-6-9-18-25
Personnel:
Karen W. Katz *(Pres & CEO)*
James E. Skinner *(CFO)*
Phillip L. Maxwell *(CIO)*
Wanda Gierhart *(CMO)*
Marita O'Dea *(Chief HR Officer & Sr VP-HR-Neiman Marcus Stores)*
John E. Koryl *(Pres-Neiman Marcus Direct)*
James J. Gold *(CEO-Bergdorf Goodman)*
Nelson A. Bangs *(Gen Counsel & Sr VP)*
Gerald Barnes *(Exec VP-Neiman Marcus Direct)*
Ken Downing *(Sr VP & Dir-Fashion)*
Wayne A. Hussey *(Sr VP-Store Dev)*
Nickelson Wooster *(Dir-Men's Fashion)*
Brands & Products:
BERGDORF GOODMAN
CHEF'S CATALOGUE
HORCHOW
NEIMAN MARCUS

NYDJ APPAREL, LLC

(Holding of Falconhead Capital, LLC)
5401 S Soto St
Vernon, CA 90058
Tel.: (323) 581-9040
Fax: (323) 581-9041
E-mail: contact@nydj.com
Web Site: www.nydj.com
Year Founded: 2003
Business Description:
Women's Designer Jeans & Other Apparel Mfr & Distr
S.I.C.: 2339; 2331; 2337; 5137
N.A.I.C.S.: 315239; 315232; 315234; 424330
Media: 6-9-11-25
Personnel:
Leslie Rudes *(Co-Founder)*
Lisa Rudes-Sandel *(Co-Founder)*
Edwin Lewis *(Chm & CEO)*
Kevin Mahoney *(Pres)*
Crystal Kong *(Mktg Mgr)*
Brands & Products:
NOT YOUR DAUGHTER'S JEANS
TUMMY TUCK

OATEY SUPPLY CHAIN SERVICES

4700 W 160th St
Cleveland, OH 44135
Tel.: (216) 267-7100
Fax: (216) 267-6538
Web Site: www.oatey.com
Sales Range: $10-24.9 Million
Approx. Number Employees: 800
Business Description:
Manufacturing Plumbing & Hardware Producers
S.I.C.: 5074
N.A.I.C.S.: 423720
Media: 2-4-7-10-13-18-19-21-22
Personnel:
John Mcmillan *(Pres)*
Brands & Products:
ALL-FLASH
CLOG BUSTER
COLOR-FLASH
THE ELIMINATOR
END-CAP
FLEX-FLASH
FLOWGUARD
FLOWGUARD GOLD
GREAT BLUE
GREAT WHITE
HIGHRISE
HOLDRITE
J-HOOK
KNOCK-OUT
MASTER FLASH
MAXWAX
MS END-CAP
NO-CALK
OATEY
OATEYWELD
PUSH CAP
QUADTRO
QUIET PIPES
R-SHINE
SAFE FLO
SURE-VENT
TUB-N-TILE
TWIST-N-SET

OLEG CASSINI, INC.

Radio City Sta
New York, NY 10101
Tel.: (212) 753-7540
Fax: (212) 308-3053
Toll Free: (800) 441-6534
E-mail: olegcassini@rcn.com
Web Site: www.olegcassini.com
Approx. Number Employees: 14
Business Description:
Apparel, Accessories & Home Furnishings; Distr of Products to Department & Specialty Stores
S.I.C.: 5137; 5136
N.A.I.C.S.: 424330; 424320
Media: 2-4-5-6-8-9-10-25
Distr.: Intl.; Natl.
Budget Set: Quarterly
Personnel:
Oleg Cassini *(Pres)*
Peggy Nestor *(Dir-Sls)*
Brands & Products:
BLACK TIE
CASSINI
OLEG CASSINI

OSCAR DE LA RENTA LTD.

550 7th Ave
New York, NY 10018
Tel.: (212) 282-0500
E-mail: info@oscardelarenta.com
Web Site: www.oscardelarenta.com
Sales Range: $650-699.9 Million
Approx. Number Employees: 100
Business Description:
Men's & Women's Clothing Designer
S.I.C.: 2335; 2339
N.A.I.C.S.: 315233; 315239
Media: 10-30
Personnel:
Oscar de la Renta *(Chm)*
Alex Bolen *(CEO)*
Nicole McCloskey *(Dir-Fragrance Mktg)*

OTOMIX, INC.

747 Glasgow Ave
Inglewood, CA 90301
Tel.: (310) 215-6100
Toll Free: (800) 597-5425
Toll Free: (800) 701-7867
Web Site: www.otomix.com
Approx. Number Employees: 30
Year Founded: 1988
Business Description:
Men & Women's Sportswear
S.I.C.: 5136; 5137
N.A.I.C.S.: 424320; 424330
Media: 4-6-8-13
Personnel:
Mitchell Bobrow *(Owner-Otomix Athletic Company)*
Brands & Products:
MARTIAL ARTS MASTERS
OTOMIX

OXFORD INDUSTRIES, INC.

222 Piedmont Ave NE
Atlanta, GA 30308
Tel.: (404) 659-2424
Fax: (404) 653-1545
E-mail: info@oxfordinc.com
Web Site: www.oxfordinc.com
Approx. Sls.: $603,947,000
Approx. Number Employees: 4,000
Year Founded: 1942
Business Description:
Consumer Apparel for Men, Women & Children Mfr, Designer & Seller
S.I.C.: 2295; 2311; 2325; 2329; 2331; 2335
N.A.I.C.S.: 313320; 315211; 315222; 315224; 315232; 315233
Import
Advertising Expenditures: $26,700,000
Personnel:
J. Hicks Lanier *(Chm & CEO)*
Thomas Caldecot Chubb III *(Pres)*
K. Scott Grassmyer *(CFO, Sr VP & Controller)*
Sheldon P. Fogel *(Pres-Tommy Hilfiger Dress Shirts & Oxford Shirtings)*
David B. Leveille *(Pres-Oxford Golf Grp)*
Corey Rowe *(Pres-Ely & Walker)*
Thomas E. Campbell *(Gen Counsel, Sec & Sr VP-Law)*
Christine B. Cole *(Sr VP-HR)*
Kyle Zitek *(Dir-Mktg-Tommy Bahama)*
Brands & Products:
928
BEN SHERMAN
CATTLEMAN
CUMBERLAND OUTFITTERS
ELY AND WALKER
ELY PLAINS
INDIGO PALMS
ISLAND SOFT
LANIER CLOTHES
OXFORD APPAREL
OXFORD INDUSTRIES
SOLITUDE
TOMMY BAHAMA
Advertising Agency:
Dircks Associates
550 N Country Rd Ste A

Key to Media (For complete agency information see *The Advertising Red Books-Agencies* edition):
1. Bus. Publs. 2. Cable T.V. 3. Catalogs & Directories. 4. Co-op Adv. 5. Consumer Mags. 6. D.M. to Bus. Estab.7. D.M. to Consumers
8. Daily Newsp. 9. Exhibits/Trade Shows 10. Foreign 11. Infomercial 12. Internet Adv.13. Multimedia 14. Network Radio
15. Network T.V. 16. Newsp. Distr. Mags. 17. Other 18. Outdoor (Posters, Transit) 19. Point of Purchase20. Premiums, Novelties
21. Product Samples 22. Special Events Mktg. 23. Spot Radio 24. Spot T.V. 25. Weekly Newsp. 26. Yellow Page Adv.

Saint James, NY 11780-1427
Tel.: (631) 584-2274
Fax: (631) 584-2043

PATAGONIA
(Sub. of Lost Arrow Corporation)
259 W Santa Clara St
Ventura, CA 93001-2545
Tel.: (805) 643-8616
Fax: (805) 653-6355
Toll Free: (800) 638-6464
Web Site: www.patagonia.com
Sales Range: $300-349.9 Million
Approx. Number Employees: 626
Year Founded: 1972
Business Description:
Outdoor Clothing
S.I.C.: 2329; 2339
N.A.I.C.S.: 315228; 315239
Export
Media: 4-8-11-13
Personnel:
Yvon Chouinard *(Founder)*
Casey Sheahan *(CEO)*
Rob BonDurant *(VP-Mktg, Mdsg & Comm)*
Dmitri Siegel *(VP-Global ECommerce)*
Martijn Linden *(Dir-Creative)*
Jen Rapp *(Dir-PR & Comm)*
Brands & Products:
COMMITTED TO THE CORE
WATERGIRL

PAULA LISHMAN LIMITED
(d/b/a Paula Lishman International)
14341 Old Scugog Rd
Blackstock, ON Canada
Tel.: (905) 986-5096
Fax: (905) 986-0764
Toll Free: (800) 263-5272
E-mail: paula@paulalishman.com
Web Site:
www.paulalishmaninternational.com
E-Mail For Key Personnel:
Sales Director: sales@paulalishman.net
Sales Range: $1-9.9 Million
Approx. Number Employees: 45
Business Description:
Knit Fur Garments & Accessories
S.I.C.: 2371; 2329; 2339
N.A.I.C.S.: 315292; 315211; 315212
Media: 1-6-10-11
Personnel:
Paula Lishman *(Pres & CEO)*
Aaron Lishman *(Gen Mgr)*
Rosalyn Jones *(Mgr-Sls & Mktg)*

PAYLESS SHOESOURCE, INC.
(Sub. of Collective Brands Inc.)
3231 SE 6th Ave
Topeka, KS 66607-2260
Tel.: (785) 233-5171
Fax: (785) 295-6689
Web Site: www.payless.com
Sales Range: $1-4.9 Billion
Approx. Number Employees: 800
Year Founded: 1998
Business Description:
Shoe Stores
S.I.C.: 5661
N.A.I.C.S.: 448210
Personnel:
LuAnn Via *(Pres & CEO)*
Vincent DeSantis *(CMO & Sr VP)*
Andrew Meyer *(Sr VP & Gen Mgr-Mdse-Women's & Accessories Bus)*
Robert Bruennig *(Sr VP & Gen Mdse Mgr)*
Stephen J. Gish *(Sr VP-Retail Ops)*
Theodore O. Passig *(Sr VP-GMM Womens Footwear & Accessories)*
Philip D. Vostrejs *(Sr VP-Mdse Plng & Franchising)*
Advertising Agency:
Lundmark Advertising + Design Inc.
104 W 9th St Ste 104
Kansas City, MO 64105
Tel.: (816) 842-5236
Fax: (816) 221-7175

PERFORM GROUP, LLC
333 E 7th Ave
York, PA 17404-2144
Mailing Address:
PO Box 20879
York, PA 17402
Tel.: (717) 852-6900
Fax: (717) 852-6995
Fax: (800) 839-1039
Toll Free: (888) 808-0801
E-mail: customerservice@tighe.com
Web Site: www.tighe.com
Approx. Number Employees: 350
Year Founded: 1946
Business Description:
Costumes & Leotards for Misses, Men, Juniors & Children Designer & Mfr
S.I.C.: 2389; 2339
N.A.I.C.S.: 315299; 315239
Export
Media: 4-6-7-10-18-21-23
Personnel:
Leroy A. King, Jr. *(Chm, Pres & CEO)*
Jane A. Deamer *(VP-Fin)*
Sara Murphy *(Sr Dir-Mdse & Design)*
Brands & Products:
ALPHA FACTOR
ALPHA FACTOR AERIALS
CURTAIN CALL COSTUMES
CURTAIN CALL FOR CLASS
PERFORM
SPIRIT BY CURTAIN CALL

PLAYTEX APPAREL, INC.
(Div. of Hanesbrands Inc.)
1000 E Haines Mill Rd
Winston Salem, NC 27105
Tel.: (336) 519-8080
Fax: (336) 519-0421
Toll Free: (800) 537-9955
E-mail: victoria.seawright@hanesbrands.com
Web Site: www.playtex.com
Sales Range: $200-249.9 Million
Approx. Number Employees: 1,900
Business Description:
Intimate Apparel Mfr
S.I.C.: 2341
N.A.I.C.S.: 315231
Media: 4-6-15-22-25
Personnel:
William Nictakis *(Pres)*
Vicki Seawright *(Dir-Mktg-Intimate Apparel)*
Brands & Products:
18 HOUR
CROSS YOUR HEART
EVERYDAY BASICS
EXPECTANT MOMENTS
FEEL BEAUTIFUL
ONLY YOU
PLAYTEX
PLAYTEX BODY ZEN
PLAYTEX SECRETS
THANK GOODNESS IT FITS
Advertising Agencies:
KraftWorks Ltd.
552 Broadway Ste 301
New York, NY 10012
Tel.: (212) 431-7501
Fax: (212) 431-7527

Starcom MediaVest Group
35 W Wacker Dr
Chicago, IL 60601-1723
Tel.: (312) 220-3535
Fax: (312) 220-6530

PLAYTEX LIMITED
(Sub. of Playtex Products, Inc.)
6755 Mississauga Rd Ste 500
Mississauga, ON L5N 7Y2, Canada
Tel.: (905) 363-2700
Fax: (905) 363-2575
Toll Free: (800) 387-1300 (Consumer Support)
Telex: 6968618 PLAYTEX TOR
Web Site:
www.playtexproductsinc.com
Sales Range: $10-24.9 Million
Approx. Number Employees: 25
Business Description:
Household, Infant & Feminine Care Products Mfr
S.I.C.: 3999
N.A.I.C.S.: 339999
Import
Media: 3-15-18-19-22-23
Distr.: Intl.; Natl.
Budget Set: Nov.
Personnel:
Rob Power *(Mgr-IT)*
Advertising Agency:
Grey Canada
1881 Yonge St Ste 800
Toronto, ON M4S 3C4, Canada
Tel.: (416) 486-0700
Fax: (416) 486-8907

PRADA U.S.A. CORP.
(Sub. of Prada SpA)
610 W 52nd St
New York, NY 10019
Tel.: (212) 307-9300
Fax: (212) 974-3467
Toll Free: (888) 977-1900
E-mail: info@prada.com
Web Site: www.prada.com
Approx. Number Employees: 180
Year Founded: 1993
Business Description:
Apparel Mfr & Retailer
S.I.C.: 2335; 5122
N.A.I.C.S.: 315233; 446120
Import Export
Media: 6-10-30
Personnel:
Francois Kresf *(Pres & CEO)*
Chris Wile *(Sr Dir-Adv & Sls)*

PRISCILLA OF BOSTON, INC.
(Div. of David's Bridal, Inc.)
40 Cambridge St
Charlestown, MA 02129-1302
Tel.: (617) 242-2677
Fax: (617) 242-9244
Web Site: www.priscillaofboston.com
Approx. Sls.: $8,500,000
Approx. Number Employees: 60
Year Founded: 1950
Business Description:
Wedding Gowns & Bridesmaid Dresses Mfr
S.I.C.: 2335; 2299
N.A.I.C.S.: 315233; 314999
Advertising Expenditures: $200,000
Media: 2-4-6-8-10
Distr.: Natl.
Personnel:
Jo Capsino *(Dir-Adv)*
Lauren Hassabou *(Dir-Salon)*
Brands & Products:
PRISCILLA BOUTIQUE
SIRI
TEENY BY PRISCILLA
THREAD
WATTERS

QUIKSILVER, INC.
15202 Graham St
Huntington Beach, CA 92649
Tel.: (714) 889-2200
Fax: (714) 889-3700
E-mail: zqk@quiksilver.com
Web Site: www.quiksilverinc.com
Approx. Rev.: $1,837,620,000
Approx. Number Employees: 6,200
Year Founded: 1976
Business Description:
Beachwear, Skiwear, Casual Sportswear, Swimwear & Snow & Skate Apparel Mfr., Designer & Distr for Young Men & Women
S.I.C.: 5136; 2326; 2329
N.A.I.C.S.: 424320; 315211; 315225; 315228
Advertising Expenditures: $106,900,000
Media: 2-6-9-15-19-22-25
Distr.: Intl.; Natl.
Budget Set: July -Aug.
Personnel:
Robert B. McKnight, Jr. *(Chm, Pres & CEO)*
Joseph Scirocco *(CFO, COO & Exec VP-Ops-Americas)*
Greg Perlot *(CMO & Exec VP)*
Charles S. Exon *(Chief Admin Officer, Gen Counsel & Sec)*
Craig Stevenson *(Pres-Quiksilver Americas & Global Mgr-Quiksilver Brand)*
Pierre Agnes *(Pres-Quiksilver Europe)*
Brad Holman *(Sr VP & Controller)*
Randy Hild *(Sr VP)*
Steve Ellingson *(VP-Sls)*
Greg Macias *(VP-Mktg)*
Brendan Murphey *(Mgr-Product Mktg, Skate, Snow & Footwear)*
Brands & Products:
BENT METAL
DC
FIDRA
GNU
GOTCHA
HAWK
HAWK CLOTHING
LEILANI
LIB TECHNOLOGIES
QUIKSILVER
QUIKSILVEREDITION
RADIO FIJI
RAISINS
ROXY
ROXY GIRL
TEENIE WAHINE
Advertising Agencies:
72andSunny
6300 Arizona Cir
Los Angeles, CA 90045

Quiksilver, Inc. — (Continued)

Tel.: (310) 215-9009
Fax: (310) 215-9012

Red Door Interactive, Inc.
350 10th Ave Set 1100
San Diego, CA 92101
Tel.: (619) 398-2670
Fax: (619) 398-2671

REGAL LAGER, INC.
1100 Cobb Pl Blvd
Kennesaw, GA 30144
Tel.: (770) 955-5060
Fax: (770) 955-1997
Toll Free: (800) 593-5522
Web Site: www.regallager.com
Approx. Number Employees: 20
Business Description:
Sales of Infant & Children's Accessories
S.I.C.: 5099
N.A.I.C.S.: 423990
Export
Media: 6
Personnel:
Bengt Lager *(Pres)*
Brands & Products:
BUILDING QUALITY BRANDS
REGAL LAGER

RETAIL VENTURES, INC.
(Holding of Schottenstein Stores Corporation)
4150 E 5th Ave
Columbus, OH 43219
Tel.: (614) 238-4148
Fax: (614) 478-2253
Web Site: www.retailventuresinc.com
Approx. Sls.: $1,822,376,000
Approx. Number Employees: 10,500
Year Founded: 2003
Business Description:
Holding Company; Retail Discount Department Stores Owner & Operator
S.I.C.: 6719; 5311; 5399
N.A.I.C.S.: 551112; 452112; 452990
Import Export
Advertising Expenditures: $100,000,000
Media: 3-8-13-14-15-19-23-24
Personnel:
Douglas J. Probst *(CFO & Exec VP)*
Kelly Cook *(VP-Customer Strategy & Engagement)*
Advertising Agency:
Zimmerman Advertising
2200 W Commercial Blvd Ste 300
Fort Lauderdale, FL 33309-3064
Tel.: (954) 644-4000
Fax: (954) 731-2977
Toll Free: (800) 248-8522

RICHARD CANTRELL
(d/b/a Hard Tail)
1661 9th St
Santa Monica, CA 90404
Tel.: (310) 399-5511
Fax: (310) 399-3931
Web Site: www.hardtailforever.com
Sales Range: $10-24.9 Million
Approx. Number Employees: 25
Business Description:
Women's & Children's Clothing
S.I.C.: 5137; 5136
N.A.I.C.S.: 424330; 424320
Media: 6
Personnel:
Richard R. Cantrell *(Founder)*

RIVERSIDE MANUFACTURING COMPANY
301 Riverside Dr
Moultrie, GA 31768-8603
Tel.: (229) 985-5210
Fax: (229) 890-2932
Toll Free: (800) 841-8677
Web Site: www.riversideuniforms.com
Approx. Number Employees: 1,600
Year Founded: 1911
Business Description:
Business Uniforms & Career Apparel Mfr
S.I.C.: 2326; 2389
N.A.I.C.S.: 315225; 315299
Export
Media: 2-4-7-8-10-20
Distr.: Natl.
Budget Set: Jan. -Aug.
Personnel:
W. Jerry Vereen *(Founder)*
H. B. Vereen *(Exec VP)*
Dana Nellums *(VP-Mktg & Admin)*
Barbara B. Vereen *(VP-Adv & Travel)*
Juliann Key *(Dir-Art)*

ROBBY LEN FASHIONS
(Div. of A.H. Schreiber Co., Inc.)
1411 Broadway 25th Fl
New York, NY 10018-3402
Tel.: (212) 391-2525
Fax: (212) 944-9746
Approx. Number Employees: 6
Business Description:
Mfr; Designer & Distr. of Women's Swimwear
S.I.C.: 5137
N.A.I.C.S.: 424330
Media: 2-4-6-7
Distr.: Natl.
Budget Set: Oct.
Personnel:
Joel Schreiber *(Pres)*
Bill Lane *(VP & Mgr-Sls)*
Brands & Products:
ROBBY LEN

RUE21, INC.
800 Commonwealth Dr Ste 100
Warrendale, PA 15086-7527
Tel.: (724) 776-9780
Fax: (724) 776-4111
Web Site: www.rue21.com
Approx. Sls.: $634,728,000
Approx. Number Employees: 1,948
Year Founded: 1974
Business Description:
Apparel & Fragrance Retailer & Mfr
S.I.C.: 5699; 2844; 5122; 5611; 5621
N.A.I.C.S.: 448190; 325620; 446120; 448110; 448120
Import Export
Advertising Expenditures: $3,936,000
Media: 8-13-19-22
Personnel:
Robert N. Fisch *(Chm, Pres & CEO)*
Keith A. McDonough *(CFO & Sr VP)*
Kim A. Reynolds *(Sr VP & Gen Mgr-Mdse)*
John P. Bugnar *(Sr VP & Dir-Stores)*
Mark K.J. Chrystal *(Sr VP-Plng & Allocation)*
Michael A. Holland *(Sr VP-IT)*
Robert R. Thomson *(Sr VP-Real Estate)*
Brands & Products:
CARBON
CARBON BLACK
CJ BLACK
PINK INCE RUE21
REVERT ECO
RUE BY RUE21
RUE21
RUE21 ETC!
SPARKLE RUE21
TAREA BY RUE21
WWW.RUE21.COM

SAFER PRINTS INC.
(d/b/a/ Safer Textile Processing)
1875 McCarter Hwy
Newark, NJ 07104
Tel.: (973) 482-6400
Fax: (973) 482-5694
Web Site: www.safertextiles.com
Business Description:
Textile Mfr
S.I.C.: 7389; 2299
N.A.I.C.S.: 561990; 314999
Media: 10
Personnel:
Albert Safer *(Pres & CEO)*

SAN FRANCISCO MERCANTILE COMPANY, INC.
(d/b/a Eileen West)
525 Brannan St Ste 410
San Francisco, CA 94107
Tel.: (415) 957-9378
E-mail: askus@eileenwest.com
Web Site: www.eileenwest.com
Business Description:
Women's Clothing Designer
S.I.C.: 5137
N.A.I.C.S.: 424330
Media: 6-10-13
Personnel:
William Laney Thornton *(Chm)*
Eileen West *(Pres)*
Brands & Products:
EILEEN WEST
E.W. STUDIO
QUEEN ANNE'S LACE

SMARTWOOL
(Sub. of The Timberland Company)
3495 Airport Cir
Steamboat Springs, CO 80487
Mailing Address:
PO Box 774928
Steamboat Springs, CO 80477
Tel.: (970) 879-2913
Fax: (970) 879-0937
E-mail: smartservice@smartwool.com
Web Site: www.smartwool.com
Sales Range: $50-74.9 Million
Approx. Number Employees: 32
Business Description:
Apparel & Accessories Mfr
S.I.C.: 2389
N.A.I.C.S.: 315999
Advertising Expenditures: $50,000
Media: 6-8-13
Personnel:
Mark Satewiez *(Pres)*
Carol Davidson *(Dir-Creative)*
Gardner Flanagan *(Dir-Mktg)*
Advertising Agencies:
Anvil Media, Inc.
310 NE Failing St.
Portland, OR 97212
Tel.: (503) 595-6050
Fax: (503) 223-1008

TDA Advertising & Design
1500 Pearl St Ste 300
Boulder, CO 80302
Tel.: (303) 247-1180
Fax: (303) 247-1214

SPANX INC.
3344 Peachtree Rd Ste 1700
Atlanta, GA 30326
Tel.: (404) 321-1608
Fax: (404) 321-4464
Toll Free: (888) 806-7311
Web Site: www.spanx.com
Approx. Number Employees: 80
Business Description:
Body-Shaping Hosiery Mfr
S.I.C.: 2341; 5699
N.A.I.C.S.: 315231; 448150
Media: 8-13
Personnel:
Sara Blakely *(Founder & Pres)*
Laurie Ann Goldman *(CEO)*
Monica Mirro *(VP-Sls)*
Maggie Adams *(Sr Mgr-PR)*
Melissa Lear *(Mgr-Online Mktg)*
Brands & Products:
ALL THE WAY
BOD-A-BING!
BRA-LLELUJAH
HIDE & SLEEK
HIGHER POWER
HIPNOTIC
MAMA SPANX
PERFECTOE
POWER MAMA
POWER PANTIES
SPANX
SPORTEASE
THIGH'M A BELIEVER
TWO-TIMIN'
UNDIE-TECTABLE
Advertising Agency:
Brogan Tennyson
887 W Marietta St NW Studio T-102
Atlanta, GA 30318-5295
Tel.: (404) 816-0094
Fax: (404) 816-0095

SPORT HALEY, INC.
4600 E 48th Ave
Denver, CO 80216-3212
Tel.: (303) 320-8800
Fax: (303) 320-8822
Toll Free: (800) 627-9211
E-mail: info@sporthaley.com
Web Site: www.sporthaley.com
Sales Range: $10-24.9 Million
Approx. Number Employees: 64
Year Founded: 1992
Business Description:
Designer & Marketer of Mid-Priced & Premium-Priced Golf Sportswear for Women
S.I.C.: 3949; 2329; 2339; 5621
N.A.I.C.S.: 339920; 315211; 315239; 448120
Advertising Expenditures: $837,000
Media: 2-4-6-7-8-10-13-19
Personnel:
Donald W. Jewell *(Pres & CEO)*
Patrick W. Hurley *(CFO)*
Catherine B. Blair *(VP-Mdsg & Design)*
Brands & Products:
BEN HOGAN
SPORT HALEY

Key to Media (For complete agency information see *The Advertising Red Books-Agencies* edition):
1. Bus. Publs. 2. Cable T.V. 3. Catalogs & Directories. 4. Co-op Adv. 5. Consumer Mags. 6. D.M. to Bus. Estab.7. D.M. to Consumers
8. Daily Newsp. 9. Exhibits/Trade Shows 10. Foreign 11. Infomercial 12. Internet Adv.13. Multimedia 14. Network Radio
15. Network T.V. 16. Newsp. Distr. Mags. 17. Other 18. Outdoor (Posters, Transit) 19. Point of Purchase20. Premiums, Novelties
21. Product Samples 22. Special Events Mktg. 23. Spot Radio 24. Spot T.V. 25. Weekly Newsp. 26. Yellow Page Adv.

SPORTIF USA INC.
1415 Greg St Ste 101
Sparks, NV 89431
Tel.: (775) 359-6400
Fax: (775) 353-3433
E-mail: info@sportif.com
Web Site: www.sportif.com
Sales Range: $10-24.9 Million
Approx. Number Employees: 50
Year Founded: 1965
Business Description:
Men's & Women's Clothing
S.I.C.: 5136; 5137
N.A.I.C.S.: 424320; 424330
Media: 4-8-13
Personnel:
John E. Kirsch *(Pres & CEO)*
Tom Williamson *(VP-Sls & Mktg)*
Brands & Products:
AVENTURA
SPORTIF
SPORTIF USA

ST. JOHN KNITS INTERNATIONAL, INC.
(Holding of Vestar/Gray Investors LLC)
17622 Armstrong Ave
Irvine, CA 92614-5726
Tel.: (949) 863-1171
Fax: (949) 223-3396
Web Site: www.stjohnknits.com
E-Mail For Key Personnel:
Sales Director: sales@stjohnknits.com
Sales Range: $350-399.9 Million
Approx. Number Employees: 3,000
Year Founded: 1962
Business Description:
Women's Fashion Apparel Mfr
S.I.C.: 2253; 2339
N.A.I.C.S.: 315191; 315239
Advertising Expenditures: $13,400,000
Media: 6-9-10-25
Distr.: Intl.
Personnel:
James Kelley *(Chm)*
Glenn McMahon *(CEO)*
Rick Chilcott *(Exec VP)*
Tiffany Anastaskis *(VP-Adv & Promo)*
Robert Green *(Dir-Sls)*
Chuck Roundtree *(Dir-Mktg)*
George Sharp *(Dir-Creative)*
Brands & Products:
ST. JOHN

STAGE STORES, INC.
10201 Main St
Houston, TX 77025
Mailing Address:
PO Box 35167
Houston, TX 77235
Tel.: (713) 667-5601
Fax: (713) 663-9780
Toll Free: (800) 579-2302
E-mail: customercomments@stagestores.com
Web Site: www.stagestores.com
E-Mail For Key Personnel:
Marketing Director: jswartz@stagestoresinc.com
Approx. Sls.: $1,470,590,000
Approx. Number Employees: 13,500
Year Founded: 1988
Business Description:
Family Clothing & Department Stores Owner & Operator
S.I.C.: 5651; 5311; 6719
N.A.I.C.S.: 448140; 452111; 551112
Import
Advertising Expenditures: $63,400,000
Media: 8-9-14-15-18-23-24-25
Personnel:
Andrew T. Hall *(Pres & CEO)*
Oded Shein *(CFO & Exec VP)*
Edward J. Record *(COO)*
Steven Hunter *(CIO & Exec VP)*
Richard A. Maloney *(Chief Mdsg Officer)*
Mike Searles *(Pres/COO-South Hill Div)*
Ron D. Lucas *(Exec VP-HR)*
Joanne Swartz *(Exec VP-Adv & Sls Promo)*
Richard E. Stasyszen *(Controller & Sr VP-Fin)*
Jon Gunnerson *(Sr VP & Dir-Stores-Houston Div)*
Gough H. Grubbs *(Sr VP-Logistics & Distr)*
Christine Johnston *(Sr VP-GMM Cosmetics & Fragrances)*
Russell A. Lundy II *(Sr VP-Stores South Hill Div)*
Mel B. Ward *(Sr VP-Real Estate)*
Brands & Products:
BEALLS
PALAIS ROYAL
PEEBLES
STAGE
Advertising Agencies:
Brownchild
2330 Dunstan, Ste. 2
Houston, TX 77005
Tel.: (713) 668-5278

Reynolds Media Services
2425 Fountainview, Ste. 355
Houston, TX 77057
Tel.: (713) 977-3778
Fax: (713) 977-3774

SUGARTOWN WORLDWIDE INC.
(Sub. of Oxford Industries, Inc.)
(d/b/a Lilly Pulitzer)
800 3rd Ave
King of Prussia, PA 19406
Tel.: (610) 878-5550
Fax: (610) 878-9039
Fax: (610) 875-5555
E-mail: publicrelations@lillypulitzer.com
Web Site: www.lillypulitzer.com
Approx. Sls.: $45,000,000
Approx. Number Employees: 50
Business Description:
Sportswear, Women's
S.I.C.: 2339; 2331
N.A.I.C.S.: 315239; 315232
Media: 4-6-8-13
Personnel:
James B. Bradbeer, Jr. *(Pres)*
Scott A. Beaumont *(CEO)*
Janie Schoenborn *(Dir-Fashion)*
Brands & Products:
LILLY PULITZER
LITTLE LILY

SUN PRECAUTIONS, INC.
2815 Wetmore Ave
Everett, WA 98201
Tel.: (425) 303-8585
Fax: (425) 303-0836
Toll Free: (800) 882-7860
E-mail: marketing@sunprecautions.com
Web Site: www.sunprecautions.com
Approx. Number Employees: 20
Business Description:
Sun Protective Clothing
S.I.C.: 5699; 5136
N.A.I.C.S.: 448150; 424320
Media: 4-6-8-13
Personnel:
Shaun Hughes *(Pres)*
Brands & Products:
SOLUMBRA
SUN PRECAUTIONS

SUNRISE BRANDS, LLC
(Holding of Sunrise Acquisition Corp.)
801 S Figueroa St Ste 2500
Los Angeles, CA 90017
Tel.: (323) 780-8250
Fax: (323) 780-0751
Toll Free: (800) 780-8250
Approx. Sls.: $195,308,000
Approx. Number Employees: 250
Year Founded: 1984
Business Description:
Private Label & Private Brand Casual Apparel Design & Sourcing Services
S.I.C.: 7389; 2321; 2329; 2331; 2335; 2339; 2389
N.A.I.C.S.: 541490; 315223; 315228; 315232; 315233; 315239; 315299
Advertising Expenditures: $2,800,000
Personnel:
Gerard Guez *(Chm)*
Todd Kay *(Vice Chm)*
Charles Turlinski *(CEO)*
Patrick Chow *(Chief Admin Officer)*
Rosa Castro *(Dir-HR)*

SUPERIOR UNIFORM GROUP, INC.
10055 Seminole Blvd
Seminole, FL 33772-2564
Mailing Address:
PO Box 4002
Seminole, FL 33775-4002
Tel.: (727) 397-9611
Fax: (727) 803-2658
Toll Free: (800) 727-8643
Web Site: www.superioruniformgroup.com
Approx. Sls.: $105,877,854
Approx. Number Employees: 626
Year Founded: 1920
Business Description:
Apparel for the Medical & Health, Industrial, Commercial, Leisure & Public Safety Markets; Industrial Laundry Bags & Operating Room Masks, Footware & Sheets; Corporate Embroidered Sportswear Mfr & Marketer
S.I.C.: 2326; 2295; 2389
N.A.I.C.S.: 315225; 313320; 315299
Advertising Expenditures: $102,000
Media: 2-4-7-13
Distr.: Natl.
Personnel:
Gerald M. Benstock *(Chm)*
Alan D. Schwartz *(Pres)*
Michael Benstock *(CEO)*
Andrew D. Demott Jr. *(CFO)*
Mark Decker *(CIO)*
Richard T. Dawson *(Gen Counsel, Sec & VP)*
Janice Henry *(VP-Mktg)*
Errol Pegler *(Sr Account Exec)*
Brands & Products:
FASHION SEAL
FASHION SEAL HEALTHCARE
MARTIN'S
SUPERIOR
TUGS!
UNIVOGUE
WORKLON

THE TALBOTS, INC.
1 Talbots Dr
Hingham, MA 02043
Tel.: (781) 749-7600
Fax: (781) 741-7734
E-mail: investor.relations@talbots.com
Web Site: www.thetalbotsinc.com
Approx. Sls.: $1,213,060,000
Approx. Number Employees: 3,484
Year Founded: 1947
Business Description:
Women's Classic Clothing Mail Order & Store Retailer
S.I.C.: 5621; 5961
N.A.I.C.S.: 448120; 454113
Advertising Expenditures: $58,900,000
Media: 4-6-8-9-13-14-15-19-23-25
Personnel:
Gary M. Pfeiffer *(Chm)*
Trudy F. Sullivan *(Pres & CEO)*
Michael Scarpa *(CFO & COO)*
John Kovac *(CIO & Sr VP)*
Lori Wagner *(CMO-Talbots Brand & Exec VP)*
Michael Smaldone *(Chief Creative Officer)*
Gregory Poole *(Chief Supply Chain Officer & Exec VP)*
Benedetta I. Casamento *(Exec VP-Fin)*
Richard T. O'Connell, Jr. *(Exec VP-Real Estate, Legal, Store Plng, Design & Construction)*
Carol Stone *(Sr VP-Fin & Controller)*
Lizanne Kindler *(Sr VP-Mdsg)*
Julie F. Lorigan *(Sr VP-IR & Media Rels)*
Ruthanne Russell *(Sr VP-HR)*
Kate Goodman *(VP-ECommerce)*
Meredith Paley *(VP-PR)*
Betsy Thompson *(Dir-Corp Comm & Community Rels)*
Brands & Products:
J JILL
TALBOTS
TALBOTS COLLECTION
TALBOTS MISSES
TALBOTS PETITES
TALBOTS WOMAN
TALBOTS WOMAN PETITES
Advertising Agency:
Publicis USA
(Sub. of Publicis, S.A., Paris, France)
4 Herald Sq 950 6th Ave
New York, NY 10001
Tel.: (212) 279-5550
Fax: (212) 279-5560

TANNER COMPANIES, LP
(d/b/a Doncaster)
537 Rock Rd
Rutherfordton, NC 28139-8125
Mailing Address:

Tanner Companies, LP — (Continued)

PO Box 1139
Rutherfordton, NC 28139-1139
Tel.: (828) 287-4205
Fax: (828) 287-8954
Toll Free: (800) 800-5857
Web Site: www.doncaster.com
Sales Range: $75-99.9 Million
Approx. Number Employees: 350
Year Founded: 1931
Business Description:
Women's Apparel
S.I.C.: 2339; 2335
N.A.I.C.S.: 315239; 315233
Import
Media: 2-4-6-9
Distr.: Natl.
Personnel:
Laura C. Kendall *(Pres)*
Brands & Products:
TANNER

THYME MATERNITY

(Sub. of Reitmans (Canada) Limited)
250 Sauve W
Montreal, QC H3L 1Z2, Canada
Tel.: (514) 385-2694
Fax: (514) 385-2683
E-mail: customers@thymematernity.com
Web Site: www.thymematernity.com
Business Description:
Maternity Clothing Retailer
S.I.C.: 5621
N.A.I.C.S.: 448120
Media: 4

TWEEN BRANDS INC.

(Sub. of The Dress Barn, Inc.)
8323 Walton Pkwy
New Albany, OH 43054
Tel.: (614) 775-3500
Fax: (614) 775-3938
Web Site: www.tweenbrands.com
Approx. Sls.: $995,062,000
Approx. Number Employees: 3,500
Year Founded: 1987
Business Description:
Fashion Retailer
S.I.C.: 5641; 5137
N.A.I.C.S.: 448130; 424330
Advertising Expenditures:
$21,400,000
Personnel:
Rolando De Aguiar *(CFO & Exec VP)*
Karen S. Etzkorn *(CIO & Sr VP)*
Scott M. Bracale *(Pres-Agency)*
Ronnie Robinson *(Exec VP-Supply Chain)*
Alan J. Hochman *(Sr VP-Real Estate & Store Plng)*
Michael Keane *(Sr VP-HR)*
Kristin Sperling *(Sr Mgr-Sourcing-Accessories)*
Brands & Products:
JUSTICE

UJENA SWIMWEAR AND FASHIONS

1931A Old Middlefield Way
Mountain View, CA 94043
Tel.: (650) 948-8901
Tel.: (650) 938-1010 (Mktg)
Fax: (650) 938-1004
Toll Free: (800) 448-5362
Web Site: www.ujena.com
Sales Range: $1-9.9 Million
Approx. Number Employees: 35
Year Founded: 1984
Business Description:
Swimwear & Casual & Active Wear Mfr & Retailer
S.I.C.: 5699; 5961
N.A.I.C.S.: 448190; 454113
Media: 4-5-8-10-13-18-20-22
Personnel:
Lisa Anderson-Wall *(Pres & Head Designer)*
Catherine Cross *(VP & Dir-PR)*
Bob Anderson *(Dir & Producer)*
Justin Wall *(Dir-Sls)*
Trisha Tompkins *(Mgr-Mktg)*
Brands & Products:
UJENA
UJENA JAM

UNIQUE VINTAGE

2013 W Magnolia Blvd
Burbank, CA 91506
Toll Free: (800) 721-6589
Web Site: www.unique-vintage.com
Business Description:
Retail of Vintage Inspired Dresses, Prom Dresses & Wedding Dresses
S.I.C.: 5621
N.A.I.C.S.: 448120
Media: 4-13
Personnel:
Katherine Echeverry *(Pres)*

VENUS SWIMWEAR, INC.

(Holding of Catalog Holdings, Inc.)
11711 Marco Beach Dr
Jacksonville, FL 32224
Tel.: (904) 645-6000
Tel.: (904) 265-8487
Fax: (904) 645-5370
Toll Free: (888) 782-2224
E-mail: email@venusswimwear.com
Web Site: www.venus.com
Sales Range: $100-124.9 Million
Approx. Number Employees: 325
Year Founded: 1982
Business Description:
Mail Order Women's Apparel & Swimsuits
S.I.C.: 5961; 5137
N.A.I.C.S.: 454113; 424330
Media: 4-8-13
Personnel:
Laura Morris *(Dir-Mktg)*
Brands & Products:
VENUS
VENUS EDGE
WINTERSILKS

VERA WANG BRIDAL HOUSE LTD.

225 W 39th St Fl 9
New York, NY 10018
Tel.: (212) 575-6400
Toll Free: (800) VEW-VERA
E-mail: inquiries@verawang.com
Web Site: www.verawang.com
Approx. Sls.: $25,000,000
Approx. Number Employees: 215
Business Description:
Bridal & Formal Gowns; Jewelry & Accessories
S.I.C.: 2335; 5621
N.A.I.C.S.: 315233; 448120
Media: 6-10-30
Personnel:
Vera Wang *(CEO)*
Alice Childress *(Dir-Adv & Creative Svcs)*
Brands & Products:
VERA WANG

VF CORPORATION

105 Corporate Center Blvd
Greensboro, NC 27408
Mailing Address:
PO Box 21488
Greensboro, NC 27420-1488
Tel.: (336) 424-6000
Fax: (336) 424-7668
E-mail: cindy_knobel@vfc.com
Web Site: www.vfc.com
E-Mail For Key Personnel:
Public Relations: Paul_Mason@vfc.com
Approx. Rev.: $7,702,589,000
Approx. Number Employees: 47,000
Year Founded: 1899
Business Description:
Apparel Mfr
S.I.C.: 2329; 2321; 2325; 2341; 5136
N.A.I.C.S.: 315211; 315223; 315224; 315231; 424320
Advertising Expenditures:
$329,100,000
Media: 2-4-5-6-14-15-20-22-23-24-30
Distr.: Natl.
Personnel:
Eric C. Wiseman *(Chm, Pres & CEO)*
Robert K. Shearer *(CFO & Sr VP)*
Martin S. Schneider *(CIO & VP)*
Bradley W. Batten *(Chief Acctg Officer, VP & Controller)*
Boyd A. Rogers *(Pres-Supply Chain & VP)*
Karl Heinz Salzburger *(Pres-Intl & VP)*
Susan Kellogg *(Pres-Contemporary Brands Coalition)*
Candace S. Cummings *(Gen Counsel, Sec & VP-Admin)*
Stephen F. Dull *(VP-Strategy)*
Michael Johnson *(VP-Mktg)*
Cindy Knoebel *(VP-Fin & Corp Comm)*
Susan Larson Williams *(VP-HR)*
Brands & Products:
20X
7 FOR ALL MANKIND
AURA
BELCOR
BESTFORM
BOLERO
BRITTANIA
BUDDY LEE
BULWARK
CHASE AUTHENTICS
CHEF DESIGNS
CHIC
CSA
CURVATION
EAGLE CREEK
EARL JEAN
EASTPAK
ELLA MOSS
THE FORCE
GEMMA
GITANO
HERO BY WRANGLER
HORACE SMALL
IMAGEWEAR
JANSPORT
JOHN VARVATOS
KIPLING
LEE
LEE NATIONAL DENIM DAY
LEE SPORT
LILY OF FRANCE
LOU
LUCY
MAJESTIC
MAVERICK
NAPAPIJRI
NAUTICA
THE NORTH FACE
OLD AXE
PENN STATE TEXTILES
RED KAP
REEF
RIDERS
RUSTLER
SPLENDID
TIMBER CREEK BY WRANGLER
VANITY FAIR
VANS
VASSARETTE
VF
VF SOLUTIONS
WE FIT YOUR LIFE.
WRANGLER
WRANGLER HERO
Advertising Agencies:
Ink & Co.
446 Broadway 4th Fl
New York, NY 10013
Tel.: (212) 334-3168
Fax: (212) 334-3167

OLSON
1625 Hennepin Ave
Minneapolis, MN 55403
Tel.: (612) 215-9800
Fax: (612) 215-9801

Story Worldwide
20 Marshall St Ste 220
South Norwalk, CT 06854
Tel.: (203) 831-8700
Fax: (203) 299-0068

WACOAL AMERICA INC.

(Sub. of Wacoal Holdings Corp.)
136 Madison Ave
New York, NY 10016-6711
Tel.: (212) 532-6100
Fax: (212) 696-5608
Web Site: www.wacoal-america.com
Approx. Number Employees: 1,000
Business Description:
Intimate Apparel, Lingerie, Bathing Suits & Sportswear Mfr
S.I.C.: 2341
N.A.I.C.S.: 315231
Media: 5-6
Distr.: Intl.; Natl.
Budget Set: Annually
Personnel:
Richard C. Murray *(Pres)*
Edward Skuller *(Dir-Creative Svcs)*
Brands & Products:
TEENFORM

THE WARNACO GROUP, INC.

501 7th Ave
New York, NY 10018
Tel.: (212) 287-8000
Fax: (212) 287-8301
E-mail: contactus@warnaco.com
Web Site: www.warnaco.com

Key to Media (For complete agency information see *The Advertising Red Books-Agencies* edition):
1. Bus. Publs. 2. Cable T.V. 3. Catalogs & Directories. 4. Co-op Adv. 5. Consumer Mags. 6. D.M. to Bus. Estab.7. D.M. to Consumers
8. Daily Newsp. 9. Exhibits/Trade Shows 10. Foreign 11. Infomercial 12. Internet Adv.13. Multimedia 14. Network Radio
15. Network T.V. 16. Newsp. Distr. Mags. 17. Other 18. Outdoor (Posters, Transit) 19. Point of Purchase20. Premiums, Novelties
21. Product Samples 22. Special Events Mktg. 23. Spot Radio 24. Spot T.V. 25. Weekly Newsp. 26. Yellow Page Adv.

Approx. Rev.: $2,295,751,000
Approx. Number Employees: 6,400
Year Founded: 1969
Business Description:
Women's & Men's Intimates & Apparel Mfr & Distr
S.I.C.: 2341; 2322
N.A.I.C.S.: 315231; 315221
Import Export
Advertising Expenditures: $100,200,000
Media: 4-5-6-9-19
Personnel:
Joseph R. Gromek *(Pres & CEO)*
Lawrence R. Rutkowski *(CFO & Exec VP)*
Helen McCluskey *(COO)*
David Cunningham *(Pres-Chaps)*
Dwight Meyer *(Pres-Global Sourcing, Distr & Logistics)*
Frank Tworecke *(Pres-Warnaco Sportswear Grp)*
Jay Dubiner *(Gen Counsel, Sec & Sr VP)*
Stanley P. Silverstein *(Exec VP-Intl Strategy & Bus Dev)*
Bob Dakin *(Sr VP)*
Elizabeth Wood *(Sr VP-HR)*
Emily Bohonos *(Dir-Mktg-Calvin Klein Underwear)*
Kate Wille *(Mgr-Mktg & Promos)*
Brands & Products:
BODY NANCY GANZ
BODYSLIMMERS
CALVIN KLEIN
LEJABY
OLGA
RASUREL
WARNACO
WARNER'S
Advertising Agency:
Agency212, LLC
(The Tucker Partnership, Inc. (Parent Company))
112 W 20th St 7th Fl
New York, NY 10011
Tel.: (212) 994-6700
Fax: (212) 994-6699

WEISSMAN THEATRICAL SUPPLY, INC.

6750 Manchester Rd
Saint Louis, MO 63139
Tel.: (314) 773-9000
Fax: (314) 773-8610
Toll Free: (800) 477-5410
E-mail: info@weissmans.net
Web Site: www.weissmans.com
Approx. Number Employees: 60
Business Description:
Dancewear
S.I.C.: 2389; 2329; 2335; 2337; 2339; 2341; 5621; 5641; 5699; 5961
N.A.I.C.S.: 315999; 315211; 315212; 315231; 315233; 315234; 448120; 448130; 448190; 454113
Media: 2-4-6-8-13
Personnel:
Howard Weissman *(Pres)*
Claudia Reed *(VP-Mktg, Dir-Sls & Adv)*
Brands & Products:
DANCEWEAR SOLUTIONS
DESIGNS FOR DANCE
WEISSMAN

WEST COAST LEATHER

290 Futter
San Francisco, CA 94108
Tel.: (415) 362-8300
Fax: (415) 362-0585
E-mail: sf@westcoastleather.com
Web Site: www.wclusa.com
Approx. Number Employees: 10
Business Description:
Leather Garments Sales
S.I.C.: 5699; 5136
N.A.I.C.S.: 448190; 424320
Media: 4-9-23
Personnel:
Skip Pas *(Dir-Fashion)*

THE WET SEAL, INC.

26972 Burbank
Foothill Ranch, CA 92610-2506
Tel.: (949) 699-3900
Fax: (949) 583-0715
Fax: (949) 699-4722
Toll Free: (800) 735-7325
Web Site: www.wetsealinc.com
Approx. Sls.: $581,194,000
Approx. Number Employees: 2,047
Year Founded: 1962
Business Description:
Retailer of Contemporary Apparel & Accessories
S.I.C.: 5621; 5699
N.A.I.C.S.: 448120; 448150
Advertising Expenditures: $3,600,000
Media: 6-19
Personnel:
Harold D. Kahn *(Chm)*
Ken Seipel *(Pres & COO)*
Sharon Hughes *(Pres & Chief Mdse Officer-Arden B Div)*
Susan P. McGalla *(CEO)*
Steve H. Benrubi *(CFO, Sec & Exec VP)*
Jon C. Kubo *(CIO & VP)*
Barbara Arneklev *(VP-HR)*
Shari Gunn *(VP-ECommerce)*
Christine Thompson *(Brand Dir)*
Brands & Products:
ARDEN B.
CONTEMPO CASUALS
WET SEAL

WHITESWAN/META

(Div. of Encompass Group LLC)
13975 Polo Trl
Lake Forest, IL 60045
Tel.: (847) 247-0380
Fax: (847) 247-0387
Toll Free: (800) 832-6300
E-mail: whiteswan@encompassgroup.net
Web Site: www.whiteswanmeta.net
Approx. Number Employees: 30
Year Founded: 1896
Business Description:
Mfr. of Healthcare Uniforms
S.I.C.: 2389
N.A.I.C.S.: 315299
Media: 2-4-7-10-17
Distr.: Natl.
Personnel:
Michael Gann *(Gen Mgr-Sls-Mktg)*
Brands & Products:
FUNDAMENTALS BY WHITE SWAN
META
WHITE SWAN

WOODEN SHIPS OF HOBOKEN

231 W 39th St Ste 711
New York, NY 10018
Tel.: (212) 221-3660
Fax: (212) 221-2329
E-mail: sales@wooden-ships.com
Web Site: www.wooden-ships.com
E-Mail For Key Personnel:
Sales Director: sales@wooden-ships.com
Approx. Sls.: $15,000,000
Approx. Number Employees: 6
Year Founded: 1992
Business Description:
Clothing Mfr & Retailer
S.I.C.: 5131; 5094
N.A.I.C.S.: 424310; 423940
Media: 4-6-10
Personnel:
Mark Donovan *(Co-Owner)*
Paola Buendia *(Pres)*
Brands & Products:
1920'S
ABBIE
ALEXANDRA
AMELIE
ANGELA
ANNABEL
ANNELISE
ANTIBES
ARGYLE
BALLET
BATIK
BEADED
BECKETT
BELLE
BIAS HOLLAND
BOATNECK
CABLE BALLET
CABLE BUTTON
CABLE V-NECK
CABLE YOKE
CAFE TOP
CANVAS CHELSEA
CANVAS HOLLAND
CAROLYN
CHARLOTTE
CHELSEA TWEED
CLAIRE
COLORBLOCK
COTTON BALLET
COTTON CAFE
COTTON COLETTE
COTTON SLIP
COTTON THEA
COUNTRY FAIR
COWL RUANA
CROSSTOWN
CUPCAKE
DAISY FLAPPER
DEIRDRE
DEVON
EARLY BIRDIE
ELLIE
ELLIOTT
EMMA-YARN CAP
FERNANDA
FINNIGAN
FLAPPER
FLEUR DE LYS
FLORAL KNIT
FRENCH STRIPE
GOSSAMER
HARPER
HEARTS
HOLLAND RAIN
HOUNDSTOOTH
INGRID
ISABEL
JAMIE
KATIE
LACE GEORGIA
LACE HOODIE
LILA
LOOSE KNIT
LORNA
MARAIS
MARGEAUX
MARLEY
MARSEILLES
MATRYOSHKA
METROPOLITAN
METROPOLITAN CANVAS
METROPOLITAN STRIPE
MONTREAL
NIGHT OWL
OVAL HOLLAND
POLKA DOT
POPCORN
REV.CANVAS FRINGED CLOCHE
RIBBED TOP
RIBBON
ROSE
RYE
SALLY
SALLY FLUTTER
SALLY SHELL
SALLY STRIPED
SALLY TIP
SARATOGA REVERSIBLE
SOLID SWING
SOPHIE
STRIPED V
SUNDRESS CARDIGAN
SWING FAIR ISLE
TAPESTRY
TENLEY
THEA DRESS
TINY CABLE
TINY FLOWER
TINY SHELL
TOGGLE
TRINITY
TUESDAY
TULIP DRAGON
VESPA
VINTAGE
WINDOWPANE
WOODEN SHIPS
WRAP CARDIGAN

Key to Media (For complete agency information see *The Advertising Red Books-Agencies* edition):
1. Bus. Publs. 2. Cable T.V. 3. Catalogs & Directories. 4. Co-op Adv. 5. Consumer Mags. 6. D.M. to Bus. Estab.7. D.M. to Consumers 8. Daily Newsp. 9. Exhibits/Trade Shows 10. Foreign 11. Infomercial 12. Internet Adv.13. Multimedia 14. Network Radio 15. Network T.V. 16. Newsp. Distr. Mags. 17. Other 18. Outdoor (Posters, Transit) 19. Point of Purchase20. Premiums, Novelties 21. Product Samples 22. Special Events Mktg. 23. Spot Radio 24. Spot T.V. 25. Weekly Newsp. 26. Yellow Page Adv.

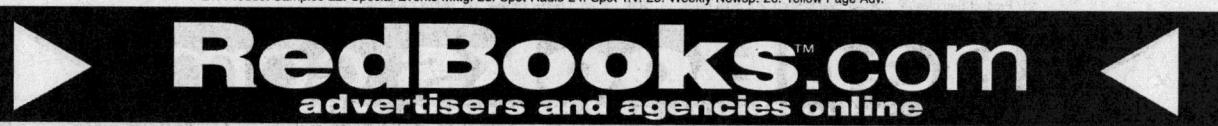

Apparel II-Men's & Boys' Wear

ABERCROMBIE & FITCH CO.
6301 Fitch Path
New Albany, OH 43054-9269
Tel.: (614) 283-6500
Fax: (614) 283-6710
Toll Free: (888) 856-4480
E-mail: investor_relations@abercrombie.com
Web Site: www.abercrombie.com
Approx. Sls.: $3,468,777,000
Approx. Number Employees: 9,000
Year Founded: 1892
Business Description:
Retail & Mail Order Casual Apparel
S.I.C.: 5651; 5611; 5621
N.A.I.C.S.: 448140; 448110; 448120
Advertising Expenditures: $17,700,000
Media: 4-6-8-31
Personnel:
Michael S. Jeffries *(Chm & CEO)*
Jonathan E. Ramsden *(CFO & Exec VP)*
David S. Cupps *(Gen Counsel, Sec & Sr VP)*
Diane Chang *(Exec VP-Sourcing)*
Leslee K. Herro *(Exec VP-Plng & Allocation)*
Brian Logan *(Sr VP-Fin)*
Erin Kamburowski *(Brand Mgr-A&F Women's)*
Brands & Products:
ABERCROMBIE
ABERCROMBIE & FITCH
ABRA
ADAMS MOUNTAIN
ADRIANA
ALANA
ALICE
ANGELINA
ANNA
AUGUR LAKE
AVA
AVALANCHE MOUNTAIN
AVALANCHE PASS SOLID OXFORD
BAILEY
BAKER MOUNTAIN
BALSAM LAKE
BARTLETT POND
BAXTER
BEACH MILL
BEAR MOUNTAIN
BEAVER RIVER
BENNI
BLACKFOOT POND
BLUFF MOUNTAIN
BOREAS MOUNTAIN
BRADLEY POND
BROOKTROUT LAKE
CADENCE
CAMERON
CARA
CAROLYN
CASEY
CASSANDRA
CASSIA
CAYLA
CELESTE
CHAMPLAIN VALLEY
CHASE LAKE
CHRISTINE
CHRISTY
CINDY
CLARIE
CLEO
COOPER KILN TRAIL
COPPER LAKE
CROOKED CREEK
CURTIS POND
DANA
DANIELLE
DARCY
DEBBIE
DEBORAH
DEEP LAKE
DEER BROOK
DENISE
DESSA
DURANT LAKE
EDDY
ELIZABETH
ELLIE
ELSIE
EMMA BOOT
EMMALINE
EVERTON FALLS
EVETTE
FAYE
FELICITY
FLOODWOOD POND
FORGE POND
FRANCESCA
GABRIELLE
GILLY HICKS
GOTHICS MOUNTAIN
GREAT RANGE
GRETA
GRETCHEN
HALLIE
HARD LAKE
HASKELL PLACE
HEATHER
HELEN
HERKIMER LANDING
HIGH PEAKS REGION
HIGH ROCK
HOFFMAN MOUNTAIN
HOLLISTER CO.
HORN LAKE
HORTON CLASSIC STRAIGHT
HORTON CLASSIC STRAIGHT DESTROYED
IRENE
ISABEL
JANE
JILLIAN
KAREN
KATARINA
KATHERINE
KATHLEEN
KEENE VALLEY
KELSEY
KERRY
KILBURN BOOT
KRISTA
LAKE CHAMPLAIN
LEAH
LESLEY
LILLIAN
LOOKOUT MOUNTAIN
LOUISA
MADISON FLARE
MAPLE RIDGE
MARIA
MARY
MCKENZIE MOUNTAIN
MEG
MEREDITH
MICAH
MICHELLE
MILLBROOK
MOORE TRAIL
MORGAN
MURIEL
NADIA
NAOMI
NATALIE
NICOLETTE
NORA
NORTH LAKE
OPHELIA
OULUSKA PASS
PAMELA
PATRICIA
PAULA
PHELPS MOUNTAIN
PINE POINT TRAIL
PREMIUM KILBURN
PRISCILLA
QUINN
RACHEL
RACQUEL
REBECCA
REDFIELD
REMSEN SELVEDGE SLIM STRAIGHT
REMSEN SLIM STRAIGHT
ROARING BROOK CREW
ROARING BROOK V-NECK
ROCKY PEAK RIDGE
ROLLINS POND
RUEHL
RUEHL NO. 925
SANDRA
SASHA
SAWTOOTH MOUNTAIN
SCHOFIELD COBBLE
SELENA
SEVEY'S CORNER
SEWARD RANGE
SHELBY
SIMONE
SLANT ROCK
SOPHIE
STACY
STREET MOUNTAIN
SUSIE
TATUM
TERRI
THERESA
TORI
TRACY
TRISHA
TRISTEN
TWITCHELL CREEK
UPPER WOLF JAW
VALERIE
WAKELY
WHEY POND
WOLF CREEK
WOODHULL LAKE
WRIGHT MOUNTAIN
ZOE

ALLESON OF ROCHESTER, INC.
(d/b/a Don Alleson Athletic)

2921 Brighton Henrietta Town Line Rd
Rochester, NY 14623
Tel.: (585) 272-0606
Fax: (585) 272-9639
Web Site: www.alleson.com
Approx. Number Employees: 150
Year Founded: 1933
Business Description:
Mfr. of Athletic Sportswear for Men, Boys & Women
S.I.C.: 2329; 2339
N.A.I.C.S.: 315228; 315239
Import Export
Advertising Expenditures: $7,900,000
Media: 2-4
Distr.: Natl.
Budget Set: May
Personnel:
Todd Levine *(Pres)*
Elena R. Oliveri *(CFO, Treas & VP-Ops)*
Michael Kretovic *(Sec & VP-Fin)*
Brands & Products:
ALLESON
ALLESON ATHLETIC

ALPHA SHIRT COMPANY

(Div. of Broder Bros., Co.)
6 Neshaminy Interplex
Trevose, PA 19053
Tel.: (215) 291-0300
Fax: (800) 845-4970
Toll Free: (800) 523-4585
E-mail: contact@alphashirt.com
Web Site: www.alphashirt.com
Year Founded: 1933
Business Description:
Blank Apparel Whslr & Distr
S.I.C.: 5136; 5137
N.A.I.C.S.: 424320; 424330
Media: 2-4-5-6-9-10-17-25
Distr.: Natl.
Brands & Products:
ALPHA

ALPS SPORTSWEAR MANUFACTURING CO., INC.

15 Union St
Lawrence, MA 01840-1823
Tel.: (978) 683-2438
Fax: (978) 686-8051
Toll Free: (800) 262-7010
E-mail: alps@alps-sportswear.com
Web Site: www.alps-sportswear.com
Sales Range: Less than $1 Million
Approx. Number Employees: 20
Year Founded: 1934
Business Description:
Men's & Women's Sweaters & Related Apparel Mfr
S.I.C.: 2253; 2339
N.A.I.C.S.: 315191; 315239
Import Export
Media: 4-5-6-10-17
Distr.: Natl.
Budget Set: Nov. -Dec.
Personnel:
Marvin Axelrod *(Pres)*
Jerry Stone *(Dir-Sls & Mktg)*
Brands & Products:
ALPS

AMERICAN EAGLE OUTFITTERS, INC.

77 Hot Metal St
Pittsburgh, PA 15203
Tel.: (412) 432-3300
Fax: (724) 779-5585
E-mail: custserv@ae.com
Web Site: www.ae.com
Approx. Sls.: $2,967,559,000
Approx. Number Employees: 6,900
Year Founded: 1957
Business Description:
Men's & Women's Outdoor Apparel Retailer
S.I.C.: 5651; 5611; 5621
N.A.I.C.S.: 448140; 448110; 448120
Import
Advertising Expenditures: $64,900,000
Media: 3-4-6-8-19-31
Personnel:
Jay L. Schottenstein *(Chm)*
Roger S. Markfield *(Vice Chm & Exec Dir-Creative)*
James V. O'Donnell *(CEO)*
Joan Holstein Hilson *(CFO & Exec VP)*
Dennis R. Parodi *(COO & Exec VP-Real Estate)*
Tana Ward *(Chief Mdsg Officer)*
Michael Rempell *(COO-New York Design Center & Exec VP)*
Thomas A. DiDonato *(Exec VP-HR)*
Joseph E. Kerin *(Exec VP)*
Cindy Hall *(Sr VP-Design)*
Steve Kubinski *(VP-Mktg)*
Ethan Holland *(Dir-Online Mktg & Analytics)*
Jessica Berlin *(Mgr-Social Media)*
Brands & Products:
77KIDS
AE
AE.COM
AERIE
AMERICAN EAGLE
AMERICAN EAGLE OUTFITTERS
LIVE YOUR LIFE
Advertising Agencies:
160over90
1 S Broad St 10th Fl
Philadelphia, PA 19107
Tel.: (215) 732-3200
Fax: (215) 732-1664

Brierley & Partners
8401 N Central Expy Ste 1000 LB-37
Dallas, TX 75225-4403
Tel.: (214) 760-8700
Fax: (214) 743-5511

GatesmanMarmion+Dave
60 S 15th St
Pittsburgh, PA 15203-1542
Tel.: (412) 381-5400
Fax: (412) 381-9770

Wink, Incorporated
126 N 3rd St #100
Minneapolis, MN 55401
Tel.: (612) 455-2642
Fax: (612) 455-2645

ANGELICA CORPORATION

(Joint Venture of Reinet Investments SCA & Trilantic Capital Management LLC)
1105 Lakewood Pkwy Ste 210
Alpharetta, GA 30009
Tel.: (678) 823-4100
Fax: (678) 823-4165
Toll Free: (800) 235-8410
E-mail: marketing@angelica.com
Web Site: www.angelica.com
Sales Range: $400-449.9 Million
Approx. Number Employees: 5,900
Year Founded: 1878
Business Description:
Uniform Rental & Laundry Services
S.I.C.: 7212; 7213; 7218; 7299
N.A.I.C.S.: 812320; 812199; 812331; 812332
Import Export
Advertising Expenditures: $3,432,000
Media: 1-2-4-7-10-20-26
Distr.: Intl.; Natl.
Personnel:
Stuart Murray *(CEO)*
Lew Belote *(CFO)*
John S. Olbrych *(Chief Admin Officer)*
Steven L. Frey *(Gen Counsel)*
Brands & Products:
ANGEL KITS
ANGEL MATS
ANGEL SLIDERS
ANGELICA

THE APPAREL GROUP

883 Trinity Dr
Lewisville, TX 75056
Tel.: (972) 960-8212
Fax: (214) 469-3257
Toll Free: (800) 626-2884
E-mail: info@enro.com
Web Site: www.enro.com
Approx. Number Employees: 800
Business Description:
Men's Suits, Sportswear & Sweaters; Ladies' Wear Mfr
S.I.C.: 2321; 2339
N.A.I.C.S.: 315223; 315239
Advertising Expenditures: $200,000
Personnel:
John Liu *(Chm & CEO)*

ARC OUTDOORS

5425 S 99th East Ave
Tulsa, OK 74146
Tel.: (877) 974-4353
Toll Free: (877) 974-4353
E-mail: cs@arcoutdoors.com
Web Site: www.arcoutdoors.com
Sales Range: $1-9.9 Million
Approx. Number Employees: 14
Year Founded: 1998
Business Description:
Sportswear & Accessories Mfr
S.I.C.: 2329
N.A.I.C.S.: 315228
Media: 10-22
Brands & Products:
ADVANCED SOLUTIONS FOR THE OUTDOOR INDUSTRY.
ARC
ARCTICSHIELD
ELEMENT 47
INNOVATIVELY THIN; UNBELIEVABLY WARM
X-SCENT
X-SYSTEM

ARMY & NAVY DEPARTMENT STORES LIMITED

74 W Cordova St
Vancouver, BC V6B 1C9, Canada
Tel.: (604) 683-9660
Fax: (604) 683-5985
E-mail: info@armyandnavy.ca
Web Site: www.armyandnavy.ca
Approx. Number Employees: 1,000
Business Description:
Clothing Retailer
S.I.C.: 5699
N.A.I.C.S.: 448190
Export
Advertising Expenditures: $200,000
Media: 8-9-13-14-23-25
Distr.: Reg.
Personnel:
Jacqui Cohen *(Pres & CEO)*

ARROW SHIRT CO.

(Sub. of Phillips Van Heusen Corporation)
200 Madison Ave
New York, NY 10016-3903
Tel.: (212) 381-3500
Fax: (212) 381-3950
E-mail: apparelonline@arrowshirt.com
Web Site: www.arrowshirt.com
Sales Range: $150-199.9 Million
Approx. Number Employees: 350
Year Founded: 1851
Business Description:
Apparel Mfr
S.I.C.: 2329
N.A.I.C.S.: 315211
Import Export
Advertising Expenditures: $10,000,000
Media: 2-3-4-5-6-8-9-11-15-16-18-19-20-24-25
Distr.: Intl.; Natl.
Budget Set: June
Personnel:
Emanuel Chirico *(Chm & CEO)*
Malcolm Robinson *(Pres-Sportswear)*
Brands & Products:
ARROW
ARROW CLASSIC
ARROW TOURNAMENT GOLF

BACHRACH CLOTHING, INC.

(Holding of Sun Capital Partners, Inc.)
1430 Broadway Ste 308
New York, NY 10018
Tel.: (212) 354-4927
Toll Free: (800) 222-4722
E-mail: customerservice@bachrach.com
Web Site: www.bachrach.com
Approx. Number Employees: 400
Year Founded: 1877
Business Description:
Men's & Boys' Clothing Retailer
S.I.C.: 5611
N.A.I.C.S.: 448110
Import Export
Media: 4-8-13
Personnel:
Brian Lipman *(Pres)*
Brands & Products:
BACHRACH

BARNEYS NEW YORK, INC.

(Holding of Istithmar PJSC)
575 5th Ave
New York, NY 10017-2429
Tel.: (212) 826-8900
Fax: (212) 450-8489
Toll Free: (800) 926-5393
Web Site: www.barneys.com
Approx. Rev.: $104,200,000
Approx. Number Employees: 1,400
Year Founded: 1923
Business Description:
Specialty Clothing Retailer

Key to Media (For complete agency information see *The Advertising Red Books-Agencies* edition):
1. Bus. Publs. 2. Cable T.V. 3. Catalogs & Directories. 4. Co-op Adv. 5. Consumer Mags. 6. D.M. to Bus. Estab.7. D.M. to Consumers
8. Daily Newsp. 9. Exhibits/Trade Shows 10. Foreign 11. Infomercial 12. Internet Adv.13. Multimedia 14. Network Radio
15. Network T.V. 16. Newsp. Distr. Mags. 17. Other 18. Outdoor (Posters, Transit) 19. Point of Purchase20. Premiums, Novelties
21. Product Samples 22. Special Events Mktg. 23. Spot Radio 24. Spot T.V. 25. Weekly Newsp. 26. Yellow Page Adv.

Barneys New York, Inc. — (Continued)

S.I.C.: 5611; 5621
N.A.I.C.S.: 448110; 448120
Import
Advertising Expenditures: $7,120,000
Media: 5-6-8-9-16-18-19-23-24-25
Distr.: Direct to Consumer; Natl.
Personnel:
Andy Watson *(Chm)*
Mark Lee *(CEO)*
Judith Collinson *(Exec VP-Womens)*
Tom Kalenderian *(Exec VP-Menswear Mdsg)*
David New *(Exec VP-Creative Svcs)*
Marc H. Perlowitz *(Exec VP-HR)*
Daniella Vitale *(Exec VP-Women's & Barneys.com Ops)*
Larry Promisel *(VP-E-Commerce)*
Amanda Brooks *(Dir-Fashion)*
Simon Doonan *(Dir-Creative)*
Heather Kaminetsky *(Dir-Internet Mktg)*
Shilpa Shenoy *(Dir-Digital Mktg-NY)*
Brands & Products:
BARNEYS NEW YORK
BARNEY'S NEW YORK CO-OP
BARNEY'S NEW YORK OUTLET

THE BASKETBALL MARKETING COMPANY INC.
(d/b/a AND 1)
101 Enterprise Ste 100
Aliso Viejo, CA 92656
Tel.: (949) 614-4300
Tel.: (949) 752-6688
Fax: (949) 756-1534
Toll Free: (800) 848-8698
E-mail: info@and1.com
Web Site: www.and1.com
Year Founded: 1993
Business Description:
Athletic Apparel Mfr
S.I.C.: 3149; 2321; 2325; 2331; 3949
N.A.I.C.S.: 316219; 315223; 315224; 315232; 339920
Media: 1-4-11-22
Brands & Products:
AND 1

BEAU TIES LTD.
69 Industrial Ave
Middlebury, VT 05753-1129
Tel.: (802) 388-0108
Fax: (802) 388-7808
Toll Free: (800) 488-8437
E-mail: customerservice@beautiesltd.com
Web Site: www.beautiesltd.com
Approx. Sls.: $1,800,000
Approx. Number Employees: 25
Business Description:
Retailer & Mail Order of Bow Ties
S.I.C.: 5961; 2323
N.A.I.C.S.: 454113; 315993
Media: 4-8-13
Personnel:
Deb Venman *(Co-Owner & Exec VP)*
Bill Kenerson *(Pres)*
Cy Tall *(Mgr-Mktg)*

BEMIDJI WOOLEN MILLS
301 Irvine Ave NW
Bemidji, MN 56601
Tel.: (218) 751-5166
Fax: (218) 751-4659
Toll Free: (888) 751-5166
E-mail: info@bemidjiwoolenmills.com
Web Site: www.bemidjiwoolenmills.com
Sales Range: $50-74.9 Million
Approx. Number Employees: 50
Year Founded: 1920
Business Description:
Woolen Apparel
S.I.C.: 5651; 5131
N.A.I.C.S.: 448140; 424310
Media: 4-13
Personnel:
Bill Batchelder *(Pres)*
Keith Johnson *(VP-Sls)*

THE BEN SILVER CORPORATION
149 King St
Charleston, SC 29401
Tel.: (843) 577-4556
Fax: (843) 723-1543
Toll Free: (800) 221-4671
E-mail: bensilver@bensilver.com
Web Site: www.bensilver.com
Approx. Number Employees: 40
Business Description:
Mfr. & Sales of Men's Clothing & Accessories
S.I.C.: 3299; 2299
N.A.I.C.S.: 327999; 314999
Import Export
Media: 4-8-13
Personnel:
Robert Prenner *(Owner)*
Sue Prenner *(Pres)*
Brands & Products:
BEN SILVER
BEN SILVER COLLECTION

BILLY REID, INC.
114 North Court St
Florence, AL 35630
Tel.: (256) 767-4692
Toll Free: (877) 757-3934
Web Site: www.billyreid.com
Business Description:
Clothing Mfr & Distr
S.I.C.: 5136
N.A.I.C.S.: 424320
Media: 8-19
Brands & Products:
BILLY REID

BLACK MOUNTAIN APPAREL
14100 US Hwy 19 N Ste 107
Clearwater, FL 33764
Tel.: (727) 527-5310
Fax: (727) 216-6423
E-mail: melissa@blackmountainapparel.com
Web Site: www.blackmountainapparel.com
Approx. Number Employees: 10
Year Founded: 1995
Business Description:
Polar Fleece, Pile Jackets, Vests, Pullovers & Accessories
S.I.C.: 2331; 2311; 2339; 2353
N.A.I.C.S.: 315232; 315222; 315239; 315991
Advertising Expenditures: $40,000
Media: 2-4-10-13
Distr.: Intl.
Personnel:
Harlan Newman *(Pres & CEO)*

BOB'S STORES CORP.
(Joint Venture of Versa Capital Management, Inc. & Crystal Capital Fund Management, L.P.)
160 Corp Ct
Meriden, CT 06450-8313
Tel.: (203) 235-5775
Fax: (203) 634-0129
Toll Free: (866) 333-BOBS
E-mail: info@bobstores.com
Web Site: www.bobstores.com
Approx. Sls.: $310,000,000
Approx. Number Employees: 2,400
Year Founded: 1954
Business Description:
Retail Apparel Stores
S.I.C.: 5651; 5699
N.A.I.C.S.: 448140; 448150
Advertising Expenditures: $15,000,000
D.M. to Consumers: $3,750,000; Daily Newsp.: $7,500,000; Other: $3,750,000
Distr.: Reg.
Budget Set: Nov.
Personnel:
Jim Smith *(CFO)*
Scott Hampson *(Sr VP & Dir-Store Ops)*
Kelly Toussaing *(Sr VP & Dir-Fin)*
Advertising Agency:
Zimmerman Advertising
2200 W Commercial Blvd Ste 300
Fort Lauderdale, FL 33309-3064
Tel.: (954) 644-4000
Fax: (954) 731-2977
Toll Free: (800) 248-8522
Bob's Stores

BOSS HOLDINGS, INC.
1221 Page St
Kewanee, IL 61443-2101
Tel.: (309) 852-2131
Fax: (309) 852-0848
Toll Free: (800) 447-4581
E-mail: bossmfg1893@bossgloves.com
Web Site: www.bossgloves.com
Approx. Sls.: $48,957,000
Approx. Number Employees: 203
Year Founded: 1893
Business Description:
Holding Company; Work Gloves, Boots & Rain Gear, Pet Products & Balloons Mfr & Distr
S.I.C.: 3151; 3069; 6719
N.A.I.C.S.: 315992; 326299; 551112
Advertising Expenditures: $789,000
Media: 4-10-20-21-22
Personnel:
G. Louis Graziadio, III *(Chm, Pres & CEO)*
Steven G. Pont *(Chief Acctg Officer, Principal Fin Officer & VP-Fin)*
James F. Sanders *(Gen Counsel & Sec)*
Brands & Products:
BOSS

BRAWN OF CALIFORNIA, INC.
(Sub. of Hanover Direct, Inc.)
Ste A 1500 Harbor Blvd
Weehawken, NJ 07086-6732
Tel.: (201) 863-7300
Fax: (201) 272-3280
Toll Free: (800) 414-1114
Web Site: www.undergear.com
Approx. Number Employees: 42
Business Description:
Men's Clothing Designer
S.I.C.: 5611; 5961
N.A.I.C.S.: 448110; 454113
Media: 4-13
Brands & Products:
INTERNATIONAL MALE
UNDER GEAR

BROOKS BROTHERS INC
(Sub. of Retail Brand Alliance, Inc.)
350 Campus Plz
Edison, NJ 08818-4016
Tel.: (732) 225-4870
Fax: (732) 225-1520
Toll Free: (800) 274-1815
E-mail: service@brooksbrothers.com
Web Site: www.brooksbrothers.com
Approx. Number Employees: 5,500
Year Founded: 1818
Business Description:
Clothing for Men & Women
S.I.C.: 5611
N.A.I.C.S.: 448110
Media: 4-6-9-13-18-19-25
Distr.: Natl.
Budget Set: Oct.
Personnel:
Claudio Del Vecchio *(Chm & CEO)*
Lou Amendola *(Sr VP & Gen Mgr-Mdsg)*
Joseph Dixon *(Sr VP-Production & Technical Svcs)*
Karl Haller *(VP-Strategy & Bus Dev)*
Brands & Products:
BROOKS BROTHERS
Advertising Agencies:
AR Media
601 W 26th St Ste 810
New York, NY 10001
Tel.: (212) 739-5500
Fax: (212) 739-5800

Razorfish Philadelphia
417 N 8th St Fl 2
Philadelphia, PA 19123-3916
Tel.: (267) 295-7100
Fax: (267) 295-7101

THE BROWN & CHURCH COMPANY
(Sub. of Individualized Apparel Group)
118 Marimorre Dr
Pilot Mountain, NC 27041
Tel.: (336) 368-5502
Fax: (336) 368-5454
Toll Free: (800) 782-7270
Web Site: www.brownandchurchco.com
Approx. Sls.: $2,000,000
Approx. Number Employees: 40
Year Founded: 1975
Business Description:
Neckties Mfr
S.I.C.: 2321
N.A.I.C.S.: 315223
Media: 8-19-21
Distr.: Natl.
Budget Set: Oct.
Personnel:
Larry Marshall *(CEO)*
Brands & Products:
BROWN & CHURCH
KEYS & LOCKWOOD
YAPRE

CARHARTT, INC.
5750 Mercury Dr
Dearborn, MI 48126-4234
Tel.: (313) 271-8460
Fax: (313) 271-3455

Key to Media (For complete agency information see *The Advertising Red Books-Agencies* edition):
1. Bus. Publs. 2. Cable T.V. 3. Catalogs & Directories. 4. Co-op Adv. 5. Consumer Mags. 6. D.M. to Bus. Estab.7. D.M. to Consumers 8. Daily Newsp. 9. Exhibits/Trade Shows 10. Foreign 11. Infomercial 12. Internet Adv.13. Multimedia 14. Network Radio 15. Network T.V. 16. Newsp. Distr. Mags. 17. Other 18. Outdoor (Posters, Transit) 19. Point of Purchase20. Premiums, Novelties 21. Product Samples 22. Special Events Mktg. 23. Spot Radio 24. Spot T.V. 25. Weekly Newsp. 26. Yellow Page Adv.

Toll Free: (800) 358-3825
E-mail: info@carhartt.com
Web Site: www.carhartt.com
Approx. Number Employees: 40
Year Founded: 1889
Business Description:
Mfr. of Utility & Work Clothes & Outer Wear
S.I.C.: 2326; 2325
N.A.I.C.S.: 315225; 315224
Export
Advertising Expenditures: $1,500,000
Consumer Mags.: $1,125,000; Exhibits/Trade Shows: $75,000; Other: $75,000; Point of Purchase: $225,000
Distr.: Natl.
Budget Set: Oct. -Nov.
Personnel:
Mark Valade *(Pres & CEO)*
Tony Ambroza *(VP-Mktg)*
Jennifer Flasher *(VP-HR)*
Brian Juszak *(Dir-Retail Mktg)*
Randy Meza *(Dir-Mktg)*
Brands & Products:
1889
CARHARTT
COOLMAX
CORDURA
EXTREMES
WORK-DRY
WORKCAMO
WORKCOMFORT
WORKFLEX
Advertising Agencies:
BDS Marketing
10 Holland
Irvine, CA 92618
Tel.: (949) 472-6700
Fax: (949) 597-2220

UPP Entertainment Marketing
3401 Winona Ave
Burbank, CA 91504
Tel.: (818) 526-0111
Fax: (818) 526-1466
Branded Integration
Celebrity Affinity Program
Product Placement
Public Relations
Work Wear

CASUAL MALE RBT, LLC
(Sub. of Casual Male Retail Group Inc.)
555 Turnpike St
Canton, MA 02021
Tel.: (781) 828-9300
Fax: (781) 821-6094
Web Site: www.casualmale.com
Sales Range: $100-124.9 Million
Business Description:
Men's Clothing Retailer
S.I.C.: 5699
N.A.I.C.S.: 448190; 448150
Personnel:
David A. Levin *(Pres & CEO)*
Advertising Agency:
Planet Propaganda, Inc.
605 Williamson St
Madison, WI 53703
Tel.: (608) 256-0000
Fax: (608) 256-1975

CASUAL MALE RETAIL GROUP INC.
555 Turnpike St
Canton, MA 02021
Tel.: (781) 828-9300
Fax: (781) 821-6094
Toll Free: (800) 767-0319
E-mail: info@casualmale.com
Web Site: www.cmrginc.com
Approx. Sls.: $393,642,000
Approx. Number Employees: 1,576
Year Founded: 1976
Business Description:
Men's Clothing Retailer
S.I.C.: 5611; 5961
N.A.I.C.S.: 448110; 454113
Import
Advertising Expenditures: $1,200,000
Media: 3-4-5-7-8-9-13-14-15-18-19-22-23-24-25-26
Distr.: Natl.
Personnel:
Seymour Holtzman *(Chm)*
David A. Levin *(CEO)*
Dennis R. Hernreich *(CFO, COO & Exec VP)*
Jack R. McKinney *(CIO & Sr VP)*
Peter Stratton, Jr. *(Chief Acctg Officer, Controller & Sr VP-Fin)*
Robert S. Molloy *(Gen Counsel)*
Mark Bean *(Sr VP-Sls & Ops)*
Richard Della Bernarda *(Sr VP-Mktg)*
Francie Nguyen *(Sr VP-Direct)*
Peter E. Schmitz *(Sr VP-Real Estate)*
Vickie S. Smith *(Sr VP-Plng & Allocation)*
Walter E. Sprague *(Sr VP-HR)*
Brands & Products:
B&T FACTORY DIRECT
CASUAL MALE XL
LIFE'S BETTER WHEN IT FITS
LIVINGXL
ROCHESTER BIG & TALL CLOTHING
SEARS CANADA-CASUAL MALE
SHOES XL

CAVENDER'S
7820 S Broadway Ave
Tyler, TX 75703-5241
Tel.: (903) 561-4992
Fax: (903) 509-9020
E-mail: webopt@cavenders.com
Web Site: www.cavenders.com
Approx. Number Employees: 600
Year Founded: 1965
Business Description:
Provider of Apparel & Accessories
S.I.C.: 5661; 5699
N.A.I.C.S.: 448210; 448190
Personnel:
James R. Cavender *(CEO)*
Advertising Agency:
Westar Advertising
2019 W SW Loop 323
Tyler, TX 75701
Tel.: (903) 561-6848
Fax: (903) 561-4849

CGS INDUSTRIES, INC.
3409 Queens Blvd
Long Island City, NY 11101
Tel.: (718) 482-0700
Fax: (718) 482-1385
E-mail: info@cgsindustries.com
Web Site: www.cgsindustries.com
Approx. Number Employees: 65
Business Description:
Sportswear for Men & Boys
S.I.C.: 5137; 5136
N.A.I.C.S.: 424330; 424320
Advertising Expenditures: $1,000,000
Bus. Publs.: $1,000,000
Distr.: Natl.
Budget Set: Dec.
Personnel:
Lal Sani *(Pres)*
Sunil Sani *(VP-Ops & Adv)*

CHAMPION ATHLETICWEAR INC.
(Div. of Hanesbrands Inc.)
1000 E Hanes Mill Rd
Winston Salem, NC 27105-1384
Mailing Address:
PO Box 1550
Winston Salem, NC 27102
Tel.: (336) 519-8080
Fax: (336) 519-7909
Toll Free: (800) 999-2249
Web Site: www.championusa.com
Sales Range: $100-124.9 Million
Approx. Number Employees: 1,200
Year Founded: 1919
Business Description:
Athletic, Casual Knitwear & Apparel Mfr & Whslr
S.I.C.: 2329; 2339
N.A.I.C.S.: 315228; 315239
Media: 3-4-5-6-7-11-13-18-19-22-24-31
Distr.: Intl.; Natl.
Personnel:
Richard Noll *(CEO)*
Claire Edgar *(Brand Mktg Dir-Champion)*
Cathy Marchant *(Sr Brand Mktg Mgr)*
Advertising Agency:
Night Agency
307 Canal St Fl 2
New York, NY 10013
Tel.: (212) 431-1945
Fax: (917) 677-8327

COUNTESS MARA, INC.
(Sub. of Randa Corp.)
120 W 45th St
New York, NY 10036
Tel.: (212) 768-8800
Fax: (212) 768-8585
Web Site: www.countessmara.com
Approx. Number Employees: 30
Year Founded: 1938
Business Description:
Mfr. of Men's Ties & Accessories
S.I.C.: 2323
N.A.I.C.S.: 315993
Advertising Expenditures: $275,000
Media: 6
Distr.: Natl.
Budget Set: Sept.
Personnel:
Jeffery Spiegel *(Pres)*
Brands & Products:
COUNTESS MARA

CUTTER & BUCK, INC.
(Sub. of New Wave Group AB)
701 N 34th St Ste 400
Seattle, WA 98103-3415
Tel.: (206) 830-6812
Fax: (206) 448-0589
E-mail: corpinfo@cutterbuck.com
Web Site: www.cutterbuck.com
Approx. Number Employees: 359
Year Founded: 1990
Business Description:
Men's & Women's Apparel Designer, Mfr & Distr
S.I.C.: 2329; 2339; 5136; 5137
N.A.I.C.S.: 315211; 315212; 424320; 424330
Advertising Expenditures: $1,700,000
Media: 2-5-7-8
Personnel:
Julie Snow *(VP-Design & Mdsg)*

DAVID PEYSER SPORTSWEAR INC.
88 Spence St
Bay Shore, NY 11706-2230
Mailing Address:
PO Box 9171
Bay Shore, NY 11706-9171
Tel.: (631) 273-8020
Fax: (631) 435-8018
E-mail: info@weatherproofco.com
Web Site: www.weatherproofco.com
Approx. Number Employees: 200
Year Founded: 1948
Business Description:
Sportswear & Athletic Clothing Supplier & Mfr
S.I.C.: 2329; 2339
N.A.I.C.S.: 315228; 315239
Media: 2-4
Personnel:
Paul Peyser *(Pres)*
Brands & Products:
MV SPORT
WEATHER PROOF

DELTA APPAREL, INC.
322 S Main St
Greenville, SC 29601
Tel.: (864) 232-5200
Fax: (864) 232-5199
E-mail: investor.relations@deltaapparel.com
Web Site: www.deltaapparel.com
E-Mail For Key Personnel:
Sales Director: sales@deltaapparel.com
Approx. Sls.: $475,236,000
Approx. Number Employees: 7,200
Year Founded: 1903
Business Description:
Knit Apparel Designer, Mfr & Marketer
S.I.C.: 5131; 2299; 2321; 2339
N.A.I.C.S.: 424310; 314999; 315223; 315239
Advertising Expenditures: $4,500,000
Media: 2-5-7-21
Personnel:
Robert W. Humphreys *(Chm, Pres & CEO)*
Deborah H. Merrill *(CFO, Treas & VP)*
Steven E. Cochran *(Pres-Activewear)*
David R. Palmer *(VP & Asst Treas)*
Brands & Products:
THE COTTON EXCHANGE
DELTA
THE GAME
INTENSITY ATHLETICS
JUNK FOOD
JUNK MAIL
KUDZU
QUAIL HOLLOW
SOFFE
SWEET AND SOUR

DOCKERS BRAND
(Unit of Levi Strauss & Co.)
1155 Battery St
San Francisco, CA 94111-1230
Tel.: (415) 501-6000
Fax: (415) 501-3939

Key to Media (For complete agency information see *The Advertising Red Books-Agencies* edition):
1. Bus. Publs. 2. Cable T.V. 3. Catalogs & Directories. 4. Co-op Adv. 5. Consumer Mags. 6. D.M. to Bus. Estab.7. D.M. to Consumers
8. Daily Newsp. 9. Exhibits/Trade Shows 10. Foreign 11. Infomercial 12. Internet Adv.13. Multimedia 14. Network Radio
15. Network T.V. 16. Newsp. Distr. Mags. 17. Other 18. Outdoor (Posters, Transit) 19. Point of Purchase20. Premiums, Novelties
21. Product Samples 22. Special Events Mktg. 23. Spot Radio 24. Spot T.V. 25. Weekly Newsp. 26. Yellow Page Adv.

Dockers Brand — (Continued)

Web Site: www.dockers.com
Approx. Number Employees: 10,000
Business Description:
Men's & Women's Apparel Mfr
S.I.C.: 5611; 5621
N.A.I.C.S.: 448110; 448120
Media: 3
Personnel:
Robert D. Haas *(Chm)*
James Calhoun *(Pres-Global Dockers)*
Advertising Agencies:
Draftfcb West
1160 Battery St Ste 250
San Francisco, CA 94111
Tel.: (415) 820-8000
Fax: (415) 820-8087

OMD Los Angeles
5353 Grosvenor Blvd
Los Angeles, CA 90066
Tel.: (310) 301-3600
Fax: (646) 278-8000

OMD-USA
195 Broadway
New York, NY 10007
Tel.: (212) 590-7100
Digital Media Buying
Traditional Media

Silverlign Group Inc.
54 N Central Ave Ste 200
Campbell, CA 95008
Tel.: (408) 792-3010
Fax: (408) 792-3014

DR. JAY'S INC.

Prince St Sta
New York, NY 10012
Tel.: (888) 437-5297
Toll Free: (888) 437-5297
E-mail: corporate@drjays.com
Web Site: www.drjays.com
Approx. Number Employees: 300
Year Founded: 1991
Business Description:
Sale of Mens & Boys Clothing; Urban Fashions
S.I.C.: 5611
N.A.I.C.S.: 448110
Import Export
Media: 13-17
Personnel:
Elliot Vetesh *(Pres)*
Mark Sutton *(Mgr-Mktg)*
Brands & Products:
DRJAYS.COM
GET DRESSED

DYNAMIC TEAM SPORTS INC.

454 Acord Ln
Downingtown, PA 19335
Tel.: (610) 518-3300
Fax: (610) 518-9200
E-mail: info@dynamicteamsports.com
Web Site:
www.dynamicteamsports.com
Approx. Number Employees: 60
Business Description:
Mfr. of Team Athletic Uniforms
S.I.C.: 2389; 2339
N.A.I.C.S.: 315299; 315239
Media: 2-4-13
Personnel:
Scott A. Samter *(Pres)*
Brands & Products:
ABERDEEN
ACE
AMERICAN
ANDORRA
ARCADIA
ARLINGTON
ASPEN
AVALANCHE
AVALON
AZTEC
BAJA
BERKELEY
BUTANE
CABO
CANNES
CAPITAL
CHAMPIONS CHOOSE DYNAMIC
CHESAPEAKE
CONCORD
CONSTITUTION
CORSICO
COSMOS
COURT
DAREDEVIL
DIAMOND
DIPLOMAT
DOME
DRAFT
DYNAMIC
EAGLE
ECLIPSE
ELIMINATOR
ELITE
ENDLINE
FLAMES
FLARE
FORWARD
FREEDOM
GUARD
HAWK
HURRICANE
ICEBERG
INDEPENDENCE
JUSTICE
LAVA
LIBERTY
MADRID
MATADOR
MATRIX
MAVERICK
MEGAVOLT
MEMORIAL
NAPLES
NATIONAL
NAVAJO
ORION
OXFORD
PARANA
PATRIOT
PHOENIX
PLAZA
POWERHOUSE
PROWLER
RAMS
RAVEN
REBOUND
ROMA
ROSWELL
SANTE FE
SCORPIONS
SEATON
SENATOR
SENECA
SHOOTER
SIDELINE
SIERRA
SLASH
STRATUS
SWOOSH
TOLEDO
UNION
VALDEZ
YORK

ECKO UNLIMITED, INC.

(Sub. of Marc Ecko Enterprises)
40 W 23rd St
New York, NY 10010
Tel.: (917) 262-1000
Fax: (917) 262-3525
Web Site: www.shopecko.com
Approx. Number Employees: 300
Year Founded: 1993
Business Description:
Casual Clothing & Accessories Designer, Mfr, Whslr & Retailer
S.I.C.: 2321; 2329; 2331; 2335; 2339; 3149; 5136; 5137; 5139; 5611; 5621; 5961
N.A.I.C.S.: 315223; 315228; 315232; 315233; 315239; 316219; 424320; 424330; 424340; 448110; 448120; 454111
Personnel:
Marc Ecko *(Co-Founder & Co-CEO)*
Seth Gerszberg *(Co-Founder & Co-CEO)*
Marci M. Tapper *(Co-Founder & Pres-Zoo York)*
Effy Zinkin *(Pres)*
Eric Wesolowski *(COO-Ecko Direct)*
Michael Golden *(CMO)*
Brands & Products:
ECKO
ECKO AEROSOL ASSAULT
ECKO ALFA
ECKO ANCIENT MYTHS
ECKO ASCENDING
ECKO ATHENA'S
ECKO AVALON
ECKO BACK TO BASICS
ECKO BASIC
ECKO BIG BLOCK
ECKO BOXED
ECKO CENTRAL ELEMENT
ECKO CHECKED UP
ECKO CREST
ECKO CRUCIFIED
ECKO DEAD LAUGHTER
ECKO DEAD PRESIDENTS
ECKO DESTINATION
ECKO DIAMOND ARCH
ECKO DIVINE
ECKO DOOM RIDER
ECKO ENTOURAGE
ECKO ETERNAL
ECKO EU PIQUE
ECKO EVIL INSIDE
ECKO FLAWLESS
ECKO FROM THE UNDERGROUND
ECKO FUEL
ECKO FUTURIST
ECKO GET THE MONEY
ECKO GOOD
ECKO GREED
ECKO HEAVEN & HELL
ECKO HI-WINDS
ECKO HIGHER STATUS
ECKO ILLUSIONAL
ECKO IMPERIAL
ECKO IN PURSUIT
ECKO IVY LEAGUE
ECKO KINGS
ECKO LATE NIGHT
ECKO MASTER OF WATCH
ECKO MASTER PIECE
ECKO MUMBAI BREAKER
ECKO OLD SKOOL
ECKO PESOS
ECKO RACER
ECKO RAW AND UNCUT
ECKO REVO
ECKO RHINO
ECKO RHINO CENTRIC
ECKO RHINO SCREENPRINT
ECKO RHOMBUS
ECKO RIDING DEMON
ECKO ROCKER
ECKO SHIELD WATCH
ECKO SHIELDED
ECKO SHOTGUN
ECKO SKETCH
ECKO SKETCH REPEATER
ECKO SMOKE
ECKO SPORTY
ECKO STREET BRIGADE
ECKO SUPERNATURAL
ECKO SURE
ECKO THE ANSEN ONCE
ECKO THE DISTINCTIVE
ECKO THE DISTINCTIVE TRACK
ECKO THE DOG TAG 2
ECKO THE ENCORE OZ
ECKO THE FIDEL
ECKO THE KING BOXED
ECKO THE OFFICIAL
ECKO THE RISEN
ECKO THE SEEKER
ECKO THE SHADOW
ECKO THE SUPREME
ECKO TRIED AND TRUE
ECKO TUMULTUOUS
ECKO UNDERGROUND SOUND
ECKO UPSIDE DOWN
ECKO VAPOR
ECKO WALLBURNER
ECKO WINGED
ECKO WINGED CROSS
ECKO WRITING ALL WRONGS
SHOPECKO
THE SUPREME
ZOO YORK
Advertising Agency:
David & Goliath
909 N Sepulveda Blvd Ste 700
El Segundo, CA 90245
Tel.: (310) 445-5200
Fax: (310) 445-5201

EDDIE BAUER, INC.

(Holding of Golden Gate Capital)
(Filed Ch 11 Bankruptcy #912100 on 06/17/09 in U.S. Bankruptcy Ct, Dist of DE, Wilmington)
10401 NE 8th St Ste 500
Bellevue, WA 98004
Tel.: (425) 755-6544
Fax: (425) 755-7694
Web Site: www.eddiebauer.com
Approx. Number Employees: 500
Year Founded: 1920
Business Description:
Men's & Women's Casual Clothing, Gear, Accessories & Footwear Mfr, Sales & Mail Order
S.I.C.: 5136; 5137; 5611; 5621; 5699; 5961
N.A.I.C.S.: 424320; 424330; 448110; 448120; 448190; 454111; 454113
Media: 31

Key to Media (For complete agency information see *The Advertising Red Books-Agencies* edition):
1. Bus. Publs. 2. Cable T.V. 3. Catalogs & Directories. 4. Co-op Adv. 5. Consumer Mags. 6. D.M. to Bus. Estab.7. D.M. to Consumers
8. Daily Newsp. 9. Exhibits/Trade Shows 10. Foreign 11. Infomercial 12. Internet Adv.13. Multimedia 14. Network Radio
15. Network T.V. 16. Newsp. Distr. Mags. 17. Other 18. Outdoor (Posters, Transit) 19. Point of Purchase20. Premiums, Novelties
21. Product Samples 22. Special Events Mktg. 23. Spot Radio 24. Spot T.V. 25. Weekly Newsp. 26. Yellow Page Adv.

Personnel:
Neil S. Fiske *(CEO)*
Christine Schultz *(CIO)*
Advertising Agency:
Fry, Inc.
650 Avis Dr
Ann Arbor, MI 48108
Tel.: (734) 741-0640
Fax: (734) 769-9918
Toll Free: (800) FRY6858

ELBECO INCORPORATED
4418 Pottsville Pike
Reading, PA 19605-1205
Tel.: (610) 921-0651
Fax: (610) 921-8651
E-mail: marketing@elbeco.com
Web Site: www.elbeco.com
Approx. Number Employees: 600
Year Founded: 1907
Business Description:
Mfr. of Professional Uniform Apparel
S.I.C.: 2326
N.A.I.C.S.: 315225
Advertising Expenditures: $450,000
Consumer Mags.: $150,000; D.M. to Consumers: $100,000; Exhibits/Trade Shows: $200,000
Distr.: Natl.
Budget Set: Jan.
Personnel:
David L. Lurio *(Pres)*
Dave Adams *(VP-Fin)*
Brands & Products:
CHECKPOINTE
COMFORTGRIP
DUTYMAX
DUTYMAXX
ELBECO
ELBECO CLASSIC
EXPRESS
FIT FOR DUTY FIT FOR YOU
LADIES CHOICE
LUXURY
LUXURY PLUS
MERIDIAN
PARAGON PLUS
PRESTIGE
PRESTIGE ADVANCE
REGULATION
REGULATION PLUS
SUMMIT DUTY
TEK TWILL
TEX-TROP
TOP AUTHORITY
TOP AUTHORITY PLUS
TRANSCONFR
UFX
WEST COAST

ELDER MANUFACTURING COMPANY, INC.
999 Executive Pkwy Ste 300
Saint Louis, MO 63141
Tel.: (314) 469-1120
Fax: (314) 336-0516
Fax: (800) 788-9891
Toll Free: (800) 824-8880
E-mail: info@elderwearwecare.com
Web Site: www.elderwearwecare.com
Approx. Number Employees: 100
Year Founded: 1988
Business Description:
Uniforms Mfr
S.I.C.: 2321; 2331
N.A.I.C.S.: 315223; 315232
Media: 5
Distr.: Natl.
Budget Set: May
Personnel:
Robert Branstetter *(CFO)*
Gregory Beile *(Exec VP)*
Gregg Hanson *(Exec VP)*
Richard Pace *(Dir-Mktg)*
Brands & Products:
BECKY THATCHER
BRUXTON
ELDER WEAR
ELDERWEAR
K-12 GEAR
MARK TWAYNE
SCHOOL DAYS
TOM SAWYER
WE CARE.

EX OFFICIO, LLC
(Sub. of Jarden Branded Consumables)
Gateway North Corporate Park 3314 S 116th St
Tukwila, WA 98168
Tel.: (206) 691-5250
Fax: (206) 286-9012
Toll Free: (800) 644-7303
E-mail: info@exofficio.com
Web Site: www.exofficio.com
Sales Range: $75-99.9 Million
Approx. Number Employees: 50
Year Founded: 1988
Business Description:
Clothing Mfr
S.I.C.: 5137; 5136
N.A.I.C.S.: 424330; 424320
Media: 5-10
Personnel:
Rick Hemmerling *(Pres)*
Steve Bendzak *(Gen Mgr)*
Bill Swan *(Dir-Admin)*
Karen Sain *(Brand Mgr)*
Brands & Products:
BUZZ OFF

THE FAIRCHILD CORPORATION
1750 Tysons Blvd Ste 1400
McLean, VA 22102-4244
Tel.: (703) 478-5800
Fax: (703) 478-5775
Web Site: www.fairchild.com/
Sales Range: $350-399.9 Million
Approx. Number Employees: 784
Year Founded: 1920
Business Description:
Protective Clothing Design & Sale
S.I.C.: 5611; 5699
N.A.I.C.S.: 448110; 448150
Export
Advertising Expenditures: $19,400,000
Media: 4-7-10
Distr.: Natl.
Budget Set: June
Personnel:
Michael L. McDonald *(CFO & Sr VP)*

THE FECHHEIMER BROTHERS COMPANY
(Holding of Berkshire Hathaway Inc.)
4545 Malsbary Rd
Cincinnati, OH 45242-5624
Tel.: (513) 793-5400
Fax: (513) 793-7819
Toll Free: (800) 543-1939
E-mail: info@fechheimer.com
Web Site: www.fechheimer.com
Sales Range: $300-349.9 Million
Approx. Number Employees: 700
Year Founded: 1842
Business Description:
Public Safety Uniforms Mfr
S.I.C.: 2326; 2389
N.A.I.C.S.: 315225; 315299
Advertising Expenditures: $395,000
Media: 6-10-13-19-20
Personnel:
Bob Getto *(Pres & CEO)*
Brands & Products:
FLYING CROSS BY FECHHEIMER

FISHMAN & TOBIN, INC.
4000 Chemical Rd Ste 500
Plymouth Meeting, PA 19462
Tel.: (610) 828-8400
Tel.: (212) 868-7920 (Adv)
Fax: (610) 828-4426
Toll Free: (800) 367-2772
E-mail: inquiries@fishmantobin.com
Web Site: www.fishmantobin.com
Sales Range: $100-124.9 Million
Approx. Number Employees: 2,500
Year Founded: 1914
Business Description:
Boys' & Men's Trousers & Clothing Distr
S.I.C.: 2311; 2321
N.A.I.C.S.: 315222; 315223
Import
Media: 4-5-6-7-10-17-18
Distr.: Natl.
Personnel:
Sylvan M. Tobin *(Chm)*
Mark Fishman *(Pres)*
Nicholas Vetere *(CFO)*

FORT INC.
(d/b/a Fort Catalog Stores)
903 Central Ave
Nebraska City, NE 68410
Tel.: (402) 873-7388
Fax: (402) 423-9369
E-mail: help@fortoutpost.com
Web Site: www.the-fort.com
Approx. Sls.: $14,858,209
Approx. Number Employees: 30
Business Description:
Clothing Retailer
S.I.C.: 5961; 5699
N.A.I.C.S.: 454113; 448190
Media: 4-8
Personnel:
Carl C. Wohlfarth *(VP & Gen Mgr)*
Brands & Products:
EXPERIENCE THE FORT
FORT WESTERN

FRUIT OF THE LOOM, INC.
(Holding of Berkshire Hathaway Inc.)
1 Fruit of the Loom Dr
Bowling Green, KY 42103-9015
Mailing Address:
PO Box 90015
Bowling Green, KY 42102-9015
Tel.: (270) 781-6400
Fax: (270) 781-6588
Web Site: www.fruit.com
E-Mail For Key Personnel:
Marketing Director: jshivel@fruit.com
Sales Director: ebaumgartner@fruit.com
Sales Range: $5-14.9 Billion
Approx. Number Employees: 33,000
Year Founded: 1851
Business Description:
Apparel Mfr
S.I.C.: 2254; 2253
N.A.I.C.S.: 315192; 315191
Import Export
Advertising Expenditures: $60,000,000
Media: 2-3-4-5-6-7-8-10-13-15-18-19-20-21-23-24
Distr.: Intl.; Natl.
Budget Set: Nov.
Personnel:
John Holland *(Pres & CEO)*
G. William Newton *(Exec VP & CFO)*
Mike Holland *(Sr VP)*
John Shivel *(Sr VP-Adv, Mktg & Corp Comm)*
Brands & Products:
BEST BY FRUIT OF THE LOOM
BVD
EASY TO WEAR
FRUIT OF THE LOOM
FUNGALS
FUNPALS
LOFTEEZ
SCREEN STARS
UNDEROOS
Advertising Agency:
The Richards Group, Inc.
8750 N Central Expy Ste 100
Dallas, TX 75231-6430
Tel.: (214) 891-5700
Fax: (214) 265-2933

G-III APPAREL GROUP, LTD.
512 7th Ave 35th Fl
New York, NY 10018-0832
Tel.: (212) 403-0500
Fax: (212) 403-0551
Web Site: www.g-iii.com
Approx. Sls.: $1,063,404,000
Approx. Number Employees: 2,154
Year Founded: 1974
Business Description:
Apparel Designer, Marketer & Mfr
S.I.C.: 2299; 2311; 2371
N.A.I.C.S.: 313312; 315222; 315292
Import Export
Advertising Expenditures: $36,400,000
Media: 5-13-17
Personnel:
Morris Goldfarb *(Chm & CEO)*
Sammy Aaron *(Vice Chm)*
Roni Seiderman *(Pres-Calvin Klein Accessories)*
Jeanette Nostra-Katz *(Pres)*
Neal S. Nackman *(CFO)*
Wayne S. Miller *(COO)*
Jeffrey Goldfarb *(Dir-Strategic Plng)*
Brands & Products:
BLACK RIVET
CALVIN KLEIN
COLE HAAN
ELIZA J
ELLEN TRACY
G-III
G-III SPORTS
G-III WOMEN
GUESS
INDUSTRIAL COTTON
JESSICA HOWARD
JONES NEW YORK
KENNETH COLE
MARVIN RICHARDS
NINE WEST
SEAN JOHN

Key to Media (For complete agency information see *The Advertising Red Books-Agencies* edition):
1. Bus. Publs. 2. Cable T.V. 3. Catalogs & Directories. 4. Co-op Adv. 5. Consumer Mags. 6. D.M. to Bus. Estab.7. D.M. to Consumers 8. Daily Newsp. 9. Exhibits/Trade Shows 10. Foreign 11. Infomercial 12. Internet Adv.13. Multimedia 14. Network Radio 15. Network T.V. 16. Newsp. Distr. Mags. 17. Other 18. Outdoor (Posters, Transit) 19. Point of Purchase20. Premiums, Novelties 21. Product Samples 22. Special Events Mktg. 23. Spot Radio 24. Spot T.V. 25. Weekly Newsp. 26. Yellow Page Adv.

G-III Apparel Group, Ltd. — (Continued)

SIENA STUDIO
TOMMY HILFIGER
WILSON'S LEATHER
Advertising Agency:
Creative Marketing Plus Inc.
4705 Center Blvd Ste 806
Long Island City, NY 11109
Tel.: (718) 606-0767
Fax: (718) 606-6345

GEM-DANDY, INC.

200 W Academy St
Madison, NC 27025
Mailing Address:
PO Box 657
Madison, NC 27025-0657
Tel.: (336) 548-9624
Fax: (336) 427-7105
Toll Free: (800) 334-5101
E-mail: customerservice@gem-dandy.com
Web Site: www.gem-dandy.com
Approx. Number Employees: 42
Year Founded: 1921
Business Description:
Distr. of Suspenders, Belts & Small Leather Products
S.I.C.: 2389
N.A.I.C.S.: 315999
Import Export
Advertising Expenditures: $350,000
Media: 4-5-6-9-10-26
Distr.: Natl.
Budget Set: Aug.
Personnel:
Brad Penn *(Pres)*
Don Wilson *(Sr VP-Ops)*
Paul Walter *(VP-Fin)*
Brands & Products:
GEM-DANDY
Advertising Agency:
Steele & Ballington Studios
Route 4 Box 33
Reidsville, NC 27320
(Danbury; Bill Blass; Ruff Hewn; Lyntone Belts & Accessories)

GEORGIA BOOT, LLC

(Sub. of Rocky Brands, Inc.)
39 E Canal St
Nelsonville, OH 45764
Tel.: (740) 753-1951
Fax: (740) 753-4024
Web Site: www.rockybrands.com
Sales Range: $450-499.9 Million
Business Description:
Outdoor & Occupational Footwear Designer, Mfr & Distr
S.I.C.: 3149; 3143; 3144
N.A.I.C.S.: 316219; 316213; 316214
Personnel:
Mike Brooks *(Chm)*
Advertising Agency:
Thompson & Company Marketing Communications
50 Peabody Pl
Memphis, TN 38103-3667
Tel.: (901) 527-8000
Fax: (901) 527-3697

GTFM LLC

(d/b/a FUBU)
350 5th Ave Ste 6617
New York, NY 10118-6617
Tel.: (212) 273-3300
Fax: (212) 273-3333
Web Site: www.fubu.com
Approx. Number Employees: 60
Year Founded: 1992
Business Description:
Clothing & Home Collection Designer
S.I.C.: 5136; 5137
N.A.I.C.S.: 424320; 424330
Media: 6-13-18-19-22-23-24
Distr.: Intl.; Natl.
Personnel:
Daymond John *(Pres & CEO)*
Brands & Products:
FUBU INTERNATIONAL
FUBU THE COLLECTION
PLATINUM FUBU

H. FREEMAN & SON, INC.

411 N Cranberry Rd
Westminster, MD 21157
Tel.: (410) 857-5774
Fax: (410) 857-1560
Toll Free: (800) 468-0689
E-mail: hfrcustserv@hfreemanco.com
Web Site: www.hfreemanco.com
Approx. Number Employees: 425
Year Founded: 1885
Business Description:
Men's Tailored Clothing Mfr
S.I.C.: 2311; 2325
N.A.I.C.S.: 315222; 315224
Media: 1-4-5-7-8-10-19-21
Distr.: Natl.
Budget Set: Jan.
Personnel:
Mark Falcone *(Gen Mgr)*
Brands & Products:
H. FREEMAN

HAGGAR CORPORATION

(Joint Venture of Perseus LLC, Symphony Holdings Limited & Infinity Associates LLC)
11511 Luna Rd
Dallas, TX 75234-6022
Tel.: (214) 352-8481
Fax: (214) 956-4367
E-mail: public.relations@haggar.com
Web Site: www.haggar.com
Sales Range: $450-499.9 Million
Approx. Number Employees: 3,300
Year Founded: 1926
Business Description:
Men's & Women's Apparel Products Marketer, Importer & Mfr
S.I.C.: 2326; 5136; 5611; 5621
N.A.I.C.S.: 315225; 424320; 448110; 448120
Export
Advertising Expenditures: $12,300,000
Media: 2-3-5-6-10-15-19-23-24
Distr.: Intl.
Budget Set: June
Personnel:
Tim Lyons *(Pres-Sls)*
Chirine Boukarroum *(Mgr-Mktg)*
Brands & Products:
COMFORT EQUIPPED
COOL 18
EXPANDOMATIC
FOREVERNEW
FREEDOM KHAKI
HAGGAR
HAGGAR BLACK LABEL
HERITAGE
STONEBRIDGE

HAMRICK INC.

742 Peachoid Rd
Gaffney, SC 29341-3440
Tel.: (864) 489-6095
Fax: (864) 489-9514
Web Site: www.hamricks.com
Approx. Number Employees: 440
Business Description:
Clothing Stores
S.I.C.: 5651; 2337
N.A.I.C.S.: 448140; 315234
Media: 8-9-13-19-23-24-25
Distr.: Reg.
Personnel:
Barry L. Hamrick *(Pres)*

HARDWICK CLOTHES INC.

3800 Old Tasso Rd
Cleveland, TN 37312
Tel.: (423) 476-6534
Fax: (423) 476-5756
E-mail: customerservice@hardwickclothes.com
Web Site: www.hardwickclothes.com
Approx. Number Employees: 300
Year Founded: 1882
Business Description:
Men's & Ladies' Clothing, Suits, Sport Coats, Slacks
S.I.C.: 2311
N.A.I.C.S.: 315222
Advertising Expenditures: $200,000
Media: 2-4-7-10-19-20
Distr.: Natl.
Budget Set: Dec.
Personnel:
Thomas H. Hopper *(Chm & Pres)*
Nancy Deakins *(Dir-Adv & Sec)*
Jim Park *(VP-Sls)*
Brands & Products:
HARDWICK CLOTHES
LADY HARDWICK

HARPER INDUSTRIES, INC.

136 Central Ave
Clark, NJ 07066-1422
Tel.: (732) 815-3200
Fax: (732) 815-3232
Approx. Number Employees: 300
Year Founded: 1946
Business Description:
Mfr. of Men's Activewear Shirts
S.I.C.: 8021
N.A.I.C.S.: 621210
Media: 4-6-16-19
Distr.: Natl.
Brands & Products:
AMY BARR
ATTITUDES ONLY
CARRIAGE WAY
COUNTRY TOUCH
GRAND BANKS OUTFITTERS
HARCREST
HARPER
SPORTE PARTS

HART SCHAFFNER & MARX

(Joint Venture of S. Kumars Nationwide Limited & Emerisque Brands UK Limited)
(d/b/a HMX, LLC)
101 N Wacker Dr
Chicago, IL 60606-1784
Tel.: (312) 357-5353
Fax: (312) 444-2674
E-mail: info@hartschaffnermarx.com
Web Site: www.hartschaffnermarx.com
Sales Range: $600-649.9 Million
Approx. Number Employees: 700
Year Founded: 1887
Business Description:
Men's Tailored Apparel Mfr
S.I.C.: 2311; 2325
N.A.I.C.S.: 315222; 315224
Media: 2-4-5-6-7-8-9-17-19-20-23-24
Distr.: Intl.; Natl.
Personnel:
Joe Faczek *(Mgr-Mktg)*
Brands & Products:
HART SCHAFFNER & MARX

HAT WORLD, INC.

(Sub. of Genesco Inc.)
7555 Woodland Dr
Indianapolis, IN 46278-1347
Tel.: (317) 334-9428
Fax: (317) 337-1428
Toll Free: (888) 564HATS
Web Site: www.lids.com
Sales Range: $25-49.9 Million
Approx. Number Employees: 900
Year Founded: 1995
Business Description:
Miscellaneous Apparel & Accessory Store
S.I.C.: 5699
N.A.I.C.S.: 448190
Import Export
Media: 4-5-13-19
Personnel:
Glenn Campbell *(Co-Founder)*
Kenneth J. Kocher *(Pres)*
Brands & Products:
WWW.HATSHACK.COM
WWW.HATWORLD.COM
WWW.LIDS.COM
WWW.LIDSKIDS.COM

HICKEY-FREEMAN CO., INC.

(Joint Venture of S. Kumars Nationwide Limited & Emerisque Brands UK Limited)
(d/b/a HMX, LLC)
1155 Clinton Ave N
Rochester, NY 14621
Mailing Address:
PO Box 30200
Rochester, NY 14603-3200
Tel.: (585) 467-7240
Fax: (585) 467-1236
Toll Free: (888) 603-8968
E-mail: info@hickeyfreeman.com
Web Site: www.hickeyfreeman.com
Sales Range: $300-349.9 Million
Approx. Number Employees: 750
Business Description:
Men's Tailored Apparel Mfr
S.I.C.: 2311; 2325
N.A.I.C.S.: 315222; 315224
Advertising Expenditures: $2,800,000
Media: 2-4-5-6-7-8-9-10-13-16-19-23
Distr.: Natl.
Budget Set: May
Personnel:
Chris Linares *(Sr VP-Retail)*
Brands & Products:
HICKEY-FREEMAN

HONEYWELL NORTH SAFETY PRODUCTS

(Div. of Honeywell Safety Products)
2000 Plainfield Pke
Cranston, RI 02921
Tel.: (401) 943-4400

Key to Media (For complete agency information see *The Advertising Red Books-Agencies* edition):
1. Bus. Publs. 2. Cable T.V. 3. Catalogs & Directories. 4. Co-op Adv. 5. Consumer Mags. 6. D.M. to Bus. Estab.7. D.M. to Consumers 8. Daily Newsp. 9. Exhibits/Trade Shows 10. Foreign 11. Infomercial 12. Internet Adv.13. Multimedia 14. Network Radio 15. Network T.V. 16. Newsp. Distr. Mags. 17. Other 18. Outdoor (Posters, Transit) 19. Point of Purchase20. Premiums, Novelties 21. Product Samples 22. Special Events Mktg. 23. Spot Radio 24. Spot T.V. 25. Weekly Newsp. 26. Yellow Page Adv.

Fax: (800) 572-6346
Fax: (401) 946-7560
Toll Free: (800) 430-4110
E-mail: marketing@honeywell.com
Web Site: www.northsafety.com
Approx. Sls.: $10,000,000
Approx. Number Employees: 200
Year Founded: 1855
Business Description:
Personal Protection Equipment Mfr
S.I.C.: 2389; 3851
N.A.I.C.S.: 315999; 339115
Media: 2-4-7-10-11-20-21
Distr.: Intl.; Natl.
Budget Set: Nov. -Dec.
Personnel:
Charles S. Ellis *(Pres)*
Sonny Hayes *(Sr VP-Mfg)*
Nino Granatiero *(VP-Product Dev)*
Ron Lee *(VP-Sls-West)*
Mark Sheehan *(VP-Fin)*
Ricardo Valdes *(VP-Sls-Latin America)*
Brands & Products:
DURABILT
V-SAFE

HONEYWELL SAFETY PRODUCTS
(Sub. of Honeywell Life Safety)
2001 Spring Rd Ste 425
Oak Brook, IL 60523-4019
Tel.: (630) 572-5715
Fax: (630) 572-8518
Approx. Sls.: $608,897,000
Approx. Number Employees: 3,055
Year Founded: 1995
Business Description:
Protective Clothing, Footwear & Equipment Mfr
S.I.C.: 3021; 2329; 2339; 2341; 2389; 3143; 3144; 5045; 5084; 5085; 7389
N.A.I.C.S.: 316211; 315211; 315212; 315231; 315999; 316213; 316214; 423830; 423840; 425110; 425120
Advertising Expenditures: $5,569,000
Personnel:
David F. Myers, Jr. *(Mgr-Bus Dev)*
Matthew A. Satnick *(Mgr)*
Craig Staub *(Mgr)*
Brands & Products:
BREATHABLE AIRMESH
MORNING PRIDE
MUCK
NORTH
NORTHERN
THE ORIGINAL MUCK BOOT CO.
PRO-WARRINGTON
RANGER
SALISBURY
SERVICE
SERVUS
TOTAL FIRE
W.H. SALISBURY
XTRATUF

HOT TOPIC, INC.
18305 E San Jose Ave
City of Industry, CA 91748
Tel.: (626) 839-4681
Fax: (626) 839-4686
Web Site: www.hottopic.com
Approx. Sls.: $708,244,000
Approx. Number Employees: 2,400
Year Founded: 1989
Business Description:
Music & Popular Culture-Inspired Clothing & Accessories Retailer
S.I.C.: 5699; 5621
N.A.I.C.S.: 448150; 448120
Advertising Expenditures: $8,500,000
Media: 4-8-9-22
Personnel:
Bruce A. Quinnell *(Chm)*
Lisa M. Harper *(CEO)*
James McGinty *(CFO)*
Gerald Cook *(COO)*
Donald Hendricks *(CIO)*
John Kirkpatrick *(Sr VP & Chief Music Officer)*
Jeff Allison *(Sr VP)*
Mark Mizicko *(Sr VP-Plng & Allocation)*
Kelly Mcguire Diehl *(VP-HR)*
Darrell Kinsley *(VP-Visual & Store Design)*
George Wehlitz Jr. *(VP-Fin)*
Brands & Products:
EVERYTING ABOUT THE MUSIC
HOT TOPIC
MORBID MAKEUP
MORBID THREADS

THE HUBBARD COMPANY
(Sub. of Tom James Company)
208 Lurgan Ave
Shippensburg, PA 17257
Tel.: (717) 532-4146
Toll Free: (800) 241-1226
E-mail: hubcustserv@thehubbardcompany.com
Web Site: www.thehubbardcompany.com
Approx. Number Employees: 150
Year Founded: 1935
Business Description:
Mfr of Men's Pants
S.I.C.: 2253; 2325
N.A.I.C.S.: 315191; 315224
Media: 2-5-6-9-19-23-24
Distr.: Natl.
Budget Set: Jan.

HUGO BOSS FASHIONS INC.
(Sub. of Hugo Boss USA Inc.)
601 W 26th St 8th Fl
New York, NY 10001
Tel.: (212) 940-0600
Fax: (212) 940-0606
E-mail: sally_tran@hugoboss.com
Web Site: www.hugoboss.com
Approx. Number Employees: 65
Business Description:
Men's & Women's Fashion Apparel Whslr
S.I.C.: 5136
N.A.I.C.S.: 424320
Media: 2-4-6-7-8-10-19-25
Distr.: Direct to Consumer; Intl.; Natl.
Personnel:
Mark S. Brashear *(Chm & CEO-Americas)*
Advertising Agency:
One Source Visual Marketing Solution
108 W 39th St 2nd Fl
New York, NY 10018
Tel.: (212) 398-0444
Toll Free: (877) 398-0444

I. SPIEWAK & SONS, INC.
469 7th Ave 10th Fl
New York, NY 10018-7605
Tel.: (212) 695-1620
Fax: (212) 629-4803
Toll Free: (800) 223-6850
Toll Free: (888) 268-6850 (Sales)
E-mail: info@spiewak.com
Web Site: www.spiewak.com
E-Mail For Key Personnel:
President: roy@spiewak.com
Approx. Number Employees: 450
Year Founded: 1904
Business Description:
Provider of Ladies', Men's, Young Men's & Boys' Outerwear, Ski & Sportswear, Insulated Clothing, Trappings, Uniforms & Industrial Jackets & Parkas
S.I.C.: 2329
N.A.I.C.S.: 315228
Import Export
Advertising Expenditures: $500,000
Media: 2-4-5-6-7-10-11-18-20-22-23-26
Distr.: Intl.; Natl.
Budget Set: Mar.
Personnel:
Jerry Spiewak *(Chm)*
Roy Spiewak *(Pres)*
Michael Spiewak *(CEO)*
Patrick Cunningham *(Controller)*
Brands & Products:
AVENEL
BIO PROTECTIVE CLOTHING
CAREER FASHION
ELBERON RAIN
EXCALIBUR
FLIGHT DECK U.S.A.
GREENBRIAR
HIDDEN AGENDA
JONES DUTY
ORTLEY
PELHAM
ROCKAWAY
SABER
SHADMORE
SPIEWAK
TITAN
VIZGUARD
WEATHER-TECH

IMP ORIGINALS, INC.
100 W 33rd St Ste 1103
New York, NY 10001-2909
Tel.: (212) 563-5510
Fax: (212) 695-0825
Web Site: www.imporiginalsinc.com
Approx. Number Employees: 85
Business Description:
Mfr of Boy's Wear
S.I.C.: 5136
N.A.I.C.S.: 424320
Media: 6
Distr.: Natl.
Budget Set: Oct.
Personnel:
Burton Stern *(Pres)*
Fran Issadopre *(Mgr-Natl Sls)*
Brands & Products:
ALEXANDER JULIAN
IMP ORIGINALS

INCOMING, INC.
244 5th Ave Ste V235
New York, NY 10001
Tel.: (917) 210-1074
Toll Free: (888) 218-4037
E-mail: info@incominginc.com
Web Site: www.incominginc.com
Approx. Rev.: $59,011
Approx. Number Employees: 4
Year Founded: 2006
Business Description:
Renewable Biofuels Mfr
S.I.C.: 1389; 2865
N.A.I.C.S.: 213112; 325192
Advertising Expenditures: $128,905
Media: 17
Personnel:
R. Samuel Bell, Jr. *(Chm & CEO)*
Victor Abi Jaoudi, II *(Pres, COO & Dir)*
Jasmine Victoria *(Exec VP & Sec)*
Eric Norris *(VP-Fin)*

IZOD
(Sub. of Phillips Van Heusen Corporation)
1001 Frontier Rd MS No 44
Bridgewater, NJ 08807
Tel.: (908) 685-0050
Toll Free: (800) 866-7292
Web Site: www.izod.com
Sales Range: $250-299.9 Million
Approx. Number Employees: 750
Business Description:
Sportswear Mfr
S.I.C.: 2389
N.A.I.C.S.: 315299
Media: 1-5-6-8-9-10-11-13-19
Distr.: Intl.; Natl.
Budget Set: Nov.
Personnel:
Cheryl Dapolito *(Pres)*
Donna Patrick *(Pres-Retail)*
Rose Butkiewicz *(Mgr-Mktg)*
Brands & Products:
IZOD

JANTZEN INC.
(Div. of Jantzen Apparel, LLC)
1411 Broadway Fl 24
New York, NY 10018-3402
Tel.: (212) 730-1622
Fax: (212) 302-2785
Web Site: www.jantzen.com
Sales Range: $50-74.9 Million
Approx. Number Employees: 5
Business Description:
Swimsuits for Women & Children
S.I.C.: 5137; 2339
N.A.I.C.S.: 424330; 315239
Brands & Products:
NIKE
ORIGINAL PENGUIN
PERRY ELLIS
Advertising Agency:
ECommerce Partners
59 Franklin St Ste 6B
New York, NY 10013
Tel.: (212) 334-3390
Fax: (503) 218-5585
Toll Free: (866) 431-6669

JHANE BARNES, INC.
140 W 57th St
New York, NY 10019
Tel.: (212) 575-2448
Fax: (212) 575-2506
Toll Free: (888) G0JHANE
E-mail: info@jhanebarnes.com
Web Site: www.jhanebarnes.com
Approx. Number Employees: 12
Business Description:
Men's Clothing & Accessories Designer
S.I.C.: 7389; 2322
N.A.I.C.S.: 561990; 315221
Media: 6-10-13
Personnel:
Jhane Barnes *(CEO)*

Key to Media (For complete agency information see *The Advertising Red Books-Agencies* edition):
1. Bus. Publs. 2. Cable T.V. 3. Catalogs & Directories. 4. Co-op Adv. 5. Consumer Mags. 6. D.M. to Bus. Estab.7. D.M. to Consumers 8. Daily Newsp. 9. Exhibits/Trade Shows 10. Foreign 11. Infomercial 12. Internet Adv.13. Multimedia 14. Network Radio 15. Network T.V. 16. Newsp. Distr. Mags. 17. Other 18. Outdoor (Posters, Transit) 19. Point of Purchase20. Premiums, Novelties 21. Product Samples 22. Special Events Mktg. 23. Spot Radio 24. Spot T.V. 25. Weekly Newsp. 26. Yellow Page Adv.

JOS. A. BANK CLOTHIERS, INC.
500 Hanover Pike
Hampstead, MD 21074-2002
Tel.: (410) 239-2700
Fax: (410) 239-5700
Toll Free: (800) 999-7472
E-mail: service@jos-a-bank.com
Web Site: www.josbank.com
Approx. Sls.: $858,128,000
Approx. Number Employees: 3,728
Year Founded: 1905
Business Description:
Men's Clothing Mfr & Sales
S.I.C.: 5611; 5961
N.A.I.C.S.: 448110; 454113
Export
Advertising Expenditures: $7,156,000
Media: 4-6-8-13-19-22-23
Personnel:
Robert N. Wildrick *(Chm)*
R. Neal Black *(Pres & CEO)*
Gary M. Merry *(CIO)*
Charles D. Frazer *(Gen Counsel, Sec & Sr VP)*
Robert B. Hensley *(Exec VP-Real Estate Dev & HR)*
James W. Thorne *(Exec VP-Mdsg & Chief Mdsg Officer)*
Jerry Deboer *(Sr VP-Mktg)*
Andrea Poling *(VP-HR)*
Brands & Products:
JOS. A. BANK
THE MIRACLE COLLECTION
TRAVELER CREASE
VACATION IN PARADISE

JUNK FOOD CLOTHING COMPANY
(Formerly Liquid Blaino Designs, Inc.)
(Sub. of Delta Apparel, Inc.)
11725 Mississippi Ave
Los Angeles, CA 90025
Tel.: (310) 445-7776
Web Site: www.junkfoodclothing.com
Sales Range: $150-199.9 Million
Business Description:
Licensed & Branded Apparel Sales
S.I.C.: 2389
N.A.I.C.S.: 315999
Media: 13-20

JUSTIN BOOT COMPANY
(Plant of Justin Brands, Inc.)
1100 Presley Dr
Cassville, MO 65625
Tel.: (417) 847-4192
Fax: (417) 847-3205
Web Site: www.justinbrands.com
Sales Range: $100-124.9 Million
Approx. Number Employees: 250
Business Description:
Footwear Mfr
S.I.C.: 3149; 3144
N.A.I.C.S.: 316219; 316214
Brands & Products:
JUSTIN BOOTS
Advertising Agency:
French/West/Vaughan, Inc.
112 E Hargett St
Raleigh, NC 27601
Tel.: (919) 832-6300
Fax: (919) 832-6360

KAZOO, INC.
(d/b/a Edwards Garment)
4900 9th St
Kalamazoo, MI 49009
Tel.: (269) 375-4900
Fax: (269) 375-8230
E-mail: edwardg@edwardsgarment.com
Web Site: www.edwardsgarment.com
Approx. Number Employees: 180
Business Description:
Men's & Women's Clothing Mfr
S.I.C.: 2326
N.A.I.C.S.: 315225
Media: 2-4-10
Distr.: Natl.
Budget Set: Dec.
Personnel:
Gary Schultz *(Pres)*
Brands & Products:
EDWARDS GARMENT
LAUNDRY PLUS

KEY INDUSTRIES, INC.
400 Marble Rd
Fort Scott, KS 66701-8639
Tel.: (620) 223-2000
Fax: (620) 223-5822
Toll Free: (800) 835-0365
E-mail: custserv@keyapparel.com
Web Site: www.keyindustriesinc.com
Approx. Number Employees: 46
Year Founded: 1908
Business Description:
Overalls, Work Clothes & Jeans Mfr
S.I.C.: 2326
N.A.I.C.S.: 315225
Import Export
Media: 3-4-5-6-8-9-18-19-20-22-23-24-25-26
Distr.: Natl.
Budget Set: Dec. -Jan.
Personnel:
William K. Pollock *(Chm)*
Jeff Sweetser *(CIO & VP)*
Michael Johnson *(Sr VP-Ops)*
Brands & Products:
BIC
KEY
MOSSY OAK
POLAR KING
TEN MILE
WOLF MOUNTAIN

KUHLMAN COMPANY INC.
420 N 5th Ave Ste 100
Minneapolis, MN 55401
Tel.: (212) 486-9300
Fax: (612) 338-5762
E-mail: info@kuhlmancompany.com
Web Site: www.kuhlmancompany.com
Sales Range: $1-9.9 Million
Approx. Number Employees: 110
Business Description:
Apparel & Accessories Retailer & Whslr
S.I.C.: 5699; 5136
N.A.I.C.S.: 448150; 424320; 448190
Advertising Expenditures: $390,000
Media: 4-8-13-19
Personnel:
Scott Kuhlman *(Chm, Pres & Chief Creative Officer)*

LEE JEANS
(Div. of VF Jeanswear Limited Partnership)
9001 W 67th St
Shawnee Mission, KS 66202
Tel.: (913) 789-0679
Fax: (913) 384-0190
Web Site: www.lee.com
Sales Range: $100-124.9 Million
Approx. Number Employees: 120
Business Description:
Clothing Mfr
S.I.C.: 2329; 2325
N.A.I.C.S.: 315211; 315224
Personnel:
Joe Dzialo *(Pres)*
Liz Cahill *(VP-Mktg-VF Jeanswear)*
Advertising Agencies:
ArnoldNYC
110 5th Ave
New York, NY 10011
Tel.: (212) 463-1000
Fax: (212) 463-1080

Barkley
1740 Main St
Kansas City, MO 64108
Tel.: (816) 842-1500
E-Commerce
Lee.com

LEHIGH OUTFITTERS, LLC
(Sub. of Rocky Brands, Inc.)
39 E Canal St
Nelsonville, OH 45764
Tel.: (740) 753-9100
Fax: (740) 753-7240
Toll Free: (800) 444-4086
E-mail: clientservices@lehighoutfitters.com
Web Site: www.lehighoutfitters.com
Sales Range: $400-449.9 Million
Approx. Number Employees: 250
Year Founded: 1922
Business Description:
Safety Footwear & Apparel Mfr
S.I.C.: 3149; 2389; 3143; 3144; 5139
N.A.I.C.S.: 316219; 315299; 316213; 316214; 424340
Media: 5-6-8-13-18-21
Personnel:
Mike Brooks *(Chm & CEO)*
Richard Simms *(Pres-Retail)*
Mark Dean *(Dir-Govt & Millitary Sls)*
Kevin Lowe *(Mgr-Investments & Cost Acctg)*

LEVI STRAUSS & CO.
1155 Battery St
San Francisco, CA 94111-1230
Tel.: (415) 501-6000
Fax: (415) 501-3939
Toll Free: (800) 872-5384
Web Site: www.levistrauss.com
E-Mail For Key Personnel:
Public Relations: questions@levi.com
Approx. Sls.: $4,325,908,000
Approx. Number Employees: 16,200
Year Founded: 1853
Business Description:
Jeans & Apparel Mfr & Marketer
S.I.C.: 2325; 2339
N.A.I.C.S.: 315224; 315239
Import Export
Advertising Expenditures: $327,800,000
Media: 3-6-15-17-18-23-24
Distr.: Intl.; Natl.
Personnel:
David Love *(Owner)*
Stephen C. Neal *(Chm)*
R. John Anderson *(Pres & CEO)*
Blake Jorgensen *(CFO)*
Rebecca Van Dyck *(CMO)*
Jill Nash *(Chief Comm Officer & Sr VP-Corp Affairs)*
Lawrence W. Ruff *(Chief Strategy Officer)*
Armin Broger *(Pres-Levi Strauss EMEA)*
Jennifer Sey *(Sr VP-Global Mktg-Dockers)*
Cathleen L. Unruh *(Sr VP)*
Paul Zadoff *(Sr VP-Wholesale Comml Ops-Americas)*
Beto Guajardo *(Global VP-Strategy)*
Christian Navarro *(Sr Mgr-Consumer Mktg-Global)*
Lisa Vargas *(Sr Mgr-Mktg)*
Brands & Products:
501 ORIGINAL
503
504
505
512
515
518
524
525
527
531
545
550
569
BOOT CUT 517
CAPITAL E
CARRIER
COMFORT FIT 560
COPPER
DOCKERS
FLARE 542
LEVI STRAUSS SIGNATURE
LEVI'S
LEVI'S 513
LEVI'S 517
LEVI'S 524
LEVI'S 560
LEVI'S ECO
MID RISE BOOT 553
MID RISE STRAIGHT 552
NEVER IRON
RED TAB
RELAXED STRAIGHT 559
SHRINK-TO-FIT
SIGNATURE BY LEVI STRAUSS & CO.
SKINNY 510
SKINNY 511
SLIM BOOT 507
SLIM STRAIGHT 514
TILTED STRAIGHT 523
ULTRA LOW BOOT 522
VINTAGE STRAIGHT 539
Advertising Agencies:
Aerial Advertising Services
333 W Jack London Blvd Hangar 241
Livermore, CA 94551
Tel.: (925) 449-0210

BBDO Korea
Sungam Building 114 Nohnhyun-Dong
Seoul, Korea (South)
Tel.: (82) 2 3449 9000
Fax: (82) 2 515 2678

EVB-Evolution Bureau
55 Union St
San Francisco, CA 94111
Tel.: (415) 281-3950
Fax: (415) 281-3957

Key to Media (For complete agency information see *The Advertising Red Books-Agencies* edition):
1. Bus. Publs. 2. Cable T.V. 3. Catalogs & Directories. 4. Co-op Adv. 5. Consumer Mags. 6. D.M. to Bus. Estab.7. D.M. to Consumers
8. Daily Newsp. 9. Exhibits/Trade Shows 10. Foreign 11. Infomercial 12. Internet Adv.13. Multimedia 14. Network Radio
15. Network T.V. 16. Newsp. Distr. Mags. 17. Other 18. Outdoor (Posters, Transit) 19. Point of Purchase20. Premiums, Novelties
21. Product Samples 22. Special Events Mktg. 23. Spot Radio 24. Spot T.V. 25. Weekly Newsp. 26. Yellow Page Adv.

OgilvyOne Worldwide
35 Robinson Road #03-01
Singapore, 068876, Singapore
Tel.: (65) 6213 7899
Fax: (65) 6213 7980
Levi's Asia Pacific Copper Jeans

OMD-USA
195 Broadway
New York, NY 10007
Tel.: (212) 590-7100
Dockers
Levi's
Media Buying & Planning

Razorfish
821 2nd Ave Ste 1800
Seattle, WA 98104-2343
Tel.: (206) 816-8800
Fax: (206) 816-8808
Go Forth Campaign - Digital

Sub Rosa
27 W 24th St Ste 501
New York, NY 10010
Tel.: (212) 414-8605
Fax: (646) 349-1685

TEQUILA
16F Cambridge House Taikoo Place
979 King's Road
Hong Kong, China
Tel.: (86) 2802 6363
Fax: (86) 2802 6262
Colour Patches

Wieden + Kennedy, Inc.
224 NW 13th Ave
Portland, OR 97209-2953
Tel.: (503) 937-7000
Fax: (503) 937-8000
(Levi's, Creative, United States)
Go Forth Campaign

LORD WEST FORMAL WEAR

257 Ritten House Cir
Bristol, PA 19007
Tel.: (215) 785-2300
Fax: (215) 785-5300
E-mail: info@flowformal.com
Web Site: www.flowformal.com
Sales Range: $25-49.9 Million
Year Founded: 1917
Business Description:
Mfr. of Men's Formalwear & Accessories
S.I.C.: 2311; 2325
N.A.I.C.S.: 315222; 315224
Export
Advertising Expenditures: $700,000
Media: 6-10-13-15-19
Distr.: Natl.
Budget Set: Dec.
Personnel:
Charles Burkhalter *(VP-Creative Svcs)*
Brands & Products:
LORD WEST

LOST ARROW CORPORATION

259 W Santa Clara St
Ventura, CA 93001
Mailing Address:
PO Box 150
Ventura, CA 93002-0150
Tel.: (805) 643-8616
Fax: (805) 653-6355
Web Site: www.patagonia.com
Sales Range: $300-349.9 Million
Approx. Number Employees: 1,000
Year Founded: 1984
Business Description:
Outdoor Clothing Designer & Distr
S.I.C.: 5941; 2339
N.A.I.C.S.: 451110; 315239
Advertising Expenditures: $600,000
Media: 4-6-8-10-13-19-21-22
Distr.: Intl.
Personnel:
Yvon Chouinard *(Owner)*
Casey Sheahan *(CEO)*
Mike Mesko *(VP-Production)*
Jen Rapp *(Dir-Pub Rels)*
Brands & Products:
LOTUS DESIGNS
PATAGONIA
WATER GIRL INT'L
Advertising Agency:
Lost Arrow Design
259 W Santa Clara
Ventura, CA 93001
Tel.: (805) 643-8616
Fax: (805) 653-6355

LULULEMON ATHLETICA INC.

1818 Cornwall Avenue
Vancouver, BC V6J 1C7, Canada
Tel.: (604) 732-6124
Web Site: www.lululemon.com
Approx. Rev.: $711,704,000
Approx. Number Employees: 4,572
Year Founded: 1998
Business Description:
Athletic Apparel Designer & Retailer
S.I.C.: 3949; 5699
N.A.I.C.S.: 339920; 448190
Media: 22-28
Personnel:
Dennis J. Wilson *(Chm & Chief Innovation/Branding Officer)*
Christine M. Day *(CEO)*
John E. Currie *(CFO)*
Kathryn Henry *(CIO)*
Chris Ladd *(Sr VP-Global e-Commerce)*
Brands & Products:
LULULEMON ATHLETICA
OQOQO

LUSKEY'S WESTERN STORES, INC.

3402 Catclaw Dr
Abilene, TX 79606
Tel.: (325) 793-9953
Fax: (325) 793-9956
Toll Free: (800) 725-7966
Web Site: www.luskeys.com
Approx. Number Employees: 12
Year Founded: 1919
Business Description:
Western Apparel Retailer
S.I.C.: 5699
N.A.I.C.S.: 448190
Export
Media: 2-4-9-10-13-23-24
Personnel:
Jerry Doty *(Owner)*
Alan Luskey *(Owner)*
Brands & Products:
LUSKEY'S/RYON'S
LUSKEY'S WESTERN STORES
RYON'S

MARKS WORK WEARHOUSE LTD.

(Sub. of Canadian Tire Corporation Limited)
30 1035 64th Ave SE Ste 30
Calgary, AB T2H 2J7, Canada
Tel.: (403) 255-9220
Fax: (403) 255-6005
Toll Free: (800) 663-6275
E-mail: customer.service@marksegain.net
Web Site: www.marks.com
Sales Range: $250-299.9 Million
Approx. Number Employees: 2,863
Year Founded: 1977
Business Description:
Retailer of Women's & Men's Workwear, Casual Wear, Custom Uniforms & Related Apparel
S.I.C.: 5699
N.A.I.C.S.: 448150
Import
Consumer Mags.: 50%; Point of Purchase: 50%
Personnel:
Michael Strachan *(Sr VP-Mdsg)*
Anna Greco-Taylor *(Brand Mgr)*
Sabrina Lalonde *(Mgr-Mktg)*
Brands & Products:
BLUE PINE
CANYON CREEK
CLOTHES THAT WORK
DAKOTA
DENVER HAYES
MOUNTAIN GEAR
ULTIMATE WORK
WIND RIVER OUTFITTING
WORK WORLD
WORKPRO

MARV HOLLAND APPAREL LTD.

10939 120th St NW
Edmonton, AB Canada
Tel.: (780) 453-5044
Fax: (780) 453-6283
E-mail: custserv@marvholland.com
Web Site: www.marvholland.com
Approx. Number Employees: 180
Year Founded: 1948
Business Description:
Business Clothing & Uniforms
S.I.C.: 2329; 2311
N.A.I.C.S.: 315211; 315222
Import
Advertising Expenditures: $300,000
Media: 2-4-7-10-21-26
Distr.: Natl.
Budget Set: Dec.
Personnel:
Marvin C. Holland *(Owner & CEO)*
Brands & Products:
CRYON
FIREWALL
IMAGE MAKER
MAGNUM
MAROX
MARV HOLLAND
NOMEX

MAUS & HOFFMAN, INC.

800 E Las Olas Blvd
Fort Lauderdale, FL 33301
Tel.: (954) 463-1472
Fax: (954) 463-1587
Toll Free: (800) MAU-MAUS
E-mail: info@mausandhoffman.com
Web Site: www.mausandhoffman.com
Approx. Number Employees: 35
Year Founded: 1940
Business Description:
Retailer of Clothing
S.I.C.: 5611; 5621
N.A.I.C.S.: 448110; 448120
Media: 4-6-8
Personnel:
John G. Maus *(Pres)*

THE MEN'S WEARHOUSE, INC.

6380 Rogerdale Rd
Houston, TX 77072-1624
Tel.: (281) 776-7200
Fax: (281) 776-7038
Toll Free: (800) 776-7848
E-mail: ir@tmw.com
Web Site: www.menswearhouse.com
Approx. Sls.: $2,102,664,000
Approx. Number Employees: 11,800
Year Founded: 1973
Business Description:
Men's Clothing Store Owner & Operator
S.I.C.: 5611; 5699
N.A.I.C.S.: 448110; 448150
Import
Advertising Expenditures: $82,000,000
Media: 3-14-15-17-23-24
Distr.: Natl.
Personnel:
George A. Zimmer *(Chm & CEO)*
David H. Edwab *(Vice Chm)*
Douglas S. Ewert *(Pres & COO)*
Neill P. Davis *(CFO, Treas & Exec VP)*
William Melvin *(CIO & Sr VP)*
Diane Ridgway-Cross *(CMO)*
Gary G. Ckodre *(Exec VP-Distr, Logistics & Tuxedo Ops & Chief Compliance Officer)*
Carole L. Souvenir *(Chief Legal Officer & Exec VP-Employee Rels)*
Jayme D. Maxwell *(Chief Adv Officer, Chief Creative Officer & Sr VP)*
Diana M. Wilson *(Chief Acctg Officer & Sr VP)*
Charles Bresler *(Exec VP-Mktg & HR)*
William C. Silveira *(Exec VP-Mfg)*
Scott Norris *(Sr VP & Gen Mgr-Mdse)*
Jamie R. Bragg *(Sr VP-Ops)*
Thomas L. Jennings *(Sr VP)*
Susan G. Neal *(Sr VP-eBus & Digital Strategies)*
Mark Neutze *(Sr VP-Stores)*
David Stevens *(Sr VP-Distr & Logistics)*
James D. Young *(Sr VP-Distr)*
James E. Zimmer *(Sr VP-Mdsg)*
Kim Owens *(VP-Mktg)*
Matt Schow *(VP-Online Mktg & Ecommerce)*
Brands & Products:
APPLE
BOSTONIAN
CANARY
CEDAR
JONES NEW YORK CITY
JOSEPH & FEISS
J.VICTOR
MARGARITAVILLE
MEN'S WEARHOUSE
POOL
PRONTO UOMO
TUXEDO

Key to Media (For complete agency information see *The Advertising Red Books-Agencies* edition):
1. Bus. Publs. 2. Cable T.V. 3. Catalogs & Directories. 4. Co-op Adv. 5. Consumer Mags. 6. D.M. to Bus. Estab.7. D.M. to Consumers 8. Daily Newsp. 9. Exhibits/Trade Shows 10. Foreign 11. Infomercial 12. Internet Adv.13. Multimedia 14. Network Radio 15. Network T.V. 16. Newsp. Distr. Mags. 17. Other 18. Outdoor (Posters, Transit) 19. Point of Purchase20. Premiums, Novelties 21. Product Samples 22. Special Events Mktg. 23. Spot Radio 24. Spot T.V. 25. Weekly Newsp. 26. Yellow Page Adv.

The Men's Wearhouse, Inc. — (Continued)

Advertising Agency:
Mullen
101 N Cherry St Ste 600
Winston Salem, NC 27101-4035
Tel.: (336) 765-3630
Fax: (336) 774-9550

MILLER INTERNATIONAL, INC.
8500 Zuni St
Denver, CO 80260-5007
Tel.: (303) 428-5696
Fax: (303) 430-1130
Toll Free: (800) 688-4525
Web Site: www.rmccjeans.com
Approx. Number Employees: 200
Business Description:
Mfr of Western Apparel
S.I.C.: 2339; 2325
N.A.I.C.S.: 315239; 315224
Import Export
Media: 2-18-19-22
Distr.: Natl.
Budget Set: Oct.
Brands & Products:
CINCH
CRUEL GIRL
ROCKIES
ROCKY MOUNTAIN

MW TUX
(Div. of The Men's Wearhouse, Inc.)
1835 Shackleford Ct
Norcross, GA 30093-2949
Tel.: (770) 448-8381
Fax: (770) 449-6707
Toll Free: (800) 955-8287
Web Site: www.afterhours.com
Sales Range: $75-99.9 Million
Year Founded: 1946
Business Description:
Men's Formal Wear Sales & Rental
S.I.C.: 7299; 5699
N.A.I.C.S.: 532220; 448190
Media: 6-13
Personnel:
Gary G. Ckodre *(Exec VP)*
Jamie R. Bragg *(Sr VP-Distr)*
Brands & Products:
CREATE-A-TUX

NAUTICA ENTERPRISES, INC.
(Sub. of VF Corporation)
40 W 57th St
New York, NY 10019-4001
Tel.: (212) 541-5757
Fax: (212) 887-8136
Web Site: www.nautica.com
Sales Range: $1-4.9 Billion
Approx. Number Employees: 3,300
Year Founded: 1984
Business Description:
Active Wear & Sportswear Mfr
S.I.C.: 2329; 2341
N.A.I.C.S.: 315228; 315231
Import
Media: 1-4-5-6-7-10-13-14-15-23-24
Personnel:
Karen Murray *(Pres)*
Tom Froehlich *(CIO)*
Lisa Whitney *(Gen Counsel & VP)*
Stephen Wilson *(Sr VP-Global Logistics)*
Nina Flood *(VP-Mktg)*
Advertising Agency:
Laird+Partners
475 10th Ave 7th Fl
New York, NY 10018
Tel.: (212) 478-8181
Fax: (212) 478-8210

NEWFIELD EXPLORATION COMPANY
363 N Sam Houston Pkwy E Ste 2020
Houston, TX 77060-2424
Tel.: (281) 847-6000
Fax: (281) 405-4242
E-mail: info@newfld.com
Web Site: www.newfld.com
Approx. Rev.: $1,883,000,000
Approx. Number Employees: 1,352
Year Founded: 1989
Business Description:
Explore, Develop & Acquire Crude Oil & Natural Gas Properties
S.I.C.: 1311; 2911
N.A.I.C.S.: 211111; 324110
Bus. Publs.: 100%
Personnel:
Lee K. Boothby *(Chm, Pres & CEO)*
Terry W. Rathert *(CFO & Exec VP)*
Gary D. Packer *(COO & Exec VP)*
John D. Marziotti *(Gen Counsel & Sec)*
Deanna L. Jones *(VP-HR)*
Mark J. Spicer *(VP-IT)*
James T. Zernell *(VP-Production)*
Brian L. Rickmers *(Controller & Asst Sec)*

NEXT INC.
7625 Hamilton Park Dr Ste 12
Chattanooga, TN 37421
Tel.: (423) 296-8213
Fax: (423) 510-7058
E-mail: info@nextinc.net
Web Site: www.nextinc.net
Approx. Sls.: $15,352,424
Approx. Number Employees: 80
Business Description:
Licensed & Branded Promotional Products & Imprinted Sportswear Designer & Distr
S.I.C.: 2389; 7336
N.A.I.C.S.: 315999; 541430
Advertising Expenditures: $3,106,000
Personnel:
Ronald J. Metz *(Chm)*
Robert M. Budd *(CEO)*
David O. Cole *(CFO, Chief Acctg Officer & Sec)*

OLD NAVY
(Div. of The Gap, Inc.)
2 Folsom St
San Francisco, CA 94105-1205
Tel.: (650) 952-4400
Web Site: www.oldnavy.com
Sales Range: $400-449.9 Million
Approx. Number Employees: 1,000
Year Founded: 1994
Business Description:
Specialty Apparel Retailer
S.I.C.: 5651; 5641
N.A.I.C.S.: 448140; 448130
Media: 3-4-8-14-15-17-22-25-31
Distr.: Reg.
Personnel:
Amy Curtis-McIntyre *(CMO & Sr VP-Mktg)*
Tom Wyatt *(Pres-Decision)*
Ann Pavey Wells *(Mgr-Ops)*
Advertising Agencies:
CP+B
3390 Mary St Ste 300
Coconut Grove, FL 33133
Tel.: (305) 859-2070
Fax: (305) 854-3419
(Seasonal Campaigns)

CP+B Boulder
6450 Gunpark Dr
Boulder, CO 80301
Tel.: (303) 628-5100
Fax: (303) 516-0227

JL Media, Inc.
1600 Rte 22 E
Union, NJ 07083-3415
Tel.: (908) 687-8700
Fax: (908) 687-9280

Old Navy Marketing
2 Folsom St
San Francisco, CA 94105
Tel.: (650) 952-4400

RealTime Media, Inc.
1060 1st Ave Ste 201
King of Prussia, PA 19406
Tel.: (610) 337-3600
Fax: (610) 337-2300

OSHKOSH B'GOSH, INC.
(Sub. of Carter's, Inc.)
206 Spate st
Oshkosh, WI 54901-5008
Tel.: (920) 231-8800
Fax: (920) 231-8621
Toll Free: (800) 282-4674
E-mail: consumerbgosh@carters.com
Web Site: www.oshkoshbgosh.com
Sales Range: $300-349.9 Million
Approx. Number Employees: 20
Year Founded: 1895
Business Description:
Infants' & Children's Wear & Accessories; Workwear & Men's Sportswear
S.I.C.: 5641; 5611
N.A.I.C.S.: 448130; 448110
Import Export
Media: 1-2-3-4-5-6-8-9-11-13-18-19-20-22-23-24-25
Distr.: Intl.; Natl.
Personnel:
Lisa A. Fitzgerald *(Exec VP & Brand Leader)*
Tanya Coventry-Strader *(Dir-Brand Strategy)*
Brands & Products:
OSHKOSH
OSHKOSH BABY
OSHKOSH B'GOSH

PAUL FREDRICK MENSTYLE INC.
223 W Poplar St
Fleetwood, PA 19522
Tel.: (610) 944-0909
Fax: (610) 944-7600
E-mail: sdrayer@paulfredrick.com
Web Site: www.paulfredrick.com
Approx. Number Employees: 102
Business Description:
Men's Mail Order Clothing Mfr
S.I.C.: 5961
N.A.I.C.S.: 454113
Export
Media: 4-6-8-11
Personnel:
Paul Sacher *(Pres & CEO)*
Angela Crouse *(Mgr-Internet Mktg)*

PERRY ELLIS INTERNATIONAL, INC.
3000 NW 107th Ave
Miami, FL 33172-2133
Tel.: (305) 592-2830
Fax: (305) 594-2307
E-mail: info@pery.com
Web Site: www.pery.com
Approx. Rev.: $790,288,000
Approx. Number Employees: 2,400
Year Founded: 1967
Business Description:
Clothing Designer & Marketer
S.I.C.: 2321; 2325; 5621
N.A.I.C.S.: 315223; 315224; 448120
Import
Advertising Expenditures: $11,600,000
Media: 4-5-6-13-18-22-30
Personnel:
George Feldenkreis *(Chm & CEO)*
Oscar Feldenkreis *(Chm & CEO)*
Anita D. Britt *(CFO)*
Brett Dean *(CMO)*
Stephen Harriman *(Pres-Divisions)*
Gary Rubin *(Pres-Retail & E-com)*
Cory Shade *(Gen Counsel & Sr VP)*
Jack F. Voith *(Exec VP)*
Thomas D'Ambrosio *(Sr VP & Controller)*
Pablo de Echevarria *(Sr VP-Mktg)*
Gail Rhodes *(Sr VP-Sls-Women's Swim)*
Kim Wagenaar *(Sr VP-Nike Swim)*
Gina Avila *(VP-Mdsg)*
Lori Medici *(VP-Mktg)*
John Crocco *(Dir-Creative)*
Bernie Keasley *(Dir-Fin-Europe)*
Brands & Products:
AXIS
AXIST
C&C CALIFORNIA
CALLAWAY GOLF
CROSSINGS
CUBAVERA
FARAH
GIRL STAR
GOTCHA
GRAND SLAM
HAVANERA CO.
JAG
JANTZEN
JOHN HENRY
LAUNDRY BY SHELLI SEGAL
MANHATTAN
MCD
MONDO DI MARCO
MUNSINGWEAR
NATURAL ISSUE
NIKE SWIM
ORIGINAL PENGUIN
PENGUIN SPORT
PERRY ELLIS
PERRY ELLIS AMERICA
PERRY ELLIS PORTFOLIO
PGA TOUR
PRO PLAYER
RED SAND
SAVANE
TRICOT ST. RAPHAEL
Advertising Agencies:
LaForce & Stevens
132 W 21st St

Key to Media (For complete agency information see *The Advertising Red Books-Agencies* edition):
1. Bus. Publs. 2. Cable T.V. 3. Catalogs & Directories. 4. Co-op Adv. 5. Consumer Mags. 6. D.M. to Bus. Estab.7. D.M. to Consumers 8. Daily Newsp. 9. Exhibits/Trade Shows 10. Foreign 11. Infomercial 12. Internet Adv.13. Multimedia 14. Network Radio 15. Network T.V. 16. Newsp. Distr. Mags. 17. Other 18. Outdoor (Posters, Transit) 19. Point of Purchase20. Premiums, Novelties 21. Product Samples 22. Special Events Mktg. 23. Spot Radio 24. Spot T.V. 25. Weekly Newsp. 26. Yellow Page Adv.

New York, NY 10011
Tel.: (212) 242-9353
Fax: (212) 242-9565

Laspata Decaro
450 W 15th St Ste 600
New York, NY 10011
Tel.: (212) 929-1998
Fax: (212) 243-5305

Lloyd & Co.
180 Varick St Ste 1018
New York, NY 10014
Tel.: (212) 414-3100
Fax: (212) 414-3113

Wilen Press
3333 SW 15th St
Deerfield Beach, FL 33442
Tel.: (954) 246-5000
Fax: (954) 246-3333

PHAT FASHIONS, LLC

(Sub. of Kellwood Company)
512 7th Ave 29th Fl
New York, NY 10018
Tel.: (212) 798-3100
Fax: (212) 798-3105
Toll Free: (866) 547-5319
Web Site: www.babyphat.com
Approx. Number Employees: 25
Year Founded: 1992
Business Description:
Clothing & Outerwear Designer & Retailer
S.I.C.: 5611; 5136; 5641
N.A.I.C.S.: 448110; 424320; 448130
Media: 6-10-13-18-19-22-23
Personnel:
Kimora Lee Simmons *(Dir-Creative)*
Brands & Products:
BABY PHAT
PHAT FARM
PHAT FARM PLUS

PHILLIPS VAN HEUSEN CORPORATION

200 Madison Ave
New York, NY 10016-3903
Tel.: (212) 381-3500
Fax: (212) 381-3950
Web Site: www.pvh.com
Approx. Rev.: $4,636,848,000
Approx. Number Employees: 10,500
Year Founded: 1881
Business Description:
Apparel & Accessories Designer, Mfr, Distr & Retailer
S.I.C.: 2326; 2311; 2321; 2322; 2323; 2325; 2339; 2389; 5136; 5611
N.A.I.C.S.: 315225; 315221; 315222; 315223; 315224; 315239; 315993; 315999; 424320; 448110
Import Export
Advertising Expenditures: $303,575,000
Media: 1-2-4-5-6-7-8-9-10-11-15-16-18-19-20-24-25
Distr.: Natl.
Budget Set: July -Dec.
Personnel:
Emanuel Chirico *(Chm & CEO)*
Francis K. Duane *(Vice Chm-Wholesale)*
Allen E. Sirkin *(Pres & COO)*
Michael A. Shaffer *(CFO & Exec VP-Fin)*
Kenneth L. Wyse *(Pres-PVH Licensing)*
Mark D. Fischer *(Gen Counsel, Sec & Sr VP)*
Pamela N. Hootkin *(Treas, Sr VP & Dir-IR)*
Michael Kelly *(Exec VP-Mktg)*
John D. Peters *(Exec VP-Logistics & Tech-Shared Svcs Div)*
Kevin Urban *(Exec VP-Logistics Svcs-Shared Svcs Div)*
Bruce Goldstein *(Sr VP & Controller)*
David F. Kozel *(Sr VP-HR)*
Cindi Mullane *(Sr VP-Ops)*
Andrea Elliott *(VP & Gen Mgr-Canadian Retail Ops-Toronto)*
Brands & Products:
ARROW
BASS
CALVIN KLEIN
EAGLE
GH BASS & CO
IZOD
PVH
VAN HEUSEN
Advertising Agencies:
5W Public Relations
888 7th Ave 12th Fl
New York, NY 10106
Tel.: (212) 999-5585
Fax: (646) 328-1711

KRT Marketing
3685 Mt Diablo Blvd Ste 255
Lafayette, CA 94549-3776
Tel.: (925) 284-0444
Fax: (925) 284-0448
Recruitment

POLO RALPH LAUREN CORPORATION

650 Madison Ave
New York, NY 10022-1029
Tel.: (212) 318-7000
Fax: (212) 888-5780
Toll Free: (800) 377-7656
E-mail: CustomerSupport@polo.com
Web Site: www.ralphlauren.com
E-Mail For Key Personnel:
Marketing Director: dlauren@polo.com
Approx. Rev.: $5,660,300,000
Approx. Number Employees: 24,000
Year Founded: 1967
Business Description:
Mfr of Men's, Women's & Children's Clothing & Accessories, Fragrances, Home Furnishings, Luggage, Furs; Retail Sales
S.I.C.: 2326; 2321; 2325; 2339; 5023; 5139
N.A.I.C.S.: 315225; 315212; 315223; 315224; 423220; 424340
Advertising Expenditures: $192,000,000
Media: 6-9-31
Distr.: Intl.; Natl.
Personnel:
Ralph Lauren *(Chm & CEO)*
Roger N. Farah *(Pres & COO)*
Tracey Thomas Travis *(CFO & Sr VP)*
Mark Daley *(Pres-Asia Pacific)*
Susie McCabe *(Pres-Factory Stores)*
Jeffrey D. Morgan *(Div Pres-Product Licensing)*
Jerry Lauren *(Exec VP-Men's Design)*
Jackwyn L. Nemerov *(Exec VP-Wholesale Brands, Licensed Products & Asia Pacific)*
Don Baum *(Sr VP)*
Mary Randolph Carter *(Sr VP)*
Mitchell A. Kosh *(Sr VP-HR & Legal)*
David Lauren *(Sr VP-Corp Comm, Adv & Mktg)*
Robbin Mitchell *(Sr VP-Bus Process Integration)*
Howard Smith *(Sr VP-Supply Chain Ops)*
Miki Racine *(VP-Mktg)*
Kristen D'Arcy *(Sr Dir-Digital Mktg)*
Janelle Bronner *(District Brand Mgr-Club Monaco)*
Brands & Products:
ALEXIS
AMANDA
AMERICAN LIVING
APRES SKI
BARTON
BIG&TALL
BIG PONY
BLACK LABEL
BLUE LABEL
CHAPS
CLUB MONACO
DOUBLE BLACK
DOUBLE RL
EXPLORER
LAUREN
LAUREN BY RALPH LAUREN
LAUREN FOR MEN
LAUREN JEANS CO.
LAUREN PETITE
LAUREN SPA
LOVE
PINK PONY
POLO
POLO BLACK
POLO BLUE
POLO BY RALPH LAUREN
POLO GOLF
POLO GULF
POLO RALPH LAUREN
POLO TENNIS
PURPLE LABEL
RALPH
RALPH BY RALPH LAUREN
RALPH HOT
RALPH LAUREN BLACK LABEL
RALPH LAUREN BLUE
RALPH LAUREN BLUE LABEL
RALPH LAUREN CHILDRENSWEAR
RALPH LAUREN GOLF
RALPH LAUREN HOME
RALPH LAUREN PAINT
RALPH LAUREN PURPLE LABEL
RALPH LAUREN WOMEN?S COLLECTION
RALPH ROCKS
RLX
ROMANCE
ROMANCE SILVER
RRL
RUGBY
SAFARI
Advertising Agency:
Roberts + Langer DDB
437 Madison Ave 8th Fl
New York, NY 10022
Tel.: (646) 289-7300
Fax: (212) 593-1286

PREMIUMWEAR, INC.

(Sub. of Deluxe Small Business Services)
5500 Feltl Rd
Minnetonka, MN 55343-7902
Tel.: (952) 979-1700
Fax: (952) 979-1717
Toll Free: (800) 248-0158
E-mail: info@riversandtrading.com
Web Site: www.pageandtuttlecorporate.com
Sales Range: $75-99.9 Million
Approx. Number Employees: 100
Year Founded: 1886
Business Description:
Specialty Apparel Designer, Embroiderer & Retailer
S.I.C.: 2321; 2329
N.A.I.C.S.: 315223; 315228
Import Export
Advertising Expenditures: $1,200,000
Catalogs & Directories: $300,000; Co-op Adv.: $500,000; Consumer Mags.: $200,000; Daily Newsp.: $100,000; Special Events Mktg.: $100,000
Distr.: Intl.; Natl.
Budget Set: Aug.
Personnel:
Dick Merhar *(CFO)*
Jan Pfeffer *(Mgr-Fin)*
Brands & Products:
MUNSINGWEAR
PAGE & TUTTLE

RANDA ACCESSORIES, LLC

(Sub. of Randa Corp.)
2009 W Hastings St
Chicago, IL 60608
Tel.: (312) 997-2358
Fax: (312) 997-2147
Toll Free: (800) 843-8455
Web Site: www.humphreysinc.com
Approx. Number Employees: 200
Business Description:
Leather Distr
S.I.C.: 2389
N.A.I.C.S.: 315999
Media: 5-7-10-19
Personnel:
John Hastings *(CFO & Exec VP)*
Brad Kovaly *(COO & VP)*
Mary Rice *(Sr VP-Sls)*
Terry Tackett *(VP-Sls & Mktg)*

RANDA CORP.

(d/b/a Randa Accessories)
120 W 45th St Ste 3801
New York, NY 10036-4041
Tel.: (212) 768-8800
Fax: (212) 768-8585
Toll Free: (800) NECKTIE
Web Site: www.randa.net
Sales Range: $75-99.9 Million
Approx. Number Employees: 361
Year Founded: 1960
Business Description:
Men's Accessories Mfr
S.I.C.: 2782; 2323
N.A.I.C.S.: 323118; 315993
Media: 6-7-10
Personnel:
Jeffrey Spiegel *(Pres & CEO)*
David Katz *(CMO & Sr VP)*
Chris Bagnall *(Pres-Market Connect Grp)*

Key to Media (For complete agency information see *The Advertising Red Books-Agencies* edition):
1. Bus. Publs. 2. Cable T.V. 3. Catalogs & Directories. 4. Co-op Adv. 5. Consumer Mags. 6. D.M. to Bus. Estab.7. D.M. to Consumers
8. Daily Newsp. 9. Exhibits/Trade Shows 10. Foreign 11. Infomercial 12. Internet Adv.13. Multimedia 14. Network Radio
15. Network T.V. 16. Newsp. Distr. Mags. 17. Other 18. Outdoor (Posters, Transit) 19. Point of Purchase20. Premiums, Novelties
21. Product Samples 22. Special Events Mktg. 23. Spot Radio 24. Spot T.V. 25. Weekly Newsp. 26. Yellow Page Adv.

Randa Corp. — (Continued)

Randy Kennedy *(Sr VP)*
Judy Person *(Sr VP-Sls)*
Melissa Lawrence *(VP-Sls)*
Advertising Agency:
Revision
37 W 28th St 7th Fl
New York, NY 10001
Tel.: (212) 889-0005
Fax: (212) 889-0006
Countess Mara

REFRIGIWEAR, INC.

54 Breakstone Dr
Dahlonega, GA 30533-6698
Tel.: (706) 864-5757
Fax: (706) 864-5898
Toll Free: (800) 645-3744
E-mail: customerservice@refrigiwear.com
Web Site: www.refrigiwear.com
Sales Range: $10-24.9 Million
Approx. Number Employees: 110
Year Founded: 1954
Business Description:
Industrial Insulated Work Clothing Mfr
S.I.C.: 2329; 2389
N.A.I.C.S.: 315228; 315999
Import Export
Advertising Expenditures: $150,000
Media: 2-4-7-10-11-21
Distr.: Intl.; Natl.
Budget Set: Jan.
Personnel:
Mark Silberman *(Owner)*
Ronald Breakstone *(Pres)*
Colin Allen *(Exec VP-Sls)*
Don Byerly *(VP-Sls)*
Larry Gross *(Gen Mgr-WeatherGuard)*
Brands & Products:
CHILLBREAKER
COOLERWEAR
IRONTUFF
REFRIGIWEAR
STEEL-BUILT
WEATHERGUARD

ROCKY OUTDOOR GEAR

(Unit of Rocky Brands, Inc.)
39 E Canal St
Nelsonville, OH 45764
Tel.: (740) 753-1951
Fax: (740) 753-4211
Toll Free: (877) 795-2410
E-mail: info@rockybrands.com
Web Site: www.rockybrands.com
Sales Range: $125-149.9 Million
Approx. Number Employees: 200
Year Founded: 1979
Business Description:
Outdoor & Occupational Footwear Designer, Mfr & Distr
S.I.C.: 3149; 3143; 3144
N.A.I.C.S.: 316219; 316213; 316214
Personnel:
Mike Brooks *(Chm)*
Advertising Agency:
Thompson & Company Marketing Communications
50 Peabody Pl
Memphis, TN 38103-3667
Tel.: (901) 527-8000
Fax: (901) 527-3697

ROOTS CANADA LTD.

1400 Castlefield Ave
Toronto, ON M6B 4C4, Canada
Tel.: (416) 781-3574
Toll Free: (888) 307-6687
E-mail: onlineservice@roots.com
Web Site: www.roots.com
Sales Range: $250-299.9 Million
Approx. Number Employees: 200
Business Description:
Leather Products Mfr
S.I.C.: 3172
N.A.I.C.S.: 316993
Media: 6-13-22
Personnel:
Don Green *(Co-Founder)*
Michael Budman *(Co-Owner)*
Robert Sarner *(Dir-Comm & Pub Affairs)*

ROYTEX, INC.

16 E 34th St Fl 17
New York, NY 10016-4328
Tel.: (212) 686-3500
Fax: (212) 686-4336
E-mail: info@roytex.com
Web Site: www.roytex.com
Approx. Sls.: $60,000,000
Approx. Number Employees: 50
Year Founded: 1955
Business Description:
Sportswear Distr
S.I.C.: 5136
N.A.I.C.S.: 424320
Advertising Expenditures: $300,000
Media: 4-6-9-10-25
Distr.: Natl.
Personnel:
Richard Mourry *(Pres)*
Dennis Mourry *(CEO)*
Brands & Products:
ROYTEX, INC.

RUSSELL ATHLETIC

(Div. of Russell Corporation)
3330 Cumberland Blvd Ste 800
Atlanta, GA 30339
Tel.: (678) 742-8000
Web Site: www.russellathletic.com
Sales Range: $50-74.9 Million
Approx. Number Employees: 100
Business Description:
Athletic Team Uniforms & Leisure Wear Mfr & Marketer
S.I.C.: 2253; 2211
N.A.I.C.S.: 315191; 313210
Media: 4-6-10-25
Distr.: Intl.; Natl.
Budget Set: Oct.
Personnel:
Gary Barfield *(Exec VP)*
Julia Neuroth *(Sr Mgr-Mktg)*

SABAS BUNCH LIMITED PARTNERSHIP

(d/b/a Sabas Arizona Original Western Store)
3270 N Colorado St Ste 101
Chandler, AZ 85225
Tel.: (480) 969-7122
Fax: (480) 833-6494
Toll Free: (877) 342-1835
E-mail: info@sabas.com
Web Site: www.sabas.com
Approx. Number Employees: 100
Year Founded: 1927
Business Description:
Quality Western Apparel
S.I.C.: 5651; 5661
N.A.I.C.S.: 448140; 448210
Advertising Expenditures: $200,000
Media: 4-6-8-9-10-23-24-25-26
Distr.: Reg.
Personnel:
Roger Saba, Sr. *(Pres)*
Roger Saba, Jr. *(VP-Mktg & Sls)*
Brands & Products:
ARIZONA'S ORIGINAL WESTERN STORE
SABA'S

SCHOTT BROTHERS, INC.

1000 Jefferson Ave
Elizabeth, NJ 07201
Tel.: (908) 527-0011
Fax: (908) 527-6185
Toll Free: (800) 631-5407
E-mail: schottnyc@schottnyc.com
Web Site: www.schottnyc.com
Approx. Number Employees: 200
Year Founded: 1913
Business Description:
Mfr. of Men's & Boys' Leather & Cloth Outerwear & Sheepskin-Lined Clothing
S.I.C.: 2371; 2329
N.A.I.C.S.: 315292; 315228
Import Export
Media: 2-4-6-7-8-10-11-17-19
Distr.: Intl.; Natl.
Brands & Products:
SCHOTT

SEAN JOHN CLOTHING, INC.

(Sub. of Bad Boy Worldwide Entertainment Group)
1710 Broadway
New York, NY 10019
Tel.: (212) 500-2200
Fax: (212) 500-2201
E-mail: careers@seanjohn.com
Web Site: www.seanjohn.com
Sales Range: $1-9.9 Million
Approx. Number Employees: 65
Year Founded: 1998
Business Description:
Men's Apparel Designer, Producer & Distr
S.I.C.: 2329; 2322; 2326
N.A.I.C.S.: 315228; 315221; 315225
Media: 6-10-14-18-23
Personnel:
Sean Combs *(Pres)*
Dawn Robertson *(Pres)*
Jeffrey Tweedy *(Exec VP & Gen Mgr)*

SEATTLE PACIFIC INDUSTRIES, INC.

21216 72nd Ave S
Kent, WA 98032
Tel.: (206) 282-8889
Fax: (253) 872-2949
E-mail: ub@unionbay.com
Web Site: www.unionbay.com
Approx. Number Employees: 380
Year Founded: 1981
Business Description:
Mfr., Designer & Retailer of Men's & Women's Sportswear
S.I.C.: 5136
N.A.I.C.S.: 424320
Import
Advertising Expenditures: $5,000,000
Media: 1-3-6-8-10-17-19-21-22-24
Distr.: Intl.; Natl.
Personnel:
Steve Ritchey *(Pres)*
Gooria Lung *(COO)*
Brands & Products:
RE-UNION
SALTAIRE
SERGIO VALENTE
SISTER MOON
UNION
UNIONBAY

SOUTHWICK CLOTHING LLC

20 Computer Dr
Haverhill, MA 01832
Tel.: (978) 686-3833
Fax: (978) 738-0802
E-mail: custserv@southwickclothing.com
Web Site: www.southwickclothing.com
Approx. Number Employees: 200
Year Founded: 1929
Business Description:
Mfr of Clothes for Men
S.I.C.: 2311; 2325
N.A.I.C.S.: 315222; 315224
Export
Advertising Expenditures: $500,000
Media: 5-6-8-9-11-18-23
Distr.: Direct to Consumer; Natl.
Budget Set: July -Sept.
Personnel:
Joseph Antista *(Dir-Training)*
Brands & Products:
NINES BY SOUTHWICK
SOUTHWICK

STANFIELD'S LIMITED

1 Logan St
PO Box 190
Truro, NS B2N 5C2, Canada
Tel.: (902) 895-5406
Fax: (902) 893-8187
E-mail: inquiries@stanfields.com
Web Site: www.stanfields.com
Approx. Number Employees: 500
Year Founded: 1856
Business Description:
Sportswear, Underwear & Lounge Wear Mfr & Seller
S.I.C.: 2325
N.A.I.C.S.: 315224
Media: 5-6-10-11-14-15-18-19-21-26
Distr.: Intl.; Natl.
Budget Set: Aug.
Personnel:
F. Thomas Stanfield *(Pres & CEO)*
Jon D. F. Stanfield *(Pres-Stanfields-Canada)*
Glen Gaudet *(VP-Sls-Ops)*
Ian Covert *(Dir-Mktg & Bus Dev)*
Cheryl Smith *(Dir-Mdsg)*
Brands & Products:
ALL CLIMATE
KERMEL
LENZING
POLAR-THERM
PROTEKTAGARD
STANFIELD'S
THE UNDERWEAR COMPANY
Advertising Agency:
John St.
172 John Street
Toronto, ON M5T 1X5, Canada
Tel.: (416) 348-0048
Fax: (416) 348-0050
— Arthur Fleischmann *(Acct Dir)*
— Robyn Crookshank *(Acct Exec)*

Key to Media (For complete agency information see *The Advertising Red Books-Agencies* edition):
1. Bus. Publs. 2. Cable T.V. 3. Catalogs & Directories. 4. Co-op Adv. 5. Consumer Mags. 6. D.M. to Bus. Estab.7. D.M. to Consumers
8. Daily Newsp. 9. Exhibits/Trade Shows 10. Foreign 11. Infomercial 12. Internet Adv.13. Multimedia 14. Network Radio
15. Network T.V. 16. Newsp. Distr. Mags. 17. Other 18. Outdoor (Posters, Transit) 19. Point of Purchase20. Premiums, Novelties
21. Product Samples 22. Special Events Mktg. 23. Spot Radio 24. Spot T.V. 25. Weekly Newsp. 26. Yellow Page Adv.

SUPERBA, INC.
(Sub. of PVH Superba/Insignia Neckwear, Inc.)
1735 S Santa Fe Ave
Los Angeles, CA 90021-2904
Mailing Address:
PO Box 21805
Los Angeles, CA 90021-0805
Tel.: (213) 688-7970
Fax: (213) 623-3226
E-mail: info@superbainc.com
Web Site: www.superbainc.com
E-Mail For Key Personnel:
President: mervynmandelbaum@superbainc.com
Marketing Director: ncrouse@superbainc.com
Sales Director: lkniola@superbainc.com
Public Relations: ncrouse@superbainc.com
Sales Range: $350-399.9 Million
Approx. Number Employees: 950
Year Founded: 1873
Business Description:
Mfr. of Men's Neckwear
S.I.C.: 2323
N.A.I.C.S.: 315993
Import Export
Media: 2-4-7-10-19
Distr.: Intl.; Natl.
Budget Set: Mar.
Personnel:
Lee Terrill *(Pres)*
Mervyn Mandelbaum *(CEO)*
John Jarratt *(Exec VP-Sls & Mktg)*
Larry Kniola *(Exec VP)*
Danielle Mandelbaum *(Exec VP-Mdsg)*
Jim Beckman *(VP & Brand Mgr)*
Russell Smith *(VP & Brand Mgr)*
John Valastro *(VP & Brand Mgr)*
Bob Bolger *(VP-IT)*
Nancy Crouse *(VP-Sls & Svc)*
Brands & Products:
SUPERBA

SYMS CORPORATION
1 Syms Way
Secaucus, NJ 07094
Tel.: (201) 902-9600
Fax: (201) 902-9874
E-mail: customerservice@syms.com
Web Site: www.syms.com
Approx. Sls.: $445,133,000
Approx. Number Employees: 1,100
Year Founded: 1959
Business Description:
Apparel & Footwear Retailer
S.I.C.: 5651
N.A.I.C.S.: 448140
Advertising Expenditures: $7,021,000
Media: 8-9-23-24
Distr.: Natl.
Budget Set: Sept.
Personnel:
Marcy Syms *(Chm & CEO)*
Joel Feigenbaum *(Pres & COO)*
Seth Udasin *(CFO, Chief Acctg Officer & Sr VP)*
Laura McCabe Brandt *(VP, Gen Counsel & Sec)*
Anne Keefe *(Sr VP-HR)*
Margaret Collord *(VP-Mktg & Adv)*
Elyse Marks *(VP-IT)*
Marilen Adraneda *(Mgr-HR)*
Brands & Products:
AN EDUCATED CONSUMER IS OUR BEST CUSTOMER
THE MORE YOU KNOW ABOUT CLOTHING, THE BETTER IT IS
NAMES YOU MUST KNOW
REDISCOVER SYMS OFF PRICE - ON STYLE
SYMS
WHERE BARGAINS WERE BORN
Advertising Agency:
Syms Advertising
1 Syms Way
Secaucus, NJ 07094-9400
Tel.: (201) 902-9600
Fax: (201) 902-9270
(Off Price Apparel)

TANDY LEATHER FACTORY, INC.
1900 SE Loop
Fort Worth, TX 76119-4337
Tel.: (817) 496-4414
Fax: (817) 496-9806
Toll Free: (800) 433-3201
E-mail: tlfhelp@leatherfactory.com
Web Site: www.tandyleatherfactory.com
Approx. Sls.: $59,892,870
Approx. Number Employees: 364
Year Founded: 1980
Business Description:
Leather Products Mfr & Distr
S.I.C.: 3199; 2371; 3161; 5199
N.A.I.C.S.: 316999; 315292; 316991; 424990
Import Export
Advertising Expenditures: $3,002,000
Media: 4-7-8-19
Personnel:
Wray Thompson *(Chm)*
Jon W. Thompson *(Pres, CEO & COO)*
Shannon L. Greene *(CFO & Treas)*
William M. Warren *(Gen Counsel & Sec)*
Brands & Products:
TANDY LEATHER FACTORY
TLF

TELEFLEX INCORPORATED
155 S Limerick Rd
Limerick, PA 19468
Tel.: (610) 948-5100
Fax: (610) 948-5101
E-mail: webmgr@teleflex.com
Web Site: www.teleflex.com
Approx. Rev.: $1,801,705,000
Approx. Number Employees: 12,500
Year Founded: 1943
Business Description:
Commercial, Medical & Aerospace Market Engineered Products Mfr & Distr
S.I.C.: 3842; 3714; 3728; 3812; 3829; 3841; 3845
N.A.I.C.S.: 339113; 334510; 334511; 334519; 336322; 336399; 336413; 339112
Export
Media: 21-23
Distr.: Intl.; Natl.
Budget Set: Dec.
Personnel:
Benson F. Smith *(Chm, Pres & CEO)*
Richard A. Meier *(CFO & Exec VP)*
Charles E. Williams *(Chief Acctg Officer & Controller)*
Vince Northfield *(Exec VP-Global Ops & Medical)*
Julie McDowell *(VP-Corp Comm)*
James J. Leyden *(Asst Sec)*
Brands & Products:
TELEFLEX

TOMMY BAHAMA
(Sub. of Oxford Industries, Inc.)
428 Westlake Ave N Ste 388
Seattle, WA 98109
Tel.: (206) 622-8688
Fax: (206) 622-4483
E-mail: info@tommybahama.com
Web Site: www.tommybahama.com
Sales Range: $250-299.9 Million
Approx. Number Employees: 300
Year Founded: 1992
Business Description:
Men's & Women's Clothing, Accessories & Home Furnishings Mfr
S.I.C.: 5651; 2321; 5137
N.A.I.C.S.: 448140; 315223; 424330
Media: 6
Personnel:
Douglas B. Wood *(Pres & COO)*
Terry R. Pillow *(CEO)*
Rob Goldberg *(Sr VP-Mktg & Restaurants)*
Jon Wright *(VP-HR & Corp Ops)*
Kyle Zitek *(Dir-Mktg)*
Brands & Products:
TOMMY BAHAMA
Advertising Agencies:
DKC
386 Park Ave S 10th Fl
New York, NY 10016
Tel.: (212) 685-4300
Fax: (212) 685-9024

Foundation Inc.
1715 E Olive Way
Seattle, WA 98120
Tel.: (206) 860-8800

Hornall Anderson
Ste 1300 710 2nd Ave
Seattle, WA 98104-1712
Tel.: (206) 467-5800
Fax: (206) 467-6411

Orsi Public Relations
1158 Greenacre Ave
Los Angeles, CA 90046
Tel.: (323) 874-4073
Fax: (323) 874-8796

TRUE RELIGION APPAREL, INC.
2263 E Vernon Ave
Vernon, CA 90058
Tel.: (323) 266-3072
Fax: (323) 266-8060
Web Site: www.truereligionbrandjeans.com
Approx. Rev.: $363,714,000
Approx. Number Employees: 1,663
Year Founded: 2002
Business Description:
Denim Apparel Mfr, Designer & Marketer
S.I.C.: 2325; 2326; 2337; 5699
N.A.I.C.S.: 315224; 315225; 315234; 448190
Advertising Expenditures: $8,000,000
Media: 2-6-8
Personnel:
Jeffrey Lubell *(Founder, Chm & CEO)*
Lynne Koplin *(Pres)*
Peter F. Collins *(CFO & Asst Sec)*
David Chiovetti *(Sr VP-Retail-North America)*
Kelly Gvildys *(Sr VP)*
Jordan Daly *(VP-Brand Strategy)*

UNDER ARMOUR, INC.
1020 Hull St 3rd Fl
Baltimore, MD 21230
Tel.: (410) 234-9820
Toll Free: (888) 427-6687
Toll Free: (888) 1-ARMOUR
E-mail: feedback@underarmour.com
Web Site: www.underarmour.com
Approx. Rev.: $1,063,927,000
Approx. Number Employees: 2,000
Business Description:
Men's, Women's & Youth Sports Apparel Mfr
S.I.C.: 2329; 2311; 2321; 2322; 2339; 2353; 3949
N.A.I.C.S.: 315211; 315221; 315222; 315223; 315239; 315991; 339920
Advertising Expenditures: $128,200,000
Media: 1-3-5-6-8-13-15-17-18-19-22-24-31
Personnel:
Kevin A. Plank *(Chm, Pres & CEO)*
Brad Dickerson *(CFO)*
Kip J. Fulks *(COO)*
Chip Adams *(Chief Performance Officer)*
James E. Calo *(Chief Supply Chain Officer)*
Peter P. Mahrer *(Pres-EMEA)*
Kevin M. Haley *(Sr VP-Consumer Insights)*
J. Scott Plank *(Exec VP-Bus Dev)*
Stephen J. Battista *(Sr VP-Brand)*
William J. Kraus *(Sr VP-Mktg)*
Gene McCarthy *(Sr VP-Footwear)*
Matthew C. Mirchin *(Sr VP-Sports Mktg)*
Adam Peake *(Sr VP-Sls)*
Melissa A. Wallace *(Sr VP-Talent)*
Dan Sawall *(VP-Retail)*
Diane Pelkey *(Sr Dir-Comm)*
Brands & Products:
10 UNIVERSITY
ACCURACY POLO
THE ADVANTAGE IS UNDENIABLE
ALLSEASONGEAR
ARBORA TANK
ARMOUR
ARMOUR STORM
BASEMAP LEGGING
BRISCOE
BURN SHORT
CAPTURE OUTFIT
CARDIO FULL
CARDIO TANK
CLICK-CLACK
COIL POLO
COLDGEAR
DCE
DELAWARE MICROSHORT
DERVOS
DIAMOND
DOG LEG POLO
THE DROPPER CREW
ELIMINATE MPZ
GRIP STRETCHFIT
GUST JACKET
GYRA II

Key to Media (For complete agency information see *The Advertising Red Books-Agencies* edition):
1. Bus. Publs. 2. Cable T.V. 3. Catalogs & Directories. 4. Co-op Adv. 5. Consumer Mags. 6. D.M. to Bus. Estab.7. D.M. to Consumers
8. Daily Newsp. 9. Exhibits/Trade Shows 10. Foreign 11. Infomercial 12. Internet Adv.13. Multimedia 14. Network Radio
15. Network T.V. 16. Newsp. Distr. Mags. 17. Other 18. Outdoor (Posters, Transit) 19. Point of Purchase20. Premiums, Novelties
21. Product Samples 22. Special Events Mktg. 23. Spot Radio 24. Spot T.V. 25. Weekly Newsp. 26. Yellow Page Adv.

Under Armour, Inc. — (Continued)

HAWAII ARMOUR
HEATGEAR
HUNDO
HUNTER'S PERFORMANCE
IGNITE SLIDE
LOCKER SLIDE
LOCKERTAG
LOFT POLO
LOOSEGEAR
MEMBER POLO
MICROSHORT
MPZ
MULTIFLECTION
NECTAR
O-FLOW
PATHWAY T
PROTO SPEED
RECHARGE COMPRESSION
SKULLCAP
SOCCER
SPIN POLO
STRETCHFIT
SURGE DUFFLE
SURGE GRAPHIC HOODY
TACTICAL
TACTICAL APPROACH
TALON
TEAMSOCK
TEXAS TECH
TEXTURED II POLO
TNP TANK
TURFGEAR
UA ANTLER T
UA ATTACK
UA BASE
UA BREAKAWAY
UA CAPTURE
UA CHIMIRA
UA CUMBERLAND II
UA DEMOLISH
UA ILLUSION
UA METAL
UA MIRAGE
UA PLAYER POLO
UA POWER
UA PROXIMO
UA PULSE
UA REVENANT
UA TECH
UNDER ARMOUR
UNDER ARMOUR METAL

Advertising Agencies:
Alexander & Tom
3500 Boston St Ste 225
Baltimore, MD 21224-5275
Tel.: (410) 327-7400
Fax: (410) 327-7403

CP+B
3390 Mary St Ste 300
Coconut Grove, FL 33133
Tel.: (305) 859-2070
Fax: (305) 854-3419
Basketball Division
Creative
Digital
Print
TV

Deutsch, Inc.
(A Lowe & Partners Company)
111 8th Ave 14th Fl
New York, NY 10011-5201
Tel.: (212) 981-7600
Fax: (212) 981-7525
Public Relations

UNIFIRST CORPORATION

68 Jonspin Rd
Wilmington, MA 01887-1090
Tel.: (978) 658-8888
Fax: (978) 657-5663
Toll Free: (800) 455-7654
E-mail: ufirst@unifirst.com
Web Site: www.unifirst.com
E-Mail For Key Personnel:
Public Relations: jbartlet@unifirst.com
Approx. Rev.: $1,025,939,000
Approx. Number Employees: 10,000
Year Founded: 1936
Business Description:
Workwear & Related Products Supplier
S.I.C.: 5137; 5136; 7218; 7299
N.A.I.C.S.: 424330; 424320; 812199; 812332
Import
Advertising Expenditures: $1,600,000
Media: 1-2-4-7-10-20-23-26
Distr.: Intl.; Natl.
Personnel:
Ronald D. Croatti *(Chm, Pres & CEO)*
Steven Sintros *(CFO & VP)*
Cynthia Croatti *(Treas & Exec VP)*
William M. Ross *(Sr VP-Asset Mgmt)*
Bruce P. Boynton *(Sr VP-Ops)*
David A. Difillippo *(Sr VP-Ops)*
Michael A. Croatti *(Reg VP)*
John R. Badey *(VP-Dist & Engrg)*
David M Katz *(VP-Sls & Mktg)*
Michael E. Ruttner *(VP)*
Brands & Products:
ARMOREX FR
BREEZE WEAVE
COMFORT FIRST
CXP NOMEX
FLEXWEAR
GREAT IMPRESSIONS
INDURA
MODERN BUSINESS MAGAZINE
PARK STREET
SOFTWILL
ULTRA SOFT
UNICLEAN
UNIFIRST
UNIMOP
UNISCRAPER
UNIWEAR
UNIWEAVE
Advertising Agency:
American Ad Management
27710 Jefferson Blvd., Ste. 102
Temecula, CA 92590
Tel.: (909) 695-7700
Yellow Page Advertising

VF IMAGEWEAR

(Branch of VF Imagewear)
4408 W Linebaugh Ave
Tampa, FL 33624-5245
Tel.: (813) 963-6153
Fax: (813) 969-6570
Web Site: www.vfc.com
E-Mail For Key Personnel:
Marketing Director: rick-becker@vfc.com
Sales Range: $550-599.9 Million
Approx. Number Employees: 1,000
Year Founded: 1986
Business Description:
Licensed Sportswear Mfr & Sales
S.I.C.: 2329; 2339
N.A.I.C.S.: 315228; 315239
Import Export
Media: 2-4-5-6-9-10-19-22-23
Distr.: Natl.
Budget Set: Oct.
Personnel:
Scott Baxter *(Pres-Grp & VP)*
Richard E. Becker *(VP-Sls)*
Dana Parker *(VP-Mdsg)*

VF JEANSWEAR LIMITED PARTNERSHIP

(Sub. of VF Corporation)
400 N Elm St
Greensboro, NC 27401-2143
Tel.: (336) 332-3400
Fax: (336) 332-3518
E-mail: info@optera.com
Web Site: www.vfc.com
Sales Range: $400-449.9 Million
Approx. Number Employees: 800
Business Description:
Men's, Women's & Children's Clothing Mfr
S.I.C.: 2325; 2321; 2329
N.A.I.C.S.: 315224; 315211; 315223
Advertising Expenditures: $20,000,000
Media: 2-5-6-7-10-15-18-19-21-23-24
Distr.: Intl.; Natl.
Budget Set: Sept.
Personnel:
Angelo Lagrega *(Pres)*
Phillip Dunn *(Pres-Jeanswear Mass Market)*
Joseph Dzialo *(Pres-Lee Brand)*
Advertising Agency:
Makin' It Work - Pronto! Hispanic Marketing & Communications
3025 G Waughtown St
Winston Salem, NC 27107
Tel.: (336) 714-2837

VINEYARD VINES LLC

37 Brown House Rd
Stamford, CT 06902
Tel.: (203) 862-0793
Fax: (800) 892-3606
Toll Free: (800) 892-4982
E-mail: tieguys@vineyardvines.com
Web Site: www.vineyardvines.com
Sales Range: $10-24.9 Million
Approx. Number Employees: 100
Year Founded: 1998
Business Description:
Clothing Designer & Mfr
S.I.C.: 2326; 5136
N.A.I.C.S.: 315225; 424320
Personnel:
Ian Murray *(Owner)*
Shep Murray *(Owner)*
Brands & Products:
VINEYARD VINES
Advertising Agency:
Deutsch, Inc.
(A Lowe & Partners Company)
111 8th Ave 14th Fl
New York, NY 10011-5201
Tel.: (212) 981-7600
Fax: (212) 981-7525

THE WALKING COMPANY HOLDINGS, INC.

(Filed Ch 11 Bankruptcy #915139 on 12/07/09 in U.S. Bankruptcy Ct, Central Dist of CA, Santa Barbara)
121 Gray Ave
Santa Barbara, CA 93101-1831
Tel.: (805) 963-8727
Fax: (805) 962-9460
Toll Free: (800) 642DOGS
Web Site: www.thewalkingcompany.com/
Sales Range: $200-249.9 Million
Approx. Number Employees: 1,100
Business Description:
Footwear Retailer, Catalog Sales & Electronic Commerce
S.I.C.: 5661; 5961
N.A.I.C.S.: 448210; 454111; 454113
Advertising Expenditures: $3,858,000
Media: 4-8-13-18
Personnel:
Andrew Feshbach *(Pres & CEO)*
Anthony Wall *(Gen Counsel, Sec & Exec VP-Bus Affairs)*
Lee M. Cox *(Sr VP-Retail Ops)*
Brands & Products:
BIG BIG DOGS
BIG DOG SPORTSWEAR
BIG DOGS
LITTLE BIG DOGS
SHOP WITH THE BIG DOGS

WILLIAMSON-DICKIE MANUFACTURING COMPANY

509 W Vickery Blvd
Fort Worth, TX 76104
Tel.: (817) 336-7201
Fax: (817) 810-4454
Toll Free: (800) 342-5437
E-mail: Pbrannan@dickies.com
Web Site: www.dickies.com
Sales Range: $800-899.9 Million
Approx. Number Employees: 350
Year Founded: 1922
Business Description:
Work Clothing Mfr
S.I.C.: 2326
N.A.I.C.S.: 315225
Import Export
Advertising Expenditures: $2,250,000
Media: 1-2-4-5-6-7-8-10-11-13-14-17-18-19-20-21-22-23
Distr.: Intl.; Natl.
Budget Set: Nov.
Personnel:
Philip C. Williamson *(Chm, Pres & CEO)*
Gail Williamson-Rawl *(Vice Chm)*
Randy Teuber *(CFO & Exec VP)*
Marett Cobb *(Exec VP-HR)*
Tad Uchtman *(Sr VP-Mktg, Mdsg, Licensing & Retail)*
Michael Polydoroff *(Sr Dir-Brand Mktg)*
Jason Prior *(Dir-Retail Mktg)*
Brands & Products:
A LEGEND IN WORK
DICKIES
DURACOMFORT
FLEXWAIST
ORIGINAL 874
STAYDARK
TRADITIONAL 874
Advertising Agency:
Goodby, Silverstein & Partners, Inc.
(Part of Omnicom Group, Inc.)
720 California St
San Francisco, CA 94108-2404
Tel.: (415) 392-0669
Fax: (415) 788-4303
Dickies Agency of Record

Key to Media (For complete agency information see *The Advertising Red Books-Agencies* edition):
1. Bus. Publs. 2. Cable T.V. 3. Catalogs & Directories. 4. Co-op Adv. 5. Consumer Mags. 6. D.M. to Bus. Estab.7. D.M. to Consumers
8. Daily Newsp. 9. Exhibits/Trade Shows 10. Foreign 11. Infomercial 12. Internet Adv.13. Multimedia 14. Network Radio
15. Network T.V. 16. Newsp. Distr. Mags. 17. Other 18. Outdoor (Posters, Transit) 19. Point of Purchase20. Premiums, Novelties
21. Product Samples 22. Special Events Mktg. 23. Spot Radio 24. Spot T.V. 25. Weekly Newsp. 26. Yellow Page Adv.

Appliances

Carpet Sweepers — Convection Ovens — Dish Washers — Disposals — Microwave Ovens — Refrigerators — Sewing Machines — Small Appliances — Stoves — Toasters — Vacuum Cleaners — Water Coolers

ADAMS MFG. CO.
9790 Midwest Ave
Cleveland, OH 44125-2425
Tel.: (216) 587-6801
Fax: (216) 587-6807
E-mail: adamsx@att.net
Web Site:
www.adamsmanufacturing.com
Approx. Number Employees: 60
Year Founded: 1945
Business Description:
Mfr. of Humidifiers
S.I.C.: 3585; 3822
N.A.I.C.S.: 333415; 334512
Import Export
Media: 2-4-5-6-7-9-10-11-13-18-19-20-25-26
Distr.: Natl.
Budget Set: June
Personnel:
Marty L. Schonberger *(Pres)*
R. Schonberger *(VP-HR)*
Brands & Products:
ADAMS
ADAMS CLEANAIRE
HUMID-AIRE
INFRA-RED
MAGNANIMALS
MAGNET MAN
NOSE MAN
QUIK-FOLD
SPEEDFLAME
UNI-PAK

AERUS LLC
5420 LBJ Fwy Ste 1010
Dallas, TX 75240
Tel.: (214) 378-4000
Fax: (214) 378-7561
Toll Free: (800) 243-9078
Web Site: www.aerusonline.com
E-Mail For Key Personnel:
President: contactceo@aerusonline.com
Sales Range: $100-124.9 Million
Approx. Number Employees: 2,500
Year Founded: 1924
Business Description:
Commercial & Retail Vacuum Cleaners & Floor Polishers Mfr & Direct Sales
S.I.C.: 3635
N.A.I.C.S.: 335212
Import Export
Advertising Expenditures: $1,330,000
Multimedia: $50,000; Bus. Publs.: $10,000; Cable T.V.: $20,000; Catalogs & Directories: $200,000; D.M. to Consumers: $100,000; Daily Newsp.: $50,000; Exhibits/Trade Shows: $500,000; Other: $50,000; Premiums, Novelties: $100,000; Product Samples: $100,000; Special Events Mktg.: $50,000; Yellow Page Adv.: $100,000
Distr.: Natl.
Personnel:
Kevin Hickey *(Pres)*
Joseph P. Urso *(CEO)*
Bob McComas *(VP-HR)*
David Wade *(VP-Info Tech)*
Brands & Products:
AIRLUX
CENTRALUX
ENCORE
EPIC SERIES
FLOOR PRO
GUARDIAN
HOME SOLUTION
LITTLE LUX
LITTLE PRO
LUX
LUX 7000 SERIES

ALLIANCE LAUNDRY HOLDINGS LLC
(Holding of Teachers' Private Capital)
Shepard St
Ripon, WI 54971-0990
Tel.: (920) 748-3121
Fax: (920) 748-4334
E-mail: Bruce.Rounds@alliancels.com
Web Site: www.comlaundry.com
Approx. Rev.: $393,220,000
Approx. Number Employees: 1,488
Business Description:
Commercial Laundry Equipment Mfr
S.I.C.: 3582; 3633
N.A.I.C.S.: 333312; 335224
Import Export
Advertising Expenditures: $3,500,000
Media: 2-7-10-20
Distr.: Intl.; Natl.
Budget Set: Nov.
Personnel:
Steve Faraone *(Chm)*
Thomas F. L'Esperance *(Vice Chm)*
Michael D. Schoeb *(Pres & CEO)*
Bruce P. Rounds *(CFO & VP)*
Scott L. Spiller *(Chief Legal Officer, Sec & VP)*
Jeffrey J. Brothers *(Sr VP-Sls-North America)*
R. Scott Gaster *(VP & Gen Mgr-Ripon Ops)*
Robert J. Baudhuin *(VP-Engrg)*
Brenda Henke *(Dir-Trng & Technical Comm)*
Robert T. Wallace *(Dir-Fin Analysis & Internal Reporting-Alliance Laundry Sys)*
Brands & Products:
AJAX
HUEBSCH
NETMASTER
SIMPLEX
SPEED QUEEN
UNIMAC
WASHALERT
Advertising Agency:
Nelson Schmidt
600 E Wisconsin Ave
Milwaukee, WI 53202
Tel.: (414) 224-0210
Fax: (414) 224-9463

ANAHEIM MANUFACTURING COMPANY
(Sub. of Western Industries, Inc.)
4240 E La Palma Ave
Anaheim, CA 92807-1816
Mailing Address:
PO Box 4146
Anaheim, CA 92803-4146
Tel.: (714) 524-7770
Fax: (714) 996-7073
Toll Free: (800) 767-6293
E-mail: info@anaheimmfg.com
Web Site: www.anaheimmfg.com
Approx. Number Employees: 100
Year Founded: 1958
Business Description:
Residential & Commercial Food Waste Disposal Mfr
S.I.C.: 3639
N.A.I.C.S.: 335228
Import Export
Advertising Expenditures: $700,000
Media: 2-4-6-10-11-13-19-20
Distr.: Direct to Consumer; Intl.; Natl.; Reg.
Budget Set: Sept.
Personnel:
Thomas P. Dugan *(Pres)*
Walter Kovacs *(VP-Engrg)*
Sergio Varela *(VP-Sls & Mktg)*
Brands & Products:
CLEAR WATER
COOL WATER
QUICK & HOT
WASTE KING
WHIRLAWAY

APPLIANCE RECYCLING CENTERS OF AMERICA, INC.
(d/b/a ARCA)
7400 Excelsior Blvd
Minneapolis, MN 55426-4517
Tel.: (952) 930-9000
Fax: (952) 930-1800
Toll Free: (800) 452-8680
E-mail: info@arcainc.com
Web Site: www.arcainc.com
Approx. Rev.: $108,162,000
Approx. Number Employees: 366
Year Founded: 1983
Business Description:
Large-Scale Collection, Resale & Recycling of Major Household Appliances in an Environmentally Sound Manner
S.I.C.: 5719; 4953; 5722
N.A.I.C.S.: 442299; 443111; 562920
Advertising Expenditures: $3,520,000
Media: 9-13-23-24-26
Personnel:
Edward R. Cameron *(Chm, Pres & CEO)*
Peter P. Hausback *(CFO & Exec VP)*
Brands & Products:
APPLIANCE $MART
APPLIANCE RECYCLING CENTERS OF AMERICA
APPLIANCESMART
ARCA
ENCORE RECYCLED APPLIANCES

APSCO APPLIANCE CENTERS
4520 E Bay Dr
Clearwater, FL 33764
Tel.: (727) 536-5542
Fax: (727) 531-7890
Web Site: www.apsco.com/
Sales Range: $10-24.9 Million
Approx. Number Employees: 35
Year Founded: 1972
Business Description:
Electric Household Appliances
S.I.C.: 5722; 7699

Key to Media (For complete agency information see *The Advertising Red Books-Agencies* edition):
1. Bus. Publs. 2. Cable T.V. 3. Catalogs & Directories. 4. Co-op Adv. 5. Consumer Mags. 6. D.M. to Bus. Estab.7. D.M. to Consumers 8. Daily Newsp. 9. Exhibits/Trade Shows 10. Foreign 11. Infomercial 12. Internet Adv.13. Multimedia 14. Network Radio 15. Network T.V. 16. Newsp. Distr. Mags. 17. Other 18. Outdoor (Posters, Transit) 19. Point of Purchase20. Premiums, Novelties 21. Product Samples 22. Special Events Mktg. 23. Spot Radio 24. Spot T.V. 25. Weekly Newsp. 26. Yellow Page Adv.

APSCO Appliance Centers — (Continued)

N.A.I.C.S.: 443111; 811412
Media: 6
Personnel:
Alfred C. Greco *(Pres & Owner)*
Darrell Hoag *(Owner)*
Jon Chaplin *(Comptroller)*

BARBEQUES GALORE, INC.
(Sub. of Grand Hall Enterprise Company Ltd.)
2173 Salk Ave Ste 200
Carlsbad, CA 92008
Tel.: (949) 597-2400
Fax: (760) 795-3499
Toll Free: (800) 752-3085
E-mail: CustomerService@bbqgalore.com
Web Site: www.bbqgalore.com
Sales Range: $200-249.9 Million
Approx. Number Employees: 1,262
Year Founded: 1977
Business Description:
Barbecue Grill & Accessories Mfr & Retailer
S.I.C.: 3631
N.A.I.C.S.: 335221
Advertising Expenditures: $9,806,442
Personnel:
Henrik Stepanyan *(COO)*
Joe Lopez *(VP-Mktg & Product)*
Brands & Products:
BAR-B-CHEF
THE BARBEQUE BIBLE
BRINKMAN SMOKER
BUILT-INS
CAPT'N COOK
COOK-ON
DEAD HEAT HOT SAUCE
GRAND TURBO
JIM BEAM MARINADE
OLYMPIA BBQ LIGHT
TURBO CLASSIC
TURBO ELITE
TURBO SELECT
TURBO STS
WEBER SMOKEY JOE

BELL NORDIQ GROUP INC.
(Sub. of Bell Aliant Inc.)
7151 Jean Talon E 7th Fl
Anjou, QC H1M 3N8, Canada
Tel.: (514) 493-5531
Fax: (514) 493-5516
E-mail: press@bellnordiq.ca
Web Site: www.bellnordiq.ca
Sales Range: $1-9.9 Million
Approx. Number Employees: 800
Year Founded: 1976
Business Description:
Telecommunications
S.I.C.: 4813
N.A.I.C.S.: 517110
Media: 7-9-11-13-23-24-25
Personnel:
Roch L. Dube *(Pres & CEO)*
Brands & Products:
BELL NORDIQ
NORTHERNTEL
TELEBEC

BERNINA OF AMERICA INC.
(Sub. of Bernina Schweiz AG)
3702 Prairie Lake Ct
Aurora, IL 60504
Tel.: (630) 978-2500
Fax: (630) 978-8214
Web Site: www.berninausa.com
Sales Range: $100-124.9 Million
Approx. Number Employees: 150
Year Founded: 1969
Business Description:
Sewing Machines & Related Items
S.I.C.: 2517
N.A.I.C.S.: 337129
Import
Advertising Expenditures: $500,000
Media: 4-5-6-8-9-10-15-25
Distr.: Natl.
Budget Set: Sept.
Personnel:
Martin Favre *(Pres)*
Brands & Products:
950 INDUSTRIAL
ACTIVA 220
ACTIVA 230 PE
ACTIVA 240
ARTISTA 165E HERITAGE EDITION
ARTISTA 185 QEE
ARTISTA 200
ARTISTA 200 E
AURORA 430 E
AURORA 440 QE
AURORA 440 QEE
BERNETTE 55
BERNETTE 80E
BERNETTE 90E
BERNINA 1008
NOTHING SEWS LIKE A BERNINA. NOTHING
VIRTUOSA 153 QE ALEX ANDERSON CLASSIC
VIRTUOSA 153 QUILTER'S EDITION
VIRTUOSA 155
Advertising Agency:
Sterling Rice Group
1801 13th St Ste 400
Boulder, CO 80302
Tel.: (303) 381-6400
Fax: (303) 444-6637

BEST BUY CANADA LTD.
(Sub. of Best Buy Co., Inc.)
8800 Glenlyon Pkwy
Burnaby, BC V5J 5K3, Canada
Tel.: (604) 435-8223
Fax: (604) 412-5280
Toll Free: (866) BEST-BUY
Web Site: www.bestbuy.ca
Sales Range: $150-199.9 Million
Approx. Number Employees: 1,500
Year Founded: 1983
Business Description:
Retailer of Consumer Goods
S.I.C.: 5064; 7629
N.A.I.C.S.: 423620; 811211
Personnel:
Christopher Ian Bennett *(Dir-Corp Comm)*
Advertising Agencies:
CP+B Canada
296 Richmond St W Ste 500
Toronto, ON M5V 1X2, Canada
Tel.: (416) 598-4944
Fax: (416) 593-4944

Media Experts
495 Wellington St W Ste 250
Toronto, ON M5V 1E9, Canada
Tel.: (416) 597-0707
Fax: (416) 597-9927
Media Buying

Weber Shandwick
207 Queen's Quay W Ste 400
Toronto, ON M5J 1A7, Canada
Tel.: (416) 964-6444
Fax: (416) 964-6611
Corporate Communications
Digital
Integrated Marketing Communications
Public Relations
Social Media
— Pascale Ares *(Acct Exec)*

BESTWAY, INC.
12400 Coit Rd Ste 950
Dallas, TX 75251
Tel.: (214) 630-6655
Fax: (972) 387-7250
Web Site: www.bestwayrto.com
Sales Range: $1-9.9 Million
Approx. Number Employees: 45
Year Founded: 1993
Business Description:
Rent-to-Own Chain
S.I.C.: 7359; 5712
N.A.I.C.S.: 532420; 442110
Advertising Expenditures: $1,725,515
Media: 8-9
Distr.: Direct to Consumer
Budget Set: Aug. -July
Personnel:
R. Brooks Reed *(Chm)*
David A. Kraemer *(CEO)*
Beth A. Durrett *(CFO & Sec)*
Brands & Products:
BESTWAY

BISSELL HOMECARE, INC.
2345 Walker Ave NW
Grand Rapids, MI 49544-2516
Tel.: (616) 453-4451
Fax: (616) 453-1383
Toll Free: (800) 237-7691
E-mail: info@bissell.com
Web Site: www.bissell.com
Approx. Number Employees: 1,400
Year Founded: 1955
Business Description:
Carpet Sweepers, Vacuum Cleaners, Home Care Devices, Chemical Floor Scrubbers, Rug Shampooers & Home Cleaning Chemical Specialties Mfr
S.I.C.: 3635; 2842; 2899
N.A.I.C.S.: 335212; 325612; 325998
Media: 2-3-4-5-6-7-8-10-12-13-15-18-19-24-25
Distr.: Natl.
Budget Set: Jan.
Personnel:
Mark J. Bissell *(CEO)*
Michael DeJong *(CIO & Dir-IT)*
James A. Krzeminski *(Pres-Bus Ventures)*
Rich Sorota *(Sr VP-Mktg & Sls)*
Brands & Products:
ACAROSAN
APOHEAT
BARBIE
BIG GREEN
BISSELL
BISSELL TO GO
BOOSTER
BUTLER
CATCHALL
CLEAN 'N LIGHT
CLEANVIEW
CLEARVIEW
DEEP CLEANING BOOSTER
DIGIPRO
DIRTLIFTER
EASY VAC
EASYMATE
EASYVAC POWERBRUSH
FEATHERWEIGHT
FLIP
FLIP-IT
FORMULA
GOVAC
GROOVY VAC
LIFT-OFF
LITTLE GREEN
ONE STEP
OXY GEN2
OXY-KIC
OXYKIC
PERFECT PASS
PERFECT SWEEP
PERFECT SWEEP TURBO
POWER PARTNER
POWER TRAK
POWERCLEARVIEW
POWERFORCE
POWERGLIDE
POWERGROOM
POWERLIFTER
POWERSTEAMER
POWERSTEAMER PRO
PRO-TECH
PROHEAT
PROHEAT PRO-TECH
PROLITE
PROPARTNER
PURE AIR
QUICK STEAMER
QUICKSTEAMER
REVOLUTION
SOFT N SAFE
SPORT LIFTER
SPOTBOT
SPOTLIFTER 2X
SPOTLILFTER
STEAM MOP
STEAM 'N CLEAN
STEAMMOP
STURDY SWEEP
SWEEP UP
SWIFT SWEEP
TANK-IN-TANK
TURBO
TURBOBRUSH
WE MEAN CLEAN.
Advertising Agencies:
Barrie D'Rozario Murphy
400 1st Ave N Ste 220
Minneapolis, MN 55401
Tel.: (612) 279-1500
Fax: (612) 332-9995

Cramer-Krasselt
225 N Michigan Ave
Chicago, IL 60601-7601
Tel.: (312) 616-9600
Fax: (312) 616-3839

CRT/tanaka
101 W Commerce Rd
Richmond, VA 23224
Tel.: (804) 675-8100
Fax: (804) 675-8183

BKI
(Div. of Standex Food Service Equipment Group)
2812 Grandview Dr
Simpsonville, SC 29680-6217
Mailing Address:
PO Box 80400
Simpsonville, SC 29680-0007

Key to Media (For complete agency information see *The Advertising Red Books-Agencies* edition):
1. Bus. Publs. 2. Cable T.V. 3. Catalogs & Directories. 4. Co-op Adv. 5. Consumer Mags. 6. D.M. to Bus. Estab.7. D.M. to Consumers
8. Daily Newsp. 9. Exhibits/Trade Shows 10. Foreign 11. Infomercial 12. Internet Adv.13. Multimedia 14. Network Radio
15. Network T.V. 16. Newsp. Distr. Mags. 17. Other 18. Outdoor (Posters, Transit) 19. Point of Purchase20. Premiums, Novelties
21. Product Samples 22. Special Events Mktg. 23. Spot Radio 24. Spot T.V. 25. Weekly Newsp. 26. Yellow Page Adv.

Tel.: (864) 963-3471
Fax: (864) 967-2787
Toll Free: (800) 927-6887
E-mail: customerservice@bkideas.com
Web Site: www.bkideas.com
Sales Range: $75-99.9 Million
Approx. Number Employees: 150
Year Founded: 1954
Business Description:
Commercial Ovens, Warmers, Fryers Filters & Refrigerated Cases Mfr
S.I.C.: 2034; 2098
N.A.I.C.S.: 311423; 311823
Export
Media: 2-4-7-10
Distr.: Intl.; Natl.
Budget Set: June
Brands & Products:
BK INDUSTRIES
BKI
WHISPERFLO
Advertising Agency:
VantagePoint, Inc
80 Villa Rd
Greenville, SC 29615
Tel.: (864) 331-1240
Fax: (864) 331-1245

BLODGETT OVEN COMPANY INC

(Sub. of The Middleby Corporation)
44 Lakeside Ave
Burlington, VT 05401
Tel.: (802) 860-3700
Fax: (802) 864-0183
Toll Free: (800) 331-5842
E-mail: info@blodgett.com
Web Site: www.blodgett.com
Sales Range: $200-249.9 Million
Approx. Number Employees: 600
Year Founded: 1848
Business Description:
Commercial Cooking Equipment
S.I.C.: 3589; 3631
N.A.I.C.S.: 333319; 335221
Import Export
Media: 4-7-10-16-19-20-22
Distr.: Intl.; Natl.
Budget Set: Sept. -Oct.
Personnel:
Gary Mick *(Pres)*
Bethany Trombley *(Mgr-Adv)*
Brands & Products:
BLODGETT COMBI
BLODGETT RANGE
BLODGETT XCEL
MARK V EXCEL

BRAUN NORTH AMERICA

(Sub. of The Gillette Company)
1 Gillette Park
Boston, MA 02127-1028
Tel.: (781) 939-8300
Toll Free: (800) 272-8611
Web Site: www.braun.com
Sales Range: $1-4.9 Billion
Business Description:
Electrical Appliances Mfr
S.I.C.: 5064
N.A.I.C.S.: 423620
Advertising Expenditures: $15,000,000
Media: 1-4-5-6-10-15-16-19-23-24-26
Distr.: Intl.; Natl.
Personnel:
Mark M. Leckie *(Pres)*
Phil Drapeau *(Brand Mgr)*
Rich Meyer *(Mgr-Adv Svcs)*
Brands & Products:
BRAUN AROMASTER
BRAUN AROMATIC
BRAUN CITROMATIC
BRAUN DENTAL CENTER
BRAUN ELECTRIC RAZOR
BRAUN INDEPENDENT 2000
BRAUN MULTIPRACTIC
BRAUN MULTIPRESS
BRAUN QUARTZ
BRAUN QUICKSTYLE
BRAUN QUICKSTYLE COMBI
BRAUN REFLEX CONTROL
BRAUN SILENTIME
BRAUN SLIMSTYLE
BRAUN VOICE CONTROL
FLEX XP
FREEGLIDER
INTERFACE EXCEL
SYNCRO SYSTEM
SYSTEM 1-2-3
Advertising Agency:
BBDO Worldwide Inc.
(Sub. of Omnicom Group, Inc.)
1285 Ave of the Americas
New York, NY 10019-6028
Tel.: (212) 459-5000
Fax: (212) 459-6645

BRAY INTERNATIONAL, INC.

13333 Westland E Blvd
Houston, TX 77041-1219
Tel.: (281) 894-5454
Fax: (281) 894-9499
Web Site: www.bray.com
Approx. Sls.: $41,600,000
Approx. Number Employees: 200
Year Founded: 1986
Business Description:
Sell Control Flow Products
S.I.C.: 3491
N.A.I.C.S.: 332911
Import Export
Media: 10
Personnel:
Frank J. Raymond, Jr. *(Founder & Chm)*
Craig C. Brown *(Founder, Pres & CEO)*
David Gent *(CIO)*
Brands & Products:
BRAY
Advertising Agency:
Prom Krog Altstiel Inc.
11053 N Towne Sq Rd
Mequon, WI 53092-5051
Tel.: (262) 241-9414
Fax: (262) 241-9454

BROTHER INTERNATIONAL CORPORATION - USA

(Sub. of Brother Industries, Ltd.)
100 Somerset Corporate Blvd
Bridgewater, NJ 08807-0911
Mailing Address:
PO Box 6911
Bridgewater, NJ 08807-0911
Tel.: (908) 704-1700
Fax: (908) 704-8235
Web Site: www.brother-usa.com
Approx. Number Employees: 1,100
Year Founded: 1954
Business Description:
Office Equipment & Sewing Machines Whslr
S.I.C.: 5044; 3579; 5064; 5084
N.A.I.C.S.: 423420; 333313; 423620; 423830
Import Export
Media: 1-2-5-6-9-10-14-15-18-20-26
Distr.: Natl.
Budget Set: Sept.
Personnel:
Tadashi Ishiguro *(Pres)*
Anthony Melfi *(CFO)*
Dean F. Shulman *(Sr VP)*
Nancy Long *(Sr Mgr-Mktg)*
Advertising Agencies:
MSA Advertising & Public Relations
475 Park Ave S 6th Fl
New York, NY 10016
Tel.: (212) 532-5151
Fax: (212) 532-5499
(Sewing & Knitting Machines, Consumer Products Div.)
— Keith Klein *(Acct. Exec.)*

PJA Advertising + Marketing
214 Grant Ave Ste 450
San Francisco, CA 94108
Tel.: (415) 200-0800
Fax: (415) 200-0801
Agency of Record
All-in-Ones
Marketing
Media Strategy, Planning & Buying
Printers

BSH HOME APPLIANCES CORPORATION

(Joint Venture of Robert Bosch GmbH & Siemens Aktiengesellschaft)
5551 McFadden Ave
Huntington Beach, CA 92649-1317
Tel.: (714) 901-6600
Fax: (714) 901-5980
Toll Free: (800) 828-9165
E-mail: info@thermador.com
Web Site: www.thermador.com
Sales Range: $500-549.9 Million
Approx. Number Employees: 215
Year Founded: 1980
Business Description:
Home Appliance Mfr & Distr
S.I.C.: 3631
N.A.I.C.S.: 335221
Import
Advertising Expenditures: $300,000
Media: 2-4-6-7-10-16-24
Distr.: Natl.
Budget Set: Nov.
Personnel:
Michael Traub *(Pres & CEO)*
Clemens Scheller *(CTO & Exec VP)*
Micaela Shaw *(Brand Mgr)*
Lonna Dayhoff *(Mgr-Electronic Mktg)*
Marni Hale *(Mgr-Mktg Rels-Thermador)*
Brands & Products:
BOSCH
GAGGENAU
THERMADOR
Advertising Agency:
Gregory Welteroth Advertising
356 Laurens Rd
Montoursville, PA 17754
Tel.: (570) 433-3366
Fax: (866) 294-5765

BUNN-O-MATIC CORPORATION

1400 Stevenson Dr
Springfield, IL 62703-4228
Tel.: (217) 529-6601
Fax: (217) 585-7699
Toll Free: (800) 637-8606
Web Site: www.bunnomatic.com
Approx. Number Employees: 400
Year Founded: 1952
Business Description:
Coffee Brewing Equipment; Iced Tea Brewers, Coffee Grinders, Hot Water Machines; Coffee & Tea Filters; Water Conditioners
S.I.C.: 3589
N.A.I.C.S.: 333319
Export
Media: 2-4-7-10-20
Distr.: Intl.; Natl.
Budget Set: Nov. -Dec.
Personnel:
Arthur H. Bunn *(Pres & CEO)*
Greg Fisher *(Sr VP-Comml Accounts)*
Kurt Powell *(Sr VP-Global Accts)*
Randy Pope *(Dir-BUNN Beverage Tech Center)*
Brands & Products:
392
AXIOM
BREW-THRU
BREWLOGIC
BREWWISE
BREWWIZARD
BUNN
BUNN ESPRESS
BUNN GOURMET ICE
BUNN-O-MATIC
BUNN POUR-O-MATIC
BUNNLINK
BUNNSERVE
COFFEE AT ITS BEST
COOL FROTH
DBC
DIGITAL BREWER CONTROL
DR. BREW
DUAL
DUAL SOFT HEAT
EASY CLEAR
EASY POUR
EASY TEA
EASYGARD
FLAVORGARD
GOURMET ICE
GOURMET JUICE
HIGH INTENSITY
THE HORIZONTAL RED LINE
IMIX
INFUSION SERIES
ITCB INFUSION
LEGENDARY FOR QUALITY
MARK OF QUALITY IN BEVERAGE EQUIPMENT WORLDWIDE
MY CAFE
NOTHING BREWS LIKE A BUNN
POUR-O-MATIC
POWERLOGIC
PULSE-BREW
PULSE WAVE
QUALITY BEVERAGE EQUIPMENT WORLDWIDE
SAFETY-FRESH
SIGNATURE SERIES
SILVER SERIES
SINGLE
SINGLE SOFT HEAT
SINGLE THERMOFRESH

Key to Media (For complete agency information see *The Advertising Red Books-Agencies* edition):
1. Bus. Publs. 2. Cable T.V. 3. Catalogs & Directories. 4. Co-op Adv. 5. Consumer Mags. 6. D.M. to Bus. Estab.7. D.M. to Consumers
8. Daily Newsp. 9. Exhibits/Trade Shows 10. Foreign 11. Infomercial 12. Internet Adv.13. Multimedia 14. Network Radio
15. Network T.V. 16. Newsp. Distr. Mags. 17. Other 18. Outdoor (Posters, Transit) 19. Point of Purchase20. Premiums, Novelties
21. Product Samples 22. Special Events Mktg. 23. Spot Radio 24. Spot T.V. 25. Weekly Newsp. 26. Yellow Page Adv.

Bunn-O-Matic Corporation — (Continued)

SMART FUNNEL
SMART HEAT
SMART HOPPER
SMARTWAVE
SOFT HEAT
SPLASHGARD
SYSTEM III
TEA AT ITS BEST
THERMOFRESH
TITAN
ULTRA GOURMET ICE

CAPRESSO INC.

81 Ruckman Rd
Closter, NJ 07624
Tel.: (201) 767-3999
Fax: (201) 767-9684
Toll Free: (800) 767-3554
E-mail: contact@capresso.com
Web Site: www.capresso.com
Approx. Number Employees: 25
Year Founded: 1994
Business Description:
Coffee Equipment
S.I.C.: 5046; 5149
N.A.I.C.S.: 423440; 424490
Media: 6
Personnel:
David Shull *(VP-Sls & Mktg)*

CASABLANCA FAN COMPANY

(Sub. of Hunter Fan Company)
7130 Goodlett Farms Pkwy Ste 400
Memphis, TN 38016
Tel.: (909) 629-1477
Fax: (909) 629-0958
Toll Free: (888) 227-2178
Web Site: www.casablancafanco.com
Approx. Rev.: $75,000,000
Approx. Number Employees: 200
Year Founded: 1974
Business Description:
Ceiling Fan Mfr
S.I.C.: 3634; 5085
N.A.I.C.S.: 335211; 423840
Import Export
Media: 2-4-5-6-10-19-24
Distr.: Intl.; Natl.
Budget Set: July
Personnel:
Joe Veering *(VP-Mktg)*
Brands & Products:
19TH CENTURY
AEGEAN CLASSIC
AVALON BLADES
BEL AIR
BEL AIR HALO
BELLA
BRESCIA
BRESCIA GALLERY
CAMPANA
CAPISTRANO
CASABLANCA
CATHAY
COMMODORE VANDERBILT
CONCENTRA
COSMOPOLITAN COLLECTION
ESTRADA
FOUR SEASONS III
FOUR SEASONS III OUTSIDER
KAWAYAN
KEY LARGO
LANAI
LE GRANDE
MALIBU STAR
MARRAKESH
METROPOLITAN
MISSION COLLECTION
MODENA
MODERNE PORTABLE
NEW ORLEANS CENTENNIAL
NOUVELLE
PANAMA
S3
SCANDIA
SOUTH SEAS COLLECTION
STEALTH
UTOPIAN
VENTURA
VERRAZANO
VICTORIAN
WAILEA
THE WILDERNESS COLLECTION
WORLD'S FINEST CEILING FAN
ZEPHAIR PORTABLE

CLEMENTS NATIONAL COMPANY

6650 S Narragansett Ave
Chicago, IL 60638
Tel.: (708) 594-5890
Fax: (708) 594-2481
Web Site: www.cadillacproducts.com
Approx. Number Employees: 50
Business Description:
Mfr. of Vacuum Cleaners, Portable Blowers, Flameless Electric Torches & Fume Collectors
S.I.C.: 3589
N.A.I.C.S.: 333319
Export
Advertising Expenditures: $200,000
Media: 2-4-7-17
Distr.: Direct to Consumer; Natl.
Budget Set: Jan.
Personnel:
Reginal Barrett *(Pres)*
Alan Walse *(Gen Mgr)*
Brands & Products:
CADILLAC
CLEMENTS NATIONAL

COMPSEE, INC.

(Div. of Control Solutions, Inc.)
5775 Soundview Dr Ste 101 E
Gig Harbor, WA 98335
Tel.: (253) 851-6500
Fax: (253) 858-2802
E-mail: sales@compsee.com
Web Site: www.compsee.com
E-Mail For Key Personnel:
Sales Director: sales@compsee.com
Approx. Number Employees: 20
Business Description:
Computerized Optical Data Collecting Services
S.I.C.: 3577
N.A.I.C.S.: 334119
Media: 7-10
Personnel:
Richard Mahmarian *(Pres)*

CONSEW

400 Veterans Blvd
Carlstadt, NJ 07072-7201
Tel.: (212) 741-7788
Fax: (212) 741-7787
Toll Free: (800) 221-8494
E-mail: consew@worldnet.att.net
Web Site: www.consew.com
Approx. Number Employees: 15
Year Founded: 1898
Business Description:
Mfr. of Industrial Sewing Machines, Clutch Motors, Parts & Related Accessories
S.I.C.: 5084
N.A.I.C.S.: 423830
Import Export
Media: 2-6-10-11
Distr.: Intl.; Natl.
Budget Set: Nov.
Personnel:
Murray Feit *(Pres)*
Doug Glenn *(Dir-Sls)*
Brands & Products:
CONSEW
CONSEW BIG LITTLE '500+ SERIES
CONSEW/ORGAN
CONSOMATICS
PREMIER
ROMCO
SUPER LUBE
TUFFY

CULLIGAN INTERNATIONAL COMPANY

(Holding of Clayton, Dubilier & Rice, LLC)
1 Culligan Pkwy
Northbrook, IL 60062-6209
Tel.: (847) 205-6000
Fax: (847) 205-6030
Fax: (847) 205-6103 (HR)
E-mail: feedback@culligan.com
Web Site: www.culligan.com
Sales Range: $700-749.9 Million
Approx. Number Employees: 5,500
Year Founded: 1936
Business Description:
Water Conditioning & Purification Equipment & Related Products Mfr
S.I.C.: 3589
N.A.I.C.S.: 333319
Advertising Expenditures: $25,700,000
Media: 6-9-10-11-18-20-23-24-26
Distr.: Intl.; Natl.
Personnel:
George W. Tamke *(Chm)*
Francis Fay *(Dir-Mktg)*
Brands & Products:
BRUNER
CULLIGAN
CULLIGAN GOLD SERIES
CULLIGANAIR
ELGA
EVERPURE

DACOR

1440 Bridgegate Dr Fl 2
Diamond Bar, CA 91765
Tel.: (626) 799-1000
Fax: (626) 441-9632
Web Site: www.dacor.com
Approx. Sls.: $29,600,000
Approx. Number Employees: 500
Business Description:
Household Cooking Equipment
S.I.C.: 3631
N.A.I.C.S.: 335221
Personnel:
S. Michael Joseph *(VP-Mktg)*
Susan Davis *(Mgr-Cooperative)*
Brands & Products:
DACOR
ELECTRIC GLIDE
EPICURE
THE LIFE OF THE KITCHEN
MILLENNIA
PREFERENCE
PURE CONVECTION
WINESTEWARD
Advertising Agency:
Domus Inc.
123 S Broad St Ste 1980
Philadelphia, PA 19109
Tel.: (215) 772-2800
Fax: (215) 772-2819

DIMPLEX NORTH AMERICA LIMITED

(Sub. of The Glen Dimplex Group)
1367 Industrial Rd
Cambridge, ON N1R 7G8, Canada
Tel.: (519) 650-3630
Fax: (519) 650-3651
Toll Free: (800) 688-6663
E-mail: info@dimplex.com
Web Site: www.dimplex.com
Approx. Number Employees: 350
Business Description:
Electric Heaters & Fireplaces Mfr
S.I.C.: 3634
N.A.I.C.S.: 335211
Media: 2-8-10-13
Personnel:
Martyn Champ *(Pres & CEO)*
Jim McLean *(VP-Prof Markets)*
Judi Tutkaluk *(Dir - Sls Admin-Mktg)*
Brands & Products:
CHROMOLOX
DIMPLEX
THE DOWNTOWN ELECTRIC FIREPLACE COMPANY
ELECTRAFLAME
ELECTROMODE
OPTIFLAME
SYMPHONY

DIXIE PRODUCTS GROUP

(Div. of Georgia-Pacific Corporation)
133 Peachtree St NE
Atlanta, GA 30303
Tel.: (404) 652-4000
Fax: (404) 230-1674
Web Site: www.dixie.com
Business Description:
Tabletop Products Mfr
S.I.C.: 2679; 3089
N.A.I.C.S.: 322299; 326199
Personnel:
Bill Donahue *(Pres)*
Sean Fallmann *(Pres-North American Consumer Products)*
Fernando Gonzalez *(VP & Gen Mgr-Retail Tabletop)*
Brands & Products:
INSULAIR
Advertising Agencies:
Eric Mower and Associates
7000 Central Pkwy NE Ste 1020
Atlanta, GA 30328-4586
Tel.: (678) 587-0301
Fax: (770) 481-1500

Howard, Merrell & Partners, Inc.
8521 Six Forks Rd 4th Fl
Raleigh, NC 27615-5278
Tel.: (919) 848-2400
Fax: (919) 848-2420

DUKE MANUFACTURING COMPANY, INC.

2305 N Broadway
Saint Louis, MO 63102-1405

Key to Media (For complete agency information see *The Advertising Red Books-Agencies* edition):
1. Bus. Publs. 2. Cable T.V. 3. Catalogs & Directories. 4. Co-op Adv. 5. Consumer Mags. 6. D.M. to Bus. Estab.7. D.M. to Consumers
8. Daily Newsp. 9. Exhibits/Trade Shows 10. Foreign 11. Infomercial 12. Internet Adv.13. Multimedia 14. Network Radio
15. Network T.V. 16. Newsp. Distr. Mags. 17. Other 18. Outdoor (Posters, Transit) 19. Point of Purchase20. Premiums, Novelties
21. Product Samples 22. Special Events Mktg. 23. Spot Radio 24. Spot T.V. 25. Weekly Newsp. 26. Yellow Page Adv.

Tel.: (314) 231-1130
Fax: (314) 231-5074
Toll Free: (800) 735-3853
E-mail: customerservice@dukemfg.com
Web Site: www.dukemfg.com
Approx. Number Employees: 500
Year Founded: 1923
Business Description:
Foodservice Equipment Mfr
S.I.C.: 3589; 3556
N.A.I.C.S.: 333319; 333294
Export
Advertising Expenditures: $500,000
Media: 2-4-7-10
Distr.: Intl.; Natl.
Personnel:
Jack J. Hake *(Pres)*
Douglas George *(Sr VP)*
Steve Shei *(VP-Engrg)*
Ron Kieffer *(Dir-Svcs)*
Brands & Products:
AEROHOT
AEROSERV
DUKE
ECONOMATE
HERITAGE
NEXT GENERATION
SOUTHERN ENGINEERING
THERMOTAINER
THURMADUKE
YOUR SOLUTIONS PARTNER
Advertising Agencies:
Direct Impact, Inc.
8420 Delmar Blvd Ste Ll6
Saint Louis, MO 63124
Tel.: (314) 567-0024

Obata Design, Inc.
1610 Menard St
Saint Louis, MO 63104
Tel.: (314) 241-1710

EAGLE COMPRESSORS INC.
(Sub. of Paratech, Inc.)
3003 Thurston Ave
Greensboro, NC 27406
Tel.: (336) 398-8000
Fax: (336) 398-8001
Telex: (336)398-8001
E-mail: eagleair@eaglecompressors.com
Web Site:
www.eaglecompressors.com
Approx. Number Employees: 30
Year Founded: 1969
Business Description:
Breathing Air Systems & Components for Safety Products
S.I.C.: 3563; 5084
N.A.I.C.S.: 333912; 423830
Media: 4-13
Personnel:
Anthony M. Gonzales *(Gen Mgr)*
Brands & Products:
EAGLE COMPRESSORS

EDWARD DON & COMPANY
2500 S Harlem Ave
North Riverside, IL 60546-1415
Tel.: (708) 442-9400
Fax: (708) 442-0436
Toll Free: (800) 777-4366
E-mail: customerservice@don.com
Web Site: www.don.com
Approx. Number Employees: 1,000
Year Founded: 1921
Business Description:
Food Service Equipment, Furnishings & Supplies Distr
S.I.C.: 5046; 5021
N.A.I.C.S.: 423440; 423210
Import Export
Media: 1-2-5-7-8-10-20-26
Distr.: Natl.
Budget Set: Jan.
Personnel:
Robert E. Don *(Chm)*
Stephen Don *(Pres & CEO)*
James P. Jones *(CFO, COO & Exec VP)*
Andre Mills *(VP-HR)*
John Seefeldt *(VP-Natl Accts)*
Jeffery Weiland *(VP-Sls)*
Brands & Products:
DON
DON D CIDE
DON O MITE
DON PINK
DYNO BRITE
EDWARD DON
FRISK PLUS
MIR O SPRAY
MIR O ZERO
PINK DISH
SUNLITE
TABLES OF CONTENT

ELECTROLUX HOME CARE PRODUCTS NORTH AMERICA
(Div. of Electrolux Home Products North America)
807 N Main St
Bloomington, IL 61701
Mailing Address:
PO Box 3900
Peoria, IL 61612
Tel.: (309) 828-2367
Fax: (309) 823-5203
Toll Free: (800) 282-2886
Web Site: www.eureka.com
Approx. Number Employees: 200
Year Founded: 1909
Business Description:
Floor Care Products, Upright & Canister Vacuum Cleaners & Lightweight Cleaners Mfr
S.I.C.: 2842
N.A.I.C.S.: 325612
Export
Media: 3-5-6-8-9-10-11-13-15-19-20-23-24-26
Distr.: Natl.
Personnel:
Russell S. Minick *(Pres & CEO)*
Cennert Steffen *(Exec VP-Opers)*
Michela Laible *(VP-HR)*
David Voigts *(VP-Product Devel & Sourcing)*
Frank Sanchez *(Gen Mgr)*
Brad Hoare *(Sr Dir-Products)*
Cheryl Waisanen *(Mgr-Mktg)*
Brands & Products:
THE BOSS
THE BOSS LITE
BRAVO! BOSS
BRAVO II BOSS PLUS
ENVIRO STEAMER
EUREKA
EUREKA HOME CLEANING SYSTEMS
HOT SHOT
MIGHTY MITE
MINI MITE
SANITAIRE
SMART VAC
STICK BROOM
WHIRLWIND
Advertising Agencies:
ARS Advertising Inc.
1001 Reads Lake Rd
Chattanooga, TN 37415-2056
Tel.: (423) 875-3743
Fax: (423) 875-5346

Deutsch New York
111 8th Ave 14th Fl
New York, NY 10011
Tel.: (212) 605-8000

ELECTROLUX HOME PRODUCTS NORTH AMERICA
(Sub. of AB Electrolux)
250 Bobby Jones Expwy
Augusta, GA 30907
Tel.: (706) 651-1751
Fax: (706) 651-7769
E-mail: info@electroluxusa.com
Web Site: www.electroluxusa.com
Approx. Number Employees: 22,000
Business Description:
Indoor Home Appliances Mfr
S.I.C.: 3639
N.A.I.C.S.: 335228
Media: 2-4-6-8-9-10-11-14-18-19-20-23-26
Distr.: Natl.
Budget Set: July -Aug.
Personnel:
Mary Kay Kopf *(VP-Mktg)*

ETS, LLC
7445 Company Dr
Indianapolis, IN 46237-9296
Tel.: (317) 554-3500
Fax: (317) 554-3693
Fax: (800) 358-7947
Toll Free: (800) 553-9590
Web Site: www.etstan.com
Sales Range: $100-124.9 Million
Approx. Number Employees: 275
Business Description:
Tanning Beds, Products & Parts Mfr & Distr
S.I.C.: 5722; 5099
N.A.I.C.S.: 443111; 423990
Media: 4-6
Personnel:
Bill Pipp *(CEO)*
Brands & Products:
ETS TAN
HYDROMASSAGE
SHINEWHITE
YOUR PARTNER IN TANNING

EURO-PRO CORPORATION
4400 Bois Franc
Saint Laurent, QC H4S IA7, Canada
Fax: (514) 842-6985
Toll Free: (800) 361-4639
Web Site: www.euro-pro.com
Approx. Number Employees: 100
Year Founded: 1950
Business Description:
Vacuum Cleaner & Household Appliance Designer, Mfr & Distr
S.I.C.: 3635; 3639
N.A.I.C.S.: 335212; 335228
Media: 13
Brands & Products:
BRAVETTI
EURO-PRO
FANTOM
QUAD BLADE
SHARK
SOLUTIONS FOR GLOBAL LIVING.
Advertising Agency:
Alpaytac Group
445 N Wells St Ste 401
Chicago, IL 60654
Tel.: (312) 245-9805
Fax: (312) 245-9807

FORTUNE BRANDS, INC.
520 Lake Cook Rd
Deerfield, IL 60069-3640
Tel.: (847) 484-4400
Fax: (847) 478-0073
E-mail: mail@fortunebrands.com
Web Site: www.fortunebrands.com
Approx. Sls.: $7,141,500,000
Approx. Number Employees: 24,600
Year Founded: 1985
Business Description:
Holding Company; Distilled Spirits, Hardware & Home Improvement Products; Office Products; Golf & Leisure Products
S.I.C.: 6719; 2085; 2434; 2542; 3088; 3429; 3496; 3949; 5182
N.A.I.C.S.: 551112; 312140; 326191; 332510; 332618; 337110; 337215; 339920; 424820
Import Export
Advertising Expenditures: $643,100,000
Media: 4-5-8-11-22-30
Personnel:
Bruce A. Carbonari *(Chm & CEO)*
Craig P. Omtvedt *(CFO & Sr VP)*
Mark Hausberg *(Treas & Sr VP-Fin)*
Patrick J. Koley *(Sr VP-Strategy & Corp Dev)*
Lauren S. Tashma *(VP, Asst Sec & Assoc Gen Counsel)*
C. Clarkson Hine *(VP-Corp Comm & Pub Affairs)*
Elizabeth R. Lane *(VP-HR)*
Brands & Products:
100 ANOS
AFTER SHOCK
ALBERTA SPRINGS
AMERICAN LOCK
ARDMORE
ARISTOKRAFT
BAKER'S
BASIL HAYDEN'S
BOOKER'S
CALVERT
CALVERT EXTRA
CANADIAN CLUB
CASTELLANA
COCKBURN'S
COURVOISIER
CRUZAN
DECORA
DEKUYPER
DIAMOND
DYC UNE
EL TESORO
EL TESORO DE DON FELIPE
FOOTJOY
FORTUNE BRANDS
FUNDADOR
FURST BISMARCK
FYPON
GILBEY'S
HARVEYS
HOMECREST

Key to Media (For complete agency information see *The Advertising Red Books-Agencies* edition):
1. Bus. Publs. 2. Cable T.V. 3. Catalogs & Directories. 4. Co-op Adv. 5. Consumer Mags. 6. D.M. to Bus. Estab.7. D.M. to Consumers 8. Daily Newsp. 9. Exhibits/Trade Shows 10. Foreign 11. Infomercial 12. Internet Adv.13. Multimedia 14. Network Radio 15. Network T.V. 16. Newsp. Distr. Mags. 17. Other 18. Outdoor (Posters, Transit) 19. Point of Purchase20. Premiums, Novelties 21. Product Samples 22. Special Events Mktg. 23. Spot Radio 24. Spot T.V. 25. Weekly Newsp. 26. Yellow Page Adv.

Fortune Brands, Inc. — (Continued)

HORNITOS
HY-LITE
JACOBI 1880
JIM BEAM
KAMCHATKA
KAMORA
KESSLER
KITCHEN CRAFT
KNOB CREEK
KUEMMERLING
LAPHROAIG
LARIOS DRY GIN
LEROUX
LORD CALVERT
MAKER'S MARK
MASTER LOCK
MASTERBRAND CABINETS
MOEN
OLD CROW
OLD GRAND-DAD
OLD OVERHOLT
OMEGA CABINETRY
PINNACLE
RED STAG
RONRICO
SALIGNAC
SAUZA
SAUZA BLANCO
SAUZA GOLD
SCHROCK
SCHROCK CABINETRY
SCOTTY CAMERON
SIMONTON WINDOWS
THE SMALL BATCH BOURBON COLLECTION
SOURZ
STARBUCKS LIQUEURS
TANGLE RIDGE
TEACHER'S
TERRY CENTENARIO
THERMA-TRU
TITLIEST
TRES CEPAS
TRES GENERACIONES
VOX
WATERLOO
WINDSOR CANADIAN
WOLFSCHMIDT

FRANKE INC.

(Sub. of Franke Holding AG)
800 Aviation PW
Smyrna, TN 37167
Tel.: (615) 287-8200
Fax: (615) 287-8260
Web Site: www.franke.com
Approx. Number Employees: 80
Business Description:
Mfr. of Stainless Steel Products
S.I.C.: 3589; 5046
N.A.I.C.S.: 333319; 423440
Personnel:
Thomas Campion *(Pres)*
Krista Rivers *(Coord-Mktg Services)*
Advertising Agency:
Catalpha Advertising & Design
6801 Loch Raven Blvd
Towson, MD 21286
Tel.: (410) 337-0066
Fax: (410) 296-2297

FRYMASTER LLC

(Sub. of Manitowoc Foodservice USA)
8700 Line Ave
Shreveport, LA 71106
Mailing Address:
PO Box 51000
Shreveport, LA 71135-1000
Tel.: (318) 865-1711
Fax: (318) 868-5987
Toll Free: (800) 995-1210
Toll Free: (800) 551-8633
Toll Free: (800) 221-4583
E-mail: salesmkt@frymaster.com
Web Site: www.frymaster.com
E-Mail For Key Personnel:
Sales Director: salesmkt@frymaster.com
Sales Range: $75-99.9 Million
Approx. Number Employees: 200
Year Founded: 1935
Business Description:
Restaurant Equipment Mfr
S.I.C.: 3556; 5046
N.A.I.C.S.: 333294; 423440
Export
Advertising Expenditures: $300,000
Media: 2-5-7-10
Distr.: Intl.; Natl.
Budget Set: Oct.

FUJITSU GENERAL AMERICA, INC.

(Sub. of Fujitsu America, Inc.)
353 Route 46 W
Fairfield, NJ 07004
Tel.: (973) 575-0380
Fax: (973) 575-2194
Toll Free: (866) 952-8324
Web Site: www.fujitsugeneral.com
Approx. Number Employees: 50
Year Founded: 1936
Business Description:
Air Conditioning Unit Mfr
S.I.C.: 3585
N.A.I.C.S.: 333415
Media: 5-6
Personnel:
Erin Mezle *(Dir-Mktg)*
Brands & Products:
PLASMAVISION SLIMSCREEN
Advertising Agency:
Della Femina & Gianettino
98 Floral Ave Ste 201
New Providence, NJ 07974
Tel.: (908) 871-0100
Fax: (908) 871-0120
Toll Free: (800) 497-0622

GE CONSUMER & INDUSTRIAL

(Div. of GE Industrial)
Appliance Park AP3-232
Louisville, KY 40225
Tel.: (502) 452-4311
Fax: (502) 452-0352
Web Site:
www.geconsumerandindustrial.com
E-Mail For Key Personnel:
Public Relations: kim_freeman@ge.com
Sales Range: $1-4.9 Billion
Approx. Number Employees: 64,000
Business Description:
Appliance & Lighting Products Mfr & Repair Services
S.I.C.: 3631; 3632; 3639; 3646; 3648; 7699
N.A.I.C.S.: 335221; 335122; 335129; 335222; 335228; 811412
Media: 1-2-3-4-5-6-7-8-9-10-15-16-19-20-23-24-25-26
Distr.: Natl.
Budget Set: Aug.
Personnel:
James P. Campbell *(Pres & CEO)*
Michael B. Petras *(CEO-GE Lighting & Pres-GE Lighting)*
Gregory L. Levinsky *(VP-IT)*
Paul A. Raymont *(VP-Tech)*
Joseph B. Ruocco *(VP-HR)*
Fritz O'Connor *(Dir-Strategic Mktg)*
Brands & Products:
GE MONOGRAM
GE PROFILE ARCTICA
GE PROFILE CUSTOMSTYLE
GE PROFILE HARMONY
GE SMARTWATER
Advertising Agencies:
JohnsonRauhoff
2525 Lake Pines Dr
Saint Joseph, MI 49085
Tel.: (269) 428-9212
Fax: (269) 428-3312
Toll Free: (800) 572-3996

OMD Worldwide
195 Broadway
New York, NY 10007
Tel.: (212) 590-7100

Power Creative
11701 Commonwealth Dr
Louisville, KY 40299-2358
Tel.: (502) 267-0772
Fax: (502) 267-1727

GEM REFRIGERATOR COMPANY, INC.

7340 Milnor St
Philadelphia, PA 19136
Tel.: (215) 426-8700
Fax: (215) 426-8731
E-mail: info@gemrefrigeratorcompany.com
Web Site:
www.gemrefrigeratorcompany.com
Sales Range: $100-124.9 Million
Approx. Number Employees: 30
Year Founded: 1925
Business Description:
Mfr. of Refrigerators, Freezers & Equipment for Commercial Use
S.I.C.: 3585; 5078
N.A.I.C.S.: 333415; 423740
Media: 2-4-7-10
Distr.: Natl.
Personnel:
Bruce Gruhler *(Pres)*
Brands & Products:
GEM REFRIGERATOR

THE GENIE COMPANY

(Sub. of Overhead Door Corporation)
22790 Lk Park Blvd
Alliance, OH 44601-3498
Tel.: (330) 821-5360
Fax: (330) 821-1927
Toll Free: (800) 354-3643
Web Site: www.geniecompany.com
Approx. Sls.: $200,000,000
Approx. Number Employees: 200
Year Founded: 1925
Business Description:
Mfr. of Residential Garage Door Opener System, Gate Openers, Wet/Dry Shop Vacuums & Garbage Trash Compactors
S.I.C.: 3699; 3635
N.A.I.C.S.: 335999; 335212
Export
Advertising Expenditures: $5,000,000
Media: 2-3-5-6-7-10-14-19-20-23-24-26
Distr.: Natl.
Budget Set: Monthly
Personnel:
Rick Johnson *(Gen Mgr)*
Brands & Products:
BLUE MAX
CHAIN GLIDE
CRYPTAR
FORCEGUARD
GENIE
HERCULES
INTELLICODE
PRO MAX
SAFE-T-BEAM
SURE TOUCH
WATCH DOG

GOLD MEDAL PRODUCTS CO.

10700 Medallion Dr
Cincinnati, OH 45241-4807
Tel.: (513) 769-7676
Fax: (513) 769-8500
Toll Free: (800) 543-0862
E-mail: info@gmpopcorn.com
Web Site: www.gmpopcorn.com
Sales Range: $75-99.9 Million
Approx. Number Employees: 350
Year Founded: 1931
Business Description:
Concession & Snack Bar Installations
S.I.C.: 3556; 3589
N.A.I.C.S.: 333294; 333319
Export
Advertising Expenditures: $700,000
Media: 2-3-4-5-7-8-9-10-11-13-19-20-21-22-25
Distr.: Intl.; Natl.
Budget Set: Nov.
Personnel:
Dan Kroeger *(Pres)*
Dave Evans *(VP-Pur)*
Sally Lloyd *(VP-HR)*
David Garretson *(Mgr-Sls-Intl)*
Stephanie Goodin *(Mgr-Mktg)*
Chris Petroff *(Mgr-Natl Sls)*
Brands & Products:
ASTRO
BIG EYE
BLIZ-WHIZ
CITATION
CONE-O-CORN
CORNADO
DELUXE WHIZ BANG
DOGEROO
ECONO-POP
EE-ZEE ADE
EE-ZEE SNO-KONE CONCENTRATE
EEZE OFF
EL NACHO GRANDE
EZ KLEEN
FLAVACOL
FLOSSUGAR
FRUSHEEZ
FRYING SAUCER
FUNNEL
GAY 90'S
GOLD MEDAL
KLEEN SWEEP
LIL SHAVER
MIDWAY'S FINEST
MOM'S HOME STYLE FUDGE
NAKS-PAK
NAKS POP
PINTO POP

Key to Media (For complete agency information see *The Advertising Red Books-Agencies* edition):
1. Bus. Publs. 2. Cable T.V. 3. Catalogs & Directories. 4. Co-op Adv. 5. Consumer Mags. 6. D.M. to Bus. Estab.7. D.M. to Consumers
8. Daily Newsp. 9. Exhibits/Trade Shows 10. Foreign 11. Infomercial 12. Internet Adv.13. Multimedia 14. Network Radio
15. Network T.V. 16. Newsp. Distr. Mags. 17. Other 18. Outdoor (Posters, Transit) 19. Point of Purchase20. Premiums, Novelties
21. Product Samples 22. Special Events Mktg. 23. Spot Radio 24. Spot T.V. 25. Weekly Newsp. 26. Yellow Page Adv.

POLAR PETE
POP-A-LOT
PRONTO PUP MIX
SERVALOT
SHAVATRON
SMOOTHIE O
SNO KONE
SNO-KONER
SNOKONETTE
SUPER DOGEROO
SUPER POLAR PETE
TITAN
TORNADO
WHIRLWIND
WHIZ BANG
Advertising Agency:
Gold Medal Direct
10700 Medallion Dr.
Cincinnati, OH 45241
Tel.: (513) 769-7676
Fax: (513) 769-8500

GRINDMASTER CORPORATION

4003 Collins Ln
Louisville, KY 40245-1643
Mailing Address:
PO Box 35020
Louisville, KY 40232-5020
Tel.: (502) 425-4776
Fax: (502) 425-4664
Toll Free: (800) 695-4500
E-mail: info@grindmaster.com
Web Site: www.grindmaster.com
Approx. Number Employees: 200
Year Founded: 1933
Business Description:
Mfr. & Distr of Beverage Makers, Dispensers, & Accessories
S.I.C.: 2099; 3556
N.A.I.C.S.: 311999; 333294
Import Export
Media: 2-4-7-10-11-13-20-26
Distr.: Intl.
Budget Set: Dec.
Personnel:
Robert Poe *(Pres)*
Brands & Products:
AMERICAN METAL WARE
CRATHCO
ESPRESSIMO
GRINDMASTER
PRECISIONBREW
WILCH

GUY GRAY SUPPLY, INC.

5235 Alben Barkley Dr
Paducah, KY 42001-6788
Tel.: (270) 554-4206
Fax: (270) 554-3912
Approx. Sls.: $2,500,000
Approx. Number Employees: 10
Business Description:
Whslr of Plumbing & Electrical Supplies
S.I.C.: 5074; 5063
N.A.I.C.S.: 423720; 423610
Media: 2-4
Personnel:
Jerry E. McElya *(Pres)*

HALSEY TAYLOR

(Sub. of Elkay Manufacturing Company)
2222 Camden Ct
Oak Brook, IL 60523-4674
Tel.: (630) 574-3500
Fax: (630) 574-3503
E-mail: sales@halseytaylor.com
Web Site: www.halseytaylor.com
E-Mail For Key Personnel:
Sales Director: sales@halseytaylor.com
Approx. Number Employees: 200
Year Founded: 1912
Business Description:
Drinking Fountains & Electric Water Coolers Mfr
S.I.C.: 3431; 3585
N.A.I.C.S.: 332998; 333415
Export
Media: 2-4-7-10-11
Distr.: Intl.; Natl.
Budget Set: Oct.
Personnel:
Jack Krecek *(VP & Gen Mgr-Product)*
Johnnie Bertella *(Dir-Sls)*
Brands & Products:
DOUBLE BUBBLER
ENDURA
ENDURA II
OVL II
PURITAN
VOYAGER
Advertising Agency:
Creative Elements
19224 Schoolhouse Rd.
Mokena, IL 60448
Tel.: (708) 478-8000

HAMILTON BEACH BRANDS, INC.

(Sub. of Housewares Holding Company)
4421 Waterfront Dr
Glen Allen, VA 23060-3375
Tel.: (804) 273-9777
Fax: (804) 527-7230
Toll Free: (800) 851-8900
E-mail: info@hamiltonbeach.com
Web Site: www.hamiltonbeach.com
E-Mail For Key Personnel:
President: mike.morecroft@hamiltonbeach.com
Sales Director: psmith@hamiltonbeach.com
Public Relations: kirby.kriz@hamiltonbeach.com
Approx. Sls.: $546,718,976
Approx. Number Employees: 545
Year Founded: 1929
Business Description:
Small Appliances Mfr
S.I.C.: 3634
N.A.I.C.S.: 335211
Import Export
Advertising Expenditures: $3,000,000
Media: 2-3-4-5-6-9-10-13-14-17-19-25
Distr.: Natl.
Personnel:
James A. Taylor *(CFO)*
Gregory H. Trepp *(CEO-Global Mktg)*
Kathleen L. Diller *(Gen Counsel, Sec & VP)*
Scott Tidey *(Sr VP-North America Sls & Mktg)*
Keith B. Burns *(VP-Engrg & IT)*
Barry Roebuck *(Dir-Creative)*
J. Norman Hall *(Asst Treas)*
Brands & Products:
2 SLICE INTELLI TOAST
4 SLICE INTELLI TOAST
AROMA EXPRESS
BAGEL SMART
BIG MOUTH
BREWSTATION
CARVE 'N SET
CHROMECLASSIC
CLEANCUT
COUNTERSCAPE YOUR KITCHEN
CUSTOM GRIND
DOUBLE DISH
DRINKMASTER
EASY FILL
ECLECTRICS
EXPRESSION
FLAVORPLUS
FLIP 'N FLUFF
FRESHCHOP
FRESHPRO
HAMILTON BEACH
HEALTHSMART
MEAL MAKER
MEAL MAKER EXPRESS
MIXMATE
MUCHAS MARGARITAS
OPENEASE
POWER DELUXE
PREPSTAR
PROCTOR-SILEX
SHORTCUT
SMOOTH EDGE
SMOOTHIES & MORE
SNOWMAN
STAY OR GO
STEAM STORM
STEPSAVOR
SUPREME STEAM
SURECUT
TURBO-TWISTER
WAFFLE STIX
WALK 'N CUT
Advertising Agency:
JohnsonRauhoff
2525 Lake Pines Dr
Saint Joseph, MI 49085
Tel.: (269) 428-9212
Fax: (269) 428-3312
Toll Free: (800) 572-3996

HAWS CORPORATION

1455 Kleppe Ln
Sparks, NV 89431
Tel.: (775) 359-4712
Fax: (775) 359-7424
E-mail: info@hawsco.com
Web Site: www.hawsco.com
Approx. Number Employees: 150
Year Founded: 1909
Business Description:
Emergency Equipment; Drinking Fountains; Water Coolers
S.I.C.: 3431
N.A.I.C.S.: 332998
Import Export
Advertising Expenditures: $455,000
Media: 4-5-6-10-11
Distr.: Intl.; Natl.
Budget Set: Oct.
Personnel:
Michael Haws Traynor *(Chm)*
Sallie R. Haws *(Pres & CEO)*
Thomas White *(Pres)*
Scot McLean *(VP-Sls)*
John Pettibone *(VP-Fin)*
Janet Hurst *(Mgr-HR)*
Brands & Products:
COOL TECH
ENVIRO-GUARD
FEATHER-FLO
HAWS
HAWS COMFORT CONTROL
OMNI-FLO
SMART SYSTEM
SOFT-FLO
STREETSMART
UNI-FLO
WARM TECH
Advertising Agency:
Global Studio
9590 Prototype Ct Ste 100
Reno, NV 89521
Tel.: (775) 853-8333
Fax: (775) 853-0200
Toll Free: (800) 932-2787

HHGREGG, INC.

4151 E 96th St
Indianapolis, IN 46240-1442
Mailing Address:
PO Box 51609
Indianapolis, IN 46251-0609
Tel.: (317) 848-8710
Fax: (317) 848-8723
Toll Free: (866) WSGREGG
E-mail: investorrelations@hhgregg.com
Web Site: www.hhgregg.com
Approx. Sls.: $2,077,651,000
Approx. Number Employees: 4,872
Year Founded: 1955
Business Description:
Home Appliances & Consumer Electronics Retailer
S.I.C.: 5731; 5712; 5722
N.A.I.C.S.: 443112; 442110; 443111
Advertising Expenditures: $40,600,000
Media: 2-3-6-8-9-13-18-19-20-21-23-24-25-26
Distr.: Reg.
Personnel:
Jerry W. Throgmartin *(Chm)*
Dennis L. May *(Pres & CEO)*
Jeremy J. Aguilar *(CFO)*
Gregg William Throgmartin *(COO & Exec VP)*
Michael D. Stout *(Chief Admin Officer)*
Michael G. Larimer *(Chief Mdsg Officer)*
Jeffrey J. McClintic *(Sr VP-Appliance Mdsg)*
Andy Giesler *(VP-Fin)*
Jeff Pearson *(VP-Mktg)*
Brands & Products:
H.H. GREGG
Advertising Agency:
Zimmerman Advertising
2200 W Commercial Blvd Ste 300
Fort Lauderdale, FL 33309-3064
Tel.: (954) 644-4000
Fax: (954) 731-2977
Toll Free: (800) 248-8522

HI-VAC CORPORATION

117 Industry Rd
Marietta, OH 45750-9355
Tel.: (740) 374-2306
Fax: (740) 374-5447
Toll Free: (800) 752-2400
E-mail: sales@hi-vac.com
Web Site: www.hi-vac.com
E-Mail For Key Personnel:
Sales Director: sales@hi-vac.com
Approx. Number Employees: 100
Year Founded: 1969
Business Description:
Industrial Vacuum Cleaners Mfr
S.I.C.: 3589; 5084

Key to Media (For complete agency information see *The Advertising Red Books-Agencies* edition):
1. Bus. Publs. 2. Cable T.V. 3. Catalogs & Directories. 4. Co-op Adv. 5. Consumer Mags. 6. D.M. to Bus. Estab.7. D.M. to Consumers 8. Daily Newsp. 9. Exhibits/Trade Shows 10. Foreign 11. Infomercial 12. Internet Adv.13. Multimedia 14. Network Radio 15. Network T.V. 16. Newsp. Distr. Mags. 17. Other 18. Outdoor (Posters, Transit) 19. Point of Purchase20. Premiums, Novelties 21. Product Samples 22. Special Events Mktg. 23. Spot Radio 24. Spot T.V. 25. Weekly Newsp. 26. Yellow Page Adv.

Hi-Vac Corporation — (Continued)

N.A.I.C.S.: 333319; 423830
Export
Media: 2-4-7-10-11-18
Distr.: Intl.
Budget Set: Jan.
Personnel:
Patrick Snyder *(VP-Sls & Mktg)*
Brands & Products:
AQUATECH
ECHO
HI-VAC
RENVAC
ULTRA VAC
X-VAC

HMI INDUSTRIES INC.

13325 Darice Pkwy Unit A
Strongsville, OH 44149
Tel.: (440) 846-7800
Fax: (440) 846-7899
Toll Free: (800) 344-1840
E-mail: marketing@filterqueen.com
Web Site: www.filterqueen.com
Sales Range: $25-49.9 Million
Approx. Number Employees: 101
Year Founded: 1928
Business Description:
Mfr. & Sales of Filtration Portable Surface Cleaners, Portable Room Air Cleaners & Central Vacuum Cleaning Systems
S.I.C.: 3635; 5722
N.A.I.C.S.: 335212; 443111
Import Export
Advertising Expenditures: $50,000
Media: 5-6-7-10-13-20
Distr.: Intl.; Natl.
Personnel:
Kirk W. Foley *(Chm & CEO)*
Daniel J. Duggan *(Pres-Sls)*
Jacqueline Purcell *(VP-Aftermarket Prods Mktg)*
Brands & Products:
CELLUPURE
DEFENDER
EMPRESS
ENVIROPURE
FILTER QUEEN
FILTER QUEEN INDOOR AIR QUALITY SYSTEM
MAJESTIC
MAJESTIC II
MEDIPURE
PRINCESS
VACU-CLEAN

HOBART FOOD EQUIPMENT GROUP CANADA

(Unit of Hobart Corporation)
716 Gordon Baker Rd Ste 206-207
North York, ON M2H 3B4, Canada
Tel.: (416) 447-6432
Fax: (416) 447-0075
Toll Free: (800) 444-4764 (service)
Telex: 966696
E-mail: customer.care@hobart.ca
Web Site: www.hobart.ca
Sales Range: $125-149.9 Million
Approx. Number Employees: 25
Business Description:
Commercial Food Equipment & Home Appliances Mfr, Sales & Service
S.I.C.: 3631; 3639; 5064; 7699
N.A.I.C.S.: 335221; 335228; 423620; 811412
Media: 10

THE HOTSY CORPORATION

(Holding of Harbour Group Ltd.)
4275 NW Pacific Rim Blvd
Camas, WA 98607
Tel.: (360) 834-0983
Fax: (800) 535-9164
Toll Free: (800) 525-1976
E-mail: info@hotsy.com
Web Site: www.hotsy.com
Approx. Number Employees: 160
Business Description:
Mfr. of High Pressure Cleaning Equipment & Related Chemicals
S.I.C.: 3589; 2841
N.A.I.C.S.: 333319; 325611
Export
Advertising Expenditures: $250,000
Media: 2-4-5-6-7-8-10-13-19-20-26
Distr.: Intl.; Natl.
Budget Set: Jan.
Brands & Products:
HOTSY
SHARK

HUNTER FAN COMPANY

(Holding of MidOcean Partners, LLP)
7130 Goodlett Farm Pkwy Ste 400
Cordova, TN 38016
Tel.: (901) 743-1360
Fax: (901) 248-2385
Web Site: www.hunterfan.com
Sales Range: $350-399.9 Million
Approx. Number Employees: 200
Year Founded: 1886
Business Description:
Ceiling Fans Mfr
S.I.C.: 3634; 3822
N.A.I.C.S.: 335211; 334512
Import Export
Media: 2-3-4-5-6-10-11-13-19-20-21-22-24-25-26
Distr.: Natl.
Budget Set: Oct.
Personnel:
Bob Pape *(Pres-Bus Innovation Grp)*
Joe Deering *(Sr VP)*
Bill Ulewicz *(Sr VP-Ops)*
Diane Burk *(VP-HR)*
Roberto Fuentes *(Dir-Mktg & Sls-Intl)*
Brands & Products:
AIR MAX
ARCHITECT
ASHBURY
AUTOSAVER
AVENTINE
BAKER STREET
BELLE MEADE
CARE FREE
CENTURY
CORAL BAY
DESIGNER'S CHOICE
DESIGNER'S CHOICE COLLECTION
ELLIPSE
FRENCH QUARTER
GALLERY EDITION
HEPATECH
HUNTER
INDIGLO
JUST RIGHT
LANCASTER
THE LANCASTER
LOW PROFILE
MILLENNIUM
MONTALCINO
MOZAMBIQUE
NITEGLO
ORLEANS
PALATINE
PENINSULA
PRESTIGE
QUIETFLO
RAINIER
RIAZZI
SAND DOLLAR
SANIBEL
SATURN
SET AND SAVE
SEVILLE
SONA
SPA SELECT
STATE STREET
STONEBRIDGE
VENTURA
VILLA
WELLESLEY
Advertising Agency:
Doner
25900 Northwestern Hwy
Southfield, MI 48075
Tel.: (248) 354-9700
Fax: (248) 827-8440

IMI CORNELIUS

(Sub. of IMI Cornelius Inc.)
500 Regency Dr
Glendale Heights, IL 60139-2285
Tel.: (630) 980-6900
Fax: (630) 980-8511
Web Site: www.cornelius.com
Approx. Number Employees: 500
Business Description:
Mfr of Refrigeration Products, Icemakers, Ice Dispensers, Refrigerated Liquid Chillers & Temperature Control Units
S.I.C.: 3585
N.A.I.C.S.: 333415
Import Export
Media: 2-7-10-11
Distr.: Intl.; Natl.
Budget Set: Nov.
Personnel:
Chris Dagiantis *(Product Mgr)*
Mike Long *(Engr-Contract)*
Brands & Products:
JET SPRAY
STATIONMASTER
XTREME ICE
Advertising Agency:
Scott, Inc. of Milwaukee (dba Scott Advertising)
1031 N Astor St
Milwaukee, WI 53202-3324
Tel.: (414) 276-1080
Fax: (414) 276-3327

IN-SINK-ERATOR

(Sub. of Emerson Electric Co.)
4700 21st St
Racine, WI 53406-5031
Tel.: (262) 554-5432
Fax: (262) 554-3530
Toll Free: (800) 558-5700
Web Site: www.insinkerator.com
Sales Range: $400-449.9 Million
Approx. Number Employees: 1,000
Year Founded: 1940
Business Description:
Garbage Disposers, Trash Compactors, Hot Water Dispensers Mfr & Sales
S.I.C.: 3639; 3621
N.A.I.C.S.: 335228; 335312
Export
Advertising Expenditures: $3,000,000
Media: 2-5-6-7-8-9-10-11-14-18-19-20-26
Distr.: Intl.; Natl.
Budget Set: Oct.
Personnel:
Jerry Ryder *(Pres)*
Dave MacNair *(VP-Mktg)*
Jack Backstrom *(Mktg Dir)*
Brands & Products:
BADGER
IN-SINK-ERATOR
JAM-BUSTER
QUICK LOCK
Advertising Agency:
Design North, Inc.
8007 Douglas Ave
Racine, WI 53402
Tel.: (262) 639-2080
Tel.: (262) 898-1090
Fax: (262) 639-5230
Toll Free: (800) 247-8494

INDUSTRIAL DIELECTRICS, INC.

407 S 7th St
Noblesville, IN 46060
Tel.: (317) 773-1766
Fax: (317) 773-3877
E-mail: plastics@idiplastic.com
Web Site: www.idiplastic.com
Approx. Sls.: $135,000,000
Approx. Number Employees: 500
Year Founded: 1966
Business Description:
Electrical Insulators & Insulation Materials Mfr
S.I.C.: 3644
N.A.I.C.S.: 335932
Import Export
Media: 4-7-10-13-16-17-22
Personnel:
Thomas K. Merrell *(Pres)*
Ramon Rodriguez *(Dir-Cost Structure Mngmt)*
Laurence R. Henss *(Treas)*
Jay Merrell *(Exec VP)*
Jon W. Coleman *(VP-Personnel)*
William Funke *(VP-Global Sls & Tech)*
Paul Rhodes *(VP-Mktg)*
Tom Flood *(Gen Mgr-IDI North America)*
Pete Jarosz *(Dir-Slitting Opers)*

JANOME AMERICA, INC.

(Sub. of Janome Sewing Machine Co., Ltd.)
10 Industrial Ave
Mahwah, NJ 07430
Tel.: (201) 825-3200
Fax: (201) 825-1488
Toll Free: (800) 631-0183
E-mail: advmgr@janome-america.com
Web Site: www.janome.com
Approx. Number Employees: 50
Business Description:
Sewing Machine Mfr & Distr
S.I.C.: 5064; 5949
N.A.I.C.S.: 423620; 451130
Export
Media: 2-6-10
Budget Set: Jan.
Personnel:
Randy Thomas *(Sr VP)*
Advertising Agency:
McKinney Johnson
1303 SW 16th

Key to Media (For complete agency information see *The Advertising Red Books-Agencies* edition):
1. Bus. Publs. 2. Cable T.V. 3. Catalogs & Directories. 4. Co-op Adv. 5. Consumer Mags. 6. D.M. to Bus. Estab.7. D.M. to Consumers
8. Daily Newsp. 9. Exhibits/Trade Shows 10. Foreign 11. Infomercial 12. Internet Adv.13. Multimedia 14. Network Radio
15. Network T.V. 16. Newsp. Distr. Mags. 17. Other 18. Outdoor (Posters, Transit) 19. Point of Purchase20. Premiums, Novelties
21. Product Samples 22. Special Events Mktg. 23. Spot Radio 24. Spot T.V. 25. Weekly Newsp. 26. Yellow Page Adv.

Portland, OR 97201
Tel.: (503) 222-0112
Fax: (503) 222-5897

JARDEN CONSUMER SOLUTIONS
(Div. of Jarden Corporation)
2381 NW Executive Ctr Dr
Boca Raton, FL 33431-7321
Tel.: (561) 912-4100
Fax: (561) 912-4567
E-mail: info@jardencs.com
Web Site: www.jardencs.com
Approx. Sls.: $400,000,000
Approx. Number Employees: 400
Year Founded: 1924
Business Description:
Small Appliances Mfr
S.I.C.: 3631; 2514
N.A.I.C.S.: 335221; 337124
Import Export
Advertising Expenditures: $25,000,000
Media: 1-2-3-4-5-6-7-8-9-10-11-13-15-16-18-19-20-23-24-25
Distr.: Intl.; Natl.
Budget Set: Apr.
Personnel:
Andrew C. Hill *(Pres & CEO)*
Alan LeFevre *(CFO & Exec VP-Ops)*
Joseph A. Tadeo *(Sr VP & Gen Mgr)*
Mary Ann Knaus *(Sr VP-Strategic Dev & Global Mktg)*
Katherine Phelps *(Mgr-Media)*
Fabio Bottallo *(Brand Mgr-Intl)*
Brands & Products:
BIONAIRE
CROCK POT
FOOD SAVER
HEALTH-O-METER
HOLMES
MR. COFFEE
OSTER
PATTON
RIVAL
SEALAMEAL
SELECTRONIC
SHEARMASTER
SHOT OF STEAM
SIMMER-SAFE
SLUMBER REST
SPORT MATE 1200
SPRAY MIST
STEAM 'N DRI
STEAM VALET
STYLE-AIRE
SUNBEAM
SUNBEAM AUTOMATIC WARMING BLANKETS
SUNBEAM CHILL-IT
SUNBEAM DENTAL CARE
SUNBEAM HEAT TO GO
SUNRON
SUPER POT
THERMO CAFE
TIGHT CURL II
TODAY
TOTAL CLEAN
TUFF GUARD
VIKING HANGING SCALES
VILLAWARE
VISTA
ZARAFINA
Advertising Agency:
Hill Holliday
53 State St
Boston, MA 02109
Tel.: (617) 366-4000

JESSUP'S APPLIANCES
1210 E Venice Ave
Venice, FL 34285
Tel.: (941) 484-9030
Approx. Number Employees: 20
Business Description:
Retailer of Major Appliances
S.I.C.: 5999
N.A.I.C.S.: 453998
Media: 8-9-24
Personnel:
Tom Jessup *(Pres)*
John Padgett *(Mgr-Sls)*

JOHNSON CONTROLS - FRICK
(Formerly York Process Systems - Frick)
(Div. of Johnson Controls Building Efficiency Group)
100 CV Ave
Waynesboro, PA 17268
Tel.: (717) 762-2121
Fax: (717) 762-8624
E-mail: info@johnsoncontrols.com
Web Site: www.johnsoncontrols.com/publish/us/en/products/building_efficiency/Commercial_and_Industrial_Refrigeration.html
Sales Range: $125-149.9 Million
Approx. Number Employees: 500
Year Founded: 1853
Business Description:
Industrial Refrigeration Equipment Mfr
S.I.C.: 3585
N.A.I.C.S.: 333415
Media: 6-9-17-25
Distr.: Intl.; Natl.; Reg.
Budget Set: Dec.
Personnel:
John Gay *(Mgr-Mktg)*
Brands & Products:
ACUAIR
POWERPAC
QUANTUM

KAZ, INC.
(Sub. of Helen of Troy Limited)
250 Turnpike Rd
Southborough, MA 01772
Tel.: (508) 490-7000
Toll Free: (800) 477-0457
E-mail: consumerrelations@kaz.com
Web Site: www.kaz.com
Sales Range: $300-349.9 Million
Approx. Number Employees: 600
Year Founded: 1926
Business Description:
Electric Vaporizers; Electric Heating Pads; Private-Label Heating Products; Electric Humidifiers; Home Steam Baths & Saunas & Heating Caps Mfr
S.I.C.: 3634; 3841
N.A.I.C.S.: 335211; 339112
Import Export
Media: 4-5-7-20
Distr.: Intl.; Natl
Budget Set: Apr.
Personnel:
Julien R. Mininberg *(Pres & CEO)*
Mark Simon *(Sr VP & Gen Mgr-North America)*
Roelof Zeijpveld *(Sr VP & Gen Mgr-EMEA)*
Rob McMillan *(Gen Mgr-Canada)*
Eleanor Mok *(Gen Mgr-Asia Pacific)*
Alvaro Avellaira *(Dir-Sls & Mktg)*
Brands & Products:
A WORLD OF HEALTH & COMFORT
CIRCU-BREEZE
COOL MIST
DYNAFILTER
ENVIRACAIRE
EXPRESS
HEALTHMIST
HEAT GIANT
HONEYWELL
INTELLICHECK
KAZ
NO DRAFT
OSCILLATOR
QUICK HEAT
QUIETCARE
SAFEGUARD
SAFETYLIGHT 2100
SAFETYLIGHT 2200
SILENTCOMFORT
SMARTHEAT
SMARTTEMP
SOLAR COMFORT
SUPER TURBO
SURESET
THERMAL MATRIX
TWINDOW
VICKS

KENT/EUROCLEAN
(Unit of Nilfisk-Advance, Inc.)
14600 21st Ave N
Plymouth, MN 55447-3408
Tel.: (763) 745-3500
Fax: (866) 261-4779
Toll Free: (800) 334-1083
Web Site: www.kenteuroclean.com
Approx. Number Employees: 3,000
Year Founded: 1913
Business Description:
Floor Maintenance Equipment Mfr
S.I.C.: 3589; 5087
N.A.I.C.S.: 333319; 423850
Import Export
Advertising Expenditures: $140,000
Media: 2-5-7-10
Distr.: Reg.
Personnel:
Christian Cornelius-Knudsen *(CEO)*
Brands & Products:
BACK VAC
CHAMPION 28
CUSTOMERZONE
DURATRAC
DURAVAC 152
DUST MAGNET
EDGE
EDGE 12
HIP VAC
HYDRODRY
KENT
KLENZOR
RAINMAKER
RAZOR
RAZOR PLUS
RELIAVAC
SELECTGLOSS 17E
SELECTGLOSS 20B
SELECTGLOSS 20E
SELECTLINE
SELECTSCRUB
SELECTSPOT
SELECTSPRAY
SELECTSPRAY 1250E
SELECTSPRAY 1500E
SELECTSPRAY 2700G
SELECTSWEEP
SELECTVAC
SIMPLE. CLEAN.
XTRAC
Advertising Agency:
Creative Communications Consultants, Inc.
111 3rd Ave S Ste 390
Minneapolis, MN 55401-2553
Tel.: (612) 338-5098
Fax: (612) 338-1398
— Susan McPherson *(Acct Exec)*

KOLPAK
(Unit of Manitowoc Foodservice USA)
2915 Tennessee Ave N
Parsons, TN 38363-5046
Tel.: (731) 847-6361
Fax: (731) 847-5638
Toll Free: (800) 826-7036
E-mail: info@kolpak.com
Web Site: www.kolpak.com
Sales Range: $100-124.9 Million
Approx. Number Employees: 300
Year Founded: 1969
Business Description:
Freezers & Refrigerators for Food Service Industry Mfr
S.I.C.: 3585
N.A.I.C.S.: 333415
Export
Advertising Expenditures: $300,000
Media: 2-4-5-10
Distr.: Natl.
Budget Set: Oct.
Personnel:
Mike Bowes *(Fin Mgr-Manitowoc)*
Jim Acee *(Sls Mgr-Inside)*
Brands & Products:
EXPRESS
KOLPAK
POLAR-PAK

LSI INDUSTRIES INC.
10000 Alliance Rd
Cincinnati, OH 45242-4706
Tel.: (513) 793-3200
Fax: (513) 984-1335
E-mail: info@lsi-industries.com
Web Site: www.lsi-industries.com
Approx. Sls.: $293,501,000
Approx. Number Employees: 1,200
Year Founded: 1976
Business Description:
Lighting, Graphics & Menu Board Systems Mfr
S.I.C.: 3648; 3646; 3993; 5063
N.A.I.C.S.: 335129; 335122; 339950; 423610
Export
Advertising Expenditures: $281,000
Media: 4-6-10-13-16-22-26
Personnel:
Robert J. Ready *(Chm, Pres & CEO)*
Ronald S. Stowell *(CFO, Treas & VP)*
James P. Sferra *(Sec & Exec VP-Mfg)*
Vicki Rea *(Mgr-Mktg)*
Brands & Products:
A COMPANY WITH A SMART VISION
ABOLITE
AEROSYSTEM
AUGUSTA
CHALLENGER
CHARLESTON
CITATION
CONDOR
COURTSIDER
CROSSOVER
CYPRESS

Key to Media (For complete agency information see *The Advertising Red Books-Agencies* edition):
1. Bus. Publs. 2. Cable T.V. 3. Catalogs & Directories. 4. Co-op Adv. 5. Consumer Mags. 6. D.M. to Bus. Estab.7. D.M. to Consumers 8. Daily Newsp. 9. Exhibits/Trade Shows 10. Foreign 11. Infomercial 12. Internet Adv.13. Multimedia 14. Network Radio 15. Network T.V. 16. Newsp. Distr. Mags. 17. Other 18. Outdoor (Posters, Transit) 19. Point of Purchase20. Premiums, Novelties 21. Product Samples 22. Special Events Mktg. 23. Spot Radio 24. Spot T.V. 25. Weekly Newsp. 26. Yellow Page Adv.

LSI Industries Inc. — (Continued)

DAKOTA
DORAL
DURAGRIP
EAGLE
ENCORE
GALLANT
GREENBRIAR
GREENLEE
HERCULEX
HERITAGE
HILTON
LITE-MART
LSI INDUSTRIES
OVATION
PARATRON
PARK AVENUE
PATRIOT
RETROFIT TO CROSSOVER
RICHMOND
SACRAMENTO
SCOTTSDALE
SOVEREIGN
STARBEAM

MAC-GRAY CORPORATION

404 Wyman St Ste 400
Waltham, MA 02451
Tel.: (781) 487-7600
Fax: (617) 492-5386
Toll Free: (800) MAC-GRAY
E-mail: ir@macgray.com
Web Site: www.mac-gray.com
Approx. Rev.: $320,011,000
Approx. Number Employees: 876
Year Founded: 1927
Business Description:
Supplier of Card & Coin-Operated Laundry Services in Multiple Housing Facilities Such As Apartment Buildings, Colleges & Universities & Public Housing Complexes
S.I.C.: 3582; 0752; 5087; 7215; 7299
N.A.I.C.S.: 333312; 423850; 812310; 812910; 812990
Advertising Expenditures: $1,153,000
Personnel:
Thomas E. Bullock *(Chm)*
Stewart Gray Macdonald, Jr. *(CEO)*
Michael J. Shea *(CFO & Exec VP)*
Linda Serafini *(Gen Counsel, Sec & VP)*
Philip Emma *(Exec VP)*
Neil F. MacLellan, III *(Exec VP-Sls)*
Robert J. Tuttle *(Exec VP-Tech & Info Svcs)*
Brands & Products:
COPICO
E-ISSUES
ENERGY STAR
INTELLIGENT LAUNDRY SOLUTIONS
LAUNDRY
LAUNDRYLINK
LAUNDRYVIEW
MAC-GRAY
MICROFRIDGE
SAFECIRCUIT
TURBOWASH
VENTSANKE
Advertising Agency:
O'Sullivan Communications
42 Davis Rd Ste 1
Acton, MA 01720
Tel.: (978) 264-0707

MANITOWOC FOODSERVICE USA

(Formerly Enodis Corporation)
(Sub. of Manitowoc Foodservice Companies, Inc.)
2227 Welbilt Blvd
New Port Richey, FL 34655-5130
Tel.: (727) 375-7010
Fax: (727) 375-0472
Web Site: www.manitowocfsusa.com
Sales Range: $25-49.9 Million
Approx. Number Employees: 40
Year Founded: 1907
Business Description:
Commercial Food Service Equipment Mfr
S.I.C.: 3589; 3585
N.A.I.C.S.: 333319; 333415
Import Export
Media: 4-7-10-17
Distr.: Natl.
Budget Set: Jan.
Personnel:
Michael J. Kachmer *(Pres)*
Brands & Products:
CLEVELAND
DEAN
GARLAND
LINCOLN
MERCO
SAVORY
U.S. RANGE
VARIMIXER

MANITOWOC ICE, INC.

(Sub. of Manitowoc Foodservice USA)
2110 S 26th St
Manitowoc, WI 54220
Mailing Address:
PO Box 1720
Manitowoc, WI 54221-1720
Tel.: (920) 682-0161
Fax: (920) 683-7879
Fax: (800) 235-9705
Toll Free: (800) 545-5720
Web Site: www.manitowocice.com
Sales Range: $125-149.9 Million
Approx. Number Employees: 400
Year Founded: 1965
Business Description:
Commercial Ice Machines & Storage Bins Mfr
S.I.C.: 3585; 5078
N.A.I.C.S.: 333415; 423740
Export
Media: 2-4-5-8-10-11-13-20-26
Distr.: Intl.; Natl.
Budget Set: Monthly
Personnel:
Dan Brandl *(VP & GM)*
Rick Showers *(VP-Mktg-Manitowoc Ice)*
Wendy Turek *(Dir-Fin)*

MERCO/SAVORY LLC

(Sub. of Manitowoc Foodservice USA)
1111 N Hadley Rd
Fort Wayne, IN 46804-5540
Tel.: (260) 459-8200
Fax: (260) 436-0735
Toll Free: (800) 547-2513
E-mail: sales@mercosavory.com
Web Site: www.mercosavory.com
E-Mail For Key Personnel:
Sales Director: sales@mercosavory.com
Sales Range: $25-49.9 Million
Approx. Number Employees: 70
Year Founded: 1834
Business Description:
Restaurant Equipment Mfr
S.I.C.: 3556
N.A.I.C.S.: 333294
Export
Advertising Expenditures: $200,000
Media: 7-10
Distr.: Intl.; Natl.
Budget Set: Sept.
Personnel:
Stephen Amos *(Owner)*
Brands & Products:
CONTEMPO
PANORAMA
ST1 MINI

MERROW MACHINE COMPANY

502 Bedford St
Fall River, MA 02720
Tel.: (508) 689-4095
Fax: (508) 689-4098
Toll Free: (800) 431-6677
E-mail: info@merrow.com
Web Site: www.merrow.com
Sales Range: $10-24.9 Million
Approx. Number Employees: 150
Year Founded: 1838
Business Description:
Industrial Sewing Machines Mfr
S.I.C.: 3559; 6512
N.A.I.C.S.: 333298; 531120
Export
Advertising Expenditures: $300,000
Media: 2-4-7-10-11-17
Distr.: Intl.; Natl.
Personnel:
Charles Merrow *(Pres)*
Brands & Products:
MERROW

THE METAL WARE CORP.

1700 Monroe St
Two Rivers, WI 54241-2928
Tel.: (920) 793-1368
Fax: (920) 793-1086
Toll Free: (800) 288-4545
E-mail: cdrumm@nesco.com
Web Site: www.nesco.com
Approx. Number Employees: 100
Year Founded: 1920
Business Description:
Electric Housewares & Appliances Marketer
S.I.C.: 3634; 3631
N.A.I.C.S.: 335211; 335221
Import Export
Media: 2-5-10-15
Distr.: Natl.
Budget Set: Dec.
Personnel:
Wesley C. Drumm *(Pres & CEO)*
Victor F. Trastek *(Sr VP)*
Brands & Products:
ADD-A-TRAY
AMERICA HARVEST
CLEAN-A-SCREEN
CONVERGE-A-FLOW
CYCLONIC COOKING
EXPANDER RING
EXPRESS
JERKY WORKS
JET-STREAM
JUMBO JERKY WORKS
KAR 'N HOME
NESCO
NESCO/AMERICAN HARVEST
NESCOTE
OPEN COUNTRY
SNACKMASTER
TRAVL-MATES
TUMBLE DRUMM

MICROFLUIDICS INTERNATIONAL CORPORATION

(Sub. of IDEX Corporation)
30 Ossipee Rd
Newton, MA 02464-9101
Mailing Address:
PO Box 9101
Newton, MA 02464-9101
Tel.: (617) 969-5452
Fax: (617) 965-1213
Toll Free: (800) 370-5452
E-mail: info@mfics.com
Web Site: www.mficcorp.com
Approx. Rev.: $15,739,000
Approx. Number Employees: 50
Year Founded: 1983
Business Description:
Mfr of High Performance Fluid Processing Equipment for the Pharmaceutical, Chemical, Biotechnology, Cosmetic/Personal Care, & Food Industries
S.I.C.: 3821; 3559
N.A.I.C.S.: 339111; 333298
Export
Advertising Expenditures: $3,093,293
Media: 2-4-7-8-10-22
Distr.: Intl.; Natl.
Budget Set: Nov.
Personnel:
George Uveges *(Chm)*
Michael C. Ferrara *(Pres & CEO)*
Robert P. Bruno *(COO)*
Peter F. Byczko *(Chief Acctg Officer & VP-Fin)*
Kent Chu *(VP-Sls-Asia Pacific)*
William J. Conroy *(VP-Ops & Engrg & Corp Officer)*
William Kober *(VP-Sls-Americas & Asia East)*
Xavier Leroy *(VP-Sls-Europe, Middle, East America & Africa)*
Mary Anne North *(VP-Customer Success)*
David Gucwa *(Product Mgr)*
Brands & Products:
EPWORTH MILL
MFIC
MICROFLUIDICS
MICROFLUIDICS REACTION TECHNOLOGY
MICROFLUIDIZER
MICROFLUIDIZER MIXER-REACTOR
MOREHOUSE-COWLES
VISCOMAX
ZINGER

MIELE INC.

(Sub. of Miele & Cie KG)
9 Independence Way
Princeton, NJ 08540
Tel.: (609) 419-9898
Fax: (609) 419-4298
Toll Free: (800) 843-7231
E-mail: hr@mieleusa.com
Web Site: www.mieleusa.com
Approx. Number Employees: 150
Year Founded: 1983

Key to Media (For complete agency information see *The Advertising Red Books-Agencies* edition):
1. Bus. Publs. 2. Cable T.V. 3. Catalogs & Directories. 4. Co-op Adv. 5. Consumer Mags. 6. D.M. to Bus. Estab.7. D.M. to Consumers
8. Daily Newsp. 9. Exhibits/Trade Shows 10. Foreign 11. Infomercial 12. Internet Adv.13. Multimedia 14. Network Radio
15. Network T.V. 16. Newsp. Distr. Mags. 17. Other 18. Outdoor (Posters, Transit) 19. Point of Purchase20. Premiums, Novelties
21. Product Samples 22. Special Events Mktg. 23. Spot Radio 24. Spot T.V. 25. Weekly Newsp. 26. Yellow Page Adv.

Business Description:
Major Household Appliances & Vacuums Sales & Services
S.I.C.: 5064
N.A.I.C.S.: 423620
Import
Media: 1-5-6-10-19-26
Distr.: Intl.; Natl.
Budget Set: Sept. -Oct.
Personnel:
Nick Ord *(Pres)*
Nadine Hanselmann *(Mgr-Mktg)*
Matthew Kueny *(Mgr-Product Dev)*
Brands & Products:
MASTER CHEF COLLECTION
MIELE
Advertising Agencies:
AGENCYSACKS
345 7th Ave 7th Fl
New York, NY 10001-5006
Tel.: (212) 826-4004
Fax: (212) 593-7824

Thacker & Frank
339 Princeton Hightstown Rd.
Cranbury, NJ 08512
Tel.: (609) 490-0999
Fax: (609) 448-4343

MONOSOL, LLC
(Holding of Catterton Partners)
707 E 80th Pl Ste 301
Merrillville, IN 46410
Tel.: (219) 762-3165
Fax: (219) 755-4062
E-mail: careers@monosol.com
Web Site: www.monosol.com
Approx. Number Employees: 500
Year Founded: 1953
Business Description:
Producer of Water-Soluble Films Used for Hospital Laundry Bags, Mold Release Agents & Packaging Films
S.I.C.: 2671
N.A.I.C.S.: 326112
Media: 7-10-13
Personnel:
Scott Bening *(Pres & CEO)*
Brands & Products:
AQUAFILM
BADGEMASTER
DISSOLVOSACK
DURAFILM
MONODOSE
MONOPAC
MONOPOL
MONOSOL
POLAFILM
TERRALOC

NATERRA INTERNATIONAL INC.
13525 Denton Dr
Dallas, TX 75234
Tel.: (972) 616-6100
Fax: (972) 620-0715
Toll Free: (800) 433-6392
Web Site:
www.beautymanfacture.com
Approx. Number Employees: 55
Year Founded: 1922
Business Description:
Perfumes, Cosmetics & Other Toilet Preparations
S.I.C.: 2844
N.A.I.C.S.: 325620
Brands & Products:
BABY MAGIC
NATERRA
SKINMILK
SUE PREE
TIME BLOCK
TREE HUT
Advertising Agency:
The Richards Group, Inc.
8750 N Central Expy Ste 100
Dallas, TX 75231-6430
Tel.: (214) 891-5700
Fax: (214) 265-2933
All That Glitters
Baby Magic
Creative
National Magazine Campaign
Strategic Planning
Tree Hut

NESCO AMERICAN HARVEST INC.
(Sub. of The Metal Ware Corp.)
1700 Monroe St
Two Rivers, WI 54241-2928
Tel.: (920) 793-1368
Fax: (920) 793-1086
E-mail: marketing@nesco.com
Web Site: www.nesco.com
Approx. Number Employees: 120
Year Founded: 1920
Business Description:
Household Cooking Appliances Mfr & Marketer
S.I.C.: 3634; 3631
N.A.I.C.S.: 335211; 335221
Import Export
Advertising Expenditures: $200,000
Media: 4-6-9-10-23-24
Distr.: Intl.; Natl.
Budget Set: Dec.
Personnel:
Wesley Drumm *(Pres)*
Mike Berger *(VP-Sls)*
Brands & Products:
BABE & KRIS
JET STREAM
OPEN COUNTRY

NOBLES MANUFACTURING, INC.
(Holding of Inverness Graham Investments)
1105 E Pine St
Saint Croix Falls, WI 54024
Tel.: (715) 483-3079
Fax: (715) 483-1884
Web Site: www.noblesmfg.com
Sales Range: $50-74.9 Million
Approx. Number Employees: 45
Year Founded: 1948
Business Description:
Ammunition Feeding System Mfr
S.I.C.: 3559; 3728
N.A.I.C.S.: 333298; 336413
Export
Media: 1-2-3-5-6-7-9-10-13-22
Distr.: Natl.
Budget Set: Jan.
Personnel:
Troy Priem *(Pres)*
Ted Priem *(CEO)*
Brands & Products:
NOBLES
NOBLES SPIN KLEEN
NOBLES TURBO
NOBLES TURBO DRYER
SPIN-KLEEN

NSS ENTERPRISES, INC.
3115 Frenchmens Rd
Toledo, OH 43607-2918
Tel.: (419) 531-2121
Fax: (419) 531-3761
E-mail: mailus@nss.com
Web Site: www.nss.com
Sales Range: $25-49.9 Million
Approx. Number Employees: 170
Year Founded: 1911
Business Description:
Floor & Carpet Cleaning Equipment Mfr
S.I.C.: 3589; 3567
N.A.I.C.S.: 333319; 333994
Import Export
Media: 2-4-5-7-10-11-20-22-26
Distr.: Intl.
Personnel:
Mark Bevington *(Pres)*
Ronald P. Tonies *(CEO & CFO)*
Brands & Products:
AERO PLUS
AQUAFORCE
BP RANGER
BRONCO
CHAMP
CHARGER
COLT
COMMANDER
DESIGNER
DESIGNER DRY
GALAXY
GALAXY DS
INTEGRITY AT WORK.
MANTA
MAVERICK
MUSTANG
NSS
OUTLAW
PACER
PONY
PORTER
PREDATOR
SIDEWINDER
STALLION
THOROUGHBRED
WRANGLER

ORECK CORPORATION
565 Marriott Dr Ste 300
Nashville, TN 37214
Tel.: (615) 316-5800
Fax: (615) 316-5839
Toll Free: (800) 408-7134
E-mail: privacy@oreck.com
Web Site: www.oreck.com
Approx. Number Employees: 1,100
Year Founded: 1963
Business Description:
Upright Consumer & Commercial Vacuum Cleaners, Air Purifiers, Water Purifiers
S.I.C.: 3635; 5722
N.A.I.C.S.: 335212; 443111
Advertising Expenditures: $200,000
Media: 2-3-6-9-14-15-16-23-24-25
Distr.: Intl.; Natl.
Budget Set: June
Personnel:
David Oreck *(Founder)*
Bill Fry *(Chm)*
Thomas A. Oreck *(Pres)*
Jeff Gray *(CFO)*
Scott Vogel *(CMO & VP-Channels)*
Linda Tilt *(Mgr-Interactive Mktg)*
Brands & Products:
BOWL BEAUTIFUL
CLOUD FREE
CORDLESS ZIP VAC
CRYSTAL AROMA II
DUTCHTECH
ELECTRIKBROOM
FULL BLOOM
GREASE LOCK
GRUNGE ATTACK
HEALTHIER, EASIER, SMARTER.
HOSPITAL CLEAN
NO RETURN
ORBITER
ORECK
ORECK ALANITE
ORECK CAR VAC
ORECK DRY CARPET
ORECK FLOOR SWEEPER
ORECK FRESH AIR
ORECK FULL RELEASE
ORECK HALO
ORECK HOUSEKEEPER
ORECK IRONMAN
ORECK LITTER EX
ORECK PREMIST
ORECK RESTAURATEUR
ORECK XL
ORECKBRITE
REVELRY
RINSE-A-MATIC STEEMER
RINSE-A-MATIC STEEMER ULTRA
SOLVE-A-SPOT
SPEED IRON
STEAM-IT
STEEMER ULTRA
STONE CLEAR TOP
TIMBERWORKS
TREWAX
TWO TOUGH
WOOD SPLENDOR
Advertising Agency:
SBC Advertising
333 W Nationwide Blvd
Columbus, OH 43215
Tel.: (614) 891-7070
Fax: (614) 255-2600
Toll Free: (866) 891-7001

P.C. RICHARD & SON
150 Price Pkwy
Farmingdale, NY 11735-1315
Tel.: (631) 843-4300
Tel.: (631) 843-4470
Fax: (631) 843-4589
Web Site: www.pcrichard.com
Approx. Number Employees: 2,173
Year Founded: 1909
Business Description:
Appliance, Electronics & Home Office Retailer
S.I.C.: 5722; 5731
N.A.I.C.S.: 443111; 443112
Advertising Expenditures: $500,000
Media: 1-4-5-6-9-13-14-15-16-18-22-23-24-25-26
Distr.: Reg.
Personnel:
Gary Richard *(Pres & CEO)*
Tom Pohmer *(CFO)*
Peter Richard *(Exec VP)*

PLASTAKET MANUFACTURING COMPANY INC.
6220 E Hwy 12
Lodi, CA 95240
Tel.: (209) 369-2154

Key to Media (For complete agency information see *The Advertising Red Books-Agencies* edition):
1. Bus. Publs. 2. Cable T.V. 3. Catalogs & Directories. 4. Co-op Adv. 5. Consumer Mags. 6. D.M. to Bus. Estab.7. D.M. to Consumers 8. Daily Newsp. 9. Exhibits/Trade Shows 10. Foreign 11. Infomercial 12. Internet Adv.13. Multimedia 14. Network Radio 15. Network T.V. 16. Newsp. Distr. Mags. 17. Other 18. Outdoor (Posters, Transit) 19. Point of Purchase20. Premiums, Novelties 21. Product Samples 22. Special Events Mktg. 23. Spot Radio 24. Spot T.V. 25. Weekly Newsp. 26. Yellow Page Adv.

Plastaket Manufacturing Company Inc. — (Continued)

Fax: (209) 369-7455
Web Site: www.championjuicer.com
E-Mail For Key Personnel:
Sales Director: sales@championjuicer.com
Approx. Number Employees: 30
Business Description:
Mfr. & Distributor of Juicers
S.I.C.: 3634; 3556
N.A.I.C.S.: 335211; 333294
Media: 6
Brands & Products:
CHAMPION

PURCELL MURRAY COMPANY INC.

185 Park Ln
Brisbane, CA 94005
Tel.: (415) 468-6620
Fax: (415) 468-0667
Toll Free: (800) 892-4040
Web Site: www.purcellmurray.com
Approx. Sls.: $75,000,000
Approx. Number Employees: 100
Year Founded: 1981
Business Description:
Large Appliances; Wholesale Distribution
S.I.C.: 5074; 5064
N.A.I.C.S.: 423720; 423620
Media: 6-7-10-11-13
Personnel:
Timothy F. Murray *(Pres)*
Don Connors *(Dir-Sls-Builder)*
Mike Maramba *(Dir-Ops)*
Kevin Murray *(Dir-Mktg)*
Kels D. Purcell *(Dir-Sls)*
Curtis Roe *(Dir-Fin)*
Anne Laluc *(Brand Mgr)*
Leticia Parraz *(Product Mgr-Home Expo)*
Cristina Lintoco *(Product Mgr-La Cornue)*
David Ariente *(Mgr-Warehouse Ops)*
Larry Chatfield *(Mgr-Technical Svcs)*
Linda Clare *(Mgr-Territory)*
Laura Clifton *(Mgr-Builder Sls Territory-SF Bay Area)*
Chalisa Dade *(Mgr-Lead Product)*
Alexis Gion *(Mgr-La Cornue)*
Virginia Gonzalez *(Mgr-Territory)*
Dan Graves *(Mgr-Territory)*
Sean Hernandez *(Mgr-IT)*
Jim Jones *(Mgr-Territory)*
Laura Marcoux *(Mgr-Territory)*
Rich Marple *(Mgr-Territory)*
Tim McLoughlin *(Mgr-Sls-Southern California)*
Debbie Rucker *(Mgr-Logisitcs)*
Heather Storm *(Mgr-Showroom)*
Larissa Taboryski *(Mgr-Showroom & Culinary)*
Steve Van Hoomisen *(Mgr-Territory)*
JePaul Wahtley *(Mgr-Credit & Collections)*
Dennis Zapata *(Mgr-Warehouse)*

QT MAILING & PACKAGING DIVISION

(Sub. of 123 Payroll Services, Inc.)
123 Main St
Philadelphia, PA 19127
Tel.: (215) 555-1212
Fax: (215) 555-1234
Approx. Number Employees: 30
Year Founded: 1977
Business Description:
Mailing Services
S.I.C.: 7389
N.A.I.C.S.: 561431
Advertising Expenditures: $200,000
Co-op Adv.: $20,000; D.M. to Bus. Estab.: $30,000; Foreign: $40,000; Internet Adv.: $10,000; Spot T.V.: $100,000
Personnel:
Janie Jones *(Sr VP)*
Barb Larson *(VP, Mgr, Copywriter & Dir-Creative)*
Yesenia Jimenez *(Dir)*
Brands & Products:
XPRESSIT

RANGE KLEEN MANUFACTURING INC.

4240 E Rd
Lima, OH 45807-1533
Tel.: (419) 331-8000
Fax: (419) 331-4538
Toll Free: (888) 391-2020
E-mail: info@rangekleen.com
Web Site: www.rangekleen.com
Approx. Number Employees: 500
Year Founded: 1971
Business Description:
Reflector Bowls & Pans Mfr
S.I.C.: 3365; 3469
N.A.I.C.S.: 331524; 332116
Export
Advertising Expenditures: $400,000
Media: 2-4-7-8-10-15-19-20-21-24
Distr.: Natl.
Budget Set: Nov.
Personnel:
Patrick O'Connor *(Pres)*
Dave Link *(CFO)*
Brands & Products:
RANGE KLEEN

REMINGTON LICENSING CORPORATION

(Sub. of Spectrum Brands, Inc.)
601 Rayovac Dr
Madison, WI 53711-2497
Mailing Address:
PO Box 44960
Madison, WI 53744-4960
Tel.: (608) 275-3340
Fax: (203) 332-4648
Toll Free: (800) 736-4648
E-mail: webmaster@remington-products.com
Web Site: www.remington-products.com
Sales Range: $400-449.9 Million
Approx. Number Employees: 1,000
Year Founded: 1979
Business Description:
Personal Care Products Licensing & Distr
S.I.C.: 6794; 5064
N.A.I.C.S.: 533110; 423620
Import Export
Media: 1-2-5-6-7-8-11-13-15-19-20-22-23-24-25
Distr.: Natl.
Budget Set: Mar.
Personnel:
Denise Lincoln *(Art Dir & Creative Dir)*
Brands & Products:
AERO SERIES
CARE SETTER
CODE
FLEX360
FUZZ AWAY
INTERCEPT
MICROFLEX
MICROSCREEN
PG-350
PRECISION
PRO AIR
REMINGTON
REMINGTON EXPRESS SET
RM PRO
SHAVER SAVER
SHEER GOLD
SHORTCUT CLIPPER
SMART SPACE SETTER
SMOOTH & SILKY
SPEED SETTER
SUPERSONIC
TCT
TIGHT CURLS
TRIM & SHAPE
TWISTERS
VOLUME MAXIMIZER
VORTEX
Advertising Agency:
Clarke Advertising
401 N Cattlemen Rd Ste 200
Sarasota, FL 34232-6439
Tel.: (941) 365-2710
Fax: (941) 366-4940
Toll Free: (800) 724-0289
(Flex360, PG-350, RM PRO, ShortCut Clipper)

RONCO INVENTIONS LLC

3850 Royal Ave
Simi Valley, CA 93063
Tel.: (805) 433-1030
Fax: (818) 775-4664
Toll Free: (800) 357-2782
Web Site: www.ronco.com
Sales Range: $200-249.9 Million
Approx. Number Employees: 30
Year Founded: 1984
Business Description:
Household Appliances Mfr & Distr
S.I.C.: 5023; 5719
N.A.I.C.S.: 423220; 442299
Import Export
Advertising Expenditures: $30,000,000
Media: 3-4-6-8-9-10-11-12-13-15-22-24-25
Distr.: Intl.
Personnel:
Terry Tigner *(Pres & CEO)*
Brands & Products:
DIAL-O-MATIC
GLH #9
POPEIL
POPEIL'S
RONCO
SHOWTIME
SIX STAR

ROTOVAC CORPORATION

17905 Bothell Everett Hwy
Mill Creek, WA 98012
Tel.: (425) 883-6746
Fax: (425) 883-8953
Toll Free: (888) 768-6822
Web Site: www.rotovac.com
Sales Range: $75-99.9 Million
Approx. Number Employees: 20
Business Description:
Carpet Cleaning System Mfr
S.I.C.: 3635
N.A.I.C.S.: 335212
Media: 6
Personnel:
Cliff Monson *(Pres)*

ROWENTA (USA), INC.

(Sub. of Rowenta Werke)
2121 Eden Rd
Millville, NJ 08332
Tel.: (781) 396-0600
Fax: (856) 825-0118
E-mail: customer@rowentausa.com
Web Site: www.rowentausa.com
Approx. Number Employees: 32
Business Description:
Marketing & Distribution of Household Appliances
S.I.C.: 5064
N.A.I.C.S.: 423620
Media: 10
Distr.: Natl.
Personnel:
John Crisostamo *(CFO)*
Danna Duffy *(Mgr-Mktg)*
Brands & Products:
ACTIPRESS
POWERGLIDE 2
POWERPRESS
PROFESSIONAL LUXE
ROWENTA
ULTRA PROFESSIONAL
Advertising Agencies:
AMP Agency
295 Devonshire St
Boston, MA 02110
Tel.: (617) 542-5587
Fax: (617) 896-1311

Cogent Public Relations
100 Tower Office Pk
Woburn, MA 01801
Tel.: (781) 937-3670
Fax: (781) 937-3575

RUSSELL HOBBS, INC.

(Div. of Spectrum Brands, Inc.)
(d/b/a Spectrum Brands, Inc. - Small Appliances Division)
3633 S Flamingo Rd
Miramar, FL 33027
Tel.: (954) 883-1000
Toll Free: (800) 231-9786
E-mail: investor.relations@russellhobbsinc.com
Web Site: www.russellhobbsinc.com
Sales Range: $650-699.9 Million
Approx. Number Employees: 575
Year Founded: 1988
Business Description:
Holding Company; Small Household Appliance Licensing, Marketing & Distr
S.I.C.: 6719; 3634; 5064; 6794
N.A.I.C.S.: 551112; 335211; 423620; 533110
Distr.: Natl.
Budget Set: Mar.
Personnel:
Terry Lee Polistina *(Pres & CEO)*
John M. Silvestri *(Pres/Gen Mgr-Pet Products Div)*
Paul J. Harber *(CIO & VP, Chief Integration Officer)*
Martin J. Burns *(Pres/Gen Mgr-Europe Div)*

Key to Media (For complete agency information see *The Advertising Red Books-Agencies* edition):
1. Bus. Publs. 2. Cable T.V. 3. Catalogs & Directories. 4. Co-op Adv. 5. Consumer Mags. 6. D.M. to Bus. Estab.7. D.M. to Consumers
8. Daily Newsp. 9. Exhibits/Trade Shows 10. Foreign 11. Infomercial 12. Internet Adv.13. Multimedia 14. Network Radio
15. Network T.V. 16. Newsp. Distr. Mags. 17. Other 18. Outdoor (Posters, Transit) 19. Point of Purchase20. Premiums, Novelties
21. Product Samples 22. Special Events Mktg. 23. Spot Radio 24. Spot T.V. 25. Weekly Newsp. 26. Yellow Page Adv.

Evanghela Hidalgo *(Pres/Gen Mgr-Americas Div)*
Lisa R. Carstarphen *(Gen Counsel, Sec & VP)*
Robert P. Schwartz *(Sr VP-Mktg)*
Steven A. Trussell *(VP-Global Sourcing & Procurement)*
Advertising Agency:
Manning Gottlieb OMD
Seymour Mews House
London, W1H 6BN, United Kingdom
Tel.: (44) 207 470 5300
Fax: (44) 207 412 0244

THE SALVAJOR COMPANY

4530 E 75th Ter
Kansas City, MO 64132-2081
Tel.: (816) 363-1030
Fax: (816) 363-4914
Toll Free: (800) 821-3136
E-mail: sales@salvajor.com
Web Site: www.salvajor.com
E-Mail For Key Personnel:
Sales Director: sales@salvajor.com
Approx. Number Employees: 50
Year Founded: 1944
Business Description:
Commercial Waste Disposers & Waste Handling Systems Mfr
S.I.C.: 3589; 3556
N.A.I.C.S.: 333319; 333294
Import Export
Media: 2-4-6-7-8-10-20
Distr.: Intl.; Natl.
Budget Set: Oct.
Personnel:
Chris Hohl *(Pres)*
Greg Wait *(VP-Sls)*
Brands & Products:
SALVAJOR
SCRAPMASTER
TROUGHVEYOR

SANDENVENDO AMERICA

(Sub. of Sanden Corporation)
10710 Sanden Dr
Dallas, TX 75238
Tel.: (214) 765-9066
Fax: (214) 221-7011
Toll Free: (800) 344-7216
E-mail: info@vendoco.com
Web Site: www.vendoco.com
Approx. Number Employees: 195
Year Founded: 1937
Business Description:
Mfr. of Vending Machines
S.I.C.: 7699
N.A.I.C.S.: 811310
Import Export
Media: 2-4-8-10-20
Distr.: Intl.
Budget Set: Dec.
Personnel:
Frank Kabei *(CEO)*
Brands & Products:
ROBO-DOOR
UNIVENDOR
UNIVENDOR-2
V-MAX

SKYE INTERNATIONAL, INC.

(Filed Ch 11 Bankruptcy #954485 on 12/16/09 in U.S. Bankruptcy Ct, Dist of NV, Las Vegas)
7701 E Gray Rd Ste 4
Scottsdale, AZ 85260-6966
Tel.: (480) 993-2300
Fax: (480) 951-6809
E-mail: info@tankless.com
Web Site: www.tankless.com
Approx. Number Employees: 9
Year Founded: 2003
Business Description:
Tankless Water Heaters Developer & Marketer
S.I.C.: 3639
N.A.I.C.S.: 335228
Advertising Expenditures: $97,936
Media: 17
Personnel:
Perry D. Logan *(Chm, Pres, CEO, Dir & Member-Corp Governance Committee)*
David P. Allen *(VP-Engrg)*

SON CHIEF ELECTRICS, INC.

41 Meadow St
Winsted, CT 06098-1438
Tel.: (860) 379-2741
Fax: (860) 379-2742
Approx. Number Employees: 10
Year Founded: 1916
Business Description:
Metal Stamper
S.I.C.: 3499; 3469
N.A.I.C.S.: 332116; 332214; 332439
Media: 7
Distr.: Natl.
Budget Set: Oct.

SPECTRUM BRANDS HOLDINGS, INC.

(Holding of Harbinger Capital Partners LLC)
601 Rayovac Dr
Madison, WI 53711
Tel.: (608) 275-3340
Web Site: www.spectrumbrands.com
Approx. Sls.: $2,567,011,000
Approx. Number Employees: 6,100
Year Founded: 2010
Business Description:
Holding Company; Electric Appliances Designer, Mfr & Whslr
S.I.C.: 6719; 3639; 5064; 6794
N.A.I.C.S.: 551112; 335228; 423620; 533110
Import
Advertising Expenditures: $37,520,000
Personnel:
David M. Maura *(Interim Chm)*
David R. Lumley *(CEO)*
Anthony L. Genito *(CFO & Exec VP)*
Terry Lee Polistina *(Pres-Small Appliances Div & Dir)*
John A. Heil *(Pres-Global Pet Supplies)*
Nathan E. Fagre *(Gen Counsel & Sec)*
John T. Wilson *(Gen Counsel)*
David A. Prichard *(VP-IR & Corp Comm)*

STANDEX INTERNATIONAL CORPORATION

11 Keewaydin Dr
Salem, NH 03079
Tel.: (603) 893-9701
Fax: (603) 893-7324
E-mail: investorrelations@standex.com
Web Site: www.standex.com
Approx. Sls.: $633,750,000
Approx. Number Employees: 4,000
Year Founded: 1955
Business Description:
Food Service Equipment, Air Distribution Products, Engineered Products, Hydraulics Products & Engraving Equipment Mfr
S.I.C.: 3556; 3443; 3585; 3679; 3714
N.A.I.C.S.: 333294; 332313; 333415; 334419; 336399
Import Export
Media: 2-5-6-8-10-19-20
Distr.: Intl.; Natl.
Budget Set: Dec.
Personnel:
Edward J. Trainor *(Chm)*
Roger L. Fix *(Pres & CEO)*
Thomas DeByle *(CFO)*
Deborah A. Rosen *(Chief Legal Officer, Sec & VP)*
Sean C. Valashinas *(Chief Acctg Officer)*
John Abbott *(Grp VP-Food Svc Grp)*
Brands & Products:
ACME
ALCO
BARBECUE KING
B.F. PERKINS
BKI
CUSTOM HOISTS
FRANK LEWIS
HARRY'S CRESTVIEW GROVES
LHERMITE
MASON
MASTER-BILT
MOLD-TECH
MULLEN
MULT-O
NOR-LAKE
ON CALL
PEMCO
PERKINS
PROCON
RED COOPER
RED GOAT
ROEHLEN
SALSA EXPRESS
SNAPPY
SPINCRAFT
STANDEX
TRIBOCOAT
UNITRAY
UNITRON 3
UNITRON 5
UNITRON 7
USECO

STAR MANUFACTURING INTERNATIONAL, INC.

10 Sunnen Dr
Saint Louis, MO 63143
Tel.: (314) 781-2777
Fax: (314) 781-3636
Fax: (800) 264-6666
Toll Free: (800) 264-7827
E-mail: tgaskill@star-mfg.com
Web Site: www.star-mfg.com
Approx. Sls.: $40,700,000
Approx. Number Employees: 60
Year Founded: 1921
Business Description:
Commercial Cooking & Foodwarming Equipment Mfr
S.I.C.: 3589; 3556
N.A.I.C.S.: 333319; 333294
Media: 6
Personnel:
Nestor Ibrahim *(Pres)*
Mike Barber *(CFO)*
Tim Gaskill *(VP-Sls & Mktg)*
Brands & Products:
JET-STAR
MINIVEYOR
PROVEYOR
STAR
STAR-MAX
ULTRA-MAX

STEAMATIC INC.

3333 Quorum Dr Ste 280
Fort Worth, TX 76137
Tel.: (817) 332-1575
Fax: (817) 332-5349
Toll Free: (800) 527-1295
E-mail: operations@steamatic.com
Web Site: www.steamatic.com
Sales Range: $50-74.9 Million
Approx. Number Employees: 14
Year Founded: 1968
Business Description:
Mfr. & Franchiser of Carpet, Furniture & Drapery Cleaning Processes, Air Duct Cleaning & Fire & Water Damage Restoration
S.I.C.: 6794; 7359
N.A.I.C.S.: 533110; 532299
Advertising Expenditures: $500,000
Media: 1-2-6-7-8-9-10-11-12-13-17-20
Distr.: Intl.; Natl.
Budget Set: Nov.
Personnel:
Bill Sims *(Pres)*
Diana Schreibel *(Asst VP-Natl Mktg)*
Jarrod Sims *(Dir-Franchise Dev)*
Frank Van Zant *(Dir-Trng)*
Brands & Products:
ALLER-RX
LAMBRITE
LINAIRE GEL
MICROBAN
ODORMATIC
STEAMATIC
STEAMATIC THE TOTAL CLEANING SERVICE
STEAMATICARE
Advertising Agency:
World Advertising & Public Relations
303 Arthur St
Fort Worth, TX 76107-2352
Tel.: (817) 332-1575
Fax: (817) 332-5349
Toll Free: (800) 433-2940
(Carpet Cleaning, Residential & Industrial & Indoor Air Quality & Restoration)

SUB-ZERO FREEZER CO., INC.

4717 Hammersley Rd
Madison, WI 53711-2708
Tel.: (608) 271-2233
Fax: (608) 270-3339
Toll Free: (800) 532-7820
E-mail: customerservice@subzero.com
Web Site: www.subzero.com
Approx. Number Employees: 1,200
Year Founded: 1945
Business Description:
Residential Refrigeration & Wine Storage Mfr
S.I.C.: 3632
N.A.I.C.S.: 335222
Export
Media: 1-2-3-4-5-6-10-19-20
Distr.: Natl.
Personnel:
James Bakke *(Pres & CEO)*
Michele Bedard *(VP-Mktg)*

Key to Media (For complete agency information see *The Advertising Red Books-Agencies* edition):
1. Bus. Publs. 2. Cable T.V. 3. Catalogs & Directories. 4. Co-op Adv. 5. Consumer Mags. 6. D.M. to Bus. Estab.7. D.M. to Consumers
8. Daily Newsp. 9. Exhibits/Trade Shows 10. Foreign 11. Infomercial 12. Internet Adv.13. Multimedia 14. Network Radio
15. Network T.V. 16. Newsp. Distr. Mags. 17. Other 18. Outdoor (Posters, Transit) 19. Point of Purchase20. Premiums, Novelties
21. Product Samples 22. Special Events Mktg. 23. Spot Radio 24. Spot T.V. 25. Weekly Newsp. 26. Yellow Page Adv.

Sub-Zero Freezer Co., Inc. — (Continued)

Steve Dunlap *(VP-Sls)*
Ed Murphy *(VP-Fin)*
Chuck Verri *(VP-HR)*
Paul Leuthe *(Mgr-Corp Mktg)*

Brands & Products:
PRO 48
SUB-ZERO
SUB-ZERO FREEZER
WINE STORAGE EQUIPMENT
WOLF

Advertising Agency:
The Richards Group, Inc.
8750 N Central Expy Ste 100
Dallas, TX 75231-6430
Tel.: (214) 891-5700
Fax: (214) 265-2933

SWING-A-WAY PRODUCTS

(Sub. of Focus Products Group, LLC)
4100 Beck Ave
Saint Louis, MO 63116-2634
Tel.: (314) 773-1487
Fax: (314) 773-5187
Approx. Number Employees: 150
Year Founded: 1938
Business Description:
Household Kitchen Appliances
S.I.C.: 3631
N.A.I.C.S.: 335221
Export
Media: 2-4-6-9-10
Distr.: Natl.

Brands & Products:
SWING-A-WAY

THERMO ELECTRON LABORATORY EQUIPMENT LLC

(Sub. of Thermo Fisher Scientific Inc.)
308 Ridgefield Ct
Asheville, NC 28806
Tel.: (828) 658-2711
Fax: (888) 618-2669
Toll Free: (800) 522-7746
E-mail: info@thermo.com
Web Site: www.thermofisher.com
Sales Range: $600-649.9 Million
Approx. Number Employees: 1,500
Year Founded: 1938
Business Description:
Products & Services for Life Science, Material Science, Bioprocessing & Drug Discovery
S.I.C.: 3821; 3826; 3829
N.A.I.C.S.: 339111; 334516; 334519
Export
Media: 2-4-6-8-10-11-13
Distr.: Intl.; Natl.
Budget Set: Nov.
Personnel:
Dan Biggs *(VP-Sls-North America)*

Brands & Products:
KENDRO
REVCO
SORVALL

THERMOS L.L.C.

2550 W Golf Rd Ste 800
Rolling Meadows, IL 60008
Tel.: (847) 439-7821
Fax: (847) 593-5570
Toll Free: (800) 243-0745
Web Site: www.thermos.com
Approx. Number Employees: 768
Year Founded: 1904
Business Description:
Steel & Glass Vacuum Ware; Foam Containers; School Lunch Kits; Ice Chests & Jugs; Foam Insulated Coolers; Insulated Coffee Carafes
S.I.C.: 3499; 3086
N.A.I.C.S.: 332439; 326140
Import Export
Advertising Expenditures: $750,000
Media: 1-2-3-4-6-7-8-10-11-12-19-20-21-24-25
Distr.: Intl.; Natl.
Budget Set: July
Personnel:
Rick Dias *(Pres & COO)*
Alex Huang *(CEO)*

Brands & Products:
B3BASICS
BRIEFCASE
COFFEE BUTLER
COLDWARE
COMPACT
ELEMENT 5
FOOGO
FRESH SERVICE
FUNTAINER
GEO TREK
HAMMERTONE
HIDE 'N SNAK
HOTTER, COOLER, FRESHER THINKING
INTAK
ISOTEC
LUNCHLUGGER
NASCAR
PINK RIBBON
RAYA
THE ROCK
SEABREEZE
SELECT-A-BREW
SNAK JAR
STAINLESS KING
STASH TOP
THERMAX
THERMOS
THERMOS NISSAN
TRADITIONAL
TWIN TRAVELER

TTI FLOOR CARE NORTH AMERICA

(Sub. of Techtronic Industries Co., Ltd.)
7005 Cochran Rd
Solon, OH 44139
Tel.: (330) 499-9499
Web Site: www.ttifloorcare.com/contact.aspx
Business Description:
Floor Care Appliances
S.I.C.: 3639
N.A.I.C.S.: 335228
Personnel:
Chris Gurreri *(Pres)*
Brian Kirkendall *(VP-Mktg-Hoover)*
Carolyn Resar *(VP-Mktg)*

Brands & Products:
HOOVER
RED DEVIL

Advertising Agency:
Empower MediaMarketing
(MEDIA THAT WORKS)
1111 Saint Gregory St
Cincinnati, OH 45202
Tel.: (513) 871-9454
Fax: (513) 871-1804
Digital
Magazines
Media Agency of Record
Media Planning and Buying
National Television

TYLER REFRIGERATION CORP.

(Sub. of Carrier Commercial Refrigeration)
1329 Lk St
Niles, MI 49120-5204
Tel.: (269) 683-2000
Fax: (269) 684-9802
Toll Free: (800) 992-3744
Sales Range: $125-149.9 Million
Approx. Number Employees: 450
Year Founded: 1927
Business Description:
Commercial Refrigeration Units Designer Mfr
S.I.C.: 3585
N.A.I.C.S.: 333415
Export
Advertising Expenditures: $500,000
Media: 2-10
Distr.: Natl.
Personnel:
Esther Johnson *(Gen Mgr)*
Dave Enos *(Dir-Sls & Natl Accounts)*
Stephen Maley *(Mgr-HR)*
Skip Muir *(Mgr-Dealer Devel)*

Brands & Products:
ENVIROGUARD
TYLER

UNITED SERVICE EQUIPMENT COMPANY

(Sub. of Standex Food Service Equipment Group)
914 Ridgely Rd
Murfreesboro, TN 37129-4912
Tel.: (615) 893-8432
Fax: (615) 890-3196
Fax: (877) 876-9665
Toll Free: (800) 251-4232
E-mail: info@useco.com
Web Site: www.useco.com
Sales Range: $10-24.9 Million
Approx. Number Employees: 2
Year Founded: 1884
Business Description:
Mfr. of Patient-Feeding Systems & Food Service Equipment for Hospitals, Institutions & Commercial Use
S.I.C.: 3589
N.A.I.C.S.: 333319
Export
Advertising Expenditures: $250,000
Media: 2-7-13
Distr.: Intl.; Natl.
Budget Set: May

Brands & Products:
ROTA-CHILL
UNITRAY
UNITRON

UNITED STATES COLD STORAGE, INC.

(Sub. of John Swire & Sons Limited)
100 Dobbs Ln Ste 102
Cherry Hill, NJ 08034-1436
Tel.: (856) 354-8181
Fax: (856) 354-8199
E-mail: info@uscold.com
Web Site: www.uscoldstorage.com
Approx. Number Employees: 30
Year Founded: 1891
Business Description:
Public Refrigerated Warehouse Operator
S.I.C.: 4222; 2097
N.A.I.C.S.: 493120; 312113
Advertising Expenditures: $225,000
Media: 2-4-5-7-10-20-26
Distr.: Natl.
Budget Set: Oct.
Personnel:
David Harlan *(Pres & CEO)*
James Slamon *(CFO & VP)*
George Cruz *(VP & Area Mgr)*
Luis Guardiola *(VP & Area Mgr)*
Rod Noll *(VP & Area Mgr)*
Tom Vaghy *(VP & Mgr-Reg Opers-Omaha)*
Gerald P. Boyle *(VP-Info Tech)*
Jerome Scherer *(VP-Natl Sls, Mktg & Govt Affairs)*
Lawrence Sokolowski *(VP-HR & Insurance)*
Charles Toogood *(VP-Engrg)*
Timothy Brennan *(Dir-IT)*
Tim Brennen *(Dir-IT)*
Althea Duncan *(Opers Mgr)*
James Marrella *(Coord-OSHA & EPA Compliance)*

Brands & Products:
E-US COLD
PDQ LOGISTICS
PDQ MEXICO
TASKMASTER
UNITED STATES COLD SOLUTIONS
UNITED STATES COLD STORAGE

VAPOR CORP.

3101 W Hallandale Blvd Ste 100
Hallandale, FL 33009
Toll Free: (888) 482-7671
Web Site: www.vapor-corp.com
Approx. Sls.: $10,917,101
Approx. Number Employees: 21
Business Description:
Vaporizers & Electronic Devices Mfr & Distr
S.I.C.: 3634; 5064
N.A.I.C.S.: 335211; 423620
Advertising Expenditures: $970,806
Personnel:
Kevin Frija *(Chm, Pres, CEO & CFO)*

Brands & Products:
EZSMOKER
FIFTY-ONE
GREEN PUFFER
KRAVE
SMOKE STAR

VEEDER-ROOT COMPANY

(Sub. of Danaher Corporation)
125 Powder Forest Dr
Simsbury, CT 06070
Mailing Address:
PO Box 2003
Simsbury, CT 06070-7684
Tel.: (860) 651-2700
Fax: (860) 651-2704
Toll Free: (888) 561-7942
E-mail: info@veeder.com
Web Site: www.veeder.com
Sales Range: $400-449.9 Million
Approx. Number Employees: 1,000
Year Founded: 1866
Business Description:
Mfr. of Underground Storage Tank Leak Detection Systems and Other Environmental Products
S.I.C.: 3823; 3824

Key to Media (For complete agency information see *The Advertising Red Books-Agencies* edition):
1. Bus. Publs. 2. Cable T.V. 3. Catalogs & Directories. 4. Co-op Adv. 5. Consumer Mags. 6. D.M. to Bus. Estab.7. D.M. to Consumers 8. Daily Newsp. 9. Exhibits/Trade Shows 10. Foreign 11. Infomercial 12. Internet Adv.13. Multimedia 14. Network Radio 15. Network T.V. 16. Newsp. Distr. Mags. 17. Other 18. Outdoor (Posters, Transit) 19. Point of Purchase20. Premiums, Novelties 21. Product Samples 22. Special Events Mktg. 23. Spot Radio 24. Spot T.V. 25. Weekly Newsp. 26. Yellow Page Adv.

N.A.I.C.S.: 334513; 334514
Export
Media: 2-10
Distr.: Intl.
Personnel:
Martin Gafinowitz *(VP-Mktg)*
Lu Ying *(Gen Mgr)*
Tay Kiat *(Dir-IT)*
Rebecca Lao *(Reg Mgr-Sls)*
Serene Koh *(Office Mgr)*
Eva Chambers *(Mgr-Commercialization)*
Brands & Products:
INFORM
TLS SERIES

VICTORY REFRIGERATION COMPANY LLC
(Sub. of The AFE Group Ltd.)
110 Woodcrest Rd
Cherry Hill, NJ 08003-3648
Tel.: (856) 428-4200
Fax: (856) 428-7299
E-mail: info@victoryrefrigeration.com
Web Site:
www.victoryrefrigeration.com
Sales Range: $25-49.9 Million
Approx. Number Employees: 150
Year Founded: 1944
Business Description:
Commercial Refrigerators, Freezers & Other Foodservice Equipment Mfr
S.I.C.: 3585; 3589
N.A.I.C.S.: 333415; 333319
Import Export
Media: 1-2-4-7-10-13-19-20
Distr.: Intl.; Natl.
Budget Set: Sept.
Personnel:
Mark Curran *(Pres)*
Mitch Cohen *(VP-Sls)*
Jim Hurston *(VP-Mktg)*
Jim Kehoe *(Dir-Engrg)*
Brands & Products:
VICTORY

VIKING RANGE CORPORATION
111 W Frnt St
Greenwood, MS 38930-4442
Tel.: (662) 455-1200
Fax: (662) 453-7939
Toll Free: (888) VIKING1
Web Site: www.vikingrange.com
Approx. Number Employees: 850
Year Founded: 1984
Business Description:
Mfr. of Commercial Gas Cooking Stoves & Other Major Appliances for the Home
S.I.C.: 3631; 3444
N.A.I.C.S.: 335221; 332322
Import Export
Media: 2-3-4-5-6-8-10-11-13-19-26-30
Distr.: Intl.
Budget Set: Oct.
Personnel:
Fred Carl, Jr. *(Chm, Pres & CEO)*
Brian Waldrop *(CFO)*
Liston Durden *(Sr VP-Mktg)*
Basil Larkin *(VP-Sls)*
Sue Bailey *(Product Mgr)*
Brands & Products:
CYCLONIC
EASY-GLIDE
GOURMET-GLO
JAM-INATOR
MAGNEQUICK
OUTDOOR RANGE
PROFLOW
QUICKCOOK
TIMEPIECE
TRUCONVEC
TRUSEAR
VARISIMMER
VERSAVENT
VIKING
VSH

VITASOY USA INC.
(Sub. of Vitasoy International Holdings Ltd.)
1 New England Way
Ayer, MA 01432
Tel.: (978) 772-6880
Toll Free: (800) 848-2769
E-mail: info@vitasoy-usa.com
Web Site: www.vitasoy-usa.com
Approx. Number Employees: 150
Business Description:
Soy Products & Other Asian Style Foods Producer & Distr
S.I.C.: 5149
N.A.I.C.S.: 424490
Personnel:
Walter M. Riglian *(Pres & CEO)*
Susan Rolnick *(VP-Mktg)*
Eugene Lye *(Dir-Asian Div & Canada)*
Mark Sherburne *(Dir-Sls)*
Advertising Agencies:
360 Public Relations LLC
140 Clareedon St Ste 401
Boston, MA 02116
Tel.: (617) 585-5770
Fax: (617) 585-5789

AMP Agency (Alloy Marketing & Promotion)
77 N Washington St
Boston, MA 02114
Tel.: (617) 723-8929
Fax: (617) 723-2188

McGovern Communications
27 Elmore St
Arlington, MA 02476
Tel.: (781) 648-7157

VON SCHRADER COMPANY
1600 Junction Ave
Racine, WI 53403-2568
Tel.: (262) 634-1956
Fax: (262) 634-2888
Toll Free: (800) 626-6916
Web Site: www.vonschrader.com
Approx. Number Employees: 50
Year Founded: 1935
Business Description:
Portable Carpet Shampoo Machines, Upholstery Cleaning Equipment, Wall & Ceiling Cleaning Equipment & Accessories, Detergents & Chemicals Mfr
S.I.C.: 5087; 5169
N.A.I.C.S.: 423850; 424690
Export
Advertising Expenditures: $390,000
Media: 2-6-10
Distr.: Intl.; Natl.
Budget Set: Jan.
Personnel:
Jeff Ranch *(CFO)*
Trudy Schatzman *(Mgr-Customer Svc)*
Brands & Products:
BEFORE
BLOCKADE
THE CHOICE OF A LIFETIME
DOLPHIN
ESPRIT
FUSION
LIQUIDATOR
LMX
MACH 12
ODOR EXPLODER
PRELIM
PRISM
PRISM CARPET COLOR REPAIR
SANITIZING MACHINE
VERSATILE
VON SCHRADER DETERGENT (BLUE LABEL)
VON SCHRADER DETERGENT (RED LABEL)
VS3

VSM SEWING INC.
(Sub. of VSM Group AB)
31000 Viking Pkwy
Westlake, OH 44145-1019
Mailing Address:
PO Box 458012
Westlake, OH 44145
Tel.: (440) 808-6550
E-mail: info@husqvarnaviking.com
Web Site: www.husqvarnaviking.com
E-Mail For Key Personnel:
Sales Director: staningraham@husqvarnaviking.com
Public Relations: nancy.jewell@husqvarnaviking.com
Approx. Number Employees: 350
Year Founded: 1986
Business Description:
Sewing Machines Distr
S.I.C.: 5064
N.A.I.C.S.: 423620
Import
Media: 6
Distr.: Natl.
Personnel:
Sue Hausmann *(Sr VP-Sewing Education)*
Calorine Weazer *(Mktg Mgr)*

VULCAN-HART
(Sub. of Illinois Tool Works Inc.)
3600 N Point Blvd
Baltimore, MD 21222
Tel.: (410) 284-0660
Fax: (410) 288-3662
Toll Free: (866) 988-5226
Web Site: www.vulcanhart.com
Sales Range: $50-74.9 Million
Approx. Number Employees: 175
Year Founded: 1890
Business Description:
Commercial Cooking Equipment Mfr & Distr
S.I.C.: 3631; 3639
N.A.I.C.S.: 335221; 335228
Media: 2-7-10-13
Personnel:
Tim Murray *(Pres)*
James J. Cullinane *(VP-Sls)*
Carrie Whitmer *(Gen Mgr)*
Chris Bauermann *(Gen Mgr)*
Rob Chiarelli *(Project Mgr)*
Harry Schildkraut *(Project Mgr)*
Mike Nunez *(Asst Mgr-Opers)*
Cynthia Flanery *(Mgr-Plant)*

WARING PRODUCTS, INC.
(Div. of Conair Corporation)
1 Cummings Point Rd
Stamford, CT 06902-7901
Tel.: (203) 975-4600
Fax: (203) 975-4660
Toll Free: (800) 492-7464
Web Site: www.waringproducts.com
E-Mail For Key Personnel:
Public Relations: mary_rodgers@conair.com
Sales Range: $25-49.9 Million
Approx. Number Employees: 400
Business Description:
Commercial & Consumer Portable Electrical Appliances Mfr
S.I.C.: 3639
N.A.I.C.S.: 335228
Import Export
Advertising Expenditures: $4,000,000
Media: 2-4-6-7-9-10-11-16-19-20-23-24-25
Distr.: Intl.; Natl.
Budget Set: Dec.
Personnel:
Jerry Rutigliano *(VP & Gen Mgr-Sls & Mktg)*
Mary J. Rodgers *(Dir-Mktg Comm)*
Joan Gioiella *(Product Mgr)*
Brands & Products:
MEGA PRO
MEGAMIX
TAILGATER
WARING
WARING BY CUISINART
WARING PRO

WARNER'S STELLIAN CO., INC.
550 Atwater Cir
Saint Paul, MN 55103-4401
Tel.: (651) 222-0011
Fax: (651) 726-1683
Web Site: www.warnersstellian.com
Approx. Sls.: $28,154,911
Approx. Number Employees: 400
Business Description:
Electric Household Appliances
S.I.C.: 5722; 5064
N.A.I.C.S.: 443111; 423620
Personnel:
Jeff Warner *(Pres)*
Carla Warner *(Dir-Sale & VP)*
Bill Warner *(Dir-Mdsg & Customer Svc)*
Bob Warner *(Dir-Ops)*
Advertising Agency:
Nemer Fieger
6250 Excelsior Blvd Ste 203
Minneapolis, MN 55416-2735
Tel.: (952) 925-4848
Fax: (952) 925-1907

WATER-RIGHT INC.
(Formerly WaterCare Corporation)
(Sub. of Water-Right, Inc.)
1900 Prospect Ct
Appleton, WI 54914
Tel.: (920) 739-9401
Fax: (920) 739-9406
E-mail: info@watercare.com
Web Site: www.watercare.com
Approx. Number Employees: 15
Year Founded: 1946

Key to Media (For complete agency information see *The Advertising Red Books-Agencies* edition):
1. Bus. Publs. 2. Cable T.V. 3. Catalogs & Directories. 4. Co-op Adv. 5. Consumer Mags. 6. D.M. to Bus. Estab.7. D.M. to Consumers 8. Daily Newsp. 9. Exhibits/Trade Shows 10. Foreign 11. Infomercial 12. Internet Adv.13. Multimedia 14. Network Radio 15. Network T.V. 16. Newsp. Distr. Mags. 17. Other 18. Outdoor (Posters, Transit) 19. Point of Purchase20. Premiums, Novelties 21. Product Samples 22. Special Events Mktg. 23. Spot Radio 24. Spot T.V. 25. Weekly Newsp. 26. Yellow Page Adv.

Water-Right Inc. — (Continued)

Business Description:
Water Filters, Softeners & Other Water Purification Equipment Mfr
S.I.C.: 3589; 5722
N.A.I.C.S.: 333319; 443111
Media: 2-4-5-8-10-13-18-20-22-23-24-26
Distr.: Natl.
Personnel:
Mary Blanchard *(Office Mgr)*
William F. Granger *(Mgr-Sls)*
Tim Rindt *(Mgr-Purchase Orders)*
Brands & Products:
CARESOFT
ELAN
HOSTESS
MICROCLEAR
PULSE EM
SENSIAL
SENSIAL METERED
WE MAKE WATER GOOD FOR LIFE

W.C. BRADLEY CO.
1017 Front Ave
Columbus, GA 31901-5260
Mailing Address:
PO Box 140
Columbus, GA 31902-0140
Tel.: (706) 571-6056
Fax: (706) 571-6084
Web Site: www.wcbradley.com
Sales Range: $150-199.9 Million
Approx. Number Employees: 2,500
Year Founded: 1885
Business Description:
Gas & Electric Outdoor Barbecue Grill Mfr
S.I.C.: 3631; 3949
N.A.I.C.S.: 335221; 339920
Import Export
Advertising Expenditures: $3,000,000
Media: 1-2-4-5-6-7-8-11-19-20-24
Distr.: Natl.
Budget Set: Aug.
Personnel:
Stephen T. Butler *(Chm)*
Marc R. Olivie *(Pres & CEO)*
W. Gregory Yates *(CFO & Exec VP-Admin)*
Rick Woodham *(VP-HR)*
Michelle Zeller *(VP-Mktg)*
Rob Schwing *(Gen Mgr-Bus Dev-Char-Broil)*
Brands & Products:
BIG EASY
CADDIE
CHAR-BROIL
THE EDGE
LAMPLIGHT
PATIO BISTRO
PATIO CADDIE
PRECISIONHEAT
QUICKSET
QUICKSET TRADITIONAL
SANTA FE
TIKI
TRADITIONAL
TRENTINO
TUSCAN COLLECTION

WEBER-STEPHEN PRODUCTS CO.
200 E Daniels Rd
Palatine, IL 60067-6266
Tel.: (847) 934-5700
Fax: (847) 934-3153
Toll Free: (800) 446-1071
E-mail: support@weberstephen.com
Web Site: www.weber.com
Approx. Number Employees: 450
Business Description:
Mfr. of Bar-B-Que Kettles; Electric Insect Killers; Gas Barbeques
S.I.C.: 3631; 5812
N.A.I.C.S.: 335221; 722110
Advertising Expenditures: $25,000,000
Media: 2-3-5-6-8-9-10-11-13-15-16-18-19-21-22-23-24-25
Distr.: Intl.; Natl.
Budget Set: Sept.
Personnel:
James Stephen *(CEO)*
Michael Kempster, Sr. *(CMO & Exec VP)*
Len Gryn *(Exec VP)*
Barbara Mark *(VP-HR)*
Brooke Jones *(Mgr-Mktg)*
Brands & Products:
BABY Q
FLAVORIZER
GENESIS
GO-ANYWHERE
ONE-TOUCH
PERFORMER
RANCH
SLIDERFRAME
SMOKEY JOE
SMOKEY MOUNTAIN COOKER
SUMMIT
WEBER
WEBER Q

WELLS/BLOOMFIELD
(Sub. of Carrier Commercial Refrigeration)
2 Erik Cir
Verdi, NV 89439
Mailing Address:
PO Box 280
Verdi, NV 89439-0280
Tel.: (775) 689-5700
Fax: (775) 689-5972
Toll Free: (800) 777-0450
E-mail: sales@wellsbloomfield.com
Web Site: www.wellsbloomfield.com
E-Mail For Key Personnel:
Sales Director: sales@wellsbloomfield.com
Approx. Rev.: $55,000,000
Approx. Number Employees: 300
Year Founded: 1932
Business Description:
Commercial Cooking Equipment
S.I.C.: 3589
N.A.I.C.S.: 333319
Import Export
Media: 2-4-7-10-26
Distr.: Intl.; Natl.
Budget Set: Oct.
Personnel:
Kevin Clark *(VP-Sls & Mktg)*
Brands & Products:
WELLS/BLOOMFIELD

WHIRLPOOL CANADA, INC.
(Sub. of Whirlpool Corporation)
1901 Minnesota Ct
Mississauga, ON L5N 3A7, Canada
Tel.: (905) 821-6400
Fax: (905) 821-7871
Web Site: www.whirlpoolcanada.com
Approx. Number Employees: 300
Business Description:
Distr of Household Appliances
S.I.C.: 5722
N.A.I.C.S.: 443111
Personnel:
Joao Brega *(Pres-Mexico & Canada)*
Joseph T. Liotine *(VP & Gen Mgr)*
Joseph M. Sanguinetti *(VP-Sls)*
Steven Maroun *(Brand Mgr-Inglis & Amana)*
Advertising Agency:
MediaCom
498 7th Ave
New York, NY 10018
Tel.: (212) 912-4200
Fax: (212) 508-4386
Cooking Moments
Media Buying Agency of Record

WHIRLPOOL CORPORATION
2000 N M-63
Benton Harbor, MI 49022-2692
Tel.: (269) 923-5000
Fax: (269) 923-3722
E-mail: info@whirlpoolcorp.com
Web Site: www.whirlpoolcorp.com
Approx. Sls.: $18,366,000,000
Approx. Number Employees: 70,758
Year Founded: 1911
Business Description:
Home Appliances Mfr
S.I.C.: 3634; 3585; 3633
N.A.I.C.S.: 335211; 333415; 335224
Import Export
Advertising Expenditures: $235,000,000
Media: 2-3-5-6-8-10-15-16-19-24-26
Distr.: Natl.
Budget Set: Aug. -Sept.
Personnel:
Jeff M. Fettig *(Chm & CEO)*
Roy W. Templin *(CFO & Exec VP)*
Bracken Darrell *(Pres-Whirlpool Europe & Exec VP)*
Jose Drummond *(Pres-Latin America & Exec VP)*
Marc R. Bitzer *(Pres-North America)*
Michael A. Todman *(Pres-Whirlpool Intl)*
Daniel F. Hopp *(Gen Counsel & Sr VP-Corp Affairs)*
David T. Szczupak *(Exec VP-Global Product Org)*
David A. Binkley *(Sr VP-HR-Global)*
John Miller *(Sr VP-Global Strategic Sourcing)*
Blair Clark *(Corp VP-Strategy & Bus Plng)*
Christian Gianni *(VP-Global Engrg & Tech)*
Jeff Noel *(VP-Comm & Pub Affairs)*
Ludovic Beaufils *(Gen Mgr-Refrigeration)*
Pam Rogers Klyn *(Gen Mgr-NAR Cooking Bus)*
Brian J. Maynard *(Dir-Brand Mktg, Premium Brands)*
Arthur Azevedo *(Dir-Fin-Special Projects)*
Blane Buckingham *(Dir-Natl Sls)*
Simone Camargo *(Dir-Competetive Intelligence)*
Mike Huie *(Dir-KitchenAid Small Appliances-Global)*
Vikas Sharma *(Dir-Category Mktg)*
Deb O'Connor *(Sr Mgr-Brand Experience)*
Monica Teague *(Sr Mgr-PR & Brand Experience & Mgr-Media Rels & Corp Comm)*
Tanu Grewal *(Sr Mgr-Mktg-Whirlpool Brand)*
Angela Seger *(Sr Mgr-Mktg)*
Sita Singhal *(Sr Mgr-Comm)*
Brandon Buckingham *(Sr Brand Mgr-Whirlpool Laundry)*
Carolyn Torres *(Brand Mgr)*
Carolyn Kelley *(Sr Brand Mgr-Amana)*
Ewa Foltynska *(Mgr-Mktg-Poland&Baltics)*
Carlos Johnson *(Mgr-Mdsg)*
Jody Lau *(Mgr-Corp Reputation Comm)*
Eileen Robinson *(Mgr-Corp Comm-Europe)*
Mark Siva *(Mgr-Brand Mktg-Italy)*
Rik Woestenenk *(Mgr-Sls & Mktg-Essentials Benelux)*
Brands & Products:
ACCUBAKE
ACCUSIMMER
ACCUWAVE
ACROS
ADMIRAL
AFFRESH
AMANA
ARTISAN
BAUKNECHT
BRASTEM
BRASTEMP
BRAVOS
BRIVA
CABRIO
CALYPSO
CENTENNIAL
CONQUEST
CONSUL
DUET
ECOSTYLE
EMBRACO
EPIC Z
EQ
ESLABON DE LUJO
ESTATE
FACILITE
FAST FORWARD ICE
FLORAL
FOR THE LOVE OF COOKING
FOR THE WAY IT'S MADE
FREEZERATOR
GEMINI
GLADIATOR
GLADIATOR CLAW
GOLD
GREEN INTELLIGENCE
ICE2O
ICEMAGIC
IN-DOOR-ICE
INGLIS
JENN-AIR
JETCLEAN
KIC
KITCHENAID
KOSMOS
LADEN
MAGIC CHEF
MAYTAG
POLARA
ROPER
SHAPE OF THE STAND MIXER
SPLIT ATIVE
STAINWASH
SUPER EASY WASH
SUPERMATIC

Key to Media (For complete agency information see *The Advertising Red Books-Agencies* edition):
1. Bus. Publs. 2. Cable T.V. 3. Catalogs & Directories. 4. Co-op Adv. 5. Consumer Mags. 6. D.M. to Bus. Estab.7. D.M. to Consumers
8. Daily Newsp. 9. Exhibits/Trade Shows 10. Foreign 11. Infomercial 12. Internet Adv.13. Multimedia 14. Network Radio
15. Network T.V. 16. Newsp. Distr. Mags. 17. Other 18. Outdoor (Posters, Transit) 19. Point of Purchase20. Premiums, Novelties
21. Product Samples 22. Special Events Mktg. 23. Spot Radio 24. Spot T.V. 25. Weekly Newsp. 26. Yellow Page Adv.

ULTIMA COOK
VELOS
WHIRLPOOL
WHIRLPOOL & YOU

Advertising Agencies:
ARS Advertising Inc.
1001 Reads Lake Rd
Chattanooga, TN 37415-2056
Tel.: (423) 875-3743
Fax: (423) 875-5346
Jenn-Air
Kitchenaid

Digitas Inc.
33 Arch St
Boston, MA 02110
Tel.: (617) 867-1000
Fax: (617) 867-1111
Jenn-Air

Digitas, Inc.
111 E Wacker Dr Ste 1500
Chicago, IL 60601-4501
Tel.: (312) 729-0100
Fax: (312) 729-0111

JohnsonRauhoff
2525 Lake Pines Dr
Saint Joseph, MI 49085
Tel.: (269) 428-9212
Fax: (269) 428-3312
Toll Free: (800) 572-3996

Peppercom
470 Park Ave S 5th Fl
New York, NY 10016
Tel.: (212) 931-6100
Fax: (212) 931-6159
Amana
Gladiator
Maytag
Public Relations Agency of Record
Whirlpool

Perry Ballard Incorporated
526 Upton Dr E
Saint Joseph, MI 49085
Tel.: (269) 983-0611
Fax: (269) 983-0747
Toll Free: (800) 800-9547

Radix Communications, Inc.
3399 S Lakeshore Dr
Saint Joseph, MI 49085
Tel.: (269) 982-7400
Fax: (269) 982-7405

Ted Barkus Company, Inc.
8017 Anderson St
Philadelphia, PA 19118
Tel.: (215) 545-0616
Amana Appliances

WORLD DRYER CORPORATION

(Sub. of Carrier Commercial Refrigeration)
5700 McDermott Dr
Berkeley, IL 60163-1102
Tel.: (708) 449-6950
Fax: (708) 449-6958
Toll Free: (800) 323-0701
Web Site: www.worlddryer.com

Sales Range: $25-49.9 Million
Approx. Number Employees: 50
Year Founded: 1950

Business Description:
Hand & Hair Dryers, Soap Dispensers, Touchless Faucets & Baby Changing Stations
S.I.C.: 3585; 3564
N.A.I.C.S.: 333415; 333412
Import Export
Media: 2-4-10-11-20
Distr.: Intl.; Natl.
Budget Set: Feb. -Mar.
Personnel:
Tom Vic *(Pres)*
Susan Fan *(VP-Engrg)*
John Potts *(VP-Sls & Pur)*
Brands & Products:
WORLD

YORK PROCESS SYSTEMS - FRICK

(Name Changed to Johnson Controls - Frick)

Key to Media (For complete agency information see *The Advertising Red Books-Agencies* edition):
1. Bus. Publs. 2. Cable T.V. 3. Catalogs & Directories. 4. Co-op Adv. 5. Consumer Mags. 6. D.M. to Bus. Estab. 7. D.M. to Consumers 8. Daily Newsp. 9. Exhibits/Trade Shows 10. Foreign 11. Infomercial 12. Internet Adv. 13. Multimedia 14. Network Radio 15. Network T.V. 16. Newsp. Distr. Mags. 17. Other 18. Outdoor (Posters, Transit) 19. Point of Purchase 20. Premiums, Novelties 21. Product Samples 22. Special Events Mktg. 23. Spot Radio 24. Spot T.V. 25. Weekly Newsp. 26. Yellow Page Adv.

Architecture, Engineering & Construction

Cement — Elevators — Fireplaces — Flooring — Glass — Grates — Iron — Kitchen Cabinets — Lath Boards — Lumber — Mirrors — Plumbing Fixtures — Prefabricated Buildings — Roofing — Steel — Store Fixtures — Swimming Pools

A&D EXTERIORS
956 S Bartlett Rd #140
Bartlett, IL 60103
Fax: (866) 902-8281
Toll Free: (800) 557-1398
Web Site: www.andexteriors.com
Business Description:
Home Remodeling Services
S.I.C.: 1531
N.A.I.C.S.: 236118
Media: 8-10-13-16-26
Personnel:
Dustin Bassi *(Pres)*

A. M. CASTLE & CO.
3400 N Wolf Rd
Franklin Park, IL 60131
Tel.: (847) 455-7111
Fax: (847) 455-2113
Web Site: www.amcastle.com
Approx. Sls.: $943,706,000
Approx. Number Employees: 1,619
Year Founded: 1890
Business Description:
Specialty Metal & Plastic Products Distr
S.I.C.: 5051; 5162
N.A.I.C.S.: 423510; 424610
Export
Advertising Expenditures: $30,000
Media: 2-4-7-9-10-20
Distr.: Natl.
Budget Set: Nov.
Personnel:
Michael H. Goldberg *(Pres & CEO)*
Scott F. Stephens *(CFO, Treas & VP-Fin)*
Patrick R. Anderson *(Chief Acctg Officer, VP & Controller)*
Robert J. Perna *(Sec, VP & Gen Counsel)*
Stephen V. Hooks *(Exec VP)*
Kevin P. Fitzpatrick *(VP-HR)*
Rick Lazzari *(VP-Procurement)*
Brands & Products:
A. M. CASTLE & CO.
CASTLE METALS
Advertising Agency:
FD U.S. - Chicago
33 N LaSalle St 18th Fl
Chicago, IL 60602
Tel.: (312) 861-4700
Fax: (312) 553-6740

A. ROUTSIS ASSOCIATES, INC.
275 Donohue Rd Ste 1
Dracut, MA 01826
Tel.: (978) 957-0700
Fax: (978) 957-1860
E-mail: info@traininginteractive.com
Web Site:
www.traininginteractive.com
Approx. Number Employees: 7
Year Founded: 1982
Business Description:
On-Site Training & Technical Support for Plastics Part Design & Production
S.I.C.: 8711
N.A.I.C.S.: 541330
Media: 2-7-10-13-22
Personnel:
Andy Routsis *(Owner)*

ABB INC.
(Sub. of ABB Ltd.)
8585 TransCanada Highway South
Saint Laurent, QC H4S 1Z6, Canada
Tel.: (514) 856-6266
Tel.: (514) 856-6222
Fax: (514) 856-6297
Web Site: www.abb.ca
Approx. Number Employees: 2,500
Year Founded: 1901
Business Description:
Power & Automation Products Mfr
S.I.C.: 3612
N.A.I.C.S.: 335311
Advertising Expenditures: $1,000,000
Media: 2-4-9-10-17-25-26
Distr.: Intl.
Personnel:
Sandy Taylor *(Pres & CEO)*
Jean Guay *(VP & Gen Mgr-Power & Indus Sys Bus)*
Greg Farthing *(VP)*
Monica Barth *(Specialist-Comm)*

ABM INDUSTRIES, INC.
551 Fifth Ave Ste 300
New York, NY 10176
Tel.: (212) 297-0200
Fax: (212) 297-0375
E-mail: info@abm.com
Web Site: www.abm.com
Approx. Rev.: $3,495,747,000
Approx. Number Employees: 96,000
Year Founded: 1909
Business Description:
Building Maintenance Services; Facility Services Contractor
S.I.C.: 7349; 6513; 7217; 8744
N.A.I.C.S.: 561720; 531110; 561210; 561740
Media: 2-10
Distr.: Natl.
Budget Set: Aug.
Personnel:
Henrik C. Slipsager *(Pres & CEO)*
Steven M. Zaccagnini *(CMO)*
Sarah Hlavinka McConnell *(Gen Counsel, Sec & Sr VP)*
James S. Lusk *(Exec VP)*
James P. McClure *(Exec VP)*
Mark Muglich *(Exec VP)*
Dean A. Chin *(Sr VP & Controller)*
Gary R. Wallace *(Sr VP & Dir-Bus Dev)*
Erin M. Andre *(Sr VP-HR)*
David L. Farwell *(Sr VP-IR)*
Tony Mitchell *(VP-Corp Comm)*

ACE ASPHALT OF ARIZONA, INC.
3030 S 7th St
Phoenix, AZ 85040
Tel.: (602) 243-4100
Fax: (602) 243-3768
E-mail: info@aceasphalt.com
Web Site: www.aceasphalt.com
E-Mail For Key Personnel:
Sales Director: sales@tdg1.com
Approx. Number Employees: 150
Business Description:
Parking Lot Construction & Maintenance
S.I.C.: 1622
N.A.I.C.S.: 237310
Media: 2-7-8-10-26
Personnel:
John Drexler *(Chm)*
Timpthy J. Drexler *(Pres & CEO)*
Gary J. Kessler *(CFO)*
Michael Moertl *(COO & VP)*
Brands & Products:
ACE ASPHALT

ACMAT CORPORATION
233 Main St
New Britain, CT 06050-2350
Mailing Address:
PO Box 2350
New Britain, CT 06050-2350
Tel.: (860) 229-9000
Fax: (860) 229-1111
E-mail: info@acmatcorp.com
Web Site: www.acmatcorp.com
Approx. Rev.: $8,063,085
Approx. Number Employees: 30
Year Founded: 1950
Business Description:
Interior Design & New Building Construction Services
S.I.C.: 7389; 1522; 1541
N.A.I.C.S.: 541410; 236210; 236220
Media: 2-7-8-15-16
Distr.: Direct to Consumer; Reg.
Budget Set: Nov.
Personnel:
Henry W. Nozko, Jr. *(Chm, Pres & CEO)*
Michael P. Cifone *(CFO & Sr VP)*
Gary M. Case *(Gen Counsel)*
Larry Chevian *(Mgr-Project)*
J. Marshall Reed *(Mgr-Project)*
Ray A. Suite *(Mgr-Estimating)*
Robert Winchell *(Mgr-Building)*

ACORN IRON & SUPPLY CO., INC.
915 N Delaware Ave
Philadelphia, PA 19123-3110
Tel.: (215) 922-7070
Fax: (215) 922-2522
E-mail: ileenback@aol.com
Web Site: www.acorniron.com
Approx. Number Employees: 5
Business Description:
Iron Platens, Stands & Accessory Tooling Distr
S.I.C.: 5051
N.A.I.C.S.: 423510
Media: 2-10
Distr.: Intl.; Natl.
Brands & Products:
ACORN

ADAMS & WESTLAKE, LTD.
PO Box 4524
Elkhart, IN 46514-0524
Tel.: (574) 264-1141
Fax: (574) 264-1146
E-mail: adlakeltd@aol.com
Web Site: www.adlake.com
Approx. Number Employees: 36
Year Founded: 1857
Business Description:
Mfr of Transportation Supplies, Railroad & Bus Parts & Sub-

Key to Media (For complete agency information see *The Advertising Red Books-Agencies* edition):
1. Bus. Publs. 2. Cable T.V. 3. Catalogs & Directories. 4. Co-op Adv. 5. Consumer Mags. 6. D.M. to Bus. Estab.7. D.M. to Consumers
8. Daily Newsp. 9. Exhibits/Trade Shows 10. Foreign 11. Infomercial 12. Internet Adv.13. Multimedia 14. Network Radio
15. Network T.V. 16. Newsp. Distr. Mags. 17. Other 18. Outdoor (Posters, Transit) 19. Point of Purchase20. Premiums, Novelties
21. Product Samples 22. Special Events Mktg. 23. Spot Radio 24. Spot T.V. 25. Weekly Newsp. 26. Yellow Page Adv.

Assemblies; Contract Manufacturing & Non-Ferrous Castings
S.I.C.: 3799; 3743
N.A.I.C.S.: 336999; 336510
Import Export
Media: 10
Distr.: Direct to Consumer; Natl.
Budget Set: Nov.
Personnel:
Randy Schneider *(Pres)*
Brands & Products:
ADLAKE
ETERNA-BRITE

ADANAC MOLYBDENUM CORPORATION
2055 152nd Street Suite 200
Surrey, BC V4A 4N7, Canada
Tel.: (604) 535-6834
Fax: (604) 536-8411
E-mail: info@adanacmoly.com
Web Site: www.adanacmoly.com/
Approx. Number Employees: 15
Year Founded: 1992
Business Description:
Molybdenum Mining Services
S.I.C.: 1099
N.A.I.C.S.: 212299
Advertising Expenditures: $201,552
Personnel:
Roger P. Taylor *(Chm)*
Leonard J. Sojka *(Pres)*
Maria L. Tejada *(CFO)*

AECOM
(Sub. of AECOM Technology Corporation)
2 Technology Park Dr
Westford, MA 01886-3140
Tel.: (978) 589-3000
Fax: (978) 589-3100
Toll Free: (800) 722-2440
Web Site: www.aecom.com
Sales Range: $75-99.9 Million
Approx. Number Employees: 400
Year Founded: 1968
Business Description:
Environmental Services
S.I.C.: 8748; 4953
N.A.I.C.S.: 541690; 562219
Media: 2-4-10-13
Personnel:
Robert C. Weber *(CEO-Environment)*
Michael Beck *(Sr VP-Sls & Mktg)*
Todd Schwendeman *(VP & Dir-Remediation-Global)*

AECOM TECHNOLOGY CORPORATION
555 S Flower St Ste 3700
Los Angeles, CA 90071-2300
Tel.: (213) 593-8000
Fax: (213) 593-8730
E-mail: info@aecom.com
Web Site: www.aecom.com
Approx. Rev.: $6,545,791,000
Approx. Number Employees: 48,100
Year Founded: 1990
Business Description:
Architectural, Engineering & Construction Management Services
S.I.C.: 8712; 8711; 8748
N.A.I.C.S.: 541310; 541330; 541618
Media: 2-4-7-10
Distr.: Natl.
Personnel:
Richard G. Newman *(Chm)*
David N. Odgers *(Vice Chm-Pro Dev)*
Daniel R. Tishman *(Vice Chm)*
John M. Dionisio *(Pres & CEO)*
Regis Damour *(Chief Risk Officer, Chief Exec-AECOM Enterprises & Sr VP)*
Michael S. Burke *(CFO & Exec VP)*
Raul Cruz *(CIO & Sr VP)*
Dean D. Luchsinger *(Chief Ethics Officer & Chief Compliance Officer)*
Paul J. Gennaro *(Chief Comm Officer & Sr VP-Corp Comm)*
Glenn R. Robson *(Chief Strategy Officer & Sr VP)*
James T. Walsh *(CTO & Sr VP)*
Gary Lawrence *(Chief Sustainability Officer & VP)*
Joseph E. Brown *(Chief Innovation Officer)*
Robert C. Weber *(CEO-Environment)*
Nancy Laben *(Gen Counsel & Sr VP-Legal)*
Jack A. Baylis *(Exec VP-Global Water)*
Jane Chmielinski *(Chief Corp Officer & Exec VP)*
James M. Jaska *(Exec VP-Govt)*
Alan P. Krusi *(Exec VP-Corp Dev)*
Nigel C. Robinson *(Exec VP-Geographies)*
Frederick W. Werner *(Exec VP-Bus Lines)*
Eric Chen *(Sr VP-Corp Fin)*
Donald D. Graul *(Sr VP-Global Alternative Delivery-Transportation Bus)*
Bob Pell *(Chief Integration Officer & Sr VP-Ops)*
Gregory Sauter *(Sr VP-Corp Svcs)*
Susan M. Frank *(VP, Asst Gen Counsel & Global Compliance)*
Alan Morris *(Dir-Building Engrg-Resource Sciences Arabia)*
Marcos Vendramini *(Dir-Transportation-Brazil)*
Advertising Agency:
Rubenstein Associates, Inc.
1345 Ave of the Americas Fl 30
New York, NY 10105-0109
Tel.: (212) 843-8000
Fax: (212) 843-9200

AETRIUM INCORPORATED
2350 Helen St N
North Saint Paul, MN 55109-2942
Tel.: (651) 770-2000
Fax: (651) 770-7975
E-mail: info@aetrium.com
Web Site: www.aetrium.com
Approx. Sls.: $16,257,902
Approx. Number Employees: 67
Year Founded: 1982
Business Description:
Mfr & Marketer of Electromechanical Handlers & Testers for the Semiconductor Industry
S.I.C.: 3824; 3559; 3825; 3829
N.A.I.C.S.: 334514; 333295; 334515; 334519
Export
Media: 1-5-7-10-11-20
Personnel:
Joseph C. Levesque *(Chm)*
John J. Pollock *(Pres & CEO)*
Douglas L. Hemer *(Chief Admin Officer & Sec)*
Dean K. Hedstrom *(VP-Tech)*
Gary A. Quasabart *(VP-Sls-Worldwide)*
W. Charles Sletten, II *(VP-Engrg)*
Brands & Products:
AETRIUM
EXPERIENCE, TECHNOLOGY, SOLUTIONS
Advertising Agency:
M.R. Danielson Advertising LLC
6 W 5th St 500
Saint Paul, MN 55102
Tel.: (651) 698-1512
Fax: (651) 698-0104

AGC FLAT GLASS NORTH AMERICA, INC.
(Sub. of AGC America, Inc.)
11175 Cicero Dr Ste 400
Alpharetta, GA 30022
Mailing Address:
PO Box 929
Kingsport, TN 37662
Tel.: (404) 446-4200
Fax: (404) 446-4221
Toll Free: (800) 251-0441
E-mail: webmaster@afgglass.com
Web Site: www.afgglass.com
Approx. Number Employees: 4,300
Year Founded: 1978
Business Description:
Flat Glass & Rolled Glass Mfr
S.I.C.: 3211; 3231
N.A.I.C.S.: 327211; 327215
Export
Advertising Expenditures: $300,000
Media: 1-2-7-10-13-19-20-21-22
Distr.: Natl.
Budget Set: Oct.
Personnel:
Mark Ishiko *(Pres & CEO)*
Tadayuki Oi *(CTO & VP-Tech Dev)*
Marc Massa *(VP-Sls)*
Brands & Products:
AQUATEX
CFD-TCO
CFR-TCO
COMFORT-E2
COMFORT TI-AC
CRYSTAL 73
FLAX
FLOREX
FLUTEX
FOREST GREEN (HA 26)
GLACIER COMFORT TI-AC
HAMMERED
INDUSTREX
KOOLVUE BRONZE
KRYSTAL FLUTES
KRYSTAL KLEAR
LOW-T GRAY
NON-GLARE EXHISITION (PATTERN 122)
OBSCURE WIRE GLASS
OLD ENGLISH (PATTERN 124)
PATTERN 62
RADIANCE
RADIANCE TI
RAIN
SOLARSHIELD
SOLATEX
SOLITE
VELVEX
WASHBOARD
Advertising Agency:
Creative Energy Group Inc
3206 Hanover Rd
Johnson City, TN 37604
Tel.: (423) 926-9494
Fax: (423) 929-7222
Toll Free: (800) 926-9454

ALABAMA METAL INDUSTRIES CORPORATION
(Div. of Gibraltar Industries, Inc.)
(d/b/a AMICO)
3245 Fayette Ave
Birmingham, AL 35208-4822
Tel.: (205) 787-2611
Fax: (205) 786-6527
Toll Free: (800) 366-2642
E-mail: sales@amico-online.com
Web Site: www.amico-online.com
E-Mail For Key Personnel:
Sales Director: sales@amico-online.com
Sales Range: $250-299.9 Million
Approx. Number Employees: 120
Year Founded: 1939
Business Description:
Mfr & Distr of Industrial Flooring, Grating & Expanded Metal Products
S.I.C.: 3446
N.A.I.C.S.: 332323
Import Export
Media: 2-8-10-20-21
Distr.: Intl.; Natl.
Budget Set: Jan.
Personnel:
Joseph D. Smith *(Pres)*
Michael Scott *(VP-Sls-Mktg)*
Brands & Products:
AMICO
AMICO-KLEMP
DIAMOND-GRIP
DUO-GRIP
GATOR-DECK
GATORGRATE
KORDEK
KORDEK II
RIV-DEXTEEL
SAFETY-TREAD
SAFTEY-GRIP
SEASAFE
SECURA FENCE
SECURA LATH
SHOT-FORM
STAY-FORM

ALCOA INC.
390 Park Ave
New York, NY 10022-4608
Tel.: (212) 836-2674 (IR)
Tel.: (212) 836-2732 (Office of Sec)
E-mail: aice.communications@alcoa.com
Web Site: www.alcoa.com
E-Mail For Key Personnel:
Public Relations: investor.relations@alcoa.com
Approx. Sls.: $21,013,000,000
Approx. Number Employees: 59,000
Year Founded: 1888
Business Description:
Primary & Fabricated Aluminum & Alumina Products Mfr, Producer & Recycler
S.I.C.: 3353; 3354; 3355
N.A.I.C.S.: 331315; 331316; 331319
Import Export
Media: 2-4-6-7-8-9-10-14-15-18-19-20-23-24-25
Distr.: Intl.; Natl.
Personnel:
Klaus-Christian Kleinfeld *(Chm & CEO)*
George King *(Co-Mng Dir & VP)*
Julia Steyn *(Co-Mng Dir & VP)*

Key to Media (For complete agency information see *The Advertising Red Books-Agencies* edition):
1. Bus. Publs. 2. Cable T.V. 3. Catalogs & Directories. 4. Co-op Adv. 5. Consumer Mags. 6. D.M. to Bus. Estab.7. D.M. to Consumers 8. Daily Newsp. 9. Exhibits/Trade Shows 10. Foreign 11. Infomercial 12. Internet Adv.13. Multimedia 14. Network Radio 15. Network T.V. 16. Newsp. Distr. Mags. 17. Other 18. Outdoor (Posters, Transit) 19. Point of Purchase20. Premiums, Novelties 21. Product Samples 22. Special Events Mktg. 23. Spot Radio 24. Spot T.V. 25. Weekly Newsp. 26. Yellow Page Adv.

Alcoa Inc. — (Continued)

Charles D. McLane, Jr. *(CFO & Exec VP)*
Ronald E. Barin *(VP & Chief Investment Officer-Pension Investments)*
Kevin J. Anton *(Chief Sustainability Officer & VP-Alcoa)*
Olivier M. Jarrault *(Pres-Engineered Products & Solutions & Exec VP)*
Alan J. Cransberg *(VP-Alcoa & Pres-Global Primary Products)*
Franklin L. Feder *(Pres-Latin America & Caribbean & VP)*
Jean-Pierre Gilardeau *(Pres-Global Primary Metals Tech/Mfg & VP)*
Raymond B. Mitchell *(Pres-Alcoa Power & Propulsion & VP)*
Michael G. Wallis *(Pres-North American Rolled Products & VP)*
Kevin Kramer *(Pres-Wheel Products)*
Glen G. Morrison *(Pres-Alcoa Building & Construction Sys)*
Kenneth P. Wisnoski *(Pres-Global Primary Products-Growth, Bauxite & Africa)*
Christopher L. Ayers *(COO-Global Primary Products Bus & Exec VP)*
Kurt R. Waldo *(Gen Counsel & VP)*
Nicholas J. DeRoma *(Chief Legal & Compliance Officer & Exec VP)*
John G. Thuestad *(Grp Pres-Global Primary Products & Exec VP)*
Helmut Wieser *(Grp Pres-Global Rolled Products & Exec VP)*
Jack Bergen *(VP-HR)*
Matthew E. Garth *(VP-Fin-Rolled Products Grp-North America)*
Tony R. Thene *(VP-Alcoa, VP-Fin, Engineered Products & Solutions)*
Roy Harvey *(Dir-IR)*
Randall Scheps *(Dir-Mktg)*
Dina Shapiro *(Dir-Mktg Comm & Branding)*
Brenda A. Hart *(Sr Counsel & Asst Sec)*
Paul A. Hayes *(Asst Treas)*
Max W. Laun *(Asst Gen Counsel-Mergers & Acq)*
Judith L. Nocito *(Asst Gen Counsel)*
Dale C. Perdue *(Asst Gen Counsel)*

Brands & Products:
AA
ACC-U-BAR
ACCU-LOK
ALCOA
ALCOA-DIRECT
ALU-PLATE
ALUMA-PERF
ARALL
AUTO-BULB
CATER-TIME
GRIP-RITE
HUCK-SPIN
INSULCLAD
ISOPORT
ISOWEB
K-FAST
L-R WALL
LEAF RELIEF
MAGNA-BULB
MAGNA-GRIP
MAGNA-LOK
OPTI-POUR
POWER SHADE
POWER WALL
RAMBOLT
STRONGHOLD
SUN SHADE
UNIT WALL
WALL SYSTEM

Advertising Agencies:
Drake Advertising, Inc.
4141 Brownsville Rd Ste 1
Pittsburgh, PA 15227
Tel.: (412) 882-4700
Fax: (412) 882-4702
Toll Free: (877) 583-7253

McCann Erickson Guangming Ltd.
21/F Huaihai Plaza
Shanghai, 200031, China
Tel.: (86) 21 2411 1488
Fax: (86) 21 2411 1468
Reynolds Aluminum Foil
Diamond Aluminum Foil

ALCOA RIGID PACKAGING

(Div. of Alcoa Inc.)
2300 N Wright Rd
Alcoa, TN 37701-3141
Tel.: (865) 977-2002
Sales Range: $150-199.9 Million
Year Founded: 1980
Business Description:
Mfr of Aluminum Sheets for Beverage & Food Cans & Can Recycling
S.I.C.: 3353
N.A.I.C.S.: 331315
Advertising Agency:
Ackermann PR
1111 Northshore Dr Ste N-400
Knoxville, TN 37919
Tel.: (865) 584-0550
Fax: (865) 588-3009
Toll Free: (866) 896-4069
Toll Free: (888) 414-7787

ALCOA WHEEL & FORGED PRODUCTS

(Div. of Alcoa Inc.)
1600 Harvard Ave
Cleveland, OH 44105-3040
Tel.: (216) 641-3600
Fax: (216) 641-4032
Toll Free: (800) 242-9898
Web Site: www.alcoa.com
Sales Range: $1-4.9 Billion
Approx. Number Employees: 5,000
Year Founded: 1916
Business Description:
Forged Aluminum Wheels for the Heavy Truck Industry; Forged & Cast Wheels for the Automotive Industry; Forged Aluminum, Titanium & Nickel-Based Alloy Parts for Aerospace & Industrial Applications
S.I.C.: 3463; 3769; 8733
N.A.I.C.S.: 332112; 336419; 541710
Export
Media: 2-4-5-7-10
Personnel:
Tim D. Myers *(Pres)*
Advertising Agencies:
The Drucker Group
1440 N Dayton St Ste 202
Chicago, IL 60642
Tel.: (312) 867-4960
Fax: (312) 867-4967

Marcus Thomas LLC
24865 Emery Rd
Cleveland, OH 44128
Tel.: (216) 292-4700
Fax: (216) 378-0396
Toll Free: (888) 482-4455

ALERIS RECYCLING & SPECIFICATION ALLOYS AMERICAS

(Div. of Aleris International, Inc.)
25825 Science Park Dr Ste 400
Beachwood, OH 44122
Tel.: (216) 910-3400
Web Site: www.aleris.com
Approx. Number Employees: 300
Year Founded: 1985
Business Description:
Aluminum Recycling & Alloying Facilities & Zinc Manufacturing Facilities
S.I.C.: 3341
N.A.I.C.S.: 331314
Media: 2
Personnel:
Terrance J. Hogan *(Sr VP & Gen Mgr)*

ALIMAK HEK INC

(Sub. of Alimak AB)
8400 Villa Dr
Houston, TX 77061
Tel.: (713) 640-8500
Toll Free: (800) 525-4625
E-mail: info@alimakamericas.com
Web Site: www.alimakhek.com
Approx. Number Employees: 74
Year Founded: 1948
Business Description:
Marketer & Sales of Elevators, Hoists & Platforms
S.I.C.: 5084; 7699
N.A.I.C.S.: 423830; 811490
Import Export
Media: 1-2-4-7-8-10-13-17-20-26
Distr.: Intl.; Natl.
Budget Set: Sept.
Personnel:
Dale Stoddard *(Pres)*
Thomas Dunn *(Sr VP-Indus Products)*
Ed Gibbs *(VP-Construction Products)*
Anthony Dragone *(Sls Mgr)*
Brands & Products:
ALICLIMBER
ALIMAK SE
SCANDO-MINI

ALLEGHENY TECHNOLOGIES INCORPORATED

1000 Six PPG Pl 10 Fl
Pittsburgh, PA 15222-5479
Tel.: (412) 394-2800
Fax: (412) 394-3034
Web Site:
www.alleghenytechnologies.com
Approx. Sls.: $4,047,800,000
Approx. Number Employees: 9,200
Year Founded: 1996
Business Description:
Steel & Alloys Mfr
S.I.C.: 3441; 3312; 3317; 3339
N.A.I.C.S.: 332312; 331111; 331210; 331419
Import Export
Media: 1-2-4-7-10-11
Distr.: Intl.; Natl.
Personnel:
Richard J. Harshman *(Chm, Pres & CEO)*
Hunter R. Dalton *(Grp Pres-ATI Long Products & Pres-ATI Allvac Bus Unit)*
Terry L. Dunlap *(Grp Pres-ATI Flat-Rolled Products & Pres-ATI Allegheny Ludlum)*
David M. Hogan *(Grp Pres-ATI Engineered Products)*
John D. Sims *(Pres-ATI Wah Chang Bus Unit)*
Robert S. Wetherbee *(Pres-Bus Unit-ATI Tungsten Matls)*
Elliot S. Davis *(Gen Counsel & VP)*
Jon D. Walton *(Exec VP-HR, Chief Legal, Compliance Officer & Corp Sec)*
Dale G. Reid *(Principal Fin Officer & Sr VP-Fin)*
Dan Greenfield *(VP-IR & Corp Comm)*
Brands & Products:
ALFA-I
ALLCORR
ALTEMP
ATI
E-BRITE
MINIMISER
OHMALOY
PRECISION ROLLED STRIP
SPECIALTY MATERIALS THAT MAKE OUR WORLD

ALLEN & HOSHALL, INC.

1661 Intl Dr Ste 100
Memphis, TN 38120-1440
Tel.: (901) 820-0820
Fax: (901) 683-1001
E-mail: ahinfo@allenhoshall.com
Web Site: www.allenhoshall.com
Approx. Number Employees: 150
Year Founded: 1915
Business Description:
Architectural, Engineering & Consulting Services
S.I.C.: 8711; 8742
N.A.I.C.S.: 541330; 541611
Media: 2-7-10-23-24
Distr.: Direct to Consumer; Intl.; Natl.
Budget Set: Jan.
Personnel:
Michael R. Young *(Pres)*
Jay Caughman *(VP & Dir-Land Surveying)*
Terry Lawson *(Mgr-Mktg)*

ALLIED BUILDING PRODUCTS CORPORATION

(Div. of Oldcastle, Inc.)
15 E Union Ave
East Rutherford, NJ 07073-2127
Tel.: (201) 507-8400
Fax: (201) 507-3842
Toll Free: (800) 541-2198
Web Site: www.alliedbuilding.com
E-Mail For Key Personnel:
Sales Director: sales@alliedbuilding.com
Approx. Number Employees: 150
Year Founded: 1950
Business Description:
Roofing, Siding, Insulation, Sheet Metal & Waterproofing
S.I.C.: 5031; 5032
N.A.I.C.S.: 423310; 423320
Advertising Expenditures: $500,000
Media: 10-22-26
Personnel:
Robert Feury, Jr. *(CEO)*

ALLVAC INCORPORATED

(Unit of Allegheny Technologies Incorporated)
2020 Ashcraft Ave

Key to Media (For complete agency information see *The Advertising Red Books-Agencies* edition):
1. Bus. Publs. 2. Cable T.V. 3. Catalogs & Directories. 4. Co-op Adv. 5. Consumer Mags. 6. D.M. to Bus. Estab.7. D.M. to Consumers
8. Daily Newsp. 9. Exhibits/Trade Shows 10. Foreign 11. Infomercial 12. Internet Adv.13. Multimedia 14. Network Radio
15. Network T.V. 16. Newsp. Distr. Mags. 17. Other 18. Outdoor (Posters, Transit) 19. Point of Purchase20. Premiums, Novelties
21. Product Samples 22. Special Events Mktg. 23. Spot Radio 24. Spot T.V. 25. Weekly Newsp. 26. Yellow Page Adv.

Monroe, NC 28111-5030
Tel.: (704) 289-4511
Fax: (704) 289-4018
E-mail: sales@allvac.com
Web Site: www.allvac.com
E-Mail For Key Personnel:
Sales Director: sales@allvac.com
Public Relations: howard.freese@allvac.com
Sales Range: $200-249.9 Million
Approx. Number Employees: 1,200
Year Founded: 1957
Business Description:
Mfr. & Designer of Machines; Nickel Titanium Alloys Specialty Steels, Tool & High Speed Steel
S.I.C.: 6061
N.A.I.C.S.: 522130
Import Export
Media: 2-4
Personnel:
Hunter R. Dalton *(Pres)*
Howard L. Freese *(Mgr-Bus Dev Biomedical)*
Brands & Products:
ALLEGHENY LUDLUM AL 6XN
ALLVAC
ALLVAC 13-8MO SUPERTOUGH
ALLVAC 718-OP
ALLVAC ALLCORR
ALLVAC ASTROLOY
ALLVAC RENE 41
ALLVAC TIOSTALLOY
ALLVAC TIOSTEUM
ALLVAC TJA-1537
ALLVAC WASPALOY
ALLVAC X-751
NICKELVAC
VASCO
VASCO JETHETE
VASCOJET
VASCOMAX

ALTAP VIENNA
1945 Old Gallows
Vienna, VA 22182
Tel.: (703) 343-6700
Sales Range: $50-74.9 Million
Business Description:
Alcholic Bvrg.
S.I.C.: 5813
N.A.I.C.S.: 722410
Advertising Expenditures: $700,000
Exhibits/Trade Shows: $100,000; Infomercial: $500,000; Spot Radio: $100,000

ALVAREZ HOMES, INC.
3617 Hudson Ln
Tampa, FL 33618
Tel.: (813) 969-3033
Fax: (813) 960-1925
E-mail: gail@alvarezhomes.com
Web Site: www.alvarezhomes.com
Approx. Number Employees: 25
Year Founded: 1983
Business Description:
Residential Home Builder
S.I.C.: 1521
N.A.I.C.S.: 236115
Media: 6
Personnel:
Bobby Alvarez *(Pres)*
Alex Socias *(Dir-Field Ops)*

AMD INDUSTRIES, INC.
4620 W 19th St
Cicero, IL 60804-2502
Mailing Address:
PO Box 286
Herington, KS 67449-0286
Tel.: (708) 863-8900
Fax: (708) 863-2065
Toll Free: (800) 367-9999
E-mail: sales@amdpop.com
Web Site: www.amdpop.com
E-Mail For Key Personnel:
Sales Director: sales@amdpop.com
Public Relations: myersm@amdpop.com
Approx. Sls.: $2,000,000
Approx. Number Employees: 55
Year Founded: 1922
Business Description:
Mfr. & Designer of Custom Point-of-Purchase Displays
S.I.C.: 3993
N.A.I.C.S.: 339950
Export
Media: 2-4-7-10-20-26
Distr.: Natl.
Budget Set: Oct. -Nov.
Personnel:
David E. Allen *(CEO)*
Mike Myers *(COO & Exec VP)*
Jerry Dohse *(Exec VP-Sls)*
Tim Norton *(Exec VP)*

AMERICAN BUILDERS & CONTRACTORS SUPPLY CO., INC.
(Holding of Hendricks Holding Company, Inc.)
(d/b/a ABC Supply Co. Inc.)
1 ABC Pkwy
Beloit, WI 53511-4466
Tel.: (608) 362-8000
Fax: (608) 362-6217
Web Site: www.abc-supply.com
Approx. Number Employees: 6,000
Year Founded: 1982
Business Description:
Roofing, Siding, Windows & Tools Distr
S.I.C.: 5033; 5031
N.A.I.C.S.: 423330; 423310
Export
Advertising Expenditures: $2,500,000
Media: 2-4-7-10
Distr.: Natl.
Budget Set: Dec.
Personnel:
Diane M. Hendricks *(Founder & Chm)*
David A. Luck *(Pres & CEO)*
Kendra A. Story *(CFO & Treas)*
Keith Rozolis *(COO & Exec VP)*
Kathy Murray *(CIO & VP)*
Lisa Indgjer *(VP-Assoc Svcs & HR)*
Steve Kubicka *(Dir-Comml Products)*
Mark Singer *(Dir-Real Estate)*
Walt Zimmerman *(Dir-Metal Products)*
Amy Lokrantz *(Mgr-Fin Analysis & Forecasting)*
Brands & Products:
ABC
Advertising Agency:
The Weinstein Organization, Inc.
1 S Wacker Dr Ste 1670
Chicago, IL 60606-4670
Tel.: (312) 214-2900
Fax: (312) 214-1120
(Roofing; Building Supplies)

AMERICAN FOLDING DOOR COMPANY
175-35 Liberty Ave
Jamaica, NY 11433-1325
Tel.: (718) 657-2000
Fax: (718) 658-5509
E-mail: amfold@earthlink.net
Web Site:
www.americanfoldingdoor.com
Approx. Number Employees: 10
Business Description:
Folding Door Mfr
S.I.C.: 3089
N.A.I.C.S.: 326199
Advertising Expenditures: $250,000
Media: 2-4-7-9-10
Distr.: Natl.
Budget Set: Mar.
Personnel:
Jack Gross *(Pres)*
Steve Casavana *(Dir-Mktg)*
Brands & Products:
AMERICAN FOLDING DOOR COMPANY
AMERIFOLD
STEELFOLD
WOVENWOOD
WOVYNFOLD

AMERICAN HOMESTAR CORPORATION
2450 S Shore Blvd Ste 300
League City, TX 77573-2997
Tel.: (281) 334-9700
Fax: (281) 334-9737
Toll Free: (888) 775-4040
Web Site:
www.americanhomestar.com
Sales Range: $100-124.9 Million
Approx. Number Employees: 570
Year Founded: 1971
Business Description:
Manufactured Homes Mfr & Distr
S.I.C.: 2451; 5271
N.A.I.C.S.: 321991; 453930
Advertising Expenditures: $1,300,000
Personnel:
Finis F. Teeter *(Pres & CEO)*
Craig A. Reynolds *(CFO, Principal Acctg Officer, Sec & Exec VP)*
Charles N. Carney Jr. *(COO-Retail Ops & VP)*
Brands & Products:
AMERICAN HOMESTAR
OAK CREEK
PLATINUM

AMERICAN MARAZZI TILE, INC.
(Sub. of Marazzi Gruppo Ceramiche S.p.A.)
359 Clay Rd
Sunnyvale, TX 75182-9710
Tel.: (972) 226-0110
Fax: (972) 226-2263
Web Site: www.marazzitile.com
Approx. Number Employees: 650
Year Founded: 1980
Business Description:
Mfr. of Ceramic Floor & Wall Tile
S.I.C.: 3253
N.A.I.C.S.: 327122
Media: 2-4-6-7
Personnel:
David Carlile *(CFO)*
Brands & Products:
AFRICA SLATE
ARTEA STONE
CAVERNS
CERAMICRAFT
COLORADO STONE
GRAND CANYON
ISOLA
POLICROMI
POSADAS
PRESIDENTIAL
TRIBAL SLATE

AMERON INTERNATIONAL CORPORATION
245 S Los Robles Ave
Pasadena, CA 91101-3638
Mailing Address:
PO Box 7007
Pasadena, CA 91109-7007
Tel.: (626) 683-4000
Fax: (626) 683-4060
E-mail: ameron-info@sip.net
Web Site: www.ameron.com
Approx. Sls.: $503,259,000
Approx. Number Employees: 2,400
Year Founded: 1929
Business Description:
Mfr. of Engineering Products for Utility Construction & Industrial Customers, Concrete Pressure Pipe; Concrete & Steel Traffic & Lighting Poles; Manufacture & Reinforcing Steel Products; Corrosion Protective Coatings, Fiberglass Pipe & Fittings, Corrosion Resistant Lining for Concrete Sewer Pipe & Sub-Surface Concrete; Acid-Resistant Cements, Spray-On Protective Surfaces
S.I.C.: 3272; 3479
N.A.I.C.S.: 327390; 327332; 332812
Export
Advertising Expenditures: $2,252,000
Personnel:
James S. Marlen *(Chm & CEO)*
Gary Wagner *(CFO, Sr VP-Fin & Admin)*
Richard Mueller *(Pres-Water Transmission Grp)*
John Szabo *(Pres-Pole Products)*
Leonard J. McGill *(Gen Counsel, Sec & Sr VP)*
James R. McLaughlin *(Treas & Sr VP-Corp Dev)*
Ralph S. Friedrich *(Sr VP-Tech)*
Terrence P. O'Shea *(VP-HR)*
Wayne Liechti *(Dir-Steel Ops)*
Wesley Olison *(Dir-Concrete Ops)*
Brands & Products:
ABC
AMERCOAT
AMERLOCK
AMERON INTERNATIONAL
AMERSHIELD
ARROW-LOCK
BONDSTRAND
CENTRON
DIMETCOTE
DUALOY
MEGAFLON
NU-KLAD
PSX
STEELBOND
STEELGUARD
T-HAB
T-LOCK
TEKALOID

Key to Media (For complete agency information see *The Advertising Red Books-Agencies* edition):
1. Bus. Publs. 2. Cable T.V. 3. Catalogs & Directories. 4. Co-op Adv. 5. Consumer Mags. 6. D.M. to Bus. Estab.7. D.M. to Consumers
8. Daily Newsp. 9. Exhibits/Trade Shows 10. Foreign 11. Infomercial 12. Internet Adv.13. Multimedia 14. Network Radio
15. Network T.V. 16. Newsp. Distr. Mags. 17. Other 18. Outdoor (Posters, Transit) 19. Point of Purchase20. Premiums, Novelties
21. Product Samples 22. Special Events Mktg. 23. Spot Radio 24. Spot T.V. 25. Weekly Newsp. 26. Yellow Page Adv.

Ameron International Corporation — (Continued)

TIDEGUARD
TRACTOL
VICTORIAN

AMETEK, INC.
1100 Cassatt Rd
Berwyn, PA 19312-1177
Mailing Address:
PO Box 1764
Paoli, PA 19301-0801
Tel.: (610) 647-2121
Fax: (215) 323-9337
Toll Free: (800) 473-1286
E-mail: webmaster@ametek.com
Web Site: www.ametek.com
Approx. Sls.: $2,470,952,000
Approx. Number Employees: 11,600
Year Founded: 1930
Business Description:
Electronic Instruments & Electromechanical Devices Mfr.
S.I.C.: 3621; 3823
N.A.I.C.S.: 335312; 334513
Import Export
Distr.: Intl.; Natl.
Personnel:
Frank S. Hermance *(Chm & CEO)*
John J. Molinelli *(CFO & Exec VP)*
William P. Lawson *(CIO & VP)*
Robert S. Feit *(Gen Counsel)*
Robert R. Mandos, Jr. *(Sr VP & Comptroller)*
Gregory J. Kelble *(Sr VP-HR)*
Matthew J. Cole *(VP & Gen Mgr-Advanced Measurement Tech Div)*
Timothy F. Croal *(VP & Gen Mgr-Programmable Power Div)*
Neil J. Desmond *(VP & Gen Mgr-Instrumentation & Specialty Controls)*
David Duffie *(VP & Gen Mgr-SCP)*
Matthew C. French *(VP & Gen Mgr-Precision Motion Control Div)*
Allan Imrie *(VP & Gen Mgr-Precision Instruments-Europe)*
Jon P. Kidder *(VP & Gen Mgr-Advanced Measurement Tech)*
Patrick J. McGeehan *(VP & Gen Mgr-Specialty Metal Products)*
Ron Oscher *(VP/Gen Mgr-Matls Analysis Div)*
James E. Visnic *(VP & Gen Mgr)*
Donald W. Carlson *(Corp VP-Strategic Procurement)*
Roger A. Smith *(VP-Mktg & Sls)*
John J. Weaver *(VP-HR)*
Herman van Eijkelenburg *(Dir-Product Mktg)*
Brands & Products:
ADVANCED INDUSTRIES
AEGIS
AEM
AEROMEDIC
AIR CONTROL
AIRSCREW
AMETEK
AMPHION
ANTAVIA
ARGANTIX
B-PAK
B/W CONTROLS
BATTERY-MATE
BRAKE
CALIFORNIA
CAMECA
CARLE
CATRAC
CDU
CERRAFLEX
CHANDLER
CHATILLON
CORE FLOW
DAVENPORT
DIXON
DRAKE AIR
DREXELBROOK
DRIVE-CHEK
DUALSTREAM
DURATEK
DYCOR
DYMAXION
EDAX
ELGAR
FLEXSIL
GEMCO
GENERAL-CERAMICS
GLASSEAL
GRABNER
GULTON STATHAM
HAMILTON
HAVEG
HCC
HDR
HERMETIC SEAL
HIGH STANDARD AVIATION
HOBART
HPM
HUGHES-TREITLER
HUNTER SPRING
INFIN-A-TEK
IROX
JEM
JOFRA
LAMB
LAND INSTRUMENTS
LER
LEVEL MATE
LLOYD
LTD
MAE
MANSFIELD & GREEN
MCG
MICRO-SET
MICROJAMMER
MINIFLASH
MINIJAMMER
MINIVAP
MOD-CAL
MOTION CONTROL GROUP
MOTOGARD
MUIRHEAD AEROSPACE
MVS
NATIONAL CONTROLS
NAUTILAIR
NCC
NEG'ATOR
NEXYGEN
ORTEC
PANALARM
PARSTAT
PATRIOT SENSOR
PETROLAB
PHANTOM CINEMAG
PITTMAN
PLASTUF
PMT
POWERCORR
POWERPULSE
POWERSINE
POWERSTEP
POWERTEN
PRECITECH
PRESTOLITE
PRINCETON APPLIED RESEARCH
PRO-STIK
PROCESS INSTRUMENTS
PROLINE
PROMAXION
PULSAR
QUADLINK
QUIK-SET
QUIZIX
READING ALLOYS
RIS
ROTOREEL
ROTRON
SAFETIMETER
SCIENTIFIC COLUMBUS
SCP
SEALTRON
SEASTREAM
SEMELEX
SIGNAL RECOVERY
SILTEMP
SOLARTRON ANALYTICAL
SOLARTRON ISA
SOLARTRON METROLOGY
SOLFRUNT
SOLIDSTATE CONTROLS
SORENSEN
SPECTRATEMP
SPECTRO
TAYLOR-HOBSON
THERMOX
TOTAL AIR PROBE
TRACE ANALYTICAL
TURBO-MASS
ULTISIL
USG
USGAUGE
VIS
VISION RESEARCH
WEST CHESTER PLASTICS
WESTERN RESEARCH
WINDJAMMER
Advertising Agency:
Lefton Company
100 Independence Mall W
Philadelphia, PA 19106-2399
Tel.: (215) 923-9600
Fax: (215) 351-4298

AMKOR TECHNOLOGY, INC.
1900 S Price Rd
Chandler, AZ 85248-1604
Tel.: (480) 821-5000
Fax: (480) 821-8276
E-mail: marketing@amkor.com
Web Site: www.amkor.com
Approx. Sls.: $2,939,483,000
Approx. Number Employees: 19,900
Year Founded: 1968
Business Description:
Semiconductor Packaging & Test Services
S.I.C.: 3559; 3674; 3825
N.A.I.C.S.: 333295; 334413; 334515
Media: 2-4-13-18
Personnel:
James J. Kim *(Chm)*
Kenneth T. Joyce *(Pres & CEO)*
Joanne Solomon *(CFO & Exec VP)*
Gil C. Tily *(Chief Admin Officer, Gen Counsel & Exec VP)*
James Fusaro *(Exec VP-Assembly & Test Product Mgmt)*
Michael Lamble *(Exec VP-Worldwide Sls)*
Greg Johnson *(Sr Dir-IR & Corp Comm)*
Jooho Kim *(Dir)*
Brands & Products:
AMKARD
AMKOR TECHNOLOGY
CASON
CHIPARRAY
CSPNL
ETCSP
EXPOSEDPAD
FCCSP
FCMBGA
FLEXBGA
FUSIONQUAD
MICROLEADFRAME
POWERQUAD
POWERSOP
SUPERBGA
SUPERFC
TAPE-SUPERBGA
TAPEARRAY
TMV
TSCSP
ULTRA CSP
VISIONPAK
WEB.DATA

ANCHOR LAMINA INC.
2590 Ouellette Ave
Windsor, ON N8X 1L7, Canada
Tel.: (519) 966-4431
Fax: (519) 972-6862
E-mail: wineng@anchorlamina.com
Web Site: www.anchorlamina.com
Approx. Number Employees: 661
Year Founded: 1960
Business Description:
Mfr of Die Sets; Suppliers of Torch Cut Steel for Plastic Injection Mould Sets; Hydraulic Motors & Portable Drills Mfr
S.I.C.: 3312; 3544
N.A.I.C.S.: 331111; 333514
Import Export
Advertising Expenditures: $600,000
Media: 2-4-6-10-20-21-26
Distr.: Intl
Budget Set: June -July
Personnel:
Roy Verstraete *(Pres & CEO)*
Paul Brisebois *(VP-Sls)*
Harvey Van Huizen *(VP-Sls-US)*

ANDERSEN CORPORATION
100 4th Ave N
Bayport, MN 55003-1096
Tel.: (651) 264-5150
Fax: (651) 264-5107
E-mail: info@andersenwindows.com
Web Site: www.andersenwindows.com
Approx. Rev.: $2,500,000,000
Approx. Number Employees: 9,000
Year Founded: 1903
Business Description:
Mfr of Wood Window Units, Patio Doors & Roof Windows
S.I.C.: 2431; 3231
N.A.I.C.S.: 321911; 327215
Import Export
Media: 1-2-4-5-6-7-8-10-15-18-19-20-21-22-23-26
Distr.: Intl.; Natl.
Budget Set: Sept. -Oct.
Personnel:
James E. Humphrey *(Chm)*
Jay Lund *(Pres & COO)*
Philip Donaldson *(CFO & Exec VP)*
Mary D. Carter *(Chief Admin Officer)*
Alan Bernick *(Gen Counsel & Sr VP)*

Mary J. Schumacher *(Sr VP-Res, Engrg & Advanced Tech)*
Laurie Bauer *(VP-Corp Comm)*
Rod Krois *(Dir-Mktg)*
Susan Roeder *(Mgr-Corp Affairs)*
Brands & Products:
400 CIRCLE TOP
400 FLEXIFRAME
400 FRENCHWOOD
400 SPRINGLINE
400 WOODWRIGHT
ANDERSEN
BEAUTY-LINE
COME HOME
FLEXIFRAME
FLEXIVENT
FRENCHWOOD
KLM BY ANDERSEN
NARROLINE
PERMA-SHIELD
PRESSURE-SEAL
RENEWAL BY ANDERSEN
SPRINGLINE
STORMWATCH
STRUTWALL
TERRATONE
WOODWRIGHT
Advertising Agencies:
The Morris + King Company
101 5th Ave
New York, NY 10003
Tel.: (212) 561-7450
Fax: (212) 561-7461
(Renewal by Andersen, Farmingdale, NY Showroom)

Zion & Zion
464 S Farmer Ave Ste 105
Tempe, AZ 85281
Tel.: (480) 751-1007
Fax: (480) 753-3177

ANDERSON HARDWOOD FLOORS

384 Torrington Rd
Clinton, SC 29325-4635
Tel.: (864) 833-6250
Fax: (864) 833-6664
Web Site: www.andersonfloors.com
Approx. Number Employees: 400
Year Founded: 1946
Business Description:
Hardwood, Veneer & Plywood Flooring Mfr
S.I.C.: 2435; 2431
N.A.I.C.S.: 321211; 321918
Advertising Expenditures: $4,000,000
Media: 2-4-7-8-10
Distr.: Intl.; Natl.
Budget Set: Jan.
Personnel:
Don Finkell *(Pres)*
Brands & Products:
ANDERSON
ANDERSON HARDWOOD FLOORS
BILTMORE ESTATE
DELLA MANO
EXOTIC COLLECTION
FREEDOM
MOUNTAIN
RHINOTUFF

ANTHONY FOREST PRODUCTS CO., INC.

309 N Washington Ave
El Dorado, AR 71730-5614
Tel.: (870) 862-3414
Fax: (870) 863-0809
Toll Free: (800) 856-2372
E-mail: info@anthonyforest.com
Web Site: www.anthonyforest.com
Approx. Number Employees: 350
Year Founded: 1965
Business Description:
Lumber & Engineered Wood Products Mfr
S.I.C.: 2421; 2431
N.A.I.C.S.: 321113; 321918
Import Export
Advertising Expenditures: $200,000
Media: 4-10-25
Distr.: Natl.
Budget Set: May
Personnel:
Beryl Anthony, Jr. *(Chm)*
Aubra Anthony, Jr. *(Pres & CEO)*
Ronnie Clay *(Treas & VP-Fin)*
Russ Anthony *(Exec VP)*
Lynda Anthony *(VP-HR, Safety & Environ)*
Kerlin Drake *(VP-Mktg)*
Chris Webb *(Mgr-Sls)*
Brands & Products:
ANTHONY LOG HOMES
ANTHONY POWER PLANK
POWER BEAM
POWER COLUMN
POWER HEADER
POWER JOIST
POWER LOG
POWER PLANK
POWER PRESERVED COLUMN
POWER PRESERVED GLULAM
POWER PRODUCTS

ANTI-HYDRO INTERNATIONAL, INC.

45 River Rd
Flemington, NJ 08822-6026
Tel.: (908) 284-9000
Fax: (908) 284-9464
Toll Free: (800) 777-1773
E-mail: sales@anti-hydro.com
Web Site: www.anti-hydro.com
E-Mail For Key Personnel:
Sales Director: sales@anti-hydro.com
Sales Range: $50-74.9 Million
Approx. Number Employees: 50
Year Founded: 1904
Business Description:
Building Construction Chemicals & Industrial Flooring Products Mfr
S.I.C.: 2821; 3241
N.A.I.C.S.: 325211; 327310
Export
Media: 2-4-5-7-10-11-21-26
Distr.: Natl.
Budget Set: Mar.
Personnel:
Piyush Patel *(Pres)*
Pankaj Desai *(CEO)*
Brands & Products:
A-H 3 WAY SEALER
A-H A-1 AGGREGATE TOPPING
A-H A-1 TOPPING PRE-MIX
A-H A-2 EMERY SHAKE-ON
A-H ACCELLO
A-H ACURICON
A-H AHCO
A-H ALOX
A-H ANCHOR-IT
A-H ANCHOR MASONRY SURFACER
A-H ANCHOR PLUG
A-H ANTI SPALLING COMPOUND
A-H ARIDOX
A-H ARIDSIL VOC
A-H ARMORTOP
A-H AXPANDCRETE
A-H CLEAR CURE
A-H COAL TAR EPOXY
A-H CRACK FILLER
A-H CURING COMPOUND
A-H EE
A-H EMERUNDUM
A-H EMERY EPOXY TOPING
A-H EPOXY BONDING
A-H EPOXY COATING
A-H EPOXY HI-BUILD
A-H EPOXY LIQUID BINDER
A-H EPOXY PRIMER
A-H FORM FREE
A-H GROOVE & CRACK FILLER
A-H HYDRO-SET 32
A-H HYDROCAP
A-H HYDROCRYLIC
A-H HYDROSEAL
A-H IRONTOP
A-H LEVELTEC PRIMER
A-H LIGHT REFLECTIVE METALLIC
A-H METALLIC HARDENER
A-H METALLIC WATERPROOFING
A-H NON-SLIP AGGREGATE WS
A-H NON-SPARKLING METALLIC
A-H OILGUARD
A-H POLITITE
A-H POLY EPOXY BONDING
A-H POLYSEALANT
A-H PVA BONDER
A-H RETARDSET
A-H SEALCOTE NY
A-H SEAMLESS MEMBRANE
A-H SILICA EPOXY TOPPING
A-H SILICARBID
A-H SQ HARDENER NATURAL
A-H SUPER P
A-H SURE STEP
A-H TRAFFIC DECK
A-H TUNG OIL
A-H URETHANE BITUMEN SEALANT JFR
A-H URETHANE FLOOR COAT
A-H URETHANE FORM COAT
ANTI-HYDRO

ANVICOM-COMMAND FEDERAL, INC.

(Div. of Command Information, Inc.)
2034 Eisenhower Ave
Alexandria, VA 22314
Tel.: (703) 224-2866
Fax: (703) 224-2881
E-mail: anvicombd@anvi.com
Web Site: www.anvi.com
Approx. Number Employees: 225
Year Founded: 1991
Business Description:
Computer Network Design & Information Technology Support Services to the U.S. Department of Defense
S.I.C.: 7373; 7371
N.A.I.C.S.: 541512; 541511
Media: 10
Personnel:
Nancy Hampton *(Gen Mgr)*
Brands & Products:
ANVICOM

APOGEE ENTERPRISES, INC.

4400 W 78th St Ste 520
Minneapolis, MN 55435
Tel.: (952) 835-1874
Fax: (952) 835-3196
Toll Free: (877) 752-3432
E-mail: webmaster@apogeeidd.com
Web Site: www.apog.com
Approx. Sls.: $582,777,000
Approx. Number Employees: 3,555
Year Founded: 1949
Business Description:
Architectural & Building Products & Services
S.I.C.: 3211; 1751; 1799
N.A.I.C.S.: 327211; 238130; 238190
Export
Advertising Expenditures: $1,000,000
Media: 2-4-7-13-17-26
Personnel:
Bernard P. Aldrich *(Chm)*
Joseph F. Puishys *(Pres & CEO)*
James S. Porter *(CFO)*
Patricia A. Beithon *(Gen Counsel & Sec)*
Brands & Products:
APOGEE
HARMON
LINETEC
PPG AUTOGLASS
TRU VUE
TUBELITE
VIRACON
VIRACON CURVLITE
VIRATEC
WAUSAU

AQUATIC

(Formerly Lasco Bathware)
(Joint Venture of Onex Corporation & Canada Pension Plan Investment Board)
8101 E Kaiser Blvd Ste 200
Anaheim, CA 92808-2261
Tel.: (714) 993-1220
Fax: (714) 998-1250
Toll Free: (800) 877-2005
Web Site: www.aquaticbath.com
Approx. Number Employees: 80
Year Founded: 1947
Business Description:
Bathware & Shower Products Mfr
S.I.C.: 3088; 1711
N.A.I.C.S.: 326191; 238220
Export
Advertising Expenditures: $200,000
Media: 4-5-6-7-8-10-20-21
Distr.: Natl.
Budget Set: May
Personnel:
Gary Anderson *(Pres)*
Ron Hussey *(VP-HR)*
Dave McKechnie *(Gen Mgr)*
Brian Burns *(Dir-Fin)*
Carmen Sjelin *(Dir-Safety & Security)*
Brands & Products:
BUILDERS CHOICE
FREEDOM LINE
LASCO
LASCO STEAM
LASCOAT
LASCOLITE
REMODELINE
Advertising Agency:
Purdie Rogers, Inc.
5447 Ballard Ave NW
Seattle, WA 98107

Key to Media (For complete agency information see *The Advertising Red Books-Agencies* edition):
1. Bus. Publs. 2. Cable T.V. 3. Catalogs & Directories. 4. Co-op Adv. 5. Consumer Mags. 6. D.M. to Bus. Estab.7. D.M. to Consumers
8. Daily Newsp. 9. Exhibits/Trade Shows 10. Foreign 11. Infomercial 12. Internet Adv.13. Multimedia 14. Network Radio
15. Network T.V. 16. Newsp. Distr. Mags. 17. Other 18. Outdoor (Posters, Transit) 19. Point of Purchase20. Premiums, Novelties
21. Product Samples 22. Special Events Mktg. 23. Spot Radio 24. Spot T.V. 25. Weekly Newsp. 26. Yellow Page Adv.

Aquatic — (Continued)

Tel.: (206) 628-7700
Fax: (206) 628-2818

ARBOR MASTERS TREE SERVICE

8250 Cole Pkwy
Shawnee, KS 66227
Tel.: (913) 441-8888
Fax: (913) 441-8922
Web Site: www.arbormasters.com
Business Description:
Tree & Landscaping Services
S.I.C.: 0782
N.A.I.C.S.: 561730
Media: 13-26
Personnel:
Ron Keith *(CEO)*

ARCELORMITTAL DOFASCO INC.

(Sub. of ArcelorMittal)
1330 Burlington St E
PO Box 2460
Hamilton, ON L8N 3J5, Canada
Tel.: (905) 544-3761
Fax: (905) 548-4935
Toll Free: (800) 363-2726
E-mail: investors@dofasco.ca
Web Site: www.dofasco.ca
E-Mail For Key Personnel:
Public Relations: gordon_forstner@dofasco.ca
Approx. Sls.: $5,122,159,840
Approx. Number Employees: 7,400
Year Founded: 1912
Business Description:
Galvanized, Tinplate & Chromium-Coated Flat Rolled Steels & Tubular Products Mfr
S.I.C.: 3312
N.A.I.C.S.: 331111
Media: 2-4-7-10-18
Distr.: Intl.; Natl.
Budget Set: Nov. -Dec.
Personnel:
Juergen G. Schachler *(Pres & CEO)*
Urmas Soomet *(Sec & Dir-Legal Svcs)*
Brian E. Aranha *(VP-Comml)*
Brad Davey *(VP-Sls & Mktg)*
Scott Maki *(VP-Fin)*
Robert W. Nuttall *(VP-Fin)*
Brands & Products:
EXTRAGAL
GALVALUME
GALVALUME PLUS
SOLUTIONS IN STEEL
ZYPLEX
Advertising Agency:
JAN Kelley Marketing
1005 Skyview Dr Ste 322
Burlington, ON L7P 5B1, Canada
Tel.: (905) 631-7934
Fax: (905) 631-8558
Toll Free: (800) 461-7304

ARCELORMITTAL STEEL USA INC.

(Sub. of ArcelorMittal Steel North America)
1 S Dearborn
Chicago, IL 60603
Tel.: (312) 899-3351
Fax: (219) 399-5544
Web Site: www.arcelormittal.com
Approx. Number Employees: 20,500
Year Founded: 1893
Business Description:
Bar & Flat-Rolled Steel Mfr
S.I.C.: 3312; 1011
N.A.I.C.S.: 331111; 212210
Import Export
Media: 1-2-4-7-10-20-22
Distr.: Natl.; Reg.
Budget Set: Sept.
Personnel:
Michael G. Rippey *(CEO-USA & Exec VP)*
Matthew Bernstein *(VP-Pur)*
Advertising Agency:
Esrock Partners
14550 S 94th Ave
Orland Park, IL 60462-2652
Tel.: (708) 349-8400
Fax: (708) 349-8471

ARCH COAL, INC.

One CityPlace Dr Ste 300
Saint Louis, MO 63141
Tel.: (314) 994-2700
Fax: (314) 994-2878
E-mail: careers@archcoal.com
Web Site: www.archcoal.com
Approx. Rev.: $3,186,268,000
Approx. Number Employees: 4,700
Year Founded: 1969
Business Description:
Mining, Production & Sale of Coal
S.I.C.: 1221; 1222; 1231; 1241; 2999
N.A.I.C.S.: 212111; 212112; 212113; 213113; 324199
Media: 2
Personnel:
Steven F. Leer *(Chm & CEO)*
John W. Eaves *(Pres & COO)*
John T. Drexler *(CFO & Sr VP)*
David E. Hartley *(CIO & VP)*
John W. Lorson *(Chief Acctg Officer & VP)*
Jennifer J. Johnson *(Pres-Arch Energy Resources Inc)*
Renato Paladino *(Pres-Arch Coal Asia-Pacific Pte. Ltd)*
Robert W. Shanks *(Pres-Ops-East)*
Robert G. Jones *(Gen Counsel, Sec & Sr VP-Law)*
Paul A. Lang *(Exec VP-Ops)*
C. Henry Besten Jr. *(Sr VP-Strategic Dev)*
David N. Warnecke *(Sr VP-Mktg & Trading)*
John Ziegler, Jr. *(Sr VP-Sls & Admin)*
Sheila B. Feldman *(VP-HR)*
Jeffrey W. Strobel *(VP-Bus Dev & Strategy)*
Advertising Agency:
Charles Ryan Associates Inc.
300 Summers St Ste 1100
Charleston, WV 25301-1631
Tel.: (304) 342-0161
Fax: (304) 342-1941

ARCHITECTURAL ART MFG. INC.

(Div. of Pittcon Industries)
6409 Rhode Island Ave
Riverdale, MD 20737
Tel.: (316) 838-4291
Fax: (316) 838-8502
Toll Free: (800) 835-0028
E-mail: archart@aamicorp.com
Web Site: www.archart.com
Approx. Number Employees: 150
Year Founded: 1948
Business Description:
Bronze, Aluminum, Stainless Steel, Component Expansion Joint Covers Railing Systems, Manhole & Trench Covers & Frames
S.I.C.: 3441; 3446
N.A.I.C.S.: 332312; 332323
Advertising Expenditures: $200,000
Media: 2-4-10-17-26
Distr.: Natl.
Budget Set: Jan. -Mar.
Personnel:
Jerry Weberman *(Gen Mgr)*

ARMSTRONG WOOD PRODUCTS, INC.

(Sub. of Armstrong World Industries, Inc.)
5465 Legacy Dr Ste 600
Plano, TX 75024
Tel.: (972) 473-8300
Tel.: (214) 887-2100 (Cabinets)
Fax: (214) 887-2428
Web Site: www.armstrong.com
Sales Range: $50-74.9 Million
Approx. Number Employees: 500
Year Founded: 1943
Business Description:
Hardwood Flooring, Kitchen & Bathroom Wood Cabinets Mfr & Distr
S.I.C.: 2431; 2434
N.A.I.C.S.: 321918; 337110
Import Export
Media: 2-5-6-10-13-26
Distr.: Natl.
Budget Set: Nov. -Dec.
Brands & Products:
BRUCE
CARUTH

ARROW GROUP INDUSTRIES, INC.

(Joint Venture of Leonard Green & Partners, L.P.)
1680 Rte 23 N
Wayne, NJ 07474
Mailing Address:
PO Box 928
Wayne, NJ 07474-0928
Tel.: (973) 696-6900
Fax: (973) 696-8539
E-mail: info@arrowsheds.com
Web Site: www.arrowsheds.com
Approx. Number Employees: 40
Business Description:
Steel, Aluminum & Wood Outdoor Storage Buildings Mfr
S.I.C.: 3448
N.A.I.C.S.: 332311
Export
Advertising Expenditures: $300,000
Media: 2-6-9-10-19-20
Distr.: Intl.; Natl.
Budget Set: Dec.
Personnel:
George J. Smith *(Pres & CEO)*
Jerry Saul *(Mgr-Adv)*
Brands & Products:
ARROW
SPACEMAKER

AS AMERICA, INC.

(Holding of Sun Capital Partners, Inc.)
(d/b/a American Standard Brands)
1 Centennial Ave
Piscataway, NJ 08855-6820
Tel.: (732) 980-3000
Toll Free: (800) 442-1902
Web Site: www.americanstandard-us.com
Business Description:
Bathroom & Kitchen Faucets, Fixtures, Furniture Mfr
S.I.C.: 3261; 3432
N.A.I.C.S.: 327111; 332913
Personnel:
Donald C. Devine *(Pres & CEO)*
Debbie Drury *(Dir-Brand Comm)*
Linda Klein *(Sr Product Mgr-Chinaware)*
Advertising Agency:
Carmichael Lynch
110 N 5th St
Minneapolis, MN 55403
Tel.: (612) 334-6000
Fax: (612) 334-6090

ASARCO INCORPORATED

(Sub. of Grupo Mexico, S.A.B. de C.V.)
8224 S 48th Ste 220
Phoenix, AZ 85044
Mailing Address:
PO Box 5747
Tucson, AZ 85703-0747
Tel.: (602) 977-6500
Fax: (602) 977-6706
E-mail: phxrecep@asarco.com
Web Site: www.asarco.com
Approx. Number Employees: 30
Year Founded: 1899
Business Description:
Producer of Nonferrous Metals Principally Copper, Lead, Zinc & Silver
S.I.C.: 1021; 1044
N.A.I.C.S.: 212234; 212222
Import Export
Advertising Expenditures: $500,000
Media: 2-7-9-10
Distr.: Natl.
Budget Set: Oct.-Nov.
Personnel:
Oscar Gonzalez *(VP, CFO)*
Joseph A. Wilhelm *(Gen Mgr-Hayden Ops)*

ASSOCIATED MATERIALS LLC

(Sub. of AMH Holdings, LLC)
3773 State Rd
Cuyahoga Falls, OH 44223
Tel.: (330) 929-1811
Fax: (330) 922-2354
Toll Free: (800) 922-6009
Web Site:
www.associatedmaterials.com
Approx. Sls.: $1,167,187,000
Approx. Number Employees: 2,472
Year Founded: 1983
Business Description:
Steel, Aluminum & Vinyl Siding, Steel Wire & Electric Cable Mfr & Distr
S.I.C.: 5033; 3315; 3325; 3354; 3357; 5211
N.A.I.C.S.: 423330; 331222; 331316; 331513; 335921; 444190
Advertising Expenditures: $12,500,000
Personnel:
Erik D. Ragatz *(Chm)*
Jerry W. Burris *(Pres & CEO)*
Thomas N. Chieffe *(Pres)*
Stephen E. Graham *(CFO, Sec & VP)*
Robert M. Franco *(Pres-AMI Distr)*
Warren J. Arthur *(Sr VP-Ops)*
Robert C. Gaydos *(Sr VP-Ops)*

Key to Media (For complete agency information see *The Advertising Red Books-Agencies* edition):
1. Bus. Publs. 2. Cable T.V. 3. Catalogs & Directories. 4. Co-op Adv. 5. Consumer Mags. 6. D.M. to Bus. Estab.7. D.M. to Consumers
8. Daily Newsp. 9. Exhibits/Trade Shows 10. Foreign 11. Infomercial 12. Internet Adv.13. Multimedia 14. Network Radio
15. Network T.V. 16. Newsp. Distr. Mags. 17. Other 18. Outdoor (Posters, Transit) 19. Point of Purchase20. Premiums, Novelties
21. Product Samples 22. Special Events Mktg. 23. Spot Radio 24. Spot T.V. 25. Weekly Newsp. 26. Yellow Page Adv.

Brad Beard *(Reg VP)*
John F. Haumesser *(VP-HR)*
Dana Schindler *(Mgr-Mktg & Siding Products)*
Brands & Products:
ALSIDE
GENTEK

ASTEC INDUSTRIES, INC.

1725 Shepherd Rd
Chattanooga, TN 37421
Tel.: (423) 899-5898
Fax: (423) 899-4456
Toll Free: (888) 451-5551
E-mail: webmaster@astecindustries.com
Web Site: www.astecindustries.com
Approx. Sls.: $771,335,000
Approx. Number Employees: 3,284
Year Founded: 1972
Business Description:
Holding Company; Asphalt, Aggregate & Mining Equipment Mfr
S.I.C.: 6719; 3531; 3532; 5082
N.A.I.C.S.: 551112; 333120; 333131; 423810
Export
Advertising Expenditures: $3,002,000
Media: 1-2-4-7-10-11-13-18
Distr.: Intl.; Natl.
Budget Set: Nov.
Personnel:
J. Don Brock *(Chm & CEO)*
Joseph P. Vig *(Pres)*
F. McKamy Hall *(CFO, Treas & VP)*
Michael A. Bremmer *(Pres-CEI Enterprises, Inc)*
Frank D. Cargould *(Pres-Breaker Tech Ltd & Breaker Tech, Inc)*
Joe K. Cline *(Pres-Astec Underground)*
Lawrence Cumming *(Pres-Peterson Pacific Corp)*
Jeffery J. Elliott *(Pres-Johnson Crushers)*
Timothy Gonigam *(Pres-Astec Mobile Screens, Inc)*
James F. Pfeiffer *(Pres-American Augers Inc)*
David L. Winters *(Pres-Carlson Paving Products)*
Stephen C. Anderson *(Sec & Dir-IR)*
Thomas R. Campbell *(Grp VP-Mobile & Underground)*
Richard A. Patek *(Grp VP-Aggregate & Mining)*
W. Norman Smith *(Grp VP-Asphalt)*
Paul G. Shelton *(Dir-Adv)*
Brands & Products:
ACCU-SWIPE
AMERICAN AUGERS
ASTEC
COMBO
DOUBLE BARREL
FAST PACK
FAST TRAX
GYRASPHERE
HEATEC
JCI
KOLBERG
M-PACK
MORE EQUIPMENT MORE INDUSTRIES
PHOENIX
PIONEER
ROAD MINER
ROADTEC
SHUTTLE BUGGY
SIX PACK
TELSMITH
TRENCOR
WHISPER JET

THE ASTRUP COMPANY

(Sub. of Glen Raven, Inc.)
2937 W 25th St
Cleveland, OH 44113-5303
Tel.: (216) 696-2820
Fax: (216) 696-8202
Web Site: www.trivantage.com
Approx. Number Employees: 282
Year Founded: 1876
Business Description:
Distr of Fabrics, Hardware & Supplies for Fabrication of Awnings, Tents, Tarps & Boat Tops
S.I.C.: 5199; 5088
N.A.I.C.S.: 424990; 423860
Import Export
Media: 2-4-7-10-13-20-21-26
Distr.: Intl.; Natl.

ATLANTA LIMITED

101 Shree Amba Shanti Chambers
Mumbai, 400059, India
Tel.: (91) 2229252929
Fax: (91) 2229252900
E-mail: mail@atlantainfra.com
Web Site: www.atlantainfra.com
Approx. Rev.: $44,726,859
Approx. Number Employees: 136
Business Description:
Infrastructure Development, Mining & Real Estate Services
S.I.C.: 1522; 1429; 1622; 1629; 6531
N.A.I.C.S.: 236220; 212319; 237310; 237990; 531390
Advertising Expenditures: $143,444
Personnel:
G. Viswanathan *(Chm)*
Rajhoo Bbarot *(Mng Dir)*
Rajeev Kumar *(CFO)*

ATLAS MINERALS & CHEMICALS, INC.

1227 Vly Rd
Mertztown, PA 19539-8827
Tel.: (610) 682-7171
Fax: (610) 682-9200
Toll Free: (800) 523-8269
E-mail: sales@atlasmin.com
Web Site: www.atlasmin.com
E-Mail For Key Personnel:
Sales Director: sales@atlasmin.com
Sales Range: $10-24.9 Million
Approx. Number Employees: 48
Year Founded: 1892
Business Description:
Corrosion-Resistant Cements, Linings, Coatings, Rigid Plastics & Pipe Jointing Compounds, Adhesive Putties
S.I.C.: 2891; 2952
N.A.I.C.S.: 325520; 324122
Import Export
Media: 1-2-4-7-10-21
Distr.: Direct to Consumer; Intl.; Natl.
Budget Set: Sept.
Personnel:
George P. Gabriel *(Chm & CEO)*
Francis X. Hanson *(Pres)*
John Im *(Mng Dir)*
Scott Gallagher *(Mgr-Mktg)*
Brands & Products:
ALKOR
ANCHOR-LOK
ATLAS
EPOXY BOND
REZKLAD

ATNA RESOURCES LTD.

14142 Denver W Pkwy Ste 250
Golden, CO 80401
Tel.: (303) 278-8464
Fax: (303) 279-3772
Toll Free: (877) 692-8182
Web Site: www.atna.com
Approx. Rev.: $30,606,900
Approx. Number Employees: 127
Business Description:
Gold Exploration & Mining Services
S.I.C.: 1041
N.A.I.C.S.: 212221
Personnel:
David H. Watkins *(Chm)*
James Hesketh *(Pres & CEO)*
Rod Gloss *(CFO & VP)*
Douglas E. Stewart *(COO)*
Advertising Agency:
Renmark Financial Communications, Inc.
1550 Metcalfe Ste 502
Montreal, QC H3A 1X6, Canada
Tel.: (514) 939-3989
Fax: (514) 939-3717

ATRIUM COMPANIES, INC.

(Joint Venture of Bank of America Corporation, Kenner & Company, Inc. & UBS Capital Americas Investments II LLC)
3890 W NW Hwy Ste 500
Dallas, TX 75220
Mailing Address:
PO Box 226957
Dallas, TX 75222-6957
Tel.: (214) 630-5757
Fax: (214) 630-5001
Fax: (214) 951-0642
E-mail: info@atrium.com
Web Site: www.atrium.com
Approx. Number Employees: 100
Year Founded: 1948
Business Description:
Doors & Windows Mfr & Distr
S.I.C.: 3442; 2431
N.A.I.C.S.: 332321; 321911
Media: 13
Personnel:
Kevin O'Meara *(Chm & CEO)*
Cary Baetz *(CFO)*
Robert E. Burns *(COO & Exec VP)*
Carl Gentile *(CIO)*
Philip J. Ragona *(Gen Counsel & Sr VP)*
Mark Gallant *(Sr VP-Mktg)*
Advertising Agency:
Purdie Rogers, Inc.
5447 Ballard Ave NW
Seattle, WA 98107
Tel.: (206) 628-7700
Fax: (206) 628-2818

THE AUSTIN COMPANY

(Sub. of Kajima International Inc.)
6095 Parkland Blvd
Cleveland, OH 44124
Tel.: (440) 544-2600
Fax: (440) 544-2690
E-mail: austin.info@theaustin.com
Web Site: www.theaustin.com
E-Mail For Key Personnel:
Public Relations: kathleen.bast@theaustin.com
Sales Range: $75-99.9 Million
Approx. Number Employees: 565
Year Founded: 1878
Business Description:
Architectural Design, Engineering, Construction Management & Consulting Services
S.I.C.: 8712; 1541; 8711; 8748
N.A.I.C.S.: 541310; 236210; 541330; 541690
Import Export
Advertising Expenditures: $150,000
Media: 1-2-4-6-7-9-10-11-17-20
Distr.: Intl.; Natl.
Budget Set: Nov.
Personnel:
Michael G. Pierce *(Pres)*
Philip J. Todd *(Sr VP-Svcs)*
Ronald D. Frattare *(VP & Mgr-Facilities Dev)*
Patrick Flanagan *(Dir & Exec Advisor)*
John Harrington *(Dir-Technical)*
Brands & Products:
THE AUSTIN COMPANY
THE AUSTIN METHOD
PROMIS

BAHNSON, INC.

(Sub. of Bahnson Holdings, Inc.)
3901 Westpoint Blvd
Winston Salem, NC 27103
Mailing Address:
PO Box 411227
Charlotte, NC 28241-1227
Tel.: (336) 760-3111
Fax: (336) 760-1548
Web Site: www.luwaamericas.com
Approx. Number Employees: 1,000
Business Description:
Air Treatment Products, Systems & Services
S.I.C.: 3564
N.A.I.C.S.: 333411
Media: 1-4-6-10-17
Distr.: Natl.
Budget Set: Jan.
Personnel:
Tim Whitener *(Pres & CEO)*
Brands & Products:
YOUR AIR. WE CARE.

BAKER CONCRETE CONSTRUCTION, INC.

900 N Garver Rd
Monroe, OH 45050-1241
Tel.: (513) 539-4000
Fax: (513) 539-4380
Web Site: www.bakerconcrete.com
Approx. Sls.: $330,000,000
Approx. Number Employees: 3,500
Year Founded: 1968
Business Description:
Concrete Construction Services
S.I.C.: 1771; 1622
N.A.I.C.S.: 238110; 237310
Media: 2
Personnel:
Daniel L. Baker *(Pres)*
Todd Wilkowski *(Gen Counsel)*
Tom Bell *(Exec VP)*
Stephen E. Martin *(Sr VP-Estimating)*
Steve Lydy *(VP-Bus Dev)*
Advertising Agency:
intrinzic marketing + design inc.
1 Levee Way Ste 3121
Newport, KY 41071
Tel.: (859) 261-2200

Key to Media (For complete agency information see *The Advertising Red Books-Agencies* edition):
1. Bus. Publs. 2. Cable T.V. 3. Catalogs & Directories. 4. Co-op Adv. 5. Consumer Mags. 6. D.M. to Bus. Estab.7. D.M. to Consumers
8. Daily Newsp. 9. Exhibits/Trade Shows 10. Foreign 11. Infomercial 12. Internet Adv.13. Multimedia 14. Network Radio
15. Network T.V. 16. Newsp. Distr. Mags. 17. Other 18. Outdoor (Posters, Transit) 19. Point of Purchase20. Premiums, Novelties
21. Product Samples 22. Special Events Mktg. 23. Spot Radio 24. Spot T.V. 25. Weekly Newsp. 26. Yellow Page Adv.

Baker Concrete Construction, Inc. —
(Continued)

Fax: (859) 261-2102

BALLARD POWER SYSTEMS, INC.
9000 Glenlyon Pkwy
Burnaby, BC V5J 5J8, Canada
Tel.: (604) 454-0900
Fax: (604) 412-4700
E-mail: investors@ballard.com
Web Site: www.ballard.com
Approx. Rev.: $65,019,000
Approx. Number Employees: 440
Year Founded: 1979
Business Description:
Fuel Cell & Fuel Cell Systems Mfr
S.I.C.: 3699; 3674
N.A.I.C.S.: 335999; 334413
Media: 2-7-10
Personnel:
Ian A. Bourne *(Chm)*
John W. Sheridan *(Pres & CEO)*
Tony Guglielmin *(CFO & VP)*
Bill Foulds *(Pres-Matl Products)*
Hans-Joachim Schoepf *(Exec VP)*
Guy McAree *(Dir-Corp Comm & Mktg)*
Brands & Products:
AVCARB
BALLARD
ECOSTAR
FC VELOCITY
NEXA
POWER TO CHANGE THE WORLD
POWERED BY BALLARD
Advertising Agency:
C&E Translation & Advertising Inc.
311-1037 West Broadway
Vancouver, BC V6H 1E3, Canada
Tel.: (604) 736-3609
Fax: (604) 736-3078

BALTEK INC.
(Sub. of 3A Composites Holding AG)
108 Fairway Ct
Northvale, NJ 07647-2401
Tel.: (201) 767-1400
Fax: (201) 367-1201
E-Mail For Key Personnel:
Sales Director: sales@alcanbaltek.com
Approx. Number Employees: 767
Year Founded: 1880
Business Description:
Structural Core Materials Mfr
S.I.C.: 2499
N.A.I.C.S.: 321999
Import Export
Advertising Expenditures: $200,000
Media: 2-4-7-10-13
Distr.: Intl.; Natl.
Personnel:
Marc Anderson *(Dir-Sls & Mktg)*
Brands & Products:
DECOLITE
Advertising Agency:
Messer & Susslin & Others, Inc.
274 N Middletown Rd
Pearl River, NY 10965-1216
Tel.: (845) 735-3030
Fax: (845) 735-2270

BARTLETT COCKE, LP
8706 Lockway St
San Antonio, TX 78217-4837
Tel.: (210) 655-1031
Fax: (210) 655-1327
Web Site: www.bartlettcocke.com
Approx. Number Employees: 400
Year Founded: 1959
Business Description:
Provider of General Contracting Services
S.I.C.: 1522
N.A.I.C.S.: 236220
Personnel:
Randall J. Pawelek *(Chm, Pres & CEO)*
Advertising Agency:
The Atkins Group
501 Soledad
San Antonio, TX 78205
Tel.: (210) 444-2500
Fax: (210) 824-8236

BATEMAN BROTHERS LUMBER CO., INC.
89 S Sand Rd
New Britain, PA 18901-5122
Mailing Address:
PO Box 1039
Doylestown, PA 18901-0017
Tel.: (215) 345-7331
Fax: (215) 345-4118
Web Site: www.batemanlumber.com
Approx. Number Employees: 30
Year Founded: 1946
Business Description:
Mfr. & Retailer of Imported & Domestic Lumber
S.I.C.: 5031
N.A.I.C.S.: 423310
Import
Media: 2-4-7-10
Distr.: Natl.
Personnel:
Edward D. Bateman *(Chm)*
George Bateman *(Pres)*

BEACON ROOFING SUPPLY, INC.
1 Lakeland Park Dr
Peabody, MA 01960
Tel.: (978) 535-7668
Fax: (978) 535-7358
Toll Free: (877) 645-7663
Web Site:
www.beaconroofingsupply.com
Approx. Sls.: $1,609,969,000
Approx. Number Employees: 2,231
Year Founded: 1928
Business Description:
Residential & Non-Residential Building Exterior & Roofing Materials Distr
S.I.C.: 5033
N.A.I.C.S.: 423330
Media: 7-10-13
Personnel:
Robert R. Buck *(Chm)*
Paul M. Isabella *(Pres & CEO)*
David R. Grace *(CFO & Exec VP)*
Christopher Nelson *(CIO & VP)*
Ross D. Cooper *(Gen Counsel, Sec & Sr VP)*
James I. MacKimm *(Exec VP)*
Patrick Murphy *(Exec VP)*
C. Munroe Best, III *(Sr VP)*
Kent C. Gardner *(Sr VP-Shelter Midwest, Shelter Southwest & Pacific Supply)*
C. Eric Swank *(Sr VP-The Roof Center & Fleet Ops)*
Robert K. Greer, Jr. *(Reg VP-West End Lumber)*
Gerard Hill *(Reg VP-Sls)*
John F. Smith, Jr. *(Reg VP-Shelter Southwest Reg)*
John P. Massarelli *(VP-Sls & Mktg)*
David Pasternak *(VP-HR)*
Ken Heitkamp *(Reg Mgr-Beacon Pacific)*

THE BECK GROUP
1807 Ross Ave Ste 500
Dallas, TX 75201-4691
Tel.: (214) 303-6200
Fax: (214) 303-6300
Web Site: www.beckgroup.com
Sales Range: $500-549.9 Million
Approx. Number Employees: 600
Year Founded: 1912
Business Description:
Building Design & Contracting Services
S.I.C.: 1522; 1541
N.A.I.C.S.: 236220; 236210
Personnel:
Peter Beck *(Mng Dir & CEO)*
Mark Collins *(Mng Dir & CFO)*
Kip E. Daniel *(Mng Dir)*
Rick del Monte *(Mng Dir)*
C. Samuel Ellison *(Mng Dir)*
Jim Gettman *(Mng Dir)*
Paul Higgins *(Mng Dir)*
Mark House *(Mng Dir)*
Brad Phillips *(Mng Dir)*
Mike Webster *(Mng Dir)*
Lawrence A. Wilson *(Dir)*
Advertising Agency:
Levenson & Brinker Public Relations
717 Harwood 20th Fl
Dallas, TX 75201
Tel.: (214) 932-6057
Tel.: (214) 932-6076
Fax: (214) 880-0628

BENCHMARK INDUSTRIES
630 Hay Ave
Brookville, OH 45309-1908
Tel.: (937) 833-4091
Fax: (937) 833-5268
Toll Free: (800) 833-4096
Web Site:
benchmarkindustriesohio.com/
E-Mail For Key Personnel:
Sales Director: sales@benchmark-homes.com
Approx. Number Employees: 70
Year Founded: 1946
Business Description:
Industrialized Housing Mfr
S.I.C.: 2452
N.A.I.C.S.: 321992
Media: 2-4-6-10-19-25
Distr.: Reg.
Personnel:
George Kirby *(VP-Production)*
David Sowers *(VP-Pur)*

BENJAMIN OBDYKE, INC.
400 Babyllon Rd Ste A
Horsham, PA 19044-1232
Tel.: (215) 672-7200
Fax: (215) 672-5204
Toll Free: (800) 523-5261 (Sales)
Toll Free: (800) 346-7655 (Customer Service)
E-mail: info@benjaminobdyke.com
Web Site: www.benjaminobdyke.com
Sales Range: $200-249.9 Million
Approx. Number Employees: 40
Year Founded: 1868
Business Description:
Provider of Building Construction Products
S.I.C.: 5075; 5072
N.A.I.C.S.: 423730; 423710
Export
Personnel:
David A. Campbell *(Pres)*
Richard J. Campbell *(CEO)*
Mike Coulton *(Gen Mgr)*
Brands & Products:
CEDAR BREATHER
FLASHMASTER
HOME SLICKER
JUMBO TEX
KWIKDEK
PLUS TYPAR
RAPID RIDGE
RIPCORD
ROLL VENT
THE WATERFALL
WATERFALL
XTRACTOR VENT
Advertising Agency:
IMRE
909 Ridgebrook Rd Ste 300
Baltimore, MD 21152
Tel.: (410) 821-8220
Fax: (410) 821-5619

THE BILCO COMPANY
37 Water St PO Box 1203
West Haven, CT 06516-3837
Tel.: (203) 934-6363
Fax: (203) 933-8478
E-mail: bilco@biloco.com
Web Site: www.bilco.com
Approx. Number Employees: 100
Year Founded: 1926
Business Description:
Mfr. of Construction Supplies & Fixtures
S.I.C.: 3442; 3446
N.A.I.C.S.: 332321; 332323
Personnel:
Robert J. Lyons Jr. *(Pres & CEO)*
Roger F. Joyce *(Exec VP)*
Brands & Products:
BILCO
LADDER UP
LADDERUP
LUMIVENT
PERMENTRY
T-CAM
VERSAMOUNT
Advertising Agency:
Catalyst Marketing Communications Inc.
2777 Summer St Ste 301
Stamford, CT 06905
Tel.: (203) 348-7541
Fax: (203) 348-5688

BLACK & VEATCH HOLDING COMPANY
8400 Ward Pkwy
Kansas City, MO 64114-2031
Tel.: (913) 458-2000
Fax: (913) 458-2934
E-mail: corporateinfo@bv.com
Web Site: www.bv.com
Approx. Rev.: $2,200,000,000
Approx. Number Employees: 9,600
Year Founded: 1915
Business Description:
Construction Services
S.I.C.: 8711; 8712

Key to Media (For complete agency information see *The Advertising Red Books-Agencies* edition):
1. Bus. Publs. 2. Cable T.V. 3. Catalogs & Directories. 4. Co-op Adv. 5. Consumer Mags. 6. D.M. to Bus. Estab.7. D.M. to Consumers
8. Daily Newsp. 9. Exhibits/Trade Shows 10. Foreign 11. Infomercial 12. Internet Adv.13. Multimedia 14. Network Radio
15. Network T.V. 16. Newsp. Distr. Mags. 17. Other 18. Outdoor (Posters, Transit) 19. Point of Purchase20. Premiums, Novelties
21. Product Samples 22. Special Events Mktg. 23. Spot Radio 24. Spot T.V. 25. Weekly Newsp. 26. Yellow Page Adv.

N.A.I.C.S.: 541330; 541310
Personnel:
Leonard C. Rodman *(Chm, Pres & CEO)*
Karen L. Daniel *(CFO)*
Jim Lewis *(Chief Admin Officer & Pres-Admin Div)*
Daniel W. McCarthy *(Pres/CEO-B & V Water)*
O. H. Oskvig *(Pres/CEO-B & V Energy)*
John Voeller *(Sr VP)*
Corrine Smith *(VP-Corp Mktg, Brand Mgmt & Comm)*
Carl Petz *(Assoc VP-Strategic Mktg & Comm)*
George Minter *(Sr Mgr-Media Rels & Commun)*
Brands & Products:
BLACK & VEATCH
BUILDING A WORLD OF DIFFERENCE
PATHFINDER
Advertising Agency:
Bernstein-Rein Advertising, Inc.
4600 Madison Ave Ste 1500
Kansas City, MO 64112-3016
Tel.: (816) 756-0640
Fax: (816) 399-6000
Toll Free: (800) 571-6246

BLACK BROTHERS COMPANY

501 9th Ave
Mendota, IL 61342-1927
Tel.: (815) 539-7451
Fax: (815) 538-2451
E-mail: info@blackbros.com
Web Site: www.blackbros.com
Approx. Number Employees: 75
Year Founded: 1882
Business Description:
Roll Coating, Glue Spreading & Laminating Equipment
S.I.C.: 3553; 3549
N.A.I.C.S.: 333210; 333518
Export
Media: 1-2-4-7-10-11-13-20
Distr.: Intl.; Natl.
Budget Set: Dec.
Personnel:
Matthew Carroll *(Pres)*
Jeffrey W. Simonton *(CFO)*
Robert F. Stachlewitz, Jr. *(COO)*
Frank Kobilsek *(Dir-Product Dev)*
H. Todd Phalen *(Dir-Sls)*
Brands & Products:
BLACK BROS

THE BLOOMFIELD MANUFACTURING CO., INC.

46 W Spring St
Bloomfield, IN 47424-1473
Tel.: (812) 384-4441
Fax: (812) 384-4592
Toll Free: (800) 233-2051
E-mail: webmaster@hi-lift.com
Web Site: www.hi-lift.com
Approx. Number Employees: 60
Year Founded: 1895
Business Description:
Jacks & Fence Products, Door Products & Cargo Tie Down Products Mfr
S.I.C.: 1721
N.A.I.C.S.: 238320
Export
Advertising Expenditures: $200,000
Media: 10-11-19
Distr.: Intl.; Natl.
Budget Set: July -Nov.
Personnel:
Eric Harrah *(CEO)*
Steve Dowden *(VP-Sls & Mktg)*
Jason Skomp *(Mgr-Adv)*
Brands & Products:
HI-LIFT

BLUE EARTH, INC.

(Formerly GENESIS FLUID SOLUTIONS HOLDINGS, INC.)
2298 Horizon Ridge Pkwy Ste 205
Henderson, NV 89052
Tel.: (702) 608-5476
Tel.: (702) 263-1808
Fax: (702) 263-1824
Approx. Number Employees: 27
Year Founded: 1994
Business Description:
Waterway Restoration & Water Remediation Technologies Designer & Developer; Energy Management Services
S.I.C.: 4941; 9511
N.A.I.C.S.: 221310; 924110
Advertising Expenditures: $46,590
Media: 17
Personnel:
Laird Q. Cagan *(Chm)*
Johnny R. Thomas *(Pres & CEO)*

BLUELINX HOLDINGS, INC.

(Holding of Cerberus Capital Management, L.P.)
4300 Wildwood Pkwy
Atlanta, GA 30339
Tel.: (770) 953-7000
Toll Free: (888) 502-BLUE
Toll Free: (866) 671-5138 (Investor Relations)
E-mail: contactus@bluelinxco.com
Web Site: www.bluelinxco.com
Approx. Sls.: $1,804,418,000
Approx. Number Employees: 1,940
Business Description:
Holding Company
S.I.C.: 5211; 5031; 6719
N.A.I.C.S.: 444190; 423310; 551112
Advertising Expenditures: $1,800,000
Personnel:
George R. Judd *(Pres & CEO)*
Steven G. Skinner *(Mng Partner)*
Howard D. Goforth *(CFO, Treas & Sr VP)*
Dean A. Adelman *(Chief Admin Officer)*
David J. Dalton *(Sr VP)*
Brands & Products:
ATLAS GLASSMASTER
ATLAS PINNACLE
ATLAS STRATFORD
BEDFORD VILLAGE
CATAWBA
CENTURA
CUTTER
ESTATE
FASTBEAM
FIBERSTRONG
G-P LAM
HIGH RIDGE
JOIST JACKETS
JUBILEE
LEDGER JACKETS
LIONITE
MCKENZIE
MOUNT VERNON
PARKSIDE
PLY-BEAD
PLYTANIUM
PRIMETRIM
SAVANNAH
STURD-FLOOR
STYLELINE
STYROFOM
TANZA
THERMOSTAT
TIMBER RIDGE
VINYL DETAILS
WEATHERBEST
WEATHERMATE
WOOD I BEAM
Advertising Agencies:
Paprocki & Co.
865 Adair Ave
Atlanta, GA 30306
Tel.: (404) 308-0019
Fax: (404) 607-1317

Red Square
202 Government St
Mobile, AL 36602
Tel.: (251) 476-1283
Fax: (251) 476-1582

BMC SELECT

720 Park Blvd Ste 200
Boise, ID 83712
Tel.: (208) 331-4300
E-mail: info@bmhc.com
Web Site: www.bmcselect.com
Sales Range: $1-4.9 Billion
Approx. Number Employees: 280
Business Description:
Holding Company; Building Materials Distr
S.I.C.: 5211; 6719
N.A.I.C.S.: 444190; 444110; 551112
Advertising Expenditures: $338,000
Media: 7-13
Personnel:
Jay B. Hunt *(Chm)*
Daniel McQuary *(CFO)*
Paul S. Street *(Chief Admin Officer & Gen Counsel)*
Eric R. Beem *(Chief Acctg Officer, VP & Controller)*
Richard M. Giesbrecht *(Sr Dir-Accounting)*
Advertising Agencies:
The Blueshirt Group
456 Montgomery St 11th Fl
San Francisco, CA 94104
Tel.: (415) 217-7722
Fax: (415) 217-7721

Stoltz Marketing Group
615 W Main St 2nd Fl
Boise, ID 83702
Tel.: (208) 388-0766
Fax: (208) 388-0764

THE BOARDMAN INC.

1135 S McKinley Ave
Oklahoma City, OK 73108
Tel.: (405) 634-5434
Fax: (405) 632-6948
E-mail: boardman@boardmaninc.com
Web Site: www.boardmaninc.com
E-Mail For Key Personnel:
President: rgrommet@boardmaninc.com
Sales Director: sales@boardmaninc.com
Approx. Number Employees: 80
Year Founded: 1986
Business Description:
Industrial Metal, Pressure Vessels & Large Diameter Pipe Mfr
S.I.C.: 3443
N.A.I.C.S.: 332313
Media: 2-4-7-10-13-26
Distr.: Natl.
Budget Set: Dec.
Personnel:
Roger Grommet *(Pres)*
Jim Hagemann *(CFO)*
Mike Ashby *(Mgr-Estimating)*
Rusty Dill *(Mgr-Engrg)*
Bob Stromer *(Mgr-Pur)*

BODYCOTE THERMAL PROCESSING

(Sub. of Bodycote International Inc.)
1975 N Ruby St
Melrose Park, IL 60160-1109
Tel.: (708) 344-4080
Fax: (708) 344-4010
E-mail: timotyh.veenbaas@bodycote.com
Web Site: www.bodycote.com
Approx. Number Employees: 1,119
Year Founded: 1922
Business Description:
Heat Treating of Metal
S.I.C.: 3398
N.A.I.C.S.: 332811
Import Export
Media: 2-7-10-11-13
Distr.: Direct to Consumer; Natl.
Personnel:
Timothy Veenbaas *(Gen Mgr)*
Brian Strebing *(Dir-Continuous Improvement)*
Craig Zimmerman *(Dir-Technical)*
Brands & Products:
CAHTS
LINDURE
THIXMOLDING

BORAL INDUSTRIES INC.

(Sub. of Boral Limited)
200 Manville Ct E Ste 310
Roswell, GA 30076
Tel.: (770) 645-4500
Fax: (770) 645-2888
Web Site: www.boralbricks.com
Approx. Sls.: $440,000,000
Approx. Number Employees: 2,400
Business Description:
Holding Company
S.I.C.: 3251; 3272
N.A.I.C.S.: 327121; 327390
Personnel:
Mike Kane *(Pres)*
Brands & Products:
BORAL
Advertising Agency:
IMRE
909 Ridgebrook Rd Ste 300
Baltimore, MD 21152
Tel.: (410) 821-8220
Fax: (410) 821-5619
Bricks

BRADEN MANUFACTURING LLC

(Sub. of Global Power Equipment Group Inc.)
5199 N Mingo Rd
Tulsa, OK 74117
Mailing Address:
PO Box 1229

Key to Media (For complete agency information see *The Advertising Red Books-Agencies* edition):
1. Bus. Publs. 2. Cable T.V. 3. Catalogs & Directories. 4. Co-op Adv. 5. Consumer Mags. 6. D.M. to Bus. Estab.7. D.M. to Consumers
8. Daily Newsp. 9. Exhibits/Trade Shows 10. Foreign 11. Infomercial 12. Internet Adv.13. Multimedia 14. Network Radio
15. Network T.V. 16. Newsp. Distr. Mags. 17. Other 18. Outdoor (Posters, Transit) 19. Point of Purchase20. Premiums, Novelties
21. Product Samples 22. Special Events Mktg. 23. Spot Radio 24. Spot T.V. 25. Weekly Newsp. 26. Yellow Page Adv.

Braden Manufacturing LLC — (Continued)

Tulsa, OK 74101-1229
Tel.: (918) 272-5371
Fax: (918) 272-7414
E-mail: sales@braden.com
Web Site: www.braden.com
E-Mail For Key Personnel:
Sales Director: sales@braden.com
Sales Range: $100-124.9 Million
Approx. Number Employees: 550
Year Founded: 1923
Business Description:
Structural Steel Fabricator
S.I.C.: 3441
N.A.I.C.S.: 332312
Export
Media: 2-4-10-11-13
Distr.: Intl.
Budget Set: Sept.
Personnel:
Gene F. Schockemoehl *(Pres)*

BRADLEY CORPORATION

W 142 N 9101 Fountain Blvd
Menomonee Falls, WI 53051-2348
Tel.: (262) 251-6000
Fax: (262) 251-5817
Toll Free: (800) BRADLEY
Web Site: www.bradleycorp.com
Approx. Number Employees: 400
Year Founded: 1921
Business Description:
Washfountains, Faucets, Safety Fixtures, Showers; Security Prison & Jail Plumbing Fixtures
S.I.C.: 3272; 3431
N.A.I.C.S.: 327390; 332998
Import Export
Media: 2-4-5-7-10-11-20-21-22-26
Distr.: Intl.; Natl.; Reg.
Budget Set: Aug.
Personnel:
Donald Mullett *(CEO)*
Diane Rudy *(VP-HR)*
Jon Dommisse *(Dir-Product Dev & Mktg)*
Kris Alderson *(Sr Mgr-Mktg)*
Valerie Bonney *(Product Mgr)*
Rebecca Geissler *(Product Mgr)*
Heather Koehn *(Product Mgr)*
Nate Kogler *(Product Mgr-Safety & Indus)*
Ryan Pfund *(Product Mgr)*
Jon Villwock *(Product Mgr)*
Brands & Products:
90-75
BRADLEY
BRADPACK
BRADSTONE
DYNAMIX
EXPRESS
FASTRAC
FREQUENCY
LABTAP
LAVCARE
MULTI-FOUNTS
ON-SITE
ONSTEP
SENTINEL
SENTRY
TERREON

BRAND ENERGY, INC.

(Holding of First Reserve Corporation)
1325 Cobb International Dr Ste A-1
Kennesaw, GA 30152
Tel.: (678) 285-1400
Fax: (770) 514-0285
Web Site: www.beis.com
Approx. Rev.: $1,089,651,000
Approx. Number Employees: 10,600
Year Founded: 1966
Business Description:
Scaffold & Industrial Construction Contracting Services
S.I.C.: 1771; 1799
N.A.I.C.S.: 238990; 238110; 238190
Media: 10-13-22
Personnel:
Timothy H. Day *(Chm)*
Paul T. Wood *(Pres & CEO)*
John A. Durkee *(Pres)*
Anthony A. Rabb *(CFO, Treas & Sr VP-Fin)*
James McGee *(Pres-Bus Dev)*
Joseph A. Sadowski *(Pres-Bus Dev)*
Stephen F. Tisdall *(Pres-Infrastructure Svcs)*
David J. Witsken *(Pres-Brand Energy Svcs)*
James R. Billingsley, Jr. *(Gen Counsel, Sec & Exec VP)*
George R. Fleck *(Exec VP-HR)*
Albert A. Reeves *(Sr VP)*

BRANDEIS MACHINERY & SUPPLY COMPANY

(Sub. of Bramco Inc.)
1801 Watterson Trl
Louisville, KY 40299-2431
Tel.: (502) 493-4300
Fax: (502) 499-4311
Web Site:
www.brandeismachinery.com
Approx. Number Employees: 62
Year Founded: 1951
Business Description:
Providers of Equipments for Construction & Mining Services
S.I.C.: 5082
N.A.I.C.S.: 423810
Import Export
Personnel:
Jay Paradis *(Chm)*
Gene Snowden, Jr. *(Pres & COO)*
Charles Leis *(CEO)*
Larry Shuck *(Sr VP & Gen Mgr-Crane & Matl Handling)*
Tony Estes *(Sr VP-Sls)*
David Coultas *(VP & Reg Mgr-Sls)*
Chuck Mueller *(VP & Reg Mgr-Sls)*
Gary Hirsch *(Gen Mgr-Crane & Matl Handling)*
Dan Brandon *(Mgr-Sls & Rental Svcs)*
Advertising Agency:
Ackermann PR
1111 Northshore Dr Ste N-400
Knoxville, TN 37919
Tel.: (865) 584-0550
Fax: (865) 588-3009
Toll Free: (866) 896-4069
Toll Free: (888) 414-7787

BRASFIELD & GORRIE, LLC

3021 7th Ave S
Birmingham, AL 35233-2939
Tel.: (205) 328-4000
Fax: (205) 251-1304
Toll Free: (800) 239-8017
Web Site: www.brasfieldgorrie.com
Sales Range: $1-4.9 Billion
Approx. Number Employees: 2,939
Year Founded: 1922
Business Description:
General Contractor
S.I.C.: 1522; 1541
N.A.I.C.S.: 236220; 236210
Media: 2
Personnel:
M. Miller Gorrie *(Chm)*
Jim Gorrie *(Pres)*
Randall J. Freeman *(CFO)*
Jeffrey I. Stone *(COO)*
Tom Garrett *(CIO)*
Rob Taylor *(Pres-East Reg)*
Charles Grizzle *(Gen Counsel)*

BROOKFIELD HOMES

(Sub. of Brookfield Homes Corporation)
12865 Pointe Del Mar Way Ste 200
Del Mar, CA 92014-3860
Tel.: (858) 481-8500
Fax: (858) 794-6185
E-mail: infosdrv@brookfieldhomes.com
Web Site: www.brookfieldhomes.com
E-Mail For Key Personnel:
Sales Director: sales@brookfieldhomes.com
Sales Range: $50-74.9 Million
Approx. Number Employees: 75
Business Description:
New Home Builders
S.I.C.: 1521
N.A.I.C.S.: 236115
Advertising Expenditures: $200,000
Media: 2-6-7-8-9-18-25
Distr.: Reg.
Budget Set: Monthly

BROOKFIELD HOMES CORPORATION

8500 Executive Park Ave Ste 300
Fairfax, VA 22031
Tel.: (703) 270-1700
Fax: (703) 270-1401
E-mail: infosf@brookfieldhomes.com
Web Site: www.brookfieldhomes.com
Approx. Rev.: $338,866,000
Approx. Number Employees: 271
Year Founded: 1953
Business Description:
Real Estate Development Company
S.I.C.: 1521
N.A.I.C.S.: 236115
Advertising Expenditures: $7,000,000
Personnel:
Robert L. Stelzl *(Chm)*
Robert Hubbel *(Pres)*
Stephen P. Doyle *(Pres-Brookfield San Diego Holdings)*
Adrian Foley *(Pres-Brookfield Homes Southland)*
Robert C. Hubbell *(Pres-Brookfield Homes)*
Richard T. Whitney *(Pres-Brookfield California Land Holdings)*
William B. Seith *(Exec VP)*
Linda T. Northwood *(Dir-IR)*
Advertising Agencies:
Bailey Gardiner Inc.
444 W. Beech St Ste 400
San Diego, CA 92101
Tel.: (619) 295-8232
Fax: (619) 295-8234
San Diego/Riverside Div.

Oxford Communications, Inc.
11 Music Mtn Blvd
Lambertville, NJ 08530
Tel.: (609) 397-4242
Fax: (609) 397-8863

BROWN AND CALDWELL

201 N Civic Dr
Walnut Creek, CA 94596-3864
Tel.: (925) 937-9010
Fax: (925) 937-9026
Toll Free: (800) 727-2224
E-mail: info@brwncald.com
Web Site:
www.brownandcaldwell.com
E-Mail For Key Personnel:
Public Relations: tpeckham@brwncald.com
Sales Range: $150-199.9 Million
Approx. Number Employees: 1,315
Year Founded: 1947
Business Description:
Environmental Consulting & Engineering Services
S.I.C.: 8711; 8999
N.A.I.C.S.: 541330; 541620
Media: 2-4-7-10-13-26
Distr.: Intl.; Natl.
Budget Set: Sept.
Personnel:
James R. Miller *(Pres & COO)*
Craig Goehring *(CEO)*
Robert Leichtner *(Gen Counsel & Sec)*
Cindy Paulson *(Sr VP)*

BSW INTERNATIONAL, INC.

1 W 3rd St Ste 800
Tulsa, OK 74103-3532
Tel.: (918) 582-8771
Fax: (918) 587-3594
Approx. Number Employees: 150
Year Founded: 1983
Business Description:
Architectural Engineering Firm
S.I.C.: 8712; 8711
N.A.I.C.S.: 541310; 541330
Import Export
Personnel:
Robert C. Workman *(Chm)*
Doug Heinrichs *(Mng Dir & VP)*
John Gigas *(CFO)*
William D. Howell *(Dir-Design)*
Advertising Agency:
Cubic
1631 S Boston Ave
Tulsa, OK 74119
Tel.: (918) 587-7888
Fax: (918) 398-9081

BUFFALO WIRE WORKS CO., INC.

1165 Clinton St
Buffalo, NY 14206-2825
Tel.: (716) 826-4666
Fax: (716) 826-8271
Toll Free: (800) 828-7028
E-mail: info@buffalowire.com
Web Site: www.buffalowire.com
Sales Range: $1-9.9 Million
Approx. Number Employees: 80
Year Founded: 1869
Business Description:
Wire Cloth; Vibrator Screen Replacements; Perforated Plate; Custom Cut Plate
S.I.C.: 3496; 3469
N.A.I.C.S.: 332618; 332116
Export
Media: 2-4-7-10-11-20-26
Distr.: Reg.
Budget Set: Mar.
Personnel:
Joseph Abramo *(CEO)*
George Ulrich *(CFO)*

Key to Media (For complete agency information see *The Advertising Red Books-Agencies* edition):
1. Bus. Publs. 2. Cable T.V. 3. Catalogs & Directories. 4. Co-op Adv. 5. Consumer Mags. 6. D.M. to Bus. Estab.7. D.M. to Consumers
8. Daily Newsp. 9. Exhibits/Trade Shows 10. Foreign 11. Infomercial 12. Internet Adv.13. Multimedia 14. Network Radio
15. Network T.V. 16. Newsp. Distr. Mags. 17. Other 18. Outdoor (Posters, Transit) 19. Point of Purchase20. Premiums, Novelties
21. Product Samples 22. Special Events Mktg. 23. Spot Radio 24. Spot T.V. 25. Weekly Newsp. 26. Yellow Page Adv.

Dominic Nasso *(Exec VP-Sls)*
Erich Steadman *(VP-Tech)*
Rick Zimmer *(VP-Engrg)*
Betsy Budzynski *(Mgr-HR)*
Beth Dajka *(Mgr-Customer Svc)*

Brands & Products:
BUFFALO HARP
BUFFALO WIRE WORKS
CLEAN SLOT
CLEAN THRU
CLEAN WEAVE
GATOR WIRE
HARDCORE

BUILDING MATERIALS CORPORATION OF AMERICA

(Sub. of G-I Holdings Inc.)
(d/b/a GAF Materials Corporation)
1361 Alps Rd
Wayne, NJ 07470-3700
Tel.: (973) 628-3000
Fax: (973) 628-3326
Web Site: www.gaf.com
Approx. Sls.: $2,748,909,000
Business Description:
Asphalt & Polymer Based Roofing Products & Accessories Mfr
S.I.C.: 2952; 3083; 5033
N.A.I.C.S.: 324122; 326130; 423330
Media: 6
Personnel:
Robert B. Tafaro *(Pres & CEO)*
John F. Rebele *(CFO, Chief Admin Officer & Sr VP)*
Richard A. Nowak *(COO & Exec VP)*
Matti Kiik *(CTO & Sr VP)*
Mike Newton *(Exec Officer)*
Daniel J. Goldstein *(Gen Counsel & Sr VP)*
Jan E. Jerger-Stevens *(Sr VP-HR)*
Advertising Agency:
White Good & Co. Advertising
226 N Arch St Ste 1
Lancaster, PA 17603
Tel.: (717) 396-0200
Fax: (717) 396-9483

BUILDING PRODUCTS OF CANADA CORP.

(Sub. of EMCO Corporation)
9510 Street Patrick Street
La Salle, QC H8R 1R9, Canada
Tel.: (514) 364-0161
Fax: (514) 364-9029
Toll Free: (800) 567-2726
E-mail: service@emcobp.com
Web Site: www.bpcan.com
E-Mail For Key Personnel:
President: YGos@emcoltd.com
Marketing Director: mabr@emcoltd.com
Sales Director: GCha@emcoltd.com
Approx. Number Employees: 250
Year Founded: 1925
Business Description:
Ceiling, Structural & Acoustical Panel Mfr; Shingle Mfr
S.I.C.: 2952; 5211
N.A.I.C.S.: 324122; 444190
Import Export
Media: 2-4-5-6-10-13-19-21
Distr.: Natl.
Budget Set: Nov. -Dec.
Personnel:
Gaetan Chamaillard *(VP-Sls)*
Jean-Marc Lemery *(Dir-Product Lines)*
Guy Moras *(Mgr-Mktg-Roofing Products)*
Carol Filso *(Mgr-Mdsg & Promos)*
Brands & Products:
AIR-GARD
BP CEILING CLASSICS
CITADEL
DAKOTA
ECLIPSE
ENERMAX
EUROPA
EVEREST
EXCEL II
HARMONY
MIRAGE
MOSAIC
NIAGARA
PRO STANDARD
RAMPART
RIDGLASS
ROOFMASTER
STARTER STRIP
TITE-LOK
TITE-ON
TRADITION
WEATHER-TITE
YUKON
Advertising Agencies:
energi PR
368 Notre Dame W Ste 402
Montreal, QC H2Y 1T9, Canada
Tel.: (514) 288-8500
Fax: (514) 288-5680
Toll Free: (888) 764-MECA

Lajeunesse Communication Marketing
807 rue Roy Est
Montreal, QC H2L 1E4, Canada
Tel.: (514) 528-8888
Fax: (514) 528-1291

BURGESS & NIPLE, INC.

5085 Reed Rd
Columbus, OH 43220
Tel.: (614) 459-2050
Fax: (614) 451-1385
E-mail: info@burnip.com
Web Site: www.burgessniple.com
Approx. Sls.: $63,000,000
Approx. Number Employees: 670
Year Founded: 1912
Business Description:
Engineering & Architectural Services
S.I.C.: 8711; 8712
N.A.I.C.S.: 541330; 541310
Advertising Expenditures: $500,000
Media: 2-13-17-26
Personnel:
Ronald R. Schultz *(Chm)*
John DeBell *(Exec VP)*
Chuck Zibbel *(Reg Dir)*

BURROUGHS & CHAPIN CO. INC.

611 Burroughs & Chapin Blvd Ste 100
Myrtle Beach, SC 29577
Tel.: (843) 448-5123
Fax: (843) 448-5138
Web Site: www.burroughschapin.com
Approx. Sls.: $38,800,000
Approx. Number Employees: 275
Business Description:
Subdivision Developers
S.I.C.: 6552; 0139
N.A.I.C.S.: 237210; 111998
Personnel:
J. Egerton E. Burroughs *(Chm)*
William F. Pritchard *(Interim Pres & CEO)*
Tony K. Cox *(Exec VP-Real Estate)*
Robert Swezy *(Exec VP)*
Mary E. Basden *(Sr VP-Human Capital)*
Patrick J. Walsh *(Sr VP-Asset Mgmt & Comml Leasing)*
Charles C. Hucks *(VP-Tech)*
Advertising Agency:
Lesnik, Himmelsbach, Wilson, & Hearl (d/b/a LHWH)
3005 Hwy 17 Bypass N
Myrtle Beach, SC 29577-6742
Tel.: (843) 448-1123
Fax: (843) 626-2390

BUSCH INDUSTRIES, INC.

900 E Paris Ave SE Ste 304
Grand Rapids, MI 49546
Tel.: (616) 957-3737
Fax: (616) 957-9951
E-mail: tech@buschindustries.com
Web Site: www.buschindustries.com
Approx. Number Employees: 5
Year Founded: 1989
Business Description:
Structural Framing Management & Engineering Services
S.I.C.: 8748; 3441
N.A.I.C.S.: 541618; 332312
Media: 2-4-7-13
Distr.: Natl.
Budget Set: Feb.
Personnel:
John H. Busch *(Pres)*

BUSINESS DEVELOPMENT BANK OF CANADA

BDC Bldg 5 Pl Ville Marie Ste 400
Montreal, QC H3B 5E7, Canada
Tel.: (514) 283-5904
Fax: (514) 283-5911
Toll Free: (888) 463-6232
E-mail: info@bdc.ca
Web Site: www.bdc.ca
Approx. Int. Income: $670,920,478
Approx. Number Employees: 1,860
Year Founded: 1944
Business Description:
Banking Services
S.I.C.: 6029; 6211
N.A.I.C.S.: 522110; 523110
Media: 2-4-6-7-9-10-25
Personnel:
John A. MacNaughton *(Chm)*
Jean-Rene Halde *(Pres & CEO)*
Paul Buron *(CFO & Exec VP)*
Louise Paradis *(Sec & Sr VP-Legal Affairs)*
Edmee Metivier *(Exec VP-Fin & Consulting)*
Jacques Simoneau *(Exec VP-Investments)*
Patrice Bernard *(Sr VP-Financing & Consulting-Quebec)*
Edwin Cumby *(Sr VP-Ops-Atlantic)*
Wellington Holbrook *(Sr VP-Ops-Prairies & Western Reg)*
Mary Karamanos *(Sr VP-HR)*
Patrick Latour *(Sr VP-Financing & Consulting-Prairies)*
Peter Lawler *(Sr VP-Financing & Consulting-Ontario)*
Jerome Nycz *(Sr VP-Strategy & Corp Dev)*
Terry Quinn *(Sr VP-Financing & Consulting-Atlantic)*
Andre St. Pierre *(Sr VP-Credit Risk Mgmt)*
Paula L. Cruickshank *(VP-Security)*
France de Gaspe Beaubien *(VP-Financing & Mktg)*
Glen R. Egan *(VP-Info & Comm Technologies)*
Roger Giraldeau *(VP-Subordinate Fin)*
Danielle Landry *(VP-Subordinate Financing-Eastern Quebec)*
Susan Rohac *(VP-Subordinate Financing-Ottawa)*
Johanne Bissonnette *(Mgr-Media Rels)*

BUTLER MANUFACTURING COMPANY

(Sub. of BlueScope Steel North America Corporation)
1540 Genessee St
Kansas City, MO 64102
Mailing Address:
PO Box 419917
Kansas City, MO 64141-6917
Tel.: (816) 968-3000
Fax: (816) 968-3720
Web Site: www.butlermfg.com
Sales Range: $750-799.9 Million
Approx. Number Employees: 4,300
Year Founded: 1901
Business Description:
Mfr of Pre-Engineered Buildings, Agricultural Buildings; Aluminum Extrusion & Finishing; Skylights & General Contracting
S.I.C.: 3448; 3442
N.A.I.C.S.: 332311; 332321
Import Export
Media: 2-10-20-26
Distr.: Intl.; Natl.
Budget Set: Oct. -Nov.
Personnel:
Pat Finan *(Pres)*
Ted Wolfe *(Pres)*
Chuck Hatch *(VP & Gen Mgr)*
Richard Cliffe *(VP-HR)*
Ron Miller *(VP-Mktg)*
Dennis Hainley *(Gen Mgr)*
Lynn Hindley *(Mgr-Mktg)*
Patricia Torres *(Reg Sls Mgr-Mexico)*
Leslie Clark *(Mgr-Mktg Comm)*
Mike McQuillen *(Mgr-Buildings HR Grp)*
Craig Miller *(Mgr-Mktg Intelligence)*
Steve Shearer *(Mgr-Accts)*
Brands & Products:
AG-MASTER
AGRI-BUILDER
AMERICAN SERIES
BUILDING PROFIT
BUTLER
BUTLER ADVANTAGE
BUTLER BUILDER
BUTLER CLASSIC
BUTLER-COTE
BUTLER ELECTRONIC SPECIFICATIONS
BUTLER LITE PANL
BUTLER REFERENCE LIBRARY
BUTLERIB II
CLEAR VUE
CMR-24
DELTA
FARMSTED
FAST ROOF
FIRE LITE

Key to Media (For complete agency information see *The Advertising Red Books-Agencies* edition):
1. Bus. Publs. 2. Cable T.V. 3. Catalogs & Directories. 4. Co-op Adv. 5. Consumer Mags. 6. D.M. to Bus. Estab.7. D.M. to Consumers 8. Daily Newsp. 9. Exhibits/Trade Shows 10. Foreign 11. Infomercial 12. Internet Adv.13. Multimedia 14. Network Radio 15. Network T.V. 16. Newsp. Distr. Mags. 17. Other 18. Outdoor (Posters, Transit) 19. Point of Purchase20. Premiums, Novelties 21. Product Samples 22. Special Events Mktg. 23. Spot Radio 24. Spot T.V. 25. Weekly Newsp. 26. Yellow Page Adv.

Butler Manufacturing Company — (Continued)

FLEX-GUIDE
LANDMARK 2000
LOCK-RIVET
MONOPANL
MR-24
NATURALITE
PANL-FRAME
PANL-LINE
PANLASTIC
PRONTO
ROLL RUNNER
ROOF RUNNER
ROOF SENTRY
SCRUBOLT
SHADOWRIB
SKY-HATCH
SKY-WEB
SKYWALL
TEXTURE-COTE
THERMAL MONOPANL
TMR
VISTAWALL
VSR
WIDESPAN

Advertising Agency:
Noble
2215 W Chesterfield Blvd
Springfield, MO 65807-8650
Tel.: (417) 875-5000
Fax: (417) 875-5051
Toll Free: (800) 662-5390
— Nancy Banasik *(Acct Supvr)*

BUZZI UNICEM USA
(Branch of Buzzi Unicem USA Inc.)
10401 N Meridian St Ste 400
Indianapolis, IN 46290
Tel.: (610) 882-5000
Fax: (317) 805-3250
Web Site: www.buzziunicem.com
Approx. Number Employees: 40
Year Founded: 1919
Business Description:
Mfr. & Importer of Cement, Clinker & Ready Mixed Concrete
S.I.C.: 3241; 3273
N.A.I.C.S.: 327310; 327320
Import
Advertising Expenditures: $610,000
Media: 2-4-7-9-20
Distr.: Natl.
Budget Set: Oct.
Personnel:
Larry Hoffis *(Gen Mgr)*
Brands & Products:
AUCEM
LONESTAR

CAMBRIDGE BRASS
(Sub. of A.Y. McDonald Manufacturing Co.)
140 Orion Pl
Cambridge, ON N1R 5V1, Canada
Mailing Address:
Box 249
Cambridge, ON N1R 5V1, Canada
Tel.: (519) 621-5520
Fax: (519) 621-8674
Toll Free: (800) 724-3906
Toll Free: (800) 265-6638
E-mail: info@cbrass.com
Web Site: www.cambridgebrass.com
Approx. Number Employees: 150
Year Founded: 1905
Business Description:
Underground Pipes & Waterworks Brass Products
S.I.C.: 1629
N.A.I.C.S.: 237990
Media: 4
Personnel:
Andy Olbrycht *(Dir-Sls & Mktg)*
Brands & Products:
CAMBRIDGE BRASS

CAMP DRESSER & MCKEE INC.
1 Cambridge Pl 50 Hampshire St
Cambridge, MA 02139
Tel.: (617) 452-6000
Fax: (617) 452-8000
Web Site: www.cdm.com
Sales Range: $650-699.9 Million
Approx. Number Employees: 4,000
Year Founded: 1947
Business Description:
Civil & Environmental Engineering, Construction & Consulting Services
S.I.C.: 8711; 1629; 8748
N.A.I.C.S.: 541330; 237990; 541690
Export
Media: 2-4-10-13
Personnel:
Richard D. Fox *(Chm & CEO)*
John D. Manning *(Pres & COO)*
Robert A. Anton *(CFO & Sr VP)*
Peter F. Palmisano *(CIO & Sr VP)*
Paul R. Brown *(CMO & Exec Dir)*
William S. Howard *(CTO & Exec VP)*
Paul G. Camell *(Chief Acctg Officer & Exec VP)*
Jonathan G. Curtis *(Pres-Federal Programs)*
Paul R. Shea *(Pres-Constructors)*
James S. Lackman *(Gen Counsel & Sec)*
Stephen Kellogg *(Sr VP-Ops)*
Charlene Allen *(VP-HR)*
Marlene Hobel *(VP-Corp Comm)*
Brands & Products:
CDM
LISTEN. THINK. DELIVER.

CANADIAN ROYALTIES INC.
(Joint Venture of Jilin Horoc Nonferrous Metal Group Co., Ltd. & Goldbrook Ventures, Inc.)
2772 Chemin Sullivan
Val d'Or, QC J9P 0B9, Canada
Tel.: (819) 824-1030
Fax: (819) 824-1003
Toll Free: (866) 219-4678
E-mail: info@canadianroyalties.com
Web Site: www.canadianroyalties.com
Approx. Rev.: $36,708
Approx. Number Employees: 150
Year Founded: 2002
Business Description:
Nickel & Copper Mining Services
S.I.C.: 1021
N.A.I.C.S.: 212234
Advertising Expenditures: $583,338
Media: 10
Personnel:
Grant Arnold *(Pres & COO)*
Gail Amyot *(Mgr-Environ & Permitting)*
Advertising Agency:
Renmark Financial Communications, Inc.
1550 Metcalfe Ste 502
Montreal, QC H3A 1X6, Canada
Tel.: (514) 939-3989
Fax: (514) 939-3717

CANTEX INC.
(Sub. of Sumitomo Corporation of America)
2101 SE 1st St
Mineral Wells, TX 76067-5601
Mailing Address:
Ste 2700 301 Commerce St
Fort Worth, TX 76102-4127
Tel.: (940) 325-3344
Fax: (817) 215-7001
Web Site: www.cantexinc.com
Approx. Number Employees: 300
Business Description:
Electrical Conduit Mfr
S.I.C.: 3084
N.A.I.C.S.: 326122
Export
Advertising Expenditures: $320,000
Media: 1-2-4-7-10-20
Distr.: Natl.
Budget Set: Nov.-Dec.
Personnel:
Don Wirtanen *(Pres & COO)*
Kathy Hines *(Mgr-Mktg)*
Brands & Products:
EZBOX
FOAMCORE

CARMEUSE NORTH AMERICA
(Sub. of Carmeuse S.A.)
11 Stanwix St 21th Fl
Pittsburgh, PA 15222-1312
Tel.: (412) 995-5500
Fax: (412) 995-5570
E-mail: info@carmeusena.com
Web Site: www.carmeusena.com
Approx. Number Employees: 100
Year Founded: 1988
Business Description:
Lime & Lime Related Environmental Technologies Mfr
S.I.C.: 3274; 1422
N.A.I.C.S.: 327410; 212312
Advertising Expenditures: $1,000,000
Media: 1-2-4-7-10-20-21-22-26
Distr.: Intl.; Natl.
Budget Set: Oct.
Personnel:
Thomas Buck *(Pres & CEO)*
Bruce Inglis *(CFO)*
Patrick Worms *(CIO)*
Kevin Whyte *(Gen Counsel & VP)*
Philip Johnson *(Sr VP-Sls & Mktg)*
Aidan Connolly *(VP & Gen Mgr-Indus Sands & Engrg)*
Bruce Routhieaux *(VP-Sls)*
James Derby *(Dir-Tech)*

CAROLINA STEEL GROUP LLC
(Div. of Hirschfeld Industries, Inc.)
101 CentrePort Dr 400
Greensboro, NC 27409
Mailing Address:
PO Box 20888
Greensboro, NC 27420-0888
Tel.: (336) 275-9711
Fax: (336) 691-5801
Toll Free: (800) 632-0286
Sales Range: $100-124.9 Million
Year Founded: 1919
Business Description:
Mfr of Structural Steel
S.I.C.: 3441
N.A.I.C.S.: 332312
Import
Media: 2
Personnel:
W. H. Reeves *(Pres)*

CARPENTER TECHNOLOGY CORPORATION
P.O. Box 14662
Reading, PA 19610-1339
Mailing Address:
PO Box 14662 Bldg #L05
Reading, PA 19612-4662
Tel.: (610) 208-2000
Fax: (610) 208-3716
Toll Free: (800) 654-6543
E-mail: webmaster@cartech.com
Web Site: www.cartech.com
E-Mail For Key Personnel:
Public Relations: LMacGregor@cartech.com
Approx. Sls.: $1,675,100,000
Approx. Number Employees: 3,500
Year Founded: 1889
Business Description:
Specialty Metals & Engineered Products Mfr, Fabricator & Distr
S.I.C.: 3325; 3312
N.A.I.C.S.: 331513; 331111
Import Export
Media: 2-4-7-10-11-13
Distr.: Intl.; Natl.
Budget Set: June
Personnel:
Gregory A. Pratt *(Chm)*
William A. Wulfsohn *(Pres & CEO)*
K. Douglas Ralph *(CFO & Sr VP)*
Sanjay Guglani *(CMO & VP)*
Thomas F. Cramsey *(Chief Acctg Officer & VP)*
James D. Dee *(Gen Counsel, Sec & VP)*
Michael L. Shor *(Exec VP)*
Mark S. Kamon *(Sr VP-Specialist Alloy Ops)*
David L. Strobel *(Sr VP-Global Ops)*
Sunil Y. Widge *(Sr VP-Strategis Bus Dev & Govt Affairs)*
Andrew T. Ziolkowski *(Sr VP-Strategic Integration)*
Michael A. Hajoist *(VP-Treasury & IR)*
Bernard M. Mara *(VP-Global Advanced Engrg)*
Russell E. Reber, Jr. *(VP-Quality, Technical & Customer Svcs)*
Joseph P. O'Donnell *(Dir-Tax & Asst Treas)*
Michael C. Haney *(Asst Treas)*
Wendy K. Pulaski *(Asst Sec)*
Brands & Products:
15-15LC
20CB-3
20MO-6
302HQ-FM
304-SCQ
309 A.B.Q.
316L-SCQ
440-XH
ACEROS FORTUNA
AERMET
ALCHROME
BETA C
BIODUR
CALLTOUGH
CARPENTER
CARPENTER 20CB-3LR
CARPENTER CCM
CARPENTER GLASS SEALING 49
CARPENTER HIGH PERMEABILITY

Key to Media (For complete agency information see *The Advertising Red Books-Agencies* edition):
1. Bus. Publs. 2. Cable T.V. 3. Catalogs & Directories. 4. Co-op Adv. 5. Consumer Mags. 6. D.M. to Bus. Estab.7. D.M. to Consumers
8. Daily Newsp. 9. Exhibits/Trade Shows 10. Foreign 11. Infomercial 12. Internet Adv.13. Multimedia 14. Network Radio
15. Network T.V. 16. Newsp. Distr. Mags. 17. Other 18. Outdoor (Posters, Transit) 19. Point of Purchase20. Premiums, Novelties
21. Product Samples 22. Special Events Mktg. 23. Spot Radio 24. Spot T.V. 25. Weekly Newsp. 26. Yellow Page Adv.

CARPENTER HYMU
CARPENTER INVAR
CARPENTER LOW EXPANSION
CARPENTER NO 158
CARPENTER POWDER PRODUCTS
CARPENTER TEMPERATURE COMPENSATOR
CCM PLUS
CHROME CORE
CONSUMET
CRB-7
CUPRON
CUSTOM 275
CUSTOM 450
CUSTOM 455
CUSTOM 465
CUSTOM 475
CUSTOM AGE 625 PLUS
CUSTOMET 286-LNI
DYNAMET
ECOLUBE-ENDURAMET
ENDURAMET
EVANOHM
EXTENDO-DIE
FREE-CUT INVAR
GALL-TOUGH
HIPERCO
HIPERNOM
HY-RA
HYMU "77"
HYMU "800"
KNIGHTCOTE
MAGNEDUR
MAXAMET
MICRO-MELT
MICROMELT 440-XH
MP35N
NEUTROSORB PLUS
NIAL
NICOSEAL
NIMARK
NO. 1 JR
NO610
NO883
PROJECT 70+
PYROMET
PYROTOOL
PYROWEAR
SCF-19
SEAFAST
SEVENSTAR
SOLAR
SPEEDSTAR
STAR MAX
TALLEY
TITANIUM UL TRABAR
TOPHEL
TOPHET
TRIMRITE
VACUMET

Advertising Agency:
tomsheehan worldwide
645 Penn St
Reading, PA 19601-3408
Tel.: (610) 478-8448
Fax: (610) 478-8449
(Specialty Metals)

CASCADES, INC.

404 Marie-Victorin Blvd
PO Box 30
Kingsey Falls, QC J0A 1B0, Canada
Tel.: (819) 363-5100
Fax: (819) 363-5155
E-mail: info@cascades.com
Web Site: www.cascades.com
Approx. Sls.: $4,033,508,380
Approx. Number Employees: 12,300
Year Founded: 1964
Business Description:
Boxboard, Fine Papers, Tissue Papers, Containerboard & Specialty Products Mfr
S.I.C.: 2653; 2631; 2679; 3089
N.A.I.C.S.: 322211; 322130; 322299; 326199
Advertising Expenditures: $47,830
Media: 2-9-25
Personnel:
Laurent Lemaire *(Chm)*
Alain Lemaire *(Pres & CEO)*
Allan Hogg *(CFO & VP)*
Mario Plourde *(COO)*
Luc Langevin *(Pres/COO-Specialty Products Grp)*
Hubert Bolduc *(VP-Comm & Pub Affairs)*
Christine Beaulieu *(Dir-Corp Comm)*
Didier Filion *(Dir-IR)*
Walter Hudson *(Dir-Natl Accts)*
Steve Hicknell *(Sls Mgr)*
Perry Pike *(Sls Mgr-Natl Accts)*
Daniele Seguin *(Sls Mgr-Quebec-Atlantic Provinces)*
Martin Taillon *(Sls Mgr)*
Johanne Fournier *(Mgr-Customer Svc)*
Brands & Products:
ARCTIKOAT
CASCADES
DELI-TRAY
ENVIRO
GREEN BY NATURE
JENSON
MICROCYCLE
NORAMPAC
ORFORD
PLASTICHANGE
PRO-ZORB
SUPERCYCLE
SYLVACYCLE
SYLVATECH
Advertising Agency:
Nurun Inc.
711 De La Commune St W
Montreal, QC H3C 1X6, Canada
Tel.: (514) 392-1900
Fax: (514) 392-0911
Toll Free: (877) 696-1292

CATTUS PET SUPPLIES, INC.

(Div. of 123 Staffing, Inc.)
5647 Springfield Avenue
Gillette, NJ 07992
Tel.: (908) 555-1212
Sales Range: $150-199.9 Million
Year Founded: 2002
Business Description:
Pet Grooming Supplies & Accessories
S.I.C.: 5999
N.A.I.C.S.: 453910
Advertising Expenditures: $800,000
D.M. to Consumers: $200,000; Product Samples: $600,000
Personnel:
Nancy Smith *(Pres)*
Julie Drew *(CEO)*

CAVCO INDUSTRIES, INC.

1001 N Central Ave Ste 800
Phoenix, AZ 85004-1962
Tel.: (602) 256-6263
Fax: (602) 256-6189
E-mail: info@cavco.com
Web Site: www.cavco.com
Approx. Sls.: $171,827,000
Approx. Number Employees: 2,450
Year Founded: 1998
Business Description:
Producer of Manufactured Housing
S.I.C.: 2451; 5271
N.A.I.C.S.: 321991; 453930
Export
Advertising Expenditures: $241,000
Media: 10-22
Personnel:
Joseph H. Stegmayer *(Chm, Pres & CEO)*
Daniel L. Urness *(CFO, Treas & VP)*
James P. Glew *(Gen Counsel & Sec)*
Brands & Products:
CAVCO HOMES
FLEETWOOD HOMES
NATIONWIDE HOMES
PALM HARBOR HOMES,

CECO DOOR PRODUCTS

(Sub. of Assa Abloy AB)
9159 Telecom Dr
Milan, TN 38358
Tel.: (731) 686-8345
Fax: (731) 686-4211
Toll Free: (800) 232-6834
E-mail: cecomarketing@cecodoor.com
Web Site: www.cecodoor.com
Approx. Number Employees: 500
Year Founded: 1912
Business Description:
Mfr. of Side-Hinged Door Systems for Commercial, Industrial & Residential Applications
S.I.C.: 3442; 2431
N.A.I.C.S.: 332321; 321911
Export
Advertising Expenditures: $7,000,000
Bus. Publs.: $3,500,000; Exhibits/Trade Shows: $3,500,000
Distr.: Natl.
Budget Set: Jan.
Personnel:
Jim Sabella *(Mgr-Mktg)*
Brands & Products:
ARMOR SHIELD
COLORTSYLE
ELECTROLYNX
FUEGO
IMPERIAL
KHEMPRO
LEGION
MADERA
MEDALLION
OMEGA
REGENT
RESTRICTDOR
SMOKE TECH
SOUND TECH
STAINLESS TECH
STORMPRO 320
STORMPRO 361
THRULITE
ULTRADOR
VERSADOOR

CEDAR SHAKE & SHINGLE BUREAU

No 2 7101 Horne St
Mission, BC V2V 7A2, Canada
Tel.: (604) 820-7700
Fax: (604) 820-0266
E-mail: info@cedarbureau.com
Web Site: www.cedarbureau.org
E-Mail For Key Personnel:
Marketing Director: lynne@cedarbureau.com
Sales Range: $10-24.9 Million
Approx. Number Employees: 10
Year Founded: 1915
Business Description:
Certi-Label Cedar Roofing & Sidewall Products
S.I.C.: 2499; 2421; 2449
N.A.I.C.S.: 321999; 321113; 321920
Media: 2-6-8-10-16-21-23
Distr.: Natl.
Budget Set: Jan.-Dec.
Personnel:
Lynne Christensen *(Dir-Ops)*
Tony Bonura *(Mgr)*
Peter Parmenter *(Mgr)*

CEMEX, INC.

(Sub. of CEMEX, S.A.B. de C.V.)
840 Gessner Ste 1400
Houston, TX 77024
Tel.: (713) 650-6200
Fax: (713) 653-6815
Web Site: www.cemexusa.com
Approx. Number Employees: 4,100
Year Founded: 1930
Business Description:
Cement, Concrete Products, Construction Aggregates & Specialty Minerals Mfr
S.I.C.: 3273; 3271
N.A.I.C.S.: 327320; 327331
Advertising Expenditures: $200,000
Media: 2-10
Distr.: Reg.
Budget Set: Sept. -Oct.
Personnel:
Gilberto Perezalonso Cifuentes *(Pres-Ops-CEMEX-US)*
Leslie S. White *(Gen Counsel & Exec VP)*
Robert Craddock *(Exec VP-Comml)*

CENTRAL STEEL & WIRE COMPANY

3000 W 51st St
Chicago, IL 60632-2122
Tel.: (773) 471-3800
Fax: (800) 232-9279
Toll Free: (800) 621-8510
E-mail: csw@centralsteel.com
Web Site: www.centralsteel.com
Approx. Number Employees: 300
Year Founded: 1909
Business Description:
Mfr. & Distributor of Processed & Unprocessed Ferrous & Nonferrous Metals
S.I.C.: 5051
N.A.I.C.S.: 423510
Media: 2-4-7-10
Distr.: Natl.
Budget Set: Sept. -Nov.
Personnel:
Michael X. Cronin *(Chm & CEO)*
Ronald V. Kazmar *(CFO, Treas & VP)*

CENTRIA ARCHITECTURAL SYSTEMS

(Div. of CENTRIA, Inc.)
1005 Beaver Grade Rd
Moon Township, PA 15108
Tel.: (412) 299-8000
Fax: (412) 299-8038
Toll Free: (800) 759-7474
E-mail: info@centria.com
Web Site: www.centria.com/CAS/default.aspx

Key to Media (For complete agency information see *The Advertising Red Books-Agencies* edition):
1. Bus. Publs. 2. Cable T.V. 3. Catalogs & Directories. 4. Co-op Adv. 5. Consumer Mags. 6. D.M. to Bus. Estab.7. D.M. to Consumers 8. Daily Newsp. 9. Exhibits/Trade Shows 10. Foreign 11. Infomercial 12. Internet Adv.13. Multimedia 14. Network Radio 15. Network T.V. 16. Newsp. Distr. Mags. 17. Other 18. Outdoor (Posters, Transit) 19. Point of Purchase20. Premiums, Novelties 21. Product Samples 22. Special Events Mktg. 23. Spot Radio 24. Spot T.V. 25. Weekly Newsp. 26. Yellow Page Adv.

CENTRIA Architectural Systems — (Continued)

Business Description:
Custom-Engineered Architectural Metal Enclosure Systems Mfr
S.I.C.: 3444; 1761
N.A.I.C.S.: 332322; 238160
Media: 10
Personnel:
Rick Brow *(Dir-Mktg)*

CENTRIA, INC.

1005 Beaver Grade Rd
Moon Township, PA 15108-2964
Tel.: (412) 299-8000
Fax: (412) 299-8317
Toll Free: (888) 265-4084
E-mail: info@centria.com
Web Site: www.centria.com
Approx. Number Employees: 100
Year Founded: 1996
Business Description:
Mfr. of Metal Clad Building Materials, Wall & Roof Panels, Industrial Ventilation Equipment
S.I.C.: 3444; 1761
N.A.I.C.S.: 332322; 238160
Import Export
Media: 2-7-10-17-26
Distr.: Natl.
Budget Set: Nov.
Personnel:
Mark Sherwin *(Pres)*
Rick Mowrey *(Dir-Mktg-Bus Dev)*
Brands & Products:
THE BETTER ROOF
CONCEPT SERIES
CURVED SRS
DIMENSION SERIES
DURACAST
DURAGARD
DURALLURE
ECONOLAP
FLUOROFINISH
FORMABOND
FORMAVUE
FORMAWALL
Q-FLOOR
STYLE-RIB
SUPER-RIB
TAPROUTE
VERSACOR
VERSAPANEL
VERSAWALL
Advertising Agency:
The Lauerer Markin Group, Inc.
1700 Woodlands Dr
Maumee, OH 43537-4043
Tel.: (419) 893-2500
Fax: (419) 893-1050
Toll Free: (800) 535-3212

CENTURY ALUMINUM OF WEST VIRGINIA, INC.

(Sub. of Century Aluminum Company)
PO Box 98
Ravenswood, WV 26164-0098
Tel.: (304) 273-7322
Fax: (304) 273-7479
Web Site:
www.centuryaluminum.com/electrical_electronic_maintainers.html
Sales Range: $350-399.9 Million
Approx. Number Employees: 750
Year Founded: 1955
Business Description:
Aluminum Mfr
S.I.C.: 3334; 3354
N.A.I.C.S.: 331312; 331316
Import Export
Media: 4-9-14-15-17
Distr.: Natl.

CENTURY FENCE COMPANY

1300 Hickory St
Pewaukee, WI 53072-5505
Mailing Address:
PO Box 727
Waukesha, WI 53072
Tel.: (262) 547-3331
Fax: (262) 691-3463
Toll Free: (800) 558-0507
E-mail: sales@centuryfence.com
Web Site: www.centuryfence.com
E-Mail For Key Personnel:
Sales Director: sales@centuryfence.com
Approx. Number Employees: 100
Year Founded: 1917
Business Description:
Chain Link Fence & Gates; Steel Beam Guard Rail; Athletic Back Stops & Tennis Courts; Interstate Highway Fencing & Signing; Traffic Pavement Markings
S.I.C.: 1799; 1721
N.A.I.C.S.: 238990; 238320
Media: 2-4-7-8-10-18-24-26
Distr.: Direct to Consumer; Reg.
Personnel:
A.W. Bryant *(Chm)*
John Connell *(Pres)*
Brands & Products:
CENTURY FENCE

CERTAINTEED CORPORATION

(Sub. of Saint-Gobain Corporation)
750 E Swedesford Rd
Valley Forge, PA 19482
Mailing Address:
PO Box 860
Valley Forge, PA 19482-0860
Tel.: (610) 341-7000
Fax: (610) 341-7777
Toll Free: (800) 233-8990
Telex: 845263
E-mail: corporate@certainteed.com
Web Site: www.certainteed.com
Sales Range: $1-4.9 Billion
Approx. Number Employees: 7,000
Year Founded: 1904
Business Description:
Insulation Products; Solid Vinyl Siding & Windows; Asphalt Roofing Materials; Polymerization; PVC Pipe; Clay Roof Tiles; Ventilation Products; Fiber Glass Reinforcements; PVC Fencing, Deck & Railing, Retractable Awning & Canopy Systems, Siding Mfr
S.I.C.: 3221; 3299
N.A.I.C.S.: 327213; 327999
Import Export
Media: 2-3-4-5-6-7-9-10-14-15-19-21-23-24-25-26
Distr.: Natl.
Budget Set: Aug. -Sept.
Personnel:
John Crowe *(Pres)*
Peter Dachowski *(CEO)*
Robert Panaro *(CFO, VP-Fin & Controller-Auster)*
Lynn E. Price *(VP & CIO)*
Mark Rayfield *(Pres-Siding Products Grp)*
Tom Smith *(Pres-CertainTeed Roofing)*
Tim Feagans *(Sr VP & Gen Counsel)*
Shawn Puccio *(Sr VP-Fin)*
Paul Batt *(Dir-Product Mktg)*
Monica Brogan *(Mgr-Sls Support & Corp Mktg)*
Brands & Products:
HORIZON SHANGLE
INDEPENDENCE SHANGLE
INSUL-SAFE
INSUL SAFE III
YELOMINE

CF ULTRA TECH

(Div. of Construction Forms, Inc.)
777 Maritime Dr
Port Washington, WI 53074-0308
Mailing Address:
PO Box 308
Port Washington, WI 53074-0308
Tel.: (262) 284-7800
Fax: (262) 284-7878
Toll Free: (800) 223-3676
Web Site: www.conforms.com
Approx. Number Employees: 150
Business Description:
Concrete Pumping Systems & Accessories
S.I.C.: 3498
N.A.I.C.S.: 332996
Media: 2-4-6-8-10-11-19-21-26
Personnel:
Alan J. Kastelic *(Pres)*

CGC INC.

(Holding of USG Corporation)
350 Burnhamthorpe Rd W Fl 5
Mississauga, ON L5B 3J1, Canada
Mailing Address:
P.O. Box 4034, Terminal A
Toronto, ON M5W 1K8, Canada
Tel.: (905) 803-5600
Fax: (905) 803-5688
Toll Free: (800) 565-6607
Web Site: www.cgcinc.com
Approx. Sls.: $400,000,000
Approx. Number Employees: 50
Year Founded: 1907
Business Description:
Gypsum Board, Compounds, Vinyl Covered Gypsum, Lath, Plaster, Industrial Gypsum, Interior & Exterior Cement Board Mfr; Ceiling Grid; Acoustical Ceiling Tile Marketer
S.I.C.: 3275
N.A.I.C.S.: 327420
Import Export
Media: 1-2-4-5-7-10-19-20-21-22
Distr.: Natl.
Personnel:
William C. Foote *(Chm & CEO-USG Corp)*
Christopher R. Griffin *(Chm)*
James S. Metcalf *(Pres & COO-USG Corp)*
Christopher Macey *(Pres)*
Rick D. Lowes *(CFO, Treas & VP & Sr VP-Bus Dev-USG Corp)*
Brands & Products:
ASTRO CLIMAPLUS
AURATONE
COMPASSO
DONN
READY-TEX
SYNKO

CH2M HILL COMPANIES, LTD.

9191 S Jamaica St
Englewood, CO 80112
Tel.: (720) 286-2000
Fax: (720) 286-9250
Toll Free: (888) 242-6445
E-mail: feedback@ch2m.com
Web Site: www.ch2m.com
Approx. Rev.: $5,422,801,000
Approx. Number Employees: 23,000
Year Founded: 1946
Business Description:
Engineering, Planning, Economics, Construction Operations & Management Services
S.I.C.: 8711; 4953
N.A.I.C.S.: 541330; 562920
Media: 2-7-10-13-22
Personnel:
Lee A. McIntire *(Chm & CEO)*
John Quarendon *(Mng Dir)*
Gabriel Ruiz *(Mng Dir)*
Michael A. Lucki *(CFO & Sr VP)*
John Madia *(Chief HR Officer & Sr VP)*
Joann Shea *(VP & Chief Acctng Officer)*
Robert G. Card *(Pres-Facilities & Infrastructure Div & Sr VP-Ops)*
Robert W. Bailey *(Pres-Water Bus Grp)*
Mark Fallon *(Pres-Nuclear Bus Grp)*
Samuel H. Iapalucci *(Sec & Exec VP)*
Gregory McIntire *(Sr VP & Dir-Commun Grp)*
David W. Miller *(Sr VP & Dir-Strategic Initiatives)*
Bob Allen *(Sr VP-Exec Leadership)*
Garry M. Higdem *(Sr VP-Ops)*
John Polcyn *(Sr VP)*
Nancy R. Tuor *(Grp VP)*
Robert H. Griffin *(VP & Global Program Mgr)*
Richard Campbell *(VP-Engrg Tech)*
Ed Aromi *(Dir-Bus Dev Lead)*
John Corsi *(Dir-Corp Comm)*
William T. Dehn *(Dir-Risk Mgmt)*
Jonathan Harris *(Dir)*
Jeff Mack *(Dir-Construction Mgmt-Transportation Grp)*
Diana Bjornskov *(Mgr-Mktg)*
Joseph Cazares *(Mgr)*
Advertising Agency:
CH2M
(House Agency)
6060 S. Willow Dr.
Greenwood Village, CO 80111-5142
Tel.: (303) 713-2435

THE CHAMBERLAIN GROUP, INC.

(Sub. of Duchossois Industries, Inc.)
845 N Larch Ave
Elmhurst, IL 60126-1114
Tel.: (630) 279-3600
Fax: (630) 530-6091
Toll Free: (800) 282-6225
E-mail: help@chamberlaingroup.com
Web Site: www.chamberlain.com
Approx. Number Employees: 4,000
Business Description:
Mfr of Garage Door Openers, Commercial Door & Gate Operators, Telephone Entry Systems & Access Control Systems
S.I.C.: 3699
N.A.I.C.S.: 335999
Export
Media: 2-3-4-5-6-7-8-9-10-11-14-15-20-23-25-26

Key to Media (For complete agency information see *The Advertising Red Books-Agencies* edition):
1. Bus. Publs. 2. Cable T.V. 3. Catalogs & Directories. 4. Co-op Adv. 5. Consumer Mags. 6. D.M. to Bus. Estab.7. D.M. to Consumers 8. Daily Newsp. 9. Exhibits/Trade Shows 10. Foreign 11. Infomercial 12. Internet Adv.13. Multimedia 14. Network Radio 15. Network T.V. 16. Newsp. Distr. Mags. 17. Other 18. Outdoor (Posters, Transit) 19. Point of Purchase20. Premiums, Novelties 21. Product Samples 22. Special Events Mktg. 23. Spot Radio 24. Spot T.V. 25. Weekly Newsp. 26. Yellow Page Adv.

Distr.: Intl.; Natl.
Budget Set: Sept.
Personnel:
Mark Karasek *(CTO & Exec VP-Engrg)*
Sarah S. Anderson *(VP-Mktg Comm & Customer Care)*
Sandy Scherschel *(VP-Sls & Mktg)*
Jenny Newman *(Mgr-HR)*
Brands & Products:
CHAMBERLAIN
CHAMBERLAIN AND WHISPER DRIVE
ELITE
LIFTMASTER
SENTEX
Advertising Agency:
Marketing Support, Inc.
200 E Randolph Dr Ste 5000
Chicago, IL 60601
Tel.: (312) 565-0044
Fax: (312) 946-6100

CHAMPION ENTERPRISES HOLDINGS, LLC
(Joint Venture of Bain Capital, LLC & Centerbridge Partners, L.P.)
(Filed Ch 11 Bankruptcy #914019 on 11/15/09 in U.S. Bankruptcy Ct, Dist of DE, Wilmington)
755 W Big Beaver Rd Ste 1000
Troy, MI 48084
Tel.: (248) 614-8200
Fax: (248) 273-4208
Web Site: www.championhomes.net
Approx. Sls.: $1,033,193,000
Approx. Number Employees: 4,100
Year Founded: 1953
Business Description:
Holding Company; Owned by Centerbridge Partners L.P., MAK Capital Fund LP & Sankaty Advisors LLC.
S.I.C.: 2451; 5271; 6719
N.A.I.C.S.: 321991; 453930; 551112
Advertising Expenditures: $4,200,000
Media: 4-6-7-8-9-18
Distr.: Natl.
Budget Set: Jan.
Personnel:
Phyllis A. Knight *(CFO)*
Roger K. Scholten *(Gen Counsel & Sr VP)*

CHASE ROYSTON LABORATORIES
(Div. of Chase Corporation)
201 Zeta Dr
Pittsburgh, PA 15238
Tel.: (412) 828-1500
Fax: (412) 828-4826
Toll Free: (800) 245-3209
E-mail: royston@chasecorp.com
Web Site: www.roystonlab.com
Sales Range: $10-24.9 Million
Approx. Number Employees: 43
Year Founded: 1940
Business Description:
Corrosion Control Products Mfr
S.I.C.: 2821; 2899
N.A.I.C.S.: 325211; 325998
Export
Media: 2-4-7-10-11-20-21
Distr.: Intl.; Natl.
Personnel:
Doug Zuberer *(Dir-Highway & Architectural Products Mfg)*
Brands & Products:
CEVA
CEVA CRETE
EASY PAVE
EVA-POX
EVAZOTE
HANDY CAP IP IP
HANDY CAP XL IP
PLASTAZOTE
ROSPHALT RX
ROYAL-GARD
TAPECOAT

CHEROKEE BRICK & TILE COMPANY
3250 Waterville Rd
Macon, GA 31206-1246
Mailing Address:
PO Box 4567
Macon, GA 31208-4567
Tel.: (478) 781-6800
Fax: (478) 781-8964
Web Site: www.cherokeebrick.com/
Approx. Number Employees: 250
Year Founded: 1908
Business Description:
Bricks Mfr
S.I.C.: 3251; 3255
N.A.I.C.S.: 327121; 327124
Advertising Expenditures: $600,000
Media: 2-4-9-10-21-23-26
Distr.: Reg.
Personnel:
Kenneth D. Sams *(Owner)*
Mike Peavy *(Pres)*
Carl Capps *(CFO)*
Brands & Products:
AUTUMN SMOKE
BEAUMONT
COVINGTON
GEORGIAN MAROON
MELROSE
MOSSTOWN
NACHEZ
OXFORD
PROVIDENCE
SAVANNAH
ST. JAMES
STRATTON
WINDSOR

CHICAGO BRIDGE & IRON COMPANY
(Sub. of Chicago Bridge & Iron Company N.V.)
2103 Research Forest Dr
The Woodlands, TX 77380-1123
Tel.: (832) 513-1600
Fax: (832) 513-1605
E-mail: media-relations@cbi.com
Web Site: www.cbi.com/contact-us/worldwide-locations
Sales Range: $1-4.9 Billion
Approx. Number Employees: 300
Business Description:
Holding Company; Corporate Administrative Office
S.I.C.: 6719; 9131
N.A.I.C.S.: 551112; 551114; 921140
Media: 2-10-13
Personnel:
Mario Valaperta *(VP & Area Dir-Fin-Western Hemisphere)*
Jan Sieving *(Dir-Corp Comm)*
Brands & Products:
CHICAGO BRIDGE AND IRON

CHILDERS CARPORTS AND STRUCTURES, INC.
11711 Brittmoore Pk Dr
Houston, TX 77041-6923
Tel.: (713) 460-2181
Fax: (713) 460-2566
E-mail: salesccsi@childersonline.com
Web Site: www.childersonline.com
E-Mail For Key Personnel:
Sales Director: salesccsi@childersonline.com
Approx. Sls.: $3,000,000
Approx. Number Employees: 23
Year Founded: 1947
Business Description:
Pre-engineered Structures, Canopies & Walkway Covers
S.I.C.: 3448; 3444
N.A.I.C.S.: 332311; 332322
Media: 2-8-10-21-26
Distr.: Natl.
Budget Set: Nov.-Dec.
Personnel:
Tod M. Babin *(Pres)*
Brands & Products:
CHILDERS

CHRONOMITE LABORATORIES, INC.
(Affil. of Acorn Engineering Company, Inc.)
1420 W 240th St
Harbor City, CA 90710-1307
Tel.: (626) 937-4270
Fax: (310) 530-1381
Toll Free: (800) 447-4962
E-mail: info@chronomite.com
Web Site: www.chronomite.com
Approx. Number Employees: 30
Year Founded: 1967
Business Description:
Mfr. of Energy Conservation Products
S.I.C.: 3822; 8733
N.A.I.C.S.: 334512; 541710
Export
Media: 1-2-4-7-10-13-18-19-20-21
Distr.: Intl.; Natl.
Brands & Products:
INSTANT-FLOW
INSTANT TEMP

CIRCOR INTERNATIONAL, INC.
Ste 130 25 Corporate Dr
Burlington, MA 01803-4238
Tel.: (781) 270-1200
Fax: (781) 270-1299
Web Site: www.circor.com
Approx. Rev.: $685,910,000
Approx. Number Employees: 2,950
Business Description:
Designs, Manufactures & Supplies Valves & Related Products & Services
S.I.C.: 3494; 1711; 3491; 3492
N.A.I.C.S.: 332919; 238220; 332911; 332912
Advertising Expenditures: $1,900,000
Personnel:
A. William Higgins *(Chm, Pres & CEO)*
Frederic M. Burditt *(CFO, Treas & VP)*
Richard A. Broughton *(CIO & VP)*
Steve Cartolano *(VP-Bus Dev & Strategy-CIRCOR Aerospace Products Grp)*
Susan M. McCuaig *(VP-HR)*
Alan J. Glass *(Asst Sec)*
Brands & Products:
CIRCOR
KF TELFORD
SSI EQUIPMENT

CLARK DOOR CO., INC.
(Sub. of Coldmatic Products International LLC)
2564 Metro Blvd
Maryland Heights, MO 63043-2417
Tel.: (314) 432-3112
Fax: (314) 432-2296
Toll Free: (800) 278-0090
Web Site: www.coldmatic.com
Approx. Number Employees: 125
Year Founded: 1933
Business Description:
Automatic Doors; Shock Absorber; Fire Doors; Door Covering; Cold Storage & Fire Door Combination Mfr
S.I.C.: 5031; 3442
N.A.I.C.S.: 423310; 332321
Media: 1-2-4-7-8-10-11-19-20-26
Distr.: Intl.; Natl.
Budget Set: Jan.
Brands & Products:
FIRECHIEF
FIREMAN

CLARK GRAVE VAULT COMPANY
375 E 5th Ave
Columbus, OH 43201-2819
Tel.: (614) 294-3761
Fax: (614) 299-2324
Toll Free: (800) 848-3570
Web Site: www.clarkvault.com
Approx. Number Employees: 150
Year Founded: 1898
Business Description:
Carbon/Galvanized Steel, Copper Grave & Urn Vaults Mfr
S.I.C.: 3995; 3316
N.A.I.C.S.: 339995; 331221
Media: 1-2-6-8-10-16-18
Distr.: Direct to Consumer; Natl.
Budget Set: Nov.
Personnel:
Douglas A. Beck *(VP-Sls & Mktg)*
Mark A. Beck *(Plant Mgr)*
Brands & Products:
CLARK

CLEAVER-BROOKS
11950 W Lk Park Dr
Milwaukee, WI 53201-0421
Tel.: (414) 359-0600
Fax: (414) 438-4930
Web Site: www.cleaver-brooks.com
E-Mail For Key Personnel:
Marketing Director: wgoggins@aqua-chem.com
Approx. Number Employees: 1,000
Year Founded: 1931
Business Description:
Packaged Boilers, Burners, Steam Boilers & Heating Equipment
S.I.C.: 3559
N.A.I.C.S.: 332410
Export
Advertising Expenditures: $1,000,000
Media: 1-2-4-5-7-10-11-20-26
Distr.: Intl.; Natl.
Budget Set: Apr.
Personnel:
David M. Tenniswood *(Chm)*
Welch Goggins *(Pres & CEO)*

Key to Media (For complete agency information see *The Advertising Red Books-Agencies* edition):
1. Bus. Publs. 2. Cable T.V. 3. Catalogs & Directories. 4. Co-op Adv. 5. Consumer Mags. 6. D.M. to Bus. Estab.7. D.M. to Consumers
8. Daily Newsp. 9. Exhibits/Trade Shows 10. Foreign 11. Infomercial 12. Internet Adv.13. Multimedia 14. Network Radio
15. Network T.V. 16. Newsp. Distr. Mags. 17. Other 18. Outdoor (Posters, Transit) 19. Point of Purchase20. Premiums, Novelties
21. Product Samples 22. Special Events Mktg. 23. Spot Radio 24. Spot T.V. 25. Weekly Newsp. 26. Yellow Page Adv.

Cleaver-Brooks — (Continued)

Robert St-Denis *(Pres-Engineered Boiler Systems)*
John M. Bodish *(Exec VP-Ops)*

CLESTRA HAUSERMAN, INC.
(Sub. of Clestra Hauserman S.A.)
259 Veterans Ln Ste 201
Doylestown, PA 18901
Tel.: (267) 880-3700
Fax: (267) 880-3705
E-mail: clestra.usa@clestra.com
Web Site: www.clestra.com
Approx. Sls.: $30,000,000
Approx. Number Employees: 14
Year Founded: 1990
Business Description:
Movable Walls & Partitions Mfr, Designer & Installer
S.I.C.: 1799
N.A.I.C.S.: 238990
Import
Media: 4-6-10-21
Distr.: Intl.; Natl.
Personnel:
David R. Harkins, Jr. *(COO)*
Brands & Products:
CINERRIO H-LINE
CINERRIO I-LINE
DESIGNER WALL
DOUBLE WALL
FACILITY WALL
KNOLL WAUBY CLESTRA HAUSERMAN
READY WALL
ULTRAMOVABLE

CLOPAY BUILDING PRODUCTS COMPANY
(Sub. of Clopay Corporation)
8585 Duke Blvd
Mason, OH 45040
Tel.: (513) 770-4800
Fax: (513) 770-3863
Toll Free: (800) 282-2260
E-mail: info@clopaydoor.com
Web Site: www.clopaydoor.com
E-Mail For Key Personnel:
Marketing Director: plohse@clopay.com
Sales Director: jpalazzolo@clopay.com
Approx. Sls.: $700,000,000
Approx. Number Employees: 225
Year Founded: 1859
Business Description:
Garage Doors Mfr, Sells Building Materials
S.I.C.: 2431; 3442
N.A.I.C.S.: 321911; 332321
Import Export
Advertising Expenditures: $7,000,000
Media: 1-2-3-4-5-6-10-19-20-21
Distr.: Intl.; Natl.
Budget Set: June
Personnel:
John Palazzolo *(Sr VP-Sls)*
Mark Westerfield *(Dir-Product Dev)*
Justin Evans *(Product Mgr-Retail)*
Brands & Products:
CLOPAY
HOLMES
IDEAL DOOR
Advertising Agency:
Empower MediaMarketing
(MEDIA THAT WORKS)
1111 Saint Gregory St
Cincinnati, OH 45202
Tel.: (513) 871-9454
Fax: (513) 871-1804

CLUNE CONSTRUCTION CO.
10 S La Salle St Ste 300
Chicago, IL 60603-1095
Tel.: (312) 726-6103
Fax: (312) 419-8139
E-mail: info@clunegc.com
Web Site: www.clunegc.com
Approx. Sls.: $175,000,000
Approx. Number Employees: 100
Year Founded: 1956
Business Description:
Provider of Construction Management & Consulting Services
S.I.C.: 8711; 8748
N.A.I.C.S.: 541330; 541618
Media: 7
Personnel:
Michael T. Clune *(Chm & CEO)*
Emmett Glynn *(Mng Dir & CFO)*
Karen Mari *(Sr VP)*

CLYDE COMPANIES INC.
730N 1500 W
Orem, UT 84057
Tel.: (801) 802-6900
Fax: (801) 802-0733
Web Site: www.clydeinc.com
Sales Range: $600-649.9 Million
Approx. Number Employees: 2,000
Year Founded: 1998
Business Description:
Highway & Street Construction
S.I.C.: 1622; 5031
N.A.I.C.S.: 237310; 423310
Personnel:
Wilford C. Clyde *(Pres)*
Don McGee *(VP-Fin)*
John Young *(VP)*
Kay Hermansen *(Dir-Corp Comm)*
Advertising Agency:
Penna Powers Brian Haynes
1706 S Major St
Salt Lake City, UT 84115
Tel.: (801) 487-4800
Fax: (801) 487-0707
Toll Free: (800) 409-9346

CO-EX CORP.
(Sub. of Bayer Corporation)
5 Alexander Dr
Wallingford, CT 06492-2429
Tel.: (203) 679-0500
Fax: (203) 679-0600
Toll Free: (800) 888-5364
E-mail: info@co-excorp.com
Web Site: www.co-excorp.com
Approx. Number Employees: 9
Year Founded: 1988
Business Description:
Plastics Sheets & Rods Mfr
S.I.C.: 5162
N.A.I.C.S.: 424610
Media: 10
Personnel:
Kurt Glaser *(Mng Dir)*
Mike Johnson *(Mng Dir)*
Cynthia Siniscalco *(CFO)*
Janice Pravorne *(Mgr-Horticultural Segment)*
Brands & Products:
MACROLUX

COGENIC, LLC
405 Lyell Ave
Rochester, NY 14606
Tel.: (585) 458-7000
Fax: (585) 458-8262
E-mail: info@cogenicllc.com
Web Site: www.cogenicllc.com
Approx. Number Employees: 30
Year Founded: 1949
Business Description:
General & Mechanical Commercial Contracting
S.I.C.: 1796; 1711
N.A.I.C.S.: 238290; 238220
Media: 2-7-13
Personnel:
Joseph Lancaster *(Pres)*
Freddy Ramos *(Gen Mgr-Mechanical-NJ)*

COLD SPRING GRANITE COMPANY
17482 Granite W Rd
Cold Spring, MN 56320-2508
Tel.: (320) 685-3621
Fax: (320) 685-8490
Toll Free: (800) 328-5040
Web Site: www.coldspringgranite.com
E-Mail For Key Personnel:
Marketing Director: marketing@coldspringgranite.com
Sales Range: $500-549.9 Million
Approx. Number Employees: 1,420
Year Founded: 1898
Business Description:
Dimensional Stone Mfr for the Construction Industry, Stone Products for the Memorial Industry, Stone Tile & Interior Products
S.I.C.: 3281; 1741
N.A.I.C.S.: 327991; 238140
Import Export
Advertising Expenditures: $500,000
Bus. Publs.: $50,000; Consumer Mags.: $200,000; D.M. to Bus. Estab.: $50,000; D.M. to Consumers: $50,000; Exhibits/Trade Shows: $100,000; Product Samples: $50,000
Distr.: Intl.; Natl.
Budget Set: Dec.
Personnel:
Patrick Alexander *(Chm & CEO)*
John Mattke *(Pres & COO)*
Dan Rea *(Sr VP-Comml Grp)*
Greg Flint *(VP-Ops & Strategy)*
Brands & Products:
A BETTER WAY...
COLD SPRING
COLD SPRING GRANITE
GRANIT BRONZ
PRIVATE ESTATES
ROYAL MELROSE

COMMERCIAL METALS COMPANY
6565 N MacArthur Blvd Ste 800
Irving, TX 75039
Mailing Address:
PO Box 1046
Dallas, TX 75221-1046
Tel.: (214) 689-4300
Fax: (214) 689-5886
E-mail: debbie.okle@cmc.com
Web Site:
www.commercialmetals.com
E-Mail For Key Personnel:
Public Relations: dokle@commercialmetals.com
Approx. Sls.: $6,306,102,000
Approx. Number Employees: 11,558
Year Founded: 1915
Business Description:
Steel, Metal Products & Related Materials Mfr, Recycler & Marketer
S.I.C.: 5051; 3312; 4953; 5093
N.A.I.C.S.: 423510; 331111; 423930; 562920
Import Export
Media: 2-20-26
Distr.: Natl.
Budget Set: June
Personnel:
Murray R. McClean *(Chm & CEO)*
Joseph Alvarado *(Pres & COO)*
Barbara R. Smith *(CFO & Sr VP)*
Tracy Nolan *(CIO & VP)*
Joseph R. Reichard *(Chief Engrg Officer)*
Hanns Zoellner *(Pres-CMC Intl & Exec VP)*
Tracy L. Porter *(Pres-CMC Americas Div & Sr VP)*
Ann J. Bruder *(Gen Counsel, Sec & Sr VP-Law, Govt Affairs & Global Trade)*
Binh Huynh *(Exec VP)*
James B. Alleman *(Sr VP-HR & Org Dev)*
Devesh Sharma *(Sr VP-Bus Dev & Bus Processes)*
Manny Rosenfeld *(VP & Dir-Internal Audit)*
Jim Forkovitch *(Gen Mgr)*
Debbie Okle *(Dir-PR)*
Jimmy R. Hodges *(Asst Controller)*
Advertising Agency:
Premisa
Heinzelova 62a
10 000
Zagreb, Croatia
Tel.: (385) 1 23 57 800
Fax: (385) 1 6180 336

CONSOLIDATED STORAGE COMPANIES, INC.
(Sub. of Capital Resource Partners)
(d/b/a Equipto)
225 Main St
Tatamy, PA 18085
Tel.: (610) 253-2775
Fax: (888) 859-2121
Toll Free: (800) 323-0801
E-mail: info@equipto.com
Web Site: www.equipto.com
Approx. Number Employees: 160
Year Founded: 1907
Business Description:
Wire & Steel Shelving & Racks, Benches, Store Fixtures, Lockers, Drawers, Cabinets, Mobile Aisle, Mezzanine & Carts Mfr
S.I.C.: 2519
N.A.I.C.S.: 337125
Media: 2-4-13
Distr.: Natl.
Budget Set: Nov.
Brands & Products:
CENTURY CONTAINERS
DESIGNLINE
EQUIPTO
EQUIPTOFLEX
IRON GRIP
LITTLE GEM
V-GRIP
ZIP-IN

Key to Media (For complete agency information see *The Advertising Red Books-Agencies* edition):
1. Bus. Publs. 2. Cable T.V. 3. Catalogs & Directories. 4. Co-op Adv. 5. Consumer Mags. 6. D.M. to Bus. Estab.7. D.M. to Consumers 8. Daily Newsp. 9. Exhibits/Trade Shows 10. Foreign 11. Infomercial 12. Internet Adv.13. Multimedia 14. Network Radio 15. Network T.V. 16. Newsp. Distr. Mags. 17. Other 18. Outdoor (Posters, Transit) 19. Point of Purchase20. Premiums, Novelties 21. Product Samples 22. Special Events Mktg. 23. Spot Radio 24. Spot T.V. 25. Weekly Newsp. 26. Yellow Page Adv.

CONSULIER ENGINEERING, INC.
2391 Old Dixie Hwy
Riviera Beach, FL 33404
Tel.: (561) 842-2492
Fax: (561) 845-3237
E-mail: contact@consulier.com
Web Site: www.consulier.com
Approx. Rev.: $2,911,975
Approx. Number Employees: 29
Year Founded: 1985
Business Description:
Soap Marketer & Distr; Development of Data-Based Emergency Room Information Systems
S.I.C.: 7372; 2841
N.A.I.C.S.: 511210; 325611
Advertising Expenditures: $269,420
Media: 10-13
Personnel:
Warren B. Mosler *(Chm, Pres & CEO)*
Alan R. Simon *(Gen Counsel, Treas & Sec)*
Brands & Products:
CONSULIER
CRA-Z SOAP
INVESTING FOR THE FUTURE

CONSUMERS KITCHENS & BATHS
717 Broadway Ave
Holbrook, NY 11741-4905
Tel.: (631) 563-3200
Fax: (631) 567-1852
E-mail: info@consumerskitchens.com
Web Site: www.consumerssupercenters.com
Approx. Number Employees: 220
Year Founded: 1976
Business Description:
Retail & Wholesale Kitchen & Bath Equipment; Ready-To-Assemble Furniture
S.I.C.: 5722; 5031
N.A.I.C.S.: 443111; 423310
Import
Advertising Expenditures: $3,500,000
Media: 1-2-4-6-7-9-10-13-18-20-22-25-26
Distr.: Reg.
Personnel:
James Baloga *(CEO)*
Thomas Frisina *(CFO)*
Joel Miller *(Dir-Mktg)*
Brands & Products:
KITCHENS & BATHS
OUR ONLY BUSINESS
Advertising Agency:
Mega Media Marketing
717 Broadway Ave.
Holbrook, NY 11741
Tel.: (516) 563-3200
Fax: (516) 567-1852

COORSTEK, INC.
16000 Table Mountain Pkwy
Golden, CO 80403-1693
Tel.: (303) 271-7000
Fax: (303) 271-7009
E-mail: info@coorstek.com
Web Site: www.coorstek.com
Sales Range: $350-399.9 Million
Approx. Number Employees: 2,400
Year Founded: 1911
Business Description:
Ceramics, Custom Made Parts, Grinding Media, High Density Ceramic, Mill Lining Brick, High Alumina Ceramic, Metallized Ceramic, Cerasurf Ceramic Brick; Vistal Translucent Ceramic, Thin & Thick Film Substrates
S.I.C.: 3264
N.A.I.C.S.: 327113
Import Export
Media: 2-10
Personnel:
John K. Coors *(Chm, Pres & CEO)*
Steve Rask *(CFO)*
J. Mark Chenoweth *(Exec VP)*
Doug Coors *(Exec VP)*
Mark A. Petty *(Exec VP)*
Harrison Hartman *(Mgr-Corp Mktg)*
Brands & Products:
AMAZING SOLUTIONS
CERA-CHECK
CERA-SLIDE
CERALASE
CERAMICELL
CERAPURE
CERASHIELD
CERASURF
COORSTEK
DURA-Z
DURASENSE
DURASTRATE
GAISER
JUNSEISET
META-PLAST
MIDFILM
MINIGROOVE
PLASMAPURE
PLASMAPURE-UC
PLASMARESIST
POLYGLYDE
PURESIC
RF PURE
RO PURE
SILKEDGE
SMOOTHEDGE
STATSAFE
SUPERCHARGE
SUPERSTRATE
TEKSERVICE
TETRA-TEMP
TETRAFLUOR
TETRALON
THERMTILE
ULTRAFINE
ULTRASIC
WILBANKS

CORE FURNACE SYSTEMS CORPORATION
100 Corp Ctr Dr
Coraopolis, PA 15108-3185
Tel.: (412) 262-2240
Fax: (412) 262-2055
Toll Free: (800) 355-4826
Telex: 247639
E-mail: info@tenovacore.com
Web Site: www.tenovacore.com
Approx. Number Employees: 120
Year Founded: 1979
Business Description:
Mill Machinery Equipment; Engineering, Furnaces, Sheet & Strip Equipment
S.I.C.: 3567
N.A.I.C.S.: 333994
Export
Media: 1-2-4-10-20
Distr.: Direct to Consumer; Natl.
Budget Set: Oct.
Brands & Products:
CONSTEEL
CORE
CORE FURNACE SYSTEMS
FASTEEL
FASTMELT
FURNANCE SYSTEM
KOESTER KT

CORNELL IRON WORKS, INC.
(Sub. of CIW Enterprises, Inc.)
100 Elmwood Ave Crestwood Industrial Park
Mountain Top, PA 18707
Tel.: (570) 474-6773
Fax: (570) 474-9973
Toll Free: (800) 233-8366
E-mail: cornell@cornelliron.com
Web Site: www.cornelliron.com
E-Mail For Key Personnel:
President: andrewc@cornelliron.com
Marketing Director: johnp@cornelliron.com
Sales Director: michaels@cornelliron.com
Sales Range: $50-74.9 Million
Approx. Number Employees: 220
Year Founded: 1828
Business Description:
Rolling Metal Door Grilles & Shutters Mfr
S.I.C.: 3442; 3446
N.A.I.C.S.: 332321; 332323
Import Export
Advertising Expenditures: $400,000
Media: 2-4-7-10-13
Distr.: Intl.
Budget Set: Oct.
Personnel:
Andrew Cornell *(Pres & CEO)*
Steve Gallacher *(VP-Mktg)*
Shawn Smith *(VP-Sls)*
Lauretta O'Hara *(Mgr-HR)*
John Polchin *(Mgr-Southwest Reg Sls)*
Brands & Products:
GRAPHICS DOOR
M100 FIREGARD SYSTEM
MATADOOR
SAF-T-GARD
SCREENGARD
SENTRY GATE
SMOKESHIELD
SPECTRASHIELD
THERMISER
VISION AIRE
VISION GLIDE
VISTA GLIDE
VISTAGARD
WEATHERGARD

COSENTINO USA
13124 Trinity Dr
Stafford, TX 77477
Tel.: (281) 494-7277
Fax: (281) 494-7299
Toll Free: (800) 291-1311
Web Site: www.silestoneusa.com
Sales Range: $150-199.9 Million
Approx. Number Employees: 550
Year Founded: 1998
Business Description:
Silestone Natural Quartz Surfaces Mfr, Distr & Marketer
S.I.C.: 3281; 5032
N.A.I.C.S.: 327991; 423320
Media: 2-4-10-23-24
Personnel:
Roberto Contreras *(CEO)*
Advertising Agency:
Freed Advertising
1650 Hwy 6 Ste 400
Sugar Land, TX 77478
Tel.: (281) 240-4949
Fax: (281) 240-4999

CPFILMS INC.
(Sub. of Solutia Inc.)
4210 The Great Rd
Fieldale, VA 24089
Mailing Address:
PO Box 5068
Martinsville, VA 24115
Tel.: (276) 627-3000
Fax: (276) 627-3032
Toll Free: (800) 345-6088
E-mail: cpfilms@cpfilms.com
Web Site: www.cpfilms.com
Sales Range: $125-149.9 Million
Approx. Number Employees: 600
Business Description:
Window Films
S.I.C.: 3081
N.A.I.C.S.: 326113
Media: 10
Personnel:
T. Michael Donnelly *(Pres & Gen Mgr-Performance Films)*
Melania Russell *(Dir-HR)*
Brands & Products:
AGHT
CLEARLES
COURTGUARD
FORMULA ONE
GILA
GOLD2000
LLUMALLOY
LLUMAR
VISTA
Z-FLEX

CRATEX MANUFACTURING CO., INC.
328 Encinitas Blvd Ste 200
Encinitas, CA 92024
Tel.: (760) 942-2877
Fax: (760) 942-4513
Fax: (800) 788-0463
Toll Free: (800) 800-4077
E-mail: sales@cratex.com
Web Site: www.cratex.com
E-Mail For Key Personnel:
Sales Director: sales@cratex.com
Approx. Number Employees: 60
Year Founded: 1935
Business Description:
Mfr. of Abrasive Products
S.I.C.: 3291
N.A.I.C.S.: 327910
Import Export
Advertising Expenditures: $250,000
Media: 2-4-6-7-8-21
Distr.: Intl.; Natl.
Budget Set: June
Personnel:
Allen McCasland *(Chm)*
R.M. McCasland *(Pres)*
John M. Rossi *(Mgr-Mktg)*
Brands & Products:
BRIGHTBOY
CRATEX

CRENLO, LLC
(Sub. of Dover Industrial Products, Inc.)

Key to Media (For complete agency information see *The Advertising Red Books-Agencies* edition):
1. Bus. Publs. 2. Cable T.V. 3. Catalogs & Directories. 4. Co-op Adv. 5. Consumer Mags. 6. D.M. to Bus. Estab.7. D.M. to Consumers
8. Daily Newsp. 9. Exhibits/Trade Shows 10. Foreign 11. Infomercial 12. Internet Adv.13. Multimedia 14. Network Radio
15. Network T.V. 16. Newsp. Distr. Mags. 17. Other 18. Outdoor (Posters, Transit) 19. Point of Purchase20. Premiums, Novelties
21. Product Samples 22. Special Events Mktg. 23. Spot Radio 24. Spot T.V. 25. Weekly Newsp. 26. Yellow Page Adv.

Crenlo, LLC — (Continued)

1600 4th Ave NW
Rochester, MN 55901-2573
Tel.: (507) 289-3371
Fax: (507) 287-3405
E-mail: cabsales@crenlo.com
Web Site: www.crenlo.com
E-Mail For Key Personnel:
Sales Director: DEstes@crenlo.com
Sales Range: $400-449.9 Million
Approx. Number Employees: 800
Year Founded: 1951
Business Description:
Sheet Metal Products, Frame Fabricators, & Electronic Modular Enclosures Mfr & Distr
S.I.C.: 3469
N.A.I.C.S.: 332116
Import Export
Advertising Expenditures: $275,000
Media: 2-4-10
Distr.: Intl.; Natl.
Budget Set: May
Personnel:
Mark Pillers *(VP-Cab Sls & Mktg)*

CRESCENT MICHAELS

5013 Grays Ave
Philadelphia, PA 19143-5812
Tel.: (215) 724-8640
Fax: (215) 729-6727
E-mail: cmilani@crescentmichaels.com
Web Site: www.crescentmichaels.com
Approx. Sls.: $4,000,000
Approx. Number Employees: 40
Year Founded: 1990
Business Description:
Bronze, Aluminum & Stainless Steel Ornamental Architectural Metal Work
S.I.C.: 3441
N.A.I.C.S.: 332312
Media: 2-4-7
Distr.: Natl.
Budget Set: Nov.-Dec.
Brands & Products:
CRESCENT MICHAELS

CSC WORLDWIDE

4401 Equity Dr
Columbus, OH 43228-3856
Tel.: (614) 850-1460
Fax: (614) 850-0741
Toll Free: (800) 848-3573
E-mail: service@cscww.com
Web Site: www.cscworldwide.com
Sales Range: $50-74.9 Million
Approx. Number Employees: 160
Year Founded: 1895
Business Description:
Mfr. of Show Cases, Wall Systems, Custom Counters, Bakery Cases, Refrigerated & Open Refrigerated Cases & Heated Merchandisers
S.I.C.: 2541; 3585
N.A.I.C.S.: 337212; 333415
Import Export
Advertising Expenditures: $240,000
Bus. Publs.: $60,000; Catalogs & Directories: $60,000; Exhibits/Trade Shows: $120,000
Distr.: Intl.; Natl.
Budget Set: Nov.
Personnel:
Chris Aschinger *(Pres & CEO)*
Nick Fortine *(Pres-CSC Specialty Retail Grp)*
Brands & Products:
AMERICAN SERIES
CLASSIQUE III
FIFTH AVENUE
LANE AVENUE
SYSTECH
WALL SELL
WALL SELL BASIC

CULTURED STONE CORPORATION

(Sub. of Owens Corning)
Hwy 29 N Tower Rd
Napa, CA 94559
Tel.: (707) 255-1727
Fax: (707) 255-5572
Web Site: www.culturedstone.com
Sales Range: $150-199.9 Million
Business Description:
Stone Mfr
S.I.C.: 2821
N.A.I.C.S.: 325211
Media: 4-10
Personnel:
John Stein *(Pres)*
Brands & Products:
COBBLESTONE
CULTURED BRICK
CULTURED STONE
PRO-FIT LEDGESTONE

CUMMINGS INCORPORATED

4560 Trousdale Dr
Knoxville, TN 37204
Tel.: (615) 244-5555
Fax: (615) 782-6699
Toll Free: (800) 489-7446
Web Site: www.cummingssign.com
Sales Range: $200-249.9 Million
Approx. Number Employees: 256
Year Founded: 1946
Business Description:
Signs & Specialty Advertising
S.I.C.: 3993
N.A.I.C.S.: 339950
Import Export
Media: 13-18
Personnel:
C. Stephen Lynn *(Chm)*
Stephen R. Kerr *(Pres)*
James Murray *(CMO & Exec VP)*
Bruce H. Cornett *(VP-Customer Svc)*
Everett Evans *(VP-Engrg & R&D)*

CUNNINGHAM-LIMP COMPANY

39300 W Twelve Mile Rd Ste 200
Farmington Hills, MI 48331-2997
Tel.: (248) 489-2300
Fax: (248) 489-2310
E-mail: info@cunninghamlimp.com
Web Site: www.cunninghamlimp.com
Approx. Number Employees: 12
Year Founded: 1940
Business Description:
Holding Company; Contracting Services
S.I.C.: 1522
N.A.I.C.S.: 236220
Media: 1-2-7-9-10
Distr.: Natl.
Personnel:
Donald R. Kegley, Jr. *(Pres)*

CURRIES COMPANY

(Sub. of McKinney Products Company)
1502 12th St NW
Mason City, IA 50401-5809
Mailing Address:
PO Box 1648
Mason City, IA 50402-1648
Tel.: (641) 423-1334
Fax: (641) 423-9104
E-mail: curries@curries.com
Web Site: www.curries.com
Approx. Number Employees: 700
Year Founded: 1958
Business Description:
Mfr. of Steel Doors & Frames
S.I.C.: 3442
N.A.I.C.S.: 332321
Export
Media: 2-4-7-10-17
Distr.: Natl.
Personnel:
Jerry N. Currie *(Pres & CEO)*
Mark Evers *(Dir-HR)*
Dean Peterson *(Dir-Sls Admin)*

CUSTOM BILT METALS

1347 Shore St
West Sacramento, CA 95691
Tel.: (916) 372-7696
Fax: (916) 372-8327
Toll Free: (800) 675-5111
E-mail: Info@custombiltmetals.com
Web Site: www.custombiltmetals.com
Sales Range: $25-49.9 Million
Approx. Number Employees: 1,000
Year Founded: 1974
Business Description:
Wholesaler of Metalworking Machinery
S.I.C.: 5084; 1761
N.A.I.C.S.: 423830; 238160
Brands & Products:
ARMOR
CANYON
COUNTRY CEDAR
GUARDIAN
MAJESTIC
TITAN
VAIL MAJESTIC
Advertising Agency:
Purdie Rogers, Inc.
5447 Ballard Ave NW
Seattle, WA 98107
Tel.: (206) 628-7700
Fax: (206) 628-2818

THE CYCLONE MFG. CO.

151 N Washington St
Urbana, IN 46990-9539
Mailing Address:
PO Box 67
Urbana, IN 46990-9539
Tel.: (260) 774-3311
Fax: (260) 774-3416
E-mail: manager@spyker.com
Web Site: www.cyclonemetalfab.com
Approx. Number Employees: 70
Year Founded: 1868
Business Description:
Metal Fabrications & Stampings
S.I.C.: 3444; 3531
N.A.I.C.S.: 332322; 333120
Export
Media: 2-10
Distr.: Natl.
Budget Set: Jan.
Personnel:
Daniel E. Speicher, III *(Pres, Mgr-Sls & Mgr-Adv)*
Robert Beck *(Mgr-Engrng)*
Brands & Products:
CYCLONE
SPYKER SPREADER

DAL-TILE COPORATION

(Sub. of Mohawk Industries, Inc.)
7834 C F Hawn Freeway PO Box 170130
Dallas, TX 75217-6529
Tel.: (214) 398-1411
Fax: (214) 309-4390
Web Site: www.daltile.com
Sales Range: $1-4.9 Billion
Approx. Number Employees: 7,900
Year Founded: 1947
Business Description:
Mfr. of Ceramic Wall & Floor Tile
S.I.C.: 3253
N.A.I.C.S.: 327122
Import
Personnel:
Harold G. Turk *(Pres)*
Michael F. McGlothlin *(CFO)*
Paul Adam *(VP-HR)*
Michael Kephart *(VP-Intl Sls & Mktg)*
Brands & Products:
AMERICAN OLEAN
DALTILE
Advertising Agencies:
Southwest Media Group
2100 Ross Ave Ste 3200
Dallas, TX 75201
Tel.: (214) 561-5543
Fax: (214) 744-1086

Square One, Inc.
1801 N Lamar Ste 375
Dallas, TX 75202
Tel.: (214) 749-1111
Fax: (214) 379-8499

DALLAS MARKET CENTER COMPANY

(d/b/a World Trade Center)
2100 N Stemmons Freeway 1000
Dallas, TX 75207
Tel.: (214) 655-6100
Fax: (214) 749-5479
E-mail: info@dmcmail.com
Web Site:
www.dallasmarketcenter.com
Sales Range: $100-124.9 Million
Approx. Number Employees: 200
Business Description:
Commercial & Industrial Building Operation
S.I.C.: 6512
N.A.I.C.S.: 531120
Personnel:
Bill Winsor *(Pres & CEO)*
Cindy Morris *(COO)*
Jane Robertson *(Exec VP-Mktg)*
Alden Clanahan *(VP-Trend Direction & Design)*
Cherie R. Marcum *(VP-Fin)*
Advertising Agency:
Firehouse, Inc.
14860 Landmark Blvd No 247
Dallas, TX 75254
Tel.: (972) 692-0911
Fax: (972) 692-0912

DAVID WEEKLEY HOMES, LP

1111 N Post Oak Rd
Houston, TX 77055-7211
Tel.: (713) 963-0500
Fax: (713) 963-0322
Web Site:
www.davidweekleyhomes.com

Key to Media (For complete agency information see *The Advertising Red Books-Agencies* edition):
1. Bus. Publs. 2. Cable T.V. 3. Catalogs & Directories. 4. Co-op Adv. 5. Consumer Mags. 6. D.M. to Bus. Estab.7. D.M. to Consumers 8. Daily Newsp. 9. Exhibits/Trade Shows 10. Foreign 11. Infomercial 12. Internet Adv.13. Multimedia 14. Network Radio 15. Network T.V. 16. Newsp. Distr. Mags. 17. Other 18. Outdoor (Posters, Transit) 19. Point of Purchase20. Premiums, Novelties 21. Product Samples 22. Special Events Mktg. 23. Spot Radio 24. Spot T.V. 25. Weekly Newsp. 26. Yellow Page Adv.

Approx. Sls.: $1,500,000,000
Approx. Number Employees: 1,500
Year Founded: 1976
Business Description:
Custom Homes Builder
S.I.C.: 1521
N.A.I.C.S.: 236115
Media: 2-6-10-16-18-25-26
Personnel:
David M. Weekley *(Chm)*
John Johnson *(CEO)*
Randy Braden *(Pres-FL)*
Rick Moore *(Pres-Houston)*
Natalie Harris *(VP-Mktg)*
Brands & Products:
DAVID WEEKLY HOMES
FLEXSPACE
LIFEDESIGN
PERSONAL BUILDER

DAVIE INDUSTRIES INC.

22 Rue George D Davie
Levis, QC G6V 8V5, Canada
Tel.: (418) 837-5841
Fax: (418) 835-1017
Web Site: www.davie.ca
Approx. Number Employees: 23
Year Founded: 1825
Business Description:
Turnkey Manufacturing; Ship Construction, Conversion & Repair; Construction of Heavy Industrial & Offshore Fabrications
S.I.C.: 3731
N.A.I.C.S.: 336611
Import Export
Media: 1-2-4-7-10-25-26
Distr.: Intl.; Natl.
Budget Set: Oct.
Personnel:
Gustav Johan Nydal *(Pres & CEO-Davie Yards)*

DAW TECHNOLOGIES, INC.

1600 W 2200 S Ste 201
Salt Lake City, UT 84119
Tel.: (801) 977-3100
Fax: (801) 973-6640
E-mail: info@dawtech.com
Web Site: www.dawtech.com
Sales Range: $10-24.9 Million
Approx. Number Employees: 25
Year Founded: 1989
Business Description:
Controlled Environmental Solutions & Cleanroom Supplier
S.I.C.: 3674
N.A.I.C.S.: 334413
Export
Media: 7-17
Personnel:
James C. Collings *(CEO)*
Pete J. Spransy *(VP-Tech)*
Brands & Products:
AIR-FRAME
DAWTECH
ENVIROZONE AIR ENTRANCE
MATRIX

THE DAY & ZIMMERMANN GROUP, INC.

1500 Spring Garden St
Philadelphia, PA 19130-3638
Tel.: (215) 299-8000
Toll Free: (800) 523-0786
Telex: 845192
E-mail: media.relations@dayzim.com
Web Site: www.dayzim.com
Sales Range: $1-4.9 Billion
Approx. Number Employees: 24,000
Year Founded: 1901
Business Description:
Holding Company; Architectural Design, Engineering, Construction Management, Facility Maintenance, Security, Munitions Production, Government & Commercial Support Services
S.I.C.: 6719; 7381; 7389; 8711; 8712; 8744
N.A.I.C.S.: 551112; 541310; 541330; 561210; 561499; 561612
Export
Personnel:
Harold L. Yoh, III *(Chm & CEO)*
Joseph J. Ucciferro *(Pres & CEO-Comml & Public Sector)*
Joseph W. Ritzel *(CFO & Sr VP-Fin)*
Anthony J. Bosco, Jr. *(CIO & Sr VP)*
William Yoh *(Chief Customer Officer)*
John DiMarco *(Pres-Govt Svcs Div)*
William R. Hamm *(Gen Counsel, Sec & Sr VP)*
Brands & Products:
DAY & ZIMMERMANN
MANAGED MAINTENANCE SOLUTIONS
WE DO WHAT WE SAY.
Advertising Agency:
Gregory FCA
27 W Athens Ave Ste 200
Ardmore, PA 19003
Tel.: (610) 642-8253
Fax: (610) 642-1258
Fax: (610) 649-9029
Toll Free: (800) 499-4734

DELAIR GROUP, LLC

(Sub. of Shapes/Arch Holdings, LLC)
8600 River Rd
Delair, NJ 08110-3328
Tel.: (856) 663-2900
Fax: (856) 663-1297
Toll Free: (800) 235-0185
E-mail: info@delairgroup.com
Web Site: www.delairgroup.com
Approx. Number Employees: 300
Year Founded: 1962
Business Description:
Swimming Pools, Pool Accessories & Aluminum Fencing Mfr
S.I.C.: 3354; 3441
N.A.I.C.S.: 331316; 332312
Export
Advertising Expenditures: $1,500,000
Media: 1-2-3-4-5-6-7-9-10-16-18-19-20-21-23-24-25-26
Distr.: Natl.
Budget Set: Sept.
Personnel:
David Stewart *(Exec VP)*
Brands & Products:
DELGARD
ESTHER WILLIAMS
INFINITY
JOHNNY WEISSMULLER
SYMPHONY SERIES

DELTA FAUCET COMPANY

(Sub. of Masco Corporation)
55 E 111th St
Indianapolis, IN 46280-1071
Tel.: (317) 848-1812
Fax: (317) 571-6513
Toll Free: (800) 345-3358
Web Site: www.deltafaucet.com
Sales Range: $125-149.9 Million
Approx. Number Employees: 300
Year Founded: 1954
Business Description:
Faucets Mfr
S.I.C.: 3432; 3494
N.A.I.C.S.: 332913; 332919
Media: 2-4-22
Personnel:
Keith Allman *(Pres)*
Rich Burkman *(CFO)*
Charlie McTargett *(Sr Dir-Mktg)*
Ken Martin *(Sr Dir-Comml Sls)*
Brands & Products:
BRILLIANCE
BRIZO
DELTA
DELTA SELECT
MONITOR
MONITOR II
SCALD GUARD
Advertising Agencies:
Gibbs & Soell, Inc.
60 E 42nd St
New York, NY 10165
Tel.: (212) 697-2600
Fax: (212) 697-2646
Pub Rels

Leo Burnett USA
35 W Wacker Dr
Chicago, IL 60601-1723
Tel.: (312) 220-5959
Fax: (312) 220-3299

Liquid Thread
1675 Broadway
New York, NY 10019
Tel.: (212) 468-4000

MSLGROUP
1675 Broadway 9th Floor
New York, NY 10019-5865
Tel.: (212) 468-4200
Fax: (212) 468-3007

DENHOLTZ MANAGEMENT CORP.

14 Cliffwood Ave
Matawan, NJ 07047
Tel.: (732) 381-1115
Tel.: (732) 388-3000
Fax: (732) 626-4300
Web Site:
www.denholtzassociates.com
Sales Range: $10-24.9 Million
Approx. Number Employees: 75
Year Founded: 1983
Business Description:
Industrial Buildings & Warehouses
S.I.C.: 1522
N.A.I.C.S.: 236220
Media: 2
Personnel:
Kristine Hurlbut *(Sr VP-Leasing)*
Brian Mac Murray *(Dir-HR)*
Robert Mahoney *(Mgr-Property)*
Advertising Agency:
Beckerman Public Relations
One University Plz Ste 507
Hackensack, NJ 07601
Tel.: (908) 781-6420
Fax: (201) 465-8040

DEUBLIN COMPANY

2050 Norman Dr W
Waukegan, IL 60085-6747
Tel.: (847) 689-8600
Fax: (847) 689-8690
E-mail: customerservice@deublin.com
Web Site: www.deublin.com
Approx. Number Employees: 100
Year Founded: 1945
Business Description:
Rotating Union Mfr
S.I.C.: 3498; 3492
N.A.I.C.S.: 332996; 332912
Import Export
Media: 2-4-7-10-13-26
Distr.: Intl.; Natl.
Personnel:
Donald L. Deubler *(Chm & CEO)*
Ron Kelner *(Pres)*
Ed Lerner *(CFO)*
Rob O'Brien *(VP-Sls & Mktg)*
Afzal Ali *(Dir-Mktg)*

DEVCON INTERNATIONAL CORP.

(Holding of Golden Gate Capital)
3880 N 28th Ter
Hollywood, FL 33020
Tel.: (954) 926-5200
Fax: (954) 926-1809
E-mail: info@devcon-security.com
Web Site: www.devcon-security.com
Sales Range: $50-74.9 Million
Approx. Number Employees: 600
Year Founded: 1950
Business Description:
Holding Company; Security System Installation & Monitoring Services
S.I.C.: 6719; 7382
N.A.I.C.S.: 551112; 561621
Advertising Expenditures: $500,000
Personnel:
Robert C. Farenhem *(Pres & CEO)*
Mark M. McIntosh *(CFO)*
Ann M. MacDonald *(Sr VP-Fin)*
Kimberly Marcil *(Sr VP-HR & Mgmt Dev)*

DIAMOND SPAS, INC.

4409 Coriolis Way
Frederick, CO 80504
Tel.: (720) 864-9115
Fax: (720) 864-9120
Toll Free: (800) 951SPAS
E-mail: customerservice@diamondspas.com
Web Site: www.diamondspas.com
Business Description:
Bath Fixture, Hot Tub & Spa Designer & Mfr
S.I.C.: 3261
N.A.I.C.S.: 327111
Media: 2-4-13
Personnel:
Stephanie Bennett *(Pres)*

DICK CORPORATION

1900 State Route 51
Large, PA 15025
Tel.: (412) 384-1000
Fax: (412) 384-1150
E-mail: jobs@dickcorp.com
Web Site: www.dickcorp.com
Approx. Number Employees: 2,500
Year Founded: 1922
Business Description:
General Contractors for Construction of Industrial & Other Nonresidential Buildings
S.I.C.: 1622

Dick Corporation — (Continued)

N.A.I.C.S.: 237310
Media: 2-9-25
Personnel:
David E. Dick *(Owner)*
Douglas P. Dick *(Chm & CEO)*
Stephen D'Angelo *(Pres)*
Roger J. Peters *(Gen Counsel)*
Shelby Gardner *(Dir-Project Support)*
Nadine Lee *(Mgr-Mktg & Proposal)*

DIPCRAFT MANUFACTURING COMPANY

111 W Braddock Ave
Braddock, PA 15104-1115
Tel.: (412) 351-2363
Fax: (412) 351-4528
Toll Free: (800) 245-6145
E-mail: fiberglass@dipcraft.com
Web Site: www.dipcraft.com
Sales Range: $1-9.9 Million
Approx. Number Employees: 2
Year Founded: 1946
Business Description:
Translucent Fiberglass, Reinforced Plastic Building Panels Mfr; Candy Wrappers & Latex Balloons Imprinter
S.I.C.: 3089; 7389
N.A.I.C.S.: 326199; 561910
Import Export
Media: 2-4-6-9-10-19-20-26
Distr.: Direct to Consumer; Natl.
Budget Set: Jan.
Personnel:
Michael Tobias *(Pres)*
Brands & Products:
DIPCRAFT

DISPLAY TECHNOLOGIES

(Sub. of Cannon Solutions)
111-01 14th Ave
College Point, NY 11356
Tel.: (718) 321-3100
Fax: (718) 321-1932
Toll Free: (800) 424-4220
Web Site: www.display-technologies.com
Year Founded: 1976
Business Description:
Point of Purchase Displays
S.I.C.: 2519; 2541
N.A.I.C.S.: 337125; 337212
Media: 19

DIVERSIFIED GLOBAL HOLDINGS GROUP, INC.

(Formerly Royal Style Design, Inc.)
800 N Magnolia Ave Ste 105
Orlando, FL 32803
Tel.: (407) 843-3344
Fax: (407) 553-0064
Approx. Rev.: $45,770,645
Approx. Number Employees: 82
Year Founded: 2006
Business Description:
Holding Company
S.I.C.: 6719
N.A.I.C.S.: 551112
Media: 8
Personnel:
Vadim Enikeev *(Chm)*
Richard Lloyd *(Pres & CEO)*
Nikolay Lobachev *(CFO)*

DMJM H&N

(Sub. of AECOM Technology Corporation)
999 Town & Country Rd
Orange, CA 92868-4713
Mailing Address:
PO Box 6240
Orange, CA 92863-6240
Tel.: (714) 567-2400
Fax: (714) 543-0985
Web Site: www.dmjmhn.com
Sales Range: $75-99.9 Million
Approx. Number Employees: 400
Year Founded: 2001
Business Description:
Engineering Services
S.I.C.: 8712; 8711
N.A.I.C.S.: 541310; 541330
Advertising Expenditures: $250,000
Media: 2-6
Distr.: Intl.; Natl.
Budget Set: Nov.
Personnel:
Dennis Deslatte *(Reg Dir-Fin)*
Brands & Products:
HOLMES & NARVER

DOMINION HOMES, INC.

4900 Tuttle Crossing Blvd
Dublin, OH 43016
Tel.: (614) 356-5000
Fax: (614) 356-6010
Web Site: www.dominionhomes.com
Sales Range: $125-149.9 Million
Approx. Number Employees: 193
Year Founded: 1952
Business Description:
New Home Builder
S.I.C.: 1522; 1521; 1531; 6552
N.A.I.C.S.: 236220; 236115; 236117; 237210
Advertising Expenditures: $3,603,000
Media: 6-8-9-18-23-24-25
Personnel:
Mark A. Nelson *(Owner)*
Douglas G. Borror *(Chm)*
David S. Borror *(Vice Chm)*
William G. Cornely *(CFO, COO & Exec VP-Fin)*
Mike Biagi *(Pres-Centennial Home Mortgage)*
Michael A. Archer *(Sr VP-Sls Ops-Ohio Div)*
Brands & Products:
THE BEST OF EVERYTHING
DOMINION
ITS YOUR HOME

THE DONALD DURHAM COMPANY

59 Forest Ave
Des Moines, IA 50314-3509
Tel.: (515) 243-0491
Fax: (515) 243-3010
E-mail: info@waterputty.com
Web Site: www.waterputty.com
Approx. Number Employees: 10
Year Founded: 1924
Business Description:
Mfr. of Water Putty
S.I.C.: 3087
N.A.I.C.S.: 325991
Media: 2-6-10
Distr.: Intl.; Natl.
Budget Set: Nov.
Personnel:
Ronald D. Lindharz *(Pres)*
Brands & Products:
ASK FOR THE ORIGINAL
DURHAM'S ROCK HARD WATER PUTTY

DOOR ENGINEERING AND MANUFACTURING LLC

400 Cherry St
Kasota, MN 56050
Tel.: (507) 931-6910
Fax: (507) 931-9318
Toll Free: (800) 959-1352
E-mail: door@doorengineering.com
Web Site: www.doorengineering.com
Sales Range: $1-9.9 Million
Approx. Number Employees: 40
Business Description:
Designer & Mfr of Building & Warehouse Doors
S.I.C.: 3442
N.A.I.C.S.: 332321
Media: 2-4-17
Personnel:
Steve Saggau *(Pres)*

DPR CONSTRUCTION, INC.

1450 Veterans Blvd
Redwood City, CA 94063
Tel.: (650) 474-1450
Fax: (650) 474-1451
E-mail: info@dprinc.com
Web Site: www.dprinc.com
Sales Range: $1-4.9 Billion
Approx. Number Employees: 2,100
Year Founded: 1990
Business Description:
Commercial Building Construction Services
S.I.C.: 1522
N.A.I.C.S.: 236220
Media: 10
Personnel:
Peter Nosler *(Founder)*
Eric Lamb *(Exec VP)*
Yumi Clevenger *(Dir-Mktg)*

D.R. HORTON/CONTINENTAL SERIES

(Sub. of Continental Homes)
7600 E Orchard Rd Ste 350F
Greenwood Village, CO 80111-2556
Tel.: (303) 488-0061
Fax: (303) 488-0206
Web Site: www.drhorton.com/corp/PhoneList.do
Sales Range: $10-24.9 Million
Approx. Number Employees: 50
Business Description:
Mortgage Service
S.I.C.: 8742
N.A.I.C.S.: 541611
Media: 9-24-25
Personnel:
Scott Davis *(Pres)*
Cheryl Jaramillo *(VP-Sls & Mktg)*
John Wayne *(VP-Pur & Land Ops)*

DRESSER TRAP ROCK, INC.

1000 E Ave
Dresser, WI 54009
Tel.: (715) 483-3216
Fax: (715) 483-3219
Web Site: www.dressertraprock.com
Approx. Number Employees: 17
Year Founded: 1914
Business Description:
Aggregates Producer
S.I.C.: 1429
N.A.I.C.S.: 212319
Media: 2-5-6-23
Distr.: Intl.; Natl.
Budget Set: June
Personnel:
Bill Lusum *(CFO)*
Lyla Demullind *(Office Mgr)*

THE D.S. BROWN COMPANY

(Sub. of Gibraltar Industries, Inc.)
300 E Cherry St
North Baltimore, OH 45872-1227
Tel.: (419) 257-3561
Fax: (419) 257-2200
E-mail: dsbrown@dsbrown.com
Web Site: www.dsbrown.com
Approx. Sls.: $50,000,000
Approx. Number Employees: 275
Year Founded: 1890
Business Description:
Engineered Products Designer, Mfr & Supplier for Bridge & Highway Construction
S.I.C.: 3061; 3441
N.A.I.C.S.: 326291; 332312
Import Export
Media: 2-10-13
Personnel:
Steve Duffy *(Pres & CEO)*
Tim Hack *(CFO)*
Chris Youngless *(Mgr-Mktg)*
Brands & Products:
CABLEGUARD
DELASTIC
DELCRETE
DELPATCH
EXODERMIC
FIBERBOND
FRM CRETE
MATRIX
MAURER
PAVESAVER
SKEWMASTER
STEELFLEX
STEELFLEX MODULAR EXPANSION JOINT SYSTEMS
STEELFLEX STRIP SEAL EXPANSION JOINT SYSTEMS
VERSIFLEX

DUGAN & MEYERS CONSTRUCTION CO., INC.

11110 Kenwood Rd
Cincinnati, OH 45242-1818
Tel.: (513) 891-4300
Fax: (513) 891-0704
E-mail: info@dugan-meyers.com
Web Site: www.dugan-meyers.com
Sales Range: $75-99.9 Million
Approx. Number Employees: 200
Year Founded: 1935
Business Description:
Holding Company; General Construction & Construction Management Services
S.I.C.: 1541; 1522
N.A.I.C.S.: 236210; 236220
Advertising Expenditures: $200,000
Media: 2-7-9-13-22-26
Distr.: Direct to Consumer; Natl.
Personnel:
Dan Dugan *(Owner)*
Jerome E. Meyers *(CEO & COO)*
Jeffrey D. Kelly *(CFO)*
Patrick Wells *(Dir-Bus Dev)*

DURASOL AWNINGS, INC.

(Sub. of Duchossois Industries, Inc.)
225 Tower Dr
Middletown, NY 10941-2049

Key to Media (For complete agency information see *The Advertising Red Books-Agencies* edition):
1. Bus. Publs. 2. Cable T.V. 3. Catalogs & Directories. 4. Co-op Adv. 5. Consumer Mags. 6. D.M. to Bus. Estab.7. D.M. to Consumers 8. Daily Newsp. 9. Exhibits/Trade Shows 10. Foreign 11. Infomercial 12. Internet Adv.13. Multimedia 14. Network Radio 15. Network T.V. 16. Newsp. Distr. Mags. 17. Other 18. Outdoor (Posters, Transit) 19. Point of Purchase20. Premiums, Novelties 21. Product Samples 22. Special Events Mktg. 23. Spot Radio 24. Spot T.V. 25. Weekly Newsp. 26. Yellow Page Adv.

Tel.: (845) 692-1100
Fax: (845) 692-1120
Toll Free: (888) 387-2765
Web Site: www.durasol.com
Approx. Number Employees: 225
Year Founded: 1984
Business Description:
Retractable Canvas Awnings Mfr
S.I.C.: 2394
N.A.I.C.S.: 314912
Media: 8-13
Personnel:
Clark Gregory *(VP-Sls & Mktg)*
Alan Pedersen *(Sls Dir-Natl)*
Debra Plock *(Mgr-Customer Support)*
Brands & Products:
DURASHADE SERIES
SUN SHELTER
SUNCATCHER
SUNGUARD

DURST CORPORATION

129 Dermody St
Cranford, NJ 07016-3217
Tel.: (908) 653-1100
Fax: (908) 789-2911
Toll Free: (800) 451-0234
E-mail: durst@durstcorp.com
Web Site: www.durstcorp.com
Approx. Number Employees: 25
Year Founded: 1901
Business Description:
Specialty Plumbing Products Mfr
S.I.C.: 5074; 3432
N.A.I.C.S.: 423720; 332913
Media: 1-4-18-23
Distr.: Natl.
Budget Set: Nov.
Personnel:
John Dillon *(Dir-Mktg)*

THE DWYER GROUP, INC.

(Holding of The Riverside Company)
1010 N University Parks Dr
Waco, TX 76707-3854
Mailing Address:
PO Box 3146
Waco, TX 76707-0146
Tel.: (254) 745-2400
Fax: (254) 745-2590
Web Site: www.dwyergroup.com
E-Mail For Key Personnel:
President: ddwyerowens@dwyergroup.com
Sales Range: $25-49.9 Million
Approx. Number Employees: 300
Year Founded: 1970
Business Description:
Diversified Franchiser Services
S.I.C.: 7699; 7629
N.A.I.C.S.: 562991; 811219
Export
Advertising Expenditures: $6,000,000
Media: 1-2-3-5-6-7-8-9-10-14-15-18-20-23-24-25-26
Distr.: Direct to Consumer; Natl.
Budget Set: Monthly
Personnel:
Dina Dwyer-Owens *(Chm & CEO)*
Mike Bidwell *(Pres & COO)*
Tom Buckley *(CFO, Treas & VP)*
Debbie Wright-Hood *(Chief Admin Officer & Sec)*
Duke Johnston *(Gen Counsel & VP-Legal & Govt Affairs)*
Robert Tunmire *(Exec VP)*
Chris Mellon *(VP-Mktg)*
Lori Johnson *(Dir-Mktg)*
Steve LaCroix *(Asst Gen Counsel)*
Brands & Products:
AIRE SERVE HEATING & AIR CONDITIONING
AMERICA'S TROUBLESHOOTER
THE CLEAN EXPERIENCE
DREAMMAKER BATH & KITCHEN
GLASS DOCTOR
MR. APPLIANCE
MR. ELECTRIC
QUICK-AS-A-WINK
RAINBOW INTERNATIONAL
SUPER KLEEN
WE FIX YOUR PANES
YOUR COMFORT COMPANY

EAGLE MANUFACTURING COMPANY

2400 Charles St
Wellsburg, WV 26070-1000
Tel.: (304) 737-3171
Fax: (304) 737-1752
E-mail: sales@eagle-mfg.com
Web Site: www.eagle-mfg.com
E-Mail For Key Personnel:
Sales Director: sales@eagle-mfg.com
Approx. Number Employees: 200
Year Founded: 1894
Business Description:
Mfr. of Metal Fabricated Products
S.I.C.: 3411; 3444
N.A.I.C.S.: 332431; 332322
Export
Media: 1-2-4-10-11-13-17-19
Distr.: Natl.
Budget Set: Oct.
Personnel:
Joe Eddy *(Pres & CEO)*
John Mitchell *(VP-Sls)*
Brands & Products:
ARMORKRAFT
CORDONATOR
DRUM BOGIE
EAGLE
EAGLE PEST
GREAT PEOPLE GREAT PRODUCTS
QUIK-DEPLOY
SAFESMOKER
YELLOWJACKET
Advertising Agency:
Gutman Advertising LLC
6743 National Rd
Triadelphia, WV 26059
Tel.: (304) 214-4700
Fax: (304) 214-4705
(Safety Can, Safety Cabinets, Haz-Mat Products)

EAGLE WINDOW & DOOR, INC.

(Sub. of Andersen Corporation)
2045 Kerper Blvd
Dubuque, IA 52001
Mailing Address:
PO Box 1072
Dubuque, IA 52004-1072
Tel.: (563) 556-2270
Fax: (563) 556-4408
Fax: (563) 556-3825
Toll Free: (800) 324-5354
E-mail: eagleinc@eaglewindow.com
Web Site: www.eaglewindow.com
E-Mail For Key Personnel:
President: dbeeken@eaglewindow.com
Approx. Number Employees: 500
Year Founded: 1977
Business Description:
Windows & Doors Mfr
S.I.C.: 2431; 3442
N.A.I.C.S.: 321911; 332321
Media: 2-4-5-6-7-8-10-19-23-24-26
Personnel:
David Beeken *(Pres & CEO)*
Sandee Peters *(Gen Mgr)*
Brands & Products:
EAGLE
TALON

EARLE M. JORGENSEN COMPANY

(Sub. of Reliance Steel & Aluminum Co.)
10650 S Alameda St
Lynwood, CA 90262
Tel.: (323) 567-1122
Fax: (323) 563-5500
Toll Free: (800) 336-5365
E-mail: comments@emjmetals.com
Web Site: www.emjmetals.com
Sales Range: $1-4.9 Billion
Approx. Number Employees: 103
Year Founded: 1915
Business Description:
Metal Bar & Tubular Products Distr
S.I.C.: 5051
N.A.I.C.S.: 423510
Export
Advertising Expenditures: $650,000
Media: 2-4-6-8-9-25-26
Distr.: Direct to Consumer; Natl.
Budget Set: Dec.
Personnel:
R. Neil McCaffery *(Pres & CEO)*
Kenneth Henry *(Exec VP)*

EATON ELECTRICAL SERVICES & SYSTEMS

(Sub. of Eaton Corporation)
380 Carlingview Dr
Toronto, ON M9W 5X9, Canada
Tel.: (416) 798-0112
Tel.: (416) 798-0754
Fax: (416) 798-3532
Fax: (416) 798-0062
Toll Free: (800) 461-9166
Web Site: www.powerware.com
Sales Range: $1-9.9 Million
Approx. Number Employees: 50
Year Founded: 1999
Business Description:
Electronic Components Mfr
S.I.C.: 3699
N.A.I.C.S.: 335999
Media: 4-7-8-10-13-18-19-20-21-22-23-26
Brands & Products:
POWERWARE

E.C. BARTON & COMPANY

(d/b/a Surplus Warehouse)
2929 Browns Ln
Jonesboro, AR 72401
Tel.: (870) 932-6673
Fax: (870) 972-1304
E-mail: webcontact@ecbarton.com
Web Site: www.ecbarton.com
Sales Range: $125-149.9 Million
Approx. Number Employees: 12
Year Founded: 1885
Business Description:
Lumber & Building Materials Whslr & Retailer
S.I.C.: 5031
N.A.I.C.S.: 423310
Media: 2-3-4-7-9-10-16-19-23-24-25-26
Distr.: Direct to Consumer
Personnel:
Niel Crowson *(Pres & CEO)*
John Tant *(VP-Trng & Dev)*
Rick Cheshier *(Dir-MIS)*
H. R. McDonough *(Dir-Mktg)*
Joe Crowson *(Mgr-Transportation)*
Kevin Wooldridge *(Mgr-Inventory)*
Brands & Products:
E. C. BARTON & COMPANY
SURPLUS WAREHOUSE

EDWARD HINES LUMBER CO.

(Holding of U.S. LBM Holdings)
1000 Corporate Grove Dr
Buffalo Grove, IL 60089-4550
Tel.: (847) 353-7700
Fax: (847) 353-7891
Toll Free: (888) EDHINES
E-mail: sales@hineslumber.com
Web Site: www.hineslumber.com
E-Mail For Key Personnel:
Sales Director: sales@hineslumber.com
Approx. Number Employees: 600
Year Founded: 1892
Business Description:
Lumber & Other Building Materials Whslr
S.I.C.: 5031
N.A.I.C.S.: 423310
Advertising Expenditures: $600,000
Media: 2-4-7-8-9-10-18-20-23
Distr.: Natl.
Budget Set: Oct.
Personnel:
Steve Svendsen *(CFO)*
Elizabeth Hines Bigelow *(Mgr-Mktg)*
Brands & Products:
EDWARD HINES LUMBER
THE SOURCE FOR ALL YOUR BUILDING NEEDS
Advertising Agency:
Hayes Marketing Services, Inc.
4519 Highcrest Rd.
Rockford, IL 61107
Tel.: (815) 227-4400

EIS, INC.

(Sub. of Genuine Parts Company)
2018 Powers Ferry Rd Ste 500
Atlanta, GA 30339
Tel.: (678) 255-3600
Fax: (678) 255-3753
Toll Free: (800) 949-9992
E-mail: salesdesk@eis-inc.com
Web Site: www.eis-inc.com
E-Mail For Key Personnel:
Sales Director: salesdesk@eis-inc.com
Sales Range: $700-749.9 Million
Approx. Number Employees: 1,200
Year Founded: 1949
Business Description:
Process Materials, Production Supplies & Industrial Motor Repair Products Distr
S.I.C.: 5063; 5065
N.A.I.C.S.: 423610; 423690
Export
Advertising Expenditures: $300,000
Media: 2-4-7-10-13-16
Distr.: Natl.
Budget Set: Oct.

Key to Media (For complete agency information see *The Advertising Red Books-Agencies* edition):
1. Bus. Publs. 2. Cable T.V. 3. Catalogs & Directories. 4. Co-op Adv. 5. Consumer Mags. 6. D.M. to Bus. Estab.7. D.M. to Consumers
8. Daily Newsp. 9. Exhibits/Trade Shows 10. Foreign 11. Infomercial 12. Internet Adv.13. Multimedia 14. Network Radio
15. Network T.V. 16. Newsp. Distr. Mags. 17. Other 18. Outdoor (Posters, Transit) 19. Point of Purchase20. Premiums, Novelties
21. Product Samples 22. Special Events Mktg. 23. Spot Radio 24. Spot T.V. 25. Weekly Newsp. 26. Yellow Page Adv.

EIS, Inc. — (Continued)

Personnel:
Robert W. Thomas *(Pres & CEO)*
Matthew C. Tyser *(CFO & Sr VP)*
Alexander Gonzalez *(Sr VP-Electrical & Assembly Bus)*
Larry L. Griffin *(Sr VP-Mktg)*
Thomas A. Jones *(Sr VP-Mfg)*
William C. Knight *(Sr VP-Ops & Logistics)*
Gary Chittaro *(Mktg Mgr)*
Tom Coin *(Mgr-Market Segment)*
Paul Currie *(Mgr-EMtkg)*
Dan Diegnan *(Mgr-Market Segment)*
David Jenkins *(Mgr-Market Segment)*
Robert Kwon *(Mgr-Strategic Supply Solutions)*

E.L. WAGNER CO., INC.

750 Wordin Ave
Bridgeport, CT 06605-2423
Tel.: (203) 335-3960
Fax: (203) 331-9430
E-mail: jcgedneyii@wagnerswimmingpools.com
Web Site: www.wagnerswimmingpools.com
Approx. Number Employees: 150
Year Founded: 1919
Business Description:
Retailer of Swimming Pools
S.I.C.: 1799; 7349
N.A.I.C.S.: 238990; 561790
Advertising Expenditures: $250,000
Media: 2-4-9-10-17-25
Distr.: Natl.
Personnel:
Mary Lou Gedney *(Mgr-Adv)*

ELCAR FENCE & SUPPLY CO.

2155 S Valentia St
Denver, CO 80231-3324
Tel.: (303) 755-5211
Fax: (303) 755-5215
Web Site: www.elcarfence.com
Approx. Number Employees: 35
Year Founded: 1946
Business Description:
Fence Builder
S.I.C.: 1799
N.A.I.C.S.: 238990
Media: 2-8-9-10-13-21-23-24-25-26
Distr.: Direct to Consumer; Reg.
Budget Set: Dec.
Personnel:
Alfred M. Ellerby *(CEO)*
Brands & Products:
ELCAR FENCE
Advertising Agency:
Page Lewis Media
1300 S Monaco Pkwy Ste 12D
Denver, CO 80224
Tel.: (303) 757-1199

ELECTRIC EEL MANUFACTURING CO., INC.

501 W Leffel Ln
Springfield, OH 45506-3529
Tel.: (937) 323-4644
Fax: (937) 323-3767
Toll Free: (800) 833-1212
E-mail: info@electriceel.com
Web Site: www.electriceel.com
Approx. Sls.: $3,000,000
Approx. Number Employees: 35
Year Founded: 1939
Business Description:
Drain & Sewer Cleaning Equipment
S.I.C.: 3589; 3423
N.A.I.C.S.: 333319; 332212
Advertising Expenditures: $200,000
Media: 2-4-7-10-11-13-17
Distr.: Intl.; Natl.
Personnel:
David Hale *(CEO & VP)*
Thomas H. Hale *(CFO & VP)*
Mark A. Speranza *(Dir-Mktg)*
Brands & Products:
EELCAM
ELECTRICEEL
HANDE
TRI-MAX

ELGIN-BUTLER BRICK COMPANY

1007 E 40th St
Austin, TX 78751-4805
Mailing Address:
PO Box 546
Elgin, TX 78621
Tel.: (512) 285-3356
Fax: (512) 281-2487
E-mail: contact@elginbutler.com
Web Site: www.elginbutler.com
Approx. Number Employees: 110
Year Founded: 1873
Business Description:
Tile, Face & Fire Brick Mfr
S.I.C.: 3251
N.A.I.C.S.: 327121
Import Export
Media: 1-4-6-10-20-21
Distr.: Natl.
Personnel:
John Russell Butler *(Pres)*
Robert Butler *(Reg Mgr-Sls)*

ELJER, INC.

(Sub. of AS America, Inc.)
14801 Quorum Dr
Dallas, TX 75254-7589
Tel.: (972) 560-2000
Toll Free: (800) 423-5537
Web Site: www.eljer.com
Sales Range: $150-199.9 Million
Approx. Number Employees: 2,000
Year Founded: 1904
Business Description:
Faucets, Kitchen & Bath Sinks, Toilets, Bidets, Tubs & Whirlpools Mfr & Whslr
S.I.C.: 3432; 3431
N.A.I.C.S.: 332913; 332998
Import Export
Media: 2-4-5-6-7-10-13-19-20-26
Distr.: Intl.; Natl.
Brands & Products:
ELJER
THOSE WHO KNOW BETTER, KNOW ELJER

ELKAY MANUFACTURING COMPANY

2222 Camden Ct
Oak Brook, IL 60523-4674
Tel.: (630) 574-8484
Fax: (630) 574-5012
E-mail: fiberglass@dipcraft.com
Web Site: www.elkay.com
Sales Range: $550-599.9 Million
Approx. Number Employees: 4,200
Year Founded: 1920
Business Description:
Sinks, Faucets, Commercial Water Coolers & Drinking Fountains Supplier & Mfr
S.I.C.: 3431; 3585
N.A.I.C.S.: 332998; 333415
Import Export
Media: 1-2-4-5-6-7-10-19-20-26
Distr.: Intl
Budget Set: Sept. -Oct.
Personnel:
Duke Piotter *(Exec VP-Mktg & Channel Dev)*
Jack Krecek *(VP & Gen Mgr-Comml Channels)*
Tom Samanic *(VP & Gen Mgr)*
Mark Whittington *(VP & Gen Mgr-Traditional Plumbing Channel)*
David Southard *(Dir-Comp & Benefits)*
Brands & Products:
ALLURE
AREZZO
CELEBRITY
ELITE
ELITE BY ELKAY
ELITE GOURMET
ELKAY
ELKAY STARLITE
ELUMINA
EZ COOLERS
FERRARA
GOURMET
HI-ARC
LUSTERTONE
MODA
NOUVEAU GOURMET
PACEMAKER
REGENCY
SPECIALTY COLLECTION
STARLITE
STARLITY
UNDERMOUNT
VIVO
WATER SENTRY
Advertising Agency:
Marketing Support, Inc.
200 E Randolph Dr Ste 5000
Chicago, IL 60601
Tel.: (312) 565-0044
Fax: (312) 946-6100
— Katie Saunders *(Acct Exec)*

EMCOR GROUP, INC.

301 Merritt Seven 6th Fl
Norwalk, CT 06851-1060
Tel.: (203) 849-7800
Fax: (203) 849-7900
Toll Free: (866) 890-7794
E-mail: emcor_info@emcorgroup.com
Web Site: www.emcorgroup.com
Approx. Rev.: $5,121,285,000
Approx. Number Employees: 24,000
Year Founded: 1987
Business Description:
Holding Company; Electrical & Mechanical Construction, Energy Infrastructure & Facilities Management Services
S.I.C.: 6719; 1731; 8744
N.A.I.C.S.: 551112; 238210; 561210
Media: 2-4-7-10-13-14-15-17
Distr.: Natl.
Personnel:
Frank T. MacInnis *(Chm)*
Anthony J. Guzzi *(Pres & CEO)*
Mark A. Pompa *(CFO & Exec VP)*
Joseph A. Puglisi *(CIO & VP)*
Kevin R. Craig *(Pres-EMCOR Site-Based Svcs)*
Sheldon I. Cammaker *(Gen Counsel, Sec & Exec VP)*
R. Kevin Matz *(Exec VP-Shared Svcs)*
William E. Feher *(VP-Fin & Compliance)*
Mava K. Heffler *(VP-Mktg & Comm)*
Brands & Products:
BUILD. POWER. SERVICE. PROTECT
EMCOR
KNOWLEDGE IN ACTION
Advertising Agencies:
The Donaldson Group
88 Hopmeadow St
Weatogue, CT 06089-9602
Tel.: (860) 658-9777
Fax: (860) 658-0533

Linden Alschuler & Kaplan, Inc.
1251 Ave of the Americas Ste 940
New York, NY 10020
Tel.: (212) 575-4545
Fax: (212) 575-0519

Mason & Kichar Recruitment Advertising
260 Amity Rd
Woodbridge, CT 06525
Tel.: (203) 392-0252
Fax: (203) 392-0255

ENERFAB, INC.

4955 Spring Grove Ave
Cincinnati, OH 45232-1925
Tel.: (513) 641-0500
Fax: (513) 641-1821
Web Site: www.enerfab.com
Approx. Number Employees: 2,600
Year Founded: 1901
Business Description:
Holding Company; Industrial Equipment Mfr, Maintenance & Contractor Services
S.I.C.: 6719; 1799; 3559; 5084
N.A.I.C.S.: 551112; 238990; 332410; 333298; 423830
Advertising Expenditures: $100,000
Media: 2-4-7-10
Distr.: Intl.; Natl.
Budget Set: Aug.
Personnel:
Dave Herche *(Chm)*
Wendell R. Bell *(Vice Chm & CEO)*
Brands & Products:
ENERFAB
LASTIGLAS
Advertising Agency:
Liaison Marketing Communications, Ltd.
2354 Kemper Ln
Cincinnati, OH 45206
Tel.: (513) 281-2301
Fax: (513) 281-2363

ENERGYCONNECT, INC.

(Sub. of EnergyConnect Group, Inc.)
5335 SW Medals Rd Ste 325
Portland, OR 97035
Tel.: (503) 419-3580
Web Site: www.energyconnectinc.com
Sales Range: $10-24.9 Million
Approx. Number Employees: 38

Key to Media (For complete agency information see *The Advertising Red Books-Agencies* edition):
1. Bus. Publs. 2. Cable T.V. 3. Catalogs & Directories. 4. Co-op Adv. 5. Consumer Mags. 6. D.M. to Bus. Estab.7. D.M. to Consumers 8. Daily Newsp. 9. Exhibits/Trade Shows 10. Foreign 11. Infomercial 12. Internet Adv.13. Multimedia 14. Network Radio 15. Network T.V. 16. Newsp. Distr. Mags. 17. Other 18. Outdoor (Posters, Transit) 19. Point of Purchase20. Premiums, Novelties 21. Product Samples 22. Special Events Mktg. 23. Spot Radio 24. Spot T.V. 25. Weekly Newsp. 26. Yellow Page Adv.

Business Description:
Energy Efficiency Solutions
S.I.C.: 7349
N.A.I.C.S.: 561790
Personnel:
Rodney M. Boucher *(Dir)*
Advertising Agency:
Rasky Baerlein Strategic Communications
70 Franklin St 3rd Fl
Boston, MA 02110
Tel.: (617) 443-9933
Fax: (617) 443-9944

ENGLOBAL CORPORATION

Ste 400 654 N Sam Houston Pkwy E
Houston, TX 77060-5914
Tel.: (281) 878-1000
Fax: (281) 821-5488
Toll Free: (800) 411-6040
E-mail: englobal@englobal.com
Web Site: www.englobal.com
Approx. Rev.: $320,615,000
Approx. Number Employees: 2,030
Year Founded: 1985
Business Description:
Engineering Services & Engineered Systems Principally for the Pipeline, Refining & Petrochemical Industries
S.I.C.: 8711; 7389
N.A.I.C.S.: 541330; 541990
Media: 2-10-13-14-15
Personnel:
William A. Coskey *(Chm)*
Edward L. Pagano *(Pres & CEO)*
John R. Beall *(Interim CFO)*
Natalie S. Hairston *(Chief Governance Officer, Sec & VP-IR)*
Tami Walker *(Gen Counsel & VP-Legal)*
Michael H. Lee *(Exec VP-Field Solutions)*
Rochelle D. Leedy *(Exec VP-Automation)*
Timothy P. Rennie *(Exec VP-Engrg & Construction)*
R. David Kelley *(Sr VP-Corp Svcs)*
Michael M. Patton *(Sr VP-Midwest Ops)*
Dennis E. Pisula *(Sr VP-Bus Dev)*
Fred Bridgewater *(Corp VP-HR)*
Robert J. Church *(Mgr-HR)*
Alex Schroeder *(Mgr-IT)*

ESSAR STEEL ALGOMA INC.

(Sub. of Essar Steel Ltd.)
105 West St
Sault Sainte Marie, ON P6A 7B4, Canada
Tel.: (705) 945-2351
Fax: (705) 945-2203
E-mail: sales@algoma.com
Web Site: www.essarsteelalgoma.com
E-Mail For Key Personnel:
Sales Director: sales@algoma.com
Approx. Sls.: $1,828,485,361
Approx. Number Employees: 3,200
Year Founded: 1901
Business Description:
Rolled Sheet & Plate Steel Mfr
S.I.C.: 3316; 3312
N.A.I.C.S.: 331221; 331111
Export
Media: 2-4-10-20
Distr.: Intl.; Natl.
Budget Set: Oct. -Nov.
Personnel:
Rakesh Kapur *(CFO)*
Pramod Kumar Shukla *(COO)*
Victoria Chiappetta *(VP-Legal)*
Rob Dionisi *(VP-Sls & Mktg)*
Brian Doherty *(VP-HR)*
Jatinder Mehra *(Dir)*
Ed Bumbacco *(Mgr-Corp Logistics & Pur & Stores)*
Brenda Stenta *(Mgr-Corp Comm)*

THE EUCLID CHEMICAL COMPANY

(Sub. of Tremco Incorporated)
19218 Redwood Rd
Cleveland, OH 44110
Tel.: (216) 531-9222
Fax: (216) 531-9396
Toll Free: (800) 321-7628
E-mail: info@euclidchemical.com
Web Site: www.euclidchemical.com
Sales Range: $125-149.9 Million
Approx. Number Employees: 250
Year Founded: 1910
Business Description:
Concrete Construction Specialty Products & Services
S.I.C.: 2891; 2851; 3272
N.A.I.C.S.: 325520; 325510; 327390
Export
Media: 2-4-7-8-10-18-21-22
Distr.: Intl.
Budget Set: Dec.
Personnel:
Moorman Scott *(Pres)*
Nicholas Adams *(VP & Gen Mgr)*
Paul Albright *(VP-Sls)*
Dave Nicholson *(VP-Sls)*
Jeff Abbuhl *(Mgr-Product-Admixture/MCP)*
Jennifer Crisman *(Mgr-Product)*
Dale Mizer *(Mgr-Product-Concrete Rehabilitation Products)*
Advertising Agency:
Market One Communications
23945 Mercantile Rd Ste C
Beachwood, OH 44122
Tel.: (216) 360-8140
Fax: (216) 360-8179

E.V. WILLIAMS, INC.

(Sub. of The Branch Group)
925 S Military Hwy
Virginia Beach, VA 23464
Tel.: (757) 420-1140
Fax: (757) 420-7250
E-mail: vpops@evwilliams.com
Web Site: www.evwilliams.com
Approx. Number Employees: 310
Year Founded: 1941
Business Description:
Concrete Paving Construction Services
S.I.C.: 1622
N.A.I.C.S.: 237310
Media: 9-18-26
Personnel:
Thomas L. Partridge *(Pres)*

EVOLVING GOLD CORP.

1075 Westroger
Vancouver, BC V6E 3C9, Canada
Tel.: (604) 685-6375
Fax: (604) 909-1163
Toll Free: (866) 604-3864
E-mail: info@evolvinggold.com
Web Site: www.evolvinggold.com
Approx. Int. Income: $131,219
Year Founded: 2003
Business Description:
Gold Mining Services
S.I.C.: 1041
N.A.I.C.S.: 212221
Personnel:
R. Stuart Angus *(Chm)*
Quinton Hennigh *(Pres & Chief Geologist)*
William Gee *(CEO)*
Charles E. Jenkins *(CFO)*
Rory Quinn *(Mgr-IR)*
Advertising Agency:
Renmark Financial Communications, Inc.
1550 Metcalfe Ste 502
Montreal, QC H3A 1X6, Canada
Tel.: (514) 939-3989
Fax: (514) 939-3717

FALCON WATERFREE TECHNOLOGIES, LLC

751 Kenmoor Ave SE
Grand Rapids, MI 49546
Tel.: (616) 954-3570
Fax: (616) 954-3579
Toll Free: (866) 975-0174
E-mail: info@falconwaterfree.com
Web Site: www.falconwaterfree.com
Approx. Number Employees: 45
Business Description:
Waterfree Urinal Systems Mfr
S.I.C.: 3432
N.A.I.C.S.: 332913
Media: 4-10-13
Personnel:
Marc Nathanson *(Chm)*
James Krug *(CEO)*
Ditmar Gorges *(Exec VP)*
Aline Daniel *(VP-Sls)*

FANSTEEL INC.

1746 Commerce Rd
Creston, IA 50801
Tel.: (641) 782-8521
Fax: (641) 782-7672
E-mail: wellmans@wellmandynamics.com
Web Site: www.fansteel.com
Sales Range: $75-99.9 Million
Approx. Number Employees: 685
Year Founded: 1907
Business Description:
Holding Company; Steel & Specialty Metal Castings & Powdered Metal Components Mfr
S.I.C.: 6719; 3324; 3363; 3364; 3499
N.A.I.C.S.: 551112; 331512; 331521; 331522; 332117
Export
Advertising Expenditures: $382,000
Media: 2-4-7
Distr.: Intl.; Natl.
Budget Set: Oct.
Personnel:
Curtis J. Zamec, II *(Pres & CEO)*
Earl F. White *(CFO)*

FIBER COMPOSITES, LLC

181 Random Dr
New London, NC 28127-8735
Tel.: (704) 463-7120
Fax: (704) 463-0405
E-mail: info@fiberondecking.com
Web Site: www.fiberondecking.com
Approx. Number Employees: 300
Business Description:
Composite Decking Materials Mfr & Distr
S.I.C.: 5039
N.A.I.C.S.: 423390
Personnel:
Doug Mancosh *(Pres)*
Advertising Agency:
Trone Inc.
4035 Piedmont Pkwy
High Point, NC 27265-9402
Tel.: (336) 886-1622
Fax: (336) 886-2174

FIBERESIN INDUSTRIES, INC.

37031 E Wisconsin Ave
Oconomowoc, WI 53066
Mailing Address:
PO Box 88
Oconomowoc, WI 53066-0088
Tel.: (262) 567-4427
Fax: (262) 567-4814
E-mail: sales@fiberesin.com
Web Site: www.fiberesin.com
E-Mail For Key Personnel:
Sales Director: sales@fiberesin.com
Approx. Number Employees: 200
Year Founded: 1946
Business Description:
Laminated Particle Board & Wood Composites Mfr
S.I.C.: 2493; 2452
N.A.I.C.S.: 321219; 321992
Import Export
Media: 2-10-17
Distr.: Natl.
Personnel:
Mike Nicholas *(Pres & CEO)*
Ken Johnson *(Exec VP-Product Dev)*
Brands & Products:
FIBERESIN

FISHER DEVELOPMENT INC.

1485 Bayshore Blvd
San Francisco, CA 94124
Tel.: (415) 468-1717
Fax: (415) 468-6241
Web Site: www.fisherinc.com
Sales Range: $100-124.9 Million
Approx. Number Employees: 175
Business Description:
Commercial & Office Building, New Construction
S.I.C.: 1522
N.A.I.C.S.: 236220
Advertising Expenditures: $10,000
Media: 2-10
Personnel:
Denise B. Sharp *(Pres)*
Dennis Kreuser *(CFO)*
Sydney Bernier *(VP-Mktg)*

FISHER HOUSE FOUNDATION, INC.

111 Rockville Pke Ste 420
Rockville, MD 20850
Tel.: (212) 940-6875
Fax: (301) 294-8562
E-mail: info@fisherhouse.org
Web Site: www.fisherhouse.org
Sales Range: $250-299.9 Million
Approx. Number Employees: 11
Business Description:
Donator of "Comfort Homes" to Military Families
S.I.C.: 5211
N.A.I.C.S.: 444110
Media: 22

Key to Media (For complete agency information see *The Advertising Red Books-Agencies* edition):
1. Bus. Publs. 2. Cable T.V. 3. Catalogs & Directories. 4. Co-op Adv. 5. Consumer Mags. 6. D.M. to Bus. Estab.7. D.M. to Consumers
8. Daily Newsp. 9. Exhibits/Trade Shows 10. Foreign 11. Infomercial 12. Internet Adv.13. Multimedia 14. Network Radio
15. Network T.V. 16. Newsp. Distr. Mags. 17. Other 18. Outdoor (Posters, Transit) 19. Point of Purchase20. Premiums, Novelties
21. Product Samples 22. Special Events Mktg. 23. Spot Radio 24. Spot T.V. 25. Weekly Newsp. 26. Yellow Page Adv.

Fisher House Foundation, Inc. — (Continued)

Personnel:
David A. Coker *(Pres)*
Mary B. Considine *(Dir-Admin)*
Pamela Lea-Maida *(Dir-Hero Miles)*

FISHER MANUFACTURING COMPANY

1900 S O St
Tulare, CA 93274
Tel.: (559) 685-5200
Fax: (559) 685-5222
Toll Free: (800) 421-6162
E-mail: info@fisher-mfg.com
Web Site: www.fisher-mfg.com
Approx. Number Employees: 49
Year Founded: 1936
Business Description:
Mfr. of Commercial Plumbing Systems
S.I.C.: 3432
N.A.I.C.S.: 332913
Personnel:
Ray Fisher, Jr. *(Pres)*
Jeff Westley *(VP-Sls)*
Melissa Hulsey *(Coord-Mktg)*
Advertising Agency:
Strahan Advertising
1940 Old Tustin Ave
Santa Ana, CA 92705
Tel.: (714) 547-6383
Fax: (714) 547-5463

FLEXTRONICS INTERNATIONAL LTD.

(Sub. of Flextronics International USA, Inc.)
637 Gibraltar Dr
Milpitas, CA 95035
Tel.: (408) 957-8500
Fax: (408) 957-6056
Web Site: www.flextronics.com
Approx. Number Employees: 230
Year Founded: 1977
Business Description:
Electronics Design, Engineering & Logistics Services
S.I.C.: 3679; 5065
N.A.I.C.S.: 334419; 423690
Import Export
Media: 2-4-7-8-22
Personnel:
Dave Purvis *(CTO & Exec VP)*
Brands & Products:
SOLECTRON

THE FLINCHBAUGH CO., INC.

245 Beshore School Rd
Manchester, PA 17345
Tel.: (717) 266-2202
Fax: (717) 266-7055
Toll Free: (800) 326-2418
Web Site: www.flinchbaugh.com
Approx. Sls.: $2,700,000
Approx. Number Employees: 29
Year Founded: 1936
Business Description:
Mfr. of Speed Reducers, Dumbwaiters, Stair Climbs, Wheelchair Lifts; Provider of Contract Machining
S.I.C.: 3599; 3534
N.A.I.C.S.: 332710; 333921
Import Export
Media: 1-2-4-6-10-13-26
Distr.: Natl.
Budget Set: Mar.
Personnel:
Gregory Jenkins *(Owner & Pres)*
Brands & Products:
BUTLER
BUTLER AUTOMATIC DUMBWAITERS
BUTLER IMPERIAL ELITE STAIR CLIMB
BUTLER WHEELCHAIR LIFT
FLINCHBAUGH

FLINN & DREFFEIN ENGINEERING COMPANY

3520 Comml Ave
Northbrook, IL 60062-1821
Tel.: (847) 272-6370
Fax: (847) 272-6450
E-mail: thauter@flinndreffein.com
Web Site: www.flinndreffein.com
Approx. Number Employees: 15
Year Founded: 1907
Business Description:
Mfr. & Designer of Industrial Furnaces & Process Controls Systems
S.I.C.: 3585; 3567
N.A.I.C.S.: 333415; 333994
Export
Media: 2-10
Distr.: Natl.
Budget Set: Aug.
Personnel:
Joe K. Balaz *(Owner)*
Rich Koomjian *(VP-Tech)*

FLORIDA SHED COMPANY

Unit A1 6425 Ulmerton Rd
Largo, FL 33771-4918
Tel.: (727) 524-9191
Fax: (727) 524-9199
Toll Free: (800) 824-5335
Web Site: www.floridashed.com
Approx. Number Employees: 5
Business Description:
Wood Shed Contractor
S.I.C.: 2452; 1799
N.A.I.C.S.: 321992; 238990
Media: 6
Personnel:
Joseph Capenella *(Owner)*

FLORIDA TILE INDUSTRIES, INC.

(Sub. of Panariagroup Industrie Ceramiche S.p.A.)
320 W Main St
Lakeland, FL 33815-1556
Mailing Address:
PO Box 447
Lakeland, FL 33802
Tel.: (863) 284-4156
Fax: (863) 683-8936
Toll Free: (800) FLA-TILE
E-mail: salesdept@floridatile.com
Web Site: www.floridatile.com
E-Mail For Key Personnel:
Sales Director: salesdept@floridatile.com
Approx. Number Employees: 800
Year Founded: 1954
Business Description:
Ceramic Wall & Floor Tile Distr & Mfr
S.I.C.: 3253; 5031
N.A.I.C.S.: 327122; 423310
Import Export
Advertising Expenditures: $600,000
Media: 2-3-4-6-7-8-13-19-21-25
Distr.: Intl.; Natl.
Budget Set: Oct.
Personnel:
Emilio Mussini *(CEO)*
Luca Setti *(CFO & Sr VP)*
Massimo Barbari *(Exec VP-Sls, Distr & Mktg)*
Jim Cuthbertson *(VP-Mktg)*
Tracy Fisher *(VP-HR)*
Brands & Products:
NATURA

FLOWSERVE CORPORATION

5215 N O'Connor Blvd Ste 2300
Irving, TX 75039-5435
Tel.: (972) 443-6500
Fax: (972) 443-6800
E-mail: exportcompliance@flowserve.com
Web Site: www.flowserve.com
Approx. Sls.: $4,032,036,000
Approx. Number Employees: 15,000
Year Founded: 1912
Business Description:
Pumps & Precision-Engineered Flow Control Equipment Developer & Mfr
S.I.C.: 3491; 3561
N.A.I.C.S.: 332911; 333911
Export
Media: 2-4-7-10
Distr.: Intl.; Natl.
Budget Set: Sept.
Personnel:
Mark A. Blinn *(Pres & CEO)*
Kyle B. Ahlfinger *(CMO & VP)*
Mark D. Dailey *(Chief Admin Officer & Sr VP)*
Richard J. Guiltinan, Jr. *(Chief Acctg Officer & Sr VP-Fin)*
Thomas E. Ferguson *(Pres-Flow Solutions Grp & Sr VP)*
Thomas L. Pajonas *(Pres-Flow Control Div & Sr VP)*
Ronald F. Shuff *(Gen Counsel, Sec & Sr VP)*
Dean P. Freeman *(Treas & Sr VP-Fin)*
Andrew J. Beall *(Sr VP)*
Jerry L. Rockstroh *(Sr VP-Supply Chain & Continuous Improvement)*
Paul W. Fehlman *(VP-Fin-FSG)*
Michael E. Conley *(Dir-IR)*
Brands & Products:
ACCORD
ACEC CENTRIFUGAL
ALDRICH
ALLPAC
AMPLIFLOW
ANCHORDARLING
APEX
ARGUS
ASEPTIK
ATOMAC
AUTOMAX
AUTOSHIFT
AVIATOR
BATTIG
BIG MAX
BUTTERFLY
BW SEALS
BYRON JACKSON
CAMERON
CENTURA
CERCOFORM
CHANNELSTREAM
CIRCPAC
CLEANFLOW
CLEANPAC
COLDFLOW
DRAIN TITAN
DUBALL
DURAMETALLIC
DURASEAL
DURCO
DURCO-CAST
DURCO-D
DURCOMETER
DURCON
DURCOPUMP
DURICHLOR
DURIRON
EDWARD
EQUIWEDGE
EUROPAC 600
EXPERIENCE IN MOTION
FIVE STAR SEAL
FLITE-FLOW
FLOWSERVE
GASPAC
GEAREX
GESTRA
GUARDIAN
HYDREX
IDP
JEUMONTSCHNEIDER
KAMMER
LIMITORQUE
LOGIX
MAGNALERT
MAXFLO 3
MCCANNA
MCCANNA-MARPAC
NAF
NAVAL
NOBLE ALLOY
NORBRO
NORDSTORM
PAC-SEAL
PACIFIC WIETZ
PANTHER
PHAROS
PHAZER
PLEUGER
PMV
POLYCHEM
POLYVALVE
QUADRA PRESS
SCHMIDT ARMATUREN
SCIENCO
SERK AUDCO
SIER-BATH
SLEEVELINE
STARPAC
SUPERCHLOR
T-LINE
TERRA-TITAN
TITAN
TKL
ULTRASWITCH
UNITED CENTRIFUGAL
VALTEK
VALTEK EMA
VOGT
WESTERN LAND ROLLER
WILSONSNYDER
WORCESTER
WORTHINGTON
Advertising Agency:
Koroberi
1506 E Franklin St Ste 300
Chapel Hill, NC 27514
Tel.: (919) 960-9794
Fax: (919) 960-8570

FLUOR CORPORATION

6700 Las Colinas Blvd
Irving, TX 75039
Tel.: (469) 398-7000
Fax: (469) 398-7255

Key to Media (For complete agency information see *The Advertising Red Books-Agencies* edition):
1. Bus. Publs. 2. Cable T.V. 3. Catalogs & Directories. 4. Co-op Adv. 5. Consumer Mags. 6. D.M. to Bus. Estab.7. D.M. to Consumers
8. Daily Newsp. 9. Exhibits/Trade Shows 10. Foreign 11. Infomercial 12. Internet Adv.13. Multimedia 14. Network Radio
15. Network T.V. 16. Newsp. Distr. Mags. 17. Other 18. Outdoor (Posters, Transit) 19. Point of Purchase20. Premiums, Novelties
21. Product Samples 22. Special Events Mktg. 23. Spot Radio 24. Spot T.V. 25. Weekly Newsp. 26. Yellow Page Adv.

Web Site: www.fluor.com
Approx. Rev.: $20,849,349,000
Approx. Number Employees: 39,229
Year Founded: 1890
Business Description:
Engineering, Procurement, Construction & Maintenance Services
S.I.C.: 8711; 1522; 1799; 6719
N.A.I.C.S.: 541330; 236220; 238190; 551112
Personnel:
David T. Seaton *(CEO)*
D. Michael Steuert *(CFO, Chief Acctg Officer & Sr VP)*
Ray F. Barnard *(CIO & VP)*
Carlos M. Hernandez *(Chief Legal Officer & Sec)*
Lee C. Tashjian *(Pres-Fluor Foundation & VP-Corp Affairs)*
David E. Constable *(Pres-Ops)*
Stephen B. Dobbs *(Sr Grp Pres-Indus & Infrastructure-Govt & Global Svcs)*
David R. Dunning *(Pres-Power Grp)*
Kirk D. Grimes *(Pres-Global Svcs Grp)*
Peter W.B. Oosterveer *(Pres-Energy & Chemicals Grp)*
Bruce A. Stanski *(Pres-Govt Grp)*
Garry Flowers *(Sr VP-Construction Svcs)*
Glenn Gilkey *(Sr VP-HR & Admin)*
David Marventano *(Sr VP-Govt Rels)*
Robert Prieto *(Sr VP)*
James A. Scotti *(Sr VP & Chief Procurement Officer)*
Ian Thomas *(Sr VP-Corp Strategy & Emerging Markets Grp)*
Suzanne Esber *(Dir-Community Rels)*
Brands & Products:
AMECO
FLUOR
FLUOR DANIEL
FLUOR FEDERAL SERVICES
FLUOR GLOBAL SERVICES
FLUOR SIGNATURE SERVICES
KNOWLEDGE@WORK
Advertising Agency:
FD Americas Public Affairs
1101 K St NW 9th Fl
Washington, DC 20005
Tel.: (202) 346-8800
Fax: (202) 346-8804

FOLLANSBEE STEEL
(Sub. of Louis Berkman Co.)
PO Box 610
Follansbee, WV 26037
Tel.: (304) 527-1260
Fax: (304) 527-1269
Toll Free: (800) 624-6906
E-mail: info@follansbeeroofing.com
Web Site: www.follansbeeroofing.com
Year Founded: 1904
Business Description:
Roofing, Stainless Steel Sheets & Alloy Coated Stainless Steel Mfr
S.I.C.: 3312; 2952
N.A.I.C.S.: 331111; 324122
Export
Media: 2-4-10-21-26
Distr.: Natl.
Budget Set: Dec. -Jan.
Personnel:
Ed Thomas *(VP & Gen Mgr)*
Brands & Products:
THE BEST ROOF MONEY CAN BUY
FOLLANSBEE
KLASSICKOLORS
TCS II
TCS SATIN
TERNE II
Advertising Agency:
Larson O'Brien Marketing Group
3591 Ridgeway Dr Ste 200
Bethel Park, PA 15102
Tel.: (412) 831-1959
Fax: (412) 833-2838

FORTIFIBER CORPORATION
300 Industrial Blvd
Fernley, NV 89451-9309
Tel.: (775) 833-6161
Fax: (775) 833-6151
Toll Free: (800) 443-4079
Web Site: www.fortifiber.com
Sales Range: $50-74.9 Million
Approx. Number Employees: 75
Year Founded: 1939
Business Description:
Building Paper, Waterproof & Reinforced Wrapping Paper, Chemically Coated & Treated Industrial Paper, Extrusion Coated Paper & Foil
S.I.C.: 2671
N.A.I.C.S.: 322221
Media: 1-10-13
Personnel:
Christopher Yount *(Pres & COO)*
Jim Rossner *(VP-Sls & Mktg)*
Brands & Products:
AQUABAR
THE BOOT
CORNER SHIELD
FORESIGHT
FORTIFIBER
FORTIFIBER BUILDING SYSTEMS GROUP
FORTIFLASH
FORTIFY
INKWORKS
JUMBO TEX
MOISTOP E-Z SEAL
MOISTOP NEXT
ORANGE LABEL SISALKRAFT
PROTECTING YOUR WORLD FROM THE ELEMENTS
SCRIBE-RITE
SEEKURE
TRI-PLI
VAPORSTOP
WEATHERSMART

FORTRESS INTERNATIONAL GROUP, INC.
7226 Lee DeForest Dr Ste 203
Columbia, MD 21046
Tel.: (410) 423-7423
Tel.: (410) 423-7438
Tel.: (410) 312-9988
Fax: (410) 423-7437
Fax: (410) 312-9979
Web Site: www.thefigi.com
Approx. Rev.: $74,903,900
Approx. Number Employees: 114
Year Founded: 2004
Business Description:
Mission Critical Facilities & Information Infrastructure Planning, Designing & Development
S.I.C.: 8742; 7379; 7382
N.A.I.C.S.: 541614; 541519; 561621
Advertising Expenditures: $100,000
Media: 17
Personnel:
John Morton, III *(Chm)*
Harvey L. Weiss *(Vice Chm)*
Gerard J. Gallagher *(Pres)*
Thomas P. Rosato *(CEO)*
Timothy C. Dec *(CFO)*

FOUR SEASONS SUNROOM
(Sub. of Ultraframe (UK) Ltd.)
5005 Veterans Memorial Hwy
Holbrook, NY 11741-4506
Tel.: (631) 563-4000
Fax: (631) 563-4010
Toll Free: (800) 368-7732
E-mail: info@fourseasonssunrooms.com
Web Site: www.four-seasons-sunrooms.com
Approx. Number Employees: 200
Year Founded: 1975
Business Description:
Mfr. & Distr of Sunrooms, Enclosures & Large-Scale Skylights
S.I.C.: 3448; 3444
N.A.I.C.S.: 332311; 332322
Import Export
Media: 1-3-4-5-6-7-8-9-10-11-12-13-15-16-18-19-24-25-26
Distr.: Intl.; Natl.
Personnel:
Shaun Kennedy *(CEO)*
James F. Ruppel *(Dir-Corp Mktg)*
Brands & Products:
FOUR SEASONS
WONDERGLASS

FRANKLIN BUILDING SUPPLY CO. INC.
11700 W Franklin Rd
Boise, ID 83709-0139
Tel.: (208) 322-4567
Fax: (208) 322-4476
Web Site:
www.franklinbuildingsupply.com
Approx. Number Employees: 250
Year Founded: 1976
Business Description:
Lumber & Other Building Materials
S.I.C.: 5031
N.A.I.C.S.: 423310
Import Export
Personnel:
Rhonda Millick *(CFO)*
Stan Buscher *(Gen Mgr)*
Erick Wadsworth *(Gen Mgr)*
Rick Lierz *(Reg Mgr)*
Advertising Agency:
CLM Marketing & Advertising
588 W Idaho St
Boise, ID 83702-5928
Tel.: (208) 342-2525
Fax: (208) 384-1906

FRONTEER GOLD INC.
(Sub. of Newmont Mining Corporation)
Ste 1650 1055 W Hastings
Vancouver, BC V6E 2E9, Canada
Tel.: (604) 632-4677
Fax: (604) 632-4678
Toll Free: (877) 632-4677
E-mail: info@fronteergroup.com
Web Site: www.fronteergroup.com
Approx. Rev.: $33,226,777
Approx. Number Employees: 44
Business Description:
Precious Metals Mining & Exploration Services
S.I.C.: 1099
N.A.I.C.S.: 212299
Export
Advertising Expenditures: $1,774,000
Personnel:
Oliver Lennox-King *(Chm)*
Mark O'Dea *(Pres & CEO)*
Sean Tetzlaff *(CFO & Sec)*
Troy J. Fierro *(COO)*
Chris Lee *(Chief Geoscientist)*

FX40 BUILDING DESIGN CORPORATION
1557 Marine Dr West
Vancouver, BC Canada
Tel.: (604) 922-6092
Tel.: (604) 617-1443
Fax: (604) 922-6081
E-mail: info@dcfurniturecollection.com
Web Site:
www.dcfurniturecollection.com
Approx. Number Employees: 10
Year Founded: 1991
Business Description:
Residential Buildings & Renovations Designer & Developer
S.I.C.: 1522; 1531
N.A.I.C.S.: 236220; 236116; 236118
Media: 6-18
Personnel:
David Christopher *(Principal)*

GAF MATERIALS CORP.
(Formerly ElkCorp)
(Sub. of Building Materials Corporation of America)
14911 Quorum Dr Ste 600
Dallas, TX 75254
Tel.: (972) 851-0500
Fax: (972) 851-0550
Web Site: www.gaf.com
Sales Range: $900-999.9 Million
Approx. Number Employees: 1,496
Year Founded: 1955
Business Description:
Roofing & Architectural Products Mfr
S.I.C.: 2952; 2541
N.A.I.C.S.: 324122; 337212
Import Export
Advertising Expenditures: $9,869,000
Media: 2-3-4-22
Personnel:
Robert B. Tafaro *(Chm, Pres & CEO)*
John F. Rebele *(CFO & Sr VP)*
Richard A. Nowak *(COO)*
Jan Jerger-Stevens *(Sr VP-HR)*
Monte Coulter *(VP-Mktg)*
Brands & Products:
CAPSTONE
CROSSTIMBERS
DOMAIN
ICEGARD
KWIKWRAP
PLYLOC
PRESTIQUE
RAILWAYS
RAINCAP
RAISED PROFILE
RIDGECREST
RIDGLASS
ROOFGARD
SEAL-A-RIDGE
SHIELDGARD
STAINGUARD
TG-2
VERSASHIELD
Z RIDGE

Key to Media (For complete agency information see *The Advertising Red Books-Agencies* edition):
1. Bus. Publs. 2. Cable T.V. 3. Catalogs & Directories. 4. Co-op Adv. 5. Consumer Mags. 6. D.M. to Bus. Estab.7. D.M. to Consumers 8. Daily Newsp. 9. Exhibits/Trade Shows 10. Foreign 11. Infomercial 12. Internet Adv.13. Multimedia 14. Network Radio 15. Network T.V. 16. Newsp. Distr. Mags. 17. Other 18. Outdoor (Posters, Transit) 19. Point of Purchase20. Premiums, Novelties 21. Product Samples 22. Special Events Mktg. 23. Spot Radio 24. Spot T.V. 25. Weekly Newsp. 26. Yellow Page Adv.

GARY WILKES, INC.

5701 Division Dr Ste A
Fort Myers, FL 33905
Tel.: (239) 694-1122
Fax: (239) 694-0116
E-mail: info@garywilkes.com
Web Site: www.garywilkes.com
Approx. Number Employees: 10
Year Founded: 1987
Business Description:
General Contractor
S.I.C.: 1522; 1541
N.A.I.C.S.: 236220; 236210
Media: 2-6
Personnel:
Gary Wilkes *(Owner)*
Jani Denison *(Comptroller)*
A. Donegan *(Project Mgr)*

GASSER & SONS, INC.

440 Moreland Rd
Commack, NY 11725
Tel.: (631) 543-6600
Fax: (631) 543-6649
E-mail: sales@gasser.com
Web Site: www.gasser.com
E-Mail For Key Personnel:
President: rfgasser@gasser.com
Sales Director: sales@gasser.com
Approx. Number Employees: 65
Year Founded: 1916
Business Description:
Deep-draw Metal Fabrication Specialists
S.I.C.: 3469; 3444
N.A.I.C.S.: 332116; 332322
Import Export
Advertising Expenditures: $200,000
Media: 2-4-10-17-21
Distr.: Natl.
Budget Set: Nov.
Personnel:
Richard F. Gasser *(Chm & Pres)*

GENERAL CABLE CORPORATION

4 Tesseneer Dr
Highland Heights, KY 41076
Mailing Address:
PO Box 9167
Highland Heights, KY 41076-9167
Tel.: (859) 572-8000
Fax: (859) 572-8458
E-mail: info@generalcable.com
Web Site: www.generalcable.com
Approx. Sls.: $4,864,900,000
Approx. Number Employees: 11,700
Year Founded: 1844
Business Description:
Wire, Cable & Associated Products Mfr
S.I.C.: 3356; 3357
N.A.I.C.S.: 331491; 335929
Advertising Expenditures: $12,000,000
Media: 2-4-10-18-19-20-21
Personnel:
Gregory B. Kenny *(Pres & CEO)*
Brian J. Robinson *(CFO, Treas & Exec VP)*
Elizabeth W. Taliaferro *(CIO & Sr VP)*
Gregory J. Lampert *(Pres/CEO-North America & Exec VP)*
Campbell Whyte *(Pres/CEO-Gen Cable-Oceania)*
Robert J. Siverd *(Gen Counsel, Sec & Exec VP)*
Roderick Macdonald *(Exec VP-Global Sls & Bus Dev)*
Roger A. Roundhouse *(Sr VP & Gen Mgr)*
James Freestone *(Sr VP-Global Tech)*
Mark A. Thackeray *(Sr VP-North American Ops)*
Thomas E. Bisson *(VP-Sls)*
Jeffrey P. Later *(VP-Sls-Electronics)*
Brian E. Moriarty *(VP-Sls-United States)*
Mike Murphy *(VP-Sls-Gepco Brand Products)*
Brands & Products:
ANACONDA
BICC
BLOLITE
BRAND REX
CAROL
CAROLPRENE
CDC
COMMAND
COMMAND LINX
COMMAND SERIES
COMMODORE
DEMAND BETTER & EXPECT MORE
DURASHEATH
EMPOWR
EXZHELLENT
FREP
FROGHIDE
GENERAL CABLE
GENPOWR
GENSPEED
GENWRAP
HELIX
HI-TEMP
LIFETIME PLUS
LO-CAP
NEXTGEN
PANGEN
PLATINUM PLUS
PLUG-IT
POLYRAD
THE POWER OF ONE
POWRMAX
POWRNET
POWRPAK
POWRSERV
PROSPARK
QUIK-PREP
RIGTUFF
SHIPLAN
SILEC
SUPER VU-TRON
SUPERCAT
T-2
TRANSPOWR
TRU-MARK
ULTRA FLEX
ULTROL
UNIBLEND
UNISHIELD
VNTC
VU-TRON

GENERAL CABLE CORPORATION

(Sub. of General Cable Corporation)
1600 W Main St
Willimantic, CT 06226-1128
Tel.: (860) 456-8000
Fax: (860) 423-8128
Web Site: www.generalcable.com
Sales Range: $125-149.9 Million
Approx. Number Employees: 300
Year Founded: 1948
Business Description:
Production of Electronic Wire & Cable Products for the Computer, Military, Aerospace, Automotive, Industrial & Local Area Network Markets
S.I.C.: 3496
N.A.I.C.S.: 332618
Export
Advertising Expenditures: $600,000
Media: 1-2-4-7-10-20
Distr.: Natl.
Budget Set: Aug.
Personnel:
Stewart Later *(VP-Sls-Electronics)*
Brands & Products:
ANACONDA
BICC
CAROL
CHEMGUARD
POLYRAD
TAPE CABLE
TELETAPE
ULTRO
VN-FLEX
VN-TC
XL-TC

GENESIS FLUID SOLUTIONS HOLDINGS, INC.

(Name Changed to BLUE EARTH, INC.)

GENOVA PRODUCTS, INC.

7034 E Ct St
Davison, MI 48423
Tel.: (810) 744-4500
Fax: (810) 744-1653
Toll Free: (800) 521-7488
E-mail: inquiry@genovaproducts.com
Web Site: www.genovaproducts.com
Approx. Number Employees: 500
Year Founded: 1962
Business Description:
Mfr. of Plumbing Pipe, Fittings & Related Products, Raingutters & Vinyl Fencing
S.I.C.: 3089; 2891
N.A.I.C.S.: 326199; 325520
Media: 1-2-4-5-6-7-10-11-14-19-20-21-23
Distr.: Natl.
Budget Set: Oct.
Personnel:
Robert M. Williams *(Founder)*
Dwight P. Van Steenkiste *(Pres)*
Jeanette Kellogg *(VP-Sls & Mktg)*
Brands & Products:
ARCTICWELD
DEBRI-SHIELD
FLOWGUARD GOLD
GENOGRIP
GENOVA
HIGHFLO
NOVACLEAN
NOVAVENT
NOVAWELD
PVC DYNAMIC DUO
RAINGO
RAINGO & REPLAK
SNAP-FIT
STREET/SOCKET
TWIST-LOK
UNCOPPER
UNCOPPER PRO

GEORGIA GULF CORPORATION

115 Perimeter Ctr Pl Ste 460
Atlanta, GA 30346
Mailing Address:
PO Box 105197
Atlanta, GA 30348-5197
Tel.: (770) 395-4500
Fax: (770) 395-4529
E-mail: investor@ggc.com
Web Site: www.ggc.com
Approx. Sls.: $2,818,040,000
Approx. Number Employees: 3,932
Year Founded: 1985
Business Description:
Chlorovinyls & Aromatics Mfr for Construction, Housing, Plastics, Pulp & Paper, Pharmaceutical & Consumer Industries
S.I.C.: 2812; 2821; 5169
N.A.I.C.S.: 325181; 325211; 424690
Export
Advertising Expenditures: $6,400,000
Personnel:
Paul D. Carrico *(Pres & CEO)*
Gregory C. Thompson *(CFO)*
Dwain Wilcox *(CIO & VP)*
Joseph C. Breunig *(Exec VP-Chemicals)*
C. Douglas Shannon *(VP-Procurement)*
James Worrell *(VP-HR)*
Alan Chapple *(Dir-Comm)*
Pat Quinlan *(Dir-Aromatics)*
Brands & Products:
GEORGIA GULF
SOLUCOR

GEORGIA MARBLE DIMENSION STONE

(Sub. of Polycor Inc.)
200 Georgia Marble Ln PO Box 238
Tate, GA 30177-0238
Tel.: (770) 735-2611
Fax: (770) 735-2236
Toll Free: (800) 334-0122
E-mail: georgiamarble@polycor.com
Web Site: www.polycor.com/eng
Approx. Number Employees: 65
Year Founded: 1884
Business Description:
Stone for Building Facades & Interiors, Memorial Monuments, Crushed & Ground Calcium Carbonate Products & Consumer Landscape Products
S.I.C.: 1411; 1422
N.A.I.C.S.: 212311; 212312
Advertising Expenditures: $500,000
Media: 5
Distr.: Natl.
Budget Set: Oct.
Brands & Products:
THE AMERICAN CLASSICS
CHEROKEE
ETOWAH
MARBLSTAL
PATHWAYS

GEOSPATIAL HOLDINGS, INC.

229 Howes Run Rd
Sarver, PA 16055
Tel.: (724) 353-3400
Fax: (724) 353-3049
E-mail: info@geospatialcorporation.com
Web Site: www.geospatialcorporation.com

Key to Media (For complete agency information see *The Advertising Red Books-Agencies* edition):
1. Bus. Publs. 2. Cable T.V. 3. Catalogs & Directories. 4. Co-op Adv. 5. Consumer Mags. 6. D.M. to Bus. Estab.7. D.M. to Consumers 8. Daily Newsp. 9. Exhibits/Trade Shows 10. Foreign 11. Infomercial 12. Internet Adv.13. Multimedia 14. Network Radio 15. Network T.V. 16. Newsp. Distr. Mags. 17. Other 18. Outdoor (Posters, Transit) 19. Point of Purchase20. Premiums, Novelties 21. Product Samples 22. Special Events Mktg. 23. Spot Radio 24. Spot T.V. 25. Weekly Newsp. 26. Yellow Page Adv.

Approx. Rev.: $825,669
Approx. Number Employees: 60
Business Description:
Pipeline Management Services
S.I.C.: 8713; 1389; 8748
N.A.I.C.S.: 541360; 213112; 541618
Advertising Expenditures: $160,554
Media: 17
Personnel:
Mark A. Smith *(Chm, Pres & CEO)*
Thomas R. Oxenreiter *(CFO)*
Todd R. Porter *(Exec VP-Worldwide Energy Ops)*
Linda M. Ward *(Exec VP-Bus Dev)*

GERBER PLUMBING FIXTURES CORPORATION

2500 Internationale Pkwy
Woodridge, IL 60517
Tel.: (630) 679-1420
Fax: (630) 679-1430
E-mail: sales@gerberonline.com
Web Site: www.gerberonline.com
E-Mail For Key Personnel:
Sales Director: sales@gerberonline.com
Sales Range: $100-124.9 Million
Approx. Number Employees: 900
Year Founded: 1932
Business Description:
Plumbing Fixtures Mfr
S.I.C.: 3432
N.A.I.C.S.: 332913
Export
Advertising Expenditures: $200,000
Media: 2-4-7-10-20-22-24
Distr.: Intl.; Natl.
Budget Set: Oct.
Personnel:
Kevin McJoynt *(Dir-Mktg)*
Brands & Products:
AQUA SAVER
CERAMAFLOW
GERBER
GERBER HARDWATER
LUXOVAL
MAURICE
MAXWELL
MIRAGE
OVAL
RESILIENCE
SAFETEMP
ULTRA FLUSH
Advertising Agency:
Kleber & Associates Marketing & Communications
1215 Hightower Trl Bldg C
Atlanta, GA 30350
Tel.: (770) 518-1000
Fax: (770) 518-2700
Plumbing Fixtures

GILBANE BUILDING COMPANY

(Sub. of Gilbane, Inc.)
7 Jackson Walkway
Providence, RI 02903-3623
Tel.: (401) 456-5800
Fax: (401) 456-5936
Toll Free: (800) GILBANE
E-mail: bolean@gilbaneco.com
Web Site: www.gilbaneco.com
E-Mail For Key Personnel:
Public Relations: wcotter@gilbaneco.com
Sales Range: $1-4.9 Billion
Approx. Number Employees: 400
Year Founded: 1873
Business Description:
Commercial Construction Management & General Contractors
S.I.C.: 1522
N.A.I.C.S.: 236220
Media: 10-17
Distr.: Natl.
Budget Set: Jan.
Personnel:
Thomas F. Gilbane, Jr. *(Chm & CEO)*
John Ruggieri *(CFO & Sr VP)*
Alfred K. Potter, II *(Chief Strategy Officer & Sr VP)*
Richard R. Roy *(Treas & Sr VP-Fin)*
George Cavallo *(Exec VP)*
Daniel P. McConaghy *(Exec VP)*
Thomas M. Laird, Jr. *(Sr VP & Reg Mgr-Central Reg)*
John V. Ros, Jr. *(Sr VP & Reg Mgr-Southwest Reg)*
Michael Bohn *(Sr VP & Reg Mgr)*
Gregory C. Stewart *(Sr VP & Reg Mgr-Delaware Valley Reg)*
Anthony O'Dea *(VP & Dir-Safety)*
Wes Cotter *(Dir-Comm)*
Kristy dosReis *(Dir-Mktg Comm)*
Scott Eckartz *(Dir-Southeast Region)*
Susan Klawans *(Dir-Client Satisfaction)*
Adam Jelen *(Mgr-Milwaukee)*
Brands & Products:
GILBANE

GLEN-GERY CORPORATION

(Sub. of Oldcastle Architectural, Inc.)
1166 Spring St
Wyomissing, PA 19610-6001
Mailing Address:
PO Box 7001
Wyomissing, PA 19610
Tel.: (610) 374-4011
Fax: (610) 374-1622
E-mail: gg@glengerybrick.com
Web Site: www.glengerybrick.com
Approx. Number Employees: 30
Year Founded: 1890
Business Description:
Mfr. & Sales of Brick & Concrete Block
S.I.C.: 3251; 3272
N.A.I.C.S.: 327121; 327332
Export
Advertising Expenditures: $456,000
Media: 1-4-6-7-8-9-10-16-17-18-19-20-21-23-24-25-26
Distr.: Direct to Consumer; Natl.
Budget Set: Dec.
Personnel:
Stephen G. Matsick *(Pres)*
Lawson Booker *(VP-HR)*
Ben Hoenich *(Mgr-Mktg)*
Brands & Products:
GLEN-GERY

THE GOLDFIELD CORPORATION

1684 W Hibiscus Blvd
Melbourne, FL 32901-3073
Tel.: (321) 724-1700
Fax: (321) 724-1163
E-mail: investorrelations@goldfieldcorp.com
Web Site: www.goldfieldcorp.com
Approx. Rev.: $33,367,979
Approx. Number Employees: 18
Year Founded: 1968
Business Description:
Mining & Milling of Copper, Zinc & Silver; Electrical Construction
S.I.C.: 1623; 1799
N.A.I.C.S.: 237110; 237130; 238910
Export
Advertising Expenditures: $4,016,653
Personnel:
John H. Sottile *(Chm, Pres & CEO)*
Stephen R. Wherry *(CFO & Sr VP)*

GRACE PERFORMANCE CHEMICALS

(Sub. of W. R. GRACE & CO.)
62 Whittemore Ave
Cambridge, MA 02140-1623
Tel.: (617) 876-1400
Fax: (617) 498-4311
Sales Range: $1-4.9 Billion
Approx. Number Employees: 2,000
Business Description:
Waterproofing, Concrete Admixtures, Thermal Barriers, Cement Processing Additives & Masonry Products
S.I.C.: 2899
N.A.I.C.S.: 325998
Advertising Expenditures: $4,000,000
Media: 10
Distr.: Intl.; Natl.
Budget Set: Sept.
Personnel:
Christine L. Welby *(Mgr-Divisional Mktg Commun)*

GRANITE CONSTRUCTION INCORPORATED

585 W Beach St
Watsonville, CA 95076
Tel.: (831) 724-1011
Fax: (831) 722-9657
E-mail: info@gcinc.com
Web Site:
www.graniteconstruction.com
Approx. Rev.: $1,762,965,000
Approx. Number Employees: 2,300
Year Founded: 1990
Business Description:
Holding Company; Heavy Civil Construction Contractor Services
S.I.C.: 6719; 1622; 1629
N.A.I.C.S.: 551112; 237310; 237990
Bus. Publs.: 100%
Personnel:
James H. Roberts *(Pres & CEO)*
Laurel J. Krzeminski *(CFO & VP)*
Terry K. Eller *(Gen Counsel, VP & Sec)*
Michael F. Donnino *(Sr VP & Grp Mgr)*
Advertising Agency:
Jeffrey/Scott Advertising
670 P St
Fresno, CA 93721-2704
Tel.: (559) 268-9741
Fax: (559) 268-9759

GRAYCOR INC.

1 Graycor Dr
Homewood, IL 60430-4618
Tel.: (708) 206-0500
Fax: (708) 206-0505
E-mail: info@graycor.com
Web Site: www.graycor.com
E-Mail For Key Personnel:
Marketing Director: brian_redington@graycor.com
Public Relations: melissa_garcia@graycor.com
Sales Range: $400-449.9 Million
Approx. Number Employees: 1,500
Year Founded: 1921
Business Description:
Holding Company; Commercial Construction Contractor
S.I.C.: 6719; 1522; 1541
N.A.I.C.S.: 551112; 236210; 236220
Advertising Expenditures: $1,000,000
Media: 2-4-7-10-17-20-26
Distr.: Natl.
Budget Set: May
Personnel:
Melvin Gray *(Chm)*
Steve F. Gray *(Vice Chm & CFO)*
John Shannon *(Bus Mgr)*
Brands & Products:
BUILDING SOMETHING MORE.
GRAYCOR
WANTED: A HARD JOB
Advertising Agency:
Tonic Blue Communications
200 E Evergreen Ste 101
Mount Prospect, IL 60056
Tel.: (847) 255-2335
Fax: (847) 255-2328

GREASE MONKEY INTERNATIONAL, INC.

7100 E Belleview Ave Ste 305
Greenwood Village, CO 80111
Tel.: (303) 308-1660
Fax: (303) 308-5906
Toll Free: (800) 822-7706
E-mail: marketing@greasemonkeyintl.com
Web Site:
www.greasemonkeyintl.com
Approx. Sls.: $6,500,000
Approx. Number Employees: 40
Year Founded: 1978
Business Description:
Owner, Operator, Franchisor of Quick Lubrication Centers
S.I.C.: 7549; 6794
N.A.I.C.S.: 811191; 533110
Export
Advertising Expenditures: $560,000
Media: 3-5-7-8-9-11-13-18-19-23-25-26
Distr.: Reg.
Budget Set: Dec.
Personnel:
Chester Stokes *(Chm)*
Rex L. Utsler *(Pres & CEO)*
Ronald Smith *(CFO)*
Lori Schneider *(VP-Mktg & Comm)*
Brands & Products:
GREASE MONKEY
PREVENTIVE MAINTENANCE PROS
Advertising Agency:
Sexton & Co.
4429 South Atchison Circle
Aurora, CO 80015
Tel.: (303) 246-0366
Fax: (303) 997-7330

GREAT GRABZ

4535 Domestic Ave Ste D
Naples, FL 34104
Tel.: (239) 435-0677
Fax: (239) 261-8255
Toll Free: (866) 478-4722
E-mail: ashley@greatgrabz.com
Web Site: www.greatgrabz.com
Approx. Number Employees: 4
Business Description:
Decorative Safety Bar Designer & Mfr
S.I.C.: 3429
N.A.I.C.S.: 332510

Key to Media (For complete agency information see *The Advertising Red Books-Agencies* edition):
1. Bus. Publs. 2. Cable T.V. 3. Catalogs & Directories. 4. Co-op Adv. 5. Consumer Mags. 6. D.M. to Bus. Estab.7. D.M. to Consumers
8. Daily Newsp. 9. Exhibits/Trade Shows 10. Foreign 11. Infomercial 12. Internet Adv.13. Multimedia 14. Network Radio
15. Network T.V. 16. Newsp. Distr. Mags. 17. Other 18. Outdoor (Posters, Transit) 19. Point of Purchase20. Premiums, Novelties
21. Product Samples 22. Special Events Mktg. 23. Spot Radio 24. Spot T.V. 25. Weekly Newsp. 26. Yellow Page Adv.

Great Grabz — (Continued)

Media: 6-7-8-13
Personnel:
Abbie J.W. Sladick *(Pres)*
Ashley Armstrong *(VP-Mktg)*
Advertising Agencies:
Aspire Internet Design
15762 W. 70th Dr
Arvada, CO 80007
Tel.: (303) 940-2537

Maven Group
1101 Kings Way
Naples, FL 34104
Tel.: (239) 384-9455
Fax: (239) 434-2791

GREAT LAKES DREDGE & DOCK CORPORATION
2122 York Rd
Oak Brook, IL 60523
Tel.: (630) 574-3000
Fax: (630) 574-2909
Web Site: www.gldd.com
Approx. Rev.: $686,922,000
Approx. Number Employees: 1,023
Year Founded: 1890
Business Description:
Dredging & Other Port Services
S.I.C.: 1629; 4499
N.A.I.C.S.: 237990; 488310
Advertising Expenditures: $100,000
Media: 2-4-6-10-18-19-20-26
Distr.: Intl.; Natl.
Personnel:
Nathan David Leight *(Chm)*
Bruce J. Biemeck *(Pres, CFO & Treas)*
Jonathan W. Berger *(CEO)*
David E. Simonelli *(Pres-Dredging Ops)*
Kyle D. Johnson *(Sr VP-Ops)*
John F. Karas *(Sr VP-Estimating & Bus Dev)*
William H. Hanson *(VP & Mgr-Bus Dev-US)*
Steven F. O'Hara *(VP, Mgr-Area)*
William F. Pagendarm *(VP-Hopper Dredging)*
Steven W. Becker *(Chief Mechanical Engr & VP-Plant Equipment)*

GREAT LAKES WINDOW, INC.
(Sub. of Ply Gem Industries, Inc.)
30499 Tracy Rd
Walbridge, OH 43465-9777
Tel.: (419) 666-5555
Fax: (419) 661-2926
Fax: (419) 666-7643
Toll Free: (800) 666-0000
E-mail: webmaster@greatlakeswindow.com
Web Site:
www.greatlakeswindow.com
Approx. Number Employees: 650
Year Founded: 1981
Business Description:
Vinyl Replacement Windows & Patio Doors
S.I.C.: 3089; 5031
N.A.I.C.S.: 326199; 423310
Advertising Expenditures: $600,000
Media: 7-8
Personnel:
Jeff Klein *(Pres)*
Ralph Pfeiffer *(Dir-Mktg)*
Brands & Products:
GREAT LAKES

GREAT PLAINS COMPANIES, INC.
1 Carlson Pkwy N Ste 120
Plymouth, MN 55447-4453
Mailing Address:
PO Box 309
Anoka, MN 55303-0309
Tel.: (763) 208-9760
Fax: (763) 258-0166
Toll Free: (800) 488-9545
Sales Range: $25-49.9 Million
Approx. Number Employees: 250
Year Founded: 1989
Business Description:
Holding Company; Residential Construction Contractors
S.I.C.: 6719; 1521
N.A.I.C.S.: 551112; 236115
Media: 5-10-20-22-23-24-25-26
Personnel:
Michael R. Wigley *(CEO)*
Dave Franze *(CFO & Controller)*

GREER STEEL COMPANY
(Sub. of Greer Industries Inc.)
624 Blvd
Dover, OH 44622
Tel.: (330) 343-8811
Fax: (330) 343-1700
Toll Free: (800) 388-2868
E-mail: sales@greersteel.com
Web Site: www.greersteel.com
E-Mail For Key Personnel:
Sales Director: sales@greersteel.com
Approx. Number Employees: 225
Year Founded: 1917
Business Description:
Cold Rolled Strip Steel & Flat Wire Mfr
S.I.C.: 3316
N.A.I.C.S.: 331221
Media: 2-4
Personnel:
Charlie Eames *(Mgr-Admin Sls)*
Cha Reanef *(Mgr-Sls-Admin)*

GREG WEBER, INC.
9220 Bonita Beach Rd Ste 200
Bonita Springs, FL 34135
Tel.: (239) 333-4001
Fax: (239) 592-5326
E-mail: greg@gregweberinc.com
Web Site: www.gregweberinc.com
Sales Range: Less than $1 Million
Approx. Number Employees: 1
Business Description:
Custom Home Designer
S.I.C.: 1521
N.A.I.C.S.: 236115
Media: 6-13-17
Personnel:
Greg Weber *(Owner)*

GREGORY POOLE EQUIPMENT COMPANY INC.
(Sub. of Panther Summit Industries Inc.)
4807 Beryl Rd PO Box 469
Raleigh, NC 27606-1406
Tel.: (919) 828-0641
Fax: (919) 890-4643
E-mail: info@gregorypoole.com
Web Site: www.gregorypoole.com
Sales Range: $25-49.9 Million
Approx. Number Employees: 650
Year Founded: 1957
Business Description:
Supplier of Construction & Mining Machinery
S.I.C.: 7353; 5084
N.A.I.C.S.: 532412; 423830
Personnel:
J. Gregory Poole, III *(Pres & COO)*
Kathy Morris *(CFO & VP)*
Richard Donnelly *(Exec VP)*
Advertising Agency:
Emery Advertising
4911 Green Rd Ste 101
Raleigh, NC 27616
Tel.: (919) 790-2600
Fax: (919) 790-2601

GROSSMANS BARGAIN OUTLET
(Sub. of E.C. Barton & Company)
90 Hawes Way
Stoughton, MA 02072
Tel.: (781) 297-3300
Fax: (781) 297-0180
E-mail: feedback@bargain-outlets.com
Web Site: www.bargain-outlets.com
Approx. Number Employees: 25
Year Founded: 1967
Business Description:
Lumber, Building Materials & Other Home Improvement Products Whslr
S.I.C.: 5031
N.A.I.C.S.: 423310
Media: 3-8-9-17-18-23-24-25-26
Distr.: Reg.
Budget Set: Sept.
Personnel:
Tom Ford *(Pres & CEO)*
Tom Dowd *(Dir-Adv)*

GUARDIAN BUILDING PRODUCTS
(Sub. of Guardian Industries Corp.)
979 Batesville Rd
Greer, SC 29651
Mailing Address:
PO Box 207
Greenville, SC 29602
Tel.: (864) 297-6101
Fax: (864) 281-3558
Toll Free: (800) 569-4262
Web Site: www.guardianbp.com
Approx. Number Employees: 285
Year Founded: 1966
Business Description:
Wholesale Distributor of Lumber & Wood Products; Building Materials
S.I.C.: 5033; 5031
N.A.I.C.S.: 423330; 423310
Import
Media: 2-4-7-10-17
Distr.: Natl.
Personnel:
John Gunn *(VP-Procurement)*
Bruce Schneider *(VP-Sls)*
Brands & Products:
BMA
BMA PLUS

GUARDIAN INDUSTRIES CORP.
2300 Harmon Rd
Auburn Hills, MI 48326-1714
Tel.: (248) 340-1800
Fax: (248) 340-9988
Web Site: www.guardian.com
Sales Range: $5-14.9 Billion
Approx. Number Employees: 18,000
Year Founded: 1932
Business Description:
Insulation, Glass & Automotive Parts Mfr
S.I.C.: 3211; 5013; 5211
N.A.I.C.S.: 327211; 441310; 444190
Export
Media: 1-2-4-6-8-10-16-21
Distr.: Natl.
Budget Set: Jan.
Personnel:
Ralph J. Gerson *(Pres & CEO)*
Jeffrey A. Knight *(CFO & Grp VP)*
Russell J. Ebeid *(Pres-Glass Grp)*
Duane Faulkner *(Pres-Building Products Grp)*
David Jaffe *(Gen Counsel)*
Scott Thomsen *(Grp VP-North American Flat Glass Ops)*
Peter S. Walters *(Grp VP)*
Martin Powell *(VP-Sls & Mktg)*
Chris Dolan *(Dir-Comml Glass)*
Amy Hennes *(Mgr-Corp Commun)*
Brands & Products:
ART-GUARD
ARTIST CHOICE
CLIMAGUARD
CLIMAGUARD RLF
CLIMAGUARD SPF
DIAMONDGUARD
ECOGUARD
EXTRACLEAR
GBP PLUS
MASTERSPEC
SHOWERGUARD
SILACOAT
SUNGUARD
ULTRA MIRROR
ULTRAWHITE
Advertising Agencies:
Carton Donofrio Partners, Inc.
100 N Charles St 15th Fl
Baltimore, MD 21201
Tel.: (410) 576-9000
Fax: (410) 528-8809

The VIA Group LLC
34 Danforth St Ste 309
Portland, ME 04101
Tel.: (207) 221-3000
Fax: (207) 761-9422

GULF STATES MANUFACTURERS, INC.
(Sub. of Nucor Building Systems)
101 Airport Rd
Starkville, MS 39759-9682
Mailing Address:
PO Box 1128
Starkville, MS 39760-1128
Tel.: (662) 323-8021
Fax: (662) 324-2984
E-mail: sales@gulfstatesmanufacturers.com
Web Site:
www.gulfstatesmanufacturers.com
E-Mail For Key Personnel:
Sales Director: sales@gulfstatesmanufacturers.com
Approx. Sls.: $45,000,000
Approx. Number Employees: 192
Year Founded: 1968
Business Description:
Pre-Engineered Steel Buildings Mfr
S.I.C.: 3448

Key to Media (For complete agency information see *The Advertising Red Books-Agencies* edition):
1. Bus. Publs. 2. Cable T.V. 3. Catalogs & Directories. 4. Co-op Adv. 5. Consumer Mags. 6. D.M. to Bus. Estab.7. D.M. to Consumers
8. Daily Newsp. 9. Exhibits/Trade Shows 10. Foreign 11. Infomercial 12. Internet Adv.13. Multimedia 14. Network Radio
15. Network T.V. 16. Newsp. Distr. Mags. 17. Other 18. Outdoor (Posters, Transit) 19. Point of Purchase20. Premiums, Novelties
21. Product Samples 22. Special Events Mktg. 23. Spot Radio 24. Spot T.V. 25. Weekly Newsp. 26. Yellow Page Adv.

N.A.I.C.S.: 332311
Export
Advertising Expenditures: $300,000
Media: 2-5-6-7-8-10-11-13-18-26
Distr.: Intl.; Natl.
Budget Set: Jan.
Personnel:
Danny Coggins *(Pres)*
Cory Montgomery *(Dir-Sls)*
Becky Roland *(Mgr-Mktg)*
Brands & Products:
GULF STATES

GULFSTREAM HOMES, INC.
6646 Willow Park Dr
Naples, FL 34109
Tel.: (239) 280-3100
Fax: (239) 280-3150
Web Site: www.gulfstreamhomes.com
Approx. Number Employees: 50
Year Founded: 1998
Business Description:
Residential Homes Designer & Builder
S.I.C.: 1521
N.A.I.C.S.: 236115
Media: 6
Personnel:
Michael J. Peel *(Co-Founder, Co-Owner & Pres)*
Stephen L. Peel *(Co-Founder, Co-Owner & VP)*
Jeneane Paula Bennett *(Dir-Sls & Mktg)*
Chris Coughlin *(Mgr-Field)*
Kirk Emery *(Mgr-Field)*
Robert Fuerstenau *(Mgr-Field)*
Dale Hogue *(Mgr-Construction)*
Tyler MacKay *(Mgr-Field)*
Virginia Madden *(Mgr-Bus)*
Jack Mathieson *(Mgr-Project)*
Walter Mulock *(Mgr-Field)*
Mark Napoli *(Mgr)*
Justin Osnes *(Mgr-Field)*
Craig Saunders *(Mgr-Field)*
Renee Uhlar *(Mgr-Acctg)*

GUY F. ATKINSON CONSTRUCTION, LLC
(Sub. of Clark Construction Group, LLC)
11001 W 120th Ave Ste 310
Broomfield, CO 80021
Tel.: (303) 410-2542
Fax: (303) 410-9705
E-mail: information@atkn.com
Web Site: www.atkn.com
Sales Range: $550-599.9 Million
Approx. Number Employees: 3,000
Year Founded: 1928
Business Description:
Heavy, Civil Construction & Manufacturing Operations
S.I.C.: 1629
N.A.I.C.S.: 237990
Import Export
Media: 1-2-4
Distr.: Natl.
Budget Set: Oct.
Personnel:
Joe Cooper *(Sr VP)*

H&E EQUIPMENT SERVICES, INC.
11100 Mead Rd Ste 200
Baton Rouge, LA 70816
Tel.: (225) 298-5200
Fax: (225) 298-5377
Toll Free: (877) 700RENT
E-mail: Imagee@he-equipment.com
Web Site: www.he-equipment.com
Approx. Rev.: $574,154,000
Approx. Number Employees: 1,616
Year Founded: 1971
Business Description:
Equipment Distributor; Rentals, Sales, Parts & Service of Construction, Mining & Industrial Equipment
S.I.C.: 1541; 5082; 7359
N.A.I.C.S.: 236210; 423810; 532411; 532490
Import Export
Advertising Expenditures: $600,000
Media: 2-7-13-26
Personnel:
Gary W. Bagley *(Chm)*
John M. Engquist *(Pres & CEO)*
Leslie S. Magee *(CFO & Sec)*
Toby Hawkins *(VP-Mktg)*
Brands & Products:
H AND E EQUIPMENT SERVICES

H-P PRODUCTS, INC.
512 W Gorgas St
Louisville, OH 44641-1332
Mailing Address:
PO Box 3912
Louisville, OH 44641-1332
Tel.: (330) 875-5556
Fax: (330) 875-7584
Toll Free: (800) 822-8356
E-mail: info@hpproducts.net
Web Site: www.hpproducts.net
Sales Range: $100-124.9 Million
Approx. Number Employees: 300
Year Founded: 1948
Business Description:
Fabricated Tubing Systems & Components, H-P Tubing, Central Vacuum Cleaning Systems & Offset Pipe Bends Mfr
S.I.C.: 3498; 3564
N.A.I.C.S.: 332996; 333411
Import Export
Advertising Expenditures: $300,000
Media: 1-3-4-6-7-9-10-19-20-23-24
Distr.: Intl.; Natl.
Budget Set: Dec.
Personnel:
Paul R. Bishop *(Chm & CEO)*
David L. Bishop *(Vice Chm)*
Allen Green *(Pres & COO)*
Greg Calderone *(VP & Gen Mgr-Floorcare)*
Amy Wesley *(Mgr-Mktg)*
Brands & Products:
FLOORVAC
H-P PRODUCTS
MAXUM
METFLO
PLATINUM FORCE
TURBOCAT
TURBOTEAM
VACUFLO
Advertising Agency:
Liggett Stashower
LS Brand Bldg 1240 Huron Rd
Cleveland, OH 44115
Tel.: (216) 348-8500
Fax: (914) 407-1475
Vacuum Systems

HANDY & HARMAN LTD.
(Formerly WHX Corporation)
(Sub. of Steel Partners, LLC)
1133 Westchester Ave Ste N222
White Plains, NY 10604
Tel.: (914) 461-1300
Fax: (914) 696-8684
E-mail: info@handyharman.com
Web Site: www.handyharman.com
Approx. Sls.: $581,515,000
Approx. Number Employees: 1,790
Year Founded: 1920
Business Description:
Black Plate Sheets & Coils, Blued Plate, Coke & Coke By-Products, Cold Rolled Sheets & Coils, Electrolytic Tin Plate Sheets & Coils, Galvanized Sheets & Coils; Hot Rolled Bands, Sheets, Coils, Plates, Pattern Design Cold Rolled Sheets & Coils, Prepainted Steel, Semi-Finished Products, Culvert Sheets Mfr
S.I.C.: 3479; 3312; 3496
N.A.I.C.S.: 332812; 331111; 332618
Import Export
Advertising Expenditures: $3,300,000
Media: 1-2-4-5-7-8-9-10-17-18-19-20-21-24
Distr.: Natl.
Budget Set: Oct.
Personnel:
Warren G. Lichtenstein *(Chm)*
Glen M. Kassan *(Vice Chm & CEO)*
James F. McCabe, Jr. *(CFO & Sr VP)*

THE HANDY/KENLIN GROUP
29 E Hintz Rd
Wheeling, IL 60090
Tel.: (847) 459-0900
Fax: (847) 459-0902
E-mail: customerservice@handykenlin.com
Web Site: www.handykenlin.com
Sales Range: $10-24.9 Million
Approx. Number Employees: 30
Year Founded: 1898
Business Description:
Mfr of Button Covering Machines, Metal Stamps & Furniture Hardware
S.I.C.: 3965; 3552
N.A.I.C.S.: 339993; 333292
Media: 2-4-7-10-19-21-26
Distr.: Natl.
Personnel:
Ken Shonfeld *(Pres & CEO)*
Michael Baritz *(CEO)*

HARROP INDUSTRIES, INC.
3470 E 5th Ave
Columbus, OH 43219
Tel.: (614) 231-3621
Fax: (614) 235-3699
E-mail: sales@harropusa.com
Web Site: www.harropusa.com
E-Mail For Key Personnel:
Sales Director: sales@harropusa.com
Approx. Number Employees: 50
Year Founded: 1919
Business Description:
Designer & Constructor of Kilns & Dryers for Ceramic Industry; Engineering Services for Feasability & Construction of Plants; Mfr of Modular Kilns & Furnaces & Thermal Analysis Testing Service Instruments
S.I.C.: 1629; 3567
N.A.I.C.S.: 237990; 333994
Export
Advertising Expenditures: $100,000
Bus. Publs.: $100,000
Distr.: Direct to Consumer; Intl.; Natl.
Budget Set: Jan.
Personnel:
James E. Houseman *(Pres)*
Terry Henderson *(Controller)*

HARSCO CORPORATION
350 Poplar Church Rd
Camp Hill, PA 17001
Mailing Address:
PO Box 8888
Camp Hill, PA 17001-8888
Tel.: (717) 763-7064
Fax: (717) 763-6424
E-mail: info@harsco.com
Web Site: www.harsco.com
Approx. Rev.: $3,038,678,000
Approx. Number Employees: 19,300
Year Founded: 1956
Business Description:
Industrial Services & Engineered Products to Steel, Construction, Gas & Energy & Railway Transportation Industries
S.I.C.: 2813; 3341; 3443; 3559; 4953; 5045; 5051; 7389
N.A.I.C.S.: 325120; 331314; 331423; 331492; 332313; 332410; 332420; 423510; 425110; 425120; 562212; 562920
Export
Media: 2-4-7-10-17
Distr.: Natl.
Budget Set: Jan.
Personnel:
Salvatore D. Fazzolari *(Chm, Pres & CEO)*
Richard C. Neuffer *(Vice Chm)*
Stephen J. Schnoor *(CFO & Chief Acctg Officer)*
Han Jansen *(CFO-Metals & Minerals)*
Douglas Eubanks *(CIO & VP)*
Mark E. Kimmel *(Chief Admin Officer, Gen Counsel, Sec & Sr VP)*
Galdino J. Claro *(CEO-Harsco Metals & Harsco Minerals Bus Grp & Exec VP)*
A. Verona Dorch *(VP, Asst Sec & Deputy Gen Counsel)*
Gerald F. Vinci *(VP-HR)*
Kenneth Julian *(Sr Dir-Comm)*
Brands & Products:
HARSCO
INSIGHT ONSITE
Advertising Agency:
Parker Advertising Service, Inc.
101 N Pointe Blvd 2nd Fl
Lancaster, PA 17601
Tel.: (717) 581-1966
Fax: (717) 581-1566
Toll Free: (800) 396-3306

HARSCO INFRASTRUCTURE
(Sub. of Harsco Corporation)
1 Mack Centre Dr
Paramus, NJ 07652-3908
Mailing Address:
650 From Road Ste 525
Paramus, NJ 07652
Tel.: (201) 261-5600
Fax: (201) 261-5544
Toll Free: (800) 969-5600
Web Site: www.harsco-i.us
E-Mail For Key Personnel:
Sales Director: sales@pcshd.com
Sales Range: $50-74.9 Million
Approx. Number Employees: 125
Business Description:
Steel & Aluminum Scaffolding, Shoring & Forming Equipment Mfr & Distr

Key to Media (For complete agency information see *The Advertising Red Books-Agencies* edition):
1. Bus. Publs. 2. Cable T.V. 3. Catalogs & Directories. 4. Co-op Adv. 5. Consumer Mags. 6. D.M. to Bus. Estab.7. D.M. to Consumers 8. Daily Newsp. 9. Exhibits/Trade Shows 10. Foreign 11. Infomercial 12. Internet Adv.13. Multimedia 14. Network Radio 15. Network T.V. 16. Newsp. Distr. Mags. 17. Other 18. Outdoor (Posters, Transit) 19. Point of Purchase20. Premiums, Novelties 21. Product Samples 22. Special Events Mktg. 23. Spot Radio 24. Spot T.V. 25. Weekly Newsp. 26. Yellow Page Adv.

Harsco Infrastructure — (Continued)

S.I.C.: 5082; 5032
N.A.I.C.S.: 423810; 423320
Advertising Expenditures: $305,000
Media: 2-4-7-10-17
Distr.: Natl.
Budget Set: Oct.
Personnel:
Ivor J. Harrington *(CEO & Exec VP)*
Michael Cubitt *(CFO)*

HARVEY INDUSTRIES, INC.

1400 Main St
Waltham, MA 02451-1601
Tel.: (781) 899-3500
Fax: (781) 398-7826
Toll Free: (800) 9HARVEY
E-mail: info@harveyind.com
Web Site: www.harveybp.com
Approx. Sls.: $485,000,000
Approx. Number Employees: 1,800
Year Founded: 1961
Business Description:
Roofing, Siding & Insulation, Metal Doors, Sash, Trim & Millwork
S.I.C.: 5033; 5031
N.A.I.C.S.: 423330; 423310
Media: 2-4-6-7-8-9-10-13-19
Distr.: Reg.
Budget Set: Aug.
Personnel:
Alan Marlow *(Pres)*
Tom Bigony *(Co-CEO)*
Erik Jarnryd *(Co-CEO)*
Frances E. Martel *(CFO & Sr VP)*
Glen Frederick *(Sr VP-Mktg)*
Tony Furlan *(VP & Mgr)*
Brands & Products:
ACOUSTIC
ENERGY STAR
HARVEY
INTERCEPT
TRU-CHANNEL

HBE CORPORATION

11330 Olive Blvd
Saint Louis, MO 63141-7149
Tel.: (314) 567-9000
Fax: (314) 567-0602
Toll Free: (800) 423-4677
Web Site: www.hbecorp.com
Sales Range: $650-699.9 Million
Approx. Number Employees: 6,000
Year Founded: 1960
Business Description:
Design & Construction Services for Hospitals, Medical Office Buildings & Financial Facilities; Owner of Hotels
S.I.C.: 7011; 6552
N.A.I.C.S.: 721110; 237210
Advertising Expenditures: $5,000,000
Media: 1-2-4-6-7-9-10-18-20-22-25
Distr.: Natl.
Budget Set: Nov.
Personnel:
Fred S. Kummer *(Founder & CEO)*
Steve Grosswald *(Sr VP-Hospital Design & Construction)*
Mark Ames *(VP-Mktg & Adv)*

HCS CORPORATION

(Sub. of Saint-Gobain Corporation)
22626 85th Pl S
Kent, WA 98031-2469
Tel.: (253) 854-4945
Fax: (253) 854-4947
E-mail: hotcell@hotcell.com
Web Site: www.hotcell.com
Approx. Sls.: $3,800,000
Approx. Number Employees: 13
Year Founded: 1997
Business Description:
Radiation Shielding Windows Mfr
S.I.C.: 3231
N.A.I.C.S.: 327215
Media: 4
Brands & Products:
SUPER CONTRYX XRAY GLASSES

HD SUPPLY, INC.

(Joint Venture of Carlyle Holding Corporation, Bain Capital, LLC & Clayton, Dubilier & Rice, LLC)
3100 Cumberland Blvd Ste 1480
Atlanta, GA 30339
Tel.: (770) 852-9000
Web Site: www.hdsupplyinc.com
Approx. Sls.: $7,477,000,000
Approx. Number Employees: 15,200
Year Founded: 1928
Business Description:
Construction & Maintenance-Related Products Wholesale Distr; Owned by Bain Capital LLC, The Carlyle Group Inc. & Clayton, Dubilier & Rice, Inc.
S.I.C.: 5039; 5063; 5074; 5162
N.A.I.C.S.: 423390; 423610; 423720; 424610
Import Export
Advertising Expenditures: $22,000,000
Personnel:
James G. Berges *(Chm)*
Joseph J. DeAngelo *(CEO)*
Ronald J. Domanico *(CFO & Sr VP)*
Michele M. Markham *(CIO & Sr VP)*
Anesa Chaibi *(Pres/CEO-HD Supply Facilities Maintenance)*
Jerry Webb *(Pres/CEO-HD Supply Waterworks)*
Vasken Altounian *(Pres-HD Supply Canada)*
Steve Ferry *(Pres-HD Supply Electrical & HD Supply Plumbing)*
Richard Fiechter *(Pres-HD Supply Repair & Remodel)*
Rick J. McClure *(Pres-Utilities)*
Michael L. Stanwood *(Pres-IPVF)*
Ricardo Nunez *(Gen Counsel, Sec & Sr VP)*
John A. Stegeman *(Exec VP)*
Vidya Chauhan *(Sr VP-Strategic Bus Dev & Integration)*
Margaret Newman *(Sr VP-HR, Mktg & Comm)*
Kathleen M. Ryan *(VP-Mktg & Comm)*

HEERY-HLM DESIGN

(Sub. of Heery International, Inc.)
820 16th St Mall
Denver, CO 80202
Tel.: (720) 946-0276
Fax: (720) 946-0277
Web Site: www.hlmdesign.com
Approx. Number Employees: 434
Year Founded: 1962
Business Description:
Architectural Design, Engineering & Construction Services
S.I.C.: 8712
N.A.I.C.S.: 541310
Media: 2-10
Personnel:
Jim Isaf *(Reg Mgr)*

HEERY INTERNATIONAL, INC.

(Sub. of Balfour Beatty Building Management & Services)
999 Peachtree St NE
Atlanta, GA 30309-3953
Tel.: (404) 881-9880
Fax: (404) 875-1283
E-mail: corporate@heery.com
Web Site: www.heery.com
Sales Range: $250-299.9 Million
Approx. Number Employees: 250
Year Founded: 1952
Business Description:
Construction Management & Design Services
S.I.C.: 8712; 8742
N.A.I.C.S.: 541310; 541611
Media: 7-10
Personnel:
Theodore E. Sak *(CFO & Exec VP)*
Richard Nikonovich-Kahn *(Gen Counsel & Sr VP)*
Greg Peirce *(Sr VP)*
Daniel P. Wise *(VP & Dir-HR)*
Allyson Gipson *(Dir-Project-West Reg)*
Martha Pacini *(Dir-Corp Commun)*
William E. Heitz *(Reg Mgr)*
Glenn Jardine *(Reg Mgr)*

HENDRICK MANUFACTURING COMPANY

1 7th Ave
Carbondale, PA 18407-2203
Tel.: (570) 282-1010
Fax: (570) 282-1506
Toll Free: (800) 225-7373
E-mail: sales@hendrickmfg.com
Web Site: www.hendrickmfg.com
E-Mail For Key Personnel:
Sales Director: sales@hendrickmfg.com
Approx. Number Employees: 150
Year Founded: 1876
Business Description:
Perforated Metal Screens, Perforated Grilles Mfr & Distr
S.I.C.: 3469; 3444
N.A.I.C.S.: 332116; 332322
Media: 4-6-10
Distr.: Direct to Consumer; Natl.
Budget Set: Apr.
Personnel:
Darren Drake *(Pres & CFO)*
Janee Ploskonka *(Mgr-Supply Chain)*
Advertising Agency:
Pilling Graphics
240 Pennsylvania Ave., Ste. 2
Scranton, PA 18503
Tel.: (570) 347-3786
Fax: (570) 347-3773
(All Products)

HENDRIX WIRE & CABLE, INC.

(Sub. of Marmon Engineered Wire & Cable)
53 Old Wilton Rd
Milford, NH 03055-3119
Tel.: (603) 673-2040
Fax: (603) 673-1497
E-mail: overhead@hendrix-wc.com
Web Site: www.hendrix-wc.com
Sales Range: $50-74.9 Million
Approx. Number Employees: 120
Year Founded: 1951
Business Description:
Underground & Overhead Electrical Distribution Cable, Cable Systems & Accessories Mfr
S.I.C.: 3357; 3699
N.A.I.C.S.: 335921; 335999
Import Export
Media: 2-4
Personnel:
Tom Brennan *(Pres)*
Karen Slattery *(VP-HR)*

HENKELS & MCCOY, INC.

985 Jolly Rd
Blue Bell, PA 19422-1903
Tel.: (215) 283-7600
Fax: (215) 283-7659
Toll Free: (888) HENKELS
E-mail: marketing@henkels.com
Web Site: www.henkels.com
Sales Range: $700-749.9 Million
Approx. Number Employees: 5,000
Year Founded: 1923
Business Description:
Communications & Energy Utility Services; Engineering, Construction & Maintenance
S.I.C.: 1623
N.A.I.C.S.: 237130
Media: 2-4-7-10-13-17
Personnel:
T. Roderick Henkels *(Pres & CEO)*
Robert Delark *(CFO & VP)*
Jonathan C. Schoff *(COO & Exec VP)*
Christine Crawford *(Gen Counsel, VP & Sec)*
Joseph Paulits *(Treas & Dir-Acctg)*
Christopher Henkels *(Dir-Info Svc & Tech)*
Rick Sutliff *(Dir-Svcs)*
Paul DeMara *(Mgr-Mktg Comm & Res)*

HERITAGE HOMES INC.

456 S Hampton Rd
Westfield, MA 01085-1327
Mailing Address:
PO Box 698
Westfield, MA 01086-0698
Tel.: (413) 568-8614
Fax: (413) 568-8616
Web Site: www.heritagehomesofma.com/
Sales Range: $10-24.9 Million
Approx. Number Employees: 15
Year Founded: 1955
Business Description:
Custom Manufactured, Personalized & Modular Homes, Custom Additions & Garages, Remodeling Services, Commercial & Light Industrial Building
S.I.C.: 1521; 1522
N.A.I.C.S.: 236115; 236220
Media: 4-9-10-18-25-26
Distr.: Reg.
Budget Set: Jan.
Personnel:
Robert T. Goyette, Jr. *(Pres)*
Linda Greskowicz *(Mgr-Office)*

HICKMAN, WILLIAMS & COMPANY

Chiquita Ctr 250 E 5th St Ste 300
Cincinnati, OH 45202
Tel.: (513) 621-1946
Fax: (513) 621-0024
Toll Free: (800) 393-5551
Web Site: www.hicwilco.com
Approx. Number Employees: 12
Year Founded: 1890
Business Description:
Brokers of Coal, Coke & Other

Key to Media (For complete agency information see *The Advertising Red Books-Agencies* edition):
1. Bus. Publs. 2. Cable T.V. 3. Catalogs & Directories. 4. Co-op Adv. 5. Consumer Mags. 6. D.M. to Bus. Estab.7. D.M. to Consumers
8. Daily Newsp. 9. Exhibits/Trade Shows 10. Foreign 11. Infomercial 12. Internet Adv.13. Multimedia 14. Network Radio
15. Network T.V. 16. Newsp. Distr. Mags. 17. Other 18. Outdoor (Posters, Transit) 19. Point of Purchase20. Premiums, Novelties
21. Product Samples 22. Special Events Mktg. 23. Spot Radio 24. Spot T.V. 25. Weekly Newsp. 26. Yellow Page Adv.

Products Used by the Foundry Industry; Coke Processing Plants
S.I.C.: 5051; 5052
N.A.I.C.S.: 423510; 423520
Export
Media: 2-4-7-10-20
Personnel:
James E. Sander *(CFO, Sec & VP)*
Sandra C. Hartman *(Mgr-Computer Ops)*

HILL INTERNATIONAL INC.
303 Lippincott Ctr
Marlton, NJ 08053-4160
Tel.: (856) 810-6200
Fax: (856) 810-0404
Web Site: www.hillintl.com
Approx. Rev.: $451,758,000
Approx. Number Employees: 2,445
Year Founded: 1976
Business Description:
Construction Management, Project Management & Construction Claims Management Services
S.I.C.: 8711; 8742; 8748
N.A.I.C.S.: 541330; 541611; 541618
Advertising Expenditures: $631,000
Personnel:
Irvin E. Richter *(Chm & CEO)*
David L. Richter *(Pres & COO)*
Bruce A. Schlaitzer *(Mng Dir & Sr VP)*
Eric C. Butterworth *(Mng Dir & VP)*
Jacek P. Zurawski *(Mng Dir & VP)*
John Fanelli III *(CFO & Sr VP)*
Michael J. Petrisko *(CIO & Sr VP)*
Catherine H. Emma *(Chief Admin Officer & Sr VP)*
Ronald F. Emma *(Chief Acctg Officer & Sr VP)*
Raouf S. Ghali *(Pres-Project Mgmt Grp)*
Frederic Z. Samelian *(Pres-Construction Claims Grp)*
Thomas J. Spearing, III *(Pres-Project Mgmt Grp-Americas)*
William H. Dengler Jr. *(Gen Counsel & Sr VP)*
James B. Biden *(Exec VP-HillStone Intl LLC)*
Mohammed Al Rais *(Mng Dir-Middle East Ops & Sr VP)*
John R. Brells *(Mng Dir-Australia & Sr VP)*
Abdo E. Kardous *(Mng Dir-Asia Pacific Ops & Sr VP)*
William Kennedy *(Sr VP & Mng Dir-Asia, Middle East & Africa)*
Robert C. Hixon, Jr. *(Sr VP & Dir-Federal Buildings Grp)*
James E. Koch *(Sr VP & Dir-Federal Svcs Grp)*
Clarke D. Pile *(Sr VP & Reg Mgr-New York)*
Stuart S. Richter *(Sr VP, Mgr-New Jersey, Southeastern US & Caribbean Reg)*
Dennis L. Allen *(Sr VP)*
James W. Palmer *(Sr VP)*
Alann M. Ramirez *(Sr VP)*
Andre B. Sassine *(Sr VP)*
John P. Paolin *(VP-Mktg & Corp Comm)*
Advertising Agency:
EASTWEST Public Relations
77B Amoy Street
Singapore, 069896, Singapore
Tel.: (65) 6222 0306
Fax: (65) 6222 0124
(Asia Pacific, Public Relations)

HIRSCHFELD INDUSTRIES, INC.
(Holding of Insight Equity Holdings LLC)
112 W 29th St
San Angelo, TX 76903-2553
Tel.: (325) 486-4201
Tel.: (325) 486-4202
Fax: (325) 486-4380
E-mail: info@hirschfeld.com
Web Site: www.hirschfeld.com
Approx. Rev.: $182,699,000
Approx. Number Employees: 885
Year Founded: 1946
Business Description:
Structural Steel Mfr
S.I.C.: 3441
N.A.I.C.S.: 332312
Personnel:
Richard Phillips *(Pres)*
Dennis C. Hirschfeld *(CEO)*
Rodney L. Goodwill *(CFO)*
W.H. Reeves *(Pres-Bridge Div)*
Jacob Balderas *(Sr VP-HR)*
Jeremy Bartz *(Mgr-HR)*
Advertising Agency:
Love Advertising Inc.
770 S Post Oak Ln Ste 101
Houston, TX 77056-1913
Tel.: (713) 552-1055
Fax: (713) 552-9155
Toll Free: (800) 544-5683

HITCHINER MANUFACTURING COMPANY INC.
117 Old Wilson Rd
Milford, NH 03055
Tel.: (603) 673-1100
Fax: (603) 673-7960
E-mail: info@hitchiner.com
Web Site: www.hitchiner.com
Sales Range: $150-199.9 Million
Approx. Number Employees: 2,500
Year Founded: 1946
Business Description:
Ferrous & Nonferrous Investment Casting
S.I.C.: 3324; 3363
N.A.I.C.S.: 331512; 331521
Export
Advertising Expenditures: $200,000
Media: 2-4-10
Distr.: Intl.; Natl.
Budget Set: Dec.-Jan.
Personnel:
Michael R. Hanrahan *(Pres)*
Randal J. Donovan *(CFO, Treas, Sec & Exec VP-Fin)*
Brands & Products:
HITCHINER
IMAGINATION IN METALLURGY

HOLCOMB & HOKE MANUFACTURING COMPANY, INC.
1545 Van Buren St
Indianapolis, IN 46203-4176
Tel.: (317) 784-2444
Tel.: (317) 784-2448
Fax: (317) 781-9164
E-mail: info@foldoor.com
Web Site: www.foldoor.com
Approx. Number Employees: 62
Year Founded: 1913
Business Description:
Mfr. of Vinyl Covered & Wood Doors & Partitions; Folding Wood & Steel Operable Walls
S.I.C.: 3089; 2431
N.A.I.C.S.: 326199; 321918
Import Export
Media: 2-4-5-7-10-13-20-21
Distr.: Natl.
Budget Set: Oct.
Brands & Products:
FOLDOOR
FOLDOOR WOOD PANEL
SOUNDGUARD
STARLINE

HOMASOTE COMPANY
932 Lower Ferry Rd
Trenton, NJ 08628-0240
Mailing Address:
PO Box 7240
Trenton, NJ 08628
Tel.: (609) 883-3300
Fax: (609) 530-1584
Toll Free: (800) 257-9491
E-mail: sales@homasote.com
Web Site: www.homasote.com
E-Mail For Key Personnel:
Sales Director: sales@homasote.com
Sales Range: $10-24.9 Million
Approx. Number Employees: 215
Year Founded: 1909
Business Description:
Insulating & Building Boards; Rigid Urethane Insulation for Roofs & Sidewalls; Nail Base Roof Insulation; Industrial Packaging Mfr
S.I.C.: 2493; 3086
N.A.I.C.S.: 321219; 326150
Import Export
Media: 2-4-7-10-21
Personnel:
Warren Flicker *(Chm & CEO)*
Ronald D. Fasano *(CFO)*
Brands & Products:
4-WAY
440 SOUNDBARRIER
COMFORTBASE
DESIGNWALL
EASY-PLY
FIRESTALL
HOMASOTE
HOMEX
ICE DECK
N.C.F.R.
NOVA CORK
PAK-LINE
PINNACLE
THERMASOTE

HUFCOR INCORPORATED
2101 Kennedy Rd
Janesville, WI 53545-0824
Tel.: (608) 756-1241
Fax: (608) 756-1246
Toll Free: (800) 356-6968
Toll Free: (800) 542-2371
E-mail: hufcor@hufcor.com
Web Site: www.hufcor.com
Approx. Number Employees: 250
Year Founded: 1900
Business Description:
Mfr. of Folding Door & Partition Systems
S.I.C.: 2519; 3442
N.A.I.C.S.: 337125; 332321
Advertising Expenditures: $500,000
Media: 2-7-10-26
Distr.: Intl.; Natl.
Budget Set: Mar.
Personnel:
John E. Hough *(Chm)*
J. Michael Borden *(CEO)*
Brands & Products:
CLASSIC
HUFCOR
HUFGUARD
NAVIGATOR
PATHFINDER
ROOMMATE
SPECTRUM
TOUCHGARD
TOUCHGUARD
UNISPAN
Advertising Agency:
MTH Design
104 South St., Ste. 206
Waunakee, WI 53597
Tel.: (608) 849-5690

HUNT BUILDING COMPANY LIMITED
4401 N Mesa St
El Paso, TX 79902-1107
Tel.: (915) 533-1122
Fax: (915) 545-2631
E-mail: development@huntbuilding.com
Web Site: www.huntcompanies.com
Sales Range: $350-399.9 Million
Approx. Number Employees: 400
Year Founded: 1947
Business Description:
Building Contractors & Land Development
S.I.C.: 1522; 6531
N.A.I.C.S.: 236116; 531210
Personnel:
M.L. Hunt *(Pres & CEO)*
William C. Sanders *(Chief Acctg Officer & Exec VP)*
Advertising Agency:
Mithoff Burton Partners
123 W Mills Ave Ste 500
El Paso, TX 79901
Tel.: (915) 544-9400
Fax: (915) 544-9426
Toll Free: (877) 335-2322

HUNT CONSTRUCTION GROUP, INC.
(Branch of Hunt Construction Group, Inc.)
2450 S Tibbs Ave
Indianapolis, IN 46241
Tel.: (317) 227-7800
Fax: (317) 227-7810
E-mail: indy@huntconstructiongroup.com
Web Site: www.huntconstructiongroup.com
Approx. Number Employees: 850
Year Founded: 1944
Business Description:
Contracting & Construction Services
S.I.C.: 1522; 1541
N.A.I.C.S.: 236220; 236210
Media: 2-4-10-16-25
Personnel:
Mike Fratianni *(Exec VP & Mgr-East Div)*
Michael J. Gausden *(Exec VP & Mgr-West Div)*

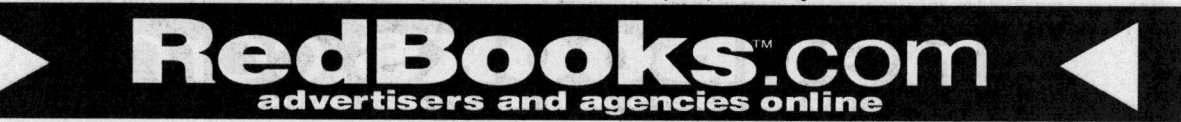

Key to Media (For complete agency information see *The Advertising Red Books-Agencies* edition):
1. Bus. Publs. 2. Cable T.V. 3. Catalogs & Directories. 4. Co-op Adv. 5. Consumer Mags. 6. D.M. to Bus. Estab.7. D.M. to Consumers 8. Daily Newsp. 9. Exhibits/Trade Shows 10. Foreign 11. Infomercial 12. Internet Adv.13. Multimedia 14. Network Radio 15. Network T.V. 16. Newsp. Distr. Mags. 17. Other 18. Outdoor (Posters, Transit) 19. Point of Purchase20. Premiums, Novelties 21. Product Samples 22. Special Events Mktg. 23. Spot Radio 24. Spot T.V. 25. Weekly Newsp. 26. Yellow Page Adv.

Hunt Construction Group, Inc. — (Continued)

Mark E. Lavoy *(Exec VP & Mgr-South Div)*
Bob Decker *(Exec VP)*
Ken Johnson *(Exec VP)*
Belinda D. Burke *(VP-Mktg & Comm)*
Troy Hoberg *(Dir-Bus Dev)*
Bob Sanders *(Dir-Bus Dev)*

THE HUNT CORPORATION
6720 N Scottsdale Rd Ste 300
Scottsdale, AZ 85253-4460
Tel.: (480) 368-4700
Fax: (480) 368-4747
Web Site: www.huntconstructiongroup.com
E-Mail For Key Personnel:
President: rghunt@thehuntcorp.com
Approx. Sls.: $2,000,000,000
Approx. Number Employees: 1,000
Year Founded: 1944
Business Description:
Commercial Construction Contractors & Construction Services
S.I.C.: 1521
N.A.I.C.S.: 236115
Media: 18-25
Personnel:
Robert G. Hunt *(Chm & CEO)*
Stephen Atkins *(CFO)*
David Smith *(CIO)*

HURD WINDOWS & DOORS INC
(Holding of Longroad Asset Management LLC)
575 S Whelen Ave
Medford, WI 54451-1738
Tel.: (715) 748-2011
Fax: (715) 748-1785
Toll Free: (800) 223-4873
Web Site: www.hurd.com
Approx. Number Employees: 1,000
Year Founded: 1919
Business Description:
Millwork Products; Wood Windows & Patio Doors; Vinyl Windows & Patio Doors Mfr & Retailer
S.I.C.: 2431
N.A.I.C.S.: 321911
Export
Advertising Expenditures: $1,500,000
Media: 2-4-5-6-7-10-20
Distr.: Natl.
Budget Set: Nov.
Personnel:
Dominic Truniger *(Pres)*
David Roberts *(VP-Sls)*
Brands & Products:
CLIMATE CONTROL
HURD
HURD COMFORTGLAZE
HURD FEELSAFE
HURD PERFORMANCEWOOD
SUMBLOCKER
SUPER SUNBLOCKER

HUTTIG BUILDING PRODUCTS, INC.
555 Maryville University Dr Ste 400
Saint Louis, MO 63141
Tel.: (314) 216-2600
Fax: (314) 216-2601
E-mail: information@huttig.com
Web Site: www.huttig.com
Approx. Sls.: $467,700,000
Approx. Number Employees: 900
Year Founded: 1885
Business Description:
Millwork, Building Materials & Wood Products Whslr For Use in New Residential Construction & Home Improvement Remodeling & Repair Work
S.I.C.: 5031; 5033; 5211
N.A.I.C.S.: 423310; 423330; 444190
Media: 2-4-5-6-7-8-9-10-19-22-25-26
Distr.: Natl.
Personnel:
R. S. Evans *(Chm)*
Jon P. Vrabely *(CEO)*
Philip W. Keipp *(CFO, Sec & VP)*
Brian D. Robinson *(CIO & VP)*
Greg W. Gurley *(VP-Product Mgmt, Mktg & Natl Accounts)*
Nikki Wildman *(Dir-Product Mgmt-Building Products & Corp Mktg)*

I.C. THOMASSON ASSOCIATES, INC.
2950 Kraft Dr Ste 500
Nashville, TN 37204-0527
Mailing Address:
PO Box 40527
Nashville, TN 37204-0527
Tel.: (615) 346-3400
Fax: (615) 346-3550
E-mail: jobs@icthomasson.com
Web Site: www.icthomasson.com
Approx. Number Employees: 140
Year Founded: 1942
Business Description:
Mechanical & Electrical Consulting Engineering Services
S.I.C.: 8711
N.A.I.C.S.: 541330
Media: 2-7-10-22
Personnel:
Bruce Mason *(Controller)*
Carolyn Martz *(Dir-HR)*
Kerry Rice *(Mgr-Computer Sys)*
Beth Davenport *(Coord-Mktg)*

IMPERIA BROS., INC.
57 Canal Rd
Pelham, NY 10803-2706
Tel.: (914) 738-0900
Fax: (914) 738-2494
Fax: (914) 738-0243 (Sls)
Toll Free: (800) 246-2569
Web Site: www.imperiamasonry.com/main.htm
Approx. Number Employees: 78
Year Founded: 1927
Business Description:
Mfr. of Concrete & Lightweight Blocks; Mason & Building Materials; Retail Home Center
S.I.C.: 5031
N.A.I.C.S.: 423310
Media: 7-9-10-14-17-23-25-26
Distr.: Natl.
Personnel:
Joseph Imperia *(Pres, Treas & Sec)*
Theresa Brandt *(Office Mgr-Acctg)*
Gerry Ferrotti *(Sls Mgr)*

INCLINATOR COMPANY OF AMERICA
601 Gibson Blvd
Harrisburg, PA 17104
Tel.: (717) 234-8065
Fax: (717) 234-0941
Toll Free: (800) 343-9007
E-mail: isales@inclinator.com
Web Site: www.inclinator.com
Approx. Number Employees: 50
Year Founded: 1923
Business Description:
Mfr. of Electric Elevators for the Home
S.I.C.: 3534
N.A.I.C.S.: 333921
Import Export
Advertising Expenditures: $380,000
Media: 2-4-5-6-9-10-23-24-26
Distr.: Intl.; Natl.
Personnel:
Steven Knock *(Pres & Mgr-Mktg)*
Steve Progin *(CFO)*
Brands & Products:
ACCESSIBILITY LIFT
BEAUTIFULLY DESIGNED. MASTERFULLY ENGINEERED.
ELEVETTE
HOMEWAITER
HYDRA RIDE II
INCLINATOR
INCLINATOR VL
INCLINETTE
SPECTRALIFT
STAIRLIFT
Advertising Agency:
Scheffey Advertising Agency
100 Foxshire Dr.
Lancaster, PA 17601
Tel.: (717) 569-8274
Fax: (717) 569-8276

INDUSTRIAL ACOUSTICS COMPANY, INC.
1160 Commerce Ave
Bronx, NY 10462-5506
Tel.: (718) 931-8000
Fax: (718) 863-1138
E-mail: info@industrialacoustics.com
Web Site: www.industrialacoustics.com
Sales Range: $75-99.9 Million
Approx. Number Employees: 200
Year Founded: 1949
Business Description:
Noise Control Equipment
S.I.C.: 3448; 1742
N.A.I.C.S.: 332311; 238310
Export
Media: 2-4-7-10-11-26
Distr.: Intl.; Natl.
Budget Set: Dec.
Personnel:
Ken Deoasho *(Gen Mgr)*
Advertising Agency:
Westchester Associates
1162 Commerce Ave
Bronx, NY 10462
Tel.: (718) 931-8000
Fax: (718) 863-1138

INSITUFORM TECHNOLOGIES INC
17988 Edison Ave
Chesterfield, MO 63005-1195
Tel.: (636) 530-8000
Fax: (636) 519-8010
Toll Free: (800) 234-2992
E-mail: feedback@insituform.com
Web Site: www.insituform.com
Approx. Rev.: $914,975,000
Approx. Number Employees: 3,200
Year Founded: 1980
Business Description:
Trenchless Pipeline Reconstruction
S.I.C.: 1629
N.A.I.C.S.: 237990
Export
Media: 1-5-10-20
Distr.: Natl.
Budget Set: July
Personnel:
J. Joseph Burgess *(Pres & CEO)*
David A. Martin *(CFO & Sr VP)*
Matthys Lourens *(CIO)*
David F. Morris *(Chief Admin Officer & Sr VP)*
Dorwin Hawn *(Sr VP-Energy & Mining)*
Charles Voltz *(Sr VP-N American Rehabilitation)*
Holly Sharp *(VP-HR, Environmental, Health, & Safety)*
Brands & Products:
CLEAN WATER FOR THE WORLD.
INSITUFORM
INSITUFORM BLUE
INSITUFORM CIPP
INSITUFORM CP
INSITUFORM PPL
INSITUFORM TECHNOLOGIES
INSITUGUARD
INSITUMAIN
IPLUS COMPOSITE
IPLUS INFUSION
ITAP
THERMOPIPE
TITE LINER

INTEGRATED ELECTRICAL SERVICES, INC.
1800 W Loop S Ste 500
Houston, TX 77027
Tel.: (713) 860-1500
Fax: (713) 860-1599
E-mail: info@ies-co.com
Web Site: www.ies-co.com
Approx. Rev.: $460,633,000
Approx. Number Employees: 2,921
Year Founded: 1997
Business Description:
Electrical & Communications Contracting Solutions
S.I.C.: 1731
N.A.I.C.S.: 238210
Advertising Expenditures: $1,547,000
Personnel:
Michael J. Hall *(Chm)*
Michael J. Caliel *(Pres & CEO)*
Terry L. Freeman *(CFO & Sr VP)*
Advertising Agency:
Pennino & Partners
19200 Space Center Blvd., Site 2611
Houston, TX 77058
Tel.: (281) 286-9398
— Laura Pennino *(Acct Exec)*

INTERNATIONAL ALUMINUM CORPORATION
(Holding of Genstar Capital, LLC)
767 Monterey Pass Rd
Monterey Park, CA 91754
Mailing Address:
PO Box 6
Monterey Park, CA 91754-0006
Tel.: (323) 264-1670
Fax: (323) 266-3838
E-mail: info@intlextrusion.com
Web Site: www.intlalum.com
Sales Range: $250-299.9 Million
Approx. Number Employees: 1,600
Year Founded: 1957
Business Description:
Aluminum & Vinyl Building Products Mfr
S.I.C.: 3442; 3446; 3448

Key to Media (For complete agency information see *The Advertising Red Books-Agencies* edition):
1. Bus. Publs. 2. Cable T.V. 3. Catalogs & Directories. 4. Co-op Adv. 5. Consumer Mags. 6. D.M. to Bus. Estab.7. D.M. to Consumers
8. Daily Newsp. 9. Exhibits/Trade Shows 10. Foreign 11. Infomercial 12. Internet Adv.13. Multimedia 14. Network Radio
15. Network T.V. 16. Newsp. Distr. Mags. 17. Other 18. Outdoor (Posters, Transit) 19. Point of Purchase20. Premiums, Novelties
21. Product Samples 22. Special Events Mktg. 23. Spot Radio 24. Spot T.V. 25. Weekly Newsp. 26. Yellow Page Adv.

N.A.I.C.S.: 332321; 332311; 332323
Import Export
Advertising Expenditures: $2,345,000
Personnel:
Richard Almy *(CEO)*

INTERNATIONAL REVOLVING DOORS
(d/b/a Evansville Metal Products)
2138 N Sixth Ave
Evansville, IN 47710-2814
Tel.: (812) 425-3311
Fax: (812) 426-2682
Toll Free: (800) 745-4726
E-mail: info@internationalrevolvingdoors.com
Web Site: www.internationalrevolvingdoors.com
Sales Range: $1-9.9 Million
Approx. Number Employees: 70
Year Founded: 1907
Business Description:
Mfr. of Revolving & Swing Doors
S.I.C.: 3442; 3231
N.A.I.C.S.: 332321; 327215
Export
Advertising Expenditures: $655,000
Media: 1-2-4-6-10-11-17-21
Distr.: Direct to Consumer; Intl.; Natl.
Budget Set: Oct.
Personnel:
Rahmi Soyugenc *(Pres)*

ITG AUTOMOTIVE SAFETY
(Div. of International Textile Group, Inc.)
41 Stevens St
Greenville, SC 29605-4408
Tel.: (864) 240-2709
Fax: (864) 240-2711
Web Site: www.safetycomponents.com
Sales Range: $250-299.9 Million
Year Founded: 1994
Business Description:
Supplier of Automotive Airbag Fabric & Cushions
S.I.C.: 3714; 2299
N.A.I.C.S.: 336399; 314999
Advertising Expenditures: $235,000
Media: 7-10-21
Brands & Products:
COMMANDER
FUSION
GLIDE II
PBI MATRIX
TRADITION
WEATHERMAX

IVAN ALLEN WORKSPACE, LLC
1000 Maritta St Ste 224
Atlanta, GA 30318
Tel.: (404) 760-8700
Fax: (404) 760-8673
E-mail: info@ivanallen.com
Web Site: www.ivanallen.com
Sales Range: $10-24.9 Million
Approx. Number Employees: 35
Year Founded: 1900
Business Description:
Office Furniture Dealer; Architectural & Design Services
S.I.C.: 6512
N.A.I.C.S.: 531120
Media: 2-4-7-10-17
Distr.: Natl.
Personnel:
Kevin Grain *(Gen Mgr)*
Brands & Products:
IVAN ALLEN WORKSPACE

IVEDA CORPORATION
(Name Changed to Iveda Solutions, Inc.)

IVEDA SOLUTIONS, INC.
(Formerly Iveda Corporation)
1201 S Alma School Ste 4450
Mesa, AZ 85210
Tel.: (480) 307-8700
Fax: (480) 962-1251
Toll Free: (800) 385-8616
E-mail: general@ivedasolutions.com
Web Site: www.ivedasolutions.com
Approx. Rev.: $940,008
Approx. Number Employees: 23
Year Founded: 2006
Business Description:
Video Hosting & Surveillance Services
S.I.C.: 7382; 3651; 7372
N.A.I.C.S.: 561621; 334310; 511210
Advertising Expenditures: $32,003
Media: 17
Personnel:
David Ly *(Pres & CEO)*
Steven G. Wollach *(CFO)*
Luz Berg *(COO, CMO & Sec)*

JACK WALTERS & SONS CORP.
(d/b/a Walters Buildings)
6600 Midland Ct
Allenton, WI 53002
Mailing Address:
PO Box 388
Allenton, WI 53002
Tel.: (262) 629-5521
Fax: (262) 629-5233
Toll Free: (800) 558-7800
E-mail: sales@waltersbuildings.com
Web Site: www.waltersbuildings.com
E-Mail For Key Personnel:
Sales Director: sales@waltersbuildings.com
Sales Range: $10-24.9 Million
Approx. Number Employees: 180
Year Founded: 1966
Business Description:
Prefabricated Metal Buildings
S.I.C.: 3448
N.A.I.C.S.: 332311
Media: 2-4-10
Personnel:
Scott Walters *(Pres)*
Jim Rollins *(Center Mgr)*
Brands & Products:
WALTERS BUILDINGS

JACOBS ENGINEERING GROUP, INC.
1111 S Arroyo Pkwy
Pasadena, CA 91105
Mailing Address:
PO Box 7084
Pasadena, CA 91109-7084
Tel.: (626) 578-3500
Fax: (626) 578-6916
E-mail: contactus@jacobs.com
Web Site: www.jacobs.com
Approx. Rev.: $9,915,517,000
Approx. Number Employees: 38,500
Year Founded: 1947
Business Description:
Architectural Engineering & Construction Services
S.I.C.: 8711; 1522; 1629
N.A.I.C.S.: 541330; 236220; 237990
Media: 2-10
Distr.: Natl.
Personnel:
Noel G. Watson *(Chm)*
Craig L. Martin *(Pres & CEO)*
Cora L. Carmody *(CIO & Sr VP)*
Rogers F. Starr *(Pres-Jacobs Technology)*
William C. Markley, III *(Gen Counsel & Sr VP)*
John W. Prosser Jr. *(Treas, Principal Fin Officer & Exec VP-Fin & Admin)*
Thomas R. Hammond *(Exec VP-Ops)*
George A. Kunberger Jr. *(Exec VP)*
Gregory J. Landry *(Exec VP-Ops)*
Nazim G. Thawerbhoy *(Sr VP & Controller)*
William J. Birkhofer *(Sr VP)*
Andrew F. Kremer *(Sr VP-Global Sls)*
John McLachlan *(Sr VP)*
Patricia H. Summers *(Sr VP-Global HR)*
Walter C. Barber, Jr. *(Grp VP)*
Robert M. Clement *(Grp VP)*
Jay Michael Coyle *(Grp VP)*
James E. Dixon *(Grp VP-Global Maintenanace Svcs)*
Arlan C. Emmert *(Grp VP)*
Michael J. Higgins *(Grp VP)*
Robert Matha *(Grp VP)*
Thomas H. Mcduffie *(Grp VP)*
Earl J. Mitchell, Jr. *(Grp VP)*
Christopher E. Nagel *(Grp VP)*
Robert G. Norfleet *(Grp VP)*
Philip J. Stassi *(Grp VP)*
Allyn B. Taylor *(Grp VP)*
Brands & Products:
JACOBS
JE

JAMISON DOOR COMPANY
55 JV Jamison Dr
Hagerstown, MD 21740
Mailing Address:
PO Box 70
Hagerstown, MD 21740
Tel.: (301) 733-3100
Fax: (301) 791-7339
Toll Free: (800) 532-3667
E-mail: dac@jamisondoor.com
Web Site: www.jamisondoor.com
E-Mail For Key Personnel:
Sales Director: sales@jamisondoor.com
Approx. Number Employees: 165
Year Founded: 1906
Business Description:
Mfr. of Cold Storage, Sound Reduction & Other Specialty Engineered Doors
S.I.C.: 3442
N.A.I.C.S.: 332321
Export
Media: 2-4-7-10
Distr.: Intl.; Natl.
Personnel:
John Williams *(Chm & CEO)*
Thomas E. Johnson *(Exec VP)*
Curtis L. Berry *(VP-Engrg)*
Dwight Clark *(VP-Sls & Mktg)*
George Hamilton *(Mgr-Mktg)*
Brands & Products:
INVISION 2000
JAMOCLEAR
JAMOLITE II
JAMOLITE III
JAMOTUF
MARK IV
PLYFOAM
PLYFOAM II
RETAIL-PRO

JARMEL KIZEL ARCHITECTS & ENGINEERS, INC.
42 Okner Pkwy
Livingston, NJ 07039
Tel.: (973) 994-9669
Fax: (973) 994-4069
E-mail: info@jkarch.com
Web Site: www.jarmelkizel.com
Sales Range: $25-49.9 Million
Approx. Number Employees: 50
Year Founded: 1975
Business Description:
Architectural & Engineering Services
S.I.C.: 8712; 8711
N.A.I.C.S.: 541310; 541330
Media: 2
Personnel:
Marvin Jarmel *(Principal)*
Matthew B. Jarmel *(Principal)*
Richard A. Jarmel *(Principal)*
Irwin H. Kizel *(Principal)*
Vladimir Ayzenberg *(Dir-MEP Engrg)*
Kordian Homentowski *(Project Mgr-HVAC/Electrical/Bldg Utilities Design)*

J.D. IRVING, LIMITED
300 Union St
Saint John, NB E2L 4M3, Canada
Tel.: (506) 632-7777
Fax: (506) 648-2205
E-mail: info@jdirving.com
Web Site: www.jdirving.com
Approx. Number Employees: 15,000
Business Description:
Holding Company; Sawmills & Home Improvement Stores; Shipbuilding & Construction
S.I.C.: 6719
N.A.I.C.S.: 551112
Personnel:
James Irving *(Pres & CEO)*
Mary Keith *(VP-Comm)*
Advertising Agency:
BarnesMcInerney Inc.
120 Adelaide St W Ste 910
Toronto, ON M5H 3L5, Canada
Tel.: (416) 367-5000
Fax: (416) 367-5390

J.E. DUNN CONSTRUCTION GROUP, INC.
929 Holmes St
Kansas City, MO 64106
Tel.: (816) 474-8600
Fax: (816) 391-2510
E-mail: info@jedunn.com
Web Site: www.jedunn.com
Approx. Number Employees: 3,200
Year Founded: 1924
Business Description:
Construction Services
S.I.C.: 1522
N.A.I.C.S.: 236220
Media: 2
Personnel:
Stephen D. Dunn *(Chm)*
Terrence P. Dunn *(Pres & CEO)*

J.E. Dunn Construction Group, Inc. — (Continued)

Gordon Lansford *(CFO & Sr VP)*
Casey S. Halsey *(Chief Risk Officer & Exec VP)*
Danna Guffey *(Mgr-Mktg Commun)*
Richard Beyer *(Mgr-HR)*

J.H. BAXTER & COMPANY
1700 S El Camino Real Ste 407
San Mateo, CA 94402
Mailing Address:
PO Box 5902
San Mateo, CA 94402-0902
Tel.: (650) 349-0201
Fax: (650) 570-6878
E-mail: info@jhbaxter.com
Web Site: www.jhbaxter.com
Sales Range: $25-49.9 Miilion
Approx. Number Employees: 220
Year Founded: 1914
Business Description:
Mfr. of Pressure Treated Poles, Piling & Lumber
S.I.C.: 6282; 2491
N.A.I.C.S.: 523920; 321114
Media: 2-4-7-10-17
Distr.: Natl.
Brands & Products:
ACQ
CHEMONITE
J H BAXTER

JOHN AGNELLI CONSTRUCTION
6000 Marina Dr Ste 107
Holmes Beach, FL 34217
Tel.: (941) 779-0765
Fax: (941) 779-0769
E-mail: agnelliconstructioninc@yahoo.com
Web Site:
www.agnelliconstruction.com
Business Description:
Construction Services
S.I.C.: 1522; 1521; 1541
N.A.I.C.S.: 236220; 236115; 236116; 236210
Media: 8-9-13-17-23-25
Personnel:
Frank Agnelli *(Owner)*

JOHN CANNON HOMES INC.
6710 Professional Pkwy W
Sarasota, FL 34240-8444
Tel.: (941) 924-5935
Fax: (941) 924-4129
E-mail: info@johncannon.com
Web Site: www.johncannon.com
Approx. Number Employees: 50
Business Description:
Residential Home Builder
S.I.C.: 1521
N.A.I.C.S.: 236115
Media: 6
Personnel:
Nancy Hielscher *(Mgr-Mktg)*

JOHNS MANVILLE CORPORATION
(Holding of Berkshire Hathaway Inc.)
717 17th St
Denver, CO 80202
Mailing Address:
PO Box 5108
Denver, CO 80217-5108
Tel.: (303) 978-2000
Fax: (303) 978-2318
Toll Free: (800) 654-3103
E-mail: iwebmaster@jm.com
Web Site: www.jm.com
Sales Range: $1-4.9 Billion
Approx. Number Employees: 800
Year Founded: 1858
Business Description:
Premium-Quality Building & Specialty Products Mfr & Marketer
S.I.C.: 3296; 2952
N.A.I.C.S.: 327993; 324122
Import Export
Advertising Expenditures: $15,000,000
Media: 1-2-4-5-6-7-8-9-10-11-13-16-18-19-20-21-22-26
Distr.: Intl.; Natl.
Personnel:
Todd Raba *(Chm, Pres & CEO)*
Mary K. Rhinehart *(CFO & Sr VP)*
Fred Stephan *(VP & Gen Mgr-Roofing Sys Bus)*
Brands & Products:
AP
APPEX 4.5M
ATTIC PROTECTOR
BESTILE
BUR
CLIMATE PRO
COMFORTTHERM
DECKPRO
DURAFOAM
DUROBOARD
DYNACLAD
DYNAFLEX
DYNAGLAS
DYNAGLAS 30 FR
DYNAGLAS FR
DYNAGRIP
DYNAKAP
DYNALASTIC 180
DYNALASTIC 250
DYNAPLY
DYNATRED
EASYFIT
ENRGY 3
FESCANT PLUS
FESCO BOARD
FESCO FOAM
FLEX-I-DRAIN
GLASBASE PLUS
GLASKAP
GLASKAP PLUS
GLASPLY
GLASPLY IV
GLASPLY PREMIER
GLASTITE
ISO 3
JM APP
NAILBOARD
PRESTO-TITE
PRIMAPLY 28
PROWRAP
RETRO-FIT
SPIDER
SUREGRIP
TAPERED ENRGY 3
TOPGARD
TOPGARD 4000
TOPGARD 5000
TRICOR M FR
TRICOR S
ULTRALOK
Advertising Agencies:
Faction Media
1730 Blake St Ste 200
Denver, CO 80202
Tel.: (303) 339-0206

GyroHSR Denver
1625 Broadway Ste 2800
Denver, CO 80202
Tel.: (303) 294-9944
Fax: (303) 294-9997
Toll Free: (800) 243-2648

Purdie Rogers, Inc.
5447 Ballard Ave NW
Seattle, WA 98107
Tel.: (206) 628-7700
Fax: (206) 628-2818

Weber Shandwick
(Sub. of The Interpublic Group of Companies)
919 3rd Ave
New York, NY 10022
Tel.: (212) 445-8000
Fax: (212) 445-8001

JOSAM COMPANY
525 W US Hwy 20
Michigan City, IN 46360
Mailing Address:
PO Box T
Michigan City, IN 46361-0360
Tel.: (219) 872-5531
Toll Free: (866) 395-6726
E-mail: info@josam.com
Web Site: www.josam.com
Approx. Number Employees: 100
Year Founded: 1987
Business Description:
Plumbing Drainage Specialties
S.I.C.: 3431; 3432
N.A.I.C.S.: 332998; 332913
Media: 4-5-10-17-20-21-22
Distr.: Intl.; Natl.
Budget Set: Jan.
Personnel:
Caswell F. Holloway, Jr. *(Chm)*
B. Scott Holloway *(Pres & CEO)*
Nick Quatrini *(CFO)*
Barry J. Hodgekins *(COO)*
Paula Bowe *(VP-Mktg & Sls)*
Paula Malandro *(VP-Mktg)*
David Szerencse *(VP-Fin)*
Brian Tubaugh *(Dir-Engrg)*
Bradd DeBello *(Reg Sls Mgr)*
Tim Dougherty *(Svc Center Mgr)*
Linda Pinkepank *(Mgr-MIS)*
Brands & Products:
ABSORBOTRON
BLUCHER-JOSAM
CHASE SAVER
FLO-SEPTOR
FLO-SET
HYDRASAN
JOSAM
KLEENATRON
LORO JOSAM
MEA-JOSAM

KAISER ALUMINUM CORPORATION
27422 Portola Pkwy Ste 350
Foothill Ranch, CA 92610-2837
Tel.: (949) 614-1740
Fax: (949) 614-1930
E-mail: sales@kaiseraluminum.com
Web Site: www.kaiseral.com
Approx. Sls.: $1,079,100,000
Approx. Number Employees: 2,300
Year Founded: 1946
Business Description:
Aluminum Products Producer & Marketer
S.I.C.: 3334; 1099; 2819
N.A.I.C.S.: 331312; 212299; 331311
Advertising Expenditures: $300,000
Media: 2-4-9
Distr.: Natl.
Personnel:
Jack A. Hockema *(Chm, Pres & CEO)*
Daniel J. Rinkenberger *(CFO & Sr VP)*
Neal West *(Chief Acctg Officer & VP)*
John M. Donnan *(Sec, Sr VP & Gen Counsel)*
John Barneson *(Sr VP-Corp Dev)*
James E. McAuliffe, Jr. *(Sr VP-IR)*
Tom P. Gannon *(VP-Mktg)*
Advertising Agency:
ARENDS
515 N River St Ste 101
Batavia, IL 60510
Tel.: (630) 482-9800
Fax: (630) 482-9833

KAWNEER COMPANY, INC.
(Sub. of Alcoa Inc.)
555 Guthridge Ct
Norcross, GA 30092
Tel.: (770) 449-5555
Fax: (770) 734-1560
Web Site: www.kawneer.com
Sales Range: $450-499.9 Million
Approx. Number Employees: 1,400
Year Founded: 1906
Business Description:
Architectural Aluminum Building Products & Systems Mfr
S.I.C.: 3442; 3446
N.A.I.C.S.: 332321; 332323
Export
Media: 2-4-10-20-21
Distr.: Intl.; Natl.
Budget Set: Dec.
Personnel:
Diana Perreiah *(Gen Mgr)*
Robert Leyland *(Dir-Sls)*
Karen Zipfel *(Dir-Mktg)*
Brands & Products:
1600 L-R WALL
1600 POWERWALL
1600 SUNSHADE
1600 WALL POWERSHADE
1600 WALL SYSTEM
2500 PG WALL
2800 TRUSSWALL
350 HEAVY WALL
350 TUFFLINE
512 VENTROW
516 ISOPORT
5500 ISOWEB
7500 WALL
ARMORLINE
CONTROLLER
DESIGN VIEW
E CUSTOMERDIRECT
ENCORE
ENTARA
EQULINE
FA-SET
FLUSHLINE
GLASSVENT
HPS
HUSKY
INLIGHTEN
INSULCLAD
ISOLOCK

Key to Media (For complete agency information see *The Advertising Red Books-Agencies* edition):
1. Bus. Publs. 2. Cable T.V. 3. Catalogs & Directories. 4. Co-op Adv. 5. Consumer Mags. 6. D.M. to Bus. Estab.7. D.M. to Consumers 8. Daily Newsp. 9. Exhibits/Trade Shows 10. Foreign 11. Infomercial 12. Internet Adv.13. Multimedia 14. Network Radio 15. Network T.V. 16. Newsp. Distr. Mags. 17. Other 18. Outdoor (Posters, Transit) 19. Point of Purchase20. Premiums, Novelties 21. Product Samples 22. Special Events Mktg. 23. Spot Radio 24. Spot T.V. 25. Weekly Newsp. 26. Yellow Page Adv.

ISOPLEX
ISOPORT
ISOSTRUT
KAWNEER
KAWNEER RUBBER & PLASTICS
NUCORE
PANELINE
PANIC GUARD
PARTNERPAK
PARTNERPAK+
THE PERFORMER
PERMADIZE
PG 123
POWERSHADE
POWERSLOPE
POWERWALL
PROFIT$MAKER
QUICKSEAL
SEALAIR
SEAMLESS MULLION
SHEERWALL
SMARTSOLUTIONS
STADIA VIEW
TRIFAB
VERSA PIVOT
VERSAGLAZE

KB ALLOYS, INC.

(Sub. of AMG Advanced Metallurgical Group N.V.)
2208 Quarry Dr Ste 201
Reading, PA 19609
Tel.: (610) 370-6585
Tel.: (610) 370-6733
Fax: (610) 370-6571
Toll Free: (800) 523-8457
E-mail: sales@kballoys.com
Web Site: www.kballoys.com
E-Mail For Key Personnel:
Sales Director: sales@kballoys.com
Approx. Number Employees: 150
Year Founded: 1950
Business Description:
Aluminum Master Alloys & Chemicals Mfr
S.I.C.: 3355; 3444
N.A.I.C.S.: 331319; 332322
Export
Media: 10
Distr.: Intl.; Natl.
Budget Set: Nov.
Personnel:
Richard J. Malliris *(Pres & CEO)*
Timothy R. Weaver *(VP-Fin)*
Tim Donnelly *(Dir-Sls & Mktg)*
Frank J. Amaturo *(Mgr-Sls Admin)*
Steve J. Halpin *(Mgr-Sls-Blaine)*
Brands & Products:
BORAL
TIBOR
TICAR
TITAL
Advertising Agency:
tomsheehan worldwide
645 Penn St
Reading, PA 19601-3408
Tel.: (610) 478-8448
Fax: (610) 478-8449

KB HOME

10990 Wilshire Blvd 7th Fl
Los Angeles, CA 90024
Tel.: (310) 231-4000
Fax: (310) 231-4222
Toll Free: (888) 524-6637
E-mail: pr@kbhome.com
Web Site: www.kbhome.com
Approx. Rev.: $1,589,996,000
Approx. Number Employees: 1,300
Year Founded: 1957
Business Description:
Homes & Commercial Project Builder
S.I.C.: 1531
N.A.I.C.S.: 236117
Advertising Expenditures: $25,900,000
Media: 8-9-10-18-23-24
Distr.: Intl.; Natl.
Budget Set: Dec.
Personnel:
Jeffrey T. Mezger *(Pres & CEO)*
Jeff Kaminski *(CFO & Exec VP)*
William R. Hollinger *(Chief Acctg Officer & Sr VP)*
Brian Woram *(Gen Counsel & Exec VP)*
Glen Barnard *(Sr VP-KBnxt Grp)*
Cory F. Cohen *(Sr VP-Tax)*
Thomas F. Norton *(Sr VP-HR)*
Brands & Products:
1-888-KB-HOMES
888-KB-HOMES
BUILT TO ORDER
THE CALIFORNIA SERIES
COLONY HOMES
DURA
DURA BUILDERS
HOUSECALL
KAUFMAN & BROAD
KB
KB HOME
KB URBAN
L'OFFICE
MY HOME MY EARTH
TRIPOLY
WHERE TRUST IS BUILT
Advertising Agencies:
The Phelps Group
901 Wilshire Blvd
Santa Monica, CA 90401-1854
Tel.: (310) 752-4400
Fax: (310) 752-4444

Shennum Green, Inc.
6160 Stoneridge Mall Rd Ste 290
Pleasanton, CA 94588
Tel.: (925) 460-8301
Fax: (925) 460-8307

KBR, INC.

601 Jefferson St Ste 9400
Houston, TX 77002
Tel.: (713) 753-2000
Fax: (713) 753-5353
E-mail: investors@kbr.com
Web Site: www.kbr.com
Approx. Rev.: $10,099,000,000
Approx. Number Employees: 35,000
Year Founded: 1901
Business Description:
Engineering, Construction & Government Contracting Services
S.I.C.: 1629; 8711
N.A.I.C.S.: 237990; 541330
Export
Media: 1-2-4-7-9-10-11-20-23
Distr.: Intl.; Natl.
Budget Set: Aug.
Personnel:
William P. Utt *(Chm, Pres & CEO)*
Susan K. Carter *(CFO & Exec VP)*
Dennis S. Baldwin *(Chief Acctg Officer & VP)*
Mitch Dauzat *(Pres-Gas Monetization)*
John Derbyshire *(Pres-Tech Bus Unit)*
Colin Elliott *(Pres-Infrastructure & Minerals)*
Roy Oelking *(Pres-Oil & Gas)*
Andrew Pringle *(Pres-Govt & Defense-Intl)*
John Quinn *(Pres-Downstream)*
John L. Rose *(Pres-Hydrocarbons Grp)*
James T. Stewart *(Pres-Power & Indus)*
Mark S. Williams *(Pres-Infrastructure, Govt & Power)*
Ted Wright *(Pres-North American Govt & Defense)*
David Zimmerman *(Pres-Svcs)*
Andrew D. Farley *(Gen Counsel & Exec VP)*
Klaudia J. Brace *(Exec VP-Admin)*
Dennis L. Calton *(Exec VP-Ops)*
Chris Barton *(Sr VP-Bus Dev-Oil & Gas Bus)*
Tom Mumford *(Sr VP-Comml)*
Chris Rhine *(Sr VP-Resource Mgmt)*
Rob Kukla, Jr. *(Dir-IR)*
Brad Lankford *(Supvr-KCM)*
Advertising Agency:
Khemistry
14-16 Brewer Street
London, W1F OSG, United Kingdom
Tel.: (44) 20 7437 4084
Fax: (44) 20 7437 4085

KEENEY MANUFACTURING COMPANY

(Sub. of United Plumbing Technologies)
1170 Main St
Newington, CT 06111
Tel.: (860) 666-3342
Fax: (860) 665-0374
Toll Free: (800) 243-0526
Web Site: www.plumbpak.com
Approx. Number Employees: 450
Year Founded: 1923
Business Description:
Mfr Construction & Replacement Plumbing/Water Supply Products
S.I.C.: 3432; 5074
N.A.I.C.S.: 332913; 423720
Import Export
Media: 4-7-10
Distr.: Natl.
Personnel:
Chris Jeffers *(Dir-Mktg)*

KEN-MAC METALS, INC.

(Sub. of ThyssenKrupp Materials NA)
17901 Englewood Dr
Cleveland, OH 44130-3454
Tel.: (440) 234-7500
Fax: (440) 234-4459
Toll Free: (800) 831-9503
E-mail: sales@kenmacmetals.com
Web Site: www.kenmacmetals.com
E-Mail For Key Personnel:
Sales Director: sales@kenmacmetals.com
Approx. Sls.: $200,000,000
Approx. Number Employees: 175
Year Founded: 1968
Business Description:
Aluminum & Stainless Metals Service Center
S.I.C.: 5051
N.A.I.C.S.: 423510
Import Export
Advertising Expenditures: $50,000
Media: 2-4-7-10-11-17
Distr.: Intl.; Natl.
Personnel:
Tim Yost *(Exec VP)*

KEYS GRANITE INC.

8788 NW 27th St
Miami, FL 33172
Tel.: (305) 477-7363
Fax: (305) 477-9567
Toll Free: (800) 8-GRANITE
E-mail: sales@keysgranite.com
Web Site: www.keysgranite.com
E-Mail For Key Personnel:
Sales Director: sales@keysgranite.com
Approx. Number Employees: 35
Business Description:
Granite & Marble Whslr
S.I.C.: 5032
N.A.I.C.S.: 423320
Media: 2-10
Personnel:
David Mansur *(Gen Mgr)*
Susan Soar *(Mgr-HR)*

KEYSTONE CONSOLIDATED INDUSTRIES, INC.

5430 LBJ Fwy Ste 1700
Dallas, TX 75240-2697
Tel.: (972) 458-0028
Fax: (972) 448-1408
Approx. Sls.: $450,745,000
Approx. Number Employees: 974
Year Founded: 1889
Business Description:
Mfr of Steel-Fabricated Wire Products, Industrial Wire & Rods
S.I.C.: 2999; 3312; 3315; 3496
N.A.I.C.S.: 324199; 331111; 331222; 332618
Advertising Expenditures: $1,400,000
Media: 17
Distr.: Natl.
Budget Set: June
Personnel:
Glenn R. Simmons *(Chm)*
David L. Cheek *(CEO)*
Bert E. Downing *(CFO)*
C. Victor Stirnaman *(COO & Exec VP)*
Brands & Products:
RED BRAND

KEYSTONE STEEL & WIRE CO.

(Div. of Keystone Consolidated Industries, Inc.)
7000 SW Adams St
Peoria, IL 61641
Tel.: (309) 697-7020
Fax: (309) 697-7422
Toll Free: (800) 447-6444
E-mail: general@keystonesteel.com
Web Site: www.keystonesteel.com
Sales Range: $50-74.9 Million
Approx. Number Employees: 70
Year Founded: 1889
Business Description:
Mfr of Steel Rods, Wire Mesh Products & Fencing
S.I.C.: 2999; 3312; 3316; 3469; 3496; 3537
N.A.I.C.S.: 324199; 331111; 331221; 332214; 332618; 333924
Import Export
Media: 1-2-4-6-7-10-13-19-20-26
Distr.: Natl.

Key to Media (For complete agency information see *The Advertising Red Books-Agencies* edition):
1. Bus. Publs. 2. Cable T.V. 3. Catalogs & Directories. 4. Co-op Adv. 5. Consumer Mags. 6. D.M. to Bus. Estab.7. D.M. to Consumers 8. Daily Newsp. 9. Exhibits/Trade Shows 10. Foreign 11. Infomercial 12. Internet Adv.13. Multimedia 14. Network Radio 15. Network T.V. 16. Newsp. Distr. Mags. 17. Other 18. Outdoor (Posters, Transit) 19. Point of Purchase20. Premiums, Novelties 21. Product Samples 22. Special Events Mktg. 23. Spot Radio 24. Spot T.V. 25. Weekly Newsp. 26. Yellow Page Adv.

Keystone Steel & Wire Co. — (Continued)

Budget Set: Oct.
Personnel:
David Cheek *(Pres & CEO)*
Vic Stirnaman *(COO & Exec VP)*
Richard Webb *(VP-Sls & Mktg-Industrial Products)*
Doug Wright *(VP-Sls & Mktg-Wire Products)*
Todd S. Mowbray *(Mgr-Sls-Wire Rod)*
Brands & Products:
KEYDECK
KEYMESH
KEYSTONE LG
KEYTWIST
RED BRAND
RED TOP
SIERRA

KIMMINS CORP.

1501 E 2nd Ave
Tampa, FL 33605
Tel.: (813) 248-3878
Fax: (813) 367-4262
E-mail: webmaster@kimmins.com
Web Site: www.kimmins.com
Approx. Number Employees: 450
Year Founded: 1922
Business Description:
Contract Construction & Demolition Services
S.I.C.: 1799
N.A.I.C.S.: 238990; 238910
Advertising Expenditures: $475,000
Media: 10
Distr.: Natl.
Personnel:
Francis Williams *(Chm)*
Joseph Williams *(Pres)*

KIRBY BUILDING SYSTEMS, INC.

(Sub. of Nucor Building Systems)
124 Kirby Dr
Portland, TN 37148
Mailing Address:
PO Box 390
Portland, TN 37148-0390
Tel.: (615) 325-4165
Fax: (800) 347-7999
E-mail: information@kirbybuildingsystems.com
Web Site:
www.kirbybuildingsystems.com
Sales Range: $75-99.9 Million
Approx. Number Employees: 200
Year Founded: 1955
Business Description:
Pre-Engineered Metal Buildings Mfr
S.I.C.: 3448
N.A.I.C.S.: 332311
Export
Media: 2-5-7-9-21-25-26
Distr.: Natl.
Budget Set: Dec.
Personnel:
Thomas McCann *(Pres)*
Brands & Products:
XPRESS

KIRRIN RESOURCES INC.

900 Elveden House 717 7th Ave SW
Calgary, AB T2P 0Z3, Canada
Tel.: (403) 205-4996
Fax: (403) 265-0608
Web Site: www.kirrinresources.com
Approx. Number Employees: 19
Year Founded: 1996
Business Description:
Diamond & Uranium Exploration & Development Services
S.I.C.: 1499; 1094
N.A.I.C.S.: 212399; 212291
Personnel:
Brian M. Benitz *(Chm)*
Derek J. Moran *(CEO)*
Peter T. Farkas *(CFO & Sec)*
Advertising Agency:
CHF Investor Relations
90 Adelaide St W Ste 600
Toronto, ON M5H 3V9, Canada
Tel.: (416) 868-1079
Fax: (416) 868-6198

KITCHEN KOMPACT, INC.

911 E 11th St
Jeffersonville, IN 47131
Mailing Address:
PO Box 868
Jeffersonville, IN 47131-0868
Tel.: (812) 282-6681
Fax: (812) 282-7880
Web Site: www.kitchenkompact.com
Sales Range: $125-149.9 Million
Approx. Number Employees: 275
Year Founded: 1937
Business Description:
Kitchen Cabinetry Mfr
S.I.C.: 2434
N.A.I.C.S.: 337110
Media: 10
Distr.: Natl.
Budget Set: Apr.
Personnel:
Dwight Gahm *(Founder)*
Walter Gahm *(Pres & CEO)*
Robert G. Wilson *(VP-Fin & Controller)*
Mike Heuser *(VP-Pur)*
Gordon Gahm *(Dir-Mktg)*
Brands & Products:
CHADWOOD
KITCHEN KOMPACT
LYNWOOD
MELLOWOOD
RICHWOOD LITE

KNEISLEY ELECTRIC COMPANY

900 West Miller Rd
Iola, KS 66749
Tel.: (620) 365-6628
Fax: (620) 365-2753
E-mail: sales@kneisley.com
Web Site: www.kneisley.com
E-Mail For Key Personnel:
Sales Director: sales@kneisley.com
Approx. Sls.: $11,576,672
Approx. Number Employees: 14
Year Founded: 1930
Business Description:
Theater Lighting Equipment Mfr
S.I.C.: 3646
N.A.I.C.S.: 335122
Media: 2-7-10
Distr.: Intl.; Natl.
Budget Set: July
Brands & Products:
KNI-TRON
XENEX I
XENEX II

KOCH ENTERPRISES, INC.

14 S 11th Ave
Evansville, IN 47712
Tel.: (812) 465-9800
Fax: (812) 465-9613
Web Site: www.kochenterprises.com
E-Mail For Key Personnel:
President: rkoch@kochenterprises.com
Sales Range: $700-749.9 Million
Approx. Number Employees: 2,000
Year Founded: 1873
Business Description:
Holding Company; Automotive Parts & Accessories & Heating & Air-Conditioning Products
S.I.C.: 3363; 5075
N.A.I.C.S.: 331521; 423730
Import Export
Advertising Expenditures: $350,000
Media: 2-4-5-6-7-8-9-10-14-18-20-23-26
Distr.: Natl.
Budget Set: Nov.
Personnel:
Robert L. Koch II *(Pres & Co-CEO)*
Susan E. Parsons *(CFO, Treas & Sec)*
James H. Muehlbauer *(Exec VP)*
Jennifer Slade *(Dir-Mktg)*

KOCH KNIGHT LLC

(Sub. of Koch Chemical Technology Group, LLC)
5385 Orchard View Dr SE
Canton, OH 44730
Tel.: (330) 488-1651
Fax: (330) 488-1656
E-mail: info@kochknight.com
Web Site: www.kochknight.com
Approx. Number Employees: 80
Year Founded: 1910
Business Description:
Chemical Equipment & Corrosion-Proof Materials Mfr
S.I.C.: 2899
N.A.I.C.S.: 325998
Export
Media: 2-4-10-21
Distr.: Intl.; Natl.
Budget Set: Dec.
Personnel:
Michael Graess *(Pres)*
Brands & Products:
FLEXERAMIC

KOHLER COMPANY

444 Highland Dr
Kohler, WI 53044-1515
Tel.: (920) 457-4441
Fax: (920) 457-1271
Toll Free: (800) 456-4537
E-mail: info@kohlerco.com
Web Site: www.kohlerco.com
Sales Range: $1-4.9 Billion
Approx. Number Employees: 30,000
Year Founded: 1874
Business Description:
Plumbing Fixtures, Furniture, Small Engines, Generators & Electrical Switchgear Mfr
S.I.C.: 3431; 3432
N.A.I.C.S.: 332998; 332913
Import Export
Media: 1-2-3-4-5-6-7-9-10-13-14-15-18-19-20-21-23-24-26
Distr.: Natl.
Budget Set: Oct.
Personnel:
David Kohler *(Owner)*
Herbert V. Kohler, Jr. *(Pres)*
Jeffrey P. Cheney *(CFO & Sr VP-Fin)*
Ralf Becker *(Pres-Europe, Middle East & Africa)*
Thomas Cromwell *(Pres-Engine Bus)*
Richard J. Fotsch *(Pres-Global Power Grp)*
Jason Struthers *(Pres-Kohler Power Sys)*
Jim Westdorp *(Pres-Kitchen & Bath Grp)*
Hugh Ekberg *(Exec VP-Kitchen & Bath-Americas Div)*
Laura E. Kohler *(Sr VP-HR)*
Jim Lewis *(VP-Mktg)*
John C. Engberg *(Dir-Comm-Rsch & Media)*
Jeff Rafter *(Mgr-Mktg)*
Carrie A. Seymour *(Mgr-Market Res & Segmentation)*
Jeff Mueller *(Engr)*
Brands & Products:
ADDISON
ALCOTT
ALENCON LACE
ALTERNA
AMARETTO
ANKARA
ANN SACKS
ANTIQUE
APERITIF
AQUIFER
ARICA
ASHLAND
ASOKA GARDEN
ASSURE
AUTEL
AVATAR
BAKER
BAKERSFIELD
BANCROFT
BARRINGTON
BAYVIEW
BODYSPA
BOL
BOTANICAL STUDY
BOTTICELLI
BOUCLE
BREVIA
BROOKFIELD
BROOKLINE
CACHET
CAMBER
CANCUN
CANTATA
CANTINA
CAPE COD
CAPE DORY
CAPE HATTERAS
CAPTIVA
CARIBBEAN
CAXTON
CERANA
CHABLIS
CHORD
CILANTRO
CIMARRON
CITY CLUB
CLAIRETTE
CLARITY
CLOSE REACH
COMFORT HEIGHT
COMPASS
CONSONANCE
CORALAIS
CRIMSON TOPAZ
DEERFIELD
DELAFIELD
DEMILAV

Key to Media (For complete agency information see *The Advertising Red Books-Agencies* edition):
1. Bus. Publs. 2. Cable T.V. 3. Catalogs & Directories. 4. Co-op Adv. 5. Consumer Mags. 6. D.M. to Bus. Estab.7. D.M. to Consumers 8. Daily Newsp. 9. Exhibits/Trade Shows 10. Foreign 11. Infomercial 12. Internet Adv.13. Multimedia 14. Network Radio 15. Network T.V. 16. Newsp. Distr. Mags. 17. Other 18. Outdoor (Posters, Transit) 19. Point of Purchase20. Premiums, Novelties 21. Product Samples 22. Special Events Mktg. 23. Spot Radio 24. Spot T.V. 25. Weekly Newsp. 26. Yellow Page Adv.

DEVONSHIRE
DICKINSON
DOCKSIDE
DOLCE VITA
EFFICIENCY
ELLERY
ELLIPSE
ENTERTAINER
ENTREE
EPERNAY
EPICUREAN
EXECUTIVE CHEF
FABLES AND FLOWERS
FAIRFAX
FALLING WATER
FARMINGTON
FINIAL
FLEUR
FLIGHT OF FANCY
FOLIO
FORTE
FREEWILL
FRENCH CURVE
GABRIELLE
GALLEON
GARAMOND
GARDEN BANDANA
GARLAND
GATHERING
GEORGES BRASS
GILFORD
GIMLET
GLEN FALLS
GLENBURY
GREEK
GUARDIAN
HARBORVIEW
HARTLAND
HATBOX
HIGHLANDS
HIGHLINE
HIRISE
HOURGLASS
HYTEC
IMPERIAL BLUE
INTERLACE
INVITATION
IRON ETCHINGS
IRON WORKS
IRON WORKS HISTORIC
JACOB DELAFON
JOURNEY
KALLISTA
KATHRYN
KITTY HAWK
KOHLER
KOI DANCE
LABOR
LADY VANITY
LAKEFIELD
LAKEWOOD
LANGLADE
LARKSPUR
LAUREATE
LEIGHTON
LIFE IN THE COUNTRY
LINIA
LOTUS POOL
LUSTRA
LYRIC
MAESTRO
MAIDEN
MAN'S LAV
MARATEA
MARCATO
MARSALA
MASTERSHOWER
MAYFIELD
MAYFLOWER
MCGUIRE
MEADOWLAND
MEMOIRS
MICKEY'S WISH
MOXIE
MYTHICAL BEASTS
NANTUCKET
NEOMEDIAM
NORTHLAND
OCEANVIEW
OCELLUS
OVERTURE
PARADOX
PARIGI
PARK FALLS
PEONIES AND IVY
PERSONA
PHEASANT
PINOIR
PINSTRIPE
PLUM BLOSSOM
POISE
PORTRAIT
POWER CLEAN
PRAIRIE FLOWERS
PRESSURE LITE
PRIMARY
PRO COOKCENTER
PRO COOKSINK
PRO TASKCENTER
PRO TASKSINK
PROAVATAR
PROFILE
PROFLEX
PROMASTER
PROVIDENCE
PROVINCIAL
PURIST
QUICK-RELEASE
QUIET-CLOSE
RADIANT
RAPPORT
RAVINIA
REVIVAL
RHYTHM
RIALTO
RICOCHET
RITE-TEMP
RIVER FALLS
RIVERBATH
RUSSIAN TEACUP
SALUTE
SAMBA
SAN RAPHAEL
SAN TROPEZ
SANIJURA
SANTA ROSA
SAREE
SAVANYO
SEA SALT
SEADREAM
SEAFORTH
SEAWALL
SENZA
SERIF
SERPENTINE BRONZE
SILKWEAVE
SMART DIVIDE
SOJOURN
SOK
SOLILOQUY
SONATA
SORBET
SPUN GLASS
STACCATO
STEEPING
STERLING
STILLNESS
SUNWARD
SWERVE
SWIFTFLO
SYMBIO
SYMBOL
SYNCHRONY
TABLEAU
TABORET
TAHOE
TAKE WING
TEA-FOR-TWO
TELLIEUR
TERCET
TERRACINA
TIDINGS
TOCCATA
TREND
TRIESTE
TRIKO
TRILOGY
TRITON
TWIRL
UNDERTONE
URBANITE
VAPOUR
VAS
VERACRUZ
VERITY
VERSE
VESSELS
VESSELS BOTTICELLI
VIBRANT
VIGORA
VILLAGER
VINNATA
VINTAGE
WATER RHYTHM
WATERCOVE
WATERHAVEN
WATER'S GROVE
WATERSCAPE
WATERTILE
WELLSPRING
WELLWORTH
WESTOVER
WHISTLING STRAITS
WOODFIELD

Advertising Agencies:
Carat
150 E 42nd St
New York, NY 10017
Tel.: (212) 689-6800
Fax: (212) 689-6005
Media Planning & Buying

Doe-Anderson
620 W Main St
Louisville, KY 40202-2933
Tel.: (502) 589-1700
Fax: (502) 587-8349

GSD&M
828 W 6th St
Austin, TX 78703-5420
Tel.: (512) 242-4736
Fax: (512) 242-4700

KOMATSU AMERICA CORP.
(Sub. of Komatsu Ltd.)
1701 West Golf Rd
Rolling Meadows, IL 60008
Tel.: (847) 437-5800
Fax: (847) 437-1016
Toll Free: (866) 513-5778
Web Site: www.komatsuamerica.com
Approx. Number Employees: 350
Year Founded: 1988
Business Description:
Heavy-Duty Construction Equipment Mfr & Importer
S.I.C.: 3531; 6141
N.A.I.C.S.: 333120; 522220
Media: 1-2-4-5-7-10-13-18-20-22-26
Distr.: Natl.
Personnel:
David W. Grzelak *(Chm & CEO)*
Jim Shinozuka *(Pres & COO)*
Gary Kaspeer *(CFO)*
Steve Cihock *(Mgr-Adv, Promotions & Events)*

THE KULJIAN CORPORATION
3700 Market St No 2
Philadelphia, PA 19104-3169
Tel.: (215) 243-1900
Fax: (215) 243-1942
E-mail: inquiry@kuljian.com
Web Site: www.kuljian.com
Sales Range: $1-9.9 Million
Approx. Number Employees: 200
Year Founded: 1941
Business Description:
Engineering Consulting Services
S.I.C.: 8711; 8748
N.A.I.C.S.: 541330; 541618
Media: 17
Distr.: Intl.; Natl.
Budget Set: Oct.
Personnel:
Ronald Szostak *(Exec VP)*
Mary Hart *(VP-Sls)*
Mike Shome *(VP-Mktg)*
Brands & Products:
KULJIAN

LADISH CO., INC.
5481 S Packard Ave
Cudahy, WI 53110
Mailing Address:
PO Box 8902
Cudahy, WI 53110
Tel.: (414) 747-2611
Fax: (414) 747-2963
E-mail: gvroman@ladishco.com
Web Site: www.ladishco.com
Approx. Sls.: $403,132,000
Approx. Number Employees: 1,250
Year Founded: 1905
Business Description:
High-Strength Forged & Cast Metal Components Developer, Mfr & Marketer
S.I.C.: 3462; 3363; 3463; 3724
N.A.I.C.S.: 332111; 331521; 332112; 336412
Media: 2-4-7-10
Distr.: Natl.
Budget Set: Dec.
Personnel:
Gary J. Vroman *(Pres & CEO)*
Wayne E. Larsen *(VP-Law & Fin & Sec)*
Douglas Roberts *(Gen Mgr-Sls & Mktg)*

LAFARGE CANADA INC.
(Div. of Lafarge North America Inc.)
334 Avro Ave
Pointe-Claire, QC H9R 5W5, Canada
Tel.: (514) 428-7300
Fax: (514) 428-0049
Fax: (514) 876-8900
Web Site:
www.lafargenorthamerica.com

Key to Media (For complete agency information see *The Advertising Red Books-Agencies* edition):
1. Bus. Publs. 2. Cable T.V. 3. Catalogs & Directories. 4. Co-op Adv. 5. Consumer Mags. 6. D.M. to Bus. Estab.7. D.M. to Consumers
8. Daily Newsp. 9. Exhibits/Trade Shows 10. Foreign 11. Infomercial 12. Internet Adv.13. Multimedia 14. Network Radio
15. Network T.V. 16. Newsp. Distr. Mags. 17. Other 18. Outdoor (Posters, Transit) 19. Point of Purchase20. Premiums, Novelties
21. Product Samples 22. Special Events Mktg. 23. Spot Radio 24. Spot T.V. 25. Weekly Newsp. 26. Yellow Page Adv.

Lafarge Canada Inc. — (Continued)

Approx. Number Employees: 5,000
Year Founded: 1909
Business Description:
Supplier of Concrete & Construction Materials
S.I.C.: 5032
N.A.I.C.S.: 423320
Import Export
Media: 2-4-7-9-10-11-13-21-26
Distr.: Intl., Natl.
Budget Set: Oct. -Nov.
Personnel:
John D. Redfern *(Chm)*
Eric Olsen *(CFO & Exec VP)*
Alvaro Lorenz *(Sr VP-Lafarge Cement)*
Oliver Merindol *(Sr VP-Corp Tech Services)*
Brands & Products:
LAFARGE SF CEMENT
MAXCEM
SUPERCEM
SUPERCEM PLUS
TERCEM 3000
TERRACEM

LAFARGE NORTH AMERICA INC.

(Sub. of Lafarge Ciments)
12950 Worldgate Dr Ste 500
Herndon, VA 20170
Tel.: (703) 480-3600
Fax: (703) 796-2214
Web Site:
www.lafargenorthamerica.com
Approx. Number Employees: 16,400
Year Founded: 1983
Business Description:
Holding Company; Production & Sale of Cement, Concrete & Related Products
S.I.C.: 3241; 3273
N.A.I.C.S.: 327310; 327320
Import
Advertising Expenditures: $300,000
Media: 2-4-6-7-10-17
Distr.: Intl., Natl.
Budget Set: Oct.
Personnel:
Bernard L.M. Kasriel *(Vice Chm)*
Eric Olsen *(CFO & VP)*
Brands & Products:
AGILIA
LAFARGE

LAFARGE NORTH AMERICA INC.

(Div. of Lafarge North America Inc.)
300 E Joppa Rd Hampton Plz
Towson, MD 21286
Tel.: (410) 847-3300
Fax: (410) 847-3266
E-mail: info@lafargenorthamerica.com
Web Site:
www.lafargenorthamerica.com
Approx. Number Employees: 60
Year Founded: 1914
Business Description:
Blast Furnace Slag, Sand & Gravel, Limestone & Iron Ore Mfr
S.I.C.: 3241
N.A.I.C.S.: 327310
Advertising Expenditures: $300,000
Media: 4-9-10-21
Distr.: Reg.
Budget Set: Nov.

LAKE SHORE INDUSTRIES, INC.

1817 Poplar St
Erie, PA 16502
Mailing Address:
PO Box 59
Erie, PA 16512-0059
Tel.: (814) 456-4277
Fax: (814) 453-4293
Toll Free: (800) 458-0463
E-mail: info@lsisigns.com
Web Site: www.lsisigns.com
Approx. Sls.: $2,000,000
Approx. Number Employees: 23
Year Founded: 1908
Business Description:
Sign Mfr
S.I.C.: 3993; 3354
N.A.I.C.S.: 339950; 331316
Export
Media: 2-6-8-13-26
Distr.: Direct to Consumer; Intl.; Natl.
Budget Set: Oct.
Personnel:
Leo Bruno *(Pres)*
Shirley Bruno *(Dir-Mktg)*
Brands & Products:
LETTER-LITE

LARKEN ASSOCIATES

390 Amelo Rd Bldg 5 Ste 507
Hillsborough, NJ 08844
Tel.: (908) 874-8686
Fax: (908) 874-6064
E-mail: info@larkenassociates.com
Web Site: www.larkenassociates.com
E-Mail For Key Personnel:
President: dgardner@larkenassociates.com
Approx. Sls.: $4,300,000
Approx. Number Employees: 20
Business Description:
Developer of Commercial & Residential Real Estate
S.I.C.: 6512; 1522
N.A.I.C.S.: 531120; 236220
Media: 2-4-13-16-26
Personnel:
Lawrence W. Gardner *(Chm & CEO)*
David Gardner *(Pres & COO)*
Babette Rutman *(CFO)*
Marilyn Cornelia *(Exec VP-Residential)*

LARSON MANUFACTURING COMPANY

2333 Eastbrook Dr
Brookings, SD 57006-2838
Tel.: (605) 692-6115
Fax: (605) 696-6403
E-mail: customerservice@larsondoors.com
Web Site: www.larsondoors.com
Approx. Number Employees: 1,050
Year Founded: 1964
Business Description:
Aluminum Storm Doors Mfr
S.I.C.: 5031; 3442
N.A.I.C.S.: 423310; 332321
Advertising Expenditures: $200,000
Media: 2-4-6-7-10-19
Distr.: Natl.
Personnel:
Jeff Rief *(COO)*
June Eng *(Dir-Mktg)*
Brands & Products:
CLASSIC-VIEW
ELEGANCE
GLASS
LIFE-CORE
LIFESTYLE
MULTI-VENT
PRESTIGE-SEAL
VALUE-CORE
VINYL-CLAD

LATI U.S.A., INC.

(Sub. of Lati Industria Termoplastici S.p.A.)
257 Deming Way
Summerville, SC 29483
Tel.: (843) 285-2200
Fax: (843) 285-2249
Toll Free: (888) USALATI
E-mail: info@us.lati.com
Web Site: www.lati.com
Approx. Number Employees: 6
Year Founded: 1996
Business Description:
Compounder Engineering Thermoplastics
S.I.C.: 3087
N.A.I.C.S.: 325991
Media: 13

LATROBE SPECIALTY STEEL COMPANY

(Holding of Bain Capital, LLC)
2626 Ligonier St
Latrobe, PA 15650-3246
Mailing Address:
PO Box 31
Latrobe, PA 15650
Tel.: (724) 537-7711
Fax: (724) 532-6316
E-mail: info@latrobesteel.com
Web Site: www.latrobesteel.com
Approx. Number Employees: 800
Year Founded: 1913
Business Description:
Specialty Steel Products Mfr
S.I.C.: 3312; 3369
N.A.I.C.S.: 331111; 331528
Export
Media: 2-4-10-20
Distr.: Intl.; Natl.
Personnel:
Thomas O. Hicks *(Co-Chm)*
Steven E. Karol *(Co-Chm)*
B. Christopher DiSantis *(Pres & CEO)*
Daniel G. Hennessy *(Sr VP-Mfg)*
Brands & Products:
BEARCAT S-7
CBS-1000 M
CBS-600
CM-50
CM-52
CORSAIR
CRUSADER
DOUBLE SIX M-2
DYNAMAX (M42)
GRAPH-AIR
GRAPH-MO
LESCALLOY 300 M VAC-ARC
LESCALLOY M50 VIM-VAR
LESCO A-6
LESCO BRAKE DIE
MGR
MP35N
OLYMPIC D-2
SELECT B (A2)
TATMO
TATMO V
TATMO V-N
VAC-ARC
VDC (H13)
VISCOUNT 44 (H13)

LAVI INDUSTRIES INC.

27810 Ave Hopkins
Valencia, CA 91355-1246
Tel.: (661) 257-7800
Fax: (661) 257-4938
Toll Free: (800) 624-6225
E-mail: sales@lavi.com
Web Site: www.lavi.com
E-Mail For Key Personnel:
President: GabrielL@lavi.com
Sales Director: sales@lavi.com
Approx. Number Employees: 150
Year Founded: 1980
Business Description:
Suppliers of Construction Materials
S.I.C.: 3446
N.A.I.C.S.: 332323
Import Export
Personnel:
Gabriel Lavi *(CEO)*
Chrissa Harris *(CFO)*
Brands & Products:
BELTRAC
DIRECTAC
DIRECTRAC
LAROSA
LIDO-LUSTER
LIDO RAIL
LIDO-TONE
LIDO-WELD
NEXTRAC
QUICKCLIP
QUICKMOUNT
Advertising Agency:
Glyphix Advertising
6964 Shoup Ave
West Hills, CA 91307
Tel.: (818) 704-3994
Fax: (818) 704-8850

LAWRENCE METAL PRODUCTS, INC.

260 Spur Dr S
Bay Shore, NY 11706-3917
Mailing Address:
PO Box 400-M
Bay Shore, NY 11706
Tel.: (631) 666-0300
Fax: (631) 647-6591
Fax: (631) 666-0336
Fax: (631) 666-3066
Toll Free: (800) 441-0019
E-mail: sales@lawrencemetal.com
Web Site: www.lawrencemetal.com
E-Mail For Key Personnel:
President: dlawrence@lawrencemetal.com
Marketing Director: bcastro@lawrencemetal.com
Sales Director: sales@lawrencemetal.com
Sales Range: $50-74.9 Million
Approx. Number Employees: 110
Year Founded: 1881
Business Description:
Mfr of Pedestrian Traffic Control Systems
S.I.C.: 3446; 5083
N.A.I.C.S.: 332323; 423820
Import Export
Media: 2-4-7-8-10-13-26
Distr.: Intl.
Budget Set: Sept. -Oct.

Key to Media (For complete agency information see *The Advertising Red Books-Agencies* edition):
1. Bus. Publs. 2. Cable T.V. 3. Catalogs & Directories. 4. Co-op Adv. 5. Consumer Mags. 6. D.M. to Bus. Estab.7. D.M. to Consumers
8. Daily Newsp. 9. Exhibits/Trade Shows 10. Foreign 11. Infomercial 12. Internet Adv.13. Multimedia 14. Network Radio
15. Network T.V. 16. Newsp. Distr. Mags. 17. Other 18. Outdoor (Posters, Transit) 19. Point of Purchase20. Premiums, Novelties
21. Product Samples 22. Special Events Mktg. 23. Spot Radio 24. Spot T.V. 25. Weekly Newsp. 26. Yellow Page Adv.

Personnel:
Alan McTherson *(CEO)*
Bill Vetter *(Gen Mgr)*
Brands & Products:
CLASSIC
CONTROL YOUR WORLD.
LAWRENCE
TENSABARRIER
TENSACLEAR
Advertising Agencies:
Epoch 5 Public Relations
755 New York Ave
Huntington, NY 11743
Tel.: (631) 427-1713
Fax: (631) 427-1740

Walter F. Cameron Advertising Inc.
350 Motor Pkwy Ste 410
Hauppauge, NY 11788-5125
Tel.: (631) 232-3033
Fax: (631) 232-3111

LEE COMPANY

331 Mallory Sta Rd
Franklin, TN 37067
Tel.: (615) 567-1000
Fax: (615) 567-1026
E-mail: leecompany@leecompany.com
Web Site: www.leecompany.com
Sales Range: $75-99.9 Million
Approx. Number Employees: 750
Year Founded: 1944
Business Description:
Plumbing Contractors & Mechanical
S.I.C.: 1711; 1731
N.A.I.C.S.: 238220; 238210
Personnel:
Richard C. Perko *(Pres)*
William B. Lee *(CEO)*
Advertising Agency:
Garmezy Media
53 Lindsley Ave
Nashville, TN 37210
Tel.: (615) 242-6878

LEHIGH CEMENT COMPANY

(Sub. of Heidelberg Cement, Inc.)
(d/b/a Lehigh Heidelberg Cement Group)
7660 Imperial Way
Allentown, PA 18195-1016
Tel.: (610) 366-4600
Fax: (610) 366-4851
Toll Free: (800) 523-5488
Telex: 510-6511020 LEHPORCEM ATW
E-mail: info@lehighcement.com
Web Site: www.lehighcement.com
Sales Range: $1-4.9 Billion
Approx. Number Employees: 130
Year Founded: 1897
Business Description:
Cement & Concrete Products Mfr
S.I.C.: 3241; 3271; 3272; 3273
N.A.I.C.S.: 327310; 327320; 327331; 327332
Import Export
Advertising Expenditures: $200,000
Media: 2-10-17-25
Distr.: Natl.
Budget Set: Nov.-Dec.
Personnel:
Daniel M. Harrington *(COO)*

LEIGH FIBERS, INC.

1101 Syphrit Rd
Wellford, SC 29385-9460
Tel.: (864) 439-4111
Fax: (864) 439-5647
Web Site: www.leighfibers.com
Approx. Sls.: $100,000,000
Approx. Number Employees: 406
Year Founded: 1922
Business Description:
Recycling of Textile Waste
S.I.C.: 2299; 2824
N.A.I.C.S.: 314999; 325222
Import Export
Personnel:
Philip Lehner *(Chm)*
Keith Taylor *(Pres)*
Carl Lehner *(CEO)*
Advertising Agency:
Brewer Associates Marketing Communications
39555 Orchard Hill Pl Ste 600
Novi, MI 48375
Tel.: (734) 458-7180

LENNAR HOMES, INC.

(Sub. of Lennar Corporation)
550 Greens Pkwy Ste 111
Houston, TX 77067
Tel.: (281) 875-1000
Web Site: www.lennar.com
Sales Range: $1-4.9 Billion
Approx. Number Employees: 6,053
Year Founded: 1954
Business Description:
Residential Construction Services
S.I.C.: 1521
N.A.I.C.S.: 236115
Media: 2-4-8-9-10-13-18-25
Distr.: Natl.
Personnel:
Stuart A. Miller *(CEO)*
Kay Howard *(Dir-Comm)*
Advertising Agency:
Zimmerman Advertising
2200 W Commercial Blvd Ste 300
Fort Lauderdale, FL 33309-3064
Tel.: (954) 644-4000
Fax: (954) 731-2977
Toll Free: (800) 248-8522

LENNOX HEARTH PRODUCTS

(Div. of Lennox International Inc.)
1110 W Taft Ave
Orange, CA 92865-4150
Tel.: (615) 925-3417
Fax: (714) 921-6149
Toll Free: (800) 9-LENNOX
Web Site: www.lennoxhearthproducts.com
Sales Range: $50-74.9 Million
Approx. Number Employees: 100
Year Founded: 1996
Business Description:
Mfr of Wood-Burning & Gas-Fired Fireplaces, Fireplace Inserts, Stoves & Chimney Systems
S.I.C.: 3272
N.A.I.C.S.: 327390
Import Export
Advertising Expenditures: $3,500,000
Bus. Publs.: $1,750,000; Catalogs & Directories: $350,000; Consumer Mags.: $175,000; Exhibits/Trade Shows: $350,000; Other: $175,000; Point of Purchase: $700,000
Distr.: Intl.
Budget Set: Dec.
Brands & Products:
CORNER
EARTH STOVE
ELITE
MERIT PLUS
PENINSULA
REFLECTIONS
SEE-THROUGH
SEREFINA
SERENE HEAT
SUPERIOR
TRADITIONS
WHITFIELD

LESTER BUILDING SYSTEMS, LLC

1111 Second Ave S
Lester Prairie, MN 55354
Tel.: (320) 395-2531
Fax: (320) 395-5393
Toll Free: (800) 826-4439
E-mail: info@lesterbuildings.com
Web Site: www.lesterbuildings.com
Sales Range: $25-49.9 Million
Approx. Number Employees: 200
Year Founded: 1947
Business Description:
Pre-Engineered Wood Frame Buildings Mfr
S.I.C.: 1522
N.A.I.C.S.: 236220
Media: 8-10-22-23-25
Personnel:
John Hill *(Pres)*
Larry Lembrich *(Sr VP-Sls)*
Tom Borgman *(Mgr-Mktg)*
Mike Kelly *(Mgr-Southeast Minnesota)*
Brands & Products:
BONANZA'S
IMPROV
INSL-WALL
LESTER
LESTER NET
LESTER QUOTE
R-CONTROL
TOWN AND COUNTRY
UNI-FRAME

LIBERTY HOMES, INC.

1101 Eisenhower Dr N
Goshen, IN 46526
Mailing Address:
PO Box 35
Goshen, IN 46527-0035
Tel.: (574) 533-0431
Fax: (574) 533-0438
Toll Free: (800) 733-0431
E-mail: info@libertyhomesinc.com
Web Site: www.libertyhomesinc.com
Sales Range: $75-99.9 Million
Approx. Number Employees: 30
Year Founded: 1941
Business Description:
Manufactured & Modular Home Designer
S.I.C.: 2452; 2451
N.A.I.C.S.: 321992; 321991
Media: 13
Personnel:
Edward J. Hussey *(Chm & CEO)*
Michael Hussey *(Pres)*
Marc Dosmann *(CFO & VP)*
Edward J. Hussey, Jr. *(VP, Sec & Asst Treas)*
Ronald Atkins *(VP-Pur)*

LIFTOMATIC MATERIAL HANDLING INC.

700 Dartmouth Ln
Buffalo Grove, IL 60089
Tel.: (847) 325-2930
Fax: (847) 325-2959
Toll Free: (800) 837-6540
E-mail: info@liftomatic.com
Web Site: www.liftomatic.com
E-Mail For Key Personnel:
Sales Director: sales@liftomatic.com
Approx. Number Employees: 12
Year Founded: 1947
Business Description:
Drum Handling Equipment Mfr
S.I.C.: 3537
N.A.I.C.S.: 333924
Import Export
Media: 2-4-5-7-11-20
Distr.: Intl.
Budget Set: Sept. -Nov.
Personnel:
Todd Berg *(Pres)*
E. Darren Berg *(VP-Sls)*
Brands & Products:
DU-SOM
ERGO-MATIC
LIFTOMATIC
PARROT-BEAK
PARTNERS1
PORTA-RAMP
QUICK-CLAW
SPEEDLOCK
STEEL-IT
TD-850 DRUMVERTER
WEATHER BEAK

LINDAL CEDAR HOMES, INC.

4300 S 104th Pl
Seattle, WA 98178
Tel.: (206) 725-0900
Fax: (206) 725-1615
E-mail: info@lindal.com
Web Site: www.lindal.com
Approx. Sls.: $48,266,000
Approx. Number Employees: 200
Year Founded: 1945
Business Description:
Custom Cedar Home & Sunroom Mfr
S.I.C.: 2452; 2541
N.A.I.C.S.: 321992; 337212
Import Export
Media: 2-6
Distr.: Intl.
Budget Set: Oct.
Personnel:
Robert W. Lindal *(Chm & CEO)*
Michael Harris *(Pres & COO)*
Dennis Greg *(CFO & VP-Fin)*
Martin J. Lindal *(Exec VP)*
Sig Benson *(VP-Mktg)*
David Nixon *(VP-Mfg & Pur)*
Brands & Products:
AFFINITY
CHALET
JUSTUS
LINDAL
LINDAL CEDAR HOMES
PROW
SUMMIT
Advertising Agency:
Golden Lasso, LLC
1520 Bellevue Ave
Seattle, WA 98107
Tel.: (006) 632-6030
Fax: (006) 838-3161

LIQUID COATING DESIGNS INC.

1262 Quarry Ln Ste D
Pleasanton, CA 94566
Tel.: (925) 931-1937

Key to Media (For complete agency information see *The Advertising Red Books-Agencies* edition):
1. Bus. Publs. 2. Cable T.V. 3. Catalogs & Directories. 4. Co-op Adv. 5. Consumer Mags. 6. D.M. to Bus. Estab.7. D.M. to Consumers 8. Daily Newsp. 9. Exhibits/Trade Shows 10. Foreign 11. Infomercial 12. Internet Adv.13. Multimedia 14. Network Radio 15. Network T.V. 16. Newsp. Distr. Mags. 17. Other 18. Outdoor (Posters, Transit) 19. Point of Purchase20. Premiums, Novelties 21. Product Samples 22. Special Events Mktg. 23. Spot Radio 24. Spot T.V. 25. Weekly Newsp. 26. Yellow Page Adv.

Liquid Coating Designs Inc. — (Continued)

Fax: (925) 931-1938
Toll Free: (866) 886-2628
E-mail: liquidstone@earthlink.net
Web Site:
www.liquidcoatingdesigns.com
Business Description:
Concrete Resurfacing Services
S.I.C.: 1771
N.A.I.C.S.: 238110
Media: 2-6-13
Personnel:
Charles Suhay *(Pres)*

L.M. SCOFIELD COMPANY

6533 Bandini Blvd
Los Angeles, CA 90040
Tel.: (323) 720-3000
Fax: (770) 920-6061
Toll Free: (800) 800-9900
Web Site: www.scofield.com
Approx. Number Employees: 140
Year Founded: 1915
Business Description:
Mfr. of Colors & Texturing Systems for Concrete
S.I.C.: 2899; 2816
N.A.I.C.S.: 325998; 325131
Media: 2-4-5-10-21
Distr.: Natl.
Budget Set: Jan.
Personnel:
Phillip Arnold *(Chm & CEO)*
Harry Moats *(Pres & COO)*
Jim Heermans *(CFO & VP)*
Cam Villar *(Dir-Mktg)*
Brands & Products:
BUILDINGCALK-3G
BUILDINGCALK-3S
CEMENTONE
CHEMSTAIN
CHROMIX
COLORCURE
COLORSTONE
COLORWAX
CONPATCH
CURESEAL
EMERCHROME
LITHOCHROME
LITHOSEAL
LITHOTEX
OVERLAY
PANELETCH
PAVECRAFTERS
REPELLO
SCOFIELD
SCOFIELD FORMULA ONE
TEXTURETOP
TINTURA
TRAFFICALK-3G
WATERCALK
WATERCALK-3G
WATERCALK-3S

THE LONGFORD GROUP, INC.

3077 East Warm Springs Rd
Las Vegas, NV 89120
Tel.: (702) 454-5300
Fax: (702) 454-8715
E-mail: info@longfordhomes.com
Web Site: www.longfordhomes.com
Approx. Sls.: $46,051,361
Approx. Number Employees: 80
Business Description:
Residential Construction
S.I.C.: 1521
N.A.I.C.S.: 236115
Personnel:
John Murtagh *(Pres)*
Advertising Agency:
The Geary Company
3136 E Russell Rd
Las Vegas, NV 89120-3463
Tel.: (702) 382-9610
Fax: (702) 382-0920

LOUISIANA-PACIFIC CORPORATION

414 Union St Ste 2000
Nashville, TN 37219-1700
Tel.: (615) 986-5600
Fax: (615) 986-5666
Toll Free: (800) 648-6893
E-mail: customer.support@lpcorp.com
Web Site: www.lpcorp.com
Approx. Sls.: $1,383,600,000
Approx. Number Employees: 3,800
Year Founded: 1973
Business Description:
Building Products; Lumber, OSB, Wood, Aluminum, Panel Products, Engineered I-Joists, Cellulose Insulation
S.I.C.: 2421; 2493
N.A.I.C.S.: 321113; 321219
Import Export
Advertising Expenditures: $16,000,000
Media: 2-3-4-6-7-8-10-11-13-15-17-18-19-21-24-26
Distr.: Intl.; Natl.
Budget Set: Dec.
Personnel:
Richard W. Frost *(CEO)*
Curtis M. Stevens *(CFO & Exec VP-Admin)*
Mark Fuchs *(Gen Counsel, Corp Sec & VP)*
Richard S. Olszewski *(Exec VP-Speciality Products, Sls & Mtkg)*
Jeff Wagner *(Exec VP-OSB)*
Brian Luoma *(VP & Gen Mgr-Engrg Wood Products)*
Brad Southern *(VP & Gen Mgr-Siding)*
David Crowe *(VP-Corp Engrg & Tech)*
Ann Harris *(VP-HR)*
Neil Sherman *(VP-Procurement, Logistics & Supply Mgmt)*
Mike Sims *(VP-Sls)*
Ben Skoog *(Brand Mgr-LP)*
Mary Cohn *(Mgr-Corp Affairs)*
Judy Musgrove *(Mgr-Corp Mktg)*
Brands & Products:
ABTCO
AQUATILE
BETTER BUILDING BEGINS HERE
BUILD WITH US.
CANEXEL
GANG-LAM
LP
LP SOLUTIONS
SMARTSIDE
SOLID START
TOP NOTCH
WEATHERBEST
Advertising Agency:
Gish, Sherwood & Friends, Inc.
(d/b/a GS&F)
4235 Hillsboro Pike
Nashville, TN 37215-3344
Tel.: (615) 385-1100
Fax: (615) 783-0500
(Public Relations)

LOZIER CORPORATION

6336 John J Pershing Dr
Omaha, NE 68110
Mailing Address:
PO Box 3448
Omaha, NE 68103-0448
Tel.: (402) 457-8000
Fax: (402) 457-8390
Toll Free: (800) 228-9882
E-mail: salesinfo@lozier.biz
Web Site: www.lozier.com
E-Mail For Key Personnel:
Sales Director: salesinfo@lozier.biz
Approx. Number Employees: 2,100
Year Founded: 1956
Business Description:
Mfr & Retailer of Retail Store Fixtures & Storage Systems
S.I.C.: 2519; 2541
N.A.I.C.S.: 337125; 337212
Export
Media: 2-4-7-10
Distr.: Intl.; Natl.
Personnel:
Steve Franz *(CFO)*
Brands & Products:
CLASSIC RX
CLASSIC RX SYSTEM
CUBE SAVER
FLEX RX
FLEX RX SYSTEM
LOZIER

LUCITE INTERNATIONAL, INC.

(Sub. of Lucite International)
The Lucite Ctr 7275 Goodlett Farms Pkwy
Cordova, TN 38016
Tel.: (901) 381-2000
Fax: (901) 381-2266
Web Site: www.luciteinternational.com
Approx. Number Employees: 300
Year Founded: 1995
Business Description:
Plastic Lighting Panels, Plastic Decorator Panels, Rigid Clear & Solar Tint Sheets In Acrylic & Styrene, Non Glare Picture Framing Panels, MMA & Higher Monomers Acrylic Polymer, Cast Acrylic Sheet & Acrylic Bead Resins
S.I.C.: 2821; 3089
N.A.I.C.S.: 325211; 326199
Export
Media: 1-2-4-5-10-11-16-19-21-23-24
Distr.: Intl.; Natl.
Budget Set: Sept.
Personnel:
Brent Long *(CFO)*
J. Jefferson Davis *(Pres-US)*
Neil Sayers *(VP-Tech)*
Kevin Burgason *(Dir-Americas Strategic Plng)*
Bob Connolly *(Dir-Bus-Monomers Americas)*
Chris Robinson *(Bus Mgr)*
Brands & Products:
LUCITE SUPERTUF
LUCITE TUFCOAT
PERSPEX
Advertising Agency:
Walker & Associates, Inc.
5100 Poplar Ave Ste 2812
Memphis, TN 38137
Tel.: (901) 522-1100
Fax: (901) 522-1101

LUMBER LIQUIDATORS HOLDINGS, INC.

3000 John Deere Rd
Toano, VA 23168-9332
Tel.: (757) 259-4280
E-mail: lumber@lumberliquidators.com
Web Site: www.lumberliquidators.com
Approx. Sls.: $620,281,000
Approx. Number Employees: 1,197
Year Founded: 1994
Business Description:
Hardwood Flooring Products Retailer
S.I.C.: 5211; 5031; 5713
N.A.I.C.S.: 444110; 423310; 442210
Advertising Expenditures: $49,797,000
Media: 4-6-8-13-18-22-25-26
Personnel:
Thomas D. Sullivan *(Chm)*
Robert M. Lynch *(Pres & COO)*
Jeffrey W. Griffiths *(CEO)*
Daniel E. Terrell *(CFO)*
William K. Schlegel *(Chief Mdsg Officer)*
E. Livingston B. Haskell *(Gen Counsel & Sec)*
Robert M. Morrison *(Sr VP-Store Ops)*
Marco Q. Pescara *(Sr VP-Direct Mktg & Adv)*
Brands & Products:
AUSTRALIAN CYPRESS
AZTEC CHERRY
BELLAWOOD
BRAZILIAN MESQUITE
GUNSTOCKOAK
THE LUMBER LIQUIDATORS
MAPLE
MOCHA OAK
MORNINGSTAR
SCHON
TUFFTEAK
TYPENNINGTON
Advertising Agency:
A. Eicoff & Co.
(Div. of Ogilvy & Mather Worldwide)
401 N Michigan Ave 4th Fl
Chicago, IL 60611-4212
Tel.: (312) 527-7183
Fax: (312) 527-7188
Toll Free: (800) 333-6605

LURIE GLASS COMPANY

(Div. of The Lurie Companies)
12000 W Wirth St
Milwaukee, WI 53222
Tel.: (414) 536-8000
Fax: (414) 977-5525
E-mail: info@lurieglass.com
Web Site: www.lurieglass.com
Approx. Sls.: $7,000,000
Approx. Number Employees: 95
Year Founded: 1918
Business Description:
Mfr. of Glass Products For Commercial, Industrial, Residential & Automotive Use
S.I.C.: 1793; 5231
N.A.I.C.S.: 238150; 444120
Advertising Expenditures: $250,000
Media: 2-4-6-7-10-13-26
Distr.: Natl.
Personnel:
Marc S. Lurie *(Pres)*

Key to Media (For complete agency information see *The Advertising Red Books-Agencies* edition):
1. Bus. Publs. 2. Cable T.V. 3. Catalogs & Directories. 4. Co-op Adv. 5. Consumer Mags. 6. D.M. to Bus. Estab.7. D.M. to Consumers
8. Daily Newsp. 9. Exhibits/Trade Shows 10. Foreign 11. Infomercial 12. Internet Adv.13. Multimedia 14. Network Radio
15. Network T.V. 16. Newsp. Distr. Mags. 17. Other 18. Outdoor (Posters, Transit) 19. Point of Purchase20. Premiums, Novelties
21. Product Samples 22. Special Events Mktg. 23. Spot Radio 24. Spot T.V. 25. Weekly Newsp. 26. Yellow Page Adv.

LYON WORKSPACE PRODUCTS LLC
(Sub. of Lyon & Dittrich Holding Company)
420 N Main St
Montgomery, IL 60538-1367
Mailing Address:
PO Box 671
Aurora, IL 60507-0671
Tel.: (630) 892-8941
Fax: (630) 892-8966
Toll Free: (800) 433-8488
E-mail: lyon@lyonworkspace.com
Web Site: www.lyonworkspace.com
Approx. Number Employees: 350
Year Founded: 1901
Business Description:
Steel Shelving, Lockers, Shop Equipment, Boxes & Tool Storage Equipment & Office Cabinets Mfr
S.I.C.: 2542
N.A.I.C.S.: 337215
Import Export
Advertising Expenditures: $1,000,000
Media: 1-2-4-5-7-10-17-20-21-26
Distr.: Natl.
Budget Set: Various
Personnel:
R. Peter Washington *(Chm & CEO)*
Chris Rubella *(Dir-Mktg)*
Brands & Products:
BINWAL
ERGO-BENCH
LIFESTYLE
LYON
MSS II
PALTIER
VALTEC

M&G DURA-VENT, INC.
(Formerly Simpson Dura-Vent Company, Inc.)
(Sub. of Muelink & Grol B.V.)
877 Cotting Ct
Vacaville, CA 95688-9354
Mailing Address:
PO Box 1510
Vacaville, CA 95696-1510
Tel.: (707) 446-1786
Fax: (707) 446-4740
Toll Free: (800) 835-4429
E-mail: customerservice@duravent.com
Web Site: www.duravent.com
E-Mail For Key Personnel:
Sales Director: jdavis@duravent.com
Sales Range: $100-124.9 Million
Approx. Number Employees: 450
Year Founded: 1982
Business Description:
Gas Vents, All-Fuel Chimneys, Stovepipes, Chimney Liners & Pellet Vents Mfr
S.I.C.: 3444; 3564
N.A.I.C.S.: 332322; 333412
Import Export
Advertising Expenditures: $650,000
Media: 2-4-5-7-10-19-20-22
Distr.: Natl.
Budget Set: July
Personnel:
Stephen P. Eberhard *(Pres & CEO)*
Todd Lampey *(Mgr-Natl Sls)*

M-D BUILDING PRODUCTS, INC.
4041 N Santa Fe Ave
Oklahoma City, OK 73118
Mailing Address:
PO Box 25188
Oklahoma City, OK 73125-0188
Tel.: (405) 528-4411
Fax: (405) 557-3668
Fax: (800) 557-3568
Toll Free: (800) 654-0007
E-mail: info@mdteam.com
Web Site: www.mdteam.com
Approx. Number Employees: 400
Year Founded: 1920
Business Description:
Building Products Mfr
S.I.C.: 1311
N.A.I.C.S.: 211111
Import Export
Media: 2-4-5-7-8-10-13
Distr.: Natl.
Budget Set: Sept. -Oct.
Personnel:
Lorin Plotkin *(Pres & CEO)*
Kathryn V. McKinny *(CFO)*
Larry Sanford *(Exec VP-Ops)*
Steve Wright *(Exec VP)*
Brands & Products:
AMERICAN LEVEL
MD
SMARTDOT
SMARTTOOL
V-FLEX

M/I HOMES, INC.
3 Easton Oval Ste 500
Columbus, OH 43219-6011
Tel.: (614) 418-8000
Fax: (614) 418-8080
Toll Free: (888) 644-4111
E-mail: comments@mihomes.com
Web Site: www.mihomes.com
Approx. Rev.: $616,377,000
Approx. Number Employees: 522
Year Founded: 1976
Business Description:
Homebuilders
S.I.C.: 1522; 1521
N.A.I.C.S.: 236220; 236115
Advertising Expenditures: $5,300,000
Media: 4-6-8-13-14-15-16-17-18
Personnel:
Robert H. Schottenstein *(Chm, Pres, CEO & Asst Sec)*
Phillip G. Creek *(CFO & Exec VP)*
Tim Hall *(Pres-Orlando Div)*
J. Thomas Mason *(Sec, Exec VP & Gen Counsel)*
Brands & Products:
M/I HOMES
MOVE UP
REALTOR
SHOWCASE HOMES

MAAX SPAS ARIZONA, INC.
(Sub. of MAAX Bath Inc.)
25605 S Arizona Ave
Chandler, AZ 85248
Tel.: (480) 895-0598
Fax: (480) 895-7926
E-mail: info@colemanspas.com
Web Site: www.colemanspas.com
E-Mail For Key Personnel:
Marketing Director: jkeller@colemanspas.com
Approx. Number Employees: 150
Year Founded: 1983
Business Description:
Sauna & Acrylic Spas Mfr
S.I.C.: 3088; 5074
N.A.I.C.S.: 326191; 423720
Export
Media: 2-3-4-5-6-9-10-12-13-22-23-24-26
Distr.: Natl.
Budget Set: Mar. -Feb.
Brands & Products:
CALIFORNIA COOPERAGE
FOOT RELIEF ZONE
HORIZON
ROLL-TOP
SPECTRUM
THERMO-LOCK IV
ZONE THERAPY

MACCAFERRI, INC.
(Sub. of Gruppo Industriale Maccaferri)
10303 Governor Ln Blvd
Williamsport, MD 21795
Tel.: (301) 223-6910
Fax: (301) 223-4590
Web Site: www.maccaferri-usa.com
Approx. Number Employees: 50
Year Founded: 1974
Business Description:
Mfr Environmental Control Products
S.I.C.: 3496
N.A.I.C.S.: 332618
Export
Media: 1-2-4-10-13-20-21-22-26
Distr.: Natl.
Budget Set: Nov.
Personnel:
Paolo Raponi *(CEO)*
Ghislain Brunet *(Dir-Mktg-Tech)*
Brands & Products:
FLEXMESH
GREEN GABIONS
MACCAFERRI GAWACWIN
MACCAFERRI GREEN TERRAMESH
MACCAFERRI TERRAWALL
MACGRID EB SERIES
MACGRID KG SERIES
MACGRID WG SERIES
MACMAT
MACSTARS 2000
MACTEX
RENO MATTRESSES
ROAD MESH
TERRAM PARADRAIN
TERRAM PARALINK
TERRAMESH
TERRAMM GRID

MAINE DRILLING & BLASTING INC.
Rte 201 Brunswick Rd
Gardiner, ME 04345
Tel.: (207) 582-2338
Fax: (207) 582-8794
E-mail: info@mdandb.com
Web Site: www.mdandb.com
Approx. Number Employees: 300
Year Founded: 1966
Business Description:
Heavy Construction & Drilling & Blasting Services
S.I.C.: 1541
N.A.I.C.S.: 236210
Import Export
Media: 4-7-13-16-20
Personnel:
William D. Purington *(Pres)*

MAINTENANCE, INC.
1051 W Liberty St
Wooster, OH 44691-0408
Mailing Address:
PO Box 408
Wooster, OH 44691
Tel.: (330) 264-6262
Fax: (800) 264-2578
Toll Free: (800) 892-6701
E-mail: bob@maintinc.com
Web Site: www.maintinc.com
Sales Estimate: $10-19 Million
Approx. Number Employees: 10
Year Founded: 1938
Business Description:
Chemical & Chemical Preparations; Pavement Maintenance Products
S.I.C.: 2992; 5169
N.A.I.C.S.: 324191; 424690
Export
Media: 2-4-7-10-21-26
Distr.: Intl.; Natl.
Budget Set: Jan.
Brands & Products:
FASS-DRI
J-16
LASTEK
MAINTENANCE
REC-TECH

MARKOVITZ ENTERPRISES, INC., FLOWLINE DIVISION
(Div. of Markovitz Enterprises, Inc.)
1400 New Butler Rd
New Castle, PA 16101
Mailing Address:
PO Box 7027
New Castle, PA 16107-7027
Tel.: (724) 658-3711
Fax: (336) 881-5838
Toll Free: (800) 245-0354
E-mail: sales@flowlinefittings.com
Web Site: www.flowlinefittings.com
E-Mail For Key Personnel:
Sales Director: sales@flowlinefittings.com
Approx. Number Employees: 200
Year Founded: 1948
Business Description:
Mfr. of Pipe Fittings
S.I.C.: 3498; 3462
N.A.I.C.S.: 332996; 332111
Export
Media: 1-2-4-6-10-21
Distr.: Intl.; Natl.
Budget Set: Dec.
Personnel:
David Ottaviani *(VP-Sls)*

MARLITE, INC.
202 Harger St
Dover, OH 44622
Tel.: (330) 343-6621
Fax: (330) 343-7296
E-mail: info@marlite.com
Web Site: www.marlite.com
Sales Range: $75-99.9 Million
Approx. Number Employees: 250
Year Founded: 1930
Business Description:
Specialty Wall Systems & Interior Building Products Mfr
S.I.C.: 2431; 5031
N.A.I.C.S.: 321911; 423310
Import Export
Media: 1-4-10-16-21
Distr.: Intl.; Natl.
Budget Set: Jan. -Dec.

Key to Media (For complete agency information see *The Advertising Red Books-Agencies* edition):
1. Bus. Publs. 2. Cable T.V. 3. Catalogs & Directories. 4. Co-op Adv. 5. Consumer Mags. 6. D.M. to Bus. Estab.7. D.M. to Consumers 8. Daily Newsp. 9. Exhibits/Trade Shows 10. Foreign 11. Infomercial 12. Internet Adv.13. Multimedia 14. Network Radio 15. Network T.V. 16. Newsp. Distr. Mags. 17. Other 18. Outdoor (Posters, Transit) 19. Point of Purchase20. Premiums, Novelties 21. Product Samples 22. Special Events Mktg. 23. Spot Radio 24. Spot T.V. 25. Weekly Newsp. 26. Yellow Page Adv.

Marlite, Inc. — (Continued)

Personnel:
John Popa *(Pres & CEO)*
Greg Triplett *(VP-Sls & Mktg)*
Kevin Krieger *(Mgr-Product Dev)*
Sherry Mason *(Supvr-Mktg Svcs)*
Brands & Products:
DIMENSIONS
DISPLAWALL
DISPLAWALL DIMENSIONS
DISPLAWALL FL
MARLITE
MARLITE FRP
MARLITE MODULES
MARLITE PLANK
SURFACE SYSTEMS
SURFACE SYSTEMS RADIUS WALL
VISPLAY
VISPLAY AIR
VISPLAY AREA
VISPLAY BEAM
VISPLAY INVISIBLE
VISPLAY MONO
VISPLAY SHUTTLE
VISPLAY STRIPES
Advertising Agency:
Whitemyer Advertising, Inc.
254 E 4th St
Zoar, OH 44697
Tel.: (330) 874-2432
Fax: (330) 874-2715
(Marlite, Displawall, Surface Systems)

MARNELL CORRAO ASSOCIATES, INC.

222 Via Marnell Way
Las Vegas, NV 89119
Tel.: (702) 739-2999
Fax: (702) 739-2005
E-mail: info@marnellcorrao.com
Web Site: www.marnellcorrao.com
Sales Range: $200-249.9 Million
Approx. Number Employees: 1,200
Year Founded: 1974
Business Description:
Commercial Building Contractor
S.I.C.: 1522
N.A.I.C.S.: 236220
Media: 2-10
Personnel:
Anthony Marnell *(Owner, Chm & CEO)*
James A. Barrett *(CFO & Treas)*
Cary Rehm *(COO)*
Brad Schnepf *(Pres-Marnell Properties)*

MARTIN DOOR MANUFACTURING, INC.

2828 S 900 West
Salt Lake City, UT 84119-2420
Mailing Address:
PO Box 27437
Salt Lake City, UT 84127-0437
Tel.: (801) 973-9310
Fax: (801) 688-8182
Fax: (801) 977-4222
E-mail: advertising@martindoor.com
Web Site: www.martindoor.com
Approx. Sls.: $15,000,000
Approx. Number Employees: 115
Year Founded: 1936
Business Description:
Steel, Sectional Overhead Garage Doors Mfr
S.I.C.: 3442; 5031
N.A.I.C.S.: 332321; 423310
Import Export
Media: 2-4-6-7-10-24
Distr.: Intl.; Natl.
Personnel:
David O. Martin *(CEO)*
Dean Clark *(CFO)*
David Haslam *(Dir-Sls-North America)*
Michael Martin *(Dir-Adv)*
Brands & Products:
CAMELOT
CARRIAGE HOUSE
FINGER SHIELD
FLUSHLINE
HI-TENSIL
MARTIN
MARTIN DOOR MANUFACTURING
MARTIN DOORS
MARTIN GARAGE DOORS
MONTANA
RANCH
ROLLER SHIELD
SUPER STEEL
WOODLINE

MASCO BATH

(Sub. of Masco Corporation)
320 Industrial Park Rd
Adamsville, TN 38310
Tel.: (731) 632-0911
Fax: (731) 632-4232
Toll Free: (800) 238-3940
Web Site: www.aquaglass.com
Sales Range: $100-124.9 Million
Approx. Number Employees: 500
Business Description:
Shower Units, Whirlpools, Steam Baths & Accessories
S.I.C.: 3088; 3842
N.A.I.C.S.: 326191; 339113
Media: 10
Personnel:
Chris Yenkovich *(CEO)*
Brands & Products:
AQUA GLASS
Advertising Agency:
Stiegler, Wells, Brunswick & Roth, Inc.
(d/b/a SWB&R)
3865 Adler Pl
Bethlehem, PA 18017-9000
Tel.: (610) 866-0611
Fax: (610) 866-8650

MASCO CONTRACTOR SERVICES

(Sub. of Masco Corporation)
2339 Beville Rd
Daytona Beach, FL 32119
Tel.: (386) 304-2222
Fax: (386) 304-2304
E-mail: info@mascocs.com
Web Site:
www.mascocontractorservices.com
Sales Range: $25-49.9 Million
Approx. Number Employees: 90
Business Description:
Building Insulation Services
S.I.C.: 1742
N.A.I.C.S.: 238310
Media: 4-10
Personnel:
Robert Buck *(Exec VP)*
Brands & Products:
ENVIRONMENTS FOR LIVING

MASCO CORPORATION

21001 Van Born Rd
Taylor, MI 48180-1340
Tel.: (313) 274-7400
Fax: (313) 792-6135
Toll Free: (888) 627-6397
E-mail: webmaster@mascohq.com
Web Site: www.masco.com
Approx. Sls.: $7,592,000,000
Approx. Number Employees: 32,500
Year Founded: 1929
Business Description:
Home Improvement Products Mfr
S.I.C.: 2519; 2434; 2449; 3432; 3494
N.A.I.C.S.: 337125; 321920; 332913; 332919; 337110
Export
Advertising Expenditures: $90,000,000
Media: 2-5-6-10-15-24
Distr.: Intl.; Natl.
Personnel:
Timothy Wadhams *(Pres & CEO)*
John G. Sznewajs *(CFO, Treas & VP)*
Donald J. DeMarie, Jr. *(COO & Exec VP)*
Timothy J. Monteith *(CIO & VP)*
David F. Brown *(Chief Procurement Officer & VP-Supply Chain)*
Melonie Colaianne *(Pres-Foundation)*
Jerry Volas *(Grp Pres-North America Retail & Wholesale Grp)*
Thomas Voss *(Grp Pres-Europe)*
W. Timothy Yaggi *(Grp Pres-North America Builder Grp)*
Gregory D. Wittrock *(Gen Counsel, Sec & VP)*
Maria C. Duey *(VP-IR & Comm)*
Charles F. Greenwood *(VP-HR)*
Karen R. Mendelsohn *(VP-Sls & Mktg)*
Jai Shah *(VP-Fin-North America Retail & Wholesale Grp)*
Brands & Products:
ALSONS
AMERICAN METAL PRODUCTS
AMERICAN SHOWER & BATH
AQUA GLASS
ARROW FASTENER
AXOR
BATH UNLIMITED
BEHR
BEHR PREMIUM PLUS
BEHR PROCESS
BRAINERD
BRASSCRAFT
BRASSTECH
BRISTAN
BRIZO
CASUAL COLORS
COBRA PRODUCTS
DAMIXA
DELTA
DELTA FAUCET
EXPRESSIONS
FIELDSTONE
FRANKLIN BRASS
FRESH
GALE INDUSTRIES
GAMCO
GINGER
GUMMERS
HAMMERITE
HANSGROHE
HERITAGE
HOT SPOT
HOT SPRING
KILZ
KRAFTMAID
LIBERTY
LIBERTY HARDWARE
MARIANI
MARVEL
MERILLAT
MILL'S PRIDE
MONITOR
NEWPORT BRASS
NEWTEAM
PEERLESS
PLUMBSHOP
SPEEDWAY
VAPOR
WATKINS
Advertising Agencies:
G&D Communications Corporation
422 Oliver Dr
Troy, MI 48084-5401
Tel.: (248) 362-2750
Fax: (248) 362-8698

Manning Selvage & Lee
222 Merchandise Mart Plz Ste 4-150
Chicago, IL 60654
Tel.: (312) 861-5200
Fax: (312) 861-5252

MASTER HALCO

(Branch of Master Halco, Inc.)
9800 Reeves Rd
Tampa, FL 33619
Tel.: (813) 626-3191
Fax: (813) 623-3401
Toll Free: (800) 669-9473
Web Site: www.fenceonline.com
Approx. Number Employees: 150
Business Description:
Mfr & Distr Fence Systems
S.I.C.: 3315
N.A.I.C.S.: 331222
Import Export
Media: 2-4-10
Distr.: Intl.; Natl.; Reg.
Budget Set: Sept.
Brands & Products:
ANCHOR FENCE PRODUCTS
CLASSIC PREMIER
COLOR LINK
COLOR PLUS
HOUND SURROUND
LEGEND
MASTER BOND
MASTER COLOR
MONUMENTAL IRON WORKS
PERMAFUSED
POSTMASTER
SILVERSHIELD
SLAT MASTER
STEELMATE

MASTER HALCO, INC.

(Sub. of ITOCHU International Inc.)
1 City Blvd W Ste 900
Orange, CA 92868
Tel.: (714) 385-0091
Fax: (714) 385-0107
Toll Free: (800) 883-8384
E-mail: info@fenceonline.com
Web Site: www.fenceonline.com
Approx. Sls.: $554,600,000
Approx. Number Employees: 1,615
Year Founded: 1961
Business Description:
Perimeter Security & Fencing Mfr & Wholesale Distr; Vinyl, Wood, Ornamental & Chain Link Fences & Automated Gates for Residential, Commercial, Industrial & High Security Applications
S.I.C.: 5039; 3315

Key to Media (For complete agency information see *The Advertising Red Books-Agencies* edition):
1. Bus. Publs. 2. Cable T.V. 3. Catalogs & Directories. 4. Co-op Adv. 5. Consumer Mags. 6. D.M. to Bus. Estab.7. D.M. to Consumers
8. Daily Newsp. 9. Exhibits/Trade Shows 10. Foreign 11. Infomercial 12. Internet Adv.13. Multimedia 14. Network Radio
15. Network T.V. 16. Newsp. Distr. Mags. 17. Other 18. Outdoor (Posters, Transit) 19. Point of Purchase20. Premiums, Novelties
21. Product Samples 22. Special Events Mktg. 23. Spot Radio 24. Spot T.V. 25. Weekly Newsp. 26. Yellow Page Adv.

N.A.I.C.S.: 423390; 331222
Media: 2-3-5-6-7-10-13-16-19-22-26
Personnel:
Ken Fishbein *(Co-CEO)*
Mona Zinman *(Co-CEO)*
Brands & Products:
CLASSIC PREMIER
ECHELON PLUS
ESTATE GATE
EVERLAST VINYL
IMPASSE
IMPRESSIONS VINYL
LEGEND VINYL
MONTAGE
MONUMENTAL COLUMN
MONUMENTAL IRON
PERMAFUSED/SPECTRA
POSTMASTER
PRO-ARC

MASTERBRAND CABINETS, INC.
(Sub. of Fortune Brands Home & Security LLC)
1 MasterBrand Cabinets Dr
Jasper, IN 47546
Mailing Address:
PO Box 420
Jasper, IN 47547-0420
Tel.: (812) 482-2527
Fax: (812) 482-9879
Web Site: www.masterbrand.com
Sales Range: $1-4.9 Billion
Approx. Number Employees: 420
Year Founded: 1926
Business Description:
Cabinetry Mfr
S.I.C.: 2434
N.A.I.C.S.: 337110
Export
Distr.: Natl.
Budget Set: Aug.
Personnel:
Greg Stoner *(Pres)*
Martin Van Doren *(Exec VP-Dealer & Wholesale Channels)*
Eric Skorge *(Sr Dir-Fin)*
Brands & Products:
ARISTOKRAFT
CAPITAL CABINET
DECORA
DIAMOND
DYNASTY
GEORGETOWN
HOMECREST
KEMPER
KITCHEN CLASSICS
KITCHEN CRAFT
MAPLE CREEK
NHB
OMEGA
SHROCK
Advertising Agency:
Vest Advertising
3007 Sprowl Rd
Louisville, KY 40299-3620
Tel.: (502) 267-5335
Fax: (502) 267-6025
(Decora, Diamond)
— Rita Vest *(Acct. Exec.)*

MAURICE L. CONDON CO., INC.
250 Ferris Ave
White Plains, NY 10603
Tel.: (914) 946-4111
Fax: (914) 946-3779
E-mail: mlc@mlcondon.com
Approx. Number Employees: 35
Year Founded: 1935
Business Description:
Lumber, Plywood & Hardwood Retailer
S.I.C.: 5031; 5211
N.A.I.C.S.: 423310; 444110
Advertising Expenditures: $80,000
Media: 2-4-6-7-8-9
Distr.: Natl.
Budget Set: Oct.
Personnel:
Condon P. Bennett *(Pres)*
Robert G. Bennett *(VP & Pur Agent)*

MAXWELL SYSTEMS INC.
1000 1st Ave Ste 200
King of Prussia, PA 19406
Tel.: (610) 277-3515
Fax: (610) 277-2081
E-mail: info@maxwellsystems.com
Web Site: www.maxwellsystems.com
Sales Range: $10-24.9 Million
Approx. Number Employees: 62
Business Description:
Mfr of Construction Industry Software
S.I.C.: 5045; 5734
N.A.I.C.S.: 423430; 443120
Personnel:
Jim Flynn *(Pres & CEO)*
Eric Foster *(VP-Tech)*
Robert Hodges *(VP-Strategic Projects)*
Lisa Stotts *(VP-Fin)*
Nancy Panko *(Dir-Mktg)*
Brands & Products:
MAXWELL SYSTEMS ESTIMATION LOGISTICS 7.3
Advertising Agency:
Gregory FCA
27 W Athens Ave Ste 200
Ardmore, PA 19003
Tel.: (610) 642-8253
Fax: (610) 642-1258
Fax: (610) 649-9029
Toll Free: (800) 499-4734
— Theresa Murray *(Acct Exec-Maxwell Systems)*

MCBRIDE & SON ENTERPRISES INC.
16091 Wingley Ridge
Chesterfield, MO 63017
Tel.: (636) 537-2000
Fax: (636) 537-2546
Web Site: www.mcbridehomes.com
Approx. Number Employees: 45
Business Description:
Provider of Home Construction Services
S.I.C.: 6531; 1521
N.A.I.C.S.: 531210; 236115
Personnel:
John Eilermann *(Chm & CEO)*
Jeffery Schlinder *(Pres-McBride Homes)*
Advertising Agency:
The Glennon Company, Inc.
716 Geyer Ste 300
Saint Louis, MO 63104
Tel.: (314) 993-6111
Fax: (314) 772-9800

MCCARTHY BUILDING COMPANIES, INC.
(Sub. of McCarthy Holdings, Inc.)
1341 N Rock Hill Rd
Saint Louis, MO 63124
Tel.: (314) 968-3300
Fax: (314) 968-4780
E-mail: stl@mccarthy.com
Web Site: www.mccarthy.com
Sales Range: $1-4.9 Billion
Approx. Number Employees: 1,700
Year Founded: 1864
Business Description:
Commercial, Institutional, Civil & Industrial Construction Services
S.I.C.: 1522; 1541; 1622; 1629
N.A.I.C.S.: 236220; 236210; 237310; 237990
Advertising Expenditures: $1,000,000
Media: 1-2-7-10-13-22-26
Personnel:
Michael D. Bolen *(Chm & CEO)*
Derek W. Glanvill *(Pres & COO)*
J. Douglas Audiffred *(VP-Fin)*
Susan Garritano *(Mgr-PR)*

MEADOW BURKE
(Plant of Meadow Burke)
5110 Santa Fe Rd
Tampa, FL 33619
Tel.: (813) 247-3663
Fax: (813) 248-0703
Web Site: www.meadowburke.com
Approx. Number Employees: 50
Business Description:
Concrete Forming & Reinforcing Products
S.I.C.: 3315
N.A.I.C.S.: 331222
Distr.: Natl.
Budget Set: Nov.
Personnel:
Rob Cox *(Mgr-Mfg Svcs Reg Distr Center)*
Advertising Agency:
Advertising Seven, Inc.
324 S Hyde Park Ave # 275
Tampa, FL 33606
Tel.: (813) 251-8520

MEDINA INTERNATIONAL HOLDINGS, INC.
1802 Pomona Rd
Corona, CA 92880
Tel.: (909) 522-4414
Fax: (909) 522-4230
E-mail: info@medinaih.com
Web Site:
www.medinainternationalholdings.com
Approx. Sls.: $541,675
Approx. Number Employees: 10
Year Founded: 1998
Business Description:
Watercraft Mfr
S.I.C.: 3732
N.A.I.C.S.: 336612
Advertising Expenditures: $3,339
Media: 17
Personnel:
Daniel Medina *(Pres)*
Madhava Rao Mankal *(CFO)*

MEG
(Div. of Hirsh Industries, Inc.)
502 S Green St
Cambridge City, IN 47327
Mailing Address:
PO Box 240
Cambridge City, IN 47327-0240
Tel.: (765) 478-3141
Fax: (765) 478-4439
Toll Free: (800) 645-3315
E-mail: meginfo@megfixtures.com
Web Site: www.megfixtures.com
E-Mail For Key Personnel:
President: thilkert@megfixtures.com
Approx. Number Employees: 700
Year Founded: 1992
Business Description:
Store Fixture Mfr
S.I.C.: 2519
N.A.I.C.S.: 337125
Import Export
Media: 4-13
Distr.: Direct to Consumer
Budget Set: Monthly
Personnel:
Tom Hilkert *(CEO)*
Rich Van Dillen *(VP-Sls & Mktg)*
Brands & Products:
MOBILE MERCHANDISING SYSTEMS
OPTIMUM

MERCHANT & EVANS, INC.
308 Connecticut Dr
Burlington, NJ 08016-4104
Mailing Address:
PO Box 1680
Burlington, NJ 08016-7280
Tel.: (609) 387-3033
Fax: (609) 387-4838
Toll Free: (800) 257-6215
Web Site: www.ziprib.com
E-Mail For Key Personnel:
Marketing Director: Marketing@ziprib.com
Sales Director: Sales@ziprib.com
Approx. Sls.: $4,000,000
Approx. Number Employees: 30
Year Founded: 1866
Business Description:
Roofing System Services
S.I.C.: 3446; 5051
N.A.I.C.S.: 332323; 423510
Media: 4
Distr.: Natl.
Budget Set: Dec.
Personnel:
Steve Buck *(Pres)*
Brands & Products:
ZIP-RIB

MERITAGE HOMES CORPORATION
17851 N 85th St Ste 300
Scottsdale, AZ 85255
Tel.: (480) 515-8100
Fax: (480) 998-9178
Toll Free: (800) 400-7888
Web Site: www.meritagehomes.com
Approx. Rev.: $941,656,000
Approx. Number Employees: 650
Year Founded: 1988
Business Description:
Single-Family Home Construction Services
S.I.C.: 1531; 1521
N.A.I.C.S.: 236118; 236115; 236117
Advertising Expenditures: $6,100,000
Personnel:
Steven J. Hilton *(Chm & CEO)*
Larry W. Seay *(CFO & Exec VP)*
Steven M. Davis *(COO & Exec VP)*
Steve C. Pardee *(CIO & VP)*
Hilla Sferruzza *(Chief Acctg Officer, VP & Controller)*
C. Timothy White *(Gen Counsel, Sec & Exec VP)*
David R. Modlin *(VP-Sls)*
Brian Kittle *(Dir-Sls)*

Key to Media (For complete agency information see *The Advertising Red Books-Agencies* edition):
1. Bus. Publs. 2. Cable T.V. 3. Catalogs & Directories. 4. Co-op Adv. 5. Consumer Mags. 6. D.M. to Bus. Estab.7. D.M. to Consumers
8. Daily Newsp. 9. Exhibits/Trade Shows 10. Foreign 11. Infomercial 12. Internet Adv.13. Multimedia 14. Network Radio
15. Network T.V. 16. Newsp. Distr. Mags. 17. Other 18. Outdoor (Posters, Transit) 19. Point of Purchase20. Premiums, Novelties
21. Product Samples 22. Special Events Mktg. 23. Spot Radio 24. Spot T.V. 25. Weekly Newsp. 26. Yellow Page Adv.

Meritage Homes Corporation — (Continued)

Brands & Products:
MERITAGE HOMES

MESSER CONSTRUCTION CO.
5158 Fishwick Dr
Cincinnati, OH 45216-2216
Tel.: (513) 242-1541
Fax: (513) 242-6467
Web Site: www.messer.com
Approx. Number Employees: 120
Year Founded: 1932
Business Description:
Provider of Contracting & Construction Services
S.I.C.: 1522
N.A.I.C.S.: 236220
Personnel:
Thomas M. Keckeis *(Pres)*
Kathleen C. Daly *(Sr VP)*
James R. Hess *(Sr VP)*
Advertising Agency:
Fahlgren Mortine
4030 Easton Station Ste 300
Columbus, OH 43219
Tel.: (614) 383-1500
Fax: (614) 383-1501

MET-CON CONSTRUCTION INC.
15760 Acorn Trl
Faribault, MN 55021
Tel.: (507) 332-2266
Fax: (507) 332-8742
Web Site: www.met-con.com
Sales Range: $300-349.9 Million
Approx. Number Employees: 175
Business Description:
Industrial Buildings & Warehouses
S.I.C.: 1522
N.A.I.C.S.: 236220
Media: 7-8-10-26
Personnel:
Thomas McDonough *(Founder & Pres)*
Jim Roush *(Gen Mgr-Met & Con Kato)*
Joel Schafer *(Dir-Sls & Mktg)*

METALICO INC.
186 N Ave E
Cranford, NJ 07016-2439
Tel.: (908) 497-9610
Fax: (908) 497-1097
E-mail: info@meltalico.com
Web Site: www.metalico.com/
Approx. Rev.: $553,253,000
Approx. Number Employees: 782
Year Founded: 1997
Business Description:
Metal Services
S.I.C.: 3341; 3356
N.A.I.C.S.: 331492; 331314; 331491
Advertising Expenditures: $391,000
Personnel:
Carlos E. Aguero *(Chm, Pres & CEO)*
Eric W. Finlayson *(CFO & Sr VP)*
Kenneth P. Mueller *(COO-Ferrous & Nonferrous Scrap Metal Recycling & Sr VP)*
Arnold S. Graber *(Gen Counsel, Sec & Exec VP)*

METALS USA BUILDING PRODUCTS - ROOFING PRODUCTS
(Div. of Metals USA Building Products, L.P.)
(d/b/a Gerard Roofing Technologies)
955 Columbia St
Brea, CA 92821-2923
Tel.: (714) 529-0407
Fax: (714) 529-6643
E-mail: gerardusa@metalsusa.com
Web Site: www.gerardusa.com
Approx. Number Employees: 100
Year Founded: 1971
Business Description:
Metal Roofing Products Mfr
S.I.C.: 3448
N.A.I.C.S.: 332311
Export
Media: 4-5-10-11-15-21
Distr.: Natl.
Personnel:
Ron Anderson *(VP-Sls & Mktg)*
Brands & Products:
CANYON SHAKE
GERARD
GRANITE RIDGE SHINGLE
GUARDIAN

METALS USA, INC.
(Sub. of METALS USA HOLDINGS CORP.)
2400 E Commercial Blvd Ste 905
Fort Lauderdale, FL 33308
Tel.: (954) 202-4000
Fax: (954) 202-0271
Toll Free: (888) 871-8701
Web Site: www.metalsusa.com
Sales Range: $1-4.9 Billion
Approx. Number Employees: 2,700
Year Founded: 1996
Business Description:
Metal Processing & Distribution Services
S.I.C.: 5051; 3441
N.A.I.C.S.: 423510; 332312
Media: 10-22
Personnel:
C. Lourenco Goncalves *(Chm, Pres & CEO)*
Robert C. McPherson, III *(CFO & Sr VP)*
Brands & Products:
ALLMET
GERARD
NATIONAL
ROYAL
TAI
VALLEY
VIKING
WESTERN

METEC INC.
(Sub. of Metecno S.p.A.)
405 Fentress Blvd
Daytona Beach, FL 32114
Tel.: (386) 255-5391
Fax: (386) 258-1693
Web Site: www.alumashield.com
Approx. Sls.: $25,700,000
Approx. Number Employees: 30
Business Description:
Sheet Metalwork
S.I.C.: 3585
N.A.I.C.S.: 333415
Advertising Agency:
Larson O'Brien Marketing Group
3591 Ridgeway Dr Ste 200
Bethel Park, PA 15102
Tel.: (412) 831-1959
Fax: (412) 833-2838
Insulated Composite Panels

METPAR CORP.
95 State St
Westbury, NY 11590-5006
Mailing Address:
PO Box 1873
Westbury, NY 11590
Tel.: (516) 333-2600
Fax: (516) 333-2618
E-mail: sales@metpar.com
Web Site: www.metpar.com
E-Mail For Key Personnel:
Sales Director: sales@metpar.com
Approx. Number Employees: 75
Year Founded: 1952
Business Description:
Toilet, Shower & Dressing Compartments Mfr
S.I.C.: 3431; 3088
N.A.I.C.S.: 332998; 326191
Import Export
Media: 2-4-6-7-10-11
Distr.: Intl.; Natl.
Personnel:
David Bonade *(CFO & Dir-Fin)*
Peter Bryan *(VP-Sls & Mktg)*
Brands & Products:
CORINTHIAN
DORIAN
FORUM
LUXOR
METPAR MULTICAM
MULTI-CAM
POLLY

MICHELS CORPORATION
817 W Main St
Brownsville, WI 53006
Mailing Address:
PO Box 128
Brownsville, WI 53006-0128
Tel.: (920) 583-3132
Fax: (920) 583-3429
E-mail: corpinfo@michels.us
Web Site: www.michels.us
Sales Range: $300-349.9 Million
Approx. Number Employees: 2,000
Year Founded: 1960
Business Description:
Utility, Engineering, Design & Construction Contractor Services
S.I.C.: 1623
N.A.I.C.S.: 237110
Media: 9
Personnel:
Patrick D. Michels *(Pres)*
Mark Hutter *(VP-Bus Dev & Mktg)*
Advertising Agency:
The Goodness Company
Cornerstone Ofc Ste 820 Baker St
Wisconsin Rapids, WI 54494
Tel.: (715) 423-1255
Fax: (715) 423-1310
Toll Free: (866) 265-1001

MID-AMERICAN ELEVATOR EQUIPMENT CO., INC.
820 N Wolcott Ave
Chicago, IL 60622
Tel.: (773) 486-6900
Fax: (773) 486-2438
E-mail: sales@mid-americanelevator.com
Web Site: www.mid-americanelevator.com
E-Mail For Key Personnel:
Sales Director: sales@mid-americanelevator.com
Approx. Sls.: $30,000,000
Approx. Number Employees: 135
Year Founded: 1974
Business Description:
Installation, Repair & Maintenance of Elevators
S.I.C.: 1796; 7699
N.A.I.C.S.: 238290; 811490
Import Export
Personnel:
Robert Bailey, III *(Pres)*
Robert Bailey, II *(CEO & CFO)*
Jackie Smith *(Mgr-Adv)*
Brands & Products:
MID-AMERICAN ELEVATOR COMPANY
WE KEEP AMERICA MOVING!
Advertising Agency:
Vaughan, Thain and Spencer, Inc.
4 Walker Ave Ste C
Clarendon Hills, IL 60514-1351
Tel.: (630) 920-0164
Fax: (630) 920-0767
— John Vaughan *(Acct Exec)*

MILLER AND SMITH HOMES, INC.
(Sub. of Miller & Smith Holding Company Inc.)
8401 Greensboro Dr Ste 300
McLean, VA 22102-3054
Tel.: (703) 821-2500
Fax: (703) 821-2040
Web Site: www.millerandsmith.com
Approx. Number Employees: 75
Year Founded: 1964
Business Description:
Home Builder & Developer
S.I.C.: 1522
N.A.I.C.S.: 236220
Advertising Expenditures: $500,000
Media: 4-8-10-13-16-19-25-26
Budget Set: Oct.
Personnel:
Gordon V. Smith *(Founder & Chm)*
Richard J. North *(Partner)*
Douglas Smith *(Partner)*
Alvin D. Hall *(CFO)*

MINAEAN INTERNATIONAL CORPORATION
Cathedral Place Suite 1304
Vancouver, BC V6C 3L2, Canada
Tel.: (604) 684-2181
Fax: (604) 682-4768
Web Site: www.minaean.com
Approx. Sls.: $2,189,669
Year Founded: 1998
Business Description:
Residential & Commercial Construction & Engineering
S.I.C.: 1522; 1531; 1623; 1791; 1799; 2451
N.A.I.C.S.: 236220; 236117; 237130; 238120; 238190; 321991
Advertising Expenditures: $134,885
Media: 17
Personnel:
Hari B. Varshney *(Chm)*
Mervyn J. Pinto *(Pres & CEO)*
Keith Scott *(CFO & Dir)*

MINERALLAC CO.
100 Gast Rd
Hampshire, IL 60140-7654
Tel.: (630) 543-7080
Fax: (630) 543-4220
E-mail: info@minerallac.com

Key to Media (For complete agency information see *The Advertising Red Books-Agencies* edition):
1. Bus. Publs. 2. Cable T.V. 3. Catalogs & Directories. 4. Co-op Adv. 5. Consumer Mags. 6. D.M. to Bus. Estab.7. D.M. to Consumers
8. Daily Newsp. 9. Exhibits/Trade Shows 10. Foreign 11. Infomercial 12. Internet Adv.13. Multimedia 14. Network Radio
15. Network T.V. 16. Newsp. Distr. Mags. 17. Other 18. Outdoor (Posters, Transit) 19. Point of Purchase20. Premiums, Novelties
21. Product Samples 22. Special Events Mktg. 23. Spot Radio 24. Spot T.V. 25. Weekly Newsp. 26. Yellow Page Adv.

Web Site: www.minerallac.com
E-Mail For Key Personnel:
President: JHalvacek@minerallac.com
Approx. Number Employees: 92
Year Founded: 1894
Business Description:
Steel & Plastic Fasteners Mfr for Electrical Telecommunications & Utility Industry
S.I.C.: 3644; 3496
N.A.I.C.S.: 335932; 332618
Import Export
Advertising Expenditures: $225,000
Media: 1-2-3-4-7-10-13-16-19-20-21-22
Distr.: Intl.; Natl.
Personnel:
Jim Halvacek *(Pres)*
Brands & Products:
BLACK CLAW
HI-C
IMPACK
IMPACT
IMPACT STAPLES
JIFFY
MIN-E
MINERALLAC
REDMOR PRODUCTS
UNIPRODUX

MISCOR GROUP, LTD.
800 Nave Rd SE
Massillon, OH 44646
Tel.: (330) 830-3500
E-mail: info@miscor.com
Web Site: www.miscor.com
Approx. Rev.: $33,065,000
Approx. Number Employees: 267
Business Description:
Electrical Contracting & Services
S.I.C.: 8711; 1731; 7629
N.A.I.C.S.: 541330; 238210; 811219
Advertising Expenditures: $36,000
Media: 17
Personnel:
Michael P. Moore *(Pres & CEO)*
Marc Valentin *(Chief Acctg Officer)*

MMI PRODUCTS, INC.
(Div. of Oldcastle, Inc.)
400 N Sam Houston Pkwy E Ste 1200
Houston, TX 77060
Tel.: (281) 876-0080
Fax: (281) 448-6302
Web Site: www.mmiproductsinc.com
Approx. Number Employees: 2,500
Year Founded: 1989
Business Description:
Fencing & Concrete Construction Products
S.I.C.: 3441; 3496; 3499
N.A.I.C.S.: 332312; 332618; 332999
Media: 2-3-9-10-23
Distr.: Natl.
Budget Set: Oct.
Personnel:
Celes Pesmaspin *(CEO)*
Brands & Products:
COLORBOND I
COLORBOND II
EASY LINER
FENCE PRO
THE FIRST NAME IN FENCE
GUARDSMAN
MEDO MESH
MMI PRO MIX
MMI PRO SET
NATURELINK
PRIVA/LINK
SAFE-T-LOAD
STEELTEX
TIMBERCRAFT
TUF-LINK
TUF WOOD
TUF WOOD "PLUS"
WOODLINK

MODERN DROP FORGE CO.
13810 S Western Ave
Blue Island, IL 60406-3229
Tel.: (708) 388-1806
Fax: (708) 597-3633
E-mail: engineering@modernforge.com
Web Site: www.modernforge.com
E-Mail For Key Personnel:
Sales Director: sales@modernforge.com
Approx. Number Employees: 300
Year Founded: 1914
Business Description:
Steel Drop Forgings Mfr
S.I.C.: 3462; 3544
N.A.I.C.S.: 332111; 333514
Import Export
Media: 2-6-8
Personnel:
Gregory Heim *(CEO & Pres)*
Richard Heim *(COO)*

MODERN TRACK MACHINERY
(Sub. of Geismar S.A.)
1415 Davis Rd
Elgin, IL 60123-1321
Tel.: (847) 697-7510
Fax: (847) 697-0136
E-mail: info@geismar-mtm.com
Web Site: www.geismar-mtm.com
Approx. Number Employees: 30
Year Founded: 1974
Business Description:
Railroad Track Construction & Maintenance Equipment
S.I.C.: 5088
N.A.I.C.S.: 423860
Import
Media: 7-10
Distr.: Natl.
Budget Set: Jan.
Personnel:
Al Reynolds *(Gen Mgr-Sls)*
Brands & Products:
MODERN TRACK MACHINERY

MODERNFOLD, INC.
(Div. of DORMA Group North America)
215 W New Rd
Greenfield, IN 46140
Tel.: (317) 468-6700
Fax: (317) 468-6760
Toll Free: (800) 869-9685
E-mail: info@modernfold.com
Web Site: www.modernfold.com
E-Mail For Key Personnel:
Marketing Director: marketing@modernfold.com
Approx. Number Employees: 75
Year Founded: 1925
Business Description:
Operable Wall Systems & Space Division Solutions for Interior Environments; Operable Partitions, Moveable Glass Walls & Accordion Doors Designer, Mfr & Servicer
S.I.C.: 2522; 2519
N.A.I.C.S.: 337214; 337125
Export
Advertising Expenditures: $373,000
Bus. Publs.: $354,350; Other: $18,650
Distr.: Intl.; Natl.
Budget Set: Nov.
Personnel:
Dave Smith *(Exec VP)*
Mike Beavers *(Dir-Mktg)*
Brands & Products:
ACOUSTI-SEAL
MODERNFOLD
SOUNDMASTER
SPACESETTER

MONIERLIFETILE LLC
(Joint Venture of Boral Limited, Lafarge S.A. & PAI Partners S.A.S.)
7575 Irvine Ctr Dr Ste 100
Irvine, CA 92618-2930
Tel.: (949) 756-1605
Fax: (949) 756-2401
Toll Free: (800) 571-8453
Web Site: www.monierlifetile.com
Approx. Number Employees: 800
Year Founded: 1997
Business Description:
Concrete Roof Tile Mfr & Whslr; Owned by Boral Limited & by MONIER Group GmbH
S.I.C.: 3251; 3272; 5033
N.A.I.C.S.: 327121; 327390; 423330
Export
Advertising Expenditures: $500,000
Media: 2-3-4-5-6-8-9-10-13-16-18-19-20-21-26
Distr.: Natl.
Budget Set: Jan.
Personnel:
Derek Taylor *(CFO & VP)*
Christian Doelle *(VP-Sls & Mktg)*
Advertising Agency:
RiechesBaird, Inc.
1 Wrigley
Irvine, CA 92618
Tel.: (949) 586-1200
Fax: (949) 586-1201

MOUNTAIN WEST, LLC
(d/b/a Mountain West Products)
4212 S Hwy 191
Rexburg, ID 83440-4251
Tel.: (208) 356-4571
Fax: (208) 356-0200
Toll Free: (800) 727-9959
Web Site: www.mwpllc.com
Sales Range: $10-24.9 Million
Approx. Number Employees: 250
Year Founded: 1980
Business Description:
Marketer of Volcanic Stone, Western Bark, Aquarium Gravel, Gas Grill Lava Rock
S.I.C.: 1429
N.A.I.C.S.: 212319
Import Export
Advertising Expenditures: $500,000
Media: 2-4-5-6-7-8-10-13-19-21-26
Distr.: Intl.
Budget Set: Nov.
Personnel:
Ernie Johnson *(Pres)*
Byron Morgan *(Gen Mgr)*
Brands & Products:
MOUNTAIN MAGIC
MWP
SOIL PEP
YARD CARE
Advertising Agency:
Banik Communications
121 4th St N Ste 1B
Great Falls, MT 59401
Tel.: (406) 454-3422
Fax: (406) 771-1418
Toll Free: (800) 823-3388

MSX INTERNATIONAL, INC.
(Sub. of Citigroup Inc.)
1950 Concept Dr
Warren, MI 48091
Tel.: (248) 829-6300
Fax: (586) 758-7217
E-mail: recruiters@msxi.com
Web Site: www.msxi.com
Sales Range: $1-4.9 Billion
Approx. Number Employees: 14,000
Year Founded: 1997
Business Description:
Business Consulting Services
S.I.C.: 8748; 7361
N.A.I.C.S.: 541618; 561310
Media: 2-4-7-10-16
Distr.: Natl.
Budget Set: Nov.
Personnel:
Frederick Minturn *(Pres & CEO)*
Wolfgang P. Kurth *(Sr VP-Ops-Europe)*
Margaret Turner *(VP-HR)*
Brands & Products:
APPLYING TECHNOLOGY, DELIVERING RESULTS.
MSX INTERNATIONAL

MUELLER WATER PRODUCTS, INC.
1200 Albernathy Rd NE Ste 1200
Atlanta, GA 30328
Tel.: (770) 206-4200
Web Site: www.muellerwaterproducts.com
Approx. Sls.: $1,337,500,000
Approx. Number Employees: 4,800
Business Description:
Water Infrastructure & Flow Control Mfr
S.I.C.: 3491; 3829
N.A.I.C.S.: 332911; 334519
Advertising Expenditures: $4,200,000
Personnel:
Gregory E. Hyland *(Chm, Pres & CEO)*
Evan L. Hart *(CFO & Sr VP)*
Robert P. Keefe *(CIO & Sr VP)*
Gregory S. Rogowski *(Pres-Mueller Company Ltd)*
Robert Barker *(Chief Compliance Officerm, Gen Counsel, Sec & Exec VP)*
Walt Smith *(Treas & Sr VP)*
Robert D. Dunn *(Sr VP-HR)*
Marietta Edmunds Zakas *(Sr VP-Strategy, Corp Dev & Comm)*
John Pensec *(Dir-Corp Comm & Public Affairs)*

MURDOCK, INC.
125 Proctor Ave
City of Industry, CA 91746
Tel.: (513) 471-7700
Fax: (626) 855-4894
E-mail: bmurdock@acorneng.com
Web Site: www.murdock-supersecur.com
Sales Range: $25-49.9 Million
Approx. Number Employees: 20
Year Founded: 1853

Key to Media (For complete agency information see *The Advertising Red Books-Agencies* edition):
1. Bus. Publs. 2. Cable T.V. 3. Catalogs & Directories. 4. Co-op Adv. 5. Consumer Mags. 6. D.M. to Bus. Estab.7. D.M. to Consumers 8. Daily Newsp. 9. Exhibits/Trade Shows 10. Foreign 11. Infomercial 12. Internet Adv.13. Multimedia 14. Network Radio 15. Network T.V. 16. Newsp. Distr. Mags. 17. Other 18. Outdoor (Posters, Transit) 19. Point of Purchase20. Premiums, Novelties 21. Product Samples 22. Special Events Mktg. 23. Spot Radio 24. Spot T.V. 25. Weekly Newsp. 26. Yellow Page Adv.

Murdock, Inc. — (Continued)

Business Description:
Mfr & Sales of Air Valves & Outdoor Anti-Freezing Hydrants, Drinking Fountains & Emergency Showers
S.I.C.: 3431
N.A.I.C.S.: 332998
Advertising Expenditures: $200,000
Media: 2-4-10
Distr.: Natl.
Budget Set: Jan.
Personnel:
Robert A. Murdock *(Pres)*
Brands & Products:
MURDOCK
Advertising Agency:
Murdock, Inc
(House Agency)
2488 River Rd.
Cincinnati, OH 45204
Tel.: (513) 471-7700
Fax: (513) 471-3299

MWH GLOBAL, INC.
380 Interlocken Crescent Ste 200
Broomfield, CO 80021
Tel.: (303) 533-1900
Fax: (303) 533-1901
Web Site: www.mwhglobal.com
E-Mail For Key Personnel:
Public Relations: cheryl.friedling@mwhglobal.com
Sales Range: $1-4.9 Billion
Approx. Number Employees: 6,200
Year Founded: 2001
Business Description:
Civil Engineering Services in the Areas of Energy, Infrastructure, Water & Wastewater
S.I.C.: 8711; 1629; 8748; 8999; 9511
N.A.I.C.S.: 541330; 237990; 541620; 541690; 924110
Import Export
Media: 2-10-18
Personnel:
Robert B. Uhler *(Chm & CEO)*
David G. Barnes *(CFO)*

MYR GROUP INC.
1701 W Golf Rd Ste 1012
Rolling Meadows, IL 60008-4270
Tel.: (847) 290-1891
Fax: (847) 290-1892
E-mail: info@myrgroup.com
Web Site: www.myrgroup.com
Approx. Rev.: $597,077,000
Approx. Number Employees: 2,800
Year Founded: 1891
Business Description:
Electrical & Mechanical Construction Services
S.I.C.: 1731; 1623; 1629
N.A.I.C.S.: 238210; 237130; 237990
Advertising Expenditures: $304,000
Media: 2-26
Personnel:
William A. Koertner *(Pres & CEO)*

NABCO ENTRANCES, INC.
(Sub. of Nabtesco Corporation)
S 82 W 18717 Gemini Dr
Muskego, WI 53150-0906
Tel.: (877) 622-2694
Tel.: (262) 679-0045
Fax: (262) 679-2505
E-mail: customerservice@nabcoentrances.com
Web Site: www.nabcoentrances.com
Approx. Number Employees: 100
Year Founded: 1969
Business Description:
Developer & Mfr of Automatic & Device Activated Entrance Systems & Doors
S.I.C.: 3442; 3699
N.A.I.C.S.: 332321; 335999
Import Export
Media: 2-10
Distr.: Natl.
Personnel:
Phil Stuckey *(Pres)*
Larry Grassmann *(VP-Sls & Mktg)*
Brands & Products:
ACUGARD 2
ACUMOTION
ACUSENSOR
GYRO TECH
NABCO

NAPLES LUMBER & SUPPLY INC.
3828 Radio Rd
Naples, FL 34104
Tel.: (239) 643-7000
Fax: (239) 643-5987
E-mail: information@napleslumber.com
Web Site: www.napleslumber.com
Sales Range: $10-24.9 Million
Approx. Number Employees: 35
Year Founded: 1971
Business Description:
Lumber & Building Materials Retailer
S.I.C.: 5031; 2439
N.A.I.C.S.: 423310; 321214
Bus. Publs.: 100%
Personnel:
Ron Labbe *(Owner)*

NASSCO HOLDINGS INCORPORATED
(Sub. of General Dynamics Marine Systems, Inc.)
(d/b/a NASSCO)
2798 Harbor Dr
San Diego, CA 92113
Mailing Address:
PO Box 85278
San Diego, CA 92186-5278
Tel.: (619) 544-3400
Fax: (619) 544-3541
E-mail: kjohnson@nassco.com
Web Site: www.nassco.com
Sales Range: $650-699.9 Million
Approx. Number Employees: 4,600
Year Founded: 1960
Business Description:
Shipbuilding & Repair Services
S.I.C.: 3731
N.A.I.C.S.: 336611
Media: 2-4-10
Distr.: Natl.
Budget Set: Jan.
Personnel:
Frederick J. Harris *(Pres)*
Christopher Barnes *(Gen Counsel & VP)*
Janice Grace *(Sr VP-Ops)*
Kevin M. Graney *(VP-Engrg)*
Tim McCue *(VP-Engrg)*
Karl Johnson *(Dir-Comm)*
Katie H. Dame *(Acct Mgr)*

NATIONAL TECHNICAL SYSTEMS INC.
24007 Ventura Blvd Ste 200
Calabasas, CA 91302
Tel.: (310) 641-7700
Fax: (818) 591-0899
Toll Free: (800) 270-2516
E-mail: customerservice@ntscorp.com
Web Site: www.ntscorp.com/
Approx. Rev.: $144,069,000
Approx. Number Employees: 1,095
Year Founded: 1961
Business Description:
Engineer & Service for the Aerospace, Defense & Commercial Industries
S.I.C.: 8734
N.A.I.C.S.: 541380
Media: 2-10-13-22
Personnel:
Aaron Cohen *(Vice Chm)*
William McGinnis *(Pres & CEO)*
Raffy Lorentzian *(CFO & Sr VP)*
Arturo Villa *(CIO)*
Douglas Briskie *(Sr VP-Dev Officer)*
Derek Coppinger *(Sr VP-Corp Dev)*
Cynthia Maher *(Sr VP)*
David C. Mann *(Gen Mgr)*
Dan Cannon *(Dir-Quality & Regulatory Affairs)*
Andrea Korfin *(Dir-Corp Organizational Devel & Strategic Alignment)*
Bill Schoneman *(Dir-Advanced Tech)*
Willie Seebertd *(Dir-Environ Health & Safety)*
Steven L. Lightsey *(Program Mgr)*
Brands & Products:
NTS
Advertising Agency:
Allen & Caron
18200 Von Karman Ave Ste 780
Irvine, CA 92612-0192
Tel.: (949) 474-4300
Fax: (949) 474-4330
(Investor & Media Relations)

NATIONWIDE HOMES, INC.
(Sub. of Palm Harbor Homes, Inc.)
1100 Rives Rd
Martinsville, VA 24112
Mailing Address:
PO Box 5511
Martinsville, VA 24115
Tel.: (276) 632-7100
Fax: (276) 666-2537
Toll Free: (800) 216-7001
Web Site: www.nationwide-homes.com
Sales Range: $25-49.9 Million
Approx. Number Employees: 350
Year Founded: 1959
Business Description:
Modular Housing Mfr
S.I.C.: 2452; 1521
N.A.I.C.S.: 321992; 236115
Media: 1-2-3-5-9-10-18-26
Distr.: Reg.
Personnel:
Andy Miller *(Pres)*
Brands & Products:
CORNERSTONE COLLECTION
THE CUMBERLAND
NATIONWIDE
SILVER SERIES
Advertising Agency:
919 Marketing Company
102 Avent Ferry Rd
Holly Springs, NC 27540
Tel.: (919) 557-7890
Fax: (919) 557-0041

NEENAH ENTERPRISES, INC.
2121 Brooks Ave
Neenah, WI 54957
Tel.: (920) 725-7000
Fax: (920) 729-3661
Toll Free: (800) 558-5075
E-mail: info@nfco.com
Web Site: www.nfco.com
Business Description:
Holding Company
S.I.C.: 6719
N.A.I.C.S.: 551112
Advertising Expenditures: $542,000
Personnel:
Ted S. Lodge *(Chm)*
Thomas J. Riordan *(Pres & CEO)*
Brent E. Johnson *(CFO)*
Frank Headington *(VP-Tech)*

NEENAH FOUNDRY COMPANY
(Holding of NEENAH ENTERPRISES, INC.)
2121 Brooks St
Neenah, WI 54956
Mailing Address:
PO Box 729
Neenah, WI 54957
Tel.: (920) 725-7000
Fax: (920) 729-3661
Toll Free: (800) 558-5075
Web Site: www.nfco.com
Sales Range: $150-199.9 Million
Year Founded: 1872
Business Description:
Construction & Industrial Iron Casting Mfr
S.I.C.: 3321
N.A.I.C.S.: 331511
Advertising Expenditures: $542,000
Personnel:
Dale E. Parker *(CFO)*
Frank Headington *(VP-Tech)*
Brands & Products:
NEENAH

NEW HOLLAND CONSTRUCTION
(Unit of CNH America LLC)
245 E N Ave
Carol Stream, IL 60188
Tel.: (262) 636-6011
Fax: (630) 462-1747
Web Site: www.newhollandconstruction.com
Approx. Number Employees: 40
Year Founded: 1999
Business Description:
Construction & Earth Moving Equipment Sales & Distr
S.I.C.: 5082
N.A.I.C.S.: 423810
Advertising Expenditures: $200,000
Media: 1-2-5-7-10
Distr.: Intl.; Natl.
Budget Set: Nov.
Brands & Products:
FIATALLIS
NEW HOLLAND CONSTRUCTION
Advertising Agency:
Slack Barshinger & Partners, Inc.
233 N Michigan Ave Ste 3050
Chicago, IL 60601
Tel.: (312) 970-5800
Fax: (312) 970-5850

Key to Media (For complete agency information see *The Advertising Red Books-Agencies* edition):
1. Bus. Publs. 2. Cable T.V. 3. Catalogs & Directories. 4. Co-op Adv. 5. Consumer Mags. 6. D.M. to Bus. Estab.7. D.M. to Consumers
8. Daily Newsp. 9. Exhibits/Trade Shows 10. Foreign 11. Infomercial 12. Internet Adv.13. Multimedia 14. Network Radio
15. Network T.V. 16. Newsp. Distr. Mags. 17. Other 18. Outdoor (Posters, Transit) 19. Point of Purchase20. Premiums, Novelties
21. Product Samples 22. Special Events Mktg. 23. Spot Radio 24. Spot T.V. 25. Weekly Newsp. 26. Yellow Page Adv.

Toll Free: (800) 888-6197

NEW YORK WIRE COMPANY
152 N Main St
Mount Wolf, PA 17347
Tel.: (717) 266-5626
Fax: (717) 266-5871
E-mail: mzammetti@newyorkwire.com
Web Site: www.newyorkwire.com
Approx. Number Employees: 500
Year Founded: 1888
Business Description:
Screening, Industrial Mesh & Drawn Wire Products
S.I.C.: 3496
N.A.I.C.S.: 332618
Export
Advertising Expenditures: $300,000
Media: 2-4-5-10-11-13-17-19
Distr.: Intl.; Natl.
Budget Set: Nov.
Personnel:
Frank T. Gaiteri *(VP-Engrg)*
Walter J. Senkowski *(VP-Fin)*
Raymond M. Hertz *(Dir-Sls-Natl)*
Teresa A. Markey *(Dir-Customer Support Svcs)*
Lori Rhinehart *(Safety Mgr)*
Brands & Products:
NEWYORKWIRE
WALLSPAN

NEW YORK WIRE COMPANY
(Branch of New York Wire Company)
500 E Middle St
Hanover, PA 17331-2027
Tel.: (717) 637-3795
Fax: (717) 637-4766
Toll Free: (800) 323-5585
Web Site: www.newyorkwire.com/company/locations.html
Sales Range: $10-24.9 Million
Approx. Number Employees: 280
Year Founded: 1944
Business Description:
Woven Wire & Screening Products
S.I.C.: 3496
N.A.I.C.S.: 332618
Export
Advertising Expenditures: $220,000
Media: 2-4-10-19-20-21
Distr.: Natl.
Budget Set: Apr.-May
Personnel:
Paul Troyer *(Mgr-Sls & Mktg)*
Brands & Products:
DURAROOF
PAW PROOF
SOLAR GUARD
STAR BRAND
STARALUM
STARBRITE
STARGLASS
STARGLASS STIFF
STARLIFE
SUNSHIELD
WALLMESH
WALLSPAN

NEWARK WIRE CLOTH CO.
160 Fornelius Ave
Clifton, NJ 07013
Tel.: (973) 778-4478
Fax: (973) 778-4481
Toll Free: (800) 221-0392
E-mail: info@newarkwire.com
Web Site: www.newarkwire.com
E-Mail For Key Personnel:
President: rwc@newarkwire.com
Sales Range: $10-24.9 Million
Approx. Number Employees: 35
Year Founded: 1911
Business Description:
Fabricated Wire Products: Wire Cloth, Filtration Equipment, Strainers & Screens Mfr
S.I.C.: 3496; 3494
N.A.I.C.S.: 332618; 332919
Import Export
Media: 2-4-7-10-21
Distr.: Intl.; Natl.
Budget Set: Oct.
Personnel:
Richard W. Campbell *(Pres)*
Brands & Products:
NEWARK
SANICLEAN STRAINERS
SUPERLA SIEVE
TENSIL BOLT
Advertising Agency:
Norman Diegnan & Associates
PO Box 298
Oldwick, NJ 08858
Tel.: (908) 832-7951
Fax: (908) 832-9650

NEWGROUND RESOURCES
15450 S Outr 40 Ste 300
Chesterfield, MO 63017-2062
Tel.: (636) 898-8100
Fax: (636) 898-8111
Toll Free: (888) 613-0001
E-mail: clientdev@newground.com
Web Site: www.newground.com
Approx. Sls.: $80,000,000
Approx. Number Employees: 150
Year Founded: 1913
Business Description:
Consultants, Designers & General Contractors Specific to the Financial Industry
S.I.C.: 1522; 8742
N.A.I.C.S.: 236220; 541611
Advertising Expenditures: $1,000,000
Media: 2-4-7-10-13-20
Distr.: Natl.; Reg.
Budget Set: Sept.
Personnel:
John T. Golitz *(Chm)*
Kevin J. Blair *(Pres & CEO)*
Charles J. Zaegel *(CFO & Exec VP)*
Larry Gandelman *(Sr VP-Program Mgmt)*
James E. Kueneke *(Exec VP-Retail)*
Robert E. Mannion *(Exec VP-Construction)*
Barry Theobald *(Sr VP-Eastern Reg)*
Thomas D. Auer *(Sr VP-Architecture)*
Jeff Glantz *(VP-Strategic Alliances)*
Scott Hilton *(VP-Mdsg Ops)*
Kayce Ansell *(Dir-Mktg)*
Rebecca Doepke *(Dir-Culture)*

NEXT LEVEL TURF MANAGEMENT
301 State Rd 60 W
Plant City, FL 33567
Tel.: (813) 651-0270
Fax: (813) 650-8621
E-mail: service@nextleveltruf.net
Web Site: www.nextleveltruf.net
Business Description:
Turf Management Services; Fertilization & Weed Control, Sprinklers & Irrigation Systems, Custom Landscaping, Sod Installation & Replacement, Hydro-Seeding, Clean Ups, Concrete Patios, Walkways, Driveways, Pavers & Decorative Curbing
S.I.C.: 0782
N.A.I.C.S.: 561730
Media: 7-8
Personnel:
Brandon Melanson *(Pres)*

NIAGARA LASALLE STEEL COMPANY
(Sub. of Niagara Corporation)
1412 150th St
Hammond, IN 46327-1743
Tel.: (219) 853-6000
Fax: (219) 853-6081
E-mail: info@niagaralasalle.com
Web Site: www.niag.com
Approx. Number Employees: 400
Year Founded: 1912
Business Description:
Cold Finished & Specialty Steel Bar Products Mfr
S.I.C.: 3316
N.A.I.C.S.: 331221
D.M. to Consumers: 80%; Exhibits/Trade Shows: 20%
Distr.: Natl.
Budget Set: Sept.
Personnel:
Frank Archer *(Pres)*
Kevin Stevick *(CEO)*
Tom Smith *(VP-Sls & Mktg)*

NIXCO PLUMBING INC.
4281 State Rt 42
Mason, OH 45040
Tel.: (513) 398-5907
Fax: (513) 770-5590
Web Site: www.nixcoplumbing.com
Business Description:
Plumbing Services
S.I.C.: 1711
N.A.I.C.S.: 238220
Media: 13-17
Personnel:
Jeff Heger *(Owner & Pres)*

NLC PRODUCTS INC.
3801 Woodland Hts Rd Ste 100
Little Rock, AR 72212
Tel.: (501) 227-9050
Fax: (501) 227-4892
Web Site: www.huntsmart.com
Approx. Number Employees: 50
Business Description:
Hunting Equipment Mfr
S.I.C.: 5091; 5961
N.A.I.C.S.: 423910; 454113
Media: 4-10-13
Personnel:
Henry Mariani *(Chm)*
Brands & Products:
NITE LITE
Advertising Agency:
Matmon.Com
303 W Capitol Ave
Little Rock, AR 72201
Tel.: (501) 375-4999

NOBILITY HOMES, INC.
3741 Southwest 7th St
Ocala, FL 34474-1948
Tel.: (352) 732-5157
Fax: (352) 622-6766
E-mail: info@nobilityhomes.com
Web Site: www.nobilityhomes.com
Approx. Sls.: $11,869,333
Approx. Number Employees: 102
Year Founded: 1967
Business Description:
Mobile Homes Designer, Mfr & Retailer
S.I.C.: 5271; 2451
N.A.I.C.S.: 453930; 321991
Advertising Expenditures: $489,583
Personnel:
Terry E. Trexler *(Pres)*
Thomas W. Trexler *(CFO & Exec VP)*
Brands & Products:
NOBILITY

NOOTER CORPORATION
(Holding of CIC Group, Inc.)
1500 S 2nd St
Saint Louis, MO 63104
Tel.: (314) 421-7200
Fax: (314) 421-7395
Telex: 044-849
E-mail: sales@nooterconstruction.com
Web Site: www.nooter.com
E-Mail For Key Personnel:
Sales Director: sales@nooterconstruction.com
Sales Range: $350-399.9 Million
Approx. Number Employees: 75
Year Founded: 1896
Business Description:
Holding Company; Engineering Services
S.I.C.: 3443; 3479
N.A.I.C.S.: 332420; 332812
Import Export
Media: 2-4-7-22
Distr.: Natl.
Personnel:
Jim Nelson *(Pres)*

NORANDEX/REYNOLDS DISTRIBUTION, INC.
(Sub. of Saint-Gobain Corporation)
300 Executive Pwy W Ste 100
Hudson, OH 44236
Tel.: (330) 656-8800
Toll Free: (800) 528-0942
E-mail: info@norandex.com
Web Site: www.norandex.com
E-Mail For Key Personnel:
Marketing Director: garber@norandex.com
Sales Range: $800-899.9 Million
Approx. Number Employees: 2,200
Year Founded: 1946
Business Description:
Building Materials Distr & Vinyl Siding Mfr
S.I.C.: 5033; 3089; 5211
N.A.I.C.S.: 423330; 326199; 444190
Advertising Expenditures: $2,000,000
D.M. to Consumers: $2,000,000
Distr.: Natl.
Budget Set: Sept.-Oct.
Personnel:
Van L. Garber *(VP-Mktg)*

NORCRAFT HOLDINGS, LP
(Joint Venture of Apax Partners LLP & Trimaran Capital Partners, LLC)
3020 Denmark Ave Ste 100
Eagan, MN 55121-2417
Tel.: (651) 234-3300
Fax: (651) 234-3398
Web Site: www.norcraftcompanies.com

Key to Media (For complete agency information see *The Advertising Red Books-Agencies* edition):
1. Bus. Publs. 2. Cable T.V. 3. Catalogs & Directories. 4. Co-op Adv. 5. Consumer Mags. 6. D.M. to Bus. Estab.7. D.M. to Consumers
8. Daily Newsp. 9. Exhibits/Trade Shows 10. Foreign 11. Infomercial 12. Internet Adv.13. Multimedia 14. Network Radio
15. Network T.V. 16. Newsp. Distr. Mags. 17. Other 18. Outdoor (Posters, Transit) 19. Point of Purchase20. Premiums, Novelties
21. Product Samples 22. Special Events Mktg. 23. Spot Radio 24. Spot T.V. 25. Weekly Newsp. 26. Yellow Page Adv.

Norcraft Holdings, LP — (Continued)

Approx. Sls.: $262,568,000
Approx. Number Employees: 1,630
Year Founded: 1974
Business Description:
Kitchen Cabinets Mfr; Owned by Apax Partners, Inc. & Trimaran Capital Partners
S.I.C.: 5031; 2434
N.A.I.C.S.: 423310; 337110
Advertising Expenditures: $400,000
Media: 2-4-5-7-10-17-19-20-26
Distr.: Natl.
Personnel:
Herbert Buller *(Chm)*
Mark Buller *(Pres & CEO)*
Leigh Ginter *(CFO)*
Simon Solomon *(Pres-UltraCraft)*
John Swedeen *(Pres-StarMark)*
Kurt Wanninger *(Pres-Mid Continent)*
Brands & Products:
BROOKWOOD CABINETRY
DESIGNER STOCK SIGNATURE SERIES
DESTINY
ENTREE
FIELDSTONE CABINETRY
MID CONTINENT CABINETRY
NORCRAFT CABINETRY
PRO SERIES
STARMARK CABINETRY
ULTRACRAFT CABINETRY
VISION

NORTEK, INC.
(Holding of Nortek Holdings, Inc.)
50 Kennedy Plz
Providence, RI 02903-2393
Tel.: (401) 751-1600
Fax: (401) 751-4610
E-mail: general@nortek-inc.com
Web Site: www.nortek-inc.com
Approx. Sls.: $1,899,300,000
Approx. Number Employees: 9,500
Year Founded: 1967
Business Description:
Residential & Commercial Building Products Mfr & Sales for the Construction, Manufactured Housing & Do-It-Yourself & Professional Remodeling & Renovation Markets
S.I.C.: 2435; 3444; 3585; 3639; 5064
N.A.I.C.S.: 321211; 332322; 333415; 335228; 423620
Import Export
Advertising Expenditures: $32,424,000
Distr.: Natl.
Budget Set: Dec.
Personnel:
Richard L. Bready *(Chm, Pres & CEO)*
Almon C. Hall, III *(CFO & Sr VP)*
Kevin W. Donnelly *(Gen Counsel, Sec & Sr VP)*
Edward J. Cooney *(Treas & Sr VP)*
Andrew W. Prete *(VP-Bus Dev & Asst Sec)*
Brands & Products:
21ST SENTRY
76 COLLECTION
ACCESS MASTER
ACCESS PRO
ALERTLINK
ASTON
BEADED SOFFIT
CHANNEL PLUS
CHATEAU
CHATEAU LEGACY
CHATEAU NOBILITY
CHEF-AIRE
CLASSIC MANOR
CLASSIC WEAVE
COLMAN
CONSERVATION ENERGY SYSTEMS
CONSUL
CUBIT
CWD
D5 SOFFIT
DEFIANT
DOUBLE CHECK
DOUBLE-GARD V
EDENAIRE
ENVOY
FINESSE
FINYL RAIL
FLAIR
GOVERNAIR
GREAT LAKES GOLD
INTERTHERM
KEEP SAFER
KROY
LOSONE
MAMMOTH
MICROMATE
MICROTEK
MILLBRIDGE
MILLER
MODUCCI
MONITOR
MT EXPRESS
MULTI CODE
NAPCO
NAPCO PREMIUM
NAPCO PRIME
NAUTILUS
NOVI
OLDE PROVIDENCE
OPEN HOUSE
POWERMISER
PROGUARD
PYRO-GUARD
QUALITAIR
REGENCY
RICHWOOD
SENSAIRE
SILENT SIGNAL
SILHOUETTE
SOLITAIRE
SOLITAIRE ULTRA SILENT
SUNNYBROOK
TEMTROL
THERMAL-GARD
TIMBERLAST
UNIFRAME
VANEE
VAPAC
VARIBEST

NORTHWEST PIPE COMPANY
5721 SE Columbia Way Ste 200
Vancouver, WA 98661
Tel.: (360) 397-6250
Fax: (360) 397-6257
Toll Free: (800) 989-9631
E-mail: employment@nwpipe.com
Web Site: www.nwpipe.com
Approx. Sls.: $386,750,000
Approx. Number Employees: 1,200
Year Founded: 1966
Business Description:
Steel Pipes Mfr
S.I.C.: 3317
N.A.I.C.S.: 331210
Advertising Expenditures: $735,000
Media: 2-4-10
Personnel:
William R. Tagmyer *(Chm)*
Richard A. Roman *(CEO)*
Robin A. Gantt *(CFO)*
Scott Montross *(COO)*
Robert L. Mahoney *(Pres-Tubular Products Grp)*
Gary A. Stokes *(Pres-Water Transmission)*
Greg Carrier *(VP-Pur)*
Kevin Gullickson *(Dir-Quality Assurance)*
Kip Bartlett *(Mgr-Sls)*
Matt Geiger *(Mgr-Ops)*
John Peterson *(Mgr-Ops)*
Randy Ridgley *(Mgr-Ops)*
Hardin Stephens *(Mgr-Sls)*
Brands & Products:
EZ-FLOW
FLAME-OUT
NORTHWEST PIPE
POWERPIPE
POZ-LOC

NOVELIS INC.
(Sub. of Hindalco Industries Ltd.)
3399 Peachtree Rd NE Lenox Bldg Ste 1500
Atlanta, GA 30326
Tel.: (404) 814-4200
Fax: (404) 814-4219
E-mail: media.relations@novelis.com
Web Site: www.novelis.com
Approx. Sls.: $8,673,000,000
Approx. Number Employees: 11,600
Year Founded: 2005
Business Description:
Aluminum Rolled Semi-Finished Products Mfr
S.I.C.: 3355; 3339; 3497
N.A.I.C.S.: 331319; 322225; 331419
Import Export
Advertising Expenditures: $1,000,000
Media: 4-7-8-10-11
Personnel:
Kumar Mangalam Birla *(Chm)*
Debnarayan Bhattacharya *(Vice Chm)*
Philip R. Martens *(Pres & CEO)*
Steven R. Fisher *(CFO & Sr VP)*
Karen K. Renner *(CIO & VP)*
Leslie J. Parrette, Jr. *(Chief Compliance Officer, Gen Counsel & Sr VP)*
Erwin Mayr *(Chief Strategy Officer & Sr VP)*
Leslie W. Joyce *(Chief People Officer & Sr VP)*
John Gardner *(Chief Sustainability Officer & VP)*
Jean-Marc Germain *(Pres-North America & Sr VP)*
Alexandre Moreira Martins de Almeida *(Pres-South America & Sr VP)*
Thomas Walpole *(Pres-Novelis Asia & Sr VP-Global Mfg Excellence)*
Antonio Tadeu Coelho Nardocci *(Pres-Novelis Europe)*
James Liu *(Mng Dir-Bus Dev-China & Dir-Sls & Mktg-Automotive Asia)*
Robert Nelson *(VP-Fin & Controller)*
Kim Adler *(VP-Comm & Govt Affairs)*
Monica Anderton *(VP-HR)*
Nick Madden *(Chief Procurement Officer & VP)*
Brenda D. Pulley *(VP-Corp Affairs & Comm)*
Robert Virtue *(VP-HR)*
Charles Belbin *(Dir-Corp Comm)*
Advertising Agency:
AutoCom Associates
74 W Long Lk Rd Ste 103
Bloomfield Hills, MI 48304-2770
Tel.: (248) 647-8621
Fax: (248) 642-2110

NUCOR CORPORATION
1915 Rexford Rd
Charlotte, NC 28211
Tel.: (704) 366-7000
Fax: (704) 362-4208
Toll Free: (800) 999-7461
Web Site: www.nucor.com
Approx. Sls.: $15,844,627,000
Approx. Number Employees: 20,500
Year Founded: 1955
Business Description:
Steel & Steel Products Mfr & Whslr
S.I.C.: 3312; 3315; 3462; 4953; 5051
N.A.I.C.S.: 331111; 331222; 332111; 423510; 562920
Import Export
Media: 2-6-7-17
Distr.: Intl.; Natl.
Budget Set: Sept.
Personnel:
Daniel R. DiMicco *(Chm & CEO)*
John J. Ferriola *(Pres & COO)*
James D. Frias *(CFO, Treas & Exec VP)*
Bob Lowe *(Pres-Buildings Grp)*
Douglas R. Gunson *(Gen Counsel)*
James R. Darsey *(Exec VP)*
Keith Brian Grass *(Exec VP)*
Ladd R. Hall *(Exec VP-Flat Rolled Products)*
Hamilton Lott Jr. *(Exec VP)*
R. Joseph Stratman *(Exec VP)*
K. Rex Query *(VP & Gen Mgr)*
James M. Coblin *(VP-HR)*
Michael D. Keller *(Controller & Gen Mgr)*
Elizabeth W. Bowers *(Gen Mgr-Taxes)*
Stephen D. Laxton *(Gen Mgr-Bus Dev & Strategic Plng)*
Norman L. Maero *(Gen Mgr-Construction)*
Bradford G. TRUE *(Gen Mgr)*
Steven J. Rowlan *(Dir-Environ Affairs)*
Pat Dreher *(Mgr-Intl Sls & Mktg)*
Brands & Products:
IT'S OUR NATURE
NUCOR
NUCOR BEARING PRODUCTS
NUCOR BUILDING SYSTEMS
NUCOR COLD FINISHED BAR
NUCOR FASTENERS
NUCOR GRINDING BALLS
NUCOR STEEL
VULCRAFT
Advertising Agency:
Eric Mower and Associates
1001 Morehead Sq Dr 5th Fl
Charlotte, NC 28203
Tel.: (704) 375-0123
Fax: (704) 375-0222
Toll Free: (800) 968-0682
— Matthew Ferguson *(Acct Exec)*
— Scott Howard *(Assoc Media Dir)*

NUPLA CORPORATION
(Sub. of Specialty Tool, Inc.)
11912 Sheldon St
Sun Valley, CA 91352-1509
Tel.: (818) 827-0718
Fax: (818) 504-9620
Toll Free: (800) 872-7661
E-mail: sales@nuplacorp.com
Web Site: www.nuplacorp.com
E-Mail For Key Personnel:
Sales Director: sales@nuplacorp.com
Approx. Number Employees: 125
Year Founded: 1938
Business Description:
Industrial Surface Protective Hammers & Related Products Mfr
S.I.C.: 3423
N.A.I.C.S.: 332212
Media: 2-3-4-7-8-10-21
Distr.: Intl.; Natl.
Budget Set: Dec.
Personnel:
Dan Harold *(Dir-Mktg & Sls)*
Sumi Gandhi *(Mgr-Intl Sls)*
Ron Ortiz *(Mgr)*
Brands & Products:
CUSH-N-GRIP
EXCALIBUR
EZ SQUEEGEE
IMPAX
MICRO-STRIKE
MICROJUST
NON-SPARKING POWER DRIVE
NON-SPARKING SPS
NON-SPARKING STRIKE
NU-POLE
NULOK
NUPLA
NUPLABOND
NUPLAFLEX
NUPLAGLAS
POWER DRIVE
POWER PYLON
SPI IMPAX
SPS
STRIKE PRO
SUPER DUTY
WE CAN HANDLE ANYTHING

NVR INCORPORATED
11700 Plaza America Dr Ste 500
Reston, VA 20190-4792
Tel.: (703) 956-4000
Fax: (703) 956-4750
E-mail: info@nvrinc.com
Web Site: www.nvrinc.com
Approx. Rev.: $2,980,758,000
Approx. Number Employees: 2,822
Year Founded: 1987
Business Description:
Builder of Houses; Financial Services Company
S.I.C.: 1531; 1521; 1522; 6082; 6141; 6159
N.A.I.C.S.: 236118; 236115; 236116; 236220; 522220; 522292; 522293; 522294; 522298
Media: 4-6-9-16-18-25
Distr.: Natl.
Budget Set: Sept.
Personnel:
Dwight C. Schar *(Chm)*
Paul C. Saville *(Pres & CEO)*
Dennis M. Seremet *(CFO & Sr VP)*
Lee Darnold *(Dir-Sls & Mktg)*
Brands & Products:
FOX RIDGE HOMES
LUXURY FOR LIFE
NV HOMES
RYAN HOMES
RYMARC HOMES
Advertising Agency:
Williams Whittle Associates, Inc.
711 Princess St
Alexandria, VA 22314-2221
Tel.: (703) 836-9222
Fax: (703) 684-3285

ODL INCORPORATED
215 E Roosevelt Ave
Zeeland, MI 49464-1239
Tel.: (616) 772-9111
Fax: (616) 772-3840
Toll Free: (800) 253-3900
Web Site: www.odl.com
Approx. Number Employees: 500
Year Founded: 1948
Business Description:
Building Products Mfr
S.I.C.: 2431; 3444
N.A.I.C.S.: 321918; 332322
Import Export
Media: 1-2-3-4-6-7-9-10-13-18-19-20-21-22-23-25
Distr.: Natl.
Budget Set: Dec.
Personnel:
Dave Killoran *(Chm)*
Mike Burke *(VP-Fin)*
Kevin Dolle *(VP-Sls & Mktg)*
Scott Harder *(VP-Sls & Mktg)*
Angelo Marasco *(Dir-Prod Dev)*
Scott Spence *(Sr Mgr-Product)*
Brands & Products:
A BETTER WAY TO TREAT A DOOR
ALLURE
AVANT
BEVELED ELEGANCE
BREAKTHROUGH
BRISTOL
BUILDING VALUE INTO BUILDING PRODUCTS
CADENCE
CHATEAU
CIRRUS
CRYSTAL GROOVED SERIES
CUT CRYSTAL
ELEGANT BEVEL SERIES
ENERGY STAR
ENTROPY
ENTRYPOINT
ESCAPADES
ETCHED AND SILK SERIES
EXPRESSIONS
HEIRLOOMS
HP PRO
IMPRESSIONS
INTERPRETATIONS
LEGACY MASTER
LIGHT-TOUCH
MAJESTIC
NOUVEAU
OAKPARK
ODL
PALAIS
PANACHE
PARIS
PRO-SERIES
QUIET ELEGANCE
RADIANT HUES
SECURE BY DESIGN
SEVERE WEATHER
SIMPLICITY
SLAM-PROOF
SMARTFRAME
SOLAR FLAIR
SOLAR LENS
TRIPOLI
VISTA
Advertising Agency:
Tilson PR
1001 Yamato Rd Ste 400
Boca Raton, FL 33431
Tel.: (561) 998-1995
Fax: (561) 998-1790
Toll Free: (888) 397-7878
EntryPoint

THE OLSON COMPANY
3010 Old Ranch Pkwy 400 Ste 100
Seal Beach, CA 90740
Tel.: (562) 596-4770
Fax: (562) 596-4703
E-mail: info@theolsonco.com
Web Site: www.theolsonco.com
Approx. Sls.: $13,700,000
Approx. Number Employees: 200
Business Description:
Single-Family Housing Construction
S.I.C.: 1521
N.A.I.C.S.: 236115
Personnel:
Stephen E. Olson *(Chm & CEO)*
Advertising Agency:
The MWW Group
1 Meadowlands Plz 6th Fl
East Rutherford, NJ 07073
Tel.: (201) 507-9500
Fax: (201) 507-0092
Depot Walk

OLYMPIC STEEL INC.
5096 Richmond Rd
Cleveland, OH 44146-1329
Tel.: (216) 292-3800
Fax: (216) 292-3974
Toll Free: (800) 321-6290
E-mail: info@olysteel.com
Web Site: www.olysteel.com
E-Mail For Key Personnel:
President: dwolfort@olysteel.com
Marketing Director: dlenzi@olysteel.com
Approx. Sls.: $805,043,000
Approx. Number Employees: 1,113
Year Founded: 1954
Business Description:
Processing & Distribution of Carbon Coated Carbon & Stainless Steel Flat-rolled Sheet, Coil & Plate Products
S.I.C.: 5051
N.A.I.C.S.: 423510
Import Export
Media: 2-4-7-22
Distr.: Natl.
Budget Set: Dec.
Personnel:
Michael D. Siegal *(Chm & CEO)*
David A. Wolfort *(Pres & COO)*
Richard T. Marabito *(CFO)*
John Brieck *(Reg VP-Southern Region)*
David Lenzi *(VP-Sls & Mktg)*
Richard A. Manson *(VP-HR & Admin)*
Dan Shepard *(Gen Mgr)*
Steven L. Larson *(Dir-Ops & Facilities)*

ON SEMICONDUCTOR CORPORATION
5005 E McDowell Rd
Phoenix, AZ 85008-4229
Tel.: (602) 244-6600
Fax: (602) 244-6071
E-mail: supplymgmt@onsemi.com
Web Site: www.onsemi.com
Approx. Rev.: $2,313,400,000
Approx. Number Employees: 14,307
Year Founded: 1999
Business Description:
Analog, Logic & Discrete Semiconductor Mfr
S.I.C.: 3674; 3559
N.A.I.C.S.: 334413; 333295
Advertising Expenditures: $125,000
Personnel:
J. Daniel McCranie *(Chm)*
Keith D. Jackson *(Pres & CEO)*
Donald A. Colvin *(CFO, Treas & Exec VP)*
William John Nelson *(COO & Exec VP)*
Hans Stork *(CTO & Sr VP)*
George H. Cave *(Gen Counsel, Chief Compliance & Ethics Officer, Se)*
Robert Charles Mahoney *(Exec VP-Sls & Mktg)*
William M. Hall *(Sr VP & Gen Mgr-Standard Products Grp)*
Bob Klosterboer *(Gen Mgr-Digital & Mixed-Signal Product Grp & Sr VP)*
William A. Schromm *(Sr VP & Gen Mgr-Computing & Consumer Products Grp)*
Michael A. Williams *(Sr VP & Gen Mgr-Automotive & Power Regulation Grp)*
Carlos Laber *(Sr Dir-Design)*
Ken Rizvi *(Dir-Fin)*
Todd Visconti *(Product Mgr)*
Brands & Products:
ON SEMICONDUCTOR
SELECTION.SERVICE.SUPPORT
Advertising Agency:
McClenahan Bruer Communications
5331 SW Macadam Ave Ste 220
Portland, OR 97239
Tel.: (503) 546-1000
Fax: (503) 546-1001
Public Relations

OPUS CORPORATION
10350 Bren Rd W
Minnetonka, MN 55343-9014
Tel.: (952) 656-4444
Fax: (952) 656-4529
Web Site: www.opuscorp.com
E-Mail For Key Personnel:
President: mark.rauenhorst@opuscorp.com
Sales Range: $1-4.9 Billion
Approx. Number Employees: 1,368
Year Founded: 1953
Business Description:
Holding Company; Real Estate Development & Construction Services
S.I.C.: 6719; 1522; 1541; 6552
N.A.I.C.S.: 551112; 236116; 236210; 236220; 237210
Personnel:
Andy Deckas *(CIO & Sr VP)*
Dan Nicol *(Gen Counsel, Sec & Sr VP)*
Carol Quam *(Dir-Mktg)*

Key to Media (For complete agency information see *The Advertising Red Books-Agencies* edition):
1. Bus. Publs. 2. Cable T.V. 3. Catalogs & Directories. 4. Co-op Adv. 5. Consumer Mags. 6. D.M. to Bus. Estab.7. D.M. to Consumers
8. Daily Newsp. 9. Exhibits/Trade Shows 10. Foreign 11. Infomercial 12. Internet Adv.13. Multimedia 14. Network Radio
15. Network T.V. 16. Newsp. Distr. Mags. 17. Other 18. Outdoor (Posters, Transit) 19. Point of Purchase20. Premiums, Novelties
21. Product Samples 22. Special Events Mktg. 23. Spot Radio 24. Spot T.V. 25. Weekly Newsp. 26. Yellow Page Adv.

OPUS Corporation — (Continued)

Brands & Products:
OPUS
OPUS SERVICENET
Advertising Agency:
Trozzolo Communications Group
802 Broadway Ste 300
Kansas City, MO 64105
Tel.: (816) 842-8111
Fax: (816) 842-8188

OREPAC HOLDING COMPANY INC.

30170 SW Ore Pac Ave
Wilsonville, OR 97070-9794
Tel.: (503) 682-5050
Fax: (503) 682-1965
Web Site: www.orepac.com
Approx. Sls.: $500,000,000
Approx. Number Employees: 900
Year Founded: 1977
Business Description:
Lumber, Plywood & Millwork
S.I.C.: 5031; 5033
N.A.I.C.S.: 423310; 423330
Import Export
Media: 5
Personnel:
Glenn Hart *(Pres & CEO)*
Alan Kirk *(CFO)*

ORION MARINE GROUP, INC.

12000 Aerospace Ste 300
Houston, TX 77034
Tel.: (713) 852-6500
Tel.: (713) 852-6506 (IR)
Fax: (713) 852-6530
E-mail: ir@orionmarinegroup.com
Web Site:
www.orionmarinegroup.com
Approx. Rev.: $353,135,000
Approx. Number Employees: 303
Year Founded: 1994
Business Description:
Marine Construction Services
S.I.C.: 1629; 1623; 3731; 3799
N.A.I.C.S.: 237990; 237120; 336611; 336999
Advertising Expenditures: $63,000
Media: 17
Personnel:
J. Michael Pearson *(Pres & CEO)*
Mark R. Stauffer *(CFO, Chief Acctg Officer & Exec VP)*
Peter R. Buchler *(Gen Counsel, Sec & Exec VP)*
James L. Rose *(Exec VP-Atlantic Seaboard & Caribbean)*
Chris DeAlmeida *(Dir-IR)*

ORLEANS HOMEBUILDERS, INC.

(Filed Ch 11 Bankruptcy #10-10684 on 3/2/10 in U.S. Bankruptcy Ct, Dist of DE, Wilmington)
3333 Street Rd Ste 101
Bensalem, PA 19020
Tel.: (215) 245-7500
Fax: (215) 633-2352
E-mail: info@orleanshomes.com
Web Site: www.orleanshomes.com
Sales Range: $500-549.9 Million
Approx. Number Employees: 544
Year Founded: 1969
Business Description:
Residential Community Developer
S.I.C.: 1521; 1531; 6552
N.A.I.C.S.: 236115; 236117; 237210
Advertising Expenditures: $5,128,000
Media: 4-6-8
Personnel:
Jeffrey P. Orleans *(Chm & CEO)*
Benjamin D. Goldman *(Vice Chm)*
Michael T. Vesey *(Pres & COO)*
Robert M. Segal *(Partner)*
David Kaplan *(Principal)*
C. Dean Amann, II *(Exec VP-Northern & Midwestern Regions)*
Kyle J. Upper *(Exec VP-Land Acq-Florida)*
Thomas R. Vesey *(Exec VP-Southern Region)*

OSMOSE, INC.

980 Ellicott St
Buffalo, NY 14209-2323
Tel.: (716) 882-5905
Fax: (716) 882-5139
E-mail: info@osmose.com
Web Site: www.osmose.com
E-Mail For Key Personnel:
President: jspengler@osmose.com
Sales Range: $250-299.9 Million
Approx. Number Employees: 1,600
Year Founded: 1934
Business Description:
Wood Preservatives, Equipment & Services
S.I.C.: 2491
N.A.I.C.S.: 321114
Import Export
Advertising Expenditures: $495,000
Media: 1-2-4-5-6-7-10-19-20-22
Distr.: Natl.
Budget Set: Oct.
Personnel:
Paul A. Goydan *(Pres)*
Michael Leach *(CFO)*
Tom Petrik *(Sr VP)*
Tom Marr *(VP-Engrng)*
Frank Robertson *(VP-Mktg)*
Tom Hobart *(Graphic Art Mgr)*
Al Heberer *(Natl Accts Mgr)*
Brands & Products:
OSMOPLASTIC
OSMOSE
OSMOSE K-33
SUNWOOD

OSMOSE, INC.

(Div. of Osmose, Inc.)
1016 Everee Inn Rd
Griffin, GA 30224-4733
Mailing Address:
PO Box O
Griffin, GA 30224-0012
Tel.: (770) 233-4200
Tel.: (770) 228-8434
Fax: (770) 412-0819
Toll Free: (800) 241-0240
E-mail: pressuretreated@osmose.com
Web Site: www.osmosewood.com
Approx. Sls.: $60,000,000
Approx. Number Employees: 50
Year Founded: 1934
Business Description:
Wood Preservatives
S.I.C.: 2491
N.A.I.C.S.: 321114
Export
Advertising Expenditures: $400,000
Distr.: Intl.
Brands & Products:
ADVANCE GUARD INSECT PROTECTED WOOD
WEATHERSHIELD
WOODSHADES

OTIS ELEVATOR COMPANY

(Group of United Technologies Corporation)
10 Farm Springs Rd
Farmington, CT 06032
Tel.: (860) 676-6000
Fax: (860) 676-5111
Toll Free: (800) 233-6847
Web Site: www.otisworldwide.com
Approx. Rev.: $10,300,000,000
Approx. Number Employees: 61,103
Year Founded: 1853
Business Description:
Installation, Inspection, Service & Repair of Elevators, Escalators, Automated People-Moving Systems & Moving Walkways
S.I.C.: 3534; 1796
N.A.I.C.S.: 333921; 238290
Media: 2-7-10
Distr.: Intl., Natl.
Personnel:
Didier Michaud-Daniel *(Pres)*
Angelo Messina *(CFO & VP)*
Johan Bill *(Gen Counsel, Sec & VP)*
Patrick Blethon *(VP-Strategy & Bus Dev)*
Xavier Savigny *(VP-HR)*
Paul Thomson *(VP-HR)*
Melanie Rener *(Mgr-PR & Comm)*
Brands & Products:
ELEVONIC
EMS PANORAMA
GEN2
NEXT STEP
OTIS
SKYWAY
TRAV-O-LATORS
Advertising Agencies:
CooperKatz & Company
205 Lexington Ave 5th Fl
New York, NY 10016
Tel.: (917) 595-3030
Fax: (917) 326-8997

Maier Advertising, Inc.
1789 New Britain Ave
Farmington, CT 06032-3317
Tel.: (860) 677-4581
Fax: (860) 677-5854
Fax: (860) 677-4898

OVERHEAD DOOR CORPORATION

(Sub. of Sanwa Holdings Corporation)
2501 S State Hwy 121 Ste 200
Lewisville, TX 75067
Tel.: (469) 549-7110
Fax: (469) 549-7268
Toll Free: (800) 275-3290
E-mail: info@overheaddoor.com
Web Site: www.overheaddoor.com
Approx. Number Employees: 150
Year Founded: 1921
Business Description:
Sectional Doors for Residential, Commercial & Industrial Installation
S.I.C.: 3442; 2431
N.A.I.C.S.: 332321; 321911
Import Export
Advertising Expenditures: $900,000
Media: 2-5-6-17
Distr.: Natl.
Budget Set: Nov. -Dec.
Personnel:
Dennis Stone *(Pres & CEO)*
Paul Leeman *(CFO)*
William A. Schochet *(Gen Counsel, Sec & VP)*
Brands & Products:
GENIE
HORTON AUTOMATICS
MCGUIRE
OVERHEAD
TODCO

OVERLY MANUFACTURING COMPANY

(Sub. of Overly Door Company)
574 W Otterman St
Greensburg, PA 15601-2148
Mailing Address:
PO Box 70
Greensburg, PA 15601-0070
Tel.: (724) 834-7300
Fax: (724) 830-2877
Toll Free: (800) 979-7300
E-mail: overly@overly.com
Web Site: www.overly.com
Approx. Number Employees: 25
Year Founded: 1888
Business Description:
Mfr & Supplier of Metal Cladding Systems & Architectural Products; Engineering & Fabrication of Custom Hollow Metal Door & Window Assemblies
S.I.C.: 3442; 3446
N.A.I.C.S.: 332321; 332323
Export
Advertising Expenditures: $300,000
Media: 2-4-7-10
Distr.: Intl., Natl.
Budget Set: Nov.
Personnel:
Charles Baugh *(Pres)*
Terry Reese *(CEO)*
Bill Hughes *(Mgr-Mktg)*
Brands & Products:
OVERLY

OWEN INDUSTRIES, INC.

501 Ave H
Carter Lake, IA 51510-1513
Tel.: (712) 347-5500
Fax: (712) 347-6166
E-mail: salesoii@owenind.com
Web Site: www.owenind.com
E-Mail For Key Personnel:
Sales Director: salesoii@owenind.com
Approx. Number Employees: 400
Year Founded: 1885
Business Description:
Fabricated Structural Metal; Metal Service Center
S.I.C.: 5051; 3441
N.A.I.C.S.: 423510; 332312
Import Export
Advertising Expenditures: $200,000
Media: 2-5-6-7-8-17-20-26
Distr.: Direct to Consumer; Reg.
Personnel:
Edward Korbel *(CFO & VP-Fin)*
Craig Bence *(CIO & VP)*
Keith Siebels *(Sr VP-Sls)*
Brad Johnson *(VP-HR)*

Key to Media (For complete agency information see *The Advertising Red Books-Agencies* edition):
1. Bus. Publs. 2. Cable T.V. 3. Catalogs & Directories. 4. Co-op Adv. 5. Consumer Mags. 6. D.M. to Bus. Estab.7. D.M. to Consumers
8. Daily Newsp. 9. Exhibits/Trade Shows 10. Foreign 11. Infomercial 12. Internet Adv.13. Multimedia 14. Network Radio
15. Network T.V. 16. Newsp. Distr. Mags. 17. Other 18. Outdoor (Posters, Transit) 19. Point of Purchase20. Premiums, Novelties
21. Product Samples 22. Special Events Mktg. 23. Spot Radio 24. Spot T.V. 25. Weekly Newsp. 26. Yellow Page Adv.

OWENS CORNING
1 Owens Corning Pkwy
Toledo, OH 43659-1000
Tel.: (419) 248-8000
Fax: (419) 248-8445
Toll Free: (800) 438-7465
Toll Free: (800) GET-PINK
Web Site: www.owenscorning.com
Approx. Sls.: $4,997,000,000
Approx. Number Employees: 15,000
Year Founded: 1938
Business Description:
Glass Composites & Building Materials Systems Mfr
S.I.C.: 3296; 2952; 3221
N.A.I.C.S.: 327993; 324122; 327213
Import Export
Advertising Expenditures: $23,000,000
Media: 2-3-4-5-6-7-8-9-10-11-13-15-19-20-21-24
Distr.: Intl.
Personnel:
Michael H. Thaman *(Chm & CEO)*
Duncan Palmer *(CFO)*
Frank C. O'Brien-Bernini *(VP & Chief Sustainability Officer)*
John Hillenbrand *(Chief Innovation Officer & VP)*
Charles E. Dana *(Grp Pres-Building Matls)*
Arnaud Genis *(Grp Pres-Composite Solutions)*
John W. Christy *(Interim Gen Counsel)*
Daniel T. Smith *(Sr VP-HR)*
Curt A. Barker *(VP-Sls & Distr)*
Achilles Karagiozisas *(Dir-Building Science)*
Billy Lee *(Sls Mgr-Hong Kong)*
Beth Winkler *(Strategist-Mktg)*
Brands & Products:
AEROFLEX
AEROFLEX PLUS
AEROMAT
ATTIC BLANKET
BASEMENT BLANKET
BILD-R-TAPE
CLASSIC
CRATEC
CRATEC PLUS
CULTURED BRICK
CULTURED STONE
DURAFLEX
ENDURAGOLD
ESSENTIALS
EUROSPAN
FASTBATT
FIBERGLAS
FINISHING ELEMENTS
FLAKEGLAS
FOAMSEALR
FOAMULAR
FOLD-FORM
GENERATIONS
GLASLOCK
INNOVATION FOR LIVING
INSUL-QUICK
INSULPINK
INTERLOCKEN
MIRAFLEX
MIRAVISTA
OAKRIDGE
OAKRIDGE PRO
OWENS CORNING
PERMAMOP
PINK FIBERGLAS
PINKCORE
PINKPLUS
PINKSEAL
PINKWRAP
PROMINENCE
PROPINK
QUIETR
QUIETZONE
RAFT-R-MATE
RELIANCE
S-2 GLASS
SELECTSOUND
SILENTEX
SOFTR
SONOBATTS
SOUNDSOAK
STRATAGUARD
SYSTEM ADVANTAGE
SYSTEM THINKING
TERRA CRAFT
THERMOMAT
THERMORANGE
TRU-BOND
TRUFLOW
TRUGUARD
TRULO
TRUMBULL
TRUMELT
TRUPAVE
TYPE 30
VENTSURE
WEATHERLOCK
YELLOW JACKET
ZENTRON
Advertising Agency:
Doner
25900 Northwestern Hwy
Southfield, MI 48075
Tel.: (248) 354-9700
Fax: (248) 827-8440

P&H MINING EQUIPMENT
(Div. of Joy Global, Inc.)
4400 W National Ave
Milwaukee, WI 53214-3639
Tel.: (414) 671-4400
Fax: (414) 671-7604
E-mail: ph-min@hii.com
Web Site: www.phmining.com
Sales Range: $125-149.9 Million
Approx. Number Employees: 1,000
Year Founded: 1884
Business Description:
Mfr. of Electric Mining Shovels & Draglines, Hydraulic Mining Shovels & Electrical Components
S.I.C.: 3531
N.A.I.C.S.: 333120
Personnel:
Randal W. Baker *(Pres & COO)*
Dian Lene *(VP-Mktg)*
Advertising Agency:
Phoenix Marketing Group, Inc.
6750 Maple Terr
Milwaukee, WI 53213
Tel.: (414) 771-1044
Fax: (414) 771-1084

PACIFIC COLUMNS, INC.
505 W Lambert Rd
Brea, CA 92821
Tel.: (714) 257-9600
Fax: (714) 257-9628
Toll Free: (800) 294-1098
Web Site: www.pacificcolumns.com
E-Mail For Key Personnel:
Sales Director: sales@pacificcolumns.com
Sales Range: $10-24.9 Million
Approx. Number Employees: 65
Year Founded: 1998
Business Description:
Interior & Exterior Architectural Columns, Wainscoting & Wood Trim Online Sales
S.I.C.: 2541
N.A.I.C.S.: 337212
Media: 4-13
Personnel:
Robert Sellek *(CEO)*
Brands & Products:
ENDURA-CLASSIC
ENDURA-CRAFT
ENDURA-LUM
ENDURA-SERIES
ENDURA-STONE
PACIFIC COLUMNS
PREMIER SERIES
PREMIERE
SIGNATURE SERIES

PACIFIC HANDY CUTTER, INC.
(Holding of AMERICAN CAPITAL, LTD.)
2968 Randolph Ave
Costa Mesa, CA 92626-4312
Mailing Address:
PO Box 10869
Costa Mesa, CA 92627-0266
Tel.: (714) 662-1033
Fax: (714) 662-7595
Toll Free: (800) 229-2233
E-mail: info@pacifichandycutter.com
Web Site: www.go-phc.com
Sales Range: $50-74.9 Million
Approx. Number Employees: 55
Year Founded: 1950
Business Description:
Carton Cutter & Razor Blade Cutting Tools Mfr
S.I.C.: 3421; 3423
N.A.I.C.S.: 332211; 332212
Import Export
Advertising Expenditures: $800,000
Media: 1-4-6-10-20-21-26
Distr.: Intl.; Natl.
Budget Set: Quarterly
Brands & Products:
BLADE BANK
HANDY CUTTERS
HANDY HOOKER
HAVANA
LAZERBLADE
PACIFIC HANDY CUTTER
PHC BLADE BANK
PHC SAFETY COIN ROLL CUTTER
PROPREP
QUICK TRASH
QUICKBLADE
RAZE
S3 SAFETY CUTTERS
SAFETY COIN ROLL
SAFETY FIRST
SAFETY GRIP
SAFETY POINT
SNAPPY HOOKER
SPECTRUM TOOLS
STEEL TRACK
SUPERLITE
Advertising Agency:
Handy Cutter Line
2968 Randolph Ave
Costa Mesa, CA 92626-4312
Tel.: (714) 662-1033
Fax: (714) 662-7595
Toll Free: (800) 969-3322

PACIFIC NATIONAL GROUP INC.
2392 S Bateman Ave
Irwindale, CA 91010-3312
Tel.: (626) 357-4400
Fax: (626) 256-9580
E-mail: info@pacific-inc.com
Web Site: www.pacific-inc.com
Approx. Sls.: $34,023,839
Approx. Number Employees: 38
Year Founded: 1954
Business Description:
Commercial Building Construction Contractor
S.I.C.: 1522; 5032
N.A.I.C.S.: 236220; 423320
Import Export
Personnel:
Arden L. Boren *(Pres & CFO)*
Dick Stover *(VP & Mgr-Construction)*
Advertising Agency:
Sprokkit
333 S Grand Ave Ste 1600
Los Angeles, CA 90071
Tel.: (213) 626-2076
Fax: (231) 232-3739

PADDOCK POOL CONSTRUCTION COMPANY
6525 E Thomas Rd
Scottsdale, AZ 85251
Tel.: (480) 947-7261
Fax: (480) 970-7456
E-mail: info@paddockpoolsandspas.com
Web Site: www.paddockpoolsandspas.com
Approx. Number Employees: 500
Year Founded: 1958
Business Description:
Pool Sales & Mfr
S.I.C.: 1799; 5999
N.A.I.C.S.: 238990; 453998
Media: 4-10-13
Distr.: Natl.
Budget Set: Nov.
Personnel:
Jim Cich *(Pres & CEO)*
Sam Louis *(Sr VP-Construction Division)*
Brands & Products:
MDX
PADDOCK
PCC2000
PERMA DECK
WE'RE ALL YOUR BACKYARD NEEDS!
Advertising Agency:
The Lavidge Company
2777 E Camelback Rd Ste 300
Phoenix, AZ 85016
Tel.: (480) 998-2600
Fax: (480) 998-5525

PAN AMERICAN SILVER CORP.
625 Howe Street Suite 1500
Vancouver, BC V6C 2T6, Canada
Tel.: (604) 684-1175
Fax: (604) 684-0147
E-mail: info@panamericansilver.com
Web Site: www.panamericansilver.com
Approx. Sls.: $631,986,000
Approx. Number Employees: 4,600
Year Founded: 1994

Key to Media (For complete agency information see *The Advertising Red Books-Agencies* edition):
1. Bus. Publs. 2. Cable T.V. 3. Catalogs & Directories. 4. Co-op Adv. 5. Consumer Mags. 6. D.M. to Bus. Estab.7. D.M. to Consumers
8. Daily Newsp. 9. Exhibits/Trade Shows 10. Foreign 11. Infomercial 12. Internet Adv.13. Multimedia 14. Network Radio
15. Network T.V. 16. Newsp. Distr. Mags. 17. Other 18. Outdoor (Posters, Transit) 19. Point of Purchase20. Premiums, Novelties
21. Product Samples 22. Special Events Mktg. 23. Spot Radio 24. Spot T.V. 25. Weekly Newsp. 26. Yellow Page Adv.

Pan American Silver Corp. — (Continued)

Business Description:
Mining Services
S.I.C.: 1044; 1041
N.A.I.C.S.: 212222; 212221
Personnel:
Ross J. Beaty *(Chm & CEO)*
Geoffrey A. Burns *(Pres & CEO)*
G. Robert Doyle *(CFO)*
Steven Busby *(COO)*
Robert P. Pirooz *(Gen Counsel)*
Michael Steinmann *(Exec VP-Geology & Exploration)*
Andres Dasso *(Sr VP-Mining Ops)*
Sean McAleer *(VP-HR & Security)*
Ignacio Couturier *(Dir-Treasury)*
Marie Mohammed *(Dir-HR)*
Hik Park *(Dir-Internal Audit)*
Wade Stogran *(Dir-Environ Affairs)*
Rick Urenda *(Dir-Safety & Trng)*
Kettina Cordero *(Coord-IR)*
Advertising Agency:
BarnesMcInerney Inc.
120 Adelaide St W Ste 910
Toronto, ON M5H 3L5, Canada
Tel.: (416) 367-5000
Fax: (416) 367-5390

PANNEAUX TEMBEC-OSB INC.
(Sub. of Arbec Forest Products Inc.)
775 122nd Street
PO Box 40
Grand-Mere, QC G9T 5K7, Canada
Tel.: (819) 538-0735
Fax: (819) 538-0595
Toll Free: (888) 343-0735
Approx. Number Employees: 140
Year Founded: 1980
Business Description:
O.S.B. Mfr
S.I.C.: 2493
N.A.I.C.S.: 321219
Export
Advertising Expenditures: $500,000
Media: 5-7-10-21-26
Distr.: Natl.
Personnel:
Pierre Gingras *(Gen Mgr)*
Brands & Products:
MALETTE XTRA

PANOLAM INDUSTRIES INTERNATIONAL, INC.
(Joint Venture of Genstar Capital, LLC & The Sterling Group, L.P.)
(Filed Ch 11 Bankruptcy #913889 on 11/05/09 in U.S. Bankruptcy Ct, Dist of DE, Wilmington)
20 Progress Dr
Shelton, CT 06484-6216
Tel.: (203) 925-1556
Fax: (203) 225-0050
Toll Free: (800) 672-6652
Toll Free: (800) 746-6483
E-mail: info@panolam.com
Web Site: www.panolam.com
Approx. Sls.: $366,709,000
Approx. Number Employees: 242
Year Founded: 1997
Business Description:
Thermally Fused Melamine & HPL Designer, Mfr & Distr; Owned by Genstar Capital LLC & The Sterling Group, LP
S.I.C.: 2493; 3089
N.A.I.C.S.: 321219; 326199
Advertising Expenditures: $2,656,000
Personnel:
Robert Muller, Jr. *(Chm, Pres & CEO)*
Vincent S. Miceli *(CFO)*
Stephen Canary *(VP-Tech)*
Brands & Products:
CONOLITE
NEVAMAR
PIONITE
PLUSWOOD

PARISI INCORPORATED
(d/b/a Royal Store Fixture)
305 Pheasant Run
Newtown, PA 18940
Tel.: (215) 968-6677
Fax: (215) 968-3580
Toll Free: (800) 722-4481
E-mail: quality@parisi-royal.com
Web Site: www.parisi-royal.com
E-Mail For Key Personnel:
President: jparisi@fast.net
Sales Director: dmoore@parisi-royal.com
Approx. Number Employees: 50
Year Founded: 1962
Business Description:
Mfr of Store Fixtures & Refrigerator Showcases
S.I.C.: 2531; 2434
N.A.I.C.S.: 337127; 337110
Export
Media: 2-4-7-10
Distr.: Natl.
Personnel:
Jack Childs *(VP-Estimating & Engrg)*
Brands & Products:
PARISI
ROYAL

PARSONS & WHITTEMORE, INC.
4 Intl Dr Ste 5
Rye Brook, NY 10573
Tel.: (914) 937-9009
Fax: (914) 937-2259
Sales Range: $1-4.9 Billion
Approx. Number Employees: 30
Year Founded: 1909
Business Description:
Holding Company; Producer of Market Pulp
S.I.C.: 2611; 8711
N.A.I.C.S.: 322110; 541330
Media: 2-25
Distr.: Intl.; Natl.
Personnel:
Peggy Jaye *(Dir-Pub Rels)*

PARSONS BRINCKERHOFF INC.
(Sub. of Balfour Beatty plc)
1 Penn Plz
New York, NY 10119-0002
Tel.: (212) 465-5000
Fax: (212) 465-5096
Telex: RCA 232 117
E-mail: pbinfo@pbworld.com
Web Site: www.pbworld.com
Approx. Rev.: $2,340,000,000
Approx. Number Employees: 15,000
Year Founded: 1885
Business Description:
Engineering Services
S.I.C.: 8711
N.A.I.C.S.: 541330
Media: 2-10
Personnel:
Richard A. Schrader *(Chm)*
George J. Pierson *(CEO)*
John Murphy *(CFO)*
Scott Ney *(Principal-Engr & Sr Project Mgr)*
Kenneth Hopson *(Treas-Global & Sr VP-Fin)*
Juan Murillo *(Sr VP & Dir-Tech-Bridges)*
Jeff Morales *(Sr VP)*
Brian Tanberg *(VP-Tampa & Dir-Ports & Marine Practice-Southeast)*
Michael Kerry *(Reg Dir)*
Roger Rodiek *(Mgr-Bus Dev)*
Kevin J. Curran *(Dir)*
David A. McAlister *(Dir-Corp Dev)*
Chris R. O'Brien *(Dir-Bus Dev)*
Nick Randles *(Dir-Power Networks-EMEA)*
Ian Scholey *(Dir-Ops-Rail Grp-Europe & Africa)*
Mary Clayton *(Area Mgr)*
Robert Brooks *(Mgr-Natl Design Ops-Sports & Entertainment)*
Nicole Bucich *(Mgr-New York Metropolitan Plng & Environmental)*
Deborah Jasper *(Mgr-HR)*
Victoria Cross Kelly *(Mgr-Strategic Ops-Northeast Reg)*
Thomas W. Malcolm *(Mgr-Corp Comm)*
W. Stephen Dale *(Asst Gen Counsel-Litigation)*

PARSONS CORPORATION
100 W Walnut St
Pasadena, CA 91124-0001
Tel.: (626) 440-2000
Fax: (626) 440-2630
Web Site: www.parsons.com
Approx. Rev.: $3,400,000,000
Approx. Number Employees: 800
Year Founded: 1944
Business Description:
Engineering & Construction Services
S.I.C.: 1629; 1622
N.A.I.C.S.: 237990; 237310
Export
Media: 2
Personnel:
Charles L. Harrington *(Chm & CEO)*
Curtis A. Bower *(Vice Chm & Chief Risk Officer-Parsons Corporation)*
George Lester Ball *(CFO, Treas & Exec VP)*
Virginia Grebbien *(Pres-Parsons Water & Infrastructure Inc.)*
Dean Harwood *(Pres-Enterprises)*
Marty Fabrick *(Exec VP)*
Ruth McMorrow *(Exec VP-Enterprises)*
Stephen M. Shive *(Sr VP & Mgr)*
Maureen C. Hayes *(Sr VP)*
Avis Russell *(VP & Dir-Contracts & Procurement-Ops Shared Svcs)*
Erin Kuhlman *(VP-Pub Rel)*
Randy Britt *(Dir-Sustainability)*

PEERLESS FAUCET COMPANY
(Sub. of Delta Faucet Company)
55 E 111th St
Indianapolis, IN 46280-0980
Tel.: (317) 848-1812
Fax: (317) 848-0713
Toll Free: (800) 438-6673
Web Site: www.deltafaucet.com
Sales Range: $125-149.9 Million
Approx. Number Employees: 300
Year Founded: 1971
Business Description:
Faucets Mfr & Marketer
S.I.C.: 3432
N.A.I.C.S.: 332913
Media: 6-13
Personnel:
Keith Allman *(Pres)*
Brands & Products:
JUST WHAT YOU'RE LOOKING FOR
PEERLESS
SCALDGARD
Advertising Agency:
Young & Laramore
407 N Fulton St
Indianapolis, IN 46202
Tel.: (317) 264-8000
Fax: (317) 264-8002

PELLA CORPORATION
102 Main St
Pella, IA 50219-2147
Tel.: (641) 621-1000
Fax: (641) 628-6070
Toll Free: (888) 847-3552
E-mail: webinfo@pella.com
Web Site: www.pella.com
Approx. Rev.: $1,300,000,000
Approx. Number Employees: 9,000
Year Founded: 1925
Business Description:
Windows, Sliding Glass Doors, Skylights & Entrance Doors Mfr & Sales
S.I.C.: 2431; 3442
N.A.I.C.S.: 321911; 332321
Import Export
Media: 1-2-3-4-5-6-7-8-9-10-11-17-18-19-20-21-22-23-24-25-26
Distr.: Natl.
Budget Set: Oct.
Personnel:
Melvin Haught *(Pres & CEO)*
Danny Van Zanten *(Pres-Pella Heritage Div)*
Chris Simpson *(Sr VP-Mktg & Sls)*
Karin Peterson *(VP-HR)*
Elaine Sagers *(VP-Mktg & Customer Support)*
Kathy Harkema *(Mgr-Corp Pub Rels)*
Terry Zeimetz *(Mgr-Comml Market)*
Brands & Products:
ARCHITECT SERIES
CENTERA BY PELLA
DESIGNER SERIES
DURACAST
ENCOMPASS BY PELLA
ENDURACLAD
EXPRESS INSTALL
PELLA
PELLA IMPERVIA
PELLA ONE-TOUCH
PELLA'S PRECISION FIT
PROLINE
ROLSCREEN
SELECT
THERMASTAR BY PELLA
VIEWED TO BE THE BEST
Advertising Agencies:
BrandBuzz
285 Madison Ave 22nd Fl
New York, NY 10017
Tel.: (212) 210-3879
Fax: (212) 210-3878

The Integer Group-Midwest
2633 Fleur Dr
Des Moines, IA 50321-1753

Key to Media (For complete agency information see *The Advertising Red Books-Agencies* edition):
1. Bus. Publs. 2. Cable T.V. 3. Catalogs & Directories. 4. Co-op Adv. 5. Consumer Mags. 6. D.M. to Bus. Estab.7. D.M. to Consumers 8. Daily Newsp. 9. Exhibits/Trade Shows 10. Foreign 11. Infomercial 12. Internet Adv.13. Multimedia 14. Network Radio 15. Network T.V. 16. Newsp. Distr. Mags. 17. Other 18. Outdoor (Posters, Transit) 19. Point of Purchase20. Premiums, Novelties 21. Product Samples 22. Special Events Mktg. 23. Spot Radio 24. Spot T.V. 25. Weekly Newsp. 26. Yellow Page Adv.

Tel.: (515) 288-7910
Fax: (515) 288-8439
Toll Free: (800) 752-2633
(In-Store, Database & Relationship Marketing & Promotions)

Ketchum Directory Advertising/Kansas City
7015 College Blvd Ste 700
Overland Park, KS 66211-1524
Tel.: (913) 344-1900
Fax: (913) 344-1960
Toll Free: (800) 922-6977

MEC - NA HQ, New York
825 7th Ave
New York, NY 10019-5818
Tel.: (212) 474-0000
Fax: (212) 474-0003
Media Buying

PELLA ENTRY SYSTEMS DIVISION

(Div. of Pella Corporation)
7100 Dixie Hwy
Fairfield, OH 45014-5543
Tel.: (513) 870-3600
Fax: (513) 870-3602
Toll Free: (800) 883-6677
Web Site: www.pella.com
Approx. Number Employees: 330
Year Founded: 1893
Business Description:
Residential Steel, Carbon Entry Systems Mfr
S.I.C.: 2431
N.A.I.C.S.: 321911
Import
Advertising Expenditures: $700,000
Media: 1-2-4-5-6-7-8-10-18-19-20-21-23
Distr.: Natl.
Budget Set: Dec.
Personnel:
Rich Allen *(Pres)*
Neil Jackman *(VP-Sls)*
Brands & Products:
EVER STRAIT
HOMESTEAD
PEASE CARBON DOOR
PEASE SHIELD

PENCO PRODUCTS, INC.

(Sub. of International Manufacturing Company LLC)
(d/b/a IMC Metal Fabrication Group)
2024 Cressman Rd
Skippack, PA 19474
Mailing Address:
PO Box 158
Skippack, PA 19474-0158
Tel.: (610) 666-0500
Fax: (610) 666-7561
Toll Free: (800) 562-1000
E-mail: general@pencoproducts.com
Web Site: www.pencoproducts.com
Approx. Number Employees: 1,500
Year Founded: 1869
Business Description:
Fabricated Metal Storage & Material Handling Products Mfr
S.I.C.: 2542; 3499
N.A.I.C.S.: 337215; 332999
Media: 2-4-10-13
Distr.: Natl.
Brands & Products:
ALL-WELDED
ANGLE IRON
CLIPPER
ERECTOMATIC
GUARDIAN
INVINCIBLE II
PATRIOT
PROTOUGH
RIVETRITE
SMARTLOCKER
STADIUM
VANGUARD
WORKSAFE

PENFLEX, INC.

105-B Industrial Dr
Gilbertsville, PA 19525
Tel.: (610) 367-2260
Fax: (610) 367-2248
Toll Free: (800) 232-3539
E-mail: sales@penflex.com
Web Site: www.penflex.com
E-Mail For Key Personnel:
Sales Director: sales@penflex.com
Approx. Sls.: $2,500,000
Approx. Number Employees: 45
Year Founded: 1902
Business Description:
Flexible Metal Hose & Wire Braid Products Mfr
S.I.C.: 5084; 3569
N.A.I.C.S.: 423830; 333999
Media: 4-13
Distr.: Intl.; Natl.
Budget Set: Aug.
Personnel:
Nate Barker *(Owner)*
Robert Barker *(Pres)*
Brands & Products:
INTERLOK
P3
PENFLEX
SQUARELOK

PENTAIR WATER POOL AND SPA, INC.

(Formerly Paragon Aquatics)
(Div. of Pentair Pool Products, Inc.)
1351 Rte 55
Lagrangeville, NY 12540
Tel.: (845) 452-5500
Fax: (845) 452-5426
Web Site: www.pentairpool.com
Sales Range: $50-74.9 Million
Approx. Number Employees: 45
Year Founded: 1956
Business Description:
Commercial Swimming Pool Equipment Mfr
S.I.C.: 3444; 3446
N.A.I.C.S.: 332322; 332323
Export
Media: 2-4-6-7-11-13-20-22
Distr.: Direct to Consumer; Intl.; Natl.
Personnel:
Rita Heady *(Dir-Mktg)*
Brands & Products:
STARK

THE PERMENTRY COMPANY

(Sub. of The Bilco Company)
37 Water St
West Haven, CT 06516-3837
Mailing Address:
PO Box 1203
New Haven, CT 06505-1203
Tel.: (203) 934-9818
Fax: (203) 933-8478
Fax: (203) 931-4365
E-mail: bilco@bilco.com
Web Site: www.bilco.com
Approx. Number Employees: 80
Year Founded: 1926
Business Description:
Industrial Doors, Ladders, Window Wells, Roof Scuttles & Building Products Mfr
S.I.C.: 3442; 3446
N.A.I.C.S.: 332321; 332323
Advertising Expenditures: $500,000
Media: 2-4-6-9-10-18-19
Distr.: Reg.
Budget Set: Dec.
Personnel:
Robert Lyons *(Chm & Pres)*
Roger Joyce *(Vice Chm)*
Stephen Weyel *(Coord-Adv & Mktg)*
Advertising Agency:
Catalyst Marketing Communications Inc.
2777 Summer St Ste 301
Stamford, CT 06905
Tel.: (203) 348-7541
Fax: (203) 348-5688

PETERSEN ALUMINUM CORPORATION

1005 Tonne Rd
Elk Grove Village, IL 60007
Tel.: (847) 228-7150
Fax: (475) 696-7968 8479567968
Fax: (800) 722-7150
Toll Free: (800) PACCLAD
E-mail: manager@petersenmail.com
Web Site: www.pac-clad.com
E-Mail For Key Personnel:
President: mfpetersen@petersenmail.com
Sales Director: sales@petersenmail.com
Sales Range: $200-249.9 Million
Approx. Number Employees: 180
Year Founded: 1965
Business Description:
Warehousing; Fabrication of Aluminum & Steel Architectural Metals, Roll Formed Building Panels & Architectural Signage
S.I.C.: 3353; 3316
N.A.I.C.S.: 331315; 331221
Import Export
Media: 2-10
Personnel:
Michael Petersen *(Pres)*
Blake Batkoff *(Dir-Mktg & Sls)*
Brands & Products:
ARCHITEX
PAC-CLAD
REDI-ROOF
SNAP-CLAD
SNAP-ON
TITE-LOC

PGT, INC.

(Holding of JLL Partners Inc.)
1070 Technology Dr
North Venice, FL 34275
Tel.: (941) 480-1600
Fax: (941) 480-1900
Web Site: www.pgtindustries.com
Approx. Sls.: $175,741,000
Approx. Number Employees: 1,200
Year Founded: 2003
Business Description:
Holding Company; Impact-Resistant Windows & Doors Mfr
S.I.C.: 6719; 3442
N.A.I.C.S.: 551112; 332321
Advertising Expenditures: $200,000
Media: 3-15
Personnel:
Paul S. Levy *(Chm)*
Rodney Hershberger *(Pres & CEO)*
Jeffrey T. Jackson *(CFO & Exec VP)*
Mario Ferrucci, III *(Gen Counsel & VP)*
Debbie L. LaPinska *(VP-Sls & Mktg)*
Brands & Products:
EZE-BREEZE
NATURESCAPE
PGT
VISIBLY BETTER
WINGUARD
Advertising Agency:
Beber Silverstein Group
3361 SW 3rd Ave
Miami, FL 33145-3911
Tel.: (305) 856-9800
Fax: (305) 854-7686

PHANTOM MFG. (INTL.) LTD.

30451 Simpson Rd PO Box 1907
Abbotsford, BC Canada
Tel.: (604) 855-3654
Fax: (604) 855-7834
Toll Free: (888) PHANTOM
E-mail: phantom@phantomscreens.com
Web Site: www.phantomscreens.com
Approx. Number Employees: 100
Year Founded: 1992
Business Description:
Retractable Screen Solutions for Doors & Windows
S.I.C.: 3442
N.A.I.C.S.: 332321
Media: 6
Personnel:
Kenneth Rooke *(Owner)*
C. Esther De Wolde *(CEO)*
Ron Somers *(VP-Sls & Mktg)*

PIKE ELECTRIC CORPORATION

100 Pike Way
Mount Airy, NC 27030-8147
Mailing Address:
PO Box 868
Mount Airy, NC 27030-0868
Tel.: (336) 789-2171
Fax: (336) 719-4566
Toll Free: (800) 424-7453
E-mail: hr@pike.com
Web Site: www.pike.com
Approx. Rev.: $593,858,000
Approx. Number Employees: 4,600
Year Founded: 1945
Business Description:
Electrical Contracting Services
S.I.C.: 1731; 1623
N.A.I.C.S.: 238210; 237130
Import Export
Advertising Expenditures: $1,180,000
Personnel:
J. Eric Pike *(Chm, Pres & CEO)*
Anthony K. Slater *(CFO & Exec VP)*
Audie G. Simmons *(COO & Exec VP-Ops)*
Jeffrey Calhoun *(Chief Acctg Officer)*
James R. Fox *(Gen Counsel, Sec & VP-Risk Mgmt)*
James T. Benfield *(Sr VP-Ops)*
Jimmy R. Hicks *(Sr VP-Engrg & Substation Construction)*

Key to Media (For complete agency information see *The Advertising Red Books-Agencies* edition):
1. Bus. Publs. 2. Cable T.V. 3. Catalogs & Directories. 4. Co-op Adv. 5. Consumer Mags. 6. D.M. to Bus. Estab.7. D.M. to Consumers
8. Daily Newsp. 9. Exhibits/Trade Shows 10. Foreign 11. Infomercial 12. Internet Adv.13. Multimedia 14. Network Radio
15. Network T.V. 16. Newsp. Distr. Mags. 17. Other 18. Outdoor (Posters, Transit) 19. Point of Purchase20. Premiums, Novelties
21. Product Samples 22. Special Events Mktg. 23. Spot Radio 24. Spot T.V. 25. Weekly Newsp. 26. Yellow Page Adv.

Pike Electric Corporation — (Continued)

Brands & Products:
KLONDYKE
PIKE
PIKE ELECTRIC
PIKE ENERGY SOLUTIONS

PIONEER PLASTICS CORPORATION

(Joint Venture of Genstar Capital, LLC & The Sterling Group, L.P.)
1 Pionite Road
Auburn, ME 04211-1014
Tel.: (207) 784-9111
Fax: (207) 784-0392
Toll Free: (800) 746-6483
E-mail: info@pionite.com
Web Site: www.pionite.com/frl/environmental/index.html
Approx. Number Employees: 700
Year Founded: 1946
Business Description:
Laminate Mfr
S.I.C.: 3083
N.A.I.C.S.: 326130
Import Export
Media: 2-4-7-10-20-21-22
Distr.: Natl.
Budget Set: Nov.
Personnel:
Robert J. Muller *(Pres & CEO)*
Advertising Agency:
The BCB Group, Inc.
10 Alexander Dr
Wallingford, CT 06492
Tel.: (203) 630-7800
Fax: (203) 630-7805

P.J. DICK-TRUMBULL-LINDY

225 North Shore Dr
Pittsburgh, PA 15212
Tel.: (412) 462-9300
Fax: (412) 807-2020
Web Site: www.pjdick.com
Approx. Number Employees: 400
Year Founded: 1979
Business Description:
Heavy Building Contractors
S.I.C.: 1522; 8748
N.A.I.C.S.: 236220; 541618
Media: 2-4-7-10
Distr.: Natl.
Personnel:
George E. Mezey *(Pres)*
Clifford R. Rowe *(CEO)*
Stephen M. Clark *(Exec VP-Fin)*
Bernie Kobosky *(Mgr-Mktg)*

PLIBRICO CO. LLC

1010 N Hooker St
Chicago, IL 60622-4220
Tel.: (312) 337-9000
Fax: (312) 337-9003
E-mail: info@plibrico-usa.com
Web Site: www.plibrico-usa.com
Sales Range: $25-49.9 Million
Approx. Number Employees: 1,100
Year Founded: 1914
Business Description:
Monolithic Refractories Mfr & Other Monolithic Refractory Technology Services
S.I.C.: 1711; 1741
N.A.I.C.S.: 238220; 238140
Advertising Expenditures: $355,000
Media: 1-2-4-7-10-20-26
Distr.: Intl.; Natl.
Budget Set: Nov.
Personnel:
Jim Eckert *(Pres)*
Joseph Milas *(CFO)*
Kevin Layton *(Gen Mgr)*
Brands & Products:
AL-SHIELD
ALL-TUFF
DEMON
EXO-SET UNO
HYMOR
HYRATE
HYREZIST
INDUC-E-COOL
INJEC-TITE
LWI
PETRO-MIX
PLI-FLOW
PLIBRICO
PLICAST
PLIGUN
PLISTIX
PLISULATE
REDI-SHAPE

PLUM CREEK TIMBER COMPANY, INC.

Ste 4300 999 3rd Ave
Seattle, WA 98104-4096
Tel.: (206) 467-3600
Fax: (206) 467-3795
Toll Free: (800) 858-5347
E-mail: info@plumcreek.com
Web Site: www.plumcreek.com
Approx. Rev.: $1,190,000,000
Approx. Number Employees: 647
Year Founded: 1989
Business Description:
Lumber Milling; Timber Tracts
S.I.C.: 0811; 2421; 2611
N.A.I.C.S.: 113110; 321912; 322110
Export
Advertising Expenditures: $1,400,000
Media: 2-7-9-19-25
Distr.: Natl.
Budget Set: Sept.
Personnel:
John F. Morgan, Sr. *(Chm)*
Rick R. Holley *(Pres & CEO)*
David W. Lambert *(CFO & Sr VP)*
Thomas M. Lindquist *(COO & Exec VP)*
James A. Kraft *(Gen Counsel, Sec & Sr VP)*
James A. Kilberg *(Sr VP-Real Estate)*
Larry D. Neilson *(Sr VP-Bus Dev)*
Barbara L. Crowe *(VP-HR)*
Joan K. Fitzmaurice *(VP-Corp Comm, Audit & IT)*
Rosemary Daszkiewicz *(Sr Dir-Law)*
Kathy Budinick *(Dir-Comm)*
Brands & Products:
GLACIER CLEAR
GLACIER GREEN
GROWING VALUE FROM EXCEPTIONAL RESOURCES
MARINE DECK
PLUM CREEK
SUPER-REFINED MDF2
ULTRA-POUR

PLY GEM SIDING GROUP

(Sub. of Alcoa Inc.)
2600 Grand Blvd Ste 900
Kansas City, MO 64108
Tel.: (412) 249-6000
Fax: (412) 249-6059
Toll Free: (800) 962-6973
Toll Free: (800) 788-1964
E-mail: support@alcoahomesinfo.com
Web Site: www.alcoahomes.com
Sales Range: $1-4.9 Billion
Approx. Number Employees: 3,000
Year Founded: 1986
Business Description:
Mfr. of Residential Aluminum & Vinyl Siding & Other Building Products.
S.I.C.: 3353; 3081
N.A.I.C.S.: 331315; 326113
Export
Media: 2-4-7-10-15
Distr.: Natl.
Personnel:
Gary Acinapura *(Pres)*
Brands & Products:
BRENTWOOD
CARVEDWOOD2 SERIES
CEDAR DISCOVERY
CHARLESTON BEADED COLLECTION
DUTCH OAK
GRAND SIERRA
HORIZON COLLECTION
LEAF RELIEF
LIBERTY ELITE
MEADOWBROOK
MILL CREEK
OASIS
QUEST
QUEST3
RUSTIC
SILHOUETTE CLASSIC
STRUCTURE
T-LOK
TRADE MARK
TRADITIONAL SELECT

POGGENPOHL U.S., INC.

(Sub. of Poggenpohl GmbH)
350 Passaic Ave
Fairfield, NJ 07004
Tel.: (973) 812-8900
Fax: (973) 812-9320
Toll Free: (800) 987-0553
E-mail: info@poggenpohl-usa.com
Web Site: www.poggenpohl-usa.com
Sales Range: $25-49.9 Million
Approx. Number Employees: 25
Year Founded: 1888
Business Description:
Kitchen & Bath Cabinets Distr
S.I.C.: 2434
N.A.I.C.S.: 337110
Media: 4-5-6-7-8-10-13-14-16-26
Distr.: Natl.
Budget Set: Sept.
Personnel:
Ted Chappel *(Pres)*
Janine Flamer *(Dir-Mktg & PR)*
Advertising Agency:
Poggenpohl Advertising Group
350 Passaic Ave
Fairfield, NJ 07004-2007
Tel.: (973) 812-8900
Fax: (973) 812-9320
Toll Free: (800) 987-0553

POLYCOR INC.

139 rue Saint-Pierre
Quebec, QC G1K 8B9, Canada
Tel.: (418) 692-4695
Fax: (418) 692-0981
E-mail: info@polycor.com
Web Site: www.polycor.com
Approx. Number Employees: 500
Year Founded: 1884
Business Description:
Natural Stone Products
S.I.C.: 1411
N.A.I.C.S.: 212311
Export
Media: 1-4-7-10-11
Personnel:
Irenee Bouchard *(Chm & CEO)*
Patrick Perus *(Pres & CEO)*
Clermont Perron *(Sr VP)*
Sandra Leclerc *(Corp Controller)*

POTTERS INDUSTRIES, INC.

(Sub. of PQ Corporation)
1200 W Swedesford Rd
Berwyn, PA 19312
Mailing Address:
PO Box 840
Valley Forge, PA 19482-0840
Tel.: (610) 651-4700
Fax: (610) 408-9724
Toll Free: (800) 55BEADS
Telex: 219054 POTTR VR
Web Site: www.pottersbeads.com
Approx. Number Employees: 650
Year Founded: 1914
Business Description:
Engineered Glass Materials Mfr
S.I.C.: 3231
N.A.I.C.S.: 327215
Import Export
Advertising Expenditures: $300,000
Media: 2-4-10-20-21-26
Distr.: Intl.; Natl.
Budget Set: Oct.
Personnel:
Scott Randolph *(Pres)*
Brands & Products:
BALLOTINI
CONDUCT-O-FIL
EXPANDING YOUR UNIVERSE
LUXSIL
Q-CEL
SPHERICEL
SPHERIGLASS
VISIBEAD
VISIGUN

POWER ENGINEERS, INC.

3940 Glenbrook Dr
Hailey, ID 83333-8446
Tel.: (208) 788-3456
Fax: (208) 788-2082
Web Site: www.powereng.com
Approx. Number Employees: 2,000
Year Founded: 1976
Business Description:
Provider of Engineering Services
S.I.C.: 8711
N.A.I.C.S.: 541330
Import Export
Personnel:
Jack Hand *(Pres)*
Advertising Agency:
Stoltz Marketing Group
615 W Main St 2nd Fl
Boise, ID 83702
Tel.: (208) 388-0766
Fax: (208) 388-0764

POWERSECURE INTERNATIONAL, INC.

1609 Heritage Commerce Ct
Wake Forest, NC 27587
Tel.: (919) 556-3056
Fax: (919) 556-3596
Toll Free: (866) 347-5455

E-mail: info@powersecure.com
Web Site: www.powersecure.com
Approx. Rev.: $97,514,000
Approx. Number Employees: 390
Year Founded: 1991
Business Description:
Gas Meter Monitoring Services
S.I.C.: 3533; 1389; 3586; 7389
N.A.I.C.S.: 561421; 213112; 333132; 333913; 541990
Advertising Expenditures: $535,000
Personnel:
Sidney Hinton *(Pres & CEO)*
Christopher T. Hutter *(CFO)*
Gary J. Zuiderveen *(Principal Acctg Officer, Treas, Sec, Controller & VP-Fin)*
Brands & Products:
POWERSECURE

PRECISION CASTPARTS CORP.
4650 SW Macadam Ave Ste 440
Portland, OR 97239-4262
Tel.: (503) 417-4800
Fax: (503) 417-4817
E-mail: info@precastcorp.com
Web Site: www.precast.com
Approx. Sls.: $6,220,100,000
Approx. Number Employees: 18,300
Year Founded: 1953
Business Description:
Metal Components, Investment Castings, Fasteners, Airfoils, Specialty Alloys, Sewer Systems & Precision Tools Mfr
S.I.C.: 3325; 3364; 3452; 3511; 3544; 3721; 3724; 3728; 8733
N.A.I.C.S.: 331513; 331522; 332722; 333511; 333514; 333611; 336411; 336412; 336413; 541710
Import Export
Media: 2-4-10-21
Distr.: Natl.
Personnel:
Mark Donegan *(Chm)*
Steven G. Hackett *(Pres & Exec VP)*
Shawn R. Hagel *(CFO & Sr VP)*
Byron J. Gaddis *(CIO & VP)*
Kenneth D. Buck *(Pres-PCC Airfoils & Wyman-Gordon & Exec VP)*
Joseph I. Snowden *(Pres-Special Metals Corp & Sr VP)*
Roger A. Cooke *(Gen Counsel & Sr VP)*
Kevin M. Stein *(Exec VP)*
John W. Ericksen *(Sr VP-Corp Trng & Org Dev)*
Brands & Products:
AEREX
ASTRO PUNCH
BRIGHTRAY
CHERRYBUCK
CHERRYMAX
E-NUT
FLEXLOC
FORCEMATE
FORCETEC
GROMEX
HI-LIFE
HI-LITE
HI-LOK
INCOLOY
INCONEL
MADE FROM SOLID
MATHREAD
MAXIBOLT
MONEL
MORTORQ
MP159
MP35N
MULTIPHASE
NILO
NIMONIC
PCC
PRECISION CASTPARTS
SLEEVBOLT
STA-LOK
TAPTITE
TELLEP
TORX
TORX-PLUS
TUKLOC
UDIMET

PRIMESOURCE BUILDING PRODUCTS, INC.
(Sub. of ITOCHU International Inc.)
2115 E Belt Line Rd
Carrollton, TX 75006-5624
Tel.: (972) 417-3701
Fax: (972) 416-3910
E-mail: webmaster@primesourcebp.com
Web Site: www.primesourcebp.com
Approx. Number Employees: 100
Business Description:
Building Products Whslr Fasteners, Tools, Compressors Hardware & Wire
S.I.C.: 5031
N.A.I.C.S.: 423310
Media: 2-9-25-26
Personnel:
Ken Fishbein *(Co-CEO)*
Mona Zinman *(Co-CEO)*
Jerry Kegley *(CFO & Sr VP)*
Linda Garziano *(Dir-Mktg)*
Advertising Agency:
Martino & Binzer
270 Farmington Ave Ste 128
Farmington, CT 06032
Tel.: (860) 678-4300
Fax: (860) 678-4301

PRO-TECH INDUSTRIES, INC.
8550 Younger Creek Dr
Sacramento, CA 95828
Tel.: (916) 504-4044
Fax: (916) 504-4048
E-mail: dgordon@pro-techind.com
Web Site: www.pro-techind.com
Approx. Rev.: $13,890,892
Approx. Number Employees: 85
Year Founded: 2007
Business Description:
Fire Protection, Life Safety, Alarm, Detection, Electrical, Voice & Data Communications Infrastructure Building Services
S.I.C.: 1731; 1623; 7382; 9224
N.A.I.C.S.: 238210; 237130; 561621; 922160
Advertising Expenditures: $22,084
Media: 17
Personnel:
Donald Gordon *(CEO & Dir)*
Michael Walsh *(CFO)*

PURE AIRE CORPORATION
2219 Agate Ct
Simi Valley, CA 93065-1839
Tel.: (805) 527-1622
Fax: (805) 527-2664
E-mail: info@pureaire.com
Web Site: www.pureaire.com
Approx. Number Employees: 8
Year Founded: 1963
Business Description:
Mfr. of Controlled Atmosphere & Semiconductor Wafer Processing Equipment
S.I.C.: 3559; 3564
N.A.I.C.S.: 333295; 333411
Export
Media: 2-13
Distr.: Natl.
Personnel:
Michael Sutcliffe *(Pres)*
Brands & Products:
PURE AIRE

PYRAMID MOULDINGS
300 S Magnolia Ave
Green Cove Springs, FL 32043
Tel.: (904) 284-5611
Fax: (904) 284-1705
E-mail: info@pyramidmouldings.com
Web Site: www.pyramidmouldings.com
Approx. Number Employees: 100
Year Founded: 1928
Business Description:
Mfr. of Roll-Formed Stainless & Carbon Steel Products for Architectural, Appliance, Luggage, Office Furniture & Other Industries
S.I.C.: 3449
N.A.I.C.S.: 332114
Media: 4-13
Distr.: Natl.
Budget Set: Nov.
Personnel:
Ronald Martin *(Pres & CEO)*
William D. Munch *(VP-Sls & Mktg)*
Erwin J. Walz *(VP-HR)*

QUEENSTON MINING INC.
Suite 1116 111 Richmond Street West
Toronto, ON M5H 2G4, Canada
Tel.: (416) 364-0001
Fax: (416) 364-5098
E-mail: info@queenston.ca
Web Site: www.queenston.ca
Approx. Rev.: $387,582
Year Founded: 1990
Business Description:
Gold & Base Metal Mining Services
S.I.C.: 1099; 1041
N.A.I.C.S.: 212299; 212221
Media: 2-9-10-23
Personnel:
Hugh D. Harbinson *(Chm)*
Charles E. Page *(Pres & CEO)*
John A. Francis *(CFO)*
Michel Leblanc *(Mgr-Exploration)*

QUIKRETE COMPANIES
3490 Piedmont Rd NE Ste 1300
Atlanta, GA 30305-4811
Tel.: (404) 634-9100
Fax: (404) 842-1424
Toll Free: (800) 282-5828
E-mail: careers@quikrete.com
Web Site: www.quikrete.com
Sales Range: $100-124.9 Million
Approx. Number Employees: 2,500
Year Founded: 1940
Business Description:
Pre-Mixed Concrete Products
S.I.C.: 3299; 3255
N.A.I.C.S.: 327999; 327124
Export
Advertising Expenditures: $1,000,000
Media: 3-6-17-18-21-26
Distr.: Natl.
Personnel:
James E. Winchester *(Pres)*
Dennis Winchester *(Exec VP)*
John O. Winchester *(Exec VP)*
Brands & Products:
AQUABLEND
AQUALIGHT
BB GUN-ITE
BBOND
BBOND MS
BLOCBOND
BOND LOK
FASTSET
GUN-ITE
GUN-ITE MS
QUIK-TUBE
QUIKRETE
QUIKTUBE
QUIKWALL
STEPMAKER
THERMO-LUBE
THIN SET
TRAFFIC TOP
TUBESAND
WALK MAKER
Advertising Agency:
Fitzgerald+CO
3060 Peachtree Rd NW
Atlanta, GA 30305
Tel.: (404) 504-6900
Fax: (404) 239-0548

RAYNOR GARAGE DOORS
(Sub. of Neisewander Enterprises Inc.)
1101 E River Rd
Dixon, IL 61021-3252
Mailing Address:
PO Box 448
Dixon, IL 61021-0448
Tel.: (815) 288-1431
Fax: (815) 288-7142
Toll Free: (800) 472-9667
E-mail: thegarage@raynor.com
Web Site: www.raynor.com
Approx. Number Employees: 755
Year Founded: 1944
Business Description:
Overhead & Garage Doors Mfr
S.I.C.: 3442; 7011
N.A.I.C.S.: 332321; 721110
Import Export
Advertising Expenditures: $1,500,000
Media: 1-2-4-5-6-7-10-13-18-19-20-21-22-23-26
Distr.: Natl.
Budget Set: Oct.
Personnel:
Ray H. Neisewander, III *(Pres & CEO)*
Denny Ruetten *(Sr VP-Ops)*
Brands & Products:
AMERICAN RIVERS
DECADE SHOWCASE WITH ENDURACOTE
FEATHERLITE
FLITE STAR
RAYNOR
SURETEST
TRI-CORE

R.D. BITZER CO. INC.
776 American Dr
Bensalem, PA 19020-7342
Tel.: (215) 604-6600
Fax: (215) 604-6601
E-mail: sales@rdbitzer.com
Web Site: www.rdbitzer.com

Key to Media (For complete agency information see *The Advertising Red Books-Agencies* edition):
1. Bus. Publs. 2. Cable T.V. 3. Catalogs & Directories. 4. Co-op Adv. 5. Consumer Mags. 6. D.M. to Bus. Estab.7. D.M. to Consumers
8. Daily Newsp. 9. Exhibits/Trade Shows 10. Foreign 11. Infomercial 12. Internet Adv.13. Multimedia 14. Network Radio
15. Network T.V. 16. Newsp. Distr. Mags. 17. Other 18. Outdoor (Posters, Transit) 19. Point of Purchase20. Premiums, Novelties
21. Product Samples 22. Special Events Mktg. 23. Spot Radio 24. Spot T.V. 25. Weekly Newsp. 26. Yellow Page Adv.

R.D. Bitzer Co. Inc. — (Continued)

E-Mail For Key Personnel:
Sales Director: sales@rdbitzer.com
Sales Range: $10-24.9 Million
Approx. Number Employees: 25
Year Founded: 1929
Business Description:
Plumbing & Heating Equipment Distr
S.I.C.: 5074; 5084
N.A.I.C.S.: 423720; 423830
Advertising Expenditures: $400,000
Media: 5-10-17-26
Distr.: Natl.
Personnel:
John H. Bitzer *(Pres)*
William Bitzer *(CEO)*
Mike Deluca *(Mgr-Acctg)*
Brian Taylor *(Mgr-Svc)*

RED METAL RESOURCES LTD.

195 Park Avenue
Thunder Bay, ON P7B 1B9, Canada
Tel.: (807) 345-5380
E-mail: invest@redmetalresources.com
Web Site: www.redmetalresources.com
Business Description:
Copper & Gold Mining Services
S.I.C.: 1021; 1041
N.A.I.C.S.: 212234; 212221
Advertising Expenditures: $111,835
Media: 17
Personnel:
Caitlin Jeffs *(Pres, CEO & Sec)*
John Da Costa *(CFO & Treas)*
Adam Rabiner *(Dir-Corp Comm)*

REDBUILT LLC

(Holding of Atlas Holdings LLC)
200 E Mallard Dr
Boise, ID 83706
Tel.: (208) 364-1316
Fax: (208) 364-1300
Web Site: www.redbuilt.com
E-Mail For Key Personnel:
President: FultonD@trusjoist.com
Sales Range: $100-124.9 Million
Approx. Number Employees: 235
Year Founded: 1969
Business Description:
Engineered Structural Wood Products Designer, Mfr & Distr
S.I.C.: 2439
N.A.I.C.S.: 321214; 321213
Export
Distr.: Intl.
Personnel:
Tom Denig *(Chm & Mgr-Comml Resources)*
William Walters *(Vice Chm & Mgr-Comml Resources)*
Kurt Liebich *(CEO & Mgr-Comml Resources)*
Bruce Murphy *(CFO & Sr VP-Comml Resources)*
Daniel Cromie *(Sec, Treas & Mgr-Comml Resources)*
Ted Osterberger *(Sr VP-Engrg & Comml Resources)*
Randy Ruim *(Sr VP-Sls & Mktg-Comml Resources)*
Brands & Products:
RED-I
REDBUILT
REDLAM
Advertising Agency:
Stoltz Marketing Group
615 W Main St 2nd Fl
Boise, ID 83702
Tel.: (208) 388-0766
Fax: (208) 388-0764

REGAL BELOIT CORPORATION

200 State St
Beloit, WI 53511-6254
Tel.: (608) 364-8800
Fax: (608) 364-8818
E-mail: regal@regal-beloit.com
Web Site: www.regalbeloit.com
Approx. Sls.: $2,237,978,000
Approx. Number Employees: 18,500
Year Founded: 1955
Business Description:
Power Transmission Systems & High-Speed Steel Rotary Cutting Tools Mfr
S.I.C.: 3621; 3566; 3568
N.A.I.C.S.: 335312; 333612; 333613
Export
Advertising Expenditures: $300,000
Multimedia: $1,000; Bus. Publs.: $49,000; Catalogs & Directories: $175,000; Co-op Adv.: $20,000; D.M. to Bus. Estab.: $30,000; Exhibits/Trade Shows: $20,000; Premiums, Novelties: $4,000; Yellow Page Adv.: $1,000
Distr.: Natl.
Budget Set: Nov.
Personnel:
Henry W. Knueppel *(Chm & CEO)*
Mark J. Gliebe *(Pres)*
Charles A. Hinrichs *(CFO & VP)*
Jonathan J. Schlemmer *(COO)*
Peter J. Rowley *(Chief Acctg Officer, VP & Corp Controller)*
Peter C. Underwood *(Gen Counsel, Sec & VP)*
Charlotte Gabet *(Brand Mgr-HVACR)*
Brands & Products:
AT THE HEART OF WHAT DRIVES YOUR WORLD
BALL SCREW ACTUATED CLUTCH
BCC TAP
BLUE MAX
CAPITOL GEARS
CARBO CLAD
CENTURY XL END MILLS
CML
CNC INTERTAP
CNC/XL
CNC/XM TAPS
CREST-KUT
DIXECON
DIXIE CARBIDE
DIXIE DYNA-DRILLS
DIXIE DYNA-MILLS
DIXIE DYNA-REAMERS
DREAM-EZE
DURST
ELECTRA-GEAR
ELECTRACK
FAST TAP
FLEX-A-DRIVE
FLEX-A-MOUNT
FLEX-IN-LINE
FLEXACLEAN
FLEXALINE
FOOTE-JONES
GLENBARD REAMERS
GROVE GEAR
HELIX 2000
HUB CITY
HYDROSMOOTH
ILLINOIS GEAR
LEESON ELECTRIC
MARATHON
MARATHON ELECTRIC
MASTERGEAR
MET-FLO
MINA GEAR
MULTI FLUTE CHAMFER-SINK
NATIONAL GOLD
NOSTER
OPPERMAN MASTERGEAR
PATERSON
RADIAL TAPER PIPE TAP
REAM-EZE
REGAL
REGAL CUTTING TOOLS
REGAL GOLD
REGAL-LINE
REGAL PREMIUM
REGAL RAPID ROUTER
RICHMOND GEAR
ROCKET TAP
SINGLE TAPERED BUSHING
SKEW-SHEAR
SOLENOID ACTUATED MECHANICAL CLUTCH COMBINATION
SUPER TUF CUT END MILLS
TANDEM UNIPASS ACME TAP
THOMSON TECHNOLOGIES
UNI-DRILL
UNICOMB
UNILINE
UNIPASS DRILL 'N' TAP
UNIPASS TAPER PIPE DRILL 'N' TAP
VELVET DRIVE
XM SERIES END MILL
XP/PM
XP/PMC
Z SERIES

THE REINFORCED EARTH COMPANY

8614 Westwood Center Dr Ste 1100
Vienna, VA 22182-2233
Fax: (703) 821-1815
Toll Free: (800) 446-5700
Web Site: www.reinforcedearth.com
Business Description:
Retaining Wall Systems, Reflective & Absorptive Sound Walls, Precast Arches & Slope Stabilization Systems Constructor
S.I.C.: 1629
N.A.I.C.S.: 237990
Media: 10
Personnel:
Kim Britton *(Mgr-HR)*

REPUBLIC SERVICES, INC.

18500 N Allied Way
Phoenix, AZ 85054
Tel.: (480) 627-2700
Toll Free: (877) 241-8396
E-mail: corporateoffice@republicservices.com
Web Site: www.republicservices.com
Approx. Rev.: $8,106,600,000
Approx. Number Employees: 30,000
Year Founded: 1996
Business Description:
Solid Waste Disposal & Recyling Services
S.I.C.: 4953; 4212; 8748
N.A.I.C.S.: 562211; 541690; 562111
Media: 10-18-22
Personnel:
James E. O'Connor *(Chm & CEO)*
Donald W. Slager *(Pres & CEO)*
Tod C. Holmes *(CFO)*
William G. Halnon *(CIO & Sr VP)*
Charles F. Serianni *(Chief Acctg Officer & Sr VP)*
Michael Rissman *(Gen Counsel, Sec & Exec VP)*
Brian A. Bales *(Exec VP-Bus Dev)*
William C. Flower *(Exec VP-Comm)*
Jeffrey A. Hughes *(Exec VP-HR)*
Gary L. Sova *(Exec VP-Mktg & Sls)*
Jeffrey D. Andrews *(Sr VP-Western Ops)*
Ronald R. Krall *(Sr VP-East Reg)*
Edward A. Lang, III *(Sr VP)*
Christopher R. Synek *(Sr VP)*
James G. Van Weelden *(Sr VP-Republic Svc)*
Brands & Products:
ADDING VALUE AT EVERY STOP!

REPUBLIC STORAGE SYSTEMS, LLC

(Holding of Versa Capital Management, Inc.)
1038 Belden Ave NE
Canton, OH 44705-1459
Tel.: (330) 438-5800
Fax: (330) 454-7772
Toll Free: (800) 477-1255
E-mail: humanres@republicstorage.com
Web Site: www.republicstorage.com
E-Mail For Key Personnel:
Marketing Director: marketing@republicstorage.com
Sales Director: sales@republicstorage.com
Sales Range: $50-74.9 Million
Approx. Number Employees: 500
Year Founded: 1886
Business Description:
Mfr of Lockers, Shelving, Metal Cabinets & Storage Racks
S.I.C.: 2542; 3441
N.A.I.C.S.: 337215; 332312
Export
Media: 1-2-4-5-7-8-10-13-20-21-26
Distr.: Direct to Consumer; Natl.
Budget Set: Oct.
Brands & Products:
CLERESPAN
REPUBLIC

RESCO PRODUCTS GREENSBORO

(Div. of Resco Products, Inc.)
3514 W Wendover Ave
Greensboro, NC 27407
Mailing Address:
PO Box 7247
Greensboro, NC 27417-0247
Tel.: (336) 299-1441
Fax: (336) 854-5916
Toll Free: (800) 334-5578
Approx. Number Employees: 85
Business Description:
Refractories Mfr
S.I.C.: 3295; 5085
N.A.I.C.S.: 327992; 423840
Import Export
Advertising Expenditures: $300,000
Bus. Publs.: $300,000
Distr.: Intl.; Natl.
Budget Set: Aug.

Key to Media (For complete agency information see *The Advertising Red Books-Agencies* edition):
1. Bus. Publs. 2. Cable T.V. 3. Catalogs & Directories. 4. Co-op Adv. 5. Consumer Mags. 6. D.M. to Bus. Estab.7. D.M. to Consumers
8. Daily Newsp. 9. Exhibits/Trade Shows 10. Foreign 11. Infomercial 12. Internet Adv.13. Multimedia 14. Network Radio
15. Network T.V. 16. Newsp. Distr. Mags. 17. Other 18. Outdoor (Posters, Transit) 19. Point of Purchase20. Premiums, Novelties
21. Product Samples 22. Special Events Mktg. 23. Spot Radio 24. Spot T.V. 25. Weekly Newsp. 26. Yellow Page Adv.

Personnel:
Kevin Frederes *(Mgr-Sls & Mktg)*
Brands & Products:
PACO

RESCO PRODUCTS, INC.
2 Penn Ctr W Ste 430
Pittsburgh, PA 15276
Tel.: (412) 494-4491
Fax: (412) 494-4571
Fax: (412) 294-1080 (Sales)
Toll Free: (888) 283-5505
E-mail: sales@rescoproducts.com
Web Site: www.rescoproducts.com
E-Mail For Key Personnel:
Sales Director: sales@rescoproducts.com
Approx. Rev.: $50,000,000
Approx. Number Employees: 75
Year Founded: 1946
Business Description:
Refractories, Brick & Ceramic Minerals Mfr & Sales
S.I.C.: 3297; 3255
N.A.I.C.S.: 327125; 327124
Export
Media: 2-4-10-20
Distr.: Intl.; Natl.
Personnel:
William K. Brown *(Pres & CEO)*
Timothy J. Powell *(CFO & VP-Fin)*
John Castilano *(COO)*
Richard W. Copp *(VP-Sls & Mktg)*
Brands & Products:
ADACOR
ADAMANT
ADAPHOS
ADASET
AL-MAX
ALKATROL
ALUMEX
ANDAFRAC
CERAMIC CLAYS
COELEX
CONDOR
CORLINE
CORMAG
CORPATCH
DIBOND
DURA-TAB
DURALITE
EAGLE
EXCELBOND
EXCELINE
EZ CAST
EZ CUBED
FERROX X
FREENFREE
FURN-A-RAM
FURNACON
FURNACUBED
FURNAL
FURNALITE
FURNASCRETE
GC SAKONITE
GREENFREE
GUIDON
HARKLASE
HELSPOR
HELSPOT
HI-ALMAX
HI-ALMAX DRY
HI-RAM
HI-STRENGTH
HILO-AL
HILOBOND
HOTZONE
KRIAL
KRICON
KRICOR
KRILENE
KRILEX
KRILINE
KRIMUL
KRITAB
KROMAG
LADLELINE
LADLEMAX
LARCOBOND
LO-ERODE
LO-SET
LO-SIL
LOFERO
LOFERO HM
MAG-FLUX
MAGNESITE
MAXBOND
MAXLINE
MEGOLITE
METALDAM
MONO
MONO GUN
NARCAL
NOVAL
NOVUS
NUCON
NULINE
OCEANITE
OXILINE
PACO
PACO MIX
PACOCAST
PATRIOT
PERATEX
PERECON
PERICLASE
PERMA-PATCH
PERMA-STAR
PERMACAST
PERMACON
PERMAGUN
PERMANENTE
PHASCAST
PHASGUN
PROCAST
PROGUN
PUROCAST
PUROCRETE
PUROLITE
PUROTAB
PYROCAST
PYROFRAC
PYROPHYL
PYROSET
PYROTROL
QUIKTURN
R-MAX
RESCAL
RESCO
RESCOAT
RESCOBOND
RESCOCAST
RESCOGUN
RESCOMAG
RESCORAM
RESCOSET
RFG MORTAR
RITEX
SAKONITE
SENECA
SERIPHYL
SPRAY MIX
SUPER ADAMANT
SUPER KRIAL
SUPER TROWLEZE
SUPERFLOW
SUREFLOW
TROWLEZE
VEE BLOCK
VIBROCAST

RESEARCH TRIANGLE FOUNDATION OF NORTH CAROLINA
12 Davis Dr
Research Triangle Park, NC 27709
Tel.: (919) 549-8181
Fax: (919) 549-8246
E-mail: info@rtp.org
Web Site: www.rtp.org
Sales Range: $10-24.9 Million
Approx. Number Employees: 15
Business Description:
High Technology Research & Design Center
S.I.C.: 8733
N.A.I.C.S.: 541710
Personnel:
Sherwood H. Smith, Jr. *(Vice Chm)*
Elizabeth Rooks *(Interim Pres & CEO)*
Advertising Agency:
Clean Design, Inc.
10 Laboratory Dr Bldg 2 Ste 200
Research Triangle Park, NC 27709
Tel.: (919) 544-2193
Fax: (919) 473-2200

REVERE PRODUCTS
(Sub. of Pioneer Manufacturing Company)
4529 Industrial Pkwy
Cleveland, OH 44135-4541
Mailing Address:
PO Box 35311
Cleveland, OH 44135-0311
Tel.: (216) 671-5500
Fax: (216) 671-5502
Fax: (216) 671-1097
Toll Free: (800) 321-1976
E-mail: info@revereproducts.com
Web Site: www.revereproducts.com
Approx. Number Employees: 90
Year Founded: 1954
Business Description:
Mfr of Roofing Materials, Floor & Concrete Patching Materials, Rust Inhibitor Coatings, Asphalt Roadway Patching Materials; Protective Coatings; Ice Removing Compounds; Building & Grounds Maintenance Materials
S.I.C.: 5087; 2952
N.A.I.C.S.: 423850; 324122
Export
Catalogs & Directories: 80%; D.M. to Bus. Estab.: 17%; D.M. to Consumers: 3%
Distr.: Natl.
Budget Set: Nov.
Personnel:
James H. Schattinger *(Chm)*
Doug Schattinger *(Pres)*
Brands & Products:
EPOXI GRIP
FIBRO-DEK
FLO GLAZE
MIRACLE SEAL
RIM
STA-FIL

RICHARDS INDUSTRIES VALVE GROUP
3170 Wasson Rd
Cincinnati, OH 45209
Tel.: (513) 533-5600
Fax: (513) 871-0105
Toll Free: (800) 543-7311
E-mail: info@richardsind.com
Web Site: www.richardsind.com
E-Mail For Key Personnel:
President: grichards@richardsind.com
Sales Range: $25-49.9 Million
Approx. Number Employees: 150
Year Founded: 1947
Business Description:
Mfr. of Industrial Valves & Related Piping Specialty Products
S.I.C.: 3491; 3494
N.A.I.C.S.: 332911; 332919
Import Export
Advertising Expenditures: $450,000
Media: 2-4-7-10-11-20-21
Distr.: Intl.
Budget Set: Aug.
Personnel:
Gilbert Richards *(Founder)*
Bruce Broxterman *(Pres)*
Jason Cooper *(CFO, VP-Acctg & MIS)*
Cheryl Koopman *(VP-HR & Dir-Community Affairs)*
Brands & Products:
BESTOBELL
BESTOBELL STEAM TRAPS
HEX
HEX VALVE
JORDAN
JORDAN VALVE
MARWIN
MARWIN BALL VALVES
SMARTWATCH

RIGIDIZED METALS CORP.
658 Ohio St
Buffalo, NY 14203-3122
Tel.: (716) 849-4760
Fax: (716) 849-0401
Toll Free: (800) 836-2580
E-mail: info@rigidized.com
Web Site: www.rigidized.com
Approx. Number Employees: 45
Year Founded: 1940
Business Description:
Deep Textured Design-strengthened Metals Mfr
S.I.C.: 3469; 3444
N.A.I.C.S.: 332116; 332322
Export
Advertising Expenditures: $400,000
Media: 2-4-7-21
Distr.: Intl.; Natl.
Budget Set: Oct.
Personnel:
R. S. Smith, III *(Pres)*
W. Andrew Brown *(Mgr-Small Quantities)*
Brands & Products:
DUOTEX
FROSTONE
PAN-IN-PAN
RIGI-BUMP
RIGI-GRIP
RIGI-TILE
RIGIDIZED
RIGIDTEX
TRIM-TEX

Key to Media (For complete agency information see *The Advertising Red Books-Agencies* edition):
1. Bus. Publs. 2. Cable T.V. 3. Catalogs & Directories. 4. Co-op Adv. 5. Consumer Mags. 6. D.M. to Bus. Estab.7. D.M. to Consumers 8. Daily Newsp. 9. Exhibits/Trade Shows 10. Foreign 11. Infomercial 12. Internet Adv.13. Multimedia 14. Network Radio 15. Network T.V. 16. Newsp. Distr. Mags. 17. Other 18. Outdoor (Posters, Transit) 19. Point of Purchase20. Premiums, Novelties 21. Product Samples 22. Special Events Mktg. 23. Spot Radio 24. Spot T.V. 25. Weekly Newsp. 26. Yellow Page Adv.

RITE-HITE CORPORATION
(Sub. of Rite-Hite Holding Corporation)
8900 N Arbon Dr
Milwaukee, WI 53223-2451
Tel.: (414) 355-2600
Fax: (414) 355-9248
Toll Free: (800) 456-0600
E-mail: info@ritehite.com
Web Site: www.ritehite.com
Approx. Number Employees: 150
Year Founded: 1965
Business Description:
Mfr. of Dock Shelters; Traffic & Powered Doors; Safety Curtains
S.I.C.: 5084; 3842
N.A.I.C.S.: 423830; 339113
Export
Advertising Expenditures: $1,060,000
Media: 2-4-10
Distr.: Natl.
Personnel:
Andy Olson *(Mktg Mgr)*
Brands & Products:
PROTECTOR

RM&L LUCKY ENTERPRISES INC.
131 Balkum Ave
Bastrop, LA 71220
Tel.: (318) 235-8566
E-mail: lomanuelcaldwell@yahoo.com
Year Founded: 2007
Business Description:
Construction
N.A.I.C.S.: 236220; 236115; 812990
Media: 2-4-7-8
Personnel:
Lomanuel Caldwell *(Owner)*
Shemei Jackson *(CEO & Pres)*

ROBBINS, INC.
4777 Eastern Ave
Cincinnati, OH 45226-2338
Tel.: (513) 871-8988
Fax: (513) 871-7998
E-mail: info@robbinsfloor.com
Web Site: www.robbinsfloor.com
Approx. Rev.: $87,000,000
Approx. Number Employees: 270
Year Founded: 1969
Business Description:
Mfr. of Hardwood Flooring, Portable Floors, Racquetball Courts, Squash Courts, Residential Wood Block & Parquet Flooring
S.I.C.: 2431; 2491
N.A.I.C.S.: 321918; 321114
Advertising Expenditures: $700,000
Media: 2-10
Distr.: Intl.; Natl.
Budget Set: Aug.
Personnel:
Ken Thomas *(VP-Mktg)*
Brands & Products:
AIR CHANNEL
AIR-CHANNEL STAR
ALL STAR
BIO-CHANNEL
BIO CHANNEL LP
BIO CUSHION
BIO TRACK
CHEMTURE PLUS
CHEMTURF
CONTEMPORARY MAPLE
CONTEMPORARY PARQUET
CONTEMPORARY PLANK
CONTEMPORARY STRIP
DURATION
DURATION PLUS
FIFTH AVENUE PLANK
LOCK-TITE
MACH
NEW HERRINGBONE
NEW JEFFERSONIAN
PRINCETON PLANK
PULASTIC
ROBBINS
SHAKEN PLANK
SPORTPLAY MX
SPORTWOOD
SPORTWOOD PLUS
SPORTWOOD PLUS ULTRA
STRIP TITE
TRADITIONAL STRIP

ROCK OF AGES CORPORATION
(Sub. of Swenson Granite Company LLC)
560 Graniteville Rd
Graniteville, VT 05654
Tel.: (802) 476-3121
Fax: (802) 476-2245
Toll Free: (800) 421-0166
E-mail: info@rockofages.com
Web Site: www.rockofages.com
Approx. Rev.: $45,521,147
Approx. Number Employees: 257
Business Description:
Quarrier, Mfr & Retailer of Granite Memorials Primarily for Cemetaries
S.I.C.: 3281; 1411; 1423; 5032
N.A.I.C.S.: 327991; 212311; 212313; 423320
Advertising Expenditures: $179,000
Media: 2-4-7-9-10-25-26
Distr.: Intl.; Natl.
Budget Set: Oct.
Personnel:
Kurt M. Swenson *(Chm)*
Donald M. Labonte *(Pres & CEO)*
Laura Plude *(CFO)*
Rich M. Urbach *(Pres/COO-Retail Div)*
Robert Campo *(VP-Sls & Mktg)*
Michael Caputo *(Dir-Product)*
Paul H. Hutchins *(Dir-HR)*
Todd Paton *(Dir-Tourism)*
Brands & Products:
AMERICAN BLACK
BARRE GRAY
BETHEL WHITE
GALACTIC BLUE
GARDENIA WHITE
ROCK OF AGES
SALISBURY PINK
STANSTEAD GRAY

ROCKY MOUNTAIN LOG HOMES
1883 US Hwy 93 S
Hamilton, MT 59840
Tel.: (406) 363-5680
Fax: (406) 363-2109
E-mail: sales@rmlh.com
Web Site: www.rmlh.com
E-Mail For Key Personnel:
Sales Director: sales@rmlh.com
Approx. Number Employees: 70
Year Founded: 1974
Business Description:
Mfr. of Log Homes
S.I.C.: 2452; 5031
N.A.I.C.S.: 321992; 423310
Export
Advertising Expenditures: $200,000
Media: 4-5-6-10-13-19-20-21-22-26
Distr.: Natl.
Budget Set: Mar.
Personnel:
James R. Schueler *(Pres & CEO)*
Brands & Products:
ROCKY MOUNTAIN
Advertising Agency:
Spiker Communications, Inc.
229 E Main St
Missoula, MT 59802-4423
Tel.: (406) 721-0785
Fax: (406) 728-8915

RODMAN INDUSTRIES
(Sub. of Fiberesin Industries, Inc.)
2601 Cleveland Ave
Marinette, WI 54143
Mailing Address:
PO Box 88
Oconomowoc, WI 53066-0088
Tel.: (715) 735-9541
Fax: (262) 569-5821
E-mail: info@rodmanindustries.com
Web Site: www.rodmanindustries.com
Approx. Number Employees: 30
Year Founded: 1965
Business Description:
Mfr of Particle Board
S.I.C.: 2493
N.A.I.C.S.: 321219
Export
Media: 2
Distr.: Natl.
Budget Set: Oct.
Brands & Products:
RESINCORE I
RESINCORE III

ROLLEX CORPORATION
800 Chase Ave
Elk Grove Village, IL 60007-5605
Tel.: (847) 437-3000
Fax: (847) 437-7561
E-mail: marketing@rollex.com
Web Site: www.rollex.com
Approx. Number Employees: 150
Year Founded: 1957
Business Description:
Mfr. of Aluminum, Vinyl & Steel Building Products
S.I.C.: 3444; 3354
N.A.I.C.S.: 332322; 331316
Media: 2-4-7-10-17
Distr.: Natl.
Personnel:
James L. Brittingham *(Chm)*
John A. Foley *(CFO)*
Brands & Products:
THE BOOM IN THE BURBS
CHESTNUT HILL
COLORSELECT
EAGLE
MANCHESTER
PRE-FIXED SOFFIT SYSTEM. FROM ROLLEX.
QUALITY FROM DAY ONE
RENDITION
ROLLEX MEANS SIDING.
SPECTRUM
SYMPHONY
WE LISTEN TO HOMEOWNERS
WE ROLL IT AND WE EX IT
WINCHESTER BAY

ROOFING BY CURRY
6245 Clark Center Ave Ste J
Sarasota, FL 34238
Tel.: (941) 921-9111
Fax: (941) 925-2916
E-mail: info@roofingbycurry.com
Web Site: www.roofingbycurry.com
Approx. Number Employees: 4
Business Description:
Roofing Contractor
S.I.C.: 1761
N.A.I.C.S.: 238160
Media: 8-13-16-23-24
Personnel:
Gary Curry *(Pres)*
Jason Smith *(Sls Rep)*

ROTO-ROOTER, INC.
(Sub. of Chemed Corporation)
255 E Fifth St Chemed Ctr Ste 2500
Cincinnati, OH 45202-4726
Tel.: (513) 762-6690
Fax: (513) 762-6590
Toll Free: (800) GETROTO
Web Site: www.rotorooter.com
Sales Range: $50-74.9 Million
Approx. Number Employees: 150
Year Founded: 1935
Business Description:
Plumbing
S.I.C.: 1711
N.A.I.C.S.: 238220
Personnel:
Paul Abrams *(Mgr-Media Rels)*
Mike Tailor *(Mgr-Svcs Mktg-Bus Dev)*
Brands & Products:
AND AWAY GO TROUBLES DOWN THE DRAIN
Advertising Agency:
Eisen Management Group
515 Monmouth St Ste 302
Newport, KY 41071
Tel.: (859) 291-4302
Fax: (859) 291-4360

THE ROTTLUND COMPANY, INC.
3065 Centre Pointe Dr
Roseville, MN 55113-1130
Tel.: (651) 638-0500
Fax: (651) 638-0501
E-mail: info@rottlundhomes.com
Web Site: www.rottlundhomes.com
Approx. Number Employees: 70
Year Founded: 1973
Business Description:
Residential Home Construction
S.I.C.: 1531; 1521
N.A.I.C.S.: 236117; 236115
Media: 1-2-4-5-6-7-8-9-13-16-18-19-22-23-24-25-26
Distr.: Natl.
Budget Set: Dec.
Personnel:
Todd M. Stutz *(Pres)*
Steven A. Kahn *(CFO)*
Brands & Products:
DAVID BERNARD HOME BUILDERS
ROTTLUND HOMES
YOUR BUILDER FOR LIFE

ROTTLUND HOMES OF FLORIDA, INC.
(Sub. of The Rottlund Company, Inc.)
2637 McCormick Dr
Clearwater, FL 33759
Tel.: (727) 669-2449

Key to Media (For complete agency information see *The Advertising Red Books-Agencies* edition):
1. Bus. Publs. 2. Cable T.V. 3. Catalogs & Directories. 4. Co-op Adv. 5. Consumer Mags. 6. D.M. to Bus. Estab.7. D.M. to Consumers 8. Daily Newsp. 9. Exhibits/Trade Shows 10. Foreign 11. Infomercial 12. Internet Adv.13. Multimedia 14. Network Radio 15. Network T.V. 16. Newsp. Distr. Mags. 17. Other 18. Outdoor (Posters, Transit) 19. Point of Purchase20. Premiums, Novelties 21. Product Samples 22. Special Events Mktg. 23. Spot Radio 24. Spot T.V. 25. Weekly Newsp. 26. Yellow Page Adv.

Fax: (727) 669-0997
Web Site: www.rottlundhomes.com
Sales Range: $10-24.9 Million
Year Founded: 1994
Business Description:
Residential Home Construction
S.I.C.: 1521
N.A.I.C.S.: 236115
Media: 6-8-18

ROUGH BROTHERS, INC.

5513 Vine St
Cincinnati, OH 45217-1003
Tel.: (513) 242-0310
Fax: (513) 242-0816
Toll Free: (800) 543-7351
Web Site: www.roughbros.com
E-Mail For Key Personnel:
President: rreilly@roughbros.com
Sales Range: $50-74.9 Million
Approx. Number Employees: 130
Year Founded: 1932
Business Description:
Mfr & Designer of Commercial & Industrial Greenhouses & Components
S.I.C.: 3448; 1522
N.A.I.C.S.: 332311; 236220
Import Export
Advertising Expenditures: $250,000
Media: 2-4-7-10-11-13
Distr.: Natl.
Budget Set: Jan.
Personnel:
Richard Reilly *(Pres)*
David Robert *(CFO)*
Bill Vietassns *(Dir-Adv)*

ROYAL GROUP TECHNOLOGIES LIMITED

(Sub. of GEORGIA GULF CORPORATION)
1 Royal Gate Blvd
Woodbridge, ON L4L 8Z7, Canada
Tel.: (905) 264-0701
Fax: (905) 264-0702
E-mail: corporate@royalgrouptech.com
Web Site: www.royalgrouptech.com
Sales Range: $1-4.9 Billion
Approx. Number Employees: 7,800
Year Founded: 1970
Business Description:
Polymer-Based Home Improvement Product Mfr
S.I.C.: 5039; 2673; 3446; 5113
N.A.I.C.S.: 423390; 326111; 332323; 424130
Media: 2-10-13
Brands & Products:
ABINGTON
ADDISON
CLEARWOOD
COLORWASH
DURA TECHNOLOGY
DURASLATE
ENER-CEL
ENVELOP
FRAME SHAPES
HEIRLOOM
LASERLITE
LYKEWOOD
NEVER ROT
PREMIER
PRO-SERIES
PROFRAME
PROSASH I-M
QUICK-TRIM
RAINTRAX
REFLECTIONS
THE ROYAL BUILDING SYSTEM
ROYAL GROUP
ROYALINEX
ROYALSIDE
ROYALWOOD
SFT ECLECTICS
SPECTRA COAT
TRENDS
TRIMPLANK
TWINWALL
VERANDA
YARDMATE

ROYAL MOULDINGS LTD.

(Sub. of Royal Group Technologies Limited)
135 Bear Creek Rd
Marion, VA 24354
Mailing Address:
PO Box 610
Marion, VA 24354
Tel.: (276) 783-8161
Fax: (276) 782-3292
Toll Free: (800) 368-3117
E-mail: info@royalmouldings.com
Web Site:
www.royalbuildingproducts.com
Sales Range: $1-4.9 Billion
Year Founded: 1968
Business Description:
Mfr. of Decorative Polymer Mouldings & Cellular Vinyl Extrusion Components & Systems
S.I.C.: 6029; 2431; 3089
N.A.I.C.S.: 522110; 321918; 326199
Export
Media: 1-2-4-5-7-10-13-19-20-21
Distr.: Natl.
Brands & Products:
CELLULAR VINYL PVC
ELEMENTS
ENVELOP
GARAGE SOLUTIONS
LYKEWOOD
NO ROT
PRO FRAME
PRO SASH
PRO SERIES
QUICK TRIM
ROYAL COLLECTION
ROYAL COLORS TRIM BOARD
SENOVIA
SMART SPACE SYSTEM
THERMO STOP
THERMO SYSTEMS
TRIMPLANK

ROYAL STYLE DESIGN, INC.

(Name Changed to Diversified Global Holdings Group, Inc.)

R.P. WILLIAMS & SONS, INC.

400 Summer St
Bristol, NH 03222-3213
Tel.: (603) 744-5446
Fax: (603) 744-2507
Toll Free: (800) 245-5446
E-mail: info@rpwilliams.com
Web Site: www.rpwilliams.com
Sales Range: Less than $1 Million
Approx. Number Employees: 21
Year Founded: 1941
Business Description:
Lumber & Building Supplies
S.I.C.: 5031
N.A.I.C.S.: 423310
Media: 2-4-7-8-10-13
Distr.: Natl.
Personnel:
Robert M. Williams, Jr. *(Pres)*

RSI HOME PRODUCTS

(Sub. of RSI Holding Corporation)
(d/b/a General Marble)
350 N Generals Blvd
Lincolnton, NC 28092-3557
Tel.: (714) 449-2200
Fax: (704) 732-5005
E-mail: custserv@rsihomeproducts.com
Approx. Number Employees: 350
Business Description:
Tufflex Cushioning & Padding; Plastic Netting Products; Insulation; Mulch; Dividers; Oil Sorbents Mfr
S.I.C.: 3281; 5031
N.A.I.C.S.: 327991; 423310
Advertising Expenditures: $245,000
Bus. Publs.: $75,000; Catalogs & Directories: $50,000; D.M. to Bus. Estab.: $80,000; Exhibits/Trade Shows: $40,000
Distr.: Natl.
Budget Set: Sept.
Personnel:
Alex Calabrese *(Pres)*
Brands & Products:
HYDRO MULCH
SODNET
TENSIONET
TUFFLEX

RUDD EQUIPMENT COMPANY INC.

4344 Poplar Level Rd
Louisville, KY 40213-1841
Tel.: (502) 456-4050
Fax: (502) 459-8695
E-mail: information@ruddequipment.com
Web Site: www.ruddequipment.com
Approx. Sls.: $175,000,000
Approx. Number Employees: 370
Year Founded: 1952
Business Description:
Construction & Mining Machinery
S.I.C.: 5082; 7353
N.A.I.C.S.: 423810; 532412
Import Export
Personnel:
Mark Burris *(Pres)*
Michael D. Rudd *(CEO)*
Bill Maggard *(Sr VP-Product Support)*
Advertising Agency:
Roberts Communications Inc.
1 N Shore Ctr 12 Federal St Ste 120
Pittsburgh, PA 15212
Tel.: (412) 535-5000
Fax: (412) 535-5006
— Bill Blume *(Dir-Media)*

RUSCO WINDOW COMPANY

(Sub. of Lawrence Transportation Systems Inc.)
872 Lee Hwy
Roanoke, VA 24019
Mailing Address:
PO Box 7667
Roanoke, VA 24019
Tel.: (540) 966-3797
Fax: (540) 966-4570
Toll Free: (800) 382-7176
E-mail: ginfo@ruscowindow.com
Web Site: www.ruscowindow.com
Approx. Sls.: $5,700,000
Approx. Number Employees: 80
Year Founded: 1979
Business Description:
Mfr. of Windows & Distributor of Home Improvement Products
S.I.C.: 4214; 4225
N.A.I.C.S.: 484210; 493110
Media: 2-4-6-7-8-10-19
Distr.: Natl.
Budget Set: Nov. -Dec.

RUSSELL SWINTON OATMAN DESIGN ASSOCIATES, INC.

132 Mirick Rd
Princeton, MA 01541-1111
Tel.: (978) 464-2360
Year Founded: 1977
Business Description:
Architectural Plans for Reproduction Houses
S.I.C.: 8712
N.A.I.C.S.: 541310
Media: 4-6-26
Personnel:
Russell S. Oatman *(Pres)*

RUTLAND PRODUCTS CO.

38 Merchants Row
Rutland, VT 05702
Tel.: (802) 775-5519
Fax: (802) 775-5262
Toll Free: (800) 544-1307
E-mail: sales@rutland.com
Web Site: www.rutland.com
E-Mail For Key Personnel:
Sales Director: sales@rutland.com
Approx. Number Employees: 20
Year Founded: 1883
Business Description:
Stove & Fireplace Products Mfr
S.I.C.: 3429
N.A.I.C.S.: 332510
Export
Advertising Expenditures: $200,000
Media: 2-4-5-10-19-21
Distr.: Natl.
Budget Set: Oct.
Personnel:
G. Miller *(CFO)*
Brands & Products:
CHIMNEY SHEILD
DAMPGONE
DURAFLAME
FIRE-UP
GRAPHO-GLAS
KWIK-SHOT
LOG BRIGHT
MASTER SWEEP
ONE MATCH
POWDERED SOOT DESTROYER
RUTLAND
RUTLAND 100S
SAFE-LITE
SOOT SWEEP
STOVO
SWEEPALL

SAE INTERNATIONAL

(Formerly Society of Automotive Engineers, Inc.)
400 Commonwealth Dr
Warrendale, PA 15096-0001
Tel.: (724) 776-4841
Fax: (724) 776-0445
Web Site: www.sae.org

Key to Media (For complete agency information see *The Advertising Red Books-Agencies* edition):
1. Bus. Publs. 2. Cable T.V. 3. Catalogs & Directories. 4. Co-op Adv. 5. Consumer Mags. 6. D.M. to Bus. Estab.7. D.M. to Consumers
8. Daily Newsp. 9. Exhibits/Trade Shows 10. Foreign 11. Infomercial 12. Internet Adv.13. Multimedia 14. Network Radio
15. Network T.V. 16. Newsp. Distr. Mags. 17. Other 18. Outdoor (Posters, Transit) 19. Point of Purchase20. Premiums, Novelties
21. Product Samples 22. Special Events Mktg. 23. Spot Radio 24. Spot T.V. 25. Weekly Newsp. 26. Yellow Page Adv.

SAE International — (Continued)
Sales Range: $50-74.9 Million
Approx. Number Employees: 300
Year Founded: 1905
Business Description:
Mobility Engineering
S.I.C.: 8711; 8611
N.A.I.C.S.: 541330; 813910
Media: 7-10-11-13-17
Personnel:
David Schutt *(CEO)*
Andrew Brown *(Exec Dir & Chief Technologist-Delphi Corporation)*
Timothy Mellon *(Dir-Govt Affairs)*
Jack Pokrzywa *(Mgr)*
Carol A. Story *(Asst Treas)*
Brands & Products:
SAE INTERNATIONAL

SAFELITE SOLUTIONS LLC
(Sub. of Belron US)
2400 Farmers Dr
Columbus, OH 43235
Tel.: (614) 210-9000
Fax: (614) 210-9491
Web Site: www.safelite.com
Approx. Number Employees: 100
Business Description:
Auto Glass Repair Claims Management Services
S.I.C.: 6411
N.A.I.C.S.: 524298
Personnel:
Melina Metzger *(Mgr-PR)*
Advertising Agencies:
Berry Network, Inc.
3100 Kettering Blvd
Dayton, OH 45439
Fax: (937) 298-1426
Toll Free: (800) 366-1264

Ron Foth Advertising
8100 N High St
Columbus, OH 43235-6400
Tel.: (614) 888-7771
Fax: (614) 888-5933

SAFWAY SERVICES, LLC
(Holding of Odyssey Investment Partners, LLC)
N19 W 24200 Riverwood Dr
Waukesha, WI 53188
Mailing Address:
PO Box 1991
Milwaukee, WI 53201
Tel.: (262) 523-6500
Fax: (262) 523-9808
Toll Free: (800) 558-4772
E-mail: marketing1@safway.com
Web Site: www.safway.com
E-Mail For Key Personnel:
President: marc.wilson@safway.com
Marketing Director: Michelle. Dalton@safway.com
Sales Director: bob.viscomi@safway.com
Sales Range: $700-749.9 Million
Approx. Number Employees: 4,000
Year Founded: 1936
Business Description:
Scaffold Sales, Rentals & Services
S.I.C.: 7359; 5082
N.A.I.C.S.: 532490; 423810
Import Export
Advertising Expenditures: $1,500,000
Bus. Publs.: $15,000; Catalogs & Directories: $30,000; D.M. to Bus. Estab.: $135,000; D.M. to Consumers: $1,170,000; Exhibits/Trade Shows: $135,000; Premiums, Novelties: $15,000
Distr.: Intl.; Natl.
Budget Set: Oct.
Personnel:
Marc J. Wilson *(Pres & CEO)*
Robert Sukalich *(CFO & VP)*
Jerry Johns *(COO & Exec VP)*
Curt Paulsen *(Gen Counsel & VP)*
Chuck Thimm *(VP-Info Sys)*
Mike Krach *(Reg Mgr-Mid Atlantic)*
Andy Reiland *(Mgr-Equipment Procurement & Asset Mgmt)*
Brands & Products:
ADJUST-A-SHORE
DURAPLANK
QUIKDECK
SAFLOAD
SAFMAX
SAFWAY
SL FRAME SYSTEM
SYSTEMS

SAINT-GOBAIN CERAMICS
(Sub. of Saint-Gobain Ceramics & Plastics)
23 Acheson Dr
Niagara Falls, NY 14303-1555
Tel.: (716) 278-6233
Fax: (716) 278-2373
E-mail: scd.sales@saint-gobain.com
Web Site: www.carbo.com
Sales Range: $50-74.9 Million
Approx. Number Employees: 200
Year Founded: 1891
Business Description:
High Temperature Ceramic Fiber Insulation & Refractory Products, Polyester Resins & Resin Components Producer
S.I.C.: 3262
N.A.I.C.S.: 327112
Export
Advertising Expenditures: $550,000
Media: 2-4-13-16-26
Distr.: Intl.; Natl.
Budget Set: Dec.
Personnel:
Curt Schmidt *(Mktg Mgr)*
Brands & Products:
HEXOLOY
Advertising Agency:
Quinlan & Company
385 N French Rd Ste 106
Amherst, NY 14228-2096
Tel.: (716) 691-6200
Fax: (716) 691-2898

SAKRETE OF NORTH AMERICA, LLC
(Sub. of Bonsal American, Inc.)
5155 Fischer Ave
Cincinnati, OH 45217
Mailing Address:
PO Box 17087
Saint Bernard, OH 45217-0087
Tel.: (513) 242-3644
Fax: (513) 242-7845
Toll Free: (866) SAKRETE
E-mail: sakrete@oldcastleapg.com
Web Site: www.sakrete.com
Sales Range: $10-24.9 Million
Approx. Number Employees: 10
Year Founded: 1936
Business Description:
Concrete Mix Mfr & Distr
S.I.C.: 3273
N.A.I.C.S.: 327320
Media: 2-7-16
Distr.: Natl.
Budget Set: Oct.
Personnel:
Johnsie Beck *(Pres)*
Eric Peterson *(Dir-Mktg)*
Bob Schmidt *(Mgr-Sakrete Product)*
Brands & Products:
SAKRETE

SAMUELS GROUP, INC.
311 Fiancial Way St 300
Wausau, WI 54401-1404
Tel.: (715) 842-2222
Fax: (715) 848-8088
E-mail: info@samuelsgroup.net
Web Site: www.samuelsgroup.net
Approx. Number Employees: 70
Business Description:
General Contractor & Construction Manager; Commercial, Industrial & Apartment Buildings Designer & Builder
S.I.C.: 1522
N.A.I.C.S.: 236220
Media: 17
Personnel:
Sid Samuels *(Founder & Pres)*
Wil Hoxie *(Dir-Safety)*
Shelley Rowe *(Coord-Mktg Comm)*
Advertising Agency:
TMA+Peritus
1 Corporate Dr Ste 404
Wausau, WI 54401
Tel.: (715) 849-4200
Fax: (715) 849-3900

SANFORD & HAWLEY, INC.
1790 Farmington Ave
Unionville, CT 06085-1209
Tel.: (860) 673-3213
Fax: (860) 675-2125
Toll Free: (800) 433-7941
E-mail: counter@sanhaw.com
Web Site: www.sanhaw.com
E-Mail For Key Personnel:
President: rps@sanhaw.com
Marketing Director: fws@sanhaw.com
Approx. Number Employees: 90
Year Founded: 1946
Business Description:
Sale of Building Materials; Lumber; Drywall; Hardware; Paint; Plywood; Windows; Doors; Mason Supplies & Roofing
S.I.C.: 5031
N.A.I.C.S.: 423310
Media: 4-7-8-9-17-18-25-26
Distr.: Direct to Consumer; Reg.
Personnel:
Robert P. Sanford *(Pres)*
Frank W. Sanford *(VP-Mktg)*

SANIJET CORP.
6200 Maple Ave
Dallas, TX 75235
Tel.: (972) 745-2283
Fax: (214) 352-0348
Toll Free: (877) 934-0477
E-mail: info@sanijet.com
Web Site: www.sanijet.com
Approx. Rev.: $5,000,000
Business Description:
Pipeless Spa Systems
S.I.C.: 3088
N.A.I.C.S.: 326191
Advertising Expenditures: $2,000,000
Personnel:
Philip Jerome Klement *(VP-Sls & Mktg)*

SAUNDERS BROTHERS
479 Main St Ste 1
Westbrook, ME 04092-4201
Tel.: (207) 854-2551
Fax: (207) 856-1295
Fax: (207) 854-1243
Toll Free: (800) 343-0675
E-mail: sales@saundersbros.com
Web Site: www.saundersbros.com
E-Mail For Key Personnel:
Sales Director: sales@saundersbros.com
Approx. Number Employees: 200
Year Founded: 1900
Business Description:
Wood Dowels, Decorative Furniture Accessories & Wood Furniture Component Parts Mfr
S.I.C.: 2499; 5099
N.A.I.C.S.: 321999; 423990
Import Export
Media: 2-4-7-10-21
Distr.: Natl.
Budget Set: Sept.
Personnel:
Beth Brooks *(Asst Mgr-Sls & Mktg)*

SCAN DESIGN OF FLORIDA INC.
1153 Bennett Dr
Longwood, FL 32750
Tel.: (407) 831-6633
Fax: (407) 831-6651
E-mail: corporate@scandesign.com
Web Site: www.scandesign.com
Approx. Number Employees: 105
Business Description:
Household Furniture
S.I.C.: 5021; 5712
N.A.I.C.S.: 423210; 442110
Media: 3-4-8-9-14-15-23-24-25
Personnel:
Jesper Knudsen *(Pres)*

SCHLEGEL SYSTEMS, INC.
(Sub. of Lupus Capital PLC)
1555 Jefferson Rd
Rochester, NY 14623-3109
Tel.: (585) 427-7200
Fax: (585) 475-9993
E-mail: schlegelus@schlegel.com
Web Site: www.schlegel.com
Approx. Number Employees: 650
Year Founded: 1885
Business Description:
Engineered Perimeter Sealing Systems
S.I.C.: 3069; 3089
N.A.I.C.S.: 326299; 326199
Import Export
Advertising Expenditures: $1,000,000
Media: 1-2-7-10-21
Distr.: Intl.; Natl.
Budget Set: Oct.
Brands & Products:
FINSEAL
LECTRA-CON
POLY-BOND
Q-LON

Key to Media (For complete agency information see *The Advertising Red Books-Agencies* edition):
1. Bus. Publs. 2. Cable T.V. 3. Catalogs & Directories. 4. Co-op Adv. 5. Consumer Mags. 6. D.M. to Bus. Estab.7. D.M. to Consumers 8. Daily Newsp. 9. Exhibits/Trade Shows 10. Foreign 11. Infomercial 12. Internet Adv.13. Multimedia 14. Network Radio 15. Network T.V. 16. Newsp. Distr. Mags. 17. Other 18. Outdoor (Posters, Transit) 19. Point of Purchase20. Premiums, Novelties 21. Product Samples 22. Special Events Mktg. 23. Spot Radio 24. Spot T.V. 25. Weekly Newsp. 26. Yellow Page Adv.

SCHLEGEL

SCHNITZER STEEL INDUSTRIES, INC.

3200 NW Yeon Ave
Portland, OR 97210
Tel.: (503) 224-9900
Fax: (503) 321-2648
E-mail: ir@schn.com
Web Site: www.schnitzersteel.com
Approx. Rev.: $2,301,240,000
Approx. Number Employees: 3,237
Year Founded: 1906
Business Description:
Steel Mfr & Scrap Steel & Iron Processor
S.I.C.: 3312; 5093
N.A.I.C.S.: 331111; 423930
Export
Personnel:
John D. Carter *(Chm)*
Tamara Adler L. Lundgren *(Pres & CEO)*
Richard D. Peach *(CFO & Sr VP)*
Vicki A. Piersall *(Chief Admin Officer-Metals Recycling Unit & VP-Strategic Plng)*
Jeffrey Dyck *(Pres-Steel Mfg Bus & Sr VP)*
Donald Hamaker *(Pres-Metals Recycling Bus & Sr VP)*
Thomas D. Klauer *(Pres-Auto Parts Bus & Sr VP)*
Richard C. Josephson *(Gen Counsel, Sec & Sr VP)*
Gary A. Schnitzer *(Exec VP-Bus Dev)*
Advertising Agency:
Gard Communications
711 SW Alder St 4th Fl
Portland, OR 97205
Tel.: (503) 221-0100
Fax: (503) 226-4854
Toll Free: (800) 800-7132

SCHOTT GEMTRON CORPORATION

(Joint Venture of Asahi Glass Co., Ltd. & Carl-Zeiss-Stiftung)
615 Hwy 68
Sweetwater, TN 37874-1911
Tel.: (423) 337-3522
Fax: (423) 337-7979
E-mail: salesinfo@gemtron.net
Web Site: www.gemtron.net
E-Mail For Key Personnel:
Sales Director: salesinfo@gemtron.net
Approx. Number Employees: 250
Year Founded: 1973
Business Description:
Mfr. of Tempered & Decorative Glass For Uses Including Shower Doors, Ovens & Shelving; Joint Venture of Schott Glaswerke & AFG Industries, Inc.
S.I.C.: 3211
N.A.I.C.S.: 327211
Export
Advertising Expenditures: $250,000
Media: 2-4-5-7-10-20-21
Distr.: Natl.
Budget Set: Nov.
Personnel:
Douglas D. Roberts *(Pres)*
Mark Delp *(Exec VP)*

SCHOTT GEMTRON CORPORATION

(Joint Venture of Asahi Glass Co., Ltd. & Carl-Zeiss-Stiftung)
2000 Chestnut St
Vincennes, IN 47591-1760
Mailing Address:
PO Box 317
Vincennes, IN 47591-0317
Tel.: (812) 882-2680
Fax: (812) 882-7679
Web Site: www.gemtron.com
Approx. Number Employees: 500
Business Description:
Glass Tempering & Tempered Glass; Ceramics
S.I.C.: 3231
N.A.I.C.S.: 327215
Import Export
Advertising Expenditures: $260,000
Media: 2-4-5-7-10-20-21
Distr.: Natl.
Budget Set: Dec.

SCHUMACHER HOMES, INC.

2715 Wise Ave NW
Canton, OH 44708
Toll Free: (800) 813-1116
Web Site:
www.schumacherhomes.com
Approx. Rev.: $2,700,000
Approx. Number Employees: 10
Year Founded: 2003
Business Description:
Custom Home Builder
S.I.C.: 1531
N.A.I.C.S.: 236117
Personnel:
Paul Schumacher *(Pres)*
Mary Schumaker Baker *(VP-Sls & Mktg)*
Jeff Gannon *(Mgr-Mktg)*
Advertising Agency:
Intrapromote LLC
591 Boston Mills Rd Ste 550
Hudson, OH 44236
Tel.: (866) 570-1785
Fax: (630) 604-7656
Search & Social Media Agency of Record

SCOTT LUMBER COMPANY

54382 National Rd
Bridgeport, OH 43912-9717
Tel.: (740) 635-2345
Fax: (740) 635-4816
E-mail: scottlmb@scottlumberco.com
Approx. Number Employees: 150
Year Founded: 1869
Business Description:
Lumber, Building Materials, Hardware, Kitchen Cabinets & Plumbing Materials Mfr
S.I.C.: 5031; 5063
N.A.I.C.S.: 423310; 423610
Media: 3-5-8-9-18-23-24-26
Distr.: Direct to Consumer; Reg.
Budget Set: Nov.

SCS ENGINEERS

3900 Kilroy Airport Way Ste 100
Long Beach, CA 90806-6816
Tel.: (562) 426-9544
Fax: (562) 427-0805
E-mail: service@scsengineers.com
Web Site: www.scsengineers.com
E-Mail For Key Personnel:
President: rstearns@scsengineers.com
Marketing Director: mmclaughlin@scsengineers.com
Sales Director: dross@scsengineers.com
Sales Range: $25-49.9 Million
Approx. Number Employees: 685
Year Founded: 1970
Business Description:
Environmental Consulting Engineers; Solid & Hazardous Waste Management
S.I.C.: 8711; 1541
N.A.I.C.S.: 541330; 236210
Export
Personnel:
Robert P. Stearns *(Chm)*
Nick Jokanovich *(CFO)*
Jay Hatho *(CIO & VP)*
Tom Barham *(Sr VP-Svcs)*
Bob Gardner *(Sr VP-Solid Waste Svcs)*
Mike McLaughlin *(Sr VP-Environ Svcs)*
Jeffrey L. Pierce *(Sr VP-Energy)*
Dave Ross *(Sr VP)*
Mark B. Beizer *(VP & Office Dir)*
Thomas D. Dong *(Dir-Environ Svcs)*
Ambrose McCready *(Dir)*
Joseph J. Miller *(Dir)*
Gary Pons *(Dir-Corp Health & Safety)*
Rich Dart *(Reg Mgr-Svcs-Long Beach)*
David Laney *(Mgr-Environ Svcs)*
John Picone *(Mgr-Corp Comm)*
Advertising Agency:
Cook & Schmid
2760 5th Ave Ste 210
San Diego, CA 92103
Tel.: (619) 814-2370
Fax: (619) 814-2375
Toll Free: (866) 615-9181
(Public Relations)

SERVICEMAGIC, INC.

(Sub. of IAC/InterActiveCorp)
14023 Denver W Pkwy Bldg 64 Ste 200
Golden, CO 80401
Tel.: (303) 963-7200
Fax: (303) 980-3003
Toll Free: (800) 474-1596
Web Site: www.servicemagic.com
Sales Range: $25-49.9 Million
Approx. Number Employees: 1,000
Year Founded: 1998
Business Description:
Contractors & Service Professionals Website Operator
S.I.C.: 8621
N.A.I.C.S.: 813920
Personnel:
Michael J. Beaudoin *(Co-Founder & Co-Chm)*
Rodney Rice *(Co-Founder & Co-Chm)*
Craig Smith *(Pres & CEO-Intl)*
Chris Terrill *(CEO)*
Ty Kasperbauer *(Sr VP-New Channel Dev)*
Ryan Sullivan *(Sr VP-Tech)*
Andy Zurcher *(Sr VP-Product Mgmt)*
Matt Zurcher *(Sr VP-Ops & Consumer Div)*
Joseph Clay *(VP-HR)*
Jim Croft *(VP-Sls-Denver)*
Tom Durant *(VP-Fin)*
Ben Little *(VP-Sls)*
Brands & Products:
IMPROVENET
Advertising Agency:
JMPR, Inc.
5850 Canoga Ave Ste 300
Woodland Hills, CA 91367
Tel.: (818) 992-4353
Fax: (818) 992-0543

SHAKERTOWN 1992, INC.

(Sub. of The Clarke Group)
1200 Kerron St
Winlock, WA 98596
Mailing Address:
PO Box 400
Winlock, WA 98596-0400
Tel.: (360) 785-3501
Fax: (360) 785-3076
Toll Free: (800) 426-8970
Web Site: www.shakertown.com
Approx. Number Employees: 65
Business Description:
Cedar Shingles Mfr
S.I.C.: 2499
N.A.I.C.S.: 321999
Advertising Expenditures: $500,000
Media: 2-6-17
Distr.: Natl.
Budget Set: Oct.
Brands & Products:
FANCY CUTS
SHAKERTOWN SIDING

SHANNON & WILSON, INC.

400 N 34th St Ste 100
Seattle, WA 98103-8600
Tel.: (206) 632-8020
Fax: (206) 695-6777
Telex: 469160
Web Site: www.shannonwilson.com
Sales Range: $25-49.9 Million
Approx. Number Employees: 300
Year Founded: 1954
Business Description:
Geotechnical & Environmental Consulting Services
S.I.C.: 8711; 8713
N.A.I.C.S.: 541330; 541360
Export
Media: 2-10
Personnel:
Gerard Buechel *(Pres)*
Atef A. Azzam *(Sr VP)*
Greg Fischer *(Office Mgr)*

SHAWMUT WOODWORKING & SUPPLY CORP.

(d/b/a Shawmut Design & Construction)
560 Harrison Ave
Boston, MA 02118
Tel.: (617) 622-7000
Fax: (617) 622-7001
E-mail: info@shawmut.com
Web Site: www.shawmut.com
Sales Range: $400-449.9 Million
Approx. Number Employees: 515
Year Founded: 1982
Business Description:
Provider of Commercial, Office & Institutional Building Contracting Services
S.I.C.: 1522
N.A.I.C.S.: 236220; 236116
Personnel:
James S. Ansara *(Chm)*
William Hughes *(Pres)*
Thomas E. Goemaat *(CEO)*

Key to Media (For complete agency information see *The Advertising Red Books-Agencies* edition):
1. Bus. Publs. 2. Cable T.V. 3. Catalogs & Directories. 4. Co-op Adv. 5. Consumer Mags. 6. D.M. to Bus. Estab.7. D.M. to Consumers
8. Daily.Newsp. 9. Exhibits/Trade Shows 10. Foreign 11. Infomercial 12. Internet Adv.13. Multimedia 14. Network Radio
15. Network T.V. 16. Newsp. Distr. Mags. 17. Other 18. Outdoor (Posters, Transit) 19. Point of Purchase20. Premiums, Novelties
21. Product Samples 22. Special Events Mktg. 23. Spot Radio 24. Spot T.V. 25. Weekly Newsp. 26. Yellow Page Adv.

Shawmut Woodworking & Supply Corp. — (Continued)

Gary Bergeron *(VP-Purchasing)*
William Pisani *(VP-Retail & Gaming)*
Advertising Agency:
Schwartz Communications, Inc.
230 3rd Ave
Waltham, MA 02451
Tel.: (781) 684-0770
Fax: (781) 684-6500

SHUR-CO, INC.
2309 Shurlock St
Yankton, SD 57078-1210
Mailing Address:
PO Box 713
Yankton, SD 57078-0713
Tel.: (605) 665-6000
Fax: (605) 665-0501
Toll Free: (888) 474-8726
E-mail: info@shurco.com
Web Site: www.shurco.com
Approx. Number Employees: 247
Year Founded: 1992
Business Description:
Mfr. of Tarps
S.I.C.: 3429; 3711
N.A.I.C.S.: 332510; 336211
Import Export
Personnel:
William Shorma *(Pres)*
Carla Ewald *(CFO)*
Mike Krajewski *(Mgr-Natl Construction Sls)*
Brands & Products:
COVER-PRO
COVER-UP
SHELTER-RITE
SHUR-CO
SHUR-LOK
SHUR-MATIC
SHUR-TRAK
SHURCO
SHURCO-LOK
TRUCKHYDE
TWIST-LOK
Advertising Agency:
Epic Multimedia
3500 S Phillips Ave Ste 127
Sioux Falls, SD 57105
Tel.: (605) 271-2598
Fax: (605) 274-0842

SICO INCORPORATED
7525 Cahill Rd
Edina, MN 55439-2738
Tel.: (952) 941-1700
Fax: (952) 941-6737
Toll Free: (800) 328-6138
E-mail: sales@sicoinc.com
Web Site: www.sicoinc.com
E-Mail For Key Personnel:
Sales Director: sales@sicoinc.com
Approx. Number Employees: 420
Year Founded: 1951
Business Description:
Mobile Folding Products Mfr; Cafeteria/Banquet Tables, Stages, Risers & Portable Dance Floors
S.I.C.: 2531; 2511
N.A.I.C.S.: 337127; 337122
Export
Media: 2-4-6-7-10-13-20
Distr.: Intl.; Natl.
Budget Set: Dec.
Personnel:
Andrew J. Shea *(Chm)*
Hal Wilson *(CEO)*
Joel Mondshane *(Mgr-Adv)*
Brands & Products:
EURO BED
INSTA-THEATRE
INSTA-WALL
SICO
SICO INSTA-WALL
SICO VERI-LITE
STARLIGHT

SIDEL INC.
(Sub. of Groupe Sidel)
5600 Sun Ct
Norcross, GA 30092
Tel.: (770) 449-8058
Tel.: (678) 221-3000
Fax: (770) 409-2208
Fax: (770) 447-0084
E-mail: sales@usa.sidel.com
Web Site: www.sidelsystems.com
E-Mail For Key Personnel:
Sales Director: sales@usa.sidel.com
Approx. Number Employees: 300
Year Founded: 1984
Business Description:
Packaging Equipment Mfr
S.I.C.: 5084
N.A.I.C.S.: 423830
Media: 2-10-13-20
Brands & Products:
ACTIS

SIERRA PACIFIC INDUSTRIES
19794 Riverside Ave
Anderson, CA 96007-4908
Tel.: (530) 378-8000
Fax: (530) 378-8109
E-mail: sierra@spi-ind.com
Web Site: www.spi-ind.com
Approx. Number Employees: 4,000
Business Description:
Lumber & Wood Products Mfr & Retailer
S.I.C.: 2421; 2431; 5031
N.A.I.C.S.: 321113; 321918; 423310
Media: 2-4-8-10-16-21-22
Distr.: Natl.
Budget Set: Annually
Personnel:
A. A. Emmerson *(Pres)*
Mark Emmerson *(CFO)*
Steve Gaston *(CIO)*
George Emmerson *(VP-Sls & Mktg)*
Brands & Products:
GROWING FORESTS FOR OUR FUTURE?
SIERRA PACIFIC INDUSTRIES

SIKA CORPORATION
(Sub. of Sika AG)
201 Polito Ave
Lyndhurst, NJ 07071-3601
Tel.: (201) 933-8800
Fax: (201) 933-6225
Fax: (201) 804-1076
Toll Free: (800) 933SIKA
E-mail: sikainfo@sika-corp.com
Web Site: www.sikausa.com
Approx. Number Employees: 900
Year Founded: 1937
Business Description:
Developer & Mfr of Specialty Chemicals; Sealants, Adhesives, Epoxies, Grouts, Mortars, Concrete Admixtures; Noise Reduction & Reinforcing Materials for Construction, Industrial Applications, Transportation, Appliances & Automotive
S.I.C.: 2891; 2851
N.A.I.C.S.: 325520; 325510
Import Export
Advertising Expenditures: $340,000
Media: 2-4-5-7-10-11-19-20-21
Distr.: Natl.
Budget Set: Sept.
Personnel:
Paul Schuler *(Pres)*
Steve Gill *(Sr VP-Fin & Admin)*
Steve Harms *(Sr VP-Ops)*
Scott Henry *(Sr VP-Industry)*
Rick Montani *(Sr VP-Construction Prods Div)*
Steve Rosenberg *(Sr VP-R&D)*
Brian Whelan *(Sr VP-Roofing)*
Rose Romaldo *(Mktg Mgr)*
Advertising Agency:
Stiegler, Wells, Brunswick & Roth, Inc.
(d/b/a SWB&R)
3865 Adler Pl
Bethlehem, PA 18017-9000
Tel.: (610) 866-0611
Fax: (610) 866-8650

SILBERLINE MANUFACTURING CO., INC.
130 Lincoln Dr
Tamaqua, PA 18252-0420
Mailing Address:
PO Box B
Tamaqua, PA 18252-0420
Tel.: (570) 668-6050
Fax: (570) 668-2621
Toll Free: (800) 348-4824
Web Site: www.silberline.com
Approx. Number Employees: 260
Year Founded: 1945
Business Description:
Aluminum Pigments Mfr
S.I.C.: 2816; 2819
N.A.I.C.S.: 325131; 325188
Media: 2-4-7-10-17
Distr.: Natl.
Personnel:
Glenn Kleppinger *(Sr VP-Global Bus Dev)*
James Ranieri *(VP-Sls-America)*
Anthony Reed *(Dir-Automotive Mktg-Global)*
Richard Rosen *(Mgr-Automotive Productive Dev-Global)*
Sean Zhou *(Mgr-Product Dev-Plastics)*
Brands & Products:
AQUASIL
AQUAVET
AQUAVEX
ETERNABRITE
GEOMETRIC PIGMENT
THE GLOBAL SUPPLIER OF EFFECT PIGMENTS
SIL-O-WET
SILBERCOTE
SILBERLINE
SILCROMA
SILVET
SILVEX
SPARKLE SILVER
STARBRITE
TUFFLAKE
ULTRA
VACCUM METALIZED FLAKE
Advertising Agency:
Keenan-Nagle Advertising
1301 S 12th St
Allentown, PA 18103-3814
Tel.: (610) 797-7100
Fax: (610) 797-8212
(Aluminum Pigments)

SILBRICO CORPORATION
6300 River Rd
Hodgkins, IL 60525-4257
Tel.: (708) 354-3350
Fax: (708) 354-6698
Toll Free: (800) 323-4287
E-mail: info@silbrico.com
Web Site: www.silbrico.com
Sales Range: $100-124.9 Million
Approx. Number Employees: 70
Year Founded: 1945
Business Description:
Perlite Products Mfr For Lightweight Insulating Construction
S.I.C.: 3295; 3296
N.A.I.C.S.: 327992; 327993
Import Export
Media: 2-4-7-8-10-19-21-26
Distr.: Natl.; Reg.
Budget Set: Dec.
Personnel:
T. Mendius *(Pres & CEO)*
Steve Garnett *(CFO)*
Brands & Products:
KRUM
RYOLEX
SIL-CELL
SIL-KLEER
SILBRICO

SILVER BULLET PLUMBING
6011 Benjamin Rd Ste 102
Tampa, FL 33634
Tel.: (813) 699-5643
Web Site: www.silverbulletplumbing.com
Business Description:
Plumbing Services
S.I.C.: 1711
N.A.I.C.S.: 238220
Media: 13
Personnel:
Eric Takebury *(Service Mgr)*
Advertising Agency:
Baum Marketing Group
6011 Benjamin Rd Ste 102
Tampa, FL 33634
Toll Free: (888) 688-4613

SIMONINI BUILDERS
1910 S Blvd Ste 200
Charlotte, NC 28203
Tel.: (704) 358-9940
Fax: (704) 358-9978
E-mail: info@simonini.com
Web Site: www.simonini.com
Sales Range: $200-249.9 Million
Approx. Number Employees: 60
Year Founded: 1996
Business Description:
Home Builder
S.I.C.: 1531; 1521; 1522
N.A.I.C.S.: 236117; 236115; 236116
Personnel:
Ray A. Killian, Jr. *(Owner, CEO & Dir)*
William E. Saint *(CFO)*
Alan C. Simonini *(Chief Creative Officer)*

Key to Media (For complete agency information see *The Advertising Red Books-Agencies* edition):
1. Bus. Publs. 2. Cable T.V. 3. Catalogs & Directories. 4. Co-op Adv. 5. Consumer Mags. 6. D.M. to Bus. Estab.7. D.M. to Consumers
8. Daily Newsp. 9. Exhibits/Trade Shows 10. Foreign 11. Infomercial 12. Internet Adv.13. Multimedia 14. Network Radio
15. Network T.V. 16. Newsp. Distr. Mags. 17. Other 18. Outdoor (Posters, Transit) 19. Point of Purchase20. Premiums, Novelties
21. Product Samples 22. Special Events Mktg. 23. Spot Radio 24. Spot T.V. 25. Weekly Newsp. 26. Yellow Page Adv.

Advertising Agency:
Loeffler Ketchum Mountjoy (LKM)
6115 Park S Dr Ste 350
Charlotte, NC 28210
Tel.: (704) 364-8969
Fax: (704) 364-8470
Toll Free: (800) 851-8436

SIMPSON DOOR COMPANY

(Sub. of Simpson Investment Company)
400 Simpson Ave
McCleary, WA 98557
Tel.: (360) 495-3291
Fax: (360) 495-3291
Web Site: www.simpsondoor.com
Approx. Number Employees: 250
Business Description:
Mfr. of Doors
S.I.C.: 2431
N.A.I.C.S.: 321911
Export
Advertising Expenditures: $1,000,000
Media: 2-4-5-6-10-17
Distr.: Natl.
Budget Set: Sept.
Personnel:
Jim Brandt *(Mgr-Mktg Svcs)*
Brad Loveless *(Mgr-Mktg)*
Brands & Products:
ADVENT
BUNGALOW SERIES
DOORS OF A LIFETIME
ENCORE
MASTERMARK
REDI-PRIME
SIMPSON
VIEWSAVER

SIMPSON LUMBER COMPANY, LLC

(Sub. of Simpson Investment Company)
917 E 11th St
Tacoma, WA 98421
Mailing Address:
PO Box 460
Shelton, WA 98584-0460
Tel.: (253) 779-6400
Fax: (253) 779-6469
Web Site: www.simpson.com
Approx. Number Employees: 2,000
Year Founded: 1890
Business Description:
Lumber, Paper & Doors Mfr
S.I.C.: 2421; 0181
N.A.I.C.S.: 321912; 111421
Import Export
Media: 2-4-7-10-22
Distr.: Intl.; Natl.
Personnel:
Laurie Creech *(Mgr-Sls, Mktg-Lumber & Fiber)*
Advertising Agencies:
Brandner Communications, Inc.
32026 32nd Ave S
Federal Way, WA 98001
Tel.: (253) 661-7333
Fax: (253) 661-7336

JayRay, a communications consultancy
535 E Dock St Ste 205
Tacoma, WA 98402-4630
Tel.: (253) 627-9128
Fax: (253) 627-6548

SIMPSON TECHNOLOGIES CORPORATION

751 Shoreline Dr
Aurora, IL 60504-6194
Tel.: (630) 978-0044
Fax: (630) 978-0068
E-mail: sales@simpsongroup.com
Web Site: www.simpsongroup.com
E-Mail For Key Personnel:
Sales Director: sales@simpsongroup.com
Sales Range: $10-24.9 Million
Approx. Number Employees: 120
Year Founded: 1912
Business Description:
Foundry Sand Mixing, Preparing, Reclaiming & Handling Equipment; Vibratory Screens
S.I.C.: 3559
N.A.I.C.S.: 333298
Media: 5-10-17-19
Distr.: Intl.
Budget Set: Nov.
Personnel:
Henry W. Dienst *(Chm & CEO)*
Bruce W. Dienst *(Pres & COO)*
Scott M. Strobl *(VP-Tech)*
Suzanne M. Bolda *(Dir-HR)*
David V. Silsby *(Product Mgr)*
Julie McMillin *(Mgr-IT Projects)*
Brands & Products:
FLEXIGAS
HARTLEY
MATCHBLOMATIC
MIX-MULLER
MULTI-COOLER
PRO-CLAIM
SIMPSON
SIMPSON MIX-MULLER
SIMPSON MULTI-MULL
SPEEDMULLOR

SKUTTLE INDOOR AIR QUALITY PRODUCTS

101 Margaret St
Marietta, OH 45750-9052
Tel.: (740) 373-9169
Fax: (740) 373-9565
Toll Free: (800) 848-9786
E-mail: customerservice@skuttle.com
Web Site: www.skuttle.com
Sales Range: $1-9.9 Million
Approx. Number Employees: 30
Year Founded: 1917
Business Description:
Mfr. of Whole-House Humidifiers, Air Cleaners & Make-up Air Controls
S.I.C.: 3634; 3564
N.A.I.C.S.: 335211; 333411
Export
Advertising Expenditures: $300,000
Media: 2-3-4-5-7-8-10-16-19-20-21-25-26
Distr.: Intl.; Natl.
Budget Set: Apr.
Personnel:
John Riley *(VP-Sls & Mktg)*
Brands & Products:
SKUTTLE

SMITH-MIDLAND CORPORATION

5119 Catlett Rd
Midland, VA 22728-2113
Tel.: (540) 439-3266
Fax: (540) 439-1232
E-mail: info@smithmidland.com
Web Site: www.smithmidland.com
Approx. Rev.: $31,709,989
Approx. Number Employees: 139
Year Founded: 1960
Business Description:
Precast Concrete Products For Construction, Utilities & Farming Industries Develops, Mfr, Marketer, Leasor, Licenser, Seller & Installer
S.I.C.: 3272
N.A.I.C.S.: 327390; 327332
Advertising Expenditures: $373,000
Media: 5-7-8-10-13-17
Personnel:
Rodney I. Smith *(Pres & CEO)*
Ashley B. Smith *(Pres & COO)*
William A. Kenter *(CFO)*
Steve Ott *(VP-Engrg)*
Brands & Products:
BEACH PRISMS
BLUE RIDGE
CONCRETE SAFETY SYSTEMS
DURAFLEX 360
EASI-BRICK
EASI-SET
EASI-SPAN
EXCELLENCE IN PRECAST CONCRETE
FAN
H2OUT
J-J HOOKS
LIFT-AND-RELEASE
NELSON
OUTBACK
SECOND NATURE
SIERRA WALL
SLENDERWALL
SMITH-MIDLAND
THERMAGUARD
Advertising Agency:
Ad Ventures
5119 Catlett Rd
Midland, VA 22728
Tel.: (540) 439-8056
Fax: (540) 439-1232

SMOOTH-ON INC.

2000 Saint John St
Easton, PA 18042-6646
Tel.: (610) 252-5800
Fax: (610) 252-6200
Toll Free: (800) 762-0744
E-mail: smoothon@smooth-on.com
Web Site: www.smooth-on.com
Approx. Number Employees: 50
Year Founded: 1895
Business Description:
Epoxy Resin Formulations; Polysulphide Rubber Formulations; Polyurethanes; Epoxy Adhesive Cements & Sealants & Flexible Mold Compounds; Metal Filled Epoxy Compounds; Non-Metallic Epoxy Compounds & Release Agents Mfr
S.I.C.: 2821; 2822
N.A.I.C.S.: 325211; 325212
Export
Media: 1-2-4-6-10
Distr.: Intl.; Natl.
Budget Set: Dec.
Personnel:
Sal A. Bianco, III *(Pres)*
Brands & Products:
ACCEL-T
ALJA-SAFE
BODY DOUBLE
BRUSH-ON
C-1508
C-1509
C-1515
C-1520
CAB-O-SIL
CLEAR FLEX
COLORMATCH
CRYPTOLYTE
CRYSTAL CLEAR
DRAGON SKIN
DRAGON SKIN Q
DUOMATRIX
DUOMATRIX-C
DUOMATRIX-G
DUOMATRIX NEO
EA-40
ECOFLEX
ENCAPSO K
EQUINOX
EVERGREEN
EZ-MIX
EZ-SPRAY
EZ-SPRAY JR.
FAST CAT
FASTCAT
FEATHER LITE
FLAME OUT
FLEXFOAM-IT!
FMC
FOAM-IT!
FORMULA 79
HYPER-FOLIC
IGNITE
IN & OUT
KICK-IT
KWIKEE
M-13
MATRIX
METALSET
MOLD MAX
MT-13
ONE STEP
OOMOO
PC-3
PLASTI-PASTE
PLAT CAT
PMC
POYO PUTTY
PRE-COTE
PSYCHO PAINT
REBOUND
REOFLEX
RUBBER GLASS
SHELL SHOCK
SIL-POXY
SILC PIG
SILICONE THINNER
SKIN TITE
SLACKER
SLO-JO
SMASH! PLASTIC
SMOOTH-CAST
SMOOTH-ON
SMOOTH-SIL
SO-CURE
SO-FLEX
SO-STRONG
SOMA FOAMA
SONITE 16
SORTA CLEAR
SORTA-CLEAR
SUN DEVIL
SUPERSEAL
TASK
THI-VEX
UNIVERSAL MOLD RELEASE

Key to Media (For complete agency information see *The Advertising Red Books-Agencies* edition):
1. Bus. Publs. 2. Cable T.V. 3. Catalogs & Directories. 4. Co-op Adv. 5. Consumer Mags. 6. D.M. to Bus. Estab.7. D.M. to Consumers
8. Daily Newsp. 9. Exhibits/Trade Shows 10. Foreign 11. Infomercial 12. Internet Adv.13. Multimedia 14. Network Radio
15. Network T.V. 16. Newsp. Distr. Mags. 17. Other 18. Outdoor (Posters, Transit) 19. Point of Purchase20. Premiums, Novelties
21. Product Samples 22. Special Events Mktg. 23. Spot Radio 24. Spot T.V. 25. Weekly Newsp. 26. Yellow Page Adv.

Smooth-On Inc. — (Continued)

URE-BOND
URE-FIL
VYTAFLEX
XTEND-IT

SNC-LAVALIN GROUP INC.
455 Rene-Levesque Blvd West
Montreal, QC H2Z 1Z3, Canada
Tel.: (514) 393-1000
Fax: (514) 866-0795
Telex: 55-61250 SNC MTL
E-mail: info@snclavalin.com
Web Site: www.snc-lavalin.com
E-Mail For Key Personnel:
Public Relations: gillian.maccormack@snclavalin.com
Approx. Rev.: $6,433,838,112
Approx. Number Employees: 23,923
Year Founded: 1911
Business Description:
Project Management, Engineering, Procurement & Construction; Technical & Socio-Economic Studies
S.I.C.: 8711
N.A.I.C.S.: 541330
Media: 2-10
Personnel:
Gwyn Morgan *(Chm)*
Pierre Duhaime *(Pres & CEO)*
Gilles Laramee *(CFO & Exec VP)*
Riadh Ben Aissa *(Exec VP)*
Feroz Ashraf *(Exec VP-Mining & Metallurgy)*
Jean Beaudoin *(Exec VP-Chemicals & Petroleum)*
Jim Burke *(Exec VP)*
Darleen Caron *(Exec VP-Global HR)*
Patrick Lamarre *(Exec VP)*
Michael Novak *(Exec VP)*
Jean Claude Pingat *(Exec VP)*
Charlie Rate *(Exec VP)*
Pat Di Lillo *(Sr VP & Controller)*
Amin Khouday *(Sr VP & Gen Mgr-Road Transportation)*
Dominick Trupia *(Sr VP & Gen Mgr-Chemicals & Petroleum Bus Unit-Houston)*
Gerry Grigoropoulos *(Sr VP-Capital)*
Luc Lainey *(Sr VP-Quality & Trng)*
Henri Madjar *(Sr VP-Project Dev & Intl)*
Diane Nyisztor *(Sr VP-Compensation & Benefits)*
Edward Ryczkowski *(VP & Gen Mgr-Manitoba)*
Nicola Angelini *(VP-Corp Strategy & Dev)*
Leslie Quinton *(VP-Global Corp Comm)*
Dominique Morval *(Dir-Comm-Global Corp Comm)*
Brands & Products:
SNC-LAVALIN

SOCIETY OF AUTOMOTIVE ENGINEERS, INC.
(Name Changed to SAE International)

SOLUTIONS OFFICE INTERIORS, INC.
(d/b/a S O I)
(Private-Parent-Single Location)
1702L Meridian Ave Ste 261
San Jose, CA 95125
Tel.: (408) 295-0101
Fax: (408) 295-0202
E-mail: info@expectsolutions.com
Web Site: www.expectsolutions.com
Approx. Rev.: $1,700,000
Approx. Number Employees: 30
Year Founded: 2001
Business Description:
Office Environment Architect
S.I.C.: 7389
N.A.I.C.S.: 541410
Media: 13
Personnel:
Sarah Laffoday *(Dir-Bus Dev)*
George Meza *(Dir-Ops)*

SOMMER METALCRAFT CORPORATION
315 Poston Dr
Crawfordsville, IN 47933
Tel.: (765) 362-6200
Fax: (765) 359-4201
Toll Free: (888) 8SOMMER
E-mail: sales@sommercorp.com
Web Site: www.sommermetalcraft.com
E-Mail For Key Personnel:
Sales Director: sales@sommercorp.com
Approx. Number Employees: 115
Year Founded: 1908
Business Description:
Mfr. of Wire Forms & Welded Wire Assembly
S.I.C.: 3496
N.A.I.C.S.: 332618
Advertising Expenditures: $300,000
Media: 2-7-10-13
Distr.: Natl.
Personnel:
Jon W. Sommer *(Chm & CEO)*
Scott Sommer *(Pres)*
Brands & Products:
SOMMER METALCRAFT

SONIC TECHNOLOGY SOLUTIONS INC.
Unit 7 8765 Ash Street
Vancouver, BC V6P 6T3, Canada
Tel.: (604) 736-2552
Fax: (604) 736-2558
Toll Free: (877) 736-2552
Web Site: www.sesi.ca
Business Description:
Soil Remediation & Environmental Cleanup Services
S.I.C.: 4953
N.A.I.C.S.: 562211; 562219
Advertising Expenditures: $46,029
Media: 17
Personnel:
Adam R. Sumel *(Co-Founder, Pres & CEO)*
Richard Ilich *(Co-Founder & Sec)*
Richard Wadsworth *(Pres & CEO)*
Lisa Sharp *(CFO)*
Brands & Products:
SONOPROCESS

SONO-TEK CORPORATION
2012 Rte 9W
Milton, NY 12547
Tel.: (845) 795-2020
Fax: (845) 795-2720
Web Site: www.sono-tek.com
Approx. Rev.: $7,242,324
Approx. Number Employees: 44
Year Founded: 1975
Business Description:
Ultrasonic Liquid Atomizing Nozzles Mfr & Sales
S.I.C.: 3593
N.A.I.C.S.: 333995
Advertising Expenditures: $206,271
Personnel:
Christopher L. Coccio *(Chm & CEO)*
Joseph Riemer *(Pres)*
Stephen J. Bagley *(CFO)*
Edward B. Bozydaj *(Dir-Ops)*
Robb Engle *(Dir-Tech Svcs)*

SOUTHERN LUMBER & MILLWORK CORP.
2031 King St Ext
Charleston, SC 29405-9419
Tel.: (843) 744-6281
Fax: (843) 747-4154
E-mail: mail@southernlumbermillwork.com
Web Site: www.southernlumbermillwork.com
Approx. Sls.: $10,000,000
Approx. Number Employees: 60
Year Founded: 1940
Business Description:
Wholesale & Retail Lumber, Custom Made Doors & Windows; Custom Millwork Building Materials
S.I.C.: 5211
N.A.I.C.S.: 444110
Import
Media: 6-9-10-23-24-25-26
Distr.: Natl.
Budget Set: Jan.
Personnel:
Joyce A. Shuler *(CEO)*
Ben Albrecht *(CEO-Mfg Ops)*

SOUTHERN PIPE & SUPPLY CO., INC.
4330 Hwy 39 N
Meridian, MS 39301
Tel.: (601) 693-2911
Fax: (601) 485-0074
Web Site: www.southernpipe.com
Sales Range: $125-149.9 Million
Approx. Number Employees: 680
Business Description:
Distr of Wholesale Plumbing & Heating Supplies
S.I.C.: 5074; 5075
N.A.I.C.S.: 423720; 423730
Advertising Expenditures: $2,000,000
Media: 2-4
Personnel:
Jay Davidson *(Pres)*
Martin Davidson *(Pres)*
James McAllister *(VP-Fin)*
Ron Black *(Dir-HR)*

SPARKMAN & STEPHENS, INC.
529 5th Ave 14th Fl
New York, NY 10017
Tel.: (212) 661-1240
Tel.: (212) 661-6170 (Brokerage)
Fax: (212) 661-1235
E-mail: info@sparkmanstephens.com
Web Site: www.sparkmanstephens.com
Approx. Number Employees: 17
Year Founded: 1929
Business Description:
Yacht Design & Brokerage
S.I.C.: 3732; 5551
N.A.I.C.S.: 336612; 441222
Media: 10
Personnel:
Bruce Johnson *(Pres & Chief Designer)*

SPEAKMAN COMPANY
400 Anchor Mill Rd Twin Spans Business Park
New Castle, DE 19720
Tel.: (302) 764-7100
Fax: (302) 764-1956
Toll Free: (800) 537-2107
E-mail: sales@speakmancompany.com
Web Site: www.speakmancompany.com
E-Mail For Key Personnel:
Sales Director: sales@speakmancompany.com
Approx. Number Employees: 110
Year Founded: 1869
Business Description:
Mfr. of Showers, Brass Plumbing, Decorative Brass Plumbing Fittings & Safety Equipment
S.I.C.: 3432; 3431
N.A.I.C.S.: 332913; 332998
Import Export
Media: 1-4-7-10-13-17-21
Distr.: Natl.
Budget Set: Nov.
Personnel:
Robert Cook *(Pres)*
Michael Trenham *(CFO)*
Robert Knoll *(COO)*
James Clark *(Mgr-Acctg)*
Kathy Sarren *(Mgr-HR)*
Brands & Products:
ANYSTREAM
COMMANDER
COSMOPOLITAN
EASY-PUSH
EYESAVER
MICROFLO
PERFECT VALVE
SAFE-T-ZONE
SENTINEL MARK II
SPEAKMAN

SPECIALIZED TECHNOLOGY RESOURCES, INC.
(Sub. of STR Holdings, Inc.)
10 Water St
Enfield, CT 06082-4899
Tel.: (860) 749-8371
Fax: (860) 749-8234
E-mail: strnet@strus.com
Web Site: www.strquality.com
E-Mail For Key Personnel:
President: dennis.jilot@strus.com
Sales Range: $25-49.9 Million
Approx. Number Employees: 150
Year Founded: 1944
Business Description:
International Network of Independent Contract Laboratories Providing Engineering, Research & Development, Testing & Quality Assurance, Labor, Health & Safety Audits, Specialty Manufacturing, Consulting & Publishing Services for Industry, Government & Trade Associations; Social Compliance Auditing
S.I.C.: 8733; 3081
N.A.I.C.S.: 541710; 326113
Export
Media: 10-13
Distr.: Natl.

Key to Media (For complete agency information see *The Advertising Red Books-Agencies* edition):
1. Bus. Publs. 2. Cable T.V. 3. Catalogs & Directories. 4. Co-op Adv. 5. Consumer Mags. 6. D.M. to Bus. Estab.7. D.M. to Consumers 8. Daily Newsp. 9. Exhibits/Trade Shows 10. Foreign 11. Infomercial 12. Internet Adv.13. Multimedia 14. Network Radio 15. Network T.V. 16. Newsp. Distr. Mags. 17. Other 18. Outdoor (Posters, Transit) 19. Point of Purchase20. Premiums, Novelties 21. Product Samples 22. Special Events Mktg. 23. Spot Radio 24. Spot T.V. 25. Weekly Newsp. 26. Yellow Page Adv.

Budget Set: Oct. -Nov.
Brands & Products:
PHOTOCAP
STR

SPECIALTY SCREEN & GLASS LLC
11144 Main St
Cincinnati, OH 45241
Tel.: (513) 563-4535
E-mail: sales@specialtyscreenandglass.com
Web Site:
www.specialtyscreenandglass.com
Business Description:
Installation & Repair of Screen & Glass Windows
S.I.C.: 1751; 1793
N.A.I.C.S.: 238350; 238150
Media: 6-16-18-26-29
Personnel:
David Clark *(Pres)*

SPEEDRACK PRODUCTS GROUP, LTD.
7903 Venture Ave NW
Sparta, MI 49345-9309
Mailing Address:
PO Box 191
Wilmington, DE 19899-0191
Tel.: (616) 887-0002
Fax: (616) 887-2693
Toll Free: (800) 752-7352
E-mail: sales@speedrack.net
Web Site: www.speedrack.net
E-Mail For Key Personnel:
Sales Director: sales@speedrack.net
Sales Range: $25-49.9 Million
Approx. Number Employees: 300
Year Founded: 1989
Business Description:
Supplier of Pallet Racking & Storage Systems
S.I.C.: 3444
N.A.I.C.S.: 332322
Media: 2-4-7-10-13-26
Distr.: Natl.
Personnel:
Jim Johnson *(Pres)*
Ron Ducharme *(CEO & Dir-Fin)*
Brands & Products:
DRIVE-IN
KEYSTONE
SPEEDRACK
SUPER CANT-LEG
SUPER TRUSS
TEARDROP

SSGI, INC.
8120 Belvedere Rd Ste 4
West Palm Beach, FL 33411
Tel.: (561) 333-3600
Fax: (561) 202-6216
Web Site:
www.surgesolutionsgroup.com
Approx. Rev.: $7,784,942
Approx. Number Employees: 21
Year Founded: 1997
Business Description:
General Construction Services Including Insurance Restoration, Petroleum Contracting & Installation Services
S.I.C.: 7349; 5172; 6411
N.A.I.C.S.: 561790; 424720; 524298
Advertising Expenditures: $54,629
Media: 17

Personnel:
Larry M. Glasscock *(Pres & CEO)*

STABLER COMPANIES, INC.
(Sub. of New Enterprise Stone & Lime Co., Inc.)
635 Lucknow Rd
Harrisburg, PA 17110-1635
Tel.: (717) 234-3106
Fax: (717) 236-1281
E-mail: info@stablercompaniesinc.com
Web Site:
www.stablercompaniesinc.com
Approx. Number Employees: 1,200
Year Founded: 1953
Business Description:
General Contractor; Highway & Street Construction; Manufacturer of Asphalt Paving Mixtures, Crushed & Broken Limestone
S.I.C.: 5032; 3089
N.A.I.C.S.: 423320; 326199
Personnel:
James van Buren *(Pres & COO)*
Craig Noll *(VP-Sls-Mktg)*
Dave Koman *(Acctg Mgr)*
Advertising Agency:
Sonnhalter
633 W Bagley Rd
Berea, OH 44017-1356
Tel.: (440) 234-1812
Fax: (440) 234-1890

STANLEY ACCESS TECHNOLOGIES, LLC
(Sub. of Stanley Security Solutions, Inc.)
65 Scott Swamp Rd
Farmington, CT 06032
Tel.: (860) 677-2861
Fax: (860) 679-6495
Toll Free: (800) 7ACCESS
Web Site:
www.stanleyaccesstechnologies.com
Sales Range: $150-199.9 Million
Business Description:
Automatic Doors & Automatic Door Operating Equipment Mfr & Distr
S.I.C.: 5031; 1751
N.A.I.C.S.: 423310; 238130
Media: 4-10
Personnel:
Justin C. Boswell *(Pres-Stanley Security Solutions)*
Brands & Products:
STANLEY

STANLEY SUPPLY & SERVICES, INC.
(Sub. of Stanley Tools Group)
335 Willow St
North Andover, MA 01845
Tel.: (978) 682-9844
Fax: (800) 743-8141
Web Site:
www.stanleysupplyservices.com
E-Mail For Key Personnel:
Sales Director: sales@stanleyworks.com
Sales Range: $75-99.9 Million
Approx. Number Employees: 200
Business Description:
High Tech Tools, Test Instruments & Personal Protection & Safety Products Mfr & Distr
S.I.C.: 5085
N.A.I.C.S.: 423840

Media: 4-7
Personnel:
Paul Kiyser *(Gen Mgr)*
Brands & Products:
JENSEN

STAR BUILDING SYSTEMS
(Sub. of NCI BUILDING SYSTEMS, INC.)
8600 S Interstate 35
Oklahoma City, OK 73149
Mailing Address:
PO Box 94910
Oklahoma City, OK 73143-4910
Tel.: (405) 636-2010
Fax: (405) 636-2419
Toll Free: (800) 879-7827
E-mail: info@starbuildings.com
Web Site: www.starbuildings.com
Approx. Number Employees: 100
Year Founded: 1927
Business Description:
Metal Building Systems & Metal Component Products Mfr
S.I.C.: 3448
N.A.I.C.S.: 332311
Import Export
Distr.: Intl.; Natl.
Budget Set: Sept. -Oct.
Personnel:
Joe Edge *(Pres)*
Jack Eskew *(VP-HR)*
Phil Symes *(VP-Sls & Mktg)*
Dustin Cole *(Dir-Engr)*
David Alexander *(Dir-Customer Svc)*
Gene Bell *(Dir-Pricing & Production Control)*
Dan DeKalb *(Dir-Quality & Product Dev)*
Bill Hood *(Dir-Drafting)*
Dave Rutherford *(Dir-Bus Affairs)*
Jeff Koos *(Mgr)*
Advertising Agency:
Star Marketing
8600 S Interstate 35
Oklahoma City, OK 73149
Tel.: (405) 636-2010

STAR LUMBER & SUPPLY COMPANY, INC.
325 S W St
Wichita, KS 67213-2105
Tel.: (316) 942-2221
Fax: (316) 942-0690
Web Site: www.starlumber.com
Sales Range: $100-124.9 Million
Approx. Number Employees: 380
Year Founded: 1939
Business Description:
Lumber & Other Building Materials Mfr & Retailer
S.I.C.: 5031
N.A.I.C.S.: 423310
Import Export
Advertising Expenditures: $300,000
Media: 2-3-5-8-9-10-13-18-19-20-21-22-23-24-26
Distr.: Reg.
Budget Set: Jan.
Personnel:
Chris Goebel *(Pres & CEO)*
Roger Voge *(Exec VP)*
Patrick Goebel *(VP-Sls & Mktg)*
Brands & Products:
STAR

STARRCO COMPANY INC.
11700 Fairgrove Indus Blvd
Maryland Heights, MO 63043-3436
Tel.: (314) 567-5533
Fax: (314) 567-7555
Toll Free: (800) 325-4259
E-mail: starrco@starrco.com
Web Site: www.starrco.com
Approx. Number Employees: 40
Year Founded: 1965
Business Description:
Mfr. of Portable Buildings, Pre-engineered Modular Office Systems, Mezzanines & Exterior Portable Buildings
S.I.C.: 3448; 3444
N.A.I.C.S.: 332311; 332322
Media: 2-4-5-6-7-10-13-18-20-21
Distr.: Natl.
Personnel:
Bryan Carey *(Pres)*
John Gilmore *(Exec VP)*
Daryl Carlson *(VP-Mktg)*
Brands & Products:
MEZZANINES
PREASSEMBLED PORTABLE BUILDINGS
STARRCO
STARRCO 2000
STARRCO 2500
STARRCO 3000
STARRCO 3500
STARRSPACE 3000
STARRSPACE 3500

STEBBINS ENGINEERING & MANUFACTURING COMPANY
363 Eastern Blvd
Watertown, NY 13601-3140
Tel.: (315) 782-3000
Fax: (315) 782-0481
E-mail: info@stebbinseng.com
Web Site: www.stebbinseng.com
Sales Range: $125-149.9 Million
Approx. Number Employees: 1,500
Year Founded: 1884
Business Description:
Mfr. & Install Reinforced Tile & Linings
S.I.C.: 1799; 3443
N.A.I.C.S.: 238990; 332313
Export
Media: 1-2-21-26
Distr.: Natl.
Personnel:
A. E. Calligaris *(Chm, Pres & CEO)*
Andrew J. Weiss *(Exec VP)*
Robert J. Storms *(Sr VP)*
Dave Honan *(VP-Engrg)*

STEEL DYNAMICS, INC.
7575 W Jefferson Blvd
Fort Wayne, IN 46804-7932
Tel.: (260) 459-3553
Fax: (260) 969-3591
E-mail: investor@steeldynamics.com
Web Site: www.steeldynamics.com
Approx. Sls.: $6,300,887,000
Approx. Number Employees: 6,180
Year Founded: 1993
Business Description:
Steel Products Mfr
S.I.C.: 3312; 3316; 3317; 3441
N.A.I.C.S.: 331111; 331210; 331221; 332312
Media: 2
Personnel:
Keith E. Busse *(Chm & CEO)*
Theresa E. Wagler *(CFO & Exec VP)*

Key to Media (For complete agency information see *The Advertising Red Books-Agencies* edition):
1. Bus. Publs. 2. Cable T.V. 3. Catalogs & Directories. 4. Co-op Adv. 5. Consumer Mags. 6. D.M. to Bus. Estab.7. D.M. to Consumers 8. Daily Newsp. 9. Exhibits/Trade Shows 10. Foreign 11. Infomercial 12. Internet Adv.13. Multimedia 14. Network Radio 15. Network T.V. 16. Newsp. Distr. Mags. 17. Other 18. Outdoor (Posters, Transit) 19. Point of Purchase20. Premiums, Novelties 21. Product Samples 22. Special Events Mktg. 23. Spot Radio 24. Spot T.V. 25. Weekly Newsp. 26. Yellow Page Adv.

Steel Dynamics, Inc. — (Continued)

Gary E. Heasley *(Exec VP-Strategic Plng & Bus Dev)*
Richard P. Teets, Jr. *(Exec VP-Steelmaking)*
Glenn A. Pushis *(VP & Gen Mgr-Flat Roll Div)*
Ben Eisbart *(VP-HR)*
Don Switzer *(Mgr-Mktg)*
Fred Warner *(Mgr-IR)*
Brands & Products:
SDI
STEEL DYNAMICS, INC

STEELCRAFT MANUFACTURING COMPANY
(Sub. of Ingersoll-Rand Company)
9017 Blue Ash Rd
Cincinnati, OH 45242-6816
Tel.: (513) 745-6400
Fax: (513) 745-6657
Fax: (513) 745-6300
Toll Free: (800) 243-9780
E-mail: info@steelcraft.com
Web Site: www.steelcraft.com
Approx. Number Employees: 800
Year Founded: 1933
Business Description:
Mfr. of Commercial Steel Doors & Door Frames
S.I.C.: 3442
N.A.I.C.S.: 332321
Export
Media: 2-4-7-10-13-16-21
Distr.: Natl.
Personnel:
Al Urbaniak *(Mgr-Tech Support)*
Brands & Products:
BROADWAY COLLECTION BY SCHLAGE
DEXTER
DIXIE-PACIFIC
DOR-O-MATIC
E-BOLT
ETC
FALCON
GLYNN-JOHNSON
HARTMANN-SANDERS
INTERFLEX
IVES
KRYPTONITE
LCN
LOCKNETICS
MONARCH
RECOGNITION SYSTEMS
SCHLAGE
STEELCRAFT
VON DUPRIN

STOCK BUILDING SUPPLY OF ARKANSAS, LLC
(Sub. of Stock Building Supply Inc.)
(d/b/a National Home Centers)
Hwy 265 N
Springdale, AR 72764-0789
Tel.: (479) 756-1700
Fax: (479) 927-5790
E-mail: info@nhci.com
Web Site: www.nhci.com
Sales Range: $100-124.9 Million
Approx. Number Employees: 500
Year Founded: 1972
Business Description:
Lumber & Other Building Materials Dealers
S.I.C.: 5211
N.A.I.C.S.: 444110
Media: 8-9-25
Distr.: Reg.
Personnel:
Jeff Newman *(Sr VP-Pur & Mgr-Mdsg)*
John Collins *(VP-Mdsg)*
Beth Epperson *(Mgr-Adv)*

STONCOR GROUP, INC.
(Sub. of RPM Industrial Holding Co.)
1000 E Park Ave
Maple Shade, NJ 08052
Tel.: (856) 779-7500
Fax: (856) 321-7510
Toll Free: (800) 854-0310
Web Site: www.stoncor.com
Approx. Rev.: $757,179,008
Approx. Number Employees: 200
Year Founded: 1922
Business Description:
Industrial & Commercial Polymer-Based Floors, Walls, Coatings, Linings & Construction Products Mfr & Retailer
S.I.C.: 2851; 3996
N.A.I.C.S.: 325510; 326192
Advertising Expenditures: $230,000
Media: 2-4-10-17
Distr.: Natl.
Budget Set: Oct.
Personnel:
David P. Reif *(Pres)*
Mike Jewell *(VP-Mktg)*
Kendall Ellis *(Mgr-Mktg)*
Brands & Products:
STONBLEND
STONCHEM
STONCLAD
STONGLAZE
STONLUX
STONSHIELD
Advertising Agency:
Signature Communications
417 N Eigth St 4th Fl Ste 401
Philadelphia, PA 19123-4226
Tel.: (215) 922-3022
Fax: (215) 922-3033

STONECUTTER MILLS CORP.
230 Spindale St
Spindale, NC 28160
Tel.: (828) 286-2341
Fax: (828) 287-7280
Web Site: www.stonecuttermills.com
Approx. Number Employees: 6
Year Founded: 1920
Business Description:
Industrial Park Manager
S.I.C.: 6531
N.A.I.C.S.: 531312
Media: 9-18
Personnel:
James R. Cowan *(CEO)*

SUBURBAN PROPANE PARTNERS, L.P.
1 Suburban Plz 240 Rte 10 W PO Box 206
Whippany, NJ 07981-0206
Tel.: (973) 887-5300
Tel.: (973) 503-9252 (Investor Relations)
Toll Free: (800) 776-7263
E-mail: ir@suburbanpropane.com
Web Site: www.suburbanpropane.com
Approx. Rev.: $1,136,694,000
Approx. Number Employees: 2,598
Year Founded: 1996
Business Description:
Liquefied Petroleum Gas Dealer
S.I.C.: 5984; 5172
N.A.I.C.S.: 454312; 424720
Import Export
Media: 8-10-13-26
Personnel:
Harold R. Logan, Jr. *(Chm-Supervisory Bd)*
Harold R. Logan, Jr. *(Supervisory Board of Directors:)*
Michael J. Dunn, Jr. *(Pres & CEO)*
Michael A. Stivala *(CFO)*
Michael A. Kuglin *(Chief Acctg Officer & Controller)*
Michael J. Dunn, Jr. *(Supervisory Board of Directors:)*
Paul E. Abel *(Gen Counsel, Sec & VP)*
Michael M. Keating *(Sr VP-Admin)*
Neil Scanlon *(Asst VP)*
Sandra Zwickel *(Asst Gen Counsel)*
Brands & Products:
HOMETOWN HEARTH AND GRILL
SUBURBAN ENERGY SERVICES
SUBURBAN PROPANE

SUMMITVILLE TILES, INC.
PO Box 73
Summitville, OH 43962-0073
Tel.: (330) 223-1511
Fax: (330) 223-1414
E-mail: webmaster@summitville.com
Web Site: www.summitville.com
Approx. Number Employees: 200
Year Founded: 1911
Business Description:
Mfr. of Glazed Wall, Decorative & Quarry Tile; Floor Brick; Glazed Porcelain Floor Tile
S.I.C.: 3253; 5211
N.A.I.C.S.: 327122; 444190
Import Export
Media: 2-4-6-7-10-17
Distr.: Natl.
Personnel:
Bruce Johnson *(Owner)*
David W. Johnson *(CEO)*
Brands & Products:
LANDMARK
OLDE TOWNE
STRATA
SUMMITVILLE

SUN BUILDING SYSTEMS, LLC
9 Stauffer Indus Pk
Taylor, PA 18517-9601
Tel.: (570) 562-0110
Fax: (570) 562-0737
Approx. Number Employees: 150
Year Founded: 1973
Business Description:
Modular Housing Mfr
S.I.C.: 2452
N.A.I.C.S.: 321992
Export
Advertising Expenditures: $500,000
Media: 2-7-9-10-16-17-19-21-25
Distr.: Natl.
Personnel:
Jim Jones *(Pres)*
Brian Kovach *(Dir-Engrg-Quality Control)*

SUNPORCH STRUCTURES INC.
495 Post Rd E
Westport, CT 06880-4400
Tel.: (203) 454-0040
Fax: (203) 454-0020
E-mail: info@sunporch.com
Web Site: www.sunporch.com
Sales Range: $200-249.9 Million
Approx. Number Employees: 50
Year Founded: 1974
Business Description:
Aluminum Greenhouses & Porches Mfr & Sales
S.I.C.: 3448
N.A.I.C.S.: 332311
Media: 4-6
Personnel:
Dean Schwartz *(Pres)*
Brands & Products:
SUNPORCH

SUNSETTER PRODUCTS, LP
184 Charles St
Malden, MA 02148
Tel.: (781) 321-9600
Fax: (781) 321-8650
Toll Free: (800) 876-2340
Web Site: www.sunsetter.com
Approx. Sls.: $50,000,000
Approx. Number Employees: 60
Business Description:
Retractable Awnings Mfr
S.I.C.: 2394; 3446
N.A.I.C.S.: 314912; 332323
Media: 6
Personnel:
Jonathan Hershberg *(Pres)*
Richard Tharpe *(Dir-Sls & Mktg)*
Brands & Products:
EASYSHADE
SOMFY
SUNSETTER
SUNSETTER OASIS
VISTA

SUNVALLEY SOLAR, INC.
398 Lemon Creek Dr Ste A
Walnut, CA 91789
Tel.: (909) 598-0618
Fax: (909) 598-6633
Web Site: www.sunvalleysolarinc.com
Approx. Rev.: $4,634,140
Approx. Number Employees: 16
Year Founded: 2007
Business Description:
Solar Power Technology & System Integration
S.I.C.: 3612
N.A.I.C.S.: 335311
Advertising Expenditures: $27,210
Media: 17
Personnel:
James Zhijian Zhang *(Pres & CEO)*
Mandy Chung *(CFO, Treas & Sec)*
Henry Hangbo Yu *(Gen Mgr)*
Shirley Liao *(Dir-Admin)*

SUPER SKY PRODUCTS, INC.
(Filed Ch 11 Bankruptcy #1047476 on 11/17/10 in U.S. Bankruptcy Ct, Northern Dist of TX, Ft Worth)
10301 N Enterprise Dr
Mequon, WI 53092-4639
Tel.: (262) 242-2000
Fax: (262) 242-7409
Toll Free: (800) 558-0467
E-mail: supersky@supersky.com

Key to Media (For complete agency information see *The Advertising Red Books-Agencies* edition):
1. Bus. Publs. 2. Cable T.V. 3. Catalogs & Directories. 4. Co-op Adv. 5. Consumer Mags. 6. D.M. to Bus. Estab.7. D.M. to Consumers 8. Daily Newsp. 9. Exhibits/Trade Shows 10. Foreign 11. Infomercial 12. Internet Adv.13. Multimedia 14. Network Radio 15. Network T.V. 16. Newsp. Distr. Mags. 17. Other 18. Outdoor (Posters, Transit) 19. Point of Purchase20. Premiums, Novelties 21. Product Samples 22. Special Events Mktg. 23. Spot Radio 24. Spot T.V. 25. Weekly Newsp. 26. Yellow Page Adv.

Web Site: www.supersky.com
Approx. Number Employees: 74
Year Founded: 1923
Business Description:
Holding Company; Skylights Mfr
S.I.C.: 6719; 3444
N.A.I.C.S.: 551112; 332322
Media: 4-5-6-10-13-16
Distr.: Intl.; Natl.
Budget Set: Nov.
Personnel:
James E. Roesing *(Pres & CEO)*
Rod Kivioja *(Dir-Sls)*
Richard Poklar *(Dir-Ops)*
Tim Staats *(Dir-Engrg)*
Julie Guetzke *(Sls Mgr-Tech)*
Cindy Selig *(Mgr-Mktg & Estimator)*
Dan Stiller *(Mgr-Pur)*
Brands & Products:
EDGE
EDGE MAX
NANOGEL
SUPER SKY

SUPERIOR TUBE COMPANY INC.

(Sub. of Superior Group, Inc.)
3900 Germantown Pike
Collegeville, PA 19426-3112
Tel.: (610) 489-5200
Fax: (610) 489-5220
E-mail: info@superiortube.com
Web Site: www.superiortube.com
Approx. Number Employees: 200
Year Founded: 1934
Business Description:
Mfr. of Small Metal Tubing
S.I.C.: 3317; 3498
N.A.I.C.S.: 331210; 332996
Import Export
Advertising Expenditures: $80,000
Media: 2-4-7-10-13
Distr.: Natl.
Budget Set: Jan.
Brands & Products:
CATHALOYS
HYPOFLEX
WELDRAWN

SWARTWOUT DIVISION

(Joint Venture of Onex Corporation & Canada Pension Plan Investment Board)
3900 Doctor Greaves Rd
Grandview, MO 64030-1134
Tel.: (816) 761-7476
Fax: (816) 765-8955
E-mail: swartwout@swartwout.com
Web Site: www.swartwout.com
Approx. Number Employees: 115
Business Description:
Ventilators, Louvers, Heat & Smoke Units & Roof Curbs Mfr
S.I.C.: 1799
N.A.I.C.S.: 238990
Advertising Expenditures: $200,000
Media: 2-4-5-7-10-20-21-22
Distr.: Intl.; Natl.
Budget Set: Mar.
Personnel:
Tom Edwards *(Pres)*
Melissa A. Wilkins *(Adv & Promo Mgr)*
Brands & Products:
AIRJECTOR
AIRLOUVER
CONTOURAMIC AIRMOVER
FIBER-AIRE
GRAVITY VENT
HEAT VALVE
HID-N-AIRE
LITE-N-AIRE
LOW-LINE
MAGNAVALVE
MODULE-AIRE
PYROJECTOR
SKYLITE PYROJECTOR
SWIRL-OUT
WHIRLOUT
Advertising Agency:
Kuhn & Associates
10000 College Blvd.
Shawnee Mission, KS 66210
Tel.: (913) 663-5999
(Fiberglass Dampers & Louvers)

SWEPCO TUBE CORPORATION

1 Clifton Blvd
Clifton, NJ 07015
Tel.: (973) 778-3000
Fax: (973) 778-9289
E-mail: info@swepcotube.com
Web Site: www.swepcotube.com
Approx. Number Employees: 100
Year Founded: 1949
Business Description:
Stainless Steel Pipe & Tubing Mfr
S.I.C.: 3356; 3317
N.A.I.C.S.: 331491; 331210
Media: 4-7-8
Distr.: Natl.
Personnel:
Kenneth Shultz *(Pres & COO)*
Holly Keller Koeppel *(CFO & VP)*
Bob Catanzariti *(VP-Sls)*
Steve Oberhelman *(VP-Fin)*
Brands & Products:
SWEPCO

SYAR INDUSTRIES, INC.

2301 Napa Vallejo Hwy
Napa, CA 94558-6242
Mailing Address:
PO Box 2540
Napa, CA 94558-0524
Tel.: (707) 252-8711
Fax: (707) 224-5932
Fax: (707) 257-2630
Sales Range: $25-49.9 Million
Approx. Number Employees: 350
Year Founded: 1933
Business Description:
Retailer of Construction & Building Materials
S.I.C.: 5032; 2951
N.A.I.C.S.: 423320; 324121
Media: 7-9
Distr.: Reg.
Budget Set: Mar.
Personnel:
James M. Syar *(Pres)*
Susie Dericco *(CFO)*

SYMMONS INDUSTRIES, INC.

31 Brooks Dr
Braintree, MA 02184-3804
Tel.: (781) 848-2250
Fax: (781) 961-9621
Fax: (800) 961-9621
Toll Free: (800) SYMMONS
E-mail: info@symmons.com
Web Site: www.symmons.com
E-Mail For Key Personnel:
Sales Director: jgalvin@symmons.com
Approx. Number Employees: 290
Year Founded: 1939
Business Description:
Pressure Balanced Safety Shower Systems, Faucets & Plumbing Specialties Mfr
S.I.C.: 3494; 3432
N.A.I.C.S.: 332919; 332913
Export
Media: 2-4-6-7-10-20-21
Distr.: Natl.
Budget Set: Oct.
Personnel:
William B. O'Keeffe *(Pres & CEO)*
Tim Okeefe *(CEO)*
Dominic Solis *(VP-Mktg & Sls)*
Brands & Products:
ALLURA
ANDORA
BALLINA
CANTERBURY
CARRINGTON
CLEAR-VUE
DELUXE TEMPTROL
EURO-FLO
FIANO
FORZA
HYDAPIPE
LAUNDRY-MATE
LUCETTA
MAXLINE
MOSCATO
NARU
OXFORD
RADIANCE
SAFETYMIX
SCOT
SERENO
SHOWEROFF
THE SMART CHOICE
SYMMETRIX
SYMMONS
SYMMONS DESIGN STUDIO
TEMPCONTROL
TEMPSIZE
TEMPTROL
TEMPTROL 2000
TEMPTROL II
THERMIXER
ULTRA-SENSE
VELLA
VISU-TEMP
WATER DANCE
WINSLET
Advertising Agency:
Circle One
10 Norden Pl
Norwalk, CT 06854
Tel.: (203) 286-0550
Fax: (203) 286-0555

T&S BRASS & BRONZE WORKS, INC.

2 Saddleback Cove
Travelers Rest, SC 29690-2232
Tel.: (864) 834-4102
Fax: (800) 868-0084
Toll Free: (800) 476-4103
E-mail: tsbrass@tsbrass.com
Web Site: www.tsbrass.com
Approx. Number Employees: 250
Year Founded: 1947
Business Description:
Plumbing Products; Faucets, Valves & Fittings for Commercial, Industrial & Institutional Projects
S.I.C.: 3432
N.A.I.C.S.: 332913
Import Export
Advertising Expenditures: $1,000,000
Media: 4-5-6-7-8-10-11-13-19-20-21-22
Distr.: Intl.
Budget Set: Nov.
Personnel:
Claude I. Theisen *(Chm)*
Rick Skelton *(CFO)*
Craig Ashton *(Exec VP)*
Eva-Marie Fox *(VP-Mktg)*
Gary Cole *(Mgr-Ops)*
Mike Orlando *(Mgr-Bus Dev)*
Brands & Products:
LAB FLO
RELIABILITY BUILT IN
SAF-T-LINK
SAGE SYSTEMS
T&S

TANKNOLOGY INC

8501 N Mopac Expy Ste 400
Austin, TX 78759
Tel.: (512) 451-6334
Fax: (512) 459-1459
E-mail: info@tanknology.com
Web Site: www.tanknology.com
Approx. Number Employees: 230
Year Founded: 1988
Business Description:
Environmental Compliance Services
S.I.C.: 8711
N.A.I.C.S.: 541330
Import Export
Media: 2-4-7-10-11
Personnel:
Allen Porter *(Pres & CEO)*
Pete DeWeese *(CFO & Exec VP)*
Richard Schnabel *(VP-Sls)*
Brad Walls *(Dir-Sls-Nonretail Fuels)*
Kevin Callaway *(Reg Mgr)*
Ignacio Allende *(Mgr-Intl Ops)*
Kevin O'Hearn *(Mgr-Sls-Gulf Coast)*

T.E. IBBERSON COMPANY

(Sub. of Ibberson, Inc.)
828 5th St S
Hopkins, MN 55343-7750
Tel.: (952) 938-7007
Tel.: (952) 939-5763 (Pres)
Tel.: (952) 939-6968 (Bus Devel)
Tel.: (952) 939-5762 (Opers)
Fax: (952) 939-0451
E-mail: tei@ibberson.com
Web Site: www.ibberson.com
E-Mail For Key Personnel:
President: skimes@ibberson.com
Approx. Number Employees: 100
Year Founded: 1881
Business Description:
Engineering & Construction Services
S.I.C.: 1629
N.A.I.C.S.: 237990
Media: 2-10
Personnel:
Steve Kimes *(Pres)*

TEMBEC INC.

800 Boulevard Rene Levesque W Ste 1050
Montreal, QC H3B 1X9, Canada
Tel.: (514) 871-0137
Fax: (514) 397-0896
Web Site: www.tembec.com
Approx. Sls.: $1,912,325,140
Approx. Number Employees: 6,727
Year Founded: 1973

Tembec Inc. — (Continued)

Business Description:
Forest Products Converting Services
S.I.C.: 2611; 2421
N.A.I.C.S.: 322110; 321912
Export
Advertising Expenditures: $4,000,000
Media: 2-4-7-9-10-23-24-25
Distr.: Natl.
Budget Set: Sept.
Personnel:
James Continenza *(Chm)*
James Lopez *(Pres & CEO)*
Michel Dumas *(CFO & Exec VP-Fin)*
Chris Black *(Pres-Paper & High-Yield Pulp Grp & Exec VP)*
Yvon Pelletier *(Pres-Specialty Cellulose & Chemical Grp & Exec VP)*
Dennis Rounsville *(Pres-Forest Products Grp & Exec VP)*
Antonio Fratianni *(Gen Counsel, Sec & VP)*
Patrick Lebel *(Gen Counsel, Sec & VP)*
John Valley *(Exec VP)*
Randy Fournier *(Sr VP-Chemical Products & Kraft Pulp)*
Eric Bergeron *(VP-HR)*
Pierre Brien *(VP-Comm & Pub Affairs)*
Paul Dottori *(VP-Energy, Environment & Tech)*
Mahendra Patel *(VP-Engrg, Pur & Svcs)*
Jacques Rochon *(VP-IT)*
Jacques Rocray *(VP-Environ-Tech)*
Brands & Products:
ARBO
FOREVER GREEN
IMPACT ZERO
JAGER BUILDING SYSTEMS
KALLIMA
MUSKOKA
THE SPIRIT OF INNOVATION
TEMBEC
TEMBOARD
TEMCELL
TEMPROFJ
VINTAGE

TENSAR CORPORATION
(Holding of Arcapita, Inc.)
5871 Glenridge Dr Ste 300
Atlanta, GA 30328-5306
Tel.: (404) 214-1700
Tel.: (404) 250-1290
Fax: (404) 250-0461
Toll Free: (888) 828-5126
E-mail: info@tensarcorp.com
Web Site: www.tensarcorp.com
Approx. Sls.: $175,827,000
Approx. Number Employees: 715
Year Founded: 1983
Business Description:
Specialty Products & Engineering Services for the Mining, Erosion Prevention & Solid Waste Industries
S.I.C.: 8711
N.A.I.C.S.: 541330
Import Export
Media: 10
Personnel:
E. Stockton Croft *(Chm)*
Jeffrey B. Johnson *(CFO & Exec VP)*
Robert F. Briggs *(Gen Counsel, Sec & Exec VP)*
John Bolton *(Dir-Mktg)*
Bryan Gee *(Product Mgr-Roadway Sys)*
Libby Hungerford *(Mgr-Sls-Central Reg)*

TETRA TECH, INC.
3475 E Foothill Blvd
Pasadena, CA 91107-6024
Tel.: (626) 351-4664
Fax: (626) 351-5291
E-mail: info@tetratech.com
Web Site: www.tetratech.com
Approx. Rev.: $2,201,232,000
Approx. Number Employees: 12,000
Year Founded: 1966
Business Description:
Environmental Engineering & Consulting Services; Client-Sponsored Research & Development & Environmental Assessment
S.I.C.: 8711; 8748
N.A.I.C.S.: 541330; 541618
Advertising Expenditures: $2,000,000
Media: 2-7-10
Personnel:
Dan L. Batrack *(Chm & CEO)*
Steven M. Burdick *(CFO & Treas)*
Craig L. Christensen *(CIO & Sr VP)*
Brian Carter *(Chief Acctg Officer, VP & Controller)*
Frank Gross *(Pres-Remediation & Construction Mgmt Segment & Exec VP)*
Janis B. Salin *(Gen Counsel, Sec & Sr VP)*
Ronald J. Chu *(Exec VP-Technical Support Svcs)*
Douglas G. Smith *(Exec VP-Engrg & Architecture Svcs)*
Michael A. Bieber *(Sr VP-Corp Dev)*
Sam W. Box *(Sr VP-Project Risk Mgmt)*
William R. Brownlie *(Chief Engr & Sr VP)*
Richard A. Lemmon *(Sr VP-Corp Admin)*
Leslie L. Shoemaker *(Sr VP-Corp Strategy)*

TEXAS INDUSTRIES, INC.
1341 W Mockingbird Ln Ste 700W
Dallas, TX 75247-6913
Tel.: (972) 647-6700
Fax: (972) 647-3878
E-mail: tlacaze@txi.com
Web Site: www.txi.com
Approx. Sls.: $621,813,000
Approx. Number Employees: 2,020
Year Founded: 1951
Business Description:
Producer of Steel & Construction Materials, Including Cement, Aggregates & Concrete; Real Estate
S.I.C.: 2999; 3241; 3312
N.A.I.C.S.: 324199; 327310; 331111
Export
Advertising Expenditures: $175,000
Media: 2-5-7-10
Personnel:
Kenneth R. Allen *(CFO & VP-Fin)*
Melvin G. Brekhus *(Pres & CEO)*
James B. Rogers *(COO & VP)*
Frederick G. Anderson *(Gen Counsel, Sec & VP)*
T. Lesley Vines *(VP, Controller & Asst Treas)*
George E. Eure *(VP-Engrg)*
Stephen D. Mayfield *(VP-Cement, Aggregates Sls & Mktg)*
J. Barrett Reese *(VP-Mktg)*
Wesley E. Schlenker *(Asst Sec)*
Brands & Products:
DIAMOND PRO
EZY-BOND
INNOVATING STANDARDS
MAXIMIZER
TXI

THEO KALOMIRAKIS THEATERS
517 W 35th St Fl 7
New York, NY 10001
Tel.: (212) 244-2404
Fax: (212) 244-7409
Toll Free: (877) TKTHEATERS
E-mail: info@tktheaters.com
Web Site: www.tktheaters.com
Sales Range: $10-24.9 Million
Approx. Number Employees: 12
Business Description:
Home Theater Design Services
S.I.C.: 7389
N.A.I.C.S.: 541410
Media: 6-10
Personnel:
Theo Kalomirakis *(Pres)*
James Theobald *(VP-Sls & Mktg)*

THERMA-TRU CORP.
(Sub. of Fortune Brands Home & Security LLC)
1750 Indian Wood Cir
Maumee, OH 43537-4049
Tel.: (419) 891-7400
Fax: (419) 891-7411
Fax: (800) 322-8688
Toll Free: (800) 537-8827
Toll Free: (800) 843-7628
Web Site: www.thermatru.com
Sales Range: $400-449.9 Million
Approx. Number Employees: 2,700
Year Founded: 1962
Business Description:
Exterior Door Systems, Fiberglass & Steel Frames Mfr
S.I.C.: 3442; 2431
N.A.I.C.S.: 332321; 321911
Import Export
Advertising Expenditures: $2,000,000
Media: 1-2-4-6-7-10-11-13-16-19-20-21-22-24-26
Distr.: Intl.; Natl.; Reg.
Budget Set: Oct.
Personnel:
David D. Haddix *(CFO)*
Carol Summersgill *(VP-HR)*
Joe Herman *(Dir-Sls Ops)*
Brands & Products:
BENCHMARK
BEVELLINE
CLASSIC-CRAFT
FIBER-CLASSIC
FIBER CRAFT
FROSTED IMAGES
MAHOGANY COLLECTION
RUSTIC COLLECTION
SMOOTH-STAR
STARLITE
STEEL-BEATER FIBERGLASS DOORS
THERMA TRU
VICTORIAN CRYSTAL
Advertising Agency:
Hitchcock Fleming & Associates, Inc.
500 Wolf Ledges Pkwy
Akron, OH 44311-1022
Tel.: (330) 376-2111
Fax: (330) 376-2220
Toll Free: (888) 376-7601

THERMAL INDUSTRIES, INC.
(Joint Venture of Bank of America Corporation, Kenner & Company, Inc. & UBS Capital Americas Investments II LLC)
5450 2nd Ave
Pittsburgh, PA 15207
Tel.: (412) 244-6400
Fax: (412) 395-1999
Toll Free: (800) 245-1540
Web Site: www.thermalindustries.com
Sales Range: $75-99.9 Million
Approx. Number Employees: 475
Year Founded: 1960
Business Description:
Mfr. of Vinyl Windows, Patio Doors & Enclosures, Decks, Docks & Railing Systems
S.I.C.: 3442
N.A.I.C.S.: 332321
Media: 2
Distr.: Natl.
Personnel:
David S. Rascoe *(Pres & COO)*
Evan Kaffenes *(VP-Fin)*
Brands & Products:
DREAM
DREAMGLAS GALLERY COLLECTION
DREAMSPACE

THERMOENERGY CORPORATION
124 W Capitol Ave Ste 880
Little Rock, AR 72201
Tel.: (501) 376-6477
Fax: (501) 244-9203
Web Site: www.thermoenergy.com
Approx. Rev.: $2,874,000
Approx. Number Employees: 25
Year Founded: 1988
Business Description:
Recycling Waste Materials
S.I.C.: 4952
N.A.I.C.S.: 221320
Advertising Expenditures: $2,720,000
Personnel:
Cary G. Bullock *(Chm, Pres & CEO)*
Teodor Klowan, Jr. *(CFO, Corp Sec & Exec VP)*

THYSSENKRUPP ACCESS INC.
(Div. of ThyssenKrupp Elevator Americas Corp.)
4001 E 138th St
Grandview, MO 64030-2837
Tel.: (816) 763-3100
Fax: (816) 763-4467
Toll Free: (800) 829-9760
E-mail: marketing@accessind.com
Web Site: www.tkaccess.com
Approx. Number Employees: 114
Year Founded: 1935
Business Description:
Accessibility Products, Stairway Elevators, Wheelchair Lifts & Vertical & Inclined Platforms Mfr.
S.I.C.: 3534; 5999
N.A.I.C.S.: 333921; 446199
Export

Key to Media (For complete agency information see *The Advertising Red Books-Agencies* edition):
1. Bus. Publs. 2. Cable T.V. 3. Catalogs & Directories. 4. Co-op Adv. 5. Consumer Mags. 6. D.M. to Bus. Estab.7. D.M. to Consumers
8. Daily Newsp. 9. Exhibits/Trade Shows 10. Foreign 11. Infomercial 12. Internet Adv.13. Multimedia 14. Network Radio
15. Network T.V. 16. Newsp. Distr. Mags. 17. Other 18. Outdoor (Posters, Transit) 19. Point of Purchase20. Premiums, Novelties
21. Product Samples 22. Special Events Mktg. 23. Spot Radio 24. Spot T.V. 25. Weekly Newsp. 26. Yellow Page Adv.

Media: 1-2-6-7-8-10-11-13
Distr.: Intl.; Natl.
Budget Set: June
Personnel:
Scott Zoetewey *(Pres)*
Lee Stockton *(Mgr-Pur)*
Brands & Products:
CARRIER LIFT
EXCEL
STAIR GLIDE

TIAX LLC
35 Hartwell Ave
Lexington, MA 02421
Tel.: (617) 498-5000
Fax: (617) 498-7200
Toll Free: (800) 677-3000
Web Site: www.tiaxllc.com
Approx. Number Employees: 301
Year Founded: 1886
Business Description:
Technology & Product Development; Environmental, Health & Safety Consulting; Management Consulting Services
S.I.C.: 8711
N.A.I.C.S.: 541330
Media: 10-22
Distr.: Intl.
Budget Set: Nov.
Personnel:
Kenan Sahin *(Founder & Pres)*
Brian Barnett *(VP-Tech)*
Twig Mowatt *(Dir-Comm)*
Bob Rancatore *(Project Mgr)*
Brands & Products:
APTAC
ARC
SUPPORTIVE HOME
TIAX

TODCO, INC.
(Div. of Overhead Door Corporation)
1332 Fairground Rd E
Marion, OH 43302
Mailing Address:
PO Box 1087
Marion, OH 43301-1108
Tel.: (740) 383-6376
Fax: (740) 383-2261
E-mail: todco@todco.com
Web Site: www.todco.com
Approx. Number Employees: 100
Year Founded: 1957
Business Description:
Truck Doors Mfr
S.I.C.: 5013; 5599
N.A.I.C.S.: 441310; 441229
Advertising Expenditures: $500,000
Media: 1-2-4-10-26
Distr.: Intl.; Natl.
Budget Set: Oct.
Personnel:
Scott Blackford *(Pres)*
Lynn Bosch *(Dir-Mktg)*
Advertising Agency:
Badertscher Communications, Inc.
137 S Prospect St
Marion, OH 43302-3713
Tel.: (740) 383-2633
Fax: (740) 383-6223
(Overhead Doors & Ramps)

TOLL BROTHERS, INC.
250 Gibraltar Rd
Horsham, PA 19044-2323
Tel.: (215) 938-8000
Fax: (215) 938-8010
Toll Free: (800) 289-8655
E-mail: info@tollbrothers.com
Web Site: www.tollbrothers.com
E-Mail For Key Personnel:
Marketing Director: kmccarron@tollbrothersinc.com
Approx. Rev.: $1,494,771,000
Approx. Number Employees: 2,117
Year Founded: 1967
Business Description:
Single-Family Detached & Attached Luxury Homes Designer, Builder & Developer
S.I.C.: 1531; 1521
N.A.I.C.S.: 236117; 236115
Advertising Expenditures: $9,200,000
Media: 1-4-6-8-9-13-18-25
Distr.: Reg.
Personnel:
Bruce E. Toll *(Owner)*
Robert I. Toll *(Chm)*
Zvi Barzilay *(Pres & COO)*
Barry A. Depew *(Reg Pres)*
Douglas C. Yearley, Jr. *(CEO)*
Martin P. Connor *(CFO & Treas)*
Kira McCarron *(CMO & Sr VP)*
John K. McDonald *(Chief Compliance Officer, Gen Counsel & Sr VP)*
Joseph R. Sicree *(Chief Acctg Officer-IR & Sr VP)*
Tom Anhut *(Grp Pres-Carolinas & Georgia)*
Kevin J. McMaster *(Sr VP & Corp Controller)*
Frederick N. Cooper *(Sr VP-Fin)*
Jonathan C. Downs *(Sr VP-HR)*
A. Stern *(Sr VP-Home Building Ops Div)*
Brands & Products:
AMERICA'S LUXURY HOME BUILDER
TOLL BROTHERS
Advertising Agency:
Geto & deMilly Inc.
276 5th Ave Ste 806
New York, NY 10001
Tel.: (212) 686-4551
Fax: (212) 213-6850

TORCON, INC.
328 Newman Springs Rd
Red Bank, NJ 07701
Tel.: (732) 704-9800
Fax: (732) 704-9810
E-mail: info@torcon.com
Web Site: www.torcon.com
Approx. Number Employees: 250
Year Founded: 1965
Business Description:
Construction Management, General Construction & Project Consultants
S.I.C.: 8748
N.A.I.C.S.: 541618
Personnel:
Benedict Torcivia, Sr. *(Chm & CEO)*
Benedict Torcivia, Jr. *(Co-Pres)*
Joseph A. Torcivia *(Co-Pres)*
Philip Fischer *(CFO)*
Richard Estrin *(Sr VP)*
Dennis Schettino *(Sr VP)*
Ken Smith *(Dir-Mktg)*
Advertising Agency:
R&J Public Relations
1140 Rte 22 E Ste 200
Bridgewater, NJ 08807
Tel.: (908) 722-5757
Fax: (908) 722-5776

TORK, INC.
1 Grove St
Mount Vernon, NY 10550-2401
Tel.: (914) 664-3542
Fax: (914) 664-5052
Telex: 131447
E-mail: service@tork.com
Web Site: www.tork.com
E-Mail For Key Personnel:
President: sshankar@tork.com
Sales Range: $10-24.9 Million
Approx. Number Employees: 100
Year Founded: 1922
Business Description:
Time Switches, Photoelectric Controls, Digital Controls, Monitoring & Control Systems
S.I.C.: 3625; 3674
N.A.I.C.S.: 335314; 334413
Import Export
Media: 1-2-4-5-7-10-11-19-20-21
Distr.: Intl.; Natl.
Budget Set: June
Personnel:
Nicholas Murlo *(VP-Engrg)*
Brands & Products:
ELITE TIMER
TORK
TORK-ALERT

TOUSA, INC.
(Sub. of Technical Olympic SA)
4000 Hollywood Blvd Ste 500 N
Hollywood, FL 33021
Tel.: (954) 364-4000
Fax: (281) 364-4010
E-mail: info@tousa.com
Web Site: www.tousa.com
Sales Range: $1-4.9 Billion
Approx. Number Employees: 1,461
Year Founded: 1983
Business Description:
Holding Company; Home Construction Services
S.I.C.: 1521; 6719; 8742
N.A.I.C.S.: 236115; 541611; 551112
Advertising Expenditures: $9,800,000
Media: 2-9-16
Personnel:
Konstantinos A. Stengos *(Chm)*
Antonio B. Mon *(Vice Chm, Pres & CEO)*
John R. Boken *(CEO & Chief Restructuring Officer)*
Tommy L. McAden *(CFO & Exec VP)*
George Yeonas *(COO & Exec VP-Homebuilding Ops)*
Brands & Products:
NEWMARK

TRACO INC.
71 Progress Ave
Cranberry Township, PA 16066
Tel.: (724) 776-7000
Fax: (724) 776-7014
Toll Free: (800) 837-7001
Web Site: www.traco.com
Sales Range: $150-199.9 Million
Approx. Number Employees: 1,800
Year Founded: 1950
Business Description:
Mfr. of Commercial & Residential Windows, Doors, Skylights, Solariums, Folding Glass Walls, Sunrooms, & Impact-Resistant Hurricane Windows & Doors
S.I.C.: 3442; 3354
N.A.I.C.S.: 332321; 331316
Media: 10
Brands & Products:
BEYOND WINDOWS BEYOND DOORS
BISCAYNE
E-GEN
HURRCULES
NEXGEN
NEXGEN ENERGY SPACER
NEXGEN THERMAL BARRIER SYSTEM
NEXGLAZE
NRG
TR-6300
TRACO
TRACO BLAST
VALU
THE WINDOWS AND DOORS THAT GREET THE WORLD

TRANE INC.
(Sub. of Ingersoll-Rand Company)
1 Centennial Ave
Piscataway, NJ 08855-6820
Mailing Address:
PO Box 6820
Piscataway, NJ 08855-6820
Tel.: (732) 652-7100
Fax: (732) 980-3340
Web Site: www.trane.com
Approx. Sls.: $7,449,600,000
Approx. Number Employees: 29,600
Year Founded: 1929
Business Description:
Holding Company; Heating, Ventilation & Air-Conditioning Systems Mfr
S.I.C.: 6719; 3433; 3585
N.A.I.C.S.: 551112; 333414; 333415
Import Export
Advertising Expenditures: $136,000,000
Media: 2-4-5-6-7-9-10-18-19
Distr.: Natl.
Budget Set: Oct.
Personnel:
Patrick Shannon *(VP-Fin & IT)*
Joyce Warrington *(Brand Dir)*
Paul Dickard *(Dir-Pub Affairs)*
Matt Biesterveld *(Mgr-Customer Direct Svc)*
Brands & Products:
TRANE
Advertising Agency:
Carmichael Lynch
110 N 5th St
Minneapolis, MN 55403
Tel.: (612) 334-6000
Fax: (612) 334-6090
Bath & Kitchen
Creative
— Andrew Pautz *(Acct Rep)*

TREESOURCE INDUSTRIES, INC.
8277 Center St SW
Tumwater, WA 98501
Mailing Address:
PO Box 14487
Tumwater, WA 98511-4487
Tel.: (360) 352-1548
Fax: (360) 570-9355
E-mail: webmaster@treesource.com
Web Site: www.treesource.com
Sales Range: $75-99.9 Million
Approx. Number Employees: 250
Year Founded: 1983

Key to Media (For complete agency information see *The Advertising Red Books-Agencies* edition):
1. Bus. Publs. 2. Cable T.V. 3. Catalogs & Directories. 4. Co-op Adv. 5. Consumer Mags. 6. D.M. to Bus. Estab.7. D.M. to Consumers 8. Daily Newsp. 9. Exhibits/Trade Shows 10. Foreign 11. Infomercial 12. Internet Adv.13. Multimedia 14. Network Radio 15. Network T.V. 16. Newsp. Distr. Mags. 17. Other 18. Outdoor (Posters, Transit) 19. Point of Purchase20. Premiums, Novelties 21. Product Samples 22. Special Events Mktg. 23. Spot Radio 24. Spot T.V. 25. Weekly Newsp. 26. Yellow Page Adv.

TreeSource Industries, Inc. — (Continued)

Business Description:
Producer of Soft & Hardwood Lumber, Wood Products & By-products
S.I.C.: 2421
N.A.I.C.S.: 321113
Export
Media: 2-26
Distr.: Intl.; Natl.
Budget Set: Apr.
Brands & Products:
TREESOURCE

TREMCO INCORPORATED
(Sub. of RPM Industrial Holding Co.)
3735 Green Rd
Beachwood, OH 44122
Tel.: (216) 292-5000
Fax: (216) 292-5167
Toll Free: (800) 852-9068
E-mail: info@tremcoinc.com
Web Site: www.tremcoinc.com
E-Mail For Key Personnel:
President: korach@tremcoinc.com
Sales Range: $400-449.9 Million
Approx. Number Employees: 1,900
Year Founded: 1928
Business Description:
Mfr of Protective Coatings, Sealants & Roofing Materials for Building Maintenance & Construction Industries
S.I.C.: 2891; 2851; 2952; 3272; 9224
N.A.I.C.S.: 325520; 324122; 325510; 327390; 922160
Media: 2-4-5-7-10-13-19-20
Distr.: Natl.
Budget Set: Oct.
Personnel:
Randall Korach *(Pres)*
Michael Drumm *(CFO & VP)*
Chuck Houk *(VP & Gen Mgr-Comml Sealants & Waterproofing)*
Brands & Products:
DYMONIC
EXOAIR
PARASEAL
PROGLAZE
SPECTREM
TEMPROOF
THC
TREMCO
VISIONSTRIP
VULKEM

TREX COMPANY, INC.
160 Exeter Dr
Winchester, VA 22603
Tel.: (540) 542-6300
Fax: (540) 542-6885
Toll Free: (800) 289-8739
E-mail: question@trex.com
Web Site: www.trex.com
Approx. Sls.: $317,690,000
Approx. Number Employees: 550
Year Founded: 1996
Business Description:
Wood-Alternative Decking, Railing & Fencing Products Mfr
S.I.C.: 2493; 2452; 3089
N.A.I.C.S.: 321219; 321992; 326199
Advertising Expenditures: $20,600,000
Media: 2-5-6-10-24
Personnel:
Andrew U. Ferrari *(Owner)*
Ronald W. Kaplan *(Chm, Pres & CEO)*
James E. Cline *(CFO & VP)*
William R. Gupp *(Chief Admin Officer, Gen Counsel & Sec)*
J. Mitchell Cox *(VP-Sls)*
Adam D. Zambanini *(VP-Mktg)*
Brands & Products:
CREATE YOUR SPACE
THE DECK OF A LIFETIME
FIBREX
HOW OUTDOOR LIVING SHOULD FEEL
TIGER CLAW
TREX
TREX ACCENTS
TREX ARTISAN SERIES RAILING
TREX BRASILIA
TREX CONTOURS
TREX DESIGNER SERIES RAILING
TREX HIDEAWAY
TREX ORIGINS
TREX SECLUSIONS
TREX SURROUNDINGS
TREXEXPRESS
TREXTRIM
Advertising Agency:
L.C. Williams & Associates, LLC
150 N Michigan Ave 38th Fl
Chicago, IL 60601-7558
Tel.: (312) 565-3900
Fax: (312) 565-1770
Toll Free: (800) 837-7123

TRI-CITY ELECTRICAL CONTRACTORS, INC.
430 W Dr
Altamonte Springs, FL 32714
Tel.: (407) 788-3500
Fax: (407) 682-7353
Toll Free: (800) 768-2489
E-mail: info@tcelectric.com
Web Site: www.tcelectric.com
Approx. Number Employees: 800
Year Founded: 1958
Business Description:
Electrical Contracting & Communication Services
S.I.C.: 1731
N.A.I.C.S.: 238210
Distr.: Reg.
Personnel:
Jack Olmstead *(Pres)*
Charles W. McFarland *(CFO & Sr VP)*
Mary Baker *(Dir-HR)*
Lynn Harden *(Mgr)*
C. L. Janeski *(Mgr)*
Tom Lancione *(Mgr-Facility)*
Kevin Neal *(Mgr-Svcs-Comm Div)*
Advertising Agency:
Cristol Marketing Company
237 Hunt Club Blvd Ste 102
Longwood, FL 32779
Tel.: (407) 774-2515
Fax: (407) 774-6647

TRI COUNTY AIR CONDITIONING-HEATING, INC.
1080 Enterprise Ct
Nokomis, FL 34275
Tel.: (941) 485-2222
Web Site: tri9285.dealerstack.net
Year Founded: 1977
Business Description:
Air Conditioning, Heating & Solar Contractor
S.I.C.: 1711
N.A.I.C.S.: 238220
Media: 1-2-3-6-7-8-9-10-13-16-18-19-20-22-23-24-25-26
Personnel:
William S. Swanson *(Pres)*

TRI-STEEL HOMES, INC.
5400 S Stemmons Fwy
Denton, TX 76210
Tel.: (940) 497-7070
Fax: (940) 497-3505
Toll Free: (800) TRI-STEEL
E-mail: info@tri-steel.com
Approx. Number Employees: 100
Year Founded: 1976
Business Description:
Mfr. of Steel Frame Homes
S.I.C.: 3448
N.A.I.C.S.: 332311
Advertising Expenditures: $360,000
Media: 2-4-6-9-25
Distr.: Intl.; Natl.
Brands & Products:
TRI-STEEL STRUCTURES

TRINITY INDUSTRIES, INC.
2525 Stemmons Fwy
Dallas, TX 75207-2401
Mailing Address:
PO Box 568887
Dallas, TX 75356-8887
Tel.: (214) 631-4420
Fax: (214) 589-8810
Telex: 62875050
E-mail: product.info@trin.net
Web Site: www.trin.net
Approx. Rev.: $2,189,100,000
Approx. Number Employees: 9,270
Year Founded: 1933
Business Description:
Energy Equipment, Railcar, Transportation Barge & Construction Products Mfr
S.I.C.: 3444; 3442; 3499; 3561; 3743; 7359
N.A.I.C.S.: 532210; 332321; 332322; 332439; 333911; 336510; 532299; 532310; 532420; 532490
Media: 2-4
Personnel:
Timothy R. Wallace *(Chm, Pres & CEO)*
Antonio Carrillo *(Pres)*
James E. Perry *(CFO & VP)*
Madhuri A. Andrews *(CIO)*
S. Theis Rice *(Chief Legal Officer & VP)*
William A. McWhirter II *(Group Pres-Construction Products Segment & Sr VP)*
D. Stephen Menzies *(Grp Pres & Sr VP)*
Donald G. Collum *(Chief Audit Exec & VP)*
Brands & Products:
SMOOTHCRETE
TRINCOOL
TRINITY
Advertising Agency:
Farrar Public Relations, Inc.
5924 Forrest Ln
Fort Worth, TX 76112-1043
Tel.: (817) 937-1557
Pub Rels

TRUE HOME VALUE, INC.
(Holding of Blackstreet Capital Management, LLC)
5611 Fern Valley Rd PO Box 34749
Louisville, KY 40228-1055
Tel.: (502) 968-2020
Fax: (502) 968-7798
Toll Free: (800) 669-2020
Web Site: www.thv.com
Sales Range: $50-74.9 Million
Approx. Number Employees: 100
Year Founded: 1998
Business Description:
Lumber & Other Building Materials Dealer
S.I.C.: 3082; 3089; 5031
N.A.I.C.S.: 326121; 326199; 423310
Import Export
Advertising Expenditures: $3,487,051
Personnel:
Stephen A. Hoffmann *(Chm)*
Charles L. Smith *(CEO)*
David A. Anderson *(CFO)*
Brands & Products:
ALTER-LITE
LEINGANG
PRIMAX
ROLOX
THERMOCOTE
THERMOVIEW
THOMAS
THV

TUBULAR STEEL INC.
(Sub. of TSI Holding Company)
1031 Executive Pkwy Dr
Saint Louis, MO 63141-6339
Tel.: (314) 851-9200
Fax: (314) 851-9336
E-mail: info@tubularsteel.com
Web Site: www.tubularsteel.com
Approx. Number Employees: 350
Year Founded: 1953
Business Description:
Steel Distr
S.I.C.: 5051
N.A.I.C.S.: 423510
Media: 7-20
Distr.: Direct to Consumer
Personnel:
Daniel Hauck *(Pres)*
Mike Birch *(Mgr-Product)*

TURBOSONIC TECHNOLOGIES, INC.
550 Parkside Dr Ste A 14
Waterloo, ON N2L 5V4, Canada
Tel.: (519) 885-5513
Fax: (519) 885-6992
E-mail: info@turbosonic.com
Web Site: www.turbosonic.com
Approx. Rev.: $13,739,297
Approx. Number Employees: 47
Business Description:
Air Pollution Control Engineering Services
S.I.C.: 8711; 3559
N.A.I.C.S.: 541330; 333298
Advertising Expenditures: $101,464
Media: 2-4-10-13
Personnel:
Ken Kivenko *(Chm)*
Egbert Q. van Everdingen *(Pres, Treas & Sec)*
Edward F. Spink *(CEO)*
Carl A. Young *(CFO)*
Robert A. Allan *(VP-Engrg)*
Richard C. Gimpel *(VP-Sls & Mktg)*
David J. Hobson *(VP-Fin & Admin)*
Dorina Aldwinckle *(Office Mgr)*

Key to Media (For complete agency information see *The Advertising Red Books-Agencies* edition):
1. Bus. Publs. 2. Cable T.V. 3. Catalogs & Directories. 4. Co-op Adv. 5. Consumer Mags. 6. D.M. to Bus. Estab.7. D.M. to Consumers 8. Daily Newsp. 9. Exhibits/Trade Shows 10. Foreign 11. Infomercial 12. Internet Adv.13. Multimedia 14. Network Radio 15. Network T.V. 16. Newsp. Distr. Mags. 17. Other 18. Outdoor (Posters, Transit) 19. Point of Purchase20. Premiums, Novelties 21. Product Samples 22. Special Events Mktg. 23. Spot Radio 24. Spot T.V. 25. Weekly Newsp. 26. Yellow Page Adv.

Brands & Products:
DRY FOG
SONICBURN
SONICHEM
SONICKLEEN
SONICOOL
SONICORE
TURBOSONIC.COM
TURBOSORB
TURBOSOX
TURBOTAK
TURBOVENTURI

TXI-RIVERSIDE CEMENT

(Sub. of Texas Industries, Inc.)
3500 Porsche Way Ste 150
Ontario, CA 91761-0079
Mailing Address:
PO Box 51479
Ontario, CA 91761-0079
Tel.: (909) 635-1800
Fax: (909) 635-1897
Toll Free: (800) 442-4910
Web Site: www.txi.com
Sales Range: $100-124.9 Million
Approx. Number Employees: 400
Year Founded: 1991
Business Description:
Cement, Pre-Engineered Metal Building Systems, Bituminous Coal & Lignite & Sheet Metal Work Mfr
S.I.C.: 3241; 3272; 3299
N.A.I.C.S.: 327310; 327332; 327390; 327999
Advertising Expenditures: $200,000
Media: 2-9
Distr.: Natl.
Budget Set: Dec.
Personnel:
Randall E. Jones *(VP-Comm & Govt Affairs)*
Ron Runnels *(Gen Mgr)*
Brands & Products:
TXI

TYLER ELEVATOR PRODUCTS, INC.

(Div. of Sematic USA, Inc.)
7852 Bavaria Rd
Twinsburg, OH 44087
Tel.: (216) 524-0100
Fax: (216) 524-9710
E-mail: after_sales@tylerelevator.com
Web Site: www.tylerelevator.com
Sales Range: $50-74.9 Million
Approx. Number Employees: 18
Year Founded: 1872
Business Description:
Mfr. of Elevators
S.I.C.: 3534
N.A.I.C.S.: 333921
Advertising Expenditures: $2,000,000
Media: 7
Distr.: Intl.; Natl.
Budget Set: Oct. -Nov.
Personnel:
Paul Metved *(Gen Mgr)*

U FILL OR WE FILL DUMPSTER SERVICE

9226 Adler St
New Port Richey, FL 34654-4502
Tel.: (727) 505-3851
Web Site: www.ufillorwefill.com
Business Description:
Construction Debris & Waste Disposal
S.I.C.: 4959
N.A.I.C.S.: 562998
Media: 13
Personnel:
Stephen Schembri *(Pres)*

ULBRICH STAINLESS STEEL & SPECIAL METALS, INC.

57 Dodge Ave
North Haven, CT 06473-1191
Tel.: (203) 239-4481
Fax: (203) 239-7479
E-mail: info@ulbrich.com
Web Site: www.ulbrich.com
Approx. Number Employees: 700
Year Founded: 1924
Business Description:
Rerolled Stainless Steel Strip & Special Metal Strip; Wire, Round, Flat, Shaped Wire
S.I.C.: 3316; 3356
N.A.I.C.S.: 331221; 331491
Import Export
Media: 2-4-7-10
Distr.: Intl.; Natl.
Budget Set: Nov.
Personnel:
Frederick Ulbrich, Jr. *(Chm)*
Chris Ulbrich *(Vice Chm & COO)*
Jay Cei *(CFO)*
Frank Best *(Grp Pres-Ulbrich Steel Div)*
Mike Petro *(VP-HR)*
Robert Giapponi *(Gen Mgr-Ops)*
Don Hennon *(Dir-Mktg)*
John Schmidt *(Dir-New Products)*
Pat Robb *(Product Assurance Mgr)*
Brands & Products:
ULBRASEAL
ULBRAVAR
ULBRICH

UNADILLA SILO COMPANY INC.

18 Clifton St
Unadilla, NY 13849-3361
Mailing Address:
PO Box K
Unadilla, NY 13849-0710
Tel.: (607) 369-9341
Fax: (607) 369-3608
E-mail: info@unalam.com
Web Site: www.unalam.com
Approx. Number Employees: 69
Year Founded: 1909
Business Description:
Mfr of Laminated Wood Arches & Beams
S.I.C.: 2439
N.A.I.C.S.: 321213
Export
Advertising Expenditures: $200,000
Media: 2-4-6-10-13
Distr.: Reg.
Budget Set: Jan. -May
Personnel:
Craig H. Van Cott *(Pres)*
Phillip Holowacz *(VP-Sls)*
Robert K. Kaseguma *(VP-Engrng)*

UNIBOARD CANADA INC.

(Sub. of Pfleiderer AG)
2540 Boulevard Daniel Johnson Suite 500
Laval, QC H7T 2S3, Canada
Tel.: (450) 682-5240
Fax: (450) 682-0550
Toll Free: (800) 263-5240
E-mail: james-hogg@uniboard.com
Web Site: www.uniboard.com
E-Mail For Key Personnel:
Marketing Director: marketing@uniboard.com
Sales Director: can@uniboard.com
Sales Range: $400-449.9 Million
Approx. Number Employees: 1,300
Year Founded: 1987
Business Description:
Provider of Melamine Panels, Medium Density Fiberboard & Particleboard
S.I.C.: 2493
N.A.I.C.S.: 321219
Import Export
Media: 2-4-10-21-26
Distr.: Intl.; Natl.
Personnel:
James Hogg *(Pres & CEO)*
Christoph Schmitz *(CFO & Exec VP)*
Erick Boily *(VP-HR)*
Brands & Products:
FORPAN
MULTILOOK
PANFIBRE
PANFOIL
PANVAL

UNIQUE TILE

1364 N Kelly
Nixa, MO 65714
Tel.: (417) 725-5515
Fax: (417) 725-4411
Toll Free: (800) 348-8453
Web Site: www.uniquetile.com
Approx. Number Employees: 35
Year Founded: 1988
Business Description:
Tile Mfr & Distr
S.I.C.: 3251
N.A.I.C.S.: 327121
Import Export
Media: 4-7-8-10-11
Personnel:
Melissa Turpin *(Pres)*

UNISTRUT CORPORATION

(Sub. of Tyco Engineered Products & Services)
4205 Elizabeth
Wayne, MI 48184
Tel.: (734) 721-4040
Fax: (734) 721-4106
Toll Free: (800) 521-7730
Web Site: www.unistrut.com
Approx. Number Employees: 200
Year Founded: 1924
Business Description:
Metal Framing Products Mfr
S.I.C.: 3448; 3446
N.A.I.C.S.: 332311; 332323
Export
Advertising Expenditures: $250,000
Media: 1-2-4-5-7-10-13
Distr.: Intl.; Natl.
Budget Set: Mar.
Personnel:
Keith Murray *(Mgr-Eastern Region)*
Glen Noble *(Mgr-Reg Sls)*
Jim Romano *(Mgr-Midwest Region)*
Brands & Products:
PRIME ANGLE
ROOFWALKS
TELESPAR
TELESTRUT
UNISTRUT
UNITED INTERLOCK

UNITED STATES AWNING COMPANY

(d/b/a US Awning)
1100 Gillespie Ave
Sarasota, FL 34236
Tel.: (941) 955-7010
Fax: (941) 366-7206
Web Site: www.unitedstatesawningco.com
E-Mail For Key Personnel:
Sales Director: sales@unitedstatesawningco.com
Approx. Rev.: $1,200,000
Approx. Number Employees: 20
Year Founded: 1965
Business Description:
Awnings Mfr & Installer
S.I.C.: 1522
N.A.I.C.S.: 236220
Media: 6-13-26
Personnel:
Ray Hautamaki *(Pres)*
Mark Schwalm *(COO & VP)*

UNITED STATES CERAMIC TILE COMPANY

11190 NW 25 St Ste100
Miami, FL 33172
Tel.: (330) 649-5000
Fax: (305) 357-6571
Toll Free: (800) 321-0684
E-mail: info@rocatilegroup.com
Web Site: www.rocatilegroup.com
Approx. Number Employees: 300
Year Founded: 1913
Business Description:
Glazed Ceramic Wall & Floor Tile Mfr & Supplier
S.I.C.: 3253
N.A.I.C.S.: 327122
Import Export
Media: 1-2-4-6-7-10-13-19-20-21-26
Distr.: Natl.
Budget Set: Nov.
Personnel:
Agustin Lopez *(CEO)*
Brands & Products:
BRIGHT GLAZE
CALIFORNIA MARBLE
CRYSTAL TONES
DECORATIVE INSERTS
DESIGNERS CHOICE
FIFTH AVENUE COLLECTION
FLAIR
GOBI
HARBOR GATE
LAUFEN
LITETONES
LUXOR
MAGMA
MATTE GLAZE
ROCK CREEK
ROMANY VILLA
ROMANY VILLA WALL & FLOOR TILE
SIERRA
TOLEDO
USCTCO
VANCOUVER
WINDRIFT
WINDRIFT REFLECTIONS
Advertising Agency:
WRL Advertising, Inc.
4470 Dressler Rd NW
Canton, OH 44718-2716
Tel.: (330) 493-8866
Fax: (330) 493-8860

Key to Media (For complete agency information see *The Advertising Red Books-Agencies* edition):
1. Bus. Publs. 2. Cable T.V. 3. Catalogs & Directories. 4. Co-op Adv. 5. Consumer Mags. 6. D.M. to Bus. Estab.7. D.M. to Consumers
8. Daily Newsp. 9. Exhibits/Trade Shows 10. Foreign 11. Infomercial 12. Internet Adv.13. Multimedia 14. Network Radio
15. Network T.V. 16. Newsp. Distr. Mags. 17. Other 18. Outdoor (Posters, Transit) 19. Point of Purchase20. Premiums, Novelties
21. Product Samples 22. Special Events Mktg. 23. Spot Radio 24. Spot T.V. 25. Weekly Newsp. 26. Yellow Page Adv.

United States Ceramic Tile Company — (Continued)

(Flair! and other Glazed Ceramic Wall & Floor Tiles)

UNITED STATES PIPE & FOUNDRY COMPANY, INC.
(Sub. of Mueller Water Products, Inc.)
3300 1st Ave N
Birmingham, AL 35222-1204
Mailing Address:
PO Box 10406
Birmingham, AL 35202-0406
Tel.: (205) 254-7000
Fax: (205) 254-7165
Toll Free: (866) 347-7473
Web Site: www.uspipe.com
Sales Range: $750-799.9 Million
Approx. Number Employees: 1,900
Year Founded: 1899
Business Description:
Ductile Iron Pressure Pipes & Fittings Mfr
S.I.C.: 3321; 3491
N.A.I.C.S.: 331511; 332911
Export
Media: 1-2-4-7-10-23
Distr.: Direct to Consumer; Intl.; Natl.
Budget Set: Oct.
Personnel:
Paul T. Ciolino *(Pres)*
Gary Crawford *(VP-Sls)*
Brands & Products:
FIELD-FLANGE 350
FIELD LOK 350
FLANGE-TYTE
METROSEAL
PERMAFUSE
TR FLEX
TR TELE FLEX
TRIM TYTE
TRIM TYTON
TYTON
TYTON JOINT
USIFLEX
XTRA FLEX

UNIVERSAL FOREST PRODUCTS, INC.
2801 E Beltline Ave NE
Grand Rapids, MI 49525-9680
Tel.: (616) 364-6161
Fax: (616) 364-5558
Web Site: www.ufpi.com
Approx. Sls.: $1,890,851,000
Approx. Number Employees: 5,100
Business Description:
Holding Company; Lumber & Composite Wood Building Products Mfr & Distr
S.I.C.: 6719; 2421; 2436; 2439; 2491; 2493; 5031
N.A.I.C.S.: 551112; 321113; 321114; 321212; 321213; 321214; 321219; 321912; 423310
Media: 7-10-13
Personnel:
William G. Currie *(Pres)*
Matthew J. Missad *(CEO)*
Michael R. Cole *(CFO & VP-Fin)*
Patrick M. Webster *(COO & Pres-Western Div)*
Ronald G. Klyn *(CIO)*
David A. Tutas *(Gen Counsel)*
Michael F. Mordell *(Exec VP-Pur)*
Robert D. Coleman *(Sr VP)*
Joseph F. Granger *(Gen Mgr-Ops & VP)*
C. Scott Greene *(Gen Mgr-Ops & VP-Mktg)*
Bob Hendricks *(VP-HR)*
Brands & Products:
CAPRICORN
DHP
EASY RISER
EQUATOR
KDAT
LATITUDES
LUMBER PRODUCTS
OPEN JOIST
PROWOOD
SIDESTEP
TECHTRIM
UNIVERSAL FOREST PRODUCT

URS CORPORATION
600 Montgomery St 26th Fl
San Francisco, CA 94111-2728
Tel.: (415) 774-2700
Fax: (415) 398-1905
Toll Free: (877) 877-8970
E-mail: investor_relations@urscorp.com
Web Site: www.urscorp.com
Approx. Rev.: $9,177,051,000
Approx. Number Employees: 47,000
Year Founded: 1951
Business Description:
Urban & Environmental Analysis, Planning & Design, Engineering, Architectural, Environmental & Economic Analysis
S.I.C.: 8711; 1629
N.A.I.C.S.: 541330; 237990
Media: 7-8-10-13-18-23-24
Personnel:
Martin M. Koffel *(Chm, Pres & CEO)*
H. Thomas Hicks *(CFO)*
Reed N. Brimhall *(Chief Acctg Officer, VP & Controller)*
Gary V. Jandegian *(Pres-Infrastructure & Environ Bus)*
Randall A. Wotring *(Pres-Federal Svcs-URS)*
Joseph Masters *(Gen Counsel, Sec & VP)*
Dhamo S. Dhamotharan *(Exec VP)*
Martin S. Tanzer *(Exec VP-Pub Sector Bus Dev)*
Hugh Blackwood *(Sr VP-Intl Ops)*
Susan B. Kilgannon *(VP-Corp Comm)*
Thomas J. Lynch *(VP-IT)*
Thomas W. Bishop *(Mgr)*
Advertising Agency:
Forget Me Knot/FMK Advertising
16 New Jersey St
Huntington Station, NY 11746
Tel.: (631) 242-9119
Fax: (631) 242-9449
Toll Free: (866) 528-5810

URS CORPORATION
(Sub. of URS Corporation)
1 Penn Plz Ste 610
New York, NY 10119-0698
Tel.: (212) 736-4444
Fax: (212) 629-4249
E-mail: sue_kilgannon@urscorp.com
Web Site: www.urscorp.com/Contact/index.php
Sales Range: $75-99.9 Million
Approx. Number Employees: 450
Business Description:
Highways, Bridges & Mass Transit Design
S.I.C.: 8711; 8712
N.A.I.C.S.: 541330; 541310
Media: 2
Personnel:
Jay M. Gewritzman *(VP & Office Mgr)*
Susan B. Kilgannon *(VP-Corp Comm)*

URS CORPORATION-WASHINGTON DIVISION
(Sub. of URS Corporation)
720 Park Blvd
Boise, ID 83712-7758
Tel.: (208) 386-5000
Fax: (208) 386-7186
Telex: 368439
Web Site: www.urscorp.com/Divisions/index.php?s=4
Approx. Rev.: $3,398,082,048
Approx. Number Employees: 25,000
Year Founded: 1912
Business Description:
Management, Engineering & Construction Services
S.I.C.: 8711; 1622; 1629
N.A.I.C.S.: 541330; 237310; 237990
Media: 1-2-4-13
Personnel:
Thomas H. Zarges *(Pres)*
Terri L. Marts *(Pres-Washington Defense)*
Greg P. Therrien *(Pres-Infrastructure Bus Unit)*

USG CORPORATION
550 W Adams St
Chicago, IL 60661-3676
Mailing Address:
PO Box 6721
Chicago, IL 60680-6721
Tel.: (312) 606-4000
Fax: (312) 606-4093
Toll Free: (800) USG4YOU
E-mail: usg4you@usg.com
Web Site: www.usg.com
E-Mail For Key Personnel:
Public Relations: publicrelations@usg.com
Approx. Sls.: $2,939,000,000
Approx. Number Employees: 9,250
Year Founded: 1902
Business Description:
Holding Company; Building Materials Mfr & Distr
S.I.C.: 3275; 1771; 5032; 5211
N.A.I.C.S.: 327420; 238110; 423320; 444190
Export
Advertising Expenditures: $15,000,000
Media: 4-5-7-10-19-21
Distr.: Natl.
Budget Set: Sept.
Personnel:
William C. Foote *(Chm)*
James S. Metcalf *(Pres & CEO)*
Richard H. Fleming *(CFO & Exec VP)*
Dominic A. Dannessa *(CTO & Sr VP)*
Brendan J. Deely *(Pres/CEO-L&W Supply Corp & Sr VP)*
Jennifer F. Scanlon *(Pres-Intl & VP)*
Stanley L. Ferguson *(Gen Counsel & Exec VP)*
Christopher R. Griffin *(Exec VP-Ops)*
Fareed A. Khan *(Exec VP-Fin & Strategy)*
Brain J. Cook *(Sr VP-HR)*
D. Rick Lowes *(Sr VP-Fin)*
Steve Bjorklund *(Dir-Tile & Flooring)*
Linda McGovern *(Dir-Mktg)*
Melissa York *(Dir-Integrated Mktg Comm)*
Brands & Products:
A-11
A/P LITE
ACRI-ADD
AIRTROL
APEX
AQUA-CAL
AQUA CAST
AQUA-TOUGH
ARIDEX
B-11
B1OS BEADEX
B1WNB BEADEX
B1XW BEADEX
B1XWEL BEADEX
B1XWELNB BEADEX
B1XWNB BEADEX
B2 BEADEX
BABY BULL
BEADEX
BEADEX B4
BEADEX B8
BEADEX B9
BEN FRANKLIN
BILLO
BLOK-TITE
BRIO
CA-5
CADRE
CAL-SEAL
CAS-20
CERAMICAL
CHAMPION
CLASSIC
CLEAN ROOM
CLIMAPLUS
COLORS OF MILAN
COLORS OF SIENA
COLORS OF VENICE
COMMITTED TO THE CRAFT
COVER COAT
CURVATURA
DANISH
DIAMOND
DIVINO
DRYSTONE
DUR-A-BEAD
DURABOND
DURACAL
DURAMOLD
DUROCK
EARLY EXPOSURE
EASY SAND
ECHELON
EL MERO MERO DRYWALERO
ENDURACAST
ENVIRO-SHIELD
ENVIROSTONE
FAST CAST
FASTEX
FIBER-ART
FIBEROCK
FIRECODE
FIVE STARSM
FORTACRETE
FROST
GARDENCAST
GEOMETRIX
GLACIER
GOLD
GYP-LAP

Key to Media (For complete agency information see *The Advertising Red Books-Agencies* edition):
1. Bus. Publs. 2. Cable T.V. 3. Catalogs & Directories. 4. Co-op Adv. 5. Consumer Mags. 6. D.M. to Bus. Estab.7. D.M. to Consumers 8. Daily Newsp. 9. Exhibits/Trade Shows 10. Foreign 11. Infomercial 12. Internet Adv.13. Multimedia 14. Network Radio 15. Network T.V. 16. Newsp. Distr. Mags. 17. Other 18. Outdoor (Posters, Transit) 19. Point of Purchase20. Premiums, Novelties 21. Product Samples 22. Special Events Mktg. 23. Spot Radio 24. Spot T.V. 25. Weekly Newsp. 26. Yellow Page Adv.

HALCYON
HUMITEK
HYDRO-STONE
HYDROCAL
HYDROMITE
HYDROPERM
IMPERIAL
K-LITE
KEMIKAL
LEVELROCK
LUNAR
MAC
MATRIX
MICHELANGELO
MICORE
MICORE MICRO BEAD
MICRO BEAD
MIDWEIGHT
MILLENNIA
MOLD TOUGH
NEXT GEN
NO-GO
NXG
ORIENTAL
ORION
PARALINE
PLUS 3
POURABLE BEFORE DRYWALL
PREMIER
PROFLOW
PURITAN
PYROFILL
QUADRA
QUICK-N-EASY
QUICK-SPRAY
QUIK-TOP
RAYITE
READYROCK
RED TOP
REGAL
ROCK FACE
ROCKLATH
SANDRIFT
SANTE-FE
SECUROCK
SHEETROCK
SHEETROCK B1
SHEETROCK B2
SHEETROCK B4
SHEETROCK B9J
SHEETROCK SLIC OS
SHEETROCK SLOC
SHEETROCK TOTAL
SHEETROCK TOTAL LITE
SILVER SET
SLC
SNOW WHITE
SOF 'N-SOIL
SOQUETE
SRB
SRM-25
STRENGTH BENEATH THE SURFACE
STRUCTO-BASE
STRUCTO-GAUGE
STRUCTOCORE
STRUCTOLITE
SUMMIT
TEXOLITE
THERMOFILL
TO THE CORE
TOPO
TUF-BASE
TUF-CAL
TUF-SET
TUF-SET LITE
TUF-SPRAY
TUF-STONE
TUF-TAPE
TUF-TEX
TUFFHIDE
ULTRA-BASE
ULTRA BEAD
ULTRACAL
ULTRACODE
USG
VALUEMESH

Advertising Agencies:
GyroHSR
60 Madison Ave Ste 1101
New York, NY 10010
Tel.: (212) 915-2490
Fax: (212) 915-2491

MC2 Marketing Inc.
13131 E 166th St
Cerritos, CA 90703-2202
Tel.: (562) 365-0200
Fax: (562) 365-0201

USG INTERIORS, INC.

(Sub. of USG Corporation)
550 W Adams St S Franklin St
Chicago, IL 60661
Mailing Address:
PO Box 4470
Chicago, IL 60680-4470
Tel.: (312) 606-4000
Fax: (312) 672-4093
E-mail: info@usg.com
Web Site: www.usg.com
Approx. Rev.: $455,000,000
Approx. Number Employees: 14,000
Year Founded: 1986
Business Description:
Commmercial & Residential Ceiling Products
S.I.C.: 3446
N.A.I.C.S.: 332323
Media: 7-10-21
Distr.: Natl.
Budget Set: Sept.
Personnel:
Bill Foote *(Chm & CEO)*

VARCO PRUDEN BUILDINGS, INC.

(Sub. of BlueScope Steel North America Corporation)
(d/b/a VP Buildings)
3200 Players Club Cir
Memphis, TN 38125-8843
Mailing Address:
PO Box 17967
Memphis, TN 38187
Tel.: (901) 748-8000
Fax: (901) 748-9323
Toll Free: (800) 238-3246
E-mail: vpsales@vp.com
Web Site: www.vp.com
Approx. Sls.: $400,000,000
Approx. Number Employees: 1,800
Business Description:
Prefabricated Metal Building Mfr
S.I.C.: 3448
N.A.I.C.S.: 332311
Import Export
Advertising Expenditures: $1,000,000
Media: 1-2-4-7-10-13-18-20-21-22-26
Distr.: Intl.; Natl.
Budget Set: Sept.
Personnel:
Chuck Haslebacher *(Pres)*
Ross E. Braithwait *(VP-Sls & Mktg)*
Jim Peckham *(Mgr)*
Doug Yancey *(Mgr-Adv)*
Brands & Products:
DECK FRAME
Advertising Agency:
Thompson & Company Marketing Communications
50 Peabody Pl
Memphis, TN 38103-3667
Tel.: (901) 527-8000
Fax: (901) 527-3697

VICEROY HOMES LIMITED

(Holding of JSC Open Investments)
414 Croft St E
Port Hope, ON L1A 4H1, Canada
Tel.: (905) 885-8600
Fax: (905) 885-8362
E-mail: info@viceroy.com
Web Site: www.viceroy.com
Sales Range: $75-99.9 Million
Approx. Number Employees: 400
Year Founded: 1955
Business Description:
Real Estate Services
S.I.C.: 6531
N.A.I.C.S.: 531390
Media: 4-6-10-22
Personnel:
Gaylord G. Lindal *(Chm, Pres & CEO)*
Bill Simpson *(VP-Fin)*
Jim Griffiths *(Dir-Mktg)*

VIKING DOOR & WINDOW

2099 S 10th St
San Jose, CA 95112
Tel.: (408) 294-5546
Fax: (408) 294-5117
E-mail: sales.manager@vikingdoor.com
Web Site: www.vikingdoor.com
E-Mail For Key Personnel:
Sales Director: sales.manager@vikingdoor.com
Business Description:
Doors & Windows & Moulding Seller
S.I.C.: 2431
N.A.I.C.S.: 321911
Media: 17
Personnel:
Kevin Collins *(Owner)*
Dave Moore *(Pres & CEO)*
Dale Miles *(Dir-Ops)*
Phyllis Dali *(Mgr-Acctg)*
Abel Juarez *(Mgr-Inside Sls)*

THE VIKING GROUP

210 N Industrial Park Rd
Hastings, MI 49058-9706
Tel.: (269) 945-9501
Fax: (269) 945-4495
Toll Free: (800) 968-9501
E-mail: techsvcs@vikingcorp.com
Web Site: www.vikinggroupinc.com
E-Mail For Key Personnel:
President: KOrtyl@vikingcorp.com
Marketing Director: JNorton@vikingcorp.com
Approx. Number Employees: 300
Year Founded: 1897
Business Description:
Fire Protection Products Mfr
S.I.C.: 3669; 3053
N.A.I.C.S.: 334290; 339991
Import Export
Media: 1-2-4-7-10-11-13-20-21-26
Distr.: Intl.; Natl.
Budget Set: Jan.
Personnel:
Mike Bosma *(Pres)*
Kevin Ortyl *(CEO)*
Janice Oshinski *(VP-Fin)*
Jess Norton *(Dir-Mktg)*
Brands & Products:
BRAMMALL
EASY RISER
FIRECYCLE
HORIZON
MICROFAST
MICROFAST HP
MICROMATIC
MIRAGE
TYDEN
VIKING

VINTAGE PARTS

120 Corporate Dr
Beaver Dam, WI 53916-3116
Tel.: (920) 887-8146
Fax: (920) 887-1764
Web Site: www.vpartsinc.com/
Approx. Number Employees: 80
Year Founded: 1971
Business Description:
Service Parts Sales & Distr
S.I.C.: 5082; 5084
N.A.I.C.S.: 423810; 423830
Media: 2-4-7-10
Distr.: Natl.
Budget Set: July
Personnel:
Darrell Armbruster *(Pres & CEO)*
Peter Fogarty *(Dir-Sls)*
Brands & Products:
VINTAGE PARTS

VIRGINIA GLASS PRODUCTS CORPORATION

(Sub. of Virginia Mirror Company Incorporated)
347 Old Sand Rd
Martinsville, VA 24148
Mailing Address:
PO Box 5431
Martinsville, VA 24115-5431
Tel.: (276) 956-3131
Fax: (276) 956-3020
Toll Free: (800) 368-3011
E-mail: info@va-glass.com
Web Site: www.va-glass.com
Approx. Number Employees: 105
Year Founded: 1956
Business Description:
Glass Products Mfr
S.I.C.: 3211; 3231
N.A.I.C.S.: 327211; 327215
Export
Advertising Expenditures: $500,000
Media: 2-6-21
Distr.: Natl.
Budget Set: Dec.
Personnel:
W. Christopher Beeler, Jr. *(CEO)*
Benjamin D. Beeler *(Exec VP)*
Brands & Products:
CERAM-SPAN
SURESEAL
TEMPAR-GLAS
TEMPAR-GLAS ALL-GLASS ENTRANCES
TEMPAR-GLAS SHOWER DOORS
TEMPAR-GLAS SLIDING DOORS
TEMPAR-GLAS SPANDREL GLASS

Key to Media (For complete agency information see *The Advertising Red Books-Agencies* edition):
1. Bus. Publs. 2. Cable T.V. 3. Catalogs & Directories. 4. Co-op Adv. 5. Consumer Mags. 6. D.M. to Bus. Estab.7. D.M. to Consumers
8. Daily Newsp. 9. Exhibits/Trade Shows 10. Foreign 11. Infomercial 12. Internet Adv.13. Multimedia 14. Network Radio
15. Network T.V. 16. Newsp. Distr. Mags. 17. Other 18. Outdoor (Posters, Transit) 19. Point of Purchase20. Premiums, Novelties
21. Product Samples 22. Special Events Mktg. 23. Spot Radio 24. Spot T.V. 25. Weekly Newsp. 26. Yellow Page Adv.

VOCON DESIGN, INC.
3142 Prospect Ave
Cleveland, OH 44115
Tel.: (216) 588-0800
Fax: (216) 588-0801
Toll Free: (866) 787-7021
E-mail: vocon@vocon.com
Web Site: www.vocon.com
Sales Range: $10-24.9 Million
Approx. Number Employees: 70
Year Founded: 1987
Business Description:
Architectural & Interior Design Services
S.I.C.: 7389; 8712
N.A.I.C.S.: 541410; 541310
Personnel:
Frank Mercuri *(CFO)*
Advertising Agency:
Falls Communications
50 Public Sq 25th Fl
Cleveland, OH 44113
Tel.: (216) 696-0229
Fax: (216) 696-0269

VULCAN MATERIALS COMPANY
1200 Urban Center Dr
Birmingham, AL 35242
Mailing Address:
PO Box 385014
Birmingham, AL 35238-5014
Tel.: (205) 298-3000
Fax: (205) 298-2960
E-mail: info@vmcmail.com
Web Site: www.vulcanmaterials.com
Approx. Rev.: $2,558,862,000
Approx. Number Employees: 7,749
Year Founded: 1909
Business Description:
Construction Aggregate Mfr
S.I.C.: 1429; 1411; 1442; 3272
N.A.I.C.S.: 212319; 212311; 212321; 327390
Import Export
Media: 2-7-8-9-13-18-25
Distr.: Natl.
Budget Set: Oct.
Personnel:
Donald M. James *(Chm & CEO)*
Daniel F. Sansone *(CFO & Exec VP)*
Ejaz A. Khan *(CIO, VP & Controller)*
Robert A. Wason IV *(Sr VP & Gen Counsel)*
Danny R. Shepherd *(Exec VP-Construction Matls)*
J. Wayne Houston *(Sr VP-HR)*
James Averitt *(Dir-Risk Mgmt)*
David Donaldson *(Dir-Community Rels)*
John English *(Mgr-Pub Affairs)*
Norman Jetmundsen, Jr. *(Asst Gen Counsel)*
Carol Maxwell *(Coord-Community Programs)*
Advertising Agencies:
Ackermann PR
1111 Northshore Dr Ste N-400
Knoxville, TN 37919
Tel.: (865) 584-0550
Fax: (865) 588-3009
Toll Free: (866) 896-4069
Toll Free: (888) 414-7787

Intermark Group, Inc.
101 25th St N
Birmingham, AL 35203
Tel.: (205) 803-0000
Fax: (205) 870-3843
Toll Free: (800) 554-0218

W.A. ROOSEVELT COMPANY
2727 Commerce St
La Crosse, WI 54603-1760
Tel.: (608) 781-2000
Fax: (608) 781-8372
E-mail: info@waroosevelt.com
Web Site: www.waroosevelt.com
Approx. Number Employees: 100
Year Founded: 1868
Business Description:
Distr. of Plumbing, Heating, Electrical, Air Conditioning & Refrigeration Supplies & Equipment
S.I.C.: 5074; 5063
N.A.I.C.S.: 423720; 423610
Media: 2-7-10-18-20-22-23
Distr.: Natl.
Budget Set: Dec.
Personnel:
Todd Eber *(Owner & Pres)*
Jim Voshart *(VP-Sls)*

WAKEFIELD THERMAL SOLUTIONS
33 Bridge St
Pelham, NH 03076-3475
Tel.: (603) 635-2800
Fax: (603) 635-1900
E-mail: info@wakefield.com
Web Site: www.wakefield.com
Approx. Sls.: $8,000,000
Approx. Number Employees: 273
Business Description:
Mfr. of Heat Sinks For the Electronic Industry
S.I.C.: 3559
N.A.I.C.S.: 332410
Advertising Expenditures: $400,000
Media: 2-4-7-10
Distr.: Natl.
Budget Set: Jan.
Personnel:
James Polakiewicz *(CFO)*
Brands & Products:
AHAM TOR
ATI

WALKER & ZANGER, INC.
8901 Bradley Ave
Sun Valley, CA 91352
Tel.: (818) 833-0848
Fax: (818) 833-4347
Toll Free: (800) 540-0235
E-mail: info@walkerzanger.com
Web Site: www.walkerzanger.com
E-Mail For Key Personnel:
President: jzanger@walkerzanger.com
Marketing Director: bbrown@walkerzanger.com
Sales Range: $100-124.9 Million
Approx. Number Employees: 300
Year Founded: 1952
Business Description:
Marble, Granite, Soapstone, Limestone, Slate, Onyx, Quartzite, Agglomerates & Ceramic Tile Distr
S.I.C.: 5032
N.A.I.C.S.: 423320
Media: 2-4-5-7-8-10-21
Distr.: Natl.
Budget Set: Nov.
Personnel:
Leon Zanger *(Chm & CEO)*
Jonathan A. Zanger *(Pres)*
Pat Petrocelli *(COO & VP)*
Mike Bastone *(VP-Sls)*
Jared Becker *(Exec Dir-Creative)*
Tristan Mcmanaman *(Dir-Mktg)*
Brands & Products:
ABISKO
ALABASTRO
ANTEQUERA
ANTIUM
AVIGNON
BORGIA
BROADWAY
CASABLANCA
CERAMICA ALHAMBRA
CORDILLERA
COTE D OR
DERUTA
DURANGO ANCIENT
FIRENZE
FIREPLACES
FUSION
FUSION GLASS
GRAMERCY PARK
GRANITE
GROOVE
IMPERIUM
INTARSIO ROMANO
JERUSALEM STONE
KASARE
LAGUNA
LIMESTONE
LIMESTONE MOLDINGS
MAISON FRANCAISE
MANTRA
MARBLE
MARSPAC
MARTILE
MATOUCHE
MEDALLIONS
MELANGE
METAL TECH
METALLISMO
MIZU
MODA MOSAIC
MONDRIAN
MONTROUGE
MOSAIC
NEWPORT
OPUS ANTICATO
ORIELLE
PARADIGM
PATINE
PAVIA ANTICO
PAVIA ANTICO PINTURA
PIETRA CAMPANIA
PIETRA DI FIANDRA
PINTERETTO
PROGRESSIVE
RAVEN HILL FORGE
ROKU
SHABUI
SKYLINE
SLATE
SOBU
SOHO
SPA GLASS
SPANISH COTTO
STEEL WORK
STONE TECH
SUMARI
TESSERA
TEXTURA
TIBERON
TRAVERTINE
TRIBECA
TUSCANY
VENEZIA
VIA FORTE
VILLA RUSTICA
VINTAGE GLASS
WALKER ZANGER
WATERFALL
WEAVE
WILLOW CREEK
XILO
YOUR LIFE'S TILE RESOURCE
ZEN GARDEN

WALPOLE WOODWORKERS, INC.
767 E St
Walpole, MA 02081
Mailing Address:
PO Box 151
Walpole, MA 02081-0151
Tel.: (508) 668-2800
Tel.: (781) 329-0770
Fax: (508) 668-7301
Toll Free: (800) 343-6948
E-mail: sales@walpolewoodworkers.com
Web Site:
www.walpolewoodworkers.com
E-Mail For Key Personnel:
Sales Director: sales@walpolewoodworkers.com
Approx. Number Employees: 250
Year Founded: 1933
Business Description:
Mfr. of Wood Products: Fences, Furniture & Prefabricated Buildings
S.I.C.: 2499; 5211
N.A.I.C.S.: 321999; 444190
Advertising Expenditures: $350,000
Media: 2-4-6-8-9-10-13-18-26
Distr.: Natl.
Budget Set: Jan.
Personnel:
Louis A. Maglio *(CEO)*
James E. Loer, Jr. *(Treas & Mgr-Admin)*
Sue Donahue *(Dir-Mktg)*
Brands & Products:
WALPOLE

WALTER ENERGY, INC.
4211 W Boy Scout Blvd
Tampa, FL 33607-5724
Tel.: (813) 871-4811
Fax: (813) 871-4399
Web Site: www.walterind.com
Approx. Rev.: $1,587,730,000
Approx. Number Employees: 2,100
Year Founded: 1946
Business Description:
Mfr. of Ductile Iron Pressure Pipe & Fittings & Coal; Production of Furnace & Foundry Coke, Chemicals & Allied Products, Various Building Materials & Industrial Products; New Construction of Single Family Homes & Financing
S.I.C.: 3312; 1222; 1521; 3321; 3498
N.A.I.C.S.: 331111; 212112; 236115; 331511; 332996
Import Export
Advertising Expenditures: $5,000,000
Media: 2-9-25
Personnel:
Walter J. Scheller, III *(CEO)*
Lisa A. Honnold *(Interim CFO, Sr VP & Controller)*
Charles C. Stewart *(Pres-Walter Minerals Walter Coke)*
Miles C. Dearden, III *(Treas & Sr VP)*

Key to Media (For complete agency information see *The Advertising Red Books-Agencies* edition):
1. Bus. Publs. 2. Cable T.V. 3. Catalogs & Directories. 4. Co-op Adv. 5. Consumer Mags. 6. D.M. to Bus. Estab.7. D.M. to Consumers 8. Daily Newsp. 9. Exhibits/Trade Shows 10. Foreign 11. Infomercial 12. Internet Adv.13. Multimedia 14. Network Radio 15. Network T.V. 16. Newsp. Distr. Mags. 17. Other 18. Outdoor (Posters, Transit) 19. Point of Purchase20. Premiums, Novelties 21. Product Samples 22. Special Events Mktg. 23. Spot Radio 24. Spot T.V. 25. Weekly Newsp. 26. Yellow Page Adv.

Larry E. Williams *(Sr VP-HR)*
Michael A. Monahan *(Dir-Corp Comm)*
Brands & Products:
TYTON JOINT
Advertising Agency:
Azzam Jordan
305 Washington Ave Ste 305
Baltimore, MD 21204
Tel.: (410) 825-1800
Fax: (410) 825-3997
— Colleen Kennedy *(Acct Exec)*

THE WARMINGTON GROUP
3090 Pullman St
Costa Mesa, CA 92626-5901
Tel.: (714) 557-5511
Fax: (714) 641-9337
Web Site:
www.warmingtonhomes.com
Sales Range: $350-399.9 Million
Approx. Number Employees: 300
Year Founded: 1972
Business Description:
Construction Services
S.I.C.: 6552
N.A.I.C.S.: 237210
Advertising Expenditures: $1,000,000
Media: 2-4-6-7-8-10-18
Distr.: Natl.
Personnel:
Allen Morris *(Sr VP)*
Jennifer Bell *(Dir-Media & PR)*
Advertising Agency:
Bayport Advertising
(House Agency)
3090 Pullman Ave., Ste. A
Costa Mesa, CA 92626
Tel.: (714) 557-5511
(New Homes)

WASCO PRODUCTS, INC.
22 Pioneer Ave
Sanford, ME 04073-3046
Tel.: (207) 324-8060
Fax: (800) 933-0593
Toll Free: (800) 388-0293
E-mail: sales@wascoproducts.com
Web Site: www.wascoproducts.com
E-Mail For Key Personnel:
Sales Director: sales@wascoproducts.com
Approx. Number Employees: 70
Year Founded: 1935
Business Description:
Skylights, Roof Windows, Heat & Smoke Vents, Patio Doors Mfr
S.I.C.: 3211; 3089
N.A.I.C.S.: 327211; 326199
Advertising Expenditures: $500,000
Media: 2-4-5-7-8-10-13-22
Distr.: Natl.
Personnel:
Jeff Frank *(CEO)*
Sara Havaid *(COO)*
Brands & Products:
CIRCULAR SKYDOMES
CLASSIC
CLUSTER
E-CLASS
LOW PROFILE
NON-THERMALIZED
PERMATHERM
PINNACLE
PYRODOME
PYROVENT
SKYDOME
SKYDOMES
SKYWINDOW
SKYWINDOWS
THERMALIZED
WASCO
Advertising Agency:
Maverick Marketing International
24 Preble St
Portland, ME 04101
Tel.: (207) 773-0802

WATKINS MANUFACTURING CORPORATION
(Sub. of Masco Corporation)
(d/b/a Hot Spring Portable Spas)
1280 Park Ctr Dr
Vista, CA 92083-8314
Tel.: (760) 598-6464
Fax: (760) 598-8910
Toll Free: (800) 999-4688
E-mail: info@hotspring.com
Web Site: www.hotspring.com
E-Mail For Key Personnel:
Marketing Director: market@watkinsmfg.com
Sales Range: $250-299.9 Million
Approx. Number Employees: 900
Year Founded: 1977
Business Description:
Spas
S.I.C.: 3088; 5091
N.A.I.C.S.: 326191; 423910
Export
Media: 5-6-10-14-19-20-22-26
Distr.: Intl.; Natl.
Budget Set: Oct.
Personnel:
Steve Hammock *(Pres)*
Mike Dunn *(Exec VP)*
Sandra Shuda *(VP-HR)*
Brands & Products:
DREAMJET
EVERFRESH WATER CARE SYSTEM
FOOTWELL
HOT SPRING
HOT SPRING CLASSIC
HOT SPRING GRANDEE
HOT SPRING JETSETTER
HOT SPRING PRODIGY
HOT SPRING SOVEREIGN
HYDROPULSE
JET-CLUSTER
JETSTREAM
LANDMARK
MOTO-MASSAGE
PRECISION
QUARTET
SOOTHING SEVEN
TIGER RIVER SPAS
Advertising Agencies:
Ocean Bridge Group
1714 16th St
Santa Monica, CA 90404
Tel.: (310) 392-3200

SiteLab International, Inc.
2223 Avenida De La Playa Ste 208
La Jolla, CA 92037-3218
Tel.: (858) 456-4720
Fax: (858) 456-4724

WAUKEE ENGINEERING CO. INC.
5600 W Florist Ave
Milwaukee, WI 53218-1621
Tel.: (414) 462-8200
Fax: (414) 462-7022
E-mail: sales@waukeemeters.com
Web Site: www.waukeemeters.com
E-Mail For Key Personnel:
Sales Director: sales@waukeemeters.com
Approx. Number Employees: 20
Year Founded: 1950
Business Description:
Flow Meters, Mixers & Compressors for Industrial Heating & Heat-Treating Industry
S.I.C.: 3824; 3823
N.A.I.C.S.: 334514; 334513
Export
Media: 2-4-7-8-10-13-20-26
Distr.: Natl.
Budget Set: Jan.
Brands & Products:
ACCURATE AND RELIABLE FLOW CONTROL
VALVE TRONIC
WAUKEE
WAUKEE FLO-ALARM
WAUKEE FLO-METER
WAUKEE FLOW TOTALIZER
WAUKEE MIXOR
WAUKEE TRONIC

WAUSAU HOMES, INC.
10805 Bus Hwy 51
Rothschild, WI 54474
Tel.: (715) 359-7272
Fax: (715) 359-2867
E-mail: info@wausauhomes.com
Web Site: www.wausauhomes.com
Approx. Number Employees: 600
Year Founded: 1960
Business Description:
Pre-Fabricated Homes
S.I.C.: 2452; 1521
N.A.I.C.S.: 321992; 236115
Advertising Expenditures: $225,000
Media: 5-6-7-8-9-10-16-18-19-20-22-23-24-25-26
Distr.: Reg.
Budget Set: Dec.
Brands & Products:
ADVANCE BUILDING SYSTEMS
REDEFINING THE BUILDING EXPERIENCE
STERLING BUILDING SYSTEMS
WAUSAU HOMES

WAXMAN INDUSTRIES, INC.
24460 Aurora Rd
Bedford, OH 44146-1728
Tel.: (440) 439-1830
Fax: (440) 439-8678
E-mail: info@waxmanind.com
Web Site: www.waxmanind.com
Sales Range: $50-74.9 Million
Approx. Number Employees: 440
Year Founded: 1934
Business Description:
Assembler, Packager & Distributor of Plumbing & Hardware Products for the Home Repair & Remodeling Markets
S.I.C.: 5074; 5072
N.A.I.C.S.: 423720; 423710
Import
Advertising Expenditures: $330,000
Media: 1-2-5-10-19-22
Distr.: Natl.
Budget Set: Jan.
Personnel:
Armond Waxman *(Co-Chm, Co-CEO & Treas)*
Melvin Waxman *(Co-Chm & Co-CEO)*
Mark W. Wester *(CFO & Sr VP)*
Patrick Ferrante *(VP & Gen Mgr)*
Michael Pendry *(VP-Fin)*
Brands & Products:
EZ CASTER
EZ MOUNT
EZSLIDERS
HYDROSPIN
KF
WAXMAN INDUSTRIES

WAYNE-DALTON CORP.
(Sub. of Overhead Door Corporation)
1 Door Dr
Mount Hope, OH 44660
Tel.: (330) 674-7015
Fax: (330) 763-8032
Web Site: www.wayne-dalton.com
Sales Range: $300-349.9 Million
Approx. Number Employees: 2,400
Year Founded: 1954
Business Description:
Mfr. of Wood, Aluminum, Fiberglass & Steel Overhead Garage Doors & Garage Door Openers
S.I.C.: 3442; 2431
N.A.I.C.S.: 332321; 321911
Import Export
Media: 22
Personnel:
Willis Mullet *(Chm)*
George Keller *(Sr VP-HR)*
Brands & Products:
AKBAR
ATLER
DECOR
DOORMASTER
FABRIC-SHIELD
FOAMCORE
IDRIVE
PLEXIGLAS
QUANTUM
SECUR-VENT
SILENTGLIDE
STYLELINE
THERMOGUARD
THERMOMARK
THERMOSPAN
THERMOWAYNE
TITAN
TORQUEMASTER
WAYNE
WAYNE-DALTON
WAYNEGARD
WAYNEGUARD
WAYNEMARK
WAYNETEC
Advertising Agency:
SBC Advertising
333 W Nationwide Blvd
Columbus, OH 43215
Tel.: (614) 891-7070
Fax: (614) 255-2600
Toll Free: (866) 891-7001

WEISER LOCK, INC.
(Sub. of Stanley Black & Decker, Inc.)
19701 Da Vinci
Lake Forest, CA 92610
Tel.: (949) 672-4000
Fax: (949) 672-4001
Toll Free: (800) 854-3151
E-mail: info@weiserlock.com
Web Site: www.weiserlock.com
Sales Range: $25-49.9 Million
Approx. Number Employees: 30
Year Founded: 1904

Key to Media (For complete agency information see *The Advertising Red Books-Agencies* edition):
1. Bus. Publs. 2. Cable T.V. 3. Catalogs & Directories. 4. Co-op Adv. 5. Consumer Mags. 6. D.M. to Bus. Estab.7. D.M. to Consumers
8. Daily Newsp. 9. Exhibits/Trade Shows 10. Foreign 11. Infomercial 12. Internet Adv.13. Multimedia 14. Network Radio
15. Network T.V. 16. Newsp. Distr. Mags. 17. Other 18. Outdoor (Posters, Transit) 19. Point of Purchase20. Premiums, Novelties
21. Product Samples 22. Special Events Mktg. 23. Spot Radio 24. Spot T.V. 25. Weekly Newsp. 26. Yellow Page Adv.

Weiser Lock, Inc. — (Continued)

Business Description:
Mfr. Residential, Mobile Home Door Locks & Related Door Hardware
S.I.C.: 3429
N.A.I.C.S.: 332510
Export
Advertising Expenditures: $1,500,000
Media: 2-4-5-6-9-10-13-19-20-23-24
Distr.: Natl.

Brands & Products:
BASICS BY WEISER LOCK
ELEMENTS SERIES
FASHION DOORWARE
POWERBOLT 1000
PRESTIGE
WEISER
WEISER BRILLIANCE
WEISERBOLT
WEISERLOCK
WELCOME HOME

THE WEITZ COMPANY

Capital Sq 400 Locust St Ste 300
Des Moines, IA 50309
Tel.: (515) 698-4260
Fax: (515) 698-4297
Web Site: www.weitz.com
E-Mail For Key Personnel:
President: destigter@weitz.com
Sales Range: $300-349.9 Million
Approx. Number Employees: 1,400
Year Founded: 1855
Business Description:
General Contractors & Construction Managers
S.I.C.: 1541
N.A.I.C.S.: 236210
Media: 2
Personnel:
Glenn H. De Stigter *(Chm)*
Leonard W. Martling, Jr. *(CEO)*
David Strutt *(Gen Counsel & Sr VP)*
Advertising Agency:
The Meyocks Group
6800 Lake Dr Ste 150
West Des Moines, IA 50266-2544
Tel.: (515) 225-1200
Fax: (515) 225-6400

WELLBORN HOLDINGS INC.

(Sub. of Wellborn Cabinet, Inc.)
215 Diller Ave
New Holland, PA 17557
Tel.: (717) 351-1700
Fax: (717) 351-1714
E-mail: info@vikingcabinetry.biz
Web Site: www.rutt.net
Approx. Number Employees: 82
Year Founded: 1951
Business Description:
Mfr. of Custom Kitchen Cabinets, Custom Bath Vanities & Office, Den & Bar Furniture
S.I.C.: 2434
N.A.I.C.S.: 337110
Advertising Expenditures: $750,000
Media: 6-10
Distr.: Natl.
Personnel:
David Roos *(CEO)*
Jerry Price *(Gen Mgr)*
Brands & Products:
FOR THOSE UNACCUSTOMED TO COMPROMISE
RUTT HANDCRAFTED CABINETRY

WELLMAN PRODUCTS GROUP

(Sub. of Carlisle Brake & Friction, Inc.)
6180 Cochron Rd
Solon, OH 44139
Tel.: (440) 528-4000
Fax: (440) 528-4098
E-mail: info@wellmanproducts.com
Web Site: www.wellmanproducts.com
Sales Range: $50-74.9 Million
Approx. Number Employees: 60
Business Description:
Metal Clutch Plates, Facings, Brake Linings and Transmission Discs Mfr
S.I.C.: 3499; 3714
N.A.I.C.S.: 332117; 336340
Advertising Expenditures: $300,000
Media: 2-4-10-11-13-18-20-26
Distr.: Natl.
Budget Set: Oct.
Personnel:
Ronald E. Weinberg *(Chm)*
Tom Sovich *(VP-Sls & Mktg)*
Brands & Products:
HAWK PERFORMANCE
VELVETOUCH

WERNER HOLDING CO.

93 Werner Rd
Greenville, PA 16125-9434
Tel.: (724) 588-8600
Fax: (724) 588-0315
Toll Free: (888) 523-3370
E-mail: frienlv@wernerco.com
Web Site: www.wernerco.com
Approx. Number Employees: 1,500
Year Founded: 1997
Business Description:
Holding Company; Aluminum Products
S.I.C.: 6719; 3355
N.A.I.C.S.: 551112; 331319
Import Export
Advertising Expenditures: $1,500,000
Media: 2-4-7-9-10-11-13-14-18-19
Personnel:
Bill Allen *(Chm & CEO)*
Larry Friend *(CFO, Treas & Exec VP)*
Ed Gericke *(Exec VP)*
Brands & Products:
ALDEK
ALFLO
ALUMA-PLANK
ALUMALOCK
CLIMBINGPRO
EDGE
GLASS MARK
HOLSTER-TOP
MULTI-LOK
PINCH-PROOF
SHU-LOK
SPILL-PROOF
TASK MASTER
TOOL-TRA-TOP
TRACTION-TRED
TRUE GRIP
TWIST-PROOF
WERNER

WEYERHAEUSER COMPANY

33663 Weyerhaeuser Way S
Federal Way, WA 98063
Mailing Address:
PO Box 9777
Federal Way, WA 98063-9777
Tel.: (253) 924-2345
Fax: (253) 924-2685
Toll Free: (800) 525-5440
E-mail: pubrelations@weyerhaeuser.com
Web Site: www.weyerhaeuser.com
Approx. Rev.: $6,552,000,000
Approx. Number Employees: 14,250
Year Founded: 1900
Business Description:
Building Products, Pulp, Paper & Packaging & Management of Timberlands
S.I.C.: 5093; 2421; 2499; 2631
N.A.I.C.S.: 423930; 321113; 321999; 322130
Import Export
Advertising Expenditures: $7,000,000
Media: 2-4-6-7-8-9-10-15-19-20-23-24-25
Distr.: Intl.; Natl.
Budget Set: Oct.
Personnel:
Daniel S. Fulton *(Pres & CEO)*
Patricia M. Bedient *(CFO & Exec VP)*
Kevin Shearer *(CIO & VP)*
Jeanne Hillman *(Chief Acctg Officer)*
Sandy McDade *(Gen Counsel & Sr VP)*
Claire S. Grace *(Sec, VP & Asst Gen Counsel)*
Thomas F. Gideon *(Exec VP-Timberlands)*
Lawrence B. Burrows *(Sr VP-Wood Products)*
Srinivasan Chandrasekaran *(Sr VP-Cellulose Fiber)*
Carlos J. Guilherme *(VP-Sls)*
Karen Andrus-Hughes *(Mgr-Mktg)*
Nancy Arend *(Mgr)*
Thomas M. Smith *(Mgr-Rail Transportation)*
Brands & Products:
ABALON BEECH
ACREAGE
BOBCAT
CAMBERLEY HOMES
CEDARONE
CHOCTAW
CHOICEPLY
CHOICETRIM
CLASSIC GLULAM
COMPARIS
COUGAR
DURAFLAKE
FIRST CHOICE
FURN-I-FRAME
HUSKY
ILEVEL
IMAGEPRINT
JAVELIN
LYNX
LYPTUS
MARACAY HOMES
MATRIX
NEXTPHASE
PARALLAM
PEARL
SONORA
STRUCTUREPAK
THINFLEX
TIMBERSTRAND
TJ-PRO
TJ-XPER
TJI
ULTRAPINE
WEATHERMATE
WILLCOPY
Advertising Agencies:
Dailey & Associates
(Sub. of The Interpublic Group of Cos., Inc.)
8687 Melrose Ave Ste G300
West Hollywood, CA 90069-5701
Tel.: (310) 360-3100
Fax: (310) 360-0810

FD Americas Public Affairs
1101 K St NW 9th Fl
Washington, DC 20005
Tel.: (202) 346-8800
Fax: (202) 346-8804

WEYERHAEUSER COMPANY LIMITED

(Sub. of Weyerhaeuser International, Inc.)
925 Georgia Street West
Vancouver, BC V6C 3L2, Canada
Tel.: (604) 661-8000
E-mail: sandy.mcdade@weyerhaeuser.com
Web Site: www.weyerhaeuser.com
Sales Range: $1-4.9 Billion
Approx. Number Employees: 12,000
Year Founded: 1966
Business Description:
Lumber, Panelboard, Integrated Forest Products & Engineered Wood
S.I.C.: 3559
N.A.I.C.S.: 333298
Export
Media: 2-25
Distr.: Intl.; Natl.
Budget Set: Oct. -Dec.
Personnel:
Anne Giardini *(Pres)*
Sandy D. McDade *(Gen Counsel & Sr VP)*

WEYERHAEUSER INTERNATIONAL, INC.

(Sub. of Weyerhaeuser Company)
33663 Weyerhaeuser Way
Federal Way, WA 98063-9777
Tel.: (253) 924-2345
Fax: (253) 924-5979
Web Site: www.weyerhaeuser.com/Company/CorporateAffairs/ContactByMail
Sales Range: $150-199.9 Million
Business Description:
Holding Company
S.I.C.: 5031
N.A.I.C.S.: 423310
Advertising Agency:
Dailey & Associates
(Sub. of The Interpublic Group of Cos., Inc.)
8687 Melrose Ave Ste G300
West Hollywood, CA 90069-5701
Tel.: (310) 360-3100
Fax: (310) 360-0810

WHEATLAND TUBE COMPANY

(Div. of John Maneely Company)
1 Council Ave
Wheatland, PA 16161-0608
Mailing Address:
PO Box 600
Collingswood, NJ 08108-0600
Tel.: (724) 346-7158
Fax: (724) 346-7260
Toll Free: (800) 257-8182
E-mail: info@wheatland.com
Web Site: www.wheatland.com
Approx. Number Employees: 1,000

Key to Media (For complete agency information see *The Advertising Red Books-Agencies* edition):
1. Bus. Publs. 2. Cable T.V. 3. Catalogs & Directories. 4. Co-op Adv. 5. Consumer Mags. 6. D.M. to Bus. Estab.7. D.M. to Consumers 8. Daily Newsp. 9. Exhibits/Trade Shows 10. Foreign 11. Infomercial 12. Internet Adv.13. Multimedia 14. Network Radio 15. Network T.V. 16. Newsp. Distr. Mags. 17. Other 18. Outdoor (Posters, Transit) 19. Point of Purchase20. Premiums, Novelties 21. Product Samples 22. Special Events Mktg. 23. Spot Radio 24. Spot T.V. 25. Weekly Newsp. 26. Yellow Page Adv.

Business Description:
Steel Pipe Mfr
S.I.C.: 3317
N.A.I.C.S.: 331210
Advertising Expenditures: $200,000
Media: 2-4-7-10
Distr.: Intl.; Natl.
Personnel:
Mickey McNamara *(Gen Counsel)*
Mark Magno *(VP-Sls)*
Gina Beach *(HR Coord)*
Advertising Agency:
Kerry Schwoyer Associates
33 N. Market St.
Lancaster, PA 17603
Tel.: (717) 393-6099
(Black & Galvanized Steel Pipes)

WHEELING CORRUGATING
(Div. of Severstal Wheeling Inc.)
1134 Mkt St
Wheeling, WV 26003
Tel.: (304) 234-2332
Fax: (304) 234-2210
Web Site:
www.wheelingcorrugating.com
Approx. Number Employees: 250
Year Founded: 1890
Business Description:
Mfr of Roll Formed Steel Products
S.I.C.: 3312; 3444; 3448
N.A.I.C.S.: 331111; 332311; 332322
Advertising Expenditures: $1,000,000
Media: 1-2-4-5-7-10-13-16-19-20-21-22
Distr.: Intl.
Budget Set: Oct.
Personnel:
Brian Robb *(Mgr-Sls)*
Brands & Products:
BARNMASTER
CENTURYDRAIN
CHANNELDRAIN
CHANNELDRAIN 2000
CULVERCOTE PLUS II
CULVERCOTE WITH TRENCHCOAT
CULVERTCOTE
PANELDRAIN
SOFTITE
TENSILFORM
TENSILVENT

WHITE RIVER HARDWOODS-WOODWORKS, INC.
1197 Happy Hollow Rd
Fayetteville, AR 72701
Tel.: (479) 442-6986
Fax: (479) 444-0406
Toll Free: (800) 558-0119
E-mail: info@whiteriver.com
Web Site: www.whiteriver.com
Approx. Number Employees: 50
Year Founded: 1979
Business Description:
Mfr of Traditional & Decorative Hardwood Millwork
S.I.C.: 2499; 3446
N.A.I.C.S.: 321999; 332323
Media: 4-7-8-10
Personnel:
Bruce Johnson *(Owner)*
Joan Johnson *(Owner)*
Richard Enrique *(Dir-Mktg)*
Brands & Products:
AUTHENTIC HAND-CARVED
ELEGANT ADDITIONS
MARBLEWOOD
METALWOOD
MON REALE
ULTRA FLEX
WHITE RIVER

THE WHITMAN COMPANIES, INC.
116 Tices Ln # B1
East Brunswick, NJ 08816
Tel.: (732) 390-5858
Fax: (732) 390-9496
E-mail: whitman@whitmanco.com
Web Site: www.whitmanco.com
Approx. Number Employees: 70
Year Founded: 1985
Business Description:
Environmental Engineering Consulting & Management Services
S.I.C.: 8748; 8711
N.A.I.C.S.: 541690; 541330
Media: 2
Personnel:
Barry Skoultchi *(Pres & CEO)*
Todd Gerber *(COO & Exec VP)*
Ira L. Whitman *(Principal)*
Michael Sylvester *(Sr VP)*
Michael Metlitz *(Dir-Environ Compliance)*

WHX CORPORATION
(Name Changed to Handy & Harman Ltd.)

WILLIAM LYON HOMES
4490 Von Karman Ave
Newport Beach, CA 92660-2008
Tel.: (949) 833-3600
Fax: (949) 476-2178
Web Site: www.lyonhomes.com
Approx. Rev.: $309,243,000
Approx. Number Employees: 195
Year Founded: 1956
Business Description:
Single Family Homes Designer, Constructor & Sales
S.I.C.: 1531
N.A.I.C.S.: 236117
Advertising Expenditures: $23,600,000
Personnel:
William Lyon, Sr. *(Chm & CEO)*
William H. Lyon *(Pres & COO)*
Colin T. Severn *(CFO, Corp Sec & VP)*
Mary J. Connelly *(Pres-Nevada Div & Sr VP)*
W. Thomas Hickcox *(Pres-Arizona Div & Sr VP)*
Brian H. Doyle *(Pres-Southern California Div & VP)*
Richard S. Robinson *(Sr VP-Fin)*
Lesley Pennington *(VP-Sls)*

W.J. RUSCOE COMPANY
485 Kenmore Blvd
Akron, OH 44301-1013
Mailing Address:
PO Box 3858
Akron, OH 44314-0858
Tel.: (330) 253-8148
Fax: (330) 253-2933
Toll Free: (800) 293-8148
E-mail: sales@ruscoe.com
Web Site: www.ruscoe.com
E-Mail For Key Personnel:
Sales Director: sales@ruscoe.com
Approx. Sls.: $6,500,000
Approx. Number Employees: 46
Year Founded: 1946
Business Description:
Adhesive Mfr & Distr
S.I.C.: 2891
N.A.I.C.S.: 325520
Advertising Expenditures: $25,000
Media: 2-4-7-8-10-19-21
Distr.: Natl.
Budget Set: Dec.
Personnel:
Paul Michalec *(Pres)*
Betty Pfaff *(Treas, Sec & Dir-HR)*
Larry Musci *(Mgr-Sls & Mktg)*
Brands & Products:
NITRILE ALUMINIZED ROOF PRIMER
PAN-L-BOND
PERMANENT-SEALER
PLIO-TAC
PLIOBOND
R
Advertising Agency:
Total Marketing Services
550 E. Nine Mile Rd.
Ferndale, MI 48220
Tel.: (248) 548-3260
(Adhesives & Sealants)

W.L. GORE & ASSOCIATES, INC.
555 Papermill Rd
Newark, DE 19711-7513
Tel.: (410) 506-7787
Toll Free: (888) 914-4673
E-mail: info@wlgore.com
Web Site: www.gore.com
Approx. Rev.: $2,000,000,000
Approx. Number Employees: 8,000
Year Founded: 1958
Business Description:
Mfr. of Artificial Arteries & Prostheses; Special Wiring & Cable for Computers In Space; Waterproof Breathable Membranes; Industrial Sealants & Filters
S.I.C.: 3357; 2821
N.A.I.C.S.: 335921; 325211
Personnel:
Terri Kelly *(Pres & CEO)*
Steve Shuster *(Brand Mgr-Global)*
Jenny Maher *(Mgr-Pub Rels)*
Thom O Hara *(Mgr-Mktg-Gore Medical)*
Brands & Products:
ABSORBOND
ACU-RATE
ACUSEAL
ADVANCED HYBRID
AIRLOCK
AIRVANTAGE
AMAZON
APTERA
ARMACOR
ASSIST
BALANCE PROJECT
BIAC
CANMORE
CARBEL
CELERUS
CHEM-SURE
CHEMPAK
CLEANSTREAM
COMTEC
CONCURVE
CONFLUENT
COOLPOWER
CORDUROY
CRESCENDO
CROSSTECH
DE-FLEX
DEXIOS
DIASTAT
DIRECT-GRIP
DRYLIFE
DRYLOFT
DUALMESH
DURAPOINT
DURAVENT
DYNACORE
ELIXIR
EMERGE
ENDURING
EXCELLERATOR
EXCLUDER
EYE-OPENER
EZA-SIT
FAIRGROUND
FIREBLOCKER
FIRELINER
FLAMEBLOCKER
FLEX-LITE
FLEX-ZONE
FLEXLIFE
GEO-FLEX
GET OUT AND STAY OUT
GFO
GORE
GORE ALL-WEATHER
GORE ARMACOR
GORE BIKE WEAR
GORE-BOND
GORE-CLAD
GORE EZE-SIT
GORE-FLEX
GORE-FLIGHT
GORE-MATE
GORE-NO STAT
GORE OSSEOQUEST
GORE PLUTO
GORE RESOLUT ADAPT
GORE-SEAM
GORE-SELECT
GORE-SHIELD
GORE SMOOTHER
GORE-SORBER
GORE-TEX
GORE-TEX BEST DEFENSE
GORE-TEX COMFORT COOL
GORE-TEX EXACTGRIP
GORE-TEX FLEX
GORE-TEX GR
GORE-TEX GUARANTEED TO KEEP YOU DRY
GORE-TEX HEAVYWEIGHT
GORE-TEX LIGHT-PLUS
GORE-TEX PARTNERS IN PERFORMANCE
GORE-TEX XCR
GORE-TRET
GORE WRAP
GUARANTEED TO KEEP YOU DRY
HELEX
HEMOBAHN
IMAGIN
IMMERSION
INFERNO
INLIGHTEN
LIGHT-PULSE
LIGHTYEAR
LYOGUARD
MICROFLAM
MICROFLAT
MIL-ENE
MULTI-STRIP
MYCROMESH

Key to Media (For complete agency information see *The Advertising Red Books-Agencies* edition):
1. Bus. Publs. 2. Cable T.V. 3. Catalogs & Directories. 4. Co-op Adv. 5. Consumer Mags. 6. D.M. to Bus. Estab.7. D.M. to Consumers 8. Daily Newsp. 9. Exhibits/Trade Shows 10. Foreign 11. Infomercial 12. Internet Adv.13. Multimedia 14. Network Radio 15. Network T.V. 16. Newsp. Distr. Mags. 17. Other 18. Outdoor (Posters, Transit) 19. Point of Purchase20. Premiums, Novelties 21. Product Samples 22. Special Events Mktg. 23. Spot Radio 24. Spot T.V. 25. Weekly Newsp. 26. Yellow Page Adv.

W.L. Gore & Associates, Inc. — (Continued)

NANOWEB
NEXT GENERATION
NLIGHTEN
OCEAN TECHNOLOGY
OLEOGARD
ONE-UP
PACLITE
PANTALOON
PARATRON
PARTELANA
PEEL N' SHIELD
PERMA-CLEAN
PERMAFLOW
PHASEFLEX
POLARCHIP
POLYWEB
PRECLUDE
PRECLUDE MVP
PREVENT
PRIMEA
PRISTYNE
PROCEL
PRODURA
PROPATEN
QUIETZONE
RASTEX
READYFLEX
RELIANT
REMEDIA
RESOLUT
REVIVEX
RIBBON-AX
RIDE ON
RIP KIT
RTS
S-KEY
SCIENCE MUSIC MAGIC
SEALING WITH CERTAINTY
SEAMGUARD
SEAMSTUFF
SEQUEL
SHOECARE MARK
SIL-KORE
SILENT LINE
SIM-PULL
SKYFLEX
SNAPSHOT
SORBER
SOUND QUALITY THAT LASTS
SPEED LINE
SPEEDBOARD
SPEEDFILM
SPUN-BOSS
STA-PURE
STORMCUFF
STORMFLAP
SUMMER TECHNOLOGY
SUPERFLEX
SUPPRESCENT
SYSCARE
TEFLON
TENARA
TETRA-BLEND
TETRA-ETCH
TETRA-PREP
THERMO-DRY
THERMOPOWER
TOMINATOR
TRIGUARD
TRIMENSIONAL
VIABAHN
VIABIL
VIACARDIA
VIADUCT
VIATORR
WINDCHILL CALCULATOR
WINDSTOPPER
WINDSTOPPER N2S
ZINTEX

Advertising Agencies:
Jung von Matt
Glashuttenstrasse 38
20357
Hamburg, Germany
Tel.: (49) 40 43210
Fax: (49) 40 43211 113
Gore-Tex

Mullin/Ashley Associates, Inc.
306 Canon St
Chestertown, MD 21620
Tel.: (410) 778-2184
Fax: (410) 778-6640
Toll Free: (888) 662-4558

Warschawski
1501 Sulgrave Ave Ste 350
Baltimore, MD 21209
Tel.: (410) 367-2700
Fax: (410) 367-2400
GORE-TEX

W.M. JORDAN COMPANY INC.
11010 Jefferson Ave
Newport News, VA 23601
Tel.: (757) 596-6341
Fax: (757) 596-7425
E-mail: info@wmjordan.com
Web Site: www.wmjordan.com
Approx. Number Employees: 332
Year Founded: 1957
Business Description:
Contracting & Construction Services
S.I.C.: 1522
N.A.I.C.S.: 236220
Personnel:
Robert T. Lawson *(Chm)*
John R. Lawson, II *(Pres & CEO)*
Advertising Agency:
Davis & Company
1705 Baltic Ave
Virginia Beach, VA 23451
Tel.: (757) 627-7373
Fax: (757) 627-4257

WOHLSEN CONSTRUCTION COMPANY
548 Steel Way
Lancaster, PA 17601-3138
Tel.: (717) 299-2500
Fax: (717) 299-3419
Web Site: www.wohlsen.com
Approx. Sls.: $140,000,000
Approx. Number Employees: 375
Year Founded: 1890
Business Description:
Nonresidential Construction Services
S.I.C.: 1522; 1541
N.A.I.C.S.: 236220; 236210
Import Export
Personnel:
J. Gary Langmuir *(Chm, Pres & CEO)*
Edward Gordon *(CFO)*
John Valen *(Exec VP)*
Brands & Products:
WOHLSEN
Advertising Agency:
The Archer Group
233 N King St
Wilmington, DE 19801
Tel.: (302) 429-9120
Fax: (302) 429-8720
Interactive Web Site

WOODWARD GOVERNOR COMPANY
1000 E Drake Rd
Fort Collins, CO 80525
Mailing Address:
PO Box 1519
Fort Collins, CO 80522-1519
Tel.: (970) 482-5811
Tel.: (970) 498-3112 (IR)
Fax: (970) 498-3058
E-mail: investorrelations@woodward.com
Web Site: www.woodward.com
Approx. Sls.: $1,457,030,000
Approx. Number Employees: 5,452
Year Founded: 1870
Business Description:
Aerospace & Industrial Energy Control Systems & Components Designer, Mfr & Servicer
S.I.C.: 3699; 3511; 3679; 3714; 3724; 3728; 3829; 5063; 7629
N.A.I.C.S.: 335999; 333611; 334419; 334519; 336322; 336412; 336413; 423610; 811219
Media: 4-7-10
Distr.: Natl.
Personnel:
Thomas A. Gendron *(Chm, Pres, CEO & Interim Pres-Aircraft Turbine Sys)*
Robert F. Weber, Jr. *(CFO & Treas)*
A. Christopher Fawzy *(Chief Compliance Officer, Gen Counsel, Corp Sec & Corp VP)*
Martin V. Glass *(Pres-Aircraft Sys)*
Gerhard Lauffer *(Pres-Electrical Power Sys)*
Chad R. Preiss *(Pres-Engine Sys)*
Jim Rudolph *(Pres-Industrial Turbomachinery Sys)*
Harlan Barkley *(Corp VP-IT)*
Steven J. Meyer *(Corp VP-Human Resources)*
Rose Briani-Burden *(Mgr-Bus Comm)*
Brands & Products:
APECS
ATLAS-II
ATLASPC
ATLASSC
CODER
COIL COMMANDER
CONTROL ASSISTANT
DSLC
DYNA
EASYGEN
EXCEL
FIREFLY
FLO-TECH
GAP
GECO
GLO-TECH
IN-PULSE
MATHWORKS
MICRONET
MICRONET TMR
MINI-GEN
NETCON
NETSIM
PEAK
PROACT
PROTECH
SMARTFIRE
SOGAV
SONICFLO
STEXCITE
STREAMLINE
SWIFT
TECJET
WATCH WINDOW
WOODWARD
XFER

WORLDWIDE WHOLESALE FLOOR COVERINGS
1055 US Hwy 1
Edison, NJ 08837
Tel.: (732) 906-1400
Fax: (732) 906-1486
Web Site:
www.worldwidewholesale.com
Approx. Sls.: $18,653,603
Approx. Number Employees: 100
Business Description:
Carpets
S.I.C.: 5713
N.A.I.C.S.: 442210
Personnel:
Alan Braunstein *(Pres)*
Brands & Products:
WORLDWIDE
Advertising Agency:
Evans Alliance, LLC
72 Cobbler Sq
Sparta, NJ 07871
Tel.: (973) 250-4040
Fax: (973) 729-2851

WORTHINGTON INDUSTRIES, INC.
200 Old Wilson Bridge Rd
Columbus, OH 43085
Tel.: (614) 438-3210
Fax: (614) 438-7948
Web Site:
www.worthingtonindustries.com
Approx. Sls.: $2,442,624,000
Approx. Number Employees: 8,400
Year Founded: 1955
Business Description:
Holding Company; Metal Cylinders, Suspended Ceiling Systems, Railcar & Industrial Castings Mfr
S.I.C.: 6719; 3312; 3354; 3356; 3364; 3443; 3499
N.A.I.C.S.: 551112; 331111; 331316; 331491; 331522; 332313; 332439; 332999
Advertising Expenditures: $3,800,000
Personnel:
John P. McConnell *(Chm & CEO)*
George P. Stoe *(Pres & COO)*
B. Andrew Rose *(CFO & VP)*
Robert J. Richardson *(CIO)*
Dale T. Brinkman *(Gen Counsel, Sec & VP-Admin)*
Ralph V. Roberts *(Sr VP-Mktg)*
Virgil L. Winland *(Sr VP-Mfg)*
Andrew Billman *(VP-Pur)*
Cathy Mayne Lyttle *(VP-Comm & IR)*
Eric M. Smolenski *(VP-HR)*
Brands & Products:
BALLOON TIME
BERNZOMATIC
MAP-PRO
SCI
WORTHINGTON PRO GRADE
Advertising Agency:
Fahlgren Mortine
4030 Easton Station Ste 300
Columbus, OH 43219
Tel.: (614) 383-1500
Fax: (614) 383-1501

Key to Media (For complete agency information see *The Advertising Red Books-Agencies* edition):
1. Bus. Publs. 2. Cable T.V. 3. Catalogs & Directories. 4. Co-op Adv. 5. Consumer Mags. 6. D.M. to Bus. Estab.7. D.M. to Consumers
8. Daily Newsp. 9. Exhibits/Trade Shows 10. Foreign 11. Infomercial 12. Internet Adv.13. Multimedia 14. Network Radio
15. Network T.V. 16. Newsp. Distr. Mags. 17. Other 18. Outdoor (Posters, Transit) 19. Point of Purchase20. Premiums, Novelties
21. Product Samples 22. Special Events Mktg. 23. Spot Radio 24. Spot T.V. 25. Weekly Newsp. 26. Yellow Page Adv.

YORK BUILDING PRODUCTS CO., INC.
950 Smile Way
York, PA 17404
Tel.: (717) 848-2831
Fax: (717) 848-5565
Fax: (717) 854-9156
Toll Free: (800) 673-2408
Web Site: www.yorkbuilding.com
Sales Range: $25-49.9 Million
Approx. Number Employees: 150
Year Founded: 1948
Business Description:
Building Blocks Mfr; Quarrying & Asphalt Processing
S.I.C.: 3271; 1442
N.A.I.C.S.: 327331; 212321
Advertising Expenditures: $200,000
Media: 2-4-7-10-17
Distr.: Natl.
Personnel:
David Stewart *(Pres)*
Dale Voorheis *(CFO)*
Jill Broome *(Mgr-Mktg)*
Brands & Products:
EARTHSTONE
GEMSTONE
IVANY
KEYSTONE
SOUND BLUX
SOUNDBLOX
SPECTRA-GLAZE
TITAN

YORKTOWNE, INC.
(Div. of Cabinetry Division)
(d/b/a Yorktowne Cabinetry)
100 Redco Ave
Red Lion, PA 17356
Mailing Address:
PO Box 231
Red Lion, PA 17356-0231
Tel.: (717) 244-4011
Fax: (717) 244-5497
Toll Free: (800) 777-0065
E-mail: cabinets@yorktwn.com
Web Site:
www.yorktownecabinetry.com
Sales Range: $75-99.9 Million
Approx. Number Employees: 500
Year Founded: 1908
Business Description:
Mfr of Kitchen Cabinets, Vanities, Countertops & Specialty Furniture
S.I.C.: 2434
N.A.I.C.S.: 337110
Media: 1-2-4-5-6-7-10-13-18-19-20-21-22-23-24-26
Budget Set: Nov.
Personnel:
Tim Jahnke *(Pres)*
Ted Fetner *(VP-Sls)*
Jim Kolefki *(VP-Fin)*
Rudy Detweiler *(Dir-Natl Sls)*
Robert Godin *(Mgr-Acctg)*
Brands & Products:
YORKTOWNE
Advertising Agency:
Stoner Bunting Advertising
210 W Grant St
Lancaster, PA 17603-3707
Tel.: (717) 291-1491
Fax: (717) 399-8197

ZOLTEK COMPANIES, INC.
3101 McKelvey Rd
Bridgeton, MO 63044
Tel.: (314) 291-5110
Fax: (314) 291-8536
Toll Free: (800) 325-4409
Web Site: www.zoltek.com
Approx. Sls.: $128,464,000
Approx. Number Employees: 1,095
Year Founded: 1975
Business Description:
Mfr & Marketer of Carbon Fibers for Use in Aircraft Brakes & Other Composite Materials
S.I.C.: 3624; 5063
N.A.I.C.S.: 335991; 423610
Advertising Expenditures: $50,000
Media: 2-10-17
Personnel:
Zsolt Rumy *(CEO)*
Andrew W. Whipple *(CFO & Chief Acctg Officer)*
Peter Kiss *(VP-Engrg)*
David Sodemann *(VP-HR)*
Timothy McCarthy *(Mgr)*
Brands & Products:
PANEX
PYRON
ZOLTEK

Key to Media (For complete agency information see *The Advertising Red Books-Agencies* edition):
1. Bus. Publs. 2. Cable T.V. 3. Catalogs & Directories. 4. Co-op Adv. 5. Consumer Mags. 6. D.M. to Bus. Estab.7. D.M. to Consumers
8. Daily Newsp. 9. Exhibits/Trade Shows 10. Foreign 11. Infomercial 12. Internet Adv.13. Multimedia 14. Network Radio
15. Network T.V. 16. Newsp. Distr. Mags. 17. Other 18. Outdoor (Posters, Transit) 19. Point of Purchase20. Premiums, Novelties
21. Product Samples 22. Special Events Mktg. 23. Spot Radio 24. Spot T.V. 25. Weekly Newsp. 26. Yellow Page Adv.

Associations, Institutions, Unions, Etc.

Boards — Commissions — Cooperatives — Councils — Dealer Associations — Federations—Guilds—Institutes—Non-Profit Membership—Organizations—Societies—Trade Associations—Unions

92ND STREET YOUNG MEN'S & YOUNG WOMEN'S HEBREW ASSOCIATION
1395 Lexington Ave
New York, NY 10128
Tel.: (212) 415-5500
Tel.: (212) 415-5470 (Exec Office)
Fax: (212) 415-5788
Web Site: www.92y.org
Year Founded: 1874
Business Description:
Youth Services
S.I.C.: 8322
N.A.I.C.S.: 624110
Media: 2-23
Personnel:
Matthew Bronfman *(Chm)*
Sol Adler *(Exec Dir)*

AARP
601 E St NW
Washington, DC 20049-0001
Tel.: (202) 434-2277
Fax: (202) 434-6548
Toll Free: (888) 687-2277
E-mail: member@aarp.org
Web Site: www.aarp.org
Approx. Sls.: $878,000,000
Approx. Number Employees: 1,800
Year Founded: 1958
Business Description:
Non-Profit, Non-Partisan Membership Organization (AARP) Representing the Needs of Americans Over 50; Product Service Information
S.I.C.: 8399; 2721
N.A.I.C.S.: 813212; 511120
Advertising Expenditures: $115,000,000
Media: 2-6-8-10-13-15-16-19-22-24
Distr.: Natl.
Personnel:
Dawn Sweeney *(Pres)*
Addison Barry Rand *(CEO)*
Robert R. Hagans *(CFO & Exec VP)*
Emilio Pardo *(Chief Brand Officer)*
James T. Kimbrough *(Pres-Kentucky)*
Steve Cone *(Exec VP)*
Lorraine Cortes-Vazquez *(Exec VP-Multicultural Markets & Engagement)*
Nancy A. LeaMond *(Exec VP)*
John Rother *(Exec VP-Policy, Strategy & Intl Affairs)*
Bill Farris *(VP)*
Patricia Lippe Davis *(VP-Mktg-Media Sls)*
Helen Baptist *(Sr Dir-Bus Dev)*
Anne Herbster *(Dir-Brand Svcs)*
Amelia Jones *(Dir-Publications)*
David Rosenberg *(Dir-Brand Adv)*
Susan Severance *(Dir-Adv)*
Nora Super *(Dir-Federal Govt Rels-Health & Long-Term Care)*
LeeAnn Steinberg *(Sr Brand Mgr)*
Heidi Sternheim *(Sr Brand Mgr)*
Brands & Products:
AARP
AARP BULLETIN
AARP SEGUNDA JUVENTUD
AARP THE MAGAZINE
THE POWER TO MAKE IT BETTER
Advertising Agencies:
802 Creative Partners, Inc.
768 S Main St PO Box 54
Bethel, VT 05032
Tel.: (802) 234-9755
Fax: (802) 234-6719

Adfero Group
1666 K St NW Ste 250
Washington, DC 20006
Tel.: (202) 333-4444
Fax: (202) 333-3231

GSD&M
828 W 6th St
Austin, TX 78703-5420
Tel.: (512) 242-4736
Fax: (512) 242-4700
(Creative, Media Buying)

Hydra Group, Inc.
8800 Wilshire Blvd 2nd Fl
Beverly Hills, CA 90211
Tel.: (310) 659-5755
Fax: (310) 659-5855

Maslansky, Luntz & Partners
1101 King St Ste 110
Alexandria, VA 22314
Tel.: (703) 358-0080
Fax: (703) 358-0089

o2kl
10 W 18th St 6th Fl
New York, NY 10011
Tel.: (646) 829-6239
Fax: (646) 839-6254

THE ACADEMY OF SCIENCE FICTION, FANTASY & HORROR FILMS
334 W 54th St
Los Angeles, CA 90037-3806
Tel.: (323) 752-5811
Web Site: www.saturnawards.org
Year Founded: 1972
Business Description:
Association Promoting Science Fiction, Fantasy & Horror Films
S.I.C.: 7812
N.A.I.C.S.: 512110
Media: 10-22
Personnel:
Robert Holguin *(Chm & Pres)*
Roger Fenton *(VP-Academy & Editor-Film)*

ACCURACY IN MEDIA, INC.
4455 Connecticut Ave NW Ste 330
Washington, DC 20008-2372
Tel.: (202) 364-4401
Fax: (202) 364-4098
E-mail: info@aim.org
Web Site: www.aim.org
Sales Range: Less than $1 Million
Approx. Number Employees: 12
Year Founded: 1969
Business Description:
News Media Monitor
S.I.C.: 7383
N.A.I.C.S.: 519110
Advertising Expenditures: $50,000
Media: 4-8-9-10-13-20-23
Distr.: Natl.
Budget Set: May -Oct.
Personnel:
Don Irvine *(Chm)*
Deborah Lambert *(Dir-Special Projects)*
Charles Rozier *(Dir-Speakers Bureau)*
Mercedes M. Amaya *(Mgr-Mailroom)*
Brands & Products:
AIM

THE ADHESIVE AND SEALANT COUNCIL, INC.
7101 Wiscosin Ave Ste 990
Bethesda, MD 20814
Tel.: (301) 986-9700
Fax: (301) 986-9795
E-mail: info@ascouncil.org
Web Site: www.ascouncil.org
Approx. Number Employees: 8
Year Founded: 1958
Business Description:
Association for Adhesives & Sealants Industry
S.I.C.: 8611
N.A.I.C.S.: 813910
Media: 10
Personnel:
Matt Croson *(Pres)*
Mark Collatz *(Dir-Govt Rels)*
Lori Crowe *(Dir-Mktg)*
Malinda Armstrong *(Sr Mgr-Fin & Admin)*

THE ADVENTURE PROJECT
320 7th Ave
Brooklyn, NY 11215
Tel.: (774) 238-7761
Web Site:
www.theadventureproject.com
Business Description:
Non Profit Adding Venture to Support Social Enterprises
N.A.I.C.S.: 813410
Media: 13-29
Personnel:
Jody Landers *(Co-Founder)*
Becky Straw *(Co-Founder)*

THE ADVERTISING COUNCIL, INC.
815 2nd Ave Fl 9
New York, NY 10017-2303
Tel.: (212) 922-1500
Fax: (212) 922-1676
Toll Free: (800) 933PSAS
E-mail: info@adcouncil.org
Web Site: www.adcouncil.org
Approx. Number Employees: 95
Year Founded: 1942
Business Description:
Public Service Campaigns Producer, Distr & Promoter
S.I.C.: 7319
N.A.I.C.S.: 541890
Media: 2-3-6-9-13-14-15-18-23-24-25-26
Distr.: Intl.; Natl.
Personnel:
Tim Armstrong *(Chm)*
Peggy Conlon *(Pres & CEO)*
John Fish *(CFO & Exec VP)*
Heidi Arthur *(Sr VP & Grp Campaign Dir)*

Key to Media (For complete agency information see *The Advertising Red Books-Agencies* edition):
1. Bus. Publs. 2. Cable T.V. 3. Catalogs & Directories. 4. Co-op Adv. 5. Consumer Mags. 6. D.M. to Bus. Estab.7. D.M. to Consumers
8. Daily Newsp. 9. Exhibits/Trade Shows 10. Foreign 11. Infomercial 12. Internet Adv.13. Multimedia 14. Network Radio
15. Network T.V. 16. Newsp. Distr. Mags. 17. Other 18. Outdoor (Posters, Transit) 19. Point of Purchase20. Premiums, Novelties
21. Product Samples 22. Special Events Mktg. 23. Spot Radio 24. Spot T.V. 25. Weekly Newsp. 26. Yellow Page Adv.

Priscilla Natkins *(Exec VP & Dir-Client Svcs)*
Barbara Leshinsky *(Exec VP-Dev)*
Paula Veale *(Exec VP-Corp Commun)*
Regina Bradley *(Sr VP & Dir-HR)*
Anthony Foleno *(Sr VP & Dir-Res)*
Danielle Linet *(Sr VP & Dir-Creative Svcs)*
Kate Emanuel *(Sr VP-Non-Profit & Govt Affairs)*
Barbara Shimaitis *(Sr VP-Interactive Svcs)*
Leith El-Hassan *(VP-Media & Mktg & Distribution Svcs)*
Ellyn Fisher *(VP-PR & Social Media)*
Danna Kuzler *(Dir-Non Profit Govt Affairs)*
Brands & Products:
ADCOUNCIL
MCGRUFF THE CRIME DOG
SMOKEY BEAR
VINCE & LARRY
Advertising Agencies:
McCann Erickson Worldwide
622 3rd Ave
New York, NY 10017-6707
Tel.: (646) 865-2000
Fax: (646) 487-9610

Neiman Group
614 N Frnt St
Harrisburg, PA 17101-1057
Tel.: (717) 232-5554
Fax: (717) 232-7998

Ogilvy & Mather Advertising
636 11th Ave
New York, NY 10036
Tel.: (212) 237-4000
Fax: (212) 237-5123
(Global Warming)

AEROSPACE INDUSTRIES ASSOCIATION
1000 Wilson Blvd Ste 1700
Arlington, VA 22209-3928
Tel.: (703) 358-1000
Fax: (703) 358-1012
Web Site: www.aia-aerospace.org
Business Description:
Trade Association Rrepresenting Aerospace & Defense Manufacturers
S.I.C.: 8611
N.A.I.C.S.: 813910
Media: 2
Personnel:
James F. Albaugh *(Chm)*
Mariion C. Blakey *(Pres & CEO)*
Ginette C. Colot *(CFO)*
Donald R. Forest *(COO)*
Francis X. Sheller *(VP-Comm)*
Alexis Allen *(Asst VP-Comm)*
Todd D. Sigler *(Asst VP-Civil Aviation)*

AFTER BANKRUPTCY FOUNDATION, INC.
9106 Fall View Dr
Fishers, IN 46037-3822
Tel.: (317) 578-7118
Fax: (317) 578-8747
E-mail: maryann@afterbankruptcy.com
Web Site: www.afterbankruptcy.org
Approx. Number Employees: 30
Business Description:
Seminars & Tools for Recovering from Bankruptcy
S.I.C.: 8299
N.A.I.C.S.: 611699
Media: 8-10
Personnel:
Stephen Snyder *(Owner)*

AFTERSCHOOL ALLIANCE
1616 H St NW Ste 820
Washington, DC 20006
Tel.: (202) 347-2030
Tel.: (202) 347-1002
Fax: (202) 347-2092
E-mail: info@afterschoolalliance.org
Web Site: www.afterschoolalliance.org
Sales Range: $10-24.9 Million
Approx. Number Employees: 10
Year Founded: 1999
Business Description:
Afterschool Programs Awareness Organizaton
S.I.C.: 8351
N.A.I.C.S.: 624410
Media: 6-13-14-15-18

ALASKA SEAFOOD MARKETING INSTITUTE
311 N Franklin St Ste 200
Juneau, AK 99801-1147
Tel.: (907) 465-5560
Fax: (907) 465-5572
Toll Free: (800) 478-2903
E-mail: info@alaskaseafood.org
Web Site: www.alaskaseafood.org
Approx. Number Employees: 20
Year Founded: 1981
Business Description:
Non-profit Trade Association Promoting Alaska Seafood: Fresh, Frozen & Canned Salmon, Halibut, Shellfish & Whitefish
S.I.C.: 9641
N.A.I.C.S.: 926140
Advertising Expenditures: $200,000
Media: 1-2-3-4-5-6-7-8-10-11-12-13-16-18-19-22-23-24
Distr.: Intl.; Natl.
Personnel:
Naresh Shrestha *(CFO)*
Ray Riutta *(Exec Dir)*
Larry Andrews *(Dir-Retail Mktg)*
Randy Rice *(Dir-Program)*
Advertising Agencies:
Andrew Brown Associates
140 High St.
Box 14
Guildford, Surrey GU1 2RH, United Kingdom
Tel.: (44) 1483 416136
Fax: (44) 1483 426662
(AK Salmon)

Markonsult
58 rue Pottier
78150
Le Chesnay, France
Tel.: (33) 1 39 23 2007
Fax: (33) 1 39 23 2017
(AK Salmon)

R & L Associates, Inc.
5-31-2 Nerima-ku
179
Tokyo, Japan
Tel.: (81) 3 3990 1767
Fax: (81) 3 3990 4725
(Seafood)

Schiedermayer & Associates
31280 Oak Crest Dr.
Westlake Village, CA 91311
Tel.: (818) 991-5985
(AK Halibut, Fresh and Frozen Whitefish)

Shanghai Shengming Trade Co.
7B Yi Cui Court
Crest Garden
Pudong
Shanghai, P.R. 200120, China
Tel.: (86) 21 6542 7622
Fax: (86) 21 6562 6660
(Alaska Seafood)

ALEXANDER GRAHAM BELL ASSOCIATION FOR THE DEAF AND HARD OF HEARING
(d/b/a AG Bell)
3417 Volta Pl NW
Washington, DC 20007
Tel.: (202) 337-5220
Fax: (202) 337-8314
E-mail: info@agbell.org
Web Site: www.agbell.org
Sales Range: $10-24.9 Million
Approx. Number Employees: 10
Business Description:
Promoter of the Use of Spoken Language by Adults & Children with Hearing Loss; Publisher of Books, Brochures, Instructional Videos, CDs & Audiocassettes
S.I.C.: 8322
N.A.I.C.S.: 624120
Media: 4-10-13
Personnel:
Alexander T. Graham *(CEO & Exec Dir)*
Judy Harrison *(Dir-Programs)*
Robin Bailey *(Mgr-Member Svcs)*
Bryan Reynolds *(Mgr-Admin Svcs)*
Gary W. Yates *(Mgr-Adv, Exhibit Sls, Sponsorships & Institutional Subscriptions)*
Brands & Products:
ALEXANDER GRAHAM BELL
THE VOLTA REVIEW
VOLTA VOICES

ALLIANCE OF CONFESSING EVANGELICALS, INC.
1716 Spruce St
Philadelphia, PA 19103-6716
Mailing Address:
PO Box 2000
Philadelphia, PA 19103
Tel.: (215) 546-3696
Fax: (215) 735-5133
Toll Free: (800) 956-2644
E-mail: alliance@alliancenet.org
Web Site: www.alliancenet.org
Approx. Number Employees: 15
Year Founded: 1949
Business Description:
Radio Programs & Conference Ministry Services; Non-Profit Publisher
S.I.C.: 7389
N.A.I.C.S.: 512290
Media: 1-4-8-10-17-22-23
Distr.: Natl.
Personnel:
Elmer Snethen *(Chm)*
Robert F. Brady *(Exec VP)*
Brands & Products:
ALLIANCE OF CONFESSING EVANGELICALS
THE BIBLE STUDY HOUR
DR. BARNHOUSE & THE BIBLE
EVERY LAST WORD
GOD'S WORD TODAY
MODERN REFORMATION
REFORMATION21
WHITE HORSE INN

AMALGAMATED LITHOGRAPHERS OF AMERICA
113 University Pl
New York, NY 10003-4527
Tel.: (212) 460-0800
Fax: (212) 673-5102
E-mail: info@litho.org
Web Site: www.litho.org
Approx. Number Employees: 100
Year Founded: 1889
Business Description:
Lithographers' Union
S.I.C.: 8631; 6512
N.A.I.C.S.: 813930; 531120
Advertising Expenditures: $650,000
Media: 2-4-6-7-8-10-18-25
Distr.: Reg.
Personnel:
Patrick LoPresti *(Pres)*
Gene Kreis *(First VP)*

AMERICA-ISRAEL CHAMBER OF COMMERCE
200 S Broad St Ste 700
Philadelphia, PA 19102-3869
Tel.: (215) 790-3722
Fax: (215) 790-3600
E-mail: aicc@greaterphilachamber.com
Web Site: www.americaisraelchamber.com
Year Founded: 1987
Business Description:
Economic Development & Trade Promotion Services
S.I.C.: 8611
N.A.I.C.S.: 813910
Media: 11-13
Personnel:
Debbie Duchwaly *(Exec Dir)*
Avner Lahat *(Dir)*

AMERICAN ARCHITECTURAL MANUFACTURERS ASSOCIATION
1827 Walden Ofc Sq Ste 550
Schaumburg, IL 60173-4268
Tel.: (847) 303-5664
Fax: (847) 303-5774
Web Site: www.aamanet.org
Approx. Number Employees: 18
Year Founded: 1936
Business Description:
Door & Window Companies Promoter
S.I.C.: 8611
N.A.I.C.S.: 813910
Media: 2-4-6-7-10
Distr.: Natl.
Budget Set: Oct.
Personnel:
Rich Walker *(Pres & CEO)*
Janice Charletta *(Dir-Association Svcs)*
Brands & Products:
AAMA
INSTALLATION MASTERS
Advertising Agency:
Point to Point Inc.
23240 Chagrin Blvd Ste 200

Key to Media (For complete agency information see *The Advertising Red Books-Agencies* edition):
1. Bus. Publs. 2. Cable T.V. 3. Catalogs & Directories. 4. Co-op Adv. 5. Consumer Mags. 6. D.M. to Bus. Estab.7. D.M. to Consumers
8. Daily Newsp. 9. Exhibits/Trade Shows 10. Foreign 11. Infomercial 12. Internet Adv.13. Multimedia 14. Network Radio
15. Network T.V. 16. Newsp. Distr. Mags. 17. Other 18. Outdoor (Posters, Transit) 19. Point of Purchase20. Premiums, Novelties
21. Product Samples 22. Special Events Mktg. 23. Spot Radio 24. Spot T.V. 25. Weekly Newsp. 26. Yellow Page Adv.

American Architectural Manufacturers Association — (Continued)

Beachwood, OH 44122
Tel.: (216) 831-4421
Fax: (216) 831-3099

AMERICAN ASSOCIATION FOR THE ADVANCEMENT OF SCIENCE

1200 New York Ave NW
Washington, DC 20005
Tel.: (202) 326-6400
Fax: (202) 789-0455
E-mail: media@aaas.org
Web Site: www.aaas.org
Approx. Number Employees: 350
Year Founded: 1848
Business Description:
Publishers of Science Magazine; Association of Professional Scientists
S.I.C.: 8621; 4522
N.A.I.C.S.: 813920; 481219
Export
Advertising Expenditures: $500,000
Media: 2-4-6-7-8-9-10-11-13-20
Distr.: Intl.; Natl.
Personnel:
Alan I. Leshner *(CEO)*
Philip Blair *(CFO)*
Monica M. Bradford *(Exec Editor-Science)*
Stephen J. Nelson *(Assoc Dir)*
Deborah Harris *(Dir-Intl Mktg)*
Ginger Pinholster *(Dir-Office-Pub Programs)*
Barbara Rice *(Associate Dir)*
Wendy Sturley *(Mktg Mgr)*
Janis Crowley *(Mgr-Adv)*
Brands & Products:
AAAS
ADVANCING SCIENCE. SERVING SOCIETY
SCIENCE

AMERICAN ASSOCIATION OF CRITICAL-CARE NURSES

101 Columbia
Aliso Viejo, CA 92656-4109
Tel.: (949) 362-2050
Fax: (949) 362-2020
Toll Free: (800) 899-2226
E-mail: info@aacn.org
Web Site: www.aacn.org
Year Founded: 1969
Business Description:
Nursing Association
S.I.C.: 8621
N.A.I.C.S.: 813920
Media: 2-8-10
Personnel:
Wanda L. Johanson *(CEO)*

THE AMERICAN BANKERS ASSOCIATION

1120 Connecticut Ave NW
Washington, DC 20036-3902
Tel.: (202) 663-5000
Fax: (202) 663-7543
Toll Free: (800) BANKERS
E-mail: custserv@aba.com
Web Site: www.aba.com
Approx. Sls.: $57,000,000
Approx. Number Employees: 325
Year Founded: 1875
Business Description:
Banking Trade Association
S.I.C.: 8611
N.A.I.C.S.: 813910
Media: 2-6-10-13
Distr.: Natl.
Budget Set: Jan.
Personnel:
Frank Keating *(Pres & CEO)*
Bob Edy *(CFO)*
Barry Epstein *(Sr VP & Controller)*
Maggie Kelly *(VP-Mktg)*
Virginia Dean *(Exec Dir-Commun)*
Brands & Products:
ABA TRUST LETTER
AMERICAN BANKERS ASSOCIATION
Advertising Agency:
IMC Strategy Lab
401 W 45th St Ste 4C
New York, NY 10036
Tel.: (917) 257-3523
Toll Free: (800) 845-3779

AMERICAN BUSINESS MEDIA

675 3rd Ave 7th Fl
New York, NY 10017-5704
Tel.: (212) 661-6360
Fax: (212) 370-0736
E-mail: info@abmmail.com
Web Site: www.americanbusinessmedia.com
E-Mail For Key Personnel:
President: g.hughes@abmmail.com
Sales Range: $10-24.9 Million
Approx. Number Employees: 16
Year Founded: 1906
Business Description:
Trade Association of Specialized Business Publications
S.I.C.: 8611
N.A.I.C.S.: 813910
Advertising Expenditures: $1,000,000
Media: 2-10-13
Distr.: Natl.
Budget Set: July
Personnel:
Charles G. McCurdy *(Chm)*
Clark Pettit *(Pres & CEO)*
Todd Hittle *(CFO & Gen Mgr)*
Mark Rothman *(CMO)*
Kate Patton *(Mgr-Mktg & Comm)*
Walter Koval *(Sr Coord-Bus Dev)*
Advertising Agency:
DiMassimo Goldstein
(d/b/a DIGO Brands)
220 E 23rd St
New York, NY 10010
Tel.: (212) 253-7500
Fax: (646) 507-5850

AMERICAN CANCER SOCIETY, INC.

250 William St
Atlanta, GA 30303
Tel.: (404) 320-3333
Fax: (404) 982-3677
Toll Free: (800) 227-2345
Web Site: www.cancer.org
Approx. Number Employees: 6,500
Year Founded: 1913
Business Description:
Non-Profit Organization Dedicated to the Elimination of Cancer
S.I.C.: 8733
N.A.I.C.S.: 541710
Media: 2-3-5-6-8-9-10-13-14-15-25
Distr.: Natl.
Personnel:
Van Velsor Wolf *(Chm)*
Christopher W. Hansen *(Pres)*
John R. Seffrin *(CEO)*
Greg Bontrager *(COO)*
Vic Ayers *(CIO)*
Scott Bennett *(CMO)*
Dave Grams *(Reg VP)*
Brian Allem *(VP-Community)*
A. Gregory Donaldson *(VP-Corp Comm-Natl)*
Andy Goldsmith *(VP-Creative & Brand Strategy)*
Alex O. Stone *(Dir-Market Dev)*
Meggan Hood *(Mgr-Adv)*
Brands & Products:
AMERICAN CANCER SOCIETY
DAFFODIL DAYS
I CAN COPE
MAKING STRIDES
RELAY FOR LIFE
Advertising Agencies:
Brodeur Partners
855 Boylston St 2nd Fl
Boston, MA 02116-2622
Tel.: (617) 587-2800
Fax: (617) 587-2828
(Public Relations)

Goodway Group
The Pavilion 261 Old York Rd Ste 930
Jenkintown, PA 19046
Tel.: (215) 887-5700
Fax: (215) 881-2239

The Martin Agency
One Shockoe Plz
Richmond, VA 23219-4132
Tel.: (804) 698-8000
Fax: (804) 698-8001

AMERICAN COLLEGE OF NURSE-MIDWIVES

8403 Colesville Rd Ste 1550
Silver Spring, MD 20910-6374
Tel.: (240) 485-1800
Fax: (240) 485-1818
E-mail: info@acnm.org
Web Site: www.midwife.org
Approx. Number Employees: 40
Year Founded: 1929
Business Description:
Women's Health Care Promoter
S.I.C.: 8621; 2721
N.A.I.C.S.: 813920; 511120
Media: 6-8-10-13
Personnel:
Melissa D. Avery *(Pres)*
Lorrie Kaplan *(Exec Dir)*
Meredith Graham *(Dir-Fin & Admin)*
George Hamilton *(Dir-Membership)*
Elaine Germano *(Mgr-Education Projects)*
Fausto Miranda *(Mgr-IT)*
Monica Greenfield *(Coord-Program)*

AMERICAN CONCRETE INSTITUTE

38800 Country Club Dr
Farmington Hills, MI 48333-9094
Tel.: (248) 848-3700
Fax: (248) 848-3701
E-mail: bkstore@concrete.org
Web Site: www.concrete.org
Approx. Number Employees: 50
Year Founded: 1904
Business Description:
Industrial Association
S.I.C.: 8621
N.A.I.C.S.: 813920
Advertising Expenditures: $900,000
Media: 2-4-7-8-10
Distr.: Intl.; Natl.
Budget Set: Aug.
Personnel:
John W. Nehasil *(Mng Dir-Certification & Chapters)*
Ronald Burg *(Exec VP)*
William R. Tolley *(Exec VP)*
Daniel W. Falconer *(Mng Dir-Engrng)*
Christopher Darnell *(Sr Dir-Creative & Mgr-Ops)*
Diane L. Baloh *(Dir-Sls & Membership)*
Barbara Cheyne *(Dir-HR)*
Renee J. Lewis *(Dir-Publ & Event Svcs)*
Kevin P. Mlutkowski *(Dir-Sustainability)*
John K. Conn *(Mgr-Certification Ops & Chapters)*
Jeri A. Kolodziej *(Mgr-Governance)*
Melinda G. Reynolds *(Mgr-Member Svcs)*
Brands & Products:
ACI MATERIALS JOURNAL
ACI STRUCTURAL JOURNAL
ADVANCING CONCRETE KNOWLEDGE
AMERICAN CONCRETE INSTITUTE
CONCRETE INTERNATIONAL
CONCRETE REPAIR BULLETIN

AMERICAN CONFERENCE OF GOVERNMENTAL INDUSTRIAL HYGIENISTS

(d/b/a ACGIH)
1330 Kemper Meadow Dr
Cincinnati, OH 45240
Tel.: (513) 742-6163
Tel.: (513) 742-2020
Fax: (513) 742-3355
E-mail: mail@acgih.org
Web Site: www.acgih.org
Approx. Number Employees: 14
Year Founded: 1938
Business Description:
Worker Health & Safety Promotion
S.I.C.: 8621; 2721
N.A.I.C.S.: 813920; 511120
Media: 4-7-10
Personnel:
A. Anthony Rizzuto *(Exec Dir)*
Brands & Products:
ACGIH
THE ACTION LEVEL
CAREER CHOICES AND CHANGES

AMERICAN COUNCIL OF LIFE INSURERS

101 Constitution Ave NW
Washington, DC 20001-2133
Tel.: (202) 624-2000
Fax: (202) 624-2319
E-mail: memberservices@acli.com
Web Site: www.acli.com
Sales Estimate: $60-79 Million
Approx. Number Employees: 200
Year Founded: 1967
Business Description:
Lobbying & Communication Representative for Life Insurance Industry
S.I.C.: 8611
N.A.I.C.S.: 813910
Advertising Expenditures: $3,500,000
Media: 1-6-9-10
Distr.: Natl.

Key to Media (For complete agency information see *The Advertising Red Books-Agencies* edition):
1. Bus. Publs. 2. Cable T.V. 3. Catalogs & Directories. 4. Co-op Adv. 5. Consumer Mags. 6. D.M. to Bus. Estab.7. D.M. to Consumers
8. Daily Newsp. 9. Exhibits/Trade Shows 10. Foreign 11. Infomercial 12. Internet Adv.13. Multimedia 14. Network Radio
15. Network T.V. 16. Newsp. Distr. Mags. 17. Other 18. Outdoor (Posters, Transit) 19. Point of Purchase20. Premiums, Novelties
21. Product Samples 22. Special Events Mktg. 23. Spot Radio 24. Spot T.V. 25. Weekly Newsp. 26. Yellow Page Adv.

Budget Set: Nov.
Personnel:
Jack Dolan *(Mng Dir & VP)*
Shawn Hausman *(Sr VP-Pub Affairs & Publr)*

AMERICAN DAIRY ASSOCIATION
(Sub. of Dairy Management, Inc.)
10255 W Higgins Rd Ste 900
Rosemont, IL 60018-5616
Tel.: (847) 803-2000
Fax: (847) 803-2077
E-mail: ilovecheese@rosedmi.com
Web Site: www.ilovecheese.com
Approx. Number Employees: 100
Year Founded: 1940
Business Description:
Dairy Advertising & Marketing Services
S.I.C.: 8743
N.A.I.C.S.: 541820
Export
Advertising Expenditures: $48,000,000
Media: 2-3-6-7-9-14-15-18-19-23-24
Distr.: Natl.
Budget Set: Aug.
Personnel:
Thomas P. Gallagher *(CEO-Dairy Mgmt, Inc)*
Brands & Products:
AHH, THE POWER OF CHEESE
ILOVECHEESE.COM
Advertising Agencies:
DDB Chicago
200 E Randolph St
Chicago, IL 60601
Tel.: (312) 552-6000
Fax: (312) 552-2370

Flair Communications Agency, Inc.
214 W Erie St
Chicago, IL 60654
Tel.: (312) 943-5959
Toll Free: (800) 621-8317

THE AMERICAN DENTAL ASSOCIATION
211 E Chicago Ave
Chicago, IL 60611
Tel.: (312) 440-2500
Fax: (312) 440-2800
E-mail: publicinfo@ada.org
Web Site: www.ada.org
Approx. Rev.: $86,000,000
Approx. Number Employees: 400
Business Description:
Dental Association
S.I.C.: 8621; 2721
N.A.I.C.S.: 813920; 511120
Advertising Expenditures: $1,000,000
Media: 2-13
Personnel:
Clayton B. Mickel *(Mng VP-Corp Relations & Strategic Mktg Alliances-JADA)*
Michael Glick *(Editor)*
David C. Sarrett *(Editor)*
Kathleen O'louthlin *(Exec Dir)*
Robert Czarnecki *(Dir-Admin)*
Dwight S. Edwards *(Dir-Dev)*
Sandra Eitel *(Dir-Mktg & Comm)*
Carol Krause *(Dir-Sls & Mktg)*
Michelle Boyd *(Mgr-Adv Sls)*
Fred Peterson *(Mgr-Media Rels)*
Sandie Rostek *(Mgr-Administrative Svcs)*

Advertising Agency:
GSP Marketing Services, Inc.
320 W Ohio St
Chicago, IL 60654
Tel.: (312) 944-3000
Fax: (312) 944-8587

AMERICAN DIABETES ASSOCIATION
1701 N Beauregard St
Alexandria, VA 22311-1717
Tel.: (703) 549-1500
Fax: (703) 739-9346
Toll Free: (800) 342-2383
E-mail: customerservice@diabetes.org
Web Site: www.diabetes.org
Sales Range: $400-449.9 Million
Approx. Number Employees: 850
Year Founded: 1940
Business Description:
Health Organization; Diabetes Research, Information & Advocacy
S.I.C.: 8621; 2721
N.A.I.C.S.: 813920; 511120
Media: 4-6-7-8-13-18-22
Personnel:
Larry Hausner *(CEO)*
Craig Elfers *(Chief Field Dev Officer)*
Dwight Holing *(Treas, Sec & Dir)*
Vaneeda Bennett *(Exec VP-Dev)*
Lois Witkop *(Sr VP-Mktg Comm)*

AMERICAN EGG BOARD
1460 Renaissance Dr Ste 301
Park Ridge, IL 60068-1348
Tel.: (847) 296-7043
Fax: (847) 296-7007
E-mail: aeb@aeb.org
Web Site: www.aeb.org
Approx. Number Employees: 20
Business Description:
Organization for the Promotion of Eggs
S.I.C.: 8611
N.A.I.C.S.: 813910
Advertising Expenditures: $10,793,627
Media: 2-3-4-6-10-11-15-23-24
Distr.: Natl.
Budget Set: July
Personnel:
Craig Willerson *(Vice Chm)*
Joanne Ivy *(Pres & CEO)*
Kevin Burkum *(Sr VP-Mktg)*
Brands & Products:
THE INCREDIBLE EDIBLE EGG
Advertising Agencies:
Starcom USA
35 W Wacker Dr
Chicago, IL 60601
Tel.: (312) 220-3535
Fax: (312) 220-6530
Media Planning & Buying

Stephan & Brady, Inc.
1850 Hoffman St
Madison, WI 53704-2541
Tel.: (608) 241-4141
Fax: (608) 241-4246
(Foodservice)

AMERICAN ENTERPRISE INSTITUTE FOR PUBLIC POLICY RESEARCH
1150 17th St NW
Washington, DC 20036-4603
Tel.: (202) 862-5800
Fax: (202) 862-7178
E-mail: info@aei.org
Web Site: www.aei.org
Sales Range: $10-24.9 Million
Approx. Number Employees: 150
Year Founded: 1943
Business Description:
Nonprofit, Nonpartisan, Publicly Supported Educational Research Organization
S.I.C.: 8733
N.A.I.C.S.: 541720; 541710
Media: 2-6-7-8-10
Distr.: Intl.; Natl.
Budget Set: Nov.
Personnel:
David Gerson *(Exec VP)*
Brands & Products:
AEI
THE AMERICAN ENTERPRISE
Advertising Agency:
Bergman Group
4880 Sadler Rd Ste 220
Glen Allen, VA 23060
Tel.: (804) 225-0600
Fax: (804) 225-0900

AMERICAN FEDERATION OF LABOR - CONGRESS OF INDUSTRIAL ORGANIZATIONS
(d/b/a AFL-CIO)
815 16th St NW
Washington, DC 20006-4101
Tel.: (202) 637-5000
Fax: (202) 637-5058
Web Site: www.aflcio.org
Sales Estimate: $40-59 Million
Approx. Number Employees: 60
Year Founded: 1951
Business Description:
Labor Organization
S.I.C.: 8631
N.A.I.C.S.: 813930
Media: 2-9-14
Distr.: Natl.
Personnel:
Richard Trumka *(Pres)*
Linda Chavez-Thompson *(CIO & Exec VP Emerita)*
John J. Sweeney *(CIO & Pres Emeritus)*
Ron Blackwell *(Dir-Corp Affairs)*
Brands & Products:
AFL-CIO
AMERICA@WORK
VOICE@WORK
WORKINGFAMILIES.COM
Advertising Agency:
Media Strategies & Research
1580 Lincoln St 510
Denver, CO 80203
Tel.: (303) 989-4700
Fax: (303) 989-1910
— Jon Hutchens *(Acct Exec)*

AMERICAN FOREST & PAPER ASSOCIATION
1111 19th St NW Ste 800
Washington, DC 20036-3603
Tel.: (202) 463-2700
Fax: (202) 463-2785
E-mail: info@afandpa.org
Web Site: www.afandpa.org
Sales Range: $10-24.9 Million
Approx. Number Employees: 60
Year Founded: 1993
Business Description:
Trade Association for Paper & Forestry Industries
S.I.C.: 8611
N.A.I.C.S.: 813910
Media: 2-3-6-9-10-23-24
Distr.: Natl.
Budget Set: Oct.
Personnel:
Richard James *(CFO)*
Advertising Agency:
The Bivings Group
2201 Wisconsin Ave NW Ste 310
Washington, DC 20007
Tel.: (202) 741-1500
Fax: (202) 741-1501

AMERICAN FORESTS
734 15th St NW Ste 800
Washington, DC 20005
Mailing Address:
PO Box 2000
Washington, DC 20013
Tel.: (202) 737-1944
Fax: (202) 955-4588
E-mail: info@amfor.org
Web Site: www.amfor.org
Sales Range: $10-24.9 Million
Approx. Number Employees: 50
Year Founded: 1875
Business Description:
Forest Conservation Agency
S.I.C.: 8641; 8748
N.A.I.C.S.: 813410; 541618
Media: 6-7-10
Personnel:
Caroline Gabel *(Chm)*
Gerald Gray *(Sr VP-Programs)*
Gary Moll *(Sr VP)*
Gregory Meyer *(VP-Mktg & Dev)*
Deborah Gangloff *(Exec Dir)*
Lydia Scalettar *(Dir-Consulting Art)*
JoAnn Williams *(Dir-Admin)*
Brands & Products:
AMERICAN FORESTS
CITYGREEN
FORESTBYTES
GLOBAL RELEAF
WILDFIRE RELEAF

THE AMERICAN GASTROENTEROLOGICAL ASSOCIATION
4930 Del Ray Ave
Bethesda, MD 20814
Tel.: (301) 654-2055
Fax: (301) 654-5920
E-mail: member@gastro.org
Web Site: www.gastro.org
Approx. Rev.: $17,000,000
Approx. Number Employees: 65
Year Founded: 1897
Business Description:
Medical Society
S.I.C.: 8399
N.A.I.C.S.: 813319
Media: 6
Personnel:
Lynn P. Robinson *(Co-Exec VP)*
Tom Serena *(Co-Exec VP)*
Dianne Bach *(Sr VP)*
Michael H. Stolar *(Sr VP)*
Richard Podgorski *(Reg VP)*
Jessica Duncan *(VP-Comm)*
Jeff Springer *(VP-Mktg & Member Svcs)*
Thoba Khumalo *(Managing Editor)*

Key to Media (For complete agency information see *The Advertising Red Books-Agencies* edition):
1. Bus. Publs. 2. Cable T.V. 3. Catalogs & Directories. 4. Co-op Adv. 5. Consumer Mags. 6. D.M. to Bus. Estab.7. D.M. to Consumers
8. Daily Newsp. 9. Exhibits/Trade Shows 10. Foreign 11. Infomercial 12. Internet Adv.13. Multimedia 14. Network Radio
15. Network T.V. 16. Newsp. Distr. Mags. 17. Other 18. Outdoor (Posters, Transit) 19. Point of Purchase20. Premiums, Novelties
21. Product Samples 22. Special Events Mktg. 23. Spot Radio 24. Spot T.V. 25. Weekly Newsp. 26. Yellow Page Adv.

The American Gastroenterological Association — (Continued)

Jennifer Conte *(Sr Dir-Tech & Reimbursement Issues)*
Stacie Gallice *(Sr Dir-Info & Plng Svcs)*
Laura Henning *(Sr Dir-Mktg)*
Ellen Silver *(Sr Dir-DDW Admin)*
Kathleen Teixeira *(Sr Dir-Govt Affairs)*
Derek Randolph *(Dir-Building Svcs)*
Leslie Waite *(Dir-Info Sys)*

AMERICAN HEART ASSOCIATION

7272 Greenville Ave
Dallas, TX 75231-5129
Tel.: (214) 373-6300
Fax: (214) 570-5930
Toll Free: (800) 242-8721
E-mail: info@americanheart.org
Web Site: www.americanheart.org
Sales Estimate: $80-99 Million
Approx. Number Employees: 380
Year Founded: 1924

Business Description:
Non-Profit Health Agency
S.I.C.: 8399; 2721
N.A.I.C.S.: 813212; 511120

Media: 2-3-6-8-9-14-15-18-23-24-25
Distr.: Natl.

Personnel:
Nancy Brown *(CEO)*
Rebecca White *(Exec Dir)*
Anu Gandhi *(Dir-Mktg)*
Jennifer Hancock *(Dir-Corp Events-Mid Michigan Region)*
Amanda Peterson *(Dir-Youth Market)*
Jennifer Pratt *(Dir-Comm)*
Linda Hood *(Mgr-Brand & Healthcare Quality)*

Advertising Agencies:
AgencyNet
300 SW 1st Ave Ste 155
Fort Lauderdale, FL 33301
Tel.: (954) 524-8800
Fax: (954) 524-8843

Bergman Group
4880 Sadler Rd Ste 220
Glen Allen, VA 23060
Tel.: (804) 225-0600
Fax: (804) 225-0900

Campbell-Ewald
30400 Van Dyke Ave
Warren, MI 48093-2368
Tel.: (586) 574-3400
Fax: (586) 575-9925

Digital Brewing Company
720 Market St 3rd Fl
San Francisco, CA 94102
Tel.: (415) 398-1333
Fax: (415) 398-2266

Gumas Advertising
99 Shotwell St
San Francisco, CA 94103-3625
Tel.: (415) 621-7575
Fax: (415) 255-8804

Lippincott Williams and Williams
351 W Camden St
Baltimore, MD 21201
Tel.: (410) 528-4000

AMERICAN HEREFORD ASSOCIATION

1501 Wyandotte St
Kansas City, MO 64108-1222
Mailing Address:
PO Box 014059
Kansas City, MO 64101-0059
Tel.: (816) 842-3757
Fax: (816) 842-6931
Telex: 42344 AHA KSC
E-mail: aha@hereford.org
Web Site: www.hereford.org
Approx. Number Employees: 30
Year Founded: 1881
Business Description:
Hereford Cattle Promotion Association
S.I.C.: 0752; 8611
N.A.I.C.S.: 115210; 813910
Media: 1-2-5-23
Distr.: Natl.
Budget Set: June
Personnel:
Leslie Mathews *(CFO)*
Craig Huffhines *(Exec VP)*
Joe Rickabaugh *(Dir-Field Mgmt & Seedstock Mktg)*
Caryn Vaught *(Mgr-Production)*
Cindy Coleman *(Supvr-Records)*

AMERICAN INSTITUTE OF CERTIFIED PUBLIC ACCOUNTANTS INC.

220 C Leigh Farm Rd
Durham, NY 27707
Tel.: (212) 596-6200
Fax: (212) 596-6213
E-mail: infotech@aicpa.org
Web Site: www.aicpa.org
E-Mail For Key Personnel:
President: bmelanson@aicpa.org
Public Relations: gpickard@aicpa.org
Approx. Rev.: $157,324,000
Approx. Number Employees: 653
Year Founded: 1887
Business Description:
Professional Membership Services to Certified Public Accountants
S.I.C.: 8621; 2721
N.A.I.C.S.: 813920; 511120
Media: 2-7-10-13-17
Personnel:
Barry C. Melancon *(Pres & CEO)*
Scott Spiegel *(CFO)*
Richard L. Miller *(Gen Counsel & Sec)*
Susan Coffey *(Sr VP-Member Quality & Intl Affairs)*
Anthony Pugliese *(Sr VP-Fin, Membership & Ops)*
Arleen Thomas *(Sr VP-Member Competency & Dev)*
Patricia Duane *(VP-HR)*
Cynthia Lund *(VP-State Societies)*
Janice Maiman *(VP-Comm & Media Channels)*
John Toman *(VP-Conferences & Sls)*
Noel Albertson *(Dir-Process Coordination & Plng)*
Joel Allegretti *(Dir-Media Rels)*
Cheryl Reynolds *(Dir-Comm Adv & Brand Mgmt)*
David Tolson *(Dir-Product Devel)*
Brands & Products:
AICPA
CPA WEB TRUST
FEED THE PIG
JOURNAL OF ACCOUNTANCY

AMERICAN INSTITUTE OF CHEMICAL ENGINEERS

3 Park Ave Fl 19
New York, NY 10016
Fax: (212) 591-8888
Toll Free: (800) 242-4363
Web Site: www.aiche.org
Approx. Sls.: $18,414,810
Approx. Number Employees: 45
Business Description:
Professional Association
S.I.C.: 8621; 2721
N.A.I.C.S.: 813920; 511120
Media: 10
Personnel:
William D. Byers *(Pres)*
Joe Kramer *(Dir-Programming)*
Bette Lawler *(Dir-Ops)*
Tim McCreight *(Dir-Mktg)*
Jeff Wood *(Dir-Meetings)*

AMERICAN IRON AND STEEL INSTITUTE

1140 Connecticut Ave NW Ste 705
Washington, DC 20036
Tel.: (202) 452-7100
Tel.: (202) 452-7116
Fax: (202) 466-7052
Fax: (202) 463-6573
E-mail: webmaster@steel.org
Web Site: www.steel.org
Approx. Number Employees: 50
Year Founded: 1905
Business Description:
Trade Association
S.I.C.: 8611
N.A.I.C.S.: 813910
Advertising Expenditures: $200,000
Media: 2-4-6-7-9-10-14-24
Distr.: Natl.
Budget Set: Monthly
Personnel:
Daniel R. DiMicco *(Chm)*
Thomas J. Gibson *(Pres & CEO)*
Larry Kavanagh *(Pres-Steel Market Dev Institute)*
Barry Solarz *(Sr VP-Trade & Economic Policy)*
David Bell *(VP-Fin & Admin)*
Nancy Gravatt *(VP-Comm)*
Brands & Products:
AMERICAN IRON AND STEEL INSTITUTE
STEELMARK

AMERICAN KENNEL CLUB, INC.

260 Madison Ave
New York, NY 10016-2401
Tel.: (212) 696-8200
Fax: (212) 696-8299
Web Site: www.akc.org
Approx. Sls.: $65,400,000
Approx. Number Employees: 411
Year Founded: 1884
Business Description:
Association for the Advancement of Purebred Dogs; Publisher & Printer of Books
S.I.C.: 8399; 2721
N.A.I.C.S.: 813312; 511120
Media: 6-13-18
Personnel:
Ronald Menaker *(Chm)*
Dennis B. Sprung *(Pres & CEO)*
James T. Stevens *(CFO)*
John Lyons *(COO)*
Charles Kneifel *(CIO & VP)*
Margaret Poindexter *(Gen Counsel)*
Gina Di Nardo *(Asst VP)*
Mari-Beth O'Neill *(Asst VP-Customer Svc)*
Bobby Birdsong *(Dir-Show Events)*
Mary Burch *(Dir-Canine Good Citizen Program & Spokesperson)*
Lisa Peterson *(Dir-Comm)*
Lisa Gonzalez *(Coord-Mktg & Communications)*
Daphna Strauss *(Coord-Bus Dev)*
Brands & Products:
AKC
AMERICAN KENNEL CLUB
CANINE GOOD CITIZEN
DOGNY
FOUNDATION STOCK SERVICE
HUMANE FUND
RALLY

AMERICAN LEGACY FOUNDATION

1724 Massachusetts Ave NW
Washington, DC 20036
Tel.: (202) 454-5555
Fax: (202) 454-5599
E-mail: info@americanlegacy.org
Web Site: www.americanlegacy.org
Approx. Rev.: $188,367,103
Approx. Number Employees: 100
Year Founded: 1999
Business Description:
Non-Profit Tobacco Education Group
S.I.C.: 8399
N.A.I.C.S.: 813319
Advertising Expenditures: $35,000,000
Media: 3-6-9-13-15-16-18-19-24
Personnel:
Cheryl Healton *(Pres & CEO)*
Anthony Thomas O'Toole *(CFO, Chief Investment Officer & Exec VP)*
Dave Dobbins *(COO)*
Ellen Vargyas *(Gen Counsel)*
Amber Hardy Thornton *(Exec VP-Program Devel)*
Eric Asche *(Sr VP-Mktg)*
Julia Cartwright *(Sr VP-Comm)*
Donna Vallone *(Sr VP-Res Evaluation)*
Anna M. Spriggs *(VP-HR)*
Christine Fritz-Kunigonis *(Asst VP-Acctg)*
Patricia McLaughlin *(Asst VP-Comm)*
Nicole Dorrier *(Sr Dir-Youth Prevention Mktg)*
Kaye Placeres *(Sr Dir-Interactive Mktg)*
Jeff Constantino *(Dir-Cessation Mktg)*
Brands & Products:
AMERICAN LEGACY FOUNDATION
EX
TRUTH
YOUTH ACTIVISM
Advertising Agencies:
Arnold Worldwide
101 Huntington Ave
Boston, MA 02199-7603
Tel.: (617) 587-8000
Fax: (617) 587-8004
Creative

GSD&M
828 W 6th St
Austin, TX 78703-5420
Tel.: (512) 242-4736
Fax: (512) 242-4700
Creative

Key to Media (For complete agency information see *The Advertising Red Books-Agencies* edition):
1. Bus. Publs. 2. Cable T.V. 3. Catalogs & Directories. 4. Co-op Adv. 5. Consumer Mags. 6. D.M. to Bus. Estab.7. D.M. to Consumers
8. Daily Newsp. 9. Exhibits/Trade Shows 10. Foreign 11. Infomercial 12. Internet Adv.13. Multimedia 14. Network Radio
15. Network T.V. 16. Newsp. Distr. Mags. 17. Other 18. Outdoor (Posters, Transit) 19. Point of Purchase20. Premiums, Novelties
21. Product Samples 22. Special Events Mktg. 23. Spot Radio 24. Spot T.V. 25. Weekly Newsp. 26. Yellow Page Adv.

PHD
(An Omnicom Company)
220 E 42nd 7th Fl
New York, NY 10017
Tel.: (212) 894-6600
Fax: (212) 894-4100
Media Buying

AMERICAN LUNG ASSOCIATION

61 Broadway 6th Fl
New York, NY 10005
Tel.: (212) 315-8700
Fax: (212) 608-3219
Toll Free: (800) LUNGUSA
Toll Free: (800) 548-8252
E-mail: info@lungusa.org
Web Site: www.lungusa.org
Sales Range: $10-24.9 Million
Approx. Number Employees: 27
Year Founded: 1904
Business Description:
Health Organization
S.I.C.: 8399
N.A.I.C.S.: 813212
Media: 2-6-7-8-13-15-22
Personnel:
Charles Dean Connor *(Pres & CEO)*
Adrienne Glasgow *(CFO & VP)*
Susan Cutter *(VP-HR & Ops)*
Carrie Martin *(VP-Comm)*
James M. Anderson *(Dir-Dev)*
Marina Tanzer *(Dir-Planned Giving)*
Gregg Tubbs *(Dir-Corp Comm)*
Brands & Products:
AMERICAN LUNG ASSOCIATION
ASTHMA WALK
BLOW THE WHISTLE ON ASTHMA
CHRISTMAS SEAL CAMPAIGN
CHRISTMAS SEALS
CLEAN AIR CHALLENGE
CLEAN AIR WEEK
FREEDOM FROM SMOKING
GOLF PRIVILEGE CARD
NOT ON TOBACCO
Advertising Agency:
Red Deluxe Brand Development
120 S Front St
Memphis, TN 38103
Tel.: (901) 522-9242
Fax: (901) 522-9890
Fighting for Air Campaign
Out-of-Home
Print
Public Service Announcement Brand Campaign
Radio
Television

AMERICAN MATHEMATICAL SOCIETY, INC.

201 Charles St
Providence, RI 02904-2213
Tel.: (401) 455-4000
Fax: (401) 331-3842
Toll Free: (800) 321-4267
E-mail: ams@ams.org
Web Site: www.ams.org
Sales Range: $10-24.9 Million
Approx. Number Employees: 222
Year Founded: 1888
Business Description:
Mathematics Books & Journals
S.I.C.: 8733; 2721; 2731; 2741
N.A.I.C.S.: 541710; 511120; 511130; 511140
Export
Media: 4-8-10-11-13-26
Distr.: Intl.; Natl.
Personnel:
James G. Glimm *(Pres)*
Brands & Products:
MATHDOC
MATHEMATICAL WORLD
MATHSCI
MATHSCINET

AMERICAN MEDICAL ASSOCIATION

(d/b/a AMA)
515 N State St
Chicago, IL 60610-4325
Tel.: (312) 464-5000
Fax: (312) 464-4184
Toll Free: (800) 621-8335
E-mail: marylou_white@ama-assn.org
Web Site: www.ama-assn.org
Sales Range: $200-249.9 Million
Approx. Number Employees: 1,125
Year Founded: 1847
Business Description:
Physicians Professional Association; Medical Journals; Medical Education Seminars; Health Information, Related Books & Products; Physician Placement Service
S.I.C.: 8621; 2721
N.A.I.C.S.: 813920; 511120
Advertising Expenditures: $300,000
Media: 1-2-4-7-8-9-10-13-16-20-23
Distr.: Natl.
Budget Set: Dec.
Personnel:
Modena H. Wilson *(Pres)*
Michael D. Maves *(CEO & Exec VP)*
Denise M. Hagerty *(CFO & SVP)*
Marietta L. Parenti *(CMO & Sr VP)*
Jeffery J. Bonistalli *(Dir-Adv & Mktg)*
Mark Daniels *(Dir-Sls & Bus Products)*
Dan Reyes *(Dir-CPT Product Dev)*
Brands & Products:
AMA EVOICE
AMA VOICE
AMERICAN MEDICAL NEWS
CPT
JAMA: JOURNAL OF THE AMERICAN MEDICAL ASSOCIATION
Advertising Agency:
The Weinstein Organization, Inc.
1 S Wacker Dr Ste 1670
Chicago, IL 60606-4670
Tel.: (312) 214-2900
Fax: (312) 214-1120
(Insurance)

AMERICAN PLASTICS COUNCIL

1300 Wilson Blvd
Arlington, VA 22209-2321
Tel.: (703) 741-5000
Fax: (703) 741-6000
Toll Free: (800) 2-HELP-90
Web Site: www.plastics.org
Approx. Number Employees: 50
Year Founded: 1905
Business Description:
Plastics Association
S.I.C.: 8611
N.A.I.C.S.: 813910
Advertising Expenditures: $24,000,000
Media: 3-6-10-14-15
Personnel:
Cal Dooley *(Pres & CEO)*
Dell Perelman *(Chief of Staff & Gen Counsel)*
Lisa B. Harrison *(VP-Commun)*
Jennifer Killinger *(Sr Dir-Sustainability, Pub Outreach & Plastics Div)*
Advertising Agency:
The Bivings Group
2201 Wisconsin Ave NW Ste 310
Washington, DC 20007
Tel.: (202) 741-1500
Fax: (202) 741-1501

AMERICAN PODIATRIC MEDICAL ASSOCIATION

9312 Old Georgetown Rd
Bethesda, MD 20814
Tel.: (301) 571-9200
Fax: (301) 530-2752
Toll Free: (800) ASK-APMA
E-mail: info@apma.org
Web Site: www.apma.org
Approx. Rev.: $9,692,925
Approx. Number Employees: 57
Business Description:
Association
S.I.C.: 8621
N.A.I.C.S.: 813920
Media: 6-7-8-10-13-17
Personnel:
Denis M. Russell *(CFO)*
Glenn B. Gastwirth *(Exec Dir)*
Jay Levrio *(Exec Dir)*
James R. Christina *(Dir-Scientific Affairs)*
Scott Haag *(Dir-Health Policy & Practice)*
Beth Shaub *(Dir-Membership Svcs)*
Rachel Richards *(Mgr-Adv)*

AMERICAN PUBLIC TRANSPORTATION ASSOCIATION

1666 K St NW Ste 1100
Washington, DC 20006-1215
Tel.: (202) 496-4800
Fax: (202) 496-4324
E-mail: mwilliams@apta.com
Web Site: www.apta.com
Approx. Number Employees: 90
Business Description:
Non Profit Organization for Public Transportation
S.I.C.: 8611
N.A.I.C.S.: 813910
Advertising Expenditures: $600,000
Media: 10-13
Personnel:
Richard Bacigalupo *(CEO)*
Lisa Burns *(Dir-Mktg)*
Thomas Elwell *(Dir-Mktg)*
Cynthia Baker *(Mktg Dir)*
Jill Cappadoro *(Mktg Dir)*
Patrick McLean *(Mktg Dir)*
Anne-Catherine Vinickas *(Mktg Dir)*
Jenny Williams *(Mktg Dir)*
Nancy Lohr *(Dir-Mktg-Customer Svc)*
Mantill Williams *(Dir-Advocacy Comm)*
Virginia Miller *(Sr Mgr-Media Rels)*
Jenny Sirnio *(Product Mgr)*
Joan Danfifer *(Mktg Mgr)*
Lori S. Hiott *(Mktg Mgr)*
Jim Macchitelli *(Mktg Mgr)*
Jennifer L. Boley *(Mgr-Mktg)*
Belinda Boyd *(Mgr-Mktg)*
Merrie DuFrene *(Mgr-Mktg)*
Melissa Hightower *(Mgr-Mktg)*

AMERICAN QUARTER HORSE ASSOCIATION

1600 Quarter Horse Dr
Amarillo, TX 79104
Mailing Address:
PO Box 200
Amarillo, TX 79168
Tel.: (806) 376-4811
Fax: (806) 349-6400
Toll Free: (800) 414RIDE
E-mail: aqha@arn.net
Web Site: www.aqha.com
Approx. Rev.: $49,883,318
Approx. Number Employees: 320
Year Founded: 1940
Business Description:
Horse Breeder Association
S.I.C.: 0752
N.A.I.C.S.: 115210
Export
Advertising Expenditures: $5,395,137
Media: 2-3-4-5-6-9-13-15-18-19-22-23-24-25
Distr.: Direct to Consumer; Intl.; Natl.
Budget Set: Mar.
Personnel:
Don Treadway *(Exec VP)*
Tom Persechino *(Exec Dir-Competition & Breed Integrity)*
Jim Campbell *(Sr Dir-Mktg & Publ)*
Duward Epps *(Dir-Production)*
Brands & Products:
THE AMERICAN QUARTER HORSE JOURNAL
THE AMERICAN QUARTER HORSE RACING JOURNAL
AMERICA'S HORSE
LIFE IS A RIDE

AMERICAN RADIO RELAY LEAGUE, INC.

225 Main St
Newington, CT 06111-1400
Tel.: (860) 594-0200
Fax: (860) 594-0259
E-mail: ads@arrl.org
Web Site: www.arrl.org
E-Mail For Key Personnel:
Marketing Director: jbee@arrl.org
Sales Director: ads@arrl.org
Approx. Number Employees: 115
Year Founded: 1914
Business Description:
Amateur Radio Association
S.I.C.: 8699; 2721
N.A.I.C.S.: 813990; 511120
Media: 4-6-8-10-13
Distr.: Natl.
Personnel:
Jim Haynie *(Pres)*
David Sumner *(CEO, Sec & Exec VP)*
Barry J. Shelley *(CFO)*
Amy Hurtabo *(Mgr-Circulation)*
Ed Hare *(Supvr)*
Brands & Products:
ARRL
NCJ
QST

AMERICAN RED CROSS

2025 E St NW
Washington, DC 20006
Tel.: (202) 737-8300
Fax: (202) 942-2024
Toll Free: (800) 435-7669
E-mail: info@usa.redcross.org

Key to Media (For complete agency information see *The Advertising Red Books-Agencies* edition):
1. Bus. Publs. 2. Cable T.V. 3. Catalogs & Directories. 4. Co-op Adv. 5. Consumer Mags. 6. D.M. to Bus. Estab.7. D.M. to Consumers
8. Daily Newsp. 9. Exhibits/Trade Shows 10. Foreign 11. Infomercial 12. Internet Adv.13. Multimedia 14. Network Radio
15. Network T.V. 16. Newsp. Distr. Mags. 17. Other 18. Outdoor (Posters, Transit) 19. Point of Purchase20. Premiums, Novelties
21. Product Samples 22. Special Events Mktg. 23. Spot Radio 24. Spot T.V. 25. Weekly Newsp. 26. Yellow Page Adv.

American Red Cross — (Continued)
Web Site: www.redcross.org
Approx. Number Employees: 35,000
Year Founded: 1881
Business Description:
Disaster Relief & Humanitarian Services
S.I.C.: 8399
N.A.I.C.S.: 813311; 813319
Advertising Expenditures: $700,000
Media: 3-6-7-8-9-14-15-18-23-24
Distr.: Intl.
Personnel:
Bonnie McElveen-Hunter *(Chm)*
Gail J. McGovern *(Pres & CEO)*
Neal Denton *(Sr VP-Govt Rels & Strategic Partnerships)*
Peggy Dyer *(CMO)*
Suzy C. DeFrancis *(Chief Pub Affairs Officer)*
Suzanne Hall *(Chief Info Security Officer)*
Mary S. Elcano *(Gen Counsel & Sec)*
Carol Miller *(Exec VP-HR)*
Roger K. Lowe *(Sr VP-Comm)*
Valerie Whyman *(Exec Dir)*
Cherae L. Bishop *(Sr Dir-Congressional Affairs)*
Carol Robinson *(Dir-Creative Resources)*
Vicki Thomas *(Dir)*
Sally Domson *(Mgr-Mktg)*
Christine Heim *(Mgr-Mktg)*
Karen Tiedt *(Mgr-Program-Mktg)*
Advertising Agencies:
Abece
404 Washington Ave Ste 620
Miami Beach, FL 33139
Tel.: (305) 604-3020
Fax: (305) 604-3099

BBDO New York
1285 Ave of the Americas 7th Fl
New York, NY 10019-6028
Tel.: (212) 459-5000
Agency of Record
B2B
Consumer Advertising
Media

BKV Inc.
10561 Barkley St Ste 200
Overland Park, KS 66212
Tel.: (913) 648-8333
Fax: (913) 648-5024

Mason & Kichar Recruitment Advertising
260 Amity Rd
Woodbridge, CT 06525
Tel.: (203) 392-0252
Fax: (203) 392-0255

TBC Inc.
900 S Wolfe St
Baltimore, MD 21231
Tel.: (410) 347-7500
Fax: (410) 986-1299

AMERICAN SHEEP INDUSTRY ASSOCIATION, INC.

9785 Maroon Cir Ste 360
Englewood, CO 80112
Tel.: (303) 771-3500
Fax: (303) 771-8200
E-mail: info@sheepusa.org
Web Site: www.sheepusa.org
Sales Range: Less than $1 Million
Approx. Number Employees: 8
Year Founded: 1865
Business Description:
US Sheep Industry National Trade Organization
S.I.C.: 8611
N.A.I.C.S.: 813910
Advertising Expenditures: $200,000
Media: 2-6-7-10-13-16
Distr.: Natl.
Personnel:
Glen Fisher *(Pres)*
Larry Kincaid *(CFO)*
Amy Trinidad *(Editor-Adv & Sheep Industry News)*
Peter Orwick *(Exec Dir)*
Rita Kourlis Samuelson *(Dir-Intl Wool-Pelt Mktg)*
Judy Malone *(Dir-Indus Info)*
Paul Rodgers *(Deputy Dir-Policy)*

AMERICAN SHORTHORN ASSOCIATION

8288 Hascall St
Omaha, NE 68124
Tel.: (402) 393-7200
Fax: (402) 393-7203
Web Site: www.shorthorn.org
Approx. Number Employees: 9
Year Founded: 1872
Business Description:
Shorthorn Beef Cattle Association
S.I.C.: 8611
N.A.I.C.S.: 813910
Import Export
Media: 2-4-5-8-9-10-20-23-25
Distr.: Intl.; Natl.
Budget Set: June
Advertising Agency:
Shorthorn Publications, Inc.
8288 Hascall St.
Omaha, NE 68124
Tel.: (402) 393-7051
Fax: (402) 393-7080
(Shorthorn Cattle)

AMERICAN SOCIETY FOR THE PREVENTION OF CRUELTY TO ANIMALS

(d/b/a ASPCA)
424 E 92nd St
New York, NY 10128
Tel.: (212) 876-7700
Fax: (212) 423-0416
E-mail: communications@aspca.org
Web Site: www.aspca.org
Approx. Rev.: $43,200,000
Approx. Number Employees: 500
Business Description:
Promoter of Humane Treatment, Cruelty Prevention & Fear & Pain Allieviation of Animals
S.I.C.: 8399; 0742; 0752
N.A.I.C.S.: 813312; 541940; 812910
Media: 6-24
Personnel:
Hoyle C. Jones *(Chm)*
Edwin Sayres *(Pres & CEO)*
Stephen Eudene *(CFO & Sr VP)*
Steven R. Hansen *(COO)*
Elizabeth J. Estroff *(Sr VP-Comm)*
Lee J. Murray *(Sr VP-HR)*
Stephen Musso *(Sr VP & Chief-Ops)*
Advertising Agency:
Rawle Murdy Associates, Inc.
2 Beaufain St
Charleston, SC 29401
Tel.: (843) 577-7327
Fax: (843) 722-3960

AMERICAN SOCIETY OF HEALTH-SYSTEM PHARMACISTS

7272 Wisconsin Ave
Bethesda, MD 20814-4836
Tel.: (301) 657-3000
Fax: (301) 657-1251
E-mail: info@ashp.org
Web Site: www.ashp.org
Approx. Rev.: $34,000,000
Approx. Number Employees: 190
Year Founded: 1942
Business Description:
National Professional Association of Pharmacists
S.I.C.: 8621
N.A.I.C.S.: 813920
Advertising Expenditures: $300,000
Media: 8-13
Personnel:
Stephen Allen *(Exec VP)*
Michael Dodd *(Dir-Mktg)*
Brian Meyer *(Dir-Govt Affairs Div)*
Karin Cushman *(Sr Mgr-Comml Mgmt)*
Brands & Products:
AHFSFIRSTFAX
AMERICAN SOCIETY OF HEALTH-SYSTEM PHARMACISTS
CLINITREND
TOGETHER WE MAKE A GREAT TEAM

AMERICAN SOCIETY OF PLASTIC SURGEONS INC.

444 E Algonquin Rd
Arlington Heights, IL 60005
Tel.: (847) 228-9900
Fax: (847) 228-9131
E-mail: media@plasticsurgery.org
Web Site: www.plasticsurgery.org
Approx. Number Employees: 80
Year Founded: 1931
Business Description:
Professional Medical Association
S.I.C.: 8621; 8322
N.A.I.C.S.: 813920; 624190
Media: 2-6-8-10-13-22
Personnel:
Michael F. McGuire *(Mng Dir)*
William M. Kuzon *(Pres-Plastic Surgery Educational Foundation)*
Paul Pomerantz *(Exec VP)*
Bonnie Burkoth *(Mgr-Exhibit)*

AMERICAN SOCIETY OF TRAVEL AGENTS, INC.

1101 King St Ste 200
Alexandria, VA 22314-2944
Tel.: (703) 739-2782
Fax: (703) 684-8319
E-mail: askasta@asta.org
Web Site: www.asta.org
Approx. Number Employees: 30
Year Founded: 1931
Business Description:
Travel Trade Association
S.I.C.: 8611
N.A.I.C.S.: 813910
Media: 7-10-20
Distr.: Intl.; Natl.
Budget Set: Aug.
Personnel:
Cris Russo *(Chm & Pres)*
Brands & Products:
ASTA
DEDICATED TO THE BUSINESS OF SELLING TRAVEL

AMERICAN WATER WORKS ASSOCIATION

6666 W Quincy Ave
Denver, CO 80235-3098
Tel.: (303) 794-7711
Fax: (303) 347-0804
Toll Free: (800) 926-7337
Telex: 45-0895 AWWA DVR
E-mail: info@awwa.org
Web Site: www.awwa.org
Approx. Rev.: $27,000,000
Approx. Number Employees: 160
Year Founded: 1881
Business Description:
Non-Profit Scientific & Educational Society For Quality Drinking Water; Books, Manuals, Standards & Periodicals
S.I.C.: 8621
N.A.I.C.S.: 813920
Export
Advertising Expenditures: $200,000
Media: 2-4-7-8-10-13-20-22
Distr.: Intl.; Natl.
Budget Set: Aug.
Personnel:
Andrew W. Richardson *(Pres)*
Jack Dozier *(Exec Dir)*
Judy L. Grycko *(Exec Dir)*
Del Haylock *(Exec Dir)*
Diane Hei *(Exec Dir)*
Carol Khare *(Exec Dir)*
Angie Monteleone *(Exec Dir)*
Dave Scott *(Exec Dir)*
Laurie A. Dougherty *(Exec Dir)*
Don Hershey *(Exec Dir)*
Mike Howe *(Exec Dir)*
Raymond J. Raposa *(Exec Dir)*
Kay Sanborn *(Exec Dir)*
Greg Kail *(Dir-Comm)*
Alan Larson *(Brand Mgr)*
Bill Selle *(Product Mgr)*
Mona E. Cavalcoli *(Mgr-Section)*
Laurie Nelson *(Mgr-Membership Mktg)*
Brands & Products:
AWWA
THE WATER LIBRARY

AMNESTY INTERNATIONAL USA

5 Penn Plz 16th Fl
New York, NY 10001
Tel.: (212) 807-8400
Fax: (212) 627-1451
E-mail: aimember@aiusa.org
Web Site: www.amnestyusa.org
Approx. Number Employees: 170
Year Founded: 1961
Business Description:
Human Rights Promotion Agency
S.I.C.: 8651; 8641; 8699
N.A.I.C.S.: 813940; 813410; 813990
Advertising Expenditures: $450,000
Media: 6-8-18
Personnel:
Jim McDonald *(Sr VP-Consumer Engagement)*
Gwen Fitzgerald *(Mng Dir-Comm)*
Larry Cox *(Exec Dir)*
Helen Garrett *(Dir-Creative Svcs & Special Projects)*

Key to Media (For complete agency information see *The Advertising Red Books-Agencies* edition):
1. Bus. Publs. 2. Cable T.V. 3. Catalogs & Directories. 4. Co-op Adv. 5. Consumer Mags. 6. D.M. to Bus. Estab.7. D.M. to Consumers
8. Daily Newsp. 9. Exhibits/Trade Shows 10. Foreign 11. Infomercial 12. Internet Adv.13. Multimedia 14. Network Radio
15. Network T.V. 16. Newsp. Distr. Mags. 17. Other 18. Outdoor (Posters, Transit) 19. Point of Purchase20. Premiums, Novelties
21. Product Samples 22. Special Events Mktg. 23. Spot Radio 24. Spot T.V. 25. Weekly Newsp. 26. Yellow Page Adv.

Brands & Products:
ACTION FOR HUMAN RIGHTS. HOPE FOR HUMANITY.
AMNESTY INTERNATIONAL USA
URGENT ACTION
Advertising Agencies:
Quiet Storm
15-16 Margaret St
London, W1W 8RW, United Kingdom
Tel.: (44) 20 7907 1140
Fax: (44) 20 7907 1150

TBA Global
21700 Oxnard St Ste 1430
Woodland Hills, CA 91367
Tel.: (818) 226-2800
Fax: (818) 226-2801
Agency of Record

ANIMAL CARE & CONTROL OF NEW YORK CITY, INC.
11 Park Pl Ste 805
New York, NY 10007
Tel.: (212) 442-7076
Web Site: www.nycacc.org
Approx. Rev.: $9,400,000
Approx. Number Employees: 154
Year Founded: 1994
Business Description:
Pet Organization
S.I.C.: 8399
N.A.I.C.S.: 813312
Media: 15-22
Personnel:
Risa Weinstock *(Gen Counsel & Dir-Admin)*
Julie Bank *(Exec Dir)*
Richard Gentles *(Dir-Dev & Comm)*
Stephen Janeczdo *(Dir-Ops)*
Advertising Agency:
Unit 7
30 Irving Pl 11th Fl
New York, NY 10003
Tel.: (212) 209-1600
Fax: (212) 209-1800

ANSWERS IN GENESIS
2800 Bullittsburg Church Rd
Petersburg, KY 41080
Mailing Address:
PO Box 510
Hebron, KY 41048
Tel.: (859) 727-2222
Toll Free: (800) 778-3390
Web Site: www.answersingenesis.org
Business Description:
Ministry
S.I.C.: 8661
N.A.I.C.S.: 813110
Media: 6-11-13-14-22
Personnel:
Ken Ham *(Pres & CEO)*

APA-THE ENGINEERED WOOD ASSOCIATION
7011 S 19th St
Tacoma, WA 98466-5333
Tel.: (253) 565-6600
Fax: (253) 565-7265
E-mail: help@apawood.org
Web Site: www.apawood.org
E-Mail For Key Personnel:
Public Relations: kevin.hayes@apawood.org
Approx. Number Employees: 75
Year Founded: 1933
Business Description:
Trade Association for the Engineered Wood Industry
S.I.C.: 8611
N.A.I.C.S.: 813910
Advertising Expenditures: $170,000
Media: 2-4-7
Distr.: Intl.; Natl.
Budget Set: Dec.
Personnel:
Dennis Hardman *(Pres)*
Brands & Products:
APA
APA PRI-400
GLULAM

APACHE SOFTWARE FOUNDATION
1901 Munsey Dr
Forest Hill, MD 21050-2747
Tel.: (410) 803-2258
Fax: (410) 803-2258
E-mail: apache@apache.org
Web Site: www.apache.org
Business Description:
Foundation
S.I.C.: 5045
N.A.I.C.S.: 423430
Media: 7-13
Personnel:
Greg Stein *(Vice Chm, Dir, VP-Subversion, Member & Developer)*

THE ASCII GROUP, INC.
7101 Wisconsin Ave Ste 1000
Bethesda, MD 20814-4881
Tel.: (301) 718-2600
Fax: (301) 718-0435
Toll Free: (800) 394-2724
E-mail: partner@ascii.com
Web Site: www.ascii.com
Approx. Number Employees: 30
Year Founded: 1984
Business Description:
Resellers of Computers & Services
S.I.C.: 5045; 3571
N.A.I.C.S.: 423430; 334111
Import Export
Media: 2-4-5-6-7-8-10-11-13-14-19-20-21-23-24
Distr.: Natl.
Personnel:
Alan D. Weinberger *(Founder & CEO)*
Jerry Koutavas *(Pres)*

ASM INTERNATIONAL
9639 Kinsman Rd
Materials Park, OH 44073-0002
Tel.: (440) 338-5151
Fax: (440) 338-4634
Toll Free: (800) 336-5152
E-mail: customerservice@asminternational.org
Web Site: www.asminternational.org
E-Mail For Key Personnel:
Sales Director: jack.hutchinson@asminternational.org
Approx. Number Employees: 80
Year Founded: 1913
Business Description:
Technical Metals & Materials Association
S.I.C.: 8611
N.A.I.C.S.: 813910
Export
Media: 1-2-4-7-8-9-10-11-13-20-23
Distr.: Intl.; Natl.
Budget Set: Aug.
Personnel:
Vladimir A. Professor *(Chm)*
Ashok K. Khare *(Pres)*
Michael DeHaemer *(Mng Dir)*
Stanley C. Theobald *(Mng Dir)*
William Kornbau *(Dir-Fin)*
Laura Marshall *(Dir-Bus Dev)*
Michael Sellaroli *(Mgr-Sls)*
Leslie Taylor *(Mgr-Exec Office)*
Brands & Products:
ADVANCED MATERIALS & PROCESSES
ALLOY DIGEST
AM&P TESTING BUYERS' GUIDE
ASM INTERNATIONAL
ASM NEWS
ELECTRONIC DEVICE FAILURE ANALYSIS
ELECTRONIC MATERIALS HANDBOOK
ENGINEERED MATERIALS HANDBOOK
ENPLOT
EVERYTHING MATERIAL
HEAT TREATING PROGRESS
HTP THERMAL SOURCEBOOK
INTERNATIONAL MATERIALS REVIEWS
JOURNAL OF FAILURE ANALYSIS & PREVENTION
JOURNAL OF MATERIALS ENGINEERING & PERFORMANCE
JOURNAL OF PHASE EQUILIBRIA & DIFFUSION
JOURNAL OF THERMAL SPRAY TECHNOLOGY
MAT.DB
MATERIALS & PROCESSES FOR MEDICAL DEVICES
METALLURGICAL & MATERIALS TRANSACTIONS
METALS ABSTRACTS
METALS HANDBOOK

ASPHALT INSTITUTE
2696 Research Park Dr
Lexington, KY 40511-8480
Tel.: (859) 288-4960
Fax: (859) 288-4999
E-mail: info@asphaltinstitute.org
Web Site: www.asphaltinstitute.org
Sales Range: $50-74.9 Million
Approx. Number Employees: 42
Year Founded: 1919
Business Description:
US-Based Association of International Petroleum Asphalt/Bitumen Producers, Manufacturers & Affiliated Businesses; Publisher of Technical Publications, Research & Education on Asphalt
S.I.C.: 8733; 8611
N.A.I.C.S.: 541710; 813910
Export
Advertising Expenditures: $200,000
Media: 2-4-5-7-10-11-13-20-22
Distr.: Intl.
Personnel:
Peter T. Grass *(Pres)*
Brian J. Clark *(Dir-Mktg & Membership)*
Crystal O'brin *(Coord-HR)*

ASPHALT ROOFING MANUFACTURERS ASSOCIATION
529 14th St Ste 700
Washington, DC 20045
Tel.: (202) 207-0917
Fax: (202) 223-9741
E-mail: info@asphaltroofing.org
Web Site: www.asphaltroofing.org
Approx. Number Employees: 10
Year Founded: 1915
Business Description:
Literature & Audiovisuals On Asphalt Roofing
S.I.C.: 8699
N.A.I.C.S.: 813990
Advertising Expenditures: $200,000
Media: 3-8-18-26
Distr.: Natl.
Budget Set: Nov.
Personnel:
Reed B. Hitchcock *(Exec VP)*

ASSOCIATION OF AMERICAN PUBLISHERS, INC.
71 5th Ave 2nd Fl
New York, NY 10003-3004
Tel.: (212) 255-0200
Fax: (212) 255-7007
Web Site: www.publishers.org
Approx. Rev.: $7,185,900
Approx. Number Employees: 25
Year Founded: 1975
Business Description:
Trade Organization for Book Publishers
S.I.C.: 8611; 2741
N.A.I.C.S.: 813910; 511199
Media: 2-6-10
Personnel:
Tom Allen *(Pres & CEO)*
John Sargent *(Treas & Dir)*
Allan R. Adler *(VP-Legal & Govt Affairs)*
Jay Diskey *(Exec Dir-Schools)*
J. Bruce Hildebrand *(Exec Dir-Higher Education)*
Luisa Simpson *(Exec Dir-Intl Copyright Enforcement & Trade Policy)*
Judith Platt *(Dir-Comm & Pub Affairs)*
Advertising Agency:
Verso Advertising, Inc.
50 W 17th St 5th Fl
New York, NY 10011-5702
Tel.: (212) 292-2990
Fax: (212) 557-2592

ASSOCIATION OF AMERICAN RAILROADS
425 3rd St SW
Washington, DC 20024
Tel.: (202) 639-2100
Fax: (202) 639-2558
Web Site: www.aar.org
Approx. Number Employees: 48
Year Founded: 1934
Business Description:
Trade Association for Railroads
S.I.C.: 8631
N.A.I.C.S.: 813930
Advertising Expenditures: $200,000
Media: 2-6-9-25
Distr.: Natl.
Budget Set: May
Personnel:
Edward R. Hamberger *(Pres & CEO)*

Association of American Railroads — (Continued)

Louis P. Warchot *(Gen Counsel & Sr VP-Law)*
John T. Gray *(Sr VP-Policy & Economics)*
Obie O'Bannon *(Sr VP-Govt Affairs)*
Jeff Marsh *(VP-Fin & Admin)*
Thomas L. Farmer *(Asst VP-Security)*

ASSOCIATION OF AMERICAN UNIVERSITY PRESSES

71 W 23rd St Ste 901
New York, NY 10010-4171
Tel.: (212) 989-1010
Fax: (212) 989-0275
E-mail: aaupny@aol.com
Web Site: www.aaupnet.org
Business Description:
Trade Association Representing 120 U.S. & International University Presses
S.I.C.: 8621; 8742
N.A.I.C.S.: 813920; 541613
Advertising Expenditures: $200,000
Media: 2-4-5-10
Distr.: Intl.; Natl.
Personnel:
Timothy Muench *(Controller & Asst Dir)*
Peter Givler *(Exec Dir)*
Brenna McLaughlin *(Dir-Electronic & Strategic Initiatives)*
Linda McCall *(Mgr-Admin)*
Susan Patton *(Mgr-Membership)*
Advertising Agency:
University Press Promotions (House Agency)
71 W. 23rd. St., Ste. 901
New York, NY 10010
Tel.: (212) 989-1010

ASSOCIATION OF NATIONAL ADVERTISERS, INC.

(d/b/a ANA)
708 3rd Ave
New York, NY 10017
Tel.: (212) 697-5950
Fax: (212) 687-7310
E-mail: info@ana.net
Web Site: www.ana.net
E-Mail For Key Personnel:
President: RLiodice@ana.net
Approx. Number Employees: 48
Year Founded: 1910
Business Description:
Trade Association
S.I.C.: 8611
N.A.I.C.S.: 813910
Media: 2-10-13-22
Personnel:
Gary Elliott *(Chm)*
Rebecca Saeger *(Chm)*
Roger W. Adams *(Vice Chm)*
Robert D. Liodice *(Pres & CEO)*
Christine Manna *(COO & Sec)*
Douglas J. Wood *(Gen Counsel)*
Barbara Bacci Mirque *(Exec VP)*
Bill Duggan *(Exec VP-Committees)*
Daniel L. Jaffe *(Exec VP-Govt Rels)*
Michael Palmer *(Exec VP-Member Rels)*
William Zengel *(Exec VP)*
Kathleen Hunter *(Sr VP)*
Keith Scarborough *(Sr VP-State Govt Rels)*
Brian Davidson *(VP & Mgr-Midwestern Reg)*
Shepard Kramer *(Sr Dir-Member Svcs)*
Kristen McDonough *(Sr Dir-Conferences)*
Mark Liebert *(Dir-Corp Trng)*
Jessica Alvarado *(Mgr-Trng)*
Mary Anne Farrell *(Mgr-Info Svcs)*
Christina Micioni *(Mgr-Conferences & Forums)*

ASSOCIATION OF OFFICIAL SEED CERTIFYING AGENCIES

(Affil. of Indiana Crop Improvement Association, Inc.)
1601 52nd Ave Ste 1
Moline, IL 61265
Tel.: (309) 736-0120
Fax: (309) 736-0115
Web Site: www.aosca.org
E-Mail For Key Personnel:
President: cboruff@aosca.org
Business Description:
Seed & Other Crop Propagation Materials Promoter
S.I.C.: 8611
N.A.I.C.S.: 813910
Media: 4-10-13-22

ATHLETES IN ACTION

651 Taylor Dr
Xenia, OH 45385
Tel.: (937) 352-1000
Web Site: www.athletesinaction.org
Sales Range: $10-24.9 Million
Approx. Number Employees: 100
Business Description:
Christian Sports Ministry
S.I.C.: 8661
N.A.I.C.S.: 813110
Media: 13
Personnel:
Mark Householder *(Pres)*

AUTOMOBILE CLUB OF SOUTHERN CALIFORNIA

2601 S Figueroa St
Los Angeles, CA 90007
Mailing Address:
PO Box 25001
Santa Ana, CA 92799-5001
Tel.: (213) 741-3686
Fax: (213) 741-4890
E-mail: webmaster@aaa-calif.com
Web Site: www.aaa-calif.com
Approx. Number Employees: 7,000
Year Founded: 1900
Business Description:
Membership, Insurance & Travel
S.I.C.: 6411; 4729
N.A.I.C.S.: 524210; 561599
Advertising Expenditures: $15,350,000
Media: 4-6-7-8
Distr.: Reg.
Budget Set: Oct.
Personnel:
Thomas V. McKernan, Jr. *(Pres & CEO)*
David Mactingly *(CFO, Treas & Sr VP-Fin-Admin)*
Windy Sabins *(Sr VP)*
Brands & Products:
AAA
AUTO CLUB OF SOUTHERN CALIFORNIA
ROAD SERVICE ONLINE
WESTWAYS
Advertising Agency:
Grey Los Angeles
3500 W Olive Ave Ste 700
Burbank, CA 91505
Tel.: (818) 531-0800
Fax: (818) 531-0701

AUTOMOTIVE SERVICE ASSOCIATION

1901 Airport Fwy Ste 100
Bedford, TX 76021
Mailing Address:
PO Box 929
Bedford, TX 76095-0929
Tel.: (817) 283-6205
Fax: (817) 685-0225
Toll Free: (800) 272-7467
E-mail: asainfo@asashop.org
Web Site: www.asashop.org
Approx. Rev.: $7,754,823
Approx. Number Employees: 35
Year Founded: 1951
Business Description:
Promotional Group for Automotive Repair Shops
S.I.C.: 8611
N.A.I.C.S.: 813910
Advertising Expenditures: $350,000
Media: 7-8-10-19-20-22
Personnel:
Denny Kahler *(Chm)*
Ron Pyle *(Pres)*
Reggie Denney *(Gen Dir)*
Brie Ragland *(Mgr-Mktg)*
Brands & Products:
AUTOMOTIVE SERVICE ASSOCIATION
CONGRESS OF AUTOMOTIVE REPAIR AND SERVICE
INTERNATIONAL AUTOBODY CONGRESS & EXPOSITION

AVON FOUNDATION

(Unit of Avon Products, Inc.)
1345 Ave of the Americas
New York, NY 10105-0196
Tel.: (212) 282-5000
Toll Free: (866) 510AVON
E-mail: info@avonfoundation.org
Web Site: www.avonfoundation.org
Sales Range: $250-299.9 Million
Year Founded: 1955
Business Description:
Foundation Focusing on Breast Cancer Research & Domestic Violence
S.I.C.: 6732
N.A.I.C.S.: 813211
Media: 6-8-22
Personnel:
Carol Kurzig *(Pres)*
Karyn Margolis *(Sr Mgr-PR & Comm)*

BARRE GRANITE ASSOCIATION, INC.

51 Church St
Barre, VT 05641-4229
Tel.: (802) 476-4131
Fax: (802) 476-4765
E-mail: bga@barregranite.org
Web Site: www.barregranite.org
Sales Range: $10-24.9 Million
Approx. Number Employees: 3
Year Founded: 1889
Business Description:
Granite Product Trade Association
S.I.C.: 8611
N.A.I.C.S.: 813910
Advertising Expenditures: $200,000
Media: 2-6-9-10-14-18-20-22
Distr.: Natl.
Brands & Products:
BARRE GUILD

BENTON FOUNDATION

1250 Connecticut NW Ste 200
Washington, DC 20036
Tel.: (202) 638-5770
Fax: (240) 235-5024
E-mail: benton@benton.org
Web Site: www.benton.org
Sales Range: Less than $1 Million
Approx. Number Employees: 2
Year Founded: 1981
Business Description:
Media Policy & Community Media Foundation
S.I.C.: 6732
N.A.I.C.S.: 813211
Media: 13
Personnel:
Charles Benton *(Chm & CEO-Trustee)*
Henry Rivera *(Gen Counsel)*
Kevin Taglang *(Editor-Comm)*
Brands & Products:
BENTON FOUNDATION
DIGITAL DIVIDE NETWORK
DIGITAL OPPORTUNITY CHANNEL
ONEWORLD UNITED STATES

THE BETTER BUSINESS BUREAU OF METROPOLITAN NEW YORK

257 Park Ave S
New York, NY 10010-7384
Tel.: (212) 533-7500
E-mail: inquiry@newyork.bbb.org
Web Site: www.newyork.bbb.org
Approx. Rev.: $270,036,000
Business Description:
Business Services
S.I.C.: 8611
N.A.I.C.S.: 813910
Media: 2-6
Personnel:
Claire Rosenzweig *(Pres & CEO)*

BOAT OWNERS ASSOCIATION OF THE UNITED STATES

(d/b/a BoatUS.com)
880 S Pickett St
Alexandria, VA 22304-4606
Tel.: (703) 461-4666
Fax: (703) 461-2847
E-mail: editor@boatus.com
Web Site: www.boatus.com
Approx. Number Employees: 500
Year Founded: 1966
Business Description:
Boating Association
S.I.C.: 8699
N.A.I.C.S.: 813990
Advertising Expenditures: $1,000,000
Media: 6-9-10-13-20-25
Personnel:
Richard Schwartz *(Founder & Chm)*
Nancy Michelman *(Pres)*
Bill Oakerson *(CEO)*
Scott Croft *(Dir-PR)*
Dina Murray *(Mgr-Membership Programs)*
Advertising Agency:
McVey Michaels
325 Riverside Dr Ste 51
New York, NY 10025
Tel.: (212) 316-0383

Fax: (212) 666-1980
(Magazine Representative)

BOY SCOUTS OF AMERICA
1325 W Walnut Hill Ln
Irving, TX 75038-3008
Mailing Address:
PO Box 152079
Irving, TX 75015
Tel.: (972) 580-2000
Fax: (972) 580-7870
Web Site: www.scouting.org
Approx. Sls.: $244,000,000
Approx. Number Employees: 1,000
Year Founded: 1911
Business Description:
National Council of Boy Scouts
S.I.C.: 8322; 5136
N.A.I.C.S.: 624110; 424320
Advertising Expenditures: $300,000
Media: 6-9-18-23-24-25
Distr.: Natl.
Budget Set: Oct.
Personnel:
William F. Cronk *(Pres)*
Ron Tozzie *(CIO)*
John Gottschalk *(Exec VP)*
Willey Ilees *(Dir-Mktg Grp)*
Stephen Medlicott *(Dir-Mktg & Comm)*
Brands & Products:
BOY SCOUTS OF AMERICA
Advertising Agencies:
Edelman
3131 Turtle Creek Blvd Ste 500
Dallas, TX 75219-5434
Tel.: (214) 520-3555
Fax: (214) 520-3458
Boy Scouts of America

Fleishman-Hillard Inc.
200 N Broadway
Saint Louis, MO 63102-2730
Tel.: (314) 982-1700
Fax: (314) 982-0586
(Hispanic Youth)

Martin/Williams Advertising Inc.
(A Member of Omnicom Group)
60 S 6th St Ste 2800
Minneapolis, MN 55402-4428
Tel.: (612) 340-0800
Fax: (612) 342-9700
Letter to the Editor

BREAST CANCER RESEARCH FOUNDATION
60 E 56th St 8th Fl
New York, NY 10022
Tel.: (646) 497-2600
Fax: (646) 497-0890
E-mail: bcrf@bcrfcure.org
Web Site: www.bcrfcure.org
Approx. Rev.: $11,000,000
Approx. Number Employees: 16
Year Founded: 1993
Business Description:
Breast Cancer Research Foundation
S.I.C.: 8733
N.A.I.C.S.: 541720
Media: 6-13-18-22
Personnel:
Evelyn H. Lauder *(Founder & Chm)*
Myra J. Biblowit *(Pres)*
Robbie Finke *(Dir-Mktg)*
Lucretia Gilbert *(Dir-Special Events)*
Margaret Mastrianni *(Dir)*
Patricia Altman *(Assoc Dir-Mktg)*
Brands & Products:
THE BREAST CANCER RESEARCH FOUNDATION
JILL ROSE
PREVENTION AND A CURE IN OUR LIFETIME

BRICK INDUSTRY ASSOCIATION
1850 Centenial Park Dr Ste 310
Reston, VA 20191
Tel.: (703) 620-0010
Fax: (703) 620-3928
E-mail: brickinfo@bia.org
Web Site: www.gobrick.com
E-Mail For Key Personnel:
President: jennison@bia.org
Marketing Director: ssears@bia.org
Sales Range: $10-24.9 Million
Approx. Number Employees: 25
Year Founded: 1935
Business Description:
Clay Products, Brick & Tile Association
S.I.C.: 8611
N.A.I.C.S.: 813910
Media: 2-3-4-6-10-20-23-24
Distr.: Natl.
Budget Set: Oct.
Personnel:
J. Gregg Borchelt *(Pres & CEO)*
Stephen Sears *(VP-Mktg & Member Svcs)*
Kathy Curtis *(Exec Dir)*
Kelly Ewell *(Dir-Mktg Svcs)*
Leroy Danforth *(Mgr-Architectural Outreach)*

BRITISH AMERICAN BUSINESS COUNCIL
200 S Broad St Ste 700
Philadelphia, PA 19102-3896
Tel.: (215) 790-3686
Fax: (215) 790-3600
E-mail: jrosenberg@greaterphilachamber.com
Web Site: www.babc.org
Business Description:
Promotes Increased Trade & Investment between the United Kingdom & United States
S.I.C.: 8611; 9199
N.A.I.C.S.: 813910; 921190
Media: 11-13
Personnel:
Carlos Gonzalez *(Treas & VP-Fin)*

BUSINESS BROKERS NETWORK
9330 LBJ Freeway Ste 740
Dallas, TX 75243
Tel.: (972) 680-8414
Fax: (972) 644-8508
E-mail: info@bbnbrokers.com
Web Site: www.bbnbrokers.com
Approx. Number Employees: 20
Year Founded: 1981
Business Description:
Business Brokerage Services
S.I.C.: 7389
N.A.I.C.S.: 541990
Media: 2-7-13
Personnel:
Gerrald Nance *(Founder & Pres)*
Zack Tannery *(Pres)*
Kenneth S. Beard *(Dir-Mktg)*
Brands & Products:
BUSINESS BROKERS NETWORK

BUSINESS SOFTWARE ALLIANCE, INC.
1150 18th St NW Ste 700
Washington, DC 20036
Tel.: (202) 872-5500
Fax: (202) 872-5501
Toll Free: (888) NO-PIRACY
E-mail: info@bsa.org
Web Site: www.bsa.org
Sales Range: $200-249.9 Million
Approx. Number Employees: 250
Year Founded: 1988
Business Description:
Safe & Digital World Promoter
S.I.C.: 8621
N.A.I.C.S.: 813920
Media: 13-17
Personnel:
Robert W. Holleyman, II *(Pres & CEO)*
Jodie L. Kelley *(Gen Counsel & VP-Anti-Piracy)*
Matt Reid *(VP-Comm)*
Lizum Mishra *(Dir-India)*
Brands & Products:
BSA
Advertising Agency:
LVT Benelux Public Relations
Kosterijland 5
3981 AJ
Bunnik, Netherlands
Tel.: (31) 30 65 65 070
Fax: (31) 30 65 65 473

BUTTE HUMANE SOCIETY
2579 Fair St
Chico, CA 95928
Tel.: (530) 343-7917
Fax: (530) 343-3734
E-mail: info@buttehumane.org
Web Site: www.buttehumane.org
Business Description:
Animal Shelter & Spade & Neuter Clinic
N.A.I.C.S.: 812910
Media: 9-13-18-23-24-25-26-29
Personnel:
Kristin Staggs *(Chm)*

CALIFORNIA AVOCADO COMMISSION
12 Mauchly Ste L
Irvine, CA 92618
Tel.: (949) 341-1955
Fax: (949) 341-1970
Web Site: www.avocado.org
Approx. Number Employees: 12
Year Founded: 1961
Business Description:
California Avocados Advertising & Promotion
S.I.C.: 8611
N.A.I.C.S.: 813910
Advertising Expenditures: $10,000,000
Media: 13-18-24
Personnel:
Rick Shade *(Chm)*
Thomas Bellamore *(Pres)*
Jan DeLyser *(VP-Mktg)*
Brands & Products:
CALIFORNIA AVOCADOS
Advertising Agency:
Integrated Marketing Works
(A Division of Bretschger & Associates)
260 Newport Ctr Dr Ste 425
Newport Beach, CA 92660
Tel.: (949) 833-3822
Fax: (949) 833-3810

CALIFORNIA CLING PEACH BOARD
531D N Alta Ave
Dinuba, CA 93618-3202
Tel.: (559) 595-1425
Fax: (559) 591-5744
Web Site: www.calclingpeach.com
Sales Range: $50-74.9 Million
Approx. Number Employees: 100
Year Founded: 1937
Business Description:
Promotion & Advertising of California Cling Peaches
S.I.C.: 9641
N.A.I.C.S.: 926140
Media: 2-6-7-10-11-16-19-21-23
Distr.: Natl.
Personnel:
J D Allen *(Mgr)*
Brands & Products:
CALIFORNIA CLING PEACH BOARD

CALIFORNIA DRIED PLUM BOARD
3840 Rosin Ct Ste 170
Sacramento, CA 95834-1699
Tel.: (916) 565-6232
Fax: (916) 565-6237
Web Site:
www.californiadriedplums.org
Sales Range: $10-24.9 Million
Approx. Number Employees: 4
Year Founded: 1952
Business Description:
Advertising, Public Relations, Sales Promotion, Market Research, Production & Processing Research & Educational Programs Through, Paid & For Growers & Handlers of Dried Prunes
S.I.C.: 8611; 8743
N.A.I.C.S.: 813910; 541820
Media: 17
Personnel:
Richard L. Peterson *(Exec Dir)*

CALIFORNIA FIG ADVISORY BOARD
600 W Shaw Ave Ste 300
Fresno, CA 93704
Tel.: (559) 243-8600
Fax: (559) 243-8605
Toll Free: (800) 588-2344
E-mail: info@californiafigs.com
Web Site: www.californiafigs.com
Approx. Number Employees: 4
Year Founded: 1954
Business Description:
California Dried Figs
S.I.C.: 8611
N.A.I.C.S.: 813910
Advertising Expenditures: $265,000
Media: 2-5-6-9-11-20-21-22-25
Distr.: Intl.; Natl.
Budget Set: Mar.
Personnel:
Carla Stockli *(dir)*

CALIFORNIA MANUFACTURED HOUSING INSTITUTE
10630 Town Ctr Dr Ste 120
Rancho Cucamonga, CA 91730-6889
Tel.: (909) 987-2599
Fax: (909) 989-0434
E-mail: info@cmhi.org
Web Site: www.cmhi.org

Key to Media (For complete agency information see *The Advertising Red Books-Agencies* edition):
1. Bus. Publs. 2. Cable T.V. 3. Catalogs & Directories. 4. Co-op Adv. 5. Consumer Mags. 6. D.M. to Bus. Estab.7. D.M. to Consumers 8. Daily Newsp. 9. Exhibits/Trade Shows 10. Foreign 11. Infomercial 12. Internet Adv.13. Multimedia 14. Network Radio 15. Network T.V. 16. Newsp. Distr. Mags. 17. Other 18. Outdoor (Posters, Transit) 19. Point of Purchase20. Premiums, Novelties 21. Product Samples 22. Special Events Mktg. 23. Spot Radio 24. Spot T.V. 25. Weekly Newsp. 26. Yellow Page Adv.

California Manufactured Housing Institute — (Continued)
Sales Range: Less than $1 Million
Approx. Number Employees: 3
Year Founded: 1977
Business Description:
Non-profit Professional & Trade Association for the Manufactured Housing Industry
S.I.C.: 8611
N.A.I.C.S.: 813910
Advertising Expenditures: $250,000
Media: 2-6-8-9-10-18-20-23-24-25
Distr.: Reg.
Budget Set: Jan.
Personnel:
Craig Fleming *(First Vice Chm)*
Jess Maxcy *(Pres)*
Connie Lamphear *(Dir-Membership Svcs)*

CALIFORNIA OLIVE COMMITTEE
1903 N Fine Ave Ste 102
Fresno, CA 93727-1510
Tel.: (559) 456-9096
Fax: (559) 456-9099
E-mail: calolive@psnw.com
Web Site: www.calolive.org
Approx. Number Employees: 3
Year Founded: 1965
Business Description:
Olive Promoter; Commodity Board
S.I.C.: 8611
N.A.I.C.S.: 813910
Media: 2-6-7-10-13-18-19-20-21-22
Distr.: Natl.
Budget Set: Dec.
Personnel:
Denise Junqueiro *(Dir-Programs & Svcs)*
Advertising Agency:
Vittles
141 Santa Rosa Ave
Sausalito, CA 94965
Tel.: (415) 332-0840
Fax: (415) 332-0841
— Patricia A. Shea *(Owner)*

CALIFORNIA REDWOOD ASSOCIATION
405 Enfrente Dr Ste 200
Novato, CA 94949-7201
Tel.: (415) 382-0662
Fax: (415) 382-8531
Toll Free: (888) CAL-REDWOOD
E-mail: info@calredwood.org
Web Site: www.calredwood.org
Year Founded: 1916
Business Description:
Lumber Trade Association
S.I.C.: 8611
N.A.I.C.S.: 813910
Media: 1-2-4-6
Distr.: Natl.
Budget Set: Jan.
Personnel:
Charles Jourdain *(Pres)*

CALIFORNIA STRAWBERRY COMMISSION
180 Westridge Dr Ste 101
Watsonville, CA 95076
Mailing Address:
PO Box 269
Watsonville, CA 95077
Tel.: (831) 724-1301
Fax: (831) 724-5973
E-mail: info@calstrawberry.com
Web Site: www.calstrawberry.com
Approx. Number Employees: 19
Year Founded: 1955
Business Description:
Marketing of Fresh & Frozen Strawberries
S.I.C.: 8611
N.A.I.C.S.: 813910
Advertising Expenditures: $530,000
Media: 2-7-19-23-24
Distr.: Natl.
Budget Set: Nov.
Personnel:
Mark Murai *(Pres)*
Advertising Agencies:
Ketchum
1050 Battery St
San Francisco, CA 94111-1209
Tel.: (415) 984-6100
Fax: (415) 984-6102

Sterling Rice Group
1801 13th St Ste 400
Boulder, CO 80302
Tel.: (303) 381-6400
Fax: (303) 444-6637

CALIFORNIA TABLE GRAPE COMMISSION
392 W Fallbrook Ave Ste 101
Fresno, CA 93711-6150
Tel.: (559) 447-8350
Fax: (559) 447-9184
E-mail: info@grapesfromcalifornia.com
Web Site: www.grapesfromcalifornia.com
Approx. Number Employees: 20
Year Founded: 1968
Business Description:
Promotion of the Table Grape Industry
S.I.C.: 8611
N.A.I.C.S.: 813910
Advertising Expenditures: $650,000
Media: 3-9-10-11-18-19-20-23
Distr.: Intl.; Natl.
Budget Set: Dec.
Personnel:
Kathleen Nave *(Pres)*
Jim Howard *(Dir-Comm)*
Advertising Agencies:
McCann Worldgroup
600 Battery St
San Francisco, CA 94111
Tel.: (415) 262-5600
Fax: (415) 262-5400

Vista Group
4561 Colorado Blvd
Los Angeles, CA 90039
Tel.: (818) 551-6789
Fax: (818) 840-6880

CANADIAN ADVANCED TECHNOLOGY ALLIANCE
(d/b/a CATAAlliance)
388 Albert St
Ottawa, ON K1R 5B2, Canada
Tel.: (613) 236-6550
Fax: (613) 236-8189
E-mail: info@cata.ca
Web Site: www.cata.ca
Approx. Number Employees: 7
Business Description:
Technology Alliance
S.I.C.: 8611; 7379
N.A.I.C.S.: 813910; 541519
Media: 7-10-13
Personnel:
John Reid *(Pres & CEO)*
Russ Roberts *(Sr VP-Tax & Fin)*
Joanne Stanley *(VP-Mktg)*
Barry Gander *(Exec Dir)*
Alice Debroy *(Co-Mgr-Office)*
Tracey Long *(Office Mgr & Mgr-Events)*
Cathi Malette *(Mgr-Member Svcs)*

CANADIAN ASSOCIATION OF INTERNET PROVIDERS
(Div. of Canadian Advanced Technology Alliance)
388 Albert St 2nd Fl
Ottawa, ON K1R 5B2, Canada
Tel.: (613) 232-2247
Fax: (613) 236-8189
E-mail: info@caip.ca
Web Site: www.caip.ca
Approx. Number Employees: 6
Year Founded: 1996
Business Description:
Technology Trade Association
S.I.C.: 8611; 7379
N.A.I.C.S.: 813910; 541519
Media: 8
Personnel:
Tom Copeland *(Chm)*
Joanne Stanley *(Mng Dir)*
John LaCalamita *(Gen Counsel)*
Alice Debroy *(Project Mgr)*
Cathi Malette *(Mgr-Member Svcs)*

CANADIAN MARKETING ASSOCIATION
1 Concorde Gate Ste 607
Toronto, ON Canada
Tel.: (416) 391-2362
Fax: (416) 441-4062
E-mail: info@the-cma.org
Web Site: www.the-cma.org
Approx. Number Employees: 40
Business Description:
Trade Association for the Direct Marketing Industry
S.I.C.: 8611
N.A.I.C.S.: 813910
Media: 2-7-10-13-17-22
Personnel:
John Gustavson *(Pres & CEO)*
Wally Hill *(VP-Pub Affairs & Comm)*
Ed Cartwright *(Sr Dir-Comm)*
Gabriele Janes *(Sr Dir-Prof Dev)*
Sandra Singer *(Sr Dir-Councils & Res)*
Colin Marsden *(Dir-IT)*
David Phillips *(Dir-Sponsorship)*
David Wilson *(Sr Mgr-Membership Mktg)*
Paddy McKenzie *(Sr Mgr-Trade Shows & Special Events)*
Stacey Lewis *(Sr Mgr-Digital Comm)*
Jeannette Soo *(Sr Mgr-Convention & Special Events)*
Sandra Stock *(Sr Mgr-Corp Svcs)*
Andra Thurton *(Sr Mgr-Events Mktg & Sls)*

CANADIAN PARKS AND WILDERNESS SOCIETY
250 City Centre Ave Ste 506
Ottawa, ON Canada
Tel.: (613) 569-7226
Fax: (613) 569-7098
Toll Free: (800) 333-WILD
E-mail: info@cpaws.org
Web Site: www.cpaws.org
E-Mail For Key Personnel:
Public Relations: media@paws.org
Approx. Number Employees: 50
Year Founded: 1963
Business Description:
Parks & Wilderness Preservation
S.I.C.: 8699; 8641
N.A.I.C.S.: 813990; 813410
Media: 6-8-13
Personnel:
Anne Levesque *(Exec Dir)*
Eric Hedert Daly *(Exec Dir-Natl)*
Ellen Adelberg *(Dir-Comm & Mktg)*
Anowara Baqi *(Mgr-Accts)*
Ursula Dechnik *(Mgr-Donor Database)*
Chris Henschel *(Mgr-Domestic & Intl Affairs-Natl)*
Sue Novotny *(Mgr-Comm)*
Aran O'Carroll *(Mgr-Legislative & Regulatory Affairs-Natl)*
Emily Smith *(Mgr-Office)*
Vicki DiMillo *(Coord-Dev)*
Jill Sturdy *(Coord-Natl Conservation & Outreach)*

CANADIAN PLASTICS INDUSTRY ASSOCIATION
(d/b/a CPIA)
5915 Airport Rd Ste 712
Mississauga, ON Canada
Tel.: (905) 678-7748
Fax: (905) 678-0774
E-mail: info@cpia.ca
Web Site: www.cpia.ca
Approx. Number Employees: 25
Business Description:
Trade Association Promoting Plastics Industry in Canada
S.I.C.: 8611; 3082; 3084; 3089
N.A.I.C.S.: 813910; 326121; 326122; 326199
Media: 10-13-16-17-22
Personnel:
Dave Birkby *(Chm)*
Mark Badger *(Pres & CEO)*
Tom Sockett *(Mgr-Event Canon Comm LLC)*
Desiree Johnston *(Coord-Shows)*

CANADIAN TOURISM COMMISSION
Ste 1400 4 Bentall Ctr
Vancouver, BC Canada
Tel.: (604) 638-8300
Fax: (604) 638-8425
E-mail: ctx_feedback@businteractive.com
Web Site: www.canadatourism.com
Approx. Number Employees: 90
Business Description:
Organization for the Promotion of Tourism in Canada
S.I.C.: 8611; 9441
N.A.I.C.S.: 813910; 923130
Advertising Expenditures: $52,454,934
Media: 2-10-25
Personnel:
Steve Allan *(Chm)*
Michele McKenzie *(Pres & CEO)*
Karin Zabel *(CFO & VP-Fin)*
Chantal Pean *(Sec & Sr VP-Corp Affairs)*
Greg Klassen *(Sr VP-Mktg Strategy & Comm)*
Siobhan Chrepien *(Exec Dir-Mktg-Americas)*

Key to Media (For complete agency information see *The Advertising Red Books-Agencies* edition):
1. Bus. Publs. 2. Cable T.V. 3. Catalogs & Directories. 4. Co-op Adv. 5. Consumer Mags. 6. D.M. to Bus. Estab.7. D.M. to Consumers
8. Daily Newsp. 9. Exhibits/Trade Shows 10. Foreign 11. Infomercial 12. Internet Adv.13. Multimedia 14. Network Radio
15. Network T.V. 16. Newsp. Distr. Mags. 17. Other 18. Outdoor (Posters, Transit) 19. Point of Purchase20. Premiums, Novelties
21. Product Samples 22. Special Events Mktg. 23. Spot Radio 24. Spot T.V. 25. Weekly Newsp. 26. Yellow Page Adv.

Gisele Danis *(Exec Dir-Global Brand Integration)*
Derek Galpin *(Dir-Mktg-China)*
Scott Pritchard *(Dir-Bus Dev & Comm)*
Daniel Vasquez *(Mgr-eMktg)*

Advertising Agencies:
DDB Canada
33 Bloor Street East Suite 1700
Toronto, ON M4W 3T4, Canada
Tel.: (416) 925-9819
Fax: (416) 925-4180
Agency of Record
Skiing & Snowboarding

Tribal DDB Vancouver
1600-777 Hornby St
Vancouver, BC V6Z 2T3, Canada
Tel.: (604) 608-4451
Fax: (604) 640-4343
Skiing & Snowboarding

THE CATFISH INSTITUTE

5420 I55 North Ste F
Jackson, MS 39211
Mailing Address:
PO Box 1669
Madison, MS 39130-1669
Tel.: (601) 977-9559
Fax: (662) 887-6857
E-mail: cawnpci@dellfouth.net
Web Site: www.catfishinstitute.com
Approx. Number Employees: 2
Year Founded: 1986
Business Description:
Farm Raised Catfish Promoter
S.I.C.: 0921
N.A.I.C.S.: 112511
Media: 2-7-10-15
Personnel:
Roger Barlow *(Pres)*
Brands & Products:
THE CATFISH INSTITUTE
THE REAL BEAUTY IS IN THE TASTE
Advertising Agency:
The Richards Group, Inc.
8750 N Central Expy Ste 100
Dallas, TX 75231-6430
Tel.: (214) 891-5700
Fax: (214) 265-2933
(U.S. Farm-Raised Catfish)

CATHOLIC RELIEF SERVICES

228 W Lexington St
Baltimore, MD 21201-3443
Tel.: (410) 625-2220
Fax: (410) 685-1635
Toll Free: (800) 736-3467
E-mail: webmaster@catholicrelief.org
Web Site: www.catholicrelief.org
E-Mail For Key Personnel:
Public Relations: egriffin@catholicrelief.org
Sales Range: $10-24.9 Million
Approx. Number Employees: 700
Year Founded: 1943
Business Description:
Catholic International Relief & Development Agency
S.I.C.: 8322
N.A.I.C.S.: 624190
Media: 3-6-13-14-15
Distr.: Intl.
Personnel:
Mark Palmer *(CFO & Exec VP)*
David Piraino *(Exec VP-HR)*
Joan Rosenhauer *(Exec VP-Ops)*
Michael Wiest *(Exec VP)*
Cameron Barry *(Editor & Writer)*

CATTLEMEN'S BEEF PROMOTION & RESEARCH BOARD

9000 E Nichols Ave St 215
Centennial, CO 80112
Tel.: (303) 220-9890
Fax: (303) 694-2851
E-mail: beefboard@beefboard.org
Web Site: www.beefboard.org
Approx. Rev.: $45,236,042
Approx. Number Employees: 9
Year Founded: 1986
Business Description:
Public Relations for Beef Industry
S.I.C.: 8743
N.A.I.C.S.: 541820
Import Export
Advertising Expenditures: $16,000,000
Media: 2-3-6-8-10-11-13-14-15-16-18-22-23-24-26
Distr.: Intl.; Natl.
Personnel:
Wesley Grau *(Chm)*
Weldon Wynn *(Vice Chm)*
Lynn Heinze *(VP-Comm)*
Basilio Aja *(Exec Dir)*
Bill Dale *(Exec Dir)*
Fred Lombardi *(Exec Dir)*
William E. Powell *(Exec Dir)*
Brands & Products:
BEEF. IT'S STILL WHAT'S FOR DINNER
BEEF. IT'S WHAT'S FOR DINNER!

CHARITY NAVIGATOR

139 Harristown Rd Ste 201
Glen Rock, NJ 07452
Tel.: (201) 818-1288
Fax: (201) 818-4694
E-mail: media@charitynavigator.org
Web Site: www.charitynavigator.org
Approx. Number Employees: 12
Year Founded: 2001
Business Description:
Charitable Giving Information Services
S.I.C.: 7389; 2741
N.A.I.C.S.: 519190; 516110
Media: 6
Personnel:
John P. Dugan *(Founder & Chm)*
Ken Berger *(Pres & CEO)*
Tim Gamory *(CIO & Mgr-HR)*

CHERRY MARKETING INSTITUTE

12800 Escanaba Dr
Dewitt, MI 48820-8680
Tel.: (517) 669-4264
Fax: (517) 669-3354
E-mail: info@choosecherries.com
Web Site: www.choosecherries.com
E-Mail For Key Personnel:
President: pkorson@cherrymkt.org
Sales Range: Less than $1 Million
Approx. Number Employees: 2
Year Founded: 1988
Business Description:
Promotion of Tart & Sweet Cherries
S.I.C.: 8611
N.A.I.C.S.: 813910
Export
Media: 2-5-7-10-11-13-18-19
Distr.: Natl.
Budget Set: Sept.
Personnel:
Randy Willmeng *(Chm)*
Philip J. Korson *(Pres & Mng Dir)*
Jeff Manning *(CMO)*
Julie Gorden *(Dir-Retail Promo)*

CHICAGO AUTOMOBILE TRADE ASSOCIATION

18 W 200 Butterfield Rd
Oakbrook Terrace, IL 60181-4810
Tel.: (630) 495-2282
Fax: (630) 495-2260
E-mail: pgrace@cata.info
Web Site: www.cata.drivechicago.com
Approx. Number Employees: 9
Year Founded: 1904
Business Description:
Trade Association for Automobile Dealers
S.I.C.: 8611
N.A.I.C.S.: 813910
Advertising Expenditures: $450,000
Media: 9-23-24
Distr.: Reg.
Personnel:
Steve Foley, Jr. *(Co-Chm)*
Mike Ettleson *(Vice Chm)*
Dave Sloan *(Pres & Gen Mgr)*
Pam Grace *(Dir & Coord)*

CHILDFUND INTERNATIONAL

2821 Emerywood Pkwy
Richmond, VA 23294-3726
Tel.: (804) 756-2700
Fax: (804) 756-2732
Toll Free: (800) 776-6767
Telex: 6844270 CCF UW
Telex: 7607731 CCF UW
E-mail: questions@childfund.org
Web Site: www.childfund.org
Approx. Rev.: $162,000,000
Approx. Number Employees: 675
Year Founded: 1938
Business Description:
International Child Development Organization
S.I.C.: 8399
N.A.I.C.S.: 813319
Media: 3-8-10-11-12-14-18-23-24
Distr.: Direct to Consumer; Intl.; Natl.
Budget Set: July -June
Personnel:
Anne Lynam Goddard *(Pres & CEO)*
James Tuite *(CFO & VP-Fin & Ops)*
Cheri Dahl *(VP-Comm & Pub Affairs)*
Linda Conley *(Dir-Global People Systems & Svcs)*
Cynthia Price *(Dir-Comm)*
Brands & Products:
CHILDALERT
CHILDWORLD
CHRISTIAN CHILDREN'S FUND
Advertising Agencies:
Bergman Group
4880 Sadler Rd Ste 220
Glen Allen, VA 23060
Tel.: (804) 225-0600
Fax: (804) 225-0900

Burford Company Advertising
125 E Main St
Richmond, VA 23219
Tel.: (804) 780-0354
Fax: (804) 780-0025

Response Media, Inc.
3155 Medlock Bridge Rd
Norcross, GA 30071-1423
Tel.: (770) 451-5478
Fax: (770) 451-4929

THE CHILDREN'S HEALTH FUND

215 W 125 St Ste 301
New York, NY 10027
Tel.: (212) 535-9400
Fax: (212) 535-7488
E-mail: cSumkin@chfund.org
Web Site: www.childrenshealthfund.org
Approx. Number Employees: 50
Year Founded: 1987
Business Description:
Non-Profit Healthcare Services for Medically Underserved Children
S.I.C.: 8399
N.A.I.C.S.: 813319
Media: 22-24-25
Distr.: Natl.
Personnel:
Irwin Redlener *(Co-Founder & Pres)*
Paul Simon *(Co-Founder)*
Robert F. Tannenhauser *(Chm)*
Ervin Revlener *(Pres)*
Jeb Weisman *(CIO)*
Arturo Brito *(Chief Medical Officer & Exec VP)*
Dennis Johnson *(Exec VP-Policy & Advocacy)*
Carol Sumkin *(Sr VP-Dev)*
Karen B. Redlener *(Exec Dir)*

CITIZENS FOR GLOBAL SOLUTIONS

418 7th St SE
Washington, DC 20003-2769
Tel.: (202) 546-3950
Fax: (202) 546-3749
E-mail: info@globalsolutions.org
Web Site: www.globalsolutions.org
Sales Range: Less than $1 Million
Approx. Number Employees: 10
Year Founded: 1947
Business Description:
Non-Profit Organization Developing New Avenues Toward World Order
S.I.C.: 7389
N.A.I.C.S.: 561499
Advertising Expenditures: $250,000
Media: 3-15-18-20-22-23-24
Distr.: Natl.
Personnel:
Marjorie Ramp *(Chm)*
Don Kraus *(CEO)*
Brands & Products:
CITIZENS FOR GLOBAL SOLUTIONS
WFA

CMI MARKETING, INC.

(d/b/a CafeMom)
401 Park Ave S
New York, NY 10016
Tel.: (646) 435-6500
Fax: (646) 435-6600
E-mail: pr@cafemom.com
Web Site: www.cafemom.com
Approx. Number Employees: 50
Year Founded: 1999
Business Description:
Membership Organization
S.I.C.: 8621
N.A.I.C.S.: 813920
Media: 13-22

Key to Media (For complete agency information see *The Advertising Red Books-Agencies* edition):
1. Bus. Publs. 2. Cable T.V. 3. Catalogs & Directories. 4. Co-op Adv. 5. Consumer Mags. 6. D.M. to Bus. Estab.7. D.M. to Consumers 8. Daily Newsp. 9. Exhibits/Trade Shows 10. Foreign 11. Infomercial 12. Internet Adv.13. Multimedia 14. Network Radio 15. Network T.V. 16. Newsp. Distr. Mags. 17. Other 18. Outdoor (Posters, Transit) 19. Point of Purchase20. Premiums, Novelties 21. Product Samples 22. Special Events Mktg. 23. Spot Radio 24. Spot T.V. 25. Weekly Newsp. 26. Yellow Page Adv.

CMI Marketing, Inc. — (Continued)

Personnel:
Andrew Shue *(Co-Founder)*
Meredith Vieira *(Co-Founder)*
Michael Sanchez *(CEO)*
Nique Fajors *(VP-Partner Mngmt)*
Alexandra Aleskovsky *(CMO)*
Laurie Basch *(Sr VP-Legal & Bus Affairs)*
Ann Lundberg *(Exec VP)*
Laura Fortner *(Sr VP-Bus Devel)*

COALITION FOR A DRUG-FREE GREATER CINCINNATI

2330 Victory Pkwy Ste 703
Cincinnati, OH 45206
Tel.: (513) 751-8000
Fax: (513) 751-8001
E-mail: info@drugfreecincinnati.org
Web Site: www.drugfreecincinnati.org
Business Description:
Coalition to Prevent Under Age Drug Use
S.I.C.: 8641
N.A.I.C.S.: 813410
Media: 22
Personnel:
Mary Haag *(Pres, CEO & Executive Dir)*
Tony Martinez *(Mgr-Environmental Prevention Strategies)*
Erika Wilson *(Coord-Special Projects)*

COIN LAUNDRY ASSOCIATION

1S660 Midwest Rd
Oakbrook Terrace, IL 60181
Tel.: (630) 963-5547
Fax: (630) 963-5864
E-mail: info@coinlaundry.org
Web Site: www.coinlaundry.org
Sales Range: Less than $1 Million
Approx. Number Employees: 12
Year Founded: 1960
Business Description:
Trade Association For Self-service Laundries & Dry Cleaning Industry
S.I.C.: 8611
N.A.I.C.S.: 813910
Media: 13
Distr.: Reg.
Budget Set: Oct. -Nov.
Personnel:
Michael Sokolowski *(Exec VP)*
Linda Theoharis *(Dir-Media Sls)*

COLOMBIAN COFFEE FEDERATION, INC.

140 E 57th St
New York, NY 10022-2703
Tel.: (212) 421-8300
Fax: (212) 758-3816
Fax: (212) 371-3489
E-mail: juan.valdez@juanvaldez.com
Web Site: www.juanvaldez.com
Sales Range: Less than $1 Million
Approx. Number Employees: 10
Year Founded: 1993
Business Description:
Colombian Coffee-Growers Association
S.I.C.: 8742
N.A.I.C.S.: 541611
Advertising Expenditures: $20,000,000
Media: 2-3-6-15-24
Distr.: Natl.
Budget Set: Jan.
Personnel:
Juan Esteban Orduz *(Pres & CEO)*
Brands & Products:
BUENDIA
GRAB LIFE BY THE BEANS
ITS THE WORLDS CUP
JUAN VALDEZ
THE RICHEST COFFEE IN THE WORLD
Advertising Agency:
Weber Shandwick
(Sub. of The Interpublic Group of Companies)
919 3rd Ave
New York, NY 10022
Tel.: (212) 445-8000
Fax: (212) 445-8001

COMMON GROUND ALLIANCE

1421 Prince St Ste 410
Alexandria, VA 22314
Tel.: (703) 836-1709
Fax: (309) 407-2244
Web Site:
www.commongroundalliance.com
Approx. Number Employees: 5
Business Description:
Promoter of Effective Damage Prevention Practices
S.I.C.: 8611; 8999
N.A.I.C.S.: 813910; 541620
Personnel:
Bob Kipp *(Pres)*
Chris McMurry *(VP & Assoc Dir-PR & Social Media Mktg)*
Khrysanne Kerr *(VP-Comm & Program Dev)*
Erika Andreasen *(Dir-Opers)*
Janell Watson *(Coord-Membership & Office)*
Advertising Agency:
MGH, Inc.
100 Painters Mill Rd Ste 600
Owings Mills, MD 21117-7305
Tel.: (410) 902-5000
Fax: (410) 902-8712

COMMUNICATIONS WORKERS OF AMERICA

501 3rd St NW
Washington, DC 20001
Tel.: (202) 434-1100
Fax: (202) 434-1279
E-mail: memberetc@cwa-union.org
Web Site: www.cwa-union.org
Approx. Number Employees: 300
Year Founded: 1940
Business Description:
Labor Union
S.I.C.: 8631
N.A.I.C.S.: 813930
Media: 1-6-9-10-14-18-20-23-24-25
Distr.: Natl.
Budget Set: Jan.
Personnel:
Larry Cohen *(Pres)*
Advertising Agency:
Greer Margolis
1010 Wisconsin Ave. N.W., Ste. 800
Washington, DC 20007
Tel.: (202) 338-8700

THE COMMUNITY PRESERVATION CORPORATION

28 E 28th St 9th Fl
New York, NY 10016-7943
Tel.: (212) 869-5300
Fax: (212) 683-0694
E-mail: info@communityp.com
Web Site: www.communityp.com
Sales Range: $300-349.9 Million
Approx. Number Employees: 150
Year Founded: 1974
Business Description:
Mortgage Bankers & Correspondents
S.I.C.: 6159
N.A.I.C.S.: 522292
Personnel:
Michael D. Lappin *(Pres & CEO)*
Ronald Schiferl *(CFO)*
Richard A. Kumro *(Gen Counsel)*
Kathleen A. Dunn *(Exec VP)*
John M. McCarthy *(Exec VP)*
Alice Dunn *(Sr VP & Head-HR)*
Carolyn Au *(Sr VP)*
Jack Greene *(Sr VP)*
Dianna Look *(Sr VP)*
Brenda Ratliff *(VP-Comm)*
Brands & Products:
CPC
Advertising Agency:
Geto & deMilly Inc.
276 5th Ave Ste 806
New York, NY 10001
Tel.: (212) 686-4551
Fax: (212) 213-6850

CONSUMER HEALTHCARE PRODUCTS ASSOCIATION

900 19th St NW Ste 700
Washington, DC 20006
Tel.: (202) 429-9260
Fax: (202) 223-6835
Web Site: www.chpa-info.org
Business Description:
Member-Based Association Representing Manufacturers & Distributors of Nonprescription, Over-the-Counter (OTC) Medicines & Nutritional Supplements
S.I.C.: 8699
N.A.I.C.S.: 813990
Media: 14-17
Personnel:
Christopher D. DeWolf *(Chm)*
Scott M. Melville *(Pres & CEO)*
Virginia Cox *(VP-Comm & Strategic Initiatives)*

COPPER DEVELOPMENT ASSOCIATION INC.

260 Madison Ave
New York, NY 10016-2401
Tel.: (212) 251-7200
Fax: (212) 251-7234
E-mail: questions@cda.copper.org
Web Site: www.copper.org
E-Mail For Key Personnel:
Marketing Director: kgeremia@cda.copper.org
Approx. Number Employees: 40
Year Founded: 1963
Business Description:
Trade Association For Copper & Copper-Alloy Products
S.I.C.: 8611
N.A.I.C.S.: 813910
Export
Media: 2-10-12
Distr.: Natl.
Budget Set: Dec.
Personnel:
Andrew G Kireta, Sr. *(Pres & CEO)*
Harold T. Michels *(Sr VP-Tech & Technical Svcs)*
Robert Weed *(VP-OEM)*
Lorraine Herzing Mills *(VP-Fin & Admin)*
David Brender *(Natl Program Mgr-EEEI/PQBW)*
David E. Hunt *(Mgr-Architectural Svcs at Revere Copper Products)*
Maki Isayama *(Mgr-Info Tech)*
Helen Lee *(Asst Mgr-Fin & Admin)*
Advertising Agencies:
communications 21
834 Inman Vlg Pky Ste 150
Atlanta, GA 30307
Tel.: (404) 814-1330
Fax: (404) 814-1332
Media Relations
Paid Search Advertising
Social Media Marketing

Marquardt & Roche and Partners
5 High Ridge Pk
Stamford, CT 06905
Tel.: (203) 327-0890
Fax: (203) 353-8487
(Copper & Brass Applications)

COUNCIL FOR BIOTECHNOLOGY INFORMATION

1201 Maryland Ave SW Ste 900
Washington, DC 20024
Tel.: (202) 962-9200
Fax: (202) 488-6301
E-mail: cbi@whybiotech.com
Web Site: www.bio.org
Approx. Number Employees: 160
Year Founded: 2000
Business Description:
Biotechnology Information Services
S.I.C.: 8611
N.A.I.C.S.: 813910
Media: 4-6-13
Personnel:
Ellen Fernandes *(Mgr-HR)*

COUNCIL ON FOREIGN RELATIONS

58 E 68th St
New York, NY 10065
Tel.: (212) 434-9400
Fax: (212) 434-9800
E-mail: communications@cfr.org
Web Site: www.cfr.org
E-Mail For Key Personnel:
Public Relations: communications@cfr.org
Sales Range: $75-99.9 Million
Approx. Number Employees: 140
Year Founded: 1921
Business Description:
Foreign Policy Information Services; Non-Profit Independent National Organization
S.I.C.: 8733; 2721
N.A.I.C.S.: 541720; 511120
Media: 8-13
Distr.: Intl.; Natl.
Personnel:
Peter G. Peterson *(Chm)*
David Kellogg *(CIO & Publr)*
James Lindsay *(Sr VP & Dir-Studies & Chm-Maurice R. Greenberg)*
Richard N. Haass *(Pres-Council-Foreign Rels)*
Jan Mowder Hughes *(VP-HR & Admin)*
Lisa Shields *(VP-Comm & Mktg)*

Key to Media (For complete agency information see *The Advertising Red Books-Agencies* edition):
1. Bus. Publs. 2. Cable T.V. 3. Catalogs & Directories. 4. Co-op Adv. 5. Consumer Mags. 6. D.M. to Bus. Estab.7. D.M. to Consumers
8. Daily Newsp. 9. Exhibits/Trade Shows 10. Foreign 11. Infomercial 12. Internet Adv.13. Multimedia 14. Network Radio
15. Network T.V. 16. Newsp. Distr. Mags. 17. Other 18. Outdoor (Posters, Transit) 19. Point of Purchase20. Premiums, Novelties
21. Product Samples 22. Special Events Mktg. 23. Spot Radio 24. Spot T.V. 25. Weekly Newsp. 26. Yellow Page Adv.

Gideon Rose *(Editor-Foreign Affairs)*
Neftali F. Alvarez *(Dir-Facility, Event & Security Mgmt)*
Jana Gasn Beauchamp *(Dir-Membership Admin & Rels)*
Janine Hill *(Dir-Fellowship Affairs & Studies Strategic Plng)*
Valerie Post *(Dir-Special Events)*
Jeffrey A. Reinke *(Dir-Special Programs)*
Anya Schmemann *(Dir-Task Force Program)*
Amy Gunning Baker *(Asst Dir-Studies Office)*
Brands & Products:
COUNCIL ON FOREIGN RELATIONS
FOREIGN AFFAIRS

COUNTRY MUSIC ASSOCIATION
1 Music Cir S
Nashville, TN 37203-4312
Tel.: (615) 244-2840
Fax: (615) 726-0314
Fax: (615) 248-1007
E-mail: marketing@cmaworld.com
Web Site: www.cmaworld.com
Sales Range: $10-24.9 Million
Approx. Number Employees: 35
Year Founded: 1958
Business Description:
Country Music Promoter
S.I.C.: 8621
N.A.I.C.S.: 813920
Media: 3-8-10-14-15-18-20-22-23-24
Personnel:
Steve Buchanan *(Chm)*
Steve Moore *(CEO)*
Athena Patterson *(Dir-Creative Svcs)*
Scott Stem *(Dir-Media Rels)*
Tammy Donham *(Mgr-Mktg)*
Brands & Products:
CMA AWARDS
CMA MUSIC FESTIVAL
CMAWORLD.COM

CREDIT UNION NATIONAL ASSOCIATION
5710 Mineral Point Rd
Madison, WI 53705-4454
Mailing Address:
PO Box 431
Madison, WI 53701-0431
Tel.: (608) 231-4000
Fax: (608) 231-4263
Toll Free: (800) 356-9655
Web Site: www.cuna.org
E-Mail For Key Personnel:
President: dmica@cuna.com
Approx. Number Employees: 278
Year Founded: 1934
Business Description:
National Trade Association
S.I.C.: 8611
N.A.I.C.S.: 813910
Export
Media: 2-7
Distr.: Natl.
Budget Set: Aug. -Sept.
Personnel:
Richard McBride *(COO)*
Joe Day *(Dir-Bus Dev)*
Julie Esser *(Dir-New Alliances)*
Brands & Products:
AMERICA'S CREDIT UNIONS
CREDIT UNION
CREDIT UNION DIRECTORS
CREDIT UNION FRONT LINE
CUNA
WHERE PEOPLE ARE WORTH MORE THAN MONEY

CRUISE LINES INTERNATIONAL ASSOCIATION, INC.
(d/b/a CLIA)
910 SE 17th St Ste 400
Fort Lauderdale, FL 33316
Tel.: (754) 224-2200
Fax: (754) 224-2250
E-mail: info@cruising.org
Web Site: www.cruising.org
E-Mail For Key Personnel:
Marketing Director: bsharak@cruiseassoc.com
Sales Range: Less than $1 Million
Approx. Number Employees: 21
Year Founded: 1975
Business Description:
Cruise Lines Trade Group
S.I.C.: 8611
N.A.I.C.S.: 813910
Advertising Expenditures: $1,000,000
Media: 2-6
Distr.: Natl.
Budget Set: Oct.
Personnel:
Howard S. Frank *(Chm)*
Christine Duffy *(Pres & CEO)*
Paul Zacharski *(CFO)*
Robert Sharak *(Exec VP-Mktg & Distr)*
Robert Fuller *(Dir-Fin & Admin)*
Jim Smith *(Dir-Mktg)*
Brands & Products:
CLIA
YOU DESERVE A CRUISE
Advertising Agency:
DDB Miami
770 S Dixie Hwy
Coral Gables, FL 33146
Tel.: (305) 529-4300
Fax: (305) 662-3166

DAIRY MANAGEMENT, INC.
10255 W Higgins Rd Ste 900
Rosemont, IL 60018-5616
Tel.: (847) 803-2000
Fax: (847) 803-2077
Web Site: www.dairyinfo.com
Approx. Number Employees: 120
Year Founded: 1915
Business Description:
Milk & Dairy Products Promoter
S.I.C.: 8611
N.A.I.C.S.: 813910
Media: 6-8-9-14-15
Personnel:
Thomas Gallagher *(CEO)*
Daniel Chavka *(Exec VP-Fin & Admin)*
Mark Leitner *(Exec VP-Sls, Mktg & Insights)*
Mark Inkrott *(Dir & Mgr-NFL Relationship)*
Brands & Products:
AMERICAN DAIRY ASSOCIATION
DMI
NATIONAL DAIRY BOARD
NATIONAL DAIRY COUNCIL
UNITED DAIRY INDUSTRY ASSOCIATION
U.S. DAIRY EXPORT COUNCIL

DARE 2 SHARE MINISTRIES INTERNATIONAL, INC.
PO Box 745323
Arvada, CO 80006-5323
Tel.: (303) 425-1606
Fax: (303) 425-1633
Toll Free: (800) 462-8355
E-mail: information@dare2share.org
Web Site: www.dare2share.org
Approx. Rev.: $2,400,000
Approx. Number Employees: 24
Year Founded: 1944
Business Description:
Youth Evangelism Training Conferences
S.I.C.: 8641
N.A.I.C.S.: 813410
Advertising Expenditures: $200,000
Media: 2-10-14-23
Distr.: Direct to Consumer; Intl.; Natl.
Personnel:
Greg Stier *(Founder & Pres)*
Debbie Bresina *(Exec VP & Exec Dir)*
Molly Bandimere *(Mgr-Event Volunteer)*
Brands & Products:
DARE 2 SHARE MINISTRIES
PARAGON PUBLISHING
SOUL FUEL

THE DARFUR FOUNDATION
315 Church St 4C
New York, NY 10013
Tel.: (206) 234-4558
E-mail: info@darfurfoundation.org
Web Site: www.darfurfoundation.org
Sales Range: $10-24.9 Million
Approx. Number Employees: 3
Business Description:
Non-Profit Organizaion Supporting Peace in Darfur, Sudan
S.I.C.: 8399
N.A.I.C.S.: 813311
Media: 1-13

THE DEAN A. MCGEE EYE INSTITUTE
608 S L Young Blvd
Oklahoma City, OK 73104
Tel.: (405) 271-6060
Tel.: (405) 232-8696
Fax: (405) 271-3013
Web Site: www.dmei.com
Sales Estimate: $1-4.9 Million
Approx. Number Employees: 40
Business Description:
Ophthalmological Services
S.I.C.: 8062
N.A.I.C.S.: 622110
Media: 9-16-25
Personnel:
Matthew D. Bown *(Exec VP)*

DEMOCRATIC NATIONAL COMMITTEE
430 S Capitol St SE
Washington, DC 20003-4024
Tel.: (202) 863-8000
Fax: (202) 863-8063
Toll Free: (877) 336-7200
E-mail: info@democrats.org
Web Site: www.democrats.org
Approx. Number Employees: 150
Year Founded: 1854
Business Description:
Political Services
S.I.C.: 8651
N.A.I.C.S.: 813940
Advertising Expenditures: $12,000,000
Media: 8-9-13-14-15-23-24-25
Distr.: Natl.
Personnel:
Debbie Wasserman Schultz *(Chm)*
Dona Brazil *(Vice Chm)*
Mark Brewer *(Vice Chm)*
Linda Chavez-Thompson *(Vice Chm)*
Mike Honda *(Vice Chm)*
Jen O'Malley *(Exec Dir)*

DETROIT METRO CONVENTION & VISITORS BUREAU
211 W Fort St Ste 1000
Detroit, MI 48226
Tel.: (313) 202-1800
Fax: (313) 202-1808
Toll Free: (800) DETROIT
E-mail: vic@visitdetroit.com
Web Site: www.visitdetroit.com
Approx. Number Employees: 50
Year Founded: 1896
Business Description:
Tourism & Travel Promoter
S.I.C.: 8611
N.A.I.C.S.: 813910
Media: 4-10-13-22
Personnel:
Timothy McCarthy *(Chm)*
Larry Alexander *(Pres & CEO)*
Michael O'Callaghan *(COO & Exec VP)*
Christopher Baum *(Sr VP-Sls & Mktg)*
Sajid Zuberi *(VP-Fin)*
Dave Beachnau *(Exec Dir)*
Carla Conner-Penzabene *(Dir-Sls)*
Harriet Carter *(Dir-Bureau Svcs)*
Joan L. Foxley *(Dir-HR)*
Renee Monforton *(Dir-Comm)*
John Francis *(Mgr-Sports & Destination Support)*
Advertising Agency:
BERLINE
70 E Long Lk Rd
Bloomfield Hills, MI 48304
Tel.: (248) 593-4744
Fax: (248) 593-4740

THE DIAN FOSSEY GORILLA FUND INTERNATIONAL
800 Cherokee Ave SE
Atlanta, GA 30315-1440
Tel.: (404) 624-5881
Fax: (404) 624-5999
Toll Free: (800) 851-0203
E-mail: 2help@gorillafund.org
Web Site: www.gorillafund.org
Sales Range: $1-9.9 Million
Approx. Number Employees: 80
Year Founded: 1978
Business Description:
Organization for the Conservation & Protection of Gorillas & Their Habitat in Africa
S.I.C.: 7389
N.A.I.C.S.: 561990
Media: 6-13-23-24
Personnel:
Clare Richardson *(Pres & CEO)*
Erika Archibald *(Dir-Comm)*
Kathryn Fawcett *(Dir-Karisoke Res Center)*
Advertising Agency:
TG Madison
3340 Peachtree Rd NE Ste 2850

Key to Media (For complete agency information see *The Advertising Red Books-Agencies* edition):
1. Bus. Publs. 2. Cable T.V. 3. Catalogs & Directories. 4. Co-op Adv. 5. Consumer Mags. 6. D.M. to Bus. Estab.7. D.M. to Consumers
8. Daily Newsp. 9. Exhibits/Trade Shows 10. Foreign 11. Infomercial 12. Internet Adv.13. Multimedia 14. Network Radio
15. Network T.V. 16. Newsp. Distr. Mags. 17. Other 18. Outdoor (Posters, Transit) 19. Point of Purchase20. Premiums, Novelties
21. Product Samples 22. Special Events Mktg. 23. Spot Radio 24. Spot T.V. 25. Weekly Newsp. 26. Yellow Page Adv.

The Dian Fossey Gorilla Fund International — (Continued)

Atlanta, GA 30326-1027
Tel.: (404) 262-2623
Tel.: (404) 267-4421 (President's Number)
Fax: (404) 237-2811

THE DIRECT MARKETING ASSOCIATION INC.

1120 Ave of the Americas
New York, NY 10036-6700
Tel.: (212) 768-7277
Fax: (212) 302-6714
E-mail: customerservice@the-dma.org
Web Site: www.the-dma.org
Approx. Rev.: $33,020,901
Approx. Number Employees: 90
Year Founded: 1917
Business Description:
Trade Association for the Direct Marketing Industry
S.I.C.: 8611
N.A.I.C.S.: 813910
Media: 4-7-10-13
Personnel:
Don McKenzie *(Vice Chm)*
Robert Allen *(Interim Pres & CEO)*
Lawrence M. Kimmel *(CEO)*
Sue R.E. Geramian *(Chief Comm Officer & Sr VP)*
Senny Boone *(Sr VP-Corp & Social Responsibility)*
Jerry Cerasale *(Sr VP-Govt Affairs)*
Ken Ebeling *(Sr VP-Member & Segment Svcs)*
Pat Kachura *(Sr VP-Corp)*
Karina Penia Gracia *(Sr Dir-Mktg)*

DIRECT SELLING ASSOCIATION

1667 K St NW Ste 1100
Washington, DC 20006
Tel.: (202) 452-8866
Fax: (202) 452-9010
E-mail: info@dsa.org
Web Site: www.dsa.org
Business Description:
Regulation of Direct Selling & Supplier Companies
S.I.C.: 8611
N.A.I.C.S.: 813910
Media: 13
Personnel:
Amy Robinson *(CMO & Sr VP)*

DIRECTORS GUILD OF AMERICA, INC.

7920 W Sunset Blvd
Los Angeles, CA 90046-3300
Tel.: (310) 289-2000
Fax: (310) 289-2029
E-mail: dga@dga.org
Web Site: www.dga.org
Approx. Sls.: $20,000,000
Approx. Number Employees: 140
Year Founded: 1936
Business Description:
Motion Picture Directors' Organization
S.I.C.: 8999; 8631
N.A.I.C.S.: 711510; 813930
Media: 1-2-10-13-15
Personnel:
Taylor Hartford *(Pres)*
Beverly Ware *(Assoc Gen Counsel)*
Darrell L. Hope *(Editor-DGA Monthly)*
Kathy Garmezy *(Exec Dir-Govt & Intl Affairs)*
Marcelo Giacusa *(Exec Dir-Theatre Ops-Awards Admin-Facility Mgmt)*
Jon Larson *(Exec Dir-Natl)*
Rodney Mitchell *(Exec Dir-Natl)*
Jay D. Roth *(Exec Dir-Natl)*
Morgan Rumpf *(Exec Dir-Comm-Natl)*
G. Bryan Unger *(Exec Dir-Western)*
Joyce Baron *(Mgr-Res)*
Barbara Berman *(Mgr-Contracts)*
Carlos Gutierrez *(Mgr-Printshop)*
Brands & Products:
DGA AWARD
DIRECTORS GUILD OF AMERICA

DISTILLED SPIRITS COUNCIL OF THE UNITED STATES, INC.

1250 Eye St NW Ste 400
Washington, DC 20005-5977
Tel.: (202) 628-3544
Fax: (202) 682-8876
E-mail: webmaster@discus.org
Web Site: www.discus.org
Approx. Number Employees: 40
Year Founded: 1973
Business Description:
Trade Association
S.I.C.: 8611
N.A.I.C.S.: 813910
Media: 2-6-9-13-16-25
Distr.: Intl.; Natl.
Budget Set: Oct.
Personnel:
Peter H. Cressy *(Pres & CEO)*
Frank Coleman *(Sr VP)*
Lynne J. Omlie *(Sr VP)*
Brands & Products:
DISTILLED SPIRITS COUNCIL OF THE UNITED STATES

DIVING EQUIPMENT & MARKETING ASSOCIATION

(d/b/a DEMA)
3750 Convoy St Ste 310
San Diego, CA 92111-3741
Tel.: (858) 616-6408
Fax: (858) 616-6495
E-mail: info@dema.org
Web Site: www.dema.org
Sales Range: Less than $1 Million
Approx. Number Employees: 6
Year Founded: 1977
Business Description:
Non-Profit Trade Association for the Diving Industry
S.I.C.: 7389
N.A.I.C.S.: 561920
Media: 2-10
Personnel:
Nicole Russell *(Mng Dir)*
Colleen Vasquez *(Controller & Assoc Dir)*
Tom Ingram *(Exec Dir)*

DOCTORS WITHOUT BORDERS USA, INC.

333 7th Ave 2nd Fl
New York, NY 10001
Tel.: (212) 679-6800
Fax: (212) 679-7016
Toll Free: (888) 392-0392
E-mail: info@doctorswithoutborders.org
Web Site: www.doctorswithoutborders.org
Approx. Rev.: $53,541,442
Approx. Number Employees: 80
Year Founded: 1971
Business Description:
Charitable Organization for Independent Medical Health & Relief Services
S.I.C.: 8399; 8641
N.A.I.C.S.: 813319; 813410
Media: 6-9-13-14-25
Personnel:
Mathew Spitzer *(Pres)*

DUCKS UNLIMITED, INC.

1 Waterfowl Way
Memphis, TN 38120-2350
Tel.: (901) 758-3825
Fax: (901) 758-3850
Toll Free: (800) 45-DUCKS
Web Site: www.ducks.org
Approx. Number Employees: 510
Year Founded: 1937
Business Description:
Wetland Conservation Organization
S.I.C.: 0971
N.A.I.C.S.: 114210
Import Export
Media: 6-9-13-14-18-25
Personnel:
Jeffrey M. Nelson *(CEO)*
James C. Boyd *(CIO)*
Randy L. Graves *(Chief Admin Officer)*
H. J. Beto *(Reg VP)*
John W. Newman *(First VP)*
Ken Babcock *(Dir-Opers)*
Beth Bryan *(Dir-Adv)*
Ryan Heiniger *(Dir-Conservation Program)*
Bob Hoffman *(Dir-Opers)*
Philip Milburn *(Dir-Dev & Natl)*
Thomas S. Moorman *(Dir-Conservation Program)*
Jon Rich *(Dir-Planning)*
Rudolph Rosen *(Dir-Opers)*
Scott Sutherland *(Dir-Governmental Affairs)*
Wayne Dierks *(Grp Mgr-HR)*
Anita Goode *(Mgr-Adv)*
W. Alan Wentz *(Mgr-Programs)*
Brands & Products:
DUCKS UNLIMITED

DUCTILE IRON PIPE RESEARCH ASSOCIATION

245 Riverchase Pkwy E Ste O
Birmingham, AL 35244
Tel.: (205) 402-8700
Fax: (205) 402-8730
Web Site: www.dipra.org
Approx. Number Employees: 20
Year Founded: 1915
Business Description:
Ductile Iron Pipe Marketer
S.I.C.: 8621
N.A.I.C.S.: 813920
Media: 2-10-13
Distr.: Natl.
Budget Set: Sept.
Personnel:
L. Gregg Horn *(Pres)*
Richard W. Bonds *(Dir-Res & Technical)*

EARTH SHARE

7735 Old Georgetown Rd Ste 900
Bethesda, MD 20814
Tel.: (240) 333-0300
Fax: (240) 333-0301
Toll Free: (800) 875-3863
Web Site: www.earthshare.org
Approx. Rev.: $72,000,000
Year Founded: 1988
Business Description:
Promoter of Environmental Education, National Environmental Federation
S.I.C.: 8399
N.A.I.C.S.: 813312
Media: 6-13
Personnel:
Kalman Stein *(Pres & CEO)*
Steven Kravitz *(CFO)*
Renny Perdue *(Sr Dir-Corp Partnerships)*
Perry Bird *(Dir-Member Svcs)*
Elizabeth Hitchcock *(Dir-Comm)*
Robin Perkins *(Dir-Comm & Mktg)*
Miriam Davidson *(Mgr-Pub Campaigns)*
Paul Fitzpatrick *(Mgr-Info Sys)*
Leslie Bethke Pope *(Mgr-Acctg)*

EDISONLEARNING, INC.

521 5th Ave 11th Fl
New York, NY 10175-0003
Tel.: (212) 419-1600
Fax: (212) 419-1604
E-mail: communications@edisonschools.com
Web Site: www.edisonlearning.com/
Approx. Rev.: $425,627,639
Approx. Number Employees: 230
Year Founded: 1992
Business Description:
Schools Operator
S.I.C.: 8211; 8748
N.A.I.C.S.: 611110; 541618
Media: 10-13
Personnel:
Jeff Wahl *(Pres & CEO)*
David Duffy *(CFO & Exec VP)*
Advertising Agencies:
Drohlich Associates, Inc.
22 Balcony
Saint Louis, MO 63141
Tel.: (314) 567-4030
Fax: (314) 567-0703

Neiman Group
614 N Frnt St
Harrisburg, PA 17101-1057
Tel.: (717) 232-5554
Fax: (717) 232-7998

EDUCATIONAL ASSISTANCE LTD.

PO Box 3021
Glen Ellyn, IL 60138-3021
Tel.: (630) 690-0010
Fax: (630) 690-0565
E-mail: 2eal@inventorydonations.org
Web Site: www.ealworks.org
Year Founded: 1982
Business Description:
Monetary Donations & Scholarships for Disadvantaged Children
S.I.C.: 8399
N.A.I.C.S.: 813319
Media: 6
Personnel:
John Saban *(Dir-Dev)*

ELECTRIC POWER RESEARCH INSTITUTE INC

3420 Hillview Ave
Palo Alto, CA 94304
Mailing Address:

Key to Media (For complete agency information see *The Advertising Red Books-Agencies* edition):
1. Bus. Publs. 2. Cable T.V. 3. Catalogs & Directories. 4. Co-op Adv. 5. Consumer Mags. 6. D.M. to Bus. Estab.7. D.M. to Consumers 8. Daily Newsp. 9. Exhibits/Trade Shows 10. Foreign 11. Infomercial 12. Internet Adv.13. Multimedia 14. Network Radio 15. Network T.V. 16. Newsp. Distr. Mags. 17. Other 18. Outdoor (Posters, Transit) 19. Point of Purchase20. Premiums, Novelties 21. Product Samples 22. Special Events Mktg. 23. Spot Radio 24. Spot T.V. 25. Weekly Newsp. 26. Yellow Page Adv.

PO Box 10412
Palo Alto, CA 94303
Tel.: (650) 855-2000
Toll Free: (800) 313-3774
E-mail: askepri@epri.com
Web Site: www.epri.com
E-Mail For Key Personnel:
Sales Director: rchapman@epri.com
Approx. Rev.: $273,839,000
Approx. Number Employees: 750
Year Founded: 1973
Business Description:
Electric Power Research Association
S.I.C.: 8733
N.A.I.C.S.: 541710
Media: 17-22
Personnel:
James L. Turner *(Vice Chm)*
Theodore U. Marston *(Sr VP-CTO)*
Norma Formanek *(Gen Counsel , Sr VP & Institute Governance)*
Salvador A. Casente, Jr. *(VP-Legal & Asst Corp Sec)*
Clark Gellings *(VP-Tech)*
Acher Mosse *(Exec Dir)*
David J. Modeen *(Dir-External Affairs-Nuclear Sector)*
Brands & Products:
EPRI

ENTERTAINMENT INDUSTRY FOUNDATION
1201 W 5th St Ste T-700
Los Angeles, CA 90017
Tel.: (213) 240-3900
Fax: (213) 481-3100
Web Site: www.eifoundation.org
Approx. Number Employees: 23
Year Founded: 1942
Business Description:
Charitable Foundation Supported by the Entertainment Industry to Raise Awareness & Funds for Critical Social Issues
S.I.C.: 8399; 8611
N.A.I.C.S.: 813319; 813910
Media: 6-7-8-10-13-17-22
Personnel:
Lisa C. Paulsen *(Pres & CEO)*
Merrily Newton *(CFO)*
Michael Balaoing *(Sr VP-Philanthropic Svcs)*
Kathleen Lobb *(Sr VP-Comm)*
Amy Banachowski *(Dir-Integrated Mktg)*
Bobby Fergerstrom *(Mgr-Grants)*
Brands & Products:
ENTERTAINMENT INDUSTRY FOUNDATION
HUNGER FREE AMERICA
NATIONAL ARTS EDUCATION INITIATIVE
NATIONAL CARDIOVASCULAR RESEARCH INITIATIVE
NATIONAL COLORECTAL CANCER RESEARCH ALLIANCE
NATIONAL WOMEN'S CANCER RESEARCH ALLIANCE
Advertising Agency:
The Designory
211 E Ocean Blvd Ste 100
Long Beach, CA 90802-4850
Tel.: (562) 624-0200
Fax: (562) 491-0140

ENVIRONMENTAL DEFENSE FUND
257 Park Ave S
New York, NY 10010
Tel.: (212) 505-2100
Fax: (212) 505-2375
Web Site: www.edf.org
Approx. Number Employees: 300
Year Founded: 1967
Business Description:
Environmental Rights Protection
S.I.C.: 8399
N.A.I.C.S.: 813312
Personnel:
Fred Krupp *(Pres)*
Peter Accinno *(CFO, Treas, VP-Fin & Admin)*
Liza Henshaw *(COO)*
Marcia Aronoff *(Sr VP-Programs)*
Cynthia Hampton *(VP-Mktg & Comm)*
Rebecca Shaw *(Assoc VP-Land, Water & Wildlife Program)*
Wade Crowfoot *(Dir-West Coast Reg)*
Laura Harnish *(Dir-Natl Strategy)*
Advertising Agencies:
Goodman Media International, Inc.
750 7th Ave 28th Fl
New York, NY 10016
Tel.: (212) 576-2700
Fax: (212) 576-2701

Ogilvy & Mather Advertising
636 11th Ave
New York, NY 10036
Tel.: (212) 237-4000
Fax: (212) 237-5123
(Global Warming)

EQUAL FOOTING FOUNDATION
2214 Rock Hill Rd Ste 300
Herndon, VA 20170
Tel.: (703) 904-7878
Fax: (703) 904-8008
E-mail: chahn@nvtc.org
Web Site: www.efooting.org
Approx. Number Employees: 24
Business Description:
Non-profit Foundation
S.I.C.: 6732
N.A.I.C.S.: 813211
Personnel:
Colleen Hahn *(Pres & Exec Dir)*
Advertising Agency:
Wills & Associates
3 Bethesda Metro Ste 700
Bethesda, MD 20814
Tel.: (301) 767-0220
Fax: (240) 465-0733

EXETER HEALTH RESOURCES
5 Alumni Dr
Exeter, NH 03833
Tel.: (603) 778-7311
Fax: (603) 580-6592
Web Site: www.exeterhospital.com
Approx. Rev.: $200,627,383
Business Description:
Healthcare Services
S.I.C.: 9431
N.A.I.C.S.: 923120
Personnel:
Kevin J. Callahan *(Pres & CEO)*
Advertising Agency:
Winsper Inc.
77 Summer St
Boston, MA 02110
Tel.: (617) 695-2900
Fax: (617) 696-2910

FACES WITHOUT PLACES
PO Box 23300
Cincinnati, OH 45223-0300
Tel.: (513) 549-3155
Tel.: (513) 421-7803, ext. 16
Web Site:
www.faceswithoutplaces.org
Business Description:
Removes Barriers to Education for Children & Youth Experiencing Homelessness in the Greater Cincinnati Area
S.I.C.: 8699
N.A.I.C.S.: 813990
Media: 13-22-29
Personnel:
Tracy Power *(Pres)*
Advertising Agency:
Eisen Management Group
515 Monmouth St Ste 302
Newport, KY 41071
Tel.: (859) 291-4302
Fax: (859) 291-4360

FAMILY FIRST
5211 W Lourel St
Tampa, FL 33607
Tel.: (813) 222-8300
Fax: (813) 222-8301
E-mail: info@familyfirst.net
Web Site: www.familyfirst.net
E-Mail For Key Personnel:
President: mark@familyfirst.net
Marketing Director: george@familyfirst.net
Approx. Number Employees: 25
Year Founded: 1991
Business Description:
Family Services
S.I.C.: 8733; 8661
N.A.I.C.S.: 541720; 813110
Media: 6-10-13
Personnel:
Mark W. Merrill *(Pres)*
Bryan Davis *(Dir-All Pro Dad)*
George Woods *(Dir-Mktg)*
Barbara Hall *(Mgr-Acctg)*
Brands & Products:
ALL PRO DAD
FAMILY FIRST
IMOM
Advertising Agency:
Digital Lightbridge, LLC
11902 Little Rd
New Port Richey, FL 34654
Tel.: (727) 863-7806
Fax: (727) 863-7816

FLORIDA AVOCADO ADMINISTRATIVE COMMITTEES
18710 SW 288th St
Homestead, FL 33030-2309
Tel.: (305) 247-0848
Fax: (305) 245-1315
E-mail: avacadocommittee@bellsouth.net
Sales Range: $10-24.9 Million
Approx. Number Employees: 3
Year Founded: 1954
Business Description:
Avocado Federal Marketing Ordering Services
S.I.C.: 8611
N.A.I.C.S.: 813910
Media: 5-7
Distr.: Reg.
Budget Set: Apr.
Personnel:
Alan Flinn *(Mgr-Committees)*

FLORIDA COUNCIL ON COMPULSIVE GAMBLING
901 Douglas Ave Ste 200
Altamonte Springs, FL 32714-2057
Tel.: (407) 865-6200
Fax: (407) 865-6103
Web Site: www.gamblinghelp.org
Approx. Number Employees: 10
Business Description:
Information, Resource Referrals & Support Services for Problem Gamblers, Their Families, Employers & Others
S.I.C.: 7389
N.A.I.C.S.: 561990
Media: 13-14-15-18
Personnel:
Paul Ashe *(Pres)*

FLORIDA FRUIT & VEGETABLE ASSOCIATION
800 Trafalgar Ct Ste 200
Maitland, FL 32751-5219
Tel.: (321) 214-5200
Fax: (321) 214-0210
E-mail: information@ffva.com
Web Site: www.ffva.com
Approx. Number Employees: 60
Year Founded: 1943
Business Description:
Agricultural Trade & Service Association
S.I.C.: 8611; 4729
N.A.I.C.S.: 813910; 561599
Advertising Expenditures: $500,000
Media: 1-2-4-6-9-10-16-19-20-22-25
Distr.: Natl.
Budget Set: Jan. -June
Personnel:
Mike Stuart *(Pres)*
Lisa Lochridge *(Dir-Public Affairs)*
Daniel A. Botts *(Dir-Environ & Pest Mngmt)*
Kerry B. Kates *(Dir-Water & Natural Resources)*

FLORIDA HOSPITAL ASSOCIATION
306 E College Ave
Tallahassee, FL 32301-1522
Tel.: (850) 222-9800
Fax: (850) 561-6230
Web Site: www.fha.org
Approx. Number Employees: 40
Business Description:
Hospital Association
S.I.C.: 8611
N.A.I.C.S.: 813910
Media: 2-9-10-13-25
Personnel:
William A. Bell *(Gen Counsel)*
Paul Belcher *(Sr VP)*
Ralph Glatfelter *(Sr VP)*
John Mines *(Sr VP)*
Rich Rasmussen *(VP-Membership Rels)*
Kathy Reep *(VP-Fin Svcs)*
Lynn Bearden *(Dir-Ops)*
Dianne L. Bennett *(Dir-Membership Svcs & Education)*
Janice Clement *(Dir-Loan Admin)*

Key to Media (For complete agency information see *The Advertising Red Books-Agencies* edition):
1. Bus. Publs. 2. Cable T.V. 3. Catalogs & Directories. 4. Co-op Adv. 5. Consumer Mags. 6. D.M. to Bus. Estab.7. D.M. to Consumers 8. Daily Newsp. 9. Exhibits/Trade Shows 10. Foreign 11. Infomercial 12. Internet Adv.13. Multimedia 14. Network Radio 15. Network T.V. 16. Newsp. Distr. Mags. 17. Other 18. Outdoor (Posters, Transit) 19. Point of Purchase20. Premiums, Novelties 21. Product Samples 22. Special Events Mktg. 23. Spot Radio 24. Spot T.V. 25. Weekly Newsp. 26. Yellow Page Adv.

Florida Hospital Association — (Continued)

Steve McGee *(Dir-Support Svcs)*
Fran Owens *(Dir-Acctg)*
Jennifer Greenhalgh *(Mgr-HIMS Ops)*
Debbie Hegarty *(Mgr-Survey & Special Projects)*
Kaye Lynn Mattern *(Mgr-Acctg Svcs)*
Luanne MacNeill *(Coord-Quality Initiatives)*

FLORIDA TOMATO COMMITTEE

800 Trafalgar Ct Ste 300
Maitland, FL 32751
Tel.: (407) 660-1949
Fax: (407) 660-1656
E-mail: info@floridatomatoes.org
Web Site: www.floridatomatoes.org
Approx. Sls.: $7,000,000
Approx. Number Employees: 5
Year Founded: 1963
Business Description:
Promoter of Florida Tomatoes; Trade Association
S.I.C.: 8611
N.A.I.C.S.: 813910
Export
Media: 2-6-9-10-15-16-19
Distr.: Natl.
Budget Set: Sept.
Personnel:
Samantha Winters *(Dir-Promo)*
Reggie Brown *(Mgr)*
Advertising Agencies:
Lewis & Neale, Inc.
320 W 13th St 7th Fl
New York, NY 10014
Tel.: (212) 420-8808
Fax: (212) 229-2867

Sena Reider, Inc.
99 Pacific St Ste 155D
Monterey, CA 93940-2484
Tel.: (831) 372-4961
Fax: (831) 375-7117

FOCUS: HOPE

1355 Oakman Blvd
Detroit, MI 48238-2849
Tel.: (313) 494-5500
Fax: (313) 494-4287
Web Site: www.focushope.edu
Year Founded: 1968
Business Description:
Civil & Human Rights Organization
S.I.C.: 8641; 8399
N.A.I.C.S.: 813410; 813311
Personnel:
Eleanor M. Josaitis *(Co-Founder)*
William F. Jones, Jr. *(CEO)*
Martha Schultz *(CFO)*
Timothy Duperron *(COO)*
Patrick O. Lindsey *(Dir-External Rels & Dev)*
Julian E. Pate, III *(Dir-Education)*
Arnold Pirtle *(Dir-Facilities & Community Affairs)*
Tim W. Sullivan *(Dir-Mfg)*
Brands & Products:
FOCUS HOPE
Advertising Agency:
AutoCom Associates
74 W Long Lk Rd Ste 103
Bloomfield Hills, MI 48304-2770
Tel.: (248) 647-8621
Fax: (248) 642-2110

FOODSERVICE & PACKAGING INSTITUTE, INC.

201 Park Washington Ct
Falls Church, VA 22046-2921
Tel.: (703) 538-3550
Fax: (703) 241-5603
E-mail: fpi@fpi.org
Web Site: www.fpi.org
Approx. Number Employees: 3
Year Founded: 1933
Business Description:
Business Association for the Single-Use Foodservice Packaging Industry
S.I.C.: 8611
N.A.I.C.S.: 813910
Media: 1-2-4-7-13
Personnel:
Lynn Dyer *(Pres)*

FORGING INDUSTRY ASSOCIATION

25 W Prospect Ave Ste 300
Cleveland, OH 44115-1000
Tel.: (216) 781-6260
Fax: (216) 781-0102
E-mail: info@forging.org
Web Site: www.forging.org
Approx. Number Employees: 15
Year Founded: 1913
Business Description:
Corporate Membership Association for the Forging Industry
S.I.C.: 8611
N.A.I.C.S.: 813910
Media: 2-10
Distr.: Natl.
Personnel:
Jay S. Gunasekera *(Chm)*
Lynn C. Outwater *(Mng Partner)*
Charles H. Hageman *(Exec VP)*
Karen Lewis *(Gen Mgr)*
Tim Dunagan *(Grp Dir-Mktg)*
Don Farley *(Dir-Mktg)*
Robin Ingols *(Dir-Mktg Components)*
George Mochnal *(Dir-R & D)*

FOUNDATION FOR BIOMEDICAL RESEARCH

818 Connecticut Ave NW Ste 900
Washington, DC 20006-2702
Tel.: (202) 457-0654
Fax: (202) 457-0659
E-mail: info@fbresearch.org
Web Site: www.fbresearch.org
Approx. Number Employees: 5
Year Founded: 1981
Business Description:
Information on the Benefits of Animal Testing
S.I.C.: 8621
N.A.I.C.S.: 813920
Media: 2-10-18-20-24
Personnel:
Frankie Trull *(Founder & Pres)*
Paul McKellips *(Exec VP)*
Michael Stebbins *(Dir-Res)*

FRENCH-AMERICAN CHAMBER OF COMMERCE

1528 Walnut St Ste 2020
Philadelphia, PA 19102
Tel.: (215) 545-0123
Fax: (215) 545-0144
E-mail: Info@faccphila.org
Web Site: www.faccphila.org
Approx. Number Employees: 1
Business Description:
Non-profit, Membership-Driven Business Association
S.I.C.: 8611
N.A.I.C.S.: 813910
Media: 11-13
Personnel:
Peter J. Tucci *(Pres)*
Molly Hoyle *(VP-Comm)*
Judith L. Ujobai *(Exec Dir)*
Bruno Casabon *(Dir-Sls)*
Daniele L. Thomas Easton *(Dir)*

FRENCH INSTITUTE ALLIANCE FRANCAISE

22 E 60th St
New York, NY 10022
Tel.: (212) 355-6100
Fax: (212) 935-4119
E-mail: info@fiaf.org
Web Site: www.fiaf.org
Approx. Number Employees: 22
Business Description:
Cultural Center Promoting French Culture; French Language Instruction
S.I.C.: 8641
N.A.I.C.S.: 813410
Media: 8-9-13-18-22-25
Personnel:
Marie M. Steckel *(Pres)*

FRESH AIR FUND

633 3rd Ave 14th Fl
New York, NY 10017-8152
Tel.: (212) 897-8900
Fax: (212) 681-0146
Toll Free: (800) 367-0003
E-mail: freshair@freshair.org
Web Site: www.freshair.org
E-Mail For Key Personnel:
Public Relations: pr@freshair.org
Approx. Rev.: $12,000,000
Approx. Number Employees: 42
Year Founded: 1877
Business Description:
Non-Profit Youth Service Organization
S.I.C.: 8399; 8641
N.A.I.C.S.: 813319; 813410
Media: 6-8-9-23-24-25
Distr.: Reg.
Budget Set: Oct.
Personnel:
Donald Newhouse *(Chm)*
Jenny Morgenthau *(Exec Dir)*
Brands & Products:
THE FRESH AIR FUND

FRIENDS OF ANIMALS, INC.

777 Post Rd Ste 205
Darien, CT 06820
Tel.: (203) 656-1522
Fax: (203) 656-0267
E-mail: contact@friendsofanimals.org
Web Site: www.friendsofanimals.org
Approx. Billings: $60,000
Approx. Number Employees: 15
Year Founded: 1957
Business Description:
Promoter of Protecting Animals from Cruelty & Abuse
S.I.C.: 8399
N.A.I.C.S.: 813312; 813319
Media: 2-6-13-26
Personnel:
Carol Fleischmann *(Chm)*
Priscilla Feral *(Pres)*
Lee Hall *(VP-Legal Affairs)*
Bob Orabona *(Dir-Ops)*

FULL GOSPEL BUSINESS MEN'S FELLOWSHIP INTERNATIONAL

3 Holland
Irvine, CA 92618-2275
Tel.: (949) 461-0100
Fax: (949) 609-0344
E-mail: international@fgbmfi.org
Web Site: www.fgbmfi.org
Approx. Number Employees: 6
Year Founded: 1951
Business Description:
Non-Profit Religious Organization
S.I.C.: 8661; 2721
N.A.I.C.S.: 813110; 511120
Advertising Expenditures: $500,000
Media: 9-13-14-15-23-24-25
Distr.: Intl.; Natl.
Personnel:
Richard Shakarian *(Pres)*
Brands & Products:
FGBMFI
VOICE

FUR COUNCIL OF CANADA

1435 Saint Alexandre Ste 1270
Montreal, QC Canada
Tel.: (514) 844-1945
Fax: (514) 844-8593
E-mail: info@furcouncil.com
Web Site: www.canadafurcouncil.com
Approx. Number Employees: 8
Year Founded: 1964
Business Description:
Fur Promoter
S.I.C.: 2371; 2329; 2339; 8641; 8699
N.A.I.C.S.: 315292; 315211; 315212; 813410; 813990
Media: 6-10-11-13
Personnel:
Teresa Eloy *(Dir-Comm)*

GIRL SCOUTS OF THE UNITED STATES OF AMERICA

420 5th Ave
New York, NY 10018-2729
Tel.: (212) 852-8000
Fax: (212) 852-6514
Fax: (212) 852-6517
Toll Free: (800) 478-7248
E-mail: international@girlscouts.org
Web Site: www.girlscouts.org
E-Mail For Key Personnel:
Marketing Director: d.scala@girlscouts.org
Sales Director: g.brown@girlscouts.org
Approx. Sls.: $116,956,000
Approx. Number Employees: 500
Year Founded: 1912
Business Description:
Girl Scout Services
S.I.C.: 8322; 5137
N.A.I.C.S.: 624110; 424330
Media: 4-5-8-19
Distr.: Direct to Consumer; Natl.
Budget Set: May
Personnel:
Patricia Diaz Dennis *(Chm)*
Kathy Cloninger *(CEO)*
Florence Corsello *(CFO-Bus Svcs & Sr VP)*
Deborah Taft *(Sr VP-Fund Dev)*
Mary P. Borba *(Second VP)*
Linda P. Foreman *(Second VP)*
Barry Horowitz *(VP-Wholesale, Retail & License Bus)*
Jamie Joyce *(VP-Interactive Mktg)*

Key to Media (For complete agency information see *The Advertising Red Books-Agencies* edition):
1. Bus. Publs. 2. Cable T.V. 3. Catalogs & Directories. 4. Co-op Adv. 5. Consumer Mags. 6. D.M. to Bus. Estab.7. D.M. to Consumers 8. Daily Newsp. 9. Exhibits/Trade Shows 10. Foreign 11. Infomercial 12. Internet Adv.13. Multimedia 14. Network Radio 15. Network T.V. 16. Newsp. Distr. Mags. 17. Other 18. Outdoor (Posters, Transit) 19. Point of Purchase20. Premiums, Novelties 21. Product Samples 22. Special Events Mktg. 23. Spot Radio 24. Spot T.V. 25. Weekly Newsp. 26. Yellow Page Adv.

Gerri Brown *(Dir-Sls)*
Daria Scala *(Mgr-Adv & Direct Mail Sls)*

Brands & Products:
GIRL SCOUT COOKIES
GIRL SCOUT GOLD AWARD
GIRL SCOUTS
WHERE GIRLS GROW STRONG

Advertising Agencies:
Amazon Advertising
30 Hotaling Pl Ste 100
San Francisco, CA 94111
Tel.: (415) 433-3004
Fax: (415) 433-3002

CRT/tanaka
101 W Commerce Rd
Richmond, VA 23224
Tel.: (804) 675-8100
Fax: (804) 675-8183
Crisis Counsel

Daniel J. Edelman, Inc.
(d/b/a Edelman)
200 E Randolph St Fl 63
Chicago, IL 60601-6705
Tel.: (312) 240-3000
Fax: (312) 240-2900
Centennial PR
Consumer Engagement
Crisis Counsel
Issues Management
Media Relations

Grupo Gallegos
401 E Ocean Blvd Ste 600
Long Beach, CA 90802
Tel.: (562) 256-3600
Fax: (562) 256-3620

THE GLADNEY CENTER FOR ADOPTION

6300 John Ryan Dr
Fort Worth, TX 76132-4122
Tel.: (817) 922-6000
Fax: (817) 922-5955
Toll Free: (800) GLADNEY
E-mail: media@gladney.org
Web Site:
www.adoptionsbygladney.com
Approx. Number Employees: 84
Year Founded: 1887
Business Description:
Adoption Services
S.I.C.: 8322
N.A.I.C.S.: 624110
Media: 10-13-14-15-16-24-26
Personnel:
Michael McMahon *(Vice Chm)*
Frank R. Garrott *(Pres & CEO)*
Heidi Cox *(Gen Counsel & Exec VP)*
Scott J. Brown *(Exec VP & Mng Dir-Africa)*
Marshall Williams *(Sr VP & Mng Dir-Eastern Europe-Latin America)*

GLAUCOMA RESEARCH FOUNDATION

251 Post St Ste 600
San Francisco, CA 94108
Tel.: (415) 986-3162
Fax: (415) 986-3763
Toll Free: (800) 826-6693
E-mail: info@glaucoma.org
Web Site: www.glaucoma.org
Sales Range: $10-24.9 Million
Approx. Number Employees: 8
Year Founded: 1978
Business Description:
Research Foundation for Glaucoma
S.I.C.: 8733; 8011
N.A.I.C.S.: 541720; 621111
Media: 6
Personnel:
Thomas M. Brunner *(Pres & CEO)*
Andrew Jackson *(Dir-Comm)*
Catalina San Agustin *(Dir-Ops)*

GODDARD SYSTEMS, INC.

(Sub. of Wind River Holdings, L.P.)
1016 W 9th Ave
King of Prussia, PA 19406
Tel.: (610) 265-8510
Fax: (610) 265-8867
E-mail: info@goddardsystems.com
Web Site: www.goddardsystems.com
Approx. Number Employees: 120
Year Founded: 1988
Business Description:
Early Childhood Learning Centers
S.I.C.: 8351
N.A.I.C.S.: 624410
Media: 6-7-8-10-14-15-18-22-23-24-26
Personnel:
Joseph Schumacher *(CEO)*
Robert Scopinich *(CFO)*
Victor Yeandel *(VP-Mktg, Adv & PR)*

GOODWILL INDUSTRIES-SUNCOAST, INC.

10596 Gandy Blvd
Saint Petersburg, FL 33702
Tel.: (727) 523-1512
Fax: (727) 576-2797
Toll Free: (888) 279-1988
E-mail: gw.marketing@goodwill-suncoast.com
Web Site: www.goodwill-suncoast.org
Sales Range: $10-24.9 Million
Approx. Number Employees: 1,200
Year Founded: 1954
Business Description:
Nonprofit Organization; Used Merchandise Store Operator; Housing & Workforce Placement Services
S.I.C.: 8641; 5932; 7361; 9531
N.A.I.C.S.: 813410; 453310; 561310; 925110
Media: 9-22
Personnel:
Martin W. Gladysz *(Chm)*
R. Lee Waits *(Pres & CEO)*
Gary Hebert *(CFO & Treas)*
Deborah A. Passerini *(COO & Exec VP)*
Michael Ann Harvey *(VP-Mktg & PR)*
Jacqui Miller *(VP-HR)*
Chris Ward *(Mgr-Mktg & Media Rels)*

GOVERNMENT EMPLOYEES HOSPITAL ASSOCIATION, INC.

(d/b/a GEHA)
17306 E 24 Hwy
Independence, MO 64056
Mailing Address:
PO Box 4665
Independence, MO 64051-4665
Tel.: (816) 257-5500
Toll Free: (800) 821-6136
Web Site: www.geha.com
Approx. Number Employees: 825
Year Founded: 1939
Business Description:
Health Insurance Services
S.I.C.: 6321
N.A.I.C.S.: 524114
Media: 8-10
Personnel:
Richard Miles *(Pres)*
Michael Gremillon *(CIO)*
Advertising Agency:
Kuhn & Wittenborn, Inc.
2405 Grand Blvd Ste 600
Kansas City, MO 64108-2519
Tel.: (816) 471-7888
Fax: (816) 471-7530

GRAIN FOODS FOUNDATION

490 Bear Cub Dr
Ridgway, CO 81432
Tel.: (970) 626-5183
Fax: (970) 626-5814
E-mail: judi.adams@grainfoundation.org
Web Site: www.grainpower.org
Year Founded: 2004
Business Description:
Milling & Baking Industry Foundation
S.I.C.: 8621
N.A.I.C.S.: 813920
Media: 6-22
Personnel:
Judi Adams *(Pres)*
Advertising Agency:
Mullen
40 Broad St
Boston, MA 02109
Tel.: (617) 226-9000
Fax: (617) 226-9100
Bread

GREATER NEW HAVEN ASSOCIATION OF REALTORS

127 Washington Ave WLL
North Haven, CT 06473
Tel.: (203) 234-7700
Fax: (203) 234-3980
E-mail: info@greaternhrealtors.com
Web Site: www.greaternhrealtors.com
Approx. Number Employees: 50
Year Founded: 1915
Business Description:
Professional Organization Monitoring Real Estate Practices
S.I.C.: 6159
N.A.I.C.S.: 522292
Media: 7-10
Personnel:
Albert Scafati *(Chm)*
Roberta N. O'Hara *(Pres)*
Kate Blake *(Dir-Membership)*
Edward Sposito *(Dir-Fin)*
Advertising Agency:
McLaughlin, DelVecchio & Casey, Inc.
1 Church St
New Haven, CT 06510-3330
Tel.: (203) 624-4151
Fax: (203) 401-6134

GREENPEACE

702 H St NW
Washington, DC 20001
Tel.: (202) 462-1177
Fax: (202) 462-4507
Web Site: www.greenpeace.org
Approx. Number Employees: 185
Business Description:
Environmental Organization
S.I.C.: 8399
N.A.I.C.S.: 813312
Personnel:
Phil Radford *(Exec Dir)*
Advertising Agencies:
Almap BBDO
Av Roque Petroni JR 999 35e 7 anderas
Sao Paulo, 04707-905, Brazil
Tel.: (55) 11 2161 5600
Fax: (55) 11 2161 5645

DDB Budapest
Dozsa Gyorgy ut 84/a 3rd Floor
H-1068
Budapest, Hungary
Tel.: (36) 1 461 2800
Fax: (36) 1 321 6270

McCann Erickson S.A.
Paseo de la Castellana 165
28046
Madrid, Spain
Tel.: (34) 91 5679 000
Fax: (34) 91 571 2098

Ogilvy & Mather Advertising Beijing
9th Floor Huali Building 58 Jinbao Street
Beijing, 100005, China
Tel.: (86) 10 8520 6688
Fax: (86) 10 8520 6060

Ogilvy Johannesburg (Pty.) Ltd.
The Brand Building 15 Sloane Street
2152
Johannesburg, 2021, South Africa
Tel.: (27) 11 709 66 00
Fax: (27) 21 700 3000

Scala/JWT
Str Trotusului Nr 39 Sector 1
012141
Bucharest, Romania
Tel.: (40) 121 224 1460
Fax: (40) 21 224 1461

HABITAT FOR HUMANITY INTERNATIONAL, INC.

121 Habitat St
Americus, GA 31709-3423
Tel.: (229) 924-6935
Fax: (229) 924-6934
Toll Free: (800) 422-4828
E-mail: publicinfo@habitat.org
Web Site: www.habitat.org
Approx. Rev.: $285,350,080
Approx. Number Employees: 300
Year Founded: 1976
Business Description:
Non-Profit Organization Promoting & Providing Housing for the Poor
S.I.C.: 8399
N.A.I.C.S.: 813319
Advertising Expenditures: $25,000
Media: 1-2-3-7-8-10-11-14-15-18-20-22-23-24
Personnel:
Ken Klein *(Chm)*
Theodore A. Dosch *(Vice Chm)*
Anugerah Pekerti *(Vice Chm)*
Jonathan Reckford *(CEO)*
Ed Quibell *(CFO & Sr VP-Admin)*
Elizabeth Kilcullen Blake *(Gen Counsel & Sr VP-Advocacy & Govt Affairs)*
Mike Carscaddon *(Exec VP-Intl Field Ops)*
Chris Clarke *(Sr VP-Comm & Mktg)*
Mark Crozet *(Sr VP-Resource Dev)*
Larry Gluth *(Sr VP-US & Canada)*
Dave McMurtry *(Sr VP-Strategy)*

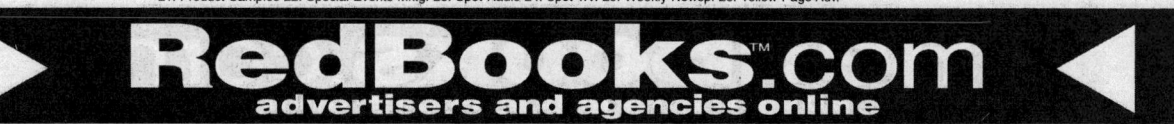

Habitat for Humanity International, Inc. — (Continued)

Connie Steward *(Sr VP-HR, Learning & Organizational Dev)*
Tina Collins *(Dir-DM Ops)*
Jessica Boatright *(Dir-Brand Strategy & Special Initiatives)*
Jeff Brock *(Dir-Staffing)*
Danielle Turnage *(Mgr-Special Events)*
Brands & Products:
HABITAT FOR HUMANITY
Advertising Agency:
Sparxoo
4400 W Spruce St # 333
Tampa, FL 44607
Tel.: (646) 345-1800

HARDWOOD PLYWOOD & VENEER ASSOCATION

1825 Michael Faraday Dr
Reston, VA 20190-5304
Tel.: (703) 435-2900
Fax: (703) 435-2537
E-mail: hpva@hpva.org
Web Site: www.hpva.org
E-Mail For Key Personnel:
President: baltman@hpva.org
Marketing Director: calt@hpva.org
Sales Range: Less than $1 Million
Approx. Number Employees: 9
Year Founded: 1921
Business Description:
Hardwood Plywood, Veneer & Engineered Flooring Industry Association
S.I.C.: 8611
N.A.I.C.S.: 813910
Media: 2-7-10
Personnel:
Kip howlet *(Pres)*
Brian Sause *(Dir-Testing & Certification)*

HEALTHCARESEEKER.COM

612 Main St
Boonton, NJ 07005
Tel.: (973) 257-1483
Fax: (973) 257-1478
Fax: (888) 453-0810
Toll Free: (888) 331-3431
Web Site: www.healthcareseeker.com
Approx. Rev.: $20,000,000
Approx. Number Employees: 25
Business Description:
Health Care Employment Agency
S.I.C.: 7361
N.A.I.C.S.: 561310
Media: 2-7
Personnel:
Stephen Halasnik *(Pres)*
Gina Halasnik *(CFO)*

HEALTHRIGHT INTERNATIONAL

80 Maiden Ln
New York, NY 10038
Tel.: (212) 226-9890
Fax: (212) 226-7026
Toll Free: (888) 817-HELP
E-mail: info@healthright.org
Web Site: www.healthright.org
Approx. Rev.: $3,800,000
Approx. Number Employees: 150
Year Founded: 1990
Business Description:
Medical & Humanitarian Services
S.I.C.: 8399
N.A.I.C.S.: 813319
Media: 6
Personnel:
Rachel Madenyika *(CFO)*
Walter Cortes *(Dir-Fin & Admin)*
Cathy Hews *(Mgr-Office & HR)*

HEALTHWISE, INCORPORATED

2601 N Bogus Basin Rd
Boise, ID 83702-0909
Tel.: (208) 345-1161
Fax: (208) 345-1897
Toll Free: (800) 706-9646
E-mail: moreinfo@healthwise.org
Web Site: www.healthwise.org
Approx. Number Employees: 220
Business Description:
Medical Information
S.I.C.: 8641
N.A.I.C.S.: 813410
Media: 2-10-13
Personnel:
Donald W. Kemper *(Chm & CEO)*
Jim giuffre *(Pres & COO)*
A. James Balkins *(CFO & Chief Strategic Officer)*
Steven Schneider *(Chief Medical Officer)*
Molly Mettler *(Sr VP)*
Brands & Products:
FOR EVERY HEALTH DECISION
HEALTHWISE
HEALTHWISE HANDBOOK
HEALTHWISE KNOWLEDGEBASE
LX

HERITAGE GALLERIES & AUCTIONEER

3500 Maple Ave 17th Fl
Dallas, TX 75219
Tel.: (214) 528-3500
Fax: (214) 409-1968
Toll Free: (800) 872-6467
Web Site: www.heritagecoin.com
Approx. Number Employees: 100
Year Founded: 1970
Business Description:
Wholesale & Retail of Rare Coins
S.I.C.: 5094
N.A.I.C.S.: 423940
Import Export
Media: 2-4-5-6-8-9-10-11-13-19-22-23-25-26
Personnel:
Leo Frese *(Exec VP)*
Debbie Rexing *(VP-Mktg)*
Carl Watson *(Sr Dir-Art & Dir-Creative)*
Brands & Products:
HERITAGE AUCTION GALLERIES
HERITAGE COMICS AUCTIONS
HERITAGE CURRENCY AUCTION OF AMERICA
HERITAGE NUMISMATICAUCTIONS.COM
HERITAGE RARE COIN GALLERIES
HERITAGE WORLD COIN AUCTIONS

HIRE HEROES USA

100 North Point Center E Ste 200
Alpharetta, GA 30022
Tel.: (678) 323-2593
Fax: (678) 248-8398
Toll Free: (866) 915HERO
Web Site: www.hireheroesusa.org
Business Description:
Transition Assistance, Job Search Assistance & Job Placement Services for Veterans & Their Families
N.A.I.C.S.: 923140
Media: 22
Personnel:
Brian Stann *(Pres)*
Nathan Smith *(Exec Dir)*
Sara Trask *(Dir-Corp Rels)*

HOLSTEIN ASSOCIATION USA, INC.

1 Holstein Pl
Brattleboro, VT 05301-3363
Tel.: (802) 254-4551
Fax: (802) 254-8251
Toll Free: (800) 952-5200
E-mail: info@holstein.com
Web Site: www.holsteinusa.com
Approx. Number Employees: 180
Year Founded: 1885
Business Description:
Dairy Cattle Breed Association
S.I.C.: 8699; 8748
N.A.I.C.S.: 813990; 541690
Media: 1-2-4-7-8-9-10-13-20-25
Distr.: Intl.; Natl.
Budget Set: Oct.
Personnel:
Richard Chichester *(Chm)*
Tom Nunes *(Pres)*
John Meyer *(CEO & Exec Sec)*
Barbara Casna *(CFO & Treas)*
Stephen Phillips *(Gen Counsel)*
Dan Meihak *(Exec Dir-Herd Advancement Svcs)*
Gerrardo Quaassdorff *(Exec Dir-Intl Mktg)*
Brands & Products:
DIARYVISIION
EASY ID
HOLSTEIN ASSOCIATION
MULTIMATE
RED BOOK PLUS

THE HUMANE SOCIETY OF THE UNITED STATES

2100 L St NW
Washington, DC 20037
Tel.: (202) 452-1100
Fax: (202) 778-6132
E-mail: membership@hsus.org
Web Site: www.hsus.org
Approx. Rev.: $85,857,349
Approx. Number Employees: 300
Year Founded: 1954
Business Description:
Humane Treatment of Animals Promoter
S.I.C.: 8399
N.A.I.C.S.: 813312
Media: 6-7-8-10-13
Personnel:
Anita W. Coupe *(Chm)*
Wayne Pacelle *(Pres & CEO)*
Thomas Wait *(CFO)*
Roger A. Kindler *(Chief Legal Officer & Gen Counsel)*
Kelly O'Meara *(Dir-Program)*
Brands & Products:
ALL ANIMALS
ANIMAL SHELTERING
THE HUMANE SOCIETY OF THE UNITED STATES
HUMANELINES
KIND NEWS
PAIN & DISTRESS REPORT
PARTY ANIMALS
PETS FOR LIFE
WILD NEIGHBORS
WILDLIFE TRACKS
Advertising Agencies:
Illume Communications
805 E Baltimore St
Baltimore, MD 21202
Tel.: (410) 783-2627
Fax: (410) 783-2650

Market Development Group, Inc.
5151 Wisconsin Ave NW 4th Fl
Washington, DC 20016
Tel.: (202) 298-8030
Fax: (202) 244-4999

IDAHO POTATO COMMISSION

661 S Rivershore Ln Ste 230
Eagle, ID 83616
Mailing Address:
PO Box 1670
Boise, ID 83616
Tel.: (208) 334-2350
Fax: (208) 334-2274
E-mail: ipc@potato.idaho.gov
Web Site: www.idahopotato.com
Approx. Number Employees: 15
Year Founded: 1937
Business Description:
Idaho Potatoes Promoter
S.I.C.: 9641
N.A.I.C.S.: 926140
Advertising Expenditures: $250,000
Media: 2-3-5-6-9-10-18-23-24
Distr.: Natl.
Personnel:
Frank W. Muir *(Pres & CEO)*
Brands & Products:
GROWN IN IDAHO
SPUDDY BUDDY
Advertising Agency:
EvansHardy & Young, Inc.
829 De La Vina St Ste 100
Santa Barbara, CA 93101-3238
Tel.: (805) 963-5841
Fax: (805) 564-4279
(Consumer Target)

IGAS, INC.

842 5th Ave
New Kensington, PA 15068
Tel.: (724) 472-9701
Fax: (267) 501-1931
E-mail: support@igas.com
Web Site: www.igas.com
Approx. Number Employees: 1,000
Year Founded: 1929
Business Description:
Professional Handwriting Analysis & Psychological Testing
S.I.C.: 7389
N.A.I.C.S.: 561990
Media: 2-6-7-9-10-14-24
Distr.: Intl.; Natl.
Budget Set: Monthly
Personnel:
Greg Greco *(Pres)*
Brands & Products:
A STROKE IS A STROKE WHEREVER YOU FIND IT
GRAPHOANALYSIS
GRAPHOANALYTIC
INTERNATIONAL GRAPHOANALYSIS SOCIETY

Key to Media (For complete agency information see *The Advertising Red Books-Agencies* edition):
1. Bus. Publs. 2. Cable T.V. 3. Catalogs & Directories. 4. Co-op Adv. 5. Consumer Mags. 6. D.M. to Bus. Estab.7. D.M. to Consumers 8. Daily Newsp. 9. Exhibits/Trade Shows 10. Foreign 11. Infomercial 12. Internet Adv.13. Multimedia 14. Network Radio 15. Network T.V. 16. Newsp. Distr. Mags. 17. Other 18. Outdoor (Posters, Transit) 19. Point of Purchase20. Premiums, Novelties 21. Product Samples 22. Special Events Mktg. 23. Spot Radio 24. Spot T.V. 25. Weekly Newsp. 26. Yellow Page Adv.

INDEPENDENT INSURANCE AGENTS & BROKERS OF AMERICA, INC.
127 S Peyton St
Alexandria, VA 22314-2803
Tel.: (703) 683-4422
Fax: (703) 683-7556
Toll Free: (800) 221-7917
E-mail: info@iiaba.org
Web Site:
www.independentagent.com
Approx. Number Employees: 70
Year Founded: 1896
Business Description:
Promotion of Independent Insurance Agents In the United States
S.I.C.: 8611; 2721
N.A.I.C.S.: 813910; 511120
Media: 2-6-14-15
Distr.: Natl.
Budget Set: Apr.
Personnel:
Robert Rusboldt *(Pres & CEO)*
Steve Cocke *(CFO)*
Debra Berkins *(Gen Counsel & Exec VP)*
Katie Potthoff Butler *(Asst VP-Comm)*
Elif Wisecup *(Dir-Mktg)*
Brands & Products:
BIG I
INDEPENDENT INSURANCE AGENT
TRUSTED CHOICE

THE INDEPENDENT LUBRICANT MANUFACTURERS ASSOCIATION
(d/b/a ILMA)
400 N Columbus St
Alexandria, VA 22314
Tel.: (703) 684-5574
Fax: (703) 836-8503
E-mail: info@ilma.org
Web Site: www.ilma.org
Approx. Number Employees: 7
Year Founded: 1948
Business Description:
Lubricant Mfr Association
S.I.C.: 8611
N.A.I.C.S.: 813910
Media: 2-13-22
Personnel:
Cathie Novack *(Pres)*
Martha Jolkovski *(Dir-Publ & Adv)*
Brands & Products:
COMPOUNDINGS
FLASHPOINT
ILMA

INDIANA CROP IMPROVEMENT ASSOCIATION, INC.
7700 Stockwell Rd
Lafayette, IN 47909
Tel.: (765) 523-2535
Fax: (765) 523-2536
E-mail: icia@indianacrop.org
Web Site: www.indianacrop.org
Approx. Number Employees: 25
Year Founded: 1900
Business Description:
Field & Laboratory Services For the Seed Industry
S.I.C.: 8734
N.A.I.C.S.: 541380
Media: 1-4-6-8-10
Distr.: Reg.
Budget Set: Feb.
Personnel:
Scott Beck *(Pres)*
Larry Svajgr *(Exec Dir)*
Joe Deford *(Dir-Field Programs)*
Susan Dadacz *(Supvr-Seed Lab Svcs & Records)*

INDUSTRIAL DESIGNERS SOCIETY OF AMERICA
45195 Business Ct Ste 250
Dulles, VA 20166
Tel.: (703) 707-6000
Fax: (703) 787-8501
E-mail: idsa@idsa.org
Web Site: www.idsa.org
Approx. Rev.: $2,414,857
Approx. Number Employees: 15
Year Founded: 1927
Business Description:
Promoter of Industrial Design Industry
S.I.C.: 8621; 8743
N.A.I.C.S.: 813920; 541820
Media: 2-4-7-10
Personnel:
Stephen Wilcox *(Principal & Founder-Design Science)*
Brian Roderman *(Co-Founder & Chief Innovation Officer-In2 Innovation)*
Keith Schacht *(CEO)*
Cooper Woodring *(Pres-Indus Designers Society of America)*
Charles Jones *(Chief Design Officer & Sr VP)*
Michael Laude *(Dir-Design)*
Steve McCallion *(Dir-Creative at ZIBA Design)*
Raymond Riley *(Dir-Design)*
Jim Kaufman *(Dept Chm & Coord-Program)*

INSTITUTE OF ELECTRICAL AND ELECTRONICS ENGINEERS, INC.
IEEE 445 Hose Ln
Piscataway, NJ 08854
Tel.: (212) 419-7900
Fax: (732) 981-9667
E-mail: customer-service@ieee.org
Web Site: www.ieee.org
Approx. Number Employees: 800
Year Founded: 1884
Business Description:
Technical Professional Information Organization
S.I.C.: 8621
N.A.I.C.S.: 813920
Media: 10-13
Personnel:
Anthony Durniak *(Chm & Dir-Adv)*
Judith L. Gorman *(Mng Dir)*
Cecelia Jankowski *(Mng Dir)*
Thomas Siegert *(CFO & Staff Exec-Bus Admin)*
Alexander Pasik *(CIO)*
Patrick D. Mahoney *(CMO)*
Barry C. Johnson *(Pres-IEEE Standards Association)*
Joseph V. Lillie *(Pres-Elect)*
Karen Kenney *(Assoc Mng Dir)*
Susan Tatiner *(Assoc Mng Dir)*
Karen McCabe *(Sr Dir-Mktg)*
Marion Delaney *(Adv Dir-IEEE Spectrum)*
Gerry Grenier *(Dir-Pub Tech)*
Jean Jennings *(Dir-Intl Sls)*
Kenneth Moore *(Dir-IEEE Book & Info Svcs)*
Sharon Nadler *(Dir-Bus Plng & Admin)*
Anita Ricketts *(Dir-Intl Corp Regulatory Compliance)*
Richard D. Schwartz *(Dir-Bus Admin)*
Fran Staples *(Dir-Sls & Customer Accts)*
Peter Tuohy *(Dir-Periodicals Production Svcs)*
James Vick *(Dir-Adv Bus)*
Fran Zappulla *(Dir-Publ Ops)*
Colleen Crary *(Mgr-Membership Program-IEEE SA)*
Josephine Germano *(Admin Mgr-IEEE Pubations)*
Rona Gertz *(Mgr)*
William Hagen *(Mgr-Intellectual Property)*
Barry Holquist *(Mgr-Academic Acct-Central)*
Jennifer McClain *(Mgr-Standard Education Program)*
Michael Petro *(Mgr-Govt Acct)*
Markus Plessel *(Mgr-Mktg)*
Joe Vaitkus *(Mgr-Academic Acct-East)*
Brands & Products:
IEEE
IEEEXPLORE

INSTITUTE OF MANAGEMENT ACCOUNTANTS, INC.
10 Paragon Dr
Montvale, NJ 07645-1718
Tel.: (201) 573-9000
Fax: (201) 474-1600
Toll Free: (800) 638-4427
Telex: 9102509487
E-mail: ima@imanet.org
Web Site: www.imanet.org
Approx. Number Employees: 100
Year Founded: 1919
Business Description:
Professional Association of Accountants
S.I.C.: 8621
N.A.I.C.S.: 813920
Media: 2-8-10-13-16-23-26
Distr.: Natl.
Budget Set: Nov.
Personnel:
Thomas B. Perry *(Chm)*
Jeffrey C. Thomson *(Pres & CEO)*
Kathy Williams *(Asst VP & Editor-in-Chief)*
Alice Schulman *(Adv & Circulation Coord)*
Brands & Products:
ADVANCING THE PROFESSION
CMA
ICMA
IMA
MANAGEMENT ACCOUNTING QUARTERLY
STRATEGIC FINANCE
STRATEGIC TECHNOTES

INSTITUTE OF REAL ESTATE MANAGEMENT
(Affil. of National Association of Realtors)
430 N Michigan Ave
Chicago, IL 60611-4011
Tel.: (312) 329-6000
Fax: (312) 661-0217
Fax: (800) 338-4736
Toll Free: (800) 837-0706
E-mail: custserv@irem.org
Web Site: www.irem.org
Approx. Number Employees: 60
Year Founded: 1933
Business Description:
Not-for-Profit Association of Certified Property Managers (CPMs)
S.I.C.: 8611; 8742
N.A.I.C.S.: 813910; 541611
Export
Advertising Expenditures: $500,000
Media: 2-4-7-9-10-11-13-22
Distr.: Intl.; Natl.
Personnel:
O. Randall Woodbury *(Pres)*
Gail P. Duke *(Sr VP)*
Michael T. Lanning *(Sr VP)*
Regina T. Mullins *(Sr VP)*
Robert B. Toothaker *(Sr VP)*
Randy L. Carnival *(Reg VP)*
Greg P. Cartwright *(Reg VP)*
Cynthia M. Clare *(Reg VP)*
Kevin Grail *(Reg VP)*
Jan R. Grosch *(Reg VP)*
Laurence C. Harmon *(Reg VP)*
Raymond J. Perkins *(Reg VP)*
Karen L. Pharr *(Reg VP)*
Mary W. Wilken *(Reg VP)*
Sharon Peters *(Mgr-Pub Rels)*
Brands & Products:
AMO
ARM
CPM
INCOME/EXPENSE ANALYSIS
IREM
JPM

INSURANCE BROKERS & AGENTS OF THE WEST
(Div. of Independent Insurance Agents & Brokers of America, Inc.)
7041 Koll Ctr Pkwy Ste 290
Pleasanton, CA 94566
Tel.: (925) 426-3300
Fax: (925) 484-6014
Toll Free: (800) 772-8998
E-mail: info@ibawest.com
Web Site: www.ibawest.com
Approx. Sls.: $10,000,000
Approx. Number Employees: 25
Year Founded: 1908
Business Description:
Insurance & Related Services Offered by Independent Insurance Brokers & Agents in California, Alaska, Oregon & Washington
S.I.C.: 6411
N.A.I.C.S.: 524210
Advertising Expenditures: $500,000
Media: 1-2-4-5-7-10-15-20-22-23-24
Distr.: Reg.
Budget Set: Jan.
Personnel:
Timothy Manaka *(Pres)*
Steve Young *(Gen Counsel & Sr VP)*
David Benesh *(VP-Mktg & Comm)*
Diana Hunnicutt *(Dir-Member Svcs)*
Constance Cohrs *(Mgr-Member Svcs)*

INTEGRITY SOLUTIONS
16430 N Scottsdale Rd Ste 125
Phoenix, AZ 85254
Tel.: (602) 253-5700
Fax: (480) 991-2016
Toll Free: (800) 896-9090
Web Site: www.integritysolutions.com
Sales Range: $10-24.9 Million
Approx. Number Employees: 20
Year Founded: 1984

Key to Media (For complete agency information see *The Advertising Red Books-Agencies* edition):
1. Bus. Publs. 2. Cable T.V. 3. Catalogs & Directories. 4. Co-op Adv. 5. Consumer Mags. 6. D.M. to Bus. Estab.7. D.M. to Consumers 8. Daily Newsp. 9. Exhibits/Trade Shows 10. Foreign 11. Infomercial 12. Internet Adv.13. Multimedia 14. Network Radio 15. Network T.V. 16. Newsp. Distr. Mags. 17. Other 18. Outdoor (Posters, Transit) 19. Point of Purchase20. Premiums, Novelties 21. Product Samples 22. Special Events Mktg. 23. Spot Radio 24. Spot T.V. 25. Weekly Newsp. 26. Yellow Page Adv.

Integrity Solutions — (Continued)

Business Description:
Employee Performance Improvement Services
S.I.C.: 8299
N.A.I.C.S.: 611430
Media: 2
Personnel:
Walt Zeglinski *(CEO & Partner)*
Steve Schmidt *(Principal & VP-Client Dev)*
Bill Kowalski *(Sr VP-Client Dev & Consulting Solutions)*
Jim Warner *(VP-Ops & Mktg)*
Dave Larter *(Dir-Client Solutions)*
Julie Ann Wessinger *(Dir-Natl Client Performance Strategies)*
Brands & Products:
BUILDING INTEGRITY INTO EVERY CUSTOMER EXPERIENCE
THE CUSTOMER
INTEGRITY COACHING
INTEGRITY SELLING
INTEGRITY SOLUTIONS
INTEGRITY SYSTEMS INC
MANAGING GOAL ACHIEVEMENT

INTERNATIONAL AIDS VACCINE INITIATIVE
110 William St 27th Fl
New York, NY 10038-3901
Tel.: (212) 847-1111
Fax: (212) 847-1112
E-mail: info@iavi.org
Web Site: www.iavi.org
Approx. Number Employees: 100
Business Description:
AIDS Vaccines Research
S.I.C.: 2836; 8733
N.A.I.C.S.: 325414; 541710
Media: 2-7-8-11
Personnel:
Seth F. Berkley *(Pres & CEO)*
Linn Dorin *(CFO & Sr VP-Fin & Admin)*
Mike Goldrich *(COO & Exec VP)*
Stephen Udem *(Sr VP-Vaccine Res, Devel & Chief Scientific Officer)*
Robert Hecht *(Sr VP-Pub Policy)*
John L. McGoldrick *(Sr VP-External Strategy Devel)*
Michael Caulfield *(Exec Dir-AIDS Vaccine Design & Dev Laboratory)*
Ronaldo Lima *(Sr Dir-IT)*
Megan McBride *(Sr Dir-Clinical Ops)*
Skip Mooney *(Sr Dir-Resource Dev)*
Anjali Nayyar *(Dir-India)*
Edward Pollack *(Dir-Bus Dev)*
Jennifer Lehrman *(Sr Mgr-Fin & Plng)*

INTERNATIONAL AIRLINE PASSENGERS ASSOCIATION
5204 Tennyson Pkwy Ste 500
Plano, TX 75024
Tel.: (972) 404-9980
Fax: (972) 233-5348
Fax: (800) 647-4272
Toll Free: (800) 821-4272
E-mail: iapa@iapausa.com
Web Site: www.iapa.com
Sales Range: $10-24.9 Million
Approx. Number Employees: 40
Year Founded: 1960
Business Description:
Airline Passengers Association
S.I.C.: 8742; 4731
N.A.I.C.S.: 541614; 488510
Advertising Expenditures: $500,000
Media: 2-3-6-7-8-9-10-11
Distr.: Intl.; Natl.
Budget Set: Oct.
Personnel:
Terry Evans *(Pres & CEO)*
Daniel Rutenberg *(VP-Mktg)*
Michael Cintron *(Mgr-CIS)*
Brands & Products:
BAG GUARD
THE FINAL DESTINATION FOR FREQUENT FLYERS
IAPA
IAPA CARD-PROTECTOR
IAPA TRAVEL GUARD

INTERNATIONAL ASSOCIATION OF PLASTICS DISTRIBUTORS
6734 W 121st St
Overland Park, KS 66209
Tel.: (913) 345-1005
Fax: (913) 345-1006
E-mail: iapd@iapd.org
Web Site: www.iapd.org
Sales Range: Less than $1 Million
Approx. Number Employees: 8
Year Founded: 1956
Business Description:
Business Association
S.I.C.: 8611
N.A.I.C.S.: 813910
Media: 4-7-10-13
Personnel:
Susan Avery *(Exec Dir)*
Janet A. Thill *(Dir-Publ)*

INTERNATIONAL DAIRY-DELI-BAKERY-ASSOCIATION
636 Science Dr
Madison, WI 53711-1073
Tel.: (608) 238-7908
Fax: (608) 238-6330
E-mail: iddba@iddba.org
Web Site: www.iddba.org
Approx. Number Employees: 24
Year Founded: 1964
Business Description:
Trade Association
S.I.C.: 8611
N.A.I.C.S.: 813910
Media: 2-7-10
Distr.: Intl.
Personnel:
Carol Christison *(Exec Dir)*
Lucie Arendt *(Dir-Membership, Exhibits & Registration & MIS)*
Mary Kay O'Connor *(Dir-Education)*
Rita Coyne *(Mgr-Meetings)*
Jeremy Johnson *(Coord-Education Sls & Mktg)*
Brands & Products:
IDDBA
SERVSAFE
Advertising Agency:
Beltrame Leffler Advertising
708 Massachusetts Ave
Indianapolis, IN 46204
Tel.: (317) 916-9930
Fax: (317) 916-9935

INTERNATIONAL FABRICARE INSTITUTE
14700 Sweitzer Ln
Laurel, MD 20707
Tel.: (301) 622-1900
Fax: (240) 295-4200
Fax: (240) 295-0685
Toll Free: (800) 638-2627
E-mail: techline@ifi.org
Web Site: www.ifi.org
Approx. Number Employees: 39
Year Founded: 1883
Business Description:
Drycleaners, Launderers & Those Concerned With Quality Clothes Cleaning Care Services, Research & Information
S.I.C.: 8641; 8611
N.A.I.C.S.: 813410; 813910
Media: 2-4-7-10-20
Distr.: Intl.; Natl.
Budget Set: Apr.
Personnel:
David Norford *(Dir-Mktg)*

INTERNATIONAL FELLOWSHIP OF CHRISTIANS & JEWS, INC.
30 N La Salle St Ste 2600
Chicago, IL 60602
Tel.: (312) 641-7200
Fax: (312) 641-7201
Toll Free: (800) 486-8844
E-mail: info@ifcj.org
Web Site: www.ifcj.org
Approx. Rev.: $40,503,403
Approx. Number Employees: 40
Year Founded: 1983
Business Description:
Community Services
S.I.C.: 8661
N.A.I.C.S.: 813110
Media: 3-4-12-13
Personnel:
Yechiel Eckstein *(Founder & Pres)*

INTERNATIONAL SPA ASSOCIATION
2365 Harrodsburg Rd Ste A325
Lexington, KY 40504-4326
Tel.: (859) 226-4326
Fax: (859) 226-4445
Toll Free: (888) 651-4772
E-mail: ispa@ispastaff.com
Web Site: www.experienceispa.com
Approx. Number Employees: 20
Business Description:
Business Association
S.I.C.: 8611
N.A.I.C.S.: 813910
Media: 6-10-13
Personnel:
Jean Kolb *(Chm)*
Lynne Walker McNees *(Pres)*
Angie Jowers *(Dir-Ops)*
Shelby Jones *(Mgr-PR)*
Lisa Mciver *(Mgr-Events)*

INTERNATIONAL WEBMASTERS ASSOCIATION
119 E Union St Ste F
Pasadena, CA 91103
Tel.: (626) 449-3709
Fax: (626) 449-8308
Web Site: www.iwanet.org
Business Description:
Trade Association
S.I.C.: 7374; 8621
N.A.I.C.S.: 518210; 813920
Media: 13

INTERNET SYSTEMS CONSORTIUM, INC.
950 Charter St
Redwood City, CA 94063
Tel.: (650) 423-1300
Fax: (650) 423-1355
E-mail: info@isc.org
Web Site: www.isc.org
E-Mail For Key Personnel:
Sales Director: sales@isc.org
Business Description:
Open Source Software Association
S.I.C.: 8611
N.A.I.C.S.: 813910
Media: 7-13
Personnel:
Paul Vixie *(Pres)*

IOWA BEEF INDUSTRY COUNCIL
2055 Ironwood Ct
Ames, IA 50014
Mailing Address:
PO Box 451
Ames, IA 50010-0451
Tel.: (515) 296-2305
Fax: (515) 296-4873
Web Site: www.iabeef.org
Year Founded: 1970
Business Description:
Iowa Beef Promotion, Education & Research
S.I.C.: 8631; 8611
N.A.I.C.S.: 813930; 813910
Media: 5-18-23
Distr.: Reg.
Budget Set: July
Personnel:
Nancy Degner *(Exec Dir)*
Michelle Baumhover *(Dir-Consumer Mktg)*
Brian Waddingham *(Dir-Industry Rels)*

ISSA
(d/b/a ISSA)
7373 N Lincoln Ave
Lincolnwood, IL 60712-1799
Tel.: (847) 982-0800
Fax: (847) 982-1012
Toll Free: (800) 225-4772
E-mail: info@issa.com
Web Site: www.issa.com
Approx. Number Employees: 25
Year Founded: 1923
Business Description:
Association of Mfr & Distr of the Sanitary Supply Industry
S.I.C.: 8611
N.A.I.C.S.: 813910
Advertising Expenditures: $200,000
Media: 2-6-10-13-22
Distr.: Intl.; Natl.
Personnel:
Scott Jarden *(Pres)*
John Garfinkel *(Exec Dir)*
Leeann Nowling *(Dir-Convention)*
Mark Armitage *(Dir-Exhibition Svcs-Europe)*
Bill Balek *(Dir-Environmental Svcs & Legislative Affairs)*
Dianna Bisswurm *(Dir-Indus Outreach)*
Joan Cooke *(Dir-Ops)*
Anthony Trombetta *(Dir-Sls)*
Lisa Veeck *(Dir-Media Comm & Publ)*
Dan Wagner *(Dir-Facility Svc Legislative Affairs)*
Lori Zarling *(Dir-Tech Svcs)*
Michael McQueen *(Asst Dir-Publications)*
Anita Foler *(Fin Mgr)*
Carl Diwby *(Mgr-Adv Sls)*

Key to Media (For complete agency information see *The Advertising Red Books-Agencies* edition):
1. Bus. Publs. 2. Cable T.V. 3. Catalogs & Directories. 4. Co-op Adv. 5. Consumer Mags. 6. D.M. to Bus. Estab.7. D.M. to Consumers 8. Daily Newsp. 9. Exhibits/Trade Shows 10. Foreign 11. Infomercial 12. Internet Adv.13. Multimedia 14. Network Radio 15. Network T.V. 16. Newsp. Distr. Mags. 17. Other 18. Outdoor (Posters, Transit) 19. Point of Purchase20. Premiums, Novelties 21. Product Samples 22. Special Events Mktg. 23. Spot Radio 24. Spot T.V. 25. Weekly Newsp. 26. Yellow Page Adv.

Donna Tode *(Mgr-Fin)*
Luis Velez *(Mgr-Graphic Project)*
Tracy Weber *(Mgr-Ops)*
Brands & Products:
CIMS
E.Z. TRAINER
ISSA
ISSA/INTERCLEAN
ISSA MEMBER THE EXPERTS ON CLEANING & MAINTENANCE
ISSAALERT
Advertising Agency:
Queue Creative Marketing Group LLC
29 S Lasalle Ste 930
Chicago, IL 60603
Tel.: (312) 564-6000
Fax: (847) 364-0270
Toll Free: (800) 935-1073

JAPAN AMERICA SOCIETY OF GREATER PHILADELPHIA
200 S Broad St Ste 700
Philadelphia, PA 19102
Tel.: (215) 790-3810
Fax: (215) 790-3805
E-mail: jasgp@greaterphilachamber.com
Web Site: www.jasgp.org
Sales Range: $25-49.9 Million
Approx. Number Employees: 3
Business Description:
Non Profit Community Association
S.I.C.: 8611
N.A.I.C.S.: 813910
Media: 11-13
Personnel:
Kazumi Teune *(Exec Dir)*

JETRO, NEW YORK
(Branch of Japan External Trade Organization)
1221 Ave of the Americas 42nd Fl
New York, NY 10020
Tel.: (212) 997-0400
Fax: (212) 997-0464
Web Site: www.jetro.org/page/offices/Itemid/224/state/NY
Approx. Number Employees: 50
Year Founded: 1958
Business Description:
Japan External Trade Promoter
S.I.C.: 9611
N.A.I.C.S.: 926110
Media: 2-7-10-13
Distr.: Natl.
Personnel:
Masaki Fujihara *(Dir-Bus Dev)*

JUVENILE DIABETES RESEARCH FOUNDATION INTERNATIONAL
26 Broadway
New York, NY 10004
Tel.: (212) 785-9500
Fax: (212) 785-9595
Toll Free: (800) 533-CURE
E-mail: info@jdrf.org
Web Site: www.jdrf.org
Approx. Rev.: $11,995,000
Approx. Number Employees: 50
Year Founded: 1970
Business Description:
Non-profit, Health Agency that Funds Research to Find a Cure for Diabetes
S.I.C.: 8399; 8733
N.A.I.C.S.: 813319; 541720
Media: 1-3-4-6-10-13-15-25

Personnel:
C. John Brady *(Chm)*
Edward Sebald *(CFO & Asst Treas)*
Robert A. Goldstein *(Sr VP-Scientific Affairs)*
Benita Shobe *(Sr VP-Field Ops)*
William Ahearn *(VP-Strategic Commun)*
Joana Casas *(Dir-Natl Media Rels)*
Laura Whitton *(Natl Mgr-Govt Relations)*
Advertising Agency:
Cone
(A Member of Omnicom Group)
855 Boylston St
Boston, MA 02116
Tel.: (617) 227-2111
Fax: (617) 523-3955

KANSAS CITY BOARD OF TRADE
4800 Main St Ste 303
Kansas City, MO 64112
Tel.: (816) 753-7500
Fax: (816) 753-3944
Toll Free: (800) 821-5228
E-mail: kcbt@kcbt.com
Web Site: www.kcbt.com
Approx. Rev.: $22,715,000
Approx. Number Employees: 20
Year Founded: 1876
Business Description:
Commodity Exchange Services
S.I.C.: 6231; 6289
N.A.I.C.S.: 523210; 523999
Media: 7-13-20
Distr.: Natl.
Personnel:
Jeffrey Borchardt *(Pres & CEO)*
Shelia A. Summers *(VP-Mktg)*
Deborah Bollman *(Asst VP-Mktg)*
Jeffery Hughes *(Asst VP-Compliance)*

LAS VEGAS INSTITUTE FOR ADVANCED DENTAL STUDIES
9501 Hillwood Dr
Las Vegas, NV 89134
Tel.: (702) 341-7978
Toll Free: (866) LVI-DOCS
E-mail: info@lvilive.com
Web Site: www.lvidocs.com
Approx. Number Employees: 100
Year Founded: 1995
Business Description:
Dental Services
S.I.C.: 8299; 8021
N.A.I.C.S.: 611699; 621210
Media: 6-15
Personnel:
William Dickerson *(Owner)*

LENOX HILL NEIGHBORHOOD HOUSE
331 E 70th St
New York, NY 10021
Tel.: (212) 744-5022
Fax: (212) 744-5150
E-mail: administration@lenoxhill.org
Web Site: www.lenoxhill.org
Approx. Rev.: $13,270,931
Approx. Number Employees: 200
Year Founded: 1894
Business Description:
Social Services & Educational Organization
S.I.C.: 8699; 8299; 8351
N.A.I.C.S.: 813990; 611710; 624410
Media: 6

Personnel:
Diana Ronan Quasha *(Chm)*
Thomas J. Edelman *(Pres)*
Warren Scharf *(Exec Dir)*

LIFEBEAT, INC.
630 9th Ave Ste 1010
New York, NY 10036-3708
Tel.: (212) 459-2590
Fax: (212) 459-2892
Toll Free: (800) AIDS-411
E-mail: info@lifebeat.org
Web Site: www.lifebeat.org
Approx. Number Employees: 5
Business Description:
Music Industry Foundation Supporting AIDS Education
S.I.C.: 8399
N.A.I.C.S.: 813319
Media: 6-22
Personnel:
Erica Banks *(Mgr-Hearts & Voices)*
Kizzy Kay-Graham *(Mgr-Outreach & Volunteer Programs)*
Brands & Products:
LIFEBEAT
THE MUSIC INDUSTRY FIGHTS AIDS

LONG GROVE BUSINESS & COMMUNITY PARTNERS
307 Old McHenry Rd
Long Grove, IL 60047
Tel.: (847) 634-0888
Web Site: www.longgroveonline.com
Business Description:
Management of Long Grove, Il's Historic District
S.I.C.: 8412
N.A.I.C.S.: 712120
Media: 3-13-17-24
Personnel:
Peg Ball *(Pres)*
John Maguire *(Dir-Community Dev)*

MAGAZINE PUBLISHERS OF AMERICA
810 7th Ave 24th Fl
New York, NY 10019
Tel.: (212) 872-3700
Fax: (212) 888-4217
Toll Free: (888) 567-3228
E-mail: mpa@magazine.org
Web Site: www.magazine.org
E-Mail For Key Personnel:
Public Relations: pr@magazine.org
Approx. Number Employees: 45
Year Founded: 1919
Business Description:
Consumer Magazine Publisher's Association
S.I.C.: 8611
N.A.I.C.S.: 813910
Advertising Expenditures: $1,500,000
Media: 2-7-10-20
Distr.: Natl.
Budget Set: Oct.
Personnel:
Michael A. Clinton *(Chm)*
Efrem Zimbalist, III *(Vice Chm-MPA, Pres & CEO-Active Interest Media)*
Nina Link *(Pres & CEO)*
Richard O'Rorke *(CFO)*
Andrew Jung *(CMO & Exec VP)*
James Cregan *(Exec VP-Govt Affairs)*
Ken Godshall *(Exec VP)*
Howard Polskin *(Exec VP-Comm, Platforms & Events)*

Rita Cohen *(Sr VP-Govt Affairs)*
Wayne Eadie *(Sr VP-Res)*
Myra Barcan *(VP-Sys & Tech)*
Barry McGrath *(Controller-Fin)*
Cristina Dinozo *(Dir-Comm & Platforms)*
Suzette Kraemer *(Dir-IMAG & Consumer Mktg)*
Miguel Baez *(Mgr-Printing)*
Ray Santana *(Mgr-Network & Tech Support)*

MAINE POTATO BOARD
744 Main St Ste 1
Presque Isle, ME 04769
Tel.: (207) 769-5061
Fax: (207) 764-4148
Toll Free: (800) 553-5516
E-mail: mainepotatoes@mainepotatoes.com
Web Site: www.mainepotatoes.com
E-Mail For Key Personnel:
President: Todd@mainepotatoes.com
Marketing Director: flannery@mainepotatoes.com
Sales Range: Less than $1 Million
Approx. Number Employees: 10
Year Founded: 1986
Business Description:
Promoter & Advertiser Maine Potatoes
S.I.C.: 8611
N.A.I.C.S.: 813910
Media: 2-9-23-24
Distr.: Direct to Consumer; Reg.
Budget Set: Aug.
Personnel:
Brandon Roope *(Pres)*
Donald E. Flannery *(Exec Dir)*
Timothy P. Hobbs *(Dir-Dev & Grower Rels)*

MAKE-A-WISH FOUNDATION OF GREATER LOS ANGELES
1875 Century Park E Ste 950
Los Angeles, CA 90067-2515
Tel.: (310) 788-9474
Fax: (310) 785-9474
Toll Free: (800) 322-9474
E-mail: info@wishla.org
Web Site: www.wishla.org
E-Mail For Key Personnel:
President: kseely@wishla.org
Approx. Rev.: $2,977,325
Approx. Number Employees: 20
Year Founded: 1983
Business Description:
Non-Profit Organization That Grants Wishes to Children with Life Threatening Illnesses
S.I.C.: 8641
N.A.I.C.S.: 813410
Media: 3-4-6-8-9-13-18-22-26
Brands & Products:
MAKE-A-WISH
OKTOBERFEST
Advertising Agencies:
Celtic, Inc.
330 S Executive Dr Ste 206
Brookfield, WI 53005-4215
Tel.: (262) 789-7630
Fax: (262) 789-9454

One to One Interactive, LLC
(d/b/a OTOi)
465 Medford St Ste 300
Charlestown, MA 02129
Tel.: (617) 425-7300

Key to Media (For complete agency information see *The Advertising Red Books-Agencies* edition):
1. Bus. Publs. 2. Cable T.V. 3. Catalogs & Directories. 4. Co-op Adv. 5. Consumer Mags. 6. D.M. to Bus. Estab.7. D.M. to Consumers
8. Daily Newsp. 9. Exhibits/Trade Shows 10. Foreign 11. Infomercial 12. Internet Adv.13. Multimedia 14. Network Radio
15. Network T.V. 16. Newsp. Distr. Mags. 17. Other 18. Outdoor (Posters, Transit) 19. Point of Purchase20. Premiums, Novelties
21. Product Samples 22. Special Events Mktg. 23. Spot Radio 24. Spot T.V. 25. Weekly Newsp. 26. Yellow Page Adv.

Make-A-Wish Foundation of Greater Los Angeles — (Continued)

Fax: (617) 242-0632

The Pollack PR Marketing Group
1901 Ave of the Stars Ste 1040
Los Angeles, CA 90067
Tel.: (310) 556-4443
Fax: (310) 286-2350
A Season of Wishes 2008

MANAGEMENT & TRAINING CORPORATION
500 N Market Pl Dr
Centerville, UT 84014-1708
Tel.: (801) 693-2600
Fax: (801) 693-2900
Toll Free: (800) 574-4682
E-mail: mtcwebmaster@mtctrains.com
Web Site: www.mtctrains.com
E-Mail For Key Personnel:
Marketing Director: mmurphy@mtctrains.com
Public Relations: cstuart@mtctrains.com
Approx. Sls.: $449,300,000
Approx. Number Employees: 7,000
Year Founded: 1981
Business Description:
Job Training & Management Services for Correctional Facilities
S.I.C.: 8299; 8331
N.A.I.C.S.: 611710; 624310
Media: 7-13
Personnel:
Scott Marquardt *(Pres)*
Lyle J. Parry *(CFO, Treas, Sec & Sr VP)*
Mike Murphy *(VP-Corrections Mrkg)*
Curtis Price, Jr. *(VP-Govt & Community Rels)*
Carl Stuart *(Corp Commun Dir)*

MAPLE FLOORING MANUFACTURERS ASSOCIATION
60 Revere Dr Ste 500
Northbrook, IL 60062
Tel.: (847) 480-9138
Fax: (847) 480-9282
E-mail: mfma@maplefloor.org
Web Site: www.maplefloor.org
Approx. Premiums: $500,000
Year Founded: 1897
Business Description:
International, Not-For-Profit Trade Organization
S.I.C.: 8611
N.A.I.C.S.: 813910
Media: 2-4-10-13
Distr.: Natl.
Budget Set: Nov.
Personnel:
Heather Gagnon *(Dir-Mktg Commun)*

MARCH OF DIMES BIRTH DEFECTS FOUNDATION
1275 Mamaroneck Ave
White Plains, NY 10605
Tel.: (914) 428-7100
Fax: (914) 428-8203
Toll Free: (888) 663-4637
E-mail: askus@marchofdimes.com
Web Site: www.marchofdimes.com
Approx. Rev.: $210,096,000
Approx. Number Employees: 1,400
Year Founded: 1938
Business Description:
Non-Profit Agency for Preventing Birth Defects & Reducing Infant Mortality
S.I.C.: 8399
N.A.I.C.S.: 813319
Media: 5-6-22-23-24
Personnel:
Richard E. Mulligan *(CFO, Treas & Sr VP-Fin-Admin)*
Jane Massey *(COO & Exec VP)*
Patricia Goldman *(CMO & VP)*
Lisa Bellsey *(Gen Counsel)*
Scott Berns *(Sr VP)*
Michael Katz *(Sr VP-Res)*
Don Schieman *(Dir-Kentucky)*
Todd Dezen *(Assoc Dir-Media Rels)*
Brands & Products:
MAMA
MARCH OF DIMES
PREGNANCY & NEWBORN HEALTH EDUCATION CENTER
WALKAMERICA
Advertising Agencies:
Barkley Public Relations
1740 Main St
Kansas City, MO 64108
Tel.: (816) 842-1500

BKV Inc.
10561 Barkley St Ste 200
Overland Park, KS 66212
Tel.: (913) 648-8333
Fax: (913) 648-5024

Leverage Marketing Group
(A GOODWICK/LIAZON Company)
117-119 S Main St
Newtown, CT 06470-2380
Tel.: (203) 270-6699
Fax: (203) 270-3491

MAX Advertising
3190 NE Expy Ste 120
Atlanta, GA 30341
Tel.: (770) 454-7100
Fax: (770) 454-7100

MARTS & LUNDY, INC.
1200 Wall St W Fl 5A
Lyndhurst, NJ 07071
Tel.: (201) 460-1660
Fax: (201) 460-0680
E-mail: info@martsandlundy.com
Web Site: www.martsandlundy.com
Approx. Rev.: $2,900,000
Approx. Number Employees: 45
Year Founded: 1960
Business Description:
Management Consulting Services
S.I.C.: 8742
N.A.I.C.S.: 541611
Personnel:
Bruce McClintock *(Chm)*
Donald M. Fellows *(Pres & CEO)*
Robert Miskura *(CFO & VP)*
Shirley Anne Peppers *(Exec Dir)*
John Wilson *(Exec Dir)*
Katherine McStowe *(Sr Fin Assoc, Asst Treas & Asst Sec)*
Advertising Agency:
Bergman Group
4880 Sadler Rd Ste 220
Glen Allen, VA 23060
Tel.: (804) 225-0600
Fax: (804) 225-0900

MEDICAL EXPRESS INC.
(Sub. of AMN Healthcare Services, Inc.)
2601 Blake St Ste 400
Denver, CO 80205
Tel.: (303) 524-6150
Fax: (800) 743-7257
Toll Free: (800) 544-7255
E-mail: info@medicalexpress.com
Web Site: www.medicalexpress.com
Sales Range: $25-49.9 Million
Approx. Number Employees: 100
Business Description:
Temporary Help Services for Healthcare Industry
S.I.C.: 7389
N.A.I.C.S.: 561499
Media: 2-8-13

MEETING PROFESSIONALS INTERNATIONAL (MPI)
3030 LBJ Freeway Ste 1700
Dallas, TX 75234-2759
Tel.: (972) 702-3000
Fax: (972) 702-3070
E-mail: feedback@mpiweb.org
Web Site: www.mpiweb.org
Approx. Number Employees: 81
Year Founded: 1972
Business Description:
Membership Organization Addressing the Meetings Profession
S.I.C.: 8742
N.A.I.C.S.: 541611
Media: 8-11
Personnel:
Greg Lohrentz *(CFO & COO)*
Jeff Busch *(VP-Commun)*
Sandra Riggins *(Dir-Governance)*
Advertising Agency:
McLaughlin, DelVecchio & Casey, Inc.
1 Church St
New Haven, CT 06510-3330
Tel.: (203) 624-4151
Fax: (203) 401-6134

MEETING PROFESSIONALS INTERNATIONAL (MPI)
(Sub. of Meeting Professionals International (MPI))
6519B Mississauga Rd
Mississauga, ON Canada
Tel.: (905) 286-4807
Fax: (905) 567-7191
Web Site: www.mpiweb.org
Business Description:
Professional Meeting Planners
S.I.C.: 8742
N.A.I.C.S.: 541611
Media: 8-11
Advertising Agency:
McLaughlin, DelVecchio & Casey, Inc.
1 Church St
New Haven, CT 06510-3330
Tel.: (203) 624-4151
Fax: (203) 401-6134

MERCHANTS ASSOCIATION OF FLORIDA, INC.
PO Box 972
Tampa, FL 33601-0972
Tel.: (813) 273-7766
E-mail: bob.krone@merchantsflorida.com
Web Site: www.merchantsflorida.com
Sales Range: $10-24.9 Million
Approx. Number Employees: 100
Year Founded: 1916
Business Description:
Business Assistance Services
S.I.C.: 7389
N.A.I.C.S.: 561499
Media: 7-10
Personnel:
T. Curtis Flynn *(Sr VP-Info Svcs Div)*
Thomas Feaster *(Mgr)*

METROPOLITAN MINISTRIES INC.
2002 N Florida Ave
Tampa, FL 33602-2204
Tel.: (813) 209-1000
Fax: (813) 209-1048
Web Site: www.metromin.org
Sales Range: $1-9.9 Million
Approx. Number Employees: 100
Business Description:
Religious Services
S.I.C.: 8322; 8661
N.A.I.C.S.: 624190; 813110
Media: 8-13-22
Personnel:
Tim Marks *(Pres & COO)*
Morris E. Hintzman *(CEO)*
Phil Signore *(CFO)*

MICHAEL J. FOX FOUNDATION FOR PARKINSON'S RESEARCH
Church St Sta PO Box 780
New York, NY 10008
Mailing Address:
PO Box 4777
New York, NY 10008
Tel.: (212) 509-0995
Toll Free: (800) 708-7644
Web Site: www.michaeljfox.org
Year Founded: 2000
Business Description:
Foundation for Parkinson's Research
S.I.C.: 8733
N.A.I.C.S.: 541710
Media: 6-24
Personnel:
Deborah Brooks *(Co-Founder)*
Michael J. Fox *(Founder)*
Katie Hood *(CEO)*
Advertising Agency:
Deutsch, Inc.
(A Lowe & Partners Company)
111 8th Ave 14th Fl
New York, NY 10011-5201
Tel.: (212) 981-7600
Fax: (212) 981-7525

MICHIGAN APPLE COMMITTEE
13750 S Sedona Pkwy
Lansing, MI 48906
Tel.: (517) 669-8353
Fax: (517) 669-9506
Toll Free: (800) 456-2753
E-mail: staff@michiganapples.com
Web Site: www.michiganapples.com
Approx. Sls.: $2,000,000
Approx. Number Employees: 8
Year Founded: 1939
Business Description:
Non-Profit Michigan Apples Promoter
S.I.C.: 8611
N.A.I.C.S.: 813910
Media: 2-7-9-10-18-19-20-23
Distr.: Natl.
Budget Set: Aug.

Key to Media (For complete agency information see *The Advertising Red Books-Agencies* edition):
1. Bus. Publs. 2. Cable T.V. 3. Catalogs & Directories. 4. Co-op Adv. 5. Consumer Mags. 6. D.M. to Bus. Estab.7. D.M. to Consumers
8. Daily Newsp. 9. Exhibits/Trade Shows 10. Foreign 11. Infomercial 12. Internet Adv.13. Multimedia 14. Network Radio
15. Network T.V. 16. Newsp. Distr. Mags. 17. Other 18. Outdoor (Posters, Transit) 19. Point of Purchase20. Premiums, Novelties
21. Product Samples 22. Special Events Mktg. 23. Spot Radio 24. Spot T.V. 25. Weekly Newsp. 26. Yellow Page Adv.

Personnel:
Diane Smith *(Dir-Fin & Admin)*
Ken Meyer *(Mgr-Mdsg)*
Brands & Products:
FLAVORBEST
GREAT LAKES, GREAT FLAVORS.
MICHIGAN APPLE

MICHIGAN ASSOCIATION OF INSURANCE AGENTS
1141 Centennial Way
Lansing, MI 48917
Tel.: (517) 323-9473
Fax: (517) 323-1629
E-mail: info@michagent.org
Web Site: www.michagent.org
Approx. Number Employees: 24
Business Description:
Independent Insurance Agents Association
S.I.C.: 8611
N.A.I.C.S.: 813910
Media: 2-10-22
Personnel:
Robert Pierce *(CEO)*
Jennifer Burnett *(Mgr-Comm, Mktg & Adv)*
Advertising Agency:
Queue Creative
410 S Cedar St Ste F
Lansing, MI 48912
Tel.: (517) 374-6600
Fax: (517) 374-4215

MICHIGAN BLUEBERRY GROWERS ASSOCIATION
04726 County Rd 215
Grand Junction, MI 49056-9218
Tel.: (269) 434-6791
Fax: (269) 434-6997
E-mail: gretchen@blueberries.com
Web Site: www.blueberries.com
E-Mail For Key Personnel:
Public Relations: mdepta@blueberries.com
Approx. Sls.: $30,000,000
Approx. Number Employees: 40
Year Founded: 1934
Business Description:
Fresh & Frozen Blueberries Growers & Marketers
S.I.C.: 5142; 5148
N.A.I.C.S.: 424420; 424480
Import Export
Advertising Expenditures: $800,000
Media: 2-7-8-10-19-20-21
Distr.: Natl.
Budget Set: Feb.
Personnel:
Frank Bragg *(CEO)*
Lorrie Ford Merker *(Asst Treas)*
Brands & Products:
GROWING SUCCESS THROUGHOUT THE WORLD

MICHIGAN CROP IMPROVEMENT ASSOCIATION
2901 Jolly Rd
Okemos, MI 48864-3552
Tel.: (517) 332-3546
Fax: (517) 332-9301
E-mail: info@michcrop.com
Web Site: www.michcrop.com
Sales Range: Less than $1 Million
Approx. Number Employees: 6
Year Founded: 1904
Business Description:
Certified Field Seeds, Seed Sampling, Inspection & Testing Services
S.I.C.: 8734
N.A.I.C.S.: 541380
Import Export
Media: 6-25
Distr.: Reg.
Budget Set: Jan.
Brands & Products:
MICHIGAN CERTIFIED SEED
MICHIGAN CROP

MICHIGAN MILK PRODUCERS ASSOCIATION
41310 Bridge St
Novi, MI 48376-3002
Tel.: (248) 474-6672
Fax: (248) 474-0924
E-mail: info@mimilk.com
Web Site: www.mimilk.com
Sales Range: $500-549.9 Million
Approx. Number Employees: 200
Year Founded: 1916
Business Description:
Dairy Cooperative; Milk Processing & Marketing
S.I.C.: 5143; 2023
N.A.I.C.S.: 424430; 311514
Media: 2-10-21
Distr.: Reg.
Budget Set: Oct.
Personnel:
Kenneth Nobis *(Pres)*
Sheila Burkhardt *(Dir-Member Rels & Pub Affairs)*

MINNESOTA GOLF ASSOCIATION
6550 York Ave S Ste 211
Edina, MN 55435-2333
Tel.: (952) 927-4643
Fax: (952) 927-9642
E-mail: info@mngolf.org
Web Site: www.mngolf.org
E-Mail For Key Personnel:
Public Relations: Joel@mngolf.org
Year Founded: 1901
Business Description:
Golf Course, Resort & Tourism Services
S.I.C.: 7997
N.A.I.C.S.: 713910
Media: 6-8-10-22-24
Personnel:
Joel Comstock *(Dir-Reg Affairs)*
Brands & Products:
EXPLORE MINNESOTA GOLF

THE MINNESOTA MINORITY SUPPLIER DEVELOPMENT COUNCIL
111 3rd Ave S Ste 240
Minneapolis, MN 55401
Tel.: (612) 465-8881
Fax: (612) 465-8887
E-mail: info@mmsdc.org
Web Site: www.mmsdc.org
Approx. Number Employees: 3
Business Description:
Minority Business Association
S.I.C.: 8611
N.A.I.C.S.: 813910
Advertising Agency:
Affinity Marketing
7505 Metro Blvd Ste 340
Edina, MN 55439
Tel.: (952) 746-5208
Fax: (952) 746-4161

MORRIS CERULLO WORLD EVANGELISM
(d/b/a Morris Cerullo Ministries)
3545 Aero Ct
San Diego, CA 92123-1710
Tel.: (858) 277-2200
Fax: (858) 277-5111
E-mail: morriscerullo@mcwe.com
Web Site: www.mcwe.com
E-Mail For Key Personnel:
President: morriscerullo@mcwe.com
Approx. Number Employees: 100
Business Description:
Religious Services
S.I.C.: 8661; 2741
N.A.I.C.S.: 813110; 511199
Export
Advertising Expenditures: $1,500,000
Media: 1-2-3-8-10-11-12-13-20-22-23-24
Distr.: Intl.
Budget Set: Nov.
Personnel:
Morris Cerullo *(Pres)*

MOTHERS AGAINST DRUNK DRIVING (MADD)
511 E John Carpenter Fwy Ste 700
Irving, TX 75062
Tel.: (214) 744-6233
Fax: (972) 869-2206
Fax: (972) 869-2207
Toll Free: (800) GETMADD
Web Site: www.madd.org
Approx. Rev.: $46,707,000
Approx. Number Employees: 340
Year Founded: 1980
Business Description:
Non-Profit Organization
S.I.C.: 8699
N.A.I.C.S.: 813990
Media: 2-3-6-9-14-15-17-18-23-24-25
Distr.: Natl.; Reg.
Budget Set: July
Personnel:
Laura Dean-Mooney *(Pres)*
Charles Hurley *(CEO)*
Brands & Products:
DRIVE FOR LIFE
DRIVEN
I'M A MADD DAD
INSIDE TRACK
IT'S A MADD HOUSE HERE
KEEP IT A SAFE SUMMER
MADD
MADD DASH
MADDVOCATE
NATIONAL YOUTH SUMMIT TO PREVENT UNDERAGE DRINKING
ON TRACK
PROMISE TO KEEP IT SAFE
RATING THE STATES
RIGHT TRACK
TAKE THE LEAD
THINK
TIE ONE ON FOR SAFETY
UMADD
VICTIM IMPACT PANEL
WALK LIKE MADD
YOUTH IN ACTION
Advertising Agencies:
Aviatech, LLC
4350 Executive Dr Ste 200
San Diego, CA 92121
Tel.: (858) 777-5000
Fax: (858) 777-5050

Clarity Coverdale Fury Advertising, Inc.
120 S 6th St Ste 1300
Minneapolis, MN 55402-1810
Tel.: (612) 339-3902
Fax: (612) 359-4399

Hospodka & White
350 N St Paul Ste 2895
Dallas, TX 75201
Tel.: (972) 421-0780
Fax: (972) 421-0783

MOTION PICTURE & TELEVISION FUND INC.
23388 Mulholland Dr
Woodland Hills, CA 91364
Tel.: (818) 876-1888
Fax: (818) 876-1079
Toll Free: (800) 876-8320
Web Site: www.mptvfund.org
Approx. Number Employees: 825
Year Founded: 1921
Business Description:
Non-profit Organization Providing Health Care & Operating Hospitals for Entertainment Industry
S.I.C.: 8062; 8059
N.A.I.C.S.: 622110; 623311
Import Export
Media: 2-22
Personnel:
Bob Pisano *(Chm)*
Bob Beitcher *(Pres & CEO)*
Frank Guererra *(CFO)*

THE NATIONAL ASSOCIATION FOR FEMALE EXECUTIVES
(Div. of Working Mother Media, Inc.)
2 PKWY 10th Fl
New York, NY 10016
Tel.: (212) 351-6451
Tel.: (212) 351-6453
Fax: (212) 219-7801
Toll Free: (800) 927-6233
Sales Range: $10-24.9 Million
Approx. Number Employees: 19
Year Founded: 1972
Business Description:
Female Executives Association & Magazine Publisher
S.I.C.: 8611
N.A.I.C.S.: 813910
Import Export
Advertising Expenditures: $2,000,000
Media: 4-5-8-10-19
Distr.: Natl.
Budget Set: Feb.
Personnel:
Betty Spence *(Pres)*
Carol Evans *(CEO)*
Paula Damiano *(Editor-NAFE E-Newsletter, Mgr-Membership Dev & Comm)*
Barbara Bella *(Acct Dir)*
Christy Ezelle *(Acct Dir)*
Valerie Elkin *(Dir-Sponsorship Sls)*
Luci Knight *(Dir-Conferences)*
Carmen Nieves *(Sls Mgr-Conferences)*
Jacqueline La Brocca *(Mgr-Conferences)*
Brands & Products:
NAFE

Key to Media (For complete agency information see *The Advertising Red Books-Agencies* edition):
1. Bus. Publs. 2. Cable T.V. 3. Catalogs & Directories. 4. Co-op Adv. 5. Consumer Mags. 6. D.M. to Bus. Estab.7. D.M. to Consumers 8. Daily Newsp. 9. Exhibits/Trade Shows 10. Foreign 11. Infomercial 12. Internet Adv.13. Multimedia 14. Network Radio 15. Network T.V. 16. Newsp. Distr. Mags. 17. Other 18. Outdoor (Posters, Transit) 19. Point of Purchase20. Premiums, Novelties 21. Product Samples 22. Special Events Mktg. 23. Spot Radio 24. Spot T.V. 25. Weekly Newsp. 26. Yellow Page Adv.

The National Association for Female Executives — (Continued)

Advertising Agency:
The Rosen Group
30 W 26th St Third Fl
New York, NY 10010-2011
Tel.: (212) 255-8455
Fax: (212) 255-8456

THE NATIONAL ASSOCIATION FOR PET CONTAINER RESOURCES
(d/b/a NAPCOR)
PO Box 1327
Sonoma, CA 95476
Tel.: (707) 996-4207
Fax: (707) 935-1998
E-mail: information@napcor.com
Web Site: www.napcor.com
Approx. Number Employees: 3
Year Founded: 1987
Business Description:
Trade Association for the Polyethylene Terephthalate (PET) Plastic Industry
S.I.C.: 8748
N.A.I.C.S.: 541690
Media: 4-10-13-26
Personnel:
Dennis M. Sabourin *(Exec Dir)*
Kate Eagles *(Dir-Comm)*
Mike Schedler *(Dir-Tech)*

NATIONAL ASSOCIATION FOR VARIABLE ANNUITIES
(d/b/a NAVA)
11710 Plaza America Dr Ste 100
Reston, VA 20190-4737
Tel.: (703) 707-8830
Fax: (703) 707-8831
E-mail: nava@navanet.org
Web Site: www.navanet.org
Sales Range: $50-74.9 Million
Approx. Number Employees: 12
Business Description:
Annuity & Variable Life Products Promoter; Educational & Informational Resources
S.I.C.: 8611
N.A.I.C.S.: 813910
Media: 2-10
Personnel:
Jane Mancini *(Vice Chm)*
Mark J. Mackey *(Pres & CEO)*
Farrell J. Dolan *(Exec VP)*
John C. Walters *(Exec VP-Product)*
David J. Robertson *(Sr VP)*
Robert Nolan *(VP-Commun)*
Chris Paulitz *(VP-Comm & Pub Affairs)*
Deborah Tucker *(Coord-Media Rels)*
Brands & Products:
NATIONAL RETIREMENT PLANNING WEEK
NAVA
NRPC NATIONAL RETIREMENT PLANNING COALITION
RETIRE ON YOUR TERMS
RETIREMENT READINESS INDEX
Advertising Agency:
Walt & Company
2105 S Bascom Ave Ste 240
Campbell, CA 95008
Tel.: (408) 369-7200
Fax: (408) 369-7201
Public Relations

NATIONAL ASSOCIATION OF CONVENIENCE STORES
(d/b/a NACS)
1600 Duke St
Alexandria, VA 22314
Tel.: (703) 684-3600
Toll Free: (800) 966-6227
Web Site: www.nacsonline.com
Business Description:
Trade Association for the Convenience & Petroleum Retailing Industry
S.I.C.: 8611
N.A.I.C.S.: 813910
Media: 6-13-22
Personnel:
Henry O'Armour *(Pres & CEO)*

NATIONAL ASSOCIATION OF ORTHOPAEDIC NURSES
401 N Michigan Ave Ste 2200
Chicago, IL 60611
Tel.: (312) 644-6610
Fax: (312) 527-6658
Toll Free: (800) 289-NAON
E-mail: naon@smithbucklin.com
Web Site: www.orthonurse.org
Approx. Number Employees: 10
Year Founded: 1980
Business Description:
Education & Research Related to Nursing
S.I.C.: 8611; 2721
N.A.I.C.S.: 813910; 511120
Media: 2-10-13
Personnel:
Julie Twiss *(Pres)*
Mary Jo Satusky *(Pres-Elect)*
Mary Faut Rodts *(Editor-in-Chief)*
Kaye Englebrecht *(Exec Dir)*
Christina Tomaso *(Mgr-Ops)*

NATIONAL AUDUBON SOCIETY
700 Broadway
New York, NY 10003-9536
Tel.: (212) 979-3000
Fax: (212) 979-3188
E-mail: education@audubon.org
Web Site: www.audubon.org
E-Mail For Key Personnel:
President: jflicker@audubon.org
Public Relations: jbianchi@audubon.org
Sales Estimate: $80-99 Million
Approx. Number Employees: 400
Business Description:
Conservation & Education Society
S.I.C.: 8641; 2721
N.A.I.C.S.: 813410; 511120
Advertising Expenditures: $3,000,000
Media: 2-4-8-10-18-23-24-25
Distr.: Natl.
Budget Set: June
Personnel:
Donal O'Brien *(Chm)*
David Yarnold *(Pres & CEO)*
Bob Perciasepe *(COO)*
Brands & Products:
AUDUBON
AUDUBON ADVISORY

NATIONAL BRAIN TUMOR SOCIETY
22 Battery St Ste 612
San Francisco, CA 94111-5520
Tel.: (415) 834-9970
Fax: (415) 834-9980
Toll Free: (800) 934-CURE
E-mail: info@braintumor.org
Web Site: www.braintumor.org
Sales Range: $10-24.9 Million
Approx. Number Employees: 50
Business Description:
Brain Tumor Health Organization
S.I.C.: 8399
N.A.I.C.S.: 813212; 813219
Media: 7-8-13-22
Personnel:
Jeffrey Kolodin *(Chm)*
Allison Jones Thomson *(Chm)*
Cord Schlobohm *(Vice Chm)*

NATIONAL CATTLEMEN'S BEEF ASSOCIATION
9110 E Nichols Ave Ste 300
Centennial, CO 80112-3450
Tel.: (303) 694-0305
Fax: (303) 694-2851
E-mail: cattle@beef.org
Web Site: www.beefusa.org
Approx. Number Employees: 120
Year Founded: 1922
Business Description:
Non-Profit, Commodity Promotion, Consumer Education, Research
S.I.C.: 8611
N.A.I.C.S.: 813910
Advertising Expenditures: $21,000,000
Media: 2-3-6-9-15-23
Distr.: Direct to Consumer; Natl.
Budget Set: Feb.
Personnel:
Forrest Roberts *(CEO)*
Kim Essex *(Sr VP-Consumer Mktg)*
Rick McCarty *(VP-Issue Analysis & Strategy)*
Mark Thomas *(VP-Consumer Mktg)*
Jim Henger *(Exec Dir-Retail Mktg)*
Jan Lyons *(Dir-KS-Manhattan)*
Advertising Agencies:
Daniel J. Edelman, Inc.
(d/b/a Edelman)
200 E Randolph St Fl 63
Chicago, IL 60601-6705
Tel.: (312) 240-3000
Fax: (312) 240-2900
(Nutrition, Online)

DeVries Public Relations
30 E 60th St 14th Fl
New York, NY 10022
Tel.: (212) 891-0400
Fax: (212) 644-0291

GolinHarris
(Part of the Interpublic Group of Companies)
111 E Wacker Dr 11th Fl
Chicago, IL 60601-4306
Tel.: (312) 729-4000
Fax: (312) 729-4010
(Safety & Environmental Public Relations)

HEILBrice
9840 Irvine Center Dr
Irvine, CA 92618
Tel.: (949) 336-8800
Fax: (949) 336-8819
The Beef Checkoff

NATIONAL COFFEE ASSOCIATION OF USA, INC.
45 Broadway Ste 1140
New York, NY 10006-5113
Tel.: (212) 766-4007
Fax: (212) 766-5815
E-mail: info@ncausa.org
Web Site: www.ncausa.org
E-Mail For Key Personnel:
Marketing Director: smwolfe@ncausa.org
Sales Range: Less than $1 Million
Approx. Number Employees: 6
Year Founded: 1911
Business Description:
Trade Association
S.I.C.: 8611
N.A.I.C.S.: 813910
Media: 2-10-14-15-23-24
Distr.: Natl.
Personnel:
Robert Nelson *(Pres & CEO)*

NATIONAL COMMITTEE FOR QUALITY ASSURANCE
11000 13L St NW Ste1000
Washington, DC 20005-4938
Tel.: (202) 955-3500
Fax: (202) 955-3599
E-mail: hediscomment@ncqa.org
Web Site: www.ncqa.org
Approx. Rev.: $23,000,000
Approx. Number Employees: 200
Year Founded: 1991
Business Description:
Measures the Performance of Managed Health Care Systems
S.I.C.: 8611
N.A.I.C.S.: 813910
Personnel:
Margaret E. O'Kane *(Pres)*
Ester Emard *(COO)*
Greg Pawlson *(Exec VP)*
Sarah Thomas *(VP-Public Policy & Comm)*
Victoria Street *(Dir-NCQA Education)*
Advertising Agency:
Crosby Marketing Communications
705 Melvin Ave Ste 200
Annapolis, MD 21401-1540
Tel.: (410) 626-0805
Fax: (410) 269-6547

NATIONAL COMMUNITY PHARMACISTS ASSOCIATION
100 Daingerfield Rd
Alexandria, VA 22314-2833
Tel.: (703) 683-8200
Fax: (703) 683-3619
Toll Free: (800) 544-7447
E-mail: info@ncpanet.org
Web Site: www.ncpanet.org
Approx. Sls.: $4,000,000
Approx. Number Employees: 70
Year Founded: 1898
Business Description:
Independent Retail Druggists Association
S.I.C.: 8611
N.A.I.C.S.: 813910
Advertising Expenditures: $250,000
Media: 2-7-10-13
Distr.: Natl.
Personnel:
Donnie Calhoun *(Chm)*
Joseph H. Harmison *(Pres)*
Douglas Hoey *(CEO & Exec VP)*
John Coster *(Sr VP-Govt Affairs & Head-Advocacy Center)*
Gerard Herpel *(Second VP)*

Michael Ford *(VP-Commun)*
Enjua M. Claude *(Dir-Production)*
Nina Dadgar *(Dir-Mktg & Sls)*

NATIONAL CONCRETE MASONRY ASSOCIATION
13750 Sunrise Valley Dr
Herndon, VA 20171-4662
Tel.: (703) 713-1900
Fax: (703) 713-1910
E-mail: ncma@ncma.org
Web Site: www.ncma.org
E-Mail For Key Personnel:
Marketing Director: jharke@ncma.org
Approx. Sls.: $4,500,000
Approx. Number Employees: 25
Year Founded: 1918
Business Description:
Concrete Block Producer Association
S.I.C.: 8611
N.A.I.C.S.: 813910
Media: 2-4-7-10
Distr.: Natl.
Budget Set: Aug.
Personnel:
Robert D. Thomas *(Pres)*
Dennis W. Graber *(Dir-Tech Publ)*
Heidi Weiss *(Mgr-Adv & Show Sls)*
Advertising Agency:
L.C. Williams & Associates, LLC
150 N Michigan Ave 38th Fl
Chicago, IL 60601-7558
Tel.: (312) 565-3900
Fax: (312) 565-1770
Toll Free: (800) 837-7123

NATIONAL COTTON COUNCIL OF AMERICA
7193 Goodlett Farms Pkwy
Cordova, TN 38016
Mailing Address:
PO Box 2995
Cordova, TN 38088-2995
Tel.: (901) 274-9030
Fax: (901) 725-0510
E-mail: info@natbat.com
Web Site: www.cotton.org
Approx. Number Employees: 100
Year Founded: 1954
Business Description:
Promoter of Cotton Usage
S.I.C.: 8611
N.A.I.C.S.: 813910
Media: 2-6-10
Distr.: Natl.
Budget Set: May
Personnel:
Jon W. Hardwick *(Chm)*
Mark D. Lange *(Pres & CEO)*
R. E. Shellabarger *(Dir-Fin Svcs)*
Ellen C. Ferrell *(Dir-Meeting & Travel Svcs)*
John Gibson *(Dir-Member Svcs)*
Marjory L. Walker *(Dir-Comm, Production & AV Svcs)*
David B. Collins *(Asst Dir-Foreign Ops)*
Michael Rochelle *(Asst Dir-Member Svcs)*

NATIONAL COUNCIL ON PROBLEM GAMBLING
730 11th St NW Ste 601
Washington, DC 20001
Tel.: (202) 547-9204
Fax: (202) 547-9206
E-mail: ncpg@ncpgambling.org
Web Site: www.ncpgambling.org
Approx. Number Employees: 4
Business Description:
Organization Servicing Problem Gambling
S.I.C.: 8699
N.A.I.C.S.: 813990
Media: 13-17

NATIONAL EATING DISORDERS ASSOCIATION
603 Stewart St Ste 803
Seattle, WA 98101
Tel.: (206) 382-3587
Fax: (206) 829-8501
Toll Free: (800) 931-2237
E-mail: info@nationaleatingdisorders.org
Web Site:
www.nationaleatingdisorders.org
Approx. Number Employees: 10
Business Description:
Not-For-Profit Organization Focusing on Eating Disorders Prevention & Treatment
S.I.C.: 8399
N.A.I.C.S.: 813212
Media: 13
Personnel:
Robbie Munn *(Chm)*
Lynn S. Grefe *(CEO)*
William Walters *(Volunteer Coord)*
Susie Roman *(Dir-Program)*
Advertising Agency:
Greenleaf & Associates
1994 Lucille Ave
Los Angeles, CA 90039
Tel.: (323) 660-5800
Pub Rels
— Karen Brundage *(Acct Exec)*

NATIONAL EDUCATION ASSOCIATION
1201 16th St NW
Washington, DC 20036
Tel.: (202) 833-4000
Fax: (202) 822-7974
Web Site: www.nea.org
Sales Range: $100-124.9 Million
Approx. Number Employees: 560
Year Founded: 1857
Business Description:
Promoter of Teaching Profession
S.I.C.: 8631; 8621
N.A.I.C.S.: 813930; 813920
Media: 2-6-8-13-15-23
Personnel:
John I. Wilson *(Exec Dir)*
Leona Hiraoka *(Dir-Media)*
Steve Snyder *(Mgr-Adv & Brdcst Svcs)*

NATIONAL ELECTRICAL MANUFACTURERS ASSOCIATION
1300 N 17th St N Ste 1752
Rosslyn, VA 22209-3801
Tel.: (703) 841-3200
Fax: (703) 841-5900
Fax: (703) 841-3384
Telex: 90477
Web Site: www.nema.org
Sales Range: $10-24.9 Million
Approx. Number Employees: 100
Year Founded: 1926
Business Description:
Trade Association; Standards, Statistics, Government Affairs
S.I.C.: 8611; 8621
N.A.I.C.S.: 813910; 813920
Media: 2-3-5-7-10-13-19-23-24
Distr.: Natl.
Budget Set: July
Personnel:
Evan Gaddis *(Pres & CEO)*
Stephen Gold *(Dir-Tech)*

NATIONAL FFA ORGANIZATION
6060 FFA Dr
Indianapolis, IN 46278-1370
Tel.: (317) 802-6060
Fax: (317) 802-6061
E-mail: webmaster@ffa.org
Web Site: www.ffa.org
Approx. Number Employees: 110
Year Founded: 1928
Business Description:
Publisher of Bi-Monthly Magazine
S.I.C.: 8641; 5961
N.A.I.C.S.: 813410; 454113
Media: 2-5-7-10-13-18-20
Distr.: Natl.
Budget Set: Aug. -Sept.
Personnel:
Dwight Armstrong *(CEO)*
Doug Loudenslager *(COO)*
Tammy Meyer *(Exec Dir)*
Frank Saldana *(Exec Dir)*
Kent Schescke *(Dir-Strategic Partnerships)*
Bill Stagg *(Dir-Strategic Comm)*
Rosalie Hunsinger *(Mgr-Program)*
Brands & Products:
FFA
FFA NEW HORIZONS

NATIONAL FIRE PROTECTION ASSOCIATION
1 Batterymarch Pk
Quincy, MA 02169-7454
Tel.: (617) 770-3000
Fax: (617) 770-0700
Toll Free: (800) 344-3555
Web Site: www.nfpa.org
Approx. Number Employees: 300
Year Founded: 1896
Business Description:
Standards Development, Publishing & Educational Organization; Fire Prevention & Safety Program
S.I.C.: 8621; 2721
N.A.I.C.S.: 813920; 511120
Media: 4-7-8-10
Distr.: Intl.
Budget Set: Aug.
Personnel:
James M. Shannon *(Pres & CEO)*
Bruce Mullen *(CFO & Sr VP-Fin)*
Brands & Products:
BUILDING AND CONSTRUCTION SAFETY CODE
COMPREHENSIVE CONSENSUS CODES
INTERNATIONAL BUILDING CODE
INTERNATIONAL MECHANICAL CODE
INTERNATIONAL PLUMBING CODE
INTERNATIONAL RESIDENTIAL CODE
LEARN NOT TO BURN
LIFE SAFETY CODE
NATIONAL ELECTRICAL CODE
NATIONAL FIRE ALARM CODE
NATIONAL FIRE CODES
NEC
NEC EXPERT
NECDIGEST
NECPLUS
NFC
NFPA
NFPA 101
NFPA 1600
NFPA 5000
NFPA 70
NFPA 70E
NFPA 72
NFPA JOURNAL
NFPA WORLD SAFETY CONFERENCE & EXPOSITION
RISKWATCH
SAFEWORK
SPARKY THE FIREDOG
STALLCUP'S
UGLY'S
UNIFORM FIRE CODE
UNIFORM MECHANICAL CODE
UNIFORM PLUMBING CODE
Advertising Agency:
Fletcher Media Group
94 Grove St
Peterborough, NH 03458
Tel.: (603) 924-6383
Fax: (603) 924-6562

NATIONAL FOOTBALL LEAGUE PLAYERS INCORPORATED
(Sub. of National Football League Players Association)
(d/b/a NFL PLAYERS)
1133 20th St NW
Washington, DC 20036
Tel.: (202) 463-2200
Fax: (202) 756-9323
Toll Free: (800) 372-5535
Web Site: www.nflplayers.com/about-us/Department--Contacts
Approx. Number Employees: 100
Year Founded: 1994
Business Description:
Professional Football Player Licensing & Marketing Services
S.I.C.: 9651; 8742
N.A.I.C.S.: 926150; 541613
Advertising Expenditures: $350,000
Media: 1-7-9-10-13-25
Distr.: Natl.
Personnel:
Keith Gordon *(Pres)*
Pam Adolph *(VP-Apparel Licensing)*
Ahmad Nassar *(VP-Bus & Legal Affairs)*
Karen Austin *(Asst VP-Non-Apparel Licensing)*
Steve Goodman *(Asst VP-Corp Partnerships)*
Felice Jones *(Asst VP-Event Mktg)*
Angela Manolakas *(Asst VP-Event Mktg)*
DeMaurice Smith *(Exec Dir)*
Scottie Graham *(Dir-Player Engagement)*
Doug Airel *(Sr Mgr-Player Svcs)*
Muneer Moore *(Sr Mgr-Player Svcs)*
Stephanie Wu Mosley *(Sr Mgr-Corp Partnerships)*
Nicole Pozzi *(Sr Mgr-Multimedia Licensing)*
Richard Medina *(Coord-Multimedia Licensing)*
Advertising Agencies:
AMP Agency (Alloy Marketing & Promotion)

Key to Media (For complete agency information see *The Advertising Red Books-Agencies* edition):
1. Bus. Publs. 2. Cable T.V. 3. Catalogs & Directories. 4. Co-op Adv. 5. Consumer Mags. 6. D.M. to Bus. Estab.7. D.M. to Consumers
8. Daily Newsp. 9. Exhibits/Trade Shows 10. Foreign 11. Infomercial 12. Internet Adv.13. Multimedia 14. Network Radio
15. Network T.V. 16. Newsp. Distr. Mags. 17. Other 18. Outdoor (Posters, Transit) 19. Point of Purchase20. Premiums, Novelties
21. Product Samples 22. Special Events Mktg. 23. Spot Radio 24. Spot T.V. 25. Weekly Newsp. 26. Yellow Page Adv.

National Football League Players Incorporated — (Continued)

77 N Washington St
Boston, MA 02114
Tel.: (617) 723-8929
Fax: (617) 723-2188
Creative
Strategy

Players Inc.
2021 L St.
Washington, DC 20036
Fax: (202) 496-2496

NATIONAL HONEY BOARD
11409 Business Park Cir Ste 10
Firestone, CO 80504
Tel.: (303) 776-2337
Fax: (303) 776-1177
Web Site: www.honey.com
Approx. Number Employees: 8
Year Founded: 1987
Business Description:
Advertising & Promotion of Honey
S.I.C.: 8743; 5812
N.A.I.C.S.: 541820; 722110
Export
Advertising Expenditures: $1,400,000
Media: 5-6-9-10-19
Distr.: Natl.
Personnel:
Bruce Boynton *(CEO)*
Sam Butler *(CFO)*
Advertising Agency:
EvansHardy & Young, Inc.
829 De La Vina St Ste 100
Santa Barbara, CA 93101-3238
Tel.: (805) 963-5841
Fax: (805) 564-4279
Industry Relations
Media Relations
Public Relations Agency of Record

NATIONAL HOT ROD ASSOCIATION
2035 Financial Way
Glendora, CA 91740
Tel.: (626) 914-4761
Fax: (626) 963-5360
E-mail: careers@nhra.com
Web Site: www.nhra.com
Approx. Number Employees: 130
Year Founded: 1951
Business Description:
Drag Racing Sanctioning Body
S.I.C.: 7948; 2711
N.A.I.C.S.: 711212; 511110
Advertising Expenditures: $3,000,000
Media: 2-5-6-8-9-10-14-15-19-20-23-24
Distr.: Natl.
Budget Set: Jan.
Personnel:
Wally Parks *(Founder)*
Dallas Gardner *(Chm)*
Tom Compton *(Pres)*
Linda Louie *(Gen Counsel & VP)*
Peter Clifford *(Exec VP & Gen Mgr)*
Graham Light *(Sr VP-Racing Ops)*
Jerry Archambeault *(VP-PR & Comm)*
Glen Cromwell *(VP-Event Mktg-Natl)*
Adriane Ridder *(VP-Publications)*
Jeff Morton *(Dir-Adv Sls)*
Jared Robinson *(Dir-IT)*
Jim Trace *(Dir-Brdcst & Video Comm)*
Anthony Vestal *(Dir-Media Rels)*
Jeff Winters *(Mktg Mgr)*
Rose Dickinson *(Mgr-Mktg & Adv)*
Brands & Products:
NATIONAL DRAGSTER
NHRA
NHRA LUCAS OIL
NHRA O'REILLY JR.
NHRA POWERADE
NHRA SUMMIT
NHRA'S YOUTH AND EDUCATION SERVICES
WALLY PARKS NHRA
Advertising Agencies:
National Hot Rod Association
2035 Financial Way
Glendora, CA 91741
Tel.: (626) 914-4761
Fax: (626) 963-5360

The Tombras Group
630 Concord St
Knoxville, TN 37919-3305
Tel.: (865) 524-5376
Fax: (865) 524-5667

NATIONAL KIDNEY FOUNDATION, INC.
30 E 33rd St 8th Fl
New York, NY 10016
Tel.: (212) 889-2210
Fax: (212) 689-9261
Toll Free: (800) 622-9010
E-mail: info@kidney.org
Web Site: www.kidney.org
Approx. Rev.: $34,159,334
Approx. Number Employees: 100
Year Founded: 1950
Business Description:
Health Organization
S.I.C.: 8733
N.A.I.C.S.: 541720; 541710
Media: 6-13-18-22-23-24
Personnel:
Bryan N. Becker *(Pres)*
John Davis *(CEO)*
Thomas Martin *(CFO)*

NATIONAL MARINE MANUFACTURERS ASSOCIATION
200 E Randolph St Ste 5100
Chicago, IL 60601-6528
Tel.: (312) 946-6200
Fax: (312) 946-0401
Web Site: www.nmma.org
E-Mail For Key Personnel:
President: tdammrich@nmma.org
Marketing Director: cblackwell@nmma.org
Approx. Number Employees: 120
Business Description:
National Association of Recreational Boating Industry; Producers of Consumer & Trade Boat Shows
S.I.C.: 8611; 7999
N.A.I.C.S.: 813910; 713990
Advertising Expenditures: $4,000,000
Media: 2-3-4-6-7-8-9-10-11-12-16-18-22-23-24-25
Budget Set: June
Personnel:
Thomas Dammrich *(Pres)*
Craig Boskey *(CFO & VP-Fin)*
Carl Blackwell *(CMO, VP-Mktg & Comm)*
Ben Wold *(Exec VP)*
David Dickerson *(Dir-State Govt Rels)*
Stephen Evans *(Dir-Svcs)*
John Marcinek *(Dir-Integrated Mktg)*
Robert Marino *(Dir-IT)*
John McKnight *(Dir-Compliance)*
Robert Newsome *(Dir-Engineering Standards)*
James Petru *(Dir-Market Statistics)*
Fernando Regueiro *(Dir-Internet Svcs)*
Bryan Welsh *(Dir-Membership)*
Brands & Products:
DISCOVER BOATING
NMMA
SHOWBOAT ADVERTISING
Advertising Agency:
The Ungar Group
333 N Michigan Ave Ste 2234
Chicago, IL 60601
Tel.: (312) 541-0000
Fax: (312) 541-0010

NATIONAL MARROW DONOR PROGRAM, INC.
3001 Broadway St Ste 500
Minneapolis, MN 55413-2195
Tel.: (612) 627-5800
Fax: (612) 627-8125
Toll Free: (800) 627-7692
Web Site: www.bethematch.org
Approx. Number Employees: 700
Business Description:
Finder of Patient Donors for People with Leukemia or Related Blood Diseases
S.I.C.: 8099
N.A.I.C.S.: 621999
Media: 6-7-8-10
Personnel:
Jeffrey Chell *(CEO)*
Gordon C. Bryan *(CFO)*
D. Michael Jones *(CIO)*
Michael Boo *(Chief Strategy Officer)*
Claudio Garcia *(Chief Mktg & Sls Officer)*
Patrick Thompson *(Pub Rel & Sr Coord-Media)*
Regan Hall Reinerth *(Sr Mgr-Mktg & Gen Pub)*
Advertising Agency:
Padilla Speer Beardsley
1101 W River Pkwy Ste 400
Minneapolis, MN 55415-1241
Tel.: (612) 455-1700
Fax: (612) 455-1060

NATIONAL NOTARY ASSOCIATION
9350 De Soto Ave
Chatsworth, CA 91311-4926
Mailing Address:
PO Box 2402
Chatsworth, CA 91313-2402
Tel.: (818) 739-1923
Fax: (800) 833-1211
Toll Free: (800) 876-6827
E-mail: services@nationalnotary.org
Web Site: www.nationalnotary.org
Approx. Number Employees: 70
Year Founded: 1957
Business Description:
Professional Association For Notaries Public
S.I.C.: 8621; 8611
N.A.I.C.S.: 813920; 813910
Advertising Expenditures: $435,000
Bus. Publs.: $25,000; Catalogs & Directories: $50,000; D.M. to Bus. Estab.: $100,000; D.M. to Consumers: $200,000; Other: $50,000; Premiums, Novelties: $10,000
Distr.: Direct to Consumer; Natl.
Budget Set: Oct.
Personnel:
Milton G. Valera *(Pres)*
Mark A. Valera *(COO & VP)*
Deborah M. Thaw *(Exec VP)*
Charles N. Faerber *(Editor & Legislative Analyst)*
Phillip W. Browne *(Mgr-Comm)*
Brands & Products:
NATIONAL NOTARY ASSOCIATION
TRUSTED NOTARY
UNIVERSAL

NATIONAL OILHEAT RESEARCH ALLIANCE
600 Cameron St Ste 206
Alexandria, VA 22314
Tel.: (703) 340-1660
E-mail: info@nora-oilheat.org
Web Site: www.nora-oilheat.org
Approx. Rev.: $16,296,296
Approx. Number Employees: 2
Year Founded: 2001
Business Description:
Oilheat Research & Development
S.I.C.: 1389
N.A.I.C.S.: 213112
Advertising Expenditures: $3,911,750
Media: 4-7-13
Personnel:
John J. Huber *(Pres)*

NATIONAL PARKS CONSERVATION ASSOCIATION
1300 19th St NW Ste 300
Washington, DC 20036
Tel.: (202) 223-6722
Fax: (202) 659-0650
Toll Free: (800) 628-7275
E-mail: npca@npca.org
Web Site: www.npca.org
Approx. Number Employees: 80
Year Founded: 1919
Business Description:
Promoter of Parks Conservation
S.I.C.: 8641; 2721
N.A.I.C.S.: 813410; 511120
Media: 6
Personnel:
Thomas C. Kiernan *(Pres)*
Elizabeth Fayad *(Gen Counsel)*
Theresa Pierno *(Exec VP)*
Craig Obey *(Sr VP-Govt Affairs)*
Ron Tipton *(Sr VP-Program)*
Karen Allen *(VP-HR)*
Linda M. Rancourt *(VP-Comm)*
Donald Barger *(Sr Dir)*
Alex Brash *(Sr Dir)*
Laura Loomis *(Sr Dir-Govt Affairs)*
Joy Oakes *(Sr Dir-Clean Air Campaign-Mid-Atlantic)*
Jim Stratton *(Sr Dir)*
Suzanne Dixon *(Reg Dir)*
Alan Spears *(Assoc Dir)*
Morgan Dodd *(Dir-Gift Plng)*
Terry Vines *(Dir-Membership Ops)*
Sonya Tynes-Shaw *(Assoc Dir)*
Joan Frankevich *(Mgr-Program)*
Steve Thompson *(Sr Program Mgr)*

NATIONAL PEANUT BOARD
Ste 210 2839 Paces Ferry Rd SE
Atlanta, GA 30339-5769

Key to Media (For complete agency information see *The Advertising Red Books-Agencies* edition):
1. Bus. Publs. 2. Cable T.V. 3. Catalogs & Directories. 4. Co-op Adv. 5. Consumer Mags. 6. D.M. to Bus. Estab.7. D.M. to Consumers 8. Daily Newsp. 9. Exhibits/Trade Shows 10. Foreign 11. Infomercial 12. Internet Adv.13. Multimedia 14. Network Radio 15. Network T.V. 16. Newsp. Distr. Mags. 17. Other 18. Outdoor (Posters, Transit) 19. Point of Purchase20. Premiums, Novelties 21. Product Samples 22. Special Events Mktg. 23. Spot Radio 24. Spot T.V. 25. Weekly Newsp. 26. Yellow Page Adv.

Tel.: (678) 424-5750
Fax: (678) 424-5751
Toll Free: (866) 825-7946
E-mail: peanuts@nationalpeanutboard.org
Web Site: www.nationalpeanutboard.org
Sales Range: $10-24.9 Million
Approx. Number Employees: 9
Year Founded: 2000
Business Description:
Peanuts Researcher & Promoter
S.I.C.: 8611
N.A.I.C.S.: 813910
Media: 1-3-4-13-18
Personnel:
Raffaela Marie Fenn *(Pres & Mng Dir)*
Ryan Lepicier *(VP-Mktg & Comm)*
Sherry Coleman Collins *(Mgr-Mktg & Comm)*
Advertising Agencies:
GolinHarris
1575 Northside Dr NW Bldg 200 Ste 200
Atlanta, GA 30318
Tel.: (404) 880-4600
Fax: (404) 523-3483

Lawler Ballard Van Durand
31 Inverness Center Pkwy Ste 110
Birmingham, AL 35242-4822
Tel.: (205) 995-1775
Fax: (205) 991-5141

NATIONAL PORK PRODUCERS COUNCIL

10664 Justin Dr
Urbandale, IA 50322-3755
Mailing Address:
PO Box 10383
Des Moines, IA 50306-0383
Tel.: (515) 278-8012
Fax: (515) 278-8011
Web Site: www.nppc.org
Approx. Number Employees: 65
Business Description:
Pork Lobbyists
S.I.C.: 8611
N.A.I.C.S.: 813910
Import Export
Advertising Expenditures: $350,000
Media: 1-10-13-15-18-20
Distr.: Natl.
Budget Set: Jan.
Personnel:
Doug Wolf *(Pres)*
Neil Dierks *(CEO)*
John Wrigley *(Dir-Resource Dev & Gen Mgr-World Pork Expo)*
Craig Boelling *(Dir-Producer Svcs)*
Doug Fricke *(Dir-Trade Show Mktg)*
Chelsie Redalen *(Dir-Govt Rels)*
Dave Warner *(Dir-Comm)*
Advertising Agency:
Charleston/Orwig, Inc.
515 W North Shore Dr
Hartland, WI 53029-8312
Tel.: (262) 563-5100
Fax: (262) 563-5101

NATIONAL POTATO PROMOTION BOARD

7555 E Hampden Ave Ste 412
Denver, CO 80231
Tel.: (303) 369-7783
Fax: (303) 369-7718
Web Site: www.uspotatoes.com
Sales Range: Less than $1 Million
Approx. Number Employees: 17
Year Founded: 1972
Business Description:
Association Promoting Potatoes
S.I.C.: 8611
N.A.I.C.S.: 813910
Advertising Expenditures: $200,000
Media: 11-18-19-23
Distr.: Intl.; Natl.
Personnel:
Tim O'Connor *(Pres & CEO)*
Diana LeDoux *(VP-Fin & IT)*
Teresa Kuwahara *(Mgr-Intl Mktg-Dehydrated)*
Susan Weller *(Mgr-Intl Mktg-Frozen)*

NATIONAL RESTAURANT ASSOCIATION

1200 17th St NW
Washington, DC 20036
Tel.: (202) 331-5900
Tel.: (202) 973-3677
Fax: (202) 331-2429
Toll Free: (800) 424-5156
Web Site: www.restaurant.org
Approx. Number Employees: 65
Business Description:
Restaurant Industry Business Association
S.I.C.: 8611
N.A.I.C.S.: 813910
Personnel:
Mike Gibbons *(Chm & Trustees)*
Sally Smith *(Chm)*
Rosalyn Mallet *(Vice Chm)*
Dawn Sweeney *(Pres & CEO)*
Marvin Irby *(CFO & Chief Admin Officer)*
Scott DeFife *(Exec VP-Policy & Gov Affairs)*
Sue Hensley *(Sr VP-Pub Affairs Comm)*
Katie Laning Niebaum *(Dir-Advocacy Comm)*
Annika Stensson *(Dir-Media Rels)*
Advertising Agencies:
Capitol Marketing Group, Inc.
4055 Chain Bridge Rd
Fairfax, VA 22030-4103
Tel.: (703) 591-0100
Fax: (703) 591-1508

Fixation Marketing
4340 E-W Hwy Ste 200
Bethesda, MD 20814
Tel.: (240) 207-2009
Fax: (301) 718-1940

Multi Media Services Corp.
915 King St 2nd Fl
Alexandria, VA 22314
Tel.: (703) 739-2160
Fax: (703) 836-9517

NATIONAL RETAIL HARDWARE ASSOCIATION

6325 Digital Way Ste 300
Indianapolis, IN 46278-1756
Tel.: (317) 290-0338
Fax: (317) 275-9403
Toll Free: (800) 772-4424
E-mail: contact@nrha.org
Web Site: www.nrha.org
Approx. Number Employees: 35
Year Founded: 1900
Business Description:
Various Retail Hardware Associations Throughout North America
S.I.C.: 2721; 8611
N.A.I.C.S.: 511120; 813910
Export
Advertising Expenditures: $2,600,000
Media: 1-2-4-6-7-10-11-13-14-15-20
Distr.: Natl.
Budget Set: Apr.
Personnel:
Bob Tatter *(Dir-Publications)*

NATIONAL RETAILERS ASSOCIATION

400 E Royal Ln Ste 201
Irving, TX 75039
Toll Free: (877) 869-7115
Web Site: www.nationalrestaurant.org
Business Description:
Business Association Related to Commerce
S.I.C.: 8611
N.A.I.C.S.: 813910
Media: 13
Personnel:
George Reich *(Pres & CEO)*

NATIONAL RIFLE ASSOCIATION

(d/b/a NRA)
11250 Waples Mill Rd
Fairfax, VA 22030-7400
Tel.: (703) 267-1000
Fax: (703) 267-3907
E-mail: nra.contact@nra.org
Web Site: www.nra.org
Approx. Number Employees: 550
Year Founded: 1871
Business Description:
Association Promoting the Responsible Use of Firearms
S.I.C.: 8641
N.A.I.C.S.: 813410
Media: 1-2-3-6-10-18
Distr.: Natl.
Personnel:
Wayne R. Lapierre, Jr. *(CEO & Exec VP)*

NATIONAL SPORTING GOODS ASSOCIATION

1601 Feehanville Dr Ste 300
Mount Prospect, IL 60056-6042
Tel.: (847) 296-6742
Fax: (847) 391-9827
E-mail: info@nsga.org
Web Site: www.nsga.org
Sales Range: $25-49.9 Million
Approx. Number Employees: 12
Year Founded: 1929
Business Description:
Promotes Sporting Goods
S.I.C.: 8611; 2721
N.A.I.C.S.: 813910; 511120
Advertising Expenditures: $350,000
Media: 2
Distr.: Natl.
Budget Set: Apr.
Personnel:
Matt Carson *(Pres & CEO)*
Chuck Suritz *(Dir-Strategic Plng & Education)*
Larry Weindruch *(Dir-NSGA Team Dealer Div)*

NATIONAL TOOLING & MACHINING ASSOCIATION

9300 Livingston Rd
Fort Washington, MD 20744-4905
Tel.: (301) 248-6200
Fax: (301) 248-7104
Toll Free: (800) 248-6862
E-mail: info@ntma.org
Web Site: www.ntma.org
Approx. Sls.: $7,000,000
Approx. Number Employees: 16
Year Founded: 1943
Business Description:
Association of Designers & Builders of Special Tooling & Precision Machining
S.I.C.: 8611
N.A.I.C.S.: 813910
Media: 2-4-7-9-10-18-25
Distr.: Natl.
Budget Set: Oct.
Personnel:
Grady Cope *(Chm)*

NATIONAL TRUST FOR HISTORIC PRESERVATION

1785 Massachusetts Ave NW
Washington, DC 20036-2117
Tel.: (202) 588-6000
Fax: (202) 588-6038
E-mail: info@nthp.org
Web Site: www.preservationnation.org
Approx. Number Employees: 150
Year Founded: 1949
Business Description:
Society for Historic Preservation
S.I.C.: 8412
N.A.I.C.S.: 712120
Media: 3
Personnel:
Stephanie Meeks *(Pres & CEO)*
Greg Coble *(CFO)*
Paul W. Edmondson *(Chief Legal Officer, Gen Counsel & VP)*
Bob Barron *(Publr)*
David A. Brown *(Exec VP)*
John Pucher *(Mgr-Magazine Bus)*
Advertising Agency:
The Ivy Group, Ltd.
1100 N Providence Rd
Media, PA 19063
Tel.: (610) 566-5680
Fax: (610) 566-5683

THE NATIONAL UNDERGROUND RAILROAD FREEDOM CENTER

50 E Freedom Way
Cincinnati, OH 45202-2739
Tel.: (513) 333-7500
Fax: (513) 333-7718
Web Site: www.freedomcenter.org
Approx. Number Employees: 29
Business Description:
Underground Railroad & the Abolitionist Movement Information
S.I.C.: 8412
N.A.I.C.S.: 712120
Personnel:
Don W. Murphey *(CEO)*
Advertising Agency:
Landor Associates
110 Shillito Pl
Cincinnati, OH 45202-2361
Tel.: (513) 419-2300
Fax: (513) 221-3532

Key to Media (For complete agency information see *The Advertising Red Books-Agencies* edition):
1. Bus. Publs. 2. Cable T.V. 3. Catalogs & Directories. 4. Co-op Adv. 5. Consumer Mags. 6. D.M. to Bus. Estab.7. D.M. to Consumers
8. Daily Newsp. 9. Exhibits/Trade Shows 10. Foreign 11. Infomercial 12. Internet Adv.13. Multimedia 14. Network Radio
15. Network T.V. 16. Newsp. Distr. Mags. 17. Other 18. Outdoor (Posters, Transit) 19. Point of Purchase20. Premiums, Novelties
21. Product Samples 22. Special Events Mktg. 23. Spot Radio 24. Spot T.V. 25. Weekly Newsp. 26. Yellow Page Adv.

NATIONAL VENTURE CAPITAL ASSOCIATION
1655 N Fort Myer Dr Ste 850
Arlington, VA 22209-3199
Tel.: (703) 524-2549
Fax: (703) 524-3940
E-mail: lturner@nvca.org
Web Site: www.nvca.org
Approx. Number Employees: 10
Business Description:
Trade Association Representing the Venture Capital Industry
S.I.C.: 8611
N.A.I.C.S.: 813910
Media: 13
Personnel:
Kate Mitchell *(Chm)*
Mark G. Heesen *(Pres)*
Molly M. Myers *(Sr VP)*
Emily A. Baker *(Dir-Federal Policy & Political Advocacy)*
Jeanne Lazarus Metzger *(Dir-Mktg)*

NATIONAL WATERMELON PROMOTION BOARD
3361 Rouse Rd Ste 150
Orlando, FL 32817
Tel.: (407) 657-0261
Fax: (407) 657-2213
E-mail: info@watermelon.org
Web Site: www.watermelon.org
Approx. Number Employees: 8
Business Description:
Promoter of Watermelons
S.I.C.: 8743
N.A.I.C.S.: 541820
Media: 4-10-13-19-22
Personnel:
Mark Arney *(Exec Dir)*
Rebekah Dossett *(Dir-Ops & Industry Affairs)*
Gordon Hunt *(Dir-Mktg & Comm)*

NATSO, INC.
1737 King St Ste 200
Alexandria, VA 22314
Tel.: (703) 549-2100
Fax: (703) 684-4525
Toll Free: (888) 275-6287
E-mail: headquarters@natso.com
Web Site: www.natso.com
Approx. Sls.: $2,800,000
Approx. Number Employees: 14
Year Founded: 1960
Business Description:
National Trade Association Representing Travel Plaza & Truckstop Owners & Operators
S.I.C.: 8611
N.A.I.C.S.: 813910
Media: 2-7
Distr.: Natl.
Personnel:
Lisa J. Mullings *(CEO)*
Bob Shuman *(Dir-Fin)*
Brands & Products:
CHECK LINK

THE NATURE CONSERVANCY
4245 N Fairfax Dr Ste 100
Arlington, VA 22203-1606
Tel.: (703) 841-5300
Fax: (703) 841-1283
Web Site: www.nature.org
Approx. Rev.: $546,000,000
Approx. Number Employees: 400
Year Founded: 1951
Business Description:
Conservation Services
S.I.C.: 8641
N.A.I.C.S.: 813410
Media: 3-6-13-14-15-22
Personnel:
John P. Morgridge *(Co-Chm)*
Mark Tercek *(Pres & CEO)*
Stephen Howell *(CFO & Chief Admin Officer)*
Brian McPeek *(COO)*
Jean-Louis Ecochard *(CIO & VP)*
Geof Rochester *(CMO)*
Karen Berky *(Chief Ethics & Chief Compliance Officer)*
Phillip Tabas *(Gen Counsel)*
Rob McKim *(Reg Dir-Central US)*
Jerry Touval *(Regional Dir-Science-Latin America)*
Robert Bendick *(Dir-External Affairs)*
Erin Dovichin *(Dir-Commun)*
Lynne Hale *(Dir)*
Richard Jeo *(Dir-Plng)*
Jeff Parrish *(Dir-Global Mediterranean Conservation)*
Chip Sutton *(Dir-Comm)*
Grady Timmons *(Dir-Comm)*
Elizabeth Ward *(Dir-Mktg Comm)*
Adrienne Egolf *(Coord-Mktg)*
Advertising Agency:
Alexander & Tom
3500 Boston St Ste 225
Baltimore, MD 21224-5275
Tel.: (410) 327-7400
Fax: (410) 327-7403

NEBRASKA ENERGY COOPERATIVE
605 12th St
Aurora, NE 68818
Tel.: (402) 694-2106
Fax: (402) 694-6943
Web Site: www.aventinerei.com
Approx. Number Employees: 100
Business Description:
Agricultural Cooperative Services
S.I.C.: 9641; 8611; 8699; 8748
N.A.I.C.S.: 926140; 541690; 813910; 813990
Media: 5-7-10

NEGOTIATION INSTITUTE, INC.
350 5th Ave Ste 5701
New York, NY 10118-7415
Tel.: (212) 888-0053
Fax: (212) 888-7775
E-mail: gerardn@negotiation.com
Web Site: www.negotiation.com
E-Mail For Key Personnel:
President: gerardn@negotiation.com
Approx. Number Employees: 20
Year Founded: 1966
Business Description:
Non-Profit Art of Negotiating Programs
S.I.C.: 8742
N.A.I.C.S.: 541611
Media: 1-2-4-6-7-8-9-10-20
Distr.: Natl.
Personnel:
Gerard Nierenberg *(Founder)*
Brands & Products:
ART OF NEGOTIATING
ERROR AWARENESS
EVERYBODY WINS
THE NEGOTIATION INSTITUTE

NEIGHBORHOOD CLEANERS ASSOCIATION INTERNATIONAL
252 W 29th St
New York, NY 10001-5271
Tel.: (212) 967-3002
Fax: (212) 967-2240
Toll Free: (800) 888-1622
E-mail: info@nca-i.com
Web Site: www.nca-i.com
Sales Range: $10-24.9 Million
Approx. Number Employees: 10
Year Founded: 1947
Business Description:
Dry Cleaners Trade Association
S.I.C.: 8611; 8249
N.A.I.C.S.: 813910; 611519
Advertising Expenditures: $400,000
Media: 1-2-10
Distr.: Reg.
Personnel:
Nora Nealis *(Exec Dir)*
Advertising Agency:
RushPRnews
1010 suite 1007 Cherrier
Montreal, QC H2L 1H8, Canada
Tel.: (514) 523-3771

NEW ENGLAND APPLE ASSOCIATION
8 Elm St
Hatfield, MA 01038
Mailing Address:
PO Box 41
Hatfield, MA 01038
Tel.: (413) 247-9966
Fax: (413) 247-9666
Web Site:
www.newenglandapples.org/
Year Founded: 1935
Business Description:
Promoter of Apples in New England
S.I.C.: 8611
N.A.I.C.S.: 813910
Media: 10-18-19-22
Distr.: Reg.
Budget Set: July
Brands & Products:
NEW ENGLAND APPLES
THE SEAL OF GOOD TASTE

NEW JERSEY BROADCASTERS ASSOCIATION
348 Applegarth Rd
Monroe Township, NJ 08831
Tel.: (609) 860-0111
Fax: (609) 860-0110
Toll Free: (888) NJBA-FONE
E-mail: njba@njba.com
Web Site: www.njba.com
Sales Range: Less than $1 Million
Approx. Number Employees: 3
Year Founded: 1946
Business Description:
Broadcasters Trade Association for the Radio & TV Stations in the State of New Jersey
S.I.C.: 8611
N.A.I.C.S.: 813910
Personnel:
Robert E. McAllan *(Chm & CEO)*
Joseph M. Bilotta *(COO & Treas)*
Advertising Agency:
D&R Advertising, Inc.
1 Bridge Plz
Fort Lee, NJ 07024
Tel.: (201) 592-0550
Fax: (201) 592-8745

NEW JERSEY HOSPITAL ASSOCIATION
PO Box 1 760 Alexander Rd
Princeton, NJ 08540-0001
Tel.: (609) 275-4000
Web Site: www.njha.com
Sales Range: $100-124.9 Million
Approx. Number Employees: 150
Business Description:
Hospital Trade Organization
S.I.C.: 8611; 8742
N.A.I.C.S.: 813910; 541611
Media: 2-6
Personnel:
Elisabeth Ryan *(Pres & CEO)*
Joseph Carr *(CEO-Cape Reg Medical Center)*
Sarah Lechner *(Gen Counsel)*
Sean Hopkins *(Sr VP-Health)*
William Kennedy *(Sr VP-NJHA Healthcare Bus Solutions)*
Kerry McKean Kelly *(VP-Comm & Member Svcs)*
Maureen Barrie *(Dir-Consulting Svcs)*

NEW JERSEY POULTRY PRODUCTS PROMOTION COUNCIL
John Fitch Plz
Trenton, NJ 08625
Mailing Address:
PO Box 330
Trenton, NJ 08625-0330
Tel.: (609) 292-5536
Fax: (609) 341-3212
Web Site: www.stat.nj.us
Approx. Number Employees: 250
Business Description:
Poultry & Fresh Eggs Promoter
S.I.C.: 9641
N.A.I.C.S.: 926140
Media: 19-23
Distr.: Reg.
Budget Set: Sept.
Personnel:
Emanuel Puglisi *(Chm)*

NEW YORK APPLE ASSOCIATION, INC.
7645 Main St
Fishers, NY 14453-0350
Tel.: (585) 924-2171
Fax: (585) 924-1629
Web Site: www.nyapplecountry.com
E-Mail For Key Personnel:
President: jimallen@nyapplecountry.com
Marketing Director: david@nyapplecountry.com
Approx. Number Employees: 5
Year Founded: 1950
Business Description:
Fresh Apples & Apple Products Promoter
S.I.C.: 8611
N.A.I.C.S.: 813910
Media: 2-6-10-19
Distr.: Natl.
Budget Set: June-Oct.
Personnel:
Jim Allen *(Pres)*
Brands & Products:
APPLE COUNTRY
NEW YORK APPLE ASSOCIATION, INC.

Key to Media (For complete agency information see *The Advertising Red Books-Agencies* edition):
1. Bus. Publs. 2. Cable T.V. 3. Catalogs & Directories. 4. Co-op Adv. 5. Consumer Mags. 6. D.M. to Bus. Estab.7. D.M. to Consumers
8. Daily Newsp. 9. Exhibits/Trade Shows 10. Foreign 11. Infomercial 12. Internet Adv.13. Multimedia 14. Network Radio
15. Network T.V. 16. Newsp. Distr. Mags. 17. Other 18. Outdoor (Posters, Transit) 19. Point of Purchase20. Premiums, Novelties
21. Product Samples 22. Special Events Mktg. 23. Spot Radio 24. Spot T.V. 25. Weekly Newsp. 26. Yellow Page Adv.

Advertising Agency:
Mason Selkowitz Marketing, Inc
400 Whitney Rd
Penfield, NY 14526
Tel.: (585) 249-1100
Fax: (585) 249-1060

NIGHTINGALE-CONANT CORPORATION

6245 W Howard St
Niles, IL 60714-3403
Toll Free: (800) 560-6081
E-mail: sales@nightingale.com
Web Site: www.nightingale.com
E-Mail For Key Personnel:
Sales Director: sales@nightingale.com
Approx. Number Employees: 145
Year Founded: 1960
Business Description:
Audio & Video Training; Self-Development Programs
S.I.C.: 8299; 7389
N.A.I.C.S.: 611710; 541990
Advertising Expenditures: $18,854,000
Bus. Publs.: $300,000; Catalogs & Directories: $6,000,000; Co-op Adv.: $50,000; Consumer Mags.: $100,000; D.M. to Bus. Estab.: $6,000,000; D.M. to Consumers: $6,000,000; Exhibits/Trade Shows: $50,000; Point of Purchase: $50,000; Product Samples: $300,000; Yellow Page Adv.: $4,000
Distr.: Intl.; Natl.
Budget Set: Mar.
Personnel:
Vic Conant *(Chm)*
Gary Chappell *(CEO)*
Brands & Products:
THE ADVANCED PROPERTY INVESTMENT SYSTEM
LEAD THE FIELD
NIGHTINGALE-CONANT
WEALTH GENERATOR SYSTEM

THE NORTH AMERICAN BLUEBERRY COUNCIL

80 Iron Point Cir Ste 114
Folsom, CA 95630
Tel.: (916) 983-2279
Fax: (916) 983-9370
E-mail: info@blueberry.org
Web Site: www.blueberry.org
Approx. Number Employees: 15
Year Founded: 1965
Business Description:
Blueberry Promotion
S.I.C.: 8621
N.A.I.C.S.: 813920
Media: 2-10-11
Personnel:
Mark Villata *(Exec Dir-Mktg)*
Advertising Agency:
Lewis & Neale, Inc.
320 W 13th St 7th Fl
New York, NY 10014
Tel.: (212) 420-8808
Fax: (212) 229-2867

NORTH SHORE ANIMAL LEAGUE, INC.

25 Davis Ave
Port Washington, NY 11050
Tel.: (516) 883-7575
Fax: (516) 883-8256
E-mail: spirof@nsalamerica.org
Web Site: www.nsalamerica.org
Sales Estimate: $80-99 Million
Approx. Number Employees: 275
Year Founded: 1944
Business Description:
Non-Profit Pet Rescue & Adoption Organization
S.I.C.: 8399
N.A.I.C.S.: 813312
Media: 2-3-6-8-9-18-20-22-23-24-25-26
Distr.: Reg.
Budget Set: Aug.
Personnel:
John Stevenson *(Pres & Dir)*
Valerie Fields *(CFO & Sr VP)*

THE NORTHWEST ONTARIO SUNSET COUNTRY TRAVEL ASSOCIATION

W Kenora
PO Box 647
Kenora, ON Canada
Tel.: (807) 468-5853
Fax: (807) 468-5484
Toll Free: (800) 665-7567
E-mail: info@ontariossunsetcountry.ca
Web Site: www.ontariossunsetcountry.ca
Approx. Number Employees: 3
Business Description:
Travel Association
S.I.C.: 4729
N.A.I.C.S.: 561599
Media: 11-18-23-24

OHIO STATE FLORIST ASSOCIATION (OFA)

2133 Steward Ct
Columbus, OH 43215
Tel.: (614) 487-1117
Fax: (614) 487-1216
E-mail: ofa@ofa.org
Web Site: www.ofa.org
Approx. Number Employees: 11
Year Founded: 1929
Business Description:
Advertising & Marketing of Fresh Flowers to Consumers
S.I.C.: 8621
N.A.I.C.S.: 813920
Import
Media: 5-6-9-13-19-20
Distr.: Natl.
Budget Set: Sept.
Personnel:
Steve Carver *(Sr Mgr-Education & Events)*
Brands & Products:
OFA
SENT WITH SPECIAL CARE

ONWARD HEALTHCARE INC.

Ste 100 64 Danbury Rd
Wilton, CT 06897-4438
Tel.: (203) 642-1400
Fax: (800) 970-5001
Toll Free: (800) 278-0332
E-mail: info@onwardhealthcare.com
Web Site: www.onwardhealthcare.com
Approx. Number Employees: 120
Year Founded: 2002
Business Description:
Healthcare Staffing Services
S.I.C.: 7361
N.A.I.C.S.: 561310
Media: 2-8-22
Personnel:
Kevin Clark *(Chm & CEO)*

OPTICIANS ASSOCIATION OF AMERICA

441 Carlisle Dr
Herndon, VA 20170
Tel.: (703) 437-8780
Fax: (703) 437-0727
E-mail: oaa@oaa.org
Web Site: www.oaa.org
Approx. Number Employees: 2
Year Founded: 1926
Business Description:
Opticians Association
S.I.C.: 5995; 8611
N.A.I.C.S.: 446130; 813910
Media: 1-6-7-10-13
Distr.: Natl.
Budget Set: May
Personnel:
Diane Charles *(Pres)*
Brands & Products:
GUILD OPTICIANS
PRESCRIPTION OPTICIANS OF AMERICA

OREGON BEEF COUNCIL

1827 NE 44th Ave Ste 315
Portland, OR 97213-1467
Tel.: (503) 274-2333
Fax: (503) 274-5405
Web Site: www.orbeef.org
Approx. Number Employees: 3
Year Founded: 1959
Business Description:
Beef Industry Education & Promotion
S.I.C.: 8611
N.A.I.C.S.: 813910
Advertising Expenditures: $500,000
Media: 3-5-6-9-10-13-14-15-19-22-23-24-25
Distr.: Reg.
Budget Set: July

OUTDOOR ADVERTISING ASSOCIATION OF AMERICA

1850 M St NW Ste 1040
Washington, DC 20036
Tel.: (202) 833-5566
Fax: (202) 833-1522
E-mail: info@oaaa.org
Web Site: www.oaaa.org
E-Mail For Key Personnel:
President: nancyfletcher@oaa.org
Public Relations: mmoller@oaaa.org
Approx. Number Employees: 15
Year Founded: 1891
Business Description:
Trade Representation Services to the Outdoor Advertising Industry
S.I.C.: 8611
N.A.I.C.S.: 813910
Advertising Expenditures: $500,000
Media: 1-2-10-13-18-22
Distr.: Natl.
Personnel:
Wally Kelly *(Chm)*
Paul Meyer *(Vice Chm)*
Richard Schaps *(Vice Chm-Comm)*
Nancy Fletcher *(Pres & CEO)*
Stephen Freitas *(CMO)*
Ken Klein *(Exec VP-Govt Rels)*
Brands & Products:
OAAA
PASS IT ON

THE OVARIAN CANCER RESEARCH FUND, INC.

14 Pennsylvania Plz Ste 1400
New York, NY 10122
Tel.: (212) 268-1002
Fax: (212) 947-5652
Toll Free: (800) 873-9569
E-mail: info@ocrf.org
Web Site: www.ocrf.org
Approx. Rev.: $2,529,636
Approx. Number Employees: 5
Business Description:
Cancer Research
S.I.C.: 8733
N.A.I.C.S.: 541710; 541720
Media: 8-15
Personnel:
Sol Schreiber *(Founder & Co-Chm)*
Faith Kates Kogan *(Pres-Board of Dir)*

PACIFIC NORTHWEST CANNED PEAR SERVICE, INC.

105 S 18th St
Yakima, WA 98901-2175
Tel.: (509) 453-4837
Fax: (509) 453-4880
E-mail: info@cannedpears.com
Web Site: www.eatcannedpears.com
E-Mail For Key Personnel:
Marketing Director: mmiller@pnwcannedpears.com
Approx. Number Employees: 5
Year Founded: 1954
Business Description:
Representation for Processed Pears in OR & WA
S.I.C.: 8743
N.A.I.C.S.: 541820
Export
Media: 2-24
Distr.: Natl.
Budget Set: July
Personnel:
Mark Miller *(Dir-Promo)*
Brands & Products:
ALWAYS RIPE, ALWAYS READY
BARTLETT
PACIFIC NORTHWEST CANNED PEARS
Advertising Agency:
Segerstrom Communications
2745 Webster St., Ste. 9
San Francisco, CA 94123
Tel.: (415) 922-6033
Fax: (415) 474-1875
Canned Pears

PARENT PROJECT MUSCULAR DISTROPHY

1012 N University Blvd
Middletown, OH 45042
Tel.: (513) 424-0696
Fax: (513) 425-9907
Toll Free: (800) 714-5437
Web Site: www.parentprojectmd.org
Approx. Number Employees: 3
Business Description:
Duchenne Muscular Distrophy Research, Advocacy, Education & Compassion
S.I.C.: 8399
N.A.I.C.S.: 813212
Media: 13
Personnel:
Pat Furlong *(Pres & CEO)*

Key to Media (For complete agency information see *The Advertising Red Books-Agencies* edition):
1. Bus. Publs. 2. Cable T.V. 3. Catalogs & Directories. 4. Co-op Adv. 5. Consumer Mags. 6. D.M. to Bus. Estab.7. D.M. to Consumers 8. Daily Newsp. 9. Exhibits/Trade Shows 10. Foreign 11. Infomercial 12. Internet Adv.13. Multimedia 14. Network Radio 15. Network T.V. 16. Newsp. Distr. Mags. 17. Other 18. Outdoor (Posters, Transit) 19. Point of Purchase20. Premiums, Novelties 21. Product Samples 22. Special Events Mktg. 23. Spot Radio 24. Spot T.V. 25. Weekly Newsp. 26. Yellow Page Adv.

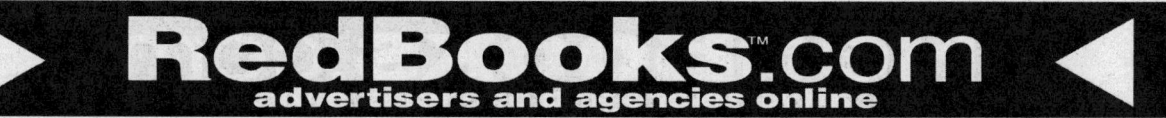

PARTNERSHIP FOR A DRUG-FREE AMERICA INC.
405 Lexington Ave Ste 1601
New York, NY 10174-0002
Tel.: (212) 922-1560
Fax: (212) 922-1570
E-mail: webmail@drugfree.org
Web Site: www.drugfree.org
Approx. Number Employees: 40
Year Founded: 1986
Business Description:
Non-Profit Organization to Prevent the Use of Illegal Drugs
S.I.C.: 8322
N.A.I.C.S.: 624190
Media: 1-6-14-15-17-18-22
Distr.: Natl.
Personnel:
Patricia Russo *(Chm)*
Stephen Pasierb *(Pres & CEO)*
Robert Caruso *(CFO & Exec VP)*
Sean Clarkin *(Exec VP & Dir-Strategy-Program Mngt)*
Hilary Baris *(Dir-Digital Media & Mktg)*
Denise Young Farrell *(Dir-Pub Affairs)*
Advertising Agencies:
Euro RSCG Worldwide
350 Hudson St
New York, NY 10014-4504
Tel.: (212) 886-2000
Fax: (212) 886-2016
Toll Free: (800) 937-0233

Wunderman
(Worldwide Headquarters)
285 Madison Ave
New York, NY 10017
Tel.: (212) 941-3000
Fax: (212) 210-5454
Time To Talk

PATROLMAN'S BENEVOLENT ASSOCIATION OF THE CITY OF NEW YORK, INC.
40 Fulton St
New York, NY 10038-1850
Tel.: (212) 233-5531
Fax: (212) 233-3952
Web Site: www.nycpba.org
Approx. Number Employees: 95
Year Founded: 1894
Business Description:
Union for Police Officers in New York City
S.I.C.: 8631
N.A.I.C.S.: 813930
Media: 3-9-17-18-23-24-25
Personnel:
Patrick J. Lynch *(Pres)*
John Puglissi *(First VP)*
Mubarak Abdul-Jabbar *(Second VP)*
Albert O'Leary *(Dir-Commun)*
Joseph Mancini *(Mgr-Pub Rels)*

PEAR BUREAU NORTHWEST
4382 SE International Way Ste A
Milwaukie, OR 97222
Tel.: (503) 652-9720
Fax: (503) 652-9721
E-mail: cmather@usapears.com
Web Site: www.usapears.com
E-Mail For Key Personnel:
President: kmoffitt@usapears.com
Approx. Number Employees: 25
Year Founded: 1931
Business Description:
Non-Profit Marketing Organization to Develop New Markets for Pears
S.I.C.: 8611; 8743
N.A.I.C.S.: 813910; 541820
Import Export
Media: 1-2-5-6-7-8-10-11-13-19-20-22-23
Distr.: Intl.; Natl.
Budget Set: June
Personnel:
Kevin D. Moffitt *(Pres & CEO)*
Jeff Correa *(Dir-Mktg)*
Cristie Mather *(Dir-Comm)*
Brands & Products:
PEARBEAR
USA PEAR BUDDIES

PENNSYLVANIA CHAMBER OF BUSINESS & INDUSTRY
417 Walnut St
Harrisburg, PA 17101-1902
Tel.: (717) 255-3252
Fax: (717) 255-3298
Toll Free: (800) 225-7224
E-mail: info@pachamber.org
Web Site: www.pachamber.org
Approx. Number Employees: 82
Year Founded: 1916
Business Description:
Business Association & State Chamber
S.I.C.: 8611; 8748
N.A.I.C.S.: 813910; 541618
Media: 2-8-13
Personnel:
Floyd W. Warner *(Pres)*
Gina Berardone *(Exec VP-Reg Accts)*
Gene Barr *(VP-Govt & Pub Affairs)*
Laurel Belding *(Dir-Bus Dev)*
Lesley Smith *(Dir-Commun)*
Susan E. Smith *(Dir-Customer Learning)*
Dick Laufer *(Mgr-Membership Retention)*
Debra Steffey *(Mgr-Membership Devel)*

PERLITE INSTITUTE, INC.
Ste A 4305 N 6th St
Harrisburg, PA 17110-1650
Tel.: (717) 238-9723
Fax: (717) 238-9985
Telex: 262167 PERLITE UR
E-mail: info@perlite.org
Web Site: www.perlite.org
Approx. Number Employees: 6
Year Founded: 1949
Business Description:
International Association of Producers of Industrial & Horticultural Products
S.I.C.: 0181
N.A.I.C.S.: 111422
Media: 2-4-8-10-13
Distr.: Intl.; Natl.
Budget Set: May

PHARMACEUTICAL RESEARCH & MANUFACTURERS OF AMERICA
950 F St NW Ste 300
Washington, DC 20004
Tel.: (202) 835-3400
Fax: (202) 835-3450
E-mail: webmaster@phrma.org
Web Site: www.phrma.org
Approx. Number Employees: 100
Year Founded: 1958
Business Description:
Trade Association for Pharmaceutical Research
S.I.C.: 8611
N.A.I.C.S.: 813910
Advertising Expenditures: $300,000
Media: 3-6-9-15
Distr.: Natl.
Budget Set: Dec.
Personnel:
John J. Castellani *(Pres & CEO)*
Christopher Viehbacher *(Chm-PhRMA Board & CEO-Sanofi-aventis)*
Chip Davis *(Exec VP-Advocacy)*
Rod Hunter *(Sr VP-Intl Advocacy)*
Alan Goldhammer *(Asst VP-Regulatory Affairs)*
Brands & Products:
HELPINGPATIENTS
LEADING THE WAY IN THE SEARCH FOR CURES
NEW MEDICINE. NEW HOPE.
PHARMAFACTS
PHATE
PHRMA
RX WORKS
TODAY'S RESEARCH. TOMORROW'S CURES
Advertising Agencies:
Captus Communications
6704 Old McLean Village Dr Ste 100
McLean, VA 22101-3906
Tel.: (703) 542-4910
Fax: (703) 917-4347

Cline, Davis & Mann, Inc.
220 E 42nd St 8th Fl
New York, NY 10017-5806
Tel.: (212) 907-4300
Fax: (212) 557-7240
Creative

Edelman
3rd Floor Toranomon 45 MT Bldg
Tokyo, 105-001, Japan
Tel.: (81) 3 6403 5200
Fax: (81) 3 6403 5201
Public Relations

Universal McCann
100 33rd St 8th Fl
New York, NY 10001
Tel.: (212) 883-4700
Media Placement

PHILADELPHIA CHURCH OF GOD
PO Box 3700
Edmond, OK 73083
Tel.: (405) 340-7474
Fax: (405) 359-6280
Toll Free: (800) 772-8577
Web Site: www.pcog.org
Sales Range: $25-49.9 Million
Approx. Number Employees: 100
Business Description:
Religious Organization
S.I.C.: 8661
N.A.I.C.S.: 813110
Advertising Expenditures: $500,000
Media: 9-13
Personnel:
Shane Granger *(Dir-Mktg)*

PHILANTHROPIC RESEARCH INC.
(d/b/a GuideStar)
427 Scotland Street
Williamsburg, VA 23185
Tel.: (757) 229-4631
Fax: (757) 229-8912
Toll Free: (800) 784-9378
E-mail: customerservice@guidestar.org
Web Site: www2.guidestar.org/
Sales Range: $1-9.9 Million
Approx. Number Employees: 47
Year Founded: 1994
Business Description:
Information & Database Services on Non-Profit Organizations
S.I.C.: 2741; 8621; 8733
N.A.I.C.S.: 511140; 516110; 541720; 813920
Advertising Expenditures: $80,000
Media: 2-13
Personnel:
Virginia A. Hodgkinson *(Founder & Vice Chm)*
Robert G. Ottenhoff *(Pres & CEO)*
Lee Glenn *(Sr VP)*
James Dobrzeniecki *(VP-IT)*
Dan Moore *(VP-Pub Affairs)*
Debra Snider *(VP-Admin & Commun)*
Karen Rayzor *(Dir-Nonprofit Rels)*
Tom C. Tinsley *(Dir-F.B. Heron Foundation)*
Pamela Jowdy *(Sr Product Mgr-Guidestar Premium & Charity Check)*
Brands & Products:
GUIDESTAR

PICKLE PACKERS INTERNATIONAL, INC.
1 Pickle & Pepper Plaza
Saint Charles, IL 60174
Mailing Address:
Ste 925 1620 I St NW
Washington, DC 20006-4035
Tel.: (630) 584-0759
Fax: (630) 584-0759
Web Site: www.ilovepickles.org
Year Founded: 1893
Business Description:
Non-Profit Trade Association for the Pickled Vegetables Industry
S.I.C.: 3824; 8611
N.A.I.C.S.: 334514; 813910
Advertising Expenditures: $200,000
Media: 2-6
Distr.: Natl.
Personnel:
John Gallo *(Pres)*

PLAN USA, INC.
155 Plan Way
Warwick, RI 02886
Tel.: (401) 738-5600
Fax: (401) 738-5608
Toll Free: (800) 556-7918
E-mail: info@planusa.org
Web Site: www.planusa.org
Approx. Number Employees: 77
Year Founded: 1937
Business Description:
Grassroots Assistance In Health, Education, Family Livelihood & Community Development to Help Sponsored Children & their Families In Developing Countries towards Long-term Goal of Self-sufficiency
S.I.C.: 8322
N.A.I.C.S.: 624110
Media: 2-3-6-8-9-12-13-15-16-23-24-25
Distr.: Natl.

Key to Media (For complete agency information see *The Advertising Red Books-Agencies* edition):
1. Bus. Publs. 2. Cable T.V. 3. Catalogs & Directories. 4. Co-op Adv. 5. Consumer Mags. 6. D.M. to Bus. Estab.7. D.M. to Consumers
8. Daily Newsp. 9. Exhibits/Trade Shows 10. Foreign 11. Infomercial 12. Internet Adv.13. Multimedia 14. Network Radio
15. Network T.V. 16. Newsp. Distr. Mags. 17. Other 18. Outdoor (Posters, Transit) 19. Point of Purchase20. Premiums, Novelties
21. Product Samples 22. Special Events Mktg. 23. Spot Radio 24. Spot T.V. 25. Weekly Newsp. 26. Yellow Page Adv.

Budget Set: Apr.
Personnel:
Carol Donnelly *(VP-HR)*
Janet Moretti *(Mgr-Corp)*
Brands & Products:
CHILDREACH
PLAN
SEE ME, SHARE MY WORLD

PLANNED PARENTHOOD FEDERATION OF AMERICA, INC.
434 W 33rd St
New York, NY 10001
Tel.: (212) 261-4300
Fax: (212) 247-6274
Web Site:
www.plannedparenthood.org
Approx. Number Employees: 150
Year Founded: 1916
Business Description:
Family Planning Information & Services
S.I.C.: 8093
N.A.I.C.S.: 621410
Advertising Expenditures: $2,000,000
Personnel:
Andrea Hagelgans *(Sr Press Officer)*
Brands & Products:
AMERICAS MOST TRUSTED NAME IN WOMEN'S HEALTH
COMPUPLAN
PLANNED PARENTHOOD
PPFA
REPUBLICANS FOR CHOICE
RESPONSIBLE CHOICES
TEENWIRE.COM
VOX
Advertising Agency:
Promark Direct Inc.
300 N Midland Ave Ste 2
Saddle Brook, NJ 07663-5723
Tel.: (201) 398-9000
Fax: (201) 398-9212
Toll Free: (800) 404-1900

THE PLASTICS PIPE INSTITUTE, INC.
(d/b/a PPI)
105 Decker Ct Ste 825
Irving, TX 75062
Tel.: (469) 499-1044
Fax: (469) 499-1063
E-mail: info@plasticpipe.org
Web Site: www.plasticpipe.org
Approx. Number Employees: 6
Year Founded: 1950
Business Description:
Trade Association Representing Plastics Piping Industry
S.I.C.: 8611
N.A.I.C.S.: 813910
Advertising Expenditures: $60,000
Media: 2-7-10-13-16
Personnel:
Tony Radoszewski *(Exec Dir)*
Stephen Boros *(Dir-Tech)*
Mike Pluimer *(Dir-Engrg)*
Camille Rubeiz *(Dir-Engrg)*

PRECAST/PRESTRESSED CONCRETE INSTITUTE
209 W Jackson Blvd Ste 500
Chicago, IL 60606-6938
Tel.: (312) 786-0300
Fax: (312) 786-0353
E-mail: info@pci.org
Web Site: www.pci.org
Approx. Sls.: $8,000,000
Approx. Number Employees: 30
Business Description:
Precast & Prestressed Concrete Institute
S.I.C.: 8611
N.A.I.C.S.: 813910
Advertising Expenditures: $1,000,000
Bus. Publs.: $1,000,000
Distr.: Natl.
Budget Set: Oct. -Nov.
Personnel:
Thomas E. D'Arcy *(Chm)*
Thomas Mczvoy *(Chm)*
James G. Toscas *(Pres)*
Jason Krohn *(Mng Dir-Tech)*
Rita L. Seraderian *(Exec Dir)*
Sidney Freedman *(Dir-Architectura, Industrial Ops & Safety)*
Colin Faul *(Mgr-Mktg)*
Advertising Agency:
James O. Ahtes, Inc.
3813 Mission Hills Road
Northbrook, IL 60062-5711
Tel.: (847) 205-5689

PRODUCE MARKETING ASSOCIATION
1500 Casho Mill Rd
Newark, DE 19711
Tel.: (302) 738-7100
Fax: (302) 731-2409
E-mail: info@pma.com
Web Site: www.pma.com
Approx. Number Employees: 75
Year Founded: 1949
Business Description:
Trade Association for Marketers of Fresh Fruits, Vegetables & Floral Products
S.I.C.: 8611; 5812
N.A.I.C.S.: 813910; 722110
Media: 4-10-19
Personnel:
Bryan Silbermann *(Pres & CEO)*
Lorna Christie *(COO & Exec VP)*
Duane Eaton *(Sr VP-Admin)*

THE PROFESSIONAL PUTTERS ASSOCIATION
(Sub. of Putt-Putt, LLC)
8105 Timberlake Rd
Lynchburg, VA 24502
Mailing Address:
5225 28th St
Lubbock, TX 79407
Tel.: (434) 237-7888
Fax: (914) 412-0483
E-mail: homeoffice@putt-putt.com
Web Site: www.proputters.com
Year Founded: 1959
Business Description:
Professional Putting Organization
S.I.C.: 8621
N.A.I.C.S.: 813920
Advertising Expenditures: $550,000
Media: 2-3-4-5-7-8-9-11-13-16-18-22-23-24-25-26
Distr.: Intl.; Natl.
Budget Set: Sept.
Personnel:
Joe Aboid *(Commissioner)*
Jim Evans *(Partner)*
Brands & Products:
APA
JPA
PPA

PROFESSIONAL RODEO COWBOYS ASSOCIATION
(d/b/a PRCA)
101 Pro Rodeo Dr
Colorado Springs, CO 80919
Tel.: (719) 593-8840
Fax: (719) 548-4876
E-mail: receptionist@prorodeo.com
Web Site: www.prorodeo.org
Sales Range: $10-24.9 Million
Approx. Number Employees: 80
Business Description:
Sports Promotion
S.I.C.: 8611; 2721
N.A.I.C.S.: 813910; 511120
Personnel:
Lewis A. Cryer *(Pres)*
Brands & Products:
PROFESSIONAL RODEO COWBOYS ASSOCIATION
Advertising Agency:
French/West/Vaughan, Inc.
112 E Hargett St
Raleigh, NC 27601
Tel.: (919) 832-6300
Fax: (919) 832-6360

QSAC INC.
253 W 35th St 16th Fl
New York, NY 10001
Tel.: (212) 244-5560
Fax: (212) 244-5561
Web Site: www.qsac.com
Approx. Number Employees: 1,000
Business Description:
Quality Services for the Autism Community
N.A.I.C.S.: 813410
Media: 28
Personnel:
Gary Maffei *(CEO)*
Paul Naranjo *(CFO)*
Cory Polshansky *(COO)*
Lisa A. Veglia *(Chief Admin Officer)*

QUALITY CHEKD DAIRIES, INC.
1733 Pk St
Naperville, IL 60563-8478
Mailing Address:
PO Box 104293
Jefferson City, MO 65110-4293
Tel.: (630) 717-1110
Fax: (630) 717-1126
Toll Free: (800) 522-7080
E-mail: qchekd@qchekd.com
Web Site: www.qchekd.com
E-Mail For Key Personnel:
Marketing Director: mmurphy@qchekd.com
Sales Range: $10-24.9 Million
Approx. Number Employees: 7
Year Founded: 1944
Business Description:
Dairy Processor
S.I.C.: 8611
N.A.I.C.S.: 813910
Export
Advertising Expenditures: $260,000
Media: 2-10-19-20-21-23
Distr.: Natl.
Budget Set: Oct.
Personnel:
Peter Horvath *(Pres)*
Molly Murphy *(Dir-Mktg)*
Brands & Products:
BLUE Q. RED CHEK. GREAT STUFF.
CHEKD FOR QUALITY
Advertising Agency:
Slack Barshinger & Partners, Inc.
233 N Michigan Ave Ste 3050
Chicago, IL 60601
Tel.: (312) 970-5800
Fax: (312) 970-5850
Toll Free: (800) 888-6197

QUALITY SERVICES FOR THE AUTISM COMMUNITY
(d/b/a QSAC)
253 W 35th St 16th Fl
New York, NY 10001
Tel.: (212) 244-5560
Fax: (212) 244-5561
Web Site: www.qsac.com
Business Description:
Educational, Habilitation, Residential, Support, & Recreational Programs to Meet the Needs of Persons with Autism & their Families
N.A.I.C.S.: 813319
Media: 9-13-23-25-29
Personnel:
Gary A. Maffei *(CEO & Exec Dir)*
Paul Naranjo *(CFO)*
Cory Polshansky *(COO & Deputy Exec Dir)*
Lisa A. Veglia *(Deputy Exec Dir & Chief Admin Officer)*

RECORDING MUSICIANS ASSOCIATION LOS ANGELES
817 Vine St Ste 209
Los Angeles, CA 90038-3715
Tel.: (323) 462-4762
E-mail: mjourgesen@rmala.org
Web Site: www.rmala.org
Business Description:
Music Recording Industry Organization
S.I.C.: 8631
N.A.I.C.S.: 813930
Media: 2-10

RECREATION VEHICLE INDUSTRY ASSOCIATION
(d/b/a Go RVing Coalition)
1896 Preston White Dr
Reston, VA 20191-4363
Tel.: (703) 620-6003
Fax: (703) 620-5071
E-mail: mailings@rvia.org
Web Site: www.rvia.org
Approx. Number Employees: 56
Year Founded: 1994
Business Description:
Information & Services for Recreational Vehicle Mfr & Suppliers
S.I.C.: 8611
N.A.I.C.S.: 813910
Media: 6-9-10-13-23
Personnel:
Gregg Fore *(Chm)*
Richard Coon *(Pres)*
James Ashurst *(CMO & VP)*
Christine Morrison *(Sr Dir-Mktg Comm)*
Kevin Broom *(Dir-Media Rels)*
Matt Wald *(Dir-Government Affairs)*
Margie Craig *(Mgr-Adv)*
CVourtney Rodney *(Mgr-Pub Rels)*
Brands & Products:
GO RVING
RVIA

Key to Media (For complete agency information see *The Advertising Red Books-Agencies* edition):
1. Bus. Publs. 2. Cable T.V. 3. Catalogs & Directories. 4. Co-op Adv. 5. Consumer Mags. 6. D.M. to Bus. Estab.7. D.M. to Consumers 8. Daily Newsp. 9. Exhibits/Trade Shows 10. Foreign 11. Infomercial 12. Internet Adv.13. Multimedia 14. Network Radio 15. Network T.V. 16. Newsp. Distr. Mags. 17. Other 18. Outdoor (Posters, Transit) 19. Point of Purchase20. Premiums, Novelties 21. Product Samples 22. Special Events Mktg. 23. Spot Radio 24. Spot T.V. 25. Weekly Newsp. 26. Yellow Page Adv.

Recreation Vehicle Industry Association — (Continued)

Advertising Agency:
Barton Gilanelli & Associates, Inc.
51 N Mascher St
Philadelphia, PA 19106-2205
Tel.: (215) 592-8601

RECYCLING COUNCIL OF BRITISH COLUMBIA
(d/b/a RCBC)
10-119 W Pender St
Vancouver, BC Canada
Tel.: (604) 683-6009
Fax: (604) 683-7255
E-mail: natalie@rcbc.bc.ca
Web Site: www.rcbc.bc.ca
Approx. Rev.: $525,864
Year Founded: 1974
Business Description:
Organization Focused on the Promotion of Recycling
S.I.C.: 8611
N.A.I.C.S.: 813910
Media: 8-10-13
Personnel:
Alan Stanley *(Pres)*
Brock MacDonald *(Exec Dir)*
Anna Rochelle *(Dir-Fin)*
Mairi Welman *(Dir-Comm)*

RHODE ISLAND COALITION AGAINST DOMESTIC VIOLENCE
422 Post Rd
Warwick, RI 02888-1524
Tel.: (401) 467-9940
Fax: (401) 467-9943
Toll Free: (800) 494-8100
E-mail: ricadv@ricadv.org
Web Site: www.ricadv.org
Approx. Rev.: $3,380,557
Approx. Number Employees: 9
Year Founded: 1979
Business Description:
Domestic Violence Assistance Services
S.I.C.: 7389; 8322
N.A.I.C.S.: 561990; 624190
Media: 3-13-18-22-23-24
Personnel:
Deborah DeBare *(Exec Dir)*
Cheryl Delekta *(Dir-Fin)*

RISE N' SHINE
417 23rd Ave S
Seattle, WA 98144
Tel.: (206) 628-8949
Web Site: www.risenshine.org
Business Description:
HIV/Aids Awareness
S.I.C.: 8399
N.A.I.C.S.: 813319
Media: 22
Personnel:
Janet L. Trinkaus *(Founder)*
Michael Dunlop *(Exec Assoc Dir-Programs)*
Rick North *(Exec Assoc Dir-Dev)*
Lauren Henry *(Mgr-Events)*
Terry Marsh *(Mgr-Mentor Programs)*

ROBINS, KAPLAN, MILLER & CIRESI LLP
2800 LaSalle Plz 800 LaSalle Ave
Minneapolis, MN 55402-3394
Tel.: (612) 349-8500
Fax: (612) 339-4181
Toll Free: (800) 553-9910
Web Site: www.rkmc.com
Approx. Number Employees: 250
Year Founded: 1938
Business Description:
Legal Services
S.I.C.: 8111
N.A.I.C.S.: 541110
Personnel:
Elliot S. Kaplan *(Partner)*
Richard J. Nigon *(CFO)*
Diane P. Frick *(Dir-HR)*
Advertising Agency:
Preston Kelly
222 First Ave NE
Minneapolis, MN 55413
Tel.: (612) 843-4000
Fax: (612) 843-3900

ROLLER SKATING ASSOCIATION INTERNATIONAL
6905 Corporate Dr
Indianapolis, IN 46278-1927
Tel.: (317) 347-2626
Fax: (317) 347-2636
E-mail: admin@rollerskating.com
Web Site: www.rollerskating.org
Sales Range: $25-49.9 Million
Approx. Number Employees: 8
Year Founded: 1937
Business Description:
Trade Association For Roller Skating Rink Operators, Roller Skating Teachers & Coaches, & Roller Skating Manufacturers
S.I.C.: 8641
N.A.I.C.S.: 813410
Media: 2-7-9-10-13
Distr.: Intl.; Natl.
Personnel:
Susan Melenchuk *(Exec Dir)*
Jennifer Wendel *(Dir-Member Svcs)*
Brands & Products:
RHCA
RSA
RSM
SCA
SRSTA

RONALD MCDONALD HOUSE CHARITIES, INC.
(Sub. of McDonald's Corporation)
One Kroc Dr
Oak Brook, IL 60523
Tel.: (630) 623-7048
Fax: (630) 623-7488
Web Site: www.rmhc.org
Sales Range: $75-99.9 Million
Approx. Number Employees: 3,000
Year Founded: 1984
Business Description:
Charity Involved in Creating, Finding & Supporting Programs that Directly Improve the Health & Well-Being of Children
S.I.C.: 8322
N.A.I.C.S.: 624110; 624190
Advertising Expenditures: $200,000
Media: 6-15-22
Personnel:
Martin J. Coyne, Jr. *(Pres & CEO)*
Kelly Thien *(Mgr-Mktg & Communications)*
Advertising Agencies:
GolinHarris
(Part of the Interpublic Group of Companies)
111 E Wacker Dr 11th Fl
Chicago, IL 60601-4306
Tel.: (312) 729-4000
Fax: (312) 729-4010

Henson Consulting
111 W Wesley Ste 5
Wheaton, IL 60187
Tel.: (630) 933-9477

The Ross Agency
201 Gibraltar Rd Ste 149
Horsham, PA 19044
Tel.: (888) 815-7536
Fax: (800) 859-2349
Toll Free: (888) 815-7536

Villing & Company, Inc.
5909 Nimtz Pkwy
South Bend, IN 46628
Tel.: (574) 277-0215
Fax: (574) 277-5513

ROTARY INTERNATIONAL
One Rotary Ctr 1560 Sherman Ave
Evanston, IL 60201
Tel.: (847) 866-3000
Fax: (847) 328-8554
Fax: (847) 328-8281
E-mail: edwinfuta@rotary.org
Web Site: www.rotary.org
Approx. Number Employees: 500
Business Description:
Humanitarian Services
S.I.C.: 8399
N.A.I.C.S.: 813311
Media: 2-7-8-10-11-13-17
Personnel:
Jessica Anderson *(Sr Coord-Program & Presidential Initiatives)*
Advertising Agency:
Rotary International
1560 Sherman Ave
Evanston, IL 60201-4818
Tel.: (847) 866-3000
Fax: (847) 328-8554

THE SALVATION ARMY
615 Slaters Ln
Alexandria, VA 22313
Tel.: (703) 684-5500
Fax: (703) 684-3478
E-mail: sa_information@usn.salvationarmy.org
Web Site: www.salvationarmyusa.org
Year Founded: 1865
Business Description:
Used Merchandise Retailer; Charity & Life Income Financial Planning Services
S.I.C.: 5932; 8641
N.A.I.C.S.: 453310; 813410
Import Export
Media: 6-9-10-23-24-25
Distr.: Natl.
Budget Set: Sept.
Personnel:
John Jones *(Dir-Brand Mgmt)*
Advertising Agencies:
Franco Public Relations Group
400 Renaissance Ctr Ste 1000
Detroit, MI 48243
Tel.: (313) 567-2300
Fax: (313) 567-4486
The Salvation Army of Southeast Michigan Adult Rehabilitation Center

Grizzard Communications
(An Omnicom Co.)
229 Peachtree St NE Ste 1400
Atlanta, GA 30303-1606
Tel.: (404) 522-8330
Fax: (404) 335-0313
Toll Free: (800) 241-9351
Direct Response Marketing
Fundraising
Integrated Marketing
Texas Division (Agency of Record)

Merkle Inc.
7001 Columbia Gateway Dr
Columbia, MD 21046
Tel.: (443) 542-4000
Fax: (443) 542-4001

The Richards Group, Inc.
8750 N Central Expy Ste 100
Dallas, TX 75231-6430
Tel.: (214) 891-5700
Fax: (214) 265-2933

SAVE THE CHILDREN FEDERATION, INC.
54 Wilton Rd
Westport, CT 06881-9948
Tel.: (203) 221-4000
Fax: (203) 222-1067
Toll Free: (800) 728-3843
E-mail: webmaster@savechildren.org
Web Site: www.savethechildren.org
Approx. Rev.: $240,241,000
Approx. Number Employees: 200
Business Description:
Fund Raiser to Aid Children
S.I.C.: 8322; 5947
N.A.I.C.S.: 624190; 453220
Media: 3-6-7-8-11-13-14-15-23-24-25
Distr.: Intl.
Personnel:
Charles F. MacCormack *(Pres & CEO)*
Jane Whitbread *(CEO)*
Carolyn Miles *(COO & Exec VP)*
Cynthia Carr *(Gen Counsel & VP-People Strategies & Corp Svcs)*
Mark K. Shriver *(Sr VP)*
Chloe O'Gara *(Assoc VP)*
David Oot *(Assoc VP-Helath & Nutrition)*
Jude Bridge *(Dir-Mktg, Campaigns & Comm)*
Rudy von Bernuth *(Dir-Humanitarian)*
Brands & Products:
SAVE THE CHILDREN
Advertising Agency:
Wieden + Kennedy UK Limited
16 Hanbury Street
London, E1 6QR, United Kingdom
Tel.: (44) 207 194 7000
Fax: (44) 207 194 7100

SAVE THE MANATEE CLUB, INC.
500 N Maitland Ave
Maitland, FL 32751
Tel.: (407) 539-0990
Fax: (407) 539-0871
E-mail: info@savethemanatee.org
Web Site: www.savethemanatee.org
Approx. Number Employees: 15
Year Founded: 1981
Business Description:
Manatee Conservation Services
S.I.C.: 8699; 8399; 8641
N.A.I.C.S.: 813990; 813319; 813410
Media: 4-6-8

Key to Media (For complete agency information see *The Advertising Red Books-Agencies* edition):
1. Bus. Publs. 2. Cable T.V. 3. Catalogs & Directories. 4. Co-op Adv. 5. Consumer Mags. 6. D.M. to Bus. Estab.7. D.M. to Consumers
8. Daily Newsp. 9. Exhibits/Trade Shows 10. Foreign 11. Infomercial 12. Internet Adv.13. Multimedia 14. Network Radio
15. Network T.V. 16. Newsp. Distr. Mags. 17. Other 18. Outdoor (Posters, Transit) 19. Point of Purchase20. Premiums, Novelties
21. Product Samples 22. Special Events Mktg. 23. Spot Radio 24. Spot T.V. 25. Weekly Newsp. 26. Yellow Page Adv.

Personnel:
Patrick Rose *(Exec Dir)*
Connie Graham *(Dir-Ops)*
Janice Nearing *(Dir-PR)*
Nancy Sadusky *(Dir-Comm)*
Katie Tripp *(Dir-Science & Conservation)*

SCOTTSDALE HEALTHCARE FOUNDATION

10001 N 92nd St Ste 121
Scottsdale, AZ 85258
Tel.: (480) 882-4517
Fax: (480) 882-6600
Toll Free: (866) 592-7423
Web Site: www.shc.org/foundation/index.htm
Sales Range: $1-9.9 Million
Approx. Number Employees: 16
Business Description:
Fundraising Organizations
S.I.C.: 7389
N.A.I.C.S.: 561990
Media: 8
Personnel:
John N. Ferree, Jr. *(Pres)*
Brands & Products:
SCOTTSDALE HEALTHCARE

SEMINOLE TRIBE OF FLORIDA, INC.

6300 Stirling Rd
Hollywood, FL 33024-2153
Tel.: (954) 966-6300
Fax: (954) 967-3600
Toll Free: (800) 683-7800
E-mail: tribune@semtribe.com
Web Site: www.semtribe.com
Sales Range: $500-549.9 Million
Approx. Number Employees: 500
Year Founded: 1984
Business Description:
American Indian Tribal Council
S.I.C.: 8641; 5812; 5813; 7011
N.A.I.C.S.: 921150; 721120; 722110; 722410
Media: 3-9-22
Personnel:
Richard Bowers *(Vice Chm & Pres)*
Jim Shore *(Gen Counsel)*
Virginia Mitchell *(Editor-in-Chief)*
Advertising Agency:
Bitner Goodman
701 W Cypress Creek Rd Ste 204
Fort Lauderdale, FL 33309-2045
Tel.: (954) 730-7730
Fax: (954) 730-7130
Public Relations

SIERRA CLUB

85 2nd St 2nd Fl
San Francisco, CA 94105
Tel.: (415) 977-5500
Tel.: (415) 977-5526 (Media)
Fax: (415) 977-5799
E-mail: information@sierraclub.org
Web Site: www.sierraclub.org
Approx. Rev.: $63,000,000
Approx. Number Employees: 500
Year Founded: 1892
Business Description:
Social Organization & Publisher
S.I.C.: 8641; 2741
N.A.I.C.S.: 813410; 511199
Media: 6
Personnel:
Carl Pope *(Chm)*
Robin Mann *(Pres)*
Dan Olinger *(Dir-Member Resources)*
Kristi Rummel *(Dir-Natl Adv)*
Chuck Baldwin *(Assoc Dir-Ops)*
Advertising Agency:
Cone
(A Member of Omnicom Group)
855 Boylston St
Boston, MA 02116
Tel.: (617) 227-2111
Fax: (617) 523-3955

SIERRA CLUB OF CANADA

412 1 Nicholas St
Ottawa, ON Canada
Tel.: (613) 241-4611
Fax: (613) 241-2292
Toll Free: (888) 810-4204
E-mail: info@sierraclub.ca
Web Site: www.sierraclub.ca
Personnel:
Kaissy Yu *(CFO)*
Advertising Agency:
Calder Bateman Communications Ltd.
10241 109th St
Edmonton, AB T5J 1N2, Canada
Tel.: (780) 426-3610
Fax: (780) 425-6646
(Dangers of Chemical Pesticides)

THE SOAP AND DETERGENT ASSOCIATION

(d/b/a SDA)
1500 K St NW Ste 300
Washington, DC 20005
Tel.: (202) 347-2900
Fax: (202) 347-4110
E-mail: info@cleaning101.com
Web Site: www.cleaning101.com
Approx. Rev.: $750,000
Approx. Number Employees: 19
Year Founded: 1926
Business Description:
Trade Association Representing the Soap & Detergent Industry
S.I.C.: 8611
N.A.I.C.S.: 813910
Media: 2
Personnel:
Jane M. Hutterly *(Chm)*
Robert Chouffot *(Vice Chm)*
Brian Sansoni *(VP-Comm & Membership)*
Richard Sedlak *(VP-Tech & Intl Affairs)*
Brands & Products:
SDA

SOCIETY OF AMERICAN FLORISTS

(d/b/a SAF)
1601 Duke St
Alexandria, VA 22314-3406
Tel.: (703) 836-8700
Fax: (703) 836-8705
E-mail: info@safnow.org
Web Site: www.safnow.org
Approx. Number Employees: 30
Year Founded: 1884
Business Description:
Promotion of Flowers & Plants at Professional Florist Shops Between Traditional Floral Buying Holidays; Trade Association For Floral Industry
S.I.C.: 8611
N.A.I.C.S.: 813910
Media: 2-7-10
Distr.: Natl.
Budget Set: Aug.
Personnel:
Robert B. Luthultz *(Chm & Pres)*
Peter J. Moran *(CEO & Exec VP)*
Leonard Bowers *(Dir-Fin)*
Jenny Stromann *(Mgr-Consumer Mktg)*

THE SOCIETY OF AMERICAN MILITARY ENGINEERS

607 Prince St
Alexandria, VA 22314-3117
Tel.: (703) 549-3800
Fax: (703) 548-6153
Toll Free: (800) 336-3097
E-mail: member@same.org
Web Site: www.same.org
E-Mail For Key Personnel:
Marketing Director: jnichols@same.org
Approx. Number Employees: 19
Year Founded: 1920
Business Description:
Engineering Society
S.I.C.: 8621
N.A.I.C.S.: 813920
Media: 2-10
Distr.: Intl.; Natl.
Budget Set: Oct.
Personnel:
Eileen L. Erickson *(Editor-in-Chief, Dir-Comm & Mktg)*
Diana Dawkins *(Dir-Membership)*

SOCIETY OF MANUFACTURING ENGINEERS

1 SME Dr
Dearborn, MI 48128-2408
Tel.: (313) 271-1500
Fax: (313) 271-2861
Fax: (313) 425-3400
Toll Free: (800) 733-4763
E-mail: service@sme.org
Web Site: www.sme.org
Approx. Number Employees: 140
Year Founded: 1969
Business Description:
Manufacturing Engineering Society; Publisher of Magazine; Promotion of Trade Related Events
S.I.C.: 8621; 8641
N.A.I.C.S.: 813920; 813410
Media: 2-7-10-13-17
Distr.: Natl.
Budget Set: Sept.
Personnel:
Mark Tomlinson *(CEO)*
George E. West *(Dir)*
Denise King *(Coord-Adv)*
Brands & Products:
CERTIFIED MANUFACTURING ENGINEER
CERTIFIED MANUFACTURING TECHNOLOGIST
JOURNAL OF MANUFACTURING PROCESSES
JOURNAL OF MANUFACTURING SYSTEMS
MANUFACTURING ENGINEERING
SOCIETY OF MANUFACTURING ENGINEERS
WHERE MANUFACTURING COMES TOGETHER

THE SOCIETY OF THE PLASTICS INDUSTRY, INC.

1667 K St NW Ste 1000
Washington, DC 20006
Tel.: (202) 974-5200
Fax: (202) 296-7005
Web Site: www.plasticsindustry.org
Approx. Sls.: $13,717,574
Approx. Number Employees: 63
Year Founded: 1937
Business Description:
Association for the Plastics Industry
S.I.C.: 8611
N.A.I.C.S.: 813910
Export
Media: 2-10-11-13
Personnel:
Paul H. Appelblom *(Pres)*
Mary Hanson *(CFO)*
Tracy Cullen *(Sr VP-Comm & Mktg)*
Lynne Harris *(Sr VP-Science & Tech)*
Jery Huntley *(Exec Dir)*
Barry Eisenberg *(Dir-Commun-Mktg Svcs)*
Tommy Southall *(Dir-Indus Info Svcs)*
Barbara Darby *(Mgr-Workforce Devel)*
Brands & Products:
PLASTICS DATA SOURCE
SPI

SOUTHERN FOREST PRODUCTS ASSOCIATION

2900 Indiana Ave
Kenner, LA 70065
Tel.: (504) 443-4464
Fax: (504) 443-6612
E-mail: mail@sfpa.org
Web Site: www.sfpa.org
E-Mail For Key Personnel:
Public Relations: rwallace@sfpa.org
Approx. Number Employees: 20
Year Founded: 1915
Business Description:
Southern Pine Lumber Trade Association
S.I.C.: 8611
N.A.I.C.S.: 813910
Media: 2-10
Distr.: Natl.
Personnel:
Digges Morgan *(Pres)*
Tami Kessler *(Sec & Dir-Admin)*
Richard Wallace *(VP-Commun)*
Eric Gee *(Dir-Expo & Forest Resources)*
Richard Kleiner *(Dir-Intl-Mktg Dev)*
Catherine Marx Kaake *(Dir-Engineered & Framing Markets)*
Brands & Products:
SOUTHERN FOREST PRODUCTS ASSOCIATION
SOUTHERN PINE BY DESIGN
SOUTHERN PINE COUNCIL
SOUTHERNPINE.COM

THE SOUTHERN POVERTY LAW CENTER

403 Washington Ave
Montgomery, AL 36104-4344
Tel.: (334) 956-8200
Fax: (334) 956-8483
Web Site: www.splcenter.org
Approx. Rev.: $36,000,000
Approx. Number Employees: 110
Year Founded: 1971
Business Description:
Non-Profit Organization for Civil Rights

Key to Media (For complete agency information see *The Advertising Red Books-Agencies* edition):
1. Bus. Publs. 2. Cable T.V. 3. Catalogs & Directories. 4. Co-op Adv. 5. Consumer Mags. 6. D.M. to Bus. Estab.7. D.M. to Consumers
8. Daily Newsp. 9. Exhibits/Trade Shows 10. Foreign 11. Infomercial 12. Internet Adv.13. Multimedia 14. Network Radio
15. Network T.V. 16. Newsp. Distr. Mags. 17. Other 18. Outdoor (Posters, Transit) 19. Point of Purchase20. Premiums, Novelties
21. Product Samples 22. Special Events Mktg. 23. Spot Radio 24. Spot T.V. 25. Weekly Newsp. 26. Yellow Page Adv.

The Southern Poverty Law Center — (Continued)

S.I.C.: 8111; 2721; 8399
N.A.I.C.S.: 541110; 511120; 813319
Media: 8
Personnel:
Morris Dees *(Founder & Chief Trial Atty)*
Joseph J. Levin, Jr. *(Co-Founder)*
James McElroy *(Chm)*
J. Richard Cohen *(Pres)*
Rhonda Brownstein *(Dir-Legal)*
Russell Estes *(Dir-Design)*
Jennifer Holladay *(Dir-Toleranceorg)*
Teenie Hutchison *(Dir-Admin & Fin)*
Mark Potok *(Dir-Intelligence Project)*
Penny Weaver *(Dir-Community Affairs)*
Sam Whalum *(Dir-HR)*
Brands & Products:
PLANET TOLERANCE
SOUTHERN POVERTY LAW CENTER
TEACHING TOLERANCE
TOLERANCE.ORG

SPECIAL OLYMPICS INTERNATIONAL, INC.

1133 19th St NW
Washington, DC 20036
Tel.: (202) 628-3630
Fax: (202) 824-0200
E-mail: info@specialolympics.org
Web Site: www.specialolympics.org
Approx. Number Employees: 150
Business Description:
Organization for Empowering Individuals with Intellectual Disabilities through Competition & Sports Training
S.I.C.: 8322
N.A.I.C.S.: 624120
Media: 6-13-14-15-18-22-23-24
Personnel:
Eunice Kennedy Shriver *(Founder)*
Timothy P. Shriver *(Chm & CEO)*
Raymond J. Lane *(Vice Chm, Mng Partner-Kleiner Perkins Caufield & Byers)*
Stephen M. Carter *(Vice Chm)*
Brady Lun *(Pres & COO)*
Ryan Eaded *(Coord-Media Rels)*
Drake Turrentine *(Chief Legal Officer & Sec)*
Kristen Seckler *(VP-Branding & Comm)*
Advertising Agencies:
Hager Sharp Inc.
1090 Vermont Ave NW 3rd Fl
Washington, DC 20005
Tel.: (202) 842-3600
Fax: (202) 842-4032

TDA Advertising & Design
1500 Pearl St Ste 300
Boulder, CO 80302
Tel.: (303) 247-1180
Fax: (303) 247-1214
(Creative, World Winter Games)

SPELNA, INC.

225 Industrial Ct
Fredericksburg, VA 22408-2420
Tel.: (540) 898-1524
Fax: (540) 898-2674
E-mail: spelnagrp@aol.com
Web Site: spelnadocstorage.com
Approx. Number Employees: 3
Year Founded: 1978
Business Description:
Management Consulting
S.I.C.: 6512; 8742
N.A.I.C.S.: 531120; 541611
Import Export
Media: 2-6-8-19
Distr.: Intl.; Natl.
Budget Set: Nov.
Personnel:
Olivier Jacqueau *(Pres-BCB)*
John Bufalari *(Gen Mgr & Mgr-HR)*

ST. PETERSBURG AREA CHAMBER OF COMMERCE

The Chamber Bldg 100 2nd Ave N Ste 150
Saint Petersburg, FL 33701
Tel.: (727) 821-4069
Fax: (727) 895-6326
Web Site: www.stpete.com
Sales Range: Less than $1 Million
Approx. Number Employees: 15
Year Founded: 1888
Business Description:
Chamber of Commerce
S.I.C.: 8611
N.A.I.C.S.: 813910
Media: 2-6-8-10-13-24
Personnel:
Chris Steinocher *(Pres & CEO)*
Brands & Products:
EXPERIENCE MORE
ST. PETERSBURG AREA CHAMBER OF COMMERCE

STEEL JOIST INSTITUTE

196 Stone Bridge Unit 1
Myrtle Beach, SC 29588-6760
Tel.: (843) 293-1995
Fax: (843) 293-7500
E-mail: sji@steeljoist.org
Web Site: www.steeljoist.org
Approx. Number Employees: 1
Year Founded: 1928
Business Description:
Non-Profit Trade Association
S.I.C.: 8611; 8711
N.A.I.C.S.: 813910; 541330
Media: 2-7-8
Distr.: Natl.
Budget Set: Jan.
Advertising Agency:
Hughes
1141 S 7th St
Saint Louis, MO 63104
Tel.: (314) 571-6300
(Technical Publications)

STEVIE AWARDS, INC.

(d/b/a American Business Awards)
11885 Grand Commons Ave Ste 210
Fairfax, VA 22030
Tel.: (703) 547-8389
Fax: (703) 991-2397
E-mail: info@stevieawards.com
Web Site: www.stevieawards.com
Approx. Sls.: $250,000
Approx. Number Employees: 2
Year Founded: 2002
Business Description:
Awards Programs
S.I.C.: 8611
N.A.I.C.S.: 813910
Advertising Expenditures: $125,000
Media: 2-7-13
Personnel:
Francois Baird *(Co-Founder & Chm)*
Michael P. Gallagher *(Pres)*
Stanford L. Kurland *(COO & Exec Mng Dir)*
Steven Cohen *(Sr VP-HR)*
Leland E. Holly *(Sr VP-HR)*
Chris Harrington *(VP-Sls)*
Jeff Penn *(VP-Sls)*
Brands & Products:
AMERICAN BUSINESS AWARDS
INTERNATIONAL BUSINESS AWARDS
THE STEVES
STEVIE AWARDS
Advertising Agency:
Michael Kaminer Public Relations
1123 Broadwy
New York, NY 10010
Tel.: (212) 627-8098

THE SUGAR ASSOCIATION, INC.

1300 L St NW Ste 1001
Washington, DC 20005
Tel.: (202) 785-1122
Fax: (202) 785-5019
E-mail: sugar@sugar.org
Web Site: www.sugar.org
Sales Range: $10-24.9 Million
Approx. Number Employees: 6
Year Founded: 1943
Business Description:
Trade Association
S.I.C.: 8611
N.A.I.C.S.: 813910
Advertising Expenditures: $3,000,000
Media: 6-10-13-19-23-24
Distr.: Natl.
Budget Set: June
Personnel:
Andrew Briscoe *(Pres & CEO)*
Charles Baker *(Chief Science Officer & Exec VP)*
Mary O'Dell *(Dir-Comml)*
Brands & Products:
SUGAR
THE SUGARMARK
SWEET BY NATURE

SUNCOAST WORKFORCE BOARD, INC.

3660 N Washington Blvd
Sarasota, FL 34234
Tel.: (941) 358-4080
Fax: (941) 358-4085
E-mail: info@swdb.org
Web Site: www.swdb.org
Approx. Rev.: $6,500,000
Approx. Number Employees: 23
Year Founded: 1983
Business Description:
Job Training & Related Services
S.I.C.: 8331
N.A.I.C.S.: 624310
Media: 9-18-22-23-24-25
Personnel:
Mary Helen Kress *(Pres & CEO)*
Robin Dawson *(CFO)*
Leslie Loveless *(COO)*
Chet Filanowski *(Dir-IT)*
Sally Hill *(Dir-Comm)*
Kathy Bouchard *(Mgr-HR)*
Clare Sauve *(Accountant)*

SURFRIDER FOUNDATION

942 Calle Negocio Ste 350
San Clemente, CA 92673
Tel.: (949) 492-8170
Fax: (949) 492-8142
Web Site: www.surfrider.org
Approx. Rev.: $3,900,000
Approx. Number Employees: 35
Year Founded: 2004
Business Description:
Civic/Social Association
S.I.C.: 8641
N.A.I.C.S.: 813410
Personnel:
Jim Moriarty *(CEO)*
Laura Mazzarella *(Mgr-Mktg)*
Kyle Lishok *(Coord-Mktg)*
Advertising Agency:
Borders Perrin Norrander Inc
808 SW 3rd Ave 8th Fl
Portland, OR 97204-2400
Tel.: (503) 227-2506
Fax: (503) 227-4827

SUSAN G. KOMEN FOR THE CURE

5005 LBJ Fwy Ste 250
Dallas, TX 75244
Tel.: (972) 855-1600
Fax: (972) 855-1605
Web Site: www.komen.org
Approx. Number Employees: 250
Year Founded: 1982
Business Description:
Non-Profit Organization for Breast Cancer Research
S.I.C.: 8399
N.A.I.C.S.: 813212
Personnel:
Nancy G. Brinker *(Founder & CEO)*
Alexine Clement Jackson *(Chm)*
Elizabeth Thompson *(Pres)*
Mark E. Nadolny *(CFO)*
Katrina McGhee *(CMO & Exec VP)*
Johnathan Blum *(Gen Counsel)*
Leslie M. Aun *(VP-Mktg & Comm)*
Susan Carter Johns *(VP-Strategic Relationships)*
Tabetha Leinweber *(Dir-Direct Mktg)*
Advertising Agencies:
Duffy & Partners
710 2nd St S Ste 602
Minneapolis, MN 55401
Tel.: (612) 548-2333
Fax: (612) 548-2334

Launch Agency
4100 Midway Rd Ste 2110
Carrollton, TX 75007
Tel.: (972) 818-4100
Fax: (972) 818-4101
Toll Free: (866) 427-5013

Merkle Inc.
7001 Columbia Gateway Dr
Columbia, MD 21046
Tel.: (443) 542-4000
Fax: (443) 542-4001

Star Group Communications, Inc.
(d/b/a The Star Group)
220 Laurel Rd
Voorhees, NJ 08043
Tel.: (856) 782-7000
Fax: (856) 782-5699
Philadelphia Affiliate

Stoltz Marketing Group
615 W Main St 2nd Fl
Boise, ID 83702
Tel.: (208) 388-0766
Fax: (208) 388-0764

Key to Media (For complete agency information see *The Advertising Red Books-Agencies* edition):
1. Bus. Publs. 2. Cable T.V. 3. Catalogs & Directories. 4. Co-op Adv. 5. Consumer Mags. 6. D.M. to Bus. Estab.7. D.M. to Consumers
8. Daily Newsp. 9. Exhibits/Trade Shows 10. Foreign 11. Infomercial 12. Internet Adv.13. Multimedia 14. Network Radio
15. Network T.V. 16. Newsp. Distr. Mags. 17. Other 18. Outdoor (Posters, Transit) 19. Point of Purchase20. Premiums, Novelties
21. Product Samples 22. Special Events Mktg. 23. Spot Radio 24. Spot T.V. 25. Weekly Newsp. 26. Yellow Page Adv.

TracyLocke
1999 Bryan St Ste 2800
Dallas, TX 75201
Tel.: (214) 259-3500
Fax: (214) 259-3550

Weber Shandwick-Dallas
1717 9th St Ste 1600
Dallas, TX 75201
Tel.: (469) 375-0200
Fax: (972) 868-7671

SWITZERLAND CHEESE ASSOCIATES INC.
(Sub. of Switzerland Cheese Marketing AG)
704 Executive Blvd
Valley Cottage, NY 10989
Tel.: (845) 268-2460
Fax: (845) 268-2480
Web Site: www.switzerland-cheesesl.es/cat/services/contact/contact.htm
Approx. Number Employees: 6
Business Description:
Whslr of Cheese & Specialty Products Related to Cheese; Promotion of Natural Cheeses from Switzerland
S.I.C.: 8611; 5143
N.A.I.C.S.: 813910; 424430
Advertising Expenditures: $100,000
Media: 2-6-8-9-10-11-13-18-21-23
Distr.: Natl.
Budget Set: Mar.
Personnel:
Steve Millard *(Exec VP-Mktg)*

SYNTHETIC ORGANIC CHEMICAL MANUFACTURERS ASSOCIATION
(d/b/a SOCMA)
1850 M St NW Ste 700
Washington, DC 20036-5810
Tel.: (202) 721-4100
Fax: (202) 296-8120
E-mail: info@socma.com
Web Site: www.socma.com
Approx. Number Employees: 30
Year Founded: 1921
Business Description:
Trade Association for the Chemicals Industry
S.I.C.: 8611
N.A.I.C.S.: 813910
Media: 2-4-5-7-10-13-20-22
Personnel:
Lawrence D. Sloan *(Pres & CEO)*
C. Tucker Helmes *(Sr Dir)*
Dolores Alonso *(Sr Dir)*
Charlena Patterson *(Sr Dir)*
Ana C. Penaranda *(Sr Dir)*
Liesa Brown *(Dir-Dept Lead & Cross-Promo)*
Holland Jordan *(Dir-ChemStewards)*
Jeff Gunnulfsen *(Sr Mgr-Govt Rels)*
Brands & Products:
CHEMICAL BOND EXPRESS
RESPONSIBLE CARE
SOCMA

TEA ASSOCIATION OF THE USA, INC.
362 5th Ave Rm 801
New York, NY 10001-0899
Tel.: (212) 986-9415
Fax: (212) 697-8658
E-mail: info@teausa.com
Web Site: www.teausa.com
E-Mail For Key Personnel:
President: simrany@teausa.com
Approx. Number Employees: 4
Year Founded: 1899
Business Description:
Tea Promotion & Trade Services
S.I.C.: 8611
N.A.I.C.S.: 813910
Media: 10-22
Distr.: Natl.
Personnel:
Victor J. Ferretti *(Chm)*
Joseph Simrany *(Pres)*

TOWERS WATSON & CO.
875 3rd Ave
New York, NY 10022
Tel.: (212) 725-7550
Web Site: www.towerswatson.com
Approx. Rev.: $2,387,829,000
Approx. Number Employees: 12,750
Business Description:
Human Resources, Risk & Financial Management Services
S.I.C.: 8748
N.A.I.C.S.: 541618
Personnel:
Mark V. Mactas *(Pres & COO)*
John J. Haley *(CEO)*
Roger F. Millay *(CFO & VP)*
Anne Donavan Bodnar *(Chief Admin Officer)*
Walter W. Bardenwerper *(Gen Counsel, Sec & VP)*
Darrell Comis *(Sr VP-Reinsurance Brokerage Bus)*
Patricia L. Guinn *(Mng Dir-Risk & Fin Svcs)*
Anthony Candito *(Head-IT)*
Sharon Clark *(Head-Mktg)*
Gordon L. Gould *(Head-Strategy & Corp Dev)*
Christine Brown *(Editor & Writer-Mktg)*
Mary Malone *(Dir-IR)*
Advertising Agency:
Stein Rogan + Partners
432 Park Ave S
New York, NY 10016-8013
Tel.: (212) 213-1112
Fax: (212) 779-7305

TOY INDUSTRY ASSOCIATION, INC.
1115 Broadway Ste 400
New York, NY 10010-2803
Tel.: (212) 675-1141
Fax: (212) 633-1429
E-mail: info@toyassociation.org
Web Site: www.toyassociation.org
Sales Range: $10-24.9 Million
Approx. Number Employees: 45
Year Founded: 1916
Business Description:
Trade Association for North American Producers & Importers of Toys, Games & Children's Entertainment Products
S.I.C.: 8611
N.A.I.C.S.: 813910
Media: 2-4-10-11
Personnel:
Carter Keithley *(Pres)*
Alan P. Kaufman *(Sr VP-Technical Affairs)*
Jean Butler *(VP-Membership)*
Brands & Products:
AMERICAN INTERNATIONAL TOY FAIR
FALL TOY PREVIEW
TOYCON
Advertising Agency:
G.S. Schwartz & Co. Inc.
470 Park Ave S 10th Fl S
New York, NY 10016-6819
Tel.: (212) 725-4500
Fax: (212) 725-9188
American International Toy Fair

TRADE COMMISSION OF SPAIN
405 Lexington Ave 44 Fl
New York, NY 10174-4499
Tel.: (212) 661-4959
Fax: (212) 972-2494
E-mail: newyork@mcx.es
Sales Range: $10-24.9 Million
Approx. Number Employees: 40
Business Description:
Spanish Wines & Food Products Advertiser & Promoter
S.I.C.: 7389
N.A.I.C.S.: 561990
Advertising Expenditures: $2,500,000
Media: 2-6-19-20-23
Distr.: Intl.; Natl.
Personnel:
Jeffrey Shaw *(Dir-Mktg)*
Paloma Marugan *(Mgr-Mktg)*

TRAVEL INDUSTRY ASSOCIATION OF AMERICA
1100 New York Ave NW Ste 450
Washington, DC 20005-3934
Tel.: (202) 408-8422
Fax: (202) 408-1255
Web Site: www.ustravel.org/
Sales Estimate: $10-19 Million
Approx. Number Employees: 80
Year Founded: 1941
Business Description:
Tourism Promoter & Facilitator; Non-profit Association
S.I.C.: 8699
N.A.I.C.S.: 813990
Media: 2-4-5-7-8-10-13-18
Personnel:
Bruce Bommarito *(Owner)*
Rodger Dow *(Pres & CEO)*
Dawn L. Drew *(Publr & VP)*
Robert Moore *(Exec VP-Sls)*
Graham W. Atkinson *(Sr VP)*
Suzanne D. Cook *(Sr VP-Res)*
Peter J. Strebel *(Sr VP)*
Adam Vance *(Sr VP-Product Devel)*
Kayoko Inoue *(Mng Dir-Intl Mktg)*
Andreas Sappok *(VP & Gen Mgr)*
Regina A. Sullivan *(VP-Pub Affairs)*
Eric Eimstad *(VP-Sls)*
Michael E. Fegley *(VP-Global Sls)*
Felicia Fisher *(VP-Sls)*
Richard Jackson *(VP-Intl Sls)*
David Mimm *(VP-Fin)*
Pamela C. Wright *(Div VP-Sls)*
LaVerne Brown *(Gen Mgr-Sls)*
Susan Bergen *(Dir-Intl Pow Wow Ops)*
Shelley Conway *(Dir-Meeting & Event Svcs)*
Karen Reinhard *(Dir-HR)*
Eiko Tanaka *(Sr Mgr-Intl Mktg)*
Cathy Keefe *(Mgr-Media Rels)*
Michael Martin *(Mgr-Intl Mktg)*
Pat Thach *(Mgr-Production)*
Brands & Products:
SEEAMERICA
U.S TRAVEL ASSOCIATION
Advertising Agency:
Chess Communications Group
901 E Fayette St
Baltimore, MD 21202-4731
Tel.: (410) 732-7400
Fax: (410) 563-0045
Toll Free: (800) 551-0158

UNITE HERE
275 7th Ave
New York, NY 10001-6708
Tel.: (212) 265-7000
Fax: (212) 265-3415
Web Site: www.uniteunion.org
Approx. Number Employees: 1,100
Year Founded: 2004
Business Description:
Labor Union
S.I.C.: 8621
N.A.I.C.S.: 813920
Media: 9-13-23-24-25
Distr.: Natl.
Personnel:
John W. Wilhelm *(Pres)*

UNITED NATIONS CHILDREN'S FUND
(d/b/a UNICEF)
3 United Nations Plz
New York, NY 10017
Tel.: (212) 326-7000
Fax: (212) 888-7465
Fax: (212) 887-7454
E-mail: info@un.org
Web Site: www.un.org
Approx. Rev.: $1,680,000,000
Approx. Number Employees: 7,200
Year Founded: 1946
Business Description:
International Foundation Helping Children in Need
S.I.C.: 8399
N.A.I.C.S.: 813319
Media: 4-7-8-11-12-13-18-22
Personnel:
Caryl Stern *(Pres/CEO-U S Fund)*
Veronica Pollard *(Sr VP-Mktg & Comm-U S Fund)*
Hilde Johnson *(Deputy Exec Dir)*
Anthony Lake *(Exec Dir)*
Matthew Cortellesi *(Mgr-Global Mktg)*
Brands & Products:
UNICEF
Advertising Agencies:
A. Eicoff & Co.
(Div. of Ogilvy & Mather Worldwide)
401 N Michigan Ave 4th Fl
Chicago, IL 60611-4212
Tel.: (312) 527-7183
Fax: (312) 527-7188
Toll Free: (800) 333-6605

BBDO Guerrero
11th Floor Insular Life Building Ayala Avenue corner
Makati, 1226, Philippines
Tel.: (63) 2 892 701
Fax: (63) 892 7501

Casanova Pendrill, LLC
275-A McCormick Ave Ste 100
Costa Mesa, CA 92626-3369
Tel.: (714) 918-8200
Fax: (714) 918-8295

Key to Media (For complete agency information see *The Advertising Red Books-Agencies* edition):
1. Bus. Publs. 2. Cable T.V. 3. Catalogs & Directories. 4. Co-op Adv. 5. Consumer Mags. 6. D.M. to Bus. Estab.7. D.M. to Consumers 8. Daily Newsp. 9. Exhibits/Trade Shows 10. Foreign 11. Infomercial 12. Internet Adv.13. Multimedia 14. Network Radio 15. Network T.V. 16. Newsp. Distr. Mags. 17. Other 18. Outdoor (Posters, Transit) 19. Point of Purchase20. Premiums, Novelties 21. Product Samples 22. Special Events Mktg. 23. Spot Radio 24. Spot T.V. 25. Weekly Newsp. 26. Yellow Page Adv.

United Nations Children's Fund — (Continued)

droga5
400 Lafayette 5th Fl
New York, NY 10003
Tel.: (917) 237-8888
Fax: (917) 237-8889

EastWest Marketing Group
401 5th Ave 4th Fl
New York, NY 10016
Tel.: (212) 951-7220
Fax: (212) 951-7201
Trick-or-Treat for Unicef
Tap Project

Outhouse Communication
22 Fairfield Pl
Fairfield, CT 06824
Tel.: (203) 255-0200
Fax: (203) 255-0209

Posner Advertising
30 Broad St 33rd Fl
New York, NY 10004
Tel.: (212) 867-3900
Fax: (212) 480-3440
Toll Free: (800) 664-3817

UNITED NEGRO COLLEGE FUND, INC.

8260 Willow Oaks Corporate Dr
Fairfax, VA 22031-4513
Tel.: (703) 205-3400
Fax: (703) 205-3446
Toll Free: (800) 331-2244
E-mail: info@uncf.org
Web Site: www.uncf.org
Approx. Rev.: $152,230,009
Approx. Number Employees: 226
Year Founded: 1944
Business Description:
Financial Assistance to Students; Funds to Member & Historically Black Colleges & Universities
S.I.C.: 8399
N.A.I.C.S.: 813319
Advertising Expenditures: $850,000
Media: 2-3-6-7-8-9-13-14-15-18-22-23-24-25
Personnel:
William F. Stasior *(Chm & Treas)*
Alfred G. Goldstein *(Vice Chm)*
Jack L. Stahl *(Vice Chm)*
Michael L. Lomax *(Pres & CEO)*
Hubert C. Graves *(CFO & VP)*
LaJuan H. Lyles *(Chief Admin Officer, Sr VP & Head-HR)*
Shari Crittendon *(Gen Counsel & VP)*
Maurice E. Jenkins *(Sr VP)*
John P. Donohue *(Exec VP)*
James N. Alston *(Sr VP-Field Ops-North)*
Carl Ware *(Sr VP)*
James H. Mayo, III *(VP-Western Field Ops)*
Woodie T. White *(VP-Midwest)*
Anthony Caldwell *(Reg Dir-Dev)*
Paulette Jackson *(Reg Dir-Dev-Overseeing Offices)*
Fred D. Mitchell *(Reg Dir-Dev)*
Cedric Mobley *(Mgr-Mktg)*
Brands & Products:
A MIND IS A TERRIBLE THING TO WASTE
UNCF

UNITED STATES BOWLING CONGRESS

621 Six Flags Dr
Arlington, TX 76011
Tel.: (817) 385-8227
Fax: (817) 385-8262
Toll Free: (800) 514-BOWL
E-mail: bowlinfo@bowl.com
Web Site: www.bowl.com
Sales Range: $10-24.9 Million
Approx. Number Employees: 210
Year Founded: 1996
Business Description:
Bowling Association
S.I.C.: 8611; 8743
N.A.I.C.S.: 813910; 541820
Media: 7-10-13-20
Distr.: Natl.
Budget Set: Sept.
Personnel:
Kevin Dornberger *(COO)*
Pete Tredwell *(Mng Dir-Media)*
Jason Overstreet *(Dir-PR & Publ)*
Brands & Products:
BOWL FOR THE CURE
BOWL WITH US
MEET FOR THE CURE
SPORT BOWLING
USBC COLLEGIATE
USBC HIGH SCHOOL
USBC JUNIOR TEAM USA
USBC TEAM USA

UNITED STATES TELECOM ASSOCIATION

607 14th St NW Ste 400
Washington, DC 20005
Tel.: (202) 326-7300
Fax: (202) 326-7333
E-mail: membership@ustelecom.org
Web Site: www.ustelecom.org
Approx. Number Employees: 40
Year Founded: 1897
Business Description:
Telecommunications Trade Association
S.I.C.: 8611
N.A.I.C.S.: 813910
Media: 2-4-7-10-13-20-22
Distr.: Natl.
Personnel:
Walter B. McCormick, Jr. *(Pres & CEO)*
Brands & Products:
USTELECOM

UNITED THROUGH READING

11750 Sorrento Valley Rd Ste 100
San Diego, CA 92121
Tel.: (858) 481-7323
Fax: (858) 481-9489
E-mail: info@unitedthroughreading.org
Web Site: www.unitedthroughreading.org
Business Description:
Non Profit Facilitating Family Bonding Through Reading
N.A.I.C.S.: 813410
Media: 22
Personnel:
Sally Ann Zoll *(CEO)*

UNTIL THERE'S A CURE FOUNDATION

560 Mtn Home Rd
Redwood City, CA 94062
Tel.: (650) 332-3200
Fax: (650) 332-3210
E-mail: info@utac.org
Web Site: www.until.org
Approx. Number Employees: 3
Business Description:
Nonprofit Organization That Raises Funds & Awareness about HIV/AIDS
S.I.C.: 8399
N.A.I.C.S.: 813319
Media: 6-22
Personnel:
Donna Allen *(Pres)*
Nora Hanna *(Exec Dir)*
Brands & Products:
THE BRACELET
UNTIL THERE'S A CURE

U.S. DAIRY EXPORT COUNCIL

(Sub. of Dairy Management, Inc.)
2101 Wilson Blvd Ste 400
Arlington, VA 22201-3061
Tel.: (703) 528-3049
Fax: (703) 528-3705
E-mail: info@usdec.org
Web Site: www.usdec.org
Approx. Number Employees: 20
Business Description:
U.S. Dairy Exports Promoter
S.I.C.: 5143
N.A.I.C.S.: 424430
Media: 6-10-11-17
Distr.: Intl.; Natl.
Personnel:
Tom Camerlo *(Chm)*
Thomas M. Suber *(Pres)*
Marc A.H. Beck *(Sr VP-Export Mktg)*
Diane Lewis *(Sr VP)*
Margaret Speich *(VP-Comm & Membership)*

USA RICE FEDERATION

4301 N Fairfax Dr Ste 425
Arlington, VA 22203
Tel.: (703) 236-2300
Fax: (703) 236-2301
E-mail: riceinfo@usarice.com
Web Site: www.usarice.com
Approx. Number Employees: 25
Year Founded: 1959
Business Description:
Association Promoting Consumption of Rice
S.I.C.: 8611
N.A.I.C.S.: 813910
Export
Media: 2-7
Distr.: Natl.
Budget Set: June
Personnel:
James W. Warshaw *(Chm)*
Bob Cummings *(Sr VP)*
David Coia *(VP-Commun)*
Lisa Gargano *(Sr Dir-HR & Admin)*
Stacy-Fitzgerald Redd *(Sr Dir-Comm)*
Johnny Broussard *(Dir-Legislative Affairs & Comm)*
Brands & Products:
RICE. A WORLD OF GREAT IDEAS
USA RICE
Advertising Agency:
Gordon Hanrahan, Inc.
150 N Michigan Ave Ste 600
Chicago, IL 60601-7570
Tel.: (312) 372-0935
Fax: (312) 372-1409
(USA Rice)

VERMONT SKI AREAS ASSOCIATION, INC.

(d/b/a Ski Vermont)
26 State St
Montpelier, VT 05602-2943
Tel.: (802) 223-2439
Fax: (802) 229-6917
E-mail: info@skivermont.com
Web Site: www.skivermont.com
Sales Range: $10-24.9 Million
Approx. Number Employees: 5
Year Founded: 1970
Business Description:
Trade Association
S.I.C.: 8611
N.A.I.C.S.: 813910
Advertising Expenditures: $400,000
Media: 6-8-9-13-23-24
Distr.: Reg.
Budget Set: May
Personnel:
Parker Riehle *(Pres)*
Liz Dohrman *(Mgr-Mktg)*
Brands & Products:
SKI VERMONT
Advertising Agencies:
802 Creative Partners, Inc.
768 S Main St PO Box 54
Bethel, VT 05032
Tel.: (802) 234-9755
Fax: (802) 234-6719

Vermont Ski Area Association
26 State St
Montpelier, VT 05601
Tel.: (802) 223-2439
Fax: (802) 229-6917

WASHINGTON STATE APPLE COMMISSION

2900 Euclid Ave
Wenatchee, WA 98801-8102
Mailing Address:
PO Box 18
Wenatchee, WA 98807-0018
Tel.: (509) 663-9600
Fax: (509) 662-5824
E-mail: info@waapple.org
Web Site: www.bestapples.com
Sales Range: $10-24.9 Million
Approx. Number Employees: 9
Year Founded: 1937
Business Description:
Washington State Apples Promoter
S.I.C.: 8611
N.A.I.C.S.: 813910
Export
Media: 11
Distr.: Intl.; Natl.
Budget Set: Sept.
Personnel:
Todd Fryhover *(Pres)*

WASHINGTON STATE DAIRY PRODUCTS COMMISSION

4201 198th St SW Ste 101
Lynnwood, WA 98036-6751
Tel.: (425) 672-0687
Fax: (425) 672-0674
Web Site: www.havemilk.com
Approx. Sls.: $4,500,000
Approx. Number Employees: 16
Year Founded: 1939
Business Description:
Dairy Products Advertiser & Promoter
S.I.C.: 8611
N.A.I.C.S.: 813910

Key to Media (For complete agency information see *The Advertising Red Books-Agencies* edition):
1. Bus. Publs. 2. Cable T.V. 3. Catalogs & Directories. 4. Co-op Adv. 5. Consumer Mags. 6. D.M. to Bus. Estab.7. D.M. to Consumers 8. Daily Newsp. 9. Exhibits/Trade Shows 10. Foreign 11. Infomercial 12. Internet Adv.13. Multimedia 14. Network Radio 15. Network T.V. 16. Newsp. Distr. Mags. 17. Other 18. Outdoor (Posters, Transit) 19. Point of Purchase20. Premiums, Novelties 21. Product Samples 22. Special Events Mktg. 23. Spot Radio 24. Spot T.V. 25. Weekly Newsp. 26. Yellow Page Adv.

Advertising Expenditures: $2,584,000
Bus. Publs.: $11,000; Co-op Adv.: $200,000; Daily Newsp.: $375,000; Network T.V.: $200,000; Outdoor (Posters, Transit): $390,000; Point of Purchase: $150,000; Premiums, Novelties: $20,000; Spot Radio: $658,000; Spot T.V.: $580,000
Distr.: Reg.
Budget Set: May
Personnel:
Stephen Matzen *(Gen Mgr)*
Debra French *(Exec Dir)*
Martha Marino *(Dir-Nutrition Affairs)*
Celeste Piette *(Dir-Ops & Bus Mgmt)*
Lynne Schmoe *(Dir-Industry Comm)*
Jeff Steele *(Dir-Retail Promos)*
Blair Thompson *(Dir-Consumer Comm)*
Cara Stayton *(Mgr-School Programs)*

WASHINGTON STATE FRUIT COMMISSION
105 S 18th St Ste 205
Yakima, WA 98901-2176
Tel.: (509) 453-4837
Fax: (509) 453-4880
E-mail: stonefruit@wastatefruit.com
Web Site: www.nwcherries.com
Sales Range: $10-24.9 Million
Approx. Number Employees: 20
Year Founded: 1947
Business Description:
Cherries, Apricots, Peaches, Nectarines, Plums & Prunes Distr & Marketer
S.I.C.: 5148; 8611
N.A.I.C.S.: 424480; 813910
Advertising Expenditures: $650,000
Media: 1-2-5-6-9-10-11-13-14-18-19-20-21-22-23-24-25
Distr.: Natl.
Budget Set: Jan.
Personnel:
B.J. Thurlby *(Pres)*
Keith Hu *(Dir-Mktg)*
Brands & Products:
NORTHWEST CHERRY GROWERS

WELLSTAR HEALTH SYSTEM, INC.
805 Sandy Plains Rd
Marietta, GA 30066
Tel.: (770) 792-7600
Fax: (770) 793-7975
Web Site: www.wellstar.org
Sales Range: $1-4.9 Billion
Approx. Number Employees: 600
Business Description:
Healthcare; Physicians, Hospitals, Hospice, Home Care Programs, Senior Living, Urgent Care Facilities
S.I.C.: 8062; 8011; 8049; 8071; 8082; 8099
N.A.I.C.S.: 622110; 621112; 621399; 621511; 621610; 621999
Media: 4-6-22
Personnel:
Janie Maddox *(Vice Chm)*
Gregory L. Simone *(Pres & CEO)*
Jim Budzinksi *(CFO & Exec VP)*
Michael Andrews *(Chief Oncology Officer)*
Bill Mayfield *(Chief Surgical Officer)*
Alan Muster *(Chief Pulmonary Officer)*

WESTAT INC.
1600 Research Blvd
Rockville, MD 20850
Tel.: (301) 251-1500
Fax: (301) 294-2040
E-mail: marketing@westat.com
Web Site: www.westat.com
E-Mail For Key Personnel:
Marketing Director: marketing@westat.com
Approx. Number Employees: 2,700
Year Founded: 1961
Business Description:
Statistical Survey Research
S.I.C.: 8732
N.A.I.C.S.: 541910
Media: 1-2-7-10-13
Distr.: Intl.; Natl.
Budget Set: Dec.
Personnel:
Thomas McKenna *(Exec VP)*
James Smith *(Sr VP)*
Bruce F. Romer *(VP & Dir-Admin)*
Peter Gill *(VP-Contracts & Acctg)*
Brands & Products:
CHESHIRE
EXCELLENCE IN RESEARCH
WESTAT
WESVAR

WESTERN WOOD PRODUCTS ASSOCIATION
522 SW 5th Ave Ste 500
Portland, OR 97204-2122
Tel.: (503) 224-3930
Fax: (503) 224-3934
Fax: (503) 224-3935
E-mail: info@wwpa.org
Web Site: www.wwpa.org
Approx. Rev.: $4,000,000
Approx. Number Employees: 50
Year Founded: 1964
Business Description:
Lumber Products Trade Association
S.I.C.: 8611
N.A.I.C.S.: 813910
Media: 1-2-7-10
Distr.: Intl.; Natl.
Budget Set: Apr.
Personnel:
Eric Schooler *(Chm)*
Duane Vaagen *(Chm)*
Kevin Binam *(Pres & CEO)*
Robert Bernhardt, Jr. *(Dir-Info Svcs)*
Robert Butch *(Dir-Info Svcs)*
Kevin C.K. Cheung *(Dir-Tech Svcs)*

THE WHAT TO EXPECT FOUNDATION
211 W 80th St Lowr Level
New York, NY 10024
Tel.: (212) 712-9764
Fax: (212) 712-9741
E-mail: info@whattoexpect.org
Web Site: www.whattoexpect.org
Sales Range: $10-24.9 Million
Approx. Number Employees: 15
Business Description:
Pregnancy Information Foundation
S.I.C.: 8641
N.A.I.C.S.: 813410
Media: 6-10-13
Personnel:
Heidi Murkoff *(Pres)*
Lisa Bernstein *(Exec Dir)*

WIKIMEDIA FOUNDATION INC.
PO Box 78350
San Francisco, CA 94107-8350
Tel.: (415) 839-6885
Fax: (415) 882-0495
E-mail: info@wikimedia.org
Web Site:
www.wikimediafoundation.org
Sales Range: $10-24.9 Million
Approx. Number Employees: 50
Business Description:
Free Educational Content Collection & Development Services
S.I.C.: 2741
N.A.I.C.S.: 516110
Personnel:
Jan-Bart de Vreede *(Vice Chm)*
Stuart West *(Vice Chm)*
Veronique Kessler *(CFO & COO)*
Cyn Skyberg *(Chief Talent Officer & Chief Culture Officer)*
Geoff Brigham *(Gen Counsel)*
Jay Walsh *(Head-Comm)*
Domas Mituzas *(Engr-Data & Performance)*
Advertising Agency:
Peppercom
470 Park Ave S 5th Fl
New York, NY 10016
Tel.: (212) 931-6100
Fax: (212) 931-6159
(5th Annual Giving Campaign)

WILDAID
744 Montgomery St Ste 120
San Francisco, CA 94111
Tel.: (415) 834-3174
Fax: (415) 834-1759
E-mail: info@wildaid.org
Web Site: www.wildaid.org
Sales Range: Less than $1 Million
Approx. Number Employees: 20
Business Description:
Wildlife Protection
S.I.C.: 8399
N.A.I.C.S.: 813312
Media: 7-8-13
Personnel:
Steve Trent *(Pres)*
Peter Knights *(Exec Dir-San Francisco)*
Advertising Agency:
JWT U.S.A., Inc.
(d/b/a JWT-Team Detroit)
550 Town Ctr Dr
Dearborn, MI 48126
Tel.: (313) 615-3100
Tel.: (313) 615-2000 (Team Detroit)
Fax: (313) 964-3191
Fax: (212) 615-4600

WINDOW & DOOR MANUFACTURERS ASSOCIATION
401 N Michigan Ave Ste 2200
Chicago, IL 60611
Tel.: (312) 321-6802
Fax: (312) 673-6922
Toll Free: (800) 223-2301
E-mail: wdma@wdma.com
Web Site: www.wdma.com
Approx. Number Employees: 7
Year Founded: 1928
Business Description:
Window & Door Manufacturers Association
S.I.C.: 8611; 5031
N.A.I.C.S.: 813910; 423310
Media: 1-2-4-5-6-7-10-13-19-22-26
Distr.: Natl.
Budget Set: Feb.
Personnel:
Michael O. Brian *(Pres & CEO)*
Advertising Agency:
James O. Ahtes, Inc.
3813 Mission Hills Road
Northbrook, IL 60062-5711
Tel.: (847) 205-5689

WISCONSIN BEEF COUNCIL, INC.
632 Grand Canyon Dr
Madison, WI 53719-2904
Tel.: (608) 833-7177
Fax: (608) 833-4725
E-mail: info@beeftips.com
Web Site: www.beeftips.com
Approx. Number Employees: 3
Year Founded: 1986
Business Description:
Promoter of Beef/Veal through Promotion, Consumer Education & Research
S.I.C.: 8611
N.A.I.C.S.: 813910
Media: 13-19-23
Personnel:
John W. Freitag *(Exec Dir)*
Angela Horkan *(Dir-Mktg)*

WISCONSIN MILK MARKETING BOARD, INC.
8418 Excelsior Dr
Madison, WI 53717
Tel.: (608) 836-8820
Fax: (608) 836-5822
Toll Free: (800) 373WMMB
E-mail: feedback@wmmb.org
Web Site:
www.eatwisconsincheese.com
Sales Range: $25-49.9 Million
Approx. Number Employees: 50
Year Founded: 1984
Business Description:
Trade Association for Milk Products
S.I.C.: 8611; 8733
N.A.I.C.S.: 813910; 541710
Advertising Expenditures: $3,450,000
Media: 10
Distr.: Natl.
Budget Set: Apr.
Personnel:
James Robson *(CEO)*
Patrick Geoghegan *(Sr VP-Corp Comm)*
Dave Bavlnka *(VP-Mktg-Fluid & Related Products)*
Advertising Agencies:
Shine Advertising
612 W Main St Ste 105
Madison, WI 53703
Tel.: (608) 442-7373
Fax: (608) 442-7374
Wisconsin Cheese

Stephan & Brady, Inc.
1850 Hoffman St
Madison, WI 53704-2541
Tel.: (608) 241-4141
Fax: (608) 241-4246
(Dairy Prod. Promo. & Adv.)

W.K. KELLOGG FOUNDATION
1 Michigan Ave E
Battle Creek, MI 49017-4005

Key to Media (For complete agency information see *The Advertising Red Books-Agencies* edition):
1. Bus. Publs. 2. Cable T.V. 3. Catalogs & Directories. 4. Co-op Adv. 5. Consumer Mags. 6. D.M. to Bus. Estab.7. D.M. to Consumers
8. Daily Newsp. 9. Exhibits/Trade Shows 10. Foreign 11. Infomercial 12. Internet Adv.13. Multimedia 14. Network Radio
15. Network T.V. 16. Newsp. Distr. Mags. 17. Other 18. Outdoor (Posters, Transit) 19. Point of Purchase20. Premiums, Novelties
21. Product Samples 22. Special Events Mktg. 23. Spot Radio 24. Spot T.V. 25. Weekly Newsp. 26. Yellow Page Adv.

W.K. Kellogg Foundation — (Continued)

Tel.: (269) 968-1611
Fax: (269) 968-0413
Web Site: www.wkkf.org
Sales Range: $125-149.9 Million
Approx. Number Employees: 205
Year Founded: 1930
Business Description:
Youth & Education Grantmaking Organization
S.I.C.: 8399
N.A.I.C.S.: 813219; 813319
Media: 22
Personnel:
Sterling K. Speirn *(Pres & CEO)*
La June Montgomery-Talley *(COO & Treas)*
Joel Wittenberg *(Chief Investment Officer & VP)*
Kara Inae Carlisle *(Program Officer)*
Susan Katz Froning *(Gen Counsel)*
James E. McHale *(Sr VP-Programs)*
Timothy L. Dechant *(Dir-Tech)*
Norman Howard *(Dir-HR)*
Reginald G. Sanders *(Dir-Investments)*
Ali Webb *(Dir)*
Advertising Agencies:
Felder Communications Group
50 Louis NW Ste 600
Grand Rapids, MI 49503
Tel.: (616) 459-1200
Fax: (616) 459-2080

Pace & Partners
1223 Turner St Ste 101
Lansing, MI 48906
Tel.: (517) 267-9800
Fax: (517) 267-9815

WORD OF LIFE FELLOWSHIP, INC.

PO Box 600
Schroon Lake, NY 12870
Tel.: (518) 494-6000
Fax: (518) 494-6306
E-mail: info@wol.org
Web Site: www.wol.org
Sales Range: $100-124.9 Million
Approx. Number Employees: 300
Business Description:
Religious Organization; Radio Progam Producer; Theatrical Producer
S.I.C.: 8661; 4832; 7361; 7389
N.A.I.C.S.: 813110; 512290; 515111; 515112; 561310
Media: 9-22-25
Personnel:
Wayne Lewis *(Founder & Dir)*
Harry Bollback *(Founder)*
Joe Jordan *(Exec Dir)*

WORKFORCE FAIRNESS INSTITUTE

607 14th St NW Ste 500
Washington, DC 20005
Tel.: (202) 354-8267
E-mail: workforcefairnessinstitute@workforcefairness.com
Web Site: www.workforcefairness.org
Approx. Number Employees: 3
Business Description:
Issue Educational Organization
S.I.C.: 9411
N.A.I.C.S.: 923110
Media: 10-13
Personnel:
Kathryn Packer *(Pres)*

WORLD GOLD COUNCIL

424 Madison Ave
New York, NY 10017
Tel.: (212) 317-3800
Fax: (212) 688-0410
E-mail: info@gold.org
Web Site: www.gold.org
Approx. Number Employees: 11
Year Founded: 1985
Business Description:
Gold & Gold-Related Products Promoter
S.I.C.: 8611
N.A.I.C.S.: 813910
Media: 1-2-5-6-7-8-9-10-16-19-22-25
Distr.: Intl.; Natl.
Personnel:
Ian Telfer *(Chm)*
Aram Shishmanian *(CEO)*
Jason Toussaint *(Mng Dir)*
Mike Pace *(VP-Mktg)*
Brands & Products:
THE GOLD FASHIONED GIRLS
THERE'S ONE LANGUAGE EVERYONE UNDERSTANDS
WORLD GOLD COUNCIL
Advertising Agency:
Cubitt Jacobs & Prosek Communications
1552 Post Rd
Stratford, CT 06824
Tel.: (203) 378-1152
Fax: (203) 375-1112

WORLD WILDLIFE FUND CANADA

(Affil. of WWF International)
(d/b/a WWF-Canada)
245 Eglinton Ave E Ste 410
Toronto, ON M4P 3J1, Canada
Tel.: (416) 489-8800
Fax: (416) 489-3611
Toll Free: (800) 267-2632
E-mail: ca-panda@wwfcanada.org
Web Site: www.wwf.ca
Sales Range: $10-24.9 Million
Approx. Number Employees: 50
Year Founded: 1967
Business Description:
Research & Conservation Projects
S.I.C.: 8399
N.A.I.C.S.: 813312
Media: 6-8-9-12-13-18-22-25
Personnel:
Patricia Koval *(Chm)*
Gerald Butts *(Pres & CEO)*
Grahame J. Cliff *(CFO, VP-Fin & Admin)*
Arlin Hackman *(VP & Chief Conservation Officer)*
Shawn Mitchell *(VP-HR & Comm)*
Davis Ross *(VP-Mktg & Donor Rels)*
Christina Topp *(Dir-Mktg)*
Maureen Harrison *(Dir-Human & Volunteer Resources)*
Josh Laughren *(Dir-Comm)*
Jenifer Jobbins *(Office Mgr)*
Advertising Agency:
Draftfcb Toronto
(Canadian Headquarters)
245 Eglinton Avenue East Suite 300
Toronto, ON M4P 3C2, Canada
Tel.: (416) 483-3600
Fax: (416) 489-8782
— Jeremy Marten *(Grp Acct Dir)*

WORLD WILDLIFE FUND, INC.

(Affil. of WWF International)
1250 24th St NW 6th Fl
Washington, DC 20037
Mailing Address:
PO Box 96555
Washington, DC 20077
Tel.: (202) 293-4800
Fax: (202) 293-9211
Toll Free: (800) 960-0993
Web Site: www.worldwildlife.org
Approx. Rev.: $160,769,961
Approx. Number Employees: 300
Business Description:
Wildlife Conservation Organization
S.I.C.: 8399
N.A.I.C.S.: 813312
Media: 6-13
Personnel:
Lawrence H. Linden *(Co-Chm)*
Roger W. Sant *(Co-Chm)*
Carter S. Roberts *(Pres & CEO)*
Michael Bauer *(CFO)*
Marcia W. Marsh *(COO)*
Terry Macko *(CMO)*
Margaret L. Ackerley *(Gen Counsel & Sr VP)*
Ginette Hemley *(Sr VP-Conservation Strategy & Sciences)*
Kerry Green Zobor *(VP-Comm)*
Steve Ertel *(Sr Dir-Media Rels & External Comm)*
Anne Topp *(Dir-Network Svcs)*
Brands & Products:
WILDFINDER
WWF
Advertising Agency:
Heller Communications
100 Jay St Unit 12 C
Brooklyn, NY 11201
Tel.: (718) 222-4800
Fax: (212) 937-2406

YELLOW PAGES INTEGRATED MEDIA ASSOCIATION

(d/b/a Yellow Pages Association)
400 Connell Dr Ste 1100
Berkeley Heights, NJ 07922
Tel.: (908) 286-2380
Fax: (908) 286-0620
Web Site: www.ypassociation.org
Sales Range: $10-24.9 Million
Approx. Number Employees: 25
Year Founded: 1988
Business Description:
Membership Services to Yellow Pages Integrated Media Industry
S.I.C.: 8611
N.A.I.C.S.: 813910
Media: 2-7-8-10-13-18-19-20-21-22
Personnel:
Negley Norton *(Pres)*
Donna G. Borowicz *(CFO)*
Stephanie Hobbs *(VP-Mktg Comm)*
Cindi Aldrich *(Dir-Membership Dev)*
Amy Healy *(Dir-Public Policy)*
Kacy Hayner *(Comm Mgr)*
Brands & Products:
ELINC
IT PAYS. WE'LL PROVE IT.
MARKETING THE MEDIUM
RATES & DATA
YELLOW PAGES ASSOCIATION
YELLOW PAGES CO-OP
YELLOW PAGES INTEGRATED MEDIA ASSOCIATION
YELLOW PAGES RESEARCH INSTITUTE
YPA CO-OP
YPA CONNECTION
YPA ELITE
YPA IRIS
YPA IRIS ONLINE
YPA RATES & DATA

YOUNG ENTREPRENEURS' ORGANIZATION

500 Montgomery St Ste 500
Alexandria, VA 22314-5501
Tel.: (703) 519-6700
Fax: (703) 519-1864 6700
E-mail: info@eonetwork.org
Web Site: www.eonetwork.org
Approx. Number Employees: 40
Business Description:
Business Organization
S.I.C.: 8611
N.A.I.C.S.: 813910
Export
Media: 2-22

ZERO - THE PROJECT TO END PROSTATE CANCER

10 G St NE Ste 601
Washington, DC 20002
Tel.: (202) 463-9455
Fax: (571) 257-8559
Toll Free: (888) 245-9455
E-mail: info@zerocancer.org
Web Site: www.zerocancer.org
Approx. Number Employees: 15
Business Description:
Prostate Cancer Foundation
S.I.C.: 8399
N.A.I.C.S.: 813212
Media: 6-7-8-10-22
Personnel:
Skip Lockwood *(CEO)*
Jamie Bearse *(COO)*
Kevin Johnson *(Sr VP-Govt Rels & Advocacy)*
Betsy London *(Sr VP-Events)*
Linwood Norman *(Dir-Comm)*
Tracy Amish *(Coord-Events)*

ZOGBY INTERNATIONAL, INC.

(Sub. of IBOPE Group)
901 Broad St
Utica, NY 13501
Tel.: (315) 624-0200
Fax: (315) 624-0210
E-mail: leads@zogby.com
Web Site: www.zogby.com
Sales Range: Less than $1 Million
Approx. Number Employees: 300
Year Founded: 1984
Business Description:
Opinion & Market Research
S.I.C.: 8742; 8732
N.A.I.C.S.: 541613; 541910
Export
Advertising Expenditures: $100,000
Media: 2-8-13
Personnel:
John Zogby *(Chm)*
Chad T. Bohnert *(CMO)*
Rebecca Wittman *(VP & Mng Editor)*
Rosemary Penz *(VP-Fin)*
Gary Smith *(Comptroller)*
Rose Kolwaite *(Mgr-Call Center)*

Key to Media (For complete agency information see *The Advertising Red Books-Agencies* edition):
1. Bus. Publs. 2. Cable T.V. 3. Catalogs & Directories. 4. Co-op Adv. 5. Consumer Mags. 6. D.M. to Bus. Estab.7. D.M. to Consumers
8. Daily Newsp. 9. Exhibits/Trade Shows 10. Foreign 11. Infomercial 12. Internet Adv.13. Multimedia 14. Network Radio
15. Network T.V. 16. Newsp. Distr. Mags. 17. Other 18. Outdoor (Posters, Transit) 19. Point of Purchase20. Premiums, Novelties
21. Product Samples 22. Special Events Mktg. 23. Spot Radio 24. Spot T.V. 25. Weekly Newsp. 26. Yellow Page Adv.

A-1 LIMOUSINE INC.
2 Emmons Dr
Princeton, NJ 08540
Tel.: (909) 951-0070
Fax: (609) 452-0816
Toll Free: (888) 215-4662
E-mail: info@a1limo.com
Web Site: www.a1limo.com
Approx. Number Employees: 423
Year Founded: 1970
Business Description:
Limousine Rental Services
S.I.C.: 4119
N.A.I.C.S.: 485320
Media: 2-9-13-23-25
Personnel:
Michael Starr *(CEO)*
Malcolm Frankel *(Dir-Sls & Mktg)*
Brands & Products:
A-1 LIMOUSINE
FOR PEOPLE GOING PLACES
Advertising Agency:
Creative Marketing Alliance Inc.
191 Clarksville Rd
Princeton Junction, NJ 08550
Tel.: (609) 297-2222
Fax: (609) 799-7032
— Kaitlin Welch *(Acct Exec)*

ADELPHI ENTERPRISES L.P.
(d/b/a Bredemann Lexus in Glenview)
2000 Waukegan Rd
Glenview, IL 60025
Tel.: (847) 729-6000
Fax: (847) 729-6090
E-mail: lexusservice@bredemann.com
Web Site: www.lexus.bredemann.com
Approx. Number Employees: 100
Year Founded: 1988
Business Description:
New & Used Car Dealers
S.I.C.: 5511
N.A.I.C.S.: 441110
Media: 8-23-24
Personnel:
Joseph Bredemann, Jr. *(Pres)*
Martin Bredemann *(Gen Mgr)*

ADVANTAGE BMW CLEAR LAKE
(Holding of Group 1 Automotive, Inc.)
400 Gulf Freeway
League City, TX 77573
Tel.: (281) 557-7000
Fax: (281) 557-7020
E-mail: info@advantagecl.com
Web Site: www.advantagecl.com
Sales Range: $50-74.9 Million
Approx. Number Employees: 100
Business Description:
New Car Dealership
S.I.C.: 5599
N.A.I.C.S.: 441229
Media: 3-8-13

ADVANTAGE BMW DOWNTOWN
(Holding of Group 1 Automotive, Inc.)
2101 San Jacinto
Houston, TX 77002
Tel.: (713) 289-1200
Fax: (713) 289-1230
Web Site: www.advantagedt.com
Sales Range: $50-74.9 Million
Approx. Number Employees: 70
Business Description:
New Car Dealership
S.I.C.: 5599
N.A.I.C.S.: 441229
Media: 3-8-13

AIRSTREAM, INC.
(Sub. of Thor Industries, Inc.)
419 W Pike St PO Box 629
Jackson Center, OH 45334-9728
Tel.: (937) 596-6111
Fax: (937) 596-7941
Web Site: www.airstream.com
Sales Range: $200-249.9 Million
Approx. Number Employees: 450
Business Description:
Recreational Vehicles & Trailers Mfr
S.I.C.: 3792; 3716
N.A.I.C.S.: 336214; 336213
Media: 5
Personnel:
Larry Huttle *(Chm)*
Robert Wheeler *(Pres & CEO)*
Mark Wahl *(Sr VP-Ops)*
Brands & Products:
AIRSTREAM MOTOR HOMES & TRAVEL TRAILERS

ALL STAR CARTS AND VEHICLES CORP.
1565D 5th Industrial Ct
Bay Shore, NY 11706
Tel.: (631) 666-5252
Fax: (631) 666-1319
Toll Free: (800) 831-3166
E-mail: info@allstarcarts.com
Web Site: www.allstarcarts.com
Approx. Number Employees: 60
Year Founded: 1971
Business Description:
Custom-Made Carts, Kiosks, Trucks & Trailer Mfr
S.I.C.: 2531; 3792
N.A.I.C.S.: 337127; 336214
Export
Media: 4-10-26
Distr.: Natl.
Budget Set: Aug.
Personnel:
Stephen L. Kronrad *(Pres & Dir-Pur)*
Robert B. Kronrad *(Sr VP & Chief Engr)*

AM GENERAL, LLC
(Joint Venture of MacAndrews & Forbes Holdings Inc. & The Renco Group Inc.)
105 N Niles Ave
South Bend, IN 46617
Mailing Address:
PO Box 7025
South Bend, IN 46617
Tel.: (574) 237-6222
Fax: (574) 284-2910
Web Site: www.amgeneral.com
Approx. Number Employees: 130
Business Description:
High-Mobility Vehicles Mfr; Owned 70% by MacAndrews & Forbes Holding Inc. & 30 % by Renco Group Inc.
S.I.C.: 3795; 3714
N.A.I.C.S.: 336992; 336399
Media: 2
Distr.: Intl.; Natl.
Budget Set: Sept. -Oct.
Personnel:
James A. Armour *(Chm)*
Robert J. Gula *(Pres)*
Paul J. Cafiero *(CFO & VP)*
Brands & Products:
EMS
HMMWV
HUMMER
HUMVEE
Advertising Agency:
Villing & Company, Inc.
5909 Nimtz Pkwy
South Bend, IN 46628
Tel.: (574) 277-0215
Fax: (574) 277-5513

AMERICAN HONDA MOTOR CO., INC.
(Sub. of Honda Motor Co., Ltd.)
1919 Torrance Blvd
Torrance, CA 90501-2722
Tel.: (310) 783-2000
Fax: (310) 783-2110
Web Site: www.honda.com
Approx. Number Employees: 35
Year Founded: 1948
Business Description:
Motorcycles, Autos & Power Products Mfr
S.I.C.: 5012; 3711
N.A.I.C.S.: 423110; 336111
Import Export
Advertising Expenditures: $1,325,000,000
Media: 3-6-9-10-13-15-16-18-22-23-24-26
Distr.: Natl.
Personnel:
Tetsuo Iwamura *(Pres & CEO)*
Shinichi Sakamoto *(Treas & VP-Fin)*
John Mendel *(Exec VP)*
Gary Kessler *(Sr VP-HR, Admin & Corp Affairs)*
Steve Center *(VP-Adv & PR)*
Susie Rossick *(Sr Mgr-Natl Adv-Acura)*
Tom Peyton *(Brand Mgr)*
Stephen Ellis *(Mgr-Fuel Cell Mktg)*
Jenny Howell *(Mgr-Acura Reg Mktg)*
Barbara Ponce *(Mgr-Corp & Diversity Adv)*
Advertising Agencies:
Concept Cafe Advertising
3930 NE 2nd Ave Ste 200
Miami, FL 33137
Tel.: (305) 856-4567
Fax: (305) 722-2219

La Agencia de Orci & Asociados
11620 Wilshire Blvd Ste 600
Los Angeles, CA 90025-1706
Tel.: (310) 444-7300
Fax: (310) 478-3587
(Hispanic Consumer Marketing)

RPA
(Rubin Postaer and Associates)
2525 Colorado Ave
Santa Monica, CA 90404
Tel.: (310) 394-4000

Key to Media (For complete agency information see *The Advertising Red Books-Agencies* edition):
1. Bus. Publs. 2. Cable T.V. 3. Catalogs & Directories. 4. Co-op Adv. 5. Consumer Mags. 6. D.M. to Bus. Estab.7. D.M. to Consumers
8. Daily Newsp. 9. Exhibits/Trade Shows 10. Foreign 11. Infomercial 12. Internet Adv.13. Multimedia 14. Network Radio
15. Network T.V. 16. Newsp. Distr. Mags. 17. Other 18. Outdoor (Posters, Transit) 19. Point of Purchase20. Premiums, Novelties
21. Product Samples 22. Special Events Mktg. 23. Spot Radio 24. Spot T.V. 25. Weekly Newsp. 26. Yellow Page Adv.

American Honda Motor Co., Inc. — (Continued)

Fax: (310) 633-7099
(Automobiles, Fit)
Media Agency of Record

AMERICAN SUZUKI MOTOR CORPORATION

(Sub. of Suzuki Motor Corporation)
3251 E Imperial Hwy
Brea, CA 92821-6722
Tel.: (714) 996-7040
Fax: (714) 524-8499
Web Site: www.suzuki.com
E-Mail For Key Personnel:
President: rsuzuki@suz.com
Public Relations: csmitharnold@suz.com
Approx. Number Employees: 350
Business Description:
Automobiles, Motorcycles & Outboard Motors Distr
S.I.C.: 5012
N.A.I.C.S.: 423110
Import
Media: 3-4-5-6-10-14-15-16-18-19-22-23-24-25-26
Distr.: Natl.
Budget Set: Apr.
Personnel:
Kinji Saito *(Pres)*
Michio Suzuki *(CEO)*
Masafumi Harano *(Exec VP-Automotive)*
Hideaki Tanaka *(VP-Opers & HR)*
Larry Vandiver *(Sr Dir-Sls & Mktg)*
Robert Elliott *(Mgr-Adv)*
Ben Hilverda *(Mgr-Adv-Automotive)*
Brands & Products:
AERIO
CCI
DUALSPORT
ESTEEM
ESTEEM WAGON
GRAND VITARA
KATANA
KING QUAD
MECHANIC TO MECHANIC
PEI
QUADRUNNER
QUADSPORT
SAVAGE
SWIFT
VITARA
XL-7
Advertising Agencies:
Academy Communications Inc.
677-C Alpha Dr Ste C
Cleveland, OH 44143
Tel.: (440) 646-9900
Fax: (440) 646-8999

Kilgannon
1360 Peachtree St Ste 700
Atlanta, GA 30309
Tel.: (404) 876-2800
Fax: (404) 876-2830

PainePR
19000 MacArthur Blvd 8 Fl
Irvine, CA 92612-1438
Tel.: (949) 809-6700
Fax: (949) 260-1116
Toll Free: (866) PAINEPR

Questus
1 Beach St Ste 103
San Francisco, CA 94133
Tel.: (415) 677-5700
Fax: (415) 677-9517
Hayabusa

Siltanen & Partners
353 Coral Cir
El Segundo, CA 90245
Tel.: (310) 321-5200
Fax: (310) 321-5270
Equator
Grarnd Vitara

AMERICAN TOWER CORPORATION

116 Huntington Ave 11th Fl
Boston, MA 02116-5749
Tel.: (617) 375-7500
Fax: (617) 375-7575
E-mail: ir@americantower.com
Web Site: www.americantower.com
Approx. Rev.: $1,985,335,000
Approx. Number Employees: 1,729
Year Founded: 1995
Business Description:
Owner, Developer & Operator of Wireless Communications Towers
S.I.C.: 4812
N.A.I.C.S.: 517212
Media: 2-10
Personnel:
James D. Taiclet, Jr. *(Chm, Pres & CEO)*
Amit Sharma *(Pres & Exec VP-Asia)*
Thomas A. Bartlett *(CFO)*
Edmund Disanto *(Chief Admin Officer, Gen Counsel & Exec VP)*
William H. Hess *(Pres-Latin America & Exec VP-Intl Ops & Intl Bus Dev)*
Steven C. Marshall *(Pres-US Tower Div & Exec VP)*

AMERICA'S CAR-MART, INC.

802 Southeast Plaza Ave Ste 200
Bentonville, AR 72712
Tel.: (479) 464-9944
Fax: (479) 273-7556
E-mail: investorinfo@car-mart.com
Web Site: www.car-mart.com
Approx. Rev.: $379,251,000
Approx. Number Employees: 1,025
Year Founded: 1981
Business Description:
Car Dealership Owner & Operator
S.I.C.: 5521
N.A.I.C.S.: 441120
Advertising Expenditures: $3,400,000
Media: 9-14-15
Personnel:
Tilman J. Falgout, III *(Chm & Gen Counsel)*
William H. Henderson *(Vice Chm, Pres & CEO)*
Jeffrey A. Williams *(CFO, Sec & VP-Fin)*
Eddie L. Hight *(COO)*
Brands & Products:
AMERICAS CAR-MART
DRIVE EASY

AMP HOLDING INC.

(Formerly TITLE STARTS ONLINE, INC.)
4540 Alpine Rd
Blue Ash, OH 45242
Tel.: (513) 360-4704
E-mail: admin@ampelectricvehicles.com
Web Site: www.ampelectricvehicles.com
Approx. Rev.: $140,707
Approx. Number Employees: 27
Year Founded: 2007
Business Description:
Automobiles & Other Vehicle Modification Mfr & Sales
S.I.C.: 3711; 5599
N.A.I.C.S.: 336111; 441229
Advertising Expenditures: $261,000
Media: 17
Personnel:
Joseph S. Paresi *(Chm)*
James E. Taylor *(Vice Chm & CEO)*
Stephen S. Burns *(Pres & Sec)*
Paul Vincent Gonzales *(CFO)*

ANCIRA ENTERPRISES INC.

6111 Bandera Rd
San Antonio, TX 78238-1643
Tel.: (210) 681-4900
Fax: (210) 681-9413
Toll Free: (800) 299-5286
Web Site: www.ancira.com
Approx. Number Employees: 300
Year Founded: 1983
Business Description:
New & Used Automobiles Retailer
S.I.C.: 5511; 6512
N.A.I.C.S.: 441110; 531120
Media: 23-24
Distr.: Reg.
Personnel:
Ernesto Ancira *(Owner)*
Betty Ferguson *(CFO)*
Greg Spence *(Exec VP)*

ASBURY AUTOMOTIVE GROUP, INC.

2905 Premiere Pkwy Ste 300
Duluth, GA 30097
Tel.: (770) 418-8200
Fax: (678) 542-2701
E-mail: info@asburyauto.com
Web Site: www.asburyauto.com
E-Mail For Key Personnel:
Public Relations: mcorey@asburyauto.com
Approx. Rev.: $3,936,000,000
Approx. Number Employees: 7,100
Year Founded: 1995
Business Description:
Car Dealership Owner & Operator
S.I.C.: 5511; 5599
N.A.I.C.S.: 441110; 441229
Advertising Expenditures: $26,400,000
Media: 3-8-9-13-16-23-24-25-26
Personnel:
Charles R. Oglesby *(Chm)*
Craig T. Monaghan *(Pres & CEO)*
Scott Krenz *(CFO & Sr VP)*
Michael S. Kearney *(COO & Exec VP)*
Bryan C. Hanlon *(Chief Acctg Officer & Controller)*
Elizabeth B. Chandler *(Gen Counsel & VP)*
Kenneth E. Jackson *(VP-HR)*
Advertising Agency:
RF Binder
950 3rd Ave 7th Fl
New York, NY 10022
Tel.: (212) 994-7600
Fax: (212) 994-7597

ASV, INC.

(Sub. of Terex Construction)
840 Lily Ln
Grand Rapids, MN 55744-4089
Mailing Address:
PO Box 5160
Grand Rapids, MN 55744-5180
Tel.: (218) 327-3434
Fax: (218) 327-9122
Toll Free: (800) 346-5954
E-mail: sales@asvi.com
Web Site: www.asvi.com
E-Mail For Key Personnel:
Sales Director: sales@asvi.com
Approx. Sls.: $264,137,000
Approx. Number Employees: 284
Year Founded: 1983
Business Description:
Track-driven Utility & Construction Vehicle Mfr & Designer
S.I.C.: 3531
N.A.I.C.S.: 333120
Export
Advertising Expenditures: $1,346,000
Media: 2-4-7-10
Personnel:
Lisa Walsh *(Dir-Corp Affairs)*
Brands & Products:
POSI-TRACK
TRACK TRUCK

AUDI OF AMERICA, INC.

(Sub. of Audi AG)
2200 Ferdinand Porsche Dr
Herndon, VA 20171
Tel.: (248) 754-5000
Fax: (248) 754-4930
Toll Free: (800) 822-2834 (Customer Relations)
Web Site: www.audiusa.com
Sales Range: $75-99.9 Million
Approx. Number Employees: 1,200
Business Description:
Motor Vehicle Distr
S.I.C.: 5012
N.A.I.C.S.: 423110
Import
Advertising Expenditures: $70,000,000
Media: 2-3-4-6-8-9-10-13-14-15-18-19-20-22-23-24-26
Distr.: Intl.; Natl.
Budget Set: Dec.
Personnel:
Johan de Nysschen *(Pres)*
Scott Keogh *(Chief Mktg Officer)*
Jeri Ward *(Gen Mgr-Mktg & Strategy)*
Peter Donnellan *(Dir-After Sls)*
Marc Trahan *(Dir-After Sls & Technical Svc)*
Carter Balkcom *(Product Mgr-Mktg Americas)*
Anthony Foulk *(Product Mgr-A6 & A7)*
DeLu Jackson *(Mgr-Dept, Digital & Relationship Mktg)*
Benny Lawrence *(Mgr-Media & Brand Innovation)*
Bradley Stertz *(Mgr-PR & Corp Comm)*
Brands & Products:
AUDI
Q7
TRUTH IN ENGINEERING
Advertising Agencies:
AKQA, Inc.
118 King St 6th Fl
San Francisco, CA 94107
Tel.: (415) 645-9400

Key to Media (For complete agency information see *The Advertising Red Books-Agencies* edition):
1. Bus. Publs. 2. Cable T.V. 3. Catalogs & Directories. 4. Co-op Adv. 5. Consumer Mags. 6. D.M. to Bus. Estab.7. D.M. to Consumers
8. Daily Newsp. 9. Exhibits/Trade Shows 10. Foreign 11. Infomercial 12. Internet Adv.13. Multimedia 14. Network Radio
15. Network T.V. 16. Newsp. Distr. Mags. 17. Other 18. Outdoor (Posters, Transit) 19. Point of Purchase20. Premiums, Novelties
21. Product Samples 22. Special Events Mktg. 23. Spot Radio 24. Spot T.V. 25. Weekly Newsp. 26. Yellow Page Adv.

Fax: (415) 645-9420
Digital Agency of Record

M80
2894 Rowena Ave
Los Angeles, CA 90039
Tel.: (323) 644-7800
Fax: (323) 644-7801
(Agency of Record)

Venables, Bell & Partners
201 Post St Ste 200
San Francisco, CA 94108
Tel.: (415) 288-3300
Fax: (415) 421-3683
(Agency of Record)
Audi A3 TDI Clean Diesel

AUTOMOTIVE SERVICE NETWORK, INC.
1011 N Wymore Rd Ste 100
Winter Park, FL 32789
Mailing Address:
PO Box 1720
Winter Park, FL 32790
Tel.: (407) 539-6500
Fax: (407) 975-0466
Fax: (407) 629-9213
Sales Range: $1-9.9 Million
Approx. Number Employees: 80
Year Founded: 1976
Business Description:
Automobile Dealership; Accounting Services & Automotive Repair
S.I.C.: 5511; 7539; 8721
N.A.I.C.S.: 441110; 541219; 811198
Media: 9-14-15-22
Personnel:
Roger Holler, Jr. *(Pres)*
Juliette Holler *(Principal)*

AUTOMOTIVE WAREHOUSE, INC.
(Sub. of CARQUEST Corporation)
(d/b/a Airport CarQuest)
2760 Waiwai Loop
Honolulu, HI 96819-1940
Tel.: (808) 836-0331
Fax: (808) 834-1525
Web Site: www.carquest.com/findDC.html
Approx. Number Employees: 30
Business Description:
Automotive Parts & Accessories
S.I.C.: 5013
N.A.I.C.S.: 423120
Media: 9-17

AUTONATION, INC.
200 SW 1st Ave
Fort Lauderdale, FL 33301
Tel.: (954) 769-6000
Fax: (954) 769-6537
E-mail: cannonm@autonation.com
Web Site: www.autonation.com
Approx. Rev.: $12,461,000,000
Approx. Number Employees: 19,000
Year Founded: 1991
Business Description:
Automotive Retail & Financing Services
S.I.C.: 5511; 5521
N.A.I.C.S.: 441110; 441120
Advertising Expenditures: $126,200,000
Media: 8-9-10-13-14-18-23-24-25
Personnel:
Michael J. Jackson *(Chm & CEO)*
Michael E. Maroone *(Pres & COO)*
Michael J. Short *(CFO & Exec VP)*
Jonathan P. Ferrando *(Gen Counsel, Sec & Exec VP)*
Marc Cannon *(Sr VP)*
Gary Marcotte *(Sr VP-eCommerce)*
Donna Parlapiano *(Sr VP-Reg Ops & Indus Relations)*
Kevin P. Westfall *(Sr VP-Sls)*
Brands & Products:
APPLEWAY
AUTONATION
AUTOWAY
AUTOWEST
BANKSTON
CHAMPION
COURTESY
DESERT
DOBBS
DRIVEN TO BE THE BEST
FOX
MAROONE
MIKE SHAD
MULLINAX
POWER
TEAM
Advertising Agency:
Zimmerman Advertising
2200 W Commercial Blvd Ste 300
Fort Lauderdale, FL 33309-3064
Tel.: (954) 644-4000
Fax: (954) 731-2977
Toll Free: (800) 248-8522

AVIS RENT A CAR SYSTEM, LLC
(Sub. of Avis Budget Group, Inc.)
6 Sylvan Way
Parsippany, NJ 07054
Tel.: (973) 496-3500
Fax: (973) 496-7999
Toll Free: (888) 777-AVIS
Web Site: www.avis.com
Sales Range: $1-4.9 Billion
Approx. Number Employees: 14,000
Business Description:
Car Rental Services
S.I.C.: 7514
N.A.I.C.S.: 532111
Media: 3-6-7-8-9-13-15-18-24-26
Personnel:
Ronald L. Nelson *(Chm & CEO)*
David B. Wyshner *(CFO & Exec VP)*
Mark J. Servodidio *(Chief Admin Officer & Exec VP)*
Scott Deaver *(Exec VP-Strategy)*
Patric Siniscalchi *(Exec VP-Intl Rels)*
Becky Alseth *(Sr VP-Mktg)*
Robert Bouta *(Sr VP-Avis Budget Grp)*
Edward Gitlitz *(Sr VP-Fleet Svcs)*
Robert Lambert *(Sr VP-Global Acct Sls)*
Darren Peacock *(Mgr-Mktg & Comm)*
Alice Pereira *(Mgr-Pub Rels)*

BEECHMONT AUTOMOTIVE GROUP
8639 Beechmont Ave
Cincinnati, OH 45255-4709
Mailing Address:
PO Box 54366
Cincinnati, OH 45254-0366
Tel.: (513) 388-3800
Fax: (513) 624-1199
E-mail: sales@theautomile.com
Web Site: www.beechmontcars.com
E-Mail For Key Personnel:
President: bwjr@theautomile.com
Sales Director: sales@theautomile.com
Approx. Number Employees: 300
Year Founded: 1980
Business Description:
Dealer, Sales & Service of New & Used Cars
S.I.C.: 5511; 7539
N.A.I.C.S.: 441110; 811118
Media: 6
Personnel:
Bill F. Woeste, Jr. *(Pres)*
Margot L. Hunley *(Mgr-Parts)*
Bob Wilder *(Mgr-Parts)*
Brands & Products:
BEECHMONT AUTOMILE

BELLA GROUP
PO Box 190816
San Juan, PR 00919-0816
Tel.: (787) 620-7010
Tel.: (878) 620-7546
Fax: (787) 620-7009
Web Site: www.bellainternational.com
Sales Range: $150-199.9 Million
Approx. Number Employees: 250
Year Founded: 1963
Business Description:
Automobile Sales
S.I.C.: 5012; 5511
N.A.I.C.S.: 423110; 441110
Import Export
Media: 10-18
Personnel:
Maria I. Esteve *(Owner)*
Jeronimo Esteve-Abril *(Chm)*
Carlos A. Lopez-Lay *(Pres & CEO)*
William Cuebas *(VP-HR & Admin)*
Viviana Fornaris *(VP-Info Sys)*
Advertising Agency:
Euro RSCG Puerto Rico
Centra Internacional de Mercade Torre 1 Ste 803
Guaynabo, PR 00968
Tel.: (787) 999-0600
Fax: (787) 999-0609

BERGSTROM AUTOMOTIVE
1 Neenah Ctr 7th Fl
Neenah, WI 54956
Tel.: (920) 725-4444
Fax: (920) 729-5145
Web Site: www.bergstromauto.com
Sales Range: $25-49.9 Million
Approx. Number Employees: 1,500
Year Founded: 1974
Business Description:
Car Dealership Owner & Operator
S.I.C.: 5511; 5521
N.A.I.C.S.: 441110; 441120
Media: 8-9-18-23-24-25
Personnel:
John F. Bergstrom *(Chm)*
Richard Bergstrom *(Gen Mgr)*
Linda Moorhead *(Dir-Corp Mktg)*

BERGSTROM CADILLAC HUMMER
(Sub. of Bergstrom Automotive)
1200 Applegate Rd
Madison, WI 53713
Tel.: (608) 271-2211
Fax: (608) 271-2266
E-mail: gclark@bergstromauto.com
Web Site:
www.bergstromcadillac.com
Approx. Sls.: $44,000,000
Approx. Number Employees: 80
Business Description:
New & Used Automobiles
S.I.C.: 5511
N.A.I.C.S.: 441110
Media: 9-25
Personnel:
George Coarvk *(Gen Mgr)*

BERT SMITH AUTOMOTIVE
3800 34th St N US 19
Saint Petersburg, FL 33714
Tel.: (727) 527-1111
Fax: (727) 522-8512
Web Site: www.bertsmith.com
Sales Range: $25-49.9 Million
Approx. Number Employees: 130
Business Description:
New & Used Car Dealership Owner & Operator
S.I.C.: 5511; 5521
N.A.I.C.S.: 441110; 441120
Media: 3-8-9-13-18-22-24-25
Personnel:
E.W. Smith, III *(Pres & CEO)*

BEUCKMAN FORD INC.
15675 Manchester Rd
Ballwin, MO 63011-2242
Tel.: (636) 227-5700
Fax: (636) 227-5743
Web Site: www.gotobo.com
Approx. Number Employees: 100
Year Founded: 1970
Business Description:
New & Used Car Dealers
S.I.C.: 5511; 5521; 7515
N.A.I.C.S.: 441110; 441120; 532112
Media: 24
Personnel:
Fred Beuckman *(Pres)*
Larry Perez *(Gen Mgr)*

BIG DOG MOTORCYCLES OF TAMPA
9528 N Florida Ave
Tampa, FL 33612
Tel.: (813) 935-4166
Tel.: (813) 377-7979
Fax: (813) 935-4155
Web Site: www.tampabdm.com
Business Description:
Motorcycle Dealership
S.I.C.: 5571; 3751
N.A.I.C.S.: 441221; 336991
Media: 8-10-13-20
Personnel:
Ben Haire *(Gen Mgr)*
Tank Sherman *(Gen Mgr)*

BILL CURRIE FORD INC.
5815 N Dale Mabry Hwy
Tampa, FL 33614
Tel.: (813) 872-5555
Fax: (813) 879-5570
Toll Free: (888) 255-1156
Web Site: www.billcurrie.com
E-Mail For Key Personnel:
Sales Director: sales@billcurrie.com
Approx. Sls.: $161,690,464
Approx. Number Employees: 300
Business Description:
Automobiles, New & Used
S.I.C.: 5511; 7538
N.A.I.C.S.: 441110; 811111
Media: 3
Personnel:
Wilmer E. Currie, III *(Pres)*

BILL HEARD ENTERPRISES, INC.
200 Brookstone Ctr Pkwy Ste 205
Columbus, GA 31904-4563
Tel.: (706) 323-1111
Fax: (706) 321-9488
E-mail: info@billheard.com
Web Site: www.billheard.com
Approx. Number Employees: 3,100
Year Founded: 1919
Business Description:
New & Used Automobiles
S.I.C.: 5511; 7515
N.A.I.C.S.: 441110; 532112
Advertising Expenditures: $1,300,000
Media: 4-8-9-13-18-19-23-24-25-26
Distr.: Natl.
Personnel:
William T. Heard *(Pres & CEO)*
Ronald A. Feldner *(CFO)*

BMW OF EL PASO
(Div. of Earnhardt's Auto Centers)
6318 Montana Ave
El Paso, TX 79925
Tel.: (915) 778-9381
Fax: (915) 779-8952
Toll Free: (888) 217-8666
Web Site: www.bmwofelpaso.com
Approx. Sls.: $37,800,000
Approx. Number Employees: 104
Business Description:
Car Dealership Operations
S.I.C.: 5511; 5521
N.A.I.C.S.: 441110; 441120
Media: 13-18

BMW OF NORTH AMERICA, LLC
(Sub. of Bayerische Motoren Werke Aktiengesellschaft)
300 Chestnut Ridge Rd
Woodcliff Lake, NJ 07675
Mailing Address:
PO Box 1227
Westwood, NJ 07675-1227
Tel.: (201) 307-4000
Fax: (201) 307-4095
Toll Free: (800) 831-1117
Web Site: www.bmwgroupna.com
Approx. Number Employees: 900
Year Founded: 1975
Business Description:
BMW Automobiles, Motorcycles, Parts & Accessories Mfr & Sales
S.I.C.: 5012; 5013; 9111
N.A.I.C.S.: 423110; 423120; 921110
Import
Advertising Expenditures: $100,000,000
Media: 2-3-6-9-10-15-17-19-20-23-24-25
Distr.: Natl.
Budget Set: June
Personnel:
Jim O'Donnell *(Pres)*
Tom Purves *(CEO)*
Peter Miles *(Exec VP-Ops)*
Dan Creed *(VP-Mktg)*
Tom Kowaleski *(VP-Corp Comm)*
Martin Birkmann *(Mgr-Brand)*
Trudy Hardy *(Mgr-Mktg-Mini Cooper)*
Patrick McKenna *(Mgr-Mktg & Comm)*
Advertising Agencies:
Baldwin&
212 W Main St Ste 105
Durham, NC 27702
Tel.: (919) 680-0900
utobahn Racing Invite-Cologne

Butler, Shine, Stern & Partners
20 Liberty Ship Way
Sausalito, CA 94965-3312
Tel.: (415) 331-6049
Fax: (415) 331-3524
Mini

Concept Farm
43 W 24th St 5th Fl
New York, NY 10010
Tel.: (212) 463-9939
Fax: (212) 463-7032

Dotglu, LLC
160 Varick St 3th Fl
New York, NY 10013
Tel.: (212) 462-1300
Fax: (212) 663-1719
Customer Relationship & Digital Marketing

Fallon Minneapolis
901 Marquette Ave Ste 2400
Minneapolis, MN 55402
Tel.: (612) 758-2345
Fax: (612) 758-2346
Toll Free: (866) 758-2345
The Hire
— Ginny Grossman *(Acct Exec)*
— Bob Molhoek *(Acct Exec)*
— Bjorn Gunnerud *(Acct Exec)*
— Bryan Chang *(Acct Exec)*
— Lisa LaVigne *(Acct Exec)*

Grey San Francisco
303 2nd St Ste 300 N Tower
San Francisco, CA 94107
Tel.: (415) 403-8000
Fax: (415) 403-8204
(Interactive, Direct, Promotional Marketing)
Regional Dealerships

kirshenbaum bond senecal + partners
160 Varick St 4th Fl
New York, NY 10013
Tel.: (212) 633-0080
Fax: (212) 463-8643
Creative

Matlock Advertising & Public Relations
107 Luckie St
Atlanta, GA 30303
Tel.: (404) 872-3200
Fax: (404) 876-4929
Marketing

Ramona
411 Lafayette St 6th Fl
New York, NY 10003
Tel.: (212) 924-2981
Fax: (212) 206-6491
USA Hispanic Agency of Record

Sanders/Wingo
2222 Rio Grande Bldg C 3rd Fl
Austin, TX 78705
Tel.: (512) 476-7949
Fax: (512) 476-7950
Diversity Marketing
Mini USA

Universal McCann
100 33rd St 8th Fl
New York, NY 10001
Tel.: (212) 883-4700
Media Agency of Record

BRAMAN MOTORS, INC.
2901 Okeechobee Blvd
West Palm Beach, FL 33409
Tel.: (305) 571-1225
Tel.: (305) 571-1200
Fax: (305) 640-0017
Web Site: www.bramanmiami.com
Approx. Number Employees: 400
Year Founded: 1976
Business Description:
New & Used Car & Truck Dealer
S.I.C.: 5511; 5521
N.A.I.C.S.: 441110; 441120
Media: 6-9-25
Personnel:
Norman Braman *(Owner)*
Ken Harte *(Gen Mgr)*

BRICKNER MOTORS, INC.
16450 County Hwy A
Marathon, WI 54448-9599
Tel.: (715) 842-5611
Fax: (715) 443-3838
Toll Free: (800) 345-5631
E-mail: littlechicago@bricknerfamily.com
Web Site: www.bricknerfamily.com
Sales Range: $25-49.9 Million
Approx. Number Employees: 50
Year Founded: 1945
Business Description:
New & Used Car Dealers
S.I.C.: 5511
N.A.I.C.S.: 441110
Import Export
Media: 5-8-9-18-23-24-25-26
Personnel:
Jerry Vickner *(Pres)*
Darin Weiks *(Mgr-Sls)*

BRUCKNER TRUCK SALES, INC.
9471 Interstate 40 E
Amarillo, TX 79118
Tel.: (806) 376-6273
Fax: (806) 349-5192
E-mail: info@brucknertruck.com
Web Site: www.brucknertruck.com
Approx. Number Employees: 550
Year Founded: 1932
Business Description:
Truck Dealership
S.I.C.: 5599
N.A.I.C.S.: 441229
Import Export
Media: 8-9-10-18-25
Personnel:
Pat Frost *(CFO)*

BUCKEYE NISSAN INC.
3820 Pkwy Ln
Hilliard, OH 43026-1217
Tel.: (614) 771-2345
Fax: (614) 771-2363
E-mail: newsales@buckeyenissan.com
Web Site: www.buckeyenissan.com
Sales Range: $350-399.9 Million
Approx. Number Employees: 60
Year Founded: 1980
Business Description:
Car Dealership Owner & Operator
S.I.C.: 5511; 5521
N.A.I.C.S.: 441110; 441120
Advertising Expenditures: $300,000
Media: 9-23-25
Distr.: Natl.
Budget Set: Dec.
Personnel:
Sean Kenney *(COO & VP)*

BUD DAVIS CADILLAC, INC.
5433 Poplar Ave
Memphis, TN 38119-3634
Tel.: (901) 761-1900
Fax: (901) 685-7431
Toll Free: (888) 664-1930
Web Site: www.buddaviscadillac.com
Sales Range: $125-149.9 Million
Approx. Number Employees: 125
Year Founded: 1975
Business Description:
Retailer of New & Used Automobiles
S.I.C.: 5511; 5521
N.A.I.C.S.: 441110; 441120
Media: 2-10-23-24-26
Personnel:
Bud Davis *(Owner)*
Wilson Croom *(Dir-Svc)*
Jon Neal *(Dir-Fin)*
John Creel *(Mgr-Sls)*
Roy Thweatt *(Mgr-Parts)*

BUEHLER MOTOR INC.
175 Southport Dr
Morrisville, NC 27560
Tel.: (919) 380-3333
Fax: (919) 380-3256
Web Site: www.buehlermotor.com
Sales Range: $50-74.9 Million
Approx. Number Employees: 150
Business Description:
Motors, Electric
S.I.C.: 3621
N.A.I.C.S.: 335312
Personnel:
Robert Riedford *(Pres)*
Advertising Agency:
XPR LLC
217 N Main St Ste 200
Santa Ana, CA 92701
Tel.: (714) 881-2310
Fax: (714) 881-2443

BUELL MOTORCYCLE COMPANY, LLC
(Sub. of Harley-Davidson, Inc.)
2799 Buell Dr
East Troy, WI 53120-1372
Tel.: (262) 642-2020
Fax: (262) 642-2030
Web Site: www.buell.com
Sales Range: $25-49.9 Million
Approx. Number Employees: 50
Year Founded: 1983
Business Description:
Performance Motorcycles
S.I.C.: 3751
N.A.I.C.S.: 336991
Media: 10-22
Personnel:
Erik Buell *(Chm & CTO)*
Jon Flickinger *(Pres & COO)*

CANEPA DESIGN GROUP
4900 Scotts Valley Dr
Scotts Valley, CA 95066-4208
Tel.: (831) 430-9940
Fax: (831) 430-9941
E-mail: info@canepa.com
Web Site: www.canepa.com
Approx. Number Employees: 25
Business Description:
Automotive Custom Design Services

Key to Media (For complete agency information see *The Advertising Red Books-Agencies* edition):
1. Bus. Publs. 2. Cable T.V. 3. Catalogs & Directories. 4. Co-op Adv. 5. Consumer Mags. 6. D.M. to Bus. Estab.7. D.M. to Consumers
8. Daily Newsp. 9. Exhibits/Trade Shows 10. Foreign 11. Infomercial 12. Internet Adv.13. Multimedia 14. Network Radio
15. Network T.V. 16. Newsp. Distr. Mags. 17. Other 18. Outdoor (Posters, Transit) 19. Point of Purchase20. Premiums, Novelties
21. Product Samples 22. Special Events Mktg. 23. Spot Radio 24. Spot T.V. 25. Weekly Newsp. 26. Yellow Page Adv.

S.I.C.: 7389; 7532
N.A.I.C.S.: 541990; 811121
Media: 6-10-13
Personnel:
Bruce Canepa *(Owner)*
Brands & Products:
CANEPA DESIGN

THE CARLSON COMPANY INC.

6045 N Broadway St
Wichita, KS 67219-2013
Tel.: (316) 744-0481
Fax: (316) 744-2144
E-mail: info@carlsoncompany.com
Web Site: www.carlsoncompany.com
Approx. Sls.: $3,000,000
Approx. Number Employees: 23
Year Founded: 1948
Business Description:
Clutches, Brakes & Seals Mfr
S.I.C.: 3714
N.A.I.C.S.: 336399
Export
Media: 7-13
Distr.: Direct to Consumer; Natl.
Budget Set: Nov.
Personnel:
Maynard N. Wood *(Pres-Sls)*
Brands & Products:
CARLSON
POWER FLO

CARMAX, INC.

12800 Tuckahoe Creek Pkwy
Richmond, VA 23238-1115
Tel.: (804) 747-0422
Fax: (804) 747-5848
E-mail: carmax@carmax.com
Web Site: www.carmax.com
Approx. Rev.: $8,975,554,000
Approx. Number Employees: 15,565
Year Founded: 1996
Business Description:
Administrative Services for Car Dealerships
S.I.C.: 5511; 5013; 5521
N.A.I.C.S.: 441110; 441120; 441310
Advertising Expenditures: $96,200,000
Media: 9-13-23-24-25
Personnel:
William R. Tiefel *(Chm)*
Thomas J. Folliard *(Pres & CEO)*
Thomas W. Reedy, Jr. *(CFO & Sr VP)*
Richard M. Smith *(CIO & Sr VP)*
Michael K. Dolan *(Chief Admin Officer & Exec VP)*
Eric M. Margolin *(Gen Counsel, Sr VP & Corp Sec)*
Keith D. Browning *(Exec VP-Fin)*
Joseph S. Kunkel *(Sr VP-Mktg & Strategy)*
William C. Wood, Jr. *(Sr VP-Sls)*
Tom Vicini *(Reg VP & Gen Mgr-Central Reg)*
Tom Marcey *(Gen Mgr & Reg VP-Mid-Atlantic Reg)*
Rodney Baker *(Reg VP)*
Chris Bartee *(Reg VP-Mdsg-Southwest Reg)*
Ron Costa *(Reg VP-Mdsg)*
John Davis *(Reg VP-Svc Ops-Mid-Atlantic Reg)*
Todd Gibbons *(Reg VP-Svc Ops-Central Reg)*
Bill McChrystal *(Reg VP-Mdsg-Florida Region)*
Marty Sberna *(Reg VP)*
Vaughn Sigmon *(Reg VP)*
Laura Donahue *(VP-Adv)*
Scott A. Rivas *(VP-HR)*
Michelle Halasz *(Asst VP & Deputy Gen Counsel)*
Veronica Hinckle *(Asst VP & Asst Controller)*
Natalie Wyatt *(Asst VP & Asst Controller)*
Mark Adams *(Asst VP-Logistics)*
Dandy Barrett *(Asst VP-IR)*
Edward Fabritiis *(Asst VP-Svc Ops HR)*
Dodie Fix *(Asst VP-Procurement)*
Chad Kulas *(Asst VP-HR)*
John Montegari *(Asst VP-Media)*
Gary Sheehan *(Asst VP-Process Engrg)*
Joe Wilson *(Asst VP-Auction Svcs & Buyer Dev)*
Brands & Products:
CARMAX
THE WAY CAR BUYING SHOULD BE
Advertising Agency:
Amalgamated Advertising LLC
145 W 30th St 7th Fl
New York, NY 10001
Tel.: (646) 878-1700
Fax: (646) 878-1787

CARQUEST CORPORATION

(Sub. of General Parts International, Inc.)
2635 E Millbrook Rd
Raleigh, NC 27604
Mailing Address:
PO Box 26929
Raleigh, NC 27611-6929
Tel.: (919) 573-3000
Fax: (919) 573-3555
E-mail: info@carquest.com
Web Site: www.carquest.com/
Approx. Number Employees: 800
Year Founded: 1974
Business Description:
Automotive Supplies & Parts
S.I.C.: 5013
N.A.I.C.S.: 423120; 441310
Media: 2-3-5-9-15-22-24-25
Personnel:
Tod Hack *(Pres)*
John Gardner *(Sr VP-Fin)*
Kevin Nelson *(Mgr-Natl Sls)*
Advertising Agency:
Ketchum Directory Advertising/Kansas City
7015 College Blvd Ste 700
Overland Park, KS 66211-1524
Tel.: (913) 344-1900
Fax: (913) 344-1960
Toll Free: (800) 922-6977

CHAMPION MOTORSPORT

3101 Centerport Cir
Pompano Beach, FL 33064
Tel.: (954) 946-2136
Fax: (954) 941-0295
Toll Free: (888) 548-8872
E-mail: sales@championmotorsport.com
Web Site: www.championmotorsport.com
E-Mail For Key Personnel:
Sales Director: sales@championmotorsport.com
Sales Range: $150-199.9 Million
Approx. Number Employees: 11
Year Founded: 1998
Business Description:
Aftermarket Automotive Parts & Accessories Designer & Mfr
S.I.C.: 5013
N.A.I.C.S.: 441310
Media: 6
Personnel:
Dave Maraj *(Owner)*
Naveen Maraj *(Pres)*
Wilson Tai *(Mgr-Mktg)*
Brands & Products:
CHAMPION
TUBI

CHRYSLER CANADA INC.

(Group of Chrysler Group LLC)
1 Riverside Dr W
Windsor, ON N9A 5K3, Canada
Mailing Address:
PO Box 1621
Windsor, ON N9A 4H6, Canada
Tel.: (519) 973-2000
Fax: (519) 973-2226
Toll Free: (800) 465-2001
Web Site: www.chryslercanada.ca
Sales Range: $1-4.9 Billion
Approx. Number Employees: 11,000
Year Founded: 1925
Business Description:
Motor Vehicles Mfr & Distr
S.I.C.: 3711; 5511
N.A.I.C.S.: 336111; 441110
Advertising Expenditures: $1,000,000
Media: 2-4-6-7-8-10-14-15-16-17-18-19-22-23-24-25
Distr.: Natl.
Budget Set: Nov. -Dec.
Personnel:
Reid Bigland *(Pres & CEO)*
Pat Dougherty *(VP-Sls)*
Mark Mallie *(Brand Mgr-Dodge Challenger)*
Brands & Products:
CHRYSLER
Advertising Agencies:
BBDO Toronto
2 Bloor St W
Toronto, ON M4W 3R6, Canada
Tel.: (416) 972-1505
Fax: (416) 972-5656

Nolin BBDO
3575 Boulevard St-Laurent Suite 300
Montreal, QC H2X 2T7, Canada
Tel.: (514) 939-4100
Fax: (514) 939-4006

Publicis
111 Queen St E Ste 200
Toronto, ON M5C 1S2, Canada
Tel.: (416) 925-7733
Fax: (416) 925-7341
Agency of Record
Chrysler
Dodge
Jeep
Ram Truck

CHRYSLER GROUP LLC

1000 Chrysler Dr
Auburn Hills, MI 48326-2766
Tel.: (248) 576-5741
Fax: (248) 576-4742
Telex: 800-334-9200
Web Site: www.chryslergroupllc.com
Approx. Rev.: $62,200,000,000
Approx. Number Employees: 54,000
Business Description:
Motor Vehicle Mfr; Owned by United Auto Workers 67.69%, Fiat S.p.A. (20%) Government of the United States (9.85%) & Government of Canada (2.46%)
S.I.C.: 3711; 7515
N.A.I.C.S.: 336111; 532112
Import Export
Media: 1-3-6-9-13-14-15-16-18-23-24
Distr.: Intl.; Natl.
Personnel:
Sergio Marchionne *(Chm & CEO)*
Pietro Gorlier *(Pres & CEO-MOPAR Brand Svc)*
James E. Press *(Deputy CEO)*
Richard Palmer *(CFO & Sr VP)*
Scott A. Sandschafer *(CIO & VP)*
Ralph V. Gilles *(Pres/CEO-Dodge Car Brand)*
Fred Diaz, Jr. *(Pres/CEO-Dodge Ram Brand)*
Olivier Francois *(Pres/CEO-Chrysler Brand)*
Michael Manley *(Pres/CEO-Jeep Brand)*
Holly E. Leese *(Gen Counsel, Sr VP & Sec)*
Doug D. Betts *(Sr VP-Quality)*
Scott Garberding *(Sr VP-Mfg & World Class Mfg)*
Michael J. Keegan *(Sr VP-Supply Chain Mgmt)*
Dan C. Knott *(Sr VP-Pur & Supplier Quality-Chrysler Grp LLC)*
Scott G. Kunselman *(Sr VP-Engrg)*
Nancy A. Rae *(Sr VP-HR)*
Gualberto Ranieri *(Sr VP-Comm)*
Joseph Trapasso *(Sr VP-External Affairs)*
Thomas J. Hadrych *(VP-Benefits)*
Thomas Hausch *(VP-Europe, Middle East & Africa)*
Bob Lee *(VP-Engine & Electrified Propulsion Sys)*
Karla E. Middlebrooks *(VP-Product, Procurement & Cost Mgmt Fin)*
Andreas Schell *(VP-EE Core)*
Paul L. Wolff *(VP-Taxation)*
John D. Plecha *(Dir-Mktg & Global Comm-Jeep & Chrysler)*
Susan Thompson *(Dir-Media)*
Judith K. Wheeler *(Dir-Adv)*
Lisa J. Wicker *(Dir-Talent Acq, Integrated Trng, Global Diversity & Compliance)*
Gu Yingjia *(Dir-Corp Comm-China)*
Mark Spencer *(Sr Mgr-Comm-Dodge Brand)*
Becky Blanchard *(Brand Mgr-Chrysler Town & Country)*
Jeff Hartley *(Brand Mgr)*
Holly Scerbo *(Mgr-Global Brand Comm)*
Eric Andrew *(Mgr-Dodge Charger & Challenger Mktg)*
Beth Paretta *(Mgr-Mktg-SRT & Motorsports Brand)*
Mike Perugi *(Mgr-Retail & Customer Svcs)*
Janice Tarachowski *(Mgr-Brand Licensing)*
Brands & Products:
CHRYSLER
CHRYSLER 300

Chrysler Group LLC — (Continued)

CHRYSLER 300 C
CHRYSLER 300 M
CHRYSLER CIRRUS
CHRYSLER CONCORDE
CHRYSLER CROSSFIRE COUPE
CHRYSLER CROSSFIRE ROADSTER
CHRYSLER FINANCIAL
CHRYSLER LHS
CHRYSLER PACIFICA
CHRYSLER PT CRUISER
CHRYSLER SEBRING
CHRYSLER TOWN & COUNTRY
CHRYSLER VOYAGER
DODGE
DODGE AVENGER
DODGE CALIBER SRT4
DODGE CARAVAN
DODGE CHALLENGER
DODGE CHARGER
DODGE DAKOTA
DODGE DURANGO
DODGE GRAND CARAVAN
DODGE INTREPID
DODGE JOURNEY
DODGE NEON
DODGE RAM
DODGE RAM WAGON & VAN
DODGE STRATUS
DODGE VIPER
GEM
HEMI
JEEP
JEEP CHEROKEE
JEEP COMMANDER
JEEP GRAND CHEROKEE
JEEP GRAND CHEROKEE LAREDO
JEEP LIBERTY
JEEP PATRIOT
JEEP WRANGLER
JOURNEY
MOPAR
PLYMOUTH PROWLER
TOWN & COUNTRY

Advertising Agencies:
Armando Testa Group
Via Luisa del Carretto 58
10131
Turin, Italy
Tel.: (39) 011 88 10111
Fax: (39) 011 88 10468

Brownstein Group
215 S Broad St 9th Fl
Philadelphia, PA 19107-5325
Tel.: (215) 735-3470
Fax: (215) 735-6298

Carlson Marketing
1405 Xenium Ln N
Plymouth, MN 55441
Tel.: (763) 445-3000

Centra360
1400 Old Country Rd Ste 420
Westbury, NY 11590-5119
Tel.: (516) 997-3147
Fax: (516) 334-7798

Duffey Petrosky
39303 Country Club Dr Ste A18
Farmington Hills, MI 48331-3482
Tel.: (248) 489-8300
Fax: (248) 994-1600
Certified Used Vehicles
Chrysler Affinity Program
Marketing to Small Business & Fleet Operators

George P. Johnson Company, Inc.
3600 Giddings Rd
Auburn Hills, MI 48326-1515
Tel.: (248) 475-2500
Fax: (248) 475-2325

Global Advertising 1st
174 Waterfront St Ste 310
Oxon Hill, MD 20745
Tel.: (240) 289-4001
Fax: (240) 289-4002

GlobalHue
Ste 1600 4000 Town Ctr
Southfield, MI 48076
Tel.: (248) 223-8900
Fax: (248) 304-8877
(African American)
Jeep
— Don Coleman *(Pres & CEO)*

PointRoll Inc.
951 E Hector St
Conshohocken, PA 19428
Tel.: (267) 558-1300
Fax: (267) 285-1141
Toll Free: (800) 203-6956

SapientNitro USA, Inc.
215 Park Ave S 2nd Fl
New York, NY 10003-1603
Tel.: (212) 206-1005
Fax: (212) 206-8510
Chrysler
Digital Agency of Record
Dodge
Interactive Duties
Jeep
Online Advertising
Ram Truck
Site Design & Development

Unicom Marketing Group
2875 S 25th Ave
Broadview, IL 60155
Tel.: (312) 738-1404
Fax: (708) 410-4501

Vibrant Media
565 5th Ave 15th Fl
New York, NY 10017
Tel.: (646) 312-6100
Fax: (212) 867-4925

Wieden + Kennedy, Inc.
224 NW 13th Ave
Portland, OR 97209-2953
Tel.: (503) 937-7000
Fax: (503) 937-8000
Born Of Fire
Dodge

THE COLLECTION, INC.

200 Bird Rd
Coral Gables, FL 33146
Tel.: (305) 444-5555
Fax: (786) 924-5504
Toll Free: (800) 252-4827
Web Site: www.thecollection.com
Approx. Number Employees: 180
Business Description:
Car Dealership Owner & Operator
S.I.C.: 5511
N.A.I.C.S.: 441110
Media: 6-8-9-22-25
Personnel:
Ken Gorin *(Pres)*
Larry Rustin *(VP-Fin)*
Michael Garilli *(Dir-Acctg & Gen Mgr-Audi Ops)*
Pete Risi *(Gen Mgr-Sls)*
Elizabeth Amador *(Dir-HR)*
Tim Coughlin *(Dir-Svc)*
Gary Moseley *(Dir-Svc)*
Paul Scott *(Dir-Fixed Ops)*
Beth Miller *(Bus Mgr-Porsche)*
Natalia Echeverry *(Bus Mgr-Audi)*
William Pena *(Bus Mgr-Certified Pre-Owned)*
Rafael Monteagudo *(Asst Mgr-Svc)*
Michael Sanchez *(Asst Mgr-Jaguar Svc)*
Noel Acevedo *(Mgr-Audi Svcs)*
Alex Akbarin *(Mgr-Porsche Sls)*
Steve Barmann *(Mgr-Sls-Aston Martin)*
Mimmo Falanga *(Mgr-Ferrari Bus)*
Mike George *(Mgr-Wholesale)*
Arnie Gonzalez *(Mgr-Audit Sls)*
George Jaile *(Mgr-Sls-Ferrari)*
Lorena Molieri *(Mgr-Bus)*
Desmond Perryman *(Mgr-Svc)*
Leticia Rios *(Mgr-Jaguar Bus)*
Kenneth Snay *(Mgr-Jaguar Sls)*
Scott Struble *(Mgr-Jaguar Svc)*
Ron Wiley *(Parts Mgr)*
Advertising Agency:
Turbulence Advertising
12000 Biscayne Blvd Ste 602
North Miami Beach, FL 33181
Tel.: (305) 892-7190
Fax: (305) 892-7194

CONFEDERATE MOTORS, INC.

2222 5th Ave S
Birmingham, AL 35222
Tel.: (205) 324-9888
Fax: (205) 324-8047
Toll Free: (877) 324-9888
E-mail: kelly@confederate.com
Web Site: www.confederate.com
Approx. Sls.: $1,860,680
Approx. Number Employees: 11
Business Description:
Motorcyle Designer & Mfr
S.I.C.: 3751
N.A.I.C.S.: 336991
Advertising Expenditures: $93,185
Media: 17
Personnel:
H. Matthew Chambers *(Chm, CEO & Mng Dir)*
Joseph Mitchell *(CFO)*

COPART, INC.

4665 Business Center Dr
Fairfield, CA 94534
Tel.: (707) 639-5000
Fax: (707) 639-5196
E-mail: investor.relations@copart.com
Web Site: www.copart.com
Approx. Rev.: $872,246,000
Approx. Number Employees: 2,825
Year Founded: 1982
Business Description:
Used & Salvage Vehicle Sales & Remarketing Services
S.I.C.: 5521; 5961
N.A.I.C.S.: 441120; 454112
Advertising Expenditures: $12,700,000
Media: 4-8-10-20
Personnel:
Willis J. Johnson *(Chm)*
Vincent W. Mitz *(Pres)*
A. Jayson Adair *(CEO)*
William E. Franklin *(CFO & Sr VP-Fin)*

COURTESY PALM HARBOR HONDA

(Sub. of Asbury Automotive Group, Inc.)
31200 US Hwy 19 N
Palm Harbor, FL 34684
Tel.: (727) 772-6600
Web Site:
www.palmharborhonda.com
Business Description:
Automobile Dealership
S.I.C.: 5012
N.A.I.C.S.: 423110
Media: 13
Personnel:
Charles Oglesby *(Pres)*

CRANE CARRIER COMPANY

(Sub. of CCI Corporation)
1925 N Sheridan Rd
Tulsa, OK 74115-3602
Mailing Address:
PO Box 582891
Tulsa, OK 74158-2891
Tel.: (918) 836-0151
Fax: (918) 832-7348
E-mail: service@cranecarrier.com
Web Site: www.cranecarrier.com
E-Mail For Key Personnel:
Sales Director: sales@cranecarrier.com
Approx. Number Employees: 250
Year Founded: 1953
Business Description:
Mfr of Heavy Duty On & Off Highway Carriers For Concrete Mixers, Refuse, Drilling Rigs & Bulk Materials Handling
S.I.C.: 3711; 5013
N.A.I.C.S.: 336211; 423120
Import Export
Advertising Expenditures: $200,000
Media: 17-19
Distr.: Intl.; Natl.
Budget Set: Apr.
Personnel:
Ken Mullen *(VP-Sls-OEM Products)*
Glenn Pochocki *(VP-Sls & Mktg-Refuse & Chassis)*
Leon Warner *(VP-Fin)*
John Sczesny *(Gen Mgr)*
Jeff Carpenter *(Dir-Svc)*
Mike Broadbooks *(Reg Mgr-Svc)*
Dale Dunn *(Reg Mgr-Svc)*
Alan Jones *(Mgr-HR)*
Brands & Products:
CENTAUR II
CENTURION
CENTURY
CORSAIR

CROWLEY AUTO GROUP

223 Broad St Rte 72
Bristol, CT 06010
Tel.: (860) 589-4444
Fax: (860) 314-6082
E-mail: rguevara@crowleyauto.net
Web Site: www.crowleyauto.com
Approx. Number Employees: 25
Year Founded: 1972
Business Description:
Sales of New & Used Automobiles

Key to Media (For complete agency information see *The Advertising Red Books-Agencies* edition):
1. Bus. Publs. 2. Cable T.V. 3. Catalogs & Directories. 4. Co-op Adv. 5. Consumer Mags. 6. D.M. to Bus. Estab.7. D.M. to Consumers
8. Daily Newsp. 9. Exhibits/Trade Shows 10. Foreign 11. Infomercial 12. Internet Adv.13. Multimedia 14. Network Radio
15. Network T.V. 16. Newsp. Distr. Mags. 17. Other 18. Outdoor (Posters, Transit) 19. Point of Purchase20. Premiums, Novelties
21. Product Samples 22. Special Events Mktg. 23. Spot Radio 24. Spot T.V. 25. Weekly Newsp. 26. Yellow Page Adv.

S.I.C.: 5511; 7538
N.A.I.C.S.: 441110; 811111
Advertising Expenditures: $350,000
Media: 3-6-9-13-15-17-18-22-23-24-25
Personnel:
Ken Crowley *(Chm)*
Steve Miller *(Exec VP)*

CROWN AUTO DEALERSHIPS INC.
(d/b/a Crown Cars)
6001 34th St N
Saint Petersburg, FL 33714-1251
Tel.: (727) 527-5731
Fax: (727) 522-4539
E-mail: info@crowncars.com
Web Site: www.crowncars.com
Sales Range: $100-124.9 Million
Approx. Number Employees: 300
Business Description:
New & Used Car Dealership Owner & Operator
S.I.C.: 5511; 5521
N.A.I.C.S.: 441110; 441120
Media: 3-5-8-9-13-18-22-23-24-25
Personnel:
Dwayne Hawkins *(Pres)*
Tom Smith *(CFO)*

CURRY ACURA
(Holding of Curry Corporation)
685 Central Ave
Scarsdale, NY 10583
Tel.: (914) 472-6800
Fax: (914) 725-5792
Toll Free: (866) 491-1024
E-mail: sales@curryacura.com
Web Site: www.curryacura.com
E-Mail For Key Personnel:
Sales Director: sales@curryacura.com
Approx. Number Employees: 400
Year Founded: 1947
Business Description:
Retailer of New & Used Vehicles
S.I.C.: 5511
N.A.I.C.S.: 441110
Media: 2-6-7-8-9-14-15-25
Distr.: Natl.
Personnel:
Mike Miele *(Gen Mgr)*

CURTIS C. GUNN, INC.
227 Broadway St
San Antonio, TX 78205-1923
Tel.: (210) 472-2501
Fax: (210) 472-2508
E-mail: info@gunnauto.com
Web Site: www.gunnauto.com
Approx. Number Employees: 900
Year Founded: 1955
Business Description:
Automobile Dealership
S.I.C.: 5511
N.A.I.C.S.: 441110
Advertising Expenditures: $3,000,000
Media: 23-24-25
Distr.: Reg.
Budget Set: Oct.
Personnel:
Curtis C. Gunn, Jr. *(Chm)*
Kelly Collins *(CFO)*
Paul Young *(Exec VP)*
Jaff Doherty *(VP-Consumer Strategy)*
Cindy Rowley *(Acctg Mgr)*

DARLING'S INC.
96 Pkwy S Unit 1
Brewer, ME 04412
Tel.: (207) 992-1740
Fax: (207) 941-1241
Toll Free: (888) 225-2805
E-mail: sales@darlings.com
Web Site: www.darlings.com
E-Mail For Key Personnel:
Sales Director: sales@darlings.com
Approx. Number Employees: 250
Year Founded: 1976
Business Description:
Retailer of New & Used Automobiles; Whslr & Distr of Motor Vehicle Parts
S.I.C.: 5511
N.A.I.C.S.: 441110
Advertising Expenditures: $200,000
Media: 6-7-8-9-15-23-25-26
Distr.: Reg.
Personnel:
Jay Darling *(Pres)*
John B. Darling *(Principal & Consultant)*
Charles Rohn *(Exec VP)*
Bob Jonah *(Gen Mgr-Darlings Honda Nissan Volvo)*
George Chiaie *(Parts Dir)*
Kerry Galeaz *(Mgr-Sls-Darlings Auto Mall)*
Joe Simpson *(Mgr-Sls)*

DAVE SYVERSON INC.
2310 E Main St
Albert Lea, MN 56007-0251
Tel.: (507) 373-1438
Fax: (507) 373-3063
Toll Free: (800) 423-6663
E-mail: email@davesyverson.com
Web Site: www.syversonford.com
Approx. Number Employees: 65
Year Founded: 1967
Business Description:
Retailer of New/Used Automobiles & Trucks; Repair Shops; Truck Leasing
S.I.C.: 5511; 7519
N.A.I.C.S.: 441110; 532120
Advertising Expenditures: $300,000
Media: 2-4-8-9-13-19-22-23-24-25-26
Personnel:
David B. Syverson *(Pres)*
Bob Syverson *(Gen Mgr)*

DAYTON ANDREWS FIVE STAR CHRYSLER PLYMOUTH JEEP, INC.
2388 Gulf to Bay Blvd
Clearwater, FL 33765-4103
Tel.: (727) 799-4539
Fax: (727) 796-0079
E-mail: sales@daytonandrews.com
Web Site: www.daytonandrews.com
E-Mail For Key Personnel:
Sales Director: sales@daytonandrews.com
Approx. Number Employees: 50
Year Founded: 1964
Business Description:
Retailer of New & Used Automobiles
S.I.C.: 5511
N.A.I.C.S.: 441110
Media: 9-24-25
Personnel:
Charley Flatley *(Dir-Svcs)*

DEAN ARBOUR CHEVROLET CADILLAC
1859 N US Hwy 23
East Tawas, MI 48730
Tel.: (989) 362-3403
Fax: (989) 362-0640
Toll Free: (866) GET-DEAN
Web Site: www.deanarbor.com
Sales Range: $10-24.9 Million
Approx. Number Employees: 100
Business Description:
Sales of New & Used Automobiles
S.I.C.: 5511; 5521
N.A.I.C.S.: 441110; 441120
Media: 9-14-18-19-20-23-25
Personnel:
Dean Arbour *(Owner)*
Harvey Harriman *(Gen Mgr & Mgr-New/Used Car)*

DESERT EUROPEAN MOTORCARS, LTD.
71387 Hwy 111
Rancho Mirage, CA 92270-4110
Tel.: (760) 773-5000
Fax: (760) 773-4406
Toll Free: (800) 347-4709
E-mail: info@deserteuropean.com
Web Site: www.deserteuropean.com
Approx. Sls.: $90,000,000
Approx. Number Employees: 100
Business Description:
Car Dealership
S.I.C.: 5511
N.A.I.C.S.: 441110
Media: 6-9-25
Personnel:
David B. Murphy *(Pres)*
Frank Hickingbotham *(CEO)*

DIMMITT LUXURY MOTORS
25191 US Hwy 19 N
Clearwater, FL 33763
Tel.: (727) 797-7070
Fax: (727) 791-4308
E-mail: info@dimmitt.com
Web Site: www.dimmitt.com
Approx. Sls.: $100,000,000
Approx. Number Employees: 150
Business Description:
Car Dealership Owner & Operator
S.I.C.: 5511; 7538
N.A.I.C.S.: 441110; 811111
Media: 6-9-18-23-24-25
Personnel:
Richard Dimmitt *(Owner)*
Chris Jordan *(CFO)*

DOLLAR THRIFTY AUTOMOTIVE GROUP, INC.
5330 E 31st St
Tulsa, OK 74153-0985
Mailing Address:
PO Box 35985
Tulsa, OK 74153-0985
Tel.: (918) 660-7700
Fax: (918) 669-2934
Web Site: www.dtag.com
Approx. Rev.: $1,537,160,000
Approx. Number Employees: 6,000
Year Founded: 1997
Business Description:
Vehicle Rental Company
S.I.C.: 7514
N.A.I.C.S.: 532111
Advertising Expenditures: $21,200,000
Media: 8-9-10-13-15
Personnel:
Richard W. Neu *(Chm)*
Scott L. Thompson *(Pres & CEO)*
H. Clifford Buster *(CFO & Sr Exec VP)*
Rick L. Morris *(CIO & Exec VP)*
Vicki Vaniman *(Gen Counsel, Sec & Exec VP)*
David Sparkman *(Exec VP)*
Jeff Cerefice *(Sr VP)*
James Duffy *(Reg VP-Ops)*
Charlie Coniglio *(VP-eCommerce, Global Distribution, Mktg & Adv)*
Fred J. Fleischner *(VP-Corp Comm)*
Jeanie Dancer *(Mgr-Strategic Partners)*
Advertising Agencies:
FKQ Advertising + Marketing
15351 Roosevelt Blvd
Clearwater, FL 33760-3534
Tel.: (727) 539-8800
Fax: (866) 707-6648
Dollar Rent-A-Car
Thrifty Car Rental

The Portsmouth Group
PO Box 71765
Dubai, United Arab Emirates
Tel.: (971) 4 369 3575

DOWNTOWN FORD SALES INC.
525 N 16th St
Sacramento, CA 95811
Tel.: (916) 442-6931
Fax: (916) 442-0800
Fax: (916) 491-3141
Toll Free: (888) 640-9949
E-mail: info@downtownfordsales.com
Web Site: www.downtownfordsales.com
Approx. Number Employees: 100
Business Description:
Automobiles Dealer
S.I.C.: 5511
N.A.I.C.S.: 441110
Media: 9-18-23-25
Distr.: Reg.
Personnel:
Ray Enos *(Pres & Principal)*
Jeff Stubblefield *(Dir-Parts-Svc)*
Dave Forbess *(Mgr-Fleet)*
Scott Ikesaki *(Mgr-New Car)*
Terry Meadows *(Mgr-Bus)*
Dave C. Sarra *(Mgr-Parts)*

DRIVETIME AUTOMOTIVE GROUP, INC.
4020 E Indian School Rd
Phoenix, AZ 85018
Tel.: (602) 852-6600
Fax: (602) 852-6686
Toll Free: (888) 418-1212
E-mail: press@drivetime.com
Web Site: www.drivetime.com
Sales Range: $1-4.9 Billion
Approx. Number Employees: 2,203
Year Founded: 1977
Business Description:
Used Car Dealership & Financing Services
S.I.C.: 5521; 6141
N.A.I.C.S.: 441120; 522291
Advertising Expenditures: $11,200,000
Media: 3-8-13-14-15-18-20-22-23-24-25
Distr.: Reg.
Budget Set: Dec.

Key to Media (For complete agency information see *The Advertising Red Books-Agencies* edition):
1. Bus. Publs. 2. Cable T.V. 3. Catalogs & Directories. 4. Co-op Adv. 5. Consumer Mags. 6. D.M. to Bus. Estab.7. D.M. to Consumers 8. Daily Newsp. 9. Exhibits/Trade Shows 10. Foreign 11. Infomercial 12. Internet Adv.13. Multimedia 14. Network Radio 15. Network T.V. 16. Newsp. Distr. Mags. 17. Other 18. Outdoor (Posters, Transit) 19. Point of Purchase20. Premiums, Novelties 21. Product Samples 22. Special Events Mktg. 23. Spot Radio 24. Spot T.V. 25. Weekly Newsp. 26. Yellow Page Adv.

DriveTime Automotive Group, Inc. — (Continued)

Personnel:
Raymond C. Fidel *(Pres & CEO)*
Colin Bachinsky *(Mng Dir)*
Mark G. Sauder *(CFO & Exec VP)*
Alan J. Appelman *(Chief Credit Officer & Exec VP)*
Jon D. Ehlinger *(Exec VP, Sec & Gen Counsel)*
Dan Packowski *(Dir-Real Estate)*
Brands & Products:
DRIVECARE
DRIVETIME
DT CHAMP
THE GO-TO-GUYS FOR CARS AND CREDIT.
MILITARY MERIT
RATEADVANTAGE
Advertising Agency:
Targeting Group
7155 Old Katy Rd Ste 100 N
Houston, TX 77024
Tel.: (713) 867-3242
Fax: (713) 869-6560

DUCATI NORTH AMERICA INC.
(Sub. of Ducati Motor Holding S.p.A.)
10443 Bandley Dr
Cupertino, CA 95014-1912
Tel.: (408) 253-0499
Fax: (408) 253-4099
E-mail: customerservice@ducati.com
Web Site: www.ducati.com/od/ducatinorthamerica/en/aboutus.jhtml
Approx. Number Employees: 45
Business Description:
Motorcycle Distr
S.I.C.: 3751
N.A.I.C.S.: 336991
Advertising Agency:
JMPR, Inc.
5850 Canoga Ave Ste 300
Woodland Hills, CA 91367
Tel.: (818) 992-4353
Fax: (818) 992-0543

EARNHARDT HONDA
(Div. of Earnhardt's Auto Centers)
10151 W Papago Freeway
Avondale, AZ 85323
Tel.: (623) 934-5211
Fax: (623) 842-0712
Toll Free: (888) 343-2497
E-mail: webmaster@earnhardt.com
Web Site: www.earnhardt.com
Approx. Number Employees: 2,000
Year Founded: 1951
Business Description:
New & Used Automobiles Retailer
S.I.C.: 5511
N.A.I.C.S.: 441110
Media: 8-9-18-19-20-23-24-26
Distr.: Direct to Consumer; Reg.
Personnel:
Joe Staples *(Gen Mgr)*
Vicky Van Dyke *(Dir-Mktg)*

EARNHARDT'S AUTO CENTERS
7300 W Orchid Ln
Chandler, AZ 85226
Tel.: (480) 893-0000
Fax: (480) 783-4666
Toll Free: (800) 357-6070
E-mail: info@earnhardt.com
Web Site: www.earnhardt.com
Approx. Sls.: $600,000,000
Approx. Number Employees: 1,650
Year Founded: 1951
Business Description:
New & Used Automobiles
S.I.C.: 5521
N.A.I.C.S.: 441120
Media: 13-25
Personnel:
Hal J. Earnhardt *(Pres)*
Robbyn McDowell *(CFO)*
John Nissen *(Gen Mgr)*
Mike Housh *(Dir)*
Vicky Van Dyke *(Dir-Mktg)*

EAST TENNESSEE NISSAN MORRISTOWN
5496 W Andrew Johnson Hwy
Morristown, TN 37814
Tel.: (423) 587-2506
Fax: (423) 587-2520
Toll Free: (800) 785-0613
E-mail: info@easttennesseenissan.com
Web Site:
www.victoryautomotivegroup.com
Approx. Number Employees: 100
Business Description:
New & Used Car Sales
S.I.C.: 5511; 5521
N.A.I.C.S.: 441110; 441120
Media: 8
Personnel:
Jeff Cappo *(Owner)*
John Booker *(Gen Mgr)*

EVELAND'S INC.
(d/b/a Scamp Trailers)
Hwy 371 N
Backus, MN 56435
Mailing Address:
PO Box 2
Backus, MN 56435
Tel.: (218) 947-4932
Fax: (218) 947-3490
Toll Free: (800) 346-4962
Web Site: www.scamptrailers.com
Sales Range: $10-24.9 Million
Approx. Number Employees: 45
Year Founded: 1971
Business Description:
Mfr. & Sales of Trailers
S.I.C.: 3792
N.A.I.C.S.: 336214
Media: 6
Personnel:
Kent Eveland *(Pres)*

EWALD AUTOMOTIVE GROUP, LLC
6319 S 108th St
Franklin, WI 53132
Tel.: (414) 258-5000
Fax: (414) 427-2015
Web Site: www.ewaldauto.com
Approx. Number Employees: 450
Year Founded: 1964
Business Description:
New & Used Automobiles Retailer
S.I.C.: 5511
N.A.I.C.S.: 441110
Media: 9-18-20-23-24-25
Distr.: Reg.
Personnel:
Craig A. Ewald *(Pres)*
Edward Fried *(CFO)*
Tom Ewald *(VP & Dir-Variable Ops)*
Jody Schutte *(Gen Mgr)*

EZ LUBE INC.
3506 W Lk Ctr Dr B
Santa Ana, CA 92704
Tel.: (714) 556-1312
Fax: (714) 556-1362
E-mail: info@ezlube.com
Web Site: www.ezlube.com
Approx. Sls.: $17,585,388
Approx. Number Employees: 193
Business Description:
Lubrication Service, Automotive
S.I.C.: 7549
N.A.I.C.S.: 811191
Personnel:
Guy Marsala *(Pres & CEO)*
Mark J. Archer *(Partner & CFO)*
Advertising Agency:
The Phelps Group
901 Wilshire Blvd
Santa Monica, CA 90401-1854
Tel.: (310) 752-4400
Fax: (310) 752-4444

FAIRWAY FORD, INC.
2323 Laurens Rd
Greenville, SC 29607-3246
Tel.: (864) 242-5060
Fax: (864) 233-1301
E-mail: info@fairwayford.com
Web Site: www.fairwayford.com
Sales Range: $25-49.9 Million
Approx. Number Employees: 100
Year Founded: 1961
Business Description:
New & Used Automobile Dealer
S.I.C.: 5511; 5521; 7538
N.A.I.C.S.: 441110; 441120; 811111
Advertising Expenditures: $480,000
Media: 5-13-15-23-25-26
Personnel:
A. Foster McKissick *(Pres)*
Gary McAlister *(Gen Mgr)*
Charlie Eassy *(Mgr-Parts)*
Fred Sizemore *(Mgr-Svc)*

FERMAN MOTOR CAR CO., INC.
(Sub. of Ferman Automotive Management)
1306 W Kennedy Blvd
Tampa, FL 33606-1849
Tel.: (813) 251-2765
Fax: (813) 254-4798
Web Site: www.fermanauto.com
E-Mail For Key Personnel:
Marketing Director: marketing@fermanauto.com
Public Relations: fnorth@fermanmail.net
Sales Range: $10-24.9 Million
Approx. Number Employees: 15
Year Founded: 1895
Business Description:
Dealer of New & Used Automobiles
S.I.C.: 5511
N.A.I.C.S.: 441110
Media: 3-5-8-9-10-13-18-19-20-22-23-24-25
Personnel:
James Laurens Ferman, Jr. *(Pres)*
Nick Boicheff *(Controller & Dir-Info Sys)*
Advertising Agency:
Ad Partners Inc.
9800 4th St N Ste 200
Saint Petersburg, FL 33702
Tel.: (727) 289-8900
Fax: (727) 289-8999

FERRARI NORTH AMERICA, INC.
(Sub. of Ferrari S.p.A.)
250 Sylvan Ave
Englewood Cliffs, NJ 07632-2500
Tel.: (201) 816-2600
Fax: (201) 816-2626
Web Site: www.ferrariusa.com
Approx. Sls.: $70,000,000
Approx. Number Employees: 75
Year Founded: 1990
Business Description:
Sports Cars Importer & Distr
S.I.C.: 5012
N.A.I.C.S.: 423110
Import
Media: 6-9-10-14-22-25-30
Distr.: Natl.
Budget Set: Aug.
Personnel:
Maurizio Parlato *(Pres & CEO)*
Joseph Marsella *(CFO & VP)*
Federica Marchionni *(Dir-Brand, Ferrari S.p.A.)*
Enrico Galliera *(Dir-Mktg & Commercial)*

FISKER AUTOMOTIVE, INC.
2811 McGraw Ave Ste B
Irvine, CA 92614
Tel.: (714) 888-4255
Fax: (949) 474-5574
E-mail: info@fiskerautomotive.com
Web Site: www.fiskerautomotive.com
Sales Range: $300-349.9 Million
Business Description:
Automobile Mfr; Owned by Quantum Fuel Systems Technologies Worldwide, Inc. & Fisker Coachbuild, LLC
S.I.C.: 3711
N.A.I.C.S.: 336111
Personnel:
Ray Lane *(Chm)*
Henrik Fisker *(CEO)*
Bernhard Koehler *(COO)*
Thomas Fritz *(Dir-Engrg)*
David Harris *(Mgr-Mktg)*
Advertising Agency:
Lambesis, Inc.
2800 Roosevelt St
Carlsbad, CA 92008-1670
Tel.: (760) 547-2333
Fax: (760) 547-2331
Agency of Record

FORCE PROTECTION, INC.
1520 Old Trolley Rd
Summerville, SC 29485
Tel.: (843) 574-7001
Tel.: (843) 574-7000
Fax: (843) 329-0380
E-mail: info@forceprotection.net
Web Site: www.forceprotection.net
Approx. Sls.: $655,973,000
Approx. Number Employees: 940
Year Founded: 1997
Business Description:
Armored Land Vehicle Mfr
S.I.C.: 3795
N.A.I.C.S.: 336992
Advertising Expenditures: $1,400,000
Personnel:
Michael Moody *(Chm & CEO)*
Charles Alexander Mathis *(CFO)*
Randy Hutcherson *(COO)*

Key to Media (For complete agency information see *The Advertising Red Books-Agencies* edition):
1. Bus. Publs. 2. Cable T.V. 3. Catalogs & Directories. 4. Co-op Adv. 5. Consumer Mags. 6. D.M. to Bus. Estab.7. D.M. to Consumers 8. Daily Newsp. 9. Exhibits/Trade Shows 10. Foreign 11. Infomercial 12. Internet Adv.13. Multimedia 14. Network Radio 15. Network T.V. 16. Newsp. Distr. Mags. 17. Other 18. Outdoor (Posters, Transit) 19. Point of Purchase20. Premiums, Novelties 21. Product Samples 22. Special Events Mktg. 23. Spot Radio 24. Spot T.V. 25. Weekly Newsp. 26. Yellow Page Adv.

James Grazioplene *(Exec VP-Total Lifecycle Support)*
Mark L. Garrell *(Sr VP-Govt Affairs & Dir-Washington Ops)*
John Wall *(Sr VP & Asst Gen Counsel)*
Shelia Boyd *(VP-HR)*
Richard Hamilton *(VP-Fin)*
Wes Harris *(Dir-IR)*

FORD MOTOR COMPANY
1 American Rd
Dearborn, MI 48126-2701
Tel.: (313) 322-3000
Fax: (313) 845-6073
Toll Free: (800) 555-5259
E-mail: info@ford.com
Web Site: www.ford.com
Approx. Sls.: $119,280,000,000
Approx. Number Employees: 198,000
Year Founded: 1903
Business Description:
Motor Vehicles Mfr
S.I.C.: 3711; 3714
N.A.I.C.S.: 336111; 336399
Import Export
Advertising Expenditures: $3,300,000,000
Media: 2-3-6-9-13-14-15-16-17-18-23-24
Distr.: Intl.; Natl.
Personnel:
William Clay Ford, Jr. *(Chm)*
Alan R. Mulally *(Pres & CEO)*
Lewis W.K. Booth *(CFO & Exec VP)*
Nicholas J. Smither *(CIO & Grp VP)*
J. C. Mays *(Chief Creative Officer & Grp VP-Design)*
Gerhard Schmidt *(CTO & VP-Rsch & Advanced Engrg)*
Michael E. Bannister *(Chm/CEO-Ford Motor Credit & Exec VP)*
Stephen T. Odell *(Chm/CEO-Ford of Europe & Grp VP)*
David L. Schoch *(Chm/CEO-China)*
Mark Fields *(Pres-Americas & Exec VP)*
Joseph R. Hinrichs *(Pres-Asia Pacific & Africa & Grp VP)*
James G. Vella *(Pres-Fund & Community Svcs)*
David G. Leitch *(Grp VP & Gen Counsel)*
Robert T. Davis *(Sr VP-Product Dev & Quality)*
Thomas K. Brown *(Grp VP-Global Pur)*
Susan M. Cischke *(Grp VP-Sustainability, Environment & Safety Engrg)*
James D. Farley *(Grp VP-Global Mktg Sls & Svc)*
Felicia J. Fields *(Grp VP-HR & Corp Svcs)*
Bennie W. Fowler *(Grp VP-Quality)*
Derrick M. Kuzak *(Grp VP-Global Product Dev)*
Ziad S. Ojakli *(Grp VP-Govt & Community Rels)*
Joseph Bakaj *(VP-Product Programs & Product Dev)*
Ken Czubay *(VP-General Mktg)*
Raymond F. Day *(VP-Comm)*
Dean Stoneley *(VP-Mktg, Sls & Svc)*
Frederiek Toney *(VP-Global Ford Customer Svc Div)*
Mike Herniak *(Gen Mgr-Canada)*
Moray Callum *(Exec Dir-Design-Americas)*
George Sharp *(Exec Dir-IR)*
Hau Thai-Tang *(Exec Dir-Global Product Programs)*
Mike Crowley *(Sls Dir)*
Matt VanDyke *(Mktg Dir-Comm-US)*
Elena Ford *(Dir-Global Mktg, Mktg Mgr)*
Nancy Gioia *(Dir-Global Electrification)*
Kevin Koswick *(Dir-North American Fleet Lease & Remarketing)*
Christine Stasiw Lazarchuk *(Dir-Market Res-Global)*
Dave Sanabria *(Dir-Adv-Asia Pacific)*
Rob Johnston *(Reg Mgr-Sls & Inventory)*
Sam De La Garza *(Brand Mgr-Ford Fiesta)*
Robert Parker *(Brand Mgr-Small Car Grp)*
Paul Russell *(Brand Mgr-Focus)*
Dan Geist *(Mgr-Mkg-Racing Tech-North America)*
Alan Hall *(Mgr-Ford Car Coom)*
Kate Pearce *(Mgr-Mktg)*
Jonathan Richards *(Mgr-Mktg-Fusion)*
Doug Scott *(Mgr-Mktg-Truck Group)*
David Gersabeck *(Product Mgr-Sync Svcs)*
Mark Bentley *(Mgr-Licensing)*
John Clinard *(Mgr-Comm-Western Reg)*
Tim Duerr *(Mgr-Motorsports Mktg-North America)*
Lori Dunn *(Mgr-Mktg-Export Ops & Global Growth)*
David Finnegan *(Mgr-Electric Vehicles & Mktg)*
Connie Fontaine *(Mgr-US Luxury & Non-Traditional Comm)*
Jeffrey Nemeth *(Mgr)*
Eric Peterson *(Mgr-Mktg)*
George Pipas *(Mgr-Sls Analysis)*
Usha Raghavachari *(Mgr-Advanced Product Mktg)*
Brian Rathsburg *(Mgr-Mktg-F Series)*
Allison Revier *(Mgr-Mustang Product Mktg)*
Thomais Zaremba *(Mgr-Car Comm)*
Brands & Products:
COMMAND SEATING
CROWN VICTORIA
ECOBOOST
EDGE
FLEX
FORD
FORD E-SERIES
FORD ECONOLINE
FORD ESCAPE
FORD ESCAPE HYBRID
FORD EXCURSION
FORD EXPEDITION
FORD EXPLORER
FORD EXPLORER SPORT
FORD EXPLORER SPORT TRAC
FORD F-150
FORD F-150 SVT
FORD F-150 SVT LIGHTNING
FORD F-150 SVT RAPTOR
FORD F-250
FORD F-350
FORD F-450
FORD FIESTA
FORD FIVE HUNDRED
FORD FOCUS
FORD FOCUS SE WAGON
FORD FREESTYLE
FORD FUSION
FORD FUSION HYBRID
FORD GT
FORD MUSTANG CONVERTIBLE
FORD MUSTANG COUPE
FORD MUSTANG GT
FORD RANGER
FORD SUPER DUTY
FORD SVT MUSTANG COBRA
FORD TAURUS
FORD TAURUS WAGON
FORD TAURUS-X
FORD THUNDERBIRD
FORD WINDSTAR
LINCOLN
MERCURY
SYNC
Advertising Agencies:
Aerial Advertising Services
333 W Jack London Blvd Hangar 241
Livermore, CA 94551
Tel.: (925) 449-0210

BBR Saatchi & Saatchi
6 Hachilason Street
Ramat Gan, 52522, Israel
Tel.: (972) 3755 2626
Fax: (972) 3755 2727

Budco Creative Services
13700 Oakland Ave
Highland Park, MI 48203
Tel.: (313) 957-5100
Fax: (313) 957-5522
Toll Free: (888) BUDCO-40

Burson-Marsteller
(Part of Young & Rubicam Brands, a Sub. of WPP Group plc)
230 Park Ave S
New York, NY 10003-1566
Tel.: (212) 614-4000
Fax: (212) 598-5407

Ervin Marketing Creative Communications
5615 Pershing Ave Ste 27
Saint Louis, MO 63112
Tel.: (314) 454-1143
Fax: (314) 454-1160

Euro RSCG Worldwide HQ
350 Hudson St
New York, NY 10014-4504
Tel.: (212) 886-2000
Fax: (212) 886-2016

imc2
12404 Park Central Ste 400
Dallas, TX 75251
Tel.: (214) 224-1000
Fax: (214) 224-1100

JWT U.S.A., Inc.
(d/b/a JWT-Team Detroit)
550 Town Ctr Dr
Dearborn, MI 48126
Tel.: (313) 615-3100
Tel.: (313) 615-2000 (Team Detroit)
Fax: (313) 964-3191
Fax: (212) 615-4600
(Ford Div. Cars & Trucks)

Ogilvy Public Relations Worldwide
636 11th Ave
New York, NY 10036
Tel.: (212) 880-5200
Fax: (212) 370-4636

Ogilvy Team Detroit
550 Town Center Dr
Dearborn, MI 48126
Tel.: (313) 615-3300
Fax: (313) 615-2000
(Ford Customer Service Division & Corp. Adv.)

PanCom International, Inc.
3701 Wilshire Blvd Ste 800
Los Angeles, CA 90010-2816
Tel.: (213) 427-1371
Fax: (213) 383-6729
Toll Free: (877) YPanCom
Asian American Market

PointRoll Inc.
951 E Hector St
Conshohocken, PA 19428
Tel.: (267) 558-1300
Fax: (267) 285-1141
Toll Free: (800) 203-6956

Sarkissian Mason
135 W 26th St 5 Fl
New York, NY 10001
Tel.: (212) 625-8212
Fax: (212) 625-8211

Uniworld Group, Inc.
1 Metro Center N 11th Fl
Brooklyn, NY 11201
Tel.: (212) 219-1600
Fax: (212) 219-6395
(African-American Advertising for Ford Division; African-American Media Buying for All Brands)

Zubi Advertising Services, Inc.
355 Alhambra Cir 10th Fl
Coral Gables, FL 33134-5006
Tel.: (305) 448-9824
Fax: (305) 460-6393
(Ford Division & Corporate Hispanic Creative & Media; Hispanic Media Buying for All Brands)
Mustang GT 500
Sync

FORD MOTOR COMPANY OF CANADA, LIMITED
(Sub. of Ford Motor Company)
The Canadian Road
PO Box 2000
Oakville, ON L6J 5E4, Canada
Tel.: (905) 845-2511
Fax: (905) 844-8085
Web Site: www.ford.ca
Sales Range: $5-14.9 Billion
Approx. Number Employees: 16,000
Year Founded: 1904
Business Description:
Mfr. of Cars, Trucks & Other Motor Vehicles
S.I.C.: 3711
N.A.I.C.S.: 336120; 336111
Import Export
Advertising Expenditures: $32,000,000
Media: 2-4-5-6-7-8-9-10-11-13-15-18-19-20-21-22-23-24-25-26
Distr.: Intl.; Natl.
Budget Set: Various
Personnel:
David Mondragon *(Pres & CEO)*
Brands & Products:
AVIATOR
E-SERIES

Key to Media (For complete agency information see *The Advertising Red Books-Agencies* edition):
1. Bus. Publs. 2. Cable T.V. 3. Catalogs & Directories. 4. Co-op Adv. 5. Consumer Mags. 6. D.M. to Bus. Estab.7. D.M. to Consumers
8. Daily Newsp. 9. Exhibits/Trade Shows 10. Foreign 11. Infomercial 12. Internet Adv.13. Multimedia 14. Network Radio
15. Network T.V. 16. Newsp. Distr. Mags. 17. Other 18. Outdoor (Posters, Transit) 19. Point of Purchase20. Premiums, Novelties
21. Product Samples 22. Special Events Mktg. 23. Spot Radio 24. Spot T.V. 25. Weekly Newsp. 26. Yellow Page Adv.

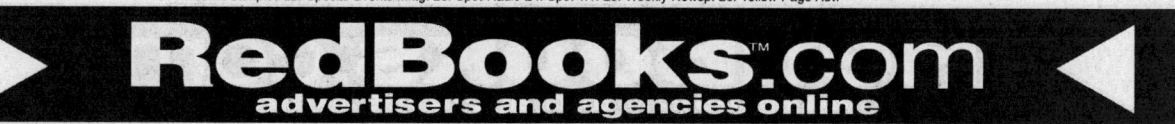

Ford Motor Company of Canada, Limited — (Continued)

ESCAPE
EXCURSION
EXPEDITION
EXPLORER SPORT TRAC
F-150
F-150 HERITAGE
F-250 SUPER DUTY
F-350 SUPER DUTY
FREESTAR
RANGER

Advertising Agency:
Y&R, Ltd.
60 Bloor Street West
Toronto, ON M4W 1J2, Canada
Tel.: (416) 961-5111
Fax: (416) 961-7890
F-Series Super Duty Pickup
Fusion
Focus
Edge

FORKLIFTS OF MINNESOTA, INC.

501 W 78th St
Bloomington, MN 55420
Tel.: (952) 887-5400
Fax: (952) 881-3030
Toll Free: (800) 752-4300
E-mail: sales@forkliftsofmn.com
Web Site: www.forkliftsofmn.com
E-Mail For Key Personnel:
Sales Director: sales@forkliftsofmn.com
Sales Range: $25-49.9 Million
Approx. Number Employees: 160
Year Founded: 1949
Business Description:
Forklift Truck Dealership; Service, Sale of Parts & Rental
S.I.C.: 5084; 5085
N.A.I.C.S.: 423830; 423840
Advertising Expenditures: $400,000
Media: 2-10-26
Budget Set: Sept. -Dec.
Personnel:
Clayton Schubert *(Co-Owner)*
Jeff Schubert *(Co-Owner)*
Larry Carpenter *(Mgr-Sls)*
Sid Lemcke *(Parts Mgr)*
Kevin Uecker *(Svc Mgr)*

FOX AUTOMOTIVE GROUP

(Sub. of AutoNation, Inc.)
(d/b/a Fox Chevrolet of Laurel)
501 Washington Blvd S 5
Laurel, MD 20707
Tel.: (301) 725-2700
Fax: (301) 483-7883
E-mail: colabuccik@autonation.com
Web Site: www.foxdealers.com
Sales Range: $50-74.9 Million
Approx. Number Employees: 84
Business Description:
Automobile Sales
S.I.C.: 5511
N.A.I.C.S.: 441110
Media: 9-25

FOX VALLEY MOTORCARS INC.

209 E Ogden Ave
Westmont, IL 60559
Tel.: (630) 654-9000
Fax: (630) 654-9001
Toll Free: (888) 883-0915
E-mail: sales@foxvalleymotorcars.com
Web Site:
www.foxvalleymotorcars.com
E-Mail For Key Personnel:
Sales Director: sales@foxvalleymotorcars.com
Approx. Number Employees: 25
Year Founded: 1998
Business Description:
Car Dealership
S.I.C.: 5511; 5521
N.A.I.C.S.: 441110; 441120
Advertising Expenditures: $148,000
Media: 5-6-13-22
Personnel:
Jim Nuccio *(Mgr-Sls)*

FREIGHTLINER LLC

(Sub. of Daimler Trucks North America LLC)
4747 N Channel Ave
Portland, OR 97217-7613
Tel.: (503) 745-8000
Fax: (503) 745-8921
E-mail: webmaster@freightliner.com
Web Site: www.freightliner.com
Year Founded: 1942
Business Description:
Diesel Trucks & Tractors Mfr
S.I.C.: 3711; 3714
N.A.I.C.S.: 336120; 336399
Media: 1-2-6-10
Distr.: Natl.
Personnel:
Roger M. Nielsen *(COO)*
Juergen Kritschgau *(CFO-Fin & Control)*
Tom Taylor *(Exec VP)*
Michael Delaney *(Sr VP-Mktg)*
Alan Mayne *(Gen Mgr-Manufacturing Opers)*
Melissa Kellogg *(Dir-Product Mktg)*
Brands & Products:
FREIGHTLINER
Advertising Agencies:
HMH
1800 SW 1st Ave Ste 250
Portland, OR 97201
Tel.: (503) 295-1922
Fax: (503) 295-1938
Toll Free: (800) 350-9355

Rains Marketing
5440 SW Westgate Dr
Portland, OR 97221
Tel.: (503) 297-1791
Fax: (503) 297-2282

GALLOWAY FAMILY OF DEALERSHIPS

1800 Boy Scout Dr
Fort Myers, FL 33907-2113
Tel.: (239) 936-3673
Fax: (239) 274-2347
E-mail: information@gallowayfamily.com
Web Site: www.gallowayfamily.com
Approx. Number Employees: 370
Year Founded: 1927
Business Description:
Automobile Dealership Services
S.I.C.: 5511
N.A.I.C.S.: 441110
Media: 3-8-9-13-18-19-23-24-26
Personnel:
Sam M. Galloway, Jr. *(Pres)*

GALPIN MOTORS, INC.

15505 Roscoe Blvd
North Hills, CA 91343-6503
Tel.: (818) 787-3800
Fax: (818) 778-2210
Toll Free: (800) 256-7137
E-mail: info@galpin.com
Web Site: www.gogalpin.com
Approx. Number Employees: 1,000
Year Founded: 1946
Business Description:
Retail Sales, Lease, Rental & Service of New & Used Motor Vehicles
S.I.C.: 5511; 5521
N.A.I.C.S.: 441110; 441120
Media: 8-9-18-23-24-25-26
Personnel:
Bert Boeckmann *(Pres)*
Phil H. Marshall *(CFO)*
Jeff Skobin *(Dir-Adv)*
Advertising Agency:
JMPR, Inc.
5850 Canoga Ave Ste 300
Woodland Hills, CA 91367
Tel.: (818) 992-4353
Fax: (818) 992-0543

GARBER MANAGEMENT GROUP INC.

(d/b/a Garber Automotive Group)
999 S Washington
Saginaw, MI 48601
Tel.: (989) 790-9090
Fax: (989) 799-9326
Web Site: www.garberbuick.com
Sales Range: $250-299.9 Million
Approx. Number Employees: 600
Year Founded: 1907
Business Description:
Car Dealership Owner & Operator
S.I.C.: 5511; 5521
N.A.I.C.S.: 441110; 441120
Import Export
Media: 3-8-9-13-16-23-24-25
Personnel:
Richard J. Garber, Jr. *(Owner & Pres)*
Scott Ellsworth *(COO)*

GARFF ENTERPRISES INC.

(d/b/a Ken Garff Automotive Group)
405 S Main Ste 1200
Salt Lake City, UT 84111-3521
Tel.: (801) 257-3400
Fax: (801) 257-3496
Web Site: www.kengarff.com
Approx. Number Employees: 2,500
Year Founded: 1949
Business Description:
Dealer of New & Used Cars
S.I.C.: 5511; 6512
N.A.I.C.S.: 441110; 531120
Import Export
Media: 9-16-18-23-24-25
Personnel:
Matt Garff *(Owner)*
Robert Garff *(Chm)*
John Garff *(Pres & CEO)*
Rick Fulkerson *(VP-Mktg)*
Brands & Products:
KEN GARFF

GATOR FORD TRUCK SALES INC.

11780 Tampa Gateway Blvd
Seffner, FL 33584
Tel.: (813) 980-3673
Fax: (813) 261-1251
E-mail: general@gatorford.com
Web Site: www.gatorford.com
Sales Range: $25-49.9 Million
Approx. Number Employees: 85
Business Description:
Car & Truck Dealership Owner & Operator
S.I.C.: 5511; 5521; 5599
N.A.I.C.S.: 441110; 441120; 441229
Media: 3-8-9-18-22-24-25
Personnel:
David Kilcoyne *(Pres)*
Pat Cooper *(Mgr-Sls)*

GENERAL ENGINES COMPANY INC.

(d/b/a Eager Beaver Trailers)
14893 Hwy 27
Lake Wales, FL 33859
Tel.: (863) 638-1421
Fax: (863) 638-2028
Toll Free: (800) 257-8163
E-mail: sales@eagerbeavertrailers.com
Web Site:
www.eagerbeavertrailers.com
E-Mail For Key Personnel:
Sales Director: sales@eagerbeavertrailers.com
Approx. Number Employees: 120
Year Founded: 1946
Business Description:
Mfr. of Trailers
S.I.C.: 3715
N.A.I.C.S.: 336212
Export
Advertising Expenditures: $250,000
Media: 1-2-4-5-6-7-8-10-11-16-19-20-26
Distr.: Natl.
Budget Set: Dec.
Personnel:
Frank Flowers *(Pres)*
Brands & Products:
ALL WHEEL ABS
EASY LOADER
ROTO-RING

GENERAL MOTORS COMPANY

300 Renaissance Ctr
Detroit, MI 48265-3000
Tel.: (313) 556-5000
Fax: (815) 282-6156
Web Site: www.gm.com
Approx. Rev.: $135,592,000,000
Approx. Number Employees: 202,000
Year Founded: 1908
Business Description:
Automobiles, Trucks, Diesel Locomotives & Engines, Aircraft Engines & Engine Parts, Automotive, Locomotive & Aircraft Components
S.I.C.: 3711; 3714; 5084
N.A.I.C.S.: 336111; 336112; 336120; 336211; 336312; 336322; 336340; 336350; 336399; 423830
Import Export
Advertising Expenditures: $4,259,000,000
Media: 2-3-5-6-9-10-11-13-14-15-18-19-22-23-24
Distr.: Intl.; Natl.
Personnel:
Daniel F. Akerson *(Chm & CEO)*
Stephen J. Girsky *(Vice Chm-Corp Strategy & Bus Dev)*
Daniel Ammann *(CFO & Sr VP)*
Terry Kline *(CIO & VP-IT)*
Sam Mancuso *(CMO)*

Key to Media (For complete agency information see *The Advertising Red Books-Agencies* edition):
1. Bus. Publs. 2. Cable T.V. 3. Catalogs & Directories. 4. Co-op Adv. 5. Consumer Mags. 6. D.M. to Bus. Estab.7. D.M. to Consumers 8. Daily Newsp. 9. Exhibits/Trade Shows 10. Foreign 11. Infomercial 12. Internet Adv.13. Multimedia 14. Network Radio 15. Network T.V. 16. Newsp. Distr. Mags. 17. Other 18. Outdoor (Posters, Transit) 19. Point of Purchase20. Premiums, Novelties 21. Product Samples 22. Special Events Mktg. 23. Spot Radio 24. Spot T.V. 25. Weekly Newsp. 26. Yellow Page Adv.

Nicholas S. Cyprus *(Chief Acctg Officer, VP & Controller)*
Mary Carpenter *(Chief Plng Officer)*
Jim Bovenzi *(Pres/Mng Dir-GM Russia)*
Grace D. Lieblein *(Pres/Mng Dir-Mexico)*
Kevin E. Wale *(Pres/Mng Dir-GM China Grp)*
Jaime Ardila *(Pres-South America & VP)*
Jonathan J. Lauckner *(Pres-Gen Motors Ventures, LLC & VP)*
Timothy E. Lee *(Pres-Intl Ops & VP)*
David N. Reilly *(Pres-Europe & VP)*
Mark I. Reuss *(Pres-North America)*
John N. Stadwick *(Pres-Middle East)*
Walter G. Borst *(CEO-Promark Global Advisors & VP)*
Michael P. Millikin *(Gen Counsel & Sr VP)*
James A. Davlin *(Treas & VP-Fin)*
Mary T. Barra *(Sr VP-Product Dev-Global)*
Alan S. Batey *(VP-Sls & Svc-Chevrolet-US)*
Stephen K. Carlisle *(VP-Global Product Plng)*
Daniel M. Hancock *(VP-Global Strategic Product Alliances)*
Kurt McNeil *(VP-Sls)*
Chris Perry *(VP-Mktg-US)*
Rick Scheidt *(VP-Mktg-Chevrolet-United States)*
Brian K. Sweeney *(VP-Sls)*
Tony DiSalle *(Head-US Mktg-Buick)*
John Schwegman *(Head-Mktg-GMC)*
Jim Bunnell *(Gen Mgr-Dealer Network & Sls Support)*
Brian Small *(Gen Mgr-Fleet & Comml Ops)*
Annette Guarisco *(Exec Dir-Federal Affairs & Govt Compliance)*
Katie Maple McBride *(Exec Dir-Internal & Exec Comm)*
Mary Sipes *(Exec Dir-Product Plng-North America)*
Clay Dean *(Dir-Design-Cadillac)*
Jon Beebe *(Dir-Digital Strategy & Integration)*
Craig Bierley *(Dir-Adv & Promos Buick)*
Jeffrey Glover *(Dir-New Bus Dev & Plng-CIS)*
Kevin Mayer *(Dir-Chevrolet Adv)*
Linda Pesonen *(Dir-Mktg)*
Steve Rosenblum *(Dir-Mktg & Adv)*
Megan Stooke *(Dir-Mktg Strategy & Ops)*
Ed Vogt *(Dir-CRM Mktg & Ops)*
Maria Rohr *(Mgr-Mktg-Buick)*
Nick Richards *(Mgr-Comm-Hummer)*
Larry Peck *(Mktg Mgr-Experiential)*
Cynthia Price *(Mktg Mgr)*
Jim Cain *(Mgr-Fin Comm)*
Ryndee Carney *(Mgr-Dealer & Adv Comm)*
Karen Cuff *(Mgr-Interactive Mktg)*
Mary Kubitskey *(Mgr-Natl Adv)*
Cindy McColley *(Mgr-Digital Adv)*
Nancy Sharkey *(Mgr-Web Strategy-Global)*
Susan Walton *(Mgr-Product Mktg, Mobile Apps)*

Brands & Products:
ACADIA
ACDELCO
ALLISION TRANSMISSION
AVALANCHE
AVEO
BUICK
CADILLAC
CADILLAC SLS
CANYON
CAPRICE
CHEVROLET
COBALT
COLORADO
CORVETTE
CTS
CTS-V
DEXRON
DTS
ENVOY
ENVOY DENALI
ENVOY XL
ENVOY XL DENALI
EPICA
EQUINOX
ESCALADE
ESCALADE ESV
ESCALADE EXT
EXPRESS CARGO
EXPRESS PASSENGER
G8
GMC
HHR
HOLDEN
IMPALA
LACROSSE
LUCERNE
ONSTAR
OPEL
SAFARI
SAVANA CARGO
SAVANA PASSENGER
SIERRA
SILVERADO
SPARK
SRX
STS
STS-V
SUBURBAN
SV6
TAHOE
TAVERA
TRAILBLAZER
VAUXHALL
VOLT
YUKON
YUKON DENALI
YUKON XL
YUKON XL DENALI

Advertising Agencies:

Aegis Group plc
10 Triton Street
London, NW1 3BF, United Kingdom
Tel.: (44) 2070707700
Fax: (44) 2070707800

Big Fuel Communications LLC
298 5th Ave 5th Fl
New York, NY 10001
Tel.: (212) 616-6300
Fax: (212) 658-9226

BroadBandagency LLC
1007 Harvard Rd
Grosse Pointe Park, MI 48230
Tel.: (313) 282-3711

Carlson Marketing
1405 Xenium Ln N
Plymouth, MN 55441
Tel.: (763) 445-3000

Deutsch LA
5454 Beethoven St
Los Angeles, CA 90066-7017
Tel.: (310) 862-3000
Fax: (310) 862-3100

Digitas Inc.
33 Arch St
Boston, MA 02110
Tel.: (617) 867-1000
Fax: (617) 867-1111
Buick
GMC
Interactive
— Barbara Goose *(Exec VP-Mktg)*

Erwin-Penland
(Owned by Hill, Holliday, Connors, Cosmopulos, Inc., Member of the Interpublic Group)
125 E Broad St
Greenville, SC 29601
Tel.: (864) 271-0500
Fax: (864) 235-5941

ES Advertising
6222 Wilshire Blvd Ste 302
Los Angeles, CA 90048
Tel.: (323) 964-9001
Fax: (323) 964-9801

Fallon Minneapolis
901 Marquette Ave Ste 2400
Minneapolis, MN 55402
Tel.: (612) 758-2345
Fax: (612) 758-2346
Toll Free: (866) 758-2345
Cadillac

Fallon Worldwide
901 Marquette Ave Ste 2400
Minneapolis, MN 55402
Tel.: (612) 758-2345
Fax: (612) 758-2346
Cadillac

General Motors R*Works
1 Woodward Ste 1200
Detroit, MI 48226
Tel.: (313) 596-9000
Fax: (313) 961-1623

Goodby, Silverstein & Partners
211 Woodside Ave
Detroit, MI 48201
Tel.: (313) 202-3700
Chevrolet

Goodby, Silverstein & Partners, Inc.
(Part of Omnicom Group, Inc.)
720 California St
San Francisco, CA 94108-2404
Tel.: (415) 392-0669
Fax: (415) 788-4303
Chevrolet - Lead Creative Agency

LaBov & Beyond, Inc.
609 E Cook Rd
Fort Wayne, IN 46825
Tel.: (260) 497-0111
Fax: (260) 497-0007

LatinWorks Marketing, Inc.
206 E 9th St Capital Tower Fl 13
Austin, TX 78701
Tel.: (512) 479-6200
Fax: (512) 479-6024

Leo Burnett Detroit, Inc.
3310 W Big Beaver Rd Ste 107
Troy, MI 48084-2809
Tel.: (248) 458-8300
Tel.: (248) 458-8519
Fax: (248) 458-8300
Pontiac Solstice
Buick
GMC
Pontiac G8
— Chris Balicki *(Grp Acct Dir)*

Leo Burnett India
Big Apple A
Mumbai, 400 012, India
Tel.: (91) 22 5663 4444
Fax: (91) 22 2417 3328
Chevrolet Spark
Chevrolet Tavera

Leo Burnett Worldwide, Inc.
35 W Wacker Dr
Chicago, IL 60601-1723
Tel.: (312) 220-5959
Fax: (312) 220-3299
Buick
GMC
— Peter McHugh *(Acct Dir-GMC)*

Martin Retail Group/Martin Advertising
2801 University Blvd Ste 200
Birmingham, AL 35233
Tel.: (205) 930-9200
Fax: (205) 933-6949
Buick
GMC

McCann Erickson
360 W Maple Rd
Birmingham, MI 48009
Tel.: (248) 203-8000
Fax: (248) 203-8010

McCann Erickson Guangming Ltd.
21/F Huaihai Plaza
Shanghai, 200031, China
Tel.: (86) 21 2411 1488
Fax: (86) 21 2411 1468
Cadillac
Buick

Mother New York
595 11th Ave
New York, NY 10036
Tel.: (212) 254-2800
Fax: (212) 254-6121
Chevrolet
The Road We're On

Perich Advertising + Design
117 N 1st St Ste 100
Ann Arbor, MI 48104-1354
Tel.: (734) 769-2215
Fax: (734) 769-2322
(Hybrid Vehicles)

PointRoll Inc.
951 E Hector St
Conshohocken, PA 19428
Tel.: (267) 558-1300
Fax: (267) 285-1141
Toll Free: (800) 203-6956

Sanders/Wingo Advertising, Inc.
221 N Kansas Ste 900
El Paso, TX 79901
Tel.: (915) 533-9583

Key to Media (For complete agency information see *The Advertising Red Books-Agencies* edition):
1. Bus. Publs. 2. Cable T.V. 3. Catalogs & Directories. 4. Co-op Adv. 5. Consumer Mags. 6. D.M. to Bus. Estab.7. D.M. to Consumers
8. Daily Newsp. 9. Exhibits/Trade Shows 10. Foreign 11. Infomercial 12. Internet Adv.13. Multimedia 14. Network Radio
15. Network T.V. 16. Newsp. Distr. Mags. 17. Other 18. Outdoor (Posters, Transit) 19. Point of Purchase20. Premiums, Novelties
21. Product Samples 22. Special Events Mktg. 23. Spot Radio 24. Spot T.V. 25. Weekly Newsp. 26. Yellow Page Adv.

General Motors Company — (Continued)

Fax: (915) 533-3601
Chevrolet

Savage
4203 Montrose Blvd.
Houston, TX 77006
Tel.: (713) 522-1555
Fax: (713) 522-1582
(Online Investor Relations Materials & Annual Reports)

Spike/DDB
55 Washington St Ste 650
Brooklyn, NY 11201
Tel.: (718) 596-5400
Fax: (212) 415-3101
African-American Agency of Record-Chevrolet

SS&K
88 Pine St 30th Fl
New York, NY 10005
Tel.: (212) 274-9500
Fax: (212) 274-9598
Toll Free: (800) 274-7765
Buick
GMC
Social Media

Starcom MediaVest Group
35 W Wacker Dr
Chicago, IL 60601-1723
Tel.: (312) 220-3535
Fax: (312) 220-6530
Buick
GMC
Media Buying

Strauss Radio Strategies, Inc.
National Press Bldg Ste 1163 529 14th St NW
Washington, DC 20045
Tel.: (202) 638-0200
Fax: (202) 638-0400

Vigilante Advertising
345 Hudson Street
New York, NY 10014
Tel.: (212) 545-2850
Fax: (212) 444-6061

Whitespeed
29672 Zuma Bay Way
Malibu, CA 90265
Tel.: (310) 869-9979
Fax: (310) 899-3199

GENERAL MOTORS OF CANADA LTD.
(Sub. of General Motors Company)
1908 Colonel Sam Dr
Oshawa, ON L1H 8P7, Canada
Tel.: (905) 644-5000
Fax: (905) 644-3873
Toll Free: (800) 263-3777 (English)
Toll Free: (800) 263-7854 (French)
Web Site: www.gmcanada.com
Approx. Number Employees: 9,000
Year Founded: 1918
Business Description:
Automotive Production & Distribution
S.I.C.: 3711
N.A.I.C.S.: 336111; 336211
Import Export
Media: 6-7-8-10-14-15-17-22-25-26
Distr.: Natl.
Budget Set: Dec.
Personnel:
Kevin W. Williams *(Pres & Mng Dir)*
Shawn Severs *(CFO & VP-Fin-General Motors of Canada)*
Frank Trivieri *(Gen Dir-Mktg)*
Neil J. MacDonald *(Gen Counsel & VP-Corp Affairs)*
Marc Comeau *(VP-Vehicle Sls, Svc & Mktg)*
Pri Bieri *(Dir-Sls-Mktg)*
Fred Lautenschlager *(Mktg Mgr-Fullsize Trucks & Utilities)*
Dan Mepham *(Product Mgr-Chevrolet Volt)*
Harry Ng *(Product Mgr-Chevrolet)*
Brian Riendeau *(Mgr-Retail Adv)*
Thomas Wilson *(Mgr-Corp Center Consolidations)*
Dayna Ryall *(Asst Mgr-Mktg)*

GLENDALE INTERNATIONAL CORP.
1155 North Service Rd West Ste 11
Oakville, ON L6M 3E3, Canada
Tel.: (905) 844-2870
Fax: (289) 291-4001
E-mail: info@glendaleint.com
Web Site: www.glendaleint.com
Approx. Sls.: $74,466,168
Approx. Number Employees: 457
Year Founded: 1970
Business Description:
Recreational Vehicles & Illuminated Cockpit Instrumentation Panels & Beveled Keyboards Mfr & Sales
S.I.C.: 5561; 3728
N.A.I.C.S.: 441210; 336413
Media: 7-10
Personnel:
Edward C. Hanna *(Chm & CEO)*
Murray L. Hannan *(CFO)*
John McCook *(Pres-Travelaire Canada)*
Terry Mullan *(Pres-Glendale Recreational Vehicles)*
Brands & Products:
GLENDALE
GOLDEN FALCON
RUSTLER
TITANIUM
TRAVELAIRE

GLOBE MOTOR CAR CORP.
1230 Bloomfield Ave
Fairfield, NJ 07004
Tel.: (973) 227-3600
Fax: (973) 575-7835
Toll Free: (877) 492-1864
E-mail: scherr@globemb.com
Web Site: www.globemotorcar.com
Approx. Number Employees: 100
Year Founded: 1967
Business Description:
Owner & Operator of Car Dealerships
S.I.C.: 5511; 5012
N.A.I.C.S.: 441110; 423110
Media: 6-8-13
Personnel:
Joseph Chnapko *(Pres)*
Peter Scherr *(Gen Mgr-Sls)*

GRAHAM MOTORS AND CONTROLS
PO Box 960607
El Paso, TX 79996
Tel.: (915) 599-2727
Fax: (915) 599-2883
Fax: (866) 471-4261
Toll Free: (888) 363-1313
Web Site: www.grahammotorsandcontrols.com
Sales Range: Less than $1 Million
Approx. Number Employees: 150
Year Founded: 1936
Business Description:
Industrial Power Transmission Equipment Mfr
S.I.C.: 3714; 5063
N.A.I.C.S.: 336350; 423610
Media: 4-7-8-13
Personnel:
Oscar Seleme *(Gen Mgr)*
Roxanna Williams *(Office Mgr)*
Brands & Products:
CYCLETROL
GRAHAM
MAGNAPAK
VARISPEED A2000
VARISPEED R400
VARISPEED S1000

GROUP 1 AUTOMOTIVE, INC.
800 Gessner Ste 500
Houston, TX 77024
Tel.: (713) 647-5700
Fax: (713) 647-5858
E-mail: investorrelations@group1auto.com
Web Site: www.group1auto.com
Approx. Rev.: $5,509,169,000
Approx. Number Employees: 7,454
Year Founded: 1995
Business Description:
New & Used Car Dealer
S.I.C.: 5511; 5013; 6141
N.A.I.C.S.: 441110; 441310; 522291
Advertising Expenditures: $45,047,000
Media: 2
Personnel:
John L. Adams *(Chm)*
Earl J. Hesterberg *(Pres & CEO)*
John C. Rickel *(CFO & Sr VP)*
Darryl M. Burman *(Gen Counsel & VP)*
Randy L. Callison *(Sr VP-Corp Dev & Ops)*
James R. Druzbik *(VP-Info Sys)*
M. Lee Mitchell *(VP-Fin Svcs)*
Gigi L. Myung *(VP-Pur)*
J. Brooks O'Hara *(VP-HR)*
Kim Paper Canning *(Mgr-IR)*

GUARANTY CHEVROLET-PONTIAC
20 Hwy 99 S
Junction City, OR 97448-9714
Tel.: (541) 998-2333
Fax: (541) 998-4292
Toll Free: (800) 766-9231
E-mail: esales@guaranty.com
Web Site: www.guaranty.com
Approx. Number Employees: 300
Year Founded: 1966
Business Description:
Retailers of Automobile
S.I.C.: 5561; 5511
N.A.I.C.S.: 441210; 441110
Media: 5-8-9-13-23-24-25-26
Distr.: Natl.
Budget Set: Dec.
Personnel:
Shannon Nill *(Owner)*
Becky Smith *(Mgr-Adv & Mktg)*

GULF STATES TOYOTA, INC.
(Sub. of Friedkin Companies Inc.)
PO Box 442168
Houston, TX 77244-2168
Mailing Address:
PO Box 40306
Houston, TX 77240-0306
Tel.: (713) 580-3300
Fax: (713) 580-3332
Sales Range: $1-4.9 Billion
Approx. Number Employees: 1,200
Year Founded: 1969
Business Description:
New Automobile & Motor Vehicle Parts Distr
S.I.C.: 5012; 5013
N.A.I.C.S.: 423110; 423120
Media: 8-9-23-24-25
Personnel:
Thomas Friedkin *(Chm)*
Toby Hynes *(Pres)*
Frank Gruen *(CFO)*
J. C. Fassino *(Sr VP-Market Representation)*
Tom Bittenbender *(VP-Sls Ops)*
Gene Brown *(VP-Mktg)*
Dominic Gallo *(VP-HR)*
David Copeland *(Dir-Admin)*
Eric Williamson *(Dir-Fleet Ops)*
Advertising Agency:
Intermark Group, Inc.
101 25th St N
Birmingham, AL 35203
Tel.: (205) 803-0000
Fax: (205) 870-3843
Toll Free: (800) 554-0218

HACKNEY INTERNATIONAL
(Div. of Hackney)
400 Hackney Ave
Washington, NC 27889-4726
Mailing Address:
PO Box 880
Washington, NC 27889
Tel.: (252) 946-6521
Fax: (252) 975-8340
Toll Free: (800) 763-0700
E-mail: hhackney@hackneyinternational.com
Web Site: www.hackneyinternational.com
Approx. Number Employees: 500
Year Founded: 1992
Business Description:
Truck Bodies & Trailers for the Beverage Industry Mfr, Emergency Services & Other Applications
S.I.C.: 3711
N.A.I.C.S.: 336211
Import Export
Media: 1-2-10
Distr.: Natl.
Budget Set: July
Personnel:
Leandro Rodriguez *(Dir-InterNatl Sls)*
Brands & Products:
DIMENSION
DOCKMASTER
PERFORMER
POLAR BEAR
SERVEND
SPRINT
STRETCH

HALREC INC.
(d/b/a Stevens Creek Toyota)
4202 Stevens Creek Blvd
San Jose, CA 95129

Key to Media (For complete agency information see *The Advertising Red Books-Agencies* edition):
1. Bus. Publs. 2. Cable T.V. 3. Catalogs & Directories. 4. Co-op Adv. 5. Consumer Mags. 6. D.M. to Bus. Estab.7. D.M. to Consumers
8. Daily Newsp. 9. Exhibits/Trade Shows 10. Foreign 11. Infomercial 12. Internet Adv.13. Multimedia 14. Network Radio
15. Network T.V. 16. Newsp. Distr. Mags. 17. Other 18. Outdoor (Posters, Transit) 19. Point of Purchase20. Premiums, Novelties
21. Product Samples 22. Special Events Mktg. 23. Spot Radio 24. Spot T.V. 25. Weekly Newsp. 26. Yellow Page Adv.

Tel.: (408) 984-1234
Fax: (408) 246-8028
Web Site: www.sctoyota.com
Approx. Sls.: $150,000,000
Approx. Number Employees: 250
Business Description:
New & Used Car Dealers
S.I.C.: 5511; 7539
N.A.I.C.S.: 441110; 811118
Personnel:
Harold Cornelius *(Chm)*
Advertising Agencies:
ABC (Advertising Business Consultants)
1334 Lincoln Ave
San Jose, CA 95125
Tel.: (408) 298-0124
Fax: (408) 298-0125

Larry Alexander Advertising
5582 Merritt Court
Concord, CA 94521-4740
Tel.: (925) 513-8904

HANSLER MANUTENTION, INC

(Sub. of Hansler Industries)
10145 Cote de Liesse
Dorval, QC H9P 1A3, Canada
Tel.: (514) 636-0453
Fax: (514) 636-8427
E-mail: dvallee@hansler.com
Web Site:
www.hanslermanutention.ca
Approx. Number Employees: 12
Business Description:
Lift Trucks Rental & Leasing Services
S.I.C.: 3537; 7359
N.A.I.C.S.: 333924; 532490
Media: 2-8-10-13
Personnel:
John Brinkworth *(Dir-Fin)*

HARLEY-DAVIDSON, INC.

3700 W Juneau Ave
Milwaukee, WI 53208
Mailing Address:
PO Box 453
Milwaukee, WI 53201-0653
Tel.: (414) 343-4680
Fax: (414) 343-8230
Web Site: www.harley-davidson.com
Approx. Rev.: $4,859,336,000
Approx. Number Employees: 6,900
Year Founded: 1903
Business Description:
Motorcycles, Parts & Accessories Mfr & Distr
S.I.C.: 3751
N.A.I.C.S.: 336991
Import Export
Advertising Expenditures: $75,800,000
Media: 4-5-6-8-10-13-15-18-19-20-22-24
Distr.: Intl.; Natl.
Personnel:
Barry K. Allen *(Chm)*
Keith E. Wandell *(Pres & CEO)*
Mark Kornetzke *(Chief Acctg Officer)*
Gail A. Lione *(Gen Counsel, Sec & Exec VP)*
Paul J. Jones *(Gen Counsel, Sec & VP)*
J. Darrell Thomas *(Treas, VP & Asst Sec)*
William J. Davidson *(Sr VP)*
Karl M. Eberle *(Sr VP-Mfg)*
Ronald M. Hutchinson *(Sr VP-Product Dev)*
Mark-Hans Richer *(Global CMO & Sr VP)*
Michael P. Heerhold *(VP & Gen Mgr-Powertrain Ops)*
Jeffrey A. Merten *(VP & Gen Mgr-North American Sls)*
Patrick Smith *(VP & Gen Mgr-Global Apparel & Mdse)*
Joanne M. Bischmann *(VP-Comm)*
Tonit Calaway *(VP-HR)*
Joan Vichmann *(VP-Comm)*
Ed Magee *(Gen Mgr-York Vehicle Ops)*
Dino Bernacchi *(Dir-Mktg Comm-North America)*
Vince Orange *(Dir-Supply Mgmt)*
Richard Steffens *(Dir-Quality)*
Brands & Products:
883 XL
ALUMINATOR
BADLANDER
BLAST
BRAG
BUELL
CAGIVA
DEUCE
DYNA
DYNA DEFENDER
DYNA GLIDE
ELECTRA GLIDE
ELECTRA-GLO
EVOLUTION
FAT BOY
FXRG
HARLEY-DAVIDSON
HARLEY OWNERS GROUP
H.O.G.
LIGHTNING
LOW RIDER
MOTORCLOTHES
THE MOUNTED OFFICER
MV AGUSTA
NIGHT TRAIN
QUEST
RIDERS EDGE
ROAD GLIDE
ROAD KING
ROAD TECH
SCREAMIN EAGLE
SOFTAIL
SPORTSTER
SPRINGER
SUNWASH
SUPER GLIDE
TLE SIDECAR
TOUR-PAK
TWIN CAM
ULTRA CLASSIC
V-ROD
VRSC
WIDE GLIDE
WILLIE G
Advertising Agencies:
303 Group
Level 3 51 Murray St
Sydney, 2009, Australia
Tel.: (61) 2 9552 2100
Fax: (61) 2 9339 6799

AVA Advertising
259 S St
Waukesha, WI 53186
Tel.: (262) 523-9200
Fax: (262) 523-9210

Larter Advertising
15243 Yonge St
Aurora, ON L4G 1L8, Canada
Tel.: (905) 727-6978
Fax: (905) 727-0103

Laughlin/Constable, Inc.
207 E Michigan St
Milwaukee, WI 53202-4998
Tel.: (414) 272-2400
Fax: (414) 270-7140

McCann Erickson Worldwide
622 3rd Ave
New York, NY 10017-6707
Tel.: (646) 865-2000
Fax: (646) 487-9610

Overdrive
38 Everett St 2nd Fl
Boston, MA 02134
Tel.: (617) 254-5000
Fax: (617) 254-5003

Red Brown Kle
840 N Old World Third St Ste 401
Milwaukee, WI 53203
Tel.: (414) 272-2600
Fax: (414) 272-2690
Toll Free: (888) 725-2041

Schawk Retail Marketing
1 N Dearborn Ste 700
Chicago, IL 60602
Tel.: (312) 666-9200
Fax: (312) 260-1970
Toll Free: (888) AMBROSI

Starcom MediaVest Group
35 W Wacker Dr
Chicago, IL 60601-1723
Tel.: (312) 220-3535
Fax: (312) 220-6530

WHITTMANHART
150 North Michigan Ave Ste 300
Chicago, IL 60601
Tel.: (312) 981-6000
Fax: (312) 981-6100

HAROLD MATTHEWS NISSAN INC.

185 Hwy 76
Clarksville, TN 37043
Tel.: (931) 552-7555
Fax: (931) 552-7634
E-mail: admin@haroldmatthewsnissan.com
Web Site:
www.haroldmatthewsnissan.com
Approx. Number Employees: 60
Business Description:
New & Used Car Dealers
S.I.C.: 5511
N.A.I.C.S.: 441110
Media: 8-16-18-22-23
Personnel:
Gary Matthews *(Pres)*
Wayne Clardy *(Office Mgr)*

HEISER AUTOMOTIVE GROUP INC.

1700 W Silverspring Dr
Glendale, WI 53209
Tel.: (414) 355-7401
Tel.: (414) 357-2166
Fax: (414) 247-8990
Fax: (414) 357-2112
Web Site: www.heiser.com
Sales Range: $125-149.9 Million
Approx. Number Employees: 320
Year Founded: 1917
Business Description:
Auto Dealership
S.I.C.: 5511; 5521
N.A.I.C.S.: 441110; 441120
Media: 9-13-23-24-25
Distr.: Reg.
Personnel:
Chris Dulla *(Pres)*
Sam Scaffidi *(Mgr)*

HERTZ GLOBAL HOLDINGS, INC.

(Joint Venture of Bank of America Corporation, Carlyle Holding Corporation & Clayton, Dubilier & Rice, LLC)
225 Brae Blvd
Park Ridge, NJ 07656-0713
Tel.: (201) 307-2000
Tel.: (201) 307-2100 (IR)
Fax: (201) 307-2644
E-mail: investorrelations@hertz.com
Web Site: www.hertz.com
Approx. Rev.: $7,562,534,000
Approx. Number Employees: 22,900
Business Description:
Holding Company; Owned by Bank of America Corporation, Carlyle Holding Corporation & Clayton, Dubilier & Rice LLC
S.I.C.: 4581; 6719; 7514
N.A.I.C.S.: 488190; 532111; 551112
Advertising Expenditures: $116,300,000
Personnel:
Mark P. Frissora *(Chm & CEO)*
Elyse Douglas *(CFO & Exec VP)*
Joseph F. Eckroth *(CIO & Sr VP-Global Customer Care)*
LeighAnne G. Baker *(Chief HR Officer & Sr VP)*
Michel Taride *(Pres-Hertz Europe & Exec VP)*
Joseph R. Nothwang *(Pres-Rentala & Leasing Americas & Pacific)*
Gerald A. Plescia *(Exec VP)*
John A. Thomas *(Exec VP-Global Supply Chain)*
Jatindar Kapur *(Controller & Sr VP-Fin)*
Robert J. Stuart *(Sr VP-Global Sls)*
Edward Hu *(VP & Gen Mgr-China)*
Gary Fulena *(Acting Gen Mgr-Advantage Rent A Car)*
Paula Rivera *(Mgr-PR)*
Advertising Agency:
Iris
Iris Towers 185 Park St
London, SE1 9DY, United Kingdom
Tel.: (44) 20 7654 7900
Fax: (44) 20 7654 7901

HOLLER DRIVER'S MART

1970 SR 436
Winter Park, FL 32792
Tel.: (407) 645-1234
Tel.: (407) 645-1331
Fax: (407) 647-3582
Toll Free: (888) 856-5771
Web Site: www.hollerdriversmart.com
Approx. Number Employees: 225
Year Founded: 1938
Business Description:
Car & Truck Dealership

Key to Media (For complete agency information see *The Advertising Red Books-Agencies* edition):
1. Bus. Publs. 2. Cable T.V. 3. Catalogs & Directories. 4. Co-op Adv. 5. Consumer Mags. 6. D.M. to Bus. Estab.7. D.M. to Consumers
8. Daily Newsp. 9. Exhibits/Trade Shows 10. Foreign 11. Infomercial 12. Internet Adv.13. Multimedia 14. Network Radio
15. Network T.V. 16. Newsp. Distr. Mags. 17. Other 18. Outdoor (Posters, Transit) 19. Point of Purchase20. Premiums, Novelties
21. Product Samples 22. Special Events Mktg. 23. Spot Radio 24. Spot T.V. 25. Weekly Newsp. 26. Yellow Page Adv.

Holler Driver's Mart — (Continued)
S.I.C.: 5511; 5521
N.A.I.C.S.: 441110; 441120
Media: 2-8-9-13-14-15-22-26
Personnel:
Roger W. Holler, Jr. *(Pres)*
Gavin Hutchinson *(Gen Mgr)*

HOMETOWN AUTO RETAILERS, INC.
1309 S Main St
Watertown, CT 06706
Tel.: (203) 756-1300
Fax: (203) 756-1339
E-mail: info@hometownautoretailers.com
Web Site: www.hometownautoretailers.com
Sales Range: $200-249.9 Million
Approx. Number Employees: 297
Year Founded: 1997
Business Description:
Car & Light Truck Dealerships
S.I.C.: 5511
N.A.I.C.S.: 441110
Advertising Expenditures: $3,400,000
Media: 5
Personnel:
Corey Shaker *(Pres, CEO & COO)*
Charles F. Schwartz *(CFO)*
William C. Muller *(Reg VP South Division)*

HONDA CANADA INC.
(Sub. of Honda Motor Co., Ltd.)
715 Milner Ave
Toronto, ON M1B 2K8, Canada
Tel.: (905) 888-8110
Fax: (416) 286-1322
Web Site: www.honda.ca
Sales Range: $1-4.9 Billion
Approx. Number Employees: 5,000
Year Founded: 1969
Business Description:
Automobiles Importer & Distr
S.I.C.: 5012
N.A.I.C.S.: 423110
Import Export
Media: 2-3-4-5-6-7-8-9-10-13-14-15-16-18-19-22-23-25-26
Distr.: Natl.
Budget Set: Jan. -Mar.
Personnel:
Takashi Sekiguchi *(Pres & CEO)*
Jerry Chenkin *(Exec VP)*
Barry Holt *(VP-Fin)*
Jean-Marc Leclerc *(Asst VP-Mktg)*
Trevor Maidment *(Sr Mgr-Adv)*
Brands & Products:
ACURA 1.7 EL
ACURA MDX
ODYSSEY
Advertising Agencies:
Grip Ltd.
179 John St 6th Fl
Toronto, ON M5T 1X4, Canada
Tel.: (416) 340-7111
Fax: (416) 340-7776

PHD Canada
96 Spadina Ave Ste 600
Toronto, ON M5V 2J6, Canada
Tel.: (416) 922-0217
Fax: (416) 922-8469
Media Placement & Strategy

HYUNDAI AUTO CANADA
(Div. of Hyundai Motor America)
75 Frontenac Drive
Markham, ON L3R 6H2, Canada
Tel.: (905) 477-0202
Fax: (905) 477-0187
Telex: 6-986306 HD PONY
E-mail: cr@hyundaicanada.com
Web Site: www.hyundaicanada.com
Approx. Number Employees: 170
Business Description:
Passenger Vehicles Whslr & Distr Through Authorized Hyundai Dealers
S.I.C.: 5013
N.A.I.C.S.: 423120
Personnel:
Steve Kelleher *(Pres & CEO)*
Oles Gadacz *(Dir-PR)*
Michael Handy *(Mgr-Mktg)*
Chad Heard *(Mgr-PR)*
Advertising Agency:
Bensimon Byrne
420 Wellington St W
Toronto, ON M5V 1E3, Canada
Tel.: (416) 922-2211
Fax: (416) 922-8590

HYUNDAI MOTOR AMERICA
(Sub. of Hyundai Motor Company)
10550 Talbert Ave
Fountain Valley, CA 92708-6031
Tel.: (714) 965-3000
Fax: (714) 965-3816
Web Site: www.hyundaiusa.com
Approx. Number Employees: 800
Year Founded: 1985
Business Description:
Automobiles Distr
S.I.C.: 5012; 5013
N.A.I.C.S.: 423110; 423120
Import
Media: 2-3-6-8-9-10-13-15-18-19-22-23-24
Distr.: Natl.
Personnel:
John Krafcik *(Pres & CEO)*
Cayne Lee *(CFO)*
Frank Ferrara *(Exec VP-Corp Plng & Customer Satisfaction)*
Steve Shannon *(VP-Mktg)*
Derrick Hatami *(Gen Mgr-Western Reg)*
Sam Brnovich *(Exec Dir-Sls Plng & Retail Ops)*
Chris Hosford *(Exec Dir-Corp Comm)*
Jacquelyn Kim *(Dir-Mktg, Strategy & Promos)*
Erwin Raphael *(Dir-Product Quality & Svc Engrg)*
Barry Ratzlaff *(Dir-Customer Satisfaction & Svc Bus Dev)*
Simon Cho *(Sr Mgr-Interactive Mktg)*
Brands & Products:
ALLEGRO
AVIVA
ELANTRA
EXCEL
HYUNDAI ADVANTAGE
SHIFTRONIC
SMARTSTOCK
TAOS
TIOGA
Advertising Agencies:
Goodby, Silverstein & Partners, Inc.
(Part of Omnicom Group, Inc.)
720 California St
San Francisco, CA 94108-2404
Tel.: (415) 392-0669
Fax: (415) 788-4303
Tucson
Santa Fe
Veracruz
Genesis

Initiative Los Angeles
5700 Wilshire Blvd Ste 400
Los Angeles, CA 90036-3648
Tel.: (323) 370-8000
Fax: (323) 370-8950

Initiative Worldwide
(Part of The Interpublic Group of Companies, Inc.)
1 Dag Hammerskjold Plz 5th Fl
New York, NY 10017
Tel.: (212) 605-7000
Fax: (212) 605-7200

Innocean Americas Worldwide
4 Park Plz Ste 950
Irvine, CA 92614
Tel.: (949) 440-2100
Media Buying

Siltanen & Partners
353 Coral Cir
El Segundo, CA 90245
Tel.: (310) 321-5200
Fax: (310) 321-5270

IMOBOLIS, INC.
8950 W Olympic Blvd Ste 350
Beverly Hills, CA 90211
Tel.: (310) 281-6094
E-mail: info@imobolis.com
Web Site: www.imobolis.com
Approx. Number Employees: 1
Year Founded: 2010
Business Description:
Automobile Sales
S.I.C.: 5012
N.A.I.C.S.: 423110
Advertising Expenditures: $97,449
Media: 17
Personnel:
Julian Spitari *(Pres, CEO, CFO & Sec)*
Ronald Chew *(Gen Counsel)*

INSURANCE AUTO AUCTIONS, INC.
(Holding of KAR Auction Services, Inc.)
2 Westbrook Corporate Ctr Ste 500
Westchester, IL 60154
Tel.: (708) 492-7000
Fax: (708) 492-7078
E-mail: cservice@iaai.com
Web Site: www.iaai.com
E-Mail For Key Personnel:
Marketing Director: marketing@iaai.com
Sales Director: sales@iaai.com
Sales Range: $550-599.9 Million
Year Founded: 1982
Business Description:
Salvage Vehicle Auction Services
S.I.C.: 5521; 5599
N.A.I.C.S.: 441120; 441229
Media: 7-10-13
Personnel:
Thomas C. O'Brien *(Pres & CEO)*
John W. Kett *(CFO & Sr VP)*
David R. Montgomery *(COO & Sr VP)*
Sidney L. Kerley *(Gen Counsel & VP)*
Peter B. Doder *(Sr VP-Market Dev)*
Donald J. Hermanek *(Chief Client Officer & Sr VP)*
Mark Walsh *(Sr VP-Sls)*
Patrick W. Walsh *(Sr VP-Bus Dev)*
Kelly Ingersoll *(Dir-Transportation & CAT Logistics)*
Brands & Products:
IAA

INTERNATIONAL TRUCK AND ENGINE CORPORATION
(Sub. of Navistar International Corporation)
4201 Winfield Rd
Warrenville, IL 60555-4025
Mailing Address:
PO Box 1488
Warrenville, IL 60555-7488
Tel.: (630) 753-5000
Fax: (630) 753-2192
Web Site: www.internationaldelivers.com
Sales Range: $450-499.9 Million
Approx. Number Employees: 1,400
Business Description:
Medium & Heavy Duty Diesel Trucks, Buses, Diesel Engines & Replacement Parts Mfr & Marketer
S.I.C.: 3711; 3714
N.A.I.C.S.: 336120; 336399
Export
Advertising Expenditures: $5,000,000
Media: 2-4-6-7-9-10-14-16-19-20-23-26
Distr.: Natl.
Personnel:
Daniel C. Ustian *(Chm, Pres & CEO)*
Jack Allen *(Pres-Engine Grp)*
Dee Kapur *(Pres-Truck Grp)*
Steven K. Covey *(Gen Counsel & Sr VP)*
Greg Elliott *(Sr VP-HR & Admin-Navistar)*
Phyllis E. Cochran *(Sr VP & Gen Mgr-Navistar Parts Grp)*
Thomas Baughman *(VP & Gen Mgr-Heavy Vehicle Center)*
Annette Freund *(VP-Compensation, Benefits & HR Support)*
Tom Grogan *(VP-Bus Sls)*
Thomas M. Hough *(VP-Strategic Initiatives)*
David Hillman *(Dir-Mktg)*
Mark Brakeall *(Mgr-Mktg-Bus Dev)*
Randy Ray *(Mgr-Mktg-Bus Dev)*
Roy Wiley *(Mgr-External Commun)*
Brands & Products:
INTERNATIONAL
Advertising Agency:
PriceWeber Marketing Communications, Inc.
10701 Shelbyville Rd
Louisville, KY 40243
Tel.: (502) 499-9220
Fax: (502) 491-5593

INTERNATIONAL TRUCK AND ENGINE CORPORATION CANADA
(Holding of Navistar International Corporation)
5500 N Service Rd
Burlington, ON L7L 5H7, Canada
Mailing Address:
PO Box 5337
Burlington, ON L7R 5A4, Canada

Key to Media (For complete agency information see *The Advertising Red Books-Agencies* edition):
1. Bus. Publs. 2. Cable T.V. 3. Catalogs & Directories. 4. Co-op Adv. 5. Consumer Mags. 6. D.M. to Bus. Estab.7. D.M. to Consumers
8. Daily Newsp. 9. Exhibits/Trade Shows 10. Foreign 11. Infomercial 12. Internet Adv.13. Multimedia 14. Network Radio
15. Network T.V. 16. Newsp. Distr. Mags. 17. Other 18. Outdoor (Posters, Transit) 19. Point of Purchase20. Premiums, Novelties
21. Product Samples 22. Special Events Mktg. 23. Spot Radio 24. Spot T.V. 25. Weekly Newsp. 26. Yellow Page Adv.

Tel.: (905) 332-3323
Fax: (905) 332-2965
Web Site: www.navistar.com
Sales Range: $1-4.9 Billion
Approx. Number Employees: 1,200
Year Founded: 1903
Business Description:
Medium & Heavy Trucks, Diesel Engines & School Buses Marketer & Distr
S.I.C.: 3519
N.A.I.C.S.: 333618
Import Export
Media: 2-4-6-8-10-13-14-18-19-22-26
Distr.: Natl.
Budget Set: Nov. -Dec.
Personnel:
Jim Schumacher *(Pres & CEO)*
Justina Morison *(Mgr-Mktg)*
Brands & Products:
INTERNATIONAL TRUCK SCHOOL BUS ENGINE
Advertising Agency:
JAN Kelley Marketing
1005 Skyview Dr Ste 322
Burlington, ON L7P 5B1, Canada
Tel.: (905) 631-7934
Fax: (905) 631-8558
Toll Free: (800) 461-7304

ISUZU MOTORS AMERICA INC.
(Sub. of Isuzu Motors Limited)
1400 S Douglas Rd Ste 100
Anaheim, CA 92806
Tel.: (714) 935-9300
Fax: (562) 229-5011
Toll Free: (800) 255-6727
E-mail: info@isuzu.com
Web Site: www.isuzu.com
Approx. Number Employees: 200
Year Founded: 1980
Business Description:
Pickup Trucks, Sports Utility Vehicles, Light/Medium-Duty Trucks & Diesel Engines Distr in the US & Canada
S.I.C.: 5012; 5084
N.A.I.C.S.: 423110; 423830
Import
Media: 2-3-5-6-7-8-9-10-13-15-18-19-22-23-24-25-26
Distr.: Natl.
Budget Set: Aug.

JAGUAR CANADA INC.
(Sub. of Jaguar Cars Limited)
8 Indell Lane
Brampton, ON L6T 4H3, Canada
Tel.: (905) 792-9400
Fax: (905) 791-2772
Toll Free: (800) 4-JAGUAR
E-mail: canadian@jaguar.com
Web Site: www.jaguar.ca
Business Description:
Automobile Marketer & Distr
S.I.C.: 5012
N.A.I.C.S.: 423110
Advertising Expenditures: $2,000,000
Media: 2-4-6-7-8-9-17-25-26-30
Distr.: Natl.
Budget Set: June
Personnel:
Gary Moyer *(Pres)*
Steve Majewski *(Mgr-Mktg-Natl)*
Advertising Agency:
Y&R, Ltd.
60 Bloor Street West
Toronto, ON M4W 1J2, Canada
Tel.: (416) 961-5111
Fax: (416) 961-7890

JAGUAR CARS NORTH AMERICA
(Sub. of Jaguar Cars Limited)
1 Premier Pl
Irvine, CA 92618
Tel.: (949) 341-5800
E-mail: info@ford.com
Web Site: www.jaguarusa.com
Year Founded: 1968
Business Description:
Automobile Marketer & Distr
S.I.C.: 5012
N.A.I.C.S.: 423110
Import
Media: 1-2-3-4-5-6-8-9-10-13-15-16-18-19-20-22-23-24-25-26
Distr.: Natl.
Personnel:
David Pryor *(VP-Brand)*
Advertising Agency:
S3
718 Main St
Boonton, NJ 07005
Tel.: (973) 257-5533
Fax: (973) 257-5543

JEFFERSON CHEVROLET CO.
2130 E Jefferson Ave
Detroit, MI 48207
Tel.: (313) 259-1200
Fax: (313) 259-5597
E-mail: info@jeffersonchevrolet.com
Web Site: www.jeffersonchevrolet.com
Approx. Number Employees: 100
Year Founded: 1942
Business Description:
New & Used Automobile & Truck Retailer
S.I.C.: 5511; 5014; 5521
N.A.I.C.S.: 441110; 441120; 441320
Media: 3-8-9
Personnel:
Brian Tellier *(Gen Mgr)*
James Tellier *(Dir-Line Grp)*
Jerry Dewaele *(Mgr-Svc)*

JENKINS AUTO SALES OF FLORIDA
4531 N Federal Hwy
Pompano Beach, FL 33064
Tel.: (954) 782-8060
Fax: (954) 782-0153
Toll Free: (877) 270-2277
E-mail: mail@jenkinsautosales.com
Web Site: www.jenkinsautosales.com
Approx. Number Employees: 4
Business Description:
Automobiles, New & Used
S.I.C.: 5511; 5012
N.A.I.C.S.: 441110; 423110
Media: 6
Personnel:
William G. Jenkins *(Pres)*

JERRY BIGGERS CHEVROLET - ISUZU INC.
1385 E Chicago St
Elgin, IL 60120
Tel.: (847) 742-9000
Fax: (847) 742-6186
Toll Free: (866) 431-1555
E-mail: info@biggerschevy.com
Web Site: www.biggerschevy.com
Approx. Number Employees: 125
Year Founded: 1970
Business Description:
New & Used Car Dealer & Services
S.I.C.: 5511; 5521
N.A.I.C.S.: 441110; 441120
Import Export
Media: 3-23
Personnel:
Celeste Jacklin *(CFO)*
James Leichter *(Principal-Dealer)*
Bob Colwell *(Gen Mgr)*
Advertising Agency:
Man Marketing
765 Kimberly Dr
Carol Stream, IL 60188
Tel.: (630) 929-5200
Fax: (630) 752-9288

JM FAMILY ENTERPRISES INC.
100 Jim Moran Blvd
Deerfield Beach, FL 33442-1702
Tel.: (954) 429-2000
Fax: (954) 429-2300
E-mail: human_resources@jmfamily.com
Web Site: www.jmfamily.com
Approx. Rev.: $11,100,000,000
Approx. Number Employees: 4,000
Year Founded: 1968
Business Description:
Diversified Automotive Corporation
S.I.C.: 5012; 5013
N.A.I.C.S.: 423110; 423120
Media: 6-9-25
Personnel:
Colin Brown *(Pres & CEO)*
Carmen S. Johnson *(Gen Counsel & Sr VP)*
Forrest Heathcott *(Exec VP)*
Ed Sheehy *(Exec VP)*
Sandra Porceng *(VP-Total Rewards)*
Brands & Products:
JM FAMILY
Advertising Agency:
Ambit Marketing Communications
2601 E Oakland Park Blvd Ste 301
Fort Lauderdale, FL 33306
Tel.: (954) 568-2100
Fax: (954) 568-2888

JOE MACHENS FORD INC.
1911 W Worley St
Columbia, MO 65203
Tel.: (573) 445-4411
Fax: (573) 445-8164
Toll Free: (866) 811-7518
E-mail: jmf@machens.com
Web Site: www.machens.com
Sales Range: $10-24.9 Million
Approx. Number Employees: 175
Year Founded: 1969
Business Description:
Car Dealership Owner & Operator
S.I.C.: 5511
N.A.I.C.S.: 441110
Media: 9-25
Personnel:
Gary R. Drewing *(Pres)*
Chris Ehase *(Gen Mgr-Sls)*
Terry Sells *(Gen Mgr-Sls)*
Mary Jo Henry *(Dir-Mktg)*
Jim Volmert *(Dir-Fin)*
Russ Berry *(Mgr-Sls)*
Gene Buck *(Mgr-Bus)*
Ralph Dumas *(Mgr-Svc)*
Barry Garrett *(Mgr-Sls)*
Keven Osborne *(Mgr-Sls)*
Marcia Rasmussen *(Mgr-Customer Rels)*
Ken Redders *(Mgr-Trng)*
Bob Tighe *(Mgr-Parts)*
Steve Veltrop, Jr. *(Mgr-Fleet)*
Steve Veltrop, Sr. *(Mgr-Fleet)*
Marc Weiner *(Mgr-Fin)*
Kevin West *(Mgr-Sls)*

JOHN EAGLE HONDA OF HOUSTON
(Holding of John Eagle Dealerships)
18787 NW Fwy
Houston, TX 77065
Tel.: (281) 955-6666
Fax: (281) 955-7487
E-mail: sales@johneaglehonda.com
Web Site: www.johneaglehonda.com
E-Mail For Key Personnel:
Sales Director: sales@johneaglehonda.com
Sales Range: $50-74.9 Million
Approx. Number Employees: 150
Year Founded: 1984
Business Description:
New & Used Car Dealer
S.I.C.: 5511; 5521; 7538
N.A.I.C.S.: 441110; 441120; 811111
Advertising Expenditures: $300,000
Media: 8-9-17-23-24-25-26
Distr.: Direct to Consumer; Reg.
Budget Set: Dec.
Personnel:
Mac DeLaup *(Pres & Mng Partner)*
Carol Rainoshek *(Comptroller)*
Glen Holender *(Gen Mgr)*
David Kent *(Dir-Svc)*
Jassen Richardson *(Dir-Parts)*
Jeff Schramme *(Dir-Fin)*
Peggy Terry *(Office Mgr)*
Greg Cypher *(Mgr-Pre-Owned Sls)*
Ammar Sheikh *(Mgr-Sls)*
Frank Amos *(Mgr-Internet Sls)*
Matt Vogtv *(Mgr-Fin)*
Adam Wiese *(Mgr-Fin)*
Brands & Products:
EAGLE EDGE
JOHN EAGLE HONDA

JOHN SULLIVAN AUTOMOTIVE GROUP
700 Automall Dr
Roseville, CA 95678
Tel.: (916) 782-1243
Fax: (916) 782-1256
Toll Free: (800) 879-5646
E-mail: sales@chevyworld.com
Web Site: www.chevyworld.com
E-Mail For Key Personnel:
Sales Director: sales@chevyworld.com
Approx. Number Employees: 200
Year Founded: 1951
Business Description:
New & Used Auto Dealer
S.I.C.: 5511; 7539
N.A.I.C.S.: 441110; 811118
Advertising Expenditures: $2,500,000
Media: 3-8-9-18-20-23-24-25
Distr.: Reg.
Personnel:
John L. Sullivan *(Pres)*
Dave Rogers *(VP & Gen Mgr)*

JOYCE MOTORS CORP.
(d/b/a Joyce Honda)
3166 State Rte 10
Denville, NJ 07834
Tel.: (973) 361-3000
Fax: (973) 361-5836

Key to Media (For complete agency information see *The Advertising Red Books-Agencies* edition):
1. Bus. Publs. 2. Cable T.V. 3. Catalogs & Directories. 4. Co-op Adv. 5. Consumer Mags. 6. D.M. to Bus. Estab.7. D.M. to Consumers 8. Daily Newsp. 9. Exhibits/Trade Shows 10. Foreign 11. Infomercial 12. Internet Adv.13. Multimedia 14. Network Radio 15. Network T.V. 16. Newsp. Distr. Mags. 17. Other 18. Outdoor (Posters, Transit) 19. Point of Purchase20. Premiums, Novelties 21. Product Samples 22. Special Events Mktg. 23. Spot Radio 24. Spot T.V. 25. Weekly Newsp. 26. Yellow Page Adv.

Joyce Motors Corp. — (Continued)

Web Site: www.joycehonda.com
Approx. Number Employees: 100
Business Description:
New & Used Car Dealer
S.I.C.: 5511
N.A.I.C.S.: 441110
Media: 3-7-8-13
Personnel:
James B. Grecco *(Principal & Pres)*

KELLEY AUTOMOTIVE GROUP
633 Ave of Autos
Fort Wayne, IN 46804
Tel.: (260) 434-4600
Fax: (260) 434-4601
Toll Free: (800) 434-4600
Web Site: www.drivekelley.com
Sales Range: $350-399.9 Million
Approx. Number Employees: 500
Year Founded: 1952
Business Description:
New & Used Automobile Dealer & Servicer
S.I.C.: 5511; 7538
N.A.I.C.S.: 441110; 811111
Media: 3-8-18-22-23-24-25
Personnel:
Thomas Kelley *(Pres & CEO)*
Gary Thelen *(CFO)*

KENWORTH TRUCK CO.
(Div. of PACCAR Inc.)
10630 NE 38th Pl
Kirkland, WA 98033-7909
Mailing Address:
PO Box 1000
Kirkland, WA 98083-1000
Tel.: (425) 828-5000
Web Site: www.kenworth.com
Sales Range: $550-599.9 Million
Approx. Number Employees: 3,400
Year Founded: 1923
Business Description:
Heavy & Medium Duty Trucks Mfr & Distr
S.I.C.: 3711; 3714
N.A.I.C.S.: 336120; 336399
Media: 2-4-7-9-10-11-14-18-19-20
Distr.: Intl.; Natl.
Budget Set: Sept.
Personnel:
Robert J. Christensen *(Sr VP)*
William Kozek *(Gen Mgr & VP-PACCAR)*
Gary Moore *(Asst Gen Mgr-Sls & Mktg)*
Scott Chowaniec *(Mgr-Natl Sls-PACCAR Parts)*
Brands & Products:
AEROCAB
AERODYNE
C500
T2000
T300
T600
T800
W900

KERBECK CADILLAC PONTIAC CHEVROLET, INC.
430 N Albany Ave
Atlantic City, NJ 08401
Tel.: (609) 344-2100
Fax: (609) 344-4105
Toll Free: (800) 578-3883
E-mail: info@kerbeck.com
Web Site: www.kerbeck.com
Approx. Sls.: $150,000,000
Approx. Number Employees: 92
Business Description:
Car Dealership
S.I.C.: 5511; 5521
N.A.I.C.S.: 441110; 441120
Media: 6-9-25
Personnel:
Charles Kerbeck *(Pres)*

KIA MOTORS AMERICA INC.
(Sub. of Kia Motors Corporation)
111 Peters Canyon Rd
Irvine, CA 92606
Mailing Address:
PO Box 52410
Irvine, CA 92619-2410
Tel.: (949) 468-4800
Fax: (949) 468-4905
E-mail: receptionist@kiausa.com
Web Site: www.kiausa.com
Approx. Number Employees: 445
Year Founded: 1992
Business Description:
Automobile Distr
S.I.C.: 5012; 5013
N.A.I.C.S.: 423110; 423120
Import
Advertising Expenditures: $240,000,000
Media: 5-8-9-10-18-19-23-24-25
Distr.: Natl.
Budget Set: Sept.
Personnel:
Byung Mo Ahn *(CEO & Grp Pres)*
David Kim *(CFO)*
John Yoon *(Gen Counsel, VP-HR & Admin)*
Keith Jun *(VP-Fin)*
Michael Sprague *(VP-Mktg & Comm)*
Tim Chaney *(Dir-Mktg)*
Scott McKee *(Dir-PR)*
Dave Schoonover *(Mgr-Customer Relationship Mktg)*
Advertising Agencies:
David & Goliath
909 N Sepulveda Blvd Ste 700
El Segundo, CA 90245
Tel.: (310) 445-5200
Fax: (310) 445-5201
Agency of Record
Borrego
Hamstar (TM) Clothing
Spectra
This or That Campaign
— Russell Wager *(Mng Partner & Acct Exec)*
— Brook Dore *(Acct Exec)*
— Jill Jagger *(Acct Exec)*

Initiative Worldwide
(Part of The Interpublic Group of Companies, Inc.)
1 Dag Hammerskjold Plz 5th Fl
New York, NY 10017
Tel.: (212) 605-7000
Fax: (212) 605-7200

Innocean Americas Worldwide
4 Park Plz Ste 950
Irvine, CA 92614
Tel.: (949) 440-2100

PointRoll Inc.
951 E Hector St
Conshohocken, PA 19428
Tel.: (267) 558-1300
Fax: (267) 285-1141
Toll Free: (800) 203-6956

KIDRON, INC.
(Div. of Specialized Vehicles Corporation)
13442 Emerson Rd
Kidron, OH 44636
Mailing Address:
PO Box 17
Kidron, OH 44636-0017
Tel.: (800) 321-5421
Fax: (330) 857-8451
Toll Free: (800) 321-5421
E-mail: kinfo@kidron.com
Web Site: www.kidron.com
E-Mail For Key Personnel:
Sales Director: ksales@kidron.com
Approx. Number Employees: 500
Year Founded: 1854
Business Description:
Refrigerated Truck Bodies & Trailers, Refrigeration Systems & Ice Cream & Food Vending Carts Mfr
S.I.C.: 4222; 3715
N.A.I.C.S.: 493120; 336212
Import Export
Media: 7-10
Distr.: Intl.; Natl.
Budget Set: Sept. -Oct.
Personnel:
John E. Sommer, Jr. *(Exec VP)*
Brands & Products:
CARGO STAR
EMPEROR
GLACIERVAN
GLACIERVAN PLUS
GLACIERVAN QS
HACKNEY CLASSIC
HACKNEY DAIRY CLASSIC
ULTRA-FOAM
ULTRA-TEMP
VARI-TEMP 2000
Advertising Agency:
Whitemyer Advertising, Inc.
254 E 4th St
Zoar, OH 44697
Tel.: (330) 874-2432
Fax: (330) 874-2715
(Ultra Glaciervan & Polarvan Truck Bodies)

THE KNAPHEIDE MANUFACTURING COMPANY
1848 Westphalia Strasse
Quincy, IL 62305
Mailing Address:
PO Box 7140
Quincy, IL 62305-7140
Tel.: (217) 222-7131
Fax: (217) 222-5939
E-mail: knapheide@knapheide.com
Web Site: www.knapheide.com
Approx. Number Employees: 600
Year Founded: 1848
Business Description:
Mfr. of Truck Bodies
S.I.C.: 3711; 5084
N.A.I.C.S.: 336120; 423830
Media: 2-6-8-10
Distr.: Intl.; Natl.
Budget Set: Various
Personnel:
H. W. Knapheide *(Pres)*
Jim Bockenfeld *(VP-Sls & Mktg)*
Brands & Products:
DURA-RAIL
E-Z MOUNT INSTALLATION
HEAVY-HAULER
HEAVY-HAULER JR
KARRY-ALL
KNAP KAP
KNAP-PACK
KNAPHEIDE
KNAPHOIST
KUV
OPTION FIT
PACESETTER
PACESETTER-X
QUICK MOUNT INSTALLATION
QUIET-LATCH
ROUGHNECK
ROUGHNECK TOOLBOX STORAGE SYSTEMS
SURE-LOCK
VALUE-MASTER
VALUE-MASTER-X

KRAMER LTD.
2360 Pasqua St N
PO Box 707
Regina, SK S4P 3A8, Canada
Tel.: (306) 545-3311
Fax: (306) 949-6277
E-mail: info@kramer.ca
Web Site: www.kramer.ca
E-Mail For Key Personnel:
President: trk@kramerltd.com
Sales Range: $10-24.9 Million
Approx. Number Employees: 200
Year Founded: 1944
Business Description:
Agricultural & Industrial Machinery Retailer & Servicer
S.I.C.: 5084; 5083
N.A.I.C.S.: 423830; 423820
Import Export
Media: 1-2-4-5-6-7-9-10-18-19-20-23-25-26
Distr.: Canada
Personnel:
Donald Kramer *(Owner)*
Timothy R. Kramer *(Pres & CEO)*
Jim Gibson *(Mgr-Sls-Lift Trucks)*
Andre Blais *(Mgr-Agriculture)*
Dwayne Fortney *(Mgr-Ops)*
Darren Mackie *(Mgr-Experienced Parts)*
Sheri Melnick *(Mgr-Credit)*
Rob Nelson *(Mgr-Info Sys)*
Robert Perry *(Mgr-Fin)*
Rob Schaffer *(Mgr-Sls-Used Equipment)*
Marcel Vindevoghel *(Mgr-Sls-Engines)*
Don White *(Mgr-Parts-Southern)*
Bera Youck *(Mgr-HR)*

KRUSE INTERNATIONAL
5540 County Rd 11 A
Auburn, IN 46706
Tel.: (260) 925-5600
Fax: (260) 925-5467
Toll Free: (800) 968-4444
E-mail: info@kruse.com
Web Site: www.kruse.com
E-Mail For Key Personnel:
Public Relations: sarah@kruse.com
Sales Range: $10-24.9 Million
Approx. Number Employees: 50
Business Description:
Auction Services
S.I.C.: 5961
N.A.I.C.S.: 454112
Media: 2-3-6-10-23-24

Key to Media (For complete agency information see *The Advertising Red Books-Agencies* edition):
1. Bus. Publs. 2. Cable T.V. 3. Catalogs & Directories. 4. Co-op Adv. 5. Consumer Mags. 6. D.M. to Bus. Estab.7. D.M. to Consumers
8. Daily Newsp. 9. Exhibits/Trade Shows 10. Foreign 11. Infomercial 12. Internet Adv.13. Multimedia 14. Network Radio
15. Network T.V. 16. Newsp. Distr. Mags. 17. Other 18. Outdoor (Posters, Transit) 19. Point of Purchase20. Premiums, Novelties
21. Product Samples 22. Special Events Mktg. 23. Spot Radio 24. Spot T.V. 25. Weekly Newsp. 26. Yellow Page Adv.

KUNI ENTERPRISES INC.
203 Southeast Park Plz Dr Ste 290
Vancouver, WA 98684
Tel.: (503) 372-7457
Tel.: (503) 748-5400
Fax: (360) 567-0970
Toll Free: (877) 277-1429
Web Site: www.kunibmw.com
Year Founded: 1970
Business Description:
Auto Dealer
S.I.C.: 5511
N.A.I.C.S.: 441110
Media: 9-22-23-24-25
Distr.: Reg.
Personnel:
Shanon Mornhinweg *(Pres & Gen Mgr)*

LAND ROVER NORTH AMERICA
(Sub. of Land Rover)
1 Premier Pl
Irvine, CA 92618
Tel.: (949) 341-6100
Toll Free: (800) 346-3493
Web Site: www.landroverusa.com
Approx. Number Employees: 100
Business Description:
Automobile Marketer & Distr
S.I.C.: 5012
N.A.I.C.S.: 423110
Media: 2-3-5-6-7-8-9-10-12-13-14-15-18-22-23-24-25-26
Distr.: Intl.
Personnel:
Chris Marchand *(Exec VP-Mktg & Sls-Land Rover)*
Finbar McFall *(VP-Mktg)*
Jeremy Render *(Brand Mgr-ReMktg-Jaguar Land Rover North America LLC)*
Advertising Agencies:
Interbrand Design Forum
7575 Paragon Rd
Dayton, OH 45459-5316
Tel.: (937) 439-4400
Fax: (937) 439-4340

Young & Rubicam Inc.
285 Madison Ave
New York, NY 10017-6401
Tel.: (212) 210-3000
Fax: (212) 490-9073
Freelander 2
Sword Collector

LARRY H. MILLER GROUP OF COMPANIES
9350 South 150 East Rte 1000
Sandy, UT 84070
Tel.: (801) 563-4100
Fax: (801) 563-4198
Web Site: www.lhm.com
Sales Range: $1-4.9 Billion
Approx. Number Employees: 5,050
Year Founded: 1979
Business Description:
Holding Company; Automobile Dealerships, Sports Franchises, Entertainment Venues, Radio & Television Media, Restaurants & Retail Stores Owner & Operator
S.I.C.: 6719; 4832; 4833; 5511; 5812; 5999; 7389; 7941
N.A.I.C.S.: 551112; 441110; 453998; 515112; 515120; 711211; 711310; 722110
Personnel:
Karen G. Miller *(Pres)*
Greg Miller *(CEO)*
Clark L. Whitworth *(CFO)*
Tony Scahnurr *(COO)*
David Carr *(CIO)*
Randy Rigby *(Pres-Utah Jazz & Larry H Miller Sports & Entertainment)*
Robert Tingey *(Gen Counsel)*
Advertising Agency:
Saxton Horne Advertising
9350 S 150 E Ste 950
Sandy, UT 84070
Tel.: (801) 304-1000
Fax: (801) 304-1008

LAZY DAYS R.V. CENTER, INC.
(Sub. of LD Holdings Inc.)
(Filed Ch 11 Bankruptcy #913911 on 11/05/09 in U.S. Bankruptcy Ct, Dist of DE, Wilmington.)
6130 Lazy Days Blvd
Seffner, FL 33584-2968
Tel.: (813) 246-4333
Fax: (813) 246-4408
Toll Free: (888) 500-5299
Web Site: www.lazydays.com
E-Mail For Key Personnel:
Sales Director: sales@lazydays.com
Approx. Rev.: $777,950,792
Approx. Number Employees: 675
Year Founded: 1976
Business Description:
Recreational Vehicle Retailer & Campground Operator
S.I.C.: 5561; 7033
N.A.I.C.S.: 441210; 721211
Advertising Expenditures: $4,994,000
Personnel:
John Horton *(Pres & CEO)*
Randy Lay *(CFO)*
Joe Wiley *(CIO)*
Dominic Calabro *(Pres-CrownClub & Mgr-Sls)*
Bob Grady *(Dir-Svc & Parts)*
Linda Stephens *(Dir-Corp Reporting & IR)*
Advertising Agency:
Schifino Lee Advertising
511 W Bay St Ste 400
Tampa, FL 33606
Tel.: (813) 258-5858
Fax: (813) 254-1146

LEXUS DIVISION
(Div. of Toyota Motor Sales, U.S.A., Inc.)
19001 S Western Ave
Torrance, CA 90501
Mailing Address:
PO Box 2991 Mail Drop L201
Torrance, CA 90501
Tel.: (310) 468-4000
Fax: (310) 468-7800
Web Site: www.lexus.com
Business Description:
Cars Mfr & Sales
S.I.C.: 3711; 5012
N.A.I.C.S.: 336111; 423110
Media: 2-3-6-13-15-18-30
Personnel:
Mark Templin *(VP & Gen Mgr)*
David Nordstrom *(VP-Mktg)*
Lynda Eguchi *(Mgr-Mktg Strategy & Life Cycle)*
Steve Jess *(Mgr-Natl Mktg Comm)*
Robin Pisz *(Mgr-Natl Adv & Media)*
Advertising Agencies:
Skinny
160 Varick St
New York, NY 10013
Tel.: (212) 561-6005
CT200h

Team One
(Sub. of Saatchi & Saatchi Advertising Worldwide)
1960 E Grand Ave
El Segundo, CA 90245-5059
Tel.: (310) 615-2000
Fax: (310) 322-7565
Agency of Record

Walton / Isaacson
4250 Wilshre Blvd
Los Angeles, CA 90010
Tel.: (323) 456-1100
Fax: (323) 456-1139
African American Marketing

LINCOLN-MERCURY
(Div. of Ford Motor Company)
16800 Executive Plaza Dr 4th Fl
Dearborn, MI 48126
Tel.: (313) 322-3000
Toll Free: (800) 392-3673
Web Site: www.lincolnvehicles.com
Sales Range: $100-124.9 Million
Approx. Number Employees: 200
Year Founded: 1945
Business Description:
Marketing of Cars & Trucks
S.I.C.: 5511
N.A.I.C.S.: 441110
Import Export
Personnel:
Hall Feder *(Gen Mgr-Sls)*
John Felice *(Gen Mgr-Mktg-Ford Motor Co)*
Brett Wheatley *(Mktg Dir-Ford Customer Svc Div-Ford Motor Co)*
Advertising Agency:
Uniworld Group, Inc.
1 Metro Center N 11th Fl
Brooklyn, NY 11201
Tel.: (212) 219-1600
Fax: (212) 219-6395
Navigator
— Shelley O'Conner *(Acct Exec)*

LINDE MATERIAL HANDLING NORTH AMERICA CORPORATION
(Joint Venture of The Goldman Sachs Group, Inc. & KKR & CO. L.P.)
2450 W 5th N St
Summerville, SC 29483-9621
Mailing Address:
PO Box 2400
Summerville, SC 29484-2400
Tel.: (843) 875-8000
Fax: (843) 875-8329
E-mail: finance@lmh-na.com
Web Site: www.lmh-na.com
Sales Range: $75-99.9 Million
Approx. Number Employees: 200
Year Founded: 1853
Business Description:
Forklifts & Industrial Trucks Mfr
S.I.C.: 3537
N.A.I.C.S.: 333924
Import Export
Media: 1-2-4-6-9-10-18-20-22-26
Distr.: Natl.
Budget Set: Sept.
Personnel:
Brian Butler *(Pres)*
Skip Somers *(VP-Sls)*
Mark Rossler *(Mgr-Gen Product)*

LITHIA MOTORS INC
360 E Jackson St
Medford, OR 97501
Tel.: (541) 776-6899
Fax: (541) 858-3279
Toll Free: (800) 866-9213 (IR)
E-mail: invest@lithia.com
Web Site: www.lithia.com
Approx. Rev.: $2,131,598,000
Approx. Number Employees: 4,039
Year Founded: 1946
Business Description:
Automobile Dealership Franchise Owner & Operator
S.I.C.: 5511; 5521; 7538
N.A.I.C.S.: 441110; 441120; 811111
Import Export
Advertising Expenditures: $27,100,000
Media: 3-5-8-9-13-23-24-25
Personnel:
Sidney B. DeBoer *(Chm & CEO)*
M.L. Dick Heimann *(Vice Chm-Corp Affairs)*
Bryan B. DeBoer *(Pres & COO)*
Chris Holzshu *(CFO & Sr VP)*
R.Bradford Gray *(Exec VP)*
John North *(Controller & VP-Fin)*
Brands & Products:
AMERICA'S CAR & TRUCK STORE
Advertising Agency:
LAD Advertising
350 E Jackson
Medford, OR 97501
Tel.: (541) 776-6868

LOTUS CARS USA, INC.
(Sub. of Group Lotus Plc)
2236 Northmont Pkwy
Duluth, GA 30096
Tel.: (770) 476-6540
Fax: (770) 476-6541
Toll Free: (800) 24LOTUS
Web Site: www.lotuscars.com
Year Founded: 1986
Business Description:
Automobile Importer & Distr
S.I.C.: 5012
N.A.I.C.S.: 423110
Import
Media: 2-6-7-8-9-16-19-20-22
Distr.: Natl.
Budget Set: June
Brands & Products:
LOTUS
Advertising Agency:
The Cimarron Group
6855 Santa Monica Blvd
Hollywood, CA 90038
Tel.: (323) 337-0300
Fax: (323) 337-0333

LOU LARICHE CHEVROLET INC.
40875 Plymouth Rd
Plymouth, MI 48170
Tel.: (734) 453-4600
Fax: (734) 455-2570
Toll Free: (800) 460-5146
E-mail: louariche@aol.com
Web Site: www.louchevy.com/
Approx. Number Employees: 75

Key to Media (For complete agency information see *The Advertising Red Books-Agencies* edition):
1. Bus. Publs. 2. Cable T.V. 3. Catalogs & Directories. 4. Co-op Adv. 5. Consumer Mags. 6. D.M. to Bus. Estab.7. D.M. to Consumers 8. Daily Newsp. 9. Exhibits/Trade Shows 10. Foreign 11. Infomercial 12. Internet Adv.13. Multimedia 14. Network Radio 15. Network T.V. 16. Newsp. Distr. Mags. 17. Other 18. Outdoor (Posters, Transit) 19. Point of Purchase20. Premiums, Novelties 21. Product Samples 22. Special Events Mktg. 23. Spot Radio 24. Spot T.V. 25. Weekly Newsp. 26. Yellow Page Adv.

Lou LaRiche Chevrolet Inc. — (Continued)

Year Founded: 1970
Business Description:
New & Used Car Dealer
S.I.C.: 5511
N.A.I.C.S.: 441110
Media: 9-13-18-20-22-23-24-25
Personnel:
Louis LaRiche *(Pres)*
Ronald Chaudoin *(Gen Mgr)*
Scott M. Schmidt *(Bus Mgr)*
Mark Rzepka *(Mgr-Parts)*

LUPIENT AUTOMOTIVE GROUP

750 Pennsylvania Ave
Golden Valley, MN 55426
Tel.: (763) 544-6666
Fax: (763) 513-5517
Web Site: www.lupient.com
Sales Range: $450-499.9 Million
Approx. Number Employees: 1,000
Business Description:
Automobile Dealership
S.I.C.: 5511; 7538
N.A.I.C.S.: 441110; 811111
Advertising Expenditures: $200,000
Media: 1-9-10-18-22
Personnel:
James W. Lupient *(Pres)*

MACK TRUCKS, INC.

(Sub. of Volvo Truck Corporation)
2100 Mack Blvd
Allentown, PA 18105
Tel.: (610) 709-3011
E-mail: webmaster@macktrucks.com
Web Site: www.macktrucks.com
E-Mail For Key Personnel:
Marketing Director: mktg.comm@macktrucks.com
Approx. Number Employees: 800
Year Founded: 1900
Business Description:
Heavy-Duty Truck Mfr
S.I.C.: 3711; 3714
N.A.I.C.S.: 336120; 336399
Import Export
Media: 2-4-8-10-11-18-19-20-22-24
Distr.: Intl.; Natl.
Budget Set: Nov.
Personnel:
Dennis R. Slagle *(Pres & CEO)*
Kevin Flaherty *(Sr VP-Sls)*
Carl Heikel *(Sr VP-Mack Intl)*
Tom Kelly *(Sr VP-Product Portfolio Mgmt)*
Bruce P Hollenbeck *(VP)*
Michael Reardon *(VP-Sls)*
Hal Dickson *(Dir-Product Remarketing)*
David McKenna *(Dir-Powertrain Sls & Mktg)*
Rick Miller *(Dir-Strategic Mktg)*
Tonyah Dillahunt *(Mgr-Mktg-Dev)*
Tom Davis *(Mgr-Northeast Reg)*
Brands & Products:
GRANITE
MACK
ONECALL
V-MAC
VISION
Advertising Agency:
Stiegler, Wells, Brunswick & Roth, Inc.
(d/b/a SWB&R)
3865 Adler Pl
Bethlehem, PA 18017-9000
Tel.: (610) 866-0611
Fax: (610) 866-8650

MAGUIRE CHEVROLET-CADILLAC

(Sub. of Maguire Automotive, LLC)
35 Cinema Dr
Ithaca, NY 14850
Tel.: (607) 272-9292
Fax: (607) 277-1940
Web Site: www.maguirecars.com/ou/ithaca-gm/
Approx. Number Employees: 26
Business Description:
Automobile Dealership
S.I.C.: 5511
N.A.I.C.S.: 441110
Media: 8-9-23-25-26
Personnel:
Phil Maguire *(Gen Mgr)*

MAITA ENTERPRISES INC.

2500 Auburn Blvd
Sacramento, CA 95821
Tel.: (916) 481-0855
Fax: (916) 483-2194
Toll Free: (888) 360-4999
E-mail: sales@maitatoyota.com
Web Site: www.maitatoyota.com
E-Mail For Key Personnel:
Sales Director: sales@maitatoyota.com
Business Description:
New & Used Automobile Retailer
S.I.C.: 5511; 5521; 7538
N.A.I.C.S.: 441110; 441120; 811111
Media: 9-13-20-23-24-25
Distr.: Reg.
Personnel:
Vincent Maita *(Owner)*
Dave Klingensmith *(Gen Mgr-Sls)*

THE MAJOR AUTOMOTIVE COMPANIES, INC.

43-40 Northern Blvd
Long Island City, NY 11101
Tel.: (718) 937-3700
Fax: (718) 937-9770
Web Site: www.majorworld.com
Sales Range: $350-399.9 Million
Approx. Number Employees: 520
Business Description:
Car Dealership Owner & Operator
S.I.C.: 5521
N.A.I.C.S.: 441120
Advertising Expenditures: $15,768,832
Media: 5-8-9-13-18
Personnel:
Bruce Bendell *(CEO)*
Andrew Jasyk *(Mgr-Mktg)*

MASERATI NORTH AMERICA, INC.

(Sub. of Maserati S.p.A.)
250 Sylvan Ave
Englewood Cliffs, NJ 07632
Tel.: (201) 816-2600
Fax: (201) 816-2626
E-mail: info@maseratiamerica.com
Approx. Number Employees: 150
Year Founded: 1977
Business Description:
Sports Cars Importer & Distr
S.I.C.: 5012; 5013
N.A.I.C.S.: 423110; 423120
Media: 2-6-10-22
Personnel:
Mark McNabb *(CEO)*
Andrea Soriani *(Head-Mktg & Comm)*

MAZDA NORTH AMERICAN OPERATIONS

(Sub. of Mazda Motor Corporation)
7755 Irvine Ctr Dr
Irvine, CA 92618
Mailing Address:
PO Box 19734
Irvine, CA 92623-9734
Tel.: (949) 727-1990
Fax: (949) 727-6101
Toll Free: (800) 222-5500
Web Site: www.mazdausa.com
Approx. Number Employees: 750
Year Founded: 1988
Business Description:
Automobile Developer Marketer, Retailer & Servicer
S.I.C.: 5012; 5013
N.A.I.C.S.: 423110; 423120
Import Export
Advertising Expenditures: $155,000,000
Media: 3-6-9-15-18-23-24
Distr.: Natl.
Budget Set: Oct.
Personnel:
James J. O'Sullivan *(Pres & CEO)*
Jim Lievois *(CFO & SVP)*
Keith Egawa *(COO & Exec VP)*
Don Romano *(Pres-Mazda Canada)*
Robert T. Davis *(Sr VP-Product Dev & Quality)*
John Abel *(Dir-Mktg)*
Jeremy Barnes *(Dir-Product Corp Comm)*
Mike Nakashima *(Dir-Mktg)*
Wendy Crane *(Mgr-Adv-Natl)*
David Harris *(Mgr-Digital & Alternative Media)*
Advertising Agencies:
Hill & Knowlton, Inc.
(Member of WPP)
825 3rd Ave 24th Fl
New York, NY 10022
Tel.: (212) 885-0300
Fax: (212) 885-0570
Agency of Record

Team Mazda
7535 Irvine Center Dr
Irvine, CA 92618
Tel.: (949) 255-9100
Agency of Record-Direct Marketing

WPP Group USA Inc.
100 Park Ave
New York, NY 10017-5529
Tel.: (212) 632-2200
Fax: (212) 632-2249

MCINERNEY INC.

14100 W Eight Mile Rd
Oak Park, MI 48237-3045
Tel.: (248) 398-8200
Fax: (248) 398-4289
Web Site: www.chryslercars.com
Sales Range: $150-199.9 Million
Approx. Number Employees: 250
Year Founded: 1963
Business Description:
Sales of Automobiles
S.I.C.: 5511
N.A.I.C.S.: 441110
Media: 9-25
Personnel:
Martin J. McInerney *(Pres)*
Joe Marino *(Gen Mgr)*

MERCEDES-BENZ CANADA INC.

(Sub. of Daimler AG)
98 Vanderhoof Ave
Toronto, ON M4G 4C9, Canada
Tel.: (416) 425-3550
Fax: (416) 423-5027
Toll Free: (800) 387-0100
Telex: 65-24232
Web Site: www.mercedes-benz.ca
Sales Range: $800-899.9 Million
Approx. Number Employees: 300
Business Description:
Sales & Service Company
S.I.C.: 5511
N.A.I.C.S.: 441110
Media: 2-3-11-13-14-15-16-18-23-24-25-30
Personnel:
Marc Boderke *(VP-Mktg)*
Christian Spelter *(VP-Fin)*
Christopher Goczan *(Natl Product Mgr)*
Advertising Agency:
BBDO Toronto
2 Bloor St W
Toronto, ON M4W 3R6, Canada
Tel.: (416) 972-1505
Fax: (416) 972-5656

MERCEDES BENZ SACRAMENTO

(Sub. of Asbury Automotive Group, Inc.)
1810 Howe Ave
Sacramento, CA 95825-1026
Tel.: (916) 924-8000
Fax: (916) 924-6718
Toll Free: (800) 721-9794
Web Site: www.mbsacramento.com
Sales Range: $75-99.9 Million
Approx. Number Employees: 125
Year Founded: 1961
Business Description:
Retail & Service of New & Used Cars; Wholesale & Retail Automotive Parts
S.I.C.: 5511; 7515
N.A.I.C.S.: 441110; 532112
Import
Media: 9-23-24-30
Personnel:
George Grinzewitsch *(Owner)*

MERCEDES-BENZ USA INC.

(Sub. of Daimler AG)
1 Mercedes Dr
Montvale, NJ 07645-1815
Tel.: (201) 573-0600
Fax: (201) 573-4394
Toll Free: (800) FORMERCEDES
Web Site: www.mbusa.com
Approx. Number Employees: 1,500
Year Founded: 1965
Business Description:
Distr of Automobiles
S.I.C.: 5012; 5013
N.A.I.C.S.: 423110; 423120
Import
Advertising Expenditures: $155,000,000
Media: 1-3-10-14-15-23-24-25-30
Distr.: Natl.
Budget Set: Oct.

Key to Media (For complete agency information see *The Advertising Red Books-Agencies* edition):
1. Bus. Publs. 2. Cable T.V. 3. Catalogs & Directories. 4. Co-op Adv. 5. Consumer Mags. 6. D.M. to Bus. Estab.7. D.M. to Consumers
8. Daily Newsp. 9. Exhibits/Trade Shows 10. Foreign 11. Infomercial 12. Internet Adv.13. Multimedia 14. Network Radio
15. Network T.V. 16. Newsp. Distr. Mags. 17. Other 18. Outdoor (Posters, Transit) 19. Point of Purchase20. Premiums, Novelties
21. Product Samples 22. Special Events Mktg. 23. Spot Radio 24. Spot T.V. 25. Weekly Newsp. 26. Yellow Page Adv.

Personnel:
Steve Cannon *(VP-Mktg)*
Alan McLaren *(VP-Customer Svcs)*
Michael Slagter *(VP-Sls)*
Andrew Gillman *(Gen Mgr-Northeast Reg)*
Tracy Matura *(Gen Mgr-Strategic Retail Dev)*
Jay Schmid *(Gen Mgr-Central Reg)*
Drew Slaven *(Gen Mgr-Mktg Svcs)*
Robert Woerner *(Gen Mgr-West Region)*
Robert Yeatman *(Gen Mgr-Sls Mgmt & Volume Plng)*
Lisa Holladay *(Brand Mgr)*
Robert Allan *(Mgr-Product-AMG)*
Eric Jillard *(Mgr-Dept-Digital Mktg)*
Beth Lange *(Mgr-Digital Mktg)*
Adam Paige *(Mgr-Brand PR)*

Advertising Agencies:
Cargo
511 Rhett St
Greenville, SC 29601
Tel.: (864) 704-1180
Fax: (864) 704-1199
Advertising
Brand Positioning
Daimler Vans USA (Agency of Record)
Freightliner Sprinter Commerical Vans
Interactive Design
Media Planning & Buying
Sprinter Commercial Vans
Strategic Planning
Trade Show Marketing

Merkley + Partners
(Sub. of Omnicom Group, Inc.)
200 Varick St
New York, NY 10014-4810
Tel.: (212) 366-3500
Fax: (212) 805-7445
Agency of Record

Razorfish New York
1440 Broadway 19th Fl
New York, NY 10018
Tel.: (212) 798-6600
Fax: (212) 798-6601
Digital Agency of Record
— Pierre Odendaal *(Grp Dir-Creative)*

MIDWEST INDUSTRIES, INC.

122 E Hwy 175
Ida Grove, IA 51445
Tel.: (712) 364-3365
Fax: (712) 364-3361
Toll Free: (800) 859-3028
E-mail: info@midwestindustries.com
Web Site:
www.midwestindustries.com
Approx. Number Employees: 300
Year Founded: 1954
Business Description:
Mfr. & Retailer of Boat Hoists, Docks & Trailers
S.I.C.: 3792; 3536
N.A.I.C.S.: 336214; 333923
Export
Media: 2-6-10-18-19
Distr.: Natl.
Personnel:
Andy Brosius *(Pres)*
Brands & Products:
FREEDOM HITCH
MIDWEST
SHORELAND'R
SHORESTATION

MIKE ALBERT LEASING, INC.

10340 Evendale Dr
Cincinnati, OH 45241-2512
Tel.: (513) 563-1400
Fax: (513) 563-9316
Toll Free: (800) 98LEASE
E-mail: customerrelations@mikealbert.com
Web Site: www.mikealbert.com
Sales Range: $25-49.9 Million
Approx. Number Employees: 350
Year Founded: 1929
Business Description:
Automobile Leasing Services
S.I.C.: 7515; 7519
N.A.I.C.S.: 532112; 532120
Advertising Expenditures: $300,000
Media: 2-8-9-25-26
Distr.: Natl.
Personnel:
Marty Betagole *(Pres)*
Robert Betagole *(CEO)*
W. Bruce Shaffer *(CFO)*
W. Patrick Stull *(COO)*
Brands & Products:
MAXFLEET
MIKE ALBERT

MIKE KASHTAN'S SUPERIOR AUTO SALES

7290 Park Blvd
Pinellas Park, FL 33781
Tel.: (727) 545-8777
Web Site: www.727cars.com
Approx. Number Employees: 6
Business Description:
Automobile Dealership
S.I.C.: 5012
N.A.I.C.S.: 423110
Media: 13
Personnel:
Mike Kashtan *(Owner)*

MILLER INDUSTRIES, INC.

8503 Hilltop Dr
Ooltewah, TN 37363
Tel.: (423) 238-4171
Fax: (423) 238-5371
Toll Free: (800) 292-0330
E-mail: sales@millerind.com
Web Site: www.millerind.com
E-Mail For Key Personnel:
Sales Director: sales@millerind.com
Approx. Sls.: $306,897,000
Approx. Number Employees: 700
Year Founded: 1990
Business Description:
Towing & Recovery Equipment Mfr
S.I.C.: 3711; 6512
N.A.I.C.S.: 336211; 531120
Export
Advertising Expenditures: $3,200,000
Media: 2-7-10-18
Distr.: Natl.
Personnel:
William G. Miller *(Chm & Co-CEO)*
Jeffrey I. Badgley *(Pres & Co-CEO)*
J. Vincent Mish *(CFO & Exec VP)*
Frank Madonia *(Gen Counsel, Sec & Exec VP)*
Randy Olson *(VP-Mktg)*
Bill Bakely *(Dir-HR)*
Brands & Products:
BONIFACE
CENTURY
CHALLENGER
CHAMPION
CHEVRON
EAGLE
EXPREE SERIES
HOLMES
JIGE
MIDNIGHT EXPRESS
SP SERIES
TITAN T-SERIES
TRAILERS
VULCAN

MITSUBISHI CANADA LIMITED

(Sub. of Mitsubishi International Corporation)
200 Granville St Ste 2800
Vancouver, BC V6C 1G6, Canada
Tel.: (604) 654-8000
Fax: (604) 654-8228
Web Site: www.mitsubishi.ca
Sales Range: $550-599.9 Million
Approx. Number Employees: 30
Business Description:
Importer & Exporter of Steel, Machinery, Metals, Food, Grains, Chemicals, Lumber & General Merchandise
S.I.C.: 2899
N.A.I.C.S.: 325998
Personnel:
Fhinji Kowasi *(Pres & CEO)*
Advertising Agency:
BBDO Toronto
2 Bloor St W
Toronto, ON M4W 3R6, Canada
Tel.: (416) 972-1505
Fax: (416) 972-5656

MITSUBISHI FUSO TRUCK OF AMERICA, INC.

(43% Owned by DaimlerChrysler AG)
2015 Ctr Square Rd
Bridgeport, NJ 08014
Tel.: (856) 467-4500
Fax: (856) 467-4695
Toll Free: (877) 829-3876
Web Site: www.mitfuso.com
Approx. Sls.: $200,000,000
Approx. Number Employees: 72
Year Founded: 1986
Business Description:
Class 3-7, Diesel Powered & Cab-Over Commercial Trucks Mfr
S.I.C.: 5012; 5013
N.A.I.C.S.: 423110; 423120
Import
Media: 1-2-3-4-5-6-7-8-9-10-13-18-19-20-22-23-26
Distr.: Natl.
Budget Set: Oct.
Personnel:
Todd Bloom *(Pres & CEO)*
Takeo Ishimaru *(CFO)*
Joshua Tregear *(Mgr-Corp Comm)*
Brands & Products:
MITSUBISHI FUSO
Advertising Agency:
Lefton Company
100 Independence Mall W
Philadelphia, PA 19106-2399
Tel.: (215) 923-9600
Fax: (215) 351-4298

MITSUBISHI INTERNATIONAL CORPORATION

(Sub. of Mitsubishi Corporation)
655 3rd Ave
New York, NY 10017
Tel.: (212) 605-2000
Fax: (212) 605-2597
E-mail: info@mitsubishicorp.com
Web Site: www.mitsubishicorp.com
Approx. Number Employees: 650
Year Founded: 1954
Business Description:
All Types of Commodities Exporter & Importer
S.I.C.: 5051; 5172
N.A.I.C.S.: 423510; 424720
Import Export
Media: 2-3-6-9-23-24
Distr.: Intl.; Natl.
Budget Set: Dec.
Personnel:
Tsutomu Awaya *(Pres & CEO-Korea)*
James E. Brumm *(Gen Counsel & Exec VP)*
Takajiro Ishikawa *(Sr VP-Indus Fin)*
Hidekazu Sakurai *(Sr VP & Head-Chemicals)*
Kenzo Takahashi *(Sr VP & Head-Living Essentials)*
Hajime Kimura *(Sr VP & Gen Mgr-Palo Alto Branch)*
Jeffrey W. Daley *(Sr VP)*
Hitoshi Inada *(Sr VP)*
Osamu Takada *(Gen Mgr-Tohoku)*
Tracy L. Austin *(Exec Dir)*
Advertising Agencies:
180 Los Angeles
1733 Ocean Ave 4th fl
Santa Monica, CA 90401
Tel.: (310) 382-1400
Fax: (310) 382-1401
Lead Creative Agecy
Live Drive

Gregory FCA
27 W Athens Ave Ste 200
Ardmore, PA 19003
Tel.: (610) 642-8253
Fax: (610) 642-1258
Fax: (610) 649-9029
Toll Free: (800) 499-4734

MITSUBISHI MOTORS NORTH AMERICA, INC.

(Sub. of Mitsubishi Motors Corporation)
6400 Katella Ave
Cypress, CA 90630-5208
Tel.: (714) 372-6000
Fax: (714) 373-1020
Toll Free: (888) MITSU2005
Web Site: www.mitsubishicars.com
Sales Range: $1-4.9 Billion
Approx. Number Employees: 1,590
Year Founded: 1981
Business Description:
Cars & Trucks Distr
S.I.C.: 5012
N.A.I.C.S.: 423110
Import
Media: 2-3-5-6-8-9-10-15-16-18-19-22-23-24-25
Distr.: Natl.
Budget Set: Jan.
Personnel:
Yoichi Yokozawa *(Pres & CEO)*
John McElroy *(Gen Counsel & Sr VP)*
Gregory Adams *(VP-Mktg & Product Plng)*
Francine Harsini *(Dir-Adv & Promos)*
Barbara Dunbar *(Mgr-Web Initiatives)*

Key to Media (For complete agency information see *The Advertising Red Books-Agencies* edition):
1. Bus. Publs. 2. Cable T.V. 3. Catalogs & Directories. 4. Co-op Adv. 5. Consumer Mags. 6. D.M. to Bus. Estab.7. D.M. to Consumers
8. Daily Newsp. 9. Exhibits/Trade Shows 10. Foreign 11. Infomercial 12. Internet Adv.13. Multimedia 14. Network Radio
15. Network T.V. 16. Newsp. Distr. Mags. 17. Other 18. Outdoor (Posters, Transit) 19. Point of Purchase20. Premiums, Novelties
21. Product Samples 22. Special Events Mktg. 23. Spot Radio 24. Spot T.V. 25. Weekly Newsp. 26. Yellow Page Adv.

Mitsubishi Motors North America, Inc. — (Continued)

Moe Durand *(Mgr-Product Comm)*
Mike Evanoff *(Mgr-Product Strategy)*
Matt Mendez *(Mgr-Adv)*

Advertising Agencies:
180 Los Angeles
1733 Ocean Ave 4th fl
Santa Monica, CA 90401
Tel.: (310) 382-1400
Fax: (310) 382-1401
Creative
Live Drive
Mitsubishi Outlander Sport

BBDO North America
1285 Ave of the Americas
New York, NY 10019-6028
Tel.: (212) 459-5000
Fax: (212) 459-6814

Organic, Inc.
555 Market St 4th Fl
San Francisco, CA 94105
Tel.: (415) 581-5300
Fax: (415) 581-5400

Possible Worldwide
5780 W Jefferson Blvd
Los Angeles, CA 90016
Tel.: (310) 202-2900
Fax: (310) 202-2910

NAPLETON SCHAUMBURG MOTORS, INC.

(Sub. of North American Automotive Services, Inc.)
(d/b/a Napleton's Schaumburg Mazda)
100 W Golf Rd
Schaumburg, IL 60195
Tel.: (847) 285-5301
Web Site:
www.schaumburgmazda.com
Approx. Number Employees: 100
Year Founded: 1987
Business Description:
New & Used Car Dealer
S.I.C.: 5511; 5521; 7538
N.A.I.C.S.: 441110; 441120; 811111
Advertising Expenditures: $300,000
Media: 9-16-24-25-26
Distr.: Reg.
Budget Set: Quarterly
Personnel:
Stephen Napleton *(Chm)*
Charles Weck *(Pres)*
Chris Napleton *(Gen Mgr-Sls)*

NAVISTAR INTERNATIONAL CORPORATION

4201 Winfield Rd
Warrenville, IL 60555-4025
Mailing Address:
PO Box 1488
Warrenville, IL 60555-7488
Tel.: (630) 753-5000
Fax: (630) 753-2303
Toll Free: (800) 448-7825
E-mail: info@navistar.com
Web Site: www.navistar.com
Approx. Rev.: $12,145,000,000
Approx. Number Employees: 18,700
Year Founded: 1902
Business Description:
Holding Company; Truck Mfr
S.I.C.: 3714; 3711; 3795
N.A.I.C.S.: 336120; 336111; 336112; 336211; 336312; 336322; 336340; 336350; 336399; 336992
Export
Advertising Expenditures: $27,000,000
Media: 2-4-6-7-9-10-14-19-20-23-26
Distr.: Intl.; Natl.
Personnel:
Daniel C. Ustian *(Chm, Pres & CEO)*
Andrew J. Cederoth *(CFO & Exec VP)*
Deepak T. Kapur *(Pres-Truck Grp)*
Archie Massicotte *(Pres-Navistar Defense)*
Phyllis E. Cochran *(Sr VP & Gen Mgr)*
Tom Grogan *(VP-Bus Sls)*
Steve Ostarello *(VP-Powertrain Product Dev)*
Jim Rumpf *(Gen Mgr-Springfield Plant)*
David Hillman *(Mktg Dir)*
Joe Leep *(Dir-Global Mfg Readiness)*
Bob Neitzel *(Mgr-Vocational Mktg)*
Roy Wiley *(Mgr-External Comm)*
Brands & Products:
INTERNATIONAL
NAVISTAR
Advertising Agencies:
Fathom Communications
(Part of Omnicom Group of Companies)
437 Madison Ave
New York, NY 10022
Tel.: (212) 817-6600
Fax: (212) 415-3514

Ketchum
E Randolph Ste 3600
Chicago, IL 60601-5925
Tel.: (312) 228-6800
Fax: (312) 228-6868

KSL Media, Inc.
367 Park Ave S 4th Fl
New York, NY 10016
Tel.: (212) 352-5800
Fax: (212) 352-5935
Media Planning & Buying

NES RENTALS HOLDINGS, INC.

5440 N Cumberland
Chicago, IL 60656
Tel.: (773) 695-3999
Fax: (773) 714-0538
E-mail: info@n-e-s.com
Web Site: www.nesrentals.com/
Sales Range: $550-599.9 Million
Approx. Number Employees: 60
Year Founded: 1996
Business Description:
Renter of Specialty & General Equipment to Industrial & Construction End-Users
S.I.C.: 7359; 7353
N.A.I.C.S.: 532490; 532412
Import Export
Personnel:
Andrew Studdert *(Chm, Pres & CEO)*
Michael Milligan *(CFO)*
Brands & Products:
NES
Advertising Agency:
Alexander Marketing
801 Broadway Ave Ste 300
Grand Rapids, MI 49504
Tel.: (616) 957-2000
Fax: (616) 957-3514

NEW COUNTRY MOTOR CAR GROUP INC.

358 Broadway Ste 403
Saratoga Springs, NY 12866
Tel.: (518) 584-7700
Fax: (518) 584-8611
E-mail: info@newcountry.com
Web Site: www.newcountry.com
Approx. Number Employees: 925
Business Description:
New & Used Automobiles Retailer
S.I.C.: 8741; 5511
N.A.I.C.S.: 561110; 441110
Advertising Expenditures: $1,250,000
Media: 8-9-18-25
Budget Set: June
Personnel:
Michael Cantanucci *(Pres)*
Carl Leuchton *(CFO)*

NISSAN FORKLIFT CORPORATION, NORTH AMERICA

(Sub. of Nissan Motor Co., Ltd.)
240 N Prospect St
Marengo, IL 60152
Tel.: (815) 568-0061
Fax: (815) 568-0179
Toll Free: (800) 846-6432
E-mail: nfcsales@nfcna.com
Web Site: www.nissanforklift.com
Sales Range: $1-4.9 Billion
Approx. Number Employees: 420
Year Founded: 1957
Business Description:
Forklift Trucks & Distr of Industrial Machinery Mfr
S.I.C.: 3537; 3519
N.A.I.C.S.: 333924; 333618
Import
Media: 2-6-10-13-25
Personnel:
Jim Radous *(VP-Sls, Mktg & Div Officer)*
Brands & Products:
LASER SERIES
NOMAD SERIES
OPTIMUM SERIES
WALKIE
WALKIE RIDER

NISSAN NORTH AMERICA, INC.

(Sub. of Nissan Motor Co., Ltd.)
One Nissan Way
Franklin, TN 37067
Mailing Address:
PO Box 685001
Franklin, TN 37068
Tel.: (615) 725-1000
Fax: (615) 967-3343
Web Site: www.nissanusa.com
Approx. Number Employees: 9,000
Year Founded: 1960
Business Description:
Cars & Trucks Mfr & Distr
S.I.C.: 5013; 3711; 8741
N.A.I.C.S.: 423120; 336111; 336112; 561110
Import Export
Advertising Expenditures: $1,441,400,000
Distr.: Natl.
Personnel:
Carlos Ghosn *(Chm & CEO)*
Carla Bailo *(Sr VP-R & D-Americas Reg)*
Scott E. Becker *(Sr VP-Admin & Fin)*
Brian Carolin *(Sr VP-Sls & Mktg)*
Bill Krueger *(Sr VP-Mfg, Pur, Supply Chain Mgmt & Total Customer Satisfaction)*
Dominique Thormann *(Sr VP-Admin & Fin)*
Scott Fessenden *(Reg VP)*
Gary Frigo *(Reg VP)*
Patrick Steiner *(Reg VP-Nissan Central)*
Al Castignetti *(VP-Sls Div)*
Richard Latek *(VP-Sls-Midwest Reg)*
David Reuter *(VP-Corp Comm-Americas)*
Mark Igo *(Gen Mgr-Infiniti)*
Walter Burchfield *(Dir-Bus Plng, Parts & Svc)*
Bob Brown *(Sr Mgr-Mktg Comm)*
Carl Phillips *(Sr Mgr-Infinti Mktg Comm)*
Peter Bedrosian *(Sr Mgr-Product Plng)*
Mike Drongowski *(Sr Mgr-Product Plng)*
Chad Jacoby *(Sr Mgr-Media Ops)*
Nat Mason *(Sr Mgr-Specialty Vehicles)*
Melissa Adams *(Mgr-CRM Programs)*
Michael Awdish *(Mgr-Mktg & Comm-Nissan)*
Phil O'Connor *(Mgr-Mktg Comm)*
Steve Petrecca *(Mgr-Interactive Mktg)*
Anita Randall *(Mgr-Mktg & Corp Media Planner)*
Doug Simpson *(Mgr-Interactive Mktg)*
Brands & Products:
G20
G35
I30 INFINITI
INFINITI
J30
MAXIMA
NISSAN
PATHFINDER
Q45 INFINITI
QUEST
QX4 INFINITI
ROGUE
SENTRA
TITAN
Advertising Agencies:
The Designory
211 E Ocean Blvd Ste 100
Long Beach, CA 90802-4850
Tel.: (562) 624-0200
Fax: (562) 491-0140

Dieste
1999 Bryan St Ste 2700
Dallas, TX 75201
Tel.: (214) 259-8000
Fax: (214) 259-8040
(Nissan, Infiniti, Multicultural Marketing)

MARCA Miami
3390 Mary St Ste 254
Coconut Grove, FL 33133
Tel.: (305) 665-5410
Tel.: (305) 423-8301
Fax: (305) 665-3533
Infiniti

OMD-USA
195 Broadway
New York, NY 10007

Tel.: (212) 590-7100
Rogue

TBWA/Chiat/Day
(Regional Headquarters)
488 Madison Ave
New York, NY 10022
Tel.: (212) 804-1000
Fax: (212) 804-1200

TBWA Chiat Day Los Angeles
5353 Grosvenor Blvd
Los Angeles, CA 90066
Tel.: (310) 305-5000
Fax: (310) 305-6000
G35
Rogue

TEQUILA U.S.
488 Madison Ave 5th Fl
New York, NY 10022
Tel.: (212) 804-1000
Fax: (212) 804-1200

True Agency
5300 Beethoven St Penthouse
Los Angeles, CA 90066
Tel.: (310) 437-8746
Fax: (310) 437-8500
Nissan
Infiniti

Zimmerman Advertising
2200 W Commercial Blvd Ste 300
Fort Lauderdale, FL 33309-3064
Tel.: (954) 644-4000
Fax: (954) 731-2977
Toll Free: (800) 248-8522

NORTH AMERICAN TRUCK & TRAILER, INC.

4500 N Cliff Ave
Sioux Falls, SD 57104-0553
Tel.: (605) 332-7112
Fax: (605) 332-8940
E-mail: jason.rush@nattinc.com
Web Site: www.northamericantrucktrailer.com
Approx. Number Employees: 500
Year Founded: 1989
Business Description:
Distr of Trucks & Trailers
S.I.C.: 5012; 7538
N.A.I.C.S.: 423110; 811111
Import Export
Media: 2-10
Personnel:
William Rush *(Pres, Treas & Sec)*

NORTHERN MOTOR COMPANY

1419 Ludington St
Escanaba, MI 49829-2836
Tel.: (906) 786-1130
Fax: (906) 786-7788
E-mail: nomoco@chartermi.net
Web Site: www.northernmotor.com
Approx. Number Employees: 25
Business Description:
Retailer of New & Used Cars
S.I.C.: 5511
N.A.I.C.S.: 441110
Media: 4-8-13
Personnel:
John Arball *(Gen Mgr-Sls)*
Deanna Lawson *(Bus Mgr)*
Marilyn Henderson *(Office Mgr)*

#1 COCHRAN, INC.

4520 William Penn Hwy
Monroeville, PA 15146-2746
Tel.: (412) 373-3333
Fax: (412) 373-4288
Toll Free: (800) 860-3337
Web Site: www.cochran.com
E-Mail For Key Personnel:
Sales Director: sales@cochran.com
Approx. Number Employees: 400
Year Founded: 1965
Business Description:
Sales of Motor Vehicles
S.I.C.: 5511; 5521
N.A.I.C.S.: 441110; 441120
Personnel:
R.E. Cochran *(Pres)*
Aaron Herbick *(Dir-HR)*
Sue Gross *(Mgr-HR)*
Advertising Agency:
RJW Media
5830 Ellsworth Ave Ste 200
Pittsburgh, PA 15232-1778
Tel.: (412) 361-6833
Fax: (412) 361-8005

O'BRIEN AUTOMOTIVE TEAM

1111 O'Brien Dr
Urbana, IL 61801
Tel.: (217) 398-1222
Fax: (217) 398-5984
Toll Free: (800) 816-5978
Web Site: www.obrienteam.com
Approx. Sls.: $15,700,000
Approx. Number Employees: 150
Business Description:
Automobile Sales
S.I.C.: 5012
N.A.I.C.S.: 423110
Media: 4-8-10-13-14-15-23-24-26
Personnel:
Joseph D. O'Brien, Jr. *(Pres)*

OSHKOSH CORPORATION

2307 Oregon St
Oshkosh, WI 54902-7062
Mailing Address:
PO Box 2566
Oshkosh, WI 54903-2566
Tel.: (920) 235-9151
Fax: (920) 233-9314
E-mail: jobline@oshtruck.com
Web Site:
www.oshkoshcorporation.com
E-Mail For Key Personnel:
Public Relations: kskyba@oshtruck.com
Approx. Sls.: $9,842,400,000
Approx. Number Employees: 12,400
Year Founded: 1917
Business Description:
Mfr, Designer & Marketer of Specialty Commercial, Fire, Emergency & Military Trucks
S.I.C.: 3711
N.A.I.C.S.: 336120; 336112; 336211
Import Export
Advertising Expenditures: $15,400,000
Media: 1-2-4-7-10-11-13-20
Distr.: Intl.; Natl.
Budget Set: Jan.
Personnel:
Charles L. Szews *(Pres & CEO)*
David M. Sagehorn *(CFO & Exec VP)*
Michael K. Rohrkaste *(Chief Acctg officer & Exec VP)*
R. Andrew Hove *(Pres-Defense & Exec VP)*
Jim Johnson *(Exec VP & Pres-Fire & Emergency Segment)*
Frank Nerenhausen *(Pres-Comml Segment & Exec VP)*
John M. Urias *(Pres-Oshkosh Defense & Exec VP)*
Wilson R. Jones *(Pres-Access Segment)*
Bryan J. Blankfield *(Gen Counsel, Sec & Exec VP)*
Gregory L. Fredericksen *(Chief Procurement Officer & Exec VP)*
Joseph H. Kimmitt *(Exec VP-Govt Ops & Industry Rels)*
Donald H. Verhoff *(Exec VP-Corp Engrg & Tech)*
Thomas J. Polnaszek *(Sr VP-Fin & Controller)*
Colleen Moynihan *(Sr VP-Total Quality Mgmt)*
Michael S. Guzowski *(VP-IT)*
Corey R. Braun *(Asst Treas)*
Brands & Products:
ALL STEER
COMMAND ZONE
GEESINK
HAWK
HERCULES
HIGHLAND
HUSKY
JERR-DAN
KIGGEN
LANCE
LOAD-SPAN
LOCKLINK
MCNEILUS
MEDTEC
NORBA
OSHKOSH
PIERCE
PROPULSE
REVOLUTION
SIDE ROLL PROTECTION
TAK-4
Advertising Agency:
Padilla Speer Beardsley
1101 W River Pkwy Ste 400
Minneapolis, MN 55415-1241
Tel.: (612) 455-1700
Fax: (612) 455-1060
Pub Rels

OURISMAN AUTOMOTIVE GROUP

4400 Branch Ave
Marlow Heights, MD 20748
Tel.: (301) 423-4028
Fax: (301) 423-5725
Web Site: www.ourisman.com
Sales Range: $750-799.9 Million
Approx. Number Employees: 1,050
Year Founded: 1921
Business Description:
Owner of Auto Dealerships & Supplier of Automobile Parts & Services
S.I.C.: 5511
N.A.I.C.S.: 441110
Media: 3-4-8-9-23-24
Personnel:
Mandell J. Ourisman *(Chm)*
John Ourisman *(Pres)*
Mohamed Reshed *(CFO)*

PACCAR INC.

PACCAR Bldg 777 106th Ave NE
Bellevue, WA 98004-5027
Mailing Address:
PO Box 1518
Bellevue, WA 98009-1518
Tel.: (425) 468-7400
Fax: (425) 468-8216
Telex: 6838005
E-mail: corporate.secretary@paccar.com
Web Site: www.paccar.com
Approx. Rev.: $9,325,100,000
Approx. Number Employees: 17,700
Year Founded: 1905
Business Description:
Heavy Duty On & Off Road Trucks Mfr; Industrial Winches Mfr & Marketer; General Automotive Parts & Accessories Marketer
S.I.C.: 3711; 3714
N.A.I.C.S.: 336120; 336399
Import Export
Advertising Expenditures: $300,000
Media: 2-4-7-10
Distr.: Natl.
Budget Set: Oct.
Personnel:
Kyle Quinn *(CIO & VP-Global Info Tech Div)*
Daniel D. Sobic *(Exec VP)*
James G. Cardillo *(Sr VP)*
Robert J. Christensen *(Sr VP)*
William D. Jackson *(VP & Gen Mgr-Peterbilt)*
Jack K. Levier *(VP-HR)*
Thomas E. Plimpton *(Mgr)*
Brands & Products:
BRADEN
CARCO
DAF
DYNACRAFT
FODEN
GEARMATIC
KENWORTH
PACCAR
PETERBILT
THE PURSUIT OF QUALITY
Advertising Agency:
Capita Technologies, Inc.
17600 Gillette Ave
Irvine, CA 92614
Tel.: (949) 260-3000
Fax: (949) 851-9875

PACE AMERICAN INC.

(Holding of Sun Capital Partners, Inc.)
2229 Lakeside Dr
Bannockburn, IL 60015
Tel.: (847) 283-9955
Web Site: www.paceamerican.com
Sales Range: $75-99.9 Million
Year Founded: 1986
Business Description:
Cargo & Utility Trailers Mfr
S.I.C.: 3715
N.A.I.C.S.: 336212
Import Export
Media: 4-7-22
Personnel:
James Tennant *(CEO)*
Nancy Boylan *(Office Mgr)*
Jason O'Neil *(Mgr-Mktg Comm)*
Brands & Products:
AEROSPORT
CARGO SPORT
CONQUEST
EXPLORER
HAMMER
JOURNEY

Key to Media (For complete agency information see *The Advertising Red Books-Agencies* edition):
1. Bus. Publs. 2. Cable T.V. 3. Catalogs & Directories. 4. Co-op Adv. 5. Consumer Mags. 6. D.M. to Bus. Estab.7. D.M. to Consumers
8. Daily Newsp. 9. Exhibits/Trade Shows 10. Foreign 11. Infomercial 12. Internet Adv.13. Multimedia 14. Network Radio
15. Network T.V. 16. Newsp. Distr. Mags. 17. Other 18. Outdoor (Posters, Transit) 19. Point of Purchase20. Premiums, Novelties
21. Product Samples 22. Special Events Mktg. 23. Spot Radio 24. Spot T.V. 25. Weekly Newsp. 26. Yellow Page Adv.

Pace American Inc. — (Continued)

LEGACY
MIDWAY
PURSUIT
RALLYE
SHADOW
SILVER ARROW
SUMMIT
WORK SPORT

PACIFICO ENTERPRISES, INC.

(d/b/a Pacifico Auto Group)
6701 Essington Ave
Philadelphia, PA 19153-3407
Tel.: (215) 492-1700
Fax: (215) 492-0983
Toll Free: (888) 475-1384
E-mail: info@pacificocars.com
Web Site: www.pacificocars.com
Sales Range: $75-99.9 Million
Approx. Number Employees: 170
Year Founded: 1923
Business Description:
New & Used Automobiles Retailer
S.I.C.: 5511; 7538
N.A.I.C.S.: 441110; 811111
Media: 3-4-7-8-9-16-18-23-24-25-26
Distr.: Direct to Consumer; Reg.
Budget Set: Jan.
Personnel:
Joe David Pacifico *(Owner)*
Kerry T. Pacifico *(Partner & Mgr)*

PARAGON ACURA

56-02 Northern Blvd
Woodside, NY 11377
Tel.: (718) 392-8882
Fax: (718) 457-4733
Toll Free: (800) PARAGON
Web Site: www.paragonacura.com
Approx. Sls.: $13,000,000
Approx. Number Employees: 50
Year Founded: 1929
Business Description:
Sales of Automobiles
S.I.C.: 5511; 5521
N.A.I.C.S.: 441110; 441120
Media: 1-3-9-10-13-16-18-22-23-24-25-26
Personnel:
Paul Singer *(Owner & Pres)*
Brian Bestonk *(VP & Gen Mgr)*

PENSKE AUTOMOTIVE GROUP, INC.

2555 Telegraph Rd
Bloomfield Hills, MI 48302-0954
Tel.: (248) 648-2500
Fax: (248) 648-2525
E-mail: info@penskeautomotive.com
Web Site:
www.penskeautomotive.com
Approx. Rev.: $10,713,585,000
Approx. Number Employees: 14,800
Year Founded: 1990
Business Description:
Holding Company; New & Used Car Dealerships Operator
S.I.C.: 6719; 5511; 5521
N.A.I.C.S.: 551112; 441110; 441120
Advertising Expenditures: $62,970,000
Media: 2-3-6-8-9-10-13-14-15-22-23-24-25
Distr.: Reg.
Personnel:
Roger S. Penske *(Chm & CEO)*
Robert H. Kurnick Jr. *(Pres)*
David K. Jones *(CFO & Exec VP)*
J. D. Carlson *(Chief Acctg Officer, Sr VP & Controller)*
Shane M. Spradlin *(Gen Counsel, Sec & Sr VP)*
George Brochick *(Exec VP-Ops-Western Reg)*
Hiroshi Ishikawa *(Exec VP-Intl Bus Dev)*
R. Whitfield Ramonat *(Exec VP-Central Ops & Fin Svcs)*
Calvin Sharp *(Exec VP-HR)*
Bernie W. Wolfe *(Exec VP-Eastern Region)*
Yoshimi Namba *(Sr VP-Intl Bus Dev)*
Anthony R. Pordon *(Sr VP-IR & Corp Dev)*
Brands & Products:
PENSKE

PENSKE CORPORATION

2555 Telegraph Rd
Bloomfield Hills, MI 48302
Tel.: (248) 648-2000
Fax: (248) 648-2005
Web Site: www.penske.com
Approx. Number Employees: 120
Business Description:
Holding Company; Truck Leasing & Auto Dealerships
S.I.C.: 7519
N.A.I.C.S.: 532120
Media: 2-4-6-16-17-19
Distr.: Natl.
Personnel:
Roger S. Penske *(Chm & CEO)*
Robert H. Kurnick Jr. *(Pres)*
J. Patrick Conroy *(CFO & Exec VP)*
Walter P. Czarnecki *(Exec VP)*

PENSKE LOGISTICS, LLC

(Joint Venture of General Electric Company & Penske Corporation)
Route 10 Green Hills PO Box 563
Reading, PA 19603
Tel.: (610) 775-6000
Fax: (610) 775-6432
Web Site: www.penskelogistics.com
Sales Range: $1-4.9 Billion
Approx. Number Employees: 15,100
Year Founded: 1969
Business Description:
Logistics, Transportation & Distribution Services
S.I.C.: 7519; 4213
N.A.I.C.S.: 532120; 484121
Media: 7-10-13
Distr.: Natl.
Budget Set: Oct.
Personnel:
Marc Althen *(Pres)*
Paul Ott *(CFO)*
Tom McKenna *(Sr VP)*
Terry Miller *(Exec VP-Ops)*
Dave Cumbo *(Sr VP-Ops-West Region)*
Jim Erdman *(Sr VP-Intl Ops)*
Joseph K. Gallick *(Sr VP-Sls)*
Jeffrey Stoicheff *(Sr VP-HR)*
Mckenna Tom *(Sr VP-Logistics Tech)*
Julie Levering *(Dir-Maintenance Svcs)*
Rohit Talwar *(Dir-Sys Architecture & IT Svcs)*
Advertising Agency:
Elevation
1027 33rd St NW Ste 260
Washington, DC 20007
Tel.: (202) 380-3230
Fax: (202) 337-1228

PENSKE TRUCK LEASING COMPANY, L.P.

(Joint Venture of General Electric Company & Penske Corporation)
Rte 10 Green Hills
Reading, PA 19607
Mailing Address:
PO Box 563
Reading, PA 19603-0563
Tel.: (610) 775-6000
Fax: (610) 775-6432
Toll Free: (800) GO-PENSKE
Web Site:
www.pensketruckleasing.com
Approx. Number Employees: 20,000
Year Founded: 1969
Business Description:
Full-Service Truck Leasing, Contract Maintenance & Commercial & Consumer Truck Rental Services; Owned by GE Equipment Services & by Penske Corporation
S.I.C.: 7519
N.A.I.C.S.: 532120
Media: 2-7-8-10-13-18-19-22
Budget Set: Oct.
Personnel:
Roger S. Penske *(Chm)*
Brian Hard *(Pres)*
Jim Feenstra *(Sr VP-Mktg)*
Bill Jacobelli *(Sr VP-Northeast Region)*
William Stobbart *(Sr VP-IT)*
Art Vallely *(Sr VP)*
Don Metcalf *(Dir-Product Mktg)*
Advertising Agencies:
Ketchum Directory Advertising/Kansas City
7015 College Blvd Ste 700
Overland Park, KS 66211-1524
Tel.: (913) 344-1900
Fax: (913) 344-1960
Toll Free: (800) 922-6977

Porter Novelli
(Sub. of Omnicom Group, Inc.)
75 Varick St 6th Fl
New York, NY 10013
Tel.: (212) 601-8000
Fax: (212) 601-8101

PETERBILT MOTORS CO.

(Div. of PACCAR Inc.)
1700 Woodbrook St
Denton, TX 76205-7864
Tel.: (940) 591-4000
Fax: (940) 591-4260
E-mail: pbcontact@peterbilt.com
Web Site: www.peterbilt.com
Sales Range: $550-599.9 Million
Approx. Number Employees: 2,300
Year Founded: 1939
Business Description:
Mfr. Heavy Duty Trucks
S.I.C.: 3537
N.A.I.C.S.: 333924
Advertising Expenditures: $1,400,000
Media: 2-3-4-5-7-8-10-11-20-26
Distr.: Intl.; Natl.
Budget Set: Nov.
Brands & Products:
AIR LEAF
AIR SWEEP
AIR TRAC
CAB AIR SUSPENSION
LOW AIR LEAF
PETERBILT
TRUCKCARE
ULTRA CAB
ULTRA-RIDE
ULTRA SLEEPER
UNIBILT
VARASHIELD

PIAGGIO USA, INC.

(Sub. of Piaggio & C. SpA)
140 E 45th St Ste 17C
New York, NY 10017
Tel.: (212) 380-4400
Fax: (212) 380-4459
Toll Free: (800) 631-1101
E-mail: info@piaggiogroupusa.com
Web Site: www.piaggiousa.com
Approx. Number Employees: 30
Year Founded: 1998
Business Description:
Scooters & Accessories Distr
S.I.C.: 3751
N.A.I.C.S.: 336991
Media: 4-10-22
Brands & Products:
APRILIA
MOTO GUZZI
SCARABEO
Advertising Agency:
CooperKatz & Company
205 Lexington Ave 5th Fl
New York, NY 10016
Tel.: (917) 595-3030
Fax: (917) 326-8997
Public Relations
— Anne Green *(Acct Exec)*

PIERCE MANUFACTURING, INC.

(Sub. of Oshkosh Corporation)
PO Box 2017
Appleton, WI 54912-2017
Tel.: (920) 832-3000
Fax: (920) 832-3617
Web Site: www.piercemfg.com
E-Mail For Key Personnel:
Public Relations: KSkiba@piercemfg.com
Sales Range: $350-399.9 Million
Approx. Number Employees: 1,500
Year Founded: 1913
Business Description:
Fire Trucks & Emergency Vehicles Mfr
S.I.C.: 3711
N.A.I.C.S.: 336120
Export
Advertising Expenditures: $200,000
Media: 2-5-7-10-22
Personnel:
Tom Adrians *(CFO)*
Jim Johnson *(Pres-Fire & Emergency Segment & Exec VP)*
Jodie Larsen *(VP-HR)*
Jim Parker *(VP-Intl Sls)*
Brands & Products:
COMMAND ZONE
CONTENDER
DASH
ENFORCER
HERCULES
HUSKY
LANCE
PIERCE
QUANTUM
SABER

Key to Media (For complete agency information see *The Advertising Red Books-Agencies* edition):
1. Bus. Publs. 2. Cable T.V. 3. Catalogs & Directories. 4. Co-op Adv. 5. Consumer Mags. 6. D.M. to Bus. Estab.7. D.M. to Consumers
8. Daily Newsp. 9. Exhibits/Trade Shows 10. Foreign 11. Infomercial 12. Internet Adv.13. Multimedia 14. Network Radio
15. Network T.V. 16. Newsp. Distr. Mags. 17. Other 18. Outdoor (Posters, Transit) 19. Point of Purchase20. Premiums, Novelties
21. Product Samples 22. Special Events Mktg. 23. Spot Radio 24. Spot T.V. 25. Weekly Newsp. 26. Yellow Page Adv.

Advertising Agency:
Added Value, Inc.
6600 France Ave S Ste 490
Minneapolis, MN 55435
Tel.: (952) 925-9566
Fax: (952) 920-4337
— Scott Anderson *(Principal & Acct. Exec.)*

PLANET AUTOMOTIVE, INC.
(d/b/a Potamkin Automotive)
6600 Cowpen Rd Ste 200
Miami, FL 33014-7618
Tel.: (305) 774-7690
Fax: (305) 774-7696
Web Site: www.planetautomotive.com
Sales Range: $1-4.9 Billion
Approx. Number Employees: 1,500
Business Description:
Holding Company for Auto Dealerships & Franchises
S.I.C.: 5511; 6719
N.A.I.C.S.: 441110; 551112
Media: 9-16-23-24-25
Personnel:
Alan Potamkin *(Co-Chm)*
Robert Potamkin *(Co-Chm)*
Barry Frieder *(Pres & COO)*
David Yusko *(CFO)*
David Winton *(Treas & Exec VP)*
Andrew Pfeifer *(Sr VP-Corp Ops)*
Lonnie Decker *(VP-Bus Dev & E-Commerce)*
David Frieder *(VP-Pur & Vendor Rels)*
Ralph Perkins *(VP-Mktg, E-Commerce & Bus Dev)*
Joel Verity *(Dir-IT)*

PORSCHE CARS NORTH AMERICA, INC.
(Sub. of Porsche Enterprises, Inc.)
980 Hammond Dr NE Ste 1000
Atlanta, GA 30328-8187
Tel.: (770) 290-3500
Fax: (770) 290-3700
E-mail: info@porsche.com
Web Site: www.porsche.com
Sales Range: $200-249.9 Million
Approx. Number Employees: 135
Year Founded: 1984
Business Description:
Cars & Parts Mfr
S.I.C.: 5012; 5013
N.A.I.C.S.: 423110; 423120
Import
Media: 2-6-9-13-14-15-18-22-26-30
Distr.: Natl.
Budget Set: July
Personnel:
Detlev von Platen *(Pres & CEO)*
Thierry Kartochian *(CFO)*
Michael Bartsch *(COO & Exec VP)*
Joseph S. Folz *(General Counsel & Sec)*
David Pryor *(Sr VP-Mktg)*
Andre Oosthuizen *(VP-Mktg)*
Bernd Harling *(Gen Mgr-Pub Rels)*
Scott Baker *(Mgr-Mktg-North America)*
Dave Engelman *(Mgr-Media Rels)*
Gary Fong *(Mgr-Product Experience)*
Tony Fouladpour *(Mgr-Bus Comm)*
Steve Janisse *(Mgr-Automotive Media Rels)*
Nick Twork *(Mgr-Product Comm)*
Advertising Agencies:
Catalano Lellos & Silverstein
137 Varick St., 6th Fl.
New York, NY 10013
Tel.: (212) 243-0700
Fax: (212) 317-2374
(Online Marketing)

Cramer-Krasselt
225 N Michigan Ave
Chicago, IL 60601-7601
Tel.: (312) 616-9600
Fax: (312) 616-3839
Creative

Goodway Group
The Pavilion 261 Old York Rd Ste 930
Jenkintown, PA 19046
Tel.: (215) 887-5700
Fax: (215) 881-2239

Omnicom Media Group
195 Broadway
New York, NY 10007
Tel.: (212) 590-7100
Global Media Planning & Buying

PRECISION TUNE AUTO CARE
(Sub. of Precision Auto Care, Inc.)
PO Box 5000
Leesburg, VA 20177-0500
Tel.: (703) 777-9095
Fax: (703) 771-7108
Web Site: www.precisiontune.com
Sales Range: $25-49.9 Million
Approx. Number Employees: 25
Year Founded: 1975
Business Description:
Franchise of Automatic Tune Up Shops
S.I.C.: 6794; 7542
N.A.I.C.S.: 533110; 811192
Personnel:
Louis M. Brown, Jr. *(Chm)*
Robert Salconi *(CEO)*
Advertising Agency:
Bradham-Hamilton Advertising, Inc.
321 Wingo Way Ste 103
Mount Pleasant, SC 29464
Tel.: (843) 971-8660
Fax: (843) 971-8663

PRO STOP TRUCK SERVICE INC.
(Unit of Dart Transit Company)
800 Lone Oak Rd
Eagan, MN 55121-2212
Tel.: (651) 452-8137
Fax: (651) 633-1302
Toll Free: (800) 729-0323
E-mail: webmaster@dart.net
Web Site: pro-stop.com
Approx. Sls.: $10,000,000
Approx. Number Employees: 100
Business Description:
Diesel Engine Repair: Automotive
S.I.C.: 7538; 5541
N.A.I.C.S.: 811111; 447190
Media: 13
Personnel:
David Oren *(Pres)*

RANDALL REED'S PRESTIGE LINCOLN MERCURY
3601 Shiloh Rd
Garland, TX 75041
Tel.: (972) 864-3673
Fax: (972) 864-3695
Web Site: www.888gorandall.com
E-Mail For Key Personnel:
Sales Director: sales@regencycars.com
Approx. Number Employees: 100
Year Founded: 1982
Business Description:
Automobile Dealership
S.I.C.: 5511
N.A.I.C.S.: 441110
Media: 9-25
Personnel:
Randall Reed *(Owner)*

RAY CATENA MOTOR CAR
910 US Hwy 1
Edison, NJ 08817
Tel.: (732) 549-6600
Fax: (732) 549-9387
Web Site: www.raycatena.com
Approx. Sls.: $47,500,000
Approx. Number Employees: 250
Business Description:
Automobiles, New & Used
S.I.C.: 5511; 7515
N.A.I.C.S.: 441110; 532112
Media: 6-9-18
Personnel:
Raymond Catena *(Pres)*
John Storm *(CFO)*

RDK TRUCK SALES & SERVICE, INC.
3214 Adamo Dr
Tampa, FL 33605
Tel.: (813) 241-0711
Fax: (813) 241-0414
E-mail: info@rdk.com
Web Site: www.rdk.com
Sales Range: $50-74.9 Million
Approx. Number Employees: 75
Business Description:
Garbage Truck Sales & Services
S.I.C.: 5599; 7539
N.A.I.C.S.: 441229; 811198
Media: 2-10-13
Personnel:
Richard Kemner *(Owner)*
Mike Kemner *(Mgr-Mktg)*

READING TRUCK BODY INC.
(Sub. of Reading Group)
Hancock Blvd & Gerry Sts
Reading, PA 19611
Mailing Address:
PO Box 650
Shillington, PA 19607-0650
Tel.: (610) 775-3301
Fax: (610) 775-3261
Toll Free: (800) 458-2226
E-mail: marketing@readingbody.com
Web Site: www.readingbody.com
Approx. Number Employees: 550
Year Founded: 1955
Business Description:
Truck Bodies & Related Parts & Accessories Mfr
S.I.C.: 3711
N.A.I.C.S.: 336211
Media: 2-4-10-13
Distr.: Intl.
Budget Set: Dec.
Personnel:
Harry Schank *(VP-HR)*
Brands & Products:
AEROTECH
CLASSIC II
HUSKY
LATCH-MATIC
LECTRO-LIFE
READING SERVICE BODY
READING STAKE BODY
READY CAP
RHINO LININGS
SADDLE MATE
SPACE CAP
STEEL FORCE
TOOL MATES
Advertising Agency:
Launch Dynamic Media, LLC
828 Penn Ave
Wyomissing, PA 19610
Tel.: (610) 898-1330
Fax: (610) 898-8262

RED MCCOMBS SUPERIOR PONTIAC
(Sub. of McCombs Enterprises)
4800 NW Loop 410
San Antonio, TX 78229
Tel.: (210) 256-5300
Fax: (210) 684-2884
E-mail: info@superiorpontiac.com
Web Site: www.superiorpontiac.com
Sales Range: $150-199.9 Million
Approx. Number Employees: 250
Year Founded: 1995
Business Description:
New & Used Automobiles Dealer
S.I.C.: 5511; 5521
N.A.I.C.S.: 441110; 441120
Advertising Expenditures: $200,000
Media: 3-5-8-9-10-13-23-24-25-26
Personnel:
Red McCombs *(Partner)*
Advertising Agency:
Mann & Mann
84 N.E. Loop 410, Ste. 126
San Antonio, TX 78216
Tel.: (210) 525-8148
Fax: (210) 525-3704

REEDMAN TOLL AUTO WORLD
1700 E Lincoln Hwy US Rte 1
Langhorne, PA 19047
Tel.: (215) 757-4961
Fax: (215) 741-4977
Toll Free: (877) 919-8200
E-mail: autos@reedman.com
Web Site: www.reedmantoll.com
Approx. Number Employees: 400
Business Description:
New & Used Cars & Trucks Whslr
S.I.C.: 5511; 5521
N.A.I.C.S.: 441110; 441120
Advertising Expenditures: $100,000
Media: 9-22
Distr.: Reg.
Personnel:
Bruce Toll *(Pres & CEO)*
William O'Flanagan *(VP & Gen Mgr)*
Trisha DeMaria *(Mgr-Adv)*

REEVES IMPORT MOTORCARS INC.
11333 N Florida Ave
Tampa, FL 33617
Tel.: (813) 933-2811
Fax: (813) 931-4073
Web Site: www.drivereeves.com
Approx. Number Employees: 200
Year Founded: 1971
Business Description:
Car Dealership Owner & Operator
S.I.C.: 5511; 5521
N.A.I.C.S.: 441110; 441120
Media: 6-8-9-13-16-18-22-23-24-25-26

Key to Media (For complete agency information see *The Advertising Red Books-Agencies* edition):
1. Bus. Publs. 2. Cable T.V. 3. Catalogs & Directories. 4. Co-op Adv. 5. Consumer Mags. 6. D.M. to Bus. Estab.7. D.M. to Consumers 8. Daily Newsp. 9. Exhibits/Trade Shows 10. Foreign 11. Infomercial 12. Internet Adv.13. Multimedia 14. Network Radio 15. Network T.V. 16. Newsp. Distr. Mags. 17. Other 18. Outdoor (Posters, Transit) 19. Point of Purchase20. Premiums, Novelties 21. Product Samples 22. Special Events Mktg. 23. Spot Radio 24. Spot T.V. 25. Weekly Newsp. 26. Yellow Page Adv.

Reeves Import Motorcars Inc. — (Continued)

Personnel:
Vivian C. Reeves *(Pres & CEO)*
Kimberly Rogers *(Mgr-Mktg)*

Advertising Agency:
Pyper Paul + Kenney, Inc.
1102 N Florida Ave
Tampa, FL 33602
Tel.: (813) 496-7000
Fax: (813) 496-7003

RELIABLE CHEVROLET
800 N Central Expwy
Richardson, TX 75080-5204
Tel.: (972) 952-1500
Fax: (972) 952-8171
Toll Free: (888) 837-0219
Web Site: www.reliablechev.com
Sales Range: $25-49.9 Million
Approx. Number Employees: 250
Year Founded: 1986
Business Description:
Automobile Dealership
S.I.C.: 5511; 7538
N.A.I.C.S.: 441110; 811111
Advertising Expenditures: $1,000,000
Media: 4-7-8-9-10-13-18-19-20-23-24-26
Distr.: Direct to Consumer; Reg.
Budget Set: June
Personnel:
Darrell McCutcheon *(Pres)*
Dave Anderson *(Gen Mgr)*
Brad Kelly *(Dir-Svc)*
Danny Needham *(Mgr)*
Jeff Power *(Mgr-Gen Sls)*
Robert Richmond *(Mgr-Svc)*

RENAULT USA
(Sub. of Renault S.A.)
411 Theodore Fremd Ave Ste 105
Rye, NY 10580
Tel.: (212) 730-0676
Fax: (212) 730-0706
Toll Free: (800) 332-1052
Telex: 4320053
E-mail: sales@RenaultUSA.com
Web Site: www.renaultusa.com
Year Founded: 1957
Business Description:
Automobile Technical Support Services
S.I.C.: 5012; 7514
N.A.I.C.S.: 423110; 532111
Advertising Expenditures: $300,000
Media: 5-7-8-9-10-14-18-19-20-23-25-26
Distr.: Natl.

RICHMOND FORD
4600 W Broad St
Richmond, VA 23230-3206
Tel.: (804) 358-5521
Fax: (804) 358-2650
E-mail: bstanley@richmondford.com
Web Site: www.richmondford.com
Approx. Number Employees: 200
Year Founded: 1920
Business Description:
Automobiles & Trucks
S.I.C.: 5012
N.A.I.C.S.: 423110
Media: 8-13-23-24
Personnel:
Ron Kody *(Pres)*

RIVERTON MOTOR COMPANY INC.
(d/b/a Riverton Chevrolet Oldsmobile)
10770 Auto Mall Dr
Sandy, UT 84070
Tel.: (801) 576-4600
Tel.: (801) 208-2761
Fax: (801) 576-4695
Web Site: www.rivertonmotor.com
Approx. Sls.: $75,575,264
Approx. Number Employees: 50
Business Description:
Car Dealership Owner & Operator
S.I.C.: 5511; 5521
N.A.I.C.S.: 441110; 441120
Media: 9
Personnel:
Christopher Page *(Pres)*

RUSH ENTERPRISES INC.
555 IH 35 S Ste 500
New Braunfels, TX 78130
Mailing Address:
PO Box 34630
New Braunfels, TX 78130
Tel.: (830) 626-5200
Fax: (830) 626-5318
Toll Free: (800) 973-7874
E-mail: webmaster@rush-enterprises.com
Web Site: www.rushenterprises.com
Approx. Rev.: $1,497,927,000
Approx. Number Employees: 3,010
Year Founded: 1965
Business Description:
Transportation & Construction Equipment Retailer
S.I.C.: 7519; 5012; 5088
N.A.I.C.S.: 532120; 423110; 423860
Import Export
Advertising Expenditures: $2,900,000
Media: 2-4-5-7-10
Personnel:
W. Marvin Rush *(Chm)*
W. M. Rush *(Pres & CEO)*
Steven L. Keller *(CFO, Treas & Sr VP)*
Derrek Weaver *(Gen Counsel, Sec & Sr VP)*
Martin A. Naegelin, Jr. *(Exec VP)*
Scott Anderson *(Sr VP-Fin & Insurance)*
Daryl J. Gorup *(Sr VP-Dealership Ops)*
David C. Orf *(Sr VP-Mktg, Fleets & Specialized Equipment Sls)*
James E. Thor *(Sr VP-Retail Sls)*
Karen S. Konecny *(Dir-Mktg)*
Brands & Products:
OFFICIAL OUTFITTERS OF THE WEST
RUSH
RUSH ENTERPRISES
RUSH EQUIPMENT CENTERS
RUSH TRUCK CENTERS
Advertising Agency:
Adam Friedman Associates
11 E 44 St 5th Fl
New York, NY 10017
Tel.: (212) 981-2529
Fax: (212) 981-8174

RUSSELL & SMITH FORD INC.
3440 S Loop W
Houston, TX 77025
Tel.: (713) 663-4111
Fax: (713) 663-4171
Web Site: www.rsford.com
Approx. Sls.: $172,541,920
Approx. Number Employees: 330
Business Description:
Automobiles, New & Used
S.I.C.: 5511
N.A.I.C.S.: 441110
Advertising Expenditures: $2,400,000
Media: 5-8-13-18-20-22-23
Personnel:
William C. Smith *(Chm)*
Advertising Agency:
Michael Lee Advertising & Design, Inc
2615 Calder Ave Ste 150
Beaumont, TX 77702
Tel.: (409) 835-7564

SAM LEMAN CHRYSLER-PLYMOUTH-DODGE
161 Detroit Ave
Morton, IL 61550
Tel.: (309) 263-2345
Fax: (309) 266-5368
E-mail: info@samlemanmorton.com
Web Site: www.samlemanmorton.com
Approx. Sls.: $19,300,000
Approx. Number Employees: 55
Business Description:
Automobiles, New & Used
S.I.C.: 5511
N.A.I.C.S.: 441110
Media: 1-4-7-10-20-22
Personnel:
Ben Leman *(Principal-Dealership)*
Tom Bauer *(Gen Mgr-Sls)*

SANDERSON FORD INC.
6400 N 51st Ave
Glendale, AZ 85301
Tel.: (623) 842-8600
Tel.: (623) 842-8685 (Service)
Fax: (623) 842-8718
E-mail: info@sandersonford.com
Web Site: www.sandersonford.com
Approx. Sls.: $160,000,000
Approx. Number Employees: 390
Business Description:
Retail Auto Dealership
S.I.C.: 5511
N.A.I.C.S.: 441110
Advertising Expenditures: $400,000
Media: 9-17-18-20-23-24-25
Distr.: Reg.
Budget Set: Nov. -Dec.
Personnel:
David Kimmerle *(Pres & CEO)*
Neil Schrock *(Gen Mgr-Sls)*
Steve Wendt *(Gen Mgr)*
Tom Collins *(Dir-F & I)*
Max Sirstins *(Dir-Adv)*
Dave Tedder *(Dir-Internet)*
Stan Wibben *(Dir-Part)*
Jerry Cremonese *(Bus Mgr)*
Rosemary Soto *(Office Mgr)*
Dave Beard *(Mgr-Parts)*
Loren Clifton *(Mgr-New Vehicle Sls)*
Larry Haidek *(Mgr-Internet Sls)*
Brian Medhurst *(Mgr-Internet Sls)*
Jerry Pena *(Mgr-Body Shop)*
Andy Reece *(Mgr-Sls)*
G. R. Stillwell *(Mgr-Internet Sls)*

SEAGRAVE FIRE APPARATUS, LLC
(Holding of FB Capital Partners, L.P.)
105 E 12th St
Clintonville, WI 54929-1518
Tel.: (715) 823-2141
Fax: (715) 823-5768
E-mail: sales@seagrave.com
Web Site: www.seagrave.com
E-Mail For Key Personnel:
Sales Director: sales@seagrave.com
Sales Range: $50-74.9 Million
Approx. Number Employees: 403
Year Founded: 1881
Business Description:
Heavy-Duty Specialized On-Off Highway Trucks & Fire Apparatus Mfr
S.I.C.: 3711; 3531
N.A.I.C.S.: 336120; 333120
Export
Media: 2-5-10-20
Distr.: Natl.
Budget Set: Sept.
Personnel:
John Neiner *(Pres & CEO)*
Brands & Products:
FWD
SEAGRAVE
Advertising Agency:
Pyramid Creative Group, Inc.
911 Delanglade St
Kaukauna, WI 54130
Tel.: (920) 759-1700
Fax: (920) 759-9424

SERVCO PACIFIC INC.
2850 Pukoloa St Ste 300
Honolulu, HI 96819
Mailing Address:
PO Box 2788
Honolulu, HI 96803-2788
Tel.: (808) 521-6511
Fax: (808) 564-2813
Web Site: www.servco.com
Sales Range: $400-449.9 Million
Approx. Number Employees: 980
Year Founded: 1919
Business Description:
Whslr & Retailer of Cars & Trucks, Home Appliances, Home Electronics, Laundry Products, Water Heaters, Musical Products, Real Estate, Insurance, Tire-Battery Accessories, Copiers, Facsimile Machines & Educational Items
S.I.C.: 5511; 5064
N.A.I.C.S.: 441110; 423620
Import Export
Media: 7-8-13-23-24-26
Personnel:
Jeffrey A. Bell *(CFO, Treas & Sr VP)*
John Harris *(CIO & Grp VP)*
Carol K. Lam *(Sr VP-Properties)*

SEWELL AUTOMOTIVE COMPANIES
3860 W NW Hwy Ste 100
Dallas, TX 75220
Tel.: (214) 902-2222
Fax: (214) 358-0652
Toll Free: (888) 878-0982
E-mail: media.inquiries@sewell.com
Web Site: www.sewell.com
Approx. Number Employees: 1,415
Year Founded: 1911
Business Description:
Retailer of Automobiles
S.I.C.: 5511; 5521
N.A.I.C.S.: 441110; 441120
Personnel:
Carl J. Sewell *(Gen Mgr)*

Key to Media (For complete agency information see *The Advertising Red Books-Agencies* edition):
1. Bus. Publs. 2. Cable T.V. 3. Catalogs & Directories. 4. Co-op Adv. 5. Consumer Mags. 6. D.M. to Bus. Estab.7. D.M. to Consumers
8. Daily Newsp. 9. Exhibits/Trade Shows 10. Foreign 11. Infomercial 12. Internet Adv.13. Multimedia 14. Network Radio
15. Network T.V. 16. Newsp. Distr. Mags. 17. Other 18. Outdoor (Posters, Transit) 19. Point of Purchase20. Premiums, Novelties
21. Product Samples 22. Special Events Mktg. 23. Spot Radio 24. Spot T.V. 25. Weekly Newsp. 26. Yellow Page Adv.

Advertising Agency:
The Richards Group, Inc.
8750 N Central Expy Ste 100
Dallas, TX 75231-6430
Tel.: (214) 891-5700
Fax: (214) 265-2933

SMART USA DISTRIBUTOR LLC
(Div. of Penske Automotive Group, Inc.)
1765 S Telegraph Rd
Bloomfield Hills, MI 48302-0161
Tel.: (248) 648-2456
Business Description:
Smart Car Distr in the US & Puerto Rico
S.I.C.: 5012
N.A.I.C.S.: 423110
Personnel:
Jill Lajdziak, *(Pres)*
Advertising Agencies:
AMCI
4755 Alla Rd Ste 1000
Marina Del Rey, CA 90292
Tel.: (310) 765-4100
Fax: (310) 822-1276

Perich Advertising + Design
117 N 1st St Ste 100
Ann Arbor, MI 48104-1354
Tel.: (734) 769-2215
Fax: (734) 769-2322

SONIC AUTOMOTIVE, INC.
6415 Idlewild Rd Ste 109
Charlotte, NC 28212-0503
Mailing Address:
PO Box 18747
Charlotte, NC 28218-0747
Tel.: (704) 566-2400
Fax: (770) 536-4665
E-mail: webmaster@sonicautomotive.com
Web Site: www.sonicautomotive.com
Approx. Rev.: $6,880,844,000
Approx. Number Employees: 9,200
Year Founded: 1997
Business Description:
Automotive Retailer
S.I.C.: 5511
N.A.I.C.S.: 441110
Advertising Expenditures: $46,900,000
Media: 8-9-14-15-22-23-24-25
Distr.: Natl.
Budget Set: Dec.
Personnel:
O. Bruton Smith *(Chm & CEO)*
David P. Cosper *(Vice Chm & CFO)*
B. Scott Smith *(Pres & Chief Strategic Officer)*
Heath Byrd *(CIO & VP)*
Rachel M. Richards *(VP-Retail Strategy & CMO)*
Jeff Dyke *(Exec VP-Ops)*
David Bruton Smith *(Exec VP)*
Wesley Pandoff *(Sr VP & Controller)*
Ben Pingry *(Dir-Mktg)*
Advertising Agency:
The Loomis Agency
17120 Dallas Pkwy Ste 200
Dallas, TX 75248-1189
Tel.: (972) 331-7000
Fax: (972) 331-7001

SONIC-PLYMOUTH CADILLAC, INC.
(Sub. of Sonic Automotive, Inc.)
(d/b/a Don Massey Cadillac)
40475 Ann Arbor Rd
Plymouth, MI 48170
Tel.: (734) 453-7500
Fax: (734) 453-0290
Fax: (734) 454-0226
Toll Free: (800) 794-7360
Web Site: www.donmasseycadillac.com
E-Mail For Key Personnel:
Sales Director: sales@masseycadillacplymouth.com
Sales Range: $75-99.9 Million
Approx. Number Employees: 140
Year Founded: 1955
Business Description:
Automobile Dealership
S.I.C.: 5511
N.A.I.C.S.: 441110
Media: 2-3-8-9-13-20-23-24-26
Distr.: Reg.

SOUTHEAST TOYOTA DISTRIBUTORS, LLC
(Sub. of JM Family Enterprises Inc.)
100 Jim Moran Blvd
Deerfield Beach, FL 33442-1702
Tel.: (954) 429-2000
Fax: (954) 429-2300
Web Site: www.jmfamily.com
Approx. Number Employees: 2,500
Business Description:
Distr of Vehicles & Automotive Parts & Accessories
S.I.C.: 5012; 8721
N.A.I.C.S.: 423110; 541219
Personnel:
Ed Sheehy *(Pres)*
Hank Grooms *(VP-Mktg & Incentives)*
Myra Adams *(Dir-Mktg Media)*
Advertising Agencies:
22Squared
401 E Jackson St Fl 36
Tampa, FL 33602-5225
Tel.: (813) 202-1200
Fax: (813) 202-1261

National Newspaper Placement Services
766 N Sun Dr Ste 2090
Lake Mary, FL 32746-2553
Tel.: (850) 521-1195
Fax: (850) 577-3646
Toll Free: (800) 742-1373

Pros Marketing of America, Inc.
611 Druid Rd E Ste 705
Clearwater, FL 33756
Tel.: (727) 461-1211
Fax: (727) 461-0109

SOUTHGATE FORD INC.
16501 Fort St
Southgate, MI 48195-1403
Tel.: (734) 282-3636
Fax: (734) 282-1770
E-mail: info@southgateford.com
Web Site: www.southgateford.com
Approx. Number Employees: 155
Year Founded: 1983
Business Description:
New & Used Automobiles Dealership
S.I.C.: 5511; 5521
N.A.I.C.S.: 441110; 441120
Media: 4-7-8-10-13

Personnel:
Walter J. Oben, Jr. *(Owner)*
Jim Jurcak *(Gen Mgr)*
Bob Lovett *(Dir-Svc)*
Sandy Spencer *(Office Mgr)*
Joan Bevak *(Asst Mgr-Svcs)*
Ken Hibbard *(Mgr-Bodyshop)*
Kim Schleicher *(Mgr-Rental)*

ST. PETE AUTO MALL
2500 34th St N
Saint Petersburg, FL 33713
Tel.: (727) 323-2277
Fax: (727) 323-7481
Approx. Number Employees: 61
Business Description:
Car Dealership
S.I.C.: 5511; 7538
N.A.I.C.S.: 441110; 811111
Media: 8-9-24-25
Personnel:
William Douglas *(Pres)*

STANDARD PARKING CORPORATION
900 N Michigan Ave Ste 1600
Chicago, IL 60611-1542
Tel.: (312) 274-2000
Fax: (312) 640-6169
Toll Free: (888) 700PARK
E-mail: info@apcoastandard.com
Web Site: www.standardparking.com
Approx. Rev.: $721,143,000
Approx. Number Employees: 6,824
Business Description:
Parking Facility Management Services
S.I.C.: 7521
N.A.I.C.S.: 812930
Advertising Expenditures: $308,000
Personnel:
Robert S. Roath *(Chm)*
James A. Wilhelm *(Pres & CEO)*
G. Marc Baumann *(CFO & Exec VP)*
Thomas L. Hagerman *(COO & Exec VP-Ops)*
Michael K. Wolf *(Chief Admin Officer, Exec VP & Assoc Gen Counsel)*
Robert N. Sacks *(Gen Counsel, Sec & Exec VP)*
John Ricchiuto *(Exec VP-Ops)*
Edward E. Simmons *(Exec VP-Ops)*
Steven A. Warshauer *(Exec VP-Ops)*
Daniel R. Meyer *(Sr VP)*
Michael E. Swartz *(Sr VP)*

STERLING MCCALL TOYOTA GROUP
(Holding of Group 1 Automotive, Inc.)
9400 SW Freeway
Houston, TX 77074-1408
Mailing Address:
PO Box 1507
Stafford, TX 77497-1507
Tel.: (713) 270-3900
Fax: (713) 270-3746
E-mail: info@sterlingmccalltoyota.com
Web Site: www.sterlingmccalltoyota.com
Sales Range: $125-149.9 Million
Approx. Number Employees: 200
Year Founded: 1956
Business Description:
Automobile Dealer
S.I.C.: 5511; 5521
N.A.I.C.S.: 441110; 441120
Media: 13-23
Distr.: Direct to Consumer

Budget Set: Jan.

STEVE FOLEY CADILLAC
100 Skokie Blvd
Northbrook, IL 60062-1610
Tel.: (847) 564-4090
Fax: (847) 564-5787
E-mail: service@stevefoley.com
Web Site: www.stevefoley.com
Approx. Number Employees: 100
Business Description:
Sales of New & Used Automobiles
S.I.C.: 7514; 5511
N.A.I.C.S.: 532111; 441110
Media: 6
Personnel:
Mercedes Foley *(Vice Chm & Sec)*
Stephen X. Foley, Jr. *(VP & Gen Mgr)*

STRUT, LLC
208 Avenida Fabricante Unit A
San Clemente, CA 92672
Tel.: (949) 361-9841
Fax: (949) 361-8976
E-mail: info@strutwear.com
Web Site: www.strutwear.com
Approx. Number Employees: 9
Business Description:
High End Automotive Accessories
S.I.C.: 3714
N.A.I.C.S.: 336399
Media: 6-10
Brands & Products:
STRUT

SUBARU CANADA, INC.
(Sub. of Fuji Heavy Industries, Ltd.)
560 Suffolk Ct
Mississauga, ON L5R 4J7, Canada
Tel.: (905) 568-4959
Fax: (905) 568-8087
Web Site: www.subaru.ca
Approx. Number Employees: 100
Business Description:
Distribution & Sales of Subaru Automobiles
S.I.C.: 5013
N.A.I.C.S.: 423120
Personnel:
Shiro Ohta *(Chm, Pres & CEO)*
Ted Lalka *(VP-Product Plng-Public Relations)*
Advertising Agency:
DDB Canada
33 Bloor Street East Suite 1700
Toronto, ON M4W 3T4, Canada
Tel.: (416) 925-9819
Fax: (416) 925-4180
Forester

SUBARU OF AMERICA, INC.
(Sub. of Fuji Heavy Industries, Ltd.)
2235 Rte 70 W
Cherry Hill, NJ 08002
Mailing Address:
PO Box 6000
Cherry Hill, NJ 08034-6000
Tel.: (856) 488-8500
Fax: (856) 488-0485
Fax: (856) 488-3196
Toll Free: (800) SUBARU3
Web Site: www.subaru.com
Sales Range: $1-4.9 Billion
Approx. Number Employees: 1,000
Year Founded: 1968
Business Description:
Automobiles Whslr
S.I.C.: 5012; 5013

Key to Media (For complete agency information see *The Advertising Red Books-Agencies* edition):
1. Bus. Publs. 2. Cable T.V. 3. Catalogs & Directories. 4. Co-op Adv. 5. Consumer Mags. 6. D.M. to Bus. Estab.7. D.M. to Consumers
8. Daily Newsp. 9. Exhibits/Trade Shows 10. Foreign 11. Infomercial 12. Internet Adv.13. Multimedia 14. Network Radio
15. Network T.V. 16. Newsp. Distr. Mags. 17. Other 18. Outdoor (Posters, Transit) 19. Point of Purchase20. Premiums, Novelties
21. Product Samples 22. Special Events Mktg. 23. Spot Radio 24. Spot T.V. 25. Weekly Newsp. 26. Yellow Page Adv.

Subaru of America, Inc. — (Continued)

N.A.I.C.S.: 423110; 423120
Media: 3-6-9-14-15-18-23-24
Distr.: Natl.
Personnel:
Yoshio Hasanuma *(Chm, Pres & CEO)*
Tom Doll *(COO & Exec VP)*
Dean Evans *(CMO)*
Sim Coldeck *(Exec VP)*
Tim Mahoney *(Sr VP)*
Dam Dalton *(VP-HR)*
Tim Bennett *(Dir-Adv)*
Michael McHale *(Dir-Corp Comm)*
Alan Bethke *(Mgr-Mktg Ops & Plng)*
John Frantz *(Mgr-Reg Market Dev)*
Dominick Infante *(Mgr-Product Comm-Natl)*
Sheriece Matias *(Mgr-Corp Comm)*

Brands & Products:
FORESTER
IMPREZA 2.5I
IMPREZA WRX
TRIBECA

Advertising Agencies:
AdAsia Communications, Inc.
85 Fifth Ave 7th Fl
New York, NY 10003
Tel.: (212) 871-6886
Fax: (212) 871-6883
Asian Americans

Carmichael Lynch
110 N 5th St
Minneapolis, MN 55403
Tel.: (612) 334-6000
Fax: (612) 334-6090

Dentsu Inc.
1-8-1 Higashi-shimbashi
Tokyo, 105-7001, Japan
Tel.: (81) 3 6216 8042
Fax: (81) 3 6217 5515

Goodway Group
The Pavilion 261 Old York Rd Ste 930
Jenkintown, PA 19046
Tel.: (215) 887-5700
Fax: (215) 881-2239

Harris, Baio & McCullough Inc.
520 S Frnt St
Philadelphia, PA 19147-1723
Tel.: (215) 440-9800
Fax: (215) 440-9812

Leo Burnett Sydney
20 Windmill st
Sydney, NSW 2060, Australia
Tel.: (61) 2 9925 3555
Fax: (61) 2 9925 3617
Tribeca
— Peter Fitzhardinge *(Acct Dir)*
— Kirsty Richards *(Acct Dir)*

The MWW Group
1212 Ave of the Americas 5th Fl
New York, NY 10036-1602
Tel.: (212) 704-9727
Fax: (212) 704-0917
Agency of Record
Lifestyle Marketing

OMD Canada
67 Richmond St W 2nd Fl
Toronto, ON M5H 1Z5, Canada
Tel.: (416) 681-5600
Fax: (416) 681-5620
Media Buying

R/GA
350 W 39th St
New York, NY 10018-1402
Tel.: (212) 946-4000
Fax: (212) 946-4010
Digital

SUPREME INDUSTRIES, INC.
2581 E Kercher Rd
Goshen, IN 46527
Mailing Address:
PO Box 463
Goshen, IN 46527-0463
Tel.: (574) 642-3070
Fax: (574) 642-4729
Toll Free: (800) 642-4889
E-mail: ir@supremecorp.com
Web Site: www.supremeind.com
Approx. Sls.: $220,888,586
Approx. Number Employees: 1,700
Year Founded: 1974
Business Description:
Specialized Commercial Truck Bodies & Related Truck Equipment Mfr, Sales & Repair
S.I.C.: 3711
N.A.I.C.S.: 336211; 336120
Advertising Expenditures: $63,345
Media: 2-4-5-6-7-8-10-26
Personnel:
Herbert M. Gardner *(Chm)*
Kim Korth *(Pres & CEO)*
Matthew W. Long *(CFO, Treas & Asst Sec)*
William J. Barrett *(Sec & Exec VP-Long-Range & Strategic Plng, Asst Treas)*
Mark Beer *(VP-Sls & Mktg)*
Bob Besse *(VP-Sls & Mktg)*
Jacqueline Daniels *(VP-HR)*
Jeffery D. Mowery *(VP-Fin)*
Ken Schafer *(Dir-Strategic Pur & Matls Mgmt)*
Brands & Products:
SUPREME INDUSTRIES

SUZUKI CANADA, INC.
(Sub. of Suzuki Motor Corporation)
100 E Beaver Creek Rd
Richmond Hill, ON L4B 1J6, Canada
Tel.: (905) 889-2600
Fax: (905) 764-1574
Telex: 622968
Web Site: www.suzuki.ca
Approx. Number Employees: 125
Business Description:
Distribution of Suzuki Automobiles, Motorcycles & Outboard Motors
S.I.C.: 7389
N.A.I.C.S.: 425120
Personnel:
Keiichi Maruyama *(Pres)*
Advertising Agency:
John St.
172 John Street
Toronto, ON M5T 1X5, Canada
Tel.: (416) 348-0048
Fax: (416) 348-0050

SYMBOLIC MOTOR CAR COMPANY
7440 La Jolla Blvd
La Jolla, CA 92037
Tel.: (858) 454-1800
Fax: (858) 454-1890
E-mail: info@symbolicmotors.com
Web Site: www.symbolicmotors.com
Approx. Number Employees: 25
Business Description:
Car Dealership
S.I.C.: 5521; 5012
N.A.I.C.S.: 441120; 423110
Media: 6-10-11-13-22
Personnel:
Patrick Van Schoote *(CEO & Gen Mgr-Classic & Competition Cars)*

SYNERGIS TECHNOLOGIES GROUP
3755 36th St
Kentwood, MI 49512
Mailing Address:
PO Box 3457
Moultrie, GA 31776-3457
Tel.: (616) 245-4400
Fax: (616) 475-3204
E-mail: info@synergis.us
Web Site: www.synergis.us
Approx. Sls.: $65,000,000
Approx. Number Employees: 250
Year Founded: 1957
Business Description:
Mfr. & Designer of Chassis & Body Stamping Dies for Car Manufacturers
S.I.C.: 7532; 3545
N.A.I.C.S.: 811121; 333515
Import Export
Media: 2-7-10-13-17
Distr.: Natl.
Personnel:
Jay Groendyke *(Pres & CEO)*

TAMPA MITSUBISHI
(Sub. of Elder Automotive Group)
11608 N Florida Ave
Tampa, FL 33612
Toll Free: (866) 980-1332
Web Site: www.tampamitsubishi.com
Business Description:
New & Used Car Dealership
S.I.C.: 5511; 5521
N.A.I.C.S.: 441110; 441120
Personnel:
Chris Warren, *(Gen Mgr)*
Advertising Agency:
Traffic Advertising, LLC
210 S Pinellas Ave Ste 112
Tarpon Springs, FL 34689
Tel.: (727) 942-3339

TEREX ROAD BUILDING
(Div. of Terex Corporation)
Interstate 40 Morgan Rd
Oklahoma City, OK 73128
Mailing Address:
PO Box 1985
Oklahoma City, OK 73101-1985
Tel.: (405) 787-6020
Fax: (405) 491-2417
E-mail: sales@cmicorp.com
Web Site: www.terexrb.com
E-Mail For Key Personnel:
Sales Director: sales@cmicorp.com
Sales Range: $800-899.9 Million
Approx. Number Employees: 1,800
Year Founded: 1964
Business Description:
Construction Equipment, Specialized Trailers for Heavy Construction Equipment, Waste Composition Equipment & Waste Reduction Grinders Mfr
S.I.C.: 5082; 3531
N.A.I.C.S.: 423810; 333120
Import Export
Advertising Expenditures: $1,085,000
Multimedia: $25,000; Bus. Publs.: $400,000; Catalogs & Directories: $20,000; Co-op Adv.: $20,000; D.M. to Bus. Estab.: $300,000; Exhibits/Trade Shows: $200,000; Other: $20,000; Premiums, Novelties: $100,000
Distr.: Direct to Consumer; Intl.; Natl.
Budget Set: Oct.
Brands & Products:
BID-WELL
CMI
JOHNSON ROSS
LOAD KING
MAGNUM
ROTO-MILL
ROTO-MIXER
TRIPLE-DRUM

TESLA MOTORS, INC.
3500 Deer Creek Rd
Palo Alto, CA 94304
Tel.: (650) 681-5000
E-mail: reservations@teslamotors.com
Web Site: www.teslamotors.com
Approx. Rev.: $116,744,000
Approx. Number Employees: 899
Year Founded: 2003
Business Description:
Electric-Powered Automobile Mfr & Sales
S.I.C.: 3711; 5012
N.A.I.C.S.: 336111; 423110
Advertising Expenditures: $3,100,000
Personnel:
Elon R. Musk *(Chm & CEO-Product Architect)*
Deepak Ahuja *(CFO)*
Peter Rawlinson *(VP & Chief Engr-Vehicle Engrg)*
Evelyn Chiang *(VP-Supply Chain & IT)*
Jim Dunlay *(VP-Powertrain Hardware Engrg)*
Ricardo Reyes *(VP-Comm)*
Mike Taylor *(VP-Fin)*
John Walker *(VP-Sls & Mktg-North America)*
Greg Zanghi *(Dir-Ops-Svc & Parts)*

THOMAS BUILT BUSES, INC.
(Sub. of Freightliner LLC)
1408 Courtesy Rd
High Point, NC 27260-7248
Mailing Address:
PO Box 2450
High Point, NC 27261-2450
Tel.: (336) 889-4871
Fax: (336) 881-6509
Web Site: www.thomasbus.com
Approx. Number Employees: 1,600
Year Founded: 1916
Business Description:
Mfr. of School & Commercial Buses
S.I.C.: 3711
N.A.I.C.S.: 336211; 336111
Import Export
Advertising Expenditures: $300,000
Media: 1-2-4-7-8-10-11-13-20
Distr.: Intl.; Natl.
Budget Set: Apr.
Personnel:
Kelley Platt *(Pres & CEO)*

Key to Media (For complete agency information see *The Advertising Red Books-Agencies* edition):
1. Bus. Publs. 2. Cable T.V. 3. Catalogs & Directories. 4. Co-op Adv. 5. Consumer Mags. 6. D.M. to Bus. Estab.7. D.M. to Consumers
8. Daily Newsp. 9. Exhibits/Trade Shows 10. Foreign 11. Infomercial 12. Internet Adv.13. Multimedia 14. Network Radio
15. Network T.V. 16. Newsp. Distr. Mags. 17. Other 18. Outdoor (Posters, Transit) 19. Point of Purchase20. Premiums, Novelties
21. Product Samples 22. Special Events Mktg. 23. Spot Radio 24. Spot T.V. 25. Weekly Newsp. 26. Yellow Page Adv.

Christine Kamps *(CFO)*
Jeff Allen *(COO)*
Ken Hedgecock *(VP-Sls & Mktg)*
Brands & Products:
BUSES-ALL-READY-TO-BUY

TOM BUSH REGENCY MOTORS INC.

9850 Atlantic Blvd
Jacksonville, FL 32225-6536
Tel.: (904) 725-0911
Tel.: (904) 371-4800
Fax: (904) 727-7917
Fax: (904) 371-4776
Toll Free: (800) 542-1996
E-mail: webmaster@tombush.com
Web Site: www.tombush.com
Sales Range: $100-124.9 Million
Approx. Number Employees: 211
Year Founded: 1970
Business Description:
New & Used Car Dealers
S.I.C.: 5511
N.A.I.C.S.: 441110
Import
Advertising Expenditures: $1,200,000
Media: 8-9-13-25-26
Personnel:
John Bush *(Pres & CEO)*
Telis Assimenios *(Gen Mgr & COO)*
Robert Hudson *(Gen Mgr-Sls)*

TOROMONT CAT

(Sub. of Toromont Industries Ltd.)
140 Inksbrook Dr
Winnipeg, MB R2R 2W3, Canada
Tel.: (204) 453-4343
Fax: (204) 475-7964
Web Site: www.toromontcat.com
Approx. Number Employees: 100
Year Founded: 1915
Business Description:
Sales of Heavy Construction Equipment
S.I.C.: 3531
N.A.I.C.S.: 333120
Import Export
Media: 7-9-10-18-19-20-25-26
Distr.: Intl.
Budget Set: Sept.
Personnel:
Scott Medhurst *(Pres)*

TOWNE HYUNDAI

3170 Rte 10 W
Denville, NJ 07834
Tel.: (973) 366-7777
Fax: (973) 366-3237
Toll Free: (866) 610-1678
Web Site: www.townehyundai.com
Approx. Sls.: $12,000,000
Approx. Number Employees: 25
Business Description:
Car Dealership
S.I.C.: 5511
N.A.I.C.S.: 441110
Media: 3-8-13

TOYOTA CANADA, INC.

(Joint Venture of Mitsui & Co., Ltd. & Toyota Motor Corporation)
1 Toyota Pl
Scarborough, ON M1H 1H9, Canada
Tel.: (416) 438-6320
Fax: (416) 431-1867
Telex: CANATOYO TOR 21
E-mail: lbalaisis@toyota.ca
Web Site: www.toyota.ca
Approx. Number Employees: 575
Year Founded: 1972
Business Description:
CBU Vehicle Import & Sales; Joint Venture of Mitsui & Co., Ltd. (50%) & Toyota Motor Corporation (50%)
S.I.C.: 5013
N.A.I.C.S.: 423120
Personnel:
Yoichi Tomihara *(Pres)*
Stephen Beatty *(Mng Dir)*
Tony Wearing *(Mng Dir)*
Warren Orton *(Dir-PR & Adv)*
Linas Balaisis *(Natl Mgr-PR & Adv)*
Advertising Agencies:
Attik
85 2nd St 6th Fl
San Francisco, CA 94105
Tel.: (415) 284-2600
Fax: (415) 284-2650

Dentsu Canada
276 King St W
Toronto, ON M5V 1J2, Canada
Tel.: (416) 929-9700
Fax: (416) 929-0128
Corolla
Scion
Tacoma
— Michael Stollar *(Acct Dir)*

TOYOTA INDUSTRIES NORTH AMERICA, INC.

(Div. of Toyota Industries Corporation)
25 NW Point Blvd Ste 925
Elk Grove Village, IL 60007
Tel.: (847) 228-8462
Fax: (847) 228-0145
Web Site: www.toyotaindustries.com
Approx. Number Employees: 25
Year Founded: 2001
Business Description:
Holding Company
S.I.C.: 6719
N.A.I.C.S.: 551112
Personnel:
Masaharu Suzuki *(Pres)*
Advertising Agencies:
The Glover Park Group
1025 F St NW 9th Fl
Washington, DC 20004-1409
Tel.: (202) 337-0808
Fax: (202) 337-9137

GolinHarris
(Part of the Interpublic Group of Companies)
111 E Wacker Dr 11th Fl
Chicago, IL 60601-4306
Tel.: (312) 729-4000
Fax: (312) 729-4010

Powell Tate-Weber Shandwick
700 13th St NW Ste 800
Washington, DC 20005
Tel.: (202) 585-2737
Fax: (202) 383-0079

Quinn Gillespie & Associates LLC
1133 Connecticut Ave NW 5th Fl
Washington, DC 20036
Tel.: (202) 457-1110
Fax: (202) 457-1130

Saatchi & Saatchi Los Angeles
3501 Sepulveda Blvd
Torrance, CA 90505-2538
Tel.: (310) 214-6000
Fax: (310) 214-6160
Avalon

TOYOTA MOTOR NORTH AMERICA, INC.

(Sub. of Toyota Motor Corporation)
9 W 57th St Ste 4900
New York, NY 10019-2701
Tel.: (212) 223-0303
Fax: (212) 759-7670
Web Site: www.toyota.com
Sales Range: $1-4.9 Billion
Approx. Number Employees: 31,543
Business Description:
Holding Company
S.I.C.: 6719
N.A.I.C.S.: 551112
Personnel:
Yoshi Inaba *(Pres & COO)*
Steve St. Angelo *(Pres-Toyota Kentucky & Exec VP-Toyota North America-Toyota)*
Dian Ogilvie *(Sr VP)*
Patricia Pineda *(Grp VP)*
Adrian Si *(Mktg Mgr-Interactive-Scion)*
Advertising Agencies:
Burrell
233 N Michigan Ave Ste 2900
Chicago, IL 60601
Tel.: (312) 297-9600
Fax: (312) 297-9601
African American

MacDonald Media
185 Madison Ave 4th Fl
New York, NY 10016
Tel.: (212) 578-8735
Fax: (212) 481-1030

Nobox Marketing Group, Inc.
Metro Parque #7 1st St Ste 303
Guaynabo, PR 00968
Tel.: (787) 792-7070
Fax: (787) 792-5454
Toyota Del Puerto Rico - Tundra

Organic, Inc.
555 Market St 4th Fl
San Francisco, CA 94105
Tel.: (415) 581-5300
Fax: (415) 581-5400

Saatchi & Saatchi Los Angeles
3501 Sepulveda Blvd
Torrance, CA 90505-2538
Tel.: (310) 214-6000
Fax: (310) 214-6160

TOYOTA MOTOR SALES, U.S.A., INC.

(Sub. of Toyota Motor North America, Inc.)
19001 S Western Ave
Torrance, CA 90501-1106
Tel.: (310) 468-4000
Fax: (310) 468-7800
Toll Free: (800) GO-TOYOTA
Web Site: www.toyota.com
Approx. Number Employees: 70,000
Year Founded: 1957
Business Description:
Passenger Cars, 4-Wheel Drive Vehicles, Trucks & Vans Distr
S.I.C.: 5012
N.A.I.C.S.: 423110
Import Export
Advertising Expenditures: $1,784,500,000
Media: 2-3-6-9-10-13-15-16-17-18-22-23-24
Distr.: Natl.
Budget Set: Oct.
Personnel:
Yoshimi Inaba *(Chm & CEO)*
James E. Lentz, III *(Pres & COO)*
Tracey C. Doi *(CFO & Grp VP)*
Zackery Hicks *(CIO & VP)*
Lee White *(Pres-Toyota Racing Dev)*
Christopher P. Reynolds *(Gen Counsel & VP)*
Robert C. Daly *(Sr VP)*
Donald V. Esmond *(Sr VP-Automotive Ops)*
Fletcher G. Davidson *(Grp VP & Gen Mgr-Toyota Customer Svcs)*
Mark Templin *(Grp VP & Gen Mgr-Lexus)*
Robert Carter *(Grp VP & Brand Mgr)*
William D. Fay *(Grp VP-Mktg)*
Christopher K. Hostetter *(Grp VP-Strategic Resources)*
Miles B. King *(Grp VP-HR)*
Randy Pflughaupt *(Grp VP-Sls Admin)*
Eric Taira *(VP & Asst Gen Counsel)*
Jeff Bracken *(VP-Sls-Toyota Div)*
Nancy L. Fein *(VP-Customer Rels)*
Cheryl Hughes *(VP-Rewards, Workforce & Tech)*
David Nordstrom *(VP-Mktg-Lexus)*
Albert A. Smith *(VP-Lexus Customer Svcs)*
Richard Valenstein *(VP-Fin)*
Chris Cento *(Gen Mgr-Boston Region)*
Kevin Cour *(Gen Mgr-Los Angeles Reg)*
D'Anne Duclos *(Gen Mgr-Lexus Southern Area)*
Clyde Dyson *(Gen Mgr-Cincinnati Region)*
Alec Hagey *(Gen Mgr-New York Reg)*
Dan Swartz *(Gen Mgr-Lexus Central Area)*
Matt Kaleba *(Asst Gen Mgr)*
Rick Lofaso *(Corp Mgr-Car Mktg)*
Dawn Ahmed *(Mgr-Scion)*
Gregg Benkendorfer *(Mgr-Natl-Product Mktg-SUVs & Crossovers)*
Dionne Colvin *(Mgr-Strategic Plng-Natl)*
Tom Deluise *(Mgr-Digital-Natl)*
Christine Duron-Yu *(Mgr-Scion Interactive Mktg)*
Kevin Higgins *(Corp Mgr-Mktg-SUV)*
Ed Laukes *(Corp Mgr-Mktg-Motorsports)*
Tim Morrison *(Mgr-Mktg Comm)*
Jim Pisz *(Mgr-Advanced Tech)*
Chris Schultz *(Mgr)*
Bob Zeinstra *(Mgr-Natl-Adv & Comm Strategy)*
Kimberly Kyaw *(Sr Media Strategist-Digital Media & Brand Integration)*
Advertising Agencies:
Attik
85 2nd St 6th Fl
San Francisco, CA 94105
Tel.: (415) 284-2600
Fax: (415) 284-2650
(Scion)

Burrell
233 N Michigan Ave Ste 2900
Chicago, IL 60601

Key to Media (For complete agency information see *The Advertising Red Books-Agencies* edition):
1. Bus. Publs. 2. Cable T.V. 3. Catalogs & Directories. 4. Co-op Adv. 5. Consumer Mags. 6. D.M. to Bus. Estab.7. D.M. to Consumers
8. Daily Newsp. 9. Exhibits/Trade Shows 10. Foreign 11. Infomercial 12. Internet Adv.13. Multimedia 14. Network Radio
15. Network T.V. 16. Newsp. Distr. Mags. 17. Other 18. Outdoor (Posters, Transit) 19. Point of Purchase20. Premiums, Novelties
21. Product Samples 22. Special Events Mktg. 23. Spot Radio 24. Spot T.V. 25. Weekly Newsp. 26. Yellow Page Adv.

Toyota Motor Sales, U.S.A., Inc. — (Continued)

Tel.: (312) 297-9600
Fax: (312) 297-9601
(African-American Advertising)

Callahan Creek, Inc.
805 New Hampshire St
Lawrence, KS 66044-2739
Tel.: (785) 838-4774
Fax: (785) 838-4033

Conill Advertising, Inc.
3501 Sepulveda Blvd
Torrance, CA 90505-2538
Tel.: (310) 214-6400
Fax: (310) 214-6409

Ervin Advertising & Design, Inc.
(d/b/a Ervin AD)
130 McCormick Ave Ste 100
Costa Mesa, CA 92626
Tel.: (949) 251-1166
Fax: (714) 966-2371

Genex
9905 Jefferson Blvd
Culver City, CA 90232
Tel.: (310) 736-2000
Fax: (310) 736-2001

Guthrie/Mayes
710 W Main St
Louisville, KY 40202-2676
Tel.: (502) 584-0371
Fax: (502) 584-0207

Intermark Group, Inc.
101 25th St N
Birmingham, AL 35203
Tel.: (205) 803-0000
Fax: (205) 870-3843
Toll Free: (800) 554-0218

interTrend Communications, Inc.
555 E Ocean Blvd
Long Beach, CA 90802-5003
Tel.: (562) 733-1888
Fax: (562) 733-1889
Matrix

Saatchi & Saatchi Los Angeles
3501 Sepulveda Blvd
Torrance, CA 90505-2538
Tel.: (310) 214-6000
Fax: (310) 214-6160
Swagger Wagon
Toyota Sienna

Trend Influence
303 Peachtree Center Ave Ste 625
Atlanta, GA 30303
Tel.: (404) 221-1188
Fax: (404) 720-8200

Zenith Media Services
(Regional Headquarters for ZenithOptimedia, the Americas)
299 W Houston St 10th Fl
New York, NY 10014-4806
Tel.: (212) 859-5100
Fax: (212) 727-9495

POWER TOYOTA CERRITOS

(Sub. of AutoNation, Inc.)
18700 Studebaker Rd
Cerritos, CA 90703-5335
Tel.: (562) 860-6561
Fax: (562) 860-9891
Web Site: www.toyotacerritos.com
Sales Range: $150-199.9 Million
Approx. Number Employees: 225
Business Description:
Auto Dealerships
S.I.C.: 5511; 5013
N.A.I.C.S.: 441110; 441310
Media: 2-3-5-6-8-9-13-23-24-25-26
Distr.: Reg.
Personnel:
Kevin Naderi *(Gen Mgr)*

TOYOTA OF MORRISTOWN

169 Ridgedale Ave
Morristown, NJ 07960
Tel.: (973) 540-1111
Fax: (973) 540-1190
E-mail: aferrara@toyotaofmorristown.com
Web Site: www.toyotaofmorristown.com
Approx. Number Employees: 150
Business Description:
Retailer of New & Used Cars
S.I.C.: 5511
N.A.I.C.S.: 441110
Media: 3-8-9-13-22-23-25-26
Personnel:
Jonathan Brauer *(Owner & Principal)*
Anthony Ferrara *(Owner & Gen Mgr)*
Advertising Agency:
The Magna Group
17-17 Rte 208 N
Fair Lawn, NJ 07410
Tel.: (201) 652-8600
Fax: (201) 652-4263

TRAILMOBILE CORPORATION

100 N Field Dr Ste 355
Lake Forest, IL 60045-2514
Tel.: (847) 504-2000
Fax: (847) 615-9863
Toll Free: (800) 877-4990
E-mail: hq@trailmobile.com
Web Site: www.trailmobile.com
Approx. Number Employees: 1,000
Business Description:
Truck Trailers Mfr; Aftermarket Replacement Parts Distr
S.I.C.: 3715; 5013
N.A.I.C.S.: 336212; 423120
Import Export
Media: 2-4-6-7-10-22-25
Distr.: Intl.; Natl.
Budget Set: Sept.
Personnel:
Timothy McDonnell *(Gen Counsel & VP)*
Brands & Products:
ADDVANTAGE
TRAILMOBILE
ULTRA PLATE

UNION CITY BODY COMPANY, LLC

(Sub. of Grand Vehicle Works Holdings Corp.)
301 S Jackson Pke
Union City, IN 47390
Mailing Address:
Ste 214 600 Central Ave
Highland Park, IL 60035-3256
Tel.: (765) 964-3121
Fax: (765) 964-3763
E-mail: info@ucbc.com
Web Site: www.ucbc.com
Approx. Number Employees: 500
Year Founded: 1898
Business Description:
Mfr. of Truck Bodies & Transportation Products & Services
S.I.C.: 3711
N.A.I.C.S.: 336211
Import Export
Media: 4-7-10-13-20-22
Distr.: Natl.
Brands & Products:
AEROMASTER WALK-IN VANS
METROMASTER
TRADEMASTER
UTILIVAN

VOLKSWAGEN CANADA, INC.

(Sub. of Volkswagen AG)
777 Bayly St W
Ajax, ON L1S 7G7, Canada
Tel.: (905) 428-6700
Fax: (905) 428-5834
Web Site: www.vw.com
Approx. Number Employees: 100
Year Founded: 1952
Business Description:
Motor Vehicle Mfr & Distr
S.I.C.: 3711
N.A.I.C.S.: 336111
Import
Media: 2-3-4-5-6-7-8-9-10-11-13-14-15-16-18-19-22-23-24-25
Distr.: Natl.
Budget Set: Nov. -Dec.
Personnel:
Klaus Leisen *(Chm)*
John White *(Pres)*
Bruce Rosen *(Dir-Mktg & Comm)*
Thomas Tetzlaff *(Manager, Public Relations)*
Peter Viney *(Mgr-Retail & Customer Relationship Mgmt Mktg)*

VOLKSWAGEN GROUP OF AMERICA, INC.

(Sub. of Volkswagen AG)
2200 Ferdinand Porsche Dr
Herndon, VA 20171
Tel.: (248) 754-5000
Tel.: (248) 340-5000
Fax: (248) 754-4930
Toll Free: (800) 374-8389
Web Site: www.volkswagengroupamerica.com
Approx. Number Employees: 800
Year Founded: 1955
Business Description:
Motor Vehicle Mfr & Distr
S.I.C.: 5012; 3711; 5013
N.A.I.C.S.: 423110; 336111; 423120
Import
Advertising Expenditures: $400,000,000
Media: 3-6-9-13-14-15-18-22-23-24
Distr.: Intl.; Natl.
Personnel:
Jonathan Browning *(Pres & CEO)*
Michael Lohscheller *(CFO & Exec VP)*
Mark Barnes *(COO)*
Falk Bell *(Exec VP-Svc & Quality)*
Tony Cervone *(Exec VP-Grp Comm)*
Jill Bratina *(VP-Comm)*
Tim Ellis *(VP-Mktg)*
Scott Vazin *(VP-PR)*
M. Toscan Bennett *(Mgr-Used Car Remarketing)*
Sara Devine *(Mgr-Digital Integrated Mktg)*
Mark Gillies *(Mgr-Product & Tech Comm)*
Advertising Agencies:
Deutsch LA
5454 Beethoven St
Los Angeles, CA 90066-7017
Tel.: (310) 862-3000
Fax: (310) 862-3100
Agency of Record-Creative
The Force
— Tom Else *(Acct Dir)*
— Chris Carter *(Acct Exec)*

Draftfcb
101 E Erie St
Chicago, IL 60611
Tel.: (312) 425-5000
Fax: (312) 425-5010
Agency of Record-CRM

VOLVO CARS OF CANADA LTD.

(Sub. of Volvo Personvagnar Holding AB)
175 Gordon Baker Rd
Toronto, ON M2H 2N7, Canada
Tel.: (416) 493-3700
Fax: (416) 496-0552
Toll Free: (800) 663-8255
Web Site: www.volvocanada.com
Approx. Number Employees: 60
Business Description:
Automotive Sales
S.I.C.: 5013
N.A.I.C.S.: 423120
Advertising Agency:
Marshall Fenn Communications Ltd.
890 Yonge St Ste 300
Toronto, ON M4W 3P4, Canada
Tel.: (416) 962-3366
Fax: (416) 962-3375

VOLVO CARS OF NORTH AMERICA LLC

(Sub. of Volvo Car Corporation)
1 Volvo Dr
Rockleigh, NJ 07647-2507
Tel.: (201) 768-7300
Fax: (201) 768-1385
Web Site: www.volvocars.com
Sales Range: $75-99.9 Million
Business Description:
Automobiles, Parts & Accessories Sales
S.I.C.: 5012
N.A.I.C.S.: 423110
Personnel:
Chris Dauerer *(VP-Customer Svc)*
John Maloney *(VP-Mktg)*
Art Battaglia *(Mgr-Product-C30)*
Greg Hembrough *(Mgr-Sls & Mktg)*
Advertising Agencies:
Centra360
1400 Old Country Rd Ste 420
Westbury, NY 11590-5119
Tel.: (516) 997-3147
Fax: (516) 334-7798

Euro RSCG Worldwide
350 Hudson St
New York, NY 10014-4504
Tel.: (212) 886-2000
Fax: (212) 886-2016
Toll Free: (800) 937-0233

Key to Media (For complete agency information see *The Advertising Red Books-Agencies* edition):
1. Bus. Publs. 2. Cable T.V. 3. Catalogs & Directories. 4. Co-op Adv. 5. Consumer Mags. 6. D.M. to Bus. Estab.7. D.M. to Consumers 8. Daily Newsp. 9. Exhibits/Trade Shows 10. Foreign 11. Infomercial 12. Internet Adv.13. Multimedia 14. Network Radio 15. Network T.V. 16. Newsp. Distr. Mags. 17. Other 18. Outdoor (Posters, Transit) 19. Point of Purchase20. Premiums, Novelties 21. Product Samples 22. Special Events Mktg. 23. Spot Radio 24. Spot T.V. 25. Weekly Newsp. 26. Yellow Page Adv.

Plan B (the agency alternative)
116 W Illinois St 2W
Chicago, IL 60654
Tel.: (312) 222-0303
Fax: (312) 222-0305
Toll Free: (866) 317-5262
Volvo XC60

VOLVO GROUP NORTH AMERICA INC.
(Sub. of AB Volvo)
570 Lexington Ave 20th Fl
New York, NY 10022-6885
Tel.: (212) 418-7400
Fax: (212) 418-7435
E-mail: info@volvo.com
Web Site: www.volvo.com
Approx. Number Employees: 6
Business Description:
Mfr. of Trucks
S.I.C.: 8742; 8748
N.A.I.C.S.: 541611; 541690
Media: 6-8-10-11-13-14-15-18-25
Personnel:
Salvatore L. Mauro *(Pres)*
John Johnston *(Mgr-Mktg-eBusiness)*

VOLVO TRUCKS NORTH AMERICA, INC.
(Sub. of Volvo Truck Corporation)
7900 National Service Rd
Greensboro, NC 27409
Mailing Address:
PO Box 26115
Greensboro, NC 27402-6115
Tel.: (336) 393-2000
Fax: (336) 393-2262
Telex: 6843027
Web Site: www.volvotrucks.us.com
Approx. Number Employees: 2,000
Year Founded: 1981
Business Description:
Mfr. & Distr of Trucks
S.I.C.: 3711; 5013
N.A.I.C.S.: 336120; 423120
Import Export
Media: 2-4-5-7-8-9-10-11-18-19-20-22-23-26
Distr.: Intl.; Natl.
Budget Set: Oct. -Nov.
Personnel:
Dennis Slagle *(Pres & CEO)*
Lars Thoren *(CFO & Exec VP)*
Ron Huibers *(Sr VP-Sls & Mktg-North America)*
Rikard Jonsson *(Sr VP-Sls & Mktg-Parts)*
Scott Kress *(VP-Sls)*
Greg Tinnel *(VP-HR)*
Brands & Products:
AUTOCAR
VOLVO
VOLVO VN
WHITEGMC AERO SERIES
WHITEGMC CONVENTIONALS
XPEDITOR
Advertising Agency:
Jennings & Company
104-A N Elliott Rd
Chapel Hill, NC 27514
Tel.: (919) 929-0225
Fax: (919) 968-8278

VT INC.
8500 Shawnee Mission Pkwy Ste 200
Merriam, KS 66202-2960
Tel.: (913) 432-6400
Web Site: www.vanenterprises.com
Sales Range: $1-4.9 Billion
Approx. Number Employees: 7,000
Year Founded: 1973
Business Description:
Holding Company; Operator of Automobile Dealerships
S.I.C.: 5511; 8742
N.A.I.C.S.: 441110; 541611
Media: 4-13-26
Personnel:
Larry Van Tuyl *(Co-CEO)*
Jim Thayer *(CFO)*

WALSER AUTOMOTIVE GROUP, INC.
4401 American Blvd W
Bloomington, MN 55437
Tel.: (952) 929-3535
Fax: (952) 929-5252
E-mail: pporter@walser.com
Web Site: www.walser.com
Approx. Number Employees: 1,000
Year Founded: 1956
Business Description:
Auto Selling & Leasing
S.I.C.: 7532
N.A.I.C.S.: 811121
Personnel:
Andrew Walser *(Pres)*
Paul Walser *(CEO)*
Advertising Agency:
Nemer Fieger
6250 Excelsior Blvd Ste 203
Minneapolis, MN 55416-2735
Tel.: (952) 925-4848
Fax: (952) 925-1907

WARNOCK AUTOMOTIVE GROUP, INC.
175 Rte 10
East Hanover, NJ 07936-2104
Tel.: (973) 884-2100
Fax: (973) 884-2737
Toll Free: (800) 927-6625
E-mail: marketing@warnockauto.com
Web Site: www.warnockauto.com
E-Mail For Key Personnel:
Marketing Director: marketing@warnockauto.com
Approx. Number Employees: 450
Year Founded: 1976
Business Description:
New & Used Car Dealership
S.I.C.: 5511; 7515
N.A.I.C.S.: 441110; 532112
Advertising Expenditures: $3,000,000
Media: 2-3-4-5-7-8-9-10-13-16-18-19-20-22-23-26
Distr.: Reg.
Budget Set: Nov.
Personnel:
Michael Critchley *(Pres & CFO)*
Tim Ryan *(Gen Mgr)*

WESTLEX INC.
(d/b/a Westside Lexus)
12000 Old Katy Rd
Houston, TX 77079
Tel.: (281) 558-3030
Fax: (281) 558-7859
E-mail: tstanberry@westsidelexus.com
Web Site: www.westsidelexus.com
Sales Range: $150-199.9 Million
Approx. Number Employees: 151
Business Description:
Automobiles, New & Used
S.I.C.: 5511; 7532
N.A.I.C.S.: 441110; 811121
Personnel:
Jack Kendall *(Pres)*
Brett Aldridge *(Gen Mgr)*
Dale McMullen *(Gen Mgr-Sls)*
Gerald Chomer *(Dir-Fin Svcs)*
Robert Parnell *(Dir-Parts & Svc)*
David Trice *(Sls Mgr)*
Rex Goodson *(Mgr-Inventory Control & Coord)*
Ronnie Brush *(Mgr-Collision Center)*
Gary Cohen *(Mgr-New Vehicle Sls)*
Gustavo Fuentes *(Mgr-Make Ready)*
Doug Gilmer *(Mgr-Preowned sls)*
Carolyn Glazer *(Mgr-Admin)*
Gina Henderson *(Mgr-Fin Svcs)*
Kevin Jacobson *(Mgr-Fin Svcs)*
Christy McGaha *(Mgr-Acctg)*
Paul Rockett *(Mgr-Fin Svcs)*
Hans Schackmann *(Mgr-Svc Drive)*
Clarice Schlinger *(Mgr-HR)*
Ty Stanberry *(Mgr-Pre-Owned)*
Ross Zuerner *(Mgr-Parts)*
Advertising Agency:
The Advertising Group
13313 SW Fwy
Sugar Land, TX 77478
Tel.: (281) 240-2114
— Phil Scott *(Acct Exec)*

WILLEY MOTORS INC.
(d/b/a Willey Honda)
2215 S 500 W
Bountiful, UT 84010
Tel.: (801) 295-4477
Fax: (801) 295-6831
Toll Free: (800) NEWHONDA
E-mail: patriciab@willeyford.com
Web Site: www.willeyhonda.com
Sales Range: $10-24.9 Million
Approx. Number Employees: 50
Business Description:
New & Used Car Dealers
S.I.C.: 5511; 5012
N.A.I.C.S.: 441110; 423110
Personnel:
Duff Willey *(Owner & Pres)*
Ron Henson *(Gen Mgr)*
Kay Grover *(Office Mgr)*
Brands & Products:
CAR DEALERSHIP
Advertising Agency:
CLM Marketing & Advertising
588 W Idaho St
Boise, ID 83702-5928
Tel.: (208) 342-2525
Fax: (208) 384-1906

WOLFINGTON BODY COMPANY, INC.
30 N Pottstown Pke
Exton, PA 19341
Mailing Address:
PO Box 218
Exton, PA 19341-0218
Tel.: (610) 458-8501
Fax: (610) 458-0293
E-mail: buses@wolfington.com
Web Site: www.wolfington.com
Approx. Number Employees: 100
Year Founded: 1876
Business Description:
Distr of School & Commercial Buses, Ambulances & Funeral Cars & Limousines
S.I.C.: 5599
N.A.I.C.S.: 441229
Export
Media: 2-4-7-10-11-17
Distr.: Direct to Consumer; Reg.
Personnel:
Richard I. Wolfington *(Pres)*
Frank K Dutcher *(Sr VP)*
Dane Colestock *(VP & Dir-Facilities)*
James E. Wolfington *(Sls Mgr)*
Advertising Agency:
JRL Advertising & Sales Promotion, Inc.
80 Orchard Rd
North East, MD 21901
Tel.: (410) 287-1336
Fax: (410) 287-1334
(Carpenter; Mid-Bus; Champion; Diamond; Corbell-Buses & Superior Funeral Coaches)
— John Landan *(Pres.)*

WORLD TOYOTA
(Holding of Group 1 Automotive, Inc.)
5800 Peachtree Industrial Blvd
Atlanta, GA 30341
Tel.: (678) 547-9000
Fax: (678) 547-9011
Toll Free: (866) 314-4459
E-mail: sales@worldtoyota.com
Web Site: www.worldtoyota.net
E-Mail For Key Personnel:
Sales Director: sales@worldtoyota.com
Sales Range: $25-49.9 Million
Approx. Number Employees: 100
Business Description:
Car Dealership
S.I.C.: 5599
N.A.I.C.S.: 441229
Media: 8-13
Personnel:
Mike Balog *(Gen Mgr)*
Jack Brennen *(Gen Mgr)*

W.W. WALLWORK, INC.
900 35th St NW
Fargo, ND 58102-3089
Mailing Address:
PO Box 1819
Fargo, ND 58107-1819
Tel.: (701) 476-7000
Fax: (701) 476-7001
Toll Free: (800) 937-3003
E-mail: sales@wallworktrucks.com
Web Site: www.wallworktrucks.com
E-Mail For Key Personnel:
Sales Director: sales@wallworktrucks.com
Approx. Number Employees: 130
Year Founded: 1921
Business Description:
Whslr & Retailer of Cars, Trucks & Parts; Truck Trailers Service & Repairs; Finance Leasing
S.I.C.: 5511; 5012
N.A.I.C.S.: 441110; 423110
Export
Media: 7-8-10-26
Personnel:
William W. Wallwork, III *(Pres)*
Cim Drewicke *(CFO)*

XTRA LEASE LLC
(Div. of XTRA Corporation)
1801 Park 270 Dr Ste 400
Saint Louis, MO 63146-4037
Tel.: (314) 579-9300
Fax: (314) 542-2150
Toll Free: (800) 325-1453

Key to Media (For complete agency information see *The Advertising Red Books-Agencies* edition):
1. Bus. Publs. 2. Cable T.V. 3. Catalogs & Directories. 4. Co-op Adv. 5. Consumer Mags. 6. D.M. to Bus. Estab.7. D.M. to Consumers
8. Daily Newsp. 9. Exhibits/Trade Shows 10. Foreign 11. Infomercial 12. Internet Adv.13. Multimedia 14. Network Radio
15. Network T.V. 16. Newsp. Distr. Mags. 17. Other 18. Outdoor (Posters, Transit) 19. Point of Purchase20. Premiums, Novelties
21. Product Samples 22. Special Events Mktg. 23. Spot Radio 24. Spot T.V. 25. Weekly Newsp. 26. Yellow Page Adv.

XTRA Lease LLC — (Continued)

Web Site: www.xtralease.com
Sales Range: $25-49.9 Million
Approx. Number Employees: 177
Business Description:
Renting & Leasing of Trailers
S.I.C.: 7519
N.A.I.C.S.: 532120
Media: 2-7-10-13
Personnel:
William H Franz *(Pres)*
Steve Zaborowski *(Sr VP)*
Kathy O'Leary *(VP-Mktg)*
Ron Kemm *(Dir-Mktg)*
Advertising Agency:
McKinney Chicago
430 W Erie Ste 400
Chicago, IL 60610
Tel.: (312) 944-6784
Fax: (312) 944-6789

YANMAR AMERICA CORPORATION

(Sub. of Yanmar Co., Ltd.)
101 International Parkway
Adairsville, GA 30103
Tel.: (770) 877-9894
Fax: (770) 877-9009
Web Site: www.yanmar.com
Sales Range: $25-49.9 Million
Approx. Number Employees: 150
Year Founded: 1912
Business Description:
Mfr of Marine & Industrial Diesel Engines
S.I.C.: 5084; 5083
N.A.I.C.S.: 423830; 423820
Advertising Expenditures: $2,000,000
Media: 2-6-8-9-10-16-18-20-23-24-25-26
Distr.: Natl.
Budget Set: Apr.
Brands & Products:
YANMAR

Key to Media (For complete agency information see *The Advertising Red Books-Agencies* edition):
1. Bus. Publs. 2. Cable T.V. 3. Catalogs & Directories. 4. Co-op Adv. 5. Consumer Mags. 6. D.M. to Bus. Estab.7. D.M. to Consumers
8. Daily Newsp. 9. Exhibits/Trade Shows 10. Foreign 11. Infomercial 12. Internet Adv.13. Multimedia 14. Network Radio
15. Network T.V. 16. Newsp. Distr. Mags. 17. Other 18. Outdoor (Posters, Transit) 19. Point of Purchase20. Premiums, Novelties
21. Product Samples 22. Special Events Mktg. 23. Spot Radio 24. Spot T.V. 25. Weekly Newsp. 26. Yellow Page Adv.

Automotive Parts & Accessories

Automobile Electronics — Bearings — Braking Systems — Ignitions — Motors — Mufflers — Part Rebuilders — Repair & Service Centers — Transmissions

A&D TECHNOLOGY INC.
(Sub. of A&D Company, Ltd.)
4622 Runway Blvd
Ann Arbor, MI 48108
Tel.: (734) 973-1111
Fax: (734) 973-1103
E-mail: info@aanddtech.com
Web Site: www.aanddtech.com
Approx. Number Employees: 100
Year Founded: 2005
Business Description:
Powertrain Testing & Measurement Equipment Distr & Engineering Services
S.I.C.: 5046; 7389; 8711
N.A.I.C.S.: 423440; 541330; 541990
Media: 10-11
Personnel:
Yoichiro Koyama *(Pres)*

AAMCO TRANSMISSIONS, INC.
(Holding of AMERICAN CAPITAL, LTD.)
201 Gibraltar Rd Ste 100
Horsham, PA 19044-2331
Tel.: (610) 668-2900
Fax: (610) 668-1308
Toll Free: (800) GOAAMCO
E-mail: wright@aamco.com
Web Site: www.aamco.com
Sales Range: $25-49.9 Million
Approx. Number Employees: 150
Year Founded: 1963
Business Description:
Automobile Transmission Repair Center Franchiser
S.I.C.: 7537
N.A.I.C.S.: 811113
Advertising Expenditures: $24,000,000
Media: 2-3-8-9-10-18-19-23-24-25-26
Distr.: Natl.
Personnel:
Mark H. Wurth *(Pres & COO)*
Keith Morgan *(CEO)*
Brian O'Donnell *(Sr VP-Sls)*
Jack Bachinsky *(VP-Mktg)*
Brands & Products:
AAMCO TRANSMISSIONS
Advertising Agencies:
Gregory FCA
27 W Athens Ave Ste 200
Ardmore, PA 19003
Tel.: (610) 642-8253
Fax: (610) 642-1258
Fax: (610) 649-9029
Toll Free: (800) 499-4734
E-85 Retrofit Program

Qorvis Communications
1201 Connecticut Ave NW Ste 500
Washington, DC 20036
Tel.: (202) 496-1000
Fax: (202) 496-1300

The Ross Agency
201 Gibraltar Rd Ste 149
Horsham, PA 19044
Tel.: (888) 815-7536
Fax: (800) 859-2349
Toll Free: (888) 815-7536

ACKLANDS-GRAINGER INC.
(Sub. of W.W. Grainger, Inc.)
90 West Beaver Creek Road
Richmond Hill, ON L4B 1E7, Canada
Tel.: (905) 731-5516
Fax: (905) 731-2497
Toll Free: (800) 668-8989
E-mail: andersonr@agi.ca
Web Site: www.acklandsgrainger.com
Approx. Sls.: $600,000,000
Approx. Number Employees: 2,200
Year Founded: 1889
Business Description:
Industrial, Automotive Fleet & Safety Products Distr
S.I.C.: 5013
N.A.I.C.S.: 441310
Import
Media: 4
Distr.: Natl.
Budget Set: Sept.
Personnel:
Sean O'Brien *(Pres)*
George McClean *(Gen Counsel & VP)*
Henry Buckley *(VP & Gen Mgr)*
Paul Rushlow *(VP)*
Steve Ince *(VP-Mktg)*
Sandro Verrelli *(VP-Sls & Mktg)*
Laurie Wright *(VP-HR)*
John Tzanopoulos *(Mgr-IT)*
Advertising Agency:
True North Inc.
630 Third Ave 12th Fl
New York, NY 10017
Tel.: (212) 557-4202
Fax: (212) 557-4204

ACTIVANT SOLUTIONS-AUTOMOTIVE GROUP
(Joint Venture of Hellman & Friedman LLC, Thoma Bravo, LLC & JMI Services, Inc.)
804 Las Cimas Pkwy
Austin, TX 78746
Tel.: (512) 328-2300
Fax: (512) 328-7255
Toll Free: (800) 678-5266
E-mail: automotive.marketing@activant.com
Web Site: www.activant.com
Approx. Number Employees: 2,100
Year Founded: 1972
Business Description:
Business Information Technologies Mfr & Management Services
S.I.C.: 7371
N.A.I.C.S.: 541511
Media: 8-10-13
Personnel:
Thomas V. Aliotti *(Sr VP & Gen Mgr-Automotive Grp)*
Brands & Products:
A-DIS
ACONNEX
ACTIVANT
BARCODEEXPERT
BUYER ASSIST
INTERCHANGE
J-CON
LABOREXPERT
LASERCAT
THE PAPERLESS WAREHOUSE
PARTEXPERT
PRISM
ULTIMATE

ACTIVANT SOLUTIONS INC.
(Joint Venture of Hellman & Friedman LLC, Thoma Bravo, LLC & JMI Services, Inc.)
7683 Southfront Rd
Livermore, CA 94551
Tel.: (925) 449-0606
Fax: (925) 449-1037
Toll Free: (888) 448-2636
E-mail: info@activant.com
Web Site: www.activant.com
Approx. Rev.: $370,756,000
Approx. Number Employees: 1,600
Year Founded: 1972
Business Description:
Business Information Technologies Mfr & Management Services; Owned by Hellman & Friedman LLC, Thoma Bravo LLC & JMI Equity
S.I.C.: 7371; 3577; 7372; 7373; 7379; 7389
N.A.I.C.S.: 541511; 334119; 511210; 541512; 541519; 561499
Export
Media: 1-2-7-8-10-13-20
Personnel:
Pervez A. Qureshi *(Pres & CEO)*
Kathleen M. Crusco *(CFO & Exec VP)*
Timothy F. Taich *(Gen Counsel)*
Kevin P. Roach *(Exec VP-Wholesale Distr Grp)*
Paul Salsgiver *(Exec VP-Hardlines, Lumber & Automotive)*
Peter Donnelly *(Sr VP-Ops)*
Scott Hanson *(Sr VP)*
David Petroni *(Sr VP-Corp Dev)*
William Wilson *(Sr VP-Product Dev)*
Steve Bieszczat *(VP-Mktg)*

ADVANCE AUTO PARTS, INC.
5008 Airport Rd
Roanoke, VA 24012-1119
Tel.: (540) 362-4911
Fax: (540) 561-1448
E-mail: shelly.whitaker@advanceautoparts.com
Web Site: www.advanceautoparts.com
Approx. Sls.: $5,925,203,000
Approx. Number Employees: 29,000
Year Founded: 1998
Business Description:
Automotive Aftermarket Sales & Service
S.I.C.: 5013; 7538
N.A.I.C.S.: 441310; 811111
Import Export
Advertising Expenditures: $65,431,000
Media: 4-14-15-16-18-19-24
Personnel:
Jimmie L. Wade *(Pres)*
Darren R. Jackson *(CEO)*
Michael A. Norona *(CFO & Exec VP)*
Kevin Freeland *(COO)*
Rick Coro *(CIO & Sr VP-IT)*
Greg Johnson *(CMO, Sr VP & Gen Mgr-DIY)*
Jim Durkin *(Pres-Autopart Intl)*

Key to Media (For complete agency information see *The Advertising Red Books-Agencies* edition):
1. Bus. Publs. 2. Cable T.V. 3. Catalogs & Directories. 4. Co-op Adv. 5. Consumer Mags. 6. D.M. to Bus. Estab.7. D.M. to Consumers 8. Daily Newsp. 9. Exhibits/Trade Shows 10. Foreign 11. Infomercial 12. Internet Adv.13. Multimedia 14. Network Radio 15. Network T.V. 16. Newsp. Distr. Mags. 17. Other 18. Outdoor (Posters, Transit) 19. Point of Purchase20. Premiums, Novelties 21. Product Samples 22. Special Events Mktg. 23. Spot Radio 24. Spot T.V. 25. Weekly Newsp. 26. Yellow Page Adv.

Advance Auto Parts, Inc. — (Continued)
Sarah Powell *(Gen Counsel, Sec & Sr VP)*
Jill Livesay *(Sr VP & Controller)*
Scott Bauhofer *(Sr VP & Gen Mgr-E-Commerce)*
Donna J. Broome *(Sr VP-Team Member Excellence)*
Gregory E. Haan *(Sr VP-Mdsg-Parts Dept)*
Carl Hauch *(Sr VP-Team Member Excellence)*
Mike Marolt *(Sr VP-Store Support)*
Judd Nystrom *(Sr VP-Fin)*
Mike Pack *(Sr VP-Ops)*
Kurt R. Schumacher *(Sr VP-Ops-Florida)*
Derrick Thomas *(Sr VP-Southeast Ops)*
Charles E. Tyson *(Sr VP-Mdsg)*
Randy Young *(Sr VP-Real Estate)*
Michael S. Fogarty *(Reg VP-Ops)*
Larry Nelson *(VP-Comml Sls-New Customer Dev)*
Tracy Cockerham *(VP-Analysis, Res & Loyalty Mktg)*
Chris Hagestad *(VP-Mdsg & Parts)*
Steve Hoeft *(VP-Comml-Sls & Natl Accounts)*
Walter Scott *(VP-E-Commerce & Comml)*
Shelly Whitaker *(Mgr-Pub Comm)*
Brands & Products:
ADVANCE AUTO PARTS
AUTOPART INTERNATIONAL
KEEP THE WHEELS TURNING
PDQ
WE'RE READY IN ADVANCE
Advertising Agencies:
The Richards Group, Inc.
8750 N Central Expy Ste 100
Dallas, TX 75231-6430
Tel.: (214) 891-5700
Fax: (214) 265-2933

Starcom USA
35 W Wacker Dr
Chicago, IL 60601
Tel.: (312) 220-3535
Fax: (312) 220-6530
Media Agency of Record

Tapestry Partners
35 W Wacker Dr
Chicago, IL 60601
Tel.: (312) 220-3535
Fax: (312) 220-6561
Multicultural Media Planning & Buying

ADVANCED PLATING INC.
1425 Cowan Ct
Nashville, TN 37207
Tel.: (615) 227-6900
Fax: (615) 262-7935
Toll Free: (800) 588-6686
E-mail: gochrome@advancedplating.com
Web Site: www.advancedplating.com
Approx. Sls.: $2,000,000
Approx. Number Employees: 50
Year Founded: 1986
Business Description:
Chrome Plating Services
S.I.C.: 3471
N.A.I.C.S.: 332813
Media: 4-10
Personnel:
Steve Tracy *(Co-Owner & Pres)*
Sheri Tracy *(Owner)*

AFFINIA GROUP INTERMEDIATE HOLDINGS INC.
(Sub. of Affinia Group Holdings Inc.)
1101 Technology Dr
Ann Arbor, MI 48108
Tel.: (734) 827-5400
Fax: (734) 827-5401
E-mail: info@affiniagroup.com
Web Site: www.affiniagroup.com
Approx. Sls.: $1,991,000,000
Approx. Number Employees: 11,835
Business Description:
Holding Company
S.I.C.: 6719
N.A.I.C.S.: 551112
Advertising Expenditures: $27,000,000
Personnel:
James A. Stern *(Chm)*
Terry R. McCormack *(Pres & CEO)*
Thomas H. Madden *(CFO & Sr VP)*
Robert Beltran *(VP-Sls-Intl)*
Thomas J. Zorn *(VP-HR)*
Edmund T. LaCross *(Dir-Tax)*

AFFINIA WIX FILTRATION PRODUCTS
(Sub. of Affinia Group Inc.)
1 Wix Way
Gastonia, NC 28054
Mailing Address:
PO Box 1967
Gastonia, NC 28053-1967
Tel.: (704) 864-6711
Tel.: (704) 864-6748 (Sales)
Fax: (704) 864-9277
Fax: (704) 853-6149
E-mail: info@wixfilters.com
Web Site: www.wixfilters.com
E-Mail For Key Personnel:
Sales Director: sales@wixfilters.com
Approx. Number Employees: 700
Year Founded: 1939
Business Description:
Air, Oil, Fuel, Hydraulic, Cooling & Specialty Filters Mfr
S.I.C.: 3714
N.A.I.C.S.: 336399
Media: 1-2-4-6-7-8-9-10-16-18-19-21-24-26
Distr.: Natl.
Budget Set: Jan.
Personnel:
David Hogue *(Dir-Intl Mktg)*

AIR LIFT COMPANY
2727 Snow Rd
Lansing, MI 48917-9595
Tel.: (517) 322-2144
Fax: (517) 322-0240
E-mail: service@airliftcompany.com
Web Site: www.airliftcompany.com
Approx. Sls.: $7,000,000
Approx. Number Employees: 50
Year Founded: 1950
Business Description:
Air Spring Suspension Products
S.I.C.: 3493; 3714
N.A.I.C.S.: 332611; 336399
Media: 2-4-6-7-8-10-13-19-20
Distr.: Natl.
Budget Set: Oct.
Personnel:
Kevin Mehigh *(Pres)*
Craig Webb *(CFO)*
Brands & Products:
AIR CELL
AIR LIFT
AIR LIFT 1000
EASYSTREET
LOAD CONTROLLER II
LOCK-N-LIFT
PRIMARY AIR
QUICK SHOT
RIDECONTROL
SLAM AIR
SMARTAIR
WIRELESSAIR

AIRTEX PRODUCTS
(Holding of United Components, Inc.)
407 W Main St
Fairfield, IL 62837-1622
Tel.: (618) 842-2111
Fax: (618) 842-4069
E-mail: airtexprodsales@airtexproducts.com
Web Site: www.airtexproducts.com
Approx. Number Employees: 800
Year Founded: 1935
Business Description:
Automobile Parts, Fuel Pumps, Water Pumps & Parts, Water Outlets, & Fan Clutches
S.I.C.: 5013
N.A.I.C.S.: 423120
Import Export
Media: 2-4-7-8
Distr.: Natl.
Budget Set: Oct.
Personnel:
Dee Monge *(Pres)*
Ray Swetman *(VP-Sls & Mktg)*
John Boyer *(Dir-Retail Sls & Product Strategy)*
Dan Williford *(Mgr-Mktg)*
Brands & Products:
AIRTEX
Advertising Agency:
Keller Crescent Advertising
1100 E Louisiana St
Evansville, IN 47711
Tel.: (812) 464-2461
Toll Free: (800) 457-3837

ALBERT TROSTEL & SONS CO.
(Holding of Everett Smith Group, Ltd.)
330 E Kilbourn Ave Ste 750
Milwaukee, WI 53202-3145
Tel.: (414) 223-1560
Fax: (414) 225-0025
Approx. Number Employees: 4,750
Year Founded: 1865
Business Description:
Holding Company
S.I.C.: 8721
N.A.I.C.S.: 541219
Advertising Expenditures: $300,000
Media: 4-17
Distr.: Natl.
Budget Set: Nov. -Dec.

ALLISON TRANSMISSION HOLDINGS, INC.
(Formerly Allison Transmission, Inc.)
(Joint Venture of Onex Corporation & Carlyle Holding Corporation)
4700 W 10th St
Speedway, IN 46222
Mailing Address:
PO Box 894
Indianapolis, IN 46206-0894
Tel.: (317) 242-5000
Fax: (317) 242-3123
Toll Free: (800) 2525ATD
E-mail: info@allisontransmission.com
Web Site: www.allisontransmission.com
Approx. Rev.: $1,926,300,000
Approx. Number Employees: 2,750
Year Founded: 1915
Business Description:
Heavy Duty Automatic & Power Shift Transmissions Designer & Mfr; Owned 49.8% by The Carlyle Group & 49.8% by Onex Corporation
S.I.C.: 3714
N.A.I.C.S.: 336350
Export
Advertising Expenditures: $800,000
Media: 2-4-7-10
Distr.: Intl.; Natl.
Personnel:
Lawrence E. Dewey *(Chm, Pres & CEO)*
David S. Graziosi *(CFO, Exec VP & Treas)*
Ryan A. Milburn *(CIO & VP)*
Eric C. Scroggins *(Gen Counsel, VP & Sec)*
Mark A. Anspach *(VP-Global Procurement & Supplier Quality)*
Michael G. Headly *(VP-Non-NAFTA Mktg, Sls & Svc)*
Randall R. Kirk *(VP-Product Engrg)*
Robert M. Price *(VP-HR)*
James L. Wanaselja *(VP-NAFTA Mktg, Sls & Svc)*
Chris Collet *(Product Mgr-Sls)*
Lou Gilbert *(Mgr-Mktg-North American)*
Brands & Products:
ALLISON TRANSMISSION
IF IT'S NOT ALLISON, IT'S NOT AUTOMATIC
Advertising Agency:
Quinlan Marketing Communications
550 Congressional Blvd Ste 350
Carmel, IN 46032
Tel.: (317) 573-5080
Fax: (317) 573-5088

ALLOMATIC PRODUCTS COMPANY
(Sub. of Powertrain Products Corp.)
102 Jericho Tpke
Floral Park, NY 11001
Mailing Address:
PO Box 267
Sullivan, IN 47882
Tel.: (516) 775-0330
Fax: (516) 775-5543
Toll Free: (800) 568-0330
E-mail: apcsales@allomatic.com
Web Site: www.allomatic.com
Year Founded: 1958
Business Description:
Friction & Reaction Plates Mfr, Transmission Filters & Automatic Transmission Parts
S.I.C.: 3714
N.A.I.C.S.: 336399
Import Export
Advertising Expenditures: $425,000
Media: 1-2-4-5-7-10-19-20-21-22

Key to Media (For complete agency information see *The Advertising Red Books-Agencies* edition):
1. Bus. Publs. 2. Cable T.V. 3. Catalogs & Directories. 4. Co-op Adv. 5. Consumer Mags. 6. D.M. to Bus. Estab.7. D.M. to Consumers
8. Daily Newsp. 9. Exhibits/Trade Shows 10. Foreign 11. Infomercial 12. Internet Adv.13. Multimedia 14. Network Radio
15. Network T.V. 16. Newsp. Distr. Mags. 17. Other 18. Outdoor (Posters, Transit) 19. Point of Purchase20. Premiums, Novelties
21. Product Samples 22. Special Events Mktg. 23. Spot Radio 24. Spot T.V. 25. Weekly Newsp. 26. Yellow Page Adv.

Distr.: Intl.; Natl.
Budget Set: Oct.
Personnel:
John A. Butz *(Pres)*
Israel Tabaksblat *(VP-Mktg & Sls)*
Charles Sanfillippo *(Mgr-Sls-Export & Domestic)*
Bob Tichy *(Mgr-Mktg Svcs)*
Brands & Products:
ALLOMATIC

ALTRA HOLDINGS, INC.
300 Granite St Ste 201
Braintree, MA 02184
Tel.: (781) 917-0600
E-mail: info@altramotion.com
Web Site: www.altramotion.com
Approx. Sls.: $520,162,000
Approx. Number Employees: 2,787
Business Description:
Mechanical Power Transmission Products Designer, Marketer & Mfr; Holding Company
S.I.C.: 3568; 6719
N.A.I.C.S.: 333613; 551112
Advertising Expenditures: $1,300,000
Personnel:
Michael L. Hurt *(Chm)*
Carl R. Christenson *(Pres & CEO-Altra Indus Motion)*
Christian Storch *(CFO)*
Todd B. Patriacca *(Chief Acctg Officer, VP- Fin, Treas & Corp Controller)*
Glenn Deegan *(Gen Counsel, Sec, VP-Legal & HR-Altra Indus Motion)*
Craig Schuele *(VP-Mktg & Bus Dev-Altra Indus Motion)*

AMBAC INTERNATIONAL CORPORATION
910 Spears Creek Ct
Elgin, SC 29045
Mailing Address:
PO Box 85
Columbia, SC 29202-0085
Tel.: (803) 462-9600
Fax: (803) 735-2280
Fax: (800) 542-8230
Toll Free: (800) 628-6894
Web Site: www.ambac.net
E-Mail For Key Personnel:
Sales Director: sales@ambac.net
Approx. Number Employees: 100
Year Founded: 1987
Business Description:
Fuel Injection Equipment Mfr
S.I.C.: 3714; 3728
N.A.I.C.S.: 336312; 336413
Advertising Expenditures: $320,000
Media: 1-2-4-5-7-10-11-13-19-20
Distr.: Intl.; Natl.
Budget Set: Dec.
Personnel:
Robert Stamm *(Pres)*
Ken Smith *(Mgr-Mktg)*
Brands & Products:
AMBAC

AMERICAN AXLE & MANUFACTURING HOLDINGS, INC.
1 Dauch Dr
Detroit, MI 48211-1198
Tel.: (313) 758-2000
Fax: (313) 758-3090
E-mail: corporaterelations@aam.com
Web Site: www.aam.com
Approx. Sls.: $2,283,000,000
Approx. Number Employees: 7,850
Year Founded: 1998
Business Description:
Holding Company; Motor Vehicle Driveline, Drivetrain, Chassis & Other Automotive Components Designer & Mfr
S.I.C.: 6719; 3462; 3599; 3714
N.A.I.C.S.: 551112; 332111; 332710; 336330; 336350; 336399
Media: 2-7-10
Distr.: Intl
Personnel:
Richard E. Dauch *(Co-Founder, Chm, & CEO)*
David C. Dauch *(Pres & COO)*
Michael K. Simonte *(CFO & Exec VP-Fin)*
Patrick S. Lancaster *(Chief Admin Officer, Sec & Exec VP)*
Steven J. Proctor *(Pres-Asia & Corp VP)*
Richard Raymond *(Gen Counsel)*
John J. Bellanti *(Exec VP-Worldwide Ops)*
Curt S. Howell *(VP-Full-Frame-Vehicle Bus Unit)*
John C. Salter *(Exec Dir-Sls & Mktg)*
Thomas J. Szymanski *(Exec Dir-Mfg Plng)*
Renee Rogers *(Mgr-Comm & Media Rels)*
Brands & Products:
AAM
DELIVERING POWER
I-RIDE
SMARTBAR
TRACRITE

AMERICAN DEFENSE SYSTEMS, INC.
230 Duffy Ave
Hicksville, NY 11801
Tel.: (516) 390-5300
Fax: (516) 390-5308
E-mail: info@adsiarmor.com
Web Site: www.adsi-armor.com
Approx. Rev.: $39,519,054
Approx. Number Employees: 41
Year Founded: 2002
Business Description:
Customized Armor Solutions for Military Tactical & Non-Tactical Transport Vehicles & Construction Equipment
S.I.C.: 3795; 3531; 3714; 9711
N.A.I.C.S.: 336992; 333120; 336399; 928110
Advertising Expenditures: $117,000
Media: 7-10-17
Personnel:
Alfred M. Gray, Jr. *(Chm)*
Anthony J. Piscitelli *(CEO)*
Gary Sidorsky *(CFO)*
Kevin J. Healy *(COO & Sec)*
Fergal Foley *(Sr VP-Govt Rels & Bus Dev)*
Charles R. Pegg *(Sr VP-Program Mgmt)*
Curtis M. Taufman *(Sr VP-Engrg)*
John F. Rutledge, III *(VP-Sls)*
Roger Ward *(VP-IR & Mktg)*

AMERICAN TIRE DISTRIBUTORS HOLDINGS, INC.
(Holding of TPG Capital, L.P.)
12200 Herbert Wayne Ct Ste 150
Huntersville, NC 28078
Mailing Address:
PO Box 3145
Huntersville, NC 28070-3145
Tel.: (704) 992-2000
Fax: (704) 992-1384
Toll Free: (800) 222-1167
Web Site: www.atd-us.com
Approx. Sls.: $2,460,174,000
Approx. Number Employees: 2,500
Year Founded: 1935
Business Description:
Tires Wheels & Related Product Distr
S.I.C.: 5014; 5012
N.A.I.C.S.: 441320; 423110; 423130
Media: 4-7-13-17
Personnel:
William E. Berry *(Pres & CEO)*
David L. Dyckman *(CFO & Exec VP)*
J. Michael Gaither *(Gen Counsel & Exec VP)*
Daniel K. Brown *(Exec VP-Sls)*
Phillip E. Marrett *(Exec VP-Procurement)*
Jim Williams *(Sr VP & Mgr-Western Div)*
Roland Boyette *(Sr VP-Sls)*
Keith Calcagno *(Sr VP-Eastern Div)*
John Flowers *(Sr VP-Ops)*
Dan Seitler *(Sr VP-Procurement)*
Jason Shannon *(Sr VP-Admin & Pricing)*
Ron Sinclair *(Sr VP-Mktg)*
Rick Anthis *(Reg VP)*
David Martin *(Dir-Sales Tool & Supply)*
Brands & Products:
AMERICAN TIRE DISTRIBUTORS
ATDONLINE
ATDSERVICEBAY
CRUISERALLOY
DRIFZ
DYNATRAC
ICW
MAGNUM
PACER
TIREBUYER.COM
TIREP ROS
Advertising Agency:
Luquire George Andrews, Inc. (dba LGA)
4201 Congress St Ste 400
Charlotte, NC 28209
Tel.: (704) 552-6565
Fax: (704) 552-1972

AMERICAN VAN EQUIPMENT INC.
149 Leheigh Ave
Lakewood, NJ 08701
Tel.: (732) 905-5900
Fax: (800) 833-8266
Toll Free: (800) 526-4743
E-mail: info@americanvan.com
Web Site: www.americanvan.com
Sales Range: $25-49.9 Million
Approx. Number Employees: 310
Business Description:
Commercial Truck & Van Accessories
S.I.C.: 5013; 3429
N.A.I.C.S.: 441310; 332510
Media: 4-13
Personnel:
Charles B. Richter *(Pres)*
Joseph W. Fallon, Sr. *(VP-Fin)*
Brands & Products:
BUCKET BOSS
DELTA PRO
EZ-PALM
GOLIGHT
GUARDIAN
POSI-LOCK
POWERRACK
POWERVERTER
PROFILER
STREAMLIGHT LITEBOX
SYSTEM ONE
VETO PRO PAC
VISOR SHELF-IT

ANGUS INDUSTRIES INC.
(d/b/a Angus-Palm)
315 Airport Dr
Watertown, SD 57201-5606
Tel.: (605) 886-5681
Fax: (605) 886-6179
E-mail: info@angus-palm.com
Web Site: www.angus-palm.com
Sales Range: $75-99.9 Million
Approx. Number Employees: 730
Year Founded: 1969
Business Description:
Industrial Trucks & Tractors
S.I.C.: 3537; 3714
N.A.I.C.S.: 333924; 336399
Import Export
Media: 2-9-10
Personnel:
Robert A. Kluver *(Pres)*
William Knese *(CFO & VP-Fin & Admin)*
Marty Comes *(Sr VP-Mktg & Sr VP-Sls)*

AP EXHAUST PRODUCTS, INC.
300 Dixie Trl
Goldsboro, NC 27530
Tel.: (919) 580-2000
Fax: (919) 580-2010
E-mail: webmaster@apexhaust.com
Web Site: www.apexhaust.com
Approx. Number Employees: 300
Year Founded: 1927
Business Description:
Automotive Exhaust & Emissions Products Mfr
S.I.C.: 3714
N.A.I.C.S.: 336399
Import Export
Media: 4-5-13
Distr.: Natl.
Budget Set: Sept. -Oct.
Personnel:
Vange Proimos *(Pres)*
Dave Mozingo *(Dir-HR)*
Gary Nix *(Dir-Mktg & Product Mgmt)*
Hope Abbott *(HR-Mgr)*
Brands & Products:
BIG MAX
CHALLENGE
DIRECT FIT
ENFORCER
ENFORCER II
GOERLICH'S
MAX FIT
MERIT
MSL
PRE-CAT
PREBENT
STRAIGHT

Key to Media (For complete agency information see *The Advertising Red Books-Agencies* edition):
1. Bus. Publs. 2. Cable T.V. 3. Catalogs & Directories. 4. Co-op Adv. 5. Consumer Mags. 6. D.M. to Bus. Estab.7. D.M. to Consumers
8. Daily Newsp. 9. Exhibits/Trade Shows 10. Foreign 11. Infomercial 12. Internet Adv.13. Multimedia 14. Network Radio
15. Network T.V. 16. Newsp. Distr. Mags. 17. Other 18. Outdoor (Posters, Transit) 19. Point of Purchase20. Premiums, Novelties
21. Product Samples 22. Special Events Mktg. 23. Spot Radio 24. Spot T.V. 25. Weekly Newsp. 26. Yellow Page Adv.

AP Exhaust Products, Inc. — (Continued)

TRUCKEX
UNIVERSAL
XLERATOR
XLERATOR BIG MAX
XLERATOR ENFORCER
XLERATOR XSS

APPLIED INDUSTRIAL TECHNOLOGIES, INC.

1 Applied Plz
Cleveland, OH 44115
Tel.: (216) 426-4000
Fax: (216) 426-4845
Toll Free: (877) 279-2799
E-mail: appliedindustrial@applied.com
Web Site: www.appliedindustrial.com
E-Mail For Key Personnel:
Public Relations: jkho@applied.com
Approx. Sls.: $2,212,849,000
Approx. Number Employees: 4,640
Year Founded: 1923
Business Description:
Industrial Fluid Power & Engineered Products & Systems Distr
S.I.C.: 5085; 5082; 5084
N.A.I.C.S.: 423840; 423810; 423830
Media: 1-2-4-5-7-10-16-18-19-20-21-22-26
Personnel:
Benjamin J. Mondics *(Pres & COO)*
Neil A. Schrimsher *(CEO)*
Mark O. Eisele *(CFO, Treas & VP)*
Michael L. Coticchia *(Chief Admin Officer & VP)*
Fred D. Bauer *(Gen Counsel, Sec & VP)*
Thomas E. Arnold *(VP-Mktg & Strategic Accts)*
Richard C. Shaw *(VP-Comm & Learning)*
Bob Boyle *(Dir-Power Transmission Products-Applied Indus Technologies)*
Vickie Molenda *(Dir-Govt Ops)*
Dave Smith *(Dir-Corp Pur)*
Andy Webb *(Dir-Trng)*
Julie Kho *(Mgr-Pub Rel)*
Jody A. Chabowski *(Asst Controller)*
Alan M. Krupa *(Asst Treas)*

ARCTIC FREEZE DISCOUNT AUTO & TRUCK REPAIR

1198 East Bay Dr
Largo, FL 33770
Tel.: (727) 585-2074
Web Site: www.arcticfreezeauto.com/
Business Description:
Automobile & Truck Repair Services
S.I.C.: 7539
N.A.I.C.S.: 811198
Media: 9-13-25-29
Personnel:
Brett O'Neill *(Pres)*

ARMORED AUTOGROUP INC.

39 Old Ridgebury Rd
Danbury, CT 06810
Tel.: (203) 205-2900
Web Site: www.armoredautogroup.com
Business Description:
Automobile Performance & Appearance Products Mfr
N.A.I.C.S.: 811198; 811121
Media: 13-29
Personnel:
Derek Gordon *(Pres)*
Dave Lundstedt *(CEO)*

ARROW SAFETY DEVICE COMPANY

17 Dixon
Seaford, DE 19975
Mailing Address:
PO Box 159
Mount Holly, NJ 08060-0159
Tel.: (609) 267-1083
Fax: (609) 267-1585
Toll Free: (800) 327-2514
E-mail: arrow@jersey.net
Web Site: www.arrowsafetydevice.com
Sales Range: $1-9.9 Million
Approx. Number Employees: 50
Year Founded: 1930
Business Description:
Vehicle Lighting Systems & Accessories Mfr
S.I.C.: 3647
N.A.I.C.S.: 336321
Import Export
Media: 2-4-7-10-13
Distr.: Natl.
Budget Set: Nov.
Personnel:
Alfred W. Hopkin, Jr. *(Chm & CEO)*
Brands & Products:
ARROW

ARVINMERITOR, INC.
(Name Changed to Meritor, Inc.)

ASHLAND INC.

(Div. of Ashland Inc.)
(d/b/a Valvoline Instant Oil Change)
3499 Blazer Pkwy
Lexington, KY 40509-1850
Tel.: (859) 357-7777
Fax: (859) 357-3133
Web Site: www.vioc.com
Sales Range: $900-999.9 Million
Approx. Number Employees: 4,500
Year Founded: 1986
Business Description:
Automobile Quick Oil Change, Oil & Lubrication Service Center & Franchise
S.I.C.: 7549; 7539
N.A.I.C.S.: 811191; 811198
Media: 3-8-9-13-19-23-24
Distr.: Direct to Consumer; Natl.

AUSCO PRODUCTS, INC.

2245 Pipestone Rd
Benton Harbor, MI 49022-2425
Mailing Address:
PO Box 8787
Benton Harbor, MI 49023-8787
Tel.: (269) 926-0700
Fax: (269) 926-0817
Toll Free: (800) 253-2860
E-mail: auscoinfo@auscoproducts.com
Web Site: www.auscoproducts.com
Sales Range: $10-24.9 Million
Approx. Number Employees: 110
Year Founded: 1908
Business Description:
Braking Equipment Mfr for Off-Highway Vehicles
S.I.C.: 3714; 3523
N.A.I.C.S.: 336340; 333111
Export
Media: 2-4-6-7
Distr.: Natl.
Budget Set: May -June
Personnel:
William R. Heinrich *(Pres & CEO)*
Brands & Products:
AUSCO
Advertising Agency:
Perry Ballard Incorporated
526 Upton Dr E
Saint Joseph, MI 49085
Tel.: (269) 983-0611
Fax: (269) 983-0747
Toll Free: (800) 800-9547

AUTO GLASS SPECIALISTS, INC.

(Sub. of Belron US)
5225 Verona Rd
Madison, WI 53711-4497
Tel.: (608) 827-0101
Fax: (608) 216-7303
Toll Free: (800) 558-1000
E-mail: info@littleredtruck.com
Web Site: www.littleredtruck.com
Approx. Number Employees: 500
Year Founded: 1961
Business Description:
Vehicle Glass Repair & Replacement Services
S.I.C.: 7536
N.A.I.C.S.: 811122
Import Export
Advertising Expenditures: $2,098,196
Media: 2-3-6-8-10-18-19-20-23-24-26
Distr.: Direct to Consumer; Intl.; Natl.
Budget Set: Sept.
Personnel:
Lonn R. Schwartz *(CFO)*
Brands & Products:
AUTO GLASS SPECIALISTS

AUTOLIV NORTH AMERICA, AMERICAN TECHNICAL CENTER

(Div. of Autoliv North America)
1320 Pacific Dr
Auburn Hills, MI 48326-1569
Tel.: (248) 475-9000
Fax: (248) 475-9011
E-mail: info@autoliv.com
Web Site: www.autoliv.com
Approx. Number Employees: 300
Business Description:
Automotive Safety Systems Developer, Mfr & Seller
S.I.C.: 3714; 3559
N.A.I.C.S.: 336399; 333298
Advertising Expenditures: $300,000
Media: 2
Personnel:
Lars Westerberg *(Chm)*
Jan Carlson *(Pres & CEO)*
Halvar Jonzon *(VP-Pur)*
Jan Olsson *(VP-Res & Engrg)*
Tom Hartman *(Sr Dir-Lean Consulting & Bus Dev)*
Ray Pekar *(Dir-IR & Bus Dev)*

AUTOMOTIVE SUPPLY ASSOCIATES, INC.

129 Manchester St
Concord, NH 03301-5118
Tel.: (603) 225-4000
Fax: (603) 225-2484
E-mail: asaprodsup@asa.sanel.com
Approx. Number Employees: 375
Year Founded: 1989
Business Description:
Wholesale Distr of Automotive & Industrial Parts & Supplies
S.I.C.: 5013; 7539
N.A.I.C.S.: 423120; 811118
Media: 3-9-14-15-23-25
Personnel:
Henry Sanel *(Chm)*
George Segal *(Pres)*

AUTOSWAGE PRODUCTS, INC.

726 River Rd
Shelton, CT 06484-4848
Tel.: (203) 929-1401
Fax: (203) 929-6187
E-mail: sales@autoswage.com
Web Site: www.autoswage.com
E-Mail For Key Personnel:
Sales Director: sales@autoswage.com
Approx. Number Employees: 20
Year Founded: 1946
Business Description:
Small Metal Components Mfr
S.I.C.: 3599; 3678
N.A.I.C.S.: 332710; 334417
Import Export
Media: 2-4-7-10
Distr.: Natl.
Budget Set: July
Personnel:
David Brenton *(Owner)*
Keith Brenton *(Pres)*

AUTOZONE, INC.

123 S Front St
Memphis, TN 38103-3607
Mailing Address:
PO Box 2198
Memphis, TN 38101-2198
Tel.: (901) 495-6500
Fax: (901) 495-8300
E-mail: customer.service@autozone.com
Web Site: www.autozoneinc.com
Approx. Sls.: $7,362,618,000
Approx. Number Employees: 35,280
Year Founded: 1979
Business Description:
Retailer of Auto Parts & Accessories
S.I.C.: 5013
N.A.I.C.S.: 441310
Advertising Expenditures: $65,500,000
Media: 7-8-9-10-15-17-23-24-25-26
Personnel:
William C. Rhodes, III *(Chm, Pres & CEO)*
William T. Giles *(CFO, Exec VP-Fin, IT & Store Dev)*
Jon A. Bascom *(CIO & Sr VP)*
Robert D. Olsen *(Corp Dev Officer)*
Harry L. Goldsmith *(Gen Counsel, Sec & Exec VP)*
Charlie Pleas III *(Sr VP & Controller)*
Timothy W. Briggs *(Sr VP-HR)*
Mark A. Finestone *(Sr VP-Mdsg)*
William W. Graves *(Sr VP-Supply Chain)*
Lisa R. Kranc *(Sr VP-Mktg)*
Thomas B. Newbern *(Sr VP-Store Ops)*
Larry Roesel *(Sr VP-Comml)*
Brands & Products:
ALBANY
AUTOZONE

Key to Media (For complete agency information see *The Advertising Red Books-Agencies* edition):
1. Bus. Publs. 2. Cable T.V. 3. Catalogs & Directories. 4. Co-op Adv. 5. Consumer Mags. 6. D.M. to Bus. Estab.7. D.M. to Consumers 8. Daily Newsp. 9. Exhibits/Trade Shows 10. Foreign 11. Infomercial 12. Internet Adv.13. Multimedia 14. Network Radio 15. Network T.V. 16. Newsp. Distr. Mags. 17. Other 18. Outdoor (Posters, Transit) 19. Point of Purchase20. Premiums, Novelties 21. Product Samples 22. Special Events Mktg. 23. Spot Radio 24. Spot T.V. 25. Weekly Newsp. 26. Yellow Page Adv.

DEUTSCH
DURALAST
DURALAST GOLD
ULTRA SPARK
VALUCRAFT

Advertising Agencies:
Doner
25900 Northwestern Hwy
Southfield, MI 48075
Tel.: (248) 354-9700
Fax: (248) 827-8440
Creative

MPG
(Div. of HAVAS)
195 Broadway 12th Fl
New York, NY 10007
Tel.: (646) 587-5000
Fax: (646) 587-5005
Media Planning

Sponge, LLC
520 W Erie St Ste 400
Chicago, IL 60654
Tel.: (312) 397-8880
Fax: (312) 397-8888
Agency of Record

AXIOM AUTOMOTIVE TECHNOLOGIES
(Div. of Transtar Industries, Inc.)
6550 Hamilton Ave
Pittsburgh, PA 15206
Tel.: (412) 441-7353
Fax: (412) 441-4242
Toll Free: (800) 999-5590
Approx. Sls.: $55,000,000
Business Description:
Motor Vehicle Supplies &Transmission Replacement Parts Distr
S.I.C.: 5013; 3714
N.A.I.C.S.: 423120; 336399
Media: 4
Personnel:
Greg Gyllstrom *(CEO)*

BASSANI MANUFACTURING
2900 E La Jolla St
Anaheim, CA 92806-1305
Tel.: (714) 630-1821
Fax: (714) 630-2980
Toll Free: (866) 782-3284
E-mail: info@bassani.com
Web Site: www.bassani.com
Approx. Number Employees: 45
Year Founded: 1969
Business Description:
Mfr. of Motorcycle Exhaust Systems, Tube Bending & Display Fixtures
S.I.C.: 3599; 3498
N.A.I.C.S.: 332710; 332996
Export
Media: 2-4-20-26
Distr.: Intl.; Natl.
Budget Set: Jan.
Personnel:
Darryl Bassani *(Pres)*
Brands & Products:
AFT-CAT
BASSANI XHAUST
EQUALIZER
THE SOUND OF POWER
X-PIPE

BEAD INDUSTRIES INC.
11 Cascade Blvd
Milford, CT 06460
Tel.: (203) 301-0270
Fax: (203) 301-0280
Toll Free: (800) 297-4851
E-mail: sales@beadindustries.com
Web Site: www.beadindustries.com
E-Mail For Key Personnel:
Sales Director: sales@beadindustries.com
Approx. Number Employees: 40
Year Founded: 1914
Business Description:
Bead Chains & Custom-Designed Contact Pins Mfr
S.I.C.: 3432; 3679
N.A.I.C.S.: 332913; 334419
Export
Advertising Expenditures: $200,000
Media: 2-4-6-8-10-21
Distr.: Intl.; Natl.
Budget Set: Nov.
Personnel:
Kenneth Bryant *(Chm & CEO)*
Ron Andreoli *(Pres)*
Jill Mayer *(Controller & Mgr-Mktg)*
Brands & Products:
BEAD
BEAD CHAIN
TANDEM-PINS

BEE LINE COMPANY
(Div. of McLaughlin Body Co.)
2700 62nd St Ct
Bettendorf, IA 52722-5575
Mailing Address:
PO Box 130
Bettendorf, IA 52722
Tel.: (563) 332-4066
Fax: (563) 332-6517
Toll Free: (800) 728-7828
E-mail: beeline@beeline-co.com
Web Site: www.beeline-co.com
Approx. Number Employees: 100
Year Founded: 1927
Business Description:
Mfr. of Truck Wheel Alignment & Wheel Correction Equipment for Autos & Heavy Duty Trucks
S.I.C.: 3559
N.A.I.C.S.: 333298
Import Export
Advertising Expenditures: $700,000
Media: 2-4-5-6-7-8-10-11-13-22-26
Distr.: Direct to Consumer; Natl.
Budget Set: Nov.
Personnel:
Charles L. Smith *(Pres)*
W.L. Storm *(CFO)*
Lee McLaughlin *(VP-Sls)*
Mick Dalton *(Dir-Mktg)*
Rick Lund *(Plant Mgr)*
Fred A. Badure *(Mgr-Training)*
Celeste Pratt *(Mgr-Accts)*
Brands & Products:
BEE LINE
BEELINER
LASER'S EDGE
MULTIPULL
RED DOT TANDEM ALIGNER
STINGER

BEHR AMERICA, INC.
(Sub. of Behr GmbH & Co. KG)
2700 Daley Dr
Troy, MI 48083
Tel.: (248) 743-3700
Fax: (248) 743-3701
Web Site: www.behrgroup.com
Approx. Number Employees: 260
Business Description:
Mfr. of Air Conditioning & Engine Cooling Products
S.I.C.: 3714
N.A.I.C.S.: 336399
Personnel:
Markus Flik *(Chm)*
Heinz Otto *(Pres & CEO)*
Indira Sadikovic *(Mgr-Comm)*
Advertising Agency:
AutoCom Associates
74 W Long Lk Rd Ste 103
Bloomfield Hills, MI 48304-2770
Tel.: (248) 647-8621
Fax: (248) 642-2110

BELANGER, INC.
1001 Doheny Ct
Northville, MI 48167-1957
Tel.: (248) 349-7010
Fax: (248) 349-2309
Toll Free: (866) 4TUNNEL
E-mail: info@belangerinc.com
Web Site: www.belangerinc.com
Approx. Number Employees: 212
Year Founded: 1969
Business Description:
Car Wash Equipment Mfr
S.I.C.: 3589
N.A.I.C.S.: 333319
Media: 2-4-7-10-13
Personnel:
Christina Alexander *(Mgr-Mktg)*
Brands & Products:
AIRBLADE
AIRCANNON
BELANGER
BUILD-A-WASH
CHAMELEON
CORRELATOR
DURASCRUBBER
DURASHINER
DURATRANS XD
ENDURO CLASS 60
FREESTYLER
GYRO WRAP
HYBRID HYDRO MITTER
INSTA-KLEEN
INTEGRA
MIXSTIR
MULTI-PURPOSE ARCH
NEON STIK
PIVOTING WHEEL STINGER
PREP JET SYSTEM
PRO CLASS 100
QUAD WAVE MITTER
QUICKFIRE
RAIN ARCH
RAPID TURNKEY
ROCKER SPIN CLEAN
SIGNATURE
SINGLE & TRIPLE FOAM PODS
SINGLE FOAM POD
TIRE WASHER
TITAN VPS
TOP WHEEL
TRIPLE FOAM POD
TRIPLE FOAM STICKS
UNI-ARCH
V-MAX
VECTOR RAPID WASH
WAVE ACROSS
WAVE FULL SIDE WASHER
WAVE LOW SIDE WASHER

BESTOP, INC.
(Sub. of Magna International Inc.)
2100 W Midway Blvd
Broomfield, CO 80020-1626
Mailing Address:
PO Box 307
Broomfield, CO 80038-0307
Tel.: (303) 465-1755
Fax: (303) 466-3436
Toll Free: (800) 845-3567
E-mail: csbestop@bestop.com
Web Site: www.bestop.com
Approx. Rev.: $65,000,000
Approx. Number Employees: 60
Year Founded: 1953
Business Description:
Soft Tops, Hard Tops & Accessories for Small Sport Utility Vehicles Mfr
S.I.C.: 3714
N.A.I.C.S.: 336399
Import Export
Media: 2-4-5-6-7-10-17-19-20-22-26
Distr.: Intl.; Natl.
Budget Set: Sept.
Personnel:
Jim Chick *(Dir-Sls & Mktg)*
Brands & Products:
EXTENDATRUNK
HALFTOP
HOSS
INSTATRUNK
REPLACE-A-TOP
SUNPORT
SUNRIDER
SUPERTOP
TIGERTOP
TRAILMAX

BG PRODUCTS, INC.
740 S Wichita St
Wichita, KS 67213
Tel.: (316) 265-2686
Fax: (316) 265-1082
Web Site: www.bgprod.com
Sales Range: $300-349.9 Million
Approx. Number Employees: 138
Year Founded: 1971
Business Description:
Fuel Additives, Lubricating Oils & Greases Mfr
S.I.C.: 2992; 2899
N.A.I.C.S.: 324191; 325998
Media: 3-4-10
Personnel:
Galen Myers *(CEO)*
Ron Garcia *(CFO)*
Rob Richardson *(COO)*
Brands & Products:
BG
BG 44K POWER ENHANCER
BG BIG DAWG
BG CF5
BG FRIGI-CHARGE
BG FRIGI-CLEAN
BG FRIGI-FLUSH
BG FRIGI-FRESH
BG INJECT-A-FLUSH
BG ISC INDUCTION SYSTEM CLEANER
BG MGC
BG MOA
BG SHEAR POWER
BG SYNCRO SHIFT
BG UNIVERSAL FRIGI-QUIET
BG UNIVERSAL SUPER COOL
WAKE RUNNER

BIG O TIRES, INC.
(Sub. of TBC Corporation)
12650 E Briarwood Ave Ste 2D
Centennial, CO 80112

Key to Media (For complete agency information see *The Advertising Red Books-Agencies* edition):
1. Bus. Publs. 2. Cable T.V. 3. Catalogs & Directories. 4. Co-op Adv. 5. Consumer Mags. 6. D.M. to Bus. Estab.7. D.M. to Consumers
8. Daily Newsp. 9. Exhibits/Trade Shows 10. Foreign 11. Infomercial 12. Internet Adv.13. Multimedia 14. Network Radio
15. Network T.V. 16. Newsp. Distr. Mags. 17. Other 18. Outdoor (Posters, Transit) 19. Point of Purchase20. Premiums, Novelties
21. Product Samples 22. Special Events Mktg. 23. Spot Radio 24. Spot T.V. 25. Weekly Newsp. 26. Yellow Page Adv.

Big O Tires, Inc. — (Continued)

Tel.: (303) 728-5500
Fax: (303) 728-5700
Toll Free: (800) 321-2446
E-mail: franchise@bigotires.com
Web Site: www.bigotires.com
E-Mail For Key Personnel:
Sales Director: sales@bigotires.com
Approx. Number Employees: 90
Year Founded: 1962
Business Description:
Franchisor of Tire Retail Centers
S.I.C.: 5014
N.A.I.C.S.: 441320
Import
Advertising Expenditures: $16,000,000
Media: 2-3-8-9-13-18-19-22-23-24-25-26
Distr.: Reg.
Personnel:
Kevin Kormondy *(COO & Exec VP)*
Susan B. Hendee *(Gen Counsel)*
Kim McBee *(Dir-Mktg)*
Advertising Agencies:
Barkley
1740 Main St
Kansas City, MO 64108
Tel.: (816) 842-1500

Big O Tires
12650 E Briarwood Ave Ste 2D
Centennial, CO 80112
Tel.: (303) 728-5500
Fax: (303) 728-5672
Toll Free: (800) 321-2446

BOMBARDIER RECREATIONAL PRODUCTS, INC.

(Holding of Bain Capital, LLC)
726 Saint-Joseph St
Valcourt, QC J0E 2L0, Canada
Tel.: (450) 532-2211
Fax: (450) 532-6303
Web Site: www.brp.com
Approx. Number Employees: 110
Business Description:
Personal Watercraft, Boats & All-Terrain Vehicles Mfr
S.I.C.: 3799; 3732
N.A.I.C.S.: 336999; 336612
Personnel:
Jose Boisjoli *(Pres-Bombardier Recreational Products)*
Johanne Denault *(Mgr-Corp Comm)*
Brands & Products:
EVINRUDE
EVINRUDE E TEC
GSX
JOHNSON
LYNX
MINI Z
ROTAX
SEA-DOO
SKI-DOO
SPEEDSTER
SPORTSTER
SUMMIT
Advertising Agencies:
Campbell-Ewald
30400 Van Dyke Ave
Warren, MI 48093-2368
Tel.: (586) 574-3400
Fax: (586) 575-9925

Cramer-Krasselt
246 E Chicago St
Milwaukee, WI 53202
Tel.: (414) 227-3500
Fax: (414) 276-8710
Evinrude

BOSTON GEAR

(Group of ALTRA INDUSTRIAL MOTION, INC.)
300 Granite St
Braintree, MA 02184
Tel.: (781) 917-0600
Fax: (781) 843-0615
Toll Free: (800) 999-9860
E-mail: info@altramotion.com
Web Site: www.bostongear.com
E-Mail For Key Personnel:
Marketing Director: marketing@bostongear.com
Sales Range: $25-49.9 Million
Approx. Number Employees: 100
Year Founded: 1877
Business Description:
Bearings, Pillow Blocks, Gears, Sprockets, Fluid Power Components, Roller Chain, Speed Reducers, Electric Motors, Clutch Brakes & Universal Joints
S.I.C.: 3566; 3728
N.A.I.C.S.: 333612; 336413
Media: 7-10-17
Personnel:
Gerald P. Ferris *(Gen Mgr-Sls & Mktg)*
Craig Schuele *(Dir-Mktg)*
Brands & Products:
BEAR-N-BRONZ
BOST-BRONZ
OPTIMOUNT
RADIOTROL

BOSTROM SEATING INC

(Sub. of Commercial Vehicle Group, Inc.)
50 Nances Creek Blvd
Piedmont, AL 36272
Mailing Address:
PO Box 566
Piedmont, AL 36272
Tel.: (256) 447-9051
Fax: (256) 447-2038
Toll Free: (800) 459-7328
Web Site: www.bostromseating.com
Sales Range: $250-299.9 Million
Approx. Number Employees: 650
Year Founded: 1935
Business Description:
Truck & Off-Highway Vehicle Suspension Seats
S.I.C.: 2396
N.A.I.C.S.: 336360
Export
Media: 2-7-13
Distr.: Intl.; Natl.
Budget Set: Aug.
Brands & Products:
LIBERTY II
ROUTEMASTER
STATIC
TRANS-AIRE
VIKING T-BAR

BRIDGESTONE/FIRESTONE NORTH AMERICAN TIRE, LLC

(Div. of Bridgestone Americas Holding, Inc.)
535 Marriott Dr Ste 140990
Nashville, TN 37214-5092
Tel.: (615) 937-1000
Fax: (615) 872-1599
Toll Free: (800) 543-5000
Web Site: www.bridgestone-firestone.com
Approx. Number Employees: 5,000
Year Founded: 1990
Business Description:
Tire Mfr & Sales
S.I.C.: 3011; 5014
N.A.I.C.S.: 326211; 441320
Personnel:
Philip Dobbs *(CMO)*
Melissa McGuire *(Gen Counsel & VP)*
Phil Pacsi *(VP-Mktg)*
Brands & Products:
TRANSFORCE
Advertising Agencies:
Dentsu America, Inc.
32 Ave of the Americas 16th Fl
New York, NY 10013
Tel.: (212) 397-3333
Fax: (212) 397-3322

Levelwing Media
35 W 31st St
New York, NY 10001
Tel.: (646) 216-8320
Fax: (917) 591-7157

BRIGGS & STRATTON CORPORATION

12301 W Wirth St
Wauwatosa, WI 53222-2110
Mailing Address:
PO Box 702
Milwaukee, WI 53201-0702
Tel.: (414) 259-5333
Fax: (414) 259-5773
Web Site: www.briggsandstratton.com
Approx. Sls.: $2,109,998,000
Approx. Number Employees: 6,716
Year Founded: 1909
Business Description:
Gasoline Engines for Outdoor Power Equipment
S.I.C.: 3511; 3524
N.A.I.C.S.: 333611; 333112
Export
Advertising Expenditures: $25,100,000
Media: 2-4-5-7-10-13-15-19-20-21-24-26
Distr.: Intl.; Natl.
Budget Set: May -Sept.
Personnel:
Todd J. Teske *(Chm, Pres & CEO)*
David J. Rodgers *(CFO & Sr VP)*
Harold L. Redman *(Pres-Products Grp & Sr VP)*
Joseph C. Wright *(Pres-Engine Grp & Sr VP)*
Robert F. Heath *(Gen Counsel, Sec & VP)*
James E. Breen *(Sr VP)*
William H. Reitman *(Sr VP-Bus Dev & Customer Svcs)*
Thomas R. Savage *(Sr VP-Admin)*
Edward J. Wadja, II *(VP & Gen Mgr-Intl)*
Randall R. Carpenter *(VP-Mktg)*
Troy Blewett *(Dir-Dealer Channel Mktg)*
Bob Hurd *(Product Mgr-Standby Power)*
Brands & Products:
BRIGGS & STRATTON
BRUTE
CLASSIC
CRAFTSMAN
FERRIS
GE
I/C
INDUSTRIAL PLUS
INTEK
JOHN DEERE
MOST VANGUARD
MURRAY
THE POWER WITHIN
Q45
SIMPLICITY
SNAPPER
SPRINT
TROY-BILT
VANGUARD
VICTA
Advertising Agencies:
Cramer-Krasselt
225 N Michigan Ave
Chicago, IL 60601-7601
Tel.: (312) 616-9600
Fax: (312) 616-3839
(Small Gasoline Engines)

Marx McClellan Thrun
(d/b/a MMT)
207 E Buffalo St Ste 643
Milwaukee, WI 53202
Tel.: (414) 277-7743
Fax: (414) 277-7784

BURGESS-NORTON MANUFACTURING COMPANY

(Div. of AMSTED Industries Incorporated)
737 Peyton St
Geneva, IL 60134-2150
Tel.: (630) 232-4100
Fax: (630) 232-3734
Web Site: www.burgessnorton.com
Approx. Number Employees: 500
Year Founded: 1903
Business Description:
Piston Pins & Powder Metal Parts, Dulcite & Gray Iron Castings & Assembled Parts Mfr
S.I.C.: 8711
N.A.I.C.S.: 541330
Export
Advertising Expenditures: $50,000
Media: 2-7
Distr.: Natl.
Budget Set: Oct.
Personnel:
Tom Stockwell, III *(Dir-Global Sls)*
Brands & Products:
BN

CANADIAN TIRE CORPORATION LIMITED

2180 Yonge Street
PO Box 770
Toronto, ON M4P 2VB, Canada
Tel.: (416) 480-3000
Fax: (416) 487-6512
E-mail: investor.relations@cantire.com
Web Site: www.canadiantire.ca
Approx. Rev.: $8,501,303,820
Approx. Number Employees: 7,689
Year Founded: 1922

Key to Media (For complete agency information see *The Advertising Red Books-Agencies* edition):
1. Bus. Publs. 2. Cable T.V. 3. Catalogs & Directories. 4. Co-op Adv. 5. Consumer Mags. 6. D.M. to Bus. Estab.7. D.M. to Consumers
8. Daily Newsp. 9. Exhibits/Trade Shows 10. Foreign 11. Infomercial 12. Internet Adv.13. Multimedia 14. Network Radio
15. Network T.V. 16. Newsp. Distr. Mags. 17. Other 18. Outdoor (Posters, Transit) 19. Point of Purchase20. Premiums, Novelties
21. Product Samples 22. Special Events Mktg. 23. Spot Radio 24. Spot T.V. 25. Weekly Newsp. 26. Yellow Page Adv.

Business Description:
Automotive Parts & Accessories Retailer
S.I.C.: 5013
N.A.I.C.S.: 441310
Advertising Expenditures: $5,500,000
Media: 4-8-10-18-19
Personnel:
Maureen J. Sabia *(Chm)*
Stephen G. Wetmore *(Pres & CEO)*
Marco Marrone *(CFO & Exec VP)*
Kristine Freudenthaler *(CIO & Sr VP-IT)*
G. Michael Arnett *(Pres-Canadian Tire Retail)*
Dean McCann *(Pres-Tire Fin Svcs-Canada)*
Paul Wilson *(Pres-Marks Work Wearhouse)*
Robyn Collver *(Gen Counsel, Sec & Sr VP)*
J. How Thomas *(VP-Fin Strategy, Performance & Officef)*
Patrick R. Sinnott *(Exec VP-Tech & Supply)*
Stanley W. Pasternak *(Sr VP-Fin)*
Sharon Patterson *(Sr VP-HR)*
Kenneth Silver *(Sr VP-Corporate Strategy & Real Estate)*
T. J. Flood *(VP-Mdsg)*
Michelle Ghandour *(Mgr-Comm)*
Brands & Products:
CANADIAN TIRE
CANADIAN TIRE COMMERCIAL LINK
CANADIAN TIRE FOUNDATION FOR FAMILIES
CANADIAN TIRE JUMPSTART
CANADIAN TIRE MONEY
FOR DAYS LIKE TODAY
MOTOMASTER
OPTIONS
YARDWORKS
Advertising Agencies:
Euro RSCG Discovery
372 Danbury Rd Ste 100
Wilton, CT 06897
Tel.: (203) 563-3300
Fax: (203) 563-3435

James Hoggan & Associates, Inc.
#510-1125 Howe St
Vancouver, BC V6Z 2K8, Canada
Tel.: (604) 739-7500
Fax: (604) 736-9902

Watt International, Inc.
300 Bayview Ave
Toronto, ON M5A 3R7, Canada
Tel.: (416) 364-9384
Fax: (416) 364-1098

CAR-X ASSOCIATES CORP.
(Sub. of Tuffy Associates Corporation)
1375 E Woodfield Rd Ste 500
Schaumburg, IL 60173
Tel.: (847) 273-8938
Fax: (847) 619-3310
Web Site: www.carx.com
Approx. Number Employees: 14
Business Description:
Automotive Repair Services
S.I.C.: 7533
N.A.I.C.S.: 811112
Media: 8-9-23-24-26
Budget Set: Nov.
Personnel:
Kenneth Smith *(Dir-Acct Svcs)*

CARFAX INC.
(Sub. of R.L. Polk & Co.)
5860 Trinity Pkwy Ste 600
Centreville, VA 20120
Tel.: (703) 934-2664
Fax: (703) 218-2853
Web Site: www.carfax.com
Approx. Number Employees: 291
Business Description:
Vehicle History Information Services
S.I.C.: 7389
N.A.I.C.S.: 519190
Media: 23-24
Personnel:
Stephen R. Polk *(Chm)*
Richard Raines *(Pres)*
Scott Fredericks *(VP-Mktg)*
Lan Luu *(VP-Fin)*
Larry Gamache *(Dir-Comm)*
Jeannie Moran *(Dir-Consumer Mktg)*
Brands & Products:
CARFAX
CARFAX BUYBACK GUARANTEE
CUSTOMER RATINGS & COMMENTS
HOT LISTINGS
LEMON CHECK
RECALL CHECK
RECORD CHECK
SAFETY & RELIABILITY REPORT
TALKING CAR
VEHICLE HISTORY REPORT
WARRANTY CHECK
Advertising Agencies:
PointRoll Inc.
951 E Hector St
Conshohocken, PA 19428
Tel.: (267) 558-1300
Fax: (267) 285-1141
Toll Free: (800) 203-6956

Zimmerman Advertising
2200 W Commercial Blvd Ste 300
Fort Lauderdale, FL 33309-3064
Tel.: (954) 644-4000
Fax: (954) 731-2977
Toll Free: (800) 248-8522

CARLISLE POWER TRANSMISSION PRODUCTS, INC.
(Unit of Carlisle Power Transmission Products, Inc.)
2601 West Butterfield Rd
Springfield, MO 65807
Mailing Address:
PO Box 630
Miamisburg, OH 45343-0630
Tel.: (417) 881-7440
Fax: (417) 881-2367
Toll Free: (866) 773-2926
Web Site: www.cptbelts.com
Sales Range: $200-249.9 Million
Approx. Number Employees: 900
Year Founded: 1905
Business Description:
Automotive & Industrial Belt Mfr
S.I.C.: 3052
N.A.I.C.S.: 326220
Export
Media: 2-6
Distr.: Natl.
Budget Set: Sept.
Personnel:
Dennis McCambridge *(VP-Sls & Mktg)*

CEQUENT TRAILER PRODUCTS, INC.
(Sub. of TRIMAS CORPORATION)
1050 Indianhead Dr
Mosinee, WI 54455
Mailing Address:
PO Box 577
West Bend, WI 53095-0577
Tel.: (877) 208-2548
Fax: (715) 693-1799
E-mail: ctpmail@cequentgroup.com
Web Site: www.cequentgroup.com
E-Mail For Key Personnel:
President: SHazlett@wesbar.com
Sales Range: $75-99.9 Million
Approx. Number Employees: 200
Year Founded: 1934
Business Description:
Mfr of Marine, Agricultural & Industrial Trailer Components; Lights, Wire Harnesses, Hub & Grease Caps & Boat Ladders
S.I.C.: 3799; 3569
N.A.I.C.S.: 336999; 333999
Import Export
Media: 2-4-5-6-10-11-13-17-19-20-22
Distr.: Natl.
Budget Set: Aug.
Brands & Products:
BEARING SAVER
STOWAWAY
TITE-LITE

CERION, LLC
2424 John Daly Rd
Inkster, MI 48141
Tel.: (313) 785-5956
Fax: (313) 785-3546
Web Site: www.cerionllc.com
Business Description:
Holding Company
S.I.C.: 6719
N.A.I.C.S.: 551112
Advertising Agency:
P2R Associates
39201 Schoolcraft Rd Ste B-15
Livonia, MI 48150
Tel.: (248) 348-2464
Fax: (248) 348-2465

CHAMPION LABORATORIES, INC.
(Holding of United Components, Inc.)
200 S 4th St
Albion, IL 62806-1313
Tel.: (618) 445-6011
Fax: (618) 445-4040
Toll Free: (800) 851-3641
E-mail: hotline@champlabs.com
Web Site: www.champlabs.com
Approx. Number Employees: 1,200
Year Founded: 1955
Business Description:
Mfr. of Oil, Air, Fuel, Transmission & Cabin Air Filters & Dust Collector Filters
S.I.C.: 3714; 3564
N.A.I.C.S.: 336399; 333412
Import Export
Advertising Expenditures: $500,000
Media: 2-4-5-7-8-9-10-17-18-19-21
Distr.: Intl.
Budget Set: Oct.
Personnel:
Wolfgang Winzer *(Pres)*
John Gaither *(VP-Engrg)*
Pete Haskell *(Dir-Heavy Duty Sls-North America)*
Don Rigg *(Dir-Product Dev)*
Michael Tate *(Dir-Heavy Duty Sls-Canada)*
Brands & Products:
CHAMP
ECORE
EUROFILTER
LUBER-FINER

CHICAGO-WILCOX MFG. COMPANY, INC.
16928 State St
South Holland, IL 60473
Tel.: (708) 339-5000
Fax: (708) 339-9876
E-mail: sales@chicagowilcox.com
Web Site: www.chicagowilcox.com
E-Mail For Key Personnel:
Sales Director: sales@chicagowilcox.com
Approx. Number Employees: 40
Year Founded: 1906
Business Description:
Gaskets, Metal Stampings Mfr
S.I.C.: 3053; 3499
N.A.I.C.S.: 339991; 332999
Media: 2-4-10
Distr.: Natl.
Budget Set: Nov.
Personnel:
Steve C. Anthony *(Pres)*
Mike Sullivan *(Dir-Mfg)*
Hank Schneider *(Mgr-Sls)*
Brands & Products:
SUPER X
WILCOID
WILSEAL
Advertising Agency:
Fred H. Ebersold, Inc.
6040 Main St
Downers Grove, IL 60516
Tel.: (630) 512-9922
Fax: (630) 512-0033
(Whole Line)

CLAUS ETTENSBERGER CORPORATION
10349 Santa Monica Blvd
West Los Angeles, CA 90025
Tel.: (310) 767-1111
Fax: (310) 203-3909
Toll Free: (800) 766-0064
E-mail: info@cecwheels.com
Web Site: www.cecwills.com
Approx. Number Employees: 45
Year Founded: 1990
Business Description:
Luxury Automotive Accessories, Customizing & Tuning
S.I.C.: 5013
N.A.I.C.S.: 423120
Media: 6-10

CLORE AUTOMOTIVE LLC
8735 Rosehill Rd Ste 220
Lenexa, KS 66215
Tel.: (913) 310-1050
Tel.: (913) 310-1053
Fax: (913) 310-1075
Fax: (800) 716-6531
Toll Free: (800) 328-2921
E-mail: sales@cloreautomotive.com
Web Site: www.cloreautomotive.com
E-Mail For Key Personnel:
Sales Director: sales@cloreautomotive.com

Key to Media (For complete agency information see *The Advertising Red Books-Agencies* edition):
1. Bus. Publs. 2. Cable T.V. 3. Catalogs & Directories. 4. Co-op Adv. 5. Consumer Mags. 6. D.M. to Bus. Estab.7. D.M. to Consumers
8. Daily Newsp. 9. Exhibits/Trade Shows 10. Foreign 11. Infomercial 12. Internet Adv.13. Multimedia 14. Network Radio
15. Network T.V. 16. Newsp. Distr. Mags. 17. Other 18. Outdoor (Posters, Transit) 19. Point of Purchase20. Premiums, Novelties
21. Product Samples 22. Special Events Mktg. 23. Spot Radio 24. Spot T.V. 25. Weekly Newsp. 26. Yellow Page Adv.

Clore Automotive LLC — (Continued)

Approx. Number Employees: 100
Business Description:
Electric Arc Welders, Battery Chargers, Antifreeze, Recycling Machines & Industrial Truck Equipment
S.I.C.: 3612; 3699
N.A.I.C.S.: 335311; 335999
Media: 2-4-5-7-8-10-13-19-26
Personnel:
Jim Chasim *(Pres & CEO)*
Mike Canipe *(CFO & Exec VP)*
Brands & Products:
BOOSTER PAC
JUMP-N-CARRY
SOLAR
T-TECH
TRANSOID
TRUCK PAC
VIPER

COLE HERSEE COMPANY
(Sub. of Littelfuse, Inc.)
20 Old Colony Ave
Boston, MA 02127-2467
Tel.: (617) 268-2100
Fax: (617) 268-9490
E-mail: marketing@colehersee.com
Web Site: www.colehersee.com
E-Mail For Key Personnel:
President: rmayer@colehersee.com
Public Relations: gmarsden@colehersee.com
Approx. Number Employees: 212
Year Founded: 1924
Business Description:
Mfr of Vehicle Electrical Components, Digital Switches, Connectors & Related Electronic Products
S.I.C.: 3643; 3613; 3714
N.A.I.C.S.: 335931; 335313; 336399
Import Export
Media: 2-4-7-13-19
Personnel:
Robert L. Mayer *(Pres)*
Gary Keefe *(Gen Mgr-Sls)*
John Wu *(Dir-Engrg)*
James Ruffin *(Mgr-Office Svcs)*
John Curry *(Mgr-Gen Acctg)*
Ray Dobry *(Mgr-Market Segment)*
Philip E. Grasso *(Mgr-Customer Svc)*
Les Johnston *(Mgr-OEM Technical Sls-Natl)*
Graeme Marsden *(Mgr-Mktg & Commun)*
Jim Mueller *(Mgr-Credit)*
Jing Rong *(Mgr-Pur)*
Mike Wilkinson *(Mgr-HR)*
Brands & Products:
CH
SURESTART
Advertising Agency:
McNeil, Gray & Rice
1 Washington Mall
Boston, MA 02108-2603
Tel.: (617) 367-0100
Fax: (617) 367-0160

COLONY TIRE CORPORATION
1415 N Broad St
Edenton, NC 27932-9613
Mailing Address:
PO Box 827
Edenton, NC 27932-0827
Tel.: (252) 482-8080
Fax: (252) 482-7626
Web Site: www.colonytire.com
Approx. Number Employees: 365
Year Founded: 1976
Business Description:
Whslr, Retailer & Servicer of Tires
S.I.C.: 5014
N.A.I.C.S.: 441320; 423130
Import Export
Media: 7-8-9-13-23-24-25
Personnel:
Charles A. Creighton *(CEO)*
Andrew Bergeron *(COO & Exec VP)*

COMMERCIAL VEHICLE GROUP, INC.
7800 Walton Pkwy
New Albany, OH 43054
Tel.: (614) 289-5360
Fax: (614) 289-5361
E-mail: info@cvgrp.com
Web Site: www.cvgrp.com
Approx. Sls.: $597,779,000
Approx. Number Employees: 5,430
Year Founded: 2002
Business Description:
Commercial Vehicle Interior Systems Supplier
S.I.C.: 3711; 2396; 3231; 3714
N.A.I.C.S.: 336211; 327215; 336360; 336399
Media: 7
Personnel:
Richard A. Snell *(Chm)*
Mervin Dunn *(Pres & CEO)*
Chad M. Utrup *(CFO)*
Gerald L. Armstrong *(Pres-Structures & Interior Trim Systems)*
Gordon Boyd *(Pres-Seating Sys)*
Kevin R. L. Frailey *(Pres-Electrical Sys)*
Milton D. Kniss *(Exec VP & Gen Mgr-Seating Sys)*
John M. Hyre *(Dir-IR & Corp Comm)*
Brands & Products:
AERODYNAMIC MOTOMIRROR
BACKCYCLER
BATLOCK
CAMERAWASH
EASY-AIRE
KEYFREE
LIGHTWASH
MOTO FOUR
MOTO MIRROR
PRUSTMAN
ROADWATCH 3
ROADWATCH SS
TRADITIONAL STYLE MOTOMIRROR
VALEO ROCKER SWITCH DPDT
VALEO ROCKER SWITCH SPST
VALEO SWITCH

COMPETITION SPECIALTIES INC.
2402 W Vly Hwy N
Auburn, WA 98001
Tel.: (253) 833-6211
Fax: (253) 833-7227
Web Site: www.compspecialties.com
Approx. Sls.: $18,000,000
Approx. Number Employees: 130
Year Founded: 1966
Business Description:
High Performance Automotive Parts & Off-Road Accessories Distr & Whslr
S.I.C.: 5013
N.A.I.C.S.: 423120
Media: 10
Personnel:
Nancy Woomer *(Chm)*
Ken Woomer *(Pres & CEO)*
Tom McClosky *(CFO, Treas & Sec)*
Tom Cline *(Mgr-Natl Sls)*
T. C. Howe *(Mgr-Canada Sls & Phone Sls)*
Tom Klein *(Mgr-Program Accts)*
Jim Lucero *(Mgr-Ops)*
Brands & Products:
CSI

CONTINENTAL AUTOMOTIVE SYSTEMS US, INC.
(Plant of Continental Automotive Systems US, Inc.)
2400 Executive Hills Blvd
Auburn Hills, MI 48326
Tel.: (248) 209-4000
Fax: (248) 209-4040
E-mail: contact_us@usa.contiteves.com
Web Site: usa.vdo.com
Approx. Number Employees: 1,500
Year Founded: 1954
Business Description:
Automotive Electronics & Safety Equipment Developer & Mfr
S.I.C.: 3714
N.A.I.C.S.: 336399
Import Export
Media: 2-4-5-7-10
Distr.: Natl.
Budget Set: Dec.

CORSA PERFORMANCE
140 Blaze Industrial Pkwy
Berea, OH 44017
Tel.: (440) 891-0999
Fax: (440) 891-1868
Toll Free: (800) 486-0999
E-mail: sales@corsaperf.com
Web Site: www.corsaperf.com
E-Mail For Key Personnel:
Sales Director: sales@corsaperf.com
Approx. Number Employees: 50
Business Description:
Exhaust System Mfr
S.I.C.: 7533
N.A.I.C.S.: 811112
Advertising Agency:
McCullough Public Relations, Inc.
3570 Executive Dr Ste 104
Uniontown, OH 44685
Tel.: (330) 244-9980
Fax: (330) 244-9981

COTTMAN TRANSMISSION, LLC
(Holding of AMERICAN CAPITAL, LTD.)
201 Gibraltar Nasa Rd Ste 150
Horsham, PA 19044
Tel.: (215) 643-5885
Fax: (215) 643-5800
Toll Free: (866) COTTMAN
E-mail: info@cottman.com
Web Site: www.cottman.com
Sales Range: $10-24.9 Million
Approx. Number Employees: 52
Year Founded: 1962
Business Description:
Franchiser of Automotive Transmission Centers
S.I.C.: 7537
N.A.I.C.S.: 811113
Media: 3-8-9-13-18-23-24-25-26
Distr.: Natl.
Brands & Products:
COTTMAN
Advertising Agencies:
Nationwide Newspapers Advertising, LLC
5955 Masters Blvd
Orlando, FL 32819
Tel.: (407) 909-1644
Fax: (407) 909-1748

The Ross Agency
201 Gibraltar Rd Ste 149
Horsham, PA 19044
Tel.: (888) 815-7536
Fax: (800) 859-2349
Toll Free: (888) 815-7536

CPI HOLDINGS, LLC
(Sub. of CASH TECHNOLOGIES, INC.)
2005 W Ave B St
Hope, AR 71801-8882
Mailing Address:
PO Box 579
Hope, AR 71802-0579
Tel.: (870) 777-8821
Fax: (870) 777-1379
E-mail: info@championparts.com
Web Site: www.championparts.com
Sales Range: $10-24.9 Million
Approx. Number Employees: 291
Year Founded: 1946
Business Description:
Automotive Truck & Tractor Parts Mfr
S.I.C.: 3714; 3711
N.A.I.C.S.: 336399; 336211
Import Export
Advertising Expenditures: $450,000
Media: 2-4-10
Distr.: Natl.
Budget Set: Nov.
Personnel:
Jerry A. Bragiel *(Pres)*

CSK AUTO CORP.
(Sub. of O'Reilly Automotive Inc.)
645 E Missouri Ave Ste 400
Phoenix, AZ 85012-1373
Tel.: (602) 265-9200
Fax: (602) 631-7321
E-mail: contactus@cskauto.com
Web Site: www.cskauto.com
Approx. Sls.: $1,851,647,000
Approx. Number Employees: 9,100
Year Founded: 1968
Business Description:
Automotive Parts & Accessories Retailer
S.I.C.: 5013
N.A.I.C.S.: 441310
Import Export
Advertising Expenditures: $50,200,000
Media: 3-9-14-15-18-19-22-23-24-26
Distr.: Reg.
Personnel:
Larry Ellis *(Sr VP-Logistics)*
Advertising Agency:
Acento Advertising, Inc.
2254 S Sepulveda Blvd
Los Angeles, CA 90064
Tel.: (310) 943-8300
Fax: (310) 943-8310

CUSTOM ACCESSORIES INC.
6440 W Howard St
Niles, IL 60714-3302

Key to Media (For complete agency information see *The Advertising Red Books-Agencies* edition):
1. Bus. Publs. 2. Cable T.V. 3. Catalogs & Directories. 4. Co-op Adv. 5. Consumer Mags. 6. D.M. to Bus. Estab.7. D.M. to Consumers 8. Daily Newsp. 9. Exhibits/Trade Shows 10. Foreign 11. Infomercial 12. Internet Adv.13. Multimedia 14. Network Radio 15. Network T.V. 16. Newsp. Distr. Mags. 17. Other 18. Outdoor (Posters, Transit) 19. Point of Purchase20. Premiums, Novelties 21. Product Samples 22. Special Events Mktg. 23. Spot Radio 24. Spot T.V. 25. Weekly Newsp. 26. Yellow Page Adv.

Tel.: (847) 966-6900
Fax: (847) 966-9650
Toll Free: (800) 962-6676
E-mail: cainfo@causa.com
Web Site: www.causa.com
Approx. Number Employees: 160
Year Founded: 1974
Business Description:
Interior & Exterior Automotive Accessories Distr
S.I.C.: 5013
N.A.I.C.S.: 423120
Import Export
Media: 4-19
Personnel:
Abe J. Matthew *(Chm)*
Kenneth S. Matthew *(Pres & CEO)*
Brands & Products:
AIR MASTER
CONCEPT XT
CUSTOM ACCESSORIES
ELECTRO-TEK
MASTER
MASTER TIRE REPAIR
SKULL
YELLOW JACKET

DANA CANADA CORPORATION
(Sub. of Dana Holding Corporation)
PO Box 3029
Saint Catharines, ON L2R 7k9, Canada
Tel.: (905) 563-2200
Fax: (905) 563-2240
Web Site: www.danacanada.com
Sales Range: $25-49.9 Million
Approx. Number Employees: 50
Year Founded: 1922
Business Description:
Automotive & Heavy Truck Parts Designer, Engineer & Mfr
S.I.C.: 3714; 3053
N.A.I.C.S.: 336399; 339991
Media: 2-4-6-10-19-21-22
Distr.: Intl.; Natl.
Budget Set: Jan.

DANA HOLDING CORPORATION
3939 Technology Dr
Maumee, OH 43537
Mailing Address:
PO Box 1000
Toledo, OH 43537-1000
Tel.: (419) 887-3000
Fax: (419) 887-5200
Toll Free: (800) 472-8810
E-mail: InvestorRelations@dana.com
Web Site: www.dana.com
E-Mail For Key Personnel:
Public Relations: gary.corrigan@dana.com
Approx. Sls.: $6,109,000,000
Approx. Number Employees: 22,500
Year Founded: 1904
Business Description:
Automotive & Heavy Truck Parts Designer, Engineer & Mfr
S.I.C.: 3053; 3711; 3714
N.A.I.C.S.: 336330; 336211; 336350; 336399; 339991
Import Export
Media: 10
Distr.: Natl.
Budget Set: Nov.
Personnel:
John M. Devine *(Chm)*
Roger J. Wood *(Pres & CEO)*
James A. Yost *(CFO & Exec VP)*
Douglas S. Tracy *(CIO & VP)*
Robert H. Marcin *(Chief Admin Officer & Exec VP)*
Rodney R. Filcek *(Chief Acctg Officer)*
Jacqueline A. Dedo *(Chief Strategy & Procurement Officer)*
Eric Schwarz *(Chief Pur Officer)*
Martin Bryant *(Pres-Light Vehicle Products)*
Mark Wallace *(Pres-Heavy Vehichle Products)*
Marc S. Levin *(Gen Counsel & Sr VP)*
Jeff Cole *(Dir-Mktg Comm)*
Bob Goldston *(Dir-Mktg)*
Charles Hartlage *(Mgr-Corp & Exec Comm)*
Brands & Products:
ADVANTEK
ATMOPLAS
CLEVITE
DANA
GLACIER VANDERVELL
PEOPLE FINDING A BETTER WAY
PERFECT CIRCLE
ROLLING CHASSIS
SPICER
VICTOR REINZ
Advertising Agency:
Gelia-Media, Inc.
390 S Youngs Rd
Williamsville, NY 14221
Tel.: (716) 629-3200
Fax: (716) 629-3299

DANFOSS GRAHAM
(Sub. of Danfoss Electronic Drives)
8800 W Bradley Rd
Milwaukee, WI 53224-9541
Mailing Address:
PO Box 245041
Milwaukee, WI 53224
Tel.: (414) 355-8800
Fax: (414) 355-6117
Toll Free: (800) 621-8806
E-mail: namc@danfoss.com
Web Site: www.danfossdrives.com
Approx. Number Employees: 200
Year Founded: 1936
Business Description:
AC Variable Frequency Drives Mfr
S.I.C.: 3625; 3566
N.A.I.C.S.: 335314; 333612
Media: 2-7-10
Distr.: Intl.; Natl.
Budget Set: Oct.
Personnel:
Arnaldo Ricca *(Pres)*
Mark Hansen *(Dir-Mktg)*

DAYCO CANADA CORP.
(Sub. of Mark IV Industries, Inc.)
46 Norelco Dr
Weston, ON M9L 1S3, Canada
Tel.: (416) 741-3900
Fax: (416) 741-3816
Web Site: www.dayco.ca
Approx. Number Employees: 200
Business Description:
Automotive Parts Mfr & Distr
S.I.C.: 3714
N.A.I.C.S.: 336340
Import Export
Media: 1-2-4-5-10-15-18-19-20-21
Distr.: Natl.
Budget Set: Mar.
Personnel:
Frank J. Reeves *(VP & Gen Mgr)*
Bill Hay *(VP-Sls)*
Donna Hicks *(Mgr-Mktg)*

DELPHI HOLDINGS L.L.P.
5725 Delphi Dr
Troy, MI 48098-2815
Tel.: (248) 813-2000
Fax: (248) 813-2670
Web Site: www.delphi.com
Sales Range: $5-14.9 Billion
Approx. Number Employees: 12,700
Year Founded: 1888
Business Description:
Automotive Parts Distr & Mfr
S.I.C.: 3711; 3714
N.A.I.C.S.: 336211; 336399
Media: 2-3-4-6-7-8-9-10-11-13-15-18-20-22-23-25
Personnel:
Rodney O'Neal *(Pres & CEO)*
Kevin P. Clark *(CFO)*
Timothy C. McCabe *(CIO & VP)*
David M. Sherbin *(Chief Compliance Officer, Gen Counsel, Sec & VP)*
James A. Bertrand *(Pres-Thermal Sys & VP)*
Francisco A. Ordonez *(Pres-Product & Service Solutions & VP)*
Jeffrey J. Owens *(Pres-Delphi Electronics & Safety & VP)*
Ronald M. Pirtle *(Pres-Powertrain Sys & VP)*
James A. Spencer *(Pres-Delphi Electrical & Electronic & South America & Mexico & VP)*
Kevin M. Butler *(VP-HR Mgmt & Global Bus Svcs)*
Karen L. Healy *(VP-Corp Affairs & Mktg)*
John Anderson *(Dir-Corp Affairs)*
Steve Clemons *(Dir-Asia Pacific Plng & Mktg Comm)*
Claudia Piccinin *(Dir-Comm, Mktg-Delphi Thermal Sys)*
Carrie Wright *(Dir-Comm & Aftermarket Global Br)*
Xochitl Diaz *(Mgr-Media Rels)*
Michael Simon *(Mgr-Natl Sls)*
Dina Vizzaccaro *(Mgr)*
Brands & Products:
AURA
DELPHI
MYFI
ROADY
SKYFI
Advertising Agency:
Chletcos/Gallagher Inc.
63 Greene St Ste 602
New York, NY 10012
Tel.: (212) 334-2455
Fax: (212) 334-2463

DELPHI PRODUCT & SERVICE SOLUTIONS
(Div. of Delphi Holdings L.L.P.)
1441 W Long Lk Rd
Troy, MI 48098
Mailing Address:
PO Box 5090
Troy, MI 48098-5090
Tel.: (248) 267-8800
E-mail: dpsscustomerservice@delphi.com
Web Site: www.delphi-pss.com
Sales Range: $150-199.9 Million
Business Description:
Aftermarket Automotive Electronics, Replacement Parts & Services
S.I.C.: 5013
N.A.I.C.S.: 423120
Import Export
Media: 10-18
Personnel:
Francisco A. Ordonez *(Pres)*
Brands & Products:
DS800
SKYFI AUDIO SYSTEM
TRUE HANDS-FREE MOBILE COMMUNICATION

DENSO SALES CALIFORNIA, INC.
(Sub. of Denso Corporation)
3900 Via Oro Ave
Long Beach, CA 90810-1868
Tel.: (310) 834-6352
Fax: (310) 513-7319
Toll Free: (800) 222-6352
Web Site: www.denso-dsca.com
Sales Range: $500-549.9 Million
Approx. Number Employees: 213
Year Founded: 1971
Business Description:
Automotive Parts Distr
S.I.C.: 5013
N.A.I.C.S.: 423120
Import Export
Advertising Expenditures: $4,250,000
Media: 1-2-4-5-6-7-8-10-12-19-20-22
Distr.: Natl.
Budget Set: Sept.
Personnel:
Max Adachi *(Pres)*
David Shushereba *(Sr Mgr)*
Brands & Products:
DENSO FIRST TIME FIT
DENSO IRIDIUM POWER
DENSO RE-ENGINEERED PRODUCTS
DENSO ROBOTICS
MOVINCOOL
ND
OFFICE PRO
Advertising Agencies:
Integrated Marketing Works
(A Division of Bretschger & Associates)
260 Newport Ctr Dr Ste 425
Newport Beach, CA 92660
Tel.: (949) 833-3822
Fax: (949) 833-3810

The Marx Group
2175 E Francisco Blvd East Ste F
San Rafael, CA 94901
Tel.: (415) 453-0844
Fax: (415) 451-0166

DENT WIZARD INTERNATIONAL CORP.
(Holding of H.I.G. Capital, LLC)
4710 Earth City Expy
Bridgeton, MO 63044
Tel.: (314) 592-1800
Fax: (314) 592-1951
Toll Free: (800) DENTWIZ
Toll Free: (800) 969HAIL
E-mail: inquiries@dentwizard.com
Web Site: www.dentwizard.com
Approx. Number Employees: 150
Year Founded: 1983

Key to Media (For complete agency information see *The Advertising Red Books-Agencies* edition):
1. Bus. Publs. 2. Cable T.V. 3. Catalogs & Directories. 4. Co-op Adv. 5. Consumer Mags. 6. D.M. to Bus. Estab.7. D.M. to Consumers 8. Daily Newsp. 9. Exhibits/Trade Shows 10. Foreign 11. Infomercial 12. Internet Adv.13. Multimedia 14. Network Radio 15. Network T.V. 16. Newsp. Distr. Mags. 17. Other 18. Outdoor (Posters, Transit) 19. Point of Purchase20. Premiums, Novelties 21. Product Samples 22. Special Events Mktg. 23. Spot Radio 24. Spot T.V. 25. Weekly Newsp. 26. Yellow Page Adv.

Dent Wizard International Corp. — (Continued)

Business Description:
Paintless Dent Removal Services
S.I.C.: 7532
N.A.I.C.S.: 811121
Media: 7-8-10-11-13

Brands & Products:
DENT WIZARD
DENTS AWAY...SAME DAY

Advertising Agency:
Barkley
304 N Broadway
Saint Louis, MO 63102
Tel.: (314) 727-9500
Fax: (314) 727-0561
Toll Free: (800) 886-0561

DETROIT DIESEL CORP.
(Sub. of Daimler Trucks North America LLC)
13400 Outer Dr W
Detroit, MI 48239
Tel.: (313) 592-5001
Fax: (313) 592-7323
Web Site: www.detroitdiesel.com
Approx. Number Employees: 2,600
Year Founded: 1938
Business Description:
Mfr & Designer of Diesel & Alternative Fuel Engines
S.I.C.: 3519; 3714
N.A.I.C.S.: 333618; 336399
Export
Media: 2-4-7-10-11-13-14-19-23-26
Distr.: Intl.
Budget Set: Oct.
Personnel:
Brad Williamson *(Mgr-Mktg Comm)*

Brands & Products:
DDEC
DETROIT DIESEL
DETROIT DIESEL & SPINNING ARROWS DESIGN
ELECTRONIC FIRE COMMANDER
EMITLESS
POWER TRAC
PROMANAGER
SERIES 2000
SERIES 4000
SERIES 50
SERIES 60
SPINNING ARROWS DESIGN

Advertising Agencies:
Landau Public Relations
700 W Saint Clair Ave Ste 414
Cleveland, OH 44113
Tel.: (216) 696-1686
Fax: (216) 771-5206

Riegner & Associates, Inc.
18481 W 10 Mile Rd
Southfield, MI 48075-2621
Tel.: (248) 569-4242
Fax: (248) 443-0690
(Diesel)

DEVILBISS AUTOMOTIVE REFINISHING
(Sub. of Illinois Tool Works Inc.)
11360 S Airfield Rd
Swanton, OH 43558
Fax: (800) 445-6643
Toll Free: (800) 445-3988
Web Site:
www.autorefinishdevilbiss.com
Sales Range: $25-49.9 Million
Approx. Number Employees: 40
Year Founded: 1888
Business Description:
Spray Guns & Related Equipment Mfr
S.I.C.: 3559
N.A.I.C.S.: 333298
Media: 4
Personnel:
Thomas White *(Mgr-Bus Unit)*

Brands & Products:
BINKS
DEVILBISS

DORMAN PRODUCTS, INC.
3400 E Walnut St
Colmar, PA 18915-9768
Mailing Address:
PO Box 1800
Colmar, PA 18915-0902
Tel.: (215) 997-1800
Fax: (215) 997-7968
E-mail: generalinquiry@dormanproducts.com
Web Site: www.dormanproducts.com
Approx. Rev.: $455,716,000
Approx. Number Employees: 1,170
Year Founded: 1978
Business Description:
Aftermarket Auto Parts Distr
S.I.C.: 3585; 3231; 3714
N.A.I.C.S.: 336391; 327215; 336399
Import
Media: 4-13
Personnel:
Steven L. Berman *(Chm & CEO)*
Mathias J. Barton *(Co-Pres)*
Joseph M. Beretta *(Co-Pres)*
Matthew S. Kohnke *(CFO)*
Thomas J. Knoblauch *(Gen Counsel, VP & Asst Sec)*
Fred V. Frigo *(Sr VP-Ops)*
Noam Chasen *(Dir-Mktg)*

Brands & Products:
AUTO GRADE
BODY-TITE!
BRASS-TITE!
CLUTCH-IN!
CONDUCT-TITE!
DEALER-PAK
DORMAN
EXPAND-TITE
FIRST STOP
HELP!
INSTALLER-PAK
KEEP-TITE!
LICENSE-TITE!
LOOK!
MIGHTY FLOW!
NEW PRODUCTS NEW SOLUTIONS NEW OPPORTUNITIES
NEW SINCE 1918
O-TITE!
OE SOLUTIONS
OIL-TITE!
PEDAL-UP!
PIK-A-NUT
QUICK DISCONNECT
SCAN-TECH
SPEEDI-BOOT!
SPINDLE-TITE!
SPRING-TITE!

DORON PRECISION SYSTEMS, INC.
150 Corporate Dr
Binghamton, NY 13904
Tel.: (607) 772-1610
Fax: (607) 772-6760
E-mail: sales@doronprecision.com
Web Site: www.doronprecision.com
E-Mail For Key Personnel:
Sales Director: sales@doronprecision.com
Approx. Number Employees: 50
Year Founded: 1973
Business Description:
Driving Simulation & Entertainment Simulation Systems
S.I.C.: 3589; 3944
N.A.I.C.S.: 333319; 339932
Export
Advertising Expenditures: $350,000
Media: 1-2-7-10-11-21-22
Distr.: Intl.
Budget Set: Aug.
Personnel:
Donald E. Wenzinger *(Pres)*

Brands & Products:
45OLE
AMOS
DORON
L-300 RA
L-300 SERIES
SRV
TRANSPORT 6
VEHICLE MANEUVERING TRAINER

DOUGLAS DYNAMICS, INC.
7777 N 73rd St
Milwaukee, WI 53233
Tel.: (414) 354-2310
Web Site: www.douglasdynamics.com
Approx. Sls.: $176,795,000
Approx. Number Employees: 450
Business Description:
Light Truck Snow & Ice Control Equipment Mfr & Sales
S.I.C.: 3714; 5013; 5078
N.A.I.C.S.: 336399; 423120; 423740
Advertising Expenditures: $2,805,000
Personnel:
Michael W. Wickham *(Chm)*
James L. Janik *(Pres, CEO & Dir)*
Robert L. McCormick *(CFO & VP)*
Mark Adamson *(VP-Sls & Mktg)*

DUFF-NORTON
(Sub. of Columbus McKinnon Corporation)
9415 Pioneer Ave
Charlotte, NC 28273-6318
Mailing Address:
PO Box 7010
Charlotte, NC 28241-7010
Tel.: (704) 588-0510
Fax: (704) 588-1994
Toll Free: (800) 477-5002
Web Site: www.duffnorton.com
Sales Range: $100-124.9 Million
Approx. Number Employees: 348
Year Founded: 1883
Business Description:
Mfr. of Lifting Jacks, Mechanical Actuators, Electromechanical Linear Actuators & Rotating Joints
S.I.C.: 3569; 3625
N.A.I.C.S.: 333999; 335314
Import Export
Advertising Expenditures: $400,000
Media: 2-4-5-8-10-11-13-20
Distr.: Natl.
Budget Set: Jan.
Personnel:
Howard B. Wentz, Jr. *(Pres-Ops)*
Charles Buie *(Product Mgr)*

Brands & Products:
BOSSMAN
DUFF-NORTON
MAXI-PAC
MINI-PAC
ROLARAM
THE ROTARY UNION
SPIRACON
SUPER-PAC

DURAKON INDUSTRIES INC.
(Joint Venture of Littlejohn & Co. LLC & Resilience Capital Partners LLC)
2101 N Lapeer Rd
Lapeer, MI 48446-8628
Tel.: (810) 664-0850
Fax: (810) 664-3957
E-mail: custserv@durakon.com
Web Site: www.penda.com
Sales Range: $150-199.9 Million
Approx. Number Employees: 532
Year Founded: 1979
Business Description:
Pickup Truck Bedliners Distr & Mfr
S.I.C.: 3714; 3711
N.A.I.C.S.: 336399; 336211
Import Export
Media: 1-2-4-5-6-7-8-10-11-16-19-20-21-22-23-24-26
Distr.: Intl.; Natl.
Budget Set: Oct.
Personnel:
James C Smith *(CFO & VP)*

Brands & Products:
ALLSTAR
BODYGARD
CARGOPRO
DURALINER
DURASPORT
DURATRUNK

DUTTON-LAINSON COMPANY
451 W 2nd St
Hastings, NE 68901-7535
Mailing Address:
PO Box 729
Hastings, NE 68902-0729
Tel.: (402) 462-4141
Fax: (402) 460-4612
E-mail: dlsales@dutton-lainson.com
Web Site: www.dutton-lainson.com
Approx. Number Employees: 310
Year Founded: 1886
Business Description:
Marine, Automotive & Agricultural Products Mfr; Plumbing & Electrical Products Wholesale Distr
S.I.C.: 3531; 5074
N.A.I.C.S.: 333120; 423720
Import Export
Advertising Expenditures: $500,000
Media: 2-4-5-10-19-20-26
Distr.: Intl.; Natl.
Budget Set: Sept.
Personnel:
Mark Bliss *(VP-Sls & Mktg)*

Brands & Products:
BUMP-ME
DL
GOLDENROD
GREASE KEEPER
HITCH-LOCK
SENTINEL
STRONGARM
TUFFPLATE

Advertising Agency:
Idea Bank Marketing
701 W Second St

Key to Media (For complete agency information see *The Advertising Red Books-Agencies* edition):
1. Bus. Publs. 2. Cable T.V. 3. Catalogs & Directories. 4. Co-op Adv. 5. Consumer Mags. 6. D.M. to Bus. Estab.7. D.M. to Consumers
8. Daily Newsp. 9. Exhibits/Trade Shows 10. Foreign 11. Infomercial 12. Internet Adv.13. Multimedia 14. Network Radio
15. Network T.V. 16. Newsp. Distr. Mags. 17. Other 18. Outdoor (Posters, Transit) 19. Point of Purchase20. Premiums, Novelties
21. Product Samples 22. Special Events Mktg. 23. Spot Radio 24. Spot T.V. 25. Weekly Newsp. 26. Yellow Page Adv.

Hastings, NE 68901
Tel.: (402) 463-0588
Fax: (402) 463-2187
(Winches, Jacks, Couplers & Related Accessories (Strongarm/D-L) Marine, Hardware, Industrial & Automotive)
— Ann Martin *(Acct. Exec.)*

EATON CORPORATION - TRUCK COMPONENTS
(Unit of Eaton Corporation)
13100 E Michigan Ave
Galesburg, MI 49053-9201
Tel.: (269) 342-3000
Fax: (269) 342-3831
Toll Free: (800) 826-HELP
Web Site: www.truck.eaton.com
Sales Range: $100-124.9 Million
Approx. Number Employees: 500
Business Description:
Commercial Vehicle Drive Train & Safety Systems Mfr
S.I.C.: 8741; 8111
N.A.I.C.S.: 561110; 541110
Import Export
Advertising Expenditures: $4,000,000
Media: 1-2-4-7-8-10-13-19-20
Distr.: Intl.; Natl.
Budget Set: Jan.
Personnel:
Don Alles *(Dir-Global Branding & Comm)*
Brands & Products:
EATON
EATON FULLER
ROADRANGER
Advertising Agency:
Gelia-Media, Inc.
390 S Youngs Rd
Williamsville, NY 14221
Tel.: (716) 629-3200
Fax: (716) 629-3299

ECOTALITY, INC.
4 Embarcadero Ctr Ste 3720
San Francisco, CA 94111
Tel.: (415) 992-3000
Fax: (415) 992-3001
E-mail: info@ecotality.com
Web Site: www.ecotality.com
Approx. Rev.: $13,736,621
Approx. Number Employees: 116
Year Founded: 1999
Business Description:
Clean Electric Transportation & Storage Mfr
S.I.C.: 3621; 3714
N.A.I.C.S.: 335312; 336322
Advertising Expenditures: $628,128
Personnel:
Jonathan R. Read *(Pres & CEO)*
H. Ravi Brar *(CFO)*
Barry S. Baer *(Sec & Asst Treas)*
Randy Carrero *(VP-Digital Media & Network Solutions)*
Susie Herrmann *(VP-Corp Fin)*
Jeanine L'Ecuyer *(VP-Mktg & Comm)*
Brands & Products:
BLINK
MINIT-CHARGER

EDELBROCK CORPORATION
2700 California St
Torrance, CA 90503-3907
Tel.: (310) 781-2222
Fax: (310) 320-1187
E-mail: edelbrock@edelbrock.com
Web Site: www.edelbrock.com
E-Mail For Key Personnel:
Sales Director: sales@edelbrock.com
Sales Range: $100-124.9 Million
Approx. Number Employees: 600
Year Founded: 1938
Business Description:
Performance Automotive Equipment, Manifolds, Carburetor Synchronizers, Camshafts, Electronic Water Injection, Chrome Signature Accessories & Valve Covers Mfr
S.I.C.: 3714; 3751
N.A.I.C.S.: 336399; 336991
Import Export
Advertising Expenditures: $10,442,000
Media: 4-5-6-8-10-18-19-20-25
Distr.: Intl.; Natl.
Budget Set: Oct. -Nov.
Personnel:
O. Victor Edelbrock, Jr. *(Chm, Pres & CEO)*
Aristedes T. Feles *(CFO & VP-Fin)*
Cathleen Edelbrock *(VP-Adv & Sec)*
Jeff Thompson *(Exec VP)*
Steve Whipple *(VP-Sls)*
Brands & Products:
ACCU-DRIVE
CLASSIC ALUMINUM
DURABLE TRFLON
EDELBROCK
ELITE
ENDURASHINE
NITROSTEEL
PERFORMER
PERFORMER LINK
PERMASTAR
POWER PACKAGE
PRO-FLO
PRO-TUNER
QUIET-FLO
RED ROCKERS
RUSSELL
SIGNATURE
SIGNATURE SERIES
SOUND DEFLECTION TECHNOLOGY
STREET TUNNEL RAMS
SURE SEAT
TEFLON
THUNDER
TI-TECH
TORKER II
THE TOTAL POWER PACKAGE
TUBULAR EXHAUST SYSTEMS
UNI-SYN
VICTOR SERIES
Advertising Agency:
Edelbrock Advertising
2700 California St
Torrance, CA 90503
Tel.: (310) 781-2222
Fax: (310) 320-1187
Toll Free: (800) 739-3737
(Automotive & Motorcycle Parts)

EMERSON POWER TRANSMISSION CORPORATION
(Sub. of Emerson Industrial Automation)
909 Lafayette St
Valparaiso, IN 46383-4210
Tel.: (219) 465-2200
Fax: (219) 465-2290
Telex: 25-8446
E-mail: salestraining@emerson-ept.com
Web Site: www.emerson-ept.com
E-Mail For Key Personnel:
Sales Director: salestraining@emerson.com
Sales Range: $500-549.9 Million
Approx. Number Employees: 1,500
Year Founded: 1905
Business Description:
Roller, Ball & Specialized Bearings Mfr
S.I.C.: 3562; 3643; 3823
N.A.I.C.S.: 332991; 334513; 335931
Advertising Expenditures: $315,000
Media: 2-4-8-10-11
Distr.: Natl.
Budget Set: Apr. -May
Personnel:
Tony Pike *(Pres & CEO)*
John Hickel *(VP & Gen Mgr)*
Jim Hoshiko *(Dir-Mktg & Sls)*
Advertising Agency:
Jaap-Orr Company
31 E 12th St 2nd Fl
Cincinnati, OH 45202
Tel.: (513) 241-2228
Fax: (513) 241-1969
(Bearings: Camrol, Cagerol, Guiderol, Sphererol)

ENERGY ABSORPTION SYSTEMS, INC.
(Sub. of Trinity Industries, Inc.)
35 E Wacker Dr
Chicago, IL 60601
Tel.: (312) 467-6750
Fax: (312) 467-1356
E-mail: customerservice@energyabsorption.com
Web Site: www.energyabsorption.com
E-Mail For Key Personnel:
Marketing Director: marketing@energyabsorption.com
Sales Range: $25-49.9 Million
Approx. Number Employees: 25
Year Founded: 1969
Business Description:
Highway Crash Cushions & Safety Products Mfr
S.I.C.: 3499; 3089
N.A.I.C.S.: 332999; 326199
Import Export
Media: 2-4-6-7-10-13-17
Distr.: Natl.
Personnel:
Leslie J. Jezuit *(Chm)*
Kim Ludwig *(Mgr-Comm)*
Brands & Products:
ABC TERMINAL
ALPHA 2001 MD TMA
ALPHA 60 MD TMA
ALPHA 70K TMA
BARRIERGATE
BRAKEMASTER 350
CUSHIONWALL II
EASI CELL CLUSTER
ENERGITE III
FASTBREAK WORK ZONE
FREEZEFREE
IMS
LS-PRO TMA
N-E-A-T
QUAD GUARD CZ
QUADGUARD
QUADGUARD ELITE
QUADGUARDLMC
QUADTREND 350
REACT 350
REACT 350 WIDE
REACT 350 WORKZONE
SAFE-HIT
SAFE-STOP 180 TMA
SAFE-STOP TMA
STOPGATE
TRITON BARRIER TL-2
TRITON BARRIER TL-3
TRITON CET WORKZONE
UNIVERSAL BARRELS

EXIDE TECHNOLOGIES
13000 Deerfield Pkwy Bldg 200
Alpharetta, GA 30004-6118
Tel.: (678) 566-9000
Fax: (678) 566-9188
E-mail: communications@exide.com
Web Site: www.exide.com
Approx. Sls.: $2,887,516,000
Approx. Number Employees: 10,027
Year Founded: 1888
Business Description:
Lead Acid Batteries Mfr & Supplier
S.I.C.: 3691; 4953; 7699
N.A.I.C.S.: 335911; 562920; 811310
Import Export
Advertising Expenditures: $258,212,000
Media: 2-4-6-7-10-19-20-26
Distr.: Natl.
Budget Set: Dec.
Personnel:
John P. Reilly *(Chm)*
Phillip A. Damaska *(CFO & Exec VP)*
Erach S. Balsara *(CIO & VP)*
Bruce A. Cole *(Pres-Exide Americas)*
Luke Lu *(Pres-Asia Pacific)*
Michael Ostermann *(Pres-Exide Europe)*
Barbara A. Hatcher *(Gen Counsel & Exec VP)*
George S. Jones, Jr. *(Exec VP-Comm)*
Edward R. Tetreault *(Exec VP-HR)*
Joseph Dowd *(VP & Gen Mgr)*
Paul G. Cheeseman *(VP-Global Engrg & Res)*
Carol Knies *(Sr Dir-IR)*
Bob Osinski *(Dir-Mktg & Adv)*
James R. Bolch *(Pres & CEO)*
Louis E. Martinez *(Chief Acctg Officer, VP & Controller)*
Brands & Products:
ABSOLYTE
CENTRA
CLASSIC
CLASSIC CSM
DETA
DRYSAFE
ELEMENT
EXIDE
EXIDE EXTREME
EXIDE NASCAR SELECT
FULMEN
GLOBAL LEADER IN STORED ELECTRICAL ENERGY
GNB
GNB FUSION
LIBERATOR
MARATHON
MEGACYCLE
NASCAR EXTREME
NASCAR SELECT
NAUTILUS
ORBITAL
PALLETPRO

Key to Media (For complete agency information see *The Advertising Red Books-Agencies* edition):
1. Bus. Publs. 2. Cable T.V. 3. Catalogs & Directories. 4. Co-op Adv. 5. Consumer Mags. 6. D.M. to Bus. Estab.7. D.M. to Consumers
8. Daily Newsp. 9. Exhibits/Trade Shows 10. Foreign 11. Infomercial 12. Internet Adv.13. Multimedia 14. Network Radio
15. Network T.V. 16. Newsp. Distr. Mags. 17. Other 18. Outdoor (Posters, Transit) 19. Point of Purchase20. Premiums, Novelties
21. Product Samples 22. Special Events Mktg. 23. Spot Radio 24. Spot T.V. 25. Weekly Newsp. 26. Yellow Page Adv.

Exide Technologies — (Continued)

POWERFIT
RELAY GEL
ROADFORCE
SONNENSCHEIN
SPRINTER
STOWAWAY
SUNLYTE
SUPER CRANK
TUBULAR-HP
TUDOR

Advertising Agency:
J. Addams & Partners, Inc.
500 Bishop St Studio B-5
Atlanta, GA 30318
Tel.: (404) 231-1132
Fax: (404) 240-0418

FAIRFIELD MANUFACTURING COMPANY, INC.

(Sub. of Oerlikon Drive Systems)
US 52 South
Lafayette, IN 47903
Tel.: (765) 772-4000
Fax: (765) 772-4001
E-mail: sales@fairfieldmfg.com
Web Site: www.fairfieldmfg.com
E-Mail For Key Personnel:
Sales Director: sales@fairfieldmfg.com
Business Description:
Custom Gears & Drive Solutions
S.I.C.: 3566
N.A.I.C.S.: 333612
Personnel:
Gary Lehman *(CEO)*
Advertising Agency:
dgs Marketing Engineers
10100 Lantern Rd Ste 225
Fishers, IN 46037
Tel.: (317) 813-2222
Fax: (317) 813-2233

FEDERAL-MOGUL CORPORATION

26555 Northwestern Hwy
Southfield, MI 48033
Tel.: (248) 354-7700
Fax: (248) 354-8648
E-mail: marie.remboulis@federalmogul.com
Web Site: www.federal-mogul.com
Approx. Sls.: $6,219,000,000
Approx. Number Employees: 42,700
Year Founded: 1899
Business Description:
Automobiles Components & Sub-Systems Supplier
S.I.C.: 3714; 3053; 3592; 3711
N.A.I.C.S.: 336399; 336211; 336311; 339991
Import Export
Advertising Expenditures: $40,000,000
Media: 2-3-4-6-7-10-15-19-20
Distr.: Intl.; Natl.
Budget Set: Sept.
Personnel:
Jose Maria Alapont *(Pres & CEO)*
Alan Haughie *(CFO & Sr VP)*
Alston German *(CIO & VP)*
Brett D. Pynnonen *(Chief Compliance Officer, Gen Counsel & Sr VP)*
Jerome Rouquet *(Chief Acctg Officer, VP & Controller)*
William S. Bowers *(Sr VP-Sls & Mktg)*
Jean Brunol *(Sr VP-Bus & Ops Strategy)*
Jay Burkhart *(Sr VP-Aftermarket-Global)*
Gerard Chochoy *(Sr VP-Powertrain Bearings & Sealings)*
Rene L. F. Dalleur *(Sr VP-Customer Satisfaction, Global Engrg & Mfg)*
Pascal Goachet *(Sr VP-HR & Org-Global)*
Ramzi Y. Hermiz *(Sr VP-Vehicle Safety & Protection)*
Rainer Jueckstock *(Sr VP-Powertrain Energy)*
Eric McAlexander *(Sr VP-Global Mfg)*
Markus Wermers *(Sr VP-Pur-Global)*
Steve Gaut *(VP-Corp Comm & Govt Rels)*
Jim Burke *(Dir-Global Comm)*
Todd Gross *(Dir-Global Customer Satisfaction)*
Tracy Neil *(Brand Mgr-ANCO)*
Brands & Products:
ABEX
AE
ANCO
BENTLEY-HARRIS
BERAL
BRICO
CARTER
CHAMPION
DEVA
DURON
FEDERAL-MOGUL
FEL-PRO
FERODO
FPDIESEL
GLYCODUR
GOETZE
METAFRAM
METAGLISS
MOOG
NATIONAL
NECTO
NURAL
PAYEN
PRECISION
RAIMSA
SEALED POWER
SPEED-PRO
THERMOQUIET
TRUVIEW
UNIPISTON
WAGNER
Advertising Agency:
Marketing Directions, Inc.
28005 Clemens Rd
Cleveland, OH 44145
Tel.: (440) 835-5550
Fax: (440) 892-9195

FLEETPRIDE, INC.

(Holding of Investcorp International, Inc.)
8708 Technology Forest Pl Ste 125
The Woodlands, TX 77381
Tel.: (832) 585-0555
Tel.: (832) 592-9953 (Mktg Comm)
Fax: (832) 592-9970
Toll Free: (866) 435-3387
E-mail: info@fleetpride.com
Web Site: www.fleetpride.com
Sales Range: $500-549.9 Million
Approx. Number Employees: 2,254
Year Founded: 1999
Business Description:
Heavy-Duty Truck & Trailer Parts Distr; Truck Repair & Maintenance Service Facilities Operator
S.I.C.: 5013; 7538; 7539
N.A.I.C.S.: 423120; 811111; 811198
Media: 10
Personnel:
Woody M. McGee *(Pres & CEO)*
John Mosunic *(CFO)*
Lee Stockseth *(COO)*
George C. Argodale *(CIO)*
Robert Lindley *(VP-Supply Chain & Gen Mgr-PDC)*
Anthony Vingiano *(VP & Reg Mgr-Northeast)*
Mark Esselman *(VP-HR)*
Pete Painter *(VP-Sls & Mktg)*
Steve Turnlund *(Reg Mgr-Western)*
Cherie Reid *(Product Mgr)*
Brands & Products:
FLEETCARE

FREE SERVICE TIRE COMPANY, INC.

126 Buffalo St
Johnson City, TN 37604-5702
Mailing Address:
PO Box 1637
Johnson City, TN 37605-1637
Tel.: (423) 979-2250
Fax: (423) 979-2263
E-mail: retail@freeservicetire.com
Web Site: www.freeservicetire.com
Approx. Number Employees: 195
Year Founded: 1919
Business Description:
Retailer of Tires; Provider of Automotive Services
S.I.C.: 7539; 5014
N.A.I.C.S.: 811198; 441320
Import
Advertising Expenditures: $600,000
Media: 2-3-5-7-8-10-13-15-22-23-24-25-26
Distr.: Reg.
Personnel:
Lewis P. Wexler, Sr. *(Chm & CEO)*
Lewis P. Wexler, Jr. *(Pres)*
Matthew Wilhjelm *(VP-Fin & Corp Admin)*
Advertising Agency:
Mincom Communications
30 E. 60th St., Ste. 401
New York, NY 10022
Tel.: (212) 355-3289

GALENA ASSOCIATES, LLC

(d/b/a Valvoline Instant Oil Change)
25 Main St 4th Fl
Hartford, CT 06106
Tel.: (860) 244-9310
Fax: (860) 548-1999
Toll Free: (800) 606LUBE
Web Site: www.vioc.com
Approx. Number Employees: 400
Business Description:
Oil Change Franchise Owner
S.I.C.: 7549
N.A.I.C.S.: 811191
Media: 7-8-9-10-20-23-25
Distr.: Natl.
Personnel:
Mike Ferri *(Owner & Pres)*
Andy Leiberman *(Dir-Mktg)*

GARLOCK SEALING TECHNOLOGIES

(Sub. of EnPro Industries, Inc.)
1666 Division St
Palmyra, NY 14522-9383
Tel.: (315) 597-4811
Fax: (315) 597-3216
Fax: (800) 543-0598
Toll Free: (800) 448-6688
Web Site: www.garlock.com
Sales Range: $400-449.9 Million
Approx. Number Employees: 1,800
Year Founded: 1887
Business Description:
Industrial Seals, Gaskets, Packing, Expansion Joints, Metal Gaskets & Mechanical Seals
S.I.C.: 3053
N.A.I.C.S.: 339991
Export
Advertising Expenditures: $300,000
Media: 2-4-7-10-13-20-21-26
Distr.: Intl.; Natl.
Budget Set: Oct.
Personnel:
Dale Herold *(Pres)*
Janet C. Jessen *(Dir-Mktg)*
Tim Hurley *(Sr Mgr-Global Product)*
Earl Rogalski *(Product Mgr)*
Jim Drago *(Mgr-Bus Dev & Integration)*
Advertising Agencies:
Bush Communications, LLC
25 N Washington St 4th Fl
Rochester, NY 14614
Tel.: (585) 244-0270
Fax: (585) 244-3046

Stiegler, Wells, Brunswick & Roth, Inc.
(d/b/a SWB&R)
3865 Adler Pl
Bethlehem, PA 18017-9000
Tel.: (610) 866-0611
Fax: (610) 866-8650

THE GATES CORPORATION

(Joint Venture of Onex Corporation & Canada Pension Plan Investment Board)
1551 Wewatta St
Denver, CO 80202
Mailing Address:
PO Box 5887
Denver, CO 80217-5887
Tel.: (303) 744-1911
Telex: 6837035
Web Site: www.gates.com
Approx. Sls.: $1,763,400,000
Approx. Number Employees: 15,000
Year Founded: 1911
Business Description:
Automotive Belts, Hoses & Other Rubber Related Products Mfr
S.I.C.: 3052; 3089
N.A.I.C.S.: 326220; 326199
Import Export
Media: 1-2-4-5-6-7-10-11-18-19-20
Distr.: Intl
Personnel:
Jeff Brekke *(Pres-N American Automotive Aftermarket Div)*
Michael Wedge *(CIO)*
Gordon Hoffman *(VP-Mktg)*
Dave Miller *(VP-Global Automotive Mktg & Corp Branding)*
Jeff Sandt *(Mgr-Bus Dev & New Bus)*

Key to Media (For complete agency information see *The Advertising Red Books-Agencies* edition):
1. Bus. Publs. 2. Cable T.V. 3. Catalogs & Directories. 4. Co-op Adv. 5. Consumer Mags. 6. D.M. to Bus. Estab.7. D.M. to Consumers 8. Daily Newsp. 9. Exhibits/Trade Shows 10. Foreign 11. Infomercial 12. Internet Adv.13. Multimedia 14. Network Radio 15. Network T.V. 16. Newsp. Distr. Mags. 17. Other 18. Outdoor (Posters, Transit) 19. Point of Purchase20. Premiums, Novelties 21. Product Samples 22. Special Events Mktg. 23. Spot Radio 24. Spot T.V. 25. Weekly Newsp. 26. Yellow Page Adv.

Brands & Products:
GATES

GENERAL BEARING CORPORATION
44 High St
West Nyack, NY 10994-2702
Tel.: (845) 358-6000
Fax: (845) 358-6277
Toll Free: (800) 431-1766
E-mail: sales@gbc.gnrl.com
Web Site: www.generalbearing.com
E-Mail For Key Personnel:
President: dgussack@gbc.gnrl.com
Marketing Director: JWilliams@gbc.gnrl.com
Sales Director: sales@gbc.gnrl.com
Public Relations: fgarner@gbc.gnrl.com
Approx. Sls.: $102,354,000
Approx. Number Employees: 971
Year Founded: 1958
Business Description:
Bearings Mfr
S.I.C.: 3562; 5085
N.A.I.C.S.: 332991; 423840
Import
Advertising Expenditures: $49,000
Media: 2-4-7-10-20-21-22
Distr.: Intl.; Natl.
Budget Set: Jan.
Personnel:
Seymour I. Gussack *(Chm)*
David Gussack *(Pres)*
Rocky Cambrea *(CFO)*
John E. Stein *(Gen Counsel & Sec)*
William Kurtz *(VP & Dir-Ops)*
Joseph Hoo *(VP-Advanced Tech & Affairs-China)*
Jeff Williams *(VP-Sls & Mktg)*
Fran Garner *(Dir-HR)*
Brands & Products:
THE GENERAL
HYATT
Advertising Agency:
Starnet Design & Litho, Inc.
50 Commerce Dr.
Allendale, NJ 07401
Tel.: (201) 760-2600
Fax: (201) 760-2550

GENERAL PARTS INTERNATIONAL, INC.
(d/b/a CARQUEST Auto Parts)
2635 E Millbrook Rd
Raleigh, NC 27604
Tel.: (919) 573-3000
Fax: (919) 573-2501
Web Site: www.carquest.com
E-Mail For Key Personnel:
Marketing Director: scott.ginsburg@gpi.com
Approx. Sls.: $2,870,000,000
Approx. Number Employees: 18,000
Year Founded: 1961
Business Description:
Automotive Parts Distribution Services
S.I.C.: 5013
N.A.I.C.S.: 423120; 441310
Personnel:
O. Temple Sloan, III *(Pres & COO)*
Matt Davis *(Mgr-Mktg)*
Brands & Products:
PROUDLY SERVING A WORLD IN MOTION
Advertising Agency:
The Stone Agency
312 W Millbrook Rd Ste 225
Raleigh, NC 27609
Tel.: (919) 645-0799

GENTEX CORPORATION
600 N Centennial St
Zeeland, MI 49464-1318
Tel.: (616) 772-1800
Fax: (616) 772-7348
Web Site: www.gentex.com
E-Mail For Key Personnel:
Public Relations: ir@gentex.com
Approx. Sls.: $816,263,414
Approx. Number Employees: 2,908
Year Founded: 1974
Business Description:
Automotive Mirrors, Smoke Detectors, Fire Alarms & Signaling Devices Mfr
S.I.C.: 3714; 3231
N.A.I.C.S.: 336399; 327215
Import Export
Advertising Expenditures: $922,000
Media: 2-4-10-13
Personnel:
Fred Bauer *(Chm & CEO)*
Steve Dykman *(CFO & VP-Fin)*
Connie Hamblin *(Sec & VP-IR & Corp Comm)*
Jim Hollars *(Sr VP-Intl)*
Enoch Jen *(Sr VP)*
Mark Newton *(Sr VP-Electronics & Pur & North American Sls)*
Bruce Los *(VP-HR)*
Craig Piersma *(Dir-Product Mktg)*
Brands & Products:
A SMARTER VISION
GENTEX
GENTEX CORPORATION
HOMELINK
NIGHT VISION SAFETY
ONSTAR
PATHPOINT
SMARTBEAM
Advertising Agency:
Felder Communications Group
50 Louis NW Ste 600
Grand Rapids, MI 49503
Tel.: (616) 459-1200
Fax: (616) 459-2080

GENUINE PARTS COMPANY
2999 Circle 75 Pkwy
Atlanta, GA 30339-3050
Tel.: (770) 953-1700
Fax: (770) 956-2211
E-mail: webmaster@genpt.com
Web Site: www.genpt.com
Approx. Sls.: $11,207,589,000
Approx. Number Employees: 29,500
Year Founded: 1928
Business Description:
Automotive Replacement Parts, Industrial Replacement Parts, Office Products & Electrical/Electronic Materials Distr & Whslr
S.I.C.: 5013
N.A.I.C.S.: 441310
Import Export
Advertising Expenditures: $36,800,000
Media: 2-3-4-5-6-7-8-9-15-17-18-19-20-22-23-24-25-26
Distr.: Natl.
Budget Set: Jan.
Personnel:
Thomas C. Gallagher *(Chm, Pres & CEO)*
Jerry W. Nix *(Vice Chm, CFO & Exec VP-Fin)*
Paul D. Donahue *(Pres-US Automotive Parts Grp & Exec VP)*
Scott C. Smith *(Corp Counsel & Sr VP)*
Frank M. Howard *(Treas & Sr VP)*
Carol B. Yancey *(Sec & Sr VP-Fin)*
Charles A. Chesnutt *(Sr VP-Tech & Process Improvement)*
R. Bruce Clayton *(Sr VP-HR)*
Michael D. Orr *(Sr VP-Ops & Logistics)*
David Haskett *(Corp Controller & Asst VP)*
Napoleon Rutledge *(Asst VP-Internal Audit)*
Eric Sundby *(Sr Dir-ITShared Svcs)*
Brands & Products:
BALKAMP
COMPUCESSORY
ELITE IMAGE
GPC
NAPA
NATURE SAVER
RAYLOC
SPARCO
Advertising Agency:
Otey White & Associates
8146 One Calais Ave
Baton Rouge, LA 70808-3155
Tel.: (225) 201-0032
Fax: (225) 761-9000

GKN AUTOMOTIVE INC.
(Sub. of GKN plc)
3300 University Dr
Auburn Hills, MI 48326-2362
Tel.: (248) 377-1200
Web Site: www.gkndriveline.com
Business Description:
Mfr. & Marketing of Constant Velocity Products & Viscous Couplings
S.I.C.: 3714; 5013
N.A.I.C.S.: 336350; 423120
Advertising Agency:
AutoCom Associates
74 W Long Lk Rd Ste 103
Bloomfield Hills, MI 48304-2770
Tel.: (248) 647-8621
Fax: (248) 642-2110

GM POWERTRAIN GROUP
(Div. of General Motors Company)
823 Joslyn Ave
Pontiac, MI 48340-2925
Tel.: (248) 857-0932
Fax: (248) 857-0105
Approx. Number Employees: 60,000
Business Description:
Engines, Transmissions, Casting & Components
S.I.C.: 3714
N.A.I.C.S.: 336399
Media: 2-10
Distr.: Natl.
Personnel:
Thomas G. Stephens *(Gen Mgr, Vice Chm & Global Chief Tech Officer)*
Brands & Products:
DURAMAX DIESEL
ECOTEC
EMOTION
HYDRA-MATIC
NORTHSTAR
POWERTRAIN
VORTEC
VTI
Advertising Agency:
Leo Burnett Detroit, Inc.
3310 W Big Beaver Rd Ste 107
Troy, MI 48084-2809
Tel.: (248) 458-8300
Tel.: (248) 458-8519
Fax: (248) 458-8300

GOLD EAGLE COMPANY
4400 S Kildare Ave
Chicago, IL 60632-4356
Tel.: (773) 376-4400
Fax: (773) 376-3245
Toll Free: (800) 621-1251
E-mail: marketing@goldeagle.com
Web Site: www.goldeagle.com
E-Mail For Key Personnel:
Marketing Director: pcomiski@goldeagle.com
Approx. Number Employees: 200
Year Founded: 1932
Business Description:
Automotive Additives, Cleaners & Fluids Developer, Mfr, Marketer & Distr
S.I.C.: 2992; 7539
N.A.I.C.S.: 324191; 811198
Media: 2-17-22
Personnel:
Robert F. Hirsch *(Chm)*
Randy Levy *(CFO)*
Manny Grijalva *(Chief Innovation Officer & Exec VP)*
Howard Donnally *(Exec VP-Sls, Customer Advocacy & Product Engrg)*
Ray Jablonski *(Exec VP-Ops)*
Rich Schwab *(VP-Sls-Intl)*
Tom Bingham *(Dir-Mktg)*
Brands & Products:
104+
ALUMASEAL
DIESELPOWER
D.O.G.G.
GOLD EAGLE
GOLDEN TOUCH
HEET
NO-LEAK
STA-BIL

GOODALL MFG. LLC
7558 Washington Ave S
Eden Prairie, MN 55344-3705
Tel.: (952) 941-6666
Fax: (952) 941-2617
Toll Free: (800) 328-7730
E-mail: info@goodallmfg.com
Web Site: www.goodallmfg.com
Sales Range: $400-449.9 Million
Approx. Number Employees: 26
Year Founded: 1962
Business Description:
Mfr. of Automotive Service Equipment, Portable Electric Light Plants, Air Hoses, Portable Airtanks, Parts Washers, Booster Air Compressors Cables & Battery Clamps, Tow Ropes & Straps, Extension Cords, Hitch Balls, Hooks, Winches, Gas Remover & Holder, Chargers, Engine Heaters, Battery, Radiator Flushers, First Aid Kits, Brushes & Scrapers
S.I.C.: 3714
N.A.I.C.S.: 336322
Media: 4-6-10-20-21
Distr.: Natl.
Budget Set: June

Key to Media (For complete agency information see *The Advertising Red Books-Agencies* edition):
1. Bus. Publs. 2. Cable T.V. 3. Catalogs & Directories. 4. Co-op Adv. 5. Consumer Mags. 6. D.M. to Bus. Estab.7. D.M. to Consumers 8. Daily Newsp. 9. Exhibits/Trade Shows 10. Foreign 11. Infomercial 12. Internet Adv.13. Multimedia 14. Network Radio 15. Network T.V. 16. Newsp. Distr. Mags. 17. Other 18. Outdoor (Posters, Transit) 19. Point of Purchase20. Premiums, Novelties 21. Product Samples 22. Special Events Mktg. 23. Spot Radio 24. Spot T.V. 25. Weekly Newsp. 26. Yellow Page Adv.

Goodall Mfg. LLC — (Continued)

Personnel:
Dave Sundet *(Chm & Pres)*
Brands & Products:
BOOST-ALL
CHARGE-ALL
CLEAN ALL
FLUSH-ALL
GAS-ALL
GOODALL
PROTECH
START-ALL
TECHGUARD
TOW-ALL
WINCH-ALL

GROTE INDUSTRIES, INC.
2600 Lanier Dr
Madison, IN 47250
Tel.: (812) 273-1296
Fax: (812) 265-8440
Toll Free: (800) 628-0809
E-mail: lora.mcmahon@grote.com
Web Site: www.grote.com
Approx. Rev.: $67,000,000
Approx. Number Employees: 688
Year Founded: 1901
Business Description:
Automotive Lighting Systems, Mirrors & Reflective Components Mfr
S.I.C.: 3647; 3231
N.A.I.C.S.: 336321; 327215
Import Export
Media: 2-4-5-7-8-10-19-21
Distr.: Intl.
Budget Set: Aug.
Personnel:
William D. Grote, III *(Chm & CEO)*
Dominic Grote *(Pres & COO)*
Jim Braun *(Exec VP)*
John Grote *(Sls Dir)*
William Stone *(Dir-Quality)*
Eric Thorstensen *(Dir-Sls)*
Chris Cammack *(Brand Mgr)*
Robert Holmes *(Mgr-OEM Sls-Southeastern Reg)*
Brands & Products:
BEEHIVE
BETT'S
BLUE CHIP
DRI-SEAL
DURAMOLD
ECONOLITE
THE FIRST NAME IN VEHICLE SAFETY SYSTEMS
FRUEHAUF
GROTE
GROTE SELECT
HI COUNT
HYLITE
METRI-PACK
MICRONOVA
NEXGEN
OBSTACLE DETECTION SYSTEM
PACK-CON
PACKARD
PER-LUX
REVERSE-A-MATIC SYSTEM
SLIDE-ON
SMART ALARM
STUD-TO-STUD
SUPERNOVA
SWITCH-TO-STARTER
TOP POST
TORSION MOUNT
TORSION MOUNT II
TURTLEBACK
TURTLEBACK II
ULTRA-BLUE-SEAL
ULTRA-NOSE-BOX
ULTRA-PIN
ULTRA-SEAL
ULTRALINK
VERSALITE
Advertising Agency:
Octane VTM
3650 Washington Blvd
Indianapolis, IN 46205
Tel.: (317) 920-6105

GUNITE CORPORATION
(Sub. of ACCURIDE CORPORATION)
302 Peoples Ave
Rockford, IL 61104-7035
Tel.: (815) 964-3301
Fax: (815) 964-0775
Toll Free: (800) 677-3786
Web Site: www.gunite.com
E-Mail For Key Personnel:
Marketing Director: tom.parsons@gunite.com
Sales Range: $250-299.9 Million
Approx. Number Employees: 664
Year Founded: 1854
Business Description:
Mfr. of Ferrous Spoke Wheels & Hubs, Brake Drums, Disc Brake Rotors & Automatic Slack Adjusters for Heavy-Duty Trucks & Trailers
S.I.C.: 3714
N.A.I.C.S.: 336399
Import Export
Media: 1-2-4-7-10-13-19
Distr.: Natl.
Budget Set: Oct.
Personnel:
Jasen Drenth *(Dir-Product Mgmt)*
Brands & Products:
GUNITE

HAHN AUTOMOTIVE WAREHOUSE, INC.
415 W Main St
Rochester, NY 14608-1944
Tel.: (585) 235-1595
Fax: (585) 235-8615
E-mail: inquiries@hahnauto.com
Web Site: www.hahnauto.com
Approx. Sls.: $125,575,000
Approx. Number Employees: 1,142
Year Founded: 1958
Business Description:
Automotive Aftermarket Warehouse Distr
S.I.C.: 5013
N.A.I.C.S.: 423120
Media: 9-18-25
Personnel:
Daniel J. Chessin *(Co-Pres)*
Eli Futerman *(Co-Pres)*
Daniel R. McDonald *(Gen Counsel & VP)*
Michael Bonacci *(Dir-Sls & Mktg)*

HAMILTON CASTER & MFG. CO.
1637 Dixie Hwy
Hamilton, OH 45011-4087
Tel.: (513) 863-3300
Fax: (513) 863-5508
Fax: (800) 232-3733
Toll Free: (888) 699-7164
E-mail: info@hamiltoncaster.com
Web Site: www.hamiltoncaster.com
Approx. Number Employees: 78
Year Founded: 1907
Business Description:
Truck Casters, Wheels & Non-Powered Floor Trucks Mfr, Supplier & Distr
S.I.C.: 3537; 3089
N.A.I.C.S.: 333924; 326199
Import Export
Advertising Expenditures: $240,000
Media: 2-7-8-10
Distr.: Natl.
Budget Set: Oct.
Personnel:
Dave Lippert *(Pres)*
Steve Lippert *(Exec VP)*
James Lippert *(VP-Sls)*
Mark J. Lippert *(VP-Mktg)*
Brands & Products:
ACE-TUF
AQUALITE
CUSH-N-AIRE
CUSH-N-FLEX
DELRIN
DURALAST
ENDURANCE
FORGEMASTER
HAMILTON
HI-LO
POLY-SOFT
POLY-TECH
POLYLAST
SUPER ENDURANCE
SUPER-FLEX
SUPER ULTRALAST
SUPERLAST
ULTRALAST
UNILAST
VERSA-TECH
VULCALITE

HASTINGS MANUFACTURING COMPANY, LLC
(Holding of The Anderson Group, LLC)
325 N Hanover St
Hastings, MI 49058-1527
Tel.: (269) 945-2491
Fax: (269) 945-4667
Toll Free: (800) 776-1088
Web Site: www.hastingsmfg.com
Sales Range: $25-49.9 Million
Approx. Number Employees: 400
Year Founded: 1915
Business Description:
Motor Vehicle Piston Rings Designer & Mfr
S.I.C.: 3592
N.A.I.C.S.: 336311
Export
Advertising Expenditures: $300,000
Media: 2-4-5-6-7-10-14-15-19-20
Distr.: Natl.
Budget Set: Sept.
Personnel:
Frederick A. Cook *(Pres & CEO)*
Robert M. Kollar *(COO)*
Brad Cousins *(Pres-China Ops)*
Richard L. Zwiernikowski, Jr. *(VP-Fin & Admin)*
Len Gawron *(Dir-OEM Sls)*
Dave Sepesi *(Dir-OEM Sls)*
Dan Titus *(Dir-OEM Sls)*
Kevin D. Willison *(Dir-IT)*
Randy Lunsford *(Mgr-Product Design & Analysis)*
Angela Tindall *(Coord-Mktg)*
Brands & Products:
FLEX-VENT
HASTINGS
HASTINGS TOUGH GUY
THE ORIGINAL RING LEADER
POWER FLEX

HAYES LEMMERZ INTERNATIONAL INC.
(Filed Ch 11 Bankruptcy #911671 on 05/11/2009 in U.S. Bankruptcy Ct, Dist of DE, Wilmington)
15300 Centennial Dr
Northville, MI 48168
Tel.: (734) 737-5000
Fax: (734) 737-2198
Toll Free: (800) 521-0515
E-mail: pr@hayes-lemmerz.com
Web Site: www.hayes-lemmerz.com
Sales Range: $1-4.9 Billion
Approx. Number Employees: 6,400
Year Founded: 1908
Business Description:
Supplier of Automotive & Commercial Highway Wheels, Brakes, Suspension & Other Components
S.I.C.: 3714; 3365; 3711
N.A.I.C.S.: 336399; 331524; 336211
Import Export
Media: 2-4-10
Personnel:
Curtis J. Clawson *(Chm, Pres & CEO)*
Mark A. Brebberman *(CFO & VP)*
Fred Bentley *(COO & Pres-Global Wheel Grp)*
Pieter Klinkers *(Pres-Europe, Africa & Asia Pacific)*
Patrick C. Cauley *(Gen Counsel, Sec & VP)*
Ed Meador *(VP-Sls & Ops)*
Christine M. Sweda *(Chief Tax Officer & Dir-Tax)*
Brands & Products:
CENTRIFUSE
CENTRULITE
CENTRUMOUNT
CENTRUSTEEL
FLEX
GEMTECH
HAYES LEMMERZ
HAYES LEMMERZ...WE KEEP THE WORLD ROLLING
NOVACHROME
VERSASTYLE

HBD INDUSTRIES, INC.
5200 Upper Metro Pl Ste 110
Dublin, OH 43017
Tel.: (614) 526-7000
Fax: (614) 526-7020
E-mail: nlaw@hbdindustries.com
Web Site: www.hbdindustries.com
Approx. Number Employees: 1,750
Year Founded: 1903
Business Description:
Automotive Hoses, Industrial & Aircraft Hoses, Ducting & Industrial Coated Fabrics, Belting, V-Belts, Rubber Bands & Urethane Rolls
S.I.C.: 3052; 3621
N.A.I.C.S.: 326220; 335312
Export
Media: 8-10
Distr.: Natl.
Budget Set: Oct.

Key to Media (For complete agency information see *The Advertising Red Books-Agencies* edition):
1. Bus. Publs. 2. Cable T.V. 3. Catalogs & Directories. 4. Co-op Adv. 5. Consumer Mags. 6. D.M. to Bus. Estab.7. D.M. to Consumers 8. Daily Newsp. 9. Exhibits/Trade Shows 10. Foreign 11. Infomercial 12. Internet Adv.13. Multimedia 14. Network Radio 15. Network T.V. 16. Newsp. Distr. Mags. 17. Other 18. Outdoor (Posters, Transit) 19. Point of Purchase20. Premiums, Novelties 21. Product Samples 22. Special Events Mktg. 23. Spot Radio 24. Spot T.V. 25. Weekly Newsp. 26. Yellow Page Adv.

Personnel:
Randy Greely *(Chm & CEO)*
Nelson K. Law *(Dir-Strategic Initiatives)*
Brands & Products:
AERODUCT
AIR POWER
AIRFLEX
ALARM
ATLAS
BELLOWSFLEX
BIG RED
BIGJOB
BLACK MAX
BLACK RACER
BLACK VALUFLEX
BLAST-FLEX
BURSTPROOF
CARIPACK
CHEVRON
CHLOROCHEM
CO-AX
COMMANDER
CONCURE
CONVERTAPIPE
CYCLONE
DURA-RED
EBONITE
EXCALIBUR
FLEX-LOC
FLEXKING
FLEXSEAL
FLEXSTRENGTH
FLIGHTMASTER
GLACIER
GLASSTEX
GOLDENAIR
GRAY SHADOW
GRIPTITE
GRIPTOP
HERCULES
HERCULES 500
HI-FLO
HI-FLO CO-AX
HI-VAC
HOT 'N COLD
HY-FLEX
HY-FLEX 200
KEVLAR
KOROWHITE
MAINLINER
MAXECON
MAXECON 300
MAXECON PLUS
MAXECON WASHDOWN
MAXIPOWER
METRIFLEX
MOVER
MULTI-CHEM
NEOFLEX
NOMEX
NYLOCK
POWERPLUS
PRIME MOVER
PUMPFLEX
PUMPFLEX I
PUMPFLEX II
RADIAL AIRE
RADIAL FLEX
RED VALUFLEX
RIBFLEX
SAFETYFLEX
SANI-KING
SANI-PURE
SANI-WHITE
SHOCKGUARD
SHOCKGUARD 300
SILFLEX
SLIDE-A-PACK
SLIPTOP
SUPERLITE
SURE-SET
SYNCHROBELT
TANKMASTER
THERMOID
TRACKMASTER
TRANSPORTER
TUFTEX
ULTRA-CHEM
ULTRAFLEX
UNICORD
VALUFLEX
VERSICON
WHITE LIGHTNING
ZEPHYR
Advertising Agency:
GWA Communications, Inc.
5200 Upper Metro Pl Ste 110
Dublin, OH 43017-5378
Tel.: (614) 526-7015
Fax: (614) 526-7020
(Thermoid, Industrial Hose, Ducting, V-Belts, Light Weight Conveyor Belting, Rubber Rolls, Rubber Bands)

HECKETHORN MANUFACTURING COMPANY, INC.

(Holding of Rosewood Acquisition Corporation)
2005 Forrest St
Dyersburg, TN 38024-3683
Tel.: (731) 285-3310
Fax: (731) 286-2739
Web Site: www.hecomfg.com
Approx. Number Employees: 400
Year Founded: 1963
Business Description:
Mfr of Automotive Component Parts; U-Bolts & Muffler Clamps
S.I.C.: 3714
N.A.I.C.S.: 336399
Export
Advertising Expenditures: $25,000
Media: 2-4
Distr.: Natl.
Budget Set: May
Personnel:
Jon Walter *(Pres & CEO)*
Tim McKinney *(VP-Pur & Matls)*
Gary Whittle *(VP-Engrg)*
Garry McArthur *(Dir-Quality Control)*
Dennis West *(Mgr-Product Design)*
Brands & Products:
HECO

HEHR INTERNATIONAL INC.

3333 Casitas Ave
Los Angeles, CA 90039-2207
Tel.: (323) 663-1261
Fax: (323) 666-2372
E-mail: cshehrla@hehrintl.com
Web Site: www.hehr-international.com
Approx. Number Employees: 1,050
Year Founded: 1946
Business Description:
Mfr. of Windows & Accessories for Mobile Homes, Recreational Vehicles, Vans, Toppers, Buses, Alternators, Generators, Battery Isolators
S.I.C.: 3442; 3231
N.A.I.C.S.: 332321; 327215
Import Export
Media: 2-4-7-10-20
Distr.: Intl.
Budget Set: July
Personnel:
Mary Utick *(Pres & CEO)*
Brands & Products:
HEHR
HEHR GLASS CO
HEHR INTERNATIONAL
HEHR POWERLINE

HEIL ENVIRONMENTAL INDUSTRIES, LTD.

(Sub. of Dover Industrial Products, Inc.)
2030 Hamilton Pl Blvd Ste 300
Chattanooga, TN 37421
Tel.: (423) 899-9100
Fax: (423) 855-3478
Toll Free: (800) 824-4345
E-mail: corp@heilco.com
Web Site: www.heil.com
Sales Range: $500-549.9 Million
Approx. Number Employees: 1,500
Year Founded: 1901
Business Description:
Refuse Collection Equipment, Dump Bodies & Hoist Mfr
S.I.C.: 3711; 3715
N.A.I.C.S.: 336211; 336212
Export
Advertising Expenditures: $650,000
Bus. Publs.: $390,000; D.M. to Consumers: $130,000; Exhibits/Trade Shows: $130,000
Distr.: Intl.; Natl.
Budget Set: Aug.
Personnel:
Pat Cerroll *(Pres)*
George Paterowski *(Gen Counsel, Sec & VP)*
Ken Daver *(Dir-Mktg)*
Anthony Henson *(Dir-North American Ops)*
Brands & Products:
DPF FORMULA
DURAPACK
FORMULA
HALF/PACK
HEIL
POWERLIFT
POWERTRACK
PT 1000
PYTHON
RAPID-RAIL
RETRIEVER
STARR

HENDRICKSON INTERNATIONAL

(Sub. of The Boler Company)
800 S Frontage Rd
Woodridge, IL 60517-4900
Tel.: (630) 910-2800
Fax: (630) 910-2899
Web Site: www.hendrickson-intl.com
Approx. Number Employees: 100
Business Description:
Truck Suspensions Mfr
S.I.C.: 3714
N.A.I.C.S.: 336399
Media: 10
Personnel:
Doug Sanford *(VP & Gen Mgr-Stamping)*
Baine Adams *(VP-Global Sls & Mktg)*
Jeff Zawacki *(Gen Mgr)*
Sean Coleman *(Dir-Sls, Truck OEM Products)*
John Morgan *(Mgr-Mktg)*

HENNESSY INDUSTRIES, INC.

(Sub. of Danaher Corporation)
1601 J P Hennessy Dr
La Vergne, TN 37086-3524
Tel.: (615) 641-7533
Fax: (615) 641-6069
Toll Free: (800) 688-6359
Web Site: www.hennessy-ind.com
Sales Range: $200-249.9 Million
Approx. Number Employees: 500
Year Founded: 1953
Business Description:
Automotive Service Equipment Mfr
S.I.C.: 3714; 3545
N.A.I.C.S.: 336399; 333515
Export
Media: 2-4-7-8-10-20
Distr.: Intl.; Natl.
Budget Set: Oct. -Nov.
Personnel:
Howard Hagan *(Reg VP)*
Kevin Keefe *(VP-Mktg)*
Brands & Products:
AMMCO
BADA
COATS
Advertising Agencies:
Conway Marketing Communications
6400 Baum Dr
Knoxville, TN 37919
Tel.: (865) 588-5731
Toll Free: (800) 882-7875

Gish, Sherwood & Friends, Inc. (d/b/a GS&F)
4235 Hillsboro Pike
Nashville, TN 37215-3344
Tel.: (615) 385-1100
Fax: (615) 783-0500

HOFFCO/COMET INDUSTRIES, INC.

358 NW F St
Richmond, IN 47374-2230
Tel.: (765) 966-8161
Fax: (765) 935-2346
Toll Free: (800) 999-8161
E-mail: aftsales@hoffcocomet.com
Web Site: www.hoffcocomet.com
Approx. Number Employees: 200
Year Founded: 1949
Business Description:
Transmissions, Clutches, Brakes & Drive System Components Mfr
S.I.C.: 3568; 3524
N.A.I.C.S.: 333613; 333112
Import Export
Advertising Expenditures: $150,000
Media: 2-5-6-10-18-19
Distr.: Intl.; Natl.
Budget Set: Various
Personnel:
John Bratt *(CEO)*
Brands & Products:
EZ HOE
HOFFCO/COMET
LI'L HOE

HOGEBUILT, INC.

(Sub. of Marmon Highway Technologies)
784 Bill Jones Industrial Dr
Springfield, TN 37172
Tel.: (626) 330-2356

Key to Media (For complete agency information see *The Advertising Red Books-Agencies* edition):
1. Bus. Publs. 2. Cable T.V. 3. Catalogs & Directories. 4. Co-op Adv. 5. Consumer Mags. 6. D.M. to Bus. Estab.7. D.M. to Consumers
8. Daily Newsp. 9. Exhibits/Trade Shows 10. Foreign 11. Infomercial 12. Internet Adv.13. Multimedia 14. Network Radio
15. Network T.V. 16. Newsp. Distr. Mags. 17. Other 18. Outdoor (Posters, Transit) 19. Point of Purchase20. Premiums, Novelties
21. Product Samples 22. Special Events Mktg. 23. Spot Radio 24. Spot T.V. 25. Weekly Newsp. 26. Yellow Page Adv.

Hogebuilt, Inc. — (Continued)

Toll Free: (800) 421-1589
E-mail: sales@hogebuilt.com
Web Site: www.hogebuilt.com
Sales Range: $300-349.9 Million
Business Description:
Truck & Trailer Spray Suppression Systems
S.I.C.: 3714
N.A.I.C.S.: 336330
Media: 2
Personnel:
Sean Swafford *(Dir-Aftermarket Sls-North America)*
Brands & Products:
HOGEBUILT

HOKE, INC.

(Sub. of CIRCOR International, Inc.)
405 Centura Ct
Spartanburg, SC 29303-6603
Tel.: (864) 574-7966
Fax: (864) 587-5608
E-mail: rtaylor@circortech.com
Web Site: www.hoke.com
Sales Range: $50-74.9 Million
Approx. Number Employees: 500
Year Founded: 1925
Business Description:
Fluid Controls Mfr
S.I.C.: 3492; 3498
N.A.I.C.S.: 332912; 332996
Media: 2-4-5-7-8-10-20-21-22
Distr.: Natl.
Budget Set: Nov.
Personnel:
Ven Robins *(VP & Gen Mgr)*
Brands & Products:
GO REGULATORS
GYROLOK
HOKE

HONEYWELL CONSUMER PRODUCTS GROUP

(Div. of Honeywell Transportation Systems)
39 Old Ridgebury Rd
Danbury, CT 06810-5109
Tel.: (203) 830-7800
Fax: (203) 830-7907
Toll Free: (800) 862-7737
Web Site: www.prestone.com
E-Mail For Key Personnel:
President: dave.lundstedt@honeywell.com
Sales Range: $1-4.9 Billion
Approx. Number Employees: 5,000
Year Founded: 1927
Business Description:
Mfr. & Distr of Antifreeze, Oil & Air Filters, Spark Plugs & Car Care Products
S.I.C.: 2899; 3714
N.A.I.C.S.: 325998; 336399
Export
Media: 2-3-4-5-6-10-15-19-20-21-23-24
Personnel:
David Lundstedt *(Pres)*
Guy Andrysic *(Sr VP-Sls)*
Jim Brown *(Dir-New Products)*
Megan Currie *(Product Mgr)*
Brands & Products:
AUTOMOTIVE STRENGTH PRESTONE
BLINK
FRAM
HOLTS
PRESTONE
PRESTONE 0 TO 60
PRESTONE BUG WASH
PRESTONE COLD START
PRESTONE JUMP IT
PRESTONE TIRE JACK
PRESTONE WINDSHIELD MELT
REDEX

HONEYWELL FRICTION MATERIALS

(Sub. of Honeywell International Inc.)
900 W Maple Rd
Troy, MI 48084
Tel.: (248) 362-7000
Fax: (248) 362-7078
Telex: 62887297 (FRAM GEN)
Web Site: www.bendixbrakes.com
Sales Range: $10-24.9 Million
Approx. Number Employees: 50
Year Founded: 1934
Business Description:
Brake Pads & Shoes Mfr & Distr
S.I.C.: 8733
N.A.I.C.S.: 541710
Import Export
Media: 2-3-5-6-7-10-13-14-15-19-20-22
Distr.: Natl.
Budget Set: Sept.
Personnel:
Rainer Bostel *(Mng Dir)*
Miquel Tintore *(VP-Sls)*
Shannon Lara *(Mgr-Mktg Svcs)*
Brands & Products:
BENDIX
BENDIX GLOBAL
ROADTUFF
Advertising Agency:
Keiler & Company
304 Main St
Farmington, CT 06032-2985
Tel.: (860) 677-8821
Fax: (860) 676-8164

HUB CITY, INC.

(Sub. of Regal Beloit Corporation)
2914 Industrial Ave
Aberdeen, SD 57401-3345
Mailing Address:
PO Box 1089
Aberdeen, SD 57402
Tel.: (605) 225-0360
Fax: (605) 225-0567
E-mail: sales@hubcityinc.com
Web Site: www.hubcityinc.com
E-Mail For Key Personnel:
Sales Director: sales@hubcityinc.com
Sales Range: $50-74.9 Million
Approx. Number Employees: 450
Year Founded: 1892
Business Description:
Mechanical Power Transmission Components Mfr
S.I.C.: 3568
N.A.I.C.S.: 333613
Import Export
Advertising Expenditures: $150,000
Media: 2-4-7-10-11-13-16-21
Distr.: Natl.
Budget Set: Oct.
Personnel:
Jim Campbell *(VP & Gen Mgr)*
Von Eschen *(VP-Engrg)*
Alton Vilhauer *(Mgr-Mktg)*
Brands & Products:
DURALINE
ILLINOIS GEAR
INDUSTRIALINE
POWERATIO
POWERTORQUE
SPARTAN

HUNTER ENGINEERING COMPANY

11250 Hunter Dr
Bridgeton, MO 63044-2306
Tel.: (314) 731-3020
Fax: (314) 731-1550
E-mail: info@hunter.com
Web Site: www.hunter.com
Approx. Number Employees: 300
Year Founded: 1946
Business Description:
Automotive Wheel Alignment Equipment, Wheel Balancers, Brake Lathes, Tire Changers, Lift Racks & Brake Testers Mfr
S.I.C.: 3559; 3829
N.A.I.C.S.: 333298; 334519
Export
Media: 1-2-4-7-10-11-13-19-20
Distr.: Intl.; Natl.
Personnel:
Stephen F. Brauer *(Chm)*
Nick Colarelli *(Exec VP)*
Dave Smith *(Sr VP)*
Beau Brauer *(VP-Mktg)*
Tom Meyer *(VP-Engrg & Matls)*
Joseph A. Staniszewski *(VP-Fin)*
Jay Zhang *(VP-Sls)*
Denny Bowen *(Dir-Product Mngmt)*
Carol Keeven *(Dir-Hunter Svc Center)*
Ron May *(Dir-Matls)*
Byron Morgan *(Dir-Trng)*
Ed Trenary *(Dir-Quality)*
Amin Alasgarli *(Reg Mgr)*
Patrick Callanan *(Mgr-Acct & Tech)*
Brands & Products:
ALIGNGUIDE
CAL-CHECK
CAMM
EXPRESSALIGN
FASTERCASTER
HUNTER
HUNTERPRO
LEVEL REMINDER
PARTHUNTER
RANGEFINDER
SERIES 511
SERIES 811
SERVODRIVE
SHIM-SELECT
SHOPRESULTS.NET
UNDERCARINFO.NET
VIDEOTECH
VIRTUAL VIEW
WEBSPECS.NET
WINALIGN
Advertising Agency:
H.E. Advertising
11250 Hunter Dr
Bridgeton, MO 63044-2306
Tel.: (314) 731-3020
Fax: (314) 731-1550
Fax: (314) 895-4432
(Auto Service Equip.)

HUTCHENS INDUSTRIES INC.

215 N Patterson Ave
Springfield, MO 65802
Tel.: (417) 862-5012
Fax: (417) 862-2317
Toll Free: (800) 654-8824
Web Site: www.hutch-susp.com
E-Mail For Key Personnel:
Marketing Director: mwhite@hutchensindustries.com
Sales Range: $100-124.9 Million
Approx. Number Employees: 300
Year Founded: 1950
Business Description:
Mfr. of Suspension Systems & Sliding Subframes for Trailers & Trucks; Custom Steel Fabrication; Stampings & Castings
S.I.C.: 3714; 3711
N.A.I.C.S.: 336399; 336211
Export
Advertising Expenditures: $100,000
Media: 2-4-10-13-20
Distr.: Intl.; Natl.
Budget Set: Mar.
Personnel:
Jeff Hutchens *(Pres & CEO)*
Russ Brazeal *(VP-Engrg)*
Jim Cantrell *(VP-Pur)*
Mike White *(VP-Sls)*
Louis King *(Mgr-Adv)*
Brands & Products:
HUTCH
Advertising Agency:
Cummings Group
New Towne Plz II 5301 E State St Ste 301
Rockford, IL 61108
Tel.: (815) 394-0184
Fax: (815) 394-0291

IAV AUTOMOTIVE ENGINEERING INC.

(Sub. of Ingenieurgesellschaft Auto und Verkehr)
15620 Technology Dr
Northville, MI 48168
Tel.: (734) 971-1070
Fax: (734) 233-3320
E-mail: info@iav-usa.com
Web Site: www.iav-usa.com
Approx. Number Employees: 80
Business Description:
Developer of Automotive Technology
S.I.C.: 8711
N.A.I.C.S.: 541330
Media: 10
Advertising Agency:
The Millerschin Group
3250 University Dr Ste 115
Auburn Hills, MI 48326
Tel.: (248) 276-1970

IMPCO TECHNOLOGIES, INC.

(Sub. of FUEL SYSTEMS SOLUTIONS, INC.)
3030 S Susan St
Santa Ana, CA 92704-6435
Tel.: (714) 656-1200
Fax: (714) 656-1400
E-mail: corporate@impcotechnologies.com
Web Site: www.impcotechnologies.com
Sales Range: $200-249.9 Million
Approx. Number Employees: 700
Year Founded: 1958
Business Description:
Alternative Gaseous Fuel Systems Technologies & Components Designer & Mfr
S.I.C.: 3519

Key to Media (For complete agency information see *The Advertising Red Books-Agencies* edition):
1. Bus. Publs. 2. Cable T.V. 3. Catalogs & Directories. 4. Co-op Adv. 5. Consumer Mags. 6. D.M. to Bus. Estab.7. D.M. to Consumers 8. Daily Newsp. 9. Exhibits/Trade Shows 10. Foreign 11. Infomercial 12. Internet Adv.13. Multimedia 14. Network Radio 15. Network T.V. 16. Newsp. Distr. Mags. 17. Other 18. Outdoor (Posters, Transit) 19. Point of Purchase20. Premiums, Novelties 21. Product Samples 22. Special Events Mktg. 23. Spot Radio 24. Spot T.V. 25. Weekly Newsp. 26. Yellow Page Adv.

N.A.I.C.S.: 333618
Import Export
Advertising Expenditures: $400,000
Media: 1-2-4-10-11-19
Distr.: Intl.; Natl.
Budget Set: Jan.
Personnel:
Peter J. Chase *(COO)*
Brands & Products:
ECLIPSE
IMPCO GASEOUS FUEL ENGINES
SPECTRUM

INDIAN HEAD INDUSTRIES, INC.
8530 Cliff Cameron Dr
Charlotte, NC 28269-9786
Tel.: (704) 547-7411
Fax: (704) 547-9367
Toll Free: (800) 527-1534
E-mail: mail@indianheadindustries.com
Web Site:
www.indianheadindustries.com
Sales Range: $50-74.9 Million
Approx. Number Employees: 650
Year Founded: 1984
Business Description:
Mfr of Heavy Duty Truck Spring Brakes
S.I.C.: 3714; 3593
N.A.I.C.S.: 336340; 333995
Import Export
Media: 2-7-10-11
Personnel:
Ronald I Parker *(Chm)*
Bryan Schrandt *(Sr VP-Worldwide Sls & Mktg)*
Rebecca Phillips-Parker *(VP-Comm & Bus Dev)*
Brands & Products:
E-STROKE
INDIAN HEAD INDUSTRIES.COM
MGM BRAKES

INTERSTATE BATTERY SYSTEM OF AMERICA INC.
12770 Merit Dr Ste 400
Dallas, TX 75251-1296
Tel.: (972) 991-1444
Fax: (972) 455-6533
E-mail: info@interstatebatteries.com
Web Site:
www.interstatebatteries.com
Sales Range: $10-24.9 Million
Approx. Number Employees: 800
Year Founded: 1991
Business Description:
Electrical Batteries Distr
S.I.C.: 3692; 3691
N.A.I.C.S.: 335912; 335911
Import Export
Media: 10-13-22
Personnel:
Norm Miller *(Chm)*
Carlos M. Sepulveda, Jr. *(Pres & CEO)*
Dennis Brown *(CMO & Sr VP)*
Chris Willis *(VP-HR & Counsel)*
Cynthia Mitchell *(Mgr-ECommerce Mktg)*
Advertising Agency:
Firehouse, Inc.
14860 Landmark Blvd No 247
Dallas, TX 75254
Tel.: (972) 692-0911
Fax: (972) 692-0912

JASON INCORPORATED
411 E Wisconsin Ave Ste 2120
Milwaukee, WI 53202
Tel.: (414) 277-9300
Fax: (414) 277-9445
E-mail: jasoninfo@jasoninc.com
Web Site: www.jasoninc.com
Approx. Sls.: $550,000,000
Approx. Number Employees: 3,400
Year Founded: 1985
Business Description:
Diversified Mfr Including Nonwoven Fabrics, Finishing Products & Precision Components
S.I.C.: 3999; 2297; 3053; 3465
N.A.I.C.S.: 339999; 313230; 336370; 339991
Import Export
Advertising Expenditures: $300,000
Distr.: Natl.
Personnel:
David C. Westgate *(Chm, Pres & CEO)*
John Hengel *(VP-Fin)*
Brands & Products:
JACKSON
JACKSONLEA
JANESVILLE
JASON
MARABOND
MARATEX
MARATEX PLUS
MILSCO
OSBORN
POLYLITE
POLYTEX
SEALEZE
SUROFLEX
TRUSPEC

JASPER ELECTRIC MOTORS
(Div. of Jasper Engine & Transmission Exchange)
733 W Division Rd
Jasper, IN 47546
Tel.: (812) 482-1660
Fax: (812) 634-1561
Toll Free: (800) 827-7470
Web Site:
www.jasperelectricmotors.com
E-Mail For Key Personnel:
Sales Director: sales@jasperengines.com
Approx. Number Employees: 15
Year Founded: 1952
Business Description:
Servicer of Industrial & Agricultural Electric Motors
S.I.C.: 7699; 5063
N.A.I.C.S.: 811310; 423610
Advertising Expenditures: $400,000
Media: 1-8-10-13-20-24
Distr.: Reg.
Budget Set: Oct.
Personnel:
Jeff Bawel *(Mgr)*
Brands & Products:
BALDOR

JASPER ENGINE & TRANSMISSION EXCHANGE
815 Wernsing Rd
Jasper, IN 47547
Tel.: (812) 482-1041
Fax: (812) 634-1820
Toll Free: (800) 827-7455
E-mail: sales@jasperengines.com
Web Site: www.jasperengines.com
E-Mail For Key Personnel:
Sales Director: sales@jasperengines.com
Sales Range: $200-249.9 Million
Approx. Number Employees: 900
Year Founded: 1942
Business Description:
Remanufacturing of Automobile & Truck Engines, Transmissions, Differentials, Marine Engines, Stern Drives & Electric Motors
S.I.C.: 5013
N.A.I.C.S.: 423120
Advertising Expenditures: $1,000,000
Media: 2-4-7-8-9-10-18-19-20-23-26
Distr.: Reg.
Budget Set: Jan.
Personnel:
Gervase Schwenk *(Chm)*
Doug Bawel *(Pres)*
Ray Schwenk *(Comptroller)*
Mike Pfau *(Mgr-Adv)*
Brands & Products:
JASPER

J.B. POINDEXTER & CO., INC.
600 Travis Ste 200
Houston, TX 77002-5218
Tel.: (713) 655-9800
Fax: (713) 951-9038
E-mail: info@jbpco.com
Web Site: www.jbpoindexter.com
Approx. Rev.: $553,561,000
Approx. Number Employees: 2,800
Year Founded: 1994
Business Description:
Motor Vehicle Body Mfr
S.I.C.: 3711; 3537; 3792
N.A.I.C.S.: 336112; 333924; 336214
Advertising Expenditures: $1,082,000
Personnel:
John B. Poindexter *(Chm & CEO)*
Michael O'Connor *(CFO)*
Robert Preston *(COO)*
Norbert Markert *(Pres/COO-Morgan Truck Body)*
Nelson Byman *(Pres-Specialty Mfg & MIC Grp)*
James Donahue *(Pres-Truck Accessories)*
Jay Krishnamurthy *(VP-IT)*

J.C. WHITNEY & CO.
(d/b/a The Riverside Group)
111 E Wacker Dr
Chicago, IL 60601
Tel.: (312) 431-6000
Fax: (312) 431-6166
Toll Free: (800) JCWHITNEY
Web Site: www.jcwhitney.com
Year Founded: 1915
Business Description:
Automotive Supplies & Equipment
S.I.C.: 5013; 4225
N.A.I.C.S.: 441310; 493110
Media: 2-4-5-10-13-26
Personnel:
Jerome Mascitti *(VP-Fin)*
Marc Delchecciolo *(Dir-Mktg-Print)*
Brands & Products:
EVERYTHING AUTOMOTIVE
J.C. WHITNEY
Advertising Agency:
Oneupweb
13561 S W Bayshore Dr Ste 3000
Traverse City, MI 49684
Tel.: (231) 922-9977
Fax: (231) 922-9966

Toll Free: (877) 568-7477

JEGS AUTOMOTIVE INC.
(d/b/a JEGS High Performance)
101 Jegs Pl
Delaware, OH 43015
Tel.: (614) 294-5050
Fax: (740) 362-7017
Toll Free: (800) 345-4545
E-mail: info@jegs.com
Web Site: www.jegs.com
Approx. Number Employees: 300
Year Founded: 1960
Business Description:
Automotive Part & Supply Mfr & Mail-Order Retailer
S.I.C.: 5013; 5961
N.A.I.C.S.: 423120; 454113
Media: 3-4-8-18-20-22

JIFFY LUBE INTERNATIONAL, INC.
(Sub. of Shell Oil Company)
910 Louisiana St
Houston, TX 77002
Tel.: (713) 546-4100
Fax: (713) 546-4101
Toll Free: (800) 252-0554, ext. 6272 (Pub Rels)
Web Site: www.jiffylube.com
Approx. Number Employees: 3,000
Year Founded: 1979
Business Description:
Oil Change Shop Owner, Operator & Franchisor
S.I.C.: 7549
N.A.I.C.S.: 811191
Media: 3-5-7-8-9-10-23-24-25
Distr.: Natl.
Personnel:
Larry Burch *(Pres)*
Brands & Products:
JIFFY LUBE
Advertising Agencies:
G2 Branding and Design
200 5th Ave
New York, NY 10010
Tel.: (212) 537-3700
Fax: (212) 537-3737

MMB
580 Harrison Ave
Boston, MA 02118
Tel.: (617) 670-9700
Fax: (617) 670-9711

JOHN BEAN
(Sub. of Snap-on Incorporated)
309 Exchange Ave
Conway, AR 72032
Tel.: (501) 450-2000
Fax: (501) 450-2085
Telex: 831-363
Web Site: www.johnbean.com
Sales Range: $75-99.9 Million
Approx. Number Employees: 200
Business Description:
Automotive Wheel Aligners & Wheel Balancers, Brake Service, Tire Changing & Truing Equipment, Engine Diagnostic Analyzers, Tools & Accessories for Auto & Truck Service
S.I.C.: 3559
N.A.I.C.S.: 333298
Media: 4

JOHNSON CONTROLS, INC.
5757 N Green Bay Ave
Milwaukee, WI 53209

Key to Media (For complete agency information see *The Advertising Red Books-Agencies* edition):
1. Bus. Publs. 2. Cable T.V. 3. Catalogs & Directories. 4. Co-op Adv. 5. Consumer Mags. 6. D.M. to Bus. Estab.7. D.M. to Consumers
8. Daily Newsp. 9. Exhibits/Trade Shows 10. Foreign 11. Infomercial 12. Internet Adv.13. Multimedia 14. Network Radio
15. Network T.V. 16. Newsp. Distr. Mags. 17. Other 18. Outdoor (Posters, Transit) 19. Point of Purchase20. Premiums, Novelties
21. Product Samples 22. Special Events Mktg. 23. Spot Radio 24. Spot T.V. 25. Weekly Newsp. 26. Yellow Page Adv.

Johnson Controls, Inc. — (Continued)

Mailing Address:
PO Box 591
Milwaukee, WI 53201-0591
Tel.: (414) 524-1200
Fax: (414) 524-2077
Telex: 4311074
E-mail: webmaster@jci.com
Web Site: www.johnsoncontrols.com
Approx. Sls.: $34,305,000,000
Approx. Number Employees: 137,000
Year Founded: 1885
Business Description:
Automotive Battery & Interior Systems Designer & Mfr; Facility Heating, Ventilation, Air Conditioning, Lighting, Fire & Safety Systems Designer, Mfr & Installer
S.I.C.: 3691; 2396; 3585; 3646; 3692; 3714; 3822; 9224
N.A.I.C.S.: 335911; 333415; 334512; 335122; 335912; 336360; 336399; 922160
Import Export
Media: 2-6-7-10-19-20-22-26
Distr.: Intl.; Natl.
Budget Set: Oct.
Personnel:
Stephen A. Roell *(Chm, Pres & CEO)*
R. Bruce McDonald *(CFO & Exec VP)*
Colin Boyd *(CIO & VP-IT)*
Giovanni Fiori *(Exec VP & Pres-Intl)*
Beda Bolzenius *(Pres-Automotive Experience & VP)*
Alex A. Molinaroli *(Pres-Power Solutions & VP)*
C. David Myers *(Pres-Building Efficiency & VP)*
Natalie A. Black *(Gen Counsel, Corp Sec & Sr VP)*
Jerome D. Okarma *(Gen Counsel, Sec & VP)*
Susan F. Davis *(Exec VP-HR)*
Bill Jackson *(Exec VP-Ops & Innovation)*
Jeff Williams *(Grp VP & Gen Mgr)*
John J. Murphy *(VP & Gen Mgr-North America Svc & Solutions)*
Susan M. Kreh *(VP-Fin-Power Solutions)*
Jacqueline F. Strayer *(VP-Corp Comm)*
Carolyn Woznicki *(VP-Pur)*
Paul Mason *(Exec Dir-Media Rels-Global)*
John Hein *(Dir-Global Mktg Comm)*
Terry Hoffmann *(Dir-Building Automation Sys Mktg)*
Paul Von Paumgartten *(Dir-Energy & Environment Affiairs)*
Debra Lacey *(Mgr-Pub Rel)*
Brands & Products:
ALL-POLYMER
AUTOVISION
BASO
BLUECONNECT
CARBOCAP
CARGOFLEX
CUTLER-HAMMER
EATON
HOMELINK
JOHNSON CONTROLS
METASYS
OPTIMA
OPTIVIEW
RAILPORT
SKYPAK
TRUERH
THE ULTIMATE POWER SOURCE
VARTA
YORK
YORK ISOFLOW
YORK LATITUDE
YORK MAXE
YORK PARAFLOW
YORK TITAN
YORKCALC
YORKWORKSCE
Advertising Agency:
Marx McClellan Thrun
(d/b/a MMT)
207 E Buffalo St Ste 643
Milwaukee, WI 53202
Tel.: (414) 277-7743
Fax: (414) 277-7784

JORDAN VALLEY AUTO BODY REPAIR
2945 W Sunshine St
Springfield, MO 65807
Tel.: (417) 227-9337
Toll Free: (866) 672-AUTO
Web Site: www.jordanvalleyabr.com
Approx. Number Employees: 18
Business Description:
Auto Body Repair & Painting
S.I.C.: 7532
N.A.I.C.S.: 811121
Media: 13-18-26

J.W. SPEAKER CORPORATION
N120 W19434 Freistadt Rd
Germantown, WI 53022-8211
Mailing Address:
PO Box 1011
Germantown, WI 53022-8211
Tel.: (262) 251-6660
Fax: (262) 251-2918
Toll Free: (800) 558-7288
E-mail: info@jwspeaker.com
Web Site: www.jwspeaker.com
Approx. Sls.: $130,000,000
Approx. Number Employees: 200
Year Founded: 1935
Business Description:
Vehicle Lighting Equipment Mfr
S.I.C.: 3647
N.A.I.C.S.: 336321
Import Export
Media: 2-4-7-8-21
Distr.: Natl.
Budget Set: Various
Personnel:
Jamie Speaker *(Co-Pres)*
Timothy J. Speaker *(Co-Pres)*
Brands & Products:
HEATAB
HIGH PERFORMANCE OVALS
SPEAKER
Advertising Agency:
Grasso & Halsey Advertising & Marketing Service
1505 11th Ave.
Grafton, WI 53024
Tel.: (262) 375-1015
Fax: (262) 375-1274

K&N ENGINEERING INC.
1455 Citrus St
Riverside, CA 92507
Mailing Address:
PO Box 1329
Riverside, CA 92502
Tel.: (951) 826-4000
Toll Free: (800) 858-3333
E-mail: tech@knfilters.com
Web Site: www.kandn.org
Approx. Number Employees: 190
Year Founded: 1967
Business Description:
Mfr. of Air Filters
S.I.C.: 3714
N.A.I.C.S.: 336399
Advertising Expenditures: $5,000,000
Media: 10
Brands & Products:
AIRCHARGER
FILTERCHARGER
K&N
PERFORMANCE GOLD

KENT AUTOMOTIVE
(Sub. of Lawson Products, Inc.)
1666 E Touhy Ave
Des Plaines, IL 60018
Tel.: (847) 827-9666
Fax: (847) 827-2084
Toll Free: (800) 654-6333
E-mail: info@kent-automotive.com
Web Site: www.kent-automotive.com
Sales Range: $200-249.9 Million
Approx. Number Employees: 500
Business Description:
Automotive Collision & Mechanical Repair Products Distr
S.I.C.: 5072; 5085
N.A.I.C.S.: 423710; 423840
Media: 2-10
Personnel:
Matt Brown *(Dir-Sls)*
Peter Mailman *(Reg Mgr)*
Alex Martinez *(Reg Mgr)*
Craig Oliveira *(Reg Mgr)*
Bill Pursel *(Reg Mgr)*
Larry Rosetti *(Reg Mgr)*
Brands & Products:
SUPERTANIUM

KEY SAFETY SYSTEMS, INC.
(Sub. of Crestview Partners, L.P.)
7000 Nineteen Mile Rd
Sterling Heights, MI 48314
Tel.: (586) 726-3800
Fax: (863) 668-6007
Web Site: www.keysafetyinc.com
Sales Range: $1-4.9 Billion
Approx. Number Employees: 9,000
Year Founded: 1987
Business Description:
Automotive Safety Systems & Electronic Components Mfr
S.I.C.: 3714; 3674
N.A.I.C.S.: 336399; 334413
Import Export
Advertising Expenditures: $300,000
Personnel:
Nick Scheele *(Chm)*
Jason Luo *(Pres & CEO)*
Dave Smith *(CFO & Sr VP-Specialty Bus Unit)*
Wendell Lane *(Pres-Seat Belts)*
Mark Wehner *(Pres-Safety Products Bus Unit)*
Larry Casey *(Sr VP-Global HR)*
Ron Feldeisen *(Sr VP-Sls & Mktg-Global)*
Greg Heald *(Sr VP-Bus Dev & Pur)*
Jim Scarpa *(Sr VP-Global Mfg & Quality)*
Tony Nardone *(VP & Gen Mgr-Gen Specialty Bus Unit)*

KEYSTONE AUTOMOTIVE INDUSTRIES, INC.
(Sub. of LKQ Corporation)
700 E Bonita Ave
Pomona, CA 91767
Tel.: (909) 624-8041
Fax: (909) 624-9136
Toll Free: (800) 772-5557
Web Site: www.keystone-auto.com
Sales Range: $700-749.9 Million
Approx. Number Employees: 4,000
Year Founded: 1947
Business Description:
Auto Parts Distr
S.I.C.: 5013; 3714
N.A.I.C.S.: 423120; 336399; 441310
Import Export
Media: 4-22
Personnel:
Joe Holsten *(Vice Chm & Co-CEO)*
Laurie Garcia *(Coord-Mktg)*
Brands & Products:
KEYSTONE
ORDERKEYSTONE.COM
PLATINUM PLUS
PLATINUM REFINISH
RAISING THE STANDARD SINCE DAY ONE

KEYSTONE AUTOMOTIVE OPERATIONS, INC.
(Holding of Platinum Equity, LLC)
44 Tunkhannock Ave
Exeter, PA 18643
Tel.: (570) 655-4514
Fax: (570) 655-4005
Toll Free: (800) 233-8321
Web Site:
www.keystoneautomotive.com
Approx. Sls.: $468,529,000
Approx. Number Employees: 1,444
Year Founded: 1971
Business Description:
Holding Company; Automotive Parts & Supplies Whslr & Retailer
S.I.C.: 6719; 5013
N.A.I.C.S.: 551112; 423120; 441310
Advertising Expenditures: $1,400,000
Media: 4-9-16-25
Personnel:
Edward H. Orzetti *(Pres & CEO)*
Richard S. Paradise *(CFO & Exec VP)*
Patrick Judge *(Exec VP & Compliance Officer)*
Kevin Canavan *(VP-Strategy, Bus Dev, RV & eCommerce)*
Rudy Esteves *(VP-HR)*
Mick O'Donovan *(VP-IT Ops)*
Chris Patti *(VP-Sls-US)*
Joe Santangelo *(VP-Consumer Ops)*
M. K. Sathya *(VP-Asset Mgmt & Mdsg)*
Greg Asselin *(Dir-Sls Tech & Master Data)*
Gerard Guler *(Dir-Process Improvement)*
Bob Hartmann *(Dir-Accts-Natl)*
Dawn Layauo *(Dir-HR Ops)*
Ivan Martinez *(Dir-Export)*
Lawrence Montante *(Dir-Category Mgmt Analysis)*
Jim Murosky *(Dir-Speed & Performance)*
Ron Travis *(Dir-Fulfillment Quality)*
Bill Voight *(Dir-Inventory Mgmt)*
Mike Isbell *(Mgr-Hard Parts)*

Key to Media (For complete agency information see *The Advertising Red Books-Agencies* edition):
1. Bus. Publs. 2. Cable T.V. 3. Catalogs & Directories. 4. Co-op Adv. 5. Consumer Mags. 6. D.M. to Bus. Estab.7. D.M. to Consumers
8. Daily Newsp. 9. Exhibits/Trade Shows 10. Foreign 11. Infomercial 12. Internet Adv.13. Multimedia 14. Network Radio
15. Network T.V. 16. Newsp. Distr. Mags. 17. Other 18. Outdoor (Posters, Transit) 19. Point of Purchase20. Premiums, Novelties
21. Product Samples 22. Special Events Mktg. 23. Spot Radio 24. Spot T.V. 25. Weekly Newsp. 26. Yellow Page Adv.

Brands & Products:
A&A AUTO PARTS

KRACO ENTERPRISES, LLC
(Holding of Sun Capital Partners, Inc.)
505 E Euclid Ave
Compton, CA 90222
Tel.: (310) 639-0666
Fax: (310) 603-2260
Toll Free: (800) 678-1910
E-mail: info@kraco.com
Web Site: www.kraco.com
E-Mail For Key Personnel:
Marketing Director: marketing@kraco.com
Sales Director: sales@kraco.com
Approx. Number Employees: 88
Year Founded: 1954
Business Description:
Automotive Floormat Mfr
S.I.C.: 3069; 5013
N.A.I.C.S.: 326299; 441310
Import Export
Advertising Expenditures: $8,500,000
Media: 2-4-5-6-9-10-14-15-18-19-23-24-25
Distr.: Natl.
Budget Set: Quarterly
Personnel:
Bob Brocoff *(Pres)*
Kent Friend *(Sr VP-Sls & Mktg)*
Bob Chaviz *(VP-Fin)*
Brands & Products:
CARGO
PREMIUM
Advertising Agency:
Kraco Enterprises
505 E Euclid Ave
Compton, CA 90224
Tel.: (310) 639-0666
Fax: (310) 603-2260
Fax: (310) 604-9838
Toll Free: (800) 678-1910
(Magazine Advertising)

KYB AMERICA LLC
(Sub. of Kayaba Industry Co., Ltd.)
140 N Mitchell Ct
Addison, IL 60101
Tel.: (630) 620-5555
Fax: (630) 620-8133
Web Site: www.kyb.com
E-Mail For Key Personnel:
Sales Director: mike@kyb.com
Approx. Number Employees: 70
Year Founded: 1974
Business Description:
Automotive Shock Absorbers, Industrial Hydraulic Motors & Components Mfr
S.I.C.: 5013; 3714
N.A.I.C.S.: 423120; 336399
Import Export
Advertising Expenditures: $500,000
Media: 1-2-4-5-6-10-13-16-19
Distr.: Intl.; Natl.
Budget Set: Dec.

LANCASTER COLONY AUTOMOTIVE GROUP
(Sub. of Lancaster Colony Corporation)
(d/b/a Rubber Queen)
437 Cambridge Rd
Coshocton, OH 43812
Tel.: (740) 622-3522
Fax: (740) 622-4915
Toll Free: (800) 837-9160
E-mail: info@rubberqueen.com
Web Site: www.rubberqueen.com
E-Mail For Key Personnel:
Marketing Director: terrin_williams@ppi-us.com
Approx. Sls.: $26,000,000
Approx. Number Employees: 260
Business Description:
Interior Automotive Accessories Including Floor Mats, Splash Guards, Consoles & Convenience Accessories Mfr
S.I.C.: 3069; 5013
N.A.I.C.S.: 326299; 441310
Import Export
Media: 2-4-5-6-8-10-19-21-24
Distr.: Natl.
Budget Set: July

THE LAS-STIK MFG. COMPANY
1441 Milburn Ave
Dayton, OH 45404
Tel.: (937) 236-6686
Fax: (937) 236-6123
Toll Free: (800) 628-9843
E-mail: info@las-stik.com
Web Site: www.las-stik.com
Approx. Number Employees: 9
Year Founded: 1915
Business Description:
Mfr. & Supplier of Wax Treated Dust Cloths, Upholstery Cleaners, Windshield Washer Solvent & Anti-Freeze
S.I.C.: 5169
N.A.I.C.S.: 424690
Media: 2-4-7-10-19-21
Distr.: Natl.
Budget Set: Mar.
Personnel:
Paul Stebel *(Pres)*
Brands & Products:
FREEMAN
GIT UM
LAS-STIK

LEE MYLES ASSOCIATES CORPORATION
650 From Rd S Lobby 4th Floor
Paramus, NJ 07652
Tel.: (610) 370-6900
Toll Free: (800) LEE-MYLES
Web Site: www.leemyles.com
Approx. Number Employees: 16
Year Founded: 1947
Business Description:
Lee Myles Transmission & AutoCare Centers Franchisor; Transmission & Automotive Repair Services
S.I.C.: 6794; 7537; 7538
N.A.I.C.S.: 533110; 811111; 811113
Advertising Expenditures: $500,000
Distr.: Reg.
Budget Set: Nov.
Personnel:
Sally A. Guido *(Pres & CEO)*
Sal Gargone *(Dir-Support & Trng)*
Advertising Agency:
Furman Roth Advertising
801 2nd Ave 14th Fl
New York, NY 10017-4706
Tel.: (212) 687-2300
Fax: (212) 687-0858
(Automotive Transmissions)
— Mark Leftkowitz *(Acct. Exec.)*

LES SCHWAB TIRE CENTERS OF OREGON, INC.
646 NW Madras Hwy PO Box 667
Prineville, OR 97754
Tel.: (541) 447-4136
Fax: (541) 416-5488
Web Site: www.lesschwab.com
Sales Range: $1-4.9 Billion
Approx. Number Employees: 7,000
Year Founded: 1952
Business Description:
Tires, Batteries, Alignment Machinery & Wheels Retailer
S.I.C.: 5013; 5014; 7534
N.A.I.C.S.: 441320; 326212; 423130; 441310
Media: 10-13-18-22-23-24-26
Personnel:
John Britton *(Pres)*
Richard B. Borgman *(CEO)*
Jim Goad *(Treas & VP-Fin)*
Brian Capp *(VP-Mktg)*
Emy Stafford *(Supvr-Media)*

LIQUID GLAZE, INC.
6017 Jordan Rd
Toccoa, GA 30577-9353
Mailing Address:
PO Box 506
Toccoa, GA 30577
Tel.: (706) 886-6853
Fax: (706) 678-1557
Toll Free: (800) 458-7873
E-mail: liquidglaze@alltel.net
Web Site: www.liquidlustre.com
Approx. Number Employees: 10
Year Founded: 1927
Business Description:
Automobile Cleaning Compound & Finish
S.I.C.: 2842; 5169
N.A.I.C.S.: 325612; 424690
Media: 2-7
Distr.: Intl.; Natl.
Budget Set: June
Personnel:
J. C. Lawson *(Pres)*
Brands & Products:
LIQUID LUSTRE
METAL LUSTRE
VINYL LUSTRE

LIQUID RESINS INTERNATIONAL, LTD.
4295 N Holly Rd
Olney, IL 62450
Tel.: (618) 392-3590
Fax: (618) 392-3202
E-mail: sales@liquidresins.com
Web Site: www.liquidresins.com
E-Mail For Key Personnel:
Sales Director: sales@liquidresins.com
Sales Range: $10-24.9 Million
Approx. Number Employees: 14
Business Description:
Windshield Repairer
S.I.C.: 7539
N.A.I.C.S.: 811198
Media: 6
Personnel:
James Pottor *(Pres)*

LOJACK CORPORATION
200 Lowder Brook Dr Ste 1000
Westwood, MA 02090-1190
Tel.: (781) 326-4700
Fax: (781) 251-4649
Toll Free: (800) 4-LOJACK
Web Site: www.lojack.com
Approx. Rev.: $146,635,000
Approx. Number Employees: 624
Year Founded: 1978
Business Description:
Stolen Vehicle & Personal Property Location & Recovery Devices
S.I.C.: 3669; 3661; 3663
N.A.I.C.S.: 334290; 334210; 334220
Export
Advertising Expenditures: $2,130,000
Media: 7-8-19-23
Distr.: Direct to Consumer; Intl.; Natl.
Personnel:
Richard T. Riley *(Chm)*
Randy L. Ortiz *(Pres & CEO)*
Donald R. Peck *(CFO & Exec VP)*
Kathleen P. Lundy *(Gen Counsel & VP)*
Timothy P. O'Connor *(Exec VP)*
Paul Joseph Weichselbaum *(Exec VP)*
Thomas M. Camp *(Sr VP & Gen Mgr-Intl)*
Kevin M. Mullins *(Sr VP & Gen Mgr-US Automotive)*
Jeremy Warnick *(Mgr-Corp Comm)*
Brands & Products:
LOJACK
LOJACK EARLY WARNING
LOJACK FOR LAPTOPS
LOJACK VEHICLE RECOVERY SYSTEM

LONG MOTOR CORPORATION
14600 W 107th St
Lenexa, KS 66215
Mailing Address:
PO Box 14991
Lenexa, KS 66215
Tel.: (913) 541-1525
Tel.: (913) 541-8500
Tel.: (913) 541-0880
Fax: (913) 599-0323
Fax: (913) 599-3299
Toll Free: (800) 255-0088
Toll Free: (800) 222-5664
Web Site: www.longmotor.com
Approx. Sls.: $106,000,000
Approx. Number Employees: 140
Year Founded: 1984
Business Description:
Automotive Supply Mail Order Retailer
S.I.C.: 5961; 5013
N.A.I.C.S.: 454113; 423120
Media: 4
Personnel:
Janet Long *(VP-Sls, Mktg & Res Dev)*
Susan Berkowitz *(Mgr-Mktg)*

LONNIE MCCURRY'S FOUR WHEEL DRIVE CENTER, INC.
(d/b/a Skyjacker)
212 Stevenson St
West Monroe, LA 71292
Mailing Address:
PO Box 1678
West Monroe, LA 71294-1678
Tel.: (318) 388-0816
Fax: (318) 388-2608
Web Site: www.skyjacker.com
Approx. Number Employees: 48
Year Founded: 1973
Business Description:
Mfr of Motor Vehicle Parts & Supplies
S.I.C.: 5013
N.A.I.C.S.: 423120
Media: 3-4-10-13-18-20-22

Key to Media (For complete agency information see *The Advertising Red Books-Agencies* edition):
1. Bus. Publs. 2. Cable T.V. 3. Catalogs & Directories. 4. Co-op Adv. 5. Consumer Mags. 6. D.M. to Bus. Estab.7. D.M. to Consumers
8. Daily Newsp. 9. Exhibits/Trade Shows 10. Foreign 11. Infomercial 12. Internet Adv.13. Multimedia 14. Network Radio
15. Network T.V. 16. Newsp. Distr. Mags. 17. Other 18. Outdoor (Posters, Transit) 19. Point of Purchase20. Premiums, Novelties
21. Product Samples 22. Special Events Mktg. 23. Spot Radio 24. Spot T.V. 25. Weekly Newsp. 26. Yellow Page Adv.

Lonnie McCurry's Four Wheel Drive Center, Inc. — (Continued)

Personnel:
Lonnie McCurry, Sr. *(Pres & CEO)*
Nell McCurry *(Chief Admin Officer)*
Cindy Acree *(Exec Dir)*
Lee McGuire *(Supvr-Mktg)*

Brands & Products:
SKYJACKER

LUND INTERNATIONAL, INC.

(Holding of Linsalata Capital Partners Inc.)
4325 Hamilton Mill Rd Ste 400
Buford, GA 30518
Tel.: (770) 339-5800
Fax: (770) 688-2057
Toll Free: (888) 588-6049
Web Site: www.lundinternational.com
Approx. Number Employees: 900
Year Founded: 1997
Business Description:
Automotive Accessory Mfr
S.I.C.: 3714
N.A.I.C.S.: 336399
Export
Advertising Expenditures: $1,000,000
Media: 1-3-4-5-6-7-10-12-13-16-17-19-21-22-24
Distr.: Intl.
Budget Set: Apr.
Personnel:
George Scherff *(Owner)*

Brands & Products:
AEROSHADE
AEROSHIELD
AEROSHIELD CUSTOM
AEROSHIELD-PLUS
AEROSHIELD WAVE
AUTO VENTSHADE
AVENGER
BACKBLADE
BACKDRAFT
BELMOR
BUGFLECTOR
BUGFLECTOR II
BUGSCREEN
CARFLECTOR
CARGO LINER
CARGO-LOGIC
CATCH-ALL
CATCH-ALL X-RACING
CATCH-ALL X-TREME
CHALLENGER
CHAMELEON
COLDFRONT
CONCEPT II
CONTENDER
DEFLECTA-SHIELD
DELTA III
DURALOADER
ECLIPSE
EZ BRACKET
FASTBACK
FRONT RUNNER
GATEKEEPER
GENESIS
HITCH HAND
HITCHSTEP
INTERCEPTOR
LUNAR
LUND
LUND SUNVISOR
MAGNUM
MOONVISOR
NIFTY
NITROWING
PREMIER
PRO-LINE
RACERBACK
RADSTEP
RUNNERS
SCREENFRONT
SEAL-TITE
SHADOW
SIDETRACKER
SLOTS
SOLAR
SPORTRAILS
SPORTREND
SPORTTUBES
STAINLESS INTERCEPTOR
STAINLESS STEPSHIELD
STEPMATES
STEPRAIL
STEPSHIELD
STYLERS
SUNFLECTOR
SUNVISOR
SUNVISOR II
SUPERSTEP
TAIL-LOADER
TAIL-LOADER II
TAILGATOR
TAILMATE
TAILSHADES
TAILSHADES2
TRAILBACK
TRAILRUNNER
TRENZ
TRIDENT
TURBO VENTS
ULTIMA
VENTA-LATORS
VENTSHADE
VENTVISOR
WINDFLOW BLADE
WINTERSHIELD
WRAPPERS
X-STEP
X-TERMINATOR

MAACO FRANCHISING, INC.

(Holding of Driven Brands, Inc.)
(d/b/a MAACO Collision Repair & Auto Painting)
610 Freedom Business Ctr Ste 200
King of Prussia, PA 19406
Tel.: (610) 265-6606
Fax: (610) 337-6113
Web Site: www.maaco.com
Approx. Sls.: $67,243,401
Approx. Number Employees: 150
Year Founded: 1972
Business Description:
Franchiser of Auto Painting & Bodywork Shops
S.I.C.: 7532
N.A.I.C.S.: 811121
Media: 3-8-9-18-23-24
Distr.: Natl.
Budget Set: Various
Personnel:
David M. Lapps *(Pres)*
Eileen Moran *(VP-Adv)*
Advertising Agency:
Printz Advertising
610 Freedom Bus Ctr Ste 200
King of Prussia, PA 19406
Tel.: (610) 265-6606
Fax: (610) 337-6189
(Maaco Auto Painting & Bodyworks; The Goddard School for Early Childhood Development)

MACNEIL AUTOMOTIVE PRODUCTS, LTD.

2435 Wisconsin Ave
Downers Grove, IL 60515
Tel.: (630) 769-1500
Fax: (630) 769-0300
Toll Free: (800) 441-6287
E-mail: sales@macneil.com
Web Site: www.weathertech.com
E-Mail For Key Personnel:
Sales Director: sales@macneil.com
Approx. Number Employees: 40
Year Founded: 1989
Business Description:
Automotive Accessories Mfr & Retailer
S.I.C.: 5013
N.A.I.C.S.: 441310; 423120
Media: 2-6-13
Personnel:
David MacNeil *(Founder & CEO)*
Sam Ezzo *(Art Dir)*
Carolyn Little *(Coord-Mktg)*
Brands & Products:
ADVANTAGE
AIRCUSHION
CLASSIC
CLEARCOVER
CLEARFRAME
CLICK AND STAY
DIGITALIFT
EASY-ON
FLOORLINER
LAMPGARD
LET THE FRESH AIR IN
MACNEIL
MAGICLIP
MATGRIP
MAX
PETSTEP
PIAA
PLATEFRAME
RACKSACK
TECHNOFLEX
WEATHERTECH

MAGNA CLOSURES

(Sub. of Magna International Inc.)
521 Newpark Blvd
Newmarket, ON L3Y 4X7, Canada
Tel.: (905) 898-2665
Fax: (905) 853-0377
E-mail: info@magnaclosures.com
Web Site: www.magnaclosures.com
Sales Range: $1-4.9 Billion
Approx. Number Employees: 250
Year Founded: 2001
Business Description:
Vehicle Interior & Closure Systems & Components Mfr
S.I.C.: 3711; 3714
N.A.I.C.S.: 336211; 336340
Import Export
Distr.: Intl.; Natl.
Budget Set: Dec.
Personnel:
Frank Seguin *(Pres)*
Brands & Products:
SHAPING THE INNER DIMENSION
Advertising Agency:
Quell Communications Group
2075 W Big Beaver Rd Ste 415
Troy, MI 48084
Tel.: (248) 649-8900

MAGNA DONNELLY CORPORATION

(Sub. of Magna International Inc.)
49 W 3rd St
Holland, MI 49423
Tel.: (616) 786-7000
Fax: (616) 786-6235
E-mail: information@magnadon.com
Web Site: www.donnelly.com
Year Founded: 1905
Business Description:
International Supplier of Automotive Parts & Component Systems
S.I.C.: 3231; 3647
N.A.I.C.S.: 327215; 336321
Import Export
Advertising Expenditures: $200,000
Media: 2-4-8-10-21-24
Distr.: Intl.; Natl.
Budget Set: Nov.
Brands & Products:
EC COMPTEMP
INTELLIGENT MIRROR
LANECHEK
PANORAMICVISION
SPM

MAGNA INTERNATIONAL INC.

337 Magna Drive
Aurora, ON L4G 7K1, Canada
Tel.: (905) 726-2462
Fax: (905) 726-7455
Telex: 6 966856
Web Site: www.magnaint.com
Approx. Sls.: $24,102,000,000
Approx. Number Employees: 96,600
Year Founded: 1961
Business Description:
Automotive Parts Mfr
S.I.C.: 3714; 3711
N.A.I.C.S.: 336399; 336211; 336340
Import Export
Media: 6-7-8-17-25-26
Distr.: Intl.; Natl.
Personnel:
Donald James Walker *(CEO)*
Vincent J. Galifi *(CFO & Exec VP)*
James J. Tobin, Sr. *(Pres-Japan/Korea & CMO)*
Jeffrey O. Palmer *(Chief Legal Officer & Exec VP)*
Herbert Demel *(Pres-China/India/Southeast Asia/South America/Africa & Exec VP)*
Manfred Eibeck *(Pres-Russia & Exec VP-Europe)*
Guenther Apfalter *(Pres-Europe)*
Thomas Schultheiss *(Gen Counsel & VP-Europe)*
Peter Koob *(Exec VP-Corp Dev)*
Marc Neeb *(Exec VP-HR-Global)*
Alon Ossip *(Exec VP)*
Gerd R. Brusius *(VP-Corp Sls & Mktg)*
Hubert Hodl *(VP-Mktg & New Bus Dev-Europe)*
Patrick W.D. McCann *(VP-Fin)*
Scott E. Paradise *(VP-Mktg & New Bus Dev-Americas)*
Brands & Products:
COSMA
DECOMA
INTIER AUTOMOTIVE
MAGNA
TESMA
WHERE IT ALL COMES TOGETHER

Key to Media (For complete agency information see *The Advertising Red Books-Agencies* edition):
1. Bus. Publs. 2. Cable T.V. 3. Catalogs & Directories. 4. Co-op Adv. 5. Consumer Mags. 6. D.M. to Bus. Estab.7. D.M. to Consumers 8. Daily Newsp. 9. Exhibits/Trade Shows 10. Foreign 11. Infomercial 12. Internet Adv.13. Multimedia 14. Network Radio 15. Network T.V. 16. Newsp. Distr. Mags. 17. Other 18. Outdoor (Posters, Transit) 19. Point of Purchase20. Premiums, Novelties 21. Product Samples 22. Special Events Mktg. 23. Spot Radio 24. Spot T.V. 25. Weekly Newsp. 26. Yellow Page Adv.

Advertising Agency:
Quell Communications Group
2075 W Big Beaver Rd Ste 415
Troy, MI 48084
Tel.: (248) 649-8900
— Michael Niederquell *(Acct Exec)*

MASTERRACKCROWN
(Sub. of Leggett & Platt, Incorporated)
7315 E Lincoln Way
Apple Creek, OH 44606
Tel.: (330) 262-6010
Fax: (330) 262-4095
Toll Free: (800) 321-4934
E-mail: info@crown-na.com
Web Site: www.crown-na.com
E-Mail For Key Personnel:
Marketing Director: angie.massaro@legplatt.com
Sales Director: mgordon@crown-na.com
Sales Range: $600-649.9 Million
Approx. Number Employees: 420
Year Founded: 1941
Business Description:
Special Vehicle Bodies & Interiors
S.I.C.: 7538
N.A.I.C.S.: 811111
Import Export
Media: 4-5-6-7-8-10-20
Distr.: Natl.
Budget Set: Jan.
Personnel:
Walter Kissinger *(Chm & CEO)*
Brands & Products:
MASTERLITE
POWERMASTER
SLIDE-DOWN

MCI SERVICE PARTS, INC.
(Sub. of Motor Coach Industries International, Inc.)
7001 Universal Coach Dr
Louisville, KY 40258
Fax: (800) 525-4569
Toll Free: (800) 323-1290
Web Site: www.mcicoach.com
Approx. Number Employees: 1,100
Year Founded: 1971
Business Description:
Bus Repair & Replacement Parts
S.I.C.: 5013
N.A.I.C.S.: 423120
Import Export
Media: 2-4-5-7-10-20-26
Distr.: Natl.
Personnel:
Derrick Anderson *(Gen Mgr)*

MEINEKE CAR CARE CENTERS, INC.
(Holding of Driven Brands, Inc.)
128 S Tryon St Ste 900
Charlotte, NC 28202
Tel.: (704) 377-8855
Fax: (704) 377-1490
Toll Free: (800) MEINEKE
Web Site: www.meineke.com
E-Mail For Key Personnel:
President: ken_walker@meineke.com
Marketing Director: john_vitagliano@meineke.com
Sales Range: $1-9.9 Million
Approx. Number Employees: 110
Year Founded: 1972
Business Description:
Muffler & Brake Repair Services
S.I.C.: 7538; 7539
N.A.I.C.S.: 811111; 811198
Media: 3-8-9-15-23-24-26
Distr.: Natl.
Budget Set: Quarterly
Personnel:
Kenneth D. Walker *(Chm & CEO)*
Keenan V. Moran *(Pres & COO)*
John Vitagliano *(VP-Mktg & Dealer Comm)*
Nancy Truesdale *(Dir-Adv)*
Brands & Products:
MEINEKE
Advertising Agencies:
ID Media
(Part of the Interpublic Group of Companies)
100 W 33rd St
New York, NY 10001
Tel.: (212) 907-7011
Fax: (212) 907-7290
Lead Agency (Print)

Wyse
668 Euclid Ave
Cleveland, OH 44114
Tel.: (216) 696-2424
Fax: (216) 736-4425
Lead Agency (Creative)
Media Planning

MERITOR, INC.
(Formerly ArvinMeritor, Inc.)
2135 W Maple Rd
Troy, MI 48084
Tel.: (248) 435-1000
Fax: (248) 435-1393
Toll Free: (866) INFO-ARM
Web Site: www.meritor.com/default.aspx
Approx. Sls.: $3,590,000,000
Approx. Number Employees: 12,514
Year Founded: 1909
Business Description:
Integrated Systems, Modules & Components Supplier to the Motor Vehicle Industry
S.I.C.: 3714; 3479; 3493; 3711
N.A.I.C.S.: 336399; 332611; 332812; 336211; 336340
Import Export
Media: 10-11-13
Personnel:
Charles G. McClure, Jr. *(Chm, Pres & CEO)*
Jeffrey A. Craig *(CFO)*
Carsten J. Reinhardt *(COO)*
Timothy E. Bowes *(Pres-Comml Truck & VP)*
Joe Mejaly *(Pres-Aftermarket & Trailer & VP)*
Vernon G. Baker II *(Gen Counsel & Sr VP)*
Linda M. Cummins *(Sr VP-Comm)*
Mary A. Lehmann *(Sr VP-Treasury, Corp Dev, Comm & IR)*
Larry Ott *(Sr VP-HR)*
Larry Burgin *(VP & Gen Mgr-Trailer Products-Worldwide)*
Krista Sohm *(VP-Comm)*
Craig Cartmill *(Gen Mgr-Ops-Comml Vehicle Aftermarke Bus-Worldwide)*
Terry Livingston *(Gen Mgr-Americas)*
John Nelligan *(Gen Mgr-OEM Sls & Natl Accts)*
Matthew Stevenson *(Gen Mgr-Field Ops & Mktg-North America)*
Krista McClure *(Sr Dir-Corp Comm)*
Brett Penzkofer *(Sr Dir-Fin-Truck Americas)*
Jerry Rush *(Sr Dir-Govt Affairs & Community Rels)*
Rick Decaire *(Dir-East Region Sls)*
Aaron Bickford *(Dir-Mktg)*
Christy Daehnert *(Dir-IR)*
David Giroux *(Dir-Global Brand Mgmt & Mktg Comm-Americas)*
Carl Anderson *(Asst Treas)*
Brands & Products:
EUCLID MEGA
EUCLID STOP MATE
FUMAGALLI
GABRIEL
LITEFLEX
LITEPEDAL
MERITOR
MXL
ONGUARD
RIDESENTRY
RPL PERMALUBE
SACHSTWINEXTEND
SMART SYSTEMS
Advertising Agencies:
Budco Creative Services
13700 Oakland Ave
Highland Park, MI 48203
Tel.: (313) 957-5100
Fax: (313) 957-5522
Toll Free: (888) BUDCO-40

The Buntin Group
1001 Hawkins St
Nashville, TN 37203-4758
Tel.: (615) 244-5720
Fax: (615) 244-6511

MICO, INCORPORATED
1911 Lee Blvd
North Mankato, MN 56003-2507
Mailing Address:
PO Box 8118
Mankato, MN 56002-8118
Tel.: (507) 625-6426
Fax: (507) 625-3212
E-mail: micomail@mico.com
Web Site: www.mico.com
Approx. Number Employees: 245
Year Founded: 1946
Business Description:
Hydraulic Brake Systems & Components Mfr
S.I.C.: 3714; 3561
N.A.I.C.S.: 336340; 333911
Export
Advertising Expenditures: $200,000
Media: 1-2-4-7-10-11-21
Distr.: Intl.; Natl.
Budget Set: Oct.
Personnel:
Brent McGrath *(Pres-MICO)*
Len Walton *(Dir-Sls & Mktg)*
Pete Marso *(Product Mgr)*
Dona Rehome *(Coord-Mktg)*
Brands & Products:
INNOVATIVE BRAKING AND CONTROLS WORLDWIDE
MICO

MIDAS, INC.
1300 N Arlington
Itasca, IL 60143
Tel.: (630) 438-3000
Fax: (630) 438-3880
Web Site: www.midas.com
Approx. Rev.: $192,400,000
Approx. Number Employees: 940
Year Founded: 1956
Business Description:
Franchisor of Muffler Shops; Automotive Aftermarket Mufflers, Exhausts, Brakes & Suspension Products & Services
S.I.C.: 5088; 7533; 7538
N.A.I.C.S.: 423860; 811111; 811112
Advertising Expenditures: $9,300,000
Media: 1-3-5-6-8-9-10-11-13-14-15-18-19-23-24-26
Distr.: Intl.; Natl.
Budget Set: Oct.
Personnel:
Alan D. Feldman *(Chm, Pres & CEO)*
William M. Guzik *(CFO & Exec VP)*
Frederick W. Dow, Jr. *(CMO & Sr VP)*
Alvin K. Marr *(Gen Counsel, Sec & Sr VP)*
Ben Parma *(VP-HR)*
Brands & Products:
MIDAS
MIDAS TOUCH
SECURESTOP
TRUST THE MIDAS TOUCH
Advertising Agency:
Euro RSCG Worldwide
36 E Grand Ave
Chicago, IL 60611-3506
Tel.: (312) 337-4400
Fax: (312) 337-5930
Fax: (312) 337-2316

MIDAS INTERNATIONAL, INC.
(Sub. of Midas, Inc.)
1300 N Arlington Hts Rd
Itasca, IL 60143-3174
Tel.: (630) 438-3000
Fax: (630) 438-3700
E-mail: info@midasinc.com
Web Site: www.midas.com/AboutMidas/AroundtheWorld/tabid/165/Default.aspx
Sales Range: $100-124.9 Million
Approx. Number Employees: 140
Business Description:
Franchisor of Muffler Shops; Automotive Aftermarket Mufflers, Exhausts, Brakes & Suspension Products & Services
S.I.C.: 5012; 5088; 7533; 7538
N.A.I.C.S.: 423110; 423860; 811111; 811112
Advertising Expenditures: $3,900,000
Personnel:
William M. Guzik *(CFO & Exec VP)*
Frederick W. Dow, Jr. *(CMO & Sr VP)*
Alvin K. Marr *(Gen Counsel, Sec & Sr VP)*
John E. Brisson Jr. *(VP & Fin-Planning)*
Ben Parma *(VP-HR)*
Lisa Wellington *(Sr Mgr-Mktg Plng)*

MIGHTY DISTRIBUTING SYSTEM OF AMERICA
650 Engineering Dr
Norcross, GA 30092-2821
Tel.: (770) 448-3900
Fax: (770) 446-8627
E-mail: editor@mightyautoparts.com
Web Site: www.mightyautoparts.com
Approx. Sls.: $76,000,000
Approx. Number Employees: 50
Year Founded: 1970

Key to Media (For complete agency information see *The Advertising Red Books-Agencies* edition):
1. Bus. Publs. 2. Cable T.V. 3. Catalogs & Directories. 4. Co-op Adv. 5. Consumer Mags. 6. D.M. to Bus. Estab.7. D.M. to Consumers
8. Daily Newsp. 9. Exhibits/Trade Shows 10. Foreign 11. Infomercial 12. Internet Adv.13. Multimedia 14. Network Radio
15. Network T.V. 16. Newsp. Distr. Mags. 17. Other 18. Outdoor (Posters, Transit) 19. Point of Purchase20. Premiums, Novelties
21. Product Samples 22. Special Events Mktg. 23. Spot Radio 24. Spot T.V. 25. Weekly Newsp. 26. Yellow Page Adv.

Mighty Distributing System of America — (Continued)

Business Description:
Franchise System of Distributing Automotive Parts to Professional Shops
S.I.C.: 6794; 5013
N.A.I.C.S.: 533110; 423120
Import Export
Advertising Expenditures: $1,500,000
Distr.: Natl.
Budget Set: Oct.
Personnel:
Ken Voelker *(Pres & COO)*
Pelham Wilder *(CFO & VP-Fin)*
Gary Vann *(Sr VP-Sls & Mktg)*
Scott Dees *(Gen Mgr)*
Brands & Products:
ENGINE GUARD II
MIC PLUS
MIGHTY
MIGHTY SYSTEM XL
MIGHTY TECSELECT
MIGHTY VS7
POWERCORE
STORM GUARD
Advertising Agency:
Agency South
3762 Old Bridge Way
Atlanta, GA 30136
Tel.: (770) 476-0709
(Auto Parts; Professional Technicians)

MILE MARKER INTERNATIONAL INC.

2121 Blunt Rd
Pompano Beach, FL 33069
Tel.: (954) 782-0604
Fax: (954) 782-0770
Toll Free: (800) 886-8647
E-mail: info@milemarker.com
Web Site: www.milemarker.com
Sales Range: $10-24.9 Million
Approx. Number Employees: 12
Year Founded: 1980
Business Description:
Automotive Supplies & Parts Mfr & Distr
S.I.C.: 3714; 5012
N.A.I.C.S.: 336399; 423110
Advertising Expenditures: $366,000
Media: 4
Personnel:
Lisa R. Aho *(Dir-Sls)*
Brands & Products:
ABUSED WORLD WIDE
MIFI TECHNOLOGY
MILE MARKER

MIRACLE POWER PRODUCTS CORP.

1101 Belt Line St
Cleveland, OH 44109-2849
Tel.: (216) 741-1388
Fax: (216) 741-1391
E-mail: info@miraclepowerproducts.com
Web Site:
www.miraclepowerproducts.com
Approx. Number Employees: 10
Year Founded: 1950
Business Description:
Mfr of Automotive, Industrial & Aircraft Lubricants
S.I.C.: 5172
N.A.I.C.S.: 424720
Export
Media: 2-4-8-10-22
Distr.: Intl.; Natl.
Budget Set: Oct.
Personnel:
Brian Fialko *(Pres)*
Brands & Products:
DFG-123
DGF
MIRACLE
MIRACLE POWER
SAF
WGF

MIZATI LUXURY ALLOY WHEELS, INC.

19929 Harrison Ave
Walnut Creek, CA 91789
Tel.: (909) 839-5118
Fax: (909) 525-1369
E-mail: sales@mizatiwheels.com
Web Site: www.mizatiwheels.com
E-Mail For Key Personnel:
Sales Director: sales@mizatiwheels.com
Approx. Rev.: $241,248
Approx. Number Employees: 3
Year Founded: 2001
Business Description:
Custom Luxury Wheels Mfr & Distr
S.I.C.: 3714; 5013
N.A.I.C.S.: 336399; 423120
Advertising Expenditures: $4,499
Media: 5-10-22
Personnel:
Hazel Chu *(Pres & CEO)*
Brands & Products:
AMORE
APOLLO
BLAST
DOUBLE D
FACE OFF
FIX
FURIOUS
FUSION
GALAN
GRAND
GRANDE
HERO
ILLUMINATI
KLICK
MAESTRO
MIZATI
MZ 1
PIPER
REBEL
ROGUE
RONIN
SAGE
SAINT
SALIENT
SAVANT
SEER
STIX
STRENGTH
TORO
ZATI

MK AUTOMOTIVE, INC.

5833 West Tropicana Ave
Las Vegas, NV 89103
Tel.: (702) 227-8324
Fax: (800) 491-1160
Toll Free: (800) 970-0793
E-mail: info@mikesmastermechanics.com
Web Site:
www.mikesmastermechanics.com
Approx. Sls.: $4,659,263
Year Founded: 2002
Business Description:
Automotive Repair Services
S.I.C.: 7538
N.A.I.C.S.: 811111
Advertising Expenditures: $42,168
Media: 17
Personnel:
Michael R. Murphy *(Pres)*

MONRO MUFFLER BRAKE, INC.

200 Holleder Pkwy
Rochester, NY 14615
Tel.: (585) 647-6400
Fax: (585) 647-0945
Toll Free: (800) 876-6676
Web Site: www.monro.com
Approx. Sls.: $636,678,000
Approx. Number Employees: 5,005
Year Founded: 1966
Business Description:
Automobile Repair Service Shops for Mufflers, Brakes, Front End & Tires
S.I.C.: 7538; 7533
N.A.I.C.S.: 811111; 811112
Media: 2-6-7-8-9-10-18-22-23-26
Distr.: Reg.
Budget Set: Mar.
Personnel:
Robert G. Gross *(Chm & CEO)*
John W. Van Heel *(Pres)*
Catherine D'Amico *(CFO, Treas & Exec VP-Fin)*
Joseph Tomarchio, Jr. *(Exec VP-Stores Ops)*
David M. Baier *(VP-Mdsg)*
Robert E. Mullen *(VP-HR)*
James P. Prinzi *(VP-Mktg & Adv)*
Brands & Products:
AUTOTIRE
MONRO
MONRO MUFFLER BRAKE & SERVICE
MR. TIRE
TIRE WAREHOUSE
TREAD QUARTERS DISCOUNT TIRE
TRUST & CONFIDENCE

MORAN INDUSTRIES, INC.

(d/b/a Mr. Transmission & Multistate Transmission)
4444 147th St
Midlothian, IL 60445-2644
Tel.: (708) 389-5922
Fax: (708) 389-9882
Toll Free: (800) 377-9247
Web Site: www.moranindustries.com
Approx. Rev.: $5,000,000
Approx. Number Employees: 20
Year Founded: 1958
Business Description:
Franchisors of Multistate Transmissions, Transmission Repair & Service Centers
S.I.C.: 7537
N.A.I.C.S.: 811113
Import Export
Media: 13
Distr.: Intl.
Budget Set: Various
Personnel:
Dennis Moran *(Chm)*
Barbara Moran *(CEO)*
Brands & Products:
ATLAS TRANSMISSION
DR. NICK'S TRANSMISSION
MILEX
MORAN INDUSTRIES
MR. TRANSMISSION
MULTISTATE TRANSMISSIONS

MOTION INDUSTRIES, INC.

(Sub. of Genuine Parts Company)
1605 Alton Rd
Birmingham, AL 35210-3770
Mailing Address:
PO Box 1477
Birmingham, AL 35201-1477
Tel.: (205) 956-1122
Fax: (205) 951-1172
Toll Free: (800) 526-9328
Web Site: www.motionindustries.com
Sales Range: $1-4.9 Billion
Approx. Number Employees: 6,320
Year Founded: 1946
Business Description:
Bearings, Power Transmission & Fluid Power Replacement Parts Distr
S.I.C.: 5085
N.A.I.C.S.: 423840
Export
Media: 1-2-4-5-7-8-10-11-13-16-20-22-26
Distr.: Intl.; Natl.
Budget Set: Aug.
Personnel:
William J. Stevens *(Pres & CEO)*
Robert J. Summerlin *(COO-Indus Products/Integrated Svcs & Exec VP-Mktg)*
Thomas L. Miller *(COO & Exec VP)*
Ellen H. Holladay *(CIO)*
G. Harold Dunaway, Jr. *(Exec VP-Fin/ Admin & Sec)*
M. Wayne Law *(Exec VP)*
Tmothy P. Breen *(Sr VP & Group Exec)*
James R. Neill *(Sr VP-HR)*
Thomas S. Robertshaw *(Sr VP)*
Kevin P. Storer *(Sr VP & Grp Exec)*
C. Jeff Rouse *(Grp VP-East)*
Gerald V. Sourbeer *(Grp VP-Bus Solutions & Svcs)*
John D. Walters *(Grp VP-Southwest)*
Linda Price *(VP-Mktg)*
William E. Horn *(Mgr-Strategic Accts)*

MOTORCAR PARTS OF AMERICA, INC.

(d/b/a MPA)
2929 California St
Torrance, CA 90503-3914
Tel.: (310) 212-7910
Fax: (310) 212-7581
E-mail: info@commercegroupcorp.com
Web Site: www.motorcarparts.com
Approx. Sls.: $161,285,000
Approx. Number Employees: 1,689
Year Founded: 1968
Business Description:
Remanufacturer of Automotive Replacement Alternators & Starters
S.I.C.: 5084; 3625; 3714
N.A.I.C.S.: 423830; 335314; 336322
Advertising Expenditures: $368,000
Personnel:
Selwyn H. Joffe *(Chm, Pres & CEO)*
David Lee *(CFO)*
Steven Kratz *(COO)*
Kevin Daly *(Chief Acctg Officer)*
Mervyn Mcculloch *(Chief Acq Officer)*
Michael Umansky *(Gen Counsel, Sec & VP)*
Alex Alvarez *(VP-Fin & Strategic Plng)*

Key to Media (For complete agency information see *The Advertising Red Books-Agencies* edition):
1. Bus. Publs. 2. Cable T.V. 3. Catalogs & Directories. 4. Co-op Adv. 5. Consumer Mags. 6. D.M. to Bus. Estab.7. D.M. to Consumers
8. Daily Newsp. 9. Exhibits/Trade Shows 10. Foreign 11. Infomercial 12. Internet Adv.13. Multimedia 14. Network Radio
15. Network T.V. 16. Newsp. Distr. Mags. 17. Other 18. Outdoor (Posters, Transit) 19. Point of Purchase20. Premiums, Novelties
21. Product Samples 22. Special Events Mktg. 23. Spot Radio 24. Spot T.V. 25. Weekly Newsp. 26. Yellow Page Adv.

John Foster *(VP-Mktg)*
Ron Lacombe *(VP-Traditional Sls)*
Rick Mochulsky *(VP-Sls)*
Brands & Products:
QUALITY-BUILT
RELIANCE
TALON
XTREME

MR. GASKET INC.
10601 Memphis Ave Ste 12
Brooklyn, OH 44144-2043
Tel.: (216) 688-8300
Fax: (216) 688-8307
Fax: (216) 688-8305
E-mail: mrgasket@mrgasket.com
Web Site: www.mrgasket.com
Sales Range: $75-99.9 Million
Approx. Number Employees: 180
Year Founded: 1965
Business Description:
Mfr of Automotive Accessories
S.I.C.: 3714; 5013
N.A.I.C.S.: 336399; 423120
Import Export
Advertising Expenditures: $2,000,000
Media: 1-2-3-4-5-6-7-10-13-18-19-21-22-24
Distr.: Natl.
Personnel:
Bob Bruegging *(VP-Sls)*

MRC BEARINGS
(Sub. of SKF USA Inc.)
402 Chandler St
Jamestown, NY 14701
Tel.: (716) 661-2600
Fax: (716) 661-2740
E-Mail For Key Personnel:
Marketing Director: steve.j.koehler@skf.com
Approx. Number Employees: 600
Year Founded: 1902
Business Description:
Ball & Roller Bearings for Aerospace Applications Mfr
S.I.C.: 3562
N.A.I.C.S.: 332991
Media: 4-6-10
Distr.: Direct to Consumer; Intl.; Natl.
Budget Set: Jan.
Personnel:
Cheryl Johnson *(Mgr-Comm)*

MULTIPLE ALLIED SERVICES, INC.
(dba Miracle Auto Painting)
(Filed Ch 11 Bankruptcy #947577 on 08/17/09 in U.S. Bankruptcy Ct, Northern Dist of CA, Oakland)
2343 Lincoln Ave
Hayward, CA 94545-1117
Tel.: (510) 887-2211
Fax: (510) 887-3092
Toll Free: (877) MIRACLE
E-mail: info@miracleautopainting.com
Web Site:
www.miracleautopainting.com
E-Mail For Key Personnel:
Marketing Director: jim@miracleautopainting.com
Sales Range: $10-24.9 Million
Approx. Number Employees: 100
Year Founded: 1953
Business Description:
Auto Painting & Body Repair Services
S.I.C.: 6794; 7532
N.A.I.C.S.: 533110; 811121
Advertising Expenditures: $450,000
Media: 2-18
Distr.: Reg.
Budget Set: Nov.
Brands & Products:
MIRACLE

MURRAY'S DISCOUNT AUTO STORES
(Sub. of O'Reilly Automotive Inc.)
8080 Haggerty Rd
Belleville, MI 48111-1643
Tel.: (734) 957-8080
Fax: (734) 957-8156
Toll Free: (877) 808-0698
Web Site: www.murraysdiscount.com
Sales Range: $200-249.9 Million
Approx. Number Employees: 2,200
Year Founded: 1972
Business Description:
Retail Automotive Services
S.I.C.: 5013
N.A.I.C.S.: 441310
Advertising Expenditures: $2,500,000
Media: 4-5-8-9-18-23-24-26
Distr.: Reg.
Brands & Products:
MURRAY'S DISCOUNT AUTO STORES

NATIONAL AUTOMOTIVE PARTS ASSOCIATION
(Div. of Genuine Parts Company - U.S. Automotive Parts Group)
(d/b/a NAPA)
2999 Cir 75 Pkwy SE
Atlanta, GA 30339-3050
Tel.: (770) 956-2200
Fax: (770) 956-2212
Web Site: www.napaonline.com
Approx. Number Employees: 31,000
Year Founded: 1925
Business Description:
Automotive Replacement Parts Mfr & Whslr
S.I.C.: 5013; 3714
N.A.I.C.S.: 423120; 336399
Media: 1-2-3-5-6-7-9-10-15-18-19-20-23-24-25-26
Distr.: Natl.
Budget Set: Aug.
Personnel:
Tom Gallagher *(Chm, Pres & CEO)*
Brands & Products:
NAPA
TRACS

NATIONAL SEATING CO.
(Sub. of Commercial Vehicle Group, Inc.)
200 National Dr
Vonore, TN 37885-2124
Tel.: (423) 884-6651
Fax: (423) 884-6166
Toll Free: (800) 222-7328
E-mail: info@cvgrp.com
Web Site: www.cvgrp.com
Sales Range: $200-249.9 Million
Approx. Number Employees: 500
Year Founded: 1920
Business Description:
Mfr of Bus & Truck Seating
S.I.C.: 3714
N.A.I.C.S.: 336399
Export
Advertising Expenditures: $100,000
Media: 4-10-26
Distr.: Intl.
Budget Set: Oct.
Personnel:
Merv Dunn *(Pres & CEO)*
Raymond Miller *(VP-Sls & Mktg)*
Chris Wilson *(Product Mgr)*
Brands & Products:
BACKCYCLER
CUSH-N-AIRE
EASY-AIRE
NATIONAL 2000

NEAPCO, INC.
(Holding of United Components, Inc.)
740 Queen St
Pottstown, PA 19464-6014
Mailing Address:
PO Box 399
Pottstown, PA 19464-0399
Tel.: (610) 323-6000
Fax: (610) 326-3857
Toll Free: (800) 821-2374
E-mail: info@neapco.com
Web Site: www.neapco.com
Approx. Number Employees: 300
Year Founded: 1921
Business Description:
U-Joints, P-T-O Shafts & Drive Line Transmission Components
S.I.C.: 3714; 3568
N.A.I.C.S.: 336350; 333613
Import Export
Media: 2-4-7-10-20-21
Distr.: Natl.
Personnel:
Robert Hawkey *(Pres & CEO)*
J. Lion *(Sr VP-Fin & Admin)*
David Scheick *(Asst Controller)*
Brands & Products:
NEAPCO

NISSAN CANADA INC.
(Sub. of Nissan Motor Co., Ltd.)
5290 Orbitor Dr
Mississauga, ON L4W 4Z5, Canada
Tel.: (905) 629-2888
Fax: (905) 629-9742
Web Site: www.nissancanada.com
Approx. Number Employees: 300
Business Description:
Car & Truck Distr
S.I.C.: 5511
N.A.I.C.S.: 441110
Media: 1-2-4-6-8-9-10-11-14-15-16-18-19-20-21-22-25-26
Distr.: Intl.; Natl.
Budget Set: Mar.
Personnel:
Allen Childs *(Pres)*
Jeff M. Parent *(VP-Sls & Mktg)*
Asgar Molu *(Gen Mgr)*
Judy Wheeler *(Dir-Mktg)*
Didier Marsaud *(Sr Mgr-Corp Comm)*
Advertising Agencies:
OMD Canada
67 Richmond St W 2nd Fl
Toronto, ON M5H 1Z5, Canada
Tel.: (416) 681-5600
Fax: (416) 681-5620

TBWA Toronto
10 Lower Spadina Ave
Toronto, ON M5V 2Z2, Canada
Tel.: (416) 260-6600
Fax: (416) 260-8088
(Infiniti, Versa)

OFF ROAD UNLIMITED CORP.
300 N Victory Blvd
Burbank, CA 91504
Tel.: (818) 848-2020
Fax: (818) 729-1919
Toll Free: (888) 365-0244
E-mail: info@offroadunlimited.com
Web Site: www.offroadunlimited.com
Approx. Number Employees: 45
Year Founded: 1977
Business Description:
Retailer of Automotive & Off Road Parts & Installation Services
S.I.C.: 5013
N.A.I.C.S.: 423120; 441310
Media: 6-10-13
Personnel:
Maurice Rozo *(Owner)*
Brands & Products:
ORU
YOU'VE EARNED IT. YOU DESERVE IT. WE HAVE IT!

ONSTAR CORPORATION
(Sub. of General Motors Company)
400 Renaissance Ctr
Detroit, MI 48243
Tel.: (248) 588-6050
Toll Free: (888) 4-ONSTAR
E-mail: info@onstar.com
Web Site: www.onstar.com
Business Description:
Automotive Safety Technology
S.I.C.: 7382
N.A.I.C.S.: 561621
Media: 2-6-10-15
Personnel:
Linda Marshall *(Pres)*
Sam Mancuso *(CMO)*
Brands & Products:
ONSTAR
Advertising Agencies:
Campbell-Ewald
30400 Van Dyke Ave
Warren, MI 48093-2368
Tel.: (586) 574-3400
Fax: (586) 575-9925

Deutsch, Inc.
(A Lowe & Partners Company)
111 8th Ave 14th Fl
New York, NY 10011-5201
Tel.: (212) 981-7600
Fax: (212) 981-7525

MVP Collaborative
1751 E Lincoln Ave
Madison Heights, MI 48071
Tel.: (248) 591-5100
Fax: (248) 591-5199

OPTIMA BATTERIES, INC.
(Sub. of Johnson Controls Power Solutions Group)
17500 E 22nd Ave
Aurora, CO 80011
Tel.: (888) 867-8462
Fax: (303) 344-9905
Toll Free: (888) 8OPTIMA
E-mail: questions@optimabatteries.com
Web Site: www.optimabatteries.com
Sales Range: $50-74.9 Million
Approx. Number Employees: 190
Year Founded: 2001
Business Description:
Automotive Batteries

Key to Media (For complete agency information see *The Advertising Red Books-Agencies* edition):
1. Bus. Publs. 2. Cable T.V. 3. Catalogs & Directories. 4. Co-op Adv. 5. Consumer Mags. 6. D.M. to Bus. Estab.7. D.M. to Consumers
8. Daily Newsp. 9. Exhibits/Trade Shows 10. Foreign 11. Infomercial 12. Internet Adv.13. Multimedia 14. Network Radio
15. Network T.V. 16. Newsp. Distr. Mags. 17. Other 18. Outdoor (Posters, Transit) 19. Point of Purchase20. Premiums, Novelties
21. Product Samples 22. Special Events Mktg. 23. Spot Radio 24. Spot T.V. 25. Weekly Newsp. 26. Yellow Page Adv.

Optima Batteries, Inc. — (Continued)

S.I.C.: 3692; 3691
N.A.I.C.S.: 335912; 335911
Media: 2-3-6-15-20
Brands & Products:
OPTIMA
OPTIMA SPIRALCELL
THE ULTIMATE POWER SOURCE
Advertising Agency:
Stir Advertising & Integrated Marketing
252 E Highland Ave
Milwaukee, WI 53202
Tel.: (414) 278-0040
Fax: (414) 278-0390

O'REILLY AUTOMOTIVE INC.
233 S Patterson Ave
Springfield, MO 65802-2210
Mailing Address:
PO Box 1156
Springfield, MO 65801-1156
Tel.: (417) 862-6708
Fax: (417) 874-7145
E-mail: orlyap@oreillyauto.com
Web Site: www.oreillyauto.com
Approx. Sls.: $4,847,062,000
Approx. Number Employees: 30,379
Year Founded: 1957
Business Description:
Automotive Aftermarket Parts, Tools, Supplies, Equipment & Accessories Distributor & Supplier to Do-it-Yourself Customers & Professional Mechanics
S.I.C.: 5013
N.A.I.C.S.: 441310
Advertising Expenditures: $72,927,000
Media: 3-5-8-9-13-14-15-18-22-23-24-25-26
Personnel:
David E. O'Reilly *(Chm)*
Charles H. O'Reilly, Jr. *(Vice Chm)*
Lawrence P. O'Reilly *(Vice Chm)*
Greg L. Henslee *(CEO & Co-Pres)*
Ted F. Wise *(COO & Co-Pres)*
Thomas McFall *(CFO & Exec VP-Fin)*
Gregory D. Johnson *(Sr VP-Distr Ops)*
Randy Johnson *(Sr VP-Inventory Mgmt)*
David McCready *(Sr VP-Distr Ops)*
Jeff Shaw *(Sr VP-Stores Sls & Ops)*
Mike Swearengin *(Sr VP-Mdse)*
Tony Bartholomew *(VP-Sls)*
Greg Beck *(VP-Pur)*
Steve Jasinski *(VP-Info Sys)*
Michelle M. Kimrey *(VP-Fin)*
Thomas Seboldt *(VP-Mdse)*
Phillip Thompson *(VP-HR)*
Douglas Adams *(Dir-Atlanta East Reg)*
Thomas Allen *(Dir-Store Computer Ops)*
Jeanene Asher *(Dir-Telecom)*
Emmitt Barina *(Dir-Safety, Environmental & Regulatory Compliance)*
Bert Bentley *(Dir-Houston)*
Robert Bodenhamer *(Dir-IT)*
David Glore *(Dir-Ozark Sls)*
Jim Maynard *(Dir-Employment & Team Member Rel)*
Curt Miles *(Dir-Indianapolis)*
Brad Oplotnik *(Dir-Sys Mgmt)*
Art Rodriguez *(Dir-Southern Div Sls)*
Chuck Rogers *(Dir-Sls & Admin)*
Denny Smith *(Dir-Springfield)*
Charlie Stallcup *(Dir-Trng)*
Wes Wise *(Dir-Mktg)*
Douglas Bragg *(Reg Mgr)*
Brands & Products:
AUTO VALUE
O'REILLY
O'REILLY AUTO PARTS
PROFESSIONAL PARTS PEOPLE
Advertising Agencies:
Carat
150 E 42nd St
New York, NY 10017
Tel.: (212) 689-6800
Fax: (212) 689-6005
O'Reilly Automotive Inc.
— Margaret Chunn *(Acct Exec-O'Reilly Automotive)*

Meridian Creative Alliance
113 E Church St
Ozark, MO 65721-8313
Tel.: (417) 581-2884
Fax: (417) 581-2906
Toll Free: (800) 955-2884

PARKHURST MANUFACTURING CO., INC.
18999 Hwy Y
Sedalia, MO 65301
Mailing Address:
PO Box 1323
Sedalia, MO 65301
Tel.: (660) 826-8685
Fax: (660) 826-8688
Toll Free: (800) 821-7380
Web Site: www.parkhurstmfg.com
E-Mail For Key Personnel:
President: rob@parkhurstmfg.com
Sales Director: sales@parkhurstmfg.com
Approx. Number Employees: 30
Year Founded: 1946
Business Description:
Truck Bodies Mfr; Machine Tooling & Custom Fabrication Services
S.I.C.: 3711
N.A.I.C.S.: 336211
Media: 4-5-7-10-13-16
Distr.: Natl.
Budget Set: Nov.
Personnel:
Mike Harris *(Pres)*
Laurie Boer *(Exec VP)*
Sam Trelow *(VP-Sls)*
Brands & Products:
PARKHURST

PARTS DEPOT, INC.
2147 Dale Ave SE
Roanoke, VA 24013-2147
Tel.: (540) 345-1001
Fax: (540) 983-7974
Web Site: www.parts-depot.com
Approx. Number Employees: 1,350
Year Founded: 1948
Business Description:
Motor Vehicle Supplies & Parts Whslr
S.I.C.: 5013
N.A.I.C.S.: 423120; 441310
Media: 2
Personnel:
Rollance E. Olson *(CEO)*

PENDA CORPORATION
(Joint Venture of Littlejohn & Co. LLC & Resilience Capital Partners LLC)
2344 W Wisconsin St PO Box 449
Portage, WI 53901
Tel.: (608) 742-5301
Fax: (608) 742-9413
E-mail: info@penda.com
Web Site: www.penda.com
Sales Range: $100-124.9 Million
Approx. Number Employees: 400
Year Founded: 1994
Business Description:
Plastic Products & Truck Accessories Mfr; Owned by Resilience Capital Partners LLC & Littlejohn & Co. LLC
S.I.C.: 5013; 3089; 3714
N.A.I.C.S.: 423120; 326199; 336399
Media: 2-7-10-13
Personnel:
Ulf Buergel *(Pres & CEO)*
Tim Williams *(VP-Sls, Mktg & Bus Dev)*
Dion Beyer *(Mgr-Quality)*
Brands & Products:
HIDE-A-HOOK
PENDA
PENDALINER
PENDALINER SR
SKID RESISTOR
SMARTDITCH
TRI-WING
TUFFLINER
VENTURE

THE PEP BOYS - MANNY, MOE & JACK
3111 W Allegheny Ave
Philadelphia, PA 19132-1116
Tel.: (215) 430-9000
Fax: (215) 430-4660
Toll Free: (800) 737-2697
E-mail: investorrelations@pepboys.com
Web Site: www.pepboys.com
Approx. Rev.: $1,988,641,000
Approx. Number Employees: 12,441
Year Founded: 1921
Business Description:
Automotive Parts, Accessories & Service
S.I.C.: 5013; 7539
N.A.I.C.S.: 441310; 811118; 811198
Import Export
Advertising Expenditures: $57,500,000
Media: 1-2-3-4-5-6-7-8-9-10-11-13-14-15-16-18-19-20-22-23-24-25-26
Distr.: Natl.
Budget Set: Feb.
Personnel:
Robert H. Hotz *(Chm)*
Michael R. Odell *(CEO)*
Raymond L. Arthur *(CFO)*
Sanjay Sood *(Chief Acctg Officer, VP & Controller)*
Bernard K. McElroy *(Chief Acctg Officer & VP)*
Brian D. Zuckerman *(Gen Counsel, Sec & Sr VP)*
William E. Shull, III *(Exec VP-Stores)*
Scott A. Webb *(Exec VP-Mdsg & Mktg)*
Joseph A. Cirelli *(Sr VP-Corp Dev)*
Troy E. Fee *(Sr VP-HR)*
James H. Fox *(VP-Mktg & Adv)*
Daniel E. King *(VP-Retail Ops-South)*
Charles M. McErlane *(VP)*
Robert P. Sammons *(VP-Mdsg)*
Ronald J. Stoupa *(VP-Mktg)*
Alberto Velez *(VP-Retail Ops-Southwest & Puerto Rico)*
Alexandra Spooner *(Mgr-Comm)*
Advertising Agencies:
Zeta Interactive
99 Pk Ave 23rd Fl
New York, NY 10016
Tel.: (646) 834-9400
Fax: (646) 834-9390

Zimmerman Advertising
2200 W Commercial Blvd Ste 300
Fort Lauderdale, FL 33309-3064
Tel.: (954) 644-4000
Fax: (954) 731-2977
Toll Free: (800) 248-8522

PERCEPTRON, INC.
47827 Halyard Dr
Plymouth, MI 48170-2461
Tel.: (734) 414-6100
Fax: (734) 414-4700
E-mail: inquiry@perceptron.com
Web Site: www.perceptron.com
Approx. Sls.: $59,271,000
Approx. Number Employees: 228
Year Founded: 1981
Business Description:
Automotive Test Products Mfr
S.I.C.: 3679; 3559; 3714; 7372
N.A.I.C.S.: 334419; 333298; 334611; 336322
Advertising Expenditures: $207,000
Personnel:
W. Richard Marz *(Chm)*
Harry T. Rittenour *(Pres & CEO)*
John H. Lowry III *(CFO & VP)*
Sylvia M. Smith *(Chief Acctg Officer & Controller)*
David W. Geiss *(Gen Counsel, Sec & VP)*
Mark S. Hoefing *(Sr VP-Indus Bus Unit)*
Eric C. Schneider *(VP-HR)*
Brands & Products:
AUTOFIT
AUTOGAUGE
AUTOGUIDE
AUTOSCAN
AUTOSPECT
AUTOSPECT QMS
BOSCH
CONTOUR PROBE
THE FOCUS ON PROCESS
GREENLEE
IPNET
LASAR
OPTIFLEX
PAINTSCAN
PERCEPTRON
ROTHENBERGER
SCANWORKS
SNAP-ON
TRICAM
VISUAL FIXTURING
WHEELWORKS

PERFORMANCE WAREHOUSE COMPANY, INC.
9440 N Whitaker Rd
Portland, OR 97217
Tel.: (503) 417-5302
Tel.: (503) 286-7130
Fax: (503) 417-5316
E-mail: company_info@pw1.com
Web Site: www.performancewarehouse.com
Approx. Number Employees: 250

Key to Media (For complete agency information see *The Advertising Red Books-Agencies* edition):
1. Bus. Publs. 2. Cable T.V. 3. Catalogs & Directories. 4. Co-op Adv. 5. Consumer Mags. 6. D.M. to Bus. Estab.7. D.M. to Consumers 8. Daily Newsp. 9. Exhibits/Trade Shows 10. Foreign 11. Infomercial 12. Internet Adv.13. Multimedia 14. Network Radio 15. Network T.V. 16. Newsp. Distr. Mags. 17. Other 18. Outdoor (Posters, Transit) 19. Point of Purchase20. Premiums, Novelties 21. Product Samples 22. Special Events Mktg. 23. Spot Radio 24. Spot T.V. 25. Weekly Newsp. 26. Yellow Page Adv.

Year Founded: 1969
Business Description:
Automotive Parts
S.I.C.: 5013
N.A.I.C.S.: 423120
Media: 2-7-8-9-10-24-25-26

THE PIERCE CO., INC.

(Sub. of Avis Industrial Corporation)
35 N 8th St
Upland, IN 46989
Mailing Address:
PO Box 2000
Upland, IN 46989-2000
Tel.: (765) 998-2712
Fax: (765) 998-3348
E-mail: pierce@thepiercecompany.com
Web Site:
www.thepiercecompany.com
Sales Range: $25-49.9 Million
Approx. Number Employees: 50
Year Founded: 1913
Business Description:
Mfr. of Engineered Assemblies for the Auto Industry; Formed Wire Products, Engine Speed Controls, Water Pumps, Aftermarket Fuel Pumps & Castings
S.I.C.: 3714; 3711
N.A.I.C.S.: 336399; 336211
Export
Advertising Expenditures: $100,000
Media: 4-10-13
Distr.: Natl.
Budget Set: Jan.
Brands & Products:
HOOF GOVERNORS
HYGRADE
PIERCE GOVERNORS

PILKINGTON NORTH AMERICA, INC.

(Sub. of Pilkington Group Limited)
811 Madison Ave
Toledo, OH 43604
Mailing Address:
PO Box 799
Toledo, OH 43697-0799
Tel.: (419) 247-3731
Fax: (419) 247-3821
E-mail: info@pilkington.com
Web Site: www.pilkington.com
Approx. Number Employees: 50
Business Description:
Automotive & Building Glass Mfr
S.I.C.: 3211
N.A.I.C.S.: 327211
Advertising Expenditures: $200,000
Media: 9-17-25-26
Distr.: Natl.
Budget Set: Sept.
Personnel:
Laurie Kruger *(Pres-Building Products-North America)*
Brands & Products:
PILKINGTON ACTIV

PLEWS/EDELMANN

(Joint Venture of Onex Corporation & Canada Pension Plan Investment Board)
1550 Franklin Grove Rd
Dixon, IL 61021
Tel.: (815) 288-3344
Fax: (815) 288-3388
Toll Free: (800) 770-4639
Web Site: www.plews-edelmann.com
E-Mail For Key Personnel:
Marketing Director: dbabics@stant.com
Approx. Number Employees: 190
Year Founded: 1909
Business Description:
Automotive Parts; Brass Fittings; Steel Brake Lines; Power Steering Products; Lubrication Tools; Grease Guns; Tire Hardware & Air Accessories; Specialty Greases & Oils Mfr
S.I.C.: 3714; 3561
N.A.I.C.S.: 336399; 333911
Import Export
Media: 2-3-4-5-6-10-19-20-21
Distr.: Natl.
Personnel:
Gordon Hoffman *(Dir-Sls & Mktg)*
David Babics *(Product Mgr)*
Brands & Products:
EDELMANN
LUBRIMATIC
PLEWS
POWERCRAFT
SUPERIOR
TRU-FLATE
Advertising Agency:
Gelia-Media, Inc.
390 S Youngs Rd
Williamsville, NY 14221
Tel.: (716) 629-3200
Fax: (716) 629-3299

PRECISION AUTO CARE, INC.

748 Miller Dr SE Ste G-1
Leesburg, VA 20175
Tel.: (703) 777-9095
Fax: (703) 771-7108
Toll Free: (800) 438-8863
E-mail: invest@precisionac.com
Web Site: www.precisiontune.com
Approx. Rev.: $15,066,991
Approx. Number Employees: 85
Year Founded: 1997
Business Description:
Automotive Maintenance Services
S.I.C.: 7532; 7538
N.A.I.C.S.: 811121; 811111
Export
Advertising Expenditures: $60,000
Media: 2-3-5-6-7-8-9-10-11-18-19-20-21-23-24-25
Distr.: Intl.
Budget Set: Monthly
Personnel:
Louis M. Brown, Jr. *(Chm)*
Robert R. Falconi *(Pres & CEO)*
Mark P. Francis *(CFO)*
Frederick F. Simmons *(Gen Counsel, Sec & Sr VP)*
Kevin Bates *(Sr VP-Mktg)*
John T. Wiegand *(Sr VP-Ops Programs & Dev)*
Joel Burrows *(VP-Trng & R&D)*
Brands & Products:
AMERICA'S NEIGHBORHOOD AUTO CARE EXPERTS
PRECISION AUTO WASH
PRECISION LUBE EXPRESS
PRECISION TUNE
PRECISION TUNE AUTO CARE
TUNED IN TO YOU.
WE KEEP IT GOING

PRIDE INTERNATIONAL, INC.

5847 San Felipe St Ste 3300
Houston, TX 77057-3195
Tel.: (713) 789-1400
Fax: (713) 789-1430
E-mail: jchastain@prideinternational.com
Web Site: www.prideinternational.com
Approx. Rev.: $1,460,100,000
Approx. Number Employees: 3,900
Year Founded: 1968
Business Description:
International Oil & Gas Contract Drilling Services
S.I.C.: 1311; 1381; 1389
N.A.I.C.S.: 211111; 213111; 213112
Media: 2-6-10-11
Personnel:
David A.B. Brown *(Chm)*
Louis A. Raspino, Jr. *(Pres & CEO)*
Brian C. Voegele *(CFO & Sr VP)*
Jenny McFarland Rub *(CIO & VP)*
W. Gregory Looser *(Chief Admin Officer & Sr VP)*
Leonard E. Travis *(Chief Acctg Officer & VP)*
Brady K. Long *(Gen Counsel, Sec & VP)*
Lonnie D. Bane *(Sr VP-HR & Admin)*
Kevin C. Robert *(Sr VP-Mktg & Bus Dev)*
Imran Toufeeq *(Sr VP-Ops, Engrg & Asset Mgmt)*
Jeffrey L. Chastain *(VP-IR & Comm)*
Mark Diehl *(VP-Engrg)*
David Douglas *(Dir-Sls & Mktg-Deepwater)*
Chris Young *(Mgr-Bus Dev)*

PURADYN FILTER TECHNOLOGIES, INC.

2017 High Ridge Rd
Boynton Beach, FL 33426
Tel.: (561) 547-9499
Fax: (561) 547-8629
Toll Free: (866) 787-2396
E-mail: info@puradyn.com
Web Site: www.puradyn.com
Approx. Sls.: $3,106,492
Approx. Number Employees: 23
Year Founded: 1987
Business Description:
Oil Filtration System Designer, Mfr & Marketer
S.I.C.: 3714; 1389
N.A.I.C.S.: 336312; 213112; 336399
Advertising Expenditures: $19,000
Media: 7-10-13
Personnel:
Joseph V Vittoria *(Chm & CEO)*
Kevin G. Kroger *(Pres & COO)*
Kathryn A. Morris *(Dir-Corp Comm)*

RADIATOR SPECIALTY COMPANY

600 Radiator Rd
Indian Trail, NC 28079-5225
Tel.: (704) 377-6555
Fax: (704) 684-1837
Toll Free: (800) 438-4532
E-mail: marketing@rscbrands.com
Web Site: www.rscbrands.com
E-Mail For Key Personnel:
Marketing Director: marketing@gunk.com
Approx. Number Employees: 350
Year Founded: 1924
Business Description:
Mfr of Automotive Sealings; Chemical & Rubber Products; Cleaning Compounds; Tools & Traffic Safety Devices
S.I.C.: 2899; 3069
N.A.I.C.S.: 325998; 326299
Import Export
Advertising Expenditures: $5,800,000
Media: 1-2-3-4-5-6-7-10-11-13-14-19-20-21-23-26
Distr.: Natl.
Budget Set: Oct.
Personnel:
John Huber *(Pres & CEO)*
David Goodson *(CFO & Controller)*
Ronald Weiner *(Gen Counsel & VP)*
Mike Guggenheimer *(VP-Sls & Mktg)*
Aaroen Martin *(Dir-Adv & Mktg)*
Don Debouse *(Mgr-Natl Sls)*
Brands & Products:
BIG PUNCTURE
CARB-MEDIC
DIESEL-TONE
ENGINE BRITE
GOO
GUNK
HOLD-ZIT
HYDROSEAL
LIQUID WRENCH
MILEMAX
MOTOR-MEDIC
PUNCTURE SEAL
SEALMASTER
SOLDER SEAL
SQUEAL MEDIC
STEERSEAL
STOP SMOKIN
SUPER OIL
THRUST
TITESEAL
TRANS-MEDIC
TRANSEAL
TRIPLE SEAL

RANDY'S RING & PINION SERVICE INC.

10411 Airport Rd
Everett, WA 98204
Tel.: (425) 347-1199
Fax: (425) 347-1440
Toll Free: (800) 292-1031
Web Site: www.ringpinion.com
Sales Range: $25-49.9 Million
Approx. Number Employees: 70
Year Founded: 1995
Business Description:
Differential Parts Distr
S.I.C.: 7539; 5013
N.A.I.C.S.: 811118; 441310
Media: 4-9-18-19-22-25
Personnel:
Pam Schmitt *(Sls Mgr)*
Kevin Weibusch *(Mgr-Mktg)*

RECARO NORTH AMERICA, INC.

(Sub. of RECARO GmbH & Co.)
3275 Lapeer Rd W
Auburn Hills, MI 48326
Tel.: (248) 364-3818
Fax: (248) 364-3804
Toll Free: (800) 8RECARO
E-mail: info@recaro-nao.com
Web Site: www.recaro-nao.com
Approx. Number Employees: 70
Year Founded: 1977
Business Description:
Automotive Commercial Components & Seats Mfr
S.I.C.: 2396; 8711
N.A.I.C.S.: 336360; 541330
Import
Advertising Expenditures: $1,000,000

Key to Media (For complete agency information see *The Advertising Red Books-Agencies* edition):
1. Bus. Publs. 2. Cable T.V. 3. Catalogs & Directories. 4. Co-op Adv. 5. Consumer Mags. 6. D.M. to Bus. Estab.7. D.M. to Consumers 8. Daily Newsp. 9. Exhibits/Trade Shows 10. Foreign 11. Infomercial 12. Internet Adv.13. Multimedia 14. Network Radio 15. Network T.V. 16. Newsp. Distr. Mags. 17. Other 18. Outdoor (Posters, Transit) 19. Point of Purchase20. Premiums, Novelties 21. Product Samples 22. Special Events Mktg. 23. Spot Radio 24. Spot T.V. 25. Weekly Newsp. 26. Yellow Page Adv.

RECARO North America, Inc. — (Continued)

Media: 6
Distr.: Natl.
Personnel:
Lisa Caleca *(Mgr-Mktg)*
Brands & Products:
RECARO

REMY INTERNATIONAL, INC.

(Holding of Citicorp Venture Capital, Ltd.)
600 Corporation Dr
Pendleton, IN 46064
Tel.: (765) 778-6499
Fax: (765) 778-6404
Toll Free: (800) 372-3555
E-mail: info@remyinc.com
Web Site: www.remyinc.com
Approx. Sls.: $1,103,799,000
Approx. Number Employees: 5,717
Year Founded: 1994
Business Description:
New & Remanufactured Starters, Alternators & Other Motor Vehicle Parts Mfr & Distr
S.I.C.: 3714; 5015
N.A.I.C.S.: 336399; 336322; 423140
Export
Media: 10
Personnel:
William P. Foley, II *(Chm)*
John H. Weber *(CEO & Dir)*
Fred Knechtel *(CFO)*
Gerald T. Mills *(Chief HR Officer & Sr Vp)*
John J. Pittas *(Sr VP)*
Jesus Sanchez *(Sr VP)*
Kent D. Jones *(VP-Global Sls & Mktg)*
Ratnam Philip *(Dir-Global Trade & Transportation)*
Advertising Agency:
Jackson Integrated
5804 Churchman Bypass
Indianapolis, IN 46203-6109
Tel.: (317) 791-9000
Fax: (317) 791-9800
Toll Free: (888) JACKSON

RENNTECH, INC.

1369 N Killian Dr
Lake Park, FL 33403
Tel.: (561) 845-7888
Fax: (561) 845-6777
E-mail: info@renntechmercedes.com
Web Site:
www.renntechmercedes.com
Approx. Number Employees: 15
Year Founded: 1989
Business Description:
Automotive Customizing Services
S.I.C.: 7532
N.A.I.C.S.: 811121
Media: 6-13
Personnel:
Hartmut Feyhl *(Pres)*

RIETER AUTOMOTIVE NORTH AMERICA, INC.

(Sub. of Rieter Holding AG)
38555 Hills Tech Dr
Farmington Hills, MI 48331
Tel.: (248) 848-0100
Fax: (248) 848-0130
E-mail: info@rieter.com
Web Site: www.rieter.com/en/group/about-rieter-group/subsidiaries-ass-comp/
Approx. Sls.: $175,000,000
Approx. Number Employees: 120
Year Founded: 1934
Business Description:
Automotive & Commercial Sound Control Materials Mfr
S.I.C.: 3714
N.A.I.C.S.: 336399
Media: 2-4-5-10-26
Distr.: Natl.
Budget Set: Dec.
Personnel:
Richard Derr *(Pres & CEO)*
Joseph Labak *(VP-Fin)*

RIETER AUTOMOTIVE SYSTEMS

(Sub. of Rieter Automotive North America, Inc.)
480 W Fifth St
Bloomsburg, PA 17815-1563
Tel.: (570) 784-4100
Approx. Number Employees: 700
Year Founded: 1997
Business Description:
Automobile Carpeting & Acoustical Parts
S.I.C.: 3714
N.A.I.C.S.: 336399
Media: 2-6-9-16-25
Distr.: Reg.
Budget Set: Nov.

ROLL COATER, INC.

(Holding of Willis Stein & Partners)
8440 Woodfield Crossing Blvd Bldg 2 5th Fl
Indianapolis, IN 46240-4347
Tel.: (317) 462-7761
Fax: (317) 467-6476
Web Site: www.rollcoater.com
Approx. Number Employees: 400
Year Founded: 1963
Business Description:
Coil Coating Services
S.I.C.: 3479
N.A.I.C.S.: 332812
Media: 6-9-10-13-14-15
Personnel:
Robert O'Neal *(Pres & CEO)*
Bill Scott *(CFO & Sr VP)*
Ben Markham *(Sr Dir-Bus Dev)*
Rick Miller *(Dir-Comml Dev)*
Brands & Products:
COILTRAK

ROLLS-ROYCE CORPORATION

(Sub. of Rolls-Royce North America Inc.)
2001 S Tibbs Ave
Indianapolis, IN 46206-0420
Mailing Address:
PO Box 420 S-7
Indianapolis, IN 46206
Tel.: (317) 230-2000
Fax: (317) 536-3204
Web Site: www.rolls-royce.com
Approx. Number Employees: 4,200
Year Founded: 1915
Business Description:
Design & Mfr. of Aircraft, Industrial & Marine Gas Turbine Engines
S.I.C.: 3724
N.A.I.C.S.: 336412
Import Export
Media: 2-9-10-18-20-22
Distr.: Intl.; Natl.
Budget Set: Aug.
Personnel:
Ken Roberts *(Pres-Helicopters)*
Jarrett Jones *(Dir-AE2100 Military Engines)*
Jolyon Nash *(Dir-Sls & Mktg-Rolls Royce Motor Cars)*
Karin Ricketts *(Mgr-Corp Comm-North America)*
Advertising Agencies:
Borshoff
47 S Pennsylvania St Ste 500
Indianapolis, IN 46204
Tel.: (317) 631-6400
Fax: (317) 631-6499

Jackson Integrated
5804 Churchman Bypass
Indianapolis, IN 46203-6109
Tel.: (317) 791-9000
Fax: (317) 791-9800
Toll Free: (888) JACKSON

kirshenbaum bond senecal + partners
160 Varick St 4th Fl
New York, NY 10013
Tel.: (212) 633-0080
Fax: (212) 463-8643
Acquisition & Loyalty Programs
Customer Relationship Management
Marketing Communications Agency of Record

RONA, INC.

220 Chermin Du Tremblay
Boucherville, QC J4B 8H7, Canada
Tel.: (514) 599-5100
Fax: (514) 599-5138
Web Site: www.rona.ca
Approx. Sls.: $4,577,637,706
Approx. Number Employees: 22,000
Year Founded: 1939
Business Description:
Retailer & Distr of Hardware, Home Improvement & Gardening Products
S.I.C.: 3429
N.A.I.C.S.: 332510
Export
Media: 2-3-7-8-10-11-13-15-18-21-24-25-26
Personnel:
Jean Gaulin *(Chm)*
Robert Dutton *(Pres & CEO)*
Dominique Boies *(CFO & Exec VP)*
France Charlebois *(Chief Legal Officer & Sec)*
Normand Dumont *(Exec VP-Mdsg)*
Claude Bernier *(Sr VP-Mktg & Customer Innovations)*
Paul Jovian *(Sr VP-Supply Chain)*
Jean-Luc Meunier *(Sr VP)*
Christian Proulx *(Sr VP-People & Culture)*
Michele Roy *(VP-Comm & Public Affairs)*
Stephane Milot *(Sr Dir-IR)*
Brands & Products:
RONA
Advertising Agency:
Bos Advertising
3970 Saint-Ambroise street
Montreal, QC H4C 2C7, Canada
Tel.: (514) 848-0010
Fax: (514) 373-2992

ROSTRA PRECISION CONTROLS, INC.

(Sub. of Aftermarket Controls Corporation)
2519 Dana Dr
Laurinburg, NC 28352
Tel.: (910) 276-4853
Fax: (910) 276-1354
Toll Free: (800) 782-3379
E-mail: info@rostra.com
Web Site: www.rostra.com
Business Description:
Automotive Accessories, Cruise Control & Lumbar Support Mfr for the Automobile Industry
S.I.C.: 3714; 3679
N.A.I.C.S.: 336399; 334419
Import Export
Media: 2-4-6-7-8-10-19
Distr.: Intl.
Personnel:
Thomas P. Petrillo *(Pres & CEO)*
Michael Douglas *(Dir-Sls)*
Scott Kirkendall *(Mgr-Engrg)*
Suzie Lossman *(Mgr-Transmission Acct)*
Sibyl Ringsdorf *(Mgr-Mktg)*
Brands & Products:
COMFORT HEAT
COMFORT SEAT
FIRE CONTROL
PARKPILOT
REARSENTRY
REARSIGHT
ROSS
ROSTRA
SAFETY BLADE
SCALABLE DETECTION SYSTEM
SDS
STUDENT DETECTION SYSTEM
ULTRACRUISE
Advertising Agency:
Lotus Advertising
497 Horse Pen Ln
Vass, NC 28394
Tel.: (910) 692-3054
Fax: (910) 692-7214
(Automotive Components)

ROTARY LIFT

(Sub. of Dover Industrial Products, Inc.)
2700 Lanier Dr
Madison, IN 47250-1753
Tel.: (812) 273-1622
Fax: (812) 273-6502
Toll Free: (800) 640-5438
Web Site: www.rotarylift.com
Sales Range: $100-124.9 Million
Year Founded: 1925
Business Description:
Mfr of Automatic Hydraulic Lifts
S.I.C.: 3581; 3559
N.A.I.C.S.: 333311; 333298
Export
Media: 2-4-7-10-11-16-20-26
Distr.: Intl.; Natl.
Budget Set: Oct.
Personnel:
Randolph W. Carson *(Sr VP)*
James E. Sweetnam *(Sr VP)*
John Rylee *(Mktg Dir)*
Brands & Products:
FASTSERVICE
INBAY
THE LIFT BUYER'S BIBLE
OILDRAULIC

Key to Media (For complete agency information see *The Advertising Red Books-Agencies* edition):
1. Bus. Publs. 2. Cable T.V. 3. Catalogs & Directories. 4. Co-op Adv. 5. Consumer Mags. 6. D.M. to Bus. Estab.7. D.M. to Consumers
8. Daily Newsp. 9. Exhibits/Trade Shows 10. Foreign 11. Infomercial 12. Internet Adv.13. Multimedia 14. Network Radio
15. Network T.V. 16. Newsp. Distr. Mags. 17. Other 18. Outdoor (Posters, Transit) 19. Point of Purchase20. Premiums, Novelties
21. Product Samples 22. Special Events Mktg. 23. Spot Radio 24. Spot T.V. 25. Weekly Newsp. 26. Yellow Page Adv.

ROTARY
SMARTLIFTS
VSS
Advertising Agency:
Badertscher Communications, Inc.
137 S Prospect St
Marion, OH 43302-3713
Tel.: (740) 383-2633
Fax: (740) 383-6223

SAF FORGED WHEELS

4315 Santa Ana St
Ontario, CA 91761
Tel.: (909) 937-3377
Fax: (909) 937-3375
E-mail: info@safforged.com
Web Site: www.safforged.com
Business Description:
Forged Wheels Mfr
S.I.C.: 3312; 5014
N.A.I.C.S.: 331111; 441320
Media: 6

SAF-HOLLAND INTERNATIONAL, INC.

(Sub. of SAF-Holland Inc.)
1950 Industrial Blvd
Muskegon, MI 49442-6114
Mailing Address:
PO Box 425
Muskegon, MI 49443-0425
Tel.: (231) 773-3271
Fax: (800) 356-3929
E-mail: info@hollandusa.com
Web Site: www.hollandusa.com
Approx. Number Employees: 115
Year Founded: 1948
Business Description:
Truck, Trailer & Recreational Vehicle Component Mfr
S.I.C.: 3714; 3715
N.A.I.C.S.: 336399; 336212
Import Export
Media: 1-2-7-10-17
Distr.: Intl.; Natl.
Budget Set: Sept.
Personnel:
Ken Griswold *(Dir-Mktg Svcs-America)*
John Johnson *(Dir-Customer Svc)*
Rob Nissen *(Dir-Field Svc)*
Darrell Thompson *(Dir-Trailer Sls)*

SANDEN INTERNATIONAL (USA), INC.

(Sub. of Sanden Corporation)
601 S Sanden Blvd
Wylie, TX 75098
Tel.: (972) 442-8400
Fax: (972) 442-8600
Web Site: www.sanden.com
Approx. Number Employees: 1,050
Year Founded: 1974
Business Description:
Mfr. of Compressors for Automotive Air Conditioning
S.I.C.: 3714; 1711
N.A.I.C.S.: 336399; 238220
Import Export
Advertising Expenditures: $450,000
Media: 2-4-7-10-17
Distr.: Intl.; Natl.
Personnel:
Mitsuya Yamamoto *(Pres)*
Michael Rouse *(Product Mgr-New Product Dev & Mgr-Sls)*
Brands & Products:
SANDEN SD

SEAL AFTERMARKET PRODUCTS

(Div. of Parker Hannifin Seal Group)
2315 SW 32nd Ave
Pembroke Park, FL 33023
Tel.: (954) 364-2400
Fax: (954) 364-2401
Sales Range: $75-99.9 Million
Approx. Number Employees: 150
Year Founded: 1961
Business Description:
Aftermarket Air Conditioning & Refrigeration
S.I.C.: 3585; 5064
N.A.I.C.S.: 333415; 423620
Export
Advertising Expenditures: $760,000
Bus. Publs.: $10,000; Catalogs & Directories: $10,000; Consumer Mags.: $120,000; D.M. to Consumers: $30,000; Exhibits/Trade Shows: $250,000; Foreign: $10,000; Internet Adv.: $3,000; Newsp. Distr. Mags.: $5,000; Point of Purchase: $15,000; Premiums, Novelties: $7,000; Product Samples: $180,000; Special Events Mktg.: $20,000; Yellow Page Adv.: $100,000
Distr.: Direct to Consumer; Intl.; Natl.
Budget Set: Aug.
Brands & Products:
BRYCO
GOLDSTAR
PROSELECT

SEATS INCORPORATED

(Holding of Nordic Group of Companies, Ltd.)
1515 Industrial St PO Box 60
Reedsburg, WI 53959
Tel.: (608) 524-8261
Fax: (608) 524-6004
E-mail: info@seatsinc.com
Web Site: www.seatsinc.com
E-Mail For Key Personnel:
President: ewsauey@seatsinc.com
Approx. Sls.: $28,000,000
Approx. Number Employees: 320
Year Founded: 1952
Business Description:
Mfr. of Industrial, Recreational & Transportational Seating
S.I.C.: 2531
N.A.I.C.S.: 337127
Export
Media: 2-4-7-10-17
Distr.: Natl.
Brands & Products:
911 SERIES
ELCAMINO
ELDORADO
ELDORADO VIP
LE
LOBOY
MAGNUM SERIES
ROAD PRO
SEATING FOR H.D. TRUCKS
SLE
SUMMIT
TRAIL BOSS
WIDE ELCAMINO
WIDE PARALLELOGRAM
XLT

SETON COMPANY

135 Horton Dr
Saxton, PA 16678
Tel.: (814) 635-2937
Fax: (814) 635-3058
Web Site: www.setonleather.com
Sales Range: $600-649.9 Million
Approx. Number Employees: 17
Year Founded: 1906
Business Description:
Mfr & Distr of Automotive Leather Products; Wrapping, Finishing, Cutting & Research & Development
S.I.C.: 3111
N.A.I.C.S.: 316110
Import Export
Personnel:
Eric Evans *(CFO & VP)*
Brands & Products:
BIG SKY
CLASSIQUE
CLASSIQUE II
FRONTIER
FUTURE VISIONS
PRESTIGE
RADIANCE PLUS
REVELATIONS
Advertising Agency:
Bianchi Public Relations Inc.
888 W Big Beaver Rd Ste 777
Troy, MI 48084
Tel.: (248) 269-1122
Fax: (248) 269-8202

SHELL LUBRICANTS

(Sub. of Shell Oil Company)
700 Milam St
Houston, TX 77010
Tel.: (713) 546-4100
Fax: (713) 546-4101
Web Site: www.shell.ca/home/content/can-en/products_services/solutions_for_businesses/shell_lubricants_tpkg/
Approx. Number Employees: 800
Year Founded: 2003
Business Description:
Oil & Auto Products Whslr & Distr
S.I.C.: 2992
N.A.I.C.S.: 324191
Media: 3-4-5-6-10-12-14-15-19-20-21-23-24
Personnel:
Steve Harman *(Pres-Lubricants-US)*
Troy Chapman *(Brand Dir-Pennzoil & Dir-Mktg-Quaker State)*
Chris Hayek *(Global Brand Mgr)*
Brands & Products:
AXIUS
BLACK MAGIC
BLUE CORAL
FIX-A-FLAT
GUMOUT
MEDO
THE OUTLAW
PENNZOIL
Q
QUAKER STATE
RAIN-X
SLICK 50
SNAP
WESTLEY'S
Advertising Agency:
Doner
25900 Northwestern Hwy
Southfield, MI 48075
Tel.: (248) 354-9700
Fax: (248) 827-8440
Pennzoil

SIERRA INTERNATIONAL INC.

(Div. of Teleflex Commercial Group)
1 Sierra Pl
Litchfield, IL 62056
Tel.: (217) 324-9400
Fax: (217) 324-2461
E-mail: onboard@sierramarine.com
Web Site: www.teleflexmarine.com
Sales Range: $100-124.9 Million
Approx. Number Employees: 250
Business Description:
Marine Engine & Drive Parts
S.I.C.: 3519
N.A.I.C.S.: 333618
Media: 4-18
Personnel:
Joe Hootchulte *(Gen Mgr)*

SKF SEALING SOLUTIONS

(Div. of SKF USA Inc.)
900 N State St
Elgin, IL 60123-2147
Tel.: (847) 742-0700
Fax: (847) 888-0002
Toll Free: (800) 882-0008
E-mail: info@skfusa.com
Web Site: www.skfusa.com
Approx. Number Employees: 700
Year Founded: 1878
Business Description:
Dynamic Fluid Sealing Devices Mfr
S.I.C.: 3053
N.A.I.C.S.: 339991
Export
Media: 2-4-5-7-10-20-21
Distr.: Natl.
Budget Set: Sept.
Personnel:
Dan Reed *(Pres)*
Dan Duffy *(Dir-Sls & Mktg)*
Doug Fike *(Mgr-Mktg)*
Brands & Products:
CR BRAKEMASTER
CR SEALS
CR U-JOINTS
SKF BEARINGS
Advertising Agency:
Harris, Baio & McCullough Inc.
520 S Frnt St
Philadelphia, PA 19147-1723
Tel.: (215) 440-9800
Fax: (215) 440-9812
(Seals, Bearings, Air Dryers, Speedi Sleeve & Wear Sleeves)

SKF USA

(Unit of SKF USA Inc.)
20 Industrial Dr
Hanover, PA 17331-9582
Tel.: (717) 637-8981
Fax: (717) 637-3395
Web Site: www.skf.com
Approx. Number Employees: 300
Year Founded: 1909
Business Description:
Ball & Roller Bearings
S.I.C.: 3562; 3053
N.A.I.C.S.: 332991; 339991
Import Export
Advertising Expenditures: $600,000
Media: 1-2-4-7-8-10-19-20-21
Distr.: Natl.
Budget Set: Sept.
Brands & Products:
GILMAN
MRC
RBI

Key to Media (For complete agency information see *The Advertising Red Books-Agencies* edition):
1. Bus. Publs. 2. Cable T.V. 3. Catalogs & Directories. 4. Co-op Adv. 5. Consumer Mags. 6. D.M. to Bus. Estab.7. D.M. to Consumers 8. Daily Newsp. 9. Exhibits/Trade Shows 10. Foreign 11. Infomercial 12. Internet Adv.13. Multimedia 14. Network Radio 15. Network T.V. 16. Newsp. Distr. Mags. 17. Other 18. Outdoor (Posters, Transit) 19. Point of Purchase20. Premiums, Novelties 21. Product Samples 22. Special Events Mktg. 23. Spot Radio 24. Spot T.V. 25. Weekly Newsp. 26. Yellow Page Adv.

SKF USA — (Continued)
Advertising Agency:
Harris, Baio & McCullough Inc.
520 S Frnt St
Philadelphia, PA 19147-1723
Tel.: (215) 440-9800
Fax: (215) 440-9812

SMK SPEEDY INTERNATIONAL, INC.
(Sub. of 578098 Alberta Ltd.)
(d/b/a Speedy Auto Service)
365 Bloor Street East Suite 1100
Toronto, ON M4W 3M7, Canada
Tel.: (416) 961-1133
Fax: (416) 960-7916
Web Site: www.speedy.com
Year Founded: 1956
Business Description:
Retail Automotive Services
S.I.C.: 7539
N.A.I.C.S.: 811198
Media: 3-6-8-14-15-16-18-23-24-26
Budget Set: Dec.
Brands & Products:
CAR-X
SPEEDY

SOMERSET TIRE SERVICE, INC.
(d/b/a STS Tire & Auto Center)
400 W Main St
Bound Brook, NJ 08805
Mailing Address:
PO Box 2001
Bound Brook, NJ 08805-1031
Tel.: (732) 356-8500
Fax: (732) 356-8821
E-mail: info@ststire.com
Web Site: www.ststire.com
Approx. Sls.: $154,631,618
Approx. Number Employees: 800
Year Founded: 1958
Business Description:
Tire Retailer & Automotive Repair Services
S.I.C.: 5014; 7538
N.A.I.C.S.: 441320; 811111
Import Export
Media: 5-8-9-13-18-20-23-24-25-26
Personnel:
William F. Caulin *(Pres)*
Henry Trani *(CFO)*
Brands & Products:
IT'S A TRUST THING
STS

SOUTH LUBES INC.
1890 Kingsley Ave Ste 104
Orange Park, FL 32073
Tel.: (904) 276-3598
Fax: (904) 276-0194
Web Site: www.jiffylubesoutheast.com
Sales Range: $1-4.9 Billion
Approx. Number Employees: 20
Business Description:
Automotive Lubrication Services
S.I.C.: 7549
N.A.I.C.S.: 811191
Media: 2-4-6-7-8-10-13-14-18-19-20-21-22-23-25
Personnel:
Louis W. Huntley *(Pres)*
Dwain Sanders *(VP-Fin & Treas)*
Advertising Agency:
Media Design
5569 Bowden Rd Ste 5
Jacksonville, FL 32216-8034
Tel.: (904) 636-5131
Fax: (904) 636-5322
— Lindsay Carpenter *(Dir-Mktg)*

SPARTAN MOTORS, INC.
1541 Reynolds Rd
Charlotte, MI 48813
Tel.: (517) 543-6400
Fax: (517) 543-9269
E-mail: info@spartanmotors.com
Web Site: www.spartanmotors.com
Approx. Sls.: $480,736,000
Approx. Number Employees: 1,517
Year Founded: 1975
Business Description:
Heavy Truck Custom Chassis Mfr
S.I.C.: 3714; 3711
N.A.I.C.S.: 336111; 336120; 336211; 336399
Import Export
Media: 7-10
Personnel:
Hugh W. Sloan, Jr. *(Chm)*
John E. Sztykiel *(CEO)*
Joseph Nowicki *(CFO & Chief Compliance Officer)*
Thomas W. Gorman *(COO)*
Thomas T. Kivell *(Gen Counsel, VP & Sec)*
Brands & Products:
A PASSION FOR LIFE, THE PURSUIT OF EXCELLENCE
AEROMASTER
CRIMSON FIRE
METROMASTER
ROAD RESCUE
SPARTAN
TRADEMASTER
UTILIMASTER
UTILIVAN
Advertising Agency:
Lambert, Edwards & Associates, Inc.
171 Monroe NW Ste 400
Grand Rapids, MI 49503
Tel.: (616) 233-0500
Fax: (616) 233-0600

SPEEDWAY MOTORS INC.
PO Box 81906
Lincoln, NE 68501
Tel.: (402) 323-3200
Fax: (402) 323-3211
E-mail: sales@speedwaymotors.com
Web Site: www.speedwaymotors.com
E-Mail For Key Personnel:
Sales Director: sales@speedwaymotors.com
Approx. Number Employees: 70
Year Founded: 1952
Business Description:
Mfr, Distr, Retailer & Mail Order of High Performance Specialty Automotive Products for the Racing & Street Rod Markets
S.I.C.: 5961; 3714
N.A.I.C.S.: 454113; 336399
Media: 4-13
Personnel:
D. William Smith *(Founder)*
Brands & Products:
AMERICA'S OLDEST SPEED SHOP
BLUE DIAMOND CLASSICS
FENTON
MR. ROADSTER
SMITH COLLECTION MUSEUM
SPEEDWAY MOTORS

SPORTRACK ACCESSORIES INC.
(Sub. of Thule, Inc.)
700 Bernard
Granby, QC J2G 9H7, Canada
Tel.: (450) 777-3773
Fax: (450) 777-3615
Toll Free: (800) 561-0716
E-mail: info@sportrack.com
Web Site: www.sportrack.com
Approx. Number Employees: 80
Year Founded: 1989
Business Description:
Automotive Exterior Accessories
S.I.C.: 3714
N.A.I.C.S.: 336399
Media: 4
Personnel:
Andre Clement *(Dir-Sourcing)*

SPX CORPORATION
13515 Ballantyne Corporate Pl
Charlotte, NC 28277
Tel.: (704) 752-4400
Fax: (704) 752-4505
E-mail: spx@spx.com
Web Site: www.spx.com
E-Mail For Key Personnel:
Public Relations: tlbetlejewski@spx.com
Approx. Rev.: $4,886,800,000
Approx. Number Employees: 15,500
Year Founded: 1911
Business Description:
Service Products Mfr & Distr for Multiple Industries
S.I.C.: 3621; 3544; 3829
N.A.I.C.S.: 335312; 333511; 334519
Import Export
Media: 1-2-7-10-11-19-20
Distr.: Intl.; Natl.
Budget Set: Oct.
Personnel:
Christopher J. Kearney *(Chm, Pres & CEO)*
Patrick J. O'Leary *(CFO & Exec VP)*
Christopher Hudel *(Chief Info Security Officer)*
Don L. Canterna *(Pres-Flow Tech)*
David A. Kowalski *(Pres-Test & Measurement)*
Drew T. Ladau *(Pres-Thermal Equipment & Svcs)*
Lee Powell *(Pres-Indus Products & Svcs)*
Ken Rodi *(Pres-SPX Flow Tech EMEA)*
Kevin L. Lilly *(Gen Counsel, Sec & Sr VP)*
Robert B. Foreman *(Exec VP-Global Bus Sys & Svcs)*
Raj Kapur *(Gen Mgr-India & Africa)*
Tara Bianco *(Dir-Global Mktg)*
Ryan Taylor *(Dir-IR)*
Advertising Agency:
DRB Partners, Inc.
2635 N 1st St Ste 204
San Jose, CA 95134-2032
Tel.: (408) 943-0515
Fax: (408) 943-1904
Toll Free: (877) 234-2094

STANDARD BENT GLASS CORPORATION
136 Lincoln Ave
Butler, PA 16029
Mailing Address:
PO Boz 469
Butler, PA 16003-0469
Tel.: (724) 285-3179
Fax: (724) 283-9836
Toll Free: (800) 634-9252
Web Site: www.standardbent.com/index.php
Sales Range: $10-24.9 Million
Approx. Number Employees: 150
Year Founded: 1947
Business Description:
Glass Mfr of Architectural & Security Glass Glazing Products
S.I.C.: 1793; 7536
N.A.I.C.S.: 238150; 811122
Import Export
Advertising Expenditures: $500,000
Media: 2-4-7-9-10-21-23-26
Distr.: Intl.; Natl.
Budget Set: Feb.
Personnel:
Kent Hartley *(COO)*
Jeff Nichols *(VP-Sls & Mktg)*
Bobby Chestnut *(Mgr-Estimating & Tech Sls)*
Debbie Porter *(Mgr-Customer Svc)*
Advertising Agency:
GatesmanMarmion+Dave
60 S 15th St
Pittsburgh, PA 15203-1542
Tel.: (412) 381-5400
Fax: (412) 381-9770

STANDARD MOTOR PRODUCTS, INC.
37-18 Northern Blvd
Long Island City, NY 11101
Tel.: (718) 392-0200
Fax: (718) 472-0122
E-mail: webmaster@smpcorp.com
Web Site: www.smpcorp.com
Approx. Sls.: $810,910,000
Approx. Number Employees: 3,200
Year Founded: 1919
Business Description:
Automotive Replacement Parts Mfr & Marketer
S.I.C.: 3714; 5084
N.A.I.C.S.: 336399; 336322; 423830
Import Export
Media: 2-4-5-7-10
Distr.: Intl.; Natl.
Budget Set: Oct.
Personnel:
Lawrence I. Sills *(Chm & CEO)*
John P. Gethin *(Pres & COO)*
James J. Burke, Jr. *(CFO & VP-Fin)*
Glen Moore *(Chief Acctg Officer)*
Robert H. Martin *(Treas & Asst Sec)*
Brands & Products:
ACI
BLUE STREAK
BWD
FACTORY AIR
FOUR SEASONS
HAYDEN
HYGRADE
IMPERIAL
NIEHOFF
SMP
STANDARD
STANDARD PLUS
Advertising Agency:
Maximum Marketing Services
833 W Jackson
Chicago, IL 60607
Tel.: (312) 226-4111
— Jennifer Tio *(Acct Exec)*

Key to Media (For complete agency information see *The Advertising Red Books-Agencies* edition):
1. Bus. Publs. 2. Cable T.V. 3. Catalogs & Directories. 4. Co-op Adv. 5. Consumer Mags. 6. D.M. to Bus. Estab.7. D.M. to Consumers 8. Daily Newsp. 9. Exhibits/Trade Shows 10. Foreign 11. Infomercial 12. Internet Adv.13. Multimedia 14. Network Radio 15. Network T.V. 16. Newsp. Distr. Mags. 17. Other 18. Outdoor (Posters, Transit) 19. Point of Purchase20. Premiums, Novelties 21. Product Samples 22. Special Events Mktg. 23. Spot Radio 24. Spot T.V. 25. Weekly Newsp. 26. Yellow Page Adv.

STRAUSS DISCOUNT AUTO
9A Brick Plant Rd
South River, NJ 08882-1097
Tel.: (732) 390-9000
Fax: (732) 390-9127
Web Site: www.straussauto.com
Approx. Number Employees: 2,000
Year Founded: 1919
Business Description:
Auto Parts Accessories & Service Chain
S.I.C.: 5013
N.A.I.C.S.: 441310
Import
Advertising Expenditures: $4,000,000
Media: 3-5-8-9-14-15-18-19-22-23-24-25-26
Distr.: Reg.
Budget Set: Jan.
Personnel:
Joe Catalano *(Pres & COO)*
Brands & Products:
STRAUSS AUTO
WE HELP YOU DRIVING

STREETGLOW, INC.
25 Mansard Ct
Wayne, NJ 07470
Tel.: (973) 709-9000
Fax: (973) 628-6046
Fax: (800) 793-6366
Toll Free: (800) 787-3384
Web Site: www.streetglow.com
Approx. Number Employees: 14
Year Founded: 1991
Business Description:
Automobile Light Accessories Mfr
S.I.C.: 3647
N.A.I.C.S.: 336321
Media: 5-10-18
Brands & Products:
AUTO-NEON
THE FAST AND THE FURIOUS
THE LEADER IN AUTO-NEON
MINI-NEON
OPTX
PC-NEON
STREETGLOW

STS TURBO, INC.
165 N 1330 W Ste A-4
Orem, UT 84057
Tel.: (801) 224-3477
E-mail: sales@ststurbo.com
Web Site: www.ststurbo.com
E-Mail For Key Personnel:
Sales Director: sales@ststurbo.com
Sales Range: $1-9.9 Million
Approx. Number Employees: 10
Business Description:
Automotive Rear-Mount Turbocharger Mfr
S.I.C.: 3511; 3714
N.A.I.C.S.: 333611; 336350
Advertising Expenditures: $120,000
Media: 3-6
Personnel:
Richard K. Squires *(Pres & CEO)*
Donna B. Squires *(Mgr-Acctg)*

SULLIVAN INVESTMENT CO. INC.
41 Accord Pk Dr
Norwell, MA 02061-1614
Tel.: (781) 982-1550
Fax: (781) 871-6250
Web Site: www.sullivantire.com
Approx. Number Employees: 50
Year Founded: 1979
Business Description:
Holding Company for Auto & Tire Services
S.I.C.: 5014; 7534
N.A.I.C.S.: 441320; 326212
Import Export
Media: 2-5-6-7-8-9-18-22-23-24-25
Personnel:
Robert D. Sullivan *(Pres)*
Brands & Products:
SULLIVAN TIRE AND AUTO

THEXTON MANUFACTURING COMPANY, INC.
1157 Valley Pk Dr Ste 150
Shakopee, MN 55379
Tel.: (952) 831-4171
Fax: (952) 831-5938
Toll Free: (800) 328-6277
E-mail: info@thexton.com
Web Site: www.thexton.com
Sales Range: $10-24.9 Million
Approx. Number Employees: 15
Year Founded: 1907
Business Description:
Automotive Service Tools, Testers & Repair Items Designer, Mfr & Supplier
S.I.C.: 3423; 7539
N.A.I.C.S.: 332212; 811198
Import Export
Media: 2-5-7-10-16-19
Distr.: Intl.; Natl.
Budget Set: Dec.
Personnel:
Brian Tichy *(Pres)*
Peter Swenson *(VP-Sls-Mktg)*
Brands & Products:
THE ACTIVATOR
CHARG-CHEK
COLD-CHEK
FAST-SPEC
PLUG-ALL
SUPER-PUNCH
THEXTONITE
WIREHAWK

THULE, INC.
(Sub. of Thule AB)
42 Silvermine Rd
Seymour, CT 06483-3907
Tel.: (203) 881-9600
Fax: (203) 888-4252
Web Site: www.thuleracks.com
Approx. Number Employees: 150
Year Founded: 1981
Business Description:
Roofrack Systems Mfr
S.I.C.: 3714; 5013; 5021
N.A.I.C.S.: 336399; 423210; 441310
Import Export
Media: 4-8-10-11
Personnel:
Fred Clark *(Pres)*
Moreen Parente *(VP-HR)*
Megan Link *(Dir-Mktg)*
Steve Doviak *(Mgr-Internet)*
Michael Mitschke *(Mgr-InterNatl Product Grp Boxes)*
Karl Wiedemann *(Mgr-PR & Comm)*
Brands & Products:
THULE
XPORTER
Advertising Agencies:
Bernard Hodes Group
534 Broadhollow Rd Ste 305A
Melville, NY 11747-3620
Tel.: (631) 753-1901
Fax: (631) 753-1914

T.D.A. Advertising
301 Main St.
Longmont, CO 80501
Tel.: (303) 651-1919
(Racks for Bikes, Sports, Etc.)

THYSSENKRUPP BUDD CO.
(Sub. of ThyssenKrupp Automotive AG)
3155 W Big Beaver Rd
Troy, MI 48084
Mailing Address:
PO Box 2601
Troy, MI 48007-2601
Tel.: (248) 643-3500
Fax: (248) 643-3687
Telex: 23-5837
Approx. Number Employees: 11,000
Year Founded: 1912
Business Description:
Automotive Stampings
S.I.C.: 3465; 3714
N.A.I.C.S.: 336370; 336399
Export
Media: 2-4-9-10-12-16-23-24-25
Distr.: Natl.
Budget Set: Nov. -Dec.
Personnel:
Robert Soulliere *(Pres & CEO)*
Harold T. Hoffman *(VP-Info Tech)*
Terry A. Hussey *(VP-HR)*
Brands & Products:
MIL-FAB
TEMRO

THE TIMKEN COMPANY
1835 Dueber Ave SW
Canton, OH 44706-0932
Tel.: (330) 438-3000
Tel.: (330) 471-7446 (Investor Relations)
Tel.: (330) 471-3514 (Media)
Fax: (330) 458-6006
Telex: 671 6470
E-mail: jeff.dafler@timken.com
Web Site: www.timken.com
Approx. Sls.: $4,055,500,000
Approx. Number Employees: 19,839
Year Founded: 1899
Business Description:
Antifriction Bearings & Related Products Mfr; Alloy Steel & Components Mfr
S.I.C.: 3562; 3568
N.A.I.C.S.: 332991; 333613
Import Export
Media: 1-2-4-7-10-11-17-19-20-22-23
Distr.: Intl.; Natl.
Budget Set: Oct.
Personnel:
Ward J. Timken, Jr. *(Chm)*
James W. Griffith *(Pres & CEO)*
Daniel E. Muller *(CIO & Sr VP-Strategy)*
Christopher A. Coughlin *(Pres-Process Indus)*
Leong Fang *(Pres-Timken China)*
Richard G. Kyle *(Pres-Mobile Indus & Aerospace)*
J. Ron Menning *(Pres-Aerospace, Defense & Positioning control)*
Salvatore J. Miraglia, Jr. *(Pres-Steel Grp)*
William R. Burkhart *(Gen Counsel & Sr VP)*
Glenn A. Eisenberg *(Exec VP-Fin & Admin)*
J. Ted Mihaila *(Sr VP & Controller)*
Philip D. Fracassa *(Sr VP-Tax & Treasury)*
Debra L. Miller *(Sr VP-Comm)*
Douglas H. Smith *(Sr VP-Tech & Quality)*
John C. Skurek *(VP-Treasury)*
Donald L. Walker *(VP-HR & Organizational Advancement)*
James Callan *(Gen Mgr-Aerospace & Defense)*
Brent J. Dorman *(Dir-Engrg-Bearings & Power Transmission Grp)*
Elaine Russell Reolfi *(Dir-Corp Comm)*
Jagdishwar P. Sinha *(Dir-Sls-Mktg)*
James W. Skelly *(Dir-Sls-Americas)*
Steve D. Tschiegg *(Dir-Capital Markets & IR)*
Jeff Dafler *(Mgr-Global Media & Govt Rels)*
Barry Harris *(Mgr-Global Products & Mtkg)*
Christina Tharp *(Mgr-Brand Mgmt & Corp Support)*
Brands & Products:
17-22-A
17-22-AS
ACRO-SET
AP
AP-2
AQUASPEXX
AXLE-SAVER
CE
DUO FACE-PLUS
DURASPEXX
ECO TURN
FAFNIR
FAST-TRACK
FORMED HUB
FRICTION MANAGEMENT SOLUTIONS
GENERATION 3
GRAP- MO
GRAPH-AIR
HDL
HYDRA-RIB
IMPACT
ISOCLASS
J-LINE
KWIK-SLEEVE
MICROTEC
MILEMATE
MINAPURE
NT
P900
PARAPREMIUM
PERFORMANCE PLUS
PINION-PAC
PLANET-PAC
RACEPAC
REDI-SEALS
REDI-SLEEVES
ROTOROLLED
SELECT-A-NALYSIS
SENDZIMIR
SENSOR-PAC
SET-RIGHT
SMART BEARINGS
SP
SPEXX
STATUSCHECK
SURE-FIT
TBS
TBS-600
TBS-9

Key to Media (For complete agency information see *The Advertising Red Books-Agencies* edition):
1. Bus. Publs. 2. Cable T.V. 3. Catalogs & Directories. 4. Co-op Adv. 5. Consumer Mags. 6. D.M. to Bus. Estab.7. D.M. to Consumers 8. Daily Newsp. 9. Exhibits/Trade Shows 10. Foreign 11. Infomercial 12. Internet Adv.13. Multimedia 14. Network Radio 15. Network T.V. 16. Newsp. Distr. Mags. 17. Other 18. Outdoor (Posters, Transit) 19. Point of Purchase20. Premiums, Novelties 21. Product Samples 22. Special Events Mktg. 23. Spot Radio 24. Spot T.V. 25. Weekly Newsp. 26. Yellow Page Adv.

The Timken Company — (Continued)

TDS-30
TDS-70
TDS-90
TIMKEN
TORRINGTON
TPS
TRACGLIDE
UNIPAC
UNIPAC-PLUS
UNIT-BEARING
V-SEALS
WHEEL BOSS
WHEEL-PAC
WHERE YOU TURN
WHS-100
WHS-130
XP
Z-SPEXX
ZERO DUPLICATION
Advertising Agencies:
Doner
25900 Northwestern Hwy
Southfield, MI 48075
Tel.: (248) 354-9700
Fax: (248) 827-8440

WRL Advertising, Inc.
4470 Dressler Rd NW
Canton, OH 44718-2716
Tel.: (330) 493-8866
Fax: (330) 493-8860

TIRE KINGDOM, INC.

(Sub. of TBC Corporation)
823 Donald Ross Rd
Juno Beach, FL 33408-1605
Tel.: (561) 383-3000
Fax: (561) 383-3035
Toll Free: (877) 908-3718
E-mail: webmaster@tirekingdom.com
Web Site: www.tirekingdom.com
Sales Range: $150-199.9 Million
Approx. Number Employees: 7,000
Year Founded: 1972
Business Description:
Operator of Tire Stores & Automotive Service Centers
S.I.C.: 5014; 7538
N.A.I.C.S.: 441320; 811111
Advertising Expenditures: $7,000,000
Media: 5-14-15-18-19-25-26
Personnel:
Orland Wolford *(Pres & CEO)*
James Rowe *(Sr VP-Pur)*
Sandy Sallman *(Mgr-Mktg)*
Advertising Agency:
Creative Dimensions
3940 Olympic Blvd.
Erlanger, KY 41018
Tel.: (859) 372-6701
Fax: (859) 372-6730
(Tires & Automotive Repair)

TITAN INTERNATIONAL, INC.

2701 Spruce St
Quincy, IL 62301-3473
Tel.: (217) 228-6011
Fax: (217) 228-3166
E-mail: sales@titan-intl.com
Web Site: www.titan-intl.com
E-Mail For Key Personnel:
Marketing Director: CJunkins@titan-intl.com
Approx. Sls.: $881,591,000
Approx. Number Employees: 2,400
Year Founded: 1983
Business Description:
Off-Highway Steel Wheels & Tires Mfr for Agricultural, Construction & Consumer Markets
S.I.C.: 3011; 3714
N.A.I.C.S.: 326211; 336399
Import Export
Advertising Expenditures: $2,000,000
Media: 1-2-3-4-7-8-10-19-23
Distr.: Intl.; Natl.
Budget Set: Oct.
Personnel:
Maurice Morry Taylor, Jr. *(Chm & CEO)*
Erwin Henryk Billig *(Vice Chm)*
Paul G. Reitz *(CFO)*
Kent W. Hackamack *(Treas & VP-Fin)*
Cara Junkins *(Dir-Mktg & Sls)*
Brands & Products:
TITAN

TOWER INTERNATIONAL, INC.

(Affil. of Cerberus Capital Management, L.P.)
17672 Laurel Park Dr N Ste 400E
Livonia, MI 48152
Tel.: (248) 675-6000
Fax: (248) 675-6494
Web Site: www.towerautomotive.com
Approx. Rev.: $1,997,058,000
Approx. Number Employees: 7,800
Year Founded: 1993
Business Description:
Automotive Vehicle Structural Components & Assemblies Designer & Mfr
S.I.C.: 3465; 3711; 3714
N.A.I.C.S.: 336370; 336211; 336330; 336399
Advertising Expenditures: $6,500,000
Media: 2-7-10
Personnel:
Mark Malcolm *(Pres & CEO)*
James C. Gouin *(CFO & Exec VP)*
Michael M. Rajkovic *(COO & Exec VP)*
Jim Bernard *(Pres-Americas)*
Gyula Meleghy *(Pres-Intl Ops)*
Jeffrey L. Kersten *(Sr VP & Controller)*
William Cook *(Sr VP-Global HR)*
Paul Radkoski *(Sr VP-Global Pur)*
Jim Cristiano *(Dir-Pur)*

TRANSTAR INDUSTRIES, INC.

(Holding of Friedman Fleischer & Lowe, LLC)
7350 Young Dr
Walton Hills, OH 44146-5357
Tel.: (440) 232-5100
Fax: (440) 232-0632
Fax: (440) 232-7898 (Intl Sales)
E-mail: infodesk@transtarindustries.com
Web Site: www.transtarindustries.com
Sales Range: $500-549.9 Million
Approx. Number Employees: 600
Year Founded: 1975
Business Description:
Automotive Transmission Kits & Accessories Distr
S.I.C.: 5013
N.A.I.C.S.: 423120
Media: 2-7-10-13-21-22
Personnel:
Greg Gyllstrom *(Pres & CEO)*
Jeff Marshall *(CFO)*
Neil Sethi *(Pres-Driveline Distribution Grp)*
Jim Berry *(VP-Mktg)*
Nancy Parker *(VP-HR)*
Mark Russell *(Dir-Complete Transmission Solutions)*
Rob Steinmetz *(Mgr-Product Div)*
Brands & Products:
STARSYSTEM
TRANSTAR

TRIANGLE SUSPENSION SYSTEMS, INC.

(Sub. of Marmon Highway Technologies)
200 E Maloney Rd
Du Bois, PA 15801
Tel.: (814) 375-7211
Toll Free: (800) 458-6077
Web Site: www.triangleusa.com
Sales Range: $75-99.9 Million
Approx. Number Employees: 220
Year Founded: 1971
Business Description:
Vehicle Undercarriage Parts
S.I.C.: 3714
N.A.I.C.S.: 336399
Media: 4
Personnel:
Don Moore *(Dir-HR & Admin)*
Brands & Products:
FLAGG
TRIANGLE AIR SPRING
TRIANGLE SPRING

TRICO MFG. CORP.

1235 Hickory St
Pewaukee, WI 53072-3999
Tel.: (262) 691-9336
Fax: (262) 691-2576
Toll Free: (800) 558-7008
E-mail: custserv@tricomfg.com
Web Site: www.tricocorp.com
E-Mail For Key Personnel:
President: bobj@tricomfg.com
Sales Director: nickk@tricomfg.com
Public Relations: lisak@tricomfg.com
Approx. Number Employees: 50
Year Founded: 1917
Business Description:
Mfr. of Micro-Dispensing Lubrication Products, Lubricating Devices, Coolant Systems, Constant Level Oilers, Liquid Level Indicators, Gravity Feed Oilers, Chain Oilers, Central Lubrication Equipment, Fluid Protection Products, Coolants & Lubricants
S.I.C.: 3569; 3613
N.A.I.C.S.: 333999; 335313
Export
Media: 1-2-4-5-7-10-11-13-16-19-21-26
Distr.: Intl.; Natl.
Budget Set: Nov.
Personnel:
Nick Kroll *(Pres)*
Robert D. Jung *(CEO)*
Brands & Products:
ATLAS
EVEN-FLO
EVER-LAST
EZI-ACTION
HYDROLERT
LI'L MISTER
MAXIMISE. OPTIMIZE. NEVER COMPROMISE.
MICRO-DROP
MISTMATIC
OIL SAFE
OPTO-MATIC
SPRAYMASTER
SPRAYMASTER II
TRI-COOL
TRICO
WATCHDOG

TRICO PRODUCTS CORPORATION

(Holding of Kohlberg & Company, LLC)
3255 W Hamlin Rd
Rochester Hills, MI 48309-3231
Tel.: (248) 371-1700
Fax: (248) 371-8300
E-mail: webmaster@tricoproducts.com
Web Site: www.tricoproducts.com
Approx. Sls.: $368,825,600
Approx. Number Employees: 200
Year Founded: 1917
Business Description:
Wiper Blades Mfr
S.I.C.: 3714; 3069
N.A.I.C.S.: 336399; 326299
Import Export
Advertising Expenditures: $1,230,000
Bus. Publs.: $175,000; Cable T.V.: $50,000; Consumer Mags.: $900,000; D.M. to Bus. Estab.: $25,000; Exhibits/Trade Shows: $20,000; Premiums, Novelties: $10,000; Spot Radio: $50,000
Distr.: Natl.
Budget Set: Apr.
Personnel:
James Finley *(Pres & CEO)*
Brands & Products:
EXACT FIT
TRICO
WINDSPOILER
Advertising Agencies:
Gelia-Media, Inc.
390 S Youngs Rd
Williamsville, NY 14221
Tel.: (716) 629-3200
Fax: (716) 629-3299

Richards Communications
3201 Enterprise Pkwy Ste 400
Beachwood, OH 44122
Tel.: (216) 514-7800
Fax: (216) 514-7801

TRIPPE MANUFACTURING COMPANY

(d/b/a Tripp Lite)
1111 W 35th St
Chicago, IL 60609-1404
Tel.: (773) 869-1111
Fax: (773) 869-1329
E-mail: info@tripplite.com
Web Site: www.tripplite.com
Approx. Number Employees: 400
Year Founded: 1922
Business Description:
Surge Suppressors & Other Power Protection Equipment for Computers
S.I.C.: 3679
N.A.I.C.S.: 334419
Export
Media: 1-2-4-5-6-7-10-11-19-20-21
Distr.: Intl.; Natl.
Personnel:
Barre Seid *(Chm & CEO)*
Glen Haeflinger *(Pres)*
Charles Lang *(CFO)*
Bill DeCicco *(Exec VP-Intl Bus)*

Key to Media (For complete agency information see *The Advertising Red Books-Agencies* edition):
1. Bus. Publs. 2. Cable T.V. 3. Catalogs & Directories. 4. Co-op Adv. 5. Consumer Mags. 6. D.M. to Bus. Estab.7. D.M. to Consumers 8. Daily Newsp. 9. Exhibits/Trade Shows 10. Foreign 11. Infomercial 12. Internet Adv.13. Multimedia 14. Network Radio 15. Network T.V. 16. Newsp. Distr. Mags. 17. Other 18. Outdoor (Posters, Transit) 19. Point of Purchase20. Premiums, Novelties 21. Product Samples 22. Special Events Mktg. 23. Spot Radio 24. Spot T.V. 25. Weekly Newsp. 26. Yellow Page Adv.

Keelin Wyman *(Exec VP-Mktg)*
Priscilla Galgan *(VP-Sls & Mktg)*
Dave Slotten *(Dir-Prod Mngmt)*
Vipin Sharma *(Dir-Bus Dev-Europe)*
Gloria Wong *(Mgr-Media & PR)*
Brands & Products:
BC PERSONAL
BC PRO
FIREWIRE
INTERNET OFFICE
INTERNET OFFICE
ISOBAR
OMNISMART
POWERALERT
POWERVERTER
SMARTPRO
SMARTRACK
SPIKECUBE
SPIKESTIK
TRAVELCUBE
TRAVELER
TRIPP LITE
TRIPP LITE OMNIPRO
TRIPP LITE OMNISMART
TRIPP LITE POWER PROTECTION
WABER
WATCHDOG

TRW AUTOMOTIVE HOLDINGS, CORP.

(Holding of The Blackstone Group L.P.)
12001 Tech Ctr Dr
Livonia, MI 48150
Tel.: (734) 855-2600
Fax: (734) 855-5702
Web Site: www.trwauto.com
Approx. Sls.: $14,383,000,000
Approx. Number Employees: 61,300
Business Description:
Automotive Components Mfr
S.I.C.: 3714; 3711
N.A.I.C.S.: 336312; 336211; 336399
Personnel:
John C. Plant *(Chm, Pres & CEO)*
Joseph S. Cantie *(CFO & Exec VP)*
Steven Lunn *(COO & Exec VP)*
Robin A. Walker-Lee *(Gen Counsel, Sec & Exec VP)*
Peter J. Lake *(Exec VP-Sls & Bus Dev)*
Neil Marchuk *(Exec VP-HR)*
Rob Smith *(VP & Gen Mgr)*
Kai-Uwe Wollenhaupt *(VP & Gen Mgr-Engineered Fasteners & Components)*
Peter R. Rapin *(VP-Treasury & Tax)*
Advertising Agencies:
Bianchi Public Relations Inc.
888 W Big Beaver Rd Ste 777
Troy, MI 48084
Tel.: (248) 269-1122
Fax: (248) 269-8202

Chletcos/Gallagher Inc.
63 Greene St Ste 602
New York, NY 10012
Tel.: (212) 334-2455
Fax: (212) 334-2463

TUFFY ASSOCIATES CORPORATION

7150 Granite Cir
Toledo, OH 43617
Tel.: (419) 865-6900
Fax: (419) 865-7343
Toll Free: (800) 22TUFFY
Web Site: www.tuffy.com
Approx. Number Employees: 45
Year Founded: 1970
Business Description:
Automobile Maintenance Services
S.I.C.: 7532; 7533
N.A.I.C.S.: 811121; 811112
Advertising Expenditures: $3,770,000
Media: 3-8-9-18-19-20-23-26
Distr.: Reg.
Budget Set: Dec.
Personnel:
Roger Hill *(Pres & CEO)*
Karen Vellequette *(CFO)*
Brian Kaufman *(Dir-Mktg)*
Brands & Products:
TUFFY
Advertising Agency:
Tuffy Advertising
7150 Granite Cir
Toledo, OH 43617
Tel.: (419) 865-6900
Fax: (419) 865-7343

TUNEX INTERNATIONAL, INC.

12608 S 125 W
Draper, UT 84020
Tel.: (801) 676-8882
Fax: (801) 676-8887
Toll Free: (800) 448-8639
E-mail: info@tunex.com
Web Site: www.tunex.com
Sales Range: Less than $1 Million
Approx. Number Employees: 6
Year Founded: 1972
Business Description:
Automotive Diagnostic & Repair Specialist Services: Automotive Service Franchise System
S.I.C.: 7539
N.A.I.C.S.: 811198
Advertising Expenditures: $104,498
Media: 2-4-5-8-13-19-23-24-25-26
Distr.: Reg.
Budget Set: Mar.
Brands & Products:
SERVING TOMORROW'S TECHNOLOGY TODAY
TUNEX

TURTLE WAX, INC.

625 Willowbrook Ctr Pkwy
Willowbrook, IL 60527-7969
Tel.: (630) 455-3700
Toll Free: (800) 887-8539
Web Site: www.turtlewax.com
Approx. Number Employees: 450
Year Founded: 1944
Business Description:
Car Care Products Mfr
S.I.C.: 2842
N.A.I.C.S.: 325612
Export
Media: 2-3-4-6-9-13-14-21-23-24-25
Distr.: Intl.; Natl.
Personnel:
Tom Healy *(Sr VP-Consumer Products)*
Michael Schultz *(Sr VP-Product Dev)*
Brands & Products:
BLAZIN GLAZE
CD-2
CLEARVUE
CRYSTAL POLYMER
F21
ICE
MARVEL MYSTERY OIL
ODOR-X
OXY POWER OUT
TOTAL TURTLE
TRANS-AID
TRIPLE SHINE
TURTLE WAX
WET'N BLACK
ZIP WAX
Advertising Agencies:
Energy BBDO
410 N Michigan Ave
Chicago, IL 60611-4213
Tel.: (312) 337-7860
Fax: (312) 337-6871

Zeno Group
200 E Randolph St Ste 5230
Chicago, IL 60601
Tel.: (312) 396-9700
Fax: (312) 222-1561
Turtle Wax, Inc.
— Ginger Werner *(Acct Exec)*

TWIN DISC, INCORPORATED

1328 Racine St
Racine, WI 53403
Tel.: (262) 638-4000
Fax: (262) 638-4481
E-mail: webmaster@twindisc.com
Web Site: www.twindisc.com
Approx. Sls.: $310,393,000
Approx. Number Employees: 941
Year Founded: 1918
Business Description:
Clutches, Transmission & Marine Gears & Torque Convertors Mfr; Heavy-Duty Off-Highway Power Transmission Equipment
S.I.C.: 3714; 1796; 3568; 5084
N.A.I.C.S.: 336350; 238290; 333613; 336399; 423830
Import Export
Advertising Expenditures: $975,000
Media: 2-4-6-7-8-10-20-26
Distr.: Intl.; Natl.
Budget Set: Mar.
Personnel:
Michael E. Batten *(Chm & CEO)*
John H. Batten *(Pres & COO)*
Christopher J. Eperjesy *(CFO, Treas & VP-Fin)*
Jeffrey S. Knutson *(Chief Acctg Officer & Controller)*
Thomas E. Valentyn *(Gen Counsel & Sec)*
James E. Feiertag *(Exec VP)*
Dean J. Bratel *(VP-Engrg)*
Denise L. Wilcox *(VP-HR)*
David H. Johnson *(Mgr-Mktg Comm)*
Brands & Products:
ARNESON
POWER COMMANDER
QUICKSHIFT
TWIN DISC
TWINNET
WE PUT HORSEPOWER TO WORK
Advertising Agency:
Quinlan Marketing Communications
550 Congressional Blvd Ste 350
Carmel, IN 46032
Tel.: (317) 573-5080
Fax: (317) 573-5088
(Marine Gears, Transmissions & Clutches)

UAP INC.

(Sub. of Genuine Parts Company - U.S. Automotive Parts Group)
(d/b/a NAPA Canada)
7025 Ontario St E
Montreal, QC H1N 2B3, Canada
Tel.: (514) 256-5031
Fax: (514) 256-8469
Web Site: www.napacanada.com
Sales Range: $1-4.9 Billion
Approx. Number Employees: 4,000
Year Founded: 1926
Business Description:
Automotive Parts & Replacement Accessories Distr, Remanufacturer & Merchandiser
S.I.C.: 5015; 5013
N.A.I.C.S.: 423140; 441310
Media: 2-3-4-6-8-10-13-18-23-26
Distr.: Natl.
Budget Set: Oct.
Personnel:
Jean E. Douville *(Chm)*
Robert Hattem *(Pres)*
Pierre Lefebvre *(Sec & VP-Fin)*
Kevin M. Chase *(Exec VP-Auto Parts)*
Michel Laberge *(VP-Info Sys)*
Frank Pipito *(VP-Fin)*
Brands & Products:
NAPA
Advertising Agencies:
Matthew Scott Data Marketing Solutions Inc.
385 Brunell Rd
Mississauga, ON L4Z 1Z5, Canada
Tel.: (905) 890-6959

SMD Communications
420 Note Dame W Ste 601
Montreal, QC H2Y 1Z3, Canada
Tel.: (514) 288-1777

UNI-SELECT INC.

170 Industriel Boulevard
Boucherville, QC J4B 2X3, Canada
Tel.: (450) 641-2440
Fax: (450) 641-3658
E-mail: garchambault@uni-select.com
Web Site: www.uni-select.com
Approx. Rev.: $1,379,816,465
Approx. Number Employees: 4,882
Year Founded: 1968
Business Description:
Motor Vehicle Parts & Accessories Distr
S.I.C.: 5013
N.A.I.C.S.: 423120
Media: 2-3-4-7-8-10-18-19-20-21-22-24
Personnel:
Jean-Louis Dulac *(Chm)*
Richard G. Roy *(Pres & CEO)*
Denis Mathieu *(CFO & VP)*
Jean-Pierre Beaulieu *(CIO & VP)*
Pierre Chesnay *(Sec & VP-Legal Affairs)*
William Alexander *(Exec VP-Corp Stores-USA)*
Gary O'Connor *(Exec VP)*
James E. Buzzard *(Sr VP-Corp Dev-USA)*
Florent Jacques *(Sr VP-Distr & Integration)*
Max Dull *(VP & Gen Mgr)*
Luc L'Esperance *(VP-HR)*
Martin Labrecque *(VP-Fin & Control)*
Michele Raymond *(VP-Comm & Strategic Dev)*
Brent Windom *(VP-Mktg & Product Dev-North America)*

Key to Media (For complete agency information see *The Advertising Red Books-Agencies* edition):
1. Bus. Publs. 2. Cable T.V. 3. Catalogs & Directories. 4. Co-op Adv. 5. Consumer Mags. 6. D.M. to Bus. Estab.7. D.M. to Consumers
8. Daily Newsp. 9. Exhibits/Trade Shows 10. Foreign 11. Infomercial 12. Internet Adv.13. Multimedia 14. Network Radio
15. Network T.V. 16. Newsp. Distr. Mags. 17. Other 18. Outdoor (Posters, Transit) 19. Point of Purchase20. Premiums, Novelties
21. Product Samples 22. Special Events Mktg. 23. Spot Radio 24. Spot T.V. 25. Weekly Newsp. 26. Yellow Page Adv.

Uni-Select Inc. — (Continued)

Brands & Products:
AUTO PLUS
AUTOXTRA
UNI-SELECT

UNIFRAX CORPORATION
(Holding of AEA Investors LP)
2351 Whirlpool St
Niagara Falls, NY 14305-2413
Tel.: (716) 278-3800
Fax: (716) 278-3900
E-mail: info@infrax.com
Web Site: www.unifrax.com
Approx. Number Employees: 1,055
Business Description:
Heat-Resistant Ceramic Fiber Mfr
S.I.C.: 3299; 3296
N.A.I.C.S.: 327999; 327993
Media: 2-4-10-13
Personnel:
William P. Kelly *(Chm & CEO)*
Mark D. Roos *(CFO & Sr VP)*
Virginia Cantara *(Mgr-Mktg Comm)*
Brands & Products:
EXCELFRAX
FIBERFRAX
FOAMFRAX
FYREWRAP
INSULFRAX
ISOFRAX

UNITED COMPONENTS, INC.
(Sub. of UCI International, Inc.)
14601 Hwy 41 N
Evansville, IN 47725
Tel.: (812) 867-4156
Fax: (812) 867-4157
E-mail: info@ucinc.com
Web Site: www.ucinc.com
Approx. Sls.: $884,954,000
Approx. Number Employees: 4,350
Year Founded: 2003
Business Description:
Automotive Parts Designer, Mfr & Distr
S.I.C.: 3714; 5013
N.A.I.C.S.: 336399; 423120
Advertising Expenditures: $1,500,000
Personnel:
David L. Squier *(Chm)*
Bruce M. Zorich *(CEO)*
Mark P. Blaufuss *(CFO)*
Keith A. Zar *(Gen Counsel & VP)*
Curtis Draper *(VP-Sls & Mktg)*
Mike Malady *(VP-HR)*

UNITY MANUFACTURING COMPANY
1260 N Clybourn Ave
Chicago, IL 60610
Tel.: (312) 943-5200
Fax: (312) 943-5681
E-mail: info@unityusa.com
Web Site: www.unityusa.com
Approx. Number Employees: 100
Year Founded: 1918
Business Description:
Mfr & Designer of Automotive, Truck & Emergency Vehicle Lighting Systems & Products
S.I.C.: 3647
N.A.I.C.S.: 336321
Export
Media: 2-4-7-10-11-13
Distr.: Natl.
Budget Set: Nov.
Personnel:
Louis E. Gross *(Chm)*
Timothy S. Gross *(Pres)*
Brands & Products:
THE BEAM
HID AND THE BEAM
NITE-EYES
SPITFIRE
UNIBEACON
UNILITE
UNITY

U.S. AUTO PARTS NETWORK, INC.
17150 S Margay Ave
Carson, CA 90746
Tel.: (310) 719-8666
Fax: (310) 632-1681
Toll Free: (888) 827-6976
Web Site: www.usautoparts.net
Approx. Sls.: $262,277,000
Approx. Number Employees: 1,612
Year Founded: 1995
Business Description:
Auto Parts Internet Sales
S.I.C.: 5013; 5961
N.A.I.C.S.: 423120; 454111
Advertising Expenditures: $16,500,000
Media: 8-13
Personnel:
Sol Khazani *(Co-Founder)*
Robert J. Majteles *(Chm)*
Shane Evangelist *(CEO)*
Theodore R. Sanders, Jr. *(CFO)*
Aaron E. Coleman *(CIO & Exec VP-Ops)*
Houman Akhavan *(VP-Mktg)*

U.S. AXLE, INC.
275 Shoemaker Rd
Pottstown, PA 19464-6433
Tel.: (610) 323-3800
Fax: (610) 970-2010
E-mail: sales@usaxle.com
Web Site: www.usaxle.com
E-Mail For Key Personnel:
Sales Director: sales@usaxle.com
Approx. Number Employees: 40
Year Founded: 1920
Business Description:
Shafts & Axle Shafts Mfr
S.I.C.: 3599; 3714
N.A.I.C.S.: 332710; 336399
Export
Media: 2-4-10-11-13-20
Distr.: Intl.; Natl.
Budget Set: Oct.
Personnel:
Ernie Inmon *(Pres)*
Brands & Products:
U.S. AXLE

U.S. TSUBAKI, INC.
(Sub. of Tsubakimoto Chain Co.)
301 E Marquardt Dr
Wheeling, IL 60090-6431
Tel.: (847) 459-9500
Fax: (847) 459-9515
Toll Free: (800) 323-7790
Web Site: www.ustsubaki.com
Sales Range: $300-349.9 Million
Approx. Number Employees: 1,000
Year Founded: 1971
Business Description:
Mfr of Drive Chains, Attachment Chains, Engineering Class Chains, Sprockets & Power Transmission Components
S.I.C.: 3568; 5085
N.A.I.C.S.: 333613; 423840
Import Export
Advertising Expenditures: $750,000
Media: 2-4-6-7-10-11-13
Distr.: Natl.
Budget Set: Dec.
Personnel:
Yoshi Kiteyama *(Pres)*
Tom Barton *(Gen Counsel,Treas & VP-HR)*
Brands & Products:
DOUBLE PLUS
ENERGY SERIES
LAMBDA
NEPTUNE
ONE-TOUCH INSPECTION DOOR
POWER-CYLINDER
POWER-LOCK
PRO-ALIGN
QD
SOLUTIONS THAT WORK
TAPER-LOCK
UNION
WP
XCEEDER

VALLEY TRUCK PARTS, INC.
1900 Chicago Dr
Wyoming, MI 49519
Tel.: (616) 241-5431
Fax: (616) 241-2299
Toll Free: (800) 783-8300
E-mail: info@valleytruckparts.com
Web Site: www.valleytruckparts.com
Approx. Number Employees: 100
Year Founded: 1954
Business Description:
Mfr. of Motor Vehicle Supplies & Parts
S.I.C.: 5013; 5015
N.A.I.C.S.: 423120; 423140
Import Export
Media: 2-5-7-8-10-18-23-24
Personnel:
Jack Goodale *(Pres)*
Gary Allen *(Gen Mgr)*
Jeff Powell *(Dir-HR)*
Mike Goodale *(Mgr-Sls)*

VAPOR BUS INTERNATIONAL
(Div. of Westinghouse Air Brake Technologies Corporation)
1010 Johnson Dr
Buffalo Grove, IL 60089
Tel.: (847) 777-6400
Fax: (847) 520-2222
E-mail: vaporbusinfo@wabtec.com
Web Site: www.vapordoors.com
Sales Range: $25-49.9 Million
Approx. Number Employees: 400
Year Founded: 1903
Business Description:
Designer & Mfr of Passenger Door Systems for Buses
S.I.C.: 3711; 5013
N.A.I.C.S.: 336211; 441310
Export
Media: 2-4-7-10-11
Distr.: Natl.
Personnel:
Robert Gallant *(VP & Gen Mgr)*
John Condon *(VP-Sls-North America)*
Dennis E. Huebner *(Dir-HR)*
Peter Buckley *(Sls Mgr-Central Reg)*
Mike O'Neill *(Sls Mgr-East Reg)*
Bill E. Urian *(Mktg Comm Mgr)*
Dorann Doyle *(Mgr-Customer Svc & Pricing)*
James R. Pearson *(Mgr-Mktg)*

VARTA MICROBATTERY, INC.
(Sub. of VARTA Microbattery GmbH)
1311 Mamaroneck Ste 120
White Plains, NY 16065
Tel.: (914) 592-2500
Fax: (914) 345-0488
Web Site: www.us.varta-microbattery.com
Approx. Number Employees: 60
Year Founded: 1975
Business Description:
Designer & Mfr of Rechargeable & Primary Battery Systems
S.I.C.: 3692
N.A.I.C.S.: 335912
Import Export
Media: 2-4-5-7-10-11-17-19-21
Distr.: Intl.; Natl.
Personnel:
Eddie Shaviv *(Pres & CEO)*
Brands & Products:
HIGH ENDURANCE
TITANIUM PLUS

VISTEON CORPORATION
1 Village Center Dr
Van Buren Township, MI 48111
Tel.: (313) 755-2800
Fax: (313) 755-7983
Toll Free: (800) 847-8366
E-mail: investor@visteon.com
Web Site: www.visteon.com
Approx. Sls.: $7,323,000,000
Approx. Number Employees: 26,500
Year Founded: 1997
Business Description:
Automotive Parts Mfr
S.I.C.: 3714
N.A.I.C.S.: 336322; 336399
Advertising Expenditures: $1,000,000
Media: 10
Personnel:
Donald J. Stebbins *(Chm, Pres & CEO)*
Martin E. Welch, III *(CFO & Exec VP)*
James S. Sistek *(CIO & VP-Bus Svcs-Global)*
Michael J. Widgren *(Chief Acctg Officer, VP & Controller)*
Robert C. Pallash *(Pres-Global Customer Grp & Sr VP)*
Joy M. Greenway *(VP & Pres-Product Grp & VP)*
Steve Meszaros *(Pres-Product Grp & VP)*
Michael K. Sharnas *(Gen Counsel & VP)*
Keith M. Shull *(Sr VP-HR)*
Julie A. Fream *(VP-North America Customer Grp, Global Strategy & Comm)*
Jim Fisher *(Dir-Corp Commun)*
Mark M. Duer *(Mgr-Market Res)*
Brands & Products:
GENPAD
MACH
VISTCONNECT
VISTEON
VISTEON VOICE TECHNOLOGY
Advertising Agencies:
Budco Creative Services
13700 Oakland Ave

Key to Media (For complete agency information see *The Advertising Red Books-Agencies* edition):
1. Bus. Publs. 2. Cable T.V. 3. Catalogs & Directories. 4. Co-op Adv. 5. Consumer Mags. 6. D.M. to Bus. Estab.7. D.M. to Consumers
8. Daily Newsp. 9. Exhibits/Trade Shows 10. Foreign 11. Infomercial 12. Internet Adv.13. Multimedia 14. Network Radio
15. Network T.V. 16. Newsp. Distr. Mags. 17. Other 18. Outdoor (Posters, Transit) 19. Point of Purchase20. Premiums, Novelties
21. Product Samples 22. Special Events Mktg. 23. Spot Radio 24. Spot T.V. 25. Weekly Newsp. 26. Yellow Page Adv.

Highland Park, MI 48203
Tel.: (313) 957-5100
Fax: (313) 957-5522
Toll Free: (888) BUDCO-40

Edelman
3rd Floor Toranomon 45 MT Bldg
Tokyo, 105-001, Japan
Tel.: (81) 3 6403 5200
Fax: (81) 3 6403 5201

WARN INDUSTRIES, INC.
(Sub. of Dover Industrial Products, Inc.)
12900 SE Capps Rd
Clackamas, OR 97015-8903
Tel.: (503) 722-1200
Fax: (503) 722-1411
Toll Free: (800) 543-9276
Web Site: www.warn.com
Sales Range: $200-249.9 Million
Approx. Number Employees: 550
Year Founded: 1948
Business Description:
Industrial Winches & Hoists, Aftermarket Self-Recovery & Utility Winches, Mounting Systems, 4-Wheel Drive Hubs, Fender Flares, Suspension Systems & Other Light Truck Equipment Mfr & Distr
S.I.C.: 3714; 3536
N.A.I.C.S.: 336399; 333923
Import Export
Media: 1-2-3-4-5-6-7-8-10-11-13-19-21-22-24-26
Distr.: Intl.; Natl.
Budget Set: Apr.
Personnel:
Violet Stephenson *(VP-HR)*
Ken Scuito *(Dir-Outbound Mtkg & Customer Svc)*
Brands & Products:
WARN
WARN INDUSTRIAL
WARN WARE
WARN WORKS

WARNER ELECTRIC, INC.
(Group of ALTRA INDUSTRIAL MOTION, INC.)
449 Gardner St
South Beloit, IL 61080
Tel.: (815) 389-3771
Fax: (815) 389-6425
Toll Free: (800) 234-3369
Web Site: www.warnerelectric.com
Approx. Sls.: $250,000,000
Year Founded: 1927
Business Description:
Mfr. of Electric Brakes, Clutches & Controls for Transportation, Industry & Agriculture, Photoelectrics, Linear Actuators & Ball Bearing Screws
S.I.C.: 3714
N.A.I.C.S.: 336340
Import Export
Media: 2-4-5-13-17-20
Distr.: Intl.; Natl.
Budget Set: Dec.
Personnel:
Stan Owens *(Gen Mgr)*
Brands & Products:
FORMSPRAG
UNIMODULE
WARNER ELECTRIC
WICHITA

WELLS MANUFACTURING, L.P.
(Holding of United Components, Inc.)
26 S Brooke St
Fond Du Lac, WI 54935-4007
Tel.: (920) 922-5900
Fax: (920) 922-3585
E-mail: info@wellsmfgcorp.com
Web Site: www.wellsmfgcorp.com
Approx. Number Employees: 800
Year Founded: 1903
Business Description:
Automotive Engine Performance Systems
S.I.C.: 3714
N.A.I.C.S.: 336322; 336399
Import Export
Media: 1-2-4-6-7-8-10-18-19-20
Distr.: Natl.
Personnel:
Dave Peace *(Pres)*
Paul Engle *(Principal)*
Steve Hildebrand *(VP-Mktg)*
Brands & Products:
WELLS

WESTIN AUTOMOTIVE PRODUCTS, INC.
5200 Irwindale Ave Ste 220
Irwindale, CA 91706-2014
Tel.: (626) 960-6762
Fax: (626) 338-1630
Toll Free: (800) 345-8476
E-mail: customerservice@westinautomotive.com
Web Site: www.westinautomotive.com
Approx. Number Employees: 150
Business Description:
Automotive Parts Mfr
S.I.C.: 5013
N.A.I.C.S.: 423120
Media: 2-4-5-10
Brands & Products:
FEY
T-MAX
THERE IS A DIFFERENCE!
WADE
WESTIN

WETHERILL ASSOCIATES INC.
1101 Enterprise Dr
Royersford, PA 19468-4251
Tel.: (484) 875-6600
Fax: (800) 948-6121
Toll Free: (800) 877-3340
E-mail: info@wai-weterill.com
Web Site: www.wai-wetherill.com
Approx. Number Employees: 500
Year Founded: 1978
Business Description:
Distributor of Motor Vehicle Supplies & New Parts
S.I.C.: 5013; 3714
N.A.I.C.S.: 423120; 336399
Import Export
Advertising Expenditures: $160,000
Media: 2-4-7-10
Personnel:
Jeff Sween *(CEO)*
Brands & Products:
FASTFIND
RENARD
WAIGLOBAL
WRS

WILLIAMS CONTROLS, INC.
14100 SW 72nd Ave
Portland, OR 97224-8009
Tel.: (503) 684-8600
Fax: (503) 684-3879
E-mail: info@wmco.com
Web Site: www.wmco.com
Approx. Sls.: $52,266,000
Approx. Number Employees: 234
Year Founded: 1937
Business Description:
Electronic Throttle Controls for Commercial Vehicles
S.I.C.: 3711; 3714
N.A.I.C.S.: 336211; 336322; 336399
Export
Media: 2-4-10
Personnel:
R. Eugene Goodson *(Chm)*
Patrick W. Cavanagh *(Pres & CEO)*
Dennis E. Bunday *(CFO & Exec VP)*
Mark S. Koenen *(VP-Sls & Mktg)*
Scott Thiel *(VP-Engrg & Dev)*
Laura Devine *(Dir-HR)*
Sajid Parvez *(Dir-Global Sourcing)*

WINNER INTERNATIONAL, LLC
32 W State St
Sharon, PA 16146
Tel.: (724) 981-1152
Fax: (724) 981-1216
Toll Free: (800) 527-3345
E-mail: info@winner-intl.com
Web Site: www.winner-intl.com
Approx. Sls.: $13,000,000
Approx. Number Employees: 80
Year Founded: 1986
Business Description:
Mfr of Car Safety Devices
S.I.C.: 3429
N.A.I.C.S.: 332510
Import
Advertising Expenditures: $35,000,000
Media: 6-9-14-15-18-25
Distr.: Natl.
Personnel:
Donna Winner *(Chm & CEO)*
Jerry Trontel *(Pres)*
Karen Winner-Hale *(COO)*
Brands & Products:
THE CLUB
THE DOOR CLUB
PADLOCK
SECURITY SERIES
THE SHEILD
STANDS FOR SECURITY
UTILITY LOCK
Advertising Agency:
Winner Advertising
(House Agency)
32 W. State St.
Sharon, PA 16146
Tel.: (724) 981-1152
(The Club; Pepper Spray; The Club Securtiy Series)

ZAP
501 4th St
Santa Rosa, CA 95401
Tel.: (707) 525-8658
Fax: (707) 525-8692
Toll Free: (800) 251-4555
E-mail: zap@zapworld.com
Web Site: www.zapworld.com
Approx. Sls.: $3,816,000
Approx. Number Employees: 35
Year Founded: 1994
Business Description:
Electric Vehicle Systems Mfr & Designer
S.I.C.: 3751; 3621; 5941
N.A.I.C.S.: 336991; 335312; 451110
Advertising Expenditures: $356,000
Media: 4-13
Personnel:
Gary Dodd *(Pres)*
William R. Hartman *(CFO)*
H. David Jones *(COO)*
Steven M. Schneider *(CEO-China)*
Alex Campbell *(Dir-Comm)*
Brands & Products:
ALIAS
POWERBIKE
POWERSKI
TURN IT ON
XEBRA
ZAP
ZAP DUDE
ZAPINO
ZAPPY
ZAPTRUCK XL
ZAPVAN SHUTTLE

ZENITH FUEL SYSTEMS LLC
(Sub. of Precision Aerospace Services, LLC)
14570 Industrial Park Rd
Bristol, VA 24202-3706
Tel.: (276) 669-5555
Fax: (276) 645-8696
Fax: (276) 669-0082
Web Site: www.zenithfuelsystems.com
Approx. Number Employees: 65
Year Founded: 1911
Business Description:
Mfr. of Carburetors & Fuel Valves & Pumps
S.I.C.: 3592
N.A.I.C.S.: 336311
Import Export
Advertising Expenditures: $350,000
Media: 1-2-10
Distr.: Intl.; Natl.
Personnel:
Darcio Giovanetti *(Pres)*
Bob Malina *(Mgr-Customer Svc)*
Paul Mulcahy *(Mgr-Pur)*
Chet Zinnanti *(Mgr-Ops)*
Brands & Products:
ZEEMS

ZERO-MAX, INC.
(Sub. of Miki Pulley Co., Ltd.)
13200 6th Ave N
Plymouth, MN 55441
Tel.: (763) 546-4300
Fax: (763) 546-8260
Toll Free: (800) 533-1731
E-mail: info@zero-max.com
Web Site: www.zero-max.com
Approx. Number Employees: 65
Year Founded: 1949
Business Description:
Mfr. & Market Mechanical Variable Speed Drives & Accessories, Couplings & Linear Actuators
S.I.C.: 3566; 3568
N.A.I.C.S.: 333612; 333613
Import Export
Media: 2-4-7-10-13-20-23
Distr.: Intl.; Natl.
Budget Set: Jan.
Personnel:
Douglas Moore *(Pres)*
William Centner *(VP-Fin-Admin)*
Bob Mainz *(Mgr-Sls-Mktg)*

Zero-Max, Inc. — (Continued)

Brands & Products:
CD
CROWN
ETP
MIKI PULLEY
POSI-LOK
ROH'LIX
SCHMIDT
SERVO CLASS
ZERO-MAX

ZIEBART INTERNATIONAL CORPORATION
1290 E Maple Rd
Troy, MI 48083-2817
Tel.: (248) 588-4100
Fax: (248) 588-1444
E-mail: info@ziebart.com
Web Site: www.ziebart.com
Approx. Number Employees: 200
Year Founded: 1959
Business Description:
Franchiser of Automotive Protection Services & Accessory Installations
S.I.C.: 5013; 7539
N.A.I.C.S.: 423120; 811198
Export
Advertising Expenditures: $10,195,000
Media: 3-5-8-9-10-17-19-20-22-23-24-26
Distr.: Intl.; Natl.
Budget Set: Sept.
Personnel:
Thomas E. Wolfe *(Pres & CEO)*
Daniel C. Baker *(Sr VP)*
Michael Pino *(Sr VP)*
Michael W. Riley *(Sr VP)*
Mark Lauzon *(Dir-Mktg & Adv)*
Brands & Products:
AQUAPEL
DIAMOND
INNERCLEAN
INNERGUARD
SPEEDY AUTOGLASS
ZIEBART
ZLINER

ZIM MANUFACTURING COMPANY
6100 W Grand Ave
Chicago, IL 60639
Tel.: (773) 622-2500
Fax: (773) 622-0269
E-mail: jeankukla@zimmfgco.com
Web Site: www.zimmfgco.com
Approx. Sls.: $3,000,000
Approx. Number Employees: 50
Year Founded: 1919
Business Description:
Automotive Tools Mfr
S.I.C.: 3423; 3823
N.A.I.C.S.: 332212; 334513
Export
Media: 2-4-10-11-26
Distr.: Natl.
Budget Set: Apr.
Personnel:
Ken Kukla *(Pres)*
Brands & Products:
ZIM

Key to Media (For complete agency information see *The Advertising Red Books-Agencies* edition):
1. Bus. Publs. 2. Cable T.V. 3. Catalogs & Directories. 4. Co-op Adv. 5. Consumer Mags. 6. D.M. to Bus. Estab.7. D.M. to Consumers 8. Daily Newsp. 9. Exhibits/Trade Shows 10. Foreign 11. Infomercial 12. Internet Adv.13. Multimedia 14. Network Radio 15. Network T.V. 16. Newsp. Distr. Mags. 17. Other 18. Outdoor (Posters, Transit) 19. Point of Purchase20. Premiums, Novelties 21. Product Samples 22. Special Events Mktg. 23. Spot Radio 24. Spot T.V. 25. Weekly Newsp. 26. Yellow Page Adv.

Aviation & Aerospace

Airplane Accessories — Electronic Equipment Maintenance & Service — Missiles — Space Vehicles

AAR CORP.
1 AAR Pl 1100 N Wood Dale Rd
Wood Dale, IL 60191
Tel.: (630) 227-2000
Fax: (630) 227-2019
Telex: 190062
E-mail: webmaster@aarcorp.com
Web Site: www.aarcorp.com
Approx. Sls.: $1,775,782,000
Approx. Number Employees: 6,100
Year Founded: 1951
Business Description:
Aviation & Aerospace Industry Services
S.I.C.: 3724; 3356; 4581
N.A.I.C.S.: 336412; 331491; 488190
Import Export
Media: 4-5-7-10-13-20
Distr.: Intl.; Natl.
Budget Set: June
Personnel:
David P. Storch *(Chm & CEO)*
Timothy J. Romenesko *(Pres & COO)*
Richard J. Poulton *(CFO, Treas & VP)*
Kevin M. Larson *(CIO & VP)*
Michael J. Sharp *(Chief Acctg Officer, VP & Controller)*
John M. Holmes *(Pres-Allen Asset Mgmt Div)*
Robert J. Regan *(Gen Counsel, Sec & VP)*
Andrew J. Schmidt *(Sr VP-Supply Chain-Allen Asset Mgmt Div)*
Donald J. Wetekam *(Sr VP-Govt & Defense Bus Dev)*
Danny Kleiman *(Grp VP-Maintenance, Repair & Overhaul)*
Randy J. Martinez *(Grp VP-Govt & Defense Svcs)*
Terry D. Stinson *(Grp VP-Structures & Sys)*
Michael K. Carr *(VP-Tax & Asst Treas)*
Jack Arehart *(VP-Comml Sls & Mktg)*
Frank Boni *(VP-Sls & Mktg)*
Timothy O. Skelly *(VP-HR)*
Stephen W. Peckham *(Gen Mgr)*
Jim Bomberger *(Dir-Sls)*
Tom Caskey *(Mgr-Sls Reg)*
Bob Tucker *(Mgr-Sls Reg)*
Advertising Agency:
Gerard Design
15 W. Jefferson Ave.
Naperville, IL 60540
Tel.: (630) 355-0775

AERO CONTROLS AVIONICS, INC.
(Sub. of Aero Controls Inc.)
5415 NW 36th St
Miami, FL 33166
Tel.: (305) 871-1300
Fax: (305) 884-1400
Web Site: www.aerosystems.com
Approx. Sls.: $12,000,000
Approx. Number Employees: 50
Business Description:
Aircraft Equipment & Supplies
S.I.C.: 5088; 7699
N.A.I.C.S.: 423860; 811310
Media: 2-7-10

AERO SYSTEMS ENGINEERING INC.
(Joint Venture of Tonka Bay Equity Partners LLC & Centerfield Capital Partners L.P.)
358 E Fillmore Ave
Saint Paul, MN 55107-1289
Tel.: (651) 227-7515
Fax: (651) 227-0519
E-mail: ase@aerosysengr.com
Web Site: www.aerosysengr.com
Sales Range: $25-49.9 Million
Approx. Number Employees: 200
Year Founded: 1967
Business Description:
Wind Tunnels, Turbine Engine Test Cells, Test Equipment Mfr & Ancillary Computer Support for Real-Time Data Acquisition & Control Systems
S.I.C.: 3569; 8733
N.A.I.C.S.: 333999; 541710
Export
Media: 2-10
Distr.: Intl
Personnel:
Charles Loux *(Pres & CEO)*
Steven Hedberg *(CFO & Sec)*

AEROJET
(Sub. of Aerojet-General Corporation)
5731 Wellington Rd
Gainesville, VA 20155
Tel.: (703) 754-5000
Fax: (703) 754-5316
Web Site: www.aerojet.com
Sales Range: $200-249.9 Million
Approx. Number Employees: 475
Year Founded: 1949
Business Description:
Mfr of Propulsion Products
S.I.C.: 3764; 3714
N.A.I.C.S.: 336415; 336322
Export
Media: 2-7-10-11
Distr.: Intl.; Natl.
Budget Set: Jan.
Personnel:
Craig Halterman *(CIO & VP)*
Brands & Products:
AEROSPACE

AEROSTAR INTERNATIONAL, INC.
(Sub. of Raven Industries, Inc.)
1814 F Ave
Sioux Falls, SD 57104-0243
Mailing Address:
PO Box 5057
Sioux Falls, SD 57117-5057
Tel.: (605) 331-3500
Fax: (605) 331-3520
E-mail: mail@aerostar.com
Web Site: www.aerostar.com
Sales Range: $10-24.9 Million
Approx. Number Employees: 280
Year Founded: 1986
Business Description:
Hot Air Balloons, Large Advertising Inflatables, Remote Control Blimps & Specialty Apparel
S.I.C.: 3721
N.A.I.C.S.: 336411
Export
Media: 2-10
Distr.: Natl.
Budget Set: Aug.
Personnel:
Lon E. Stroschein *(VP & Gen Mgr-Aerostar Div-Raven Industries)*
Brands & Products:
AD UPS
ADVERBLIMPS
AEROBLIMPS
AEROSTAR

AEROVIRONMENT, INC.
181 W Huntington Dr Ste 202
Monrovia, CA 91016
Tel.: (626) 357-9983
Fax: (626) 359-9628
E-mail: info@avinc.com
Web Site: www.avinc.com
Approx. Rev.: $292,503,000
Approx. Number Employees: 768
Year Founded: 1971
Business Description:
Small Unmanned Aircraft Systems Designer, Developer & Producer
S.I.C.: 3721
N.A.I.C.S.: 336411
Export
Advertising Expenditures: $979,000
Media: 10
Personnel:
Timothy E. Conver *(Chm, Pres & CEO)*
Jikun Kim *(CFO)*
Michael Bissonette *(Sr VP & Gen Mgr-Efficient Energy Sys)*
Tom Herring *(Sr VP & Gen Mgr-Unmanned Aircraft Sys Bus Segment)*
Cathleen S. Cline *(Sr VP-Admin)*
Patrick Dellario *(VP & Gen Mgr-PosiCharge Sys)*
Brands & Products:
AEROVIRONMENT
DRAGON EYE
DREAM
EV SOLUTIONS
EXOSKELETON
GLOBAL OBSERVER
GO
JOINT TACTICAL
MINELOADER
POINTER
POSICHARGE
PUMA
RAVEN
SUAV
SUNRAYCER
SWITCHBLADE
WASP
Advertising Agencies:
The Boyer Syndicate, Inc.
1800 Century Park E Ste 600
Los Angeles, CA 90067
Tel.: (310) 229-5956
Fax: (310) 455-1817

Brightspear Armed Services Consultancy
820 G St Ste 111
San Diego, CA 92101
Tel.: (619) 819-8722
Toll Free: (877) 567-4688

Key to Media (For complete agency information see *The Advertising Red Books-Agencies* edition):
1. Bus. Publs. 2. Cable T.V. 3. Catalogs & Directories. 4. Co-op Adv. 5. Consumer Mags. 6. D.M. to Bus. Estab.7. D.M. to Consumers 8. Daily Newsp. 9. Exhibits/Trade Shows 10. Foreign 11. Infomercial 12. Internet Adv.13. Multimedia 14. Network Radio 15. Network T.V. 16. Newsp. Distr. Mags. 17. Other 18. Outdoor (Posters, Transit) 19. Point of Purchase20. Premiums, Novelties 21. Product Samples 22. Special Events Mktg. 23. Spot Radio 24. Spot T.V. 25. Weekly Newsp. 26. Yellow Page Adv.

AIR INDUSTRIES GROUP, INC.
1479 N Clinton Ave
Bay Shore, NY 11706
Tel.: (631) 968-5000
Fax: (631) 968-5377
E-mail: airindmc@airindmc.com
Web Site:
www.airindustriesgroup.com
Sales Range: $25-49.9 Million
Approx. Number Employees: 180
Business Description:
Aircraft Structural Parts Mfr
S.I.C.: 3728
N.A.I.C.S.: 336413
Advertising Expenditures: $34,987
Media: 7-10
Personnel:
Peter D. Rettaliata *(CEO & Dir)*
Dario A. Peragallo *(Exec VP)*

ALLEN AIRCRAFT PRODUCTS, INC.
6168 Woodbine Rd
Ravenna, OH 44266-9665
Tel.: (330) 296-9621
Fax: (330) 296-5532
E-mail: info@allenaircraft.com
Web Site: www.allenaircraft.com
Sales Range: $10-24.9 Million
Approx. Number Employees: 135
Year Founded: 1947
Business Description:
Airplane Fluid Systems Component Mfr
S.I.C.: 3728; 3471
N.A.I.C.S.: 336413; 332813
Export
Media: 2-4-7-10-17
Distr.: Natl.
Personnel:
Neil W. Mann, Jr. *(Pres & Treas)*
Brands & Products:
ALLEN AIRCRAFT
DYNA-AIR

AMERICAN EUROCOPTER, LLC
(Sub. of EADS North America, Inc.)
2701 Forum Dr
Grand Prairie, TX 75052-7027
Tel.: (972) 641-0000
Fax: (972) 641-3550
E-mail: info@eurocopterusa.com
Web Site: www.eurocopterusa.com
Sales Range: $300-349.9 Million
Approx. Number Employees: 500
Year Founded: 1992
Business Description:
Helicopters Mfr & Marketing
S.I.C.: 3721; 5088
N.A.I.C.S.: 336411; 423860
Import Export
Advertising Expenditures: $505,000
Multimedia: $15,000; Bus. Publs.: $125,000; Exhibits/Trade Shows: $300,000; Internet Adv.: $15,000; Special Events Mktg.: $50,000
Distr.: Natl.
Budget Set: Nov.
Personnel:
Marc Paganini *(Pres & CEO)*
Romain Trapp *(CFO & Exec VP)*
Eric Walden *(Sr VP-Bus Dev)*
Anthony J. DiNota *(VP-Comml Sls, Mktg & Customer Support)*
Treg Manning *(VP-Sls)*
Brenda Reuland *(VP-Comm & PR)*
Don Baenen *(Dir-Oil & Gas Mktg)*
Patrice Royer *(Dir-Bus & Private Aviation)*
Jane Tischler *(Dir-Supply Svcs)*
Kris DeSoto *(Mgr-Mktg-Northeast Reg)*
Glenn Murray *(Mgr-Mktg-Midwest Reg)*
Brands & Products:
ASTAR
DAUPHIN
EC120
EC135
EC155
SUPER PUMA
TWINSTAR

AMR CORPORATION
4333 Amon Carter Blvd
Fort Worth, TX 76155-2605
Mailing Address:
Mail Drop 5675 HDQ
Dallas, TX 75261-9616
Tel.: (817) 963-1234
Fax: (817) 967-9641
E-mail: investor.relations@aa.com
Web Site: www.aa.com
Approx. Rev.: $22,170,000,000
Approx. Number Employees: 78,250
Year Founded: 1982
Business Description:
Airline Holding Company
S.I.C.: 4512; 4513; 6719
N.A.I.C.S.: 481111; 492110; 551112
Advertising Expenditures: $165,000,000
Media: 2-3-6-9-15-16-17-18-23-24
Distr.: Intl.; Natl.
Personnel:
Gerard J. Arpey *(Chm & CEO)*
Thomas W. Horton *(Pres)*
Isabella D. Goren *(CFO & Sr VP)*
Gary F. Kennedy *(Chief Compliance Officer, Gen Counsel & Sr VP)*
Virasb Vahidi *(Chief Comml Officer & Sr VP-Mktg & Plng)*
Robert W. Reding *(Exec VP-Ops)*
C. David Cush *(Sr VP-Global Sls)*
Thomas R. Del Valle *(Sr VP-Airport Svcs-American Airlines Inc)*
Peter J. Dolara *(Sr VP-Miami, Caribbean & Latin America-American Airli)*
Monte E. Ford *(Sr VP-IT-American Airlines)*
George Hazy *(Sr VP-Customer Svc)*
Craig S. Kreeger *(Sr VP-Customer Experience)*
William K. Ris, Jr. *(Sr VP-Govt Affairs-American Airlines)*
Roger Frizzell *(VP-Corp Commun & Adv-American Airlines Inc)*
Douglas G. Herring *(VP-Ops-Fin & Strategic Plng)*
John R. MacLean *(VP-Pur-American Airlines Inc)*
Randall H. Phillips *(VP-Engrng & Quality Assurance)*
Nora Linville *(Dir-Women's Sls & Mktg)*
Steve Schlachter *(Dir-Worldwide Adv & Promos)*
Advertising Agencies:
Ketchum Directory Advertising/Kansas City
7015 College Blvd Ste 700
Overland Park, KS 66211-1524
Tel.: (913) 344-1900
Fax: (913) 344-1960
Toll Free: (800) 922-6977

Pantin/Beber Silverstein Public Relations
(Part of the Beber Silverstein Group)
3361 SW 3rd Ave
Miami, FL 33145-3911
Tel.: (305) 856-9800
Fax: (305) 857-0027

TM Advertising
1717 Main St Ste 2000
Dallas, TX 75201
Tel.: (972) 556-1100
Fax: (972) 830-2619
(American Airlines, Creative, Media Buying)
Agency of Record

Universal McCann
100 33rd St 8th Fl
New York, NY 10001
Tel.: (212) 883-4700
(American Airlines)

ASTRONAUTICS CORPORATION OF AMERICA
4115 N Teutonia Ave
Milwaukee, WI 53209
Tel.: (414) 449-4000
Fax: (414) 447-8231
E-mail: busdev@astronautics.com
Web Site: www.astronautics.com
Sales Range: $125-149.9 Million
Approx. Number Employees: 2,600
Year Founded: 1959
Business Description:
Aircraft Instruments, Flight Control Systems, Guidance & Navigation Systems, Robotics, Thermal Magnetic Refrigeration, Avionic Displays & Display Processors & Systems Integrators Mfr
S.I.C.: 3812; 3571
N.A.I.C.S.: 334511; 334111
Export
Media: 2-4-10
Distr.: Intl.; Natl.
Personnel:
Nathaniel K. Zelazo *(Co-Founder)*
Ronald E. Zelazo *(Chm & CEO)*
Michael Russek *(Pres)*
Stephen Givant *(CFO)*
Brands & Products:
ASTRONAUTICS
CENTURION
PATTON

ATLANTIC AVIATION CORPORATION
(Sub. of Executive Air Support Inc.)
6504 International Pkwy Ste 2400
Plano, TX 75093-8236
Tel.: (972) 447-4200
Fax: (972) 447-4229
Toll Free: (800) 283-8076
Web Site: www.atlanticaviation.com
Approx. Number Employees: 300
Year Founded: 1927
Business Description:
Charters & Aircraft Management
S.I.C.: 4581
N.A.I.C.S.: 488190
Media: 2-4-5-7-10-13
Distr.: Natl.
Budget Set: Sept.
Personnel:
Sue Sommers *(VP-Sls & Mktg)*
George Bacigalupo *(Gen Mgr)*
John Carlen *(Gen Mgr-Pittsburgh)*
Jay Hamby *(Reg Dir)*
Traci Fremin *(Reg Mgr-Sls)*

AVANTAIR, INC.
4311 General Howard Dr
Clearwater, FL 33762
Tel.: (727) 539-0071
Fax: (727) 539-7007
E-mail: info@avantair.com
Web Site: www.avantair.com
Approx. Rev.: $143,006,574
Approx. Number Employees: 450
Year Founded: 2002
Business Description:
Fractional Aircraft Ownership & Management Services
S.I.C.: 8711; 7359
N.A.I.C.S.: 541330; 532411
Advertising Expenditures: $2,260,782
Personnel:
Robert J. Lepofsky *(Chm)*
Steven F. Santo *(CEO)*
Richard Pytak, Jr. *(CFO)*
Kevin Beitzel *(COO)*
John Colucci *(Exec VP)*
Kevin V. McKamey *(Exec VP)*
John Blatchley *(Dir-Sls-Northeast Reg)*
Heather Dynes *(Dir-Mktg)*

AVIALL, INC.
(Sub. of Boeing Commercial Aviation Services)
2750 Regent Blvd
Dallas, TX 75261-9048
Mailing Address:
PO Box 619048
Dallas, TX 75261-9048
Tel.: (972) 586-1000
Fax: (972) 586-1361
Toll Free: (800) 284-2551
E-mail: aviallnz@aviall.com
Web Site: www.aviall.com
Sales Range: $1-4.9 Billion
Approx. Number Employees: 1,009
Year Founded: 1993
Business Description:
New Aviation Parts, Supply-Chain Management & Other Aerospace Aftermarket Related Services
S.I.C.: 3728; 3559; 5088; 7629; 7699
N.A.I.C.S.: 336413; 333298; 423860; 811219; 811310
Media: 5-7-10-13-17
Personnel:
Dan P. Komnenovich *(Chm, Pres & CEO)*
Colin Cohen *(CFO)*
Edward Dolanski *(Exec VP & COO)*
Robin Everly *(Gen Counsel, Sr VP-Law, HR & Sec)*
Jacqueline Collier *(Sr VP & CAO)*
Joseph Lacik *(Sr VP-Info Svcs)*
Perry Scott *(Sr VP-Sls & Mktg)*
Eric Strafel *(Sr VP-Ops)*
Curt Brusto *(VP-HR)*
Brands & Products:
AVIALL

AVOX SYSTEMS INC.
(Sub. of Zodiac US Corporation)
225 Erie St
Lancaster, NY 14086-9501
Tel.: (716) 683-5100
Fax: (716) 681-1089
Telex: 91-394
Web Site: www.avoxsys.com

Key to Media (For complete agency information see *The Advertising Red Books-Agencies* edition):
1. Bus. Publs. 2. Cable T.V. 3. Catalogs & Directories. 4. Co-op Adv. 5. Consumer Mags. 6. D.M. to Bus. Estab.7. D.M. to Consumers 8. Daily Newsp. 9. Exhibits/Trade Shows 10. Foreign 11. Infomercial 12. Internet Adv.13. Multimedia 14. Network Radio 15. Network T.V. 16. Newsp. Distr. Mags. 17. Other 18. Outdoor (Posters, Transit) 19. Point of Purchase20. Premiums, Novelties 21. Product Samples 22. Special Events Mktg. 23. Spot Radio 24. Spot T.V. 25. Weekly Newsp. 26. Yellow Page Adv.

E-Mail For Key Personnel:
Sales Director: tharmon@scottaviation.com
Approx. Sls.: $100,000,000
Approx. Number Employees: 350
Year Founded: 1932
Business Description:
Mfr. & Designer of Respiratory Protective Equipment for the Civil & Military Aerospace Markets
S.I.C.: 3443; 3842
N.A.I.C.S.: 332313; 339113
Import Export
Media: 2-4-5-7-9-10-11-13-20-21-26
Distr.: Intl.; Natl.
Budget Set: Oct.
Brands & Products:
AIR-PAK
AVIOX
EAGLE IMAGER
PIDDLE-PAK
PRESUR-PAK
QUIK-DON
SCOTT
SCOTT-ALERT
SCOTT-O-VISTA
SCOTTORAMIC
SCRAM
SKAT-PAK
SKY MASK
SLING-PAK
SPEAK-EZEE
VIBRALERT
Advertising Agency:
Stand Advertising, LLC
2351 N Forest Rd Ste 102
Buffalo, NY 14068
Tel.: (716) 210-1065
Fax: (716) 210-1069

BANNER AEROSPACE, INC.
(Sub. of The Fairchild Corporation)
1750 Tysons Blvd Ste 1400
McLean, VA 22102
Tel.: (703) 478-5900
Fax: (703) 478-5767
E-mail: info@banner.com
Web Site: www.banner.com
Sales Range: $25-49.9 Million
Approx. Number Employees: 50
Business Description:
Supplier of Aircraft Parts & Related Support Services; Rotables & Engines
S.I.C.: 5088
N.A.I.C.S.: 423860
Media: 9-17
Personnel:
Jeffrey J Steiner *(CEO)*
Eugene W. Juris *(CFO & VP)*
Warren D. Persavich *(COO & Sr VP)*
Eric I. Steiner *(Sr VP)*
Bradley T. Lough *(VP-Fin)*

BE AEROSPACE, INC.
1400 Corporate Center Way
Wellington, FL 33414-2105
Tel.: (561) 791-5000
Fax: (561) 791-7900
Web Site: www.beaerospace.com
Approx. Rev.: $1,984,200,000
Approx. Number Employees: 6,650
Year Founded: 1987
Business Description:
Commercial & General Aviation Aircraft Cabin Interior Products & Equipment Mfr, Designer & Retailer
S.I.C.: 2396; 3728
N.A.I.C.S.: 336360; 336413
Import Export
Media: 2-7
Personnel:
Amin J. Khoury *(Chm & CEO)*
Werner Lieberherr *(Pres & COO)*
Thomas P. McCaffrey *(CFO & Sr VP)*
Ryan M. Patch *(Gen Counsel, Sec & VP-Law)*
Wayne R. Exton *(Grp VP & Gen Mgr-Bus Jet Segment)*
Wick Sharte *(Grp VP & Gen Mgr-Consumables Mgmt Grp)*
Stephen R. Swisher *(VP-Fin & Controller)*
Norris Powell *(VP-HR)*
Advertising Agency:
Walt Klein Advertising
2000 S Colorado Blvd Ste 10200
Denver, CO 80222
Tel.: (303) 298-8015
Fax: (303) 298-8194

BELL HELICOPTER TEXTRON, INC.
(Sub. of Textron Inc.)
600 E Hurst Blvd
Fort Worth, TX 76101
Mailing Address:
PO Box 482
Fort Worth, TX 76101-0482
Tel.: (817) 280-2011
Fax: (817) 280-8221
Telex: 758313
Web Site:
www.bellhelicopter.textron.com
Sales Range: $1-4.9 Billion
Approx. Number Employees: 8,000
Year Founded: 1935
Business Description:
Helicopter Mfr
S.I.C.: 3721; 3728
N.A.I.C.S.: 336411; 336413
Import Export
Advertising Expenditures: $2,000,000
Media: 2-5-6-7-8-9-10-11-13-18-20-23-24-25-26
Distr.: Intl.; Natl.
Budget Set: Oct.
Personnel:
John L. Garrison *(Pres & CEO)*
Robert Hastings *(Sr VP-Comm)*
Larry D. Roberts *(Sr VP-Comml Bus)*
Michael Cox *(VP-Comm)*
Jeffrey L. Angelos *(Dir-Comml Sls-North America)*
Kathleen C. Searle *(Dir-Brand & Enterprise Comm)*
Brands & Products:
206B-3
206L-4
210
407
412EP
427
430
AB139
AH-1Z
BA609
EAGLE EYE
HUEY II
UH-1Y
V-22

BEMCO INC.
2255 Union Pl
Simi Valley, CA 93065
Tel.: (805) 583-4970
Fax: (805) 583-5033
E-mail: info@bemcoinc.com
Web Site: www.bemcoinc.com
Sales Range: $10-24.9 Million
Approx. Number Employees: 26
Year Founded: 1951
Business Description:
Environmental Test Equipment & Space Simulation Systems Mfr
S.I.C.: 3826; 3829
N.A.I.C.S.: 334516; 334519
Export
Media: 2-4-26
Distr.: Direct to Consumer; Intl.; Natl.
Budget Set: Mar.
Personnel:
Barry Bruskrud *(Pres)*
Bill Pennock *(Mgr-Sls)*

THE BOEING COMPANY
100 N Riverside Plz
Chicago, IL 60606-1501
Tel.: (312) 544-2000
Fax: (312) 544-2082
Telex: 329430
E-mail: investor.relations@boeing.com
Web Site: www.boeing.com
Approx. Rev.: $64,306,000,000
Approx. Number Employees: 160,500
Year Founded: 1916
Business Description:
Commercial & Military Aircraft, Missiles, Space Exploration Equipment, Defense Electronic Systems, Computer Services & Large-Scale Information Networks Developer
S.I.C.: 3724; 3577; 3721; 3761; 3764; 3812; 9661
N.A.I.C.S.: 336412; 334119; 334511; 336411; 336414; 336415; 927110
Import Export
Advertising Expenditures: $13,000,000
Media: 1-2-6-9-11-13-15-18-24
Distr.: Intl.; Natl.
Budget Set: Oct.
Personnel:
W. James McNerney, Jr. *(Chm, Pres & CEO)*
James A. Bell *(Pres, CFO & Exec VP)*
James F. Albaugh *(Pres, CEO-Comml Airplanes & Exec VP)*
Elizabeth M. Tulach *(Mng Dir-Alternatives)*
Kim Hammonds *(CIO & VP-IT Org)*
Mark A. Schmid *(Chief Investment Officer & VP)*
John J. Tracy *(CTO & Sr VP-Engrg, Ops & Tech)*
Michael J. Cave *(Pres-Boeing Capital Corp & Sr VP-The Boeing Co)*
Robert J. Pasterick *(Pres-Shared Svcs Grp)*
J. Michael Luttig *(Gen Counsel & Exec VP)*
David Dohnalek *(Treas & VP-Fin Plng)*
Scott E. Carson *(Sr VP)*
Wanda Denson-Low *(Sr VP-Internal Governance)*
Shephard W. Hill *(Sr VP-Bus Dev & Strategy)*
Tod R. Hullin *(Sr VP-Comm)*
Timothy J. Keating *(Sr VP-Govt Ops)*
Richard D. Stephens *(Sr VP-HR & Admin)*
Harry S. McGee, III *(VP-Fin & Corp Controller)*
Gregory Smith *(VP-Fin & Controller)*
Jean Chamberlin *(VP & Gen Mgr-Mobility Div)*
Matthew Ganz *(VP & Gen Mgr-Boeing Res & Tech)*
Mary Armstrong *(VP-Environ, Health, Safety, Engrg, Ops & Tech)*
Federico Genoese-Zerbi *(VP)*
Rob Laird *(VP-Sls-India)*
Diana Sands *(VP-IR & Fin Plng & Analysis)*
Kevin Schemm *(VP-Sls-North America)*
Dennis D. Swanson *(VP-Intl Bus Dev-Boeing Defence, Space & Security-India)*
Randy Tinseth *(VP-Mktg-Comml Airplanes)*
Michael Arndt *(Mktg Dir)*
Anthony Lombardi *(Mktg Dir)*
Marcello Bruni *(Dir-Comm)*
Chantal Dorange *(Dir-Corp Comm-Europe, Middle East & Africa)*
Fritz Johnston *(Dir-Adv & Brand Mgmt)*
David Schumacher *(Dir-State & Local Govt Rels)*
Tom Young *(Dir-Brand Mgmt & Adv)*
Janice Llereza *(Sr Mgr-Alternative Investments)*
Stuart Kramlich *(Program Mgr-Flight Tests)*
Paige Pace *(Mgr-Comm)*
Erik Simonsen *(Mgr-Comm-Sys)*
Amy Hartweger *(Specialist-Comm)*
Brands & Products:
636
707
727
737
747
757
767
777
BOEING
BOEING BUSINESS JET
DASH
DREAMLINER
FLEET TEAM
Advertising Agencies:
Draftfcb
101 E Erie St
Chicago, IL 60611-2812
Tel.: (312) 425-5000
Fax: (312) 425-5010
(Horizon Campaign)

Maslansky, Luntz & Partners
1101 King St Ste 110
Alexandria, VA 22314
Tel.: (703) 358-0080
Fax: (703) 358-0089

THE BOEING COMPANY - HELICOPTER DIVISION
(Div. of The Boeing Company)
5000 E McDowell Rd
Mesa, AZ 85215-9707
Tel.: (480) 891-3000
Fax: (480) 891-6830
Web Site: www.boeing.com
Sales Range: $450-499.9 Million
Approx. Number Employees: 4,200
Year Founded: 1934
Business Description:
Helicopter Mfr, Research & Development, Systems Integration, Aerospace Support

The Boeing Company - Helicopter Division — (Continued)

S.I.C.: 3721
N.A.I.C.S.: 336411
Export
Media: 2-7-8-10-11-24
Distr.: Intl.; Natl.
Budget Set: Nov.
Personnel:
Edward Koopman *(Gen Mgr)*

BRENDAN AIRLINES

(d/b/a USA3000 Airlines)
335 Bishop Hollow Rd
Newtown Square, PA 19073
Tel.: (610) 325-1280
Fax: (610) 325-1285
E-mail: info@usa3000airlines.com
Web Site: www.usa3000.com
Approx. Number Employees: 100
Business Description:
Commercial Airline
S.I.C.: 4512
N.A.I.C.S.: 481111
Media: 6-20
Personnel:
John J. Mullen *(Chm)*
Steven E. Harfst *(CEO-USA3000 Airlines)*

CAE INC.

8585 Cote de Liesse
Saint Laurent, QC H4T 1G6, Canada
Tel.: (514) 341-6780
Fax: (514) 341-7699
Toll Free: (800) 760-0667
E-mail: investor.relations@cae.com
Web Site: www.cae.com
Approx. Rev.: $1,659,657,780
Approx. Number Employees: 7,500
Year Founded: 1947
Business Description:
Simulation, Modelling & Training Solutions for Civil Aviation & Military
S.I.C.: 5063; 8299
N.A.I.C.S.: 423610; 611512
Import Export
Media: 2-10-13
Distr.: Intl.; Natl.
Budget Set: Mar.
Personnel:
Lynton R. Wilson *(Chm)*
Marc Parent *(Pres & CEO)*
Martin Gagne *(Grp Pres-Simulation Products, Trng & Svcs)*
Jeffrey G. Roberts *(Grp Pres-Civil Simulation Products, Trng & Svcs)*
Stephane Lefebvre *(CFO & VP-Fin)*
Keyvan Fard *(Pres-Helicopter Solutions & Exec VP-Bus Dev & OEM Alliances)*
Andrew Arnovitz *(VP-IR & Strategy)*
Chris Stellwag *(Dir-Mktg & Commun)*
Brands & Products:
AUGMENTED ENGINEERING ENVIRONMENT
CAE
CAE-ASTT
CAE AVS
CAE C2-SIM
CAE DEPLOY
CAE ENVISION
CAE GESI
CAE INFRONT 3D
CAE MAD
CAE PROFILE
CAE SELECT
CAE SIMFINITY
CAE TRUE
DUAL PROFILE
DURACHROME
DURASHELL
GLADIATOR
LITHOS
LS
MACROFLOW
MAXVUE
MEDALLION
MEDALLION-S
MILL HOST
MOTIF COMPOSITING
MSHATF
ONEPLATFORM
PANELMSR
RAVE
SIMFINITY
STRIVE
SUPERFLOW
TROPOS
VARI PROFILE

CAE USA, INC.

(Sub. of CAE INC.)
4908 Tampa W Blvd
Tampa, FL 33634-2411
Mailing Address:
PO Box 15000
Tampa, FL 33684-5000
Tel.: (813) 885-7481
Fax: (813) 887-1439
E-mail: info@cae.com
Web Site: www.cae.com
Approx. Rev.: $100,000,000
Approx. Number Employees: 425
Year Founded: 1939
Business Description:
High Fidelity Flight Simulators
S.I.C.: 3589; 7373
N.A.I.C.S.: 333319; 541512
Import Export
Media: 2-7-10-20
Distr.: Direct to Consumer; Intl.; Natl.
Budget Set: Oct.
Personnel:
John Lenyo *(Pres & Gen Mgr)*
Alain Raquepas *(CFO & VP-Fin)*
John Atkinson *(Treas & Dir-Fin)*
Michael Fedele *(Gen Mgr-Trng)*
Chris Stellwag *(Dir-Commun & PR)*

CESSNA AIRCRAFT COMPANY

(Sub. of Textron Inc.)
1 Cessna Blvd
Wichita, KS 67215-1400
Mailing Address:
PO Box 7704
Wichita, KS 67277-7704
Tel.: (316) 517-6000
Fax: (316) 206-7328
Toll Free: (800) 423-7762
Web Site: www.cessna.com
Approx. Sls.: $4,200,000,000
Approx. Number Employees: 10,000
Year Founded: 1927
Business Description:
Mfr. of General Aviation Aircraft
S.I.C.: 3721
N.A.I.C.S.: 336411
Export
Media: 1-2-4-5-6-7-8-9-10-11-13-18-19-20-22-25-26
Distr.: Intl.; Natl.
Budget Set: Oct.
Personnel:
Scott A. Ernest *(Pres & CEO)*
Eric Salander *(CFO & Sr VP)*
Sue Ronshagen *(CIO)*
Dave Brant *(Sr VP-Product Engrg)*
Eric Cardinali *(Sr VP-Integrated Supply Chain)*
Mark Paolucci *(Sr VP-Sls & Mktg)*
Brad Thress *(Sr VP-Customer Svc)*
Jim Walters *(Sr VP-HR)*
Andrew Kasowski *(VP-Product Dev)*
Paul McGartoll *(VP-Strategy & Bus Dev)*
Rhonda Fullerton *(Dir-Mktg Ops)*
Lori Lucion *(Dir-Mktg Comm)*
Roger Martin *(Dir-Mktg Ops)*
Angela Banldwin *(Mgr-Media Rels)*
Brands & Products:
CARAVAN
CITATION
SKYHAWK
SKYLANE
STATIONAIR
TURBO SKYLANE
TURBO STATIONAIR
Advertising Agencies:
Bailey Lauerman
1299 Farnam St Ste 930
Omaha, NE 68102-1157
Tel.: (402) 514-9400
Fax: (402) 514-9401
The Ten. Video

LaBov & Beyond, Inc.
609 E Cook Rd
Fort Wayne, IN 46825
Tel.: (260) 497-0111
Fax: (260) 497-0007

Mediassociates, Inc.
1 Ives St
Danbury, CT 06810-2605
Tel.: (203) 797-9500
Fax: (203) 797-1400
Toll Free: (800) 522-1660
(Media Buying/Planning)

CIRCOR AEROSPACE, INC.

(Sub. of CIRCOR International, Inc.)
2301 Wardlow Cir
Corona, CA 92880
Tel.: (951) 270-6200
Fax: (951) 270-6201
E-mail: contactus@circoraerospace.com
Web Site: www.circoraerospace.com
Approx. Sls.: $35,000,000
Approx. Number Employees: 235
Year Founded: 1947
Business Description:
Valves & Controls for Aerospace, Military & Industrial Applications Mfr
S.I.C.: 3491; 3494
N.A.I.C.S.: 332911; 332919
Export
Media: 2-4-10
Distr.: Intl.; Natl.
Budget Set: Oct.
Personnel:
Mike Terrell *(VP-Sls)*
Michael Dill *(Grp VP)*

CIRRUS DESIGN CORPORATION

(Holding of Arcapita, Inc.)
4515 Taylor Cir
Duluth, MN 55811
Tel.: (218) 727-2737
Fax: (218) 727-2148
Toll Free: (888) 750-9925
Web Site: www.cirrusdesign.com
Approx. Number Employees: 1,000
Year Founded: 1984
Business Description:
Aircraft Mfr
S.I.C.: 3721
N.A.I.C.S.: 336411
Media: 6-10
Personnel:
Dale Klapmeier *(Chm)*
Brent Wouters *(Pres & CEO)*
David Coleal *(Exec VP-Mfg)*

CLARY CORPORATION

150 E Huntington Dr
Monrovia, CA 91016-4847
Tel.: (626) 359-4486
Fax: (626) 305-0254
Toll Free: (800) 442-5279
E-mail: sales@clary.com
Web Site: www.clary.com
E-Mail For Key Personnel:
Sales Director: sales@clary.com
Sales Range: $1-9.9 Million
Approx. Number Employees: 40
Year Founded: 1939
Business Description:
Uninterruptible Power Systems Mfr
S.I.C.: 3663; 3651; 3679; 5211
N.A.I.C.S.: 334220; 334310; 334418; 334419; 444190
Import Export
Media: 2-7-10-26
Distr.: Natl.
Budget Set: Sept.
Personnel:
John G. Clary *(Pres & Dir-Mktg)*
Craig Bolden *(Sls Mgr & Sr Applications Engr)*
Brands & Products:
CA UNICENTER TNG
CLARY
THE CONTINUOUS POWER COMPANY
HP OPENVIEW
NIDEX
OUTPOST
RUPS
SIGNAL POWER
SYSTEMS ENHANCEMENT
VISX

CONTINENTAL MOTORS

(Sub. of Aviation Industry Corporation of China)
2039 S Broad St
Mobile, AL 36615
Mailing Address:
PO Box 90
Mobile, AL 36601-0090
Tel.: (251) 438-3411
Fax: (251) 432-7352
Toll Free: (800) 718-3411
Web Site: www.tcmlink.com
Sales Range: $125-149.9 Million
Approx. Number Employees: 350
Year Founded: 1905
Business Description:
Power Plants for Manned & Unmanned Aircraft, New & Rebuilt General Aviation Piston Engines
S.I.C.: 3724
N.A.I.C.S.: 336412
Media: 2-10
Distr.: Natl.
Budget Set: Oct.
Personnel:
Rhett C. Ross *(Pres)*

Key to Media (For complete agency information see *The Advertising Red Books-Agencies* edition):
1. Bus. Publs. 2. Cable T.V. 3. Catalogs & Directories. 4. Co-op Adv. 5. Consumer Mags. 6. D.M. to Bus. Estab.7. D.M. to Consumers 8. Daily Newsp. 9. Exhibits/Trade Shows 10. Foreign 11. Infomercial 12. Internet Adv.13. Multimedia 14. Network Radio 15. Network T.V. 16. Newsp. Distr. Mags. 17. Other 18. Outdoor (Posters, Transit) 19. Point of Purchase20. Premiums, Novelties 21. Product Samples 22. Special Events Mktg. 23. Spot Radio 24. Spot T.V. 25. Weekly Newsp. 26. Yellow Page Adv.

Brands & Products:
TOPCARE CYLINDERS

CRANE CO.
100 First Stamford Pl
Stamford, CT 06902
Tel.: (203) 363-7300
Fax: (203) 363-7295
E-mail: webmaster@craneco.com
Web Site: www.craneco.com
Approx. Sls.: $2,217,825,000
Approx. Number Employees: 10,500
Year Founded: 1855
Business Description:
Aerospace & Electronic Components, Controls, Valves, Composite Materials, Fluid Handling Systems & Automated Vending Machines
S.I.C.: 3492; 2821; 3491; 3561; 3594; 3721; 3728; 3821; 3823; 3824; 3829; 3873; 8733
N.A.I.C.S.: 332912; 325211; 332911; 333911; 333996; 334513; 334514; 334518; 334519; 336411; 336413; 339111; 541710
Import Export
Advertising Expenditures: $750,000
Bus. Publs.: $500,000; Catalogs & Directories: $20,000; D.M. to Bus. Estab.: $40,000; Exhibits/Trade Shows: $40,000; Yellow Page Adv.: $150,000
Distr.: Intl.; Natl.
Budget Set: Oct.
Personnel:
Eric C. Fast *(Pres & CEO)*
Thomas J. Perlitz *(Pres-Controls & VP-Corp Strategy)*
David E. Bender *(Pres-Electronics)*
Max H. Mitchell *(Pres-Fluid Handling)*
Mike Rofito *(Pres-Aerospace)*
Michael Romito *(Pres-Aerospace Grp)*
Augustus I. duPont *(Gen Counsel, Sec & VP)*
Elise M. Kopczick *(VP-HR)*
Richard E. Koch *(Dir-IR)*
Brands & Products:
AIRWEIGHS
CRANE
DURATUF
FILON
GLASBORD
HYDROLOK
KEMLITE
NOBLE
SEQUENTIA
VENDMAX

CURTISS-WRIGHT FLIGHT SYSTEMS, INC.
(Sub. of Curtiss-Wright Controls, Inc.)
201 Old Boling Spring World
Shelby, NC 28152
Tel.: (704) 481-1150
Fax: (704) 481-2230
E-mail: info@cwflightsystems.com
Web Site: www.cwflightsystems.com
Sales Range: $25-49.9 Million
Approx. Number Employees: 300
Business Description:
Motion Control Integrated Systems & Components Designer & Mfr for the Aerospace, Defense & Industrial Markets
S.I.C.: 3724
N.A.I.C.S.: 336412
Media: 2-4-7-10
Distr.: Intl.; Natl.

CUTTER AVIATION, INC.
2802 E Old Twr Rd
Phoenix, AZ 85034
Tel.: (602) 273-1237
Fax: (602) 275-4010
Toll Free: (800) 234-5382
E-mail: infophoenix@cutteraviation.com
Web Site: www.cutteraviation.com
Sales Range: $75-99.9 Million
Approx. Number Employees: 300
Year Founded: 1928
Business Description:
Charter & Air Craft Management Services
S.I.C.: 5599; 5088
N.A.I.C.S.: 441229; 423860
Advertising Expenditures: $200,000
Media: 2-7-10-13
Personnel:
W. R. Cutter *(Owner)*
W. W. Cutter *(Pres & CEO)*
Steve Prieser *(CFO & VP)*
Rachel Goldie *(Mgr-Parts)*

D-VELCO MANUFACTURING OF ARIZONA INC.
(Sub. of Northstar Aerospace, Inc.)
401 S 36th St
Phoenix, AZ 85034-2812
Tel.: (602) 275-4406
Fax: (602) 275-1071
E-mail: webmaster@dvelco.com
Web Site: www.dvelco.com
Approx. Number Employees: 210
Year Founded: 1954
Business Description:
Precision Machined Aerospace Products, Assemblies & Fabrications Mfr
S.I.C.: 3599; 3812
N.A.I.C.S.: 332710; 334511
Media: 10
Personnel:
John N. Maris *(Pres & Gen Mgr-Northstar-Phoenix)*
Phil Mazur *(VP-Fin)*
Kenneth N. Clark *(Dir-Sls & Mktg)*
Mark Butler *(Mgr-Sls Acct)*

DASSAULT FALCON JET CORP.
(Sub. of Dassault Falcon Jet Corp.)
Teterboro Airport PO Box 2000
South Hackensack, NJ 07606-0620
Tel.: (201) 440-6700
Fax: (201) 541-4401
Web Site: www.dassaultfalcon.com
Approx. Number Employees: 1,727
Year Founded: 1972
Business Description:
Mfr., Sale & Service of Business Jets
S.I.C.: 5088; 3721
N.A.I.C.S.: 423860; 336411
Import Export
Advertising Expenditures: $2,500,000
Media: 1-2-6-7-10-11
Distr.: Intl.; Natl.
Budget Set: Oct.
Personnel:
John Rosanvallon *(Pres & CEO)*
Ralph Aceti *(Dir-Comm)*
Pierre-Henri Messiah *(Dir-Mktg-Falcon)*
Brands & Products:
FALCON 2000
FALCON 2000 EX
FALCON 50EX
FALCON 900C
FALCON 900EX

DAYTON INTERNATIONAL AIRPORT
3600 Terminal Dr Ste 300
Vandalia, OH 45377-3313
Tel.: (937) 454-8200
Fax: (937) 454-8284
Web Site: www.flydayton.com
Sales Range: $10-24.9 Million
Approx. Number Employees: 165
Year Founded: 1936
Business Description:
Airport & Air Facilities Operator
S.I.C.: 4581; 4512
N.A.I.C.S.: 488119; 481111
Media: 9-18-24-25
Personnel:
Mark Carpenter *(Mgr-Airport Rescue Fire Fighters)*
Advertising Agencies:
Interspace Airport Advertising
4635 Crackersport Rd
Allentown, PA 18104
Toll Free: (877) 422-8326

Neo Communications
42 E Rahn Rd
Dayton, OH 45429
Tel.: (937) 439-2737

EADS NORTH AMERICA, INC.
(Div. of European Aeronautic Defence & Space Company EADS N.V.)
1616 N Ft Myer Dr Ste 1600
Arlington, VA 22209
Tel.: (703) 236-3300
Fax: (703) 236-3301
Web Site:
www.eadsnorthamerica.com
Approx. Number Employees: 130
Business Description:
Holding Company
S.I.C.: 6719
N.A.I.C.S.: 551112
Media: 2-4-10
Personnel:
Ralph D. Crosby, Jr. *(Chm)*
Sean O'Keefe *(CEO)*
Christopher Emerson *(CFO)*
David R. Oliver, Jr. *(COO)*
James F Mulato *(Pres-EADS North America Test & Svcs)*
Pierre Cardin *(Gen Counsel)*
Samuel D. Adcock *(Sr VP-Govt Rels)*
Michael Cosentino *(VP-Tanker Ops)*
Randy Hutcherson *(VP & Mgr-Programs-Tankers)*
Carlaine Blizzard *(VP-Homeland Security Programs)*
Marc Bouvier *(VP-Strategy & Integration)*
David M. Fink *(VP-HR & Admin Svcs)*
Guy Hicks *(VP-Comm & PR)*
Ted Mickevicius *(Dir-Bus Dev-Reserve Component Forces)*
Advertising Agency:
Quinn Gillespie & Associates LLC
1133 Connecticut Ave NW 5th Fl
Washington, DC 20036
Tel.: (202) 457-1110
Fax: (202) 457-1130

ECLIPSE AEROSPACE, INC.
2503 Clark Carr Loop SE
Albuquerque, NM 87106
Tel.: (505) 245-7555
Fax: (505) 241-8803
Web Site: www.eclipseaerospace.net
Sales Range: $25-49.9 Million
Year Founded: 1998
Business Description:
Commercial Aircraft Mfr
S.I.C.: 3721
N.A.I.C.S.: 336411
Media: 10
Personnel:
Mason R. Holland, Jr. *(Chm & CEO)*
Kenneth Ross *(Pres-Svc Div)*
Ekim Alptekin *(Exec VP-Europe)*
Michael Press *(Exec VP)*
Tony Parker *(Sr VP & Chief Engr)*
Cary A. Winter *(Chief Svc Engr & Sr VP)*
Edward M. Lundeen *(Sr VP-Bus Ops)*
Jack Harrington *(Sr Dir)*

EMBRAER AIRCRAFT HOLDING INC.
(Sub. of Embraer-Empresa Brasileira de Aeronautica S/A)
276 SW 34th St
Fort Lauderdale, FL 33315-3603
Tel.: (954) 359-3700
Fax: (954) 359-3701
Web Site: www.embraer.com
Approx. Number Employees: 300
Business Description:
Aircraft Mfr
S.I.C.: 5088
N.A.I.C.S.: 423860
Media: 2-6-7-8-10-11
Distr.: Intl.
Personnel:
Mauricio Botelho *(Chm)*
Frederico Fleury Curado *(Pres & CEO)*
Carlos Villela *(Gen Counsel & VP)*
Romualdo Barros *(Exec VP-Defense Market)*
Horacio Forjaz *(Exec VP-Corp Commun)*
Satoshi Yokota *(Exec VP-Dev)*
Robert Stangarone *(VP-Corp Comm-North America)*
Gordon Preston *(Mgr-Airline Mktg)*

EMIVEST AEROSPACE CORPORATION
(Sub. of Emirates Investment & Development Company PSC)
1770 Skyplace Blvd
San Antonio, TX 78216
Tel.: (210) 258-3900
Fax: (210) 258-3917
Toll Free: (888) JET7530
E-mail: ssacsj30@aol.com
Web Site:
www.emivestaerospace.com
Approx. Number Employees: 300
Year Founded: 1995
Business Description:
Aircraft Designer & Mfr
S.I.C.: 3721
N.A.I.C.S.: 336411
Export
Advertising Expenditures: $500,000
Media: 1-2-4-10-17
Distr.: Intl.; Natl.
Personnel:
Buti Saeed Al Ghandi *(Chm)*
Anthony Power *(CEO & Board Dir)*
Mark Fairchild *(VP-Mktg & Sls)*
Brands & Products:
SJ 30-2
SWEARINGEN

Key to Media (For complete agency information see *The Advertising Red Books-Agencies* edition):
1. Bus. Publs. 2. Cable T.V. 3. Catalogs & Directories. 4. Co-op Adv. 5. Consumer Mags. 6. D.M. to Bus. Estab.7. D.M. to Consumers 8. Daily Newsp. 9. Exhibits/Trade Shows 10. Foreign 11. Infomercial 12. Internet Adv.13. Multimedia 14. Network Radio 15. Network T.V. 16. Newsp. Distr. Mags. 17. Other 18. Outdoor (Posters, Transit) 19. Point of Purchase20. Premiums, Novelties 21. Product Samples 22. Special Events Mktg. 23. Spot Radio 24. Spot T.V. 25. Weekly Newsp. 26. Yellow Page Adv.

ENGINE COMPONENTS, INC.

(Sub. of Danbury AeroSpace, Inc.)
9503 Middlex Dr
San Antonio, TX 78217-5915
Tel.: (210) 820-8101
Tel.: (210) 820-8146 (HR)
Fax: (210) 820-8102
Fax: (210) 820-2402 (HR)
E-mail: sales-service@eci.aero
Web Site: www.eci.aero
E-Mail For Key Personnel:
Sales Director: sales-service@eci.aero
Year Founded: 1943
Business Description:
Aircraft Engine & Engine Parts Mfr & Distr, Repair & Engineering Services
S.I.C.: 3724; 4581; 8711
N.A.I.C.S.: 336412; 488190; 541330
Media: 2-7-8-10-26
Distr.: Natl.
Personnel:
Gary H. Garvens *(CEO)*
Christy Nichols Quinn *(Dir-Mktg)*
Steve Thatcher *(Product Mgr-Fuel Sys)*
James K. Ball *(Mgr-Customer Svc & Sls-Northeast)*
Joel Longoria *(Mgr-Southeastern Territory)*
Tim Morland *(Mgr-Territory)*
Joe Trampota *(Mgr-Central Territory Sls)*
Brands & Products:
ECI
TITAN

FIRST AVIATION SERVICES INC.

15 Riverside Ave
Westport, CT 06880-4214
Tel.: (203) 291-3300
Fax: (203) 291-3330
E-mail: first@firstaviation.com
Web Site: www.firstaviation.com
Sales Range: $100-124.9 Million
Approx. Number Employees: 200
Year Founded: 1995
Business Description:
Aircraft Parts & Components Supplier & Distr
S.I.C.: 3728; 3724
N.A.I.C.S.: 336413; 336412
Advertising Expenditures: $174,000
Media: 2-7-10-22
Personnel:
Aaron P. Hollander *(Chm & CEO)*
James G. Howell, II *(CFO & VP)*
Ahmed M. Metwalli *(COO)*
Brands & Products:
FAVS
FIRST AVIATION

GE AVIATION

(Div. of GE Technology Infrastructure)
1 Neumann Way
Cincinnati, OH 45215-1915
Tel.: (513) 243-2000
Fax: (513) 243-0645
Toll Free: (800) 626-2004
Web Site: www.geae.com
Sales Range: $5-14.9 Billion
Approx. Number Employees: 10,000
Year Founded: 1948
Business Description:
Mfr of Commercial & Military Jet Engines & Components; Mfr of Aircraft Electrical & Mechanical Systems
S.I.C.: 3724; 3721; 3728
N.A.I.C.S.: 336412; 336411; 336413
Media: 2-4-7-10
Personnel:
David L. Joyce *(Pres & CEO)*
John M. Seral *(CIO & VP)*
Bradley Mottier *(VP & Gen Mgr-Bus & Gen Aviation)*
Colleen Athans *(VP & Gen Mgr-Assembly, Test & Overhaul)*
Bill Fitzgerald *(VP & Gen Mgr-Genx Product Line)*
Thomas Gentile *(VP & Gen Mgr-Svcs)*
Jeanne M. Rosario *(VP & Gen Mgr-Engrg)*
Roger N. Seager *(VP & Gen Mgr-Comml Aircraft Programs-China)*
Paul McElhinney *(VP-Legal & Bus Dev)*
Jack F. Ryan *(VP-HR)*
Doug Folsom *(Gen Mgr-Unison Engine Components)*
Advertising Agency:
Power Creative
11701 Commonwealth Dr
Louisville, KY 40299-2358
Tel.: (502) 267-0772
Fax: (502) 267-1727

GE CAPITAL AVIATION SERVICES

(Div. of General Electric Capital Corporation)
(d/b/a GECAS)
777 Long Ridge Rd
Stamford, CT 06927
Tel.: (203) 585-2700
Fax: (203) 316-7865
Web Site: www.gecas.com
Sales Range: $200-249.9 Million
Approx. Number Employees: 150
Business Description:
Financing & Leasing Services to the Commercial Aviation Industry
S.I.C.: 6289; 7359
N.A.I.C.S.: 523999; 532490
Media: 2-7-13
Personnel:
Norman C.T. Liu *(Pres & CEO)*
Seamus O'Donnell *(VP-Sls & Mktg-Asset Mgmt Svcs)*
Dan Whitney *(Dir-Global Comm)*

GENERAL DYNAMICS CORPORATION

2941 Fairview Park Dr Ste 100
Falls Church, VA 22042-4510
Tel.: (703) 876-3000
Fax: (703) 876-3125
E-mail: gdwebmaster@generaldynamics.com
Web Site: www.generaldynamics.com
E-Mail For Key Personnel:
Public Relations: RDoolittle@generaldynamics.com
Approx. Sls.: $32,466,000,000
Approx. Number Employees: 90,000
Year Founded: 1952
Business Description:
Military Aircraft, Submarines, Marine Systems, Space Vehicles, Electric Motors & Armored Vehicles Mfr
S.I.C.: 3761; 3711; 3731; 3795
N.A.I.C.S.: 336414; 336211; 336611; 336992
Export
Media: 2-4-10-18
Distr.: Intl.; Natl.
Budget Set: Oct.
Personnel:
Jay L. Johnson *(Chm & CEO)*
Patrick Sullivan *(Mng Dir)*
L. Hugh Redd *(CFO & Sr VP)*
Joseph T. Lombardo *(Pres-Gulfstream & Exec VP-Aerospace)*
John P. Casey *(Pres-Electric Boat & VP)*
Jeffrey Geiger *(Pres-Bath Iron Works & VP)*
Frederick J. Harris *(Pres-Nassco & VP)*
S. Daniel Johnson *(Pres-IT & VP)*
Christopher Marzilli *(Pres-C4 Sys & VP)*
John C. Ulrich *(Pres-European Land Combat Systems & VP)*
Lewis F. Von Thaer *(Pres-Advanced Info Sys & VP)*
Michael S. Wilson *(Pres-Ordnance, Tactical Sys & VP)*
Thomas W. Merrell *(Pres-American Overseas Marine)*
Daniel G. Clare *(CFO-Gulfstream Aerospace & Sr VP)*
Gregory S. Gallopoulos *(Gen Counsel, Sec & Sr VP)*
Ira P. Berman *(Gen Counsel-Gulfstream Aerospace, Sr VP-Admin & VP)*
Gerard J. Demuro *(Exec VP-Info Sys & Tech)*
Larry R. Flynn *(Sr VP-Mktg & Sls-Gulfstream Aerospace)*
Robert W. Helm *(Sr VP-Plng & Dev)*
Preston A. Henne *(Sr VP-Programs, Engrg & Test-Gulfstream Aerospace)*
Walter M. Oliver *(Sr VP-HR & Admin)*
Ernest J. Babcock *(VP & Deputy Gen Counsel)*
Tommy R. Augustsson *(VP-IT)*
Henry Eickelberg *(VP-HR & Shared Svcs)*
Kendell Pease *(VP-Govt Rels & Comm)*
David Ibbetson *(Gen Mgr-Canada)*
Brands & Products:
GENERAL DYNAMICS

GEOEYE, INC.

21700 Atlantic Blvd
Dulles, VA 20166
Tel.: (703) 480-7500
Fax: (703) 450-9570
E-mail: info@geoeye.com
Web Site: www.geoeye.com
Approx. Rev.: $330,345,000
Approx. Number Employees: 723
Business Description:
Satellite & Aerial Imagery & Geospatial Information Services
S.I.C.: 3812; 3769; 4899; 8713
N.A.I.C.S.: 334511; 336419; 517410; 541360
Advertising Expenditures: $600,000
Personnel:
James A. Abrahamson *(Chm)*
Matthew M. O'Connell *(Pres & CEO)*
Joseph F. Greeves *(CFO & Exec VP)*
William Schuster *(COO)*
William L. Warren *(Gen Counsel, Sec & Exec VP)*
Tony Frazier *(Sr VP-Mktg)*
Chris Tully *(Sr VP-Sls)*
Carl A. Alleyne *(VP-Engrg)*
Steven R. Balthazor *(VP-Fin & Plng)*
Paolo E. Colombi *(VP-Intl Sls)*
James M. Craig *(VP-Special Projects & Treasury Ops)*
Ray Helmering *(VP-Product Engrg)*
Michael Harbour *(Asst Controller)*
Mark Brender *(Exec Dir)*
Chris Wilson *(Sr Dir)*
Charmaine Pavelko *(Dir-Tax)*
Brands & Products:
GEOEYE
GEOEYE FOUNDATION
IKONOS
ORBVIEW
SEASTAR

GOODRICH CORPORATION

Four Coliseum Centre 2730 W Tyvola Rd
Charlotte, NC 28217-4578
Tel.: (704) 423-7000
Fax: (704) 423-7002
E-mail: corporate.communications@goodrich.com
Web Site: www.goodrich.com
E-Mail For Key Personnel:
Public Relations: Lisa.Bottle@goodrich.com
Approx. Sls.: $6,966,900,000
Approx. Number Employees: 25,600
Year Founded: 1870
Business Description:
Aerospace & Engineered Industrial Products Mfr & Marketer
S.I.C.: 3728; 3724
N.A.I.C.S.: 336413; 336412
Import Export
Media: 2-10-11-17-25
Distr.: Intl.; Natl.
Budget Set: Oct.
Personnel:
Marshall O. Larsen *(Chm, Pres & CEO)*
Scott E. Kuechle *(CFO & Exec VP)*
Brian Brandewie *(Pres-Aircraft Wheels & Brakes Div)*
John J. Carmola *(Pres-Actuation & Landing Segment)*
Marc Duvall *(Pres-Aerostructures Div)*
Cynthia M. Egnotovich *(Pres-Nacelles & Interior Sys Segment)*
Mike Gardiner *(Pres-Actuation Sys)*
Greg Peters *(Pres-Goodrich Aerostructures)*
Curtis Reusser *(Pres-Electronic Sys Segment)*
Bob Yancey *(Pres-Engine Control & Electrical Power Sys)*
Terrence G. Linnert *(Gen Counsel & Exec VP-Admin)*
Jennifer Pollino *(Sr VP-HR)*
Sally L. Geib *(VP, Asst Sec & Assoc Gen Counsel)*
Lisa Bottle *(VP-Corp Comm)*
Mike Lobb *(Sr Dir-Mktg & Bus Dev-Goodrich ISR)*
David Easton *(Dir-Bus Dev)*
Krister Holladay *(Dir-Govt Affairs)*
Anthony Lynch *(Dir-Bus Dev)*
Bruce Woodruff *(Dir-Mktg Business Solutions)*
Paul Dain *(Reg Mgr-Sls)*
George Corwin *(Mgr-Bus Dev-Integrators)*
Matthew DeRosier *(Mgr-Bus Dev)*
Teresa Flihan *(Mgr-Sys Quality)*
Janet Slakman *(Asst Sec)*

Key to Media (For complete agency information see *The Advertising Red Books-Agencies* edition):
1. Bus. Publs. 2. Cable T.V. 3. Catalogs & Directories. 4. Co-op Adv. 5. Consumer Mags. 6. D.M. to Bus. Estab.7. D.M. to Consumers 8. Daily Newsp. 9. Exhibits/Trade Shows 10. Foreign 11. Infomercial 12. Internet Adv.13. Multimedia 14. Network Radio 15. Network T.V. 16. Newsp. Distr. Mags. 17. Other 18. Outdoor (Posters, Transit) 19. Point of Purchase20. Premiums, Novelties 21. Product Samples 22. Special Events Mktg. 23. Spot Radio 24. Spot T.V. 25. Weekly Newsp. 26. Yellow Page Adv.

Brands & Products:
DURACARB
DURATHERM
EDL
FASTPROP
GOODRICH
GRID-LOCK
RHO-COR
RIGHT INNOVATION RIGHT HERE RIGHT NOW
Advertising Agency:
Chletcos/Gallagher Inc.
63 Greene St Ste 602
New York, NY 10012
Tel.: (212) 334-2455
Fax: (212) 334-2463

GULFSTREAM AEROSPACE CORPORATION

(Sub. of General Dynamics Aerospace Group)
500 Gulfstream Rd
Savannah, GA 31407-9643
Mailing Address:
PO Box 2206
Savannah, GA 31402-2206
Tel.: (912) 965-3000
Fax: (912) 965-3775
Toll Free: (800) 810-4853
E-mail: info@gulfstream.com
Web Site: www.gulfstream.com
Sales Range: $750-799.9 Million
Approx. Number Employees: 5,000
Year Founded: 1958
Business Description:
Designer, Developer, Producer & Marketer of Large-Cabin & Business Jet Aircraft
S.I.C.: 3721; 4581
N.A.I.C.S.: 336411; 488190
Export
Media: 2-6-7-9-10-11-20-22-25
Distr.: Intl.; Natl.
Budget Set: Sept.
Personnel:
Joseph T. Lombardo *(Pres)*
Daniel G. Clare *(CFO & Sr VP)*
Mark Burns *(Pres-Product Support)*
Ira P. Berman *(Gen Counsel & Sr VP-Admin)*
Larry Flynn *(VP-Gen Dynamics Corp, Sr VP-Mktg & Sls)*
Preston A. Henne *(VP-Gen Dynamics Corp, Sr VP-Programs & Engrg & Test)*
Buddy Sams *(Sr VP-Govt Programs & Sls)*
Roger Sperry *(Sr VP-Sls-Intl)*
Dennis Stuligross *(Sr VP-Ops)*
Pete Buresh *(Reg VP-Africa)*
Peter Jacobi *(Reg VP-Intl Military Sls)*
Jennifer Giffen *(VP-HR)*
Tarek Ragheb *(VP-Intl Sls-EMEA)*
Dalton Allen *(Dir-Strategic Bus Pursuits)*
Neil Clark *(Dir-Govt Sls Support)*
Bill Colleran *(Dir-Technical Info Svcs)*
Greg Collett *(Dir-New Product Dev & Mfg Ops)*
Joanne Davis *(Dir-Govt Contracts)*
Jamie Fields *(Dir-Repair & Overhaul Svcs)*
Franz Gilbert *(Dir-HR Technologies)*
Greg Hammerstein *(Dir-Field Svc & Autorized Warranty Facilities)*
Brad Kraft *(Dir-Completion Engrg)*
Mike Rowland *(Dir-Govt Bus Dev)*
Christine Manka Williams *(Sr Mgr-Refurbishment Ops)*
John Cooreman *(Sls Mgr-Avionics-Natl)*
Heidi Fedak *(Mgr-Corp Comm)*
Terry Freeman *(Mgr-Product Support Warranty)*
Brands & Products:
GULFSTREAM G150
GULFSTREAM G200
GULFSTREAM G250
GULFSTREAM G350
GULFSTREAM G450
GULFSTREAM G500
GULFSTREAM G550
GULFSTREAM G650
GULFSTREAM SERVICE CARE
GULFSTREAM SHARES

HAMILTON SUNDSTRAND CORPORATION

(Group of United Technologies Corporation)
1 Hamilton Rd
Windsor Locks, CT 06096-1010
Tel.: (860) 654-4361
Fax: (860) 654-2399
Web Site: www.hamiltonsundstrandcorp.com
Sales Range: $1-4.9 Billion
Approx. Number Employees: 16,000
Year Founded: 1919
Business Description:
High-Technology Aircraft & Industrial Systems Including Electric Power, Environmental Control, Actuation, Propulsion & Engine Controls Mfr, Supplier & Sevicer
S.I.C.: 3621; 3829
N.A.I.C.S.: 335312; 334519
Media: 2-4-7-9-10
Distr.: Intl.; Natl.
Budget Set: Aug.
Personnel:
Timothy Morris *(Pres-Aerospace Power Sys)*
John Triompo *(Co-Pres-Aerospace Power Sys)*
Alain M. Bellemare *(Pres)*
Robert Leduc *(Pres-Space Sys)*
Stephen Oswald *(Pres-Indus)*
Peter Longo *(Controller & VP-Fin)*
Dennis Charest *(VP-IT & Bus)*
Joseph Adams *(VP-Tech)*
Tatsuo Shirane *(VP-HR)*

HARTWELL CORPORATION

(Sub. of McKechnie Aerospace DE, Inc.)
900 S Richfield Rd
Placentia, CA 92870-6732
Tel.: (714) 993-4200
Fax: (714) 579-4419
E-mail: info@hartwellcorp.com
Web Site: www.hartwellcorp.com
Approx. Number Employees: 200
Year Founded: 1939
Business Description:
Aerospace & Industrial Latches, Fasteners, Hinges, Flush Handles, Quick Release Pins & Accessories Mfr, Adjustable Container Latches & Motion Dampeners
S.I.C.: 3429; 3728
N.A.I.C.S.: 332510; 336413
Export
Advertising Expenditures: $100,000
Media: 1-2-4-7-10-21
Distr.: Intl.; Natl.
Budget Set: Dec.
Personnel:
Don Scott *(Pres)*

HEICO CORPORATION

3000 Taft St
Hollywood, FL 33021-4441
Tel.: (954) 987-4000
Fax: (954) 987-7585
E-mail: info@heico.com
Web Site: www.heico.com
Approx. Sls.: $617,020,000
Approx. Number Employees: 2,300
Year Founded: 1957
Business Description:
Aircraft Components Mfr
S.I.C.: 3724; 3721; 3728; 8733
N.A.I.C.S.: 336412; 336411; 336413; 541710
Export
Media: 10
Personnel:
Laurans A. Mendelson *(Chm & CEO)*
Eric A. Mendelson *(Co-Pres)*
Victor H. Mendelson *(Co-Pres)*
Thomas S. Irwin *(CFO & Exec VP)*
Joseph W. Pallot *(Gen Counsel)*
Brands & Products:
HEICO
IRWINDOWS
MIRAGE

HONEYWELL AEROSPACE

(Group of Honeywell International Inc.)
1944 E Sky Harbor Cir N
Phoenix, AZ 85034-3442
Tel.: (602) 365-3099
Fax: (602) 365-3343
Toll Free: (800) 601-3099
Web Site: www51.honeywell.com/aero
Approx. Number Employees: 59,000
Year Founded: 1987
Business Description:
Develops & Manufactures Products for Aircraft, Missile & Commercial Applications
S.I.C.: 7629; 4581
N.A.I.C.S.: 811219; 488119
Personnel:
Garrett Mikita *(Pres-Air Transport & Reg Strategic Bus Unit)*
Carl Esposito *(VP-Mktg & Product Mgmt)*
Timothy Mahoney *(Sr Mgr-Program)*
Brands & Products:
AIRESEARCH
BENDIX/KING
GARRETT
Advertising Agency:
Chletcos/Gallagher Inc.
63 Greene St Ste 602
New York, NY 10012
Tel.: (212) 334-2455
Fax: (212) 334-2463

HONEYWELL AEROSPACE ELECTRONIC SYSTEMS

(Div. of Honeywell Aerospace)
21111 N 19th Ave
Phoenix, AZ 85027-2708
Tel.: (602) 365-3099
Fax: (602) 822-7000
Telex: RCA 286144
E-mail: info@honeywell.com
Web Site: www.honeywell.com
Sales Range: $1-4.9 Billion
Approx. Number Employees: 17,000
Year Founded: 1947
Business Description:
Aerospace & Electronic Systems
S.I.C.: 9661
N.A.I.C.S.: 927110
Media: 2
Distr.: Intl.; Natl.
Budget Set: Nov.
Personnel:
Tim Mahoney *(Pres & CEO)*
Adrian Paull *(VP-Customer & Product Support)*
Laura Schultz *(VP-Mktg)*
Sabine Chmielewski *(Dir-Commun)*
Darrell Davis *(Dir-Product)*
Tom Henderson *(Mgr-Tech Sls)*
Peter Jofriet *(Product Mgr-Asset Mngmt)*
Morris Mike *(Tech Product Mktg Mgr)*
John Riley *(Mktg Mgr-Svcs)*
Robert Donohoe *(Mgr-External Comm)*
Brands & Products:
ACCELEREX
ADRAS
AFIS
FLEXCOMM
FLITECOMM
FLITEFONE
MINI-PAL
Q-FLEX
RAPID SCAN
SCIRAS
SETS
SNAPSHOT
SUPERFLEX

HONEYWELL COMMERCIAL ELECTRONIC SYSTEMS

(Unit of Honeywell Aerospace)
1 Technology Ctr 23500 W 105th St
Olathe, KS 66061
Tel.: (913) 782-0400
Fax: (913) 712-1302
Telex: 669916 KINGRAD
Web Site: www51.honeywell.com
Sales Range: $450-499.9 Million
Approx. Number Employees: 1,300
Business Description:
Aircraft Electronics Mfr
S.I.C.: 3724; 3812
N.A.I.C.S.: 336412; 334511
Media: 2-8-10-11-13-20
Distr.: Intl.; Natl.
Budget Set: Sept.
Personnel:
Dan Barks *(Dir-Mktg)*
Brands & Products:
VERTICAL PROFILE

HONEYWELL LTD.

(Div. of Honeywell Canada, Inc.)
3333 Unity Drive
Mississauga, ON L5L 3S6, Canada
Tel.: (905) 608-6000
Fax: (905) 608-6254
Web Site: www.honeywell.ca
Sales Range: $400-449.9 Million
Approx. Number Employees: 1,500
Year Founded: 1930
Business Description:
Measuring & Controlling Products Mfr
S.I.C.: 3829
N.A.I.C.S.: 334519
Advertising Expenditures: $200,000
Media: 6-24
Distr.: Natl.

Key to Media (For complete agency information see *The Advertising Red Books-Agencies* edition):
1. Bus. Publs. 2. Cable T.V. 3. Catalogs & Directories. 4. Co-op Adv. 5. Consumer Mags. 6. D.M. to Bus. Estab.7. D.M. to Consumers 8. Daily Newsp. 9. Exhibits/Trade Shows 10. Foreign 11. Infomercial 12. Internet Adv.13. Multimedia 14. Network Radio 15. Network T.V. 16. Newsp. Distr. Mags. 17. Other 18. Outdoor (Posters, Transit) 19. Point of Purchase20. Premiums, Novelties 21. Product Samples 22. Special Events Mktg. 23. Spot Radio 24. Spot T.V. 25. Weekly Newsp. 26. Yellow Page Adv.

Honeywell Ltd. — (Continued)

Budget Set: Sept.

HONEYWELL PROCESS SOLUTIONS
(Div. of Honeywell Automation & Control Solutions)
2500 W Union Hills Dr
Phoenix, AZ 85027
Tel.: (602) 313-5000
Fax: (602) 822-7000
Toll Free: (800) 822-7673
Web Site: hpsweb.honeywell.com
Sales Range: $400-449.9 Million
Approx. Number Employees: 1,000
Year Founded: 1885
Business Description:
Automation & Process Control Systems Developer
S.I.C.: 3822
N.A.I.C.S.: 334512
Export
Media: 2-4-7-10-11-20
Distr.: Intl.
Budget Set: Annually
Personnel:
Norm Gilsdorf *(Pres-Process Solutions Bus)*
Elizabeth Stairs *(Gen Counsel & VP)*
Jon Lippin *(VP & Gen Mgr-Asia Pacific)*
Henri Tausch *(VP & Gen Mgr-Honeywell Field Solutions)*
Edwin Van den Maagdenberg *(VP & Gen Mgr-EMEA)*
David Sanchez *(VP & Dir-Fin)*
Harsh Chitale *(VP-Strategy & Global Mktg)*
Donna Lee Scaggs *(VP-Tech)*
Frank Whitsura *(VP-Tech & Ops)*
Ged Blenkharn *(Reg Gen Mgr-Middle East)*
Brands & Products:
ASSET MAX
EXPERION
PLANT SCAPE
SMART LINE INSTRUMENTS
TOTAL PLANT SOLUTION

HONEYWELL SENSING & CONTROL
(Sub. of Honeywell Sensing & Control)
11 W Spring St
Freeport, IL 61032-4316
Tel.: (815) 235-5500
Fax: (815) 235-5574
Toll Free: (800) 537-6945
Sales Range: $600-649.9 Million
Approx. Number Employees: 2,300
Year Founded: 1937
Business Description:
Mfr. of Sensors, Switches & Control Products for System Critical Applications in the Automotive, Information Technology, Consumer, Aviation & Industrial Markets
S.I.C.: 3613; 3644
N.A.I.C.S.: 335313; 335932
Media: 2-4-7-10-20-21
Distr.: Direct to Consumer; Natl.
Budget Set: Sept.
Personnel:
Beth Wozniak *(Pres)*
Kimbery Anderberg *(Dir-eBus Programs)*
Jeff Kirkwold *(Product Mgr)*
Brands & Products:
HONEYWELL
Advertising Agencies:
Ackerman McQueen, Inc.
1100 The Tower 1601 NW Expy
Oklahoma City, OK 73118
Tel.: (405) 843-7777
Fax: (405) 848-1932

M45 Marketing Services
524 W Stephenson St Ste 100
Freeport, IL 61032
Tel.: (815) 232-2121
Fax: (815) 297-0166

HYDRO-AIRE INC.
(Unit of Crane Aerospace Group)
3000 Winona Ave
Burbank, CA 91504-2540
Mailing Address:
PO Box 7722
Burbank, CA 91510-7722
Tel.: (818) 526-2600
Fax: (818) 842-6117
E-mail: info@hydroaire.com
Web Site: www.craneae.com
E-Mail For Key Personnel:
Marketing Director: marketing@hydroaire.com
Sales Range: $200-249.9 Million
Approx. Number Employees: 500
Year Founded: 1943
Business Description:
Fuel & Hydraulic Systems for Aircraft & Missile Industry Mfr
S.I.C.: 3728
N.A.I.C.S.: 336413
Export
Advertising Expenditures: $250,000
Media: 2-4-6-7-10-11-13-16-22-26
Distr.: Intl.; Natl.
Personnel:
Greg Ward *(Pres-Aerospace Grp)*
Mike Brady *(VP-Fin)*
Ron Kato *(VP-Mktg)*
Michael Smalley *(Mgr-Mktg & Commun)*
Brian Ramsey *(Mgr-Aftermarket Field Svcs)*
Brands & Products:
HYTROL

KAISER OPTICAL SYSTEMS, INC.
(Sub. of Rockwell Collins, Inc.)
371 Parkland Plz
Ann Arbor, MI 48103
Tel.: (734) 665-8083
Fax: (734) 665-8199
E-mail: sales@kosi.com
Web Site: www.kosi.com
E-Mail For Key Personnel:
Sales Director: sales@kosi.com
Sales Range: $10-24.9 Million
Approx. Number Employees: 70
Year Founded: 1979
Business Description:
Spectrographic Instrumentation & Applied Holographic Technology
S.I.C.: 3827
N.A.I.C.S.: 333314
Media: 10
Personnel:
Bruno Lenain *(Dir-Europe)*
Harry Owen *(Dir-Bus Dev)*
Ian Lewis *(Mgr-Mktg)*

KAMAN CORPORATION
1332 Blue Hills Ave
Bloomfield, CT 06002
Mailing Address:
PO Box 1
Bloomfield, CT 06002-0001
Tel.: (860) 243-7100
Fax: (860) 243-6365
E-mail: info.kaman-corp@kaman.com
Web Site: www.kaman.com
E-Mail For Key Personnel:
Public Relations: jkn-corp@kaman.com
Approx. Sls.: $1,318,513,000
Approx. Number Employees: 4,269
Year Founded: 1945
Business Description:
Aerospace Component & Industrial Supplies Mfr & Distr
S.I.C.: 5085; 1796; 3721
N.A.I.C.S.: 423840; 238290; 336411
Import Export
Media: 2-7-10-17
Personnel:
Neal J. Keating *(Chm, Pres & CEO)*
William C. Denninger *(CFO & Sr VP)*
Ronald M. Galla *(CIO & Sr VP)*
Candace A. Clark *(Chief Legal Officer, Sec & Sr VP)*
Gregory L. Steiner *(Pres-Aerospace Grp)*
Glenn M. Messemer *(Gen Counsel & VP)*
Lowell J. Hill *(VP-HR)*
John J. Tedone *(VP-Fin)*
Patricia C. Goldenberg *(Asst VP & Asst Treas)*
Janna L. Drake *(Asst VP-Internal Audit)*
Gary L. Tong *(Asst VP-Corp Risk, Safety & Environ Mgmt)*
Christopher Simmons *(Dir-Internal Audit)*
Brands & Products:
ADAMAS
APPLAUSE
GIBRALTER
GRETSCH
HAMER
K-MAX
KAFLEX
KARON
LATIN PERCUSSION
LP
OVATION
SABIAN
SOUND
TAKAMINE
TOCA

KAMAN INDUSTRIAL TECHNOLOGIES CORP.
(Sub. of Kaman Corporation)
1 Waterside Crossing
Windsor, CT 06095
Tel.: (860) 687-5000
Fax: (860) 687-5170
Web Site: www.kamandirect.com
Sales Range: $750-799.9 Million
Approx. Number Employees: 1,337
Business Description:
Industrial Supplies Distr
S.I.C.: 5085; 5084
N.A.I.C.S.: 423840; 423830
Personnel:
Steven J. Smidler *(Pres)*
Roger S. Jorgensen *(VP-Fin)*
David Mayer *(VP-Mktg)*
Theodore M. Clayton *(Mgr-Mktg-Energy & Power Mgmt Svcs)*
Advertising Agency:
Adams & Knight Advertising/Public Relations
80 Avon Meadow Ln
Avon, CT 06001
Tel.: (860) 676-2300
Fax: (860) 676-1940

KEARFOTT GUIDANCE & NAVIGATION CORPORATION
(Sub. of Astronautics Corporation of America)
1150 McBride Ave
Little Falls, NJ 07424-2500
Tel.: (973) 785-6000
Fax: (973) 785-6025
Telex: 133440
E-mail: info@kearfott.com
Web Site: www.kearfott.com
E-Mail For Key Personnel:
Marketing Director: marketing@kearfott.com
Sales Director: marketing@kearfott.com
Approx. Number Employees: 1,400
Year Founded: 1917
Business Description:
Inertial Navigation Systems for Land, Sea, Air & Space Designer, Developer, Mfr & Servicer
S.I.C.: 3812; 3714
N.A.I.C.S.: 334511; 336399
Export
Media: 2-7-10-11
Distr.: Intl.; Natl.
Personnel:
R. E. Zelazo *(Pres)*
Stephen Givant *(VP-Fin & HR)*
Brands & Products:
CONEX
GYROFLEX
MILNAV
SEADEVIL
SEANAV
TARA I
TARA III

L-3 COMMUNICATIONS ELECTRONIC SYSTEMS
(Sub. of L-3 Communications Corporation)
25 City View Dr
Toronto, ON M9W 5A7, Canada
Tel.: (416) 249-1231
Fax: (416) 246-2001
Web Site: www.l-3com.com/es/
Approx. Sls.: $95,000,000
Approx. Number Employees: 750
Year Founded: 1961
Business Description:
Aviation Systems
S.I.C.: 3812
N.A.I.C.S.: 334511
Export
Media: 2-4-6-10
Distr.: Natl.
Personnel:
Trevor Ratcliffe *(Pres)*
Richard D. Ackerman *(VP)*
Anne Straker *(VP-HR)*

L-3 MAS CANADA
(Sub. of L-3 Communications Corporation)

Key to Media (For complete agency information see *The Advertising Red Books-Agencies* edition):
1. Bus. Publs. 2. Cable T.V. 3. Catalogs & Directories. 4. Co-op Adv. 5. Consumer Mags. 6. D.M. to Bus. Estab.7. D.M. to Consumers
8. Daily Newsp. 9. Exhibits/Trade Shows 10. Foreign 11. Infomercial 12. Internet Adv.13. Multimedia 14. Network Radio
15. Network T.V. 16. Newsp. Distr. Mags. 17. Other 18. Outdoor (Posters, Transit) 19. Point of Purchase20. Premiums, Novelties
21. Product Samples 22. Special Events Mktg. 23. Spot Radio 24. Spot T.V. 25. Weekly Newsp. 26. Yellow Page Adv.

10000 Helen Bristol St
Mirabel, QC J7N 1H3, Canada
Tel.: (450) 476-4000
Fax: (450) 476-4460
E-mail: info.marketing@l-3com.com
Web Site: www.mas.l-3com.com
Approx. Rev.: $400,000,000
Approx. Number Employees: 1,200
Business Description:
Airplane & Internal Combustion Engines Maintenance
S.I.C.: 3519
N.A.I.C.S.: 333618
Media: 2
Personnel:
Sylvain Bedard *(Pres)*
Benoit Beaulieu *(VP-HR, Organizational Effectiveness, Info Sys & Technologies)*
Stephane Germain *(VP-Bus Dev & Strategic Plng)*
Goose Jaulin *(Dir-Mktg & Bus Dev)*
Jeremy Cartlidge *(Mgr-Mktg & Bus Dev)*

LEAR CORPORATION

21557 Telegraph Rd
Southfield, MI 48034-4248
Mailing Address:
PO Box 5008
Southfield, MI 48086-5008
Tel.: (248) 447-1500
Fax: (248) 447-1524
Web Site: www.lear.com
Approx. Sls.: $11,954,600,000
Approx. Number Employees: 86,800
Year Founded: 1917
Business Description:
Automobile & Truck Parts Mfr
S.I.C.: 5013; 2396; 3711
N.A.I.C.S.: 441310; 336211; 336360
Media: 2-7-10-11
Personnel:
Matthew J. Simoncini *(Pres & CEO)*
James M. Brackenbury *(Sr VP & Pres-European Ops)*
Louis R. Salvatore *(Sr VP & Pres-Global Seating Sys)*
Raymond E. Scott *(Sr VP & Pres-Global Electrical Power Mgmt Sys)*
Terrence B. Larkin *(Gen Counsel, Sec & Sr VP)*
Wendy L. Foss *(Sec, VP-Fin & Admin)*
Jason M. Forcier *(VP & Gen Mgr-Global Electronics)*
Dave Mullin *(VP-Sls & Mktg)*
Liam E. Hart *(Deputy Gen Counsel)*
Ed Lowenfeld *(Asst Treas)*
Brands & Products:
ADVANCE RELENTLESSLY
AVENTINO
CAR2U
CLEARVIEW
CRAFTEDCLIP
EASY ENTRY
INTELLITIRE
INTERTRONICS
LEAR CORPORATION
OASYS
OCCUSENSE
PROTEC
PVI METHOD
SMARTFOLD
SONOTEC
SOYFOAM
TOUCHTEC
ULTRAFLOOR
VISIONTEC

Advertising Agency:
AutoCom Associates
74 W Long Lk Rd Ste 103
Bloomfield Hills, MI 48304-2770
Tel.: (248) 647-8621
Fax: (248) 642-2110

LOCKHEED MARTIN CORPORATION

6801 Rockledge Dr
Bethesda, MD 20817-1877
Tel.: (301) 897-6000
Fax: (301) 897-6704
Web Site: www.lockheedmartin.com
Approx. Sls.: $45,803,000,000
Approx. Number Employees: 132,000
Year Founded: 1995
Business Description:
Space, Defense, Electronics, Communications, Information Systems, Data Management & Energy Products Designer, Developer, Mfr & Integrator
S.I.C.: 3812; 3721; 3761
N.A.I.C.S.: 334511; 336411; 336414
Import Export
Media: 2-3-7-9-10-11-13-15
Distr.: Intl.
Personnel:
Robert J. Stevens *(Chm & CEO)*
Christopher E. Kubasik *(Pres & COO)*
Roger Rose *(CEO)*
Bruce L. Tanner *(CFO & Exec VP)*
Christopher J. Gregoire *(Chief Acctg Officer, VP & Controller)*
William Clark *(Pres/CEO-Savi Tech)*
David Heywood *(Gen Counsel-Tax & VP-Taxes)*
Charles T. Burbage *(Exec VP)*
Linda R. Gooden *(Exec VP-Info Systems & Global Svc)*
Ralph D. Heath *(Exec VP-Aeronautics)*
Joanne M. Maguire *(Exec VP-Space Sys)*
Gregory R. Dahlberg *(Sr VP-Ops-Washington)*
Patrick M. Dewar *(Sr VP-Corp Strategy & Bus Dev)*
John Lucas *(Sr VP-HR)*
Ronald T. Rand *(Sr VP-Comm)*
Nettie R. Johnson *(VP-Media Rels)*
Thomas Jurkowsky *(VP-Media Rels)*
Anne Marie Squeo *(VP-Comm-Electronic Sys)*
Martin T. Stanislav *(VP-Fin & Bus Ops-IS & GS)*
Jennifer Warren *(VP-Govt Rel)*
Jeff Adams *(Dir-Worldwide Media Rels)*
Shamala N. Littlefield *(Dir-IR)*
Marina Williams *(Dir-Diversity & Inclusion-IS&GS)*
Ray Johnson *(Engr)*
Brands & Products:
A2100
ABOVE & BEYOND
ACTRAVIS
AEGIS
AEROCRAFT
AEROSPACEWARRIOR
AIMPOINT
AIR EXPRESS
ALAM
ALERT
ALTAIR
AMERICA'S SILENT HERO
AN/APG-67
AN/APS-145
ANALYTYX
ARGMATCH
ARMY TACTICAL MISSILE SYSTEM
ARQUEST
ARROWHEAD
ARTEMIS
ASTROLINK
ATACMS
ATHENA
ATLAS
ATLAS A
ATLAS III
ATLAS V
AUP
AUTOGRAPHICS
AWARENET
B-24
BIOUNIQUE
BLACKBIRD
BLU-109
BSY-2
C-130
C-141
C-5
CASS
CAVP
CBREWS
CENTAUR
CHALLENGER MARINE
CHAPARRAL
CODE ONE
COMPU-SCENE
COMSAT
COMSAT STAR
CONSTELLATION
CONSTITUTION
DAIWATCH
DEFINING MOMENTS
DFT
DISPLAY BROKER
DSMAC
E-SATCENTRAL
EAGLE SPEED
EASISTAR
EDGE FACTORY
ELECTRA
EMBRACE SPACE
ERR
ESAR
ESTARS
ETOC
ETRACK IT
EXAMINER 3DX
EXPLORER
F-104
F-117
F-16
F-16 FIGHTING FALCON
F-22
F-35
F-80
F-94
F/A-22 RAPTOR
FALCONSAR
FAST HULL
FASTRAK
FCS MULE
THE FIGHTER ENTERPRISE
FIGHTING FALCON
FIRST LOOK
FUTUREPOINT
GMLRS
GRAIL
HAVE LITE
HAWKEYE
HELLFIRE
HERCULES
HI GAIN
HIGH TIDE
HIMARS
HUDSON
IEP-CAM
IGUIDES
ILS
IMAGER
INTELLIGENT LIBRARY SYSTEM
INVENTIT
JASSM
JETSTAR
JOINT STRIKE FIGHTER
JSF
KINEMAP
L-1011
LANTIRN
LASER UT
LASERNET FINES
LIBERATOR
LIGHT MOVER
LINCOCITY
LINE-OF-SIGHT ANTITANK
LINKOSITY
LM-EXPRESS
LM PEOPLE
LM-STAR
LMC
LMCO
LOCAAS
LOCKHEED
LOCKHEED MARTIN
LODESTAR
LONGBOW
LONGBOW HELLFIRE
LONGSHOT
LOSAT
LUNAR PROSPECTOR
MA-25S
MARINE ENDURANCE
MARS FLYING BOAT
MAXIPLAN
MAXIPURGE
MAXISORT
MAXISTAR
MAXISTAR ONSCHEDULE
METEOSTAR
METROGUARD
MEWSS PIP
MH-60R
MI-15
MICAD
MICROCAT-HX
MILLENNIUM DRIVER TRAINER SYSTEM
MILSTAR
MISSION SUCCESS
MLRS
MMSR
MOONRISE
MSTAR
MTOC
MULE
MULTIPLE LAUNCH ROCKET SYSTEM
NEPTUNE
NETFIRES
NIGHTHAWK
NXTRAIN
OCEAN 21
OMNISTAR
ORION
P-2V
P-3
P-38 LIGHTNING
P-38J LIGHTNING

Key to Media (For complete agency information see *The Advertising Red Books-Agencies* edition):
1. Bus. Publs. 2. Cable T.V. 3. Catalogs & Directories. 4. Co-op Adv. 5. Consumer Mags. 6. D.M. to Bus. Estab.7. D.M. to Consumers 8. Daily Newsp. 9. Exhibits/Trade Shows 10. Foreign 11. Infomercial 12. Internet Adv.13. Multimedia 14. Network Radio 15. Network T.V. 16. Newsp. Distr. Mags. 17. Other 18. Outdoor (Posters, Transit) 19. Point of Purchase20. Premiums, Novelties 21. Product Samples 22. Special Events Mktg. 23. Spot Radio 24. Spot T.V. 25. Weekly Newsp. 26. Yellow Page Adv.

Lockheed Martin Corporation — (Continued)

P-80
P-TEN
PAC-3
PAL
PANTERA
PATHMAKER
PGMM
PIBOX
PIRA
POLAR
PREDATOR
PS-59
PSTAR
PTC
PTI
PUREVISION
RADIANT MERCURY
RADIANT TRUST
RAINBOW
RAPTOR
RASTER MATE
RATE
RRPR
S-3
S-3B
SAFE
SATCENTER
SATELLITE CONTROL SYSTEM 21
SATS
SATURN
SEA SENTINEL
SEA TALON
SEASTAR
SECUREDGE
SENTRY OWL
SHIELD
SHOOTING STAR
SILENT KEYER
SILENT SENTRY
SIRIUS
SKY SPIRIT
SKYLINE
SKYTRACKER
SLICE
SNAKE EYES
SNIFFERSTAR
SNIPER
SNIPER XR
SOE INSTITUTE
SOLUTION 21
SPEAR
SR-71
ST3000
STABILITE
STARFIRE
STARLIFTER
SUPER CONSTELLATION
SYGENEX
SYNCHRONETICS
T3
TACMS
TADS/PNVS
TALARIA
TARAS
TBMCS
TEAM WIN-T
THAAD
TITAN
TOPSCENE
TOUCH N' GO CALIBRATION
TRIDENT
U-2
UNITED SPACE ALLIANCE
V2
VALIANT
VALIDIAN
VEGA HARPOON
VEGA VENTURA
VENTURE VISION
VERS L'UNIVERS
VIEU STAR
VIKING
VISTA
VLA
VOUGHT
VTMIS
WCMD
WE NEVER FORGET WHAT WE'RE WORKING FOR
WE NEVER FORGET WHO WE'RE WORKING FOR
WELDALITE
X-35
XD
XR
ZIP SEAL
ZIP-STRIP

Advertising Agencies:
Erwin-Penland
(Owned by Hill, Holliday, Connors, Cosmopulos, Inc., Member of the Interpublic Group)
125 E Broad St
Greenville, SC 29601
Tel.: (864) 271-0500
Fax: (864) 235-5941

Keiler & Company
304 Main St
Farmington, CT 06032-2985
Tel.: (860) 677-8821
Fax: (860) 676-8164

LOCKHEED MARTIN SIMULATION, TRAINING & SUPPORT

(Unit of Lockheed Martin Sippican, Inc.)
12506 Lake Underhill Rd
Orlando, FL 32825
Tel.: (407) 306-1000
Web Site: www.lockheedmartin.com/sts
Sales Range: $400-449.9 Million
Approx. Number Employees: 2,800
Business Description:
Military & Aerospace Training Solutions
S.I.C.: 8299
N.A.I.C.S.: 611430; 611512
Media: 10
Personnel:
Bruce L. Tanner *(CFO & Exec VP)*
Joanne M. Maguire *(Exec VP-Space Sys)*

LORAL SPACE & COMMUNICATIONS INC.

600 3rd Ave
New York, NY 10016
Tel.: (212) 697-1105
Fax: (212) 338-5662
Telex: 644018
E-mail: investor.relations@hq.loral.com
Web Site: www.loral.com
Approx. Rev.: $1,158,985,000
Approx. Number Employees: 2,700
Business Description:
Telecommunications Satellites Owner & Operator; Commercial & Military Satellites & Satellite Systems Designer & Mfr
S.I.C.: 4899; 3663
N.A.I.C.S.: 517410; 334220
Media: 1-2-4-6-7-8-9-10-11-17-18-20-25
Distr.: Intl.; Natl.
Budget Set: Feb.
Personnel:
Michael B. Targoff *(Vice Chm, Pres & CEO)*
Harvey B. Rein *(CFO & Sr VP)*
Avi Katz *(Gen Counsel, Sec & Sr VP)*
Richard P. Mastoloni *(Treas & Sr VP-Fin)*
Arnold Friedman *(VP, Sr VP-Worldwide Mktg, Sls-Space Sys & Loral)*
John Rakow *(Sr VP-Legal and Bus Affairs)*
John Stack *(Asst Treas)*
Advertising Agency:
Fleishman-Hillard Canada Inc.
3575 Saint Laurent Blvd Ste 200
Montreal, QC H2X 2T7, Canada
Tel.: (514) 866-6776
Fax: (514) 86-6 8981

MACQUARIE AVIATION NORTH AMERICA GROUP

(Sub. of Macquarie Bank Limited)
(d/b/a AvPorts)
1501 Lee Hwy Ste 180
Arlington, VA 22209
Tel.: (703) 807-1088
Fax: (703) 807-1030
E-mail: info@atlanticaviation.com
Web Site: www.atlanticaviation.com
Approx. Number Employees: 3
Business Description:
Owner, Operator & Developer of Airports, Fixed-Base Operations & Aviation-Related Facilities
S.I.C.: 6512; 4581
N.A.I.C.S.: 531120; 488119
Import Export
Media: 5-13-17-19-20
Personnel:
Clive Lowe *(Exec VP)*

MCCAULEY PROPELLER SYSTEMS

(Div. of Cessna Aircraft Company)
7751 E Pawnee
Wichita, KS 67218
Mailing Address:
PO Box 7704
Wichita, KS 67277-7704
Tel.: (316) 831-4021
Fax: (316) 831-3858
Toll Free: (800) 621-PROP
E-mail: sales@mccauley.textron.com
Web Site: www.mccauley.textron.com
E-Mail For Key Personnel:
Sales Director: sales@mccauley.textron.com
Sales Range: $10-24.9 Million
Approx. Number Employees: 25
Year Founded: 1938
Business Description:
Airplane Propeller Designer & Mfr
S.I.C.: 8711; 1629
N.A.I.C.S.: 541330; 237990
Export
Media: 4-7-10-20
Distr.: Intl.; Natl.
Budget Set: Jan.
Personnel:
Scott Hickman *(Mgr-Product Support)*
Brands & Products:
BLACKMAC

MINT TURBINES LLC

(Sub. of M International Inc.)
2915 N State Hwy 99 PO Box 460
Stroud, OK 74079-0460
Tel.: (918) 968-9561
Fax: (918) 968-9564
Toll Free: (800) 284-0606
Web Site: www.mintturbines.com
E-Mail For Key Personnel:
President: gmartin@pt6t.com
Approx. Number Employees: 43
Year Founded: 1981
Business Description:
Overhaul & Repair of Aircraft Engines
S.I.C.: 7629
N.A.I.C.S.: 811219
Advertising Expenditures: $53,000
Media: 2-10
Personnel:
Rich Kasabula *(Gen Mgr)*
Wayne Bond *(Reg Mgr)*
Rick DeLorme *(Reg Mgr)*
Alonso Fonseca *(Reg Mgr)*
John Grant *(Reg Mgr)*
Dave Wark *(Reg Mgr)*
Gary Benson *(Mgr-Production)*
Joni Cole *(Mgr-Logistics)*
Jeff Frasco *(Mgr-IT)*
Danny Hickman *(Mgr-Quality Assurance)*
Thad Wages *(Mgr-Customer Support)*
Trenton Whitehouse *(Mgr-Bus Dev)*

MONOGRAM SYSTEMS

(Sub. of Air Cruisers Company, Inc.)
1500 Glenn Curtiss St
Carson, CA 90746-4012
Mailing Address:
PO Box 11189
Carson, CA 90749-1189
Tel.: (310) 884-7000
Fax: (310) 884-7300
E-mail: monogram@monogram.zodiac.com
Web Site:
www.monogramsystems.com
Approx. Number Employees: 300
Year Founded: 1941
Business Description:
Commercial Aircraft Interior Equipment Mfr, Including Passenger Seats, Lavatories, Toilets, On-Board Airstairs & Military Aircraft Escape Systems
S.I.C.: 3728
N.A.I.C.S.: 336413
Import Export
Advertising Expenditures: $1,300,000
Media: 2-4-7-10
Distr.: Intl.; Natl.
Budget Set: July
Personnel:
Michael Rozenelatt *(CEO)*
Larry Shum *(CFO)*

MOOG INC.

300 Jamison Rd
East Aurora, NY 14052-0018
Mailing Address:
PO Box 18
East Aurora, NY 14052-0018
Tel.: (716) 652-2000
Fax: (716) 687-4457
E-mail: web.admin@moog.com
Web Site: www.moog.com
E-Mail For Key Personnel:

Key to Media (For complete agency information see *The Advertising Red Books-Agencies* edition):
1. Bus. Publs. 2. Cable T.V. 3. Catalogs & Directories. 4. Co-op Adv. 5. Consumer Mags. 6. D.M. to Bus. Estab.7. D.M. to Consumers 8. Daily Newsp. 9. Exhibits/Trade Shows 10. Foreign 11. Infomercial 12. Internet Adv.13. Multimedia 14. Network Radio 15. Network T.V. 16. Newsp. Distr. Mags. 17. Other 18. Outdoor (Posters, Transit) 19. Point of Purchase20. Premiums, Novelties 21. Product Samples 22. Special Events Mktg. 23. Spot Radio 24. Spot T.V. 25. Weekly Newsp. 26. Yellow Page Adv.

Public Relations: ALuhr@moog.com
Approx. Sls.: $2,114,252,000
Approx. Number Employees: 10,117
Year Founded: 1951
Business Description:
Aircraft, Satellite & Missile Propulsion Systems & Controls; Industrial Machinery & Component Developer & Mfr
S.I.C.: 3491; 3532; 3559; 3728; 3764; 3812; 3823
N.A.I.C.S.: 332911; 333131; 333298; 334511; 334513; 336413; 336415
Export
Media: 10
Personnel:
Robert T. Brady *(Chm & CEO)*
John R. Scannell *(Pres & COO)*
Donald R. Fishback *(CFO)*
Sean Gartland *(Pres-Indus Grp & VP)*
Jay K. Hennig *(Pres-Space & Defense)*
Timothy P. Balkin *(Treas & Grp VP)*
Lawrence J. Ball *(VP & Gen Mgr)*
Anne Luhr *(Dir-IR)*
Keith J. Cosco *(Sr Counsel-Aircraft Grp)*
Brands & Products:
ENDURA-TRAC
MOOG
POWERSHIFT
POWERSHOT
SERVOJET
SILENCER
Advertising Agency:
Mobium
360 N Michigan Ave 12th Fl
Chicago, IL 60601
Tel.: (312) 422-8960

MOONEY AIRPLANE COMPANY, INC.
(Sub. of Mooney Aerospace Group, Ltd.)
165 S Al Mooney Rd N
Kerrville, TX 78028
Tel.: (830) 896-6000
Fax: (830) 792-4801
Toll Free: (800) 336-3880
Toll Free: (800) 456-3033
E-mail: sales@mooney.com
Web Site: www.mooney.com
E-Mail For Key Personnel:
Marketing Director: DCopeland@mooney.com
Sales Director: sales@mooney.com
Public Relations: croth@mooney.com
Approx. Number Employees: 300
Year Founded: 1946
Business Description:
Mfr. of 4-Place, Single Engine, High Performance Aircraft & Parts
S.I.C.: 3721; 3724
N.A.I.C.S.: 336411; 336412
Export
Advertising Expenditures: $304,000
Bus. Publs.: $240,000; Daily Newsp.: $2,000; Exhibits/Trade Shows: $60,000; Internet Adv.: $2,000
Distr.: Intl.
Personnel:
Steven E. Karol *(Chm)*
Sol Meyer *(CEO)*
Brands & Products:
BRAVO
EAGLE
EAGLE 2
OVATION
OVATION 2

NORGREN, INC.
(Sub. of IMI plc)
5400 S Delaware St
Littleton, CO 80120-1663
Tel.: (303) 794-2611
Fax: (303) 798-4856
E-mail: support@usa.norgren.com
Web Site: www.usa.norgren.com
Approx. Number Employees: 550
Year Founded: 1926
Business Description:
Mfr. of Compressed Air Filters, Regulators, Lubricators, Rodless Cylinders, Dryers & Mufflers
S.I.C.: 3492
N.A.I.C.S.: 332912
Import Export
Advertising Expenditures: $300,000
Media: 2-4-5-7-8-10-13-19-21-22
Distr.: Natl.
Budget Set: Jan.
Personnel:
Jim Mannebach *(Pres & CEO)*
Brands & Products:
DESIGNER LINE
EXCELON
LINTRA
OLYMPIAN
PROSPECTOR

NORTHROP GRUMMAN CORPORATION
1840 Century Park E
Los Angeles, CA 90067-2199
Tel.: (310) 553-6262
E-mail: randy.belote@ngc.com
Web Site: www.northropgrumman.com
Approx. Rev.: $34,757,000,000
Approx. Number Employees: 117,100
Year Founded: 1939
Business Description:
Holding Company; Defense & Commercial Electronics, Ship Building & Repairing, Information Technology, Mission Systems, Systems Integration & Space Technology Products & Services
S.I.C.: 6719; 3489; 3679; 3721; 3724; 3728; 3731; 3761; 3764; 3769; 3812; 7371; 7379; 7629; 9661
N.A.I.C.S.: 551112; 332995; 334419; 334511; 336411; 336412; 336413; 336414; 336415; 336419; 336611; 541511; 541519; 811219; 927110
Media: 2-4-10-23-24
Distr.: Intl.; Natl.
Budget Set: Nov.
Personnel:
Wesley G. Bush *(Pres & CEO)*
James F. Palmer *(CFO & Corp VP)*
Bernard P. McVey *(CIO)*
Kenneth N. Heintz *(Chief Acctg Officer, Controller & Corp VP)*
Timothy McKnight *(Chief Info Security Officer & VP)*
James L. Cameron *(Pres-Tech Svcs Sector & Corp VP)*
Gary W. Ervin *(Pres-Aerospace Sys Sector & Corp VP)*
Gloria A. Flach *(Pres-Enterprise Shared Svcs & Corp VP)*
Linda A. Mills *(Pres-Info Sys Sector & VP)*
James F. Pitts *(Pres-Electronic Sys Sector & Corp VP)*
Sheila C. Cheston *(Gen Counsel & VP)*
Joseph F. Coyne, Jr. *(VP & Deputy Gen Counsel)*
Darryl M. Fraser *(Corp VP-Comm)*
Gaston Kent *(VP-Fin)*
Daniel J. McClain *(VP-Enterprise Comm)*
Charles S. Phalen, Jr. *(VP-Corp & Enterprise Shared Svcs Indus Security)*
Vincent F. Gwiazdowski *(Dir-Intl)*
Lon Rains *(Dir-Sector-Strategic Comm)*
David E. Ricci *(Corp Dir-Pricing, Estimating & Program Control)*
Wayne S. Watanabe *(Dir-Internal Audit)*
Tom Henson *(Mgr-Media Rels)*
Douglas P. Larsen *(Asst Gen Counsel-Govt Contracts & Govt Rels)*
Advertising Agency:
McGarry Bowen, LLC
601 W 26th St Ste 1150
New York, NY 10001
Tel.: (212) 598-2900
Fax: (212) 598-2996
Creative
Media

NORTHSTAR AEROSPACE, INC.
105 Bedford Rd
Toronto, ON M5R 2K4, Canada
Tel.: (708) 728-2000
Fax: (416) 362-5334
E-mail: info@nsaero.com
Web Site: www.nsaero.com
E-Mail For Key Personnel:
President: dkj@derlan.com
Approx. Rev.: $216,985,000
Approx. Number Employees: 900
Year Founded: 1984
Business Description:
Aerospace Industries Products Mfr
S.I.C.: 3728
N.A.I.C.S.: 336413
Import Export
Media: 2-6-7-8-10
Distr.: Natl.
Budget Set: Nov.
Personnel:
Donald K. Jackson *(Chm)*
Glenn E. Hess *(Pres & CEO)*
Greg A. Schindler *(CFO)*
Craig Yuen *(Chief Strategy Officer)*
Peter Jackson *(Pres-Ops-Cananda)*
John Maris *(Pres-Phoenix)*
Harry Schmink *(Pres-Gears & Transmissions)*
David A. Anderson *(Gen Counsel)*
Allan Dorman *(Gen Mgr-Windsor)*
William Corley *(Dir-HR)*
David Fisher *(Dir-New Programs)*
Bryon Marks *(Dir-Supply Chain)*
Jim Smith *(Dir-SHEA & Facilities)*
Steven Stell *(Dir-IT)*

OMNIFLIGHT, INC.
16415 Addison Rd
Addison, TX 75001
Tel.: (972) 776-0130
Fax: (972) 715-4697
E-mail: info@omniflight.com
Web Site: www.omniflight.com
Approx. Number Employees: 500
Year Founded: 1962
Business Description:
Holding Company
S.I.C.: 4512; 4522
N.A.I.C.S.: 481111; 481219
Media: 2-7-10-11-22
Distr.: Direct to Consumer; Intl.; Natl.
Budget Set: Nov.
Personnel:
James F. Nieves *(VP-HR)*
Brands & Products:
OMNICOMX
OMNIFLEX
OMNIFLIGHT
OMNIRX

PALL CORPORATION
25 Harbor Park Dr
Port Washington, NY 11050
Tel.: (516) 484-5400
Fax: (516) 484-5228
Toll Free: (866) 898-7255
E-mail: info-belux@pall.com
Web Site: www.pall.com
E-Mail For Key Personnel:
Public Relations: melinda_yaklin@pall.com
Approx. Sls.: $2,401,932,000
Approx. Number Employees: 10,400
Year Founded: 1946
Business Description:
Filtration, Separation & Purification Products for Fluid Management
S.I.C.: 3824; 3569; 3841; 3842
N.A.I.C.S.: 334514; 333999; 339112; 339113
Export
Media: 3-4-7-9-10-11-14-15-23-24
Distr.: Intl.; Natl.
Budget Set: July
Personnel:
Eric Krasnoff *(Pres & CEO)*
Lisa McDermott *(CFO & Treas)*
Roberto Perez *(COO)*
Wolfgang Platz *(Pres-Indus & Grp VP)*
James Western *(Pres-Aerospace & Transportation)*
Sandra Marino *(Gen Counsel, Sec & Sr VP)*
Joseph S. Cervia *(Dir & Sr VP)*
Greg Collins *(Sr VP-Water & Energy Bus Grp)*
Vivien Krygier *(Sr VP)*
Saied Tousi *(Sr VP)*
Patricia Iannucci *(VP-Corp Comm & IR)*
Melinda Yaklin *(Dir-Mktg Comm-Biopharm)*
Christian Martin *(Product Mgr)*
Monica Cardona *(Mktg Mgr)*
Brands & Products:
ACCUSEP
ACCUWIK
ACRO
ACROCAP
ACRODISC
ACROPAK
ACROPREP
ACROVENT
ACROWELL
AEROLITH
ANALYSLIDE
AQUASAFE
AQUASEP
AUTOVENT
BIODYNE

Key to Media (For complete agency information see *The Advertising Red Books-Agencies* edition):
1. Bus. Publs. 2. Cable T.V. 3. Catalogs & Directories. 4. Co-op Adv. 5. Consumer Mags. 6. D.M. to Bus. Estab.7. D.M. to Consumers 8. Daily Newsp. 9. Exhibits/Trade Shows 10. Foreign 11. Infomercial 12. Internet Adv.13. Multimedia 14. Network Radio 15. Network T.V. 16. Newsp. Distr. Mags. 17. Other 18. Outdoor (Posters, Transit) 19. Point of Purchase20. Premiums, Novelties 21. Product Samples 22. Special Events Mktg. 23. Spot Radio 24. Spot T.V. 25. Weekly Newsp. 26. Yellow Page Adv.

Pall Corporation — (Continued)

BIOTRACE
BRANDOL
CARBO
CARDIOPLEGIA PLUS
CENTRAMATE
CHAMBERKLEEN
CLARIS
DEAE
DELTADYNE
DFT CLASSIC
DIA-FILTROPLAST
DIA-SCHUMALITH
DIRT-FUSE
DUO-FINE
ECOFLUX
EMFLON
ENCHANT
ENCORE
ENVIROCHECK
EPOCEL
FALCON
FLUORO-PLUS
FLUORYTE
FLURODYNE
GARDIAN
GASKET-SERT
GASKLEEN
HEPARIN HYPERD
HYPERCEL
IMMUNODYNE
INTERVENE
IONKLEEN
JUMBOSEP
KLEEN-CHANGE
KLEENPAK
LEUKOGUARD
LIPIGUARD
LIPIPOR
LOPRODYNE
MACROSEP
MARKSMAN
MEGA
MEGAPLAST
MEMBRALOX
MICRO-CARBON
MICROCHECK
MICROFUNNEL
MICROPAK
MINI PROFILE
MINIM
MINIMATE
MUSTANG
NANOSEP
NEXIS
NOVASIP
NYLAFLO
NYLASORB
OENOCLEAR
OENOPURE
OMEGA
PALL
PALL ADVANTA
PALL-AQUASAFE
PALL-ARIA
PALL DISC TUBE
PALL-FIT
PALLCELL
PALLCHEK
PALLSEP
PALLTRONIC
PHARMASSURE
PHASESEP
PHOTOKLEEN
PL50
POLY-FINE
POLYPURE
POSEIDON
POSIDYNE
PRE-BYPASS PLUS
PREFLOW
PROFILE
PUMPKLEEN
PURECELL
RESOLUTE
RIGIMESH
SEALKLEEN
SEPRASOL
SOLVAC
SPHERODEX
SPHEROSIL
STARCLEAR
STARKLEEN
STAT PRIME
SUPOR
SUPRACAP
SUPRADISC
SUPRAMESH
TRI-STAR
TRISACRYL
TUFFRYN
ULTIKLEEN
ULTIPLEAT
ULTIPOR
ULTRABIND
ULTRALAB
ULTRAMET-L
ULTRARESERVOIR
ULTRASETTE
ULTROGEL
VACUCAP
VACUSHIELD
VARAFINE
VARI-SEAL
VELADISC
VERICEL
VERSACAP
VERSAPOR
VIVID
WATER-FINE
Z-BIND

Advertising Agency:
ANEW Marketing Group
811 W Jericho Tpke Ste 109E
Smithtown, NY 11787
Tel.: (631) 982-4000
Fax: (631) 434-1129

PASSUR AEROSPACE, INC.

1 Landmark Sq
Stamford, CT 06901
Tel.: (203) 622-4086
Fax: (203) 629-2970
Toll Free: (866) 472-7787
E-mail: jeffdevaney@passur.com
Web Site: www.passur.com
Approx. Rev.: $10,958,202
Approx. Number Employees: 30
Year Founded: 1967
Business Description:
Flight Tracking Information & Decision Support Software to the Aviation Industry
S.I.C.: 7372; 3577; 4581; 7379
N.A.I.C.S.: 511210; 334119; 488190; 541519
Advertising Expenditures: $27,000
Media: 2-4-7-8-10-13-20
Distr.: Intl.; Natl.
Budget Set: Oct.
Personnel:
G.S. Beckwith Gilbert *(Chm)*
James T. Barry *(Pres & CEO)*
Jeffrey P. Devaney *(CFO & Sec)*
Tina W. Jonas *(Exec VP-Ops)*
John R. Keller *(Exec VP)*
James A. Cole *(Sr VP-R&D)*
Ron Dunsky *(Sr VP-Mktg & Comm)*
Tom White *(Sr VP-Tech & Air Traffic Mgmt)*

Brands & Products:
AIRPORTMONITOR
FIND-FLIGHT
FLIGHTLINK
FLIGHTNEWS LIVE
FLIGHTPERFORM
FLIGHTSURE
IROPSNET
KNOW NOW
LIVEALERTS
MEGADATA
OPSNET
PASSUR
PASSUR INSIGHT
PASSUR PULSE
PORTAL
RAPIDRESPONSE
STACKVIEW
TRUETRACKING
THE WORLD'S MOST RELIABLE ARRIVAL SYSTEM

PIPER AIRCRAFT, INC.

(Holding of Imprimis Limited)
2926 Piper Dr
Vero Beach, FL 32960-1955
Tel.: (772) 567-4361
Fax: (772) 979-6584
Web Site: www.piper.com
Approx. Number Employees: 600
Year Founded: 1995
Business Description:
Personal, Training, Utility & Business Aircraft Mfr
S.I.C.: 3721; 3728
N.A.I.C.S.: 336411; 336413
Export
Advertising Expenditures: $2,000,000
Media: 2-5-6-7-8-10-11-13-26
Distr.: Intl.; Natl.
Budget Set: Sept.
Personnel:
Jackie Carlon *(Dir-Mktg)*
Rorie Ainbinder *(Mgr-Mktg)*

Brands & Products:
ARCHER III
ARROW
MERIDIAN
MIRAGE
PIPER
SARATOGA
SEMINOLE
SENECA
WARRIOR

P.L. PORTER CONTROLS, INC.

(Unit of Crane Aerospace Group)
3000 Winona Ave
Burbank, CA 91510-7722
Mailing Address:
PO Box 7722
Burbank, CA 91510-7722
Tel.: (818) 526-2600
Fax: (818) 842-6117
E-mail: sales@plporter.com
Web Site: www.craneae.com
E-Mail For Key Personnel:
Sales Director: sales@plporter.com
Sales Range: $25-49.9 Million
Approx. Number Employees: 200
Year Founded: 1947
Business Description:
Position Control Mechanisms Mfr
S.I.C.: 3728
N.A.I.C.S.: 336413
Import Export
Media: 2-10
Personnel:
David E. Bender *(Pres-Electronics Grp)*
Nancy Pinkston *(Sr VP)*

PRATT & WHITNEY

(Group of United Technologies Corporation)
400 Main St
East Hartford, CT 06108-0968
Tel.: (860) 565-4321
Web Site: www.pw.utc.com
Approx. Rev.: $11,100,000,000
Approx. Number Employees: 38,442
Business Description:
Design, Development, Marketing & Support of Commercial Aircraft Engines
S.I.C.: 3724
N.A.I.C.S.: 336412
Personnel:
David Hess *(Pres-Pratt & Whitney)*
Peter A. Gutermann *(Gen Counsel & VP)*
David Galuska *(Sr VP-Module Centers & Ops)*
Rajeev Bhalla *(VP-Fin)*
Neeta Patel *(Dir-Future Programs)*
Advertising Agency:
Qorvis Communications
1201 Connecticut Ave NW Ste 500
Washington, DC 20036
Tel.: (202) 496-1000
Fax: (202) 496-1300

RAYTHEON COMPANY

870 Winter St
Waltham, MA 02451-1449
Tel.: (781) 522-3000
Fax: (781) 522-3001
Toll Free: (877) 786-7070
Telex: 92-3455
E-mail: invest@raytheon.com
Web Site: www.raytheon.com
Approx. Sls.: $25,183,000,000
Approx. Number Employees: 72,000
Year Founded: 1922
Business Description:
Developer & Mfr of Defense & Aerospace Technologies
S.I.C.: 3812; 3663; 3721; 3724; 3728; 3731; 3761; 3764; 3769; 4899
N.A.I.C.S.: 334511; 334220; 336411; 336412; 336413; 336414; 336415; 336419; 336611; 517410
Import Export
Media: 10-18-22
Distr.: Natl.
Budget Set: Oct.
Personnel:
William H. Swanson *(Chm & CEO)*
David C. Wajsgras *(CFO & Sr VP)*
Rebecca B. Rhoads *(CIO & VP)*
Michael J. Wood *(Chief Acctg Officer & VP)*
Lynn A. Dugle *(Pres-Intelligence & Info Sys)*
Edward Hanlon, Jr. *(Pres-Raytheon International, Inc)*
John D. Harris, II *(Pres-Tech Svcs Co)*
Richard R. Yuse *(Pres-Space & Airborne Sys)*

Jay B. Stephens *(Gen Counsel, Sec & Sr VP)*
Thomas M. Culligan *(Sr VP-Bus Dev)*
William J. Lynn *(Sr VP-Govt Ops & Strategy)*
Keith J. Peden *(Sr VP-HR)*
T.W. Scott *(VP & Gen Mgr-Mission Operation Solutions)*
Jane P. Chappell *(VP-Bus Dev & Strategy)*
Mitch Kugler *(VP-Strategy)*
Pamela A. Wickham *(VP-Corp Affairs & Comm)*
Mark A. Hebeisen *(Dir-Technical)*
Corrine Kovalsky *(Dir-PR)*
Jim Singer *(Dir-IR)*

Brands & Products:
AESA
AMRAMM
AN/PAS-13 THERMAL WEAPON SIGHT
ASMR
ASTOR
BEECHCRAFT
CENTURION
COMMAND VIEW
CONFLUENSE
CUSTOMER SUCCESS IS OUR MISSION
DASR
DD(X)
ECLIPSE
GBS
GEOSERVER
HAWK/AMRAAM
HISAR
HYPEX
JAVELIN
JSOW
KEI
LIVELINK
LIVELINK HLA
LUNAR PENGUIN
MALD
MATH MOVES U
MAVERICK
MICROLIGHT
MICROROUTER
NAUTOCONNING
NAUTOPILOT
NO DOUBT
PAVEWAY
PHALANX
PHOENIX
PRA TOOLKIT
RAYTHEON
RAYTHEON SIX SIGMA
SEA RAM
SEA VUE
SECUREIT
SENSOR TEXTURE MAPS
SENTRY
STARS
STINGER
SVPLUME
TACLINK
THAAD RADAR
TOMAHAWK
VISIG

Advertising Agency:
The Boston Group
500 Harrison Ave 3F
Boston, MA 02118
Tel.: (617) 350-7020
Fax: (617) 350-7021

REINHOLD INDUSTRIES INC.

(Holding of The Jordan Company, L.P.)
12827 E Imperial Hwy
Santa Fe Springs, CA 90670-4713
Tel.: (562) 944-3281
Fax: (562) 944-7238
E-mail: vedleriii@reinhold-ind.com
Web Site: www.reinhold-ind.com
Sales Range: $25-49.9 Million
Approx. Number Employees: 117
Year Founded: 1928
Business Description:
Structural Composites; Ablative Composites; Reinforced Plastics
S.I.C.: 3728; 3089
N.A.I.C.S.: 336413; 326199
Media: 2-7-10-26
Personnel:
Vern Edler, III *(VP-Sls & Mktg)*

ROBINSON HELICOPTER COMPANY

2901 Airport Dr
Torrance, CA 90505-6115
Tel.: (310) 539-0508
Fax: (310) 539-5198
E-mail: info@robinsonheli.com
Web Site: www.robinsonheli.com
Approx. Number Employees: 900
Year Founded: 1973
Business Description:
Mfr. of Helicopters
S.I.C.: 3721
N.A.I.C.S.: 336411
Export
Media: 1-2-4-7-10-13
Distr.: Intl.; Natl.
Budget Set: Dec.
Personnel:
Kurt Robinson *(Pres)*
Tim Goetz *(CFO)*
Wayne Walden *(VP-Production)*
Julie Stembridge *(Mgr-Personnel)*
Brands & Products:
BETA II
CLIPPER II
RAVEN
ROBINSON HELICOPTER COMPANY
ROBINSON R22
ROBINSON R44

ROGERSON AIRCRAFT CORPORATION

2201 Alton Pkwy
Irvine, CA 92606-5033
Tel.: (949) 660-0666
Fax: (949) 442-2312
E-mail: rogersont@rogerson.com
Web Site: www.rogerson.com
Approx. Number Employees: 300
Year Founded: 1975
Business Description:
Aircraft Fuel Valves, Auxiliary Fuel Tanks, AMLCD Electronic Flight Instrument Systems, Pressure Gauges, Fuel Quantity Measurement System, Engine Instrument Display Systems & Vacuum Lavatory Systems Mfr
S.I.C.: 3728; 3721; 3812; 8733
N.A.I.C.S.: 336413; 334511; 336411; 541710
Export
Media: 2-4-6-10-17
Distr.: Natl.
Personnel:
Dan Solvales *(Dir-Mktg & Adv)*
Brands & Products:
ROGERSON AIRCRAFT
Advertising Agency:
The King Group
20250 Acacia St., Ste. 220
Newport Beach, CA 92660
Tel.: (949) 253-0999

SARGENT CONTROLS AND AEROSPACE

(Sub. of Avborne Accessory Group, Inc.)
5675 West Burlingame Rd
Tucson, AZ 85743-9453
Tel.: (520) 744-1000
Fax: (520) 744-9494
E-mail: sca@sargentaerospace.com
Web Site: www.sargentcontrols.com
Sales Range: $100-124.9 Million
Approx. Number Employees: 200
Year Founded: 1930
Business Description:
Hydraulic & Mechanical Actuators & Valves Mfr
S.I.C.: 3451; 3728
N.A.I.C.S.: 332721; 336413
Personnel:
Scott Still *(Pres)*
Advertising Agency:
Sullivan Higdon & Sink Incorporated
6801 Whittier Ave Ste 301
McLean, VA 22101-4549
Tel.: (703) 752-7845
Fax: (703) 752-7849

SCHNELLER, INC.

6019 Powdermill Rd
Kent, OH 44240-7109
Tel.: (330) 673-1400
Fax: (330) 673-6374
Web Site: www.schneller.com
Approx. Number Employees: 140
Year Founded: 1964
Business Description:
Mfr. of Aircraft Interiors
S.I.C.: 2295; 2672
N.A.I.C.S.: 313320; 322222
Import Export
Media: 2-4-7-10-17
Distr.: Intl.; Natl.
Personnel:
Richard C. Organ *(Pres & CEO)*
Brands & Products:
ABSKYN
AERFILM
AERFORM
AERLAM
AERMAT
AERTRIM
EXCEED
GT FORM
INDURA
MIRAGE
PANFLOR
SCHNELLER
Advertising Agency:
Hitchcock Fleming & Associates, Inc.
500 Wolf Ledges Pkwy
Akron, OH 44311-1022
Tel.: (330) 376-2111
Fax: (330) 376-2220
Toll Free: (888) 376-7601

SIGNATURE FLIGHT SUPPORT CORP.

(Group of BBA Aviation plc)
201 S Orange Ave Ste 1100-S
Orlando, FL 32801
Tel.: (407) 648-7200
Fax: (407) 206-8428
E-mail: marketing@signatureflight.com
Web Site: www.signatureflight.com
Approx. Number Employees: 1,300
Year Founded: 1992
Business Description:
Private Aircraft Ground Support Services
S.I.C.: 4581
N.A.I.C.S.: 488119; 488190
Media: 2-4-8-10-13-20
Distr.: Natl.
Budget Set: Oct.
Personnel:
S. Michael Scheeringa *(Pres)*
Mark Johnstone *(CFO)*
Maria A. Sastre *(COO)*
Connie Alden *(VP-HR)*
Patrick Sniffen *(VP-Mktg)*
Brands & Products:
CONCIAIR
FILL & FLY
GOLD CAP
HYPER POWER
NET POWER
WEEKEND TAKEOFF

SPACEDEV INC.

(Sub. of Sierra Nevada Corporation)
13855 Stowe Dr
Poway, CA 92064-6800
Tel.: (858) 375-2000
Fax: (858) 375-1000
Fax: (858) 375-1050
Toll Free: (877) 375-1004
E-mail: info@spacedev.com
Web Site: www.spacedev.com
Approx. Sls.: $34,697,613
Approx. Number Employees: 173
Year Founded: 1997
Business Description:
Space Technology Systems, Subsystems, Products & Services
S.I.C.: 9661; 3663; 3679; 3761; 3764; 3769
N.A.I.C.S.: 927110; 334220; 334419; 336414; 336415; 336419
Media: 10-13-20
Personnel:
Mark N. Sirangelo *(Chm & CEO)*
Richard B. Slansky *(Pres & CFO)*
James S. Voss *(VP-Engrg)*
Mark Bailey *(Dir-Mktg & Bus Team Mgr-Components & Mechanisms)*

SPIRIT AIRLINES, INC.

2800 Executive Way
Miramar, FL 33025
Tel.: (954) 447-7920
Tel.: (954) 447-7965
Fax: (954) 447-7979
Toll Free: (800) 772-7117
E-mail: spiritair@mailnj.custhelp.com
Web Site: www.spiritair.com
E-Mail For Key Personnel:
Public Relations: lynnek@spiritair.com
Approx. Rev.: $700,037,000
Approx. Number Employees: 2,224
Year Founded: 1964
Business Description:
Air Passenger Carrier
S.I.C.: 4512
N.A.I.C.S.: 481111
Advertising Expenditures: $2,400,000

Key to Media (For complete agency information see *The Advertising Red Books-Agencies* edition):
1. Bus. Publs. 2. Cable T.V. 3. Catalogs & Directories. 4. Co-op Adv. 5. Consumer Mags. 6. D.M. to Bus. Estab.7. D.M. to Consumers 8. Daily Newsp. 9. Exhibits/Trade Shows 10. Foreign 11. Infomercial 12. Internet Adv.13. Multimedia 14. Network Radio 15. Network T.V. 16. Newsp. Distr. Mags. 17. Other 18. Outdoor (Posters, Transit) 19. Point of Purchase20. Premiums, Novelties 21. Product Samples 22. Special Events Mktg. 23. Spot Radio 24. Spot T.V. 25. Weekly Newsp. 26. Yellow Page Adv.

Spirit Airlines, Inc. — (Continued)

Personnel:
Bill Franke *(Chm)*
B. Ben Baldanza *(Pres & CEO)*
David Lancelot *(CFO & Sr VP)*
Ken McKenzie *(COO)*
Craig MacCubbin *(CIO)*
Barry Biffle *(CMO)*
Thomas Canfield *(Gen Counsel, Sec & Sr VP)*
Tony Lefebvre *(Sr VP-Ops)*
Charlie Rue *(VP-Fin Plng & Analysis)*

Brands & Products:
FREE SPIRIT
SPIRIT

Advertising Agencies:
Cohn & Wolfe
200 Fifth Ave
New York, NY 10010
Tel.: (212) 798-9700
Fax: (212) 329-9900

Visions Advertising Media, LLC
426 Shore Rd Ste B
Atlantic City, NJ 08401
Tel.: (609) 926-6358
Fax: (609) 926-6358

SPRECHER & SCHUH, INC.

(Div. of Rockwell Automation, Inc.)
15910 Intl Plz Dr
Houston, TX 77032-2439
Tel.: (281) 442-9000
Fax: (281) 442-1570
E-mail: customerservice@ssusa.cc
Web Site: www.ssusa.cc
Sales Range: $25-49.9 Million
Approx. Number Employees: 50
Year Founded: 1980
Business Description:
Motor Control Mfr
S.I.C.: 3721; 8733
N.A.I.C.S.: 336411; 541710
Media: 2-7

TALON AIR, INC.

8300 Republic Airport Rte 109
Farmingdale, NY 11735
Tel.: (631) 753-8881
Fax: (631) 753-6681
E-mail: info@talonairjets.com
Web Site: www.talonairjets.com
Sales Range: $10-24.9 Million
Approx. Number Employees: 60
Business Description:
Private Jet Charter Services
S.I.C.: 4522
N.A.I.C.S.: 481211
Personnel:
Adam Katz *(Founder, Pres & CEO)*
Paul St. Lucia *(Dir-Sls)*
Frank D'Angelone *(Mgr-Charters)*
Advertising Agency:
Susan Magrino Agency
641 Lexington Ave 28th Fl
New York, NY 10022
Tel.: (212) 957-3005
Fax: (212) 957-4071

TELEDYNE BROWN ENGINEERING, INC.

(Sub. of Teledyne Technologies Incorporated)
300 Sparkman Dr Cummings Research Pk
Huntsville, AL 35805-1912
Mailing Address:
PO Box 070007
Huntsville, AL 35807-7007
Tel.: (256) 726-1000
Fax: (256) 726-3570
E-mail: info@tbe.com
Web Site: www.tbe.com
Sales Range: $250-299.9 Million
Approx. Number Employees: 1,750
Year Founded: 1953
Business Description:
Systems Engineering & Technology Solutions to Defense, Space, Environmental & Information Problems
S.I.C.: 8733
N.A.I.C.S.: 541710
Import Export
Media: 2-4-10-16
Distr.: Natl.
Budget Set: Oct.
Personnel:
Rex D. Geveden *(Pres)*
Janice L. Hess *(CFO & Exec VP)*
George Bobb *(Gen Counsel)*
John A. Braun *(VP-Washington Ops)*
James L. Whisenant *(VP-Fin & Procurement)*
Joseph Genovese *(Dir-Bus Dev)*
Eileen Heaton *(Dir-Comm)*
Deborah McGriff *(Dir-Fin Analysis)*
Carolyn Walker *(Dir-HR)*
Kimberlee J. Williams *(Dir-Quality Mgmt Sys)*
Brands & Products:
POCKET IETM
POCKET RESPONDER
WATERSABRE

TEXTRON INC.

40 Westminster St
Providence, RI 02903
Tel.: (401) 421-2800
Fax: (401) 421-2220
E-mail: pr@textron.com
Web Site: www.textron.com
Approx. Rev.: $10,525,000,000
Approx. Number Employees: 32,000
Year Founded: 1923
Business Description:
Manned & Unmanned Aircraft & Vehicles, Turf Equipment, Tools, Fuel Systems & Electrical Testing Systems Mfr; Financial Services
S.I.C.: 3721; 3714; 3724; 3795
N.A.I.C.S.: 336411; 336399; 336412; 336992
Import Export
Advertising Expenditures: $6,000,000
Media: 9-10-11-13-15-25
Distr.: Natl.
Personnel:
Scott C. Donnelly *(Chm & CEO)*
John L. Garrison, Jr. *(Pres & CEO-Bell Helicopter)*
Frank T. Connor *(CFO & Exec VP)*
Gary Cantrell *(CIO & VP)*
Kenneth C. Bohlen *(CIO)*
Frederick K. Butler *(Chief HR Officer & Exec VP-Admin)*
John D. Butler *(Chief HR Officer & Exec VP-Admin)*
J. Scott Hall *(Pres-Indus Segment)*
Terrence O'Donnell *(Gen Counsel, Corp Sec & Exec VP)*
Richard L. Yates *(Sr VP & Corp Controller)*
Robert O. Rowland *(Sr VP-Washington Ops)*
Arnold Friedman *(VP & Deputy Gen Counsel)*
Cathy A. Streker *(VP-HR)*
Adele Suddes *(VP-Corp Comm)*
Karen Gordon Quintal *(Dir-Comm)*
Brands & Products:
AVDEL
BOB-CAT
BOESNER
BROUWER
BSK
BUNTON
CAMCAR
CARGOMASTER
CHERRY
CHESILVALE
CITATION
CUSHMAN
CUSHMAN COMMANDER
DELIGHT
E-Z-GO
ELCO
IMAP
INTESYS
JACOBSEN
JETANGER
KLAUKE
LANCET
LULL
MAPRI
OELSCHLAGER
POWERLINK
PROADVANTAGE
PROGRESSIVE ELECTRONICS
QUICK CHANGE ARBOR
QUICK DRAW
QUICK HITCH SYSTEM
RANSOMES
RIFOCS
RING SCREW
RYAN
SKY TRAK
SKYCATCHER
SNORKEL
STEINER
THE TERMINATORS
TEXTRON
TITAN
TRI-STAR
WEARMAX
Advertising Agency:
(Add) Ventures
117 Chapman St
Providence, RI 02905
Tel.: (401) 453-4748
Fax: (401) 453-0095

TEXTRON SYSTEMS CORPORATION

(Sub. of Textron Inc.)
201 Lowell St
Wilmington, MA 01887-4113
Tel.: (978) 657-5111
Fax: (978) 657-6644
E-mail: info@textron.com
Web Site: www.systems.textron.com
Sales Range: $500-549.9 Million
Approx. Number Employees: 1,000
Business Description:
Weapons Systems, Aircraft Control Component, Surveillance System, Intelligence Software & Military Vehicle Mfr
S.I.C.: 3812; 3483; 3721
N.A.I.C.S.: 334511; 332993; 336411
Export
Advertising Expenditures: $280,000
Bus. Publs.: $30,000; Catalogs & Directories: $50,000; Exhibits/Trade Shows: $200,000
Distr.: Natl.
Budget Set: Nov.
Personnel:
Fred Strader *(Pres & CEO)*
Jack Cronin *(Chief Strategy Officer & Exec VP)*
Tom McNamara *(CTO & Sr VP)*
Ellen Lord *(Sr VP & Gen Mgr)*
Kevin J. Cosgriff *(Sr VP-Intl Bus & Govt)*
Ian Walsh *(Chief Innovation Officer, Chief of Staff & Sr VP)*

THALES ATM, INC.

(Joint Venture of Siemens Aktiengesellschaft & Thales S.A.)
23501 W 84th St
Shawnee, KS 66227-3296
Tel.: (913) 422-2600
Fax: (913) 422-2962
E-mail: info@thalesgroup.com
Web Site: www.thalesatm.com
Approx. Number Employees: 90
Year Founded: 1931
Business Description:
Mfr. of Navigation Equipment, ILS Instrument Landing System, VOR VHF Omnirange, DME Distance Measuring Equipment, Differential Global Positioning Systems, Wide Area Augmentation Systems
S.I.C.: 3812; 3663
N.A.I.C.S.: 334511; 334220
Export
Media: 2-4-10-11
Distr.: Intl.; Natl.
Budget Set: Sept.
Personnel:
Kylie Allen *(CFO)*

THERMOTRON INDUSTRIES

(Div. of Venturedyne, Ltd.)
291 Kollen Pk Dr
Holland, MI 49423
Tel.: (616) 392-1491
Fax: (616) 392-5643
E-mail: info@thermotron.com
Web Site: www.thermotron.com
Approx. Number Employees: 350
Year Founded: 1962
Business Description:
Environmental Test Chambers, Vibration Test Equipment, Failure Monitoring & Detection Equipment, Software & Peripherals
S.I.C.: 3569; 3826
N.A.I.C.S.: 333999; 334516
Export
Media: 2-4-7-10-13-20
Personnel:
Ron Lampen *(Pres)*
Lynn Ternan *(VP-Sls)*
Brands & Products:
THERMOTRON

TIMCO AVIATION SERVICES, INC.

623 Radar Rd
Greensboro, NC 27410-6221
Tel.: (336) 668-4410
Fax: (954) 538-6610
E-mail: webmaster@timcogso.com
Web Site: www.timco.aero
Sales Range: $300-349.9 Million
Approx. Number Employees: 3,400

Key to Media (For complete agency information see *The Advertising Red Books-Agencies* edition):
1. Bus. Publs. 2. Cable T.V. 3. Catalogs & Directories. 4. Co-op Adv. 5. Consumer Mags. 6. D.M. to Bus. Estab.7. D.M. to Consumers 8. Daily Newsp. 9. Exhibits/Trade Shows 10. Foreign 11. Infomercial 12. Internet Adv.13. Multimedia 14. Network Radio 15. Network T.V. 16. Newsp. Distr. Mags. 17. Other 18. Outdoor (Posters, Transit) 19. Point of Purchase20. Premiums, Novelties 21. Product Samples 22. Special Events Mktg. 23. Spot Radio 24. Spot T.V. 25. Weekly Newsp. 26. Yellow Page Adv.

Business Description:
Maintenance Repair & Overhaul Services for Planes & Equipment
S.I.C.: 9621; 4581; 5088
N.A.I.C.S.: 488111; 423860; 488190
Advertising Expenditures: $100,000
Media: 2-7-11-22
Personnel:
Kevin Carter *(CEO)*
John Wells *(CIO & VP)*
R. Gene House *(CMO & Exec VP)*
Rick Salanitri *(Pres-Aerosystems & Brice Seating & Exec VP)*
Bill Norman *(Pres-MRO Svcs)*
Elizabeth Taylor *(Gen Counsel & Exec VP)*
John Eichten *(Sr VP-Sls & Mktg)*
Ray Hauck *(Sr VP-Military Bus)*
Leonard Kazmerski *(VP-Mktg & Bus Dev)*
Jeff Luedeke *(VP-Sls & Mktg)*
Fred Rasch *(VP-Maintenance, Repair & Overhaul Sls)*
Mike Anderson *(Gen Mgr-Greensboro MRO Facility)*
Lance Applegate *(Gen Mgr-Line Maintenance)*
Mark Snook *(Gen Mgr-Lake City MRO Facility)*
Keith Statzer *(Gen Mgr-Macon MRO Facility)*

TRIUMPH THERMAL SYSTEMS, INC.
(Sub. of Triumph Aerospace Systems Group)
200 Railroad St
Forest, OH 45843-9193
Tel.: (419) 273-2511
Fax: (419) 273-3285
E-mail: info@triumphgroup.com
Web Site: www.triumph-thermal.com
Sales Range: $50-74.9 Million
Approx. Number Employees: 140
Year Founded: 1986
Business Description:
Aerospace; Heat Transfer Components & Liquid Cooling Systems Mfr
S.I.C.: 3728; 3585
N.A.I.C.S.: 336413; 333415
Export
Advertising Expenditures: $900,000
Media: 2-4-8-13
Distr.: Direct to Consumer; Natl.
Budget Set: Oct.
Personnel:
Michael Perhay *(Pres)*
Mike Giangiordano *(VP-Fin & Ops)*
Stanley Coughlin *(Dir-Mfg Support, Purchasing & Plng)*
Kenneth Jackson *(Dir-HR)*
Robin Miller *(Dir-Ops)*
Bill Nostadt *(Dir-Bus Dev)*
Cris Rick *(Mgr-Aftermarket Svcs)*

UNISON INDUSTRIES, LLC
(Sub. of GE Aviation)
7575 Baymeadows Way
Jacksonville, FL 32256
Tel.: (904) 739-4000
Fax: (904) 739-4006
E-mail: mediarelations@unison.ae.ge.com
Web Site: www.unisonindustries.com
Sales Range: $300-349.9 Million
Approx. Number Employees: 700
Year Founded: 1980
Business Description:
Mfr of Aircraft Engine Electrical & Mechanical Components
S.I.C.: 3724; 3728
N.A.I.C.S.: 336412; 336413
Import Export
Media: 2-4-5-7-10-11
Distr.: Intl.; Natl.
Personnel:
Pablo Penaloza *(CFO)*
Bill Bussa *(VP-HR)*
Paul Theofan *(VP-Mktg & Sales)*
Chuck Currier *(Dir-Customer Svcs)*
David Conklin *(Mgr-Product Support)*
Brands & Products:
AUTOLITE
SLICK AIRCRAFT PRODUCTS
UNISON

UNITED TECHNOLOGIES CORPORATION
(d/b/a UTC Corp.)
United Technologies Bldg 1 Financial Plz
Hartford, CT 06101
Tel.: (860) 728-7000
Fax: (860) 728-7979
Web Site: www.utc.com
Approx. Sls.: $54,326,000,000
Approx. Number Employees: 208,200
Year Founded: 1934
Business Description:
Building Systems & Aerospace Products Mfr
S.I.C.: 8733; 3534; 3585; 3724; 3822
N.A.I.C.S.: 541710; 333415; 333921; 334512; 336412
Import Export
Media: 2-4-7-10
Personnel:
Louis R. Chenevert *(Chm & CEO)*
Gregory J. Hayes *(CFO & Sr VP)*
Nancy M. Davis *(CIO & VP)*
Jothi Purushotaman *(Pres-India)*
Charles D. Gill, Jr. *(Gen Counsel & Sr VP)*
J. Thomas Bowler, Jr. *(Sr VP-HR & Org)*
J. Michael McQuade *(Sr VP-Science & Tech)*
David E. Parekh *(VP-Res & Dir-United Tech Res Center)*
Julie A. Nizik *(Mgr-Adv & Mktg Comm)*
Brands & Products:
CARRIER
HAMILTON SUNDSTRAND
OTIS
PRATT & WHITNEY
SIKORSKY
UNITED TECHNOLOGIES
Advertising Agencies:
Bernard Hodes Group
790 E Broward Blvd Fl 4 Ste 400
Fort Lauderdale, FL 33301
Tel.: (954) 966-3500
Fax: (954) 989-3085

DDB New York
437 Madison Ave
New York, NY 10022-7001
Tel.: (212) 415-2000
Fax: (212) 415-3506

Ketchum
(Part of Omnicom)
1285 Ave of the Americas
New York, NY 10019
Tel.: (646) 935-3900
Fax: (646) 935-4482

Maier Advertising, Inc.
1789 New Britain Ave
Farmington, CT 06032-3317
Tel.: (860) 677-4581
Fax: (860) 677-5854
Fax: (860) 677-4898

Prometheus
225 N Michigan Ave
Chicago, IL 60601
Tel.: (312) 324-7000
Tel.: (312) 419-5252
Fax: (312) 324-8204

US GLOBAL NANOSPACE, INC.
2533 N Carson St Ste 5107
Carson City, NV 89706
Tel.: (775) 841-3246
Fax: (775) 883-4874
E-mail: info@usgn.com
Web Site: www.usgn.com
Sales Range: Less than $1 Million
Business Description:
Nanotechnology & Nanomaterial Product Mfr
S.I.C.: 8733; 2299; 2655
N.A.I.C.S.: 541710; 313312; 322214
Media: 7-11

WOODWARD HRT
(Formerly HR Textron Inc.)
(Sub. of Woodward Governor Company)
25200 W Rye Canyon Rd
Santa Clarita, CA 91355-1265
Tel.: (661) 294-6000
Fax: (661) 259-9622
Toll Free: (800) 235-3330
Web Site: woodwardhrt.woodward.com
Sales Range: $250-299.9 Million
Approx. Number Employees: 900
Year Founded: 1933
Business Description:
Hydraulic, Pneumatic, Fuel Management & Electromechanical Products & Solutions
S.I.C.: 3492; 3625
N.A.I.C.S.: 332912; 335314
Export
D.M. to Consumers: 50%; Other: 50%
Distr.: Natl.
Personnel:
Frank Tempesta *(Pres)*

XEBEC ADSORPTION INC.
730 Boulevard Industriel
Blainville, QC J7C 3V4, Canada
Tel.: (450) 979-8700
Fax: (450) 979-7869
Toll Free: (877) 469-3232
E-mail: sales@xebecinc.com
Web Site: www.xebecinc.com
E-Mail For Key Personnel:
Sales Director: sales@xebecinc.com
Approx. Rev.: $18,295,236
Approx. Number Employees: 163
Year Founded: 1996
Business Description:
Gas & Compressed Air Purification, Separation, Dehydration & Filtration Equipment Mfr
S.I.C.: 3563
N.A.I.C.S.: 333912
Personnel:
Kurt Sorschak *(Chm, Pres & CEO)*
Ginette Gagne *(CFO & VP)*
John Fyfe *(VP-Sls & Mktg)*
Daryl Musselman *(VP-Engrg & Tech Dev)*
Advertising Agencies:
Buchanan Communications Ltd.
107 Cheapside
London, EC2V 6DN, United Kingdom
Tel.: (44) 20 7466 5000
Fax: (44) 20 7466 5001

Edelman
1035 Cambie St 2nd Fl
Vancouver, BC V6B 5L7, Canada
Tel.: (604) 623-3007
Fax: (604) 687-4304

Key to Media (For complete agency information see *The Advertising Red Books-Agencies* edition):
1. Bus. Publs. 2. Cable T.V. 3. Catalogs & Directories. 4. Co-op Adv. 5. Consumer Mags. 6. D.M. to Bus. Estab.7. D.M. to Consumers 8. Daily Newsp. 9. Exhibits/Trade Shows 10. Foreign 11. Infomercial 12. Internet Adv.13. Multimedia 14. Network Radio 15. Network T.V. 16. Newsp. Distr. Mags. 17. Other 18. Outdoor (Posters, Transit) 19. Point of Purchase20. Premiums, Novelties 21. Product Samples 22. Special Events Mktg. 23. Spot Radio 24. Spot T.V. 25. Weekly Newsp. 26. Yellow Page Adv.

Beer, Ale & Soft Drinks

Ale — Beer — Ginger Ale — Malt Syrup — Mineral Water — Soft Drinks

7-ELEVEN CANADA, INC.
(Sub. of 7-Eleven, Inc.)
Ste 2400 13450 102nd Ave
Surrey, BC 53T0C3, Canada
Tel.: (604) 586-0711
Fax: (604) 586-1506
Toll Free: (800) 255-0711
Web Site: www.7-Eleven.com
Sales Range: $600-649.9 Million
Approx. Number Employees: 5,400
Year Founded: 1969
Business Description:
Convenience Store Operator
S.I.C.: 5411
N.A.I.C.S.: 445120
Personnel:
Stephanie Kilner *(Mgr-HR)*
Advertising Agencies:
Hot Tomali Communications Inc
1441 E Pender St
Vancouver, BC Canada V5L 1V7
Tel.: (604) 893-8347
Fax: (604) 893-8346
Slurpee Frozen Drinks

Watermark Advertising Design
815 17th Ave SW Ste 290
Calgary, AB T2T 0A1, Canada
Tel.: (403) 228-7949
Fax: (403) 245-5443
Agency of Record
Digital Advertising
Marketing
Traditional Advertising

ABITA BREWING COMPANY
21084 Hwy 36
Abita Springs, LA 70433
Mailing Address:
PO Box 1510
Abita Springs, LA 70420
Tel.: (985) 893-3143
Fax: (985) 898-3546
Toll Free: (800) 737-2311
E-mail: contact@abita.com
Web Site: www.abita.com
Sales Range: $10-24.9 Million
Approx. Number Employees: 45
Year Founded: 1986
Business Description:
Brewery
S.I.C.: 2082
N.A.I.C.S.: 312120
Media: 4-18-21-22-23-24-27-28-29
Personnel:
David Blossman *(Pres)*
Brands & Products:
ABITA AMBER
ABITA GOLDEN
ABITA LIGHT
JOCKAMO I.P.A.
PURPLE HAZE
RESTORATION PALE ALE
TURBODOG
Advertising Agency:
Innovative Advertising
403 N Columbia St
Covington, LA 70433
Tel.: (985) 809-1975

ALL MARKET, INC.
39 W 14th St
New York, NY 10011
Tel.: (212) 206-0763
Web Site: www.vitacoco.com
Business Description:
Coconut Water Processor & Distr
N.A.I.C.S.: 312112
Media: 28-29
Personnel:
Michael Kirban *(Co-CEO)*
Ira Liran *(Co-CEO)*
Brands & Products:
VITA COCO

ANHEUSER-BUSCH COMPANIES, INC.
(Sub. of Anheuser-Busch InBev N.V./ S.A.)
1 Busch Pl
Saint Louis, MO 63118-1849
Tel.: (314) 577-2000
Fax: (314) 577-2900
Toll Free: (800) 342-5283
E-mail: info@anheuser-busch.com
Web Site: www.anheuser-busch.com
Approx. Number Employees: 30,849
Year Founded: 1875
Business Description:
Holding Company; Beer & Malt Beverage Mfr & Distr
S.I.C.: 6719; 2082; 5181
N.A.I.C.S.: 551112; 312120; 424810
Import Export
Media: 3-6-9-14-15-16-18-23-24
Distr.: Intl.; Natl.
Budget Set: Sept.
Personnel:
David A. Peacock *(Pres)*
Gary L. Rutledge *(Gen Counsel & VP)*
Thomas J. Adamitis *(VP-Procurement)*
David Almeida *(VP-Fin)*
Paul Chibe *(VP-Mktg)*
Juan Torres *(Dir-Mktg)*
Megan McIntyre *(Sr Mgr-Emerging Media & Print)*
Julia Mize *(Brand Mgr)*
Adam Jacobs *(Mgr-Sports Mktg)*
Brands & Products:
ANHEUSER-BUSCH
BLACK & TAN
BUD DRY
BUD EXTRA
BUD ICE
BUD ICE LIGHT
BUD LIGHT
BUD LIGHT GOLDEN WHEAT
BUDWEISER
BUDWEISER SELECT
BUSCH
BUSCH ICE
BUSCH LIGHT
BUSCH NA
DEVON'S SHANDY
DOC OTIS'
HURRICANE HIGH GRAVITY
HURRICANE ICE
HURRICANE MALT LIQUOR
JACK'S PUMPKIN SPICE ALE
KING COBRA
KING OF BEERS
MICHELOB
MICHELOB AMBERBOCK
MICHELOB GOLDEN DRAFT
MICHELOB GOLDEN DRAFT LIGHT
MICHELOB HONEY LAGER
MICHELOB LIGHT
MICHELOB PORTER
MICHELOB ULTRA
MICHELOB ULTRA AMBER
MICHELOB ULTRA FRUIT
NATURAL ICE
NATURAL LIGHT
O'DOULS
PACIFIC RIDGE PALE ALE
RED WOLF
RHUMBA
ROLLING ROCK
ROLLING ROCK LIGHT
ROLLING ROCK PREMIUM
SELECT 55
SHOCK TOP BELGIAN WHITE
SPYKES
STONE MILL PALE ALE
SUN DOG AMBER WHEAT
TEQUIZA
ZIEGEN LIGHT
ZIEGENBOCK
Advertising Agencies:
Anomaly Communications LLC
536 Broadway 11th Fl
New York, NY 10012
Tel.: (917) 595-2200
Fax: (917) 595-2299
Budweiser

Busch Media Group
1 Busch Pl
Saint Louis, MO 63118-1849
Tel.: (314) 577-2000
Fax: (314) 577-2900

Cannonball
8251 Maryland Ave Ste 200
Saint Louis, MO 63105
Tel.: (314) 445-6400
Fax: (314) 726-3359

Concept Chaser Co., Inc.
222 N Sepulveda Blvd Ste 1518
El Segundo, CA 90245
Tel.: (310) 615-0700
Fax: (310) 615-0300

Downtown Partners Chicago
200 E Randolph St 34th Fl
Chicago, IL 60601
Tel.: (312) 552-5800
Tel.: (312) 552-5804
Fax: (312) 552-2330

Fusion Idea Lab
506 N Clark St
Chicago, IL 60654
Tel.: (312) 670-9060
Fax: (312) 670-9061

LatinWorks Marketing, Inc.
206 E 9th St Capital Tower Fl 13
Austin, TX 78701
Tel.: (512) 479-6200
Fax: (512) 479-6024

Lopito, Ileana & Howie, Inc.

Key to Media (For complete agency information see *The Advertising Red Books-Agencies* edition):
1. Bus. Publs. 2. Cable T.V. 3. Catalogs & Directories. 4. Co-op Adv. 5. Consumer Mags. 6. D.M. to Bus. Estab.7. D.M. to Consumers
8. Daily Newsp. 9. Exhibits/Trade Shows 10. Foreign 11. Infomercial 12. Internet Adv.13. Multimedia 14. Network Radio
15. Network T.V. 16. Newsp. Distr. Mags. 17. Other 18. Outdoor (Posters, Transit) 19. Point of Purchase20. Premiums, Novelties
21. Product Samples 22. Special Events Mktg. 23. Spot Radio 24. Spot T.V. 25. Weekly Newsp. 26. Yellow Page Adv.

Metro Office Park #13 First St
Guaynabo, PR 00968
Tel.: (787) 783-1160
Fax: (787) 783-2273

Maslansky, Luntz & Partners
1101 King St Ste 110
Alexandria, VA 22314
Tel.: (703) 358-0080
Fax: (703) 358-0089

Open Minds
(An RPA Co.)
2525 Colorado Ave
Santa Monica, CA 90401
Tel.: (949) 255-4300
Fax: (949) 255-4400

PALM + HAVAS
1253 McGill College Ave 3rd Fl
Montreal, QC H3B 2Y5, Canada
Tel.: (514) 845-7256
Fax: (514) 845-0975

ARROWHEAD MOUNTAIN SPRING WATER COMPANY

(Sub. of Nestle Waters North America Inc.)
777 W Putnam Ave
Greenwich, CT 06830-5091
Tel.: (203) 531-4100
Fax: (203) 863-0256
Web Site: www.arrowheadwater.com
Approx. Number Employees: 500
Year Founded: 1888
Business Description:
Water Purification Systems for Home & Office, Bottled Water Service, Drinking Cups, Electric Water Coolers
S.I.C.: 5149
N.A.I.C.S.: 424490
Media: 2-4-7-10-13-15-16-19-22-26
Distr.: Reg.
Budget Set: Jan.
Personnel:
Bill Pearson *(CFO)*
Bob Davino *(VP-Mktg)*

BIG ROCK BREWERY INCOME TRUST

5555 76th Ave SE
Calgary, AB T2C 4L8, Canada
Tel.: (403) 720-3239
Fax: (403) 236-7523
Toll Free: (800) 242-3107
E-mail: beer@bigrockbeer.com
Web Site: www.bigrockbeer.com
Approx. Rev.: $45,979,347
Approx. Number Employees: 160
Year Founded: 1984
Business Description:
Beer Brewer & Marketer
S.I.C.: 2082
N.A.I.C.S.: 312120
Media: 10-21-22
Personnel:
Edward E. McNally *(Chm & CEO)*
Bill McKenzie *(Pres)*
Barbara Feit *(CFO)*
Brands & Products:
ALBERTA
BIG ROCK BREWERY
BLACK AMBER
GRASSHOPPER
HONEY BROWN
JACKRABBIT
KOLD GLACIER LAGER
MCNALLY'S EXTRA
PALE ALE
ROCK CREEK CIDER
TRADITIONAL
WARTHOG
XO LAGER

THE BOSTON BEER COMPANY, INC.

One Design Center Ste 850
Boston, MA 02210
Tel.: (617) 368-5000
Fax: (617) 368-5500
Toll Free: (800) 372-1131
Web Site: www.bostonbeer.com
Approx. Rev.: $505,870,000
Approx. Number Employees: 780
Year Founded: 1985
Business Description:
Beer Brewer
S.I.C.: 2082
N.A.I.C.S.: 312120
Advertising Expenditures: $135,737,000
Media: 2-3-10-14-15-17-18-20-21-23-24
Distr.: Natl.
Personnel:
C. James Koch *(Chm)*
Martin F. Roper *(Pres & CEO)*
William F. Urich *(CFO & Treas)*
Frederick Grein *(Gen Counsel)*
John C. Geist *(VP-Sls)*
Jon London *(Sr Dir-Mktg)*
Brands & Products:
AMERICA'S WORLD-CLASS BEER
HARDCORE CIDER COMPANY
OREGON ALE AND BEER COMPANY
OREGON ORGINALS BRAND
SAMUEL ADAMS
SAMUEL ADAMS BOSTON LAGER
SAMUEL ADAMS UTOPIAS
SAMUEL ADAMS UTOPIAS MMII
TWISTED TEA
TWISTED TEA BREWING COMPANY
Advertising Agencies:
CM Communications, Inc.
20 Park Plz Ste 821
Boston, MA 02116
Tel.: (617) 536-3400
Fax: (617) 536-3424

Zenith Media Services
(Regional Headquarters for ZenithOptimedia, the Americas)
299 W Houston St 10th Fl
New York, NY 10014-4806
Tel.: (212) 859-5100
Fax: (212) 727-9495
(Media Buying & Planning)

BROOKLYN BREWERY CORPORATION

79 N 11th St
Brooklyn, NY 11211
Tel.: (718) 486-7422
Fax: (718) 486-7440
E-mail: info@brooklynbrewery.com
Web Site: www.brooklynbrewery.com
Approx. Sls.: $14,500,000
Approx. Number Employees: 16
Year Founded: 1987
Business Description:
Beer & Ale
S.I.C.: 5181; 2082
N.A.I.C.S.: 424810; 312120
Personnel:
Steve Hindy *(Co-Founder & Pres)*
Tom Potter *(Co-Founder)*
Mike Vitale *(VP-Sls)*
Eric Ottaway *(Gen Mgr)*
Robin Ottaway *(Mgr-Sls)*
Brands & Products:
BLACK CHOCOLATE STOUT
BLUNDERBUSS OLD ALE
BROOKLYN BREWERY
BROOKLYN BROWN ALE
BROOKLYN CUVEE DE CARDOZ
BROOKLYN LAGER
BROOKLYN PENNANT ALE 55
BROOKLYN PILSNER
BROOKLYNER WEISSE
BROOKYLN LOCAL 1
BROOKYLN LOCAL 2
BROOKYLNER SCHNEIDER HOPFEN WEISSE
EAST INDIA PALE ALE
INTENSIFIED COFFEE STOUT
MONSTER ALE
OKTOBERFEST
POST ROAD PUMPKIN ALE
SUMMER ALE
WINTER ALE
Advertising Agency:
Blenderbox Inc.
26 Dobbin St 3rd Fl
Brooklyn, NY 11222
Tel.: (718) 963-4594
Digital Agency of Record

CAPITAL BREWERY CO., INC.

7734 Ter Ave
Middleton, WI 53562-3163
Tel.: (608) 836-7100
Fax: (608) 831-9155
E-mail: capbrew@capital-brewery.com
Web Site: www.capital-brewery.com
Sales Range: $25-49.9 Million
Approx. Number Employees: 20
Year Founded: 1986
Business Description:
Beer Mfr
S.I.C.: 2082
N.A.I.C.S.: 312120
Media: 1-2-3-4-6-7-8-9-10-16-17-18-19-20-21-22-24-25-26
Distr.: Reg.
Personnel:
Carl Nolen *(Pres & CEO)*
Brands & Products:
CAPITAL 1900
CAPITAL AUTUMNAL FIRE
CAPITAL BAVARIAN LAGER
CAPITAL BLONDE DOPPELBOCK
CAPITAL BREWERY
CAPITAL BROWN ALE
CAPITAL DARK
CAPITAL DARK DOPPELBOCK
CAPITAL KLOSTER WEIZEN
CAPITAL MAIBOCK
CAPITAL OKTOBERFEST
CAPITAL SPECIAL PILSNER
CAPITAL WEIZEN DOPPELBOCK
CAPITAL WILD RICE
CAPITAL WINTER SKAL
CAPITAL WISCONSIN AMBER
Advertising Agency:
Glowac, Harris, Madison Inc.
330 S Whitney Way Ste 300
Madison, WI 53705
Tel.: (608) 232-9696
Fax: (608) 232-9636

CAROLINA BEVERAGE CORPORATION

1413 Jake Alexander Blvd S
Salisbury, NC 28146-8359
Tel.: (704) 637-5881
Fax: (704) 633-7491
E-mail: custserv@cheerwine.com
Web Site: www.cheerwine.com
Approx. Sls.: $3,000,000
Approx. Number Employees: 10
Year Founded: 1917
Business Description:
Soft Drinks Mfr
S.I.C.: 2086
N.A.I.C.S.: 312111
Export
Advertising Expenditures: $50,000
Media: 14-15-18-19-22-23-24
Personnel:
Cliff Richie *(Pres)*
Jim Leland *(VP-Sls)*
Brands & Products:
BLUE MIST
CHEERWINE
COOL MOON

CASTLE BRANDS INC.

122 E 42nd St Ste 4700
New York, NY 10168
Tel.: (646) 356-0200
Fax: (646) 356-0222
E-mail: info@castlebrandsinc.com
Web Site: www.castlebrandsinc.com
Approx. Sls.: $31,997,276
Approx. Number Employees: 40
Year Founded: 2003
Business Description:
Vodka, Rum, Irish Whiskey & Liqueurs Importer & Marketer
S.I.C.: 5182
N.A.I.C.S.: 424820
Advertising Expenditures: $1,660,545
Personnel:
Mark Andrews *(Chm)*
Richard J. Lampen *(Interim Pres & CEO)*
Alfred J. Small *(CFO, Treas, Sec & Sr VP)*
John S. Glover *(COO)*
Alejandra Pena *(Sr VP-Mktg & Brand Dir-Pallini)*
T. Kelley Spillane *(Sr VP-Sls-US)*
Brands & Products:
A. DE FUSSIGNY
BETTS & SCHOLL
BORU
BRADY'S IRISH CREAM
BRITISH ROYAL NAVY IMPERIAL RUM
CASTLE BRANDS
CELTIC CROSSING LIQUEUR
CLONTARF IRISH
GOSLING'S
JEFFERSON'S
JEFFERSON'S RESERVE
KNAPPOGUE CASTLE WHISKEY
KNAPPOGUE CASTLE WHISKEY 1951
PALLINI
SEA WYNDE RUM
TIERRAS
TRAVIS HASSE?S ORIGINAL PIE
Advertising Agencies:
Fathom Communications
(Part of Omnicom Group of Companies)
437 Madison Ave

Key to Media (For complete agency information see *The Advertising Red Books-Agencies* edition):
1. Bus. Publs. 2. Cable T.V. 3. Catalogs & Directories. 4. Co-op Adv. 5. Consumer Mags. 6. D.M. to Bus. Estab.7. D.M. to Consumers
8. Daily Newsp. 9. Exhibits/Trade Shows 10. Foreign 11. Infomercial 12. Internet Adv.13. Multimedia 14. Network Radio
15. Network T.V. 16. Newsp. Distr. Mags. 17. Other 18. Outdoor (Posters, Transit) 19. Point of Purchase20. Premiums, Novelties
21. Product Samples 22. Special Events Mktg. 23. Spot Radio 24. Spot T.V. 25. Weekly Newsp. 26. Yellow Page Adv.

Castle Brands Inc. — (Continued)

New York, NY 10022
Tel.: (212) 817-6600
Fax: (212) 415-3514
Boru Vodka

STC Associates
245 Fifth Ave 24th Fl
New York, NY 10016
Tel.: (212) 725-1900
Fax: (212) 725-1975
Website

CELSIUS HOLDINGS, INC.
2424 N Federal Hwy Ste 208
Boca Raton, FL 33431
Tel.: (561) 276-2239
Fax: (561) 276-2268
Web Site: www.celsius.com
Approx. Rev.: $8,312,960
Approx. Number Employees: 31
Year Founded: 2005
Business Description:
Beverages Producer, Marketer & Distr
S.I.C.: 2037
N.A.I.C.S.: 311411
Advertising Expenditures: $10,600,000
Media: 9-16-18-19-22-23-25
Personnel:
Stephen C. Haley *(Chm & CEO)*
Geary W. Cotton *(CFO & Dir)*
Irina Lorenzi *(VP-Mktg & Innovation)*
Brands & Products:
CELSIUS

CENTRAL EUROPEAN DISTRIBUTION CORPORATION
3000 Atrium Way Ste 265
Mount Laurel, NJ 08054
Tel.: (856) 273-6980
E-mail: info@cedc.com.pl
Web Site: www.ced-c.com
Approx. Sls.: $1,573,702,000
Approx. Number Employees: 4,153
Year Founded: 1990
Business Description:
Alcoholic Beverages Distr
S.I.C.: 5181; 5182
N.A.I.C.S.: 424810; 424820
Advertising Expenditures: $106,800,000
Media: 5
Personnel:
William V. Carey *(Chm, Pres & CEO)*
Christopher Biedermann *(CFO)*
Evangelos Evangelou *(COO & VP)*
James Archbold *(Sec, VP & Dir-IR)*
Richard S. Roberts *(Dir)*

COASTAL EXTREME BREWING COMPANY
293 JT Connell Rd
Newport, RI 02840
Tel.: (401) 849-5232
E-mail: info@newportstorm.com
Web Site: www.newportstorm.com
Approx. Sls.: $2,000,000
Approx. Number Employees: 20
Year Founded: 1999
Business Description:
Beer Mfr
S.I.C.: 2082
N.A.I.C.S.: 312120
Advertising Expenditures: $2,000,000
Media: 13-14-15-18-19
Personnel:
Brent Ryan *(Pres)*
Brands & Products:
ALYSSA
BLIZZARD PORTER
BRENT
CHLOE
DEREK
ELLE
FRANK
GLORIA
HENRY
HURRICANE AMBER ALE
JAMES
MAELSTROM IPA
NEWPORT STORM
REGENSCHAUER OKTOBERFEST
THUNDERHEAD IRISH RED

COCA-COLA BOTTLING CO. CONSOLIDATED
4100 Coca Cola Plz
Charlotte, NC 28211-3481
Tel.: (704) 557-4400
Fax: (704) 551-4646
Web Site: www.cokebottling.com
Approx. Sls.: $1,514,599,000
Approx. Number Employees: 5,200
Year Founded: 1902
Business Description:
Soft Drink Bottling, Canning & Marketing Services
S.I.C.: 2086
N.A.I.C.S.: 312111
Media: 2-3-4-6-7-8-9-13-14-15-16-18-23-24-25
Personnel:
J. Frank Harrison, III *(Chm & CEO)*
Henry W. Flint *(Vice Chm)*
William B. Elmore *(Pres & COO)*
James E. Harris *(CFO & Sr VP)*
William J. Billiard *(Chief Acctg Officer, VP & Controller)*
Melvin F. Landis *(Chief Retail Sales Officer)*
Norman C. George *(Pres-ByB Brands)*
Steven D. Westphal *(Exec VP-Ops & Sys)*
Robert G. Chambless *(Sr VP-Sls & Mktg)*
Umesh M. Kasbekar *(Sr VP-Plng & Admin)*
Advertising Agency:
1HQ Limited
The Old Brewery 22 Russell St
Windsor, Berkshire SL4 1HQ, United Kingdom
Tel.: (44) 1753 856400
Fax: (44) 1753 857971

THE COCA-COLA BOTTLING CO. OF NEW YORK, INC.
(Sub. of Coca-Cola Refreshments USA, Inc.)
3 Skyline Dr
Hawthorne, NY 10532-2174
Mailing Address:
PO Box 1230
Elmsford, NY 10523-0930
Tel.: (914) 345-3900
Fax: (914) 789-1153
Sales Range: $75-99.9 Million
Approx. Number Employees: 200
Year Founded: 1904
Business Description:
Soft Drinks Distr & Bottler
S.I.C.: 2086
N.A.I.C.S.: 312111
Media: 2-5-6-9-24-25
Distr.: Natl.
Budget Set: Sept.-Oct.

THE COCA-COLA COMPANY
1 Coca Cola Plaza
Atlanta, GA 30313-2420
Mailing Address:
PO Box 1734
Atlanta, GA 30301-1734
Tel.: (404) 676-2121
Fax: (404) 676-6792
Toll Free: (800) 468-7856
E-mail: pressinquiries@na.ko.com
Web Site: www.thecoca-colacompany.com
Approx. Rev.: $35,119,000,000
Approx. Number Employees: 139,600
Year Founded: 1896
Business Description:
Soft Drinks, Noncarbonated Beverage Concentrates & Syrups, Waters, Juices & Juice Drinks, Teas, Coffees, Energy & Sports Drinks Producer, Marketer & Distr
S.I.C.: 2086; 2087
N.A.I.C.S.: 312111; 311930
Import Export
Advertising Expenditures: $2,791,000,000
Media: 3-5-6-9-11-13-14-15-16-17-18-19-20-22-23-24
Distr.: Natl.
Budget Set: June
Personnel:
Muhtar Kent *(Chm & CEO)*
Gary P. Fayard *(CFO & Exec VP)*
Edmund R. Steinike *(CIO & VP)*
Jean-Michel R. Ares *(CIO)*
Joseph V. Tripodi *(CMO, Chief Comml Officer & Exec VP)*
Alexander Benedict Cummings, Jr. *(Chief Admin Officer & Exec VP)*
Guy Wollaert *(CTO & Sr VP)*
John M. Farrell *(Chief Strategy Officer & VP)*
Robert P. Leechman *(Chief Comml Officer & VP, Chief Customer Officer)*
Rhona Applebaum *(Chief Scientific & Regulatory Officer)*
Ceree Eberly *(Chief People Officer & Sr VP)*
Jose Octavio Reyes Lagunes *(Pres/COO-Latin America Grp)*
Irial Finan *(Pres-Bottling Investments & Exec VP)*
Ahmet C. Bozer *(Pres-Eurasia & Africa Group)*
J. Alexander M. Douglas, Jr. *(Pres-North America)*
Glenn G. Jordan *(Pres-Pacific Grp)*
Atul Singh *(Pres-India & South West Asia Bus Unit)*
Kelvin Balogun *(CEO-Coca-Cola Nigeria Limited)*
Geoffrey J. Kelly *(Gen Counsel & Sr VP)*
Penny McIntyre *(Sr VP-General Mgr-Water, Tea, Coffee)*
Harry L. Anderson *(Sr VP-Global Bus & Technical Svcs)*
Wendy Clark *(Sr VP-Integrated Mktg Comm & Capabilities)*
Shay Drohan *(Sr VP-Sparkling Beverages)*
Ingrid Saunders Jones *(Sr VP-Global Community Connections)*
Matt Kahn *(Sr VP-Mktg-Glaceau)*
Clyde C. Tuggle *(Sr VP-Global Pub Affairs & Comm)*
Jerry S. Wilson *(Chief Customer & Comml Officer & Sr VP)*
Scott K. McCune *(VP-Media, Sports & Entertainment Mktg-Worldwide)*
Andrew McMillin *(VP-Mktg)*
Scott Vitters *(Gen Mgr-PlantBottle Packaging Platform)*
Karen Wong *(Reg Dir-Global Platforms-Pacific Grp)*
Rafael Acevedo *(Brand Dir-Sprite-Global)*
Cristina Bondolowski *(Brand Dir)*
Augusto Elias *(Brand Dir-Sprite)*
Yemisi Emiola *(Global Brand Dir-Diet Coke/Coca-Cola Light)*
Shane Grant *(Brand Dir-Global)*
Sarah Armstrong *(Dir-Worldwide Agency Ops)*
Linda Cronin *(Dir-Media & Interactive Integrated Comm)*
Shelley De Villiers *(Dir-Mktg-Juice Drinks Platforms)*
Michael Donnelly *(Dir-Worldwide Interactive Mktg)*
Stephanie Eaddy *(Dir-Mktg Capabilities)*
John Egan *(Dir-Sports Mktg)*
Nick Felder *(Dir-Film/Music Production-Global/Corp Div)*
Bill Gray *(Dir-Global Brand Mgmt-Fanta)*
Angela D. Harrell *(Dir-Comm)*
Peggy Loos *(Dir-Media & Interactive Mktg)*
Ellen Lucey *(Dir-Sports Mktg)*
Warner Maney *(Dir-Creative)*
Katie Baillie Miller *(Dir-Mktg Assets Strategy & Activation Grp)*
Doug Rollins *(Dir)*
Jed Selkowitz *(Dir-Entertainment Mktg)*
Emmanuel Seuge *(Dir-Worldwide Sports & Entertaiment Mktg)*
Judith Snyder *(Dir-Global Mktg Comm)*
Kevin Tressler *(Dir-Global Comml Capability)*
Chip York *(Dir)*
Jose Serafin *(Sr Brand Mgr-Hydration & Energy-Hispanic Market)*
Stephanie Adams *(Sr Mgr-Media & Interactive)*
Ryan Anderson *(Sr Mgr-Interactive Mktg)*
Keith Berman *(Sr Mgr-Mktg)*
Rand Carpenter *(Sr Mgr-The Coca-Cola Company)*
Karen Lee *(Sr Mgr-Media)*
Roberto Mastrocola *(Sr Mgr-Media & Interactive)*
Anita Rajendra *(Sr Mgr-Interactive Mktg)*
A.J. Brustein *(Brand Mgr-Coca Cola-Global)*
Miguel Nigrinis *(Sr Brand Mgr-Hispanic Mktg)*
Bobby Oliver *(Brand Mgr-Sprite)*
Tutul Rahman *(Brand Mgr-NOS Energy Drink)*
Christy Amador *(Mgr-Global Digital Mktg)*
Tom Daly *(Mgr-Global Interactive Mktg & Strategy & Plng)*
Tim Goudie *(Grp Mgr-Interactive Mktg)*
Jackie Hroch *(Mgr-Brand Activation-Minute Maid)*
Jason Hsu *(Mgr-Mktg Procurement-Media Agency Svcs)*

Key to Media (For complete agency information see *The Advertising Red Books-Agencies* edition):
1. Bus. Publs. 2. Cable T.V. 3. Catalogs & Directories. 4. Co-op Adv. 5. Consumer Mags. 6. D.M. to Bus. Estab.7. D.M. to Consumers
8. Daily Newsp. 9. Exhibits/Trade Shows 10. Foreign 11. Infomercial 12. Internet Adv.13. Multimedia 14. Network Radio
15. Network T.V. 16. Newsp. Distr. Mags. 17: Other 18. Outdoor (Posters, Transit) 19. Point of Purchase20. Premiums, Novelties
21. Product Samples 22. Special Events Mktg. 23. Spot Radio 24. Spot T.V. 25. Weekly Newsp. 26. Yellow Page Adv.

Jen Miller *(Mgr-Social Media Mktg)*
Brian Rudolph *(Mgr-Capabilities, Comm & Connections-Global)*
Jacquie Wansley *(Mgr-Mktg-World of Coca-Cola)*
Sharon Waters *(Mgr-Comm)*

Brands & Products:
A&W
ACUEDUCTO
ADES
ALI
ALIVE
AMBASA
AMEYAL
AMORINO
ANDINA
ANDINA FORTIFIED
ANDINA FRESH
ANDINA FRUT
ANDINA FRUT LIGHT
ANDINA LIGHT
ANDINA NECTAR
ANDINA NECTAR LIGHT
APOLLINARIS
AQUA
AQUABONA
AQUACTIVEDE AQUARIUS
AQUANA
AQUARIUS
AQUARIUS ACTIVE DIET
AQUARIUS FREESTYLE
ARWA
AYATAKA
AYBAL-KIN
BAJORU GIRA
BANKIA
BARQ'S
BEAT
BEAUTIA
BEVERLY
BIBO
BIG CRUSH
BIG TAI
BIMBO
BIMBO BREAK
BINGOOO
BISTRA
BISTRONE
BJARE
BLACK CHERRY VANILLA COKE
BLACKFIRE
BOCO
BOGADERA
BOM BIT MAESIL
BONAQUA
BPM
BRAZZI
BRIGHT & EARLY
BU
BUBBLY
BURN
BUZZ
CAFE ZU
CAFFEINE-FREE BARQ'S
CAFFEINE-FREE COCA-COLA
CAFFEINE-FREE COCA-COLA LIGHT
CAFFEINE-FREE DIET COKE
CALYPSO
CAPPY
CAPRICE
CARIOCA
CARVER'S
CEPITA
CHAQWA
CHARRUA
CHAUDFONTAINE
CHEERS
CHERRY COKE
CHERRY COKE ZERO
CHINOTTO
CIEL
CITRA
COCA COLA
COCA-COLA
COCA-COLA BLACK CHERRY VANILLA
COCA-COLA BLAK
COCA-COLA C2
COCA-COLA CITRA
COCA-COLA CLASSIC
COCA-COLA LIGHT
COCA-COLA LIGHT CITRA
COCA-COLA LIGHT WITH LEMON
COCA-COLA LIGHT WITH LIME
COCA-COLA WITH LEMON
COCA-COLA WITH LIME
COCA-COLA WITH RASPBERRY
COCA-COLA ZERO
COCOTEEN
COKE II
COKE ZERO
COUNTRY CLUB
CRESTA
CRISTAL
CRUSH
CRYSTAL
DAIZU NO SUSUME
DAMLA
DANNON
DASANI
DASANI ACTIVE
DASANI BALANCE
DASANI FLAVORS
DASANI NUTRIWATER
DASANI PLUS
DEL VALLE
DELAWARE PUNCH
DIET A&W
DIET ANDINA FRUT
DIET ANDINA NECTAR
DIET BARQ'S
DIET CANADA DRY
DIET CHERRY COKE
DIET COKE
DIET COKE BLACK CHERRY VANILLA
DIET COKE CITRA
DIET COKE PLUS
DIET COKE SWEETENED WITH SPLENDA
DIET COKE WITH LEMON
DIET COKE WITH LIME
DIET COKE WITH RASPBERRY
DIET CRUSH
DIET DR PEPPER
DIET FANTA
DIET FRESKYTA
DIET INCA KOLA
DIET KIA ORA
DIET KREST
DIET LIFT
DIET LILT
DIET MASTER POUR
DIET MELLO YELLO
DIET MR. PIBB
DIET NESTEA
DIET NORTHERN NECK
DIET OASIS
DIET QUATRO
DIET SCHWEPPES
DIET SPRITE
DIET SPRITE ZERO
DIET SQUIRT
DIET TAI
DIET VANILLA COKE
DIVA
DOBRIY
DOGADAN
DORNA
DR PEPPER
DR PEPPER ZERO
E2
EARTH & SKY
EIGHT O'CLOCK
EIGHT O'CLOCK FUNCHUM
EL RAYEK
ENVIGA
ESCUIS
EVA WATER
FANTA
FANTA FREE
FANTA LIGHT
FANTA VERDIA
FANTA ZERO
FAR COAST
FINLEY
FIORAVANTI
FIRE
FIVE ALIVE
FLAVOR RAGE
FONTANA
FRESCA
FRESCA 1
FRESCOLITA
FRESKYTA
FRESQUINHA
FRESS
FRISCO
FRUGOS
FRUGOS FRESH
FRUIT SOLUTIONS
FRUITIA
FRUITOPIA
FRUKTIME
FRUTINA
FRUTONIC
FULL THROTTLE
FULL THROTTLE BLUE DEMON
FULL THROTTLE COFFEE
FULL THROTTLE SUGAR FREE
FURUSATO DAYORI
FUZE HEALTHY INFUSIONS
GEORGIA
GEORGIA CLUB
GEORGIA COFFEE
GEORGIA GOLD
GEORGIA GRANDE
GINI
GIRIOS GIRA
GLACEAU FRUITWATER
GLACEAU SMARTWATER
GLACEAU VITAMINENERGY
GLACEAU VITAMINWATER
GLADIATOR
GOLD PEAK
GOLD SPOT
GOLDEN CRUSH
GOULBURN VALLEY
GRAPETTE
GREAT TASTE HAS ITS BENEFITS
GROOVY
GUARANA KUAT LIGHT
GUARANA KUAT ZERO
HAJIME
HARU NO MINT SHUKAN
HAWAI
HEALTHWORKS
HEAVEN & EARTH
HEPPINGER
HERO
HI-C
HI SPOT
HIT
HORIZON
HOT POINT
HUANG
ICE DEW
ILLY CAFE
INCA KOLA
IPSEI
IZVORUL ALB
JAZ COLA
JERICHO
JET TONIC
JOLLY JUICE
JOY
JOYA
JUST JUICE
KAPO
KARADA MEGURI-CHA
KELOCO
KERI
KIA ORA
KILIMANJARO
KIN
KINLEY
KOCHAKADEN
KOLA INGLESA
KREST
KROPLA BESKIDU
KUAT
KUAT GUARANA
KUAT LIGHT
KULI
KYUN
LA JOLLA
LEAO GREEN TEA
LEAO GUARANA POWER
LEAO ICED TEA
LIFT
LIFT LIGHT
LIFT PLUS
LIFT PLUS LIGHT
LILT
LILT ZERO
LIMCA
LIMELITE
LIMONADE
LINNUSE
LION
LOVE BODY
MAAZA
MAD RIVER
MAGNOLIA
MALVERN
MANANTIAL
MANZANA MIA
MARE ROSSO
MAROCHA
MASTER CHILL
MASTER POUR
MATTE LEAO
MATUSOV PRAMEN
MAZOE
MELLO
MELLO YELLO
MER
MEZZO
MEZZO MIX
MIAMI
MIGORO-NOMIGORO
MINAQUA
MINUTE MAID
MINUTE MAID ACTIVE
MINUTE MAID ANTIOX
MINUTE MAID DELI
MINUTE MAID DUOFRUTAS

Key to Media (For complete agency information see *The Advertising Red Books-Agencies* edition):
1. Bus. Publs. 2. Cable T.V. 3. Catalogs & Directories. 4. Co-op Adv. 5. Consumer Mags. 6. D.M. to Bus. Estab.7. D.M. to Consumers 8. Daily Newsp. 9. Exhibits/Trade Shows 10. Foreign 11. Infomercial 12. Internet Adv.13. Multimedia 14. Network Radio 15. Network T.V. 16. Newsp. Distr. Mags. 17. Other 18. Outdoor (Posters, Transit) 19. Point of Purchase20. Premiums, Novelties 21. Product Samples 22. Special Events Mktg. 23. Spot Radio 24. Spot T.V. 25. Weekly Newsp. 26. Yellow Page Adv.

The Coca-Cola Company — (Continued)

MINUTE MAID FRUIT PLUS
MINUTE MAID HEART WISE
MINUTE MAID JUICES TO GO
MINUTE MAID JUST 10
MINUTE MAID LIGHT
MINUTE MAID MAIS
MINUTE MAID MULTI-VITAMIN
MINUTE MAID NUTRI+
MINUTE MAID PREMIUM
MINUTE MAID SOFT DRINK
MINUTE MAID SOJAPLUS
MINUTE MAID SPLASH
MIREILLE
MISSION
MONE
MONTEFIORE
MORI NO MIZUDAYORI
MORNING DELI
MOTHER
MR. PIBB
MULTIVITA
NADA
NAGOMI
NALU
NAMTHIP
NANAIRO ACHA
NATURAQUA
NECTARIN
NESTEA
NESTEA COOL
NEVADA
NEVERFAIL
NEXT
NICO
NORDIC MIST
NORTHEN NECK
NOS ENTENDEMOS
ODWALLA
OLIMPIJA
ONSIDE
PAANI
PAMPA
PARLE
PEARONA
PEATS RIDGE
PIBB XTRA
PIBB ZERO
PIKO
PILSKANIA
PLAY ENGERY DRINK
POCKET DR
POIANA NEGRI
POLAR BREW
POMS
PONKANA
POP
PORTELLO
POWERADE
POWERADE ADVANCE
POWERADE ALIVE
POWERADE AQUA+
POWERADE BALANCE
POWERADE LIGHT
POWERADE OPTION
POWERADE ZERO
POWERPLAY
PRESTA
PRESTA LIGHT
PULP ORANGE
PUMP
PUMPED ENHANCED HYDRATION
QOO
QUATRO
QUATRO LIGHT
QUWAT JABAL
RAMBLIN'
REAL GOLD
RED FLASH
REHAB
RELENTLESS
RICH
RICHY
RIWA
ROSALTA
ROSES
ROYAL TRU
ROYAL TRU LIGHT
SAFETY FIRST
SAFIA
SAHTAIN
SAMANTHA
SAMURAI
SAN LUIS
SARSI
SARYUSAISAI
SCHWEPPES
SEAGRAMS
SELTZ
SENSATION
SENSUN GAZOZ
SENZAO
SHOCK
SIGNATURE
SIM
SIMBA
SIMPLY APPLE
SIMPLY GRAPEFRUIT
SIMPLY LEMONADE
SIMPLY LIMEADE
SIMPLY ORANGE
SMART
SOBO
SOKENBICHA
SOLO
SONFIL
SOONSOO
SOUTHERN SUN
SPARKLE
SPARKLETTS
SPARLETTA
SPARLETTA IRON BREW
SPLASH
SPLICE
SPORT
SPRING!
SPRITE
SPRITE 3G
SPRITE DUO
SPRITE ICE
SPRITE LIGHT
SPRITE REMIX
SPRITE ZERO
SPUR
SQUIRT
STONEY GINGER BEER
SU VOCE
SUCOS MAIS
SUNFILL
SURGE
SVALI
SWEECHA
SWERVE
TAB
TAB ENERGY
TAB X-TRA
TADAS
TAI
TAI LIGHT
TEN REN
THEXTONS
THUMS UP
TIAN TEY
TIAN YU DI
TIKY
TOKA
TOP
TOPPUR
TOP'S
TROPI
TROPICAL
TURKUAZ
URGE
URUN
VALPRE
VALSER
VALSER VIVA
VANILLA COKE
VANILLA COKE ZERO
VAULT
VAULT ZERO
VEGITABETA
VICA
VIO
VITA
VITAL
VITAL O
VITAMINWATER
VITAMINWATER ZERO
VITAMINWATER10
VITINGO
VIVA
THE WELLNESS FROM COCA-COLA
WILKINS
WINK
YANGGUANG
YANGGUANG JUICY T
YOUKI
ZERO

Advertising Agencies:

Anomaly Communications LLC
536 Broadway 11th Fl
New York, NY 10012
Tel.: (917) 595-2200
Fax: (917) 595-2299
Gold Peak

BBH New York
32 Avenue of the Americas 19th Fl
New York, NY 10013
Tel.: (212) 812-6600
Fax: (212) 242-4110
Sprite

Burson-Marsteller
(Part of Young & Rubicam Brands, a Sub. of WPP Group plc)
230 Park Ave S
New York, NY 10003-1566
Tel.: (212) 614-4000
Fax: (212) 598-5407

CP+B
3390 Mary St Ste 300
Coconut Grove, FL 33133
Tel.: (305) 859-2070
Fax: (305) 854-3419
Coke Zero

Creative Artists Agency
2000 Ave of the Stars
Los Angeles, CA 90067
Tel.: (424) 288-2000
Fax: (424) 288-2900

Definition 6
2115 Monroe Dr Ste 100
Atlanta, GA 30324
Tel.: (404) 870-0323
Fax: (404) 897-1258

Coca Cola Happiness Machine Campaign

Deutsch LA
5454 Beethoven St
Los Angeles, CA 90066-7017
Tel.: (310) 862-3000
Fax: (310) 862-3100

Doner
25900 Northwestern Hwy
Southfield, MI 48075
Tel.: (248) 354-9700
Fax: (248) 827-8440
(Holiday Advertising & Simply Orange Brand Juice)

Fallon Worldwide
901 Marquette Ave Ste 2400
Minneapolis, MN 55402
Tel.: (612) 758-2345
Fax: (612) 758-2346

French/West/Vaughan, Inc.
112 E Hargett St
Raleigh, NC 27601
Tel.: (919) 832-6300
Fax: (919) 832-6360
(Simply Orange)

Initiative Bangkok
195 Empire Tower 28/F South Sathorn Road
Bangkok, 10120, Thailand
Tel.: (66) 2 674 5900
Fax: (66) 2 674 5909
Fanta
Minute Maid
Sprite
Schweppes
Coke Classic
Coke Zero
Coke Light

Iris
Iris Towers 185 Park St
London, SE1 9DY, United Kingdom
Tel.: (44) 20 7654 7900
Fax: (44) 20 7654 7901

Isobar US
200 Clarendon St 23rd Fl
Boston, MA 02116
Tel.: (617) 449-4100
Fax: (617) 449-4200
Sprite

kirshenbaum bond senecal + partners
160 Varick St 4th Fl
New York, NY 10013
Tel.: (212) 633-0080
Fax: (212) 463-8643

Lapiz
35 W Wacker Dr 12th Fl
Chicago, IL 60601
Tel.: (312) 220-5000
Fax: (312) 220-6212

Lean Mean Fighting Machine Ltd.
4-8 Rodney St
London, N1 9JH, United Kingdom
Tel.: (44) 020 7278 5400

Leo Burnett Worldwide, Inc.
35 W Wacker Dr
Chicago, IL 60601-1723

Key to Media (For complete agency information see *The Advertising Red Books-Agencies* edition):
1. Bus. Publs. 2. Cable T.V. 3. Catalogs & Directories. 4. Co-op Adv. 5. Consumer Mags. 6. D.M. to Bus. Estab.7. D.M. to Consumers
8. Daily Newsp. 9. Exhibits/Trade Shows 10. Foreign 11. Infomercial 12. Internet Adv.13. Multimedia 14. Network Radio
15. Network T.V. 16. Newsp. Distr. Mags. 17. Other 18. Outdoor (Posters, Transit) 19. Point of Purchase20. Premiums, Novelties
21. Product Samples 22. Special Events Mktg. 23. Spot Radio 24. Spot T.V. 25. Weekly Newsp. 26. Yellow Page Adv.

Tel.: (312) 220-5959
Fax: (312) 220-3299
(Minute Maid, Fruitopia, Surge, Hi-C)

Linkstorm
34 W 22nd St 3rd fl
New York, NY 10010
Tel.: (646) 649-8799
Fax: (646) 649-8795

Madre Buenos Aires
Rodney 234
Buenos Aires, 1427, Argentina
Tel.: (54) 11 4857 4040
Powerade
Still Beverages (Hispanic Agency of Record)

McCann Erickson Worldwide
622 3rd Ave
New York, NY 10017-6707
Tel.: (646) 865-2000
Fax: (646) 487-9610
(Coke Classic, Cherry Coke)

McCann Worldgroup
622 3rd Ave
New York, NY 10017
Tel.: (646) 865-2000
Fax: (646) 487-9610
Asia/Pacific Creative
Coke Light
Coke Zero

Mother New York
595 11th Ave
New York, NY 10036
Tel.: (212) 254-2800
Fax: (212) 254-6121
Full Throttle
Powerade

Ogilvy & Mather
(Sub. of WPP Group plc)
636 11th Ave
New York, NY 10036
Tel.: (212) 237-4000
Fax: (212) 237-5123

Publicis-Mojopartners
Bond Store 3 30 Windmill St
Sydney, NSW 2000, Australia
Tel.: (61) 2 9258 9000
Fax: (61) 2 9258 9001
Diet Coke

Publicis USA
(Sub. of Publicis, S.A., Paris, France)
4 Herald Sq 950 6th Ave
New York, NY 10001
Tel.: (212) 279-5550
Fax: (212) 279-5560
Vault

Research Development & Promotions
(d/b/a RDP)
360 Menores Ave
Coral Gables, FL 33134
Tel.: (305) 445-4997
Fax: (305) 445-4221

Santo Buenos Aires
Darwin 1212
Buenos Aires, C 1414, Argentina
Tel.: (54) 114 777 7757

Sapient Corporation
131 Dartmouth St 3rd Fl
Boston, MA 02116
Tel.: (617) 621-0200
Fax: (617) 621-1300
Powerade

Studiocom
191 Peachtree St NE Ste 4025
Atlanta, GA 30303
Tel.: (404) 541-9555

Venables, Bell & Partners
201 Post St Ste 200
San Francisco, CA 94108
Tel.: (415) 288-3300
Fax: (415) 421-3683
Nestea

Wieden + Kennedy - Amsterdam
Herengracht 258
1015 CJ
Amsterdam, Netherlands
Tel.: (31) 20 712 6500
Fax: (31) 20 712 6699
Happiness Factory

Wieden + Kennedy, Inc.
224 NW 13th Ave
Portland, OR 97209-2953
Tel.: (503) 937-7000
Fax: (503) 937-8000
Diet Coke

COCA-COLA ENTERPRISES LAKESHORE DIVISION

(Sub. of Coca-Cola Refreshments USA, Inc.)
7400 N Oak Pk Ave
Niles, IL 60714-3818
Tel.: (847) 647-0200
Fax: (847) 647-7104
E-mail: info@coca-cola.com
Web Site: www.coca-cola.com
Sales Range: $750-799.9 Million
Approx. Number Employees: 3,000
Year Founded: 1986
Business Description:
Soft Drinks Bottling Company
S.I.C.: 2086; 5149
N.A.I.C.S.: 312111; 424490
Media: 19-22

COCA-COLA REFRESHMENTS USA, INC.

(Formerly Coca-Cola Enterprises Inc.)
(Div. of The Coca-Cola Company)
2500 Windy Ridge Pkwy
Atlanta, GA 30339-5677
Mailing Address:
PO Box 723040
Atlanta, GA 31139-0040
Tel.: (770) 989-3000
Fax: (770) 989-3788
E-mail: ccemail@cokecce.com
Web Site: www.cokecce.com
Approx. Rev.: $21,645,000,000
Approx. Number Employees: 70,000
Year Founded: 1986
Business Description:
Marketer, Bottler & Distr of Beverages
S.I.C.: 2086; 2087
N.A.I.C.S.: 312111; 311930
Advertising Expenditures: $2,475,000,000
Media: 3-5-14-15-18-19-20-21-22-23-24
Personnel:
Steve Cahillane *(Pres & CEO)*
Edward J. Lopez *(Chief Diversity Officer)*
Laura Brightwell *(Sr VP-Pub Affairs & Comms)*
Daniel J. Markle *(Sr VP-Comml & Franchise Ops)*
Mark W. Schortman *(Sr VP & Reg Gen Mgr)*
Terrance A. Fitch *(VP & GM-WBU)*
Julie Francis *(VP & Gen Mgr-Midwest Bus Unit)*
Suzanne N. Forlidas *(VP, Deputy Gen Counsel & Asst Sec)*
Terri L. Purcell *(VP, Deputy Gen Counsel & Asst Sec)*
Tom A. Barlow *(VP-Vending & Wholesale-North America)*
David M. Katz *(VP-Customer Supply Chain & Strategy)*
Debbie Moody *(VP-Pub Affairs & Comm)*
Kate Rumbaugh *(VP-Pub Affairs & Comm)*
Fred Roselli *(Head-Media Rels)*
Sarah Armstrong *(Dir-Worldwide Agency Ops)*
Martin J. Miller *(Mgr-EDI Implementations)*
Advertising Agencies:
BBH New York
32 Avenue of the Americas 19th Fl
New York, NY 10013
Tel.: (212) 812-6600
Fax: (212) 242-4110

Cresta Group
1050 N State St
Chicago, IL 60610
Tel.: (312) 944-4700
Fax: (312) 944-1582

Leo Burnett Worldwide, Inc.
35 W Wacker Dr
Chicago, IL 60601-1723
Tel.: (312) 220-5959
Fax: (312) 220-3299

Manning Selvage & Lee
1170 Peachtree St NE Ste 400
Atlanta, GA 30309-7677
Tel.: (404) 875-1444
Fax: (404) 892-1274
(Public Relations)

The Martin Agency
One Shockoe Plz
Richmond, VA 23219-4132
Tel.: (804) 698-8000
Fax: (804) 698-8001

COLUMBIA CREST WINERY

14111 NE 145th St
Woodinville, WA 98072
Tel.: (425) 488-1133
Fax: (425) 415-3657
E-mail: media@columbia-crest.com
Web Site: www.columbia-crest.com
Business Description:
Wine Mfr
S.I.C.: 2084
N.A.I.C.S.: 312130
Media: 21-22
Personnel:
Brett Scallan *(Sr Mgr-Product)*
Advertising Agency:
GolinHarris
601 W 5th St 4th Fl
Los Angeles, CA 90071-2004
Tel.: (213) 623-4200
Fax: (213) 895-4746

COORS BREWING COMPANY

(Joint Venture of Molson Coors Brewing Company & SABMiller plc)
12th St & Ford St
Golden, CO 80401-1295
Mailing Address:
PO Box 4030
Golden, CO 80401
Tel.: (303) 279-6565
Tel.: (303) 277-2555 (Media)
Fax: (303) 277-5415
Toll Free: (800) 642-6116
E-mail: mediainquiries@coors.com
Web Site: www.coors.com
Approx. Rev.: $2,700,000,000
Approx. Number Employees: 3,800
Year Founded: 1873
Business Description:
Brewery
S.I.C.: 2082
N.A.I.C.S.: 312120
Media: 1-6-10-11-15-18-19-22-23
Personnel:
Mauricio Cardenas *(Chief Officer-Latin America & US Multi-Cultural)*
Ed McBrien *(Chief Revenue Officer)*
Stevie Benjamin *(Dir-Media)*
Ken Hehir *(Dir-Mktg)*
Kimberly Courtney *(Mgr-Mktg Ops)*
Advertising Agencies:
Bromley Communications
401 E Houston St
San Antonio, TX 78205-2615
Tel.: (210) 244-2000
Fax: (210) 244-2442

Carol H. Williams Advertising
875 N Michigan Ave Ste 2750
Chicago, IL 60611
Tel.: (312) 836-7900
Fax: (312) 836-7919

CarryOn
5670 Wilshire Blvd
Los Angeles, CA 90036
Tel.: (323) 848-4300
Fax: (323) 848-4310
Toll Free: (888) 838-NEWS

TAXI New York
455 Broadway 3rd Fl
New York, NY 10013
Tel.: (212) 414-8294
Fax: (212) 414-8444

COUNTRY PURE FOODS, INC.

681 W Waterloo Rd
Akron, OH 44314-1587
Tel.: (330) 753-2293
Fax: (330) 745-7838
Toll Free: (877) 99JUICE
Web Site: www.juice4u.com
Sales Range: $100-124.9 Million
Approx. Number Employees: 200
Year Founded: 1995
Business Description:
Mfr. of Fruit Drinks
S.I.C.: 2033; 2037
N.A.I.C.S.: 311421; 311411
Import Export
Advertising Expenditures: $1,000,000
Media: 2-4-13-14-15-16-17
Personnel:
Raymond K. Lee *(CEO)*

Country Pure Foods, Inc. — (Continued)

Rick Conrad *(VP-Sls)*
Paul Ponsot *(Dir-Accts-Natl)*
Jay Kucyk *(Sls Mgr)*
Brands & Products:
ARDMORE FARMS
GLACIER VALLEY
K-PAK
NATURAL COUNTRY

CRAFT BREWERS ALLIANCE, INC

929 N Russell St
Portland, OR 97227
Tel.: (503) 331-7270
Fax: (503) 331-7264
E-mail: investor.relations@craftbrewers.com
Web Site: www.redhook.com
Approx. Sls.: $140,852,000
Approx. Number Employees: 600
Year Founded: 1981
Business Description:
Beer Brewer
S.I.C.: 2082
N.A.I.C.S.: 312120
Advertising Expenditures: $9,500,000
Media: 2-4-5-6-7-8-9-13-14-15-18-19-20-22-23-24-25-26
Personnel:
Kurt R. Widmer *(Chm)*
Terry E. Michaelson *(CEO)*
Mark D. Moreland *(CFO)*
Danial Ketcher *(VP-Mktg)*
V. Sebastian Pastore *(VP-Brewing Ops & Tech)*
Martin J. Wall, IV *(VP-Sls)*
Robert Rentsch *(Brand Mgr)*
Jennifer Talley *(Mgr-Brewing)*
Brands & Products:
BLACKHOOK PORTER
BROKEN HALO IPA
COPPERHOOK
DROP TOP AMBER ALE
INDIA PALE ALE
LATE HARVEST
LONG HAMMER IPA
REDHOOK BLONDE ALE
REDHOOK ESB
REDHOOK NUT BROWN ALE
SLIM CHANCE
SUNRYE ALE
WIDMER HEFEWEIZEN
WINTERHOOK
Advertising Agencies:
McCann Erickson Seattle
1741 1st Ave S
Seattle, WA 98134
Tel.: (206) 971-4200
Fax: (206) 971-4299

TM Advertising
1717 Main St Ste 2000
Dallas, TX 75201
Tel.: (972) 556-1100
Fax: (972) 830-2619
Long Hammer IPA
Liquid Goodness Campaign
Print
Online
Out-of-Home
Point of Purchase

CROWN IMPORTS LLC

(Joint Venture of Constellation Brands, Inc.)
1 S Dearborn St Ste 1700
Chicago, IL 60603
Tel.: (312) 873-9600
Fax: (312) 873-9630
E-mail: info@crownimportsllc.com
Web Site: www.crownimportsllc.com
Sales Range: $350-399.9 Million
Approx. Number Employees: 500
Year Founded: 2007
Business Description:
Beer Importer
S.I.C.: 5181
N.A.I.C.S.: 424810
Personnel:
William Hackett *(Pres)*
Jim Sabia *(CMO & Exec VP)*
John Nichols *(Brand Mgr-St Pauli Girl)*
Steve Nichols *(Brand Mgr-Pacifico)*
Tom Willett *(Mgr-Mktg)*
Advertising Agencies:
Cramer-Krasselt
225 N Michigan Ave
Chicago, IL 60601-7601
Tel.: (312) 616-9600
Fax: (312) 616-3839
Corona Extra (Agency of Record)

Goodby, Silverstein & Partners, Inc.
(Part of Omnicom Group, Inc.)
720 California St
San Francisco, CA 94108-2404
Tel.: (415) 392-0669
Fax: (415) 788-4303
Corona Light
Creative
Modelo Especial

GSD&M
828 W 6th St
Austin, TX 78703-5420
Tel.: (512) 242-4736
Fax: (512) 242-4700
Creative
General Market Consumer Positioning
Pacifico
Victoria

Horizon Media, Inc.
75 Varick St
New York, NY 10013
Tel.: (212) 220-5000
Toll Free: (800) 633-4201

La Comunidad
6400 Biscayne Blvd
Miami, FL 33138
Tel.: (305) 993-5700
Tel.: (305) 865-9600
Fax: (305) 865-9609
Hispanic

CRYSTAL GEYSER WATER COMPANY

(Sub. of Otsuka Pharmaceutical Co., Ltd.)
501 Washington St
Calistoga, CA 94515-1425
Mailing Address:
PO Box 304
Calistoga, CA 94515-0304
Tel.: (707) 942-0500
Tel.: (415) 616-9590 (marketing)
Fax: (707) 942-0647
E-mail: webmaster@crystalgeyser.com
Web Site: www.crystalgeyserr.com
Approx. Number Employees: 125
Year Founded: 1977
Business Description:
Soft Drinks Mfr
S.I.C.: 2086
N.A.I.C.S.: 312112
Export
Media: 4-6-9-14-17-18-19-20-22-23-25
Distr.: Natl.
Personnel:
Peter Gordon *(Pres)*
Shawn Fitzpatrick *(Brand Mgr & Mgr-Special Projects)*
Brands & Products:
CRYSTAL GEYSER
JUICE SQUEEZE
TEJAVA
THE ULTIMATE REFRESHER

CRYSTAL ROCK HOLDINGS, INC.

(Formerly Vermont Pure Holdings, Ltd.)
1050 Buckingham St
Watertown, CT 06795
Tel.: (860) 945-0661
Fax: (203) 728-4614
Toll Free: (800) 525-0070
Web Site: www.crystalrock.com
Approx. Sls.: $67,780,639
Approx. Number Employees: 330
Year Founded: 1990
Business Description:
Bottled Water, Coffee, Ancillary Products & Other Office Refreshment Products Marketer & Distr
S.I.C.: 5149; 2086; 5141; 5499
N.A.I.C.S.: 424490; 312112; 424410; 445299
Advertising Expenditures: $1,449,902
Media: 5-10-13-14-15-18-21-22-26
Personnel:
Ross S. Rapaport *(Chm)*
Peter K. Baker *(Pres & CEO)*
Bruce S. MacDonald *(CFO & VP)*
John B. Baker *(Exec VP)*
Brands & Products:
CRYSTAL ROCK
VERMONT PURE
WHAT EVERYBODY NEEDS

DESCHUTES BREWERY INC.

901 Southwest Simpson Ave
Bend, OR 97702
Tel.: (541) 385-8606
Fax: (541) 383-4505
Toll Free: (888) 892-2337
E-mail: info@deschutesbrewery.com
Web Site: www.deschutesbrewery.com
Sales Range: $10-24.9 Million
Approx. Number Employees: 150
Business Description:
Producer of Alcoholic Beverages
S.I.C.: 2082; 5812
N.A.I.C.S.: 312120; 722110
Personnel:
Gary D. Fish *(Founder & Pres)*
Michael Lalonde *(COO & CFO)*
Brands & Products:
BACHELOR
BLACK BUTTE
BOND STREET BROWN
CASCADE
DESCHUTES BEER
MIRROR POND
OBSIDIAN
PUB WEAR
QUAIL SPRINGS
Advertising Agency:
North
1515 NW 19th Ave
Portland, OR 97209
Tel.: (503) 222-4117
Fax: (503) 222-4118

DIAGEO NORTH AMERICA INC.

(Div. of Diageo North America, Inc.)
530 5th Ave
New York, NY 10036
Tel.: (646) 223-2000
Fax: (646) 223-2001
E-mail: aisa.aiyer@diageo.com
Web Site: www.diageo.com
Business Description:
Spirits & Wines Producer, Importer & Marketer
S.I.C.: 5181
N.A.I.C.S.: 424810
Media: 6-18-19-20-21-22
Personnel:
Rob Warren *(Sr VP-Global Tequilas)*
Simon Burch *(Global Brand Dir-Smirnoff)*
Adam Rosen *(Brand Dir-Scotch Whisky)*
Aisa Ayer *(Assoc Brand Mgr)*
Advertising Agencies:
BBDO New York
1285 Ave of the Americas 7th Fl
New York, NY 10019-6028
Tel.: (212) 459-5000

BBH New York
32 Avenue of the Americas 19th Fl
New York, NY 10013
Tel.: (212) 812-6600
Fax: (212) 242-4110
Johnnie Walker

J. Walter Thompson Company
(d/b/a JWT)
466 Lexington Ave
New York, NY 10017-3140
Tel.: (212) 210-7000
Fax: (212) 210-7299
Smirnoff

Mother New York
595 11th Ave
New York, NY 10036
Tel.: (212) 254-2800
Fax: (212) 254-6121
Tanqueray Gin

Ogilvy & Mather Advertising
636 11th Ave
New York, NY 10036
Tel.: (212) 237-4000
Fax: (212) 237-5123

Saatchi & Saatchi
(Sub. of Publicis Groupe S.A.)
(Worldwide Headquarters)
375 Hudson St
New York, NY 10014-3660
Tel.: (212) 463-2000
Fax: (212) 463-9856

Wunderman
(Worldwide Headquarters)
285 Madison Ave
New York, NY 10017
Tel.: (212) 941-3000
Fax: (212) 210-5454

Key to Media (For complete agency information see *The Advertising Red Books-Agencies* edition):
1. Bus. Publs. 2. Cable T.V. 3. Catalogs & Directories. 4. Co-op Adv. 5. Consumer Mags. 6. D.M. to Bus. Estab.7. D.M. to Consumers 8. Daily Newsp. 9. Exhibits/Trade Shows 10. Foreign 11. Infomercial 12. Internet Adv.13. Multimedia 14. Network Radio 15. Network T.V. 16. Newsp. Distr. Mags. 17. Other 18. Outdoor (Posters, Transit) 19. Point of Purchase20. Premiums, Novelties 21. Product Samples 22. Special Events Mktg. 23. Spot Radio 24. Spot T.V. 25. Weekly Newsp. 26. Yellow Page Adv.

Whisky

DOUBLE-COLA CO.-USA
537 Market St Ste 100
Chattanooga, TN 37402-1229
Tel.: (423) 267-5691
Fax: (423) 267-0793
E-mail: info@double-cola.com
Web Site: www.double-cola.com
Approx. Number Employees: 20
Year Founded: 1927
Business Description:
Soft Drinks Mfr
S.I.C.: 2087
N.A.I.C.S.: 311930
Import Export
Media: 6-9-10-21-23
Distr.: Intl.; Natl.
Budget Set: Oct.
Personnel:
Noorally K. Dhanani *(Chm)*
Alnoor Dhanani *(Pres)*
Brands & Products:
CAFFEINE FREE SKI
CHASER
CHERRY SKI
DIET CHASER
DIET DOUBLE-COLA
DIET SKI
DOUBLE-COLA
DOUBLE-DRY
JUMBO
SKI

DR PEPPER SNAPPLE GROUP, INC.
5301 Legacy Dr
Plano, TX 75024
Tel.: (972) 673-7000
Fax: (972) 673-7980
Web Site:
www.drpeppersnapplegroup.com
Approx. Sls.: $5,636,000,000
Approx. Number Employees: 19,000
Year Founded: 2003
Business Description:
Carbonated & Non-Carbonated Soft Drink Bottler, Mfr & Distr
S.I.C.: 2086
N.A.I.C.S.: 312111
Advertising Expenditures:
$409,000,000
Personnel:
Wayne R. Sanders *(Chm)*
Larry D. Young *(Pres & CEO)*
Martin M. Ellen *(CFO)*
Tom Farrah *(CIO)*
Rodger L. Collins *(Pres-Packaged Beverages)*
James J. Johnston, Jr. *(Pres-Concentrate Sls)*
James L. Baldwin, Jr. *(Gen Counsel & Exec VP)*
Tina S. Barry *(Exec VP-Corp Affairs)*
Derry L. Hobson *(Exec VP-Supply Chain)*
Lawrence N. Solomon *(Exec VP-HR)*
David J. Thomas *(Exec VP-R&D)*
James R. Trebilcock *(Exec VP-Mktg)*
Aly Noormohamed *(Sr VP & Gen Mgr-Warehouse Direct Bus Unit)*
Lauren Radcliffe *(Dir-Brand)*
Olivia Vela *(Dir-Multicultural Mktg)*
Derek Dabrowski *(Brand Mgr)*
Mike Bueno *(Mgr-Bacon Innovation)*
Whitney Kempf *(Assoc Mgr-Interactive Media)*
Richard Lyons *(Mgr-Interactive Mktg)*
Brands & Products:
7UP
A&W
AQUAFIEL
CANADA DRY
CLAMATO
CRUSH
DEJA BLUE
DR PEPPER
HAWAIIAN PUNCH
MISTIC
MOTT'S
MR & MRS T
NANTUCKET NECTARS
PENAFIEL
RC
REALEMON
SCHWEPPES
SNAPPLE
SQUIRT
VENOM
VIDA23
Advertising Agencies:
Circle One
10 Norden Pl
Norwalk, CT 06854
Tel.: (203) 286-0550
Fax: (203) 286-0555

Deutsch LA
5454 Beethoven St
Los Angeles, CA 90066-7017
Tel.: (310) 862-3000
Fax: (310) 862-3100
(Diet Dr. Pepper, Fountain Classics, Snapple)
— Frank Dattalo *(Sr VP & Grp Dir-Creative)*

Initiative Worldwide
(Part of The Interpublic Group of Companies, Inc.)
1 Dag Hammerskjold Plz 5th Fl
New York, NY 10017
Tel.: (212) 605-7000
Fax: (212) 605-7200
Americas Beverages

Lopez Negrete Communications, Inc.
3336 Richmond Ave Ste 200
Houston, TX 77098
Tel.: (713) 877-8777
Fax: (713) 877-8796
(Dr. Pepper, 7-UP, Sunkist, Squirt)

McGarry Bowen, LLC
601 W 26th St Ste 1150
New York, NY 10001
Tel.: (212) 598-2900
Fax: (212) 598-2996
A&W
Canada Dry
Creative Assignment
Sunkist

VML, Inc.
250 Richards Rd
Kansas City, MO 64116-4279
Tel.: (816) 283-0700
Fax: (816) 283-0954
Toll Free: (800) 990-2468

Young & Rubicam Brands, Southern California
2010 Main St Ste 800
Irvine, CA 92614
Tel.: (949) 754-2000
Fax: (949) 754-2001
Accelerade

DS WATERS OF AMERICA, INC.
(Holding of Kelso & Company, L.P.)
5660 New Northside Dr Ste 500
Atlanta, GA 30328-5826
Tel.: (770) 933-1400
Fax: (770) 956-9495
Toll Free: (866) 669-3402
Web Site: www.water.com
Year Founded: 2003
Business Description:
Produces & Markets Bottled Water & Sports Drinks
S.I.C.: 2086
N.A.I.C.S.: 312112
Advertising Expenditures:
$10,000,000
Bus. Publs.: $1,000,000; Catalogs & Directories: $1,000,000; Consumer Mags.: $1,000,000; D.M. to Bus. Estab.: $1,000,000; D.M. to Consumers: $1,000,000; Daily Newsp.: $1,000,000; Exhibits/Trade Shows: $1,000,000; Other: $1,000,000; Point of Purchase: $1,000,000; Premiums, Novelties: $1,000,000
Distr.: Natl.
Personnel:
K. Dillon Schickli *(CEO)*
Tom Harrington *(COO)*
Bob Bramski *(CIO)*
Gilbert Gibson *(Pres-Div)*
Gary Dumas *(VP & Gen Mgr-North East Reg)*
Jim Lewandowski *(VP & Gen Mgr)*
Jeff Thompson *(VP & Gen Mgr)*
Joseph Silva *(Dir-Mktg)*

EIGHT O'CLOCK COFFEE
(Sub. of Tata Coffee)
155 Chestnut Rdg
Montvale, NJ 07645
Tel.: (201) 571-0300
Fax: (201) 571-0331
Web Site: www.eightoclock.com
Sales Range: $25-49.9 Million
Approx. Number Employees: 200
Year Founded: 1859
Business Description:
Coffee Mfr
S.I.C.: 2095
N.A.I.C.S.: 311920
Personnel:
Barbara Roth *(Pres)*
David Allen *(VP-Mktg)*
Alisa Jacoby *(Brand Mgr)*
Brands & Products:
EIGHT O'CLOCK
Advertising Agencies:
Respond2 Cmedia
207 NW Park Ave
Portland, OR 97209
Tel.: (503) 222-0025
Fax: (503) 222-0049

S3
718 Main St
Boonton, NJ 07005
Tel.: (973) 257-5533
Fax: (973) 257-5543

EMPIRE DISTRIBUTORS, INC.
(Sub. of McLane Company, Inc.)
3755 Atlanta Indus Pkwy
Atlanta, GA 30331
Tel.: (404) 572-4100
Fax: (404) 346-4609
Toll Free: (800) 282-9395
E-mail: webmaster@empiredist.com
Web Site: www.empiredist.org
Approx. Number Employees: 300
Year Founded: 1940
Business Description:
Wholesale Distr of Wine, Spirits, Beer, & Bar Beverages
S.I.C.: 5182
N.A.I.C.S.: 424820
Media: 2-10-13-22
Personnel:
David Kahn *(Pres)*
Jim Schwarvkofs *(CFO)*

FADO PUBS INC.
2964 Peachtree Rd Ste 600
Atlanta, GA 30305
Tel.: (404) 848-8433
Fax: (404) 848-9984
Web Site: www.fadoirishpub.com
Approx. Number Employees: 8
Year Founded: 1996
Business Description:
Resturant & Bar
S.I.C.: 5813; 5812
N.A.I.C.S.: 722410; 722110
Personnel:
Kieran McGill *(Pres & CEO)*
John Piccirillo *(Dir-Mktg & Dev)*
Advertising Agency:
Breen Smith Advertising
255 Trinity Ave SW 2nd Fl
Atlanta, GA 30303
Tel.: (404) 352-9507

FAYGO BEVERAGES, INC.
(Sub. of National Beverage Corp.)
3579 Gratiot Ave
Detroit, MI 48207-1829
Tel.: (313) 925-1600
Fax: (313) 571-7611
Toll Free: (800) 347-6591
Web Site: www.faygo.com
Sales Range: $150-199.9 Million
Approx. Number Employees: 400
Business Description:
Soft Drinks Mfr
S.I.C.: 2086
N.A.I.C.S.: 312111
Media: 5-9-18-19-20-21-23-24
Distr.: Reg.
Budget Set: Mar.
Personnel:
Al Chittaro *(Exec VP)*
Matt Rosenthal *(Dir-Mktg)*
Advertising Agency:
Rosenthal and Company Advertising
3579 Gratiot Ave.
Detroit, MI 49207
Tel.: (313) 925-1600
Fax: (313) 571-7611
(Soft Drinks)

FEROLITO, VULTAGGIO & SONS
60 Crossways Park Dr W
Woodbury, NY 11797
Tel.: (516) 812-0300
Fax: (516) 326-4988
Toll Free: (800) 832-3775
Web Site: www.drinkarizona.com
Approx. Number Employees: 200
Business Description:
Soft Drink Distr

Key to Media (For complete agency information see *The Advertising Red Books-Agencies* edition):
1. Bus. Publs. 2. Cable T.V. 3. Catalogs & Directories. 4. Co-op Adv. 5. Consumer Mags. 6. D.M. to Bus. Estab.7. D.M. to Consumers 8. Daily Newsp. 9. Exhibits/Trade Shows 10. Foreign 11. Infomercial 12. Internet Adv.13. Multimedia 14. Network Radio 15. Network T.V. 16. Newsp. Distr. Mags. 17. Other 18. Outdoor (Posters, Transit) 19. Point of Purchase20. Premiums, Novelties 21. Product Samples 22. Special Events Mktg. 23. Spot Radio 24. Spot T.V. 25. Weekly Newsp. 26. Yellow Page Adv.

Ferolito, Vultaggio & Sons — (Continued)

S.I.C.: 2082; 2086
N.A.I.C.S.: 312111; 312112; 312120
Media: 5-7-8-11-13-19
Brands & Products:
ARIZONA
BLUE LUNA
CAUTION ENERGY
CRAZY HORSE
KAHULA
MISSISSIPPI MUD
PALM BEACH
RX HERBAL

FIJI WATER LLC
(Sub. of Roll International Corporation)
11444 W Olympic Blvd Ste 210
Los Angeles, CA 90064
Tel.: (310) 312-2850
Fax: (310) 312-2828
Toll Free: (888) 426-3454
Web Site: www.fijiwater.com
Approx. Number Employees: 50
Year Founded: 1996
Business Description:
Supplier of Bottled Water
S.I.C.: 2086
N.A.I.C.S.: 312112
Media: 6
Personnel:
David Ricanati *(Pres)*
Jenna Robin *(Dir-Social Media Mktg)*
Brands & Products:
FIJI
THE TASTE OF PARADISE

FLYING DOG BREWERY
2401 Blake St
Denver, CO 80205
Tel.: (303) 292-5027
Fax: (303) 296-0164
Web Site: www.flyingdogales.com
Approx. Rev.: $1,900,000
Approx. Number Employees: 22
Year Founded: 1994
Business Description:
Brewery
S.I.C.: 2082
N.A.I.C.S.: 312120
Media: 13-22

FREDERICK P. WINNER, LTD.
7001 Quad Ave
Rosedale, MD 21237
Tel.: (410) 646-5500
Fax: (410) 646-4927
Web Site: www.indigowinegroup.com
Approx. Number Employees: 300
Year Founded: 1960
Business Description:
Beer, Wine & Spirits Distr
S.I.C.: 5181; 5182
N.A.I.C.S.: 424810; 424820
Import Export
Advertising Expenditures: $500,000
Media: 2-16
Personnel:
Mark M. Winner *(Pres & CEO)*
Ron Ward *(CFO)*

THE F.X. MATT BREWING CO.
811 Edward St
Utica, NY 13502-4001
Tel.: (315) 624-2400
Fax: (315) 624-2442
Toll Free: (800) 690-3181
E-mail: info@saranac.com
Web Site: www.saranac.com
Sales Range: $25-49.9 Million
Approx. Number Employees: 140
Year Founded: 1888
Business Description:
Brewer of Malt Beverages
S.I.C.: 2082
N.A.I.C.S.: 312120
Export
Advertising Expenditures: $1,000,000
Media: 2-6-7-9-10-11-13-18-19-20-23-25-26
Distr.: Reg.
Budget Set: Jan.
Personnel:
Alfred D. Matt *(VP-Mktg & Sls)*
Brands & Products:
12 BEERS A FALLING
12 BEERS OF SUMMER
ADIRONDACK BLACK FOREST
ADIRONDACK DIET ROOT
ADIRONDACK INDIA PALE ALE
ADIRONDACK LAGER
ADIRONDACK ROOT BEER
BLACK AND TAN
BROWN ALE
JED'S HARD PINK-LEMONADE
LAGER
ORANGE CREAM
POMEGRANATE WHEAT
SARANAC
SARANAC AMBER WHEAT
SARANAC BELGIAN WHITE
SARANAC BLACK & TAN
SARANAC CARMEL PORTER
SARANAC DIET ROOT BEER
SARANAC DUNKEL
SARANAC GINGER BEER
SARANAC HEFEWEIZEN
SARANAC MOCHA STOUT
SARANAC NUT BROWN ALE
SARANAC ORANGE CREAM
SARANAC ROOT BEER
SARANAC SCOTCH ALE
SARANAC SEASON'S BEST
SARANAC SINGLE MALT
SARANAC STOUT
SARANAC TRADITIONAL LAGER
SHIRLEY TEMPLE
UTICA CLUB LIGHT
Advertising Agency:
Trainor Associates Inc.
135 Oxford Rd.
New Hartford, NY 13413
Tel.: (315) 797-7970
Fax: (315) 797-7975

THE GATORADE COMPANY
(Sub. of PepsiCo Beverages Americas)
555 W Monroe St
Chicago, IL 60661-3605
Mailing Address:
PO Box 049003
Chicago, IL 60604-9003
Tel.: (312) 821-1000
Toll Free: (800) 884-2867
Web Site: www.gatorade.com
Sales Range: $550-599.9 Million
Approx. Number Employees: 1,210
Business Description:
Energy Drinks Mfr
S.I.C.: 2086
N.A.I.C.S.: 312112
Media: 1-11-13-14-15-18-21-22-23-24
Personnel:
Sarah Robb O'Hagan *(Pres & Global Chief Mktg Officer)*
Brands & Products:
GATORADE FROST
GATORADE ICE
GATORADE X-FACTOR
GATORADE XTREMO
RAIN
Advertising Agencies:
BBDO CentroAmerica
Edificio Via Lindora Santa Ana
San Jose, Costa Rica
Tel.: (506) 205 4000

BBDO Worldwide Inc.
(Sub. of Omnicom Group, Inc.)
1285 Ave of the Americas
New York, NY 10019-6028
Tel.: (212) 459-5000
Fax: (212) 459-6645

Fleishman-Hillard Inc.
John Hancock Ctr Ste 3300 875 N Michigan Ave
Chicago, IL 60611-1901
Tel.: (312) 751-8878
Fax: (312) 751-8191
G Series

Goodby, Silverstein & Partners, Inc.
(Part of Omnicom Group, Inc.)
720 California St
San Francisco, CA 94108-2404
Tel.: (415) 392-0669
Fax: (415) 788-4303
Propel

TBWA Chiat Day Los Angeles
5353 Grosvenor Blvd
Los Angeles, CA 90066
Tel.: (310) 305-5000
Fax: (310) 305-6000

TPN Inc.
9400 N Central Expwy Ste 1500
Dallas, TX 75231-5044
Tel.: (214) 692-1522
Fax: (214) 692-8316
— Daniel Warhaftig *(Acct Dir-Gatorade)*

Ziggurat Brands
8-14 Vine Hill
London, EC1R 5DX, United Kingdom
Tel.: (44) 20 7969 7777
Fax: (44) 20 7969 7788

THE GREAT WESTERN BREWING COMPANY
519 Second Ave N
Saskatoon, SK S7K 2C6, Canada
Tel.: (306) 653-4653
Fax: (306) 653-2166
E-mail: info@greatwesternbrewing.com
Web Site: www.greatwesternbrewing.com
Approx. Sls.: $40,000,000
Approx. Number Employees: 200
Year Founded: 1989
Business Description:
Brewery
S.I.C.: 2082
N.A.I.C.S.: 312120
Media: 14-15-22
Personnel:
Michael Micovcin *(CEO)*
Joanne Mortenson *(Dir-Mktg)*

GREEN MOUNTAIN BEVERAGE, LLC
153 Pond Ln
Middlebury, VT 05753
Tel.: (802) 388-0700
Fax: (802) 388-0600
E-mail: gmbinfo@gmbeverage.com
Web Site: www.gmbeverage.com
Approx. Number Employees: 35
Business Description:
Hard Cider Mfr & Distr
S.I.C.: 7999
N.A.I.C.S.: 532292
Media: 13-20-22
Personnel:
Walter A. Scott *(Chm & CEO)*
Brands & Products:
CIDER JACK
GREEN MOUNTAIN BEVERAGE
STRONGBOW
WOODCHUCK AMBER
WOODCHUCK DARK & DRY CIDER
WOODCHUCK DRAFT CIDER
WOODCHUCK PEAR CIDER
WOODPECKER CIDER
Advertising Agency:
Nail Communications
63 Eddy St
Providence, RI 02903
Tel.: (401) 331-6245
Fax: (401) 331-2987

GREEN SPOT, INC.
100 S Cambridge Ave
Claremont, CA 91711-4842
Tel.: (909) 625-8771
Fax: (909) 621-4634
Toll Free: (800) 456-3210
E-mail: info@greenspotusa.com
Web Site: www.greenspotusa.com
Approx. Sls.: $4,000,000
Approx. Number Employees: 15
Year Founded: 1934
Business Description:
Fruit Drink Concentrates & Flavors Mfr & Distr
S.I.C.: 5149
N.A.I.C.S.: 424490
Import Export
Advertising Expenditures: $80,000
Media: 2-4-10-11-21
Personnel:
Don Koury *(CFO)*
Terry Hughes *(VP-Sls)*
Brands & Products:
CENTURY
GREEN SPOT
GS-5
KILO
PRIVATE-PAK
SELECT
SUPREME
TRU-VAL
Advertising Agency:
Echelon Design
1442 Morton Cir
Claremont, CA 91711
Tel.: (909) 621-2122
Fax: (909) 624-4033

H2O TO GO/OPAL SPRINGS WATER COMPANY INC.
815 B St
Colver, OR 97734

Key to Media (For complete agency information see *The Advertising Red Books-Agencies* edition):
1. Bus. Publs. 2. Cable T.V. 3. Catalogs & Directories. 4. Co-op Adv. 5. Consumer Mags. 6. D.M. to Bus. Estab.7. D.M. to Consumers 8. Daily Newsp. 9. Exhibits/Trade Shows 10. Foreign 11. Infomercial 12. Internet Adv.13. Multimedia 14. Network Radio 15. Network T.V. 16. Newsp. Distr. Mags. 17. Other 18. Outdoor (Posters, Transit) 19. Point of Purchase20. Premiums, Novelties 21. Product Samples 22. Special Events Mktg. 23. Spot Radio 24. Spot T.V. 25. Weekly Newsp. 26. Yellow Page Adv.

Tel.: (541) 389-1773
Fax: (541) 546-7664
Sales Range: Less than $1 Million
Approx. Number Employees: 5
Year Founded: 1986
Business Description:
Bottled Spring Water Mfr
S.I.C.: 2086
N.A.I.C.S.: 312112
Media: 2-4-7-10-17
Personnel:
Ardena Lonien *(Office Mgr)*
Daryl Lonien *(Mgr-Opers)*
Brands & Products:
H2O TO GO
OPAL SPRINGS PREMIUM WATER

HANS HOLTERBOSCH, INC.

375 Park Ave
New York, NY 10152-0002
Tel.: (212) 421-3800
Fax: (212) 755-5271
Approx. Number Employees: 5
Business Description:
Beer Importer
S.I.C.: 5181
N.A.I.C.S.: 424810
Media: 2-6-7-8-9-10-11-14-18-20-23-24-25
Distr.: Natl.
Budget Set: Jan.-Dec.
Personnel:
H.D. Holterbosch *(Pres)*
Brands & Products:
HOFBRAU

HANSEN NATURAL CORPORATION

550 Monica Cir Ste 201
Corona, CA 92880
Tel.: (951) 739-6200
Fax: (909) 739-6220
Toll Free: (800) 426-7367
E-mail: info@hansens.com
Web Site: www.hansens.com
Approx. Sls.: $1,303,942,000
Approx. Number Employees: 833
Year Founded: 1990
Business Description:
Holding Company; Fruit Juices, Natural Sodas & Energy Drinks Developer, Mfr & Marketer
S.I.C.: 6719; 2086
N.A.I.C.S.: 551112; 312111
Advertising Expenditures: $86,700,000
Media: 2-4-6-9-10-13-16-17-18-23-24-25-26
Personnel:
Rodney C. Sacks *(Chm & CEO)*
Hilton H. Schlosberg *(Vice Chm)*
Mark Hall *(Pres-Monster Beverage Division)*
Thomas J. Kelly *(Sec-HBC & VP-Fin)*
Blower Kirk *(Sr VP-Hansen Beverage)*
Michael B. Schott *(Sr VP-Natl Sls-Monster Beverage)*
Geoff Bremmer *(Dir-Mktg-Monster Energy Brand)*
Jaime Phan *(Sr Brand Mgr)*
Brands & Products:
A NEW KIND A BUZZ
ACE
ANTI-OX
APPLE JUICE
B-WELL
BLUE SKY
CALIFORNIA
D-STRESS
DEFENSE
DIET RED ENERGY
ENERGADE
ENERGY
ENERGY WATER
HANSEN'S
HANSEN'S BLASTS
HANSEN'S DIET RED ENERGY
HANSEN'S JR. JUICE
HANSEN'S JUICE SLAM
HANSEN'S NATURAL
HANSEN'S NATURAL SODAS
HANSEN'S STAMINA
IMMUNEJUICE
JOKER MAD ENERGY
JUNIOR JUICE
LIQUIDFRUIT
LOST
MEDICINE MAN
MONSTER ENERGY
NATURAL CHOICE
NATURAL MULTI-VITAMIN JUICE SLAM
POWER FORMULA
THE REAL DEAL
RED ROCKER
RUMBA
SIGNATURE
SLIMDOWN
SPLENDA
UNBOUND ENERGY
UNLEASH THE BEAST!
Advertising Agency:
PondelWilkinson Inc.
1880 Century Park E Ste 350
Los Angeles, CA 90067
Tel.: (310) 279-5980
Fax: (310) 279-5988

HEINEKEN USA INC.

(Sub. of Heineken N.V.)
360 Hamilton Ave Ste 1103
White Plains, NY 10601-1811
Tel.: (914) 681-4100
Fax: (914) 681-1900
Toll Free: (800) 643-6733
E-mail: info@heinekenusa.com
Web Site: www.heinekenusa.com
Approx. Number Employees: 150
Business Description:
Importer of European Beer
S.I.C.: 5181
N.A.I.C.S.: 424810
Import
Advertising Expenditures: $100,000,000
Media: 2-6-13-14-15-22-23-24
Distr.: Natl.
Personnel:
Dolf van den Brink *(Pres & CEO)*
Lesya Lysyj *(CMO)*
Julie Kinch *(Chief Legal Officer & Sr VP)*
Daniel T. Tearno *(Chief Corp Rels Officer & Sr VP)*
John Nicolson *(Pres-Heineken Americas)*
Alex Jackson *(Sr VP-Ops)*
John Kennedy *(VP-Sls Strategy & Channel Mktg)*
Kheri Holland Tillman *(VP-Mktg)*
Colin Westcott-Pitt *(VP-Mktg-Dos Equis, Newcastle & Amstel Light)*
Allan O'Neil *(Gen Mgr-Western Region)*
Nick Lake *(Sr Dir-Category Mgmt)*
Luis Duran *(Reg Dir-Mktg)*
Carlos Boughton *(Brand Dir)*
Marime Riancho *(Sr Brand Mgr-Multicultural Markets)*
Carolyn Concepcion *(Brand Mgr-The Spot by Heineken)*
Brands & Products:
HEINEKEN
Advertising Agencies:
Dieste
1999 Bryan St Ste 2700
Dallas, TX 75201
Tel.: (214) 259-8000
Fax: (214) 259-8040
Heineken
Heineken Premium Light
Amstel Light
Buckler
Tecate
Tecate Light
Dos Equis
Bohemia
Ambar
Sol
Carta Blanca

Euro RSCG Worldwide
350 Hudson St
New York, NY 10014-4504
Tel.: (212) 886-2000
Fax: (212) 886-2016
Toll Free: (800) 937-0233
Dos Equis
Heineken
Heineken Light

Grupo Gallegos
401 E Ocean Blvd Ste 600
Long Beach, CA 90802
Tel.: (562) 256-3600
Fax: (562) 256-3620

MediaVest USA
1675 Broadway
New York, NY 10019
Tel.: (212) 468-4000
Fax: (212) 468-4110
Media Planning & Buying

NMA Entertainment & Marketing
11059 Sherman Way
Sun Valley, CA 91352
Tel.: (818) 982-3505
Fax: (818) 503-1936
Amstel Light
Dos Equis
Entertainment Marketing Agency of Record
Heineken
Heineken Light
Newcastle Brown Ale
Public Relations
Tecate
Tecate Light

The Vidal Partnership
228 E 45th St 11th Fl
New York, NY 10017-3303
Tel.: (646) 356-6600
Fax: (212) 661-7650
(Spanish Language Advertising)

Wieden + Kennedy-New York
150 Varick St Fl 7
New York, NY 10013-1218
Tel.: (917) 661-5200
Fax: (917) 661-5500
Creative
Heineken Light
Traditional & Digital

HINCKLEY SPRINGS

(Div. of DS Waters of America, Inc.)
6055 S Harlem Ave
Chicago, IL 60638-3984
Tel.: (773) 586-8600
Fax: (773) 586-8613
Web Site: www.hinckleysprings.com
Approx. Number Employees: 200
Year Founded: 1888
Business Description:
Pure Drinking, Distilled, Nursery & Artesian Spring Bottled Water & Water Coolers, Instant Beverages & Coffee Service
S.I.C.: 2086; 5149
N.A.I.C.S.: 312112; 424490
Export
Media: 3-5-7-8-9-10-18-19-20-21-22-23-24-25
Distr.: Reg.
Budget Set: Nov.

HONEST TEA

(Sub. of The Coca-Cola Company)
4827 Bethesda Ave
Bethesda, MD 20814
Tel.: (301) 652-3556
Fax: (301) 652-3557
E-mail: sethandbarry@honesttea.com
Web Site: www.honesttea.com
Approx. Sls.: $47,000,000
Approx. Number Employees: 108
Year Founded: 1998
Business Description:
Beverage Mfr
S.I.C.: 2086
N.A.I.C.S.: 312111
Personnel:
Seth Goldman *(Co-Founder, Pres & CEO)*
Barry Nalebuff *(Owner)*
Peter Kaye *(VP-Mktg)*
Kelly Cardmone *(Mgr-PR)*
Advertising Agencies:
Formula PR
810 Parkview Dr N
El Segundo, CA 90245
Tel.: (310) 578-7050
Fax: (310) 578-7077
Public Relations Agency of Record

SS&K
88 Pine St 30th Fl
New York, NY 10005
Tel.: (212) 274-9500
Fax: (212) 274-9598
Toll Free: (800) 274-7765
Digital Strategy
Social Marketing
Social Media & Digital Agency of Record

SS+K Agency
88 Pine St 30th Fl
New York, NY 10005
Tel.: (212) 274-9500
The Honest Store
— Alex Mailman *(Acct Dir)*
— Laura Blackburn *(Acct Exec)*

JACOB LEINENKUGEL BREWING CO.

(Joint Venture of Molson Coors Brewing Company & SABMiller plc)

Key to Media (For complete agency information see *The Advertising Red Books-Agencies* edition):
1. Bus. Publs. 2. Cable T.V. 3. Catalogs & Directories. 4. Co-op Adv. 5. Consumer Mags. 6. D.M. to Bus. Estab.7. D.M. to Consumers 8. Daily Newsp. 9. Exhibits/Trade Shows 10. Foreign 11. Infomercial 12. Internet Adv.13. Multimedia 14. Network Radio 15. Network T.V. 16. Newsp. Distr. Mags. 17. Other 18. Outdoor (Posters, Transit) 19. Point of Purchase20. Premiums, Novelties 21. Product Samples 22. Special Events Mktg. 23. Spot Radio 24. Spot T.V. 25. Weekly Newsp. 26. Yellow Page Adv.

Jacob Leinenkugel Brewing Co. — (Continued)

1 Jefferson Ave
Chippewa Falls, WI 54729-1318
Tel.: (715) 723-5557
Tel.: (715) 723-5558
Fax: (715) 723-7158
Toll Free: (888) LEINIES
Web Site: www.leinie.com
Approx. Number Employees: 92
Year Founded: 1867
Business Description:
Brewery
S.I.C.: 2082
N.A.I.C.S.: 312120
Media: 6-7-9-13-18-19-20-22-23
Distr.: Reg.
Budget Set: Nov.
Personnel:
Jake Leinenkugel *(Pres)*
Brands & Products:
LEINENKUGEL

JONES SODA COMPANY

234 9th Ave N
Seattle, WA 98109-3357
Tel.: (206) 624-3357
Fax: (206) 624-6857
Toll Free: (800) 656-6050
Web Site: www.jonessoda.com
Approx. Rev.: $17,526,000
Approx. Number Employees: 40
Business Description:
Soda & Beverage Mfr
S.I.C.: 2086
N.A.I.C.S.: 312111
Advertising Expenditures: $1,100,000
Media: 5-13-18-19-20-21-22
Personnel:
William R. Meissner *(CEO)*
Jennifer Cue *(Interim CFO)*
Mike Spear *(Dir-Mktg)*
Chris Milberger *(Mgr-Inventory Control)*
Brands & Products:
24C
JONES
JONES ENERGY
JONES GABA
JONES NATURALS
JONES ORGANICS
JONES PURE CANE SODA
Advertising Agencies:
Cole & Weber United
221 Yale Ave N Ste 600
Seattle, WA 98109
Tel.: (206) 447-9595
Fax: (206) 233-0178
— Britt Peterson *(Acct Exec-Jones Soda)*

Duo PR
3609 1st Ave NW
Seattle, WA 98107
Tel.: (206) 706-0508
Fax: (206) 706-0668

Ricochet Partners, Inc.
521 SW 11th Ave Ste 400
Portland, OR 97205
Tel.: (503) 220-0212
Fax: (503) 220-0213
(Jones GABA)

KIRIN BREWERY OF AMERICA, LLC

(Sub. of Kirin Brewery Company, Limited)
970 W 190th St Ste 890
Torrance, CA 90502-1057
Tel.: (310) 354-2400
Fax: (310) 354-5955
Web Site: www.kirin.com
Approx. Sls.: $13,000,000
Year Founded: 1996
Business Description:
Beer Importer & Whslr
S.I.C.: 5181
N.A.I.C.S.: 424810
Import
Media: 26
Distr.: Natl.
Budget Set: Aug.

KRAFT FOODS GEVALIA

(Div. of Kraft Foods Global)
Holmparken Sq
Dover, DE 07015-6276
Fax: (302) 430-7279
Toll Free: (800) 438-2542
E-mail: customer_service@gevalia.com
Web Site: www.gevalia.com
Sales Range: $250-299.9 Million
Business Description:
Coffee & Tea Distr
S.I.C.: 2095
N.A.I.C.S.: 311920
Advertising Agency:
Draftfcb
101 E Erie St
Chicago, IL 60611
Tel.: (312) 425-5000
Fax: (312) 425-5010

KRIER FOODS, INC.

520 Wolf Rd
Random Lake, WI 53075
Tel.: (920) 994-2469
Fax: (414) 355-5577
Web Site: www.krierfoods.com
Approx. Number Employees: 90
Year Founded: 1913
Business Description:
Fruit Juices & Nonalcoholic Carbonated Beverages
S.I.C.: 2033; 2086
N.A.I.C.S.: 311421; 312111
Import
Advertising Expenditures: $35,000
Media: 21-25
Distr.: Natl.
Personnel:
B. Bruce Krier *(Pres)*
Thomas Bretza *(Treas & VP-Fin)*
Steve Ihrcke *(Dir-Purchasing & Contract Packaging)*
Sue Hornacen *(Mgr-DP)*
Brands & Products:
FRUITLAND
JOLLY GOOD

LABATT BREWING COMPANY LIMITED

(Sub. of Anheuser-Busch InBev N.V./S.A.)
(d/b/a Labatt Breweries of Canada)
207 Queens Quay West Suite 299
Toronto, ON M5J 1A7, Canada
Tel.: (416) 361-5050
Fax: (416) 361-5200
E-mail: guest@labatt.com
Web Site: www.labatt.com
Approx. Number Employees: 3,000
Year Founded: 1930
Business Description:
Brewing Company
S.I.C.: 2082
N.A.I.C.S.: 312120
Media: 2-4-5-6-8-10-14-15
Personnel:
Michael Rodgers *(VP-HR)*
Christine Hamilton *(Assoc Brand Mgr-Budweiser)*
Brands & Products:
ALEXANDER KEITH'S
JOHN LABATT CLASSIC
KOOTENAY
LABATT
LABATT 50
LABATT LITE
LABATT STERLING
SCHOONER
Advertising Agencies:
AGENCY59
(A Communications Partnership)
1910 Yonge St 4th Fl
Toronto, ON M4S 1Z5, Canada
Tel.: (416) 484-1959
Fax: (416) 484-9846

Grip Ltd.
179 John St 6th Fl
Toronto, ON M5T 1X4, Canada
Tel.: (416) 340-7111
Fax: (416) 340-7776
Labatt Blue
Labatt Blue Light

Lexicon Communications Corp.
520 Bellmore Way
Pasadena, CA 91103
Tel.: (626) 683-9200
Fax: (622) 628-1960

MacLaren McCann Canada Inc.
10 Bay St
Toronto, ON M5J 2S3, Canada
Tel.: (416) 594-6000
Fax: (416) 643-7030
Fax: (416) 643-7027

Marketel
(Assoc. with McCann Erickson WorldGroup)
1100 Rene-Levesque Boulevard West
19th Floor
Montreal, QC H3B 4N4, Canada
Tel.: (514) 935-9445
Fax: (514) 935-1964

Nolin BBDO
3575 Boulevard St-Laurent Suite 300
Montreal, QC H2X 2T7, Canada
Tel.: (514) 939-4100
Fax: (514) 939-4006

Publicis Toronto
(Sub. of Publicis SA)
111 Queen St E Ste 200
Toronto, ON M5C 1S2, Canada
Tel.: (416) 925-7733
Fax: (416) 925-7341

LABATT USA LLC

(Sub. of North American Breweries, Inc.)
50 Fountain Plaza Ste 900
Buffalo, NY 14202
Tel.: (716) 604-1050
Fax: (716) 604-1055
Web Site: labattblue.com
Approx. Number Employees: 250
Business Description:
Beer Importer & Distr
S.I.C.: 5181
N.A.I.C.S.: 424810
Media: 2-4-5-6-7-8-9-10-18-19-20-23-24-26
Distr.: Reg.
Budget Set: Oct.
Personnel:
Thomas Cardella *(VP-Sls)*
Bryan Semkuley *(VP-Mktg)*

LANCER CORPORATION

(Sub. of Hoshizaki America, Inc.)
6655 Lancer Blvd
San Antonio, TX 78219
Tel.: (210) 310-7000
Fax: (210) 310-7183
Toll Free: (800) 729-1565
E-mail: generalinfo@lancercorp.com
Web Site: www.lancercorp.com
Sales Range: $100-124.9 Million
Approx. Number Employees: 1,188
Year Founded: 1967
Business Description:
Beverage Dispensing Systems Mfr & Marketer
S.I.C.: 3556
N.A.I.C.S.: 333294
Media: 8-10
Brands & Products:
ACCUFREEZE
AIR MIX
DELTA
DELTA III
ESCORT
EXTREME
ICE LINK
INLINECARBONATO
LEV
MOOCINO
PURE LINK
RAPIDFREEZE
SURE-FILL
VOLUMETRIC VALVE

LEONARD KREUSCH, INC.

200 Legrand Ave
Northvale, NJ 07647-0910
Tel.: (201) 784-2500
Fax: (201) 784-0951
E-mail: usa-sales@kreuschwines.com
Web Site:
www.leonardkreuschwines.com
Approx. Number Employees: 36
Year Founded: 1950
Business Description:
Wine Importer
S.I.C.: 5182
N.A.I.C.S.: 424820
Import
Advertising Expenditures: $750,000
Media: 1-2-3-4-5-9-10-11-13-14-16-18-19-20-21-22-23-25
Distr.: Natl.
Personnel:
Paul P. Kreusch *(Pres & CEO)*
Brands & Products:
CASAL BORDINA WINES ITALY
DESCHAUX BRANDY
DESMOND & DUFF SCOTCH
GERHARD SCHULZ
GLEN BURDINE

Key to Media (For complete agency information see *The Advertising Red Books-Agencies* edition):
1. Bus. Publs. 2. Cable T.V. 3. Catalogs & Directories. 4. Co-op Adv. 5. Consumer Mags. 6. D.M. to Bus. Estab.7. D.M. to Consumers
8. Daily Newsp. 9. Exhibits/Trade Shows 10. Foreign 11. Infomercial 12. Internet Adv.13. Multimedia 14. Network Radio
15. Network T.V. 16. Newsp. Distr. Mags. 17. Other 18. Outdoor (Posters, Transit) 19. Point of Purchase20. Premiums, Novelties
21. Product Samples 22. Special Events Mktg. 23. Spot Radio 24. Spot T.V. 25. Weekly Newsp. 26. Yellow Page Adv.

GLENDROSTAN SCOTCH
GRAND CARDINAL SPARKLING
GRAZIOSI
KARL MARX VODKA
LEONARD KREUSCH
LEONARDINI
LUCIEN DESCHAUX
PELLER ESTATES CANADA
PINES BROOK VINTNERS
PRESTIGE VODKA
SANTA ANITA
SANTA ISABEL ARGENTINA
ST. LEONARD
STAUB COGNAC
TIO SOTO
VILLA JOLADA ITALY
YVES ROCHE

THE LION BREWERY, INC.

700 N Pennsylvania Ave
Wilkes Barre, PA 18705-2451
Tel.: (570) 823-8801
Fax: (570) 823-6686
Toll Free: (800) 233-8327
E-mail: info@lionbrewery.com
Web Site: www.lionbrewery.com
E-Mail For Key Personnel:
President: clawson@lionbrewery.com
Approx. Number Employees: 130
Year Founded: 1905
Business Description:
Brewer & Bottler of Malt Beverages & Specialty Soft Drinks
S.I.C.: 2082; 2086
N.A.I.C.S.: 312120; 312111
Media: 2-10-13-18-19-21-25-26
Distr.: Natl.; Reg.
Budget Set: Jan.
Personnel:
Patrick E. Balardi *(CFO & VP)*
Michael Luksic *(VP-Mktg)*
David Givler *(Dir-Supply Chain)*
Leo Orlandini *(Dir-Ops & Master Brewer)*
Brands & Products:
BARTELS
CARAMEL PORTER
ESSLINGER PREMIUM
GIBBONS
LIEBOTSCHONER
THE LION BREWERY
LION BREWERY
LION BREWERY ROOT BEER
LIONSHEAD
OLDE PHILADELPHIA
OLDE PHILADELPHIA BLACK CHERRY
OLDE PHILADELPHIA CREAM
OLDE PHILADELPHIA DIET CREAM
OLDE PHILADELPHIA GRAPE
OLDE PHILADELPHIA ORANGE CREAM
POCONO
POCONO LAGER
POCONO PALE ALE
STEIGMAIER
STEIGMAIER PORTER
STEIGMAIER SEASONALS

MANHATTAN SPECIAL BOTTLING CORP.

342 Manhattan Ave
Brooklyn, NY 11211-2404
Tel.: (718) 388-4144
Fax: (718) 384-0244
E-mail: comments@manhattanspecial.com
Web Site: www.manhattanspecial.com
Approx. Number Employees: 28
Year Founded: 1895
Business Description:
Espresso & Iced Coffee Drinks & Sodas Distr
S.I.C.: 2086
N.A.I.C.S.: 312111
Export
Media: 2-4-10-19
Distr.: Natl.
Budget Set: Jan.
Personnel:
Aurora Passaro *(Pres)*
Louis Passaro *(Exec VP)*
Brands & Products:
MANHATTAN SPECIAL

MENDOCINO BREWING COMPANY

1601 Airport Rd
Ukiah, CA 95482
Tel.: (707) 463-6610
Toll Free: (800) 733-3871
E-mail: questions@mendobrew.com
Web Site: www.mendobrew.com
Approx. Sls.: $35,912,800
Approx. Number Employees: 60
Business Description:
Beer Brewer & Distr
S.I.C.: 2082; 5181
N.A.I.C.S.: 312120; 424810
Advertising Expenditures: $1,355,600
Media: 8-10-13-18-19-21-22
Personnel:
Vijay Mallya *(Chm)*
Yashpal Singh *(Pres & CEO)*
N. Mahadevan *(CFO & Sec)*
Tim Howard *(Area Mgr-Sls-North Bay)*
Victor Bacerra *(Mgr-Sls & Mktg-Western States)*
Michael J. Gentile *(Mgr-Sls & Mktg-Eastern States)*
John Scahill *(Mgr-Project & Maintenance)*
Keith Stevenson *(Mgr-Adv)*
Don Tubbs *(Mgr-Brewing)*
Carlos Swinney *(Webmaster)*
Lisa Jansen *(Coord-Sls & Accts)*
Brands & Products:
BLACK HAWK STOUT
BLUE HERON PALE ALE
EYE OF THE HAWK
MENDOCINO BREWING COMPANY
PEREGRINE GOLDEN ALE
RED TAIL ALE
RED TAIL LAGER
WHITE HAWK SELECT IPA

MILLER BREWING COMPANY

(Joint Venture of Molson Coors Brewing Company & SABMiller plc)
3939 W Highland Blvd
Milwaukee, WI 53208-2816
Tel.: (414) 931-2000
Fax: (414) 931-3735
Web Site: www.millerbrewing.com
Approx. Sls.: $3,900,000,000
Approx. Number Employees: 6,500
Year Founded: 1855
Business Description:
Brewery
S.I.C.: 2082
N.A.I.C.S.: 312120
Import Export
Media: 2-3-5-6-7-9-10-13-14-15-18-19-20-22-23-24-25
Distr.: Natl.
Personnel:
Thomas Cardella *(Pres, CEO-Tenth & Blake Beer Company)*
Denis Puffer *(Chief Ops Officer & Exec VP)*
D. Michael Jones *(Gen Counsel, Sec & Sr VP)*
Jonathan Stern *(Sr Dir-Brand PR)*
Robert T Brennan *(Dir-Strategic Project)*
Sharon McLenahan *(Dir-Emerging Brands)*
Evan Cohen *(Brand Mgr-Pilsner Urquell-US)*
Kevin Oglesby *(Sr Brand Mgr-Miller High Life)*
Kevin Rutherford *(Brand Mgr-Milwaukee's Best Light)*
Kim O'Malley *(Mgr-Mktg-Icehouse)*
Brands & Products:
FOSTER'S LAGER
FOSTER'S SPECIAL BITTER
FREDRICK MILLER CLASSIC CHOCOLATE LAGER
HAMM'S
HAMM'S DRAFT
HAMM'S SPECIAL LIGHT
HENRY WEINHARD'S AMBER ALE
HENRY WEINHARD'S BLUE BOAR PALE ALE
HENRY WEINHARD'S CLASSIC DARK
HENRY WEINHARD'S HEFEWEIZEN
HENRY WEINHARD'S NORTHWEST TRAIL BLONDE LAGER
HENRY WEINHARD'S PRIVATE RESERVE
HENRY WEINHARD'S SUMMER WHEAT
ICEHOUSE 5.0
ICEHOUSE 5.5
ICEHOUSE LIGHT
LEINENKUGEL'S APPLE SPICE
LEINENKUGEL'S BALLYARD BREWERY
LEINENKUGEL'S BERRY WEISS
LEINENKUGEL'S BIG BUTT DOPPELBOCK
LEINENKUGEL'S CREAMY DARK
LEINENKUGEL'S HONEY WEISS
LEINENKUGEL'S LEINIE'S RED
LEINENKUGEL'S LIGHT
LEINENKUGEL'S ORIGINAL PREMIUM
LEINENKUGEL'S RED LAGER
LEINENKUGEL'S SUNSET WHEAT
MAGNUM MALT LIQUOR
MGD 64
MICKEY'S ICE
MICKEY'S MALT LIQUOR
MILLER CHILL
MILLER GENUINE DRAFT
MILLER GENUINE DRAFT 64
MILLER GENUINE DRAFT LIGHT
MILLER HIGH LIFE
MILLER HIGH LIFE LIGHT
MILLER LITE
MILWAUKEE'S BEST
MILWAUKEE'S BEST ICE
MILWAUKEE'S BEST LIGHT
OLDE ENGLISH 800 MALT LIQUOR
OLDE ENGLISH HG800
OLDE ENGLISH HG800 7.5
PERONI NASTRO AZZURRO
PILSNER URQUELL
RED DOG
SHARP'S
SHEAF STOUT
SOUTHPAW LIGHT
SPARKS
SPARKS LIGHT
SPARKS PLUS 6%
SPARKS PLUS 7%
SPARKS RESERVE HIGH GRAVITY
SPARKS RESERVE HIGH GRAVITY 6.0
SPARKS RESERVE TRIPLE EXPORT 8.1%
STEEL SIX
ULTIMATE LIGHT BEER BY DESIGN
Advertising Agencies:
Arc Worldwide, North America
35 W Wacker 15th Fl
Chicago, IL 60601
Tel.: (312) 220-3200
Fax: (312) 220-6212
Miller Genuine Draft

Digitas, Inc.
111 E Wacker Dr Ste 1500
Chicago, IL 60601-4501
Tel.: (312) 729-0100
Fax: (312) 729-0111

Frankel & Co.
123 William St.
New York, NY 10038-3898
Tel.: (212) 267-2200
Fax: (212) 349-5208

Jacobson Rost
233 N Water St 6th Fl
Milwaukee, WI 53202
Tel.: (414) 220-4888
Fax: (414) 220-4889
Miller Lite Brewers Collection

La Comunidad
6400 Biscayne Blvd
Miami, FL 33138
Tel.: (305) 993-5700
Tel.: (305) 865-9600
Fax: (305) 865-9609

Leo Burnett USA
35 W Wacker Dr
Chicago, IL 60601-1723
Tel.: (312) 220-5959
Fax: (312) 220-3299
Miller Genuine Draft

Lopez Negrete Communications, Inc.
3336 Richmond Ave Ste 200
Houston, TX 77098
Tel.: (713) 877-8777
Fax: (713) 877-8796
Miller Lite
Hispanic Marketing

MarketVision
8647 Wurzbach Ste J100
San Antonio, TX 78240
Tel.: (210) 222-1933
Fax: (210) 222-1935

Red Brown Kle
840 N Old World Third St Ste 401
Milwaukee, WI 53203
Tel.: (414) 272-2600
Fax: (414) 272-2690
Toll Free: (888) 725-2041

Saatchi & Saatchi

Key to Media (For complete agency information see *The Advertising Red Books-Agencies* edition):
1. Bus. Publs. 2. Cable T.V. 3. Catalogs & Directories. 4. Co-op Adv. 5. Consumer Mags. 6. D.M. to Bus. Estab.7. D.M. to Consumers 8. Daily Newsp. 9. Exhibits/Trade Shows 10. Foreign 11. Infomercial 12. Internet Adv.13. Multimedia 14. Network Radio 15. Network T.V. 16. Newsp. Distr. Mags. 17. Other 18. Outdoor (Posters, Transit) 19. Point of Purchase20. Premiums, Novelties 21. Product Samples 22. Special Events Mktg. 23. Spot Radio 24. Spot T.V. 25. Weekly Newsp. 26. Yellow Page Adv.

Miller Brewing Company — (Continued)

(Sub. of Publicis Groupe S.A.)
(Worldwide Headquarters)
375 Hudson St
New York, NY 10014-3660
Tel.: (212) 463-2000
Fax: (212) 463-9856
Miller High Life
Miller Chill

Starcom MediaVest Group
35 W Wacker Dr
Chicago, IL 60601-1723
Tel.: (312) 220-3535
Fax: (312) 220-6530
(Special Campaign Coordination, Media Planning & Local & Hispanic Media Buying)

Starcom USA
35 W Wacker Dr
Chicago, IL 60601
Tel.: (312) 220-3535
Fax: (312) 220-6530

Stephan & Brady, Inc.
1850 Hoffman St
Madison, WI 53704-2541
Tel.: (608) 241-4141
Fax: (608) 241-4246
(Trade Communications, Media, Public Relations & Direct Mail)

Weber Shandwick-Saint Louis
555 Washington Ave
Saint Louis, MO 63101
Tel.: (314) 436-6565
Fax: (314) 622-6212
Toll Free: (800) 551-5971
Pilsner Urquell
— Agatha Thaller *(Acct Exec)*

Young & Rubicam Chicago
233 N Michigan Ave 16th Fl
Chicago, IL 60601-5519
Tel.: (312) 596-3000
Fax: (312) 596-3130
(Leinenkugels; Miller High Life; Icehouse; Magnum; Meister Brau; Milwaukee's Best; Molson)

MILLERCOORS LLC

(Joint Venture of Molson Coors Brewing Company & SABMiller plc)
250 S Wacker Dr
Chicago, IL 60606-6301
Tel.: (312) 496-2700
Fax: (312) 496-5884
E-mail: mediainquiries@millercoors.com
Web Site: www.millercoors.com

Approx. Rev.: $7,000,000,000
Approx. Number Employees: 10,000
Business Description:
Beer Brewer & Distr; Owned by Molson Coors Brewing Company & SABMiller plc
S.I.C.: 2082; 5181
N.A.I.C.S.: 312120; 424810
Advertising Expenditures: $400,000,000

Personnel:
Tom Long *(CEO)*
Gavin Hattersley *(CFO & Exec VP)*
Dennis Puffer *(COO & Exec VP)*
Karen Alber *(CIO)*
Andrew J. England *(CMO & Exec VP)*
Nehl Horton *(Chief Comm, Strategy & Govt Affairs Officer)*
Karen Ripley *(Chief Legal Officer)*
N. Cornell Boggs, III *(Chief Responsibility & Ethics Officer)*
Tim Wolf *(Chief Integration Officer)*
Ed McBrien *(Pres-Sls & Distr Ops)*
Patrick Edson *(VP-Mktg, Innovation & Brands)*
Rick Gomez *(VP-Brand Mktg)*
Al Patel *(Sr Dir-Multicultural Mktg)*
Joe Abegg *(Dir-Category Mgmt On-Premise)*
Arturo Nava *(Brand Mgr-Above Premium & Innovation)*
Brendan Noonan *(Brand Mgr-Miller High Life)*
Rene Ramos *(Brand Mgr)*
Peter H. Coors *(Mgr-Quality)*
Karina Diehl *(Mgr-External Comm)*
Tom Gonzales *(Mgr-Media)*
Richard Leinenkugel *(Mgr-Bus Dev-Tenth & Blake Beer)*
Sam Wehrs *(Mgr-Digital Media)*

Advertising Agencies:
Arc Worldwide
2001 The Embarcadero
San Francisco, CA 94133
Tel.: (312) 220-1177
Miller High Life

Arc Worldwide
(Sub. of Publicis Groupe S.A.)
35 W Wacker Dr 15th Fl
Chicago, IL 60601
Tel.: (312) 220-3200
Fax: (312) 220-1995
Beer

Bromley Communications
401 E Houston St
San Antonio, TX 78205-2615
Tel.: (210) 244-2000
Fax: (210) 244-2442
Latino Advertising Agency of Record for Coors Light

Dig Communications
549 W Randolph Ste 201
Chicago, IL 60661
Tel.: (312) 577-1750
Fax: (312) 577-1760
Miller High Life

Digitas, Inc.
111 E Wacker Dr Ste 1500
Chicago, IL 60601-4501
Tel.: (312) 729-0100
Fax: (312) 729-0111

Draftfcb
101 E Erie St
Chicago, IL 60611
Tel.: (312) 425-5000
Fax: (312) 425-5010

Kinetic
222 Merchandise Mart Plz Ste 250
Chicago, IL 60654
Tel.: (312) 205-0054

Landor Associates
1001 Front St
San Francisco, CA 94111
Tel.: (415) 365-1700
Fax: (415) 365-3190
Miller High Life
— J. P. Sabarots *(Acct Exec)*

Proxy Partners LLC
1099 18th St Ste 500
Denver, CO 80202
Tel.: (303) 293-3020
Fax: (303) 296-3410

Razorfish
821 2nd Ave Ste 1800
Seattle, WA 98104-2343
Tel.: (206) 816-8800
Fax: (206) 816-8808
Coors Lite

Saatchi & Saatchi
(Sub. of Publicis Groupe S.A.)
(Worldwide Headquarters)
375 Hudson St
New York, NY 10014-3660
Tel.: (212) 463-2000
Fax: (212) 463-9856
Miller High Life-Super Bowl 2010

MOLSON COORS BREWING COMPANY

1225 17th St Ste 3200
Denver, CO 80202
Mailing Address:
PO Box 4030
Golden, CO 80401-0030
Tel.: (303) 927-2337
Fax: (303) 277-6246
Toll Free: (800) 642-6116
E-mail: gminvestorrelations@molsoncoors.com
Web Site: www.molsoncoors.com
Approx. Sls.: $4,703,100,000
Approx. Number Employees: 14,660
Year Founded: 1873
Business Description:
Holding Company
S.I.C.: 2082; 6719
N.A.I.C.S.: 312120; 551112
Import Export
Advertising Expenditures: $361,600,000
Media: 2-3-6-9-15-16-18-19-22-23-24
Distr.: Natl.
Personnel:
Andrew T. Molson *(Chm)*
Peter H. Coors *(Vice Chm)*
Peter Swinburn *(Pres & CEO)*
Torsten Kuenzlen *(CMO-Molson Coors Intl)*
William G. Waters *(Chief Acctg Officer, Chief Strategy Officer & Controller)*
Samuel D. Walker *(Chief Legal Officer-Global & Sec)*
Celso White *(Chief Supply Chain Officer-Molson Coors Intl)*
Mark Hunter *(Pres/CEO-Molson Coors-UK)*
Dave Perkins *(Pres/CEO-Molson Coors-Canada)*
Krishnan Anand *(Pres-Molson Coors Intl)*
Lee Reichert *(Gen Counsel-Molson Coors Intl)*
Chris McDonough *(Dir-Mktg)*
David Preston *(Dir-Comml Innovation)*
Sherri Heckel Kuhlmann *(Deputy Gen Counsel)*
Brands & Products:
99 CALORIE CARLING
BITTERSWEET PARTNERSHIP
BLUE MOON
BLUE MOON BELGIAN WHITE ALE
BOHEMIAN
CAFFREY'S
CARLING
CARLING BLACK LABEL
CARLING C2
COORS
COORS BANQUET
COORS LIGHT
CREEMORE SPRINGS
GEORGE KILLIAN'S IRISH RED
GROLSCH
GROLSCH WEIZEN
KASTEEL CRU
KEYSTONE ICE
KEYSTONE LIGHT
KEYSTONE PREMIUM
MOLSON CANADIAN
MOLSON COORS
MOLSON DRY
MOLSON EXPORT
MOLSON GOLDEN
PILSNER
RICKARD'S RED
SOL
TORNADE
WILLIAM WORTHINGTON'S WHITE SHIELD
WORTHINGTON'S CREAMFLOW
Advertising Agencies:
Carol H. Williams Advertising
1400 65th St Ste 200
Emeryville, CA 94608
Tel.: (510) 763-5200
Fax: (510) 763-9266

VCCP
Greencoat House
London, SW1P 1DH, United Kingdom
Tel.: (44) 20 7592 9331
Fax: (44) 20 7592 7465
Coors Light

ZenithOptimedia
(Worldwide Headquarters)
24 Percy Street
London, W1T 2BS, United Kingdom
Tel.: (44) 207 961 1000
Fax: (44) 207 961 1113
Coors Light

MOLSON COORS CANADA INC.

(Sub. of Molson Coors Brewing Company)
1555 Notre-Dame Street East
Montreal, QC H2L 2R5, Canada
Tel.: (514) 521-1786
Fax: (514) 521-6951
E-mail: consumers@molson.com
Web Site: www.molson.com
Sales Range: $900-999.9 Million
Approx. Number Employees: 3,500
Year Founded: 1786
Business Description:
Brewing & Beer & Ale Distribution
S.I.C.: 2082
N.A.I.C.S.: 312120
Import Export
Media: 1-3-6-14-15
Distr.: Intl.
Budget Set: Sept. -Nov.
Personnel:
Dave Perkins *(Pres & CEO)*
Jay Wells *(CFO)*
Kelly Brown *(Chief Legal Officer)*

Key to Media (For complete agency information see *The Advertising Red Books-Agencies* edition):
1. Bus. Publs. 2. Cable T.V. 3. Catalogs & Directories. 4. Co-op Adv. 5. Consumer Mags. 6. D.M. to Bus. Estab.7. D.M. to Consumers
8. Daily Newsp. 9. Exhibits/Trade Shows 10. Foreign 11. Infomercial 12. Internet Adv.13. Multimedia 14. Network Radio
15. Network T.V. 16. Newsp. Distr. Mags. 17. Other 18. Outdoor (Posters, Transit) 19. Point of Purchase20. Premiums, Novelties
21. Product Samples 22. Special Events Mktg. 23. Spot Radio 24. Spot T.V. 25. Weekly Newsp. 26. Yellow Page Adv.

Ferg Devins *(Chief Pub Affairs Officer)*
Cathy Noonan *(Chief Supply Chain Officer)*
Ian Freedman *(Sr VP & Gen Mgr-Quebec)*
Veronique Simard *(Sr Brand Mgr-Molson M)*
Stephanie Daley *(Brand Mgr-Miller Chill)*
Jamie Sprules *(Sr Brand Mgr)*
Brands & Products:
CANADIAN
CANADIAN ICE
CANADIAN LIGHT
EX LIGHT
EXPORT
MOLSON DRY
MOLSON M
MOLSON SMOOTH DRY
MOLSON ULTRA
PILSNER
RICKARD'S
Advertising Agency:
BBDO Toronto
2 Bloor St W
Toronto, ON M4W 3R6, Canada
Tel.: (416) 972-1505
Fax: (416) 972-5656
Miller Chill Lemon

MOLSON INC.

(Sub. of Molson Coors Canada Inc.)
(d/b/a Molson Brewery)
1555 Notre Dame St
Montreal, QC H2L 2R5, Canada
Tel.: (514) 521-1786
Fax: (514) 598-6866
Toll Free: (800) 665-7661
Web Site: www.Molson.com
Sales Range: $50-74.9 Million
Approx. Number Employees: 150
Year Founded: 1786
Business Description:
Breweries, Sports & Entertainment
S.I.C.: 2082
N.A.I.C.S.: 312120
Export
Media: 1-3-4-6-14-15
Personnel:
Susan Niles *(Chief People Officer)*
Ian Freedman *(Sr VP & Gen Mgr-Molson Coors Quebec)*
Aaron Bilyea *(Brand Mgr)*
Benoit Maillette *(Mgr-Toronto Brewery)*

THE MONARCH BEVERAGE COMPANY, INC.

1123 Zonolite Rd Ste 10
Atlanta, GA 30306
Tel.: (404) 262-4040
Fax: (404) 262-4001
Toll Free: (800) 241-3732
E-mail: info@monarchbeverages.com
Web Site:
www.monarchbeverages.com
Approx. Number Employees: 25
Year Founded: 1965
Business Description:
Mfr & Distr of Branded & Custom Beverage Products
S.I.C.: 2086
N.A.I.C.S.: 312111
Export
Advertising Expenditures: $500,000
Media: 1-2-5-7-9-10-11-13-19-20-23-24
Distr.: Intl.; Natl.
Budget Set: Oct.
Personnel:
Jacques Bombal *(Pres & CEO)*
Brands & Products:
ALL SPORT BODY QUENCHER
ALL SPORT PLUS
AMERICAN COLA
BUBBLE-UP
DAD'S OLD FASHIONED ROOT BEER
DR. WELLS
KICKAPOO JOY JUICE
MASON'S
MOXIE
PLANET COLA
QUENCH
REAKTOR
RUSH! ENERGY
SUNCREST

MOUNTAIN VALLEY SPRING COMPANY

150 Central Ave
Hot Springs National Park, AR 71902
Mailing Address:
PO Box 1610
Hot Springs National Park, AR 71902-1610
Tel.: (501) 624-1635
Fax: (501) 623-5135
Toll Free: (800) 828-0836
E-mail: info@mountainvalleyspring.com
Web Site:
www.mountainvalleyspring.com
Sales Range: $25-49.9 Million
Approx. Number Employees: 150
Year Founded: 1871
Business Description:
Bottled Water Mfr & Distr
S.I.C.: 2086; 5149
N.A.I.C.S.: 312112; 424490
Export
Media: 2-8-9-10-11-13-19-20-23-25
Distr.: Natl.
Personnel:
Breck Speed *(Pres & CEO)*
Brad Forberg *(CMO)*

NATIONAL BEVERAGE CORP.

8100 SW 10th St Ste 4000
Fort Lauderdale, FL 33324
Tel.: (954) 581-0922
Fax: (954) 473-4710
Toll Free: (877) 622-3499
E-mail: asknbc@nationalbeverage.com
Web Site: www.nbcfiz.com
Approx. Sls.: $600,193,000
Approx. Number Employees: 1,200
Year Founded: 1985
Business Description:
Holding Company; Beverage Products Developer, Mfr, Marketer & Distr
S.I.C.: 2086
N.A.I.C.S.: 312111
Export
Advertising Expenditures: $35,600,000
Media: 6-9-14-15-23-24-25
Distr.: Natl.
Personnel:
Nick A. Caporella *(Chm & CEO)*
Joseph G. Caporella *(Pres)*
George R. Bracken *(CFO & Sr VP-Fin)*
Dean A. McCoy *(Chief Acctg Officer & Sr VP)*
Raymond J. Notarantonio *(Exec Dir-IT)*
Gregory J. Kwederis *(Sr Dir-Bus Intelligence)*
Richard S. Berkes *(Dir-Risk Mgmt)*
Brent R. Bott *(Dir-Consumer Mktg)*
John Scherzinger *(Dir-Credit Mgmt)*
Vanessa C. Walker *(Dir-Strategy & Brand Dev)*
Brands & Products:
ASANTE
BIG SHOT
CASCADIA
CASCADIA ONLY 2 CALORIES
CASCADIA SPARKLING CLEAR
CLEARFRUIT
CRYSTAL BAY
EVERFRESH
FAYGO
HOME JUICE
LACROIX
MEGA SPORT
MR. PURE
MT. SHASTA
NUTRAFIZZ
OHANA
POWERBLAST
RIP IT
RITZ
SHASTA
ST. NICK'S

THE NEDLOG COMPANY

92 Messner Dr
Wheeling, IL 60090-6448
Tel.: (847) 541-0924
Fax: (847) 541-1046
Toll Free: (800) 323-6201
E-mail: nedlog@nedlog.com
Web Site: www.nedlog.com
Sales Range: $10-24.9 Million
Approx. Number Employees: 5
Year Founded: 1930
Business Description:
Mfr. of Fruit Juice Drink Bases, Fruit Flavored & Artificially Flavored Fruit Drink Bases, Low Calorie Fruit Flavored Drink Bases
S.I.C.: 2086; 2087
N.A.I.C.S.: 312111; 311930
Media: 13-19-26
Distr.: Natl.
Personnel:
Grant Golden *(Chm & CEO)*
Glenn Golden *(Pres & COO)*
Karyl G. Golden *(Pres-Admin Svcs)*
Brands & Products:
BEST TASTE. NATURALLY
NEDLOG
TAMARINDO

NESTLE WATERS NORTH AMERICA INC.

(Sub. of Nestle Waters S.A.S.)
900 Long Ridge Rd Bldg 2
Stamford, CT 06902-1138
Tel.: (203) 531-4100
Toll Free: (866) 676-1672
Web Site: www.nestle-watersna.com
Approx. Rev.: $615,000,000
Approx. Number Employees: 500
Business Description:
Importers of Mineral Water & Bottlers of Domestic Water
S.I.C.: 5149
N.A.I.C.S.: 424490
Import
Advertising Expenditures: $500,000
Media: 6-15-16-18-23-24-26
Distr.: Natl.
Budget Set: Sept.
Personnel:
Kim E. Jeffery *(Pres & CEO)*
Bill Pearson *(CFO & VP-Fin)*
Dimitrios Smyrnios *(Exec VP-Retail Ops)*
Dave Muscato *(Exec VP-NestIT Direct)*
Tim Brown *(VP & Gen Mgr-Retail Ops)*
Bob Davino *(VP-Mktg)*
Michael T. Swinton *(VP-HR)*
Ty Brannen *(Reg Dir-Supply Chain-Ozarka Brand)*
Larry Cooper *(Sr Mgr-Mktg)*
Carolina Rodriguez *(Sr Brand Mgr)*
Mark Evans *(Mgr-Packaging)*
Brands & Products:
ACQUA PANNA
DEER PARK
IYEMON CHA
VOLVIC
Advertising Agencies:
McCann Erickson Worldwide
622 3rd Ave
New York, NY 10017-6707
Tel.: (646) 865-2000
Fax: (646) 487-9610

MRM Worldwide
622 3rd Ave
New York, NY 10017-6707
Tel.: (646) 865-6230
Fax: (646) 865-6264
(Arrowhead, Calistoga, Deer Park, Ozarka, Poland Spring & Zephyrhills Bottled Water)

Ogilvy & Mather
(Sub. of WPP Group plc)
636 11th Ave
New York, NY 10036
Tel.: (212) 237-4000
Fax: (212) 237-5123

NEW BELGIUM BREWING COMPANY, INC.

500 Linden
Fort Collins, CO 80524
Tel.: (970) 221-0524
Fax: (970) 221-0535
E-mail: nbb@newbelgium.com
Web Site: www.newbelgium.com
Approx. Sls.: $96,000,000
Approx. Number Employees: 360
Year Founded: 1991
Business Description:
Brewery
S.I.C.: 2082
N.A.I.C.S.: 312120
Advertising Expenditures: $1,100,000
Media: 6
Personnel:
Kim Jordan *(Co-Founder & CEO)*
Greg Owsley *(Chief Branding Officer)*
Brands & Products:
1554
2 BELOW
ABBEY
BLUE PADDLE
FAT TIRE AMBER ALE
FRAMBOZEN
LA FOLIE
MIGHTY ARROW
MOTHERSHIP WIT
SKINNY DIP

Key to Media (For complete agency information see *The Advertising Red Books-Agencies* edition):
1. Bus. Publs. 2. Cable T.V. 3. Catalogs & Directories. 4. Co-op Adv. 5. Consumer Mags. 6. D.M. to Bus. Estab.7. D.M. to Consumers 8. Daily Newsp. 9. Exhibits/Trade Shows 10. Foreign 11. Infomercial 12. Internet Adv.13. Multimedia 14. Network Radio 15. Network T.V. 16. Newsp. Distr. Mags. 17. Other 18. Outdoor (Posters, Transit) 19. Point of Purchase20. Premiums, Novelties 21. Product Samples 22. Special Events Mktg. 23. Spot Radio 24. Spot T.V. 25. Weekly Newsp. 26. Yellow Page Adv.

New Belgium Brewing Company, Inc. — (Continued)

SPRINGBOARD
SUNSHINE WHEAT
TRIPPEL
Advertising Agency:
Cultivator Advertising & Design
2737 Larimer St Ste B
Denver, CO 80205
Tel.: (303) 444-4134
Fax: (800) 783-4152

NEW CENTURY BREWING CO.
PO Box 163
Boston, MA 02128
Tel.: (781) 963-4007
Fax: (781) 658-2640
E-mail: info@newcenturybrewing.com
Web Site: www.edisonbeer.com
Approx. Sls.: $250,000
Approx. Number Employees: 15
Year Founded: 2001
Business Description:
Beer Marketer & Mfr
S.I.C.: 5181; 2082
N.A.I.C.S.: 424810; 312120
Advertising Expenditures: $50,000
Media: 2-10-13-22-23
Personnel:
Rhonda Kallman *(Founder & CEO)*
Brands & Products:
BREWED TO BE LIGHT
EDISON

NEW ORLEANS COFFEE CO., INC.
PO Box 55985
Metairie, LA 70055-5985
Tel.: (504) 488-2665
Fax: (504) 488-2685
Toll Free: (800) 293-3765
Web Site: www.coolbrew.com
Approx. Number Employees: 50
Year Founded: 1989
Business Description:
Coffee Products Mfr & Retailer
S.I.C.: 2095
N.A.I.C.S.: 311920
Advertising Expenditures: $40,000
Media: 2-6-10-13-16-18-19-20-21-22
Personnel:
Philip McCrory *(Pres & CEO)*
Brands & Products:
ALWAYS FRESH
BANANA HAZE
CAFE AU LAIT
COOLBREW
FRESH COFFEE IN AN INSTANT
FROSTY LEPRECHAUN
WHITE ALLIGATOR

NOR-CAL BEVERAGE CO., INC.
2286 Stone Blvd
West Sacramento, CA 95691-4050
Tel.: (916) 372-0600
Fax: (916) 374-2609
E-mail: norcal1@ncbev.com
Web Site: www.ncbev.com
Sales Range: $100-124.9 Million
Approx. Number Employees: 620
Year Founded: 1937
Business Description:
Bottler & Whslr of Soft Drinks, Fruit Juices & Beer; Full Line Vending Operations, Food Service & Trucking
S.I.C.: 2086; 5181
N.A.I.C.S.: 312111; 424810
Export
Media: 4-7-10-11-20-26
Distr.: Reg.
Personnel:
Donald R. Deary *(Chm & Pres)*
Mike Matroni *(COO)*
Shelly Ingrim *(VP-Sls & Mktg)*
Advertising Agency:
Clark & Associates
11180 Sun Center Dr Ste 100
Rancho Cordova, CA 95670
Tel.: (916) 635-2424
Fax: (916) 635-0531
Toll Free: (877) 888-4040
(Dr. Pepper, Squirt, RC Cola, Canada Dry)

NORTH AMERICAN BREWERIES, INC.
(Holding of KPS Capital Partners, L.P.)
445 Saint Paul St
Rochester, NY 14605-1726
Tel.: (585) 546-1030
Web Site: www.nabreweries.com
Approx. Number Employees: 450
Year Founded: 2009
Business Description:
Holding Company; Breweries & Alcoholic Beverage Distr
S.I.C.: 6719; 2082; 5181
N.A.I.C.S.: 551112; 312120; 424810
Personnel:
Richard Lozyniak *(CEO)*
Advertising Agency:
The VIA Group LLC
34 Danforth St Ste 309
Portland, ME 04101
Tel.: (207) 221-3000
Fax: (207) 761-9422

PABST BREWING COMPANY
(Holding of C. Dean Metropoulos & Co.)
9014 Heritage Pkwy Ste 308
Woodridge, IL 60517
Tel.: (630) 972-3830
Fax: (630) 972-3838
Toll Free: (800) 935-BEER
E-mail: products@pabst.com
Web Site: www.pabstbrewingco.com
Sales Range: $50-74.9 Million
Approx. Number Employees: 700
Year Founded: 1844
Business Description:
Beer Mfr
S.I.C.: 2082
N.A.I.C.S.: 312120
Export
Advertising Expenditures: $500,000
Media: 2-5-6-9-10-15-18-19-20-23-24
Distr.: Natl.
Budget Set: Oct. -Nov.
Personnel:
Chris Steffanci *(COO)*
Bryan Crowley *(CMO)*
Brands & Products:
BALLANTINE
BLATZ
CARLING BLACK LABEL
CHAMPALE
COLT 45
COUNTRY CLUB
FALSTAFF
KINGSBURY
LONE STAR
LONE STAR LIGHT
LUCKY LAGER
NATIONAL BOHEMIAN
OLD MILWAUKEE
OLD STYLE
OLYMPIA
PABST BLUE RIBBON
PEARL
PIELS LIGHT
PRIMO ISLAND
RAINIER
SCHAEFER
SCHLITZ
SILVER THUNDER
SOUTHHAMPTON
SPECIAL EXPORT
ST. IDES
STAG
STROH'S
Advertising Agency:
Cole & Weber United
221 Yale Ave N Ste 600
Seattle, WA 98109
Tel.: (206) 447-9595
Fax: (206) 233-0178
Rainier Beer

PEARLSTINE DISTRIBUTORS INC.
1600 Charleston Regional Pkwy
Charleston, SC 29492
Tel.: (843) 388-6800
Fax: (843) 388-6799
Toll Free: (800) 922-1048
E-mail: contact@pearlstine.net
Web Site: www.pearlstine.net
Sales Range: $10-24.9 Million
Approx. Number Employees: 250
Year Founded: 1865
Business Description:
Beer Distr
S.I.C.: 5181
N.A.I.C.S.: 424810
Media: 18-19-22
Personnel:
Jan Pearlstine Lipov *(Co-Owner)*
Susan Pearlstine *(Co-Owner)*
Larry Lipov *(Pres)*
Alan Fine *(CFO)*
Alton Hutto *(VP-Sls)*
Tom Sahey *(VP-Sls)*
Chuck Marquardt *(Gen Mgr)*

PEPSI BEVERAGES COMPANY
(Formerly The Pepsi Bottling Group, Inc.)
(Div. of PepsiCo Americas Beverages)
1 Pepsi Way
Somers, NY 10589-2212
Tel.: (914) 767-6000
Fax: (914) 767-7761
Web Site: www.pepsico.com
Approx. Rev.: $13,219,000,000
Approx. Number Employees: 64,900
Year Founded: 1898
Business Description:
Soft Drink Mfr & Distr
S.I.C.: 2086; 2037; 2095
N.A.I.C.S.: 312111; 311411; 311920; 312112
Advertising Expenditures: $403,000,000
Media: 5
Distr.: Intl.; Natl.
Budget Set: Apr.
Personnel:
Eric J. Foss *(CEO)*
Thomas R. Greco *(Chief Comml Officer & Exec VP)*
Joshua Rabenovets *(Sr Brand Mgr-Diet Pepsi)*
Jaime Mahoney *(Dir-Mktg, TM Pepsi)*
Gary So *(Dir-Mktg, Pepsi Max)*
Advertising Agencies:
CRN International, Inc.
1 Circular Ave
Hamden, CT 06514-4002
Tel.: (203) 288-2002
Fax: (203) 281-3291
Toll Free: (800) 688-CRN1

Guide Publications
422 Morris Ave Ste 5
Long Branch, NJ 07740
Tel.: (732) 263-9675
Fax: (732) 263-0494

OSL Communications
1100 Ave des Canadiens Gare
Windsor Bureau C-18
Montreal, QC H3B 2S2, Canada
Tel.: (514) 849-9627
Fax: (514) 849-7935

T.D. Wang Advertising Group, LLC
1023 NE 66th St Ste B
Seattle, WA 98115
Tel.: (206) 674-9466
Fax: (206) 695-2788

PEPSI-COLA BOTTLING OF WORCESTER
90 Indus Dr
Holden, MA 01520
Tel.: (508) 829-6551
Fax: (508) 829-5680
Web Site: www.pepsiworcester.com
Sales Range: $10-24.9 Million
Approx. Number Employees: 100
Business Description:
Soft Drink Mfr & Bottler
S.I.C.: 2086
N.A.I.C.S.: 312111
Personnel:
Robert H. Rauh, Sr. *(Pres)*
Jim Carceo *(Head-Sls)*
Judy Holeman *(Mgr-HR)*
Advertising Agency:
Davis Advertising, Inc.
306 Main St
Worcester, MA 01608-1550
Tel.: (508) 752-4615
Fax: (508) 421-8001

PEPSI-COLA NORTH AMERICA
(Sub. of PepsiCo Beverages Americas)
700 Anderson Hill Rd
Purchase, NY 10577
Tel.: (914) 253-2000
Fax: (914) 253-2070
E-mail: info@pepsico.com
Web Site: www.pepsico.com/Contacts.html
Sales Range: $5-14.9 Billion
Approx. Number Employees: 1,589
Business Description:
Bottling Operations Management Services
S.I.C.: 7389
N.A.I.C.S.: 561499
Personnel:
Angelique Krembs *(Mng Dir)*
Joan Pertak *(CIO)*

Key to Media (For complete agency information see *The Advertising Red Books-Agencies* edition):
1. Bus. Publs. 2. Cable T.V. 3. Catalogs & Directories. 4. Co-op Adv. 5. Consumer Mags. 6. D.M. to Bus. Estab.7. D.M. to Consumers 8. Daily Newsp. 9. Exhibits/Trade Shows 10. Foreign 11. Infomercial 12. Internet Adv.13. Multimedia 14. Network Radio 15. Network T.V. 16. Newsp. Distr. Mags. 17. Other 18. Outdoor (Posters, Transit) 19. Point of Purchase20. Premiums, Novelties 21. Product Samples 22. Special Events Mktg. 23. Spot Radio 24. Spot T.V. 25. Weekly Newsp. 26. Yellow Page Adv.

Frank Cooper, III *(CMO-Portfolio Brands & VP)*
Peter Land *(Sr VP-Comm)*
Tom Silk *(VP-Mktg-Hydration & Juice Brands)*
John Vail *(Dir-Digital Production & Agency Mgmt)*
Lawrence DiCapua *(Dir-Consumer Engagement Optimization)*
Michael T. McMillan *(Dir-Marketplace Dev)*
Carlos Zepeda *(Dir-Mktg-Diet Pepsi)*
Martha Bermudez *(Sr Mgr-Mktg)*
Jason Thalappillil *(Mgr-Interactive Mktg)*

Advertising Agencies:
Arnell
7th World Trade Ctr
New York, NY 10007
Tel.: (212) 219-8400
Fax: (212) 334-0975
(Pepsi, Diet Pepsi)

TBWA Chiat Day Los Angeles
5353 Grosvenor Blvd
Los Angeles, CA 90066
Tel.: (310) 305-5000
Fax: (310) 305-6000
(Pepsi, Diet Pepsi)

PEPSICO INC.

700 Anderson Hill Rd
Purchase, NY 10577-1401
Tel.: (914) 253-2000
Fax: (914) 253-2070
Telex: 62848
Web Site: www.pepsico.com
Approx. Rev.: $57,838,000,000
Approx. Number Employees: 294,000
Year Founded: 1965

Business Description:
Snacks, Carbonated & Non-Carbonated Beverages & Food Mfr, Marketer & Distr
S.I.C.: 2086; 2096
N.A.I.C.S.: 312111; 311919; 312112
Import Export
Advertising Expenditures: $1,900,000,000
Media: 1-2-3-6-9-13-14-15-16-18-20-22-23-24
Distr.: Intl.; Natl.

Personnel:
Indra K. Nooyi *(Chm & CEO)*
Hugh F. Johnston *(CFO)*
Julie Hamp *(Chief Comm Officer & Sr VP)*
Mehmood Khan *(Chief Scientific Officer & CEO-Global Nutrition Grp)*
Grace M. Puma *(Chief Procurement Officer & Sr VP)*
Saad Abdul-Latif *(CEO-Asia, Middle East & Africa)*
Enderson Guimaraes *(Pres-Global Ops)*
Jaya Kumar *(Pres-Global Nutrition Platforms & PepsiCo Global Nutrition Grp)*
Zein Abdalla *(CEO-PepsiCo Europe)*
John C. Compton *(CEO-PepsiCo Americas Foods)*
Massimo Fasanella d'Amore *(CEO-Beverages Americas)*
Maura Abeln Smith *(Gen Counsel, Sec & Exec VP-Govt Affairs)*
Tessa Hilado *(Treas & Sr VP-Fin)*
Salman Amin *(Exec VP-Sls & Mktg)*
Timothy P. Cost *(Exec VP-Global Corp Affairs)*
Thomas R. Greco *(Exec VP-Sls-North America Beverages)*
Cynthia M. Trudell *(Chief Personnel Officer & Exec VP-HR)*
Peter A. Bridgman *(Sr VP & Controller)*
Heidi Kleinbach-Sauter *(Sr VP-R & D Global Foods)*
Sarah McGill *(Sr VP- Tax)*
Jonathan McIntyre *(Sr VP-R & D Global Beverages)*
Vivek Sankaran *(Sr VP-Corp Strategy & Dev)*
Clay G. Small *(Sr VP-Law)*
Kristina Mangelsdorf *(VP-Mktg-Natural & Flavored Sodas)*
Michael Fox *(Sr Dir-Strategy & Mktg-Frito-Lay Growth Ventures)*
Mark Rooks *(Dir-Sports Mktg)*
Jeffrey Barth *(Dir-Portal & Collaboration Svcs)*
B. Bonin Bough *(Dir-Digital & Social Media)*
Boderick Hall *(Dir-Digital Media)*
Michael Hammer *(Dir-Venture Capital Strategy)*
Marisol Tamaro *(Dir-Mktg-Mountain Dew)*
Derek Yach *(Dir-Global Health Policy)*
Bill Wyman *(Sr Mgr-Mktg-Pepsi Brand)*
Martha Bermudez *(Sr Mgr-Mktg)*
Noel Clarke *(Sr Brand Mgr-Pepsi)*
Paul Hyde *(Intl Brand Mgr-Pepsico Beverages Australasia)*
Ariadne Karpathak *(Brand Mgr-Lipton Iced Tea, Water IVI & Gatorade)*
Brett O'Brien *(Brand Mgr-Amp)*

Brands & Products:
AQUAFINA
AQUAFINA SPARKLING
BAKEN-EATS
BOCABITS
CAFFEINE FREE DIET PEPSI
CAFFEINE FREE MOUNTAIN DEW
CAFFEINE FREE PEPSI
CAP'N CRUNCH
CHEETOS
CHESTER
CHURRUMAIS
COPELLA
COQUEIRO
CRACKER JACK
CRUESLI
CRUJITOS
DIET MOUNTAIN DEW
DIET MOUNTAIN DEW CODE RED
DIET MOUNTAIN DEW ULTRAVIOLET
DIET PEPSI
DIET PEPSI FREE
DIET PEPSI LIME
DIET PEPSI MAX
DIET PEPSI TWIST
DIET PEPSI VENNILA
DIET SIERRA MIST
DIET SLICE
DORITOS
ELMA CHIPS
FANDANGOS
FRESCAVENA
FRITO-LAY
FRITOS
FRUITWORKS
FRUIVITA
GAMESA
GATORADE
GATORADE FIERCE
GATORADE FROST
GATORADE G2
GATORADE ICE
GATORADE ICE THIRST
GATORADE THIRST
GATORADE X-FACTOR
GATORADE XTREMO
GO SNACKS
GRANDMA'S
HAMKA
HARVEST CRUNCH
HICKORY
HOSTESS
HOT OAT
HOW DEW DOES DIET
KURKURE
LAY'S
LAY'S KETTLE
LIFE
LIPTON BRISK
LIPTON'S ICED TEA
MAGICO
MANZANITA SOL
MATUTANO
MOUNTAIN DEW
MOUNTAIN DEW CODE RED
MOUNTAIN DEW LIVEWIRE
MOUNTAIN DEW MDX
MOUNTAIN DEW VOLTAGE
MUG
MUNCHOS
NATURAL CHEETOS
NATURAL LAYS
NATURAL RUFFLES
NATURAL TOSTITOS
NEAR EAST
NIKNAK
OBERTO
PASO DE LOS TOROS
PASTA RONI
PEPSI
PEPSI BLUE
PEPSI-COLA
PEPSI LIGHT
PEPSI LIME
PEPSI LIMON
PEPSI MAX
PEPSI ONE
PEPSI TWIST
PEPSI VANILLA
PEPSICO
PEPSIECOCHALLENGE.COM
PEPSIRECYCLING.COM
PROPEL
QUAKER
QUAKER CHEWY
QUAKER DIPPS
QUAKER OATMEAL
QUAKER QUAKES
QUAKER SQUARES
QUAVERS
QUISP
RADICAL FRUIT
RED ROCK
RICE-A-RONI
ROLD GOLD
RUFFLES
RUSTLERS
SABRITAS
SCOTT
SIERRA MIST
SIERRA MIST CRANBERRY SPLASH
SIERRA MIST FREE CRANBERRY SPLASH
SIMBA
SLICE
SMART FOOD
SMITHS
SNACK A JACKS
SOBE
SONRIC
SPUDZ
SUN CHIPS
TIGER COOL FUSION
TIGER QUITE STORM
TIGER RED DRIVE
TODDYNHO
TOSTITOS
TROPICANA
TROPICANA LEMONADE & PUNCHES
TROPICANA LIGHT LEMONADE & PUNCHES
TROPICANA SMOOTHIES
TROPICANA TWISTER
TROPICANA TWISTER SODAS
WALKER FRENCH
WALKER MONSTER
WALKERS
WALKERS SQUARE
WAVY LAY'S
WILD CHERRY PEPSI
WOTSITS

Advertising Agencies:
BBDO New York
1285 Ave of the Americas 7th Fl
New York, NY 10019-6028
Tel.: (212) 459-5000
Mountain Dew
Game Fuel
Pepsi-Cola Stuff

DDB Chicago
200 E Randolph St
Chicago, IL 60601
Tel.: (312) 552-6000
Fax: (312) 552-2370
Creative
Sierra Mist

Firstborn
630 9th Ave Ste 910
New York, NY 10036
Tel.: (212) 581-1100
Fax: (212) 765-7605
Digital Creative
Sierra Mist
SoBe

The Food Group
589 8th Ave 4th Fl
New York, NY 10018
Tel.: (212) 725-5766
Fax: (212) 686-2901

The Geppetto Group
95 Morton St 8th Fl
New York, NY 10014-3336
Tel.: (212) 462-8140
Fax: (212) 462-8197

Goodby, Silverstein & Partners, Inc.
(Part of Omnicom Group, Inc.)
720 California St
San Francisco, CA 94108-2404
Tel.: (415) 392-0669
Fax: (415) 788-4303
Cheetos
Propel
Sierra Mist
Tostitos

Key to Media (For complete agency information see *The Advertising Red Books-Agencies* edition):
1. Bus. Publs. 2. Cable T.V. 3. Catalogs & Directories. 4. Co-op Adv. 5. Consumer Mags. 6. D.M. to Bus. Estab.7. D.M. to Consumers
8. Daily Newsp. 9. Exhibits/Trade Shows 10. Foreign 11. Infomercial 12. Internet Adv.13. Multimedia 14. Network Radio
15. Network T.V. 16. Newsp. Distr. Mags. 17. Other 18. Outdoor (Posters, Transit) 19. Point of Purchase20. Premiums, Novelties
21. Product Samples 22. Special Events Mktg. 23. Spot Radio 24. Spot T.V. 25. Weekly Newsp. 26. Yellow Page Adv.

PepsiCo Inc. — (Continued)

Grip Ltd.
179 John St 6th Fl
Toronto, ON M5T 1X4, Canada
Tel.: (416) 340-7111
Fax: (416) 340-7776
Sun Chips

Grow Marketing
1606 Union St
San Francisco, CA 94123
Tel.: (415) 440-4769
Fax: (415) 440-4779

GSD&M
828 W 6th St
Austin, TX 78703-5420
Tel.: (512) 242-4736
Fax: (512) 242-4700
Tropicana Pure Pemium

Juniper Park
2 Bloor St W 6th Fl
Toronto, ON M4W 3R6, Canada
Tel.: (416) 413-7301
Fax: (416) 972-5486
Tropicana Pure Premium

MG&G Advertising, Inc.
69 5th Ave 5th Fl
New York, NY 10003
Tel.: (646) 638-1447
Fax: (646) 638-1455

Mindshare
2 Ploenchit Ctr 23rd Fl Sukhumvit Rd
Bangkok, 10110, Thailand
Tel.: (66) 2 629 6000
Fax: (66) 2 629 6091

OMD-USA
195 Broadway
New York, NY 10007
Tel.: (212) 590-7100
Aquafina
Diet Mountain Dew
Mountain Dew MDX
Mountain Dew
Pepsi
Diet Pepsi
Sierra Mist
Game Fuel

PeraltaStrawberryFrog
Avenida Mofarrej 1200
Sao Paulo, 05311-000, Brazil
Tel.: (55) 11 3834 8344
Fax: (55) 11 3834 8344

R.K. Swamy BBDO
(Headquarters)
Film Chamber Bldg 604 Anna Salai
Chennai, 600006, India
Tel.: (91) 44 3988 3500
Fax: (91) 44 2829 2314
7UP

Seed Gives Life
27 W 24th St Ste 501
New York, NY 10010
Tel.: (212) 414-8605
Fax: (646) 349-1685
Mountain Dew

TBWA Chiat Day Los Angeles
5353 Grosvenor Blvd
Los Angeles, CA 90066
Tel.: (310) 305-5000
Fax: (310) 305-6000
G2
Gatorade
Pepsi
Pepsi Refresh Project
Tropicana Pure Premium
— David Dryer *(Acct Exec)*
— Kristen Latto *(Acct Exec)*

Tribal DDB Worldwide
437 Madison Ave 8th Fl
New York, NY 10022
Tel.: (212) 515-8600
Fax: (212) 515-8660

PITTSBURGH BREWING COMPANY

(Sub. of Keystone Brewers, Inc.)
3340 Liberty Ave
Pittsburgh, PA 15201-1321
Tel.: (412) 682-7400
Fax: (412) 692-1103
Fax: (412) 682-2379
E-mail: info@pittsburghbrewingco.com
Web Site: www.pittsburghbrewingco.com
E-Mail For Key Personnel:
President: jpiccirilli@pittsburghbrewingco.com
Marketing Director: cantone@pittsburghbrewingco.com
Sales Director: tferraro@pittsburghbrewingco.com
Approx. Sls.: $40,000,000
Year Founded: 1861
Business Description:
Brewery
S.I.C.: 2082
N.A.I.C.S.: 312120
Export
Media: 5-18-19-21-23-24
Distr.: Reg.
Budget Set: Oct.
Personnel:
Tony Ferraro *(VP-Sls)*
Christine Antone *(Dir-Mktg)*
Angelia Umbaugh *(Dir-Art)*
Brands & Products:
AMERICAN
AUGUSTINER
BRIGADE
I.C. LIGHT
IRON CITY
MUSTANG
OLD DUTCH
OLD GERMAN

POLAND SPRING CORPORATION

(Sub. of Nestle Waters North America Inc.)
777 W Putnam Ave
Greenwich, CT 06830-5091
Tel.: (203) 531-4100
Fax: (203) 863-0297
E-mail: info@polandspring.com
Web Site: www.nestle-watersna.com
Approx. Number Employees: 550
Year Founded: 1888
Business Description:
Bottler of Spring Water
S.I.C.: 5149
N.A.I.C.S.: 424490
Advertising Expenditures: $275,000
Media: 2-6-9-10-19-21-22-23-24-25
Distr.: Intl.; Natl.
Budget Set: Apr.
Personnel:
Kim Jeffrey *(Pres)*
Bob Davino *(VP-Mktg)*
Brands & Products:
POLAND SPRING
Advertising Agencies:
Goodway Group
The Pavilion 261 Old York Rd Ste 930
Jenkintown, PA 19046
Tel.: (215) 887-5700
Fax: (215) 881-2239

Zenith Media Services
(Regional Headquarters for ZenithOptimedia, the Americas)
299 W Houston St 10th Fl
New York, NY 10014-4806
Tel.: (212) 859-5100
Fax: (212) 727-9495

POLAR BEVERAGES

1001 Southbridge St
Worcester, MA 01610-2218
Mailing Address:
PO Box 15011
Worcester, MA 01615-0011
Tel.: (508) 753-4300
Fax: (508) 793-0813
Toll Free: (800) 225-7410
E-mail: info@polarbev.com
Web Site: www.polarbev.com
Sales Range: $350-399.9 Million
Approx. Number Employees: 1,000
Year Founded: 1882
Business Description:
Carbonated Beverages & Bottled Water
S.I.C.: 2086; 5149
N.A.I.C.S.: 312111; 424490
Export
Advertising Expenditures: $1,000,000
Media: 2-5-9-10-18-19-20-23-24-26
Distr.: Reg.
Budget Set: Various
Personnel:
Ralph Crowley *(Pres & CEO)*
Mike Mulrain *(CFO)*
Christopher Crowley *(Exec VP)*
Gerald Martin *(Dir-Mktg)*
Emilie Beley *(Asst Dir-Mktg)*
Brands & Products:
POLAR
Advertising Agency:
Palley Advertising Inc.
100 Grove St Ste 403
Worcester, MA 01605-2627
Tel.: (508) 792-6655
Fax: (508) 792-6626
Media Buying

PYRAMID BREWERIES INC.

(Sub. of Magic Hat Brewing Co. & Performing Arts Center Inc.)
91 S Royal Brougham Way
Seattle, WA 98134-1219
Tel.: (206) 682-8322
Fax: (206) 682-8420
E-mail: host@pyramidbrew.com
Web Site: www.pyramidbrew.com
Approx. Sls.: $47,684,000
Approx. Number Employees: 502
Year Founded: 1984
Business Description:
Ales, Lagers & Soda Mfr; Restaurant Operator
S.I.C.: 2082; 2099; 5812
N.A.I.C.S.: 312120; 311942; 722110
Advertising Expenditures: $718,000
Media: 5-13-22
Personnel:
Alan S. Newman *(Chief Creative Officer)*
Brands & Products:
AMBER WEIZEN
HEFEWEIZEN
INDIA PALE
PYRAMID ALEHOUSE
SNOW CAP
THOMAS KEMPER

RED BULL NORTH AMERICA, INC.

(Sub. of Red Bull GmbH)
1740 Stuart St
Santa Monica, CA 90404-3596
Tel.: (310) 393-4647
Fax: (310) 230-2361
Web Site: www.redbullusa.com
Approx. Number Employees: 600
Business Description:
Distributor of Beverages
S.I.C.: 2086; 5149
N.A.I.C.S.: 312111; 424490
Media: 6-13-19-21-22-24-31
Personnel:
Nate Warner *(Head-Social Media)*
Wendy Herm *(Dir-Mktg)*
David Brooks *(Mgr-Digital Mktg)*
Samuel Keene *(Mgr-Digital Mktg)*
Advertising Agencies:
Carat
150 E 42nd St
New York, NY 10017
Tel.: (212) 689-6800
Fax: (212) 689-6005
U.S. Media Assignment

Kastner & Partners
150 Pico Blvd
Santa Monica, CA 90405
Tel.: (310) 458-2000
Fax: (310) 458-6300
(Media)

REED'S, INC.

13000 S Spring St
Los Angeles, CA 90061-1634
Tel.: (310) 217-9400
Fax: (310) 217-9411
Toll Free: (800) 997-3337
E-mail: info@reedsinc.com
Web Site: www.reedsgingerbrew.com
Approx. Sls.: $20,376,000
Approx. Number Employees: 57
Year Founded: 1987
Business Description:
Natural Carbonated Beverages, Candy, Ice Cream & Various Other Food Beverage & Food Products Mfr
S.I.C.: 2086; 2024; 2037; 2099
N.A.I.C.S.: 312111; 311340; 311411; 311520; 311999
Advertising Expenditures: $171,000
Media: 2-7-10-13-19
Personnel:
Christopher J. Reed *(Chm, Pres & CEO)*
James Linesch *(CFO)*
Thierry Foucaut *(COO)*
Mark Reed *(Exec VP-Sls)*
Neal Cohane *(Sr VP-Sls & Mktg)*
Eric Scheffer *(VP & Mgr-Natl Sls-Natural Foods)*

Key to Media (For complete agency information see *The Advertising Red Books-Agencies* edition):
1. Bus. Publs. 2. Cable T.V. 3. Catalogs & Directories. 4. Co-op Adv. 5. Consumer Mags. 6. D.M. to Bus. Estab.7. D.M. to Consumers
8. Daily Newsp. 9. Exhibits/Trade Shows 10. Foreign 11. Infomercial 12. Internet Adv.13. Multimedia 14. Network Radio
15. Network T.V. 16. Newsp. Distr. Mags. 17. Other 18. Outdoor (Posters, Transit) 19. Point of Purchase20. Premiums, Novelties
21. Product Samples 22. Special Events Mktg. 23. Spot Radio 24. Spot T.V. 25. Weekly Newsp. 26. Yellow Page Adv.

Rory Ahearn *(VP-Sls)*
Robert Lyon *(VP-Sls-Special Projects)*

REPUBLIC NATIONAL DISTRIBUTING COMPANY
8045 Northcourt Rd
Houston, TX 77040
Tel.: (832) 782-1000
Fax: (832) 782-1010
Web Site: www.rndc-usa.com
Sales Range: $1-4.9 Billion
Approx. Number Employees: 6,000
Year Founded: 1935
Business Description:
Spirits & Wine Wholesale Distr
S.I.C.: 5182
N.A.I.C.S.: 424820
Media: 2-7-22
Personnel:
Edward L. Block *(Chm)*
Tom Cole *(Pres)*
Bob Hendrickson *(Exec VP-Sls & Mktg)*
Bill Blackwell *(VP-Fin & Acctg)*
Greg Bowdish *(VP-Natl Accts & Mktg)*
Robert Olivares *(Dir-Mktg)*
Sam Ray *(Mgr-Natl Acct)*
Michael Thomas *(Mgr-Mktg)*

ROCKSTAR INC.
101 Convention Center Dr Ste 777
Las Vegas, NV 89109
Mailing Address:
PO Box 27740
Las Vegas, NV 89126
Tel.: (702) 939-5535
Fax: (702) 221-0904
E-mail: info@rockstar69.com
Web Site: www.rockstar69.com
Business Description:
Energy Drink Mfr & Marketer
S.I.C.: 2086
N.A.I.C.S.: 312111
Media: 6-13-18-20-22-23
Personnel:
Frank Guernsey *(VP-Mktg)*
Brands & Products:
PARTY LIKE A ROCKSTAR!
ROCKSTAR
ROCKSTAR JUICED
ROCKSTAR SUGAR FREE
ZERO CARB

ROYAL CROWN, SEVEN UP
(Sub. of Dr Pepper Snapple Group, Inc.)
1100 Independence Ave
Evansville, IN 47714-4549
Mailing Address:
PO Box 2870
Evansville, IN 47728-0870
Tel.: (812) 423-4483
Fax: (812) 421-3038
Sales Range: $75-99.9 Million
Approx. Number Employees: 200
Business Description:
Soft Drinks
S.I.C.: 2086
N.A.I.C.S.: 312111
Import Export
Media: 2-4-5-11-13-22
Personnel:
Dave Brown *(Mktg Dir)*

SARATOGA BEVERAGE GROUP, INC.
(Holding of North Castle Partners, L.L.C.)
11 Geyser Rd
Saratoga Springs, NY 12866-9038
Tel.: (518) 584-6363
Fax: (518) 584-0380
Web Site:
www.saratogaspringwater.com
Sales Range: $50-74.9 Million
Approx. Number Employees: 25
Year Founded: 1872
Business Description:
Bottler of Mineral & Spring Water
S.I.C.: 5149
N.A.I.C.S.: 424490
Export
Advertising Expenditures: $3,000,000
Media: 1-2-4-6-7-9-10-13-18-19-20-21-22
Distr.: Natl.
Brands & Products:
JUST PIK'T FROZEN JUICE
SARATOGA ESSENCE
SARATOGA SPLASH
SARATOGA SPRINGS
ULTIMATE JUICE
ZERO CALORIE

SEATTLE COFFEE COMPANY
(Sub. of Starbucks Corporation)
2401 Utah Ave S
Seattle, WA 98101-2078
Tel.: (206) 447-1575
Fax: (206) 447-0828
Web Site: www.seattlesbest.com
Sales Range: $25-49.9 Million
Approx. Number Employees: 45
Business Description:
Coffee Distr
S.I.C.: 2095
N.A.I.C.S.: 311920
Advertising Expenditures: $200,000
Media: 6-8-13-18-21
Brands & Products:
SEATTLE'S BEST COFFEE
TORREFAZIONE ITALIA

SHASTA, INC.
(Sub. of National Beverage Corp.)
8100 SW 10th St Ste 4000
Plantation, FL 33324
Tel.: (954) 581-0922
Fax: (954) 473-4710
Web Site: www.shastapop.com
Sales Range: $25-49.9 Million
Approx. Number Employees: 58
Business Description:
Beverage Mfr
S.I.C.: 2086; 5149
N.A.I.C.S.: 312111; 424490
Media: 1-6-7-9-14-15-23-24-25
Distr.: Natl.
Budget Set: June
Personnel:
Brent Bott *(Dir-Mktg)*

SIERRA NEVADA BREWING CO.
1075 E 20th St
Chico, CA 95928
Tel.: (530) 893-3520
Fax: (530) 893-1275
E-mail: info@sierranevada.com
Web Site: www.sierranevada.com
Approx. Number Employees: 500
Year Founded: 1980
Business Description:
Brewery
S.I.C.: 2082
N.A.I.C.S.: 312120
Personnel:
Ken Grossman *(Founder, Owner & CEO)*
Joe Whitney *(Dir-Sls & Mktg)*
Advertising Agency:
Carmichael Lynch Spong
110 N 5th St
Minneapolis, MN 55403
Tel.: (612) 375-8555
Fax: (612) 375-8501

SLEEMAN BREWERIES, LTD.
(Sub. of Sapporo Holdings Limited)
551 Clair Rd W
Guelph, ON N1L 1E9, Canada
Tel.: (519) 822-1834
Fax: (519) 822-0430
Toll Free: (800) 268-8537
E-mail: sleemanir@sleeman.ca
Web Site: www.sleeman.com
Sales Range: $150-199.9 Million
Approx. Number Employees: 1,000
Year Founded: 1984
Business Description:
Developer, Producer, Importer, Marketer & Distr of Beer
S.I.C.: 2082
N.A.I.C.S.: 312120
Media: 3-14-18
Personnel:
John Sleeman *(Founder & Chm)*
Shige Yokoi *(Pres & CEO)*
Stephane Duval *(VP-Mktg)*
Greg Newbrough *(VP-Sls)*
Skazuhiko Panaka *(VP-Fin & Devel)*
Brands & Products:
SLEEMAN CREAM ALE
Advertising Agency:
Dentsu Canada
276 King St W
Toronto, ON M5V 1J2, Canada
Tel.: (416) 929-9700
Fax: (416) 929-0128
Sapporo

SLEEMAN UNIBROUE QUEBEC
(Sub. of Sleeman Breweries, Ltd.)
80 Rue Des Carrieres
Chambly, QC J3L 2H6, Canada
Tel.: (450) 658-7658
Fax: (450) 658-9195
E-mail: info@unibroue.com
Web Site: www.unibroue.com
Approx. Number Employees: 130
Year Founded: 1990
Business Description:
Brewery
S.I.C.: 5921
N.A.I.C.S.: 445310
Media: 6-10-19-20
Brands & Products:
11
1837
BLANCHE DE CHAMBLY
DON DE DIEU
EAU BENITE
EPHEMERE
FIN DU MONDE
FRINGANTE
LA BOLDUE
LA GAILLARDE
MAUDITE
QUELQUE CHOSE
RAFTMAN
ST-HUBERT
TERRIBLE
TROIS PISTOLES
U
U2

SPRECHER BREWING COMPANY
701 W Glendale Ave
Glendale, WI 53209
Tel.: (414) 964-7837
Fax: (414) 964-2462
E-mail: beer@sprecherbrewery.com
Web Site: www.sprecherbrewery.com
Approx. Sls.: $5,000,000
Approx. Number Employees: 50
Year Founded: 1985
Business Description:
European-Style Beer & Gourmet Sodas Brewery
S.I.C.: 2082; 2086
N.A.I.C.S.: 312120; 312111
Advertising Expenditures: $50,000
Media: 5-6-10-19-21-22-23-25
Distr.: Natl.
Personnel:
Randy Sprecher *(Owner)*
Anne Sprecher *(Dir-HR)*
Brands & Products:
ABBEY TRIPLE
BLACK BAVARIAN
CREAM
DOPPLE BOCK
GENERATION PORTER
GINGER ALE
HEFE WEISS
IMPERIAL STOUT
IRISH STOUT
LO-CAL
MAI BOCK
MICRO-LIGHT
OKTOBERFEST
ORANGE DREAM
ORANGE DREAM SODA
PALE LAGER
PIZZA BEER
PUB ALE
PUMA KOLA
RAVIN' RED
RAVIN' RED SODA
SPECIAL AMBER
WINTER BREW

SUMMIT BREWING CO.
910 Montreal Cir
Saint Paul, MN 55102
Tel.: (651) 265-7800
Fax: (651) 265-7801
Web Site: www.summitbrewing.com
Sales Range: $10-24.9 Million
Approx. Number Employees: 45
Business Description:
Brewery
S.I.C.: 2082
N.A.I.C.S.: 312120
Media: 23
Personnel:
Mark O. Stutrud *(Founder)*

UNITED STATES BEVERAGE LLC
700 Canal St
Stamford, CT 06902
Tel.: (203) 961-8215
Fax: (203) 961-8216
Web Site:
www.unitedstatesbeverage.com
Approx. Sls.: $17,200,000
Approx. Number Employees: 25

Key to Media (For complete agency information see *The Advertising Red Books-Agencies* edition):
1. Bus. Publs. 2. Cable T.V. 3. Catalogs & Directories. 4. Co-op Adv. 5. Consumer Mags. 6. D.M. to Bus. Estab.7. D.M. to Consumers 8. Daily Newsp. 9. Exhibits/Trade Shows 10. Foreign 11. Infomercial 12. Internet Adv.13. Multimedia 14. Network Radio 15. Network T.V. 16. Newsp. Distr. Mags. 17. Other 18. Outdoor (Posters, Transit) 19. Point of Purchase20. Premiums, Novelties 21. Product Samples 22. Special Events Mktg. 23. Spot Radio 24. Spot T.V. 25. Weekly Newsp. 26. Yellow Page Adv.

United States Beverage LLC — (Continued)

Business Description:
Beer & Other Fermented Malt Liquors
S.I.C.: 5181; 2082
N.A.I.C.S.: 424810; 312120
Personnel:
Joseph J. Fisch, Jr. *(Pres & CEO)*
Paul Moorehead *(VP & Dir-Creative Mktg)*
Brands & Products:
26000 VODKA
BARONS
BLACK DOG ALE
ESTRELLA DAMM
SLO BREWING CO.
TEQUILOCO
TONA CERVEZA
USB
ZAMKOWE
Advertising Agency:
5W Public Relations
888 7th Ave 12th Fl
New York, NY 10106
Tel.: (212) 999-5585
Fax: (646) 328-1711

VERMONT PURE HOLDINGS, LTD.
(Name Changed to CRYSTAL ROCK HOLDINGS, INC.)

VISAGE MOBILE, INC.
500 Sansome St Ste 300
San Francisco, CA 94111
Tel.: (415) 200-2888
E-mail: jvlahos@visagemobile.com
Web Site: www.visagemobile.com
Sales Range: $1-9.9 Million
Business Description:
Wireless Technology
S.I.C.: 4812
N.A.I.C.S.: 517212
Personnel:
Timothy Weingarten *(Chm)*
Bzur Haun *(Pres & CEO)*
Dean Alms *(VP-Strategy)*
Jim Bertram *(VP-Sls)*
Maggie Mosteller *(Sr Dir-Mktg)*
Advertising Agency:
Kulesa Faul Inc.
107 S B St Ste 330
San Mateo, CA 94401
Tel.: (650) 340-1979
Fax: (650) 340-1849

VITALITY FOODSERVICE INC.
(Sub. of Nestle USA, Inc.)
400 N Tampa St Ste 1500
Tampa, FL 33602-4793
Tel.: (813) 301-4600
Fax: (813) 301-4760
Toll Free: (888) 863-6726
Web Site:
www.vitalityfoodservice.com
Sales Range: $200-249.9 Million
Approx. Number Employees: 700
Year Founded: 1989
Business Description:
Dispensing Equipment & Non-Carbonated Juice Beverages Mfr & Whslr
S.I.C.: 5149; 3586
N.A.I.C.S.: 424490; 333913
Media: 2-4-7-10-13
Personnel:
Kim Johnson *(CFO & Exec VP)*
Jerry Desmond *(VP-Sls-US)*
Bing Smith *(VP-Sls-Canada)*
Brands & Products:
EXPRESS PAK
VITALITY

WARSTEINER IMPORTERS AGENCY, INC.
(Sub. of Warsteiner International KG)
9359 Allen Rd
West Chester, OH 45069
Tel.: (513) 942-9872
Fax: (513) 942-9874
E-mail: hq@warsteiner-usa.com
Web Site: www.warsteiner-usa.com
Approx. Number Employees: 35
Year Founded: 1981
Business Description:
Beer Importer & Distr
S.I.C.: 5181
N.A.I.C.S.: 424810
Import
Media: 2-3-5-9-10-15-16-18-19-20-21-22-23
Distr.: Natl.
Brands & Products:
BECAUSE LIFE IS TOO SHORT TO DRINK CHEAP BEER
WARSTEINER
WARSTEINER PREMIUM DUNKEL
WARSTEINER PREMIUM FRESH
WARSTEINER PREMIUM VERUM

WET PLANET BEVERAGE CO.
130 Linden Oaks Ste C
Rochester, NY 14625-2834
Tel.: (585) 381-3560
Fax: (585) 381-4025
E-mail: webmaster@wetplanet.com
Web Site: www.joltenergy.com
Sales Range: $75-99.9 Million
Approx. Number Employees: 20
Year Founded: 1985
Business Description:
Soft Drinks Mfr & Distr
S.I.C.: 5149
N.A.I.C.S.: 424490
Export
Personnel:
C. J. Rapp *(Founder)*
Brands & Products:
AUTUMN FROST
BLU BOTOL NATURAL WATERS
DNA
FIRST TEE
JOLT
JUMPER CABLE
KRANK2O
MARTINELLI'S
NAPA VALLEY
PIRATES KEG GOURMET SODAS
PJ'S LOGANBERRY
POKER
THORNWOOD
XTC
Advertising Agencies:
COLANGELO
120 Tokeneke Rd
Darien, CT 06820
Tel.: (203) 662-6600
Fax: (203) 662-6601

Makai
211 Nevada St
El Segundo, CA 90245
Tel.: (310) 546-9585
Fax: (310) 321-7933
Jolt

WHITE ROCK PRODUCTS CORP.
14107 20th Ave Ste 403
Whitestone, NY 11357-3055
Tel.: (718) 746-3400
Fax: (718) 767-0413
Toll Free: (800) 969-7625
E-mail: info@whiterockbev.com
Web Site:
www.whiterockbeverages.com
Approx. Number Employees: 16
Year Founded: 1871
Business Description:
Mfr. of Sparkling/Spring Water, Carbonated/Natural Teas & Flavored Beverages
S.I.C.: 5149
N.A.I.C.S.: 424490
Export
Advertising Expenditures: $1,000,000
Media: 2-6-7-10-13-18-20-21
Distr.: Natl.
Budget Set: Nov.
Personnel:
Lawrence Bodkin *(Pres)*
Al Brazinskas *(CFO)*
Brands & Products:
OLDE BROOKLYN
SIOUX CITY
WHITE ROCK
Advertising Agency:
Beltrame Leffler Advertising
708 Massachusetts Ave
Indianapolis, IN 46204
Tel.: (317) 916-9930
Fax: (317) 916-9935

WILD GOOSE BREWING, LLC
(Sub. of Flying Dog Brewery)
4607 Wedgewood Blvd
Frederick, MD 21703-7120
Tel.: (301) 694-7899
Fax: (301) 694-2971
E-mail: info@wildgoosebrewery.com
Web Site:
www.wildgoosebrewery.com
Sales Range: $1-9.9 Million
Approx. Number Employees: 18
Year Founded: 1992
Business Description:
Beer & Ale Brewer
S.I.C.: 2082
N.A.I.C.S.: 312120
Media: 6-9-18-22-23
Distr.: Reg.
Personnel:
Jim Caruso *(Pres)*
Brands & Products:
IPA INDIA PALE ALE
WILD GOOSE BROWN LAGER
WILD GOOSE OATMEAL STOUT
XPA EXTRA PALE ALE

Key to Media (For complete agency information see *The Advertising Red Books-Agencies* edition):
1. Bus. Publs. 2. Cable T.V. 3. Catalogs & Directories. 4. Co-op Adv. 5. Consumer Mags. 6. D.M. to Bus. Estab.7. D.M. to Consumers 8. Daily Newsp. 9. Exhibits/Trade Shows 10. Foreign 11. Infomercial 12. Internet Adv.13. Multimedia 14. Network Radio 15. Network T.V. 16. Newsp. Distr. Mags. 17. Other 18. Outdoor (Posters, Transit) 19. Point of Purchase20. Premiums, Novelties 21. Product Samples 22. Special Events Mktg. 23. Spot Radio 24. Spot T.V. 25. Weekly Newsp. 26. Yellow Page Adv.

Broadcasting, Cable, Film & Video

Broadcasting Equipment — Cable TV — Educational Films — Industrial Films — Production & Post-Production Studios & Services — Radio Stations — TV Stations — Video Rental Stores — Video Tapes

1070 WIBC
(Div. of Emmis Indiana Broadcasting, L.P.)
40 Monument Cir Ste 400
Indianapolis, IN 46204
Tel.: (317) 266-9422
Fax: (317) 631-3750
E-mail: ir@emmis.com
Web Site: www.wibc.com
Sales Range: $75-99.9 Million
Approx. Number Employees: 300
Business Description:
Radio Broadcasting Services
S.I.C.: 4832
N.A.I.C.S.: 515112
Media: 13-18-20-22-23
Personnel:
Jeffrey Smulyan *(Chm)*
Patrick Walch *(CFO)*
Charlie Morgan *(Gen Mgr)*
Eric Wunnenberg *(Gen Mgr-Sls)*
Taylor Bennett *(Editor-Assignment & Editor-News)*
Sarah Cole *(Dir-Community Advancement)*
John Emerson *(Dir-Network Opers)*
Sean Matthews *(Dir-Production)*
Kent Sterling *(Dir-Program)*
Patty England *(Mgr-Natl Sls)*

20TH CENTURY FOX FILM CORP.
(Sub. of Fox Entertainment Group, Inc.)
10201 W Pico Blvd
Los Angeles, CA 90035
Mailing Address:
PO Box 900
Beverly Hills, CA 90213-0900
Tel.: (310) 369-1000
Tel.: (310) 277-2211
Fax: (310) 203-1558
Web Site: www.fox.com
Sales Range: $1-4.9 Billion
Approx. Number Employees: 5,000
Business Description:
Motion Picture & Television Production & Distribution
S.I.C.: 7812; 7819; 7822; 7829
N.A.I.C.S.: 512110; 512120; 512191; 512199
Advertising Expenditures: $43,000,000
Media: 2-3-6-9-14-15-18-23-24
Distr.: Intl.; Natl.
Personnel:
Thomas E. Rothman *(Co-Chm)*
Robert Harper *(Vice Chm)*
Oren Aviv *(CMO & Co-Pres-Domestic Theatrical Mktg)*
Tony Sella *(Chief Creative Officer & Co-Pres-Domestic Theatrical Mktg)*
John Herbert *(CIO & Exec VP-Ops Strategy)*
Chris Petrikin *(Exec VP-Corp Comm & Publicity)*
Bumble Ward *(Exec VP-Domestic Publicity)*
Zachery Eller *(Sr VP-Partnership Mktg & Promos-Mktg Unit)*
Anna Roca *(Sr VP-Promos-Intl)*
Peter Stougaard *(Sr VP-Creative Adv)*
Rodney Brown *(Exec Dir-New Release Mktg)*
Lisa DelMonte *(Dir-Online Adv)*
Alycia Marrapodi *(Dir-Digital Mktg)*
Ira Rubenstein *(Dir-Digital Mktg)*
Dougal Strachan *(Dir-Digital Mktg)*
Geoff Calnan *(Mgr-Creative Svcs)*
Hiro Kamegaya *(Mgr-Theatrical Promos-Intl)*
Brands & Products:
20TH CENTURY FOX
Advertising Agencies:
Maslansky, Luntz & Partners
1101 King St Ste 110
Alexandria, VA 22314
Tel.: (703) 358-0080
Fax: (703) 358-0089

Posterscope
2 Park Ave., 24th Fl
New York, NY 10016
Tel.: (917) 621-3250
Fax: (562) 695-1310

20TH CENTURY FOX HOME ENTERTAINMENT, INC.
(Sub. of 20th Century Fox Film Corp.)
2121 Ave of the Stars 25th Fl
Los Angeles, CA 90067-5010
Mailing Address:
PO Box 900
Beverly Hills, CA 90213-0900
Tel.: (310) 369-3900
Tel.: (310) 369-1000
Fax: (310) 369-3318
Fax: (310) 369-5262
Web Site: www.foxhome.com
Sales Range: $350-399.9 Million
Approx. Number Employees: 450
Year Founded: 1979
Business Description:
Motion Picture & Television Program Video Marketer & Distr
S.I.C.: 7822
N.A.I.C.S.: 512120
Advertising Expenditures: $310,000
Media: 2-3-4-6-7-10-15-23-24
Distr.: Intl.; Natl.
Personnel:
Paul Chambers *(Exec VP)*
Laura Cook *(Exec VP-Bus & Legal Affairs)*
Jennifer Chai *(Sr VP-Mktg)*
Gary Ferguson *(Sr VP-Emerging Markets)*
James Finn *(Sr VP-Corp & Consumer Comm)*
Advertising Agencies:
Hill & Knowlton, Inc.
(Member of WPP)
825 3rd Ave 24th Fl
New York, NY 10022
Tel.: (212) 885-0300
Fax: (212) 885-0570

PointRoll Inc.
951 E Hector St
Conshohocken, PA 19428
Tel.: (267) 558-1300
Fax: (267) 285-1141
Toll Free: (800) 203-6956

A&E TELEVISION NETWORKS INTERNATIONAL L.P.
(Joint Venture of Comcast Corporation, The Walt Disney Company, General Electric Company & The Hearst Corporation)
235 E 45th St
New York, NY 10017
Tel.: (212) 210-1400
Fax: (212) 850-9370
Web Site: www.aetn.com
Approx. Sls.: $885,800,000
Approx. Number Employees: 650
Business Description:
Holding Company; Cable Television Networks; Owned 42.5% by The Hearst Corporation, 42.5% by ABC, Inc. & 15% by NBC Universal, Inc.
S.I.C.: 6719; 4841
N.A.I.C.S.: 551112; 515210
Media: 1-2-3-6-9-11-13-14-18-20-22-23-24-25
Distr.: Intl.; Natl.
Budget Set: Oct.
Personnel:
Abbe Raven *(Pres & CEO)*
Gerard Gruosso *(CFO & Exec VP)*
Robert DeBitetto *(Pres-AE & Bio Channel)*
Melvin Berning *(Exec VP-Natl Ad Sls)*
Whitney Goit, II *(Exec VP)*
Steve Ronson *(Exec VP-Enterprises)*
Rob Sharenow *(Exec VP-Programming)*
Michael Feeney *(Sr VP-Corp Comm)*
Mark Garner *(Sr VP-Bus Dev & Distr Mktg)*
Thomas Moody *(Sr VP-Program Planning & Acq)*
Don Robert *(Sr VP-Res)*
Guy Slattery *(Sr VP-Mktg)*
Mona Tropeano *(Sr VP-Ad Sls Ops & Admin)*
Nancy Alpert *(VP & Deputy Gen Counsel)*
Michael Katz *(VP-Programming & Production-Intl)*
Marcela Tabares *(VP-Sls Res)*
Julya Fridman *(Sr Dir-Bus Dev & Strategic Insights)*
Madeleine Lowinger *(Dir-Music Svcs)*
Brands & Products:
A&E
BIOGRAPHY
BIOGRAPHY CHANNEL
HISTORY CHANNEL
Advertising Agencies:
Venables, Bell & Partners
201 Post St Ste 200
San Francisco, CA 94108
Tel.: (415) 288-3300
Fax: (415) 421-3683

ZENO Group
(An Affiliate of Daniel J. Edelman Company)
200 Park Ave S Ste 1603
New York, NY 10003
Tel.: (212) 299-8888
Fax: (212) 462-1026

ABC CABLE NETWORKS GROUP
(Sub. of The Walt Disney Company)
500 S Buena Vista St

Key to Media (For complete agency information see *The Advertising Red Books-Agencies* edition):
1. Bus. Publs. 2. Cable T.V. 3. Catalogs & Directories. 4. Co-op Adv. 5. Consumer Mags. 6. D.M. to Bus. Estab.7. D.M. to Consumers 8. Daily Newsp. 9. Exhibits/Trade Shows 10. Foreign 11. Infomercial 12. Internet Adv.13. Multimedia 14. Network Radio 15. Network T.V. 16. Newsp. Distr. Mags. 17. Other 18. Outdoor (Posters, Transit) 19. Point of Purchase20. Premiums, Novelties 21. Product Samples 22. Special Events Mktg. 23. Spot Radio 24. Spot T.V. 25. Weekly Newsp. 26. Yellow Page Adv.

ABC Cable Networks Group — (Continued)

Burbank, CA 91521
Tel.: (818) 569-7500
Fax: (818) 563-3892
Sales Range: $100-124.9 Million
Approx. Number Employees: 450
Business Description:
Cable Television Programming
S.I.C.: 4841
N.A.I.C.S.: 515210
Media: 2-3-6-8-9-13-18-22-23-24-25
Distr.: Natl.
Personnel:
Jewell Engstrom *(CFO & Exec VP)*
Albert Cheng *(Exec VP-Digital Media)*
Judy Taylor *(Sr VP-Casting & Talent Rels)*
Karin Timpone *(Sr VP-Product Strategy & Mktg)*
Beth Johnson *(VP-Digital Media-Disney ABC Television Grp)*
Advertising Agency:
Initiative Los Angeles
5700 Wilshire Blvd Ste 400
Los Angeles, CA 90036-3648
Tel.: (323) 370-8000
Fax: (323) 370-8950

ABC FAMILY CHANNEL
(Div. of ABC Family)
500 S Buena Vista St
Burbank, CA 91521-9078
Tel.: (818) 560-1000
Web Site: www.abcfamily.go.com
Sales Range: $350-399.9 Million
Approx. Number Employees: 400
Year Founded: 1977
Business Description:
Family-Oriented National Cable Network Services
S.I.C.: 7812; 4841
N.A.I.C.S.: 512110; 515210
Media: 2-3-5-6-9-10-14-15-16-18-19-20-23-24-25
Distr.: Natl.
Personnel:
Michael Riley *(Pres)*
Danielle Mullin *(VP-Mktg)*
Brands & Products:
CABLE HEALTH CLUB
FAM
THE FAMILY CHANNEL
THE FAMILY CHANNEL SEAL OF QUALITY
INTERNATIONAL FAMILY CHANNEL, INC.
Advertising Agency:
M/K Advertising Partners, Ltd. (d/b/a MK)
28 W 25th St 9th Fl
New York, NY 10010
Tel.: (212) 367-9225
Fax: (212) 242-7008

ABC, INC.
(Sub. of The Walt Disney Company)
77 W 66th St
New York, NY 10023-6201
Tel.: (212) 456-7777
Fax: (212) 456-1424
Web Site: www.abc.com
Sales Range: $5-14.9 Billion
Approx. Number Employees: 10,000
Year Founded: 1943
Business Description:
Television Networks
S.I.C.: 4833; 4832
N.A.I.C.S.: 515120; 515112
Advertising Expenditures: $64,973,000
Media: 2-3-6-9-14-15-16-18-23-24
Distr.: Intl.; Natl.
Personnel:
James L. Hedges *(CFO & Exec VP)*
Michael Shaw *(Pres-Ad Sls & Mktg)*
Michael Benson *(Exec VP-Mktg)*
Marla Provencio *(Exec VP-Mktg-ABC Entertainment)*
T. Scott Fain *(Sr VP & Deputy Gen Counsel)*
Sue Binford *(Sr VP-Corp Commun)*
Daniel Longest *(Sr VP-Disney Unlimited)*
Susan Dumond *(VP-HR)*
Advertising Agency:
Rubenstein Associates, Inc.
1345 Ave of the Americas Fl 30
New York, NY 10105-0109
Tel.: (212) 843-8000
Fax: (212) 843-9200

ABC NEWS, INC.
(Sub. of ABC News & Sports)
77 W 66th St
New York, NY 10023-6201
Tel.: (212) 456-7777
Fax: (212) 456-4297
E-mail: info@abcnews.go.com
Web Site: www.abcnews.go.com
Sales Range: $10-24.9 Million
Approx. Number Employees: 65
Business Description:
News Syndicate
S.I.C.: 7383
N.A.I.C.S.: 519110
Media: 3-6-9-14-15-18-23-24-25
Distr.: Natl.
Personnel:
Patricia J Matson *(Vice Chm)*
Paul Friedman *(Exec VP)*
Paul Slavin *(Sr VP-Digital)*
Catherine Sullivan *(Sr VP-ABC NEWS Sls)*
Cathie Levine *(VP-Comm)*
Brands & Products:
20/20
20/20/ DOWNTOWN
ABC NEWS
NIGHTLINE

ACCUWEATHER, INC.
385 Science Pk Rd
State College, PA 16803-2215
Tel.: (814) 237-0309
Fax: (814) 238-1339
E-mail: webhelp@accuweather.com
Web Site: www.accuweather.com
E-Mail For Key Personnel:
Marketing Director: rainey@accuwx.com
Approx. Number Employees: 325
Year Founded: 1962
Business Description:
Weather Information Supplier
S.I.C.: 7383; 8231
N.A.I.C.S.: 519110; 519120
Media: 2-4-6-7-8-10-13-15-20-23
Personnel:
Joel N. Myers *(Founder, Chm & Pres)*
Barry Lee Myers *(CFO)*
Lee Myers *(CFO)*
Evan Myers *(COO & Sr VP)*
Jim Candor *(Sr VP-New Media)*
Michael Steinberg *(Sr VP)*
Lee Rainey *(VP-Mktg)*
Scott Homan *(Exec Dir)*
Michael Sylvie *(Dir-User Experience)*
Brands & Products:
ACCUHELP
ACCUMALL
ACCUPOP
ACCUWEATHER
ACCUWEATHER REALFEEL TEMPERATURE
ACCUWEATHER.COM
AGRI-WEATHER
THE BEST WEATHER ON THE WEB
GALILEO
SNOW WARNING SERVICE
THE WORLD'S WEATHER AUTHORITY

ACME COMMUNICATIONS, INC.
2101 E 4th St Ste 202
Santa Ana, CA 92705-3825
Tel.: (714) 245-9499
Fax: (714) 245-9494
E-mail: ir@acmecommunications.com
Web Site: www.acmecommunications.com
Approx. Rev.: $26,848,000
Approx. Number Employees: 141
Business Description:
Holding Company; Owner & Operator of Broadcast Television Stations
S.I.C.: 4833
N.A.I.C.S.: 515120
Advertising Expenditures: $1,849,000
Personnel:
Thomas D. Allen *(Co-Founder)*
Jamie Kellner *(Chm)*
Douglas Gealy *(Pres & CEO)*
Jutta Gebauer *(CFO-Acting)*
Stan Gill *(COO)*
John Hannon *(Exec VP)*
John Greenwood *(VP & Gen Mgr)*
Sharon Weiler *(VP & Dir-Sls)*

AIRVANA, INC.
19 Alpha Rd
Chelmsford, MA 01824
Tel.: (978) 250-3000
Fax: (978) 250-3910
Toll Free: (866) 344-7437
E-mail: information@airvana.com
Web Site: www.airvana.com
Approx. Rev.: $64,594,000
Approx. Number Employees: 600
Year Founded: 2000
Business Description:
Network Infrastructure Products Mfr
S.I.C.: 3661; 3663; 4812
N.A.I.C.S.: 334210; 334220; 517212
Advertising Expenditures: $693,000
Personnel:
Vedat M. Eyuboglu *(Co-Founder & CTO)*
Sanjeev Verma *(Co-Founder & Exec VP-Corp Dev)*
Merle L. Gilmore *(Chm)*
Randall S. Battat *(Pres & CEO)*
Peter C. Anastos *(Gen Counsel & VP)*
Michael E. Clark *(Gen Mgr-Femtocell Bus)*
Mark W. Rau *(Gen Mgr-Airvana Network Solutions)*

ALASKA COMMUNICATIONS SYSTEMS GROUP, INC.
600 Telephone Ave
Anchorage, AK 99503-6091
Tel.: (907) 297-3000
Fax: (907) 297-3052
Web Site: www.acsalaska.com
Approx. Rev.: $341,524,000
Approx. Number Employees: 834
Year Founded: 1998
Business Description:
Telecommunications & Internet Services
S.I.C.: 4813; 4812; 7375
N.A.I.C.S.: 517310; 517110; 517212; 518111
Import Export
Advertising Expenditures: $7,360,000
Personnel:
Anand Vadapalli *(Pres & CEO)*
Wayne Graham *(CFO)*
Leonard A. Steinberg *(Chief Ethics Officer, Gen Counsel, Corp Sec & VP)*
Michael Todd *(Sr VP-Tech)*
Michael Wynschenk *(Sr VP-Sls)*
Laurie Butcher *(Controller & VP-Fin)*
Russell Girten *(VP-IT & Svc Mgmt)*
Heather Cavanaugh *(Dir-Corp Comm)*
Advertising Agency:
VITRO
(An MDC Partners Company)
625 Broadway Fl 4
San Diego, CA 92101-5403
Tel.: (619) 234-0408
Fax: (619) 234-4015
Agency of Record

ALIEN TECHNOLOGY CORPORATION
18220 Butterfield Blvd
Morgan Hill, CA 95037
Tel.: (408) 782-3900
Fax: (408) 782-3910
E-mail: ir@alientechnology.com
Web Site: www.alientechnology.com
Sales Range: $10-24.9 Million
Approx. Number Employees: 241
Year Founded: 1994
Business Description:
Radio Frequency Identification Mfr
S.I.C.: 3663
N.A.I.C.S.: 334220
Advertising Expenditures: $1,385,000
Media: 10-13
Personnel:
John Stephen Smith *(Founder & CTO)*
Duane E. Zitzner *(Chm)*
Peter Green *(CEO)*
Charles G. Alvarez *(CFO & VP-Fin)*
Natalino Camilleri *(COO)*
David Aaron *(Chief Legal Officer & VP-Bus Dev)*
Patrick Ervin *(VP-World Wide Mktg & Sls)*
Mike Frieswyk *(VP-Sls & Mktg)*

ALLIED ENTERTAINMENT GROUP, INC.
PO Box 2035
Industry, CA 91746
Tel.: (626) 330-0600
Fax: (626) 961-0411
E-mail: info@alliedartists.net
Web Site: www.alliedartists.net
Approx. Sls.: $60,000,000
Approx. Number Employees: 325
Business Description:
Motion Picture & Video Production

Key to Media (For complete agency information see *The Advertising Red Books-Agencies* edition):
1. Bus. Publs. 2. Cable T.V. 3. Catalogs & Directories. 4. Co-op Adv. 5. Consumer Mags. 6. D.M. to Bus. Estab.7. D.M. to Consumers
8. Daily Newsp. 9. Exhibits/Trade Shows 10. Foreign 11. Infomercial 12. Internet Adv.13. Multimedia 14. Network Radio
15. Network T.V. 16. Newsp. Distr. Mags. 17. Other 18. Outdoor (Posters, Transit) 19. Point of Purchase20. Premiums, Novelties
21. Product Samples 22. Special Events Mktg. 23. Spot Radio 24. Spot T.V. 25. Weekly Newsp. 26. Yellow Page Adv.

S.I.C.: 7812
N.A.I.C.S.: 512110
Media: 4-8-10-13-15-18

ALLIED VAUGHN INC.
7951 Computer Ave
Minneapolis, MN 55435
Tel.: (952) 832-3100
Fax: (952) 832-3203
Toll Free: (800) 323-0281
E-mail: info@alliedvaughn.com
Web Site: www.alliedvaughn.com
Sales Range: $10-24.9 Million
Approx. Number Employees: 60
Year Founded: 1999
Business Description:
Provider of Investment Holding Services
S.I.C.: 6719
N.A.I.C.S.: 551112
Media: 7-10-13
Personnel:
Doug Olzenak *(Pres, VP-Sls & Acct Exec)*
David Willette *(CEO)*
Chuck Rhinehart *(CFO)*

ALLUMINATION FILMWORKS LLC
(Sub. of Peace Arch Home Entertainment Inc.)
21250 Califa St Ste 102
Woodland Hills, CA 91367
Tel.: (818) 712-9000
Fax: (818) 712-9074
E-mail: info@alluminationfilmworks.com
Web Site: www.alluminationfilmworks.com
Approx. Number Employees: 20
Year Founded: 2002
Business Description:
Motion Picture & Home Entertainment Distr
S.I.C.: 7822; 4841
N.A.I.C.S.: 512120; 517510
Media: 4-10-13
Personnel:
Dewitt Kerry McCluggage *(Chm)*
Jeff Sagansky *(Chm)*
Cheryl Freeman *(CEO)*
Joseph Duey *(CFO)*

ALPHA VIDEO & AUDIO, INC.
7711 Computer Ave
Edina, MN 55435
Tel.: (952) 896-9898
Fax: (952) 896-9899
E-mail: Stans@alphavideo.com
Web Site: www.alphavideo.com
Sales Range: $10-24.9 Million
Approx. Number Employees: 70
Year Founded: 1970
Business Description:
Video & Digital Media Content Creation, Distribution & Management Products Mfr
S.I.C.: 3651
N.A.I.C.S.: 334310
Media: 10
Personnel:
Stan Sanek *(CEO)*
Kevin Groves *(COO & Dir-Sls)*

AMERICAN URBAN RADIO NETWORKS
960 Penn Ave Ste 200
Pittsburgh, PA 15222-3811
Tel.: (412) 456-4000
Fax: (412) 456-4022
E-mail: information@aurn.com
Web Site: www.aurnol.com
Approx. Sls.: $2,800,000
Approx. Number Employees: 60
Year Founded: 1972
Business Description:
Radio Network
S.I.C.: 4832
N.A.I.C.S.: 515112
Advertising Expenditures: $250,000
Media: 2-4-6-7-8-9-10-20-23
Distr.: Intl.; Natl.
Budget Set: Dec.
Personnel:
Ronald R. Davenport *(Chm)*
Jerry Lopes *(Pres-Program Ops & Affiliations)*
Brands & Products:
AMERICAN URBAN RADIO NETWORKS
SBN

AMERICANLIFE TV NETWORK
(Holding of ComStar Networks, LLC)
808 E Abram St
Arlington, TX 76010
Tel.: (202) 289-6633
Tel.: (571) 730-6115
Fax: (202) 289-6632
Web Site: www.americanlifetv.com
Year Founded: 1984
Business Description:
Cable Television Network
S.I.C.: 4841
N.A.I.C.S.: 515210
Media: 2-3-4-6-9-13-18-20-22-23-24-25
Distr.: Natl.
Budget Set: Sept. -Oct.
Personnel:
Chris Wyatt *(Pres & CEO)*
Aaron Norris *(Pres-Dev)*
Brands & Products:
ALN AMERICAN LIFE NETWORK
EMBASSY CHEFS
FLEA MARKET MANIA
Advertising Agency:
Worldlink Media
380 Lexington Ave 41st Fl
New York, NY 10168
Tel.: (917) 267-1900

ANCHOR BAY ENTERTAINMENT, INC.
(Sub. of Starz Media, LLC)
2401 W Big Beaver Ste 200
Troy, MI 48084-4501
Tel.: (248) 816-0909
Fax: (248) 816-3335
Web Site: www.anchorbayentertainment.com
Sales Range: $10-24.9 Million
Approx. Number Employees: 50
Year Founded: 1985
Business Description:
Home Entertainment Video Distr
S.I.C.: 7822
N.A.I.C.S.: 512120
Media: 4-6-13-20
Personnel:
Bill Clark *(Pres)*
Ray Gagnon *(Sr VP-Sls)*
Erin McGregor *(Sr VP-Opers)*
Sally Seraphim *(Sr VP)*
Kevin J. Carney *(Exec Dir-Mktg)*
Brands & Products:
ANCHOR BAY ENTERTAINMENT

ANIMAL PLANET, LLC
(Sub. of Discovery Communications, Inc.)
1 Discovery Pl
Silver Spring, MD 20910-3354
Tel.: (240) 662-2000
Fax: (240) 662-1862
Web Site: www.discovery.com
Sales Range: $125-149.9 Million
Approx. Number Employees: 500
Business Description:
Cable Television Broadcaster
S.I.C.: 4841
N.A.I.C.S.: 515210
Personnel:
John F. Hendricks *(Founder & CEO)*
Marjorie Kaplan *(Pres & Gen Mgr)*
Victoria Lowell *(Sr VP-Mktg & Ops-Media)*
Jason Carey *(VP-Production)*
Advertising Agency:
mono
(Partially Owned by MDC Partners)
3036 Hennepin Ave
Minneapolis, MN 55408
Tel.: (612) 822-4135
Fax: (612) 454-4950

ANTON/BAUER INCORPORATED
14 Progress Dr
Shelton, CT 06484
Tel.: (203) 929-1100
Fax: (203) 929-9935
Fax: (203) 925-4988
Toll Free: (800) 422-3473
E-mail: info@antonbauer.com
Web Site: www.antonbauer.com
Approx. Number Employees: 100
Business Description:
Cameras & Related Equipment
S.I.C.: 3861; 3692
N.A.I.C.S.: 333315; 335912
Media: 4-8-11
Personnel:
Michael Accardi *(Pres)*
Brands & Products:
ANTON/BAUER
DIONIC
GOLD MOUNT
HYTRON
HYTRON 100
HYTRON 50
INTERACTIVE
LEXAN
NEXUS
PRO PAC
REAL TIME
STASIS
TITAN
TITAN T2
TITAN TWIN
TRIMPAC
ULTRALIGHT
ULTRALIGHT 2
THE WORLDWIDE STANDARD

APEXTALK HOLDINGS, INC.
637 Howard St
San Francisco, CA 94105
Tel.: (415) 462-0901
Fax: (415) 777-3646
Toll Free: (800) 610-1328
E-mail: info@apextalkholdings.com
Web Site: www.apextalkholdings.com
Approx. Rev.: $14,112,549
Approx. Number Employees: 52
Business Description:
Global Communication Services
S.I.C.: 4813; 4812
N.A.I.C.S.: 517110; 517212
Advertising Expenditures: $155,302
Media: 17
Personnel:
George Ma *(Chm)*
Yibiao Chen *(Vice Chm)*
Hui Liu *(CEO)*
Shan Liu *(CFO)*
Edward Seo *(Dir-Mktg)*

ARCHIE COMICS ENTERTAINMENT, LLC
488 Main Ave
Norwalk, CT 06851
Tel.: (203) 846-2277
Web Site: www.archiecomics.com
Year Founded: 2003
Business Description:
Television, Film, Home Video, Music, Live Events & Internet Developer, Producer & Distr
S.I.C.: 7812; 7389
N.A.I.C.S.: 512110; 711320
Media: 1-10-13-16-19-20-22
Personnel:
Victor Gorelick *(Co-Pres & Editor-in-Chief)*
Fred Mausser *(Co-Pres & Dir-Circulation)*
Steve Herman *(Co-Pres)*
Chuck Grimes *(CEO)*

ARCOT SYSTEMS INC.
(Sub. of CA, Inc.)
455 W Maude Ave Ste 210
Sunnyvale, CA 94085
Tel.: (408) 969-6100
Fax: (408) 969-6290
E-mail: info@arcot.com
Web Site: www.arcot.com
Approx. Number Employees: 165
Year Founded: 1997
Business Description:
Custom Computer Programming Services
S.I.C.: 7371
N.A.I.C.S.: 541511
Personnel:
David Kaplan *(CFO)*
R. Vaidhyanathan *(Chief Product Officer)*
Chris Mckay *(Principal & Dir-Board)*
Nat D. Natraj *(Exec VP-Field Ops-Worldwide)*
Sanjay Vyas *(VP & Gen Mgr-Managed Svcs)*
Carol Stone Alexander *(VP-Mktg)*
Suril Desai *(VP-Engrg)*
Bill Moore *(VP-Strategic Relations)*
Advertising Agency:
ZENO Group
(An Affiliate of Daniel J. Edelman Company)
200 Park Ave S Ste 1603
New York, NY 10003
Tel.: (212) 299-8888
Fax: (212) 462-1026

ARNCO CORPORATION
(Div. of A-D Technologies)
860 Garden St
Elyria, OH 44035
Tel.: (440) 322-1000

Key to Media (For complete agency information see *The Advertising Red Books-Agencies* edition):
1. Bus. Publs. 2. Cable T.V. 3. Catalogs & Directories. 4. Co-op Adv. 5. Consumer Mags. 6. D.M. to Bus. Estab.7. D.M. to Consumers
8. Daily Newsp. 9. Exhibits/Trade Shows 10. Foreign 11. Infomercial 12. Internet Adv.13. Multimedia 14. Network Radio
15. Network T.V. 16. Newsp. Distr. Mags. 17. Other 18. Outdoor (Posters, Transit) 19. Point of Purchase20. Premiums, Novelties
21. Product Samples 22. Special Events Mktg. 23. Spot Radio 24. Spot T.V. 25. Weekly Newsp. 26. Yellow Page Adv.

ARNCO Corporation — (Continued)

Fax: (440) 322-1001
Toll Free: (800) 321-7914
E-mail: info@adtechnologies.com
Web Site: www.adtechnologies.com
Business Description:
Cable Installation Products
S.I.C.: 3663
N.A.I.C.S.: 334220
Media: 4-10
Personnel:
Paresh Chari *(Pres & CEO)*

ARNOLD SHAPIRO PRODUCTIONS, INC.

12925 Riverside Dr Fl 4
Sherman Oaks, CA 91423
Tel.: (818) 487-5125
Fax: (818) 487-5181
E-mail: asproductions@aol.com
Web Site:
www.arnoldshapiroprods.com
Sales Range: $10-24.9 Million
Approx. Number Employees: 40
Year Founded: 1981
Business Description:
Television & Motion Pictures Production & Distribution
S.I.C.: 7812
N.A.I.C.S.: 512110
Media: 3-15
Personnel:
Arnold Shapiro *(Pres & Exec Producer)*

ARTS ALLIANCE AMERICA

304 Hudson St 7th Fl
New York, NY 10013
Tel.: (212) 475-2888
Fax: (212) 475-5487
Year Founded: 2003
Business Description:
DVD & Home Video Distr
S.I.C.: 7822
N.A.I.C.S.: 512120
Media: 2-6-13
Personnel:
Joe Amodei *(Pres & CEO)*
Craig Van Gorp *(Exec VP-Sls)*
Sarah Guzman *(Controller)*
Loreto Penaloza *(Asst Controller)*

ASCENT MEDIA CORPORATION

12300 Liberty Blvd
Englewood, CO 80112
Tel.: (720) 875-5622
Web Site:
www.ascentmediacorporation.com
Approx. Rev.: $139,462,000
Approx. Number Employees: 1,330
Year Founded: 2008
Business Description:
Holding Company; Content & Creative Services for Media & Entertainment Industries
S.I.C.: 6719; 7319; 7389; 7812; 7829; 7999
N.A.I.C.S.: 551112; 512110; 512199; 519190; 541890; 713990
Advertising Expenditures: $607,000
Personnel:
William R. Fitzgerald *(Chm, Pres & CEO)*
George C. Platista *(CFO & Exec VP)*
William E. Niles *(Gen Counsel, Sec & Exec VP)*
Michael R. Haislip *(Exec VP)*
Michael R. Meyers *(Sr VP)*
John A. Orr *(Sr VP-Corp Dev)*
Bill Romeo *(Sr VP-ETV Svcs)*

ASTRAL MEDIA INC.

2100 Rue Sainte Catherine West
Bureau 1000
Montreal, QC H3A 3G6, Canada
Tel.: (514) 939-5000
Fax: (514) 939-1515
E-mail: corpcomm@corp.astral.com
Web Site: www.astralmedia.com
Approx. Rev.: $940,471,354
Approx. Number Employees: 2,800
Business Description:
Specialty & Pay-Per-View Television Services; Broadcasting, Video Mfr & Marketing & Technical Services
S.I.C.: 7812
N.A.I.C.S.: 512110
Media: 14-15-18-23-24
Personnel:
Andre Bureau *(Chm)*
Ian Greenberg *(Pres & CEO)*
Claude V. Gagnon *(CFO & Sr VP)*
Marc-Andre Renaud *(CIO & VP)*
Jacques Parisien *(COO-Astral Media Inc, Pres-Astral Radio & Exec VP)*
John Riley *(Pres-Television Networks & Tele Reseaux)*
Pierre Roy *(Pres-The Astral Television Networks & Pres-MusiquePlus Inc.)*
Luc Sabbatini *(Pres-Out-of-Home)*
Brigitte K. Catellier *(Sec & VP-Legal Affairs)*
Claude Lizotte *(Exec VP-TVPlus)*
Arnold Chiasson *(VP-HR)*
Robert Fortier *(VP-Fin)*
Sylvia Morin *(VP-Br& Mgmt & Corp Comm)*
Lyne Nault *(Dir-Sls-Natl)*
Brands & Products:
ASTRAL MEDIA
ENTERTAINMENT FOR YOUR WORLD
Advertising Agency:
Bos Advertising
3970 Saint-Ambroise street
Montreal, QC H4C 2C7, Canada
Tel.: (514) 848-0010
Fax: (514) 373-2992

ASTRAL MEDIA RADIO

(Sub. of Astral Media Inc.)
300 1110 Center St NE
Calgary, AB T2E 2R2, Canada
Tel.: (403) 240-5800
Fax: (403) 240-5801
E-mail: calgarysales@astral.com
Web Site: www.astralmediaradio.com
Sales Range: $1-9.9 Million
Approx. Number Employees: 60
Business Description:
Radio Broadcasting
S.I.C.: 4832
N.A.I.C.S.: 515112
Media: 18-20-22-23
Personnel:
Tom Peacock *(VP & Gen Mgr)*
Sandi Leonard *(Gen Mgr-Sls)*
Chad Nartin *(Program Dir, Mgr-Ops)*
Angela Beers *(Dir-Creative)*

ATEP RADIO INC.

(Sub. of Salem Communications Corporation)
(d/b/a Kdar)
500 E Esplanade Dr Ste 1500
Oxnard, CA 93036
Tel.: (805) 656-5327
Fax: (805) 656-5330
E-mail: radiomail@kdar.com
Web Site: www.kdar.com
Sales Range: $200-249.9 Million
Business Description:
Radio Broadcasting Stations
S.I.C.: 4832
N.A.I.C.S.: 515112
Media: 8-13-23
Personnel:
Richard Trejo *(Gen Mgr)*
Brands & Products:
KDAR.FM
KKLA.FM
KKRA.AM

ATLANTIC RECORDS GROUP

(Sub. of Warner Music Group Corp.)
1290 Ave of the Americas
New York, NY 10104-0101
Tel.: (212) 707-2978
Fax: (212) 707-2000
Fax: (212) 405-5475
Web Site: www.atlanticrecords.com
Sales Range: $50-74.9 Million
Approx. Number Employees: 230
Year Founded: 1947
Business Description:
Music Based Content Company
S.I.C.: 5735
N.A.I.C.S.: 451220
Media: 2-3-4-5-6-7-8-9-13-14-15-16-18-19-22-23-24-25
Distr.: Intl.; Natl.
Budget Set: Quarterly
Personnel:
Craig Kallman *(Co-Chm & CEO)*
Julie Greenwald *(Co-Chm & COO)*
Samantha Schwam *(CFO)*
Michael Kyser *(Pres-Black Music)*
Camille Hackney *(Sr VP-Brand Partnerships & Comml Licensing)*
L. Camille Hackney *(Sr VP-Brand Partnerships & Comml Licensing)*

ATOM ENTERTAINMENT INC.

(Sub. of MTV Networks Company)
Fl 12 225 Bush St
San Francisco, CA 94104-4254
Tel.: (415) 503-2400
Fax: (415) 503-2401
E-mail: info@atomentertainment.com
Web Site:
www.atomentertainment.com
Approx. Number Employees: 85
Year Founded: 1998
Business Description:
Licenser & Distributor of Short Films, Animations & Digital Media Via Television, Airlines, Theaters, Home Video & DVD, the Internet & Broadband Services
S.I.C.: 5734; 7313
N.A.I.C.S.: 443120; 541840
Media: 1-10-13-22
Personnel:
David Williams *(Sr VP & Gen Mgr-Nickelodeon Kids & Family Games Grp)*
Brands & Products:
ATOM

AUTOMAT PICTURES, INC.

3255 Wilshire Blvd
Los Angeles, CA 90010
Tel.: (213) 351-0444
Web Site: www.automatpictures.com
Sales Range: $1-9.9 Million
Approx. Number Employees: 10
Year Founded: 2001
Business Description:
Film Producer & Distr
S.I.C.: 7812; 7822
N.A.I.C.S.: 512110; 512120
Personnel:
Jeffrey Schwarz *(Pres & CEO)*
Advertising Agency:
Asbury Communications
9615 Brighton Way Ste 201
Beverly Hills, CA 90210
Tel.: (310) 859-1831
Fax: (310) 859-9658

AVATAR STUDIOS

2675 Scott Ave Ste G
Saint Louis, MO 63103
Tel.: (314) 533-2242
Fax: (314) 533-3349
E-mail: info@avatar-studios.com
Web Site: www.avatar-studios.com
E-Mail For Key Personnel:
President: bfaris@avatar-studios.com
Approx. Number Employees: 35
Year Founded: 1973
Business Description:
Video Production
S.I.C.: 7812
N.A.I.C.S.: 512110
Media: 4
Distr.: Natl.
Personnel:
Bill Faris *(Pres)*
Doug Hastings *(Dir-Photography)*
Carrie Zuzenak *(Mgr-Products)*

BACK TO THE BIBLE

6400 Cornhusker Hwy
Lincoln, NE 68507-3160
Tel.: (402) 464-7200
Fax: (402) 464-7474
Toll Free: (800) 759-6655
E-mail: info@backtothebible.org
Web Site: www.backtothebible.org
Approx. Number Employees: 90
Year Founded: 1939
Business Description:
Biblical Broadcaster & Publisher
S.I.C.: 4832; 2721
N.A.I.C.S.: 515112; 511120
Media: 3-4-6-8-9-10-14-15-20-21-23-25
Distr.: Natl.
Personnel:
Harold J. Berry *(Chm)*
Woodrow Kroll *(Pres & Sr Teacher-Bible)*
Tami Weissert *(Co-Host & Exec VP)*
Brands & Products:
BACK TO THE BIBLE

BAD BOY WORLDWIDE ENTERTAINMENT GROUP

1710 Broadway
New York, NY 10019
Tel.: (212) 381-1540
Fax: (212) 381-1599
Web Site: www.badboyonline.com
Sales Range: $300-349.9 Million
Approx. Number Employees: 600
Year Founded: 1994

Key to Media (For complete agency information see *The Advertising Red Books-Agencies* edition):
1. Bus. Publs. 2. Cable T.V. 3. Catalogs & Directories. 4. Co-op Adv. 5. Consumer Mags. 6. D.M. to Bus. Estab.7. D.M. to Consumers
8. Daily Newsp. 9. Exhibits/Trade Shows 10. Foreign 11. Infomercial 12. Internet Adv.13. Multimedia 14. Network Radio
15. Network T.V. 16. Newsp. Distr. Mags. 17. Other 18. Outdoor (Posters, Transit) 19. Point of Purchase20. Premiums, Novelties
21. Product Samples 22. Special Events Mktg. 23. Spot Radio 24. Spot T.V. 25. Weekly Newsp. 26. Yellow Page Adv.

Business Description:
Music & Entertainment Producer; Advertising & Marketing Services; Restaurant Owner; Men's Clothing Designer
S.I.C.: 7929; 2329; 5812; 7311; 7389; 8742
N.A.I.C.S.: 711130; 315211; 512290; 541613; 541810; 722110
Media: 3-6-10-13-14-15-18-19-22-23-24
Personnel:
Sean Combs *(CEO)*
Jon Cropper *(CMO)*
Brands & Products:
BAD BOY ENTERTAINMENT
BAD BOY RECORDS
BLUE FLAME MARKETING + ADVERTISING
JUSTIN'S
SEAN JOHN

BARRINGTON BROADCASTING GROUP LLC

(d/b/a Barrington Group)
2500 W Higgins Rd Ste 155
Hoffman Estates, IL 60169
Tel.: (847) 884-1877
Fax: (847) 755-3045
E-mail: info@barringtontv.com
Web Site: www.barringtontv.com
Approx. Rev.: $112,539,000
Approx. Number Employees: 903
Business Description:
TV Broadcasting Services
S.I.C.: 4833
N.A.I.C.S.: 515120
Personnel:
K. James Yager *(Co-Founder, Pres & CEO)*
Chris Cornelius *(Co-Founder & COO)*
Mary Flodin *(Co-Founder & Sr VP-Fin & Admin)*
Warren Spector *(CFO)*
Keith Bland *(Sr VP)*
Advertising Agency:
Marchex, Inc.
520 Pike St Ste 2000
Seattle, WA 98101
Tel.: (206) 331-3300
Fax: (206) 331-3695

B.A.S.S., INC.

(Sub. of ESPN Outdoors)
PO Box 10000
Lake Buena Vista, FL 32830
Tel.: (407) 566-2277
Fax: (407) 566-2436
Toll Free: (877) BASSUSA
E-mail: customerservice@bassmaster.com
Web Site: www.bassmaster.com
Approx. Rev.: $50,000,000
Approx. Number Employees: 68
Year Founded: 1968
Business Description:
Magazine Publisher
S.I.C.: 2721; 7991
N.A.I.C.S.: 511120; 713940
Import
Media: 2-3-5-6-7-8-9-10-13-15-18-19-20-21-22-23-24-25
Distr.: Direct to Consumer
Budget Set: Oct.
Personnel:
Dave Precht *(Sr Dir-Publ)*
Michael Cassidy *(Dir-Sls)*
Hunter Cole *(Dir-Sponsorships)*
Bruce Mathis *(Dir-Events)*
Don McPherson *(Dir-Publication Sls)*
Steve Puckett *(Dir-Ops)*
Trip Weldon *(Dir-Tournaments)*
Brands & Products:
B.A.S.S. FISHING TECHNIQUES
B.A.S.S. TIMES
BASSMASTER
BASSMASTER CLASSIC REPORT
BASSMASTER ELITE 50 SERIES
BASSMASTER TOP BASS DESTINATIONS
THE BASSMASTER TOUR
BASSMASTER TOURNAMENT TRAIL
THE BASSMASTERS
CASTING KIDS
FISHING TACKLE RETAILER

BAY NEWS 9

(Unit of Bright House Networks LLC)
700 Carillon Pkwy Ste 9
Saint Petersburg, FL 33716
Tel.: (727) 329-2300
Fax: (727) 329-2434
E-mail: desk@baynews9.com
Web Site: www.baynews9.com
Approx. Number Employees: 120
Business Description:
Cable Television News
S.I.C.: 4841
N.A.I.C.S.: 515210
Media: 3-13-18-22
Personnel:
Linda Granger *(Dir-Mktg)*

BBC WORLDWIDE AMERICA INC.

(Sub. of BBC Worldwide Limited)
747 3rd Ave Fl 7
New York, NY 10017-2803
Tel.: (212) 705-9300
Fax: (212) 705-0576
E-mail: info@bbcamerica.com
Web Site: www.bbcamerica.com
Approx. Number Employees: 90
Business Description:
Radio & TV Broadcaster
S.I.C.: 7812
N.A.I.C.S.: 512110
Media: 6
Personnel:
Herb Scannell *(Pres)*
Ann M. Sarnoff *(COO)*
Mark Gall *(Exec VP-Media Sls)*
Matt Stein *(VP-Promo, Mktg & Creative Svcs)*
Perry Simon *(Gen Mgr)*
James Fox *(Dir-Creative)*
Andrew Jackson *(Mgr-Comm)*
Advertising Agency:
bite communications
38 W 21st St 6th Fl
New York, NY 10010
Tel.: (212) 857-9370
Fax: (212) 857-9371

BEACHBODY, LLC

(Formerly Product Partners LLC)
3301 Exhibition Blvd
Santa Monica, CA 90404
Tel.: (323) 904-5600
Web Site: www.beachbody.com
Sales Range: $75-99.9 Million
Approx. Number Employees: 70
Year Founded: 1998
Business Description:
Fitness Videos & DVDs Producer, Marketer & Distr
S.I.C.: 7812; 7822
N.A.I.C.S.: 512110; 512120
Media: 6-12-13-22
Personnel:
Carl Daikeler *(Chm & CEO)*
Jon Congdon *(Pres)*
Ericka Gettman *(Sr Dir-Mktg)*
Monica Ciociola *(Dir-Database Mktg)*
Bryan Carney *(Brand Mgr & Mgr-Mktg)*
Jude Buglewicz *(Mgr-Mktg)*
Brands & Products:
MYBEACHBODY
P90X
POWER 90
PROJECT YOU
SLIM IN 6
TURBO JAM
WOWY
YOGA BOOTY BALLET
Advertising Agencies:
Dailey & Associates
(Sub. of The Interpublic Group of Cos., Inc.)
8687 Melrose Ave Ste G300
West Hollywood, CA 90069-5701
Tel.: (310) 360-3100
Fax: (310) 360-0810
(Infomercials, Creative, Online)

Diamond Media & Marketing, Inc.
7070 E 3rd Ave
Scottsdale, AZ 85251
Tel.: (480) 481-2960
Fax: (480) 481-2971
Toll Free: (877) 481-2960

BEASLEY BROADCAST GROUP, INC.

3033 Riviera Dr Ste 200
Naples, FL 34103
Tel.: (239) 263-5000
Fax: (239) 263-8191
E-mail: email@bbgi.com
Web Site: www.beasleybroadcasting.com
Approx. Rev.: $97,971,404
Approx. Number Employees: 418
Year Founded: 1961
Business Description:
Radio Broadcasting
S.I.C.: 4832
N.A.I.C.S.: 515111; 515112
Media: 3-5-6-8-9-13-14-17-18-22-23-25
Personnel:
George G. Beasley *(Chm & CEO)*
Bruce G. Beasley *(Pres & COO)*
Caroline Beasley *(CFO & Exec VP)*
Joyce N. Fitch *(Gen Counsel)*
Denyse S. Mesnik *(VP-Corp Comm)*
Marie Tedesco *(VP-Fin)*
John Brown *(Dir-IT)*

BELO CORP.

400 S Record St
Dallas, TX 75202-4841
Mailing Address:
PO Box 655237
Dallas, TX 75265-5237
Tel.: (214) 977-6606
Fax: (214) 977-6603
E-mail: invest@belo.com
Web Site: www.belo.com
Approx. Rev.: $687,395,000
Approx. Number Employees: 2,374
Year Founded: 1842
Business Description:
Holding Company; Newspaper Publishing, Television Broadcasting, Cable News & Electronic Media
S.I.C.: 6719; 2711; 4833; 4841
N.A.I.C.S.: 551112; 511110; 515120; 515210; 519130
Advertising Expenditures: $4,673,000
Media: 2-7-9-13-22
Distr.: Reg.
Budget Set: Aug.
Personnel:
Dunia A. Shive *(Pres & CEO)*
Carey P. Hendrickson *(CFO & Sr VP)*
Peter L. Diaz *(Pres-Media Ops)*
Russell F. Coleman *(Gen Counsel, Sr VP & Asst Sec)*
Guy H. Kerr *(Sec & Exec VP-Law & Govt)*
Daniel J. Blizzard *(Sec & Sr VP)*
Katherine E. Clements *(Sr VP-Media Ops)*
Richard J. Keilty *(Sr VP)*
Steven Mcintosh *(VP & Gen Mgr-Belo Adv Customer Svcs)*
David S. Starr *(VP & Deputy Gen Counsel)*
William L. Hamersly *(VP-HR)*
W. Craig Harper *(VP-Tech)*
Joe Weir *(Gen Mgr-Interactive)*
Jill Matthews *(Dir-Corp Comm & IR)*

BET HOLDINGS LLC

(Sub. of Viacom, Inc.)
(d/b/a BET Networks)
1 BET Plz 1235 W St NE
Washington, DC 20018-1211
Tel.: (202) 608-2000
Fax: (202) 608-2484
Web Site: www.bet.com
E-Mail For Key Personnel:
Marketing Director: marketing@bet.com
Sales Director: adsales@bet.com
Approx. Number Employees: 685
Year Founded: 1990
Business Description:
Holding Company; Cable Television Network & Other Media Products & Services
S.I.C.: 6719; 4832; 4833; 4841; 7389; 7812; 7822; 7829
N.A.I.C.S.: 551112; 512110; 512120; 512199; 512290; 515111; 515120; 515210; 517510; 519130
Media: 2-3-9-10-13-14-23
Distr.: Natl.
Budget Set: Jan. -Feb.
Personnel:
Debra L. Lee *(Chm & CEO)*
Scott Mills *(CFO & Exec VP)*
Paxton K. Baker *(Pres-Event Productions & Exec VP/Gen Mgr-BET J & D)*
Louis Carr *(Pres-Media Sls & Adv)*
Loretha Jones *(Pres-Original Programming)*
Denmark West *(Pres-Digital Media Grp)*
Michael Pickrum *(COO-BET Interactive LLC & Sr VP)*
Darrell E. Walker *(Gen Counsel & Exec VP)*
Raymond Goulbourne *(Exec VP-Brdcst Media Sls)*

Key to Media (For complete agency information see *The Advertising Red Books-Agencies* edition):
1. Bus. Publs. 2. Cable T.V. 3. Catalogs & Directories. 4. Co-op Adv. 5. Consumer Mags. 6. D.M. to Bus. Estab.7. D.M. to Consumers
8. Daily Newsp. 9. Exhibits/Trade Shows 10. Foreign 11. Infomercial 12. Internet Adv.13. Multimedia 14. Network Radio
15. Network T.V. 16. Newsp. Distr. Mags. 17. Other 18. Outdoor (Posters, Transit) 19. Point of Purchase20. Premiums, Novelties
21. Product Samples 22. Special Events Mktg. 23. Spot Radio 24. Spot T.V. 25. Weekly Newsp. 26. Yellow Page Adv.

BET Holdings LLC — (Continued)

Stephen G. Hill *(Exec VP-Entertainment & Music Programming)*
Jeanine Liburd *(Exec VP-Comm & Pub Affairs)*
Barbara Zaneri *(Exec VP-Programming & Strategy & Acq)*
John Gordon *(Sr VP-Fin & Controller)*
Michael D. Armstrong *(Sr VP & Gen Mgr-Intl)*
Matthew Barnhill *(Sr VP-Market Res)*
Quinton Bowman *(Sr VP-HR)*
Essie Chambers *(Sr VP-Original Programming-Centric)*
Depelsha McGruder *(Sr VP-Bus Ops-Centric)*
Martez Moore *(Sr VP-Bus Dev)*
Brandon Lucas *(VP & Gen Mgr-Mobile)*
Cybelle Brown *(VP-Sls & Bus Dev-Digital & Event Productions)*
Tom Reynolds *(VP-Bus Dev & Strategy)*
Shannon Cunningham *(Coord-Mktg)*

Brands & Products:
BET
BET J

Advertising Agency:
Harmelin Media
525 Righters Ferry Rd
Bala Cynwyd, PA 19004-1315
Tel.: (610) 668-7900
Fax: (610) 668-9548
— Suzanne Longo *(Acct Exec)*

BIG BEACH FILMS
41 Great Jones 5th Fl
New York, NY 10012
Tel.: (212) 473-5800
Fax: (212) 473-5805
E-mail: info@bigbeachfilms.com
Web Site: www.bigbeachfilms.com
Business Description:
Film Production Company
S.I.C.: 7829
N.A.I.C.S.: 512199
Personnel:
Marc Turtletaub *(Co-Founder & Partner)*
Advertising Agency:
Sunshine Sachs & Associates
149 5th Ave 7th Fl
New York, NY 10010
Tel.: (212) 691-2800

BIG IDEA, INC.
230 Franklin Rd 2A
Franklin, TN 37064
Tel.: (615) 224-2200
Fax: (615) 224-2250
Web Site: www.bigidea.com
Approx. Sls.: $34,300,000
Approx. Number Employees: 172
Year Founded: 1993
Business Description:
Family Media Services
S.I.C.: 7812
N.A.I.C.S.: 512110
Media: 4-6-7-10-22
Personnel:
Terry Pefanis *(COO)*
Brands & Products:
321 PENGUINS
BIG IDEA
GRUNTLY & IGGY
LARRY-BOY
SUNDAY MORNING VALUES, SATURDAY MORNING FUN
VEGGIETALES
VEGGIETOWN VALUES
VEGGIETUNES

BLAIR & ASSOCIATES, LTD.
(d/b/a VCI Entertainment)
11333 E 60th Pl
Tulsa, OK 74146
Tel.: (918) 254-6337
Fax: (918) 254-6117
Toll Free: (800) 331-4077
E-mail: vci@vcientertainment.com
Web Site: www.vcientertainment.com
Sales Range: $1-9.9 Million
Approx. Number Employees: 50
Business Description:
Video & DVD Producer & Distr
S.I.C.: 7822; 7812
N.A.I.C.S.: 512120; 512110
Media: 4-6-8-13
Personnel:
Robert A. Blair *(Pres)*

BLOCKBUSTER INC.
(Sub. of DISH Network Corporation)
1201 Elm St
Dallas, TX 75270-2102
Tel.: (214) 854-3000
Fax: (214) 854-4848
E-mail: investor.relations@blockbuster.com
Web Site: www.blockbuster.com
Approx. Rev.: $4,062,400,000
Approx. Number Employees: 25,000
Year Founded: 1985
Business Description:
Video Rental Retail Superstore Owner
S.I.C.: 7841; 5735
N.A.I.C.S.: 532230; 451220
Advertising Expenditures: $73,100,000
Media: 2-4-6-9-13-17-18-19-23-24
Distr.: Intl.
Personnel:
James W. Keyes *(Chm & CEO)*
Michael Kelly *(Pres)*
Dennis McGill *(CFO & Exec VP)*
Eileen M. Terry *(Exec VP-Franchise, Emerging Brands & Global Diversity Officer)*
Jeffery Stegenga *(Chief Restructuring Officer)*
Christopher J. Wyatt *(Pres-Intl & Exec VP)*
Rod J. McDonald *(Gen Counsel, Sec & VP)*
Mary Bell *(Sr VP-IR & Corp Treas)*
Kevin Lewis *(Sr VP-Digital Entertainment)*
Kathleen Walsh *(Sr VP-IT)*
Joyce Woodward *(Sr VP)*
Jeffrey Calman *(VP)*
Brands & Products:
BLOCKBUSTER VIDEO
QUIK DROP
Advertising Agencies:
Brendy Barr Communications LLC
144 Knorrwood Ct
Oakland Township, MI 48306
Tel.: (248) 651-4858
Fax: (248) 651-4868

Camelot Communications, Inc.
8140 Walnut Hill Ln Ste 700
Dallas, TX 75231
Tel.: (214) 373-6999
Fax: (214) 373-6854

DVA Media & Marketing
4515 Van Nuys Blvd Ste 402
Sherman Oaks, CA 91403
Tel.: (818) 995-0050
Fax: (818) 995-0250

The King Group
1801 Northhampton Ste 410
Desoto, TX 75115
Tel.: (214) 720-9046
Fax: (214) 720-1435

PointRoll Inc.
951 E Hector St
Conshohocken, PA 19428
Tel.: (267) 558-1300
Fax: (267) 285-1141
Toll Free: (800) 203-6956

BRAVO NETWORK
(Joint Venture of Comcast Corporation & General Electric Company)
30 Rockefeller Plz
New York, NY 10112
Tel.: (212) 664-4444
Fax: (212) 664-4085
Toll Free: (800) 531-0002
Web Site: www.bravotv.com
Sales Range: $200-249.9 Million
Business Description:
Film & Arts Network Featuring American & International Films, Theater, Dance, Documentaries, Original Children's & Cult TV Services
S.I.C.: 4841
N.A.I.C.S.: 515210
Media: 3-6-13-15
Distr.: Natl.
Personnel:
Lauren Zalaznick *(Pres)*
Frances Berwick *(Pres-Media)*
Lisa Hsia *(Exec VP-Digital Media)*
Cameron Blanchard *(Sr VP-NBC Universal Women & Lifestyle Ent Networks Comm)*
Tony Cardinale *(Sr VP-Res & Strategic Insights)*
Andrew Cohen *(Sr VP-Original Programming & Dev)*
Shari Levine *(Sr VP-Production)*
Susan Malfa *(Sr VP)*
Ellen Stone *(Sr VP-Mktg)*
Christian McLaughlin *(VP-Production)*
Advertising Agencies:
Asphalt Media
114 W 17th St
New York, NY 10011
Tel.: (212) 924-5332
Fax: (212) 989-3783

Conrad, Phillips & Vutech, Inc.
1398 Goodale Blvd
Columbus, OH 43212
Tel.: (614) 224-3887
Fax: (614) 222-0737

Zenzi Communications
646 Valley Ave Ste C
Solana Beach, CA 92075
Tel.: (858) 523-9020
Fax: (858) 523-9670

BRIGHT HOUSE NETWORKS LLC
(Sub. of Advance Publications, Inc.)
700 Carillon Pkwy Ste 6
Saint Petersburg, FL 33716-1101
Tel.: (727) 329-2000
Fax: (727) 329-2869
Web Site: www.mybrighthouse.com
Approx. Number Employees: 2,000
Business Description:
Cable Television & Internet Services
S.I.C.: 4841; 4899; 7375
N.A.I.C.S.: 515210; 517910; 518111
Media: 3-6-8-9-13-18-22-25
Personnel:
Robert J. Miron *(Chm)*
Steve Miron *(CEO)*
Mike Robertson *(Pres-Tampa Bay Div)*
Kevin Hyman *(Exec VP-Cable Ops)*
Stephen Colafrancesco *(Corp VP-Mktg & Sls)*
Pam Hagan *(VP-HR)*
Kimberly Maki *(VP-Corp Comm)*
Michelle Stuart *(VP-Mktg)*
Melinda Bacon *(Dir-Mktg)*
Michael Betts *(Dir-Mktg)*
Keith James *(Dir-Community Rels)*
Advertising Agency:
Fry/Hammond/Barr Incorporated
600 E Washington St
Orlando, FL 32801-2938
Tel.: (407) 849-0100
Fax: (407) 849-0817

BRISTOL BROADCASTING CO. INC.
PO Box 1389
Bristol, VA 24203-1389
Tel.: (276) 669-8112
Fax: (276) 669-0541
Web Site:
www.bristolbroadcasting.com
Approx. Sls.: $10,200,000
Approx. Number Employees: 60
Business Description:
Radio Broadcasting Stations
S.I.C.: 4832; 7389
N.A.I.C.S.: 515112; 711410
Media: 23
Personnel:
Lisa Hale *(Pres)*

BUCKLEY BROADCASTING CORP.
15545 Devonshire St Ste 311
Mission Hills, CA 91345
Tel.: (818) 365-5935
Fax: (818) 898-4051
Web Site: www.buckleyradio.com
Approx. Number Employees: 4
Business Description:
Radio Broadcasting Stations Operator
S.I.C.: 4832
N.A.I.C.S.: 515112
Media: 20-22-24
Personnel:
Richard D. Buckley, Jr. *(Pres)*
Steve Darnell *(Gen Mgr)*

CABLE IN THE CLASSROOM
(d/b/a CITC)
25 Massachusetts Ave NW Ste 100
Washington, DC 20001
Tel.: (202) 222-2335
Fax: (202) 222-2336
Toll Free: (800) 244-9049
E-mail: citc@cableducation.ca
Web Site: www.ciconline.org
Approx. Number Employees: 3
Year Founded: 1995

Business Description:
Commercial-Free Educational Television Programming
S.I.C.: 4841
N.A.I.C.S.: 515210; 517510
Media: 13
Personnel:
Dan McKeen *(CEO)*
Frank Gallager *(Exec Dir)*
Kat Stewart *(Dir-Strategic Initiatives)*

CABLEVISION SYSTEMS CORPORATION
1111 Stewart Ave
Bethpage, NY 11714
Tel.: (516) 803-2300
Fax: (515) 803-3134
E-mail: investor@cablevision.com
Web Site: www.cablevision.com
Approx. Rev.: $7,231,249,000
Approx. Number Employees: 16,350
Year Founded: 1973
Business Description:
Holding Company
S.I.C.: 6719; 4841; 7389
N.A.I.C.S.: 551112; 517510; 711310
Advertising Expenditures: $253,925,000
Media: 8-10-13-14-22
Personnel:
Charles F. Dolan *(Chm)*
Hank J. Ratner *(Vice Chm)*
James L. Dolan *(Pres & CEO)*
Gregg Seibert *(CFO & Exec VP)*
Thomas M. Rutledge *(COO)*
Tad Smith *(Pres-Local Media)*
Victoria D. Salhus *(Sec, Sr VP & Deputy Gen Counsel)*
Thomas C. Dolan *(Exec VP-Strategy, Dev & Dir)*
James A. Blackley *(Exec VP-Corp Engrg & Tech)*
Barry Frey *(Exec VP)*
Lisa Rosenblum *(Exec VP-Govt & Pub Affairs)*
John Trierweiler *(Exec VP-Product Mgmt)*
John Machalski *(Sr VP-Direct Sls)*
Todd Brecher *(Sr VP & Assoc Gen Counsel-Bus Affairs)*
Donna Alda *(Sr VP-TeleMktg Sls)*
Patricia Armstrong *(Sr VP)*
Kristin Aigner Dolan *(Sr VP-Strategic Product Dev)*
Tom Donohue *(Sr VP-Tech-Local Media Grp)*
Brian G. Sweeney *(Sr VP-eMedia)*
Valerie Green *(VP-Mktg, Product Strategy & Brand Mgmt)*
Joe Leonard *(VP-Mktg & Adv)*
Nancy Olsen *(Dir-Mass Mktg)*
Angelo Lomonte *(Dir-Media Strategy)*
Ken Martin *(Dir-IR)*
Susan Nicholson *(Mgr-Mktg)*
Advertising Agencies:
GroupM North America & Corporate HQ
498 Seventh Ave
New York, NY 10018
Tel.: (212) 297-8181
Fax: (212) 297-7001

Initiative Worldwide
(Part of The Interpublic Group of Companies, Inc.)
1 Dag Hammerskjold Plz 5th Fl
New York, NY 10017
Tel.: (212) 605-7000
Fax: (212) 605-7200

MediaVest USA
1675 Broadway
New York, NY 10019
Tel.: (212) 468-4000
Fax: (212) 468-4110

Sard Verbinnen & Co.
630 3rd Ave 9th Fl
New York, NY 10017
Tel.: (212) 687-8080
Fax: (212) 687-8344

Sloane & Company LLC
(d/b/a Sloane & Company)
7 Times Sq Tower 17th Fl
New York, NY 10036
Tel.: (212) 486-9500
Fax: (212) 486-9094

Starcom USA
35 W Wacker Dr
Chicago, IL 60601
Tel.: (312) 220-3535
Fax: (312) 220-6530

TBWA Chiat Day New York
488 Madison Ave
New York, NY 10022
Tel.: (212) 804-1000
Fax: (212) 804-1200

THE CANADIAN BROADCASTING CORPORATION
181 Queen St
Ottawa, ON K1P 1K9, Canada
Tel.: (613) 288-6000
Fax: (613) 288-6455
Web Site: www.cbc.ca
Sales Range: $500-549.9 Million
Approx. Number Employees: 10,000
Year Founded: 1936
Business Description:
Television & Radio Networks Broadcaster
S.I.C.: 4833
N.A.I.C.S.: 515120
Import Export
Advertising Expenditures: $200,000
Media: 6-13-14-15-18
Personnel:
Timothy W. Casgrain *(Chm)*
Hubert T. Lacroix *(Pres & CEO)*
Suzanne Morris *(CFO & VP)*
Steven Guiton *(Chief Regulatory Officer & VP)*
Pierre Nollet *(Chief Legal Officer, Sec & VP)*
Sylvain Lafrance *(Exec VP-French Svcs)*
Kirstine Stewart *(Exec VP)*
George C.B. Smith *(Sr VP-HR & Org)*
William B. Chambers *(VP-Brand, Comm & Pub Affairs)*
Bridget Hoffer *(Exec Dir-Commun, Brand & Promotions)*
Rachel Nixon *(Dir-Digital Media)*
Advertising Agency:
Veritas Communications, Inc.
370 King St W Ste 800
PO Box 46
Toronto, ON M5V 1J9, Canada
Tel.: (416) 482-2248
Fax: (416) 482-2483
Publicity & Promotions Agency of Record

CAPITOL BROADCASTING COMPANY, INC.
2619 Western Blvd
Raleigh, NC 27606
Mailing Address:
PO Box 12800
Raleigh, NC 27605-2800
Tel.: (919) 890-6000
Fax: (919) 890-6095
Web Site: www.cbc-raleigh.com
Approx. Number Employees: 900
Year Founded: 1937
Business Description:
TV & Radio Broadcasting; Satellite Services
S.I.C.: 4833; 4832
N.A.I.C.S.: 515120; 515112
Media: 2-4-7-10-17-23-24
Distr.: Natl.
Personnel:
James F. Goodmon *(Pres & CEO)*
Mike Hill *(Gen Counsel & VP)*
Daniel P. McGrath *(Treas & VP)*
Steve Hannel *(VP & Gen Mgr)*
Sam Matheny *(Gen Mgr-Mktg)*
Jim Rothschild *(Dir-Adv)*
Thomas McLaughlin *(Asst Treas)*

CAPITOL RECORDS, INC.
(Unit of The Capitol Music Group)
1750 Vine St
Hollywood, CA 90028-5209
Tel.: (323) 462-6252
Fax: (323) 467-5267
Web Site: www.capitolrecords.com
Approx. Number Employees: 200
Business Description:
Music Publisher & Distr
S.I.C.: 2741; 8999
N.A.I.C.S.: 512230; 512210
Advertising Expenditures: $7,000,000
Media: 2-5-6-7-9-14-15-16-18-19-20-22-23-24-25
Distr.: Direct to Consumer; Natl.
Budget Set: June
Brands & Products:
PRIORITY RECORDS

CARMIKE CINEMAS, INC.
Carmike Plz 1301 1st Ave
Columbus, GA 31901
Mailing Address:
PO Box 391
Columbus, GA 31902-0391
Tel.: (706) 576-3400
Fax: (706) 576-2812
E-mail: webmaster@carmike.com
Web Site: www.carmike.com
Approx. Rev.: $491,262,000
Approx. Number Employees: 615
Year Founded: 1982
Business Description:
Motion Picture Theaters
S.I.C.: 7832; 7999
N.A.I.C.S.: 512131; 713990
Advertising Expenditures: $3,860,000
Personnel:
Roland C. Smith *(Chm)*
S. David Passman, III *(Pres & CEO)*
Richard B. Hare *(CFO & Sr VP)*
Fred W. Van Noy *(COO & Sr VP)*
Lee Champion *(Gen Counsel, Sec & Sr VP)*
H. Madison Shirley *(Sr VP-Concessions)*
Jeffrey A. Cole *(Controller & Asst VP)*
Brands & Products:
HOLLYWOOD CONNECTION

THE CARTOON NETWORK, LP
(Sub. of Turner Broadcasting System, Inc.)
1050 Techwood Dr NW
Atlanta, GA 30318-5604
Tel.: (404) 885-2263
Fax: (404) 575-5267
Web Site: www.cartoonetwork.com
Sales Range: $50-74.9 Million
Approx. Number Employees: 200
Year Founded: 1992
Business Description:
Twenty-Four Hour a Day Animated Network Featuring Classic & Orginal Cartoons & Animated Programs
S.I.C.: 4833
N.A.I.C.S.: 515120
Media: 3-6-9-13-14-15-18-23-24
Distr.: Natl.
Budget Set: May
Personnel:
Stuart Snyder *(Pres)*
Rob Sorcher *(Chief Content Officer)*
John O'Hara *(Exec VP, Gen Sls Mgr-Cartoon Network Ad Sales & Mktg)*
Michael Ouweleen *(Sr VP & Dir-Creative)*
Dennis Adamovich *(Sr VP-Mktg)*
Phyllis Ehrlich *(Sr VP-Sls & Mktg & Promo)*
Josh Feldman *(Sr VP-Adv Sls)*
Stacy Isenhower *(Sr VP-Programming & Scheduling)*
Mike Lazzo *(Sr VP-Adult Swim)*
James Anderson *(VP-Pub Rels)*
William Blair *(VP-Sls, Promos & Mktg)*
Nathania Seales *(VP-Production-Creative Grp)*
Vivek Krishnani *(Dir-Mktg)*
Brands & Products:
ADULT SWIM
COURAGE THE COWARDLY DOG
DEXTER'S LABORATORY
ED, EDD 'N EDDY
FOSTER'S HOME FOR IMAGINARY FRIENDS
JOHNNY BRAVO
JUSTICE LEAGUE
KIDS NEXT DOOR
MIGUZI
POWERPUFF GIRLS
PUFFY AMI YUMI
SAMURAI JACK
SCOOBY-DOO
TEEN TITANS
TOONAMI
Advertising Agency:
RET Media
1050 Techwood Dr.
Atlanta, GA 30318
Tel.: (404) 878-7003
Media Buying

CBC AMERICA CO., LTD.
(Sub. of CBC Co., Ltd.)
(Los Angeles Representative Office)
20521 Earl St
Torrance, CA 90503-3006
Tel.: (310) 793-1500
Fax: (310) 793-1506
Web Site: www.cbcamerica.com
Approx. Number Employees: 12

Key to Media (For complete agency information see *The Advertising Red Books-Agencies* edition):
1. Bus. Publs. 2. Cable T.V. 3. Catalogs & Directories. 4. Co-op Adv. 5. Consumer Mags. 6. D.M. to Bus. Estab.7. D.M. to Consumers 8. Daily Newsp. 9. Exhibits/Trade Shows 10. Foreign 11. Infomercial 12. Internet Adv.13. Multimedia 14. Network Radio 15. Network T.V. 16. Newsp. Distr. Mags. 17. Other 18. Outdoor (Posters, Transit) 19. Point of Purchase20. Premiums, Novelties 21. Product Samples 22. Special Events Mktg. 23. Spot Radio 24. Spot T.V. 25. Weekly Newsp. 26. Yellow Page Adv.

CBC America Co., Ltd. — (Continued)

Business Description:
Distributor of Security Camera Lenses, Tubes & Products
S.I.C.: 3663
N.A.I.C.S.: 334220
Brands & Products:
COMPUTAR
COMPUTOR
Advertising Agency:
Hart Associates, Inc.
1915 Indian Wood Cir
Maumee, OH 43537-4002
Tel.: (419) 893-9600
Fax: (419) 893-9070

CBS BROADCASTING INC.

(Sub. of CBS Corporation)
(d/b/a CBS Television Network)
51 W 52nd St
New York, NY 10019
Tel.: (212) 975-4321
E-mail: info@cbs.com
Web Site: www.cbs.com
Approx. Number Employees: 8,000
Year Founded: 1927
Business Description:
Television & Radio Broadcasting Services
S.I.C.: 4833
N.A.I.C.S.: 515120
Media: 1-2-6-7-8-9-10-11-13-14-15-16-18-20-23-24-25
Distr.: Natl.
Budget Set: Aug.
Personnel:
Bruce Taub *(CFO & Exec VP)*
Martin Messinger *(Chief Compliance Officer)*
Jo Ann Ross *(Pres-Sls)*
George Schweitzer *(Pres-Mktg)*
Dana Wilkin *(Pres-Affiliate Rels)*
David Wisnia *(Exec VP-Affiliate Rels)*
Advertising Agencies:
Jack Myers Media Business Report
PO Box 27740
Las Vegas, NV 89126
Tel.: (201) 572-8675
Fax: (973) 267-1514

OMD-USA
195 Broadway
New York, NY 10007
Tel.: (212) 590-7100

CBS CORPORATION

(Group of National Amusements, Inc.)
51 W 52 St
New York, NY 10019-6188
Tel.: (212) 975-4321
Fax: (212) 975-4516
Web Site: www.cbscorporation.com
Approx. Rev.: $14,059,800,000
Approx. Number Employees: 25,380
Year Founded: 2005
Business Description:
Mass Media Company; Television, Radio, Advertising, Amusement Parks, Publishing & Digital Media Services
S.I.C.: 4833; 2731; 2741; 4832; 7996
N.A.I.C.S.: 515120; 511130; 515111; 515112; 516110; 713110
Advertising Expenditures: $433,600,000
Personnel:
Sumner M. Redstone *(Chm)*
Shari E. Redstone *(Vice Chm)*
Leslie Moonves *(Pres & CEO)*
Joseph R. Ianniello *(CFO & Exec VP)*
Gil Schwartz *(Exec VP & Chief Comm Officer)*
Larry Liding *(Chief Acctg Officer, Sr VP & Controller)*
David F. Poltrack *(Chief Res Officer)*
Ezra Kucharz *(Pres-Local Digital Media)*
George Schweitzer *(Pres-CBS Mktg Grp)*
Louis J. Briskman *(Gen Counsel & Exec VP)*
Angeline C. Straka *(Sec, Deputy Gen Counsel & Sr VP)*
Garen van de Beek *(Exec VP-On-Air Promotion & Dir-Creative-Mktg Grp)*
Anthony G. Ambrosio *(Exec VP-HR & Admin)*
Martin D. Franks *(Exec VP-Plng, Policy & Govt Relations)*
Martin M. Shea *(Exec VP-IR)*
Adam Townsend *(Exec VP-IR)*
Dan Harrison *(Sr VP-Strategic Dev)*
Richard M. Jones *(Sr VP & Gen Tax Counsel)*
Scott Koondel *(Sr VP-Corp Licensing & Distr)*
Zander Lurie *(Sr VP-Strategic Dev)*
Lori Shefa *(Sr VP-On-Air Promotion)*
Jeremy Murphy *(VP-Comm)*

CBS ENTERTAINMENT DIVISION

(Div. of CBS Broadcasting Inc.)
51 W 52nd St
New York, NY 10019
Tel.: (212) 975-4321
Fax: (212) 975-4516
Web Site: www.cbs.com
Year Founded: 1977
Business Description:
Entertainment Programming Schedules Creator
S.I.C.: 4833
N.A.I.C.S.: 515120
Media: 2-3-6-13-14-15-16-18-23-24
Distr.: Natl.
Personnel:
Nina Tassler *(Pres)*
Martin Garcia *(Pres-Intl)*
Peter Golden *(Exec VP-Talent & Casting)*
Jennifer Bresnan *(Sr VP-Alternative Programming)*
Gary D. Silver *(Sr VP-Bus Affairs)*

CBS RADIO INC.

(Sub. of CBS Corporation)
1515 Broadway 46th Fl
New York, NY 10036
Tel.: (212) 846-3939
Fax: (212) 314-9228
Fax: (212) 846-2315
Web Site: www.cbsradio.com
Approx. Number Employees: 500
Business Description:
Radio Broadcasting Services
S.I.C.: 4832
N.A.I.C.S.: 515112
Personnel:
Dan Mason *(Pres & CEO)*
Anton Guitano *(CFO, Sr Exec VP-Fin & Ops)*
David Goodman *(Pres-CBS Interactive Music Grp)*
Michael Weiss *(Pres-Sls)*
Scott Herman *(Exec VP-Ops)*
Richard Lobel *(Exec VP)*
Steve Carver *(Sr VP & Mgr-Market)*
Sue McNamara *(Sr VP-Sls)*
Greg Strassell *(Sr VP-Programming)*
Glynn Walden *(Sr VP-Engrng)*
Mark Zulli *(Sr VP-HR)*
Karen L. Mateo *(VP-Comm)*
Kerry Tucker *(VP-Strategic Sls)*
James M. Robinson *(Mgr-Sls)*
Allison Mandara *(Comm Coord)*
Brands & Products:
FREE FM
JACK
Advertising Agency:
The VIA Group LLC
34 Danforth St Ste 309
Portland, ME 04101
Tel.: (207) 221-3000
Fax: (207) 761-9422

CBS SPORTS DIVISION

(Div. of CBS Broadcasting Inc.)
51 W 52nd St
New York, NY 10019
Tel.: (212) 975-4321
Fax: (212) 975-4516
Web Site: www.sportsline.com
Approx. Number Employees: 150
Year Founded: 1977
Business Description:
Sports Programming Producer
S.I.C.: 4833
N.A.I.C.S.: 515120
Media: 14-15-24
Personnel:
Sean McManus *(Pres)*
Ken Aagaard *(Exec VP-Ops, Engrg & Production Svcs)*
Michael L. Aresco *(Exec VP-Programming)*
John Bogusz *(Exec VP)*
Rob Correa *(Exec VP-Programming)*
Marty Kaye *(Sr VP-Fin)*
Leslieanne Wade *(Sr VP-Comm)*
Harold Bryant *(VP-Production)*

CC MEDIA HOLDINGS, INC.

200 East Basse Rd
San Antonio, TX 78209
Tel.: (210) 822-2828
Web Site: www.clearchannel.com
Approx. Rev.: $5,865,685,000
Approx. Number Employees: 20,283
Year Founded: 2007
Business Description:
Diversified Media Holding Company; Owned by Bain Capital Partners, LLC & by Thomas H. Lee Partners, L.P.
S.I.C.: 6719
N.A.I.C.S.: 551112
Advertising Expenditures: $82,000,000
Personnel:
L. Lowry Mays *(Founder)*
Mark P. Mays *(Chm)*
Randall T. Mays *(Vice Chm)*
Robert W. Pittman *(CEO)*
Thomas W. Casey *(CFO)*
Andrew W. Levin *(Chief Legal Officer, Sec & Exec VP)*
Scott D. Hamilton *(Chief Acctg Officer & Sr VP)*
Robert H. Walls, Jr. *(Gen Counsel & Exec VP)*
Advertising Agencies:
Brainerd Communicators, Inc.
521 5th Ave 8th Fl
New York, NY 10175
Tel.: (212) 986-6667
Fax: (212) 739-6301

The Gary Group
2040 Broadway
Santa Monica, CA 90404-2910
Tel.: (310) 264-1700
Fax: (310) 264-9744

CECO INTERNATIONAL CORP.

440 W 15th St
New York, NY 10011-7002
Tel.: (212) 206-8280
Fax: (212) 727-2144
E-mail: info@cecostudios.com
Web Site: www.cecostudios.com
Approx. Sls.: $3,000,000
Approx. Number Employees: 50
Year Founded: 1985
Business Description:
Sales & Rental of Motion Picture, Television & Theatre Equipment
S.I.C.: 7359
N.A.I.C.S.: 532490
Media: 2-4-6-7-8-10-20
Personnel:
Donald Kline *(Chm, Pres & CEO)*
Renee Burke *(Controller)*

CENTRAL FLORIDA COX COMMUNICATIONS

(Sub. of Cox Communications, Inc.)
6020 NW 43rd St
Gainesville, FL 32653-3338
Tel.: (888) 269-9693
Fax: (352) 378-2790
Toll Free: (888) 269-9693
Web Site: www.cox.com
Approx. Number Employees: 250
Year Founded: 1962
Business Description:
Cable Television
S.I.C.: 4841; 7375
N.A.I.C.S.: 515210; 518111
Media: 2-4-8-10-24
Personnel:
Mike Giampietro *(Mgr-Sys)*
Advertising Agency:
Group 5
1215 NW 14th Ave
Gainesville, FL 32601
Tel.: (352) 377-1338
Fax: (352) 373-1939

CFAN RADIO

(Unit of Maritime Broadcasting System Ltd.)
(d/b/a The River 99.3 FM)
396 Pleasant St
Miramichi Bay, NB E1V 1X3, Canada
Tel.: (506) 622-3311
Fax: (506) 627-0335
E-mail: cfannews@mbsradio.com
Web Site: www.theriver993.com
Approx. Number Employees: 5
Business Description:
Radio Station
S.I.C.: 4832
N.A.I.C.S.: 515112
Media: 23
Brands & Products:
MBS

CFCO RADIO AM

(Sub. of Blackburn Radio Inc)
117 Keil Dr
PO Box 100
Chatham, ON N7M 5K1, Canada

Key to Media (For complete agency information see *The Advertising Red Books-Agencies* edition):
1. Bus. Publs. 2. Cable T.V. 3. Catalogs & Directories. 4. Co-op Adv. 5. Consumer Mags. 6. D.M. to Bus. Estab.7. D.M. to Consumers 8. Daily Newsp. 9. Exhibits/Trade Shows 10. Foreign 11. Infomercial 12. Internet Adv.13. Multimedia 14. Network Radio 15. Network T.V. 16. Newsp. Distr. Mags. 17. Other 18. Outdoor (Posters, Transit) 19. Point of Purchase20. Premiums, Novelties 21. Product Samples 22. Special Events Mktg. 23. Spot Radio 24. Spot T.V. 25. Weekly Newsp. 26. Yellow Page Adv.

Tel.: (519) 351-2326
Fax: (519) 354-2880
E-mail: info@630cfco.com
Web Site: www.630cfco.com
Approx. Number Employees: 10
Year Founded: 1926
Business Description:
Radio Station
S.I.C.: 4832
N.A.I.C.S.: 515112
Media: 20-22-23
Personnel:
Walter Ploegman *(Mgr-Ops)*

CFNY-FM RADIO
(Sub. of Corus Entertainment Inc.)
1 Dundas St W Ste 1600
Toronto, ON M5G 1Z3, Canada
Tel.: (416) 408-3343
Fax: (416) 847-3300
E-mail: info@edge.ca
Web Site: www.edge.ca
Sales Range: $10-24.9 Million
Approx. Number Employees: 200
Business Description:
Radio Broadcasting
S.I.C.: 4832
N.A.I.C.S.: 515112
Media: 23
Personnel:
Kelly Beveridge *(Dir-Prog & Interactions)*
Tina Crispo *(Dir-Promos)*
Rob Johnston *(Dir-Creative)*
Don Mitchell *(Dir-Music)*
Victor Giacomelli *(Mgr-Sls)*

CHARTER COMMUNICATIONS, INC.
12405 Powerscourt Dr
Saint Louis, MO 63131
Tel.: (314) 965-0555
Fax: (314) 965-9745
E-mail: webmaster@chartercom.com
Web Site: www.chartercom.com
Approx. Rev.: $7,059,000,000
Approx. Number Employees: 16,600
Year Founded: 1993
Business Description:
Cable Television, Internet & Telecommunications Services
S.I.C.: 4841; 4813; 7375
N.A.I.C.S.: 517510; 517110; 518111
Advertising Expenditures: $282,000,000
Personnel:
Michael J. Lovett *(Pres & CEO)*
Christopher L. Winfrey *(CFO & Exec VP)*
Robert E. Quicksilver *(Chief Admin Officer & Exec VP)*
Jay A. Rolls *(CTO & Sr VP)*
Kevin D. Howard *(Chief Acctg Officer, Sr VP & Controller)*
Donald F. Detampel, Jr. *(Pres-Comml Svcs & Exec VP-Tech)*
Steven Apodaca *(Pres-Ops)*
Joshua L. Jamison *(Pres-East Operating Grp)*
Richard R. Dykhouse *(Gen Counsel, Sec & Sr VP)*
John A. Birrer *(Sr VP-Customer Experience)*
Rich DiGeronimo *(Sr VP-Product & Strategy)*
Jim McGann *(Sr VP)*
Gregory Rigdon *(Sr VP-Bus Dev & Procurement)*
Allan Singer *(Sr VP-Programming)*
Todd A. Stewart *(VP-Natl Adv & Sls Dev)*
Anita Lamont *(Sr Dir-Comm)*
Kristina B. Hill *(Sr Mgr-Comm)*
Jessica Myers *(Sr Mgr-Comm)*
Brands & Products:
CHARTER
THE CHARTER BUNDLE
CHARTER CABLE TV
CHARTER COMMUNICATIONS
CHARTER CONNECT
CHARTER DIGITAL CABLE
CHARTER DIGITAL TV
CHARTER DVR
CHARTER HDTV
CHARTER HIGH-SPEED
CHARTER SECURITY SUITE
CHARTER TELEPHONE
Advertising Agencies:
CWMedia
1517 Spearmint Cir
Jamison, PA 18929
Tel.: (215) 491-5742
Fax: (775) 618-9128

Davis Advertising, Inc.
306 Main St
Worcester, MA 01608-1550
Tel.: (508) 752-4615
Fax: (508) 421-8001

Sway, Inc.
8313 Greenway Blvd Ste 100
Middleton, WI 53562-4763
Tel.: (608) 833-0088
Fax: (608) 833-9029

CHICAGOLAND TELEVISION NEWS, INC.
(Div. of WGN Continental Broadcasting Company)
(d/b/a CLTV News)
2501 W Bradley Pl
Chicago, IL 60618-4718
Tel.: (773) 528-2311
Web Site: cltv.trb.com
Approx. Number Employees: 75
Year Founded: 1992
Business Description:
Cable Television News Network
S.I.C.: 4841
N.A.I.C.S.: 515210
Advertising Expenditures: $200,000
Media: 3-6-9-14-15-18-25
Distr.: Reg.
Personnel:
Steve Farber *(Gen Mgr)*

CHILDREN'S HOSPITAL LOS ANGELES
4650 Sunset Blvd
Los Angeles, CA 90027
Tel.: (323) 660-2450
Web Site: www.chla.org
Business Description:
Children's Hospital
N.A.I.C.S.: 622310
Media: 13-23-24-29
Personnel:
Richard D. Cordova *(Pres & CEO)*
Diemlan Tonnu *(CFO & Sr VP)*
Rodney B. Hanners *(COO & Sr VP)*
Steven R. Garske *(CIO & VP)*
Lawrence L. Foust *(Gen Counsel & Sr VP)*
Claudia Looney *(Sr VP-Dev)*
DeAnn Marshall *(VP-Mktg & Comm)*
Hugo Santos *(VP-HR)*
Advertising Agency:
Ideaology Advertising Inc.
4223 Glencoe Ave Ste A 127
Marina Del Rey, CA 90292
Tel.: (310) 306-6501
Fax: (310) 306-6508

THE CHRISTIAN BROADCASTING NETWORK INC.
977 Centerville Tpke
Virginia Beach, VA 23463-7701
Tel.: (757) 226-7000
Fax: (757) 226-2017
Web Site: www.cbn.com
Approx. Number Employees: 927
Year Founded: 1960
Business Description:
Operator of Television Broadcasting Stations
S.I.C.: 8661; 4833
N.A.I.C.S.: 813110; 515120
Import Export
Media: 3-13
Personnel:
Pat Robertson *(Founder & Chm)*
Michael Little *(Pres & COO)*
Gordon Robertson *(CEO)*
Craig V. Buseck *(Dir-Conferences)*

CINEMARK USA, INC.
(Sub. of Cinemark Holdings, Inc.)
3900 Dallas Pkwy Ste 500
Plano, TX 75093-7871
Tel.: (972) 665-1000
Fax: (972) 665-1004
Toll Free: (800) 246-3627
E-mail: lmitchell@cinemark.com
Web Site: www.cinemark.com
Approx. Number Employees: 6,122
Year Founded: 1987
Business Description:
Motion Picture Exhibition Operator
S.I.C.: 7812; 7832
N.A.I.C.S.: 512110; 512131
Advertising Expenditures: $17,252,000
Personnel:
Lee Roy Mitchell *(Chm)*
Timothy Warner *(Pres & COO)*
Alan W. Stock *(CEO)*
Robert Copple *(CFO, Treas, Exec VP & Asst Sec)*
Tandy Mitchell *(Exec VP & Asst Sec)*
Robert Carmony *(Sr VP-New Tech)*
Michael Cavalier *(Sr VP)*
Frank Gonzales *(Mgr-Mktg)*
Brands & Products:
CINEMARK

CINEPLEX ENTERTAINMENT LP
(Sub. of Cineplex Galaxy Income Fund)
1303 Yonge St
Toronto, ON M4T 2Y9, Canada
Tel.: (416) 323-6600
Fax: (416) 323-6616
Web Site: www.cineplex.com
Approx. Rev.: $509,000,000
Approx. Number Employees: 130
Year Founded: 1979
Business Description:
Movie Theater Operator
S.I.C.: 7832
N.A.I.C.S.: 512131
Advertising Expenditures: $1,000,000
Media: 2-8-9-13-25
Distr.: Natl.
Budget Set: Oct. -Dec.
Personnel:
Ellis Jacob *(Pres & CEO)*
Gordon Nelson *(CFO)*
Dan McGrath *(COO)*
Anne Fitzgerald *(Chief Legal Officer)*
Salah Bachir *(Pres-Cineplex Media)*
Michael Kennedy *(Exec VP-Filmed Entertainment)*
Michael McCartney *(Exec VP-Film Programming)*
Heather Briant *(Sr VP-HR)*
Susan Mandryk *(Sr VP-Customer Strategies)*
Paul Nonis *(Sr VP-Ops)*
Fab Stanghieri *(Sr VP-Real Estate & Construction)*
Susan Campbell *(VP-Fin)*
Pat Marshall *(VP-Comm & IR)*
Ian Shaw *(VP-Pur)*
Brands & Products:
CINEPLEX
CINEPLEX ODEON THEATRES
GALAXY
RKO CENTURY WARNER THEATRES
WALTER READE THEATRES
WASHINGTON CIRCLE THEATRES
Advertising Agency:
Cineplex Media
102 Atlantic Ave Ste 100
Toronto, ON M6K 1X9, Canada
Tel.: (416) 323-6728

CINRAM INTERNATIONAL INC.
(Sub. of Cinram International Income Fund)
2255 Markham Road
Scarborough, ON M1B 2W3, Canada
Tel.: (416) 298-8190
Fax: (416) 298-0612
Web Site: www.cinram.com
Sales Range: $1-4.9 Billion
Business Description:
Pre-Recorded Multimedia Products Mfr
S.I.C.: 3651; 7812
N.A.I.C.S.: 334310; 512110
Media: 13-14-15-23-24
Personnel:
John Tino *(VP-Fin)*

CIOK/CJYC/CFBC RADIO
(Unit of Maritime Broadcasting System Ltd.)
226 Union
Saint John, NB E2L 1B1, Canada
Tel.: (506) 658-5100
Fax: (506) 658-5116
E-mail: mailbag@k100.ca
Web Site: www.k100.ca
Approx. Number Employees: 15
Business Description:
Radio Station
S.I.C.: 4832
N.A.I.C.S.: 515112
Media: 8-23
Personnel:
Kelly O'Neill *(Gen Mgr-Sls)*

CITADEL BROADCASTING COMPANY
(Sub. of CITADEL BROADCASTING CORPORATION)

Key to Media (For complete agency information see *The Advertising Red Books-Agencies* edition):
1. Bus. Publs. 2. Cable T.V. 3. Catalogs & Directories. 4. Co-op Adv. 5. Consumer Mags. 6. D.M. to Bus. Estab.7. D.M. to Consumers
8. Daily Newsp. 9. Exhibits/Trade Shows 10. Foreign 11. Infomercial 12. Internet Adv.13. Multimedia 14. Network Radio
15. Network T.V. 16. Newsp. Distr. Mags. 17. Other 18. Outdoor (Posters, Transit) 19. Point of Purchase20. Premiums, Novelties
21. Product Samples 22. Special Events Mktg. 23. Spot Radio 24. Spot T.V. 25. Weekly Newsp. 26. Yellow Page Adv.

Citadel Broadcasting Company — (Continued)

7201 W Lk Mead Blvd Ste 400
Las Vegas, NV 89128-8366
Tel.: (702) 804-5200
Fax: (702) 804-8250
Web Site: www.citadelbroadcasting.com
Sales Range: $700-749.9 Million
Year Founded: 1984
Business Description:
Radio Network & Broadcasting Stations Operator
S.I.C.: 4832
N.A.I.C.S.: 515112; 515111
Media: 13-14-18-23
Personnel:
Farid Suleman *(Pres & CEO)*
Randy L. Taylor *(CFO & Sr VP)*
Judith A. Ellis *(COO)*
Mike Pallad *(Exec VP-Sls)*

CITADEL BROADCASTING CORPORATION

Cheyenne Corp Ctr Ste 220 7690 W Cheyenne Ave
Las Vegas, NV 89129
Tel.: (702) 804-5200
Fax: (702) 804-8250
Web Site: www.citadelbroadcasting.com
Approx. Rev.: $739,566,000
Approx. Number Employees: 2,600
Business Description:
Holding Company; Radio Networks & Broadcasting Stations Owner & Operator
S.I.C.: 6719; 4832
N.A.I.C.S.: 551112; 515111; 515112
Personnel:
John L. Sander *(Chm)*
Farid Suleman *(Pres & CEO)*
Randy L. Taylor *(CFO & Sr VP)*
Judith A. Ellis *(COO)*
Hilary E. Glassman *(Gen Counsel & Sr VP)*
Mike Pallad *(Exec VP-Sls)*
Patrica Stratford *(Sr VP-Fin/Admin & Asst Sec)*
Advertising Agency:
SCA Promotions, Inc.
3030 LBJ Freeway Ste 300
Dallas, TX 75234
Tel.: (214) 860-3700
Fax: (214) 860-3723
Toll Free: (888) 860-3700

CJCW RADIO

(Unit of Maritime Broadcasting System Ltd.)
6 Marble St
PO Box 5900
Sussex, NB E0E 1P0, Canada
Tel.: (506) 432-2529
Fax: (506) 433-4900
E-mail: cjcw@nbnet.nb.ca
Web Site: www.favourites590.com
Approx. Number Employees: 5
Business Description:
Radio Broadcasting
S.I.C.: 4832
N.A.I.C.S.: 515112
Media: 14-17-18-23
Personnel:
Lou McNamara *(Gen Mgr & Mgr-Sls)*
Brands & Products:
CJCW
FAVOURITES590

CLEAR CHANNEL COMMUNICATIONS, INC.

(Holding of CC Media Holdings, Inc.)
200 E Basse Rd
San Antonio, TX 78209-8328
Tel.: (210) 822-2828
Fax: (210) 822-2299
E-mail: lisacdollinger@clearchannel.com
Web Site: www.clearchannel.com
Sales Range: $5-14.9 Billion
Approx. Number Employees: 19,450
Year Founded: 1972
Business Description:
Holding Company; Radio Broadcasting Stations Operator & Media Advertising Services
S.I.C.: 6719; 4832; 7319
N.A.I.C.S.: 551112; 515112; 541850; 541890
Advertising Expenditures: $353,200,000
Media: 3-15-18-23-24
Personnel:
Mark Pitman Mays *(Chm)*
Randall T. Mays *(Vice Chm)*
John Partilla *(Pres & Exec VP)*
Tom Casey *(CFO & Exec VP)*
David Wilson *(CIO & Sr VP)*
Scott D. Hamilton *(Chief Acctg Officer & Sr VP)*
John E. Hogan *(Pres/CEO-Radio)*
Charlie Rahilly *(Pres-Intl Ad Platforms)*
Robert H. Walls, Jr. *(Gen Counsel, Sec & Exec VP)*
Brian Coleman *(Sr VP & Treas)*
Julie Hill *(Sr VP-Fin)*
Kathryn Johnson *(Sr VP-Corp Rels)*
Andy Rosen *(Reg VP-Clear Channel Radio-New York)*
Patricia M. Jarmek *(Gen Mgr-Sls)*
Advertising Agency:
Brainerd Communicators, Inc.
521 5th Ave 8th Fl
New York, NY 10175
Tel.: (212) 986-6667
Fax: (212) 739-6301

CNBC

(Joint Venture of Comcast Corporation & General Electric Company)
900 Sylvan Ave
Englewood Cliffs, NJ 07632
Tel.: (201) 735-2622
Fax: (201) 735-3200
Toll Free: (877) 251-5685
E-mail: info@cnbc.com
Web Site: www.cnbc.com
Sales Range: $100-124.9 Million
Approx. Number Employees: 400
Year Founded: 1989
Business Description:
Business News & Personal Finance Talk Shows Producer
S.I.C.: 4841
N.A.I.C.S.: 515210; 517510
Media: 2-3-6-8-10-13-22
Distr.: Intl.; Natl.
Personnel:
Mark Hoffman *(Pres)*
Anthony Lilleyman *(CFO & VP-Bus Dev-EMEA)*
Brian Steel *(Sr VP-PR)*
Lou Tosto *(Sr VP-Digital & Mobile Ad Sls)*
Thomas Clendenin *(VP-Mktg)*
Torsten de Riese *(Dir-Digital-EMEA Reg)*
Advertising Agency:
Euro RSCG Dallas
2800 N. Dallas Pkwy, Ste 300
Plano, TX 75093
Tel.: (972) 473-5600
Fax: (972) 473-5601

CNN HEADLINE NEWS

(Sub. of Cable News Network LP)
1 CNN Ctr Northwest Box 105366
Atlanta, GA 30303-2762
Tel.: (404) 878-2276
Fax: (404) 827-3484
Web Site: www.headlinenews.cnn.com
Sales Range: $50-74.9 Million
Approx. Number Employees: 200
Business Description:
Cable TV News Program
S.I.C.: 4833
N.A.I.C.S.: 515120
Media: 2-3-6-9-14-15-18-23
Distr.: Intl.; Natl.
Budget Set: Nov.-Dec.
Personnel:
Jim Walton *(Pres)*
Tony Maddox *(Mng Dir-CNN Intl & Exec VP)*
Wayne Pace *(CFO)*
Greg D'Alba *(COO & Exec VP-Adv Sls)*
Scot M. Safon *(CMO & Exec VP)*
Mark Whitaker *(Exec VP & Mng Editor)*
Advertising Agency:
Digitas Inc.
33 Arch St
Boston, MA 02110
Tel.: (617) 867-1000
Fax: (617) 867-1111

COLUMBIA TRISTAR MOTION PICTURE GROUP

(Unit of Sony Pictures Entertainment Inc.)
10202 W Washington Blvd
Culver City, CA 90232-3119
Tel.: (310) 244-4000
Fax: (310) 244-2626
Approx. Number Employees: 3,000
Business Description:
Motion Pictures Producer & Distr
S.I.C.: 7822
N.A.I.C.S.: 512120
Advertising Expenditures: $40,000,000
Media: 2-6-7-8-9-11-14-15-18-19-20-24
Distr.: Intl.; Natl.
Personnel:
Jeffrey Blake *(Chm)*
Stefanie Napoli *(Exec VP-Media)*
Steve Elzer *(Sr VP-Media Rels)*
Loren Schwartz *(Sr VP-Creative Adv)*

COMCAST CABLE COMMUNICATIONS, INC.

(Sub. of Comcast Corporation)
1500 Market St
Philadelphia, PA 19102-2100
Tel.: (856) 638-4000
Fax: (215) 981-7712
Web Site: www.comcast.com
Sales Range: $15-24.9 Billion
Approx. Number Employees: 59,000
Year Founded: 1981
Business Description:
Developer, Manager & Operator of Broadband Communications Networks
S.I.C.: 4841
N.A.I.C.S.: 515210
Personnel:
Neil Smit *(Pres)*
David N. Watson *(COO & Exec VP)*
Andrew Baer *(CIO)*
Tony G. Werner *(CTO & Exec VP)*
Kevin M. Casey *(Pres-Northern Div)*
William Connors *(Pres-Central Div)*
John H. Ridall *(Pres-Southern Div)*
William R. Stemper *(Pres-Bus Svcs)*
Charles W. Thurston *(Pres-Comcast Spotlight)*
Steven White *(Pres-Western Div)*
Douglas Gaston *(Gen Counsel)*
D'Arcy F. Rudnay *(Sr VP-Corp Comm)*
Ken Carrig *(Exec VP-HR)*
Alan Dannenbaum *(Exec VP-Satellite Svcs)*
John Schanz *(Exec VP-Natl Engrg & Tech Ops)*
Catherine Avgiris *(Sr VP & Gen Mgr-Comm & Data Svcs)*
Mitch Bowling *(Sr VP & Gen Mgr-New Bus)*
Greg R. Butz *(Sr VP-Product Dev & Gen Mgr-Media Svcs)*
Rick Germano *(Sr VP-Customer Ops)*
Grace Killelea *(Sr VP-Talent)*
Peter Kiriacoulacos *(Chief Procurement Officer & Sr VP)*
Steve Margosian *(Sr VP-Mktg Solutions & Sports Sls-Comcast Sports Sls Unit)*
Tom Prigoda *(Sr VP)*
W. Mark Schweitzer *(Sr VP-Mktg Bus Svcs)*
Steven L. Dvoskin *(Reg VP-Ops)*
Kavita Vazirani *(VP-Media Strategy)*
Sarah Gitchell *(VP & Deputy Gen Counsel)*
David Marcus *(VP & Deputy Gen Counsel)*
Lindsay Johnston *(VP-HR)*
Advertising Agency:
Ameredia, Inc.
101 Howard St Ste 380
San Francisco, CA 94105
Tel.: (415) 788-5100
Fax: (415) 449-3411

COMCAST CORPORATION

1 Comcast Ctr
Philadelphia, PA 19103-2838
Tel.: (215) 665-1700
Fax: (215) 981-7790
Toll Free: (800) 266-2678
E-mail: corporate_communications@comcast.com
Web Site: www.comcast.com
Approx. Rev.: $37,937,000,000
Approx. Number Employees: 102,000
Year Founded: 1963
Business Description:
Cable Television, Internet & Digital Phone Services
S.I.C.: 4841
N.A.I.C.S.: 515210; 517510
Advertising Expenditures: $1,359,000
Media: 2-3-6-8-9-25
Distr.: Natl.
Budget Set: Oct.

Key to Media (For complete agency information see *The Advertising Red Books-Agencies* edition):
1. Bus. Publs. 2. Cable T.V. 3. Catalogs & Directories. 4. Co-op Adv. 5. Consumer Mags. 6. D.M. to Bus. Estab.7. D.M. to Consumers 8. Daily Newsp. 9. Exhibits/Trade Shows 10. Foreign 11. Infomercial 12. Internet Adv.13. Multimedia 14. Network Radio 15. Network T.V. 16. Newsp. Distr. Mags. 17. Other 18. Outdoor (Posters, Transit) 19. Point of Purchase20. Premiums, Novelties 21. Product Samples 22. Special Events Mktg. 23. Spot Radio 24. Spot T.V. 25. Weekly Newsp. 26. Yellow Page Adv.

Personnel:
Brian L. Roberts *(Chm, Pres & CEO)*
Michael J. Angelakis *(CFO)*
Lawrence J. Salva *(Chief Acctg Officer, Sr VP & Controller)*
Amy L. Banse *(Pres-Interactive Media & Sr VP)*
Sam Schwartz *(Pres-Converged Products)*
Stephen B. Burke *(CEO-NBCUniversal & Exec VP-Comcast Corporation)*
Arthur R. Block *(Gen Counsel, Sec & Sr VP)*
William E. Dordelman *(Treas & Sr VP)*
Charisse R. Lillie *(Exec VP-Comcast Foundation & VP-Community Investment)*
Madison Bond *(Exec VP-Content Acq)*
David L. Cohen *(Exec VP)*
Duccio Donati *(Exec VP)*
Scott Calloway *(Sr VP-Ops-Southern Div)*
Mark A. Coblitz *(Sr VP-Strategic Plng)*
Kristine Dankenbrink *(Sr VP-Taxation)*
Mike DeCandido *(Sr VP-Call Center Ops)*
Marlene S. Dooner *(Sr VP-IR)*
Cynthia Hook *(Sr VP & General Auditor)*
Melissa Maxfield *(Sr VP-Federal Govt Affairs)*
Ron Phillips *(Sr VP-Employee Engagement)*
Robert S. Pick *(Sr VP-Corp Dev)*
D'Arcy F. Rudnay *(Sr VP-Corp Comm)*
Robert S. Victor *(Sr VP-Strategic & Fin Plng)*
Tina Waters *(Sr VP-Human Performance)*
Kathryn A. Zachem *(Sr VP-Regulatory & State Legislative Affairs)*
Kirk Dale *(Reg VP-Ops)*
John D. Foote *(Reg VP-Customer Care)*
Tracy Baumgartner *(VP-PR)*
Sue Gibbs *(VP-Fin)*
Charles Goodman *(VP-Mktg & Sls)*
Jennifer Khoury *(VP-Corp Comm)*
Brian Lanier *(VP-Engrg)*
Maria Weber *(VP-PR & Community Affairs)*
Maria G. Arias *(Exec Dir-Diversity & Inclusion)*
Nigel Ponder *(Exec Dir-Adv Sls-EMEA)*
Rudy Brioche *(Sr Dir & Policy Counsel)*
Alana Davis *(Sr Dir-Video Bus)*
Charlie Douglas *(Sr Dir-Corp Comm)*
Peter Filon *(Sr Dir-Federal Govt Affairs)*
Jordan Goldstein *(Sr Dir-Regulatory Affairs)*
Jenni Moyer *(Sr Dir-Corp Comm Network & Ops)*
Joe Trahern *(Sr Dir-Federal Govt Affairs)*
Andrea Agnew *(Dir-Diversity & Inclusion)*
John Demming *(Dir-Corp & Fin Comm)*

Brands & Products:
COMCAST
COMCAST DIGITAL VOICE

Advertising Agencies:
Bauza & Associates
11 Asylum St
Hartford, CT 06103
Tel.: (860) 246-2100
Fax: (860) 246-2101

Berlin Cameron United
100 Ave of the Americas 2nd Fl
New York, NY 10013
Tel.: (212) 824-2000
Fax: (212) 268-8454
Business Services

Digitas Inc.
33 Arch St
Boston, MA 02110
Tel.: (617) 867-1000
Fax: (617) 867-1111
Acquisition Marketing
Interactive

Goodby, Silverstein & Partners, Inc.
(Part of Omnicom Group, Inc.)
720 California St
San Francisco, CA 94108-2404
Tel.: (415) 392-0669
Fax: (415) 788-4303
Internet Service
Triple Play Service

Grupo Gallegos
401 E Ocean Blvd Ste 600
Long Beach, CA 90802
Tel.: (562) 256-3600
Fax: (562) 256-3620

Huge
45 Main St Ste 220
Brooklyn, NY 11201
Tel.: (718) 625-4843
Fax: (718) 625-5157
Comcast.com (Digital Agency of Record)

MediaVest USA
1675 Broadway
New York, NY 10019
Tel.: (212) 468-4000
Fax: (212) 468-4110

Starcom MediaVest Group
35 W Wacker Dr
Chicago, IL 60601-1723
Tel.: (312) 220-3535
Fax: (312) 220-6530
E!
The Style Network

COMCAST SPECTACOR, L.P.

(Sub. of Comcast Corporation)
3601 S Broad St
Philadelphia, PA 19148-5250
Tel.: (215) 336-3600
Tel.: (215) 389-9560 (Info Operator)
Fax: (215) 389-9506
Web Site: www.comcast-spectacor.com
Sales Range: $1-4.9 Billion
Year Founded: 1996

Business Description:
Sports & Entertainment Holding Company
S.I.C.: 6719; 7389; 7941
N.A.I.C.S.: 551112; 711211; 711310
Media: 5-7-8-9-18-20-22-23-24

Personnel:
Edward M. Snider *(Chm)*
Fred A. Shabel *(Vice Chm)*
Peter A. Luukko *(Pres & COO)*
Sanford Lipstein *(Officer)*
Phil Weinberg *(Gen Counsel & Exec VP)*
Michel F. Sauers *(Sr VP-Bus Dev)*
Lane Miller *(VP-HR)*
John Braun *(Sls Mgr-Natl)*

COMCAST SPORTSNET

(Sub. of Comcast Corporation)
3601 S Broad St
Philadelphia, PA 19148
Tel.: (215) 336-3500
Fax: (215) 952-5756
E-mail: askcsn@comcastsportsnet.com
Web Site: www.comcastsportsnet.com
Approx. Rev.: $96,000,000
Approx. Number Employees: 200
Year Founded: 1997

Business Description:
Broadcaster of Philadelphia Regional & Other Sports Programming & Information
S.I.C.: 4833
N.A.I.C.S.: 515120
Advertising Expenditures: $1,500,000
Other: $1,500,000
Distr.: Natl.

Personnel:
Ed Snider *(Chm)*
Jerry Reinsdorf *(Vice Chm)*
Jack Williams *(Pres & CEO)*
Bill Daly *(Chief Legal Officer & VP)*
Ray Warren *(Chief Revenue Officer & Exec VP)*
Steve Raab *(Pres-SportsNet New York)*
Philip I. Weinberg *(Exec VP & Gen Counsel-Comcast)*
Rebecca O'Sullivan-Schulte *(Sr VP & Gen Mgr)*
Stephanie Smith *(Sr VP & Gen mgr)*
April Carty-Sipp *(Sr VP-Creative Svcs)*
Princell Hair *(Sr VP-News Ops)*
Bill Giles *(VP & Gen Mgr)*
Nancy Larkin *(VP-Mktg)*
Alice Marini *(VP-HR)*
Cynthia Weiss *(VP-Mktg)*
Bob Clarke *(Asst Gen Mgr)*
Tim Taylor *(Gen Mgr)*
Rick Hahn *(Sr Dir-Personnel)*
Michelle Murray *(Sr Dir-News Programming)*
Tony Burke *(Dir-News)*
Mark Jordan *(Dir-Programming Dev)*
Brian MacLellan *(Dir-Personnel)*

Brands & Products:
SPORTSNET

Advertising Agency:
Red Tettemer & Partners
1 S Broad St 24th Fl
Philadelphia, PA 19107
Tel.: (267) 402-1410
Fax: (267) 402-1458
— Ed Tettemer *(Principal)*

COMEDY PARTNERS

(Sub. of MTV Networks Company)
(d/b/a Comedy Central)
345 Hudson
New York, NY 10014
Tel.: (212) 767-8600
Fax: (212) 767-8592
E-mail: advertising@comedycentral.com
Web Site: www.comedycentral.com
Sales Range: $25-49.9 Million
Approx. Number Employees: 209
Year Founded: 1991

Business Description:
All Comedy Network Owner & Operator
S.I.C.: 4841
N.A.I.C.S.: 515210
Media: 3-6-8-9-11-13-14-15-16-18-25
Distr.: Natl.
Budget Set: Aug. -Sept.

Personnel:
Michele Ganeless *(Pres-Network-Comedy Central)*
Lauren Corrao *(Pres-Original Programming & Devel)*
Peter Risafi *(Sr VP-Brand Mktg & Exec Dir-Creative)*
Chris Pergola *(Sr VP-Fin)*
David Bernath *(Exec VP-Program Strategy & Multiplatform-Comedy Central)*
Erik Flannigan *(Exec VP)*
Val Boreland *(Sr VP-Programming, Promo & Multiplatform Strategy)*
Steve Grimes *(Sr VP-Digital Media)*
Joella West *(Sr VP-Bus Affairs)*
Paul Beddoe-Stephens *(VP-Digital Media-Comedy Central)*
Glenn Ginsberg *(VP-Interactive Sls-Comedy Central)*
Jeff Lucas *(Head-Sls)*

Advertising Agency:
Jack Myers Media Business Report
PO Box 27740
Las Vegas, NV 89126
Tel.: (201) 572-8675
Fax: (973) 267-1514

COMMSCOPE, INC.

(Holding of The Carlyle Group, LLC)
1100 CommScope Pl SE
Hickory, NC 28602
Tel.: (828) 324-2200
Toll Free: (800) 982-1708
E-mail: investor.relations@commscope.com
Web Site: www.commscope.com
Approx. Sls.: $3,024,859,000
Approx. Number Employees: 12,500
Year Founded: 1953

Business Description:
High Speed, High Bandwidth Cables & Other Telecommunications Applications Mfr
S.I.C.: 3663; 3357
N.A.I.C.S.: 334220; 335929
Advertising Expenditures: $8,500,000
Media: 10

Personnel:
Frank M. Drendel *(Chm)*
Marvin S. Edwards Jr. *(Pres & CEO)*
Jearld L. Leonhardt *(CFO & Exec VP)*
Kap K. Kim *(CIO & Sr VP)*
Edward A. Hally *(Chief Comml Officer & Exec VP)*
Frank B. Wyatt II *(Gen Counsel, Sec & Sr VP)*
Randall W. Crenshaw *(Chief Supply Officer & Exec VP)*
Christopher A. Story *(Exec VP-Coaxial Cable & Antenna Ops)*
Philip Armstrong, Jr. *(Sr VP-Fin & VP-IR & Corp Comm)*

Key to Media (For complete agency information see *The Advertising Red Books-Agencies* edition):
1. Bus. Publs. 2. Cable T.V. 3. Catalogs & Directories. 4. Co-op Adv. 5. Consumer Mags. 6. D.M. to Bus. Estab.7. D.M. to Consumers 8. Daily Newsp. 9. Exhibits/Trade Shows 10. Foreign 11. Infomercial 12. Internet Adv.13. Multimedia 14. Network Radio 15. Network T.V. 16. Newsp. Distr. Mags. 17. Other 18. Outdoor (Posters, Transit) 19. Point of Purchase20. Premiums, Novelties 21. Product Samples 22. Special Events Mktg. 23. Spot Radio 24. Spot T.V. 25. Weekly Newsp. 26. Yellow Page Adv.

CommScope, Inc. — (Continued)

James R. Hughes *(Sr VP-Worldwide Broadband Sls)*
Rick Aspan *(Dir-Corp Comm)*
Dave Baldwin *(Mgr-SOX Internal Audit)*

Brands & Products:
ANDREW
ARID-CORE
BLUE HIGHWAY
BRIGHTPATH
BRIGHTWIRE
CABLE GUARD
THE CABLE IN CABLE TV
CABLEPAK
CALC U LOSS
CELL REACH
COMM/SCOPE
COMMFLEX
COMMSCOPE
COMMSCOPE WIRELESS
COMMSHIELD
CONNECTED BY COMMSCOPE
CONQUEST
CRD
DIGICABLE
E-Z PAK REEL
EXTREMEFLEX
EZ-PAK
EZ STA K
EZ-SWIVEL
FIBER FEEDER
FIBER OPTIMA FIBER OPTICS BY COMMSCOPE
HELIAX
HOW INTELLIGENCE TRAVELS
MIGRAHEAL
MULTIREACH
NXG
OPTICAL REACH
P-III
P3
PARAMETER III
PLENAIR
POWER DROP
POWER FEEDER
QR
QR EXPRESS
QUANTUM REACH
REEL SMART
SIGNAL VISION
SPANMASTER
SYSTIMAX
TRANSGRIP
TRANSPLICE
TRANSWRENCH
TRIATHLON
ULTRA II
ULTRAHOME
ULTRALINK
ULTRAPIPE
UNIPRISE
WBC

Advertising Agencies:
M/C/C
8131 Lyndon B Johnson Fwy Ste 275
Dallas, TX 75251-1352
Tel.: (972) 480-8383
Fax: (972) 669-8447

MC Communications
(d/b/a M/C/C)
8131 LBJ Fwy Ste 275
Dallas, TX 75251
Tel.: (972) 480-8383
Fax: (972) 669-8447

VantagePoint, Inc
80 Villa Rd
Greenville, SC 29615
Tel.: (864) 331-1240
Fax: (864) 331-1245

COMMUNITY BROADCASTING SERVICE

(Sub. of Diversified Communications)
35 Hildreth St
Bangor, ME 04401
Tel.: (207) 947-8321
Fax: (207) 941-9378
Approx. Number Employees: 64
Business Description:
Television Broadcasting; CBS Affiliate
S.I.C.: 4833; 4832
N.A.I.C.S.: 515120; 515112
Media: 24
Personnel:
Mike Young *(VP & Gen Mgr)*

COMMUNITY TELEVISION FOUNDATION OF SOUTH FLORIDA, INC.

(d/b/a WPBT Channel 2)
14901 NE 20th Ave
Miami, FL 33181
Tel.: (305) 949-8321
Fax: (305) 944-4211
E-mail: channel2@channel2.org
Web Site: www.channel2.org
Approx. Number Employees: 135
Year Founded: 1953
Business Description:
Television Broadcasting Stations
S.I.C.: 4833
N.A.I.C.S.: 515120
Media: 8
Personnel:
Jack Lowell *(Vice Chair & Chair-Elect)*
Ramon A. Rodriguez *(Chm)*
Laurie S. Silvers *(Vice Chm)*
Rick Schneider *(Pres & CEO)*
Jim Rasmussen *(Dir)*

COMMUNITY TELEVISION OF SOUTHERN CALIFORNIA

4401 W Sunset Blvd
Los Angeles, CA 90027
Tel.: (323) 666-6500
Fax: (323) 953-5347
E-mail: info@kcet.org
Web Site: www.kcet.org
Approx. Number Employees: 175
Business Description:
Television Broadcasting Stations
S.I.C.: 4833
N.A.I.C.S.: 515120
Media: 8-15-22
Personnel:
Al Jerome *(Pres & CEO)*
Deborah Hinton *(CFO & Exec VP)*
Susan Erburu Reardon *(Chief Dev Officer, Gen Counsel & Exec VP)*
Mary Mazur *(Chief Content Officer & Exec VP)*
Nancy Rishagen *(Exec VP-Dev)*
Jacqueline Kain *(Sr VP-New Media)*
Laurel Lambert *(Dir-Adv)*

CONNECTICUT PUBLIC BROADCASTING CORP.

1049 Asylum Ave
Hartford, CT 06105
Tel.: (860) 278-5310
Fax: (860) 275-7500
E-mail: info@cpbi.org
Web Site: www.cpbi.org
Sales Range: $25-49.9 Million
Approx. Number Employees: 75
Year Founded: 1962
Business Description:
Television & Radio Broadcasting Stations Owner & Operator
S.I.C.: 4833; 4832
N.A.I.C.S.: 515120; 515112
Media: 8-9-23-24-25
Personnel:
Jerry L. Franklin *(Pres & CEO)*
Nancy Bauer *(VP-Sls & Corp Sponsorships)*
Jennifer Boyd *(Dir)*
John Dankosky *(Dir-News)*

THE COOKIE JAR COMPANY

(d/b/a The Cookie Jar Group of Companies)
266 King St W 2nd Fl
Toronto, ON Canada
Tel.: (416) 977-3238
Fax: (416) 977-4526
E-mail: info@thecookiejarcompany.com
Web Site: www.thecookiejarcompany.com
Business Description:
Holding Company; Children's Entertainment Media Production, Consumer Products Licensing & Educational Publishing Services
S.I.C.: 6719; 2731; 6794; 7812; 7822
N.A.I.C.S.: 551112; 511130; 512110; 512120; 533110
Media: 4-7-8-10-11-13-14-15-23-24
Personnel:
Toper Taylor *(Pres & COO)*
Michael Hirsh *(CEO)*
Scott McCaw *(CFO)*
Greg Gilhooly *(Gen Counsel)*
Cindy Davis *(Sr VP-Licensing-CPLG US)*
John Vandervelde *(Sr VP-Bus Dev & Co-Production-Intl)*
Mark Chernin *(VP-Bus & Legal Affairs)*
Pamela Slavin *(VP-Production)*
Brands & Products:
CINAR ANIMATION
COOKIE JAR
FOR THE KIDS INSIDE
Advertising Agency:
Gorilla Nation Media, LLC
5140 W Goldleaf Cir Fl 3
Los Angeles, CA 90056
Tel.: (310) 449-1890
Fax: (310) 449-1891
Children's Entertainment

CORUS ENTERTAINMENT INC.

Corus Quay 25 Dockside Drive
Toronto, ON M5A 0B5, Canada
Tel.: (416) 479-7000
Fax: (416) 642-3779
Web Site: www.corusent.com
Approx. Rev.: $818,392,768
Approx. Number Employees: 1,768
Year Founded: 1999
Business Description:
Media & Entertainment Services
S.I.C.: 4833; 4832; 7829
N.A.I.C.S.: 515120; 512199; 515111
Advertising Expenditures: $425,749,288
Personnel:
Heather A. Shaw *(Exec Chm)*
Julie M. Shaw *(Vice Chm)*
John M. Cassaday *(Pres & CEO)*
Scott Dyer *(Exec VP-Shared Svcs & CTO)*
Doug Murphy *(Pres-Television & Exec VP)*
Chris Pandoff *(Pres-Corus Radio & Exec VP)*
Gary A. Maavara *(Gen Counsel & Exec VP)*
Kathleen McNair *(Exec VP-HR & Corp Comm)*
Hal Blackadar *(VP-HR)*
Tracy Ewing *(VP-Corp Comm)*
Thomas C. Peddie *(CFO & Sr VP)*
Brands & Products:
CFNY
CFOX
CORUS

COUNTRY MUSIC TELEVISION, INC.

(Sub. of MTV Networks Company)
(d/b/a CMT)
330 Commerce St
Nashville, TN 37201
Tel.: (615) 335-8400
Tel.: (615) 335-8552
Fax: (615) 335-8614
Web Site: www.cmt.com
Approx. Number Employees: 20
Business Description:
Country Music Cable Network
S.I.C.: 4841
N.A.I.C.S.: 515210
Media: 3-6
Personnel:
Brian Phillips *(Pres)*
Jayson Dinsmore *(Exec VP-Dev & Programming)*
Eliot Goldberg *(Sr VP-Dev & Programming)*
Neil Holt *(Sr VP-Natl Ad Sls)*
Suzanne Norman *(Sr VP-Strategy)*
Lewis Bogach *(VP-Program Devel & Production)*
Amanda Murphy *(Dir-Media Rels)*
Paul Villadolid *(Mgr-Program Dev)*
Advertising Agency:
Media Storm LLC
99 Washington St
South Norwalk, CT 06854
Tel.: (203) 852-8001
Fax: (203) 852-5592
Media Buying & Planning Agency of Record
True Blue Campaign

COX COMMUNICATIONS, INC.

(Sub. of Cox Enterprises, Inc.)
1400 Lk Hearn Dr
Atlanta, GA 30319
Mailing Address:
PO Box 105353
Atlanta, GA 30348-5353
Tel.: (404) 843-5000
Fax: (404) 847-6258
Web Site: www.cox.com
Approx. Number Employees: 22,530
Business Description:
Telecommunications Services
S.I.C.: 4841; 4813; 4899; 7375
N.A.I.C.S.: 515210; 517310; 517410; 517910; 518111
Media: 1-3-7-15
Personnel:
Patrick J. Esser *(Pres)*
Mark F. Bowser *(CFO & Exec VP)*

Leo W. Brennan *(COO & Exec VP)*
Mark Greatrex *(CMO & Sr VP)*
Kevin Hart *(CTO & Exec VP)*
Mae A. Douglas *(Exec VP & Chief People Officer)*
William J. Fitzsimmons *(Chief Acctg Officer & Sr VP-Corp Fin)*
Dominique Reiniche *(Pres-European Group & Sr VP)*
Len Barlik *(Exec VP-Product Dev & Mgmt)*
David A. Bialis *(Sr VP & Gen Mgr-California)*
Marilyn Burrows *(Sr VP & Gen Mgr-Las Vegas & Nevada)*
Paul J. Cronin *(Sr VP & Gen Mgr-New England & Cleveland)*
Gary T. McCollum *(Sr VP & Gen Mgr-Virginia)*
Jill Campbell *(Sr VP-Ops)*
Kimberly C. Edmunds *(Sr VP-Customer Ops)*
F. William Farina *(Sr VP-Cox Media)*
Keith L. Gregory *(Sr VP-Florida & Georgia)*
Mark A. Kaish *(Sr VP-Tech Ops)*
Philip G. Meeks *(Sr VP-Cox Bus)*
David Pugliese *(Sr VP-Product Mgmt & Mktg)*
Joseph J. Rooney *(Sr VP-Brand Mktg, Adv & Social Media)*
Alexandra M. Wilson *(Sr VP-Pub Policy & Regulatory Affairs)*
Robert C. Wilson *(Sr VP-Programming)*
Kristine Faulkner *(VP-Product Dev & Mngmt-Cox Bus)*
Jennifer Garrett *(VP-Sls)*
Andrew Goldberg *(VP-Strategic Plng & Analysis)*
Steve M. Gorman *(VP-Web Strategy & Interactive Media)*
Tracy Nolan *(VP-Retail)*
Philip Nutsugah *(VP-Voice Product Mgmt)*
Robin H. Sangston *(VP-Legal Affairs)*
Rob Smallwood *(VP-Enterprise Dev-Tech Org)*
Larry Steelman *(VP-Sls Channels & Programs)*
Scott Wise *(VP-Call Centers)*
Mike Melton *(Exec Dir-Mktg Res & Analysis)*
Beth Denning *(Exec Dir-Mktg Ops)*
Tony Matthews *(Exec Dir-Mktg)*
Catherine Mitchell *(Exec Dir-Video Product Mgmt)*
Brad Grundmeyer *(Dir-Government & Pub Affairs)*
Randy O'Neal *(Dir)*
Juergen Barbusca *(Mgr-Comm)*
Tamar Hoapili *(Mgr-Community Rels & Video Production)*

Brands & Products:
COX HIGH SPEED INTERNET
YOUR FRIEND IN THE DIGITAL AGE

Advertising Agencies:
Doner
25900 Northwestern Hwy
Southfield, MI 48075
Tel.: (248) 354-9700
Fax: (248) 827-8440
Creative

PM Publicidad
1776 Peachtree St Ste N600
Atlanta, GA 30309
Tel.: (404) 870-0099
Fax: (404) 870-0321

Vigilante Advertising
345 Hudson Street
New York, NY 10014
Tel.: (212) 545-2850
Fax: (212) 444-6061

COX COMMUNICATIONS-PHOENIX

(Sub. of Cox Communications, Inc.)
1550 W Data Vly Rd
Phoenix, AZ 85027
Mailing Address:
PO Box 78071
Phoenix, AZ 85062-8071
Tel.: (623) 594-0505
Tel.: (623) 594-1000
Fax: (623) 322-7500
E-mail: info@cox.com
Web Site: www.cox.com
Approx. Number Employees: 3,500
Business Description:
Cable Television Services
S.I.C.: 4841; 7375
N.A.I.C.S.: 515210; 518111
Advertising Agency:
Cramer-Krasselt
1850 N Central Ave Ste 1800
Phoenix, AZ 85004-4561
Tel.: (602) 417-0600
Fax: (602) 258-1446
(Branding, Advertising, Online Marketing, Media)

COX ENTERPRISES, INC.

6205 Peachtree Dunwoody Rd
Atlanta, GA 30328
Mailing Address:
PO Box 105357
Atlanta, GA 30348-5357
Tel.: (678) 645-0000
Fax: (404) 847-6352
Toll Free: (877) 426-9639
E-mail: contactus@coxenterprises.com
Web Site: www.coxenterprises.com
Approx. Rev.: $14,700,000,000
Approx. Number Employees: 66,000
Year Founded: 1996
Business Description:
Cable Television, Telephone & Internet Services; Automotive Publication & Newspaper Publisher; Radio & Television Broadcasting; Vehicle Auctions
S.I.C.: 2711; 2721; 2741; 4813; 4832; 4833; 4841; 5599; 7375
N.A.I.C.S.: 511110; 441229; 511120; 515112; 515120; 515210; 516110; 517110; 518111
Personnel:
James C. Kennedy *(Chm)*
Jimmy W. Hayes *(Pres & CEO)*
John M. Dyer *(CFO & Exec VP)*
Gregory B. Morrison *(CIO & Sr VP)*
Doug E. Franklin *(Pres-Cox Media Grp)*
Sanford Schwartz *(Pres-Manheim)*
Shauna Sullivan Muhl *(Sec & VP-Legal)*
Marybeth N. Leamer *(Exec VP-HR & Admin)*
Maria Friedman *(Sr VP-Corp Tax)*
R. Dale Hughes *(Sr VP-Strategic Investments & Real Estate)*
J. Lacey Lewis *(Sr VP-Fin)*
Alexandra M. Wilson *(Sr VP-Public Policy & Regulatory Affairs)*
Judith A. Henke *(VP-HR Dev)*
Robert I. Jimenez *(VP-Corp Comm & Pub Affairs)*
Duane Ritter *(VP-Corp Security)*
Alexander R. Stickney *(VP-Internal Audit)*
Mark Leuenberger *(Asst VP)*
Kimbrel Arculeo *(Sr Dir-Corp Comm)*
Robert Cahn *(Dir-Leadership Dev, Diversity & Trng)*
Vasant Kamath *(Dir-Bus Dev)*
Matt Kuhn *(Dir-Vehicle Ops)*
Kalpana Oommen *(Dir-Advisory & Assurance)*
Advertising Agency:
LBi
1888 Emery St NW Ste 400
Atlanta, GA 30318
Tel.: (404) 267-7600
Fax: (404) 267-7625

COX RADIO, INC.

(Sub. of Cox Enterprises, Inc.)
6205 Peachtree Dunwoody Rd
Atlanta, GA 30319-1464
Tel.: (678) 645-0000
Tel.: (678) 645-4312
Fax: (678) 645-5294
E-mail: cxr.info@cox.com
Web Site: www.coxradio.com
Approx. Rev.: $410,239,000
Approx. Number Employees: 1,375
Year Founded: 1995
Business Description:
Radio Broadcasting Stations
S.I.C.: 4832
N.A.I.C.S.: 515112; 515111
Advertising Expenditures: $6,800,000
Media: 7-14
Personnel:
James C. Kennedy *(Chm & CEO-Enterprises)*
G. Dennis Berry *(Vice Chm)*
Robert F. Neil *(Pres & CEO)*
Charles Odom *(CFO)*
Marc W. Morgan *(COO & Exec VP)*
Richard A. Reis *(Grp VP)*
Caroline Devine *(Reg VP)*
Kimberly Guthrie *(Reg VP)*
Robert B. Reed *(Reg VP)*
Gregg A. Lindahl *(VP-Interactive & New Tech)*

CROWN MEDIA HOLDINGS INC.

12700 Ventura Blvd
Studio City, CA 91604
Tel.: (818) 755-2400
E-mail: ncarr@hallmarkchannel.com
Web Site: www.crownmedia.net
Approx. Rev.: $287,272,000
Approx. Number Employees: 170
Business Description:
Cable & Other Pay Television Services
S.I.C.: 4841
N.A.I.C.S.: 515210
Advertising Expenditures: $6,600,000
Media: 2-3-6-10-13-14-15-18-23-24
Personnel:
Herbert A. Granath *(Co-Chm)*
Donald J. Hall, Jr. *(Co-Chm)*
William Abbott *(Pres & CEO)*
Andrew Rooke *(CFO & Exec VP)*
Edward Georger *(Exec VP-Adv Sls)*
Charles L. Stanford *(Exec VP-Legal & Bus Affairs)*
Annie Howell *(Sr VP-Comm & Media Rels)*
Cindy Kelly *(Sr VP-Natl Adv Sls)*
Stephanie Versichelli *(Sr VP-Eastern Sls)*
Melissa Lugo *(Coord-Mktg)*
Brands & Products:
HALLMARK CHANNEL

CTV INC.

(Sub. of CTVglobemedia Inc.)
9 Channel 9 Ct
Toronto, ON M1S 4B5, Canada
Mailing Address:
PO Box 9
Toronto, ON M4A 2M9, Canada
Tel.: (416) 332-5000
Fax: (416) 332-5022
E-mail: info@ctv.ca
Web Site: www.ctv.ca
Approx. Number Employees: 2,600
Year Founded: 1971
Business Description:
Holding Company; Television Broadcasting Stations Operator
S.I.C.: 6719; 4833
N.A.I.C.S.: 551112; 515120
Advertising Expenditures: $2,027,480
Media: 6-9-13-14-15-18-22-25
Distr.: Natl.
Budget Set: June
Personnel:
Ivan Fecan *(Pres & CEO)*
Susanne Boyce *(Pres-Creative, Content & Channels)*
Rick Brace *(Pres-Revenue, Bus Plng & Sports)*
Robert Hurst *(Pres-News & Current Affairs)*
Phil King *(Pres-sports,& Exec V.P.-PROGRAMING)*
Alon Marcovici *(Exec VP-Digital Media)*
Andrea Goldstein *(Dir-Comm)*
Willy Hanssen *(Product Mgr-CTV)*
Brands & Products:
CTV

CUMULUS MEDIA INC.

3280 Peachtree Rd NW Ste 2300
Atlanta, GA 30305
Tel.: (404) 949-0700
Fax: (404) 949-0740
E-mail: marty@cumulus.com
Web Site: www.cumulus.com
Approx. Rev.: $263,333,000
Approx. Number Employees: 2,318
Year Founded: 1997
Business Description:
Holding Company; Radio Broadcasting Stations Owner & Operator
S.I.C.: 6719; 4832
N.A.I.C.S.: 551112; 515112
Media: 13-14-18-22-23
Personnel:
Lewis W. Dickey, Jr. *(Chm, Pres & CEO)*
Joseph Patrick Hannan *(CFO, Treas & Sr VP)*
John W. Dickey *(Co-COO & Exec VP)*
Jonathan G. Pinch *(Co-COO & Exec VP)*
Linda A. Hill *(Chief Acctg Officer & Controller)*
Richard Denning *(Gen Counsel, Sec & Sr VP)*
Jan Jeffries *(Sr VP-Programming)*

Key to Media (For complete agency information see *The Advertising Red Books-Agencies* edition):
1. Bus. Publs. 2. Cable T.V. 3. Catalogs & Directories. 4. Co-op Adv. 5. Consumer Mags. 6. D.M. to Bus. Estab.7. D.M. to Consumers
8. Daily Newsp. 9. Exhibits/Trade Shows 10. Foreign 11. Infomercial 12. Internet Adv.13. Multimedia 14. Network Radio
15. Network T.V. 16. Newsp. Distr. Mags. 17. Other 18. Outdoor (Posters, Transit) 19. Point of Purchase20. Premiums, Novelties
21. Product Samples 22. Special Events Mktg. 23. Spot Radio 24. Spot T.V. 25. Weekly Newsp. 26. Yellow Page Adv.

Cumulus Media Inc. — (Continued)

Mike McVay *(Sr VP-Programming)*
William Bungeroth *(VP & Mgr-Market-San Francisco)*
Leslie Brimeyer *(VP-Fin Ops)*
Kevin Garrity *(Mgr-Sls-Northeast Reg)*

CURRENT MEDIA, INC.
118 King St
San Francisco, CA 94107
Tel.: (415) 995-8200
Fax: (415) 995-8201
E-mail: info@current.com
Web Site: www.current.com
Sales Range: $50-74.9 Million
Approx. Number Employees: 391
Year Founded: 2002
Business Description:
Cable Television Channel Featuring Viewer-Created Content
S.I.C.: 4841
N.A.I.C.S.: 515210
Advertising Expenditures: $4,140,000
Media: 7
Personnel:
Albert Arnold Gore, Jr. *(Co-Founder & Chm)*
Joel Z. Hyatt *(Co-Founder & CEO)*
Paul Hollerbach *(CFO)*
Joanna Drake Earl *(COO)*
Keith Olbermann *(Chief News Officer)*
Jason Odell *(Exec VP-Tech)*
Ken Ripley *(Exec VP-Adv Sls)*
Michael Streefland *(Sr VP-Mktg)*
John Arianas *(VP-Sls-East Coast)*
Karl Lewis *(VP-Ad Sls)*

CURTIS MEDIA GROUP
3012 Highwoods Blvd Ste 200
Raleigh, NC 27604-1031
Tel.: (919) 790-9942
Fax: (919) 790-8369
E-mail: info@curtismedia.com
Web Site: www.curtismedia.com
Approx. Number Employees: 200
Year Founded: 1991
Business Description:
Radio Broadcasting Stations
S.I.C.: 4832
N.A.I.C.S.: 515112
Media: 20-22-23
Personnel:
Donald W. Curtis *(Chm & CEO)*
Phil Zachary *(Pres & COO)*
Adam Maisano *(Sr VP & Dir-Sls)*
Jon Bloom *(VP & Gen Mgr)*
Mike Hartel *(VP & Gen Mgr)*
Rick Heilmann *(VP & Gen Mgr)*
David Stuckey *(VP & Gen Mgr)*
Dean Linke *(VP-Mktg & Sports Broadcaster)*
Tom Hamilton *(Gen Mgr-Sls)*
Bill Johnston *(Gen Mgr-Sls)*
Jay Nachlis *(Dir-Program)*
Trip Savery *(Dir-Sls)*

CWK NETWORK, INC.
6849 Peachtree NE Ste 4-150
Atlanta, GA 30328
Tel.: (404) 459-8081
Fax: (404) 459-8070
Toll Free: (888) 891-6020
E-mail: info@cwknetwork.com
Web Site: www.connectingwithkids.com
Approx. Sls.: $2,000,000
Approx. Number Employees: 30
Year Founded: 1998
Business Description:
Reality-Based Broadcast Programming & Educational Products Focusing on Children Broadcasting Services
S.I.C.: 8299; 4833
N.A.I.C.S.: 611699; 515120
Media: 13
Personnel:
Gary W. DeWitt *(Co-Founder, CFO & COO)*
Stacey Dewitt *(CEO)*
Brands & Products:
CONNECT TV
CONNECT WITH KIDS
KIDS MD

DANJAQ LLC
2400 Broadway St Ste 310
Santa Monica, CA 90404
Tel.: (310) 449-3185
Fax: (310) 449-3189
Approx. Sls.: $2,000,000
Approx. Number Employees: 20
Year Founded: 1962
Business Description:
Motion Pictures Producer
S.I.C.: 7812
N.A.I.C.S.: 512110
Media: 17
Personnel:
Michael Wilson *(Pres)*
David Pope *(CEO)*
Keith Snelgrove *(VP-Mktg)*
Brands & Products:
007
JAMES BOND

DATA TRANSMISSION NETWORK CORPORATION
(Holding of Veronis Suhler Stevenson Partners LLC)
9110 W Dodge Rd
Omaha, NE 68114-3316
Tel.: (402) 390-2328
Fax: (402) 390-7188
Toll Free: (800) 485-4000
E-mail: careers@dtn.com
Web Site: www.dtn.com
Sales Range: $150-199.9 Million
Approx. Number Employees: 1,000
Year Founded: 1984
Business Description:
Provides Information & Communication Services for the Agriculture, Automotive, Energy, Farm Implement, Financial, Produce, Golf, Turf Management, Construction, Aviation, Emergency Management & Other Weather Related Industries
S.I.C.: 7375
N.A.I.C.S.: 518111
Export
Media: 2-13
Personnel:
Amy Eggen *(VP-Mktg)*
Brands & Products:
DTN
DTN AGDAILY
DTN AGDAYTA
DTN CHAMELEON
DTN FIRSTRATE
DTN INFOMAIL
DTN REAL TIME
DTN WALL STREET
DTN WEATHER CENTER
DTNERGY
DTN.IQ
DTNSTANT
EXPERTFOLIO
ROVER

DELMARVA BROADCASTING CO. INC.
2727 Shipley Rd
Wilmington, DE 19810
Tel.: (302) 478-2700
Fax: (302) 478-0100
Web Site: www.delmarvabroadcasting.com
Approx. Number Employees: 70
Business Description:
Radio Broadcasting Stations
S.I.C.: 4832
N.A.I.C.S.: 515112
Media: 20-22-23
Personnel:
Julian H. Booker *(Pres & CEO)*

DELUXE LABORATORIES, INC.
(Sub. of MacAndrews & Forbes Holdings Inc.)
1377 N Serrano Ave
Hollywood, CA 90027
Tel.: (323) 960-3600
Fax: (323) 960-7016
Toll Free: (800) 2DELUXE
E-mail: info@bydeluxe.com
Web Site: www.bydeluxe.com
Year Founded: 1915
Business Description:
Motion Picture Film Processing, Production & Distribution Services
S.I.C.: 7819; 7812; 7822; 7829
N.A.I.C.S.: 512191; 512110; 512120; 512199
Export
Media: 2-9-20-22
Distr.: Natl.
Budget Set: Oct.
Personnel:
Cyril Drabinsky *(Pres & CEO)*
Warren Stein *(COO)*
Cathy Main *(VP-Mktg)*
Brands & Products:
COLOR BY DELUXE

DEPASSE ENTERTAINMENT
9200 W Sunset Blvd Ste 520
Hollywood, CA 90069
Tel.: (310) 858-3734
Fax: (323) 965-2598
Approx. Number Employees: 15
Year Founded: 1989
Business Description:
Television Show Producer
S.I.C.: 4833
N.A.I.C.S.: 515120
Media: 2
Personnel:
Suzanne DePasse *(CEO)*

DETROIT EDUCATIONAL TV FOUNDATION
Riley Broadcast Ctr 1 Clover Ct Wixom
Detroit, MI 48393
Tel.: (248) 305-3788
Fax: (248) 305-3990
Web Site: www.wtvs.org
Approx. Number Employees: 72
Business Description:
Television Broadcasting Stations
S.I.C.: 4833
N.A.I.C.S.: 515120
Media: 7-8
Personnel:
Richard Homberg *(Pres & Gen Mgr)*
John Wenzel *(CFO)*
Daniel Alpert *(Sr VP)*

DIALOGIC INC.
(Formerly Veraz Networks, Inc.)
926 Rock Ave
San Jose, CA 95131
Tel.: (408) 750-9400
Fax: (408) 546-0081
Toll Free: (800) 755-4444
E-mail: marketing.americas@dialogic.com
Web Site: www.dialogic.com
Approx. Rev.: $178,772,000
Approx. Number Employees: 935
Year Founded: 2001
Business Description:
Internet Protocol, Media Gateways & Digital Compression Products Mfr
S.I.C.: 3663; 7373
N.A.I.C.S.: 334220; 541512
Advertising Expenditures: $900,000
Personnel:
Nick Jensen *(Chm & CEO)*
Douglas A. Sabella *(Pres & COO)*
John T. Hanson *(CFO & Exec VP)*
Anthony Housefather *(Chief Admin Officer & Exec VP)*
Eric C. Schlezinger *(Gen Counsel, Exec VP & Sec)*
Kevin Cook *(Exec VP-Worldwide Field Ops)*
D.M. Hogh *(VP-Mktg)*
Denise Pierre *(VP-Global HR)*

DIC ENTERTAINMENT CORPORATION
(Sub. of The Cookie Jar Company)
4100 W Alameda Ave 4th Fl
Burbank, CA 91505
Tel.: (818) 955-5400
Fax: (818) 955-5696
E-mail: info@dicentertainment.com
Web Site: www.dicentertainment.com
Approx. Rev.: $74,716,000
Approx. Number Employees: 70
Year Founded: 1971
Business Description:
Family-Based Television Entertainment Programming & Brand Management Services
S.I.C.: 4833; 6794
N.A.I.C.S.: 515120; 533110
Advertising Expenditures: $452,000
Media: 2-3-7-8-10-11-13-14-15-18-19-20-21-22-23-24
Distr.: Intl.; Natl.
Budget Set: Quarterly
Personnel:
Andy Heyward *(Chm & CEO)*
Mike Maliani *(Chief Creative Officer)*
Kirk Bloomgarden *(Exec VP-Global Sls)*
Robby London *(Exec VP-Creative Affairs)*
Karl Kuechenmeister *(Sr VP-Adv Sls)*
Dan Waite *(VP-Latin America & Reg Mgr-Latin America)*
Leslie Nelson *(Dir-Mng)*
Brands & Products:
INSPECTOR GADGET
LIBERTY'S KIDS
MADELINE
SAILOR MOON
STRAWBERRY SHORTCAKE
SUPER DUPER SUMOS

Key to Media (For complete agency information see *The Advertising Red Books-Agencies* edition):
1. Bus. Publs. 2. Cable T.V. 3. Catalogs & Directories. 4. Co-op Adv. 5. Consumer Mags. 6. D.M. to Bus. Estab. 7. D.M. to Consumers 8. Daily Newsp. 9. Exhibits/Trade Shows 10. Foreign 11. Infomercial 12. Internet Adv. 13. Multimedia 14. Network Radio 15. Network T.V. 16. Newsp. Distr. Mags. 17. Other 18. Outdoor (Posters, Transit) 19. Point of Purchase 20. Premiums, Novelties 21. Product Samples 22. Special Events Mktg. 23. Spot Radio 24. Spot T.V. 25. Weekly Newsp. 26. Yellow Page Adv.

TROLLZ

DICK CLARK PRODUCTIONS, INC.
(Joint Venture of Six Flags Entertainment Corp. & Red Zone LLC)
2900 Olympic Blvd
Santa Monica, CA 90404
Tel.: (310) 255-4600
Fax: (310) 255-4601
E-mail: info@dickclarkproductions.com
Web Site: www.dickclarkproductions.com
Sales Range: $25-49.9 Million
Approx. Number Employees: 100
Year Founded: 1957
Business Description:
Television Programming & Network Production Services; Owned 58.8% by Red Zone LLC & 39.2% by Six Flags, Inc.
S.I.C.: 4833; 7389
N.A.I.C.S.: 515120; 711310
Network T.V.: 100%
Distr.: Natl.
Personnel:
Orly Adelson *(Pres)*
Mark S. Shapiro *(CEO)*
Barry Adelman *(Exec VP-Television)*
Angela Cannon *(Controller & VP-Fin)*
Brands & Products:
AMERICAN BANDSTAND
AMERICAN MUSIC AWARDS
BLOOPERS
DICK CLARK'S NEW YEAR'S ROCKIN' EVE
SO YOU THINK YOU CAN DANCE

DIRECTV
2230 E Imperial Hwy
El Segundo, CA 90245-0956
Mailing Address:
PO Box 956
El Segundo, CA 90245-0956
Tel.: (310) 964-5000
Fax: (310) 535-5225
E-mail: jtgieselman@directv.com
Web Site: www.directv.com
Approx. Rev.: $24,102,000,000
Approx. Number Employees: 23,200
Year Founded: 1985
Business Description:
Digital TV Entertainment, Satellite Services & Satellite-Based Private Business Networks; Owned 39% by Fox Entertainment Group
S.I.C.: 4812; 4841; 4899
N.A.I.C.S.: 517212; 515210; 517410; 517910
Advertising Expenditures: $317,000,000
Media: 2-3-9-13-18
Distr.: Intl.; Natl.
Budget Set: Jan.
Personnel:
Michael D. White *(Chm, Pres & CEO)*
Patrick T. Doyle *(CFO & Exec VP)*
Stephen Tucker *(CFO)*
Michael R. Benson *(CIO & Exec VP)*
Paul Guyardo *(CMO & Exec VP)*
Romulo G. Pontual *(CTO & Exec VP)*
Joe Bosch *(Chief HR Officer & Exec VP)*
Bruce Churchill *(Pres-DIRECTV Latin America & Exec VP)*
Derek Chang *(Exec VP-Content Strategy & Dev)*
John F. Murphy *(Sr VP & Controller)*
Ellen Filipiak *(Sr VP-Customer Svc)*
Jon Gieselman *(Sr VP-Adv & Comm)*
Chris Long *(Sr VP)*
Andrew Reinsdorf *(Sr VP-Govt Affairs)*
Bob Riordan *(Sr VP-Adv Sls)*
David Elgas *(Dir-Product Mgmt, Mktg & Adv Prod)*
Sherry Kang *(Dir-Online Mktg)*
Robert Mercer *(Dir-PR)*
Maria Requesto *(Dir-Consumer Insights)*
Angela Chen *(Sr Mgr-Acq Mktg)*
Jade Ekstedt *(Mgr-PR)*
Brands & Products:
DIRECTV
Advertising Agencies:
Deutsch, Inc.
(A Lowe & Partners Company)
111 8th Ave 14th Fl
New York, NY 10011-5201
Tel.: (212) 981-7600
Fax: (212) 981-7525
Lead Creative
Media Buying

Euro RSCG Latino
350 Hudson St 8th Fl
New York, NY 10014-4504
Tel.: (212) 886-4100
Fax: (212) 886-4415
Spanish Language Programming

Grey New York
777 3rd Ave
New York, NY 10017-1401
Tel.: (212) 546-2000
Fax: (212) 546-1495
Brand Image
Customer Relationship Marketing
Direct Marketing
Robots
Submarine
— Alison Monk *(Acct Exec)*

NYCA
1010 S Coast Hwy Ste 101
Encinitas, CA 92024
Tel.: (760) 436-7033
Fax: (760) 436-7047

Rapp Los Angeles
222 N Sepulveda Blvd Ste 500
El Segundo, CA 90245-5644
Tel.: (310) 563-7200
Fax: (310) 563-7297

DIRECTV HOLDINGS LLC
(Unit of DIRECTV)
2230 E Imperial Hwy
El Segundo, CA 90245
Tel.: (310) 964-5000
Fax: (310) 535-5225
Toll Free: (800) DIRECTV
Web Site: www.directv.com
Approx. Rev.: $20,268,000,000
Approx. Number Employees: 16,000
Year Founded: 1994
Business Description:
Satellite Services
S.I.C.: 4899
N.A.I.C.S.: 517410
Advertising Expenditures: $222,000,000
Media: 3-8-13-15
Distr.: Natl.
Personnel:
Patrick T. Doyle *(CFO & Exec VP)*
Paul Guyardo *(CMO & Chief Sls Officer)*
John F. Murphy *(Chief Acctg Officer, Sr VP & Controller)*
Larry D. Hunter *(Gen Counsel & Exec VP)*
Derek Chang *(Exec VP)*
Michael W. Palkovic *(Exec VP-Ops)*
Jon Gieselman *(Sr VP-Adv & PR)*
Beth Schwendt *(Mgr-Adv & Sponsorships)*
Advertising Agencies:
Deutsch, Inc.
(A Lowe & Partners Company)
111 8th Ave 14th Fl
New York, NY 10011-5201
Tel.: (212) 981-7600
Fax: (212) 981-7525
Media Planning

Ketchum Directory Advertising/Kansas City
7015 College Blvd Ste 700
Overland Park, KS 66211-1524
Tel.: (913) 344-1900
Fax: (913) 344-1960
Toll Free: (800) 922-6977

THE DISCOVERY CHANNEL
(Sub. of CTV Inc.)
9 Channel 9 Ct
Scarborough, ON M1S 4B5, Canada
Tel.: (416) 332-5000
Tel.: (416) 332-4254
Fax: (416) 332-4230
Web Site: www.discoverychannel.ca
Approx. Number Employees: 5,000
Business Description:
Television Station
S.I.C.: 4833
N.A.I.C.S.: 515120
Media: 13
Personnel:
Clark Bunting *(Pres & Gen Mgr-Discovery Channel)*
Andrea Golstein *(Mng Dir)*
Wonya Y. Lucas *(COO & Exec VP)*
Steve McGowan *(Sr VP-Res)*
Liz Brach *(VP-Production)*
Chad Beamish *(Mgr-Mktg)*
Advertising Agency:
ad 2-one
246 Westminster Bridge Rd
London, SE1 7PD, United Kingdom
Tel.: (44) 207 401 0333
Fax: (44) 207 4010366

DISCOVERY COMMUNICATIONS, INC.
1 Discovery Pl
Silver Spring, MD 20910
Tel.: (240) 662-2000
Fax: (240) 662-1868
Web Site: corporate.discovery.com
Approx. Rev.: $3,773,000,000
Approx. Number Employees: 4,200
Year Founded: 1985
Business Description:
Cable TV Networks Operator
S.I.C.: 4841
N.A.I.C.S.: 515210
Advertising Expenditures: $104,000,000
Media: 2-3-4-5-6-7-8-9-10-11-13-14-15-16-17-18-20-21-22-23-24-25-26
Distr.: Natl.
Personnel:
John S. Hendricks *(Founder & Chm)*
David M. Zaslav *(Pres & CEO)*
Bradley E. Singer *(CFO & Sr Exec VP)*
Peter Liguori *(COO)*
Bruce L. Campbell *(Chief Dev Officer & Gen Counsel)*
John Honeycutt *(Exec VP & Head-Intl Bus Ops-Discovery Networks Intl)*
Jean-Briac Perrette *(Chief Digital Officer)*
Bill Goodwyn *(Pres-Global Distr & CEO-Discovery Education)*
Mark Hollinger *(Pres/CEO-Discovery Networks Intl)*
W. Clark Bunting *(Pres/Gen Mgr-Discovery Channel)*
Joseph Abruzzese *(Pres-Adv Sls)*
Eileen O'Neill *(Grp Pres-Discovery & TLC Networks)*
Kelly Day *(COO-Digital Media, Commerce & Exec VP)*
Adria Alpert-Romm *(Sr Exec VP-HR)*
Lee Bartlett *(Exec VP-Global Production Mgmt, Bus & Legal Affair)*
Clara Kim *(Exec VP-Bus Affairs, Programming Legal, Production Mgmt & Talent)*
Glenn Oakley *(Exec VP-Media Tech, Ops & Production)*
Eric Phillips *(Exec VP-Discovery Education)*
Kevin Bennett *(Sr VP-Programming-Discovery Channel)*
Douglas Craig *(Sr VP-Digital Media Ops)*
Laurie Goldberg *(Sr VP-Comm)*
Meg Lowe *(Sr VP-Domestic Distr)*
Dan Bragg *(VP-Dir-Creative)*
Chance Patterson *(VP-Comm-Intl)*
Joshua Weinberg *(VP-Comm-Discovery Channel & Science Channel)*
Paul Gasek *(Editor)*
Danelle Sabathier *(Dir-Digital Media & Mktg)*
Shellie Marshall *(Mgr-Media)*
Brands & Products:
ANIMAL PLANET
DISCOVERY CHANNEL
DISCOVERY HEALTH CHANNEL
DISCOVERY TIMES CHANNEL
PLANET GREEN
TLC
THE TRAVEL CHANNEL
Advertising Agencies:
72andSunny
6300 Arizona Cir
Los Angeles, CA 90045
Tel.: (310) 215-9009
Fax: (310) 215-9012

Amalgamated Advertising LLC
145 W 30th St 7th Fl
New York, NY 10001
Tel.: (646) 878-1700
Fax: (646) 878-1787
Planet Green

Barker/DZP
455 Broadway
New York, NY 10013
Tel.: (212) 226-7336
Fax: (212) 226-7937

Colle+McVoy

Key to Media (For complete agency information see *The Advertising Red Books-Agencies* edition):
1. Bus. Publs. 2. Cable T.V. 3. Catalogs & Directories. 4. Co-op Adv. 5. Consumer Mags. 6. D.M. to Bus. Estab.7. D.M. to Consumers
8. Daily Newsp. 9. Exhibits/Trade Shows 10. Foreign 11. Infomercial 12. Internet Adv.13. Multimedia 14. Network Radio
15. Network T.V. 16. Newsp. Distr. Mags. 17. Other 18. Outdoor (Posters, Transit) 19. Point of Purchase20. Premiums, Novelties
21. Product Samples 22. Special Events Mktg. 23. Spot Radio 24. Spot T.V. 25. Weekly Newsp. 26. Yellow Page Adv.

Discovery Communications, Inc. — (Continued)

400 1st Ave N Ste 700
Minneapolis, MN 55401-1954
Tel.: (612) 305-6000
Fax: (612) 305-6500

PHD
(An Omnicom Company)
220 E 42nd 7th Fl
New York, NY 10017
Tel.: (212) 894-6600
Fax: (212) 894-4100

ViewPoint Studios Boston
254 2nd Ave
Needham, MA 02494
Tel.: (781) 449-5858
Fax: (781) 449-7272

DISH NETWORK CORPORATION

9601 S Meridian Blvd
Englewood, CO 80112
Tel.: (303) 723-1000
Fax: (303) 723-1399
E-mail: info@echostar.com
Web Site: www.dishnetwork.com
Approx. Rev.: $12,640,744,000
Approx. Number Employees: 22,000
Year Founded: 1980
Business Description:
Satellite Television Broadcasting
S.I.C.: 4841
N.A.I.C.S.: 517510; 515210
Media: 2-8-10-18-19-23-24
Personnel:
Charles W. Ergen *(Chm, Pres & CEO)*
Robert E. Olson *(CFO & Exec VP)*
Bernard L. Han *(COO)*
Ira Bahr *(CMO & Sr VP)*
Stephen W. Wood *(Chief HR Officer & Exec VP)*
R. Stanton Dodge *(Gen Counsel, Sec & Exec VP)*
W. Erik Carlson *(Exec VP-Ops)*
Thomas A. Cullen *(Exec VP-Corp Dev)*
Nolan O. Daines *(Exec VP-Strategic Initiatives)*
James DeFranco *(Exec VP-Sls, Distr & Mktg)*
Paul W. Orban *(Sr VP & Controller)*
David Kummer *(Sr VP-Engrg & Systems)*
Warren Schlichting *(VP-Media Sls)*
Scott Higgins *(Dir-iTV)*
Carolina Padilla *(Dir-Multicultural Mktg)*
Jos? Romero *(Mgr-Mktg)*
Brands & Products:
DISH NETWORK
Advertising Agencies:
DCI Group
1828 L St NW Ste 400
Washington, DC 20036
Tel.: (202) 546-4242
Fax: (202) 546-4243

Horizon Media, Inc.
75 Varick St
New York, NY 10013
Tel.: (212) 220-5000
Toll Free: (800) 633-4201
Media Buying
Media Planning
Out of Home
Radio
Television

DIVERSIFIED BROADCASTING, INC.

(Sub. of Diversified Communications)
WCJB TV 6220 NW 43rd St
Gainesville, FL 32653
Tel.: (352) 377-2020
Fax: (352) 373-6516
E-mail: comments@wcjb.com
Web Site: www.wcjb.com
Approx. Number Employees: 85
Business Description:
Television Broadcasting Services
S.I.C.: 4833; 7313
N.A.I.C.S.: 515120; 541840
Media: 24
Personnel:
Carolyn Barrett *(Pres)*

DIVERSIFIED COMMUNICATIONS

121 Free St
Portland, ME 04112-7437
Tel.: (207) 842-5400
Fax: (207) 842-5503
E-mail: custserv@divcom.com
Web Site: www.divcom.com
Sales Range: $50-74.9 Million
Approx. Number Employees: 200
Year Founded: 1970
Business Description:
Communications; Broadcasting, Publishing, Expositions
S.I.C.: 4833; 4841
N.A.I.C.S.: 515120; 515210
Media: 2-7-8-9-10-20-22-23
Personnel:
Horace A. Hildreth, Jr. *(Chm)*
Nancy Hasselback *(Pres & CEO-Diversified Comm)*
Paul Clancy *(CFO & Exec VP-Diversified Comm)*
Carolyn Barrett *(Pres-Brdcst Div)*
Brands & Products:
DIVERSIFIED COMMUNICATIONS
INTERNATIONAL BOSTON SEAFOOD SHOW
NATIONAL FISHERMAN MAGAZINE

DIY NETWORK

(Sub. of Scripps Networks Inc.)
9721 Sherrill Blvd
Knoxville, TN 37932
Tel.: (865) 694-2700
Fax: (865) 531-0799
Web Site: www.diynetwork.com
Sales Range: $50-74.9 Million
Year Founded: 1999
Business Description:
Cable Television Network
S.I.C.: 4841
N.A.I.C.S.: 515210
Media: 2-3-5-10-13-20-22
Personnel:
Gary Herman *(Sr VP-Ad Sls)*
Ross Babbithas *(Gen Mgr)*
Bob Baskerville *(Gen Mgr-Scripps Networks Intl)*
Sandy Moussapour *(Dir-Ad Sls & Mktg)*

D'OH!, INC.

5030 Roosevelt Way NE
Seattle, WA 98105
Tel.: (206) 524-8554
Fax: (206) 524-4851
E-mail: press@scarecrow.com
Web Site: www.scarecrow.com
Approx. Number Employees: 28
Business Description:
Video & DVD Rental & Retail
S.I.C.: 7841; 7822
N.A.I.C.S.: 532230; 512120
Media: 2-6-10-13-22-25
Personnel:
Carl Tostevin *(Owner)*
Brands & Products:
SCARECROW
SCARECROW VIDEO

DOLBY LABORATORIES, INC.

100 Potrero Ave
San Francisco, CA 94103-4813
Tel.: (415) 558-0200
Fax: (415) 863-1373
E-mail: info@dolby.com
Web Site: www.dolby.com
Approx. Rev.: $922,713,000
Approx. Number Employees: 1,244
Year Founded: 1965
Business Description:
Sound Processing & Noise Reduction Technology Developer
S.I.C.: 3089; 3663; 6794
N.A.I.C.S.: 326199; 334220; 533110
Approx. Advertising Expenditures: $14,600,000
Media: 10-13
Personnel:
Peter Gotcher *(Chm)*
Kevin J. Yeaman *(Pres & CEO)*
Murray J. Demo *(CFO & Exec VP)*
Craig Todd *(CTO & Sr VP)*
Andy Sherman *(Gen Counsel, Sec & Exec VP)*
Ramzi Haidamus *(Exec VP-Sls & Mktg)*
Michael Rockwell *(Exec VP-Products & Tech)*
Ioan Allen *(Sr VP)*
Eric Cohen *(Sr VP-Corp Dev)*
Andrew Dahlkemper *(Sr VP-HR)*
Steve E. Forshay *(Sr VP-Res)*
J. Stuart Mitchell *(Sr VP-Sls)*
Robin Selden *(Sr VP-Mktg)*
Jeff Reese *(Sr Dir-Brand Strategy & Mktg-Global)*
Brands & Products:
DOLBY
Advertising Agencies:
bite communications
345 Spear St Ste 750
San Francisco, CA 94105
Tel.: (415) 365-0222
Fax: (415) 365-0223

mPRm Public Relations
5670 Wilshire Blvd Ste 2500
Los Angeles, CA 90036
Tel.: (323) 933-3399
Fax: (323) 939-7211

DOMINION VIDEO SATELLITE INC.

(d/b/a Sky Angel)
1300 Googlette Rd N
Naples, FL 34102
Tel.: (239) 403-9130
Fax: (239) 403-9104
Toll Free: (888) 759-2643
E-mail: pr@skyangel.com
Web Site: www.skyangel.com
Approx. Number Employees: 125
Year Founded: 1981
Business Description:
High-Powered DBS Satellite TV & Radio Programming
S.I.C.: 4833; 4832
N.A.I.C.S.: 515120; 515112
Media: 6-8-9-10-13-19-20-22-23-24-25
Personnel:
Thomas Scott *(Pres & COO)*
Robert W. Johnson, Jr. *(CEO)*
Kevin Alexander *(Sr VP-Mktg)*
Violet Avedisfian *(VP-Customer Contact)*
Glen Christopher *(VP-Tech Svcs)*
Veronica Grahl *(VP-HR)*
Ray LaRue *(VP-Engrg)*
Marv Weisbert *(VP-IT)*
Brands & Products:
ANGEL ONE
ANGEL TWO
KTV
SKYANGEL

DON CORNELIUS PRODUCTIONS, INC.

9255 W Sunset Blvd
Los Angeles, CA 90069
Tel.: (310) 858-8232
Fax: (310) 859-2844
E-mail: webmaster@soultrain.com
Web Site: www.soultrain.com
Approx. Number Employees: 12
Year Founded: 1970
Business Description:
Television & Music Production Services
S.I.C.: 7812
N.A.I.C.S.: 512110
Media: 6-13-15
Brands & Products:
SOUL TRAIN

DREAMWORKS ANIMATION SKG, INC.

1000 Flower St
Glendale, CA 91201
Tel.: (818) 695-5000
Fax: (818) 695-9944
E-mail: ir@dreamworksanimation.com
Web Site: www.dreamworksanimation.com
Approx. Rev.: $784,791,000
Approx. Number Employees: 2,100
Business Description:
Computer-Generated Animated Feature Films Producer & Developer
S.I.C.: 7812
N.A.I.C.S.: 512110
Media: 6-9-10-18-20-23-24-25
Personnel:
Roger A. Enrico *(Chm)*
Lewis W. Coleman *(Pres & CFO)*
John Batter *(Co-Pres-Production)*
William Damaschke *(Co-Pres-Production for Feature Animation & Pres-Live Theatrical)*
Jeffrey Katzenberg *(CEO)*
Ann Daly *(COO)*
Philip M. Cross *(Chief Acctg Officer)*
Anne Globe *(Head-Worldwide Mktg & Consumer Products)*
Rich Sullivan *(Head-Corp Fin)*
Brands & Products:
DREAMWORKS ANIMATION SKG

Key to Media (For complete agency information see *The Advertising Red Books-Agencies* edition):
1. Bus. Publs. 2. Cable T.V. 3. Catalogs & Directories. 4. Co-op Adv. 5. Consumer Mags. 6. D.M. to Bus. Estab.7. D.M. to Consumers
8. Daily Newsp. 9. Exhibits/Trade Shows 10. Foreign 11. Infomercial 12. Internet Adv.13. Multimedia 14. Network Radio
15. Network T.V. 16. Newsp. Distr. Mags. 17. Other 18. Outdoor (Posters, Transit) 19. Point of Purchase20. Premiums, Novelties
21. Product Samples 22. Special Events Mktg. 23. Spot Radio 24. Spot T.V. 25. Weekly Newsp. 26. Yellow Page Adv.

Advertising Agencies:
Big Spaceship
45 Main St Ste 716
Brooklyn, NY 11201
Tel.: (718) 222-0281
Fax: (718) 971-1062

Hauser Advertising Inc.
309 Bellino Dr
Pacific Palisades, CA 90272
Tel.: (310) 459-5911
Fax: (310) 459-5919

JB West
1316 3rd St Ste 109
Santa Monica, CA 90401
Tel.: (310) 458-1952
Fax: (310) 584-1534

StruckAxiom
159 W Broadway Ste 200
Salt Lake City, UT 84101
Tel.: (801) 531-0122
Fax: (801) 531-0123

Turbine
21 Charles St
Westport, CT 06880
Tel.: (203) 226-2400
Fax: (203) 226-2417
Social Media
Television Ads
USDA's Forest Service Movie Tie-In
Shrek Forever After
Web Site

E1 ENTERTAINMENT U.S. LP
22 Harbor Pk Dr
Port Washington, NY 11050
Tel.: (516) 484-1000
Fax: (516) 484-4746
Approx. Number Employees: 130
Year Founded: 1993
Business Description:
Music, Videos & DVDs Distr
S.I.C.: 5099; 3652
N.A.I.C.S.: 423990; 334612
Import Export
Media: 4-13
Personnel:
Michael Rosenberg *(Pres)*
Michael Koch *(CEO)*
Rob McDonald *(VP-Sls)*
Carolyn Prudente *(VP-Fin)*
Charles Book *(Dir-Intl Sls & Licensing)*
Laura Lombardi *(Dir-Retail Mktg-E1 Music)*
Sejin Park *(Dir-Worldwide Acquisitions)*
Tom Briggs *(Product Mgr)*
Brands & Products:
KOCH ENTERTAINMENT
THE MAJOR ALTERNATIVE
Advertising Agency:
Brashe Advertising, Inc.
420 Jericho Tpke
Jericho, NY 11753-1344
Tel.: (516) 935-5544
Fax: (516) 931-1722

EAGLE COMMUNICATIONS INC.
2703 Hall St Ste 15
Hays, KS 67601
Tel.: (785) 625-4000
Fax: (785) 625-8030
E-mail: info@eaglecom.net
Web Site: www.eaglecom.net
Sales Range: $10-24.9 Million
Approx. Number Employees: 200
Business Description:
Radio Broadcasting Stations, Cable TV Stations & Internet Services
S.I.C.: 4832; 4841
N.A.I.C.S.: 515112; 515210
Media: 3-7-8-13-20-22-23-24
Personnel:
Robert E. Schmidt *(Chm)*
Gary D. Shorman *(Pres & CEO)*
Travis Kohlrus *(Dir-Community Rels & Product Dev)*
Brands & Products:
EAGLE
EVERYTHING YOU IMAGINE

EDUCATIONAL MEDIA FOUNDATION
5700 W Oaks Blvd
Rocklin, CA 95765
Tel.: (916) 251-1600
Fax: (916) 251-1650
E-mail: info@klove.com
Web Site: www.klove.com/about/contact.aspx
Approx. Number Employees: 300
Business Description:
Radio Broadcasting Services
S.I.C.: 4832
N.A.I.C.S.: 515112
Media: 18-20-22
Personnel:
Mike Novak *(Pres & CEO)*
David Atkinson *(VP-Fin)*
Richard Allison *(Mgr-Bus)*
Brands & Products:
AIR ONE RADIO
CHRISTIAN MUSIC PLANET
EMF BROADCASTING
K LOVE
WORLD WIDE WORSHIP

EDUCATIONAL PRODUCTS FOR INFANCY, INC.
(d/b/a Baby BumbleBee)
405 S Pinellas Ave
Tarpon Springs, FL 34689
Tel.: (727) 938-8799
Fax: (727) 938-8939
Toll Free: (888) 984-5500
Web Site: www.babybumblebee.com
Approx. Number Employees: 8
Year Founded: 1999
Business Description:
Educational Videos & DVDs Mfr
S.I.C.: 5192
N.A.I.C.S.: 424920
Media: 2-4-6-7-8-10-13
Personnel:
Elizabeth Iftikhar *(Pres)*
Patricia Ferry *(Mgr-Customer Svc)*
Brands & Products:
ACTION WORDS
ALL ABOUT ME
ALPHABET PHONICS AND FUN
BABY BUMBLEBEE
BABY MATH
BEE SMART BABY
CRAZY FOR COLORS
KICSFLIX
KICSFLIX CLASSIC TALES
MOTORIZED MADNESS
NUMERACY
OLIVIA AND OTIS AT THE PARK
OPPOSITES AND MORE
SEQUENCING
VOCABULARY BUILDER

EDUCATIONAL TELEVISION ASSOCIATION
(Name Changed to ideastream)

EMMIS COMMUNICATIONS CORPORATION
One Emmis Plaza 40 Monument Cir Ste 700
Indianapolis, IN 46204-3011
Tel.: (317) 266-0100
Fax: (317) 631-3750
E-mail: ir@emmis.com
Web Site: www.emmis.com
E-Mail For Key Personnel:
Public Relations: kate@emmis.com
Approx. Rev.: $251,314,000
Approx. Number Employees: 870
Year Founded: 1979
Business Description:
Radio & Television Broadcasting; Magazine Publishing
S.I.C.: 4832; 2721; 4833
N.A.I.C.S.: 515112; 511120; 515111; 515120
Advertising Expenditures: $5,100,000
Media: 6-8-11-13-18-22-23-24
Personnel:
Jeffrey H. Smulyan *(Chm, Pres & CEO)*
Patrick M. Walsh *(CFO, COO & Exec VP)*
Paul Brenner *(CTO & Sr VP)*
Greg Loewen *(Chief Strategy Officer)*
Richard F. Cummings *(Pres-Radio Programming)*
J. Scott Enright *(Gen Counsel & Exec VP)*
Ryan Hornaday *(Treas & Sr VP-Fin)*
Tracy Thompson *(Exec VP-HR)*
Ian Arnold *(VP, Asst Sec & Assoc Gen Counsel)*
Traci Thomson *(VP-HR)*
Nick Cavarra *(Dir-New Bus Dev)*
Brands & Products:
NETWORK INDIANA

EMS TECHNOLOGIES, INC.
660 Engineering Dr
Norcross, GA 30092-7700
Tel.: (770) 263-9200
Fax: (770) 263-9207
E-mail: hostmaster@ems-t.com
Web Site: www.ems-t.com
Approx. Sls.: $355,225,000
Approx. Number Employees: 1,160
Year Founded: 1968
Business Description:
Wireless Systems; Antenna, Microwave, Digital Command & Control, Optical & Broadband Products Mfr
S.I.C.: 3663; 7373
N.A.I.C.S.: 334220; 541512
Media: 8-10
Personnel:
John Byard Mowell *(Chm)*
Neilson A. Mackay *(Pres & CEO)*
Gary Shell *(CFO, Treas & Sr VP-Fin)*
David M. Sheffield *(Chief Acctg Officer & VP-Fin)*
Timothy C. Reis *(Gen Counsel & VP)*
Marion Van Fosson *(VP & Gen Mgr-Defense & Space Bus Unit)*
Gary M. Hebb *(VP-Innovation & Strategy)*
Nils Helle *(VP & Chief of Staff)*
Dan Monahan *(VP-Fin)*
Perry D. Tanner *(VP-Mktg & Info Mgmt)*
Clifford Topham *(VP-Sls & Mktg)*
Brands & Products:
ACCUFIRE
CALQUEST
CASSINI
COBRA
DARPA
DATANEX
DSCS
DUAL-DUALPOL
DUALPOL
DVB-RCS
EKOLINK
EKOLINK II
EKOLITE
EKOMINI
EMPG
EMS TECHNOLOGIES
ENCOMPASS
ENFUSION
ENVISAT
GEOLUT
INMARSAT
INTELSAT
JSTARS
LEOLUT
LXE
MICRO-ACCELLERATOR
MILSTAR
MIRRORCELL
NEMA
PCS
THE PERFORMANCE LEADER
PHALANX
POSEIDON
QUAD
RADARSAT
RFTERM
SARMASTER
SATCOM
SEAWINDS
SELECTACELL
SLIMGEM
SPIRE
TDRS
TELSTAR
TOUGHTALK
WAVELINK
XCELERATOR

ENTRAVISION COMMUNICATIONS CORPORATION
2425 Olympic Blvd Ste 6000 W
Santa Monica, CA 90404-4056
Tel.: (310) 447-3870
Fax: (310) 447-3899
Web Site: www.entravision.com
Approx. Rev.: $200,476,000
Approx. Number Employees: 876
Year Founded: 2000
Business Description:
Radio & Television Broadcasting Stations
S.I.C.: 4833; 4832
N.A.I.C.S.: 515120; 515112
Advertising Expenditures: $300,000
Media: 18-23-24
Personnel:
Walter F. Ulloa *(Chm & CEO)*
Philip C. Wilkinson *(Pres & COO)*
Christopher T. Young *(CFO, Treas & Exec VP)*
Jeffery A. Liberman *(Pres-Radio Div)*

Key to Media (For complete agency information see *The Advertising Red Books-Agencies* edition):
1. Bus. Publs. 2. Cable T.V. 3. Catalogs & Directories. 4. Co-op Adv. 5. Consumer Mags. 6. D.M. to Bus. Estab.7. D.M. to Consumers 8. Daily Newsp. 9. Exhibits/Trade Shows 10. Foreign 11. Infomercial 12. Internet Adv.13. Multimedia 14. Network Radio 15. Network T.V. 16. Newsp. Distr. Mags. 17. Other 18. Outdoor (Posters, Transit) 19. Point of Purchase20. Premiums, Novelties 21. Product Samples 22. Special Events Mktg. 23. Spot Radio 24. Spot T.V. 25. Weekly Newsp. 26. Yellow Page Adv.

Entravision Communications Corporation — (Continued)

Mark A. Boelke *(Gen Counsel, Sec & VP-Legal Affairs)*
Ryan Mulligan *(Publr-Web Content)*
Larry E. Safir *(Exec VP)*
Russell Sakamoto *(Sr VP & Controller)*
Brian Reed *(VP-Sls)*
Jeff Apodaca *(Gen Mgr)*
Mario M. Carrera *(Gen Mgr)*
Karl Alonso Meyer *(Gen Mgr-Radio Stations-LA)*
Aaron Scoby *(Gen Mgr)*
Margarita Wilder *(Gen Mgr-Television)*

Advertising Agency:
Vista Media Group
5700 Wilshire Blvd Ste 250
Los Angeles, CA 90036
Tel.: (323) 900-6169
Fax: (323) 900-6126

EPOCH FILMS INC.

435 Hudson St Fl 3
New York, NY 10014
Tel.: (212) 226-0661
Fax: (212) 226-4893
E-mail: info@epochfilms.com
Web Site: www.epochfilms.com
Approx. Number Employees: 30
Business Description:
Motion Picture & Video Production
S.I.C.: 7812
N.A.I.C.S.: 512110
Media: 15-18-24
Personnel:
Mindy Goldberg *(Owner)*
Margaret Capossela *(CFO)*
Tara Averill *(Exec Dir-Sls & New Media)*
Jessica Sanders *(Comml Rep)*

ESPN, INC.

(Group of ABC, Inc.)
ESPN Plz 545 Middle St
Bristol, CT 06010-7454
Tel.: (860) 766-2000
Fax: (860) 766-2213
E-mail: askespntv@espn.pwcc.com
Web Site: www.espn.com
E-Mail For Key Personnel:
Sales Director: sales@espn.com
Sales Range: $1-4.9 Billion
Approx. Number Employees: 5,000
Year Founded: 1979
Business Description:
Holding Company; Sports Entertainment Multimedia Broadcaster & Publisher
S.I.C.: 6719; 2721; 4832; 4841
N.A.I.C.S.: 551112; 511120; 515111; 515210; 519130
Media: 3-6-9-10-13-15-22-23-24-25
Distr.: Natl.
Personnel:
George W. Bodenheimer *(Pres)*
Christine F. Driessen *(CFO & Exec VP)*
Chuck Pagano *(CTO & Exec VP)*
Edward Erhardt *(Pres-Mktg & Sls-Consumer)*
Sean Bratches *(Exec VP-Sls & Mktg)*
Edwin M. Durso *(Exec VP-Admin)*
John Skipper *(Exec VP)*
Morris Davenport *(Sr VP & Gen Mgr)*
John Kosner *(Sr VP & Gen Mgr)*
John Zehr *(Sr VP & Gen Mgr-ESPN Mobile Properties)*
Artie Bulgrin *(Sr VP-Res & Analytics)*
Keith Clinkscales *(Sr VP-Content Dev & Enterprises)*
Marie Donoghue *(Sr VP)*
Rosa Gatti *(Sr VP-Corp Comm & Outreach)*
Traug Keller *(Sr VP-Production Bus Unites-Guia)*
Carol Kruse *(Sr VP-Mktg)*
Chris LaPlaca *(Sr VP)*
Matt Murphy *(Sr VP-Sls)*
Paul Richardson *(Sr VP-HR)*
David Roberts *(VP & Gen Mgr-ESPN 10 Radio/New York)*
Moira Davis *(VP-Mktg)*
Lino Garcia *(Gen Mgr-Deportes)*
Gary Belsky *(Editor-in-Chief)*
John Dahl *(Exec Producer-ESPN Content Dev)*
Pete Gianesini *(Sr Dir-Programming)*
Seth Ader *(Sr Dir-Mktg)*
Cherie Cohen *(Sr Dir-Multi-Media Sls)*
Jim D'Antoni *(Sr Dir)*
Jim Kiernan *(Sr Dir-Digital Sls Strategy)*
Randy McKelvey *(Sr Dir-Digital Media)*
Mary Sheehan *(Sr Dir-Media & Strategy)*
Lisa Stancati *(Asst Gen Counsel)*
Jim Bowdon *(Coord Producer-ESPN Studio Production)*
Jack Obringer *(Sr Coord Producer-Studio Production)*

Brands & Products:
AROUND THE HORN
ESPN
ESPN CLASSIC
ESPN DEPORTES
ESPN FANTASY BASEBALL IS FREE. AND IT ROCKS.
ESPN NEWS
ESPN RADIO
ESPN THE MAGAZINE
ESPN ZONE
ESPN360.COM
ESPYS
PARDON THE INTERRUPTION
PLAYMAKERS
ROME IS BURNING
SPORTSCENTER
WINTER X GAMES
X GAMES

Advertising Agencies:
Almighty
300 Western Ave
Boston, MA 02134
Tel.: (617) 782-1511
Fax: (617) 782-1611

Arnold Worldwide
101 Huntington Ave
Boston, MA 02199-7603
Tel.: (617) 587-8000
Fax: (617) 587-8004

Bernard Hodes Group
534 Broadhollow Rd Ste 305A
Melville, NY 11747-3620
Tel.: (631) 753-1901
Fax: (631) 753-1914

Duffy & Shanley, Inc.
10 Charles St
Providence, RI 02904
Tel.: (401) 274-0001
Fax: (401) 274-3535
(Great Outdoor Games)

The Martin Agency
One Shockoe Plz
Richmond, VA 23219-4132
Tel.: (804) 698-8000
Fax: (804) 698-8001
X Games

Sarkissian Mason
135 W 26th St 5 Fl
New York, NY 10001
Tel.: (212) 625-8212
Fax: (212) 625-8211
ESPN The Magazine Web Site

Wieden + Kennedy-New York
150 Varick St Fl 7
New York, NY 10013-1218
Tel.: (917) 661-5200
Fax: (917) 661-5500
(NBA Games, Monday Night Football, SportsCenter)
2010 FIFA World Cup
This is SportsCenter

EUE SCREEN GEMS LTD.

1223 N 23rd St
Wilmington, NC 28405
Tel.: (910) 343-3500
Fax: (910) 343-3574
E-mail: info@screengemsstudios.com
Web Site:
www.screengemsstudios.com
Sales Range: $50-74.9 Million
Approx. Number Employees: 150
Business Description:
Television & Film Production
S.I.C.: 7829
N.A.I.C.S.: 512199
Media: 6
Personnel:
Bill Vassar *(Exec VP)*

EUPHONIX, INC.

(Sub. of Avid Technology, Inc.)
1330 W Middlefield Rd
Mountain View, CA 94043
Tel.: (650) 237-1604
Fax: (650) 969-3510
E-mail: info@euphonix.com
Web Site: www.euphonix.com
Sales Range: $10-24.9 Million
Approx. Number Employees: 111
Year Founded: 1988
Business Description:
Digital Audio Mixing Consoles Mfr
S.I.C.: 3651
N.A.I.C.S.: 334310
Media: 4-7-10-13-22
Personnel:
Richard McKernan *(Dir-Western Region)*
Ken Lancashire *(Mgr-Technical Svc)*

EVATONE, INC.

4801 Ulmerton Rd
Clearwater, FL 33762-4148
Tel.: (727) 572-7000
Fax: (727) 572-6214
Toll Free: (800) 382-8663
E-mail: sales@eva-tone.com
Web Site: www.eva-tone.com
E-Mail For Key Personnel:
Sales Director: sales@eva-tone.com
Sales Range: $25-49.9 Million
Approx. Number Employees: 75
Year Founded: 1925
Business Description:
CDs & Optical Media; Cassette Duplication; CD-ROM Development; Multimedia & E-Business Development; Commercial Printing & Packaging & Trade Binder Services; Direct Mail; Fulfillment
S.I.C.: 3652; 2752
N.A.I.C.S.: 334612; 323110
Import Export
Media: 2-7-9-10-25
Distr.: Intl.; Natl.
Budget Set: Oct.
Brands & Products:
COLLATERAL MANAGEMENT SYSTEM
EVAQUICK
EVATONE
NOTEWORTHY CDS
RE:SOURCE RABBIT

EXTREME NETWORKS INC

3585 Monroe St
Santa Clara, CA 95051-1450
Tel.: (408) 579-2800
Fax: (408) 579-3000
Toll Free: (888) 257-3000
E-mail: support@extremenetworks.com
Web Site: www.extremenetworks.com
Approx. Rev.: $334,428,000
Approx. Number Employees: 732
Year Founded: 1996
Business Description:
Broadband Network Solutions
S.I.C.: 3663; 3661
N.A.I.C.S.: 334220; 334210
Advertising Expenditures: $100,000
Media: 5-10
Personnel:
Edward B. Meyercord, III *(Chm)*
Oscar Rodriguez *(Pres & CEO)*
James T. Judson *(CFO & Interim VP)*
David Ginsburg *(CMO)*
Frank Blohm *(Chief Quality Officer & VP-Worldwide Ops)*
Diane C. Honda *(Gen Counsel, Sec & VP)*
Mimi Gigoux *(Sr VP-HR)*
Gavin Cato *(VP-Engrg)*
Greg Cross *(Mgr-PR & Worldwide)*
Brands & Products:
ALPINE
ALPINE 3800
ALTITUDE
ALTITUDE 350-2
ALTITUDE 450
ALTITUDE 451
BE EXTREME
BLACKDIAMOND
BLACKDIAMOND 10808
BLACKDIAMOND 12800R
BLACKDIAMOND 20809
BLACKDIAMOND 8800
BLACKDIAMOND12804C
EDGE
EPICENTER
EPICENTER V6.0
EXTREME NETWORKS
EXTREMEWARE
EXTREMEWARE EDGE
EXTREMEXOS
THE FUTURE ARRIVED EARLY
INNOVATING WITH EXTREME
THE NEXT GENERATION DATA CENTER
REACHNXT
SENTRIANT
SENTRIANT AG200

Key to Media (For complete agency information see *The Advertising Red Books-Agencies* edition):
1. Bus. Publs. 2. Cable T.V. 3. Catalogs & Directories. 4. Co-op Adv. 5. Consumer Mags. 6. D.M. to Bus. Estab.7. D.M. to Consumers
8. Daily Newsp. 9. Exhibits/Trade Shows 10. Foreign 11. Infomercial 12. Internet Adv.13. Multimedia 14. Network Radio
15. Network T.V. 16. Newsp. Distr. Mags. 17. Other 18. Outdoor (Posters, Transit) 19. Point of Purchase20. Premiums, Novelties
21. Product Samples 22. Special Events Mktg. 23. Spot Radio 24. Spot T.V. 25. Weekly Newsp. 26. Yellow Page Adv.

SERVICEWATCH
SUMMIT
SUMMIT WM100
SUMMIT WM20
SUMMIT WM200
SUMMIT WM2000
SUMMIT X150
SUMMIT X250E
SUMMIT X350
SUMMIT X450A
SUMMIT X450E
SUMMIT X650
SUMMIT48SI
UNIFIED ACCESS ARCHITECTURE
XOS

Advertising Agency:
Lux Communications
1127 S Genevieve Ln
San Jose, CA 95128
Tel.: (408) 244-1880

FIRST LOOK STUDIOS, INC.

(Sub. of First Look Holdings, LLC)
2000 Ave of the Stars Ste 410
Los Angeles, CA 90067
Tel.: (424) 202-5000
Fax: (424) 202-5310
E-mail: info@firstlookstudios.com
Web Site: www.firstlookstudios.com
Approx. Number Employees: 52
Year Founded: 1980
Business Description:
Motion Picture, Video & Television Program Producer & Distr
S.I.C.: 7812; 7822; 7829
N.A.I.C.S.: 512110; 512120; 512199
Advertising Expenditures: $3,000,000
Media: 1-3-13-14-15-16
Personnel:
Bill Lee *(Acting CEO)*
Dean Wilson *(COO)*
Sean Quigley *(Sr VP-Fin Plng & Analysis)*

FISHER COMMUNICATIONS, INC.

100 4th Ave N Ste 510
Seattle, WA 98109
Tel.: (206) 404-7000
Fax: (206) 404-7050
Fax: (206) 404-6037
E-mail: info@fsci.com
Web Site: www.fsci.com
Approx. Rev.: $133,664,000
Approx. Number Employees: 837
Year Founded: 1910
Business Description:
Television & Radio Station Operator
S.I.C.: 4833; 4832
N.A.I.C.S.: 515120; 515112
Advertising Expenditures: $2,400,000
Media: 5-8-13-18-23-24
Personnel:
Michael D. Wortsman *(Chm)*
Colleen B. Brown *(Pres & CEO)*
Hassan N. Natha *(CFO & Sr VP)*
Christopher J. Bellavia *(Gen Counsel, Sec & Sr VP)*
Robert I. Dunlop *(Exec VP-Ops)*
Randa E. Minkarah *(Sr VP-Bus Dev)*
John N. Tamerlano *(Sr VP-Reg Television)*
Larry Roberts *(Reg VP)*
Matt Spragins *(VP & Gen Mgr-Fisher Interactive Network)*
Brian McHale *(VP-Tech)*
Sherry Pelletier *(VP-HR)*
Jenny Kuglin *(Dir-Social Media-Fisher Interactive Network)*

FLOORGRAPHICS INC.

242 Princeton Ave
Hamilton, NJ 08619
Tel.: (609) 528-9200
Fax: (609) 689-0204
Toll Free: (888) 356-6723
E-mail: info@floorgraphics.com
Web Site: www.floorgraphics.com
Sales Range: $50-74.9 Million
Approx. Number Employees: 85
Year Founded: 1996
Business Description:
Designers of Billboards on Floors
S.I.C.: 7319
N.A.I.C.S.: 541850
Media: 7-11-13-18
Brands & Products:
FLOOR GRAPHICS

FLORIDA WEST COAST PUBLIC BROADCASTING, INC.

(d/b/a WEDU-TV)
1300 N Blvd
Tampa, FL 33607-5699
Tel.: (813) 254-9338
Fax: (813) 253-0826
Toll Free: (800) 354-9338
Web Site: www.wedu.org
Sales Range: $1-9.9 Million
Year Founded: 1958
Business Description:
Public Television Station
S.I.C.: 4833; 5261
N.A.I.C.S.: 515120; 444220
Advertising Expenditures: $100,000
Media: 7-8-9-22-24-25
Personnel:
Richard M. Lobo *(Pres & CEO)*
Larry Jopek *(VP-Mktg & Community Partnerships)*
Laura Turner *(VP-Comm)*
Rob Lorei *(Affairs Dir)*

FOCUS FEATURES

(Joint Venture of Comcast Corporation & General Electric Company)
100 Universal City Plz
Universal City, CA 91608
Tel.: (818) 777-1000
Tel.: (818) 777-7373
Fax: (818) 866-3600
Web Site: focusfeatures.com/
Sales Range: $50-74.9 Million
Business Description:
Motion Picture Producer & Distr
S.I.C.: 7812; 3652
N.A.I.C.S.: 512110; 334612
Media: 2-5-6-9-15-16-18-23-24
Distr.: Intl.; Natl.
Personnel:
Marc Shmuger *(Vice Chm)*
Scott Stuber *(Vice Chm-Production-Worldwide)*
Rick Finkelstein *(Pres & COO)*
Louis A. Feola *(Pres-Home Entertainment-Worldwide)*
Kathy Nelson *(Pres-Film Music)*
Maria Pekurovskaya *(Exec VP-Creative Adv)*
Steven Scott *(Exec VP-Music Publ & Music Opers)*
Stephanie Sperber *(Exec VP-Partnerships)*
Suzanne Cole *(Sr VP-Media)*
Erica Steinberg *(Sr VP-Prod)*
Jeff Kirschenbaum *(VP-Production)*
Ana Raab *(Mgr-Field Mktg & Adv)*

FOOD NETWORK

(Sub. of Scripps Networks Inc.)
75 9th Ave
New York, NY 10011
Tel.: (212) 398-8836
Fax: (212) 736-7716
Web Site: www.foodnetwork.com
Sales Range: $25-49.9 Million
Approx. Number Employees: 100
Year Founded: 1994
Business Description:
Cable Television Network
S.I.C.: 4841
N.A.I.C.S.: 515210
Media: 3-13-18-23-24
Distr.: Intl.; Natl.
Personnel:
Susie Fogelson *(Sr VP-Mktg, Creative Svcs & Brand Strategy)*
Karen Grinthal *(Sr VP-Adv Sls Food Network & Cooking Channel-Scripps Networks)*
Thomas Killoy *(Sr VP-Ops)*
Bruce Seidel *(Sr VP-Program Plng & Special Productions)*
Jon Steinlauf *(Sr VP-Adv Sls)*
Bob Tuschman *(Gen Mgr)*
Advertising Agencies:
Centra360
1400 Old Country Rd Ste 420
Westbury, NY 11590-5119
Tel.: (516) 997-3147
Fax: (516) 334-7798

PointRoll Inc.
951 E Hector St
Conshohocken, PA 19428
Tel.: (267) 558-1300
Fax: (267) 285-1141
Toll Free: (800) 203-6956

Radio Direct Response
1400 N Providence Rd Ste 4000
Media, PA 19063
Tel.: (610) 892-7300
Fax: (610) 892-1899
Toll Free: (800) 969-AMFM

FOX BROADCASTING COMPANY

(Sub. of Fox Entertainment Group, Inc.)
10201 W Pico Blvd
Los Angeles, CA 90064
Tel.: (310) 369-1000
E-mail: privacy@fox.com
Web Site: www.fox.com
Sales Range: $1-4.9 Billion
Approx. Number Employees: 30,000
Year Founded: 1986
Business Description:
Television Programming
S.I.C.: 4833; 7812
N.A.I.C.S.: 515120; 512110
Export
Media: 2-3-6-7-8-9-10-11-13-14-15-18-20-22
Distr.: Natl.
Personnel:
Roger Ailes *(Chm & CEO)*
David Devoe *(CFO & Sr Exec VP)*
Rupert Merdhoch *(COO)*
Toby Byrne *(Pres-Sls)*
Mike Darnell *(Pres-Alternative Entertainment)*
Joseph Earley *(Pres-Mktg & Comm)*
Kevin Reilly *(Pres-Fox Entertainment)*
Arthur M. Siskind *(Gen Counsel & Sr Exec VP)*
Preston Beckman *(Exec VP-Strategic Program Plng & Res)*
Laurel Bernard *(Exec VP-Mktg)*
Brian Dollenmayer *(Exec VP-On Air Promo & Mktg Ops)*
Jennifer Nicholson Salke *(Exec VP-Creative Affairs-20th Century Fox TV)*
Marcy Ross *(Exec VP-Current Programming)*
Shannon Ryan *(Exec VP-Mktg & Comm)*
Marsha Shulman *(Exec VP-Casting)*
Melva Benoit *(Sr VP-Consumer Insight & Audience Res)*
Matthew Glotzer *(Sr VP-Fox Digital Media)*
Missy Halprin *(Sr VP-New Talent)*
Susan Levison *(Sr VP-Drama Dev)*
Tom Morrissey *(Sr VP-Design)*
Preston Padden *(Sr VP-Affilates)*
Paul Rittenberg *(Sr VP-Adv Sls-Fox News)*
Audrey Steele *(Sr VP-Sls Res & Mktg)*
Minna Taylor *(Sr VP-Legal Affairs)*
Todd Yasui *(Sr VP)*
Jeff Misenti *(VP-Fox News Digital & Gen Mgr)*
Don Wilcox *(VP & Gen Mgr-Branded Entertainment)*
Bob Flood *(VP-Integrated Sls/Insights-Fox News & Fox Bus Network)*
John McCann *(VP-Adv Sls-Fox Bus Network)*
Susan Graham *(Exec Dir-Integrated Mktg & Promos-Natl)*
Ann Taniguchi *(Dir-Media-Natl)*
Eugene A. Brookhart *(Mgr-Transmission Scheduling Engrg & Ops)*
Brands & Products:
FOX

FOX ENTERTAINMENT GROUP, INC.

(Sub. of News Corporation)
10201 W Pico Blvd
Los Angeles, CA 90035-2606
Tel.: (310) 369-1000
Fax: (310) 969-0757
Web Site: www.fox.com
Sales Range: $1-4.9 Billion
Approx. Number Employees: 6,000
Business Description:
Holding Company; Motion Picture & Television Production, Distribution, Programming & Broadcasting Services
S.I.C.: 6719; 7812; 7819; 7822
N.A.I.C.S.: 551112; 512110; 512120; 512191
Advertising Expenditures: $1,300,000,000
Personnel:
David F. DeVoe *(CFO & Sr Exec VP)*
Jon Nesvig *(Pres-Adv Sls)*
Jean Rossi *(Pres-Fox One)*
Nick Belperio *(Sr VP-Affiliate Mktg)*
Michelle Garry *(VP-Affiliate Mktg)*
Advertising Agencies:
Dailey & Associates
(Sub. of The Interpublic Group of Cos., Inc.)

Key to Media (For complete agency information see *The Advertising Red Books-Agencies* edition):
1. Bus. Publs. 2. Cable T.V. 3. Catalogs & Directories. 4. Co-op Adv. 5. Consumer Mags. 6. D.M. to Bus. Estab.7. D.M. to Consumers 8. Daily Newsp. 9. Exhibits/Trade Shows 10. Foreign 11. Infomercial 12. Internet Adv.13. Multimedia 14. Network Radio 15. Network T.V. 16. Newsp. Distr. Mags. 17. Other 18. Outdoor (Posters, Transit) 19. Point of Purchase20. Premiums, Novelties 21. Product Samples 22. Special Events Mktg. 23. Spot Radio 24. Spot T.V. 25. Weekly Newsp. 26. Yellow Page Adv.

Fox Entertainment Group, Inc. — (Continued)

8687 Melrose Ave Ste G300
West Hollywood, CA 90069-5701
Tel.: (310) 360-3100
Fax: (310) 360-0810

Zenith Media
2049 Century Park E Ste 1300
Los Angeles, CA 90067
Tel.: (310) 551-3500
Fax: (310) 551-4119
— Julie Rieger *(Acct Exec)*

FOX SPORTS NET

(Sub. of Fox Broadcasting Company)
10000 Santa Monica Blvd
Los Angeles, CA 90067
Mailing Address:
PO Box 900
Beverly Hills, CA 90213-0900
Tel.: (310) 369-1000
Web Site: www.foxsports.com
Sales Range: $10-24.9 Million
Approx. Number Employees: 30
Business Description:
Cable Television Services
S.I.C.: 4833
N.A.I.C.S.: 515120
Personnel:
David Hills *(Chm & CEO)*
Ed Goren *(Vice Chm)*
Eric Shanks *(Pres)*
David Rone *(Exec VP)*
Robert Gottlieb *(Sr VP & Dir-Creative)*
Jerry Steinberg *(Sr VP-Field Ops)*
Mike Dimond *(VP & Gen Mgr)*
Andrew Hossom *(VP-Mktg)*
Bob Ferguson *(Gen Mgr)*
Samantha Ankeny *(Dir-Mktg & Sls Promo-Detroit)*
Brands & Products:
FOX SPORTS
Advertising Agency:
Tom, Dick & Harry Advertising
350 W Erie 2nd Fl
Chicago, IL 60654
Tel.: (312) 327-9500
Fax: (312) 327-9501

FOX TELEVISION STATIONS INC.

(Sub. of Fox Broadcasting Company)
(d/b/a Fox News)
2044 Armacost Ave
Los Angeles, CA 90925
Tel.: (310) 571-2000
Fax: (212) 301-4220
E-mail: foxnews@foxnews.com
Web Site: www.foxnews.com
Sales Range: $50-74.9 Million
Approx. Number Employees: 200
Business Description:
Television Stations Operator
S.I.C.: 4833
N.A.I.C.S.: 515120
Media: 2-3-5-9-16-18-24-25
Distr.: Natl.
Budget Set: July
Personnel:
Roger Ailes *(Chm & CEO)*
Preston Beckman *(Exec VP-Strategic Program Plng)*
Brian Lewis *(Exec VP-Corp Commun)*
Jamia Bigalow *(Sr VP-Affiliate Mktg)*
Ron Stitt *(Grp VP, Digital Media)*
Erica Keane *(VP-Media Rels)*
Dianne Smith *(VP-Legal/FCC Compliance)*

FREMANTLEMEDIA NORTH AMERICA INC.

(Sub. of FremantleMedia Ltd)
28 E 28th St
New York, NY 10016
Tel.: (212) 541-2800
Fax: (212) 541-2810
Web Site: www.fremantlemedia.com
Approx. Number Employees: 15
Business Description:
Production & Distribution of Motion Pictures & Television Programs; Marketing of Commercial Time to National Television Advertisers
S.I.C.: 7822
N.A.I.C.S.: 512120
Personnel:
Bob Higgins *(Sr VP-Children's & Family)*
Jeff Tahler *(Sr VP-Acq & Dev-Enterprises-Americas)*
Advertising Agencies:
Rogers & Cowan
8687 Melrose Ave 7th Fl
Los Angeles, CA 90069
Tel.: (310) 854-8100
Fax: (310) 854-8106

Sunshine Sachs & Associates
149 5th Ave 7th Fl
New York, NY 10010
Tel.: (212) 691-2800

FUSE NETWORKS LLC

(Sub. of Madison Square Garden, L.P.)
11 Penn Plz 17th Fl
New York, NY 10001
Tel.: (212) 324-3400
Fax: (212) 324-3445
E-mail: fuseinfo@fuse.tv
Web Site: www.fuse.tv
Sales Range: $10-24.9 Million
Approx. Number Employees: 120
Year Founded: 2003
Business Description:
Music Television Network
S.I.C.: 4841
N.A.I.C.S.: 515210
Media: 3-13
Personnel:
Joe Glennon *(Sr VP-Affiliate Distr)*
Sal LoCurto *(Sr VP-Programming)*
Jason Miller *(Sr VP-Adv Sls)*
Amy Stevens *(Sr VP-Strategic Alliances-Fuse TV)*
Lisbeth Cassaday *(VP-Media Rels)*
Donna Wolfe *(VP-Production)*
Advertising Agencies:
The Brooklyn Brothers
18 E 17th St 6th Fl
New York, NY 10003
Tel.: (212) 242-0200
Fax: (212) 242-0217

Initiative
1 Dag Hammarskjold Plz
New York, NY 10017
Tel.: (212) 605-7000
Fax: (917) 305-4003
Media Buying

FX NETWORKS, LLC

(Sub. of Fox Broadcasting Company)
10201 W Pico Blvd
Los Angeles, CA 90067
Mailing Address:
PO Box 900
Beverly Hills, CA 90213-0900
Tel.: (310) 369-1000
E-mail: user@fxnetworks.com
Web Site: www.fxnetworks.com
E-Mail For Key Personnel:
Public Relations: jsolberg@fxnetworks.com
Sales Range: $50-74.9 Million
Approx. Number Employees: 200
Year Founded: 1994
Business Description:
Cable Television Network & Programming Services
S.I.C.: 4841
N.A.I.C.S.: 515210
Advertising Expenditures: $4,000,000
Media: 1-3-6-9-14-15-18-23-24
Distr.: Natl.
Budget Set: July -Aug.
Personnel:
John Solberg *(Pres)*
Carl Saftler *(Exec VP & Gen Mgr)*
Sally Daws *(Exec VP)*
Lindsay Gardner *(Exec VP-Affiliate Sls)*
Stephanie Gibbons *(EVP-Mktg & On-Air)*
Michael Brochstein *(Sr VP-Adv Sls)*
Nicholas Grad *(Sr VP-Series Devel)*
John Varvi *(Sr VP-On-Air Promotions)*

G4 MEDIA, INC.

(Sub. of Comcast Corporation)
5750 Wilshire Blvd, 4th Floor
Los Angeles, CA 90036-7201
Tel.: (310) 979-5000
E-mail: info@g4media.com
Web Site: www.g4tv.com
Sales Range: $200-249.9 Million
Year Founded: 2002
Business Description:
Cable Network
S.I.C.: 4841
N.A.I.C.S.: 515210
Personnel:
Neal Tiles *(Pres)*
Steve Dolcemaschio *(COO)*
David Angehrn *(VP-Mktg & Strategic Planning)*
Gil Breakman *(VP-Fin)*
Advertising Agency:
72andSunny
6300 Arizona Cir
Los Angeles, CA 90045
Tel.: (310) 215-9009
Fax: (310) 215-9012

GAIAM

(Div. of Gaiam, Inc.)
350 Madison Ave 17th Fl
New York, NY 10017
Tel.: (212) 951-3000
Fax: (212) 951-9319
E-mail: information@gaiam.com
Sales Range: $250-299.9 Million
Approx. Number Employees: 800
Year Founded: 1984
Business Description:
Multimedia Entertainment
S.I.C.: 3695; 5735
N.A.I.C.S.: 334613; 451220
Advertising Expenditures: $13,000,000
Bus. Publs.: $3,000,000; Infomercial: $10,000,000
Distr.: Natl.
Personnel:
Jovi Stephenson *(VP-Mktg)*
Brands & Products:
BERENSTEIN BEARS
COPA
THE FIRM
HEROES AND LEGENDS OF THE BIBLE
JEKYLL & HYDE
LITTLE HOUSE ON THE PRAIRIE
PETER RABBIT AND FRIENDS
RUDOLPH, THE RED-NOSED REINDEER
SMOKEY JOE'S CAFE
TURBO COOKER
THE WIND IN THE WILLOWS

GALAVISION

(Sub. of Univision Communications Inc.)
605 3rd Ave 12th Fl
New York, NY 10158-1299
Tel.: (212) 455-5200
Fax: (212) 867-6710
E-mail: bm-latraffic@univision.net
Web Site: www.galavision.com
Approx. Number Employees: 120
Year Founded: 1979
Business Description:
International Network & Basic Cable Service
S.I.C.: 4841
N.A.I.C.S.: 515210
Media: 9-18
Distr.: Natl.
Budget Set: Sept.

GAME SHOW NETWORK LLC

(Joint Venture of Sony Corporation & Liberty Media Corporation)
2150 Colorada Ave
Santa Monica, CA 90404
Tel.: (310) 255-6800
Fax: (310) 255-6810
E-mail: help@gsn.com
Web Site: www.corp.gsn.com
Sales Range: $200-249.9 Million
Approx. Number Employees: 130
Business Description:
Cable Television Network (50% Owned by Liberty Media Holding & 50% Owned by Sony Pictures Entertainment)
S.I.C.: 4841
N.A.I.C.S.: 515210
Personnel:
David Goldhill *(Pres & CEO)*
Christian Meyer *(Sr VP & Gen Mgr-GSN Digital Solutions)*
John Zaccario *(Sr VP-Adv Sls)*
Mindy Hamilton *(VP-Strategic Partnerships & Promos)*
Advertising Agency:
Molecular
The Arsenal of the Charles 343 Arsenal St
Watertown, MA 02472
Tel.: (617) 218-6500
Fax: (617) 218-6700
(GSN.com)

Key to Media (For complete agency information see *The Advertising Red Books-Agencies* edition):
1. Bus. Publs. 2. Cable T.V. 3. Catalogs & Directories. 4. Co-op Adv. 5. Consumer Mags. 6. D.M. to Bus. Estab.7. D.M. to Consumers
8. Daily Newsp. 9. Exhibits/Trade Shows 10. Foreign 11. Infomercial 12. Internet Adv.13. Multimedia 14. Network Radio
15. Network T.V. 16. Newsp. Distr. Mags. 17. Other 18. Outdoor (Posters, Transit) 19. Point of Purchase20. Premiums, Novelties
21. Product Samples 22. Special Events Mktg. 23. Spot Radio 24. Spot T.V. 25. Weekly Newsp. 26. Yellow Page Adv.

GAMESVILLE, INC.
(Div. of Lycos, Inc.)
100 5th Ave
Waltham, MA 02451-2000
Tel.: (781) 370-2700
Fax: (781) 370-2703
Web Site: www.gamesville.com
Approx. Number Employees: 200
Business Description:
Online Gaming
S.I.C.: 7373; 7379
N.A.I.C.S.: 541512; 541519
Media: 13
Personnel:
Christopher Cummings *(Gen Mgr)*
Ron Le Blanc *(Mgr-Adv Sls)*
Brands & Products:
GAMESVILLE
MATCHMAKER
TRIPOD

GOODRICH RADIO AND THEATERS INC.
4417 Broadmoor Ave SE
Grand Rapids, MI 49512-5367
Tel.: (616) 698-7733
Fax: (616) 698-7220
Toll Free: (800) 473-3523
E-mail: goodrich@gqti.com
Web Site: www.gqti.com
Approx. Number Employees: 1,200
Year Founded: 1960
Business Description:
Motion Picture Theaters
S.I.C.: 7832; 4832
N.A.I.C.S.: 512131; 515112
Media: 20-23
Personnel:
Robert Emmett Goodrich *(Pres & Sec)*
Ross Pettinga *(CFO & Treas)*

GRAND OLE OPRY
(Sub. of Gaylord Entertainment Company)
2802 Opryland Dr
Nashville, TN 37214
Tel.: (615) 316-6000
Fax: (615) 316-6128
Toll Free: (800) SEEOPRY
Web Site: www.opry.com
Sales Range: $450-499.9 Million
Approx. Number Employees: 5,000
Year Founded: 1925
Business Description:
Entertainment & Hospitality Services
S.I.C.: 7996; 7011
N.A.I.C.S.: 713110; 721110
Media: 3-10-13-22-23
Distr.: Reg.
Personnel:
Pete Fisher *(VP & Gen Mgr)*
Brands & Products:
GRAND OLE OPRY

GRANITE BROADCASTING CORPORATION
(Sub. of Silver Point Capital, L.P.)
767 3rd Ave 34th Fl
New York, NY 10017-2023
Tel.: (212) 826-2530
Fax: (212) 826-2858
E-mail: ann@granitetv.com
Web Site: www.granitetv.com
Sales Range: $125-149.9 Million
Approx. Number Employees: 749
Year Founded: 1995
Business Description:
Television Broadcasting Services
S.I.C.: 4833
N.A.I.C.S.: 515120
Advertising Expenditures: $497,000
Media: 3-6-8-9-13-18-23-25-26
Personnel:
Peter Markham *(Chm)*
Mark Desantis *(Pres & Gen Mgr-Peoria Operation)*
Lawrence I. Wills *(CFO & Sr VP)*
Duane A. Lammers *(COO)*
Dan Hoffman *(Dir-Sls)*

GRAY TELEVISION, INC.
(d/b/a Gray Television Group)
4370 Peachtree Rd NE
Atlanta, GA 30319
Tel.: (404) 504-9828
Fax: (404) 261-9607
Web Site:
www.graycommunications.com
Approx. Rev.: $346,058,000
Approx. Number Employees: 1,942
Year Founded: 1897
Business Description:
Owner & Operator of Television Stations & Newspapers
S.I.C.: 4833; 2711
N.A.I.C.S.: 515120; 511110
Advertising Expenditures: $800,000
Personnel:
William E. Mayher, III *(Chm)*
Hilton H. Howell, Jr. *(Vice Chm & CEO)*
Robert S. Prather, Jr. *(Pres & COO)*
James C. Ryan *(CFO & Sr VP)*
Jackson S. Cowart, IV *(Chief Acctg Officer)*
Jason Effinger *(Reg VP-Texas & Gen Mgr-KAKE)*
Tracey Jones *(Reg VP & Gen Mgr-WHSV)*
Wayne M. Martin *(Reg VP & Gen Mgr-WKYT)*
Don Ray *(Reg VP & Gen Mgr-WSAZ)*
Bob Smith *(Reg VP & Gen Mgr-WMTV)*
Nick Waller *(Reg VP & Gen Mgr-WCTV)*
Charlie Peterson *(Reg VP)*

GREAT AMERICAN COUNTRY, INC.
(Sub. of Scripps Networks Inc.)
49 Music Square W Ste 301
Nashville, TN 37203
Tel.: (615) 327-7527
Fax: (615) 329-8770
Web Site: www.gactv.com
Sales Range: $10-24.9 Million
Approx. Number Employees: 50
Business Description:
Cable Television Network
S.I.C.: 4841
N.A.I.C.S.: 515210
Media: 3-13
Personnel:
Ed Hardy *(Pres)*
Sarah Trahern *(Sr VP-Programming)*
Scott Durand *(VP-Mktg)*
Suzanne Gordon *(Dir-Programming)*

GUTHY-RENKER CORPORATION
41550 Eclectic St Ste 200
Palm Desert, CA 92260-1967
Tel.: (760) 773-9022
Fax: (760) 773-9016
E-mail: info@guthy-renker.com
Web Site: www.guthy-renker.com
Sales Range: $1-4.9 Billion
Approx. Number Employees: 825
Year Founded: 1988
Business Description:
Infomercials Producer
S.I.C.: 7812
N.A.I.C.S.: 512110
Media: 3-6-8-12-13-15
Distr.: Direct to Consumer; Intl.
Personnel:
Bill Guthy *(Co-CEO)*
Kevin Knee *(Co-CEO)*
Greg Renker *(Co-CEO)*
Bennet Van De Bunt *(Co-CEO)*
Georg Richter *(COO)*
Seth D. Radwell *(CMO)*
Christy Hadzick *(Sr VP-Mktg)*
Brands & Products:
COMPREHENSIVE FORMULA
CORE SECRETS
GET THE EDGE
GUTHY-RENKER
MEANINGFUL BEAUTY
NATURAL ADVANTAGE
PERFECT ABS
PRINCIPAL SECRET
PROACTIV
SHEER COVER
WINSOR PILATES
YOUTHFUL ESSENCE
Advertising Agency:
PHD
(An Omnicom Company)
220 E 42nd 7th Fl
New York, NY 10017
Tel.: (212) 894-6600
Fax: (212) 894-4100

HALL COMMUNICATIONS INC.
40 Cuprak Rd
Norwich, CT 06360
Tel.: (860) 887-3511
Fax: (860) 886-7649
E-mail: info@hallradio.com
Web Site: www.hallradio.com
Approx. Number Employees: 28
Business Description:
Radio Broadcasting Stations
S.I.C.: 4832
N.A.I.C.S.: 515112
Media: 20-22-23
Personnel:
Bonnie Hall Rowbotham *(Chm)*
Arthur Rowbotham *(Pres)*
Jamie Reed *(VP-Production)*
William Baldwin *(Mgr-Natl Sls)*

HERE MEDIA INC.
10990 Wilshire Blvd Penthouse
Los Angeles, CA 90024
Tel.: (310) 806-4288
Fax: (310) 806-4268
Web Site: www.heremedia.com
Approx. Rev.: $26,920,000
Approx. Number Employees: 156
Business Description:
Cable Network Operator; Book & Magazine Publisher
S.I.C.: 4841; 2721; 2731
N.A.I.C.S.: 517510; 511120; 511130
Advertising Expenditures: $2,379,000
Personnel:
Stephen P. Jarchow *(Chm)*
Paul A. Colichman *(CEO)*
Tony Shyngle *(CFO)*
Robert Ames *(Chief Performance Officer)*
Joe Landry *(Grp Publisher & Sr VP)*
Johnathan Aubry *(VP-Publr-Advocate)*
Josh Rosenzweig *(Sr VP-Integrated Mktg)*
Reva Stark *(Sr Dir-Adv-Western Reg)*
Mark Umbach *(Sr Mgr-Corp Comm & Publicity)*

THE HISTORY CHANNEL
(Joint Venture of Comcast Corporation, The Walt Disney Company, General Electric Company & The Hearst Corporation)
235 E 45th St
New York, NY 10017
Tel.: (212) 210-1400
Fax: (212) 907-9481
Web Site: www.historychannel.com
Sales Range: $200-249.9 Million
Year Founded: 1995
Business Description:
History Programming Cable Network
S.I.C.: 4841
N.A.I.C.S.: 515210
Media: 3-6-9-13-14-18-23-24-25
Distr.: Natl.
Personnel:
Nancy Dubuc *(Pres & Gen Mgr)*
Melvin Berning *(Exec VP-Ad Sls-Natl)*
Chris Moseley *(Exec VP-Mktg)*
Amy Baker *(Sr VP-Sls)*
David McKillop *(Sr VP-Dev & Programming)*
Mike Mohamad *(Sr VP-Mktg)*
Michael Peretz *(VP-Integrated Adv Sls & Strategic Partnerships)*
Ann Marie Granite *(Sr Dir-Consumer Mktg)*
Vicky Kahn *(Dir-PR)*
Brands & Products:
HISTORYCHANNEL.COM
Advertising Agencies:
Asphalt Media
114 W 17th St
New York, NY 10011
Tel.: (212) 924-5332
Fax: (212) 989-3783

The Brooklyn Brothers
18 E 17th St 6th Fl
New York, NY 10003
Tel.: (212) 242-0200
Fax: (212) 242-0217

Dunning Eley Jones
31 Oval Rd
London, NW1 7EA, United Kingdom
Tel.: (44) 020 74289491
Fax: (44) 020 72675228

Smash Advertising
361 Newbury St
Boston, MA 02115
Tel.: (617) 912-7117

HOME & GARDEN TELEVISION
(Sub. of Scripps Networks Inc.)
(d/b/a HGTV)
9721 Sherrill Blvd
Knoxville, TN 37932
Tel.: (865) 694-2700
Fax: (865) 531-1588
Web Site: www.hgtv.com
Sales Range: $200-249.9 Million
Approx. Number Employees: 536
Year Founded: 1994
Business Description:
Cable Television Network
S.I.C.: 4841

Key to Media (For complete agency information see *The Advertising Red Books-Agencies* edition):
1. Bus. Publs. 2. Cable T.V. 3. Catalogs & Directories. 4. Co-op Adv. 5. Consumer Mags. 6. D.M. to Bus. Estab.7. D.M. to Consumers
8. Daily Newsp. 9. Exhibits/Trade Shows 10. Foreign 11. Infomercial 12. Internet Adv.13. Multimedia 14. Network Radio
15. Network T.V. 16. Newsp. Distr. Mags. 17. Other 18. Outdoor (Posters, Transit) 19. Point of Purchase20. Premiums, Novelties
21. Product Samples 22. Special Events Mktg. 23. Spot Radio 24. Spot T.V. 25. Weekly Newsp. 26. Yellow Page Adv.

Home & Garden Television — (Continued)

N.A.I.C.S.: 515210
Media: 3
Personnel:
Jim Samples *(Pres)*
Susan Packard *(Pres-Brand Outreach)*
Kathleen Finch *(Sr VP & Gen Mgr)*
Lori D. Asbury *(Sr VP-Mktg & Creative Svcs)*
Freddy James *(Sr VP-Program Dev & Production)*
Jillian St. Charles *(VP & Site Dir)*
Charity Curley *(VP-HGTVcom)*
Annette Lindstrom *(VP-Mktg)*
Emily C. Yarborough *(Mgr-Pub Rels)*
Advertising Agencies:
Dera, Roslan & Campion Public Relations
Rm 619 132 Nassau St
New York, NY 10038-2432
Tel.: (212) 966-4600
Fax: (212) 966-5763
Pub Rels

Media Storm LLC
99 Washington St
South Norwalk, CT 06854
Tel.: (203) 852-8001
Fax: (203) 852-5592
Media Buying

HOME BOX OFFICE, INC.
(Sub. of Time Warner Inc.)
1100 Ave of the Americas
New York, NY 10036-6712
Tel.: (212) 512-1000
Fax: (212) 512-5335
Telex: 825 649
E-mail: webmaster@hbo.com
Web Site: www.hbo.com
Sales Range: $550-599.9 Million
Approx. Number Employees: 1,738
Year Founded: 1972
Business Description:
Pay Cable Programming Service
S.I.C.: 4841
N.A.I.C.S.: 515210; 517510
Import Export
Media: 7-8-9-10-11-13-18-19-23-24-25
Distr.: Natl.
Personnel:
Bill Nelson *(Chm & CEO)*
Eric Kessler *(Co-Pres)*
Richard L. Plepler *(Co-Pres)*
Robert Roth *(CFO & Exec VP)*
Michael Gabriel *(CIO & Exec VP-IT)*
Robert M. Zitter *(CTO & Exec VP-Tech Ops)*
Michael Lombardo *(Pres-HBO Programming)*
Sue Naegle *(Pres-HBO Entertainment)*
Sheila Nevins *(Pres-Documentary Films)*
Charles Schreger *(Pres-Programming Sls)*
Simon Sutton *(Pres-HBO Intl & Content Distr)*
David Baldwin *(Exec VP-Program Plng)*
Steve Davidson *(Exec VP-Affiliate Sls)*
Bruce Givetti *(Exec VP-Bus Affairs & Production)*
Courteney Monroe *(Exec VP-Consumer Mktg)*
Quentin Schaffer *(Exec VP-Corp Comm)*
Michael Durange *(Dir-New Media Res)*
Cindy Matero *(Dir-Brand Mktg)*
Brands & Products:
5STARMAX
ACTIONMAX
AMERICA UNDERCOVER
ARLI$$
BOXING AFTER DARK
CARNIVALE
CINEMAX
CINEMAX ON DEMAND
CURB YOUR ENTHUSIASM
FATE: THE CARNIVALE GAME
HBO
HBO COMEDY
HBO EXPRESS
HBO FAMILY
HBO LATINO
HBO/MAX PAK
HBO ON DEMAND
HBO PPV
HBO SIGNATURE
HBO SPORTS
HBO WORLD CHAMPIONSHIP BOXING
HBO ZONE
HOME BOX OFFICE
IT'S NOT TV. IT'S HBO.
MIND OF THE MARRIED MAN
MOREMAX
MULTIMAX
OUTERMAX
OZ
SEX AND THE CITY
SIX FEET UNDER
THE SOPRANOS
TAXICAB CONFESSIONS
THRILLERMAX
THE WIRE
WMAX
Advertising Agencies:
BBDO New York
1285 Ave of the Americas 7th Fl
New York, NY 10019-6028
Tel.: (212) 459-5000
True Blood

Campfire
62 White St 3E
New York, NY 10013
Tel.: (212) 612-9600
Fax: (212) 625-9255
Game Of Thrones
Trueblood

Creature
1508 10th Ave
Seattle, WA 98122
Tel.: (206) 625-6994
Fax: (206) 625-6904

Earthquake Media, LLC
15 E 26th St Ste 802
New York, NY 10010-1505
Tel.: (212) 204-9200
Fax: (212) 967-1210

Heat
Pier 33 S 3rd Fl
San Francisco, CA 94111
Tel.: (415) 477-1999
Fax: (415) 477-1990

HSN, INC.
1 HSN Dr
Saint Petersburg, FL 33729
Tel.: (727) 872-1000
Tel.: (727) 872-7790 (Pub Rels)
Fax: (727) 872-6615
Toll Free: (800) 284-3100
Web Site: www.hsn.com
Approx. Sls.: $2,996,780,000
Approx. Number Employees: 5,000
Year Founded: 1985
Business Description:
Discount Consumer Products Retail Television Station
S.I.C.: 4833; 4841; 5961
N.A.I.C.S.: 515120; 454111; 454113; 515210
Import
Advertising Expenditures: $209,200,000
Media: 2-3-6-8-9-23-24
Distr.: Natl.
Budget Set: Sept.
Personnel:
Arthur C. Martinez *(Chm)*
Mindy Grossman *(CEO)*
Judy Schmeling *(CFO & Exec VP)*
Gregory J. Henchel *(Gen Counsel, Sec & Exec VP)*
Brian Bradley *(Exec VP-HSNcom & Advanced Svcs)*
Jill Braff *(Exec VP-Digital Commerce)*
Bill Brand *(Exec VP-Programming & Mktg & Bus Dev)*
Lynne Ronon *(Exec VP-Mdsg)*
Rob Solomon *(Exec VP-Ops)*
Anne Frazer *(Sr VP-Bus Plng & Integration)*
Mitchell Hara *(Sr VP-Corp Strategy & Merger & Acq)*
Felise Glantz Kissell *(Sr VP-IR & Strategy)*
Arthur Lewis *(Sr VP-Mdsg & Digital Commerce)*
Mia Carbonell *(VP-Corp Comm)*
John McDevitt *(VP-Fin)*
Betsy Olum *(Gen Mgr-Beauty & Mdsg Strategy)*
Brad Bohnert *(Dir-PR)*
Michelle McFarland Voorhies *(Sr Mgr-Product)*
Brands & Products:
HSN
HSN.COM

HUBBARD BROADCASTING, INC.
3415 University Ave
Saint Paul, MN 55114-1019
Tel.: (651) 646-5555
Fax: (651) 642-4172
Web Site: www.kstp.com
Approx. Number Employees: 1,100
Year Founded: 1962
Business Description:
Television & Radio Broadcasting Properties Owner & Operator
S.I.C.: 4833
N.A.I.C.S.: 515120
Media: 9-17-18-23-24
Distr.: Natl.
Budget Set: Jan.
Personnel:
Stanley S. Hubbard *(Chm, Pres & CEO)*
Robert W. Hubbard *(Grp Pres-Hubbard TV & Exec VP)*
Ginny Morris *(Pres-Radio)*
Suzanne Cook *(VP-HR)*
Tom Newberry *(VP-Fin)*
Brands & Products:
HUBBARD

IAC/INTERACTIVECORP
555 W 18th St
New York, NY 10011
Tel.: (212) 314-7300
Fax: (212) 314-7309
E-mail: info@iac.com
Web Site: www.iac.com
Approx. Rev.: $1,636,815,000
Approx. Number Employees: 3,200
Year Founded: 1986
Business Description:
Internet Services & Retailing
S.I.C.: 4833; 2741; 4729; 5961; 8999
N.A.I.C.S.: 515120; 454111; 454113; 516110; 518112; 561599
Advertising Expenditures: $349,300,000
Media: 3-5-13-15
Personnel:
Barry Diller *(Chm)*
Victor A. Kaufman *(Vice Chm)*
Gregory R. Blatt *(CEO)*
Thomas J. McInerney *(CFO & Exec VP)*
Jason Stewart *(Chief Admin Officer & Sr VP)*
Jay Herratti *(CEO-CityGrid Media)*
Craig Smith *(CEO-ServiceMagic)*
Nick Stoumpas *(Treas & Sr VP-IR)*
Michael Schwerdtman *(Sr VP & Controller)*
Joanne Hawkins *(Sr VP & Deputy Gen Counsel)*
Gregg Bernard *(Sr VP-Bus Dev-Vimeo)*
Shana Fisher *(Sr VP-Strategy & Mergers & Acq)*
Greg Morrow *(Sr VP-Tax)*
Kara Nortman *(Sr VP-Publ-Citysearch)*
Dae Mellencamp *(Gen Mgr-Vimeo)*
Brands & Products:
ADMISSION
ALSTO'S
ASK KIDS
ASK SERVICE LISTING
ASK.COM
BAGSBUY.COM
BALLARD DESIGN
BILETIX
BLOGLINES
BUSTEDTEES
CARD BOILED
CHEMISTRY.COM
CITY SEARCH
COLLEGEHUMOR.COM
CORNERSTONE BRANDS, INC.
COTTONBLEND
CURSORMANIA
CV
THE DAILY BEAST
DICTIONARY.COM
DOMANIA
DOWN TO EARTH
ECHOMUSIC
EVITE
EXCITE
FILIFE
FRONTGATE
GARAGE GAMES
GARNEY HILL
GIFTS.COM

Key to Media (For complete agency information see *The Advertising Red Books-Agencies* edition):
1. Bus. Publs. 2. Cable T.V. 3. Catalogs & Directories. 4. Co-op Adv. 5. Consumer Mags. 6. D.M. to Bus. Estab.7. D.M. to Consumers
8. Daily Newsp. 9. Exhibits/Trade Shows 10. Foreign 11. Infomercial 12. Internet Adv.13. Multi-Media 14. Network Radio
15. Network T.V. 16. Newsp. Distr. Mags. 17. Other 18. Outdoor (Posters, Transit) 19. Point of Purchase20. Premiums, Novelties
21. Product Samples 22. Special Events Mktg. 23. Spot Radio 24. Spot T.V. 25. Weekly Newsp. 26. Yellow Page Adv.

GIRLSENSE
GRANDIN ROAD
GREEN.COM
IAC
IAC ADVERTISING SOLUTIONS
IMPROVEMENTS
INEST
INSIDERPAGES
INSTANT ACTION
ISABELLA BIRD
IWON!
KAZULAH
LIFE123
LIVEDAILY
M SERVICE MAGIC
MATCH.COM
MINDSPARK
MY FUN CARDS
OUTLETBUY.COM
POPULARSCREENSAVERS
PRONTO.COM
REFERENCE.COM
RESERVE AMERICA
SENDORI
SERVICEMAGIC
SHOEBUY.COM
SHOP CHANNEL
SMILEY CENTRAL
SMITH+NOBLE
THE TERRITORY AHEAD
THESAURUS.COM
TODAY'S BIG THING
TVSN
URBANSPOON
VIMEO
WEBFETTI
ZWINKY
ZWINKY CUTIES
Advertising Agency:
Sunshine Sachs & Associates
149 5th Ave 7th Fl
New York, NY 10010
Tel.: (212) 691-2800

IDEASTREAM
(Formerly Educational Television Association)
(d/b/a WVIZ/PBS)
1375 Euclid Ave
Cleveland, OH 44134-1191
Tel.: (216) 916-6100
Fax: (216) 749-2560
Toll Free: (877) 399-3307
Web Site: www.ideastream.org
Approx. Sls.: $13,098,521
Approx. Number Employees: 100
Year Founded: 1965
Business Description:
Educational Television Broadcasting Stations
S.I.C.: 4833; 4832
N.A.I.C.S.: 515120; 515112
Media: 24
Personnel:
Edward P. Campbell *(Vice Chm & Treas)*
Jerry Wareham *(Pres & CEO)*
Robert Calsin *(CFO)*
Kathryn P. Jensen *(COO)*
Dan Shellenbarger *(Sr Dir-Ohio Channel & Exec Dir)*
Terry Krivak *(Exec Dir)*
George Viebranz *(Exec Dir)*
Thomas P. Furnas *(Sr Dir-Tech)*
Kent Geist *(Sr Dir-Community Dev)*
Maurine Paschke *(Sr Dir-Grants Dev)*
Mark Smukler *(Sr Dir-Content)*
Nancy Burce *(Dir-Staff & Svcs)*
David Kanzeg *(Dir-Programming)*
John Ramicone *(Dir-Distance Learning)*
Duane Trabert *(Mgr-Opers)*
Dick Barnick *(Engr)*
Dale Kwait *(Engr)*
Sally Lewis *(Engr)*
Dave Rodriguez *(Engr)*
Nancy Tatulinski *(Engr)*

ILOOP MOBILE, INC.
55 Metro Dr Ste 210
San Jose, CA 95110
Tel.: (408) 907-3360
Fax: (408) 824-1398
Web Site: www.iloopmobile.com
Business Description:
Mobile Technology & Services for Interactive, SMS-Based Mobile Marketing, Enterprise Solutions & Content Distribution
S.I.C.: 7373; 4812
N.A.I.C.S.: 541512; 517212
Media: 10-13-27
Personnel:
Jorgen Larsen *(Chm)*
Matthew R. Harris *(CEO)*
James O'Brien *(CFO)*
Michael Ahearn *(VP-Mktg)*

IMAGE ENTERTAINMENT, INC.
20525 Nordhoff St Ste 200
Chatsworth, CA 91311-6104
Tel.: (818) 407-9100
Fax: (818) 407-9151
E-mail: investors@image-entertainment.com
Web Site: www.image-entertainment.com
E-Mail For Key Personnel:
Marketing Director: iemarketing@image-entertainment.com
Sales Director: wholesale@image-entertainment.com
Approx. Rev.: $88,959,000
Approx. Number Employees: 69
Year Founded: 1975
Business Description:
DVD Licenser & Distr
S.I.C.: 3652; 5099; 7822
N.A.I.C.S.: 334612; 423990; 512120
Advertising Expenditures: $2,358,000
Media: 1-2-4-5-6-7-8-9-10-13-14-15-17-19
Distr.: Natl.
Personnel:
Theodore S. Green *(Chm & CEO)*
John W. Hyde *(Vice Chm)*
John P. Avagliano *(CFO & COO)*
William V. Bromiley *(Chief Acq Officer)*
Garrett M. Lee *(Sr VP-Product Dev)*
Michael B. Bayer *(VP-Bus/Legal Affairs & Assoc Gen Counsel)*
Brands & Products:
EGAMI MEDIA
IMAGE
IMAGE ENTERTAINMENT
IMAGE MUSIC GROUP
THE MUSIC DISC
VOCAL IMAGES

IMAGICA CORP. OF AMERICA
(Sub. of IMAGICA Corp.)
1840 Century Park E
Los Angeles, CA 90067
Tel.: (310) 277-1790
Fax: (310) 277-1791
Web Site: www.imagica-la.com/aboutus/about_us.htm
Approx. Sls.: $5,000,000
Approx. Number Employees: 5
Year Founded: 1987
Business Description:
Film Production Services
S.I.C.: 5043; 7699
N.A.I.C.S.: 423410; 811490
Exhibits/Trade Shows: 100%
Brands & Products:
CINECURE
IMAGER XE

IMAGINE ENTERTAINMENT
9465 Wilshire Blvd 7th Fl
Beverly Hills, CA 90212
Tel.: (310) 858-2000
Fax: (310) 858-2020
E-mail: info@imagine-entertainment.com
Web Site: www.imagine-entertainment.com
Approx. Number Employees: 43
Year Founded: 1963
Business Description:
Motion Picture & Television Production
S.I.C.: 7812
N.A.I.C.S.: 512110
Media: 3-6-15-18-24
Personnel:
Brian Grazer *(Co-Chm)*
Ron Howard *(Co-Chm)*
Karen Kehela *(Co-Chm-Imagine Films)*

INGRAM ENTERTAINMENT INC.
2 Ingram Blvd
La Vergne, TN 37089
Tel.: (615) 287-4000
Fax: (615) 287-4982
Toll Free: (800) 621-1333
Web Site:
www.ingramentertainment.com
E-Mail For Key Personnel:
President: david.ingram@ingramentertainment.com
Approx. Rev.: $1,030,000,000
Approx. Number Employees: 950
Year Founded: 1980
Business Description:
Pre-recorded Video Cassette Products Distr
S.I.C.: 7822; 3652
N.A.I.C.S.: 512120; 334612
Advertising Expenditures: $2,000,000
Media: 2-4-5-10-18-20
Distr.: Natl.
Budget Set: Dec.
Personnel:
David B. Ingram *(Chm & Pres)*
William D. Daniel *(CFO & Exec VP)*
Bob Webb *(Exec VP-Ops & Pur)*
Robert W. Webb *(Exec VP-Pur & Ops)*
Jeffrey D. Skinner *(Sr VP & Controller)*
Bob Geistman *(Sr VP-Sls & Mktg)*
Dan Norem *(VP-Mktg)*
Brands & Products:
ACCESSINGRAM.COM
ENTERTAINMENT PREVIEW
ENTERTAINMENT UPDATE
IEI
MONARCH HOME VIDEO
MYVIDEOSTORE.COM

INNER CITY BROADCASTING CORPORATION
(d/b/a WBLS)
3 Pk Ave 41st Fl
New York, NY 10016
Tel.: (212) 447-1000
Fax: (212) 447-5211
E-mail: info@wbls.com
Web Site: www.wbls.com
Approx. Number Employees: 265
Year Founded: 1972
Business Description:
Radio Broadcasting Stations
S.I.C.: 4832; 4841
N.A.I.C.S.: 515112; 515210
Import Export
Advertising Expenditures: $400,000
Media: 10-13-18-22-23
Personnel:
Pierre M. Sutton *(Chm & CEO)*
Hal Jackson *(Group Chm)*
Skip Finley *(Vice Chm)*
Charles Warfield *(Pres & COO)*
Bill Cooper *(CFO)*
Lois Wright *(Corp Counsel & Exec VP)*
Deon Levingston *(VP & Gen Mgr)*
Leon Van Gelder *(Gen Mgr-Sls)*
Mark Neiman *(Dir-Event Mktg)*
Koren Vaughan *(Asst Dir-Mktg & Dir-Promotions)*
Jennifer LaMontagne *(Mgr-Sls-Local)*
Brands & Products:
CIRCLE OF SISTERS
RADIO HEARD HERE
WBLS
WILB

INOVERIS, LLC
(Holding of ComVest Group Holdings, Inc.)
7001 Discovery Blvd
Dublin, OH 43017
Tel.: (614) 761-2000
Fax: (614) 761-3146
Toll Free: (888) 638-2832
E-mail: info@inoveris.com
Web Site: www.inoveris.com
Approx. Sls.: $49,694,924
Approx. Number Employees: 250
Business Description:
CD-ROM & DVD Production & Digital Distribution Services
S.I.C.: 3695; 7374
N.A.I.C.S.: 334613; 518210
Media: 4-7-10-11

INSIGHT COMMUNICATIONS COMPANY, INC.
810 7th Ave
New York, NY 10019
Tel.: (917) 286-2254
Fax: (917) 286-2301
E-mail: info@insight-com.com
Web Site: www.insight-com.com
Approx. Rev.: $6,373,410,000
Approx. Number Employees: 17,000
Year Founded: 1985
Business Description:
Cable Television & Internet Services
S.I.C.: 4841
N.A.I.C.S.: 517510; 515210
Media: 1-8-9-18-19-21-24-25
Personnel:
Sidney R. Knafel *(Chm)*
Michael S. Willner *(Vice Chm & CEO)*
Dinni Jain *(Pres & COO)*
John Abbot *(CFO & Exec VP)*
Hamid Heidary *(CTO & Exec VP-Central Ops)*
Daniel Mannino *(Chief Acctg Officer & Sr VP)*

Key to Media (For complete agency information see *The Advertising Red Books-Agencies* edition):
1. Bus. Publs. 2. Cable T.V. 3. Catalogs & Directories. 4. Co-op Adv. 5. Consumer Mags. 6. D.M. to Bus. Estab.7. D.M. to Consumers
8. Daily Newsp. 9. Exhibits/Trade Shows 10. Foreign 11. Infomercial 12. Internet Adv.13. Multimedia 14. Network Radio
15. Network T.V. 16. Newsp. Distr. Mags. 17. Other 18. Outdoor (Posters, Transit) 19. Point of Purchase20. Premiums, Novelties
21. Product Samples 22. Special Events Mktg. 23. Spot Radio 24. Spot T.V. 25. Weekly Newsp. 26. Yellow Page Adv.

Insight Communications Company, Inc. — (Continued)

Elliot Brecher *(Gen Counsel & Sr VP)*
Christopher Slattery *(Exec VP-Field Ops)*
Keith Hall *(Sr VP & Deputy Gen Counsel)*
Sandra D. Colony *(Sr VP-Corp Comm)*
Kevin Dowell *(Sr VP-Insight Media)*
Gregory B. Graff *(Sr VP-Field Ops)*
Melani Griffith *(Sr VP-Programming & Video Svcs)*
Pamela Euler Halling *(Sr VP-Brand)*
John W. Hutton *(Sr VP-Ops)*
Paul Meltzer *(Sr VP-Product Mgmt)*
Jim Morgan *(Sr VP-HR)*
Scott M. Schneiderman *(Sr VP-Operational Fin)*
Steve Eliasof *(VP-Mktg)*
Jerry Knights *(VP-Engrg)*
Ian Brown *(Dir-Operational Fin)*
Ellen Call *(Dir-Community Rel)*
Scott Dant *(Dir-Tax)*
Ben Halliwell *(Dir-Strategic Mktg)*
Jeff Talente *(Dir-Fixed Assets & Pur)*
Diego Jaramillo *(Mgr-Change)*
Neil Fladeland *(Engr)*

Brands & Products:
INSIGHT
INSIGHT BROADBAND
INSIGHT BROADBAND 20.0
INSIGHT DOUBLE PLAY
INSIGHT TRIPLE PLAY
INSIGHTBB
INSIGHTDIGITAL
INSIGHTPHONE

Advertising Agencies:
o2kl
10 W 18th St 6th Fl
New York, NY 10011
Tel.: (646) 829-6239
Fax: (646) 839-6254

PK Network Communications
11 E 47th St 4th Fl
New York, NY 10017-7915
Tel.: (212) 888-4700
Fax: (212) 688-8832

Red Ball Tiger
660 Mission St 3rd Fl
San Francisco, CA 94105
Tel.: (415) 905-0392
Fax: (415) 905-0399

INTERNATIONAL LUTHERAN LAYMEN'S LEAGUE
(d/b/a Lutheran Hour Ministries)
660 Mason Rdg Ctr Dr
Saint Louis, MO 63141-8557
Tel.: (314) 317-4100
Fax: (314) 317-4299
Toll Free: (800) 944-3450
Telex: 590083
E-mail: lh_min@lhm.org
Web Site: www.lhm.org
Approx. Number Employees: 150
Year Founded: 1917
Business Description:
Religious Organization
S.I.C.: 8661
N.A.I.C.S.: 813110
Media: 3-8-10-13-22
Personnel:
Mick Onnen *(Pres)*
Larry Pritchett *(COO)*
Bruce Wurdeman *(Exec Dir)*
Brands & Products:
THE LUTHERAN HOUR
LUTHERAN HOUR MINISTRIES
MEN'S NETWORK
PEOPLE OF CHRIST WITH THE MESSAGE OF HOPE
THE PUZZLE CLUB
WOMAN TO WOMAN

INTERSCOPE GEFFEN & A&M RECORDS
(Unit of Universal Music Group)
2220 Colorado Ave
Santa Monica, CA 90404
Tel.: (310) 865-1000
E-mail: feedback@igamail.com
Web Site: www.interscope.com
Approx. Number Employees: 300
Business Description:
Recorded Music & Video Mfr & Distr
S.I.C.: 3652
N.A.I.C.S.: 512220
Media: 6-9-16-18-23-24-25
Distr.: Intl.; Natl.
Personnel:
Jimmy Iovine *(Chm)*
Steve Berman *(Pres-Mktg)*

ION MEDIA NETWORKS, INC.
601 Clearwater Park Rd
West Palm Beach, FL 33401
Tel.: (561) 659-4122
Fax: (561) 659-4252
Web Site: www.ionmedia.tv
Sales Range: $200-249.9 Million
Approx. Number Employees: 453
Year Founded: 1998
Business Description:
Holding Company; Network Television Broadcasting Services
S.I.C.: 6719; 4833
N.A.I.C.S.: 551112; 515120
Media: 2-3-6-9-14-15-18-23-25
Personnel:
R. Brandon Burgess *(Chm & CEO)*
Jeff Quinn *(CFO)*
Stephen P. Appel *(Pres-Sls & Mktg)*
John Ford *(Pres-Programming & Ion Television)*
David A. Glenn *(Pres-Engrg)*
Joseph Koker *(Pres-Station Grp & DOT)*
Marc Zand *(Exec VP-Digital Networks & Bus Affairs)*
Lisa Fischer *(Sr VP-Network Adv Sls)*
Kristine Hunsinger *(Sr VP-Plng, Scheduling & Acq)*
Blaine Rominger *(Sr VP-Natl, Local & Cable Long-Form Sls)*
Robert A. Marino *(VP-Network Sls & Dir-Network Sls)*
Todd Ackley *(VP-Long Form-Natl)*
Lauren Gellert *(VP-Production & Dev)*
Ian Mahoney *(VP-Network Sl)*
Laura J. Diefenbach *(Acct Exec)*
Brands & Products:
ION MEDIA NETWORKS
PAXWAY

IRIDIUM COMMUNICATIONS INC.
1750 Tysons Blvd Ste 1400
McLean, VA 22102
Tel.: (703) 287-7400
Fax: (703) 287-7450
Toll Free: (866) 947-4348
Web Site: www.iridium.com
Approx. Rev.: $348,173,000
Approx. Number Employees: 174
Year Founded: 2007
Business Description:
Satellite Communications Services
S.I.C.: 4899
N.A.I.C.S.: 517410
Advertising Expenditures: $600,000
Personnel:
Robert H. Niehaus *(Chm)*
Matthew J. Desch *(CEO)*
Thomas J. Fitzpatrick *(CFO)*
Eric H. Morrison *(CFO)*
Thomas D. Hickey *(Chief Legal Officer)*
John Howard Campbell *(Exec VP-Govt Programs-Iridium Satellite)*

ITERIS, INC.
1700 Carnegie Ave
Santa Ana, CA 92705
Tel.: (949) 270-9400
Fax: (949) 270-9401
Toll Free: (800) 695-6599
E-mail: pr@iteris.com
Web Site: www.iteris.com
Approx. Rev.: $59,443,000
Approx. Number Employees: 276
Year Founded: 1969
Business Description:
Traffic Control & Safety Machine Vision Systems & Sensors Mfr
S.I.C.: 3625; 3651; 3669
N.A.I.C.S.: 335314; 334290; 334310
Import Export
Advertising Expenditures: $224,000
Media: 11-17
Personnel:
Gregory A. Miner *(Chm)*
Abbas Mohaddes *(Pres & CEO)*
James S. Miele *(CFO & VP-Fin)*
Alan Clelland *(Sr VP-Transportation Sys)*
Todd Kreter *(Sr VP-Dev & Ops-Sensors)*
Gregory McKhann *(Sr VP-Sls, Mktg & Bus Dev-Roadway Sensors)*
Melvyn Haxby *(Mgr-Bus Dev-Intl)*
Roger Koehler *(Mgr-Product Mktg)*
Brands & Products:
ABACUS
AUTOVUE
CVIEW PLUS
EDGE
ITERIS
SAFETYDIRECT
SYSTEMVIEW
VANTAGE
VANTAGEVIEW
VERSICAM

JBI, INC.
1783 Allanport Road
Thorold, ON L0S 1K0, Canada
Tel.: (905) 354-7222
Web Site: www.plastic2oil.com
Approx. Sls.: $12,419,168
Approx. Number Employees: 65
Business Description:
Chemical Process & Telecommunications Products
S.I.C.: 2899; 3663
N.A.I.C.S.: 325998; 334220
Advertising Expenditures: $124,497
Media: 17
Personnel:
John Bordynuik *(Pres & CEO)*
Ronald C. Baldwin, Jr. *(CFO)*
Jacob Smith *(COO)*
John Colin Robbins *(Sr VP)*
Amy Bradshaw *(VP-Mktg & Comm)*

JERRY BRUCKHEIMER FILMS INC.
1631 10th St
Santa Monica, CA 90404
Tel.: (310) 664-6260
Fax: (310) 664-6261
Web Site: www.jbfilms.com
Approx. Number Employees: 25
Business Description:
Motion Picture & Television Producer & Distr
S.I.C.: 7812
N.A.I.C.S.: 512110
Media: 3-6-11-13-15-18
Personnel:
Jerry Bruckheimer *(Pres)*

THE JIM HENSON COMPANY
1416 N La Brea Ave
Hollywood, CA 90028
Tel.: (323) 802-1500
Fax: (323) 802-1825
Web Site: www.henson.com
Approx. Number Employees: 300
Year Founded: 1958
Business Description:
Children & Family Entertainment Television Programming & Movie Production
S.I.C.: 7812; 4841
N.A.I.C.S.: 512110; 515210
Media: 3-6
Personnel:
Brian Henson *(Chm)*
Peter Schube *(Pres & COO)*
Lisa Henson *(CEO)*
Laurie Don *(Exec VP-Ops & Fin)*
Dan Scharf *(Sr VP-Bus Affairs & Assoc Gen Counsel)*
Joe Henderson *(Sr VP-Admin)*
Melissa Segal *(Sr VP-Global Consumer Products)*
Brittan Brown *(Dir-Production Fin, Production Acct)*
Tamara Sutyak *(Mgr-HR & Admin)*

THE JOY FM
6469 Parkland Dr
Sarasota, FL 34243
Tel.: (941) 753-0401
Fax: (941) 753-2963
Web Site: www.thejoyfm.com
Business Description:
Radio Station; Contemporary Christian Music
S.I.C.: 4832
N.A.I.C.S.: 515112
Personnel:
Jeff MacFarlane *(Gen Mgr)*
Advertising Agency:
Digital Lightbridge, LLC
11902 Little Rd
New Port Richey, FL 34654
Tel.: (727) 863-7806
Fax: (727) 863-7816

KABC-TV INC.
(Sub. of ABC Owned Television Stations)
500 Cir Seven Dr
Glendale, CA 91201
Tel.: (818) 863-7777
Fax: (818) 863-7080
E-mail: info@abc7.com
Web Site: www.abc7.com

Key to Media (For complete agency information see *The Advertising Red Books-Agencies* edition):
1. Bus. Publs. 2. Cable T.V. 3. Catalogs & Directories. 4. Co-op Adv. 5. Consumer Mags. 6. D.M. to Bus. Estab.7. D.M. to Consumers
8. Daily Newsp. 9. Exhibits/Trade Shows 10. Foreign 11. Infomercial 12. Internet Adv.13. Multimedia 14. Network Radio
15. Network T.V. 16. Newsp. Distr. Mags. 17. Other 18. Outdoor (Posters, Transit) 19. Point of Purchase20. Premiums, Novelties
21. Product Samples 22. Special Events Mktg. 23. Spot Radio 24. Spot T.V. 25. Weekly Newsp. 26. Yellow Page Adv.

Sales Range: $75-99.9 Million
Approx. Number Employees: 350
Business Description:
Television Broadcasting
S.I.C.: 4833
N.A.I.C.S.: 515120
Media: 23-24
Personnel:
Arnold J Kleiner *(Pres & Gen Mgr)*

KATZ MEDIA GROUP, INC.
(Sub. of Clear Channel Communications, Inc.)
125 W 55th St
New York, NY 10019-5366
Tel.: (212) 424-6000
Fax: (212) 424-6489
E-mail: info@katz-media.com
Web Site: www.katz-media.com
Sales Range: $250-299.9 Million
Approx. Number Employees: 600
Year Founded: 1888
Business Description:
Holding Company; Electronic Media Advertising Representative Services
S.I.C.: 6719; 7313
N.A.I.C.S.: 551112; 541840
Media: 2-3-14-23
Distr.: Natl.
Budget Set: Dec.
Personnel:
Robert Damon *(CFO)*
Joe Brewer *(CIO)*
Jim Beloyianis *(Pres-Katz Television Grp)*
Mark Gray *(Pres-Katz Radio Grp)*
Gerry Boehme *(Exec VP-Strategic Plng & IT Svcs)*
Brian Knox *(Sr VP & Dir-Corp Diversity)*
Barbara Kurka *(Sr VP & Dir-HR)*
Michael Sherman *(Sr VP & Dir-Comm)*
Patrick McGee *(VP-Political Sls & Strategy)*
Brands & Products:
CHRISTAL RADIO
CONTINENTAL TELEVISION SALES
EAGLE TELEVISION SALES
KATZ RADIO
MILLENNIUM SALES & MARKETING
UNIVISION RADIO SALES

KCNC-TV
(Unit of CBS Television Stations Inc.)
(d/b/a CBS4)
1044 Lincoln St
Denver, CO 80203
Tel.: (303) 861-4444
Fax: (303) 830-6380
E-mail: wfdehaven@cbs.com
Web Site: www.cbs4denver.com
Approx. Sls.: $22,900,000
Approx. Number Employees: 215
Year Founded: 1953
Business Description:
Television Broadcasting Station
S.I.C.: 4833; 2741
N.A.I.C.S.: 515120; 516110
Media: 24
Personnel:
Walt DeHaven *(VP & Gen Mgr)*
Kevin Dorsey *(Dir-Sls)*
Tim Wieland *(Dir-News)*
Kristine Strain *(Asst Dir-News)*
Debbie Cdebaca *(Mgr- Bus Dev & Sports Sls)*
John Montgomery *(Mgr-News Ops)*
Jesse Sarles *(Mgr-Web)*

KCRA-TV
(Unit of Hearst-Argyle Television, Inc.)
3 Television Cir
Sacramento, CA 95814-0794
Tel.: (916) 446-3333
Fax: (916) 325-3731
Web Site: www.kcra.com
Approx. Number Employees: 150
Year Founded: 1955
Business Description:
Television Broadcasting Station
S.I.C.: 4833
N.A.I.C.S.: 515120
Media: 8-10-13-15-24
Distr.: Natl.
Personnel:
Elliott Troshinsky *(Pres & Gen Mgr)*

KCRG TV STATION
(Sub. of Gazette Communications, Inc.)
501 2nd Ave SE
Cedar Rapids, IA 52401
Tel.: (319) 398-8422
Fax: (319) 398-8378
E-mail: newsroom@kcrg.com
Web Site: www.kcrg.com
Sales Range: $1-9.9 Million
Approx. Number Employees: 150
Business Description:
Television/Radio Stations
S.I.C.: 4832; 4833
N.A.I.C.S.: 515112; 515120
Media: 20-22-23-24
Personnel:
Tom Hurn *(Sls Mgr)*

KENS-TV
(Sub. of Belo Corp.)
5400 Fredericksburg Rd
San Antonio, TX 78229
Mailing Address:
PO Box TV5
San Antonio, TX 78299-0500
Tel.: (210) 366-5000
Fax: (210) 377-0740
E-mail: info@kens5.com
Web Site: www.kens5.com
Sales Range: $50-74.9 Million
Approx. Number Employees: 200
Business Description:
Television Broadcasting
S.I.C.: 4833
N.A.I.C.S.: 515120
Media: 13-15-24
Personnel:
Bob McGann *(Pres & Gen Mgr)*
Alan Lansing *(Dir-Creative Svcs)*

KFAX SAN FRANCISCO
(Sub. of Salem Communications Corporation)
(d/b/a Kfax AM 1100)
4880 Santa Rosa Rd Ste 300
Camarillo, CA 93012
Mailing Address:
PO Box 8125
Fremont, CA 94537
Tel.: (510) 713-1100
Fax: (510) 505-1448
Web Site: www.kfax.com
Approx. Rev.: $5,200,000
Approx. Number Employees: 40
Business Description:
Radio Broadcasting Stations
S.I.C.: 4832
N.A.I.C.S.: 515112
Media: 23
Personnel:
Edward G. Atsinger, III *(Pres & CEO)*
Brands & Products:
THE SPIRIT OF THE BAY

KFDM-TV
(Unit of Freedom Broadcasting, Inc.)
2955 Interstate 10 E
Beaumont, TX 77702
Mailing Address:
PO Box 7128
Beaumont, TX 77726
Tel.: (409) 892-6622
Fax: (409) 892-6665
E-mail: info@kfdm.com
Web Site: www.kfdm.com
Approx. Number Employees: 67
Year Founded: 1956
Business Description:
Television Station
S.I.C.: 4833
N.A.I.C.S.: 515120
Media: 5-13-15-20-22-24
Personnel:
Larry Beaulieu *(VP & Gen Mgr)*
Gina Hinson *(Dir-Promo)*
David Lowell *(Dir-News)*
Jennifer Bossier *(Mgr)*
Rix Garey *(Mgr-Sls)*
Brands & Products:
KFDM-TV

KFOR-TV
(Unit of Local TV LLC)
444 E Britton Rd
Oklahoma City, OK 73114-7515
Tel.: (405) 424-4444
Fax: (405) 478-6206
E-mail: news4@kfor.com
Web Site: www.kfor.com
Approx. Number Employees: 150
Business Description:
Television Broadcasting Station
S.I.C.: 4833
N.A.I.C.S.: 515120
Media: 1-15-22-23
Personnel:
Jim Boyer *(Pres & Gen Mgr)*
Wes Milbourn *(Exec VP & Mgr-Station)*
Mary Ann Eckstein *(Dir-News)*
Jill Fraim *(Dir-Sls Mktg Res)*

KFSN-TV INC.
(Sub. of ABC Owned Television Stations)
1777 G St
Fresno, CA 93706-1616
Tel.: (559) 442-1170
Fax: (559) 233-5844
E-mail: kfsndesk@abc.com
Web Site: www.abc30.com
Sales Range: $25-49.9 Million
Approx. Number Employees: 110
Business Description:
Television Broadcasting
S.I.C.: 4833
N.A.I.C.S.: 515120
Media: 18-23-24
Personnel:
Tracey Watkowski *(Dir-News)*
Brands & Products:
ABC30 KFSN TV

KGAN-TV
(Sub. of Sinclair Television Group, Inc.)
600 Old Marion Rd NE
Cedar Rapids, IA 52402
Mailing Address:
PO Box 3131
Cedar Rapids, IA 52406
Tel.: (319) 395-9060
Fax: (319) 395-0987
Toll Free: (800) 642-6140
E-mail: news@kgan.com
Web Site: www.kgan.com
Sales Range: $25-49.9 Million
Approx. Number Employees: 80
Business Description:
Television Station
S.I.C.: 4833
N.A.I.C.S.: 515120
Media: 24
Personnel:
Kerry Johnson *(Gen Mgr)*
Greg Stuart *(Dir-Programming)*
Randy Schildmeyer *(Engr)*

KGO-AM RADIO
(Unit of San Francisco Radio, LLC)
900 Front St
San Francisco, CA 94111-1427
Tel.: (415) 954-8118
Tel.: (415) 954-8671 (Mktg & Promos)
Fax: (415) 391-2795 (Mktg & Promos)
Web Site: www.kgoam810.com
Sales Range: $25-49.9 Million
Approx. Number Employees: 100
Business Description:
Radio Broadcasting Station
S.I.C.: 4832
N.A.I.C.S.: 515112
Media: 14-22-23
Personnel:
Deidra Lieberman *(Pres & Gen Mgr)*

KGO TELEVISION, INC.
(Sub. of ABC Owned Television Stations)
(d/b/a KGO-TV (ABC 7))
900 Frnt St
San Francisco, CA 94111-1427
Tel.: (415) 954-7777
Fax: (415) 956-6402
Web Site: www.abc7news.com
Sales Range: $25-49.9 Million
Approx. Number Employees: 100
Business Description:
Television Broadcasting Station
S.I.C.: 4833
N.A.I.C.S.: 515120
Media: 14
Personnel:
Valari Staab *(Pres & Gen Mgr)*

KGUN-TV
(Div. of Journal Broadcast Group Inc.)
7280 E Rosewood St
Tucson, AZ 85710-1350
Tel.: (520) 722-5486
Fax: (520) 733-7050
E-mail: webmaster@kgun9.com
Web Site: www.kgun9.com
Sales Range: $25-49.9 Million
Approx. Number Employees: 112
Year Founded: 1955
Business Description:
Television Broadcasting Operations
S.I.C.: 4833
N.A.I.C.S.: 515120
Media: 13-18-20-22-24

Key to Media (For complete agency information see *The Advertising Red Books-Agencies* edition):
1. Bus. Publs. 2. Cable T.V. 3. Catalogs & Directories. 4. Co-op Adv. 5. Consumer Mags. 6. D.M. to Bus. Estab.7. D.M. to Consumers 8. Daily Newsp. 9. Exhibits/Trade Shows 10. Foreign 11. Infomercial 12. Internet Adv.13. Multimedia 14. Network Radio 15. Network T.V. 16. Newsp. Distr. Mags. 17. Other 18. Outdoor (Posters, Transit) 19. Point of Purchase20. Premiums, Novelties 21. Product Samples 22. Special Events Mktg. 23. Spot Radio 24. Spot T.V. 25. Weekly Newsp. 26. Yellow Page Adv.

KGUN-TV — (Continued)

Personnel:
Scott Rein *(Mgr-Sls Production)*

KHON-TV
(Unit of New Vision Television, LLC)
88 Piikoi St
Honolulu, HI 96814-4917
Tel.: (808) 591-2222
Fax: (808) 593-8479
E-mail: news@khon2.com
Web Site: www.khon.com
Approx. Number Employees: 100
Business Description:
Television Station
S.I.C.: 4833
N.A.I.C.S.: 515120
Media: 13-18-20-24
Personnel:
Susii Hearst *(Gen Mgr-Sls)*
Joe McNamara *(Gen Mgr)*
Kyle Funaski *(Dir-Mktg)*
Lori Silva *(Dir-News)*
Bob Vaillancourt *(Dir-Engrg)*

KHOU-TV, INC.
(Sub. of KHOU Holdings, Inc.)
1945 Allen Pkwy
Houston, TX 77019
Tel.: (713) 526-1111
Fax: (713) 521-4326
E-mail: assingments@khou.com
Web Site: www.khou.com
Sales Range: $50-74.9 Million
Approx. Number Employees: 210
Business Description:
Television Broadcasting
S.I.C.: 4833
N.A.I.C.S.: 515120
Media: 3-13-23-24
Personnel:
Susan McEldoon *(Pres & Gen Mgr)*
Keith Connors *(Exec Dir-News)*
Miles Cathey *(Mgr-Sls)*
Kali Gipson *(Mgr-Mktg)*
Tim Roth *(Mgr-Interactive Sls)*
Brands & Products:
KHOU.COM

KING WORLD PRODUCTIONS, INC.
(Sub. of CBS Television Distribution)
2401 Colorado Ave Ste 110
Santa Monica, CA 90404
Tel.: (310) 264-3300
Fax: (310) 264-3301
E-mail: contactus@kingworld.com
Web Site: www.kingworld.com
Approx. Number Employees: 400
Year Founded: 1964
Business Description:
Feature Films & Television Production Distr
S.I.C.: 7822; 4833; 7812
N.A.I.C.S.: 512120; 512110; 515120
Media: 2-4-5-7-10-11-18-20-22-24
Distr.: Intl.; Natl.
Personnel:
John Nogawski *(Pres)*
Nestor Gonzalez *(CIO)*
Joe DiSalvo *(Pres-Domestic Television Sls)*
Steven R. Hirsch *(Pres-Media Sls)*
Scott Koondel *(Pres-Distr)*
Armando Nunez, Jr. *(Pres-CBS Paramount Intl Television)*
Terry Wood *(Pres-Creative Affairs)*
Ralph Goldberg *(VP & Assoc Gen Counsel)*
Delilah Loud *(Sr VP-Adv & Promo)*
Dale Casterline *(VP-Media Sls)*
Alex Ignon *(VP-Mktg)*
Advertising Agency:
PointRoll Inc.
951 E Hector St
Conshohocken, PA 19428
Tel.: (267) 558-1300
Fax: (267) 285-1141
Toll Free: (800) 203-6956

KINO INTERNATIONAL CORP.
333 W 39th St
New York, NY 10018
Tel.: (212) 629-6880
Fax: (212) 714-0871
Toll Free: (800) 562-3330
E-mail: contact@kino.com
Web Site: www.kino.com
Sales Range: $1-9.9 Million
Approx. Number Employees: 12
Year Founded: 1977
Business Description:
Classic & Foreign Language Art Films Distr
S.I.C.: 7822
N.A.I.C.S.: 512120
Media: 4-6-8-13
Personnel:
Donald Krim *(Pres)*
Brands & Products:
THE BEST IN WORLD CINEMA
KINO INTERNATIONAL
KINO ON VIDEO

KJRH
(Sub. of The E.W. Scripps Company)
3701 S Peoria Ave
Tulsa, OK 74105
Mailing Address:
PO Box 2
Tulsa, OK 74101-0002
Tel.: (918) 743-2222
Fax: (918) 748-1460
E-mail: news@kjrh.com
Web Site: www.kjrh.com
Sales Range: $25-49.9 Million
Approx. Number Employees: 120
Business Description:
Television Broadcasting Station
S.I.C.: 4833
N.A.I.C.S.: 515120
Media: 2-3-8-24
Personnel:
Donna Wilson *(VP & Gen Mgr)*
Samantha Knowlton *(Dir-Creative Svcs)*
Steve Weinstein *(Dir-News)*
Dale Vennes *(Engr)*

KLOS-FM RADIO, LLC
(Sub. of Citadel Broadcasting Company)
3321 S La Cienega Blvd
Los Angeles, CA 90016-3114
Tel.: (310) 840-4800
Fax: (310) 840-4846
Web Site: www.955klos.com
Sales Range: $10-24.9 Million
Business Description:
Radio Broadcasting Station
S.I.C.: 4832
N.A.I.C.S.: 515112
Media: 15-18-23
Personnel:
Bob Moore *(Pres & Gen Mgr)*
Dave Severino *(Gen Sls Mgr & Dir-Sls-Los Angeles)*
Eric Derise *(Dir-Sls-Digital)*
Vernon L. Copp *(Sls Mgr-Local)*

KMSB-TV, INC.
(Sub. of Belo Corp.)
1855 N Sixth Ave
Tucson, AZ 85705-5601
Tel.: (520) 770-1123
Fax: (520) 629-7185
E-mail: news@fox11az.com
Web Site: www.fox11az.com
Approx. Rev.: $4,800,000
Approx. Number Employees: 37
Year Founded: 1997
Business Description:
Television Broadcasting Station
S.I.C.: 4833
N.A.I.C.S.: 515120
Media: 13-15
Personnel:
Robert M. Simone *(Pres & Gen Mgr)*
Lee-Ann Clement *(Dir-HR)*
Betsy Green *(Dir-Market Dev)*

KNXV-TV
(Sub. of The E.W. Scripps Company)
(d/b/a ABC-15)
515 N 44th St
Phoenix, AZ 85008-6511
Tel.: (602) 273-1500
Fax: (602) 685-3000
E-mail: assignmentdesk@abc15.com
Web Site: www.abc15.com
Sales Range: $50-74.9 Million
Approx. Number Employees: 162
Business Description:
Television Station
S.I.C.: 4833
N.A.I.C.S.: 515120
Media: 24
Personnel:
Janice Todd *(VP & Gen Mgr)*

KOB-TV, INC.
(Sub. of Hubbard Broadcasting, Inc.)
4 Broadcast Plz SW
Albuquerque, NM 87104-1000
Tel.: (505) 243-4411
Fax: (505) 764-2456
Telex: 910 989 1682
E-mail: news@kob.com
Web Site: www.kob.com
Approx. Number Employees: 200
Business Description:
TV Station
S.I.C.: 4833
N.A.I.C.S.: 515120
Media: 24
Personnel:
Robert W. Hubbard *(Pres)*
Michael Burgess *(VP & Gen Mgr)*

KOFY, INC.
(Sub. of Granite Broadcasting Corporation)
(d/b/a KOFY TV 20)
2500 Marin St
San Francisco, CA 94124
Tel.: (415) 821-2020
Fax: (415) 821-1518
Web Site: www.kofytv.com
Sales Range: $10-24.9 Million
Approx. Number Employees: 40
Business Description:
TV Station
S.I.C.: 4833; 4832
N.A.I.C.S.: 515120; 515112
Media: 13-20-22-23-24
Personnel:
Craig Coane *(Pres & Gen Mgr)*
Roy Moore *(Dir-Engrg & Ops)*

KOTV INC.
(Sub. of Griffin Communications, LLC)
302 S Frankfort Ave
Tulsa, OK 74120
Mailing Address:
PO Box 6
Tulsa, OK 74101
Tel.: (918) 732-6000
Fax: (918) 732-6016
Fax: (918) 732-6032
Web Site: www.newson6.com
Approx. Number Employees: 140
Business Description:
Television Broadcaster
S.I.C.: 4833
N.A.I.C.S.: 515120
Media: 15
Personnel:
Rob Krier *(COO & VP)*

KPRZ 1210AM RADIO INC
(Sub. of Salem Communications Corporation)
(d/b/a KPRZ)
9255 Towne Centre Dr Ste 535
San Diego, CA 92121
Tel.: (858) 535-1210
Fax: (858) 535-1212
E-mail: info@kprz.com
Web Site: www.kprz.com
Approx. Rev.: $2,300,000
Approx. Number Employees: 40
Business Description:
Christian Talk Radio Broadcasting
S.I.C.: 4832; 8661
N.A.I.C.S.: 515112; 813110
Media: 22-23
Personnel:
Edward G. Atsinger, III *(Pres)*
Ron Babiarz *(Gen Mgr-Sls)*

KPWR-FM
(Div. of Emmis Radio, L.L.C.)
2600 W Olive Ave Ste 800
Burbank, CA 91505-4553
Tel.: (818) 953-4200
Fax: (818) 848-0961
E-mail: power106info@power106.com
Web Site: www.power106.com
Sales Range: $25-49.9 Million
Approx. Number Employees: 100
Business Description:
Radio Broadcasting Services
S.I.C.: 4832
N.A.I.C.S.: 515112
Media: 1-2-3-13-14-15-18-20-22-23
Personnel:
Rick Cummings *(Pres-Radio Div)*
Val Maki *(Gen Mgr)*
Dianna Jason *(Sr Dir-Mktg & Promos)*
Dennis Martin *(Chief Engr)*

KQED INC.
2601 Mariposa St
San Francisco, CA 94110-1426
Tel.: (415) 864-2000
Fax: (415) 553-2352
E-mail: pressroom@kqed.org
Web Site: www.kqed.org
Sales Range: $200-249.9 Million
Approx. Number Employees: 275
Year Founded: 1954

Key to Media (For complete agency information see *The Advertising Red Books-Agencies* edition):
1. Bus. Publs. 2. Cable T.V. 3. Catalogs & Directories. 4. Co-op Adv. 5. Consumer Mags. 6. D.M. to Bus. Estab.7. D.M. to Consumers
8. Daily Newsp. 9. Exhibits/Trade Shows 10. Foreign 11. Infomercial 12. Internet Adv.13. Multimedia 14. Network Radio
15. Network T.V. 16. Newsp. Distr. Mags. 17. Other 18. Outdoor (Posters, Transit) 19. Point of Purchase20. Premiums, Novelties
21. Product Samples 22. Special Events Mktg. 23. Spot Radio 24. Spot T.V. 25. Weekly Newsp. 26. Yellow Page Adv.

Business Description:
Television & Radio Broadcasting Services
S.I.C.: 4833; 4832
N.A.I.C.S.: 515120; 515112
Media: 20-22-23-24
Personnel:
James E. Canales *(Vice Chm)*
Anne Casscells *(Mng Dir)*
Donald W. Derheim *(COO & Exec VP)*
Traci A. Eckels *(Chief Dev Officer-KQED Pub Media)*
Bill Lowery *(Gen Counsel & Sec)*
Jo Anne Wallace *(VP & Gen Mgr-Pub Radio)*
Joanne Carder *(VP-HR & Labor Rels)*
Tim Olson *(VP-Interactive & Educational Svcs)*
Raul Ramirez *(Exec Dir-News & Pub Affairs)*
Earl Blauner *(Sr Dir-Gift Plng & Endowment)*
Robin Grotch *(Dir-Major Gifts)*
Robin Smith *(Dir-Individual Giving)*
Tim Wu *(Writer & Contributer)*

KRQE-TV
(Sub. of LIN TV Corp.)
13 Broadcast Plz W
Albuquerque, NM 87104-1056
Tel.: (505) 243-2285
Fax: (505) 248-1464
Toll Free: (800) 283-4227
E-mail: krqe@krqe.com
Web Site: www.krqe.com
Sales Range: $25-49.9 Million
Approx. Number Employees: 100
Business Description:
Television Broadcasting Services
S.I.C.: 4833
N.A.I.C.S.: 515120
Media: 13-18-24
Personnel:
William S. Anderson *(VP & Gen Mgr)*
Frank Lilley *(Dir-Engrg)*

KSCI-TV
1990 S Bundy Dr Ste 850
Los Angeles, CA 90025-5245
Tel.: (310) 478-1818
Fax: (310) 479-8118
E-mail: info@kscitv.com
Web Site: www.la18.tv
Approx. Number Employees: 60
Year Founded: 1977
Business Description:
Asian Language Television Broadcasting Stations
S.I.C.: 4833
N.A.I.C.S.: 515120
Media: 1-3-18-22
Personnel:
Peter Mathes *(CEO)*
Alice Lee *(VP-R & D & Dir-Mktg)*
Bill Welty *(VP-Engrg)*

KSEE TELEVISION, INC.
(Sub. of Granite Broadcasting Corporation)
5035 E McKinley Ave
Fresno, CA 93727
Tel.: (559) 454-2424
Fax: (559) 454-2496
E-mail: newsdesk@ksee.com
Web Site: www.ksee24.com
Sales Range: $25-49.9 Million
Approx. Number Employees: 130
Business Description:
TV Station
S.I.C.: 4833
N.A.I.C.S.: 515120
Media: 9-13-18-20-23-24-25
Personnel:
Matt Rosenfeld *(Pres & Gen Mgr)*

KSHE-FM
(Div. of Emmis Radio, L.L.C.)
800 St Louis Union Sta
Saint Louis, MO 63103
Tel.: (314) 621-0095
Fax: (314) 621-3428
E-mail: info@kshe95.com
Web Site: www.kshe95.com
Sales Range: $25-49.9 Million
Approx. Number Employees: 120
Business Description:
Radio Broadcasting Services
S.I.C.: 4832
N.A.I.C.S.: 515112
Media: 1-4-14-15-20-22
Personnel:
John Beck *(Sr VP)*
Katie Sorensen *(Coord-Sls)*

KSTC-TV CHANNEL 45
(Sub. of Hubbard Broadcasting, Inc.)
3415 University Ave W
Saint Paul, MN 55114-1019
Tel.: (651) 645-4500
Fax: (651) 642-4636
Web Site: www.kstc45.com
Approx. Number Employees: 25
Year Founded: 2000
Business Description:
Television Broadcaster
S.I.C.: 4833
N.A.I.C.S.: 515120
Media: 3-10-13-20-23-24
Personnel:
Stanley S. Hubbard *(Chm & CEO)*
Rob Hubbard *(Pres & Gen Mgr)*
Suzanne Cook *(VP-HR)*
Andy Stavast *(Gen Mgr-Sls)*
Joe Johnston *(Mktg Dir)*
Monica Doyle *(Dir-Ops)*
Dick Rice *(Dir-Engrg)*
Susan Wenz *(Mgr-Station)*

KSTP-FM, LLC
(Sub. of Hubbard Broadcasting, Inc.)
3415 University Ave
Saint Paul, MN 55114-1019
Tel.: (651) 646-5555
Tel.: (651) 642-4141
Fax: (651) 647-2904
E-mail: comments@ks95.com
Web Site: www.ks95.com
Approx. Number Employees: 29
Business Description:
FM Radio Station
S.I.C.: 4832
N.A.I.C.S.: 515112
Media: 20-23
Personnel:
Stanley Hubbard *(CEO)*
Ginny Morris *(Pres-Radio Div)*
Melanie Miltz *(Dir-Mktg & Promotions)*
Brands & Products:
KSTP-AM
WSMP-FM

KSTP-TV, LLC
(Div. of Hubbard Broadcasting, Inc.)
3415 University Ave W
Saint Paul, MN 55114-2099
Tel.: (651) 646-5555
Fax: (651) 642-4172
Web Site: www.kstp.com
E-Mail For Key Personnel:
Marketing Director: promotion@kstp.com
Sales Director: advertising@kstp.com
Approx. Number Employees: 200
Year Founded: 1948
Business Description:
Television Broadcaster
S.I.C.: 4833
N.A.I.C.S.: 515120
Media: 2-3-9-18-23-24-26
Distr.: Reg.
Personnel:
Stanley S. Hubbard *(Chm, Pres & CEO)*
Robert W. Hubbard *(Pres-TV)*
Dixie Hansen *(VP & Bus Mgr)*
Suzanne Cook *(VP-HR)*
Andrea Creech *(Mktg Dir)*
Paul Gaulke *(Dir-Mktg)*
Brands & Products:
5 EYEWITNESS NEWS

KTRK TELEVISION, INC.
(Sub. of ABC Owned Television Stations)
3310 Bissonnet St
Houston, TX 77005-2114
Tel.: (713) 666-0713
Fax: (713) 664-0013
Web Site: www.abc13.com
Approx. Sls.: $22,500,000
Approx. Number Employees: 250
Year Founded: 1996
Business Description:
Broadcasting
S.I.C.: 4833
N.A.I.C.S.: 515120
Media: 14-15
Personnel:
Bon Allen *(Dir-Sports)*
Tim Melton *(Dir-Weekend Sports)*

KTVE-TV
(Unit of Mission Broadcasting, Inc.)
200 Pavilion Rd
West Monroe, LA 71292
Tel.: (318) 323-1972
Fax: (318) 322-0926
Toll Free: (800) 613-0095
Web Site: www.myarklamiss.com
Approx. Number Employees: 65
Business Description:
Television Broadcasting Station
S.I.C.: 4833
N.A.I.C.S.: 515120
Media: 3-13-24
Personnel:
Jerry Jones *(VP & Gen Mgr)*
Susie Tumtton *(Gen Mgr-Sls)*

KTVI-TV
(Unit of Local TV LLC)
(d/b/a FOX 2 KTVI)
2250 Ball Dr
Saint Louis, MO 63146
Tel.: (314) 647-2222
Fax: (314) 644-7419
Web Site: www.fox2now.com
Business Description:
Television Broadcasting Station
S.I.C.: 4833
N.A.I.C.S.: 515120
Media: 1-2-9-13-14-15
Personnel:
Spencer Koch *(Gen Mgr)*
Audrey Prywitch *(Dir-News)*
Jay Meyers *(Mgr-Web Sls)*
Steve Mills *(Mgr-Local Sls)*
Cindy Solomon *(Mgr-Natl Sls)*

KTVK-TV, INC.
5555 N 7th Ave
Phoenix, AZ 85013-1701
Tel.: (602) 207-3333
Fax: (602) 207-3327
Fax: (602) 207-3477
Fax: (602) 207-3237
E-mail: 3tvnews@azfamily.com
Web Site: www.azfamily.com
Approx. Number Employees: 290
Year Founded: 1955
Business Description:
Television Broadcasting
S.I.C.: 4833
N.A.I.C.S.: 515120
Media: 24
Personnel:
Rick Soltesz *(Mgr-Sls)*
Mike Stone *(Mgr-Info Sys)*
Tina Tran *(Mgr-Ops)*

KTVL-TV
(Unit of Freedom Broadcasting, Inc.)
1440 Rossanley Dr
Medford, OR 97501
Tel.: (541) 773-7373
Fax: (541) 779-0451
E-mail: ktvl@ktvl.com
Web Site: www.ktvl.com
Sales Range: $100-124.9 Million
Approx. Number Employees: 40
Year Founded: 1961
Business Description:
Television Station
S.I.C.: 4833
N.A.I.C.S.: 515120
Media: 7-8-13-20-22-24
Personnel:
Kingley Kelley *(VP & Gen Mgr)*
Manny Fantis *(Dir-News)*
Mike Gantenbein *(Dir-Creative Svcs)*
Lila Hampton *(Mgr-Natl Sls)*
Carl Randall *(Engr)*

KTVT BROADCASTING COMPANY LP
(Unit of CBS Television Stations Inc.)
10111 N Central Expy
Dallas, TX 75231
Tel.: (817) 451-1111
Fax: (817) 457-1897
Web Site: www.cbs11tv.com
Approx. Sls.: $32,300,000
Approx. Number Employees: 300
Business Description:
Television Broadcasting Stations
S.I.C.: 4833
N.A.I.C.S.: 515120
Media: 24
Personnel:
Steve Mauldin *(Pres Gen Mgr)*
David Hershey *(VP-Creative Svcs & Online Promo)*
Lori Conrad *(Dir-Commun)*
Ken Foote *(Dir-Programming)*
Mike Stewart *(Mgr-Promo)*

KVUE-TV
(Sub. of Belo Corp.)
3201 Steck Ave
Austin, TX 78757-8026

Key to Media (For complete agency information see *The Advertising Red Books-Agencies* edition):
1. Bus. Publs. 2. Cable T.V. 3. Catalogs & Directories. 4. Co-op Adv. 5. Consumer Mags. 6. D.M. to Bus. Estab.7. D.M. to Consumers 8. Daily Newsp. 9. Exhibits/Trade Shows 10. Foreign 11. Infomercial 12. Internet Adv.13. Multimedia 14. Network Radio 15. Network T.V. 16. Newsp. Distr. Mags. 17. Other 18. Outdoor (Posters, Transit) 19. Point of Purchase20. Premiums, Novelties 21. Product Samples 22. Special Events Mktg. 23. Spot Radio 24. Spot T.V. 25. Weekly Newsp. 26. Yellow Page Adv.

KVUE-TV — (Continued)

Tel.: (512) 459-6521
Fax: (512) 533-2233
E-mail: news@kvue.com
Web Site: www.kvue.com
Sales Range: $50-74.9 Million
Approx. Number Employees: 200
Business Description:
Television Broadcasting
S.I.C.: 4833
N.A.I.C.S.: 515120
Media: 13-15
Personnel:
Patti C. Smith *(Pres & Gen Mgr)*
Mike Barnes *(Dir-Sports)*
Jill Fredericks *(Dir-Sls)*
Frank Volpicella *(Dir-News)*
Brands & Products:
KVUE.COM
Advertising Agencies:
H.R.P. Advertising
805 Third St
New York, NY 10022
Tel.: (212) 756-3600
Fax: (212) 756-3680

Mediaminds Inc.
300 Lakeside Dr Ste 160
Horsham, PA 19044
Tel.: (215) 293-9777

KWWL-TV

(Sub. of Quincy Newspapers Inc.)
500 E 4th St
Waterloo, IA 50703-5798
Tel.: (319) 291-1240
Fax: (319) 291-1255
E-mail: kwwl@kwwl.com
Web Site: www.kwwl.com
E-Mail For Key Personnel:
President: dwoods@kwwl.com
Approx. Number Employees: 100
Year Founded: 1953
Business Description:
Television Station
S.I.C.: 4833
N.A.I.C.S.: 515120
Media: 15
Distr.: Reg.
Budget Set: Nov.
Personnel:
John Huff *(Gen Mgr-Sls)*
Chris Hussey *(Mgr-Mktg)*
Shelly Davis *(Mgr-Local Sls)*
Kim Leer *(Mgr-Station)*
Don Morehead *(Mgr-Sls-Natl)*
Jarrett Liddicoat *(Engr)*

LA RADIO, LLC

(Sub. of Citadel Broadcasting Company)
(d/b/a KABC-AM Radio)
3321 S La Cienega Blvd
Los Angeles, CA 90016-3114
Tel.: (310) 840-4900
Tel.: (310) 840-4955 (Adv Sls)
Fax: (310) 840-2822
Web Site: www.kabc.com
Sales Range: $10-24.9 Million
Business Description:
Radio Broadcasting Station
S.I.C.: 4832
N.A.I.C.S.: 515112
Media: 13-14
Personnel:
Bob Moore *(Pres & Gen Mgr)*
Eric Derise *(Dir-Sls-Digital)*
Dave Severino *(Dir-Sls-Los Angeles)*
Vernon L. Copp *(Sls Mgr-Local)*

LANDMARK MEDIA ENTERPRISES LLC

150 W Brambleton Ave
Norfolk, VA 23510-2075
Mailing Address:
PO Box 449
Norfolk, VA 23510-0449
Tel.: (757) 446-2010
Fax: (757) 446-2489
Toll Free: (800) 446-2004
Telex: 757-446-2489
Sales Range: $1-4.9 Billion
Approx. Number Employees: 11,750
Year Founded: 1932
Business Description:
Holding Company; Newspaper Publishing, Television Broadcasting, Cable Programming & Specialty Periodical Publishing
S.I.C.: 2711; 4833
N.A.I.C.S.: 511110; 515120
Import
Media: 9-10-13
Distr.: Natl.
Budget Set: Sept.
Personnel:
Frank Batten, Jr. *(Chm & CEO)*
Richard F. Barry, III *(Vice Chm)*
Decker Anstrom *(Pres & COO)*
R. Bruce Bradley *(Pres)*
Guy R. Friddell, III *(Gen Counsel, Sec & Exec VP)*
Charlie W. Hill *(Exec VP-HR)*
Colleen Pittman *(VP-Tax, Audit & Analysis)*

LANTERN LANE ENTERTAINMENT LTD.

PO Box 8187
Calabasas, CA 91372-8187
Tel.: (818) 222-2309
Fax: (818) 224-4028
E-mail: info@lanternlane.com
Web Site: www.lanternlane.com
E-Mail For Key Personnel:
President: dgarber@lanternlane.com
Approx. Number Employees: 4
Year Founded: 1998
Business Description:
Motion Pictures & Videos Distr & Marketer
S.I.C.: 5961
N.A.I.C.S.: 454113
Media: 2-10
Personnel:
David L. Garber *(CEO)*
Enid Garber *(CFO)*
Van Nuys *(Exec VP-Television & New Media)*

LEARFIELD COMMUNICATIONS, INC.

505 Hobbs Rd
Jefferson City, MO 65109-6829
Tel.: (573) 893-7200
Fax: (573) 893-2321
E-mail: info@learfield.com
Web Site: www.learfield.com
Sales Range: $25-49.9 Million
Approx. Number Employees: 190
Year Founded: 1972
Business Description:
News & Sports Multimedia Syndicate
S.I.C.: 7383; 6794
N.A.I.C.S.: 519110; 533110
Media: 20-22-23
Personnel:
Clyde G. Lear *(Chm)*
Roger Gardner *(Vice Chm)*
Paul Schofer *(CFO)*
Joyce Steinman *(VP & Asst Mgr-Sls)*
Phil Atkinson *(VP-IT)*
Matt Lane *(Dir-Prof Dev)*
Jeff Martin *(Dir-HR)*
Lynette Morasch *(Asst Controller)*

LIBERMAN BROADCASTING CORPORATION

1845 Empire Ave
Burbank, CA 91504
Tel.: (818) 729-5300
Fax: (818) 729-5678
E-mail: lbiinfo@lbimedia.com
Web Site: www.lbimedia.com
Sales Range: $50-74.9 Million
Approx. Number Employees: 300
Business Description:
Radio Broadcasting Services
S.I.C.: 4832
N.A.I.C.S.: 515112
Media: 20-22-23
Personnel:
Jose Liberman *(Co-Founder)*
Wisdom W. Lu *(CFO)*
Lenard Liberman *(Sec & Exec VP)*
John Heffron *(Exec VP-Network & Digital Content)*
Mike Reid *(Exec VP-Sls-Estrella TV)*
Andrew Wallace *(VP & Dir-Midwest network Sls)*
Mariano Amador *(VP-Sls)*
Brands & Products:
ESTRELLA TV

LIFETIME ENTERTAINMENT SERVICES LLC

(Joint Venture of Comcast Corporation, The Walt Disney Company, General Electric Company & The Hearst Corporation)
(d/b/a Lifetime Television)
111 8th Ave
New York, NY 10011-7316
Tel.: (212) 424-7000
Fax: (212) 957-4449
Web Site: www.mylifetime.com
Sales Range: $750-799.9 Million
Approx. Number Employees: 300
Year Founded: 1984
Business Description:
Operator of Cable Television Network with Informational Programming About Lifestyles, Relationships, Personal Development & Health
S.I.C.: 4841
N.A.I.C.S.: 515210
Import Export
Media: 3-6-9-14-15-18-23-24
Distr.: Natl.
Personnel:
Nancy Dubuc *(Pres & Gen Mgr-Lifetime Networks)*
James Wesley *(CFO & Exec VP)*
Bob Bibb *(Co-CMO)*
Lewis Goldstein *(Co-CMO)*
David Gross *(Pres-Reality Programming)*
JoAnn Alfano *(Exec VP-Entertainment)*
Lori Conkling *(Exec VP-Distr)*
Mike Greco *(Exec VP-Res)*
Patricia Langer *(Exec VP-Legal, Bus Affairs & HR)*
Meredith Wagner *(Exec VP-PR)*
Richard Basso *(Sr VP-Pricing & Plng)*
Danielle Carrig *(Sr VP-Advocacy & Pub Affairs)*
David DeSocio *(Sr VP)*
Brands & Products:
LIFETIME
TELEVISION FOR WOMEN
Advertising Agency:
Horizon Media, Inc.
75 Varick St
New York, NY 10013
Tel.: (212) 220-5000
Toll Free: (800) 633-4201

LIN TV CORP.

One West Exchange St Ste 5A
Providence, RI 02903
Tel.: (401) 454-2880
Fax: (401) 454-6990
E-mail: information@lintv.com
Web Site: www.lintv.com
Approx. Rev.: $420,047,000
Approx. Number Employees: 1,825
Year Founded: 1966
Business Description:
Television Station & Interactive Television Website Operator
S.I.C.: 4833; 2741
N.A.I.C.S.: 515120; 516110
Advertising Expenditures: $3,400,000
Media: 3-7-8-13-14-15
Personnel:
Richard J. Schmaeling *(CFO & Sr VP)*
Vincent L. Sadusky *(Pres/CEO-LIN Media)*
Denise M. Parent *(Gen Counsel, Sec & VP)*
Scott M. Blumenthal *(Exec VP-Television)*
Robert S. Richter *(Sr VP-New Media)*
Mark Higgins *(VP & Gen Mgr)*
Dan Donohue *(VP-HR)*
John Viall *(VP-Engrg & Ops)*
Les Garrenton *(Dir-Engrg & Brdcst Sys)*
Courtney Guertin *(Mgr-Corp Comm)*
Katherine M. Whalen *(Asst Gen Counsel)*

LIONS GATE ENTERTAINMENT CORP.

2700 Colorado Ave Ste 200
Santa Monica, CA 90404
Tel.: (310) 449-9200
Fax: (310) 255-3870
Toll Free: (877) 848-3866
E-mail: general-inquiries@lionsgate.com
Web Site: www.lionsgate.com
Approx. Rev.: $1,582,720,000
Approx. Number Employees: 486
Year Founded: 1997
Business Description:
Producer & Distr of Motion Pictures, Television Programming, Home Entertainment, Family Entertainment, Video-On-Demand & Digitally Delivered Content
S.I.C.: 7812; 4833; 7822
N.A.I.C.S.: 512110; 512120; 515120
Advertising Expenditures: $346,300,000
Media: 3-6-9-10-13-15-17-18-24
Personnel:
Jon Feltheimer *(Co-Chm & CEO)*
Harald Ludwig *(Co-Chm)*
Michael R. Burns *(Vice Chm)*

Key to Media (For complete agency information see *The Advertising Red Books-Agencies* edition):
1. Bus. Publs. 2. Cable T.V. 3. Catalogs & Directories. 4. Co-op Adv. 5. Consumer Mags. 6. D.M. to Bus. Estab.7. D.M. to Consumers 8. Daily Newsp. 9. Exhibits/Trade Shows 10. Foreign 11. Infomercial 12. Internet Adv.13. Multimedia 14. Network Radio 15. Network T.V. 16. Newsp. Distr. Mags. 17. Other 18. Outdoor (Posters, Transit) 19. Point of Purchase20. Premiums, Novelties 21. Product Samples 22. Special Events Mktg. 23. Spot Radio 24. Spot T.V. 25. Weekly Newsp. 26. Yellow Page Adv.

Steve Beeks *(Pres & Co-COO)*
James Keegan *(CFO)*
Joseph Drake *(Co-COO & Pres-Motion Picture Grp)*
Jason Constantine *(Pres-Acq & Co-Productions-Motion Picture Grp)*
Jay Faires *(Pres-Music)*
Sarah Greenberg *(Pres-Publicity)*
Jim Packer *(Pres-Worldwide Television Distr & Digital Ops)*
Tim Palen *(Pres-Mktg)*
Wayne Levin *(Gen Counsel & Exec VP-Corp Ops)*
Ron Schwartz *(Exec VP & Gen Mgr)*
Julie Fontaine *(Exec VP-Theatrical Publicity)*
David Nonaka *(Exec VP-Bus & Legal Affairs)*
Anne Parducci *(Exec VP-Mktg)*
Lawrence Szabo *(Exec VP-Television Sls-North America)*
Bob Wenokur *(Exec VP-Post Production & Delivery Svcs)*
Danielle De Palma *(Sr VP-Digital Mktg-Lionsgate Theatrical Mktg)*
Jim Miller *(Sr VP-Motion Picture Production)*
Priscilla Pesci *(Sr VP-TV Mktg)*
Michael Rathauser *(Sr VP)*
Erika Schimik *(Sr VP-Media & Res)*
Danny St. Pierre *(Sr VP-Distr Svcs)*
Russell Ziecker *(Sr VP-Television, Music, Artists & Repertoire)*
Kristin Moss *(VP-Mktg-Home Entertainment Div)*
Brands & Products:
THE BLAIR WITCH PROJECT
DIRTY DANCING
FEARNET
LIONGATE ENTERTAINMENT
LIONGATE HOME ENTERTAINMENT
LIONGATE TELEVISION
LIONSGATE
RESERVOIR DOGS
TRIMARK
Advertising Agencies:
MEC - EMEA HQ
1 Paris Garden
London, SE1 8NU, United Kingdom
Tel.: (44) 20 7803 2000
Fax: (44) 20 7803 2001

The Visionaire Group
4221 Redwood Ave
Los Angeles, CA 90066
Tel.: (310) 823-1800
Fax: (310) 823-1822

LOUISIANA EDUCATIONAL TELEVISION AUTHORITY
(d/b/a Louisiana Public Broadcasting)
7733 Perkins Rd
Baton Rouge, LA 70810
Tel.: (225) 767-5660
Fax: (225) 767-4421
Toll Free: (800) 272-8161
Web Site: www.lpb.org
Approx. Number Employees: 90
Year Founded: 1971
Business Description:
State Network of Six Non-Commercial Television Stations
S.I.C.: 4833
N.A.I.C.S.: 515120
Media: 7-8
Personnel:
Beth Courtney *(Pres & CEO)*
Dorothy Efferson *(Dir-HR)*
Clay Fourrier *(Dir)*
Jason Viso *(Dir-Programming)*
Randy Ward *(Dir-Engrg)*
Ellen Wydra *(Dir-Educational Television & Tech)*
Bob Neese *(Mgr-Promos)*

LOUISIANA TELEVISION BROADCASTING CORPORATION
(d/b/a WBRZ-TV)
1650 Highland Rd
Baton Rouge, LA 70802
Mailing Address:
PO Box 2906
Baton Rouge, LA 70802
Tel.: (225) 387-2222
Fax: (225) 336-2246
E-mail: news@wbrz.com
Web Site: www.wbrz.com
E-Mail For Key Personnel:
Marketing Director: denise@wbrz.com
Sales Range: $10-24.9 Million
Approx. Number Employees: 150
Year Founded: 1955
Business Description:
Television Broadcasting Station
S.I.C.: 4833
N.A.I.C.S.: 515120
Media: 2-3-5-6-9-13-18-20-22-23-24-25-26
Distr.: Direct to Consumer; Reg.
Personnel:
Richard Manship *(Pres & CEO)*
Denise Akers *(Dir-Mktg)*
Jamie Politz *(Dir-HR)*

LUCASFILM, LTD.
1110 Gorgas PO Box 29901
San Francisco, CA 94129
Tel.: (415) 662-1800
Fax: (415) 662-7437
Web Site: www.lucasfilm.com
E-Mail For Key Personnel:
Public Relations: publicity@lucasfilm.com
Approx. Number Employees: 1,500
Year Founded: 1971
Business Description:
Motion Picture Producer & Distr
S.I.C.: 7812; 6794
N.A.I.C.S.: 512110; 533110
Personnel:
George W. Lucas, Jr. *(Chm)*
Micheline Chau *(Pres & COO)*
David J. Anderman *(Gen Counsel)*
Ivan Askwith *(Sr Dir-Digital Media)*
Lynne Hale *(Dir-Comm)*
Advertising Agency:
Big Spaceship
45 Main St Ste 716
Brooklyn, NY 11201
Tel.: (718) 222-0281
Fax: (718) 971-1062
Digital

MACNEIL/LEHRER PRODUCTIONS
2700 S Quincy St
Arlington, VA 22206
Tel.: (703) 998-2111
Fax: (703) 824-6592
E-mail: neewhour@tbs.org
Web Site: www.pbs.org
Approx. Number Employees: 110
Business Description:
Television Film Production
S.I.C.: 7812
N.A.I.C.S.: 512110
Personnel:
Crystal Kurtz *(Dir-HR)*
Brands & Products:
NEWS HOUR
Advertising Agency:
Goodman Media International, Inc.
750 7th Ave 28th Fl
New York, NY 10016
Tel.: (212) 576-2700
Fax: (212) 576-2701
(Newshour with Jim Lehrer)

MADISON SQUARE GARDEN NETWORK
(Sub. of Madison Square Garden, L.P.)
2 Pennsylvania Plz 14th fl
New York, NY 10121
Tel.: (212) 465-6000
Fax: (212) 465-6011
E-mail: advertising@thegarden.com
Web Site: www.msgnetwork.com
E-Mail For Key Personnel:
Public Relations: msgnetpr@msgnetwork.com
Sales Range: $50-74.9 Million
Approx. Number Employees: 150
Year Founded: 1969
Business Description:
Sports & Entertainment Broadcasting
S.I.C.: 4833; 7389
N.A.I.C.S.: 515120; 711310
Advertising Expenditures: $2,000,000
Media: 2-3-6-9-10-13-18-20-23-24
Distr.: Natl.
Personnel:
Melissa Miller Ormond *(COO-MSG Entertainment)*
Andrea Greenberg *(Exec VP-MSG Media)*
Lois Friedman *(Sr VP-Insights & Plng)*
Bob Shea *(Sr VP-Reg Bookings & Special Projects-MSG Entertainment)*
Don Simpson *(Sr VP-Bus Dev-MSG Entertainment)*
Gail Stern *(Sr VP-Mdsg & Licensing)*
Lee Weinberg *(Sr VP-Strategy & Bus Plng)*
Chris DeLauro *(VP-Ops & Engrg)*
Brian Hoffman *(VP-Mktg Solutions)*
Steve Mars *(VP-Mktg)*
Jennifer Bretschneider *(Dir-Special Events)*
Advertising Agency:
Initiative Worldwide
(Part of The Interpublic Group of Companies, Inc.)
1 Dag Hammerskjold Plz 5th Fl
New York, NY 10017
Tel.: (212) 605-7000
Fax: (212) 605-7200

MAINE PUBLIC BROADCASTING NETWORK
1450 Lisbon St
Lewiston, ME 04240
Tel.: (207) 783-9101
Fax: (207) 783-5193
Toll Free: (800) 884-1717
Web Site: www.mpbn.net
Approx. Number Employees: 75
Business Description:
Public Television Broadcasting Stations
S.I.C.: 4833
N.A.I.C.S.: 515120
Media: 7-8
Personnel:
Craig N. Denekas *(Chm)*
John Isacke *(CFO & VP-Governmental Affairs)*
Gil Maxwell *(CTO & Sr VP)*
Irwin Gratz *(Program Dir)*
Suzanne Nance *(Dir-Music)*
Susan Sharon *(Dir-News)*
Keith Shortall *(Dir-News & Pub Affairs)*

MANGA ENTERTAINMENT, INC.
(Sub. of Anchor Bay Entertainment, Inc.)
1699 Stutz Dr
Troy, MI 19820
Tel.: (248) 816-0909
E-mail: info@manga.com
Web Site: www.manga.com
Sales Range: $100-124.9 Million
Year Founded: 1994
Business Description:
Japanese Animation Video Producer, Marketer & Distr
S.I.C.: 7822
N.A.I.C.S.: 512120
Media: 4-7-10-13
Personnel:
Bill Clark *(Exec VP & Gen Mgr)*

MDTV MEDICAL NEWS NOW, INC.
3 Morris Ct
Boonton, NJ 07005
Tel.: (973) 334-6277
Fax: (973) 334-6211
Fax: (866) 329-6388
Toll Free: (877) MDTV-NOW
E-mail: wecare@mdtvnow.com
Web Site: www.mdtvnow.com
Approx. Number Employees: 16
Business Description:
Medical News & Information
S.I.C.: 4833
N.A.I.C.S.: 515120
Media: 6
Personnel:
Maria Villalonga *(Pres)*
Paul G. Argen *(CEO & Exec Producer)*
James Walsh *(Dir)*
Brands & Products:
DTCE
MDTV
MDTV SELECT

MEDIA GENERAL, INC.
333 E Franklin St
Richmond, VA 23219-2213
Mailing Address:
PO Box 85333
Richmond, VA 23293-0001
Tel.: (804) 649-6000
Fax: (804) 649-6066
E-mail: corporatecommunications@mediageneral.com
Web Site: www.mediageneral.com
Approx. Rev.: $678,115,000
Approx. Number Employees: 4,650
Year Founded: 1969
Business Description:
Newspaper Publishing & Television Broadcasting Services
S.I.C.: 4833; 2711

Key to Media (For complete agency information see *The Advertising Red Books-Agencies* edition):
1. Bus. Publs. 2. Cable T.V. 3. Catalogs & Directories. 4. Co-op Adv. 5. Consumer Mags. 6. D.M. to Bus. Estab.7. D.M. to Consumers
8. Daily Newsp. 9. Exhibits/Trade Shows 10. Foreign 11. Infomercial 12. Internet Adv.13. Multimedia 14. Network Radio
15. Network T.V. 16. Newsp. Distr. Mags. 17. Other 18. Outdoor (Posters, Transit) 19. Point of Purchase20. Premiums, Novelties
21. Product Samples 22. Special Events Mktg. 23. Spot Radio 24. Spot T.V. 25. Weekly Newsp. 26. Yellow Page Adv.

Media General, Inc. — (Continued)
N.A.I.C.S.: 515120; 511110
Media: 1-2-7-8-9-10-13-17-20-21-22-23-24-25
Distr.: Natl.
Budget Set: Sept.
Personnel:
Marshall N. Morton *(Pres & CEO)*
John A. Schauss *(CFO & VP-Fin)*
O. Reid Ashe, Jr. *(COO & Exec VP)*
Stephen Y. Dickinson *(Chief Acctg Officer & VP)*
C. Kirk Read *(Pres-Interactive & VP)*
Daniel J. Bradley *(Pres-Ohio/Rhode Island Market)*
James R. Conschafter *(Pres-Market Leader-North Carolina)*
Marilyn L. Hammond *(Pres-North Carolina Market)*
George L. Mahoney *(Gen Counsel, Sec & VP)*
Lou Anne J. Nabhan *(VP & Dir-Corp Comm)*
LeRoy Emerson *(VP-Sls Dev & Trng)*
Andrew Lobred *(VP-Sls & Mktg)*
Rebecca Adams *(Dir-User Experience & User Interface Design-Digita)*
Ray Kozakewicz *(Mgr-Corp Comm)*
Jo Ross *(Acct Rep-Adv)*
Brands & Products:
BOXERJAM
MEDIA GENERAL
RICHMOND TIMES-DISPATCH
THE TAMPA TRIBUNE
WFLA-TV
WINSTON-SALEM JOURNAL
WSPA-TV

MEDIACOM LLC
(Sub. of Mediacom Communications Corporation)
100 Crystal Run Rd
Middletown, NY 10941
Tel.: (845) 695-2600
Fax: (845) 695-2679
Web Site: mediacomcable.com/cc.html
Approx. Rev.: $651,326,000
Approx. Number Employees: 1,773
Business Description:
Interactive Fiber Networks Operations; Cable Television Services
S.I.C.: 4841; 7375
N.A.I.C.S.: 515210; 517510; 517919; 518111
Advertising Expenditures: $16,967,000
Personnel:
Rocco B. Commisso *(CEO)*

MEGATRAX PRODUCTION MUSIC, INC.
7629 Fulton Ave
North Hollywood, CA 91605
Tel.: (818) 255-7100
Fax: (818) 255-7199
Toll Free: (888) 555MEGA
E-mail: info@megatrax.com
Web Site: www.megatrax.com
Approx. Sls.: $5,000,000
Approx. Number Employees: 30
Year Founded: 1992
Business Description:
Music Production
S.I.C.: 7389; 5736
N.A.I.C.S.: 512290; 451140
Advertising Expenditures: $400,000
Media: 2-4-7-10-13-20-22
Personnel:
Ron Mendelsohn *(Pres, CEO & Exec Producer)*
Stezen Naugle *(CFO)*
Philip Macko *(VP-Sls)*
Jonathan Weiner *(Dir-Mktg)*
Scott Linn *(Office Mgr)*
Chuck Hamshaw *(Mgr-Corp, New Media, Post & Prod)*
Brands & Products:
MEGASONICS SOUNDESIGN
MEGATRAX
MUSIC + INNOVATION
THE PROMO COLLECTION
THE SCENE
Advertising Agency:
Kaplan Communications
1236 Vly Rd
Fairfield, CT 06825
Tel.: (203) 259-2279
Fax: (203) 259-1982

METRO-GOLDWYN-MAYER INC.
(d/b/a MGM Inc.)
(Filed Ch 11 Bankruptcy #1015850 on 11/3/10 in U.S. Bankruptcy Ct, Southern Dist of NY, NY)
10250 Constellation Blvd
Los Angeles, CA 90067
Tel.: (310) 449-3000
E-mail: homeentertainment@mgm.com
Web Site: www.mgm.com
Sales Range: $1-4.9 Billion
Approx. Number Employees: 445
Year Founded: 1924
Business Description:
Holding Company; Motion Picture, Television, Home Video & Theatrical Production & Distribution Services
S.I.C.: 6719; 7812; 7822; 7829
N.A.I.C.S.: 551112; 512110; 512120; 512199
Export
Advertising Expenditures: $20,000,000
Media: 8-9-24-25
Distr.: Intl.; Natl.
Personnel:
Jim Packer *(Co-Pres-Worldwide Television)*
Harry E. Sloan *(CEO)*
Dene Stratton *(CFO)*
Charles Cohen *(COO & Sr Exec VP)*
Erik Lomis *(Pres-Worldwide Distr, Home Entertainment & Acq)*
Gary Marenzi *(Pres-Worldwide Television)*
Bruce Tuchman *(Pres-MGM Worldwide Networks)*
Steve Hendry *(Sr Exec VP-Fin)*
Alison Kmetko *(Sr VP-Media)*
Justin Slobig *(Sr VP-Theatrical Adv)*
Advertising Agencies:
Ocean Bridge Group
1714 16th St
Santa Monica, CA 90404
Tel.: (310) 392-3200

RPA
(Rubin Postaer and Associates)
2525 Colorado Ave
Santa Monica, CA 90404
Tel.: (310) 394-4000
Fax: (310) 633-7099

WHITTMANHART
4500 Wilshire Blvd 2nd Fl
Los Angeles, CA 90010
Tel.: (310) 788-1900
Fax: (310) 788-2718
American Gladiators Web Site

MICI INC.
22320 130th Ave
Cadillac, MI 49601
Tel.: (231) 775-3478
Fax: (231) 775-3671
Web Site: www.9and10news.com
Approx. Number Employees: 105
Business Description:
Television Broadcasting Stations
S.I.C.: 4833
N.A.I.C.S.: 515120
Media: 8-13-15-24
Personnel:
Mario F. Iacobelli *(Pres)*
William Kring *(Gen Mgr)*

MIDCONTINENT COMMUNICATIONS CO.
(Joint Venture of Comcast Corporation & Midcontinent Media Inc.)
410 S Phillips Ave PO Box 5010
Sioux Falls, SD 57102
Tel.: (605) 357-5510
Fax: (605) 339-4419
Toll Free: (800) 888-1300
E-mail: mccomm@midco.net
Web Site: www.midcocomm.com
Sales Range: $125-149.9 Million
Approx. Number Employees: 500
Business Description:
Cable Television, Telephone, High-speed Internet Access, Cable Advertising, & Data Network Services; Joint Venture of Comcast Corporation (50%) & Midcontinent Media Inc (50%)
S.I.C.: 4841
N.A.I.C.S.: 515210
Media: 13-25-26

MILLENNIUM RADIO NEW JERSEY
(Sub. of Millennium Radio Group, LLC)
109 Walters Ave
Trenton, NJ 08638
Tel.: (609) 771-8181
Fax: (609) 406-7956
E-mail: nj1015@nj1015.com
Web Site: www.nj1015.com
Approx. Number Employees: 40
Business Description:
Radio Station
S.I.C.: 4832
N.A.I.C.S.: 515112
Media: 2-18-22
Personnel:
Ray Handel *(Dir-Mktg & Promo)*
Eric Johnson *(Dir-Program)*

MINDFIRE ENTERTAINMENT
3740 Overland Ave Ste E
Los Angeles, CA 90034
Tel.: (310) 204-4481
Fax: (310) 204-5882
Web Site: www.mindfireentertainment.com
E-Mail For Key Personnel:
President: mgottwald@mindfireentertainment.com
Approx. Number Employees: 100
Year Founded: 1997
Business Description:
Film, Television, Multi-Media & Music Publisher & Producer
S.I.C.: 7812
N.A.I.C.S.: 512110
Media: 10-22
Personnel:
Mark Gottwald *(Chm)*
Mark A. Altman *(CEO)*

MORRIS DESERT MEDIA RADIO GROUP
(Unit of Morris Communications Company LLC)
1321 N Gene Autry Trl
Palm Springs, CA 92262
Tel.: (760) 322-7890
Fax: (760) 322-5493
Approx. Number Employees: 70
Business Description:
Radio Station Owner & Operator
S.I.C.: 4832
N.A.I.C.S.: 515112; 515111
Media: 18-20-22-23
Personnel:
Norm Feuer *(Gen Mgr)*
Jamie Kanai *(Mgr-Mktg)*

MOUNT MANSFIELD TELEVISION INC.
(d/b/a WCAX-TV Channel 3)
30 Joy Dr
South Burlington, VT 05403
Tel.: (802) 652-6300
Fax: (802) 652-6319
E-mail: channel3@wcax.com
Web Site: www.wcax.com
Approx. Number Employees: 99
Business Description:
Television Broadcasting Stations
S.I.C.: 4833
N.A.I.C.S.: 515120
Media: 24
Personnel:
Peter Martin *(Pres & Gen Mgr)*
Mike McCune *(Dir-Sports)*
Anson Tebbetts *(Dir-News)*
Brands & Products:
AIR NETWORK AND SYNDICATED PROGRAM
TELEVISION PROGRAMS

MOVIE GALLERY, INC.
(Filed Ch 11 Bankruptcy #10-30696 on 02/03/2010 in U.S. Bankruptcy Ct, Eastern District of VA, Richmond)
900 W Main St
Dothan, AL 36301-1410
Tel.: (334) 677-2108
Fax: (334) 794-4688
E-mail: webmaster@moviegallery.com
Web Site: www.moviegallery.com
Sales Range: $250-299.9 Million
Approx. Number Employees: 7,900
Year Founded: 1985
Business Description:
Video Tape Rental Services
S.I.C.: 7841; 5735
N.A.I.C.S.: 532230; 451220
Import Export
Advertising Expenditures: $43,700,000
Media: 1-5-8-9-13-15-16-19-23-24-25
Personnel:
Wesley D. Sand *(Pres & COO)*
Michelle Lewis *(Sr VP-Fin & Dir-IR)*

Key to Media (For complete agency information see *The Advertising Red Books-Agencies* edition):
1. Bus. Publs. 2. Cable T.V. 3. Catalogs & Directories. 4. Co-op Adv. 5. Consumer Mags. 6. D.M. to Bus. Estab.7. D.M. to Consumers 8. Daily Newsp. 9. Exhibits/Trade Shows 10. Foreign 11. Infomercial 12. Internet Adv.13. Multimedia 14. Network Radio 15. Network T.V. 16. Newsp. Distr. Mags. 17. Other 18. Outdoor (Posters, Transit) 19. Point of Purchase20. Premiums, Novelties 21. Product Samples 22. Special Events Mktg. 23. Spot Radio 24. Spot T.V. 25. Weekly Newsp. 26. Yellow Page Adv.

Brands & Products:
MOVIE GALLERY
MOVIEBEAM
PLAY ON
VIDEOBUZZ

MSNBC CABLE, LLC
(Joint Venture of Comcast Corporation, General Electric Company & Microsoft Corporation)
30 Rockefeller Plaza
New York, NY 10112
Tel.: (212) 664-4444
Fax: (212) 664-4085
E-mail: cable@msnbc.com
Web Site: www.msnbc.com
Approx. Number Employees: 6,150
Business Description:
Internet & Television News & Information Services; Owned 50% by Microsoft Corporation and 50% by NBC Universal, Inc.
S.I.C.: 4833
N.A.I.C.S.: 515120
Media: 1-2-3-6-9-13-15-25
Personnel:
Phil Griffin *(Pres)*
Charles Tillinghast *(Pres)*
Val Nichols *(Sr VP-Adv & Promos)*
Jason Trubowitz *(VP-Comm)*
Bill Fink *(Editor-Science & Tech Dept)*
Advertising Agency:
SS&K
88 Pine St 30th Fl
New York, NY 10005
Tel.: (212) 274-9500
Fax: (212) 274-9598
Toll Free: (800) 274-7765
(Creative, Media Buying)

MTI HOME VIDEO
14216 SW 136th St
Miami, FL 33186
Tel.: (305) 255-8684
Fax: (305) 233-6943
E-mail: mti@mtivideo.com
Web Site: www.mtivideo.com
E-Mail For Key Personnel:
President: lbrahms@mtivideo.com
Sales Director: jgrossman@mtivideo.com
Approx. Number Employees: 12
Year Founded: 1984
Business Description:
Movie Videos Distr
S.I.C.: 7822
N.A.I.C.S.: 512120
Media: 4-6-13
Personnel:
Larry Brahms *(Pres & CEO)*
Paul Eyres *(COO & Sr VP)*
Nora Gonzalez *(VP-Sls)*
Jay Grossman *(VP-Sls & Acq)*
Alice de Buhr *(Mgr-Natl Accts)*

MTV NETWORKS COMPANY
(Sub. of Viacom, Inc.)
1515 Broadway
New York, NY 10036
Tel.: (212) 258-8000
Fax: (212) 846-1804
E-mail: info@mtv.com
Web Site: www.mtv.com
Sales Range: $5-14.9 Billion
Business Description:
Cable Television Programming Services
S.I.C.: 4841
N.A.I.C.S.: 515210
Media: 2-3-6-7-8-9-18-20-23-24-25-31
Distr.: Natl.
Personnel:
Bill Roedy *(Vice Chm)*
Paul Rourke *(Sr VP & CFO)*
Rich Eigendorff *(COO)*
David Kline *(CIO & Sr VP-Tech)*
Colleen Fahey Rush *(Chief Res Officer & Exec VP)*
Robert M. Bakish *(Pres-MTVN Intl)*
Marjorie Cohn *(Pres-Original Programming & Dev-Nickelodeon/MTVN Kids & Family)*
Doug Herzog *(Pres-Entertainment Grp)*
Larry W. Jones *(Pres-TV Land)*
Van Toffler *(Pres-Music & Logo Grp)*
George Cheeks *(Gen Counsel & SVP-Bus Affairs)*
Dave Sibley *(Exec VP & Mng Dir-Viacom Brand Solutions Intl-MTV Networks Intl)*
Kevin Arrix *(Exec VP-Digital Adv Sls)*
Tina Exarhos *(Exec VP-Mktg)*
Tanya Giles *(Exec VP-Strategic Insights & Res-Entertainment Grp)*
Peter Griffin *(Exec VP)*
Catherine Houser *(Exec VP, HR)*
Dermot McCormack *(Exec VP-Music & Logo)*
Sean Moran *(Exec VP-360 Brand Sls)*
Casey Patterson *(Exec VP-Event Production, Talent Dev & Studio Rels)*
Dario Spina *(Exec VP-Integrated Mktg-Music & Entertainment)*
Karen A. Maloney *(Sr VP & Controller-Worldwide)*
Joshua Dern *(Sr VP, Gen Mgr-Social Media & MTVN Global Digital Media)*
Huang Ping *(Sr VP & Gen Mgr-MTV China)*
Jason Witt *(Sr VP & Gen Mgr-Digital Fusion)*
Kerry Taylor *(Sr VP & Dir-Television-UK)*
Doug Cohn *(Sr VP-Music & Talent-Nickelodeon MTVN Kids & Family Grp)*
Samantha Cooper *(Sr VP-Content Distr)*
David Cox *(Sr VP-Sls & WW Ops at MTV Games)*
Eddie Dalva *(Sr VP-Content-MTVN Entertainment Grp)*
Chris Ficarra *(Sr VP-Mktg MTV Music Grp)*
Michael Greenspan *(Sr VP-Digital Ad Sls Ops)*
Heather Hopkins *(Sr VP-Mktg & Sls Dev)*
Mark Jones *(Sr VP-Viacom Brand Solutions)*
Suzanne McDonnell *(Sr VP-Digital Fusion)*
Philip Bourchier O'Ferrall *(Sr VP-Digital Media-Intl)*
Jeannie Scalzo *(Sr VP-Integrated Mktg Grp)*
Nick Shore *(Sr VP-Strategic Consumer Insights)*
Jon Slusser *(Sr VP)*
Melody Tan *(Sr VP-Strategy & Bus Ops-Content Distribution & Mktg)*
Nancy Tellet *(Sr VP-Res & Consumer Analytics-Latin America)*
Jose Tolosa *(Sr VP-Strategy & Bus Dev-MTVNI & MTVLA)*
Jeremiah Zinn *(Sr VP-Digital Products)*
Scott Robson *(VP & Gen Mgr-NextMovie)*
Alexis Rodriguez *(VP-Integrated Mktg)*
Ian Rowe *(VP-Pub Affairs & Strategic Partnerships)*
Andrew Sarnow *(VP-Digital Integrated Mktg-Entertainment Grp)*
Samantha Greene Woodruff *(VP-Strategy & Bus Dev-Nickelodeon/MTVN Kids)*
Jeff Lucas *(Head-Sls-Music & Entertainment)*
Kristin Frank *(Gen Mgr)*
Stephen K. Friedman *(Gen Mgr)*
Breanne Heldman *(Sr Editor-NextMovie)*
Brooke Tarnoff *(Sr Editor-NextMovie)*
David Crane *(Sr Dir-Games Res & Dev)*
Alec Hendry *(Dir-Digital Media Ops & Dev)*
Luisa Fairborne *(Dir-Ad Sls)*
Samantha Newman *(Dir-Integrated Mktg-Entertainment Grp)*
Advertising Agencies:
Atlas
315 5th Ave S Ste 500
Seattle, WA 98104
Tel.: (206) 816-8000

Prime Access
345 7th Ave
New York, NY 10001
Tel.: (212) 868-6800
Fax: (212) 868-9495

Young & Rubicam Inc.
285 Madison Ave
New York, NY 10017-6401
Tel.: (212) 210-3000
Fax: (212) 490-9073

MTVN VIDEO HITS INC.
(Sub. of MTV Networks Company)
(d/b/a VH1)
1515 Broadway
New York, NY 10036-8901
Tel.: (212) 258-7800
Web Site: www.vh1.com
Approx. Number Employees: 210
Business Description:
Cable Television Broadcasting Services
S.I.C.: 4841
N.A.I.C.S.: 515210
Media: 2-3-6-7-8-9-14-15-18-20-23-24-25-31
Personnel:
Tom Calderone *(Pres-VH1)*
Nigel Cox-Hagan *(Sr VP-Creative Grp & Consumer Mktg)*
Bill Flanagan *(Exec VP & Editorial Dir-MTVN)*
Rick Krim *(Exec VP-Talent & Music Programming-VH1)*
Sean Moran *(Exec VP-Linear, Digital Ad Sls & Integrated Mktg)*
Tina Imm *(Sr VP & Gen Mgr-VH1 Digital)*
Stacy Alexander *(Sr VP-Talent & Casting)*
Traci Terrill *(VP-Editorial & Creative & Consumer Mktg Grp-VH1)*
Tony Carbone *(VP-Digital Content & Programming)*
Stacey Kaufman *(VP-Digital Mktg-Nickelodeon/MTVN Kids & Family)*

MUZAK HOLDINGS LLC
(Sub. of Mood Media Corporation)
3318 Lakemont Blvd
Fort Mill, SC 29708
Tel.: (803) 396-3000
Fax: (803) 396-3266
Toll Free: (800) 331-3340
E-mail: muzak@muzak.com
Web Site: www.muzak.com
Approx. Rev.: $248,600,000
Approx. Number Employees: 1,261
Year Founded: 1934
Business Description:
Satellite Delivered & On-Premises Music Services & In-Store Audio Marketing
S.I.C.: 7389
N.A.I.C.S.: 512290
Import Export
Advertising Expenditures: $500,000
Media: 1-2-4-7-20-26
Distr.: Intl.; Natl.
Budget Set: Sept.
Personnel:
R. Dodd Haynes *(CFO)*
Thomas J. Gantert *(COO)*
Brands & Products:
FOREGROUND MUSIC ONE
MUSIC PLUS
MUZAK
MUZAK DISH NETWORK FOR BUSINESS
STIMULUS PROGRESSION
TONES
Advertising Agencies:
Anderson Marketing Group
7420 Blanco Rd Ste 200
San Antonio, TX 78216
Tel.: (210) 223-6233
Fax: (210) 223-9692

Oneupweb
13561 S W Bayshore Dr Ste 3000
Traverse City, MI 49684
Tel.: (231) 922-9977
Fax: (231) 922-9966
Toll Free: (877) 568-7477

NASSAU BROADCASTING PARTNERS, LP
619 Alexander Rd Fl 3
Princeton, NJ 08540-6003
Tel.: (609) 452-9696
Fax: (609) 452-6017
Web Site:
www.nassaubroadcasting.com
Approx. Sls.: $50,000,000
Approx. Number Employees: 250
Year Founded: 1986
Business Description:
Operates Radio Stations
S.I.C.: 4832
N.A.I.C.S.: 515112
Advertising Expenditures: $200,000
Media: 17
Personnel:
Louis F. Mercatanti, Jr. *(Chm & CEO)*
Peter D. Tonks *(CFO & Exec VP)*
Donald E. Dalesio *(COO & Exec VP)*
Rick Musselman *(COO & Exec VP)*
Michelle Stevens *(Exec VP-Programming & Mktg)*

Key to Media (For complete agency information see *The Advertising Red Books-Agencies* edition):
1. Bus. Publs. 2. Cable T.V. 3. Catalogs & Directories. 4. Co-op Adv. 5. Consumer Mags. 6. D.M. to Bus. Estab.7. D.M. to Consumers
8. Daily Newsp. 9. Exhibits/Trade Shows 10. Foreign 11. Infomercial 12. Internet Adv.13. Multimedia 14. Network Radio
15. Network T.V. 16. Newsp. Distr. Mags. 17. Other 18. Outdoor (Posters, Transit) 19. Point of Purchase20. Premiums, Novelties
21. Product Samples 22. Special Events Mktg. 23. Spot Radio 24. Spot T.V. 25. Weekly Newsp. 26. Yellow Page Adv.

NATIONAL AMUSEMENTS, INC.

846 University Ave
Norwood, MA 02062
Tel.: (781) 461-1600
Fax: (781) 407-0052
E-mail: customer_service@national-amusements.com
Web Site: www.nationalamusements.com
Approx. Number Employees: 133,247
Business Description:
Holding Company for Television & Motion Picture Companies, Cable Systems, Television & Radio Stations & Multiplex Cinemas
S.I.C.: 6719; 4832; 4833; 4841; 7822; 7832
N.A.I.C.S.: 551112; 512120; 512131; 515112; 515120; 515210; 517510
Media: 5-9-10-11-13-14-15-18-23-24-26
Personnel:
Shari E. Redstone *(Pres)*
Sumner M. Redstone *(CEO)*
Joseph Mollo *(CIO & VP-IT)*
Tad Jankowski *(Gen Counsel & Sr VP)*
John Bilsborough *(Sr VP-Ops)*
George Levitt *(Sr VP-Film)*
Richard Sherman *(Sr VP-Fin & Admin)*
Elaine Urban Purdy *(VP-Global Promos, Adv & Pubity)*
Robert J. Steele *(VP-Strategy & Corp Dev)*

NATIONAL FILM BOARD OF CANADA

3155 Chemin de la Cote-de-Liesse
Saint Laurent, QC H4N 2N4, Canada
Tel.: (514) 283-9000
Fax: (514) 283-7564
Toll Free: (800) 267-7710
E-mail: info@nfb.ca
Web Site: www.nfb.ca
Sales Range: $50-74.9 Million
Approx. Number Employees: 500
Year Founded: 1939
Business Description:
Film Promoter, Producer, Distr & Retailer
S.I.C.: 7812; 7822
N.A.I.C.S.: 512110; 512120
Advertising Expenditures: $2,920,528
Personnel:
Tom Perlmutter *(Commissioner-Govt Film)*
Claude Bonin *(Acting Dir Gen-French Program)*
Nathalie Courville *(Dir Gen-Mktg & Commun)*

NATIONAL GEOGRAPHIC CHANNEL

(Div. of National Geographic Society)
1145 17th St NW
Washington, DC 20036-4688
Tel.: (202) 857-7027
E-mail: comments@natgeochannel.com
Web Site: channel.nationalgeographic.com
Approx. Number Employees: 100
Business Description:
Television Broadcasting
S.I.C.: 4833
N.A.I.C.S.: 515120
Media: 3-6-13-15-20-22
Personnel:
Steve Schiffman *(Pres)*
David Haslingden *(CEO)*
Steve Burns *(Exec VP-Content)*
Rafael Sandor *(Exec VP-Mktg & Creative)*
Maryanne Culpepper *(Sr VP-Editorial Dev-Natl Geographic Television)*
Brad Dancer *(Sr VP-Res & Digital Media)*
Paul Brake *(Controller & VP-Fin)*
Stephen Hunter *(VP-Production)*
Advertising Agency:
Digitaria
533 F St 3rd Fl
San Diego, CA 92101
Tel.: (619) 325-0224
Fax: (619) 237-5269
Field Expedition: Mongolia

NBC UNIVERSAL, INC.

(Joint Venture of Comcast Corporation & General Electric Company)
30 Rockefeller Plz
New York, NY 10112
Tel.: (212) 664-4444
Fax: (212) 664-4085
Web Site: www.nbcuniversal.com
Sales Range: $5-14.9 Billion
Approx. Number Employees: 25,000
Year Founded: 1926
Business Description:
Holding Company; Television Programming, Broadcasting & Syndication; Owned 51% by Comcast Corporation & 49% by General Electric Company
S.I.C.: 6719; 4833; 4841; 7812; 7822
N.A.I.C.S.: 551112; 512110; 512120; 515120; 517510; 519130
Media: 1-2-3-4-5-6-9-13-14-15-18-20-22-23-24
Distr.: Natl.
Personnel:
Jeff Gaspin *(Chm-Television Entertainment)*
Michael Moses *(Co-Pres-Mktg)*
Ron Meyer *(Pres & COO-Universal Studios)*
Vivi Zigler *(Pres)*
Stephen B. Burke *(CEO)*
Stuart Epstein *(CFO)*
Craig Robinson *(Chief Diversity Officer & Exec VP)*
Bridget Baker *(Pres-TV Networks Distr)*
Steve Capus *(Pres-NBC News)*
John W. Eck *(Pres-Media Works-NBCUniversal)*
Marianne Gambelli *(Pres-NBC Network Adv Sls)*
Marc Graboff *(Pres-West Coast Bus Ops-NBC Entertainment)*
Mark Hoffman *(Pres-CNBC)*
Nicholas Lehman *(Pres-Digital-Entertainment, Digital Networks & Integrated Media)*
Salil Mehta *(Pres-Bus Ops, Strategy & Dev)*
Jennifer Salke *(Pres-Entertainment)*
Peter Smith *(Pres-NBC Universal-Intl)*
Adam Stotsky *(Pres-Mktg)*
Paul Telegdy *(Pres-Alternative & Late Night Programming)*
John P. Wallace *(Pres-NBC Local Media)*
Alan Wurtzel *(Pres-Res & Media Dev)*
Frederick Huntsberry *(CFO-Television Group & Exec VP-TV Distr)*
Edward Swindler *(COO-Ad Sls & Exec VP)*
Rick Cotton *(Gen Counsel & Exec VP)*
Maria Pekurovskaya *(Exec VP & Head-Creative Mktg)*
Matt Bond *(Exec VP-Content Distr)*
Brandon Burgess *(Exec VP-Bus Dev)*
Marc Chini *(Exec VP-HR)*
Patricia Fili-Krushel *(Exec VP)*
Allison Gollust *(Exec VP-Corp Comm)*
Adam Miller *(Exec VP-Corp Affairs)*
Peter Naylor *(Exec VP-Digital Media Sls)*
Anna Perez *(Exec VP-Comm)*
Cory Shields *(Exec VP-Global Policy Strategies & Alliances)*
Page Thompson *(Exec VP-Strategic Integration)*
Mark French *(Sr VP & Gen Mgr-NBC Everywhere-NBC Local Media Div)*
Scott Abraham *(Sr VP-Creative Adv)*
Meredith Ahr *(Sr VP)*
Michael Bass *(Sr VP-Strategic Initiatives)*
Barbara Blangiardi *(Sr VP-Creative Partnership & Innovation)*
Sari DeCesare *(Sr VP-TV Network & Cable Audience Res)*
Jackson George *(Sr VP-Creative Adv)*
Bruce Kallner *(Sr VP-Strategic Sls & Mktg)*
Curt King *(Sr VP)*
Joe Lagani *(Sr VP-Digital Sls iVillage)*
Vivian Mayer *(Sr VP-Publicity)*
Donna Mills *(Sr VP-Mktg, Comm & Affiliate Rels)*
Debbie Reichig *(Sr VP-Market Dev)*
Colleen Rooney *(Sr VP)*
Nicole Sabatini *(Sr VP-Mktg-The Style Network)*
Hilary Smith *(SVP, Women & Lifestyle Entertainment Networks Comm)*
Ken Wilkey *(Sr VP)*
Trez Thomas *(VP-Brand Strategy & Dir-Creative-Bravo Media)*
James Spence *(VP & Dir-Creative-Syfy)*
Dave Barrington *(VP-Daytime & Late-Night Sls)*
Jennifer Boudreaux *(VP-Digital Distr)*
Josh Cole *(VP-Mktg)*
Nick Johnson *(VP-Digital Media Sls)*
Stacy Melle *(VP-Mktg)*
Shari Post *(VP-Prime-Time Adv Sls)*
Alexis Rouse *(VP-Comm)*
Michael Schreiber *(VP-Digital Distr)*
Andrew Ault *(Exec Creative Dir-Integrated Sls Mktg)*
Jake Katz *(Dir-Trends & Primary Res)*
Brian Matthews *(Dir-Digital Media Sls)*
Aaron Rogers *(Dir-Adv & Publicity)*
Arnold Klein *(Mgr-Social Media Mktg-Universal Studios Hollywood)*
Matthew Beaton *(Sr Acct Exec-NBCOlympicscom)*
Brands & Products:
13TH STREET
CNBC
MSNBC
NBC
SCI FI CHANNEL UK
TELEMUNDO
Advertising Agencies:
Fallon Worldwide
901 Marquette Ave Ste 2400
Minneapolis, MN 55402
Tel.: (612) 758-2345
Fax: (612) 758-2346

Massivemedia
34 W 27th St 6 Fl
New York, NY 10001
Tel.: (212) 730-7222
Fax: (212) 730-7444

Naked Communications New York
96 Greene St Ste 3
New York, NY 10012
Tel.: (212) 625-3082
Fax: (212) 625-3087
(NBC Entertainment)

PK Network Communications
11 E 47th St 4th Fl
New York, NY 10017-7915
Tel.: (212) 888-4700
Fax: (212) 688-8832

Spark Communications
222 Merchandise Mart Plz Ste 550
Chicago, IL 60654-1032
Tel.: (312) 970-8400
Fax: (312) 970-8464
Fax: (312) 970-8409

Sparxoo
4400 W Spruce St # 333
Tampa, FL 44607
Tel.: (646) 345-1800

NBC UNIVERSAL TELEVISION NETWORKS GROUP

(Joint Venture of Comcast Corporation & General Electric Company)
30 Rockefeller Plz
New York, NY 10112
Tel.: (212) 664-4444
Web Site: www.nbcuni.com
Sales Range: $200-249.9 Million
Business Description:
National Television Broadcasting Company; Television Programs Producer & Syndicator; Television Stations Operator; Cable Network Programmer
S.I.C.: 4833
N.A.I.C.S.: 515120
Advertising Expenditures: $140,000,000
Media: 3-17
Personnel:
Jeff Gaspin *(Pres & COO-NBC Universal Television Grp)*
John Miller *(CMO)*
John P. Wallace *(Pres-NBC Local Media)*
Mark Lund *(Exec VP-Sls-NBC Local Media)*
Steve Mandala *(Exec VP-Sls & Mktg-Cable Networks)*
Dan Weiss *(Exec VP)*
Frances Manfredi *(Sr VP & Gen Mgr-Sls-Cable & Non-Theatrical)*
Pauline Bohm *(Sr VP-Intl Mktg)*
Alyssa Corcoran *(Sr VP-Comm-TV Networks & Digital Distr)*
Jeff Dellin *(Sr VP-Market Rsch)*
Jim Slattery *(VP-Bus & Legal Affairs)*
Ariana L. Squar *(Dir-Brand Integration)*
Rachel Mansson *(Mktg Dir-Promos)*

Key to Media (For complete agency information see *The Advertising Red Books-Agencies* edition):
1. Bus. Publs. 2. Cable T.V. 3. Catalogs & Directories. 4. Co-op Adv. 5. Consumer Mags. 6. D.M. to Bus. Estab.7. D.M. to Consumers
8. Daily Newsp. 9. Exhibits/Trade Shows 10. Foreign 11. Infomercial 12. Internet Adv.13. Multimedia 14. Network Radio
15. Network T.V. 16. Newsp. Distr. Mags. 17. Other 18. Outdoor (Posters, Transit) 19. Point of Purchase20. Premiums, Novelties
21. Product Samples 22. Special Events Mktg. 23. Spot Radio 24. Spot T.V. 25. Weekly Newsp. 26. Yellow Page Adv.

Jennifer Chastain *(Dir-Field Sls & Mktg)*
Wendy Gross *(Dir-Field Sls & Mktg)*
Emily Powers *(Dir-Bus Dev & Strategy)*
Brad Trullinger *(Dir-Bus Dev-Digital & TV Networks Distr)*
Advertising Agencies:
Fallon Worldwide
901 Marquette Ave Ste 2400
Minneapolis, MN 55402
Tel.: (612) 758-2345
Fax: (612) 758-2346

Ignited
2221 Park Pl
El Segundo, CA 90245
Tel.: (310) 773-3100
Fax: (310) 773-3101
(Media Planning & Buying)

NETWORK CHICAGO
(Div. of Window to the World Communications, Inc.)
5400 N Saint Louis Ave
Chicago, IL 60625-4623
Tel.: (773) 583-5000
Fax: (773) 583-3046
Web Site: www.networkchicago.com
Approx. Number Employees: 250
Year Founded: 1955
Business Description:
Television Station
S.I.C.: 4833; 4832
N.A.I.C.S.: 515120; 515112
Media: 8-9-13-18-20-22-23-25
Distr.: Reg.
Budget Set: Mar.
Personnel:
Daniel J. Schmidt *(Pres & CEO)*

NEULION, INC.
1600 Old Country Rd
Plainview, NY 11803
Tel.: (516) 622-8300
E-mail: info@jumptv.com
Web Site: www.jumptv.com
Approx. Rev.: $33,173,748
Approx. Number Employees: 315
Year Founded: 2000
Business Description:
Internet Television Broadcasting Services
S.I.C.: 2741; 4833
N.A.I.C.S.: 516110; 515120
Advertising Expenditures: $918,228
Personnel:
Charles B. Wang *(Chm)*
G. Scott Paterson *(Vice Chm)*
Nancy Li *(Pres & CEO)*
Arthur J. McCarthy *(CFO)*
Roy E. Reichbach *(Gen Counsel & Corp Sec)*
Michael Her *(Exec VP-R & D)*
Ronald Nunn *(Exec VP-Ops)*
Marc Sokol *(Exec VP-Mktg & Bus Dev)*
J. Christopher Wagner *(Exec VP-Marketplace Strategy)*
Advertising Agency:
KCSA Strategic Communications
(Kanan, Corbin, Schupak & Aronow, Inc.)
880 3rd Ave 6th Fl
New York, NY 10022
Tel.: (212) 682-6300
Fax: (212) 697-0910

NEW DIMENSIONS WORLD BROADCASTING NETWORK
PO Box 569
Ukiah, CA 95482
Tel.: (707) 468-5215
E-mail: info@newdimensions.org
Web Site: www.newdimensions.org
Approx. Number Employees: 4
Business Description:
Radio Broadcasting Services
S.I.C.: 4832; 2731
N.A.I.C.S.: 515112; 511130
Media: 6-14
Personnel:
Michael Toms *(Co-Founder & Co-Pres)*
Rose Holland *(Office Mgr)*

NEW FRONTIER MEDIA, INC.
7007 Winchester Cir Ste 200
Boulder, CO 80301-3505
Tel.: (303) 444-0900
Fax: (303) 938-8388
Toll Free: (888) 875-0632
Web Site: www.noof.com
Approx. Rev.: $48,709,000
Approx. Number Employees: 165
Year Founded: 1993
Business Description:
Adult-Themed & General Motion Picture Entertainment Producer & Distr
S.I.C.: 7822; 4841; 7829
N.A.I.C.S.: 512120; 512199; 515210
Advertising Expenditures: $2,400,000
Media: 1-10-22
Personnel:
Michael A. Weiner *(Chm, Pres, CEO & Sec)*
Grant H. Williams *(CFO)*
Scott A. Piper *(CIO)*
Marc Callipari *(Gen Counsel)*
Brands & Products:
FOR PEOPLE WHO LIKE TO WATCH
NEW FRONTIER MEDIA

NEW HORIZONS PICTURE CORP.
11600 San Vicente Blvd
Los Angeles, CA 90049-5102
Tel.: (310) 820-6733
Fax: (310) 207-6716
E-mail: info@newhorizonspix.com
Web Site: www.newhorizonspictures.com
Approx. Number Employees: 250
Year Founded: 1983
Business Description:
Motion Picture & Video Production Services
S.I.C.: 7812
N.A.I.C.S.: 512110
Import Export
Media: 3-18-22
Personnel:
Julie Corman *(Co-Founder & VP)*
Roger Corman *(Pres)*
Tom Krentzin *(CFO)*

NEW LINE CINEMA
(Div. of New Line Cinema Corporation)
825 N San Vicente Blvd
West Hollywood, CA 90069-4505
Tel.: (310) 967-6700
Fax: (310) 967-6701
Web Site: www.newline.com
Sales Range: $25-49.9 Million
Approx. Number Employees: 100
Year Founded: 1997
Business Description:
Motion Picture And Video Production
S.I.C.: 7812
N.A.I.C.S.: 512110
Advertising Agency:
Hauser Advertising Inc.
309 Bellino Dr
Pacific Palisades, CA 90272
Tel.: (310) 459-5911
Fax: (310) 459-5919

NEW LINE CINEMA CORPORATION
(Sub. of Time Warner Inc.)
888 7th Ave 20th Fl
New York, NY 10106-0001
Tel.: (212) 649-4900
Fax: (212) 649-4966
Web Site: www.newline.com
Sales Range: $10-24.9 Million
Approx. Number Employees: 86
Year Founded: 1967
Business Description:
Theatrical Motion Pictures Independent Producer & Distr
S.I.C.: 7812
N.A.I.C.S.: 512110
Media: 1-7
Distr.: Intl.; Natl.
Personnel:
Robert K. Shaye *(Co-Chm & Co-CEO)*
Jeffrey L. Bewkes *(Pres & COO)*
Chris Carlisle *(Pres-Domestic Theatrical Mktg)*
Ben Zinkin *(Sr Exec VP-Bus & Legal Affairs)*
Christina Kounelias *(Exec VP-Mktg)*
Advertising Agency:
PointRoll Inc.
951 E Hector St
Conshohocken, PA 19428
Tel.: (267) 558-1300
Fax: (267) 285-1141
Toll Free: (800) 203-6956

NEW NORTHWEST BROADCASTERS, LLC
315 5th Ave S Ste 700
Seattle, WA 98104
Tel.: (206) 204-0213
Fax: (206) 204-0214
E-mail: info@nnbradio.com
Web Site: www.nnbradio.com
Approx. Number Employees: 7
Business Description:
Radio Broadcasting Stations
S.I.C.: 4832
N.A.I.C.S.: 515112
Media: 20-22-23
Personnel:
Trila Bumstead *(Pres & CEO)*
Tom Freel *(VP & Gen Mgr)*

NEWSCHANNEL 5
(Sub. of Landmark Broadcasting Inc.)
474 James Robertson Pkwy
Nashville, TN 37219-1212
Tel.: (615) 244-5000
Fax: (615) 248-5353
E-mail: news@newschannel5.com
Web Site: www.newschannel5.com
Approx. Number Employees: 150
Business Description:
Television Broadcast Station
S.I.C.: 4833
N.A.I.C.S.: 515120
Media: 13-24
Personnel:
Debbie Turner *(Gen Mgr)*
Hope Hines *(Dir-Sports)*
Natalie Ryman *(Sls Mgr)*

NEXSTAR BROADCASTING GROUP, INC.
(Holding of ABRY Partners LLC)
5215 N O'Connor Blvd Ste 1400
Irving, TX 75039
Tel.: (972) 373-8800
Fax: (972) 373-8888
Web Site: www.nexstar.tv
Approx. Rev.: $313,350,000
Approx. Number Employees: 1,857
Year Founded: 1996
Business Description:
Holding Company; Television Broadcasting Stations Owner & Operator
S.I.C.: 6719; 4833
N.A.I.C.S.: 551112; 515120
Advertising Expenditures: $1,700,000
Personnel:
Perry A. Sook *(Chm, Pres & CEO)*
Thomas E. Carter *(CFO & Exec VP)*
Timothy C. Busch *(Co-COO & Exec VP)*
Brian Jones *(Co-COO & Exec VP)*
Elizabeth Hammond *(Gen Counsel & VP)*
Rick Rogala *(Sr VP & Reg Mgr)*
Blake Russell *(Sr VP-Station Ops)*
Richard Stolpe *(VP & Dir-Engrg)*

NEXT 1 INTERACTIVE, INC.
2400 N Commerce Pkwy Ste 105
Weston, FL 33326
Tel.: (954) 888-9779
Fax: (954) 888-9082
E-mail: investorrelations@nxoi.com
Web Site: www.nxoi.com
Approx. Sls.: $1,320,225
Approx. Number Employees: 25
Business Description:
Video Advertising Services
S.I.C.: 7319; 7829
N.A.I.C.S.: 541890; 512199
Advertising Expenditures: $439,573
Media: 13
Personnel:
William Kerby *(Chm & CEO)*
Adam Friedman *(CFO & Sec)*

NFL FILMS, INC.
(Sub. of National Football League)
1 NFL Plz
Mount Laurel, NJ 08054-1201
Tel.: (856) 222-3500
Fax: (856) 866-4848
E-mail: comments@films.nfl.com
Web Site: www.nflfilms.com
Approx. Number Employees: 262
Business Description:
Mfr., Promote & Distribute Films about the National Football League
S.I.C.: 7812
N.A.I.C.S.: 512110
Media: 4-10-20-22
Distr.: Natl.
Personnel:
Steve Sabol *(Pres)*
Barry Wolper *(CFO)*
Howard Katz *(COO)*

NICKELODEON DIRECT INC.
(Sub. of MTV Networks Company)
1515 Broadway

Nickelodeon Direct Inc. — (Continued)

New York, NY 10036-8901
Tel.: (212) 258-6003
Fax: (212) 846-7676
Web Site: www.viacom.com
Approx. Number Employees: 2,000
Year Founded: 1979
Business Description:
Cable Television Broadcasting Services
S.I.C.: 4841
N.A.I.C.S.: 515210
Media: 1-2-3-5-6-7-8-9-10-11-18-19-20-22-23-24-25
Distr.: Intl.; Natl.
Personnel:
Albie Hecht *(Founder & CEO-Worldwide Biggies)*
Herb Scannell *(Pres)*
Jeff Dunn *(COO)*
Leigh Anne Brodsky *(Pres-Nickelodeon & Viacom Consumer Products)*
Brown Johnson *(Pres-Animation-Nickelodeon/MTVN Kids & Family Grp)*
Cyma Zarghami *(Pres-Nickelodeon/MTV Networks Kids/Family Grp)*
Antonious Porch *(Sr VP & Deputy Gen Counsel)*
Pamela Kaufman *(Exec VP-Mktg & Promos-Worldwide)*
Jim Perry *(Exec VP-360 Brand Sls)*
Marva A. Smalls *(Exec VP-Pub Affairs)*
Howard Smith *(Exec VP-Nickelodeon Recreation)*
Steve Youngwood *(Exec VP-Digital Media)*
Jean Philippe Randisi *(Sr VP & Mng DirNVCP-Europe, Canada, Latin America)*
Indra Suharjono *(Sr VP & Mng Dir-Licensing Ops-Asia/Middle East)*
Nelson Boyce *(Sr VP-Digital Adv Sls-Nickelodeon Kids & Family Grp)*
Kevin Ellman *(Sr VP-Bus & Legal Affairs-Nickelodeon/MTVN Kids & Family)*
Tracy Katsky *(Sr VP-Dev & Original Programming)*
Samantha Maltin *(Sr VP-Partnerships-Global)*
Stuart Rosenstein *(Sr VP-Resorts & Theatricals)*
Hal Snik *(Sr VP-Consumer Products)*
Frank Tanki *(Sr VP-Partnership Mktg & Ops)*
Manuel Torres *(Sr VP-MD Global Toys, Video Games & Consumer Electronics)*
Sherice Torres *(Sr VP-Global Entertainment)*
Jim Tricarico *(Sr VP-Adv Sls-Nickelodeon/MTVN Kids & Family)*
John Paul Geurts *(VP & Dir-Creative-Nickelodeon Recreation)*
Nicole Bradley *(VP-Corp Comm)*
Jose Carbonell *(VP-Brand Mktg)*
Jennifer Tracy *(VP-Digital Promos Mktg)*
Chad Ghastin *(Dir-Digital CRM)*
Alyssa Gochis *(Dir-Adv)*
Lori Silfen *(Atty-Bus & Legal Affairs)*
Advertising Agencies:
The Martin Agency
One Shockoe Plz
Richmond, VA 23219-4132
Tel.: (804) 698-8000
Fax: (804) 698-8001

Underwired Amaze Limited
22 Newman St
London, W1T 1PH, United Kingdom
Tel.: (44) 20 70 600 400
Fax: (44) 20708436593

NIELSEN MEDIA RESEARCH, INC.

(Div. of VNU Media Measurement & Information Group)
770 Broadway
New York, NY 10003
Tel.: (646) 654-8300
E-mail: info@nielsenmedia.com
Web Site: www.nielsenmedia.com
Approx. Number Employees: 2,100
Year Founded: 1950
Business Description:
Television Audience Measurement & Advertising Information Services
S.I.C.: 8732
N.A.I.C.S.: 541910
Advertising Expenditures: $1,000,000
Bus. Publs.: $1,000,000
Distr.: Natl.
Personnel:
James M. O'Hara *(Pres-Media Product Leadership)*
Jane Rode *(VP & Partner-Fin Bus)*
Sabrina Crow *(Mng Dir & Sr VP)*
Robert Luff *(CTO & Exec VP)*
Bruce Hoynoski *(Chief Res Officer)*
Sara Exec VP-Client SvcsErichson *(Pres-Client Svcs)*
Dave Thomas *(Pres-Media Client Svcs)*
David A. Schwartz-Leeper *(Gen Counsel & Sr VP)*
Dave Harkness *(Sr VP & Mng Dir-Local Television Client Svcs)*
Catherine Herkovic *(Sr VP & Mng Dir-Television Client Svcs-Natl)*
Terrie Brennan *(Sr VP)*
Douglas Darfield *(Sr VP-Multicultural Measurement)*
Eric Lange *(Sr VP-HR)*
Howard Shimmel *(Sr VP-Client Insights)*
Michelle Stein *(Sr VP-Client Engagement)*
Annie Touliatos *(Dir-Mktg & Product Placement)*
Brands & Products:
NEW MEDIA SERVICES
NIELSEN ADVERTISER SERVICES
NIELSEN HISPANIC TELEVISION SERVICES
NIELSEN HOMEVIDEO INDEX
NIELSEN MONITOR PLUS
NIELSEN SPORTS MARKETING SERVICE
NIELSEN STATION INDEX
Advertising Agency:
The Phelps Group
901 Wilshire Blvd
Santa Monica, CA 90401-1854
Tel.: (310) 752-4400
Fax: (310) 752-4444

NY 1 NEWS

(Div. of Time Warner Cable Inc.)
75 9th Ave
New York, NY 10011-4276
Tel.: (212) 379-3456
Fax: (212) 379-3575
Web Site: www.ny1.com
Sales Range: $50-74.9 Million
Approx. Number Employees: 180
Year Founded: 1992
Business Description:
Twenty-Four Hour News Channel for NYC Featuring Local News, Lifestyle Reports, Sports & Weather
S.I.C.: 4833
N.A.I.C.S.: 515120
Media: 1-2-3-4-6-8-9-18-20-23-25
Distr.: Reg.
Personnel:
Steve Paulus *(Sr VP)*
Bernie Han *(Dir-News)*
Brad Shapiro *(Dir-IT)*
Marc Nathanson *(Exec Producer-NY1com)*

NY RADIO, LLC

(Sub. of Citadel Broadcasting Company)
(d/b/a WABC-AM Radio)
2 Penn Plz 17th Fl
New York, NY 10121
Tel.: (212) 613-3800 (Switchboard)
Tel.: (212) 613-3888
Fax: (212) 613-3890
Web Site: www.wabcradio.com
Sales Range: $50-74.9 Million
Approx. Number Employees: 200
Year Founded: 1921
Business Description:
Radio Broadcasting Station
S.I.C.: 4832
N.A.I.C.S.: 515112
Media: 10-13-18-23
Personnel:
Steve Borneman *(Pres & Gen Mgr)*

OPTELECOM-NKF INC.

(Sub. of TKH Group N.V.)
12920 Cloverleaf Center Dr
Germantown, MD 20874
Tel.: (301) 444-2200
Fax: (301) 444-2299
Toll Free: (800) 293-4237
E-mail: sales.us@optelecom-nkf.com
Web Site: www.optelecom-nkf.com
Approx. Rev.: $36,177,000
Approx. Number Employees: 160
Year Founded: 1975
Business Description:
Supplier of Fiber Optic Transport Equipment
S.I.C.: 3663; 3661; 3827
N.A.I.C.S.: 334220; 333314; 334210
Advertising Expenditures: $924,000
Personnel:
Edmund D. Ludwig *(CEO)*
Cathy Mizell *(CFO & VP)*
Coen Hooghiemstra *(VP-Engrg)*
Daniel Connole *(Sr Dir)*
Charles Queri *(Dir-Sls-Americas)*
Brands & Products:
OPERATOR OFFICE
OPTELECOM-NKF
OPTELICAM
OPTELIDOME
SIQURA
SPECTRASTREAM

THE OUTDOOR CHANNEL

(Sub. of Outdoor Channel Holdings, Inc.)
43445 Business Park Dr Ste 103
Temecula, CA 92590-3670
Tel.: (951) 699-6991
Fax: (951) 699-6313
Toll Free: (800) 770-5750
E-mail: info@outdoorchannel.com
Web Site: www.outdoorchannel.com
Sales Range: $200-249.9 Million
Year Founded: 1993
Business Description:
Television Programming, Hunting, Fishing, Shooting Sports & Off-Road Motor Sports
S.I.C.: 4841
N.A.I.C.S.: 515210
Media: 6-7-8-9-10-14-18-20-23
Personnel:
Roger L. Werner, Jr. *(Pres & CEO)*
Tom Allen *(CFO & Chief Acctg Officer)*
Thomas E. Hornish *(COO, Gen Counsel, Sec & Exec VP)*
Randy Brown *(Exec VP-Affiliate Sls & Mktg)*
Gregory M. Harrigan *(Exec VP-Adv Sls)*
Jason Brist *(Sr VP-Central Reg)*
Mark Romano *(VP-Affiliate Sls & Mktg-Eastern Div)*
Vicki Windham *(VP-HR)*
Stacy Cerny *(Exec Dir-Pricing & Plng)*
Michael Dorsey *(Dir-Programming & Production)*
Kim Ransom *(Dir-Traffic)*
Jesi Steward *(Dir-Bus Dev)*
Scott E. Fink *(Mgr-Natl Acct-Western Reg)*
Allison Hill *(Mgr-Natl Acct)*
Brands & Products:
THE OUTDOOR CHANNEL

OUTDOOR CHANNEL HOLDINGS, INC.

43445 Business Park Dr Ste 103
Temecula, CA 92590-3671
Tel.: (951) 699-6991
Fax: (909) 699-6313
Fax: (951) 699-1849
E-mail: info@outdoorchannel.com
Web Site: www.outdoorchannelholdings.com
Approx. Rev.: $83,342,000
Approx. Number Employees: 190
Year Founded: 2000
Business Description:
Holding Company; Owns & Operates a National Television Network Geared Towards Hunting, Fishing, Shooting Sports & Off-Road Motor Sports
S.I.C.: 4841; 6719
N.A.I.C.S.: 515210; 551112
Advertising Expenditures: $3,500,000
Media: 2-3-10-20
Personnel:
Perry T. Massie *(Chm)*
Thomas H. Massie *(Vice Chm)*
Roger L. Werner, Jr. *(Pres & CEO)*
Douglas J. Langston *(CFO & Chief Acctg Officer)*
Thomas D. Allen *(CFO & Exec VP)*
Thomas E. Hornish *(COO, Gen Counsel, Sec & Exec VP)*
Todd Merkow *(Pres-Digital Media)*
Denise Conroy-Galley *(Exec VP-Mktg & Res)*
Gregory M. Harrigan *(Exec VP-Adv Sls)*
Brands & Products:
OUTDOOR CHANNEL

Key to Media (For complete agency information see *The Advertising Red Books-Agencies* edition):
1. Bus. Publs. 2. Cable T.V. 3. Catalogs & Directories. 4. Co-op Adv. 5. Consumer Mags. 6. D.M. to Bus. Estab.7. D.M. to Consumers 8. Daily Newsp. 9. Exhibits/Trade Shows 10. Foreign 11. Infomercial 12. Internet Adv.13. Multimedia 14. Network Radio 15. Network T.V. 16. Newsp. Distr. Mags. 17. Other 18. Outdoor (Posters, Transit) 19. Point of Purchase20. Premiums, Novelties 21. Product Samples 22. Special Events Mktg. 23. Spot Radio 24. Spot T.V. 25. Weekly Newsp. 26. Yellow Page Adv.

OXYGEN MEDIA LLC
(Joint Venture of Comcast Corporation & General Electric Company)
75 9th Ave
New York, NY 10011
Tel.: (212) 651-2000
Fax: (212) 651-2099
E-mail: info@oxygen.com
Web Site: www.oxygen.com
Sales Range: $350-399.9 Million
Approx. Number Employees: 400
Year Founded: 1998
Business Description:
Cable Television & Internet Production Services
S.I.C.: 7812; 4841
N.A.I.C.S.: 512110; 517510
Media: 2-3-4-6-7-8-10-13-15-16-19-20-22-24
Personnel:
Lauren Zalaznick *(Pres)*
Cynthia Chu *(CFO)*
Mary Murano *(Pres-Distr)*
Cori Abraham *(Sr VP-Dev)*
Amy Introcaso-Davis *(Sr VP-Original Programming & Dev)*
Galen Jones *(Sr VP-Oxygen Res)*
Susan Malfa *(Sr VP)*
Michelle Niven *(Sr VP-Affiliate Ad Sls)*
Jane Olson *(Sr VP-Mktg & Brand Strategy)*
Michael DuPont *(VP)*
Julie Rothman *(VP-Comm)*
Brie Miranda Bryant *(Dir-Dev & Production)*
Brands & Products:
LIVE OUT LOUD
OXYGEN ALONE
OXYGEN MEDIA
Advertising Agency:
Jack Myers Media Business Report
PO Box 27740
Las Vegas, NV 89126
Tel.: (201) 572-8675
Fax: (973) 267-1514

PACKETVIDEO CORPORATION
(Sub. of NTT DoCoMo, Inc.)
10350 Science Center Dr Ste 210
San Diego, CA 92121-1138
Tel.: (858) 731-5300
Fax: (858) 731-5301
E-mail: press@packetvideo.com
Web Site: www.packetvideo.com
Sales Range: $10-24.9 Million
Approx. Number Employees: 135
Year Founded: 1998
Business Description:
Mobile Video Transmission Services
S.I.C.: 4899; 7372; 7374
N.A.I.C.S.: 517910; 511210; 518210
Personnel:
James C. Brailean *(Founder, Pres & CEO)*
Jeff Wright *(CFO)*
Osama Alshaykh *(CTO)*
Joel Espelien *(Chief Bus Officer, Gen Counsel & Exec VP-Strategy)*
Cheuk Chan *(Exec VP-Engrg & Core Client Products)*
Barbara Emond *(Exec VP-Engrg & Customer Products)*
Mark R. Banham *(Sr VP-Engrg)*
Corbett Kull *(Sr VP-Sls & Dev)*
Neil Sharma *(Sr VP-Strategic Initiatives)*
Dann Wilkens *(Sr VP-Design)*
Rick Schwartz *(Dir-Connected Home Software)*
Brands & Products:
PACKETVIDEO
Advertising Agency:
Finn Partners
11400 W Olympic Blvd Ste 850
Los Angeles, CA 90064-1544
Tel.: (310) 479-9929
Fax: (310) 479-9989

PAMAL BROADCASTING LTD.
6 Johnson Rd
Latham, NY 12110
Tel.: (518) 786-6600
Fax: (518) 786-6610
Web Site: www.pamal.com
Approx. Sls.: $27,000,000
Approx. Number Employees: 175
Year Founded: 1996
Business Description:
Radio Broadcasting Stations
S.I.C.: 4832
N.A.I.C.S.: 515112
Media: 20-22-23
Personnel:
James J. Morrell *(Chm & CEO)*
Chuck Benfer *(Gen Mgr-Albany Brdcst)*

PARAMOUNT PICTURES CORPORATION
(Sub. of Viacom, Inc.)
5555 Melrose Ave
Los Angeles, CA 90038
Tel.: (323) 956-5000
Fax: (323) 862-3775
Web Site: www.paramount.com
Approx. Number Employees: 1,700
Year Founded: 1912
Business Description:
Motion Pictures Production Services
S.I.C.: 7812
N.A.I.C.S.: 512110
Advertising Expenditures: $550,000,000
Media: 1-2-3-4-5-6-9-10-11-13-14-15-16-18-19-20-22-23-24-25
Distr.: Intl.; Natl.
Personnel:
Brad Grey *(Chm & CEO)*
Rob Moore *(Vice Chm)*
Frederick Huntsberry *(COO)*
Josh Greenstein *(CMO)*
Megan Colligan *(Pres-Domestic Mktg & Distr)*
Michael Corcoran *(Pres-Consumer Products & Recreation Grp)*
Andrew Cripps *(Pres-Intl)*
Adam Goodman *(Pres-Motion Picture Grp)*
Dennis Maguire *(Pres-Home Video Unit)*
Hal Richardson *(Pres-Television Distr)*
David Stainton *(Pres-Animation)*
Mark Badagliacca *(CFO-Paramount Pictures & Exec VP)*
Rebecca Prentice *(Gen Counsel & Sr VP)*
David H. Johnson *(Asst Exec VP-Bus Affairs)*
Steve Siskind *(Exec VP-Mktg & Adv-Worldwide)*
LeeAnne Stables *(Exec VP-Worldwide Mktg Partnerships)*
Dina Marovich *(Sr VP-Media & Interactive Mktg)*
Charles Myers *(Sr VP)*
Heath Tyldesley *(VP-Interactive Mktg)*
Mickey Worsnup *(VP-Creative)*
Mary Parent *(Producer)*
Robb Dickehut *(Exec Dir-Interactive Mktg)*
Stephanie Simard *(Exec Dir-Creative-Interactive Mktg)*
Megan Wahtera *(Dir-Creative)*
Latham Arneson *(Mgr-Anaytics)*
Sungmi Choi *(Mgr-Creative-Interactive Mktg)*
Alyson Grove *(Mgr-Interactive Media)*
Advertising Agencies:
Arenas Entertainment
3375 Barham Blvd
Los Angeles, CA 90068
Tel.: (323) 785-5555
Fax: (323) 785-5560
(Dreamworks/Paramount Pictures)

Hauser Advertising Inc.
309 Bellino Dr
Pacific Palisades, CA 90272
Tel.: (310) 459-5911
Fax: (310) 459-5919

Joule
10 E 40th St 37th Fl
New York, NY 10016
Tel.: (212) 796-8382
Creative
Mobile Media
— Greg Crockart *(Grp Acct Dir)*

MEC
5700 Wilshire Blvd Ste 550
Los Angeles, CA 90036
Tel.: (323) 761-1400
Fax: (323) 817-1870

MEC, Global HQ, New York
825 7th Ave
New York, NY 10019-6014
Tel.: (212) 474-0000
Fax: (212) 474-0020
Fax: (212) 474-0003

PK Network Communications
11 E 47th St 4th Fl
New York, NY 10017-7915
Tel.: (212) 888-4700
Fax: (212) 688-8832

PEACE ARCH ENTERTAINMENT GROUP INC.
1867 Yonge Street Ste 650
Toronto, ON M4S 1Y5, Canada
Tel.: (647) 777-1177
Fax: (647) 777-1178
Toll Free: (888) 588-3608
E-mail: info@peacearch.com
Sales Range: $50-74.9 Million
Approx. Number Employees: 90
Year Founded: 1983
Business Description:
Holding Company; Motion Picture Producer & Distr
S.I.C.: 6719; 7812; 7822
N.A.I.C.S.: 551112; 512110; 512120
Personnel:
Robert Essery *(Chm)*
John Flock *(Pres)*
Mara Di Pasquale *(CFO & COO)*
Julie Sultan *(Pres-Intl Sls & Distr)*
Roy Bodner *(VP-Pub Rels)*
Caroline Dulbourg *(VP-Intl Sls & Distr)*
Jennifer Graham *(VP-Sls & Acq)*
Terese Linden Kohn *(VP-Intl Sls & Distr)*
Brands & Products:
PEACE ARCH
Advertising Agency:
The Lippin Group
6100 Wilshire Blvd Ste 400
Los Angeles, CA 90048-5109
Tel.: (323) 965-1990
Fax: (323) 965-1993

PENNS WOODS BANCORP, INC.
300 Market St
Williamsport, PA 17701
Mailing Address:
PO Box 967
Williamsport, PA 17703-0967
Tel.: (570) 322-1111
Tel.: (570) 320-2029
Fax: (570) 320-2046
Toll Free: (877) 520-2265
Web Site: www.jssb.com
Approx. Rev.: $43,821,000
Approx. Number Employees: 182
Year Founded: 1983
Business Description:
Bank Holding Company
S.I.C.: 6712; 6029
N.A.I.C.S.: 551111; 522110
Advertising Expenditures: $388,000
Media: 7-17
Personnel:
Richard A. Grafmyre *(Pres & CEO)*
Brian L. Knepp *(CFO)*
Ann M. Riles *(Sr VP & Chief Credit Officer)*
Paul R. Mamolen *(COO-Comprehensive Fin Grp & Sr VP)*
G. David Gundy *(Sr VP & Mgr-Customer Sls & Svcs)*
Stephen M. Tasselli *(Sr VP & Mgr-Comml Loan)*

PERSONA COMMUNICATIONS CORPORATION
17 Duffy Pl
Saint John's, NL A1B 4L1, Canada
Tel.: (709) 754-3775
Fax: (709) 754-3883
Web Site: www.personainc.ca
Sales Range: $100-124.9 Million
Approx. Number Employees: 50
Year Founded: 2001
Business Description:
Cable Television Services
S.I.C.: 4841
N.A.I.C.S.: 515210
Media: 23

THE PHOENIX LEARNING GROUP, INC.
2349 Chaffee Dr
Saint Louis, MO 63146-3306
Tel.: (314) 569-0211
Fax: (314) 569-2834
Toll Free: (800) 221-1274
Web Site: www.phoenixlearninggroup.com
Approx. Number Employees: 30
Year Founded: 1973
Business Description:
Educational Media, Videos, Films, CD-Roms & Books Publishers
S.I.C.: 7812; 2731

Key to Media (For complete agency information see *The Advertising Red Books-Agencies* edition):
1. Bus. Publs. 2. Cable T.V. 3. Catalogs & Directories. 4. Co-op Adv. 5. Consumer Mags. 6. D.M. to Bus. Estab.7. D.M. to Consumers 8. Daily Newsp. 9. Exhibits/Trade Shows 10. Foreign 11. Infomercial 12. Internet Adv.13. Multimedia 14. Network Radio 15. Network T.V. 16. Network Distr. Mags. 17. Other 18. Outdoor (Posters, Transit) 19. Point of Purchase20. Premiums, Novelties 21. Product Samples 22. Special Events Mktg. 23. Spot Radio 24. Spot T.V. 25. Weekly Newsp. 26. Yellow Page Adv.

The Phoenix Learning Group, Inc. — (Continued)

N.A.I.C.S.: 512110; 511130
Media: 4-20
Personnel:
Heinz Gelles *(Pres)*
Kathy Longsworth *(VP-Sls & Market Dev)*

PHOENIX PICTURES INC.
9415 Culver Blvd
Culver City, CA 90232
Tel.: (424) 298-2788
Fax: (424) 298-2588
Web Site: www.phoenixpictures.com
Sales Range: $50-74.9 Million
Approx. Number Employees: 25
Business Description:
Motion Picture & Video Production
S.I.C.: 7812
N.A.I.C.S.: 512110
Media: 3-6-15-18-24
Personnel:
Arnold W. Messer *(Pres & COO)*
Bradley Fischer *(Co-Pres-Production)*
David Thwaites *(Co-Pres-Production)*
Christopher Trunkey *(CFO & Exec VP)*

PIKES PEAK TELEVISION INC.
399 S Eighth St
Colorado Springs, CO 80905-1803
Tel.: (719) 632-1515
Fax: (719) 632-0054
Web Site: www.krdo.com
Approx. Number Employees: 273
Year Founded: 1954
Business Description:
Television Broadcasting Stations
S.I.C.: 4833; 4832
N.A.I.C.S.: 515120; 515112
Import Export
Media: 23-24
Personnel:
Tim Larson *(Gen Mgr)*
Jerry Killion *(Dir-Design & Creative Svcs Dir)*
Mike Lewis *(Dir-Program)*
Joe Reed *(Engr)*

PIXAR ANIMATION STUDIOS
(Sub. of The Walt Disney Company)
1200 Park Ave
Emeryville, CA 94608
Tel.: (510) 922-3000
Fax: (510) 922-3151
Web Site: www.pixar.com
E-Mail For Key Personnel:
Public Relations: publicity@pixar.com
Sales Range: $250-299.9 Million
Approx. Number Employees: 850
Year Founded: 1992
Business Description:
Animated Motion Pictures Producer & Animation Software Mfr
S.I.C.: 7812; 7372
N.A.I.C.S.: 512110; 511210
Advertising Expenditures: $5,126,000
Personnel:
Ed Catmull *(Co-Founder & Pres)*
Shannon Nicosia *(Dir-Mktg & Promotions)*
Brands & Products:
RENDERMAN
RENDERMAN ARTIST TOOLS
RENDERMAN FOR MAYA
RENDERMAN PRO SERVER

PLAYBOY TV & VIDEO ENTERPRISES, INC.
(Sub. of Playboy Entertainment Group, Inc.)
2706 Media Ctr Dr
Los Angeles, CA 90065-3732
Tel.: (323) 276-4000
Fax: (323) 276-4500
Web Site: www.playboy.com
Sales Range: $400-449.9 Million
Approx. Number Employees: 150
Business Description:
Domestic & Foreign Video Production Services
S.I.C.: 7812
N.A.I.C.S.: 512110
Personnel:
Richard S. Rosenzweig *(Exec VP)*
Gary Rosenson *(Sr VP & Gen Mgr-Playboy Entertainment Group)*
Craig O'Neal *(Office Mgr)*
Advertising Agency:
PK Network Communications
11 E 47th St 4th Fl
New York, NY 10017-7915
Tel.: (212) 888-4700
Fax: (212) 688-8832

POINT.360, INC.
2777 N Ontario St
Burbank, CA 91504
Mailing Address:
PO Box 1830
Hollywood, CA 90028
Tel.: (818) 565-1400
Fax: (818) 569-3659
Web Site: www.point360.com
Approx. Rev.: $39,735,000
Approx. Number Employees: 287
Year Founded: 1990
Business Description:
Video Duplication & Distribution; Distributor of National Television Spot Advertising, Trailers, Infomercials, Syndicated Programming & Electronic Press Kits to Broadcast Outlets
S.I.C.: 7829; 3652; 7822
N.A.I.C.S.: 512199; 334612; 512120
Media: 2-10-13-22
Personnel:
Haig S. Bagerdjian *(Chm, Pres & CEO)*
Alan R. Steel *(CFO, Exec VP-Fin & Admin)*
John Knowles *(Sr VP-Sls)*
Dick Millais *(VP-Mktg)*

PORCHLIGHT ENTERTAINMENT INC.
11050 Santa Monica Blvd 3rd Fl
Los Angeles, CA 90025
Tel.: (310) 477-8400
Fax: (310) 477-5555
E-mail: info@porchlight.com
Web Site: www.porchlight.com
E-Mail For Key Personnel:
President: bjohnson@porchlight.com
Approx. Sls.: $3,000,000
Approx. Number Employees: 24
Business Description:
Producer & Distr Television Programs & Films
S.I.C.: 7812; 7372
N.A.I.C.S.: 512110; 511210
Export
Media: 2-7-10-11-13-15
Personnel:
Bruce Johnson *(Pres & CEO)*

POWER MUSIC, INC.
132 S 600 E Ste 23
Salt Lake City, UT 84101
Tel.: (801) 359-1005
Fax: (801) 328-8885
Toll Free: (800) 777-2328
E-mail: customercare@powermusic.com
Web Site: www.powermusic.com
Approx. Number Employees: 20
Year Founded: 1987
Business Description:
Step, Aerobic, Yoga & Pilates & Massage Music
S.I.C.: 3652; 5735
N.A.I.C.S.: 334612; 451220
Media: 10
Personnel:
Richard Petty *(Pres)*
Micheal Babbitt *(Exec VP-Product Devel)*

POWERLINX INC.
3225 S Macdill Ave Ste 129-123
Tampa, FL 33629-8171
Tel.: (813) 321-0966
Tel.: (813) 321-0978
Fax: (877) 866-5205
Toll Free: (888) POWERLX
E-mail: general@power-linx.com
Web Site: www.power-linx.com
Sales Range: $1-9.9 Million
Approx. Number Employees: 17
Year Founded: 1993
Business Description:
Voice, Video, Audio & Data Power Line Transmission Product Mfr
S.I.C.: 3669; 3651; 7382
N.A.I.C.S.: 334290; 334310; 561621
Advertising Expenditures: $174,501
Media: 18-19
Personnel:
Michael Tomlinson *(Pres & CEO)*

PRESS COMMUNICATIONS, LLC
1329 Campus Pkwy
Neptune, NJ 07753-6822
Tel.: (732) 751-1119
Tel.: (732) 774-4755 (Adv)
Fax: (732) 751-1726
E-mail: rosev@pcllcradio.com
Web Site: www.presscommradio.com/
Approx. Number Employees: 50
Year Founded: 1997
Business Description:
Operating Radio Stations
S.I.C.: 4833; 4832
N.A.I.C.S.: 515120; 515112
Advertising Expenditures: $2,000,000
Media: 2-3-4-5-7-8-9-13-16-18-20-22-23-24-25-26
Distr.: Reg.
Personnel:
Mark Lass *(Pres)*
Robert E. McAllan *(CEO)*
Rich Morena *(CFO)*
Jules L. Plangere, III *(Sr VP)*
John Furno *(Gen Mgr-Sls)*
Rose Van Brunt *(Mgr-HR)*

PRODUCT INFORMATION NETWORK
(Sub. of Access Television Network)
2600 Michelson Dr Ste 1650
Irvine, CA 92612
Tel.: (949) 263-9900
Fax: (949) 622-6295
Toll Free: (888) 643-8746
E-mail: info@pinnet.com
Web Site: www.pinnet.com
Approx. Number Employees: 13
Year Founded: 1993
Business Description:
Cable Television Advertising Services
S.I.C.: 4833; 7319
N.A.I.C.S.: 515120; 541890
Media: 2-4-5-6-8-9-10-12-22
Distr.: Natl.
Budget Set: Oct.
Personnel:
Kathy Tran *(Dir-Affiliate Sls)*
Brands & Products:
PRODUCT INFORMATION NETWORK

PRODUCT PARTNERS LLC
(Name Changed to Beachbody, LLC)

PROGRAM PARTNERS, INC.
818 Hampton Dr Ste 1
Venice, CA 90291
Tel.: (310) 399-4499
Fax: (310) 399-6336
E-mail: info@programpartners.com
Web Site: www.programpartners.com
Sales Range: $50-74.9 Million
Approx. Number Employees: 50
Business Description:
Independent TV Distribution Company
S.I.C.: 4833
N.A.I.C.S.: 515120
Brands & Products:
CROSSWORDS
PROGRAM PARTNERS
Advertising Agencies:
Entertainment Works
11050 Sumac Ln Ste 1
Camarillo, CA 93012
Tel.: (805) 491-6072

Priority Public Relations
2118 Wilshire Blvd Ste 835
Santa Monica, CA 90403
Tel.: (310) 954-1375
Fax: (661) 964-0344
Public Relations
— Melissa Ford *(Acct Exec)*

PROVIDENT MUSIC GROUP
(Sub. of RCA Music Group)
741 Cool Springs Blvd E
Franklin, TN 37067
Tel.: (615) 261-6500
Fax: (615) 261-3380
Toll Free: (800) 333-9000
E-mail: info@providentmusic.com
Web Site: www.providentmusic.com
Approx. Number Employees: 100
Year Founded: 1997
Business Description:
Recorded Music & Entertainment Producer & Mfr
S.I.C.: 2741
N.A.I.C.S.: 512230
Media: 4-8-13
Distr.: Intl.; Natl.
Personnel:
Terry Hemmings *(Pres & CEO)*
Mike Craft *(COO)*

Key to Media (For complete agency information see *The Advertising Red Books-Agencies* edition):
1. Bus. Publs. 2. Cable T.V. 3. Catalogs & Directories. 4. Co-op Adv. 5. Consumer Mags. 6. D.M. to Bus. Estab.7. D.M. to Consumers
8. Daily Newsp. 9. Exhibits/Trade Shows 10. Foreign 11. Infomercial 12. Internet Adv.13. Multimedia 14. Network Radio
15. Network T.V. 16. Newsp. Distr. Mags. 17. Other 18. Outdoor (Posters, Transit) 19. Point of Purchase20. Premiums, Novelties
21. Product Samples 22. Special Events Mktg. 23. Spot Radio 24. Spot T.V. 25. Weekly Newsp. 26. Yellow Page Adv.

Brands & Products:
PROVIDENT

PUBLIC BROADCASTING SERVICE

(d/b/a PBS)
2100 Crystal Dr
Arlington, VA 22202-1649
Tel.: (703) 739-5000
Fax: (703) 739-5134
Telex: 910-350-1854
E-mail: info@pbs.org
Web Site: www.pbs.org
Sales Range: $500-549.9 Million
Approx. Number Employees: 500
Year Founded: 1969
Business Description:
TV Programming & Related Services
S.I.C.: 4833
N.A.I.C.S.: 515120
Advertising Expenditures: $3,500,000
Media: 2-3-6-8-9-14-15-20-22-23
Distr.: Natl.
Budget Set: Feb.
Personnel:
John E. Porter *(Chm)*
Paula A. Kerger *(Pres & CEO)*
Barbara Landes *(CFO, Treas & Sr VP-Corp Svcs)*
John F. Wilson *(CEO-TV Programming & Sr VP)*
Lesli Rotenberg *(Sr VP-Childrens Media, Brand Mngmt & Promo)*
Rob Lippincott *(Sr VP-Education)*
Ben Grimley *(Sr Dir-Interactive Bus)*
Angela Lunter *(Dir-Online Sponsorship)*
Brands & Products:
ADULT LEARNING SATELLITE SERVICE
ADULT LEARNING SERVICE
THE BUSINESS CHANNEL
ELEMENTARY/SECONDARY SERVICE
NATIONAL DATACAST
PBS DIRECT
PBS HOME VIDEO
PBS HOME VIDEO SUPPORT SERVICES
PBS VIDEO
VDR
Advertising Agencies:
The Media Kitchen
160 Varick St
New York, NY 10013
Tel.: (212) 633-0080
Fax: (212) 633-0080

MGH, Inc.
100 Painters Mill Rd Ste 600
Owings Mills, MD 21117-7305
Tel.: (410) 902-5000
Fax: (410) 902-8712
(Make Em Laugh Documentary)

QVC INC

(Sub. of Liberty Media LLC)
1200 Wilson Dr
West Chester, PA 19380-4267
Tel.: (484) 701-1000
Fax: (484) 701-8336
Fax: (484) 701-1499
Fax: (484) 701-1443
E-mail: webmaster@qvc.com
Web Site: www.qvc.com
Approx. Rev.: $7,000,000,000
Approx. Number Employees: 11,000
Year Founded: 1986
Business Description:
Electronic Retailing Services
S.I.C.: 5961; 5399
N.A.I.C.S.: 454113; 452990
Media: 2-3-4-5-6-7-8-9-10-12-13-15-19-22-23-24
Distr.: Direct to Consumer; Natl.
Budget Set: Nov.
Personnel:
Michael George *(Pres & CEO)*
Daniel O'Connell *(CFO & Exec VP)*
Meade Rudasill *(COO)*
John Sullivan *(CIO & Exec VP)*
David Frey *(Pres-Intl)*
Claire Watts *(CEO-US)*
Angie Simmons *(Exec VP-Multichannel Platforms)*
John Misko *(Sr VP & Controller)*
Mike Appleby *(Sr VP-Programming & Plng)*
Rod Birkins *(Sr VP)*
Mary Campbell *(Sr VP-Mdsg)*
Tom Clardy *(Sr VP-HR)*
Dan McDermott *(Sr VP-Customer Svcs)*
Robert Myers *(Sr VP)*
Doug Rose *(Sr VP-Programming & Mktg)*
Beth Rubino *(Sr VP-HR)*
Jeff Taraschi *(Sr VP)*
Al Ulozas *(Sr VP)*
Jim Powel *(VP-Consumer Insights & Bus Intelligence)*
David Apostolico *(VP-Affiliate Sls & Mktg)*
Paul Capelli *(VP-Corp Comm & Community Affairs)*
Jack Comstock *(VP-Talent)*
Karen Fonner *(VP-Strategic Content)*
Larry Hayes *(VP-Legal)*
John Kelly *(VP-Home Mdsg)*
Alex Miller *(VP-E-Commerce & E-Mktg)*
Charles C. Pulcini *(VP)*
Todd Sprinkle *(VP-Media Tech)*
Mark J. Tabak *(VP-Fin & Admin)*
Denise Wine *(Dir-Event & Partnership Mktg)*
Cindi Freeburn *(Dir)*
Rich Yoegel *(Dir-Off-Air Programming)*
Marguerite Carr *(Mgr-Event Mktg)*
Laurie Raphael *(Mgr-Digital Commerce Ops)*
Christian Rivell *(Mgr-Online Mktg)*
Kayce Cashman *(Sr Publicist)*
Brands & Products:
QUALITY. VALUE. CONVENIENCE.
Advertising Agencies:
Stephens Francis Whitson
Greencoat House
London, SW1P 1DH, United Kingdom
Tel.: (44) 20 7592 7500

Zimmerman Advertising
2200 W Commercial Blvd Ste 300
Fort Lauderdale, FL 33309-3064
Tel.: (954) 644-4000
Fax: (954) 731-2977
Toll Free: (800) 248-8522

RADIO CITY ENTERTAINMENT

(Sub. of Madison Square Garden, L.P.)
2 Pennsylvania Plz
New York, NY 10121
Tel.: (212) 465-6000
Fax: (212) 631-4339
E-mail: JBretschneider@radiocity.com
Web Site: www.radiocity.com
Sales Range: $10-24.9 Million
Approx. Number Employees: 26
Business Description:
Producer of Entertainment
S.I.C.: 7941; 7389
N.A.I.C.S.: 711211; 711310
Advertising Expenditures: $2,000,000
Media: 1-2-3-5-6-7-8-9-10-13-17-18-19-23-24-25-26
Distr.: Reg.
Budget Set: Nov. -Dec.
Personnel:
Timothy Hassett *(Exec VP-Facilities)*
James Sanna *(VP-Mktg)*
Brands & Products:
BACKSTAGE ACCESS
HEADLINER
RADIO CITY CHRISTMAS SPECTACULAR
RADIO CITY MUSIC HALL
RADIO CITY ROCKETTES
RADIO CITY SPRING SPECTACULAR
ROCKETTES
Advertising Agency:
kirshenbaum bond senecal + partners
160 Varick St 4th Fl
New York, NY 10013
Tel.: (212) 633-0080
Fax: (212) 463-8643

RADIO ONE

(Formerly WNOU-FM)
(Unit of Radio One, Inc.)
40 Monument Cir Ste 600
Indianapolis, IN 46204-3011
Tel.: (317) 266-9600
Sales Range: $75-99.9 Million
Approx. Number Employees: 300
Business Description:
Radio Broadcasting Station
S.I.C.: 4832
N.A.I.C.S.: 515112
Media: 18-20-22-23
Personnel:
Chris Edge *(Program Dir)*
Shannone Dunlap *(Mgr-Gen Sls)*
Patty England *(Mgr-Natl Sls)*
Dave Hood *(Chief Engr)*

RADIO ONE, INC.

5900 Princess Garden Pkwy 7th Fl
Lanham, MD 20706-2969
Tel.: (301) 306-1111
Fax: (301) 306-9426
E-mail: info@radio-one.com
Web Site: www.radio-one.com
Approx. Rev.: $279,906,000
Approx. Number Employees: 867
Year Founded: 1980
Business Description:
Holding Company; Radio Broadcasting Stations & Other Media Properties Owner & Operator
S.I.C.: 6719; 4832; 4833
N.A.I.C.S.: 551112; 515112; 515120; 519130
Advertising Expenditures: $5,200,000
Personnel:
Catherine L. Hughes *(Founder, Chm & Sec)*
Alfred C. Liggins, III *(Pres, CEO & Treas)*
Peter D. Thompson *(CFO & Exec VP)*
Leslie C. Bauer *(CIO)*
Linda J. Eckard Vilardo *(Chief Admin Officer, VP & Asst Sec)*
Barry A. Mayo *(Pres-Radio Div)*
Mike Plantamura *(Gen Counsel & VP)*
Rick Porter *(Sr VP & Reg Mgr)*
Pamela B. Somers *(Sr VP-Corp Sls)*
Jay Stevens *(Sr VP-Programming Content)*
Doug Abernethy *(Reg VP)*
Bruce Demps *(Reg VP)*
Gary Weiss *(Reg VP)*
Jackie Kindall *(VP-HR)*
John W. Mathews *(VP-Engrg)*
Anthony K. Washington *(VP-Corp Sls)*
David Carberry *(Dir-Digital Sls-Baltimore-Washington)*
Steve Harris *(Mgr-Ops)*
Advertising Agency:
Dan Klores Communications
(d/b/a dkc)
386 Park Ave S 10th Fl
New York, NY 10016
Tel.: (212) 685-4300
Fax: (212) 685-9024

RAINBOW MEDIA HOLDINGS LLC

(Sub. of Cablevision Systems Corporation)
11 Penn Plz
New York, NY 10001
Tel.: (212) 324-8500
Fax: (516) 803-3003
E-mail: webmaster@rainbow-media.com
Web Site: www.rainbow-media.com
Sales Range: $800-899.9 Million
Approx. Number Employees: 2,000
Year Founded: 1980
Business Description:
Holding Company for Cable Television Channels
S.I.C.: 4841; 7812
N.A.I.C.S.: 515210; 512110
Personnel:
Joshua Sapan *(Pres & CEO)*
Kim Martin *(Pres & Gen Mgr-We Network)*
Robert Wolf *(CFO & Treas)*
Larry Aidem *(Pres-Rainbow Ventures)*
Patrick Dolan *(Pres-News 12 Networks)*
James Gallagher *(Gen Counsel & Exec VP)*
Steve Luttinger *(Exec VP-Sls Strategy, Ops, Sr VP-Sls & Revenue Mgmt)*
Daniel Ronayne *(Exec VP & Gen Mgr-LIFESKOOL & SPORTSKOOL)*
Manny Almeida *(Exec VP)*
Mike DiPasquale *(Exec VP-Ops)*
John Huffman *(Exec VP-Fin)*
Ellen Kroner *(Exec VP-Comm)*
Bill Rosolie *(Exec VP-Adv Sls-Rainbow National Services)*
Harold Gronenthal *(Sr VP, Gen Mgr-Program Acq & Dev-Intl)*
Rob Battles *(Sr VP-Creative Svcs)*
Allison Clarke *(Sr VP-Ad Sls-WE tv & Wedding Central-Eastern Reg)*
Scott Collins *(Sr VP-Natl Adv Sls-WE TV & AMC)*
David Evans *(Sr VP-Broadband)*
Steven Pontillo *(Sr VP-Brdcst, IS & Tech)*

Key to Media (For complete agency information see *The Advertising Red Books-Agencies* edition):
1. Bus. Publs. 2. Cable T.V. 3. Catalogs & Directories. 4. Co-op Adv. 5. Consumer Mags. 6. D.M. to Bus. Estab.7. D.M. to Consumers
8. Daily Newsp. 9. Exhibits/Trade Shows 10. Foreign 11. Infomercial 12. Internet Adv.13. Multimedia 14. Network Radio
15. Network T.V. 16. Newsp. Distr. Mags. 17. Other 18. Outdoor (Posters, Transit) 19. Point of Purchase20. Premiums, Novelties
21. Product Samples 22. Special Events Mktg. 23. Spot Radio 24. Spot T.V. 25. Weekly Newsp. 26. Yellow Page Adv.

Rainbow Media Holdings LLC — (Continued)

Christine Bragan *(VP-Mktg & Comm)*
Jason Miller *(VP-Sls)*
John Toohey *(VP-Fin & Strategic Plng)*
Greg Moyer *(Gen Mgr-VOOM HD Originals)*
Olivia Dupuis *(Dir-Corp Comm)*
Kathy Newberger *(Adv & Acct Exec)*
Brands & Products:
AMC
LIFESKOOL
NEWS 12 NETWORKS
SPORTSKOOL
VICTORY ON DEMAND
WE
Advertising Agency:
filter Advertising
160 Pearl St 2nd Fl
New York, NY 10005
Tel.: (212) 248-3028
WE

RCN TELECOM SERVICES, LLC.
(Holding of ABRY Partners LLC)
196 Van Buren St Ste 300
Herndon, VA 20170-5337
Tel.: (703) 434-8200
Toll Free: (800) RING-RCN
Web Site: www.rcn.com
Approx. Rev.: $763,770,000
Approx. Number Employees: 1,500
Year Founded: 1996
Business Description:
Telephone & Cable Services
S.I.C.: 4813; 4841
N.A.I.C.S.: 517110; 515210; 517310; 517510
Advertising Expenditures: $12,300,000
Media: 7-8-9-10-13-17-18-19-23-24-26
Distr.: Direct to Consumer; Reg.
Personnel:
Lee S. Hillman *(Chm)*
Brands & Products:
THE LIVE WIRE
RCN
RCN ESSENTIALS
WE ARE FOCUSED ON YOU
Advertising Agency:
Lippert/Heilshorn & Associates, Inc.
800 Third Ave 17th Fl
New York, NY 10022
Tel.: (212) 838-3777
Fax: (212) 838-4568

RELATIVITY MEDIA, LLC
8899 Beverly Blvd Ste 500
West Hollywood, CA 90048
Tel.: (310) 859-1250
Fax: (310) 859-1254
E-mail: hr@relativitymediallc.com
Web Site: www.relativitymediallc.com
Approx. Number Employees: 400
Business Description:
Motion Picture Production & Distribution Services
S.I.C.: 7812; 7822
N.A.I.C.S.: 512110; 512120
Personnel:
Michael Joe *(Pres)*
Ryan Kavanaugh *(CEO)*
Steve Bertram *(COO)*
Terry Curtin *(Pres-Theatrical Mktg)*
Andrew Marcus *(Pres-Corp Dev & Strategy)*
Tucker Tooley *(Pres-Worldwide Production)*
Coco Jones *(Exec VP-Mktg Partnerships)*
Advertising Agency:
Carat
875 Howard St 64
San Francisco, CA 94107
Tel.: (415) 541-2700
Fax: (415) 975-0850
U.S. Media Planning & Buying

RENDA BROADCASTING CORPORATION
(d/b/a WSHH-FM)
900 Parish St
Pittsburgh, PA 15220
Tel.: (412) 875-1800
Fax: (412) 875-1801
E-mail: info@wshh.com
Web Site: www.wshh.com
Approx. Number Employees: 75
Business Description:
Radio Station
S.I.C.: 4832
N.A.I.C.S.: 515112
Media: 20-22
Personnel:
Susan Kelly *(Gen Mgr-Sls)*

RENTRAK CORPORATION
One Airport Ctr 7700 NE Ambassador Pl
Portland, OR 97220
Mailing Address:
PO Box 18888
Portland, OR 97218-0888
Tel.: (503) 284-7581
Fax: (503) 282-9017
Toll Free: (800) 929-8000
E-mail: sales@rentrak.com
Web Site: www.rentrak.com
Approx. Rev.: $97,088,000
Approx. Number Employees: 307
Year Founded: 1977
Business Description:
Home Video Distribution, Information Tracking Software & Management Services
S.I.C.: 7812; 7372
N.A.I.C.S.: 512110; 511210
Advertising Expenditures: $1,700,000
Media: 2-6-7-10-13
Personnel:
William P. Livek *(Vice Chm & CEO)*
Cathy S. Hetzel *(Pres & Pres-Advanced Media & Info Div)*
David I. Chemerow *(CFO & COO)*
Amir Yazdani *(CIO & Exec VP-IT)*
Bruce Goerlich *(Chief Res Officer)*
Ronald Giambra *(Pres-Theatrical Worldwide)*
Marty Graham *(Pres-Home Entertainment Div)*
Chris Wilson *(Pres-Natl Linear Television Div)*
David Algranati *(Sr VP-Product Innovation & Analytical Solutions)*
Timothy Erwin *(Sr VP-Sls & Customer Rels-Home Entertainment Div)*
Evan Goldfarb *(Sr VP-Sls)*
Carol M. Hinnant *(Sr VP)*
Christopher Roberts *(Sr VP-Home Entertainment Media & Digital)*
Michael J. Vinson *(Sr VP-Statistical Sciences & Analytics)*
Dawne Richards *(VP-Product Strategy-Advanced Media & Info Div)*
Nancy Beall *(Dir-Local Sls)*
Laura Beecroft *(Dir-Mktg)*
Steve Buck *(Dir-Bus Rels)*
Philip Duddy *(Dir-Client Svcs)*
Brad Nimmons *(Dir-Client Svcs)*
Cory Sher *(Dir-Bus Dev)*
Sherri Lee *(Mgr-TV Essentials Svc)*
Brands & Products:
ACTIVE HOME VIDEO
ADESSENTIALS
BLOWOUT VIDEO
BOX OFFICE ESSENTIALS
BROADBAND ESSENTIALS
BUDGETMAKER
BUSINESS INTELLIGENCE ESSENTIALS
DATATRAK
DIGITAL DOWNLOAD ESSENTIALS
ENTERTAINMENT ESSENTIALS
ESSENTIALS
FASTRAK
FORMOVIES
FORMOVIES.COM
GAMETRAK
GOTTA HAVE IT GUARANTEE
HOME ENTERTAINMENT ESSENTIALS
HOME VIDEO ESSENTIALS
INTERNET TV ESSENTIALS
MOBILE ESSENTIALS
MOBILE ONDEMAND ESSENTIALS
MOBILE TV ESSENTIALS
MOVIE WIZARD
MOVIES FOR THE HUNGRY MIND
MULTI-SCREEN MEDIA MEASUREMENT
ONDEMAND ADESSENTIALS
ONDEMAND ESSENTIALS
ONTRAK
PAY PER TRANSACTION
PPT
PRIZE FIND
RENTRAK
RETAIL ESSENTIALS
RPM
SPORTRAK
STATIONVIEW ESSENTIALS
SUPPLY CHAIN ESSENTIALS
TV ESSENTIALS
UNLESS YOU'RE RICH ENOUGH ALREADY
VIDALERT
VIDEO GAME ESSENTIALS
VIDEOLINK

REVOLUTION STUDIOS
2900 Olympic Blvd
Santa Monica, CA 90404
Tel.: (310) 255-7000
Fax: (310) 255-7001
Web Site: www.revolutionstudios.com
Approx. Sls.: $40,000,000
Approx. Number Employees: 10
Year Founded: 2000
Business Description:
Motion Picture & Video Production
S.I.C.: 7812
N.A.I.C.S.: 512110
Media: 6-15
Personnel:
Joe Roth *(Founder & Chm)*

RHI ENTERTAINMENT DISTRIBUTION, LLC
(Filed Ch 11 Bankruptcy #10-16536 on 12/13/10 in U.S. Bankruptcy Ct, Southern Dist of NY, NY)
1325 Ave of the Americas 21st Fl
New York, NY 10019
Tel.: (212) 977-9001
Tel.: (212) 261-9100
Web Site: www.rhifilms.com
Approx. Rev.: $77,772,000
Approx. Number Employees: 80
Business Description:
Made-For-Television Movies, Mini-Series & Other Television Programming Developer, Producer & Distr
S.I.C.: 7812; 7822; 7829
N.A.I.C.S.: 512110; 512120; 512199
Advertising Expenditures: $398,000
Personnel:
Robert Halmi, Sr. *(Founder)*
Jeffrey Sagansky *(Chm)*
Henry S. Hoberman *(Gen Counsel, Sec & Exec VP)*
Susan Sheppard *(Sr VP-Bus & Legal Affairs)*
Advertising Agency:
Sayles & Winnikoff Communications
1201 Broadway Ste 904
New York, NY 10001
Tel.: (212) 725-5200
Fax: (212) 679-7368

ROAD RUNNER CORP.
(Div. of Time Warner Cable Inc.)
13241 Woodland Pk Dr
Herndon, VA 20171-3000
Tel.: (703) 345-2500
Fax: (703) 345-2515
E-mail: jobs@rr.com
Web Site: www.rr.com
Sales Range: $150-199.9 Million
Approx. Number Employees: 600
Year Founded: 1998
Business Description:
High Speed Internet Connection Services
S.I.C.: 7375
N.A.I.C.S.: 518111
Media: 8-13
Personnel:
Trudy Yamasaki-Viela *(VP-Sls & Mktg)*
Nancy L. Barton *(Mktg Mgr)*

ROOMLINX, INC.
2150 W 6th Ave Unit H
Broomfield, CO 80020
Tel.: (303) 544-1111
Fax: (303) 544-1110
E-mail: info@roomlinx.com
Web Site: www.roomlinx.com
E-Mail For Key Personnel:
Public Relations: kfrey@roomlinx.com
Approx. Rev.: $4,495,196
Approx. Number Employees: 31
Year Founded: 1998
Business Description:
In-Room Media, Entertainment & Networking Solutions to Hotels, Resorts & Time Share Properties
S.I.C.: 7999
N.A.I.C.S.: 517919; 713990
Advertising Expenditures: $78,630
Media: 10

Key to Media (For complete agency information see *The Advertising Red Books-Agencies* edition):
1. Bus. Publs. 2. Cable T.V. 3. Catalogs & Directories. 4. Co-op Adv. 5. Consumer Mags. 6. D.M. to Bus. Estab.7. D.M. to Consumers 8. Daily Newsp. 9. Exhibits/Trade Shows 10. Foreign 11. Infomercial 12. Internet Adv.13. Multimedia 14. Network Radio 15. Network T.V. 16. Newsp. Distr. Mags. 17. Other 18. Outdoor (Posters, Transit) 19. Point of Purchase20. Premiums, Novelties 21. Product Samples 22. Special Events Mktg. 23. Spot Radio 24. Spot T.V. 25. Weekly Newsp. 26. Yellow Page Adv.

Personnel:
Michael S. Wasik *(CEO, Interim CFO & Board Member)*
Edouard Garneau *(CFO)*
Bob Wagener *(VP-Sls & Mktg)*

ROUNDER RECORDS CORPORATION
(Joint Venture of Village Roadshow Limited & Clarity Partners, L.P.)
1 Rounder Rd
Burlington, MA 01803
Tel.: (617) 354-0700
Fax: (617) 491-1970
Toll Free: (800) 769-6337
E-mail: info@rounder.com
Web Site: www.rounder.com
Approx. Sls.: $25,000,000
Approx. Number Employees: 110
Year Founded: 1970
Business Description:
Pre-Recorded Records & Tapes
S.I.C.: 3652; 7389
N.A.I.C.S.: 334612; 711410
Import Export
Media: 6-13-17-22
Personnel:
Marian Leighton Levy *(Owner)*
John Virant *(Pres)*

RUSH COMMUNICATIONS, INC.
512 7th Ave Ste 43-45
New York, NY 10018-4603
Tel.: (212) 840-9399
Fax: (212) 840-9390
E-mail: info@rushcommunications.com
Web Site:
www.rushcommunications.com
Approx. Rev.: $100,500,000
Approx. Number Employees: 175
Year Founded: 1979
Business Description:
Media Entertainment Company
S.I.C.: 7929
N.A.I.C.S.: 711190
Media: 3-6-8-10-13-15-19-22-23-24
Personnel:
Russell Simmons *(Founder & Chm)*
Rich Slomovitz *(CFO)*
Brands & Products:
PHAT FARM

SALEM COMMUNICATIONS CORPORATION
4880 Santa Rosa Rd Ste 300
Camarillo, CA 93012
Tel.: (805) 987-0400
Fax: (805) 384-4520
E-mail: ir@salem.cc
Web Site: www.salem.cc
Approx. Rev.: $206,922,000
Approx. Number Employees: 1,104
Business Description:
Radio Broadcasting Stations
S.I.C.: 4832
N.A.I.C.S.: 515112; 515111
Advertising Expenditures: $89,003,000
Media: 13-22-23
Personnel:
Stuart W. Epperson *(Chm)*
Edward G. Atsinger, III *(CEO)*
Evan D. Masyr *(CFO & Sr VP)*
Greg R. Anderson *(Pres-Salem Radio Network)*
David A. R. Evans *(Pres-New Bus Dev & Interactive & Publ)*
David Santrella *(Pres-Radio Div)*
Robert C. Adair *(Sr VP-Ops)*
Allen Power *(Sr VP)*
Brian Taylor *(VP & Gen Mgr)*
Russ Whitnah *(VP & Gen Mgr)*
Andrew Adams *(Gen Mgr)*
Sean O'Neill *(Gen Mgr)*
Ron Stone *(Gen Mgr-Twin Cities)*
Peter Thiele *(Mgr-Ops & Dir-Program)*
John Butler *(Dir-Natl Program-News Talk)*
Mike Moran *(Mgr-Ops)*
Brands & Products:
CCM MAGAZINE
CHRISTIANITY.COM
CHRISTIANJOBS.COM
CHURCHSTAFFING.COM
CROSSCARDS.COM
CROSSDAILY.COM
CROSSWALK.COM
LIGHTSOURCE.COM
ONEPLACE.COM
SALEM COMMUNICATIONS
SALEM MUSIC NETWORK
SALEM NEWS NETWORK
SALEM PUBLISHING
SALEM RADIO NETWORK
SALEM RADIO REPRESENTATIVES
SALEM WEB NETWORK
SERMONSEARCH.COM
THEFISH.COM
TOWNHALL.COM

SAMUEL GOLDWYN FILMS
9570 W Pico Blvd Ste 400
Los Angeles, CA 90035-1216
Tel.: (310) 860-3100
Fax: (310) 860-3195
E-mail: info@samuelgoldwyn.com
Web Site:
www.samuelgoldwynfilms.com/
Approx. Number Employees: 10
Business Description:
Motion Pictures & Videos Producer & Distr
S.I.C.: 7812
N.A.I.C.S.: 512110
Media: 1-2-4-5-6-7-8-9-10-11-14-15-18-19-22-25
Distr.: Intl.; Natl.
Personnel:
Samuel Goldwyn, Jr. *(Chm & CEO)*
Meyer Gottlieb *(Pres)*

SARKES TARZIAN INC.
205 N College Ave 8th Fl
Bloomington, IN 47404
Mailing Address:
PO Box 62
Bloomington, IN 47402-0062
Tel.: (812) 332-7251
Fax: (812) 331-4575
Approx. Number Employees: 250
Year Founded: 1949
Business Description:
Radio & TV Broadcasting Services
S.I.C.: 4833; 4832
N.A.I.C.S.: 515120; 515112
Media: 2-7-9-18-23-24
Distr.: Natl.
Personnel:
Thomas Tarzian *(Chm & Pres)*
Valerie Carney *(Gen Counsel & Sr VP)*
Thomas Tolar *(Exec VP)*
Robert W. Davis, II *(Sr VP-Acct & Fin)*
Brands & Products:
SARKES TARZIAN

SCRIPPS NETWORKS INC.
(Sub. of Scripps Networks Interactive, Inc.)
9721 Sherrill Blvd
Knoxville, TN 37932-3330
Mailing Address:
PO Box 51210
Knoxville, TN 37950-0970
Tel.: (865) 694-2700
Fax: (865) 690-9964
Web Site: www.scrippsnetworks.com
Sales Range: $700-749.9 Million
Approx. Number Employees: 1,400
Year Founded: 1994
Business Description:
Cable TV Networks Operator
S.I.C.: 4841
N.A.I.C.S.: 515210
Media: 2-3-6-9-13-14-15-18
Distr.: Intl.; Natl.
Personnel:
John F. Lansing *(Pres)*
Jim Clayton *(CFO & Exec VP)*
Mark S. Hale *(CTO & Exec VP-Ops)*
Burton Jablin *(Exec VP)*
Christopher R. Powell *(Exec VP-HR)*
Ron Feinbaum *(Sr VP, Gen Mgr-Consumer Product-HGTV & DIY Network)*
Vikki Neil *(Sr VP & Gen Mgr-Digital)*
Soheila Ataei *(Sr VP-HR)*
Laura Galietta *(Sr VP-Ad Sls Mktg)*
Kristen Jorden *(Sr VP-Dev-Intl)*
Cindy McConkey *(Sr VP-Comm)*
Jeff Meyer *(Sr VP-Interactive Sls)*
N. J. Pesci *(Sr VP-HR)*
Dina Roman *(Sr VP-Interactive Adv Sls)*
Chuck Rosenzweig *(Sr VP-Legal Affairs)*
Jon Steinlauf *(Sr VP)*
Jerilyn Bliss *(VP-Corp Comm)*
Kevin Chorlins *(VP-Mktg & Comm)*
Jeffery Kissinger *(VP-Digital Mktg & Audience Dev)*
Bob Baskerville *(Gen Mgr-Scripps Networks Intl)*
Sergei Kuharsky *(Gen Mgr-New Enterprises-Food Network)*
Lee Hall *(Dir-Corp Comm)*
Katie Allison Granju *(Mgr-Social Media)*
Mark Richardson *(Mgr-Sls-Southeast)*
Advertising Agency:
Trylon SMR
41 East 11th St
New York, NY 10003
Tel.: (212) 725-2295
Fax: (212) 725-2243

SESAME WORKSHOP
1 Lincoln Plz
New York, NY 10023-7129
Tel.: (212) 595-3456
Fax: (212) 875-6088
E-mail: privacy@sesameonline.org
Web Site: www.sesameworkshop.org
Approx. Number Employees: 375
Year Founded: 1969
Business Description:
Producer of Children's Entertainment & Educational Television
S.I.C.: 7812; 2731
N.A.I.C.S.: 512110; 511130
Media: 5-6-17
Personnel:
Gary E. Knell *(Pres & CEO)*
Daryl Mintz *(CFO)*
Melvin Ming *(COO)*
Sherrie Rollins Westin *(CMO & Exec VP)*
Susan Kolar *(Chief Admin Officer & Exec VP)*
Liz Nealon *(Exec VP & Dir-Creative)*
Terry Fitzpatrick *(Exec VP-Distr)*
Maura Regan *(Sr VP & Gen Mgr-Global Consumer Products)*
Scott Chambers *(Sr VP-Media Distr-Worldwide)*
Jennifer Ahearn *(VP-Licensing & Strategic Partner Rels)*
Suzann Duncan *(VP-Corp Mktg)*
Jennifer Perry *(VP-Publ)*
Steven C. McDonald *(Asst VP-Corp Sponsorship)*
Risa Nelson *(Asst VP-Intl Licensing)*
Sharon Stulberg *(Asst VP-Brand Stewardship & Mktg)*
Daniel N. Lewis *(Dir-New Media Comm)*
Susanna Phillips *(Dir-Mktg-Sls)*
James Williams-Ness *(Dir-Media Res)*
Brands & Products:
DRAGON TALES
SAGWA
SESAME STREET
Advertising Agency:
mono
(Partially Owned by MDC Partners)
3036 Hennepin Ave
Minneapolis, MN 55408
Tel.: (612) 822-4135
Fax: (612) 454-4950
— Erin Keeley *(Acct Dir)*

SF VIDEO, INC.
1000 Sansome St
San Francisco, CA 94111
Tel.: (415) 288-9400
Fax: (415) 288-9410
Toll Free: (800) 545-5865
E-mail: steven@sfvideo.com
Web Site: www.sfvideo.com
Approx. Number Employees: 9
Year Founded: 1990
Business Description:
Video Duplicating Services
S.I.C.: 3652
N.A.I.C.S.: 334612
Media: 2
Personnel:
Steven Feinberg *(Pres)*
Michael Brandon *(Exec VP)*

SHAW COMMUNICATIONS INC.
630 3rd Ave SW Ste 900
Calgary, AB T2P 4L4, Canada
Tel.: (403) 750-4500
Fax: (403) 750-4501
Toll Free: (888) 750-7429
E-mail: Investor.relations@sjrb.ca
Web Site: www.shaw.ca
Approx. Rev.: $3,638,321,194
Approx. Number Employees: 10,000
Year Founded: 1966
Business Description:
Entertainment, Information & Communications Services
S.I.C.: 4841
N.A.I.C.S.: 515210
Advertising Expenditures: $64,727,938
Media: 3-5-8-23-24

Key to Media (For complete agency information see *The Advertising Red Books-Agencies* edition):
1. Bus. Publs. 2. Cable T.V. 3. Catalogs & Directories. 4. Co-op Adv. 5. Consumer Mags. 6. D.M. to Bus. Estab.7. D.M. to Consumers
8. Daily Newsp. 9. Exhibits/Trade Shows 10. Foreign 11. Infomercial 12. Internet Adv.13. Multimedia 14. Network Radio
15. Network T.V. 16. Newsp. Distr. Mags. 17. Other 18. Outdoor (Posters, Transit) 19. Point of Purchase20. Premiums, Novelties
21. Product Samples 22. Special Events Mktg. 23. Spot Radio 24. Spot T.V. 25. Weekly Newsp. 26. Yellow Page Adv.

Shaw Communications Inc. — (Continued)

Personnel:
Peter J. Bissonnette *(Pres)*
Bradley S. Shaw *(CEO)*
Steve Wilson *(CFO & Sr VP)*
Jean Brazeau *(Sr VP-Regulatory Affairs)*
Jay Mehr *(Sr VP-Ops)*
Ken C. C. Stein *(Sr VP-Corp & Regulatory Affairs)*
Rhonda D. Bashnick *(Grp VP-Fin)*
Cam Kernahan *(Grp VP-Wireless & Bus)*
Dennis Steiger *(Grp VP-Engrg)*
Jackie L. Altwasser *(VP-Fin)*
Doug McEwen *(VP-Engrg & Telecom Sys)*
Peter Taylor *(VP-IT)*
Roxanne Thompson *(Mgr-Adv)*
Brands & Products:
HIGH-SPEED
HIGH-SPEED LITE
I-GUIDE
POWERBOOST
SHAW
SHAW BUSINESS INTERNET
SHAW MESSENGER
SHAW MUSIC
SHAW PHOTO SHARE
SHAW SECURE
SHAW SPAM FILTER
SHAW WEBMAIL
SHAW WEBSPACE
WARP
XTREME-1
Advertising Agency:
BBDO Toronto
2 Bloor St W
Toronto, ON M4W 3R6, Canada
Tel.: (416) 972-1505
Fax: (416) 972-5656

SHAW MEDIA INC.
(Formerly CanWest Media Group)
(Sub. of Shaw Communications Inc.)
121 Bloor St E Ste 1500
Toronto, ON M4W 3M5, Canada
Tel.: (416) 967-1174
Fax: (416) 960-0971
E-mail: corporate.inquiries@shawmedia.ca
Web Site: www.shawmedia.ca
Sales Range: $1-4.9 Billion
Year Founded: 1983
Business Description:
Film, Television Production & Broadcasting
S.I.C.: 7812; 4833
N.A.I.C.S.: 512110; 515120
Export
Media: 6-8-9-14-15-18-25
Distr.: Natl.
Personnel:
Paul Robertson *(Pres)*
Errol Da-Re *(Exec VP-Sls)*
Lori Legault *(VP-Sls)*
Greg McLelland *(VP-Sls)*
Jason Keown *(Sr Dir-Mktg-Global Entertainment)*
Chris McDowall *(Dir-Publicity-Global Television)*
Brands & Products:
ALLIANCE ATLANTIS
HISTORY TELEVISION
HOME GARDEN TELEVISION
ODEON
SHOW CASE

SHOWTIME NETWORKS INC.
(Sub. of CBS Corporation)
1633 Brdwy
New York, NY 10019-6708
Tel.: (212) 708-1600
Fax: (212) 708-1217
Web Site: www.sho.com
Approx. Number Employees: 500
Year Founded: 1976
Business Description:
Premium Cable Television Services
S.I.C.: 4841
N.A.I.C.S.: 515210
Export
Media: 2-3-5-6-8-9-10-14-15-16-18-19-22-23-24-25-26
Distr.: Natl.
Personnel:
Matthew C. Blank *(Chm & CEO)*
Jerome Scro *(CFO & Sr VP)*
David Nevins *(Pres-Entertainment)*
Trisha Cardoso *(Exec VP-Corp Comm)*
Len Fogge *(Exec VP-Creative, Mktg, Res & Digital Media)*
Gary Levine *(Exec VP-Original Programming)*
Robert Hayes *(Sr VP & Gen Mgr-Digital Media)*
Don Buckley *(Sr VP-Digital Svcs)*
Amy Israel *(Sr VP-Original Programming)*
Johanna Fuentes *(VP-Corp Pub Rels)*
Jeff Klein *(Mgr-Digital Distributor Mktg)*
Brands & Products:
THE MOVIE CHANNEL
THE MOVIE CHANNEL ON DEMAND
SHOWTIME
SHOWTIME EN ESPANOL
SHOWTIME EVENT
SHOWTIME HD
SHOWTIME ON DEMAND

SI TV
700 N Central Ave Ste 600
Glendale, CA 91203
Tel.: (323) 256-8900
Web Site: www.sitv.com
Business Description:
Cable TV Network Catering to Bicultural Latinos
S.I.C.: 4833
N.A.I.C.S.: 515120
Media: 3-22-23-24
Personnel:
Michael Schwimmer *(CEO)*
Craig Geller *(Sr VP-Adv Sls)*

SINCLAIR BROADCAST GROUP, INC.
10706 Beaver Dam Rd
Hunt Valley, MD 21030
Tel.: (410) 568-1500
Fax: (410) 568-1533
E-mail: comments@sbgi.net
Web Site: www.sbgi.net
Approx. Rev.: $767,186,000
Approx. Number Employees: 2,350
Year Founded: 1986
Business Description:
Holding Company; Television Broadcasting Stations Owner & Operator
S.I.C.: 6719; 4833; 6794
N.A.I.C.S.: 551112; 515120; 533110
Advertising Expenditures: $3,900,000
Media: 5-17
Personnel:
David D. Smith *(Chm, Pres & CEO)*
David B. Amy *(CFO & Exec VP)*
Steven M. Marks *(COO & VP)*
David R. Bochenek *(Chief Acctg Officer & VP)*
Barry M. Faber *(Gen Counsel & Exec VP)*
Lucy A. Rutishauser *(Treas & VP-Corp Fin)*
Nat S. Ostroff *(VP-New Tech)*
Delbert R. Parks, III *(VP-Ops & Engrg)*
David Schwartz *(VP-Sls)*
Darren Shapiro *(VP-New Bus Sls)*
Gregg Siegel *(VP-Sls-Natl)*
Jeff Sleete *(VP-Mktg)*
Donald H. Thompson *(VP-HR)*
Thomas I. Waters, III *(VP-Pur)*
Advertising Agencies:
Cellit
213 W Institute Pl Ste 603
Chicago, IL 60610
Tel.: (312) 492-4128
Fax: (866) 856-3936
Toll Free: (800) 790-6597

Media Works, Ltd.
11915 Park Hts Ave
Owings Mills, MD 21117
Tel.: (410) 363-0637
Fax: (410) 356-6410

RPM-Right Place Media
437 Lewis Hargett Cir Ste 130
Lexington, KY 40503
Tel.: (859) 685-3800
Fax: (859) 685-3801

SIRIUS CANADA INC.
(Joint Venture of The Canadian Broadcasting Corporation & Sirius XM Radio Inc.)
135 Liberty St 4 Fl
Toronto, ON M6K 1A7, Canada
Tel.: (416) 513-7434
Web Site: www.siriuscanada.ca
Sales Range: $200-249.9 Million
Business Description:
Satellite Radio & Products; Owned 49% by Sirius XM Radio Inc, 40% by the Canadian Broadcasting Corporation & 11% by Slaight Communications Inc.
S.I.C.: 4899; 4832
N.A.I.C.S.: 517410; 515111
Personnel:
Mark Redmond *(Pres & CEO)*
Advertising Agencies:
BBDO Toronto
2 Bloor St W
Toronto, ON M4W 3R6, Canada
Tel.: (416) 972-1505
Fax: (416) 972-5656
(Creative, TV)

OMD Canada
67 Richmond St W 2nd Fl
Toronto, ON M5H 1Z5, Canada
Tel.: (416) 681-5600
Fax: (416) 681-5620
(Media Buying)

Proximity Canada
2 Bloor W 29th Floor
Toronto, ON M4W 3R6, Canada
Tel.: (416) 323-9162
Fax: (416) 944-7886
(Online)

SIRIUS XM RADIO INC.
1221 Ave of the Americas
New York, NY 10020-1001
Tel.: (212) 584-5100
Fax: (212) 584-5200
E-mail: genfeedback@sirius-radio.com
Web Site: www.siriusradio.com
Approx. Rev.: $2,816,992,000
Approx. Number Employees: 1,479
Business Description:
Radio Broadcasting Via Satellite
S.I.C.: 4832; 4899
N.A.I.C.S.: 515112; 515111; 517410
Advertising Expenditures: $110,050,000
Media: 3-6-15
Personnel:
Eddy W. Hartenstein *(Chm)*
Scott Greenstein *(Pres & Chief Content Officer)*
Melvin Alan Karmazin *(CEO)*
David J. Frear *(CFO & Exec VP)*
Cynthia Ricciardi *(CMO)*
Dara F. Altman *(Chief Admin Officer & Exec VP)*
James E. Meyer *(Pres-Ops & Sls)*
Patrick L. Donnelly *(Gen Counsel & Exec VP)*
Thomas D. Barry *(Sr VP & Controller)*
Bette Rockmore *(Sr VP-Adv Sls)*
Elaine Griffith *(Dir-Strategic Sourcing-Global)*
Lori Robinson *(Sr Mgr-Direct to Consumer Mktg)*
Advertising Agencies:
BDS Marketing
10 Holland
Irvine, CA 92618
Tel.: (949) 472-6700
Fax: (949) 597-2220

Joele Frank, Wilkinson Brimmer Katcher
140 E 45th St 37th Fl
New York, NY 10017
Tel.: (212) 355-4449
Fax: (212) 355-4554

SMALL FRY PRODUCTIONS INC.
460 Brogdan Rd
Atlanta, GA 30024
Tel.: (678) 339-1990
Fax: (678) 339-1991
Toll Free: (800) 521-5311
Web Site: www.small-fry.com
Approx. Number Employees: 10
Year Founded: 1995
Business Description:
Video Producer
S.I.C.: 7812
N.A.I.C.S.: 512110
Media: 4-13
Personnel:
Dennis Fedoruk *(Founder, Pres & CEO)*
Brands & Products:
LEARNING FOR A LIFETIME
SMALL FRY PRODUCTIONS

SONIC SOLUTIONS
(Sub. of Rovi Corporation)
7250 Redwood Blvd Ste 300
Novato, CA 94945

Key to Media (For complete agency information see *The Advertising Red Books-Agencies* edition):
1. Bus. Publs. 2. Cable T.V. 3. Catalogs & Directories. 4. Co-op Adv. 5. Consumer Mags. 6. D.M. to Bus. Estab.7. D.M. to Consumers 8. Daily Newsp. 9. Exhibits/Trade Shows 10. Foreign 11. Infomercial 12. Internet Adv.13. Multimedia 14. Network Radio 15. Network T.V. 16. Newsp. Distr. Mags. 17. Other 18. Outdoor (Posters, Transit) 19. Point of Purchase20. Premiums, Novelties 21. Product Samples 22. Special Events Mktg. 23. Spot Radio 24. Spot T.V. 25. Weekly Newsp. 26. Yellow Page Adv.

Tel.: (415) 893-8000
Fax: (415) 893-8008
E-mail: info@sonic.com
Web Site: www.sonic.com
Approx. Rev.: $104,345,000
Approx. Number Employees: 490
Year Founded: 1986
Business Description:
Digital Media Management Software Developer & Publisher
S.I.C.: 7372; 7371; 7379
N.A.I.C.S.: 511210; 541511; 541519
Advertising Expenditures: $3,649,000
Media: 2-10-13
Personnel:
Robert J. Doris *(Chm)*
David C. Habiger *(Pres & CEO)*
Paul F. Norris *(CFO, Gen Counsel & Exec VP)*
Mark Ely *(Pres-Strategy)*
A. Clay Leighton *(Pres-Ops)*
Matthew S. DiMaria *(Exec VP & Gen Mgr-Roxio Products Grp)*
Rolf Hartley *(Sr VP & Gen Mgr-Prof Products Grp)*
Koki Terui *(Sr VP-Strategic Initiatives)*
Jim Taylor *(Gen Mgr-Advanced Tech Grp & Chief Technologist)*
Chris Taylor *(Dir-Mktg Comm)*
Sam Orton-Jay *(Product Mgr)*
Brands & Products:
AUTHORSCRIPT
AUTOCADENCE
AUTODVD
BACKONTRACK
BACKUP MYPC
BOOM BOX
CINEPLAYER
CONSTANTQ
CRUNCH
DIGITAL MEDIA STUDIO
DIGITAL MEDIA SUITE
DRIVE LETTER ACCESS
DVD FUSION
DVDIT
EASY CD & DVD CREATOR
EASY CD CREATOR
EASY DVD COPY
EDIT-ON-DVD
EDVD
FIRST IN DVD
HYPERMUX DL
MYDVD
MYDVD STUDIO
MYTV TOGO
NONOISE
ONECLICK DVD
OPENDVD
PHOTOSHOW
PHOTOSUITE
PLANTDIRECT
POPCORN
PREPLAY
PRIMETIME
QFLIX
RECORDNOW
REELDVD
ROM FORMATTER
SCENARIST
SCENARIST STUDIO
SIMPLE BACKUP
THE SMARTEST WAY TO PUBLISH ON DVD
SONIC
SONIC DVD CREATOR
SONIC JUMPSAFE
SONIC PRIMETIME
SONIC SMARTBALANCE
SONIC SOLUTIONS
SONICCARE
SONICPOWERED
TOAST
TOAST WITH JAM
TRUE DVD
TRUE DVD SLIDESHOW
VIDEOWAVE
WINONCD
WRITEDIRECT

SONY MUSIC ENTERTAINMENT

(Sub. of Sony Corporation of America)
550 Madison Ave
New York, NY 10022-3211
Tel.: (212) 833-8000
Tel.: (212) 833-5047 (Pub Rels)
Fax: (212) 833-4818
E-mail: info@sonybmg.com
Web Site: www.sonybmg.com
Sales Range: $5-14.9 Billion
Approx. Number Employees: 10,000
Business Description:
Recorded Music Production, Record Mfr & Distr
S.I.C.: 8999; 3652; 7389
N.A.I.C.S.: 512210; 334612; 512240
Media: 2-3-6-7-8-9-14-15-16-18-19-23-24-25-26
Distr.: Intl.; Natl.
Personnel:
Doug Morris *(CEO)*
Kevin Kelleher *(CFO & Exec VP)*
Bob Morelli *(Exec VP & Gen Mgr-Sls)*
Stuart Bondell *(Exec VP-Bus, Legal Affairs & Intl)*
Mel Lewinter *(Exec VP-Label Strategy)*
David Griffith *(Sr VP-Mktg)*
Ben Howard *(Sr VP-Mktg & Sls)*
Larry Kanusher *(Sr VP-Bus & Legal Affairs)*
Sheldra Khahaifa *(Sr VP-Fin-Comml Music Grp)*
Stuart Rubin *(Sr VP-Intl Catalog Mktg Grp)*
Danny Wynn *(Sr VP-Bus & Legal Affairs)*
Brian Garrity *(VP-Corp Comm)*
Howard Lau *(VP-Fin & Strategic Plng)*
Kyle Sherwin *(VP-Media & Creative Grp)*
Pat O'Brien *(Dir-Adv)*
Brands & Products:
ARISTA RECORDS
BMG CLASSICS
BMG HERITAGE
BMG INTERNATIONAL
COLUMBIA
EPIC
J RECORDS
LAFACE RECORDS
LEGACY RECORDINGS
PROVIDENT MUSIC
RCA RECORDS
RCA VICTOR
RLG NASHVILLE
SO SO DEF RECORDS
SONY CLASSICAL
SONY MUSIC INTERNATIONAL
SONY MUSIC NASHVILLE
SONY URBAN MUSIC
SONY WONDER
VERITY RECORDS

Advertising Agencies:
Mozes, Inc.
260 Sheridan Ave Ste 320
Palo Alto, CA 94306
Tel.: (650) 328-1962
Toll Free: (888) 669-3711

Universal McCann
100 33rd St 8th Fl
New York, NY 10001
Tel.: (212) 883-4700

SONY PICTURES ENTERTAINMENT INC.

(Sub. of Sony Corporation of America)
10202 Washington Blvd
Culver City, CA 90232-3119
Tel.: (310) 244-4000
Fax: (310) 244-2626
Web Site: www.sonypictures.com
Sales Range: $5-14.9 Billion
Approx. Number Employees: 3,000
Business Description:
Diversified Motion Picture, Television & Communications Services
S.I.C.: 7812; 7822
N.A.I.C.S.: 512110; 512120
Advertising Expenditures: $125,000,000
Media: 2-6-7-8-9-11-14-15-18-19-20-24
Distr.: Intl.; Natl.
Personnel:
Michael Lynton *(Co-Chm & CEO)*
Amy Pascal *(Co-Chm)*
Jeff Blake *(Vice Chm)*
David Hendler *(CFO & Exec VP)*
Ron McNair *(Chief Acctg Officer & EVP-Fin)*
Dwight Caines *(Pres-Worldwide Digital Mktg & Exec VP- Digital Mktg Strategy)*
Peter Schlessel *(Pres-Worldwide Affairs)*
Marc Weinstock *(Pres-Worldwide Mktg)*
Leah Esther Weil *(Gen Counsel & Sr Exec VP)*
Simon Baker *(Treas & Sr VP)*
Pamela Kunath *(Exec VP & Gen Mgr)*
Corii Berg *(Exec VP & Deputy Gen Counsel)*
Shelly Bunge *(Exec VP)*
John Calkins *(Exec VP-Global Digital & Comml Innovation)*
Suzanne Criley *(Exec VP-Admin)*
Jeff Hargleroad *(Exec VP-Corp Ops)*
David Kaminow *(Exec VP-Mktg)*
Jim Kennedy *(Exec VP-Global Comm)*
George Leon *(Exec VP-Consumer Mktg)*
Jaideep Janakiram *(Sr VP-Intl Bus & Head-North America)*
Superna Kalle *(Sr VP-Networks & Gen Mgr)*
Richard Berger *(Sr VP-Global Digital Strategy & Ops)*
Paul Friedman *(Sr VP-Music Affairs Grp)*
Sheraton Kalouria *(Sr VP)*
Audrey Lee *(Sr VP-Distr-Legal Affairs)*
David K. Mannix *(Sr VP-Worldwide Facilities & Admin Svcs)*
Elias Plishner *(Sr VP-Digital Media-Worldwide)*
Spencer Stephens *(Sr VP-Tech Svcs)*
Lara Thompson *(Sr VP-Acq)*
Ann Junod Burkart *(VP-Global Comm)*
Randy Nellis *(VP-Creative)*
Scott Shooman *(Exec Dir-Acq)*
Kristie Alarcon *(Dir-Mktg & Promos)*
Petra Hughes *(Dir-Compensation & Benefits-EMEA)*
Sam Notowitz *(Dir-Mobile & Partner Mktg)*
Brands & Products:
TRIUMPH PICTURES

SONY PICTURES HOME ENTERTAINMENT

(Unit of Sony Pictures Entertainment Inc.)
10202 W Washington Blvd
Culver City, CA 90232-3119
Tel.: (310) 244-4000
Fax: (310) 244-2626
Web Site: www.spe.sony.com
Approx. Number Employees: 4,500
Year Founded: 1980
Business Description:
Video & DVD Distr
S.I.C.: 7822
N.A.I.C.S.: 512120
Media: 1-2-3-5-6-9-10-13-15-18-19-20-22-23-24-25
Distr.: Intl.; Natl.
Personnel:
David Bishop *(Pres)*
Lexine Wong *(Sr Exec VP-Worldwide Mktg)*
Matt Brown *(Exec VP-Intl)*
Don Eklund *(Exec VP-Advanced Technologies)*
Alison Biggers *(Sr VP-Worldwide Mktg)*
Fritz Friedman *(Sr VP-Worldwide Publicity)*
Tracey Garvin *(Sr VP-Mktg)*
Melanie Watson *(Dir-Mktg-New Release)*
Christine Migita *(Mgr-Digital Mktg)*

SONY PICTURES RELEASING CORPORATION

(Unit of Sony Pictures Entertainment Inc.)
10202 W Washington Blvd
Culver City, CA 90232-3119
Tel.: (310) 244-4000
Fax: (310) 244-2626
Web Site: www.spe.sony.com
Approx. Number Employees: 3,500
Business Description:
Motion Picture Distr
S.I.C.: 7822
N.A.I.C.S.: 512120
Personnel:
Michael Lynton *(Chm & CEO)*
Eileen Rumble Lomis *(VP-Fin Svcs)*
Advertising Agency:
Universal McCann
100 33rd St 8th Fl
New York, NY 10001
Tel.: (212) 883-4700

SOUTH CAROLINA EDUCATIONAL TELEVISION COMMISSION

1101 George Rogers Blvd
Columbia, SC 29201
Tel.: (803) 737-3240
Fax: (803) 737-3526
E-mail: rschaller@scetv.org
Web Site: www.scetv.org
Approx. Number Employees: 150

Key to Media (For complete agency information see *The Advertising Red Books-Agencies* edition):
1. Bus. Publs. 2. Cable T.V. 3. Catalogs & Directories. 4. Co-op Adv. 5. Consumer Mags. 6. D.M. to Bus. Estab.7. D.M. to Consumers 8. Daily Newsp. 9. Exhibits/Trade Shows 10. Foreign 11. Infomercial 12. Internet Adv.13. Multimedia 14. Network Radio 15. Network T.V. 16. Newsp. Distr. Mags. 17. Other 18. Outdoor (Posters, Transit) 19. Point of Purchase20. Premiums, Novelties 21. Product Samples 22. Special Events Mktg. 23. Spot Radio 24. Spot T.V. 25. Weekly Newsp. 26. Yellow Page Adv.

South Carolina Educational Television Commission — (Continued)

Year Founded: 1960
Business Description:
Television Broadcasting Stations
S.I.C.: 4833; 4832
N.A.I.C.S.: 515120; 515112
Media: 7-8-10-13-22
Personnel:
Dean Bird *(Sr VP-Education)*
Hap Griffin *(VP-Engrg)*
Rob Schaller *(Dir-Comm)*

SOUTH CENTRAL COMMUNICATIONS CORPORATION

20 NW 3rd St
Evansville, IN 47708
Tel.: (812) 463-7950
Fax: (812) 426-7928
Web Site:
www.southcentralcommunications.net
Approx. Number Employees: 300
Year Founded: 1946
Business Description:
Radio Broadcasting Stations
S.I.C.: 4832; 4833; 7389
N.A.I.C.S.: 515112; 512290; 515120
Import Export
Media: 7-20-22-23-24
Personnel:
John D. Engelbrecht *(Chm & Pres)*
J. P. Engelbrecht *(CEO)*
Robert Shirel *(CFO, Treas & Sec)*
Tim Hulsing *(Gen Mgr)*

SPACENET, INC.

(Sub. of Gilat Satellite Networks Ltd.)
1750 Old Meadow Rd
McLean, VA 22102-4327
Tel.: (703) 848-1000
Fax: (703) 848-1012
E-mail: info@spacenet.com
Web Site: www.spacenet.com
Approx. Number Employees: 220
Year Founded: 1981
Business Description:
Designs, Develops & Manages Services for Wireline & Wireless Broadband Network Solutions
S.I.C.: 4812; 3663; 4899
N.A.I.C.S.: 517212; 334220; 517410; 517910
Media: 7-10
Personnel:
Glenn Katz *(Pres & COO)*
Andreas M. Georghiou *(CEO)*
Susan Miller *(CEO-Spacenet Integrated Govt Solutions Div)*
Mark Bresnahan *(Gen Counsel & VP)*
David Kagan *(Sr VP-Bus Dev)*
Adrienne Loftin *(VP-HR)*
Datta Sapre *(Dir-Bus Application Delivery)*

SPANISH BROADCASTING SYSTEM INC.

2601 S Bayshore Dr PH II
Coconut Grove, FL 33133
Tel.: (305) 441-6901
Fax: (305) 446-5148
E-mail: idavidson@sbscorporate.com
Web Site:
www.spanishbroadcasting.com
Approx. Rev.: $136,122,000
Approx. Number Employees: 394
Year Founded: 1983
Business Description:
Radio Broadcasting Stations Owner & Operator
S.I.C.: 4832
N.A.I.C.S.: 515111; 515112
Import Export
Advertising Expenditures: $100,000
Media: 13-17-22-23
Personnel:
Raul Alarcon, Jr. *(Chm, Pres & CEO)*
Joseph A. Garcia *(CFO, Chief Admin Officer, Sec & Sr Exec VP)*
Peter Remington *(VP & Mgr-Market)*
Gerardo Reyes *(Gen Mgr-Sls-MegaTV KTBU Channel 55-Houston)*
Albert Rodriguez *(Chief Revenue Officer-Consolidated Operation & GenMgr-MegaTV)*
Isidro Gonzalez *(Dir-Sls)*
Rene Rodriguez *(Dir-Sports Mktg-Mega TV)*
Carlos Herrera *(Reg Mgr-Sls-MegaTV)*
Camilo Bernal *(Mgr-Affiliate Rel-Mega TV)*
Juan Fina *(Mgr-Natl Sls & SBS Miami Radio Stations)*
Jacki Nosti Cambo *(VP/Gen Mgr-Radio Cluster-Miami & Mgr-Forensic Ops)*
Claudia Trejos *(General Producer-MEGA SPORTS)*
Brands & Products:
AMOR 93.1 FM
CLASICA 92.3 FM
EL ZOL 95.7 FM
ESTEREOTEMPO
LA LEY 107.9 FM
LA MEGA
LA RAZA 93.3 FM
LA RAZA 97.9 FM
LA ZETA
LATINO 96.3 FM
MEGA 97.9 FM
REGGAETON 94
ROMANCE 106.7 FM
SBS
Advertising Agencies:
Castells & Asociados
865 S Figueroa St Ste 1100
Los Angeles, CA 90017-2543
Tel.: (213) 688-7250
Fax: (213) 688-7067

Maranon & Associates Advertising
2103 Coral Way Ste 604
Miami, FL 33145
Tel.: (305) 854-2002
Fax: (305) 476-5010

SPELLING TELEVISION INC.

(Sub. of Paramount Pictures Corporation)
5700 Wilshire Blvd
Los Angeles, CA 90036
Tel.: (310) 264-3430
Fax: (323) 965-5895
Web Site: www.paramount.com
Approx. Number Employees: 50
Business Description:
Television Series, Pilots & Movies Producer
S.I.C.: 7929
N.A.I.C.S.: 711190
Media: 3-4-8-10-11-13
Distr.: Intl.; Natl.
Brands & Products:
SPELLING TELEVISION

SPIKE TV

(Sub. of MTV Networks Company)
1515 Broadway 37th Fl
New York, NY 10036
Tel.: (212) 846-4095
Fax: (212) 846-1926
Web Site: www.spiketv.com
Business Description:
Cable Television Broadcasting Services
S.I.C.: 4841
N.A.I.C.S.: 515210
Personnel:
Kevin Kay *(Pres)*
Niels Schuurmans *(Sr VP & Dir-Creative)*
John Griffin *(Sr VP-Programming)*
Jon Slusser *(Sr VP-Sports & Multi-Platform Programming)*
Todd Ames *(VP-Consumer Mktg)*
Kimberly Maxwell *(Sr Dir-Brand & Consumer Res)*
Advertising Agencies:
Asphalt Media
114 W 17th St
New York, NY 10011
Tel.: (212) 924-5332
Fax: (212) 989-3783

Mother New York
595 11th Ave
New York, NY 10036
Tel.: (212) 254-2800
Fax: (212) 254-6121

SPORTING NEWS RADIO

(Unit of American City Business Journals, Inc.)
2800 28th St Ste 308
Santa Monica, CA 90405
Tel.: (310) 452-7100
Web Site: radio.sportingnews.com
Approx. Number Employees: 75
Year Founded: 1991
Business Description:
Sports Radio Network
S.I.C.: 4832
N.A.I.C.S.: 515112
Media: 13-14
Brands & Products:
SPORTING NEWS RADIO

STARZ ENTERTAINMENT, LLC

(Sub. of Starz, LLC)
8900 Liberty Cir
Englewood, CO 80112-7057
Tel.: (720) 852-7700
Web Site: www.starz.com
E-Mail For Key Personnel:
Public Relations: eric.becker@starzencore.com
Sales Range: $150-199.9 Million
Approx. Number Employees: 500
Year Founded: 1991
Business Description:
Cable Television Programming
S.I.C.: 4841; 4833
N.A.I.C.S.: 515210; 515120
Media: 6-8-10-13-18-24
Personnel:
Robert B. Clasen *(Chm & CEO)*
William D. Myers *(Pres)*
Steve Beabout *(Gen Counsel & Exec VP)*
Edward L. Huguez *(Exec VP)*
Nancy A. McGee *(Exec VP-Mktg)*
Stephan Shelanski *(Exec VP-Programming)*
Michael Thornton *(Exec VP-Bus & Legal Affairs)*
Sheryl Anderson *(Sr VP-HR & Admin)*
Kelly Bumann *(Sr VP-Consumer Mktg)*
Christine Carrier *(Sr VP)*
Debbie Egner *(Sr VP-Affiliate Sls & Support)*
Andrew M. Nigolian *(Sr VP)*
Michelle Parker *(Sr VP-Bus & Legal Affairs)*
Tom Southwick *(Sr VP)*
Eric Becker *(VP-Corp Comm)*
Tom Gove *(VP-Sls & Mktg)*
Randall McCurdy *(VP)*
James Porter *(VP-Post-Production & Broadcast Ops)*
Suzanne Sell *(VP-Mktg, Sls, & Corp Res)*
Neal Massey *(Exec Dir-Mktg, Sls & Corp Res)*
Steve Waldo Belgard *(Sr Dir-Programming Pubity)*
Steve Waldo *(Sr Dir-Entertainment Publicity)*
Paul Suggett *(Dir-Copy)*
Brands & Products:
ENCORE EDGE
ENCORE HD
LOVE STORIES
MOVIEPLEX
STARZ!
STARZ! CINEMA
STARZ! FAMILY
STARZ! HD
STARZ IN BLACK
STARZ! KIDS
STARZ ON DEMAND
STARZ SUPER PAK
STARZ! THEATER
STARZ TICKET
STARZ WAM
TRUE STORIES
VONGO
WAM!

SUNBEAM TELEVISION CORP.

1401 79th St Causeway
Miami, FL 33141-4104
Tel.: (305) 751-6692
Fax: (305) 757-2266
E-mail: webfeedback@wsvn.com
Web Site: www.wsvn.com
Approx. Number Employees: 475
Year Founded: 1953
Business Description:
Television Broadcasting Station Services
S.I.C.: 4833; 6512
N.A.I.C.S.: 515120; 531120
Import Export
Media: 24
Personnel:
Edmund Ansin *(Pres)*
Roger Metcalf *(CFO)*
Robert Lieder *(Gen Mgr)*

SUNDANCE INSTITUTE

1825 Three Kings Dr
Park City, UT 84060
Tel.: (801) 328-3456
Fax: (435) 658-3457
E-mail: institute@sundance.org
Web Site: www.sundance.org
Sales Range: $10-24.9 Million
Approx. Number Employees: 50
Year Founded: 1981

Key to Media (For complete agency information see *The Advertising Red Books-Agencies* edition):
1. Bus. Publs. 2. Cable T.V. 3. Catalogs & Directories. 4. Co-op Adv. 5. Consumer Mags. 6. D.M. to Bus. Estab.7. D.M. to Consumers 8. Daily Newsp. 9. Exhibits/Trade Shows 10. Foreign 11. Infomercial 12. Internet Adv.13. Multimedia 14. Network Radio 15. Network T.V. 16. Newsp. Distr. Mags. 17. Other 18. Outdoor (Posters, Transit) 19. Point of Purchase20. Premiums, Novelties 21. Product Samples 22. Special Events Mktg. 23. Spot Radio 24. Spot T.V. 25. Weekly Newsp. 26. Yellow Page Adv.

Business Description:
Non-Profit Organization Dedicated to Providing Assistance to Independent Film & Theatre Artists
S.I.C.: 7829; 8699
N.A.I.C.S.: 512199; 813990
Media: 2-6-9-18-23-24-25
Personnel:
Robert Redford *(Pres)*
John Nein *(Gen Mgr)*
Keri Putnam *(Exec Dir)*
Jennifer Arceneaux *(Dir-External Rel)*

SUNRISE BROADCASTING OF NEW YORK, INC.
(d/b/a WGNY-AM/FM)
661 Little Britain Rd
New Windsor, NY 12553-6150
Tel.: (845) 561-2131
Fax: (845) 561-2138
E-mail: faxradio@wgny.net
Web Site: www.wgny.us
Sales Range: $1-9.9 Million
Approx. Number Employees: 25
Business Description:
Radio Broadcasting Stations
S.I.C.: 4832
N.A.I.C.S.: 515112
Import Export
Media: 20-22-23
Personnel:
Joerg G. Klebe *(Pres & CEO)*
Robert DeFelice *(Mgr-Mktg)*
Brands & Products:
WGNY-AM
WGNY-FM

SWANK MOTION PICTURES INC.
1795 Watson Rd
Saint Louis, MO 63127
Tel.: (314) 534-6300
Fax: (314) 909-0879
Toll Free: (800) 876-5577
E-mail: mail@swank.com
Web Site: www.swank.com
Approx. Number Employees: 1,000
Year Founded: 1937
Business Description:
Motion Picture & Tape Distr
S.I.C.: 7829; 7822
N.A.I.C.S.: 512199; 512120
Media: 10
Personnel:
Timothy K. Swank *(Chm)*

SYFY
(Joint Venture of Comcast Corporation & General Electric Company)
30 Rockefeller Plz
New York, NY 10112
Tel.: (212) 664-4444
Fax: (212) 413-6509
E-mail: feedback@nbcuni.com
Web Site: www.nbcuni.com
Sales Range: $75-99.9 Million
Approx. Number Employees: 300
Business Description:
Cable Television Network Operator
S.I.C.: 4841
N.A.I.C.S.: 515210; 519130
Media: 3-13-15-24
Personnel:
Dave Howe *(Pres)*
Mark Stern *(Pres-Original Content)*
Michael Engleman *(Exec VP-Mktg & Global Brand Strategy)*
Adam Stotsky *(Exec VP-Market Dev)*
Craig Engler *(Gen Mgr & Sr VP-Syfy Digital)*
Mark Miller *(Sr VP-Cable Entertainment Sls)*
Brands & Products:
SCIFI.COM
Advertising Agencies:
Fallon Worldwide
901 Marquette Ave Ste 2400
Minneapolis, MN 55402
Tel.: (612) 758-2345
Fax: (612) 758-2346

Ignited
2221 Park Pl
El Segundo, CA 90245
Tel.: (310) 773-3100
Fax: (310) 773-3101

The Media Kitchen
160 Varick St
New York, NY 10013
Tel.: (212) 633-0080
Fax: (212) 633-0080
(Media Buying & Planning)

TALK RADIO NETWORK
PO Box 3755
Central Point, OR 97502
Tel.: (541) 474-2297
Fax: (541) 471-1663
Toll Free: (888) 383-3733
E-mail: info@talkradionetwork.com
Web Site: www.talkradionetwork.com
Approx. Number Employees: 200
Year Founded: 1992
Business Description:
Nationally Syndicated Talk Radio Network
S.I.C.: 4832
N.A.I.C.S.: 515112
Media: 7-8-23
Personnel:
Phil Boyce *(Pres)*
Mark Masters *(CEO)*
Bill Crawford *(COO)*
Brands & Products:
LAURA INGRAHAM
THE SAVAGE NATION
TRN

TAPESTRY FILMS
9328 Civic Center Dr
Beverly Hills, CA 90210
Tel.: (310) 275-1191
Fax: (310) 275-1266
Approx. Rev.: $1,100,000
Approx. Number Employees: 10
Year Founded: 1987
Business Description:
Motion Picture/Video Production
Motion Picture/Tape Distribution
S.I.C.: 7812
N.A.I.C.S.: 512110
Media: 17
Personnel:
Michael Schreiber *(Pres)*
Peter Abrams *(Partner)*
Robert Levy *(Partner)*

TECHNICOLOR, INC.
(Sub. of Technicolor S.A.)
3233 Mission Oaks Blvd
Camarillo, CA 93012-5047
Tel.: (805) 445-1122
Fax: (805) 445-4340
E-mail: info@technicolor.com
Web Site: www.technicolor.com
E-Mail For Key Personnel:
Marketing Director: carrie.bissell@technicolor.com
Sales Range: $25-49.9 Million
Approx. Number Employees: 2,500
Business Description:
Worldwide Color Processing & Special Services for the Motion Picture & Television Industry; Videocassette Duplication
S.I.C.: 3651; 3652
N.A.I.C.S.: 334310; 334612
Media: 2-4-5-7-8-9-10-18-19-20-25-26
Distr.: Intl.; Natl.
Personnel:
Lanny Raimondo *(Pres & CEO)*
Lyndon J. Faulkner *(Pres-Optical Media)*
Tim Sarnoff *(Pres-Technicolor Digital Productions)*
Chris Saito *(Sr VP-Mktg Digital-Worldwide)*
Brands & Products:
TECHNICOLOR
Advertising Agency:
Hauser Advertising Inc.
309 Bellino Dr
Pacific Palisades, CA 90272
Tel.: (310) 459-5911
Fax: (310) 459-5919

TECHNOLOGICAL CINEVIDEO SERVICES, INC.
Fl 4 341 W 38th St
New York, NY 10018-9693
Tel.: (212) 247-6517
Fax: (212) 489-4886
E-mail: office@tcsfilm.com
Web Site: www.tcsfilm.com
Approx. Number Employees: 8
Year Founded: 1978
Business Description:
Video Sales, Rentals & Services for Motion Pictures
S.I.C.: 5731; 7359
N.A.I.C.S.: 443112; 532490
Media: 2-10-13
Personnel:
Eric Schietinger *(Pres)*

TELEMUNDO NETWORK INC.
(Joint Venture of Comcast Corporation & General Electric Company)
2290 W 8th Ave
Hialeah, FL 33010-2017
Mailing Address:
PO Box 2290
Hialeah, FL 33010
Tel.: (305) 884-8200
Fax: (305) 889-7320
Toll Free: (800) 688-8851
E-mail: info@telemundo.com
Web Site: www.telemundo.com
Sales Range: $550-599.9 Million
Approx. Number Employees: 1,700
Year Founded: 1986
Business Description:
Television Broadcasting & Marketing Services
S.I.C.: 4833
N.A.I.C.S.: 515120
Media: 1-2-3-6-7-9-10-11-14-18-20-22-23-24-25
Distr.: Natl.
Budget Set: Dec.
Personnel:
Emilio Romano *(Pres)*
Javier Maynulet *(CFO & Sr VP-Fin)*
Jacqueline Hernandez *(COO)*
Manuel Martinez *(Pres-Telemundo 51)*
Patricio Wills *(Pres-Telemundo Television Studios)*
Jorge Hidalgo *(Sr Exec VP-Sports)*
Peter Blacker *(Exec VP-Digital Media & Emerging Bus)*
Derek Bond *(Exec VP-Studios & Brdcst Ops)*
Ramon Escobar *(Exec VP-News)*
Susan Solano Vila *(Exec VP-Mktg)*
Michelle Bella *(Sr VP-Mktg & Promotions)*
Millie Carrasquillo *(Sr VP-Res)*
Anjelica Cohn *(Sr VP-Bus Affairs)*
Lee Flaster *(Sr VP-Plng, Strategy & Bus Ops-Telemundo Ad Sls)*
Johanna Guerra *(Sr VP-News)*
Alexandra Mccauley *(Sr VP-HR)*
Enrique J. Perez *(Sr VP-Sls)*
Alfredo Richard *(Sr VP-Corp Comm & Talent Strategy)*
Mike Rodriguez *(Sr VP-Sls)*
Ken Wilkey *(Sr VP-Brdcst Network Ops & TV Stations Tech)*
Alonso Galvez *(VP-Production)*
Suzette Millo *(VP-Publicity & Talent Strategy)*
Diana Mogollon *(VP-Programming & Mktg)*
Tania Paz *(VP-Digital Media Ops & Tech)*
Borja Perez *(VP-Integrated Solutions & Digital Media)*
Joanna Popper *(VP-Mktg)*
Christian Riehl *(VP-Production)*
Mera Abramson *(Dir-Pricing & Plng)*
Tapias Mansfield *(Dir-Strategic Mktg Partnerships-West Coast)*
Alina Berriz *(Mgr-Sls & Mktg Ops-Telemundo Station Grp)*
Eliz Gazarian-Semerjian *(Mgr-Natl Sls-Los Angeles)*
Advertising Agencies:
La Comunidad
6400 Biscayne Blvd
Miami, FL 33138
Tel.: (305) 993-5700
Tel.: (305) 865-9600
Fax: (305) 865-9609
Mun2

Research Development & Promotions
(d/b/a RDP)
360 Menores Ave
Coral Gables, FL 33134
Tel.: (305) 445-4997
Fax: (305) 445-4221

TEMPE ENTERTAINMENT
6401 Riverton Ave Apt 205
North Hollywood, CA 91606
Tel.: (818) 762-4950
Web Site: www.tempevideo.com
Year Founded: 1985
Business Description:
Video & DVD Producer
S.I.C.: 7812
N.A.I.C.S.: 512110
Media: 4-6
Personnel:
J.R. Bookwalter *(Owner)*
Ernest Prell *(Mgr-Web Svcs)*

TEXAS CABLE NEWS
(Sub. of Belo Corp.)
570 Young St

Texas Cable News — (Continued)

Dallas, TX 75202-4860
Tel.: (214) 977-4500
Fax: (214) 977-4643
Web Site: www.txcn.com
Approx. Rev.: $6,100,000
Approx. Number Employees: 35
Year Founded: 1999
Business Description:
Television Broadcasting
S.I.C.: 4833
N.A.I.C.S.: 515120
Media: 3-13

TIME WARNER CABLE INC.
60 Columbus Cir
New York, NY 10023
Tel.: (212) 364-8200
Web Site: www.timewarnercable.com
Approx. Rev.: $18,868,000,000
Approx. Number Employees: 47,500
Business Description:
Cable Television Services
S.I.C.: 4841
N.A.I.C.S.: 515210; 517510
Advertising Expenditures:
$664,000,000
Media: 2-3-6-8-9-13-18-22-23-24-25
Personnel:
Glenn A Britt *(Chm & CEO)*
Robert D. Marcus *(Pres, Acting CFO & COO)*
Jeffrey Hirsch *(CMO & Exec VP-Residential Svcs)*
Ellen M. East *(Chief Comm Officer & Exec VP)*
Michael L. Lajoie *(CTO & Exec VP)*
Peter C. Stern *(Chief Strategy Officer & Exec VP)*
Gail MacKinnon *(Chief Govt Affairs Officer & Exec VP)*
Melinda Witmer *(Chief Programming Officer & Exec VP)*
Joan Gillman *(Pres-Time Warner Cable Media & Exec VP)*
Carl U.J. Rossetti *(Pres-Ventures & Exec VP)*
Bob Barlow *(Pres-Div)*
Marc Lawrence-Apfelbaum *(Gen Counsel, Sec & Exec VP)*
Gerry Campbell *(Exec VP-Bus Svcs)*
Rossetti Carl *(Exec VP)*
Michael Hayashi *(Exec VP-Architecture, Dev & Engrg)*
Barry S. Rosenblum *(Exec VP)*
William F. Osbourn, Jr. *(Sr VP & Controller)*
Craig Collins *(Sr VP-Mktg & Sls)*
Mark FitzPatrick *(Sr VP-Fin)*
Paul Lang *(Sr VP-Bus Svcs)*
Thomas Mathews *(Sr VP-HR)*
Thomas Robey *(Sr VP-IR)*
Michael Roudi *(Sr VP-Mobile Svcs)*
Nate Smith *(Sr VP-Bus Dev)*
Matthew Zelesko *(Sr VP-Web Svcs & Tech)*
William Tyson *(Reg VP-Bus Svcs)*
Bobby Amirshahi *(VP-Comm)*
Susan Leepson *(VP-Comm-East Reg)*
Mary Anne Jacobs *(Sr Dir-Govt Rels)*
Roni Howell *(Dir-Employee Rels)*
Ryan Kelly *(Mgr-Media Rels)*
Lori Wolfe *(Mgr-Competitive Intelligence)*
Advertising Agency:
BDS Marketing
10 Holland
Irvine, CA 92618
Tel.: (949) 472-6700
Fax: (949) 597-2220

TIME WARNER INC.
1 Time Warner Ctr
New York, NY 10019
Tel.: (212) 484-8000
E-mail: info@timewarner.com
Web Site: www.timewarner.com
Approx. Rev.: $26,888,000,000
Approx. Number Employees: 31,000
Year Founded: 2001
Business Description:
Cable Television & Home Internet Services, Periodical Publishing, Subscription Television & Music Programming & Film Production
S.I.C.: 4841; 2721; 7375; 7812
N.A.I.C.S.: 515210; 511120; 512110; 517510; 518111
Advertising Expenditures:
$5,682,000,000
Media: 3-6-9-11-13-14-15-16-18-23-24
Distr.: Intl.; Natl.
Budget Set: Dec.
Personnel:
Jeffrey L. Bewkes *(Chm & CEO)*
John K. Martin, Jr. *(CFO & Chief Admin Officer)*
Bill Krivoshik *(CIO & Sr VP)*
Paul T. Cappuccio *(Gen Counsel & Exec VP)*
Edward B. Ruggiero *(Treas & Sr VP)*
James E. Burtson *(Sr VP-IR)*
Gary Ginsberg *(Exec VP-Corp Affairs & Mktg)*
Carol A. Melton *(Exec VP-Global Pub Policy)*
Olaf Olafsson *(Exec VP)*
Pascal Desroches *(Controller & Sr VP)*
Michael Del Nin *(Sr VP-Intl & Corp Strategy)*
Lisa Quiroz *(Sr VP)*
Tom Santiago *(Sr VP-Global Real Estate)*
Keith Cocozza *(VP-Corp Comm)*
Mikki Taylor *(Dir-Beauty & Cover)*
Brands & Products:
AOL
AOL TIME WARNER FOUNDATION
ENTERTAINMENT WEEKLY
ESSENCE
HANNA-BARBERA
HBO
LITTLE BROWN
NETSCAPE
NEW LINE
TIME INC.
TIME WARNER
TIME WARNER CABLE
TIME WARNER TRADE PUBLISHING
TURNER BROADCASTING SYSTEMS
WARNER BROS.
Advertising Agency:
The Barbarian Group
129 S St 2nd Fl
Boston, MA 02111
Tel.: (617) 424-8887
Fax: (617) 437-9499
CNN.com

TIMES-SHAMROCK, INC.
149 Penn Ave Fl 5
Scranton, PA 18503
Tel.: (570) 346-6555
Fax: (570) 346-6038
Web Site: www.rock107.com
Approx. Sls.: $16,700,000
Approx. Number Employees: 300
Business Description:
Radio Broadcasting Stations
S.I.C.: 4832; 7812
N.A.I.C.S.: 515112; 512110
Media: 8-9-20-22-23-24-25
Personnel:
William R. Lynett *(Pres)*
Mark Hoover *(Dir-Promotion)*
Jim Morris *(Mgr-Sls)*

TIVO INC.
2160 Gold St
Alviso, CA 95002
Mailing Address:
PO Box 2160
Alviso, CA 95002-2160
Tel.: (408) 519-9100
Fax: (408) 519-5330
E-mail: employment@tivo.com
Web Site: www.tivo.com
Approx. Rev.: $219,608,000
Approx. Number Employees: 611
Year Founded: 1997
Business Description:
Digital Video Recorder Equipment & Services
S.I.C.: 4841
N.A.I.C.S.: 515210
Advertising Expenditures: $3,800,000
Media: 14-23
Personnel:
James Barton *(Co-Founder, CTO & Sr VP)*
Thomas S. Rogers *(Pres & CEO)*
Anna Brunelle *(CFO & VP)*
Matthew Zinn *(Gen Counsel, Chief Privacy officer & Sr VP)*
Jeffrey Klugman *(Sr VP & Gen Mgr-Products & Revenue)*
Tara Maitra *(Sr VP, Gen Mgr-Content & Media Sls)*
Naveen Chopra *(Sr VP-Corp Dev & Strategy)*
Nancy Kato *(Sr VP-HR)*
Joe Miller *(Sr VP-Retail Sls & Mktg)*
Dan Phillips *(Sr VP-Engrg & Ops)*
Joshua Danovitz *(VP & Gen Mgr-Intl)*
Doug Bieter *(VP-Retail Sls)*
David Sandford *(VP-Mktg & Product Mgmt)*
Dennis Dunphy *(Dir-Sls)*
Mark Risis *(Dir-Interactive Ad Sls)*
Brands & Products:
JUMP
MY TIVO GETS ME
OVERTIME SCHEDULER
POWERIIWATCH
SEASON PASS
SWIVEL
THUMBS DOWN
THUMBS UP
TIVO
TIVO CENTRAL
TIVO DVR
TIVOLUTION
TIVOTOGO
WISHLIST
Advertising Agencies:
Carat
875 Howard St 64
San Francisco, CA 94107
Tel.: (415) 541-2700
Fax: (415) 975-0850

The Direct Impact Company
99 Canal Center Plz Ste 450
Alexandria, VA 22314-1588
Tel.: (703) 684-1245
Fax: (703) 684-1249

The Kaplan Thaler Group
825 8th Ave 34th Fl
New York, NY 10019
Tel.: (212) 474-5000
Fax: (212) 474-5702
Creative

The Ruder Finn Group
301 E 57th St
New York, NY 10022-2900
Tel.: (212) 593-6400
Fax: (212) 593-6397
Public Relations
— Andrew Pray *(Acct Exec)*

Sloane & Company LLC
(d/b/a Sloane & Company)
7 Times Sq Tower 17th Fl
New York, NY 10036
Tel.: (212) 486-9500
Fax: (212) 486-9094

TLA ENTERTAINMENT GROUP, INC.
234 Market St
Philadelphia, PA 19106
Tel.: (215) 733-0608
Fax: (215) 733-0637
Toll Free: (800) 333-8521
Web Site: www.tlavideo.com
Approx. Number Employees: 175
Business Description:
Sales & Rentals of Video Tapes & DVDs
S.I.C.: 7841; 5735
N.A.I.C.S.: 532230; 451220
Media: 1-2-3-4-6-8-10-11-13-15-18-21-22
Personnel:
Raymond Murray *(Pres)*
Brian Sokel *(Mng Dir)*
Claire Brown-Kohler *(CFO)*

TOWNSQUARE MEDIA, INC.
(Holding of Oaktree Capital Management, L.P.)
240 Greenwich Ave
Greenwich, CT 06830
Tel.: (203) 861-0900
Web Site: townsquaremedia.com
Approx. Rev.: $84,141,000
Approx. Number Employees: 820
Year Founded: 1968
Business Description:
Holding Company; Radio Broadcasting Stations Owner & Operator
S.I.C.: 6719; 4832
N.A.I.C.S.: 551112; 515112
Advertising Expenditures: $1,100,000
Media: 13-18-22-23
Personnel:
Steven Price *(Chm & CEO)*
Stuart Rosenstein *(Pres & CFO)*
Bill Wilson *(Exec VP)*
Alex Berkett *(Sr VP-Bus Dev, Mergers & Acq)*
Bill Hanlon *(Sr VP-Sls)*
Erik Hellum *(Sr VP-Town Div)*
George Laughlin *(Sr VP)*

Key to Media (For complete agency information see *The Advertising Red Books-Agencies* edition):
1. Bus. Publs. 2. Cable T.V. 3. Catalogs & Directories. 4. Co-op Adv. 5. Consumer Mags. 6. D.M. to Bus. Estab.7. D.M. to Consumers
8. Daily Newsp. 9. Exhibits/Trade Shows 10. Foreign 11. Infomercial 12. Internet Adv.13. Multimedia 14. Network Radio
15. Network T.V. 16. Newsp. Distr. Mags. 17. Other 18. Outdoor (Posters, Transit) 19. Point of Purchase20. Premiums, Novelties
21. Product Samples 22. Special Events Mktg. 23. Spot Radio 24. Spot T.V. 25. Weekly Newsp. 26. Yellow Page Adv.

Dhruv A. Prasad *(Sr VP-Strategy & Ops)*
Scott Schatz *(VP-Fin & IT)*
Ben Hoffman *(Mgr-Station & Dir-Sls)*

TRANS WORLD ENTERTAINMENT CORPORATION

38 Corporate Cir
Albany, NY 12203
Tel.: (518) 452-1242
Fax: (518) 862-9519
Telex: 518-452-7848
E-mail: corpcomm@twec.com
Web Site: www.twec.com
Approx. Sls.: $652,416,000
Approx. Number Employees: 1,800
Year Founded: 1972
Business Description:
Retailer of Music, Pre-Recorded Videocassettes, DVD's & Related Products
S.I.C.: 5735
N.A.I.C.S.: 451220
Export
Advertising Expenditures: $8,900,000
Media: 3-9-16-19-23-24-25
Distr.: Direct to Consumer; Natl.
Personnel:
Robert J. Higgins *(Chm & CEO)*
Mike Honeyman *(Pres & COO)*
John J. Sullivan *(CFO, Exec VP & Sec)*
Bruce J. Eisenberg *(Exec VP-Real Estate)*
Brands & Products:
COCONUTS MUSIC & MOVIES
FYE
SATURDAY MATINEE
SPEC'S
SUNCOAST
TRANS WORLD ENTERTAINMENT
WE ARE ENTERTAINMENT
WHEREHOUSE MUSIC

TRANS WORLD RADIO INC.

300 Gregson Dr
Cary, NC 27511-6444
Tel.: (919) 460-3700
Fax: (919) 460-3702
E-mail: info@twr.org
Web Site: www.twr.org
E-Mail For Key Personnel:
President: tlowell@twr.org
Approx. Rev.: $36,911,004
Approx. Number Employees: 500
Year Founded: 1952
Business Description:
Radio Broadcasting Stations
S.I.C.: 4832
N.A.I.C.S.: 515112
Import Export
Media: 20-22-23
Personnel:
Thomas J. Lowell *(Chm)*
Lauren Libby *(Pres)*
Steve Hippe *(CFO)*
Kris Carraway *(Dir-HR)*

TRAVEL CHANNEL LLC

(Sub. of Scripps Networks Inc.)
5425 Wisconsin Ave
Chevy Chase, MD 20815
Tel.: (240) 662-2000
Fax: (240) 662-1854
Web Site: www.travel.discovery.com
Year Founded: 1987
Business Description:
Cable Network Programming Services
S.I.C.: 4833
N.A.I.C.S.: 515120
Media: 3-6-9-13-14-18-19-21-23-26
Personnel:
Laureen Ong *(Pres)*
John Barry *(Sr VP-Adv Sls-Eastern Reg)*
Scott Felenstein *(Sr VP-Adv Sls-Eastern Reg)*
Lisa Fischer *(Sr VP-Adv Sls-Eastern Reg)*
Harold Morgenstern *(Sr VP-Adv Sls-Eastern Reg)*
Ben Price *(Sr VP-Natl Adv Sls)*
Greg Regis *(Sr VP-Ad Sls & Media Partnerships)*
Evan Sternschein *(Sr VP-Natl Adv Sls)*
Scott Kohn *(VP-Adv Sls-Midwest Reg)*
Andrew Singer *(Head-Programming & Production)*
Jonathan Sichel *(Gen Mgr)*
Catherine Breza *(Dir-Mktg Production & Ops)*

TRIAD BROADCASTING CO. LLC

2511 Garden Rd Ste A104
Monterey, CA 93940
Tel.: (831) 655-6350
Fax: (831) 655-6355
Web Site: www.triadbroadcasting.com
Approx. Sls.: $19,600,000
Approx. Number Employees: 8
Business Description:
Radio Broadcasting Stations
S.I.C.: 4832
N.A.I.C.S.: 515112
Media: 20-22-23
Personnel:
David J. Benjamin *(Pres & CEO)*
James Graber *(CFO & VP)*

TRIBUNE ENTERTAINMENT COMPANY

(Div. of Tribune Broadcasting Company)
5800 W Sunset Blvd
Los Angeles, CA 90028-6607
Tel.: (323) 460-5800
Fax: (323) 460-3858
Web Site: www.tribune.com
Approx. Number Employees: 400
Year Founded: 1982
Business Description:
Television Show Production & Syndication
S.I.C.: 7819
N.A.I.C.S.: 512191
Media: 2-3-5-10-17-18-22-23-24
Personnel:
Sean Compton *(Sr VP-Programming & Entertainment)*

TRISTAR PRODUCTS INC.

492 Rte 46 E
Fairfield, NJ 07004
Tel.: (973) 575-5400
Fax: (973) 575-6708
E-mail: infotp@tristarproductsinc.com
Web Site: www.tristarproductsinc.com
Sales Range: $10-24.9 Million
Approx. Number Employees: 30
Year Founded: 1993
Business Description:
Celebrity-Endorsed Consumer Goods Marketing & Sales
S.I.C.: 5199
N.A.I.C.S.: 424990
Import Export
Personnel:
Kishore Mirchandani *(Pres & CEO)*
Steven Sowers *(CFO & VP)*
Paul DiLonardo *(VP-Sls)*
Parker Bliss *(Dir-Art)*
Rosa Campagnuolo *(Dir-Client Svcs)*
Lynda Gentile *(Dir-Creative)*
Joe Urbay *(Dir-Intl Sls)*
Marie Skavinsky *(Mgr-Accts Receivable & Credit)*
Advertising Agency:
Diamond Media & Marketing, Inc.
7070 E 3rd Ave
Scottsdale, AZ 85251
Tel.: (480) 481-2960
Fax: (480) 481-2971
Toll Free: (877) 481-2960

TROMA ENTERTAINMENT INC.

3640 11th St
Long Island City, NY 11106
Tel.: (718) 391-0110
Fax: (718) 391-0255
E-mail: films@troma.com
Web Site: www.troma.com
Approx. Sls.: $9,000,000
Approx. Number Employees: 50
Business Description:
Producer & Distr. of Motion Pictures
S.I.C.: 7812
N.A.I.C.S.: 512110
Media: 10-13
Personnel:
Lisa Borhoum *(Dir-Intl Sls)*

TRUTV

(Joint Venture of Time Warner Inc. & Liberty Media Corporation)
600 3rd Ave
New York, NY 10016-1901
Tel.: (212) 973-2800
Fax: (212) 973-3210
Toll Free: (800) COURT-56
Web Site: www.trutv.com
Approx. Sls.: $32,300,000
Approx. Number Employees: 250
Year Founded: 1991
Business Description:
Television Cable Network; Joint Venture of AOL Time Warner Inc. 50% & Liberty Media Corporation 50%
S.I.C.: 4833
N.A.I.C.S.: 515120
Media: 3-9-14-15-17-18-25
Distr.: Natl.
Personnel:
Art Bell *(Pres & COO)*
Mary Corigliano *(Sr VP-Brand Strategy, Digital Content & Multi-Platform Dev)*
Rob Pumo *(Sr VP-Ops Grp)*
Brian Compare *(VP-Programming & Mktg Res)*
Jason Valentzas *(VP-Digital Content & Multi-Platform Dev)*
Mark Juris *(Gen Mgr)*

TURNER BROADCASTING SYSTEM, INC.

(Sub. of Time Warner Inc.)
1 CNN Ctr NW
Atlanta, GA 30303-2762
Tel.: (404) 827-1700
Fax: (404) 878-0891
E-mail: cnn.feedback@turner.com
Web Site: www.turner.com
Sales Range: $1-4.9 Billion
Approx. Number Employees: 6,500
Year Founded: 1965
Business Description:
Broadcasting & Cable Production
S.I.C.: 4833; 4841
N.A.I.C.S.: 515120; 515210
Import Export
Media: 3-6-9-14-15-18-23-24-25
Distr.: Intl.; Natl.
Budget Set: Jan.
Personnel:
Philip I. Kent *(Chm & CEO)*
Louise Sams *(Pres & Exec VP)*
Coleman Breland *(COO-Turner Network Sls)*
Brenda Freeman *(CMO-Turner Animation, Young Adults & Kids Media)*
Jeff Gregor *(CMO)*
Scott Teissler *(CTO & Chief Digital Tech Strategist)*
Jim McCaffrey *(Chief Strategy Officer & Exec VP-Ops & Strategy)*
Jack Wakshlag *(Chief Res Officer)*
David R. Levy *(Pres-Sls, Distr & Sports)*
Jim Walton *(Pres-CNN Worldwide)*
Greg D'Alba *(COO-Sls & Mktg)*
Kelly Regal *(Exec VP)*
Michael Wright *(Exec VP-Programming)*
Molly Battin *(Sr VP-Brand Dev & Digital Platforms)*
Deborah K. Bradley *(Sr VP-Program Acquisitions)*
Lisa Chang *(Sr VP-HR, Intl, Tech, Strategy & Ops)*
Andrea Ching *(Sr VP-Mktg & Promotions, Turner SI Digital)*
Paul Condolora *(Sr VP-Digital-Animation, Young Adults & Kids Media)*
Tricia Garrett Melton *(Sr VP-Mktg)*
Jeremy Legg *(Sr VP)*
Jeff Matteson *(Sr VP-Comm)*
Christina Miller *(Sr VP-Sports Mktg, Programming & Strategy)*
Mark Norman *(Sr VP-Entertainment Strategy)*
Jill Shields *(Sr VP-Mktg & Promos-Animation/Young Adults & Kids)*
Misty Skedgell *(Sr VP-Corp Comm)*
Jacqueline M. Welch *(Sr VP-HR)*
Tracy Barash *(VP-Brand Dev-Cartoon Network)*
Amy Cohn *(VP-Corp Comm)*
Vicky Free *(VP-360 Consumer Mktg)*
Rebecca Rusk Lim *(VP-Interactive Experience)*
Susan Nathan *(Corp VP-Media Currency)*
Kathryn Szumowski *(Sr Dir-Media)*
Justin Williams *(Sr Dir-Bus Ops-NASCAR.com)*
Stephen Bishop *(Dir-Media)*
Keith Duprey *(Dir-Innovation & Strategy-The Sponsor Shop)*
James Wilcox *(Assoc Dir-Media-Digital & Social)*
Lisa Menendez *(Mgr-Mktg)*
Advertising Agencies:
Hauser Advertising Inc.
309 Bellino Dr
Pacific Palisades, CA 90272
Tel.: (310) 459-5911
Fax: (310) 459-5919

Key to Media (For complete agency information see *The Advertising Red Books-Agencies* edition):
1. Bus. Publs. 2. Cable T.V. 3. Catalogs & Directories. 4. Co-op Adv. 5. Consumer Mags. 6. D.M. to Bus. Estab.7. D.M. to Consumers
8. Daily Newsp. 9. Exhibits/Trade Shows 10. Foreign 11. Infomercial 12. Internet Adv.13. Multimedia 14. Network Radio
15. Network T.V. 16. Newsp. Distr. Mags. 17. Other 18. Outdoor (Posters, Transit) 19. Point of Purchase20. Premiums, Novelties
21. Product Samples 22. Special Events Mktg. 23. Spot Radio 24. Spot T.V. 25. Weekly Newsp. 26. Yellow Page Adv.

Turner Broadcasting System, Inc. — (Continued)

Mother New York
595 11th Ave
New York, NY 10036
Tel.: (212) 254-2800
Fax: (212) 254-6121

Saatchi & Saatchi
(Sub. of Publicis Groupe S.A.)
(Worldwide Headquarters)
375 Hudson St
New York, NY 10014-3660
Tel.: (212) 463-2000
Fax: (212) 463-9856

Starcom MediaVest Group
35 W Wacker Dr
Chicago, IL 60601-1723
Tel.: (312) 220-3535
Fax: (312) 220-6530
Cartoon Network
CNN
Digital, TV, Print & Out of Home
TBS
TNT
Turner Movie Classics
Turner Sports

TVA FILMS
(Div. of TVA Group, Inc.)
1 600 boul de Maisonneuve est 8e etage
Montreal, QC H2L 4P2, Canada
Tel.: (514) 284-2525
Fax: (514) 985-4461
E-mail: info@tvafilms.com
Web Site: www.tvafilms.com
Approx. Number Employees: 3
Year Founded: 2002
Business Description:
Home Video & Theatrical Programming Distr
S.I.C.: 7822
N.A.I.C.S.: 512120
Media: 6-9-13-14-15-18-25
Distr.: Natl.
Personnel:
Karynn Austin *(Dir-Mktg)*
Brands & Products:
TVAFILMS
Advertising Agencies:
Communication Popcorn
438 McGill
Montreal, QC H2Y 2G1, Canada
Tel.: (514) 448-5656
Fax: (514) 448-5868

Media Express
20 Eglinton Avenue West Ste 1250
Toronto, ON M4R 1K8, Canada
Tel.: (416) 484-5300
Fax: (416) 484-5307
Media Buying

TVA GROUP, INC.
(Sub. of Quebecor Media Inc.)
1600 de Maisonneuve Boulevard East
Montreal, QC H2L 4P2, Canada
Tel.: (514) 526-9251
Tel.: (514) 790-0461
Fax: (514) 598-2894
Fax: (514) 598-6085
E-mail: tva@tva.ca
Web Site: www.tva.canoe.ca
Approx. Rev.: $456,626,973
Approx. Number Employees: 1,250
Business Description:
Network Television Broadcasting & Multimedia Publishing Services
S.I.C.: 4833
N.A.I.C.S.: 515120
Media: 15
Personnel:
Pierre Dion *(Pres & CEO)*
Denis Rozon *(CFO & VP)*
Jocelyn Comtois *(Pres-Publ)*
Richard Gauthier *(VP-HR)*
Edith Perreault *(VP-Sls & Mktg)*
Maxime Bedard *(Dir-Legal Affairs)*
Christian Marcoux *(Asst Sec)*

TWIN CITIES PUBLIC TELEVISION, INC.
172 E 4th St
Saint Paul, MN 55101
Tel.: (651) 222-1717
Fax: (651) 229-1282
E-mail: viewerservices@tpt.org
Web Site: www.tpt.org
Sales Range: $10-24.9 Million
Approx. Number Employees: 150
Year Founded: 1955
Business Description:
Television Broadcasting Stations
S.I.C.: 4833
N.A.I.C.S.: 515120
Media: 7-8
Personnel:
James R. Pagliarini *(Pres & CEO)*
Stephen Usery *(CMO & Chief Fundraising Officer)*
Allen Giles *(Gen Counsel & Sr VP-Legal)*
Jenny Masters-Wolfe *(Sr VP-HR & Organizational Effectiveness)*
Barbara Van Loenen *(Sr VP-Fin & Bus Admin)*
Lisa K. Johnson *(Dir-Sls-Mktg)*
Brands & Products:
TPT

TWISTED SCHOLAR, INC.
3241 35th Ave SW
Seattle, WA 98126
Tel.: (206) 254-9215
Fax: (240) 266-7600
Toll Free: (888) 949-2628
E-mail: info@twistedscholar.com
Web Site: www.twistedscholar.com
Sales Range: Less than $1 Million
Approx. Number Employees: 5
Business Description:
Videos for Broadcast & Home Video Distribution Producer
S.I.C.: 7812
N.A.I.C.S.: 512110
Media: 6
Personnel:
Marty Riemer *(Owner)*

UAV CORPORATION
2200 Carolina Pl
Fort Mill, SC 29708
Tel.: (803) 548-7300
Fax: (803) 548-3335
Toll Free: (800) 486-6782
E-mail: webmaster@uavco.com
Web Site: www.uavco.com
Approx. Number Employees: 400
Year Founded: 1984
Business Description:
Wholesaler of Video & Audio Tapes, DVDs & Software
S.I.C.: 3652; 5099
N.A.I.C.S.: 334612; 423990
Advertising Expenditures: $50,000
Media: 2-8-9-10-13-25-26
Distr.: Natl.
Brands & Products:
KARAOKE BAY
STERLING

UNION RADIO, INC.
350 NE 71st St
Miami, FL 33138
Tel.: (305) 759-7280
Web Site: www.wocn.net
Approx. Rev.: $1,000,000
Approx. Number Employees: 10
Year Founded: 1984
Business Description:
Radio Station
S.I.C.: 4832
N.A.I.C.S.: 515112
Media: 14

UNIVERSAL MOTOWN RECORDS
(Unit of Universal Music Group)
1755 Broadway
New York, NY 10019
Tel.: (212) 841-8000
Fax: (212) 841-8624
Web Site: www.universalmotown.com
Approx. Sls.: $100,000,000
Approx. Number Employees: 160
Year Founded: 1959
Business Description:
Mfr. & Marketer of Records
S.I.C.: 5735
N.A.I.C.S.: 451220
Advertising Expenditures: $1,000,000
Media: 2-4-6-8-9-18-19-23-24
Distr.: Intl.; Natl.
Budget Set: Jan.
Personnel:
Sylvia Rhone *(Pres)*
Andrew Kronfeld *(Exec VP-Mktg-Intl-Universal Music Grp Intl)*
Todd Glassman *(Sr VP-Promo)*
Steve Gawley *(Sr VP-Legal)*
Karen Kwak *(Sr VP-Opers)*
Margeaux Rawson *(Sr VP-Media Rel)*
Rio Caraeff *(VP & Gen Mgr)*
Maria Ho *(VP-Corp Commun)*
Heath Kudler *(VP-Legal)*
Phylicia Fant *(Sr Dir-PR)*
Brands & Products:
MOJAZZ
MOTOWN
Advertising Agencies:
Big Spaceship
45 Main St Ste 716
Brooklyn, NY 11201
Tel.: (718) 222-0281
Fax: (718) 971-1062

Universal Music Group Advertising & Media Services
825 8th Ave
New York, NY 10019-7416
Tel.: (212) 333-8000
Fax: (877) 804-2230

UNIVERSAL STUDIOS HOLLYWOOD
(Joint Venture of Comcast Corporation & General Electric Company)
100 Universal City Plz
Universal City, CA 91608
Tel.: (818) 622-3801
Fax: (818) 622-0152
Web Site: www.universalstudioshollywood.com/
Sales Range: $25-49.9 Million
Year Founded: 1964
Business Description:
Amusement Theme Park Services
S.I.C.: 7996
N.A.I.C.S.: 713110
Media: 2-3-5-6-7-9-10-16-18-23-24-25
Distr.: Natl.
Budget Set: Sept.
Personnel:
Larry Kurzweil *(Pres & COO)*
Jennifer Cabalquinto *(CFO)*
Brian Bacica *(Sr VP-Food & Retail)*
Xiomara Wiley *(Sr VP-Sls & Mktg)*
Thomas See *(VP-Sls)*
Eliot Sekuler *(VP-PR)*
Tari Garza *(Dir-Partnership Mktg)*
Thomas L. Williams *(Supvr)*
Brands & Products:
UNIVERSAL CITY STUDIO TOURS
Advertising Agencies:
The Cimarron Group
6855 Santa Monica Blvd
Hollywood, CA 90038
Tel.: (323) 337-0300
Fax: (323) 337-0333

David & Goliath
909 N Sepulveda Blvd Ste 700
El Segundo, CA 90245
Tel.: (310) 445-5200
Fax: (310) 445-5201

DDB Los Angeles
340 Main St
Venice, CA 90291
Tel.: (310) 907-1500
Fax: (310) 907-1571

UNIVERSAL STUDIOS, INC.
(Joint Venture of Comcast Corporation & General Electric Company)
100 Universal City Plz
Universal City, CA 91608-1002
Tel.: (818) 777-1000
Fax: (818) 866-3600
Web Site: www.universalstudios.com
Approx. Number Employees: 7,000
Business Description:
Television, Home Video, Record, Tape & Video Products Producer & Distr; Licensing, Merchandising Rights & Film Property Publishing Rights Services; Gift Merchandise Retailer; Book Publisher; Toy Products Mfr; Recreation Services
S.I.C.: 7812; 3652
N.A.I.C.S.: 512110; 334612
Media: 3-6-9-14-15-18-23-24
Distr.: Natl.
Personnel:
Adam Fogelson *(Co-Chm)*
Marc Shmuger *(Chm)*
Larry Kurzweil *(Co-Pres & COO)*
Jim Watters *(Pres & Gen Mgr-Ops Grp)*
Jennifer Cabalquinto *(CFO & Exec VP)*
Karen Randall *(Gen Counsel & Exec VP)*
Hilary Hoffman *(Exec VP-Mktg)*
Kenneth Kahrs *(Exec VP-HR)*
Pamela Tuscany-Warren *(Exec VP, IT & HR)*

Key to Media (For complete agency information see *The Advertising Red Books-Agencies* edition):
1. Bus. Publs. 2. Cable T.V. 3. Catalogs & Directories. 4. Co-op Adv. 5. Consumer Mags. 6. D.M. to Bus. Estab.7. D.M. to Consumers
8. Daily Newsp. 9. Exhibits/Trade Shows 10. Foreign 11. Infomercial 12. Internet Adv.13. Multimedia 14. Network Radio
15. Network T.V. 16. Newsp. Distr. Mags. 17. Other 18. Outdoor (Posters, Transit) 19. Point of Purchase20. Premiums, Novelties
21. Product Samples 22. Special Events Mktg. 23. Spot Radio 24. Spot T.V. 25. Weekly Newsp. 26. Yellow Page Adv.

Scott Abraham *(Sr VP-Creative Svcs)*
Susan Fleishman *(Sr VP-Corp Comm & Pub Affairs)*
Doug Neil *(Sr VP-Digital Mktg)*
Jeanne Cordova *(VP-Mktg, Publicity & Special Events)*
Kristin Johnson *(VP-Media)*
Joe Eibert *(Dir-Digital Mktg)*
Tara O'Donnell *(Mgr)*
Brands & Products:
UNIVERSAL STUDIOS

U.S. MUSIC CORPORATION

(Sub. of Jam Industries Ltd.)
444 E Courtland St
Mundelein, IL 60060
Tel.: (847) 949-0444
Fax: (847) 949-8444
Toll Free: (800) 877-6863
Web Site: www.usmusiccorp.com
Sales Range: $50-74.9 Million
Approx. Number Employees: 140
Year Founded: 1883
Business Description:
Musical Instrument & Sound Equipment Mfr; Guitars, Amplifiers & Sound Engineering Equipment
S.I.C.: 3931; 3651
N.A.I.C.S.: 339992; 334310
Export
Media: 2-4-6-7-8-9-10-13-25
Distr.: Natl.
Budget Set: June
Personnel:
Barry Ryan *(Pres)*
Brands & Products:
EDEN
OSCAR SCHMIDT
PARKER
RANDALL
SOUNDTECH
U.S. MUSIC
WASHBURN

USA NETWORKS

(Joint Venture of Comcast Corporation & General Electric Company)
30 Rockefeller Plz 21st Fl
New York, NY 10112
Tel.: (212) 413-5000
Fax: (212) 413-6509
E-mail: feedback@usanetwork.com
Web Site: www.usanetwork.com
Sales Range: $200-249.9 Million
Year Founded: 1980
Business Description:
Cable Television Network Operator
S.I.C.: 4841
N.A.I.C.S.: 515210
Media: 2-3-6-7-9-10-16-18-23-24-25
Distr.: Intl.; Natl.
Budget Set: Sept.
Personnel:
Bonnie Hammer *(Pres)*
Jeff Wachtel *(Co-Pres)*
Jackie De Crinis *(Exec VP-Original Scripted Programming)*
Chris McCumber *(Exec VP-Mktg, Digital & Brand Strategy)*
Jason Holzman *(Sr VP-Brand Creative)*
Heather Olander *(Sr VP-Alternative Programming Dept)*
Alex Sepiol *(Dir)*
Advertising Agencies:
filter Advertising
160 Pearl St 2nd Fl
New York, NY 10005
Tel.: (212) 248-3028

The Media Kitchen
160 Varick St
New York, NY 10013
Tel.: (212) 633-0080
Fax: (212) 633-0080
(Media Buying & Planning)

VAN VLIET MEDIA

Apt 6L 420 E 55th St
New York, NY 10022-5147
Tel.: (212) 486-6577
Fax: (212) 980-9826
Toll Free: (800) 722-7340
E-mail: vanvlietmedia@att.net
Web Site: www.vanvlietmedia.com
Approx. Number Employees: 3
Year Founded: 1975
Business Description:
Video & Hard Drive to Film Digitization; Film & Video Tape Distr; Educational Films & Entertainment Films for TV; Pre & Post Motion Picture Production & Video Consulting
S.I.C.: 7812; 7822
N.A.I.C.S.: 512110; 512120
Import Export
Media: 2-7-13
Distr.: Intl.; Natl.
Budget Set: Dec.
Brands & Products:
BEBELL

VERAZ NETWORKS, INC.

(Name Changed to Dialogic Inc.)

VERSTANDIG BROADCASTING

1820 Heritage Cener Way
Harrisonburg, VA 22801
Tel.: (540) 434-0331
E-mail: smyers@valleyradio.com
Web Site: www.valleyradio.com
Approx. Sls.: $15,100,000
Approx. Number Employees: 3
Business Description:
Radio Broadcasting Stations
S.I.C.: 4832; 5961
N.A.I.C.S.: 515112; 454113
Media: 20-22-23
Personnel:
Dennis Burchill *(Gen Mgr-Sls)*
Susanne Myers *(Gen Mgr)*
Bill Phipps *(Dir)*

VERSUS, L.P.

(Joint Venture of Comcast Corporation & General Electric Company)
2 Stamford Plz 281 Tresser Blvd
Stamford, CT 06901
Tel.: (203) 406-2500
Fax: (203) 406-2534
Web Site: www.versus.tv
Sales Range: $10-24.9 Million
Approx. Number Employees: 60
Business Description:
Cable Sports & Entertainment Network
S.I.C.: 4841
N.A.I.C.S.: 515210
Personnel:
Gavin Harvey *(Pres-Comcast)*
Marc Fein *(Exec VP-Programming & Bus Ops)*
Meier Raivich *(VP-Comm)*
Advertising Agency:
Concept Farm
43 W 24th St 5th Fl
New York, NY 10010
Tel.: (212) 463-9939
Fax: (212) 463-7032
2008 Tour de France

VIACOM, INC.

(Group of National Amusements, Inc.)
1515 Broadway
New York, NY 10036-8901
Tel.: (212) 258-6000
Fax: (212) 258-6464
E-mail: investor.relations@viacom.com
Web Site: www.viacom.com
Approx. Rev.: $9,337,000,000
Approx. Number Employees: 10,900
Year Founded: 1971
Business Description:
Television Network & Motion Picture Services
S.I.C.: 4841; 4833; 7812
N.A.I.C.S.: 515210; 512110; 515120
Advertising Expenditures: $869,000,000
Media: 2-7-8-9-10-11-13-14-15-23-24
Distr.: Intl.; Natl.
Budget Set: Aug.
Personnel:
Sumner M. Redstone *(Founder & Exec Chm)*
Shari E. Redstone *(Vice Chm)*
Philippe P. Dauman *(Pres & CEO)*
James W. Barge *(CFO & Exec VP)*
Michael Pickrum *(Exec VP & CFO)*
Thomas E. Dooley *(COO)*
David Kline *(CIO & Sr VP-Tech)*
Brad Grey *(CEO-Paramount Pictures Corp)*
Michael D. Fricklas *(Gen Counsel, Sec & Exec VP)*
George Nelson *(Treas & Sr VP)*
Wade Davis *(Exec VP-Strategy & Corp Dev)*
Carl D. Folta *(Exec VP-Corp Comm)*
Vicky Free *(Exec VP-Mktg-BET Networks)*
Scott Guthrie *(Exec VP-Sls & Acct Mgmt)*
Dede Lea *(Exec VP-Govt Affairs)*
Walter Levitt *(Exec VP-Mktg-Comedy Central)*
Denise White *(Exec VP-HR & Admin)*
Katherine Gill-Charest *(Sr VP & Controller)*
James Bombassei *(Sr VP- IR)*
Dominique Crosby *(Sr VP-Strategy & Bus Dev)*
Jay Kushner *(Sr VP-Tax & Fin-Intl)*
Henry T. A. Moniz *(Sr VP)*
Teryl Brown *(VP-Ad Sls-TV Land)*
Jeremy Zweig *(VP-Corp Comm)*
Tyriel Wright *(Sr Mgr-Digital Media & Analyst-Market Res)*
Brands & Products:
LOGO
Advertising Agency:
The1stMovement
1010 E Union St Ste 120
Pasadena, CA 91106
Tel.: (626) 689-4993
Fax: (626) 628-1991

VIDEO MONITORING SERVICES OF AMERICA, LP

1500 Broadway 6th Fl
New York, NY 10036-6902
Tel.: (212) 736-2010
Fax: (212) 329-5292
Web Site: www.vmsinfo.com
Approx. Number Employees: 250
Year Founded: 1996
Business Description:
Information Retrieval Services
S.I.C.: 7375
N.A.I.C.S.: 518111
Import Export
Advertising Expenditures: $1,000,000
Media: 2-7-10-13-18
Personnel:
David Stephens *(CEO)*
Laila Sayad *(CFO)*
Gerry Louw *(CIO)*
Roy McInnis *(Sr VP-Sls-News Monitoring, Measurement & Analysis)*
Michael Giovia *(VP-Sls-News Div)*
Brands & Products:
INSIGHT
KNOW BETTER
PRTRAK
QUICKVIEW
REALTIME
VMS
VMS BROADCASTCENTER
VOICETRAK
THE WORLD LEADER IN INTEGRATED MEDIA INTELLIGENCE.
Advertising Agency:
Stein Rogan + Partners
432 Park Ave S
New York, NY 10016-8013
Tel.: (212) 213-1112
Fax: (212) 779-7305

VIDEOTRON LTD.

(Sub. of Quebecor Media Inc.)
612 Saint Jacques Street
Montreal, QC H3C 4M8, Canada
Tel.: (514) 380-7000
Fax: (514) 380-1919
Toll Free: (800) 561-4248
Web Site: www.videotron.com
Approx. Rev.: $2,161,920,758
Approx. Number Employees: 5,670
Year Founded: 1991
Business Description:
Cable TV, Internet & Wireless Telephone Services
S.I.C.: 4841; 4812; 7375
N.A.I.C.S.: 515210; 517212; 518111
Advertising Expenditures: $17,800,000
Media: 2-4-7-8-9-10-13-18-19-20-21-22-23-24-25-26
Personnel:
Serge Gouin *(Chm)*
Robert T. Depatie *(Pres & CEO)*
Marie-Josee Marsan *(CFO & VP-Fin)*
Andre Gascon *(CIO & VP-Wireless Technologies, VP-Info Technologies)*
Isabelle Dessureault *(Pres-VOX & VP-Corp Affairs)*
Donald Lizotte *(Pres-Le SuperClub Videotron & VP-Retail Sls)*
Jean Novak *(Pres-Bus Svc)*
Marc Labelle *(Dir & Principal-Comm Corporatives)*
Manon Brouillette *(Exec VP-Strategy & Market Dev)*
Daniel Proulx *(Sr VP-Engrg)*
Michel Allard *(VP-Engrg & Tech Dev)*
Sylvain Brosseau *(VP-Customer Svc-Consumer Div)*
Eric Champagne *(VP-Mktg-Bus Solutions)*

Key to Media (For complete agency information see *The Advertising Red Books-Agencies* edition):
1. Bus. Publs. 2. Cable T.V. 3. Catalogs & Directories. 4. Co-op Adv. 5. Consumer Mags. 6. D.M. to Bus. Estab.7. D.M. to Consumers 8. Daily Newsp. 9. Exhibits/Trade Shows 10. Foreign 11. Infomercial 12. Internet Adv.13. Multimedia 14. Network Radio 15. Network T.V. 16. Newsp. Distr. Mags. 17. Other 18. Outdoor (Posters, Transit) 19. Point of Purchase20. Premiums, Novelties 21. Product Samples 22. Special Events Mktg. 23. Spot Radio 24. Spot T.V. 25. Weekly Newsp. 26. Yellow Page Adv.

Videotron Ltd. — (Continued)

Myrianne Collin *(VP-Mktg-Consumer Sector)*
Serge Legris *(VP-Engrg-Wireless Access)*
Roger Martel *(VP-Internal Audit)*
Pierre Roy Poretta *(VP-IP Tech)*
Normand Vachon *(VP-HR)*
Denis Veilleux *(VP-Customer Svc, Pricing & Ops Support & Bus Solutions)*
Brigitte Hebert *(Gen Mgr)*

VOICE OF PROPHECY, INC.

101 W Cochran St
Simi Valley, CA 93065-6217
Tel.: (805) 955-7611
Fax: (805) 955-7703
E-mail: gospel@vop.com
Web Site: www.vop.com
Sales Range: $1-9.9 Million
Approx. Number Employees: 30
Year Founded: 1929
Business Description:
Broadcaster & Bible Study Courses
S.I.C.: 4833; 4832
N.A.I.C.S.: 515120; 515112
Advertising Expenditures: $2,600,000
Media: 6-8-10-20-23
Distr.: Direct to Consumer; Natl.
Budget Set: Aug.
Personnel:
Jim Gilley *(Chm)*
Fred Kinsey *(Dir-Speakers)*
Brands & Products:
KINGS HERALDS
VOICE OF PROPHECY
Advertising Agency:
AMS Agency
101 W Cochran St
Simi Valley, CA 93065
Tel.: (805) 955-7606

VULCAN PRODUCTIONS INC.

(Div. of Vulcan Inc.)
505 5th Ave S Ste 900
Seattle, WA 98104-3821
Tel.: (206) 342-2000
Tel.: (206) 342-2277
Fax: (206) 342-3277
E-mail: info@vulcan.com
Web Site:
www.vulcanproductions.com
Approx. Number Employees: 150
Business Description:
Independent Film Production
S.I.C.: 7812; 6371
N.A.I.C.S.: 512110; 525990
Export
Advertising Expenditures: $1,000,000
Media: 7-11
Personnel:
Paul G. Allen *(Founder & Chm)*
Jody Allen Patton *(Pres)*
Bonnie Benjamin-Phariss *(Dir-Documentary Productions)*

WABC-TV INC.

(Sub. of ABC Owned Television Stations)
7 Lincoln Sq
New York, NY 10023-5998
Tel.: (212) 456-7000
Web Site: www.7online.com
Sales Range: $75-99.9 Million
Business Description:
Television Programming
S.I.C.: 4833; 4832
N.A.I.C.S.: 515120; 515112
Media: 8-11-13-14-15-24
Personnel:
J. David Davis *(Pres & Gen Mgr)*
Debra O'Connell *(Sr VP-Mktg & Bus Devel)*
Ken Plotnik *(VP & Dir-News)*
Scott Simensky *(Gen Mgr-Sls)*

WACKY WORLD STUDIOS, LLC

148 E Douglas Rd
Oldsmar, FL 34677-2939
Tel.: (813) 818-8277
Fax: (813) 818-8396
Web Site: www.wackworld.tv
Approx. Number Employees: 27
Business Description:
Animation Studio
S.I.C.: 7819; 7812
N.A.I.C.S.: 512191; 512110
Media: 6
Personnel:
Bruce Barry *(Founder & Pres)*

WALDEN MEDIA, LLC

(Sub. of Anschutz Film Group, LLC)
1888 Century Park E 14th Fl
Los Angeles, CA 90067
Tel.: (310) 887-1000
Fax: (310) 887-1001
Web Site: www.walden.com
Approx. Number Employees: 60
Year Founded: 1997
Business Description:
Motion Picture & Video Production; Book Publisher
S.I.C.: 7812; 2731
N.A.I.C.S.: 512110; 511130
Media: 13-17-22
Personnel:
Michael Flaherty *(Co-Founder & Pres)*
Michael Bostick *(CEO)*
Francis Xavier Flaherty, Jr. *(Publr-Walden Pond & Exec VP)*
Debbie Kovacs *(Sr VP & Editorial Dir-Walden Pond Press)*

THE WALT DISNEY COMPANY

500 S Buena Vista St
Burbank, CA 91521-0001
Tel.: (818) 560-1000
Fax: (818) 560-1930
E-mail: TWDC.Corp.Communications@disney.com
Web Site: disney.go.com
Approx. Rev.: $38,063,000,000
Approx. Number Employees: 149,000
Year Founded: 1923
Business Description:
Motion Pictures, Radio & Television Programs Producer; Outdoor Recreation, Consumer Products & Educational Media Services
S.I.C.: 7996; 4832; 4833; 7812
N.A.I.C.S.: 713110; 512110; 515111; 515120
Advertising Expenditures: $2,600,000,000
Media: 1-3-6-9-10-11-13-14-15-16-18-19-20-22-23-24-25
Personnel:
John E. Pepper, Jr. *(Chm)*
Robert A. Iger *(Pres & CEO)*
James A. Rasulo *(CFO & Sr Exec VP)*
Mary Jayne Parker *(Chief HR Officer & Exec VP)*
Sean Bailey *(Pres-Motion Picture Production-Walt Disney Studios)*
Carolina Lightcap *(Pres-Channels-Worldwide)*
Alan N. Braverman *(Gen Counsel, Sec & Exec VP)*
Christine M. McCarthy *(Treas, Exec VP-Real Estate & Fin)*
Suzanne Murphy *(VP & Publr-Books & Disney Publ-Worldwide)*
Lowell Singer *(Sr VP-IR)*
Rita Ferro *(Exec VP-Disney Media Sls & Mktg)*
Kevin A. Mayer *(Exec VP-Corp Strategy, Bus Dev & Tech)*
Zenia Mucha *(Exec VP-Corp Comm)*
Preston Padden *(Exec VP-Govt Relations)*
Tricia Wilber *(Exec VP-Ad Sls & Mktg)*
Peter Fitton *(Sr VP-Ad Sls & Promos-EMEA)*
Ronald L. Iden *(Sr VP-Security)*
Kathryn Kranhold *(Sr VP-Corp Comm)*
Adam Sanderson *(Sr VP-Franchise Mgmt-Disney & ABC Television Grp)*
Brent Woodford *(Sr VP-Plng & Control)*
Aparna Pande *(VP & Gen Mgr-US Magazines)*
Tendo Nagenda *(VP-Production-Walt Disney Studios Motion Pictures)*
Chris M Williams *(Gen Mgr-T180 Studios)*
Tim Claxton *(Dir-Product Mgmt)*
Samantha Garry *(Dir-Digital Mktg & Publicity)*
Jim Mollica *(Dir-New Media-Global)*
Jenny Whitlock *(Dir-Mktg Strategy & Comm)*
Jeff Nuzzi *(Sr Mgr)*
Teresa Martin *(Program Mgr-Mktg-CRM/CMR)*
Connie Chen *(Mgr-Mktg Strategy Reg)*
Julius Harper *(Mgr-Product Strategy-Disney XD Digital Media)*
Jessica Plisek *(Mgr-New Product Mgmt)*
Brands & Products:
ADVENTURELAND
ASTRO ORBITER
AUDIO-ANIMATRONICS
BEAR IN THE BIG BLUE HOUSE
BLIZZARD BEACH
DARKWING DUCK
THE DISNEY CHANNEL
DISNEY CRUISE LINE
DISNEY PRESS
DISNEYLAND
DISNEY'S ACTIVITY CENTER
DONALD DUCK
THE DUCKS
ESPN ZONE
EXTRATERRORESTRIAL ALIEN ENCOUNTER
FANTASYLAND
FRONTIERLAND
GONZO
GOOFY
HOLLYWOOD RECORDS
IMAGINEERING
INNOVENTIONS
JUST FOR KIDS
KERMIT THE FROG
LAKE BUENA VISTA
THE LION KING
LYRIC STREET RECORDS
MAGIC KINGDOM
MAIN STREET, U.S.A.
MAMMOTH RECORDS
MDISNEY
MICKEY MOUSE
MICKEY'S TOONTOWN
MINNIE MOUSE
MISS PIGGY
MOUSE WORKS
MUPPETS
MY FIRST READ-ALONG
NEW ORLEAN'S SQUARE
PIXIE DUST
SILLY SYMPHONY
SPACE MOUNTAIN
SPECTROMAGIC
STARWAVE MOBILE
TALE SPIN
TEAMBOAT SPRINGS
TOMORROWLAND
TOONTOWN
TOUCHSTONE
WALT DISNEY
WALT DISNEY COMICS
WALT DISNEY MASTERPIECE COLLECTION
WALT DISNEY RECORDS
WALT DISNEY WORLD
Advertising Agencies:
ad 2-one
246 Westminster Bridge Rd
London, SE1 7PD, United Kingdom
Tel.: (44) 207 401 0333
Fax: (44) 207 4010366

Almighty
300 Western Ave
Boston, MA 02134
Tel.: (617) 782-1511
Fax: (617) 782-1611

The Designory
211 E Ocean Blvd Ste 100
Long Beach, CA 90802-4850
Tel.: (562) 624-0200
Fax: (562) 491-0140

Digitas Inc.
33 Arch St
Boston, MA 02110
Tel.: (617) 867-1000
Fax: (617) 867-1111

interTrend Communications, Inc.
555 E Ocean Blvd
Long Beach, CA 90802-5003
Tel.: (562) 733-1888
Fax: (562) 733-1889

ISM
745 Boylston St 7th Fl
Boston, MA 02116
Tel.: (617) 353-1822
Fax: (617) 266-1890

The Kaplan Thaler Group
825 8th Ave 34th Fl
New York, NY 10019
Tel.: (212) 474-5000
Fax: (212) 474-5702

Ketchum
(Part of Omnicom)
1285 Ave of the Americas
New York, NY 10019
Tel.: (646) 935-3900
Fax: (646) 935-4482

Lapiz

Key to Media (For complete agency information see *The Advertising Red Books-Agencies* edition):
1. Bus. Publs. 2. Cable T.V. 3. Catalogs & Directories. 4. Co-op Adv. 5. Consumer Mags. 6. D.M. to Bus. Estab.7. D.M. to Consumers 8. Daily Newsp. 9. Exhibits/Trade Shows 10. Foreign 11. Infomercial 12. Internet Adv.13. Multimedia 14. Network Radio 15. Network T.V. 16. Newsp. Distr. Mags. 17. Other 18. Outdoor (Posters, Transit) 19. Point of Purchase20. Premiums, Novelties 21. Product Samples 22. Special Events Mktg. 23. Spot Radio 24. Spot T.V. 25. Weekly Newsp. 26. Yellow Page Adv.

35 W Wacker Dr 12th Fl
Chicago, IL 60601
Tel.: (312) 220-5000
Fax: (312) 220-6212

Starcom USA
35 W Wacker Dr
Chicago, IL 60601
Tel.: (312) 220-3535
Fax: (312) 220-6530
Alice in Wonderland (Media Agency)

ZenithOptimedia
1-4/F900 Huai Hai Zhong Road
Shanghai, China
Tel.: (86) 21 6133 8399
Fax: (86) 21 6133 8398
(Disney English)

WARNER BROS. ANIMATION INC.

(Sub. of Warner Bros. Entertainment Inc.)
4000 Warner Blvd
Burbank, CA 91522
Tel.: (818) 977-8700
Fax: (818) 977-8070
Web Site: www.warnerbros.com
Approx. Sls.: $45,000,000
Approx. Number Employees: 10,000
Business Description:
Movie & TV Animation Services
S.I.C.: 7812
N.A.I.C.S.: 512110
Media: 2-3-6-9-20-23-24-25
Distr.: Intl.; Natl.
Personnel:
Sam Register *(Pres & Exec VP-Creative Affairs)*
Ed Adams *(Sr VP-Bus, Legal Affairs & Admin)*
Peter Girardi *(Sr VP-Series & Alternative Animation)*
Anthony Eastman *(Mgr-CRM & Loyalty)*
Brands & Products:
HANNA-BARBERA

WARNER BROS. ENTERTAINMENT INC.

(Sub. of Time Warner Inc.)
4000 Warner Blvd
Burbank, CA 91522
Tel.: (818) 954-6000
Web Site: www.warnerbros.com
Sales Range: $5-14.9 Billion
Approx. Number Employees: 9
Business Description:
Holding Company
S.I.C.: 6719; 4841; 7812; 7822; 7829
N.A.I.C.S.: 551112; 512110; 512120; 512199; 515210
Personnel:
Barry M. Meyer *(Chm & CEO)*
Alan F. Horn *(Pres & COO)*
Edward A. Romano *(CFO & Exec VP)*
Chris Cookson *(Pres-Tech Ops)*
Dan Fellman *(Pres-Domestic Distr-Warner Bros)*
Doug Frank *(Pres-Music Ops-Warner Bros Pictures)*
Jon Gilbert *(Pres-Studio Facilities)*
Simon Kenney *(Pres-Digital Distr)*
Sue Kroll *(Pres-Worldwide Mktg-Warner Bro)*
Veronika Kwan-Rubinek *(Pres-Distr)*
Hilary Estey McLoughlin *(Pres-Telepictures Productions)*
Diane Nelson *(Pres-DC Entertainment)*
Millard Ochs *(Pres-Intl Cinemas)*
Steve Papazian *(Pres-Worldwide Physical Production)*
Jeff Robinov *(Pres-Warner Bros Pictures Grp)*
Sander Schwartz *(Pres-Animation)*
Steven Spira *(Pres-Worldwide Bus Affairs)*
Susan Fleishman *(Exec VP-Corp Comm & Pub Affairs)*
Gary Credle *(Exec VP-Admin & Studio Ops)*
Richard J. Fox *(Exec VP-Intl)*
Lynne Frank *(Exec VP-Intl Mktg)*
Thomas Ballard *(Sr VP-Digital Games)*
Amit Desai *(Sr VP-Franchise Mgmt-DC Entertainment)*
Sharan Magnuson *(Sr VP-Publicity-Worldwide Television Mktg)*
Dean Marks *(Sr VP-Intellectual Property)*
Paul McGuire *(Sr VP-Corp Comm-Worldwide)*
Tammy Golihew *(VP-Publicity)*
Trevor Albery *(Head-Anti-Piracy-EMEA)*
Giulia Erickson *(Exec Dir-Mktg)*
Matt Meeks *(Dir-Audience Dev)*
Steve Mellano *(Dir-Market Res)*
Stacy Parr *(Dir-Mktg, Digital Mktg & Production Svcs)*
Gregory Salter *(Dir-Corp Bus Dev & Strategy)*
Sharmistha Chatterjee *(Mgr-Mktg)*
Whitney Rosenthal *(Mgr-Interactive Production)*
Bridget Groller *(Specialist-Mktg)*
Kristal Harwood *(Strategist-Social Media Mktg)*
Brittany Cohen *(Coord-Mktg)*
Advertising Agencies:
AvatarLabs
5500 Balboa Blvd
Encino, CA 91316
Tel.: (818) 784-2200
Fax: (818) 784-2204

Omnicom Media Group
195 Broadway
New York, NY 10007
Tel.: (212) 590-7100
Media Planning & Buying
New Line Cinemas
Time Warner Video

WARNER HOME VIDEO INC.

(Sub. of Warner Bros. Home Entertainment Group)
4000 Warner Blvd
Burbank, CA 91522
Tel.: (818) 954-6000
Fax: (818) 977-7333
E-mail: info@warnervideo.com
Web Site: www.warnervideo.com
Sales Range: $100-124.9 Million
Business Description:
Video Distr
S.I.C.: 7822
N.A.I.C.S.: 512120
Personnel:
Ronald Sanders *(Pres)*
Mark Horak *(Pres-North America)*
Dan Miron *(Exec VP-Worldwide Supply Chain Mgmt)*
Dorinda Marticorena *(Sr VP-High Definition-Worldwide)*
Richard Siao *(Sr VP-Sls Plng & Ops)*
Mike Takac *(Sr VP-Domestic Sls)*
Allison Ceppi *(Dir-Mktg)*
Dennis Chung *(Dir-Demand Plng & Initial Distr)*
Kathi Kakehashi *(Dir-Creative Svcs)*
Jack Walker *(Dir-Product Online Film Mktg-Global)*
Pamela Duell *(Mgr-Creative Adv-Theatrical New Release)*
Advertising Agency:
Vertical Marketing Network LLC
15147 Woodlawn Ave
Tustin, CA 92780
Tel.: (714) 258-2400, ext. 420
Fax: (714) 258-2409

WASHINGTON EDUCATIONAL TELECOMMUNICATIONS ASSOCIATION

(d/b/a WETA)
2775 S Quincy St
Arlington, VA 22206
Tel.: (703) 998-2600
Fax: (703) 998-2034
E-mail: info@weta.org
Web Site: www.weta.org
Sales Range: $50-74.9 Million
Approx. Number Employees: 194
Business Description:
Television & Radio Broadcasting Stations
S.I.C.: 4833; 4832
N.A.I.C.S.: 515120; 515112
Media: 7-8-10-13-18-22-23-24
Personnel:
Sharon Percy Rockefeller *(Pres & CEO)*
Joseph B. Bruns *(COO)*
Dalton Delan *(Chief Programming Officer & Exec VP)*
Polly Povejsil Heath *(CFO, Corp Treas & Sr VP)*

WBBB-FM

(Unit of Curtis Media Group)
3012 Highwoods Blvd Ste 200
Raleigh, NC 27604
Tel.: (919) 790-9392
Fax: (919) 790-8369
Toll Free: (800) 272-6404
Web Site: www.96rockonline.com
Approx. Number Employees: 22
Business Description:
Radio Broadcasting Station
S.I.C.: 4832
N.A.I.C.S.: 515112
Media: 20-22-23
Personnel:
Michael Hartel *(Gen Mgr)*

WBNS TELEVISION

(Holding of The Dispatch Broadcast Group)
770 Twin Rivers Dr
Columbus, OH 43215-1127
Tel.: (614) 460-3700
Web Site: www.wbns10tv.com
Approx. Number Employees: 100
Year Founded: 1949
Business Description:
Television & Radio Broadcasting Services
S.I.C.: 4833
N.A.I.C.S.: 515120
Media: 10-18-23-24
Personnel:
Tom Griesdorn *(Pres & Gen Mgr)*
Chuck DeVendra *(Dir-Sls)*
Patty Williams *(Dir-Fin)*
Frank Willson *(Dir-Mktg)*
Holly Beardsley *(Mgr-Sls)*

WBOC INC.

(Sub. of Draper Holdings Business Trust)
1729 N Salisbury Blvd
Salisbury, MD 21801
Tel.: (410) 749-1111
Fax: (410) 749-2361
E-mail: wboc@wboc.com
Web Site: www.wboc.com
Approx. Rev.: $9,400,000
Approx. Number Employees: 100
Business Description:
Television Broadcasting Stations
S.I.C.: 4833
N.A.I.C.S.: 515120
Media: 20-22-24
Personnel:
Thomas Draper *(Chm-Owner)*
Laura Baker *(COO & VP)*

WCHS-TV

(Sub. of Sinclair Television Group, Inc.)
1301 Piedmont Rd
Charleston, WV 25301-1426
Mailing Address:
PO Box 11138
Charleston, WV 25339-1138
Tel.: (304) 346-5358
Fax: (304) 345-1849
E-mail: info@wchstv.com
Web Site: www.wchstv.com
Sales Range: $25-49.9 Million
Approx. Number Employees: 105
Year Founded: 1954
Business Description:
Television Broadcasting Stations
S.I.C.: 4833
N.A.I.C.S.: 515120
Media: 13-18-23-24
Personnel:
Harold Cooper *(Mgr-Gen Sls)*

WCPO-TV

(Sub. of The E.W. Scripps Company)
1720 Gilbert Ave
Cincinnati, OH 45202
Tel.: (513) 721-9900
Fax: (513) 721-7717
E-mail: news@wcpo.com
Web Site: www.wcpo.com
Sales Range: $50-74.9 Million
Approx. Number Employees: 180
Business Description:
Television Broadcasting Station
S.I.C.: 4833
N.A.I.C.S.: 515120
Media: 18-23-24
Personnel:
Steve Thaxton *(VP & Gen Mgr)*
Bill Bullock *(Dir-New Media)*
Denise Eck *(Dir-Asst News)*
Bob Morford *(Dir-News)*
Mona Morrow *(Dir-Pub Affairs)*
Dom Nardo *(Dir-Mktg & Creative Svcs)*

WCWJ-TV

(Unit of Nexstar Broadcasting, Inc.)
9117 Hogan Rd
Jacksonville, FL 32216-4647
Mailing Address:
PO Box 17000

Key to Media (For complete agency information see *The Advertising Red Books-Agencies* edition):
1. Bus. Publs. 2. Cable T.V. 3. Catalogs & Directories. 4. Co-op Adv. 5. Consumer Mags. 6. D.M. to Bus. Estab.7. D.M. to Consumers
8. Daily Newsp. 9. Exhibits/Trade Shows 10. Foreign 11. Infomercial 12. Internet Adv.13. Multimedia 14. Network Radio
15. Network T.V. 16. Newsp. Distr. Mags. 17. Other 18. Outdoor (Posters, Transit) 19. Point of Purchase20. Premiums, Novelties
21. Product Samples 22. Special Events Mktg. 23. Spot Radio 24. Spot T.V. 25. Weekly Newsp. 26. Yellow Page Adv.

WCWJ-TV — (Continued)

Jacksonville, FL 32245-7000
Tel.: (904) 641-1700
Fax: (904) 642-7201
Web Site: www.yourjax.com
E-Mail For Key Personnel:
Marketing Director: JHalfon@wjwb.com
Sales Director: TBecker@wjwb.com
Year Founded: 1966
Business Description:
Television Broadcasting Station
S.I.C.: 4833
N.A.I.C.S.: 515120
Advertising Expenditures: $600,000
Media: 3-7-13-18-20-22-23
Distr.: Direct to Consumer; Reg.
Personnel:
Marc Hefner *(VP & Gen Mgr)*
Mark Marshman *(Head-Engrg)*
Dave Hall *(Dir-Creative Svcs)*
Gray Soapes *(Mgr-Local Sls)*
Advertising Agency:
WideGroup Interactive
9701 Wilshire Blvd Ste 1000
Beverly Hills, CA 90212
Tel.: (818) 344-9703

WDIO-TV
(Sub. of Hubbard Broadcasting, Inc.)
10 Observation Rd
Duluth, MN 55811
Tel.: (218) 727-6864
Fax: (218) 727-4415
E-mail: news@wdio.com
Web Site: www.wdio.com
Approx. Number Employees: 60
Business Description:
Television Broadcasting Station
S.I.C.: 4833
N.A.I.C.S.: 515120
Media: 24
Personnel:
George Couture *(VP & Gen Mgr)*
Steve Goodspeed *(Dir-News)*
David Poirier *(Dir-Program)*
Advertising Agency:
Petry Television Inc.
110 Plz
New York, NY 10119-3178
Tel.: (212) 230-5600
Fax: (212) 230-5608

THE WEATHER CHANNEL INC.
(Joint Venture of Comcast Corporation, General Electric Company, The Blackstone Group L.P. & Bain Capital, LLC)
300 Interstate N Pkwy SE
Atlanta, GA 30339-2403
Tel.: (770) 226-0000
Fax: (770) 226-2930
Web Site: www.weather.com
Sales Range: $200-249.9 Million
Approx. Number Employees: 800
Year Founded: 1982
Business Description:
Live Weather Forecasting for Cable Television; Owned by General Electric Company, by Vivendi S.A., by Bain Capital, LLC & by The Blackstone Group L.P.
S.I.C.: 4841
N.A.I.C.S.: 515210
Media: 2-3-6-7-8-9-13-17-18-20-23
Distr.: Natl.
Personnel:
Michael J. Kelly *(Pres & CEO)*
Jerry Elliott *(CFO & Chief Admin Officer)*
Brian Shield *(CIO & Exec VP)*
Paul Iaffaldano *(Exec VP & Gen Mgr-TWC Media Solutions Grp)*
Bob Walker *(Exec VP & Gen Mgr-Networks)*
Shirley Powell *(Exec VP-Corp Comm)*
Lynn Brindell *(Sr VP-Mktg)*
Sheila Buckley *(Sr VP-Digital Ad Sls)*
BobDeichert *(Sr VP-Digital Adv Ops)*
Michael Dingley *(Sr VP-Content & Dev)*
Indra K. Venkat *(Sr VP-Res)*
Barbara Brown *(VP-Adv Sls-Detroit & Mgr-Reg)*
Bill Drolet *(VP-Digital Ad Sls)*
Kaz Oplustil *(VP-Sls-Eastern Reg)*
Sheri Ferguson *(Dir-Adv Sales)*
Dawn Fiore *(Dir-Adv Sls-New York)*
David Blumenthal *(Dir-PR)*
Brands & Products:
THE WEATHER CHANNEL
WEATHER.COM
Advertising Agency:
Media Storm LLC
99 Washington St
South Norwalk, CT 06854
Tel.: (203) 852-8001
Fax: (203) 852-5592

WEIGEL BROADCASTING CO.
(d/b/a WCIU TV Channel 26)
26 N Halsted St
Chicago, IL 60661
Tel.: (312) 705-2600
Fax: (312) 705-2656
Web Site: www.wciu.com
Approx. Number Employees: 100
Business Description:
Television Broadcasting Stations
S.I.C.: 4833
N.A.I.C.S.: 515120
Media: 24
Personnel:
Norman Shapiro *(Pres)*
Harvey Moshman *(Exec Producer-Program Dev)*
Brands & Products:
TELEVISION STATION

WEQR-FM
(Unit of Curtis Media Group)
2581 US Hwy 70 W
Goldsboro, NC 27530
Tel.: (919) 736-1150
Fax: (919) 736-3876
Web Site: www.wgbr.com
Approx. Number Employees: 400
Business Description:
Radio Broadcasting Station
S.I.C.: 4832
N.A.I.C.S.: 515112
Media: 17-20-22-23
Personnel:
Bill Johnston *(Gen Mgr)*

WESTWOOD ONE, INC.
1166 Ave of the Americas
New York, NY 10036
Tel.: (212) 641-2000
Fax: (212) 641-2122
E-mail: wonwebmaster@westwoodone.com
Web Site: www.westwoodone.com
E-Mail For Key Personnel:
Marketing Director: PSessa@westwoodone.com
Approx. Rev.: $362,546,000
Approx. Number Employees: 1,500
Year Founded: 1976
Business Description:
Radio Programs Including News, Sports, Music, Talk, Entertainment Programs, Features, Live Events, 24-Hour Formats & Shadow Broadcast Services
S.I.C.: 3663; 4832; 7389; 7999
N.A.I.C.S.: 334220; 512290; 515111; 713990
Export
Advertising Expenditures: $2,158,000
Media: 2-7-10-13-14-20-22
Distr.: Intl.; Natl.
Personnel:
Mark R. Stone *(Vice Chm)*
Roderick M. Sherwood, III *(Pres & CFO)*
Luis Rodriguez *(CIO)*
David Hillman *(Chief Admin Officer, Gen Counsel & Sec & Ex VP-Bus Affairs)*
Edward A. Mammone *(Principal Acctg Officer & Sr VP-Fin)*
Steven Kalin *(Pres/COO-Metro Networks Traffic Div)*
Jonathan S. Marshall *(Pres/Gen Mgr-Television & Exec VP-Strategic Bus Dev)*
Fred Bennett *(Pres/ Gen Mgr-Metro Television)*
Dennis Green *(Exec VP-Affiliate Sls)*
Stephen Chessare *(Sr VP-Network Radio Sales)*
Richard J. Kosinski *(Sr VP & Chief Digital Officer)*
Max Krasny *(Sr VP-Entertainment)*
Beth Robinson *(Sr VP-Engrg & Ops)*
Bart Tessler *(Sr VP-News & Talk Programming)*
Terry Schoppmann *(VP & Mgr-New York)*
Alan Gaynor *(VP-HR)*
Peter Sessa *(VP-Mktg & Comm)*
Mark Wilson *(VP-Entertainment Div)*
Michael Schreck *(Dir-Sports Sls)*
Brands & Products:
WESTWOOD ONE

WEWS-TV
(Sub. of The E.W. Scripps Company)
3001 Euclid Ave
Cleveland, OH 44115-2516
Tel.: (216) 431-5555
Fax: (216) 361-1762
E-mail: feedback5@newsnet5.com
Web Site: www.newsnet5.com
Sales Range: $50-74.9 Million
Approx. Number Employees: 100
Business Description:
Television Broadcasting
S.I.C.: 4833
N.A.I.C.S.: 515120
Media: 3-22-23-24
Personnel:
Sam Rosenwasser *(VP & Gen Mgr)*
Jill Manuel *(Dir-News)*

WFAA-TV
(Sub. of WFAA Holdings, Inc.)
606 Young St
Dallas, TX 75202
Tel.: (214) 748-9631
Fax: (214) 977-6585
Web Site: www.wfaa.com
Sales Range: $100-124.9 Million
Approx. Number Employees: 400
Business Description:
Television Broadcasting
S.I.C.: 4833; 7313
N.A.I.C.S.: 515120; 541840
Media: 8-13-15
Personnel:
Mike Devlin *(Pres & Gen Mgr)*
David Walther *(Dir-Program)*
Doug Boehner *(Mgr-Ops)*

WFOR-TV
(Unit of CBS Television Stations Inc.)
8900 NW 18th Ter
Miami, FL 33172
Tel.: (305) 591-4444
Fax: (305) 639-4448
E-mail: newsfor@wfor.cbs.com
Web Site: www.wfor.com
Approx. Number Employees: 400
Year Founded: 1967
Business Description:
Television Broadcasting Services
S.I.C.: 4833
N.A.I.C.S.: 515120
Media: 7-9-18-20-23-24
Distr.: Reg.
Budget Set: Nov.
Personnel:
Cesar Aldama *(Dir-News)*
Judy Flook *(Dir-Design)*
Lee Zimmerman *(Dir-Commun)*
Amber Statler-Matthews *(Mgr-Special Projects)*

WFTS-TV
(Sub. of The E.W. Scripps Company)
(d/b/a Tampa Bay Television, Inc.)
4045 N Himes Ave
Tampa, FL 33607-6651
Tel.: (813) 354-2828
Fax: (813) 870-2828
Toll Free: (800) 920-2828
E-mail: newstips@wfts.com
Web Site: www.wfts.com
Sales Range: $50-74.9 Million
Approx. Number Employees: 200
Year Founded: 1981
Business Description:
Television Station
S.I.C.: 4833
N.A.I.C.S.: 515120
Media: 24

WGBR-AM
(Unit of Curtis Media Group)
2581 US 70 W
Goldsboro, NC 27530-1934
Mailing Address:
PO Box 207
Goldsboro, NC 27533-0207
Tel.: (919) 734-3336
Tel.: (919) 736-1150
Fax: (919) 736-3876
E-mail: waynecounty@curtismedia.com
Web Site: www.wgbr.com
Approx. Number Employees: 20
Business Description:
Radio Broadcasting Station
S.I.C.: 4832
N.A.I.C.S.: 515112
Media: 20-22-23
Personnel:
Bill Johnston *(Gen Mgr)*

Key to Media (For complete agency information see *The Advertising Red Books-Agencies* edition):
1. Bus. Publs. 2. Cable T.V. 3. Catalogs & Directories. 4. Co-op Adv. 5. Consumer Mags. 6. D.M. to Bus. Estab.7. D.M. to Consumers
8. Daily Newsp. 9. Exhibits/Trade Shows 10. Foreign 11. Infomercial 12. Internet Adv.13. Multimedia 14. Network Radio
15. Network T.V. 16. Newsp. Distr. Mags. 17. Other 18. Outdoor (Posters, Transit) 19. Point of Purchase20. Premiums, Novelties
21. Product Samples 22. Special Events Mktg. 23. Spot Radio 24. Spot T.V. 25. Weekly Newsp. 26. Yellow Page Adv.

WGME, INC.
(Sub. of Sinclair Television Group, Inc.)
1335 Washington Ave
Portland, ME 04103-3638
Tel.: (207) 797-1313
Fax: (207) 878-3505
E-mail: tvmail@wgme.com
Web Site: www.wgme.com
Sales Range: $25-49.9 Million
Approx. Number Employees: 85
Business Description:
Television Station
S.I.C.: 4833
N.A.I.C.S.: 515120
Media: 23
Personnel:
Tom Humpage *(Gen Mgr)*
Dave Eid *(Dir-Sports)*

WHAM-TV
(Unit of Newport Television LLC)
4225 W Henrietta Rd
Rochester, NY 14623
Tel.: (585) 334-8700
Fax: (585) 334-8719
E-mail: ddiprosa@13wham.com
Web Site: www.13wham.com
Approx. Number Employees: 105
Business Description:
Television Broadcasting Station
S.I.C.: 4833
N.A.I.C.S.: 515120
Media: 9-13-23-24-25
Personnel:
Chuck Samuel *(VP & Gen Mgr)*
David DiProsa *(Dir-Sls)*
Matt Malyn *(Dir-News)*
Jeff Starkweather *(Dir-Mktg)*

WHBF-TV
(Unit of Citadel Communications Company, Ltd.)
231 18th St
Rock Island, IL 61201
Tel.: (309) 786-5441
Fax: (309) 788-4975
E-mail: newsroom@cbs4qc.com
Web Site: www.cbs4qc.com
Year Founded: 1950
Business Description:
Television Broadcasting Station
S.I.C.: 4833
N.A.I.C.S.: 515120
Media: 1-8-15
Personnel:
Marshall Porter *(Gen Mgr)*
Heather Voudrie *(Dir-News)*
Sarah Gramenz *(Bus Mgr)*
Dan Englund *(Sls Mgr-Local)*
Angie Moye *(Sls Mgr-Natl)*
Barb Coffin *(Mgr-Traffic)*
Patty Gilbert *(Mgr-Promo)*

WHEC-TV LLC
(Sub. of Hubbard Broadcasting, Inc.)
191 E Ave
Rochester, NY 14604-2605
Tel.: (585) 546-5670
Fax: (585) 454-7433
E-mail: news@watc.com
Web Site: www.10nbc.com
Approx. Number Employees: 130
Business Description:
Television Station
S.I.C.: 4899; 4833
N.A.I.C.S.: 517410; 515120
Media: 24
Personnel:
Derek Dalton *(VP & Gen Mgr)*
Lauren Burruto *(Gen Mgr-Sls)*

WHIT-TV & WWVR RADIO
(Div. of Emmis Indiana Broadcasting, L.P.)
918 Ohio St
Terre Haute, IN 47808-1486
Tel.: (812) 232-9481
Fax: (812) 234-0089
E-mail: hi99@wthi.emmis.com
Web Site: www.wwvr.net
Sales Range: $10-24.9 Million
Approx. Number Employees: 21
Business Description:
Radio Broadcasting Services
S.I.C.: 4832
N.A.I.C.S.: 515112
Media: 13-18-20-22-23
Personnel:
James Conner *(Mgr-Station)*

WHYY INC.
150 N 6th St
Philadelphia, PA 19106-1521
Tel.: (215) 351-1200
Fax: (215) 351-1211
E-mail: info@whyy.org
Web Site: www.whyy.org
Sales Range: $100-124.9 Million
Approx. Number Employees: 200
Year Founded: 1954
Business Description:
Radio & Television Broadcasting Stations
S.I.C.: 4832; 4833
N.A.I.C.S.: 515112; 515120
Import Export
Media: 7-8-13-18-20
Personnel:
William J. Marrazzo *(Pres & CEO)*
Kyra G. McGrath *(COO & Exec VP)*
William J. Weber *(VP-Tech & Engrg Admin)*

WIBW-AM
(Unit of Kansas Radio Networks)
1210 SW Executive Dr
Topeka, KS 66615
Tel.: (785) 228-3456
Fax: (785) 272-7282
Web Site: www.am580wibw.com
Business Description:
Radio Broadcasting Services
S.I.C.: 4832
N.A.I.C.S.: 515112; 515111
Media: 20-22-23
Personnel:
Kelly Lenz *(Dir-Agriculture)*
Dan Lindquist *(Dir-Client Mktg Svcs & Certified Radio Mktg Consultant)*
Liz Montano *(Dir-News)*

WIBW-FM
(Unit of Kansas Radio Networks)
1210 SW Executive Dr
Topeka, KS 66615-3850
Tel.: (785) 272-3456
Fax: (785) 228-7282
Web Site: www.94country.com
Approx. Number Employees: 45
Business Description:
Radio Broadcasting Services
S.I.C.: 4832
N.A.I.C.S.: 515112; 515111
Media: 20-22-23
Personnel:
Dan Linquist *(Dir-Client Svcs)*

WICD-TV
(Sub. of Sinclair Television Group, Inc.)
250 S Country Fair Dr
Champaign, IL 61821-2920
Tel.: (217) 351-8500
Fax: (217) 351-6056
E-mail: sales@wicd15.com
Web Site: www.wicd15.com
E-Mail For Key Personnel:
Sales Director: sales@wicd15.com
Sales Range: $10-24.9 Million
Approx. Number Employees: 53
Year Founded: 1967
Business Description:
Television Station
S.I.C.: 4833
N.A.I.C.S.: 515120
Media: 24
Personnel:
Holly Jones *(Dir-Creative Svcs)*
Doug Quick *(Dir-Pub Affairs)*
Gene Konradi *(Mgr-Sls)*
Jim Wnek *(Chief Engr)*

WICS-TV
(Sub. of Sinclair Television Group, Inc.)
2680 E Cook St
Springfield, IL 62703-1902
Tel.: (217) 753-5620
Fax: (217) 753-8177
E-mail: news@wics.com
Web Site: www.wics.com
E-Mail For Key Personnel:
Sales Director: sales@wics.com
Sales Range: $25-49.9 Million
Approx. Number Employees: 100
Year Founded: 1953
Business Description:
Television Station
S.I.C.: 4833; 4832
N.A.I.C.S.: 515120; 515112
Media: 8-10-13-14-15
Personnel:
Steve Cramblit *(Dir-Sls)*

WINDSTREAM CORPORATION
4001 Rodney Parham Rd
Little Rock, AR 72212-2442
Tel.: (501) 748-7000
Toll Free: (866) 445-3402
Web Site: www.windstream.com
Approx. Rev.: $3,712,000,000
Approx. Number Employees: 10,086
Year Founded: 2006
Business Description:
Business & Residential Local & Long-Distance Phone Service, Broadband Data Transmission & Internet Access
S.I.C.: 4813; 4899
N.A.I.C.S.: 517110; 517910
Advertising Expenditures: $70,900,000
Personnel:
Dennis E. Foster *(Chm)*
Jeffery R. Gardner *(Pres & CEO)*
Anthony W. Thomas *(CFO)*
Brent K. Whittington *(COO)*
Cindy Nash *(CIO)*
Ric Crane *(CMO & Exec VP)*
John P. Fletcher *(Gen Counsel & Exec VP)*
Robert G. Clancy *(Treas & Sr VP)*
John Leach *(Exec VP-Bus Sls)*
Grant Raney *(Exec VP-Network Ops)*
Susan Bradley *(Sr VP-HR)*
Joe Marano *(Sr VP-Customer Svcs)*
Michael D. Rhoda *(Sr VP-Govt Affairs)*
Gregg Richey *(Sr VP-Consumer Sls)*
David Avery *(Dir-Corp Comm)*
Clint Highfill *(Dir-Regulatory Counsel)*
Mary Michaels *(Dir-Capital Markets & IR)*
Daryl Barron *(Mgr-Ops-Moultrie)*
Brooke Hicks *(Mgr-Capital Markets & IR)*
Brands & Products:
BROADBAND PROTECTION PLUS
WINDSTREAM

WISCONSIN EDUCATIONAL COMMUNICATIONS BOARD
3319 W Beltline Hwy
Madison, WI 53713-2834
Tel.: (608) 264-9600
Fax: (608) 264-9664
E-mail: info@ecb.org
Web Site: www.ecb.org
Sales Range: $10-24.9 Million
Approx. Number Employees: 45
Year Founded: 1971
Business Description:
Provider of Radio & TV Broadcasting Services
S.I.C.: 4832; 4833
N.A.I.C.S.: 515112; 515120
Media: 7-8
Personnel:
Gene Purcell *(Exec Dir)*
Brands & Products:
ECB
WISCONSIN PUBLIC RADIO
WISCONSIN PUBLIC TELEVISION

WJBF-TV
(Unit of Media General Broadcast Group)
1001 Reynolds St
Augusta, GA 30901-1105
Mailing Address:
PO Box 1404
Augusta, GA 30903-1404
Tel.: (706) 722-6664
Fax: (706) 722-0022
E-mail: info@wjbf.com
Web Site: www.wjbf.com
Sales Range: $10-24.9 Million
Approx. Number Employees: 68
Year Founded: 1953
Business Description:
Television Station
S.I.C.: 4833
N.A.I.C.S.: 515120
Media: 2-4-6-13-14-15-17-23-24
Distr.: Reg.
Personnel:
Bill Stewart *(VP & Gen Mgr)*
Robert Pipen *(Dir-Mktg)*
John Hart *(Dir-Sports)*
Mary Jones *(Dir-Programming)*
Roberto Vasquez *(Dir-Results)*
Scott Elledge *(Mgr-Production)*
Cary Hale *(Chief Engr)*

WJLA & TBD
(Div. of Allbritton Communications Company)
1100 Wilson Blvd
Arlington, VA 22209
Tel.: (703) 236-9628
Fax: (703) 236-2336
Web Site: www.tbd.com
Approx. Number Employees: 150
Year Founded: 1991

Key to Media (For complete agency information see *The Advertising Red Books-Agencies* edition):
1. Bus. Publs. 2. Cable T.V. 3. Catalogs & Directories. 4. Co-op Adv. 5. Consumer Mags. 6. D.M. to Bus. Estab.7. D.M. to Consumers 8. Daily Newsp. 9. Exhibits/Trade Shows 10. Foreign 11. Infomercial 12. Internet Adv.13. Multimedia 14. Network Radio 15. Network T.V. 16. Newsp. Distr. Mags. 17. Other 18. Outdoor (Posters, Transit) 19. Point of Purchase20. Premiums, Novelties 21. Product Samples 22. Special Events Mktg. 23. Spot Radio 24. Spot T.V. 25. Weekly Newsp. 26. Yellow Page Adv.

WJLA & TBD — (Continued)
Business Description:
News Broadcasting Station
S.I.C.: 4833
N.A.I.C.S.: 515120
Media: 3-9-10-13-18-20-22-23-24
Distr.: Reg.
Personnel:
Robert Skutari *(Gen Mgr-Sls)*
Polly Sherard *(Mgr-New Bus)*

WJR-AM RADIO
(Unit of Detroit Radio, LLC)
3011 W Grand Blvd Fisher Bldg Ste 800
Detroit, MI 48202
Tel.: (313) 875-4440
Fax: (313) 875-8760
Fax: (313) 873-9729 (Sales)
E-mail: wjr@wjr.com
Web Site: www.wjr.com
Sales Range: $25-49.9 Million
Year Founded: 1922
Business Description:
Radio Broadcasting Station
S.I.C.: 4832
N.A.I.C.S.: 515112
Advertising Expenditures: $250,000
Media: 9-18-23-24-26
Distr.: Reg.
Personnel:
Matt Hanlon *(Acting Pres & Gen Mgr)*
Bridget Burns *(Dir-Mktg & Promos)*

WJRT, INC.
(Sub. of ABC Owned Television Stations)
(d/b/a WJRT-TV)
2302 Lapeer Rd
Flint, MI 48503-4221
Tel.: (810) 233-3130
Fax: (810) 257-2812
E-mail: abc12news@abc12.com
Web Site: www.abc12.com
Sales Range: $10-24.9 Million
Approx. Number Employees: 50
Business Description:
Television Broadcasting Station
S.I.C.: 4833
N.A.I.C.S.: 515120
Media: 18-23-24
Personnel:
Tom Bryson *(Gen Mgr)*
Jim Bleicher *(Dir-News)*
Ryan Renz *(Mgr-Web Ops)*

WJZ-TV
(Unit of CBS Television Stations Inc.)
3725 Malden Ave
Baltimore, MD 21211
Tel.: (410) 466-0013
Tel.: (410) 578-7500 (Adv & Sls)
Fax: (410) 578-0642
E-mail: newsroom@wjz.com
Web Site: www.wjz.com
Approx. Number Employees: 165
Year Founded: 1958
Business Description:
Television Broadcasting Services
S.I.C.: 4833
N.A.I.C.S.: 515120
Media: 9-13-15-23-24
Distr.: Reg.
Personnel:
Jay B. Newman *(VP & Gen Mgr)*
Ruth Heltne-Carlin *(Dir-Station Mktg Devel)*
K. C. Robertson *(Dir-Creative Svcs)*
Brenda Comfort *(Asst Controller)*

WKQX-FM
(Div. of Emmis Radio, L.L.C.)
230 Merchandise Mart Plz
Chicago, IL 60654-3101
Tel.: (312) 527-8348
Fax: (312) 527-3620
E-mail: info@q101.com
Web Site: www.q101.com
Sales Range: $10-24.9 Million
Approx. Number Employees: 10
Business Description:
Radio Station
S.I.C.: 4832
N.A.I.C.S.: 515112
Media: 13-18-20-22-23
Personnel:
Marv Nyren *(VP-Mgr & Mktg)*

WLAJ-TV
(Unit of Freedom Broadcasting, Inc.)
5815 S Pennsylvania Ave
Lansing, MI 48911
Tel.: (517) 394-5300
Fax: (517) 887-0077
E-mail: info@wlaj.com
Web Site: www.wlaj.com
Approx. Number Employees: 25
Year Founded: 1990
Business Description:
Television Station
S.I.C.: 7389
N.A.I.C.S.: 711310
Media: 13-15-20-22-24
Brands & Products:
WLAJ-TV

WLHK-FM
(Div. of Emmis Indiana Broadcasting, L.P.)
40 Monument Cir Ste 600
Indianapolis, IN 46204-3011
Tel.: (317) 266-9700
Fax: (317) 684-2021
Web Site: www.wens.com
Sales Range: $200-249.9 Million
Business Description:
FM Radio Broadcasting Services
S.I.C.: 4832
N.A.I.C.S.: 515112
Media: 22-23

WLNE-TV
(Unit of Global Broadcasting, LLC)
10 Orms St
Providence, RI 02904
Tel.: (401) 453-8000
Fax: (401) 331-4401
E-mail: news@abc6.com
Web Site: www.abc6.com
Year Founded: 1963
Business Description:
Television Station
S.I.C.: 4833
N.A.I.C.S.: 515120
Media: 13-20-22-24
Personnel:
Chris Tzianabos *(VP & Gen Mgr)*
Jim Brown *(Dir-Engrg & Ops)*
Marc Fauci *(Dir-Sls)*
B. J. Finnell *(Dir-News)*
Melissa Manfre *(Dir-Digital Media)*
Anne Marie Menard *(Mgr-Bus)*

WLS TELEVISION, INC.
(Sub. of ABC Owned Television Stations)
190 N State St
Chicago, IL 60601-3302
Tel.: (312) 750-7777
Fax: (312) 889-9801
E-mail: wls.desk@abc.com
Sales Range: $150-199.9 Million
Approx. Number Employees: 600
Business Description:
Television Broadcasting
S.I.C.: 4833
N.A.I.C.S.: 515120
Media: 15
Personnel:
Emily Barr *(Pres & Gen Mgr)*
Kal Hassan *(VP & Dir-Engrg)*

WLUK-TV
(Sub. of LIN TV Corp.)
787 Lombardi Ave
Green Bay, WI 54304-3925
Mailing Address:
PO Box 19011
Green Bay, WI 54307-9011
Tel.: (920) 494-8711
Fax: (920) 494-9109
E-mail: wlukbox11@wluk.com
Web Site: www.wluk.com
Sales Range: $25-49.9 Million
Approx. Number Employees: 125
Business Description:
Television Station
S.I.C.: 4833
N.A.I.C.S.: 515120
Media: 18-20-22-24
Personnel:
Jay Zollar *(Gen Mgr)*
Pat Krohlow *(Dir-Mktg)*
Tori Grant-Welhouse *(Mgr-Gen Sls)*

WMAL-AM RADIO
(Unit of DC Radio, LLC)
4400 Jenifer St NW
Washington, DC 20015-2113
Tel.: (202) 686-3100 (Switchboard)
Tel.: (202) 895-2344 (Sales)
Fax: (202) 686-3070
Web Site: www.630wmal.com
Year Founded: 1925
Business Description:
Radio Broadcasting Station
S.I.C.: 4832
N.A.I.C.S.: 515112
Media: 18-22-23
Personnel:
Jeff Boden *(Pres & Gen Mgr)*

WMAR-TV
(Sub. of The E.W. Scripps Company)
6400 York Rd
Baltimore, MD 21212-2117
Tel.: (410) 377-2222
Fax: (410) 377-3010
Web Site: www.abc2news.com
Sales Range: $25-49.9 Million
Approx. Number Employees: 149
Business Description:
Television Broadcasting
S.I.C.: 4833
N.A.I.C.S.: 515120
Media: 24
Personnel:
Bill Hooper *(VP & Gen Mgr)*
Darlene Dorman *(Dir-Programming)*
Omari Hughes *(Dir-New)*
Harry Kakel *(Mgr-Production)*

WMYD-TV
(Sub. of Granite Broadcasting Corporation)
27777 Franklin Rd Ste 1220
Southfield, MI 48034
Tel.: (248) 355-2020
Fax: (248) 355-0368
E-mail: news@tv20detroit.com
Web Site: www.tv20detroit.com
Sales Range: $25-49.9 Million
Approx. Number Employees: 100
Business Description:
TV Station
S.I.C.: 4833
N.A.I.C.S.: 515120
Media: 9-13-18-20-23-24-25
Personnel:
Sharon McClendon *(Dir-Community Affairs)*
Dan Riley *(Engr)*

WNET.ORG
450 W 33rd St
New York, NY 10001
Tel.: (212) 560-1313
Fax: (212) 560-1314
E-mail: programming@thirteen.org
Web Site: www.thirteen.org
Sales Range: $125-149.9 Million
Approx. Number Employees: 550
Business Description:
Television Broadcasting Services
S.I.C.: 4833
N.A.I.C.S.: 515120
Media: 6-7-8-20
Personnel:
Steven Rattner *(Chm)*
Neal Shapiro *(Pres & CEO)*
Roslyn Davis *(Pres/Acting Gen Mgr-Educational Broadcasting Corp)*
Robert Clauser *(CFO, Treas & VP)*
Ken Devine *(CIO)*
Eleanor S. Applewhaite *(Gen Counsel, Sec & VP)*
Tamara E. Robinson *(VP & Dir-Programming)*
Stephen Segaller *(VP-Content)*
Charlene Shapiro *(VP & Dir-HR)*
Dan Greenberg *(Gen Mgr)*
Dan Goldman *(Exec Dir-Interactive & Broadband)*
Ranfi Rivera *(Exec Dir-Bus Dev & Institutional Strategy)*
Michael Dominick *(Dir-Local Sponsorship)*
Andy Halper *(Dir-Production)*
Richard Siegmeister *(Dir-Bus Dev & Institutional Strategy)*
Advertising Agency:
Initiative Worldwide
(Part of The Interpublic Group of Companies, Inc.)
1 Dag Hammerskjold Plz 5th Fl
New York, NY 10017
Tel.: (212) 605-7000
Fax: (212) 605-7200

WNYT-TV
(Sub. of Hubbard Broadcasting, Inc.)
715 N Pearl St
Albany, NY 12204-1819
Tel.: (518) 436-4791
Fax: (518) 426-9463
E-mail: info@wnyt.com
Web Site: www.wnyt.com
Approx. Number Employees: 130
Business Description:
Television Broadcasting Station

Key to Media (For complete agency information see *The Advertising Red Books-Agencies* edition):
1. Bus. Publs. 2. Cable T.V. 3. Catalogs & Directories. 4. Co-op Adv. 5. Consumer Mags. 6. D.M. to Bus. Estab.7. D.M. to Consumers
8. Daily Newsp. 9. Exhibits/Trade Shows 10. Foreign 11. Infomercial 12. Internet Adv.13. Multimedia 14. Network Radio
15. Network T.V. 16. Newsp. Distr. Mags. 17. Other 18. Outdoor (Posters, Transit) 19. Point of Purchase20. Premiums, Novelties
21. Product Samples 22. Special Events Mktg. 23. Spot Radio 24. Spot T.V. 25. Weekly Newsp. 26. Yellow Page Adv.

S.I.C.: 4833
N.A.I.C.S.: 515120
Media: 23-24
Personnel:
Steve P. Baboulis *(VP & Gen Mgr)*
Tony Mcmanus *(Dir-Sls)*
Steve Robbins *(Dir-Ops & Web Svcs)*
Maryann Ryan *(Dir-Pub Affairs, Programming & Special Promos)*
Carla Clark *(Mgr-Bus)*
Brands & Products:
WNYT

WORLDGATE COMMUNICATIONS, INC.
3800 Horizon Blvd Ste 103
Trevose, PA 19053
Tel.: (215) 354-5100
Tel.: (215) 354-5455 (Sales & PR)
Tel.: (215) 354-5312 (IR)
Fax: (215) 354-1049
Web Site: www.wgate.com
Approx. Rev.: $21,863,000
Approx. Number Employees: 49
Year Founded: 1995
Business Description:
Personal Video Telephony Mfr; 65% Owned by WGI Investor LLC
S.I.C.: 3661; 3651; 3669
N.A.I.C.S.: 334210; 334290; 334310
Export
Advertising Expenditures: $4,000
Media: 2-3-10-13-15-20-21-22-24
Personnel:
Robert Stevanovski *(Chm)*
Allan M. Van Buhler *(Chief Admin Officer & Sr VP-Sls, Mktg & Bus Dev)*
Christopher V. Vitale *(Gen Counsel, Sec & Sr VP-Legal & Regulatory)*
Joseph Calarco *(Controller & VP-Fin)*
Brands & Products:
OJO
WORLDGATE

WPCM-AM
(Unit of Curtis Media Group)
1109 Tower Dr
Burlington, NC 27215-4425
Tel.: (336) 584-0126
Fax: (336) 584-0739
Web Site: www.920wpcm.com
Business Description:
Radio Broadcasting Station
S.I.C.: 4832
N.A.I.C.S.: 515112
Media: 20-22-23
Personnel:
Bill Whitley *(Gen Mgr)*

WPEC-TV
(Unit of Freedom Broadcasting, Inc.)
1100 Fairfield Dr
West Palm Beach, FL 33407
Tel.: (561) 844-1212
Fax: (561) 842-1212
E-mail: newsdesk@cbs12.com
Web Site: www.cbs12.com
Approx. Number Employees: 120
Year Founded: 1954
Business Description:
Television Station
S.I.C.: 4833
N.A.I.C.S.: 515120
Media: 13-15-20-22-24
Personnel:
Tom Herwitz *(Pres)*
Brands & Products:
WPEC-TV

WPIX, INC.
(Sub. of Tribune Broadcasting Company)
(d/b/a WPIX-CW11)
220 E 42nd St
New York, NY 10017
Tel.: (212) 949-1100
Fax: (212) 986-1032
Web Site: www.wpix.com
Approx. Number Employees: 300
Year Founded: 1948
Business Description:
Television Broadcasting Station
S.I.C.: 4833
N.A.I.C.S.: 515120
Media: 2-6-7-9-18-23-24
Distr.: Reg.
Personnel:
Eric Meyrowitz *(VP & Gen Mgr)*
Bob Marra *(Gen Mgr-Sls)*
V. Jean Maye *(Dir-HR)*
Karen Scott *(Dir-News)*
Imani Laners *(Mgr-Interactive Sls)*
Advertising Agency:
JL Media, Inc.
1600 Rte 22 E
Union, NJ 07083-3415
Tel.: (908) 687-8700
Fax: (908) 687-9280
(Radio Placement)

WPLJ RADIO, LLC
(Sub. of Citadel Broadcasting Company)
(d/b/a WPLJ-FM Radio)
2 Penn Plz 17th Fl
New York, NY 10121
Tel.: (212) 613-8900
Tel.: (212) 613-8909 (Adv & Sls)
Fax: (212) 613-8950
Web Site: www.wplj.com
Sales Range: $50-74.9 Million
Approx. Number Employees: 200
Business Description:
Radio Broadcasting Station
S.I.C.: 4832
N.A.I.C.S.: 515112
Media: 18-23
Personnel:
Steve Borneman *(Pres & Gen Mgr)*

WPTF-AM
(Unit of Curtis Media Group)
3012 Highwoods Blvd
Raleigh, NC 27604-1037
Tel.: (919) 876-0674
Fax: (919) 790-8369
Toll Free: (800) 662-7979
E-mail: info@wptf.com
Web Site: www.wptf.com
Approx. Number Employees: 100
Business Description:
Radio Broadcasting Station
S.I.C.: 4832
N.A.I.C.S.: 515112
Media: 20-22-23
Personnel:
Donald W. Curtis *(Chm & CEO)*
Phil Zachary *(Pres & COO)*

WPTV
(Sub. of The E.W. Scripps Company)
1100 Banyon Blvd
West Palm Beach, FL 33401
Tel.: (561) 655-5455
Fax: (561) 653-5619
Fax: (561) 653-5719
E-mail: newstip@wptv.com
Web Site: www.wptv.com
Sales Range: $25-49.9 Million
Approx. Number Employees: 140
Business Description:
Television Broadcasting Station
S.I.C.: 4833
N.A.I.C.S.: 515120
Media: 24
Personnel:
Steve Wasserman *(VP & Gen Mgr)*
Dave Peterson *(Dir-New Media)*

WPVI-TV INC.
(Sub. of ABC Owned Television Stations)
4100 City Line Ave
Philadelphia, PA 19131-1610
Tel.: (215) 878-9700
Fax: (215) 581-4530
Web Site: www.6abc.com
Sales Range: $75-99.9 Million
Approx. Number Employees: 260
Business Description:
Television Broadcasting
S.I.C.: 4833
N.A.I.C.S.: 515120
Media: 23-24
Personnel:
Bernie Prazenica *(Pres & Gen Mgr)*
Paula McDermott *(Mgr-Mktg)*
Advertising Agency:
Tierney Communications
(A Div. of the Interpublic Group of Companies)
The Bellevue 200 S Broad St
Philadelphia, PA 19102-3803
Tel.: (215) 790-4100
Fax: (215) 790-4363

WQDR-FM
(Unit of Curtis Media Group)
3012 Highwoods Blvd
Raleigh, NC 27604-1037
Tel.: (919) 790-9392
Fax: (919) 790-8369
Toll Free: (800) 233-9470
Web Site: www.wqdr.net
Approx. Number Employees: 100
Business Description:
Radio Broadcasting Station
S.I.C.: 4832
N.A.I.C.S.: 515112
Media: 20-22-23
Personnel:
Don Curtis *(CEO)*
Phil Zachary *(CFO & VP)*
Trip Savery *(Gen Mgr)*
Lisa Mckay *(Prog Dir)*
Adam Maisano *(Mgr National Sls)*

WQHT-FM
(Div. of Emmis Radio, L.L.C.)
395 Hudson St 7th Fl
New York, NY 10014-3669
Tel.: (212) 229-9797
Fax: (212) 929-8559
E-mail: hot97@hot97.com
Web Site: www.hot97.com
Sales Range: $200-249.9 Million
Business Description:
Radio Broadcasting Services
S.I.C.: 4832
N.A.I.C.S.: 515112
Media: 13-18-20-22-23-24
Personnel:
Alex Cameron *(Gen Mgr)*

WRGB-TV
(Unit of Freedom Broadcasting, Inc.)
1400 Balltown Rd
Schenectady, NY 12309-4301
Tel.: (518) 346-6666
Fax: (518) 346-6249
E-mail: news@cbs6albany.com
Web Site: www.cbs6albany.com
Approx. Number Employees: 65
Year Founded: 1928
Business Description:
Television Station
S.I.C.: 4833
N.A.I.C.S.: 515120
Media: 3-18-20-22-24
Personnel:
Vincent Nelson *(VP & Gen Mgr)*
Bob Hewitt *(Mgr-Natl Sls)*

WRQX-FM RADIO
(Unit of DC Radio, LLC)
4400 Jenifer St NW
Washington, DC 20015-2113
Tel.: (202) 686-3100 (Switchboard)
Fax: (202) 686-3070
Web Site: www.mix1073fm.com
Sales Range: $25-49.9 Million
Business Description:
Radio Broadcasting Station
S.I.C.: 4832
N.A.I.C.S.: 515112
Media: 8-18-22-23
Personnel:
Jeff Boden *(Pres & Gen Mgr)*
Brands & Products:
WRQX-FM

WSAZ-TV
(Unit of Gray Television, Inc.)
645 5th Ave
Huntington, WV 25701
Tel.: (304) 697-4780
Fax: (304) 690-3066
E-mail: newschannel3@wsaz.com
Web Site: www.wsaz.com
Sales Range: $25-49.9 Million
Approx. Number Employees: 85
Business Description:
Television Broadcasting Station
S.I.C.: 4833
N.A.I.C.S.: 515120
Media: 3-13-20-22-24
Personnel:
Grover Tadlock *(Editor-News)*
Scott Saxton *(Dir-News)*
Anna Baxter *(Asst Dir-News)*
Shanan Mayhugh *(Sls Mgr)*
Beth Stiles *(Sls Mgr-Gen & Local)*
Charlie Boush *(Mgr-Sls-Natl)*
Edwin Lake *(Mgr-Ops)*
Mike Waterhouse *(Mgr-Ops)*
Aaron Withrow *(Chief Engr & Mgr-Engrg)*

WSTR-TV
(Sub. of Sinclair Television Group, Inc.)
5177 Fishwick Dr
Cincinnati, OH 45216
Tel.: (513) 641-4400
Fax: (513) 242-2633
Web Site: www.wb64.net
Sales Range: $10-24.9 Million
Approx. Number Employees: 30
Business Description:
TV Station
S.I.C.: 4833
N.A.I.C.S.: 515120

Key to Media (For complete agency information see *The Advertising Red Books-Agencies* edition):
1. Bus. Publs. 2. Cable T.V. 3. Catalogs & Directories. 4. Co-op Adv. 5. Consumer Mags. 6. D.M. to Bus. Estab.7. D.M. to Consumers 8. Daily Newsp. 9. Exhibits/Trade Shows 10. Foreign 11. Infomercial 12. Internet Adv.13. Multimedia 14. Network Radio 15. Network T.V. 16. Newsp. Distr. Mags. 17. Other 18. Outdoor (Posters, Transit) 19. Point of Purchase20. Premiums, Novelties 21. Product Samples 22. Special Events Mktg. 23. Spot Radio 24. Spot T.V. 25. Weekly Newsp. 26. Yellow Page Adv.

WSTR-TV — (Continued)

Personnel:
John Liwhead *(Mgr)*

Advertising Agency:
Holland Advertising:Interactive
700 Walnut St Ste 205
Cincinnati, OH 45202-2011
Tel.: (513) 744-3000
Fax: (513) 721-1269

WTVC-TV
(Unit of Freedom Broadcasting, Inc.)
4279 Benton Dr
Chattanooga, TN 37406-1244
Tel.: (423) 756-5500
Fax: (423) 757-7400
E-mail: news@newschannel9.com
Web Site: www.newschannel9.com
Approx. Number Employees: 100
Year Founded: 1958
Business Description:
Television Station
S.I.C.: 4833; 3663
N.A.I.C.S.: 515120; 334220
Media: 7-13-15-20-22-24
Personnel:
Michael Costa *(VP & Gen Mgr)*
Brands & Products:
WTVC

WTVD-TV INC.
(Sub. of ABC Owned Television Stations)
411 Liberty St
Durham, NC 27701-3407
Tel.: (919) 683-1111
Fax: (919) 682-7476
E-mail: general.manager@abc.com
Web Site: www.abc11tv.com
Sales Range: $50-74.9 Million
Approx. Number Employees: 200
Business Description:
Television Broadcasting
S.I.C.: 4833
N.A.I.C.S.: 515120
Media: 23-24
Personnel:
John H. Idler *(Pres & Gen Mgr)*
Tim Alwran *(Gen Mgr-Sls)*
Darren Pieh *(Mgr-Local Sls)*
Brands & Products:
WTVD

WTVG, INC.
(Sub. of ABC Owned Television Stations)
(d/b/a WTVG-TV)
4247 Dorr St
Toledo, OH 43607-2134
Tel.: (419) 531-1313
Fax: (419) 531-1399
E-mail: wtvg.webmaster@abc.com
Web Site: www.13abc.com
Sales Range: $10-24.9 Million
Approx. Number Employees: 120
Year Founded: 1995
Business Description:
Television Broadcasting Station
S.I.C.: 4833
N.A.I.C.S.: 515120
Media: 23-24
Personnel:
John Christianson *(Pres)*
Mary F. Gerken *(Gen Mgr-Sls)*
Mary Carrera *(Dir-Internet & Digital Sls)*
Tammy Guest *(Dir-Internet & Digital Sls)*
Hillary Drezner *(Sr Mgr-Digital Sls)*
Ben Fuller-Rowell *(Sr Mgr-Digital Sls)*
Bob Silver *(Mgr-Local Sls)*

WTVH, LLC
(Sub. of Granite Broadcasting Corporation)
980 James St
Syracuse, NY 13203
Tel.: (315) 425-5555
Fax: (315) 425-5513
Web Site: www.wtvh.com
Sales Range: $25-49.9 Million
Approx. Number Employees: 100
Business Description:
TV Station
S.I.C.: 4833
N.A.I.C.S.: 515120
Media: 9-13-18-20-23-24-25

WTWC NBC 40
(Sub. of Sinclair Television Group, Inc.)
8440 Dear Lk Rd
Tallahassee, FL 32312
Tel.: (850) 893-4140
Fax: (850) 893-6974
E-mail: info@wtwc40.com
Web Site: www.wtwc40.com
Sales Range: $25-49.9 Million
Approx. Number Employees: 90
Business Description:
TV Broadcast Station
S.I.C.: 4833
N.A.I.C.S.: 515120
Media: 24
Personnel:
Barbara Agramonte *(Mgr-Bus)*
Brands & Products:
WTWC
WTXL

WVEC-TELEVISION, INC.
(Sub. of Belo Corp.)
613 Woodis Ave
Norfolk, VA 23510-1017
Tel.: (757) 625-1313
Fax: (757) 628-6530
E-mail: news@wvec.com
Web Site: www.wvec.com
Sales Range: $50-74.9 Million
Approx. Number Employees: 160
Business Description:
Television Broadcasting
S.I.C.: 4833
N.A.I.C.S.: 515120
Media: 15
Personnel:
Tod A. Smith *(Pres & Gen Mgr)*
John Dolive *(Dir-Tech)*
Amy Warren *(Dir-Sls & Mktg)*

WWL-TV, INC.
(Sub. of Belo Corp.)
1024 N Rampart St
New Orleans, LA 70116-2406
Tel.: (504) 529-4444
Fax: (504) 529-6470
E-mail: pressrelelase@wwltv.com
Web Site: www.wwltv.com
Sales Range: $50-74.9 Million
Approx. Number Employees: 190
Year Founded: 1957
Business Description:
Television Broadcasting Station
S.I.C.: 4833
N.A.I.C.S.: 515120
Media: 13-15-24
Personnel:
Bud Brown *(Gen Mgr)*
Mike Zikmund *(Exec Dir-Sls)*
Tom Planchet *(Mgr-News & Ops)*

WWMT-TV
(Unit of Freedom Broadcasting, Inc.)
590 W Maple St
Kalamazoo, MI 49008
Tel.: (269) 388-3333
Tel.: (269) 388-3748 (Sls)
Fax: (616) 388-8228
Toll Free: (800) 875-3333
E-mail: promo@wwmt.com
Web Site: www.wwmt.com
Approx. Number Employees: 100
Year Founded: 1950
Business Description:
Television Station
S.I.C.: 4833
N.A.I.C.S.: 515120
Media: 13-15-20-22-24
Personnel:
Jim Lutton *(VP & Gen Mgr)*
Melissa Broderick *(Editor-Assignment)*
Ed Kengerski *(Dir)*
Jim Steffey *(Dir-Engrg)*
Brands & Products:
WWMT-TV

WWOR-TV, INC.
(Unit of Fox Television Stations Inc.)
9 Broadcast Plz
Secaucus, NJ 07094-2913
Tel.: (201) 348-0009
Fax: (201) 330-2180
Web Site: www.upn9.com
Sales Range: $25-49.9 Million
Approx. Number Employees: 150
Year Founded: 1992
Business Description:
Television Broadcasting Station
S.I.C.: 4833
N.A.I.C.S.: 515120
Media: 24

WXYZ-TV
(Sub. of The E.W. Scripps Company)
(d/b/a Channel 7 of Detroit, Inc.)
20777 W 10 Mile Rd
Southfield, MI 48037
Mailing Address:
PO Box 789
Southfield, MI 48037-0789
Tel.: (248) 827-7777
Fax: (248) 827-9444
Toll Free: (800) 825-0770
E-mail: talkback@wxyz.com
Web Site: www.wxyz.com
Sales Range: $75-99.9 Million
Approx. Number Employees: 250
Business Description:
Television Station
S.I.C.: 4833; 7829
N.A.I.C.S.: 515120; 512199
Media: 1-8-10-24
Personnel:
Eduardo Fernandez *(VP & Gen Mgr)*
Mike Murri *(Dir-Sls)*
Don Shane *(Dir-Sports)*

WZVN TV ABC 7
(Sub. of Waterman Broadcasting Corp.)
3719 Central Ave PO Box 7087 33911
Fort Myers, FL 33901
Tel.: (239) 939-2020
Fax: (239) 939-3244
Fax: (239) 939-2076
E-mail: webmaster@abc-7.com
Web Site: www.abc-7.com
Sales Range: $10-24.9 Million
Business Description:
Television Broadcasting Stations
S.I.C.: 4833
N.A.I.C.S.: 515120
Media: 3-9-23-24
Personnel:
Lara Kunkler *(Owner)*
Bob Beville *(Gen Mgr-Sls)*
Brian Colleran *(Dir-Sports)*
Bob Hannon *(Dir-Production)*
Bill Beard *(Mgr-Sls)*

XANADOO COMPANY
225 City Line Ave Ste 200
Bala Cynwyd, PA 19004-1724
Tel.: (610) 934-7000
Fax: (610) 934-7072
Toll Free: (888) 438-7488
Web Site: www.xanadoo.com
Sales Range: $1-9.9 Million
Approx. Number Employees: 73
Year Founded: 1991
Business Description:
Wireless Internet Services
S.I.C.: 4833
N.A.I.C.S.: 515120
Advertising Expenditures: $800,000
Media: 3-7-17-22
Personnel:
Marshall W. Pagon *(Chm, Pres & CEO)*
Andrew Smith *(CFO)*
Howard E. Verlin *(Exec VP)*
Brands & Products:
XANADOO

XM SATELLITE RADIO HOLDINGS INC.
(Sub. of Sirius XM Radio Inc.)
1221 Ave of the Americas 36th Fl
New York, NY 10020
Tel.: (212) 584-5100
E-mail: listenercare@xmradio.com
Web Site: www.xmradio.com
Approx. Rev.: $1,297,341,000
Year Founded: 1992
Business Description:
Holding Company; Satellite Radio Network Developer & Operator
S.I.C.: 6719; 4832; 4899
N.A.I.C.S.: 551112; 515111; 517410
Advertising Expenditures: $147,640,000
Media: 3-6-9-13-15-25
Personnel:
Joe Zarella *(Chief Svc Officer)*
Melvin Alan Karmazin *(CEO-Sirius XM Radio Inc)*
My-Chau Nguyen *(Sr VP-Mktg-Customer Programs & Ops)*
Steve Cook *(Grp VP & Gen Mgr-Automotive Div-SIRIUS XM Radio)*
Brands & Products:
XM
XM NAVTRAFFIC
Advertising Agencies:
Asphalt Media
114 W 17th St
New York, NY 10011
Tel.: (212) 924-5332
Fax: (212) 989-3783

Key to Media (For complete agency information see *The Advertising Red Books-Agencies* edition):
1. Bus. Publs. 2. Cable T.V. 3. Catalogs & Directories. 4. Co-op Adv. 5. Consumer Mags. 6. D.M. to Bus. Estab.7. D.M. to Consumers 8. Daily Newsp. 9. Exhibits/Trade Shows 10. Foreign 11. Infomercial 12. Internet Adv.13. Multimedia 14. Network Radio 15. Network T.V. 16. Newsp. Distr. Mags. 17. Other 18. Outdoor (Posters, Transit) 19. Point of Purchase20. Premiums, Novelties 21. Product Samples 22. Special Events Mktg. 23. Spot Radio 24. Spot T.V. 25. Weekly Newsp. 26. Yellow Page Adv.

CPM USA
7425 16th St E Ste 101
Sarasota, FL 34243-5568
Tel.: (941) 953-3866
Fax: (941) 358-3384

Goodman Media International, Inc.
750 7th Ave 28th Fl
New York, NY 10016
Tel.: (212) 576-2700
Fax: (212) 576-2701

Millsport
1999 Bryan St Ste 1800
Dallas, TX 75201
Tel.: (214) 259-3200
Fax: (214) 259-3201
Sports Marketing & Promotions

RAPP
437 Madison Ave 3rd Fl
New York, NY 10022
Tel.: (212) 817-6800
Fax: (212) 590-8400

YANKEES ENTERTAINMENT & SPORTS NETWORK, LLC

(d/b/a YES Network)
405 Lexington Ave 36th Fl
New York, NY 10174-3699
Tel.: (646) 487-3600
Fax: (646) 487-3612
E-mail: info@yesnetworktv.com
Web Site: www.yesnetwork.com
Approx. Number Employees: 50
Business Description:
Sports & Entertainment Programming Network
S.I.C.: 4841; 7819
N.A.I.C.S.: 515210; 512191
Media: 3-9-13-18-20-22-23-24
Personnel:
Tracy Dolgin *(Pres & CEO)*
John Filippelli *(Pres-Production & Programming)*
Mike Wach *(Exec VP-Adv Sls)*
Matthew Cacciato *(Sr VP-Affiliate Sls)*
Howard Levinson *(Sr VP-Adv Sls)*
Pat Cavanaugh *(VP-Fin & Controller)*
Woody Freiman *(VP-Production & Programming)*
Michael Spirito *(Dir-Digital Media & Bus Dev)*
Advertising Agencies:
M/K Advertising Partners, Ltd.
(d/b/a MK)
28 W 25th St 9th Fl
New York, NY 10010
Tel.: (212) 367-9225
Fax: (212) 242-7008

Rubenstein Associates, Inc.
1345 Ave of the Americas Fl 30
New York, NY 10105-0109
Tel.: (212) 843-8000
Fax: (212) 843-9200
Pub Rels

YOUNG BROADCASTING OF KNOXVILLE, INC.

(Sub. of Young Broadcasting, LLC)
(d/b/a WATE-TV)
1306 Broadway NE
Knoxville, TN 37917-6501
Mailing Address:
PO Box 2349
Knoxville, TN 37901
Tel.: (865) 637-6666
Fax: (865) 525-4091
E-mail: newsroom@wate.com
Web Site: www.wate.com
Sales Range: $25-49.9 Million
Approx. Number Employees: 110
Year Founded: 1953
Business Description:
Television Broadcasting Station
S.I.C.: 4833
N.A.I.C.S.: 515120
Media: 13-18-22-24
Personnel:
Tony Kahl *(Dir-Adv & Sls)*
Luwis Snyder *(Mgr-Station Bus)*

YOUNG BROADCASTING OF LOUISIANA, INC.

(Sub. of Young Broadcasting, LLC)
(d/b/a KLFY-TV)
1808 Eraste Landry Rd
Lafayette, LA 70506-1911
Mailing Address:
PO Box 90665
Lafayette, LA 70509
Tel.: (337) 981-4823
Fax: (337) 984-8323
E-mail: klfy@klfy.com
Web Site: www.klfy.com
Sales Range: $25-49.9 Million
Approx. Number Employees: 75
Year Founded: 1955
Business Description:
Television Broadcasting Station
S.I.C.: 4833
N.A.I.C.S.: 515120
Media: 1-6-10-13-14-20-25
Personnel:
Nanette Lavergne *(CFO & Controller)*
Spencer Bievenu *(Gen Mgr-Sls)*
Mike Barras *(Dir-News)*
Brands & Products:
KLFY

YOUNG BROADCASTING OF SAN FRANCISCO, INC.

(Sub. of Young Broadcasting, LLC)
(d/b/a KRON-TV)
1001 Van Ness Ave
San Francisco, CA 94109-6913
Tel.: (415) 441-4444
Fax: (415) 561-8136
E-mail: 4listens@kron4.com
Web Site: www.kron4.com
Sales Range: $75-99.9 Million
Approx. Number Employees: 300
Year Founded: 1949
Business Description:
Television Broadcasting Station
S.I.C.: 4833
N.A.I.C.S.: 515120
Advertising Expenditures: $1,000,000
Media: 3-5-6-9-18-20-22-23-25
Distr.: Direct to Consumer; Natl.
Budget Set: Oct.
Personnel:
Brian Greif *(Gen Mgr & VP-News)*
Aaron Pero *(Dir-News)*
Gary Radnich *(Dir-Sports)*

YOUNG BROADCASTING OF SIOUX FALLS, INC.

(Sub. of Young Broadcasting, LLC)
(d/b/a KELO-TV)
501 S Phillips Ave
Sioux Falls, SD 57104-6820
Tel.: (605) 336-1100
Fax: (605) 334-3447
E-mail: kelotv@keloland.com
Web Site: www.keloland.com
Sales Range: $25-49.9 Million
Approx. Number Employees: 125
Year Founded: 1953
Business Description:
Television Broadcasting Station
S.I.C.: 4833
N.A.I.C.S.: 515120
Media: 1-14-16-22-23
Personnel:
Jay Huizenga *(Gen Mgr)*
Paul Farmer *(Dir-Promo & Mktg)*

ZOCO PRODUCTIONS, LLC

30 Rockefeller Plz
New York, NY 10112
Tel.: (212) 259-1500
Web Site: www.doctoroz.com
Business Description:
Television Production Company
S.I.C.: 4833
N.A.I.C.S.: 515120
Media: 9-13-15-18-25
Personnel:
Laurie Rich *(Exec-Production)*
Brands & Products:
THE DOCTOR OZ SHOW
WWW.DOCTOROZ.COM

ZORAN CORPORATION

1390 Kifer Rd
Sunnyvale, CA 94086
Tel.: (408) 523-6500
Fax: (408) 523-6501
Web Site: www.zoran.com
E-Mail For Key Personnel:
Sales Director: sales@zoran.com
Approx. Rev.: $357,342,000
Approx. Number Employees: 1,532
Year Founded: 1983
Business Description:
Integrated Circuits Mfr, Developer & Marketer
S.I.C.: 3674; 7372
N.A.I.C.S.: 334413; 511210
Advertising Expenditures: $800,000
Media: 4-8-10-13-22
Personnel:
Uzia Galil *(Chm)*
Levy Gerzberg *(Pres & CEO)*
Karl Schneider *(CFO & Sr VP-Fin)*
Isaac Shenberg *(Sr VP-Corp Mktg & Bus Dev)*
Connie Fredrickson-Bray *(VP-HR)*
Kevin Andresen *(Dir-Product Mktg)*
Betty Watkins *(Dir-Corp Comm)*
Brands & Products:
ACTIVA
APPROACH 5C
APPROACH 7
CAMMINI
COACH
GENERATION 9-ELITE
MAESTROLINK
QUATRO
VADDIS
ZORAN

Key to Media (For complete agency information see *The Advertising Red Books-Agencies* edition):
1. Bus. Publs. 2. Cable T.V. 3. Catalogs & Directories. 4. Co-op Adv. 5. Consumer Mags. 6. D.M. to Bus. Estab.7. D.M. to Consumers 8. Daily Newsp. 9. Exhibits/Trade Shows 10. Foreign 11. Infomercial 12. Internet Adv.13. Multimedia 14. Network Radio 15. Network T.V. 16. Newsp. Distr. Mags. 17. Other 18. Outdoor (Posters, Transit) 19. Point of Purchase20. Premiums, Novelties 21. Product Samples 22. Special Events Mktg. 23. Spot Radio 24. Spot T.V. 25. Weekly Newsp. 26. Yellow Page Adv.

Cleaning Agents

Bleaches — Cleaners — Detergents — Dyes — Fabric Softeners — Insecticides — Polish — Shoe Polishes — Soaps

ADCO, INC.
(Sub. of Mentor Partners LLC)
900 W Main St
Sedalia, MO 65301-3709
Tel.: (660) 826-3300
Fax: (660) 826-1361
Toll Free: (800) 821-7556
E-mail: info@adco-inc.com
Web Site: www.adco-inc.com
Sales Range: $10-24.9 Million
Approx. Number Employees: 95
Year Founded: 1908
Business Description:
Dry Cleaning & Laundry Products Researcher, Developer, Mfr & Marketer
S.I.C.: 2842; 3582
N.A.I.C.S.: 325612; 333312
Export
Media: 2-10
Distr.: Intl.; Natl.
Personnel:
Ken Bazille *(Mgr-Sls)*
Brands & Products:
ADCO
ADCO BOOSTER
ADCO-LITE CHARGE
ADCO SILK-RESTORER
ADCO TIGER
ADVANCE KLEEN
AMAGE
AMAZE
AMYL ACETATE
AQUA SUNSHINE FRESH
BOILER COMPOUND
BOOSTER
D-F-B XTRA
DISCOVER
DYANITE
DYANITE 2000
DYANITE DOUBLE
EASY-OUT
FABRISOFT
FASHION FINISH
FASHION FLAKES
GENERAL FORMULA
GLUEAWAY
H-2-O SIZE
HORIZON
HYDRO SPOT
KNOCK OUT
LANA-LOTION
LANALIN OIL
LEATHER SHEEN
LEATHER SHEEN II
NEUTRA
NO-LINT
NOX-SPOTS
OLD BLUE
PALE OIL
PERK SHEEN
PERK SHEEN 324
PLASTICIZER
PURO
RENEW
RYNEX
SB POG
SELF-SERVE
SEMI-WET
SOFT KLEEN
SOFT KLEEN XTRA
SPEE-DEE
SPRA-DRI
SPRAY SIZING
STAR ANTISTAT
STEVA
SUNSHINE FRESH
SUPER SPRAY
SUPER-TAN
SWADCOTE
TEXTURE LIFE 2000
TIGER
TOP CAT
TRIPLE PLAY 2000
TRIPLE X
TRIPLE X DRI-SHEEN
UNIFORM EMULSIFIER
VIVIA
WATER WHITE
WETCLEANING
WETSPOT
WHITE N BRITE
ZIP-SLICK
Advertising Agency:
Callis & Assoc.
113 E. Third
Sedalia, MO 65301
Tel.: (660) 826-2822
(Dry Cleaning Chemicals)

A.J. FUNK & CO. INC.
1471 Timber Dr
Elgin, IL 60123-1827
Tel.: (847) 741-6760
Fax: (847) 741-6767
Toll Free: (877) 225-3865
E-mail: info@glasscleaner.com
Web Site: www.glasscleaner.com
Approx. Number Employees: 15
Year Founded: 1946
Business Description:
Glass Cleaner Mfr
S.I.C.: 2842; 5169
N.A.I.C.S.: 325612; 424690
Media: 3-5-13-20-23
Distr.: Natl.
Budget Set: Nov.
Personnel:
Richard Lane *(Pres)*
Brands & Products:
SPARKLE

A.L. WILSON CHEMICAL CO.
1050 Harrison Ave
Kearny, NJ 07032-5941
Tel.: (201) 997-3300
Fax: (201) 997-5122
Toll Free: (800) 526-1188
Web Site: www.alwilson.com
Approx. Number Employees: 15
Year Founded: 1928
Business Description:
Mfr. of Laundry & Dry Cleaning Stain Removal Specialty Chemicals
S.I.C.: 2842; 2841
N.A.I.C.S.: 325612; 325611
Export
Media: 2-7-10-20
Distr.: Intl.; Natl.
Personnel:
Frederick G. Schwarzmann *(Pres)*
Brands & Products:
BONGO
COLORGO CHEMICAL
DRO GO
GO-LINE
NOVEL
QWIKGO
RITEGO
RUSTGO
SOGO
SOGO RECLAMATION SYSTEM
SPOTSGO
TARGO
YELLOWGO

ALCONOX, INC.
30 Glenn St Ste 309
White Plains, NY 10603-3252
Tel.: (914) 948-4040
Fax: (914) 948-4088
E-mail: cleaning@alconox.com
Web Site: www.alconox.com
Approx. Number Employees: 25
Year Founded: 1946
Business Description:
Specialty Detergent Mfr for Pharamceutical, Laboratory & Healthcare Cleaning; Powders & Liquids for Manual Cleaning Methods, Mechanical Glassware & Instrument Washing Machines; Tablet Detergent for Syphon Type Pipette & Test-Tube Rinsers
S.I.C.: 2841
N.A.I.C.S.: 325611
Export
Media: 2-4-5-7-8-10-11-13-21
Distr.: Intl.; Natl.
Budget Set: Annually
Personnel:
Stewart Katts *(Pres)*
Elliot M. Lebowitz *(COO)*
Stuart Raetzman *(VP-Mktg (Global) & Area Pres-US)*
Brands & Products:
ALCOJET
ALCONOX
ALCOTABS
CITRAJET
CITRANOX
DET-O-JET
DETERGENT 8
LIQUINOX
LUMINOX
SOLUJET
TERG-A-ZYME
TERGAJET
Advertising Agency:
Morris-Lee Group
Cane Farm Bldg. 3
Rosemont, NJ 08556
Tel.: (609) 397-1911
(Detergent for Critical Cleaning)

ALEN AMERICAS INC.
(Sub. of Industrias Alen S.A. de C.V.)
9326 Baythorn Dr
Houston, TX 77041
Tel.: (832) 484-1508
Fax: (832) 484-1180
Toll Free: (888) 253-6263
E-mail: info@alen.com.mx
Web Site: www.alen.com
Approx. Number Employees: 35
Business Description:
Household Cleaning Products Mfr & Distr

Key to Media (For complete agency information see *The Advertising Red Books-Agencies* edition):
1. Bus. Publs. 2. Cable T.V. 3. Catalogs & Directories. 4. Co-op Adv. 5. Consumer Mags. 6. D.M. to Bus. Estab.7. D.M. to Consumers
8. Daily Newsp. 9. Exhibits/Trade Shows 10. Foreign 11. Infomercial 12. Internet Adv.13. Multimedia 14. Network Radio
15. Network T.V. 16. Newsp. Distr. Mags. 17. Other 18. Outdoor (Posters, Transit) 19. Point of Purchase20. Premiums, Novelties
21. Product Samples 22. Special Events Mktg. 23. Spot Radio 24. Spot T.V. 25. Weekly Newsp. 26. Yellow Page Adv.

S.I.C.: 5169
N.A.I.C.S.: 424690
Media: 9-10-19-21-24
Personnel:
Erwin Salazar *(Mgr-Mktg)*
Brands & Products:
CLORALEN
FESTIVAL
PINEALEN
XTRA DRAIN
XTRA LEMON
XTRA PINE
Advertising Agency:
RPR Marketing Solutions
310 W 18th St Ste 5B
New York, NY 10011
Tel.: (212) 352-9090
Fax: (212) 352-9099

ALUMIN-NU CORPORATION
9513 Woodland Ave
Cleveland, OH 44104-2413
Mailing Address:
PO Box 24359
Lyndhurst, OH 44124
Tel.: (216) 421-2116
Fax: (216) 791-8018
E-mail: info@aluminnuaol.com
Web Site: www.aluminnu.com
Approx. Number Employees: 3
Year Founded: 1963
Business Description:
Liquid Cleaning Compounds for Aluminum, Vinyl & Wood; Septic Cleaner; Gutter Cleaner; Drain Cleaner; Marine Cleaners; Lake & Pond Restoration Clean-Up Mfr
S.I.C.: 2842
N.A.I.C.S.: 325612
Export
Media: 2-3-5-6-9-10-13-19-23-24-25
Distr.: Intl.; Natl.
Budget Set: Feb.
Personnel:
Howard Kaufman *(Chm & Pres)*
Brands & Products:
ALUMIN-NU
DISPOZ-ALL
NICE 'N EASY
POWER SEPTIC
Advertising Agency:
Romanini Advertising
(House Agency)
PO Box 24359
Cleveland, OH 44124
Tel.: (440) 461-2717

AMERICAN SPECIALTIES INC.
(d/b/a ASI)
441 Saw Mill River Rd
Yonkers, NY 10701-4913
Tel.: (914) 476-9000
Fax: (914) 476-0688
E-mail: info@americanspecialties.com
Web Site:
www.americanspecialties.com
Approx. Number Employees: 2,100
Year Founded: 1961
Business Description:
Washroom/Hospital Accessories, Public Telephone Enclosures & Mall Kiosks Mfr
S.I.C.: 3431; 3446
N.A.I.C.S.: 332998; 332323
Import Export
Media: 2-4-7-10-20-21
Distr.: Intl.; Natl.
Budget Set: Dec.
Personnel:
Peter M. Rolla *(CEO)*
Gary Drossman *(CFO)*
Charles V. Labarbera *(COO)*
Brands & Products:
ASI
Advertising Agency:
Catalyst Marketing Communications Inc.
2777 Summer St Ste 301
Stamford, CT 06905
Tel.: (203) 348-7541
Fax: (203) 348-5688

AMERICO MANUFACTURING CO., INC.
6224 N Main St
Acworth, GA 30101-3330
Tel.: (770) 974-7000
Fax: (770) 974-0614
E-mail: info@americomfg.com
Web Site: www.americomfg.com
E-Mail For Key Personnel:
President: rrones@americomfg.com
Sales Range: $10-24.9 Million
Approx. Number Employees: 200
Business Description:
Mfr. & Distributor of Janitorial Supplies
S.I.C.: 3291; 5087
N.A.I.C.S.: 327910; 423850
Import Export
Media: 2-4-7-8-10-19-20
Distr.: Intl.; Natl.
Budget Set: June
Personnel:
Richard L. Rones *(Pres)*
Lenny Shutzberg *(CEO)*
John Miller *(Exec VP-Sls & Mktg)*
Becky Boggio *(Art Dir)*
Sandy Pangle *(Dir-Engrg)*
Douglas Evenson *(Dir-Adv)*
Tom Owens *(Dir-Technical Svcs)*
David Sprayberry *(Dir-Info Sys)*
Marc DuCharme *(Sls Mgr-Natl)*
Kenneth Bryant *(Mgr-Quality Control)*
Nicole Bryant *(Mgr-Sls)*
Fran Caldwell *(Mgr-Credit)*
Julie Charyna *(Mgr-HR)*
Lynne Dyszuk *(Mgr-Pur)*
Vanecia Lord *(Mgr-Customer Svc)*
Jo Anne Newlove *(Mgr-Sls Admin)*
David Whitaker *(Mgr-Inventory)*
Brands & Products:
AMERICO
CHAMPAGNE
COMBO
IMAGE-BEIGE
IMPRESS
LUSTER LITE
OCTOPUS
POLY-FLO
SCRUBBA
SUPER PEA
TWISTER

AMWAY CORPORATION
(Sub. of Alticor Inc.)
7575 Fulton St E
Ada, MI 49355-0001
Tel.: (616) 787-1000
Tel.: (616) 787-7565
Fax: (616) 682-2400
Web Site: www.amway.com
E-Mail For Key Personnel:
Public Relations: amwaypr@amway.com
Approx. Number Employees: 5,000
Year Founded: 1959
Business Description:
Sale of Home & Personal Health, Beauty & Nutrition Products; Household Cleaning Products; Housewares
S.I.C.: 5169; 5122
N.A.I.C.S.: 424690; 424210
Import Export
Media: 1-2-3-4-6-11-13-18-22-26
Distr.: Intl.; Natl.
Budget Set: Sept.
Personnel:
Steve Van Andel *(Chm)*
Doug DeVos *(Pres)*
Eva Cheng *(Exec VP-Greater China)*
Jim Payne *(Exec VP-Sls & Amway Regions)*
Jori Hartwig *(VP-Mktg)*
Jorge Calvachi *(Dir-Insights-Global)*
Yogesh Chavda *(Dir-Consumer & Market Insights)*
Beth Dornan *(Lead-Social Media & PR)*
Brands & Products:
ARTISTRY
DETER
DISH DROPS
DURAMIC
ESPRING
GLISTER
ICOOK
L.O.C.
MINT CONDITION
NUTRILITE
OPTITEMP
POSITRIM
PURSUE
SA8
SATINIQUE
SCENTSCAPES
SUN PACER
VITALOK
VITASOY
Advertising Agencies:
Brandtrust
John Hancock Bldg 875 N Michigan Ave Ste 2945
Chicago, IL 60611
Tel.: (312) 440-1833
Fax: (312) 440-9987

Fitzgerald+CO
3060 Peachtree Rd NW
Atlanta, GA 30305
Tel.: (404) 504-6900
Fax: (404) 239-0548

GSP Marketing Services, Inc.
320 W Ohio St
Chicago, IL 60654
Tel.: (312) 944-3000
Fax: (312) 944-8587

OMD Guangzhou
Rm 3707 Tower B Ctr Plz
Guangzhou, 510610, China
Tel.: (86) 20 3825 1088
Fax: (86) 20 3825 1603
(Artistry, Vitasoy, Media Buying/ Planning)

Weber Shandwick-Minneapolis
8000 Norman Ctr Dr Ste 400
Minneapolis, MN 55437
Tel.: (952) 832-5000
Fax: (952) 831-8241

ARM & HAMMER CONSUMER PRODUCTS
(Unit of Church & Dwight Domestic Consumer Products)
469 N Harrison St
Princeton, NJ 08543-5297
Tel.: (609) 683-5900
Fax: (609) 497-7208
Web Site: www.armhammer.com
Sales Range: $1-4.9 Billion
Approx. Number Employees: 5,000
Year Founded: 1846
Business Description:
Mfr. of Baking Soda, Washing Soda, Heavy Duty Laundry Detergents, Bleaches, Fabric Softener Sheets, Carpet Deodorizers, Deodorizer Sprays, Toothpastes, Deodorant Antiperspirants, Deodorants, Gum & Cat Litter Deodorizer
S.I.C.: 2841; 2812
N.A.I.C.S.: 325611; 325181
Export
Media: 3-6-8-10-15-19-21-24
Distr.: Natl.
Budget Set: Oct.
Personnel:
James R. Craigie *(Chm & CEO)*
Jackie Bravo *(Exec VP-HR)*
David Cohen *(VP-Mktg)*

AXEL PLASTICS RESEARCH LABORATORIES, INC.
PO Box 770855
Woodside, NY 11377
Tel.: (718) 672-8300
Fax: (718) 565-7447
Toll Free: (800) 332-AXEL
E-mail: info@axelplastics.com
Web Site: www.axelplastics.com
Approx. Number Employees: 30
Business Description:
Mold Release Agents, Process Aid Additives, Cleaners & Sealants Designer, Mfr & Marketer for the Plastic & Rubber Industries
S.I.C.: 2992; 2821
N.A.I.C.S.: 324191; 325211
Media: 10
Personnel:
Jacob Axel *(Pres)*
Frank Axel *(CEO)*
Thomas Preisel *(Dir-Sls & Mktg)*
Brands & Products:
AXEL
CLEANWIZ
MOLDWIZ
PASTE WIZ
XTEND
Advertising Agency:
Messer & Susslin & Others, Inc.
274 N Middletown Rd
Pearl River, NY 10965-1216
Tel.: (845) 735-3030
Fax: (845) 735-2270

BI-O-KLEEN INDUSTRIES, INC.
PO Box 820689
Vancouver, WA 98682
Tel.: (360) 576-0064
Fax: (360) 576-0065
Toll Free: (800) 477-0188
E-mail: sales@bi-o-kleen.com
Web Site: www.biokleenhome.com

Key to Media (For complete agency information see *The Advertising Red Books-Agencies* edition):
1. Bus. Publs. 2. Cable T.V. 3. Catalogs & Directories. 4. Co-op Adv. 5. Consumer Mags. 6. D.M. to Bus. Estab.7. D.M. to Consumers
8. Daily Newsp. 9. Exhibits/Trade Shows 10. Foreign 11. Infomercial 12. Internet Adv.13. Multimedia 14. Network Radio
15. Network T.V. 16. Newsp. Distr. Mags. 17. Other 18. Outdoor (Posters, Transit) 19. Point of Purchase20. Premiums, Novelties
21. Product Samples 22. Special Events Mktg. 23. Spot Radio 24. Spot T.V. 25. Weekly Newsp. 26. Yellow Page Adv.

Bi-O-Kleen Industries, Inc. — (Continued)

E-Mail For Key Personnel:
Sales Director: sales@bi-o-kleen.com
Approx. Number Employees: 5
Business Description:
Cleaning Agents
S.I.C.: 5087
N.A.I.C.S.: 423850
Media: 4-6-7-13
Personnel:
Jim Rimer *(Founder & Pres)*
Cindy Rimer *(Mgr-Sls & Mktg)*
Brands & Products:
BAC-OUT
BI-O-KLEEN
CITRUS LAUNDRY LIQUID
LEMON THYME DISHWASH LIQUID
OXYGEN BLEACH PLUS
SOY BLENDS
TOUGH ON DIRT, GENTLE ON THE EARTH

BLUE CROSS LABORATORIES

20950 Ctr Point Pkwy
Saugus, CA 91350-2621
Tel.: (661) 255-0955
Fax: (661) 255-3628
E-mail: bluecrosslabs@bc-labs.com
Web Site: www.bc-labs.com
Approx. Number Employees: 100
Year Founded: 1951
Business Description:
Household Cleaning Products Mfr
S.I.C.: 2842
N.A.I.C.S.: 325612
Export
Advertising Expenditures: $610,000
Media: 10-17-25
Distr.: Natl.
Personnel:
Darrell Mahler *(Pres & Mgr-Sls & Adv)*
Brands & Products:
ADMIRE
ALPINE PINE
AMAZIN
AQUA
ARCTIC ICE
AROMA SPA
BABY DAYS
BAHAMA BALM
BALSAM
BLUE CROSS LABORATORIES
BLUE TOO
CARESSA
CARPET CARE
CHOLESTROL
CLEAN SWEEP
COLOR-EZ
DE LA RITZ
DERMA CARE
DERMA CLEAN
DR. FOOT
DRAIN OPENER
EXTREME HEAT
FAB FACE
FABRIC REFRESHER
FIELDBREEZE
FLEES AWAY
FORMULA-4-ALL
FRESH PLUS
GRABS-ALL
HAND RX
HEALTH ALLWAYS
HERBAL BOUQUET
IMPRESS
KIDS TIME BUBBLE BATH
KITCHEN RX
KLEEN POWER
LA BOUTIQUE
LADIES DAY
LOOK 'N' FINE
MACHO
MAJOR BRITE
MEN'S CHOICE
MOP & SHINE
NATURE'S BEST
NOW YOU'RE STYLIN
OIL OF LIFE
OUT-U-SCUM
PAN PAL
PET STAIN
PINE FOREST
PRESCRIPTION CARE
PRO POWER
REGATTA
RELIEF
ROYAL FLUSH
RUG RELIEF
SALON DESIGNS
SCENT-SATION
SENSATION
SHOWER BRITE
SOIL & STAIN
SPEEDER
SUAVECITO
SWEET TALK
TAB-BLU
TILE POWER
TOILET BRITE
TRUE PINE
TRUE POTPURRI
ULTRA DISH
ULTRA FLUFFY
ULTRA OXY
VITASILK
WINDOW CLEAR
WOOL 'N CARE
XCESS

BRONDOW, INC.

68 Marbledale Rd
Tuckahoe, NY 10707-3420
Tel.: (914) 961-9026
Fax: (914) 961-9216
E-mail: info@brondow.com
Web Site: www.brondow.com
Approx. Number Employees: 20
Year Founded: 1947
Business Description:
Mfr. of Household Cleaners, Disinfectants & Deodorizers
S.I.C.: 2842
N.A.I.C.S.: 325612
Export
Advertising Expenditures: $200,000
Media: 5-9-19
Distr.: Reg.
Budget Set: June
Personnel:
Timothy E. Kelley *(Pres)*
Brands & Products:
BREATH-O-PINE
CLEAN AND FRESH
CLEAN PINE
FRESCO

BURNISHINE PRODUCTS

(Div. of Weiman Products, LLC)
755 Tri Sta Pkwy
Gurnee, IL 60031
Tel.: (847) 263-3500
Fax: (847) 263-3700
Toll Free: (800) 837-8140
Web Site: www.weimanburnishine.com
E-Mail For Key Personnel:
President: cdemasi@burnishine.com
Approx. Number Employees: 50
Year Founded: 1887
Business Description:
Chemical Products Mfr
S.I.C.: 2899
N.A.I.C.S.: 325998
Media: 2-4-5-8-10-13-19-21
Distr.: Natl.
Budget Set: Dec.
Personnel:
Carl DeMasi *(Pres & CEO)*
Patty Vick *(Mgr-Natl Sls)*
Brands & Products:
AQUA BLUE
CLEAR GEL
CRA-Z-SOAP
EPI-SAFE BARRIER CREAM
FLEXO CLEANER
GOLD MIRACLE
PLATE-SAV-UR
PRINTERS PRIDE-FOUNTAIN SOLUTIONS
PUTZ-POMADE
SAFETY FOUNT
THUMBS-UP
TONE-A-WAY
ULTRA FOUNT

CELLO PROFESSIONAL PRODUCTS

(Sub. of Carroll Company)
1354 Old Post Rd
Havre De Grace, MD 21078-3802
Tel.: (410) 939-1234
Fax: (410) 939-3028
Toll Free: (800) 638-4850
Web Site: www.cello-online.com
Approx. Number Employees: 42
Year Founded: 1977
Business Description:
Mfr of Industrial Cleaning Products
S.I.C.: 2842
N.A.I.C.S.: 325612
Export
Media: 4-10
Distr.: Natl.
Budget Set: Jan.
Personnel:
Rosie Blankinship *(Mgr-Customer Svc)*
Brands & Products:
CELLO

CHEMED CORPORATION

2600 Chemed Ctr 255 E 5th St
Cincinnati, OH 45202-4726
Tel.: (513) 762-6900
Fax: (513) 762-6919
Toll Free: (800) GET-ROTO
E-mail: info@rotorooter.com
Web Site: www.chemed.com
Approx. Rev.: $1,280,545,000
Approx. Number Employees: 13,058
Year Founded: 1935
Business Description:
Plumbing & Drain Cleaning Services to Residential & Commercial Customers
S.I.C.: 1711; 7699; 8744
N.A.I.C.S.: 238220; 561210; 562991
Export
Advertising Expenditures: $27,000,000
Media: 2-3-5-7-8-9-13-14-15-18-23-24-25-26
Distr.: Natl.
Budget Set: July -Nov.
Personnel:
George J. Walsh, III *(Chm)*
Kevin J. McNamara *(Pres & CEO)*
David P. Williams *(CFO & Exec VP)*
Lisa A. Reinhard *(Chief Admin Officer)*
Spencer S. Lee *(Exec VP)*
Timothy S. O'Toole *(Exec VP)*
Brands & Products:
CHEMED
ROTO-ROOTER
VITAS

THE CLOROX COMPANY

1221 Broadway
Oakland, CA 94612-1888
Mailing Address:
PO Box 24305
Oakland, CA 94623-1305
Tel.: (510) 271-7000
Fax: (510) 832-1463
Telex: 336-423
E-mail: clorox.investor.relations@clorox.com
Web Site: www.thecloroxcompany.com
Approx. Sls.: $5,534,000,000
Approx. Number Employees: 8,300
Year Founded: 1913
Business Description:
Cleaning Products, Housewares, Personal Care & Pet Products Mfr
S.I.C.: 2842; 0752
N.A.I.C.S.: 325612; 812910
Export
Advertising Expenditures: $518,000,000
Media: 3-6-7-8-13-14-15-16-20-23-24-25
Distr.: Intl.; Natl.
Personnel:
Donald R. Knauss *(Chm & CEO)*
Stephen M. Robb *(CFO & Sr VP)*
Thomas P. Britanik *(CMO & Sr VP)*
Wayne L. Delker *(Chief Innovation Officer & Sr VP-Global R & D)*
Laura Stein *(Gen Councel & Sr VP)*
Frank A. Tataseo *(Exec VP-Strategy, Growth & Partnerships)*
Benno Dorer *(Sr VP & Gen Mgr-Cleaning Div)*
George C. Roeth *(Sr VP & Gen Mgr-Specialty Div)*
James Foster *(Chief Product Supply Officer & Sr VP)*
Jacqueline P. Kane *(Sr VP-HR & Corp Affairs)*
Grant J. LaMontagne *(Chief Customer Officer & Sr VP)*
Sara Edel *(Dir-Insights, Brand Insights & Specialty Div-Global)*
Mary O'Connell *(Dir-Digital Media)*
Hilda S. West *(Dir-Client Svcs)*
David Kargas *(Sr Mgr-PR)*
Michelle Roberts *(Sr Mgr-Interactive Mktg)*
Carole Louie *(Sr Grp Mgr-Media Plng)*
Sumi Cate *(Mgr-Res & Dev)*
Drew McGowan *(Mgr)*
Nicholas Meyer *(Mgr-Mktg)*
Christa Patrylak *(Mgr-Digital Mktg)*
Brands & Products:
ADVANTAGE
ANT RID

ARCO IRIS
ARELA
ARMOR ALL
ARMOR ALL FIERCE SHINE TIRE FOAM
ASTRA
AYUDIN
BLACK FLAG
BLANQUITA
BLEACH PEN
BLUEBELL
BON BRIL
BRIMAX
BRITA
BURT'S BEES
CERACOL
CHUX
CLEAN-UP
CLORINDA
CLORISOL
CLOROX
CLOROX 2
CLOROX ANYWHERE
CLOROX ANYWHERE HARD SURFACE
CLOROX BLEACH PEN
CLOROX CLEAN-UP
CLOROX COMMERCIAL SOLUTIONS
CLOROX FRESHCARE
CLOROX GENTLE
CLOROX PLUS
CLOROX SCOOBA
CLOROX STAIN OUT
CLOROX ULTIMATE CARE
CLOROX2
COLOUR MORE
COMBAT
EMPERATRIZ
EVER CLEAN
EVERCLEAN
EVERFRESH
FLEUR
FLUSS
FORMULA 409
FRESH SCENT CLOROX
FRESH SCENT TILEX
FRESH STEP
FRESH STEP PLUS DUAL ACTION CRYSTALS
GLAD
GLAD-LOCK
GLADWARE
GREEN WORKS
GUMPTION
HANDI-WIPES
HANDYANDY
HEAVY-WIPES
HIDDEN VALLEY
HOME MAT
HOMEKEEPER
JETS
JONNY CAT
K.C. MASTERPIECE
KINGSFORD
KINGSFORD BBQ BAG
KINGSFORD MATCH LIGHT
KITCHEN BOUQUET
LAVENDER CLEAN PINE-SOL
LEMON FRESH CLOROX
LEMON FRESH PINE-SOL
LEMON MILDEW ROOT
LESTOIL
LIMPIDO
LIQUID-PLUMR
LIQUID-PLUMR FOAMING PIPE SNAKE
LOS CONEJOS
LUMINOSA
LUSTRILLO
MAXFORCE
MISTOLIN
MONO
MORTIMER
MOUNTAIN ENERGY PINE-SOL
OOMPH!
ORANGE ENERGY PINE-SOL
OSO
OXI MAGIC
OXIMAGIC
PERFEX
PINE-SOL
PINEXO
PINOLUZ
POETT
PROFESSIONAL STRENGTH LIQUID-PLUMR
RAIN DANCE
READYMOP
ROOMATE
ROTA
SABRA
SANI
SBP
SCOOP AWAY
SELLO ROJO
SELTON
SNAP LOCK
SOFT SCRUB
S.O.S.
SPARKLING WAVE PINE-SOL
STP
STP SON OF A GUN
SUPER GLOBO
TILEX
TILEX MILDEW ROOT
TOILETWAND
TRENET
TUFF STUFF
TUFFY
ULTRA CLOROX2
WASH 'N DRI
WAX-IT-DRY
WE MAKE EVERYDAY LIFE BETTER, EVERY DAY.
WILD FLOWER PINE-SOL
XLO
YUHANROX

Advertising Agencies:

AKQA, Inc.
118 King St 6th Fl
San Francisco, CA 94107
Tel.: (415) 645-9400
Fax: (415) 645-9420
Digital Media

Big Fuel Communications LLC
298 5th Ave 5th Fl
New York, NY 10001
Tel.: (212) 616-6300
Fax: (212) 658-9226

DDB Budapest
Dozsa Gyorgy ut 84/a 3rd Floor
H-1068
Budapest, Hungary
Tel.: (36) 1 461 2800
Fax: (36) 1 321 6270

DDB Canada
33 Bloor Street East Suite 1700
Toronto, ON M4W 3T4, Canada
Tel.: (416) 925-9819
Fax: (416) 925-4180

DDB San Francisco
555 Market St 5th Fl
San Francisco, CA 94105
Tel.: (415) 732-3600
Fax: (415) 732-3636
(Laundry Additive & Home Cleaning Products, Glad & Armor All)
Green Works

Dieste
1999 Bryan St Ste 2700
Dallas, TX 75201
Tel.: (214) 259-8000
Fax: (214) 259-8040
Pine-Sol

Don Jagoda Associates, Inc.
100 Marcus Dr
Melville, NY 11747-4229
Tel.: (631) 454-1800
Fax: (631) 454-1834
(Promotions)

Edelman
525 Market St Ste 1400
San Francisco, CA 94105
Tel.: (415) 222-9944
Fax: (415) 222-9924
(Brita, Environmental)

Euro RSCG 4D Impact
2885 Pacific Dr Ste A
Norcross, GA 30071-1807
Tel.: (888) 788-5918
Fax: (770) 248-9014
Toll Free: (888) 788-5918

Euro RSCG EDGE
915 SW Stark St 2nd Fl
Portland, OR 97205-3017
Tel.: (503) 228-5555
Fax: (503) 228-0560

OMD Canada
67 Richmond St W 2nd Fl
Toronto, ON M5H 1Z5, Canada
Tel.: (416) 681-5600
Fax: (416) 681-5620

OMD-USA
195 Broadway
New York, NY 10007
Tel.: (212) 590-7100
Scoop Away

Porter Novelli-Los Angeles
10960 Wilshire Blvd Ste 1750
Los Angeles, CA 90024-3715
Tel.: (310) 444-7000
Fax: (310) 444-7004

Tribal DDB San Francisco
555 Market St Ste 500
San Francisco, CA 94105
Tel.: (415) 732-2200
Fax: (415) 732-2295
Armor All
Clorox
Fresh Step
Glad
Tilex

CONNOISSEURS PRODUCTS CORPORATION

17 Presidential Dr
Woburn, MA 01801
Tel.: (781) 932-3949
Fax: (781) 932-4755
Toll Free: (800) 851-5333
Web Site: www.connoisseurs.com
Approx. Sls.: $19,600,000
Approx. Number Employees: 90
Year Founded: 1997
Business Description:
Jewelry & Silver Care Products Mfr
S.I.C.: 2842; 3291
N.A.I.C.S.: 325612; 327910
Media: 6
Personnel:
Douglas Dorfman *(Owner)*
John Archambault *(Exec VP-Fin & Admin)*
Brands & Products:
BEAUTY SPAS
BEAUTY TREATMENTS FOR JEWELRY
CLEANSING GEL AND BRUSH
CONNOISSEURS
GENUINE LEATHER CARRIERS
JEWELRY SOAP
JEWELRY WIPES
JUST WIPE'N SERVE
LA SONIC
LEATHERETTE CARRYALLS
METAL POLISH
SILVER POLISH
SILVER WIPES
SPAS
ULTRASOFT

CONTICO MANUFACTURING, L.L.C.

(Sub. of Katy Industries, Inc.)
305 Rock Industrial Park Dr
Saint Louis, MO 63044
Tel.: (314) 739-8585
Fax: (800) 327-5492
Toll Free: (800) 831-7077
Web Site: www.continentalcommercialproducts.com
Sales Range: $250-299.9 Million
Approx. Number Employees: 1,600
Year Founded: 1964
Business Description:
Sanitary Maintenance Equipment & Supplies; Tool & Storage Boxes, Shutters & Other Molded Plastic Houseware & Hardware Items; Plastic & Metal Pickup Truck Accessories; Plastic Industrial Containers; Plastic Trigger Sprayers & Dispensers
S.I.C.: 3089; 3082; 3084; 5122
N.A.I.C.S.: 326199; 326121; 326122; 446120
Import Export
Advertising Expenditures: $2,000,000
Media: 2-4-10-26
Distr.: Intl.; Natl.
Personnel:
David C. Cooksey *(CFO & VP-Fin)*
Jim Shaffer *(CFO & VP-Fin)*
Trish Vonder Haar *(Mgr-Mktg Commun)*
Brands & Products:
CONTICO

COPPER-BRITE, INC.

1482 E Valley Rd Ste 29
Santa Barbara, CA 93108-1200
Tel.: (805) 565-1566
Fax: (805) 565-1394
E-mail: adbrite@copperbrite.com
Web Site: www.copperbrite.com
E-Mail For Key Personnel:
Sales Director: tkbrite@copperbrite.com

Key to Media (For complete agency information see *The Advertising Red Books-Agencies* edition):
1. Bus. Publs. 2. Cable T.V. 3. Catalogs & Directories. 4. Co-op Adv. 5. Consumer Mags. 6. D.M. to Bus. Estab.7. D.M. to Consumers
8. Daily Newsp. 9. Exhibits/Trade Shows 10. Foreign 11. Infomercial 12. Internet Adv.13. Multimedia 14. Network Radio
15. Network T.V. 16. Newsp. Distr. Mags. 17. Other 18. Outdoor (Posters, Transit) 19. Point of Purchase20. Premiums, Novelties
21. Product Samples 22. Special Events Mktg. 23. Spot Radio 24. Spot T.V. 25. Weekly Newsp. 26. Yellow Page Adv.

Copper-Brite, Inc. — (Continued)
Approx. Number Employees: 2
Year Founded: 1951
Business Description:
Cleaners & Insecticides Mfr
S.I.C.: 2879; 2842
N.A.I.C.S.: 325320; 325612
Export
Media: 2-6-9-15-16-23-25
Distr.: Natl.
Personnel:
Alan D. Brite *(Pres & CEO)*
Terry K. Brite *(Exec VP)*
Brands & Products:
COPPER BRITE
ROACH PRUFE
TERMITE PRUFE
Advertising Agency:
Terry Brite Advertising-Division/Copper Brite Inc.
1482 E Valley Rd Ste 29
Santa Barbara, CA 93108-1200
Tel.: (805) 565-1566
Fax: (805) 565-1394
(Roach Prufe, Copper Brite, & Termite Prufe)

COVE CLEANERS, INC.
1400 Fruitville Rd
Sarasota, FL 34236
Tel.: (941) 365-8448
Fax: (941) 924-6764
E-mail: info@covecleaners.com
Web Site: www.covecleaners.com
Approx. Rev.: $1,500,000
Approx. Number Employees: 32
Year Founded: 1993
Business Description:
Drycleaners
S.I.C.: 7212
N.A.I.C.S.: 812320
Media: 13-18-24-26
Personnel:
Allan Loring *(CEO)*

CRC INDUSTRIES, INC.
(Sub. of Berwind Corporation)
885 Louis Dr
Warminster, PA 18974-0586
Tel.: (215) 674-4300
Fax: (215) 674-2196
E-mail: crcwebmaster@crcindustries.com
Web Site: www.crcindustries.com
Sales Range: $125-149.9 Million
Approx. Number Employees: 150
Year Founded: 1958
Business Description:
Mfr. of Electrical, Industrial, Marine, Aviation and Automotive Chemicals, Oil & Gasoline Additives, Cleaning Compounds, Starting Fluid, De-Icer, Battery Cleaner, Penetrants, Undercoatings, Diesel Products, Degreasers, Hand Cleaner & Appearance Products
S.I.C.: 2992; 3471
N.A.I.C.S.: 324191; 332813
Export
Media: 2-4-5-6-10-19-20-21
Distr.: Natl.
Budget Set: Sept.
Personnel:
Scott J. Grey *(Pres)*
Wayne King *(VP-Indus Sls-Mktg)*
Ken Cantwell *(Dir-Mktg)*
Greg DelGozzo *(Mgr-Natl Accts)*
Brands & Products:
2-26
3-36
DUSTER
HYDROFORCE
ICE-OFF
MINUTE MEND
PERMANENT METALLIC
POWERLUBE
SCREWLOOSE
SMOKE TEST
STA-LUBE
STOPLIGHT
SUPER DEGREASER
WASP & HORNET KILLER PLUS

CRITZAS INDUSTRIES, INC.
4041 Park Ave
Saint Louis, MO 63110-2319
Tel.: (314) 773-8510
Fax: (314) 773-4837
Toll Free: (877) 266-1290
E-mail: sales@goophandcleaner.com
Web Site: www.goophandcleaner.com
E-Mail For Key Personnel:
Sales Director: sales@goophandcleaner.com
Sales Range: $10-24.9 Million
Approx. Number Employees: 30
Year Founded: 1949
Business Description:
Towels, Soaps & Hand Lotion Mfr
S.I.C.: 2842; 7389
N.A.I.C.S.: 325612; 561910
Export
Media: 4-5-10-13-19-21-22
Distr.: Intl.; Natl.
Personnel:
Blake Critzas *(Owner & Pres)*
Brands & Products:
GOOP
GOOP FIRST CHOICE
GOOP ORIGINAL FORMULA
GOOP PRINTER'S FRIEND
GOOP PUM-X
GROOMER'S GOOP
MOM'S GOOP
ORANGE GOOP

CRYSTAL CLEANING BY LAVINA, INC.
8420 Ulmerton Rd
Largo, FL 33771
Tel.: (727) 709-3558
Web Site:
www.crystalcleaningbylavina.com
Business Description:
Residential & Commercial Cleaning Services
S.I.C.: 7217
N.A.I.C.S.: 561740
Media: 13
Personnel:
Lavina Dos Santos *(Pres)*

CUSTOM CHEMICAL FORMULATORS, INC.
8707 Millergrove Dr
Santa Fe Springs, CA 90670
Tel.: (562) 699-5070
Fax: (562) 699-8953
E-mail: stacy@customchem.com
Web Site: www.customchem.com
E-Mail For Key Personnel:
Sales Director: sales@customchem.com
Approx. Number Employees: 45
Year Founded: 1964
Business Description:
Cleaning Preparations & Industrial Chemicals Mfr
S.I.C.: 2842
N.A.I.C.S.: 325612
Media: 4
Personnel:
Stacy Roselli *(Dir-Mktg & Sls)*

DURACLEAN INTERNATIONAL, INC.
220 Campus Dr
Arlington Heights, IL 60004-1498
Tel.: (847) 704-7100
Fax: (847) 704-7101
Toll Free: (800) 251-7070
E-mail: franchise@duraclean.com
Web Site: www.duraclean.com
Approx. Number Employees: 20
Year Founded: 1930
Business Description:
Cleaning Services
S.I.C.: 6794; 2842
N.A.I.C.S.: 533110; 325612
Export
Media: 2-6-10-11-13-20-22-26
Distr.: Intl.; Natl.
Budget Set: Jan. -Dec.
Personnel:
Vince Caffarello *(Pres)*
Wilbur A. Gage *(Exec VP)*
Brands & Products:
DURACLEAN
DURAPROOF
DURASHIELD PLUS
EXTRACTOVATOR
FABRICRAFTER
FLOWER FRESH
ROSE SYMBOL
SPOTCRAFT
SPRAYMASTER

DURASOL DRUG CHEMICAL CO.
1 Oakland St
Amesbury, MA 01913-3013
Tel.: (978) 388-2020
Fax: (978) 388-9762
Toll Free: (800) 370-0683
E-mail: durasol@verizon.net
Web Site: www.durasolcorp.com
Sales Range: $10-24.9 Million
Approx. Number Employees: 15
Year Founded: 1938
Business Description:
Mfr. & Supplier of Adhesives, Gum Erasers, Cleaning Solutions & Eyeglass Cleaners
S.I.C.: 5047; 5912
N.A.I.C.S.: 423450; 446110
Import Export
Advertising Expenditures: $290,000
Media: 5-8-10-13-21
Distr.: Intl.; Natl.
Budget Set: Jan.
Personnel:
Lisa J. Israel *(Pres)*
Sally P. Israel *(Mng Dir)*
Walter H. Israel *(Treas & Mgr-Adv)*
Jane E. Israel *(Exec VP)*
Brands & Products:
CONCREDAMP
DURASOL
ENDSLIP
Advertising Agency:
Walter Lyons & Associates
7 Charles Rd
Swampscott, MA 01907-1619
Tel.: (978) 388-2032
Fax: (978) 388-9762
(Dental Plate Adhesives)

EARTH FRIENDLY PRODUCTS
(Sub. of Venus Laboratories Inc.)
111 S Rohlwing Rd
Addison, IL 60101
Tel.: (847) 446-4441
Fax: (847) 446-4437
E-mail: contact@ecos.com
Web Site: www.ecos.com
Year Founded: 1993
Business Description:
Environmentally Safe Cleaning Products Mfr
S.I.C.: 2842; 3586
N.A.I.C.S.: 325612; 333913
Media: 6-13
Personnel:
John Vlahakis *(Pres)*
Val Osakada *(Dir-Mktg)*

ECOLAB INC.
Ecolab Ctr 370 N Wabasha St
Saint Paul, MN 55102
Tel.: (651) 293-2233
Fax: (651) 293-2092
Toll Free: (800) 232-6522
Telex: 910 563 3739
E-mail: ecolab@ecolab.com
Web Site: www.ecolab.com
Approx. Sls.: $6,089,700,000
Approx. Number Employees: 26,494
Year Founded: 1923
Business Description:
Cleaning, Food Safety & Health Protection Products & Services
S.I.C.: 2841; 0752; 2879; 4959
N.A.I.C.S.: 325611; 115210; 325320; 562998
Export
Personnel:
Douglas M. Baker, Jr. *(Chm, Pres & CEO)*
Steven L. Fritze *(CFO)*
Robert P. Tabb *(CIO)*
Larry L. Berger *(CTO & Sr VP)*
Daniel J. Schmechel *(Chief Transformation Officer)*
Thomas W. Handley *(Pres-Global Food & Beverage & Asia Pacific Latin America)*
Phillip J. Mason *(Pres-EMEA Sector)*
James A. Miller *(Pres-Institutional Sector)*
Susan K. Nestegard *(Pres-Global Healthcare)*
James H. White *(Pres-Sector-Intl)*
Lawrence T. Bell *(Gen Counsel)*
Michael A. Hickey *(Exec VP)*
Thomas W. Schnack *(Exec VP)*
William C. Snedeker *(Exec VP-Global Svcs Sector)*
Tim Mulhere *(Sr VP & Gen Mgr-Food & Beverage NA)*
Michael L. Meyer *(Sr VP-HR)*
Tom Arata *(VP-Mktg, Global Antimicrobial & Hand Care Programs)*
William W. Goetz *(VP-Corp Mktg)*
Roger Tippet *(VP-R&D & Engrg-Water & Energy Mgmt)*
Jennifer Kirscher *(Supvr-Mktg Comm)*
Brands & Products:
ABSORBIT
ADDITIVE 601
ADVACARE

Key to Media (For complete agency information see *The Advertising Red Books-Agencies* edition):
1. Bus. Publs. 2. Cable T.V. 3. Catalogs & Directories. 4. Co-op Adv. 5. Consumer Mags. 6. D.M. to Bus. Estab.7. D.M. to Consumers
8. Daily Newsp. 9. Exhibits/Trade Shows 10. Foreign 11. Infomercial 12. Internet Adv.13. Multimedia 14. Network Radio
15. Network T.V. 16. Newsp. Distr. Mags. 17. Other 18. Outdoor (Posters, Transit) 19. Point of Purchase20. Premiums, Novelties
21. Product Samples 22. Special Events Mktg. 23. Spot Radio 24. Spot T.V. 25. Weekly Newsp. 26. Yellow Page Adv.

AIRDEFENSE
BLACK MAGIC
BLUE CORAL
CENTRAMATIC 52
CHECKPOINT
DECARBONIZER
DECARBONIZER MXP
DETERGENT 101
ECO-TEMP
ECO2000
ECOLAB
ECOSURE
EZ DRY
FORCE 5
GROUNDFORCE
HSRA
HUNTINGTON
INNSPECT BED BUG SERVICE
KLENZ-GLIDE
MIKRO-SPRAY
OASIS
OXY-GARD
PROGUARD
SENSO-MATIC
SOFISTICARTS
SOILAX
STEALTH
SURGI-BAC
S.W.A.T.
TRI-CHEM
TRI-STAR
TRI-STAR L
TRU-FEED 50
TURBO
WING COMMAND

Advertising Agencies:
The Aristos Group
750 E Lake St
Wayzata, MN 55391
Tel.: (952) 449-4100
Fax: (952) 449-4119

Paulsen Marketing Communications, Inc.
(d/b/a Paulsen AgriBranding)
3510 S 1st Ave Cir
Sioux Falls, SD 57105-5807
Tel.: (605) 336-1745
Fax: (605) 336-2305

ECOLAB INC.-FOOD & BEVERAGE DIVISION

(Div. of Ecolab Inc.)
Ecolab Ctr 370 N Wabasha St
Saint Paul, MN 55102
Tel.: (651) 293-2233
Fax: (651) 293-2092
Toll Free: (800) 352-5326
Sales Range: $1-4.9 Billion
Business Description:
Environment Sanitation Products & Services
S.I.C.: 2841; 0752; 4959
N.A.I.C.S.: 325611; 115210; 562998
Media: 2-7-10-19-20
Distr.: Natl.
Budget Set: Nov.
Personnel:
Nicholas Alfano *(VP-Corp Sls)*

ECOLAB INTERNATIONAL DIVISION

(Div. of Ecolab Inc.)
Ecolab Ctr 370 N Wabasha St
Saint Paul, MN 55102
Tel.: (651) 293-2233
Fax: (651) 225-2092
Web Site: www.ecolab.com/Directory/Country.asp?c=US
Sales Range: $200-249.9 Million
Business Description:
Cleansers & Sanitizers Mfr & Distr
S.I.C.: 2841; 2842
N.A.I.C.S.: 325611; 325612
Media: 6-11
Personnel:
Thomas Schnack *(Exec VP-Food & Beverage, Water Care, Ecovation, North)*

EVERGREEN LABS, INC.

4 W Rees Ave
Walla Walla, WA 99362
Tel.: (509) 527-0607
Fax: (509) 522-0351
Toll Free: (888) 946-3292
E-mail: info@wineaway.com
Web Site: www.wineaway.com
E-Mail For Key Personnel:
President: staci@hscis.net
Marketing Director: cherylc@hscis.net
Sales Director: cherylc@hscis.net
Sales Range: Less than $1 Million
Approx. Number Employees: 20
Business Description:
Cleaning & Sanitation Supplies Whslr
S.I.C.: 5169
N.A.I.C.S.: 424690
Media: 6-10-13
Personnel:
Staci Wanichek *(Pres-Domestic)*
Cheryl Corn *(VP & Dir-Mktg, Sls & Intl)*
Brands & Products:
RED ERASE
WINE AWAY

FAULTLESS STARCH/BON AMI COMPANY

1025 W 8th St
Kansas City, MO 64101-1207
Tel.: (816) 842-1230
Fax: (816) 842-3417
E-mail: info@faultless.com
Web Site: www.faultless.com
Approx. Number Employees: 400
Year Founded: 1887
Business Description:
Mfr. & Marketer of Laundry & Household Cleaning Products
S.I.C.: 2842
N.A.I.C.S.: 325612
Import Export
Media: 1-3-6-8-9-10-11-15-16-18-19-20-23-24-25
Distr.: Intl.; Natl.
Personnel:
Gordon T. Beaham, III *(Chm & Co-CEO)*
Robert B. Beaham *(Vice Chm, Co-CEO & Treas)*
David G. Beaham *(Pres & Co-CEO)*
Shannan Habiger *(VP-Fin)*
Benjamin Stark *(VP-Mktg)*
Brands & Products:
BON AMI
BRIGHT LINE
COBRA
FAULTLESS
FOLD-FLAT
FOLD-FLAT CART
GARDEN CLAW
GARDEN CLAW GOLD
GARDEN WEASEL
GARDEN WEASEL EDGER
HANDYBAR
HOT IRON
KLEEN KING
LAWN-CLAW
MAGIC
MAGIC PREMIUM STARCH
MAGIC SIZING
PRIVATE GARDENS
RUXXAC
SILVER SATIN
STAR BRIGHT
STARPOWER
STEEL GLO
THATCHMASTER
TOUCH UP
TRAPP
TRAPP PRIVATE GARDENS
WEASEL YOUR WAY OUT OF YARD WORK
WEED POPPER

FINE ORGANICS CORPORATION

420 Kuller Rd
Clifton, NJ 07015-2277
Tel.: (973) 478-1000
Fax: (973) 478-6120
Toll Free: (800) 526-7480
E-mail: chembiz@aol.com
Web Site: www.fineorganicscorp.com
Approx. Number Employees: 13
Year Founded: 1939
Business Description:
Specialty & Maintenance Cleaners Mfr
S.I.C.: 2842
N.A.I.C.S.: 325612
Export
Media: 2-7-21
Distr.: Direct to Consumer; Natl.
Budget Set: Oct.
Personnel:
William J. Reidy *(Chm & CEO)*
Gary F. Straub *(Pres & COO)*
Lewis Goldberg *(Mgr-Sls)*
Brands & Products:
ENVIROSOLV
FO
MEGAPOWER
OMEGA
ZODIAC PRODUCTS

THE FULLER BRUSH COMPANY

(Holding of Buckingham Capital Partners, L.P.)
1 Fuller Way
Great Bend, KS 67530
Mailing Address:
PO Box 729
Great Bend, KS 67530-0729
Tel.: (620) 792-1711
Fax: (620) 792-1906
Fax: (800) 538-3332
Toll Free: (800) 551-3030
E-mail: info@fuller.com
Web Site: www.fuller.com
Approx. Number Employees: 230
Year Founded: 1906
Business Description:
Mfr. of Products for Commercial Use, Household Cleaning & Personal Care
S.I.C.: 2842; 3991
N.A.I.C.S.: 325612; 339994
Import Export
Advertising Expenditures: $4,155,000
Media: 4-8-10-13-23-24
Distr.: Catalog; Direct to Consumer; Direct to Retailer; Natl.
Budget Set: Oct. -Nov.
Personnel:
Larry H. Gray *(VP-Consumer Sls & Mktg)*
Mike Whelan *(Art Dir)*
Brands & Products:
BATLIGHT
BIG WALLY
CUSHION SOFT
DIAMOND CUT
FORMULA 21
FULLPOWER
NATURE'S CHOICE
SPRAY 'N SPARKLE

HERCULES CHEMICAL CO., INC.

111 S St
Passaic, NJ 07055-7901
Tel.: (973) 778-5000
Fax: (800) 333-3456
Toll Free: (800) 221-9330
E-mail: info@herchem.com
Web Site: www.herchem.com
Approx. Number Employees: 100
Year Founded: 1915
Business Description:
Plumbing & Industrial Chemicals & Equipment Solders & Fluxes; Drain & Waste System Cleaners; Boiler & Heating System Cleaners; Oils; Stop-Leak Chemicals; Root Destroyers; Paints; Brushes & Accessories; Plastic Pipe Cements; Bowl Settings; Gaskets; Bolts; Anti-Freeze; Access Doors; Sealants for Threaded Pipe
S.I.C.: 2899; 3432
N.A.I.C.S.: 325998; 332913
Export
Advertising Expenditures: $580,000
Media: 2-4-5-7-10-19-20-21
Distr.: Natl.
Budget Set: Dec.
Personnel:
David Siegal *(Pres & CEO)*
Leonard A. Ruvolo *(CFO & VP-Admin)*
Wayne A. Merrifield *(Dir-Tech)*
John Domanico *(Mgr-IS)*
Erastus Muchioki *(Mgr-Safety)*
Carmen Santoro *(Mgr-Distr)*
Brands & Products:
AID-OX
BACTA-LIFE
BASE HIT
BASE HIT II
BLACK MAGIC
BLAZEMASTER
BLOCK
BLOT-O
BLOT-O PLUS
BREAK-THRU
CLEAN 'N FRIENDLY
CLIMATE SMOOTH
CLOBBER
CLORO-DOSER
CLOROBEN
CLOROBEN BACTA-LIFE
CLOROBEN DE
CLOROBEN DRAIN SNAKE
CLOROCLEAN
CORZAN
CRYO-TEK
DOUBLE AGENT

Key to Media (For complete agency information see *The Advertising Red Books-Agencies* edition):
1. Bus. Publs. 2. Cable T.V. 3. Catalogs & Directories. 4. Co-op Adv. 5. Consumer Mags. 6. D.M. to Bus. Estab.7. D.M. to Consumers 8. Daily Newsp. 9. Exhibits/Trade Shows 10. Foreign 11. Infomercial 12. Internet Adv.13. Multimedia 14. Network Radio 15. Network T.V. 16. Newsp. Distr. Mags. 17. Other 18. Outdoor (Posters, Transit) 19. Point of Purchase20. Premiums, Novelties 21. Product Samples 22. Special Events Mktg. 23. Spot Radio 24. Spot T.V. 25. Weekly Newsp. 26. Yellow Page Adv.

Hercules Chemical Co., Inc. — (Continued)

DUCK BUTTER
DUPONT
FLIP-STICK
GLUG
GRIP
GRIT-ROLL
GRRIP
GRRIP LITE
H2O
H2OFLUX
HERCULES
HERCULES FOR HANDS
IRON IKE
JEL-FLUX
JOHN RING
JOHNI BOLT
JOHNI-BOLT XL
JOHNI-BOLTS
JOHNI QUICK BOLT
JOHNI-RING
JUMBO JOHNI-RING
KEVLAR
LIQUID GLUG
MEGABUBBLE
MEGALOC
OPEN MESH ABRASIVE
OPEN WIDE
PLASTIC POXY
PLASTIC SEAL
PLUMBERS CAULK
PLUMBERS FIRESTOP SEALANT
POWER FLOW
PRO DOPE
PRO-PORT
PRO POXY
PROPOXY 20
PT-4
PT BIO 1
R-D
REAL TUFF
REAL-TUFF
ROOT DESTROYER
ROOT FORCE
SCORE
SCOUT
SEPTIC-FLOW
SIZZLE
SLUDGE TREAT
STA PUT
STA PUT ULTRA
SWIF
SWIF 95
TAPE DOPE
TEFLON TAPE DOPE
TFE TAPE
TUFF-SEAL
WHAM

HILLYARD, INC.
302 N 4th St
Saint Joseph, MO 64501-1720
Tel.: (816) 233-1321
Fax: (816) 232-0089
Toll Free: (800) 365-1555
Web Site: www.hillyard.com
Sales Range: $100-124.9 Million
Approx. Number Employees: 1,000
Year Founded: 1907
Business Description:
Floor Care Products, Maintenance Equipment & Cleaners Mfr
S.I.C.: 5169; 5087
N.A.I.C.S.: 424690; 423850
Export
Media: 1-4-6-7-8-9-10-13-20-21-26
Distr.: Intl.; Natl.
Budget Set: Sept.
Personnel:
Robert W. Roth *(Pres)*
Neil T. Ambrose *(CFO & Treas)*
Bruce Windsor *(VP-Sls & Dir-Natl Accounts)*
Jon Martin *(VP-Credit)*
Brands & Products:
ADSPRAY
AFRC
AIR SCOOP
AIRFLEXTRA
AQUAMATIC SELECTRIC
ARSENAL
ASSAULT
ASSURANCE
AUTOFLUSH
AUTOHYGIENE
BRITE-BAK
BRITEN-ZIT
BRUTE
CARPETRIEVER
CARPETWIN
CEM-SEAL
CITRUS-SCRUB
CLEAN ACTION
CLEAN ASSIST
CLEAN RELEASE
CLEAN SCRUB
THE CLEANING RESOURCE
COACH VAC
CONCRETE DEFENSE
CONTENDER
CONVERTAMATIC
CONVERTAMAX
COURT GUARD
CUTBACK
DE/CL-100
DEEP ACTION
DEVASTATOR
DISCOVERY 2000
ENDEAVOUR
EPOXY 350
EXPEDITER
EXPLORER
FLEXI-DUSTER
GARDS
GLUTTON
GOLD MEDALIST
GREEN SELECT
GRIPPER
GUM-GO
HAND DEFENSE
HAPPY FEET
HCL-145
HEAVY DUTY C.V. WASH
HIDUSTER
HIL-GLO
HIL-MIST
HIL-PAC
HIL-PHENE
HIL-SHEEN
HIL-TEX
HIL-TREAT
HILLYARD
HILLYARD - FIRST IN GYM FINISHES
H.R. 2000
HYDRO-RETRIEVER
HYDRODY
I-FORCE
I.D. 200
IMPROVED TERRAZZINE
INTEGRA
INVADER
KA
KA-NB CLEANER/DEGREASER
KLEAN KUT
KLEEN-UP SOLVENT
KUT-A-WAY
LIQUID GUM-GO
LIQUID SWABBY
LIQUID TRAP SHOOTER
LOK-GARD
LUSTRE-MIST
MARINER
MEGAVAC
MERIT
MICROMATIC
MRD 2
NEUTONE
NORTH STAR
NUTRA-RINSE
ODYSSEY
ONE PLUS
ONEX-SEAL
PALLETOTE
PINE-O-CIDE
POWER-FLO
POWER STRIP
PRISM SONTARA
PURPOSE MATADOR
Q.T.
QT-TB
QUARTERVAC
QUICK & CLEAN
QWIK-OFF
RE-JUV-NAL
RENOVATOR
RESILIENCE
RESTORER
SAFETY SCRAPE
SAFTI-GRIP
SALVATION
SANISAC
SCOTCH
SEAL 341
SELECTVAC
SHADOW
SHOWER FOAM
SOIL-STOP
SORB-IT
SPRITE AIR SCOOP
STRIP-ALL
STRONG GUARD
SUPER GREASE BUSTER
SUPER HIL-AIRE
SUPER HIL-BRITE
SUPER HIL-TONE
SUPER SHINE-ALL
SUPER Z
SUPROX
SURFCOAT
TACK-IT
TAILVAC
TAKE DOWN
TERRAZZINE
TIP-OFF
TOP CLEAN
TOP SHAPE
TRAP SHOOTER
TRAPPER
TRILOGY
TRIPLE
TROPHY
TUF SEAL
TWISTER
TYPHOON
ULTRATHANE
UPHOLD
VAC PAC
VERSAMATIC
VINDICATOR
VINDICATOR +
VOYAGER
WHIRLAMATIC
WINDO-CLEAN
X-TRA
ZIZ-O

THE HOPE COMPANY INC.
12777 Pennridge Dr
Bridgeton, MO 63044-1236
Tel.: (314) 739-7254
Fax: (314) 739-7786
E-mail: info@hopecompany.com
Web Site: www.hopecompany.com
Approx. Number Employees: 10
Year Founded: 1973
Business Description:
Household Chemical Products, Refinisher, Tung & Lemon Oils & Specialty Polishes Mfr
S.I.C.: 2842
N.A.I.C.S.: 325612
Media: 2-4-5-9-10-23
Distr.: Natl.
Personnel:
Tracy LaVanchy *(Office Mgr)*
Gregory Thomas *(Mgr-Plant)*
Brands & Products:
HOPE'S
PERFECT COUNTERTOP
PERFECT GLASS
PERFECT GRANITE
PERFECT STAINLESS

HOWELL BROTHERS CHEMICAL LABORATORIES, INC.
PO Box 28024
Philadelphia, PA 19131-4603
Tel.: (215) 477-0260
Fax: (215) 477-4525
Approx. Number Employees: 7
Year Founded: 1950
Business Description:
Detergents & Hair Cosmetics Mfr
S.I.C.: 5169; 2844
N.A.I.C.S.: 424690; 325620
Export
Advertising Expenditures: $200,000
Media: 2-5-6-7-9-10-18-23-24-25-26
Distr.: Natl.
Budget Set: Oct.
Personnel:
Douglas C. Howell *(Pres)*
Brands & Products:
HOWBRO
VITA CURL
VITA-D
VITA-E-GRO

INTERWOOD DIRECT
5225 Orbitor Dr Unit 23
Mississauga, ON L4W 4Y8, Canada
Tel.: (416) 250-1665
Fax: (416) 250-1443
Web Site: www.interwood.com
E-Mail For Key Personnel:
President: robw@interwood.com
Marketing Director: silvynn@interwood.com
Sales Range: Less than $1 Million
Approx. Number Employees: 9
Year Founded: 1974
Business Description:
Proprietary & Licensed Direct Response Products Sales, Marketing & Distribution
S.I.C.: 5961
N.A.I.C.S.: 454113

Key to Media (For complete agency information see *The Advertising Red Books-Agencies* edition):
1. Bus. Publs. 2. Cable T.V. 3. Catalogs & Directories. 4. Co-op Adv. 5. Consumer Mags. 6. D.M. to Bus. Estab.7. D.M. to Consumers
8. Daily Newsp. 9. Exhibits/Trade Shows 10. Foreign 11. Infomercial 12. Internet Adv.13. Multimedia 14. Network Radio
15. Network T.V. 16. Newsp. Distr. Mags. 17. Other 18. Outdoor (Posters, Transit) 19. Point of Purchase20. Premiums, Novelties
21. Product Samples 22. Special Events Mktg. 23. Spot Radio 24. Spot T.V. 25. Weekly Newsp. 26. Yellow Page Adv.

Import Export
Media: 3-4-8-10-12-13-23-24
Distr.: Intl.; Natl.
Personnel:
Rob Woodrooffe *(Pres)*
Silvyn Naidoo *(COO)*
Nigel Mott *(Dir-Ops-Europe)*
Allyson Woodrooffe *(Mgr-Web)*
Brands & Products:
CHEMEASE
DIDISEVEN
DUZZIT
ECO STEAM BUDDY
GT88
INTERWOOD DIRECT
MAGIC MITER
MAGIC MITRE
NOWET WONDER FOAM
QFX PAINT PARTNER
QUICKSAND
SLENDERTONE
TWISTER SWEEPER
VITADETOX
VITAFRUIT
VITAJOINTS
VITAVEGGIES

ITW CHEMTRONICS

(Sub. of Illinois Tool Works Inc.)
8125 Cobb Center Dr
Kennesaw, GA 30152
Tel.: (770) 424-4888
Fax: (770) 424-4267
Toll Free: (800) 645-5244
E-mail: askchemtronics@chemtronics.com
Web Site: www.chemtronics.com
Sales Range: $25-49.9 Million
Approx. Number Employees: 100
Year Founded: 1958
Business Description:
Electronic Maintenance & Repair
S.I.C.: 2899; 3571
N.A.I.C.S.: 325998; 334111
Export
Media: 10-11
Brands & Products:
CHAMOIS TIPS
CHEM-STEP
CHEM-WIK
CHEMASK
CHEMPAD
CHEMSWAB
CHEMTRONICS
CIRCUITWORKS
CONTROLWIPES
COTTONTIPS
COVENTRY
ELECTRO-WASH
FLEXTIPS
FLUX-OFF
FOAMTIPS
FREEZE-IT
GOLD GUARD
HEAD CLEANER
KONFORM
KONTACT RESTORER
MICROTIPS
THE MIGHTY LIQUID
NOTHING CLEANS LIKE CHEMTRONICS
OPTIC PREP
OPTICWIPES
POW-R-WASH
QBE
SCREEN PREP
SODER-WICK
STATIC FREE
TUN-O-WASH
TUNER RENU
TWILLWIPES
ULTRAJET

ITW TEXWIPE

(Sub. of Illinois Tool Works Inc.)
1210 South Park Dr
Kernersville, NC 27284
Tel.: (336) 996-7046
Fax: (336) 996-6563
Toll Free: (800) 839-9473
E-mail: info@texwipe.com
Web Site: www.texwipe.com
Sales Range: $10-24.9 Million
Approx. Number Employees: 14
Year Founded: 1964
Business Description:
Contamination Control Supplies & Cleaning Products Mfr
S.I.C.: 2842
N.A.I.C.S.: 325612
Export
Media: 2-10
Brands & Products:
ABSORBOND
ALPHA
ALPHALITE
ALPHAMOP
ALPHASEAL
ALPHASORB
ALPHAWIPE
BAG-WITHIN-A BAG
BETAMOP
BETAWIPE
BLUEWIPE
CLEANCOTTON
CLEANFOAM
CLEANPAK
COMFORTMASK
FABWIPE
FACEMASK
FOAMWIPE
HYDROCELL
HYDROSPONGE
MIRACLEWIPE
STERILE ALPHASAT
STERILE POLYSAT
STERILE TECHNISAT
STERILEWIPE
TECHNICLOTH
TEXPURE
TEXSHIELD
TEXWIPE
TEXWRITE
THERMASEAL
TRANSPLEX
VECTRA
VERSAWIPE
XCLEAN

J.A. WRIGHT & CO.

(Div. of Weiman Products, LLC)
755 Tri State Pkwy
Gurnee, IL 60031
Mailing Address:
PO Box 566
Keene, NH 03431-0566
Tel.: (847) 263-3500
Fax: (847) 263-3700
Toll Free: (800) 922-2625
E-mail: pat_ina@jawright.com
Web Site: www.jawright.com
Year Founded: 1873
Business Description:
Metal Care Products Mfr
S.I.C.: 2842
N.A.I.C.S.: 325612
Media: 17
Distr.: Natl.
Brands & Products:
WRIGHT'S ANTI-TARNISH SILVER POLISH
WRIGHT'S COOKTOP CLEANER
WRIGHT'S COPPER CREAM
WRIGHT'S JEWELRY CARE
WRIGHT'S SILVER CREAM

JELMAR COMPANY

5550 Touhy Ave Ste 200
Skokie, IL 60077
Tel.: (847) 675-8400
Fax: (847) 675-8780
Toll Free: (800) 323-5497
E-mail: jelmar@jelmar.com
Web Site: www.jelmar.com
E-Mail For Key Personnel:
President: agutterman@jelmar.com
Sales Range: $10-24.9 Million
Approx. Number Employees: 12
Year Founded: 1949
Business Description:
Mfr. of Tarnish Remover
S.I.C.: 5169
N.A.I.C.S.: 424690
Export
Advertising Expenditures: $10,000,000
Media: 3-5-10-15-24
Distr.: Intl.; Natl.
Personnel:
Arthur Gutterman *(Chm)*
Alison Gutterman *(Pres)*
Fredrick Edmonds *(COO)*
Adrienne Czech *(Dir-Mktg)*
Brands & Products:
CLR
CLR BATHROOM & KITCHEN CLEANER
CLR OUTDOOR FURNITURE CLEANER
GREASE MAGNET
TARN-X
TARN-X COPPER GLAZE
TARN-X SILVER GLAZE
Advertising Agency:
A. Eicoff & Co.
(Div. of Ogilvy & Mather Worldwide)
401 N Michigan Ave 4th Fl
Chicago, IL 60611-4212
Tel.: (312) 527-7183
Fax: (312) 527-7188
Toll Free: (800) 333-6605
(CLR/TARN-X)

JENNY PRODUCTS, INC.

850 N Pleasant Ave
Somerset, PA 15501
Tel.: (814) 445-3400
Fax: (814) 445-2280
E-mail: info@jennyproducts.com
Web Site: www.steamjenny.com
Sales Range: Less than $1 Million
Approx. Number Employees: 30
Year Founded: 1927
Business Description:
Steam Cleaners, Pressure Washers, Car Washers & Cleaning Chemicals Mfr
S.I.C.: 3589
N.A.I.C.S.: 333319
Export
Advertising Expenditures: $230,000
Bus. Publs.: $89,000; Catalogs & Directories: $40,000; Co-op Adv.: $3,000; D.M. to Consumers: $7,000; Exhibits/Trade Shows: $30,000; Point of Purchase: $2,000; Premiums, Novelties: $3,000; Yellow Page Adv.: $56,000
Distr.: Natl.
Personnel:
Peter Leiss *(Pres)*
Jodell Antram *(Mgr-Acctg)*
Brands & Products:
HYPRESSURE JENNY
JENNY
STEAM JENNY

KYZEN CORPORATION

430 Harding Industrial Dr
Nashville, TN 37211
Tel.: (615) 831-0888
Fax: (615) 831-0889
E-mail: kyzen@kyzen.com
Web Site: www.kyzen.com
Approx. Number Employees: 30
Year Founded: 1990
Business Description:
Precision Cleaning Chemicals, Processes & Equipment for Industrial Manufacturing Operations
S.I.C.: 2842; 3559
N.A.I.C.S.: 325612; 333298
Export
Media: 2-7-8-10
Personnel:
Kyle J. Doyel *(Owner)*
Thomas Forsythe *(VP-Sls & Mktg)*
Debbie Alavezos-Carboni *(Mgr-Natl Sls)*
R. Erik Miller *(Mgr-Asia Pacifc)*
Sherry Stepp *(Mgr-Mktg)*
Brands & Products:
AQUANOX
BOOSTER
CYBERSOLV
DERMAKLENZ
IONOX
KYZEN
LONOX
METALNOX
MICRONOX
OPTISOLV
RINSE
SONIC BOOST
SYNERGYCCS

THE LIBMAN COMPANY

220 N Sheldon St
Arcola, IL 61910
Tel.: (217) 268-4200
Fax: (217) 268-3439
E-mail: info@libman.com
Web Site: www.libman.com
Approx. Number Employees: 250
Year Founded: 1896
Business Description:
Brooms, Brushes & Mops Mfr
S.I.C.: 3991
N.A.I.C.S.: 339994
Media: 3-6-10-15-19-22
Personnel:
Robert Libman *(Pres)*
William Libman *(CFO)*
Andrew Libman *(VP-Mktg)*
Brian Sowinski *(Dir-Mktg)*
Brands & Products:
GATOR
LIBMAN
NITTY GRITTY
PRECISION ANGLE
SCRUBSTER

Key to Media (For complete agency information see *The Advertising Red Books-Agencies* edition):
1. Bus. Publs. 2. Cable T.V. 3. Catalogs & Directories. 4. Co-op Adv. 5. Consumer Mags. 6. D.M. to Bus. Estab.7. D.M. to Consumers
8. Daily Newsp. 9. Exhibits/Trade Shows 10. Foreign 11. Infomercial 12. Internet Adv.13. Multimedia 14. Network Radio
15. Network T.V. 16. Newsp. Distr. Mags. 17. Other 18. Outdoor (Posters, Transit) 19. Point of Purchase20. Premiums, Novelties
21. Product Samples 22. Special Events Mktg. 23. Spot Radio 24. Spot T.V. 25. Weekly Newsp. 26. Yellow Page Adv.

The Libman Company — (Continued)

TORNADO
WONDER

Advertising Agency:
Element 79
(Part of the Omincom Group)
200 E Randolph St 33rd Fl
Chicago, IL 60601
Tel.: (312) 233-8100
Fax: (312) 233-8298

MAPA SPONTEX, INC.
(Sub. of Mapa Spontex S.A.)
100 Spontex Dr
Columbia, TN 38401
Tel.: (931) 388-5632
Fax: (931) 388-3714
Toll Free: (800) 537-2897
E-mail: sales@mapaglove.com
Web Site: www.mapaglove.com
E-Mail For Key Personnel:
Sales Director: sales@mapaglove.com
Approx. Number Employees: 160
Year Founded: 1981
Business Description:
Mfr of Cellulose Sponges, Synthetic Cleaners/Polishers, Sponge Scrubbers, Spot-lifters, Spot Removers & Latex Gloves
S.I.C.: 3069; 2842
N.A.I.C.S.: 326299; 325612
Import Export
Advertising Expenditures: $560,000
Catalogs & Directories: $112,000; Consumer Mags.: $28,000; D.M. to Bus. Estab.: $56,000; Exhibits/Trade Shows: $112,000; Point of Purchase: $224,000; Premiums, Novelties: $28,000
Distr.: Natl.
Budget Set: Sept.
Personnel:
Marc Boussemirt *(Pres)*
Richard Brand *(Dir-Bus Dev)*
Buddy Ware *(Mgr-Mktg Svcs)*

Brands & Products:
K2R
SPONTEX

MARTIN FRANCHISES INC.
422 Wards Corner Rd
Loveland, OH 45140
Tel.: (513) 351-6211
Fax: (513) 731-0818
Toll Free: (800) 827-0207
E-mail: cleanup@martinizing.com
Web Site: www.martinizing.com
Approx. Number Employees: 13
Year Founded: 1949
Business Description:
Martinizing Dry Cleaning Stores Franchisor
S.I.C.: 6794; 5087
N.A.I.C.S.: 533110; 423850
Media: 2-8-9-10-13-25
Distr.: Intl.; Natl.
Personnel:
George L. Strike *(CEO)*
Jerald E. Laesser *(VP-Mktg)*
Tom Moehringer *(Mgr-Mktg)*

Brands & Products:
MARTINIZING
ONE HOUR MARTINIZING

MAXONS RESTORATIONS
280 Madison Ave
New York, NY 10016
Tel.: (212) 447-6767
Fax: (212) 447-6251
Toll Free: (800) 3MAXONS
Web Site: www.maxons.com
Approx. Number Employees: 32
Business Description:
Full-Service Disaster Restoration Specialists
S.I.C.: 7699; 7217
N.A.I.C.S.: 811490; 561740
Media: 17-26
Personnel:
Damon Gersh *(Pres & CEO)*
Howard White *(Exec VP)*
Brands & Products:
EYE OF THE STORM
MAXONS
THE PROBLEM SOLVERS
QUICKSCOPE

METHOD PRODUCTS INC.
637 Commercial St Ste 300
San Francisco, CA 94111
Tel.: (415) 931-3947
Fax: (415) 568-4693
Toll Free: (866) 9-METHOD
E-mail: info@methodhome.com
Web Site: www.methodhome.com
Sales Range: $25-49.9 Million
Approx. Number Employees: 57
Year Founded: 2001
Business Description:
Biodegradable Laundry Detergent, Dish Soap, Spray Cleaners & Scented Plug-Ins Mfr
S.I.C.: 2841; 2842
N.A.I.C.S.: 325611; 325612
Personnel:
Adam Lowry *(Co-Founder)*
Eric Ryan *(Co-Founder)*
Tim Koogle *(Chm)*
Andrew Fraser *(Pres & CEO)*
Matthew Loyd *(VP-Brand Experience)*
Brands & Products:
A CLEANER CLEAN
BEST IN GLASS
CREATES PRODUCTS FOR PEOPLE AGAINST DIRTY.
DAILY GRANITE
DAILY SHOWER
LE SCRUB
LIL' BOWL BLU
METHOD
METHODBABY
OMOP
SMARTY DISH
SQUEEKY GREEN
TUBE 'N TILE
WOOD FOR GOLD
Advertising Agencies:
droga5
400 Lafayette 5th Fl
New York, NY 10003
Tel.: (917) 237-8888
Fax: (917) 237-8889

Euro RSCG Worldwide - San Francisco
1355 Sansome St
San Francisco, CA 94111
Tel.: (415) 345-7700
Fax: (415) 345-7705
Digital Marketing

MINUTEMAN INTERNATIONAL, INC.
(Sub. of Hako-Werke GmbH)
14 th N 845 US Rd 20
Pingree Grove, IL 60140
Tel.: (630) 627-6900
Fax: (847) 683-5121
Toll Free: (800) 323-9420
E-mail: info@minutemanintl.com
Web Site: www.minutemanintl.com
Sales Range: $50-74.9 Million
Approx. Number Employees: 100
Year Founded: 1951
Business Description:
Mfr & Distr Commercial Industrial Floor & Carpet Care Equipment & Cleaning Products
S.I.C.: 3589
N.A.I.C.S.: 333319
Import Export
Advertising Expenditures: $574,000
Media: 2-4-13-19-26
Distr.: Direct to Consumer; Intl.; Natl.
Budget Set: Nov.
Personnel:
Steve Liew *(CEO)*

MOC PRODUCTS COMPANY, INC.
12306 Montague St
Pacoima, CA 91331
Tel.: (818) 896-2258
Fax: (818) 794-3694
E-mail: info@mocproducts.com
Web Site: www.mocproducts.com
Approx. Number Employees: 200
Year Founded: 1954
Business Description:
Mfr & Distr Automotive Care Products; Automotive Industry Solutions
S.I.C.: 2842; 5169
N.A.I.C.S.: 325612; 424690
Media: 10
Personnel:
Mark Waco *(Pres)*
Dave Waco *(VP-Sls)*
Brands & Products:
A/C QUIET
ADHESIVE REMOVER
ALL-SEASON WASHER SOLVENT
BANANA WAX
BIG BANG
BLUE GLOSS
BODY SHINE
BUBBLE GUM
BUG-B-GONE
CLEAN-UP SOLVENT
CLEANS ALL
COOL OFF
COOLING-SYSTEM MULTI-TREATMENT
DOUBLE CLEAN
EXTERIOR BODY SOLVENT
FABRIC SEAL
FINISH PLUS
FORMULA
FORMULA 2000
GEAR GUARD
GREEN STUFF
HEAVY-DUTY PREP SOLVENT
KNOCKOUT DRESSING
LIQUID WONDER
MAGNA BRIGHT
MAGNA BUFF
MAGNA CRYSTAL
MAGNA GLAZE
MAGNA SEAL
MEGA BLUE
METAL BRITE
MICRO FINISH
MOC
MOISTURE SHIELD
MULTI-CLEAN
MULTI-TREATMENT
ORANGE DEGREASER
PARTS WASH
POLY SEAL
POWER RED DEGREASER
POWER SHINE
PREMIUM FUEL GUARD
PURPLE STUFF
QUIET BRAKES
QUIET COAT SOUNDSHIELD
SHINE N' GUARD
SPECIAL
SPOT REMOVER
SPRAY N' GLOSS
STAY-BRITE
SUNRISE SPECIAL
SUPERCOTE
TOUCH OF ORANGE
TUNNEL WASH
ULTRA COTE
VACU FLUSH
WASH N' WAX
WASHER SOLVENT
W.W.SPECIAL

MT. HOOD SOLUTIONS
14546 N Lombard
Portland, OR 97203
Tel.: (503) 227-3505
Fax: (503) 225-9143
Toll Free: (800) 547-2594
Web Site: www.mthoodchem.com
Approx. Number Employees: 96
Year Founded: 1902
Business Description:
Detergent & Industrial Products Mfr
S.I.C.: 2841
N.A.I.C.S.: 325611
Media: 2-4-6
Distr.: Reg.
Budget Set: Nov.
Personnel:
Thomas E. Mulflur *(Pres)*
Mike Mulflur *(Exec VP)*
Brands & Products:
APPROVE
AWESOME
BALANCE
BIOSAN
C-20
C-THRU
CHEM KLEEN
CHERRY-O
CINNAMINT
CLEAR
CONTROL
COR-AIRE
CRUSADER
CRYSTAL
CULTURE SHOCK
DERMA PRO ANTIMICROBIAL
DERMA PRO LOTION
DRI WALK
DUZ IT ALL II
ELEGANCE
ENVIRO AID
FORMULA 510
FREEDOM
GLEEM
GREAT FEELING
HOSPIT ALL
HOSPIT ALL II

Key to Media (For complete agency information see *The Advertising Red Books-Agencies* edition):
1. Bus. Publs. 2. Cable T.V. 3. Catalogs & Directories. 4. Co-op Adv. 5. Consumer Mags. 6. D.M. to Bus. Estab.7. D.M. to Consumers 8. Daily Newsp. 9. Exhibits/Trade Shows 10. Foreign 11. Infomercial 12. Internet Adv.13. Multimedia 14. Network Radio 15. Network T.V. 16. Newsp. Distr. Mags. 17. Other 18. Outdoor (Posters, Transit) 19. Point of Purchase20. Premiums, Novelties 21. Product Samples 22. Special Events Mktg. 23. Spot Radio 24. Spot T.V. 25. Weekly Newsp. 26. Yellow Page Adv.

HOSPIT ALL III
KREME N KLEEN
LEMON
LEMON CRUSH
LEMON SQUEEZE
MAINTAINER
MAX ALL PURPOSE
MAX DISINFECTANT
MAX FOAMING TUB & TILE
MAX SPEARMINT
MAX VANILLA
MHBC
MICRO ONE
NEW BOWL
NICE & FRESH
NON-AMMONIATED FLOOR STRIPPER
PEACHY
PINEX
PINK PEARL
POWER
PRO CITRUS
PUFF
RAISE
REFRESH
SANI GUARD
SCRAM
SPEARMINT
SPOT GONE
STRIP-EAZE
SUN DRY 44
SURFACE GUARD
SURGATOL
SURGI KLEEN
TOP COAT
TRI TEX
ULTRA
UNDERCOVER
UNIQUE
VANILLA
WHISPER
YUZU
ZING

MWDC TEXAS INC.

(Sub. of The Men's Wearhouse, Inc.)
(d/b/a MWCleaners)
3641 Westheimer Rd
Houston, TX 77027
Tel.: (713) 850-7474
Fax: (713) 850-7474
Web Site: www.mwcleaners.com
Sales Range: $25-49.9 Million
Approx. Number Employees: 200
Year Founded: 1965
Business Description:
Dry Cleaning Services
S.I.C.: 7212; 7215
N.A.I.C.S.: 812320; 812310
Advertising Expenditures: $250,000
Media: 8-9-23-24-25-26
Distr.: Direct to Consumer; Reg.
Budget Set: Jan.
Personnel:
Mike E. Nesbit *(Pres)*
Ron Garrett *(Gen Mgr)*

NILFISK-ADVANCE, INC.

(Sub. of Nilfisk-Advance A/S)
14600 21st Ave N
Plymouth, MN 55447-4648
Tel.: (763) 745-3500
Fax: (763) 745-3718
Fax: (800) 989-6566
Toll Free: (800) 989-2235
E-mail: info@advance-us.com
Web Site: www.advance-us.com
Approx. Number Employees: 493
Year Founded: 1929
Business Description:
Floor Care Equipment Mfr
S.I.C.: 3589; 5087
N.A.I.C.S.: 333319; 423850
Advertising Expenditures: $380,000
Media: 2-10-20
Distr.: Intl.; Natl.
Budget Set: Dec.
Personnel:
Christian Cornelius-Knudson *(CEO)*
Scott Lunger *(CFO-Americas & Sr VP)*
Steven Kelley *(Gen Counsel & VP)*
Jeff Oldenkamp *(VP-Fin)*
Brands & Products:
ADVANCE ADVENGER
AQUAMAX
AQUARIDE
AQUASPOT
CAPTOR
CMAX
CONVERTAMATIC
CONVERTAMAX
DURALINE
DURATRAC
DURAVAC
EUROCLEAN
MICROMAX
MICROSTAT
NILFISK
NILFISK ACTION PLUS
NILFISK AERO
NILFISK BUDDY
NILFISK CENTIX
NILFISK COMBAT
NILFISK COMBAT ULTRA
NILFISK COMPACT
NILFISK COUPE
NILFISK EXTREME
NILFISK EXTREME ECO
NILFISK GM 80
NILFISK POWER
NILFISK SOPRA
POWERONE
POWERWAND
QUENCHER
RAZOR
SELECT LINE
SELECTVAC
SETTING STANDARDS
SPRITE
STEAMTEC
TERRA
TOTAL CLEAN
Advertising Agencies:
Creative Communications Consultants, Inc.
111 3rd Ave S Ste 390
Minneapolis, MN 55401-2553
Tel.: (612) 338-5098
Fax: (612) 338-1398

Schubert Communications, Inc.
112 Schubert Dr
Downingtown, PA 19335-3382
Tel.: (610) 269-2100
Fax: (610) 269-2275

NILODOR, INC.

10966 Industrial Pkwy NW
Bolivar, OH 44612-8991
Tel.: (330) 874-1017
Fax: (330) 874-3366
Toll Free: (800) 443-4321
E-mail: info@nilodor.com
Web Site: www.nilodor.com
Approx. Number Employees: 30
Year Founded: 1954
Business Description:
Deodorizers & Cleaners; Carpet Care Services
S.I.C.: 2842
N.A.I.C.S.: 325612
Export
Media: 2-7-9-10-13-19-20-21-22
Distr.: Natl.
Budget Set: Nov.
Personnel:
Les W. Mitson *(Pres)*
Kurt Peterson *(VP-Sls)*
Todd Sauser *(Dir-Mktg)*
Brands & Products:
2001
CHEWNOT
DOCTOR STAIN
KENNEL WASH
NATURAL TOUCH
NIL-O-FRESH
NIL-O-LITTER
NILIUM
NILODOR
NILODOR CONCENTRATE
NILOSOL
NILOTEX
NILOTRON
ODOR-BANE
OXY-FORCE
SUPER N
TAP-A-DROP

PCI, INC.

10800 Baur Blvd
Saint Louis, MO 63132-1629
Tel.: (314) 872-9333
Fax: (314) 872-9104
Toll Free: (800) 752-7657
E-mail: sales@purochem.com
Web Site: www.pcistl.com
E-Mail For Key Personnel:
Sales Director: sales@purochem.com
Approx. Sls.: $9,500,000
Approx. Number Employees: 25
Year Founded: 1930
Business Description:
Cleaning & Beauty Care Items
S.I.C.: 2842; 2844
N.A.I.C.S.: 325612; 325620
Media: 10-21
Distr.: Natl.
Personnel:
Charles B. von Doersten *(Pres)*

PENETONE CORPORATION

(Sub. of West Chemical Products, Inc.)
700 Gotham Pkwy
Carlstadt, NJ 07072
Tel.: (201) 567-3000
Fax: (201) 510-3973
Toll Free: (800) 631-1652
Web Site: www.west-penetone.com
Approx. Number Employees: 60
Year Founded: 1933
Business Description:
Mfr. and Sales of Industrial Chemicals
S.I.C.: 2842; 2992
N.A.I.C.S.: 325612; 324191
Export
Advertising Expenditures: $200,000
Media: 4-7-10-13
Distr.: Natl.
Personnel:
Bruce Muretta *(VP-Fin, Gen Mgr & Admin)*
Mike Bradford *(VP-Sls & Mktg)*
Ralph Santoro *(Mgr-Ops)*
Brands & Products:
CITRIKLEEN AEROSOL
CITRIKLEEN CA
CITRIKLEEN HD
CITRIKLEEN MIL
CITRIKLEEN NST
CITRIKLEEN RI
CITRIKLEEN XPC
FORMULA 990
FORMULA 991
FOUR-WAY
INHIBISOL OS
LUBRISIL OS
LUMABRITE HD
PENAIR HD-1 RTU
PENAIR HD-4 RTU
PENAIR M5572B RTU
PENBLAST 214M
PENBLAST 322L
PENBLAST 510M
PENETONE
PENETONE AFW1
PENETONE ET
PENSOLV L805
PENSOLV L945
PENSOLV SAFE 100
PENSOLV SAFE 101
PENSOLV SAFE PB2000
PENSOLVE SAFE 150
PL 998
TPC SOLVENT
WEDAC
WESTPINE
WINDOW JETKLEER
YOUR CLEANING SOLUTIONS RESOURCE

THE PROCTER & GAMBLE COMPANY

1 Procter & Gamble Plaza
Cincinnati, OH 45202
Mailing Address:
PO Box 599
Cincinnati, OH 45202-0599
Tel.: (513) 983-1100
Fax: (513) 983-9369
E-mail: Shareholders.IM@pg.com
Web Site: www.pg.com
Approx. Sls.: $78,938,000,000
Approx. Number Employees: 127,000
Year Founded: 1837
Business Description:
Household, Laundry, Cleaning, Personal Care, Food, Industrial & Pharmaceuticals Products Mfr
S.I.C.: 2841; 2047; 2099; 2834; 2844; 2899
N.A.I.C.S.: 325611; 311111; 311999; 325412; 325620; 325998
Import Export
Advertising Expenditures: $8,576,000,000
Media: 2-3-4-5-6-7-8-9-11-13-14-15-16-17-18-19-20-21-22-23-24-25
Distr.: Intl.; Natl.
Personnel:
Robert A. McDonald, III *(Chm, Pres & CEO)*
Werner Geissler *(Vice Chm-Global Ops)*
E. Dimitri Panayotopoulos *(Vice Chm-Global Household Care)*

Key to Media (For complete agency information see *The Advertising Red Books-Agencies* edition):
1. Bus. Publs. 2. Cable T.V. 3. Catalogs & Directories. 4. Co-op Adv. 5. Consumer Mags. 6. D.M. to Bus. Estab.7. D.M. to Consumers
8. Daily Newsp. 9. Exhibits/Trade Shows 10. Foreign 11. Infomercial 12. Internet Adv.13. Multimedia 14. Network Radio
15. Network T.V. 16. Newsp. Distr. Mags. 17. Other 18. Outdoor (Posters, Transit) 19. Point of Purchase20. Premiums, Novelties
21. Product Samples 22. Special Events Mktg. 23. Spot Radio 24. Spot T.V. 25. Weekly Newsp. 26. Yellow Page Adv.

The Procter & Gamble Company — (Continued)

Edward D. Shirley *(Vice Chm-Global Beauty & Grooming)*
Filippo Passerini *(CIO & Pres-Global Bus Svcs)*
Deborah P. Majoras *(Chief Legal Officer & Sec)*
Jon R. Moeller *(Chief Legal Officer & Sec)*
Robert L. Fregolle, Jr. *(Global Design Officer)*
R. Keith Harrison, Jr. *(Global Product Supply Officer)*
Christopher Hassall *(Global External Relations Officer)*
Joan Lewis *(Global Consumer & Market Knowledge Officer)*
Moheet Nagrath *(Global HR Officer)*
Marc S. Pritchard *(Global Brand Building Officer)*
Charles V. Bergh *(Grp Pres-Global Male Grooming)*
Steven D. Bishop *(Pres-Global Feminine Care)*
Giovanni Ciserani *(Pres-Western Europe)*
Christopher de Lapuente *(Pres-Global Hair Care, Beauty & Grooming Grp)*
Virginia C. Drosos *(Pres-Global Female Beauty & Grooming)*
Mary Lynn Ferguson-McHugh *(Pres-Family Care)*
Thomas M. Finn *(Pres-Global Health Care)*
John P. Goodwin *(Pres-Global Braun, Beauty & Grooming)*
Melanie L. Healey *(Grp Pres-North America)*
Deborah A. Henretta *(Grp Pres-Asia)*
Robert Jongstra *(Pres-Global Salon Prof, Beauty & Grooming)*
Patrice Louvet *(Pres-Global Prestige)*
Jorge S. Mesquita *(Pres-Global Fabric Care Grp)*
Laurent L. Philippe *(Grp Pres-Central Europe & EMEA)*
Charles E. Pierce *(Pres-Global Oral Care)*
Martin Riant *(Pres-Global Baby Care Grp)*
Daniela Riccardi *(Pres-Greater China)*
Jeffrey K. Schomburger *(Pres-Global Wal-Mart Team)*
Shannan Stevenson *(Pres-Greater China)*
David S. Taylor *(Grp Pres-Global Home Care)*
Jorge A. Uribe *(Pres-Latin America)*
Teri L. List *(Treas & Sr VP)*
Valarie L. Sheppard *(Sr VP, Comptroller-Global Household Care Fin & Acctg)*
Linda W. Clement-Holmes *(Sr VP-Global Diversity & Bus Svcs)*
Esi Eggleston Bracey *(VP & Gen Mgr-Cosmetics)*
April Anslinger *(Brand Mgr-Head & Shoulders-North America)*
Carla Sia *(Brand Mgr-Head & Shoulders)*
Edgar Sandoval *(Gen Mg-Mktg-North America)*
Mary Pochobradsky *(Dir-Mktg-Downy)*
Matt Smith *(Dir-Mktg)*
Cindy Tripp *(Mktg Dir-Global Design)*
Willie Alvarado *(Dir-Enterprise Infrastructure Svcs)*
Pete Carter *(Dir-Brand Building Integrated Comm-Americas)*
Laurie Heltsley *(Dir-Strategic Initiatives)*
Kevin Hochman *(Dir-Mktg-Ivory)*
Damon Jones *(Dir-Global External Rels-Shave Care)*
Bruce Katsman *(Dir-Mktg)*
Bernadette King *(Dir-Mktg)*
Ted McConnell *(Dir-Digital Innovation)*
Darrin Smith *(Dir-IT)*
Peter White *(Dir-Global Sustainability)*
Jay Gooch *(Assoc Dir)*
Eric Huston *(Assoc Dir-Global Fabric Care)*
Carl Stealey *(Assoc Dir-Mktg-Old Spice)*
Suzanne Watson *(Assoc Dir-Mktg-Tide)*
Sunny Jain *(Sr Brand Mgr-Crest Whitestrips)*
Mark Benedict *(Asst Brand Mgr-P & G Professional)*
Eric Admiral *(Brand Mgr-Olay)*
Scott Beal *(Brand Mgr)*
Heather Burgess *(Brand Mgr-Max Factor)*
Mark Christenson *(Brand Mgr-Tide North America)*
Sarah Clark *(Brand Mgr-Max Factor)*
Ami Desai *(Brand Mgr-North America Oral Care)*
Ryan Dullea *(Brand Mgr)*
Mandy Earnshaw *(Relationship Brand Mgr-Tide)*
Sara Farenkamp *(Brand Mgr-US Direct Mktg & Promotions)*
Suzanne Geist *(Brand Mgr-Tide-US)*
Becky Godlove *(Asst Brand Mgr-Mr Clean)*
Jacques Hagopian *(Brand Mgr-Charmin North America)*
Bryan Hamilton *(Brand Mgr)*
Blake Hughes *(Brand Mgr)*
David Lee *(Brand Mgr)*
Bruce Lux *(Mgr-Global eCommerce & Brand Mgr)*
Guerin McClure *(Asst Brand Mgr-Swiffer)*
Kenyatte Nelson *(Brand Mgr)*
Marshall Sims *(Brand Mgr & Mgr-Kroger Customer Team Mktg)*
Maame Stephens *(Asst Brand Mgr-P & G Professional)*
Shannon Taylor *(Brand Mgr)*
Ciare Thorn *(Asst Brand Mgr-Febreze)*
Marty Vanderstelt *(Brand Mgr)*
Carolina Varela *(Brand Mgr-Hispanic Hair Care)*
Kisha Mitchell Williams *(Brand Mgr-Multicultural)*
Andrea Zuhensky *(Asst Brand Mgr-Crest Pro Health)*
Alejandro Bethlen *(Brand Mgr-Tide)*
Chad Brizendine *(Brand Mgr-Febreze)*
Andy Cipra *(Brand Mgr-Vicks-North America)*
Eric Higgs *(Brand Mgr-Bounty)*
Patrick Kraus *(Brand Mgr)*
Ihsan Leggett *(Asst Brand Mgr-Bounty)*
Tara Murphy *(Brand Mgr-Era, Cheer & Dreft)*
Jay Sethi *(Brand Mgr-Ivory)*
Samir Sheth *(Brand Mgr)*
Elena Taylor *(Brand Mgr)*
Stephanie Waugh *(Brand Mgr-Global Respiratory Innovation)*
Tracy L. Long *(Mgr-Global Beauty Comm)*
Jean Berberich *(Mgr-Mobile Mktg Innovation)*
Fina di Salvo *(Mgr-Comm Plng & Media)*
David L. Dombrowski *(Mgr-Principle Design & Product Innovator Retail Hair Color)*
Lara Green *(Mgr-Digital Mktg)*
Michael Griffiin *(Mgr)*
Stan Joosten *(Mgr-Innovation & Holistic Consumer Comm)*
Mailynn Karaus *(Mgr-IT Sys)*
Matt Kemme *(Mgr-NA Vicks Brand)*
Eric Lieb *(Mgr-Interactive Mktg)*
Annie Ligibel *(Mgr-Digital Mktg)*
Myrna Overstreet *(Mgr-Mktg-Branded Entertainment)*
Randy Peterson *(Mgr-Digital Mktg Innovation)*
Anelsie Ramos *(Mgr-External Rels)*
Dylan Rebillot *(Mgr-Digital Mktg)*
Kathryn Reule *(Mgr-Interactive Mktg)*
Kash Shaikh *(Mgr-External Relations-Tide)*
Mauricio Troncoso *(Supervisor)*
Lucas Watson *(Global Team Leader-Digital Bus Strategy)*

Brands & Products:
A TOUCH OF SUN
ACE
ACTIVAIR EASYTAB
ACTONEL
ALIGN
ALLDAYS
ALOMATIK
AMBI PUR
AMMENS
ANNA SUI
ARIEL
ASACOL
ATTENTO
AUSONIA
AUSSIE
AYUDIN
AZ
BALDESSARINI
BALSAM
BESS
BLEND A DENT
BLEND-A-MED
BLENDAX
BOLD
BONUS
BONUX
BOSS
BOSS SKIN
BOUNCE
BOUNTY
BRAUN
BUFFETTE
CAMAY
CASCADE
CASCADE COMPLETE ALL-IN-1 ACTIONPACS
CHARMIN
CHARMIN PLUS
CHARMIN ULTRA
CHEER
CHEFF
CHILDREN'S PEPTO
CHRISTINA AGUILERA
CIERTO
CIRC
CLEARBLUE EASY
COVERGIRL
COVERGIRL QUEEN COLLECTION
COVERGIRL WETSLICKS AMAZEMINT
CREST
CREST GLIDE
CREST PRO-HEALTH
CREST WHITESTRIPS
CRISTAL
CUTIE
DAILY DEFENSE
DASH
DAWN
DAWN BOTANICALS
DAWN DIRECT FOAM
DAWN PLUS ODOR ERASER
DAWN PLUS POWER SCRUBBERS
DAWN POWER DISSOLVER
DAWN SIMPLE PLEASURES
DAWN ULTRA
DAYQUIL
DAYQUIL PLUS VITAMIN C
DAZ
DDF
DIDRONEL
DODOT
DOWNY
DOWNY TROPICAL BLOOM
DREFT
DRYEL
DUNHILL
DURACELL
ELA
ELLEN BETRIX
ENABLEX
ERA
ESCADA
ESCUDO
EUKANUBA
EVAX
FAIRY
FEBREZE
FEBREZE AIR FRESHENERS
FEBREZE REFRESHERS
FEKKAI
FIBERSURE
FIXODENT
GAIN
GAIN FABRIC SOFTENER
GAIN WHITE WATER FRESH
GILLETTE
GILLETTE COMPLETE SKINCARE
GILLETTE FUSION
GILLETTE FUSION POWER
GILLETTE M3POWER
GILLETTE M3POWER NITRO
GILLETTE MACH3
GILLETTE MACH3 TURBO
GILLETTE SATINCARE
GILLETTE VENUS
GIORGIO
GIORGIO BEVERLY HILLS
GLEEM
GLIDE
GLIDE WHITENING PLUS SCOPE
HEAD & SHOULDERS
HEAD & SHOULDERS INTENSIVE TREATMENTS
HERBAL ESSENCES
HIPOGLOS
HOME CAFE
HUGO
HYDRIENCE
IAMS
INFASIL

Key to Media (For complete agency information see *The Advertising Red Books-Agencies* edition):
1. Bus. Publs. 2. Cable T.V. 3. Catalogs & Directories. 4. Co-op Adv. 5. Consumer Mags. 6. D.M. to Bus. Estab.7. D.M. to Consumers
8. Daily Newsp. 9. Exhibits/Trade Shows 10. Foreign 11. Infomercial 12. Internet Adv.13. Multimedia 14. Network Radio
15. Network T.V. 16. Newsp. Distr. Mags. 17. Other 18. Outdoor (Posters, Transit) 19. Point of Purchase20. Premiums, Novelties
21. Product Samples 22. Special Events Mktg. 23. Spot Radio 24. Spot T.V. 25. Weekly Newsp. 26. Yellow Page Adv.

INFUSIUM
INFUSIUM 23
INNER SCIENCE
IPANA
IVORY
IVORY CANADA
JAR
JEAN PATOU
JOY
KOLESTONE
KUKIDENT
LADYSAN
LASTING COLOR
LAURA BIOGIOTTI
LAVASAN
LENOR
LINES
LINIDOR
LORETO
LUNCH
LUVS
MACROBID
MACRODANTIN
MAESTRO
MAESTRO LIMPIO
MAGIA BLANCA
MAGISTRAL
MAX FACTOR
MEN'S CHOICE
METAMUCIL
MEXX
MILLSTONE
MISS CLAIROL
MOTIF
MR. CLEAN
MR. CLEAN AUTODRY
MR. PROPER
MUM
MUSE
MYTH
NATURAL INSTINCTS
NICE 'N EASY
NUANCES
NYQUIL
NYQUIL PLUS VITAMIN C
OLAY
OLAY DEFINITY
OLD SPICE
ORAL-B
ORAL-B ADVANTAGES FLOSS PICK
ORAL-B TRIUMPH SMARTGUIDE
P&G
PAMPERS
PAMPERS KANDOO
PAMPERS SIMPLY DRY
PAMPERS UNDERJAMS
PANTENE
PANTENE PRO-V
PEPTO-BISMOL
PERFECT 10
PERLA
PHYSIQUE
POP
PRINGLES
PRINGLES MINIS
PRINGLES SELECT
PRINGLES STIX
PUFFS
PUFFS PLUS WITH THE SCENT OF VICKS
PUMA
PUR
REJOICE
REJOY
REPLAY
RINDEX
SAFEGUARD
SALVO
SATINCARE
SCENTSTORIES BY FEBREZE
SCOPE
SCOPE WHITE
SECRET
SENIOR
SHOCKWAVES
SINEX
SK-II
SUPREMO
SWASH BY TIDE
SWIFFER
TAMPAX
TESS
TIDE
TIDE 2X ULTRA
TIDE SIMPLE PLEASURES
TIDE TO GO PEN
TOM TAILOR
TORENGOS
TOTAL CARE
TOUCHING LIVES IMPROVING LIFE
TRAS
ULTRESS
UNDERJAMS
UNIJAB
VENCEDOR
VIAKAL
VICKS
VICKS EARLY DEFENSE
VIDAL SASSOON
VITAPYRENA
VIZIR
WELLA
WHISPER
YES
ZEST
ZOOTH

Advertising Agencies:

Acme Idea Company
1 Marshall St
Norwalk, CT 06854-2262
Tel.: (203) 299-5490
Fax: (203) 299-5495
Duracell

Admerasia, Inc.
159 W 25th St 6th Fl
New York, NY 10001-7203
Tel.: (212) 686-3333
Fax: (212) 686-8998

Aim Straight Up
222 E 14th St
Cincinnati, OH 45202
Tel.: (513) 381-8787

AM/PM Advertising Inc.
345 Claremont Ave Ste 26
Montclair, NJ 07042
Tel.: (973) 824-8600
Fax: (646) 366-1168

Arc Worldwide, North America
35 W Wacker 15th Fl
Chicago, IL 60601
Tel.: (312) 220-3200
Fax: (312) 220-6212

Barefoot Proximity
700 W Pete Rose Way
Cincinnati, OH 45203
Tel.: (513) 861-3668
Fax: (513) 487-6855

BBDO EMEA
151 Marylebone Rd
London, NW1 5QE, United Kingdom
Tel.: (44) 207 616 3670
Fax: (44) 207 616 3495
Gillette
Gillette Fusion Power Razor

BBDO New York
1285 Ave of the Americas 7th Fl
New York, NY 10019-6028
Tel.: (212) 459-5000

BBDO North America
1285 Ave of the Americas
New York, NY 10019-6028
Tel.: (212) 459-5000
Fax: (212) 459-6814
Venus

Beanstalk
220 E 42nd St 15th Fl
New York, NY 10017
Tel.: (212) 421-6060
Fax: (212) 421-6388
Pampers
Always
Max Factor

BMWW
17 Governors Ct Ste 150
Baltimore, MD 21244-2713
Tel.: (410) 298-0390
Fax: (410) 298-8716

Burrell
233 N Michigan Ave Ste 2900
Chicago, IL 60601
Tel.: (312) 297-9600
Fax: (312) 297-9601
(Crest Toothpaste, Tide Detergent, Crisco Shortening)

Carat Brand Experience
201 E 5th St Ste 1340
Cincinnati, OH 45202
Tel.: (513) 322-3892
Fax: (513) 255-9831

CO-OP PROMOTIONS
2301 S Ocean Dr Ste 2504
Hollywood, FL 33019
Tel.: (954) 922-2323

Creative Artists Agency
2000 Ave of the Stars
Los Angeles, CA 90067
Tel.: (424) 288-2000
Fax: (424) 288-2900

The Creative Department
1209 Sycamore St
Cincinnati, OH 45202
Tel.: (513) 651-2901
Fax: (513) 651-2902

DeVries Public Relations
30 E 60th St 14th Fl
New York, NY 10022
Tel.: (212) 891-0400
Fax: (212) 644-0291
Tide
Vicks DayQuil Mucus Control
Vicks DayQuil Mucus Control DM
— Taryn Levy *(Acct Exec)*
— Kerri Bergman *(Acct Exec)*
— Alyson Mazzarelli *(Acct Exec)*
— Liza Martindale *(Acct Exec-Tide)*
— Kathy Casciani *(Acct Exec-Tide)*

Digitas, Inc.
111 E Wacker Dr Ste 1500
Chicago, IL 60601-4501
Tel.: (312) 729-0100
Fax: (312) 729-0111

Digitas Inc.
33 Arch St
Boston, MA 02110
Tel.: (617) 867-1000
Fax: (617) 867-1111
(Oral-B Pulsonic, Crest)
Downy Fabric Softener
Tide

D.L. Blair Inc.
1051 Franklin Ave
Garden City, NY 11530
Tel.: (516) 746-3700
Fax: (516) 746-3889

EMAK Worldwide, Inc.
6330 San Vicente Blvd
Los Angeles, CA 90048-5425
Tel.: (323) 932-4300
Fax: (323) 932-4400

Euro RSCG Worldwide HQ
350 Hudson St
New York, NY 10014-4504
Tel.: (212) 886-2000
Fax: (212) 886-2016

G2 Worldwide
200 5th Ave
New York, NY 10010
Tel.: (212) 537-3700
Fax: (212) 546-2425

Grey: Callegari Berville Grey
92 Avenue Des Ternes
75017
Paris, France
Tel.: (33) 1 44 09 15 15
Fax: (33) 1 44 09 15 00
Escada
Hugo Boss
Jean Patou
Lacoste

Grey Group
200 5th Ave
New York, NY 10010
Tel.: (212) 546-2020
Fax: (212) 546-2001
Downey

Grey Hong Kong
1901 Devon House Taikoo Place
Quarry Bay, China (Hong Kong)
Tel.: (852) 2510 6888
Fax: (852) 2510 7541

Holland Advertising:Interactive
700 Walnut St Ste 205
Cincinnati, OH 45202-2011
Tel.: (513) 744-3000
Fax: (513) 721-1269

The Kaplan Thaler Group
825 8th Ave 34th Fl
New York, NY 10019
Tel.: (212) 474-5000
Fax: (212) 474-5702

Key to Media (For complete agency information see *The Advertising Red Books-Agencies* edition):
1. Bus. Publs. 2. Cable T.V. 3. Catalogs & Directories. 4. Co-op Adv. 5. Consumer Mags. 6. D.M. to Bus. Estab.7. D.M. to Consumers
8. Daily Newsp. 9. Exhibits/Trade Shows 10. Foreign 11. Infomercial 12. Internet Adv.13. Multimedia 14. Network Radio
15. Network T.V. 16. Newsp. Distr. Mags. 17. Other 18. Outdoor (Posters, Transit) 19. Point of Purchase20. Premiums, Novelties
21. Product Samples 22. Special Events Mktg. 23. Spot Radio 24. Spot T.V. 25. Weekly Newsp. 26. Yellow Page Adv.

The Procter & Gamble Company — (Continued)

Dawn

Kellen Communications
1100 Johnson Ferry Rd Ste 300
Atlanta, GA 30342
Tel.: (404) 252-3663
Fax: (404) 252-0774

KRT Marketing
3685 Mt Diablo Blvd Ste 255
Lafayette, CA 94549-3776
Tel.: (925) 284-0444
Fax: (925) 284-0448
Recruitment

Landor Associates
1001 Front St
San Francisco, CA 94111
Tel.: (415) 365-1700
Fax: (415) 365-3190
Eukanuba
Global Handwashing Day

Lapiz
35 W Wacker Dr 12th Fl
Chicago, IL 60601
Tel.: (312) 220-5000
Fax: (312) 220-6212
Bounty Paper Towels

Leo Burnett-Hong Kong
6th Fl City Plaza 3 14 Taikoo Wan Road
Quarry Bay, China (Hong Kong)
Tel.: (852) 2567 4333
Fax: (852) 2885 3209
Pert
Rejoice
— Antonio d'Esterre *(Global Head-Pert & Rejoice)*

Leo Burnett Worldwide, Inc.
35 W Wacker Dr
Chicago, IL 60601-1723
Tel.: (312) 220-5959
Fax: (312) 220-3299
(Secret, Head & Chest Cold Medicines, Cheer, Era, Gleem, Pert, Dandruff Control Pert Plus, White Cloud Tissue, TempoLuvs, Crest Super Cool, Prell, Ultra Cheer, Noxema Skin Care Products)
SK-II
Always

LPK
19 Garfield Pl
Cincinnati, OH 45202
Tel.: (513) 241-6401
Fax: (513) 241-1423
Herbal Essences

Marina Maher Communications
830 3rd Ave
New York, NY 10022
Tel.: (212) 485-6800
Fax: (212) 355-6318
Head & Shoulders

MSLGROUP
1675 Broadway 9th Floor
New York, NY 10019-5865
Tel.: (212) 468-4200
Fax: (212) 468-3007
Bounty

Febreze
— Meghan McGurkin *(Acct Exec)*
— Marisa Abdoo *(Acct Exec)*

National Retail Services
51 Sugar Hollow Rd
Danbury, CT 06810
Tel.: (203) 790-1744
Fax: (203) 798-1644

Northlich
Sawyer Point Bldg 720 Pete Rose Way
Cincinnati, OH 45202
Tel.: (513) 421-8840
Fax: (513) 455-4749

Nurun/China Interactive
162 Yong Nian Rd
Shanghai, 200025, China
Tel.: (86) 21 5383 4038
Fax: (86) 21 5383 4050
Olay
Vidal Sassoon
Pantene
Safeguard
Braun
Gillette
Pringles

OgilvyAction
22 W 19th St 10th Fl
New York, NY 10011-4204
Tel.: (212) 627-4101
Fax: (212) 627-4106
Toll Free: (800) 343-4101

Padilla Speer Beardsley
1101 W River Pkwy Ste 400
Minneapolis, MN 55415-1241
Tel.: (612) 455-1700
Fax: (612) 455-1060

PainePR
660 S Figueroa St 20th Fl
Los Angeles, CA 90017-3442
Tel.: (213) 430-0480
Fax: (213) 430-0494

PainePR
19000 MacArthur Blvd 8 Fl
Irvine, CA 92612-1438
Tel.: (949) 809-6700
Fax: (949) 260-1116
Toll Free: (866) PAINEPR
Ivory
Pampers
— Vicky Nave *(Acct Exec)*
— Lauren Yacker *(Acct Exec-Luvs)*
— Amanda Teitler *(Acct Exec-Luvs)*

Photosound Communications
1000 Wyckoff Ave
Mahwah, NJ 08536
Tel.: (609) 514-5366
Fax: (609) 514-5377

PointRoll Inc.
951 E Hector St
Conshohocken, PA 19428
Tel.: (267) 558-1300
Fax: (267) 285-1141
Toll Free: (800) 203-6956

Porter Novelli
(Sub. of Omnicom Group, Inc.)
75 Varick St 6th Fl
New York, NY 10013
Tel.: (212) 601-8000
Fax: (212) 601-8101

Possible Worldwide
302 W Third St Ste 900
Cincinnati, OH 45202
Tel.: (513) 381-1380
Fax: (513) 381-0248
Pringles

Publicis Groupe S.A.
133 Ave des Champs-Elysee
75008
Paris, France
Tel.: (33) 1 44 43 70 00
Fax: (33) 1 44 43 75 25
Oral-B

Publicis New York
4 Herald Sq 950 6th Ave
New York, NY 10001
Tel.: (212) 279-5550
Fax: (212) 279-5560
Bounty
Crest 3D Whitestrips
Pepto-Bismol
Scope Mouthwash

Publicis USA
(Sub. of Publicis, S.A., Paris, France)
4 Herald Sq 950 6th Ave
New York, NY 10001
Tel.: (212) 279-5550
Fax: (212) 279-5560
(Oral-B Pulsonic, ThermaCare)

Quigley-Simpson
11601 Wilshire Blvd Ste 710
Los Angeles, CA 90025
Tel.: (310) 996-5800
Fax: (310) 943-1414

RED212
5509 Fair Lane
Cincinnati, OH 45227
Tel.: (513) 772-1020
Fax: (513) 772-6849

Saatchi & Saatchi
(Sub. of Publicis Groupe S.A.)
(Worldwide Headquarters)
375 Hudson St
New York, NY 10014-3660
Tel.: (212) 463-2000
Fax: (212) 463-9856
Tide

Saatchi & Saatchi
3D River Valley Rd 03-01 Clarke quay
179023
Singapore, Singapore
Tel.: (65) 6339 4733
Fax: (65) 6339 3916

Saatchi & Saatchi X
605 Lakeview Dr
Springdale, AR 72764
Tel.: (479) 575-0200
Fax: (479) 725-1136
Febreze

SMG United
1675 Broadway
New York, NY 10019
Tel.: (212) 468-4000
Tide

Starcom Guangzhou
2&3A/F SanXin Plz No 33 W Huangpu Ave
Guangzhou, 510620, China
Tel.: (86) 20 3820 1900
Fax: (86) 20 3820 1891
(Gillette, Oral B)

Starcom MediaVest Group
35 W Wacker Dr
Chicago, IL 60601-1723
Tel.: (312) 220-3535
Fax: (312) 220-6530
Downy
Media Buying
Tide

Strata-G Communications
830 Main St 10th Fl
Cincinnati, OH 45202
Tel.: (513) 381-8855
Fax: (513) 381-0385
Toll Free: (800) 540-6986

Tapestry Partners
35 W Wacker Dr
Chicago, IL 60601
Tel.: (312) 220-3535
Fax: (312) 220-6561

TBWA Chiat Day New York
488 Madison Ave
New York, NY 10022
Tel.: (212) 804-1000
Fax: (212) 804-1200
Pur

Upshot
350 N Orleans St 5th Fl
Chicago, IL 60654
Tel.: (312) 943-0900
Fax: (312) 943-9699

USMP
4721 Alla Rd
Marina Del Rey, CA 90292
Tel.: (310) 754-3000
Fax: (310) 754-3001
Toll Free: (800) 454-8382
Iams

Wieden + Kennedy, Inc.
224 NW 13th Ave
Portland, OR 97209-2953
Tel.: (503) 937-7000
Fax: (503) 937-8000
Ivory
Old Spice
— Danielle Flagg *(Dir-Creative-Ivory & Dir-Art)*

Wieden + Kennedy-New York
150 Varick St Fl 7
New York, NY 10013-1218
Tel.: (917) 661-5200
Fax: (917) 661-5500
"The man your man could smell like"
Graham Webb
Old Spice

Young & Laramore
407 N Fulton St
Indianapolis, IN 46202
Tel.: (317) 264-8000
Fax: (317) 264-8002

Key to Media (For complete agency information see *The Advertising Red Books-Agencies* edition):
1. Bus. Publs. 2. Cable T.V. 3. Catalogs & Directories. 4. Co-op Adv. 5. Consumer Mags. 6. D.M. to Bus. Estab.7. D.M. to Consumers 8. Daily Newsp. 9. Exhibits/Trade Shows 10. Foreign 11. Infomercial 12. Internet Adv.13. Multimedia 14. Network Radio 15. Network T.V. 16. Newsp. Distr. Mags. 17. Other 18. Outdoor (Posters, Transit) 19. Point of Purchase20. Premiums, Novelties 21. Product Samples 22. Special Events Mktg. 23. Spot Radio 24. Spot T.V. 25. Weekly Newsp. 26. Yellow Page Adv.

PROCTER & GAMBLE INC.
(Sub. of The Procter & Gamble Company)
4711 Yonge Street
North York, ON M2N 6K8, Canada
Mailing Address:
PO Box 355 Station A
Toronto, ON M5W 1C5, Canada
Tel.: (416) 730-4711
Fax: (416) 730-4415
Web Site: www.pgcanada.ca
Sales Range: $1-4.9 Billion
Approx. Number Employees: 3,500
Year Founded: 1885
Business Description:
Household Products, Food Products, Toiletries, Paper Products Mfr & Distr
S.I.C.: 2841; 2844
N.A.I.C.S.: 325611; 325620
Media: 6-8-9-18-23-24
Distr.: Natl.
Budget Set: Mar.
Personnel:
Vivienne Bechtold *(Dir-Mktg)*
Katie Elder *(Brand Mgr-Febreze)*
Tanya Stephens *(Mgr-Digital Mktg)*
Advertising Agencies:
Proximity Canada
2 Bloor W 29th Floor
Toronto, ON M4W 3R6, Canada
Tel.: (416) 323-9162
Fax: (416) 944-7886
Razor

Saatchi & Saatchi
2 Bloor St E Ste 600
Toronto, ON M4W 1A8, Canada
Tel.: (416) 359-9595
Fax: (866) 411-1
Cascade, Comet, Ivory (Bar), Ivory Liquid, Tide, Oxydol

PULLMAN-HOLT CORPORATION
10702 N 46th St
Tampa, FL 33617
Tel.: (813) 971-2223
Fax: (813) 971-6090
Fax: (800) 833-8875
Toll Free: (800) 237-7582
E-mail: customerservice@pullmanholtcorp.com
Web Site: www.pullman-holt.com
E-Mail For Key Personnel:
Sales Director: beukovich@pullmanholtcorp.com
Approx. Number Employees: 75
Business Description:
Industrial Cleaning Equipment Mfr
S.I.C.: 3589
N.A.I.C.S.: 333319
Media: 2-4-8
Distr.: Natl.
Budget Set: Apr.
Personnel:
Ron Underwood *(Owner)*
Thomas R. Halluska *(CFO & VP-Fin)*
Robert Eukovich *(VP-Sls & Mktg)*
John D. Castellana *(Dir-Admin Ops)*
Michael W. Worden *(Dir-Engrg & Mfg)*
Karen M. Johnson *(Mgr-HR)*
Brands & Products:
EVACUATOR
GLOSS BOSS
MAGNET SPRAY
POULTICE
PULLMAN-HOLT

PURAFIL, INC.
(Sub. of Kaydon Corporation)
2654 Weaver Way
Doraville, GA 30340-1554
Tel.: (770) 662-8545
Fax: (770) 263-6922
Toll Free: (800) 222-6367
Telex: 707436
E-mail: purafil@purafil.com
Web Site: www.purafil.com
Sales Range: $25-49.9 Million
Approx. Number Employees: 65
Year Founded: 1969
Business Description:
Air & Odor Purification Systems Mfr
S.I.C.: 3564; 5084
N.A.I.C.S.: 333411; 423830
Export
Media: 2-7-17-20-26
Distr.: Intl.; Natl.
Budget Set: Dec.
Personnel:
James W. Mash *(Pres & CEO)*
Richard Corel *(Bus Dir-Europe)*
Christopher O. Muller *(Dir-Tech)*
Thomas Ramsey *(Dir-Bus Dev)*
Andrew Weiller *(Dir-Purafil Asia)*
Paula Westmoreland *(Reg Mgr-Inside Sls)*
H. Christopher Moon *(Bus Mgr-USA)*
William G. England *(Mgr-Laboratory/R&D)*
Diego Schaefer *(Mgr-Global Engrg & Replacement Media)*
Brands & Products:
FIRST IN CLEAN AIR
J-TRACK
MEDIAPIK
ONGUARD
PURAFIL
PURAFILTER

PURESAFE WATER SYSTEMS, INC.
25 Fairchild Ave Ste 250
Plainview, NY 11803
Tel.: (516) 208-8250
Fax: (516) 208-8252
Web Site: www.puresafe-watersystems.com
Approx. Number Employees: 4
Year Founded: 1987
Business Description:
Mobile Water Decontamination & Purification Systems Mfr
S.I.C.: 4941; 4959
N.A.I.C.S.: 221310; 562998
Advertising Expenditures: $22,500
Media: 17
Personnel:
Leslie J. Kessler *(Chm & CEO)*
Terry L. Lazar *(CFO)*
Gerard R. Stoehr *(COO)*

PURITAN SERVICES, INC.
(Sub. of Ecolab Inc.)
370 N Wabasha St
Saint Paul, MN 55102
Tel.: (651) 293-2233
Sales Range: $75-99.9 Million
Approx. Number Employees: 250
Year Founded: 1920
Business Description:
Mfr. & Sales of Polishing Compounds, Soaps, Detergents, Disinfectants, Sanitary & Industrial Maintenance Chemicals, Supplies & Equipment
S.I.C.: 2842
N.A.I.C.S.: 325612
Export
Advertising Expenditures: $200,000
Media: 4-7-10
Distr.: Direct to Consumer; Reg.
Budget Set: Oct.
Personnel:
Douglas M. Baker *(Pres)*
Brands & Products:
PURITAN
QUINTET
SPEEDET

RIO TINTO BORAX
(Div. of Rio Tinto Minerals)
8051 E Maplewood Ave Bldg 4
Greenwood Village, CO 80111
Mailing Address:
PO Box 926
Valencia, CA 91380-9026
Tel.: (303) 713-5000
Fax: (303) 713-5769
Web Site: www.borax.com
Approx. Number Employees: 1,500
Year Founded: 1872
Business Description:
Mfr of Industrial Chemical Products Including Borax, Boric Acid & Various Inorganic Boron Compounds
S.I.C.: 1474; 2819
N.A.I.C.S.: 212391; 325188
Export
Media: 2-6-7-9
Distr.: Intl.; Natl.
Budget Set: Jan.
Personnel:
Gary J. Goldberg *(CEO)*
Jeff Olsen *(CFO)*
Chris Robison *(COO)*
Susan Keefe *(Mgr-Commun)*
Brands & Products:
DEHYBOR
NEOBOR
OPTIBOR
POLYBOR

ROCHESTER MIDLAND CORPORATION
333 Hollenbeck St
Rochester, NY 14621-3258
Mailing Address:
PO Box 31515
Rochester, NY 14603-1515
Tel.: (585) 336-2200
Fax: (585) 467-4406
Toll Free: (800) 836-1627
E-mail: webmaster@rochestermidland.com
Web Site: www.rochestermidland.com
Approx. Number Employees: 1,100
Year Founded: 1888
Business Description:
Mfr. of Disinfectants, Liquid & Powder Soaps, Liquid Wax, Insecticides, Soap Dispensers, Water Treatment Chemicals, Industrial Maintenance Products, Sanitary Napkins & Tampons; Distributor of Vending Machines
S.I.C.: 2842; 2676
N.A.I.C.S.: 325612; 322291
Export
Media: 2-10
Distr.: Direct to Consumer; Natl.
Personnel:
Harlan D. Calkins *(Chm & CEO)*
Karen Durbin *(Mgr-Mktg)*
Liz Taylor *(Mgr-Corp Mktg Comm)*
Brands & Products:
AUDITGUARD
BRANDGUARD
CHEMGUARD
DRAINGUARD
ENVIRO CARE
FLOORGUARD
HANDGUARD
HANDSFREE
MICRODYNE
MID BRITE
NATURELLE
OVEN GLO
PROXI
REST ASSURED
RMC
RMC QUICK DRY
RODOX
SANISAC
SANOR
SCENTSATIONS
SNAP!
SPECTRUM
STAYFREE
SURFACEGUARD
T-BEAR
THERMO GLOSS
ULTRA MARATHON

THE ROOTO CORPORATION
3505 W Grand River Ave
Howell, MI 48843-7604
Tel.: (517) 546-8330
Fax: (517) 548-5162
Web Site: rootocorp.com
Approx. Number Employees: 20
Business Description:
Drain Cleaning Chemicals Mfr
S.I.C.: 2842; 2899
N.A.I.C.S.: 325612; 325998
Media: 2-6-9-10-21
Distr.: Natl.
Budget Set: Oct.
Personnel:
Joon S. Moon *(Pres)*

SAINT-GOBAIN ABRASIVES CANADA INC.
(Sub. of Compagnie de Saint-Gobain SA)
3 Beach Rd
Hamilton, ON L8L 7Y5, Canada
Tel.: (905) 547-2551
Fax: (905) 547-9194
E-mail: universal@recorder.ca
Web Site: www.saint-gobain.com/en/directory/company/search/country
Approx. Rev.: $9,338,000
Approx. Number Employees: 86
Year Founded: 1992
Business Description:
Abrasive Products Mfr
S.I.C.: 3291
N.A.I.C.S.: 327910
Media: 10-13
Brands & Products:
UNIVERSAL

SANITIZED, INC.
(Sub. of Sanitized AG)
57 Litchfield Rd Rte 202
New Preston Marble Dale, CT 06777
Tel.: (860) 868-9491
Approx. Number Employees: 9
Year Founded: 1934
Business Description:
Bacteriostats, Fungistats & Mildewstats

Key to Media (For complete agency information see *The Advertising Red Books-Agencies* edition):
1. Bus. Publs. 2. Cable T.V. 3. Catalogs & Directories. 4. Co-op Adv. 5. Consumer Mags. 6. D.M. to Bus. Estab.7. D.M. to Consumers
8. Daily Newsp. 9. Exhibits/Trade Shows 10. Foreign 11. Infomercial 12. Internet Adv.13. Multimedia 14. Network Radio
15. Network T.V. 16. Newsp. Distr. Mags. 17. Other 18. Outdoor (Posters, Transit) 19. Point of Purchase20. Premiums, Novelties
21. Product Samples 22. Special Events Mktg. 23. Spot Radio 24. Spot T.V. 25. Weekly Newsp. 26. Yellow Page Adv.

Sanitized, Inc. — (Continued)

S.I.C.: 2836
N.A.I.C.S.: 325414
Import Export
Advertising Expenditures: $500,000
Media: 2-4-6-9-23-26
Distr.: Intl.; Natl.
Personnel:
Stewart E. Klein *(Pres)*
Brands & Products:
ACTIFRESH
ACTIGARD
DURA FRESH
EVERFRESH
FRESHGARD
MICRO-GUARD

SARA LEE HOUSEHOLD & BODY CARE

(Div. of Sara Lee Corporation)
707 Eagleview Blvd
Exton, PA 19341-1159
Tel.: (610) 321-1220
Fax: (610) 321-1440
Toll Free: (800) 289-5494
Web Site: www.saralee.com/ContactUs.aspx
Sales Range: $200-249.9 Million
Approx. Number Employees: 400
Year Founded: 1954
Business Description:
Shoe Polishes, Floor Wax , Bowl Cleaner, Laundry Detergent Booster, Skin Care Products & Fabric Dye Mfr
S.I.C.: 2842; 2841
N.A.I.C.S.: 325612; 325611
Import Export
Media: 2-6-7
Distr.: Natl.
Personnel:
Gregory Hopkins *(VP-Sls & Mktg-North America)*
Stan Stoltfus *(Dir-Mktg)*
Bob Clark *(Dir-Mktg)*
Brands & Products:
CAVALIER
MIRACLE WHITE
TINTEX
WOOD PREEN

S.C. JOHNSON & SON, INC.

1525 Howe St
Racine, WI 53403-2237
Tel.: (262) 260-2000
Fax: (262) 260-6004
Toll Free: (800) 494-4855
Telex: 264429 JON WAX RCN
Web Site: www.scjohnson.com
Approx. Sls.: $6,500,000,000
Approx. Number Employees: 12,000
Year Founded: 1886
Business Description:
Household Cleaning Products & Products for Home Storage, Personal Care & Insect Control Mfr
S.I.C.: 2842; 2844
N.A.I.C.S.: 325612; 325620
Import Export
Media: 3-6-9-13-14-15-16-17-18-19-20-21-23-24
Distr.: Natl.
Budget Set: June -Nov.
Personnel:
H. Fisk Johnson *(Chm & CEO)*
Patrick O'Brien *(Pres-Europe, Africa & Near East Reg)*
David L. May *(Pres-North America)*
Steven P. Stanbrook *(Pres-Developing Markets)*
David Hecker *(Gen Counsel & Sec & Exec VP)*
Jane M. Hutterly *(Exec VP-Worldwide Corp & Environmental Affairs)*
John Rote *(VP-Mktg)*
Maria Campbell *(Dir-Diversity)*
Patricia Penman *(Dir-IMC & Fragrance Strategy Air Care)*
Gina Shaffer *(Sr Mgr-Relationship Mktg)*
Jeffrey Wolf *(Sr Brand Mgr-Edge)*
Mike Colucci *(Sr Research Scientist)*
Brands & Products:
ALPINE SPICE
ARMSTRONG
AUTAN
BAYGONE
BON AMI
BRISE
BRISE AUTO
BRISE CIRCUL AIR
BRISE HOME FRAGRANCE
BRISE ON & ON
BRISE TOUCH & FRESH
BRITE
CARNU
CARPET SCIENCE
COUNTRY GARDEN
DAILY PURE
DEEP WOODS OFF!
DRANO
DRANO BUILD-UP
DRANO CRYSTAL
DRANO LIQUID
DRANO MAX GEL
DRANO PROFESSIONAL STRENGTH
DUSTER PLUS
FANTASTIK
FANTASTIK ALL-PURPOSE
FANTASTIK BLEACH
FANTASTIK LEMON POWER
FANTASTIK MULTI-SURFACE WIPE
FANTASTIK ORANGE ACTION
FANTASTIK ORANGE WIPE
FANTASTIK OXY POWER
FAVOR
FIZZ-ITS
FUTURE
GLADE
GLADE PLUGINS
GLEID
GLO-COAT
GLORY
GRAB-IT
GRAB-IT CLOTHS
GRAB-IT MATTS
GRAB-IT MOP
GRAB-IT SWEEPER
GRAB-IT WIPE
GRAND PRIX
GREEN LIST
JUBILEE
KABBIKILLER
KIT
KLEAN'N SHINE
KLEAR
MR. MUSCLE
NATURE'S SOURCE
OFF!
ORANGE ACTION
OUST
OXY POWER
PLEDGE
PLEDGE AEROSOL
PLEDGE DUST
PLEDGE EXTRA MOISTURIZING
PLEDGE FLOOR CARE
PLEDGE GRAB-IT
PLEDGE LEMON TRIGGER
PLEDGE ORANGE OIT
PLEDGE WIPES
PLIZ
PRONTO
RAID
RALLY
SARAN WRAP
SC JOHNSON
SCRUBBING BUBBLES
SCRUBBING BUBBLES AEROSOL
SCRUBBING BUBBLES FIZZ-ITS
SCRUBBING BUBBLES FLUSHABLE
SCRUBBING BUBBLES FRESH BRUSH
SCRUBBING BUBBLES GEL BOWL
SCRUBBING BUBBLES LEMON
SCRUBBING BUBBLES MILDEW STAIN
SCRUBBING BUBBLES SHOWER SHINE
SCRUBBING BUBBLES SOAP SCUM
SHOUT
SHOUT ACTION GEL
SHOUT AEROSOL
SHOUT COLOR CATCHER
SHOUT GEL
SHOUT OXYPOWER
SHOUT TRIGGER & LIQUID
SHOUT WIPE
SHOUT WIPES
SHOWER SHINE
SKINGUARD AQUA
SKINTASTIC
STEP SAVER
SUMMER SPLASH
TEMPO
TOILET DUCK
VANISH
WE WORK HARD SO YOU DON'T HAVE TO!
WINDEX
WINDEX BEST ON GLASS
WINDEX GLASS AND SURFACE WIPE
WINDEX KITCHEN & GLASS
WINDEX MOUNTAIN BERRY
WINDEX NO DRIP
WINDEX OUTDOOR
WINDEX POWERIZED FOAMING
WINDEX SPARKLING ORANGE
WINDEX VINEGAR
WINDEX VINEGAR WIPE
ZIPLOC
ZIPLOC CONTAINERS
ZIPLOC DOUBLE-GUARD
Advertising Agencies:
BBDO North America
1285 Ave of the Americas
New York, NY 10019-6028
Tel.: (212) 459-5000
Fax: (212) 459-6814
Home Storage Products
Pest Control
Raid
Ziploc

Ogilvy & Mather
(Sub. of WPP Group plc)
636 11th Ave
New York, NY 10036
Tel.: (212) 237-4000
Fax: (212) 237-5123
Glade
Home Cleaning
Home Fragrance
Windex

Universal McCann
100 33rd St 8th Fl
New York, NY 10001
Tel.: (212) 883-4700

S.C. JOHNSON CANADA

(Sub. of S.C. Johnson & Son, Inc.)
1 Webster Street
Brantford, ON N3T 5R1, Canada
Tel.: (519) 756-7900
Fax: (519) 758-6608
Toll Free: (877) 506-7352
Web Site: www.scjohnson.ca
Approx. Number Employees: 385
Year Founded: 1920
Business Description:
Consumer Products Mfr
S.I.C.: 2841
N.A.I.C.S.: 325611
Import Export
Advertising Expenditures: $2,500,000
Media: 1-6-9-14-15-19-23-24
Distr.: Natl.

SCHOLLER, INC.

95 James Way Ste 100
Southampton, PA 18966-3847
Tel.: (215) 942-0200
Fax: (215) 942-0255
E-mail: truk@scholler.com
Web Site: www.scholler.com
Approx. Number Employees: 29
Year Founded: 1907
Business Description:
Textile Finishes, Resins, Softeners, Detergents; Water & Energy Treatments Mfr
S.I.C.: 2819; 2869
N.A.I.C.S.: 325188; 325199
Media: 2-4-7
Distr.: Direct to Consumer; Natl.
Personnel:
Karl L. Vonder Schmalz *(Pres)*
Brands & Products:
BROSCO
CREAMOYL
DURA BEAU
TRI-A-NOL
TRISCO
TRISULPHOIL

SCOTT'S LIQUID GOLD-INC.

4880 Havana St
Denver, CO 80239-2416
Mailing Address:
PO Box 39 S
Denver, CO 80239-0019
Tel.: (303) 373-4860
Fax: (303) 371-2725
Toll Free: (800) 447-1919
E-mail: dvaughn@slginc.com
Web Site: www.scottsliquidgold.com
E-Mail For Key Personnel:
Marketing Director: jhinkle@slginc.com
Approx. Sls.: $14,396,600
Approx. Number Employees: 64
Year Founded: 1954
Business Description:
Mfr. of Wood Preservatives, Fine Furniture & Wood Polish & Room Air Fresheners
S.I.C.: 2841; 2499; 2531; 2844; 3111; 3589; 3999

Key to Media (For complete agency information see *The Advertising Red Books-Agencies* edition):
1. Bus. Publs. 2. Cable T.V. 3. Catalogs & Directories. 4. Co-op Adv. 5. Consumer Mags. 6. D.M. to Bus. Estab.7. D.M. to Consumers 8. Daily Newsp. 9. Exhibits/Trade Shows 10. Foreign 11. Infomercial 12. Internet Adv.13. Multimedia 14. Network Radio 15. Network T.V. 16. Newsp. Distr. Mags. 17. Other 18. Outdoor (Posters, Transit) 19. Point of Purchase20. Premiums, Novelties 21. Product Samples 22. Special Events Mktg. 23. Spot Radio 24. Spot T.V. 25. Weekly Newsp. 26. Yellow Page Adv.

N.A.I.C.S.: 325611; 316110; 321999; 325620; 333319; 337127; 339999
Export
Advertising Expenditures: $405,200
Media: 3-5-8-9-13-15-17-19
Distr.: Intl.; Natl.
Budget Set: Monthly
Personnel:
Mark E. Goldstein *(Chm, Pres & CEO)*
Brian L. Boberick *(CFO)*
Jeffrey R. Hinkle *(VP-Mktg & Sls)*
Brands & Products:
CLEAN SCREEN
CUBE SCENTS
MOLD CONTROL 500
NEOTERIC
SCOTT'S LIQUID GOLD
TOUCH-OF-SCENT
TOUCH-OF-SCENT-TOO
Advertising Agencies:
A. Eicoff & Co.
(Div. of Ogilvy & Mather Worldwide)
401 N Michigan Ave 4th Fl
Chicago, IL 60611-4212
Tel.: (312) 527-7183
Fax: (312) 527-7188
Toll Free: (800) 333-6605

Scott's Liquid Gold- Advertising Promotions, Inc.
4880 Havana St
Denver, CO 80239-2416
Tel.: (303) 373-4860
Fax: (303) 373-1161

SENORET CHEMICAL COMPANY
566 Leffingwell Ave
Kirkwood, MO 63122-6453
Tel.: (314) 966-2394
Fax: (314) 966-0572
Toll Free: (800) 837-7644
Web Site: www.terro.com
Approx. Number Employees: 35
Year Founded: 1893
Business Description:
Insecticides
S.I.C.: 2842; 2879
N.A.I.C.S.: 325612; 325320
Import Export
Media: 6-7-9-13-14-23-25
Distr.: Natl.
Budget Set: Mar.
Personnel:
Thomas D. Kraatz *(Pres)*
Brands & Products:
CARPENTER ANT & TERMITE AEROSOL
FRUIT FLY TRAP
LIQUID ANT BAITS
TERRO

THE SERVICEMASTER COMPANY
(Sub. of ServiceMaster Global Holdings)
860 Ridge Lake Blvd
Memphis, TN 38120
Tel.: (901) 597-1400
Toll Free: (866) 782-6787
E-mail: customercare@servicemaster.com
Web Site: www.servicemaster.com
Approx. Rev.: $3,365,902,000
Approx. Number Employees: 27,000
Year Founded: 1947
Business Description:
Facilities Maintenance Services
S.I.C.: 1623; 0782; 7342; 7349
N.A.I.C.S.: 237130; 561710; 561720; 561730
Advertising Expenditures: $152,700,000
Media: 2-3-4-6-7-8-9-10-13-14-16-18-20-22-23-24-25
Distr.: Direct to Consumer; Intl.; Natl.
Personnel:
Hank Mullany *(CEO)*
Roger A. Cregg *(CFO & Sr VP-Fin)*
Linda Goodspeed *(CIO & Sr VP)*
Greer McMullen *(Gen Counsel & Sr VP)*
Mark Peterson *(Treas & Sr VP)*
Steven B. Bono *(Sr VP-Corp Comm)*
Pete Tosches *(Sr VP-Corp Comm)*
Chris Curran *(Dir-PR & Issues Mgmt)*
Donna Infurchia *(Dir-Intl)*
Sandra Lewis *(Mgr-Mktg)*
Charlie Ngo *(Mgr-Strategy & Bus Dev)*
Teresa Tyler *(Mgr-Intl Market Expansion)*
Brands & Products:
AMERICAN HOME SHIELD
AMERICAN RESIDENTIAL SERVICES/RESCUE ROOTER
AMERISPEC
FURNITURE MEDIC
MERRY MAIDS
RESCUE ROOTER
SERVICE MASTER HOME SERVICE CENTER
SERVICEMASTER
SERVICEMASTER CLEAN
TERMINIX
TRUGREEN-CHEMLAWN
TRUGREEN LANDCARE
Advertising Agencies:
Acento Advertising, Inc.
2254 S Sepulveda Blvd
Los Angeles, CA 90064
Tel.: (310) 943-8300
Fax: (310) 943-8310

archer malmo
65 Union Ave Ste 500
Memphis, TN 38103-5137
Tel.: (901) 523-2000
Fax: (901) 523-7654
Toll Free: (800) 535-8943

Leapfrog Online
807 Greenwood St
Evanston, IL 60201
Tel.: (847) 492-1968
Fax: (847) 492-1990

Signature Advertising
1755 Kirby Pkwy Ste 200
Memphis, TN 38120
Tel.: (901) 754-2200
Fax: (901) 754-9118

SEVENTH GENERATION, INC.
60 Lake St
Burlington, VT 54015-5218
Tel.: (802) 658-3773
Fax: (802) 658-1771
Toll Free: (800) 456-1191
E-mail: marketing@seventhgeneration.com
Web Site: www.seventhgeneration.com
Sales Range: $150-199.9 Million
Approx. Number Employees: 130
Business Description:
Environmentally Safe Cleaning Products Mfr
S.I.C.: 5199
N.A.I.C.S.: 424990
Media: 10-13-22
Personnel:
Jeffrey Hollender *(Founder)*
Peter Graham *(Chm)*
John B. Replogle *(Pres & CEO)*
Joey Bergstein *(CMO)*
Julie Atwood *(Exec VP-Fin & Admin)*
Jeff M. Phillips *(Exec VP)*
Jay LeDuc *(Sr VP-Ops)*
John Murphy *(Sr VP-Sls & Customer Mktg)*
Chrystie Heimert *(Dir-Comm)*
Peter Swaine *(Dir-Global Stategic Sourcing)*
Sarah Thompson *(Mgr-Web Bus)*

SPONGETECH DELIVERY SYSTEMS, INC.
10 W 33rd St Ste 518
New York, NY 10001
Tel.: (212) 695-7850
Fax: (212) 695-9342
Toll Free: (877) 776-6438
E-mail: info@spongetech.com
Web Site: www.spongetech.com
Sales Range: $1-9.9 Million
Year Founded: 2002
Business Description:
Motor Vehicle Cleaning Systems Mfr, Distr & Marketer
S.I.C.: 2842; 3471; 5013
N.A.I.C.S.: 325612; 332813; 423120
Media: 10-12-13
Personnel:
Michael Metter *(Chm, Pres & CEO)*
Steven Y. Moskowitz *(COO)*

STARBRITE CORP.
(Sub. of Ocean Bio Chem, Inc.)
4041 SW 47th Ave
Fort Lauderdale, FL 33314-4023
Tel.: (954) 587-6280
Fax: (954) 587-2813
Toll Free: (800) 327-8583
Web Site: www.starbrite.com
E-Mail For Key Personnel:
President: peter@starbrite.com
Public Relations: jeff@starbrite.com
Sales Range: $10-24.9 Million
Approx. Number Employees: 20
Year Founded: 1973
Business Description:
Mfr. of Marine, Automotive & RV Chemical Appearance Products; Brushes, Straps, Tie Downs
S.I.C.: 2842
N.A.I.C.S.: 325612
Import Export
Media: 6-7-9-10-11-15-18-21-24
Distr.: Intl.; Natl.
Budget Set: Jan.
Personnel:
Peter G. Dornau *(Pres)*
Bill Lindsey *(Mgr-Mktg)*
Advertising Agency:
D&S Advertising, Inc.
4041 SW 47th Ave
Fort Lauderdale, FL 33314-4023
Tel.: (954) 587-6280
Fax: (954) 587-2813
(Star Brite Marine & RV Care Products)

STATE INDUSTRIAL PRODUCTS CORPORATION
3100 Hamilton Ave
Cleveland, OH 44114-3701
Tel.: (216) 861-7114
Fax: (216) 861-5213
E-mail: webmaster@stateindustrial.com
Web Site: www.stateindustrial.com
Sales Range: $50-74.9 Million
Approx. Number Employees: 1,300
Year Founded: 1911
Business Description:
Cleaning Products Mfr
S.I.C.: 2841; 5072
N.A.I.C.S.: 325611; 423710
Import Export
Media: 10
Personnel:
Harold Uhrman *(CEO)*
Brands & Products:
ACIDINE
ACTION WRAP
APPLE ORCHARD
BLUE BASE
COOL-ADE
D-STROY
LIQUA-GRO
LIQUI-DAM
LIQUI-PILLOW
PARCH
SEAT DOCTOR
SPOT BLASTER
STATE

THE SUN PRODUCTS CORPORATION
(Holding of Vestar Capital Partners, Inc.)
60 Danbury Rd
Wilton, CT 06897
Tel.: (203) 254-6700
Fax: (203) 256-0585
Web Site: www.sunproductscorp.com
Sales Range: $1-4.9 Billion
Approx. Number Employees: 100
Year Founded: 2008
Business Description:
Soap & Detergent Mfr
S.I.C.: 2841
N.A.I.C.S.: 325611
Personnel:
Jeff Ansell *(Pres)*
Neil P. DeFeo *(CEO)*
Kris Kelley *(CFO & Exec VP)*
Robert F. Waldron *(CMO)*
Beth Hecht *(Gen Counsel, Sec & Sr VP)*
Gretchen Crist *(Sr VP-HR)*
Shannon Silsby *(Sr Mgr-Mktg Excellence)*
Brands & Products:
ALL
SNUGGLE
SUNLIGHT
SURF
WISK
Advertising Agencies:
Merkley + Partners
(Sub. of Omnicom Group, Inc.)
200 Varick St
New York, NY 10014-4810
Tel.: (212) 366-3500
Fax: (212) 805-7445

Mindshare
498 7th Ave

Key to Media (For complete agency information see *The Advertising Red Books-Agencies* edition):
1. Bus. Publs. 2. Cable T.V. 3. Catalogs & Directories. 4. Co-op Adv. 5. Consumer Mags. 6. D.M. to Bus. Estab.7. D.M. to Consumers 8. Daily Newsp. 9. Exhibits/Trade Shows 10. Foreign 11. Infomercial 12. Internet Adv.13. Multimedia 14. Network Radio 15. Network T.V. 16. Newsp. Distr. Mags. 17. Other 18. Outdoor (Posters, Transit) 19. Point of Purchase20. Premiums, Novelties 21. Product Samples 22. Special Events Mktg. 23. Spot Radio 24. Spot T.V. 25. Weekly Newsp. 26. Yellow Page Adv.

The Sun Products Corporation — (Continued)

New York, NY 10018
Tel.: (212) 297-7000
Fax: (212) 297-7001

TracyLocke
1999 Bryan St Ste 2800
Dallas, TX 75201
Tel.: (214) 259-3500
Fax: (214) 259-3550
Agency of Record - Shopper Marketing
Wisk
Wisk-it Facebook Application

SUNSHINE MAKERS, INC.

15922 Pacific Coast Hwy
Huntington Beach, CA 92649-1806
Tel.: (562) 795-6000
Fax: (562) 592-3034
Toll Free: (800) 228-0709
E-mail: info@simplegreen.com
Web Site: www.simplegreen.com
Approx. Number Employees: 88
Year Founded: 1975
Business Description:
Mfr. of Cleaning Products
S.I.C.: 2842
N.A.I.C.S.: 325612
Export
Advertising Expenditures: $2,000,000
Media: 3-6-9-10-13-14-15-21-22
Personnel:
Bruce FaBrizio *(Founder & Pres)*
Greg Frankenfield *(VP-Retail Sls)*
Jeff Hyder *(VP-Sls & Ops)*
Milt Krause *(VP-Tech)*
Pat Sheehan *(VP-Global Sls)*
Fred Waterfall *(VP-Shows & Promos)*
Jessica Franson *(Dir-Internet Mktg)*
Norman Lao *(Dir-Creative)*
Brands & Products:
AROMA CLEAN
SAFETY TOWELS
SIMPLE GREEN
SIMPLE GREEN D PRO 3
SIMPLE GREEN NATURALS
Advertising Agency:
Ocean Bridge Group
1714 16th St
Santa Monica, CA 90404
Tel.: (310) 392-3200

SURCO PRODUCTS, INC.

RIDC Indus Pk 292 Alpha Dr
Pittsburgh, PA 15238
Tel.: (412) 252-7000
Fax: (412) 252-1005
Toll Free: (800) 556-0111
E-mail: odorstop@earthlink.net
Web Site: www.surcopt.com
Approx. Number Employees: 75
Year Founded: 1946
Business Description:
Mfr. of Air Fresheners, Deodorants, Odor Control Systems & Fan Deodorizers
S.I.C.: 3564; 2844
N.A.I.C.S.: 333411; 325620
Import Export
Media: 7-8-10
Distr.: Reg.
Budget Set: Various
Personnel:
Arnold Zlotnik *(Pres)*
Ray Czapko *(Dir-Mktg)*
Brands & Products:
2-IN-1
24 HOUR ODOR ABSORBER
AIR-SAVERS
AIR-SCENT
AM/PM
C-7B
CH
DRIP-O-MATIC
END SMOKE
ERASE-ITT
FRESH-AS-A-BABY
GARB-O-FLAKES
HIDE-A-DISC
METAZENE
NATURE SCENT
ODOMASTER
ONCE-A-DAY
POTTY FRESH
ROUND-THE-CLOCK
RUG AROMA
SANI-FLAKES
SANI-MATIC
SANI-SCENT
SCATTER
SCENT FLO
SO FRESH
SPRINKLE
STIMULAIRE
SUPER S
SURCO
SURCOTECH
SURCOTTA
ULTRA DEO BASE
UNDO
ZORB-IT-ALL

SYSCO GUEST SUPPLY, LLC

(Sub. of Sysco Corporation)
4301 US Hwy 1 PO Box 902
Monmouth Junction, NJ 08852-0902
Tel.: (609) 514-9696
Fax: (609) 514-2692
Fax: (800) 480-7878
Toll Free: (800) 772-7676
E-mail: eservice@guestsupply.com
Web Site: www.guestsupply.com
Sales Range: $75-99.9 Million
Approx. Number Employees: 150
Year Founded: 1979
Business Description:
Toiletries, Personal Care Products, Housekeeping, Hotel Amenities & Supplies Mfr & Distr
S.I.C.: 2844; 2676; 2842; 7213
N.A.I.C.S.: 325620; 322291; 325612; 812331
Import Export
Media: 4-7-13
Personnel:
Clifford W. Stanley *(Pres & CEO)*
Paul T. Xenis *(Exec VP)*
Teri E. Unsworth *(VP-Mktg)*
Kathleen Hatrak *(Dir-Mktg)*

THE TERMINIX INTERNATIONAL COMPANY LIMITED PARTNERSHIP

(Sub. of The ServiceMaster Company)
860 Rdg Lk Blvd
Memphis, TN 38120-9421
Tel.: (901) 766-1400
Toll Free: (800) TERMINEX
Web Site: www.terminix.com
Year Founded: 1927
Business Description:
Residential & Commercial Termite & Pest Control
S.I.C.: 7342
N.A.I.C.S.: 561710
Personnel:
Vic Charles *(Partner)*
Ped Shultz *(CFO)*
Thomas Brackett *(COO)*
Brad Cumings *(CMO)*
Advertising Agency:
Publicis Dallas
7300 Lonestar Dr
Plano, TX 75024
Tel.: (972) 628-7500
Fax: (972) 628-7864

THETFORD CORPORATION

(Holding of The Dyson-Kissner-Moran Corporation)
7101 Jackson Rd
Ann Arbor, MI 48103
Mailing Address:
PO Box 1285
Ann Arbor, MI 48106
Tel.: (734) 769-6000
Fax: (734) 769-2023
Toll Free: (800) 521-3032
Telex: 810-223-6010
Web Site: www.thetford.com
Sales Range: $75-99.9 Million
Approx. Number Employees: 300
Year Founded: 1963
Business Description:
Sanitation Products & Systems For Recreation Vehicles Mfr & Whslr
S.I.C.: 3632; 3089
N.A.I.C.S.: 335222; 326199
Import Export
Advertising Expenditures: $450,000
Media: 1-2-4-5-6-8-10-17-19-20-21-22-24
Distr.: Intl.; Natl.
Budget Set: Sept.-Oct.
Personnel:
Mark Schlei *(CFO)*
William Croonenberg *(Sr VP-European Opers)*
Kevin Phillips *(VP-Sls & Mktg)*
Mary Burrows *(Mgr-Chemical Dev)*
Brands & Products:
AQUA BOWL
AQUA-KEM
AQUA-KEM TOSS-TABS
AQUA-MAGIC
AQUA-MATE
AQUA SOFT
AQUA ZYME
AQUAMAGIC IV
ARIA
BRAVURA
CAMPA CHEM
DRAIN VALVE LUBRICANT
ELECTRA MAGIC
GREY WATER ODOR CONTROL
LEVEL GAUGE CLEANER
PAK-A-POTTI
PORTA POTTI
RV/MARINE TOILET TISSUE
SOAP STAYTION
THETFORD 735MSD
THETFORD 775MSD
TISSUE DIGESTER
Advertising Agency:
AutoCom Associates
74 W Long Lk Rd Ste 103
Bloomfield Hills, MI 48304-2770
Tel.: (248) 647-8621
Fax: (248) 642-2110

UNITED AIR SPECIALISTS, INC.

(Sub. of CLARCOR, Inc.)
4440 Creek Rd
Cincinnati, OH 45242-2802
Tel.: (513) 891-0400
Fax: (513) 891-4171
Fax: (513) 891-4882
Toll Free: (800) 252-4647
E-mail: uas@uasinc.com
Web Site: www.uasinc.com
Sales Range: $25-49.9 Million
Approx. Number Employees: 70
Year Founded: 1966
Business Description:
Air Purification System Mfr
S.I.C.: 3564; 3563
N.A.I.C.S.: 333411; 333912
Import Export
Media: 2-7-10-13
Distr.: Intl.; Natl.
Personnel:
Steve Trame *(VP-Sls & Mktg)*
Brands & Products:
DUST-CAT
DUST-HOG
FRESH-X-CHANGER
FUME-GATOR
KLEENTEK
SMOG-HOG
SMOKEETER
TOTALSTAT
VISIONAIR

WALTER G. LEGGE COMPANY, INC.

(d/b/a Legge Systems)
444 Central Ave
Peekskill, NY 10566-0591
Tel.: (914) 737-5040
Fax: (914) 737-2636
Fax: (800) 332-2636
Toll Free: (800) 345-3443
E-mail: info@leggesystems.com
Web Site: www.leggesystems.com
Sales Range: $10-24.9 Million
Approx. Number Employees: 15
Year Founded: 1928
Business Description:
Nonslip Floor Polishes & Cleaners, Germicides & Anti-Static Products & Systems Mfr. & Sales
S.I.C.: 2842
N.A.I.C.S.: 325612
Export
Media: 13
Distr.: Intl.; Natl.
Budget Set: Sept. -Oct.
Brands & Products:
ADJUST-A-STAT
ALOE-STAT
ALOESEPT
BOOTSTAT
CARPET SHAMPOO 877
CITRONEX
DEEP SEAL
ELIMSTAPH NO. 2
ELIMSTAT
ELIMSTAT ATS
ELIMSTAT LX
ELIMSTAT SD
ELIMSTAT SDEC
ELIMSTAT SDSC
ELIMSTAT UXM-60P
ELIMSTATX SDSC
FLOORSHINE R20
FOAM-END

Key to Media (For complete agency information see *The Advertising Red Books-Agencies* edition):
1. Bus. Publs. 2. Cable T.V. 3. Catalogs & Directories. 4. Co-op Adv. 5. Consumer Mags. 6. D.M. to Bus. Estab.7. D.M. to Consumers 8. Daily Newsp. 9. Exhibits/Trade Shows 10. Foreign 11. Infomercial 12. Internet Adv.13. Multimedia 14. Network Radio 15. Network T.V. 16. Newsp. Distr. Mags. 17. Other 18. Outdoor (Posters, Transit) 19. Point of Purchase20. Premiums, Novelties 21. Product Samples 22. Special Events Mktg. 23. Spot Radio 24. Spot T.V. 25. Weekly Newsp. 26. Yellow Page Adv.

GRIPTEX
HEELSTAT
LEGCIDE .5
LEGCIDE HB PLUS
LEGCLEAN
LEGGE-ACY
LEGGE SYSTEMS
LEGPHENE
LEGSOLVE
LEGSOLVE-IT
LEGSTAT
NEUTRAL CLEANER
PALMSTAT
PRESS PAK
SOLESTAT
STAT-LES
STATICO
STATSHINE
TEXINOL
TEXSPAR
TEXSPAR PLUS
URE-STAT
WINDO BRITE
WRISTAT
YOU ALWAYS HAVE LEGGE TO STAND ON

WD-40 COMPANY

1061 Cudahy Pl
San Diego, CA 92110-3929
Mailing Address:
PO Box 80607
San Diego, CA 92138-0607
Tel.: (619) 275-1400
Fax: (619) 275-5823
Toll Free: (888) 324-7596
Web Site: www.wd40.com
Approx. Sls.: $321,516,000
Approx. Number Employees: 316
Year Founded: 1953
Business Description:
Lubricant & Rust Preventive Compounds Mfr
S.I.C.: 2899; 2879; 2911; 2992; 5169
N.A.I.C.S.: 325998; 324110; 324191; 325320; 424690
Export
Advertising Expenditures: $40,500,000
Media: 2-4-5-6-7-10-13-19-21-22-24
Distr.: Intl.; Natl.
Budget Set: Mar.
Personnel:
Neal E. Schmale *(Chm)*
Garry O. Ridge *(Pres & CEO)*
Jay Rembolt *(CFO, Treas & VP-Fin)*
Graham P. Milner *(Chief Branding Officer & Exec VP-Global Dev)*
Michael L. Freeman *(Pres-The Americas Div)*
Michael J. Irwin *(Exec VP-Strategic Dev)*
Tim Lesmeister *(VP-Mktg)*
Linda Cernik-Price *(Brand Mgr)*
Ross Cooling *(Brand Mgr)*
Brandy Lamb *(Brand Mgr)*
Brands & Products:
2000 FLUSHES
3-IN-ONE
3 OZ HANDY
BIG BLAST CAN
CARPET FRESH
LAVA
NO-MESS PEN
SMART STRAW
SOLVOL
SPOTSHOT
TRIGGER PRO
WD-40
WD-40 BIG BLAST
WD-40 NO-MESS PEN
Advertising Agencies:
Alcone Marketing Group
(Division of Omnicom Group, Inc.)
4 Studebaker
Irvine, CA 92618-2012
Tel.: (949) 770-4400
Fax: (949) 770-2957

Geary Interactive
401 W A St Ste 360
San Diego, CA 92101
Tel.: (619) 756-6700
Fax: (619) 234-8668
Web Sites

O'Leary and Partners
5000 Birch St Ste 1000
Newport Beach, CA 92660
Tel.: (949) 833-8006
Fax: (949) 833-9155

WEIMAN PRODUCTS, LLC

755 Tri State Pkwy
Gurnee, IL 60031
Tel.: (847) 263-3500
Fax: (847) 263-3700
Toll Free: (800) 837-8140
Toll Free: (888) 281-6400
Web Site: www.weiman.com
E-Mail For Key Personnel:
President: cdemasi@weiman.com
Approx. Number Employees: 80
Year Founded: 1963
Business Description:
Specialty Chemicals
S.I.C.: 2842; 2899
N.A.I.C.S.: 325612; 325998
Import Export
Media: 8-10-13-21
Distr.: Natl.
Personnel:
Carl DeMasi *(Pres & CEO)*
John Brennan *(Sr VP-Sls)*
Libby Gerberi *(Mgr-Mktg)*
Brands & Products:
AQUA BLUE
COOK TOP
CRA-Z SOAP
E-TRONIC
EPI-SAFE BARRIER CREAM
FLEXO CREAMER
GOLD MIRACLE
PERFECT PLANET
PLATE SAV-UR
PRINTERS PRIDE
PUTZ POMADE
ROYAL STERLING
SAFETY FOUNT
THUMBS UP
TONE-A-WAY
UFS SM
UFS SM PLUS
ULTRA FOUNT
WEIMAN
WRIGHT'S
Advertising Agency:
SWEENEY
20325 Center Rdg Rd Ph Ste
Cleveland, OH 44116
Tel.: (440) 333-0001
Fax: (440) 333-0005
Wright's
Perfect Planet

WEST CHEMICAL PRODUCTS, INC.

(Sub. of Penetone Corporation)
1000 Herrontown Rd
Princeton, NJ 08540
Tel.: (609) 921-0501
Fax: (609) 924-4308
Web Site: www.west-penetone.com
Sales Range: $50-74.9 Million
Approx. Number Employees: 5
Year Founded: 1882
Business Description:
Mfr. of Specialty Chemicals, Holding Company
S.I.C.: 2842
N.A.I.C.S.: 325612
Export
Advertising Expenditures: $1,000,000
Catalogs & Directories: $200,000;
D.M. to Consumers: $800,000
Distr.: Direct to Consumer; Indus.; Natl.
Budget Set: Nov.
Personnel:
Bruce Muretta *(VP-Fin, Gen Mgr & Admin)*
Mike Bradford *(VP-Sls-Mktg)*
Ralph Santoro *(Ops Mgr)*
Brands & Products:
GERM WARFARE
GRAFIKLEEN
PENPOWER
RAPIDYNE

W.J. HAGERTY & SONS, LTD., INC.

3801 Linden Ave
South Bend, IN 46619-1844
Mailing Address:
PO Box 1496
South Bend, IN 46624-1496
Tel.: (574) 288-4991
Fax: (574) 288-4994
Toll Free: (800) 348-5162
E-mail: hagerty100@aol.com
Web Site: hagertyusa.com
E-Mail For Key Personnel:
President: shelleys4@aol.com
Public Relations: hagerty100@aol.com
Approx. Number Employees: 65
Year Founded: 1895
Business Description:
Mfr. of Precious Metal Care Products, Jewelry Cleaners, Silver Storage Bags & Kits
S.I.C.: 2842; 3471
N.A.I.C.S.: 325612; 332813
Import Export
Media: 2-3-4-5-6-7-9-15-19-22-24-26
Distr.: Intl.; Natl.
Budget Set: May
Personnel:
Tom Batalis *(VP & Dir-Mktg)*
Brands & Products:
JEWEL CLEAN
JEWELRY KEEPER
R-22
SILVER FOAM
SILVER KEEPERS
SILVERSMITHS' POLISH
SILVERSMITHS' WASH

W.M. BARR & COMPANY, INC.

2105 Channel Ave
Memphis, TN 38113
Mailing Address:
PO Box 1879
Memphis, TN 38101-1879
Tel.: (901) 775-0100
Fax: (901) 775-5468
Fax: (800) 621-9508
Toll Free: (888) 577-1710
E-mail: klnstrp@wmbarr.com
Web Site: www.wmbarr.com
E-Mail For Key Personnel:
Sales Director: brandedsales@wmbarr.com
Sales Range: $150-199.9 Million
Approx. Number Employees: 350
Year Founded: 1946
Business Description:
Producer & Retailer of Specialty Cleaning & Polishing Agents
S.I.C.: 2851
N.A.I.C.S.: 325510
Export
Media: 1-2-4-5-6-7-9-10-12-13-14-15-19-20-23
Distr.: Natl.
Personnel:
Richard Loomis *(Pres & CEO)*
Ann Allard *(VP-HR)*
Brands & Products:
ARMOR ALL
BRITE
CITRISTRIP
EL PICO
EXXON CLEAR LITE
GILLESPIE
HOUSEBRITE
KLEAN STRIP
KWIK
PAINTERS' HELPER

ZEP INC.

1310 Seaboard Industrial Blvd NW
Atlanta, GA 30318
Mailing Address:
PO Box 2015
Atlanta, GA 30301-2015
Tel.: (404) 355-3120
Fax: (404) 603-7958
E-mail: webmaster@zep.com
Web Site: www.zepinc.com
Approx. Sls.: $568,512,000
Approx. Number Employees: 2,350
Year Founded: 1937
Business Description:
Holding Company; Commercial, Industrial & Institutional Cleaning & Maintenance Chemical Products Mfr & Marketer
S.I.C.: 6719; 2841; 2842; 2879; 2891; 2899; 2992; 5169
N.A.I.C.S.: 551112; 324191; 325320; 325520; 325611; 325612; 325998; 424690
Advertising Expenditures: $2,400,000
Personnel:
John K. Morgan *(Chm, Pres & CEO)*
Mark R. Bachmann *(CFO & Exec VP)*
Jeffrey J. Sorensen *(CMO)*
Robert P. Collins *(Chief Admin Officer & VP)*
Cedric M. Brown *(Chief Procurement Officer)*
Philip A. Theodore *(Gen Counsel, Sec & VP)*
Mari Hayes *(VP-Product Dev, Mktg & Retail)*
Brands & Products:
ENFORCER
GREENLINE

Zep Inc. — (Continued)

GREENLINK
NATIONAL CHEMICALS
SUPERIOR SOLUTIONS
ZEP
ZEP COMMERCIAL
ZEP PROFESSIONAL

ZOOTS CORPORATION

153 Needham St
Newton Upper Falls, MA 02464
Tel.: (617) 558-9666
Fax: (617) 558-9667
Toll Free: (888) 558-5588
E-mail: homedelivery@zoots.com
Web Site: www.zoots.com
Sales Range: $25-49.9 Million
Approx. Number Employees: 1,000
Year Founded: 1998
Business Description:
Drycleaning Delivery Services
S.I.C.: 7212
N.A.I.C.S.: 812320
Media: 8-13
Personnel:
James Franklin *(CMO & Chief Sls Officer)*
Brands & Products:
ZOOTS
Advertising Agency:
Cercone Brown Curtis
77 N Washington St Ste 304
Boston, MA 02114-1913
Tel.: (617) 248-0680
Fax: (617) 248-0688

Key to Media (For complete agency information see *The Advertising Red Books-Agencies* edition):
1. Bus. Publs. 2. Cable T.V. 3. Catalogs & Directories. 4. Co-op Adv. 5. Consumer Mags. 6. D.M. to Bus. Estab.7. D.M. to Consumers 8. Daily Newsp. 9. Exhibits/Trade Shows 10. Foreign 11. Infomercial 12. Internet Adv.13. Multimedia 14. Network Radio 15. Network T.V. 16. Newsp. Distr. Mags. 17. Other 18. Outdoor (Posters, Transit) 19. Point of Purchase20. Premiums, Novelties 21. Product Samples 22. Special Events Mktg. 23. Spot Radio 24. Spot T.V. 25. Weekly Newsp. 26. Yellow Page Adv.

Computers & Office Equipment, Supplies & Services

Adding Machines — Business Forms — Calculators — Cash Registers — Computers — Computer Services — Copiers — Data Storage Systems — Office Furniture — Office & School Supplies — Safes — Software — Typewriters — Word Processors — Writing — Writing Instruments

123 STAFFING, INC.
121 Chanlon Rd S Bldg 1st Fl
New Providence, NJ 07974-1541
Tel.: (908) 665-3955
Fax: (908) 771-8618
E-mail: info@123staffing.com
Web Site: www.123staffing.com
Approx. Rev.: $2,400,000,000
Approx. Number Employees: 1,000
Year Founded: 1973
Business Description:
Temporary Staffing Services
S.I.C.: 7363
N.A.I.C.S.: 561320
Distr.: Natl.
Budget Set: Nov.
Personnel:
Felicity Tabworth *(Chm & Pres)*
Laura Napier *(Co-CEO-Business Data Grp)*
Martin Greggs *(CEO)*
Claire Simmons *(Deputy Mng Dir)*
Diane Hurst *(CFO)*
James Livingstone *(CIO)*
Mike Thomas *(Chief Legal Officer)*
J. Charles Wade *(Sr Gen Counsel)*
Elizabeth Monroe *(Exec VP-Sls)*
Brendan Hurst *(Sr VP-Ops-US)*
Tanya Smith *(VP-Sls)*
Jenny Farrell *(Asst VP)*
Kelly Taylor *(Asst VP)*
Brands & Products:
123 CLEANING SERVICES
123 EAST
123 HOME HEALTHCARE
123 PAYCHECKS
123 STAFFING
123 WEST
Advertising Agency:
Browning Advertising, Inc.
121 Chanlon Rd
New Providence, NJ 07974
Tel.: (908) 464-0000
Fax: (908) 790-5405
— Eric Miller *(Acct Exec)*
— Kieran Kern *(Acct Exec)*
— T. Johnson *(VP)*

3D SYSTEMS CORPORATION
333 Three D Systems Cir
Rock Hill, SC 29730
Tel.: (803) 326-3900
Toll Free: (888) 337-9786
E-mail: moreinfo@3dsystems.com
Web Site: www.3dsystems.com
Approx. Rev.: $159,868,000
Approx. Number Employees: 484
Year Founded: 1986
Business Description:
Solid Imaging Systems Designed to Rapidly Produce 3-D Objects Mfr, Developer & Marketer
S.I.C.: 7372; 3577
N.A.I.C.S.: 511210; 334119
Advertising Expenditures: $816,000
Media: 1-2-4-7-10-13
Personnel:
G. Walter Loewenbaum, II *(Chm)*
Abraham N. Reichental *(Pres & CEO)*
Kevin P. McAlea *(VP & Gen Mgr-Rapid Mfr Solutions)*
Damon Gregoire *(CFO)*
Charles W. Hull *(CTO & Exec VP)*
Robert M. Grace, Jr. *(Gen Counsel, Sec & VP)*
Lee Dockstader *(VP & Gen Mgr-Stereolithography Bus Unit)*
Brands & Products:
3D LIGHTYEAR
3D MANAGE
3D PRINT
3D SYSTEMS
ACCUDUR
ACCUGEN
ACCURA
AMETHYST
BUILDSTATION
CASTFORM
DURAFORM
INVISION
IPRO
LASERFORM
PROCLEAN
PROCURE
PROJET
REAL MONITOR
SINTERSCAN
SINTERSTATION
SINTERSTATION HIQ
SLA
SLS
SPRO
THERMOJET
V-FLASH
VATMAN
VIPER

3M TOUCH SYSTEMS, INC.
(Sub. of 3M Company)
501 Griffin Brook Park Dr
Methuen, MA 01844-1873
Tel.: (978) 659-9000
Toll Free: (866) 407-6666 (Sales)
E-mail: touch@mmm.com
Web Site: www.3mtouch.com
Sales Range: $350-399.9 Million
Approx. Number Employees: 300
Year Founded: 2001
Business Description:
Touch Screen Products Mfr
S.I.C.: 3577
N.A.I.C.S.: 334119
Import Export
Advertising Expenditures: $500,000
Media: 2-4-7-10-17
Distr.: Natl.
Personnel:
Tim Holt *(Dir-Mktg Comm)*
Brands & Products:
CLEARTEK

3PAR INC.
(Sub. of Hewlett-Packard Company)
4209 Technology Dr
Fremont, CA 94538
Tel.: (510) 413-5999
Fax: (510) 413-5699
E-mail: salesinfo@3par.com
Web Site: www.3par.com
Approx. Rev.: $194,284,000
Approx. Number Employees: 657
Business Description:
Utility Storage Services
S.I.C.: 3572
N.A.I.C.S.: 334112
Advertising Expenditures: $208,000
Media: 10-13
Personnel:
Jeffrey A. Price *(Co-Founder & CTO-Sys Design)*
Adriel G. Lares *(CFO & VP-Fin)*
Ashok Singhal *(Co-Founder & CTO-Sys Architecture)*
Alastair A. Short *(Gen Counsel & VP)*
Peter Slocum *(VP-Engrg)*

3T SYSTEMS, INC.
999 18th St Ste 2100
Denver, CO 80202
Tel.: (303) 858-8800
Fax: (303) 790-9784
E-mail: support@3tsystems.com
Web Site: www.3tsystems.com
Sales Range: $10-24.9 Million
Approx. Number Employees: 180
Business Description:
IT Consulting Services
S.I.C.: 7373; 7371; 8748
N.A.I.C.S.: 541512; 541511; 541690
Media: 10
Personnel:
Ciaran Dwier *(CEO)*

4-PROFIT, LLC
5800 Arlington Ave Ste 10B
Riverdale, NY 10471
Tel.: (917) 661-4180
Web Site: www.4-profit.com
E-Mail For Key Personnel:
President: larry@ltbn.com
Year Founded: 1994
Business Description:
Business Support Services
S.I.C.: 8748; 7389
N.A.I.C.S.: 541618; 512290
Media: 10
Personnel:
Larry Kesslin *(Pres)*

A-D TECHNOLOGIES
(Holding of Audax Management Company, LLC)
11400 Parkside Dr Ste 300
Knoxville, TN 37934
Tel.: (865) 218-3460
Fax: (865) 223-5085
E-mail: moreinfo@adtechnologies.com
Web Site: www.adtechnologies.com
Approx. Number Employees: 200
Year Founded: 1971
Business Description:
Telecommunications Conduit Products
S.I.C.: 3663
N.A.I.C.S.: 334220
Distr.: Intl.
Personnel:
Paresh Chari *(Pres & CEO)*
Brands & Products:
FIREJACKET
SILICORE
Advertising Agency:
Sonnhalter
633 W Bagley Rd
Berea, OH 44017-1356
Tel.: (440) 234-1812
Fax: (440) 234-1890

A. T. CROSS COMPANY
1 Albion Rd
Lincoln, RI 02865-3703

Key to Media (For complete agency information see *The Advertising Red Books-Agencies* edition):
1. Bus. Publs. 2. Cable T.V. 3. Catalogs & Directories. 4. Co-op Adv. 5. Consumer Mags. 6. D.M. to Bus. Estab.7. D.M. to Consumers
8. Daily Newsp. 9. Exhibits/Trade Shows 10. Foreign 11. Infomercial 12. Internet Adv.13. Multimedia 14. Network Radio
15. Network T.V. 16. Newsp. Distr. Mags. 17. Other 18. Outdoor (Posters, Transit) 19. Point of Purchase20. Premiums, Novelties
21. Product Samples 22. Special Events Mktg. 23. Spot Radio 24. Spot T.V. 25. Weekly Newsp. 26. Yellow Page Adv.

A. T. CROSS COMPANY — (Continued)

Tel.: (401) 333-1200
Fax: (401) 334-2861
Toll Free: (800) 282-7677
E-mail: investorrelations@cross.com
Web Site: www.cross.com
Approx. Sls.: $158,312,000
Approx. Number Employees: 950
Year Founded: 1846
Business Description:
Writing Instruments Mfr
S.I.C.: 3951; 3577; 5112
N.A.I.C.S.: 339941; 334119; 424120
Import Export
Advertising Expenditures: $11,100,000
Media: 2-4-5-6-7-9-10-13-19
Distr.: Natl.
Budget Set: Jan.
Personnel:
Russell A. Boss *(Chm)*
David G. Whalen *(Pres & CEO)*
Kevin F. Mahoney *(CFO, Treas & Sr VP-Fin)*
Charles R. MacDonald *(Pres-Cross Optical Grp)*
Charles S. Mellen *(Pres-Cross Accessory Div)*
Tina C. Benik *(Sec, VP-Legal & HR)*
Sue Coffland *(VP-Mktg)*
Robin Boss Dorman *(VP-Retail Stores)*
Mark Ivory *(VP-Global Sls)*
Stephen A. Perreault *(VP-Global Ops & IT)*
Joseph V. Bassi *(Dir-Fin)*
Steve Seaver *(Mgr-Sls-Natl)*
Brands & Products:
APOGEE
APOGEE EXECUTIVE
ATX
AUTOCROSS
BRYON
CENTURY
CENTURY COLORS
CENTURY II
CENTURY SIGNET
CENTURY SPORT
CHICAGO
CLANCY
CLASSIC
COMPACT
COSTA DEL MAR
CROSS
FAULKNER
JOYCE
KENSINGTON
KNIGHTSBRIDGE
MANHATTAN
MAYFAIR
MILAN
MORPH2
OXFORD
PARIS
PARIS TONNEAU
SAUVAGE
SELECTIP
SHELLEY
TECH3
TOWNSEND
VAPOR
VERVE
VICE
WALKER
Advertising Agencies:
Arnold Worldwide
101 Huntington Ave
Boston, MA 02199-7603
Tel.: (617) 587-8000
Fax: (617) 587-8004

Imarketing Ltd, Inc.
20 Nassau St Ste 250E
Princeton, NJ 08542
Tel.: (609) 921-0400
Affiliate & Search Engine Marketing Campaigns
Agency of Record
Creative Development

ABSOLUTE SOFTWARE CORPORATION

Suite 1600 1055 Dunsmuir St
Vancouver, BC V7X 1K8, Canada
Tel.: (604) 730-9851
Fax: (604) 730-2621
Toll Free: (800) 220-0733
E-mail: info@absolute.com
Web Site: www.absolute.com
Approx. Rev.: $62,709,693
Approx. Number Employees: 350
Business Description:
Laptop Computers Mfr
S.I.C.: 3571
N.A.I.C.S.: 334111
Personnel:
John Livingston *(Chm & CEO)*
Errol Olsen *(CFO)*
Rob Chase *(COO)*
Gareth Mason *(Sr VP-Ops)*
Matthew Desharnais *(VP-Legal)*
John Sarantakes *(VP-Sls-North America)*
Dave Everitt *(Gen Mgr-Europe, Middle East & Africa)*
Advertising Agency:
Lewis PR
(d/b/a Lewis Pr Global)
Millbank Tower
London, SW1P 4RS, United Kingdom
Tel.: (44) 207 802 2626
Fax: (44) 207 802 2627

ACCELRYS, INC.

10188 Telesis Ct Ste 100
San Diego, CA 92121
Tel.: (858) 799-5000
Fax: (858) 799-5100
E-mail: jobs@accelrys.com
Web Site: www.accelrys.com
Approx. Rev.: $82,959,000
Approx. Number Employees: 362
Business Description:
Molecular Modeling & Simulation Software
S.I.C.: 7372
N.A.I.C.S.: 334611; 511210
Advertising Expenditures: $300,000
Media: 7
Personnel:
Max Carnecchia *(Pres & CEO)*
Michael A. Piraino *(CFO & Exec VP)*
Mathew A. Hahn *(CTO & Sr VP)*
Frank K. Brown *(Chief Science Officer & Sr VP)*
David R. Mersten *(Gen Counsel, Sec & Sr VP)*
Trevor Heritage *(Exec VP-Software Products)*
Todd Johnson *(Exec VP-Sls & Mktg & Svcs)*
Judith Ohrn Hicks *(VP-HR)*

ACCESS SYSTEMS USA, INC.

(Sub. of Access Co., Ltd.)
1188 E Arques Ave
Sunnyvale, CA 94085
Tel.: (408) 400-1900
Fax: (408) 400-1500
Web Site: www.access-company.com
Business Description:
Operating Systems for Handheld Computers
S.I.C.: 7371
N.A.I.C.S.: 541511
Advertising Expenditures: $700,000
Brands & Products:
GRAFFITI
HOTSYNC
PALM OS

ACCO BRANDS CORPORATION

300 Tower Pkwy
Lincolnshire, IL 60069-3640
Tel.: (847) 541-9500
Fax: (847) 484-4492
Toll Free: (800) 222-6462
E-mail: info@acco.com
Web Site: www.accobrands.com
Approx. Sls.: $1,330,500,000
Approx. Number Employees: 4,200
Year Founded: 1922
Business Description:
Office Supplies, Binders, Fasteners, Staplers, Staples, Punches, Clips, Time Management Products, Presentation Aids, Computer-Related Supplies Mfr
S.I.C.: 2782; 2653; 3577; 3579; 5943
N.A.I.C.S.: 323118; 322211; 333313; 334119; 453210
Import Export
Advertising Expenditures: $94,900,000
Media: 4-5-7-8-13-22
Distr.: Natl.
Personnel:
Robert J. Keller *(Chm & CEO)*
Boris Y. Elisman *(Pres, COO & Pres-Americas)*
Neal V. Fenwick *(CFO & Exec VP)*
David L. Kaput *(Chief HR Officer & Sr VP)*
Thomas P. O'Neill, Jr. *(Sr VP-Fin & Acctg & Chief Acctg Officer)*
Christopher M. Franey *(Pres-ACCO Brands Intl & Kensington & Exec VP)*
Thomas W. Tedford *(Pres-ACCO Brands Americas & Exec VP)*
Steven D. Rubin *(Gen Counsel, Sec & Sr VP)*
Mark C. Anderson *(Sr VP-Corp Dev)*
Richard Nelson *(VP-Corp Comm)*
Katherine Riley *(Brand Mgr-Swingline)*
Brands & Products:
ACCO
APOLLO
BOONE
DOX
EASTLIGHT
GBC
GBC JAM FREE
GBC SHREDMASTER
KENSINGTON
MARBIG
REXEL
SWINGLINE
WILSON JONES
Advertising Agency:
WDMP Ltd.
116 Putney Bridge Rd
London, SW15 2NQ, United Kingdom
Tel.: (44) 020 8870 9200
Fax: (44) 020 8875 5619

ACCU-SORT SYSTEMS, INC.

(Sub. of Danaher Corporation)
511 School House Rd
Telford, PA 18969-1148
Tel.: (215) 723-0981
Fax: (215) 721-5551
Toll Free: (800) BARCODE
E-mail: info@accusort.com
Web Site: www.accusort.com
Sales Range: $100-124.9 Million
Approx. Number Employees: 250
Year Founded: 1971
Business Description:
Mfr. of Optical Scanners & Computer Systems for Scanners
S.I.C.: 3577
N.A.I.C.S.: 334119
Import Export
Media: 2-7-10-13-22
Personnel:
Kevin Sutherby *(Pres)*
Adnan Ahmed *(VP-Mktg)*
Maik Fuchs *(Sls Mgr-EMEA)*
Andrew Ross *(Mgr-Product Mktg)*
Brands & Products:
ACCU-SORT
ACCUVISION
DRX
SOLUTIONS WITH VISION
Advertising Agency:
Goldstein Group Communications
6000 Freedom Square Dr., Ste. 165
Cleveland, OH 44131
Tel.: (216) 573-2300
Fax: (216) 573-9964
— Mark Johnson *(Acct Exec)*

ACCURATE COMMUNICATIONS, INC.

2215 Harney St
Omaha, NE 68131-3620
Tel.: (402) 342-5555
Fax: (402) 345-7700
Toll Free: (800) 779-5505
Web Site: www.accurate800.com
Approx. Number Employees: 45
Business Description:
Answering & Order Entry Services
S.I.C.: 7389
N.A.I.C.S.: 561421
Media: 2-10-20
Personnel:
Jeffrey Zindel *(Pres)*

ACD SYSTEMS INTERNATIONAL INC.

1312 Blanshard Street Suite 200
Victoria, BC V8W 2J1, Canada
Tel.: (250) 419-6700
Fax: (250) 419-6745
E-mail: pr@acdsee.com
Web Site: www.acdsystems.com
Sales Range: $10-24.9 Million
Approx. Number Employees: 141
Year Founded: 1993
Business Description:
Digital Imaging & Communications Software Products
S.I.C.: 7371; 7372
N.A.I.C.S.: 541511; 511210
Consumer Mags.: 80%; Exhibits/Trade Shows: 10%; Premiums, Novelties: 10%

Key to Media (For complete agency information see *The Advertising Red Books-Agencies* edition):
1. Bus. Publs. 2. Cable T.V. 3. Catalogs & Directories. 4. Co-op Adv. 5. Consumer Mags. 6. D.M. to Bus. Estab.7. D.M. to Consumers 8. Daily Newsp. 9. Exhibits/Trade Shows 10. Foreign 11. Infomercial 12. Internet Adv.13. Multimedia 14. Network Radio 15. Network T.V. 16. Newsp. Distr. Mags. 17. Other 18. Outdoor (Posters, Transit) 19. Point of Purchase20. Premiums, Novelties 21. Product Samples 22. Special Events Mktg. 23. Spot Radio 24. Spot T.V. 25. Weekly Newsp. 26. Yellow Page Adv.

Personnel:
Douglas Vandekerkhove *(CEO)*
Frank Lin *(Gen Mgr & CTO)*
Brands & Products:
ACD
ACD FOTOANGELO
ACD FOTOCANVAS
ACD FOTOSLATE
ACD VIDEOMAGIC
ACDINTOUCH
ACDSEE
ACDZIP
AUTOSHARE
CANVAS
FOTOANGELO
FOTOCANVAS
FOTOSLATE
FOTOVAC
IMAGE FOX
IMAGEFOX
IMAGESHARK
LURAWAVE
MPOWER TOOLS
PHOTOPRO
PHOTOSEE
PICAVIEW
REALOPTIMIZER
ROBOENHANCER
VIDEOGENESIS

ACER AMERICA CORPORATION
(Sub. of Acer Incorporated)
333 W San Carlos Street
San Jose, CA 95110
Tel.: (408) 533-7700
Fax: (408) 533-4555
E-mail: webmaster@acer.com
Web Site: www.acer.com
Approx. Number Employees: 180
Year Founded: 1977
Business Description:
Computer Sales & Service
S.I.C.: 3571; 3575; 3577
N.A.I.C.S.: 334111; 334113; 334119
Import Export
Advertising Expenditures: $1,500,000
Media: 2-4-5-6-10-11-16-19-20-21-22
Distr.: Intl.; Natl.
Personnel:
Ming Wang *(CFO)*
Sumit Agnihotry *(VP)*
Gregg Prendergast *(VP-Comml Sls & Mktg)*
Mark Hill *(Gen Mgr)*
Joe Castillo *(Sr Dir-US Consumer Sls & Mktg)*
Chris White *(Sr Dir-Product Mgmt-US)*
Richard Black *(Dir-Mktg)*
Amy Lee *(Dir-Fulfillment-Pan America)*
Lenny Pollak *(Dir-HR)*
Alan Wang *(Dir-IT)*
Irene Chan *(Sr Bus Mgr-Consumer Desktops)*

ACHIEVEGLOBAL INC.
(Sub. of Institute for International Research, Inc.)
8875 Hidden River Pkwy Ste 400
Tampa, FL 33637
Tel.: (813) 631-5799
Fax: (813) 631-5796
Toll Free: (800) 566-0630
Web Site: www.achieveglobal.com
Approx. Number Employees: 1,600
Business Description:
Training & Consulting Services
S.I.C.: 8748; 8742
N.A.I.C.S.: 541618; 541611
Media: 2-4-7-10-13-22
Personnel:
Sharon M. Daniels *(Pres & CEO)*
Michelle Bonterre *(VP-Mktg)*
Steve Carlson *(VP-Sls)*
Myron A. Harmon *(VP-HR)*
Mark Fears *(Product Mgr)*

ACI WORLDWIDE INC.
(Div. of ACI Worldwide, Inc.)
6060 Coventry Dr
Elkhorn, NE 68022
Tel.: (402) 390-7600
Fax: (402) 772-2579
Web Site: www.aciworldwide.com
Sales Range: $200-249.9 Million
Approx. Number Employees: 1,111
Year Founded: 1975
Business Description:
Developer, Designer & Marketer of Electronic Funds Transfer Applications Software
S.I.C.: 7372; 5045
N.A.I.C.S.: 511210; 423430
Export
Media: 2-4-7-10
Distr.: Natl.
Budget Set: June
Personnel:
Ann Cunningham *(Dir-Americas Mktg)*
Ileen Pinhasi *(Product Mgr)*
Karin Brown *(Mgr-Lead Product)*
Kay Hughes *(Mgr-Online Mktg)*
Brands & Products:
BASE24
BASE24-ATM
BASE24-CARD
BASE24-CHECK AUTH
BASE24-ES
BASE24-FREQUENT SHOPPER
BASE24-INFOBASE
BASE24-POS
BASE24-REFUNDS
BASE24-TELLER

ACME STAPLE COMPANY, INC.
87 Hill Rd
Franklin, NH 03235
Tel.: (603) 934-2320
Fax: (603) 934-6199
Toll Free: (800) 258-3778
E-mail: info@acmestaple.com
Web Site: www.acmestaple.com
Approx. Number Employees: 20
Year Founded: 1894
Business Description:
Staple Machines & Staples Designer, Mfr & Distr
S.I.C.: 3496; 3579; 3952; 5112
N.A.I.C.S.: 332618; 333313; 339942; 424120
Import Export
Media: 2-4-7-10
Distr.: Natl.
Personnel:
Richard L. Gold *(Pres)*
Onno F. Boswinkel *(VP & Gen Mgr)*

ACNIELSEN CORPORATION
(Div. of VNU Marketing Information, Inc.)
770 Broadway
New York, NY 10003
Tel.: (646) 654-5000
Fax: (646) 654-5002
Toll Free: (800) 553-3727
Web Site: www.nielsen.com
Approx. Number Employees: 21,000
Year Founded: 1923
Business Description:
Developer of Diagnostic, Market Measurement, Opportunity Identification & Market Analysis Products & Services
S.I.C.: 8732; 8733; 8742
N.A.I.C.S.: 541910; 541613; 541720
Advertising Expenditures: $20,000,000
Personnel:
Michael Whelan *(CFO)*
John Moses *(Chief HR Officer)*
Jason Kramer *(Exec VP-Res & Analysis)*
Amit Seth *(Exec VP)*
Matt Carey *(Sr VP)*
Will Thoretz *(Sr VP)*
Deepak Varma *(Sr VP)*
Andy Carrington *(Dir-Mktg)*
Michaela L. Hockenberger *(Dir-Mktg)*
Mensing Nieuwe *(Dir-Commun)*
Brands & Products:
HOMESCAN
MARKETTRACK
NETDISPATCH
PRICEMAN
SCANTRACK
SPACEMAN

ACORN ENERGY, INC.
4 W Rockland Rd
Montchanin, DE 19710
Tel.: (302) 656-1707
Web Site: www.acornfactor.com
Approx. Rev.: $35,694,000
Approx. Number Employees: 178
Year Founded: 1996
Business Description:
Holding Company
S.I.C.: 6719; 3812; 3845; 6289; 7373; 7379; 8748
N.A.I.C.S.: 551112; 334510; 334511; 523999; 541512; 541519; 541690
Advertising Expenditures: $66,000
Media: 2
Personnel:
John A. Moore *(Chm, Pres & CEO)*
Michael Barth *(CFO)*
Hal Davis *(Chief Strategy Officer)*

ACSIS, INC.
(Holding of Saints Capital Management LLC)
9 East Stow Rd
Marlton, NJ 08053
Tel.: (856) 489-4900
Fax: (856) 810-3597
E-mail: info@acsisinc.com
Web Site: www.acsisinc.com
Approx. Number Employees: 90
Business Description:
Supply Chain Software & Services
S.I.C.: 7373; 7371
N.A.I.C.S.: 541512; 541511
Personnel:
Marc Friend *(Chm)*
Neil Thall *(Pres & CEO)*
Stacy McDowell *(VP-Sls-WorldWide)*
Stephny Seibel *(VP-Fin)*
Nick Angelucci *(Dir-Pro Svcs)*
Kelly Kuchinski *(Dir-Product Mktg)*
Advertising Agency:
PAN Communications
300 Brickstone Sq 7th Fl
Andover, MA 01810
Tel.: (978) 474-1900
Fax: (978) 474-1903

ACT TELECONFERENCING, INC.
1526 Cole Blvd Ste 300
Golden, CO 80401
Tel.: (303) 233-3500
Fax: (303) 238-0096
E-mail: astone@acttel.com
Web Site: www.acttel.com
Sales Range: $50-74.9 Million
Approx. Number Employees: 350
Year Founded: 1989
Business Description:
Audio, Video & Web Conferencing Services
S.I.C.: 4899
N.A.I.C.S.: 517910
Advertising Expenditures: $96,000
Media: 7-8-10-13-22
Personnel:
Peter E. Salas *(Chm & CEO)*
Fran Ross *(CFO)*
Mark K. Kelly *(COO)*
Marina Bogard *(Chief Sls & Mktg Officer)*
Jennie McQuade *(Gen Counsel & VP-HR)*
Brands & Products:
ACT
ACT CONFERENCING
CLARIONCALL
CONFERENCECAST
ELITE
MAKING DISTANCE OBSOLETE
READY CONNECT
READYCONNECT

ACTION INSTRUMENTS, INC.
(Sub. of Eurotherm Limited)
44621 Guilford Dr Ste 100
Ashburn, VA 20147
Tel.: (703) 443-0000
Fax: (703) 724-7300
Toll Free: (800) 854-1076
E-mail: info@actionio.com
Web Site: www.actionio.com
Approx. Sls.: $14,000,000
Approx. Number Employees: 125
Year Founded: 1972
Business Description:
Electronic Instrumentation for Measurement & Control
S.I.C.: 3823; 8742
N.A.I.C.S.: 334513; 541611
Export
Advertising Expenditures: $500,000
Media: 2-7-8-10
Distr.: Intl.; Natl.
Personnel:
Dan Dudici *(Product Mgr)*
Brands & Products:
ACTION I/O
ACTION PAK
BARBER-COLMAN
CHESSELL
CONTINENTAL
EUROTHERM CONTROLS
FIELD PAK
TRANSPAK
ULTRA SLIMPAK
VISIPAK

Key to Media (For complete agency information see *The Advertising Red Books-Agencies* edition):
1. Bus. Publs. 2. Cable T.V. 3. Catalogs & Directories. 4. Co-op Adv. 5. Consumer Mags. 6. D.M. to Bus. Estab.7. D.M. to Consumers 8. Daily Newsp. 9. Exhibits/Trade Shows 10. Foreign 11. Infomercial 12. Internet Adv.13. Multimedia 14. Network Radio 15. Network T.V. 16. Newsp. Distr. Mags. 17. Other 18. Outdoor (Posters, Transit) 19. Point of Purchase20. Premiums, Novelties 21. Product Samples 22. Special Events Mktg. 23. Spot Radio 24. Spot T.V. 25. Weekly Newsp. 26. Yellow Page Adv.

ACTION MARKETS
1710 Hwy 35
Oakhurst, NJ 07755-2910
Tel.: (732) 531-2212
Fax: (732) 531-4798
Toll Free: (800) 622-6245
E-mail: info@actionmarkets.com
Web Site: www.actionmarkets.com
Approx. Number Employees: 10
Year Founded: 1970
Business Description:
Data Processing & Direct Marketing Services
S.I.C.: 7331
N.A.I.C.S.: 541860
Advertising Expenditures: $300,000
Media: 2-4-6-10-16-20-21-26
Distr.: Direct to Consumer
Budget Set: June
Personnel:
Donald Nissim *(Pres)*
Brands & Products:
THE ACTION MARKET DIFFERENCE

ACTIONTEC ELECTRONICS, INC.
760 N Mary Ave
Sunnyvale, CA 94085-2908
Tel.: (408) 752-7700
Fax: (408) 541-9003
E-mail: bizdev@actiontec.com
Web Site: www.actiontec.com
Approx. Sls.: $70,000,000
Approx. Number Employees: 200
Year Founded: 1993
Business Description:
Developers of Broadband-Powered Solutions
S.I.C.: 3672
N.A.I.C.S.: 334412
Import Export
Personnel:
Dean Chang *(Pres & CEO)*
Brian Paul *(CFO)*
Brands & Products:
ACTIONTEC
CREATIVE SOLUTIONS FOR THE DIGITAL LIFE.
KID DEFENDER
MEGAPLUG
VOSKY
Advertising Agency:
S&S Public Relations, Inc.
2700 Patriot Blvd
Glenview, IL 60026-8021
Tel.: (847) 955-0700
Fax: (847) 955-7720
Toll Free: (800) 287-2279

ACTIVIDENTITY CORPORATION
(Sub. of HID Global Corporation)
6623 Dumbarton Cir
Fremont, CA 94555
Tel.: (510) 574-0100
Fax: (510) 574-0101
Toll Free: (800) 529-9499
Web Site: www.actividentity.com
Approx. Rev.: $57,706,000
Approx. Number Employees: 218
Business Description:
Corporate Security Services
S.I.C.: 7372; 7371
N.A.I.C.S.: 511210; 334611; 541511
Media: 7-10-13
Personnel:
Jerome Becquart *(VP & Gen Mgr)*
Yves Le Net *(VP-Engrg)*
Karl Weintz *(VP-Sls & ops)*
Brands & Products:
4TRESS
ACTIVCARD GOLD
ACTIVCLIENT
ACTIVID
ACTIVIDENTITY
ACTIVKEY
ACTIVPACK
ACTIVREADER
SECURELOGIN
SMARTREADER

ACTUATE CORPORATION
2207 Bridgepointe Pkwy Ste 500
San Mateo, CA 94404
Tel.: (650) 645-3000
Fax: (650) 645-3700
Toll Free: (800) 914-2259
E-mail: info@actuate.com
Web Site: www.actuate.com/
Approx. Rev.: $131,472,000
Approx. Number Employees: 569
Year Founded: 1993
Business Description:
Corporate Data Reporting Software
S.I.C.: 7372
N.A.I.C.S.: 511210; 334611
Advertising Expenditures: $287,000
Media: 2-7-10-13-17-21
Personnel:
Nicolas C. Nierenberg *(Chm & Chief Architect)*
Peter I. Cittadini *(Pres & CEO)*
Daniel A. Gaudreau *(CFO & Sr VP-Ops)*
Thomas E. McKeever *(Chief Compliance Officer, Gen Counsel, Sec & Sr VP-Corp Dev)*
N. Nobby Akiha *(Sr VP-Mktg)*
Mark A. Coggins *(Sr VP-Engrg)*
Bernard Skomra *(Global VP & Gen Mgr)*
Brands & Products:
ACTUATE
ACTUATE ANALYTICS
BIRT
E.ANALYSIS
E.REPORT DESIGNER
E.REPORT OPTION
E.REPORTS
E.SPREADSHEET
ISERVER
THE LEADER IN ENTERPRISE INFORMATION APPLICATIONS
PERFORMANCESOFT ONPERFORMANCE
PERFORMANCESOFT ROOT CAUSE ANALYSIS
PERFORMANCESOFT TRACK
PERFORMANCESOFT VIEWS

ACXIOM CORPORATION
601 E 3rd St PO Box 8180
Little Rock, AR 72201
Tel.: (501) 342-1000
Fax: (501) 342-3913
Toll Free: (888) 322-9466
E-mail: infoau@acxiom.com
Web Site: www.acxiom.com
Approx. Rev.: $1,159,970,000
Approx. Number Employees: 6,600
Year Founded: 1969
Business Description:
Data Services & Technology Products Mfr
S.I.C.: 7374; 7375
N.A.I.C.S.: 518210; 518111
Advertising Expenditures: $7,600,000
Media: 2-7-10
Distr.: Intl.; Natl.
Budget Set: Jan. -Mar.
Personnel:
Catherine L. Hughes *(Chm)*
Scott E. Howe *(Pres & CEO)*
Cameron Thompson *(Grp Mng Dir)*
John A. Adams *(COO & Exec VP)*
Tim Suther *(CMO & Sr VP)*
Shawn Donovan *(Chief Sls Officer & Exec VP)*
Jerry C. Jones *(Chief Legal Officer, Sr VP & Asst Sec)*
Yousef Hamidaddin *(CEO-Middle East & North Africa)*
Stephen Whyte *(CEO-Europe)*
Cindy K. Childers *(Sr VP-HR)*
Scott Sutton *(Head-Acct-Retail & CPG)*
Vicki Poon *(Dir-Agency Svcs)*
Kirk Ward *(Dir-Product Devel)*
Josh Herman *(Product Mgr)*
Brands & Products:
ABILITEC
ACXIOM
CDI-X
CHOMONICX
IDENTIFY-X
IMPACT-X
INFOBASE
INFOBASE-X
INTELLIGENCE DRIVEN SOLUTIONS
OPTICX
PERSONICX
PERSONICX GEO
PERSONICX VISIONSCAPE
RELEVANCE-X
WE MAKE INFORMATION INTELLIGENT
Advertising Agency:
The Sells Agency, Inc.
513 Center St Ste 200
Little Rock, AR 72201
Tel.: (501) 666-8926
Fax: (501) 663-0329

ACXIOM CORPORATION
(Div. of Acxiom Corporation)
1501 Opus Pl
Downers Grove, IL 60515
Tel.: (630) 964-1501
Fax: (630) 719-0447
Toll Free: (800) 729-1501
Web Site: www.acxiom.com
Sales Range: $200-249.9 Million
Approx. Number Employees: 800
Year Founded: 1947
Business Description:
Information Management Services, Database Marketing Services (Strategic Analysis, Database Design, Enhancement & Warehousing; Modeling & Analysis) & Information Technology Outsourcing
S.I.C.: 7374; 7331
N.A.I.C.S.: 518210; 541860
Advertising Expenditures: $700,000
Media: 2-4-7-10-17-26
Distr.: Natl.
Budget Set: Sept.
Personnel:
Kathy Hecht *(VP-Mktg)*
Leslie Price *(Product Mgr)*
Brands & Products:
POWER STATION
QUIDDITY

ADC TELECOMMUNICATIONS, INC.
(Sub. of TE Connectivity Ltd.)
13625 Technology Dr
Eden Prairie, MN 55344
Mailing Address:
PO Box 1101
Minneapolis, MN 55440-1101
Tel.: (952) 938-8080
Fax: (952) 917-1717
Toll Free: (800) 366-3889
E-mail: investor@adc.com
Web Site: www.adc.com
E-Mail For Key Personnel:
Marketing Director: rob_clark@adc.com
Public Relations: investor@adc.com
Approx. Sls.: $1,156,600,000
Approx. Number Employees: 9,300
Year Founded: 1935
Business Description:
Network Equipment, Software & Integration Services for Broadband, Multiservice Networks that Deliver Data & Video & Voice Communications by Telephone, Cable Television, Internet, Broadcast, Wireless & Enterprise Networks
S.I.C.: 3679; 3661; 7372; 7373; 7379
N.A.I.C.S.: 334418; 334210; 334611; 511210; 541512; 541519
Export
Media: 2-4-5-7-10-13-21-26
Distr.: Intl.; Natl.
Budget Set: Oct.
Personnel:
James G. Mathews *(CFO)*
Patrick D. O'Brien *(Pres-Global Connectivity Solutions & VP)*
Ron Hartkemeyer *(Dir-Customer Svc)*
Brands & Products:
ADC
DSXI
ENCASER
EXTEND
FIBER MATE
FIBERGUIDE
FLEXDSX
HIGAIN
LOOPSTAR
MINIMATE
OMNIREACH
PATCHMATE
PATCHSWITCH
PG-FLEX
POWERWORX
PRO PATCH
PROAX
PXPLUS
RF WORX
SELECT SERIES
SIGNALON
SONEPLEX
SUPERFILTER
SUPERPOWER
TRACERLIGHT
TRUENET
UNIPATCH
WORLDSL
Advertising Agency:
Padilla Speer Beardsley
1101 W River Pkwy Ste 400
Minneapolis, MN 55415-1241

Key to Media (For complete agency information see *The Advertising Red Books-Agencies* edition):
1. Bus. Publs. 2. Cable T.V. 3. Catalogs & Directories. 4. Co-op Adv. 5. Consumer Mags. 6. D.M. to Bus. Estab.7. D.M. to Consumers 8. Daily Newsp. 9. Exhibits/Trade Shows 10. Foreign 11. Infomercial 12. Internet Adv.13. Multimedia 14. Network Radio 15. Network T.V. 16. Newsp. Distr. Mags. 17. Other 18. Outdoor (Posters, Transit) 19. Point of Purchase20. Premiums, Novelties 21. Product Samples 22. Special Events Mktg. 23. Spot Radio 24. Spot T.V. 25. Weekly Newsp. 26. Yellow Page Adv.

Tel.: (612) 455-1700
Fax: (612) 455-1060
Public Relations

ADE CORPORATION
(Sub. of KLA-Tencor Corporation)
80 Wilson Way
Westwood, MA 02090-1806
Tel.: (781) 467-3500
Fax: (781) 467-0500
E-mail: support@ade.com
Web Site: www.ade.com
Approx. Rev.: $103,448,000
Approx. Number Employees: 410
Year Founded: 1967
Business Description:
Automated Metrology & Inspection Systems for Semiconductor Wafer & Computer Disk Producers
S.I.C.: 3829
N.A.I.C.S.: 334519
Media: 10
Brands & Products:
ACUMAP
CONSTELLATION
DEVICE TOOLBOX
DISKMAPPER
INFOHUB
INFOTOOLS
MICROSENSE
MICROXAM
MINIFIZ
NANOMAPPER
REPORTTOOLS
ULTRAGAGE
ULTRASCAN
WAFERCHECK
WAFERSIGHT

ADECCO USA, INC.
(Sub. of Adecco S.A.)
175 Broadhollow Rd
Melville, NY 11747-4902
Tel.: (631) 844-7800
Fax: (631) 844-7577
Toll Free: (800) 836-7723
E-mail: usadecco.mail@adecci.com
Web Site: www.adeccousa.com
Approx. Number Employees: 600
Year Founded: 1950
Business Description:
Temporary Personnel & Healthcare Services
S.I.C.: 7363; 7361
N.A.I.C.S.: 561320; 561310
Media: 2-3-4-6-7-8-9-10-13-14-16-18-20-22-23-24-25-26
Distr.: Direct to Consumer; Natl.
Budget Set: Nov.
Personnel:
Joyce Russell *(Pres & Exec VP)*
Brane Acamann *(CIO)*
Ed Blust *(CMO-Mktg, Comm & PR)*
Joe Sabia *(Sr VP)*
Andrea Sugden *(Sr VP-Southern Div)*
Kristy Willis *(Sr VP-Southwest Div)*
Advertising Agency:
The MWW Group
1 Meadowlands Plz 6th Fl
East Rutherford, NJ 07073
Tel.: (201) 507-9500
Fax: (201) 507-0092

ADERANT HOLDINGS, INC.
(Holding of Vista Equity Partners LLC)
3525 Piedmont Rd Bldg 6 Ste 620
Atlanta, GA 30305
Tel.: (404) 720-3600
Fax: (404) 720-3674
Toll Free: (877) 608-4369
E-mail: info@aderant.com
Web Site: www.aderant.com
Approx. Number Employees: 40
Business Description:
Software Business Solutions
S.I.C.: 7372; 7319; 7389
N.A.I.C.S.: 511210; 541870; 561439; 561990
Personnel:
Chris Giglio *(CEO)*
Deane S. Price *(CFO & Sr VP)*
Michael Barry *(Sr VP-R&D)*
Jeff Boyce *(Sr VP-Prof Svcs & Support)*
Don Howren *(Sr VP-Sls & Mktg)*
John Callahan *(VP-Sls-North America)*
Advertising Agency:
Arketi Group
2801 Buford Hwy Druid Chase Ste 375
Atlanta, GA 30329
Tel.: (404) 929-0091
Fax: (404) 321-3397
Agency of Record

ADMINISTAFF, INC.
(Name Changed to Insperity, Inc.)

ADOBE SYSTEMS INCORPORATED
345 Park Ave
San Jose, CA 95110-2704
Tel.: (408) 536-6000
Fax: (408) 537-6000
Toll Free: (800) 833-6687
E-mail: info@adobe.com
Web Site: www.adobe.com
Approx. Rev.: $3,800,000,000
Approx. Number Employees: 9,117
Year Founded: 1982
Business Description:
Software Solutions for Network Publishing Including Web, Print, ePaper, Video, Wireless & Broadband Applications
S.I.C.: 7372; 6794
N.A.I.C.S.: 511210; 334611; 533110
Advertising Expenditures: $65,900,000
Media: 1-2-4-5-7-10-11-17-20-21-22-27
Distr.: Natl.
Personnel:
Charles M. Geschke *(Co-Founder & Chm)*
John E. Warnock *(Chm)*
Shantanu Narayen *(Pres & CEO)*
Mark S. Garrett *(CFO & Exec VP)*
Gerri Martin-Flickinger *(CIO & Sr VP)*
Doug Winnie *(Principal & Product Mgr-Adobe Edge)*
Karen O. Cottle *(Gen Counsel, Sec & Sr VP)*
Naresh Gupta *(Mng Dir-R&D-India & Sr VP-Print, Classic Publ Solutions)*
Rob M. Tarkoff *(Sr VP & Gen Mgr-Bus Productivity Solutions)*
David Wadhwani *(Sr VP & Gen Mgr-Creative & Interactive Solutions Bus Unit)*
Stephen Frieder *(Sr VP-Sls Americas-Omniture Bus)*
Digby Horner *(Sr VP-Engrg Tech Grp)*
Ann Lewnes *(Sr VP-Global Mktg)*
Tom Malloy *(Chief Software Architect & Sr VP)*
Donna Morris *(Sr VP-HR)*
Matthew Thompson *(Sr VP-Worldwide Field Ops)*
Paul Weiskopf *(Sr VP-Corp Dev)*
Brad Rencher *(VP & Gen Mgr)*
Christine Castro *(VP-Corp Comm)*
Aseem Chandra *(VP-Mktg-Omniture Bus Unit)*
John F. Mellor *(VP-Bus Dev & Strategy-Omniture)*
Bridget Perry *(VP-Mktg-Americas)*
Abdallah Saqqa *(Gen Mgr)*
Mikel Chertudi *(Sr Dir-Media & Demand Mktg-Global)*
Matthew Langie *(Sr Dir-Product Mktg)*
Erik Larson *(Sr Dir-Customer Experience Mgmt Product & Strategy)*
Christopher Parkin *(Sr Dir-Genesis Solutions)*
Mark Phibbs *(Sr Dir-APAC Mktg)*
Bill Rusitzky *(Sr Dir-Strategic & Tech Partner Alliances)*
Mike Barton *(Dir-Mktg)*
Sheryl Ehrlich *(Dir-Strategic Res)*
Mark Grilli *(Dir-Product Mktg-Acrobat Solutions)*
Nick Jordan *(Dir-Product Mgmt)*
Michael Londgren *(Dir-Product Mktg-Adobe Connect)*
Yonn Samuels *(Dir-Dev)*
Ashley Still *(Dir-Product Mgmt & Video)*
Nissa Henslee *(Sr Mgr-Multi-Channel Comm Enablement)*
Laura Laney *(Sr Mgr-Mktg & Demand Generation)*
Denise Lu *(Sr Mgr-Mktg & Education)*
Mike Peterson *(Sr Mgr-ISV Sls)*
Mike Ward *(Sr Mgr-Online & Demand Mktg)*
Danielle Beaumont *(Grp Product Mgr-Muse)*
Robert Christensen *(Product Mgr-Flash Runtimes)*
Tom Hogarty *(Product Mgr)*
Bryan O'Neil Hughes *(Sr Product Mgr-Adobe Photoshop)*
Mark Lewiecki *(Sr Product Mgr-Adobe PDF Print Engine)*
Julie Heiser *(Mgr-Res)*
Natalie Jenkins *(Mgr-Mktg Automation & Nurturing Program)*
Grace Kim *(Mgr-Principal Res, Mktg Insights & Ops)*
Jay Middleton *(Mgr-Search Mktg-Worldwide)*
Prabhjeet Singh *(Mgr-Mktg-India)*
Stacey Taylor *(Mgr-Principal Mktg & Ops)*
Ben Watson *(Mgr-Principal Mktg-Customer Experience)*
Mark Randall *(Strategist-Digital Media)*
Brands & Products:
ACROBAT
ACROBAT 9 PRO EXTENDED
ACROBAT CAPTURE
ACROBAT CONNECT
ACROBAT CONNECT PRO
ACROBAT DISTILLER
ACROBAT E-BOOK READER
ACROBAT MESSENGER
ADOBE
ADOBE AFTER EFFECTS
ADOBE ATMOSHERE
ADOBE CREATIVE SUITE
ADOBE ENCORE
ADOBE FRAMEMAKER
ADOBE MEDIA PLAYER
ADOBE ONLOCATION
ADOBE PREMIERE
AUDITION
AUTHORWARE
BREEZE
BRIDGE
CAPTIVATE
CENTRAL
COLDFUSION
CONTENT SERVER
CONTRIBUTE
DEVICE CENTRAL
DIGITAL EDITIONS
DIRECTOR
DOCUMENT CENTER
DREAMWEAVER
DYNAMIC LINK
ELEARNING SUITE
ENCORE
EXTREME
FIREWORKS
FLASH
FLASH LITE
FLASH MEDIA
FLASH PLAYER
FLASH REMOTING
FLASH VIDEO STREAMING SERVICE
FLASHCAST
FLASHPAPER
FLEX
FONT FOLIO
FRAMEMAKER
FREEHAND
GOLIVE
GRAPHICS SERVER
HOMESITE
ILLUSTRATOR
INCONTEXT EDITING
INCOPY
INDESIGN
JOBREADY
JRUN
KULER
LIVECYCLE
MACROMEDIA
OMNITURE ONLINE MARKETING SUITE
OUTPUT DESIGNER
OUTPUT PAK FOR MYSAP.COM
OVATION
PAGEMAKER
PHOTOSHOP
PREMIER
PRESENTER
PRINT ENGINE
READER
ROBOINFO
SCENE7
SHOCKWAVE PLAYER
SOUNDBOOTH
TECHNICAL COMMUNICATION SUITE
VISUAL COMMUNICATOR
WEB OUTPUT PAK
Advertising Agencies:
Big Spaceship
45 Main St Ste 716
Brooklyn, NY 11201
Tel.: (718) 222-0281
Fax: (718) 971-1062
The Expressive Web

Heat

Key to Media (For complete agency information see *The Advertising Red Books-Agencies* edition):
1. Bus. Publs. 2. Cable T.V. 3. Catalogs & Directories. 4. Co-op Adv. 5. Consumer Mags. 6. D.M. to Bus. Estab.7. D.M. to Consumers 8. Daily Newsp. 9. Exhibits/Trade Shows 10. Foreign 11. Infomercial 12. Internet Adv.13. Multimedia 14. Network Radio 15. Network T.V. 16. Newsp. Distr. Mags. 17. Other 18. Outdoor (Posters, Transit) 19. Point of Purchase20. Premiums, Novelties 21. Product Samples 22. Special Events Mktg. 23. Spot Radio 24. Spot T.V. 25. Weekly Newsp. 26. Yellow Page Adv.

Adobe Systems Incorporated — (Continued)

Pier 33 S 3rd Fl
San Francisco, CA 94111
Tel.: (415) 477-1999
Fax: (415) 477-1990

Text 100 Public Relations
(Part of the Next Fifteen Group)
77 Maiden Ln 3rd Fl
San Francisco, CA 94108
Tel.: (415) 593-8400
Fax: (415) 593-8401
— Melissa Chanslor *(Acct Exec)*

The1stMovement
1010 E Union St Ste 120
Pasadena, CA 91106
Tel.: (626) 689-4993
Fax: (626) 628-1991

Traction Corporation
1349 Larkin St
San Francisco, CA 94109
Tel.: (415) 962-5823
Fax: (415) 962-5815

ADPT CORPORATION

691 S Milpitas Blvd
Milpitas, CA 95035
Tel.: (408) 945-8600
Fax: (408) 262-2533
Telex: 910-338-0060
Web Site: www.adptco.com
E-Mail For Key Personnel:
Sales Director: sales@adaptec.com
Approx. Rev.: $73,682,000
Approx. Number Employees: 187
Year Founded: 1981
Business Description:
Investment Services
S.I.C.: 6289
N.A.I.C.S.: 523999
Media: 1-2-3-4-5-6-7-8-9-10-11-18-20-21-22-23-24-25
Distr.: Direct to Consumer; Intl.; Natl.; Reg.
Personnel:
Warren G. Lichtenstein *(Chm)*
John J. Quicke *(Interim Pres & CEO)*
Mary Dotz *(VP & CFO)*
Brands & Products:
ADAPTEC
ALTA
ALTRA
EISA MULTICHANNEL
EZ-SCSI LITE
IOWARE
ISCSI
MULTIMEDIA CONNECTION
MULTIMEDIA ENGINE
NIOBE
PHASE ENGINE
TOTAL ADVANTAGE
TOTAL CONNECT
TOTAL DATA
TWIN CHANNEL
UNIFIED SERIALS
Advertising Agency:
Walt & Company
2105 S Bascom Ave Ste 240
Campbell, CA 95008
Tel.: (408) 369-7200
Fax: (408) 369-7201

ADTRAN, INC.

901 Explorer Blvd
Huntsville, AL 35806-2807
Tel.: (256) 963-8000
Fax: (256) 963-7916
Toll Free: (800) 923-8726
E-mail: info@adtran.com
Web Site: www.adtran.com
Approx. Sls.: $605,674,000
Approx. Number Employees: 1,663
Year Founded: 1986
Business Description:
Mfr. of Digital Telephone Transmission Equipment
S.I.C.: 3661; 3663
N.A.I.C.S.: 334210; 334220
Advertising Expenditures: $2,700,000
Media: 2-7-10
Personnel:
Thomas R. Stanton *(Chm & CEO)*
James E. Matthews *(CFO, Treas, Sec & Sr VP-Fin)*
Raymond R. Schansman *(Sr VP & Gen Mgr-Enterprise Networks)*
James D Wilson, Jr. *(Sr VP & Gen Mgr-Carrier Networks)*
Michael Foliano *(Sr VP-Global Ops)*
Gary Bolton *(VP-Mktg-Global)*
Ted Cole *(VP)*
Don Brannen *(Quality Dir)*
Steve Shipley *(Dir-Product Qualification)*
Brands & Products:
4X4 DDS
ACES
ACT 1900/2300
ACT1241
ADTRAN
ADTRAN HAS THE FORMULA FOR BUSINESS SUCCESS
ADTRAN SOLUTIONS = BUSINESS SUCCESS
ADVISION
ATLAS
BR1/10
DSU
DSU 56/64
DSU 5600
DSU III AR
DSU III S2W
DSU III S4W
DSU III TDM
DSU IQ
DSU IV ESP
EAI-530
EASYMENU
ESU
ESU 120E
ESUE
EXPERTS CHOOSE ADTRAN
EXPRESS 3000 SERIES
EXPRESS 3010
EXPRESS 3100
EXPRESS 3110
EXPRESS 5000 SERIES
EXPRESS 5100
EXPRESS 5200
EXPRESS 5210
EXPRESS 6000 SERIES
EXPRESS 6200
EXPRESS 6500
EXPRESS 6503
EXPRESS 6530
EXPRESS 6531
HDSLX/T1
IQ
IQ 710
IQ VIEW
ISU
ISU 128
ISU 2X64
ISU 512
ISU 512E
MULTIPORT DBU MODULE
MX 2800
MX2800
N-COMMAND
N-FORM
N-SHAPE
N-SPECT
NETVANTA
NT1 ACE
NT1 ACE3
NX56/64K V.35 MODULE
OCU 45
OPTI-3
OPTI-6100
OSU 300
SAFE-T-NET
SMART 16/16E SHELVES
SMART SOLUTIONS FOR A CONNECTED WORLD.
T-WATCH PRO
T1 CSUS
T1 ESF CSU
T1CSU ACE
T3SU 300
TAPP
TOTAL ACCESS
TOTAL ACCESS ELEMENT MANAGEMENT SYSTEM
TOTAL ACCESS OPTI-3
TOTAL REACH
TRACER
TSCAN
TSU
TSU 100
TSU 100E
TSU 120
TSU 120E
TSU 600
TSU 600 VP24 E&M
TSU 600 VP24 FXO
TSU 600 VP24 FXS
TSU 600E
TSU ACE
TSU ESP
TSU IQ
TSU IQ+
TSU LT
TSUS
Advertising Agency:
MRB Public Relations
106 Apple St Ste 200G
Tinton Falls, NJ 07724
Tel.: (732) 758-1100
Fax: (732) 933-0993

ADVANCED MICRO DEVICES, INC.-MARKHAM

(Holding of Advanced Micro Devices, Inc.)
1 Commerce Valley Dr E
Markham, ON L3T 7X6, Canada
Tel.: (905) 882-2600
Fax: (905) 882-2620
E-mail: sales@amd.com
Web Site: www.amd.com/us-en/Corporate/AboutAMD/0,,51_52_502,00.html
E-Mail For Key Personnel:
Sales Director: sales@amd.com
Sales Range: $75-99.9 Million
Approx. Number Employees: 200
Year Founded: 1985
Business Description:
Designer, Mfr & Marketer of Multimedia Solutions & Graphics Components for Personal Computers
S.I.C.: 3575
N.A.I.C.S.: 334113
Advertising Expenditures: $500,000
Media: 2-6-10-13-18-19-20-21-22
Personnel:
Rick Bergman *(Sr VP & Gen Mgr)*
John Docherty *(Sr VP-Mfg Ops)*
Geoff Phillips *(VP & Gen Mgr-DTV Bus)*
Benjamin Bar-Haim *(Corp VP)*
Peter Hourihan *(VP-IT)*
Jason Peterson *(VP-Fin)*
Jim Seto *(VP-Engrg Ops)*
Daniel Eiref *(Dir-Mktg)*
Janet Craig *(Dir-Investor Rels)*
Chris Evenden *(Dir-Pub Rels)*
Reuven Soraya *(Dir-Sls, ATI Graphics & Chipset reuven)*
Brands & Products:
ALL-IN-WONDER
CATALYST
E-HOME WONDER
FIREGL
HDTV WONDER
HYDRAVISION
IMAGEON
MOBILITY
MOBILITY FIREGL
MOBILITY RADEON
MULTIMEDIA CENTER
PCI EXPRESS
RADEON
RAGE
REMOTE WONDER
THEATER
TV WONDER
XILLEON

ADVENT SOFTWARE, INC.

600 Townsend St Ste 500
San Francisco, CA 94103
Tel.: (415) 543-7696
Fax: (415) 543-5070
Toll Free: (800) 685-7688
E-mail: info@advent.com
Web Site: www.advent.com
Approx. Rev.: $283,501,000
Approx. Number Employees: 1,051
Year Founded: 1983
Business Description:
Stand Alone & Client/Server Software Products, Data Interfaces & Related Services that Automate Securities Trade Orders & Integrate Certain Mission-Critical Functions
S.I.C.: 7371; 7372; 7373
N.A.I.C.S.: 541511; 511210; 541512
Advertising Expenditures: $700,000
Media: 7-10-13-20
Personnel:
John H. Scully *(Chm)*
David Peter F. Hess *(Pres)*
Stephanie G. DiMarco *(CEO)*
James S. Cox *(CFO & Sr VP)*
Lily S. Chang *(CTO & Exec VP)*
Anthony Sperling *(Sr VP-Svcs & Gen Mgr)*
John P. Brennan *(Sr VP-HR & Facilities)*
Todd Gottula *(VP-Product Dev, Client Svcs & Support & Co Head-Global Acct Bus U)*
Chris Momsen *(VP-Sls, Gen Mgr & Mktg)*

Key to Media (For complete agency information see *The Advertising Red Books-Agencies* edition):
1. Bus. Publs. 2. Cable T.V. 3. Catalogs & Directories. 4. Co-op Adv. 5. Consumer Mags. 6. D.M. to Bus. Estab.7. D.M. to Consumers
8. Daily Newsp. 9. Exhibits/Trade Shows 10. Foreign 11. Infomercial 12. Internet Adv.13. Multimedia 14. Network Radio
15. Network T.V. 16. Newsp. Distr. Mags. 17. Other 18. Outdoor (Posters, Transit) 19. Point of Purchase20. Premiums, Novelties
21. Product Samples 22. Special Events Mktg. 23. Spot Radio 24. Spot T.V. 25. Weekly Newsp. 26. Yellow Page Adv.

Mike Lobosco *(Dir-Advent OnDemand)*
Tim Decker *(Mgr-Product-Electronic Trading Connectivity)*
Brands & Products:
ADVENT
ADVENT BROWSER REPORTING
ADVENT CORPORATE ACTIONS
ADVENT CUSTODIAL DATA
ADVENT INX
ADVENT MARKET DATA MANAGER
ADVENT OFFICE
ADVENT PACKAGER
ADVENT PARTNER
ADVENT PORTFOLIO EXCHANGE
ADVENT REPORT CENTER
ADVENT REVENUE CENTER
ADVENT TRUSTEDNETWORK
ADVENT WAREHOUSE
AXYS
DATAEXCHANGE
GENEVA
MOXY
MYADVENT
PORTFOLIO EXCHANGE
THE PROFESSIONAL PORTFOLIO
QUBE
REX
SMARTCLICK
TAMALE RMS
WEALTHLINE

ADVERTISING CHECKING BUREAU INCORPORATED
2 Pk Ave 18th Fl
New York, NY 10016-5675
Tel.: (212) 684-3377
Fax: (212) 684-3381
Toll Free: (800) 222-2667
E-mail: sales@acbcoop.com
Web Site: www.acbcoop.com
E-Mail For Key Personnel:
Marketing Director: mweissler@acbcoop.com
Sales Director: sales@acbcoop.com
Approx. Number Employees: 300
Year Founded: 1917
Business Description:
Co-op & Trade Promotion Marketing Services, Competitive Ad Tracking Services, Internet Ad Tracking, Retailer Ad Verification, Spiff, Rebate & Fulfillment Program Management, Customized Web Application & ASP Development
S.I.C.: 8748; 7319
N.A.I.C.S.: 541618; 541890
Advertising Expenditures: $350,000
Media: 2-7
Distr.: Natl.
Budget Set: Oct.
Personnel:
Brian McShane *(Pres)*
Michael Bookman *(Exec VP)*
John Portelli *(VP-Sls)*
Brands & Products:
ACB
ADSMART
PARANET!
PARASCOPE!
READI-ACCESS
SPIFFNET!
WEBFACTS

ADVERTISING DISTRIBUTORS OF AMERICA INC.
230 Adams Ave
Hauppauge, NY 11788-3612
Tel.: (631) 231-5700
Fax: (631) 434-1063
E-mail: debraa@advdistofam.com
Approx. Number Employees: 300
Year Founded: 1921
Business Description:
Direct Mail Services
S.I.C.: 7331; 8742
N.A.I.C.S.: 541860; 541611
Media: 2-7-9-26
Distr.: Natl.
Personnel:
John Baratelli *(Exec VP)*
Debra Aji *(VP-Sls & Client Svcs)*

AESP, INC.
16295 NW 13th Ave Ste A
Miami, FL 33169
Tel.: (305) 944-7710
Fax: (305) 949-4483
Toll Free: (800) 446-2377
E-mail: sstein@aesp.com
Web Site: www.aesp.com
E-Mail For Key Personnel:
President: sstein@aesp.com
Sales Range: $10-24.9 Million
Approx. Number Employees: 20
Year Founded: 1983
Business Description:
Computer Connectivity & Networking Devices Designer, Mfr & Marketer
S.I.C.: 3661; 3357; 3643; 3663
N.A.I.C.S.: 334210; 334220; 335921; 335931
Advertising Expenditures: $573,000
Media: 2-7
Personnel:
Slav Stein *(Pres & CEO)*
Roman Briskin *(Exec VP)*
Brands & Products:
AESP
SIGNAMAX

AFA PROTECTIVE SYSTEMS, INC.
(Div. of AFA Protective Systems, Inc.)
161 Forbes Rd Ste 201 Natl Account Div
Braintree, MA 02184
Tel.: (781) 848-6200
Fax: (781) 380-3694
Web Site: www.afaprotectivesystems.com
Approx. Number Employees: 25
Business Description:
National Business Security Monitoring Services
S.I.C.: 5087
N.A.I.C.S.: 423850
Advertising Agency:
DB Associates Advertising
222 Forbes Rd Ste 204
Braintree, MA 02184-2706
Tel.: (781) 843-0181
Fax: (781) 356-0735

AFFILIATED COMPUTER SERVICES, INC.
(Sub. of Xerox Corporation)
2828 N Haskell Ave
Dallas, TX 75204-2954
Tel.: (214) 841-6111
Fax: (214) 821-8315
E-mail: info@acs-inc.com
Web Site: www.acs-inc.com
Sales Range: $5-14.9 Billion
Approx. Number Employees: 72,600
Year Founded: 1988
Business Description:
Information Technology Services Including E-Solutions, Business Process Outsourcing, Technology Outsourcing, Consulting & Systems Integration Services
S.I.C.: 7372; 7374; 7389
N.A.I.C.S.: 511210; 518210; 561990
Media: 1-2-4-6-7-9-10-13-16-18-20-22-25
Distr.: Reg.
Personnel:
Lynn R. Blodgett *(Pres & CEO)*
Kevin Kyser *(CFO & Exec VP)*
Thomas Burlin *(COO)*
Lora Villarreal *(Exec VP & Chief People Officer)*
Christopher Leach *(Chief Info Security Officer)*
Richard Schnacker *(Pres-Fin Svcs-Grp)*
Jon Puckett *(CFO-Govt Healthcare Solutions & Sr VP)*
Tom Blodgett *(COO-Comml Ops & Exec VP)*
Dave Amoriell *(Exec VP & Grp Pres-Transportation Solutions)*
Joseph Doherty, Jr. *(Exec VP & Grp Pres-Govt Solutions)*
Connie Harvey *(Exec VP & Grp Pres-Healthcare, Fin & Insurance)*
Derrell James *(Exec VP & Grp Pres-ITO Svcs)*
Tas Panos *(Exec VP)*
John Rexford *(Exec VP-Corp Dev)*
Tracy Tolbert *(Exec VP-Sls)*
Ann Vezina *(Exec VP & Group Pres-Comml)*
Mark L. Boxer *(Sr VP & Grp Pres-Govt Healthcare Solutions)*
Chad Harris *(Sr VP & Grp Pres-Healthcare Provider & Applications Bus)*
Rebecca Scholl *(Sr VP-Corp Mktg & Comm)*
Kevin Shelly *(Sr VP-Sls-Govt Solutions Grp)*
Chris Tranquill *(Sr VP & Grp Pres-Bus Process Solution)*
Kevin Lightfoot *(VP-Corp Comm)*
Vikki Farrah *(Dir-Mktg)*
Ken Ericson *(Dir-Corp Comm)*
Carrie Hyun *(Dir-Corp Comm)*
Brands & Products:
ACS
EXPERTISE IN ACTION
PEOPLE MAKING TECHNOLOGY WORK
Advertising Agency:
E-Storm International, Inc.
(d/b/a E-Storm)
530 Bush St Ste 600
San Francisco, CA 94108
Tel.: (415) 352-1214
Fax: (415) 352-1254

AHEARN & SOPER INC.
100 Woodbine Downs Blvd
Rexdale, ON M9W 5S6, Canada
Tel.: (416) 675-3999
Fax: (416) 675-3457
Toll Free: (800) 263-4258
Web Site: www.ahearn.com
E-Mail For Key Personnel:
Sales Director: sales@ahearn.com
Approx. Sls.: $27,132,000
Approx. Number Employees: 150
Year Founded: 1881
Business Description:
Industrial Barcode Equipment Including Barcode Computers, Scanners, Printers & Label Applicators Mfr, Sales & Services
S.I.C.: 3577; 7378
N.A.I.C.S.: 334119; 811212
Import Export
Advertising Expenditures: $200,000
Media: 2-7-8-10-13-20
Distr.: Natl.
Budget Set: Dec.
Personnel:
John Paul *(Pres)*
Kamal Rashid *(CFO)*
Paul Pope *(VP & Gen Mgr)*

AHERN RENTALS, INC.
4241 S Arville St
Las Vegas, NV 89103
Tel.: (702) 362-0623
Fax: (702) 362-9316
Toll Free: (800) 400-1610
E-mail: info@ahernrentals.com
Web Site: www.ahern.com
Approx. Rev.: $284,321,000
Approx. Number Employees: 485
Year Founded: 1953
Business Description:
Construction Equipment Rentals, Sales, Parts & Maintenance Services
S.I.C.: 7353; 5013; 5015; 5082; 7359; 7539; 7699
N.A.I.C.S.: 532412; 423120; 423140; 423810; 532490; 811118; 811198; 811310
Advertising Expenditures: $669,000
Personnel:
Don F. Ahern *(Pres & CEO)*
Howard L. Brown *(CFO)*
Mark S. Brown *(CFO)*
Michael S. Stigler *(CIO & VP)*
Evan B. Ahern *(Exec VP)*
Timothy N. Lotspeich *(Sr VP-Risk Mgmt)*
Kirk D. Hartle *(VP-Fin)*
Ronald L. Lyster *(VP-Sls & Mktg)*
Richard L. Weaver *(VP-Pur)*

AIGNER INDEX, INC.
218 MacArthur Ave
New Windsor, NY 12553-7011
Tel.: (845) 562-4510
Fax: (845) 562-2638
Toll Free: (800) 242-3919
E-mail: holdex@frontiernet.net
Web Site: www.holdex.com
E-Mail For Key Personnel:
President: aigner@frontiernet.net
Approx. Rev.: $1,800,000
Approx. Number Employees: 11
Year Founded: 1907
Business Description:
Label Holders, Index Tabs, Pre-Cut Tabs & Magnetic Label Holders Mfr
S.I.C.: 2679
N.A.I.C.S.: 322299
Import Export
Media: 2-4-6-7-8-10-21-22
Distr.: Direct to Consumer; Intl.; Natl.
Budget Set: Nov.
Brands & Products:
ADAPT-A-STRIP
ANGLE-VISION
BIN-BUDDY

Key to Media (For complete agency information see *The Advertising Red Books-Agencies* edition):
1. Bus. Publs. 2. Cable T.V. 3. Catalogs & Directories. 4. Co-op Adv. 5. Consumer Mags. 6. D.M. to Bus. Estab.7. D.M. to Consumers 8. Daily Newsp. 9. Exhibits/Trade Shows 10. Foreign 11. Infomercial 12. Internet Adv.13. Multimedia 14. Network Radio 15. Network T.V. 16. Newsp. Distr. Mags. 17. Other 18. Outdoor (Posters, Transit) 19. Point of Purchase20. Premiums, Novelties 21. Product Samples 22. Special Events Mktg. 23. Spot Radio 24. Spot T.V. 25. Weekly Newsp. 26. Yellow Page Adv.

Aigner Index, Inc. — (Continued)

BIND-X
CHARGED-CARD
ECONOHOLDER
FRIG-ID
HI-LO
HOL-DEX
MAG-PRINT
OPEN-EDGE
SHELF-CLIP
SHELF LABELING STRIPS
SLIP-STRIP
SNAP-LABEL
SUPERSCAN
WIRE-RAC
WIRE-RAC MAX
WIRE-RAC MED
ZIP-SEAL

Advertising Agencies:
BBG&G Advertising
33 Hill Rd
Middletown, NY 10941
Tel.: (845) 695-1880
Fax: (845) 695-1996

Messer & Susslin & Others, Inc.
274 N Middletown Rd
Pearl River, NY 10965-1216
Tel.: (845) 735-3030
Fax: (845) 735-2270
(Label Holders)

AIRIQ, INC.

1815 Ironstone Manor, Unit 10.
Pickering, ON L1W 3W9, Canada
Tel.: (905) 831-6444
Fax: (905) 831-0567
E-mail: info@airiq.com
Web Site: www.airiq.com
Approx. Rev.: $5,144,921
Approx. Number Employees: 32
Business Description:
Wireless Location-Based Fleet Management Services
S.I.C.: 7389; 4899
N.A.I.C.S.: 561990; 517910
Media: 10
Personnel:
Donald R. Gibbs *(Pres & CEO)*
Michael J. Robb *(CFO)*
Stephen Masarovich *(Mgr-IT Ops & Support)*
Brands & Products:
AIRIQ
MOBILEIQ
THE ROAD AHEAD IS INTELLIGENT

AIRSPAN NETWORKS INC.

777 Yamato Rd Ste 310
Boca Raton, FL 33431
Tel.: (561) 893-8670
Fax: (561) 893-8671
E-mail: supportinfo@airspan.com
Web Site: www.airspan.com
Approx. Rev.: $70,351,000
Approx. Number Employees: 207
Year Founded: 1992
Business Description:
Wireless Communications Systems Sales & Solutions
S.I.C.: 4812; 3663; 4813
N.A.I.C.S.: 517212; 334220; 517310
Advertising Expenditures: $100,000
Media: 17
Personnel:
Eric D. Stonestrom *(Pres & CEO)*
David Brant *(CFO & Sr VP)*
Uzi Shalev *(COO)*
Declan Byrne *(CMO)*
Paul Senior *(CTO)*
Henrik Smith Petersen *(Pres-Global Bus Dev)*
Dori Erann *(Sr Dir-Mktg Comm)*
Brands & Products:
AIRSPAN
AIRSPANACCESS
AS3010
AS3030
AS3030 PTP
AS4000
AS4020
AS4030
AS.MAX
AS.NET
AS.TONE
BACKHAUL
BWA
EASYST
EASYST-WI-FI
FLEXNET
HIPERMAX
ITONE
MACROMAX
MACROMAXE
MICROMAX
MIMAX
NETSPAN
PRIMEMAX
PROST
PROST-WI-FI
PROXIMITY
SITESPAN
VIANET
WIMAX FORUM
WIPLL
WIPMANAGE

AIRWIDE SOLUTIONS

(Sub. of Airwide Solutions)
20 Burlington Mall Rd Ste 420
Burlington, MA 01803
Tel.: (781) 229-2406
Fax: (781) 229-2790
Web Site: www.airwidesolutions.com
Business Description:
Developer of Mobile Messaging & Security Software for Wireless Communication Products
S.I.C.: 3663
N.A.I.C.S.: 334220
Personnel:
Brenda Suarez *(Head-Corp Comm)*
Advertising Agency:
PAN Communications
300 Brickstone Sq 7th Fl
Andover, MA 01810
Tel.: (978) 474-1900
Fax: (978) 474-1903

AJILON NORTH AMERICA, LLC

(Sub. of Adecco USA, Inc.)
175 Broad Hollow Rd
Melville, NY 11747
Tel.: (631) 844-7800
Fax: (410) 321-7918
Toll Free: (800) 320-2342
E-mail: info@ajilon.com
Web Site: www.ajilonconsulting.com
Sales Range: $400-449.9 Million
Approx. Number Employees: 4,000
Business Description:
Business Information Technology Services
S.I.C.: 7373; 8742
N.A.I.C.S.: 541512; 541611
Advertising Expenditures: $200,000
Media: 6-13
Personnel:
Jeff Rupp *(Pres & COO)*
Carl Deal *(Sr VP)*
Robert Knight *(Sr VP-Natl Sls)*
Thomas McKenty *(Sr VP-North East)*
Walt Strausbaugh *(Sr VP-Field Ops)*
Marty Sylvester *(Sr VP)*

ALACRA, INC.

100 Broadway Ste 1101
New York, NY 10005-4512
Tel.: (212) 363-9620
Fax: (212) 363-9630
E-mail: info@alacra.com
Web Site: www.alacra.com
Sales Range: $10-24.9 Million
Approx. Number Employees: 45
Year Founded: 1996
Business Description:
Online Business Information Aggregator
S.I.C.: 7375
N.A.I.C.S.: 518111
Media: 7-10-13-20
Personnel:
Steven Goldstein *(Chm & CEO)*
Michael Angle *(Pres & COO)*
Craig Kissel *(CFO)*
Colin duSaire *(VP-Info Mgmt)*
Francine Falchook *(VP-Sls & Mktg)*
Gail Jewsbury *(Dir-Sls-Europe)*
Carol Ann Thomas *(Mgr-Mktg)*
Brands & Products:
ALACRA
ALACRA BOOK
ALACRA COMPLIANCE
ALACRA CONCORDANCE
ALACRA CONNECTIONS
ALACRA CORPORATE CONNECTIONS
ALACRA CURRENT AWARENESS
ALACRA PCAN
ALACRA PORTALS
ALACRA PREMIUM
ALACRA PULSE

ALACRITECH, INC.

1995 N First St Ste 200
San Jose, CA 95112
Tel.: (408) 287-9997
Fax: (408) 287-6142
E-mail: info@alacritech.com
Web Site: www.alacritech.com
Business Description:
Computer Server & Storage Technology
S.I.C.: 3572
N.A.I.C.S.: 334112
Media: 10
Personnel:
Larry Boucher *(Founder, Pres & CEO)*
Esther Lee *(CFO)*
Richard Blackborow *(VP-Engrg)*
Doug Rainbolt *(VP-Mktg)*
Brands & Products:
ACCELERATING DATA DELIVERY
ALACRITECH
DYNAMIC TCP OFFLOAD
SCALABLE NETWORK ACCELERATORS

ALANCO TECHNOLOGIES, INC.

15575 N 83rd Way Ste 3
Scottsdale, AZ 85260
Tel.: (480) 607-1010
Fax: (480) 607-1515
E-mail: alanco@alanco.com
Web Site: www.alanco.com
Approx. Sls.: $14,632,400
Approx. Number Employees: 43
Year Founded: 1969
Business Description:
RFID Tracking & Asset Management Solutions
S.I.C.: 3572
N.A.I.C.S.: 334112
Advertising Expenditures: $169,600
Media: 2-7-10-13
Personnel:
Robert R. Kauffman *(Chm & CEO)*
Greg M. Oester *(Pres)*
John A. Carlson *(Exec VP & CFO)*
Everett E. Bell *(COO & CTO)*
Thomas A. Robinson *(Exec VP)*
Adel McIntosh *(Dir-Admin Svcs)*

ALDON COMPUTER GROUP

(Holding of Marlin Equity Partners, LLC)
6001 Shellmound St Ste 600
Emeryville, CA 94608
Tel.: (510) 839-3535
Fax: (510) 839-2894
Toll Free: (800) 825-5858
E-mail: info@aldon.com
Web Site: www.aldon.com
Approx. Number Employees: 100
Year Founded: 1979
Business Description:
Application Lifecycle Management Software Developer
S.I.C.: 7372
N.A.I.C.S.: 511210
Advertising Expenditures: $75,000
Media: 2-7-10-22
Personnel:
Matt Scholl *(Pres & COO)*
Alison Ishimaru *(VP-Mktg & Product Mgmt)*
Debi Smulyan *(VP-Product Dev)*
Craig Tobey *(VP-Sls-US)*
Brands & Products:
ALDON AFFINITI
ALDON CMS

ALIENWARE CORPORATION

(Sub. of Dell Inc.)
14591 SW 120th St
Miami, FL 33186
Tel.: (305) 251-9797
Fax: (786) 388-5719
Toll Free: (800) 254-3692
E-mail: info@alienware.com
Web Site: www.alienware.com
Sales Range: $10-24.9 Million
Approx. Number Employees: 200
Year Founded: 1996
Business Description:
Computer Gaming Machines, DV Systems & High Performance Workstations Mfr
S.I.C.: 3571
N.A.I.C.S.: 334111
Media: 2-6-13
Personnel:
Brain De Layas *(VP-Mktg)*
Brands & Products:
ALIENGUISE
ALIENICE
ALIENWARE
ALIENWARE BOT
AREA
AREA-51

Key to Media (For complete agency information see *The Advertising Red Books-Agencies* edition):
1. Bus. Publs. 2. Cable T.V. 3. Catalogs & Directories. 4. Co-op Adv. 5. Consumer Mags. 6. D.M. to Bus. Estab.7. D.M. to Consumers 8. Daily Newsp. 9. Exhibits/Trade Shows 10. Foreign 11. Infomercial 12. Internet Adv.13. Multimedia 14. Network Radio 15. Network T.V. 16. Newsp. Distr. Mags. 17. Other 18. Outdoor (Posters, Transit) 19. Point of Purchase20. Premiums, Novelties 21. Product Samples 22. Special Events Mktg. 23. Spot Radio 24. Spot T.V. 25. Weekly Newsp. 26. Yellow Page Adv.

AREA-51 SENTIA
AREA-51M
AURORA
PLEXTOR
ROSWELL
SENTIA
WESTERN DIGITAL

ALL ABOUT STAFFING INC.
(Sub. of HCA HOLDINGS, INC.)
1000 Sawgrass Corporate Pkwy Fl 6
Sunrise, FL 33323-0907
Tel.: (954) 858-1833
Fax: (954) 858-1941
Toll Free: (800) 737-8661
E-mail: info@allaboutstaffing.com
Web Site: www.allaboutstaffing.com
Approx. Number Employees: 150
Business Description:
Employment Agency
S.I.C.: 7361
N.A.I.C.S.: 561310
Media: 2-8
Personnel:
Jack Lisle *(CEO)*
Tony Pentangelo *(COO)*
Advertising Agency:
Bayard Advertising Agency, Inc.
902 Broadway 10th Fl
New York, NY 10010-6002
Tel.: (212) 228-9400
Fax: (212) 228-9999
Creative Marketing
Recruitment Agency of Record
Strategic Sourcing

ALL LANGUAGES LTD.
421 Bloor St E Ste 306
Toronto, ON Canada
Tel.: (416) 975-5000
Fax: (416) 975-0505
Toll Free: (800) 567-8100 (Canada)
Toll Free: (888) 975-9544
E-mail: info@alllanguages.com
Web Site: www.alllanguages.com
Approx. Number Employees: 35
Year Founded: 1971
Business Description:
Translation & Interpreting Services
S.I.C.: 7389
N.A.I.C.S.: 561499
Advertising Expenditures: $500,000
Media: 4-7-10-13-26
Distr.: Intl.
Personnel:
Adele Saldagne *(Pres)*

ALLEGIANT TRAVEL COMPANY
8360 S Durango Dr
Las Vegas, NV 89113
Tel.: (702) 851-7300
Fax: (702) 256-7209
Web Site: www.allegiantair.com
Approx. Rev.: $663,641,000
Approx. Number Employees: 1,427
Business Description:
Travel Agency
S.I.C.: 4512; 4724
N.A.I.C.S.: 481111; 561510
Advertising Expenditures: $4,742,000
Personnel:
Maurice J. Gallagher, Jr. *(Chm & CEO)*
Andrew C. Levy *(Pres)*
Scott Sheldon *(CFO & Sr VP)*
Kris B. Bauer *(Sr VP-Ops)*
Tyri Squyres *(VP-Mktg & Sls)*
Eric Gust *(Dir-Safety)*

ALLEN COMMUNICATION LEARNING SERVICES, INC.
175 W 200 S Ste 100
Salt Lake City, UT 84101
Tel.: (801) 537-7800
Fax: (801) 537-7805
Toll Free: (866) 310-7800
E-mail: info@allencomm.com
Web Site: www.allencomm.com
Sales Estimate: $10-19 Million
Approx. Number Employees: 41
Year Founded: 1981
Business Description:
Multi-Media Training Courses
Interactive Software Producer
S.I.C.: 8299; 7389
N.A.I.C.S.: 611699; 711410
Media: 10-13
Personnel:
Ron Zamir *(Pres & CEO)*
Paul Zackrison *(CFO & COO)*

ALLEN SYSTEMS GROUP, INC.
(d/b/a ASG)
1333 3rd Ave S
Naples, FL 34102-6400
Tel.: (239) 435-2200
Fax: (239) 263-3692
Fax: (800) 325-2555
Toll Free: (800) 932-5536
E-mail: info@asg.com
Web Site: www.asg.com
E-Mail For Key Personnel:
Sales Director: sales@asg.com
Sales Range: $150-199.9 Million
Approx. Number Employees: 1,000
Year Founded: 1986
Business Description:
Software & Professional Services for Information, Operations & Applications Management
S.I.C.: 7371; 7372
N.A.I.C.S.: 541511; 511210
Media: 1-7-8-10-13-22-26
Personnel:
Arthur L. Allen *(Pres & CEO)*
Ernest J. Scheidemann *(CFO & Exec VP)*
Alan Bolt *(CIO & Exec VP)*
John Connor *(CTO & Sr VP-Bus Dev)*
Derek Eckelman *(Gen Counsel & Exec VP)*
Tom Romnios *(Exec VP-Global HR)*
Richard Vance *(Exec VP-Ops)*
Jim Bladich *(Sr VP-Sls Ops)*
Scott McCurdy *(Sr VP-Prod Mgmt, Bus Solutions & Partnerships)*
Pat Pullen *(Sr VP)*
Brands & Products:
ASG
ASG-ADDERS
ASG-ADMIN
ASG-AUTOCHANGE
ASG-BATCH BRIDGE
ASG-BECUBIC
ASG-BIP
ASG-BRIDGE
ASG-CATS
ASG-CORTEX-MS
ASG-CORTEX-OMS
ASG-CORTEX-PDB
ASG-CORTEX-PLAN
ASG-CORTEX-PREP
ASG-CORTEX-RE
ASG-CYPRESS
ASG-DBOL
ASG-DOC-AID
ASG-ECORA
ASG-ENCORE
ASG-ENTACT
ASG-ENTACT ID
ASG-ESTIMATE
ASG-FAST ACCESS
ASG-FOCAL POINT
ASG-IMPACT WEB
ASG-INSIGHT
ASG-INTELLITEST
ASG-JCLPREP
ASG-JOURNAL MANAGER
ASG-KEYPLUS
ASG-LIFE CYCLE MANAGER
ASG-MANAGER PRODUCT
ASG-MANAGERVIEW
ASG-MOBILECONTROL ADMINISTRATOR
ASG-MQENTERPRISE
ASG-NAVIGRAPH
ASG-NAVIPLEX
ASG-ODE
ASG-OPSCENTRAL
ASG-OUTBOUND ENTERPRISE
ASG-PATHPOINT
ASG-PREALERT
ASG-RADIANTONE
ASG-RECAP
ASG-REPLICATION SUITE
ASG-REPORT.WEB
ASG-ROCHADE
ASG-SAFARI
ASG-SAFARI.OLAP
ASG-SENTRY
ASG-SMARTDOT
ASG-SMARTEDIT
ASG-SMARTFILE
ASG-SMARTSCOPE
ASG-SMARTTEST
ASG-SMARTTUNE
ASG-SPACEFINDER
ASG-SYNC
ASG-TAPEFINDER
ASG-TEVISTA
ASG-TMON
ASG-TOTAL RECALL
ASG-TRACER
ASG-TRACKBIED
ASG-VALIDDATE
ASG-VIRTUAL DB
ASG-VISUAL PROCESS
ASG-WEB ENABLER
ASG-WEBDOCUMENTZ
ASG-WORKLOAD ANALYZER
ASG-WORKLOAD OPTIMIZATION SUITE
ASG-WORKLOAD PLANNER
ASG-WORKLOAD SCHEDULER
ASG-ZACK
ASG-ZARA
ASG-ZEBB
ASG-ZEKE
ASG-ZEKE AGENTS
ASG-ZENA
ASG-ZEUS

ALLIANCE DATA SYSTEMS CORPORATION
7500 Dallas Pkwy Ste 700
Plano, TX 75024
Tel.: (214) 494-3000
E-mail: corporatecommunications@alliancedatasystems.com
Web Site: www.alliancedata.com
Approx. Rev.: $2,791,421,000
Approx. Number Employees: 7,600
Year Founded: 1996
Business Description:
Network Services, Payment Systems & Database Services
S.I.C.: 2741; 8721
N.A.I.C.S.: 511140; 541214
Advertising Expenditures: $115,500,000
Personnel:
Robert A. Minicucci *(Chm)*
Edward J. Heffernan *(Pres & CEO)*
Bryan A. Pearson *(Pres & Exec VP)*
Charles L. Horn *(CFO & Exec VP)*
Alan M. Utay *(Chief Admin Officer, Gen Counsel, Sec & Exec VP)*
Laura Santillan *(Chief Acctg Officer & Sr VP)*
Michael L. Iaccarino *(Pres-Mktg Svcs & Exec VP)*
Ivan M. Szeftel *(Pres-Retail Credit Svcs & Exec VP)*
Robert P. Armiak *(Treas & Sr VP)*
Richard E. Schumacher *(Sr VP-Tax)*
Tony Good *(VP-Corp Comm)*
Jim Walz *(Dir-Mobile Strategy & Svcs)*
Advertising Agencies:
Conrad, Phillips & Vutech, Inc.
1398 Goodale Blvd
Columbus, OH 43212
Tel.: (614) 224-3887
Fax: (614) 222-0737

Ologie
447 E Main St
Columbus, OH 43215
Tel.: (614) 221-1107
Fax: (614) 221-1108
Toll Free: (800) 962-1107

Resource Interactive
343 N Front St
Columbus, OH 43215-2219
Tel.: (614) 621-2888
Fax: (614) 621-2873
Toll Free: (800) 550-5815

ALLIN CORPORATION
381 Mansfield Ave
Pittsburgh, PA 15220
Tel.: (412) 928-8800
Fax: (412) 928-0887
E-mail: webcorporate@allin.com
Web Site: www.allin.com
Approx. Rev.: $14,894,000
Approx. Number Employees: 79
Year Founded: 1996
Business Description:
Software Technology Designer & Marketer
S.I.C.: 7373; 8742
N.A.I.C.S.: 541512; 541613
Advertising Expenditures: $71,000
Media: 10-22
Personnel:
Richard W. Talarico *(Chm & CEO)*
Dean C. Praskach *(CFO & VP-Fin)*
John Troutwine *(Sr VP-Bus Dev)*

ALLSOP, INC.
4201 Meridian St
Bellingham, WA 98226
Mailing Address:
PO Box 23
Bellingham, WA 98227-0023
Tel.: (360) 734-9090
Fax: (360) 734-9858
Toll Free: (800) 426-4303
E-mail: info@allsop.com
Web Site: www.allsop.com

Key to Media (For complete agency information see *The Advertising Red Books-Agencies* edition):
1. Bus. Publs. 2. Cable T.V. 3. Catalogs & Directories. 4. Co-op Adv. 5. Consumer Mags. 6. D.M. to Bus. Estab.7. D.M. to Consumers 8. Daily Newsp. 9. Exhibits/Trade Shows 10. Foreign 11. Infomercial 12. Internet Adv.13. Multimedia 14. Network Radio 15. Network T.V. 16. Newsp. Distr. Mags. 17. Other 18. Outdoor (Posters, Transit) 19. Point of Purchase20. Premiums, Novelties 21. Product Samples 22. Special Events Mktg. 23. Spot Radio 24. Spot T.V. 25. Weekly Newsp. 26. Yellow Page Adv.

Allsop, Inc. — (Continued)
Approx. Number Employees: 100
Year Founded: 1964
Business Description:
Electronic Audio, Video & Computer Accessories; Office Care Products Mfr
S.I.C.: 3572; 3651
N.A.I.C.S.: 334112; 334310
Import Export
Advertising Expenditures: $200,000
Media: 2-4-7-8-10-13-16-19-26
Distr.: Intl.; Natl.
Budget Set: Sept.
Brands & Products:
ACCUTRACK
ALLSOP
BOOT-IN
DVD CARBON EDGE PRO
HARD TOP
METAL ART
MICROFIBRE
ORBITRAC 2
PROFESSIONAL
RAINDROP
SOFT TOP
SOFTSWEEP
ULTREEN
WHEELEASY

ALPHA CTP SYSTEM

10 Columbia Dr
Amherst, NH 03031
Tel.: (603) 689-1101
Fax: (603) 689-1197
Web Site: www.alfactp.com
Approx. Number Employees: 12
Year Founded: 1881
Business Description:
Electronic, Professional Composition & Image Setting Systems
S.I.C.: 2759; 8742
N.A.I.C.S.: 323119; 541611
Export
Advertising Expenditures: $380,000
Media: 2-4-10
Distr.: Intl.; Natl.
Budget Set: July
Personnel:
Tony Ford *(Gen Mgr)*
Brands & Products:
PANTHER
PANTHER FASTRAK

ALSTATE PROCESS SERVICE INC.

(d/b/a AllCounty Legal Support)
60 Burt Dr
Deer Park, NY 11729-5702
Tel.: (631) 667-1800
Fax: (631) 667-0302
E-mail: info@alstateprocessservice.com
Web Site: www.alstateprocessservice.com
Approx. Number Employees: 43
Business Description:
Court Maintenance & Legal Advertising Services
S.I.C.: 7389
N.A.I.C.S.: 541199
Advertising Expenditures: $200,000
Media: 9-25
Distr.: Reg.
Personnel:
Thomas M. Kurinsky *(Founder)*
Rosemary A. LaManna *(Office Mgr)*

ALTA RESOURCES CORPORATION

120 N Commercial St
Neenah, WI 54956
Tel.: (920) 751-5800
Fax: (920) 727-9954
Web Site: www.altaresources.com
Approx. Sls.: $16,000,000
Approx. Number Employees: 700
Business Description:
Telemarketing Services
S.I.C.: 7389; 7361
N.A.I.C.S.: 561422; 541612
Personnel:
Jim Bere *(Chm & CEO)*
Kim Peterson *(VP-Mktg & Strategy)*
Craig Huff *(Dir-IT)*
Jason Schubring *(Mgr-E-Bus)*
Advertising Agency:
MarketSense
7020 High Grove Blvd
Burr Ridge, IL 60527-7599
Tel.: (630) 654-0170
Fax: (630) 654-0302
Toll Free: (800) 827-0170

ALTEC LANSING LLC

(Holding of Prophet Equity L.P.)
Rte 6 & 209
Milford, PA 18337-0277
Tel.: (570) 296-4434
Fax: (570) 296-6887
Toll Free: (866) 570-5702
Web Site: www.alteclansing.com
Sales Range: $50-74.9 Million
Approx. Number Employees: 1,500
Year Founded: 1961
Business Description:
Audio Entertainment Equipment Mfr
S.I.C.: 3651
N.A.I.C.S.: 334310
Import Export
Media: 1-2-4-5-6-9-10-11-13-18-19-22-23
Distr.: Intl.; Natl.
Budget Set: Nov.
Personnel:
Vicki Marion *(Pres)*
Brendon Stead *(VP-Product & Engrg)*
Rudy Pantoja *(Gen Mgr-Ops-Asia)*
Mitch Wenger *(Sr Dir-Mktg)*
Steve Schlangen *(Sr Product Mgr)*
Brands & Products:
ALTEC LANSING
EXPRESSIONIST
IM MINI
INMOTION
MOONDANCE

ALTERA CORPORATION

101 Innovation Dr
San Jose, CA 95134
Tel.: (408) 544-7000
Tel.: (408) 544-7707 (Investor Relations)
Fax: (408) 544-6408 (Investor Relations)
E-mail: inv_rel@altera.com
Web Site: www.altera.com
Approx. Sls.: $1,954,426,000
Approx. Number Employees: 2,666
Year Founded: 1983
Business Description:
CMOS Integrated Circuits, Logic Software & Hardware Mfr, Designer, Developer & Marketer
S.I.C.: 3674; 7372
N.A.I.C.S.: 334413; 511210
Import Export
Advertising Expenditures: $6,000,000
Media: 2-5-7-11-13-18-20-22
Personnel:
John P. Daane *(Chm, Pres & CEO)*
Ronald J. Pasek *(CFO, Chief Acctg Officer & Sr VP-Fin)*
Katherine E. Schuelke *(Gen Counsel, Sec & Sr VP)*
Jordan S. Plofsky *(Sr VP & Gen Mgr-Altera Penang)*
Danny Biran *(Sr VP-Mktg)*
Misha R. Burich *(Sr VP-R & D)*
William Y. Hata *(Sr VP-Worldwide Ops & Engrg)*
Lance M. Lissner *(Sr VP-Bus Dev)*
Kevin H. Lyman *(Sr VP-HR)*
George A. Papa *(Sr VP-Sls-Worldwide)*
Anthony Dalleggio *(VP-Mktg)*
Francois Gregoire *(VP-Tech)*
Steven G. Tsukichi *(VP-Mktg)*
Luanne Schirrmeister *(Sr Dir-Product Plng & Product Mktg)*
Paul Ekas *(Dir-Component Product Plng)*
Joel Martinez *(Sr Mgr-Product Mktg)*
Brands & Products:
ACEX
ACEX 1K
ALTERA
APEX
APEX 20K
APEX 20KC
APEX 20KE
APEX II
ARRIA
ARRIA GX
CLASSIC
CYCLONE
CYCLONE II
DSP BUILDER
EXCALIBUR
FASTTRACK
FINELINE BGA
FLASHLOGIC
FLEX
FLEX 10K
FLEX 10KA
FLEX 10KE
FLEX 6000
FLEX 6000A
FLEX 8000
HARDCOPY
LOGICLOCK
MAX
MAX 3000
MAX 3000A
MAX 5000
MAX 7000
MAX 7000A
MAX 7000B
MAX 7000S
MAX 9000
MAX 9000A
MAX II
MAX PLUS
MAX PLUS II
MEGACORE
MERCURY
MODELSLIM
MULTIVOLT
NIOS
NIOS II
QUARTUS
QUARTUS II
SIGNALPROBE
SIGNALTRAP
SOPC BUILDER
STRATEX GX
STRATIX
STRATIX II
STRATIX III
STRATIX IV

ALTERIAN, INC.

(Sub. of Alterian Plc)
35 E Wacker Dr Ste 200
Chicago, IL 60601
Tel.: (312) 704-1700
Fax: (312) 704-1701
E-mail: info@alterian.com
Web Site: www.alterian.com
Approx. Number Employees: 46
Year Founded: 1997
Business Description:
Marketing & Consumer Research Software Services
S.I.C.: 7371
N.A.I.C.S.: 541511
Media: 7-10
Personnel:
David Eldridge *(CEO)*
Joseph Fuller *(COO)*
Michael Fisher *(Sr VP-Sls & Mktg-America)*
Advertising Agency:
Finn Partners
211 E Ontario St Ste 1600
Chicago, IL 60611-3297
Tel.: (312) 644-8600
Fax: (312) 932-0367

ALTEX ELECTRONICS, LTD.

11342 IH 35 N
San Antonio, TX 78233
Tel.: (210) 655-8882
Fax: (210) 637-3276
E-mail: sales@altex.com
Web Site: www.altex.com
E-Mail For Key Personnel:
Sales Director: sales@altex.com
Approx. Sls.: $33,000,000
Approx. Number Employees: 150
Year Founded: 1980
Business Description:
Wholesaler of Computer & Networking Equipment
S.I.C.: 5065; 5063
N.A.I.C.S.: 423690; 423610
Media: 4-13
Personnel:
Mike Meyers *(Pres)*
Coco Cates *(Mgr-Adv Dept)*
Brands & Products:
ALTEX

AMANO CINCINNATI, INC.

(Sub. of Amano Corporation)
140 Harrison Ave
Roseland, NJ 07068
Tel.: (973) 403-1900
Fax: (973) 364-1086
Toll Free: (800) 526-2559
E-mail: info@amano.com
Web Site: www.amano.com
Approx. Number Employees: 100
Year Founded: 1992
Business Description:
Development, Mfr & Sales of Time Recording, Time Information & Parking Equipment
S.I.C.: 3873; 3559
N.A.I.C.S.: 334518; 333298
Export

Key to Media (For complete agency information see *The Advertising Red Books-Agencies* edition):
1. Bus. Publs. 2. Cable T.V. 3. Catalogs & Directories. 4. Co-op Adv. 5. Consumer Mags. 6. D.M. to Bus. Estab.7. D.M. to Consumers 8. Daily Newsp. 9. Exhibits/Trade Shows 10. Foreign 11. Infomercial 12. Internet Adv.13. Multimedia 14. Network Radio 15. Network T.V. 16. Newsp. Distr. Mags. 17. Other 18. Outdoor (Posters, Transit) 19. Point of Purchase20. Premiums, Novelties 21. Product Samples 22. Special Events Mktg. 23. Spot Radio 24. Spot T.V. 25. Weekly Newsp. 26. Yellow Page Adv.

Advertising Expenditures: $1,000,000
Media: 2-4-5-7-10-13-20
Distr.: Intl.; Natl.
Budget Set: Sept. -Oct.
Personnel:
Michael John Lee *(Pres & CEO)*
Brands & Products:
EXPRESSPARC
TIME ATTENDANT
TIME-BASED SOLUTIONS FOR YOUR BUSINESS
TIME GUARDIAN
TRUTIME

AMBERWAVE SYSTEMS
13 Garabedian Dr
Salem, NH 03079
Tel.: (603) 870-8700
Fax: (603) 870-8607
E-mail: info@amberwave.com
Web Site: www.amberwave.com
Approx. Number Employees: 23
Year Founded: 1998
Business Description:
Semiconductor Mfr
S.I.C.: 3674
N.A.I.C.S.: 334413
Personnel:
Richard J. Faubert *(Chm)*
Advertising Agency:
Shelton Group
12400 Coit Rd Ste 650
Dallas, TX 75251
Tel.: (972) 239-5119
Fax: (972) 239-2292

AMDOCS INC.
(Corporate Headquarters of Amdocs Limited)
1390 Timberlake Manor Pkwy
Chesterfield, MO 63017-6041
Tel.: (314) 212-7000
Fax: (314) 212-7500
E-mail: dox_info@amdocs.com
Web Site: www.amdocs.com
Approx. Number Employees: 500
Year Founded: 1982
Business Description:
Operations Support Software for Telecommunications Services
S.I.C.: 7372; 7373
N.A.I.C.S.: 511210; 541512
Media: 2-10-11-13-27
Personnel:
Bruce K. Anderson *(Chm)*
Thomas G. O'Brien *(VP-Fin & IR)*
Brian Schnack *(Product Dir-Mgmt)*
Advertising Agency:
Weber Shandwick-Los Angeles
8687 Melrose Ave 7th Fl
Los Angeles, CA 90069
Tel.: (310) 854-8200
Fax: (310) 854-8201

AMERICAN APPRAISAL ASSOCIATES, INC.
411 E Wisconsin Ave Ste 1900
Milwaukee, WI 53202-4466
Tel.: (414) 271-7240
Fax: (414) 221-7065
Toll Free: (800) 558-8650
E-mail: moreinfo@american-appraisal.com
Web Site: www.american-appraisal.com
E-Mail For Key Personnel:
President: JZvesper@american-appraisal.com
Marketing Director: lbrophy@american-appraisal.com
Approx. Number Employees: 150
Year Founded: 1896
Business Description:
Professional Valuation Services
S.I.C.: 8748; 7389
N.A.I.C.S.: 561499; 541618; 541990
Media: 2-4-7-9-10-13-20-22-26
Distr.: Intl.; Natl.; Reg.
Budget Set: Mar.
Personnel:
Joseph P. Zvesper *(Chm & CEO)*
Pavlos Zeccos *(CEO & Mng Dir-American Appraisal (Hellas) Limited)*
Les E. Kiehnau *(Sr Mng Dir & Sr VP-Real Estate Advisory Practice)*
Herbert W. Saunders *(Mng Dir)*
Kimberly Russo *(CFO & Sr VP)*
Lee P. Hackett *(Exec VP)*
Paul T. Hartnett *(Sr VP-Property Appraisal Svcs Grp)*
Richard J. Siladi *(Sr VP-North America)*
Laura Brophy *(VP-Mktg)*
Peter S. Huck *(Asst VP-Telecomm)*
Brands & Products:
AMERICAN APPRAISAL
AMERICAN APPRAISAL CANADA
LEADING/THINKING/PERFORMING
REAG
THE WORLD'S ONLY TRULY GLOBAL VALUATION FIRM

AMERICAN BUSINESS SOLUTIONS, INC.
(d/b/a Employee Professionals)
6754 Willowbrook Park Dr Ste 200
Houston, TX 77066
Tel.: (281) 398-1955
Fax: (281) 398-1960
Web Site: www.employeepro.com
Approx. Sls.: $100,000,000
Approx. Number Employees: 5,000
Year Founded: 1990
Business Description:
Employee Leasing Company
S.I.C.: 7374; 6411
N.A.I.C.S.: 518210; 524210
Media: 2
Personnel:
Carol Crean *(Dir-Houston Reg)*
Esther Reiling *(Dir-Strategic Initiatives)*

AMERICAN ELECTRIC TECHNOLOGIES, INC.
6410 Long Dr
Houston, TX 77087
Tel.: (713) 644-8182
E-mail: info@aeti.com
Web Site: www.aeti.com
Approx. Sls.: $38,963,744
Approx. Number Employees: 332
Business Description:
Telecommunications Network Infrastructure Solutions
S.I.C.: 3433; 3441; 3442; 3444; 3661; 3679
N.A.I.C.S.: 333414; 332312; 332321; 332322; 334210; 334419
Media: 2-4-10
Personnel:
Arthur G. Dauber *(Chm)*
Charles M. Dauber *(Pres & CEO)*
Frances Powell Hawes *(CFO & Sr VP)*
Neal T. Hare *(CTO & Sr VP)*
Timothy C. Adams *(Pres-American Access Technologies & VP)*
Carl Vitanza *(VP & Gen Mgr-Power Distr & Control)*
Erik W. Wiisanen *(VP-Sls & Mktg)*
Frank Davis *(Dir-Oil & Gas Bus Dev)*
Dean Swift *(Mgr-Beaumont Svcs)*
Robert Thomson *(Mgr-Renewable Energy Svcs)*
Brands & Products:
AETI
AMERICAN ELECTRIC TECHNOLOGIES

AMERICAN LIST COUNSEL, INC.
4300 US Hwy 1 CN 5219
Princeton, NJ 08543
Tel.: (609) 580-2800
Fax: (609) 580-2864
Fax: (609) 580-2888
Toll Free: (800) 252-5478
E-mail: info@alc.com
Web Site: www.alc.com
Sales Range: $150-199.9 Million
Approx. Number Employees: 182
Year Founded: 1978
Business Description:
Direct Mail Advertising Services
S.I.C.: 7331
N.A.I.C.S.: 541860
Import Export
Media: 2-7
Personnel:
Donn Rappaport *(Chm)*
Susan Rice Rappaport *(Pres & CEO)*
David Dotson *(Mng Partner)*
Peter DeRosa *(CFO)*
Fran Green *(Pres-SMART Data Solutions)*
Mary Ann Buoncristiano *(Exec VP)*
Laurie Cole *(Exec VP-Customer Acq)*
Kim Lowenthal *(Exec VP)*
Heather Maylander *(Exec VP)*
Pat Stecher *(Exec VP-Bus Svcs)*
Britt Vatne *(Exec VP)*
Rachel Mercer *(Sr VP)*
Susan Rudy *(Sr VP)*
Capri Guerrini *(Dir-Mktg)*
Megan Corigliano *(Mgr-Client Mktg)*
Rich DiVirgilio *(Mgr-Client Mktg)*

AMERICAN MARKING SYSTEMS, INC.
1015 Paulison Ave
Clifton, NJ 07011-3610
Tel.: (973) 478-5600
Fax: (973) 478-0039
Toll Free: (800) 782-6766
E-mail: info@ams-stamps.com
Web Site: www.ams-stamps.com
Approx. Number Employees: 80
Year Founded: 1898
Business Description:
Mfr. of Marking Devices & ID Products such as Rubber, Self-Inking & Pre-Inked Stamps, Signs, Name Plates, Badges, Daters, Seals, Other Office Products & Industrial Marking Products
S.I.C.: 3953
N.A.I.C.S.: 339943
Advertising Expenditures: $100,000
Media: 2-4-6-7-8-13-26
Distr.: Natl.
Budget Set: Jan.
Personnel:
John A. Collins *(Pres)*
Bill Teegan *(Gen Mgr)*
Ronald Cochran *(Mgr-Mktg & Sls)*
Brands & Products:
AMERICAN MARKING SYSTEMS
AMS
PROMARK

AMERICAN SLIDE-CHART CORPORATION
25 W 550 Geneva Rd
Carol Stream, IL 60188
Tel.: (630) 665-3333
Fax: (630) 665-3491
Toll Free: (800) 323-4433
E-mail: info2@americanperrygraf.com
Web Site: www.americanperrygraf.com
Approx. Number Employees: 140
Business Description:
Custom Dimensional Marketing Products Mfr
S.I.C.: 3829; 3579
N.A.I.C.S.: 334519; 333313
Export
Advertising Expenditures: $500,000
Media: 2-7-10-13-26
Distr.: Intl.; Natl.
Brands & Products:
AMERICANSLIDECHART
FOLD OUT
MAGIC WINDOW
POP-UP
SLIDE CHART
WE PUT YOUR MESSAGE IN MOTION
WHEEL-CHART
Advertising Agency:
ASC Advertising
25 W 550 Geneva Rd
Carol Stream, IL 60188
Tel.: (800) 323-4433
Fax: (630) 665-3491
Toll Free: (800) 323-4433
(Slide Charts, Wheel Charts)

AMERICAN SOFTWARE, INC.
470 E Paces Ferry Rd NE
Atlanta, GA 30305-3301
Tel.: (404) 261-4381
Fax: (404) 264-5206
Toll Free: (800) 726-2946
E-mail: askasi@amsoftware.com
Web Site: www.amsoftware.com
Approx. Rev.: $75,276,000
Approx. Number Employees: 291
Year Founded: 1970
Business Description:
Development, Marketing & Support of Business Application Software
S.I.C.: 7372
N.A.I.C.S.: 334611; 511210
Advertising Expenditures: $1,700,000
Distr.: Intl.; Natl.
Budget Set: Feb.
Personnel:
James C. Edenfield *(Pres, CEO & Treas)*
Vincent C. Klinges *(CFO)*
Jeffrey W. Coombs *(COO & Exec VP)*
J. Michael Edenfield *(CEO-Logility & Exec VP)*
James R. McGuone *(Gen Counsel & Corp Sec)*
Brands & Products:
AMERICAN SOFTWARE
E-INTELLIPRISE
FLOW MANUFACTURING

Key to Media (For complete agency information see *The Advertising Red Books-Agencies* edition):
1. Bus. Publs. 2. Cable T.V. 3. Catalogs & Directories. 4. Co-op Adv. 5. Consumer Mags. 6. D.M. to Bus. Estab.7. D.M. to Consumers 8. Daily Newsp. 9. Exhibits/Trade Shows 10. Foreign 11. Infomercial 12. Internet Adv.13. Multimedia 14. Network Radio 15. Network T.V. 16. Newsp. Distr. Mags. 17. Other 18. Outdoor (Posters, Transit) 19. Point of Purchase20. Premiums, Novelties 21. Product Samples 22. Special Events Mktg. 23. Spot Radio 24. Spot T.V. 25. Weekly Newsp. 26. Yellow Page Adv.

AMERICAN STATIONERY CO., INC.
100 N Park Ave
Peru, IN 46970-1701
Tel.: (765) 473-4438
Fax: (765) 472-8510
Fax: (800) 253-9054
Toll Free: (800) 822-2577
E-mail: custserv@americanstationery.com
Web Site: www.americanstationery.com
Approx. Number Employees: 175
Year Founded: 1919
Business Description:
Fine Stationery & Personalized Paper Products Distr & Mfr
S.I.C.: 2678; 2679
N.A.I.C.S.: 322233; 322299
Media: 4-5-13
Personnel:
Michael Bakehorn *(Chm & CEO)*
Jerry Cowan *(Pres & COO)*
Jennifer Hutton *(Dir-Mktg, Wedding Division)*
Advertising Agency:
LH Advertising Agency Inc.
200 N Central Ave Ste 220
Hartsdale, NY 10530
Tel.: (914) 285-3456
Fax: (914) 285-3450

AMERICAN THERMOPLASTIC COMPANY
106 Gamma Dr
Pittsburgh, PA 15238-2920
Tel.: (412) 967-0900
Fax: (412) 967-9990
Toll Free: (800) 456-6602
E-mail: atc@binders.com
Web Site: www.binders.com
Approx. Number Employees: 160
Year Founded: 1954
Business Description:
Looseleaf Binders & Related Products Mfr
S.I.C.: 2782
N.A.I.C.S.: 323118
Media: 2-7-10-17
Distr.: Natl.
Budget Set: Apr.
Personnel:
Steve Silberman *(Pres)*
Joe Sprumont *(Mgr-Adv)*
Brands & Products:
CLASSIC TOUCH
CLEARLY BOUND
ENVIRONMENTALLY BOUND
FUSION
GREATCOLOR
MYLAR
NEON
POLY PRINTS
QUICKSHIP 1
QUICKSHIP 6

AMERICA'S CALL CENTER, INC.
(d/b/a WebCallUSA)
7901 Baymeadows Way Ste 14
Jacksonville, FL 32256
Tel.: (904) 224-2000
Fax: (904) 737-1107
Toll Free: (800) 564-4860
E-mail: info@webcallusa.com
Web Site: www.webcallusa.com
Approx. Sls.: $1,500,000
Approx. Number Employees: 27
Year Founded: 1987
Business Description:
Telemarketing Services
S.I.C.: 7389
N.A.I.C.S.: 561422
Media: 2
Personnel:
Dick Emberson *(Pres)*

AMERICOM GOVERNMENT SERVICES, INC.
(Sub. of SES AMERICOM, Inc.)
2 Research Way
Princeton, NJ 08540
Tel.: (609) 987-4500
Fax: (609) 987-4411
E-mail: ags-info.americom@americom-gs.com
Web Site: www.americom-gs.com
Business Description:
Satellite Telecommunications
S.I.C.: 4899
N.A.I.C.S.: 517410
Personnel:
Ran Frazier *(VP-Sls & Program Mngmt)*
William F. LaShell *(VP-Dept of Defense Sls)*
Angela Steever *(Dir-Contracts)*
Advertising Agency:
August, Lang & Husak, Inc.
4630 Montgomery Ave Ste 400
Bethesda, MD 20814-3443
Tel.: (301) 657-2772
Fax: (301) 657-9895

AML COMMUNICATIONS, INC.
1000 Avenida Acaso
Camarillo, CA 93012
Tel.: (805) 388-1345
Fax: (805) 484-2191
E-mail: ir@amlj.com
Web Site: www.amlj.com
E-Mail For Key Personnel:
Sales Director: sales@amlj.com
Approx. Sls.: $16,317,000
Approx. Number Employees: 88
Year Founded: 1986
Business Description:
Wireless Communication Amplifier Mfr
S.I.C.: 3669; 3663; 3679
N.A.I.C.S.: 334290; 334220; 334419
Advertising Expenditures: $76,000
Media: 2-7-10
Personnel:
Jacob Inbar *(Chm, Pres & CEO)*
Heera Lee *(Principal Fin Officer)*
Tiberiu Mazilu *(Exec VP-Engrg)*
Edwin J. McAvoy *(Exec VP-Sls & Mktg)*

AMS SERVICES
(Sub. of Vertafore Inc.)
3737 Park East Dr Ste 202
Beachwood, OH 44122-4347
Tel.: (216) 464-2180
Fax: (216) 464-2439
Toll Free: (800) 888-8144
Web Site: www.ams-services.com
Approx. Number Employees: 75
Year Founded: 1983
Business Description:
Developer of Comparative Rating Insurance Software for Personal & Commercial Use
S.I.C.: 7371
N.A.I.C.S.: 541511
Advertising Agency:
Square Tomato
900 1st Ave South Ste 411
Seattle, WA 98134
Tel.: (206) 264-0644

AMX CORPORATION
(Sub. of Duchossois Industries, Inc.)
3000 Research Dr
Richardson, TX 75082-3546
Tel.: (469) 624-7605
Fax: (469) 624-7153
Toll Free: (800) 222-0193
E-mail: service@amx.com
Web Site: www.amxcorp.com
E-Mail For Key Personnel:
Marketing Director: rashid.skaf@amx.com
Sales Range: $75-99.9 Million
Approx. Number Employees: 346
Year Founded: 1982
Business Description:
Electronic Equipment & Software
S.I.C.: 3571
N.A.I.C.S.: 334111
Media: 4
Personnel:
Rashid M. Skaf *(Pres & CEO)*
Chris Apple *(CFO & VP)*
Michael L. Olinger *(VP-Sls-Intl)*
Jim Pautler *(VP-Engrng)*
Mike Ramoz *(Dir-Sls, Ops & Customer Svc)*
George Grech *(Mgr-Natl Sls)*
Brands & Products:
ASSETMANAGER
CAFE DUET
DYNAMO
EXPERIENCE
INCONCERT
MAX
MEETINGMANGER
PANELBUILDER
PANELPREVIEW
TAKENOTE
XPRESS PRO

ANACOMP, INC.
15378 Ave of Science
San Diego, CA 92128
Tel.: (858) 716-3400
Fax: (858) 716-3775
E-mail: sales@anacomp.com
Web Site: www.anacomp.com
E-Mail For Key Personnel:
President: Howa.Dratler@anacomp.com
Sales Director: sales@anacomp.com
Sales Range: $150-199.9 Million
Approx. Number Employees: 1,200
Year Founded: 1968
Business Description:
Document-Management Outsourcing Services, Field Maintenance Services & Document-Management Systems & Supplies
S.I.C.: 7338; 2759; 3861
N.A.I.C.S.: 561410; 323115; 333315
Export
Media: 16
Personnel:
Michael E. Tennenbaum *(Chm)*
Thomas P. Cunningham *(CEO)*
Jeffrey S. Cartwright *(CFO & Sr VP)*
Paul J. Najar *(Gen Counsel & Exec VP)*
Bill Shute *(Sr VP & Gen Mgr-Federal Sector)*
Marie Hickey *(VP-Strategic Dev)*
Brands & Products:
ALOS
ANACOMP
DATAGRAPHIX
DATAMASTER
DOCHARBOR
GARTNER
IDP1600
IMAGE DIRECT
MICRON
SCANPRO
SUNRISE
XFP2000

ANALYSTS INTERNATIONAL CORPORATION
3601 W 76th St Ste 200
Minneapolis, MN 55435-3000
Tel.: (952) 835-5900
Fax: (952) 897-4555
Toll Free: (800) 800-5044
E-mail: inquiries@analysts.com
Web Site: www.analysts.com
Approx. Rev.: $106,688,000
Approx. Number Employees: 909
Year Founded: 1966
Business Description:
Information Technology & Business Consulting Services
S.I.C.: 8748
N.A.I.C.S.: 541690; 541618
Media: 2
Personnel:
Douglas C. Neve *(Chm)*
Brittany B. McKinney *(Pres & CEO)*
Randy W. Strobel *(CFO & Sr VP)*
Eric Educate *(Sr VP-Sls)*
Randy Hall *(Sr VP-South Reg)*
Virgil Pint *(Sr VP-North Reg)*

ANSOFT CORPORATION
(Sub. of ANSYS, Inc.)
225 W Station Sq Dr Ste 200
Pittsburgh, PA 15219-1119
Tel.: (412) 261-3200
Fax: (412) 471-9427
E-mail: info@ansoft.com
Web Site: www.ansoft.com
Sales Range: $100-124.9 Million
Approx. Number Employees: 314
Year Founded: 1984
Business Description:
Develops, Markets & Supports EDA Software Solutions
S.I.C.: 7372; 7371
N.A.I.C.S.: 334611; 511210; 541511
Advertising Expenditures: $31,506,000
Media: 2-7-10-13-21
Personnel:
Shane Emswiler *(VP & Gen Mgr-Electronics Bus Unit)*
Josh Fredberg *(VP-Mktg)*
Joe Skirbanks *(VP-Sls & Support)*
Brands & Products:
ANSOFT DESIGNER
ENSEMBLE
HFSS
MAXWELL
NEXXIM
PEXPRT
Q3D EXTRACTOR
SERENADE

Key to Media (For complete agency information see *The Advertising Red Books-Agencies* edition):
1. Bus. Publs. 2. Cable T.V. 3. Catalogs & Directories. 4. Co-op Adv. 5. Consumer Mags. 6. D.M. to Bus. Estab.7. D.M. to Consumers 8. Daily Newsp. 9. Exhibits/Trade Shows 10. Foreign 11. Infomercial 12. Internet Adv.13. Multimedia 14. Network Radio 15. Network T.V. 16. Newsp. Distr. Mags. 17. Other 18. Outdoor (Posters, Transit) 19. Point of Purchase20. Premiums, Novelties 21. Product Samples 22. Special Events Mktg. 23. Spot Radio 24. Spot T.V. 25. Weekly Newsp. 26. Yellow Page Adv.

SIMPLORER
SIWAVE

ANTEC INCORPORATED

47900 Fremont Blvd
Fremont, CA 94538
Tel.: (510) 770-1200
Fax: (510) 770-1288
E-mail: customerservice@antec-inc.com
Web Site: www.antec-inc.com
Approx. Number Employees: 50
Year Founded: 1986
Business Description:
Mfr. of Computer Hardware
S.I.C.: 3577; 5734
N.A.I.C.S.: 334119; 443120
Media: 6
Brands & Products:
ANTEC
ARIA
LANBOY
LIFESTYLE
MINUET
NEOPOWER
OVERTURE
PERFORMANCE II
PERFORMANCE PLUS
PHANTOM
SMARTBLUE
SMARTCOOL
SOLUTION
SONATA
TRICOOL
TRUE BLUE
TRUECONTROL
TRUEPOWER

AON HEWITT

(Formerly Hewitt Associates, Inc.)
(Sub. of Aon Corporation)
100 Half Day Rd
Lincolnshire, IL 60069
Tel.: (847) 295-5000
Fax: (847) 295-7634
Web Site: www.aon.com
Approx. Rev.: $3,073,560,000
Approx. Number Employees: 23,000
Year Founded: 1940
Business Description:
Human Resource Consulting
S.I.C.: 7361; 8742
N.A.I.C.S.: 561310; 541611; 541612
Media: 1-2-7-13-29
Personnel:
John L. Ryan *(Chief Legal Officer & Sr VP)*
Sanjiv K. Anand *(CTO)*
Julie S. Gordon *(Chief Client Officer)*
Yvan Legris *(CEO-UK & EMEA)*
Kristi Savacool *(CEO-Benefits Admin)*
Brad Anderson *(Sr VP-Benefits Admin)*
Mark Stach *(Gen Mgr-Strategic Bus)*
Michelle Calderon-Johns *(Dir-Insurance Ops)*
Bianca Miller *(Dir-Corp Treasury & Risk Mgmt)*
Advertising Agency:
McCormack Group
744 Cleveland Rd
Hinsdale, IL 60521
Tel.: (630) 325-1808
Fax: (630) 325-0039

AONIX NORTH AMERICA INC.

(Sub. of Aonix S.A.)
5930 Cornerstone Ct W Ste 250
San Diego, CA 92121
Tel.: (858) 457-2700
Fax: (858) 824-0212
Toll Free: (800) 97-AONIX
E-mail: info@aonix.com
Web Site: www.aonix.com
Approx. Number Employees: 35
Year Founded: 1996
Business Description:
Software Developer
S.I.C.: 7372
N.A.I.C.S.: 334611; 511210
Media: 10
Advertising Agency:
Hughes Communications, Inc.
PO Box 157
Mansfield Center, CT 06250
Tel.: (705) 751-9740
Fax: (860) 256-8374

APAC CUSTOMER SERVICES, INC.

Bannockburn Lake Office Plz 2201
Waukegan Rd Ste 300
Bannockburn, IL 60015
Tel.: (847) 374-4980
Fax: (847) 374-4991
Toll Free: (800) 688-7687
E-mail: abszafran@apacmail.com
Web Site:
www.apaccustomerservices.com
Approx. Rev.: $325,958,000
Approx. Number Employees: 13,400
Year Founded: 1973
Business Description:
Telephone-Based Sales, Marketing & Customer Management Solutions for Corporate Clients
S.I.C.: 7389; 7322; 8742
N.A.I.C.S.: 561499; 541613; 561422; 561440
Media: 2-10
Personnel:
Theodore G. Schwartz *(Founder & Chm)*
Kevin T. Keleghan *(Pres & CEO)*
Andrew B. Szafran *(CFO & Sr VP)*
Mark McDermott *(CIO & VP)*
Robert B. Nachwalter *(Gen Counsel, Sec & Sr VP)*
Christopher H. Crowley *(Sr VP-Sls)*
Arthur D. DiBari *(Sr VP-Ops)*
James C. Gari *(VP-Fin)*
Michael V. Hoehne *(VP-HR)*
Brands & Products:
APAC CUSTOMER SERVICES
ATHOME
E.PAC
ON THE LINE FOR YOUR SUCCESS
SERVICEPAC
WE HELP OUR CLIENTS SERVE THEIR CUSTOMERS BETTER

APC-MGE

(Sub. of Schneider Electric USA, Inc.)
132 Fairgrounds Rd
West Kingston, RI 02892
Mailing Address:
PO Box 278
West Kingston, RI 02892-0278
Tel.: (401) 789-5735
Fax: (401) 789-3710
Toll Free: (800) 788-2208
Web Site: www.apcc.com
Approx. Number Employees: 7,580
Year Founded: 1981
Business Description:
Electrical Power Protection Products & Services
S.I.C.: 5063; 3699
N.A.I.C.S.: 423610; 335999
Import Export
Advertising Expenditures: $52,500,000
Media: 2-4-6-7-9-10-13-18-23-24-25-26
Distr.: Intl.; Natl.
Personnel:
Laurent Vernerey *(Pres & CEO)*
Aaron L. Davis *(CMO)*
Philippe Arsonneau *(Pres-Asia Pacific & Japan)*
David R. Johnson *(Sr VP-Home & Bus Networks)*
Edward Machala *(Sr VP-Supply Chain, Mfg & Pur)*
Brands & Products:
APC
BACK-UPS
BACK-UPS OFFICE
BACK-UPS PRO
CYBERFORT
INFRASTRUXURE
LEGENDARY RELIABILITY
LINE-R
MAGNUM
MASTERSWITCH
MATRIX-UPS
NETSHELTER
NETWORKAIR
POWERCHUTE
POWERMANAGER
POWERNET
POWERSHIELD
PROTECTNET
SILCON
SMART-UPS
SURGEARREST
SYMMETRA
TRAVELPOWER
Advertising Agency:
PriMedia Inc.
1775 Bald Hill Rd
Warwick, RI 02886-4210
Tel.: (401) 826-3600
Fax: (401) 826-3644
Toll Free: (800) 397-5804

APERTURE TECHNOLOGIES INC.

(Div. of Emerson Network Power)
9 Riverbend Dr S
Stamford, CT 06907
Tel.: (203) 357-0800
Fax: (203) 351-1249
E-mail: info@aperture.com
Web Site: www.aperture.com
Sales Range: $1-9.9 Million
Approx. Number Employees: 120
Year Founded: 1987
Business Description:
Corporate IT Data Center Management Software & Services
S.I.C.: 7372; 7371; 7379; 8748
N.A.I.C.S.: 511210; 541511; 541519; 541690
Personnel:
Eileen Spellman *(VP-Fin)*
Steve Yellen *(VP-Sls & Mktg)*
Brands & Products:
APERTURE
APERTURE VIEW
VISTA
VISUAL WEB SOLUTION
Advertising Agency:
Fahlgren Mortine
4030 Easton Station Ste 300
Columbus, OH 43219
Tel.: (614) 383-1500
Fax: (614) 383-1501

API HEALTHCARE CORP.

(Formerly API Software, Inc.)
(Holding of Francisco Partners Management, LLC)
1550 Innovation Way
Hartford, WI 53027-8720
Tel.: (262) 673-6815
Fax: (262) 673-2650
Web Site: www.apihealthcare.com/
Approx. Number Employees: 350
Business Description:
Healthcare Business Management Software & Services
S.I.C.: 7372
N.A.I.C.S.: 511210
Media: 6-10-13
Personnel:
J.P. Fingado *(Pres & CEO)*
Patrick Pomroy *(CFO)*
Brands & Products:
ACTIVESTAFFER
API LABORWORKX
EDTRAK
PAYROLLMATION
SECURALL
STAFFMETRICS

API SOFTWARE, INC.

(Name Changed to API Healthcare Corp.)

APPARENT NETWORKS, INC.

400 321 Water St
Vancouver, BC Canada
Tel.: (604) 433-2333
Fax: (604) 433-2311
Toll Free: (800) 508-5233
E-mail: info@apparentnetworks.com
Web Site:
www.apparentnetworks.com
Approx. Sls.: $3,929,200
Approx. Number Employees: 40
Business Description:
Developer of Network Intelligence Software
S.I.C.: 7372; 7373; 7379
N.A.I.C.S.: 334611; 511210; 541512; 541519
Export
Media: 2-4-7-13
Personnel:
Fred Klassen *(Co-Founder & VP-Networking Technologies)*
Irfhan Rajani *(Co-Founder)*
Jim Melvin *(CEO)*
Keith Bartlett *(Exec VP-Bus Dev)*
Gregg Ammirati *(VP-Sls)*
Brands & Products:
APPARENET
APPARENET NETWORKS
APPCRITICAL
TRUPATH
Advertising Agency:
Waggener Edstrom
225 108th Ave NE Ste 700
Bellevue, WA 98004-5737
Tel.: (425) 638-7000
Fax: (425) 638-7001

Key to Media (For complete agency information see *The Advertising Red Books-Agencies* edition):
1. Bus. Publs. 2. Cable T.V. 3. Catalogs & Directories. 4. Co-op Adv. 5. Consumer Mags. 6. D.M. to Bus. Estab.7. D.M. to Consumers
8. Daily Newsp. 9. Exhibits/Trade Shows 10. Foreign 11. Infomercial 12. Internet Adv.13. Multimedia 14. Network Radio
15. Network T.V. 16. Newsp. Distr. Mags. 17. Other 18. Outdoor (Posters, Transit) 19. Point of Purchase20. Premiums, Novelties
21. Product Samples 22. Special Events Mktg. 23. Spot Radio 24. Spot T.V. 25. Weekly Newsp. 26. Yellow Page Adv.

APPLE CANADA INC.
(Sub. of Apple Inc.)
7495 Birchmount Rd
Markham, ON L3R 5G2, Canada
Tel.: (905) 513-5800
Fax: (905) 477-6305
Fax: (905) 477-8668
Telex: 416-477-6305
Web Site: www.apple.ca
Sales Range: $50-74.9 Million
Approx. Number Employees: 120
Business Description:
Retailer of Personal Computers, Portable Digital Music Players & Mobile Communication Devices
S.I.C.: 6719
N.A.I.C.S.: 551114
Media: 2-4-6-9-14-25
Distr.: Natl.
Budget Set: Dec.
Personnel:
John Hagias *(VP-Fin & Controller)*
Marion Manalo *(Mgr-Channel Programmes)*

APPLE INC.
1 Infinite Loop
Cupertino, CA 95014-2083
Tel.: (408) 996-1010
Fax: (408) 974-2113
Telex: 171567
E-mail: media.help@apple.com
Web Site: www.apple.com
Approx. Sls.: $65,225,000,000
Approx. Number Employees: 46,600
Year Founded: 1976
Business Description:
Mfr of Personal Computers, Portable Digital Music Players & Mobile Communication Devices
S.I.C.: 3577; 3571; 3663; 5045
N.A.I.C.S.: 334119; 334111; 334220; 423430
Advertising Expenditures: $501,000,000
Media: 2-3-5-6-7-8-9-10-13-14-15-18-19-23-24-31
Distr.: Intl.; Natl.
Personnel:
Timothy D. Cook *(CEO)*
Peter Oppenheimer *(CFO & Sr VP)*
Betsy Rafael *(Chief Acctg Officer, VP & Controller)*
Bruce Sewell *(Gen Counsel & Sr VP-Legal & Govt Affairs)*
Eddy Cue *(Sr VP-Internet Software & Svcs)*
Scott Forstall *(Sr VP-iPhone Software Engrg & Platform Experience)*
Jonathan Ive *(Sr VP-Indus Design)*
Ronald B. Johnson *(Sr VP-Retail)*
Robert Mansfield *(Sr VP-Mac Hardware Engrg)*
Philip W. Schiller *(Sr VP-Worldwide Product Mktg)*
Sina Tamaddon *(Sr VP-Applications)*
Jeff Williams *(Sr VP-Ops)*
Craig Federighi *(VP-Mac Software Engrg)*
Theo Theodorou *(Head-Sls-EMEA)*
Todd Tran *(Gen Mgr-Mob Ad Ops-Europe)*
Steve Dowling *(Sr Dir-Corp PR)*
Natalie Kerris *(Sr Dir-Music Pub Rels)*
Nancy Paxton *(Sr Dir-IR)*
Peter Ziatek *(Dir-Info Security)*
Joan Hoover *(Sr Mgr-IR)*
Richard Ng *(Product Mgr-Mktg)*
Benjamin Vigier *(Product Mgr-Mobile Commerce)*
Ashley Krueger *(Mgr-iAd Client Svcs & Adv)*
Warner Yuen *(Engr-Sls & Solutions Architect)*
Brands & Products:
A COMPREHENSIVE STUDY OF FINAL CUT PRO
A COMPREHENSIVE STUDY OF ILIFE
A COMPREHENSIVE STUDY OF MOTION
A COMPREHENSIVE STUDY OF SHAKE
A/ROSE
A/UX
ACOT (APPLE CLASSROOMS OF TOMORROW)
ACTC BOOT CAMP
ADMINISTERING FINAL CUT SERVER
ADVANCED EDITING TECHNIQUES IN FINAL CUT PRO
ADVANCED TECHNIQUES IN LOGIC PRO
AIRMAC
AIRPORT
AIRPORT EXPRESS
AIRPORT EXTREME
AIRTUNES
AN INTRODUCTION TO ADMINISTERING FINAL CUT SERVER
AN INTRODUCTION TO APERTURE
AN INTRODUCTION TO COLOR
AN INTRODUCTION TO DVD STUDIO PRO
AN INTRODUCTION TO FINAL CUT EXPRESS
AN INTRODUCTION TO FINAL CUT PRO
AN INTRODUCTION TO GARAGEBAND
AN INTRODUCTION TO ILIFE
AN INTRODUCTION TO IWORK
AN INTRODUCTION TO LOGIC EXPRESS & LOGIC PRO
AN INTRODUCTION TO SOUNDTRACK PRO
AN OVERVIEW OF FINAL CUT PRO
A.PACK
APERTURE
APPLE
APPLE CINEMA DISPLAY
APPLE CONSULTANTS NETWORK
APPLE DESKTOP SERVICE CERTIFICATION
APPLE DESKTOP SERVICE LAB
APPLE IIGS
APPLE ISERVICES
APPLE MEDIA SERIES
APPLE PORTABLE SERVICE CERTIFICATION
APPLE PORTABLE SERVICE LAB
APPLE REMOTE DESKTOP
APPLE STORE
APPLE STUDIO DISPLAY
APPLE TECHSTEP
APPLE TV
APPLECARE
APPLECAT
APPLECD SC
APPLEFUND
APPLELINK
APPLESCRIPT
APPLESCRIPT STUDIO
APPLESHARE
APPLETALK
APPLEVISION
APPLEWORKS
AQUA
AUDIO UNITS
BACK TO MY MAC
BENTO
BONJOUR
BOOT CAMP
CAPITALS
CARBON
CHARCOAL
CHICAGO
CINEMA TOOLS
CLARIS
CLARIS EMAILER
CLARIS ORGANIZER
CLARISDRAW
CLARISIMPACT
CLARISWORKS
COCOA
COCOA TOUCH
COLOR SYNC
COLORSHARE
COLORSYNC
COMPLETE MY ALBUM
CONVOMANIA
COVER FLOW
CYBERDOG
DASHCODE
DISK FIRST AID
DOUBLEVISION
DVD@CCESS
DVD STUDIO PRO
EDUCATOR ADVANTAGE
EDVIEW
EMAC
EMATE
EN PASSANT
ENCYCLOMEDIA
ENTERPRISE OBJECTS
ENTERPRISE OBJECTS FRAMEWORK
ETHERTALK
EXPOSE
EXTENSIONS MANAGER
FAIRPLAY
FILEVAULT
FINAL CUT
FINAL CUT PRO
FINALCUT STUDIO
FINDER
FIREWIRE
FIREWIRE SYMBOL
FONTSYNC
GADGET
GARAGEBAND
GENEVA
GENIUS BAR
GEOPORT
GRAYSHARE
GS/OS
HYPERCARD
HYPERTALK
IBOOK
ICAL
ICHAT
IDISK
IDVD
ILIFE
IMAC
IMAGEWRITER
IMOVIE
INDIE SPOTLIGHT
INFORMATION ALLEY
INKWELL
INSTRUMENTS
INTER-POLL
INTRODUCTION TO MAC OS X
IPHONE
IPHOTO
IPOD
IPOD CLASSIC
IPOD HI-FI
IPOD NANO
IPOD SHUFFLE
IPOD SOCKS
IPOD TOUCH
ISIGHT
ITUNES
ITUNES MUSIC STORE
ITUNES PLUS
ITUNES STORE
IWEB
IWORK
JAM PACK
KEYCHAIN
KEYNOTE
LASERWRITER
LEOPARD
LINKSAVER
LIVETYPE
LOCALTALK
LOGIC
LOGIC STUDIO
.MAC
MAC
MAC OS
MAC OS X
MAC OS X ADVANCED ADMINISTRATION
MAC OS X DEPLOYMENT
MAC OS X DIRECTORY SERVICES
MAC OS X SERVER ESSENTIALS
MAC OS X SUPPORT ESSENTIALS
MACAPP
MACAPPC
MACBOOK
MACBOOK AIR
MACDNS
MACINTALK
MACINTOSH
MACINTOSH PRODUCTS GUIDE
MACPAD
MACTCP
MACTEST
MACWORKSTATION
MADE FOR IPOD
MAGSAFE
MAINSTAGE
MESSAGEPAD
MOBILE ME
MONACO
MOTION GRAPHICS & EFFECTS IN FINAL CUT STUDIO
MPW
MULTI-TOUCH
NANO
NETINFO
NEW YORK
NEWTON
NEWTONMAIL
NUMBERS
OBJECTIVE-C
OFFLINE RT
ONESCANNER
ONETOONE
OPEN DIRECTORY
OPENCL
OPENDOC
OPENPLAY
PAGES
PANTHER

Key to Media (For complete agency information see *The Advertising Red Books-Agencies* edition):
1. Bus. Publs. 2. Cable T.V. 3. Catalogs & Directories. 4. Co-op Adv. 5. Consumer Mags. 6. D.M. to Bus. Estab.7. D.M. to Consumers 8. Daily Newsp. 9. Exhibits/Trade Shows 10. Foreign 11. Infomercial 12. Internet Adv.13. Multimedia 14. Network Radio 15. Network T.V. 16. Newsp. Distr. Mags. 17. Other 18. Outdoor (Posters, Transit) 19. Point of Purchase20. Premiums, Novelties 21. Product Samples 22. Special Events Mktg. 23. Spot Radio 24. Spot T.V. 25. Weekly Newsp. 26. Yellow Page Adv.

PHOTO BOOTH
PHOTOCASTING
PIPPIN
PIXLET
PLAINTALK
POWER MAC
POWER MACINTOSH
POWERBOOK
POWERBOOK DUO
POWERLATCH
POWERPC
POWERSCHOOL
POWERSHARE
POWERTALK
PROCARE
PRODOS
QUARTZ
QUICK TIME
QUICKDRAW
QUICKSTART
QUICKTAKE
QUICKTIME
QUICKTIME BROADCASTER
QUICKTIME TV
RENDEZVOUS
RESEDIT
ROSETTA
SADE
SAFARI
SAND
SCANTEST
SHAKE
SHERLOCK
SHOP DIFFERENT
SHUFFLE
SKIA
SNAPBACK
SNOW LEOPARD
SOUNDTRACK
SOURCEBUG
SPACES
SPOTLIGHT
STUDIO
STYLEWRITER
SUPERDRIVE
TECHNO
TEXTILE
THINK DIFFERENT
TIGER
TIME CAPSULE
TIME MACHINE
TOKENTALK
TOOLSERVER
TREMOR
TRUETYPE
TUBES
ULTRABEAT
VELOCITY ENGINE
VINGLE
WAVEBURNER
WEBOBJECTS
WEBSCRIPT
WORKS WITH IMOVIE
WORKS WITH IPHONE
WORLDSCRIPT
XCODE
XGRID
XSAN
XSAN 2 ADMINISTRATION
XSAN 2 FOR PRO VIDEO
XSAN FOR PRO VIDEO
XSERVE
ZEAL

Advertising Agencies:
Cresta Group
1050 N State St
Chicago, IL 60610
Tel.: (312) 944-4700
Fax: (312) 944-1582

Eleven Inc.
445 Bush St 8th Fl
San Francisco, CA 94108
Tel.: (415) 707-1111
Fax: (415) 707-1100

mono
(Partially Owned by MDC Partners)
3036 Hennepin Ave
Minneapolis, MN 55408
Tel.: (612) 822-4135
Fax: (612) 454-4950
iPad

TBWA Chiat Day Los Angeles
5353 Grosvenor Blvd
Los Angeles, CA 90066
Tel.: (310) 305-5000
Fax: (310) 305-6000
iMac
iPhone
iPod
Media Buying

APPLIED GLOBAL TECHNOLOGIES
(d/b/a AGT)
1006 Pathfinder Way
Rockledge, FL 32955
Tel.: (321) 638-2007
Fax: (321) 690-2211
E-mail: info@appliedglobal.com
Web Site: www.appliedglobal.com
Sales Range: $25-49.9 Million
Approx. Number Employees: 98
Year Founded: 1993
Business Description:
Outsourcing & Managed Services Within Voice, Video & Data Collaboration Networks
S.I.C.: 7373
N.A.I.C.S.: 541512
Media: 2-7-10-13
Personnel:
Michael J. Valletutti *(Chm & CEO)*
J. Ben Atha *(Pres & CTO)*
Craig Nickerson *(CFO)*
Mark Cray *(Exec VP)*
Mike Garvey *(Exec VP)*
Todd Jacobson *(VP-Product Devel)*
Brands & Products:
AGT
ANALYTICS
ENCORE
FATHOM
PERSPECTIVE
PRISM
WINCATS

APPLIED PRECISION, INC.
(Holding of Telegraph Hill Partners)
1040 12th Ave NW
Issaquah, WA 98027
Tel.: (425) 557-1000
Fax: (425) 557-1055
E-mail: hotline@api.com
Web Site: www.api.com
Approx. Number Employees: 150
Year Founded: 1986
Business Description:
Developer of Image Acquisition & Analysis Systems for Life Science Industry
S.I.C.: 3826
N.A.I.C.S.: 334516
Media: 13-17
Personnel:
Joe Victor *(Pres & CEO)*
Stephen D. Reichenbach *(CFO)*
Rick Loya *(Mgr-Sls-Worldwide)*
Brands & Products:
APPLIEDPRECISION
ARRAYWORX
CELLWORX
DELTAVISION
FLOWPOINT
NANOMOTION
PRECISIONPOINT
PRECISIONWORX
PROBEWORX
SOFTWORX
WAFERWORX
WAVETUNER

APPLIED SOFTWARE TECHNOLOGY, INC.
2801 Buford Hwy Druid Chase Ste 100
Atlanta, GA 30329
Tel.: (404) 633-8660
Fax: (404) 634-7390
E-mail: info@asti.com
Web Site: www.asti.com
Approx. Number Employees: 50
Business Description:
Software Consulting, Implementation, Customization & Training Services
S.I.C.: 7379; 8243
N.A.I.C.S.: 541519; 611420
Personnel:
Richard Burroughs *(Pres)*
Mark Wagasky *(VP-Sls)*
Josh Oakley *(Dir-Applied BIM Svcs)*
Advertising Agency:
Carabiner Communications
4372 Misty Morning Ln
Lilburn, GA 30047
Tel.: (770) 923-8332
Fax: (888) 686-7688
Autodesk Resale

APPLIED SYSTEMS INC.
(Holding of Bain Capital, LLC)
200 Applied Pkwy
University Park, IL 60466-4110
Tel.: (708) 534-5575
Fax: (708) 534-8016
Web Site: www.appliedsystems.com
Approx. Number Employees: 700
Year Founded: 1976
Business Description:
Management Systems Technology
S.I.C.: 7371; 5045
N.A.I.C.S.: 541511; 423430
Media: 10
Personnel:
James P. Kellner *(Chm)*
Reid French *(CEO)*
Colleen E. Mikuce *(CFO)*
Irv Kantar *(Mgr-Carrier Relationship)*
Brands & Products:
THE AGENCY MANAGER
THE DIAMOND SYSTEM
TAM CENTRAL

APRIMO, INCORPORATED
(Sub. of Teradata Corporation)
900 E 96th St Ste 400
Indianapolis, IN 46240
Tel.: (317) 803-4300
Fax: (317) 803-4251
E-mail: info@aprimo.com
Web Site: www.aprimo.com
Approx. Sls.: $51,592,000
Approx. Number Employees: 355
Year Founded: 1998
Business Description:
Marketing Software & Services
S.I.C.: 7371; 7372
N.A.I.C.S.: 541511; 511210
Advertising Expenditures: $128,000
Media: 13-17
Personnel:
William M. Godfrey *(Pres)*
Lisa Burris Arthur *(CMO)*
Robert C. Boehnlein *(Chief Customer Officer)*
John J. Stammen *(Exec VP-Worldwide Sls & Alliances)*
Brands & Products:
ACCELERATING MARKETING PRODUCTIVITY
APRIMO
APRIMO AGENCY
APRIMO ENTERPRISE
APRIMO PROFESSIONAL
ENTERPRISE MARKETING BACKBONE

APROPOS TECHNOLOGY INC.
(Sub. of Syntellect, Inc.)
1 Tower Ln 28th Fl
Oakbrook Terrace, IL 60181
Tel.: (630) 472-9600
Fax: (630) 472-9745
E-mail: info@apropos.com
Web Site: www.apropos.com
Sales Range: $10-24.9 Million
Approx. Number Employees: 99
Business Description:
Customer Interaction Computer Software
S.I.C.: 7372; 8711
N.A.I.C.S.: 511210; 541330
Media: 5-7
Brands & Products:
APROPOS

APTIFY
1850 K St NW 3rd Fl Ste350
Washington, DC 20006-1605
Tel.: (202) 223-2600
Fax: (202) 223-8800
Toll Free: (800) 355-6738
E-mail: support@aptify.com
Web Site: www.aptify.com
E-Mail For Key Personnel:
Sales Director: sales@aptify.com
Public Relations: Lou.Baccam@aptify.com
Approx. Number Employees: 65
Year Founded: 1993
Business Description:
Enterprise & E-Commerce Software Mfr
S.I.C.: 7372; 8748
N.A.I.C.S.: 511210; 541618
Media: 10
Personnel:
Amith Nagarajan *(Chm & CEO)*
Brands & Products:
APTIFY

ARBITRON INC.
9705 Patuxent Woods Dr
Columbia, MD 21046-1572
Tel.: (410) 312-8000
E-mail: investor.relations@arbitron.com
Web Site: www.arbitron.com

Key to Media (For complete agency information see *The Advertising Red Books-Agencies* edition):
1. Bus. Publs. 2. Cable T.V. 3. Catalogs & Directories. 4. Co-op Adv. 5. Consumer Mags. 6. D.M. to Bus. Estab.7. D.M. to Consumers
8. Daily Newsp. 9. Exhibits/Trade Shows 10. Foreign 11. Infomercial 12. Internet Adv.13. Multimedia 14. Network Radio
15. Network T.V. 16. Newsp. Distr. Mags. 17. Other 18. Outdoor (Posters, Transit) 19. Point of Purchase20. Premiums, Novelties
21. Product Samples 22. Special Events Mktg. 23. Spot Radio 24. Spot T.V. 25. Weekly Newsp. 26. Yellow Page Adv.

Arbitron Inc. — (Continued)

Approx. Rev.: $395,397,000
Approx. Number Employees: 1,113
Year Founded: 1949
Business Description:
Media & Marketing Research Services
S.I.C.: 7311; 7372; 7374; 8732
N.A.I.C.S.: 541810; 511210; 518210; 541910
Advertising Expenditures: $2,300,000
Media: 2-7-10
Distr.: Natl.
Personnel:
Philip Guarascio *(Chm)*
William T. Kerr *(Pres & CEO)*
Richard J. Surratt *(CFO & Exec VP-Fin)*
Sean R. Creamer *(COO & Exec VP)*
Carol Hanley *(CMO, Chief Sls Officer & Exec VP)*
Timothy T. Smith *(Exec VP-Bus Dev, Strategy & Chief Legal Officer)*
V. Scott Henry *(Exec VP-Tech Svcs)*
Marilou Legge *(Exec VP-Organizational Effectiveness & Corp Comm)*
Gregg Lindner *(Exec VP-Svc Innovation & Chief Res Officer)*
Carol Edwards *(Sr VP-Cross & Platform Media Measurement)*
Paul Krasinski *(Sr VP-Digital Media & Analytics)*
William J. McKenna *(Sr VP-New Media Ventures)*
Bill Rose *(Sr VP-Mktg)*
Ed Cohen *(VP-Res Policy & Comm)*
Julian Davis *(Dir-Urban Outreach)*
David Forr *(Dir-US Encoding Ops)*
David Oglevee *(Sr Mgr-Western Accts)*
Rick Resing *(Sr Mgr-Northeastern Accts)*
Jessica Benbow *(Mgr-Corp Comm)*
Joanna Douglas *(Mgr-Natl PPM Acct)*
Stacy Perrus *(Mgr-Mktg Comm)*
Brands & Products:
ARBITRENDS
ARBITRON
ARBITRON DATA EXPRESS
ARBITRON EBOOK
ARBITRON ON DEMAND
ARBITRON PORTABLE PEOPLE METER
ARBITRON PPM
CORPORATE ROLL-UP
CUMULATOR
CUSTOM COVERAGE
GEO-BREAK
GRID ONE
IRS
LOCALMOTION
MANAGEMENT REPORTER
MAPMAAKER DIRECT
MAPMAKER DIRECT
MARKETING RESOURCES PLUS
MAXIMISER
MAXIMISER PLUS
MAXQUALITATIVE
MEDIA PROFESSIONAL
MEDIA PROFESSIONAL PLUS
MEDIAMASTER
MRP
MUSICTESTER
NEXT GENERATION ELECTRONIC MEASUREMENT
NEXT GENERATION ELECTRONIC RATINGS
PD ADVANTAGE
PPM
PPM ANALYSIS TOOL
PPM WEEKLIES
PRINTPLUS
PRINTSCAN
PROSPECTOR
QUALITAP
QUALIZIP
RADIO COUNTY COVERAGE
REPORT DESIGNER
RETAIL DIRECT
RETAIL PROFILING SYSTEM
RETAIL SPENDING POWER
RETAILDIRECT
SCHEDULE-IT
SMARTPLUS
SMARTREPORTS
SUPERPANEL
SUPERPANELIST
TAPMEDIA
TARGETONE
TRAFFICLINK

ARCADE MARKETING, INC.

(Joint Venture of KKR & CO. L.P. & Credit Suisse Group AG)
1700 Broadway Ste 2500
New York, NY 10019
Tel.: (212) 541-2600
Fax: (212) 489-3026
Web Site: www.arcadeinc.com
Sales Range: $1-9.9 Million
Approx. Number Employees: 28
Year Founded: 1902
Business Description:
Fragrance Sampling, Scent Sampling & Interactive Product Sampling Technologies
S.I.C.: 2752
N.A.I.C.S.: 323110
Import Export
Media: 2-6-8-17-21
Distr.: Natl.
Budget Set: Dec.
Personnel:
Debra Yale-Litman *(Pres)*
Steve Greenland *(Sr VP-R&D)*
Brands & Products:
AROMALACQUER
BEAUTISEAL
BEAUTITOUCH
DISCCOVER
LIQI-SEAL
LIQUITOUCH
MICRODOT
POWDASCENT
SCENTSEAL
SCENTSTRIP
SELECTASHADE
SHADESEAL

ARCSIGHT, INC.

(Sub. of Hewlett-Packard Company)
5 Results Way
Cupertino, CA 95014
Tel.: (408) 864-2600
Fax: (408) 342-1615
E-mail: info@arcsight.com
Web Site: www.arcsight.com
Approx. Rev.: $181,384,000
Approx. Number Employees: 512
Business Description:
Security & Compliance Management Solutions
S.I.C.: 7373; 7382
N.A.I.C.S.: 541512; 561621
Advertising Expenditures: $200,000
Media: 5-7-10-13-17
Personnel:
Stewart Grierson *(CFO)*
Hugh S. Njemanze *(CTO & Exec VP-R&D)*
Tram T. Phi *(Gen Counsel)*
Joni Kahn *(Sr VP-Svcs & Support)*
Kevin P. Mosher *(Sr VP-Field Ops-Worldwide)*
Jeffrey Scheel *(Sr VP-Bus Dev)*
Gail Boddy *(VP-HR)*
Haiyan Song *(VP-Engrg)*
Laura Tom *(VP-Customer Support)*

ARCSOFT, INC.

46601 Fremont Blvd
Fremont, CA 94538
Tel.: (510) 440-9901
Fax: (510) 440-1270
E-mail: webmaster@arcsoft.com
Web Site: www.arcsoft.com
Sales Range: $10-24.9 Million
Approx. Number Employees: 395
Business Description:
Multimedia Software Developer for OEM Customers
S.I.C.: 7371
N.A.I.C.S.: 541511
Media: 10
Personnel:
Michael Deng *(Founder & CEO)*

ARI NETWORK SERVICES, INC.

10850 W Pk Pl Ste 1200
Milwaukee, WI 53224
Tel.: (414) 973-4300
Fax: (414) 973-4357
E-mail: employment@arinet.com
Web Site: www.arinet.com
Approx. Rev.: $21,484,000
Approx. Number Employees: 147
Business Description:
Business-to-Business E-Commerce Solutions Services
S.I.C.: 8748; 7371; 7375
N.A.I.C.S.: 541690; 518111; 541511
Advertising Expenditures: $132,000
Media: 2-4-5-7
Personnel:
Brian E. Dearing *(Chm, Chief Corp Dev Officer & Chief Strategy Officer)*
Roy W. Olivier *(Pres & CEO)*
Darin Janecek *(CFO & VP-Fin)*
Michael T. Tenpas *(VP-Global Sls & Mktg)*
Brands & Products:
ARI
ARI MAILSMART
COMPASS PARTNERS
EMPART
EMPART PUBLISHER
EMPART VIEWER
EMPART WEB
EMPARTPUBLISHER
EMPARTVIEWER
EMPARTWEB
GARDENPOINT.COM
MAILSMART
PARTSMART
PARTSMART CART
PARTSMART CLASSIC
PARTSMART DATA MANAGER
PARTSMART DATA PUBLISHER
PARTSMART DIY
PARTSMART WEB
SEARCHENGINESMART
SERVICESMART
TRADEROUTE
WEBSITESMART
WEBSITESMART PRO
WINNING THROUGH INNOVATION

ARIBA, INC.

807 11th Ave
Sunnyvale, CA 94089
Tel.: (650) 390-1000
Fax: (650) 390-1100
Toll Free: (866) 772-7422
E-mail: prrequest@ariba.com
Web Site: www.ariba.com
Approx. Rev.: $361,146,000
Approx. Number Employees: 1,804
Year Founded: 1996
Business Description:
Spend Management Solutions
Computer Software Developer
S.I.C.: 7372
N.A.I.C.S.: 511210; 334611
Advertising Expenditures: $769,000
Media: 1-2-13-17
Personnel:
Robert M. Calderoni *(Chm & CEO)*
Kevin Costello *(Pres)*
Ahmed Rubaie *(CFO)*
Kent Parker *(COO)*
Tim Minahan *(CMO)*
Daryl T. Rolley *(Sr VP & Gen Mgr-North America & Asia)*
Sanish Mondkar *(Sr VP-Engrg & Hosting Ops)*
Gregory Spray *(Sr VP-Solutions Mgmt)*
Matthew Zack *(Sr VP-Corp Dev & HR)*
Michael J. Arenth *(VP & Gen Mgr-European Ops)*
Karen Master *(Dir-Corp Comm)*
Patrick McCarthy *(Dir-Sls)*
Brands & Products:
ARIBA
ARIBA ANALYSIS
ARIBA BUYER
ARIBA CATEGORY MANAGEMENT
ARIBA CATEGORY PROCUREMENT
ARIBA CONTENT PROCUREMENT
ARIBA CONTRACT COMPLIANCE
ARIBA CONTRACT MANAGEMENT
ARIBA CONTRACT WORKBENCH
ARIBA CONTRACTS
ARIBA DATA ENRICHMENT
ARIBA EFORMS
ARIBA ELECTRONIC INVOICE PRESENTMENT & PAYMENT
ARIBA INVOICE
ARIBA LIVE
ARIBA PAYMENT
ARIBA PROCURE-TO-PAY
ARIBA PUNCHOUT
ARIBA QUICKSOURCE
ARIBA READY
ARIBA SETTLEMENT
ARIBA SOLUTIONS DELIVERY
ARIBA SOURCING
ARIBA SPEND MANAGEMENT
ARIBA SPEND MANAGEMENT. FIND IT. GET IT. KEEP IT.
ARIBA SPEND MANAGEMENT KNOWLEDGE BASE
ARIBA SPEND VISIBILITY
ARIBA SUPPLIER CONNECTIVITY
ARIBA SUPPLIER NETWORK
ARIBA SUPPLIER PERFORMANCE MANAGEMENT
ARIBA SUPPLY LINES
ARIBA SUPPLY MANAGER
ARIBA. THIS IS SPEND MANAGEMENT

Key to Media (For complete agency information see *The Advertising Red Books-Agencies* edition):
1. Bus. Publs. 2. Cable T.V. 3. Catalogs & Directories. 4. Co-op Adv. 5. Consumer Mags. 6. D.M. to Bus. Estab.7. D.M. to Consumers 8. Daily Newsp. 9. Exhibits/Trade Shows 10. Foreign 11. Infomercial 12. Internet Adv.13. Multimedia 14. Network Radio 15. Network T.V. 16. Newsp. Distr. Mags. 17. Other 18. Outdoor (Posters, Transit) 19. Point of Purchase20. Premiums, Novelties 21. Product Samples 22. Special Events Mktg. 23. Spot Radio 24. Spot T.V. 25. Weekly Newsp. 26. Yellow Page Adv.

ARIBA TRAVEL & EXPENSE
ARIBA WORKFORCE
ARIBA.COM
ARIBA.COM NETWORK
ARIBALIVE
IT'S TIME FOR SPEND MANAGEMENT
PO-FLIP
SUPPLYWATCH

Advertising Agency:
PAN Communications
300 Brickstone Sq 7th Fl
Andover, MA 01810
Tel.: (978) 474-1900
Fax: (978) 474-1903

ARRIS GROUP, INC.

3871 Lakefield Dr
Suwanee, GA 30024-1292
Tel.: (678) 473-2000
Fax: (678) 473-8770
Toll Free: (800) 469-6569
E-mail: jim.bauer@arrisi.com
Web Site: www.arrisi.com
Approx. Sls.: $1,087,506,000
Approx. Number Employees: 1,942
Year Founded: 2001
Business Description:
Communications Technology; Broadband Network Products Designer, Mfr & Distr
S.I.C.: 3669; 3661; 3663
N.A.I.C.S.: 334290; 334210; 334220
Advertising Expenditures: $800,000
Media: 2-4-10-22
Personnel:
Robert J. Stanzione *(Chm, Pres & CEO)*
James Alan Chiddix *(Vice Chm)*
David B. Potts *(CFO, CIO & Exec VP)*
John O. Caezza *(Pres-Access, Transport & Supplies)*
Ronald M. Coppock *(Pres-ARRIS Worldwide Sls)*
Bryant K. Isaacs *(Pres-Media & Comm Sys)*
James D. Lakin *(Pres-Advanced Tech & Svcs)*
Bruce McClelland *(Pres-Broadband Comm Sys)*
Lawrence A. Margolis *(Chief Counsel, Sec & Exec VP-Admin, Legal, HR & Strategy)*
John Boland *(Sr VP-Media & Comm Solutions Grp)*
Stan Brovont *(Sr VP-Mktg & Bus Dev)*
Sandra K. Howe *(Sr VP-Strategic Market Dev)*
Dan Whalen *(Sr VP-Sls)*
Robert Puccini *(VP & Gen Mgr)*
Alex Swan *(VP-Corp Comm)*
Don Toft *(VP-Sls)*
Connie Walters *(Sr Dir-Mktg)*
Marilyn Altman *(Dir-Tech Svcs)*
Brands & Products:
ARRIS
ATOGA
C3
C4
CABLELABS
CADANT
CORNERSTONE
DIGICON
FLEXPULL
KEYSTONE
MONARCH
PACKETCABLE
Q5
REGAL
TELEWIRE
TELEWIRE SUPPLY
TOUCHSTONE
VOICE PORT

ART TECHNOLOGY GROUP, INC.-SEATTLE

(Branch of Art Technology Group, Inc.)
1601 5th Ave Ste 1801
Seattle, WA 98101-3615
Tel.: (206) 834-8100
Fax: (206) 834-8125
Toll Free: (800) 277-4427
Web Site: www.atg.com
Sales Range: $25-49.9 Million
Approx. Number Employees: 181
Business Description:
Business Oriented Computer Software
S.I.C.: 7372
N.A.I.C.S.: 511210
Media: 7-9-25
Personnel:
Dorian Daley *(CEO)*

ARTHUR BROWN & BRO., INC.

2 W 45th St
New York, NY 10036-4502
Tel.: (212) 575-5555
Fax: (212) 575-5825
Toll Free: (800) 772PENS
E-mail: penshop@artbrown.com
Web Site: www.artbrown.com
Approx. Sls.: $1,700,000
Approx. Number Employees: 25
Year Founded: 1924
Business Description:
Writing Instruments & Artists & Drafting Supplies Distr
S.I.C.: 5999; 5199
N.A.I.C.S.: 453998; 424990
Import Export
Media: 4-5-6-7-8-9-10-26
Distr.: Intl.; Natl.
Budget Set: Jan.
Personnel:
B. Warren Brown *(Owner)*
David Brown *(VP-Corp Sls)*

ARTNET WORLDWIDE CORPORATION

(Sub. of Artnet AG)
61 Broadway 23rd Fl
New York, NY 10006-2701
Tel.: (212) 497-9700
Fax: (212) 497-9707
Web Site: www.artnet.com
Approx. Number Employees: 100
Year Founded: 1989
Business Description:
Research Services for Fine & Decorative Arts
S.I.C.: 3291; 5999
N.A.I.C.S.: 327910; 453998
Media: 2-10-13
Personnel:
Hans Neuendorf *(Chm & CEO)*
Bill Fine *(Pres)*
Jacob Pabst *(CIO)*
Brian McConville *(Exec VP)*
Karin Gardner *(VP-Fin & Controller)*
Walter Robinson *(Editor-in-Chief-Artnet Magazine)*
Advertising Agencies:
Oneupweb
13561 S W Bayshore Dr Ste 3000
Traverse City, MI 49684
Tel.: (231) 922-9977
Fax: (231) 922-9966
Toll Free: (877) 568-7477
Online Auctions
Pay-Per-Click Campaign

Winstar Interactive Media
307 7th Ave Ste 2003
New York, NY 10001
Tel.: (212) 916-0713

ARUBA NETWORKS, INC.

1344 Crossman Ave
Sunnyvale, CA 94089-1113
Tel.: (408) 227-4500
Fax: (408) 227-4550
Toll Free: (866) 552-7822
E-mail: info@arubanetworks.com
Web Site: www.arubanetworks.com
Approx. Rev.: $266,534,000
Approx. Number Employees: 681
Year Founded: 2002
Business Description:
Wireless & Wireline Enterprise Network Mobility Services
S.I.C.: 4812; 7379
N.A.I.C.S.: 517212; 541519
Advertising Expenditures: $100,000
Media: 2-10
Personnel:
Keerti Melkote *(Founder & CTO)*
Dominic P. Orr *(Pres & CEO)*
Michael Galvin *(CFO)*
Hitesh Sheth *(COO)*
Ben Gibson *(CMO)*
Alexa King *(Gen Counsel)*
Aaron Bean *(VP-HR)*
Michael Kirby *(VP-Worldwide Sls)*
Brands & Products:
ARUBA NETWORKS

ASA INTERNATIONAL LTD.

10 Speen St
Framingham, MA 01701-4661
Tel.: (508) 626-2727
Fax: (508) 626-0645
E-mail: webmaster@asaint.com
Web Site: www.asaint.com
Approx. Rev.: $19,805,092
Approx. Number Employees: 110
Year Founded: 1969
Business Description:
Business Software & Systems
S.I.C.: 7373; 7371; 7372
N.A.I.C.S.: 541512; 511210; 541511
Advertising Expenditures: $401,000
Media: 7-10-22
Brands & Products:
ASA
ASA TIRE SYSTEMS
KHAMELEON SOFTWARE
RAINMAKER
VERTICENT

ASI CORPORATION

48289 Fremont Blvd
Fremont, CA 94538-6522
Tel.: (510) 226-8000
Fax: (510) 226-8858
Toll Free: (800) 200-0274
E-mail: info@asipartner.com
Web Site: www.asipartner.com
Sales Range: $900-999.9 Million
Approx. Number Employees: 541
Year Founded: 1987
Business Description:
Computer Hardware & Software Distr
S.I.C.: 5045
N.A.I.C.S.: 423430
Media: 4-10-20
Personnel:
Christine Liang *(Founder & Pres)*
Marcel Liang *(CEO)*
Vince Tartalia *(Dir-Technical Svcs)*

ASPECT SOFTWARE, INC.

300 Apollo Dr
Chelmsford, MA 01824
Tel.: (978) 250-7900
Fax: (978) 244-7410
Web Site: www.aspect.com/
Approx. Number Employees: 325
Year Founded: 1981
Business Description:
Call Center Software & Equipment Mfr
S.I.C.: 7371; 7373
N.A.I.C.S.: 541511; 541512
Export
Media: 2-4-7-10-13-26
Personnel:
James D. Foy *(Pres & CEO)*
Michael J. Provenzano *(CFO & Exec VP-Fin)*
Jamie Ryan *(CIO & Sr VP-IT)*
David Reibel *(Gen Counsel & Sr VP)*
Kevin Schwartz *(Exec VP-Pro Svcs-Global)*
Mike Sheridan *(Exec VP-Worldwide Sls)*
Gwen Braygreen *(Sr VP-Aspect Technical Svcs & Continuing Engrg)*
Laurie Cairns *(Sr VP-Mktg)*
James F. Mitchell *(Sr VP-Tech Office)*
Lui Simhua *(Sr VP)*
Brands & Products:
ASPECT
CONCERTO CONVERSATIONS
CONCERTO ENSEMBLEPRO
CONCERTO ENTERPRISE SUITE
CONCERTO RIGHTFORCE
CONCERTO SOFTWARE
CONCERTO SPECTRUM
CONCERTO UNIFIED EDITION
CONCERTO UNISON
Advertising Agency:
The Bateman Group
1550 Bryant St Ste 770
San Francisco, CA 94103
Tel.: (415) 503-1818
Fax: (415) 503-1880

ASPECT SOFTWARE, INC.

(Branch of Aspect Software, Inc.)
1310 Ridder Park Dr
San Jose, CA 95131-2313
Tel.: (408) 325-2200
Fax: (408) 325-2260
Web Site: www.aspect.com
Sales Range: $350-399.9 Million
Approx. Number Employees: 1,254
Year Founded: 1985
Business Description:
Developer of Contact Center Products & Services Software
S.I.C.: 7372; 7373
N.A.I.C.S.: 511210; 541512
Advertising Expenditures: $1,000,000
Media: 2-6-13
Personnel:
Michael J. Provenzano *(CFO & Exec VP-Fin)*
Jamie Ryan *(CIO & Sr VP-IT)*
James F. Mitchell *(Sr VP-Tech Office)*

Key to Media (For complete agency information see *The Advertising Red Books-Agencies* edition):
1. Bus. Publs. 2. Cable T.V. 3. Catalogs & Directories. 4. Co-op Adv. 5. Consumer Mags. 6. D.M. to Bus. Estab.7. D.M. to Consumers
8. Daily Newsp. 9. Exhibits/Trade Shows 10. Foreign 11. Infomercial 12. Internet Adv.13. Multimedia 14. Network Radio
15. Network T.V. 16. Newsp. Distr. Mags. 17. Other 18. Outdoor (Posters, Transit) 19. Point of Purchase20. Premiums, Novelties
21. Product Samples 22. Special Events Mktg. 23. Spot Radio 24. Spot T.V. 25. Weekly Newsp. 26. Yellow Page Adv.

Aspect Software, Inc. — (Continued)

Advertising Agency:
Madison, Sproul & Partners
165 10th St
San Francisco, CA 94103
Tel.: (415) 541-4102

ASPEN TECHNOLOGY, INC.

(d/b/a AspenTech)
200 Wheeler Rd
Burlington, MA 01803
Tel.: (781) 221-6400
Fax: (781) 221-6410
E-mail: info@aspentech.com
Web Site: www.aspentec.com
Approx. Rev.: $198,154,000
Approx. Number Employees: 1,269
Year Founded: 1981
Business Description:
Software & Services for the Pharmaceutical, Petro Chemical, Petroleum, Metal, Electric Power, Pulp & Paper Industries
S.I.C.: 7371
N.A.I.C.S.: 541511
Advertising Expenditures: $2,500,000
Media: 2-7-8-10-22
Personnel:
Stephen M. Jennings *(Chm)*
Mark E. Fusco *(Pres & CEO)*
Mark P. Sullivan *(CFO & Exec VP)*
Frederic G. Hammond *(Gen Counsel & Sr VP)*
Manolis E. Kotzabasakis *(Exec VP-Products)*
Antonio Pietri *(Exec VP-Field Ops)*
John W. Hague *(Sr VP)*
Joanna Nikka *(Sr VP-HR)*
Richard Packwood *(Sr VP-Bus Dev)*
Paul Taylor *(Sr VP-EMEA)*
Michele Triponey *(Sr VP-Global Customer Support & Trng)*
Blair Wheeler *(Sr VP-Mktg)*
Alison Smith *(VP-Strategic Plng)*
Willie K. Chan *(Dir)*
Brands & Products:
ACCOUNTING.21
ADSIM
ADVISOR
AEROTRAN
APLE
APOLLO
ASPEN 1QMODEL POWERTOOLS
ASPEN ADSORPTION
ASPEN ADVISOR
ASPEN AEROTRAN
ASPEN AIR COOLED EXCHANGER
ASPEN APOLLO
ASPEN ASSETBUILDER
ASPEN ATOMS
ASPEN AUDIT COMPLIANCE MANAGER
ASPEN BASIC ENGINEERING
ASPEN BATCH DISTILLATION
ASPEN BATCH PROCESS DEVELOPER
ASPEN BATCH.21
ASPEN BLEND
ASPEN BUSINESS PROCESS
ASPEN CALC
ASPEN CAPABLE-TO-PROMISE
ASPEN CAPITAL COST ESTIMATOR
ASPEN CATREF
ASPEN CHROMATOGRAPHY
ASPEN CIM-IO
ASPEN COLLABORATIVE DEMAND MANAGEMENT
ASPEN COLLABORATIVE FORECASTING
ASPEN COMPLIANCE.21
ASPEN CUSTOM MODELER
ASPEN DECISION ANALYZER
ASPEN DISTIL
ASPEN DISTILLATION SYNTHESIS
ASPEN DYNAMICS
ASPEN EBRS
ASPEN ECONOMIC EVALUATION
ASPEN ENERGY ANALYZER
ASPEN ENTERPRISECONNECT
ASPEN EVENT.21
ASPEN FCC
ASPEN FIRED HEATER
ASPEN FLARE SYSTEM ANALYZER
ASPEN FRAMEWORK
ASPEN GENEALOGY
ASPEN HETRAN
ASPEN HTFS RESEARCH NETWORK
ASPEN HTFS+
ASPEN HYDROTREATER
ASPEN HYSYS AMINES
ASPEN HYSYS CRUDE
ASPEN HYSYS DYNAMICS
ASPEN HYSYS PIPELINE HYDRAULICS
ASPEN HYSYS PIPELINE HYDRAULICS-OLGAS 2-PHASE
ASPEN HYSYS UPSTREAM
ASPEN ICARUS
ASPEN ICARUS PROCESS EVALUATOR
ASPEN ICARUS PROJECT MANAGER
ASPEN IN-PLANT COST ESTIMATOR
ASPEN INFOPLUS.21
ASPEN INTEGRATION INFRASTRUCTURE
ASPEN INVENTORY PLANNER
ASPEN IQ
ASPEN MBO
ASPEN MIMI
ASPEN MODEL RUNNER
ASPEN MULTIVARIATE
ASPEN MUSE
ASPEN ONLINE DEPLOYMENT
ASPEN OPERATIONS DOMAIN MODEL
ASPEN OPSKPI
ASPEN ORION
ASPEN ORION XT
ASPEN OTISS
ASPEN PERFORMANCE SCORECARD
ASPEN PETROVANTAGE
ASPEN PIMS
ASPEN PINCH
ASPEN PLANT SCHEDULER
ASPEN PLATE EXCHANGER
ASPEN PLATE FIN EXCHANGER
ASPEN PLUS
ASPEN PLUS DYNAMICS
ASPEN PLUS ONLINE
ASPEN POLYMERS
ASPEN PROCESS ECONOMIC ANALYZER
ASPEN PROCESS EXPLORER
ASPEN PROCESS MANUAL
ASPEN PROCESS RECIPE
ASPEN PROCESS TOOLS
ASPEN PROPERTIES
ASPEN Q SERVER
ASPEN RATE-BASED DISTILLATION
ASPEN REFSYS
ASPEN RETAIL
ASPEN RICHARDSON
ASPEN ROLE-BASED VISUALIZATION
ASPEN SHELL & TUBE MECHANICAL
ASPEN SHELL TUBE EXCHANGER
ASPEN SIMULATION WORKBOOK
ASPEN SMARTSEP ADVANCED
ASPEN SMARTSIM
ASPEN SMARTSTEP
ASPEN STRATEGIC ANALYZER
ASPEN SUPPLY PLANNER
ASPEN TRANSITION MANAGER
ASPEN UTILITIES OPERATIONS
ASPEN UTILITIES PLANNER
ASPEN WATCH
ASPEN WATER
ASPEN WEB.21
ASPEN WEBMODELS
ASPEN WINRACE DATABASE
ASPEN ZYGAD
ASPENONE
ASPENTECH
ASSETBUILDER
B2B FOUNDATION
BATCH CONNECT
BATCHCAD
BATCHSEP
CALC
CAPABLE-TO-PROMISE
CATREF
COLLABORATIVE FORECASTING
COMTHERMO
DECISION ANALYZER
DMC PLUS
DYNAMICS
E!ASSIST
E!CEMS
ENTERPRISECONNECT
FIHR
FRAN
GCS
GENEALOGY
GRAPHICAL CONSOLE SYSTEM
HTFS RESEARCH NETWORK
HYDROCRACKER
HYSYS
HYSYS NEURAL NET
HYSYS OLI INTERFACE
HYSYS OPTIMIZER
HYSYS TACITE
INVENTORY PLANNER
IQMODEL POWERTOOLS
PIPE
PROFES
PROFILE.21
PUMPER LOG
SULSIM
TANK MANAGEMENT
TASC-MECHANICAL
TRAFLOW
WINRACE DATABASE

ASPYRA, INC.

4360 Park Terrace Dr Ste 220
Westlake Village, CA 91361
Tel.: (818) 880-6700
Fax: (818) 880-4398
Toll Free: (800) 437-9000
E-mail: coinfo@aspyra.com
Web Site: www.aspyra.com
Sales Range: $1-9.9 Million
Approx. Number Employees: 69
Year Founded: 1978
Business Description:
Healthcare Industry Clinical Information Systems Designer
S.I.C.: 7373; 7378
N.A.I.C.S.: 541512; 811212
Media: 7-10-13
Personnel:
Ademola Lawal *(CEO)*
Marina Varela *(Chief Acctg Officer & Sec)*
Brands & Products:
ASPYRA
CYBERLAB
CYBERMATE
CYBERMED
CYBERPATH
CYBERRAD
EXTENDING YOUR REACH

ASTEA INTERNATIONAL INC.

240 Gibraltar Rd
Horsham, PA 19044-2306
Tel.: (215) 682-2500
Fax: (215) 682-2515
Toll Free: (800) 347-7334
E-mail: info@astea.com
Web Site: www.astea.com
Approx. Rev.: $21,386,000
Approx. Number Employees: 175
Year Founded: 1979
Business Description:
Customer Relations Management Software & Services Developer, Marketer & Supporter
S.I.C.: 7372
N.A.I.C.S.: 334611; 511210
Export
Advertising Expenditures: $158,000
Media: 7
Personnel:
Zack B. Bergreen *(Chm & CEO)*
John Tobin *(Pres)*
Frederic Etskovitz *(CFO & Treas)*
Debbie Geiger *(VP-Mktg)*
Brands & Products:
ALLIANCE BIZ TALK
ALLIANCE BUSINESS INTELLIGENCE
ALLIANCE CONTACT CENTER
ALLIANCE CUSTOMER PORTAL
ALLIANCE DEPOT REPAIR
ALLIANCE DSE
ALLIANCE FIELD SERVICE
ALLIANCE GLOBAL DATABASE
ALLIANCE LINK
ALLIANCE LOGISTICS
ALLIANCE MARKETING
ALLIANCE MOBILE
ALLIANCE PROFESSIONAL SERVICES
ALLIANCE REPORTING
ALLIANCE SALES
ALLIANCE STUDIO
ASTEA
SERVICE SMART ENTERPRISE PROVEN

ASURE SOFTWARE, INC.

110 Wild Basin Dr Ste 100
Austin, TX 78746
Tel.: (512) 437-2700
Fax: (512) 437-2365
Toll Free: (888) 323-8835
E-mail: info@asuresoftware.com
Web Site: www.asuresoftware.com
Approx. Rev.: $10,033,000
Approx. Number Employees: 56
Year Founded: 1985
Business Description:
Software Developer
S.I.C.: 7373; 3669

Key to Media (For complete agency information see *The Advertising Red Books-Agencies* edition):
1. Bus. Publs. 2. Co-op T.V. 3. Catalogs & Directories. 4. Co-op Adv. 5. Consumer Mags. 6. D.M. to Bus. Estab.7. D.M. to Consumers 8. Daily Newsp. 9. Exhibits/Trade Shows 10. Foreign 11. Infomercial 12. Internet Adv.13. Multimedia 14. Network Radio 15. Network T.V. 16. Newsp. Distr. Mags. 17. Other 18. Outdoor (Posters, Transit) 19. Point of Purchase20. Premiums, Novelties 21. Product Samples 22. Special Events Mktg. 23. Spot Radio 24. Spot T.V. 25. Weekly Newsp. 26. Yellow Page Adv.

N.A.I.C.S.: 541512; 334290
Advertising Expenditures: $25,000
Media: 2-5-11-13
Distr.: Intl.; Natl.
Personnel:
David A. Sandberg *(Chm)*
Pat Goepel *(CEO)*
David Scoglio *(CFO)*
Brands & Products:
FORGENT

AT&T GOVERNMENT SOLUTIONS
(Unit of AT&T Communications Corp.)
1900 Gallows Rd
Vienna, VA 22182-3865
Tel.: (703) 506-5000
Fax: (703) 448-6890
Web Site: www.att.com/gov
Sales Range: $400-449.9 Million
Approx. Number Employees: 4,000
Year Founded: 1961
Business Description:
Integrated & Network-Enabled Information Technology Services
S.I.C.: 8748; 8742
N.A.I.C.S.: 541690; 541611
Media: 2-6-10-17
Distr.: Intl.; Natl.
Budget Set: May
Personnel:
Don Herring *(Sr VP)*
Xavier Williams *(Sr VP-Pub Sector & Healthcare)*
Gail Coles-Johnson *(Dir-HR)*

@XI COMPUTER CORPORATION
980 Calle Negocio
San Clemente, CA 92673
Tel.: (949) 498-0858
Fax: (949) 498-0257
Toll Free: (800) 432-0486
E-mail: sales@xicomputer.com
Web Site: www.xicomputer.com
E-Mail For Key Personnel:
Sales Director: sales@xicomputer.com
Sales Range: $50-74.9 Million
Approx. Number Employees: 30
Year Founded: 1987
Business Description:
Computer Systems Whslr
S.I.C.: 5734; 5045
N.A.I.C.S.: 443120; 423430
Export
Media: 6-13
Personnel:
Robert Bragaglia *(Pres & CEO)*
Brands & Products:
@XI
XI BLADERAIDER
XI MTOWER
XI NETRAIDER
XI NTOWER
XI POWERGO
XI WEBRAIDER
XICOMPUTER.COM

ATARI, INC.
(Sub. of Atari S.A.)
417 5th Ave
New York, NY 10016-2204
Tel.: (212) 726-6500
Fax: (212) 679-3424
E-mail: info@us.infogrames.com
Web Site: www.atari.com
Sales Range: $75-99.9 Million
Approx. Number Employees: 66
Year Founded: 1992
Business Description:
Creates, Publishes & Merchandises Interactive Entertainment & Consumer Software
S.I.C.: 7372; 5045
N.A.I.C.S.: 511210; 334611; 423430
Advertising Expenditures: $12,900,000
Personnel:
Jim Wilson *(CEO)*
Robert Mattes *(CFO)*
Kristen Keller *(Gen Counsel)*
Thom Kozik *(Exec VP)*
Yves Blehaut *(Sr VP)*
Owais Farooqui *(Sr VP-Digital Publ)*
Lee Jacobson *(Sr VP-Bus Dev & Licensing)*
Pierre Hintze *(VP-Product Dev)*
Lucas Bean *(Sr Dir-Online Mktg)*
Yollanda Bulla *(Mgr-Payroll, HR & Benefits)*
Advertising Agency:
Deep Focus
345 Hudson St 5th Fl
New York, NY 10014
Tel.: (212) 792-6800
Fax: (212) 792-6899

ATEX MEDIA COMMAND, INC.
(Sub. of Atex Group Ltd.)
5 Burlington Woods Dr Ste 100
Burlington, MA 01803
Tel.: (781) 275-2323
Fax: (781) 685-3276
E-mail: info@atex.com
Web Site: www.atex.com
Approx. Sls.: $11,900,000
Approx. Number Employees: 25
Business Description:
Computer Software Development
S.I.C.: 7371
N.A.I.C.S.: 541511
Media: 10
Personnel:
John Hawkins *(Grp CEO)*
Brands & Products:
ENTERPRISE SUITE
MULTI-MEDIA COMMAND
PRESTIGE
WORLD CLASS

ATS AUTOMATION TOOLING SYSTEMS INC.
250 Royal Oak Rd
Cambridge, ON N3H 4R6, Canada
Tel.: (519) 653-6500
Fax: (519) 653-6533
E-mail: info@atsautomation.com
Web Site: www.atsautomation.com
E-Mail For Key Personnel:
Sales Director: sales@atsautomation.com
Approx. Rev.: $717,859,553
Approx. Number Employees: 2,970
Year Founded: 1978
Business Description:
Turnkey Factory Automation Systems Mfr & Designer
S.I.C.: 7373
N.A.I.C.S.: 541512
Import Export
Media: 6-9-10-25
Distr.: Intl.
Budget Set: Sept.
Personnel:
David McAusland *(Chm)*
Anthony Caputo *(CEO)*
Maria Perrella *(CFO)*
Ronald Keyser *(CIO)*
Thierry Miremont *(CEO/Mng Dir-Photowatt France)*
Stewart McCuaig *(Gen Counsel, Corp Sec & VP)*
Hans-Dieter Baumtrog *(Sr VP-Life Sciences-ASG)*
Helmut Hock *(Sr VP-ASG Transportation)*
Marcus Horn *(Sr VP-ASG Products)*
Eric Kiisel *(Sr VP-ASG Energy & Industry)*
John Sun *(VP & Gen Mgr-Asg Asia)*
Chris Waters *(VP & Gen Mgr-Photowatt Ontario)*
Mike Fisher *(VP-Sls & Bus Dev)*
Patrice Pelletier *(VP-Sls & Mktg-Global)*
Hans Reidl *(VP-Fin)*
Ryan Mushlitz *(Mgr-Regional Sls-West Coast)*
Brands & Products:
AMPUSCAN
ATS AUTOMATION
COMPLIANT SOLUTIONS
FACTORY AUTOMATION SOLUTIONS
FLEXSYS
FLEXSYSPAK
FLEXTROLLEY
LYOSCAN
PHOTOWATT
ROTOFLEX
ROTOPER
SERVOCHASSIS
SMARTVISION
SUPERBOT
SUPERTRAK
TRAY HANDLER
TURN 6 LC

ATTACHMATE CORPORATION
(Joint Venture of Golden Gate Capital, Francisco Partners Management, LLC & Thoma Bravo, LLC)
1500 Dexter Ave N
Bellevue, WA 98109
Tel.: (206) 217-7100
Fax: (206) 217-7515
Toll Free: (800) 872-2829
E-mail: marketing@attachmate.com
Web Site: www.attachmate.com
Sales Range: $400-449.9 Million
Approx. Number Employees: 230
Year Founded: 1982
Business Description:
Developer of Host Connectivity, Systems Management, Security Management & Personal Computer Lifecycle Management Products & Services; Owned by Francisco Partners, Golden Gate Capital & Thoma Bravo LLC
S.I.C.: 7373; 7371; 7372; 7379; 8243
N.A.I.C.S.: 541512; 511210; 541511; 541519; 611420
Export
Advertising Expenditures: $3,000,000
Media: 2-4-5-8-10-13-17
Distr.: Direct to Consumer; Intl.; Natl.; Reg.
Budget Set: Dec.
Personnel:
Jeff Hawn *(Chm & CEO)*
Charles Sansbury *(CFO & COO)*
Robert Flynn *(Pres/Gen Mgr-Host Connectivity Solutions Bus Unit)*
Jay Gardner *(Pres/Gen Mgr-NetIQ Bus Unit)*
Ton Musters *(VP & Gen Mgr-EMEA)*
Kathleen Owens *(VP-Sls-North America)*
Eric Varness *(VP-Products & Mktg)*
Tom Gdowik *(Dir-Federal Sales)*
Brands & Products:
ATTACHMATE
ATTACHMATE FTPLUS
CRYPTOCONNECT ENCRYPTION TRANSPORT SYSTEM
DATABRIDGE
E-VANTAGE
EXTRA!
FILEXPRESS-XST
HOSTPRINT SERVER
INFOCONNECT
KEA! X
MYEXTRA!
MYEXTRA! SMART CONNECTOR ENTERPRISE EDITION
NETIQ
NETWIZARD
REFLECTION
SDK
SMART CONNECTOR
SYNAPTA
VERASTREAM
VIEWMASTER

AUCTIONS SYSTEMS AUCTIONEERS & APPRAISERS, INC.
951 W Watkins St
Phoenix, AZ 85007
Tel.: (602) 252-4842
Fax: (602) 275-8548
Toll Free: (800) 801-8880
E-mail: info@auctionandappraise.com
Web Site: www.auctionandappraise.com
Approx. Number Employees: 27
Year Founded: 1995
Business Description:
Auctioning Services
S.I.C.: 8748; 8111
N.A.I.C.S.: 541618; 541110
Media: 10-13
Personnel:
Deb Weidenhamer *(Pres)*

AUDIOCODES USA
(Sub. of AudioCodes Ltd.)
27 World's Fair Dr
Somerset, NJ 08873
Tel.: (732) 469-0880
Fax: (732) 469-2298
Toll Free: (800) 648-3647
E-mail: sales@ai-logix.com
Web Site: www.ai-logix.com
E-Mail For Key Personnel:
Sales Director: sales@ai-logix.com
Year Founded: 1991
Business Description:
Designer & Mfr of Computer Hardware & Software Communication Solutions Products
S.I.C.: 3577; 7373; 7379
N.A.I.C.S.: 334119; 541512; 541519
Media: 4-10

Key to Media (For complete agency information see *The Advertising Red Books-Agencies* edition):
1. Bus. Publs. 2. Cable T.V. 3. Catalogs & Directories. 4. Co-op Adv. 5. Consumer Mags. 6. D.M. to Bus. Estab.7. D.M. to Consumers 8. Daily Newsp. 9. Exhibits/Trade Shows 10. Foreign 11. Infomercial 12. Internet Adv.13. Multimedia 14. Network Radio 15. Network T.V. 16. Newsp. Distr. Mags. 17. Other 18. Outdoor (Posters, Transit) 19. Point of Purchase20. Premiums, Novelties 21. Product Samples 22. Special Events Mktg. 23. Spot Radio 24. Spot T.V. 25. Weekly Newsp. 26. Yellow Page Adv.

AudioCodes USA — (Continued)

Personnel:
Ron Romanchik *(VP-Call Recording Products)*

AUTHENTIDATE HOLDING CORP.

300 Connell Dr 5th Fl
Berkeley Heights, NJ 07922
Tel.: (908) 787-1700
Fax: (908) 673-9920
E-mail: help@authentidatehc.com
Web Site: www.authentidate.com
Approx. Rev.: $6,746,000
Approx. Number Employees: 59
Year Founded: 1985
Business Description:
Holding Company; Web-Based Authentication Services for Digital Documents
S.I.C.: 6719; 7372; 7379
N.A.I.C.S.: 551112; 511210; 541519
Advertising Expenditures: $37,000
Personnel:
J. Edward Sheridan *(Chm)*
O'Connell Benjamin *(Pres)*
Jan C. E. Wendenburg *(CEO)*
William A. Marshall *(CFO & Treas)*
Paul Skinner *(VP-Sls & Client Svcs)*
Gavin Stewart *(Sr Dir-Bus Dev)*
Zachary Madrigal *(Dir-Sls-Western Reg)*
Brands & Products:
AUTHENTIDATE
DOCSTAR
EPM
INSCRYBE
MDKEYBANK
Advertising Agencies:
Gigante Vaz Partners Advertising, Inc.
295 Lafayette St Fl 7
New York, NY 10012
Tel.: (212) 343-0004
Fax: (212) 343-0776

Rueckert Advertising
638 Albany Shaker Rd
Albany, NY 12211
Tel.: (518) 446-1091
Fax: (518) 446-1094
Toll Free: (800) 200-5236

AUTHORIZE.NET HOLDINGS, INC.

(Sub. of CyberSource Corporation)
808 E Utah Valley Dr
American Fork, UT 84003
Tel.: (801) 492-6450
Fax: (801) 492-6489
E-mail: resellersupport@authorize.net
Web Site: www.authorize.net
Sales Range: $75-99.9 Million
Approx. Number Employees: 200
Year Founded: 1987
Business Description:
Develops, Markets & Supports Integrated Products & Services for Customer Acquisition, Retention & Fraud Prevention Processes
S.I.C.: 6099; 8748
N.A.I.C.S.: 522320; 541690
Advertising Expenditures: $400,000
Media: 2-7-10

AUTODESK INC.

111 McInnis Pkwy
San Rafael, CA 94903-2773
Tel.: (415) 507-5000
Fax: (415) 507-5100
Web Site: usa.autodesk.com
Approx. Rev.: $1,951,800,000
Approx. Number Employees: 6,800
Year Founded: 1982
Business Description:
Digital Design Software & Services
S.I.C.: 7372
N.A.I.C.S.: 511210; 334611
Import Export
Advertising Expenditures: $18,800,000
Media: 2-4-5-6-7-8-10-13-17-22-26
Distr.: Intl.; Natl.
Personnel:
Crawford W. Beveridge *(Chm)*
Carl Bass *(Pres & CEO)*
Mark J. Hawkins *(CFO & Exec VP)*
Chris Bradshaw *(CMO & Sr VP)*
Pascal di Fronzo *(Gen Counsel, Sec & Sr VP)*
Jan Becker, Sr. *(Sr VP-HR & Corp Real Estate)*
Jay Bhatt *(Sr VP-Architecture, Engrg & Construction)*
Steve Blum *(Sr VP-Worldwide Sls & Svcs)*
Moonhie Chin *(Sr VP-Strategic Plng & Ops)*
Amar Hanspal *(Sr VP-Platform Solutions & Emerging Bus)*
Robert Buzz Kross *(Sr VP-Mfg Solutions)*
Marc Petit *(Sr VP-Media & Entertainment)*
Sue Pirri *(VP-Fin)*
Pam Pollace *(VP-Corp Comm)*
Douglas D. Eberhard *(Sr Dir-AEC Sls Dev)*
Maura Ginty *(Sr Mgr-Strategic Res & Innovation)*
W. Davis Smith *(Mgr-Utility Solutions)*
Daniel Zucker *(Mgr-Social Media)*
Brands & Products:
3-DEC
3DS MAX
ADI
AEC AUTHORITY
ALGOR
ALIAS
ALIASSTUDIO
ATC
AUGI
AUTOCAD
AUTOCAD LEARNING ASSISTANCE
AUTOCAD REVIT SERIES
AUTOCAD SIMULATOR
AUTOCAD SQL EXTENSION
AUTOCAD SQL INTERFACE
AUTODESK
AUTODESK DESIGN REVIEW
AUTODESK DWF
AUTODESK ENVISION
AUTODESK INTENT
AUTODESK INVENTOR
AUTODESK LAND DESKTOP
AUTODESK MAP 3D
AUTODESK MAPGUIDE
AUTODESK MOLDFLOW ADVISER
AUTODESK MOLDFLOW COMMUNICATOR
AUTODESK MOLDFLOW INSIGHT
AUTODESK ONSITE ENTERPRISE
AUTODESK ONSITE VIEW
AUTODESK PRE-PLAN
AUTODESK PRODUCTSTREAM
AUTODESK RASTER DESIGN
AUTODESK REALDWG
AUTODESK REVIT BUILDING
AUTODESK REVIT STRUCTURE
AUTODESK STREAMLINE
AUTODESK VAULT
AUTODESK VIZ
AUTOLISP
AUTOSHAPES
AUTOSKETCH
AUTOSNAP
AUTOTRACK
BACKBURNER
BURN
BUZZSAW
CAICE
CHARACTER STUDIO
CINESTREAM
CIVIL 3D
CLEANER
CLEANER CENTRAL
CLEARSCALE
COLOUR WARPER
COMBUSTION
CONSTRUCTWARE
CONTENT EXPLORER
DEC
DESIGN DOCTOR
DESIGN SERVER
DESIGN WEB FORMAT
DESIGNCENTER
DESIGNKIDS
DESIGNPROF
DESIGNSTUDIO
DISCREET
DWG
DWG TRUECONVERT
DWG TRUEVIEW
DXF
ECOTECT
FACE ROBOT
FBX
FEMPRO
FILMBOX
FIRE
FLAME
FMDESKTOP
FREEWHEEL
FROST
GMAX
GREEN BUILDING STUDIO
HEIDI
HUMANIK
I-DROP
IMAGEMODELER
IMOUT
INCINERATOR
INFERNO
INVENTOR
INVENTOR LT
KYNAPSE
LANDXPLORER
LUSTRE
MATCHMOVER
MAYA
MECHANICAL DESKTOP
MOLDFLOW
MOLDFLOW PLASTICS INSIGHT
MOTIONBUILDER
MOVIMENTO
MUDBOX
NAVISWORKS
OBJECTARX
OPTICORE
POLARSNAP
PORTFOLIOWALL
PROJECTPOINT
REACTOR
REAL-TIME ROTO
REALVIZ
RETIMER
ROBOT
SHOWCASE
SHOWMOTION
SKETCHBOOK
SMOKE
SOFTIMAGE
STEERINGWHEELS
STITCHER
STONE
TOPOBASE
TOXIK
TRUSTEDDWG
U-VIS
VIEWCUBE
VISUAL CONSTRUCTION
VISUAL LISP
VISUAL SURVEY
VOICE REALITY
VOLO
VTOUR
WIRE
WIRETAP
WIRETAPCENTRAL
XSI
Advertising Agencies:
Landis Communications Inc.
1388 Sutter St Ste 901
San Francisco, CA 94109
Tel.: (415) 561-0888
Fax: (415) 561-0778

Wikreate
145 Vallejo St Ste 6
San Francisco, CA 94111
Tel.: (415) 362-0440
Fax: (415) 362-0430

AUTOMATIC DATA PROCESSING, INC.

1 ADP Blvd
Roseland, NJ 07068-1728
Tel.: (973) 974-5000
Fax: (973) 974-3334
Toll Free: (800) 225-5237
E-mail: public_relations@adp.com
Web Site: www.adp.com
Approx. Rev.: $9,879,500,000
Approx. Number Employees: 51,000
Year Founded: 1949
Business Description:
Computerized Transaction Processing, Record Keeping & Information Services
S.I.C.: 7374; 7379; 7389; 8721
N.A.I.C.S.: 518210; 541219; 541519; 561499
Media: 2-4-7-10-13
Distr.: Natl.
Budget Set: May
Personnel:
Gary C. Butler *(Pres & CEO)*
Carlos A. Rodriguez *(Pres & COO)*
David Marini *(Mng Dir-Strategic Advisory Svcs Grp)*
Leon Busch *(VP & Gen Mgr-Procure-to-Pay Solutions)*
Jennifer Pineda *(Dir-Mktg)*
James Fabin *(Sr Mgr-Product Mktg)*
Michael Gerard Quigley *(Mgr-Major Accounts District)*

Brands & Products:
ADP
THE BUSINESS BEHIND BUSINESS
Advertising Agencies:
Cohn & Wolfe
200 Fifth Ave
New York, NY 10010
Tel.: (212) 798-9700
Fax: (212) 329-9900

Manning Selvage & Lee
1170 Peachtree St NE Ste 400
Atlanta, GA 30309-7677
Tel.: (404) 875-1444
Fax: (404) 892-1274

Promark Direct Inc.
300 N Midland Ave Ste 2
Saddle Brook, NJ 07663-5723
Tel.: (201) 398-9000
Fax: (201) 398-9212
Toll Free: (800) 404-1900

St. Jacques Marketing
60 Washington St Ste 203
Morristown, NJ 07960
Tel.: (973) 829-0858
Fax: (973) 624-3836
Toll Free: (800) 708-9467

Zeta Interactive
716 Main St
Boonton, NJ 07005
Tel.: (973) 316-9696
Fax: (973) 316-8006

AUTOMATION MAILING AND SHIPPING SOLUTIONS, INC.
1138-58 W 9th St
Cleveland, OH 44113-1060
Tel.: (216) 241-4487
Fax: (216) 241-5918
Toll Free: (800) 883-7935
E-mail: service@mailshipsolutions.com
Web Site: www.mailshipsolutions.com
Approx. Sls.: $2,000,000
Approx. Number Employees: 16
Year Founded: 1943
Business Description:
Electronic Postage Meters, Interfaced Electronic Scales, Postal Bar Coding Software/Hardware, InkjetBar Code Addressing Systems, Folders/ Inserters, Tabbers/Labelers, Letter Openers, Mailroom Design & Furniture, Stapling, Tacking & Stitching Machines, Staples, Stitching Wire, Pressure Sensitive Tapes, Water Activated Tapes
S.I.C.: 5085; 5113
N.A.I.C.S.: 423840; 424130
Import Export
Media: 2-4-5-6-7-9-10-21-26
Distr.: Direct to Consumer; Natl.
Personnel:
James W. Johnson *(Pres & CEO)*
Brands & Products:
AMSS
DUPLO
FRANCOTYP-POSTALIA
SENCO

AUTONOMY, INC.
(Sub. of Autonomy Corporation plc)
1 Market Plz 19th Fl Spear Twr
San Francisco, CA 94105
Tel.: (415) 243-9955
Fax: (415) 243-9984
E-mail: autonomy@autonomy.com
Web Site: www.autonomy.com
Sales Range: $125-149.9 Million
Approx. Number Employees: 554
Year Founded: 1988
Business Description:
Portal Infrastructure Software Mfr
S.I.C.: 7372; 7371
N.A.I.C.S.: 511210; 541511
Media: 2-4-7-10-13-22
Personnel:
Stouffer Egan *(CEO)*
Greg Neustaetter *(Product Dir-Mgmt-eDiscovery)*
Brands & Products:
COLLABORATIVE CLASSIFIER
EXTRACTOR
FEDERATOR
K2 CATALOG
K2 DEVELOPER
K2 ENTERPRISE
K2 SPIDER
KEYVIEW
LIQUIDOFFICE
MEDICLAIM
PROFILER
PUBLISHER
RESPONSE
TELEFORM
ULTRASEEK
VERITY

AUTONOMY PLEASANTON
(Formerly ZANTAZ Inc.)
(Sub. of Autonomy Corporation plc)
5758 West Las Positas Blvd
Pleasanton, CA 94588
Tel.: (925) 598-3000
Fax: (925) 598-3145
Toll Free: (800) 636-0095
E-mail: autonomy@autonomy.com
Web Site: www.autonomy.com
Approx. Sls.: $23,500,000
Approx. Number Employees: 300
Year Founded: 1996
Business Description:
Information Retention & Discovery Management Solutions
S.I.C.: 3572; 7389
N.A.I.C.S.: 334112; 519190
Media: 10
Personnel:
Michael Sullivan *(CEO-Autonomy Protect-Enterprise Market)*
Frank Frazier *(Sr Product Mgr)*
Brands & Products:
DIGITAL SAFE
EAS
INTROSPECT
TRUSTED. PROVEN.

AVAMAR TECHNOLOGIES, INC.
(Sub. of EMC Corporation)
135 Technology Dr Ste 100
Irvine, CA 92618-2350
Tel.: (949) 743-5100
Fax: (866) 818-9864
Web Site: www.emc.com
Sales Range: $25-49.9 Million
Approx. Number Employees: 105
Year Founded: 2000
Business Description:
Data Storage, Management & Protection Software
S.I.C.: 7371
N.A.I.C.S.: 541511
Media: 13
Personnel:
Jedidiah Yueh *(Founder)*
Scott Bledsoe *(Sr VP-Worldwide Sls)*
Brands & Products:
AVAMAR
AXION
BACKUP AND BEYOND
REPLICATOR

AVANADE INC.
818 Stewart St Ste 400
Seattle, WA 98101
Tel.: (206) 239-5600
Fax: (206) 239-5605
Web Site: www.avanade.com
Sales Range: $50-74.9 Million
Approx. Number Employees: 8,000
Business Description:
Information Technology Consultants
S.I.C.: 8243
N.A.I.C.S.: 611420
Personnel:
Adam Warby *(CEO)*
Andrew White *(COO)*
Chris Miller *(CIO)*
Howard Kilman *(Chief Leadership Officer)*
Ashish Kumar *(Pres-Europe)*
Aziz Virani *(Pres-North America)*
Ian Jordan *(Exec VP-Global Sls & Mktg)*
Joe Mendel *(Exec VP-HR)*
Mick Slattery *(Exec VP-Global Delivery)*
Advertising Agency:
Bradham-Hamilton Advertising, Inc.
321 Wingo Way Ste 103
Mount Pleasant, SC 29464
Tel.: (843) 971-8660
Fax: (843) 971-8663

AVANT TECHNOLOGIES OF PR, INC.
Rd 156 Caguas W Industrial Park
Bldg 39
Caguas, PR 00725
Tel.: (787) 746-9191
Fax: (787) 746-7131
E-mail: atsales@avantpr.com
Web Site: www.avantworld.com
Approx. Number Employees: 120
Business Description:
Computer Mfr; Networked Digital Video Surveillance Systems Mfr & Designer
S.I.C.: 3571; 7382
N.A.I.C.S.: 334111; 561621
Media: 10
Personnel:
Luis Diaz *(CEO)*
Alberto Diaz *(Mgr-Mktg)*
Brands & Products:
AVANT TECHNOLOGIES
CITY SENTINAL
DVR ATM
EVIDENT
VIDEO SENTINEL
VZIP RACK

AVATAR SYSTEMS, INC.
2801 Network Blvd Ste 210
Frisco, TX 75034
Tel.: (972) 720-1800
Fax: (972) 720-1900
E-mail: cshreve@avatarsystems.net
Web Site: www.avatarsystems.net
Sales Range: $1-9.9 Million
Approx. Number Employees: 29
Year Founded: 1996
Business Description:
Oil & Gas Computer Applications
S.I.C.: 7372; 7373
N.A.I.C.S.: 511210; 541512
Media: 7-10
Personnel:
Robert C. Shreve, Jr. *(Chm, Pres & CEO)*

AVATECH SOLUTIONS, INC.
(Name Changed to RAND WORLDWIDE, INC.)

AVECTRA INC.
No 5 7901 Jones Branch Dr
McLean, VA 22102-3338
Tel.: (703) 394-0980
Fax: (703) 394-0985
E-mail: info@avectra.com
Web Site: www.avectra.com
Sales Range: $25-49.9 Million
Approx. Number Employees: 140
Year Founded: 1993
Business Description:
Computer Software Development & Applications
S.I.C.: 7371
N.A.I.C.S.: 541511
Personnel:
Richard Davis *(Chm & CEO)*
Barry Malek *(CEO)*
Patrick Dorsey *(VP-Mktg)*
Brands & Products:
AVECTRA
NETFORUM
Advertising Agency:
Strategic Communications Group
1400 Spring St Ste 330
Silver Spring, MD 20910
Tel.: (301) 408-4500
Fax: (301) 408-4506
(On-Demand Membership Management Software)

AVERICOM LLC
The Bowman Center 1156 Bowman Rd Ste 200
Mount Pleasant, SC 29464
Toll Free: (866) 910-9610
E-mail: info@avericom.com
Web Site: www.avericom.com
Approx. Number Employees: 4
Year Founded: 2000
Business Description:
Internet Development & Support Services
S.I.C.: 7375
N.A.I.C.S.: 518111
Media: 2-13
Personnel:
Peter W. Bowman *(Pres)*

AVF CONSULTING, INC.
1220-C E Joppa Rd Ste 514
Baltimore, MD 21286
Tel.: (410) 296-5100
Fax: (410) 296-5330
E-mail: info@avfconsulting.com
Web Site: www.avfconsulting.com
E-Mail For Key Personnel:
Marketing Director: ktran@avfconsulting.com
Approx. Rev.: $255,000
Approx. Number Employees: 25
Year Founded: 1986

Key to Media (For complete agency information see *The Advertising Red Books-Agencies* edition):
1. Bus. Publs. 2. Cable T.V. 3. Catalogs & Directories. 4. Co-op Adv. 5. Consumer Mags. 6. D.M. to Bus. Estab.7. D.M. to Consumers 8. Daily Newsp. 9. Exhibits/Trade Shows 10. Foreign 11. Infomercial 12. Internet Adv.13. Multimedia 14. Network Radio 15. Network T.V. 16. Newsp. Distr. Mags. 17. Other 18. Outdoor (Posters, Transit) 19. Point of Purchase20. Premiums, Novelties 21. Product Samples 22. Special Events Mktg. 23. Spot Radio 24. Spot T.V. 25. Weekly Newsp. 26. Yellow Page Adv.

AVF Consulting, Inc. — (Continued)

Business Description:
ERP Business Management Applications & IT Solutions
S.I.C.: 7373; 7372
N.A.I.C.S.: 541512; 511210
Media: 2-10
Personnel:
Andrew Fass *(Pres)*
Larry Caudill *(CFO & Cotroller)*
Jeremy Fass *(Exec VP)*
Karen Tran *(Mgr-Mktg)*

AVNET TECHNOLOGY SOLUTIONS

(Div. of Avnet, Inc.)
8700 S Price Rd
Tempe, AZ 85284-2608
Tel.: (480) 794-6900
Fax: (480) 794-6890
Toll Free: (800) 409-1483
E-mail: ats-info@avnet.com
Web Site: www.ats.avnet.com
Sales Range: $1-4.9 Billion
Approx. Number Employees: 1,800
Year Founded: 1989
Business Description:
Computer Products, Software, Networking & Enterprise Solutions Distr
S.I.C.: 5734
N.A.I.C.S.: 443120
Advertising Expenditures: $800,000
Media: 2-4-5-7-10-13-19-20-21-22
Personnel:
Richard Hamada *(Pres & COO)*
Jeff Bawol *(Pres-Americas)*
K. P. Tang *(Pres-Asia Pacific)*
Graeme Watt *(Pres-EMEA)*
Erin Lewin *(Gen Counsel & VP)*
Fred Cuen *(Sr VP, Gen Mgr-IBM Solutions & Avnet Canada)*
Sergio Farache *(Sr VP & Gen Mgr-Latin America & Carribbean)*
Tony Vottima *(Sr VP & Gen Mgr-HP Solutions)*
Rick Alvarez *(Sr VP-Sls Acceleration)*
Philip Gallagher *(Sr VP-Avnet Inc., Global Pres-Avnet Tech Solutions)*
Dennis O'Connell *(Sr VP-Ops)*
Ger Purcell *(Sr VP-Global Info Sys)*
Steve Chlupsa *(Grp VP-Fin)*
Darren Adams *(VP & Gen Mgr-Cisco Solutions)*
Larry Fulop *(VP & Gen Mgr-Enterprise OEM)*
Steve Kedzior *(VP & Gen Mgr-Svcs)*
Chris Swahn *(VP & Gen Mgr-Oracle Solutions)*
Michael Douglass *(VP-Sls)*
Jim Kebert *(VP-Fin Solutions)*
Phyllis McCullagh *(VP-Field Sls-HP Bus Unit)*
Jack Morris *(VP-Sls)*
Kaylene Moss *(VP-HR)*
Cheryl Neal *(VP-Mktg)*
Cookie Serrano *(VP-Fin-US & Canada)*
Alison Challman *(Dir-Strategic Mktg)*
Henry Godwin *(Dir-Middle East & Africa Reg)*
Julie Jones *(Dir-Mktg & Sls Acceleration)*
Matt Wight *(Mgr-Svcs Dev)*
Brands & Products:
ENTERPRISE SOLUTIONS
HALLMARK
PARTNER SOLUTIONS
Advertising Agency:
Off Madison Ave
5555 E Van Buren St Ste 215
Phoenix, AZ 85008
Tel.: (480) 505-4500
Fax: (480) 505-4501

AVOCENT CORPORATION

(Div. of Emerson Network Power)
4991 Corporate Dr
Huntsville, AL 35805-6201
Tel.: (256) 430-4000
Fax: (256) 430-4030
Toll Free: (866) 286-2368
E-mail: sales@avocent.com
Web Site: www.avocent.com
E-Mail For Key Personnel:
Sales Director: sales@avocent.com
Approx. Sls.: $657,134,000
Approx. Number Employees: 1,099
Year Founded: 1981
Business Description:
Computer Peripheral Products Mfr
S.I.C.: 3577; 7373
N.A.I.C.S.: 334119; 541512
Advertising Expenditures: $7,517,000
Media: 2-4-5-10-13
Personnel:
Doyle C. Weeks *(Pres & COO)*
Eugene F. Mulligan *(Sr VP-Ops)*
Julie C. Yarbrough *(VP-HR)*
Brands & Products:
ACS
ADMINWORKS
ALWAYS ON. ALWAYS AVOCENT.
AMIQ
AMWORKS
AMX
AUTOTUNING
AUTOVIEW
AVOCENT
AVOCENT CARE
AVRIQ
CCM
COMMANDER
COMPANION
CONNECTIONS
CPS
CYCLADES
CYCLADES CS
DAMBRACKAS VIDEO COMPRESSION
DS1800
DSADMIN
DSAUTH
DSI5100
DSR
DSRIQ
DSVIEW
DSWEBVIEW
DWORKS
EMERGE
ESP
EVR
HMIQDHDD
HMIQDI
HMIQSHDI
HMX
HMX 1050
HMX 1070
HMX 2050
HMX MANAGER
INTEGRATOR
KVM
KVM/NET
KVM/NETPLUS
LANDESK
LONGVIEW
LONGVIEW IP
LONGVIEW WIRELESS
MERGEPOINT
ONBOARD
ONSITE
OSCAR
OUTLOOK
PM
THE POWER OF BEING THERE
SECURE RACK MANAGEMENT
SONICSENTINEL
SONIVADMIN
SPC
SWITCHVIEW
SWITCHVIEW IP
TAKE COMMAND
VCONSOLE
XP

AXEDA SYSTEMS INC.

Unit 3 25 Forbes Blvd
Foxboro, MA 02035-2873
Tel.: (508) 337-9200
Fax: (508) 337-9201
E-mail: info@axeda.com
Web Site: www.axeda.com
Approx. Number Employees: 116
Business Description:
Device Relationship Management Software Developer
S.I.C.: 7373
N.A.I.C.S.: 541512
Advertising Expenditures: $435,000
Media: 2
Personnel:
Dale Calder *(Founder)*
Rachael T. McCarthy *(CFO)*
Brian Anderson *(VP-Mktg)*
Brands & Products:
ACCESS
ADMINISTRATION
AGENT
AGENT PROJECT CREATION
AXEDA
AXEDA ACCESS
AXEDA ADMINISTRATION
AXEDA AGENT CUSTOMIZATION
AXEDA APPLICATION ADMINISTRATION
AXEDA DASHBOARD
AXEDA DEVICE
AXEDA DEVICE RELATIONSHIP MANAGEMENT SYSTEM
AXEDA DRM
AXEDA ENTERPRISE
AXEDA ENTERPRISE SDK
AXEDA POLICY MANGER
AXEDA QUERY STUDIO
AXEDA REPORT
AXEDA SERVICE
AXEDA SERVICELINK
AXEDA SERVICELINK BASICS
AXEDA SOFTWARE MANAGEMENT
AXEDA USAGE
ENTERPRISE SDK
FACTORYSOFT OPC
FIREWALL-FRIENDLY
GLOBALACCESSSERVER
POLICY MANAGER
SERVICE
SMARTLINK
SOFTWARE MANAGEMENT
USAGE

AXS-ONE INC.

(Div. of Unify Corporation)
Meadow Office Complex 301 Rte 17 N
Rutherford, NJ 07070
Tel.: (201) 935-3400
Fax: (201) 935-7678
Toll Free: (800) 828-7660
E-mail: info@axsone.com
Web Site: www.axsone.com
Approx. Rev.: $13,423,000
Approx. Number Employees: 81
Business Description:
Electronic Commerce Solutions
S.I.C.: 7372; 7371; 7373; 7376; 7379
N.A.I.C.S.: 511210; 541511; 541512; 541513; 541519
Media: 7-10
Personnel:
Mark T. Bygraves *(Sr VP & Gen Mgr)*
Kevin R. Kane *(VP-Sls)*
Debbie Thornton *(VP-Corp Mktg)*
Diederik Jordaan *(Gen Mgr-Prof Svcs)*
Brands & Products:
ACCESS TOMORROW TODAY
ACCOUNTS PAYABLE
AXS-LINK FOR FILE SYSTEM ARCHIVING
AXS-ONE
AXS-ONE CASE MANAGEMENT
AXS-ONE CLARITY
AXS-ONE CONNECTORS
AXS-ONE SUPERVISION
AXS-POINT
AXS-POINT CENTRAL
BUDGET CYCLE MANAGEMENT (BCM)
CENTRAL
COMPLIANCE PLATFORM
DYNAMIC DATA MIGRATOR
E-CELLERATOR
GENERAL LEDGER
INVENTORY CONTROL
MICROSOFT EXCHANGE
PROCUREMENT CYCLE MANAGEMENT
.PST MANAGEMENT
RAPID-AXS
THE RECORDS COMPLIANCE MANAGEMENT COMPANY
RETENTION MANAGER
SAP
SMART
SWIFT AXS
TRANSAXS CUSTOMER
TRANSAXS PROCUREMENT
XML USER INTERFACE

AZUL SYSTEMS, INC.

1600 Plymouth St
Mountain View, CA 94043
Tel.: (650) 230-6500
Fax: (650) 230-6600
E-mail: info@azulsystems.com
Web Site: www.azulsystems.com
Approx. Number Employees: 150
Year Founded: 2002
Business Description:
Data Processing Services; Data Networking
S.I.C.: 7374
N.A.I.C.S.: 518210
Personnel:
Scott Sellers *(Co-Founder, Pres & CEO)*
Gil Tene *(Co-Founder, CTO & VP-Tech)*
Shyam Pillalamarri *(Co-Founder & VP-Software Engrg)*

Advertising Agency:
The Hoffman Agency
70 N 2nd St
San Jose, CA 95113-1204
Tel.: (408) 286-2611
Fax: (408) 286-0133

B2SYSTEMS, INC.

5951 Encina Rd Ste 107
Goleta, CA 93117
Tel.: (805) 692-2222
Fax: (805) 964-4666
Toll Free: (800) 563-9220
E-mail: info@b2systems.com
Web Site: www.b2systems.com
Approx. Sls.: $3,000,000
Approx. Number Employees: 5
Year Founded: 1994
Business Description:
Data Integration Services
S.I.C.: 7373; 7371
N.A.I.C.S.: 541512; 541511
Export
Media: 10
Brands & Products:
B2 SYSTEMS
IDEO
REPORTPAINTER
SMARTSTAR
SQL INTEGRATOR

BACKUPWORKS.COM INC.

3621 MacArthur Blvd Ste 107
Santa Ana, CA 92704-6843
Tel.: (714) 751-2636
Fax: (714) 751-2637
E-mail: info@backupworks.com
Web Site: www.backupworks.com
Year Founded: 1999
Business Description:
Data Storage Products & Services
S.I.C.: 7373; 5932
N.A.I.C.S.: 541512; 453310
Media: 4-13
Brands & Products:
ADAPTEC
BACKUPWORKS.COM
CERTANCE/SEAGATE
LTO ULTRIUM

BADGER AIR BRUSH COMPANY

9128 W Belmont Ave
Franklin Park, IL 60131-2806
Tel.: (847) 678-3104
Fax: (847) 671-4352
Toll Free: (800) 247-2787
E-mail: info@badgerairbrush.com
Web Site: www.badgerairbrush.com
Approx. Number Employees: 70
Year Founded: 1963
Business Description:
Airbrushes & Related Accessories Mfr
S.I.C.: 3952
N.A.I.C.S.: 339942
Import Export
Media: 2-3-4-5-6-7-8-10-11-17-19-23-24-26
Distr.: Intl.; Natl.
Personnel:
Kenneth Schlotfeldt *(Pres)*
Brands & Products:
AIR-OPAQUE
AIR-TEX
ANTHEM
BADGER
BAKERY
BILLION-AIR
BRITE WHITE
CRESCENDO
CYCLONE
FAST BLAST
FOTO
FREAKFLEX
FRISKET
HOBBY PAL
HYBRID
IMAGINE AIR
MILLION-AIR
MODEL PAL
MODELFLEX
NAIL FLAIR
NEON
NEON FABRIC
NO-TACK
OMNI
PROPEL
RE-COIL
RENEGADE
SOTAR
SPECTRA-TEX
THAYER & CHANDLER
TOTALLY TATTOO
TRILLION-AIR
UNIVERSAL
VEGA
WHIRLWIND
X-AIR

BAE SYSTEMS-COMMUNICATION, NAVIGATION, IDENTIFICATION & RECONNAISSANCE

(Branch of BAE Systems-Communications, Navigation, Identification & Reconnaissance)
450 Pulaski Rd
Greenlawn, NY 11740-1606
Tel.: (631) 261-7000
Fax: (631) 262-8020
Web Site:
www.eis.na.baesystems.com
Approx. Number Employees: 600
Business Description:
Avionics, Navigation & Military Communication Services
S.I.C.: 3812
N.A.I.C.S.: 334511
Media: 2-4-7-10-17
Distr.: Intl.; Natl.
Budget Set: Jan.
Advertising Agencies:
The Podesta Group
1001 G St NW Ste 900 E
Washington, DC 20001
Tel.: (202) 393-1010
Fax: (202) 393-5510
Public Affairs

Weber Shandwick-Minneapolis
8000 Norman Ctr Dr Ste 400
Minneapolis, MN 55437
Tel.: (952) 832-5000
Fax: (952) 831-8241
Agency of Record

BAE SYSTEMS MOBILITY & PROTECTION SYSTEMS

(Sub. of BAE Systems Products Group)
9113 LeSaint Dr
Fairfield, OH 45014-5453
Tel.: (513) 881-9800
Fax: (513) 881-1840
Toll Free: (800) 697-0307
Web Site: www.baesystem.com
Approx. Number Employees: 700
Year Founded: 1896
Business Description:
Armored Vehicles; Personal, Industrial, Corporate & Government Security
S.I.C.: 7381
N.A.I.C.S.: 561613
Media: 2-7-8-10
Personnel:
Matt Foster *(Dir-Category & Firearms Accessories)*
Ava Keller *(Dir-Mktg & PR)*

BAE SYSTEMS PRODUCTS GROUP

(Group of BAE Systems Inc.)
13386 International Pkwy
Jacksonville, FL 32218
Tel.: (904) 741-5400
Fax: (904) 741-5403
Toll Free: (800) 654-9943
Web Site: www.baesystems.com/WorldwideLocations/UnitedStates/Locations/JacksonvilleFlorida/bae_facil_prodgroup_jax.html
Approx. Rev.: $2,360,884,000
Approx. Number Employees: 8,150
Year Founded: 1996
Business Description:
Security & Business Intelligence Solutions
S.I.C.: 3842; 3699; 7382
N.A.I.C.S.: 339113; 335999; 561621
Export
Advertising Expenditures: $1,000,000
Media: 2-7-10-13-17-22
Personnel:
Scott O'Brien *(Pres)*
Brands & Products:
911EP
AMERICAN BODY ARMOR
AUTOLOCK
B-SQUARE
BIANCHI
BLUE LIGHTNING
BLUE WONDER
BODY BUNKER
BOR-CAP
B.O.S.S.
BREAK-FREE
BREAK FREE CLP
CENTURION
CLP
DEFENSE TECHNOLOGY
DUTY GEAR
EVI-PAQ
EXOTECH
FEDERAL LABORATORIES
FIRST DEFENSE
FLEX-CUF
FRISKMASTER
GREGORY
HATCH
IDENTICATOR
KEY-CUFF
KLEEN BORE
LIGHTNING POWDER
MACE
MONADNOCK
NIK
ODV
OPERATOR
PORTAL LADDER
PR-24
PROTECH
QUIKSTEP
RADARVISION
RADORVISION
SAFARILAND
SPEEDFEED
SPIT NET
THERMAL AIR
TRANZPORT HOOD
TREADPRINT
V-TOP
WETWOP
X11
XTREME
ZERO-G
Advertising Agencies:
Dalton Agency
140 W Monroe St
Jacksonville, FL 32202
Tel.: (904) 398-5222
Fax: (904) 398-5220
Toll Free: (888) 409-2691

Integrated Corporate Relations, Inc.
761 Main Ave
Norwalk, CT 06851
Tel.: (203) 682-8200
Fax: (203) 682-8201

BAGS & BOWS

(Formerly VeriPack.com, Inc.)
(Sub. of Deluxe Small Business Services)
500 Main St
Groton, MA 01471
Toll Free: (800) 225-8155
Web Site:
www.bagsandbowsonline.com
Sales Range: $10-24.9 Million
Approx. Number Employees: 30
Business Description:
Packing & Shipping Services
S.I.C.: 7389
N.A.I.C.S.: 561439
Media: 4
Personnel:
Claire Poulin *(VP-Mktg)*

BANCTEC, INC.

(Holding of Welsh Carson Anderson & Stowe, LLC)
2701 E Grauwyler Rd
Irving, TX 75061-3414
Mailing Address:
PO Box 660204
Dallas, TX 75266-0204
Tel.: (972) 821-4000
Fax: (972) 821-4877
Toll Free: (800) 226-2832
E-mail: inquiries@banctec.com
Web Site: www.banctec.com
Approx. Rev.: $379,479,008
Approx. Number Employees: 2,670
Year Founded: 1972
Business Description:
Document & Content Processing, Payment Processing & Information Technology Services
S.I.C.: 7374; 7373; 7389
N.A.I.C.S.: 518210; 541512; 561499
Export
Media: 7-10-13
Distr.: Intl.; Natl.
Personnel:
J. Coley Clark *(Chm & CEO)*
Jeffrey D. Cushman *(CFO & Sr VP)*
Mark D. Fairchild *(CTO & Pres-BancTec Technologies)*
Michael Peplow *(Pres-Europe, Middle East & Africa, Sr VP)*

Key to Media (For complete agency information see *The Advertising Red Books-Agencies* edition):
1. Bus. Publs. 2. Cable T.V. 3. Catalogs & Directories. 4. Co-op Adv. 5. Consumer Mags. 6. D.M. to Bus. Estab.7. D.M. to Consumers
8. Daily Newsp. 9. Exhibits/Trade Shows 10. Foreign 11. Infomercial 12. Internet Adv.13. Multimedia 14. Network Radio
15. Network T.V. 16. Newsp. Distr. Mags. 17. Other 18. Outdoor (Posters, Transit) 19. Point of Purchase20. Premiums, Novelties
21. Product Samples 22. Special Events Mktg. 23. Spot Radio 24. Spot T.V. 25. Weekly Newsp. 26. Yellow Page Adv.

BancTec, Inc. — (Continued)

Bob Robinson *(Gen Counsel, Sec & VP)*
Chuck Corbin *(VP-Healthcare Industry Grp)*
Malcolm J. Gurney *(Gen Mgr)*

Brands & Products:
BANCTEC

BANDWIDTH.COM, INC.

4001 Weston Pkwy
Cary, NC 27513
Tel.: (919) 297-1100
Fax: (919) 238-9917
Toll Free: (800) 808-5150
E-mail: customercare@bandwidth.com
Web Site: www.bandwidth.com
Sales Range: $10-24.9 Million
Approx. Number Employees: 80
Year Founded: 1999
Business Description:
Business Telecommunications Services
S.I.C.: 4812; 7379
N.A.I.C.S.: 517212; 541519
Media: 10-13
Personnel:
Henry Kaestner *(Co-Founder & Exec Chm)*
David Morken *(Co-Founder, Pres & CEO)*
Joe Campbell *(Sr VP & Gen Mgr-Internet Svcs)*
Steve Leonard *(Sr VP & Gen Mgr-iNetwork)*
Advertising Agency:
Dukas Public Relations, Inc.
100 W 26th St 2nd Fl
New York, NY 10001
Tel.: (212) 704-7385
Fax: (212) 242-3646

BARCODING INC.

2220 Boston St
Baltimore, MD 21231
Tel.: (410) 385-8532
Fax: (410) 385-8559
Toll Free: (888) 860-7226
E-mail: info@barcoding.com
Web Site: www.barcoding.com
Approx. Number Employees: 55
Year Founded: 1998
Business Description:
Barcoding Services - Identification & Data Collection
S.I.C.: 7374
N.A.I.C.S.: 518210
Advertising Expenditures: $500,000
Media: 4-10-13
Personnel:
Jay Steinmetz *(Pres)*
Jeffrey Gillis *(CFO & COO)*
Shane Snyder *(VP-Sls)*
Joe Santini *(Dir-Pro Svcs)*

BARE BONES SOFTWARE, INC.

PO Box 1048
Bedford, MA 01730
Tel.: (781) 687-0700
Fax: (781) 687-0711
E-mail: sales@barebones.com
Web Site: www.barebones.com
E-Mail For Key Personnel:
Sales Director: sales@barebones.com
Approx. Number Employees: 12
Year Founded: 1994
Business Description:
Software Publisher
S.I.C.: 7371; 7372
N.A.I.C.S.: 541511; 511210
Media: 10-13-20
Personnel:
Rich Siegel *(Founder, Pres & CEO)*
Meredith Taitz *(Dir-Mktg)*
Brands & Products:
BARE BONES
BBEDIT
IT DOESN'T SUCK.
MAILSMITH
SUPER GET INFO
TEXTWRANGLER

BARRETT BUSINESS SERVICES, INC.

8100 NE Parkway Dr Ste 200
Vancouver, WA 98662
Tel.: (360) 828-0700
Fax: (360) 828-0701
Toll Free: (800) 494-5669
Web Site: www.barrettbusiness.com
Approx. Rev.: $273,123,000
Approx. Number Employees: 40,935
Year Founded: 1965
Business Description:
Human Resource Management Services
S.I.C.: 7363; 7361
N.A.I.C.S.: 561320; 561310
Media: 8-9-10-13-25
Personnel:
Anthony Meeker *(Chm)*
Michael L. Elich *(Pres & CEO)*
James D. Miller *(CFO)*
Gregory R. Vaughn *(VP & Asst Sec)*

BARRISTER GLOBAL SERVICES NETWORK, INC.

42548 Happywoods Dr
Hammond, LA 70401
Tel.: (985) 365-0400
Fax: (985) 365-0401
E-mail: sales@barrister.com
Web Site: www.barrister.com
E-Mail For Key Personnel:
President: DBower@barrister.com
Sales Director: sales@barrister.com
Sales Range: $10-24.9 Million
Approx. Number Employees: 97
Year Founded: 1982
Business Description:
Multi-Vendor IT Services
S.I.C.: 7379
N.A.I.C.S.: 541519
Export
Media: 2-7
Distr.: Natl.
Budget Set: Feb.
Personnel:
John S. Bowers, III *(Pres)*
Byron Cain *(CFO & Sr VP)*
Rose S. Neas *(VP & Gen Mgr-Services)*
Brands & Products:
ADVANTAGE SERVICES
BARRISTER
NATIONWIDE IT SERVICES PROVIDER
WEB SERVICES MANAGER

BARTLETT, INC.

(Sub. of Bartlett Nuclear Inc.)
7633 E 63rd Pl Ste 400
Tulsa, OK 74133-1272
Tel.: (918) 252-9111
Fax: (918) 459-3494
Toll Free: (800) 556-7572
Web Site: www.bartlett.com
Approx. Number Employees: 1,171
Year Founded: 1973
Business Description:
Personnel Support & Services for Nuclear Safety
S.I.C.: 7363
N.A.I.C.S.: 561320
Media: 2-4-7-10
Distr.: Natl.
Brands & Products:
OUR POWER IS IN OUR PEOPLE

BASES

(Div. of The Nielson Company Advisory Services)
50 W Rivercenter Blvd Ste 600
Covington, KY 41011-5813
Tel.: (859) 905-4000
Fax: (859) 905-5000
E-mail: info@bases.com
Web Site: www.bases.com
Approx. Number Employees: 650
Year Founded: 1989
Business Description:
Pre-Market Consumer Opinion Research, New Product Sales Forecasting, Competitor Analysis & Target Market Research Services
S.I.C.: 8732; 8742
N.A.I.C.S.: 541910; 541613
Media: 4-7
Distr.: Intl.; Natl.
Brands & Products:
BASES I/II
BASES LX
BASES XRX
PRE-BASES
PRICE ACCEPTANCE BASES
RESTAGER BASES
SPECTRA BASES

BAUMFOLDER CORPORATION

(Sub. of Heidelberg Postpress Deutschland GmbH)
1660 Campbell Rd
Sidney, OH 45365
Mailing Address:
PO Box 728
Sidney, OH 45365
Tel.: (937) 492-1281
Fax: (937) 492-7280
Toll Free: (800) 543-6107
E-mail: baumfolder@baumfolder.com
Web Site: www.baumfolder.com
Approx. Number Employees: 135
Year Founded: 1917
Business Description:
Mfr. of Paper Folding Machines, Paper Cutters, Paper Drills, Gluers & Bindery
S.I.C.: 3554; 3579
N.A.I.C.S.: 333291; 333313
Advertising Expenditures: $300,000
Media: 1-2-4-5-7-10-17-20
Distr.: Intl.; Natl.
Budget Set: Oct.
Personnel:
Ulrik Nygaard *(Pres & CEO)*
Janice A. Benanzer *(CFO & VP-Admin)*
Robert Kinson *(VP-Engrng & Quality)*
Mark Pellman *(Mgr-Mktg)*
Brands & Products:
BAUM
BAUMFOLDER GRAPHIC ARTS EQUIPMENT
Advertising Agency:
By George Advertising
14545 Mendenhall Rd.
Yorkshire, OH 45388
Tel.: (419) 582-3864

BBI-SOURCE SCIENTIFIC, INC.

(Sub. of Pressure BioSciences, Inc.)
7390 Lincoln Way
Garden Grove, CA 92841
Tel.: (714) 898-9001
Fax: (714) 891-1229
Toll Free: (800) 888-9285
Sales Range: $10-24.9 Million
Approx. Number Employees: 25
Year Founded: 1981
Business Description:
Mfr. of Biomedical Laboratory Instruments
S.I.C.: 3841
N.A.I.C.S.: 339112
Export
Media: 2-4-10-19

BEARINGPOINT, INC.

Tyson's Tower 1676 International Dr
McLean, VA 22102-4832
Tel.: (703) 747-3000
Fax: (703) 747-8500
Toll Free: (866) BRNGPNT
Web Site: www.bearingpoint.com
Sales Range: $1-4.9 Billion
Approx. Number Employees: 17,100
Year Founded: 1999
Business Description:
Business Consulting & Systems Integration Services
S.I.C.: 8742; 8748
N.A.I.C.S.: 541611; 541618; 541690
Advertising Expenditures: $20,681,000
Media: 2-10
Personnel:
Peter N. Mockler *(Mng Partner)*
Matthew Costello *(Mng Dir)*
David Johnston *(CFO)*
Hendrik J. Ansink *(Exec VP-Ops)*
Betsy Palmer *(Exec VP-Mktg & Comm)*
Elizabeth S. Palmer *(Exec VP-Mktg & Comm)*
Francesca Luthi *(Head-Global IR & Comm)*
Gina Giamanco *(Dir-Global Comm)*
Charles White *(Sr Mgr)*
Advertising Agency:
Dentsu America, Inc.
32 Ave of the Americas 16th Fl
New York, NY 10013
Tel.: (212) 397-3333
Fax: (212) 397-3322

BEHAVIOR TECH COMPUTER (US) CORPORATION

(Sub. of Behavior Tech Computer Corporation)
4180 Business Center Dr
Fremont, CA 94538-6354
Tel.: (510) 657-3956
Fax: (510) 657-3965
E-mail: sales@btcusa.com
Web Site: www.btcusa.com
Approx. Number Employees: 20
Year Founded: 1982

Key to Media (For complete agency information see *The Advertising Red Books-Agencies* edition):
1. Bus. Publs. 2. Cable T.V. 3. Catalogs & Directories. 4. Co-op Adv. 5. Consumer Mags. 6. D.M. to Bus. Estab.7. D.M. to Consumers 8. Daily Newsp. 9. Exhibits/Trade Shows 10. Foreign 11. Infomercial 12. Internet Adv.13. Multimedia 14. Network Radio 15. Network T.V. 16. Newsp. Distr. Mags. 17. Other 18. Outdoor (Posters, Transit) 19. Point of Purchase20. Premiums, Novelties 21. Product Samples 22. Special Events Mktg. 23. Spot Radio 24. Spot T.V. 25. Weekly Newsp. 26. Yellow Page Adv.

Business Description:
Mfr. & Sales of Personal Computer Peripherals, Keyboards, Optical Devices & Sound Cards
S.I.C.: 5045
N.A.I.C.S.: 423430
Export
Advertising Expenditures: $300,000
Media: 2-7-10-17
Distr.: Intl.; Natl.
Personnel:
Steel Su *(Chm)*
Daniel Yu *(Pres)*
Mei Hsu *(VP-Sls & Mktg)*
Brands & Products:
BTC

BENTLEY SYSTEMS, INC.

685 Stockton Dr
Exton, PA 19341-0678
Tel.: (610) 458-5000
Fax: (610) 458-1060
Toll Free: (800) BENTLEY
Web Site: www.bentley.com
E-Mail For Key Personnel:
President: greg.bentley@bentley.com
Marketing Director: charley.ferrucci@bentley.com
Sales Director: john.riddle@bentley.com
Sales Range: $450-499.9 Million
Approx. Number Employees: 2,800
Year Founded: 1984
Business Description:
Software Products Mfr
S.I.C.: 7372
N.A.I.C.S.: 511210
Export
Advertising Expenditures: $1,500,000
Media: 2-6-10-22
Distr.: Natl.
Budget Set: Oct.
Personnel:
Gregory Bentley *(CEO)*
David Hollister *(CFO)*
Malcolm Walter *(COO & Sr VP)*
Keith Bentley *(CTO & Dir)*
David Nation *(Gen Counsel, Sec & Sr VP-Corp Affairs)*
Barry Bentley *(Exec VP & Dir)*
Raymond B. Bentley *(Exec VP-Software Engrng)*
Alton B. Cleveland *(Sr VP-Applied Res)*
Ted Lamboo *(Sr VP-Civil & Geospatial Global Ops)*
Jean-Baptiste Monnier *(Sr VP-Bentley Asia Ops)*
Gabe Norona *(Sr VP)*
John Riddle *(Sr VP-Ops-N America)*
Bhupinder Singh *(Sr VP-Software)*
Charles Ferrucci *(VP)*
George Castle *(Dir-Partner Dev)*
Glenn Cox *(Dir-AssetWise Power, Process & Nuclear)*
Dru Crawley *(Dir-Building Performance Products)*
Brands & Products:
AUTOPIPE
AUTOPLANT
BE MAGAZINE
BENTLEY
BENTLEY ARENIUM
BENTLEY AXSYS
BENTLEY SELECT
CIVILSTORM
CLOUDWORX
CULVERTMASTER
DARWIN CALIBRATOR
DARWIN DESIGNER
DIGITAL INTERPLOT
ELEMENTARY ELECTRICAL DIAGRAMS
EXPERTDESIGNER
FLEXUNITS
FLOWMASTER
GEO WEB
GEOMACAO
GEOPAK
GISCONNECT
HAESTAD METHODS
HAMMER
HEC-PACK
HEVACOMP
INRAIL
INROADS
LEAP BRIDGE
LEAP PC-HELP
LEAP PRESTO
LEAP VERTEX
MICROSTATION
MXRAIL
MXRENEW
MXROAD
MXSITE
MXURBAN
NAVIGATOR
PLANTFLOW
PLANTSPACE
PONDPACK
POWERCIVIL
POWERMAP
POWERREBAR
POWERSURVEY
PROCONCRETE
PROJECTWISE
PROSTEEL
PUMPMASTER
SCADACONNECT
SELECT
SEWERCAD
SEWERGEMS
STAAD
STORMCAD
STORMGEMS
SUPERLOAD
WATERCAD
WATERGEMS
WATERSAFE
WINNOZL
Advertising Agency:
Hanson Associates, Inc.
4112A Station St
Philadelphia, PA 19127
Tel.: (215) 487-7051
Fax: (215) 487-7052

BGP CORP.

(A Member of PHI Group)
630 Central Ave
New Providence, NJ 07974
Mailing Address:
PO Box 1
New Providence, NJ 07974
Tel.: (908) 673-0000
Fax: (908) 673-0001
Toll Free: (800) 123-4567
E-mail: bglenford@bgp.com
E-Mail For Key Personnel:
President: t.perelli@bgp.com
Marketing Director: l.hillman@bgp.com
Sales Director: j.robbins@bgp.com
Public Relations: g.tiller@bgp.com
Approx. Rev.: $1,500,000
Approx. Number Employees: 25
Year Founded: 1986
Business Description:
Reprographics
S.I.C.: 8741
N.A.I.C.S.: 561110
Advertising Expenditures: $250,000
Multimedia: $50,000; Consumer Mags.: $9,000; D.M. to Bus. Estab.: $1,000; Internet Adv.: $100,000; Network Radio: $40,000; Premiums, Novelties: $25,000; Special Events Mktg.: $25,000
Distr.: Direct to Consumer
Budget Set: Jan. -Dec.
Personnel:
Brandon Glen *(Chm)*
Tina Perelli *(Pres & CEO)*
Robyn Green *(Dir-Creative)*
Lori Hillman *(Dir-Mktg)*
Tara Kwan *(Dir-Media)*
Jenna Robbins *(Dir-Sls)*
Sam Morrison *(Mgr-Production)*
Gregg Tiller *(Mgr-PR)*
Kieran O'Brien Kern *(Coord-Mktg)*
Brands & Products:
COPYIT
COPYQ
REPRORIGHT
Advertising Agency:
Chana & Associates
(Filed Chapter 11 Bankruptcy Protection 08/31/11)
121 Chanlon Rd
New Providence, NJ 07974
Tel.: (908) 486-6801
Fax: (908) 790-5405
Toll Free: (800) 340-3467
Mr. Jones Magic Eraser, Autumn Auto, CopyQ, CopyIt, Perfect Parchment, Perfect Paper, Trilox Desktops, Trilox Laptops, Trilox Flash Drives, Trilox DVD Burners
— Frances Smith *(Acct Exec)*
— Jim Long *(Assoc Acct Exec)*
— Bonnie Jones *(Acct Mgr)*

BIC CORPORATION

(Sub. of Societe BIC S.A.)
1 BIC Way Ste 1
Shelton, CT 06484
Tel.: (203) 783-2000
Fax: (203) 783-2081
E-mail: webmaster@bicworldusa.com
Web Site: www.bicworldusa.com
Approx. Number Employees: 300
Year Founded: 1958
Business Description:
Stationery Products, Lighters & Shavers Mfr
S.I.C.: 3951; 2678; 2899
N.A.I.C.S.: 339941; 322233; 325998
Import Export
Advertising Expenditures: $4,500,000
Media: 2-3-6-11-15
Distr.: Natl.
Budget Set: Oct.
Advertising Agencies:
MediaCom
498 7th Ave
New York, NY 10018
Tel.: (212) 912-4200
Fax: (212) 508-4386
Wite-Out

Worx Branding & Advertising
18 Waterbury Rd
Prospect, CT 06712-1215
Tel.: (203) 758-3311
Fax: (203) 758-6847

BILLIAN PUBLISHING INC.

(d/b/a Billian's HealthDATA Group)
2100 Powers Ferry Rd Ste 300
Atlanta, GA 30339-5014
Tel.: (770) 955-8484
Tel.: (770) 955-5656
Fax: (770) 955-8485
Fax: (770) 952-0669
Toll Free: (800) 533-8484
E-mail: info@billian.com
Web Site: www.billian.com
E-Mail For Key Personnel:
Sales Director: JBrooke@billian.com
Approx. Number Employees: 55
Business Description:
Consumer Magazines, Trade Magazines, Databases & Directories
S.I.C.: 2721; 2741
N.A.I.C.S.: 511120; 511140; 511199
Media: 6-7-8-10-13
Brands & Products:
ART & ANTIQUES
ASSISTED LIVING & EXTENDED CARE
BILLIAN PUBLISHING
BOATING WORLD
DICCIONARIO TEXTIL
GROUP PURCHASING ORGANIZATIONS
HOSPITAL BLUEBOOK
TEXTILE WORLD
TEXTILE WORLD ASIA
TEXTILE WORLD BLUE BOOK
TEXTILES PANAMERICANOS

BITSTREAM INC.

500 Nickerson Rd
Marlborough, MA 01752-4695
Tel.: (617) 497-6222
Fax: (617) 868-0784
Fax: (617) 868-4732
Toll Free: (800) 522-3668
E-mail: invrel@bitstream.com
Web Site: www.bitstream.com
E-Mail For Key Personnel:
Sales Director: sales@bitstream.com
Approx. Rev.: $23,144,000
Approx. Number Employees: 148
Year Founded: 1981
Business Description:
Software Developer
S.I.C.: 7372; 7371
N.A.I.C.S.: 511210; 541511
Media: 2-6-7-8-10-13
Personnel:
Amos Kaminski *(Chm & Interim CEO)*
James P. Dore *(CFO & VP)*
Costas Kitsos *(VP-Engrg)*
Brands & Products:
BITSTREAM
BOLT
BOLTBROWSER
BTX2
CYBERBIT
FONT FUSION
MYFONTS
PAGEFELX CHART
PAGEFLEX
PANORAMA
T2K
TDIS

Key to Media (For complete agency information see *The Advertising Red Books-Agencies* edition):
1. Bus. Publs. 2. Cable T.V. 3. Catalogs & Directories. 4. Co-op Adv. 5. Consumer Mags. 6. D.M. to Bus. Estab.7. D.M. to Consumers 8. Daily Newsp. 9. Exhibits/Trade Shows 10. Foreign 11. Infomercial 12. Internet Adv.13. Multimedia 14. Network Radio 15. Network T.V. 16. Newsp. Distr. Mags. 17. Other 18. Outdoor (Posters, Transit) 19. Point of Purchase20. Premiums, Novelties 21. Product Samples 22. Special Events Mktg. 23. Spot Radio 24. Spot T.V. 25. Weekly Newsp. 26. Yellow Page Adv.

BITSTREAM INC. — (Continued)

THUNDERHAWK
TRUE DOC

BLACK BOX CORPORATION

1000 Park Dr
Lawrence, PA 15055-1018
Tel.: (724) 746-5500
Fax: (724) 746-0746
Toll Free: (877) 877-2269
E-mail: info@blackbox.com
Web Site: www.blackbox.com
Approx. Rev.: $1,068,229,000
Approx. Number Employees: 4,413
Year Founded: 1976
Business Description:
Computer Network Infrastructure Services
S.I.C.: 3577; 7379; 7629
N.A.I.C.S.: 334119; 541519; 811213
Import Export
Advertising Expenditures: $5,621,000
Media: 4-7-8-13
Distr.: Intl.
Personnel:
Thomas G. Greig *(Chm)*
R. Terry Blakemore *(Pres & CEO)*
Michael McAndrew *(CFO, Treas, Sec & VP)*
Jeffrey D. Murray *(Sr VP & Gen Mgr)*
Francis W. Wertheimber *(Sr VP-Pacific Rim & Far East)*
Julie Lyda *(Gen Mgr-North America)*
Josh Whitney *(Dir-Product Mgmt)*
Brands & Products:
BLACK BOX
DIAMOND
KVM SERVSWITCH
Advertising Agency:
Asia-Pacific Connections Pte Ltd
9 Stevens Road
Singapore, 257820, Singapore
Tel.: (65) 6334 9045
Fax: (65) 6235 1428

BLACKBAUD, INC.

2000 Daniel Island Dr
Charleston, SC 29492
Tel.: (843) 216-6200
Fax: (843) 216-6111
Toll Free: (800) 443-9441
E-mail: solutions@blackbaud.com
Web Site: www.blackbaud.com
Approx. Rev.: $327,094,000
Approx. Number Employees: 2,065
Year Founded: 1982
Business Description:
Developer of Software Products for Non-Profit Organizations
S.I.C.: 7372
N.A.I.C.S.: 511210
Import Export
Advertising Expenditures: $1,100,000
Media: 7-10-22
Personnel:
Andrew M. Leitch *(Chm)*
Marc E. Chardon *(Pres & CEO)*
Timothy V. Williams *(CFO, Sr VP-Fin & Admin)*
Charles T. Cumbaa *(Pres-Enterprise Customer Bus Unit)*
Brad Holman *(Pres-Intl Markets)*
Kevin W. Mooney *(Pres-Gen Markets Bus Unit)*
Jon W. Olson *(Gen Counsel & VP)*
Heidi H. Strenck *(Sr VP & Controller)*
Louis J. Attanasi *(Sr VP-Products)*
Jana Eggers *(Sr VP-Product Mgmt & Mktg)*
Lee W. Gartley *(Sr VP)*
Charles L. Longfield *(Chief Scientist & Sr VP)*
John J. Mistretta *(Sr VP-HR)*
Gerard J. Zink *(Chief Customer Satisfaction Officer & Sr VP-Customer Support)*
Joel Wilhite *(VP-Fin)*
Rachel Hutchisson *(Dir-Corp Rels & Philanthropy)*
Steve MacLaughlin *(Dir-Internet Solutions)*
Melanie Mathos *(Mgr-PR)*
Andrew Payne *(Mgr-Product Line)*
Brands & Products:
BLACKBAUD
BLACKBAUD DIRECT MARKETING
BLACKBAUD ENTERPRISE CRM
BLACKBAUD STUDENT INFORMATION SYSTEM
THE EDUCATION EDGE
ETAPESTRY
THE FINANCIAL EDGE
THE INFORMATION EDGE
MAKE THE WORLD A BETTER PLACE.
THE PATRON EDGE
THE PATRON EDGE ONLINE
PROSPECT RATING SYSTEM
THE RAISER'S EDGE
THE RAISER'S EDGE ENTERPRISE
TARGET ANALYTICS
TEAM APPROACH
WEALTHPOINT

BLUE COAT SYSTEMS, INC.

420 N Mary Ave
Sunnyvale, CA 94085
Tel.: (408) 220-2200
Fax: (408) 220-2250
Toll Free: (866) 30BCOAT
E-mail: bcs.info@bluecoat.com
Web Site: www.bluecoat.com
Approx. Rev.: $487,113,000
Approx. Number Employees: 1,333
Year Founded: 1996
Business Description:
Integrated Computer Systems Design
S.I.C.: 3577; 3572; 7373
N.A.I.C.S.: 334119; 334112; 541512
Advertising Expenditures: $1,100,000
Personnel:
David W. Hanna *(Chm)*
Gregory S. Clark *(Pres & CEO)*
Gordon C. Brooks *(CFO & Sr VP)*
Steve Daheb *(CMO & Sr VP)*
Betsy E. Bayha *(Gen Counsel, Sec & Sr VP)*
James W. Vogt *(Sr VP & Gen Mgr-Cloud Svcs Bus Unit)*
Marc Andrews *(Sr VP-Field Ops)*
Darrell Long *(VP & Gen Mgr-Security Product Grp)*
Tom Shea *(VP & Gen Mgr-Acceleration Product Grp)*
Sharon Jordan *(VP-HR)*
Steve Rowland *(VP-Sls)*
John Shoop *(VP-Worldwide Svc Provider Sls)*
James Whitchurch *(VP-Engrg & Tech)*
Nidal Taha *(Reg Dir-Middle East)*
Tom Clare *(Product Mgr)*
Brands & Products:
BLUE COAT
PROXYAV
PROXYSG
SCOPE
SPYWARE INTERCEPTOR
Advertising Agency:
Merritt Group
11600 Sunrise Valley Dr Ste 320
Reston, VA 20191-1416
Tel.: (703) 390-1500
Fax: (703) 860-2080

BLUE FROG MEDIA

520 Pike St 24th Fl
Seattle, WA 98101
Tel.: (206) 652-4481
Fax: (206) 652-4466
E-mail: pr@bluefrogmedia.com
Web Site: www.bluefrog-media.com/
Sales Range: $1-9.9 Million
Approx. Number Employees: 52
Business Description:
Mobile Content Products Developer
S.I.C.: 7373; 7299; 7379
N.A.I.C.S.: 541512; 541519; 812990
Media: 1-6
Personnel:
Melissa M. Millburn *(VP-Corp Commun & Mktg)*
David B. Theobald *(Controller)*

BLUEARC CORPORATION

50 Rio Robles
San Jose, CA 95134-1806
Tel.: (408) 576-6600
Fax: (408) 576-6601
E-mail: info@bluearc.com
Web Site: www.bluearc.com
Sales Range: $25-49.9 Million
Approx. Number Employees: 212
Year Founded: 1998
Business Description:
Network Storage Systems
S.I.C.: 3572
N.A.I.C.S.: 334112
Media: 10
Personnel:
Michael B. Gustafson *(Pres & CEO)*
Rick Martig *(CFO)*
Christopher J. McBride *(Sr VP-Global Customer Ops)*
Bridget Warwick *(Sr VP-Mktg)*
Carlo F. Garbagnati *(VP-Engrg)*
Jean Okawaki *(VP-HR)*
Chris White *(VP-Global Channel Sls)*
Brands & Products:
BLUEARC
DATA MIGRATOR
ISCSI
TITAN

BMC INDUSTRIAL EDUCATIONAL SERVICES

2831 Maffett St
Muskegon Heights, MI 49444-2153
Tel.: (231) 733-1206
Fax: (231) 733-2116
E-mail: bmc@mail.com
Web Site: www.bmclab.com
Approx. Number Employees: 20
Year Founded: 1970
Business Description:
Scientific Laboratory Furniture, Fume Hoods & Hospital Casework
S.I.C.: 5047; 3821
N.A.I.C.S.: 423450; 339111
Export
Advertising Expenditures: $25,000
Media: 2-4-10
Distr.: Natl.
Budget Set: Nov.
Personnel:
Barry Kennedy *(Mgr-Natl Sls)*

BMC SOFTWARE, INC.

2101 Citywest Blvd
Houston, TX 77042-2827
Tel.: (713) 918-1371
Tel.: (713) 918-8880
Fax: (713) 918-8000
Toll Free: (800) 841-2031
E-mail: investor@bmc.com
Web Site: www.bmc.com
Approx. Rev.: $2,065,300,000
Approx. Number Employees: 6,200
Year Founded: 1980
Business Description:
Systems Software Products & Enterprise Management Solutions
S.I.C.: 7372; 7371
N.A.I.C.S.: 511210; 334611; 541511
Export
Media: 1-2-4-7-10-11-13-26
Distr.: Intl.; Natl.
Budget Set: Mar.
Personnel:
Robert E. Beauchamp *(Chm & CEO)*
Stephen B. Solcher *(CFO & Sr VP)*
T. Cory Bleuer *(Chief Acctg Officer, VP & Controller)*
William D. Miller *(Pres-Mainframe Svc Mgmt & Gen Mgr)*
Denise M. Clolery *(Gen Counsel, Sec & Sr VP)*
James W. Grant *(Sr VP & Gen Mgr)*
John McMahon *(Sr VP-Worldwide Sls & Svcs)*
Mike Vescuso *(Sr VP-Admin)*
Luca Lazzaron *(VP & Gen Mgr-EMEA)*
Kasey Holman *(Assoc VP-Global Comm)*
Daniel G. Trevino, Jr. *(Sr Mgr-Product Mktg)*
Rick Weaver *(Product Mgr-DB2 Solutions)*
Arpil Hickel *(Sr Product Mgr-Middleware)*
David J. Easter *(Mgr-Product Mgmt-Remedy Platform)*
Amy Stuart *(Acct Exec-Sls)*
Brands & Products:
3270 SUPEROPTIMIZER/CICS
ACTION REQUEST SYSTEM
ALARMPOINT
ALTER
AMP
ANALYTICS
APC FOR INTUNE
APPLICATION PROBLEM RESOLUTION SYSTEM
APPLICATION RESTART CONTROL
APPSIGHT
APPSIGHT APPLICATION PROBLEM RESOLUTION SYSTEM
APPTUNE
AR SYSTEM
ARS LINK
ATRIUM
AUTOOPERATOR ACCESS NV
AUTOPILOT
BACKUP & RECOVERY SOLUTION
BATCH DISCOVERY
BATCH IMPACT MANAGER
BLACK BOX
BMC
BMC SOFTWARE
BUSINESS PACKAGE

Key to Media (For complete agency information see *The Advertising Red Books-Agencies* edition):
1. Bus. Publs. 2. Cable T.V. 3. Catalogs & Directories. 4. Co-op Adv. 5. Consumer Mags. 6. D.M. to Bus. Estab.7. D.M. to Consumers 8. Daily Newsp. 9. Exhibits/Trade Shows 10. Foreign 11. Infomercial 12. Internet Adv.13. Multimedia 14. Network Radio 15. Network T.V. 16. Newsp. Distr. Mags. 17. Other 18. Outdoor (Posters, Transit) 19. Point of Purchase20. Premiums, Novelties 21. Product Samples 22. Special Events Mktg. 23. Spot Radio 24. Spot T.V. 25. Weekly Newsp. 26. Yellow Page Adv.

CATALOG MANAGER
CHANGE ACCUMULATION PLUS
CHANGE MANAGEMENT APPLICATION & AR SYSTEM
CHANGE MANAGEMENT DASHBOARD
CHANGE MANAGER
CHECK PLUS
CMF MONITOR
CONFIGURATION DISCOVERY
CONFIGURATION MANAGER
CONFIGURATION MANAGER EXPRESS
CONTENT DISTRIBUTION
CONTROL-D
CONTROL-D/AGENT
CONTROL-D/IMAGE
CONTROL-D/PAGE ON DEMAND
CONTROL-D/WEBACCESS SERVER
CONTROL-M/ANALYZER
CONTROL-M/ASSIST
CONTROL-M BUSINESS PROCESS INTEGRATION SUITE
CONTROL-M/CM
CONTROL-M/END USER
CONTROL-M/ENTERPRISE MANAGER
CONTROL-M/FORECAST
CONTROL-M/FULL ADMIN USER
CONTROL-M INTEGRATION MODULE
CONTROL-M/LINKS
CONTROL-M OPTION
CONTROL-M PLUS MODULE
CONTROL-M/RESTART
CONTROL-M SMART PLUG-IN
CONTROL-M/TAPE
CONTROL-M/WEB & PLANNING USER
CONTROL-O
CONTROL-SA
CONTROL-SA/PROVISIONING MODULE
CONTROL-V
COPY PLUS
DASD MANAGER PLUS
DATA ACCELERATOR COMPRESSION
DATA PACKER
DATABASE INTEGRITY PLUS
DATABASE PERFORMANCE
DBXRAY
DELTA PLUS VIRTUAL TERMINAL
DISCOVERY SERVICES
ENCRYPTION
ENERGIZER
EVAILABILITY
EVENT MANAGER
EVENT MANAGER BASE
EVENT MANAGER - ENTERPRISE BASE
EXPLORER
EXTENDED BUFFER MANAGER
FAST PATH
FOUNDATION DISCOVERY
IDENTITY
IMAGE COPY PLUS
IMPACT DATABASE GATEWAY
IMPACT EXPLORER
IMPACT INTEGRATION
IMPLEMENTATION ASSISTANCE
INTUNE
IOA
IT SERVICE MANAGEMENT SUITE
KNOWLEDGE MANAGEMENT
KNOWLEDGE MANAGEMENT EXPRESS
LOADPLUS
LOCAL COPY PLUS
LOGMASTER
MAGIC
MAINVIEW
MARIMBA
MASTERCELL EXCHANGE
MASTERNAVIGATOR
MAXM
MAXM DATABASE ADVISOR
MAXM REORG/EP
MAXM REORG/EP EXPRESS
MESSAGE ADVISOR
MOBILE REACH SPLITWARE
NETWORK & END-TO-END PERFORMANCE STARTER PACK
OPERTUNE
PACLOG
PATCH MANAGER
PATROL
PATROL CENTRAL ALERTS - WEB EDITION
PATROL DASHBOARD
PERFORMANCE ANALYSIS
PERFORMANCE ASSURANCE SUITE
PERFORMANCE MANAGER PORTAL
PERFORMANCE PERCEIVER
PERFORMANCE PREDICTOR
POINTER CHECKER PLUS
POOL ADVISOR
PROACTIVE SERVICE DESK PACKAGE
R+/CHANGE ACCUM
RECOVER PLUS
RECOVERY MANAGEMENT
RECOVERY MANAGER
RECOVERY UTILITY
REMEDY
REORG PLUS
REPORTS IMPACT MANAGER
ROUTES TO VALUE
SERVICE DESK EXPRESS
SLM & AR SYSTEM & FLASHBOARDS
SMARTDBA
SNAPSHOT UPGRADE FEATURE
SOFTWARE CAPITAL
SOFTWARE USAGE
SPACE EXPERT
SQL-BACKTRACK
SQL EXPLORER
SQL-PROGRAMMER
SYSCHANGE
SYSTEM CHANGE
SYSTEM EXPLORER
SYSTEM PERFORMANCE
TM APPLICATION RESPONSE TIME EXECUTION SERVER
TOPOLOGY DISCOVERY
TOPOLOGY EXTENSION
TRANSACTION MANAGEMENT
TRANSFORMING IT THROUGH AUTOMATION
TRAPBLASTER
ULTRAOPT
UNLOAD
UNLOAD PLUS
UTILITY SUITE ACCELERATORS

Advertising Agencies:
JWT Atlanta
(East Coast Office)
10B Glenlake Pkwy Ste 400
Atlanta, GA 30328
Tel.: (404) 365-7300
Fax: (770) 668-5707

Ogilvy PR
111 Sutter St 11th Fl
San Francisco, CA 94104-4541
Tel.: (415) 677-2700
Fax: (415) 677-2770
Analyst Relations
Corporate Communications
Digital
Global PR Agency of Record
Media Relations
Social Media

BNA SOFTWARE

(Div. of Tax Management, Inc.)
1231 25th St NW
Washington, DC 20037-1157
Tel.: (202) 728-7962
Fax: (202) 728-7964
Toll Free: (800) 424-2938
E-mail: software@bna.com
Web Site: www.bnasoftware.com
Approx. Number Employees: 70
Year Founded: 1983

Business Description:
Publisher of PC-based Software Applications for Tax & Financial Professionals
S.I.C.: 7373; 8111
N.A.I.C.S.: 541512; 541110
Media: 2-4-7-10-13
Distr.: Natl.

Personnel:
Paul Wojcik *(Chm & CEO)*
Michael Smith *(Gen Mgr)*
Rashid Nur *(Dir-Project Mgmt Office)*
John P. Barnes *(Sr Product Mgr)*
Susan S. Jones *(Mgr-Mktg Comm & Tax)*

Brands & Products:
BNA SOFTWARE

BOOZ ALLEN HAMILTON INC

(Sub. of Booz Allen Hamilton Holding Corporation)
8283 Greensboro Dr
McLean, VA 22102-4904
Tel.: (703) 902-5000
Fax: (703) 902-3333
Web Site: www.boozallen.com
Approx. Sls.: $4,100,000,000
Approx. Number Employees: 18,000
Year Founded: 1914

Business Description:
Management & Technology Consulting Services
S.I.C.: 8742
N.A.I.C.S.: 541611
Media: 2-4-7-9-23-24-25
Distr.: Natl.

Personnel:
Ralph W. Shrader *(Chm, Pres & CEO)*
Ronald T. Kadish *(Partner & Sr VP)*
Cesare R. Mainardi *(Mng Dir)*
Samuel R. Strickland *(CFO & Exec VP)*
Horacio Rozanski *(COO & Exec VP)*
C.G. Appleby *(Chief Legal Officer & Exec VP)*
Chris Foster *(Principal)*
Joseph E. Garner *(Exec VP)*
Fred Blackburn *(Sr VP)*
Nancy Hardwick *(Sr VP)*
Paul Kocourek *(Sr VP)*
Jim Manchisi *(Sr VP)*
Frank S. Smith, III *(Sr VP)*
Betty Thompson *(Sr VP)*

Advertising Agencies:
ENC Marketing & Communications
1430 Spring Hill Rd Ste 575
McLean, VA 22102
Tel.: (703) 288-1620
Fax: (703) 288-1637

Sefiani Communications Group
Level 2 68 York St
Sydney, NSW 2000, Australia
Tel.: (61) 2 8920 0700
Fax: (61) 2 8920 0688

THE BOSTON CONSULTING GROUP, INC.

Exchange Pl 31 Fl
Boston, MA 02109
Tel.: (617) 973-1200
Fax: (617) 973-1339
E-mail: contactus@bcg.com
Web Site: www.bcg.com
Sales Range: $1-4.9 Billion
Approx. Number Employees: 4,450
Year Founded: 1963

Business Description:
Management Consulting
S.I.C.: 8742
N.A.I.C.S.: 541611
Media: 2

Personnel:
Richard Lesser *(Chm)*
Hans-Paul Burkner *(Pres & CEO)*
Mike Deimler *(Mng Dir & Sr Partner)*
Michel Fredeau *(Sr Partner & Mng Dir)*
Ross Love *(Sr Partner & Mng Dir)*
Michael Silverstein *(Sr Partner & Mng Dir)*
Lars Faeste *(Partner, Mng Dir & Head-BCG Nordics)*
Reggie Gilyard *(Partner & Mng Dir)*
Thomas Herbeck *(Partner & Mng Dir)*
Alexander Roos *(Partner & Mng Dir)*
Chuck Scullion *(Partner & Mng Dir)*
Alan Wise *(Partner & Mng Dir)*
Harsh Vardhan *(Partner & Dir)*
Wolfgang Thiel *(Partner)*
Andrew Clark *(Sr Partner & Mng Dir)*
Nicholas Glenning *(Sr Partner & Mng Dir)*
Jeffrey Kotzen *(Sr Partner & Mng Dir)*
Rainer Strack *(Sr Partner & Mng Dir)*
James Andrew *(Sr Partner & Mng Dir)*
Thierry Chassaing *(Mng Dir & Sr Partner)*
Paul Gordon *(Mng Dir & Sr Partner)*
Steven Gunby *(Sr Partner & Mng Dir)*
Dieter Heuskel *(Mng Dir & Sr Partner)*
Nicolas Kachaner *(Mng Dir & Sr Partner)*
Nicholas Keuper *(Mng Dir & Sr Partner)*
Martin Koehler *(Mng Dir & Sr Partner)*
Craig Lawton *(Mng Dir & Sr Partner)*
Heino Meerkatt *(Mng Dir & Sr Partner)*
Antonella Mei-Pochtler *(Mng Dir & Sr Partner)*
Takashi Mitachi *(Mng Dir & Sr Partner)*
Xavier Mosquet *(Mng Dir & Sr Partner)*
Carl Stern *(Sr Partner & Mng Dir)*
Georg Sticher *(Mng Dir & Sr Partner)*
Debbie Simpson *(CFO)*
Todd Dubner *(Principal)*
Olivier Tardy *(Sr VP)*
Guido Crespi *(VP & Dir)*
Ron Nicol *(Head-Tech, Media & Telecom Practice)*
Oliver Steen *(Mgr-Houston)*

BOTTOMLINE TECHNOLOGIES INC.
(Sub. of Bottomline Technologies (de), Inc.)
3015 Windward Plz Fairways 2
Alpharetta, GA 30005
Tel.: (770) 576-3500
Fax: (770) 576-3699
E-mail: info@bottomline.com
Web Site: www.bottomline.com/contact/directions.html#Alpharetta
Approx. Rev.: $28,677,000
Approx. Number Employees: 182
Year Founded: 1981
Business Description:
Document & Payment Processing Services
S.I.C.: 6099; 7371; 7374
N.A.I.C.S.: 522320; 518210; 541511
Export
Advertising Expenditures: $926,000
Media: 7-10-11
Brands & Products:
DATA TAGS SOLUTION KIT
DESIGNSTUDIO
E.COMINTEGRATE
E.COMPRESENT
HIP AA-SMART
IMAGING SOLUTIONS
MEDEX
MEDFORMS
OPTIO DESIGNSTUDIO
OPTIO E.COMINTEGRATE
OPTIO E.COMPRESENT
OPTIO ENTERPRISE PROCESSPACKS
OPTIO HEALTHCARE PROCESSPACKS
OPTIO MEDEXFLEX
OPTIO MEDFORMS
OPTIODCS
OPTIOFAX
PRINT MANAGER
QUICKCHART
QUICKDELIVERY
QUICKRECORD
QUICKRECORD INTELLIGENT HUB
QUICKSCAN
QUICKSIGN
RAPID DOCUMENT DESIGN
XML SOLUTION KIT

BPO MANAGEMENT SERVICES, INC.
1290 N Hancock St Ste 200
Anaheim, CA 92807
Tel.: (714) 974-2670
Fax: (714) 970-1342
E-mail: info@bpoms.com
Web Site: www.bpoms.com
Sales Range: $25-49.9 Million
Approx. Number Employees: 100
Year Founded: 1982
Business Description:
Software Solutions for Healthcare Benefits Administration & Distribution
S.I.C.: 7371
N.A.I.C.S.: 541511
Advertising Expenditures: $1,139,000
Media: 8-10-13
Personnel:
Patrick A. Dolan *(Chm & CEO)*
James Cortens *(Pres & COO)*
David Frear *(CFO)*

BRADY CORPORATION
6555 W Good Hope Rd
Milwaukee, WI 53223
Mailing Address:
PO Box 571
Milwaukee, WI 53201
Tel.: (414) 358-6600
Fax: (414) 358-6798
Toll Free: (800) 541-1686
E-mail: investor@bradycorp.com
Web Site: www.bradycorp.com
Approx. Sls.: $1,339,597,000
Approx. Number Employees: 6,500
Year Founded: 1914
Business Description:
Informational & Safety Signs, Identification Products, Specialty Tapes & Traffic Control Products Mfr
S.I.C.: 3993; 2672; 3089; 3577; 3699; 3861; 3999
N.A.I.C.S.: 339950; 322222; 326199; 333315; 334119; 335999; 339999
Import Export
Advertising Expenditures: $72,000,000
Media: 1-2-4-5-7-10-13-18-19-20-21-26
Distr.: Intl.; Natl.
Personnel:
Frank M. Jaehnert *(Pres & CEO)*
Thomas J. Felmer *(CFO & Sr VP)*
Bentley Curran *(CIO & VP-IT)*
Kathleen M. Johnson *(Chief Acctg Officer & VP-Fin)*
Stephen Millar *(Pres-Asia-Pacific)*
Peter C. Sephton *(Pres-Brady Europe)*
Matthew O. Williamson *(Pres-Brady Americas)*
Allan J. Klotsche *(Sr VP-HR)*
Brands & Products:
BIG
BRADY
BRADY PEOPLE ID
BRADYPRINTER
CODESOFT
ID PAL
JAM
LABELMARK
PROMOVISION
QUO-LUCK
SENTINEL
SIGNMARK
STOPWARE
TEMTEC
TISCOR
VARITRONICS
WHEN PERFORMANCE MATTERS MOST
Advertising Agency:
Marketing Images
144 W Broadway St
Waukesha, WI 53186
Tel.: (262) 523-3940
Fax: (262) 523-3945
Toll Free: (800) 523-9307

BRADY/TISCOR, INC.
(Sub. of Brady Corporation)
10815 Rancho Bernardo Rd Ste 205
San Diego, CA 92127
Tel.: (858) 524-7700
Fax: (858) 312-7186
Toll Free: (800) 227-6379
E-mail: tiscor@tiscor.com
Web Site: www.tiscor.com
Sales Range: $10-24.9 Million
Approx. Number Employees: 50
Year Founded: 1982
Business Description:
Wireless & Internet-Enabled Mobile Workforce Automation Solutions
S.I.C.: 7373; 7371
N.A.I.C.S.: 541512; 541511
Media: 2-10
Personnel:
Mark Chebib *(Dir-Sls)*
Gus Sakas *(Dir-Sls)*
Lucia Morales *(Mgr-Mktg)*
Don Wickstrom *(Mgr-Fin-Mexico & Tiscor)*

BRADY VARITRONICS
(Sub. of Brady Corporation)
6835 Winnetka Cir
Brooklyn Park, MN 55428-1538
Tel.: (763) 536-6400
Fax: (800) 543-8966
Toll Free: (800) 637-5461
Web Site: www.varitronicsystems.com
Sales Range: $100-124.9 Million
Approx. Number Employees: 250
Year Founded: 1983
Business Description:
Specialty Business Machines & Lettering Systems
S.I.C.: 2679; 2672
N.A.I.C.S.: 322299; 322222
Import Export
Media: 2-4-7-9-10-19-25-26
Distr.: Intl.; Natl.
Personnel:
David Grey *(VP & Gen Mgr)*
Brands & Products:
GALARIO
IMAGE 1
MERLIN
MERLIN EXPRESS
MERLIN EXPRESS ELITE
MERLIN EXPRESS XT
MERLIN II
POSTER PRINTER
PROFINISH
PROLMAGE
TYPESTYLER
VARITRONICS
VISIMATE
WONDERBAR

BRAINSTORM GROUP, INC.
386 W Main St
Northborough, MA 01532-2128
Tel.: (508) 475-0475
Fax: (508) 393-8845
Web Site: www.brainstorm-group.com
Approx. Number Employees: 10
Year Founded: 1997
Business Description:
Full Service Conference & Event Management
S.I.C.: 8742
N.A.I.C.S.: 541613
Media: 2-10-13-22
Personnel:
Marion L. Elledge *(Sr VP-Commun)*
Stacey Murphy *(Mktg Dir)*
Raymond Kyle *(Dir-Accts-Natl)*

BRAINWARE, INC.
20110 Ashbrook Pl Ste 150
Ashburn, VA 20147
Tel.: (703) 948-5800
Fax: (703) 948-5887
E-mail: info@brainware.com
Web Site: www.brainware.com
Approx. Number Employees: 100
Business Description:
High-Volume Document Processing & Data Extraction Services
S.I.C.: 7374
N.A.I.C.S.: 518210
Personnel:
Carl Mergele *(CEO)*
Stephen Xeller *(Sr VP-Sls-Worldwide)*
Mark Helwege *(VP-Sls-Worldwide)*
Charlie Kaplan *(VP-Mktg)*
John Craig *(Dir-Strategic Alliances)*
Rick Lowe *(Dir-Ops)*
Leslie Stefranik *(Dir-Mktg)*
Werner Voegeli *(Dir-R&D)*
Omi Yadav *(Dir-Ops-EMEA)*
Allan Pich *(Mgr-Sls Assoc)*
Advertising Agency:
Euro RSCG Discovery
400 E Pratt St 10th Fl
Baltimore, MD 21202-6174
Tel.: (410) 230-3700
Fax: (410) 752-6689

BRANDVIA ALLIANCE, INC.
2159 Bering Dr
San Jose, CA 95131
Tel.: (408) 955-0500
Fax: (408) 955-0506
E-mail: info@brandvia.com
Web Site: www.brandvia.com
Sales Range: $1-9.9 Million
Approx. Number Employees: 25
Business Description:
Promotional Marketing Services
S.I.C.: 7319
N.A.I.C.S.: 541890
Media: 7-8-13-26
Personnel:
Jim Childers *(Pres)*

BRIDGELINE DIGITAL, INC.
10 6th Rd
Woburn, MA 01801
Tel.: (781) 376-5555
Fax: (781) 376-5033
Web Site: www.bridgelinedigital.com
Approx. Rev.: $23,558,000
Approx. Number Employees: 166
Business Description:
Web Software Tools & Applications
S.I.C.: 7372; 7371
N.A.I.C.S.: 511210; 541511
Advertising Expenditures: $578,000
Media: 10
Personnel:
Thomas L. Massie *(Chm)*
Michael D. Prinn *(CFO)*
Erez Katz *(COO & Exec VP)*
Brett Zucker *(CTO & Exec VP)*
Tracey Greene *(Chief Creative Officer & VP-Interface Design)*
Brian Lantz *(Gen Mgr & Exec VP)*
Michael Matteo *(Exec VP & Gen Mgr-NY)*
Tony Pietrocola *(Exec VP-Bus Dev)*
Pip Winslow *(Exec VP-HR)*
Brian Bolton *(VP-Mktg)*

BRIDGELINE SOFTWARE, INC.
(Name Changed to Bridgeline Digital, Inc.)

BRIDGESTONE MULTI MEDIA GROUP
300 N McKemy Ave
Chandler, AZ 85226
Tel.: (480) 940-5777
Fax: (480) 735-7984

Key to Media (For complete agency information see *The Advertising Red Books-Agencies* edition):
1. Bus. Publs. 2. Cable T.V. 3. Catalogs & Directories. 4. Co-op Adv. 5. Consumer Mags. 6. D.M. to Bus. Estab.7. D.M. to Consumers 8. Daily Newsp. 9. Exhibits/Trade Shows 10. Foreign 11. Infomercial 12. Internet Adv.13. Multimedia 14. Network Radio 15. Network T.V. 16. Newsp. Distr. Mags. 17. Other 18. Outdoor (Posters, Transit) 19. Point of Purchase20. Premiums, Novelties 21. Product Samples 22. Special Events Mktg. 23. Spot Radio 24. Spot T.V. 25. Weekly Newsp. 26. Yellow Page Adv.

Toll Free: (800) 523-0988
E-mail: info@aop.com
Web Site: www.aop.com
Approx. Sls.: $6,000,000
Approx. Number Employees: 250
Year Founded: 1987
Business Description:
Mfr of Computer Software, Consumer Electronics & Homeschool Curriculum
S.I.C.: 7812; 2731
N.A.I.C.S.: 512110; 511130
Media: 2-3-4-8-10-13-15-20-23-24
Distr.: Natl.
Personnel:
Robert J. Campbell, Jr. *(Pres & CEO)*

BRIGHTPOINT, INC.

7635 Interactive Way
Indianapolis, IN 46278
Tel.: (317) 707-2355
Fax: (317) 707-2521
Toll Free: (800) 952-2355
E-mail: info@brightpoint.com
Web Site: www.brightpoint.com
Approx. Rev.: $3,593,239,000
Approx. Number Employees: 3,909
Year Founded: 1994
Business Description:
Mobile Phones & Wireless Accessories Distr
S.I.C.: 5065
N.A.I.C.S.: 423690
Media: 2-8-10
Personnel:
Robert J. Laikin *(Chm & CEO)*
Vincent Donargo *(CFO, Treas & Exec VP)*
Jac Currie *(CIO & Exec VP)*
Robert L. Colin *(Chief Acctg Officer, Sr VP & Controller)*
Anurag Gupta *(Pres-Europe, Middle East & Africa)*
Eric Hamburger *(Pres-Brightpoint Latin America)*
J. Mark Howell *(Pres-Americas)*
Bashar Nejdawi *(Pres-Mobile Enhancement Bus)*
R. Bruce Thomlinson *(Pres-Asia Pacific)*
Craig M. Carpenter *(Gen Counsel, Sec & Exec VP)*
Alex Paskoff *(Exec VP-Bus Dev, Sr VP-Intl Ops, Exec VP-Sls & Mktg)*
Annette Cyr *(Sr VP-HR)*
Brands & Products:
BRIGHTPOINT
BRIGHTPOINT ONLINE
YOUR SUCCESS IS OUR BUSINESS

THE BRINK'S COMPANY

1801 Bayberry Ct
Richmond, VA 23226-3771
Mailing Address:
PO Box 18100
Richmond, VA 23226-8100
Tel.: (804) 289-9600
Fax: (804) 289-9758
E-mail: info@brinkscompany.com
Web Site: www.brinkscompany.com
Approx. Rev.: $3,121,500,000
Approx. Number Employees: 71,000
Year Founded: 1930
Business Description:
Holding Company; Security Guard & Armored Car Services
S.I.C.: 6719; 7381
N.A.I.C.S.: 551112; 561612; 561613
Import Export
Media: 2-7-13-15-26
Distr.: Intl.; Natl.
Personnel:
Michael T. Dan *(Chm, Pres & CEO)*
Michael J. Cazer *(Pres, CEO-Europe, Middle East & Africa)*
Joseph W. Dziedzic *(CFO & VP)*
Frank T. Lennon *(Chief Admin Officer & VP)*
McAlister C. Marshall *(Gen Counsel & VP)*
Ed Cuningham *(Dir-IR & Corp Comm)*
Brands & Products:
BRINK'S
BRINK'S HOME SECURITY
SECURE LOGISTICS WORLDWIDE
Advertising Agency:
ID Media
(Part of the Interpublic Group of Companies)
100 W 33rd St
New York, NY 10001
Tel.: (212) 907-7011
Fax: (212) 907-7290

BROADCOM CORPORATION

5300 California Ave
Irvine, CA 92617-3038
Mailing Address:
PO Box 57013
Irvine, CA 92619-7013
Tel.: (949) 926-5000
Fax: (949) 926-5203
E-mail: scottc@broadcom.com
Web Site: www.broadcom.com
Approx. Rev.: $6,818,319,000
Approx. Number Employees: 8,950
Year Founded: 1991
Business Description:
Wired & Wireless Broadband Communications Semiconductors
S.I.C.: 3674; 3663; 3679
N.A.I.C.S.: 334413; 334220; 334419
Export
Advertising Expenditures: $200,000
Media: 2-13-17
Personnel:
Henry Samueli *(Founder & CTO)*
John E. Major *(Chm)*
Scott A. McGregor *(Pres & CEO)*
Eric K. Brandt *(CFO & Exec VP)*
Kenneth E. Venner *(CIO & Exec VP)*
Robert L. Tirva *(Principal Acctg Officer, Sr VP & Controller)*
Arthur Chong *(Gen Counsel, Sec & Exec VP)*
Scott A. Bibaud *(Exec VP & Gen Mgr-Mobile Platform Grp)*
Daniel A. Marotta *(Exec VP & Gen Mgr-Broadband Comm Grp)*
Rajiv Ramaswami *(Exec VP & Gen Mgr-Enterprise Networking Grp)*
Robert A. Rango *(Exec VP & Gen Mgr-Wireless Connectivity Grp)*
Neil Y. Kim *(Exec VP-Ops & Central Engrg)*
Thomas F. Lagatta *(Exec VP-Sls-Worldwide)*
Terri L. Timberman *(Exec VP-HR)*
Nariman Yousefi *(Sr VP)*
T. Peter Andrew *(VP & Asst Treas)*
Bill Blanning *(VP-Global Media Rels)*
Vinod Lakhani *(Gen Mgr-Broadcoms High & Speed Controller Grp)*
Chris Zegarelli *(Dir-IR)*
Brands & Products:
54G
AIRFORCE
AIRFORCE ONE
AIRFORCE XPRESS
ALTI-PHY
ALTIMA
BLADERUNNER
BLUTONIUM
BROADCOM
BROADCORE
BROADRANGE
BROADVOICE
CABLEMEDEA
CABLEXCHANGE
CALISTO
CELLAIRTY
CHAMPION
CONNECTING EVERYTHING
CRYPTONETX
DIGI-PHY
DOCSIS
DOCSIS 1.1
DOCSIS 2.0
DUAL PHY
EURO-DOCSIS
EYEOPENER
FULCRUM
GRAND CHAMPION
HEX-PHY
HIGIG
HYPERTRANSPORT
INCONCERT
INSIDELINE
INTENSI-F
NETLINK
NETXTREME
OCTAL-PHY
ONEDRIVER
PACKETSYNC
PCI-EXPRESS
PROPANE
QAMLINK
QUAD-PHY
QUADSQUAD
RAIDCORE
ROBO-HS
ROBOSWITCH
ROBOSWITCH HS
SENTRYS
SIBYTE
SIGNI-PHY
SMARTRADIO
STRATA
STRATASWITCH
STRATAXGS
TURBOGIG
TURBOQAM
V-THERNET
WIDCOMM
X-PHY
XAUI
XELCORE
XPRESS
ZEEVO
Advertising Agency:
PointRoll Inc.
951 E Hector St
Conshohocken, PA 19428
Tel.: (267) 558-1300
Fax: (267) 285-1141
Toll Free: (800) 203-6956

BROADRIVER COMMUNICATIONS CORPORATION

(Sub. of Integracore, Inc.)
1000 Hemphill Ave
Atlanta, GA 30318
Tel.: (404) 961-1000
Fax: (404) 961-1899
E-mail: info@broadriver.com
Web Site: www.broadriver.com
Approx. Number Employees: 12
Year Founded: 1987
Business Description:
Voice Over IP Web Hosting
S.I.C.: 7375
N.A.I.C.S.: 518111
Media: 7-13-17-25
Personnel:
Michael L. Oken *(Founder & CTO)*
Allen Oken *(Chm)*
Kevin Beebe *(Gen Mgr)*
Brands & Products:
BROADRIVER

BROADVIEW NETWORKS HOLDINGS, INC.

(Holding of MCG Capital Corporation)
800 Westchester Ave Ste N-501
Rye Brook, NY 10573-1332
Tel.: (914) 922-7000
Fax: (646) 619-1596
Toll Free: (800) BROADVIEW
Web Site: www.broadviewnet.com
Approx. Rev.: $407,704,000
Approx. Number Employees: 950
Year Founded: 1996
Business Description:
Telephone, Data, Internet & IP-based Communications Services & Network Operator
S.I.C.: 4813; 4899; 7374; 7375
N.A.I.C.S.: 517310; 517110; 517910; 518111; 518210
Advertising Expenditures: $1,713,000
Personnel:
Steven F. Tunney *(Chm)*
Michael K. Robinson *(Pres & CEO)*
Corey Rinker *(CFO, Treas & Asst Sec)*
Brian P. Crotty *(COO)*
Kenneth A. Shulman *(CTO & CIO)*
Charles C. Hunter *(Gen Counsel, Sec & Exec VP)*
Terrence J. Anderson *(Exec VP-Corp Dev & Asst Treas)*
Jeff Blackey *(Sr VP-Mktg)*
Brands & Products:
BROADVIEW NETWORKS

BROADVISION, INC.

1600 Seaport Blvd Ste 550 N Bldg
Redwood City, CA 94063
Tel.: (650) 331-1000
Fax: (650) 542-5900
Toll Free: (866) 287-6669 (Sales)
E-mail: ir1@broadvision.com
Web Site: www.broadvision.com
E-Mail For Key Personnel:
Marketing Director: Tina.Wong@broadvision.com
Approx. Rev.: $21,817,000
Approx. Number Employees: 169
Year Founded: 1993
Business Description:
Large-Scale, Personalized Business on the Global Internet, Intranets & Extranets Application Solution Supplier
S.I.C.: 7372

Key to Media (For complete agency information see *The Advertising Red Books-Agencies* edition):
1. Bus. Publs. 2. Cable T.V. 3. Catalogs & Directories. 4. Co-op Adv. 5. Consumer Mags. 6. D.M. to Bus. Estab.7. D.M. to Consumers 8. Daily Newsp. 9. Exhibits/Trade Shows 10. Foreign 11. Infomercial 12. Internet Adv.13. Multimedia 14. Network Radio 15. Network T.V. 16. Newsp. Distr. Mags. 17. Other 18. Outdoor (Posters, Transit) 19. Point of Purchase20. Premiums, Novelties 21. Product Samples 22. Special Events Mktg. 23. Spot Radio 24. Spot T.V. 25. Weekly Newsp. 26. Yellow Page Adv.

BroadVision, Inc. — (Continued)

N.A.I.C.S.: 334611; 511210
Advertising Expenditures: $45,000
Media: 4-10-17
Personnel:
Pehong Chen *(Chm, Pres & CEO)*
Shin-Yuan Tzou *(CFO)*
David Boyer *(Sr VP-Engrg & Tech Support)*
Ralph Lentz *(VP & Gen Mgr-Americas)*
Brands & Products:
BROADVISION
BROADVISION COMMAND CENTER
BROADVISION ONE-TO-ONE COMMERCE
BROADVISION ONE-TO-ONE ENTERPRISE
BROADVISION ONE-TO-ONE PORTAL
E-BUSINESS FOR EVERYONE
IGUIDE

BROCADE COMMUNICATIONS SYSTEMS, INC.

130 Holger Way
San Jose, CA 95134
Tel.: (408) 333-8000
Fax: (408) 487-8101
E-mail: info@brocade.com
Web Site: www.brocade.com
Approx. Rev.: $2,094,363,000
Approx. Number Employees: 4,651
Year Founded: 1995
Business Description:
Computer Peripheral Equipment Mfr
S.I.C.: 3571; 3572; 3577
N.A.I.C.S.: 334111; 334112; 334119
Advertising Expenditures: $7,900,000
Media: 10
Personnel:
David L. House *(Chm)*
Michael Klayko *(CEO)*
Richard Deranleau *(CFO & VP-Fin)*
John McHugh *(CMO & VP)*
Tyler Wall *(Gen Counsel, Sec & VP)*
Ian Whiting *(Sr VP-Sls-Worldwide)*
Raymond Lee *(VP-Ops & IT)*
Jeff Seltzer *(VP-Mktg)*
Alex Lenke *(Dir-IR)*
Michelle Leach *(Mgr-PR)*
Brands & Products:
BROCADE
DCX
FABRIC OS
FILE LIFECYCLE MANAGER
MYVIEW
SAN HEALTH
SILKWORM
STORAGEX
Advertising Agency:
Ogilvy Public Relations Worldwide
636 11th Ave
New York, NY 10036
Tel.: (212) 880-5200
Fax: (212) 370-4636
— Ian Yellin *(Acct Exec)*

BROCADE CORPORATION

(Sub. of Brocade Communications Systems, Inc.)
4 Brocade Pkway
Broomfield, CO 80021-5059
Tel.: (720) 558-8000
Fax: (720) 566-8999
Toll Free: (800) 545-5773
E-mail: info@brocade.com
Web Site: www.brocade.com
Approx. Rev.: $614,433,024
Approx. Number Employees: 1,447
Year Founded: 1982
Business Description:
Enterprise Switches & Software for Storage Area Networks
S.I.C.: 3669; 3672
N.A.I.C.S.: 334290; 334412
Advertising Expenditures: $6,100,000
Media: 2-10-13
Personnel:
Randy Scheer *(Controller & Chief Acctg Officer)*
Bruce Chumley *(VP-Channel Sls)*
Jeff Vogel *(VP-Corp Devel & Strategy)*
Brands & Products:
DELL
ECLIPSE
FABRICENTER
FICON
INTREPID
MATRIX
MCDATA
NETWORKING THE WORLD'S BUSINESS DATA
SANAVIGATOR
SANTEGRITY
SANVERGENCE
SPHEREON
ULTRANET

BRODART CO.

500 Arch St
Williamsport, PA 17701-7809
Tel.: (570) 326-2461
Fax: (570) 326-1479
E-mail: bookinfo@brodart.com
Web Site: www.brodart.com
Approx. Number Employees: 1,000
Year Founded: 1940
Business Description:
Automated Library Information Systems; Books & Book Services; Library Equipment, Supplies & Furniture
S.I.C.: 5192; 5942
N.A.I.C.S.: 424920; 451211
Advertising Expenditures: $3,150,000
Media: 1-2-4-5-7-10-13-18-20-22-26-31
Distr.: Distr.; Natl.
Budget Set: Aug. -Sept.
Personnel:
Joseph Largen *(Chm, Pres, CEO & COO)*
Richard Dill *(CFO & VP)*
Tim Gage *(VP-HR)*
Chris Frantz *(Dir-Mktg & Sls)*
Emily-Anne Schulte *(Product Mgr-Mktg)*
Peter Salomone *(Mgr-Acct)*

BROOKS AUTOMATION - SYNETICS SOLUTIONS DIVISION

(Div. of Brooks Automation, Inc.)
18870 NE Riverside Pkwy
Portland, OR 97230
Tel.: (503) 465-6000
Fax: (503) 465-6393
Web Site: www.brooks.com
Sales Range: $75-99.9 Million
Approx. Number Employees: 189
Year Founded: 2000
Business Description:
Customized Automation & Airflow Management Solutions for Semiconductor Equipment Manufacturers
S.I.C.: 3559
N.A.I.C.S.: 333295
Media: 10
Personnel:
Bruce S. MacGibbon *(VP-Ops & Tech-Extended Factory Grp)*

BSQUARE CORPORATION

110 110th Ave NE Ste 202
Bellevue, WA 98004-5840
Tel.: (425) 519-5900
Fax: (425) 519-5999
Toll Free: (888) 820-4500
E-mail: sales@bsquare.com
Web Site: www.bsquare.com
Approx. Rev.: $96,774,000
Approx. Number Employees: 215
Business Description:
Computer Software Development
S.I.C.: 7371; 7372
N.A.I.C.S.: 541511; 511210
Advertising Expenditures: $93,000
Media: 2-4-5-7-10-22
Personnel:
Elliott H. Jurgensen, Jr. *(Chm)*
Brian T. Crowley *(Pres & CEO)*
Scott C. Mahan *(CFO, VP-Fin & Ops)*
Mark McMillan *(VP-Worldwide Sls & Mktg)*
Brands & Products:
BSQUARE
DEV KIT OMAP2530
DEV KIT OMAP3530
DEV KIT PXA255
DEV KIT PXA270
DEV KITPXA255
DEVICE VALIDATION TESTSUITE
FLASH UI EXTENDER
MARVELL PXA3XX
MEDIA+
THE MOBILE & EMBEDDED SYSTEM EXPERTS
NIGHTLIGHT
PRODUCTIVITY+
SCHEMABSP
SDIO HX
SOLIDCORE
TARGET DESIGNER
TI OMAP3
TI OMAP3 EVM

BT INFONET

(Sub. of British Telecommunications plc)
2160 E Grand Ave
El Segundo, CA 90245
Tel.: (310) 335-4700
Fax: (310) 335-4507
Web Site: www.bt.com
Sales Range: $600-649.9 Million
Approx. Number Employees: 1,085
Year Founded: 1970
Business Description:
Global Communications
S.I.C.: 4899; 7373
N.A.I.C.S.: 517910; 541512
Import Export
Advertising Expenditures: $8,600,000
Media: 4-6-7-10
Personnel:
Peter C. Sweers *(COO)*
John C. Hoffman *(Exec VP-Commun-Sls & Svc)*
Antti Kaunonen *(Sr VP-Mktg)*
Robert Passaretti *(VP-HR)*
Brands & Products:
GLOBAL CONNECT
INSIGHT MATTERS
THE WORLD NETWORK

BUGOPOLIS, INC.

207 Bridgeway St
Sausalito, CA 94965-2430
Tel.: (415) 324-5033
E-mail: sales@bugopolis.com
Web Site: www.bugopolis.com
E-Mail For Key Personnel:
President: jimw@bugopolis.com
Marketing Director: bonnie@bugopolis.com
Sales Director: sales@bugopolis.com
Approx. Number Employees: 5
Year Founded: 2002
Business Description:
Application Appliances Software Mfr & Distr
S.I.C.: 7372
N.A.I.C.S.: 511210
Media: 10-13
Personnel:
Bonnie Walters *(Co-Founder)*
Jim Walters *(Co-Founder)*
Brands & Products:
BUGOPOLIS
BUGSTATION
BUGZONE
PROJECTSTATION
PROJECTZONE

BULLSEYE TELECOM INC.

25900 Greenfield Rd Ste 330
Oak Park, MI 48237
Tel.: (248) 784-2500
Fax: (248) 784-2501
E-mail: customerservice@bullseyetelecom.com
Web Site: www.bullseyetelecom.com
Approx. Number Employees: 100
Business Description:
Data & Voice Telephone Communication Services
S.I.C.: 4813; 4812
N.A.I.C.S.: 517310; 517212
Media: 7-8-10-13
Personnel:
William H. Oberlin *(Chm & CEO)*
Tom Tisko *(Exec VP)*
Jerry Franks *(VP-Sls)*
Peter K. LaRose *(VP-Fin)*
Brands & Products:
AMPLIFY
BULLSEYE TELECOM INC
CORPORATE ADVANTAGE
POWERPLUS
SHORT STOP

BUSINESS VITALS

1401 Main St Ste 700
Columbia, SC 29201
Tel.: (803) 753-5200
Fax: (803) 753-5205
Toll Free: (888) 287-8483
E-mail: info@businessvitals.com
Web Site: www.businessvitals.com
Sales Range: $1-9.9 Million
Approx. Number Employees: 19
Year Founded: 2001
Business Description:
Information Technology Security Services

Key to Media (For complete agency information see *The Advertising Red Books-Agencies* edition):
1. Bus. Publs. 2. Cable T.V. 3. Catalogs & Directories. 4. Co-op Adv. 5. Consumer Mags. 6. D.M. to Bus. Estab.7. D.M. to Consumers
8. Daily Newsp. 9. Exhibits/Trade Shows 10. Foreign 11. Infomercial 12. Internet Adv.13. Multimedia 14. Network Radio
15. Network T.V. 16. Newsp. Distr. Mags. 17. Other 18. Outdoor (Posters, Transit) 19. Point of Purchase20. Premiums, Novelties
21. Product Samples 22. Special Events Mktg. 23. Spot Radio 24. Spot T.V. 25. Weekly Newsp. 26. Yellow Page Adv.

S.I.C.: 7389; 7371
N.A.I.C.S.: 561499; 541511
Media: 10
Personnel:
Jeff Brewer *(Pres & CEO)*
Brands & Products:
BUSINESS VITALS
CONFIDENTIALITY, INTEGRITY, AVAILABILITY
IT RISK MANAGEMENT LIFECYCLE
NOT E-BUSINESS. JUST BUSINESS.
OUTSOURCE YOUR TECHNOLOGY RISK

BUTLER AMERICA
2 Trap Falls Rd Ste 204
Shelton, CT 06484
Tel.: (203) 926-2700
E-mail: webmaster@butler.com
Web Site: www.butler.com
E-Mail For Key Personnel:
President: ekopko@butler.com
Sales Range: $300-349.9 Million
Approx. Number Employees: 3,600
Year Founded: 1985
Business Description:
Holding Company; Contract Technical Services
S.I.C.: 7361; 7363; 7389; 8744
N.A.I.C.S.: 561310; 541990; 561210; 561320
Media: 2-4-6-9-10-16-17-22-25-26
Distr.: Intl.; Natl.
Budget Set: Jan.
Personnel:
Tina Ciocca *(Pres)*
Brands & Products:
MINDPOWER FOR A CHANGING WORLD

BYTEX CORPORATION
495 Commerce Pk Ste S6
Milford, MA 01757
Tel.: (508) 422-9422
Fax: (508) 422-9410
E-mail: info@bytex.com
Web Site: www.bytex.com
E-Mail For Key Personnel:
Sales Director: sales@bytex.com
Approx. Number Employees: 25
Year Founded: 1980
Business Description:
Mfr. & Designer of Fault Tolerant Electronic Matrix Switching Systems & ATM Firewalls
S.I.C.: 5045
N.A.I.C.S.: 425110
Export
Media: 7-10-20
Distr.: Intl.; Natl.
Budget Set: Jan.
Personnel:
Bill Way *(Pres & CEO)*
Brands & Products:
ATLAS
AUTOSWITCH
BYTEX
NET.CARE
UNITY

CA, INC.
1 CA Plz
Islandia, NY 11749-7000
Tel.: (631) 342-6000
Fax: (631) 342-6800
Toll Free: (800) 225-5224
Telex: 981393
E-mail: cainfo@ca.com
Web Site: www.ca.com
E-Mail For Key Personnel:
Public Relations: daniel.kaferle@ca.com
Approx. Rev.: $4,429,000,000
Approx. Number Employees: 13,400
Year Founded: 1976
Business Description:
E-Business Computer Systems Management
S.I.C.: 7372
N.A.I.C.S.: 511210
Export
Media: 2-4-6-7-9-10-11-20-22-23-24-25
Distr.: Natl.
Personnel:
Russell M. Artzt *(Founder & Vice Chm)*
Arthur F. Weinbach *(Chm)*
William E. McCracken *(CEO)*
Richard Beckert *(CFO & Exec VP)*
Greg Valdez *(CIO)*
Donald F. Ferguson *(CTO & Exec VP)*
Phillip J. Harrington, Jr. *(Chief Admin Officer & Exec VP-Risk)*
Stephen Savage *(Chief Govt Rels Officer)*
Amy Fliegelman Olli *(Gen Counsel & Exec VP)*
Clifford H. R. DuPree *(Sec & Sr VP-Corp Governance)*
David C. Dobson *(Exec VP & Grp Exec-Customer Solutions Grp)*
Adam Elster *(Exec VP-Global Bus Ops & Bus Transformation)*
George Fischer *(Exec VP-Worldwide Sls & Ops)*
Ajei S. Gopal *(Exec VP-Products & Tech Grp)*
Peter J. L. Griffiths *(Exec VP-Tech & Dev Grp)*
Jacob Lamm *(Exec VP-Strategy & Corp Dev)*
Chris O'Malley *(Exec VP-Cloud Products & Solutions Bus Line)*
John Ruthven *(Exec VP-Growth & Emerging Markets)*
Una O'Neill *(Sr VP & Gen Mgr-Tech Svcs)*
Kelsey Doherty *(Sr VP-IR)*
Dan Kaferle *(Sr VP-PR-Worldwide)*
Jonathan Kissane *(Sr VP-Corp Dev)*
Gilbert Lacroix *(Sr VP-Channel Sls-EMEA)*
Bill Lispin *(Sr VP-Global Channel Sls)*
Mark Thompson *(Gen Mgr & Mng Dir-Major Markets)*
Brian Bell *(Gen Mgr-Svc & Portfolio Mgmt)*
Terrence Clark *(Gen Mgr-CA ecoSoftware)*
Christopher Cook *(Gen Mgr-Svc Assurance)*
Mike Crest *(Gen Mgr-Data Mgmt)*
Michael Denning *(Gen Mgr-Security Bus)*
Adam Famularo *(Gen Mgr-Cloud Computing Bus)*
Jon Hunter *(Gen Mgr-Sls-North America)*
Roger Pilc *(Gen Mgr-Virtualization & Automation)*
Dayton Semerjian *(Gen Mgr-Mainframe)*
Peter Stapleton *(Sr Principal & Product Mgr)*
John Ulery *(Sr Principal & Product Mgr)*
Brands & Products:
ALLFUSION
APPLOGIC
ASENTINEL
BRIGHTSTOR
CA
CA 1 TAPE MANAGEMENT
CA 11 WORKLOAD AUTOMATION RESTART & TRACKING
CA 2E
CA 3TERA
CA 7WORKLOAD AUTOMATION
CA ACCESS CONTROL
CA ACCUCHEK
CA ACF2
CA ADS
CA AION BUSINESS RULES EXPERT
CA ALLOCATE DASD SPACE & PLACEMENT
CA ANTI-SPYWARE FOR THE ENTERPRISE
CA ANTI-VIRUS FOR THE ENTERPRISE
CA APAS INSIGHT MONITOR FOR ADABAS
CA APPLICATION PERFORMANCE MANAGEMENT
CA ARCOT RISKFORT
CA ARCOT WEBFORT
CA ARCSERVE
CA ASM2 BACKUP & RESTORE
CA ASSET CONVERTER FOR MICROSOFT SMS
CA ASSET INTELLIGENCE
CA ASSET PORTFOLIO MANAGEMENT
CA ASTEX PERFORMANCE
CA AUDIT
CA AUDITOR FOR Z/OS
CA AUTOMATION POINT
CA AUTOMATION SUITE
CA AUTOSYS WORKLOAD AUTOMATION
CA BALANCING REPORT CONTROL
CA BIND ANALYZER FOR DB2 FOR Z/OS
CA BUNDL
CA CHANGE MANAGER ENTERPRISE WORKBENCH
CA CICSORT
CA CLARITY
CA CLEANUP
CA COHESION APPLICATION CONFIGURATION MANAGER
CA COMPLIANCE MANAGER FOR Z/OS
CA COMPRESS DATA COMPRESSION
CA CONFLICTS MANAGER
CA CONSOLE MANAGEMENT FOR OPENVMS
CA CREWS CATALOG RECOVERY
CA CULPRIT
CA DADS PLUS FOR CICS
CA DATA COMPRESSOR FOR DB2 FOR Z/OS
CA DATABASE ANALYZER FOR DB2 FOR Z/OS
CA DATABASE ANALYZER FOR IMS FOR Z/OS
CA DATABASE COMMAND CENTER
CA DATABASE COPIER FOR IMS FOR Z/OS
CA DATABASE ORGANIZER FOR IMS FOR Z/OS
CA DATACOM
CA DATAMACS
CA DATE SIMULATOR
CA DC MONITOR EXTENSIONS FOR IMS FOR Z/OS
CA DELIVER
CA DESKTOP MANAGEMENT SUITE FOR WINDOWS
CA DESKTOP MIGRATION MANAGER
CA DETECTOR FOR DB2 FOR Z/OS
CA DIRECTORY
CA DISK BACKUP & RESTORE
CA DISPATCH
CA DLP
CA DUO
CA DYNAM/D DISK MANAGEMENT FOR VSE
CA DYNAM FASTVTOC
CA DYNAM/FI FILE INDEPENDENCE
CA DYNAM/T TAPE MANAGEMENT FOR VSE
CA DYNAM/T TAPE MANAGEMENT FOR Z/VM
CA EARL
CA EASYTRIEVE
CA EHEALTH FOR VOICE
CA EHEALTH PERFORMANCE MANAGER
CA EMBEDDED ENTITLEMENTS MANAGER
CA ENDEVOR SOFTWARE CHANGE MANAGER
CA ENTERPRISE LOG MANAGER
CA EPIC FOR Z/VSE
CA ERWIN
CA ERWIN SAPHIR OPTION
CA ESP WORKLOAD AUTOMATION
CA EXPLORE PERFORMANCE MANAGEMENT
CA EXPLORE PERFORMANCE MANAGEMENT FOR Z/VM
CA EXPRESSPRINT
CA EXTEND/DASD VSAM COMPRESSION
CA FAQS AUTOMATED SYSTEMS OPERATION
CA FAQS PRODUCTION CONTROL SYSTEM
CA FAST CHECK
CA FAST INDEX
CA FAST LOAD
CA FAST RECOVER
CA FAST UNLOAD
CA FAVER VSAM DATA PROTECTION
CA FEDERATION MANAGER
CA FILE MASTER PLUS
CA FILE SYSTEM MANAGER
CA FILEAGE
CA FILESAVE RCS AUTOMATED RECOVERY
CA GATEWAY SECURITY
CA GEN
CA GEN/OL
CA GOVERNANCE, RISK & COMPLIANCE MANAGER
CA GRC MANAGER ON DEMAND
CA HIGH PERFORMANCE RECOVERY FOR IMS FOR Z/OS
CA HOST-BASED INTRUSION PREVENTION SYSTEM
CA HYPER-BUF VSAM BUFFER OPTIMIZER
CA IDEAL

Key to Media (For complete agency information see *The Advertising Red Books-Agencies* edition):
1. Bus. Publs. 2. Cable T.V. 3. Catalogs & Directories. 4. Co-op Adv. 5. Consumer Mags. 6. D.M. to Bus. Estab.7. D.M. to Consumers
8. Daily Newsp. 9. Exhibits/Trade Shows 10. Foreign 11. Infomercial 12. Internet Adv.13. Multimedia 14. Network Radio
15. Network T.V. 16. Newsp. Distr. Mags. 17. Other 18. Outdoor (Posters, Transit) 19. Point of Purchase20. Premiums, Novelties
21. Product Samples 22. Special Events Mktg. 23. Spot Radio 24. Spot T.V. 25. Weekly Newsp. 26. Yellow Page Adv.

CA, Inc. — (Continued)

CA IDENTITY MANAGER
CA IDMS
CA INDEX EXPERT FOR DB2 FOR Z/OS
CA INFOREFINER
CA INFOSESSION
CA INFOTRANSPORT
CA INFRASTRUCTURE MANAGEMENT
CA INSIGHT PERFORMANCE MONITOR FOR DB2 FOR Z/OS
CA INSTANT RECOVERY ON DEMAND
CA INTERTEST BATCH
CA INTERTEST FOR CICS
CA INTROSCOPE
CA IT ASSET MANAGER
CA IT CLIENT MANAGER
CA IT INVENTORY MANAGER
CA IT PROCESS AUTOMATION MANAGER
CA JARS RESOURCE ACCOUNTING
CA JCLCHECK WORKLOAD AUTOMATION
CA JMR
CA JOB MANAGEMENT FOR OPENVMS
CA JOBTRAC JOB MANAGEMENT
CA LIBRARIAN
CA LOG ANALYZER
CA LOGCOMPRESS
CA MAINFRAME CHORUS
CA MERGE/MODIFY
CA MESSAGE MANAGER
CA MICS RESOURCE MANAGEMENT
CA MIGRATE COBOL
CA MIM RESOURCE SHARING
CA MOBILE DEVICE MANAGEMENT
CA NETCOMPRESS DATA STREAM COMPRESSION
CA NETMAN
CA NETMASTER FILE TRANSFER MANAGEMENT
CA NETMASTER NETWORK MANAGEMENT
CA NETSPY NETWORK PERFORMANCE
CA NETVIZ
CA NSM
CA OPERA
CA OPTIMIZER/II
CA OUTPUT MANAGEMENT WEB VIEWER
CA PANAPT
CA PANAUDIT PLUS
CA PANEXEC
CA PANVALET
CA PARTITION EXPERT
CA PATCH MANAGER
CA PDSMAN PDS LIBRARY MANAGEMENT
CA PLAN ANALYZER
CA PLEX
CA PMA CHARGEBACK
CA PMO RUNTIME PERFORMANCE OPTIMIZER
CA QUICKFETCH RUNTIME PERFORMANCE OPTIMIZER
CA RAMIS
CA RAPID REORG
CA RAPS
CA RC/COMPARE
CA RC/EXTRACT
CA RC/MIGRATOR
CA RC/QUERY
CA RC/SECURE
CA RC/UPDATE
CA RECORDS MANAGER
CA RECOVERY ANALYZER
CA REMOTE CONSOLE
CA REMOTE CONTROL
CA REPORT FACILITY
CA SAN DESIGNER
CA SAN MANAGER
CA SCHEDULER JOB MANAGEMENT
CA SCHEDULER JOB MANAGEMENT FOR Z/VSE
CA SECURITY COMMAND CENTER
CA SERVICE ACCOUNTING
CA SITEMINDER
CA SMF DIRECTOR
CA SMR
CA SOA SECURITY MANAGER
CA SOFTWARE CHANGE MANAGER
CA SOFTWARE COMPLIANCE MANAGER
CA SOLVE:ACCESS SESSION MANAGEMENT
CA TECHNOLOGIES
CA VIRTUAL SUITE
CLEVERPATH
RECOVERY MANAGEMENT
TRANSFORMING IT MANAGEMENT.

Advertising Agencies:
Communication by Design
Victoria Street W
PO Box 90 349
Auckland, 1142, New Zealand
Tel.: (64) 9 357 6626
Fax: (64) 9 357 6619

Dircks Associates
550 N Country Rd Ste A
Saint James, NY 11780-1427
Tel.: (631) 584-2274
Fax: (631) 584-2043

CACI INTERNATIONAL INC.

1100 N Glebe Rd
Arlington, VA 22201-4798
Tel.: (703) 841-7800
Fax: (703) 841-7882
Telex: 824416
E-mail: nhogan@caci.com
Web Site: www.caci.com
E-Mail For Key Personnel:
Public Relations: jbrown@caci.com
Approx. Rev.: $3,577,780,000
Approx. Number Employees: 13,700
Year Founded: 1962
Business Description:
Information Technology & Communications Services
S.I.C.: 7373; 7371; 8711; 8742; 9711
N.A.I.C.S.: 541512; 541330; 541511; 541614; 928110
Media: 10
Personnel:
Jack Phillip London *(Chm)*
Paul M. Cofoni *(Pres & CEO)*
Thomas A. Mutryn *(CFO, Treas & Exec VP)*
Deborah B. Dunie *(CTO & Exec VP)*
H. Robert Boehm *(Chief HR Officer & Exec VP)*
Keith L. Salzman *(Chief Medical Info Officer)*
Gregory R. Bradford *(Pres-Info Solutions Grp)*
William M. Fairl *(Pres-Ops-United States)*
Jody A. Brown *(Exec VP-PR & Bus Comm)*
Albert M. Calland, III *(Exec VP-Security & Intelligence Integration)*
Gilbert B. Guarino *(Exec VP-Transformation Solutions Bus Grp)*
Lowell E. Jacoby *(Exec VP-Natl Solutions Bus Grp)*
Karl Johnson *(Exec VP-Mission Sys Bus Grp)*
Richard F. G. Miller *(Exec VP)*
Daniel E. Porter *(Exec VP-Enterprise Tech & Svcs)*
Ronald A. Schneider *(Exec VP-Bus Dev)*
Robert B. Turner *(Exec VP-HR)*
Steven H. Weiss *(Exec VP-Govt Bus Ops)*
Louis E. Andre *(Sr VP-Intl Bus Strategy)*
David L. Dragics *(Sr VP-IR)*
Carl Muller *(Sr VP)*
Jane Shaw *(Mgr)*
Brands & Products:
ACQUILINE
CACI
CACIHEALTH
COMPRIZON
EVER VIGILANT
FEDSELECT
HIGHVIEW
MOMENTUM
NETWORK II.5
QUICKBID
REGENERATE
RENOVATE
SACONS
SACONS-FEDERAL
SIMFORCE
SIMPROCESS
SIMSCRIPT
VISION & SOLUTION CENTER
XEN CORPORATION

CADENCE DESIGN SYSTEMS, INC.

2655 Seely Ave Bldg 5
San Jose, CA 95134
Tel.: (408) 943-1234
Fax: (408) 428-5001
Toll Free: (800) 746-6223
E-mail: investor_relations@cadence.com
Web Site: www.cadence.com
E-Mail For Key Personnel:
Sales Director: salesinfo@cadence.com
Approx. Rev.: $935,954,000
Approx. Number Employees: 4,600
Year Founded: 1988
Business Description:
Electronic Design Automation Software & Hardware Products Developer & Mfr
S.I.C.: 7372; 3577
N.A.I.C.S.: 511210; 334119; 334611
Export
Advertising Expenditures: $8,600,000
Media: 7-10-13-17
Distr.: Intl.
Budget Set: Dec.
Personnel:
John B. Shoven *(Chm)*
Lip-Bu Tan *(Pres & CEO)*
Geoff Ribar *(CFO & Sr VP)*
John Bruggeman *(CMO & Sr VP)*
James J. Cowie *(Gen Counsel, Sec & Sr VP)*
Chi-Ping Hsu *(Sr VP-Res, Dev & Silicon Realization Grp)*
Charlie Huang *(Sr VP-Field Ops-Worldwide)*
Tina Jones *(Sr VP-Global HR)*
Nimish H. Modi *(Sr VP-Res, Dev, System & SoC Realization Grp)*
Alan Lindstrom *(Dir-IR)*
Brands & Products:
ALLEGRO
ASSURA
CADENCE
CONNECTIONS
ENCOUNTER
FIRST ENCOUNTER
FIRST SILICON SYSTEM
INCISIVE
INSTALLSCAPE
MASKCOMPOSE
NANOROUTE
OPENBOOK
ORCAD
PSPICE
SKILL
SPEEDBRIDGE
VIRTUOSO
VOLTAGESTORM
Advertising Agency:
Text 100 London Ltd.
Level 5 The Triangle
5-17 Hammersmith Grove
London, W6 0LG, United Kingdom
Tel.: (44) 20 8846 0700
Fax: (44) 20 8846 0800

CALIBRUS, INC.

1225 W Washington St Ste 213
Tempe, AZ 85281
Tel.: (602) 778-7500
Tel.: (602) 778-7516
Fax: (602) 778-7569
E-mail: info@calibrus.com
Web Site: www.calibrus.com
Approx. Rev.: $3,745,876
Approx. Number Employees: 50
Year Founded: 1999
Business Description:
Third Party Verification, Hosted Call Recording & Interactive Voice Response/Voice Recognition Unit (IVR/VRU) Services
S.I.C.: 7373; 7389
N.A.I.C.S.: 541512; 517919; 561499
Advertising Expenditures: $22,000
Media: 2-6-10-13-23
Personnel:
Greg W. Holmes *(Pres & Sec)*
Jeff W. Holmes *(CEO)*
Kevin J. Asher *(CFO)*
Glenda Hampton *(Dir-HR)*
Kelly M. Robinson *(Dir-Ops)*

CALIPER CORPORATION

506 Carnegie Ctr Ste 300
Princeton, NJ 08540
Tel.: (609) 524-1200
Fax: (609) 524-1201
E-mail: info@calipercorp.com
Web Site: www.caliperonline.com
Sales Range: $10-24.9 Million
Approx. Number Employees: 125
Business Description:
Management Consulting Services
S.I.C.: 7361
N.A.I.C.S.: 541612
Media: 2-7

Key to Media (For complete agency information see *The Advertising Red Books-Agencies* edition):
1. Bus. Publs. 2. Cable T.V. 3. Catalogs & Directories. 4. Co-op Adv. 5. Consumer Mags. 6. D.M. to Bus. Estab.7. D.M. to Consumers
8. Daily Newsp. 9. Exhibits/Trade Shows 10. Foreign 11. Infomercial 12. Internet Adv.13. Multimedia 14. Network Radio
15. Network T.V. 16. Newsp. Distr. Mags. 17. Other 18. Outdoor (Posters, Transit) 19. Point of Purchase20. Premiums, Novelties
21. Product Samples 22. Special Events Mktg. 23. Spot Radio 24. Spot T.V. 25. Weekly Newsp. 26. Yellow Page Adv.

Personnel:
Herbert Greenberg *(Founder & CEO)*
James Harmon *(CFO)*
Mark Greenberg *(COO)*
Amy Yates *(VP-Mktg)*

CALLIDUS SOFTWARE INC.
6200 Stoneridge Mall Rd Ste 500
Pleasanton, CA 94588
Tel.: (925) 251-2200
E-mail: pr@callidussoftware.com
Web Site: www.callidussoftware.com
Approx. Rev.: $70,880,000
Approx. Number Employees: 260
Year Founded: 1996
Business Description:
Software Developer
S.I.C.: 7371; 7372
N.A.I.C.S.: 541511; 511210
Advertising Expenditures: $17,000
Media: 2
Personnel:
Charles M. Boesenberg *(Chm)*
Leslie J. Stretch *(Pres & CEO)*
Ronald J. Fior *(CFO, Sr VP-Fin & Ops)*
V. Holly Albert *(Gen Counsel, Sec & Sr VP)*
Meredith Calvert *(Sr VP-Customer Svc & Support)*
Jimmy Duan *(Sr VP-Asia Pacific & Latin America)*
Michael Graves *(Sr VP-Engrg)*
Lorna Heynike *(Sr VP-Mktg)*
Saied Karamooz *(Sr VP-Client Svcs)*
Brands & Products:
CALLIDUS SOFTWARE
CALLIDUS TRUEANALYTICS
TRUEALLOCATION
TRUECHANNEL
TRUECOMP
TRUECOMP ARCHITECTURE
TRUECOMP DATAMART
TRUECOMP GRID
TRUECOMP MANAGER
TRUECONNECTION
TRUEFOUNDATION
TRUEINFORMATION
TRUEINTEGRATION
TRUEMBO
TRUEPERFORMANCE
TRUEPERFORMANCE INDEX
TRUEPERFORMANCE INDICATOR
TRUEPRODUCER
TRUEQUOTA
TRUEREFERRAL
TRUERESOLUTION
TRUESERVICE
TRUESERVICE+
TRUESUPPORT
TRUETARGET

CAM COMMERCE SOLUTIONS, INC.
(Holding of Great Hill Partners, LLC)
17075 Newhope St Ste A
Fountain Valley, CA 92708-4262
Tel.: (714) 241-9241
Fax: (714) 241-9241
Toll Free: (800) 726-3282
Web Site: www.camcommerce.com
Approx. Rev.: $32,229,000
Approx. Number Employees: 196
Year Founded: 1983
Business Description:
Mfr of Point-of-Sale Equipment & Software for Sales & Inventory Tracking
S.I.C.: 7373; 7378
N.A.I.C.S.: 541512; 811212
Advertising Expenditures: $578,000
Media: 1-2-7-8-10-13
Brands & Products:
A-TRADE
CAM COMMERCE SOLUTIONS
CAM32
I.CAM32
I.STAR
MICROBIZ
RETAIL ICE
RETAIL STAR
SAGE MAS 90
X-CHARGE

CAMBEX CORPORATION
337 Turnpike Rd
Southborough, MA 01772
Tel.: (508) 281-0209
Fax: (508) 281-0214
Toll Free: (800) 325-5565
E-mail: info@cambex.com
Web Site: www.cambex.com
Sales Range: $1-9.9 Million
Approx. Number Employees: 14
Year Founded: 1968
Business Description:
Computer Enhancement & Data Storage Products & Solutions Designer, Developer, Mfr & Retailer
S.I.C.: 3572
N.A.I.C.S.: 334112
Import Export
Media: 2-7-10-13
Personnel:
Joseph F. Kruy *(Chm, Pres & CEO)*
Brands & Products:
A GOOD PLACE TO PUT YOUR INFORMATION
CENTURION
DYNAMIC PATH FAILOVER
FIBREQUIK
STOR
VERSACACHE

CAMO SOFTWARE, INC.
1 Woodbridge Ctr
Woodbridge, NJ 07095
Tel.: (732) 726-9203
Fax: (973) 556-1229
E-mail: camous@camo.com
Web Site: www.camo.com
Sales Range: $10-24.9 Million
Approx. Number Employees: 50
Year Founded: 1984
Business Description:
Computer Consulting Services
S.I.C.: 7373
N.A.I.C.S.: 541512
Media: 11-13
Personnel:
Halvor Svartdal *(Chm)*
Paal Braathen *(CEO)*
Ravi Upadhyaya *(VP-Product Dev)*
Brands & Products:
CAMO
MARKET SIZZLE
THE UNSCRAMBLER
UNSCRAMBLER CLASSIFIER
UNSCRAMBLER ONLINE
UNSCRAMBLER OPTIMIZER
UNSCRAMBLER PREDICTOR

CANADA POST CORPORATION
2701 Riverside Dr
Ottawa, ON K1A 0B1, Canada
Tel.: (613) 734-7575
Fax: (613) 734-7432
Toll Free: (866) 607-6301
E-mail: communications@canadapost.ca
Web Site: www.canadapost.ca
Approx. Number Employees: 71,433
Year Founded: 1981
Business Description:
Postal Service
S.I.C.: 4311
N.A.I.C.S.: 491110
Personnel:
Gordon J. Feeney *(Chm)*
Moya Greene *(CEO & Dir)*
Jacques Cote *(COO)*
Douglas Greaves *(Chief Investment Officer & VP-Pension Fund)*
Laurene Cihosky *(Sr VP-Direct Mktg/ Adv & Publ Bus)*
Cal Hart *(Sr VP-Postal Transformation)*
Peter Melanson *(Sr VP-Sls)*
Louis F. O'Brien *(Chief Customer Officer & Sr VP)*
Cheryl A. Persad *(Sr VP-Transaction Mail)*
Philip Ventura *(Sr VP-Strategy)*
Clary Ottman *(Comptroller & VP-Fin)*
Mhoire Murdoch *(VP-Customer Svc)*
Anthony Wilson-Smith *(VP-Comm)*
Jean-Mark Nantais *(Gen Mgr-Mktg Svcs)*
Alain Leduc *(Mgr-Production)*
Brands & Products:
CANADA POST
FETCH
FROM ANYWHERE...TO ANYONE
Advertising Agencies:
French/West/Vaughan, Inc.
112 E Hargett St
Raleigh, NC 27601
Tel.: (919) 832-6300
Fax: (919) 832-6360
Maple Grove

Porter Novelli-Toronto
33 Bloor Street East Suite 1450
Toronto, ON M4W 3H1, Canada
Tel.: (416) 423-6605
Fax: (416) 423-5154
— Briana D'Archi *(Acct Exec)*

CANDELIS, INC.
(Sub. of Candle Acquisition Corporation)
18821 Bardeen Ave
Irvine, CA 92612
Tel.: (949) 852-1000
Fax: (949) 752-7317
Toll Free: (800) 800-8600
E-mail: info@candelis.com
Web Site: www.candelis.com
E-Mail For Key Personnel:
Marketing Director: hossein.pourmand@candelis.com
Sales Range: $25-49.9 Million
Approx. Number Employees: 25
Year Founded: 1987
Business Description:
Medical Image Storage Devices
S.I.C.: 3572
N.A.I.C.S.: 334112
Media: 2-10-13-22
Personnel:
Mazi Razmjoo *(VP-Sls)*
Alex Razmjoo *(Dir)*
Brands & Products:
DATAFORCE
IMAGEGRID
NETFORCE
PROMOBILE
TAURUS
Advertising Agency:
XPR LLC
217 N Main St Ste 200
Santa Ana, CA 92701
Tel.: (714) 881-2310
Fax: (714) 881-2443

CAPE SYSTEMS GROUP, INC.
100 Allentown Pky
Allen, TX 75002
Toll Free: (800) 229-3434
E-mail: sales@capesystems.com
Web Site: www.capesystems.com
Sales Range: $1-9.9 Million
Approx. Number Employees: 23
Business Description:
Supply Chain Software & Computer Systems Integration Services
S.I.C.: 7372; 7373
N.A.I.C.S.: 511210; 541512
Advertising Expenditures: $78,000
Media: 17
Personnel:
Hugo H. Biermann *(Chm)*
Nicholas R.H. Toms *(CEO)*
Brad Leonard *(VP-Sls & Ops)*
Brands & Products:
APPLY & COMPLY
CAPE
CAPE PACK
CARTRITE
LEADING THE WAY IN PACKAGING SOFTWARE
PICRITE
PUTRITE
RFID APPLY AND COMPLY
RFID TAG LOCATOR
TRUCKFILL
TURNRITE

CAPGEMINI U.S.
(Sub. of Capgemini S.A.)
623 5th Ave 33rd Fl
New York, NY 10022
Tel.: (212) 314-8000
Fax: (212) 314-8001
E-mail: webmaster@capgemini.com
Web Site: www.us.capgemini.com
Approx. Number Employees: 3,000
Year Founded: 1968
Business Description:
Information Technology Consulting Services
S.I.C.: 8748
N.A.I.C.S.: 541618
Advertising Expenditures: $700,000
Media: 2-6-9-10-11-25
Distr.: Natl.
Budget Set: Dec.
Personnel:
Lanny Cohen *(CEO)*
Navin Goel *(CEO-Sogeti USA & India)*
Michael Chayet *(Gen Counsel)*
Tim Bridges *(VP-Media & Entertainment)*
Douglas Charles *(VP-Mktg Dev & Sls-North America)*
John Manos *(Mgr-Mktg)*
Brands & Products:
CAP GEMINI AMERICA

Capgemini U.S. — (Continued)

Advertising Agency:
Impressions-A.B.A. Industries, Inc.
393 Jericho Tpk
Mineola, NY 11501
Tel.: (516) 739-3210
Fax: (516) 739-9246

CAPITOL OFFICE SOLUTIONS

(Sub. of Global Imaging Systems, Inc.)
12301 Kiln Ct
Beltsville, MD 20705-6307
Tel.: (301) 210-4380
Fax: (301) 210-3040
Toll Free: (888) 937-2345
Web Site:
www.capitolofficesolutions.com
Sales Range: $100-124.9 Million
Approx. Number Employees: 72
Business Description:
Office Equipment, Copy Products & Office Furniture Distr
S.I.C.: 5999; 5731; 5943
N.A.I.C.S.: 453910; 443112; 453210
Media: 9-25-26
Distr.: Natl.
Budget Set: June

CAPTECH VENTURES, INC.

1118 W Main St
Richmond, VA 23220
Tel.: (804) 355-0511
Fax: (804) 355-4220
Web Site:
www.captechconsulting.com
Approx. Number Employees: 65
Business Description:
Information Systems Manager, Designer & Builder; Consulting Services
S.I.C.: 7373; 8742
N.A.I.C.S.: 541512; 541611
Personnel:
Sandy Williamson *(Founding Principal & CEO)*
Errol Restelli *(Mng Dir)*
Slaughter Fitz-Hugh *(Founding Principal & Chief Ops Officer)*
Advertising Agency:
Corder Philips, Inc.
508 W 5th St Ste 100
Charlotte, NC 28202
Tel.: (704) 333-3924
Fax: (704) 358-0134

CARBONITE, INC.

334 Boylston St 3rd Fl
Boston, MA 02116
Tel.: (617) 587-1100
Toll Free: (877) 665-4466
Web Site: www.carbonite.com
Sales Range: $10-24.9 Million
Business Description:
Online Data Backup Services
S.I.C.: 7374
N.A.I.C.S.: 518210
Media: 14-23
Personnel:
David Friend *(Co-Founder, Chm & CEO)*
Jeff Flowers *(Co-Founder & CTO)*
Andrew Keenan *(CFO & VP-Fin & Admin)*
Peter T. Lamson *(Sr VP & Gen Mgr-Small Bus Div)*
Oussama El-Hilali *(Sr VP-Engrg)*
Tom Murray *(VP-Mktg)*
Jeffrey Robison *(VP)*
Swami Kumaresan *(Gen Mgr-Consumer Group)*
David Hauser *(Dir)*
Advertising Agency:
Airfoil Public Relations
1000 Town Ctr Dr Ste 600
Southfield, MI 48075
Tel.: (248) 304-1400
Fax: (248) 304-1401
Toll Free: (866) AIRFOIL

CAREER BLAZERS INC.

(Holding of Global Employment Holdings, Inc.)
590 W 37th St 5th FL
New York, NY 10018
Tel.: (212) 719-3232
Fax: (212) 221-0452
Web Site: www.careerblazers.com
Sales Range: $10-24.9 Million
Approx. Number Employees: 50
Year Founded: 1949
Business Description:
Temporary & Permanent Job Placement Services
S.I.C.: 7361
N.A.I.C.S.: 561310
Media: 7-17
Personnel:
Caress Kennedy *(Pres)*

CARLSON JPM STORE FIXTURES

(Formerly Dann Dee Display Fixtures)
(Sub. of Stein Industries, Inc.)
7147 Northland Dr
Brooklyn Park, MN 55428
Tel.: (763) 504-3547
Fax: (847) 588-1620
Toll Free: (800) 888-8515
Web Site: www.carlson-store-fixtures.com
Sales Range: $25-49.9 Million
Approx. Number Employees: 100
Year Founded: 1945
Business Description:
Store Fixtures & Accessories Whslr
S.I.C.: 5046; 7389
N.A.I.C.S.: 423440; 541410
Import
Media: 2-4-7-10-22-26
Distr.: Natl.
Budget Set: July
Personnel:
Eric Ramberg *(Pres)*
Brands & Products:
DANN DEE DISPLAY FIXTURES

CAROLINA WHOLESALE OFFICE MACHINE COMPANY, INC.

425 E Arrowhead Dr
Charlotte, NC 28213-6378
Tel.: (704) 598-8101
Fax: (800) 356-9169
Toll Free: (800) 521-4600
Web Site: www.cwholesale.com
Sales Range: $25-49.9 Million
Approx. Number Employees: 50
Business Description:
Office Machines Whslr & Distr
S.I.C.: 5044
N.A.I.C.S.: 423420
Media: 2-4-7-10-13
Personnel:
Larry L. Huneycutt *(Owner)*
Marty Wilson *(CFO & VP)*

CASESTACK, INC.

2850 Ocean Pk Blvd Ste 100
Santa Monica, CA 90405
Tel.: (310) 473-8885
Fax: (310) 943-4137
E-mail: info@casestack.com
Web Site: www.casestack.com
E-Mail For Key Personnel:
Marketing Director: JWeston@casestack.com
Approx. Number Employees: 110
Year Founded: 2000
Business Description:
Logistics Outsourcing Services; Warehousing, Fulfillment & Transportation Infrastructure Services
S.I.C.: 8742; 4225; 4731
N.A.I.C.S.: 541614; 488510; 493110
Media: 10-13
Personnel:
Daniel A. Sanker *(Pres & CEO)*
Polly Rebich *(VP-Engrng)*

THE CASEY GROUP

77 E Halsey Rd
Parsippany, NJ 07054-3704
Tel.: (973) 299-4700
Fax: (973) 299-6484
E-mail: sales@caseygrp.com
Web Site: www.caseygrp.com
E-Mail For Key Personnel:
Sales Director: sales@caseygrp.com
Approx. Number Employees: 75
Year Founded: 1989
Business Description:
Computer Software Development, Management Consulting & Applications Outsourcing Services
S.I.C.: 7371; 8742
N.A.I.C.S.: 541511; 541611
Media: 2-7-22-26
Personnel:
Richard P. Casey *(Chm & CEO)*
Daniel G. Henderson *(Pres & COO)*
Jerry Auriemma *(Chief Mktg & Sls Officer)*
Holly Jamros *(VP-HR)*
Brands & Products:
CASEY
DRIVE VALUE. DELIVER SUCCESS.
PROJECT TURNAROUND

CASIO, INC.

(Sub. of Casio Computer Co., Ltd.)
570 Mount Pleasant Ave
Dover, NJ 07801-1620
Mailing Address:
PO Box 7000
Dover, NJ 07802-7000
Tel.: (973) 361-5400
Fax: (973) 537-8926
Toll Free: (800) 836-8580
Web Site: www.casio.com
Sales Range: $450-499.9 Million
Approx. Number Employees: 300
Year Founded: 1970
Business Description:
Consumer Electronics Mfr
S.I.C.: 5044; 5045
N.A.I.C.S.: 423420; 423430
Import
Advertising Expenditures: $8,800,000
Bus. Publs.: $1,000,000; Cable T.V.: $1,000,000; Co-op Adv.: $500,000; Consumer Mags.: $2,000,000; Exhibits/Trade Shows: $1,000,000; Outdoor (Posters, Transit): $200,000; Point of Purchase: $1,000,000; Premiums, Novelties: $100,000; Spot T.V.: $2,000,000
Distr.: Intl.; Natl.
Budget Set: Nov.
Personnel:
Larry Sampey *(Gen Mgr-System Products Div)*
Connie Bearfield *(Mgr-Mktg Svcs)*
Brands & Products:
CASIOTONE
CASIOTRON

CATALINA MARKETING CORPORATION

(Holding of Hellman & Friedman LLC)
200 Carillon Pkwy
Saint Petersburg, FL 33716
Tel.: (727) 579-5000
Fax: (727) 556-2700
Toll Free: (888) 322-3814
Web Site:
www.catalinamarketing.com
Approx. Rev.: $417,745,984
Approx. Number Employees: 1,200
Year Founded: 1983
Business Description:
Strategic Targeted Marketing Solutions for Consumer Goods Companies, Pharmaceutical Mfr & Retailers
S.I.C.: 7319
N.A.I.C.S.: 541890; 541870
Advertising Expenditures: $1,400,000
Media: 4-7-13-20-23-24
Distr.: Direct to Consumer; Intl.; Natl.; Reg.
Personnel:
George Off *(Founder)*
Tom Buehlmann *(Pres & Exec VP)*
Jamie Egasti *(CEO)*
Rick P. Frier *(CFO & Exec VP)*
Eric Williams *(CIO & Exec VP)*
Edward Kuehnle *(Pres-Catalina Svcs)*
Renee Selman *(Pres-Health Resource)*
Claire DeMatteis *(Gen Counsel & Exec VP)*
Deborah Booth *(Exec VP-Bus Support Svcs)*
Barry Brindise *(Sr VP-Fin)*
Sharon Glass *(Grp VP)*
Jim Flanagan *(VP-Fin)*
Rachel Keener *(Sr Dir-Corp Comm)*
Carrie Stec *(Dir-Bus Dev)*
Steve Lane *(Mgr-UK)*
Brands & Products:
CATALINA MARKETING
CHECKOUT COUPON
QUICK CASH

CAVIUM NETWORKS, INC.

805 E Middlefield Rd
Mountain View, CA 94043
Tel.: (650) 623-7000
Fax: (650) 625-9751
E-mail: info@caviumnetworks.com
Web Site: www.caviumnetworks.com
Approx. Rev.: $206,500,000
Approx. Number Employees: 633
Business Description:
Semiconductor Products Mfr; 30% Owned by Menlo Ventures
S.I.C.: 5734; 3674
N.A.I.C.S.: 443120; 334413
Advertising Expenditures: $396,000

Key to Media (For complete agency information see *The Advertising Red Books-Agencies* edition):
1. Bus. Publs. 2. Cable T.V. 3. Catalogs & Directories. 4. Co-op Adv. 5. Consumer Mags. 6. D.M. to Bus. Estab.7. D.M. to Consumers
8. Daily Newsp. 9. Exhibits/Trade Shows 10. Foreign 11. Infomercial 12. Internet Adv.13. Multimedia 14. Network Radio
15. Network T.V. 16. Newsp. Distr. Mags. 17. Other 18. Outdoor (Posters, Transit) 19. Point of Purchase20. Premiums, Novelties
21. Product Samples 22. Special Events Mktg. 23. Spot Radio 24. Spot T.V. 25. Weekly Newsp. 26. Yellow Page Adv.

Media: 7-10-11
Personnel:
Syed B. Ali *(Pres & CEO)*
Arthur Chadwick *(CFO & VP-Fin & Admin)*
Rajiv Khemani *(COO)*
Muhammad Raghib Hussain *(CTO & Corp VP-Software)*
Andrew J. Rava *(VP-Sls & Field Applications)*
Angel Atondo *(Mgr-Mktg Program)*

CBAYSYSTEMS HOLDINGS LIMITED
(Name Changed to MEDQUIST HOLDINGS INC.)

CBS INTERACTIVE INC.
(Sub. of CBS Corporation)
235 2nd St
San Francisco, CA 94105
Tel.: (415) 344-2000
Web Site: www.cbsinteractive.com
Approx. Rev.: $405,895,000
Approx. Number Employees: 3,500
Year Founded: 1995
Business Description:
Online Consumer Technology, News & Information Publisher
S.I.C.: 2741
N.A.I.C.S.: 516110
Advertising Expenditures: $17,400,000
Personnel:
Jim Lanzone *(Pres)*
Mary M. Hentges *(CFO)*
Mickey McClay Wilson *(CMO)*
David S. Morris *(Chief Client Officer)*
Adam Power *(Pres-Intl)*
Stephen Colvin *(Exec VP)*
Joseph Gillespie *(Exec VP-CNET Bus)*
Marc DeBevoise *(Sr VP & Gen Mgr-Entertainment Div)*
Greg Mason *(Sr VP & Gen Mgr)*
Dan Farber *(Sr VP-ZDNet)*
Candice Meyers *(Sr VP)*
Jose Martin *(Photographer & Editor-Photo)*
Sam Parker *(Dir-Product)*
Brands & Products:
BNET
CHOW
CNET
CNET DOWNLOADS
CNET NEWS
GAMEFAQS
GAMESPOT
MP3.COM
MYSIMON
TECHREPUBLIC
TV.COM
URBANBABY
ZDNET

CCC INFORMATION SERVICES, INC.
(Holding of Investcorp International, Inc.)
World Trade Ctr Chicago 444 Merchandise Mart
Chicago, IL 60654
Tel.: (312) 222-4636
Fax: (312) 527-2298
Toll Free: (800) 621-8070
Web Site: www.cccis.com
E-Mail For Key Personnel:
Public Relations: jharris@cccis.com
Sales Range: $150-199.9 Million
Approx. Number Employees: 1,120
Year Founded: 1980
Business Description:
Claims Management Information & Services
S.I.C.: 7371; 7372; 7379
N.A.I.C.S.: 541511; 511210; 541519
Personnel:
Githesh Ramamurthy *(Chm & CEO)*
Gary Newman *(Chief HR Officer & Sr VP)*
James A. Dickens *(Sr VP-Automotive Svcs Grp)*
John Harris *(Mgr-Strategic & PR)*
Brands & Products:
CCC ACCUMARK
CCC ACCUMARK REINSPECTION
CCC AUTOVERSE
CCC AUTOVERSE CLAIM MANAGEMENT
CCC CONNECT
CCC INTELLISPHERE
CCC INTELLISPHERE INSURANCE REPORTING
CCC PATHWAYS
CCC PATHWAYS APPRAISAL SOLUTION
CCC VALUESCOPE
CCC VALUESCOPE CLAIM SERVICES
QUALITY ADVISOR
RECYCLED PARTS SERVICES
Advertising Agency:
ThunderWheel Communications
3200 E Guasti Rd Ste 100
Ontario, CA 91761
Tel.: (909) 435-8622

CDS GLOBAL, INC.
(Sub. of Hearst Magazines)
1901 Bell Ave
Des Moines, IA 50315-1099
Tel.: (515) 247-7500
Fax: (515) 246-6805
E-mail: salesinfo@cds-global.com
Web Site: www.cds-global.com
E-Mail For Key Personnel:
Sales Director: salesinfo@cds-global.com
Approx. Number Employees: 3,000
Business Description:
Magazine & Media Subscription Data Management & Fulfillment Services
S.I.C.: 7374; 5045; 7389
N.A.I.C.S.: 518210; 425110; 561499
Media: 2
Personnel:
Malcolm Netburn *(Chm & CEO)*
Kenneth J. Barloon *(CFO & Sr VP)*
Dave Dutch *(Sr VP-Bus Solutions)*
Nancy Gessmann *(Sr VP-Enterprise Solutions)*
Christine Simpson *(VP & Gen Mgr-Canada)*
Mike Luksan *(VP-Sls, Magazines & Media)*
Sarah Nesland *(VP-Natl Sls)*
Beth Roy *(VP-Magazines & Media)*
Eileen White *(VP-Global Mktg & Comm)*
David Donnelly *(Dir-Global Comm)*

CDW CORPORATION
(Holding of Madison Dearborn Partners, LLC)
200 N Milwaukee Ave
Vernon Hills, IL 60061
Tel.: (847) 465-6000
Fax: (847) 465-3444
Toll Free: (800) 797-4239
Web Site: www.cdw.com
Approx. Sls.: $8,801,200,000
Approx. Number Employees: 6,850
Year Founded: 1984
Business Description:
Brandname Technology Services & Computer Products Reseller
S.I.C.: 5734; 5045; 5961; 5963
N.A.I.C.S.: 443120; 423430; 454111; 454390
Advertising Expenditures: $106,000,000
Media: 2-4-10-13
Distr.: Natl.
Budget Set: Nov.
Personnel:
John A. Edwardson *(Chm & CEO)*
Thomas E. Richards *(Pres & COO)*
Matthew A. Troka *(VP-Product & Partner Mgmt)*
Jonathan J. Stevens *(CIO & Sr VP-Ops)*
Christina V. Rother *(Pres-CDW Govt LLC)*
Christine A. Leahy *(General Counsel, Corp Sec & Sr VP)*
Robert J. Welyki *(Treasurer, VP & Asst Sec)*
Dennis Berger *(Chief Coworker Services Officer & Sr VP)*
Christina M. Corley *(Sr VP-Sls)*
Douglas E. Eckrote *(Sr VP-Ops & Canada)*
Bill Weaver *(Grp VP)*
Collin Kebo *(VP-Fin)*
Theresa Reinhard *(Sr Dir-Organizational Capability)*
Gary Ross *(Dir-Corp Comm)*
Heather Kline *(Coord-Marketing Project)*
Brands & Products:
SMART SEARCH
Advertising Agency:
Ogilvy PR
350 W Mart Ctr Dr 11th Fl
Chicago, IL 60654
Tel.: (312) 397-6000
Fax: (312) 397-8841
— Anshula Ahluwalia *(Acct Exec)*

CELERIT CORPORATION
216 Atkins Rd
Little Rock, AR 72211
Tel.: (501) 312-2900
Fax: (501) 312-0864
Toll Free: (888) 841-6799
E-mail: info@celerit.com
Web Site: www.celerit.com
Approx. Number Employees: 40
Year Founded: 1985
Business Description:
Information Technology Solutions & Staffing Services
S.I.C.: 7371; 8742
N.A.I.C.S.: 541511; 541611
Media: 10
Personnel:
Terry Rothwell *(CEO)*

CENTER FOR WINE ORIGINS
1850 M St NW Ste 800
Washington, DC 20036
Tel.: (202) 777-3544
Fax: (202) 289-4141
E-mail: info@wineorigins.com
Web Site: www.wineorigins.com
Approx. Number Employees: 50
Business Description:
Educational Campaign to Protect Wine Place Names
S.I.C.: 9411
N.A.I.C.S.: 923110
Media: 6

CERIDIAN CORPORATION
(Joint Venture of Thomas H. Lee Partners, L.P. & Fidelity National Financial, Inc.)
3311 E Old Shakopee Rd
Minneapolis, MN 55425
Tel.: (952) 853-8100
Fax: (952) 853-8199
Toll Free: (800) 729-7655
Telex: 160323
E-mail: info@ceridian.com
Web Site: www.ceridian.com
Approx. Rev.: $1,565,300,000
Approx. Number Employees: 8,776
Year Founded: 2000
Business Description:
Payroll Processing & Human Resource Services; Owned 33% by Fidelity National Financial, Inc. & 67% by Thomas H. Lee Partners, LP
S.I.C.: 8721; 8742; 9441
N.A.I.C.S.: 541214; 541611; 923130
Media: 17
Personnel:
Stuart C. Harvey, Jr. *(Pres & CEO)*
Gregory J. Macfarlane *(CFO & Exec VP)*
Michael F. Shea *(COO & Exec VP)*
Mike Degeneffe *(CTO & Sr VP)*
Jim Burns *(Pres-Ceridian Intl & Exec VP)*
Michael W. Sheridan *(Gen Counsel, Sec & Exec VP)*
Kairus K. Tarapore *(Exec VP-HR)*
Albert J. Bart *(Sr VP & Asst Gen Counsel)*
Craig G. Manson *(Sr VP)*
Jayson Saba *(VP-Mktg Strategy & Indus Analyst Rels)*
Lydia Ophaug *(Sr Product Mgr-Health & Welfare)*
Advertising Agencies:
Adkins Design Visual Communications LLC
35 Corporate Drive Suite 1090
Trumbull, CT 06614
Tel.: (203) 375-2887
Fax: (203) 386-1203

Ketchum Canada
33 Bloor St E Ste 1607
Toronto, ON M4W 3H1, Canada
Tel.: (416) 355-7400
Fax: (416) 355-7420

CERTICOM CORP.
(Sub. of Research In Motion Ltd.)
5520 Explorer Dr 4th Fl
Mississauga, ON L4W 5L1, Canada
Tel.: (905) 507-4220
Fax: (905) 507-4230
E-mail: info@certicom.com
Web Site: www.certicom.com
Approx. Rev.: $16,615,000
Approx. Number Employees: 112
Year Founded: 1985
Business Description:
Hardware & Software Cryptography
S.I.C.: 7373; 7372; 7382

Key to Media (For complete agency information see *The Advertising Red Books-Agencies* edition):
1. Bus. Publs. 2. Cable T.V. 3. Catalogs & Directories. 4. Co-op Adv. 5. Consumer Mags. 6. D.M. to Bus. Estab.7. D.M. to Consumers
8. Daily Newsp. 9. Exhibits/Trade Shows 10. Foreign 11. Infomercial 12. Internet Adv.13. Multimedia 14. Network Radio
15. Network T.V. 16. Newsp. Distr. Mags. 17. Other 18. Outdoor (Posters, Transit) 19. Point of Purchase20. Premiums, Novelties
21. Product Samples 22. Special Events Mktg. 23. Spot Radio 24. Spot T.V. 25. Weekly Newsp. 26. Yellow Page Adv.

Certicom Corp. — (Continued)

N.A.I.C.S.: 541512; 511210; 561621
Media: 5-10-22
Personnel:
Scott A. Vanstone *(Founder & Exec VP-Strategic Tech)*
Ross Bennett *(Sr Dir-Product Dev)*

Brands & Products:
CERTICOM
CERTICOM CODESIGN
CERTICRYPT
CODESIGN
CRYPTO
DIGITAL RIGHTS MANAGEMENT
EMBEDDED TRUST SERVICES
EPKI
IPSEC
KEYINJECT
MOVIANCRYPT
MOVIANDM
MOVIANMAIL
MOVIANVPN
SECURE SOCKETS LAYER
SECURITY BUILDER
SECURITY BUILDER DRM
SECURITY BUILDER ETS
SECURITY BUILDER GSE
SECURITY BUILDER PKI
SECURITY BUILDER SSL
TRUSTPOINT

CGI GROUP INC.

1130 Sherbrooke St W 7th Fl
Montreal, QC H3A 2M8, Canada
Tel.: (514) 841-3200
Fax: (514) 841-3299
Web Site: www.cgi.com
Approx. Rev.: $3,652,548,266
Approx. Number Employees: 31,000
Year Founded: 1981
Business Description:
Information Technology & Business Process Services; Consulting Services
S.I.C.: 8748; 7371; 7373; 7376; 7379; 8742
N.A.I.C.S.: 541690; 541511; 541512; 541513; 541519; 541611
Media: 2-6-7-10-11
Personnel:
Andre Imbeau *(Founder, Exec Vice Chm & Corp Sec)*
Serge Godin *(Founder & Exec Chm)*
Michael E. Roach *(Pres & CEO)*
David Anderson *(CFO & Exec VP)*
Luc Pinard *(CTO, Chief Quality Officer & Exec VP)*
Daniel Rocheleau *(Chief Bus Engrg Officer & Exec VP)*
Douglas McCuaig *(Pres-Canada)*
Donna S. Morea *(Pres-US, Europe & Asia)*
Hicham Adra *(Sr VP & Gen Mgr)*
Eva Maglis *(Sr VP & Gen Mgr-Tech & Infrastructure)*
Claude Marcoux *(Sr VP, Gen Mgr-Quebec & Ottawa)*
Nazzic Turner *(Sr VP & Gen Mgr-US Enterprise Markets)*
Benoit Dube *(VP-Legal Affairs)*
Louise Leonard *(Dir-Pub Rels)*
Angela Morris *(Dir-Commun)*
Ronald White *(Dir-IR)*

CGI TECHNOLOGIES & SOLUTIONS INC.

(Sub. of CGI Group Inc.)
1130 Random Hills
Fairfax, VA 22033
Tel.: (703) 267-8679
Fax: (703) 267-5073
E-mail: info@cgi.com
Web Site: www.cgi.com
Sales Range: $900-999.9 Million
Approx. Number Employees: 6,500
Business Description:
Systems Integration & Consulting Services
S.I.C.: 7373; 8748
N.A.I.C.S.: 541512; 541690
Advertising Expenditures: $1,000,000
Media: 2-4-9-10-14-16-23-25
Personnel:
Donna S. Morea *(Pres)*
Brands & Products:
ADVANCED CONSUMER LENDING SYSTEM (ACLS)
ADVANTAGE DESKTOP
AMS ACCESS GATEWAY
AUTOMATED CREDIT APPLICATION PROCESSING SYSTEM
BANKERS ACCEPTANCE PORTFOLIO SYSTEM (BAPS)
BUREAULINK
CLAIMSFLO
COLLECTION MANAGEMENT SYSTEM (CMS)
COLLECTIONS PROCESSING SYSTEM (CPS)
COMPUTER ASSISTED COLLECTION SYSTEM/PLUS (CACPLUS)
CUSTOMER ACCOUNT MANAGEMENT SYSTEM (CAMS)
ENCOUNTER
FACILITIES MANAGEMENT SYSTEM FMS
FEDERAL FINANCIAL SYSTEM (FFS)
FFS
FIELD ACTIVITY MATERIAL MANAGEMENT SYSTEM (FAMMS)
LETTER OF CREDIT SYSTEM (LCS)
MESSAGE PROCESSING SYSTEM (MPS)
MOBILE-2000
OBJECT CORE
ONLINE APPRAISAL & STATISTICAL INFORMATION SYSTEM
OPEN FFS
PATIENTLINK
PHOENIX STRATEGIC MAINTENANCE INITIATIVE (SMI)
PROCUREMENT DESKTOP (PDT)
QUICKSTART FOR DATA ENTRY
RECORDLINK
SECURITIES LENDING & BORROWING
SERVICE ORDER MANAGEMENT SYSTEM (SOMS)
STRATA
STUDENT INFORMATION SYSTEM (SIS)
TAX REVENUE ACCOUNTING CONTROL & ENFORCEMENT
TIELINE
USAGE PRICING SYSTEM (UPS)

CHDT CORPORATION

350 Jim Moran Blvd Ste 120
Deerfield Beach, FL 33442
Tel.: (954) 252-3440
Fax: (954) 474-0228
Web Site: www.chdtcorp.com
Approx. Rev.: $5,287,261
Approx. Number Employees: 9
Year Founded: 1989
Business Description:
Holding Company; Product Development, Manufacturing, Distribution, Logistics & Product Placement
S.I.C.: 6719; 1799; 3999; 7389; 8741; 8742
N.A.I.C.S.: 551112; 238990; 339999; 541614; 561110; 561499
Advertising Expenditures: $128,214
Media: 5-7-8-13
Personnel:
Howard Ullman *(Chm)*
Stewart Wallach *(CEO)*
Gerry McClinton *(COO)*

CHECKPOINT SYSTEMS INC.

(Sub. of Checkpoint Systems, Inc.)
1901 Wolf Dr
Thorofare, NJ 08086
Tel.: (973) 451-0456
Fax: (856) 848-0933
Toll Free: (800) 524-0029
Telex: 200472 Elst Ur
Web Site: www.checkpointsystems.com
Sales Range: $800-899.9 Million
Approx. Number Employees: 2,700
Business Description:
Price Marking Equipment, Direct Thermal & Thermal Transfer Printers, Continuous Feed Barcode Laser Printers, Label & Tag Stock Supplies
S.I.C.: 2679; 3577
N.A.I.C.S.: 322299; 334119
Import Export
Advertising Expenditures: $300,000
Media: 2-4-10-17
Distr.: Intl.; Natl.
Budget Set: Oct.
Personnel:
Rob van der Merwe *(Chm, Pres & CEO)*
Brands & Products:
METO

CHICAGO SHOW INC.

851 Asbury Dr
Buffalo Grove, IL 60089
Tel.: (847) 955-0200
Fax: (847) 955-9996
E-mail: jsnediker@chicagoshow.com
Web Site: www.chicagoshow.com
Approx. Number Employees: 20
Year Founded: 1902
Business Description:
Creative Designers & Producers of Point-of-Sale Advertising Displays & Merchandising Programs
S.I.C.: 3993
N.A.I.C.S.: 339950
Import
Media: 2-4-10-19
Distr.: Intl.; Natl.
Budget Set: Dec.
Personnel:
Robert R. Snediker, Jr. *(Pres)*
James M. Snediker *(CEO)*
Philip Marco *(VP-Creative)*
Brands & Products:
CHICAGO SHOW

CHISWICK, INC.

(Sub. of Deluxe Small Business Services)
33 Union Ave
Sudbury, MA 01776-2246
Tel.: (978) 443-9592
Fax: (978) 443-1707
Toll Free: (800) 225-8708
Web Site: www.chiswick.com
Sales Range: $100-124.9 Million
Approx. Number Employees: 180
Year Founded: 1974
Business Description:
Industrial & Retail Packaging, Shipping & Warehouse Product Marketer & Distr
S.I.C.: 5113
N.A.I.C.S.: 424130
Media: 4-7
Brands & Products:
CHISWICK

CHORDIANT SOFTWARE, INC.

(Name Changed to Pegasystems Inc.)

CHYRON CORPORATION

5 Hub Dr
Melville, NY 11747
Tel.: (631) 845-2000
E-mail: support@chyron.com
Web Site: www.chyron.com
Approx. Rev.: $27,727,000
Approx. Number Employees: 114
Year Founded: 1969
Business Description:
Broadcast Graphics Hardware, Software & Associated Services
S.I.C.: 7372; 3577; 3651; 3663; 7336; 7379
N.A.I.C.S.: 511210; 334119; 334220; 334310; 541430; 541519
Export
Advertising Expenditures: $17,000
Media: 1-2-4-7-10-11-20-22
Distr.: Intl.; Natl.
Personnel:
Roger L. Ogden *(Chm)*
Michael Wellesley-Wesley *(Pres & CEO)*
Jerry Kieliszak *(CFO & Sr VP)*
Peter Morrone *(Sr VP-Engrg & Product Mgmt)*
Mark Bachmore *(VP-Sls)*
Aldo Campisi *(VP-Sls-Latin America)*
Joe Foxton *(VP-Strategic Product Architecture)*
Bruce Levine *(VP-Sls-North America)*
Chuck Motta *(Gen Mgr-Govt Sys)*
Gary Chapman *(Dir-Broadcast Grp Bus)*
Carol Keane *(Dir-Sls Ops)*
William Payne *(Dir-Sls-Asia Pacific)*
Gary Schutte *(Dir-Channel Sls-North America)*
Juan Gonzalez *(Mgr-Sls-Latin America Reg)*
Jean Rene Georges *(Sr Acct Exec-Northeast & Mid-Atlantic)*
Brands & Products:
AXIS NEWS
BIZGRAPH
C-MIX
CALBOX
CAMIO
CHANNEL BOX
CHYRON
THE CHYRON CODI
CODISTRATOR
THE COMPANY THE WHOLE WORLD WATCHES

Key to Media (For complete agency information see *The Advertising Red Books-Agencies* edition):
1. Bus. Publs. 2. Cable T.V. 3. Catalogs & Directories. 4. Co-op Adv. 5. Consumer Mags. 6. D.M. to Bus. Estab.7. D.M. to Consumers 8. Daily Newsp. 9. Exhibits/Trade Shows 10. Foreign 11. Infomercial 12. Internet Adv.13. Multimedia 14. Network Radio 15. Network T.V. 16. Newsp. Distr. Mags. 17. Other 18. Outdoor (Posters, Transit) 19. Point of Purchase20. Premiums, Novelties 21. Product Samples 22. Special Events Mktg. 23. Spot Radio 24. Spot T.V. 25. Weekly Newsp. 26. Yellow Page Adv.

DIGIBOX CODI
DUET
DYNACRAWL
EAS-HD
FAST CHART
FAST MAPS
FAST QUOTE
FAST WX
HARVESTER PRO
HYPERX
INFINIT
INTERFUSE
IRB
LEIF
LEX
LEX2
LYRIC
MICROCLYPS
MICROX
MOS2WAP
NEWSCRAWL
OMS
QUARTERBACK
RGB TOOLS
SOLO2
TWISTER
WAPSTR
X-CLYPS

Advertising Agency:
Allen & Caron
18200 Von Karman Ave Ste 780
Irvine, CA 92612-0192
Tel.: (949) 474-4300
Fax: (949) 474-4330

CIBER, INC.

6363 S Fiddler's Green Cir Ste 1400
Greenwood Village, CO 80111
Tel.: (303) 220-0100
Fax: (303) 267-3899
Toll Free: (800) 242-3799
E-mail: jmatuschek@ciber.com
Web Site: www.ciber.com
E-Mail For Key Personnel:
President: mslingerlend@ciber.com
Marketing Director: rcaputo@ciber.com
Approx. Rev.: $1,071,343,000
Approx. Number Employees: 7,500
Year Founded: 1974
Business Description:
Computer Consulting Services
S.I.C.: 7371; 7373; 8748
N.A.I.C.S.: 541511; 541512; 541690
Media: 2-7-11
Personnel:
David C. Peterschmidt *(CEO)*
Claude J. Pumilia *(CFO, Treas & Exec VP)*
Eric D. Goldfarb *(CIO & Exec VP)*
Christopher L. Loffredo *(Chief Acctg Officer & VP)*
Marcia M. Kim *(Pres-Federal Govt Solutions Div & Sr VP)*
Terje Laugerud *(CEO-CIBER InterNatl & Exec VP)*
Susan Keesen *(Gen Counsel & VP)*
Rick Genovese *(Exec VP-North America)*
Bruce Douglas *(Sr VP-Sls & Bus Dev)*
Tony Ferrigno *(Sr VP-Strategy-Global)*
Joseph A. Mancuso *(Sr VP-Ops)*
Daniel Diefendorf *(VP)*
Cyndi Geiger *(VP & Area Dir-Pacific Northwest)*
Dan Hoover *(VP-Healthcare)*
Tod Kerr *(VP)*
Heather Morris Kyer *(VP)*
John Morrissey *(VP & Dir-Area)*
Steve Bill *(VP-Bus Mgmt)*
Robin Caputo *(VP-Mktg & PR)*
Scott Frock *(VP-Managed Svcs)*
Michael Haws *(VP-Strategic Solution Sls)*
Christine Locklin *(VP-Sls-Northeast)*
Dan Russell *(VP-Sls-Southeast)*
Jon Scarpelli *(VP-Tech)*
Paul Cmiel *(Sr Dir-Global Healthcare Vertical)*
Mark Hollingsead *(Dir)*
Petra Konrad *(Dir-Intl Sls & Alliances)*
Goodney Zapp *(Dir-Area)*
Raye LaPlante *(Mgr-Client Delivery)*
Brands & Products:
ALWAYS ABLE
BIT
CIBER
CIBER JOBS
CIBERSPACE
E-ACCELERATION
RAPID RETAIL

CICERO INC.

8000 Regency Pkwy
Cary, NC 27518
Tel.: (919) 380-5000
Fax: (919) 380-5121
Web Site: www.ciceroinc.com
E-Mail For Key Personnel:
Sales Director: sales@ciceroinc.com
Approx. Rev.: $2,976,000
Approx. Number Employees: 31
Year Founded: 1988
Business Description:
Application Integration Products & Services
S.I.C.: 7371
N.A.I.C.S.: 541511
Advertising Expenditures: $439,000
Media: 2-4-5-6-7-9-10-11-13-17-22-26
Distr.: Intl.
Personnel:
John L. Steffens *(Chm)*
John P. Broderick *(CEO)*
Thomas Aiello *(Sr VP-Worldwide Sls)*
Keith Anderson *(Dir-Client Svcs)*
Clint Babcock *(Dir-Pre Sls)*
Neil Crane *(Dir-Product Strategy)*
Hal Harris *(Dir-Prof Svcs)*
Brands & Products:
CICERO
ENSUREDMAIL
GENEVA INTEGRATION BROKER

CIMETRIX INCORPORATED

6979 S High Tech Dr
Salt Lake City, UT 84047-3757
Tel.: (801) 256-6500
Fax: (801) 256-6510
E-mail: investors@cimetrix.com
Web Site: www.cimetrix.com
Approx. Rev.: $6,807,000
Approx. Number Employees: 25
Business Description:
Software Products for Electronics & Semiconductor Industries
S.I.C.: 7372
N.A.I.C.S.: 511210
Advertising Expenditures: $34,000
Media: 2-10-17
Personnel:
Robert H. Reback *(Pres & CEO)*
Jodi M. Juretich *(CFO, Treas & Sec)*
David P. Faulkner *(Exec VP-Sls & Mktg)*
Paul A. Johnson *(VP-Software Engrg)*
Brands & Products:
CIM116-EQUIPMENT PERFORMANCE TRACKING
CIM40-PROCESS JOB
CIM87-CARRIER MANAGEMENT
CIM90-SUBSTRATE TRACKING
CIM94-CONTROL JOB
CIMFOUNDATION
EDACONNECT
SECSCONNECT
TESTCONNECT

CINCOM SYSTEMS, INC.

55 Merchant St
Cincinnati, OH 45246-3732
Tel.: (513) 612-2300
Fax: (513) 612-2000
Toll Free: (800) 224-6266
E-mail: info@cincom.com
Web Site: www.cincom.com
Approx. Number Employees: 1,000
Year Founded: 1968
Business Description:
Mfr. of Computer Software
S.I.C.: 7373
N.A.I.C.S.: 541512
Import Export
Media: 2-4-6-7-8-10-11-13-17-19-26
Distr.: Intl.; Natl.
Budget Set: Nov.
Personnel:
Thomas M. Nies *(Founder & CEO)*
Kenneth L. Byrne *(Gen Counsel)*
Dave Schwarber *(Sr Dir-Mfg Indus)*
Ralph Schwarz *(Sr Dir-Product)*
Brian Bish *(Dir-Transatlantic-Smalltalk Grp)*
Dennis Creech *(Dir-North American Professional Svcs)*
Dave Decker *(Dir-Sls-Natl)*
Patrick J. Dowling, Jr. *(Dir-US Sls-Document Solutions)*
Ron Hank *(Dir-Customer Rel Mgmt & Global Bus Dev)*
Steve Kayser *(Dir-Pub Rel)*
Jay McKeever *(Dir-Worldwide Mktg)*
Daniel J. Vogel *(Dir-Fin)*
Ron Weeks *(Dir-Bus Plng & Res)*
Ken Cremers *(Mgr-Support Svcs)*
Sherrie Eimer *(Mgr-N America Customer Contact Center)*
Joy Warden *(Mgr-Trade Show & Events)*
Brands & Products:
AD ADVANTAGE
CINCOM
ENVIRON
INTELLIGENT DOCUMENT SOLUTIONS
IOUTSOURCE
MANTIS
OBJECTSTUDIO
OVERC
SIMPLIFICATION THROUGH INNOVATION
SMALLTALK
SOCRATES
SUPRA
SYNCHRONY
VISUALWORKS

CINEDIGM DIGITAL CINEMA CORP.

55 Madison Ave Ste 300
Morristown, NJ 07960
Tel.: (973) 290-0080
Fax: (197) 329-00081
E-mail: info@cinedigm.com
Web Site: www.cinedigm.com
Approx. Rev.: $79,915,000
Approx. Number Employees: 188
Business Description:
Storage, Electronic Delivery & Software Services
S.I.C.: 3572
N.A.I.C.S.: 334112
Advertising Expenditures: $811,000
Personnel:
Chris McGurk *(Chm & CEO)*
Adam M. Mizel *(CFO & COO)*
Jill Newhouse Calcaterra *(CMO)*
Jeffrey M. Butkovsky *(CTO & Sr VP)*
Gary S. Loffredo *(Pres-Digital Cinema Svcs & Gen Counsel)*
John Brownson *(Pres-UniqueScreen Media)*
Jonathan Dern *(Pres-Entertainment Grp)*
Chuck Goldwater *(Pres-Media Svcs Grp)*
Gerd A. Jakuszeit *(Pres-Digital Media Svcs)*
Jim Miller *(Pres-Software)*
B. Scott Cassell *(Sr VP-Tech)*
Brian D. Pflug *(Sr VP-Acctg & Fin)*
Alison Choppelas *(VP-Bus Affairs)*
Brands & Products:
THEATRE COMMAND CENTER
THEATRICAL DISTRIBUTION SYSTEM

CINTAS CORPORATION

6800 Cintas Blvd
Cincinnati, OH 45262-5737
Tel.: (513) 459-1200
Fax: (513) 573-4130
Toll Free: (800) CINTAS1
E-mail: info@cintas.com
Web Site: www.cintas-corp.com
Approx. Rev.: $3,810,384,000
Approx. Number Employees: 30,000
Year Founded: 1929
Business Description:
Specialized Business Support Services
S.I.C.: 2326; 7218; 7389
N.A.I.C.S.: 315225; 561499; 812332
Import Export
Advertising Expenditures: $2,500,000
Media: 2-4-6-7-10-11-13-23-26
Distr.: Natl.
Budget Set: May
Personnel:
Richard T. Farmer *(Founder)*
Robert J. Kohlhepp *(Chm)*
J. Phillip Holloman *(Pres & COO)*
Scott D. Farmer *(CEO)*
William C. Gale *(CFO & Sr VP)*
David Pollak *(CMO & Sr VP)*
William W. Goetz *(Pres/COO-Global Accts & Strategic Markets)*
Thomas Frooman *(VP, Gen Counsel & Sec)*
Todd M. Schneider *(Sr VP-Sls)*
Michael L. Thompson *(Sr VP-Facility Svcs)*
Richard F. Doggett *(Dir)*
Brands & Products:
CINTAS
THE SERVICE PROFESSIONALS
THE UNIFORM PEOPLE

Key to Media (For complete agency information see *The Advertising Red Books-Agencies* edition):
1. Bus. Publs. 2. Cable T.V. 3. Catalogs & Directories. 4. Co-op Adv. 5. Consumer Mags. 6. D.M. to Bus. Estab.7. D.M. to Consumers
8. Daily Newsp. 9. Exhibits/Trade Shows 10. Foreign 11. Infomercial 12. Internet Adv.13. Multimedia 14. Network Radio
15. Network T.V. 16. Newsp. Distr. Mags. 17. Other 18. Outdoor (Posters, Transit) 19. Point of Purchase20. Premiums, Novelties
21. Product Samples 22. Special Events Mktg. 23. Spot Radio 24. Spot T.V. 25. Weekly Newsp. 26. Yellow Page Adv.

Cintas Corporation — (Continued)

Advertising Agency:
Castells & Asociados
865 S Figueroa St Ste 1100
Los Angeles, CA 90017-2543
Tel.: (213) 688-7250
Fax: (213) 688-7067

CISCO SYSTEMS, INC.

170 W Tasman Dr
San Jose, CA 95134
Tel.: (408) 526-4000
Fax: (408) 526-4100
Toll Free: (800) 553-6387
Web Site: www.cisco.com
E-Mail For Key Personnel:
Public Relations: investor-relations@cisco.com
Approx. Sls.: $43,218,000,000
Approx. Number Employees: 71,825
Year Founded: 1984
Business Description:
Networking & Other Products & Services Related to the Communications & Information Technology Industry
S.I.C.: 3577; 3669
N.A.I.C.S.: 334119; 334290
Advertising Expenditures: $290,000,000
Media: 2-6-15
Distr.: Intl.
Personnel:
John T. Chambers *(Chm & CEO)*
Frank A. Calderoni *(CFO & Exec VP)*
Gary B. Moore *(COO & Exec VP)*
Rebecca J. Jacoby *(CIO & Sr VP)*
Blair Christie *(CMO-Worldwide Govt Affairs & Corp Comm)*
Ned Hooper *(Chief Strategy Officer & Sr VP)*
Padmasree Warrior *(CTO & Sr VP-Engrg)*
Prat Bhatt *(Principal Acctg Officer, VP & Controller)*
Wim Elfrink *(Chief Globalization Officer & Exec VP-Cisco Svcs)*
Chris Dedicoat *(Pres-European Markets)*
Paul S. Mountford *(Pres-Emerging Markets)*
Mark Chandler *(Gen Counsel, Sec & Sr VP-Legal Svcs)*
Robert W. Lloyd *(Exec VP-Worldwide Ops)*
Randy Pond *(Exec VP-Ops, Processes & Sys)*
Laura K. Ipsen *(Sr VP & Gen Mgr-Connected Energy)*
John F. McCool *(Sr VP & Gen Mgr-Data Center, Switching & Svcs Grp)*
Enrique Rodriguez *(Sr VP & Gen Mgr-Svc Provider Video Tech Grp)*
Gregory Neal Akers *(Sr VP-Res & Advanced Dev)*
Debra Chrapaty *(Sr VP-Collaboration Software)*
Brett D. Galloway *(Sr VP-Network Svcs Grp)*
Keith Goodwin *(Sr VP-Worldwide Channels)*
Angel L. Mendez *(Sr VP-Customer Value Chain Mgmt)*
Barry O'Sullivan *(Sr VP-Voice Tech Grp)*
Donald R. Proctor *(Sr VP)*
Manny Rivelo *(Sr VP-Enterprise Sys & Ops)*
Brian Schipper *(Sr VP-HR)*
Tae Yoo *(Sr VP-Corp Affairs)*
Marc Randall *(VP & Gen Mgr-Core Routing Bus Unit)*
Terry Anderson *(VP-Corp Comm)*
Jere King *(VP-Mktg)*
Mark Papermaster *(VP)*
Atchison Frazer *(Dir-Enterprise Svcs Mktg)*
Yeanchen Huang *(Dir-Sys)*
Kelly Kunka *(Dir-Intl Bus Dev)*
Steven Li *(Dir-Product Mgmt)*
Santosh Srinivasan *(Dir-Connected Bus Ops)*
Lisa Johnstone *(Sr Mgr-Digital Mktg)*
Paula Wang *(Sr Mgr)*
Kristy Demarco *(Sr Brand Mgr)*
Mark Balch *(Sr Product Mgr-Data Center Solutions)*
Paul Kohler *(Sr Product Mgr)*
Samuel Pasquier *(Product Mgr)*
Christine Johansen *(Mgr-PR & Networking Infrastructure)*
Heather Sblendorio *(Mgr-Intl Mktg)*
Brands & Products:
ACCESS REGISTRAR
ACE
ACE GSS 4400
ACE MODULE
ACE XML
AIRONET
ANM
AON MODULE
AVS 3100
BRINGING THE MEETING TO YOU
CALLMANAGER
CATALYST 6500
CCDA
CCDE
CCENT
CCIE
CCNA
CCSI
CCSP
CHANGING THE WAY WE WORK,LIVE,PLAY & LEARN
CISCO
CISCO HEALTHPRESENCE
CISCO IOS
CISCO LUMIN
CISCO NEXUS
CISCO NURSE CONNECT
CISCO STACKPOWER
CISCO STADIUMVISION
CISCO STORE
CISCO TELEPRESENCE
CISCOS EOS
COLLABORATION WITHOUT LIMITATION
CONFIGMAKER
DCE
ETHERFAST
ETHERSWITCH
EVENT CENTER
FORMSHARE
GIGADRIVE
HOMELINK
INTERNET QUOTIENT
IOS
IPHONE
IRONPORT
LAN2LAN
LIGHTSTREAM
MEDIATONE
MEETINGPLACE
MGX
NETWORK REGISTRAR
NETWORKERS
NETWORKING ACADEMY
PIX
POWERPANELS
PROCONNECT
SENDERBASE
SMARTNET
STACKWISE
TRANSPATH
TRANSPORT MANAGER
VFRAME
WAN
WEBEX
WELCOME TO THE HUMAN NETWORK.
Advertising Agencies:
CMD
1631 NW Thurman St
Portland, OR 97209-2558
Tel.: (503) 223-6794
Fax: (503) 223-2430

The Coakley Heagerty Advertising & Public Relations Co.
1155 N 1st St Ste 201
San Jose, CA 95112-4925
Tel.: (408) 275-9400
Fax: (408) 995-0600

GENERAL LEVITATION
1635 Tower Grove Dr
Beverly Hills, CA 90210
Tel.: (310) 454-1188

Interprose Inc.
2635 Steeplechase Dr
Reston, VA 20191
Tel.: (703) 860-0577
Fax: (703) 860-1623

Stephenson Group
37 Hollow Brook Rd
Califon, NJ 07830
Tel.: (908) 439-3660
Fax: (908) 439-3268

CITIZEN SYSTEMS AMERICA CORPORATION

(Sub. of Citizen Watch Co., Ltd.)
363 Van Ness Way Ste 404
Torrance, CA 90501-6282
Tel.: (310) 781-1460
Fax: (310) 781-9152
Toll Free: (800) 421-6516
Web Site: www.citizen-systems.com
E-Mail For Key Personnel:
Sales Director: sales@citizen-systems.com
Approx. Number Employees: 15
Year Founded: 1969
Business Description:
Business Machines, Citizen Dot Matrix Printers, Thermal Printers, Calculators, Audio Products LCD Products & Portable Hand-Held Televisions Distr & Mfr
S.I.C.: 5044; 5064
N.A.I.C.S.: 423420; 423620
Import Export
Advertising Expenditures: $1,000,000
Media: 4-5-6-7-8
Distr.: Natl.
Budget Set: Apr.
Personnel:
Max Yamazaki *(Pres & CEO)*

CITRIX SYSTEMS, INC.

851 W Cypress Creek Rd
Fort Lauderdale, FL 33309-6123
Tel.: (954) 267-3000
Fax: (954) 267-9319
Toll Free: (800) 424-8749
Web Site: www.citrix.com
Approx. Rev.: $1,874,662,000
Approx. Number Employees: 5,637
Year Founded: 1989
Business Description:
Supplier of Server-Based Computing Products & Technologies
S.I.C.: 7372; 7371
N.A.I.C.S.: 334611; 511210; 541511
Advertising Expenditures: $123,000,000
Media: 2-6-7-10-11-13-18-23
Personnel:
Thomas F. Bogan *(Chm)*
Mark B. Templeton *(Pres & CEO)*
Scott Herren *(Mng Dir & VP-Europe, Middle East & Africa)*
David J. Henshall *(CFO & Sr VP)*
Wes R. Wasson *(CMO & Sr VP)*
David R. Friedman *(Gen Counsel, Sec & Sr VP-HR)*
Gordon Payne *(Sr VP & Gen Mgr-Desktop Div)*
Brett Caine *(Sr VP-Online Svcs Div)*
Peter J. Levine *(Sr VP-Strategy)*
Al J. Monserrat *(Sr VP-Sls & Svcs)*
Lou Shipley *(VP & Gen Mgr)*
Michael Cristinziano *(Corp VP)*
Eduardo Fleites *(Sr Dir-IR)*
Andrew Susa *(Sr Dir-Partner Org-Asia Pacific)*
Eric Armstrong *(Dir-Corp Comm)*
Ed Bezooijen *(Dir-Mktg-Benelux)*
Kurt Svenson *(Dir-Sls Dev & Mktg-Nordic)*
Cailin Pitcher *(Sr Mgr-Mktg)*
Liz Kegg *(Sr Mgr-Corp Comm)*
Shelly Cobb *(Mgr-Product Mktg-GoToAssist)*
Matt Crawford *(Mgr-Lead Product Mktg)*
Carrie Shin *(Mgr-Channel Mktg-Asia Pacific)*
Brands & Products:
ALL YOU CAN MEET
APPCACHE
APPCOMPRESS
AUTOOPTIMIZER
BRANCH REPEATER
CITIRX PROGRAM NEIGHBORHOOD
CITRIX
CITRIX ACCESS ESSENTIALS
CITRIX ACCESS GATEWAY
CITRIX ACCESS SUITE
CITRIX APPLICATION FIREWALL
CITRIX APPLICATION GATEWAY
CITRIX AUTHORIZED LEARNING CENTER
CITRIX CERTIFIED ADMINISTRATOR
CITRIX CERTIFIED ENTERPRISE ADMINISTRATOR
CITRIX CERTIFIED INSTRUCTOR
CITRIX CERTIFIED INTEGRATION ARCHITECT
CITRIX CERTIFIED SALES PROFESSIONAL
CITRIX CLOUD CENTER
CITRIX COMMUNICATION GATEWAY

Key to Media (For complete agency information see *The Advertising Red Books-Agencies* edition):
1. Bus. Publs. 2. Cable T.V. 3. Catalogs & Directories. 4. Co-op Adv. 5. Consumer Mags. 6. D.M. to Bus. Estab.7. D.M. to Consumers
8. Daily Newsp. 9. Exhibits/Trade Shows 10. Foreign 11. Infomercial 12. Internet Adv.13. Multimedia 14. Network Radio
15. Network T.V. 16. Newsp. Distr. Mags. 17. Other 18. Outdoor (Posters, Transit) 19. Point of Purchase20. Premiums, Novelties
21. Product Samples 22. Special Events Mktg. 23. Spot Radio 24. Spot T.V. 25. Weekly Newsp. 26. Yellow Page Adv.

CITRIX DELIVERY CENTER
CITRIX DESKTOP RECEIVER
CITRIX DESKTOP SERVER
CITRIX DEVELOPER NETWORK
CITRIX EASYCALL
CITRIX EDUCATION
CITRIX ESSENTIALS
CITRIX EXTRANET
CITRIX GOTOASSIST
CITRIX GOTOMEETING
CITRIX GOTOMYPC CORPORATE
CITRIX ICA
CITRIX MERCHANDISING SERVER
CITRIX PARTNER NETWORK
CITRIX PASSWORD MANAGER
CITRIX PRESENTATION SERVER
CITRIX PROVISIONING SERVER
CITRIX READY
CITRIX RECEIVER
CITRIX REPEATER
CITRIX STREAMING SERVER
CITRIX SUBSCRIPTION ADVANTAGE
CITRIX SYNERGY
CITRIX TECHNICAL SUPPORT
CITRIX WINFRAME
CITRIX WORKFLOW STUDIO
CITRIX XENAPP
DAZZLE
DESKTOPSTREAMING
EDGESIGHT
EXPERTCITY
G2A
G2AX
G2M
G2T
G2W
GOTOASSIST CORPORATE
GOTOASSIST EXPRESS
GOTOMYPC POCKETVIEW
GOTOTRAINING
GOTOWEBINAR
GOVIEW
GTA
GTAX
GTM
GTT
GTW
HDX
HIDEF CONFERENCING
METAFRAME
METAFRAME XP
MPX
NCORE
NETSCALER
NETWORKLINK
NFUSE
POCKETVIEW
REQUEST SWITCHING
SECUREICA
SIMPLER IS BETTER
SMARTACCESS
SMOOTHROAMING
SPEEDSCREEN
STORAGELINK
SUPPORT SMARTER
VPX
WANSCALER
XEN
XEN DATA CENTER
XEN SOURCE
XENCENTER
XENDESKTOP
XENENTERPRISE
XENMOTION
XENSERVER
XENSUMMIT
XENSUPPORT

Advertising Agencies:
Human Capital Management, Inc.
1000 Corporate Dr Ste 300
Fort Lauderdale, FL 33334
Tel.: (954) 318-2300
Fax: (954) 318-2301

i-on interactive, Inc.
124 E Boca Raton Rd
Boca Raton, FL 33432-3912
Tel.: (561) 394-9484
Fax: (561) 394-9773
Toll Free: (888) 466-4332

Mediasmith
274 Brannan St Ste 601
San Francisco, CA 94107-2000
Tel.: (415) 252-9339
Fax: (415) 252-9854

Starmark International, Inc.
1815 Griffin Rd
Dania Beach, FL 33004
Tel.: (954) 874-9000
Fax: (954) 874-9010
Toll Free: (888) 280-9630

CLARITAS, INC.

(Branch of Claritas, Inc.)
1525 Wilson Blvd Ste 1200
Arlington, VA 22209
Tel.: (703) 812-2700
Fax: (703) 812-2701
E-mail: info@claritas.com
Web Site: www.claritas.com
Approx. Number Employees: 100
Year Founded: 1971
Business Description:
Marketing Consulting Services
S.I.C.: 8732; 8742
N.A.I.C.S.: 541910; 541613
Media: 2-7-10-13-18-20-22-26

CLAVEL, LTD.

3 Crafts Rd
Gloucester, MA 01930-2135
Mailing Address:
PO Box 687
Ipswich, MA 19380-0687
Tel.: (978) 356-7100
Fax: (978) 281-0810
E-mail: clavelltd@aol.com
Web Site: www.clavelltd.com
Approx. Number Employees: 1
Business Description:
Promotional Gifts & Stationery Products Mfr
S.I.C.: 5199
N.A.I.C.S.: 424990
Media: 2-4-7-10-13
Distr.: Natl. Intl.
Personnel:
Throop Bergh *(Gen Mgr)*

CLEAN HARBORS, INC.

42 Longwater Dr
Norwell, MA 02061-9149
Mailing Address:
PO Box 9149
Norwell, MA 02061-9149
Tel.: (781) 792-5000
Fax: (781) 848-1632
Toll Free: (800) 282-0058
E-mail: customerservice@cleanharbors.com
Web Site: www.cleanharbors.com/
Approx. Rev.: $1,731,244,000
Approx. Number Employees: 6,840
Year Founded: 1980
Business Description:
Environment & Hazardous Waste Management Services
S.I.C.: 7389; 4212; 4959; 8711; 8999
N.A.I.C.S.: 541990; 541330; 541620; 562111; 562112; 562910
Advertising Expenditures: $300,000
Personnel:
Alan S. McKim *(Chm, Pres & CEO)*
James M. Rutledge *(CFO & Exec VP)*
Michael Twohig *(Chief Admin Officer & Exec VP)*
David T. Musselman *(Gen Counsel & Sr VP)*
George L. Curtis *(Exec VP-Pricing & Proposals)*
Deirdre J. Evens *(Exec VP-Corp Sls & Mktg & Bus Dev)*
Eric W. Gerstenberg *(Exec VP-Environmental Svcs)*
David M. Parry *(Exec VP-Energy & Industrial Svcs)*
Brian P. Weber *(Exec VP-Corp Plng & Dev)*
Simon R. Gerlin *(Sr VP-Fin)*
William F. O'Connor *(Sr VP-Risk Mngmt)*
Brands & Products:
CLEAN PACK
Advertising Agency:
Crossbow Group, LLC
136 Main St
Westport, CT 06880
Tel.: (203) 222-2244
Fax: (203) 226-7838
Strategic Communications

CLEAR CHANNEL OUTDOOR HOLDINGS, INC.

(Div. of Clear Channel Communications, Inc.)
200 E Basse Rd
San Antonio, TX 78209
Tel.: (201) 832-3700
Web Site:
www.clearchanneloutdoor.com
Approx. Rev.: $2,797,994,000
Approx. Number Employees: 7,270
Year Founded: 1997
Business Description:
Holding Company; Out-of-Home Display Advertising Products & Services
S.I.C.: 6719; 7319
N.A.I.C.S.: 551112; 541850; 541890
Advertising Expenditures: $12,000,000
Personnel:
Ronald H. Cooper *(Pres & CEO)*
Scott D. Hamilton *(Chief Acctg Officer & Sr VP)*
William Eccleshare *(Pres/CEO-Intl)*
Augusto Claux *(Pres-Latin America)*
Rod Firestone *(Pres-Midwest Grp)*
Hubert Janvier *(Pres-Southern Europe)*
Barry Sayer *(Pres-United Kingdom, Ireland & Africa)*
Chet Kwasniak *(CFO-Americas & Exec VP)*
Robert H. Walls, Jr. *(Gen Counsel & Exec VP-Clear Channel Comm)*
Franklin G. Sisson, Jr. *(Exec VP-Sls & Mktg)*
Laura C. Toncheff *(Sr VP & Deputy Gen Counsel)*
Debbie Reiching *(Sr VP-Bus Dev & Mktg)*
Pru Parkinson *(Dir-Mktg-Intl)*

CLEARPOINT BUSINESS RESOURCES, INC.

(Filed Ch 11 Bankruptcy #1012038 on 06/23/2010 in U.S. Bankruptcy Ct, Dist of DE, Wilmington)
1600 Manor Dr Ste 110
Chalfont, PA 18914
Tel.: (215) 997-7710
Fax: (215) 997-7711
Web Site: www.clear-point.com
Approx. Rev.: $5,241,706
Approx. Number Employees: 14
Business Description:
Business & Staffing Solutions & Services
S.I.C.: 7389; 7361
N.A.I.C.S.: 561499; 561310
Advertising Expenditures: $31,674
Media: 10
Personnel:
Michael D. Traina *(Owner)*
John G. Phillips *(CFO, Treas & Sec)*

CLOUDMARK, INC.

128 King St 2nd Fl
San Francisco, CA 94107
Tel.: (415) 946-3800
Fax: (415) 946-3871
E-mail: pr@cloudmark.com
Web Site: www.cloudmark.com
Approx. Number Employees: 200
Business Description:
Developer of Electronic Messaging Security Products
S.I.C.: 7373; 7372
N.A.I.C.S.: 541512; 511210
Personnel:
Hugh McCartney *(CEO)*
Leon Rishniw *(Sr VP-Engrg)*
Jacinta Tobin *(Sr VP-Sls & Bus Dev-Worldwide)*
Jlolbert Washten *(VP-Fin & Acctg)*
Advertising Agency:
Schwartz Communications, Inc.
595 Market St Ste 2000
San Francisco, CA 94105
Tel.: (415) 512-0770
Fax: (415) 882-5787

CMC ELECTRONICS INC.

(Sub. of Esterline Technologies Corporation)
600 Dr Frederik Philips Blvd
Saint Laurent, QC H4M 2S9, Canada
Tel.: (514) 748-3148
Fax: (514) 748-3100
Web Site: www.cmcelectronics.ca
Sales Range: $150-199.9 Million
Approx. Number Employees: 800
Year Founded: 1903
Business Description:
Aviation Electronics & Components Mfr
S.I.C.: 3812; 3728; 5065
N.A.I.C.S.: 334511; 336413; 423690
Media: 4-7-10
Personnel:
Gregory Yeldon *(Pres)*
Claude Chidiac *(VP-Customer Support & Strategic Dev)*

Key to Media (For complete agency information see *The Advertising Red Books-Agencies* edition):
1. Bus. Publs. 2. Cable T.V. 3. Catalogs & Directories. 4. Co-op Adv. 5. Consumer Mags. 6. D.M. to Bus. Estab.7. D.M. to Consumers
8. Daily Newsp. 9. Exhibits/Trade Shows 10. Foreign 11. Infomercial 12. Internet Adv.13. Multimedia 14. Network Radio
15. Network T.V. 16. Newsp. Distr. Mags. 17. Other 18. Outdoor (Posters, Transit) 19. Point of Purchase20. Premiums, Novelties
21. Product Samples 22. Special Events Mktg. 23. Spot Radio 24. Spot T.V. 25. Weekly Newsp. 26. Yellow Page Adv.

CMC Electronics Inc. — (Continued)

Sylvie Desjardins *(VP-Fin)*
Zbig Jaskierny *(Product Mgr)*
Janka Dvornik *(Mgr-PR & Comm)*

Brands & Products:
CMC

COCC

135 Darling Dr
Avon, CT 06001
Tel.: (860) 678-0444
Fax: (860) 677-1169
E-mail: info@cocc.com
Web Site: www.cocc.com
Approx. Number Employees: 287
Year Founded: 1967
Business Description:
Real Banking Technology Solutions
S.I.C.: 7374; 6029
N.A.I.C.S.: 518210; 522110
Media: 7-10
Personnel:
Richard Leone *(Pres & CEO)*
David K. Christie *(CFO & Sr VP)*
Stephen M. Kayser *(CMO & Sr VP-Mktg)*
Joseph D. Lockwood *(CTO & Sr VP)*
Mark B. Shaw *(Sr VP & Chief Svcs Officer)*
Jotham F. Trafton *(Chief Strategies Officer & Sr VP)*
Sue W. Kittredge *(Sec & Asst VP-Admin)*
Marco F. Bernasconi, Jr. *(First VP-Customer Svcs)*
Brent Biernat *(First VP)*
Wendy W. DeMore *(First VP-Product Mgmt)*
John P. Huber *(First VP-Sys & Programming)*
Gardiner W. Bassett *(Asst VP-Sys & Programming)*

COGENT, INC.

(Sub. of 3M Company)
639 N Rosemead Blvd
Pasadena, CA 91107
Tel.: (626) 325-9600
Fax: (626) 325-9700
E-mail: info@cogentsystems.com
Web Site: www.cogentsystems.com
Approx. Rev.: $129,583,000
Approx. Number Employees: 434
Year Founded: 1990
Business Description:
Automated Fingerprint Identification Systems & Other Fingerprint Biometrics Solutions
S.I.C.: 7382; 7371; 7373
N.A.I.C.S.: 561621; 541511; 541512
Media: 10-17
Personnel:
Ming Hsieh *(Founder & CEO)*
Paul Kim *(CFO)*
James Jasinski *(Exec VP)*
Brands & Products:
BEYOND COMPARISON
BIOSWIPE
BIOTRUST
BLUECHECK
CAFIS
CAPFIS
CAPFIS PRIME
CLS1
COGENT
COGENT SYSTEMS
LIVE-ID
LIVESCAN
MAG-GATE
MUGSHOTS
PMA
PROGRAMMABLE MATCHING ACCELERATOR
SC-GATE
SEARCH-GATE
SMART-GATE
WEB ID
WEBCHECK
Advertising Agency:
The Blueshirt Group
456 Montgomery St 11th Fl
San Francisco, CA 94104
Tel.: (415) 217-7722
Fax: (415) 217-7721

COGNIZANT TECHNOLOGY SOLUTIONS CORPORATION

Glenpointe Ctr W 500 Frank W Burr Blvd
Teaneck, NJ 07666-6804
Tel.: (201) 801-0233
Fax: (201) 801-0243
Toll Free: (888) 937-3277
E-mail: inquiry@cognizant.com
Web Site: www.cognizant.com
E-Mail For Key Personnel:
Sales Director: saleseast@cognizant.com
Approx. Rev.: $4,592,389,000
Approx. Number Employees: 104,000
Year Founded: 1994
Business Description:
Information Technology, Consulting & Business Outsourcing Services
S.I.C.: 7376; 7389; 8748
N.A.I.C.S.: 541513; 541690; 541990; 561499
Export
Media: 7-10-11-13
Personnel:
John E. Klein *(Chm)*
Francisco D'Souza *(Pres & CEO)*
Gordon J. Coburn *(CFO & COO)*
Ramakrishnan Chandrasekaran *(Pres/Mng Dir-Global Delivery)*
Bonnie Burkert *(Mgr-Life Sciences)*
Advertising Agencies:
Athorn, Clark & Partners
38 E 32nd St 11th Fl
New York, NY 10016
Tel.: (212) 457-6140
Fax: (212) 457-6161

FD U.S. Communications, Inc.
(d/b/a Financial Dynamics)
Wall St Plz 88 Pine St 32nd Fl
New York, NY 10005
Tel.: (212) 850-5600
Fax: (212) 850-5790

THE COLAD GROUP, INC.

(Sub. of Bindagraphics Inc.)
801 Exchange St
Buffalo, NY 14210-1434
Tel.: (716) 961-1776
Fax: (716) 961-1753
Toll Free: (800) 950-1755
Web Site: www.colad.com
E-Mail For Key Personnel:
Marketing Director: PWachter@colad.com
Sales Range: $10-24.9 Million
Approx. Number Employees: 90
Year Founded: 1946
Business Description:
Custom Office Supply Mfr
S.I.C.: 2759; 2675; 2752; 5112; 7389
N.A.I.C.S.: 323119; 322231; 323110; 424120; 561910
Import
Advertising Expenditures: $200,000
Media: 2-4-6-7-8-10-21-26
Distr.: Intl.; Natl.
Budget Set: Oct.
Personnel:
Todd Anson *(Pres)*
Brands & Products:
DIAMOND COAT

COLLECTORS UNIVERSE INC.

1921 E Alton Ave
Santa Ana, CA 92705
Tel.: (949) 567-1234
Fax: (949) 833-7955
E-mail: investorrelations@collectors.com
Web Site: www.collectors.com
Approx. Rev.: $39,763,000
Approx. Number Employees: 190
Business Description:
Authentication, Grading, Appraisal, Information & Exchange Services
S.I.C.: 7389
N.A.I.C.S.: 561990; 541990; 561499
Advertising Expenditures: $469,000
Media: 2-10
Personnel:
A. Clinton Allen *(Chm)*
David G. Hall *(Pres)*
Michael J. McConnell *(CEO)*
Joseph J. Wallace *(CFO)*
Kristen Chapman *(Coord-Mktg)*

COMFORCE CORPORATION

(Holding of ABRY Partners LLC)
415 Crossways Park Dr
Woodbury, NY 11797-2061
Mailing Address:
PO Box 9006
Woodbury, NY 11797
Tel.: (516) 437-3300
Fax: (516) 437-3392
Toll Free: (877) 266-3672
E-mail: comforce@charterinternet.com
Web Site: www.comforce.com
Approx. Sls.: $563,788,000
Approx. Number Employees: 532
Year Founded: 1995
Business Description:
Telecommunications, Contingent Staffing, Human Resources Outsourcing & Consulting Solutions
S.I.C.: 7363; 4899; 7361
N.A.I.C.S.: 561320; 517910; 541612; 561310
Media: 2-6-7-8-9-10-13-25-26
Personnel:
John C. Fanning *(Chm & CEO)*
Harry V. Maccarrone *(CFO, Sec & Exec VP)*
Kevin Reilly *(VP-Info Svcs & CIO)*
Arthur A. Feltman *(Gen Counsel & VP)*
Evan Burks *(Exec VP)*
Bradley Turkin *(Exec VP)*
Robert F. Ende *(Sr VP-Fin)*
Allison Gross *(Sr VP-IT Svcs-Southern)*
Pete Petix *(Sr VP)*
Robert Senatore *(Sr VP-IT Svcs-Northwest)*
Teresa Golio *(Controller & VP-Fin)*
Advertising Agency:
Communications Advertising, Inc.
2363 Deer Creek Trl
Deerfield Beach, FL 33442-1323
Tel.: (954) 481-1930
Fax: (954) 481-1939

COMMAND SECURITY CORPORATION

Rte 55 Lexington Park
Lagrangeville, NY 12540
Tel.: (845) 454-3703
Fax: (845) 454-0075
E-mail: EKondysar@CommandSecurity.com
Web Site: www.commandsecurity.com
Approx. Rev.: $146,490,159
Approx. Number Employees: 5,150
Year Founded: 1980
Business Description:
Security Services for Commercial, Industrial & Governmental Clients
S.I.C.: 7381
N.A.I.C.S.: 561612
Advertising Expenditures: $67,969
Media: 7
Personnel:
Peter T. Kikis *(Chm)*
Barry I. Regenstein *(Pres & CFO)*
Martin C. Blake, Jr. *(COO)*
Lynda B. Blake *(VP-Sls & Mktg)*
Robert Sagginario *(VP-HR & Trng)*
Brands & Products:
COMMAND SECURITY CORPORATION
CSC
CSC PLUS
SMART GUARD
SMART TRACKER
SMART WHEEL
STAIRS
TAKING COMMAND OF YOUR SECURITY NEEDS

COMMENCE CORPORATION

200 Tornillo Way Ste 200
Tinton Falls, NJ 07712
Tel.: (732) 380-9100
Tel.: (732) 660-1010
Fax: (732) 380-9170
Toll Free: (877) COMMENCE
E-mail: info@commence.com
Web Site: www.commence.com
Approx. Sls.: $2,000,000
Approx. Number Employees: 10
Business Description:
Customer Relationship Management Applications & e-Business Solutions
S.I.C.: 7371; 7372
N.A.I.C.S.: 541511; 511210
Media: 2
Personnel:
Larry Caretsky *(CEO)*
Advertising Agency:
The Devon Group
1715 Hwy 35 N Ste 106
Middletown, NJ 07748
Tel.: (732) 224-1000
Fax: (732) 706-0199

COMMUNICATIONS SPECIALTIES, INC.

55 Cabot Ct
Hauppauge, NY 11788
Tel.: (631) 273-0404
Fax: (631) 273-1638
E-mail: info@commspecial.com
Web Site: www.commspecial.com

Key to Media (For complete agency information see *The Advertising Red Books-Agencies* edition):
1. Bus. Publs. 2. Cable T.V. 3. Catalogs & Directories. 4. Co-op Adv. 5. Consumer Mags. 6. D.M. to Bus. Estab.7. D.M. to Consumers
8. Daily Newsp. 9. Exhibits/Trade Shows 10. Foreign 11. Infomercial 12. Internet Adv.13. Multimedia 14. Network Radio
15. Network T.V. 16. Newsp. Distr. Mags. 17. Other 18. Outdoor (Posters, Transit) 19. Point of Purchase20. Premiums, Novelties
21. Product Samples 22. Special Events Mktg. 23. Spot Radio 24. Spot T.V. 25. Weekly Newsp. 26. Yellow Page Adv.

E-Mail For Key Personnel:
President: johnl@commspecial.com
Approx. Number Employees: 30
Year Founded: 1983
Business Description:
Mfr. of Computer Video Peripherals & Fiber Optic Transmission Systems
S.I.C.: 3577; 3661
N.A.I.C.S.: 334119; 334210
Export
Media: 2-10-13-22
Personnel:
Lawrence M. Shulman *(Owner)*
John Lopinto *(Pres & CEO)*
Joehan Tohkingkeo *(Mng Dir)*
Paul Seiden *(Dir-Sls)*
Brands & Products:
CSI
DECISPLIT
DEUCE
FIBERLINK
HEXISPLIT
OCTOSPLIT
PURE DIGITAL FIBERLINK
QUADSWITCH
SCAN DO
TWINSPLIT

COMMVAULT SYSTEMS, INC.
2 Crescent Pl Bldg B
Oceanport, NJ 07757-1221
Mailing Address:
PO Box 900
Oceanport, NJ 07757-0900
Tel.: (732) 870-4000
Fax: (732) 870-4525
Web Site: www.commvault.com
Approx. Rev.: $314,776,000
Approx. Number Employees: 1,268
Year Founded: 1988
Business Description:
Data Management Software Applications & Related Services
S.I.C.: 7372; 7373
N.A.I.C.S.: 511210; 541512
Import Export
Advertising Expenditures: $3,819,000
Personnel:
N. Robert Hammer *(Chm, Pres & CEO)*
Louis F. Miceli *(CFO)*
Alan G. Bunte *(COO & Exec VP)*
Brian Carolan *(Chief Acctg Officer & VP-Fin)*
Warren H. Mondschein *(Gen Counsel & VP)*
William Beattie *(VP-HR)*
Jane F. Greenman *(VP-Worldwide HR)*
Brian D. McAteer *(VP-Sls Ops)*
Ron Miiller *(VP-Sls-America)*
David West *(VP-Mktg & Bus Dev)*
Dani Kenison *(Sr Dir-Global Corp Comm)*
Bob Carapezzi *(Dir-Pro Svcs-Americas)*
Michael Picariello *(Dir-IR)*
Brands & Products:
COMMCELL
COMMNET
COMMSERVE
COMMVAULT
GALAXY
GRIDSTOR
INNERVAULT
QSNAP
QUICK RECOVERY
QUICK SNAP
RECOVERY DIRECTOR
ROMS
SIM
SIMPANA
SOLVING FORWARD
UNIFIED DATA MANAGEMENT
VAULT TRACKER

THE COMPANY CORPORATION
(Sub. of Corporation Service Company)
2711 Centerville Rd Ste 400
Wilmington, DE 19808-1660
Tel.: (302) 636-5430
Fax: (302) 636-5454
Toll Free: (800) 877-4224
E-mail: info@corporate.com
Web Site: www.incorporate.com
Approx. Number Employees: 100
Year Founded: 1899
Business Description:
Business Services
S.I.C.: 8748
N.A.I.C.S.: 541618
Advertising Expenditures: $300,000
Media: 2-13
Personnel:
John Meyer *(Dir-Mktg)*

COMPELLENT TECHNOLOGIES, INC.
(Sub. of Dell Inc.)
7625 Smetana Ln
Eden Prairie, MN 55344
Tel.: (952) 294-3300
Fax: (952) 294-3333
E-mail: info@compellent.com
Web Site: www.compellent.com
Approx. Rev.: $125,275,000
Approx. Number Employees: 387
Business Description:
Network Storage Solutions
S.I.C.: 7372; 3572
N.A.I.C.S.: 511210; 334112
Advertising Expenditures: $3,500,000
Personnel:
Philip E. Soran *(Pres)*
John R. Judd *(CFO)*
John P. Guider *(COO)*
Brian P. Bell *(VP-Sls-Worldwide)*

COMPONENTSOURCE HOLDING CORPORATION
3391 Town Point Dr NW Ste 350
Kennesaw, GA 30144
Tel.: (770) 250-6100
Fax: (770) 250-6199
Web Site:
www.componentsource.com
Approx. Sls.: $8,000,000
Approx. Number Employees: 70
Year Founded: 1995
Business Description:
Software Sales
S.I.C.: 7372
N.A.I.C.S.: 511210
Media: 4-8-13
Personnel:
Sam Patterson *(CEO)*
Nigel Farnworth *(CFO)*
Brands & Products:
BACK-2-BACK SUPPORT
COMPONENTSOURCE

COMPREHENSIVE NETWORK, INC.
1663 E 17th St
Brooklyn, NY 11229
Tel.: (718) 339-9700
Fax: (718) 339-8433
Web Site:
www.comprehensivenet.com
Approx. Sls.: $1,500,000
Approx. Number Employees: 30
Business Description:
Health Care Staffing Services
S.I.C.: 8099; 8742
N.A.I.C.S.: 621999; 541613
Media: 2

COMPUCOM SYSTEMS, INC.
(Holding of Court Square Capital Partners, L.P.)
7171 Forest Ln
Dallas, TX 75230-2306
Tel.: (907) 562-4488
Fax: (972) 856-5395
Web Site: www.compucom.com
Sales Range: $1-4.9 Billion
Approx. Number Employees: 7,800
Year Founded: 1987
Business Description:
Information Technology, Hardware, Software & Application Services
S.I.C.: 7379; 7371; 7372; 7373; 7376; 8748
N.A.I.C.S.: 541519; 511210; 541511; 541512; 541513; 541690
Media: 2-5-7-8-9-10-25-26
Distr.: Natl.
Budget Set: Dec.
Personnel:
James W. Dixon *(Pres & CEO)*
Michael W. Simpson *(CFO)*
Jeffrey E. Frick *(COO)*
John Douglas *(CIO)*
William D. Barry *(Sr VP-Enterprise Sls)*
Dick Boynton *(Sr VP-Remote Svcs)*
Rocco J. Musumeche *(Sr VP-Bus Dev-IT Outsourcing Svcs)*
Kevin A. Shank *(Sr VP-Sls & Delivery Svcs)*
Timothy Shea *(Sr VP-HR & Corp Dev)*
Joe Valdes *(Sr VP-HR)*
Jim Arnold *(VP-Mktg)*
Dottie Tabor *(Mgr)*

COMPUMED, INC.
5777 W Century Blvd Ste 360
Los Angeles, CA 90045
Tel.: (310) 258-5000
Fax: (310) 645-5880
Toll Free: (800) 421-3395
E-mail: invest@compumed.net
Web Site: www.compumed.net
E-Mail For Key Personnel:
Sales Director: salesadmin@compumed.net
Public Relations: ir@compumed.net
Approx. Rev.: $1,762,000
Approx. Number Employees: 9
Year Founded: 1973
Business Description:
Computer Aided Diagnostic Systems
S.I.C.: 2835; 3841; 7373
N.A.I.C.S.: 325413; 339112; 541512
Media: 2-7-8-10-20
Distr.: Natl.
Budget Set: Aug.
Personnel:
Mark Stolper *(Chm)*
Maurizio Vecchione *(Pres & CEO)*
Phuong Dang *(CFO & Sec)*
Brands & Products:
CARDIOGRAM
COMPUMED
OSTEOCARE
OSTEOGRAM

COMPUSA INC.
(Div. of Tiger Direct, Inc.)
7795 W Flagler St Ste 35
Miami, FL 33144
Tel.: (305) 415-2200
Fax: (305) 415-2202
E-mail: sales_support@compusa.com
Web Site: www.compusa.com
E-Mail For Key Personnel:
Sales Director: sales_support@compusa.com
Sales Range: $125-149.9 Million
Year Founded: 1984
Business Description:
Computers, Computer Software & Computer Accessories Retailer
S.I.C.: 5734; 5045
N.A.I.C.S.: 443120; 423430
Media: 1-2-3-4-5-6-7-8-9-10-11-14-15-18-19-20-22-23-24
Distr.: Natl.
Advertising Agency:
Firehouse, Inc.
14860 Landmark Blvd No 247
Dallas, TX 75254
Tel.: (972) 692-0911
Fax: (972) 692-0912

COMPUSERVE INTERACTIVE SERVICES, INC.
(Sub. of AOL Inc.)
5000 Arlington Centre Blvd
Columbus, OH 43220-2913
Tel.: (614) 457-8600
Fax: (614) 457-0348
Web Site: www.compuserve.com
Sales Range: $100-124.9 Million
Approx. Number Employees: 450
Year Founded: 1969
Business Description:
Computer Information & Communications Services; Software Products; Internet, Intranet & Online Services
S.I.C.: 7375
N.A.I.C.S.: 518111
Media: 3-6-9-13-14-15-23-24-25
Personnel:
Ron Bernstein *(VP-Adv Sls)*

COMPUTER ASSOCIATES
(Div. of CA, Inc.)
52 2nd Ave
Waltham, MA 02451-1127
Tel.: (781) 890-1700
Fax: (781) 487-7791
Toll Free: (800) 325-9870
E-mail: info-emea@netegrity.com
Web Site: www.netegrity.com
Sales Range: $75-99.9 Million
Approx. Number Employees: 400
Year Founded: 1983
Business Description:
Developer & Integrator of Network Security Products & Services
S.I.C.: 7372
N.A.I.C.S.: 511210
Export
Media: 7-8-10
Distr.: Intl.; Natl.

Key to Media (For complete agency information see *The Advertising Red Books-Agencies* edition):
1. Bus. Publs. 2. Cable T.V. 3. Catalogs & Directories. 4. Co-op Adv. 5. Consumer Mags. 6. D.M. to Bus. Estab.7. D.M. to Consumers 8. Daily Newsp. 9. Exhibits/Trade Shows 10. Foreign 11. Infomercial 12. Internet Adv.13. Multimedia 14. Network Radio 15. Network T.V. 16. Newsp. Distr. Mags. 17. Other 18. Outdoor (Posters, Transit) 19. Point of Purchase20. Premiums, Novelties 21. Product Samples 22. Special Events Mktg. 23. Spot Radio 24. Spot T.V. 25. Weekly Newsp. 26. Yellow Page Adv.

Computer Associates — (Continued)

Brands & Products:
IDENTITYMINDER
SITEMINDER
TRANSACTIONMINDER

COMPUTER ASSOCIATES, INC.
(Sub. of CA, Inc.)
100 Staples Dr
Framingham, MA 01702-4479
Tel.: (508) 628-8000
Fax: (508) 481-9772
Toll Free: (800) 851-8725
Sales Range: $100-124.9 Million
Approx. Number Employees: 443
Business Description:
Information Technology Management Software Developer
S.I.C.: 7372
N.A.I.C.S.: 334611
Media: 2-13-22
Advertising Agency:
Fleishman-Hillard Inc.
855 Boylston St 5th Fl
Boston, MA 02116
Tel.: (617) 267-8223
Fax: (617) 267-5905

COMPUTER PROGRAMS & SYSTEMS, INC.
(d/b/a CPSI)
6600 Wall St
Mobile, AL 36695
Tel.: (251) 639-8100
Fax: (251) 639-8214
Toll Free: (800) 711-2774
E-mail: sales@cpsinet.com
Web Site: www.cpsinet.com/default_IE.php
Approx. Rev.: $153,247,244
Approx. Number Employees: 1,194
Year Founded: 1979
Business Description:
Computerized Information Technology Systems & Services Designer, Developer, Marketer, Installer & Supporter for Hospitals, Clinics, & Other Small or Midsized Health Care Facilities
S.I.C.: 7371; 7373
N.A.I.C.S.: 541511; 541512
Advertising Expenditures: $15,000
Media: 2-7-10-18-20
Personnel:
David A. Dye *(Chm, CFO, Sec & VP-Fin)*
J. Boyd Douglas *(Pres & CEO)*
Michael K. Muscat Jr. *(Sr VP-Product Dev)*
Thomas W. Peterson *(Sr VP-Clinical Svcs)*
Victor S. Schneider *(Sr VP-Corp & Bus Dev)*
Robert D. Hinckle *(VP-Fin Software Svcs)*
Troy D. Rosser *(VP-Sls)*
Brands & Products:
CHARTLINK
CLIENTWARE
CODEFINDER
DIRECT DEPOSIT
IMAGELINK
Advertising Agency:
Red Square
202 Government St
Mobile, AL 36602
Tel.: (251) 476-1283
Fax: (251) 476-1582

COMPUTER RESEARCH INC.
10170 Church Ranch Way Ste 300
Westminster, CO 80021-6061
Tel.: (303) 297-9200
Fax: (303) 292-3324
Approx. Rev.: $9,000,000
Approx. Number Employees: 45
Year Founded: 1961
Business Description:
Data Processing Services
S.I.C.: 7374
N.A.I.C.S.: 518210
Media: 2-7
Personnel:
Greg Lembree *(Pres)*
Brands & Products:
BANK-BOA
BID-BOA
INSTANT-BOA
OVERNITE-BOA

COMPUTER SCIENCES CORPORATION
(d/b/a CSC)
3170 Fairview Park Dr
Falls Church, VA 22042
Tel.: (703) 876-1000
E-mail: investorrelations@csc.com
Web Site: www.csc.com
Approx. Rev.: $16,042,000,000
Approx. Number Employees: 91,000
Year Founded: 1959
Business Description:
Computer Products & Services
S.I.C.: 7373; 7376; 7379; 8742
N.A.I.C.S.: 541512; 541513; 541519; 541611
Export
Media: 1-2-7-9-10-11-13-22-26
Distr.: Intl.
Personnel:
Michael W. Laphen *(Chm, Pres & CEO)*
Joe Amato *(Mng Dir)*
Michael J. Mancuso *(CFO & VP)*
Robert Wah *(VP & Chief Medical Officer-North American Pub Sector)*
Peter A. Allen *(Pres-Global Sls & Mktg & Acting Pres-Managed Svcs Sector)*
Vivek Chopra *(Pres-India Grp)*
James Dennis Cook *(Pres-Bus Solutions & Svcs Sector)*
Mike Gaffney *(Pres-Civil Grp-North America Pub Sector)*
Guy Hains *(Pres-Intl)*
Walter Howell *(Pres-Global Bus Dev)*
Mary Jo Morris *(Pres-Tech & Consumer Grp)*
Russ Owen *(Pres-Strategic Acct Dev)*
James W. Sheaffer *(Pres-North American Pub Sector)*
Michael Shove *(Pres-Asia Grp)*
Leif Ulstrup *(Pres-Federal Consulting Practice)*
Alan Weakley *(Pres-Applied Tech Grp-Pub Sector-North America)*
Andy Williams *(Pres-Northern Europe Bus Ops)*
Rich Wunder *(Pres-Consulting Grp)*
David W. Zolet *(Pres-Bus Dev-North American Pub Sector)*
William L. Deckelman, Jr. *(Gen Counsel, Sec & VP)*
Muralee Bhaskar *(Sr VP)*
Stephen Nicholas *(Sr VP-Automotive, Mfg & Telecom)*
Alisoun Moore *(VP & Gen Mgr-Health Svcs-North American Pub Sector)*
Harold Smith *(VP & Gen Mgr-Intelligenc Grp)*
Sheri Thureen *(VP & Gen Mgr)*
M. Louise Turilli *(VP, Deputy Gen Counsel & Asst Sec)*
Sharon Hays *(VP-Science & Engrg)*
Carl H. McNair, Jr. *(VP-Corp Comm & Mktg)*
Carlos C. Solari *(VP-Cyber Technologies & Svcs)*
Steve Sparling *(VP-Tech & Consumer Grp)*
Michael Dickerson *(Media Dir-Rels)*
Theresa McDermit *(Brand Dir-Digital Mktg)*
Mark Rasch *(Dir-Cybersecurity & Privacy Consulting)*
Brands & Products:
APPLIED ENTERPRISE
CARESTEPP
CHECKVISION
CKE
CLAIMS MANAGEMENT ACCELERATOR
COLOSSUS
COREXCELLENCE
CSC
CSC CONNECT
CSC CYBERCARE
CSC POWERSOLUTIONS
CSCXPRESS
CUSTOMER INTELLIGENCE
CUSTOMER SERVICE ACCELERATOR
DSDM
EASI SOLUTIONS
ENTERPRISE ADVANTAGE PROGRAM
EPOWERMHS
EXCEED
EXCEED POLICY
FAULT EVALUATOR
FRAUD EVALUATOR
FRAUDVISION
FUTURE FIRST
GRAPHTALK
GRAPHTALK AIA
GRAYWOLF
HOGAN
INFOSTEPP
INFRASHIELD
JETS
LEGAL EBILL
LEGAL SOLUTIONS SUITE
LEVEL IV
MYWORKSTYLE
NBACCELERATOR
NEW BUSINESS ACCELERATOR
OFAC EVALUATOR
PATRIOT PROTECTOR
PERFORMANCE PLUS
POINT IN
POWERMHS
POWERSTEPP
PRODUCT ACCELERATOR
RESULTS-DRIVEN COMPUTING
RISK GRADIENT
SECURITYSIGHT
SICS/NT
SMART SPEND
SMARTWORKPLACE
SUREVIEW
UMBPLEX
VANTAGE-ONE
Advertising Agencies:
Jeffrey Alec Communications
149 S Barrington Ave Ste 331
Los Angeles, CA 90049
Tel.: (310) 476-6700
Fax: (310) 476-6770

Mullen
40 Broad St
Boston, MA 02109
Tel.: (617) 226-9000
Fax: (617) 226-9100
Creative
Media Buying/Planning

COMPUTER SOFTWARE INNOVATIONS INC.
900 E Main St Ste T
Easley, SC 29642
Tel.: (864) 855-3900
Fax: (864) 855-6266
E-mail: investorrelations@csioutfitters.com
Web Site: www.csioutfitters.com
Approx. Rev.: $52,673,000
Approx. Number Employees: 219
Business Description:
Computer Software Solutions
S.I.C.: 7371; 7373
N.A.I.C.S.: 541511; 541512
Advertising Expenditures: $425,000
Media: 8-10-13
Personnel:
Anthony Sobel *(Chm)*
Nancy K. Hedrick *(Pres & CEO)*
David Dechant *(CFO)*
William J. Buchanan *(Sr VP-Technical Delivery & Support)*
Thomas P. Clinton *(Sr VP-Strategic Rels)*
Beverly N. Hawkins *(Sr VP-Product Dev)*

COMPUTER TASK GROUP, INC.
(d/b/a CTG)
800 Delaware Ave
Buffalo, NY 14209-2006
Tel.: (716) 882-8000
Fax: (716) 887-7464
Toll Free: (800) 992-5350
E-mail: partners@ctg.com
Web Site: www.ctg.com
Approx. Rev.: $331,407,000
Approx. Number Employees: 3,400
Year Founded: 1966
Business Description:
IT Application Management, Consulting, Software Development & Integration, & Staffing Solutions
S.I.C.: 7371; 7373
N.A.I.C.S.: 541511; 541512
Media: 2-4-9-20-25
Distr.: Intl.
Budget Set: Oct.
Personnel:
Brendan M. Harrington *(CFO)*
Peter P. Radetich *(Sec & Sr VP)*
Arthur W. Crumlish *(Sr VP & Gen Mgr)*
Filip J.L. Gyde *(Sr VP & Gen Mgr-CTG Europe)*
Michael J. Colson *(Sr VP)*
Paul F. Dimouro *(Sr VP-Strategic Stafffing)*
Thomas J. Neihaus *(Sr VP)*
N. Clair Detraz *(VP-Strategic Plng & Mktg-CTGHS)*
Michael E. Lippman *(VP-Sls-CTGHS)*

Key to Media (For complete agency information see *The Advertising Red Books-Agencies* edition):
1. Bus. Publs. 2. Cable T.V. 3. Catalogs & Directories. 4. Co-op Adv. 5. Consumer Mags. 6. D.M. to Bus. Estab.7. D.M. to Consumers 8. Daily Newsp. 9. Exhibits/Trade Shows 10. Foreign 11. Infomercial 12. Internet Adv.13. Multimedia 14. Network Radio 15. Network T.V. 16. Newsp. Distr. Mags. 17. Other 18. Outdoor (Posters, Transit) 19. Point of Purchase20. Premiums, Novelties 21. Product Samples 22. Special Events Mktg. 23. Spot Radio 24. Spot T.V. 25. Weekly Newsp. 26. Yellow Page Adv.

Brands & Products:
CTG EUROPE
CTG HEALTHCARE SOLUTIONS
CTG IT SOLUTIONS
CTG RETAIL SOLUTIONS
CTG STRATEGIC STAFFING SERVICES

COMPUTERIZED MEDICAL SYSTEMS, INC.
(Sub. of Elekta AB)
(d/b/a CMS)
13723 Riverport Dr Ste 100
Maryland Heights, MO 63043
Tel.: (314) 993-0003
Fax: (314) 993-0075
Toll Free: (800) 878-4267
E-mail: sales-na@cms-stl.com
Web Site: www.cmsrtp.com
E-Mail For Key Personnel:
Sales Director: sales-na@cms-stl.com
Approx. Number Employees: 100
Year Founded: 1979
Business Description:
Radiation Treatment Planning Systems Mfr
S.I.C.: 3841; 3577
N.A.I.C.S.: 339112; 334119
Export
Media: 2-10-13
Personnel:
Thomas Tuufepp *(Pres & CEO)*
Tim Mortenson *(CFO & Sr VP-Fin & Admin)*
Tim Rooney *(Sr VP-Intl Sls)*
Dave Reissig *(Sr VP-Ops)*
David Murphy *(Sr Dir-Mktg & Comm)*
Brands & Products:
ACCUSEED
CMS
FOCAL
FOCAL 4D
FOCAL DVS
FOCUS SYSTEMS
I-BEAM
IMRT
INTERPLANT
MONACO
PHYSICS
XIO

COMPUWARE CORPORATION
1 Campus Martius
Detroit, MI 48226
Tel.: (313) 227-7300
Toll Free: (800) 521-9353
Toll Free: (800) 538-7822 (Customer Svc)
Telex: 235559
E-mail: compuware.info@compuware.com
Web Site: www.compuware.com
Approx. Rev.: $928,930,000
Approx. Number Employees: 4,396
Year Founded: 1973
Business Description:
Data Processing, Professional Services & System Software Products
S.I.C.: 7372; 7371
N.A.I.C.S.: 334611; 511210; 541511
Export
Media: 2-13
Distr.: Intl.; Natl.
Personnel:
Peter Karmanos, Jr. *(Chm & CEO)*
Robert C. Paul *(Pres & COO)*
Laura L. Fournier *(CFO, Treas & Exec VP)*
Paul A. Czarnik *(CTO & Exec VP)*
Denise A. Knobblock Starr *(Chief Admin Officer & Exec VP)*
Daniel S. Follis, Jr. *(Gen Counsel, Sec & VP)*
Bruce Reading *(Sr VP & Gen Mgr-APM)*
Bob O'Brien *(Dir-Worldwide Field Mktg)*
Lloyd Bloom *(Product Mgr)*
Colin Mason *(Product Mgr-Web Load Testing)*
Brands & Products:
ABEND-AID
CARS
CHANGEPOINT
COMPUWARE
COVISINT
DEVPARTNER
DRIVERSTUDIO
FILE-AID
GOMEZ
HIPERSTATION
OPTIMALFLOW
OPTIMALJ
OPTIMALVIEW
POINTFORWARD
QACENTER
QADIRECTOR
STROBE
UNIFACE
VANTAGE
XPEDITER
Advertising Agency:
JWT U.S.A., Inc.
(d/b/a JWT-Team Detroit)
550 Town Ctr Dr
Dearborn, MI 48126
Tel.: (313) 615-3100
Tel.: (313) 615-2000 (Team Detroit)
Fax: (313) 964-3191
Fax: (212) 615-4600

COMSYS IT PARTNERS, INC.
(Sub. of MANPOWER INC.)
4400 Post Oak Pkwy Ste 1800
Houston, TX 77027-3421
Tel.: (713) 386-1400
Fax: (713) 961-0719
Web Site: www.comsys.com
Approx. Rev.: $649,307,000
Approx. Number Employees: 832
Year Founded: 1969
Business Description:
Information Technology Services, IT Staffing & Project Implementation Services
S.I.C.: 8748; 7363; 7371; 7374
N.A.I.C.S.: 541690; 518210; 541511; 561320
Media: 7-9-10-13-14-15-23-24-25
Personnel:
Joseph C. Tusa *(CFO & Sr VP)*
Ralph Kirkland *(VP-Mktg & Trng)*

COMTECH TELECOMMUNICATIONS CORP.
68 S Service Rd Ste 230
Melville, NY 11747-3833
Tel.: (631) 962-7000
Fax: (631) 777-8877
E-mail: info@comtechtel.com
Web Site: www.comtechtel.com
E-Mail For Key Personnel:
President: fkornberg@comtechtel.com
Approx. Sls.: $612,379,000
Approx. Number Employees: 1,268
Year Founded: 1967
Business Description:
Innovative Products, Systems & Services for Advanced Communications Solutions Designer, Developer, Producer & Marketer
S.I.C.: 3663; 3669
N.A.I.C.S.: 334220; 334290
Export
Media: 2
Personnel:
Fred Kornberg *(Chm, Pres & CEO)*
Michael D. Porcelain *(CFO & Sr VP)*
Richard L. Burt *(Sr VP)*
Larry Konopeko *(Sr VP)*
Larry Konopelko *(Sr VP)*
Robert L. McCollum *(Sr VP)*
Robert Rouse *(Sr VP-Strategy & M&A)*
Dan Wood *(Sr VP)*
Brands & Products:
AHA
CODEC
COMTECH
COMTECH EF DATA
COMTECH PST
COMTECH TELECOMMUNICATION CORP
HILL ENGINEERING
MEMOTEC
RADYNE
STAMPEDE
VERSO
VIPERSAT

CONCURRENT COMPUTER CORPORATION
4375 River Green Pkwy Ste 100
Duluth, GA 30096-8319
Tel.: (678) 258-4000
Fax: (678) 258-4300
Toll Free: (877) 978-7363
E-mail: info@ccur.com
Web Site: www.ccur.com
E-Mail For Key Personnel:
Marketing Director: marketing@ccur.com
Public Relations: pr@ccur.com
Approx. Rev.: $66,800,000
Approx. Number Employees: 298
Year Founded: 1966
Business Description:
Computer & Software Systems for the Real-Time Operating Systems/ Productivity Tools Market & The Video-On-Demand Market
S.I.C.: 3571; 7373
N.A.I.C.S.: 334111; 541512
Media: 2-7-10-22
Distr.: Intl.
Personnel:
Steve G. Nussrallah *(Chm)*
Dan Mondor *(Pres & CEO)*
Emory O. Berry *(CFO & Exec VP-Ops)*
David King *(CMO & Sr VP-Video Solutions)*
Gary Brust *(Sr VP-Sls & Mktg-Worldwide)*
Suzanne Smith *(Sr VP-HR & Admin)*
Kirk L. Somers *(Exec VP-Corp Affairs)*
Paul Haddad *(Sr VP-Media Data & Adv Solutions)*
Kshitij Kumar *(Sr VP-New Ventures)*
Jim Denenny *(VP & Gen Mgr-Web & Mobile Video Solutions)*
Andy Huang *(VP-Engrg)*
Brands & Products:
CONCURRENT
IHAWK
IMAGEN
LABORATORY WORKBENCH
MEDIAHAWK
NIGHTSTAR
POWER HAWK
POWERMAX
REDHAWK
RT-LAB RLX
SIGNAL WORKBENCH
SIMULATION WORKBENCH

CONDRE INC.
15151 Technology Dr
Eden Prairie, MN 55344
Tel.: (952) 294-4900
Fax: (952) 937-8365
E-mail: info@condre.com
Web Site: www.condre.com
Approx. Number Employees: 17
Business Description:
Computer Hardware & Software Distr & Integrator with a Focus on Data Storage
S.I.C.: 3651
N.A.I.C.S.: 334310
Media: 6
Personnel:
Dennis Maetzold *(Owner)*

CONEXANT SYSTEMS, INC.
(Holding of Golden Gate Capital)
4000 MacArthur Blvd
Newport Beach, CA 92660-3095
Tel.: (949) 483-4600
Toll Free: (888) 855-4562
E-mail: literature@conexant.com
Web Site: www.conexant.com
Approx. Rev.: $240,726,000
Approx. Number Employees: 596
Year Founded: 1998
Business Description:
Communication Semiconductor, Integrated Circuits & Subsystems Mfr & Distr
S.I.C.: 3674
N.A.I.C.S.: 334413
Media: 10
Personnel:
Sailesh Chittipeddi *(Pres & CEO)*
Carl Mills *(CFO)*
Mark D. Peterson *(Chief Legal Officer, Sec & Sr VP)*
Christian Scherp *(Exec VP-Global Sls)*
Bernd Lienhard *(Sr VP & Gen Mgr-Imaging & PC Media)*
Scott L. Allen *(Sr VP-Comm & IR)*
Michael H. Vishny *(Sr VP-HR)*
Steven Bakos *(VP-Worldwide Sls)*

CONNECTSHIP, INC.
(Sub. of United Parcel Service Co.)
8282 S Memorial Ste 400
Tulsa, OK 74133
Tel.: (918) 461-4460
Fax: (918) 461-4480
Toll Free: (866) 461-4460
E-mail: info@connectship.com
Web Site: www.connectship.com
Sales Range: $10-24.9 Million
Approx. Number Employees: 50
Year Founded: 1980

Key to Media (For complete agency information see *The Advertising Red Books-Agencies* edition):
1. Bus. Publs. 2. Cable T.V. 3. Catalogs & Directories. 4. Co-op Adv. 5. Consumer Mags. 6. D.M. to Bus. Estab.7. D.M. to Consumers
8. Daily Newsp. 9. Exhibits/Trade Shows 10. Foreign 11. Infomercial 12. Internet Adv.13. Multimedia 14. Network Radio
15. Network T.V. 16. Newsp. Distr. Mags. 17. Other 18. Outdoor (Posters, Transit) 19. Point of Purchase20. Premiums, Novelties
21. Product Samples 22. Special Events Mktg. 23. Spot Radio 24. Spot T.V. 25. Weekly Newsp. 26. Yellow Page Adv.

ConnectShip, Inc. — (Continued)

Business Description:
Third-Party Multi-Carrier Shipment, Rating & Tracking System
S.I.C.: 7373; 4731
N.A.I.C.S.: 541512; 488510
Advertising Expenditures: $750,000
Media: 2-7-13
Personnel:
A. R. Tandy *(Gen Mgr)*

CONNECTUS SOFTWARE

420H Chinquapin Round Rd
Lanham, MD 21401
Mailing Address:
PO Box 6607
Annapolis, MD 21401
Tel.: (410) 292-6323
Fax: (443) 782-0291
Toll Free: (866) 890-7485
E-mail: customer_service@connectus.net
Web Site: www.connectus.net
Approx. Number Employees: 10
Business Description:
Communications Software Solutions; Software as a Service (SAAS), Writing, Consulting, Research Support, Data Distribution, Market Intelligence & Public Advocacy
S.I.C.: 7372; 5045
N.A.I.C.S.: 511210; 423430
Media: 2-7-9-13-25
Personnel:
Gary C. Pick *(Pres & CEO)*

CONOLOG CORPORATION

5 Columbia Rd
Somerville, NJ 08876
Tel.: (908) 722-8081
Fax: (908) 722-5461
E-mail: conolog@conolog.com
Web Site: www.conolog.com
Approx. Rev.: $1,178,673
Approx. Number Employees: 15
Year Founded: 1969
Business Description:
Electronics Engineering, Design & Manufacturing
S.I.C.: 3679; 3678
N.A.I.C.S.: 334419; 334417
Import Export
Advertising Expenditures: $37,521
Media: 7-10-11
Personnel:
Thomas Fogg *(VP-Engrg)*

CONSONUS TECHNOLOGIES, INC.

(Sub. of MIDAS MEDICI GROUP HOLDINGS, INC.)
301 Gregson Dr
Cary, NC 27511
Tel.: (919) 379-8000
Fax: (919) 379-8100
Toll Free: (866) 872-4784
Web Site: www.consonus.com
Sales Range: $75-99.9 Million
Year Founded: 1988
Business Description:
Data Center, IT Managed Services & Infrastructure Solutions
S.I.C.: 7373; 7371; 7376; 7379; 8742; 8748
N.A.I.C.S.: 541512; 541511; 541513; 541519; 541611; 541618
Advertising Expenditures: $300,000
Media: 9-17
Personnel:
Nana Baffour *(Chm)*
Robert F. Mccarthy *(Pres)*

CONSTANT CONTACT, INC.

Reservoir Pl 1601 Trapelo Rd Ste 329
Waltham, MA 02451
Tel.: (781) 472-8100
Fax: (781) 472-8101
Toll Free: (866) 876-8464
Web Site: www.constantcontact.com
Approx. Rev.: $174,231,000
Approx. Number Employees: 734
Year Founded: 1995
Business Description:
Web-Based Services for E-Mail Marketing Campaigns
S.I.C.: 7389
N.A.I.C.S.: 561499
Advertising Expenditures: $39,214,000
Media: 2-6-10-13-23
Personnel:
Gail F. Goodman *(Chm, Pres & CEO)*
Harpreet S. Grewal *(CFO, Treas & Exec VP)*
Rick W. Jensen *(Chief Sls & Mktg Officer & Sr VP)*
Robert P. Nault *(Gen Counsel & VP)*
Ellen M. Brezniak *(Sr VP-Product Strategy)*
Eric S. Groves *(Sr VP-Worldwide Strategy & Market Dev)*
Thomas C. Howd *(Sr VP-Customer Ops)*
John J. Walsh, Jr. *(Sr VP-Engrg & Ops)*

CONTINENTAL AUCTION GROUP, INC.

11575 US Hwy 1 Ste 25
North Palm Beach, FL 33408-3039
Tel.: (561) 472-6333
Fax: (240) 201-7676
E-mail: info@auctionsaleinfo.com
Web Site: www.auctionsaleinfo.com
Approx. Number Employees: 10
Business Description:
Auction House
S.I.C.: 5961
N.A.I.C.S.: 454112
Advertising Expenditures: $350,000
Media: 4-6-8-9-17-25
Distr.: Natl.
Budget Set: Oct.
Personnel:
Randy L. Fridkis *(Pres)*

CONVERGYS CORPORATION

201 E 4th St
Cincinnati, OH 45202
Tel.: (513) 723-7000
Fax: (513) 421-8624
Toll Free: (888) 284-9900
E-mail: investor@convergys.com
Web Site: www.convergys.com
Approx. Rev.: $2,203,400,000
Approx. Number Employees: 70,000
Year Founded: 1998
Business Description:
Holding Company; Business & Operational Support Systems, Automated & Agent Assisted Customer Service Support & Human Resource Outsourcing Services
S.I.C.: 6719; 7361; 7373; 7374; 7376; 7379; 7389; 8748
N.A.I.C.S.: 551112; 518210; 541512; 541513; 541519; 541612; 541690; 541990; 561499
Media: 2-9-25
Personnel:
Jeffrey H. Fox *(Pres & CEO)*
Earl C. Shanks *(CFO)*
Jim Goetz *(CIO)*
Andrea J. Ayers *(Pres-Customer Mgmt)*
Michael J. Betzer *(Pres-Relationship Tech Mgmt/Customer Interaction)*
James P. Boyce *(Pres-Global Sls & Svcs)*
Jean-Herve Jenn *(Pres-Intl)*
Robert A. Lento *(Pres-Smart Revenue)*
Andre Valentine *(Sr VP-Fin & Controller)*
John Pratt *(Sr Dir-Natl Media Rels)*
Jeff Hazel *(Dir-Corp Comm)*
Amy Williams *(Specialist-PR)*
Brands & Products:
ATLYS
ICOMS
OUT THINKING. OUT DOING.
WIZARD
Advertising Agencies:
The CC Group
Floor 3 Imperium Imperial Way
Reading, Berkshire RG2 0TD, United Kingdom
Tel.: (44) 118 920 7650
Fax: (44) 118 986 7148

Success Communications Group
(Sub. of the Cherenson Group)
26 Eastmans Rd
Parsippany, NJ 07054
Tel.: (973) 535-9300
Fax: (973) 992-7543
Toll Free: (800) 848-4323

CONVERSION SERVICES INTERNATIONAL INC.

100 Eagle Rock Ave
East Hanover, NJ 07936
Tel.: (973) 560-9400
Fax: (973) 560-9500
Toll Free: (888) 274-5036
E-mail: info@csiwhq.com
Web Site: www.csiwhq.com
Approx. Rev.: $17,717,402
Approx. Number Employees: 70
Year Founded: 1990
Business Description:
Data Warehousing, Business Intelligence & Data Management Consulting Services
S.I.C.: 7371; 7374; 8748
N.A.I.C.S.: 541511; 518210; 541690
Advertising Expenditures: $36,102
Media: 2-7-10-13-17
Personnel:
Lori Cohen *(Pres & CEO)*
Bill Hendry *(CFO)*

CONVIO, INC.

11501 Domain Dr Ste 200
Austin, TX 78758
Tel.: (512) 652-2600
Fax: (512) 652-2699
Toll Free: (888) 528-9501
E-mail: info@convio.com
Web Site: www.convio.com
Approx. Rev.: $69,744,000
Approx. Number Employees: 367
Year Founded: 1999
Business Description:
Fund-Raising & Constituent Management Software for Nonprofit Organizations
S.I.C.: 7373; 6371; 8742
N.A.I.C.S.: 541512; 525990; 541611
Advertising Expenditures: $249,000
Personnel:
Vinay K. Bhagat *(Founder & Chief Strategy Officer)*
William G. Bock *(Chm)*
Gene Austin *(CEO)*
James R. Offerdahl *(CFO & VP)*
Sara E. Spivey *(CMO)*
Bethany Little *(VP-Enterprise Client Svcs)*
Angela G. McDermott *(VP-HR)*
Randall N. Potts *(VP-Sls)*
B. Hayden Stewart *(VP-IT)*

COPYTELE, INC.

900 Whitman Rd
Melville, NY 11747
Tel.: (631) 549-5900
Fax: (631) 549-5974
E-mail: ir@copytele.com
Web Site: www.copytele.com
Approx. Rev.: $730,675
Approx. Number Employees: 20
Year Founded: 1982
Business Description:
Flat Panel, Video Display & Encryption Device Mfr
S.I.C.: 3577; 3663; 8733
N.A.I.C.S.: 334119; 334220; 541710
Media: 2-10
Personnel:
Denis A. Krusos *(Chm & CEO)*
Henry P. Herms *(CFO)*
Brands & Products:
COPYTELE
CRYPTELE
DCS-1800
LVND
THURAYA
USS

CORBIS CORPORATION

710 2nd Ave Ste 200
Seattle, WA 98104
Tel.: (206) 373-6000
Fax: (206) 373-6100
E-mail: sales@corbis.com
Web Site: www.corbis.com
E-Mail For Key Personnel:
Sales Director: sales@corbis.com
Sales Range: $100-124.9 Million
Approx. Number Employees: 300
Year Founded: 1989
Business Description:
Customer Computer Programming Commercial Photography
S.I.C.: 7371; 7335
N.A.I.C.S.: 541511; 541922
Media: 2-4-6-7-8-13-16-20-22
Personnel:
Barry Allen *(Pres & COO)*
Gary Shenk *(CEO)*
Nairn Nerland *(Exec VP-Mktg & Gen Mgr)*
Vivian Farris *(Sr VP-HR)*
Barak Ronen *(Sr VP-Media Products-Corbis Images-London)*
Don Wieshlow *(Sr VP-Products)*
Dan Perlet *(Dir-Comm-Global)*
Amber Calo *(Sr Mgr-Creative Intelligence)*

Key to Media (For complete agency information see *The Advertising Red Books-Agencies* edition):
1. Bus. Publs. 2. Cable T.V. 3. Catalogs & Directories. 4. Co-op Adv. 5. Consumer Mags. 6. D.M. to Bus. Estab.7. D.M. to Consumers
8. Daily Newsp. 9. Exhibits/Trade Shows 10. Foreign 11. Infomercial 12. Internet Adv.13. Multimedia 14. Network Radio
15. Network T.V. 16. Newsp. Distr. Mags. 17. Other 18. Outdoor (Posters, Transit) 19. Point of Purchase20. Premiums, Novelties
21. Product Samples 22. Special Events Mktg. 23. Spot Radio 24. Spot T.V. 25. Weekly Newsp. 26. Yellow Page Adv.

Brands & Products:
CORBIS
Advertising Agencies:
Creature
1508 10th Ave
Seattle, WA 98122
Tel.: (206) 625-6994
Fax: (206) 625-6904

Trylon SMR
41 East 11th St
New York, NY 10003
Tel.: (212) 725-2295
Fax: (212) 725-2243

CORBY INDUSTRIES, INC.
812 N Gilmore St
Allentown, PA 18109
Tel.: (610) 433-1412
Fax: (610) 435-1963
Toll Free: (800) OKCORBY
E-mail: sales1@corby.com
Web Site: www.corby.com
E-Mail For Key Personnel:
Sales Director: sales1@corby.com
Sales Range: $10-24.9 Million
Approx. Number Employees: 30
Year Founded: 1972
Business Description:
Card & Digital Access Controls for Security Industry, Security Software Packages & Time & Attendance Software Turnkey Systems Mfr
S.I.C.: 3625; 3829
N.A.I.C.S.: 335314; 334519
Import Export
Advertising Expenditures: $275,000
Media: 5-8-10-16
Distr.: Natl.
Personnel:
Glenn M. Matz *(Pres)*
Kathleen S. Matz *(VP-Fin)*

COREL CORPORATION
(Holding of Vector Capital Corp.)
1600 Carling Ave
Ottawa, ON K1Z 8R7, Canada
Tel.: (613) 728-0826
Fax: (613) 728-9790
Toll Free: (800) 772-6735
Web Site: www.corel.com
Approx. Rev.: $268,230,000
Approx. Number Employees: 1,040
Year Founded: 1985
Business Description:
Software Products Mfr, Development, Licensing & Sales
S.I.C.: 7372
N.A.I.C.S.: 334611; 511210
Advertising Expenditures: $191,000
Media: 5-7-10
Personnel:
Alexander Slusky *(Chm)*
Kris Hagerman *(CEO)*
Thomas Peter Berquist *(CFO)*
Christopher DiFrancesco *(Gen Counsel, Sec & Sr VP-Legal)*
Amanda Bedborough *(Exec VP-Global Sls)*
Joe Roberts *(Exec VP-Global Products & Consultant)*
Nick Davies *(Sr VP & Gen Mgr-Graphics & Productivity)*
Shawn Cadeau *(Sr VP-Global Mktg)*
Jeremy Liang *(Sr VP-Digital Media Dev)*
Kevin Thornton *(Sr VP-Sls & Mktg)*
Catherine Hughes *(VP-Comm)*
Jessica Gould *(Sr Mgr-PR)*
Jennifer Nichol *(Mgr-Sls-Latin America)*
Greg Wood *(Mgr-Product Mktg-Digital Media)*
Brands & Products:
COREL GALLERY MAGIC
COREL PAINTER
COREL PARADOX 8
COREL PHOTO-PAINT 8
COREL PRESENTATIONS
COREL PRINT HOUSE MAGIC
COREL QUATTRO PRO
COREL VENTURA 8
COREL WORDPERFECT
CORELCENTRAL
CORELDRAW
CORELDRAW 8
CORELDRAW GRAPHICS SUITE 12
CORELVIDEO
GO FURTHER
PAINT SHOP
WORDPERFECT 12 PRODUCTIVITY
WORDPERFECT MAIL
WORDPERFECT OFFICE 12
Advertising Agency:
fama PR, Inc.
1 Broadway 16th Fl Kendall Sq
Cambridge, MA 02142
Tel.: (617) 758-4141
Fax: (617) 758-4101
Toll Free: (866) 326-2552
The Painter Factory (Online Community)

CORPORATE EXPRESS, INC.
(Sub. of Corporate Express N.V.)
1 Environmental Way
Broomfield, CO 80021-3415
Tel.: (303) 664-2000
Fax: (303) 664-3474
Web Site: www.corporateexpress.com
E-Mail For Key Personnel:
Public Relations: vanhindes@cexp.com
Sales Range: $5-14.9 Billion
Approx. Number Employees: 14,500
Year Founded: 1986
Business Description:
Office & Computer Products Supplier
S.I.C.: 5044
N.A.I.C.S.: 423420
Media: 4-21-25
Personnel:
Robert VanHees *(CFO-North America)*
Lex Elkins *(VP-Sls)*
Advertising Agency:
GroundFloor Media, Inc.
1923 Market St
Denver, CO 80202
Tel.: (303) 865-8110
Fax: (303) 253-9763

CORPORATION SERVICE COMPANY
2711 Centerville Rd Ste 400
Wilmington, DE 19808-1645
Tel.: (302) 636-5400
Fax: (302) 636-5454
Toll Free: (800) 927-9800
Web Site: www.cscglobal.com
Approx. Number Employees: 1,000
Year Founded: 1899
Business Description:
Public Record Document Filing, Retrieval & UCC Services; Litigation, Domain Name & Entity Mgmt; Registered Agent
S.I.C.: 7389
N.A.I.C.S.: 541199
Advertising Expenditures: $200,000
Media: 2-4-7-13-19-20-21-22-26
Personnel:
Dan Butler *(Chm)*
Bruce Winn *(Pres & CEO)*
Julie Rader *(Mgr-Interactive Mktg & Product Dev)*
Brands & Products:
CSC

CORSAIR COMPONENTS, INC.
46221 Landing Pkwy
Fremont, CA 94538
Tel.: (510) 657-8747
Fax: (510) 657-8748
Toll Free: (888) 222-4346
E-mail: robertp@corsair.com
Web Site: www.corsair.com
Approx. Rev.: $325,633,000
Approx. Number Employees: 383
Year Founded: 1994
Business Description:
Personal Computer & Gaming Hardware High-Performance Components Designer, Mfr & Supplier
S.I.C.: 3577; 5045
N.A.I.C.S.: 334119; 423430
Advertising Expenditures: $800,000
Media: 10-13-17-19
Personnel:
George R. Elliott *(Chm)*
Andrew J. Paul *(Pres & CEO)*
Nicholas B. Hawkins *(CFO)*
Jose R. Flahaux *(Sr VP-Worldwide Ops)*
Brands & Products:
CORSAIR

CORVU CORPORATION
(Sub. of Rocket Software, Inc.)
3400 W 66th St Ste 445
Edina, MN 55435-2111
Tel.: (952) 944-7777
Fax: (952) 944-7447
Toll Free: (800) 610-0769
E-mail: info@corvu.com
Web Site: www.corvu.com
Approx. Rev.: $15,392,396
Approx. Number Employees: 86
Year Founded: 1990
Business Description:
Management Software
S.I.C.: 7372; 7373
N.A.I.C.S.: 334611; 511210; 541512
Export
Advertising Expenditures: $130,000
Media: 7-10-11-13
Personnel:
Justin M. Macintosh *(Mng Dir)*
Richard Whomes *(Exec Officer-EMEA-Bus Area)*
Brands & Products:
CORBUSINESS
CORBUSINESS5
CORLNCENTIVE
CORMANAGE
CORPLANNING5
CORPORTFOLIO
CORRISK
CORRISK5
CORSERVER
CORSTRATEGY
CORSTRATEGY5
CORSTRATEGY.FINANCE
CORSTRATEGY.RISK
CORSTRATEGY.SCORECARD
CORTISK
CORVISION
CORVU
DYNAMART
HYPERVU
PERFORMANCE REVU
RAPIDAPPS
RAPIDROI
RAPIDSCORECARD
YOUR WINDOW INTO THE FUTURE

COVER-ALL TECHNOLOGIES, INC.
Ste 300 55 Lane Rd
Fairfield, NJ 07004-1015
Tel.: (973) 461-5200
Fax: (973) 461-5257
E-mail: info@cover-all.com
Web Site: www.cover-all.com
Approx. Rev.: $17,456,825
Approx. Number Employees: 82
Year Founded: 1981
Business Description:
Insurance Software Mfr & Distr
S.I.C.: 7372
N.A.I.C.S.: 511210; 334611
Advertising Expenditures: $243,136
Media: 2-7-10-13-16-20-21-22
Personnel:
John W. Roblin *(Chm & CEO)*
Manish D. Shah *(Pres & CTO)*
Ann F. Massey *(CFO, Sec & Controller)*
Maryanne Z. Gallagher *(COO & Exec VP)*
Miguel Edwards *(Sr VP)*
Brands & Products:
CLASSIC PRODUCT LINE
COVER-ALL
INSURANCE POLICY DATABASE
MY INSURANCE CENTER

CRAY INC.
901 Fifth Ave Ste 1000
Seattle, WA 98164
Tel.: (206) 701-2000
Fax: (206) 701-2500
E-mail: ir@cray.com
Web Site: www.cray.com
E-Mail For Key Personnel:
Public Relations: pr@cray.com
Approx. Rev.: $319,388,000
Approx. Number Employees: 885
Year Founded: 1987
Business Description:
Supercomputers Mfr
S.I.C.: 3571; 7371
N.A.I.C.S.: 334111; 541511
Advertising Expenditures: $853,000
Personnel:
Stephen C. Kiely *(Chm)*
Peter J. Ungaro *(Pres & CEO)*
Brian C. Henry *(CFO & Exec VP)*
Steven L. Scott *(CTO & Sr VP)*
Charles Fairchild *(Chief Acctg Officer, VP & Controller)*
Duncan Roweth *(Principal Engr-CTO Office)*
Wayne J. Kugel *(Sr VP-Ops & Customer Support)*
Margaret A. Williams *(Sr VP-R&D)*
Paul C. Ciernia *(VP-Sls Ops)*
Larry Hoelzeman *(VP-Sls-Worldwide)*
Linda J. Howitson *(VP-HR)*

Key to Media (For complete agency information see *The Advertising Red Books-Agencies* edition):
1. Bus. Publs. 2. Cable T.V. 3. Catalogs & Directories. 4. Co-op Adv. 5. Consumer Mags. 6. D.M. to Bus. Estab.7. D.M. to Consumers
8. Daily Newsp. 9. Exhibits/Trade Shows 10. Foreign 11. Infomercial 12. Internet Adv.13. Multimedia 14. Network Radio
15. Network T.V. 16. Newsp. Distr. Mags. 17. Other 18. Outdoor (Posters, Transit) 19. Point of Purchase20. Premiums, Novelties
21. Product Samples 22. Special Events Mktg. 23. Spot Radio 24. Spot T.V. 25. Weekly Newsp. 26. Yellow Page Adv.

Cray Inc. — (Continued)

Charles A. Morreale *(VP-Custom Engrg)*
Christy Adkinson *(Dir-Corp Marketing)*
Paul Hiemstra *(Dir-Treasury, IR & Risk Mgmt)*
Robert Pencek *(Dir-Intelligence Accts)*
Nick Davis *(Mgr-PR)*

Brands & Products:
AUTOTASKING
CRAY
CRAY-1
CRAY-2
CRAY-3
CRAY ANIMATION THEATER
CRAY C90
CRAY C90D
CRAY CF90
CRAY CHANNELS
CRAY CX1
CRAY EL
CRAY J90
CRAY J90SE
CRAY J916
CRAY J932
CRAY MTA
CRAY SV1
CRAY SX-6
CRAY T3D
CRAY T3E
CRAY X1
CRAY X1E
CRAY XD1
CRAY XMS
CRAY XMT
CRAY XT
CRAY XT4
CRAY XT5
CRAY XT5H
CRAY XT5M
CRAYDOC
CRAYLINK
CRAYPACS
CRAYPAT
CRAYPORT
CRAYSOFT
CRAYTUTOR
CRINFORM
DGAUSS
DOCVIEW
EMDS
GIGARING
HEXAR
HYPERTRANSPORT
LIBSCI
OLNET
RAPIDARRAY
SEASTAR
SEGLDR
SMARTE
SUPERCLUSTER
SUPERLINK
UNICOS
UNICOS MAX

Advertising Agency:
Interprose Inc.
2635 Steeplechase Dr
Reston, VA 20191
Tel.: (703) 860-0577
Fax: (703) 860-1623

CREATIVE AMUSEMENT SERVICES, INC.

602 S 3rd Ave
Mount Vernon, NY 10550
Tel.: (914) 668-2100
Fax: (668) 914-2080
E-mail: phil@creativenames.com
Web Site: www.creativenames.com
Approx. Sls.: $5,000,000
Approx. Number Employees: 200
Year Founded: 1977
Business Description:
Customized Computer Systems & Personalized Gift Related Software Developer & Supplier
S.I.C.: 3577; 7371
N.A.I.C.S.: 334119; 541511
Media: 2
Personnel:
Kenneth A. Kendes *(Pres)*

CREATIVE AUTOMATION COMPANY INC.

220 Fencl Ln
Hillside, IL 60162-2002
Tel.: (708) 449-2800
Fax: (708) 449-3282
Toll Free: (800) 773-1588
E-mail: info@cauto.com
Web Site: www.cauto.com
Sales Range: $50-74.9 Million
Approx. Number Employees: 350
Year Founded: 1969
Business Description:
Data Base Management, Merge Purge Processing, Address Delivery Improvement, E-Marketing Forms, Printing Personalization, Demographics & Data Processing Services
S.I.C.: 7374; 7371
N.A.I.C.S.: 518210; 541511
Import Export
Media: 2-7-8-13
Personnel:
Martin Kurpiel *(Pres, CTO & CMO)*
Arun Veluchamy *(Pres)*
Rich Czupowski *(CFO)*
Abe Zayed *(Exec VP)*
Gail Peterson *(Dir-HR)*
Brands & Products:
CREATIVE AUTOMATION
DQE
DQS
IN2VIEW

CREATIVE LABS, INC.

(Sub. of Creative Technology Ltd.)
1901 McCarthy Blvd
Milpitas, CA 95035-7427
Tel.: (408) 428-6600
Fax: (408) 428-6611
Web Site: www.creativelabs.com
Approx. Number Employees: 120
Year Founded: 1988
Business Description:
Computer Peripherals, Consumer Electronics & Home Entertainment Devices Mfr
S.I.C.: 5045; 5734
N.A.I.C.S.: 423430; 443120
Media: 2-4-6-9-10-11-25
Distr.: Intl.
Personnel:
Craig McHugh *(Pres)*
Phil O'Shaughnessy *(VP-Corp Comm)*

CTI GROUP HOLDINGS INC.

333 N Alabama St Ste 240
Indianapolis, IN 46204-1767
Tel.: (317) 262-4666
Fax: (317) 262-4849
Toll Free: (877) CTI-KNOWS
E-mail: info@ctigroup.com
Web Site: www.ctigroup.com
Approx. Rev.: $15,236,306
Approx. Number Employees: 120
Year Founded: 1968
Business Description:
Telemanagement & Billing Software
S.I.C.: 7371; 7372
N.A.I.C.S.: 511210; 334611; 541511
Import Export
Advertising Expenditures: $156,845
Media: 4-11-13
Personnel:
John Birbeck *(Chm, Pres & CEO)*
Fred Hanuschek *(CFO)*
Bill Miller *(COO)*
Susan Terry *(VP-Channel Sls & Mktg-US)*
Brands & Products:
ANALYSIS 5
CTIGROUP
EMPULSE
PROTEUS
SMARTBILL
SMARTRECORD
SMARTSPEND
TRANSACT

CYBERDEFENDER CORPORATION

617 W 7th St 10th Fl
Los Angeles, CA 90017
Tel.: (213) 689-8631
Fax: (213) 689-8639
E-mail: ir@cyberdefender.com
Web Site: www.cyberdefender.com
Approx. Rev.: $45,568,545
Approx. Number Employees: 379
Year Founded: 2003
Business Description:
Internet Security Software
S.I.C.: 7372; 7382
N.A.I.C.S.: 511210; 561621
Advertising Expenditures: $18,600,000
Media: 12-13
Personnel:
Gary Guseinov *(Chm)*
Greg Thomas *(CEO)*
Kevin Harris *(CFO)*
Igor Barash *(COO)*
Neil Evans *(Sr VP-Ops)*
Jeff Gove *(Sr VP-Call Center Ops)*
Sarah B. Hicks *(Sr VP-Product Dev)*
Brian Yoder *(VP-Engrg & Threat Res)*
Brands & Products:
CYBERDEFENDER
EARLYNETWORK
Advertising Agency:
The Bohle Company
1625 Stanford St
Santa Monica, CA 90404
Tel.: (310) 785-0515
Fax: (310) 277-2066

CYBERRESEARCH INC.

25 Business Park Dr
Branford, CT 06405
Tel.: (203) 483-8815
Fax: (203) 483-9024
Toll Free: (800) 341-2525
E-mail: info@cyberresearch.com
Web Site: www.cyberresearch.com
Approx. Number Employees: 30
Year Founded: 1983
Business Description:
Rack-Mount PCs, Motion Control Systems, Industrial & Scientific Computers Specialists
S.I.C.: 5045; 7373
N.A.I.C.S.: 423430; 541512
Media: 4-10-13
Personnel:
Robert C. Molloy *(Founder & Pres)*
Daniel Dunphy *(CFO)*
Robert Annesley *(Mgr-Sls)*
Mike Mathis *(Mgr-Application Engrg)*
Brands & Products:
ATDAQ
CYDAS
CYMOD
CYRAQ
FOLDAWAY
MICROBOX
MICROCAGE
PCIDAQ
POWERDAS
SLIMPACK
SUPERTRIM

CYBERSOURCE CORPORATION

(Sub. of Visa, Inc.)
1295 Charleston Rd
Mountain View, CA 94043
Tel.: (650) 965-6000
Fax: (650) 625-9145
E-mail: sales@cybersource.com
Web Site: www.cybersource.com
Approx. Rev.: $265,136,000
Approx. Number Employees: 654
Year Founded: 1997
Business Description:
Electronic Payment Processing Services
S.I.C.: 7374; 6022; 7372
N.A.I.C.S.: 518210; 511210; 522190
Advertising Expenditures: $38,000
Media: 10
Personnel:
William S. McKiernan *(Exec Chm & Founder)*
Michael A. Walsh *(Pres & CEO)*
Steven D. Pellizzer *(CFO & Sr VP-Fin)*
Perry S. Dembner *(CMO & Sr VP)*
David J. Kim *(Gen Counsel & VP)*
Michael Orlando *(Sr VP-Global Sls & Svcs)*
Bruce Frymire *(Dir-Corp Comm)*
Brands & Products:
AUTHORIZE.NET
BILL ME LATER
CYBERSOURCE
CYBERSOURCE CONNECT
INTELLIGENT REVIEW TECHNOLOGY
PAYMENTECH
THE POWER OF MANAGEMENT
TOTALCOLLECT

D&H DISTRIBUTING CO., INC.

2525 N 7th St
Harrisburg, PA 17110-2511
Mailing Address:
PO Box 5967
Harrisburg, PA 17110-0967
Tel.: (717) 236-8001
Fax: (717) 255-7838
Toll Free: (800) 877-1200
E-mail: info@dandh.com
Web Site: www.dandh.com

Key to Media (For complete agency information see *The Advertising Red Books-Agencies* edition):
1. Bus. Publs. 2. Cable T.V. 3. Catalogs & Directories. 4. Co-op Adv. 5. Consumer Mags. 6. D.M. to Bus. Estab.7. D.M. to Consumers 8. Daily Newsp. 9. Exhibits/Trade Shows 10. Foreign 11. Infomercial 12. Internet Adv.13. Multimedia 14. Network Radio 15. Network T.V. 16. Newsp. Distr. Mags. 17. Other 18. Outdoor (Posters, Transit) 19. Point of Purchase20. Premiums, Novelties 21. Product Samples 22. Special Events Mktg. 23. Spot Radio 24. Spot T.V. 25. Weekly Newsp. 26. Yellow Page Adv.

Sales Range: $1-4.9 Billion
Approx. Number Employees: 850
Year Founded: 1918
Business Description:
Computer & Home Office Electronic Products Distr
S.I.C.: 5045; 5065
N.A.I.C.S.: 423430; 423690
Export
Media: 2-4-7-10-17
Distr.: Natl.
Personnel:
Daniel Schwab *(Co-Pres)*
Michael Schwab *(Co-Pres)*
Israel Schwab *(CEO)*
Jeff Davis *(Sr VP-Sls)*
Robert J. Miller, Jr. *(Sr VP-Fin & Logistics)*
Mary Campbell *(VP-Mktg & Adv)*
Rob Eby *(VP-Pur)*
Tina Fisher *(Sr Dir-Pur)*
Mark Bowser *(Dir-Pur Ops)*

D-LINK SYSTEMS, INC.
(Sub. of D-Link Corporation, Inc.)
17595 Mount Herrmann St
Fountain Valley, CA 92708
Tel.: (714) 885-6000
Fax: (866) 743-4905
Toll Free: (800) 326-1688
E-mail: support@dlink.com
Web Site: www.dlink.com
Approx. Number Employees: 3,200
Year Founded: 1986
Business Description:
Networking Connectivity & Data Communications Products Mfr
S.I.C.: 5045; 3577
N.A.I.C.S.: 423430; 334119
Media: 13
Personnel:
Todd Bollenbacher *(VP-Customer Svc)*
William Brown *(Assoc VP-Product Dev)*
Daniel Kelley *(Assoc VP-Consumer Mktg)*
Maurice Famularo *(Dir-Mktg-Australia & New Zealand)*
Joe Melfi *(Product Mgr-Cloud Bus Solutions)*
Bal Phull *(Mgr-Mktg Comm)*
Advertising Agency:
Stein Rogan + Partners
432 Park Ave S
New York, NY 10016-8013
Tel.: (212) 213-1112
Fax: (212) 779-7305
Creative & Marketing Services

D.A. KOPP & ASSOCIATES, INC.
(Joint Venture of Milestone Partners Ltd.)
(d/b/a Dydacomp)
11-D Commerce Way
Totowa, NJ 07512-1154
Tel.: (973) 237-9415
Tel.: (973) 237-0300 (Tech Support)
Fax: (973) 237-9043
Toll Free: (800) 858-3666
E-mail: info@dydacomp.com
Web Site: www.dydacomp.com
E-Mail For Key Personnel:
Sales Director: sales@dydacomp.com
Approx. Number Employees: 50
Year Founded: 1983
Business Description:
Mail Order & E-Commerce Management Software Publisher
S.I.C.: 7372
N.A.I.C.S.: 511210
Media: 2-10
Personnel:
Robert Coon *(Pres)*
Lisa R. Gittleman *(Coord-Mktg & PR)*

DAHLE USA
(Sub. of Dahle Burotechnik GmbH)
49 Vose Farm Rd
Peterborough, NH 03458-1792
Tel.: (603) 924-0003
Fax: (603) 924-1616
Toll Free: (800) 243-8145
E-mail: info@dahle.com
Web Site: www.dahle.com
Approx. Number Employees: 15
Year Founded: 1976
Business Description:
Mfr. of Art & Photo Tools & Other Office Related Products
S.I.C.: 3589; 3554
N.A.I.C.S.: 333319; 333291
Import Export
Media: 1-2-4-6-16-17-20-21
Distr.: Natl.
Personnel:
Greg Rillings *(Reg Mgr-Sls)*
Chris Jackson *(Mgr-Mktg & Customer Rels)*
Brands & Products:
20300 SERIES
20400 SERIES
20500 SERIES
20600 SERIES
20800 SERIES
DAHLE

DASSAULT SYSTEMS ENOVIA
(Sub. of Dassault Systemes of America Corp.)
900 Chelmsford St Tower 2 Fl 5
Lowell, MA 01851
Tel.: (978) 442-2500
Fax: (978) 442-1000
Web Site: www.3ds.com/products/enovia
E-Mail For Key Personnel:
Public Relations: sharon.rodger@3ds.com
Sales Range: $100-124.9 Million
Approx. Number Employees: 200
Year Founded: 1983
Business Description:
Product Lifecycle Management Application Software Mfr
S.I.C.: 7372; 7371
N.A.I.C.S.: 334611; 541511
Advertising Expenditures: $44,638,000
Media: 2-4-7-10
Personnel:
Ludovic Monchal *(CFO)*
Michael Segal *(Sr VP-Sls & Svcs-Global)*
Brands & Products:
ADAPLET
APPLICATION EXCHANGE FRAMEWORK
EMATRIX
MATRIXONE
MATRIXONE DESIGNER CENTRAL
MATRIXONE DOCUMENT CENTRAL
MATRIXONE ENGINEERING CENTRAL
MATRIXONE LIBRARY CENTRAL
MATRIXONE MATERIALS COMPLIANCE CENTRAL
MATRIXONE PROGRAM CENTRAL
MATRIXONE SUPPLIER CENTRAL
MATRIXONE TEAM CENTRAL
SYNCHRONICITY DEVELOPER SUITE
SYNCHRONICITY DIGITAL DEVELOPER SUITE
SYNCHRONICITY PHYSICAL DEVELOPER SUITE
SYNCHRONICITY PUBLISHER AND CONSUMER SUITES
Advertising Agency:
LVT Benelux Public Relations
Kosterijland 5
3981 AJ
Bunnik, Netherlands
Tel.: (31) 30 65 65 070
Fax: (31) 30 65 65 473

DATA DOMAIN LLC
(Sub. of EMC Corporation)
2421 Mission College Blvd
Santa Clara, CA 95054
Tel.: (408) 980-4800
Fax: (480) 980-8620
Toll Free: (866) WE-DDUPE
E-mail: info@datadomain.com
Web Site: www.datadomain.com
E-Mail For Key Personnel:
Sales Director: sales@datadomain.com
Public Relations: press@datadomain.com
Sales Range: $250-299.9 Million
Approx. Number Employees: 777
Year Founded: 2001
Business Description:
Information Technology Data Deduplication Appliances & Software Developer & Mfr
S.I.C.: 3572; 7372
N.A.I.C.S.: 334112; 511210
Advertising Expenditures: $1,200,000
Media: 10
Personnel:
Kai Li *(Co-Founder Chief Scientist)*
Michael P. Scarpelli *(CFO & VP)*
Nick Bacica *(Sr VP-Mfg)*
David L. Schneider *(VP-Sls-Worldwide)*
Beth L. White *(VP-Mktg)*
Graham Breeze *(Engr-Systems)*

DATA I/O CORPORATION
6464 185th Ave NE Ste 101
Redmond, WA 98052-2545
Mailing Address:
PO Box 97046
Redmond, WA 98073-9746
Tel.: (425) 881-6444
Fax: (425) 869-7423
Toll Free: (800) 426-1045
Telex: 15-2167
E-mail: investorrelations@dataio.com
Web Site: www.dataio.com
Approx. Sls.: $26,396,000
Approx. Number Employees: 95
Year Founded: 1972
Business Description:
Customized Software Mfr, Developer & Marketer
S.I.C.: 3824; 3674; 3679
N.A.I.C.S.: 334514; 334413; 334419
Export
Advertising Expenditures: $197,000
Media: 2-7-10-11-13
Distr.: Direct to Consumer; Intl.; Natl.
Budget Set: Oct.
Personnel:
Paul A. Gary *(Chm)*
Frederick R. Hume *(Pres & CEO)*
Joel S. Hatlen *(CFO & VP)*
Qinghua Ma *(Gen Mgr-Ops-China)*
Phil Christenson *(Dir-Mktg)*
Brands & Products:
ABEL
DATA I/O
DATAIO
DELIVERING THE WORLD'S BEST IDEA IN SILICON
FLASHCORE
FLASHPAK
FUTURENET
OCTAL
PLDTEST PLUS
PROLINE-ROADRUNNER
PROMLINK
PS 300
QUAD
SERIAL NUMBER SERVER
TASKLINK
UNIPAK
UNISITE

DATA LISTING SERVICE LLC
(d/b/a The Connection)
11351 Rupp Dr
Burnsville, MN 55337
Tel.: (952) 948-5488
Fax: (952) 948-5498
Toll Free: (800) 883-5777
E-mail: sales@the-connection.com
Web Site: www.the-connection.com
E-Mail For Key Personnel:
Sales Director: sales@the-connection.com
Approx. Number Employees: 1,700
Year Founded: 1982
Business Description:
Telemarketing Services
S.I.C.: 7389; 4729
N.A.I.C.S.: 561422; 561599
Advertising Expenditures: $200,000
Media: 2-10-13
Personnel:
Fredrick Weiner *(Pres & CEO)*
John Meier *(CFO & VP)*
Tim Austrums *(VP-Sls & Mktg)*

DATACARD CORPORATION
(d/b/a DataCard Group)
11111 Bren Rd W
Minnetonka, MN 55343-9015
Tel.: (952) 933-1223
Fax: (952) 933-7971
Toll Free: (800) 328-8623
E-mail: info@data.com
Web Site: www.datacard.com
Approx. Rev.: $400,000,000
Approx. Number Employees: 1,400
Year Founded: 1969
Business Description:
Secure ID & Card Personalization Solutions
S.I.C.: 3579; 3089
N.A.I.C.S.: 333313; 326199
Export
Media: 2-7-10-17-22
Distr.: Intl.; Natl.
Budget Set: Dec.
Personnel:
Todd G. Wilkinson *(Pres & CEO)*
Kurt Ishaug *(CFO)*

DataCard Corporation — (Continued)

Wim Tappij Gielen *(Sr VP)*
Jeffrey Smolinski *(Sr VP-Ops)*
Russell St. John *(Sr VP-Global Mktg)*

Brands & Products:
AFFINA
ARTISTA
CARTIVA
DATACARD
DATACARD GROUP
DURAGARD
FLASHCREDIT
ID WORKS
IMAGE CARD
IMAGECARD IV
MAGNA PLATINUM
SNOOPER
ULTRAGRAFIX
VIANET

DATADIRECT TECHNOLOGIES CORP.

(Sub. of Progress Software Corporation)
3005 Carrington Mill Blvd Ste 400
Morrisville, NC 27560
Tel.: (919) 461-4200
Fax: (301) 461-4526
Toll Free: (800) 876-3101
Web Site: www.datadirect.com
Sales Range: $75-99.9 Million
Approx. Number Employees: 200
Business Description:
Computer Peripheral Equipment
S.I.C.: 3577
N.A.I.C.S.: 334119
Media: 10-11-13
Personnel:
Lindsey Anderson *(VP-Sls-Americas)*
Terence Cooke *(VP-Intl Sls)*
Asher Aremband *(Sr Dir-R&D)*
Nancy Vodicka *(Mgr-Product Mktg)*
Gregg Willhoit *(Chief Software Architect)*

Brands & Products:
DATADIRECT
DATADIRECT CONNECT
DATADIRECT JXTRANSFORMER
DATADIRECT SPY
DATADIRECT TEST
SEQUELINK
SUPPORTLINK

DATAFLUX CORPORATION

(Sub. of SAS Institute Inc.)
940 Cary Pkwy Ste 201
Cary, NC 27513
Tel.: (877) 846-3589
Fax: (919) 447-3100
E-mail: marketing@dataflux.com
Web Site: www.dataflux.com
Sales Range: $1-9.9 Million
Approx. Number Employees: 100
Year Founded: 2000
Business Description:
Developer of Computer Software
S.I.C.: 7371
N.A.I.C.S.: 541511
Media: 2-7-8-10-13
Personnel:
Scott Gidley *(Founder & CTO)*
Tony F. Fisher *(Pres & CEO)*
Steve Leitch *(CFO)*
Steve Balk *(Exec VP)*
Katie Fabiszak *(VP-Mktg & Intl Ops)*
Mazhar Leghari *(Sr Dir-Market Strategy)*
Gavin Day *(Dir-IT)*
Dan Soceanu *(Mgr-Product Mktg)*

Brands & Products:
SOFT

DATAKEY ELECTRONICS, INC.

12730 Creek View Ave
Savage, MN 55378
Tel.: (952) 746-4066
Fax: (952) 746-4061
Toll Free: (800) 328-8828
E-mail: info@datakeyelectronics.com
Web Site: www.datakey.com
Approx. Number Employees: 32
Year Founded: 1976
Business Description:
Portable Memory Products
S.I.C.: 3679
N.A.I.C.S.: 334419
Media: 2-4-10
Personnel:
Eric Jennings *(Pres)*

Brands & Products:
AXIS
DATAKEY
GUARDIAN II
THE KEY TO MAKING YOUR JOB EASIER.
THE KEY TO SUCCESS
MANAGED-MEMORY
MATING KEYCEPTACLES
RAPID DEPLOY TECHNOLOGY

DATALINK CORPORATION

8170 Upland Cir
Chanhassen, MN 55317-8589
Tel.: (952) 944-3462
Fax: (952) 944-7869
Toll Free: (800) 448-6314
E-mail: einvestor@datalink.com
Web Site: www.datalink.com
Approx. Sls.: $293,679,000
Approx. Number Employees: 299
Year Founded: 1958
Business Description:
Data Storage Systems Mfr
S.I.C.: 7373
N.A.I.C.S.: 541512
Advertising Expenditures: $15,100,000
Media: 10
Personnel:
Paul F. Lidsky *(Pres & CEO)*
Gregory T. Barnum *(CFO & VP-Fin)*
Tom Sylvester *(CIO)*
M. Shawn O'Grady *(Exec VP-Strategy & Field Ops)*
Kevin Campbell *(Reg Dir-Engrg)*

Brands & Products:
DATALINK
DATALINK.COM

Advertising Agency:
Padilla Speer Beardsley
1101 W River Pkwy Ste 400
Minneapolis, MN 55415-1241
Tel.: (612) 455-1700
Fax: (612) 455-1060

DATAMIRROR CORPORATION

(Sub. of IBM Software Group)
3100 Steeles Avenue East Suite 1100
Markham, ON L3R 8T3, Canada
Tel.: (905) 415-0310
Fax: (905) 415-0340
Toll Free: (800) 362-5955
E-mail: info@datamirror.com
Web Site: www.datamirror.com
Approx. Rev.: $43,852,729
Approx. Number Employees: 235
Year Founded: 1993
Business Description:
Real-Time Data Integration & Data Protection Solutions
S.I.C.: 7373; 7374; 7382
N.A.I.C.S.: 541512; 518210; 561621
Media: 2-10
Personnel:
Marcia Cardamore *(Exec Mng Dir-Org Dev)*
Stewart A. Ritchie *(Sr VP-Worldwide Sls)*
Jennifer St. Louis *(Mktg Mgr)*
Jennifer Lefevre-Khan *(Coord-Mktg Commun)*

Brands & Products:
CONSTELLAR HUB
DATAMIRROR
DB/XML TRANSFORM
HIGH AVAILABILITY SUITE
ICLUSTER
IDELIVER
IREFLECT
LIVEAUDIT
LIVECONNECTOR
PERVASIVE GATEWAY
POINTBASE
TRANSFORMATION SERVER

DATARAM CORPORATION

P.O.Box 7528
Princeton, NJ 08543-7528
Mailing Address:
PO Box 7528
Princeton, NJ 08543-7528
Tel.: (609) 799-0071
Fax: (609) 799-6734
Toll Free: (800) 328-2726
E-mail: webmaster@dataram.com
Web Site: www.dataram.com
E-Mail For Key Personnel:
Sales Director: usasales@dataram.com
Approx. Rev.: $46,847,000
Approx. Number Employees: 91
Year Founded: 1967
Business Description:
Computer Memory Products for Minicomputers & Workstations Mfr, Designer & Marketer
S.I.C.: 3572
N.A.I.C.S.: 334112
Export
Media: 2-5-7-10-13-17
Distr.: Intl.; Natl.
Budget Set: Jan.
Personnel:
Roger C. Cady *(Chm)*
John H. Freeman *(Pres & CEO)*
Mark E. Maddocks *(CFO & VP-Fin)*
Mark R. Bresky *(VP-IT)*
Jeffrey H. Duncan *(VP-Mfg & Engrg)*
Philip P. Marino, Jr. *(VP-Worldwide Sls)*
Jeff Goldenbaum *(Sr Mgr-Product)*

Brands & Products:
DATARAM

DATATRAK INTERNATIONAL, INC.

6150 Parkland Blvd Ste 100
Mayfield Heights, OH 44124
Tel.: (440) 443-0082
Fax: (440) 442-3482
Toll Free: (888) 677-3282
E-mail: company@datatrak.net
Web Site: www.datatrak.net/
Sales Range: $1-9.9 Million
Approx. Number Employees: 47
Year Founded: 1995
Business Description:
Software Development
S.I.C.: 7372; 8733
N.A.I.C.S.: 334611; 511210; 541710
Advertising Expenditures: $230,000
Media: 2-10
Personnel:
Laurence P. Birch *(Pres & CEO)*
Raymond J. Merk *(CFO & COO)*
Varnesh Sritharan *(VP-Legal Affairs & Sec)*

Brands & Products:
CLINICAL TRIAL MANAGEMENT SYSTEM (CTMS)
DATAARCHITECT
DATATRAK
DATATRAK ECLINICAL
DATATRAK EDC
DATATRAK INTERNATIONAL
DATATRAK MEDICAL CODING SYSTEM
DATATRAK PORTAL
EPRO
ESAT
PHASE IV
STUDYTRAK
TECHNOLOGY MEETS MEDICINE

DATAVIZ, INC.

Merritt Corporate Woods 612
Wheelers Farms Rd
Milford, CT 06461
Tel.: (203) 874-0085
Fax: (203) 874-4345
Toll Free: (800) 733-0030
E-mail: info@dataviz.com
Web Site: www.dataviz.com
Approx. Number Employees: 100
Year Founded: 1984
Business Description:
File Compatibility & Wireless Computer Software Developer
S.I.C.: 7371
N.A.I.C.S.: 541511
Media: 2-4-7-8-10-11-13-16-18
Personnel:
Dick Fontana *(Pres & CEO)*
David Conrad *(CFO)*
Kathleen McAneany *(Mgr-Documents To Go Bus)*

Brands & Products:
BEYOND CONTACTS
CONVERSIONS PLUS
DATAVIZ
DESKTOP TO GO
DOCUMENTS TO GO TOTAL OFFICE
DOSE-A-DAY
EPHPOD
HOLD'EM HIGH
INBOX TO GO
INBOX TO GO WIRELESS
MACLINKPLUS
MACOPENER
PASSWORDS PLUS
PDA PLAYGROUND
ROADSYNC
SMARTLIST TO GO
SNAPLIST

DATAWATCH CORPORATION

Quorum Office Park 271 Mill Rd
Chelmsford, MA 01824-4105
Tel.: (978) 441-2200
Fax: (978) 441-1114

Key to Media (For complete agency information see *The Advertising Red Books-Agencies* edition):
1. Bus. Publs. 2. Cable T.V. 3. Catalogs & Directories. 4. Co-op Adv. 5. Consumer Mags. 6. D.M. to Bus. Estab.7. D.M. to Consumers
8. Daily Newsp. 9. Exhibits/Trade Shows 10. Foreign 11. Infomercial 12. Internet Adv.13. Multimedia 14. Network Radio
15. Network T.V. 16. Newsp. Distr. Mags. 17. Other 18. Outdoor (Posters, Transit) 19. Point of Purchase20. Premiums, Novelties
21. Product Samples 22. Special Events Mktg. 23. Spot Radio 24. Spot T.V. 25. Weekly Newsp. 26. Yellow Page Adv.

Toll Free: (800) 445-3311
E-mail: sales@datawatch.com
Web Site: www.datawatch.com
Approx. Rev.: $17,674,000
Approx. Number Employees: 93
Year Founded: 1985
Business Description:
Report Mining Software Mfr
S.I.C.: 7372
N.A.I.C.S.: 511210
Advertising Expenditures: $151,000
Media: 2-4-5-6-7-8-10-11-13-17-22
Distr.: Natl.
Personnel:
Michael A. Morrison *(Pres & CEO)*
Murray P. Fish *(CFO & VP-Fin)*
Darrin Christensen *(VP-Sls-North America)*
Lisa G. Kilpatrick *(Dir-Mktg)*
Brands & Products:
DATAWATCH BDS
DATAWATCH ES
DATAWATCH MAIL MANAGER
ERAMS
INFORMATION MADE EASY
MONARCH
MONARCH BI SERVER
MONARCH DATA PUMP
MONARCH DATA PUMP PRO
MONARCH/ES
MONARCH PRO
MONARCH REPORT MINING SERVER
MONARCH RMS
VISUAL HD
VISUAL HELP DESK
VISUAL INSIGHT
VORTEXML DESIGNER
VORTEXML SERVER
Advertising Agency:
Greenough Communications
9 Harcourt St
Boston, MA 02116
Tel.: (617) 275-6500
Fax: (617) 275-6501

DAWSON GEOPHYSICAL COMPANY
508 W Wall St Ste 800
Midland, TX 79701-5034
Tel.: (432) 684-3000
Fax: (432) 684-3030
Toll Free: (800) 332-9766
E-mail: info@dawson3d.com
Web Site: www.dawson3d.com
Approx. Rev.: $205,272,000
Approx. Number Employees: 1,170
Year Founded: 1952
Business Description:
Seismic Data Acquirer, Processor & Interpreter
S.I.C.: 1389; 8713
N.A.I.C.S.: 213112; 541360
Advertising Expenditures: $256,000
Media: 2
Personnel:
L. Decker Dawson *(Chm)*
Stephen C. Jumper *(Pres & CEO)*
Christina W. Hagan *(CFO & Exec VP)*
C. Ray Tobias *(COO & Exec VP)*
Howell W. Pardue *(Exec VP-Data Processing)*
Kermit S. Forsdick *(Sr VP)*
Sam Dobbs *(VP-DP)*
Robert C. Chandler *(Dir-Engrg Technical Support)*
Brands & Products:
DAWSON

DDI CORP.
1220 N Simon Cir
Anaheim, CA 92806-1827
Tel.: (714) 688-7200
Fax: (714) 688-7400
Toll Free: (800) 491-9766
E-mail: info@ddiglobal.com
Web Site: www.ddiglobal.com
Approx. Sls.: $267,784,000
Approx. Number Employees: 1,676
Year Founded: 1978
Business Description:
Printed Circuit Board Engineering, Fabrication & Mfg
S.I.C.: 3672; 3679; 8711
N.A.I.C.S.: 334412; 334418; 541330
Advertising Expenditures: $70,000
Media: 10-22
Personnel:
Bryant R. Riley *(Founder & Chm)*
Mikel H. Williams *(Pres & CEO)*
Wayne Slomsky *(Interim CFO)*
Michael R. Mathews *(COO & Sr VP)*
Coleman C. Barner *(Chief Acctg Officer)*
Kurt Scheuerman *(Gen Counsel & VP)*
Gerald P. Barnes *(Sr VP-Sls)*
Brands & Products:
DDI
FLAT-WRAP
SMV
THERMALVIA

DEE SIGN COMPANY
6163 Allen Rd
West Chester, OH 45069-3855
Tel.: (513) 779-3333
Fax: (513) 779-3344
Toll Free: (800) DEESIGN
E-mail: sales@deesigncompany.com
Web Site: www.deesigncompany.com
E-Mail For Key Personnel:
Sales Director: sales@deesigncompany.com
Approx. Number Employees: 175
Year Founded: 1967
Business Description:
Real Estate Signs Mfr
S.I.C.: 3993
N.A.I.C.S.: 339950
Media: 2-4-7-10-13
Distr.: Natl.
Personnel:
Brad Huenefeld *(Pres)*
Joe Kolks *(CFO)*
Craig Dixon *(Gen Mgr)*
Will Kriedler *(Mgr-Mktg)*

D.E.I. MANAGEMENT GROUP, INC.
250 W 57th St Ste 2217
New York, NY 10107
Tel.: (212) 581-7390
Fax: (212) 245-7897
Toll Free: (800) 224-2140
E-mail: contactus@dei-sales.com
Web Site: www.dei-sales.com
Approx. Number Employees: 5
Year Founded: 1979
Business Description:
Sales Training Programs & Revenue Solutions
S.I.C.: 8742
N.A.I.C.S.: 541613
Advertising Expenditures: $240,000
Media: 2-6-10-22-26
Brands & Products:
AUTOMATED PROSPECT MANAGEMENT BOARD

DELL FORCE10 NETWORKS, INC.
350 Holger Way
San Jose, CA 95134-1362
Tel.: (408) 571-3500
Fax: (408) 571-3550
Toll Free: (866) 571-2600
E-mail: info@force10networks.com
Web Site: www.force10networks.com
Approx. Rev.: $119,070,000
Approx. Number Employees: 571
Year Founded: 1999
Business Description:
Computer Networking Products Mfr
S.I.C.: 3571
N.A.I.C.S.: 334111
Advertising Expenditures: $500,000
Media: 2-5-7-10-13-17
Personnel:
Dixon R. Doll *(Chm)*
Henry Wasik *(Pres & CEO)*
William Zerella *(CFO)*
James Hanley *(Pres-Field Ops)*
Leah Maher *(Gen Counsel & VP)*
Mary Cole *(VP-HR)*
Clive Hallatt *(Sr Dir-Bus Dev)*

DELL INC.
1 Dell Way
Round Rock, TX 78682-7000
Tel.: (512) 338-4400
Fax: (512) 283-6161
Toll Free: (800) 289-3355
Toll Free: (800) WWW-DELL
Web Site: www.dell.com
Approx. Rev.: $61,494,000,000
Approx. Number Employees: 100,300
Year Founded: 1984
Business Description:
Computer Products Developer, Mfr & Sales
S.I.C.: 3571; 5045; 5734
N.A.I.C.S.: 334111; 423430; 443120
Import Export
Advertising Expenditures: $730,000,000
Media: 2-3-4-6-7-8-13-15-16-19-24
Distr.: Intl.
Personnel:
Michael S. Dell *(Chm & CEO)*
Jeffrey W. Clarke *(Vice Chm-Ops & Tech)*
Lawrence Pentland *(Pres)*
Brian T. Gladden *(CFO & Sr VP)*
Karen Quintos *(CMO & Sr VP)*
Paul-Henri Ferrand *(CMO-Dell Consumer, Small & Medium Bus)*
Thomas W. Sweet *(Chief Acctg Officer & VP)*
Ashlen Cherry *(Officer-Americas Privacy)*
Paul D. Bell *(Pres-Pub & Large Enterprise)*
Stephen J. Felice *(Pres-Consumer, Small & Medium Bus)*
Ronald G. Garriques *(Pres-Comm Solutions)*
Stephen F. Schuckenbrock *(Pres-Svcs)*
Lawrence P. Tu *(Gen Counsel & Sr VP)*
Brad R. Anderson *(Sr VP-Enterprise Product Grp)*
Andrew Esparza *(Sr VP-HR)*
David A. Marmonti *(Sr VP-Dell)*
Ronald V. Rose *(Sr VP-Dellcom)*
Aongus Hegarty *(VP & Gen Mgr-Consumer & SME Sector EMEA)*
Steve Lalla *(VP & Gen Mgr)*
Andy Lark *(VP & Gen Mgr-Large Enterprise Mktg & Online)*
Bill Rodrigues *(VP & Gen Mgr-Global Bus)*
Dario Zamarian *(VP & Gen Mgr-Networking Bus)*
Janet B. Wright *(Asst Sec & VP-Corp, Securities & Fin Counsel)*
Mark J. Gambill *(VP-Mktg, Consumer, Small & Medium Bus)*
Kelly McGinnis *(VP-Corp Comm-Global)*
Michael Tatelman *(VP-Global Consumer Sls & Mktg)*
Atul Vohra *(VP-Mktg)*
Dave Brooke *(Gen Mgr-Middle East)*
Darren Thomas *(Gen Mgr)*
Michael J. Beach *(Exec Dir-Sls Ops)*
Bob Magee *(Dir-Procurement)*
Michael Murphy *(Dir-Environmental Affairs)*
Liam Quinn *(Dir-Tech)*
Lorrie Schultz *(Dir-BSD Mktg Comm)*
Jay Turner *(Dir-Channel Bus-Australia & New Zealand)*
Robert Williams *(Dir-IR)*
Kristen Nolte *(Sr Mgr-Americas CRM)*
John Robles *(Sr Mgr-Product Mktg)*
LeAnn Levering *(Strategist-Mktg)*
Brands & Products:
ADAMO
BE DIRECT
BUSINESSCARE
BUSINESSEASE
COMPLETECARE
CONNECTDIRECT
CRITICAL CARE
DELL
DELL DIMENSION
DELL DOLLARS
DELL INK MANAGEMENT SYSTEM
DELL OPENMANAGE
DELL PRECISION
DELL TALK
DELL THEFT
DELL TONER MANAGEMENT SYSTEM
DELL XPS ONE
DELLGUARD
DELLWARE
DELLWARE FACTS LINE
DESKDOCK
DIMENSION
DIRECTLINE
E
EASYCARE
EQUALLOGIC
EVERDREAM
EXPRESSCHARGE
FREEDOM QUEUE
HYPERCOOL
IMAGECARE
IMAGEWATCH
INSPIRON
LANSOLVE
LATITUDE
OPENFRAME
OPENLINE
OPTIPLEX

Key to Media (For complete agency information see *The Advertising Red Books-Agencies* edition):
1. Bus. Publs. 2. Cable T.V. 3. Catalogs & Directories. 4. Co-op Adv. 5. Consumer Mags. 6. D.M. to Bus. Estab.7. D.M. to Consumers
8. Daily Newsp. 9. Exhibits/Trade Shows 10. Foreign 11. Infomercial 12. Internet Adv.13. Multimedia 14. Network Radio
15. Network T.V. 16. Newsp. Distr. Mags. 17. Other 18. Outdoor (Posters, Transit) 19. Point of Purchase20. Premiums, Novelties
21. Product Samples 22. Special Events Mktg. 23. Spot Radio 24. Spot T.V. 25. Weekly Newsp. 26. Yellow Page Adv.

Dell Inc. — (Continued)

THE POWER OF TWO
POWERCONNECT
POWEREDGE
POWERVAULT
PREMIER ACCESS
PREMIER PAGES
QUIETKEY
RAMRIGHT
RAPID RESPONSE
READYWARE
SAFESITE
SELECTCARE
STRIKE ZONE
ULTRASCAN
VOSTRO
WWW.DELL.COM

Advertising Agencies:
Arnold Worldwide
101 Huntington Ave
Boston, MA 02199-7603
Tel.: (617) 587-8000
Fax: (617) 587-8004
Global Agency of Record
— Matt Belson *(VP & Acct Dir-Dell)*

Barrie D'Rozario Murphy
400 1st Ave N Ste 220
Minneapolis, MN 55401
Tel.: (612) 279-1500
Fax: (612) 332-9995

Carat International
Parker Tower 43-49 Parker St
London, WC2B 5PS, United Kingdom
Tel.: (44) 207 430 6000
Fax: (44) 207 430 6299

Cohn & Wolfe Austin
327 Congress Ave Ste 500
Austin, TX 78701-3656
Tel.: (512) 472-4122
Fax: (512) 472-5970
Toll Free: (800) 472-4122

Critical Mass Inc.
402 11th Ave SE
Calgary, AB T2G 0Y4, Canada
Tel.: (403) 262-3006
Fax: (403) 262-7185

FKM
1800 W Loop S Ste 2100
Houston, TX 77027
Tel.: (713) 862-5100
Fax: (713) 869-6560

HC&B Healthcare Communications
701 Brazos St Ste 1450
Austin, TX 78701-2581
Tel.: (512) 320-8511
Fax: (512) 320-8990

MediaCom
498 7th Ave
New York, NY 10018
Tel.: (212) 912-4200
Fax: (212) 508-4386
Media Buying
Wide Open Campaign-Media Buying & Planning

Merkle Inc.
7001 Columbia Gateway Dr
Columbia, MD 21046
Tel.: (443) 542-4000
Fax: (443) 542-4001
— Cyndie Beckwith *(VP)*

Mother New York
595 11th Ave
New York, NY 10036
Tel.: (212) 254-2800
Fax: (212) 254-6121
Dell XPS One

Public Strategies, Inc.
98 San Jacinto Blvd Ste 1200
Austin, TX 78701
Tel.: (512) 474-8848
Fax: (512) 474-0120
Wide Open Campaign - Public Relations

SicolaMartin
206 E 9th Ste 1800
Austin, TX 78701
Tel.: (512) 343-0264
Fax: (512) 343-0659

Springbox, Ltd.
706 Congress Ave Ste A
Austin, TX 78701
Tel.: (512) 391-0065
Fax: (512) 391-0064

Tocquigny Advertising, Interactive & Marketing Inc.
401 Congress Ave Ste 1700
Austin, TX 78701
Tel.: (512) 532-2800
Fax: (512) 328-5645
Toll Free: (800) 363-6566

WPP Group USA Inc.
100 Park Ave
New York, NY 10017-5529
Tel.: (212) 632-2200
Fax: (212) 632-2249

Wunderman
(Worldwide Headquarters)
285 Madison Ave
New York, NY 10017
Tel.: (212) 941-3000
Fax: (212) 210-5454

Young & Rubicam Inc.
285 Madison Ave
New York, NY 10017-6401
Tel.: (212) 210-3000
Fax: (212) 490-9073
Wide Open Campaign-Advertising & Online

DELL, INC.
(Div. of Dell Inc.)
6591 Dumbarton Cir
Fremont, CA 94555-3619
Tel.: (510) 818-5500
Fax: (510) 818-5510
E-mail: info@everdream.com
Web Site: www.everdream.com

Sales Range: $25-49.9 Million
Approx. Number Employees: 115
Year Founded: 1998

Business Description:
IT Desktop Management Services
S.I.C.: 7373
N.A.I.C.S.: 541512

Media: 2-7-10-13-22

DELL, INC.
(Div. of Dell Inc.)
110 Spit Brook Rd, Bld ZKO2
Nashua, NH 03062
Tel.: (603) 579-9762
Fax: (603) 589-5914
Toll Free: (888) 579-9762
Web Site: www.equallogic.com
E-Mail For Key Personnel:
Sales Director: sales@equallogic.com
Approx. Sls.: $68,064,000
Approx. Number Employees: 300
Year Founded: 2001
Business Description:
Internet Protocol-Based Data Storage Systems Developer
S.I.C.: 7376; 7379
N.A.I.C.S.: 541513; 541519
Advertising Expenditures: $24,000
Media: 10
Personnel:
Bob Skelley *(Exec Dir-Global Certified Partner Program & Channel)*
Timothy Sherbak *(Sr Mgr-Virtulization Solutions Mktg)*
Dylan Locsin *(Mgr-Technical Mktg)*

DELPHAX TECHNOLOGIES INC.
6100 W 110th St
Bloomington, MN 55438-2664
Tel.: (952) 939-9000
Fax: (952) 939-1151
E-mail: info@delphax.com
Web Site: www.delphax.com
Sales Range: $25-49.9 Million
Approx. Number Employees: 280
Year Founded: 1981
Business Description:
Digital Document Printing Equipment Mfr
S.I.C.: 3555; 7629
N.A.I.C.S.: 333293; 811219
Import Export
Advertising Expenditures: $500,000
Media: 2-4-7-10-22-26
Distr.: Intl.; Natl.
Budget Set: Aug.
Personnel:
Kenneth E. Overstreet *(Chm)*
Dieter P. Schilling *(Pres & CEO)*
Gregory S. Furness *(CFO)*
Kevin Howes *(VP-Sls, Mktg & Customer Svc)*
Les B. Weibye *(VP-HR)*
Michael A. Wroblewski *(VP-Engrg, Procurement & Mfg)*
Bob Rieger *(Dir-Sls Support & Customer Applications)*
Brands & Products:
CHECKTRONIC
DELPHAX
FOLIOTRONIC
IMAGGIA II
INTELLI-PICK
PS155 MICR
PS75 MICR

DELTEK, INC.
(Holding of New Mountain Capital, LLC)
13880 Dulles Corner Ln
Herndon, VA 20171
Tel.: (703) 734-8606
Fax: (703) 734-1146
Toll Free: (800) 456-2009
Web Site: www.deltek.com
Approx. Rev.: $279,648,000
Approx. Number Employees: 1,600
Year Founded: 1983
Business Description:
Project Management Software & Services
S.I.C.: 7371; 7372
N.A.I.C.S.: 541511; 511210
Advertising Expenditures: $303,000
Personnel:
Kevin T. Parker *(Pres & CEO)*
Michael P. Corkery *(CFO & Exec VP)*
Deborah K. Fitzgerald *(Sr VP & CIO)*
Kevin Iaquinto *(CMO & Sr VP)*
David R. Schwiesow *(Gen Counsel & Sr VP)*
Tom Mazich *(Exec VP & Gen Mgr-GovCon Bus Unit)*
Namita Dhallan *(Exec VP-Product Strategy & Mgmt)*
Garland Hall *(Sr VP-Customer Care)*
Holly C. Kortright *(Sr VP-HR)*
Brands & Products:
COBRA
COSTPOINT
DELTEK
DELTEK VISION
DELTEK WINSIGHT
GCS PREMIER
OPEN PLAN
WELCOMHOME
WINSIGHT

DELUXE SMALL BUSINESS SERVICES
(Sub. of Deluxe Corporation)
500 Main St
Groton, MA 01471
Tel.: (978) 448-6111
Fax: (800) 234-4324
Fax: (978) 449-3841
E-mail: customerservice@nebs.com
Web Site: www.nebs.com
Sales Range: $550-599.9 Million
Approx. Number Employees: 600
Year Founded: 1952
Business Description:
Check, Envelope, Label, Greeting Card, Sign, Stationery & Related Printing Services
S.I.C.: 5112
N.A.I.C.S.: 424120
Media: 2-4-7-10-13-21
Distr.: Intl.; Natl.
Budget Set: Apr.

DEMANDTEC, INC.
1 Franklin Pkwy Bldg 910
San Mateo, CA 94403
Tel.: (650) 645-7100
E-mail: info@demandtec.com
Web Site: www.demandtec.com
E-Mail For Key Personnel:
Sales Director: sales@demandtec.com
Approx. Rev.: $82,418,000
Approx. Number Employees: 340
Year Founded: 1999
Business Description:
Demand Based Management Software Developer & Retailer
S.I.C.: 7371; 7372
N.A.I.C.S.: 541511; 511210
Advertising Expenditures: $319,000
Media: 10
Personnel:
Daniel R. Fishback *(Pres & CEO)*
Mark A. Culhane *(CFO & Exec VP)*

Key to Media (For complete agency information see *The Advertising Red Books-Agencies* edition):
1. Bus. Publs. 2. Cable T.V. 3. Catalogs & Directories. 4. Co-op Adv. 5. Consumer Mags. 6. D.M. to Bus. Estab.7. D.M. to Consumers
8. Daily Newsp. 9. Exhibits/Trade Shows 10. Foreign 11. Infomercial 12. Internet Adv.13. Multimedia 14. Network Radio
15. Network T.V. 16. Newsp. Distr. Mags. 17. Other 18. Outdoor (Posters, Transit) 19. Point of Purchase20. Premiums, Novelties
21. Product Samples 22. Special Events Mktg. 23. Spot Radio 24. Spot T.V. 25. Weekly Newsp. 26. Yellow Page Adv.

William Phelps *(COO & Exec VP)*
Michael A. Bromme *(Sr VP-Retail)*
Tom Croke *(Sr VP-Worldwide Retail Sls)*
Kevin Sterneckert *(VP & Gen Mgr-Retail)*
Rob Culin *(VP-Shopper Insights & Strategic Programs)*
Steve Feller *(VP-HR & Admin)*
Brands & Products:
ADVANCED DEAL MANAGEMENT
ASSORTMENT OPTIMIZATION
DEAL/BILLING DATA EXPORT
DEAL MANAGEMENT
DEMADTEC PLATFORM
DEMANDTEC TRADEPOINT NETWORK
EVERYDAY PRICE MANAGEMENT
EVERYDAY PRICE OPTIMIZATION
FUNDS TRACKER
LIFECYCLE PRICE OPTIMIZATION
MARKDOWN OPTIMIZATION
OPENLINK
PRESENTATION BUILDER
PROMOTION PLANNING & OPTIMIZATION
TRADE PLANNING & OPTIMIZATION

DEMCO INC.
4810 Forest Run Rd
Madison, WI 53704-7336
Mailing Address:
PO Box 7488
Madison, WI 53707
Tel.: (608) 241-1201
Fax: (608) 241-1799
Toll Free: (800) 279-1586
E-mail: custserv@demco.com
Web Site: www.demco.com
Approx. Number Employees: 350
Year Founded: 1905
Business Description:
Business, Educational & Library Supplies Distr
S.I.C.: 5021; 2531
N.A.I.C.S.: 423210; 337127
Advertising Expenditures: $350,000
Media: 4-6-7-8-10
Distr.: Natl.
Budget Set: Oct.
Personnel:
John E. Wall *(Chm)*
William Stroner *(Pres & CEO)*
Don Rogers *(Treas & VP-Fin)*
Kyle Anderson *(VP-Sls-Mktg)*
Sue Sippola *(Dir-HR)*
Peter Williams *(Dir-Media Svcs)*
Brands & Products:
DEMCO-BOUND
DEMCOTE
FASTAPE
NORBOND

DIAGRAPH
(Sub. of Illinois Tool Works Inc.)
1 Missouri Research Pk Dr
Saint Charles, MO 63304-5685
Tel.: (636) 300-2000
Fax: (636) 300-2005
Toll Free: (800) 722-1125
E-mail: info@diagraph.com
Web Site: www.diagraph.com
E-Mail For Key Personnel:
Sales Director: sales@diagraph.com
Sales Range: $75-99.9 Million
Approx. Number Employees: 400
Year Founded: 1893
Business Description:
Product Identification & Bar Coding Systems Mfr
S.I.C.: 3953
N.A.I.C.S.: 339943
Export
Media: 2-4-7-10
Distr.: Intl.; Natl.
Budget Set: May
Personnel:
Kevin Gold *(Gen Mgr-Labeling)*
John Campbell *(Mgr-Sls)*
Bill Myers *(Mgr-Mktg)*
Brands & Products:
ALP/4500
DIAGRAPH
IJ/3000
IV/700
LA/1000
PA/5000
PEL/CIDS SE

DIALOG, LLC
(Sub. of ProQuest, LLC)
2250 Perimeter Park Dr Ste 300
Morrisville, NC 27560
Tel.: (919) 804-6400
Fax: (919) 804-6410
Toll Free: (800) 3DIALOG
Web Site: www.dialog.com
Sales Range: $25-49.9 Million
Approx. Number Employees: 1,100
Year Founded: 1972
Business Description:
Business, Finance, Science & Legal Information Services
S.I.C.: 2741; 7389
N.A.I.C.S.: 516110; 519190
Media: 2-7-8-10-11-19-20-21-26
Personnel:
Libby Trudell *(VP-Mktg)*
Brands & Products:
DATASTAR
DIALOG
INTELLIGENCE DATA
INTELLISCOPE
NEWSEDGE
PROFOUND

DIEBOLD, INCORPORATED
5995 Mayfair Rd
Canton, OH 44720-1550
Mailing Address:
PO Box 3077
Canton, OH 44720-8077
Tel.: (330) 490-4000
Fax: (330) 490-3794
Toll Free: (800) 999-3600
E-mail: productinfo@diebold.com
Web Site: www.diebold.com
Approx. Sls.: $2,823,793,000
Approx. Number Employees: 16,124
Year Founded: 1859
Business Description:
ATM & Security Solutions Services
S.I.C.: 7382; 3575; 3577
N.A.I.C.S.: 561621; 334113; 334119
Import Export
Advertising Expenditures: $8,782,000
Media: 1-2-7-9-10-13-26
Personnel:
Thomas W. Swidarski *(Pres & CEO)*
Bradley C. Richardson *(CFO & Exec VP)*
Scott M. Angelo *(CIO & VP)*
John M. Deignan *(CMO & VP)*
David J. Kennedy *(Chief Info Security Officer)*
Warren W. Dettinger *(Gen Counsel, Sec & VP)*
James L. M. Chen *(Exec VP-Intl Ops)*
Charles E. Ducey Jr. *(Exec VP-Ops-North America)*
George S. Mayes Jr. *(Exec VP-Global Ops)*
Mike J. Lee *(Sr VP)*
Alex Brown *(VP-Corp Strategy & Dev)*
NABradley J. Stephenson *(VP-Security Div-Global)*
Wico van Genderen *(VP-Mktg & Product Mgmt-Global)*
Robert J. Warren *(VP-Corp Dev & Fin)*
Michael Jacobsen *(Sr Dir-Corp Comm)*
Christopher Bast *(Dir-IR)*
Tim O'Neill *(Product Mgr)*
Jim Pellegrene *(Sr Product Mgr-Vaults)*
Brands & Products:
ACCUVOTE-OS
ADVISOR
AGILIS
THE AGILIS
AGILIS 3X
AGILIS 91X
AGILIS EMPOWER
AGILIS NDX
AGILIS POWER
AMERICAN
ASSURE
COINCOUNT
CS GOLD 4.0
DIEBOLD
EASYAIRE
EXPRESS DELIVERY
EXPRESS DELIVERY XT
GEMS
I SERIES
IMAGEWAY
INNOVATION DELIVERED
INTELLIGENT DEPOSITORY MODULE
INVOLVE
IX SERIES
LINX
MERCHANT BANKING CENTER
NEXUS
OPTEVA
OPTEVIEW
PASSVAULT
PAYSTATION
PRESIDER
RECOVERY PLUS
REMOTETELLER
REVISOR
SECURESTAT
SECUROMATIC
SITE SENTRY
TITAN
VISION DIRECT
VISUAL AUTO TELLER
WEDGE-LOCK
XAPWARE PLUS
Advertising Agencies:
Dix & Eaton Incorporated
200 Public Sq Ste 1400
Cleveland, OH 44114
Tel.: (216) 241-0405
Fax: (216) 241-3070
(Corp.)

SmileyHanchulak Marketing Communications
47 N Cleveland Massillon Rd
Akron, OH 44333-2420
Tel.: (330) 666-0868
Fax: (330) 666-5762

Zoar Interactive
254 E 4th St
Zoar, OH 44697
Tel.: (330) 874-0313
Fax: (330) 874-2715

DIETZGEN
(Unit of Nashua Corporation)
250 S NW Hwy Ste 203
Park Ridge, IL 60068
Tel.: (847) 318-1700
Fax: (847) 692-9818
Toll Free: (800) 473-1270
E-mail: contact@dietzgen.com
Web Site: www.nashua.com
Sales Range: $25-49.9 Million
Approx. Number Employees: 11
Year Founded: 1885
Business Description:
Reprographic Equipment & Supplies Mfr
S.I.C.: 3861; 2672; 2679; 3579
N.A.I.C.S.: 333315; 322222; 322299; 333313
Import Export
Media: 2-4-20-26
Distr.: Intl.; Natl.
Budget Set: Jan.
Brands & Products:
DIETZGEN

DIGI INTERNATIONAL INC.
11001 Bren Rd E
Minnetonka, MN 55343-9605
Tel.: (952) 912-3444
Fax: (952) 912-4952
Toll Free: (800) 344-4273
E-mail: info@digi.com
Web Site: www.digi.com
Approx. Sls.: $182,548,000
Approx. Number Employees: 648
Year Founded: 1985
Business Description:
Data Communications, Computer Hardware & Software Mfr & Distr
S.I.C.: 3571; 3577; 7372
N.A.I.C.S.: 334111; 334119; 511210
Export
Advertising Expenditures: $28,600,000
Media: 1-2-10
Personnel:
Joseph T. Dunsmore *(Chm, Pres & CEO)*
Steven E. Snyder *(CFO, Sr VP)*
Joel K. Young *(CTO & Sr VP-R & D)*
Larry Kraft *(Sr VP-Sls & Mktg)*
Tracy Roberts *(VP-HR & IT)*
Brands & Products:
ACCELEPORT
ACCELPORT RAS
ANYWHEREUSB
CLASSICBOARD
CONNECT
CONNECTCORE
CONNECTPORT
CONNECTWARE
DATA FIRE
DATAFIRE
DIGI
DIGI CM
DIGI CONNECT
DIGI INTERNATIONAL
DIGI NEO
DIGI ONE

Key to Media (For complete agency information see *The Advertising Red Books-Agencies* edition):
1. Bus. Publs. 2. Cable T.V. 3. Catalogs & Directories. 4. Co-op Adv. 5. Consumer Mags. 6. D.M. to Bus. Estab.7. D.M. to Consumers 8. Daily Newsp. 9. Exhibits/Trade Shows 10. Foreign 11. Infomercial 12. Internet Adv.13. Multimedia 14. Network Radio 15. Network T.V. 16. Newsp. Distr. Mags. 17. Other 18. Outdoor (Posters, Transit) 19. Point of Purchase20. Premiums, Novelties 21. Product Samples 22. Special Events Mktg. 23. Spot Radio 24. Spot T.V. 25. Weekly Newsp. 26. Yellow Page Adv.

Digi International Inc. — (Continued)

DIGI PASSPORT
DIGI SHOWBOX
DIGI TRANSPORT
DIGIMESH
EASYPOWER
EDGEPORT
EDGEUSB
ETHERLITE
HUBPORT
IDIGI
MAKING WIRELESS M2M EASY
MAXSTREAM
NEO
ONE
PORTSERVER
PYTHON
RABBIT SEMICONDUCTOR
RAPIDPORT
RAPIDPORT/4
REALPORT
WATCHPORT
WAVESPEED
XBEE
XBEE-PRO
XCITE
XPRESS
XSTREAM
XTEND
ZIGBEE

Advertising Agency:
Mulberry Marketing Communications Chicago
308 W Erie St Ste 701
Chicago, IL 60654
Tel.: (312) 664-1532
Fax: (312) 664-1532

DIGITAL ANGEL CORPORATION
490 Villaume Ave
South Saint Paul, MN 55075
Tel.: (651) 455-1621
E-mail: info@digitalangel.com
Web Site: www.digitalangel.com
Approx. Rev.: $37,720,000
Approx. Number Employees: 162
Business Description:
GPS & RFID Technology Development Services
S.I.C.: 3669; 7371; 7374
N.A.I.C.S.: 334290; 518210; 541511
Import Export
Advertising Expenditures: $200,000
Media: 2-4-10
Personnel:
Daniel E. Penni *(Chm)*
Joseph J. Grillo *(Pres & CEO)*
Jason G. Prescott *(CFO, Treas & VP-Fin-Destron Fearing)*
Brands & Products:
DIGITAL ANGEL
SECURITY THROUGH INNOVATION
THERMO LIFE
Advertising Agency:
DCI Group
1828 L St NW Ste 400
Washington, DC 20036
Tel.: (202) 546-4242
Fax: (202) 546-4243

DIGITAL DEVELOPMENT PARTNERS, INC.
17800 Castleton St Ste 300
City of Industry, CA 91748
Tel.: (626) 581-3335
Fax: (626) 581-4121
Web Site: www.digitaldevelopmentpartners.com
Approx. Rev.: $691,600
Year Founded: 2006
Business Description:
Digital-Related Services
S.I.C.: 7379
N.A.I.C.S.: 541519
Advertising Expenditures: $77,383
Media: 17
Personnel:
Jack Jie Qin *(Pres & CEO)*
William E. Sluss *(CFO & Chief Acctg Officer)*

DIMENSIONAL INSIGHT, INC.
60 Mall Rd
Burlington, MA 01803
Tel.: (781) 229-9111
Fax: (781) 229-9113
Toll Free: (800) 379-5899
E-mail: info@dimins.com
Web Site: www.dimins.com
Approx. Sls.: $10,000,000
Approx. Number Employees: 30
Year Founded: 1989
Business Description:
Database & File Management Software Development & Sales
S.I.C.: 7372
N.A.I.C.S.: 511210
Media: 10
Personnel:
Frederick A. Powers *(Co-Founder & CEO)*
Stanley R. Zanarotti *(Co-Founder & CTO)*
Ed O'Brien *(VP-Health care sls)*
Lauren McCollem *(Dir-Mktg)*

DIRECT INSITE CORP.
13450 W Sunrise Blvd
Sunrise, FL 33323
Tel.: (631) 873-2900
Fax: (631) 563-8085
Toll Free: (800) 619-0757
E-mail: sales@directinsite.com
Web Site: www.directinsite.com
E-Mail For Key Personnel:
Sales Director: sales@directinsite.com
Approx. Rev.: $9,052,000
Approx. Number Employees: 38
Year Founded: 1993
Business Description:
Electronic Invoice Management & Workflow Compliance Reconciliation for Accounts Payable & Accounts Receivable
S.I.C.: 7373; 6099; 7372
N.A.I.C.S.: 541512; 511210; 522320
Advertising Expenditures: $41,000
Media: 17
Personnel:
James A. Cannavino *(Chm)*
Matthew E. Oakes *(Pres & CEO)*
Arnold P. Leap *(CTO & Exec VP-Sls/Mktg)*
Sandra Wallace *(Acting CFO & VP-Fin)*

DIRECT MEDIA, LLC
(Sub. of Direct Media Millard, Inc.)
(d/b/a Direct Media Millard - Connecticut)
200 Pemberwick Rd
Greenwich, CT 06831
Tel.: (203) 532-1000
Web Site: www.dmminfo.com/Contact-Us/Office-Locations-and-Directions.aspx
Sales Range: $50-74.9 Million
Approx. Number Employees: 200
Year Founded: 1969
Business Description:
List Management & Brokerage Services
S.I.C.: 7331
N.A.I.C.S.: 541860
Media: 2-13
Personnel:
Dolores Ryan Babcock *(Exec VP)*
Karen Mayhew *(Exec VP-List Mgmt Div)*
Mike Mayhew *(Exec VP-Bus-to-Bus List Mgmt)*
Mary Ellen Quirk *(Exec VP)*
Carolyn Woodruff *(Exec VP)*
Larry May *(Sr VP-Strategic Dev)*
Thom Hansen *(VP-Mktg-Intl)*

DIRECTORY DISTRIBUTING ASSOCIATES, INC.
1602 Park 370 Ct
Hazelwood, MO 63042-3814
Tel.: (314) 592-8600
Fax: (314) 592-8792
Toll Free: (800) 325-1964
E-mail: dda@directrac.com
Web Site: www.ddai.com
Approx. Number Employees: 1,500
Year Founded: 1947
Business Description:
Telephone Directory Distribution, Telemarketing, Warehousing & Fulfillment Services
S.I.C.: 4212; 5192
N.A.I.C.S.: 484110; 424920
Export
Media: 2-13
Personnel:
John W. Runk *(Chm)*
Michael W. Shelton *(CFO, Treas & VP)*
Jim Fowler *(Exec VP-Ops)*
Brands & Products:
DDA

DISKEEPER CORPORATION
7590 N Glenoaks Blvd
Burbank, CA 91504-1052
Tel.: (818) 771-1600
Fax: (818) 252-5514
Toll Free: (800) 829HELP
E-mail: info@executive.com
Web Site: www.diskeeper.com
Approx. Number Employees: 160
Year Founded: 1981
Business Description:
Systems Software Mfr
S.I.C.: 7372; 5734
N.A.I.C.S.: 511210; 443120
Export
Media: 2-4-6-7-8-10-13-21
Personnel:
Craig Jensen *(Founder & Chm)*
Jerry Baldwin *(CEO)*
Manuel Vianna *(CFO)*
Dawn Richcreek *(VP-PR & Mktg)*
Danny Chadwell *(Dir-Corp Affairs)*
Damian Giannunzio *(Product Mgr)*
Michael Materie *(Product Mgr)*
John Repetto *(Mgr-Govt Reseller-North American Channel Unit)*
Dan Soliz *(Mgr-Corp Reseller-North American Channel Unit)*
Brands & Products:
DISKALERT FOR WINDOWS NT2000
DISKEEPER
EXECUTIVE SOFTWARE
FRAGSHIELD
I/O EXPRESS
PROTECTION
PUSHLNSTALLER
SECUREDELETE
SET IT AND FORGET IT
SITEKEEPER
TERABYTE VOLUME ENGINE
UNDELETE

DISPLAYTECH, INC.
2602 Clover Basin Dr
Longmont, CO 80503
Tel.: (303) 772-2191
Fax: (303) 772-2193
Toll Free: (800) 397-8124
E-mail: info@displaytech.com
Web Site: www.displaytech.com
Sales Range: $25-49.9 Million
Approx. Number Employees: 47
Year Founded: 1984
Business Description:
Microdisplays
S.I.C.: 3674; 3679
N.A.I.C.S.: 334413; 334419
Media: 5-7
Personnel:
Robert L. Burr *(Chm)*
Bruce Spenner *(Exec VP)*
Brands & Products:
DISPLAYTECH
LIGHTVIEW
WE MAKE LIGHT WORK

DIVERSIFIED BUSINESS COMMUNICATIONS
(Sub. of Diversified Communications)
121 Free St
Portland, ME 04101-3919
Tel.: (207) 842-5500
Fax: (207) 842-5503
E-mail: custserv@divcom.com
Web Site: www.divbusiness.com
Approx. Number Employees: 150
Business Description:
Industry Related Trade Shows & Publications
S.I.C.: 4833; 4841
N.A.I.C.S.: 515120; 515210
Media: 10
Personnel:
Nancy Hasselback *(Pres & CEO)*
Kendra Lavigne *(Coord-Bus Dev)*

DIXON TICONDEROGA COMPANY
(Sub. of Fabbrica Italiana Lapis ed Affini S.p.A.)
195 International Pkwy
Heathrow, FL 32746-5007
Tel.: (407) 829-9000
Fax: (407) 829-2574
Toll Free: (800) 824-9430
E-mail: info@dixonticonderoga.com
Web Site: www.dixonticonderoga.com
Sales Range: $75-99.9 Million
Approx. Number Employees: 1,403
Year Founded: 1795
Business Description:
Writing & Drawing Materials Mfr & Marketer
S.I.C.: 3952; 3951
N.A.I.C.S.: 339942; 339941
Import Export

Key to Media (For complete agency information see *The Advertising Red Books-Agencies* edition):
1. Bus. Publs. 2. Cable T.V. 3. Catalogs & Directories. 4. Co-op Adv. 5. Consumer Mags. 6. D.M. to Bus. Estab.7. D.M. to Consumers 8. Daily Newsp. 9. Exhibits/Trade Shows 10. Foreign 11. Infomercial 12. Internet Adv.13. Multimedia 14. Network Radio 15. Network T.V. 16. Newsp. Distr. Mags. 17. Other 18. Outdoor (Posters, Transit) 19. Point of Purchase20. Premiums, Novelties 21. Product Samples 22. Special Events Mktg. 23. Spot Radio 24. Spot T.V. 25. Weekly Newsp. 26. Yellow Page Adv.

Media: 2-4-5-6-7-8-10-11-20-21
Distr.: Intl.; Natl.
Budget Set: Oct.
Personnel:
Massimo Candela *(Chm)*
Donald S. Currie *(CEO)*
Lillian Gonzales *(Sec & Dir-HR)*
Brands & Products:
DIXON
HYGIEIA
PRANG
REDIMARK
REDISHARP
SENSE-A-MARK
SENSEMATIC
TICONDEROGA
VINCI
WEAREVER

DOCUMENT SECURITY SYSTEMS, INC.

28 Main St E Ste 1525
Rochester, NY 14614
Tel.: (585) 325-3610
Fax: (585) 325-2977
E-mail: robin@documentsecurity.com
Web Site: www.documentsecurity.com
Approx. Rev.: $13,381,581
Approx. Number Employees: 104
Business Description:
Anti-Scanning, Anti-Counterfeiting Technologies for Homeland Security
S.I.C.: 7373; 9711
N.A.I.C.S.: 541512; 928110
Advertising Expenditures: $23,000
Media: 7-10-20
Personnel:
Robert B. Fagenson *(Chm)*
Robert B. Bzdick *(Pres & COO)*
Patrick J. White *(CEO & Dir)*
Philip Jones *(CFO)*
Robert McAleavey *(Pres-Security Printing Div)*
Jeffrey D'Angelo *(Gen Counsel & VP)*
David M Wicker *(VP-Ops & Tech)*
Kenneth Wicker *(VP-Emerging Tech & Ops)*
Advertising Agency:
Dixon Schwabl Advertising
1595 Moseley Rd
Victor, NY 14564
Tel.: (585) 383-0380
Fax: (585) 383-1661

DON BELL SIGNS LLC

365 Oak Pl
Port Orange, FL 32127-4388
Tel.: (386) 788-8084
Fax: (386) 767-0968
E-mail: info@donbellsigns.com
Web Site: www.donbellsigns.com
Sales Estimate: $5-9.9 Million
Approx. Number Employees: 80
Year Founded: 1947
Business Description:
Hi-Tech Computer Driven Video Displays & Signs Designer, Installer & Mfr
S.I.C.: 1731; 3993
N.A.I.C.S.: 238210; 339950
Media: 10-26
Personnel:
Cecil Ward *(VP-Sls & Qualifying Agent)*

DOT HILL SYSTEMS CORP.

1351 S Sunset St
Longmont, CO 80501
Tel.: (303) 845-3200
E-mail: pr@dothill.com
Web Site: www.dothill.com
Approx. Rev.: $252,494,000
Approx. Number Employees: 293
Year Founded: 1984
Business Description:
Data Storage System Designer & Mfr
S.I.C.: 3572
N.A.I.C.S.: 334112
Advertising Expenditures: $1,100,000
Media: 2-7-10
Personnel:
Charles F. Christ *(Chm)*
Dana W. Kammersgard *(Pres & CEO)*
Hanif I. Jamal *(CFO & Sr VP)*
Ernest Hafersat *(Sr VP-Mfg, Ops & Supply Base Mgmt-Worldwide)*
James E. Kuenzel *(Sr VP-Engrg)*
Scott Brooks *(VP-Customer Svcs & Sls)*
Brad Painter *(VP-Worldwide Channel Sls)*
Ruth Macdonald *(Mgr-Mktg Comm)*
Brands & Products:
ARTECON
ASSUREDSNAP
AXIS STORAGE MANAGER
BOX HILL
DOT HILL
ECOSTOR
LYNXARRAY II
LYNXSTACK
MODBOX
R/EVOLUTION
RAIDCORE
RIO
RIO XTREME
RIVA
RIVA FC
SANMAN
SANNET
SANnet II FC
SANpath
SANSCAPE
SIMULCACHE
TANNET

DOUGLAS-GUARDIAN SERVICES CORPORATION

14800 St Marys Ln Ste 200
Houston, TX 77079-2936
Tel.: (281) 531-0500
Fax: (281) 531-1777
Toll Free: (800) 227-4644
E-mail: sales@douglasguardian.com
Web Site: www.douglasguardian.com
E-Mail For Key Personnel:
President: bruce@douglasguardian.com
Marketing Director: jryan@douglasguardian.com
Sales Director: sales@douglasguardian.com
Approx. Number Employees: 300
Year Founded: 1932
Business Description:
Collateral Management Services & Inventory Equipment Verification to Financial Institutions
S.I.C.: 7389; 6531
N.A.I.C.S.: 561499; 531210
Advertising Expenditures: $300,000
Media: 2-17-22
Distr.: Natl.
Budget Set: Jan.
Personnel:
Bruce E. Lurie *(Pres)*
Jack F. Ryan *(Sr VP)*
Woodley Simon *(Mgr-IT)*
Brands & Products:
DOUGLAS-GUARDIAN

DOW JONES BUSINESS & RELATIONSHIP INTELLIGENCE

(Unit of Dow Jones Enterprise Media)
Six Clock Tower Pl Ste 120
Maynard, MA 01754
Tel.: (978) 823-5260
Fax: (978) 823-5261
Toll Free: (888) 823-8823
E-mail: sales@generateinc.com
Web Site: www.generateinc.com
Sales Range: $50-74.9 Million
Approx. Number Employees: 55
Year Founded: 2004
Business Description:
Relationship-Mapping Technology & Business Intelligence Solutions
S.I.C.: 7371; 7374; 7375
N.A.I.C.S.: 541511; 518111; 518210
Media: 10
Personnel:
Benoit Julien *(VP-Tech)*
Michael J. Lukaszevicz *(VP-Tech)*
Brands & Products:
GENERATE
GENERATE GCLICK
GENERATE GDAILY
GENERATE GPIPE

DPAC TECHNOLOGIES CORP.

5675 Hudson Industrial Park
Hudson, OH 44236
Tel.: (330) 655-9000
Fax: (330) 655-9020
Toll Free: (800) 553-1170
E-mail: sales@dpactech.com
Web Site: www.dpactech.com
E-Mail For Key Personnel:
Sales Director: sales@dpactech.com
Approx. Sls.: $7,847,465
Approx. Number Employees: 22
Year Founded: 1983
Business Description:
Computer Memory Module Mfr
S.I.C.: 3674; 3669
N.A.I.C.S.: 334413; 334290
Advertising Expenditures: $77,000
Media: 17
Personnel:
Steven D. Runkel *(Pres & CEO)*
Stephen J. Vukadinovich *(CFO)*
Kevin Kline *(VP-Sls & Mktg)*
Brands & Products:
AIRBORNE
AIRBORNEDIRECT
DPAC TECHNOLOGIES

DRI MARK PRODUCTS, INC.

15 Harbor Pk Dr
Port Washington, NY 11050-4604
Tel.: (516) 484-6200
Fax: (516) 484-6279
Toll Free: (800) 645-9118
E-mail: info@drimark.com
Web Site: www.drimark.com
Approx. Rev.: $7,719,000,000
Approx. Number Employees: 17,500
Year Founded: 1960
Business Description:
Promotional Products Mfr
S.I.C.: 3951; 5112
N.A.I.C.S.: 339941; 424120
Import Export
Media: 4-6-7-8-10-15-20-21-24
Distr.: Natl.
Personnel:
Charles Reichmann *(Owner)*
Cathy Williams-Owen *(Pres & CFO)*
Andre Reichmann *(COO)*
Mark Dobbs *(VP-Sls)*
Susan Adam *(Mgr-IT)*
Siohan Lucidi *(Mgr-Pur)*
Lydia Mojica *(Mgr-HR)*
Connie Villamor *(Mgr-Plant)*
Brands & Products:
COMMUNICATOR
DRIMARK
METALLIC COLORS
MINI HIGHLIGHTER
SMART MONEY
STAX
TRI MARK

DRIVESAVERS DATA RECOVERY, INC.

400 Bel Marin Keys Blvd
Novato, CA 94949
Tel.: (415) 382-2000
Fax: (415) 883-0780
Toll Free: (800) 440-1904
E-mail: pr@drivesavers.com
Web Site: www.drivesavers.com
Sales Range: $10-24.9 Million
Approx. Number Employees: 50
Year Founded: 1985
Business Description:
Data Recovery & Retrieval Services
S.I.C.: 7389; 7374
N.A.I.C.S.: 519190; 518210
Media: 6
Personnel:
Scott Gaidano *(Co-Founder & Pres)*
Mike Cobb *(Dir-Engrg)*

DST SYSTEMS, INC.

333 W 11th St
Kansas City, MO 64105-1773
Mailing Address:
PO Box 219591
Kansas City, MO 64121-9591
Tel.: (816) 435-1000
Fax: (816) 435-8618
Toll Free: (888) 378-4636
E-mail: webmaster@dstsystems.com
Web Site: www.dstsystems.com
Approx. Rev.: $2,328,500,000
Approx. Number Employees: 11,200
Year Founded: 1969
Business Description:
Information Processing & Software Services & Products
S.I.C.: 7372; 6099; 7371; 7374
N.A.I.C.S.: 511210; 518210; 522320; 541511
Media: 2-10
Personnel:
Stephen C. Hooley *(Pres & COO)*
Thomas A. McDonnell *(CEO)*
Kenneth V. Hager *(CFO, Treas & VP)*
Gregg W. Givens *(Chief Acctg Officer & VP)*
Randall D. Young *(Gen Counsel, Sec & VP)*
Jonathan J. Boehm *(Exec VP)*
Robert L. Tritt *(Exec VP)*
Brands & Products:
AUTOMATED WORK DISTRIBUTOR
AWD

Key to Media (For complete agency information see *The Advertising Red Books-Agencies* edition):
1. Bus. Publs. 2. Cable T.V. 3. Catalogs & Directories. 4. Co-op Adv. 5. Consumer Mags. 6. D.M. to Bus. Estab.7. D.M. to Consumers
8. Daily Newsp. 9. Exhibits/Trade Shows 10. Foreign 11. Infomercial 12. Internet Adv.13. Multimedia 14. Network Radio
15. Network T.V. 16. Newsp. Distr. Mags. 17. Other 18. Outdoor (Posters, Transit) 19. Point of Purchase20. Premiums, Novelties
21. Product Samples 22. Special Events Mktg. 23. Spot Radio 24. Spot T.V. 25. Weekly Newsp. 26. Yellow Page Adv.

DST Systems, Inc. — (Continued)

AWD BUSINESS INTELLIGENCE
AWD/CONTACT
AWD/EMAIL
AWD/ICR
AWD/KNOWLEDGE ENABLER
AWD/NETSERVER
AWD/RIP
AWD/SCAN
AWD/ST
AWD/THIN CLIENT
AWD/VOICE
DST
DST SYSTEMS
ENCORR
FAN
FAN MAIL
FAN WEB
FINANCIAL ACCESS NETWORK
GLOBAL PORTFOLIO SYSTEM
GPS
INFOQUEST
PLANTRAC
POWERSTORE
SECURITIES TRANSFER SYSTEMS
STS
TA2000
TA2000 DESKTOP
TA2000/VOICE
TRAC
TRAC AUTOVANTAGE
TRAC WEB
VISION

DUPONT COLOR PROOFING

(Div. of E.I. du Pont de Nemours & Company)
Barley Mill Plaza Rts 141 & 48
Wilmington, DE 19880-0030
Tel.: (302) 892-1064
Fax: (302) 992-2133
Toll Free: (800) 345-9999
E-mail: info@dupont.com
Web Site: www.dupont.com/proofing
Sales Range: $100-124.9 Million
Business Description:
Print Production Services
S.I.C.: 3555; 8742
N.A.I.C.S.: 333293; 541611
Advertising Expenditures: $600,000
Media: 2-7-10
Distr.: Natl.
Budget Set: Dec. -Jan.
Brands & Products:
CROMALIN
CROMANET
CROMAPRO XP
THERMAL DYLUX
WATERPROOF

DURO ART INDUSTRIES, INC.

1832 W Juneway Ter
Chicago, IL 60626-1016
Tel.: (773) 743-3430
Fax: (773) 743-3882
E-mail: duroart@msn.com
Approx. Number Employees: 25
Business Description:
Art Supplies Mfr
S.I.C.: 3952
N.A.I.C.S.: 339942
Import Export
Media: 2-4-6-7-9-10-17-21-26
Distr.: Natl.
Personnel:
Thomas C. Rathslag, Jr. *(Owner)*
Kurt Rathslag *(Mgr-Key Accts)*
Brands & Products:
LYONS ARTIST CANVAS

DYNTEK, INC.

4440 Von Karman Ave Ste 200
Newport Beach, CA 92660
Tel.: (949) 271-6700
Fax: (949) 271-6794
E-mail: corporate@dyntek.com
Web Site: www.dyntek.com
Sales Range: $75-99.9 Million
Approx. Number Employees: 237
Year Founded: 1989
Business Description:
Information Technology Solutions & Business Process Outsource Services
S.I.C.: 7371; 7389
N.A.I.C.S.: 541511; 561499
Advertising Expenditures: $103,000
Media: 2-10
Personnel:
James Michael Gullard *(Chm)*
Ron Ben-Yishay *(Pres & CEO)*
Karen S. Rosenberger *(CFO & COO)*
Jeff Brambir *(Dir-Trng)*
Brands & Products:
DYNTEK
FLEXCARE
NETPULSE
PRODUCTIVIT
READYCARE

EA ENGINEERING, SCIENCE & TECHNOLOGY, INC.

11019 McCormick Rd Ste 400
Hunt Valley, MD 21031
Tel.: (410) 584-7000
Fax: (410) 771-1625
E-mail: info@eaest.com
Web Site: www.eaest.com
E-Mail For Key Personnel:
President: ldj@eaest.com
Approx. Number Employees: 400
Year Founded: 1973
Business Description:
Environmental, Health, Safety & Engineering Consulting Services Supplier
S.I.C.: 8748; 8711
N.A.I.C.S.: 541690; 541330
Catalogs & Directories: 10%; D.M. to Consumers: 25%; Exhibits/Trade Shows: 35%; Other: 10%; Special Events Mktg.: 10%; Yellow Page Adv.: 10%
Distr.: Natl.
Budget Set: July
Personnel:
Loren D. Jensen *(Founder, Chm & CEO)*
Ian MacFarlane *(Pres & CEO)*
Peter Ney *(CFO)*
George D. O'Brien *(Sr VP)*
Kathryn Kuwabara *(Dir-Mktg)*
Brands & Products:
EA

EAGLE POINT SOFTWARE CORPORATION

4131 Westmark Dr
Dubuque, IA 52002-2627
Tel.: (563) 556-8392
Fax: (563) 556-5321
Toll Free: (800) 678-6565
Toll Free: (800) 477-0909
E-mail: sales@eaglepoint.com
Web Site: www.eaglepoint.com
E-Mail For Key Personnel:
Sales Director: sales@eaglepoint.com
Sales Range: $10-24.9 Million
Approx. Number Employees: 40
Year Founded: 1983
Business Description:
Business & Process Improvement Services & Technologies For Land Development Professionals
S.I.C.: 7371; 8742; 8748
N.A.I.C.S.: 541511; 541611; 541618
Media: 2-4-7-8-10-13
Personnel:
John Biver *(Pres & CEO)*
Randy K. Ambrosy *(Exec VP-Bus Dev)*
Brands & Products:
AUTOCAD
BRICSCAD
COLORFAST
EAGLE POINT
LANDCADD
LANDXML
MICROSTATION
ROADCALC
SMI
VIRTUAL SIMULATOR

EASYLINK SERVICES INTERNATIONAL CORPORATION

6025 The Corners Pkwy Ste 100
Norcross, GA 30092-3328
Tel.: (678) 533-8000
Fax: (770) 246-4697
Toll Free: (888) 393-6848
Web Site: www.easylink.com
Approx. Rev.: $81,443,212
Approx. Number Employees: 282
Business Description:
Content & Document Management Software & Information & Records Management Services
S.I.C.: 4899; 7338; 7371; 7372; 7373; 7374; 7379
N.A.I.C.S.: 517910; 511210; 518210; 541511; 541512; 541519; 561410
Media: 10-22
Personnel:
Kim D. Cooke *(Chm)*
Thomas J. Stallings *(CEO)*
Glen E. Shipley *(CFO & Sec)*
Teresa A. Deuel *(Exec VP-Customer Support-Worldwide)*
Kevin R. Maloney *(Exec VP-Global Sls & Mktg)*
James J. Walsh *(VP-Sls & Mktg)*
David Hubbard *(Mgr-Dev)*
Brands & Products:
EASYLINK

ECHELON CORPORATION

550 Meridian Ave
San Jose, CA 95126
Tel.: (408) 938-5200
Fax: (408) 790-3800
Toll Free: (888) ECHELON
E-mail: lonworks@echelon.com
Web Site: www.echelon.com
Approx. Rev.: $111,037,000
Approx. Number Employees: 318
Year Founded: 1988
Business Description:
Hardware & Software Marketer & Developer
S.I.C.: 1731; 1389; 3571; 3669; 7371
N.A.I.C.S.: 238210; 213112; 334111; 334290; 541511
Media: 2-4-7-8-10-13
Personnel:
Armas Clifford Markkula, Jr. *(Vice Chm)*
Ronald A. Sege *(Pres & CEO)*
Oliver R. Stanfield *(CFO & Exec VP)*
Kathleen B. Bloch *(Gen Counsel & Sr VP)*
Russell Harris *(Sr VP-Ops)*
Michael Anderson *(Sr VP-Utility Sls & Market Dev)*
Anders B. Axelsson *(Sr VP-Comml Sls & Market Dev)*
Robert W. Hon *(Sr VP-Engrg)*
Brands & Products:
3120
3150
DIGITAL HOME
ECHELON
I.LON
LNS
LON
LONBUILDER
LONEWS
LONLINK
LONMAKER
LONMAKER INTEGRATION TOOL
LONMANAGER
LONMARK
LONPOINT
LONRESPONSE
LONSCANNER
LONSUPPORT
LONTALK
LONUSERS
LONWORKS
LONWORLD
NEURON
NODEBUILDER
OPEN LDV
OPEN SYSTEMS ALLIANCE
PANORAMIX
SHORTSTACK

ECHO METRIX, INC.

(Name Changed to PROTEXT MOBILITY, INC.)

ECLINICALWORKS, LLC

Westborough Executive Pk 112 Turnpike Rd
Westborough, MA 01581
Tel.: (508) 836-2700
Fax: (508) 475-3011
Toll Free: (866) 888MYCW
E-mail: pr@eclinicalworks.com
Web Site: www.eclinicalworks.com
Sales Range: $25-49.9 Million
Approx. Number Employees: 315
Year Founded: 1999
Business Description:
Software Developer for Medical-Practice Billing & Recordkeeping
S.I.C.: 7372
N.A.I.C.S.: 511210
Media: 10
Personnel:
Girish Kumar Navani *(Founder & CEO)*
Brands & Products:
ECLINICALWORKS

ECORA SOFTWARE CORPORATION

(Sub. of Versata Enterprises Inc.)
6011 W Courtyard Dr Ste 300
Austin, TX 78730
Tel.: (603) 287-4130
E-mail: media@ecora.com
Web Site: www.ecora.com

Key to Media (For complete agency information see *The Advertising Red Books-Agencies* edition):
1. Bus. Publs. 2. Cable T.V. 3. Catalogs & Directories. 4. Co-op Adv. 5. Consumer Mags. 6. D.M. to Bus. Estab.7. D.M. to Consumers
8. Daily Newsp. 9. Exhibits/Trade Shows 10. Foreign 11. Infomercial 12. Internet Adv.13. Multimedia 14. Network Radio
15. Network T.V. 16. Newsp. Distr. Mags. 17. Other 18. Outdoor (Posters, Transit) 19. Point of Purchase20. Premiums, Novelties
21. Product Samples 22. Special Events Mktg. 23. Spot Radio 24. Spot T.V. 25. Weekly Newsp. 26. Yellow Page Adv.

E-Mail For Key Personnel:
Marketing Director: MJudge@ecora.com
Sales Director: sales@ecora.com
Sales Range: $10-24.9 Million
Approx. Number Employees: 80
Year Founded: 1999
Business Description:
Software Publisher
S.I.C.: 7371; 7372
N.A.I.C.S.: 541511; 511210
Advertising Expenditures: $200,000
Media: 2-10-13
Personnel:
Atanas Popov *(CEO)*
Andrew Price *(CFO)*
Frank Kopas *(Sr VP-Sls)*
Brands & Products:
AUDITOR PROFESSIONAL
ECORA ENTERPRISE AUDITOR
EXECUTIVE DASHBOARD
PATCH MANAGER

EDGEWATER TECHNOLOGY, INC.
20 Harvard Mill Sq
Wakefield, MA 01880
Tel.: (781) 246-3343
Fax: (781) 246-5903
E-mail: makewaves@edgewater.com
Web Site: www.edgewater.com
Approx. Rev.: $88,545,000
Approx. Number Employees: 380
Year Founded: 1996
Business Description:
Staffing, Information Technology, Professional Consulting & Solution Services
S.I.C.: 8748; 7361; 7371; 7373; 8742
N.A.I.C.S.: 541690; 541511; 541512; 541611; 541612
Media: 5-7-10
Personnel:
Shirley Singleton *(Chm, Pres & CEO)*
Tim Oakes *(CFO)*
David Clancey *(CTO, Exec VP & Chief Strategy Officer)*
John Flavin *(Sr VP-Strategic Svcs & Accts)*
Kristin Zaepfel *(VP-HR)*

EDUPOINT EDUCATIONAL SYSTEMS, LLC
23282 Mill Creek Dr Ste 310
Laguna Hills, CA 92653
Tel.: (480) 833-2900
Fax: (949) 458-0901
Toll Free: (800) 338-7646
E-mail: sales@edupoint.com
Web Site: www.edupoint.com
Approx. Number Employees: 30
Year Founded: 1997
Business Description:
Educational Software
S.I.C.: 5734
N.A.I.C.S.: 443120
Media: 13-17
Personnel:
Robert E. Weathers *(Founder & CEO)*
Rob Wilson *(Pres & COO)*
Joe Kirkman *(CEO)*
Thomas McGrew *(CTO & Exec VP)*
Brands & Products:
GENED
GENESEA
GENESIS
PARENTCONNECTXP
SASI
SASIXP

EF JOHNSON TECHNOLOGIES, INC.
(Holding of Francisco Partners Management, LLC)
1440 Corporate Dr
Irving, TX 75038
Tel.: (972) 819-0700
Fax: (972) 819-0639
Toll Free: (800) 328-3911
E-mail: sales@efji.com
Web Site: www.efjohnsontechnologies.com
Approx. Rev.: $92,341,000
Approx. Number Employees: 267
Year Founded: 1978
Business Description:
Communications Equipment Designer & Mfr
S.I.C.: 3663; 4812
N.A.I.C.S.: 334220; 517212
Media: 2-7-10
Personnel:
Norman Stout *(Chm)*
Andrew L. Adams *(Pres & CEO)*
Jana Ahlfinger Bell *(CFO & Exec VP)*
Ed Pierson *(CIO & VP-Performance Excellence)*
Kyle Connor *(Sr VP-Sls)*
Brands & Products:
FLASHCALL
TRANSCRYPT

EGENERA, INC.
165 Forest St
Marlborough, MA 01752
Tel.: (508) 858-2600
Fax: (508) 481-3114
Toll Free: (800) 316-3976
E-mail: info@egenera.com
Web Site: www.egenera.com
Approx. Number Employees: 325
Year Founded: 2000
Business Description:
Software Solutions & Services
S.I.C.: 7371; 7372
N.A.I.C.S.: 541511; 511210
Media: 10
Personnel:
Pete Manca *(Pres & CEO)*
Jim Bandanza *(COO & Exec VP)*
Scott Geng *(Sr VP-Engrg)*
John Humphreys *(VP-Mktg)*
Brands & Products:
BLADEFRAME
CONTROL BLADE
EGENERA
PAN MANAGER
PROCESSING BLADE
SWITCH BLADE

ELECTION SERVICES CORPORATION
990 Stewart Ave Ste 500
Garden City, NY 11530-2925
Tel.: (516) 248-4200
Fax: (516) 248-4770
E-mail: info@electionservicescorp.com
Web Site:
www.electionservicescorp.com
Approx. Number Employees: 25
Year Founded: 1999
Business Description:
Election Software & Services Supplier; Voter Registration & Database Management, Polling Site & Remote Electronic Voting, Advanced Security Solutions, Accurate Tabulation, Demographic Reporting & Related Membership Services
S.I.C.: 7389
N.A.I.C.S.: 561990
Media: 7-10-13
Personnel:
Mel Schrieberg *(Chm)*
Frank Fatone *(Pres & CEO)*
Maralin Falik *(Pres)*
Janet Gagliardo *(CFO)*
Gregg W. McGilvray *(CIO)*
Brands & Products:
ELECTNET
PROXYSTREET

ELECTRO RENT CORPORATION
6060 Sepulveda Blvd
Van Nuys, CA 91411-2512
Tel.: (818) 787-2100
Fax: (818) 786-4354
Toll Free: (800) 688-1111 (Sales)
E-mail: western.sales@electrorent.com
Web Site: www.electrorent.com
E-Mail For Key Personnel:
Sales Director: cjones@electrorent.com
Approx. Rev.: $228,729,000
Approx. Number Employees: 371
Year Founded: 1965
Business Description:
Electronic Test & Measurement Equipment, Workstations & Personal Computers Sales, Rental & Lease
S.I.C.: 7359
N.A.I.C.S.: 532420; 532210
Export
Advertising Expenditures: $780,000
Media: 2-4-7-10-13
Distr.: Intl.; Natl.
Budget Set: June
Personnel:
Daniel Greenberg *(Chm & CEO)*
Steven Markheim *(Pres)*
Craig R. Jones *(CFO)*
Herb Ostenberg *(Sr VP-Sls-North America)*
John Hart *(VP-Sls)*
Tanya Jamison *(Dir-Mktg-Worldwide)*

ELECTRO STANDARDS LABORATORIES INC.
36 W Indus Dr
Cranston, RI 02921-3403
Tel.: (401) 943-1164
Fax: (401) 946-5790
Toll Free: (877) 943-1164
E-mail: eslab@electrostandards.com
Web Site: www.electrostandards.com
Sales Range: $10-24.9 Million
Approx. Number Employees: 99
Year Founded: 1976
Business Description:
Data Communication Products Mfr & Designer
S.I.C.: 3661; 7373
N.A.I.C.S.: 334210; 541512
Advertising Expenditures: $200,000
Media: 2-4-10-23-24-25
Personnel:
Raymond B. Sepe, Sr. *(Pres)*
Jeannette Gouin *(Mgr-Mktg)*
Brands & Products:
ADVANCED SYSTEMS DESIGN & SERVICES
CELLMITE
ELECTRO STANDARDS
ESLTEST
PATHWAY
QUICKSWITCH
SURE-GUARD
TEDS-TAG
TRISTATE BOX

ELECTRONIC TELE-COMMUNICATIONS, INC.
1915 MacArthur Rd
Waukesha, WI 53188-5702
Tel.: (262) 542-5600
Fax: (262) 542-5924
Toll Free: (888) 746-4382
E-mail: etccorp@etcia.com
Web Site: www.etcia.com
E-Mail For Key Personnel:
President: dean@etcia.com
Approx. Sls.: $1,658,605
Approx. Number Employees: 15
Year Founded: 1980
Business Description:
Designs, Manufactures, Programs, Markets, & Leases Digital Voice Response Systems, Call Processing Systems, & Related Computer Software Services
S.I.C.: 3661; 3669
N.A.I.C.S.: 334210; 334290
Export
Media: 10-11-13-26
Personnel:
Dean W. Danner *(Pres & CEO)*
Bonita M. Danner *(Treas & VP-Engrg)*
Joseph A. Voight, Jr. *(VP-Sls & Mktg)*
Jeff Hunholz *(Mgr-Technical Svcs)*
Debbie Scott *(Mgr-Customer Svc)*
Steve Thompson *(Mgr-Data Processing & Weather Center)*
Brands & Products:
AEC
ARIS
AUDICHRON
AUDICHRON 410
CMS-JR
CMS-SR
DIGICEPT
DIGICEPT EMCEE
ETC
MAX
MESSENGER
PARTITIONED ARCHITECTURE
SYSTEM 3
USA TIME
THE VOICE OF THE NETWORK
WEATHERTEL

ELECTRONICS FOR IMAGING, INC.
303 Velocity Way
Foster City, CA 94404-4803
Tel.: (650) 357-3500
Fax: (650) 357-3907
E-mail: investor.relations@efi.com
Web Site: www.efi.com
Approx. Rev.: $504,007,000
Approx. Number Employees: 1,886
Year Founded: 1989
Business Description:
Printing & Prepress Management Software
S.I.C.: 3577; 7372
N.A.I.C.S.: 334119; 511210
Export
Advertising Expenditures: $5,200,000

Key to Media (For complete agency information see *The Advertising Red Books-Agencies* edition):
1. Bus. Publs. 2. Cable T.V. 3. Catalogs & Directories. 4. Co-op Adv. 5. Consumer Mags. 6. D.M. to Bus. Estab.7. D.M. to Consumers 8. Daily Newsp. 9. Exhibits/Trade Shows 10. Foreign 11. Infomercial 12. Internet Adv.13. Multimedia 14. Network Radio 15. Network T.V. 16. Newsp. Distr. Mags. 17. Other 18. Outdoor (Posters, Transit) 19. Point of Purchase20. Premiums, Novelties 21. Product Samples 22. Special Events Mktg. 23. Spot Radio 24. Spot T.V. 25. Weekly Newsp. 26. Yellow Page Adv.

Electronics For Imaging, Inc. — (Continued)

Media: 10-13
Personnel:
Gill Cogan *(Chm & Gen Partner-Opus Capital)*
Fred Rosenzweig *(Pres)*
Guy Gecht *(CEO)*
Vincent Pilette *(CFO)*
Bryan Ko *(Gen Counsel)*
Toby Weiss *(Sr VP & Gen Mgr-Fiery Div)*
Sean Skelly *(VP & Gen Mgr-EFI Jetrion)*
Gordon Heneweer *(Interim CFO & VP-Fin)*
Stefan Spiegel *(Gen Mgr)*
Brands & Products:
BALANCE
COLOR PROFILER SUITE
DIGITAL STOREFRONT
DOCSTREAM
DROP ON DEMAND
EDOX
EFI
ES-1000
FIERY
FIERY CENTRAL
FIERY SYSTEM 8E
HAGEN
JETRION
LOGIC
MICROPRESS
PRINT TO WIN
PRINTME
PRINTSMITH
PSI
SDK
SPLASH
VELOCITY
VUTEK

ELMA ELECTRONIC INC.

(Sub. of Elma Electronic AG)
44350 Grimmer Blvd
Fremont, CA 94538
Tel.: (510) 656-3400
Fax: (510) 653-3783
E-mail: sales@elma.com
Web Site: www.elma.com
E-Mail For Key Personnel:
Sales Director: sales@elma.com
Approx. Number Employees: 155
Year Founded: 1962
Business Description:
Electronic Enclosure & Passive Electronic Component Designer & Mfr
S.I.C.: 3571; 5065
N.A.I.C.S.: 334111; 423690
Media: 10
Personnel:
Fred Ruegg *(Pres)*
Peter Brunner *(VP-Fin)*
Ram Rajan *(VP-Engrg)*
Eric Gittings *(Reg Mgr-NE)*

ELOYALTY CORPORATION

150 N Field Dr Ste 250
Lake Forest, IL 60045
Tel.: (847) 582-7000
Fax: (847) 582-7001
Toll Free: (877) 235-6925
Toll Free: (877) 2-ELOYAL
E-mail: euro@eloyalty.com
Web Site: www.eloyalty.com
Approx. Rev.: $88,104,000
Approx. Number Employees: 369
Year Founded: 1999
Business Description:
Customer Relationship Management Consulting & Systems Integration Services
S.I.C.: 7371; 7373; 8742; 8748
N.A.I.C.S.: 541511; 541512; 541611; 541618
Media: 10
Personnel:
Tench Coxe *(Chm)*
Kelly D. Conway *(Pres & CEO)*
Bill Noon *(CFO)*
Christine Carsen *(Chief Privacy Officer, Corp Sec, VP & Assoc Gen Counsel)*
Brands & Products:
BEHAVIORAL ANALYTICS
DESKTOP ANALYTICS
ELOYALTY
REVOLUTIONARY ANALYTICS BREAKTHROUGH RESULTS

EMC CORPORATION

176 South St
Hopkinton, MA 01748
Tel.: (508) 435-1000
Fax: (508) 497-6912
Toll Free: (800) 782-4362
Web Site: www.emc.com
Approx. Rev.: $17,015,126,000
Approx. Number Employees: 48,500
Year Founded: 1979
Business Description:
Information Storage Systems, Software Mfr & Data Management Services
S.I.C.: 3572; 3577; 7371; 7372; 7373; 7374; 7379
N.A.I.C.S.: 334112; 334119; 511210; 518210; 541511; 541512; 541519
Import Export
Advertising Expenditures: $23,500,000
Media: 1-2-4-7-10-21-26
Distr.: Intl.; Natl.
Personnel:
Joseph M. Tucci *(Chm, Pres & CEO)*
William J. Teuber, Jr. *(Vice Chm)*
David I. Goulden *(CFO & Exec VP)*
Sanjay Mirchandani *(CIO & COO-Global Centers of Excellence)*
Jeremy Burton *(CMO & Exec VP)*
Jeffrey M. Nick *(CTO & Sr VP)*
Mark S. Lewis *(Chief Strategy Officer-Info Infrastructure Products Bus)*
Jeetu Patel *(Chief Strategy Officer)*
Denis G. Cashman *(COO-Fin & Chief Acctg Officer)*
Howard D. Elias *(Pres/COO-Cloud Svcs)*
Patrick Gelsinger *(Pres/COO-Info Infrastructure Products)*
Rick Devenuti *(Pres-Info Intelligence Grp)*
Rainer Erlat *(Pres-Europe, Middle East & Africa)*
Jonathan S. Huberman *(Pres-Consumer)*
Harel Kodesh *(Pres-Cloud Infrastructure Bus)*
Paul T. Dacier *(Gen Counsel & Exec VP)*
Irina Simmons *(Treas & Sr VP)*
Arthur W. Coviello, Jr. *(Exec VP & Exec Chm-Security Div)*
Frank M. Hauck *(Exec VP)*
John T. Mollen *(Exec VP-HR)*
Bill Scannell *(Exec VP-Americas & Global Sls Programs)*
Harry L. You *(Exec VP-Office of the Chm)*
Terry Breen *(Sr VP-Strategic Relationships)*
Mark A. Link *(Sr VP-New Ventures)*
Daniel R. McGee *(Sr VP-Engrg)*
Prasad L. Rampalli *(Sr VP-Global Solutions)*
Rob Emsley *(Sr Dir-Product Mktg-Backup Recovery Sys Div)*
John M. Custer *(Dir-Federal Strategic Missions & Programs)*
Deirdre Wassell *(Dir-Solutions Mktg)*
Tyler Altrup *(Mgr-Social Media)*
Lisa Dry *(Mgr-Program)*
Jeffrey Chaffin *(Sr Acct Exec-BRS Div)*
Brands & Products:
ACARTUS
ACCESS LOGIX
ADVANTEDGE
ALPHASTOR
APPLICATIONXTENDER
ARCHIVEXTENDER
ATMOS
AUTHENTIC PROBLEMS
AUTHENTICA
AUTOMATED RESOURCE MANAGER
AUTOSTART
AUTOSWAP
AVALONIDM
AVAMAR
C-CLIP
CAPTIVA
CATALOG SOLUTION
CELERRA
CELERRA REPLICATOR
CENTERA
CENTERSTAGE
CENTRASTAR
CLAIMPACK
CLAIMSEDITOR
CLARALERT
CLARIION
CLIENTPAK
CO-STANDBYSERVER
CODEBOOK CORRELATION TECHNOLOGY
CODELINK
COMMON INFORMATION MODEL
CONFIGURESOFT
CONNECTRIX
CONTROLCENTER
COPYCROSS
COPYPOINT
CX
DANTZ
DATA DOMAIN
DATABASEXTENDER
DIGITAL MAILROOM
DIRECT MATRIX
DIRECT MATRIX ARCHITECTURE
DISKXTENDER
DISKXTENDER 2000
DOCUMENT SCIENCES
DOCUMENTUM
E-LAB
EDM
EINPUT
EMAILXAMINER
EMAILXTENDER
EMC
EMC AUTOMATED NETWORKED STORAGE
EMC CENTERA
EMC CONTROLCENTER
EMC DEVELOPERS PROGRAM
EMC ENTERPRISE STORAGE
EMC ENTERPRISE STORAGE NETWORK
EMC LIFELINE
EMC ONCOURSE
EMC PROVEN
EMC RECOVERPOINT
EMC SNAP
EMC SOURCEONE
EMC STORAGE ADMINISTRATOR
EMC2
ENGINUITY
EROOM
EVENT EXPLORER
FARPOINT
FIRSTPASS
FLARE
FORMWARE
GEOSYNCHRONY
GLOBAL FILE VIRTUALIZATION
GRAPHIC VISUALIZATION
HIGHROAD
HOMEBASE
INFINIFLEX
INFOMOVER
INFOSCAPE
INFRA
INPUTACCEL
INPUTACCEL EXPRESS
INVISTA
IONIX
ISIS
LEGATO
MAX RETRIEVER
MEDIASTOR
MIRRORVIEW
MOZY
MOZYENTERPRISE
MOZYHOME
MOZYPRO
NAVISPHERE
NETWIN
NETWORKER
NLAYERS
ONALERT
OPENSCALE
PIXTOOLS
POWERLINK
POWERPATH
POWERSNAP
QUICKSCAN
RAINFINITY
REPLICARE
REPLISTOR
RESOURCEPAK
RETROSPECT
RSA
SAFELINE
SAN ADVISOR
SAN COPY
SAN MANAGER
SDMS
SMARTS
SNAPIMAGE
SNAPSURE
SNAPVIEW
SRDF
STORAGESCOPE
SUPPORTMATE
SYMMAPI
SYMMENABLER
SYMMETRIX
SYMMETRIX DMX
SYMMETRIX VMAX

Key to Media (For complete agency information see *The Advertising Red Books-Agencies* edition):
1. Bus. Publs. 2. Cable T.V. 3. Catalogs & Directories. 4. Co-op Adv. 5. Consumer Mags. 6. D.M. to Bus. Estab.7. D.M. to Consumers
8. Daily Newsp. 9. Exhibits/Trade Shows 10. Foreign 11. Infomercial 12. Internet Adv.13. Multimedia 14. Network Radio
15. Network T.V. 16. Newsp. Distr. Mags. 17. Other 18. Outdoor (Posters, Transit) 19. Point of Purchase20. Premiums, Novelties
21. Product Samples 22. Special Events Mktg. 23. Spot Radio 24. Spot T.V. 25. Weekly Newsp. 26. Yellow Page Adv.

TELESTREAM FLIPFACTORY
TERASAM
TIMEFINDER
ULTRAFLEX
ULTRAPOINT
ULTRASCALE
UNISPHERE
VELOCITY
VIEWLETS
VIEWPOINT
VIRTUAL MATRIX
VIRTUAL MATRIX ARCHITECTURE
VIRTUAL PROVISIONING
VISUALSAN
VISUALSRM
VMAX
VMWARE
VNX
VNX5100
VNXE
VNXE3100
VOYENCE
VSAM-ASSIST
VSAM ASSISTANT
WEBXTENDER
WHERE INFORMATION LIVES
XPRESSION
XPRESSO
YOTTAYOTTA

Advertising Agencies:
OutCast Communications
123 Townsend St Ste 500
San Francisco, CA 94107
Tel.: (415) 392-8282
Fax: (415) 392-8281

Razorfish
821 2nd Ave Ste 1800
Seattle, WA 98104-2343
Tel.: (206) 816-8800
Fax: (206) 816-8808

EMPLOYER MANAGEMENT SOLUTIONS, INC.

300 S Hyde Pk Ave Ste 201
Tampa, FL 33606-2293
Tel.: (813) 287-2486
Fax: (813) 286-9564
Web Site: www.consultems.com
Sales Range: $10-24.9 Million
Approx. Number Employees: 12
Year Founded: 1998
Business Description:
Business & Technology Consulting Services
S.I.C.: 7371
N.A.I.C.S.: 541511
Media: 10
Personnel:
Elaine Myrback *(Pres & CEO)*
Doug Myrback *(Sr VP)*

EMPLOYMENT ENTERPRISES INC.

10328 Battleview Pkwy
Manassas, VA 20109
Tel.: (703) 361-2220
Fax: (703) 368-0795
Web Site: www.eeihr.com
Sales Range: $50-74.9 Million
Approx. Number Employees: 50
Business Description:
Human Resource Staffing
S.I.C.: 7363; 8721
N.A.I.C.S.: 561320; 541214
Personnel:
Lovey L. Hammel *(Pres)*
Jana W. Yeates *(CEO)*
Brands & Products:
EMPLOYMENT ENTERPRISES
POWERED BY PEOPLE-DRIVEN BY SOLUTIONS
Advertising Agency:
LeapFrog Solutions, Inc.
10467 White Granite Dr Ste 100
Oakton, VA 22124
Tel.: (703) 273-7900
Fax: (703) 273-7902

EMPLOYMENT GROUP HOLDING CORP.

4625 Beckley Rd Bldg 200
Battle Creek, MI 49016
Tel.: (269) 979-9778
Fax: (269) 979-4442
Web Site:
www.employmentgroup.com
Approx. Number Employees: 80
Year Founded: 1986
Business Description:
Help Supply Services
S.I.C.: 7363; 7361
N.A.I.C.S.: 561320; 561310
Import Export
Personnel:
Mark J. Lancaster *(Pres & CEO)*
Brands & Products:
EMPLOYMENT GROUP
MEASURABLY BETTER EMPLOYEES.
Advertising Agency:
Lambert, Edwards & Associates, Inc.
171 Monroe NW Ste 400
Grand Rapids, MI 49503
Tel.: (616) 233-0500
Fax: (616) 233-0600

EMTEC FEDERAL, INC.

(Sub. of Emtec, Inc.)
11 Diamond Rd
Springfield, NJ 07081-3101
Tel.: (973) 376-4242
Fax: (973) 376-8846
Toll Free: (800) 800-8805
Web Site: www.emtec.com
E-Mail For Key Personnel:
Marketing Director: d_singer@westcomp.com
Sales Range: $50-74.9 Million
Approx. Number Employees: 85
Year Founded: 1964
Business Description:
Military & Government Technical Consulting & Information Technology Services
S.I.C.: 7379; 8742; 8748
N.A.I.C.S.: 541519; 541611; 541690
Media: 2-4-10-17
Distr.: Natl.
Personnel:
Keith Grabel *(Pres)*
David Singer *(VP-Mktg)*

EMTEC, INC.

11 Diamond Rd
Springfield, NJ 07081
Tel.: (973) 376-4242
Fax: (973) 376-8846
Toll Free: (800) 800-8805
E-mail: investor_relations@emtecinc.com
Web Site: www.emtecinc.com
Approx. Rev.: $224,602,000
Approx. Number Employees: 649
Year Founded: 1981
Business Description:
Integrated Computer Systems Design & Information Technology Services
S.I.C.: 3577; 7373; 7379
N.A.I.C.S.: 334119; 541512; 541519
Advertising Expenditures: $1,000,000
Personnel:
Dinesh R. Desai *(Chm, Pres & CEO)*
Gregory P. Chandler *(CFO & Pres-Application Svcs Div)*
Siva Natarajan *(CIO)*
Sunil Misra *(Chief Strategy & Delivery Officer)*
Jeff Clapper *(Exec VP-Comml Sector)*
Stephen C. Donnelly *(Exec VP-Bus Planning & Analysis, HR & Corp Dev)*
Ronald A. Seitz *(Exec VP-Education)*
Sam Bhatt *(VP-Fin)*

EMULEX CORPORATION

3333 Susan St
Costa Mesa, CA 92626
Tel.: (714) 662-5600
Fax: (714) 241-0792
Toll Free: (800) EMULEX-1
E-mail: pr@emulex.com
Web Site: www.emulex.com
E-Mail For Key Personnel:
Marketing Director: marketing@emulex.com
Approx. Rev.: $452,543,000
Approx. Number Employees: 972
Year Founded: 1979
Business Description:
Storage, Server & Network Connector Products
S.I.C.: 3577; 3661; 3669
N.A.I.C.S.: 334119; 334210; 334290
Advertising Expenditures: $5,300,000
Media: 2-4-6-7-8-10-11-17
Distr.: Intl.; Natl.
Personnel:
Paul F. Folino *(Chm)*
Jeffrey W. Benck *(Pres & COO)*
James M. McCluney *(CEO)*
Michael J. Rockenbach *(CFO & Exec VP)*
Dave Goff *(CIO & VP)*
Raju Vegesna *(Chief Strategy Officer)*
Randall G. Wick *(Sr VP & Gen Counsel)*
Bob Whitson *(Sr VP & Gen Mgr)*
Susan H. Bowman *(Sr VP-HR & Facilities)*
Jeff Hoogenboom *(Sr VP-Sls-Worldwide)*
John Warwick *(Sr VP-Ops)*
Frank Yoshino *(VP-Fin)*
Katherine Lane *(Dir-Corp Comm)*
Jolene Bonina *(Mgr-PR)*
Brands & Products:
AUTOPILOT
CONVERGENCE
EMULEX
FIBRESPY
HBANYWARE
INSPEED
LIGHTPULSE
VMPILOT
VMWARE
VSPHERE 4
Advertising Agency:
Schwartz Communications, Inc.
230 3rd Ave
Waltham, MA 02451
Tel.: (781) 684-0770
Fax: (781) 684-6500

ENABLE HOLDINGS, INC.

8725 W Higins Rd Ste 900
Chicago, IL 60631
Tel.: (773) 272-5000
Fax: (773) 272-4000
E-mail: miguel.martinez@enableholdings.com
Web Site: www.ubid.com
Approx. Rev.: $18,128,000
Approx. Number Employees: 41
Business Description:
Excess Inventory Solutions
S.I.C.: 6719; 5961
N.A.I.C.S.: 454112; 454111; 551112
Advertising Expenditures: $992,000
Personnel:
Steven Sjoblad *(Chm)*

ENEIGHBORHOODS INC.

(Sub. of Dominion Enterprises)
1 Park Pl Ste 500
Boca Raton, FL 33487
Tel.: (561) 981-9700
Fax: (561) 981-9800
Fax: (561) 981-5999 (Sls)
Toll Free: (800) 975-9742
E-mail: sales@eneighborhoods.com
Web Site: www.eneighborhoods.com
Approx. Number Employees: 225
Year Founded: 2000
Business Description:
Real Estate Marketing & Information Services
S.I.C.: 7319; 2741; 6531; 7389
N.A.I.C.S.: 541890; 516110; 519190; 531390
Media: 13
Personnel:
Andy Woolley *(VP & Gen Mgr)*
Mike Couvillion *(VP-Engrg)*
Shawn Brown *(Exec Dir-Bus Ops)*
Melissa Crow *(Exec Dir-Technical Ops)*
Craig Gill *(Exec Dir-Info Tech)*
Michael Hayes *(Exec Dir-Enterprise Svcs)*
Mark Mathi *(Exec Dir-Broker & Agent Svcs)*
Brands & Products:
BUYERSTOUR
CMAPRO
ENEIGHBORHOODS AERIALS
ENEIGHBORHOODS FLYERS
ENEIGHBORHOODS MAPS
ENEIGHBORHOODS NEWSLETTER
HOMEBOOK
MLS ALLIANCE
MLSCONNECT
WYLDFYRE

ENERGY & POWER SOLUTIONS, INC.

150 Paularino Ave Ste A120
Costa Mesa, CA 92626
Tel.: (714) 586-8002
Fax: (714) 957-1093
Toll Free: (866) 377-7834
E-mail: productinfo@epsway.com
Web Site: www.epsway.com
Approx. Rev.: $12,024,000
Approx. Number Employees: 93
Year Founded: 2002
Business Description:
Energy Management Software & Services
S.I.C.: 7372; 8742; 8748
N.A.I.C.S.: 511210; 541611; 541690
Advertising Expenditures: $300,000

Key to Media (For complete agency information see *The Advertising Red Books-Agencies* edition):
1. Bus. Publs. 2. Cable T.V. 3. Catalogs & Directories. 4. Co-op Adv. 5. Consumer Mags. 6. D.M. to Bus. Estab.7. D.M. to Consumers
8. Daily Newsp. 9. Exhibits/Trade Shows 10. Foreign 11. Infomercial 12. Internet Adv.13. Multimedia 14. Network Radio
15. Network T.V. 16. Newsp. Distr. Mags. 17. Other 18. Outdoor (Posters, Transit) 19. Point of Purchase20. Premiums, Novelties
21. Product Samples 22. Special Events Mktg. 23. Spot Radio 24. Spot T.V. 25. Weekly Newsp. 26. Yellow Page Adv.

Energy & Power Solutions, Inc. — (Continued)

Personnel:
Jay B. Zoellner *(Pres & CEO)*
Peter Ludlum *(CFO)*
Iyad Darcazallie *(COO & EVP-Corp Dev)*
Julie Moran *(Exec VP & Gen Mgr-ChangePoint)*
Brands & Products:
THE EPS WAY
XCHANGE POINT

ENHERENT CORP.

33 Wood Ave S Ste 116
Iselin, NJ 08830
Tel.: (732) 321-1004
Fax: (732) 603-3868
E-mail: lstanley@enherent.com
Web Site: www.enherent.com
Approx. Rev.: $10,762,736
Approx. Number Employees: 62
Business Description:
IT Consulting & Staffing Services
S.I.C.: 7371; 7361; 7363; 7373; 8748
N.A.I.C.S.: 541511; 541512; 541690; 561310; 561320
Advertising Expenditures: $35,000
Media: 7-10-13
Personnel:
Pamela Fredette *(Chm, Pres & CEO)*
Thomas Minerva *(Vice Chm)*
Roger DiPiano *(COO)*
Lori Stanley *(Gen Counsel, Sec & VP-HR)*
Arunava De *(Controller & VP-Fin)*
Bruce Morgan *(VP-Sls)*

ENNIS, INC.

2441 Presidential Pkwy
Midlothian, TX 76065
Tel.: (972) 775-9801
Fax: (972) 775-9820
Toll Free: (800) 752-5386
Toll Free: (800) 097-28339
E-mail: pr@ennis.com
Web Site: www.ennis.com
Approx. Sls.: $549,999,000
Approx. Number Employees: 5,812
Year Founded: 1909
Business Description:
Business Forms & Apparel Mfr
S.I.C.: 2761
N.A.I.C.S.: 323116
Export
Advertising Expenditures: $1,300,000
Media: 4
Distr.: Natl.
Budget Set: Jan. -Mar.
Personnel:
Keith S. Walters *(Chm, Pres & CEO)*
Richard L. Travis, Jr. *(CFO & VP-Fin)*
Irshad Ahmad *(Pres-Alstyle Apparel & CTO)*
Michael D. Magill *(Exec VP)*
Terry Pennington *(VP-Sls-Print Segment)*
Steve Osterloh *(Dir-Mktg-Natl)*
Brands & Products:
360 DEGREES CUSTOM LABELS
ADAMS MCCLURE
ADMORE
ALSTYLE APPAREL
AMERICAN DIAMOND
BLOCK GRAPHICS
CALIBRATED
DIAMOND STAR
ENFUSION
ENNIS
GAZIANI
GENFORMS
GFS
HYLAND
NORTHSTAR
ROYAL BUSINESS FORMS
SPECIALIZED PRINTED FORMS
TENNESSEE RIVER
TRADE ENVELOPES
UNCOMPROMISED CHECK SOLUTIONS
WITT PRINTING

ENTERPRISE INFORMATICS INC.

(Sub. of Bentley Systems, Inc.)
10052 Mesa Ridge Ct Ste 100
San Diego, CA 92121-2916
Tel.: (858) 625-3000
Fax: (858) 625-3010
Toll Free: (800) 992-6784
E-mail: info@enterpriseinformatics.com
Web Site: www.enterpriseinformatics.com
Approx. Rev.: $8,974,000
Approx. Number Employees: 37
Year Founded: 1981
Business Description:
Business Information & Document Management Software Developer & Marketer
S.I.C.: 7372; 7338; 7389
N.A.I.C.S.: 511210; 561410; 561499
Export
Media: 7-10-11-13
Personnel:
John W. Low *(CFO & Sec)*
Brands & Products:
EB
EB FOR ENTERPRISE
ENTERPRISE INFORMATICS

ENTIGO CORPORATION

Ste 206 495 Thomas Jones Way
Exton, PA 19341-2553
Mailing Address:
PO Box 561
Exton, PA 19341-0561
Tel.: (484) 359-8362
Toll Free: (888) 734-9291
E-mail: info.request@entigo.com
Web Site: www.entigo.com
Approx. Number Employees: 75
Year Founded: 1995
Business Description:
Mfr. & Designer of E-Commerce Software Warranty Solutions
S.I.C.: 7371
N.A.I.C.S.: 541511
Advertising Expenditures: $300,000
Media: 2-7-10
Personnel:
Stephen Layne *(Chm & CEO)*
Brands & Products:
ENTIGO
ENTIGO REALITY
ENTIGO WARRANTY

ENTROPIC COMMUNICATIONS INC.

6290 Sequence Dr
San Diego, CA 92121
Tel.: (858) 768-3600
Fax: (858) 768-3601
E-mail: info@entropic.com
Web Site: www.entropic.com
Approx. Rev.: $210,237,000
Approx. Number Employees: 300
Business Description:
Home Entertainment & Multimedia Fabless Semiconductor Designer, Developer & Marketer
S.I.C.: 3674
N.A.I.C.S.: 334413
Advertising Expenditures: $86,000
Personnel:
Anton Monk *(Co-Founder & VP-Tech)*
Umesh Padval *(Chm)*
Patrick Henry *(Pres & CEO)*
David Lyle *(CFO)*
Lance Bridges *(Gen Counsel & VP)*
William R. Bradford *(Sr VP-Worldwide Sls)*
Vinay Gokhale *(Sr VP-Mktg & Bus Dev)*
Dale Hancock *(VP-Engrg)*
Suzanne Zoumaras *(VP-HR)*
Vince Ferrante *(Dir-Sls-North America-West)*
Debra Hart *(Dir-IR)*
Robbin Lynn *(Mgr-Mktg Comm)*
Advertising Agency:
GlobalFluency
101 Ave of the Americas 15th Fl
New York, NY 10013
Tel.: (212) 213-5400
Fax: (212) 213-4415

ENTRUST, INC.

(Holding of Thoma Bravo, LLC)
One Lincoln Centre 5400 LBJ Fwy Ste 1340
Dallas, TX 75240
Tel.: (972) 728-0447
Fax: (972) 728-0440
Toll Free: (888) 690-2424
E-mail: entrust@entrust.com
Web Site: www.entrust.com
Sales Range: $75-99.9 Million
Approx. Number Employees: 411
Year Founded: 1997
Business Description:
Secure Digital Identity Software Publisher
S.I.C.: 7372
N.A.I.C.S.: 511210
Advertising Expenditures: $2,831,000
Media: 1-2-4-7-10
Personnel:
F. William Conner *(Pres & CEO)*
David J. Wagner *(CFO & Sr VP)*
Bill Holtz *(COO & Sr VP)*
David Rockvam *(CMO & VP)*
Peter Bello *(Sr VP & Gen Mgr-US Federal Govt)*
Robert VanKirk *(VP-Sls & Svc-US)*
Brands & Products:
ENTRUST
ENTRUST AUTHORITY
ENTRUST AUTHORITY PKCS
ENTRUST CERTIFICATE SERVICES
ENTRUST ENTELLIGENCE
ENTRUST GETACCESS
ENTRUST READY
ENTRUST SECURE TRANSACTION PLATFORM
ENTRUST TRUEPASS
ENTRUST USB TOKENS
SECURING DIGITAL IDENTITIES & INFORMATION

ENVIRONMENTAL SYSTEMS RESEARCH INSTITUTE INC.

380 New York St
Redlands, CA 92373-8118
Tel.: (909) 793-2853
Fax: (909) 307-3082
E-mail: info@esri.com
Web Site: www.esri.com
Approx. Number Employees: 3,100
Year Founded: 1969
Business Description:
Geographic Information Systems
S.I.C.: 5045; 7371
N.A.I.C.S.: 423430; 541511
Import Export
Media: 1-7-10
Personnel:
Thomas Pickett *(CFO)*
Jack Dangermond *(Pres-Esri)*
Linda Hecht *(Dir-Mktg)*
Bill Meehan *(Dir-Utility Solutions)*
Paul Hardy *(Product Mgr)*
Arthur F. Lange *(Product Mgr)*
Karl Terrey *(Product Mgr-Logistics)*
Debra VanGorden *(Mgr-Mktg)*
Terry Bills *(Mgr-ESRI)*
Jeanne Foust *(Mgr)*
Randy Frantz *(Mgr-Telecom Indus Solutions)*
Dirk Gorter *(Mgr-Bus Dev)*
Karen Hurlbut *(Mgr-Mktg Comm)*
Dewey Marino *(Bus Dev Mgr)*
Brands & Products:
ACORN
ARCATLAS
ARCCAD
ARCCATALOG
ARCCOGO
ARCDATA
ARCDOC
ARCEDIT
ARCEDITOR
ARCEUROPE
ARCEXPLORER
ARCEXPRESS
ARCGIS
ARCGLOBE
ARCGRID
ARCIMS
ARCINFO
ARCLOCATION
ARCLOGISTICS
ARCNETWORK
ARCNEWS
ARCOBJECTS
ARCOPEN
ARCPAD
ARCPLOT
ARCPRESS
ARCQUEST
ARCREADER
ARCSCAN
ARCSCENE
ARCSCHOOL
ARCSDE
ARCSDL
ARCSKETCH
ARCSTORM
ARCSURVEY
ARCTOOLBOX
ARCTOOLS
ARCUSA
ARCUSER
ARCVIEW
ARCVOYAGER
ARCWATCH
ARCWEB

Key to Media (For complete agency information see *The Advertising Red Books-Agencies* edition):
1. Bus. Publs. 2. Cable T.V. 3. Catalogs & Directories. 4. Co-op Adv. 5. Consumer Mags. 6. D.M. to Bus. Estab.7. D.M. to Consumers 8. Daily Newsp. 9. Exhibits/Trade Shows 10. Foreign 11. Infomercial 12. Internet Adv.13. Multimedia 14. Network Radio 15. Network T.V. 16. Newsp. Distr. Mags. 17. Other 18. Outdoor (Posters, Transit) 19. Point of Purchase20. Premiums, Novelties 21. Product Samples 22. Special Events Mktg. 23. Spot Radio 24. Spot T.V. 25. Weekly Newsp. 26. Yellow Page Adv.

ARCWORLD
ARCXML
ATLAS GIS
ATLASWARE
AVENUE
BUSINESS ANALYST ONLINE
BUSINESSMAP
COMMUNITY
COMMUNITY CODER
COMMUNITY TAPESTRY
COMMUNITYINFO
ESRI
ESRI DEVELOPER NETWORK
ESRI IMAGE SERVER
GEODATABASE TOOLSET
GIS DATA REVIEWER
GIS PORTAL TOOLKIT
GIS WEB SERVICES
MAP PRODUCTION SYSTEM
MAPBEANS
MAPCAFE
MAPDATA
MAPLEX
MAPOBJECTS
MAPSTUDIO
MODELBUILDER
MOLE
NETENGINE
OLAP
PORTFOLIO
RENT-A-TECH
ROUTEMAP IMS
SITEREPORTER
SPATIAL DATABASE ENGINE
STREETEDITOR
TRACKING SERVER

ENVIRONMENTAL WASTE SOLUTIONS LLC

950 S Tamiami Trl Ste 210
Sarasota, FL 34236
Tel.: (941) 953-2200
Fax: (941) 951-7790
Toll Free: (800) 650-5225
E-mail: info@wasteconsulting.com
Web Site: www.environmental-waste.com
Sales Range: $25-49.9 Million
Approx. Number Employees: 30
Year Founded: 1994
Business Description:
Environmental Consulting Services
S.I.C.: 8999
N.A.I.C.S.: 541620
Media: 6
Personnel:
Darwyn Williams *(Pres & CEO)*
Diana Shapiro *(COO)*
Russell Williams *(Dir-Acct Svcs Team)*

ENVISION TELEPHONY INC.

(d/b/a Envision)
520 Pike St Ste 1600
Seattle, WA 98101
Tel.: (206) 225-0800
Fax: (206) 225-0801
E-mail: info.request@envisioninc.com
Web Site: www.envisioninc.com
Approx. Number Employees: 100
Year Founded: 1994
Business Description:
Software Developer
S.I.C.: 7371
N.A.I.C.S.: 541511
Advertising Expenditures: $200,000
Media: 2-4-7-10-22
Personnel:
Rodney Kuhn *(Founder & CEO)*
Mark C. Perrin *(Exec VP-Sls, Svcs & Mktg-Worldwide)*
Arun Thomas *(Dir-Engrg)*
Brands & Products:
CLICK2COACH
CLICK2COACH MULTISITE ADDITION
ENVISION
ENVISION BUSINESS INTELLIGENCE
ENVISION ELEARNING
ENVISION FULL-TIME RECORDING
ENVISION PERFORMANCE SUITE
ENVISION QUALITY MONITORING
ENVISION QUIZTEST
ENVISION REPORT SERVER
ENVISION WORKFORCE MANAGEMENT
SMARTAGENT
SPEECHMINER

ENWISEN, INC.

(Sub. of Lawson Software, Inc.)
7250 Redwood Blvd Ste 109
Novato, CA 94945
Tel.: (415) 897-0728
Fax: (415) 897-3863
E-mail: info@enwisen.com
Web Site: www.enwisen.com
Approx. Number Employees: 50
Year Founded: 1994
Business Description:
Human Resources & Business Solutions
S.I.C.: 7373
N.A.I.C.S.: 541512
Media: 2-7-10
Personnel:
Walter Smith *(Gen Mgr)*
John McLaughlin *(CFO)*
Barry A. Maxon *(VP-Sls)*
Michael Gantos *(Gen Mgr-Ops & Engrg-Sls)*
Elvira Echevarria *(Dir-Practice Delivery)*
Katie Neckermann Goldberg *(Dir-Svcs America)*
Barbara Levin *(Dir-Mktg & Customer Community)*
Melanie Lougee *(Dir-Product Strategy)*
Adit Vohra *(Dir-Customer Delivery)*
Roger Woehl *(Dir-Product Dev)*

EPICOR SOFTWARE CORPORATION

18200 Von Karman Ave Ste 1000
Irvine, CA 92612
Tel.: (949) 585-4000
Fax: (949) 585-4091
Toll Free: (800) 999-1809
E-mail: info@epicor.com
Web Site: www.epicor.com
Approx. Rev.: $440,283,000
Approx. Number Employees: 2,571
Year Founded: 1984
Business Description:
Integrated Enterprise & E-Business Software Solutions Designer, Developer & Marketer
S.I.C.: 7372
N.A.I.C.S.: 334611; 511210
Advertising Expenditures: $977,000
Media: 2
Personnel:
George L. Klaus *(Chm, Pres & CEO)*
Michael Pietrini *(CFO & Exec VP-Fin & Admin)*
Lauri Klaus *(Exec VP-Worldwide Sls & Consulting)*
Brad Rucker *(VP-Svcs & Support, Retail)*
Scott Hays *(Dir-Product Mktg)*
Lisa Preuss *(Dir-PR)*
Brands & Products:
AVANTE
CLIENTELE
DATAFLO
EPICOR
EPICOR ENTERPRISE
EPICOR FOR SERVICE ENTERPRISES
EPICOR ITSM
EPICOR RETAIL
ISCALA
MANAGE
MANFACT
TRUE SOA
VANTAGE
VISTA

EPROOFT, LLC

6514 McNeil Rd Bldg 1 Ste 100
Austin, TX 78729
Tel.: (512) 219-9277
Fax: (512) 219-9218
Toll Free: (877) 577-6630
E-mail: info@eprooft.com
Web Site: www.eprooft.com
Business Description:
Online Inventory Management Services
S.I.C.: 2741
N.A.I.C.S.: 516110
Media: 2-7-8-10-13-23
Personnel:
Erik Vicars *(CEO)*
Lindsey Vicars *(Exec Dir)*

EPSON AMERICA INC.

(Sub. of Seiko Epson Corporation)
3840 Kilroy Airport Way MS 4-30
Long Beach, CA 90806-2452
Tel.: (562) 981-3840
Fax: (562) 290-5220
Fax: (562) 290-5182
E-mail: info@epson.com
Web Site: www.epson.com
Approx. Sls.: $1,957,075,632
Approx. Number Employees: 500
Year Founded: 1975
Business Description:
Printer, Scanner & Component Product Marketer & Distr
S.I.C.: 5045; 3577; 5044
N.A.I.C.S.: 423430; 334119; 423420
Export
Media: 6-8-9-10-11-13
Distr.: Natl.
Personnel:
John D. Lang *(Pres & CEO)*
Alan Pound *(CFO)*
Judith Bain *(Gen Counsel & VP)*
Keith Kratzberg *(Sr VP-Comml Sls & Mktg)*
Alberto Arrendondo *(VP-Intl Mktg)*
Tetsuya Mizuno *(VP-Fin & Acctg)*
Mike Sion *(VP-Info Sys & Distr Svcs)*
Gregg Brunnick *(Grp Product Mgr-Consumer Ink Jets)*
Richard Day *(Product Mgr)*
Sean Gunduz *(Product Mgr-Projectors)*
Heather Litus Johnston *(Product Mgr-K-12 Education Mktg)*
Larry Kaufman *(Product Mgr-Pro Imaging)*
Sara Kim *(Assoc Product Mgr)*
Kristi Lanzit *(Product Mgr-Consumer Ink Jets)*
Robynne Lee *(Product Mgr)*
Jason Meyer *(Product Mgr)*
Richard Miller *(Product Mgr)*
Jason Palmer *(Product Mgr)*
Claudine Wolas-Shiva *(Sr Product Mgr)*
Brands & Products:
DFX-5000+
DFX-8000
EXPRESSION 636
EXPRESSION 836XL COLOR SCANNER
FX-1170
FX-880
LQ-1070+
LQ-1170
LQ-2550
LQ-570+
LQ-870
LX-300
PERFECTION 600
PHOTO PC 550
PHOTO PC 600
POWERLITE 5000XB
POWERLITE 7000XB
POWERLITE 7300
POWERLITE 822+
POWERLITE 83+
STYLUS COLOR 1520
STYLUS COLOR 3000
STYLUS COLOR 400
STYLUS COLOR 600
STYLUS COLOR 800
STYLUS PHOTO 700 EX
STYLUS PRO 5000
Advertising Agencies:
Butler, Shine, Stern & Partners
20 Liberty Ship Way
Sausalito, CA 94965-3312
Tel.: (415) 331-6049
Fax: (415) 331-3524
Consumer Printers
Home & Business Projectors

DDB Los Angeles
340 Main St
Venice, CA 90291
Tel.: (310) 907-1500
Fax: (310) 907-1571

iCrossing, Inc.
15169 N Scottsdale Rd Ste C400
Scottsdale, AZ 85254
Tel.: (480) 505-5800
Fax: (480) 505-5801
Toll Free: (866) 620-3780

Walt & Company
2105 S Bascom Ave Ste 240
Campbell, CA 95008
Tel.: (408) 369-7200
Fax: (408) 369-7201

EPSON CANADA LIMITED

(Sub. of Epson America Inc.)
3771 Victoria Park Ave
Scarborough, ON M1W 3Z5, Canada
Tel.: (416) 498-9955
Fax: (416) 498-4574
Web Site: www.epson.ca

Key to Media (For complete agency information see *The Advertising Red Books-Agencies* edition):
1. Bus. Publs. 2. Cable T.V. 3. Catalogs & Directories. 4. Co-op Adv. 5. Consumer Mags. 6. D.M. to Bus. Estab.7. D.M. to Consumers
8. Daily Newsp. 9. Exhibits/Trade Shows 10. Foreign 11. Infomercial 12. Internet Adv.13. Multimedia 14. Network Radio
15. Network T.V. 16. Newsp. Distr. Mags. 17. Other 18. Outdoor (Posters, Transit) 19. Point of Purchase20. Premiums, Novelties
21. Product Samples 22. Special Events Mktg. 23. Spot Radio 24. Spot T.V. 25. Weekly Newsp. 26. Yellow Page Adv.

Epson Canada Limited — (Continued)

Approx. Rev.: $450,000,000
Approx. Number Employees: 90
Year Founded: 1983
Business Description:
Computer Printers & Accessories Mfr
S.I.C.: 5734
N.A.I.C.S.: 443120
Import
Media: 2-4-5-6-7-8-9-10-20-22-25
Distr.: Direct to Consumer; Natl.
Budget Set: Dec.
Personnel:
Don Saunders *(VP)*
Lynne Lyon *(Mgr-HR)*
Andrew Patrick *(Mgr-Professional Imaging)*
Tamara Walsh *(Mgr-Mktg)*
Advertising Agency:
DDB Canada
33 Bloor Street East Suite 1700
Toronto, ON M4W 3T4, Canada
Tel.: (416) 925-9819
Fax: (416) 925-4180

EQUINIX, INC.

One Lagoon Dr 4th Fl
Redwood City, CA 94065
Tel.: (650) 598-6000
Fax: (650) 598-6900
E-mail: info@equinix.com
Web Site: www.equinix.com
Approx. Rev.: $1,220,334,000
Approx. Number Employees: 1,921
Year Founded: 1998
Business Description:
Designs, Builds & Operates Neutral Internet Business Exchange Centers
S.I.C.: 4813; 4899; 5045
N.A.I.C.S.: 517110; 425110; 517310; 517910
Personnel:
Peter F. Van Camp *(Chm)*
Stephen M. Smith *(Pres & CEO)*
Keith D. Taylor *(CFO)*
Brian Lillie *(CIO)*
Jarrett Appleby *(CMO)*
Samuel Lee *(Pres-Asia-Pacific)*
Charles J. Meyers *(Pres-North America)*
Eric Schwartz *(Pres-Europe)*
Brandi Galvin Morandi *(Gen Counsel & Sec)*
Keri Crask *(Sr VP-HR)*
Howard Horowitz *(Sr VP-Real Estate-Global)*
Doug Oates *(VP-Sls-Equinix Asia-Pacific)*
Dan Walker *(VP-Sls-North America)*
Jason Starr *(Sr Dir-IR)*
Jacqueline Hendy *(Dir-HR & Ops-North America)*
Lane Patterson *(Chief Technologist)*
Brands & Products:
DIRECT
EQUINIX
EQUINIX EXCHANGE
GIGE EXCHANGE
IBXFLEX
INTERNET BUSINESS EXCHANGE
IXIP
SMART HANDS
YOUR BUSINESS HAS ARRIVED
Advertising Agency:
Lewis PR
575 Market St Ste 2550
San Francisco, CA 94105
Tel.: (415) 992-4400

EQUINIX OPERATING CO, LLC

(Sub. of Equinix, Inc.)
1715 N Westshore Blvd Ste 650
Tampa, FL 33607
Tel.: (813) 207-7700
Fax: (813) 207-7701
Toll Free: (800) 455-9922
E-mail: info@equinix.com
Web Site: www.equinix.com
E-Mail For Key Personnel:
Sales Director: sales@switchanddata.com
Public Relations: pr@switchanddata.com
Approx. Rev.: $205,438,000
Approx. Number Employees: 376
Year Founded: 1998
Business Description:
Data Communication Services
S.I.C.: 4899
N.A.I.C.S.: 517910
Personnel:
Charles D. Browning *(Sr VP-Ops)*
William Roach *(Sr VP-Sls)*
Mario L. Galvez *(VP-Mktg)*
Ernie Sampera *(VP-Mktg-North America)*
P. J. Sheil, III *(VP-Fin)*
Ed Agar *(Dir-Bus Dev)*
Bob Marzi *(Dir-Ops)*
Advertising Agency:
Lewis PR
575 Market St Ste 2550
San Francisco, CA 94105
Tel.: (415) 992-4400

ERGOTRON, INC.

(Sub. of Nortek, Inc.)
1181 Trapp Rd
Saint Paul, MN 55121-1325
Tel.: (651) 681-7600
Fax: (651) 681-7715
Toll Free: (800) 888-8458
E-mail: sales@ergotron.com
Web Site: www.ergotron.com
E-Mail For Key Personnel:
Sales Director: sales@ergotron.com
Approx. Number Employees: 170
Year Founded: 1982
Business Description:
Designer, Mfr & Marketer of Ergonomic Mounting & Mobility Products for Computers
S.I.C.: 3577
N.A.I.C.S.: 334119
Export
Media: 4-6-7-10-11-13
Personnel:
Joel Hazzard *(Pres & CEO)*
Greg A. Mohwinkel *(CFO)*
Dan Miller *(COO)*
Jane Payfer *(CMO)*
Pete Segar *(Pres-Ergotron Branded Products)*
Jim Fischer *(Sr VP-Info Svcs-Global)*
Jonathan Pyenson *(Sr VP-EMEA Bus Ops)*
Diane Richardson *(Sr VP-OEM Grp)*
Lee Schalk *(Sr VP-Global Comm Sls)*
Craig Thomas *(VP-China Ops & Gen Mgr)*
John Deutsch *(VP-ODM Sls-Global)*
Diane M. Kaufman *(VP-HR-Global)*
C.Y. Wong *(Dir-Asia Channel Sls)*
Brands & Products:
ERGOTRON
NEO-FLEX
STYLEVIEW
TEACHWELL

ESCALATE RETAIL-DELRAY BEACH

(Branch of Escalate Retail, Inc.)
1615 S Congress Ave Ste 100
Delray Beach, FL 33445-6368
Tel.: (561) 265-2700
Fax: (561) 454-4803
Toll Free: (888) 777-68111
Web Site: www.escalateretail.com
Approx. Number Employees: 260
Business Description:
Retail Enterprise Software Developer
S.I.C.: 7371
N.A.I.C.S.: 541511
Advertising Expenditures: $1,100,000
Media: 2-4-13
Personnel:
Rob Neibauer *(Sr VP-Worldwide Sls)*
Ron Franks *(VP)*

ESET, LLC

610 W Ash St Ste 1900
San Diego, CA 92101
Tel.: (619) 876-5400
Fax: (619) 876-5845
Toll Free: (866) 343-3738
E-mail: cdale@eset.com
Web Site: www.eset.com
Sales Range: $100-124.9 Million
Approx. Number Employees: 250
Year Founded: 1992
Business Description:
Security Software Development & Sales
S.I.C.: 7372
N.A.I.C.S.: 511210
Personnel:
Anton Zajac *(Pres)*
Andrew Lee *(CEO)*
Dan Clark *(VP-Mktg & Res)*
Matthew McManus *(VP-Sls & Customer Care)*
Christopher Dale *(Mgr-PR)*
Advertising Agency:
Red Door Interactive, Inc.
350 10th Ave Set 1100
San Diego, CA 92101
Tel.: (619) 398-2670
Fax: (619) 398-2671

ESKER, INC.

(Sub. of Esker S.A.)
Ste 350 1212 Deming Way
Madison, WI 53717-1984
Tel.: (608) 828-6000
Fax: (608) 273-8227
Toll Free: (800) 368-5283
E-mail: info@esker.com
Web Site: www.esker.com
Approx. Number Employees: 120
Year Founded: 1982
Business Description:
Developer of Computer Network Connectivity Software
S.I.C.: 7371
N.A.I.C.S.: 541511
Media: 10
Personnel:
Renee Thomas *(Dir-Field Mktg-Americas)*

ESS TECHNOLOGY, INC.

(Sub. of Imperium Partners Group, LLC)
48401 Fremont Blvd
Fremont, CA 94538-6581
Tel.: (510) 492-1088
Fax: (510) 492-1098
E-mail: webmstr@esstech.com
Web Site: www.esstech.com
Approx. Rev.: $68,331,000
Approx. Number Employees: 143
Year Founded: 1984
Business Description:
Designs, Markets & Sells Highly Integrated Multimedia Semiconductor & Software Solutions for the Personal Computers & Consumer Electronics Markets
S.I.C.: 3674
N.A.I.C.S.: 334413
Advertising Expenditures: $1,876,000
Media: 2-7-10
Personnel:
Robert L. Blair *(Pres & CEO)*
John Marsh *(CFO)*
Brands & Products:
VANTAGE
VIBRATTO
VISBA

ESSELTE BUSINESS CORP

(Div. of Esselte UK Ltd.)
48 S Service Rd Ste 400
Melville, NY 11747
Tel.: (631) 675-5700
Fax: (800) 331-0231
E-mail: info@esselte.com
Web Site: www.esselte.com
Approx. Number Employees: 2,300
Year Founded: 1882
Business Description:
Filing Equipment Systems & Office Supplies Mfr
S.I.C.: 2675
N.A.I.C.S.: 322231
Import Export
Media: 4-7-11
Distr.: Intl.; Natl.
Budget Set: Oct. -Nov.
Personnel:
Gary J. Brooks *(Pres & CEO)*
Richard Douville *(CFO & Exec VP)*
Mervat El Shawarby *(Sr VP-HR)*
Candice Harris *(VP-Mktg)*
Nate Kvamme *(Gen Mgr)*
Brands & Products:
BOORUM & PEASE
CURTIS
DYMO
MEDIA MATE
OXFORD
PENDAFLEX

EVANS & SUTHERLAND COMPUTER CORPORATION - DIGITAL THEATER DIVISION

(Div. of Evans & Sutherland Computer Corporation)
770 Komas Dr
Salt Lake City, UT 84108-1229
Tel.: (801) 588-1000
Fax: (801) 588-4520
Web Site: www.es.com
Sales Range: $75-99.9 Million
Approx. Number Employees: 150

Key to Media (For complete agency information see *The Advertising Red Books-Agencies* edition):
1. Bus. Publs. 2. Cable T.V. 3. Catalogs & Directories. 4. Co-op Adv. 5. Consumer Mags. 6. D.M. to Bus. Estab.7. D.M. to Consumers 8. Daily Newsp. 9. Exhibits/Trade Shows 10. Foreign 11. Infomercial 12. Internet Adv.13. Multimedia 14. Network Radio 15. Network T.V. 16. Newsp. Distr. Mags. 17. Other 18. Outdoor (Posters, Transit) 19. Point of Purchase20. Premiums, Novelties 21. Product Samples 22. Special Events Mktg. 23. Spot Radio 24. Spot T.V. 25. Weekly Newsp. 26. Yellow Page Adv.

Business Description:
Digital Theatre Systems for Planetariums, Science Centers & Domed Theatres
S.I.C.: 3571; 3577
N.A.I.C.S.: 334111; 334119
Media: 2-4-7-10
Personnel:
Kirk Johnson *(VP & Gen Mgr)*
Brands & Products:
DIGISTAR III
DIGISTAR IIISP

EVEREST SOFTWARE INC.
(Sub. of Versata Enterprises Inc.)
6011 W Courtyard Dr Ste 300
Austin, TX 78730
Tel.: (703) 234-6600
Fax: (703) 991-1494
Toll Free: (800) 599-5303
E-mail: info@everestsoft.com
Web Site:
www.everestsoftwareinc.com
Approx. Number Employees: 380
Year Founded: 1994
Business Description:
Computer Software Development Services
S.I.C.: 7372
N.A.I.C.S.: 511210
Brands & Products:
EVEREST
UNPARALLELED VIEW OF YOUR BUSINESS
Advertising Agency:
Strategic Communications Group
1400 Spring St Ste 330
Silver Spring, MD 20910
Tel.: (301) 408-4500
Fax: (301) 408-4506

EVOLUTIONARY TECHNOLOGIES INTERNATIONAL, INC.
(Sub. of Versata Enterprises Inc.)
6011 W Courtyard Dr Ste 300
Austin, TX 78730
Tel.: (512) 377-9700
Fax: (512) 874-8900
E-mail: information@eti.com
Web Site: www.eti.com
Approx. Rev.: $9,600,000
Approx. Number Employees: 75
Year Founded: 1991
Business Description:
Software Products for Data Integration Management
S.I.C.: 7372
N.A.I.C.S.: 511210
Media: 2-10-13-20
Personnel:
Chris Ney *(CEO)*
Audrey Montgomery *(Dir-Product Dev)*
Brands & Products:
ANSWERLINK
DIALOGUE COACH
ETI
ETI DATA CLEANSER
ETI DATA MONITOR
ETI DATA PROFILER
ETI EXTRACT
HIGH PERFORMANCE DATA INTEGRATION
ICENTER
METASTORE
SUCCESS FIRST

EVOLVING SYSTEMS, INC.
9777 Pyramid Ct Ste 100
Englewood, CO 80112
Tel.: (303) 802-1000
Fax: (303) 802-1420
E-mail: info@evolving.com
Web Site: www.evolving.com
Approx. Rev.: $37,306,000
Approx. Number Employees: 248
Year Founded: 1985
Business Description:
Software & Services to Fixed-Line, Wireless & IP Customers
S.I.C.: 7371; 7372; 7373
N.A.I.C.S.: 541511; 511210; 541512
Advertising Expenditures: $500,000
Personnel:
Thaddeus Dupper *(Chm, Pres & CEO)*
Brian R. Ervine *(CFO, Chief Admin Officer & Exec VP)*
Anita T. Moseley *(Gen Counsel & Sr VP)*
Steve Farnsworth *(VP-Worldwide Customer Support)*
James King *(VP-Worldwide Mktg & Sls)*
Ram Asare Dwivedi *(Gen Mgr-Evolving Sys India)*
Sarah Hurp *(Mgr-Mktg)*
Brands & Products:
DYNAMIC SIM ALLOCATION
EVIDENT
EVOLVING SYSTEMS
LNP DATA SERVER
LSMSXPRESS
MEDIATION CENTRAL
NETVANTAGE
NUMERITRACK
ORDERPATH
PORTEXCHANGE
SERVICELINK
SERVICEXPRESS
TERTIO
VERIFY
VERIPORT

EXAR CORPORATION
48720 Kato Rd
Fremont, CA 94538
Tel.: (510) 668-7000
Fax: (510) 668-7001
Web Site: www.exar.com
Approx. Sls.: $146,005,000
Approx. Number Employees: 477
Year Founded: 1971
Business Description:
High Bandwidth Analog & Mixed Signal Silicon Solutions Designer, Developer & Marketer
S.I.C.: 3674; 3571
N.A.I.C.S.: 334413; 334111
Export
Advertising Expenditures: $1,000,000
Media: 4-7-10-11-13-22
Personnel:
Richard Louis Leza, Sr. *(Chm)*
Pete P. Rodriguez *(Pres & CEO)*
Kevin S. Bauer *(CFO & Sr VP)*
Trong Vu *(CIO & VP-IT)*
George Apostol *(CTO & Exec VP-Engrg)*
Thomas R. Melendrez *(Gen Counsel, Sec & Exec VP-Bus Dev)*
Christopher R. Dingley *(Exec VP-Sls-Worldwide)*
Paul Pickering *(Exec VP-Mktg)*
Frank Marazita *(Sr VP-Worldwide Ops, Reliability & Quality Assurance)*
Jiebing Wang *(VP-Acceleration Tech & Gen Mgr-China Dev Center)*
Diane Hill *(VP-HR)*
David Matteucci *(VP-Power Mgmt Products)*
Timothy Maloney *(Sr Dir-Digital Power Mktg)*
Greg Kaufman *(Dir-Mktg Comm)*
Brands & Products:
EXAR
EXPERIENCE OUR CONNECTIVITY
POWERING CONNECTIVITY

EXIGEN INC.
(d/b/a Exigen Group)
505 Montgomery St # 2300 345 CAI St 10th FL
San Francisco, CA 94104
Tel.: (415) 402-2600
Fax: (415) 402-2000
E-mail: info@exigengroup.com
Web Site: www.exigengroup.com
Approx. Sls.: $42,900,000
Approx. Number Employees: 120
Business Description:
Computer Software Development & Applications
S.I.C.: 7371
N.A.I.C.S.: 541511
Export
Media: 4-7-10-11
Personnel:
Greg Shenkman *(Mng Partner)*
Alec Miloslavsky *(Partner)*
Brands & Products:
BACKBONE

EZENIA! INC.
14 Celina Ave Ste 17
Nashua, NH 03063
Tel.: (603) 589-7600
Fax: (603) 880-4795
E-mail: helpdesk@infoworkspace.com
Web Site: www.ezenia.com
Approx. Rev.: $2,681,000
Approx. Number Employees: 13
Year Founded: 1991
Business Description:
Networking Equipment & Associated Software for Conferencing
S.I.C.: 3575; 3571; 3661; 3669
N.A.I.C.S.: 334113; 334111; 334210; 334290
Advertising Expenditures: $23,000
Media: 10
Personnel:
Khoa D. Nguyen *(Chm & CEO)*
Thomas J. McCann *(CFO)*
Brands & Products:
ENCOUNTER
EZENIA
INFOWORKSPACE

F5 NETWORKS, INC.
401 Elliott Ave W
Seattle, WA 98119
Tel.: (206) 272-5555
Fax: (206) 272-5556
Toll Free: (888) 882-4447
E-mail: info@f5.com
Web Site: www.f5.com
Approx. Rev.: $881,972,000
Approx. Number Employees: 2,012
Year Founded: 1996
Business Description:
Network Traffic Routing & Management Software
S.I.C.: 7372; 3577; 7371
N.A.I.C.S.: 511210; 334119; 541511
Advertising Expenditures: $2,100,000
Media: 1-7-10-13
Personnel:
Alan J. Higginson *(Chm)*
John McAdam *(Pres & CEO)*
Andy Reinland *(CFO & Sr VP)*
Kirby Wadsworth *(CMO)*
Karl Triebes *(CTO & Sr VP-Product Dev)*
John Rodriguez *(Chief Acctg Officer & Sr VP)*
Jeffrey A. Christianson *(Gen Counsel & Sr VP)*
Mark Anderson *(Sr VP-Worldwide Sls)*
Edward J. Eames *(Sr VP-Bus Ops)*
Dean Darwin *(VP-Worldwide Channel Sls)*
Kathleen Ferraro *(VP-Product Mgmt & Prod Mktg Data Solutions)*
Brands & Products:
3-DNS
ACOPIA
ACOPIA NETWORKS
ADVANCED CLIENT AUTHENTICATION
ADVANCED ROUTING
APPLICATION ACCELERATOR
ASM
BIG-IP
DATAGUARD
DEVACENTRAL
EDGE-FX
F5
F5 ACOPIA
F5 MANAGEMENT PACK
F5 NETWORKS
FAST APPLICATION PROXY
FAST CACHE
FIREPASS
FREEDOMFABRIC
GLOBAL-SITE
GTM
ICONTROL
INTERNET CONTROL ARCHITECTURE
IP APPLICATION SWITCH
IRULES
IT AGILITY. YOUR WAY.
NETCELERA
ONECONNECT
PACKET VELOCITY
SYN CHECK
TMOS
TRAFFICSHIELD
VIPRION
WANJET
WEBACCELERATOR
ZONERUNNER
Advertising Agencies:
Connect Public Relations
80 E 100 N
Provo, UT 84606
Tel.: (801) 373-7888
Fax: (801) 373-8680

Hodgson/Meyers
10210 NE Points Dr Ste 220
Kirkland, WA 98033-7872
Tel.: (425) 827-2506
Fax: (425) 822-0155

Key to Media (For complete agency information see *The Advertising Red Books-Agencies* edition):
1. Bus. Publs. 2. Cable T.V. 3. Catalogs & Directories. 4. Co-op Adv. 5. Consumer Mags. 6. D.M. to Bus. Estab.7. D.M. to Consumers
8. Daily Newsp. 9. Exhibits/Trade Shows 10. Foreign 11. Infomercial 12. Internet Adv.13. Multimedia 14. Network Radio
15. Network T.V. 16. Newsp. Distr. Mags. 17. Other 18. Outdoor (Posters, Transit) 19. Point of Purchase20. Premiums, Novelties
21. Product Samples 22. Special Events Mktg. 23. Spot Radio 24. Spot T.V. 25. Weekly Newsp. 26. Yellow Page Adv.

FACTORY CARD & PARTY OUTLET CORP.
(Joint Venture of Advent International Corporation, Berkshire Partners LLC & Weston Presidio Capital)
2727 W Diehl Rd
Naperville, IL 60563-8720
Tel.: (630) 579-2000
Fax: (630) 579-2576
Toll Free: (888) 840-8066
E-mail: customer@factorycard.com
Web Site: www.factorycard.com
Approx. Sls.: $244,232,000
Approx. Number Employees: 2,500
Year Founded: 1985
Business Description:
Party Supplies, Greeting Cards, Gift Wrap, Balloons & Other Special Occasion Merchandise Mfr & Retailer
S.I.C.: 5947; 5999
N.A.I.C.S.: 453220; 453998
Advertising Expenditures: $9,580,000
Media: 8-13
Brands & Products:
FACTORY CARD & PARTY OUTLET
FACTORY CARD OUTLET
PARTYMANIA

FAIR ISAAC CORP.
(Sub. of Fair Isaac Corporation)
20 W Kinzie St Ste 1600
Chicago, IL 60610-6398
Tel.: (312) 984-7000
Fax: (312) 984-7033
Web Site: www.fairisaac.com
Sales Range: $25-49.9 Million
Approx. Number Employees: 3,000
Business Description:
Business Decision Systems, Security Software & Credit Scoring Services
S.I.C.: 7389; 6099; 7319; 7373; 7379
N.A.I.C.S.: 561499; 522320; 541512; 541519; 541870; 561439; 561990
Advertising Expenditures: $1,200,000

FALCONSTOR SOFTWARE, INC.
2 Huntingdon Quadrangle Ste 2S01
Melville, NY 11747-3800
Tel.: (631) 777-5188
Fax: (631) 501-7633
E-mail: info@falconstor.com
Web Site: www.falconstor.com
E-Mail For Key Personnel:
Marketing Director: markting@falconstor.com
Sales Director: sales@falconstor.com
Approx. Rev.: $82,843,746
Approx. Number Employees: 501
Year Founded: 2000
Business Description:
Network Storage Management Software
S.I.C.: 7371; 7372
N.A.I.C.S.: 511210; 334611; 541511
Export
Media: 10-11-22
Personnel:
James P. McNiel *(Pres & CEO)*
James Weber *(CFO, Interim COO, Treas & VP)*
Seth Horowitz *(Gen Counsel, Sec & VP)*
Alan Chen *(VP & Gen Mgr-Asia Pacific Ops)*
Eric Chen *(VP & Gen Mgr-Ops-Asia Pacific)*
Guillaume Imberti *(VP & Gen Mgr-Ops-EMEA)*
Alex Jiang *(VP-Global Mktg)*
Abbas Meghjee *(VP-Sls-North America)*
Brands & Products:
CONTINUOUS DATA PROTECTOR
DYNAPATH
FALCONSTOR
FALCONSTOR SOFTWARE
HOTZONE
IPSTOR
TIMEMARK
TIMEVIEW
TOTALLY OPEN

FASTAFF
(Sub. of US Nursing Corporation)
6501 S Fiddlers Green Cir Ste 200
Greenwood Village, CO 80111
Tel.: (303) 692-1818
Fax: (888) 508-7854
Toll Free: (877) 912-9478 (USA)
Toll Free: (888) 857-9724 (Canada)
E-mail: hiring@fastaff.com
Web Site: www.fastaff.com
Approx. Number Employees: 250
Year Founded: 1996
Business Description:
Nursing & Medical Staffing Services
S.I.C.: 7361
N.A.I.C.S.: 561310
Media: 2
Personnel:
Greg Mikkelsen *(Vice Chm)*

FASTENAL COMPANY
2001 Theurer Blvd
Winona, MN 55987-1500
Mailing Address:
PO Box 978
Winona, MN 55987-0978
Tel.: (507) 454-5374
Fax: (507) 453-8049
E-mail: info@fastenal.com
Web Site: www.fastenal.com
Approx. Sls.: $2,269,471,000
Approx. Number Employees: 13,285
Year Founded: 1967
Business Description:
Industrial & Construction Products Whslr & Distr
S.I.C.: 3452; 5072; 5085; 5198; 5211
N.A.I.C.S.: 332722; 423710; 423840; 424950; 444190
Import
Media: 2-4-7-10-13-18-19-20-21-22-23-26
Personnel:
Robert A. Kierlin *(Chm)*
Willard D. Oberton *(Pres & CEO)*
Daniel L. Florness *(CFO & Exec VP)*
Nicholas J. Lundquist *(COO & Exec VP)*
John J. Milek *(Gen Counsel)*
Steven A. Rucinski *(Sr VP & Exec VP-Intl Sls)*
Michael Camp *(Exec VP-Product & Procurement)*
Leland J. Hein *(Exec VP)*
James C. Jansen *(Exec VP-Internal Ops)*
Ashok Singh *(Exec VP-IT)*
Steven L. Appelwick *(VP-Product Procurement, Mktg & Logistics)*
Brad Carter *(Mgr-Bus Dev)*
Brands & Products:
FASTENAL
GROWTH THROUGH CUSTOMER SERVICE

FEDEX OFFICE & PRINT SERVICES, INC.
(Sub. of FedEx Corporate Services, Inc.)
3 Galleria Tower 13155 Noel Rd Ste 1600
Dallas, TX 75240
Tel.: (214) 550-7000
Fax: (214) 550-7001
Sales Range: $900-999.9 Million
Approx. Number Employees: 1,000
Year Founded: 1970
Business Description:
Photocopying, Duplicating & Printing Services, Ground & Express Shipping Services, High-Speed Internet Access & Computer Usage, WiFi Services, Videoconferencing, Signs, Graphics & Photo Services
S.I.C.: 2752; 2759; 4215; 4513; 5943; 7336; 7384
N.A.I.C.S.: 323114; 323112; 323113; 323115; 323119; 453210; 492110; 492210; 541430; 812921; 812922
Media: 6-13-17-25-26
Personnel:
Brian D. Philips *(Pres & CEO)*
Leslie Benner *(CFO & Sr VP)*
Kim Dixon *(COO & Exec VP)*
Frederic C. Liskow *(Gen Counsel & Sr VP)*
Tracy Brightman *(Sr VP-HR)*
Carole Woodward *(VP-IT)*
Steve Pacheco *(Dir-Adv)*
Advertising Agency:
OMD-USA
195 Broadway
New York, NY 10007
Tel.: (212) 590-7100

FEI.COM, INC.
7257 Pkwy Dr Ste 200
Hanover, MD 21076
Tel.: (443) 270-5100
Fax: (410) 712-0220
E-mail: fei@feinfo.com
Web Site: www.feinfo.com
Approx. Sls.: $3,500,000
Approx. Number Employees: 50
Year Founded: 1998
Business Description:
Technology Consulting Services to Health Care & Government Contractors
S.I.C.: 7373
N.A.I.C.S.: 541512
Media: 2-10-21
Personnel:
Jiao Gu *(Owner)*

FELLOWES, INC.
1789 Norwood Ave
Itasca, IL 60143-1059
Tel.: (630) 893-1600
Fax: (630) 893-1648
E-mail: info@fellowes.com
Web Site: www.fellowes.com
Sales Range: $500-549.9 Million
Approx. Number Employees: 1,500
Year Founded: 1917
Business Description:
Computer & Office Accessories Mfr
S.I.C.: 3579; 2522
N.A.I.C.S.: 333313; 337214
Export
Advertising Expenditures: $500,000
Media: 2-4-5-10-11-19-21-22
Distr.: Intl.; Natl.
Personnel:
James Fellowes *(Chm & CEO)*
Joseph Koch *(Pres & COO)*
James Lewis *(Exec VP & Chief Supply Chain Officer)*
Maureen Moore *(Dir-Corp Mktg Commun)*
Brands & Products:
BONUS
DATA-PAK
HIGH-STAK
LIBERTY
MAGIC
POLYLOCK
POWERSHRED
SILHOUETTE
STAX-ON-STEEL
STOR/DRAWER
SYSTEMATIC
WORKSTATION
Advertising Agency:
Slack Barshinger & Partners, Inc.
233 N Michigan Ave Ste 3050
Chicago, IL 60601
Tel.: (312) 970-5800
Fax: (312) 970-5850
Toll Free: (800) 888-6197

FIDELITY NATIONAL INFORMATION SERVICES
(Sub. of Fidelity National Information Services, Inc.)
2 W Liberty Ste 300
Malvern, PA 19355
Tel.: (610) 296-8877
Fax: (484) 595-5101
Toll Free: (800) 874-7359
E-mail: info@fidelityinfoservices.com
Web Site: www.sanchez.com
Sales Range: $75-99.9 Million
Approx. Number Employees: 500
Year Founded: 1979
Business Description:
Financial Software Development & Services
S.I.C.: 7371
N.A.I.C.S.: 541511
Media: 7-10
Personnel:
Michael A. Sanchez *(Chm)*
Brands & Products:
CMAX
GT.M
PROFILE
PROFILE FOR WINDOWS
SANCHEZ
SANCHEZ E-PROFILE
SANCHEZ FMS
SANCHEZ PROFILE
SANCHEZ WEALTHWARE
SANCHEZ WEBCLIENT
SANCHEZ WEBCSR
SANCHEZ XPRESS
WEALTHWARE
WEBCLIENT
WEBCSR
XPRESS

FIDELITY NATIONAL INFORMATION SERVICES, INC.
601 Riverside Ave
Jacksonville, FL 32204
Tel.: (904) 854-5000
Fax: (904) 357-1105

Key to Media (For complete agency information see *The Advertising Red Books-Agencies* edition):
1. Bus. Publs. 2. Cable T.V. 3. Catalogs & Directories. 4. Co-op Adv. 5. Consumer Mags. 6. D.M. to Bus. Estab.7. D.M. to Consumers 8. Daily Newsp. 9. Exhibits/Trade Shows 10. Foreign 11. Infomercial 12. Internet Adv.13. Multimedia 14. Network Radio 15. Network T.V. 16. Newsp. Distr. Mags. 17. Other 18. Outdoor (Posters, Transit) 19. Point of Purchase20. Premiums, Novelties 21. Product Samples 22. Special Events Mktg. 23. Spot Radio 24. Spot T.V. 25. Weekly Newsp. 26. Yellow Page Adv.

Toll Free: (888) 323-0310
E-mail: moreinformation@fisglobal.com
Web Site: www.fisglobal.com
E-Mail For Key Personnel:
Marketing Director: fnfis.marketing@fnf.com
Approx. Rev.: $5,269,500,000
Approx. Number Employees: 33,000
Business Description:
Card Issuing Services & Check Risk Management
S.I.C.: 6099
N.A.I.C.S.: 522320
Media: 2-4-7-10-11-13
Distr.: Intl.
Personnel:
William P. Foley, II *(Chm)*
Frank R. Martire *(Pres & CEO)*
Michael D. Hayford *(CFO & Exec VP)*
Gary A. Norcross *(COO & Exec VP)*
Michael P. Oates *(Chief HR Officer & Exec VP)*
Brent Bannister Bickett *(Exec VP-Bus Dev)*
Ram Chary *(Exec VP-Global Comml Svcs)*
Frank G. D'Angelo *(Exec VP-Payment Solutions)*
Mark Davey *(Exec VP-Intl)*
Brian C. Hurdis *(Exec VP-Tech Svcs)*
Anthony Jabbour *(Exec VP-Fin Solutions)*
Francis R. Sanchez *(Exec VP-Strategic Solutions)*
James Susoreny *(Exec VP-Bus Dev)*
Marcia Danzeisen *(Sr VP-Global Mktg & Comm)*
Mary K. Waggoner *(Sr VP-IR)*
Advertising Agency:
Stephenson Group
37 Hollow Brook Rd
Califon, NJ 07830
Tel.: (908) 439-3660
Fax: (908) 439-3268

FIDO INC.
(Sub. of Rogers Wireless Inc.)
800 de la Gauchetiere St W Ste 4000
Montreal, QC H5A 1K3, Canada
Tel.: (514) 937-2121
Fax: (514) 937-2554
Toll Free: (888) 481-3436
E-mail: info@fido.ca
Web Site: www.fido.ca
Approx. Number Employees: 2,200
Business Description:
Secure Digital Voice Transmissions, Caller Identification, Text Messaging & Fax Products Mfr
S.I.C.: 4812
N.A.I.C.S.: 517212
Advertising Expenditures: $30,000,000
Media: 19
Personnel:
Gui Bourgeois *(Dir-Mktg Comm)*
Brands & Products:
FIDO

FIRST DATABANK, INC.
(Sub. of Hearst Business Media)
701 Gateway Blvd Ste 600
San Francisco, CA 94080
Tel.: (650) 588-5454
Fax: (650) 246-2829
Toll Free: (800) 633-3453
Web Site: www.firstdatabank.com
Approx. Number Employees: 400
Year Founded: 1975
Business Description:
Pharmaceutical, Medical & Nutritional Information Database Publisher
S.I.C.: 2741
N.A.I.C.S.: 511140; 519130
Media: 2-4-7-10-20
Distr.: Intl.
Budget Set: Oct.
Personnel:
Gregory H. Dorn *(Pres & CEO)*
Patrick Lupinetti *(Sr VP & Dir-Editorial)*
Jim Schultz *(VP-Fin & Ops, Gen Mgr-Indianapolis)*
Joseph E. Heins *(VP-Global Product Mgmt & Mktg)*
Bob Katter *(VP-Sls & Customer Rels)*
Dave Stephens *(VP-IT)*
Kevin Weber *(Sr Dir-Corp Transformation & Project Mgmt)*
David Manin *(Mktg Dir)*
Leesa Bolin *(Dir-HR)*
Lisa Geller *(Product Mgr)*
Brands & Products:
AHFS FIRST WEB
AHFS FRAMEWORK
DRUG INFORMATION FRAMEWORK
DRUG INFORMATION FRAMEWORK TRANSACTION OBJECTS
EVALUATIONS OF DRUG INTERACTIONS
FIRST TOX
INTERNATIONAL DRUG DATA FILE PLUS
THE KNOWLEDGE INSIDE
MEDICAL REFERENCE FRAMEWORK
NATIONAL DRUG DATA FILE PLUS
NUTRITION KNOWLEDGE BASE
NUTRITIONIST PRO
NUTRITIONIST PRO FOOD LABELING
PRICE PROBE
PRICEPOINT RX
RXWEB

FIRSTBANK DATA CORPORATION
(Sub. of Firstbank Holding Company of Colorado, Inc.)
12345 W Colfax Ave
Lakewood, CO 80215-3742
Tel.: (303) 232-3000
Fax: (303) 235-1041
E-mail: firstbank@efirstbank.com
Web Site: www.firstbank.com
Approx. Number Employees: 275
Year Founded: 1980
Business Description:
Data Processing & Preparation
S.I.C.: 7374
N.A.I.C.S.: 518210
Import Export
Personnel:
John Ikard *(Pres & CEO)*
Don Thuente *(CFO)*
Brands & Products:
THE COLORADO BANK FOR YOU
Advertising Agency:
TDA Advertising & Design
1500 Pearl St Ste 300
Boulder, CO 80302
Tel.: (303) 247-1180
Fax: (303) 247-1214

FIRSTWAVE TECHNOLOGIES INC.
7000 Central Pkwy NE Ste 330
Atlanta, GA 30328
Tel.: (678) 672-3100
Fax: (678) 672-3130
Toll Free: (800) 540-6061
E-mail: info@firstwave.net
Web Site: www.firstwave.com
Sales Range: $1-9.9 Million
Approx. Number Employees: 16
Year Founded: 1984
Business Description:
Software & Customer Relationship Management Solutions
S.I.C.: 7372; 7371
N.A.I.C.S.: 334611; 511210; 541511
Export
Media: 2-4-7-10
Distr.: Intl.; Natl.
Personnel:
Richard T. Brock *(CEO)*
Lisa J. Cramer *(CMO & Chief Sls Officer)*
Meredith A. Smith *(Mgr-Mktg Comm)*
Brands & Products:
BE FIRST IN MIND.
CORE IDE
ECRM
FIRST-MARKET
FIRST-PROJECT
FIRST-QUALITY
FIRST-SALES
FIRST-SUPPORT
FIRST-SURVEY
FIRST-WEB
FIRSTWAVE
FIRSTWAVE TECHNOLOGY
INTEGRATED DEVELOPMENT ENVIRONMENT
KNOWLEDGENOW
LEADTRACKER
NEWSWAVE
TAKECONTROL
WAVE CUSTOMER MODULE
WAVE CUSTOMER PORTAL
WAVE MARKET FEEDBACK MODULE
WAVE MARKETING MODULE
WAVE SALES MODULE
WAVE SUPPORT MODULE
WAVEMAILS

FISERV, INC.
255 Fiserv Dr
Brookfield, WI 53045-5815
Mailing Address:
PO Box 979
Brookfield, WI 53008-0979
Tel.: (262) 879-5000
Fax: (262) 879-5013
Toll Free: (800) 872-7882
E-mail: general_info@fiserv.com
Web Site: www.fiserv.com
Approx. Rev.: $4,133,000,000
Approx. Number Employees: 19,000
Year Founded: 1984
Business Description:
Financial Data Processing & Information Management Services
S.I.C.: 7374; 6099; 7371
N.A.I.C.S.: 518210; 522320; 541511
Export
Media: 1-2-3-4-6-7-9-10-11-13
Distr.: Intl.; Natl.
Budget Set: Oct.
Personnel:
Donald F. Dillon *(Chm)*
Peter J. Kight *(Vice Chm)*
Jeffery W. Yabuki *(Pres & CEO)*
Thomas J. Hirsch *(CFO, Treas & Exec VP)*
Mark A. Ernst *(COO & Exec VP)*
Maryann Goebel *(CIO & Exec VP)*
Don MacDonald *(CMO & Exec VP)*
Thomas W. Warsop, III *(Chief Sls Officer & Exec VP)*
Michael Gianoni *(Pres-Fin Institutions Grp & Exec VP)*
Sean Gallagher *(Pres-Investment Svcs Div)*
Rahul Gupta *(Pres-Digital Payment Solutions Grp)*
Mark Sievewright *(Pres-Credit Union Solutions Div)*
Charles W. Sprague *(Gen Counsel, Sec & Exec VP)*
James Cox *(Exec VP-Ccrp Dev)*
Lance F. Drummond *(Exec VP-HR & Shared Svcs)*
Christopher Bell *(Sr VP)*
Chris Capdevila *(VP-Product Mgmt, Strategy, Risk & Compliance Solutions)*
Tom Tobin *(VP-Product Dev, Risk & Compliance Group)*
Judy DeRango Wicks *(VP-Comm)*
Lori Stafford *(Asst VP-Comm)*
Lilly Straith *(Dir-Sls-Community Banks & Credit Unions)*
Laura Clary *(Product Mgr-Global Payment Solutions)*
Brands & Products:
BANKLINK
FISERV
GALAXYPLUS
INTEGRASYS
PPOONE
REMITSTREAM
SOURCE CAPTURE OPTIMIZATION
SUMMIT
VISION
Advertising Agency:
BBDO Minneapolis
150 S 5th St Ste 3500
Minneapolis, MN 55402-4200
Tel.: (612) 338-8401
Fax: (612) 656-0602

FLEXERA SOFTWARE INC.
(Holding of Thoma Bravo, LLC)
1000 E Woodfield Rd Ste 400
Schaumburg, IL 60173-5145
Tel.: (847) 466-4000
Fax: (847) 619-0788
Toll Free: (800) 374-4353
Web Site: www.flexerasoftware.com
Approx. Number Employees: 250
Year Founded: 1987
Business Description:
Software Developer
S.I.C.: 7372
N.A.I.C.S.: 511210
Import Export
Media: 2-4-7-8-10-13-18-21-22
Personnel:
Mark Bishof *(CEO)*
Joseph Freda *(CFO)*
Robert Doyle *(Sr VP-Engrg)*
Randy Littleson *(Sr VP-Mktg)*
Richard Northing *(Sr VP-Global Scvs)*
Vincent Smyth *(Gen Mgr-EMEA Sls)*

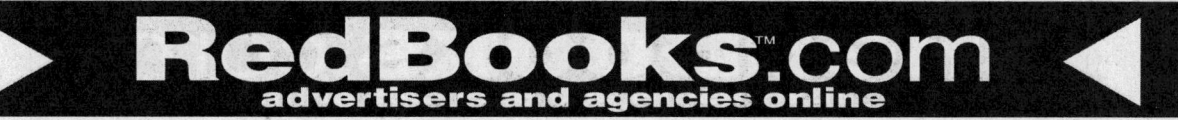

Key to Media (For complete agency information see *The Advertising Red Books-Agencies* edition):
1. Bus. Publs. 2. Cable T.V. 3. Catalogs & Directories. 4. Co-op Adv. 5. Consumer Mags. 6. D.M. to Bus. Estab.7. D.M. to Consumers 8. Daily Newsp. 9. Exhibits/Trade Shows 10. Foreign 11. Infomercial 12. Internet Adv.13. Multimedia 14. Network Radio 15. Network T.V. 16. Newsp. Distr. Mags. 17. Other 18. Outdoor (Posters, Transit) 19. Point of Purchase20. Premiums, Novelties 21. Product Samples 22. Special Events Mktg. 23. Spot Radio 24. Spot T.V. 25. Weekly Newsp. 26. Yellow Page Adv.

Flexera Software Inc. — (Continued)

Brands & Products:
ADMINSTUDIO
DEMOSHIELD
FLEXNET
INSTALLSHIELD
MACROVISION
UPDATE SERVICE

FOCALEX INC.
(Sub. of Fox Interactive Media, Inc.)
90 Bridge St
Newton, MA 02458
Tel.: (617) 559-0155
Fax: (617) 559-0475
Toll Free: (877) FOCALEX
Web Site: www.focalex.com
Sales Range: $10-24.9 Million
Approx. Number Employees: 17
Year Founded: 1998
Business Description:
Performance-Based Advertising Services
S.I.C.: 7319; 7371
N.A.I.C.S.: 541890; 541511
Media: 13
Personnel:
Russ Moore *(Pres)*

FOCUS ENHANCEMENTS INC.
(Sub. of VITEC Multimedia, Inc.)
931 Benecia Ave
Sunnyvale, CA 94085
Tel.: (650) 230-2400
Fax: (408) 739-1706
Toll Free: (800) 338-3348
E-mail: support@focusinfo.com
Web Site: www.focusinfo.com
Sales Range: $25-49.9 Million
Approx. Number Employees: 100
Year Founded: 1992
Business Description:
Wireless Technology, Video Conversion & Digital Media Services
S.I.C.: 3577; 3674; 7812
N.A.I.C.S.: 334119; 334413; 512110
Advertising Expenditures: $483,000
Media: 10
Personnel:
Norman Schlomka *(Sr VP-European Ops)*
Kevin McDonald *(VP-Mktg)*
Brands & Products:
CENTERSTAGE
COMMANDPOST
DART
FIREFLY
FIREFLY MC
FIRESTORE
FOCUS ENHANCEMENTS
HARMONY
ITVIEW MAC
MANTIS
MEDIA MESSENGER
MM-1
MMC-5 HD
MXPRODV
PERSONAL TITLEMAKER
PROXSYS
TITLEMAKER
TVIEW
TVIEW GOLD
TVIEW MICRO
TVIEW SILVER
Advertising Agency:
FutureWorks Inc.
2860 Zanker Rd Ste 108
San Jose, CA 95134
Tel.: (408) 428-0895
Fax: (408) 428-0896
Public Relations

FOLEY HOAG LLP
Seaport World Trade Ctr W 155
Seaport Blvd
Boston, MA 02210-2600
Tel.: (617) 832-1000
Fax: (617) 832-7000
E-mail: info@foleyhoag.com
Web Site: www.foleyhoag.com
Approx. Number Employees: 500
Personnel:
Robert S. Sanoff *(Partner)*
Advertising Agencies:
Cramer Productions Inc.
425 Univ Ave
Norwood, MA 02062
Tel.: (781) 278-2300
Fax: (781) 255-0721

Nicolazzo & Associates
101 Federal St Ste 710
Boston, MA 02110
Tel.: (617) 951-0000
Fax: (617) 439-9980

THE FORUM CORPORATION
265 Franklin St 4th Fl
Boston, MA 02110-3113
Tel.: (617) 523-7300
Fax: (617) 371-3300
Toll Free: (800) 367-8611
E-mail: webmaster@forum.com
Web Site: www.forum.com
Sales Range: $25-49.9 Million
Approx. Number Employees: 100
Year Founded: 1971
Business Description:
Professional Development & Training Services
S.I.C.: 8299
N.A.I.C.S.: 611430
Advertising Expenditures: $3,100,000
Media: 2-4-7-10-17-23-26
Distr.: Intl.; Natl.
Personnel:
Alyson Brandt *(Exec VP-Global Sls)*
Jocelyn Davis *(Exec VP-R & D)*
Tom Atkinson *(Dir-Res)*

FRANCORP, INC.
20200 Governor's Dr
Olympia Fields, IL 60461
Tel.: (708) 481-2900
Fax: (708) 481-5885
E-mail: info@francorp.com
Web Site: www.francorp.com
Approx. Sls.: $5,600,000
Approx. Number Employees: 28
Business Description:
Franchise Consulting Services
S.I.C.: 8742
N.A.I.C.S.: 541611
Media: 2
Personnel:
Eduardo Chianea *(Gen Mgr, Dir & Partner)*
Joseph Busch *(VP-Trng-Franchise Sls)*
Brands & Products:
FRANCORP

FRANKLIN ELECTRONIC PUBLISHERS, INC.
1 Franklin Plz
Burlington, NJ 08016
Tel.: (609) 386-2500
Fax: (609) 239-5948
Toll Free: (800) 266-5626
E-mail: service@franklin.com
Web Site: www.franklin.com
Sales Range: $25-49.9 Million
Approx. Number Employees: 133
Year Founded: 1981
Business Description:
Hand-Held Electronic Information Device Designer, Developer, Retailer & Publisher
S.I.C.: 3579; 2741; 5065
N.A.I.C.S.: 333313; 423690; 511199
Export
Advertising Expenditures: $3,055,000
Media: 1-2-4-5-7-8-10-13
Distr.: Natl.
Personnel:
Howard Lee Morgan *(Chm)*
Barry J. Lipsky *(Pres & CEO)*
Frank A. Musto *(CFO & VP)*
Toshihide Hokari *(COO & Sr VP)*
Gregory J. Winsky *(Exec VP)*
Brands & Products:
EBOOKMAN
ELECTRONIC ENCYCLOPEDIA
ELECTRONIC HOLY BIBLE
FRANKLIN
LANGUAGE MASTER
NEXT CENTURY
OFFICIAL SCRABBLE PLAYERS' DICTIONARY
PAGEMARK
POCKET PREP
ROLODEX
SPANISH MASTER
SPEAKING ACE
SPEAKING WORDMASTER
SPELLING ACE
SPELLMASTER
WORDMASTER

FREEMAN DECORATING CO.
(d/b/a The Freeman Companies)
1600 Viceroy Ste 100
Dallas, TX 75235
Tel.: (214) 445-1000
Fax: (214) 445-0200
Web Site: www.freemanco.com
Sales Range: $800-899.9 Million
Approx. Number Employees: 3,300
Year Founded: 1927
Business Description:
Convention & Trade Show Organizing Services
S.I.C.: 7389
N.A.I.C.S.: 561920; 561499
Personnel:
Donald S. Freeman, Jr. *(Chm)*
Carrie Freeman Parsons *(Vice Chm)*
John F. O'Connell, Jr. *(Pres)*
Joseph V. Popolo, Jr. *(CEO)*
Toby Purdy *(CMO & Exec VP)*
Advertising Agency:
imc2
12404 Park Central Ste 400
Dallas, TX 75251
Tel.: (214) 224-1000
Fax: (214) 224-1100

FREESCALE SEMICONDUCTOR, INC.
(Sub. of Freescale Semiconductor Holdings I, Ltd.)
6501 William Cannon Dr W
Austin, TX 78735
Tel.: (800) 521-6274
Fax: (512) 895-2652
E-mail: glaston@freescale.com
Web Site: www.freescale.com
Year Founded: 1953
Business Description:
Semiconductor Designer & Mfr
S.I.C.: 3674; 5065; 8733
N.A.I.C.S.: 334413; 423690; 541710
Media: 7-10-22
Personnel:
Richard M. Beyer *(Chm & CEO)*
Alan Campbell *(CFO & Sr VP)*
Sam Coursen *(CIO & VP)*
Henri P. Richard *(Chief Sls/Mktg Officer & Sr VP)*
Daryl E. Raiford *(Chief Acctg Officer & VP-Fin)*
Tom Deitrich *(Sr VP & Gen Mgr-Cellular Products)*
Lisa T. Su *(Sr VP & Gen Mgr, Networking & Multimedia)*
Jeff Bock *(Dir-Product Mktg)*
Andy Mastronardi *(Dir-Freescale University Programs-Worldwide)*
Matt Maupin *(Product Mgr)*
Andy R. North *(Mgr-Corp PR)*
Marlan Winter *(Mgr-Product, Bus & Tools Ecosystem)*
Brands & Products:
C-PORT
COLDFIRE
DRAGONBALL
FREESCALE
MOBILEGT
POWERPC
POWERQUICC
PRO LOGIC
SURROUND
ZIGBEE
Advertising Agency:
Godfrey Q & Partners
100 California St 9th Fl
San Francisco, CA 94111
Tel.: (415) 217-2800
Fax: (415) 217-2898

FRONTIER COMMUNICATIONS OF NEW YORK, INC.
(Sub. of Frontier Communications Corporation)
180 S Clinton Ave Frontier Ctr
Rochester, NY 14646-0700
Tel.: (585) 777-1000
Fax: (716) 232-8154
Web Site: www.frontieronline.com
Sales Range: $1-4.9 Billion
Approx. Number Employees: 2,600
Year Founded: 1899
Business Description:
Telephone Communications
S.I.C.: 4813
N.A.I.C.S.: 517310
Media: 2-3-4-7-8-9-10-13-15-18-19-22-23-24-25-26
Distr.: Direct to Consumer; Reg.
Budget Set: Oct.
Personnel:
Mary Agnes Wilderotter *(Pres & CEO)*
Tom Grooms *(Reg Dir-Mktg)*
Jack Yovanovich *(Reg Dir-Mktg)*
Patricia Amendola *(Mgr-Comm)*
Stephanie Beasly *(Mgr-Comm)*
Stephanie Schifano *(Mgr-Local Mktg & Community Rels)*
Brands & Products:
THE WAY YOU WANT IT

Key to Media (For complete agency information see *The Advertising Red Books-Agencies* edition):
1. Bus. Publs. 2. Cable T.V. 3. Catalogs & Directories. 4. Co-op Adv. 5. Consumer Mags. 6. D.M. to Bus. Estab.7. D.M. to Consumers
8. Daily Newsp. 9. Exhibits/Trade Shows 10. Foreign 11. Infomercial 12. Internet Adv.13. Multimedia 14. Network Radio
15. Network T.V. 16. Newsp. Distr. Mags. 17. Other 18. Outdoor (Posters, Transit) 19. Point of Purchase20. Premiums, Novelties
21. Product Samples 22. Special Events Mktg. 23. Spot Radio 24. Spot T.V. 25. Weekly Newsp. 26. Yellow Page Adv.

Advertising Agency:
Dixon Schwabl Advertising
1595 Moseley Rd
Victor, NY 14564
Tel.: (585) 383-0380
Fax: (585) 383-1661

FRONTRANGE SOLUTIONS INC.
(Holding of Francisco Partners Management, LLC)
5675 Gibraltar Dr
Pleasanton, CA 94588
Tel.: (925) 404-1800
Fax: (925) 398-1305
Toll Free: (800) 776-7889
Web Site: www.frontrange.com
Approx. Number Employees: 650
Year Founded: 2000
Business Description:
Sales, Marketing & Customer Support Software & Services
S.I.C.: 7372
N.A.I.C.S.: 511210
Media: 2
Personnel:
Michael J. McCloskey *(CEO)*
Greg Higham *(CIO & VP)*
Franklin P. Huang *(Gen Counsel & VP)*
Steve Baker *(VP-Fin & Admin)*
David R. Smith *(VP-Sls)*
Advertising Agency:
Horn Group Inc.
612 Howard St Ste 100
San Francisco, CA 94105
Tel.: (415) 905-4000
Fax: (415) 905-4001

FUJITSU COMPUTER PRODUCTS OF AMERICA, INC.
(Sub. of Fujitsu America, Inc.)
1255 E Arques Ave
Sunnyvale, CA 94085-4701
Tel.: (408) 746-7000
Fax: (408) 746-6910
Toll Free: (800) 626-4686
E-mail: info@fcpa.fujitsu.com
Web Site: www.fcpa.fujitsu.com
Approx. Number Employees: 350
Year Founded: 1991
Business Description:
Scanners, Magneto-Optical Drives, Ethernet Switches, Biometric Devices, Degaussers Mfr
S.I.C.: 5045; 3577
N.A.I.C.S.: 423430; 334119
Media: 4-5-6-10-13
Distr.: Natl.; Quality Resellers
Personnel:
Etsuro Sato *(Pres & CEO)*
Victor Kan *(COO & Exec VP)*
Lorne Wilson *(Sr VP)*
Ron Polluconi *(VP-Post Sls Engrng & Opers)*
Scott Francis *(Sr Dir-Product Mktg)*
Brands & Products:
DYNAMO
MHT-AH
MHT-AT
SCANPARTNER 15C
SCANPARTNER 620C
SCANPARTNER FI 4120C
SCANPARTNER FI 4220C
Advertising Agencies:
Rabuck Stranger
3221 Hutchison Ave Ste H
Los Angeles, CA 90034-3299
Tel.: (310) 815-8225
Fax: (310) 815-0770

Round2/SF
101 Second St Ste 1250
San Francisco, CA 94105
Tel.: (415) 442-0680
Fax: (415) 618-0053

FUJITSU COMPUTER SYSTEMS CORPORATION
(Sub. of Fujitsu Limited)
1250 E Arques Ave
Sunnyvale, CA 94088-3470
Tel.: (408) 746-6000
Fax: (408) 737-5999
Toll Free: (800) 831-3183
Telex: 3716812
E-mail: computers@us.fujitsu.com
Sales Range: $125-149.9 Million
Approx. Number Employees: 1,100
Year Founded: 1970
Business Description:
Computer Sales & Service
S.I.C.: 7379
N.A.I.C.S.: 541519
Import Export
Media: 1-2-4-7-10-11-13-20-26
Distr.: Intl.; Natl.
Budget Set: Mar.
Personnel:
Ari Hovsepyan *(CFO & Sr VP)*
Bipin Badani *(CIO & Sr VP)*
William King *(Exec VP-US Bus)*
Ryosuke Mori *(Exec VP-Japanese Bus Dev, Fujitsu America)*
Dave Egan *(Sr VP-Storage)*
Don Klenner *(Sr VP-Field Engrg & Support)*
Richard McCormack *(Sr VP-Mktg)*
Gloria Veon *(Sr VP-HR)*
Kevin Wrenn *(Sr VP-PC Bus & Ops)*
Al Zmyslowski *(Sr VP-Engrg)*
Paul Moore *(Sr Dir-Mobile Product Mktg)*
Advertising Agencies:
Catapult Direct
1700 Winchester Blvd
Campbell, CA 95008
Tel.: (408) 369-8111

Eastwick Communications
2700 Garcia Ave Ste 200
Mountain View, CA 94063
Tel.: (650) 480-4040
Fax: (650) 396-4430
Toll Free: (877) 314-0873

Just Media, Inc.
2550 Ninth St Ste 101
Berkeley, CA 94710
Tel.: (510) 540-5757
Fax: (510) 540-5353

FUJITSU CONSULTING
(Sub. of Fujitsu Computer Systems Corporation)
1000 Sherbrooke St W Ste 1400
Montreal, QC H3A 3R2, Canada
Tel.: (514) 877-3301
Fax: (514) 877-3351
Web Site: www.dmr.ca
Sales Range: $200-249.9 Million
Approx. Number Employees: 200
Year Founded: 1973
Business Description:
Information Management & Technology
S.I.C.: 7373
N.A.I.C.S.: 541512
Media: 2
Personnel:
Andre Pouliot *(Pres & CEO)*

FUTURELOGIC, INC.
425 E Colorado St Ste 100
Glendale, CA 91205
Tel.: (818) 244-4700
Fax: (818) 244-4764
E-mail: info@futurelogic-inc.com
Web Site: www.futurelogic-inc.com
Approx. Number Employees: 98
Business Description:
Standard & Customized Printer Solutions
S.I.C.: 2759
N.A.I.C.S.: 323119
Personnel:
Mark Meyerhofer *(Founder & Co-CTO)*
Eric Meyerhofer *(CEO & CTO)*
John Huntley *(CFO)*
John Edmunds *(VP-Sls-Intl)*
Nick Micalizzi *(VP-Domestic Sls & Mktg)*
Corralee Clark *(Sr Dir-Ops)*
Emilio Machado *(Mgr-Bus Dev-South America)*
Advertising Agency:
WelComm, Inc.
7975 Raytheon Rd Ste 340
San Diego, CA 92111-1622
Tel.: (858) 279-2100
Fax: (858) 279-5400
Toll Free: (888) WELCOMM
— Mat Naraghi *(Pres)*

FUTURESTEP
(Sub. of Korn/Ferry International)
1900 Ave Of The Stars Ste 2600
Los Angeles, CA 90067
Tel.: (713) 285-2500
Fax: (310) 553-6452
E-mail: info@futurestep.com
Web Site: www.futurestep.com
Sales Range: $100-124.9 Million
Year Founded: 1998
Business Description:
Executive Recruitment Services
S.I.C.: 7361
N.A.I.C.S.: 541612
Media: 13
Personnel:
Byrne Mulrooney *(CEO)*
Andrew Watt *(COO)*
Michael Di Stefano *(CMO)*
William Sebra *(Pres-North America)*
Kelly Cartwright *(VP & Gen Mgr-The Newman Grp)*
Jeanne MacDonald *(VP & Gen Mgr-Recruitment Process Outsourcing-US)*
Marisa Kacary *(Global VP-Mktg)*
Masao Sasaki *(VP-Fin)*
Dave Marzo *(Gen Mgr-Consulting Solutions-North America)*
Tanya Bennett *(Leader-Global Ops)*

G4S SECURE SOLUTIONS USA
(Formerly The Wackenhut Corporation)
(Sub. of G4S PLC)
1395 University Dr
Jupiter, FL 33458
Tel.: (561) 622-5656
Fax: (561) 691-6423
Approx. Number Employees: 400
Year Founded: 1954
Business Description:
Security Services Including Armed Guards, Background Investigations, Security Consulting & Program Development, Fire & Rescue Services & Specialized Security for Airports, Nuclear Power Plants & US Embassies
S.I.C.: 7381; 7382; 7389
N.A.I.C.S.: 561612; 561621; 561990
Media: 2-9-10-24-25-26
Distr.: Intl.; Natl.
Budget Set: Dec.
Personnel:
Susanne Jorgensen *(CFO)*
Drew Levine *(Pres-Security Svcs)*
Julie Payne *(Gen Counsel & Sr VP)*
Ian Green *(VP-Taxes)*
Dean Saunders *(Dir-Pur)*
Suzanne McKeon *(Mgr-Creative Svcs)*

THE GALLUP ORGANIZATION
The Gallup Bldg 901 F St NW
Washington, DC 20004
Tel.: (202) 715-3030
Fax: (202) 715-3041
Toll Free: (877) 242-5587
E-mail: sarah_van_allen@gallup.com
Web Site: www.gallup.com
Approx. Number Employees: 2,000
Year Founded: 1935
Business Description:
Marketing Research, Public Opinion Polling & Management Consulting Services
S.I.C.: 8732; 8742; 8748
N.A.I.C.S.: 541910; 541613; 541618
Media: 2-7-8-13-22
Personnel:
James K. Clifton *(Chm & CEO)*
James R. Krieger *(Vice Chm & CFO)*
Jane E. Miller *(COO & Exec VP)*
Jennifer Forsman *(VP-Sls)*

GAMESTOP CORP.
625 Westport Pkwy
Grapevine, TX 76051
Tel.: (817) 424-2000
Fax: (817) 424-2002
E-mail: investorrelations@gamestop.com
Web Site: www.gamestop.com
Approx. Sls.: $9,473,700,000
Approx. Number Employees: 17,000
Year Founded: 1983
Business Description:
Consumer Software & Video Game Entertainment Retailer
S.I.C.: 5734; 5945; 5961
N.A.I.C.S.: 443120; 451120; 454113
Advertising Expenditures: $83,700,000
Personnel:
Daniel A. DeMatteo *(Chm)*
Tony D. Bartel *(Pres)*
Julian Paul Raines *(CEO)*
Robert A. Lloyd *(CFO)*
Troy W. Crawford *(Chief Acctg Officer & Sr VP)*
David W. Carlson *(Exec VP-Fin & Asst Sec)*
Michael K. Mauler *(Exec VP-GameStop Intl)*
Bruce Kulp *(Sr VP-Supply Chain & Refurbishment)*

Key to Media (For complete agency information see *The Advertising Red Books-Agencies* edition):
1. Bus. Publs. 2. Cable T.V. 3. Catalogs & Directories. 4. Co-op Adv. 5. Consumer Mags. 6. D.M. to Bus. Estab.7. D.M. to Consumers
8. Daily Newsp. 9. Exhibits/Trade Shows 10. Foreign 11. Infomercial 12. Internet Adv.13. Multimedia 14. Network Radio
15. Network T.V. 16. Newsp. Distr. Mags. 17. Other 18. Outdoor (Posters, Transit) 19. Point of Purchase20. Premiums, Novelties
21. Product Samples 22. Special Events Mktg. 23. Spot Radio 24. Spot T.V. 25. Weekly Newsp. 26. Yellow Page Adv.

GameStop Corp. — (Continued)

Chris Petrovic *(Gen Mgr-Digital Ventures)*
Michelle Hagen *(Dir-Digital Mktg)*

Brands & Products:
EB GAMES
ELECTRONICS BOUTIQUE
FUNCOLAND
GAME INFORMER
GAMESTOP
POWER TO THE PLAYERS

Advertising Agencies:
The Marketing Arm
1999 Bryan St Ste 1800
Dallas, TX 75201-3125
Tel.: (214) 259-3200
Fax: (214) 259-3201
Promotional Agency of Record

The Richards Group, Inc.
8750 N Central Expy Ste 100
Dallas, TX 75231-6430
Tel.: (214) 891-5700
Fax: (214) 265-2933

GATEWAY, INC.
(Sub. of Acer Incorporated)
7565 Irvine Center Dr
Irvine, CA 92618
Tel.: (949) 471-7000
Fax: (949) 471-7041
Web Site: www.gateway.com
Approx. Sls.: $3,980,803,000
Approx. Number Employees: 1,645
Year Founded: 1985
Business Description:
Personal Computer Products Mfr
S.I.C.: 3571
N.A.I.C.S.: 334111
Import Export
Advertising Expenditures: $41,000,000
Media: 1-2-3-5-6-7-8-10-11-13-14-15-18-22-23-24
Personnel:
Kim Phipps *(Dir-Mktg)*
Bryan Sherlock *(Mgr-Adv)*
Brands & Products:
1-800-GATEWAY
A BETTER WAY
CONTINUING SENSING TECHNOLOGY
EMACHINES
GATEWAY
GATEWAY AUTHORIZED RESELLER
GATEWAY BUSINESS SOLUTION
GATEWAY EASYPAY
GATEWAY GOBACK
GATEWAY GOLD
GATEWAY GUIDE
GATEWAY PLATINUM
GATEWAY PROFILE
GATEWAY SELECT
GATEWAY.COM
GATEWAY.NET
LEARN WITH GATEWAY
YOU'VE GOT A FRIEND IN THE BUSINESS
Advertising Agency:
Acxiom Digital
1051 Hillsdale Blvd Ste 400
Foster City, CA 94404
Tel.: (650) 356-3400
Fax: (650) 356-3410
E-Mail Marketing

GDT TEK, INC.
(Formerly Seamless Corporation)
555 Winderely Pl Ste 300
Orlando, FL 32751
Tel.: (407) 574-4740
E-mail: info@gdttek.com
Web Site: www.gdttek.com/
Sales Range: Less than $1 Million
Approx. Number Employees: 2
Business Description:
Mobile Hardware & Software Products
S.I.C.: 4812; 7372; 7373
N.A.I.C.S.: 517212; 511210; 541512
Advertising Expenditures: $155,135
Media: 17
Personnel:
Albert Reda *(CEO)*

GE ENERGY
(Sub. of GE Energy)
1990 W NASA Blvd
Melbourne, FL 32904-2309
Tel.: (321) 435-5100
Web Site: www.gepower.com
Sales Range: $50-74.9 Million
Approx. Number Employees: 250
Year Founded: 1997
Business Description:
Energy Management Systems
S.I.C.: 7374
N.A.I.C.S.: 518210
Export
Advertising Expenditures: $400,000
Media: 2-4-10
Distr.: Intl.; Natl.
Budget Set: Oct.
Personnel:
Martin Liptrot *(Head-Comm)*
Ram Shetty *(Mgr-Mktg)*

GE FANUC EMBEDDED SYSTEMS
(Sub. of GE Fanuc Automation, Inc.)
7401 Snaproll NE
Albuquerque, NM 87109
Tel.: (505) 875-0600
Fax: (505) 798-1400
Toll Free: (800) 727-1553
E-mail: info.embeddedsystems@gefanuc.com
Web Site:
www.gefanucembedded.com
Sales Range: $150-199.9 Million
Approx. Number Employees: 900
Year Founded: 1986
Business Description:
Embedded Computing & Networking Components Mfr
S.I.C.: 3571; 3577; 3679
N.A.I.C.S.: 334111; 334119; 334419
Media: 10-17
Personnel:
Rubin Dhillon *(Mgr-Comm Products)*

GE HEALTHCARE
(Sub. of GE Healthcare Technologies)
40 IDX Dr
Burlington, VT 05402
Mailing Address:
PO Box 1070
Burlington, VT 05402-1070
Tel.: (802) 862-1022
Fax: (802) 859-6025
Web Site: www.gehealthcare.com
Sales Range: $500-549.9 Million
Approx. Number Employees: 2,409
Year Founded: 1969
Business Description:
Healthcare Information Systems
S.I.C.: 7389
N.A.I.C.S.: 519190
Media: 2-7-10
Personnel:
Vishal Wanchoo *(Pres & CEO)*
Jean-Michel Cossery *(VP & CMO)*
Kieran Murphy *(Pres/CEO-Life Sciences)*
Thomas G. Horton *(Sr VP)*
Michael J. Simpson *(Sr VP & Gen Mgr)*
John A. Kane *(Sr VP-Fin & Admin)*
Christopher Powell *(VP, Gen Mgr-Sls-HCIT Americas)*
Patricia Kondor *(Controller)*
Brian McKaig *(Mgr-Media Rels)*
Brands & Products:
CARECAST
EDIX
FLOWCAST
GROUPCAST
IDX
IMAGECAST
MAKING A DIFFERENCE IN HEALTHCARE

GEARWORKS, INC.
(Sub. of Xora, Inc.)
2770 Blue Water Rd Ste 400
Eagan, MN 55121-1500
Tel.: (651) 209-0350
Fax: (651) 209-0351
Toll Free: (800) 735-3457
E-mail: info@gearworks.com
Web Site: www.gearworks.com
E-Mail For Key Personnel:
Marketing Director: Doug@gearworks.com
Approx. Number Employees: 40
Year Founded: 1999
Business Description:
Mobile Telecommunications & Wireless Software Application Development
S.I.C.: 3625
N.A.I.C.S.: 335314
Media: 10
Personnel:
Steve Synder *(CFO)*
Brands & Products:
APPMOSPHERE
ETRACE
GEARWORKS
OPENAIRMARKET
SOLARSYSTEM

GEEK SQUAD
(Sub. of Best Buy Stores L.P.)
7601 Penn Ave
Richfield, MN 55423
Tel.: (612) 291-1000
Fax: (612) 292-2195
E-mail: danffahey@geeksquad.com
Web Site: www.geeksquad.com
Sales Range: $650-699.9 Million
Approx. Number Employees: 6,000
Business Description:
Computer Support Services
S.I.C.: 7379
N.A.I.C.S.: 541519
Advertising Expenditures: $40,000,000
Media: 18-24
Personnel:
Richard Schultz *(Founder)*
Daniel Reiter *(Mgr-Customer Experience)*
Advertising Agencies:
CP+B
3390 Mary St Ste 300
Coconut Grove, FL 33133
Tel.: (305) 859-2070
Fax: (305) 854-3419

Organic, Inc.
555 Market St 4th Fl
San Francisco, CA 94105
Tel.: (415) 581-5300
Fax: (415) 581-5400

GEEKS ON CALL HOLDINGS, INC.
814 Kempsville Rd Ste 106
Norfolk, VA 23502
Tel.: (757) 466-3448
Fax: (757) 466-3457
Toll Free: (800) 905-GEEK
E-mail: info@geeksoncall.com
Web Site: www.geeksoncall.com
Sales Range: $1-9.9 Million
Approx. Number Employees: 55
Business Description:
Computer Services & Solutions
S.I.C.: 7379
N.A.I.C.S.: 541519
Advertising Expenditures: $3,299,944
Media: 5-8-13-17-18-26
Personnel:
Richard T. Cole *(Owner)*
Brands & Products:
1-800-905-GEEK
GEEKS ON CALL

GEM SOLUTIONS, INC.
870 111th Ave N Ste 8
Naples, FL 34108
Tel.: (239) 592-1816
Fax: (239) 592-0941
Toll Free: (866) 700-7557
E-mail: sales@gem-si.com
Web Site: www.gem-si.com
E-Mail For Key Personnel:
Sales Director: sales@gem-si.com
Sales Range: Less than $1 Million
Approx. Number Employees: 30
Business Description:
E-Mail Migration Services
S.I.C.: 7379
N.A.I.C.S.: 541519
Advertising Expenditures: $223,439
Personnel:
John E. Baker *(Owner)*
Brands & Products:
GEM

GEMCOM SOFTWARE INTERNATIONAL INC.
(Joint Venture of Carlyle Holding Corporation, JMI Services, Inc. & Pala Investments AG)
1066 W Hastings St Ste 1100
Vancouver, BC V6E 3X1, Canada
Tel.: (604) 684-6550
Fax: (604) 684-3541
Toll Free: (866) 560-5846
E-mail: info@gemcomsoftware.com
Web Site: www.gemcomsoftware.com
Approx. Rev.: $34,147,807
Approx. Number Employees: 121
Year Founded: 1985
Business Description:
Mining & Mineral Exploration Industry Software Publisher; Owned by JMI Services, Inc., by Carlyle Holding Corporation & by Pala Invesments AG

Key to Media (For complete agency information see *The Advertising Red Books-Agencies* edition):
1. Bus. Publs. 2. Cable T.V. 3. Catalogs & Directories. 4. Co-op Adv. 5. Consumer Mags. 6. D.M. to Bus. Estab.7. D.M. to Consumers 8. Daily Newsp. 9. Exhibits/Trade Shows 10. Foreign 11. Infomercial 12. Internet Adv.13. Multimedia 14. Network Radio 15. Network T.V. 16. Newsp. Distr. Mags. 17. Other 18. Outdoor (Posters, Transit) 19. Point of Purchase20. Premiums, Novelties 21. Product Samples 22. Special Events Mktg. 23. Spot Radio 24. Spot T.V. 25. Weekly Newsp. 26. Yellow Page Adv.

S.I.C.: 7372; 7371
N.A.I.C.S.: 511210; 541511
Media: 2-6-7-10
Personnel:
Richard Moignard *(Pres & CEO)*
Eric Palmer *(CFO)*
Julian A. Diering *(VP-Advance Tech)*
Robert W. Selzler *(VP-Mktg)*
John Vandermay *(VP-Product Dev)*
Charlie Forrest *(Product Mgr-InSite)*
Brands & Products:
GEMS
INSITE
MINESCHED
MINEX
PCBC
SURPAC
WHITTLE

GEMSTONE SYSTEMS, INC.
(Sub. of SpringSource Global, Inc.)
1260 NW Waterhouse Ave Ste 200
Beaverton, OR 97006-5794
Tel.: (503) 533-3000
Fax: (503) 533-3230
Toll Free: (800) 243-4772
E-mail: info@gemstone.com
Web Site: www.gemstone.com
Approx. Number Employees: 55
Year Founded: 1982
Business Description:
Java-Based Applications & Server Software for E-Commerce
S.I.C.: 7372
N.A.I.C.S.: 511210
Media: 10
Personnel:
Richard Lamb *(Pres)*
Dan Ware *(Exec VP-Worldwide Sls)*
Juan Menendez *(Sr VP-Bus Dev & Alliances)*
Makarand Gokhale *(Gen Mgr-Engrg & Tech Delivery)*
Brands & Products:
GEMBUILDER
GEMCONNECT
GEMFIRE
GEMFIRE ENTERPRISE
GEMFIRE REAL-TIME EVENTS
GEMSTONE
GEMSTONE FACETS
GEMSTONE/S

GENERAL DATACOMM INDUSTRIES, INC.
6 Rubber Ave
Naugatuck, CT 06770-4117
Tel.: (203) 729-0271
Fax: (203) 723-2883
Telex: 643357
E-mail: webmaster@gdc.com
Web Site: www.gdc.com
Approx. Rev.: $8,700,000
Approx. Number Employees: 61
Year Founded: 1969
Business Description:
Network Access Equipment Designer, Developer & Mfr
S.I.C.: 3661; 7629
N.A.I.C.S.: 334210; 811211
Import Export
Advertising Expenditures: $60,000
Media: 2
Distr.: Intl.
Budget Set: Sept.
Personnel:
Howard S. Modlin *(Chm, Pres, CEO & Sec)*
William G. Henry *(CFO & VP)*
Frank Giannone *(Dir-Mktg Comm)*
Brands & Products:
THE BEST CONNECTION IN THE BUSINESS
GDC
GENERAL DATACOMM
INNOVX
METROPLEX
TEAM

GENERAL EMPLOYMENT ENTERPRISES, INC.
(Holding of PSQ, LLC)
1 Tower Ln Ste 2200
Oakbrook Terrace, IL 60181
Tel.: (630) 954-0400
Fax: (630) 954-0447
E-mail: invest@genp.com
Web Site: www.generalemployment.com
Approx. Rev.: $11,917,000
Approx. Number Employees: 68
Year Founded: 1893
Business Description:
Regular, Full-Time & Contract Staffing Services, Specializing in Information Technology, Placement Engineering & Accounting
S.I.C.: 7361; 7363
N.A.I.C.S.: 561310; 561320
Advertising Expenditures: $370,000
Media: 7-8-9-13-25
Personnel:
Salvatore J. Zizza *(CEO)*
James R. Harlan *(CFO)*
Brands & Products:
BUSINESS MANAGEMENT PERSONNEL
GENERAL EMPLOYMENT
GENERAL EMPLOYMENT ENTERPRISES
GENERATION TECHNOLOGIES, INC.
OMNI ONE
TRIAD PERSONNEL SERVICES
WE DON'T MAKE PROMISES, WE DELIVER RESULTS

GENERAL PENCIL CO.
(Sub. of General Pencil Company)
3168 Bay Rd
Redwood City, CA 94063-0311
Tel.: (650) 369-4889
Fax: (650) 369-7169
E-mail: info@generalpencil.com
Web Site: www.generalpencil.com
Approx. Number Employees: 20
Year Founded: 1889
Business Description:
Mfr. of Lead Pencils
S.I.C.: 4225; 5112
N.A.I.C.S.: 493110; 424120
Media: 6-7-8-10-19-20-21
Distr.: Natl.
Personnel:
Kate Weissenborn *(Dir-Mktg)*
Brands & Products:
GENERAL

GENESIS WORLDWIDE INC.
125 Traders Boulevard East, Unit 2
Mississauga, ON L5N 6S2, Canada
Tel.: (905) 285-9909
Fax: (090) 528-59931
E-mail: investors@genesisworldwide.com
Web Site: www.genesisworldwide.com
Approx. Rev.: $12,616,914
Approx. Number Employees: 68
Business Description:
Structural Building Software & Technology Applications
S.I.C.: 7373
N.A.I.C.S.: 541512
Media: 7-10-13
Personnel:
Richard Pope *(Chm, Pres, CEO & Sec)*
William Lindgren *(CFO)*
Michael Tancredi *(VP-Engrg, R & D)*

GENSYM CORPORATION
(Sub. of Versata Enterprises Inc.)
52 26011 West Courtyard Drive
Austin, TX 78730
Tel.: (512) 377-9700
Fax: (512) 874-8900
E-mail: info@gensym.com
Web Site: www.gensym.com
Approx. Rev.: $16,935,000
Approx. Number Employees: 65
Year Founded: 1986
Business Description:
E-Infrastructure Software Products
S.I.C.: 7372; 7371
N.A.I.C.S.: 334611; 511210; 541511
Export
Media: 2-7-10-13
Personnel:
Stephen D. Allison *(CFO)*
Brands & Products:
E-SCOR
G2
G2 E-SCOR
G2 INTEGRITY
G2 NEURON-LINE
G2 OPTEGRITY
G2 RETHINK
INTEGRITY
NEURON-LINE
OPTEGRITY
RETHINK

GEORGE LITTLE MANAGEMENT, LLC
(Sub. of DMG World Media (Canada) Inc.)
1133 Westchester Ave Ste N136
White Plains, NY 10604
Tel.: (914) 421-3200
Fax: (914) 948-6180
Toll Free: (800) 272-SHOW
E-mail: info@glmshows.com
Web Site: www.glmshows.com
E-Mail For Key Personnel:
President: jeff_little@glmshows.com
Marketing Director: alan_steel@glmshows.com
Sales Director: phil_robinson@glmshows.com
Approx. Number Employees: 100
Year Founded: 1924
Business Description:
Trade Shows & Conference Management Producers
S.I.C.: 7389
N.A.I.C.S.: 561920
Advertising Expenditures: $750,000
Media: 2-4-7-10-13
Distr.: Natl.
Personnel:
Mike Cooke *(Chm, CEO-DMG & Pres-B2R)*
Alan Steel *(Exec VP)*
Dorothy Belshaw *(Sr VP)*
Richard Pasternak *(Sr VP)*
Phil D. Robinson *(Sr VP)*
Advertising Agency:
Eric Mower and Associates
211 West Jefferson St.
Syracuse, NY 13202
Tel.: (315) 466-1000
Fax: (315) 466-2000

GEORGE S. MAY INTERNATIONAL COMPANY
303 S NW Hwy
Park Ridge, IL 60068-4232
Tel.: (847) 825-8806
Fax: (847) 825-7937
Toll Free: (800) 999-3020
E-mail: info@georgesmay.com
Web Site: www.georgesmay.com
Approx. Number Employees: 1,200
Year Founded: 1925
Business Description:
Management Consultant Services
S.I.C.: 8742
N.A.I.C.S.: 541611
Advertising Expenditures: $550,000
Media: 1-2-4-7-10-20-22-26
Distr.: Intl.; Natl.
Budget Set: Jan.
Personnel:
Israel Kushnir *(Pres)*
Paul Rauseo *(Mng Dir)*
Israel Kufhnir *(CFO)*
Thomas Vestal *(Dir-Client Rels)*
Donna V. Werner *(Dir-Corp Commun)*
Advertising Agency:
Cushman/Amberg Communications
1 E Wacker Dr Ste 3750
Chicago, IL 60601-7478
Tel.: (312) 263-2500
Fax: (312) 263-1197

GERSTEN SAVAGE LLP
600 Lexington Ave
New York, NY 10022
Tel.: (212) 752-9700
Fax: (212) 980-5192
Web Site: www.gerstensavage.com
Approx. Number Employees: 30
Personnel:
J. Kapoowitz *(Partner)*
Advertising Agency:
Rubenstein Public Relations
1345 Ave of the Americas
New York, NY 10105
Tel.: (212) 843-8000
Fax: (212) 843-9200

GFI BUSINESS SOLUTIONS INC.
(Sub. of GFI Informatique S.A.)
75 Queen Street
Montreal, QC H3C 2M6, Canada
Tel.: (514) 288-7161
Fax: (514) 843-4095
E-mail: info@gfisolutions.com
Web Site: www.gfisolutions.com
Sales Range: $25-49.9 Million
Approx. Number Employees: 1,000
Year Founded: 1977
Business Description:
Integrated Enterprise Resource Planning Software Mfr
S.I.C.: 7372
N.A.I.C.S.: 334611
Media: 2-7-10

Key to Media (For complete agency information see *The Advertising Red Books-Agencies* edition):
1. Bus. Publs. 2. Cable T.V. 3. Catalogs & Directories. 4. Co-op Adv. 5. Consumer Mags. 6. D.M. to Bus. Estab.7. D.M. to Consumers
8. Daily Newsp. 9. Exhibits/Trade Shows 10. Foreign 11. Infomercial 12. Internet Adv.13. Multimedia 14. Network Radio
15. Network T.V. 16. Newsp. Distr. Mags. 17. Other 18. Outdoor (Posters, Transit) 19. Point of Purchase20. Premiums, Novelties
21. Product Samples 22. Special Events Mktg. 23. Spot Radio 24. Spot T.V. 25. Weekly Newsp. 26. Yellow Page Adv.

GIGAFAST INC.
2033 Gateway Pl Ste 500
San Jose, CA 95110
Tel.: (408) 392-2333
Fax: (909) 992-3026
E-mail: gfeusa@gigafast.com
Web Site: www.gigafast.com
Approx. Sls.: $4,000,000
Approx. Number Employees: 25
Year Founded: 1997
Business Description:
Mfr. of Networking Products
S.I.C.: 3572
N.A.I.C.S.: 334112
Media: 6

GIGOPTIX, INC.
2300 Geng Rd Ste 250
Palo Alto, CA 94303
Tel.: (650) 424-1937
Fax: (650) 424-1938
E-mail: pr@gigoptix.com
Web Site: www.gigoptix.com
E-Mail For Key Personnel:
Sales Director: sales@gigoptix.com
Approx. Rev.: $26,876,000
Approx. Number Employees: 83
Year Founded: 2007
Business Description:
Semiconductor & High-Speed Circuits Designer & Mfr
S.I.C.: 3674; 3679
N.A.I.C.S.: 334413; 334418
Advertising Expenditures: $30,000
Media: 17
Personnel:
Andrea Betti Berutto *(Founder & CTO)*
Avishay S. Katz *(Chm, Pres & CEO)*
Jeff Parsons *(CFO-Acting)*
Julie Tipton *(Sr VP-Ops)*
Raluca Dinu *(VP & Gen Mgr-Lx Product Line)*
Jorg Wieland *(VP & Gen Mgr-HX Product Line)*
Parker Martineau *(Mgr-Corp Comm)*
Advertising Agency:
S&S Public Relations, Inc.
2700 Patriot Blvd
Glenview, IL 60026-8021
Tel.: (847) 955-0700
Fax: (847) 955-7720
Toll Free: (800) 287-2279
Global Public Relations Agency of Record

GLASSHOUSE TECHNOLOGIES, INC.
200 Crossing Blvd
Framingham, MA 01702
Tel.: (508) 879-5729
Fax: (508) 879-7319
E-mail: info@glasshouse.com
Web Site: www.glasshouse.com
E-Mail For Key Personnel:
Sales Director: sales@glasshouse.com
Public Relations: pr@glasshouse.com
Sales Range: $75-99.9 Million
Approx. Number Employees: 501
Business Description:
Information Technology Infrastructure Consulting Services
S.I.C.: 7373; 7371; 8748
N.A.I.C.S.: 541512; 541511; 541690
Media: 1-2-10-11
Personnel:
Mark Shirman *(Chm, Pres & CEO)*
Kenneth Hale *(CFO)*
Andrew Norman *(COO)*
Richard Scannell *(Sr VP)*
Debralee Donovan *(Mgr-Mktg Events)*
Advertising Agency:
Racepoint Group, Inc.
404 Wyman St Ste 375
Waltham, MA 02451
Tel.: (781) 487-4600
Fax: (781) 890-5822

GLOBAL 360, INC.
5400 LBJ Freeway 3rd Fl Ste 300
Dallas, TX 75240
Tel.: (214) 520-1660
Fax: (214) 219-0476
Toll Free: (877) 825-8259
E-mail: information@global360.com
Web Site: www.global360.com
Approx. Number Employees: 340
Year Founded: 2000
Business Description:
Business Process Management & Analysis Solutions
S.I.C.: 8742
N.A.I.C.S.: 541611
Media: 10-13
Personnel:
David Mitchell *(Pres & CEO)*
George H. Ellis *(CFO)*
Steve R. Russell *(CTO & Sr VP-R & D)*
Patricia McArdle *(Gen Counsel & VP)*
Lucy Norris *(Sr VP-Customer Care-Worldwide)*
Robert Shapiro *(Sr VP-Res)*
Craig Hopkins *(VP-IT)*
Brands & Products:
ANALYSTVIEW
CASE360
EISTREAM
EMVISION360
EXECUTE360
FILE360
GLOBAL 360 IMAGING FOR WINDOWS
GLOBAL 360 SCAN MANAGER
GLOBAL360
INSIGHT360
KEYFILE
KEYFLOW
MANAGERVIEW
PROCESS360
VIEWPOINT
VIEWSTAR

GLOBAL EMPLOYMENT HOLDINGS, INC.
10375 Park Meadows Dr Ste 375
Lone Tree, CO 80124
Tel.: (303) 216-9500
Fax: (303) 216-9533
E-mail: contactus@gesnetwork.com
Web Site: www.gesnetwork.com
Approx. Rev.: $168,476,000
Approx. Number Employees: 15,000
Year Founded: 1998
Business Description:
Staffing, Executive Search & Human Resource Consulting Services
S.I.C.: 7363; 7361
N.A.I.C.S.: 561320; 541612
Advertising Expenditures: $755,000
Personnel:
Howard Brill *(Pres & CEO-Global Employment Solutions)*

GLOBAL EPOINT INC.
339 S Cheryl Ln
City of Industry, CA 91789
Tel.: (909) 869-1688
Fax: (909) 598-2936
E-mail: info@globalepoint.com
Web Site: www.globalepoint.com
Sales Range: $25-49.9 Million
Approx. Number Employees: 91
Business Description:
Computers, Computing Solutions & Digital Video Products
S.I.C.: 3699; 5045; 7699
N.A.I.C.S.: 335999; 423430; 811310
Advertising Expenditures: $222,000
Media: 7-10-13
Personnel:
John Pan *(Chm, Pres, Sec & CFO)*
Toresa Lou *(CEO)*

GLOBAL IMAGING SYSTEMS, INC.
(Sub. of Xerox Corporation)
3820 Northdale Blvd Ste 200A
Tampa, FL 33624-1856
Mailing Address:
PO Box 273478
Tampa, FL 33688-3478
Tel.: (813) 960-5508
Fax: (813) 264-7877
Toll Free: (888) 628-7834
E-mail: gisx@mindspring.com
Web Site: www.global-imaging.com
Approx. Rev.: $1,030,584,000
Approx. Number Employees: 4,230
Year Founded: 1994
Business Description:
Office Imaging Solutions
S.I.C.: 5044; 5045
N.A.I.C.S.: 423420; 423430
Advertising Expenditures: $1,795,000
Media: 5
Personnel:
Michael E. Shea, Jr. *(CEO)*
Ed Bass *(CFO & Sr VP)*
Lawrence Paine *(Gen Counsel, Sec & Sr VP)*
Dan Cooper *(Exec VP-Field Ops)*
Tom Salierno, Jr. *(Exec VP-Corp Ops)*
Peter Shoemaker *(Exec VP-Strategy & Ops)*
Dan Brady *(Sr VP-Field Ops)*
Dick Peterson *(Sr VP-Field Ops)*
Bob Brooslin *(VP-HR)*

GLOBAL LEARNING SYSTEMS LLC
(Sub. of Bancroft Technology Group, Inc.)
5300 Westview Dr Ste 405
Frederick, MD 21703
Tel.: (301) 624-5590
Fax: (301) 624-1733
Toll Free: (800) 949-5590
E-mail: sales@globallearningsystems.com
Web Site: www.globallearningsystems.com
E-Mail For Key Personnel:
Sales Director: sales@globallearningsystems.com
Approx. Number Employees: 16
Year Founded: 1999
Business Description:
Information Technology, New Media & Internet Training for Corporations
S.I.C.: 8243
N.A.I.C.S.: 611420
Media: 10-13
Personnel:
Lawrence Cates *(Pres & CEO)*
Robert Kingyens *(COO & CTO)*

GLOBAL PAYMENT TECHNOLOGIES, INC.
170 Wilbur Pl
Bohemia, NY 11716
Tel.: (631) 563-2500
Fax: (631) 563-2630
Toll Free: (800) 472-2506
E-mail: customerservice@gptx.com
Web Site: www.gptworld.com
Sales Range: $10-24.9 Million
Approx. Number Employees: 30
Year Founded: 1988
Business Description:
Paper Currency Validators & Related Stackers Mfr & Retailer
S.I.C.: 3589; 3581
N.A.I.C.S.: 333319; 333311
Media: 2-5-10-13
Personnel:
Andrew Soussa *(CEO)*
Brands & Products:
ADVANTAGE
ARGUS
AURORA
FALCON
GPT
SA-4
Advertising Agency:
PR Financial Marketing LLC
6311 Indiangrass Ct
Katy, TX 77494
Tel.: (281) 394-2504

GLOBAL RESPONSE CORPORATION
777 S State Rd 7
Margate, FL 33068
Tel.: (954) 973-7300
Fax: (954) 969-2400
Toll Free: (800) 537-8000
E-mail: sales@globalresponse.com
Web Site: www.globalresponse.com
E-Mail For Key Personnel:
Sales Director: sales@globalresponse.com
Approx. Number Employees: 500
Year Founded: 1974
Business Description:
Customer Contact & Fulfillment Services
S.I.C.: 7389
N.A.I.C.S.: 561421
Media: 2-10
Personnel:
Herman Shooster *(Chm)*
Frank Shooster *(Exec Dir)*

GLOBAL TURNKEY SYSTEMS, INC.
2001 Rte 46
Parsippany, NJ 07054-1315
Tel.: (973) 331-1010
Fax: (973) 331-0042
Toll Free: (800) 221-1746
E-mail: sales@gtsystems.com
Web Site: www.gtsystems.com
E-Mail For Key Personnel:
Sales Director: sales@gtsystems.com
Approx. Number Employees: 50
Year Founded: 1969

Key to Media (For complete agency information see *The Advertising Red Books-Agencies* edition):
1. Bus. Publs. 2. Cable T.V. 3. Catalogs & Directories. 4. Co-op Adv. 5. Consumer Mags. 6. D.M. to Bus. Estab.7. D.M. to Consumers 8. Daily Newsp. 9. Exhibits/Trade Shows 10. Foreign 11. Infomercial 12. Internet Adv.13. Multimedia 14. Network Radio 15. Network T.V. 16. Newsp. Distr. Mags. 17. Other 18. Outdoor (Posters, Transit) 19. Point of Purchase20. Premiums, Novelties 21. Product Samples 22. Special Events Mktg. 23. Spot Radio 24. Spot T.V. 25. Weekly Newsp. 26. Yellow Page Adv.

Business Description:
Developer of Systems & Software for the Publishing Industry
S.I.C.: 7372; 5045
N.A.I.C.S.: 511210; 423430
Advertising Expenditures: $100,000
Media: 2-7-10-13-20
Distr.: Natl.
Budget Set: Sept.
Personnel:
Al Alteslane *(Pres & CEO)*
Brands & Products:
GLOBAL TURNKEY SYSTEMS
UNISON SYSTEM

GLOBAL WIRELESS DATA, LLC
1600 Oakbrook Dr Ste 580
Norcross, GA 30093-1855
Tel.: (770) 447-4990
Fax: (770) 447-1680
Web Site: www.wireless-data.com
Approx. Number Employees: 50
Year Founded: 1997
Business Description:
Reseller & Distributor of Wireless Data Communication Products
S.I.C.: 5065
N.A.I.C.S.: 423690
Personnel:
Thomas French *(CEO)*
Catherine Spornick *(COO)*
Doug Erbig *(Regl Sls Mgr)*
Jeff Hagadone *(Sls Mgr)*
Advertising Agency:
Calysto Communications
861 Sapphire Ln Sugar Hill
Atlanta, GA 30518
Tel.: (404) 266-2060
Fax: (404) 266-2041

GLOBALLOGIC, INC.
8605 Westwood Ctr Dr Ste 401
Vienna, VA 22182
Tel.: (703) 847-5900
Fax: (703) 847-5901
E-mail: info@globallogic.com
Web Site: www.globallogic.com
Sales Range: $25-49.9 Million
Approx. Number Employees: 3,000
Year Founded: 2006
Business Description:
Software Publishing & Development
S.I.C.: 7372
N.A.I.C.S.: 511210
Personnel:
Mike Daniels *(Chm)*
Shashank Samant *(Pres)*
Peter Harrison *(CEO)*
C. Wayne Grubbs *(CFO)*
Jim Dellamore *(COO)*
Johan Broekhuysen *(Sr VP & Controller)*
Andrew J. Nash *(Sr VP & Gen Mgr-Consumer & Enterprise Bus Unit)*
Boris Shnayder *(Sr VP & Gen Mgr-Telecom & Healthcare)*
Brands & Products:
GLOBALLOGIC
GLOBALLOGIC VELOCITY
Advertising Agency:
Atomic Public Relations
735 Market St 4th Fl
San Francisco, CA 94103
Tel.: (415) 402-0230
Fax: (415) 402-0237

GLOBALSCAPE INC.
4500 Lockhill-Selma Ste 150
San Antonio, TX 78249
Tel.: (210) 308-8267
Fax: (210) 308-8297
Toll Free: (800) 474-0116
Web Site: www.globalscape.com
Approx. Rev.: $18,565,000
Approx. Number Employees: 83
Year Founded: 1996
Business Description:
Secure File Management Software Developer
S.I.C.: 7372; 7371
N.A.I.C.S.: 511210; 334611; 541511
Advertising Expenditures: $624,000
Personnel:
Thomas W. Brown *(Chm)*
James R. Morris *(Pres & CEO)*
Mendy Marsh *(CFO)*
Craig A. Robinson *(COO)*
William Buie *(Exec VP-Sls & Mktg)*
Doug Conyers *(Sr VP-Engrg)*
Ellen Ohlenbusch *(VP-Mktg & Strategic Alliances)*
Brands & Products:
CUTEFTP HOME
CUTEFTP LITE
CUTEFTP MACPRO
CUTEFTP PRO
CUTEHTML
CUTEMX
CUTESITE
CUTESITE BUILDER
CUTEZIP
EFT SERVER
GLOBALSCAPE
GLOBALSCAPE CDP
GLOBALSCAPE EFT
GLOBALSCAPE SECURE FTP
GLOBALSCAPE WAFS
MAIL EXPRESS
PLAN AHEAD

GLOBALSTAR, INC.
300 Holiday Square Blvd
Covington, LA 70433
Tel.: (985) 335-1500
E-mail: pr.group@globalstar.com
Web Site: www.globalstar.com
Approx. Rev.: $67,941,000
Approx. Number Employees: 322
Year Founded: 1991
Business Description:
Voice & Data Communication Services
S.I.C.: 4812; 4813
N.A.I.C.S.: 517212; 517310
Import Export
Advertising Expenditures: $2,600,000
Personnel:
James Monroe, III *(Chm)*
Peter J. Dalton *(CEO)*
Dirk J. Wild *(CFO & Sr VP)*
Joseph F. Barnett *(Chief Acctg Officer & VP)*
Anthony J. Navarra *(Pres-Global Ops)*
Paul A. Monte *(VP-Engrg & Product Dev)*
Katie Schoeben *(Dir-Mktg Intl)*
Brands & Products:
GAC-1700
GBT-1700
GCK-1410
GDT-1700
GHB-1700
GIK-1700
GLOBALSTAR
GNC-1700
GNP-1700
GO FURTHER. DO MORE.
GPB-1700
GPDK-1410
GRC-1700
GSP-2900
GVC-1700

GLOWPOINT, INC.
430 Mountain Ave Ste 301
New Providence, NJ 07974
Tel.: (973) 855-3411
Fax: (973) 391-1901
Toll Free: (866) 456-9764
E-mail: info@glowpoint.com
Web Site: www.glowpoint.com
Approx. Rev.: $27,550,000
Approx. Number Employees: 109
Year Founded: 2000
Business Description:
Video Conferencing Services
S.I.C.: 4813
N.A.I.C.S.: 517310
Advertising Expenditures: $178,000
Media: 10
Personnel:
Joseph Laezza *(Pres & CEO)*
John R. McGovern *(CFO & Exec VP)*
Anil Balani *(Sr VP-Product & Strategy)*
Thomas Brown *(Sr VP-Sls)*
Shane Bouslough *(VP-Info Sys & Tech)*
Darren Podrabsky *(VP-Mktg)*
Tolga Sakman *(VP-Corp Dev & Strategy)*
Brands & Products:
ALL YOU CAN SEE AND SAY
CUSTOMERPOINT
EXPAND YOUR VISION
GLOWPOINT
GROW YOUR VINE
INSTANT VIDEO EVERYWHERE
PARTNERPOINT
QUICKBRIDGE
SCHEDULEPOINT
Advertising Agency:
Rocket Red
1700 Pacific Ave Ste 250
Dallas, TX 75201
Tel.: (972) 776-0022
Fax: (972) 776-0023
Agency of Record

GOMEZ, INC.
(Sub. of Compuware Corporation)
10 Maguire Rd Ste 330
Lexington, MA 02421-3110
Tel.: (781) 778-2700
Fax: (781) 778-2799
E-mail: answers@gomez.com
Web Site: www.gomez.com
Sales Range: $25-49.9 Million
Approx. Number Employees: 270
Year Founded: 1997
Business Description:
Internet Performance Management Solutions & Professional Services
S.I.C.: 7375; 7374
N.A.I.C.S.: 518111; 518210
Advertising Expenditures: $184,000
Media: 2-5-7-10-13-17-20
Personnel:
Richard M. Darer *(CFO, Treas & Sr VP)*
Edward F. Murray *(Sr VP-Network Ops, R&D)*
Bruce M. Reading *(Sr VP-Field Ops-Worlwide)*
Samatha McGarray *(Dir-PR)*
Denis Goodwin *(Product Mgr)*
Brands & Products:
ACTIVE LAST MILE XF
ACTIVE NETWORK XF
ACTUAL EXPERIENCE XF
GOMEZ
LAST MILE
REALITY LOAD XF
REALITY VIEW XF

GOSS INTERNATIONAL AMERICAS, INC
(Sub. of Goss International Corp.)
121 Technology Dr
Dover, NH 03824
Tel.: (603) 749-6600
Fax: (603) 749-3301
E-mail: info@gossinternational.com
Web Site: www.gossinternational.com
Approx. Number Employees: 1,000
Business Description:
Web Offset Printing Presses & High Volume Finishing & Mail Room Equipment Mfr For Commercial, Publication, Insert, Directory & Newspaper Markets
S.I.C.: 3555
N.A.I.C.S.: 333293
Import Export
Media: 1-2-4-7-10-11-13-20-22
Distr.: Intl.; Natl.

GRAPHIC CONTROLS LLC
400 Exchange St
Buffalo, NY 14204-2064
Mailing Address:
PO Box 1271
Buffalo, NY 14240-1271
Tel.: (716) 853-7500
Fax: (800) 347-2420
Toll Free: (800) 669-1535
E-mail: info@graphiccontrols.com
Web Site: www.graphiccontrols.com
Approx. Number Employees: 300
Business Description:
Recording Supplies & Tickets Mfr
S.I.C.: 2752; 3951
N.A.I.C.S.: 323110; 339941
Import Export
Media: 2-4-8-10-19-21
Distr.: Natl.
Personnel:
Sam Heleba *(Pres)*
Brandon Hoffman *(VP-Sls & Mktg)*
Brands & Products:
ACCULAB
ACTA
BONDTEX
DATAGRAPHIC
EASYGRAF
FULSCOPE
GC WIRELINE
GRAPHIC CONTROLS
MICROLAB
REPROVEL
SERVO
SURE CODE
SURE MARK
SURE SCAN
TRIDENT
WINDOGRAF

GREAT LAKES CASE & CABINET CO., INC.

PO Box 551
Edinboro, PA 16412
Tel.: (814) 734-7303
Fax: (814) 734-3907
Toll Free: (866) TRY-GLCC
E-mail: glcc@greatcabinets.com
Web Site: www.greatcabinets.com
Approx. Number Employees: 100
Year Founded: 1985
Business Description:
Cabinet Enclosures, Racks & Open-Frame Workstations Mfr
S.I.C.: 3499; 2522
N.A.I.C.S.: 332999; 337214
Media: 4-7-10-13
Personnel:
Carrie L. Lowther *(Pres)*
Marcia Dias-Chase *(Mgr-Mktg)*
Brands & Products:
ADVANTAGE
CO-LO
GREAT LAKES
LAKE EFFECT
WE RACK YOUR WORLD!

GREENVIEW DATA, INC.

8178 Jackson Rd
Ann Arbor, MI 48103
Mailing Address:
PO Box 1586
Ann Arbor, MI 48106-1586
Tel.: (734) 426-7500
Fax: (734) 426-7510
Toll Free: (800) 458-3348
Web Site: www.greenviewdata.com
E-Mail For Key Personnel:
Sales Director: sales@vedit.com
Approx. Sls.: $1,000,000
Approx. Number Employees: 10
Year Founded: 1980
Business Description:
Computer Software & Systems Integration
S.I.C.: 7371
N.A.I.C.S.: 541511
Export
Media: 2-6-7-8-10-13-15-21-22-23-24
Distr.: Intl.; Natl.
Budget Set: Dec.
Personnel:
Ted Green *(Pres & CEO)*
Joel Abramson *(COO)*
Philippe Green *(CTO & Exec VP)*
Ted Annis *(Dir-Mktg)*
Brands & Products:
VEDIT
VEDIT PLUS

GROSSMAN MARKETING GROUP

30 Cobble Hill Rd
Somerville, MA 02143
Tel.: (617) 623-8000
Fax: (617) 623-8058
Toll Free: (800) 368-1368
E-mail: massenv@massenvplus.com
Web Site:
www.grossmanmarketing.com
Approx. Number Employees: 60
Year Founded: 1910
Business Description:
Full Service Marketing Communications Materials & Promotional Products
S.I.C.: 5112; 2759
N.A.I.C.S.: 424120; 323119
Advertising Expenditures: $250,000
Bus. Publs.: $40,000; D.M. to Bus. Estab.: $60,000; Exhibits/Trade Shows: $5,000; Premiums, Novelties: $5,000; Product Samples: $20,000; Special Events Mktg.: $50,000; Spot Radio: $10,000; Spot T.V.: $40,000; Yellow Page Adv.: $20,000
Distr.: Reg.
Advertising Agency:
Gill Fishman Associates
955 Massachusetts Ave
Cambridge, MA 02139
Tel.: (617) 492-5666
Fax: (617) 492-5408
(Specialty Products-Folders, Binders, Disk Mailers, Point-of-Purchase)

GTCO CALCOMP, INC.

(Sub. of Interwrite Learning)
7125 Riverwood Dr
Columbia, MD 21046
Tel.: (410) 381-6688
Fax: (410) 290-9065
Toll Free: (800) 344-4723
E-mail: gtco.sales@gtcocalcomp.com
Web Site: www.gtcocalcomp.com
E-Mail For Key Personnel:
Sales Director: sales@gtcocalcomp.com
Approx. Sls.: $35,000,000
Approx. Number Employees: 120
Year Founded: 1975
Business Description:
Mfr. of Computer Equipment & Graphic Measurement Devices, Desktop Productivity Tools & Collaboration Solutions
S.I.C.: 3571; 7371
N.A.I.C.S.: 334111; 541511
Export
Media: 2-4-5-6-7-10-22
Distr.: Natl.
Personnel:
Beki Mucci *(Mgr-Intl Sls Admin)*
Brands & Products:
ACCUTAB
ACCUTAB II
CADPRO
CALCOMP
DRAWINGBOARD
DRAWINGBOARD III
DRAWINGBOARD III BACKLIT
DRAWINGBOARD IV
DRAWINGBOARD IV JUMBO
FREEPOINT
FREEPOINT 3D
GP9
GTCO
GTCO CALCOMP
INTERWRITE
INTERWRITE IPANEL
INTERWRITE MEETINGBOARD
INTERWRITE MEETINGPAD
INTERWRITE PRS
INTERWRITE SCHOOLBOARD
INTERWRITE SCHOOLPAD
INTERWRITE SOFTWARE
JETIMAGE
QUIKRULER
ROLL-UP
ROLL-UP III
SCANPLUS
SCANPLUS IV
SMART MENU
SUMMAGRAPHICS
SUMMAGRID
SUMMAGRID VI
SUMMASKETCH
SUMMASKETCH III
SUPER L
SUPER L III
SURFACE-LIT ACCUTAB
TEMPLATEWORKS
WIDEIMAGE

GTECH CORPORATION

(Sub. of Lottomatica S.p.A.)
10 Memorial Blvd
Providence, RI 02903
Tel.: (401) 392-1000
Fax: (401) 392-1234
E-mail: info@gtech.com
Web Site: www.gtech.com
E-Mail For Key Personnel:
Public Relations: Robert.Vincent@gtech.com
Approx. Rev.: $1,304,806,000
Approx. Number Employees: 5,300
Year Founded: 1981
Business Description:
Gaming System Technology & Software Developer
S.I.C.: 7371; 7372; 7373; 7999
N.A.I.C.S.: 541511; 511210; 541512; 713290
Import Export
Advertising Expenditures: $9,300,000
Media: 2-7-13
Distr.: Natl.
Budget Set: June
Personnel:
Donald R. Sweitzer *(Chm)*
Jaymin B. Patel *(Pres & CEO)*
Alan Eland *(COO & Sr VP)*
Cornelia Laverty O'Connor *(CMO & Sr VP)*
Stefano Bortoli *(CFO-Lottomatica Grp & Sr VP)*
Declan Harkin *(COO-GTECH Intl & Sr VP)*
Michael K. Prescott *(Gen Counsel, Sec & Sr VP)*
Fabio Celadon *(Sr VP-Strategic Plng)*
Ross Dalton *(Sr VP)*
Robert Vincent *(Sr VP-Corp Affairs)*
Matthew Whalen *(Sr VP-Global Tech Solutions)*
Thomas E. Walsh *(Mgr-Govt Rels)*
Brands & Products:
AGENT BUCK
ALIEN ATTACK
ALTURA
AURA
BEAVER FEVER
BIG CATCH BONUS HUNTER
BINGOVISION
BULLFROGGIN
CASH CLIMB
CASHSQUATCH
CHOP SOOEY
DIRECT
DREAMPORT
ENTERPRISE SERIES
EQPYTIAN QUEST
EUROPRINT/IGI
FIREBALL KENO
FROST AND FIRE
GAMEGUARD
GAMEPOINT
GAMESCAPE
GTECH
IGI EUROPRINT
INTERLOTT
ISYS
KNIGHT'S QUEST
LILHCO
MAGIC MOONS
MEGA MART
PICK-2 DOUBLE-UP POKER
PLAYER EXPRESS
POLCARD
POWER STATION
PRO: SYS
ROYAL WAY KENO
SPIELO
SPLITLEVEL
TRIPLE IT
UWIN
VIDEOSITE
WEALTHY WIZARD
WILD 2'S POKER
Advertising Agency:
DCI Group
1828 L St NW Ste 400
Washington, DC 20036
Tel.: (202) 546-4242
Fax: (202) 546-4243

GTSI CORP

2553 Dulles View Dr Ste 100
Herndon, VA 20171-5219
Tel.: (703) 502-2000
Fax: (703) 222-5204
Toll Free: (800) 999-GTSI
E-mail: webmaster@gtsi.com
Web Site: www.gtsi.com
Approx. Sls.: $666,711,000
Approx. Number Employees: 433
Year Founded: 1983
Business Description:
Infrastructure Technology Solutions
S.I.C.: 5734; 5045; 7378
N.A.I.C.S.: 443120; 423430; 811212
Media: 2-4-5-6-9-10-13-23-25
Personnel:
John M. Toups *(Chm)*
Sterling E. Phillips, Jr. *(CEO)*
Peter Whitfield *(CFO & Sr VP)*
Jeremy Wensinger *(COO)*
Denise L. Harrison *(CIO & VP)*
Joe Uglialoro *(Gen Counsel & VP)*
Mohamed Elrefai *(Sr VP-Sls & Mktg Ops)*
Bill Collins *(VP & Gen Mgr)*
Bridget Atkinson *(VP-HR & Org Dev)*
Chris Kiernan *(VP-Sls)*
Scott Spencer *(Gen Mgr-DoD Sls & Ops)*
Brands & Products:
GTSI
ONE MISSION YOURS
Advertising Agency:
White & Partners
13665 Dulles Technology Dr Ste 150
Herndon, VA 20171-4607
Tel.: (703) 793-3000
Fax: (703) 793-1495
Toll Free: (800) 211-0874

GUARDSMARK, LLC

10 Rockefeller Plz 12th Fl
New York, NY 10020
Tel.: (212) 765-8226
Fax: (901) 522-6013
Web Site: www.guardsmark.com
Sales Range: $500-549.9 Million
Approx. Number Employees: 18,500
Year Founded: 1963

Key to Media (For complete agency information see *The Advertising Red Books-Agencies* edition):
1. Bus. Publs. 2. Cable T.V. 3. Catalogs & Directories. 4. Co-op Adv. 5. Consumer Mags. 6. D.M. to Bus. Estab.7. D.M. to Consumers
8. Daily Newsp. 9. Exhibits/Trade Shows 10. Foreign 11. Infomercial 12. Internet Adv.13. Multimedia 14. Network Radio
15. Network T.V. 16. Newsp. Distr. Mags. 17. Other 18. Outdoor (Posters, Transit) 19. Point of Purchase20. Premiums, Novelties
21. Product Samples 22. Special Events Mktg. 23. Spot Radio 24. Spot T.V. 25. Weekly Newsp. 26. Yellow Page Adv.

Business Description:
Security Officer, Investigative, Consulting & Background Screening Services
S.I.C.: 7381; 2721
N.A.I.C.S.: 561612; 511120
Media: 2-4-6
Distr.: Natl.
Budget Set: Oct.
Personnel:
Ira A. Lipman *(Founder, Chm & Pres)*
Gustave K. Lipman *(COO & Sr Exec VP)*
John F. Clark, Jr. *(Sr VP & Mgr-Security Div Sls)*
Joshua S. Lipman *(Sr VP)*
M. Benjamin Lipman *(Sr VP-Sls)*
Don K. Pettus *(Sr VP & Grp Exec)*
Robert W. Overman *(VP & Mgr-HR)*
Brands & Products:
DAY TO DAY
EXCELLENCE IN SECURITY SOLUTIONS
GUARDSMARK
HOW TO PROTECT YOURSELF FROM CRIME
THE LIPMAN REPORT
MAXIMUM VALUE PARTNERSHIP
Advertising Agency:
Makovsky & Company, Inc.
16 E 34th St 15th Fl
New York, NY 10016
Tel.: (212) 508-9600
Fax: (212) 751-9710

GUIDELINE, INC.

(Sub. of Opinion Research Corporation)
(d/b/a ORC Guideline)
625 Ave of the Americas
New York, NY 10011-2020
Tel.: (212) 645-4500
Fax: (212) 645-7681
Web Site: www.guideline.com
Sales Range: $25-49.9 Million
Approx. Number Employees: 240
Year Founded: 1969
Business Description:
Integrated Business Research & Analysis
S.I.C.: 7389; 8742; 8748
N.A.I.C.S.: 561499; 541611; 541618
Media: 7-10-13-17
Personnel:
Christine W. Dalzell *(Sr Mng Dir)*
Walter Dempsey *(Sr VP & Gen Mgr)*
David Magnani *(Sr VP & Gen Mgr)*
Robert Reitter *(Sr VP)*
Sierra Hartley *(VP-Sls)*
Brands & Products:
FIND
INTERNET ADVISORY TEAM
PROFIT FROM OUR KNOWLEDGE

H&S BUSINESS EXPRESS INC.

(d/b/a PC America)
One Blue Hill Plaza, 2nd Fl
Pearl River, NY 10965
Mailing Address:
PO Box 1546
Pearl River, NY 10965-8546
Tel.: (845) 920-0800
Fax: (845) 920-0880
Toll Free: (800) 722-6374
E-mail: sales@pcamerica.com
Web Site: www.pcamerica.com
Approx. Sls.: $1,300,000
Approx. Number Employees: 12
Business Description:
Computer System Design Services for Retail & Restaurant
S.I.C.: 7373
N.A.I.C.S.: 541512
Media: 2

HALIFAX CORPORATION OF VIRGINIA

(Holding of Global Equity Capital, LLC)
5250 Cherokee Ave
Alexandria, VA 22312-2052
Tel.: (703) 750-2202
Fax: (703) 658-2478
Toll Free: (800) 944-2543
E-mail: info@hxcorp.com
Web Site: www.hxcorp.com
Approx. Rev.: $34,048,000
Approx. Number Employees: 284
Year Founded: 1967
Business Description:
Information Technology Services
S.I.C.: 7371; 8748
N.A.I.C.S.: 541511; 541690
Media: 7-10
Personnel:
John H. Grover *(Chm)*
Charles L. McNew *(Pres & CEO)*
Robert W. Drennen *(VP-Fin)*
Charles A. Harper *(VP-Field Svcs)*
Jamie P. Cox *(Dir-Sys Dev)*

HALLMARK INSIGHTS

(Sub. of Hallmark Cards, Inc.)
121 S 8th St Ste 700
Minneapolis, MN 55402-2841
Tel.: (612) 672-8600
Fax: (612) 672-8601
Toll Free: (800) 765-GIFT
E-mail: Marketing_Team@hallmarkinsights.com
Web Site: www.hallmarkinsights.com
Approx. Number Employees: 100
Year Founded: 1990
Business Description:
Gift Certificates & Awards
S.I.C.: 5947; 8741
N.A.I.C.S.: 453220; 561110
Media: 2
Personnel:
Keith A. Fenhaus *(Pres)*
Eileen Nemitz *(CFO & Sr VP)*
Zarir Erani *(VP-IT)*
Kimberly Hanson *(VP-Sls)*
Brands & Products:
PREMIERE CHOICE AWARD

HARMONIC, INC.

4300 N First St
San Jose, CA 95134
Tel.: (408) 542-2500
Fax: (408) 542-2511
Toll Free: (800) 788-1330
E-mail: sarah.lum@harmonicinc.com
Web Site: www.harmonicinc.com
Approx. Rev.: $423,344,000
Approx. Number Employees: 1,106
Year Founded: 1988
Business Description:
Fiber Optic & Wireless Network Transmission Products to Enable Video-on-Demand Services
S.I.C.: 3663; 2741; 3651; 3823; 7829
N.A.I.C.S.: 334220; 334310; 334513; 512199; 516110
Personnel:
Patrick J. Harshman *(Pres & CEO)*
Carolyn V. Aver *(CFO)*
Shahar Bar *(Sr VP-Corp Dev)*
Nimrod Ben-Natan *(Sr VP-Product Mktg, Solutions & Strategy)*
Charles J. Bonasera *(Sr VP-Ops)*
Neven Haltmayer *(Sr VP-R&D, Distr & Delivery Products)*
Peter E. Hilliard *(Sr VP-HR)*
Ron Howe *(Sr VP-Svc & Support)*
Geoff Stedman *(Sr VP-Corp Mktg)*
Mark Carrington *(VP-Worlwide Sls)*
Ian Graham *(VP-Sls & Svc-EMEA)*
Jim Marino *(VP-Sls-North America Cable & Telco)*
Brands & Products:
BROADCAST NETWORK GATEWAY
CHERRYPICKER
CLEARCUT
CODICO
DIVICOM
DIVITRACKIP
DIVITRACKXE
ELECTRA
ENRGY
FLXLINK
GIGALIGHT
INTERSECT
MAXLINK
MEDIANODE
METROLINK
NARROWCAST SERVICES GATEWAY
NETWATCH
NMX DIGITAL SERVICE MANAGER
NSG
PROCIPHER
PROSTREAM
PROVIEW
PWRBLAZER
PWRLINK
REDEFINING VIDEO LIBRARY
SIMULCRYPT
SUPRALINK
TERAYON
THESYS
VPON
Advertising Agency:
AxiCom Cohn & Wolfe
AxiCom Court 67 Barnes High Street
London, SW13 9LE, United Kingdom
Tel.: (44) 20 8392 4050
Fax: (44) 20 8392 4055

HARTER

(Unit of JSJ Furniture Corp.)
11451 Harter Dr
Middlebury, IN 46540-9663
Tel.: (574) 825-5871
Fax: (574) 825-3464
Toll Free: (800) 543-5449
E-mail: info@harter.com
Web Site: www.harter.com
Approx. Number Employees: 160
Year Founded: 1927
Business Description:
Mfr. of Custom Office Furniture; Office Chairs
S.I.C.: 2522; 2521
N.A.I.C.S.: 337214; 337211
Import Export
Media: 2-4-7-10
Distr.: Intl.; Natl.
Budget Set: Nov.
Brands & Products:
ALIESA
ANTHROSPIRIT
AXIOM
CALLIOPE
CATCH
CLIO
COLLEAGUE
CYCLUS
HARTER
INTUITION
LASSITER
MILLENNIUM
NEOCLASSIC
QUEST
TESO
VALET
WALLABY
Advertising Agency:
The Moderns
900 Broadway Ste 903
New York, NY 10003
Tel.: (212) 387-8852
Fax: (212) 387-8824

HAUPPAUGE DIGITAL, INC.

91 Cabot Ct
Hauppauge, NY 11788-3717
Tel.: (631) 434-1600
Fax: (631) 434-3198
E-mail: sales@hauppauge.com
Web Site: www.hauppauge.com
E-Mail For Key Personnel:
Sales Director: sales@hauppauge.com
Approx. Sls.: $56,918,617
Approx. Number Employees: 167
Year Founded: 1985
Business Description:
Analog Video, Digital Video, TV & Data Broadcast Receiver Products Mfr & Developer
S.I.C.: 3577; 3651; 3669; 3679
N.A.I.C.S.: 334119; 334290; 334310; 334418
Advertising Expenditures: $263,363
Media: 5-10-11-13
Distr.: Intl.; Natl.
Personnel:
Kenneth H. Plotkin *(Chm, Pres, CEO & COO)*
Gerald Tucciarone *(CFO)*
John Casey *(VP-Tech)*
Brands & Products:
DV-WIZARD
DV-WIZARD PRO
HAUPPAUGE!
HD PVR
IMPACTVCB
MEDIAMVP
MYCAPTURE
MYCAPTURE II
MYTV
MYTV/FM
MYTV2GO
MYTV.PVR
MYTVTOGO-FM
MYVIDEO
POWERBOOK
SOFTPVR
USB-LIVE
WINTV
WINTV-D
WINTV-DBX
WINTV-GO
WINTV-GO-FM
WINTV-GO-PLUS
WINTV-HD
WINTV HVR
WINTV-HVR-950Q
WINTV-NEXUS-S
WINTV-NOVA-S PCI

Key to Media (For complete agency information see *The Advertising Red Books-Agencies* edition):
1. Bus. Publs. 2. Cable T.V. 3. Catalogs & Directories. 4. Co-op Adv. 5. Consumer Mags. 6. D.M. to Bus. Estab.7. D.M. to Consumers
8. Daily Newsp. 9. Exhibits/Trade Shows 10. Foreign 11. Infomercial 12. Internet Adv.13. Multimedia 14. Network Radio
15. Network T.V. 16. Newsp. Distr. Mags. 17. Other 18. Outdoor (Posters, Transit) 19. Point of Purchase20. Premiums, Novelties
21. Product Samples 22. Special Events Mktg. 23. Spot Radio 24. Spot T.V. 25. Weekly Newsp. 26. Yellow Page Adv.

HAUPPAUGE DIGITAL, INC. — (Continued)

WINTV-NOVA-S USB
WINTV-NOVA-T PCI
WINTV-PVR
WINTV-PVR-250
WINTV-PVR-250MCE
WINTV-PVR-350
WINTV-PVR-USB
WINTV-RADIO
WINTV-THEATER
WINTV-USB
WINTV-USB-FM
WINTV-USB2
WMVP

HAWORTH, INC.

1 Haworth Ctr
Holland, MI 49423-9570
Tel.: (616) 393-3000
Fax: (616) 393-3420
Fax: (616) 393-1033
Fax: (616) 393-1570
Toll Free: (800) 344-2600
E-mail: publicrelations@haworth.com
Web Site: www.haworth.com
E-Mail For Key Personnel:
Sales Director: sales@haworth.com
Public Relations: publicrelations@haworth.com
Approx. Number Employees: 7,500
Year Founded: 1948
Business Description:
Office Furniture Systems & Seating
Mfr & Distr
S.I.C.: 2522; 2521
N.A.I.C.S.: 337214; 337211
Import Export
Media: 2-4-7-9-10-13-19-20-22-25-26
Distr.: Intl.; Natl.
Budget Set: Sept.
Personnel:
Richard G. Haworth *(Chm)*
Franco Bianchi *(Pres & CEO)*
Frank Rexach *(VP & Gen Mgr-Asia-Pacific)*
Pamela Wright Armstrong *(VP-Global HR)*
Mabel Casey *(VP-Global Mktg)*
Ann Harten *(VP-Global Info Svcs & HR)*
J. Todd James *(VP-Sls-Global)*
John Mooney *(VP-Fin-Global)*
Georgianna D. Olivieri *(VP-Architecture & Design)*
Jeff Reuschel *(Dir-Global Design)*
Fred Rutan *(Dir-Pur)*
Phil Todd *(Dir-Sls Support)*
Susan Wray *(Mgr-Corp Comm)*
Tom DeBoer *(Product Mgr)*
Brands & Products:
ACCOLADE
ADAPTABLE WORKSPACE
ARCHITECTURAL ELEMENTS
ASCENT
ASHVILLE
AVARI
BERKSHIRE
BERLIN
THE BEST POSTURE IS THE NEXT POSTURE
BOOGIE
CASTELLI
CATALYST
CAUSEWAY
CAVENDISH
CHANGE BY DESIGN
CLOCKWORK
COMFORTO
COMPOSE
COMPOSITES
CROSSINGS
DENDHUR
DESIGNED PERFORMANCE
ENCLOSE
ENTROPY
ERA-1
ESSEX
ETON
EUROPA
FORENZE
GALERIE
HAWORTH
HAWORTH ARCHITECTURAL INTERIORS
HAWORTH HELPS YOU DESIGN GREAT
HELLO
HIGH-TAP
IF
IMPROV
JUMP
KATIA
KINETICS
LAURA
LOOK
MARIA
MONACO
MOXIE
MUELLER
MYRTLE
NEON
NOTTINGHAM
OCTOBER
OFFICEGARDEN
ONETOUCH
ORLANDO
PAL
PLACES
THE POWER BASE
POWER WEB
POWERBEAM
PREMISE
PRESCOTT
RACE
RICHMOND
S-CON
SCAMPS
SERIES K
SHERBROOKE
SOURCEBOOK
SYSTEMSEATING
TACTICS
TALLY
TAS
TECFLOR
TECRETE
TEMPO
TODO
TOUGH FURNITURE. TOTAL SERVICE.
TRIPOLI
TRUEMATCH
TRUENET
TUSCANY
TUXEDO
UNIGROUP
V SERIES
VANCOUVER
VARIA
VIDENE
WELLSLEY
WORKSPACE EXCHANGE
X SERIES
X99
ZODY

HDI SOLUTIONS, INC.

1510 Pumphrey Ave
Auburn, AL 36832-0529
Tel.: (334) 821-0947
Fax: (334) 821-0647
Toll Free: (800) 282-0999
Web Site: www.hdinfo.com
Sales Range: $50-74.9 Million
Approx. Number Employees: 150
Year Founded: 1981
Business Description:
Data Management Software
S.I.C.: 7374
N.A.I.C.S.: 518210
Media: 4
Personnel:
Jim Wilkerson *(Exec VP)*
Brands & Products:
ACCUAUDIO PLUS
ACCUCAPTURE PLUS
ACCUDB PLUS
ACCUENTRY PLUS
ACCUIMAGE PLUS
ACCUMINE PLUS
ACCUPLUS
ACCUTITLES PLUS
ACCUVERIFY
ECASEMANAGER
ENSURE SMART
ETAGMANAGER
HDI SOLUTIONS
PACTRAC
YOUR SOLUTIONS SOURCE

HEADSTRONG CORPORATION

(Sub. of Genpact Limited)
4035 Ridge Top Rd Ste 300
Fairfax, VA 22030
Tel.: (703) 272-6700
Fax: (703) 272-2000
E-mail: information@headstrong.com
Web Site: www.headstrong.com
Approx. Number Employees: 2,000
Year Founded: 1981
Business Description:
Application Outsourcing, Systems Integration & Consulting Services
S.I.C.: 8748; 7374
N.A.I.C.S.: 541618; 518210
Media: 5-7-10-11
Personnel:
Arjun Malhotra *(Chm)*
Sandeep Sahai *(Pres & COO)*
Adarsh Mehra *(Mng Dir & Global Head-Fin)*
Alphonse Valbrune *(Gen Counsel & Corp Sec)*

HEALTH BENEFITS DIRECT CORPORATION

(Name Changed to INSPRO TECHNOLOGIES CORPORATION)

HEALTHPORT, INC.

(Joint Venture of ABRY Partners LLC & Thurston Group, LLC)
120 Bluegrass Valley Pkwy
Alpharetta, GA 30005
Tel.: (770) 360-1700
Fax: (770) 360-1740
Toll Free: (800) 367-1500
Web Site: www.healthport.com
Approx. Rev.: $188,169,000
Approx. Number Employees: 2,865
Year Founded: 1976
Business Description:
Medical Office Practice Management & Document Management Software & Information Services
S.I.C.: 7372; 2741; 7389; 8742
N.A.I.C.S.: 511210; 516110; 541611; 561499
Advertising Expenditures: $600,000
Personnel:
Patrcik J. Haynes, III *(Chm)*
Mike Labedz *(Pres & CEO)*
Brian Grazzini *(CFO)*
Gene Guertin *(CIO)*
William Matits *(Sr VP-Sls)*
Brands & Products:
DOCUSTORE
EDISCLOSE
EMRWEB
ESMARTLOG
NOTIFYME
QUICKVIEW
SAM
SMARTLINK
SMARTLOG
SMARTPARTNER
SMARTWORKS

HEALTHTRIO INC.

1010 N FInance Center Dr Ste 210
Tucson, CO 85710
Tel.: (303) 397-3000
Fax: (520) 571-2014
E-mail: healthtrioadmin@healthtrio.com
Web Site: www.healthtrio.com
Approx. Sls.: $11,000,000
Approx. Number Employees: 100
Business Description:
Communications Platforms for Healthcare Industry
S.I.C.: 7373; 7379
N.A.I.C.S.: 541512; 541519
Media: 6-10-13
Personnel:
Malik M. Hasan *(CEO)*
Asma Hasan *(Chief Legal Officer)*
Ritch Haynes *(Exec VP)*
Joseph T. Pro *(VP-Sls)*
Dave Syposs *(VP-Mktg & Bus Partnerships)*
Brands & Products:
EXCHANGE. KNOW. ACT
HEALTHTRIO
HEALTHTRIO CONNECT
HEALTHTRIO XPRESS
Advertising Agency:
Amendola Communications
9280 E Raintree Dr Ste 104
Scottsdale, AZ 85260
Tel.: (480) 664-8412
Fax: (480) 659-3531

HEALTHVISION INC.

(Sub. of Lawson Software, Inc.)
(d/b/a Healthvision - Software & Solutions)
5030 Riverside Dr St 300
Irving, TX 75039
Tel.: (972) 819-4000
Fax: (469) 420-3890
Toll Free: (800) 446-1800
E-mail: info@healthvision.com
Web Site: www.healthvision.com
Sales Range: $75-99.9 Million
Approx. Number Employees: 200
Year Founded: 1989

Key to Media (For complete agency information see *The Advertising Red Books-Agencies* edition):
1. Bus. Publs. 2. Cable T.V. 3. Catalogs & Directories. 4. Co-op Adv. 5. Consumer Mags. 6. D.M. to Bus. Estab.7. D.M. to Consumers 8. Daily Newsp. 9. Exhibits/Trade Shows 10. Foreign 11. Infomercial 12. Internet Adv.13. Multimedia 14. Network Radio 15. Network T.V. 16. Newsp. Distr. Mags. 17. Other 18. Outdoor (Posters, Transit) 19. Point of Purchase20. Premiums, Novelties 21. Product Samples 22. Special Events Mktg. 23. Spot Radio 24. Spot T.V. 25. Weekly Newsp. 26. Yellow Page Adv.

Business Description:
Health Care Industry Software & Services
S.I.C.: 7372; 7373
N.A.I.C.S.: 511210; 541512
Advertising Expenditures: $1,000,000
Media: 2-7-10-13-20
Personnel:
Paul Bellamy *(Sr VP-Intl Ops)*
May Hu *(Sr VP-R & D)*
Brands & Products:
CLOVERLEAF
INSURENET
QUOVADX

HEALTHWAREHOUSE.COM, INC.

100 Commerce Blvd
Cincinnati, OH 45140
Tel.: (513) 618-0911
Fax: (866) 821-3784
Toll Free: (866) 885-0508
E-mail: support@healthwarehouse.com
Web Site: www.healthwarehouse.com
Approx. Sls.: $5,691,765
Approx. Number Employees: 31
Year Founded: 1982
Business Description:
Online Pharmaceuticals Retailer
S.I.C.: 5961; 5912
N.A.I.C.S.: 454111; 446110
Advertising Expenditures: $450,687
Media: 13
Personnel:
Lalit P. Dhadphale *(Co-Founder, Chm, Pres & CEO)*
Patrick E. Delaney *(CFO)*

HEINN/TREND CORPORATION

4041 N Richards St
Milwaukee, WI 53212-1232
Tel.: (414) 906-3060
Fax: (414) 906-3070
Toll Free: (800) 456-8852
E-mail: info@heinntrendcorp.com
Web Site: www.heinntrendcorp.com
Approx. Sls.: $8,000,000
Approx. Number Employees: 60
Year Founded: 1896
Business Description:
Mfr. of Looseleaf Binders & Indexes
S.I.C.: 2782
N.A.I.C.S.: 323118
Import
Media: 2-4-8-10-20
Distr.: Direct to Consumer; Natl.
Budget Set: Nov.-Dec.
Personnel:
Charles Tuff *(Pres)*
Brands & Products:
HEINN/TREND

HENKEL CONSUMER ADHESIVES, INC.

(Sub. of Henkel AG & Co. KGaA)
26235 First St
Westlake, OH 44145
Tel.: (440) 937-7000
Fax: (440) 937-7077
Toll Free: (866) 591-2178
Web Site: www.stickwithhenkel.com
Approx. Sls.: $445,000,000
Approx. Number Employees: 400
Year Founded: 1971
Business Description:
Developer & Marketer of Home & Office Repair & Adhesive Products
S.I.C.: 2672; 3083
N.A.I.C.S.: 322222; 326130
Export
Media: 1-2-3-4-5-6-7-8-10-13-19-20-21-22-23-24-26
Distr.: Intl.
Budget Set: Oct.
Personnel:
Dan Brogan *(Pres)*
John Kahl *(CEO)*
Brands & Products:
CARE MAIL
DRAFT BUSTERS
DUCK TAPE
EASY LINER
KIDSCRAFT
LEPAGE
LOCTITE
ONE TOUCH
PRO PAINTER'S PLUS
SMOOTH TOP
SOFTEX
Advertising Agencies:
DigiKnow
3615 Superior Ave Bldg 44 4th Fl
Cleveland, OH 44114
Tel.: (216) 325-1800
Fax: (216) 325-1801

Liggett Stashower
LS Brand Bldg 1240 Huron Rd
Cleveland, OH 44115
Tel.: (216) 348-8500
Fax: (914) 407-1475

HEWITT ASSOCIATES

(Sub. of Aon Hewitt)
120 S Riverside Plz 17th Fl
Chicago, IL 60606
Tel.: (312) 279-7000
Fax: (847) 554-1367
Toll Free: (800) 429-2674
Web Site: www.hewitt.com
Sales Range: $25-49.9 Million
Approx. Number Employees: 300
Year Founded: 1974
Business Description:
Human Resources Software & Payroll Software
S.I.C.: 7372; 7371
N.A.I.C.S.: 511210; 541511
Media: 2-7-10-11-13-26
Personnel:
Christa Davies *(CFO & Exec VP)*
Gregory J. Besio *(Chief Admin Officer, Exec VP & Head-Global Strategy)*
Peter Lieb *(Exec VP & Gen Counsel)*
Thomas M. Brown *(Mgr-Mainframe Enabling Tech)*
Mary Beth Riordan *(Mgr-Shared Svcs)*
Brands & Products:
CYBORG SOLUTION SERIES SOFTWARE

HEWITT ASSOCIATES, INC.

(Name Changed to Aon Hewitt)

HEWLETT-PACKARD COMPANY

3000 Hanover St
Palo Alto, CA 94304-1185
Tel.: (650) 857-1501
Tel.: (650) 857-2246 (Investor Relations)
Fax: (650) 857-5518
E-mail: investor.relations@hp.com
Web Site: www.hp.com
Approx. Rev.: $126,033,000,000
Approx. Number Employees: 324,600
Year Founded: 1939
Business Description:
Computer Equipment & Software Mfr
S.I.C.: 3577; 2893; 3555; 3571; 7372
N.A.I.C.S.: 334119; 325910; 333293; 334111; 511210
Advertising Expenditures: $1,000,000,000
Media: 2-3-6-7-8-9-10-13-14-15-17-18-22-23-24-31
Distr.: Intl.; Natl.
Budget Set: July
Personnel:
Raymond J. Lane *(Chm)*
Meg Whitman *(Pres & CEO)*
Richard T. Geraffo, Jr. *(Mng Dir & Sr VP)*
Francesco Serafini *(Mng Dir & Sr VP-TSG-EMEA)*
Arturo Lee *(Mng Dir)*
Catherine A. Lesjak *(CFO & Exec VP)*
Randall D. Mott *(CIO & Exec VP)*
Martin Homlish *(CMO & Exec VP)*
Shane V. Robison *(CTO, Chief Strategy Officer & Exec VP)*
Donald C. Grantham *(Chief Sls Officer & Sr VP)*
Lynn Anderson *(Interim Chief Comm Officer)*
Peter Bocian *(Chief Admin Officer & Exec VP)*
Mathew Thomas *(Principal-Tech Svcs)*
Michael J. Holston *(Exec VP & Gen Counsel)*
John McMullen *(Treas & Sr VP)*
David A. Donatelli *(Exec VP & Gen Mgr-Enterprise Servers, Storage & Networking)*
R. Todd Bradley *(Exec VP-Personal Sys Grp)*
Vyomesh Joshi *(Exec VP-Imaging & Printing Grp)*
Tracy S. Keogh *(Exec VP-HR)*
Ann M. Livermore *(Exec VP-Enterprise Bus)*
William L. Veghte *(Exec VP-Software & Solutions)*
James T. Murrin *(Sr VP & Controller)*
Marius Haas *(Sr VP & Gen Mgr-ProCurve Networking)*
Prith Banerjee *(Sr VP-Res & Dir-HP Labs)*
Bruce Dahlgren *(Sr VP-Managed Enterprise Solutions-Imaging and Printing Grp)*
Richard Gerstein *(Sr VP-Strategy & Mktg-HP PSG)*
Brian Humphries *(Sr VP-Strategy & Bus Dev)*
Ari Jaaksi *(Sr VP)*
Ahmed Mahmoud *(Sr VP-Global IT)*
Deborah Nelson *(Sr VP-Mktg & Enterprise Bus)*
Randy Seidl *(Sr VP-Americas, Enterprise Servers, Storage & Networking)*
Neal Woods *(Sr VP-Ops-Worldwide)*
Jan Riecher *(VP & Gen Mgr-Graphics Solutions Bus-Americas)*
Paul T. Porrini *(VP & Deputy Gen Counsel & Asst Sec)*
Fred Bullock *(VP-Mktg-Americas)*
Jim Burns *(VP-Fin-Enterprise Bus)*
Chris Curtin *(VP-Digital Strategy & Corp Mktg)*
Gary Elliott *(VP)*
Tariq Hassan *(VP-Mktg & Comm-Worldwide)*
John M. Renfro *(VP-HR)*
Marc Chapman *(Gen Mgr-ePrint Center)*
Melika Carroll *(Exec Dir-Global Pub Policy)*
Alyson Griffin *(Dir-Mktg-Worldwide)*
Kristy Birney *(Dir-World Wide Integrated Mktg)*
Ken Fleming *(Dir-LaserJet & Enterprise Solutions Mktg)*
Amar Maletira *(Dir-IR)*
Jeannette Robinson *(Dir-HR)*
Rob Sbarra *(Dir-Americas Strategy & Ops-Tech Svcs Grp)*
Mark Lewis *(Sr Mgr-Mktg)*
Heidrun Gross *(Product Mgr-Imaging & Printing Grp)*
Victoria Voinigescu *(Product Mgr-Software)*
Wendy Cole *(Mgr-Digital Media-Worldwide)*
Kathleen Haley *(Mgr-Comm)*
Scott Hancock *(Mgr-Adv-Worldwide)*
Amin Kayal *(Mgr-MEMA Reg-HP Networking)*
Georgia Lalazari *(Mgr-Consumer Mktg)*
Samantha Singh *(Mgr-WW PR-HP Networking)*
Rob Walker *(Engr-Component)*
Brands & Products:
COMPAQ
HEWLETT-PACKARD
HP
HP DESKJET
HP DESKJET PLUS
HP LASERJET
HP LEFTHAND P4000 SAN
HP OFFICEJET
HP P4000 SAN
HP PAVILION
HP SCANJET
IPAQ
MEDIA CENTER
NONSTOP
NUTSIE
OPENVIEW
PAVILION
PHOTOSMART
PROCURVE
PROLIANT
Advertising Agencies:
72andSunny
6300 Arizona Cir
Los Angeles, CA 90045
Tel.: (310) 215-9009
Fax: (310) 215-9012

Acxiom Digital
1051 Hillsdale Blvd Ste 400
Foster City, CA 94404
Tel.: (650) 356-3400
Fax: (650) 356-3410

BBDO New York
1285 Ave of the Americas 7th Fl
New York, NY 10019-6028
Tel.: (212) 459-5000
Printing Business

BBDO Worldwide Inc.
(Sub. of Omnicom Group, Inc.)

Key to Media (For complete agency information see *The Advertising Red Books-Agencies* edition):
1. Bus. Publs. 2. Cable T.V. 3. Catalogs & Directories. 4. Co-op Adv. 5. Consumer Mags. 6. D.M. to Bus. Estab.7. D.M. to Consumers 8. Daily Newsp. 9. Exhibits/Trade Shows 10. Foreign 11. Infomercial 12. Internet Adv.13. Multimedia 14. Network Radio 15. Network T.V. 16. Newsp. Distr. Mags. 17. Other 18. Outdoor (Posters, Transit) 19. Point of Purchase20. Premiums, Novelties 21. Product Samples 22. Special Events Mktg. 23. Spot Radio 24. Spot T.V. 25. Weekly Newsp. 26. Yellow Page Adv.

Hewlett-Packard Company — (Continued)

1285 Ave of the Americas
New York, NY 10019-6028
Tel.: (212) 459-5000
Fax: (212) 459-6645
Imaging & Printing Group

The Bivings Group
2201 Wisconsin Ave NW Ste 310
Washington, DC 20007
Tel.: (202) 741-1500
Fax: (202) 741-1501

Carol H. Williams Advertising
1400 65th St Ste 200
Emeryville, CA 94608
Tel.: (510) 763-5200
Fax: (510) 763-9266

Davie Brown Entertainment
4721 Alla Rd
Marina Del Rey, CA 90292
Tel.: (310) 979-1980
Fax: (310) 754-1783

Denuo
35 W Wacker Dr
Chicago, IL 60601
Tel.: (312) 220-5959
Fax: (312) 220-6050

Goodby, Silverstein & Partners, Inc.
(Part of Omnicom Group, Inc.)
720 California St
San Francisco, CA 94108-2404
Tel.: (415) 392-0669
Fax: (415) 788-4303
Summit on the Summit

Leo Burnett Worldwide, Inc.
35 W Wacker Dr
Chicago, IL 60601-1723
Tel.: (312) 220-5959
Fax: (312) 220-3299

Linkstorm
34 W 22nd St 3rd fl
New York, NY 10010
Tel.: (646) 649-8799
Fax: (646) 649-8795

McCann Erickson Worldwide
622 3rd Ave
New York, NY 10017-6707
Tel.: (646) 865-2000
Fax: (646) 487-9610

McGarry Bowen, LLC
601 W 26th St Ste 1150
New York, NY 10001
Tel.: (212) 598-2900
Fax: (212) 598-2996

Omnicom Media Group
195 Broadway
New York, NY 10007
Tel.: (212) 590-7100
Media Planning & Buying

Porter Novelli
(Sub. of Omnicom Group, Inc.)
75 Varick St 6th Fl
New York, NY 10013
Tel.: (212) 601-8000
Fax: (212) 601-8101
Eprint
Printer

Porter Novelli-Bay Area-San Francisco
550 3rd St
San Francisco, CA 94107
Tel.: (415) 975-2200
Fax: (415) 975-2201
— Cynthia Kong *(Acct Exec)*

Publicis (Malaysia) Sdn. Bhd.
M1 Mezanine Fl Wisme LYL
46100
Petaling Jaya, Selangor Malaysia
Tel.: (60) 3 7952 2222
Fax: (60) 3 7952 2220

Publicis Modem
2001 The Embarcadero
San Francisco, CA 94133
Tel.: (415) 293-2570
Fax: (415) 293-2621

RAPP
437 Madison Ave 3rd Fl
New York, NY 10022
Tel.: (212) 817-6800
Fax: (212) 590-8400

Source Communications
433 Hackensack Ave 8th Fl
Hackensack, NJ 07601-6319
Tel.: (201) 343-5222
Fax: (201) 343-5710

THE HIBBERT GROUP

400 Pennington Ave
Trenton, NJ 08618
Tel.: (609) 394-7500
Fax: (609) 394-6278
Toll Free: (800) 888-HIBBERT
Web Site: www.hibbertgroup.com
Approx. Number Employees: 650
Year Founded: 1881
Business Description:
Marketing Support Services
S.I.C.: 7331; 7389
N.A.I.C.S.: 541860; 561499
Media: 7-10-13
Personnel:
Timothy J. Moonan *(Co-Chm & CEO)*
Thomas J. Moonan *(Co-Chm)*
Bill Scerenci *(Sr VP-Fin)*
Ron Arellano *(Sr VP-Denver)*
George Dowvbia *(Sr VP-Fin)*
Rosemary M. Hober *(Sr VP-Client Svcs)*
Kenneth J. Swiatkowski *(Sr VP-IT)*
Paul A. Zukowski *(Sr VP-Production)*
Diane Allen *(VP-HR)*
Rose Yacovone *(Mgr-Mktg)*
Brands & Products:
ORDER2U.COM

HIRSH INDUSTRIES, INC.

11229 Aurora Ave
Urbandale, IA 50322-7906
Tel.: (515) 299-3200
Fax: (515) 299-3374
Toll Free: (888) 781-9559 (Comml Prods)
Toll Free: (888) 781-9283 (Consumer Prods)
E-mail: contact@hirshindustries.com
Web Site: www.hirshindustries.com
Approx. Number Employees: 800
Year Founded: 1945
Business Description:
Mfr of Metal Office Furniture & Shelving
S.I.C.: 2522; 2434
N.A.I.C.S.: 337214; 337110
Media: 5-10
Personnel:
Wayne Stewart *(Pres & CEO)*
Brands & Products:
BASIC FILE
HIRSH INDUSTRIES
OFFICE DESIGNS
THE ORGANIZER
READY FILE
SMART FILE
SPACE SOLUTIONS
ULTRA FILE

HITACHI DATA SYSTEMS CORPORATION

(Sub. of Hitachi America, Ltd.)
750 Central Expy
Santa Clara, CA 95050-2627
Tel.: (408) 970-1000
E-mail: info@hds.com
Web Site: www.hds.com
Approx. Number Employees: 2,500
Business Description:
Mainframe Peripheral Products & Storage Devices Service & Distr
S.I.C.: 5045; 7378
N.A.I.C.S.: 423430; 811212
Personnel:
Minoru Kosuge *(Chm)*
Jack Domme *(CEO)*
Miklos Sandorfi *(Chief Strategy Officer-File & Content Svcs)*
Kevin Eggleston *(Sr VP & Gen Mgr-Asia Pacific)*
Niel Svennigsen *(Sr VP & Gen Mgr-EMEA)*
Brian Householder *(Sr VP-Worldwide Mktg & Bus Dev)*
John Mansfield *(Sr VP-Global Solutions Strategy & Dev)*
Frans van Rijn *(Sr VP-Logistics-Global)*
Michael Vath *(Sr VP-Global Bus Innovation)*
Michael Walkey *(Sr VP-Channels-Global)*
Lynn McLean *(VP-Sls)*
Asim Zaheer *(VP-Corp & Product Mktg-Worldwide)*
Christophe Bertrand *(Sr Dir-Product Mktg)*
Mary Ann Gallo *(Sr Dir-Corp Mktg & Comm)*
Helen Calthrop-Owen *(Sr Mgr-Pub Rel-EMEA)*
Gene Donlan *(Product Mgr)*
Brian McCann *(Mgr)*
Roberta Pezzo *(Mgr-Volume Channel-Italy)*
Brands & Products:
HITACHI
Advertising Agency:
Ogilvy PR
111 Sutter St 11th Fl
San Francisco, CA 94104-4541
Tel.: (415) 677-2700
Fax: (415) 677-2770

HONEYWELL INTERNATIONAL INC.

101 Columbia Rd
Morristown, NJ 07962
Tel.: (973) 455-2000
Fax: (973) 455-4807
Toll Free: (800) 601-3095
E-mail: rob.ferris@honeywell.com
Web Site: www.honeywell.com
Approx. Sls.: $33,370,000,000
Approx. Number Employees: 130,000
Year Founded: 1920
Business Description:
Aerospace, Automotive, Engineered Materials, Automation & Control Products Mfr & Distr
S.I.C.: 3822; 3714; 3724; 3812; 3823
N.A.I.C.S.: 334512; 334511; 334513; 336399; 336412
Import Export
Media: 2-7-8-10-11-13
Distr.: Intl.; Natl.
Budget Set: Oct.
Personnel:
David M. Cote *(Chm & CEO)*
Andreas Kramvis *(Pres & CEO-Specialty Matls)*
David J. Anderson *(CFO & Sr VP)*
Roger Fradin *(Pres/CEO-Automation & Control Solutions)*
Katherine L. Adams *(Gen Counsel & Sr VP)*
Mark R. James *(Sr VP-HR & Comm)*
Rhonda G. Germany *(VP-Strategy & Bus Dev)*
Michael Androutsos *(Dir-M&A-EMEA)*
Chris Benich *(Dir-Regulatory Affairs)*
Kelly Reed *(Dir-Brand & Mktg Comm-Global)*
John A. Weaver *(Dir-Mktg)*
Duane E. Wiedor *(Dir-Quality Mgmt)*
Les Renn *(Engr-Principal APQP Supplier Quality)*
Brands & Products:
ACCUFILL
ACCUFLO
ACCUGLASS
ACLAR
ACLON
ADEMCO
AEGIS
ANSO
APEX
AUTOLITE
BENDIX
BIOSYN
BURDICK AND JACKSON
CAPRAN
CARBENIX
CERAMETALIX
COMBO-SPREADER
DUO SPIN-ON
ECAE
ENOVATE
EXPERION
FOCUSPRO
FRAM
GENESOLV
GENETRON
HANDLELOCK
HEPA
HERCULINE
HOLTS
HYSYS
JURID
LOOP SCOUT
LUMILUX
LYNX
MAP-SHIELD
METGLAS
NANOGLASS
NOTIFIER
NOVAR
NOWPAK
OMNI
OPTIFLEX

Key to Media (For complete agency information see *The Advertising Red Books-Agencies* edition):
1. Bus. Publs. 2. Cable T.V. 3. Catalogs & Directories. 4. Co-op Adv. 5. Consumer Mags. 6. D.M. to Bus. Estab.7. D.M. to Consumers 8. Daily Newsp. 9. Exhibits/Trade Shows 10. Foreign 11. Infomercial 12. Internet Adv.13. Multimedia 14. Network Radio 15. Network T.V. 16. Newsp. Distr. Mags. 17. Other 18. Outdoor (Posters, Transit) 19. Point of Purchase20. Premiums, Novelties 21. Product Samples 22. Special Events Mktg. 23. Spot Radio 24. Spot T.V. 25. Weekly Newsp. 26. Yellow Page Adv.

OPTIVISION
OVATION
OXYSHIELD
PACNET
PRESTONE
PROCESS KNOWLEDGE SYSTEM
PROFIT
PROFITMAX
QUIETCLEAN
REDEX
RHEOCHEM
ROADTUFF
SECURUS
SELECT
SHADOW PLANT
SHADOWPLANT
SICURA
SIMONIZ
SPECTRA
SPECTRA SHIELD
SPOTGLO
STARTE PILOTE
STAYGARD
SURSENSE
TOTALPLANT
TRIGLO
TRU-BALLISTIC
UNIFORMANCE
UNISIM
UOP
VISIONPRO
VISTA
XTREME SPORT
XTREME START
Advertising Agency:
Richards Communications
3201 Enterprise Pkwy Ste 400
Beachwood, OH 44122
Tel.: (216) 514-7800
Fax: (216) 514-7801

HOUGHTON MIFFLIN HARCOURT LEARNING TECHNOLOGY

(Div. of Houghton Mifflin Harcourt Publishing Company)
222 Berkeley St
Boston, MA 02116
Tel.: (617) 351-5000
Fax: (617) 351-1100
E-mail: hmlearningtechnology@hmco.com
Web Site: hmlt.hmco.com
Approx. Number Employees: 490
Year Founded: 1995
Business Description:
Education & Consumer Software
S.I.C.: 7372
N.A.I.C.S.: 511210
Media: 4-11-13

HP COLORSPAN

(Unit of HP Imaging & Printing Group)
11311 K-Tel Dr
Minnetonka, MN 55343
Tel.: (952) 944-9330
Fax: (952) 944-9583
Fax: (952) 943-8622
Toll Free: (800) 477-7714 (Printer Sales)
Toll Free: (800) 723-3002 (Supplies Sales)
Web Site: www.hp.com
Sales Range: $100-124.9 Million
Approx. Number Employees: 90
Business Description:
Laser Printer & Display Systems, Subsystems for Electronic Printing & High-Resolution Plain-paper Typesetters Mfr, Sales & Marketer
S.I.C.: 3555; 2759; 5085
N.A.I.C.S.: 333293; 323115; 423840
Media: 2-7-10
Brands & Products:
BIG COLOR
THE BIG COLOR COMPANY
BIG INK
COLORMARK
COLORSPAN
DESIGNWINDER
DISPLAYMAKER
ENDURA CHROME
GICLEE PRINTMAKERFA
HALON
LASERMASTER
PERMA CHROME
PRESSMATE
RIP SAVER
THERMALRES
TURBORES
VIDEONET
WINJET
WINPRINT
WINPRINTER

HP ENTERPRISE SERVICES, LLC

(Group of Hewlett-Packard Company)
5400 Legacy Dr
Plano, TX 75024-3105
Tel.: (972) 605-6000
Fax: (972) 605-2643
Toll Free: (800) 566-9337
Web Site: h10134.www1.hp.com
Sales Range: $1-4.9 Billion
Year Founded: 1962
Business Description:
Information Technology Applications & Business Process Outsourcing Services
S.I.C.: 7372; 7371; 7374; 7379; 8748
N.A.I.C.S.: 511210; 518210; 541511; 541519; 541690
Distr.: Bus.-to-Bus; Natl.
Personnel:
Sean Kenny *(Pres-Industry Svcs)*
Ann M. Livermore *(Exec VP)*
John Visentin *(Exec VP)*
Jan Zadak *(Exec VP-Sls & Mktg)*
Andy Mattes *(Sr VP & Gen Mgr-HP Enterprise Svcs-Americas Reg)*
Mark Angelino *(Sr VP-Global Distr)*
Salvatore Como *(Sr VP-Infrastructure Tech Outsourcing)*
Robert Grisham *(Sr VP-Global Sls)*
David J. Shirk *(Sr VP-Worldwide Mktg)*
Joe Bottazzi *(VP & Gen Mgr-Tech Svcs-Americas)*
Robb Rasmussen *(VP & Gen Mgr-Best Shore)*
Paul Tsaparis *(VP-Tech)*
Advertising Agency:
Burson-Marsteller
(Part of Young & Rubicam Brands, a Sub. of WPP Group plc)
230 Park Ave S
New York, NY 10003-1566
Tel.: (212) 614-4000
Fax: (212) 598-5407

HQ GLOBAL WORKPLACES

(Sub. of Regus plc)
15305 Dallas Pkwy Ste 1400
Addison, TX 75001
Tel.: (972) 361-8100
Fax: (972) 361-8005
Web Site: www.hq.com
Approx. Sls.: $200,000,000
Approx. Number Employees: 2,000
Year Founded: 1969
Business Description:
Office & Business Services & Franchises; Leased Executive Suites; Video Conference Centers
S.I.C.: 6519
N.A.I.C.S.: 531190
Advertising Expenditures: $1,700,000
Media: 2-4-5-6-7-8-9-10-11-12-16-20-22-25-26
Distr.: Intl.
Budget Set: Nov.

HRN SERVICES INC.

8383 Wilshire Blvd Ste 258
Beverly Hills, CA 90211
Tel.: (323) 951-1450
Fax: (323) 951-1456
Toll Free: (800) 476-5561
E-mail: corpinfo@hrnservices.com
Web Site: www.hrnservices.com
Sales Range: $50-74.9 Million
Approx. Number Employees: 50
Year Founded: 1974
Business Description:
Nurses' Registry
S.I.C.: 7361
N.A.I.C.S.: 561310
Media: 2
Personnel:
Arthur Flaster *(Pres)*
Brands & Products:
GATEWAY TO TRAVEL
HRN

HTC GLOBAL SERVICES INC.

3270 W Big Beaver Rd
Troy, MI 48084-1840
Tel.: (248) 786-2500
Fax: (248) 530-2617
E-mail: contact@htcinc.com
Web Site: www.htcinc.com
Approx. Number Employees: 400
Year Founded: 1990
Business Description:
Computer Related Services
S.I.C.: 7373
N.A.I.C.S.: 541512
Import Export
Media: 10-13-22
Personnel:
Madhava Reddy *(Pres & CEO)*
Vikas Bhutada *(Exec VP)*
Brands & Products:
CAMPUSERP
CONNECTIT
DOCUSTACK
EBAP
EGRAMS
HTC
PPMA
REACHING OUT ... THROUGH IT

HTC INC.

3480 Hwy 701 N
Conway, SC 29526-5702
Tel.: (843) 365-2151
Fax: (843) 365-1111
Web Site: www.htcinc.net
Approx. Number Employees: 700
Year Founded: 1952
Business Description:
Provider of Telephone Services
S.I.C.: 4813
N.A.I.C.S.: 517310
Personnel:
Mike Hagg *(CEO)*
O'Neal Miller *(CFO)*
Tom Vitt *(Dir-Mktg)*
Advertising Agency:
Deutsch LA
5454 Beethoven St
Los Angeles, CA 90066-7017
Tel.: (310) 862-3000
Fax: (310) 862-3100

HURCO COMPANIES, INC.

1 Technology Way
Indianapolis, IN 46268-0180
Mailing Address:
PO Box 68180
Indianapolis, IN 46268-0180
Tel.: (317) 293-5309
Fax: (317) 328-2811
Toll Free: (800) 634-2416
E-mail: info@hurco.com
Web Site: www.hurco.com/usa/Pages/default.aspx
Approx. Sls.: $105,893,000
Approx. Number Employees: 440
Year Founded: 1968
Business Description:
Computerized Metal Component Production Services
S.I.C.: 7371; 3541
N.A.I.C.S.: 541511; 333512
Import Export
Media: 1-2-4-5-7-8-10-11-13-20-22
Distr.: Intl.; Natl.
Personnel:
Michael Doar *(Chm, Pres & CEO)*
John G. Oblazney *(CFO)*
Greg Volovic *(Exec VP-Engrg, Software & Tech)*
Rick Ritter *(Mgr-Mktg)*
Brands & Products:
ACROLOC
AUTOBEND
HURCO
MAX
ULTIMAX
ULTINET
ULTIPATH
ULTIPOCKET
WINMAX

HUTCHINSON TECHNOLOGY INC.

40 W Highland Park Dr NE
Hutchinson, MN 55350-9784
Tel.: (320) 587-3797
Tel.: (320) 587-1605 (Investor Relations)
Fax: (320) 587-1645
E-mail: hti.investors.relations@hti.htch.com
Web Site: www.htch.com
E-Mail For Key Personnel:
Public Relations: CPautz@hti.htch.com
Approx. Sls.: $347,189,000
Approx. Number Employees: 2,546
Year Founded: 1965
Business Description:
Disk Drive Suspension Assemblies Mfr
S.I.C.: 3679; 3826; 3827; 3841; 3845
N.A.I.C.S.: 334419; 333314; 334510; 334516; 339112
Import Export
Media: 10
Distr.: Intl.

Key to Media (For complete agency information see *The Advertising Red Books-Agencies* edition):
1. Bus. Publs. 2. Cable T.V. 3. Catalogs & Directories. 4. Co-op Adv. 5. Consumer Mags. 6. D.M. to Bus. Estab.7. D.M. to Consumers
8. Daily Newsp. 9. Exhibits/Trade Shows 10. Foreign 11. Infomercial 12. Internet Adv.13. Multimedia 14. Network Radio
15. Network T.V. 16. Newsp. Distr. Mags. 17. Other 18. Outdoor (Posters, Transit) 19. Point of Purchase20. Premiums, Novelties
21. Product Samples 22. Special Events Mktg. 23. Spot Radio 24. Spot T.V. 25. Weekly Newsp. 26. Yellow Page Adv.

Hutchinson Technology Inc. — (Continued)

Personnel:
Jeffrey W. Green *(Chm)*
Wayne M. Fortun *(Pres & CEO)*
David P. Radloff *(CFO & VP)*
Richard J. Penn *(Pres-Disk Drive Components Div & Sr VP)*
Peter J. Ollmann *(VP-Engrg & Ops-Disk Drive Components Div)*
Connie L. Pautz *(VP-HR)*
Charles Ives *(Dir-IR)*
Brands & Products:
HUTCHINSON TECHNOLOGY
INSPECTRA

HYLAND SOFTWARE, INC.

(Holding of Thoma Bravo, LLC)
28500 Clemens Rd
Westlake, OH 44145
Tel.: (440) 788-5000
Fax: (440) 788-5100
E-mail: hyland@onbase.com
Web Site: www.hyland.com
E-Mail For Key Personnel:
Marketing Director: marketing@onbase.com
Sales Director: sales@onbase.com
Approx. Number Employees: 275
Year Founded: 1991
Business Description:
Enterprise Content Management Software Developer
S.I.C.: 7372; 7371
N.A.I.C.S.: 511210; 541511
Advertising Expenditures: $2,671,000
Media: 10
Personnel:
A. J. Hyland *(Pres & CEO)*
Chris Hyland *(CFO & Exec VP)*
Bill Priemer *(COO & Exec VP)*
Miguel A. Zubizarreta *(CTO & Exec VP)*
Tim Pembridge *(Gen Counsel & VP)*
Debbie Connelly *(VP-HR)*
Brenda Kirk *(VP-Strategy)*
John Opdycke *(VP-Mktg)*
Steven Thomas *(Mgr-Web Experience)*
Brands & Products:
ENGAGE. EMPOWER. EVOLVE
HYLAND

HYNIX SEMICONDUCTOR AMERICA INC.

(Sub. of Hynix Semiconductor Inc.)
3101 N First St
San Jose, CA 95134
Tel.: (408) 232-8000
Fax: (408) 232-8103
Telex: 278841 HEA UR
Web Site: hsa.hynix.com
Approx. Number Employees: 75
Year Founded: 1983
Business Description:
Semiconductor Mfr & Distr
S.I.C.: 3674; 5045
N.A.I.C.S.: 334413; 423430
Import Export
Advertising Expenditures: $8,040,000
Multimedia: $50,000; Bus. Publs.: $1,000,000; Cable T.V.: $50,000; Catalogs & Directories: $50,000; Co-op Adv.: $3,600,000; Consumer Mags.: $1,000,000; Daily Newsp.: $1,000,000; Exhibits/Trade Shows: $500,000; Other: $50,000; Point of Purchase: $300,000; Premiums, Novelties: $20,000; Product Samples: $100,000; Spot Radio: $20,000; Yellow Page Adv.: $300,000
Distr.: Intl.; Natl.
Personnel:
Paul Palonsky *(Sr VP-Sls)*
Brands & Products:
NORTHBRIDGE
SAVI

I-MANY, INC.

(Holding of LLR Partners, Inc.)
12th Fl 399 Thornall St
Edison, NJ 08837
Tel.: (732) 452-1515
Toll Free: (800) 832-0228
E-mail: info@imany.com
Web Site: www.imany.com
Approx. Rev.: $34,397,000
Approx. Number Employees: 167
Year Founded: 1989
Business Description:
Computer Related Contract & Transaction Compliance Management Solutions
S.I.C.: 7372; 7371; 8748
N.A.I.C.S.: 334611; 511210; 541511; 541690
Media: 10-17
Personnel:
Paul Winn *(Chm)*
P. Kevin Kilroy *(Pres & CEO)*
Kevin M. Harris *(CFO)*
David H. Rode *(Sr VP-Global Ops)*
Mel Walker *(VP & Gen Mgr-Professional Svcs & Support)*
Brands & Products:
EMPOWER YOURSELF
I-MANY CARS
I-MANY CARS BI
I-MANY CARS ENTERPRISE
I-MANY CHARGEBACK VERIFICATION
I-MANY COLLECTIONS MANAGER
I-MANY COMPLIANCE MANAGER
I-MANY CONTRACT ADVISOR
I-MANY CONTRACT ANALYTICS
I-MANY CONTRACT MANAGER
I-MANY CONTRACTSPHERE
I-MANY DEDUCTIONS MANAGER
I-MANY DEMAND MANAGEMENT
I-MANY FFS MANAGEMENT
I-MANY GOVERNMENT PRICING
I-MANY INCENTIVES
I-MANY MASTER DATA MANAGER
I-MANY MEDICAID
I-MANY MEDICAID REBATES
I-MANY MEDICAID STATE & SUPPLEMENTAL
I-MANY SELF SERVICE
I-MANY VALIDATA
IMANY

I/OMAGIC CORPORATION

4 Marconi
Irvine, CA 92618
Tel.: (949) 707-4800
Fax: (949) 855-3550
Web Site: www.iomagic.com
E-Mail For Key Personnel:
Sales Director: sales@iomagic.com
Approx. Sls.: $10,331,740
Approx. Number Employees: 30
Business Description:
Data Storage, Digital Entertainment & Personal Computer, & Peripheral Products Retailer
S.I.C.: 3572; 5044
N.A.I.C.S.: 334112; 423420
Advertising Expenditures: $1,251,282
Media: 5-19-22
Personnel:
Thomas L. Gruber *(CFO & COO)*

IANYWHERE SOLUTIONS, INC.

(Sub. of Sybase, Inc.)
1 Sybase Dr
Dublin, CA 94568-7976
Tel.: (519) 886-3700
Fax: (519) 747-4971
Toll Free: (800) 801-2069
E-mail: contact_us@ianywhere.com
Web Site: www.ianywhere.com
Sales Range: $75-99.9 Million
Approx. Number Employees: 300
Year Founded: 2000
Business Description:
Wireless Mobile Telecommunications Services
S.I.C.: 7371
N.A.I.C.S.: 541511
Media: 2-7-9-10-13-22
Personnel:
Terry M. Stepien *(Pres)*
Brian Vink *(VP-Mktg)*
Juergen Mueller *(VP-Worldwide Sls)*
David Neudoerffer *(VP-Engrg)*
Mike Paola *(Dir-Product Mgmt)*
David Jonker *(Product Mgr)*
Lubos Parobek *(Sr Product Mgr)*
Brands & Products:
AVANTGO
IANYWHERE
IANYWHERE SOLUTIONS
MAIL ANYWHERE STUDIO
MANAGE ANYWHERE STUDIO
PYLON
PYLON APPLICATION SERVER
PYLON CONDUIT
PYLON PRO
SQL ANYWHERE

IBIQUITY DIGITAL CORPORATION

6711 Columbia Gtwy Dr Ste 500
Columbia, MD 21046
Tel.: (410) 872-1530
Fax: (443) 539-4298
E-mail: info@ibiquity.com
Web Site: www.ibiquity.com
Sales Range: $10-24.9 Million
Approx. Number Employees: 94
Year Founded: 2000
Business Description:
Developer & Licenser of HD Radio Technology
S.I.C.: 3663; 4899
N.A.I.C.S.: 334220; 517410
Media: 3-13-16-18-23-24
Personnel:
Robert J. Struble *(Pres & CEO)*
James Spencer *(CFO & Sr VP)*
Jeffrey P. Jury *(COO)*
Brian W. Kroeger *(Mgr & Chief Scientist)*
Albert D. Shuldiner *(Gen Counsel & Sr VP)*
Joseph D'Angelo *(Sr VP-Broadcast Programs & Advanced Svcs)*
Gene Parrella *(Sr VP-Core Engrg)*
Peter Brady *(VP-Mktg & Brand Mgmt)*
Judith L. Kennedy *(VP-HR)*
Walter Berger *(Dir-iChannel Web)*
Richard Greenhut *(Dir-Brdcst Sls-US)*
Gregory Clark *(Sr Mgr-OEM Mktg)*
Brands & Products:
HD DIGITAL RADIO
HD RADIO
IBIQUITY DIGITAL

IBM CANADA LIMITED

(Sub. of International Business Machines Corporation)
3600 Steeles Avenue East
Markham, ON L3R 9Z7, Canada
Tel.: (905) 316-5000
Fax: (905) 316-2535
Toll Free: (800) 426-4968
Web Site: www.ibm.com/ca
Sales Range: $150-199.9 Million
Business Description:
Computers & Computer Products Sales & Services
S.I.C.: 5045; 7378
N.A.I.C.S.: 423430; 811212
Media: 2-6-9-10-13-23-24
Distr.: Natl.
Personnel:
Mike Boden *(Dir-Media Rel)*
Pam Aziz *(Mgr-Demand Programs Mktg)*
Halya Rudiak *(Mgr-Market Segment)*

IBM INTERNET SECURITY SYSTEMS, INC.

(Sub. of IBM Global Technology Services)
6303 Barfield Rd NE
Atlanta, GA 30328-4233
Tel.: (404) 236-2600
Fax: (404) 236-2626
Toll Free: (800) 776-2362
E-mail: support@iss.net
Web Site: www.iss.net
Sales Range: $300-349.9 Million
Approx. Number Employees: 1,252
Year Founded: 1994
Business Description:
Network Security Monitoring, Detection & Response Software & Services
S.I.C.: 7372; 7371
N.A.I.C.S.: 334611; 511210; 541511
Advertising Expenditures: $2,947,000
Media: 2-7-10-13
Personnel:
Raghavan Rajaji *(CFO & Sr VP-Fin)*
Peter Evans *(Sr VP-Mktg)*
Katie Lin *(Mktg Mgr)*
Heidi Litner *(Mgr-Pub Rel)*
Brands & Products:
ACTIVEALERT
ADDME
AHEAD OF THE THREAT
ALERTCON
BLACKICE
DATABASE SCANNER
DYNAMIC THREAT PROTECTION
FIRECELL
FLEXCHECK
INTERNET SCANNER
INTERNET SECURITY SYSTEMS
ONLINE SCANNER
PROVENTIA
REALSECURE
SAFESUITE
SECURE STEPS
SECUREPARTNER
SECUREU
SECURITYFUSION
SITEPROTECTOR
SYSTEM SCANNER
VIRTUAL PATCH

Key to Media (For complete agency information see *The Advertising Red Books-Agencies* edition):
1. Bus. Publs. 2. Cable T.V. 3. Catalogs & Directories. 4. Co-op Adv. 5. Consumer Mags. 6. D.M. to Bus. Estab.7. D.M. to Consumers 8. Daily Newsp. 9. Exhibits/Trade Shows 10. Foreign 11. Infomercial 12. Internet Adv.13. Multimedia 14. Network Radio 15. Network T.V. 16. Newsp. Distr. Mags. 17. Other 18. Outdoor (Posters, Transit) 19. Point of Purchase20. Premiums, Novelties 21. Product Samples 22. Special Events Mktg. 23. Spot Radio 24. Spot T.V. 25. Weekly Newsp. 26. Yellow Page Adv.

WIRELESS SCANNER
X-FORCE
X-PRESS UPDATE

ICEWEB, INC.

22900 Shaw Rd Ste 111
Sterling, VA 20166
Tel.: (517) 287-2388
Tel.: (517) 287-2380
Fax: (517) 287-2396
Toll Free: (800) 465-4637
E-mail: info@iceweb.com
Web Site: www.iceweb.com
Approx. Sls.: $3,353,286
Approx. Number Employees: 23
Year Founded: 1969
Business Description:
Data Storage Products Mfr
S.I.C.: 3572
N.A.I.C.S.: 334112
Advertising Expenditures: $162,862
Media: 2-6-10-13
Personnel:
John R. Signorello *(Chm & CEO)*
Mark B. Lucky *(CFO)*
Karl Chen *(Sr VP-Worldwide Sls & Mktg)*
Dave Skinner *(Sr VP-Engrg & Ops)*
Gina Batali-Brooks *(Dir-Channel Mktg)*
Tracey Floming *(Dir-Corp Mktg)*
Timothy J. McNamee *(Dir-Bus Dev)*
Brands & Products:
ICEWEB

IDEO, INC.

(Sub. of Steelcase Inc.)
100 Forest Ave
Palo Alto, CA 94301
Tel.: (650) 289-3400
Fax: (650) 289-3707
Toll Free: (800) 600-4336
E-mail: reception-paloalto@ideo.com
Web Site: www.ideo.com
Sales Range: $50-74.9 Million
Approx. Number Employees: 200
Business Description:
Design Consultancy Services
S.I.C.: 7389
N.A.I.C.S.: 541990
Media: 6
Personnel:
David Kelley *(Founder & Chm)*
Tim Brown *(Pres & CEO)*
Paul Bennett *(Mng Partner-Europe & Chief Creative Officer)*
David Strong *(CFO & COO)*
Whitney Mortimer *(Sr VP)*

IDT CANADA INC.

(Sub. of Integrated Device Technology, Inc.)
603 March Rd
Kanata, ON K2K 2M5, Canada
Tel.: (613) 592-0714
Fax: (613) 592-1320
Web Site: www.idt.com
Approx. Rev.: $69,245,572
Approx. Number Employees: 276
Business Description:
Semiconductors & Modules for Networking & Communications Markets
S.I.C.: 3674
N.A.I.C.S.: 334413
Advertising Expenditures: $253,232
Media: 2-4-7-10
Personnel:
Tracy Richardson *(VP-Mktg)*
Alan Coady *(Dir-Engrg)*
Brands & Products:
POWERPRO
POWERSPAN
QSPAN
RAPIDIO
SCV64
TSI106
TSI107
TSI148
TSI310
TSI400
TSI500
UNIVERSE

IFCO SYSTEMS NORTH AMERICA

(Sub. of IFCO Systems N.V.)
13100 NW Freeway Ste 625
Easton, TX 77040
Tel.: (713) 332-6145
Fax: (713) 332-6146
E-mail: info@ifcosystems.com
Web Site: www.ifcosystems.com
Approx. Number Employees: 80
Year Founded: 1996
Business Description:
International Logistics Services
S.I.C.: 2449; 2656; 5085
N.A.I.C.S.: 321920; 322215; 423840
Import Export
Advertising Expenditures: $1,000,000
Personnel:
David S. Russell *(Pres)*
Rich Hamlin *(CFO & Sr VP)*
Mike Hachtman *(Sr VP-Sls & Bus Dev)*
Chris Tiesman *(Sr VP-Fin & Acctg)*
Brands & Products:
PALLETS

IGATE CORPORATION

6528 Kaiser Dr
Fremont, CA 94555
Tel.: (510) 896-3015
E-mail: investor@igate.com
Web Site: www.igate.com
Approx. Rev.: $280,597,000
Approx. Number Employees: 8,120
Year Founded: 1986
Business Description:
Holding Company; Information Technology Services
S.I.C.: 7371; 8711
N.A.I.C.S.: 541511; 541330
Media: 2-10
Distr.: Natl.
Personnel:
Ashok Trivedi *(Co-Chm)*
Sunil Wadhwani *(Co-Chm)*
Phaneesh Murthy *(Pres & CEO)*
Sujit Sircar *(CFO)*
Hari Murthy *(Chief Sls & Mktg Officer)*
Sean Narayanan *(Chief Delivery Officer)*

IGT

(Sub. of International Game Technology)
9295 Prototype Dr
Reno, NV 89521
Tel.: (775) 688-0100
Fax: (775) 448-0960
Web Site: www.igt.com
Approx. Sls.: $115,000,000
Approx. Number Employees: 2,200
Business Description:
North America Traditional Casino & Newer Public Gaming Markets
S.I.C.: 3999; 5099
N.A.I.C.S.: 339999; 423990
Advertising Agencies:
The Glenn Group
50 Washington St
Reno, NV 89503-5603
Tel.: (775) 686-7777
Fax: (775) 686-7750

Masterminds
6727 Delilah Rd
Egg Harbor Township, NJ 08234
Tel.: (609) 484-0009
Fax: (609) 484-1909

IKON OFFICE SOLUTIONS, INC.

(Sub. of Ricoh Americas Corporation)
70 Valley Stream Pkwy
Malvern, PA 19355-1407
Mailing Address:
PO Box 834
Valley Forge, PA 19482-0834
Tel.: (610) 296-8000
Fax: (610) 408-7084
Toll Free: (888) ASK-IKON
Toll Free: (888) 456-6457
Web Site: www.ikon.com
Approx. Rev.: $4,168,344,000
Approx. Number Employees: 25,000
Year Founded: 1952
Business Description:
Office Products & Computer & Software Retailer & Distr
S.I.C.: 5045; 5044
N.A.I.C.S.: 423430; 423420
Import Export
Media: 2-4-5-6-7-9-10-11-13-14-18-22-25-26
Personnel:
Jeffrey W. Hickling *(Pres & COO)*
Martin Brodigan *(VP-Corp Fin)*
Wendy Pinckney *(Dir-Comm)*
Brands & Products:
BUSINESS BOOSTER PACK
DOCUMENT EFFICIENCY AT WORK
IKON OFFICE SOLUTIONS
Advertising Agency:
Allen & Gerritsen
The Arsenal on the Charles 311 Arsenal St 4th Fl
Watertown, MA 02472
Tel.: (617) 926-4005
Fax: (617) 926-0133

ILINC COMMUNICATIONS, INC.

2999 N 44th St Ste 650
Phoenix, AZ 85018-7273
Tel.: (602) 952-1200
Fax: (602) 952-0544
Toll Free: (866) 297-9161
E-mail: customerservice@ilinc.com
Web Site: www.ilinc.com
E-Mail For Key Personnel:
Sales Director: sales@ilinc.com
Sales Range: $1-9.9 Million
Approx. Number Employees: 45
Year Founded: 1988
Business Description:
Web Conferencing Software & Audio Conferencing Solutions
S.I.C.: 7373; 3651; 7372
N.A.I.C.S.: 511210; 334310; 334611; 541512
Advertising Expenditures: $125,000
Personnel:
James M. Powers, Jr. *(Chm, Pres & CEO)*
Ethan Abrams *(VP-Product Dev)*
Brands & Products:
CONFERENCELINC
EVENTPLUS
ILINC
LEARNLINC
MEETINGLINC
ON-DEMAND
SUPPORTLINC
WEB & VIDEO CONFERENCING
WEB CONFERENCING
Advertising Agency:
Sacks Public Relations
1641 E Osborn Rd Ste 7
Phoenix, AZ 85016
Tel.: (602) 619-4444
Fax: (602) 357-3405

ILLUMINA, INC.

9885 Towne Centre Dr
San Diego, CA 92121
Tel.: (858) 202-4500
Fax: (858) 202-4545
E-mail: info@illumina.com
Web Site: www.illumina.com
Approx. Rev.: $902,741,000
Approx. Number Employees: 2,100
Year Founded: 1998
Business Description:
Large-scale Genetic Variation & Biological Function Analytical Technologies & Systems Developer, Mfr & Marketer
S.I.C.: 3826; 8733
N.A.I.C.S.: 334516; 541710
Advertising Expenditures: $4,200,000
Media: 10
Personnel:
William H. Rastetter *(Chm)*
Jay T. Flatley *(Pres & CEO)*
Kevin Williams *(Mng Dir)*
Christian O. Henry *(CFO, Sr VP & Gen Mgr-Life Sciences Bus Unit)*
Scott D. Kahn *(CIO)*
Mostafa Ronaghi *(CTO & Sr VP)*
Tristan Orpin *(Chief Comml Officer & Sr VP)*
Christian G. Cabou *(Gen Counsel & Sr VP)*
Gregory F. Heath *(Sr VP & Gen Mgr-Diagnostics Business Unit)*
Bill Bonnar *(Sr VP-Ops)*
Mark Lewis *(Sr VP-Dev)*
Nicholas J. Naclerio *(Sr VP-Corp Dev)*
Mike Bouchard *(VP-Fin & Acctg)*
Paulette Cabral *(VP-HR)*
Robert Kain *(VP-Engrg & Tech Strategy)*
Kirk D. Malloy *(VP-Global Customer Solutions)*
Scott Dawson *(Sr Dir-Treasury)*
Michal Lebl *(Sr Dir)*
Karen Possemato *(Sr Dir-Corp Mktg)*
Maurissa Bornstein *(Mgr-Pub Rel)*
Brands & Products:
ARRAY OF ARRAYS
BEADARRAY
BEADSTATION
BEADSTUDIO
BEADXPRESS
CASAVA
CSPRO
DASL
GOLDENGATE

Key to Media (For complete agency information see *The Advertising Red Books-Agencies* edition):
1. Bus. Publs. 2. Cable T.V. 3. Catalogs & Directories. 4. Co-op Adv. 5. Consumer Mags. 6. D.M. to Bus. Estab.7. D.M. to Consumers 8. Daily Newsp. 9. Exhibits/Trade Shows 10. Foreign 11. Infomercial 12. Internet Adv.13. Multimedia 14. Network Radio 15. Network T.V. 16. Newsp. Distr. Mags. 17. Other 18. Outdoor (Posters, Transit) 19. Point of Purchase20. Premiums, Novelties 21. Product Samples 22. Special Events Mktg. 23. Spot Radio 24. Spot T.V. 25. Weekly Newsp. 26. Yellow Page Adv.

Illumina, Inc. — (Continued)
ILLUMINA
INFINIUM
ISCAN
MAKING SENSE OUT OF LIFE
OLIGATOR
OLIGATOR FARM
SENTRIX
SHERLOCK
VERACODE

IMAGE SENSING SYSTEMS, INC.

1600 University Ave W Ste 500
Saint Paul, MN 55104-3828
Tel.: (651) 603-7700
Fax: (651) 603-7795
E-mail: iss@imagesensing.com
Web Site: www.imagesensing.com
E-Mail For Key Personnel:
Public Relations: EWood@flowtraffic.com
Approx. Rev.: $31,681,000
Approx. Number Employees: 123
Year Founded: 1984
Business Description:
Developer & Marketer of Video Image Processing Technology & Products
S.I.C.: 3824; 3829
N.A.I.C.S.: 334514; 334519
Export
Advertising Expenditures: $153,000
Media: 2-10-13
Distr.: Intl.
Budget Set: Jan. -Dec.
Personnel:
James Murdakes *(Chm)*
Kenneth R. Aubrey *(Pres & CEO)*
Gregory R.L. Smith *(CFO)*
Ken Partyka *(Principal & Engr-Hardware Design)*
Durga Panda *(Sr VP-Sls & Mktg)*
Brands & Products:
AIS CAMERA
AUTOSCOPE
AUTOSCOPE ATLAS
AUTOSCOPE RACKVISION
AUTOSCOPE SOLO
AUTOSCOPE SOLO PRO
IMAGE SENSING SYSTEMS
RTMS

IMAGEWARE SYSTEMS, INC.

10883 Thornmint Rd
San Diego, CA 92127
Tel.: (858) 673-8600
Fax: (858) 673-1770
Toll Free: (800) 842-4199
E-mail: sales@iwsinc.com
Web Site: www.iwsinc.com
E-Mail For Key Personnel:
Sales Director: sales@iwsinc.com
Sales Range: $1-9.9 Million
Approx. Number Employees: 58
Year Founded: 1987
Business Description:
Computer Systems Analyst & Design Services
S.I.C.: 7372
N.A.I.C.S.: 334611; 511210
Media: 2-5-10
Personnel:
S. James Miller, Jr. *(Chm & CEO)*
Wayne G. Wetherell *(CFO & Sr VP-Admin)*
Brands & Products:
BIOMETRIC ENGINE
DESKTOP SECURITY
EPI SUITE
IWS
IWS EPI BUILDER
IWS EPI ID
IWS EPI XPRESS
IWS GREEN SCREEN
IWS LAW ENFORCEMENT
IWS PC EVENT
IWS PC PRO
IWS PROLAB
IWS SCHOOL DAYS PLUS
IWS STUDIO
WINBADGE

IMATION CORP.

1 Imation Way
Oakdale, MN 55128-3414
Tel.: (651) 704-4000
Fax: (888) 704-4200
Toll Free: (888) 466-3456
E-mail: info@imation.com
Web Site: www.imation.com
Approx. Rev.: $1,460,900,000
Approx. Number Employees: 1,115
Year Founded: 1996
Business Description:
Information Storage Device Mfr
S.I.C.: 3695; 3572
N.A.I.C.S.: 334613; 334112
Import Export
Advertising Expenditures: $6,000,000
Media: 1-2-3-4-5-6-7-9-10-13-14-15-18-19-21-22-25
Distr.: Intl.
Budget Set: Sept.
Personnel:
Mark E. Lucas *(Pres & CEO)*
Paul R. Zeller *(CFO & Sr VP)*
Subodh K. Kulkarni *(CTO & Sr VP-Global Comml Bus)*
John L. Sullivan *(Gen Counsel, Sec & Sr VP)*
Greg J. Bosler *(Sr VP-Global Bus Mgmt)*
Ian Williams *(VP-Global Mktg & Product Mgmt)*
Thomas Lally *(Gen Mgr)*
Robert L. Garthwaite *(Gen Mgr-Imation Electronic Products)*
Rusty Rosenberger *(Global Product Dir-SMB Storage)*
Jess Walton *(Dir-Global Brand Mgmt)*
Dean Delserro *(Mgr-Product-Flash & Security Products-Global)*
Jason Elles *(Mgr-Imation Global Brand)*
Brands & Products:
BLACK WATCH
DATAGUARD
DISC STAKKA
DLTTAPE
EARTHWISE
IMATION
MATCHPRINT
MEMOREX IWAKE
OPDITRACKER
RAINBOW
SUPER DLTTAPE
SUPERDISK
TRAVAN
Advertising Agencies:
Brodeur Partners
855 Boylston St 2nd Fl
Boston, MA 02116-2622
Tel.: (617) 587-2800
Fax: (617) 587-2828
Memorex
— Jamie Ernst *(Acct Exec)*
— Josie Lee *(Acct Exec)*

GEM Group
7090 Shady Oak Rd
Eden Prairie, MN 55344
Tel.: (952) 831-6313
Fax: (952) 653-5900

OLSON
1625 Hennepin Ave
Minneapolis, MN 55403
Tel.: (612) 215-9800
Fax: (612) 215-9801
Memorex
TDK Life
WeTime Campaign

TDA Advertising & Design
1500 Pearl St Ste 300
Boulder, CO 80302
Tel.: (303) 247-1180
Fax: (303) 247-1214
(Memorex)

IMERGENT, INC.

1615 S 52nd St
Phoenix, AZ 85281
Tel.: (623) 242-5959
Fax: (775) 530-3955
E-mail: investor_relations@imergentinc.com
Web Site: www.imergentinc.com
Approx. Rev.: $65,793,000
Approx. Number Employees: 297
Year Founded: 1995
Business Description:
Web-Based Technology Solutions
S.I.C.: 7372; 2741; 7373; 7375
N.A.I.C.S.: 511210; 516110; 518111; 541512
Advertising Expenditures: $32,044,000
Personnel:
Steven G. Mihaylo *(CEO)*
Jonathan Erickson *(CFO)*
Jeffrey G. Korn *(Chief Legal Officer)*
David H. Krietzberg *(Chief Admin Officer)*
Clint Sanderson *(Sr VP)*
Jeffrey T. Jarvie *(VP-Fin & Controller)*
Che Oliver *(VP-Mktg)*
Brands & Products:
IMERGENT
STORESONLINE 4.0

IMMERSION CORPORATION

801 Fox Ln
San Jose, CA 95131
Tel.: (408) 467-1900
Fax: (408) 467-1901
Web Site: www.immersion.com
Approx. Rev.: $31,124,000
Approx. Number Employees: 82
Business Description:
Haptic Feedback Technology Developer & Licensor
S.I.C.: 3695; 7374
N.A.I.C.S.: 334613; 518210
Advertising Expenditures: $13,000
Media: 5-10
Personnel:
Jack L. Saltich *(Chm)*
Victor A. Viegas *(Pres & CEO)*
Shum Mukherjee *(CFO)*
Janice Passarello *(VP-HR)*
Brands & Products:
ACCUTOUCH
CAT
CATHSIM
CYBERFORCE
CYBERGLOVE
CYBERGRASP
CYBERIMPACT
CYBERTOUCH
EFEEL
FEEL THE GAME
FEELTHEWEB
FORCE MOUSE
FORCE STICK
GRASPPACK
HAPTIC PROFILER
HAPTICCAD
IMMERSION
IMMERSION STUDIO
IMMERSION TOUCHSENSETECHNOLOGY
IMPULSE ENGINE 2000
IMPULSE STICK
JOLTSTICK
LAPAROSCOPY SIMULATOR
MICROSCRIBE
SOFTMOUSE
TOUCHSENSE
TOUCHWARE
VIBETONE
VIBETONZ
VIRTUALHAND

IMN INCORPORATED

200 Fifth Ave
Waltham, MA 02451
Tel.: (781) 890-4700
Fax: (781) 890-4701
E-mail: marketing@imninc.com
Web Site: www.imninc.com
E-Mail For Key Personnel:
Sales Director: sales@imninc.com
Approx. Number Employees: 20
Year Founded: 1999
Business Description:
Facilitator of E-marketing Strategies
S.I.C.: 8742; 5734
N.A.I.C.S.: 541613; 443120
Media: 10-13
Personnel:
David A. Fish *(Pres)*
Ben Levitan *(CEO)*
Chris Ellis *(VP-Fin & Admin)*
Kimo Kong *(VP-Global Sls)*
Craig Samara *(Exec Dir-Automotive Svcs Grp)*
Lori Fisher *(Dir-Opers)*
Michelle Larter *(Dir-Worldwide Direct Selling)*
Gary Van Houten *(Dir-Natl Sls-OEM)*
Brands & Products:
DIRECTBLOG
ELETRA
IMAKENEWS
IMN
LOYALTY DRIVER
THE MORE YOU USE IT, THE SMARTER YOU GET.
PARTY PULSE

IMPAC MEDICAL SYSTEMS, INC.

(Sub. of Elekta AB)
100 Methilda Pl
Sunnyvale, CA 94086

Key to Media (For complete agency information see *The Advertising Red Books-Agencies* edition):
1. Bus. Publs. 2. Cable T.V. 3. Catalogs & Directories. 4. Co-op Adv. 5. Consumer Mags. 6. D.M. to Bus. Estab.7. D.M. to Consumers
8. Daily Newsp. 9. Exhibits/Trade Shows 10. Foreign 11. Infomercial 12. Internet Adv.13. Multimedia 14. Network Radio
15. Network T.V. 16. Newsp. Distr. Mags. 17. Other 18. Outdoor (Posters, Transit) 19. Point of Purchase20. Premiums, Novelties
21. Product Samples 22. Special Events Mktg. 23. Spot Radio 24. Spot T.V. 25. Weekly Newsp. 26. Yellow Page Adv.

Tel.: (650) 623-8800
Fax: (408) 830-8003
Web Site: www.impac.com
Approx. Number Employees: 200
Business Description:
Computer Software Development
S.I.C.: 7372
N.A.I.C.S.: 511210
Export
Advertising Expenditures: $542,000
Media: 4-7-10-11
Personnel:
James P. Hoey *(Co-founder & COO)*
Scott T. Soehl *(Sr VP-Oncology Sls)*
Todd M. Powell *(VP-Engrg)*
Suzanne M. Hoey *(Product Mgr)*
Brands & Products:
ACCOUNT
ECHART
INTELLILAB
POWERPATH
SUPPORT PLUS

IMPRESO, INC.
652 Southwestern Blvd
Coppell, TX 75019-4419
Mailing Address:
PO Box 506
Coppell, TX 75019-0506
Tel.: (972) 462-0100
Fax: (972) 462-7764
Fax: (800) 562-5359
Toll Free: (800) 527-2878
E-mail: service@tstimpreso.com
Web Site: www.tstimpreso.com
Approx. Sls.: $62,158,536
Approx. Number Employees: 200
Year Founded: 1976
Business Description:
Holding Company; Manifold Business Forms Mfr
S.I.C.: 2761; 6719
N.A.I.C.S.: 323116; 551112
Import Export
Advertising Expenditures: $1,100,000
Media: 2-4-13
Personnel:
Marshall D. Sorokwasz *(Chm, Pres, CEO & Treas)*
Susan M. Atkins *(CFO & VP-Fin)*
Jeffrey Boren *(VP-Sls & Mktg)*
Dwight Staubs *(Mgr-Reg Sls)*
Brands & Products:
IMPRESO
LAZER BOND
LAZER CUT SHEETS

INCENTRA LLC
(Name Changed to Presilient, LLC)

INCONTACT, INC.
7730 S Union Park Ave Ste 500
Midvale, UT 84047
Tel.: (801) 320-3200
Fax: (801) 320-3330
Toll Free: (800) 999-7691
E-mail: info@incontact.com
Web Site: www.incontact.com
Approx. Rev.: $82,155,000
Approx. Number Employees: 330
Year Founded: 1997
Business Description:
Business Telecommunications & Software Products
S.I.C.: 4813; 3663; 4899; 7372
N.A.I.C.S.: 517310; 334220; 511210; 517110; 517910
Advertising Expenditures: $650,000
Personnel:
Theodore Stern *(Chm)*
Paul Jarman *(CEO)*
Gregory S. Ayers *(CFO & Exec VP)*
Scott Welch *(COO, Chief Security Officer & Exec VP)*
Sunny Gosain *(Chief Product Officer & Exec VP)*
Frank Maylett *(Exec VP-Sls & Global Alliances)*
Jim Tanner *(Exec VP-Product & Strategy)*
Durinda Biesman *(Sr VP-Global Svc Delivery)*
Bassam Salem *(Sr VP-Prof Svcs)*
Shanna Lelli *(VP-HR)*
Jason Williams *(Sr Mgr-Product)*
Brands & Products:
ECHO
INCONTACT
INTOUCH
Advertising Agency:
SNG PR
14193 S Minuteman Dr Ste 100
Salt Lake City, UT 84020
Tel.: (801) 208-1100
Fax: (801) 208-1109

INDUS CORPORATION
1951 Kidwell Dr 8th Fl
Vienna, VA 22182
Tel.: (703) 506-6700
Fax: (703) 506-6776
Web Site: www.induscorp.com
Approx. Sls.: $19,997,056
Approx. Number Employees: 130
Business Description:
Custom Computer Programming Services
S.I.C.: 7371; 7372
N.A.I.C.S.: 541511; 511210
Personnel:
Shivram Krishnan *(Chm & CEO)*
Don Fulford *(Sr VP)*
Brian Geehan *(Sr VP-Defense & Intelligence Bus Unit)*
Patty Nunn *(Sr VP-Defense & Intelligence Sector)*
Richard McKay *(Dir-Health Informatics & Tech)*
Advertising Agency:
Focused Image
2941 Fairview Park Dr Ste 650
Falls Church, VA 22042
Tel.: (703) 739-8803
Fax: (703) 739-8809

INDUSTRIAL DISTRIBUTION GROUP, INC.
(Holding of Luther King Capital Management)
2100 The Oaks Pkwy
Belmont, NC 28012
Mailing Address:
PO Box 1127
Belmont, NC 28012
Tel.: (704) 398-5600
Fax: (704) 398-5610
Toll Free: (800) 476-3555
E-mail: contactus@idg-corp.com
Web Site: www.idg-corp.com
Approx. Sls.: $537,456,000
Approx. Number Employees: 1,240
Year Founded: 1997
Business Description:
Supplier of Procurement Solutions for Manufacturers
S.I.C.: 3821; 1796; 3531; 3559; 5084; 5085
N.A.I.C.S.: 339111; 238290; 333120; 333298; 423830; 423840
Export
Advertising Expenditures: $573,000
Personnel:
Charles A. Lingenfelter *(Pres & CEO)*
Brands & Products:
INDUSTRIAL DISTRIBUTION

INFERX CORPORATION
46950 Jennings Farm Dr Ste 290
Sterling, VA 20164
Tel.: (703) 444-6030
E-mail: sales@inferx.com
Web Site: www.inferx.com
Approx. Rev.: $4,712,299
Approx. Number Employees: 38
Business Description:
Predictive Analytics & Business Intelligence Solutions
S.I.C.: 7372
N.A.I.C.S.: 511210
Advertising Expenditures: $32,205
Media: 17
Personnel:
B. K. Gogia *(Founder & Chm)*
Jerzy W. Bala *(Co-Founder & CTO)*
Vijay Suri *(Pres & CEO)*
Ray Piluso *(COO)*
Ben Chou *(Dir-Sls)*

INFOCROSSING, INC.
(Sub. of Wipro Limited)
2 Christie Heights St
Leonia, NJ 07605
Tel.: (201) 840-4700
Fax: (201) 840-7100
Toll Free: (888) 757-7501
E-mail: info@infocrossing.com
Web Site: www.infocrossing.com
E-Mail For Key Personnel:
Sales Director: sales@infocrossing.com
Approx. Rev.: $229,207,000
Approx. Number Employees: 882
Year Founded: 1984
Business Description:
Information Technology Services, Data Center Outsourcing, Infrastructure Management Consulting & Internet Data Center & Colocation Services
S.I.C.: 7374
N.A.I.C.S.: 518210
Media: 5-7-10
Personnel:
Sameer Kishore *(Pres)*
Nicholas J. Letizia *(Gen Counsel & Sr VP)*
Lindsey Stava *(Exec VP-Mktg & Bus Dev)*
Garry Lazarewicz *(Sr VP-R&D)*
Brands & Products:
INFOCROSSING

INFOGIX INC.
1240 E Diehl Rd Ste 400
Naperville, IL 60563
Tel.: (630) 505-1800
Fax: (630) 505-1812
E-mail: info@infogix.com
Web Site: www.infogix.com
Sales Range: $25-49.9 Million
Approx. Number Employees: 150
Business Description:
Business Oriented Computer Software
S.I.C.: 7372; 8742
N.A.I.C.S.: 511210; 541611
Personnel:
Madhavan Nayar *(Pres)*
Ramon Nayar *(Sr VP-Svcs)*
Brands & Products:
ACR/DETAIL
ACR ESSENTIALS
ACR/FILE
ACR/INMATCH
ACR/INSTREAM
ACR/PC WORKBENCH
ACR/SUMMARY
ACR/WEBVIEW
CONTROLSINSIGHT
INFORMATION INTEGRITY
Advertising Agency:
Daniel J. Edelman, Inc.
(d/b/a Edelman)
200 E Randolph St Fl 63
Chicago, IL 60601-6705
Tel.: (312) 240-3000
Fax: (312) 240-2900
— Brittany Morris *(Acct Exec)*

INFOLOGIX, INC.
101 E County Line Rd
Hatboro, PA 19040
Tel.: (215) 604-0691
Fax: (215) 604-0695
Web Site: www.infologixsys.com
Approx. Rev.: $86,916,000
Approx. Number Employees: 168
Year Founded: 2004
Business Description:
Holding Company; Electronic Medical Record & Supply Chain Implementation Services
S.I.C.: 6719; 5045; 7374; 7379; 7389
N.A.I.C.S.: 551112; 425110; 518210; 519190; 541519
Advertising Expenditures: $508,000
Personnel:
David T. Gulian *(Pres & CEO)*
John A. Roberts *(CFO)*
Eric N. Rubino *(COO)*
Gerry Bartley *(Mng Dir-Healthcare Consulting & Exec VP)*
Brian Thorn *(Sr VP-Enterprise)*
Philip Ballai *(VP-Tech)*
Jason Fradin *(VP-Mktg & Comm)*
Advertising Agency:
Porter Novelli-Boston
2 Seaport Ln Ste 900
Boston, MA 02110
Tel.: (617) 897-8200
Fax: (617) 897-8203

INFONOW CORPORATION
1875 Lawrence St Ste 1200
Denver, CO 80202
Tel.: (303) 293-0212
Fax: (303) 293-0213
Toll Free: (866) 868INOW
E-mail: info@infonow.com
Web Site: www.infonow.com
Sales Range: $10-24.9 Million
Approx. Number Employees: 85
Year Founded: 1990
Business Description:
Enterprise Channel Management Software & Services
S.I.C.: 5045; 7371
N.A.I.C.S.: 423430; 541511
Media: 5-7-10-11-13

Key to Media (For complete agency information see *The Advertising Red Books-Agencies* edition):
1. Bus. Publs. 2. Cable T.V. 3. Catalogs & Directories. 4. Co-op Adv. 5. Consumer Mags. 6. D.M. to Bus. Estab.7. D.M. to Consumers
8. Daily Newsp. 9. Exhibits/Trade Shows 10. Foreign 11. Infomercial 12. Internet Adv.13. Multimedia 14. Network Radio
15. Network T.V. 16. Newsp. Distr. Mags. 17. Other 18. Outdoor (Posters, Transit) 19. Point of Purchase20. Premiums, Novelties
21. Product Samples 22. Special Events Mktg. 23. Spot Radio 24. Spot T.V. 25. Weekly Newsp. 26. Yellow Page Adv.

InfoNow Corporation — (Continued)

Personnel:
Mark Geene *(CEO)*
Michelle Yates *(VP-Sls-LocationInsight)*
Brandon Brancato *(Dir-Admin & Fin)*

Brands & Products:
ANALYTICINSIGHT
CHANNELINSIGHT
DATACONNECT
INOFNOW
LOCATIONINSIGHT
VISIBILITY THROUGH INSIGHT

INFOR

(Formerly Infor Global Solutions, Inc.)
(Joint Venture of Summit Partners L.P. & Golden Gate Capital)
13560 Morris Rd Ste 4100
Alpharetta, GA 30004
Tel.: (678) 319-8000
Fax: (678) 393-5001
Toll Free: (800) 260-2640
E-mail: inforinfo@infor.com
Web Site: www.infor.com
Sales Range: $1-4.9 Billion
Approx. Number Employees: 8,100
Business Description:
Enterprise Software Mfr; Owned by Golden Gate Capital, Inc. & Summit Partners LP
S.I.C.: 5045
N.A.I.C.S.: 423430
Export
Media: 4-8-10-13

Personnel:
Jim Schaper *(Chm)*
Charles E. Phillips, Jr. *(CEO)*
Kevin Samuelson *(CFO)*
Pam Murphy *(COO)*
Bruce Richardson *(Chief Strategy Officer & Sr VP)*
Gregory M. Giangiordano *(Gen Counsel, Sec & Sr VP)*
Marylon McGinnis *(Sr VP-Global Support)*
Cindy Cronin *(VP & Gen Mgr-Process Grp)*
Sandra Hofmann *(VP-Mktg Comm)*
Rick Parker *(VP-Global Mktg)*

INFORMATICA CORPORATION

100 Cardinal Way
Redwood City, CA 94063-4755
Tel.: (650) 385-5000
Fax: (650) 385-5500
Toll Free: (800) 653-3871
Toll Free: (800) 970-1179
E-mail: information@information.com
Web Site: www.informatica.com
Approx. Rev.: $650,076,000
Approx. Number Employees: 2,126
Year Founded: 1993
Business Description:
Enterprise Data Integration Software & Services
S.I.C.: 7372; 7371
N.A.I.C.S.: 511210; 334611; 541511
Advertising Expenditures: $2,000,000
Media: 2-10-13

Personnel:
Sohaib Abbasi *(Chm & CEO)*
Earl E. Fry *(CFO, Chief Admin Officer & Exec VP-Global Customer Support)*
Tony Young *(CIO & Sr VP)*
Chris Boorman *(CMO & Sr VP-Education & Enablement)*
James Markarian *(CTO & Exec VP)*
Paul J. Hoffman *(Exec VP & Pres-Worldwide Field Ops)*
Ivan Chong *(Exec VP-Data Quality Product Div)*
Girish Pancha *(Exec VP-Data Integration Product)*
Ansa Sekharan *(Sr VP-Global Customer Support)*
Tonya Nicholson-Chung *(Mgr-IR)*
Jill Sugita-Hulme *(Mgr-Mktg Campaigns)*

Brands & Products:
ANALYTIC BUSINESS COMPONENTS
THE DATA INTEGRATION COMPANY
INFORMATICA
INFORMATICA BUSINESS OPERATIONS ANALYTICS
INFORMATICA CUSTOMER RELATIONSHIP ANALYTICS
INFORMATICA DATA EXPLORER
INFORMATICA DATA INTEGRATION PLATFORM
INFORMATICA DATA QUALITY
INFORMATICA FINANCIAL ANALYTICS
INFORMATICA HUMAN RESOURCE ANALYTICS
INFORMATICA IDENTITY SOLUTION
INFORMATICA SUPERGLUE
INFORMATICA SUPPLY CHAIN ANALYTICS
INFORMATICA WAREHOUSE
INFORMATICA WEB CHANNEL ANALYTICS
MX
MX2
NOW YOU KNOW
POWERANALYZER
POWERANALYZER INSIGHT
POWERANALYZER MOBILE
POWERBRIDGE
POWERCAPTURE
POWERCENTER
POWERCENTER CONNECT
POWERCHANNEL
POWERCONNECT
POWEREXCHANGE
POWERMART
POWERPARTNER
POWERPLUG
TURNING INTEGRATION INTO INSIGHT
VELOCITY

INFORMATION BUILDERS INC.

2 Penn Plz
New York, NY 10121-0101
Tel.: (212) 736-4433
Fax: (212) 967-6406
Toll Free: (800) 969-4636
E-mail: askinfo@ibi.com
Web Site: www.informationbuilders.com
Sales Range: $300-349.9 Million
Approx. Number Employees: 1,750
Year Founded: 1975
Business Description:
Computer Software Developers
S.I.C.: 7373; 6794
N.A.I.C.S.: 541512; 533110
Export
Advertising Expenditures: $7,000,000
Media: 2-4-7-10-12-13-22
Distr.: Intl.; Natl.
Budget Set: Nov.

Personnel:
Gerald D. Cohen *(Founder, Pres & CEO)*
Harry Lerner *(CFO & Sr VP)*
Michael Corcoran *(CMO & Sr VP)*
Timothy Benthall *(Sr VP-Sys & Comm)*
Bob Gabriel *(Sr VP-Prof Svcs)*
Peter Mittelman *(Sr VP-FOCUS Div)*
Monte Roy *(Sr VP-Sls)*
David Sandel *(Sr VP-Bus Intelligence Products Grp)*
John G. Senor *(Sr VP-Channels & Dev)*
David Small *(Sr VP-Intl)*
David Watson *(Sr VP-iWay Software)*
Dennis Bartels *(VP-Sls-EMEA)*
Rich Hall *(VP-Sls-Western Area)*
Ryan Irwin *(VP-Sls-Central Area)*
Bill Macy *(VP-Sls)*
Dennis McLaughlin *(VP-Sls-iWay Software)*
Melissa Treier *(VP-Sls-WebFocus)*
Dave Upton *(VP-Sls-Southern Area)*
Gregory Dorman *(Gen Mgr-iWay Software Div)*
Joe Lui *(Dir-Agent Ops & Intl)*
Elizabeth Whitelock *(Dir-Sls & Mktg)*

Brands & Products:
EDA/SQL
ENTERPRISE DATA ACCESS/SQL
ETL
FOCAUDIT
FOCMAN
FOCUS
FOCUS/ELS
FOCUS FOR WINDOWS
FOCUS FUSION
INFORMATION BUILDERS
LEVEL 5 OBJECT
WEBFOCUS

Advertising Agency:
Lewis PR
535 Boylston St Ste 603
Boston, MA 02116
Tel.: (617) 226-8840
Fax: (617) 421-8619

INFORMATION RESOURCES, INC.

(Sub. of Symphony Technology Group, LLC)
150 N Clinton St
Chicago, IL 60661
Tel.: (770) 308-2341
Fax: (312) 726-0360
Toll Free: (800) 317-6245
E-mail: info@infores.com
Web Site: www.infores.com
Sales Range: $700-749.9 Million
Approx. Number Employees: 4,000
Year Founded: 1983
Business Description:
Computer Based Systems & Services for Collection & Analysis of Detailed Market Information on Sales of Consumer Packaged Goods
S.I.C.: 8732; 7373; 8742
N.A.I.C.S.: 541910; 541512; 541613
Export
Advertising Expenditures: $1,000,000
Media: 1-2-4-7-10
Distr.: Natl.
Budget Set: Sept. -Nov.

Personnel:
Romesh T. Wadhwani *(Chm)*
John Freeland *(Pres & CEO)*
Mike Duffey *(CFO)*
Jane Altobelli *(Exec VP-HR & Chief People Officer)*
Thom Blischok *(Pres-Innovation & Strategy)*
Nigel Howlett *(Pres-IRI Intl)*
Thomas E. Peterson *(Pres-Retail Grp)*
Robert I. Tomei *(Pres-Consumer & Shopper Mktg)*
Mike Kaskie *(Exec VP & Gen Mgr-Market Info Grp)*
Lynda Gammell *(Exec VP-European Tech-Symphony IRI Grp)*
Scott Pearce *(Exec VP-IRI Ops & Client Svc-Symphony IRI Grp)*
J.P. Beauchamp *(Sr VP)*
John McIndoe *(Sr VP-Mktg)*
Alexander Arbouw *(Dir-Bus & Consumer Insights-Symphony IRI Grp)*
Shelley Hughes *(Dir-PR)*
Tom Newitt *(Brand Mgr)*

Brands & Products:
APOLLO
BEHAVIOR SCAN
EUROPANEL
INFOSCAN

INGRAM MICRO INC.

1600 E Saint Andrew Pl
Santa Ana, CA 92799-5125
Tel.: (714) 566-1000
Fax: (714) 566-9440
E-mail: investor.relations@ingrammicro.com
Web Site: www.ingrammicro.com
Approx. Sls.: $34,588,984,000
Approx. Number Employees: 15,650
Year Founded: 1979
Business Description:
Information Technology Hardware, Software, Peripherals & Accessories Wholesale Distr
S.I.C.: 5044; 5045
N.A.I.C.S.: 423420; 423430
Export
Media: 5-7-8-10-13-17
Distr.: Natl.
Budget Set: Nov.

Personnel:
Dale R. Laurance *(Chm)*
Alain Monie *(Pres & COO)*
Gregory M. E. Spierkel *(CEO)*
William D. Humes *(CFO & Sr Exec VP)*
Mario F. Leone *(CIO & Exec VP)*
Keith W. F. Bradley *(Pres-North America & Sr Exec VP)*
Shailendra Gupta *(Pres-Asia Pacific & Sr Exec VP)*
Alain Maquet *(Pres-EMEA & Exec VP)*
Lisa Locklear *(CFO-North America & Sr VP)*
Larry C. Boyd *(Gen Counsel, Sec & Exec VP)*
Paul Bay *(Exec VP-North America)*
Robert K. Gifford *(Exec VP-Logistics-Global)*
Lynn Jolliffe *(Exec VP-HR, Worldwide)*
Ria M. Carlson *(Sr VP-Comm & Brand Mgmt)*
Sam Kamel *(Sr VP-Corp Strategy)*
Brian Wiser *(Sr VP-Comml & Consumer Markets Divs)*
Ken Bast *(VP & Gen Mgr-Advanced Tech Div)*
Justin Scopaz *(VP & Gen Mgr)*
Mark Snider *(VP & Gen Mgr-Canada)*

Key to Media (For complete agency information see *The Advertising Red Books-Agencies* edition):
1. Bus. Publs. 2. Cable T.V. 3. Catalogs & Directories. 4. Co-op Adv. 5. Consumer Mags. 6. D.M. to Bus. Estab.7. D.M. to Consumers
8. Daily Newsp. 9. Exhibits/Trade Shows 10. Foreign 11. Infomercial 12. Internet Adv.13. Multimedia 14. Network Radio
15. Network T.V. 16. Newsp. Distr. Mags. 17. Other 18. Outdoor (Posters, Transit) 19. Point of Purchase20. Premiums, Novelties
21. Product Samples 22. Special Events Mktg. 23. Spot Radio 24. Spot T.V. 25. Weekly Newsp. 26. Yellow Page Adv.

Kirk Robinson *(VP-Channel Mktg-North America)*
Daniel Sheehan *(Dir-Market Dev)*
Chris Balentine *(Mgr-Vendor Bus-Consumer Electronics Div)*

Brands & Products:
INGRAM MICRO

Advertising Agencies:
760 Media, Inc.
6965 El Camino Real Ste 105-543
Carlsbad, CA 92011
Tel.: (760) 603-8133
Fax: (760) 603-8138
Toll Free: (888) 760-4332

Capita Technologies, Inc.
17600 Gillette Ave
Irvine, CA 92614
Tel.: (949) 260-3000
Fax: (949) 851-9875

WhiteFox Marketing & Communications
1038 E Bastanchury Rd Ste 311
Fullerton, CA 92835
Tel.: (714) 680-0335
Fax: (949) 666-5059

INITIATE SYSTEMS, INC.

(Sub. of International Business Machines Corporation)
200 W Madison St Ste 2300
Chicago, IL 60606
Tel.: (312) 759-5030
Fax: (312) 759-5026
Toll Free: (800) 992-0300
E-mail: info@initiatesystems.com
Web Site: www.initiate.com
Sales Range: $25-49.9 Million
Approx. Number Employees: 241
Business Description:
Real-Time Data Management Systems
S.I.C.: 7374; 7372; 7389
N.A.I.C.S.: 518210; 511210; 519190
Media: 7-10-13-17
Personnel:
Ronald H. Galowich *(Chm)*
William M. Conroy *(Pres)*
Dan Kossman *(CFO)*
Jeffrey A. Galowich *(Exec VP)*
Scott Schumacher *(Sr VP & Chief Scientist)*
Gina Sandon *(VP-Mktg)*
David J. Wilkinson *(VP-Engrg)*

INSIGHT ENTERPRISES, INC.

6820 S Harl Ave
Tempe, AZ 85283-4318
Tel.: (480) 333-3000
Toll Free: (800) INSIGHT
E-mail: slabour@insight.com
Web Site: www.insight.com
Approx. Sls.: $4,809,930,000
Approx. Number Employees: 5,115
Year Founded: 1988
Business Description:
Information Technology Products, Services & Solutions
S.I.C.: 7373; 5045; 7379
N.A.I.C.S.: 541512; 423430; 541519
Advertising Expenditures: $23,736,000
Media: 2-3-4-5-7-10-13-22
Personnel:
Timothy A. Crown *(Founder & Chm)*
Kenneth T. Lamneck *(Pres & CEO)*
Glynis A. Bryan *(CFO)*
Steven Robert Andrews *(Chief Admin Officer, Gen Counsel & Sec)*
David C. Olsen *(Chief Acctg Officer, Sr VP & Controller)*
Helen K. Johnson *(Treas & Sr VP)*
Erich Jacobs *(Sr VP-Software Svcs)*
Stephen Speidel *(Sr VP-Ops)*

INSIGHT ENTERPRISES, INC.

(Sub. of Insight Enterprises, Inc.)
444 Scott Dr
Bloomingdale, IL 60108
Tel.: (630) 924-6700
Fax: (630) 351-7497
Toll Free: (800) 321-2437
Web Site: www.insight.com
Sales Range: $700-749.9 Million
Approx. Number Employees: 1,364
Year Founded: 1977
Business Description:
Distributor of Computer Media & Peripheral Equipment
S.I.C.: 5045
N.A.I.C.S.: 423430
Advertising Expenditures: $3,800,000
Distr.: Reg.

INSIGHT ENTERPRISES, INC.

(Sub. of Insight Enterprises, Inc.)
3480 Lotus Dr
Plano, TX 75075
Tel.: (469) 443-3900
Fax: (720) 567-0111
Toll Free: (800) 624-0503
Web Site: www.insight.com
Sales Range: $1-4.9 Billion
Approx. Number Employees: 1,200
Year Founded: 1983
Business Description:
Business Software Reseller
S.I.C.: 5045
N.A.I.C.S.: 423430
Media: 2-6-7-10-18
Distr.: Natl.
Budget Set: July
Personnel:
Ken Lamneck *(Pres & CEO)*

Brands & Products:
SOFTWARE SPECTRUM

INSPERITY, INC.

(Formerly Administaff, Inc.)
19001 Crescent Springs Dr
Kingwood, TX 77339-3802
Tel.: (281) 358-8986
Fax: (281) 348-3718
Toll Free: (800) 237-3170
Web Site: www.insperity.com
Approx. Rev.: $1,719,752,000
Approx. Number Employees: 1,900
Year Founded: 1986
Business Description:
Personnel Management Services
S.I.C.: 8742; 7363
N.A.I.C.S.: 541611; 561320; 561330
Advertising Expenditures: $16,447,000
Media: 7-8-10
Personnel:
Paul J. Sarvadi *(Chm & CEO)*
Richard G. Rawson *(Pres)*
Douglas S. Sharp *(CFO, Treas & Sr VP-Fin)*
A. Steve Arizpe *(COO & Exec VP-Client Svcs)*
Daniel D. Herink *(Gen Counsel, Sec & Sr VP-Legal)*
Jay E. Mincks *(Exec VP-Sls & Mktg)*
Mark W. Allen *(Sr VP-Strategic Plng)*
Gregory R. Clouse *(Sr VP-Svc Ops)*
Betty L. Collins *(Sr VP-Corp HR)*
Jason Cutbirth *(Sr VP-Mktg & Corp Comm)*
Samuel G. Larson *(Sr VP-Enterprise & Tech Solutions)*
Ronald M. McGee *(Sr VP-Property & Casualty Products Svcs)*
Martin K. Scirratt *(Sr VP-Sls)*

Brands & Products:
EMPLOYEE SERVICE CENTER
GOOD FOR SMALL BUSINESS
MARKETPLACE
PERSONNEL MANAGEMENT SYSTEM

Advertising Agencies:
MichaelsWilder
7773 W Golden Ln
Peoria, AZ 85345-7977
Tel.: (623) 334-0100
Fax: (623) 334-0200
Toll Free: (800) 423-6468

NEXTMedia Inc.
3625 N Hall St Ste 1100
Dallas, TX 75219
Tel.: (214) 252-1782
Fax: (214) 525-4852

INSPRO TECHNOLOGIES CORPORATION

(Formerly HEALTH BENEFITS DIRECT CORPORATION)
150 N Radnor-Chester Rd Ste B-101
Radnor, PA 19087
Tel.: (484) 654-2200
E-mail: info@inspro.com
Web Site: www.inspro.com
Approx. Rev.: $6,077,358
Approx. Number Employees: 46
Business Description:
Life & Health Insurance Software Products
S.I.C.: 7372; 6411
N.A.I.C.S.: 511210; 524298
Advertising Expenditures: $4,357,986
Personnel:
Donald R. Caldwell *(Chm)*
Warren V. Musser *(Vice Chm)*
Anthony R. Verdi *(CFO)*

Brands & Products:
INSURINT

INTCOMEX, INC.

3505 NW 107th Ave
Miami, FL 33178
Tel.: (305) 477-6230
Fax: (305) 477-5694
E-mail: info@intcomex.com
Web Site: www.intcomex.com.
Approx. Rev.: $1,013,272,000
Approx. Number Employees: 1,438
Year Founded: 1989
Business Description:
Computer Software Wholesale Distr
S.I.C.: 7389
N.A.I.C.S.: 425120
Media: 4-10-11-22
Personnel:
Anthony Shalom *(Chm)*
Michael Shalom *(Pres, CEO & Dir)*
Russell Olson *(CFO, Treas & Sec)*
Arturo Esguerra *(Mgr-Mktg & Comm)*

INTEC OUTSOURCING SERVICES, INC.

(Sub. of Intec Billing, Inc.)
301 Perimeter Ctr N Ste 200
Atlanta, GA 30346
Tel.: (404) 705-2800
Fax: (404) 705-2805
E-mail: info@intecbilling.com
Web Site: www.intecbilling.com
Approx. Number Employees: 200
Year Founded: 1960
Business Description:
Billing & Revenue Management Software & Services
S.I.C.: 7374; 8721
N.A.I.C.S.: 518210; 541219
Media: 7-10-11

INTEGRACORE, INC.

3822 W 1987 S
Salt Lake City, UT 84104
Tel.: (801) 975-9411
Fax: (801) 975-9394
Toll Free: (800) 732-3475
E-mail: info@integracore.com
Web Site: www.integracore.com
Approx. Sls.: $14,000,000
Approx. Number Employees: 100
Year Founded: 1987
Business Description:
Outsource Solutions
S.I.C.: 7379; 2752
N.A.I.C.S.: 541519; 323110
Media: 6

INTEGRAL SYSTEMS, INC.

6721 Columbia Gateway Dr
Columbia, MD 21046
Tel.: (443) 539-5008
Toll Free: (800) 295-4233
E-mail: earthdata@integ.com
Web Site: www.integ.com
E-Mail For Key Personnel:
Sales Director: sales@integ.com
Approx. Rev.: $177,895,000
Approx. Number Employees: 690
Year Founded: 1982
Business Description:
Satellite Ground Systems for Satellite Command & Control, Payload Processing & Integration & Test
S.I.C.: 3572; 7371; 7373
N.A.I.C.S.: 334112; 541511; 541512
Export
Advertising Expenditures: $600,000
Media: 2-7-10
Distr.: Intl.; Natl.
Personnel:
John M. Albertine *(Chm)*
Paul G. Casner, Jr. *(Pres & CEO)*
Christopher B. Roberts *(CFO & Treas)*
R. Miller Adams *(Gen Counsel & Exec VP-Corp Affairs)*
Stuart C. Daughtridge *(Exec VP-Space Comm Sys Grp)*
James B. Kramer *(Sr VP & Gen Mgr-Civil & Comml Sys)*
Robert F. Wright, Jr. *(Sr VP, Gen Mgr-Military & Intelligence Grp)*
Ernest L. Dickens *(VP & Gen Mgr-Integral Sys Svc Solutions)*
Mark Hayes *(VP-Strategic Bus Dev)*
Kathryn J. Herr *(VP-Mktg & Comm)*
Hemi Lee-Gallagher *(VP-Fin)*

Brands & Products:
ABE
ARCHIVE MANAGER
ARES

Key to Media (For complete agency information see *The Advertising Red Books-Agencies* edition):
1. Bus. Publs. 2. Cable T.V. 3. Catalogs & Directories. 4. Co-op Adv. 5. Consumer Mags. 6. D.M. to Bus. Estab.7. D.M. to Consumers 8. Daily Newsp. 9. Exhibits/Trade Shows 10. Foreign 11. Infomercial 12. Internet Adv.13. Multimedia 14. Network Radio 15. Network T.V. 16. Newsp. Distr. Mags. 17. Other 18. Outdoor (Posters, Transit) 19. Point of Purchase20. Premiums, Novelties 21. Product Samples 22. Special Events Mktg. 23. Spot Radio 24. Spot T.V. 25. Weekly Newsp. 26. Yellow Page Adv.

Integral Systems, Inc. — (Continued)

EPOCH
EPOCH CLIENT
EPOCH T&C
EPOCH TRIGGERS
EPOCH TRIGGERS SERVICE
EPOCH VERSION 4
EPOCH WEB SERVER
ESCRIBE
GSA
INTEGRAL SYSTEMS
OASYS
OPSLOG
TASK INITIATOR
TRECS

INTEGRATED SOFTWARE DESIGN, INC.

171 Forbes Blvd
Mansfield, MA 02048
Tel.: (508) 339-4928
Fax: (508) 339-2257
Toll Free: (800) 600-2242
E-mail: info2005@isdweb.com
Web Site: www.isdweb.com
Approx. Sls.: $2,500,000
Approx. Number Employees: 26
Year Founded: 1982
Business Description:
Software & Systems Integration Products
S.I.C.: 7371
N.A.I.C.S.: 541511
Export
Advertising Expenditures: $200,000
Media: 4-6-7-8-10-13
Distr.: Intl.; Natl.
Personnel:
Ramin Khoshatefeh *(CEO)*
Brands & Products:
ENLABEL
INTEGRATED SOFTWARE DESIGN
KNOWLEDGE ON
MY TATTOO
ON-TAP
ON-TAP PLUS
TATTOO EXPRESS
TATTOO ID
TATTOO ID BUSINESS
TATTOO ID ENTERPRISE
TATTOO LABEL
TATTOO POSTSCRIPT
TATTOO PS

INTEGRATED SYSTEMS ANALYSTS, INC.

Ste 600 2001 N Beauregard St
Alexandria, VA 22311-1722
Tel.: (703) 824-0700
Tel.: (703) 578-2583
Fax: (703) 379-6321
Toll Free: (800) 929-3436
E-mail: itsales@isa.com
Web Site: www.isa.com
E-Mail For Key Personnel:
Sales Director: sales@isa.com
Approx. Number Employees: 650
Year Founded: 1980
Business Description:
Systems Engineering; Information Systems Services, Corrosion Engineering; Computer & Network Maintenance, Repair & Installation
S.I.C.: 7373; 1731
N.A.I.C.S.: 541512; 238210
Media: 2
Personnel:
C. Michael Gooden *(Chm & CEO)*
Brands & Products:
INTEGRATED SYSTEMS ANALYSTS

INTELIUS, INC.

500 108th Ave NE 25th Fl
Bellevue, WA 98004
Tel.: (425) 974-6100
Fax: (425) 974-6199
E-mail: informationandfeedback@intelius.com
Web Site: www.intelius.com
Sales Range: $50-74.9 Million
Approx. Number Employees: 139
Year Founded: 2003
Business Description:
Security, Background Checks & Identity Theft Solutions
S.I.C.: 7382; 7299; 7374
N.A.I.C.S.: 561621; 518210; 812990
Advertising Expenditures: $30,300,000
Media: 4-7-8-10-13-14-15-18-20-22-26
Personnel:
John K. Arnold *(Co-Founder & Exec VP)*
Edward O. Peterson *(Co-Founder)*
Naveen K. Jain *(Chm & CEO)*
Paul T. Cook *(CFO)*
Susan K. Koehler *(CMO)*
Jim Adler *(Chief Privacy Officer)*
William R. Kerr *(Chief Corp Officer)*
William H. Beaver, Jr. *(Gen Counsel)*
Chandan S. Chauhan *(Sr VP-Product Mktg)*
Advertising Agencies:
Cole & Weber United
221 Yale Ave N Ste 600
Seattle, WA 98109
Tel.: (206) 447-9595
Fax: (206) 233-0178

Fitch
1218 3rd Ave Ste 620
Seattle, WA 98101-3275
Tel.: (206) 624-0551
Fax: (206) 624-0875

INTELLICHECK MOBILISA, INC.

191 Otto St
Port Townsend, WA 98368
Tel.: (360) 344-3233
Fax: (360) 344-3323
Toll Free: (888) 942-6624
E-mail: investor-relations@icmobil.com
Web Site: www.intellicheck.com
E-Mail For Key Personnel:
Marketing Director: marketing@intellicheck.com
Approx. Rev.: $12,291,551
Approx. Number Employees: 47
Year Founded: 1994
Business Description:
Document & Age Verification Products Developer & Distr
S.I.C.: 7372; 3577; 7373; 7382
N.A.I.C.S.: 511210; 334119; 541512; 561621
Media: 2-8-10-17
Personnel:
Nelson Ludlow *(Chm)*
Steven D. Williams *(CEO)*
Peter J. Mundy *(CFO)*
Clifford D. Link *(Sr VP-Homeland Security Solutions)*
Bonnie Ludlow *(Sr VP)*
Terry Thiele *(Dir-Sls)*
Brands & Products:
C-LINK
DEFENSE ID
ID-CHECK
INTELLICHECK MOBILISA

INTELLICORP, INC.

Ste 221 2900 Lakeside Dr
Santa Clara, CA 95054-2817
Tel.: (650) 965-5500
Fax: (650) 965-5647
Toll Free: (888) 663-3573
E-mail: investors@intellicorp.com
Web Site: www.intellicorp.com
Approx. Rev.: $10,000,000
Approx. Number Employees: 60
Year Founded: 1980
Business Description:
Developing & Marketing Software Products & Solutions for Enterprise Resource Planning Customers
S.I.C.: 7371
N.A.I.C.S.: 541511
Media: 2-7-10-13
Personnel:
Norman J. Wechsler *(Chm)*
Jerome Klajbor *(CEO)*
Brands & Products:
ASSESSOR
INTELLICORP
LIVECAPTURE
LIVECOMPARE
LIVEINTERFACE
LIVEMODEL
LIVEMONITOR
NETPROCESS
SOLO

THE INTELLIGENCE GROUP

1545 US Hwy 206 Ste 202
Bedminster, NJ 07921
Tel.: (908) 901-0112
Fax: (908) 901-0115
Toll Free: (800) 798-1303
E-mail: inquiries@intell-group.com
Web Site: www.intell-group.com
Approx. Number Employees: 20
Business Description:
Research, Investigations & Forensic Services
S.I.C.: 7381; 8733
N.A.I.C.S.: 561611; 541710
Media: 2
Personnel:
Dennis P. Farley *(Pres & CEO)*
Evans Edouard *(Mng Dir-Environ)*

INTELLIGROUP INC.

(Sub. of NTT DATA International LLC)
5 Independence Way Ste 220
Princeton, NJ 08540
Tel.: (646) 810-7400
Tel.: (646) 810-7405 (Mktg)
Fax: (646) 810-7500
Toll Free: (800) 535-0156
E-mail: contactus@intelligroup.com
Web Site: www.intelligroup.com
E-Mail For Key Personnel:
Marketing Director: corporatemarketing@intelligroup.com
Approx. Rev.: $126,518,000
Approx. Number Employees: 2,101
Year Founded: 1987
Business Description:
Consulting, Technology & Outsourcing Services
S.I.C.: 8748; 7373; 7379
N.A.I.C.S.: 541690; 541512; 541519
Advertising Expenditures: $100,000
Media: 1-10
Personnel:
Vikram Gulati *(Pres & CEO)*
Alok Bajpai *(CFO)*
Madhu Poomalil *(CFO)*
Kalyan Sundaram Mahalingam *(COO)*
Bhalachandra Bhosale *(Sr VP-Global SAP Practice)*
Marcelo Casas *(Sr VP-Empower Solutions Div)*
Pankit Desai *(Sr VP-Worldwide Sls)*
Alok Pant *(Sr VP-Global Mktg & Alliances)*
Prakash Shah *(Sr VP-Client Svcs)*
Satish Subramaniam *(Sr VP-Enterprise Svcs Grp)*
Vikram Samant *(VP-Strategic Accts-North America)*
Pat Gray *(Dir-Mktg)*
Brands & Products:
4SIGHT
4SIGHT PLUS
ARCHIVEPAC
ASPPLUS
CATEAZY
CREATING THE INTELLIGENT ENTERPRISE
D2ECONNECT
EZ PATH
HOTPAC ANALYZER
IMS
INTELLIGROUP
LMC
MYADVISOR
PHARMA EXPRESS
POWER UP SERVICES
SPEED
SYNERGY
UPTIMIZER

INTELLISYNC CORPORATION

(Sub. of Nokia Inc.)
2550 N 1st St Ste 500
San Jose, CA 95131-1038
Tel.: (408) 321-7650
Fax: (408) 321-3886
Web Site: www.intellisync.com
E-Mail For Key Personnel:
Sales Director: sales@intellisync.com
Sales Range: $50-74.9 Million
Approx. Number Employees: 456
Business Description:
Software Infrastructure Services
S.I.C.: 7372; 7371
N.A.I.C.S.: 334611; 511210; 541511
Advertising Expenditures: $2,055,000

INTERACTIVE INTELLIGENCE, INC.

7601 Interactive Way
Indianapolis, IN 46278
Tel.: (317) 872-3000
Fax: (317) 872-3000
Fax: (317) 715-8100 (Marketing)
E-mail: info@inin.com
Web Site: www.inin.com
Approx. Rev.: $166,315,000
Approx. Number Employees: 849
Year Founded: 1994

Key to Media (For complete agency information see *The Advertising Red Books-Agencies* edition):
1. Bus. Publs. 2. Cable T.V. 3. Catalogs & Directories. 4. Co-op Adv. 5. Consumer Mags. 6. D.M. to Bus. Estab.7. D.M. to Consumers 8. Daily Newsp. 9. Exhibits/Trade Shows 10. Foreign 11. Infomercial 12. Internet Adv.13. Multimedia 14. Network Radio 15. Network T.V. 16. Newsp. Distr. Mags. 17. Other 18. Outdoor (Posters, Transit) 19. Point of Purchase20. Premiums, Novelties 21. Product Samples 22. Special Events Mktg. 23. Spot Radio 24. Spot T.V. 25. Weekly Newsp. 26. Yellow Page Adv.

Business Description:
Developer of Interaction Management Software
S.I.C.: 7372; 7371
N.A.I.C.S.: 511210; 334611; 541511
Advertising Expenditures: $1,400,000
Media: 2-7-10-13
Personnel:
Donald E. Brown *(Chm, Pres & CEO)*
Stephen R. Head *(CFO, Sec, Treas, Sr VP-Fin & Admin)*
Joseph A. Staples *(CMO & Sr VP-Mktg)*
Michael D. Gagle *(Chief Scientist)*
Gary R. Blough *(Exec VP-Worldwide Sls)*
Richard Brown *(VP-Sls-EMEA)*
Pamela J. Hynes *(VP-Comm-Worldwide)*
Paul Weber *(VP-Enterprise Sales)*
Christine Holley *(Dir-Mktg Comm)*
Ty Baldwin *(Dir-Sls-Central Reg)*
Steve Kaplan *(Dir-Sls-Eastern Reg)*
Mark Piskadlo *(Dir-Sls-Western Reg)*
Gary Romeo *(Dir-Strategic Accts-Southeast)*
Brands & Products:
CUSTOMER INTERACTION CENTER
DELIBERATELY INNOVATIVE
E-FAQ KNOWLEDGE MANAGER
ICNOTIFY
INTERACTION ADMINISTRATOR
INTERACTION ATTENDANT
INTERACTION CENTER PLATFORM
INTERACTION CLIENT
INTERACTION DESIGNER
INTERACTION DESKTOP
INTERACTION DIALER
INTERACTION DIRECTOR
INTERACTION EASYSCRIPTER
INTERACTION FAQ
INTERACTION FAX VIEWER
INTERACTION FEEDBACK
INTERACTION GATEWAY
INTERACTION INTELLIGENCE
INTERACTION MARQUEE
INTERACTION MEDIA SERVER
INTERACTION MELDER
INTERACTION MESSAGE INDICATOR
INTERACTION MIGRATOR
INTERACTION MOBILE OFFICE
INTERACTION MONITOR
INTERACTION OPTIMIZER
INTERACTION RECORDER
INTERACTION SCREEN RECORDER
INTERACTION SCRIPTER
INTERACTION SERVER
INTERACTION SIP PROXY
INTERACTION SUPERVISOR
INTERACTION TRACKER
INTERACTION VOICEMAIL PLAYER
INTERACTION WEB PORTAL
INTERACTIVE INTELLIGENCE
INTERACTIVE INTELLIGENCE LIVE CONFERENCE
INTERACTIVE UPDATE
INTERACTIVELEASE
ION
MESSAGIN INTERACTION CENTER
WIRELES INTERACTION CLIENT
WIRELESS INTERACTION CLIENT

INTERCALL, INC.
(Joint Venture of Thomas H. Lee Partners, L.P. & Quadrangle Group LLC)
8420 Bryn Mawr Ste 400
Chicago, IL 60631
Tel.: (773) 399-1600
Fax: (773) 399-1588
Toll Free: (800) 374-2441
E-mail: info@intercall.com
Web Site: www.intercall.com
Approx. Number Employees: 1,200
Year Founded: 1991
Business Description:
Audio, Video & Web Conferencing Services
S.I.C.: 4812
N.A.I.C.S.: 517212
Export
Media: 2-7-10-13
Personnel:
J. Scott Etzler *(Pres)*
Larry Schensky *(Gen Counsel & VP)*
Marty Dunne *(Exec VP-Sls)*
Michael Nessler *(Exec VP-Global Ops)*
Heather Welborn *(Exec VP-Natl Sls)*
Robert Wise *(Exec VP-Strategic Bus Dev)*
Rob Ewing *(Sr VP-Sys & Tech)*
Kathleen Finato *(Sr VP-Mktg & Products)*
Philip Grybas *(Sr VP-Acctg)*
Herbert Pyles *(Sr VP-Global Customer Svc, Support & Ops)*
Dan Veytsman *(VP-HR)*
Brands & Products:
CONFERENCE PLACE
DIRECT EVENT
ENCORE
FACTS COMPLETE
LEADER-VIEW

INTERDENT, INC.
222 N Sepulveda Blvd Ste 740
El Segundo, CA 90245
Tel.: (310) 765-2400
Fax: (310) 765-2456
E-mail: info@interdent.com
Web Site: www.interdent.com
Sales Range: $200-249.9 Million
Approx. Number Employees: 1,800
Year Founded: 1990
Business Description:
Accounting, Hiring, Training, Marketing, Scheduling & Information Management Services for Dentists
S.I.C.: 6321; 8021
N.A.I.C.S.: 524114; 621210
Media: 2-10-17-23-24
Personnel:
H. Wayne Posey *(Pres & CEO)*

INTERIM HEALTHCARE INC.
(Holding of Sentinel Capital Partners LLC)
1601 Sawgrass Corporate Expy
Sunrise, FL 33323
Tel.: (954) 858-6000
Toll Free: (800) 338-7786
Web Site: www.interimhealthcare.com
Sales Range: $25-49.9 Million
Approx. Number Employees: 45
Year Founded: 1966
Business Description:
Medical Staffing Services
S.I.C.: 7363; 8082
N.A.I.C.S.: 561320; 621610
Media: 2-10-23
Personnel:
Kathleen Gilmartin *(Pres & CEO)*
Michael Slupecki *(CFO & Treas)*
Barbara A. McCann *(Chief Indus Officer)*
Jane Hinton *(Sr VP-New Franchise On-Boarding & Implementation)*
Linda Shaub *(VP-Mktg)*
Lowell Wright *(VP-Home Care Sls)*
Brands & Products:
ACROSS THE STREET. ACROSS THE COUNTRY.
INTERIM
INTERIM HOMESTYLE SERVICES
Advertising Agency:
bfw Advertising + Interactive
6700 NW Broken Sound Pkwy Ste 100
Boca Raton, FL 33487
Tel.: (561) 962-3300
Fax: (561) 962-3339

INTERLINK ELECTRONICS, INC.
546 Flynn Rd
Camarillo, CA 93012
Tel.: (805) 484-8855
Fax: (805) 484-9457
E-mail: corpcomm@interlinkelec.com
Web Site: www.interlinkelectronics.com
E-Mail For Key Personnel:
Sales Director: sales@InterlinkElectronics.com
Sales Range: $25-49.9 Million
Approx. Number Employees: 107
Year Founded: 1985
Business Description:
Intuitive Interface Components & Solution Services
S.I.C.: 3695; 3577
N.A.I.C.S.: 334613; 334119
Advertising Expenditures: $191,000
Media: 7-10
Personnel:
Steven N. Bronson *(Chm & CEO)*
John R. Schneider *(Pres & COO)*
Steven P. Leone *(CFO)*
Trevor Bray *(VP-Sls & Mktg)*
Louann Negrete *(VP-Fin)*
Jeff Solis *(Mktg Mgr)*
Brands & Products:
CLICKTRIGER
CUSTOM FSR
DURAPOINT
DURAPOINT OEM
EPAD
ESIGN ANYWHERE
FORCE SENSING RESISTORS
FREEBEAM
FREEDOM WRITER
FSR
GOSPEAK
INTEGRISIGN
INTEGRISIGN EXPRESS
INTERACTIVE REMOTE CONTROL
INTERLINK ELECTRONICS
INTUITOUCH
INTUIVISION
MICRO JOYSTICK SOLUTION KIT
MICROJOYSTICK
MICROMODULE
MICROMODULE SOLUTION KIT
MICROMODULE VP5005
MICROMODULE VP5500
MICROMODULE VP5505
MICROMODULE VP5510
MICROMODULE VP5515
MICRONAV
MICRONAV 360
MICRONAV ARRAY
MICRONAV RING
MICRONAV STRIP
MICRONAVE PAD
PROPOINT
REMOTELINK
REMOTEPOINT
REMOTEPOINT NAVIGATOR
STANDARD 400 FSR
STANDARD 402 FSR
STANDARD 406 FSR
STANDARD 408 FSR
VERSAPAD
VERSAPOINT
VERSAPOINT COMMUNICATOR

INTERMAP TECHNOLOGIES CORPORATION
736 8th Ave SW Ste 1000
Calgary, AB T2P 1H4, Canada
Tel.: (403) 266-0900
Fax: (403) 265-0499
E-mail: info@intermap.com
Web Site: www.intermap.com
Sales Range: $10-24.9 Million
Approx. Number Employees: 250
Business Description:
Mapping & Surveying Services
S.I.C.: 8711; 8713
N.A.I.C.S.: 541330; 541360
Media: 10
Personnel:
Brian L. Bullock *(Chm)*
Todd Oseth *(Pres & CEO)*
Nigel Jackson *(Pres & Dir-PT ExsaMap Asia)*
David Cunningham *(Sr VP-Sls)*
Adam Denman *(VP & Gen Mgr-Europe)*
Kevin J. Thomas *(VP-Mktg)*
Ted Garlock *(Dir-Global Mktg Comm)*
Hugh MacKay *(Dir-European Sls)*
Monica Moore *(Dir-Mktg)*
Mark Stanley *(Dir-Sls , UK, Irelanf, Denmark & Netherlands)*
Marc Wride *(Dir-Federal Civil Accts US)*
Ian Wosiski *(Reg Mgr-Sls-Southwest US)*
Brands & Products:
ACCUTERRA
GLOBAL TERRAIN
INTERMAP
NEXTMAP
STAR-3I
TOPOSAR
Advertising Agency:
AutoCom Associates
74 W Long Lk Rd Ste 103
Bloomfield Hills, MI 48304-2770
Tel.: (248) 647-8621
Fax: (248) 642-2110

INTERMEC INC.
6001 36th Ave W
Everett, WA 98203-1264
Tel.: (425) 348-2600
Fax: (425) 267-2983
E-mail: invest@intermec.com
Web Site: www.intermec.com
Approx. Rev.: $679,111,000
Approx. Number Employees: 1,745
Year Founded: 1997
Business Description:
Mfr & Marketer of Automated Data Collection & Mobile Computing Systems for Supply Chain Technology Solutions

Key to Media (For complete agency information see *The Advertising Red Books-Agencies* edition):
1. Bus. Publs. 2. Cable T.V. 3. Catalogs & Directories. 4. Co-op Adv. 5. Consumer Mags. 6. D.M. to Bus. Estab.7. D.M. to Consumers 8. Daily Newsp. 9. Exhibits/Trade Shows 10. Foreign 11. Infomercial 12. Internet Adv.13. Multimedia 14. Network Radio 15. Network T.V. 16. Newsp. Distr. Mags. 17. Other 18. Outdoor (Posters, Transit) 19. Point of Purchase20. Premiums, Novelties 21. Product Samples 22. Special Events Mktg. 23. Spot Radio 24. Spot T.V. 25. Weekly Newsp. 26. Yellow Page Adv.

Intermec Inc. — (Continued)

S.I.C.: 3577; 7372
N.A.I.C.S.: 334119; 334611
Export
Advertising Expenditures: $1,000,000
Media: 2-4-7-10-11
Personnel:
Patrick J. Byrne *(Pres & CEO)*
Robert J. Driessnack *(CFO & Sr VP)*
Janis L. Harwell *(Gen Counsel, Corp Sec, Sr VP & Sr VP-Corp Strategy)*
Dennis A. Faerber *(Sr VP-Global Supply Chain Ops)*
Jim P. McDonnell *(Sr VP-Global Sls)*
Earl R. Thompson *(Sr VP-Mobile Solutions Bus Unit)*
Mike Muller *(VP & Gen Mgr-Asia Pacific)*
Peter Fausel *(VP-Sls-North America)*
Jeanne Lyon *(VP-HR)*
Chris Ranger *(Sr Dir-Svc & Support-EMEA)*
Kevin P. McCarty *(Dir-IR)*
Brands & Products:
INTERMEC
SABRE
SMARTSYSTEMS

INTERMEC TECHNOLOGIES CORPORATION

(Sub. of Intermec Inc.)
6001 36th Ave W
Everett, WA 98203-1264
Tel.: (425) 348-2600
Fax: (425) 355-9551
Toll Free: (800) 347-2636
E-mail: info@intermec.com
Web Site: www.intermec.com
Sales Range: $650-699.9 Million
Approx. Number Employees: 2,700
Year Founded: 1966
Business Description:
Mfr of Barcode Symbology Including Products, Services & Systems
S.I.C.: 3577; 2759
N.A.I.C.S.: 334119; 323119
Export
Media: 2-7-10-11-13-22
Distr.: Intl.; Natl.
Budget Set: Feb.
Personnel:
Allen J. Lauer *(Chm)*
Patrick J. Byrne *(Pres & CEO)*
Sue Taylor *(VP-HR)*
David Jones *(Mgr-USAF & Defense Logistics Agency Strategic Account)*
Brands & Products:
CROSSBAR
INTELLITAG
INTERMEC
JANUS
NORAND
TRAKKER

INTERMEC TECHNOLOGIES CORPORATION

(Div. of Intermec Technologies Corporation)
550 2nd St SE
Cedar Rapids, IA 52401-2023
Tel.: (319) 369-3100
Fax: (319) 369-3453
Toll Free: (800) 452-2757
E-mail: info@intermec.com
Web Site: www.intermec.com
Sales Range: $600-649.9 Million
Approx. Number Employees: 2,500
Year Founded: 1968
Business Description:
Mobile & Wireless Computing Systems
S.I.C.: 3571; 5045
N.A.I.C.S.: 334111; 423430
Export
Media: 2-4-7-10-13-20-22-26
Distr.: Intl.
Budget Set: July -Aug.
Advertising Agency:
Mobium
360 N Michigan Ave 12th Fl
Chicago, IL 60601
Tel.: (312) 422-8960

INTERMETRO COMMUNICATIONS, INC.

2685 Park Center Dr Bldg A
Simi Valley, CA 93065
Tel.: (805) 433-8000
Fax: (805) 582-1006
Toll Free: (800) 44METRO
E-mail: info@intermetro.net
Web Site: www.intermetro.net
Approx. Rev.: $28,034,000
Approx. Number Employees: 29
Business Description:
Enhanced Voice & Data Services
S.I.C.: 4899
N.A.I.C.S.: 517910
Advertising Expenditures: $3,000
Media: 7-8-10
Personnel:
Charles Rice *(Chm, Pres & CEO)*
David Olert *(CFO)*

INTERNAP NETWORK SERVICES CORPORATION

250 Williams St
Atlanta, GA 30303
Tel.: (404) 302-9700
Fax: (404) 475-0520
E-mail: gen_info@internap.com
Web Site: www.internap.com
Approx. Rev.: $244,164,000
Approx. Number Employees: 416
Year Founded: 1996
Business Description:
High-Speed Computer Networking & Internet Solutions
S.I.C.: 7371; 4899; 7373; 7375
N.A.I.C.S.: 541511; 517910; 518111; 541512
Advertising Expenditures: $1,300,000
Media: 7-10-13
Personnel:
Eric Cooney *(Pres & CEO)*
George E. Kilguss, III *(CFO)*
Peter M. Evans *(Sr VP-Mktg)*
Michael Higgins *(Sr VP-Data Center Svcs)*
Patricia L. Higgins *(Sr VP)*
Steven Orchard *(Sr VP-Ops & Support)*
Randal Thompson *(Sr VP-Global Sls)*
Robert Minnear *(VP-Engrg)*
Andrew McBath *(Dir-Fin & IR)*
Brands & Products:
FLO CONTROL PLATFORM
FLOW CONTROL XCELERATOR
FLOWVIEW PLATFORM
INTERNAP
P-NAP
PERFORMANCE IP

Advertising Agency:
Davies Murphy Group
200 Wheeler Rd N Tower
Burlington, MA 01803
Tel.: (781) 418-2400
Fax: (781) 418-2480

INTERNATIONAL BUSINESS MACHINES CORPORATION

(d/b/a IBM Corporation)
1 New Orchard Rd
Armonk, NY 10504
Tel.: (914) 499-1900
Fax: (914) 765-7382
Web Site: www.ibm.com
Approx. Rev.: $99,870,000,000
Approx. Number Employees: 426,751
Year Founded: 1911
Business Description:
Advanced Information Processing Technologies, Software & Networking Systems Developer & Mfr
S.I.C.: 3571; 3577; 3579; 7371; 7372; 7373; 7379
N.A.I.C.S.: 334111; 333313; 334119; 511210; 541511; 541512; 541519
Advertising Expenditures: $1,337,000,000
Media: 2-3-4-6-7-8-9-10-11-13-14-15-18-19-22-23-24-25
Distr.: Intl.; Natl.
Personnel:
Samuel J. Palmisano *(Chm, Pres & CEO)*
Mark Loughridge *(CFO & Sr VP)*
Patrick Toole *(CIO & VP)*
Alan Ganek *(CTO & VP-Strategy & Tech-IBM Software Grp)*
Harriet P. Pearson *(Chief Privacy Officer & VP-Regulatory Policy)*
Dah-Chuen Chien *(CEO-China, Hong Kong & Taiwan)*
Robert C. Weber *(Gen Counsel, Sr VP-Legal & Regulatory Affairs)*
Andrew Bonzani *(Sec, Sr VP & Asst Gen Counsel)*
John E. Kelly, III *(Sr VP & Dir-IBM Res)*
Rodney C. Adkins *(Sr VP-IBM Sys & Tech Grp)*
Colleen F. Arnold *(Sr VP-Application Mgmt Svcs-IBM Global Bus Svcs)*
Michael E. Daniels *(Sr VP-Global Tech Svcs)*
J. Bruce Harreld *(Sr VP)*
Jon C. Iwata *(Sr VP-Mktg & Comm)*
Frank R. Kern *(Sr VP-Global Bus Svcs)*
R. Frankin Kern, III *(Sr VP-Global Bus Svcs)*
Robert J. LeBlanc *(Sr VP-Middleware Software-IBM Software Grp)*
Steven A. Mills *(Sr VP & Grp Exec-Software Grp)*
Michael D. Rhodin *(Sr VP-IBM Software Solutions Grp)*
Virginia M. Rometty *(Sr VP-IBM Global Sls & Distr)*
Linda S. Sanford *(Sr VP-Enterprise On Demand Transformation & IT)*
Timothy S. Shaughnessy *(Sr VP-Svcs Delivery)*
Edward Barbini *(VP-External Rels)*
Deirdre Bigley *(VP-Worldwide Adv & Interactive)*
Karstin Bodell *(VP-Mktg-Gen Bus)*
John Kennedy *(VP-Corp Mktg)*
Chris MacLaughlin *(VP-Mktg & Comm)*
James Sciales *(VP-Corp External Rels)*
Marjorie Tenzer *(VP-Mktg & Communications)*
Jason Han *(Head-Sls & Enterprise Mktg Mgmt-Western Reg)*
June Yee Felix *(Gen Mgr-Banking & Fin Markets)*
Leslie Reiser *(Program Dir-Interactive Mktg-Worldwide)*
Lori Bosio *(Dir-Media Rels-Software Grp)*
Tim Breuer *(Dir-Media Rels-Sys & Tech Grp)*
John Buscemi *(Dir-Media Rels-Global Bus Svcs)*
Jennifer N. Galitz McTighe *(Dir-Media Rels-IBM Res & Tech)*
Steve Malkiewicz *(Dir-Mkg & Comm-IBM Res & Intellectual Property)*
Michael Moeller *(Dir-External Rels)*
Judy Parkes *(Product Mgr-CDC)*
Fred Clarke *(Mgr-Media Rels-IBM Global Fin)*
Scott Cook *(Mgr-External Comm)*
David Manzo *(Mgr-Media Strategy)*
Clint Roswell *(Mgr-Media Rels-North America)*
Susan Emerick *(Strategist-Digital & Social Media Mktg-Global)*
Brands & Products:
ACCESS360
ACTIVE MEMORY
ACTIVEINSIGHT
ACTIVEMEMORY
AD/CYCLE
ADDME
ADVANCED 36
ADVANCED FUNCTION PRESENTATION
ADVANCED FUNCTION PRINTING
ADVANCED MICRO-PARTITIONING
AF/OPERATOR
AF/REMOTE
AFS
AGLETS
AHEAD OF THE THREAT
AIX
AIX 5L
AIX 6
AIX/ESA
AIX/L
AIX PVME
ALERT ON LAN
ALERTCON
ALLOY
ALPHABLOX
ALPHAWORKS
ANALYSTSTUDIO
ANYNET
ANYPLACE
APL2
APL2/6000
APPLICATION ADVANTAGE
APPLICATION MINING
APPLICATION REGION MANAGER
APPLICATION SYSTEM/400
APPLICATIONS ON DEMAND
APPROACH
APPSCAN
ARGUS
AS/400
AS/400E
ASCENDANT
ASCENTIAL
ASCENTIAL AUDITSTAGE
ASCENTIAL DATASTAGE

Key to Media (For complete agency information see *The Advertising Red Books-Agencies* edition):
1. Bus. Publs. 2. Cable T.V. 3. Catalogs & Directories. 4. Co-op Adv. 5. Consumer Mags. 6. D.M. to Bus. Estab.7. D.M. to Consumers
8. Daily Newsp. 9. Exhibits/Trade Shows 10. Foreign 11. Infomercial 12. Internet Adv.13. Multimedia 14. Network Radio
15. Network T.V. 16. Newsp. Distr. Mags. 17. Other 18. Outdoor (Posters, Transit) 19. Point of Purchase20. Premiums, Novelties
21. Product Samples 22. Special Events Mktg. 23. Spot Radio 24. Spot T.V. 25. Weekly Newsp. 26. Yellow Page Adv.

ASCENTIAL ENTERPRISE INTEGRATION SUITE
ASCENTIAL METASTAGE
ASCENTIAL PROFILESTAGE
ASCENTIAL QUALITYSTAGE
ASCENTIAL RTI
ASSETNET
ASSOCIATION/400
ATLAS
AUDIOVATION
BALANCED WAREHOUSE
BATCHPIPES
BETAWORKS
BIO-DICTIONARY
BLADECENTER
BLOX
BLUE CLOUD
BLUE GENE
BLUE LIGHTNING
BLUE LOGIC
BLUEDREKAR
BOOKMANAGER
BOOKMASTER
BOOLEDOZER
BOOLESEYE
BUILD FORGE
BUSINESSASSURE
BUSLOGIC
C/370
C/400
C BEAM
C-ISAM
C/MVS
C/VM
C++/MVS
C++/VM
CALIBRATED VECTORED COOLING
CALLFLOW
CAMPAIGN DESIGNER
CANDLE
CANDLE CIRCUIT
CANDLE COMMAND CENTER
CANDLE EDELIVERY
CANDLE ELECTRONIC CUSTOMER SUPPORT
CANDLE MANAGEMENT SERVER
CANDLE MANAGEMENT WORKSTATION
CANDLELIGHT
CANDLENET
CANDLENET COMMAND CENTER
CANDLENET PORTAL
CD SHOWCASE
CHANGE INTEGRATION
CHIPBENCH
CHIPHOPPER
CHIPKILL
CICS
CICS/400
CICS/6000
CICS CONNECTION
CICS/ESA
CICS EXPLORER
CICS/MVS
CICS OS/2
CICS/VM
CICS/VSE
CICSPLEX
CL/CONFERENCE
CL/SUPERSESSION
CLEARCASE
CLEARCASE ATTACHE
CLEARCASE MULTISITE
CLEARDDTS
CLEARQUEST
CLEARTRACK
CLINWARE
CLOUDSCAPE
CLUSTERPROVEN
COBION
COBOL/2
COBOL/370
COBOL/400
COGNOS
COLLABORATIVE INNOVATION
COMMON PLATFORM
COMMON USER ACCESS
COMPONENT BUSINESS MODEL
CONFIGNIA
CONNEXIS
CONSTELLAR
CONTENTCONNECT
CORECONNECT
CROSSACCESS
CROSSWORLDS
CT
CT/2
CT/DS
CUBE VIEWS
CURRENT
CYANEA
CYANEA AND DOTS DERVICE
CYANEA/ONE
CYANEA WITHIN
DAMOCLES
DATA ACE
DATA CENTER FAMILY
DATA COLLECTION CONNECTION
DATA COLLECTION SOLUTION
DATA DRIVES BUSINESS.
DATABASE 2
DATABEACON
DATABLADE
DATAHIDING
DATAHUB
DATAJOINER
DATAMIRROR
DATAMIRROR TRANSFORMATION SERVER
DATAPOWER
DATAPOWER DEVICE
DATAPROPAGATOR
DATAREFRESHER
DATASTAGE
DB2
DB2 ALPHABLOX
DB2 CLIENT APPLICATION ENABLERS
DB2 CONNECT
DB2 EXTENDERS
DB2 OLAP SERVER
DB2 UNIVERSAL DATABASE
DCCONNECT
DECISION ADVANTAGE
DEEP BLUE
DEFECT REDUCTION METHOD
DESIGNFLOW
DESKTOP ON-CALL
DEVELOPERWORKS
DEXAN
DFDSM
DFS
DFSMS/MVS
DFSMS/VM
DFSMSDFP
DFSMSDSS
DFSMSHSM
DFSMSRMM
DFSORT
DILIGENT
DILIGENT TECHNOLOGIES
DIRECTTALK
DIRECTTALK/2
DIRECTTALK/6000
DIRMAINT
DISCOVERYLINK
DISPLAYWRITE
DISTRIBUTED DATABASE CONNECTION SERVICES
DISTRIBUTED RELATIONAL DATABASE ARCHITECTURE
DOCUMENT RETRIEVAL ASSISTANT
DOMINO
DOMINO DESIGNER
DOMINO DOCUMENT MANAGER
DOORS
DPI
DRDA
DS4000
DS6000
DS8000
DUALSTOR
DXT
DXT/D1
DYNAMIC CONNECT
DYNAMIC INFRASTRUCTURE
DYNAMIC WORKPLACES
DYNIX
DYNIX/PTX
E-BUSINESS HOSTING
E-BUSINESS ON DEMAND
EASYSTRIKE
EASYSYNC
EBA
EBUSINESS AT THE SPEED OF LIGHT
ECKD
EDMSUITE
EDUQUEST
EIA
EINSTIMER
ELECTRONIC SERVICE AGENT
ELX
ENCINA
ENERGYSCALE
THE ENGINES OF E-BUSINESS
ENTERPRISE ASSET MANAGEMENT
ENTERPRISE COBOL
ENTERPRISE DOCUMENT MANAGEMENT SYSTEM
ENTERPRISE PL/I
ENTERPRISE STORAGE SERVER
ENTERPRISE SYSTEM/3090
ENTERPRISE SYSTEM/4381
ENTERPRISE SYSTEM/9000
ENTERPRISE SYSTEMS ARCHITECTURE/370
ENTERPRISE SYSTEMS ARCHITECTURE/390
ENTERPRISE SYSTEMS CONNECTION ARCHITECTURE
EOCF/2
EPILOG
ERP BENEFITS REALIZATION
ERPBRIDGE
ES/3090
ES/4381
ES/9000
ES/9370
ESCON
ESERVER
ESRA
ETE
ETEWATCH
ETHERJET
ETHERSTREAMER
EVENT MINING
EVERYPLACE
THE EXPERIENCE OF NOW.
EXPRESS ADVANTAGE
EXPRESS MIDDLEWARE
EXPRESS PORTFOLIO
EXPRESS SERVERS
EXPRESS SERVERS AND STORAGE
EXPRESS SERVICES
EXPRESS STORAGE
EXTENDED I/O
EXTREME BLUE
FAXCONCENTRATOR
FFST
FFST/2
FICON
FILENET
FIRST FAILURE SUPPORT TECHNOLOGY
FIRST FAILURE SUPPORT TECHNOLOGY/2
FIRST RUN
FLASHCOPY
FLEXIMOVE
FLOWMARK
FOUNDATIONS
FREELANCE GRAPHICS
FULL ECONOMY MODEL
GARSXCHANGE
GDDM
GDPS
GENELCO
GENELCO ADMINISTRATION+
GENELCO CLAIMS+
GENELCO ENTERPRISE SUITE+
GENELCO GROUP+
GENELCO GROUPWEB+
GENELCO LEDGER+
GENELCO LIFE+
GENELCO LIFEVIEW
GENELCO PAYOUT
GENELCO REINSURANCE
GEOGRAPHICALLY DISPERSED PARALLEL SYSPLEX
GEOINTERFACE
GEOMANAGER
GIGAPROCESSOR
GLOBAL INNOVATION OUTLOOK
GPFS
GUARDEDNET
GXT1000
GXT150L
GXT150M
HACMP
HACMP/6000
HEALTHLINK & DEVICE
HEALTHLINK CONNECT
HEALTHVILLAGE
HELPCENTER
HELPWARE
HIPERBATCH
HIPERSOCKETS
HIPERSPACE
HOLOSOFX
HOME DIRECTOR
HOTMEDIA
HOW E DO YOU WANT TO BE?
HPR CHANNEL CONNECTIVITY
HUMMINGBIRD
HYPERFACTOR
HYPERFACTOR TECHNOLOGY
HYPERSWAP
I-LMS
I5/OS
IBM
IBM BESTEAM
IBM BUSINESS PARTNER EMBLEM
IBM CERTIFIED USED EQUIPMENT
IBM CLUB

Key to Media (For complete agency information see *The Advertising Red Books-Agencies* edition):
1. Bus. Publs. 2. Cable T.V. 3. Catalogs & Directories. 4. Co-op Adv. 5. Consumer Mags. 6. D.M. to Bus. Estab.7. D.M. to Consumers
8. Daily Newsp. 9. Exhibits/Trade Shows 10. Foreign 11. Infomercial 12. Internet Adv.13. Multimedia 14. Network Radio
15. Network T.V. 16. Newsp. Distr. Mags. 17. Other 18. Outdoor (Posters, Transit) 19. Point of Purchase20. Premiums, Novelties
21. Product Samples 22. Special Events Mktg. 23. Spot Radio 24. Spot T.V. 25. Weekly Newsp. 26. Yellow Page Adv.

International Business Machines Corporation — (Continued)

IBM COMPONENT BUSINESS MODEL
IBM CONSUMER WALLET
IBM DIAGNOSTICS VIEW
IBM FACTORY OPERATIONS EXECUTIVE
IBM FLEXIBLE CREDIT
IBM PAYMENT REGISTRY
IBM PAYMENT SERVER
IBM PEEL-BACK
IBM POWERXCELL
IBM PROJECT FINANCING
IBM RECEIVABLES PURCHASE
IBM REGISTRY
IBM SOLUTION CONNECTION
IBM SPEECH TO SPEECH TRANSLATOR
IBM TOTALSTORAGE PROVEN
IBM VIRTUAL INNOVATION CENTER
IBM.COM
IBMLINK
ICING
ICLUSTER
IDATAPLEX
IDELIVER
IMAGEPLUS
IMPROMPTU
IMPROVEMENT DRIVEN ORGANIZATION
IMS
IMS CS/2
IMS/ESA
INDEPENDENCE SERIES
INFINIBLUE
INFOCOLOR
INFOPRINT
INFORMATION AGENDA
INFORMIX
INFORMIX-NEWERA
INFOSPEED
INFOWINDOW
INK MANAGER
INOTES
INOTION
INSTITUTE FOR ELECTRONIC GOVERNMENT
INTEGRATED LANGUAGE ENVIRONMENT
INTEGRATED SYSTEMS SOLUTIONS
INTELLIGENT DEVICE DISCOVERY
INTELLIGENT MINER
INTELLIGENT PRINTER DATA STREAM
INTELLISTATION
INTELLIWATCH
INTELLIWATCH PINNACLE
INTERNET POSTCARDS
INTERNET SCANNER
INTERSPACE
IP PRINTWAY
IPDS
IQ-LINK
ISERIES
ITERATIONS
IW MANAGER
JAZZ
JCENTRAL
K-STATION
KNOWLEDGEX
LAN CLIENT CONTROL MANAGER
LAN DISTANCE
LANDP
LANGUAGE ENVIRONMENT
LANSTREAMER
LEARNING SOLUTIONS
LEARNINGSPACE
LIBRARY READER
LIVEAUDIT
LOADLEVELER
LOGISCOPE
LOTUS
LOTUS DEVCON
LOTUS DISCOVERY SERVER
LOTUS ENTERPRISE INTEGRATOR
LOTUS FASTSITE
LOTUS KNOWLEDGE DISCOVERY SYSTEM
LOTUS NOTES
LOTUS ORGANIZER
LOTUS WORKFLOW
LOTUSPHERE
LOVEM
LPDA
MAESTRO
MAGSTAR
MAKE IT ALL COUNT.
MANAGE. ANYTHING. ANYWHERE
MANAGING THE WORLD'S INFRASTRUCTURE
MAXIMIZING IT VALUES.
MAXIMO
MDP
MEASURE WHAT MATTERS.
MEDIASTREAMER
MENTORPLACE
METAARCHITECT
METABROKER
METACUBE
METAMERGE
METASTAGE
METRICA
MICRO CHANNEL
MICRO-PARTITIONING
MICROMUSE
MICROMUSE AND DESIGN
MIDRANGE EXPRESS
MINDSPAN
MIXED OBJECT DOCUMENT CONTENT ARCHITECTURE
MM DESIGN
MOBILE NOTES
MO:DCA
MONO-LITH
MQINTEGRATOR
MQSERIES
MRO SOFTWARE
MULTIMEDIA PRESENTATION MANAGER/2
MULTIPRISE
MVS
MVS/DFP
MVS/ESA
MVS/SP
MVS/XA
MWAVE
NAMEGENDERIZER
NAMEHUNTER
NAMEPARSER
NAMETRANSLITERATOR
NAMEVARIATIONGENERATOR
NAVCODE
NETBAY3
NET.COMMERCE
NETCOOL
NET.DATA
NETFINITY
NETFINITY MANAGER
NETREXX
NETSERVER
NETSPOOL
NETVIEW
NETVISTA
NETWORK STATION
NETWORKED LIVING
THE NEXT UTILITY
NEXTRA
NITIX
NOID
NOTES
NUMA-Q
NUMACENTER
NWAYS
OBJECT-ORIENTED RECORDING
OBJECT TESTING
OBJECTGRID
OBJECTORY
OBJECTTIME
OFFICEVISION
OFFICEVISION/400
OFFICEVISION/MVS
OFFICEVISION/VM
OMEGAMON
OMNIFIND
ON DEMAND COMMUNITY
ON-FILE
ON-MAIL
ONFOREVER
OPEN BLUEPRINT
OPEN CLASS
OPENEDITION
OPERATING SYSTEM/2
OPERATING SYSTEM/400
OPTIM
ORCHESTRATE
OS/2 WARP
OS/390
OS/400
PARALLEL SYSPLEX
PARTNERWORLD
PASSPORT ADVANTAGE
PC 100
PC 300
PC 700
PEARL DIVER
PEOPLE WHO THINK.PEOPLE WHO DO.PEOPLE WHO GET IT.
PERFORM
PERFORMANCESTUDIO
PETROCONNECT
PHOTOMOTION
PLANETRIDER
POET
POINTBASE
POLICY TESTER
PORTMASTER
POWER
POWER ARCHITECTURE
POWER EVERYWHERE
POWER GT1
POWER GT3
POWER GT3I
POWER GT4
POWER GT4E
POWER GT4i
POWER GT4X
POWER GT4XI
POWER GTO
POWER HYPERVISOR
POWER PC 603
POWER PC 604
POWER VISUALIZATION SYSTEM
POWER WITHIN
POWER2
POWER2 ARCHITECTURE
POWER3
POWER4
POWER4+
POWER5
POWER5+
POWER6
POWERCALC
POWERED BY S/390
POWERHA
POWERHOUSE
POWERING E-BUSINESS
POWERNP
POWEROPEN
POWERPC
POWERPC 401
POWERPC 403
POWERPC 601
POWERPC 603
POWERPC 603E
POWERPC 604
POWERPC 750
POWERPC ARCHITECTURE
POWERPC REFERENCE PLATFORM
POWERPLAY
POWERPRS
POWERSERVER
PR/SM
PREDICTIVE FAILURE ANALYSIS
PRINT SERVICES FACILITY
PRINTMANAGER
PRINTWAY
PROBRANCH
PROCESSMASTER
PROCESSOR RESOURCE/ SYSTEMS MANAGER
PRODUCTPAC
PROFIT SEEKER
PROFS
PROJECTCONSOLE
PROMAP4
PROSPECT
PROTECT MORE. STORE LESS
PROTECT MORE. STORE LESS.
PROTECTIER
PROVENTIA
PROVISO
PROXML
PS/2
PSERIES
PTX
PTX/ADMIN
PURECOVERAGE
PUREXML
PURIFY
PURIFY'D
PURIFYPLUS
QBIC
QMF
QUALLABY
QUANTIFY
QUICKPLACE
QUICKR
RAA
RACF
RAMAC
RAPID RESTORE
RAPIDIMPACT
RAPIDPATH
RATIONAL
RATIONAL APEX
RATIONAL DEVELOPER NETWORK
RATIONAL PROCESS WORKBENCH
RATIONAL ROSE
RATIONAL SUITE
RATIONAL SUITE CONTENTSTUDIO
RATIONAL SUMMIT
RATIONAL TEST REALTIME
RATIONAL UNIFIED PROCESS
RATIONAL VISUAL TEST
RDN

Key to Media (For complete agency information see *The Advertising Red Books-Agencies* edition):
1. Bus. Publs. 2. Cable T.V. 3. Catalogs & Directories. 4. Co-op Adv. 5. Consumer Mags. 6. D.M. to Bus. Estab.7. D.M. to Consumers 8. Daily Newsp. 9. Exhibits/Trade Shows 10. Foreign 11. Infomercial 12. Internet Adv.13. Multimedia 14. Network Radio 15. Network T.V. 16. Newsp. Distr. Mags. 17. Other 18. Outdoor (Posters, Transit) 19. Point of Purchase20. Premiums, Novelties 21. Product Samples 22. Special Events Mktg. 23. Spot Radio 24. Spot T.V. 25. Weekly Newsp. 26. Yellow Page Adv.

READING COMPANION
READINGCOMPANION
REAL SECURE
REALHUNTER
REBUS
RED BRICK
RED BRICK VISTA
REDBEANS
REDBOOKS
REGENCY SERVICES
REMOTE COPY MANAGEMENT FACILITY
REPORTNET
REQUISITEPRO
RESCUE AND RECOVERY
RESOURCE LINK
RETAIN
RHAPSODY
RISC SYSTEM/6000
RISQL
RMF
RPG/400
RS/6000
RT PERSONAL COMPUTERS
RUP
S/360
S/370
S/390
S/390 PARALLEL ENTERPRISE SERVER
S3
SAA
SAMETIME
SANERGY
SB+
SBCLIENT
SCALABLE POWERPARALLEL SYSTEMS
SCRIPTASSURE
SCROLLPOINT
SEARCHMANAGER
SEASCAPE
SECURE24
SECUREWAY
SECUREWORLD
SECURITYFUSION
SEQUENT
SEQUENTLINK
SERVER ADVANTAGE
SERVERAID
SERVERGUIDE
SERVERPROVEN
SERVICE DIRECTOR
SERVICE DIRECTOR/2
SERVICEASSURE
SERVICEPAC
SERVICESUITE
SEVEN KEYS TO SUCCESS
SITECHECK
SITELOAD
SLAMTRACKER
SLC
SMART SOA
SMARTSUITE
SMARTWARE
SMOOTHSTART
SNAP/SHOT
SODA
SOFTAUDIT
SOFTWARE IS THE SOUL OF E-BUSINESS
SOFTWARE MALL
SOLID
SOLIDDB
SOLUTIONS FOR A SMALL PLANET
SOM
SOMOBJECTS
SPEECHVIEWER
SQL/400
SQL/DS
STATEMATE
STORAGE TANK
STORAGESMART
STOREPAY
STOREPROVEN
SUCCESSLEASE
SUPPORTPAC
SUREBASE
SUREMARK
SUREONE
SUREPATH
SUREPOINT
SUREPOS
SURF SHACK
SURFAID ANALYTIC
SYSBACK
SYSPLEX TIMER
SYSTEM/36
SYSTEM/360
SYSTEM/370
SYSTEM/38
SYSTEM/390
SYSTEM I
SYSTEM I5
SYSTEM P
SYSTEM P5
SYSTEM PROVEN
SYSTEM STORAGE DS
SYSTEM X
SYSTEM Z
SYSTEM Z10
SYSTEM Z9
SYSTEMBUILDER
SYSTEMPAC
SYSTEMS APPLICATION ARCHITECTURE
SYSTEMVIEW
SYSTEMXTRA
TALKLINK
TCS
TDMF
TEAM UNIFYING PLATFORM
TEAMCONNECTION
TECHCONNECT
TELCO FRIENDLY
TESTFACTORY
TESTFOUNDATION
TESTMATE
TESTSTUDIO
THINK CONTROL
THINK EXPRESS
THINK LEADERSHIP
THINKLIGHT
THINKPLACE
TIVOLI
TIVOLI ENTERPRISE CONSOLE
TIVOLI MANAGEMENT ENVIRONMENT
TIVOLI/SENTRY
TME 10
TOPPAGE
TOTALOGISTICS
TOTALSTORAGE
TOTALSTORAGE PROVEN
TRACKPOINT
TRANSACTION CONNECTION
TRANSFORMATION SERVER
TRANSNOTE
TRIGO
TURBOWAYS
TXSERIES
UC2
ULTRABAY
ULTRACONNECT
ULTRAMEDIA
ULTRANAV
ULTRAPORT
UNIDATA
UNIVERSE
UNYTE
VADS
VERITRAN
VERSATILE STORAGE SERVER
VIAVOICE
VIDEOCHARGER
VIRTUALBLADE
VIRTUALIZATION ENGINE
VISIBILITY. CONTROL. AUTOMATION.
VISUAL WAREHOUSE
VISUALAGE
VISUALGEN
VISUALINFO
VISUALIZATION DATA EXPLORER
VM/ESA
VSE/ESA
VTAM
WAKE ON LAN
WATCHPAD
WEBEXPLORER
WEBINTERPOINT
WEBINTERTALK
WEBSPHERE
WEBSPHERE MQ
WEBSYNERGY
WEBXACT
WHEELWRITER
WINTEGRATE
WORD PRO
WORKLOAD PARTITIONS MANAGER
WORKPAD
WORKPLACE MANAGED CLIENT
WORKPLACE MESSAGING
WORKPLACE SHELL
WORKSTATION APL2
WORLD REGISTRY
WRITING TO READ
X-ARCHITECTURE
X-FORCE
XDE
XIV
XSERIES
XSP PRIME
XTREMECACHE
XTREMEMCACHE
YOU TALK IT TYPES
Z/ARCHITECTURE
Z/OS
Z/VM
Z9
ZSERIES

Advertising Agencies:

Clean Design, Inc.
10 Laboratory Dr Bldg 2 Ste 200
Research Triangle Park, NC 27709
Tel.: (919) 544-2193
Fax: (919) 473-2200

Euro RSCG Worldwide
350 Hudson St
New York, NY 10014-4504
Tel.: (212) 886-2000
Fax: (212) 886-2016
Toll Free: (800) 937-0233

Euro RSCG Worldwide HQ
350 Hudson St
New York, NY 10014-4504
Tel.: (212) 886-2000
Fax: (212) 886-2016
Digital

FD Americas Public Affairs
1101 K St NW 9th Fl
Washington, DC 20005
Tel.: (202) 346-8800
Fax: (202) 346-8804

Jack Morton Worldwide
(A Member of the Interpublic Group of Companies)
142 Berkeley St
Boston, MA 02116
Tel.: (617) 585-7000
Fax: (617) 585-7171

Mindshare
498 7th Ave
New York, NY 10018
Tel.: (212) 297-7000
Fax: (212) 297-7001

NAVAJO Company
1164 Cadillac Ct
Milpitas, CA 95035
Tel.: (408) 957-3800
Fax: (408) 957-3809

Ogilvy & Mather
(Sub. of WPP Group plc)
636 11th Ave
New York, NY 10036
Tel.: (212) 237-4000
Fax: (212) 237-5123
— Jason Marks *(Grp Dir-Creative-IBM)*

Ogilvy Public Relations Worldwide
10 Cabot Square Canary Wharf
London, E14 4QB, United Kingdom
Tel.: (44) 20 7345 3000
Fax: (44) 20 7345 9000

PointRoll Inc.
951 E Hector St
Conshohocken, PA 19428
Tel.: (267) 558-1300
Fax: (267) 285-1141
Toll Free: (800) 203-6956

Response Media, Inc.
3155 Medlock Bridge Rd
Norcross, GA 30071-1423
Tel.: (770) 451-5478
Fax: (770) 451-4929

Velocity Sports & Entertainment
230 East Ave 3rd Fl
Norwalk, CT 06855
Tel.: (203) 831-2000
Fax: (203) 831-2300

VSA Partners, Inc.
600 W Chicago Ave
Chicago, IL 60654
Tel.: (312) 427-6413
Toll Free: (877) 422-1311

INTERNATIONAL DATACASTING CORPORATION

50 Frank Nighbor Place
Kanata, ON K2V 1B9, Canada
Tel.: (613) 596-4120
Fax: (613) 596-4863
E-mail: info@datacast.com
Web Site: www.datacast.com
E-Mail For Key Personnel:

Key to Media (For complete agency information see *The Advertising Red Books-Agencies* edition):
1. Bus. Publs. 2. Cable T.V. 3. Catalogs & Directories. 4. Co-op Adv. 5. Consumer Mags. 6. D.M. to Bus. Estab.7. D.M. to Consumers
8. Daily Newsp. 9. Exhibits/Trade Shows 10. Foreign 11. Infomercial 12. Internet Adv.13. Multimedia 14. Network Radio
15. Network T.V. 16. Newsp. Distr. Mags. 17. Other 18. Outdoor (Posters, Transit) 19. Point of Purchase20. Premiums, Novelties
21. Product Samples 22. Special Events Mktg. 23. Spot Radio 24. Spot T.V. 25. Weekly Newsp. 26. Yellow Page Adv.

International Datacasting Corporation —
(Continued)

Marketing Director: marketing@intldata.ca
Sales Director: sales@intldata.ca
Approx. Rev.: $22,826,966
Approx. Number Employees: 125
Year Founded: 1984
Business Description:
Systems & Services for Broadband Satellite Distribution of Digital Data
S.I.C.: 4899
N.A.I.C.S.: 517410
Media: 10
Personnel:
Adam E. Adamou *(Chm)*
Frederick L. Godard *(Pres & CEO)*
Cory Garbolinsky *(Acting CFO & VP-Fin)*
Diana Cantu *(Exec Dir-Bus Dev-US)*
Brands & Products:
DATACASTING XD
FLEXROUTE
INTERNATIONAL DATACASTING
SUPERFLEX

INTERNATIONAL DECISION SYSTEMS

1500 IDS Ctr 80th S 8th St
Minneapolis, MN 55402
Tel.: (612) 851-3200
Fax: (612) 851-3207
E-mail: info@idsgrp.com
Web Site: www.idsgrp.com
Sales Range: $25-49.9 Million
Approx. Number Employees: 385
Year Founded: 1974
Business Description:
Business Oriented Computer Software & Services
S.I.C.: 7372; 7373; 7379; 7389
N.A.I.C.S.: 511210; 541512; 541519; 561499
Media: 2-5-10-13-22
Personnel:
Richard Barnes *(CFO & COO)*
Kristopher Schmidt *(Gen Counsel & VP-HR & Info Svcs)*
Gerry Perham *(VP-Products Svcs & Support)*
Steve Pittman *(VP-Sls)*

INTERPHASE CORPORATION

2901 N Dallas Pkwy Ste 200
Plano, TX 75093
Tel.: (214) 654-5000
Fax: (214) 654-5500
Toll Free: (800) FASTNET
E-mail: fastnet@iphase.com
Web Site: www.iphase.com
Approx. Rev.: $18,207,000
Approx. Number Employees: 83
Year Founded: 1977
Business Description:
Telecom & Server I/O Solutions
S.I.C.: 3669; 3577
N.A.I.C.S.: 334290; 334119
Export
Advertising Expenditures: $9,000
Media: 2-10
Personnel:
Gregory B. Kalush *(Chm, Pres & CEO)*
S. Thomas Thawley *(Vice Chm & Sec)*
Thomas N. Tipton Jr. *(CFO, Treas & VP-Fin)*
Marc E. Devinney *(VP-Engrg)*
Randall McComas *(VP-Global Sls & Customer Support)*
Yoram Solomon *(VP-Corp Strategy & Bus Dev)*
Brands & Products:
ADVANCED MC
ADVANCED TCA
DESIGNED TO PERFORM. DESIGNED TO LAST.
GATEWAY
INAV
INTERPHASE
ISPAN
IWARE
PCI
PCI EXPRESS
PMC
POWERSAN
SLOTOPTIMIZER
TCA
WINPATH
WINTEGRA

INTERPLAY ENTERTAINMENT CORP.

12301 Wilshire Blvd Ste 502
Los Angeles, CA 90025
Tel.: (310) 979-7070
E-mail: info@interplay.com
Web Site: www.interplay.com
E-Mail For Key Personnel:
President: hcaen@interplay-usa.com
Sales Director: sales@interplay.com
Public Relations: pr@interplay.com
Approx. Rev.: $1,380,000
Approx. Number Employees: 11
Year Founded: 1982
Business Description:
Entertainment Software Developer & Publisher
S.I.C.: 7372
N.A.I.C.S.: 511210; 334611
Advertising Expenditures: $245,000
Media: 2-4-7-8-10-13
Personnel:
Eric Caen *(Pres)*
Herve Caen *(CEO & Interim CFO)*

INTERVALZERO INC.

400 5th Ave
Waltham, MA 02451
Tel.: (781) 996-4481
Fax: (781) 795-0158
Toll Free: (800) 334-8649
E-mail: sales@intervalzero.com
Web Site: www.intervalzero.com
E-Mail For Key Personnel:
Sales Director: sales@intervalzero.com
Sales Range: $10-24.9 Million
Approx. Number Employees: 20
Year Founded: 1980
Business Description:
Embedded Computing Software Developer
S.I.C.: 7372
N.A.I.C.S.: 511210
Advertising Expenditures: $500,000
Media: 2-4-7-8-10-13-19
Personnel:
Jeffrey D. Hibbard *(CEO)*
Brands & Products:
ARDENCE
BOOT-NIC
BXP
EMBEDHEAD
ETS
PHAR LAP
PHAR LAP SOFTWARE
READYON
RT TCP/IP
RTX
TNT DOS-EXTENDER
TNT EMBEDDED TOOL SUITE
VENTURCOM
YOUR VISION, OUR SOFTWARE

INTERVOICE, INC.

(Sub. of Convergys Corporation)
17811 Waterview Pkwy
Dallas, TX 75252-8016
Tel.: (972) 454-8000
Fax: (972) 454-8707
Toll Free: (800) 700-0122
E-mail: ir@intervoice.com
Web Site: www.intervoice.com
E-Mail For Key Personnel:
Marketing Director: mktg@intervoice-brite.com
Approx. Sls.: $202,435,000
Approx. Number Employees: 736
Year Founded: 1983
Business Description:
Speech-Enabled Interactive Information Solutions
S.I.C.: 7372; 4899; 7379; 7389
N.A.I.C.S.: 511210; 517910; 541519; 561421
Advertising Expenditures: $2,600,000
Media: 1-2-4-7-10-11-17-22
Distr.: Intl.; Natl.
Personnel:
Dean C. Howell *(Gen Counsel, Sec & Sr VP)*
Mark Harris *(Sr VP-Svcs-Global & America)*
Brands & Products:
AGENTCONNECT
BRITE
BRITE OA&M
BRITECONNECT
BRITEDEBIT
CALLINGCARD
CONNECTLINK
FONERAC
FONETOWER
INAGENT
IN*CONTROL
INTERDIAL
INTERFONE
INTERFORM
INTERGEN
INTERSOFT
INTERVOICE
INTERWAY
INTEXT
INVISION
LEAVEWORD
NAMEDIAL
NSP-5000
OMVIA
OMVIA SPEECH
ONEVOICE
PULSEDIAL
REALCARE
RESOURCECARD
ROBOTOPERATOR
SCREENSCAN
TELESCAPE
VIRTUALVOICE
VISUALCONNECT
VOCALCARD
VOICEDIAL
VOICEEDIT
VOICEPLEX
VOICERAC
WRITE-1
YOUR VOICE

INTERWOVEN INC.

(Sub. of Autonomy Corporation plc)
(d/b/a/ Autonomy Interwoven)
160 E Tasman Dr
San Jose, CA 95134
Tel.: (408) 774-2000
Fax: (408) 774-2002
E-mail: info@interwoven.com
Web Site: www.atonomy.com
Approx. Rev.: $260,288,000
Approx. Number Employees: 1,012
Year Founded: 1995
Business Description:
Content Management Software Products & Services
S.I.C.: 7372; 7374
N.A.I.C.S.: 511210; 334611; 518210
Advertising Expenditures: $392,000
Media: 7
Brands & Products:
CONTROLHUB
ENCONNECT
LIVESITE
MEDIABIN
METATAGGER
OPENDEPLOY
OPTIMOST
RECORDSMANAGER
SCRITTURA
TEAMSITE
UNIVERSALSEARCH
WORKSITE

INTRADO INC.

(Joint Venture of Thomas H. Lee Partners, L.P. & Quadrangle Group LLC)
1601 Dry Creek Dr
Longmont, CO 80503
Tel.: (720) 494-5800
Fax: (720) 494-6600
E-mail: info@intrado.com
Web Site: www.intrado.com
E-Mail For Key Personnel:
Marketing Director: rebecca.bessette@intrado.com
Sales Range: $125-149.9 Million
Approx. Number Employees: 776
Year Founded: 1979
Business Description:
9-1-1 Service Delivery & Other Telecommunication Products Mfr
S.I.C.: 4899
N.A.I.C.S.: 517910
Media: 5-7-10
Personnel:
George Heinrichs *(Pres)*
Michael D. Dingman, Jr. *(CFO)*
Lawrence P. Jennings *(COO)*
Craig W. Donaldson *(Sr VP-Regulatory & Govt Affairs)*
Rebecca Bessette *(Dir-Mktg)*
Brands & Products:
9-1-1 NET
INTELLIBASE
INTELLICAST
INTELLIGENT EMERGENCY NETWORK
INTELLIVECTOR
INTRADO
PALLADIUM

INTRALINKS INC.

(Sub. of IntraLinks Holdings, Inc.)
150 E 42nd St 8th Fl

Key to Media (For complete agency information see *The Advertising Red Books-Agencies* edition):
1. Bus. Publs. 2. Cable T.V. 3. Catalogs & Directories. 4. Co-op Adv. 5. Consumer Mags. 6. D.M. to Bus. Estab.7. D.M. to Consumers
8. Daily Newsp. 9. Exhibits/Trade Shows 10. Foreign 11. Infomercial 12. Internet Adv.13. Multimedia 14. Network Radio
15. Network T.V. 16. Newsp. Distr. Mags. 17. Other 18. Outdoor (Posters, Transit) 19. Point of Purchase20. Premiums, Novelties
21. Product Samples 22. Special Events Mktg. 23. Spot Radio 24. Spot T.V. 25. Weekly Newsp. 26. Yellow Page Adv.

New York, NY 10017
Tel.: (212) 543-7700
Fax: (212) 543-7725
Fax: (212) 543-7978
E-mail: info@intralinks.com
Web Site: www.intralinks.com
Sales Range: $125-149.9 Million
Approx. Number Employees: 214
Business Description:
Data Communication Services
S.I.C.: 4899; 7372; 7375
N.A.I.C.S.: 517910; 511210; 518111
Personnel:
Patrick J. Wack, Jr. *(Chm)*
J. Andrew Damico *(Pres, CEO & Dir)*
Anthony C. Plesner *(CFO & Chief Admin Officer)*
Gregory S. Kenepp *(CMO)*
Robert Mullen *(Exec VP)*
Jody Tracey *(Exec VP-HR)*
Warwick Kirby *(Sr VP-Australia & New Zealand)*
Brands & Products:
INTRALINKS COURIER
INTRALINKS EXCHANGES
INTRALINKS INC
Advertising Agency:
KCSA Strategic Communications
(Kanan, Corbin, Schupak & Aronow, Inc.)
880 3rd Ave 6th Fl
New York, NY 10022
Tel.: (212) 682-6300
Fax: (212) 697-0910

INUVO, INC.
15550 Lightwave Dr 3rd Fl
Clearwater, FL 33760
Tel.: (727) 324-0046
E-mail: info@inuvo.com
Web Site: www.thinkpartnership.com
Approx. Rev.: $48,969,847
Approx. Number Employees: 46
Year Founded: 1987
Business Description:
Marketing & Technological Business Solutions
S.I.C.: 7371; 7379; 7389; 8742
N.A.I.C.S.: 541511; 541519; 541613; 561499
Advertising Expenditures: $126,000
Media: 17
Personnel:
Mitchell Tuchman *(Chm)*
Richard K. Howe *(Pres & CEO)*
Wally Ruiz *(CFO)*
Stan Antonuk *(COO & Sr VP-Direct)*

INVENTHELP
(Sub. of Technosystems Consolidated Corporation)
217 9th St
Pittsburgh, PA 15222-3506
Tel.: (412) 288-1300
Fax: (412) 288-1354
Toll Free: (800) 622-9855
E-mail: inventinfo@inventhelp.com
Web Site: www.inventhelp.com
Approx. Number Employees: 250
Year Founded: 1984
Business Description:
Inventor Services
S.I.C.: 8742
N.A.I.C.S.: 541611
Advertising Expenditures: $1,000,000
Media: 2-3-6-8-12-13-14-15-23-24
Distr.: Natl.
Personnel:
Elaine Angert *(Dir-Adv)*
Liv Dobo *(Mgr-Interactive Adv)*
Patrick Marino *(Coord-Adv)*
Brands & Products:
INPEX
Advertising Agency:
Innovative Communications
217 9th St
Pittsburgh, PA 15222-3506
Tel.: (412) 288-1300
Fax: (412) 338-0480
(Invention Submission Corporation)

INVENTION TECHNOLOGIES INC.
(d/b/a Invent Tech)
2655 S Lejeune Rd Ste 550
Miami, FL 33134
Tel.: (786) 425-4000
Tel.: (786) 437-8801
E-mail: info@invent-tech.com
Web Site: www.invent-tech.com
Approx. Sls.: $10,000,000
Approx. Number Employees: 45
Business Description:
Market Analysis, Business, & Economic Research
S.I.C.: 8732
N.A.I.C.S.: 541910
Media: 10-24
Personnel:
Gray Kooritzky *(Pres)*
Brands & Products:
INVENT-TECH
INVENTION-TECHNOLOGIES
THE LAUNCHPAD FOR NEW IDEAS

INVESTMENT SEMINARS, INC.
(d/b/a InterShow)
The Githler Ctr 1258 N Palm Ave
Sarasota, FL 34236
Tel.: (941) 955-0323
Fax: (941) 366-5755
Toll Free: (800) 970-4355
E-mail: intershow@intershow.com
Web Site: www.intershow.com
Approx. Number Employees: 65
Year Founded: 1978
Business Description:
Conference (Trade Show) Producer for Individual Investors, Active Traders & Financial Advisors
S.I.C.: 7389
N.A.I.C.S.: 561920
Media: 2-10
Personnel:
Kim Githler *(Pres & CEO)*
Aaron West *(Sr VP-Media & Platform Relships-US)*
Jennifer Bruce *(Mgr-Adv)*
Brands & Products:
CRUISE SEMINARS
THE FINANCIAL ADVISOR SYMPOSIUM
THE FOREX TRADING EXPO
INTERSHOW
THE MONEY SHOW
MONEY SHOW DIGEST
THE TRADERS EXPO
THE WORLD MONEY SHOW

INVINCIBLE OFFICE FURNITURE
842 S 26th St
Manitowoc, WI 54220
Tel.: (920) 682-4601
Fax: (920) 683-2970
Toll Free: (800) 558-4417
E-mail: sales@invincible.cc
Web Site: www.invinciblefurniture.com
E-Mail For Key Personnel:
Sales Director: sales@invincible.com
Approx. Number Employees: 100
Year Founded: 1904
Business Description:
Steel Office Furniture Mfr
S.I.C.: 2522
N.A.I.C.S.: 337214
Import Export
Advertising Expenditures: $500,000
Media: 1-2-3-4-5-6-8-10-13-15-16-17-20-21-22-23-26
Distr.: Natl.
Budget Set: Jan.
Personnel:
James Leiser *(Pres & CEO)*
Brands & Products:
CLASSIC SERIES
DETENTE
INVINCIBLE
M-LINE
S-LINE
SPIRIT
VISTA
VISTA 2000 EXTRA

INX INC.
6401 Southwest Fwy
Houston, TX 77074
Tel.: (713) 795-2000
Fax: (713) 795-2001
E-mail: info@inxi.com
Web Site: www.inxi.com
Sales Range: $250-299.9 Million
Approx. Number Employees: 433
Business Description:
IT Services & Related Hardware & Software
S.I.C.: 7373; 5045; 7372
N.A.I.C.S.: 541512; 423430; 511210
Advertising Expenditures: $80,000
Media: 2-10
Personnel:
James H. Long *(Chm)*
Mark T. Hilz *(Pres & CEO)*
Philip Rydzewski *(CFO & Sr VP)*
William E. Casper *(Chief Acctg Officer, VP & Controller)*
Andrew Cadwell *(Sr VP-Sls & Field Ops)*
David DeYoung *(Sr VP-Bus Dev)*
Mike French *(Sr VP-Mktg)*
Jonathan Groves *(Sr VP-Tech)*
Paul Klotz *(Sr VP-Ops)*
Deborah Simpson *(Mgr-Employee Svcs)*

INX INTERNATIONAL INK CO.
(Sub. of INX Corporation)
150 N Martingale Rd Ste 700
Schaumburg, IL 60173
Tel.: (630) 382-1800
Fax: (847) 969-9754
Toll Free: (800) 631-7956
E-mail: inxinfo@inxintl.com
Web Site: www.inxink.com
E-Mail For Key Personnel:
Public Relations: stromberg@inxink.com
Approx. Number Employees: 100
Year Founded: 1992
Business Description:
Printing Inks Mfr
S.I.C.: 2893
N.A.I.C.S.: 325910
Import Export
Media: 2-10
Distr.: Natl.
Personnel:
Joe Cichon *(Sr VP-Mfg)*
David Sambo *(VP-OSF Sls)*
Jim Wegemer *(Dir-Accts-Natl)*
Brands & Products:
COLORTRAC
ECON O MIST
INX
INXCURE
INXFLEX
INXFRESH
LAMIALL

IOGEAR, INC.
23 Hubble Dr
Irvine, CA 92618
Tel.: (949) 453-8782
Fax: (949) 453-8785
E-mail: pr@iogear.com
Web Site: www.iogear.com
Approx. Number Employees: 80
Business Description:
Solutions & Support for Computer Connectivity
S.I.C.: 5045
N.A.I.C.S.: 423430
Media: 6-10-20
Personnel:
Sampson Yang *(CEO)*
Bill Nguyen *(Sr Mgr-Mktg)*

IOMEGA CORPORATION
(Sub. of EMC Consumer/Small Business Products)
3721 Valley Centre Dr Ste 200
San Diego, CA 92130
Tel.: (858) 314-7000
Fax: (858) 314-7001
E-mail: investorrelations@iomega.com
Web Site: www.iomega.com
Approx. Sls.: $336,614,000
Approx. Number Employees: 243
Year Founded: 1980
Business Description:
Mfr & Marketer of High Performance Removable Media Disk Drives & Subsystems; Computer Peripherals; Network Attached Storage (NAS)
S.I.C.: 3572; 7371
N.A.I.C.S.: 334112; 541511
Export
Advertising Expenditures: $1,700,000
Media: 2-4-5-6-7-8-11-13-25
Distr.: Intl.; Natl.
Budget Set: Nov.
Personnel:
Mike Nikzad *(COO)*
Ron S. Zollman *(Gen Counsel)*
Jan Jensen *(VP-Sls-Intl)*
Chris Romoser *(Sr Dir-Comm & PR-Worldwide)*
Loren Bryner *(Product Mgr-Global)*
Samer Sayed *(Mgr-BtoB Sls-Middle East & Africa Reg)*
Brands & Products:
ARCSERVE
BRIGHTSTOR
DISK-MAC
DITTO
FOLDERSHARE
FOTOSHOW
HIPZIP

Key to Media (For complete agency information see *The Advertising Red Books-Agencies* edition):
1. Bus. Publs. 2. Cable T.V. 3. Catalogs & Directories. 4. Co-op Adv. 5. Consumer Mags. 6. D.M. to Bus. Estab.7. D.M. to Consumers
8. Daily Newsp. 9. Exhibits/Trade Shows 10. Foreign 11. Infomercial 12. Internet Adv.13. Multimedia 14. Network Radio
15. Network T.V. 16. Newsp. Distr. Mags. 17. Other 18. Outdoor (Posters, Transit) 19. Point of Purchase20. Premiums, Novelties
21. Product Samples 22. Special Events Mktg. 23. Spot Radio 24. Spot T.V. 25. Weekly Newsp. 26. Yellow Page Adv.

Iomega Corporation — (Continued)

HOTBURN
IOMEGA
IOMEGAWARE
JAZ
LIFEWORKS
MICRO MINI
MICRODRIVE
NOTEBOOK ZIP
PEERLESS
POCKETZIP
PREDATOR
QUIKSYNC
QUIKTOUCH
REV
ZIP

IPSOS-ASI, INC.

(Sub. of Ipsos Group S.A.)
301 Merit 7
Norwalk, CT 06851
Tel.: (203) 840-3400
Fax: (203) 840-3450
E-mail: naminfo@ipsos-asi.com
Web Site: www.ipsos-asi.com
Approx. Number Employees: 50
Year Founded: 1962
Business Description:
Market Research
S.I.C.: 8732
N.A.I.C.S.: 541910
Media: 13
Personnel:
Gerald C. Lukeman *(Chm)*
Brad Bane *(Sr VP)*
Donna Wydra *(Sr VP)*
Brands & Products:
AD*GRAPH
EQUITY*BUILDER
NEXT*IDEA
NEXT*KIDS
NEXT*PRINT
NEXT*TV
POST*TESTING

IPSWITCH, INC.

10 Maguire Rd Ste 220
Lexington, MA 02421
Tel.: (781) 676-5700
Fax: (781) 676-5710
E-mail: pr@ipswitch.com
Web Site: www.ipswitch.com
E-Mail For Key Personnel:
Sales Director: sales@ipswitch.com
Public Relations: pr@ipswitch.com
Approx. Number Employees: 140
Year Founded: 1991
Business Description:
Internet Productivity Software Developer & Retailer
S.I.C.: 7372
N.A.I.C.S.: 511210
Media: 2-10-13
Personnel:
Roger Greene *(CEO)*
Azmi Jafarey *(CIO)*
Gary Shottes *(Pres-File Transfer Div)*
Al James *(Dir-Sls Ops, Network Mgmt Div)*
Brands & Products:
IPSWITCH
WS-FTP PROFESSIONAL
WS-FTP SERVER
Advertising Agency:
Kirk Communications
1 New Hampshire Ave Ste 125
Portsmouth, NH 03801
Tel.: (603) 766-4945
Fax: (603) 766-1901
Analyst Relations
New Product Announcements
New Product Introductions
North American Public Relations
Agency of Record
Press Relations
Product Placements
Social Networking
Trade Show Press

IRON MOUNTAIN INCORPORATED

745 Atlantic Ave
Boston, MA 02111-2735
Tel.: (617) 535-4766
Fax: (617) 350-7881
Toll Free: (800) 935-6966
E-mail: karin.pespisa@ironmountain.com
Web Site: www.ironmountain.com
Approx. Rev.: $3,055,134,000
Approx. Number Employees: 19,400
Year Founded: 1951
Business Description:
Records Management, Data Protection & Information Destruction Solutions & Services
S.I.C.: 7379; 4953; 7372; 8748
N.A.I.C.S.: 541519; 511210; 541618; 562219
Advertising Expenditures: $57,198,000
Media: 2-7-10-26
Personnel:
C. Richard Reese *(Chm)*
Brian P. McKeon *(CFO & Exec VP)*
Tasos Tsolakis *(CIO & Exec VP)*
Marc Duale *(Pres-Intl)*
Harold E. Ebbighausen *(Pres-North America)*
Robert G. Miller *(Pres-Asia Pacific Grp)*
Annie S. Drapeau *(Exec VP-HR)*
Jerry Rulli *(Exec VP-Sls-Worldwide)*
William Brown *(Sr VP-Global Compliance Process & Interim Head-Info Security)*
David Bayer *(Product Dir-Solutions Mktg)*
Ric Buskirk *(Reg Mgr-Digital Solutions)*
Dan O'Neill *(Sr Mgr-PR)*
Laura Sudnik *(Sr Mgr-PR)*
Brands & Products:
1-800-FASTFILE
BACKUPCARE
COMPASS
DELTA BLOCK
DIGITAL RECORD CENTER
ECUSTOMIZE
ENTERPRISE VALUE ARCHIVES ARCHITECTURE
EVAA
GROUPTRAK
INCONTROL
INFORMATION PROTECTION & STORAGE
IRON MOUNTAIN
IRON MOUNTAIN CONNECT
MEDIACARE
MYROAM
RECORDS COLLECTOR
SAASPROTECT ESCROW SERVICE
SAFEKEEPERPLUS
SAFEKEEPERPLUS.COM
SECUREBASE
SECURESYNC
SENDONCE
SHIPTRAK
SURE-DNS
TLD MONITOR
Advertising Agency:
Wallwork Curry McKenna
10 City Sq 5th Fl
Charlestown, MA 02129
Tel.: (617) 266-8200
Fax: (617) 266-8270

IRONPORT SYSTEMS

(Sub. of Cisco Systems, Inc.)
950 Elm Ave
San Bruno, CA 94066
Tel.: (650) 989-6500
Fax: (650) 989-6543
E-mail: info@ironport.com
Web Site: www.ironport.com
Sales Range: $150-199.9 Million
Approx. Number Employees: 700
Year Founded: 2000
Business Description:
Email & Web Security Products
S.I.C.: 7372
N.A.I.C.S.: 511210
Media: 10
Personnel:
Keith Valory *(Gen Counsel & VP-Corp Dev)*
Tom Gillis *(Sr VP-Mktg)*
Patrick Peterson *(VP-Tech)*
Brands & Products:
IRONPORT
IRONPORT M-SERIES
IRONPORT S-SERIES
IRONPORT SENDERBASE

ISLAND PACIFIC

(Sub. of 3Q Holdings Limited)
17310 Redhill Ave Ste 320
Irvine, CA 92614
Tel.: (949) 476-2212
Fax: (949) 476-0177
Toll Free: (800) 99-GETIP
E-mail: info@islandpacific.com
Web Site: www.islandpacific.com
Approx. Sls.: $25,513,000
Approx. Number Employees: 185
Year Founded: 1977
Business Description:
Software & E-Commerce Business Solutions Mfr & Retailer
S.I.C.: 7372; 7371
N.A.I.C.S.: 511210; 541511
Advertising Expenditures: $3,000
Media: 2-10-13
Personnel:
Davy Rosen *(CEO)*
Richard Gaetano *(COO)*
Brands & Products:
SYNARO

ITAGROUP, INC.

4800 Westown Pkwy Ste 300
West Des Moines, IA 50266-6719
Tel.: (515) 326-3400
Fax: (515) 221-8108
Toll Free: (800) 257-1985
Web Site: www.itagroup.com
E-Mail For Key Personnel:
Marketing Director: BSchelske@itagroup.com
Sales Range: $150-199.9 Million
Approx. Number Employees: 420
Year Founded: 1963
Business Description:
Performance Marketing Programs
S.I.C.: 7361
N.A.I.C.S.: 541612
Media: 2-7-10-26
Distr.: Reg.
Budget Set: June
Personnel:
Tom Mahoney *(Pres & CEO)*
Richard Rue *(CFO & Sr VP)*
Mary Bussone *(Sr VP-Event Mgmt)*
John Rose *(VP-IT)*
Elizabeth Brower *(Strategist-Mktg)*
Brands & Products:
IDEA TO ACTION
INTERNATIONAL TRAVEL ASSOCIATES
ITAGROUP

ITRON INC.

2111 N Molter Rd
Liberty Lake, WA 99019
Tel.: (509) 924-9900
Fax: (509) 891-3355
Toll Free: (800) 635-5461
Web Site: www.itron.com
Approx. Rev.: $2,259,271,000
Approx. Number Employees: 9,500
Year Founded: 1977
Business Description:
Energy Information & Communications Solutions to Utility Industries Worldwide
S.I.C.: 3663; 3571; 3825
N.A.I.C.S.: 334220; 334111; 334515
Import Export
Advertising Expenditures: $1,200,000
Media: 2-7-8-10-18-22
Personnel:
Jon E. Eliassen *(Chm)*
LeRoy D. Nosbaum *(Pres & CEO)*
Steven M. Helmbrecht *(CFO & Sr VP)*
Chuck McAtee, Jr. *(CIO & VP-IT)*
Philip C. Mezey *(Pres/COO-Energy)*
Marcel Regnier *(Pres/COO-Water)*
John W Holleran *(Gen Counsel, Sec & Sr VP)*
Russell E. Vanos *(VP-Mktg)*

ITT CANNON

(Div. of ITT Defense Electronics & Services)
666 E Dyer Rd
Santa Ana, CA 92705-5612
Mailing Address:
PO Box 929
Santa Ana, CA 92705
Tel.: (714) 557-4700
Fax: (714) 628-2142
Toll Free: (800) 854-3028
Web Site: www.ittcannon.com
Sales Range: $550-599.9 Million
Approx. Number Employees: 700
Year Founded: 1915
Business Description:
International Supplier of Connectors, Interconnectors, Cable Assemblies, Switches, Multi-Function Grips, I/O Card Kits, Smart Card Systems & LAN Components; Network Systems & Services
S.I.C.: 3678; 5065
N.A.I.C.S.: 334417; 423690
Import Export
Advertising Expenditures: $6,000,000
Media: 2-4-5-7-10-20
Distr.: Intl.; Natl.
Budget Set: Dec.

Key to Media (For complete agency information see *The Advertising Red Books-Agencies* edition):
1. Bus. Publs. 2. Cable T.V. 3. Catalogs & Directories. 4. Co-op Adv. 5. Consumer Mags. 6. D.M. to Bus. Estab.7. D.M. to Consumers
8. Daily Newsp. 9. Exhibits/Trade Shows 10. Foreign 11. Infomercial 12. Internet Adv.13. Multimedia 14. Network Radio
15. Network T.V. 16. Newsp. Distr. Mags. 17. Other 18. Outdoor (Posters, Transit) 19. Point of Purchase20. Premiums, Novelties
21. Product Samples 22. Special Events Mktg. 23. Spot Radio 24. Spot T.V. 25. Weekly Newsp. 26. Yellow Page Adv.

Personnel:
Bill Taylor *(Pres)*

IVT SOFTWARE, INC.
(d/b/a HWI Global)
3840 S Water St
Pittsburgh, PA 15203
Tel.: (412) 884-3028
Fax: (412) 884-3029
E-mail: info@hwicleanrooms.com
Web Site: www.hwicleanrooms.com
Approx. Rev.: $3,948,907
Year Founded: 2006
Business Description:
Cleanroom Systems Designing, Engineering, Manufacturing, Installing & Servicing
S.I.C.: 3585; 1711; 5075
N.A.I.C.S.: 333415; 238220; 423730
Advertising Expenditures: $29,603
Media: 17
Personnel:
Deric Haddad *(Chm, Pres & CEO)*
Richard Smith *(CFO)*

IWCO DIRECT
(Sub. of IWCO Direct)
75 Marcus Dr
Melville, NY 11747-4210
Tel.: (631) 694-1919
Fax: (631) 694-7493
Toll Free: (800) 700-FALA
Approx. Number Employees: 500
Year Founded: 1916
Business Description:
Direct Mail Communication Services
S.I.C.: 7331; 7374
N.A.I.C.S.: 541860; 518210
Import Export
Media: 2-7

IXIA
26601 W Agoura Rd
Calabasas, CA 91302
Tel.: (818) 871-1800
Fax: (818) 871-1805
Toll Free: (877) 367-4942
E-mail: info@ixiacom.com
Web Site: www.ixiacom.com
E-Mail For Key Personnel:
Sales Director: sales@ixiacom.com
Approx. Rev.: $276,815,000
Approx. Number Employees: 1,100
Year Founded: 1997
Business Description:
High Speed, Multi-Port Network Performance Analysis Systems Mfr
S.I.C.: 3825; 3699; 4899; 7389
N.A.I.C.S.: 334515; 335999; 517910; 541990
Advertising Expenditures: $1,000,000
Media: 2-10-13-22
Personnel:
Errol Ginsberg *(Chm & Chief Innovation Officer)*
Atul Bhatnagar *(Pres & CEO)*
Thomas B. Miller *(CFO)*
Ron Buckly *(Gen Counsel)*
Victor Alston *(Sr VP-Product Dev)*
Alan Grahame *(Sr VP-Sls Svc & Support)*
Maik Lankau *(VP-Carriers Sls North America & Global Alliances)*
Christopher L. Williams *(VP-HR)*
Daisy Sun *(Product Mgr)*
Brands & Products:
IXACCESS
IXADMIN
IXANALYZE
IXANVL
IXAUTHENTICATE
IXAUTOMATE
IXCHARIOT
IXDEFEND
IXEXPLORER
IXGREEN
IXIA
IXLOAD
IXNETWORK
IXRAVE
IXROUTER
IXSAN
IXSCRIPTMATE
IXVERIFY
IXVOICE
IXVPN
IXWLAN
LINUX SDK
OPTIXIA
REAL WORLD TRAFFIC
SCRIPTGEN
TCL API
XENPAK

IXIA
(Sub. of Ixia)
26601 W Agoura rd
Calabasas, CA 91302
Tel.: (650) 960-1025
Fax: (818) 871-1805
Web Site: www.ixiacom.com
Approx. Rev.: $37,911,000
Approx. Number Employees: 205
Year Founded: 1985
Business Description:
High Speed, Multi-Port Network Performance Analysis Systems Mfr
S.I.C.: 3825; 3661; 7372; 7389
N.A.I.C.S.: 334515; 334210; 334611; 541990
Media: 7-10
Brands & Products:
CHAMELEON
DCT 2000
MGTS
POWER PCI
POWERPCI
Advertising Agency:
Emery Advertising
4911 Green Rd Ste 101
Raleigh, NC 27616
Tel.: (919) 790-2600
Fax: (919) 790-2601

IXYS CORPORATION
1590 Buckeye Dr
Milpitas, CA 95035
Tel.: (408) 457-9000
Fax: (408) 496-0670
E-mail: admins@ixys.net
Web Site: www.ixys.com
E-Mail For Key Personnel:
Sales Director: sales@ixys.net
Approx. Rev.: $363,273,000
Approx. Number Employees: 1,244
Year Founded: 1983
Business Description:
Power Semiconductors & Power Modules Mfr
S.I.C.: 3674
N.A.I.C.S.: 334413
Advertising Expenditures: $547,000
Media: 2-10-13
Personnel:
Nathan Zommer *(Founder, Chm & CEO)*
Uzi Sasson *(Pres & CFO)*
Bradley Green *(VP-Intl Sls & Gen Mgr-Switzerland)*
Thea Kern *(Gen Mgr-Germany)*
Jeroen van Zeeland *(Gen Mgr-Germany)*
John Harris *(Mgr-Facilities)*
Brands & Products:
COOLMAS
EFFICIENCY THROUGH TECHNOLOGY
HIPERDYN
HIPERFRED
ISOPLUS
ISOPLUS I4-PAC
IXOLAR
IXYS
SONIC-FRD
WIMAX

JABIL CIRCUIT, INC.
10560 Dr Martin Luther King Jr St N
Saint Petersburg, FL 33716
Tel.: (727) 577-9749
Fax: (727) 579-8529
E-mail: investor_relations@jbail.com
Web Site: www.jabil.com
E-Mail For Key Personnel:
Marketing Director: beth_walters@jabil.com
Public Relations: beth_walters@jabil.com
Approx. Rev.: $13,409,411,000
Approx. Number Employees: 69,000
Year Founded: 1966
Business Description:
Mfr of Printed Circuit Boards
S.I.C.: 3679; 3672
N.A.I.C.S.: 334418; 334412
Export
Media: 4-8-11
Personnel:
William D. Morean *(Chm)*
Thomas A. Sansone *(Vice Chm)*
Timothy L. Main *(Pres & CEO)*
Forbes I.J. Alexander *(CFO)*
Mark T. Mondello *(COO)*
David Couch *(CIO)*
William E. Peters *(Reg Pres-America & Sr VP-Human Devel)*
Hartmut Liebel *(CEO-Aftermarket Svcs Grp & Exec VP)*
John P. Lovato *(CEO-Consumer Div & Exec VP)*
William D. Muir Jr. *(CEO-EMS Div & Exec VP)*
Robert L. Paver *(Gen Counsel & Sec)*
Joseph A. McGee *(Exec VP-Strategic Plng & Dev)*
Meheryar Mike Dastoor *(Sr VP & Controller)*
Maurice Dunlop *(Sr VP-Global Bus Units)*
Michael J. Matthes *(Sr VP-Ops-Worldwide)*
Donald J. Myers *(Sr VP-Corp Dev)*
Teck Ping Yuen *(Sr VP-Worldwide Ops)*
Courtney J. Ryan *(Sr VP-Global Bus Unit)*
Beth A. Walters *(Sr VP-Comm & IR)*
Teck Ping Yuen *(Sr VP-HR-Asia)*
David S. Emerson *(VP-Sector Sls-Worldwide)*
Linda G. Munsey *(Dir-Advanced Quality)*
Advertising Agency:
NAVAJO Company
1164 Cadillac Ct
Milpitas, CA 95035
Tel.: (408) 957-3800
Fax: (408) 957-3809

JACK HENRY & ASSOCIATES, INC.
663 W Hwy 60
Monett, MO 65708
Mailing Address:
PO Box 807
Monett, MO 65708
Tel.: (417) 235-6652
Fax: (417) 235-4281
Web Site: www.jackhenry.com
Approx. Rev.: $836,586,000
Approx. Number Employees: 4,528
Year Founded: 1976
Business Description:
Integrated Computer Systems for In-House & Service Bureau Data Processing to Banks & Other Financial Institutions
S.I.C.: 7373; 5045; 7372
N.A.I.C.S.: 541512; 423430; 511210
Media: 2-10-13
Distr.: Natl.
Personnel:
Michael E. Henry *(Chm)*
Jerry D. Hall *(Vice Chm & Exec VP)*
Tony L. Wormington *(Pres)*
John F. Prim *(CEO)*
Kevin D. Williams *(CFO & Treas)*
Debbie Wood *(Gen Mgr-Mktg & Industry Res)*
John San Filippo *(Mgr-Mktg-Symitar)*
Dennis Jones *(Mgr-Mktg-Jack Henry Banking)*
Jacqueline Scheider *(Mgr-Mktg-ProfitStars)*
Brands & Products:
4 SIGHT
ACH
ACS
ALLIANCE CHECK IMAGE SOLUTIONS
APS
ARCHIV
BANK BUSINESS RECOVERY SERVICE
CASHCONNECT
CENTURION BUSINESS RECOVERY CONSULTING GROUP
CIF 20/20
CIF 36
CIF 38
CONDUCTOR
CORE DIRECTOR
DDA
DO THE RIGHT THING.DO WHATEVER IT TAKES.HAVE FUN
EAR
FAS
FORMSMART
GRAPHICAL ACCESS FOR JHA PLATFORM SYSTEM
HBK
ICI
INTOUCH VOICE RESPONSE
IPAY TECHNOLOGIES
JACK HENRY & ASSOCIATES
JACK HENRY BANKING
LCG
LIBERTY
MEMBERCONNECT WEB

Key to Media (For complete agency information see *The Advertising Red Books-Agencies* edition):
1. Bus. Publs. 2. Cable T.V. 3. Catalogs & Directories. 4. Co-op Adv. 5. Consumer Mags. 6. D.M. to Bus. Estab.7. D.M. to Consumers 8. Daily Newsp. 9. Exhibits/Trade Shows 10. Foreign 11. Infomercial 12. Internet Adv.13. Multimedia 14. Network Radio 15. Network T.V. 16. Newsp. Distr. Mags. 17. Other 18. Outdoor (Posters, Transit) 19. Point of Purchase20. Premiums, Novelties 21. Product Samples 22. Special Events Mktg. 23. Spot Radio 24. Spot T.V. 25. Weekly Newsp. 26. Yellow Page Adv.

Jack Henry & Associates, Inc. — (Continued)

MLA
NETFORUMS
NETTELLER ONLINE BANKING
PASSPORT.ATM
PC CONTINGENCY
PINPOINT REPORT RETRIEVAL
PROFITSTARS
REAL TIME
SECTOR
SIGMASTER
STREAMLINE PLATFORM AUTOMATION
SYMITAR
TIMETRACK PAYROLL SYSTEM
VERTEX TELLER AUTOMATION SYSTEM

JACOBY & MEYERS LLP

436 Robinson Ave
Newburgh, NY 12550-3341
Tel.: (212) 445-7000
Fax: (212) 267-2804
Toll Free: (800) 975-3425
Toll Free: (866) USJACOBY
E-mail: contact@jacoby-meyers.com
Web Site: www.jacoby-meyers.com
Approx. Number Employees: 36
Year Founded: 1972
Business Description:
Law Offices (Personal Injury)
S.I.C.: 8111
N.A.I.C.S.: 541110
Advertising Expenditures: $3,000,000
Media: 3-8-9-13-15-18-22-24-25-26
Budget Set: Sept. -Oct.
Personnel:
Gail Koff *(Owner)*
Michael Catuto *(CFO)*
Danielle Mackey *(Dir-Mktg)*
Brands & Products:
JACOBY & MEYERS
Advertising Agency:
HN Media & Marketing
275 Madison Ave Ste 2200
New York, NY 10016
Tel.: (212) 490-1300
Fax: (212) 490-0777

JADE SYSTEMS CORPORATION

3377 Rte 9
Cold Spring, NY 10516
Tel.: (845) 265-3798
Fax: (845) 265-3972
Web Site: www.jadenet.com
Approx. Number Employees: 135
Year Founded: 1993
Business Description:
Retail Computers Peripherals & Software
S.I.C.: 5045; 7378
N.A.I.C.S.: 423430; 811212
Import Export
Media: 2-8-10-13-22-26

JAMS, THE RESOLUTION EXPERTS

1920 Main St at Gillette Ave Ste 300
Irvine, CA 92614
Tel.: (949) 224-1810
Fax: (949) 224-1818
Web Site: www.jamsadr.com
Sales Range: $50-74.9 Million
Approx. Number Employees: 125
Business Description:
Alternate Dispute Resolution Services
S.I.C.: 6799
N.A.I.C.S.: 523910
Media: 2-4-9-10-13-22
Personnel:
Julie Sager *(CFO & Exec VP)*
William Zauner *(CIO & VP)*
Kimberly Taylor *(CTO & Sr VP)*
John Welsh *(Gen Counsel & Exec VP)*
Laura A. Martinez *(VP-HR)*
Brands & Products:
JAMS
THE RESOLUTION EXPERTS

JC TECHNOLOGY, INC.

(d/b/a Ace Computers)
1425 E Algonquin Rd
Arlington Heights, IL 60005
Tel.: (847) 952-6900
Fax: (847) 952-6901
Toll Free: (877) ACE-COMP
Web Site: www.acecomputers.com
Sales Range: $25-49.9 Million
Approx. Number Employees: 30
Year Founded: 1983
Business Description:
IT Solutions
S.I.C.: 7373; 7359; 8748
N.A.I.C.S.: 541512; 532420; 541690
Media: 10
Personnel:
Marianne Samborski *(Pres)*

JDA SOFTWARE

(Div. of JDA Software Group, Inc.)
9715 Key W Ave
Rockville, MD 20850
Tel.: (301) 255-5000
Fax: (301) 255-5370
Toll Free: (877) 331-0728
E-mail: info@jda.com
Web Site: www.jda.com
Approx. Rev.: $176,192,000
Approx. Number Employees: 270
Year Founded: 1969
Business Description:
Computer Software & Services
S.I.C.: 7372
N.A.I.C.S.: 334611; 511210
Advertising Expenditures: $5,000,000
Media: 2
Distr.: Intl.
Personnel:
Heather Loisel *(Sr VP-Mktg-Worldwide)*
Brands & Products:
MANUGISTICS NETWORKS
STATGRAPHICS

JDA SOFTWARE GROUP, INC.

14400 N 87th St
Scottsdale, AZ 85260-3653
Tel.: (480) 308-3000
Fax: (480) 308-3001
Toll Free: (800) 438-5301
E-mail: info@jda.com
Web Site: www.jda.com
Approx. Rev.: $617,209,000
Approx. Number Employees: 3,000
Year Founded: 1985
Business Description:
Software Solutions, Software Licensing, Consulting & Maintenance Services
S.I.C.: 7371; 7372
N.A.I.C.S.: 541511; 511210
Media: 1-2-4-7-10-22
Personnel:
James D. Armstrong *(Chm)*
Hamish N. J. Brewer *(Pres & CEO)*
Peter S. Hathaway *(CFO & Exec VP)*
Laurent F. Ferrere, II *(CMO, Sr VP-Product Mgmt & Mktg)*
Aditya Srivastava *(CTO & Sr VP)*
G. Michael Bridge *(Gen Counsel & Sr VP)*
Thomas Dziersk *(Exec VP-Sls & Mktg)*
David Gai *(Exec VP-Svcs)*
David R. King *(Exec VP-Product Dev & Mgmt)*
Brian Boylan *(Sr VP-HR)*
David J. Johnston *(Sr VP-Supply Chain)*
Salil Joshi *(Sr VP-Center of Excellence)*
Duane Kotsen *(Sr VP-Implementation Svcs)*
Kelly Thomas *(Sr VP-Mfg)*
Wayne Usie *(Sr VP-Retail)*
Kenneth Williams *(Sr VP-Support)*
Andy Archer *(Reg VP-Pricing & Revenue Mgmt Grp)*
Stephen McNulty *(Reg VP-Asia Pacific)*
Brian Mort *(Reg VP-EMEA)*
Brands & Products:
ALLOCATION
ARTHUR
CATEGORYADVISOR
DEMAND CLASSIFICATION
DEMAND DECOMPOSITION
DYNAMIC DEMAND RESPONSE
ELECTRONIC DYNAMIC AGREEMANT
IDEAS
INTACTIX
INTACTIX KNOWLEDGE BASE
INTEGRATOR
INTELLECT
JDA AIRLINE REVENUE OPTIMIZER
JDA CARGO REVENUE OPTIMIZER
JDA CARRIER
JDA CHANNEL CLUSTERING
JDA CRUISE REVENUE OPTIMIZER
JDA FLOOR PLANNING
JDA FREIGHT PAY
JDA MARKDOWN OPTIMIZATION
JDA MARKETPLACE
JDA MASTER PLANNING
JDA PLANOGRAM GENERATOR
JDA PRICE OPTIMIZER
JDA PROMOTIONS OPTIMIZATION
JDA RAIL REVENUE OPTIMIZER
JDA ROUTING
JDA SEQUENCING
JDA SHELF ASSORTMENT
JDA SHELF PRICE OPTIMIZATION
JDA SPACE AUTOMATION
JDA STORE PORTAL
JDA SUPPLY
JDA TOUR REVENUE OPTIMIZER
JDA TRANSPORT RFQ
MARKET MANAGER
MARKETPLACE REPLENISH
NETWORK OPTIMIZATION
OPTIMIZE ON DEMAND
ORDER OPTIMIZATION
PORTFOLIO
PORTFOLIO CRM
PORTFOLIO DATA SYNCHRONIZATION
PORTFOLIO MERCHANDISE MANAGEMENT
PORTFOLIO MOBILE ACCESS
PORTFOLIO POS
PORTFOLIO REGISTRY
PORTFOLIO WORKFORCE MANAGEMENT
SPACE PLANNING
TRADE EVENT MANAGEMENT
VENDOR MANAGED INVENTORY
VISTACPG

JDSU COMMUNICATIONS TEST & MEASUREMENT DIVISION

(Div. of JDS Uniphase Corporation)
1 Milestone Ctr Ct
Germantown, MD 20876-4092
Tel.: (240) 404-1550
Fax: (240) 404-1198
Toll Free: (800) 543-1550
Sales Range: $450-499.9 Million
Approx. Number Employees: 2,840
Year Founded: 1959
Business Description:
Test & Measurement Equipment Mfr
S.I.C.: 3825
N.A.I.C.S.: 334515
Import Export
Media: 2-7-10
Personnel:
David Heard *(Pres & CEO)*
Helmut Berg *(Sr VP-Telecom Product Div)*
John D'Anna *(Sr VP-Global Sls)*
Bill McDaniel *(Sr VP-Global HR)*
Steve Whigham *(Sr VP-Global Order Fulfillment & Quality)*
Zvonimir Turcinov *(Dir-Mktg)*
Jim Monroe *(Dir-Corp Commun)*
Sudeep Bose *(Mgr-Product Mktg)*
Brands & Products:
CENTEST
FIREBERD
NETOPTIMIZE

JONES DAY

North Point Bldg 901 Lakeside Ave
Cleveland, OH 44114-1190
Tel.: (216) 586-3939
Fax: (216) 579-0212
Web Site: www.jonesday.com
Approx. Number Employees: 4,850
Year Founded: 1893
Business Description:
Legal Services
S.I.C.: 8111; 7389
N.A.I.C.S.: 541110; 541199
Advertising Expenditures: $400,000
Media: 2-9-11-22-25
Personnel:
Stephen J. Brogan *(Partner & Mng Partner)*
David F. Adler *(Partner)*
David B. Alden *(Partner)*
Mark J. Andreini *(Partner)*
Brett P. Barragate *(Partner)*
Gregory A. Bauer *(Partner)*
Richard J. Bedell, Jr. *(Partner)*
Mark A. Belasic *(Partner)*
John V. Biernacki *(Partner)*
Carl E. Black *(Partner)*
Jennifer Hanley Boyce *(Partner)*
Kevin D. Boyce *(Partner)*
Thomas A. Briggs *(Partner)*
Robert L. Canala *(Partner)*
Denise A. Carkhuff *(Partner)*
Dan T. Carter *(Partner)*
Terri Chase *(Partner)*
Stephanie D. Clouston *(Partner)*

Key to Media (For complete agency information see *The Advertising Red Books-Agencies* edition):
1. Bus. Publs. 2. Cable T.V. 3. Catalogs & Directories. 4. Co-op Adv. 5. Consumer Mags. 6. D.M. to Bus. Estab.7. D.M. to Consumers
8. Daily Newsp. 9. Exhibits/Trade Shows 10. Foreign 11. Infomercial 12. Internet Adv.13. Multimedia 14. Network Radio
15. Network T.V. 16. Newsp. Distr. Mags. 17. Other 18. Outdoor (Posters, Transit) 19. Point of Purchase20. Premiums, Novelties
21. Product Samples 22. Special Events Mktg. 23. Spot Radio 24. Spot T.V. 25. Weekly Newsp. 26. Yellow Page Adv.

David B. Cochran *(Partner)*
Douglas R. Cole *(Partner)*
Daniel T. Conrad *(Partner)*
William H. Coquillette *(Partner)*
James Cox *(Partner)*
John D. Currivan *(Partner)*
Thomas C. Daniels *(Partner)*
Bryan E. Davis *(Partner)*
Thomas Demitrack *(Partner)*
John P. Dunn *(Partner)*
Robert S. Faxon *(Partner)*
Regan J. Fay *(Partner)*
F. Drexel Feeling *(Partner)*
Michelle K. Fischer *(Partner)*
Timothy P. Fraelich *(Partner)*
Lyle G. Ganske *(Partner-Cleveland Office)*
Stephen Q. Giblin *(Partner)*
Calvin P. Griffith *(Partner)*
Theodore M. Grossman *(Partner)*
Gina K. Gunning *(Partner)*
Daniel C. Hagen *(Partner)*
Thomas A. Hamilton *(Partner)*
Charles W. Hardin, Jr. *(Partner)*
Joseph D. Hatina *(Partner)*
David G. Heiman *(Partner)*
William A. Herzberger *(Partner)*
Christopher J. Hewitt *(Partner)*
Kenneth G. Hochman *(Partner)*
Thomas A. Howley *(Partner)*
Peter E. Izanec *(Partner)*
Ronald R. Janke *(Partner)*
Carl M. Jenks *(Partner)*
Stephen J. Kaczynski *(Partner)*
Robert C. Kahrl *(Partner)*
Sanjiv K. Kapur *(Partner)*
Gregory G. Katsa *(Partner)*
Christopher M. Kelly *(Partner)*
Paul D. Koethe *(Partner)*
David A. Kutik *(Partner)*
Dennis W. Labarre *(Partner)*
Colleen Laduzinski *(Partner)*
Jeffrey S. Leavitt *(Partner)*
Patrick J. Leddy *(Partner)*
Jonathan Leiken *(Partner)*
Heather Lennox *(Partner)*
Barbara J. Leukart *(Partner)*
John Q. Lewis *(Partner)*
David M. Maiorana *(Partner)*
Bernadette Mihalic Mast *(Partner)*
Patrick F. McCartan *(Partner)*
Ryan B. McCrum *(Partner)*
Bruce J. McDonald *(Partner)*
Evan Miller *(Partner)*
Stephen C. Mixter *(Partner)*
Anthony R. Moore *(Partner)*
Eric H. Mosier *(Partner)*
Cassandra G. Mott *(Partner)*
Fran A. Muracca, II *(Partner)*
Dennis L. Murphy *(Partner)*
Warren L. Nachlis *(Partner)*
John M. Newman, Jr. *(Partner)*
Edward J. O'Connell *(Partner)*
Timothy O'Hearn *(Partner)*
Kevin O'Mara *(Partner)*
Michael S. Owendoff *(Partner)*
Zachary T. Paris *(Partner)*
Scott Pierpont *(Partner)*
Robert A. Profusek *(Partner)*
Phillip A. Proger *(Partner)*
Rachel L. Rawson *(Partner)*
Robert H. Rawson, Jr. *(Partner)*
John A. Rego *(Partner)*
Jeanne M. Rickert *(Partner)*
Geoffrey J. Ritts *(Partner)*
Lisa A. Roberts-Mamone *(Partner)*
Veerle Roovers *(Partner)*
Louis Rorimer *(Partner)*
James A. Rydzel *(Partner)*
John M. Saada, Jr. *(Partner)*
Steven J. Sacher *(Partner)*
Tracy Schaffer *(Partner)*
Edward J. Sebold *(Partner)*
Gary Short *(Partner)*
Steven E. Sigalow *(Partner & Practice Leader-Insurance Recovery)*
Stephen G. Sozio *(Partner)*
Stephen J. Squeri *(Partner)*
Richard G. Stuhan *(Partner)*
Brian F. Toohey *(Partner)*
Katherine U *(Partner)*
Jeffery D. Ubersax *(Partner)*
Robert S. Walker *(Partner)*
James L. Wamsley, III *(Partner)*
Stanley Weiner *(Partner)*
Carson Wen *(Partner)*
Richard B. Whitney *(Partner)*
Meredith M. Wilkes *(Partner)*
Paula Batt Wilson *(Partner)*
James E. Young *(Partner)*
David R. Petrou *(Mgr-Global Comm)*

Brands & Products:
JONES DAY

Advertising Agency:
Teague Communication
28005 Smyth Dr Ste 112
Valencia, CA 91355
Tel.: (661) 297-5292
Fax: (661) 702-9705

THE JUDGE GROUP, INC.

4 Falls Corp Ctr 300 Conshohocken State Rd
West Conshohocken, PA 19428-2949
Tel.: (610) 667-7700
Fax: (610) 668-8210
E-mail: djudge@judge.com
Web Site: www.judge.com
Sales Range: $75-99.9 Million
Approx. Number Employees: 677
Year Founded: 1970
Business Description:
Employment & Staffing Services
S.I.C.: 7361
N.A.I.C.S.: 541612
Advertising Expenditures: $550,000
Media: 2-4-6-13-16
Personnel:
Martin E. Judge, Jr. *(CEO & Founder)*
Gary R. Morris *(Pres)*
Robert G. Alessandrini *(CFO)*
Katharine A. Wiercinski *(COO)*
Ken Krieger *(CIO)*
John M. Work *(Chief Acctg Officer & Controller)*
Raj Singh *(Pres/COO-Judge Intl)*
Amy E. Feldman *(Gen Counsel)*

Brands & Products:
BERKELEY TRAINING CENTER
EAZYTYME
EHCM
JUDGE
RESULTS THROUGH THE POWER OF EXPERIENCE.

JUNIPER NETWORKS

(Sub. of Juniper Networks, Inc.)
1 Rogers St 6th Fl
Cambridge, MA 02142-1102
Tel.: (617) 497-6339
Fax: (617) 547-1031
Toll Free: (800) 828-4146
Web Site: www.juniper.net
Sales Range: $25-49.9 Million
Approx. Number Employees: 80
Year Founded: 1982
Business Description:
Network Access Software Developer
S.I.C.: 7372; 7373
N.A.I.C.S.: 511210; 541512
Advertising Expenditures: $500,000
Media: 2-5-6-7-8-10
Distr.: Intl.; Natl.

K MICRO INC.

(d/b/a CorpInfo Services)
2050 S Westgate Ave
Los Angeles, CA 90025-6119
Tel.: (310) 442-3200
Fax: (310) 442-3201
E-mail: webmaster@corpinfo.com
Web Site: www.corpinfo.com
Sales Range: $25-49.9 Million
Approx. Number Employees: 150
Year Founded: 1983
Business Description:
IT Infrastructure Services
S.I.C.: 7373
N.A.I.C.S.: 541512
Media: 10
Personnel:
Michael Sabourian *(Pres)*

KARL'S RENTAL CENTER INC.

7000 S Tenth St
Oak Creek, WI 53154-1421
Tel.: (414) 831-7069
Fax: (414) 831-7080
Toll Free: (800) 383-6332
E-mail: info@karls.com
Web Site: www.karls.com
Approx. Sls.: $6,000,000
Approx. Number Employees: 300
Year Founded: 1966
Business Description:
Party & Event Equipment Rental
S.I.C.: 7359; 7213
N.A.I.C.S.: 532299; 812331
Media: 4-26
Personnel:
Ron Creten *(Pres & COO)*

KEANE, INC.

(Branch of Keane, Inc.)
100 City Sq
Boston, MA 02129
Tel.: (617) 241-9200
E-mail: info@keane.com
Web Site: www.keane.com
E-Mail For Key Personnel:
Public Relations: pr@keane.com
Approx. Number Employees: 9,586
Year Founded: 1965
Business Description:
Information Technology & Business Process Services
S.I.C.: 7371; 7373; 7389
N.A.I.C.S.: 541511; 541512; 561499

Advertising Agency:
Gutenberg Communications
555 Eighth Ave Ste 1002
New York, NY 10018
Tel.: (212) 239-8475
Fax: (212) 239-8476
Public Relations

KELLY SERVICES, INC.

999 W Big Beaver Rd
Troy, MI 48084-4782
Tel.: (248) 362-4444
Fax: (248) 244-4360
Toll Free: (888) 465-3559
E-mail: kfirst@kellyservices.com
Web Site: www.kellyservices.com
Approx. Rev.: $4,950,300,000
Approx. Number Employees: 8,000
Year Founded: 1946
Business Description:
Temporary Staffing Services
S.I.C.: 7363
N.A.I.C.S.: 561320; 561330
Advertising Expenditures: $7,000,000
Media: 2-3-6-7-8-9-10-11-13-14-18-20-22-23-24-25-26
Distr.: Intl.
Budget Set: Nov.
Personnel:
Carl T. Camden *(Pres & CEO)*
Patricia A. Little *(CFO & Exec VP)*
George S. Corona *(COO)*
Joseph Drouin *(CIO & Sr VP)*
Michael L. Durik *(Chief Admin Officer & Exec VP)*
Michael E. Debs *(Chief Acctg Officer & Controller)*
Daniel T. Lis *(Gen Counsel & Corp Sec)*
Dhiren Shantilal *(Sr VP& Gen Mgr-APAC)*
Steven S. Armstrong *(Sr VP-Tech Svcs Grp)*
Pamela M. Berklich *(Sr VP-Sls-Americas)*
James H. Bradley *(Sr VP-Admin)*
Teresa S. Carroll *(Sr VP & Global CWO Practice Leader-Outsourcing & Consulting Grp)*
Rolf E. Kleiner *(Sr VP)*
Michael S. Morrow *(Sr VP-Mktg-Global)*
Peter W. Quigley *(Sr VP-Strategic Customer Relationships)*
Nina M. Ramsey *(Sr VP-HR-Global)*
Bernard Tommasini *(Sr VP-Outsourcing Consulting Grp-EMEA)*
James Hoen *(VP & Mgr-Div Kelly Govt Solutions)*
Leif Agneus *(Gen Mgr-EMEA)*
Shaun C. Fracassi *(Gen Mgr-US Comml)*
Jonathon D. Means *(Gen Mgr-KellyConnect)*
W. Edward Meisenheimer *(Gen Mgr-Comml-US)*
Michael S. Webster *(Gen Mgr-Americas)*
Katie Ivie *(Dir-HR)*
Kasey Wilson *(Sr Mgr-Mktg)*

Brands & Products:
KELLY SERVICES

Advertising Agency:
Wyse
668 Euclid Ave
Cleveland, OH 44114
Tel.: (216) 696-2424
Fax: (216) 736-4425

KENEXA

(Branch of Kenexa Technology, Inc.)
343 Winter St
Waltham, MA 02451
Tel.: (781) 530-5000
Fax: (781) 530-5500
Toll Free: (877) WEBHIRE
Sales Range: $25-49.9 Million
Approx. Number Employees: 100
Year Founded: 1982

Key to Media (For complete agency information see *The Advertising Red Books-Agencies* edition):
1. Bus. Publs. 2. Cable T.V. 3. Catalogs & Directories. 4. Co-op Adv. 5. Consumer Mags. 6. D.M. to Bus. Estab.7. D.M. to Consumers
8. Daily Newsp. 9. Exhibits/Trade Shows 10. Foreign 11. Infomercial 12. Internet Adv.13. Multimedia 14. Network Radio
15. Network T.V. 16. Newsp. Distr. Mags. 17. Other 18. Outdoor (Posters, Transit) 19. Point of Purchase20. Premiums, Novelties
21. Product Samples 22. Special Events Mktg. 23. Spot Radio 24. Spot T.V. 25. Weekly Newsp. 26. Yellow Page Adv.

Kenexa — (Continued)

Business Description:
Workforce Recruitment, Selection & Placement Software & Services
S.I.C.: 7361; 7372
N.A.I.C.S.: 561310; 511210
Media: 2-4-7-10-13
Personnel:
Timothy L. Geisert *(CMO)*
Russell Becker *(Exec VP & Head-Sls-Global)*
Benedetto A. Miele *(VP-Sls)*
Abby Euler *(Product Mgr-Mktg-Social Solutions & Dir)*
Michael Gegg *(Dir-Events & Mktg-Intl)*
Sheila Doherty *(Sr Mgr-Product Mktg)*
Christopher Rogers *(Sr Mgr-Mktg Comm)*
Sunita Iyengar *(Mgr-Product Mktg)*
Brands & Products:
WEBHIRE
WEBHIRE HEALTHCARE
WEBHIRE RECRUITER, CORPORATE EDITION
WEBHIRE RECRUITER, PROFESSIONAL EDITION
WEBHIRECONNECT

KENEXA CORPORATION

650 E Swedesford Rd 2nd Fl
Wayne, PA 19087
Tel.: (610) 971-9171
Fax: (610) 971-9181
Toll Free: (877) 971-9171
E-mail: contactus@kenexa.com
Web Site: www.kenexa.com
Approx. Rev.: $196,353,000
Approx. Number Employees: 1,963
Year Founded: 1987
Business Description:
Corporate Communications, Recruitment, Strategic Planning/ Research
S.I.C.: 7361; 7372; 7389; 8742; 8748
N.A.I.C.S.: 541612; 511210; 541611; 541618; 561310; 561499
Advertising Expenditures: $803,000
Media: 2-7-10-13
Personnel:
Nooruddin S. Karsan *(Chm & CEO)*
Troy A. Kanter *(Pres & COO)*
Donald F. Volk *(CFO)*
Tim Geisert *(CMO)*
Kevin Horigan *(Pres-Global HR Tech Div)*
Eric Lochner *(Pres-Global Talent Mgmt)*
Philip R. Stewart *(Pres-RPO)*
Jack W. Wiley *(Exec Dir-Res Institute)*
Brands & Products:
HR SUCCESS MULTIPLIED
INSIGHT
INTERVIEWBUILDER
IXES
KENEXA
KENEXA CAREERTRACKER
KENEXA RECRUITER
KENEXA STOREFRONT
PEOPLEQUEST
PROVE IT!

KENSINGTON TECHNOLOGY GROUP

(Div. of ACCO Brands Corporation)
333 Twin Dolphin Dr 6th Fl
Redwood City, CA 94065
Tel.: (650) 572-2700
Fax: (650) 267-2800
Toll Free: (800) 535-4242
Web Site: www.kensington.com
Sales Range: $100-124.9 Million
Approx. Number Employees: 100
Year Founded: 1981
Business Description:
Computer Accessories Mfr & Designer
S.I.C.: 3577
N.A.I.C.S.: 334119
Media: 4-7-8-13
Personnel:
Christopher M. Franey *(Pres)*
Greg Avera *(VP-Sls-Mktg)*
Christine Dumery *(Dir-Mktg Comm)*
Orlantha Boeker *(Mgr-Product Mktg)*

KEPNER-TREGOE, INC.

17 Research Rd
Skillman, NJ 08558
Tel.: (609) 921-2806
Fax: (609) 497-0130
Toll Free: (800) 537-6378
E-mail: kt-us@kepner-tregoe.com
Web Site: www.kepner-tregoe.com
Approx. Number Employees: 200
Year Founded: 1958
Business Description:
Management Consulting & Human Resource Development Services
S.I.C.: 8742; 8299
N.A.I.C.S.: 541611; 611699
Export
Media: 1-2-7-10
Personnel:
Andy Cook *(Chm)*
Andrew Graham *(Pres)*
Ray Baxter *(CEO)*
Michael W. Curran-Hays *(Partner)*
Kevin Duffy *(Partner & Global VP-Indus Practice)*
Chris Geraghty *(Partner & VP-Indus Practice-Asia Pacific)*
Christoph Goldenstern *(Partner & Global VP-Tech Practice)*
Barbara Stoeber *(Partner & Dir-Mgmt Info Sys)*
Samuel M. Bernstine *(Partner)*
William B. Baldwin *(CFO)*
David Drew *(Dir-Worldwide Alliances, Partnerships & Commercialization)*
David Kossoss *(Dir-Mktg)*
Brands & Products:
ETHINK
KT
KT WAY
PROJECT LOGIC
Advertising Agencies:
Fairbrother & Company LLC
32 Main St
Chatham, NY 12037
Tel.: (518) 392-7700
Fax: (518) 392-2723

R&J Public Relations
1140 Rte 22 E Ste 200
Bridgewater, NJ 08807
Tel.: (908) 722-5757
Fax: (908) 722-5776

KEY TRONIC CORPORATION

(d/b/a KeyTronicEMS Co.)
N 4424 Sullivan Rd Lower Level
Spokane, WA 99216-1593
Mailing Address:
PO Box 14687
Spokane, WA 99214-0687
Tel.: (509) 928-8000
Fax: (509) 927-5383
E-mail: marketing@keytronic.com
Web Site: www.keytronicems.com
Approx. Sls.: $253,846,000
Approx. Number Employees: 1,997
Year Founded: 1969
Business Description:
Electronic Contracts Mfr; PCB Assembly, Plastic Molding & Full Product Assembly
S.I.C.: 3679; 3577; 3672
N.A.I.C.S.: 334418; 334119; 334412
Import Export
Advertising Expenditures: $1,800,000
Media: 1-2-3-4-5-6-10-13-19-20-21
Distr.: Intl.; Natl.
Budget Set: June
Personnel:
Dale F. Pilz *(Chm)*
Craig D. Gates *(Pres & CEO)*
Ronald F. Klawitter *(CFO, Treas & Exec VP-Admin)*
Douglas G. Burkhardt *(Exec VP-Worldwide Ops)*
Brett R. Larsen *(VP-Fin & Controller)*
Lawrence J. Bostwick *(VP-Engrg & Quality)*
Brands & Products:
KEY TRONIC
KEYTRONICEMS
TRUST. COMMITMENT. RESULTS.

KEYNOTE SYSTEMS INCORPORATED

777 Mariners Island Blvd
San Mateo, CA 94404
Tel.: (650) 403-2400
Fax: (650) 403-5500
Toll Free: (888) 539-6683
E-mail: blx.info@keynote.com
Web Site: www.keynote.com
E-Mail For Key Personnel:
Public Relations: press@keynote.com
Approx. Rev.: $79,851,000
Approx. Number Employees: 323
Year Founded: 1995
Business Description:
Internet Performance Management Services
S.I.C.: 7379; 7374
N.A.I.C.S.: 541519; 518210
Advertising Expenditures: $2,400,000
Personnel:
Umang Gupta *(Chm & CEO)*
Curtis Smith *(CFO)*
David Peterson *(Chief Acctg Officer)*
Donald Aoki *(Sr VP-Prof Svcs)*
Jeffrey Kraatz *(Sr VP-Sls & Svcs-Worldwide)*
Anshu Agarwal *(VP-Mktg)*
Krishna Khadloya *(VP-Engrg)*
Nisheeth Mohan *(Sr Mgr-Product)*
Brands & Products:
KEYNOTE
LIFELINE
THE MOBILE & INTERNET PERFORMANCE AUTHORITY
MYKEYNOTE
PERSPECTIVE
Advertising Agency:
Connecting Point Communications
665 3rd St Ste 100
San Francisco, CA 94107
Tel.: (415) 442-2400
Fax: (415) 442-0288
— Susan Vander May *(Acct Exec-Keynote Systems)*

KINETICSYSTEMS COMPANY, LLC

900 N State St
Lockport, IL 60441
Tel.: (815) 838-0005
Fax: (815) 838-4424
Toll Free: (800) DATA-NOW
Web Site: www.kscorp.com
E-Mail For Key Personnel:
Sales Director: sales@kscorp.com
Approx. Number Employees: 20
Year Founded: 1970
Business Description:
Data Acquisition & Control Systems Designer, Mfr & Marketer
S.I.C.: 7373; 7379
N.A.I.C.S.: 541512; 541519
Export
Media: 10-13
Personnel:
William A. Boston *(Chm, Pres & CEO)*
Eric Schroeder *(CFO)*
Patrick T. Cassady *(Exec VP)*
Patricia Ramazinski *(Dir-HR)*
Wayne G. Coppe *(Mgr-Ops)*
Brands & Products:
CAMAC
CPCI/PXI
DAQ DIRECTOR
GRAND INTERCONNECT
KINETIC SYSTEMS
VERSADAQ
VXI

KINGSTON TECHNOLOGY COMPANY, INC.

17600 Newhope St
Fountain Valley, CA 92708-4220
Tel.: (714) 435-2600
Fax: (714) 435-2699
Toll Free: (877) 546-4786
Toll Free: (877) KINGSTON
E-mail: sales@kingston.com
Web Site: www.kingston.com
E-Mail For Key Personnel:
Sales Director: sales@kingston.com
Approx. Sls.: $4,500,000,000
Approx. Number Employees: 4,500
Year Founded: 1987
Business Description:
Computer Memory & Storage Products Mfr
S.I.C.: 3577; 3572
N.A.I.C.S.: 334119; 334112
Import Export
Media: 6-7
Personnel:
John Tu *(Co-Founder & Pres)*
David Sun *(Co-Founder)*
John Holland *(VP-Sls-US)*
Mark Leathem *(Dir-Sls & Mktg)*
Ramiro Leon *(Product Mgr)*
Soledad Reinares *(Product Mgr)*
Hans Voss *(Product Mgr)*
Holly Hubbard-Miller *(Mgr-Mktg)*
Jaja Lin *(Mgr-Flash Memory Mktg)*
Nicole Trochez *(Mgr-Mktg)*
David Leong *(Specialist-PR)*
Brands & Products:
DATATRAVELER
HYPERX
KINGSTON
VALUERAM

Key to Media (For complete agency information see *The Advertising Red Books-Agencies* edition):
1. Bus. Publs. 2. Cable T.V. 3. Catalogs & Directories. 4. Co-op Adv. 5. Consumer Mags. 6. D.M. to Bus. Estab.7. D.M. to Consumers
8. Daily Newsp. 9. Exhibits/Trade Shows 10. Foreign 11. Infomercial 12. Internet Adv.13. Multimedia 14. Network Radio
15. Network T.V. 16. Newsp. Distr. Mags. 17. Other 18. Outdoor (Posters, Transit) 19. Point of Purchase20. Premiums, Novelties
21. Product Samples 22. Special Events Mktg. 23. Spot Radio 24. Spot T.V. 25. Weekly Newsp. 26. Yellow Page Adv.

Advertising Agencies:
Just Media Ltd.
90 Whitfield St
London, W1T 4EZ, United Kingdom
Tel.: (44) 207 803 4400
Fax: (44) 207 021 0858

KLR Communications, Inc.
19 Corporate Plz Dr Ste 200
Newport Beach, CA 92660
Tel.: (949) 509-1888
Fax: (413) 410-9042

Lewis PR
(d/b/a Lewis Pr Global)
Millbank Tower
London, SW1P 4RS, United Kingdom
Tel.: (44) 207 802 2626
Fax: (44) 207 802 2627

KINTERA, INC.
(Sub. of Blackbaud, Inc.)
9605 Scranton Rd Ste 240
San Diego, CA 92121
Tel.: (858) 795-3000
Fax: (858) 795-3010
E-mail: info@kintera.com
Web Site: www.kintera.com
Approx. Rev.: $44,935,000
Approx. Number Employees: 281
Business Description:
Software Developer
S.I.C.: 7372
N.A.I.C.S.: 334611; 511210
Advertising Expenditures: $226,000
Media: 2-7-8-10-13
Personnel:
Richard LaBarbera *(CEO)*
Michael Rahman *(VP & Chief Patent Officer)*
Brands & Products:
FRIENDS ASKING FRIENDS
THE GIVING EXPERIENCE
KINTERA
KINTERA CONTACT
KINTERA FUNDWARE
KINTERA GIVINGFUND
KINTERA PIN ELECTRONIC SCREENING
KINTERA SPHERE

KNOLL, INC.
1235 Water St
East Greenville, PA 18041
Tel.: (215) 679-7991
Fax: (215) 679-1755
Toll Free: (800) 343-5665
E-mail: info@knoll.com
Web Site: www.knoll.com
Approx. Sls.: $809,467,000
Approx. Number Employees: 3,006
Year Founded: 1938
Business Description:
Office Furniture & Textiles Designer & Mfr
S.I.C.: 2531; 2299; 2521; 2522
N.A.I.C.S.: 337127; 314999; 337211; 337214
Export
Advertising Expenditures: $3,000,000
Media: 6-10
Distr.: Natl.
Budget Set: Sept.
Personnel:
Burton B. Staniar *(Chm)*
Andrew B. Cogan *(CEO)*
Barry L. McCabe *(CFO & Exec VP)*
Lynn M. Utter *(Pres/COO-North America)*
Jeffrey R. Blom *(Sr VP-Supply Chain-North America)*
David E. Bright *(Sr VP-Comm)*
Marcia A. Thompson *(VP-HR)*
Robert Waligunda *(Dir-Mktg)*
Brands & Products:
AUTOSTRADA
BULLDOG
CHADWICK
COPELAND LIGHT
CURRENTS
DIVIDENDS
DIVIDENDS HORIZON
EQUITY
ESSENTIALS
GRAHAM COLLECTION
HALLEY
INTERACTION
KNOLL SPACE
KNOLLEXTRA
KNOLLSTUDIO
KNOLLTEXTILES
LAPJACK
LIFE
MAGNUSSON
MORRISON
PROPELLER
REFF
RPM
SAPPER
SOHO
SPINNEYBECK
UPSTART
VISOR
WA
WISHBONE

KNOWLOGY CORPORATION
105 W Broad St 5th Fl
Falls Church, VA 22046-4233
Tel.: (703) 532-1000
Fax: (703) 532-1001
E-mail: info@knowlogy.com
Web Site: www.knowlogy.com
E-Mail For Key Personnel:
Sales Director: mghazzawi@knowlogy.com
Approx. Number Employees: 60
Year Founded: 1986
Business Description:
Computer Technical Training
S.I.C.: 8331
N.A.I.C.S.: 624310
Media: 7-10
Personnel:
Hassan Judah *(Pres)*
Brands & Products:
KNOWLOGY
TECHNOLOGY SMART

KONICA MINOLTA DANKA IMAGING
(Sub. of Konica Minolta Business Solutions USA, Inc.)
11101 Roosevelt Blvd N
Saint Petersburg, FL 33716
Tel.: (727) 622-2100
Toll Free: (800) 653-2652
Web Site: www.danka.com
Approx. Sls.: $450,000,000
Approx. Number Employees: 2,000
Business Description:
Photocopiers & Related Supplies Sales
S.I.C.: 5044
N.A.I.C.S.: 423420
Media: 13
Distr.: Intl.; Natl.
Budget Set: Sept.
Personnel:
William E. Troxil *(Pres & COO-Danka Field Ops)*

KOPIN CORPORATION
200 John Hancock Rd
Taunton, MA 02780
Tel.: (508) 824-6696
Fax: (508) 824-6958
E-mail: info@kopin.com
Web Site: www.kopin.com
Approx. Rev.: $120,385,766
Approx. Number Employees: 353
Year Founded: 1984
Business Description:
Mfr Lightweight, Power Efficient, Ultra-Small Liquid Crystal Displays (LCDs) & Heterojunction Bipolar Transistors (HBTs)
S.I.C.: 3674
N.A.I.C.S.: 334413
Import Export
Media: 4-7-10-11-13
Personnel:
John C.C. Fan *(Chm, Pres & CEO)*
Richard A. Sneider *(CFO & Treas)*
Bor-Yeu Tsaur *(Exec VP-Display Ops)*
Daily S. Hill *(Sr VP-Gallium Arsenide Ops)*
Wayne Johnson *(VP-Tech)*
Chris Parkinson *(Mgr-Golden-i Software)*
Brands & Products:
ALGAAS HBT
BDM
BDM-230K
BDM-922K
CYBERDISPLAY
CYBERDISPLAY 1280M
CYBERDISPLAY 640M
CYBERDISPLAY 800M
CYBERDISPLAY SVGA
CYBERDISPLAY SXGA LVR
CYBERDISPLAY VGA
CYBEREVF
CYBERLITE
DIGITAL IVISION
THE EYE
GAIN HBT
GAIN-HBT
HBT
INGAP HBT
KOPIN
THE NANOSEMICONDUCTOR COMPANY
WAFER-ENGINEERED
THE WAFER-ENGINEERING COMPANY

KROLL INC.
(Sub. of Altegrity, Inc.)
1166 6th Ave
New York, NY 10036
Tel.: (212) 593-1000
Fax: (212) 593-2631
Toll Free: (888) 209-9526
E-mail: info@kroll.com
Web Site: www.kroll.com
Sales Range: $1-4.9 Billion
Approx. Number Employees: 3,800
Year Founded: 1972
Business Description:
Business Consulting, Corporate Advisory, Intelligence Investigation, Background Screening & Security Services
S.I.C.: 7381; 8748
N.A.I.C.S.: 561611; 541618
Advertising Expenditures: $2,986,000
Media: 2-7-10
Personnel:
Jules B. Kroll *(Founder)*
William J. Bratton *(Chm)*
Rich Plansky *(Sr Mng Dir)*
Donald Buzinkai *(CFO)*
Tony Brierley *(COO & Exec VP)*
Tim Whipple *(Pres-Consulting Svcs Grp)*
Sabrina Perel *(Gen Counsel)*
James Bucknam *(Exec VP-Risk Mgmt & Compliance)*
Jim Kelly *(VP-HR)*
Mike Hellreigel *(Head-Fin)*
Patricia Pizzo *(Dir-Toxicology)*

KRONOS INCORPORATED
(Holding of Hellman & Friedman LLC)
297 Billerica Rd
Chelmsford, MA 01824
Tel.: (978) 250-9800
Fax: (978) 367-5900
Toll Free: (800) 225-1561
E-mail: pr@kronos.com
Web Site: www.kronos.com
Sales Range: $550-599.9 Million
Approx. Number Employees: 3,400
Year Founded: 1977
Business Description:
Software & Hardware for Labor Management, Human Resources & Payroll Development
S.I.C.: 7372; 3577
N.A.I.C.S.: 511210; 334119
Advertising Expenditures: $145,643,000
Media: 1-5-7-10-11
Personnel:
Mark S. Ain *(Founder & Chm)*
Aron J. Ain *(CEO)*
Mark Julien *(CFO)*
James J. Kizielewicz *(CMO & Sr VP)*
Peter C. George *(CTO, Sr VP-Products & Tech)*
Charlie Dickson *(Chief Admin Officer)*
Alyce Moore *(Gen Counsel & VP)*
Christopher Todd *(Sr VP-Svcs)*
Patrick Moquin *(VP-HR)*
John O'Brien *(VP-Sls-North America)*
Brands & Products:
ALTITUDE
CLARITYMATTERS
GATEKEEPER
INTRASPECT ANALYTICS
ISERIES CENTRAL
KRONOS
KRONOS 4500
KRONOS 4500 TOUCH ID
KRONOS E-CENTRAL
KRONOS ISERIES CENTRAL
SHIFTLOGIC
TIMEKEEPER CENTRAL
VISIONWARE
WEBTA
WORKFORCE CENTRAL
WORKFORCE CONNECT
WORKFORCE HR
WORKFORCE MOBILETIME
WORKFORCE PAYROLL
WORKFORCE RECRUITER

Key to Media (For complete agency information see *The Advertising Red Books-Agencies* edition):
1. Bus. Publs. 2. Cable T.V. 3. Catalogs & Directories. 4. Co-op Adv. 5. Consumer Mags. 6. D.M. to Bus. Estab.7. D.M. to Consumers 8. Daily Newsp. 9. Exhibits/Trade Shows 10. Foreign 11. Infomercial 12. Internet Adv.13. Multimedia 14. Network Radio 15. Network T.V. 16. Newsp. Distr. Mags. 17. Other 18. Outdoor (Posters, Transit) 19. Point of Purchase20. Premiums, Novelties 21. Product Samples 22. Special Events Mktg. 23. Spot Radio 24. Spot T.V. 25. Weekly Newsp. 26. Yellow Page Adv.

Kronos Incorporated — (Continued)

WORKFORCE SCHEDULER
WORKFORCE TELETIME
WORKFORCE TIMEKEEPER
Advertising Agency:
Oceanos Marketing, Inc.
99 Derby St Ste 305
Hingham, MA 02043
Tel.: (781) 804-1010
Fax: (617) 687-8008

KROY LLC
(Sub. of Pubco Corporation)
3830 Kelley Ave
Cleveland, OH 44114
Tel.: (216) 426-5600
Fax: (216) 426-5601
Toll Free: (888) 888-5769
E-mail: info@kroy.com
Web Site: www.kroy.com
Approx. Number Employees: 35
Year Founded: 1953
Business Description:
Designer, Mfr & Distr of Labeling Machines, Interior Architectural Sign Systems, Bar Code Printers & Supplies
S.I.C.: 3579; 3993
N.A.I.C.S.: 333313; 339950
Export
Media: 2-4-5-7-10-13-21
Distr.: Intl.; Natl.
Budget Set: Nov.
Personnel:
Stephen Kalette *(Gen Counsel & VP)*
Benny Bonanno *(VP-Sls & Mktg)*
Brands & Products:
DURATYPE 240SE
DURATYPE 244RS
K182
K3000-PC
K4100
K4350
K5100
K6416

KRUEGER ASSOCIATES INC.
(d/b/a National Fulfillment Services)
100 Pine Ave Bldg 4
Holmes, PA 19043
Tel.: (610) 532-4700
Fax: (610) 586-3232
Toll Free: (800) NFS-1306
E-mail: tkrueger@nfsrv.com
Web Site: www.nfsrv.com
Approx. Number Employees: 200
Business Description:
Direct Marketing Services
S.I.C.: 7374
N.A.I.C.S.: 518210
Media: 2
Personnel:
Tom Krueger *(VP-Mktg)*

KYOCERA MITA AMERICA, INC.
(Sub. of Kyocera Mita Corporation)
225 Sand Rd
Fairfield, NJ 07004
Tel.: (973) 808-8444
Fax: (973) 882-6000
E-mail: info@kyoceramita.com
Web Site: www.kyoceramita.com
E-Mail For Key Personnel:
Public Relations: daniel_butler@kyoceramita.com
Sales Range: $550-599.9 Million
Approx. Number Employees: 500
Year Founded: 1973
Business Description:
Copiers, Printers, Facsimiles & Imaging Products Mfr
S.I.C.: 3861; 5065
N.A.I.C.S.: 333315; 423690
Import Export
Advertising Expenditures: $20,000,000
Bus. Publs.: $1,000,000; Cable T.V.: $8,000,000; Co-op Adv.: $10,000,000; Exhibits/Trade Shows: $200,000; Internet Adv.: $500,000; Outdoor (Posters, Transit): $300,000
Distr.: Intl.; Natl.
Personnel:
Norihiko Ina *(Pres)*
Michael Pietrunti *(CEO)*
Gary Bonomoloc *(VP-HR)*
Peter Hendrick *(VP-Mktg)*
Terry Knopsnyder *(VP-Engrg)*
Dan Butler *(Dir-Mktg Comm & Trng)*
Akisa Matsuda *(Dir-Software Solutions)*
William Cassidy *(Assoc Dir-Product & Solutions Mktg)*
Richard Heckelmann *(Mgr-Product & Solutions Mktg)*
Advertising Agencies:
The Ruder Finn Group
301 E 57th St
New York, NY 10022-2900
Tel.: (212) 593-6400
Fax: (212) 593-6397
— Chris Fallon *(Acct Exec)*

Seiter & Miller Advertising, Inc.
460 Park Ave S
New York, NY 10016
Tel.: (212) 843-9900
Fax: (212) 843-9901
Printers

L-1 IDENTITY SOLUTIONS, INC.
177 Broad St 12th Fl
Stamford, CT 06901
Tel.: (203) 504-1100
Fax: (203) 504-1150
Web Site: www.l1id.com
Approx. Rev.: $450,128,000
Approx. Number Employees: 2,438
Year Founded: 2006
Business Description:
Personal Identity & Asset Security Services, Technologies Developer & Mfr
S.I.C.: 7382; 3577; 3699; 7371; 7372; 7379
N.A.I.C.S.: 561621; 334119; 335999; 511210; 541511; 541519
Advertising Expenditures: $200,000
Personnel:
Robert V. LaPenta *(Chm, Pres & CEO)*
B. G. Beck *(Vice Chm)*
James A. DePalma *(CFO, Treas & Exec VP)*
Joseph S. Paresi *(CMO & Exec VP)*
Mark S. Molina *(Chief Legal Officer, Sec & Exec VP)*
Vince A. D'Angelo *(Chief Acctg Officer & Sr VP-Fin)*
Joseph Atick *(Chief Strategic Officer & Exec VP)*
Doni Fordyce *(Exec VP-Corp Comm)*

LABEL-AIRE, INC.
(Sub. of Impaxx, Inc.)
550 Burning Tree Rd
Fullerton, CA 92833-1400
Tel.: (714) 441-0700
Fax: (714) 526-0300
Toll Free: (800) 959-2425
E-mail: info@label-aire.com
Web Site: www.label-aire.com
Approx. Number Employees: 130
Year Founded: 1976
Business Description:
High-Speed Label Application Equipment Mfr
S.I.C.: 3565
N.A.I.C.S.: 333993
Export
Media: 1-2-4-7-10-11-16-20-25-26
Distr.: Intl.; Natl.
Budget Set: Dec.
Personnel:
George Allen *(Pres)*
Ejvind Olesen *(Gen Mgr-Sls)*
William Claproth *(Dir-Mktg)*
Sue Farrah *(Mgr-HR)*
Phil Wignall *(Mgr-Technical Svcs)*
Brands & Products:
LABEL-AIRE

LAMB SIGN
11979 Falling Creek Dr
Manassas, VA 20112
Tel.: (703) 791-7960
Fax: (703) 791-7961
E-mail: lambsign@aol.com
Web Site: www.lambsign.com
Sales Range: Less than $1 Million
Approx. Number Employees: 6
Year Founded: 1900
Business Description:
Signs, Seals & Stencils
S.I.C.: 5943; 3953
N.A.I.C.S.: 453210; 339943
Media: 26
Distr.: Natl.
Personnel:
Rosemary Schneider *(Pres)*

LANDACORP, INC.
(Sub. of SHPS, Inc.)
2080 E 20th St Ste 170
Chico, CA 95973
Tel.: (530) 891-0853
Fax: (530) 891-8428
Toll Free: (877) 629-2000
E-mail: sales@landacorp.com
Web Site: www.landacorp.com
E-Mail For Key Personnel:
Sales Director: sales@landacorp.com
Approx. Number Employees: 30
Year Founded: 1980
Business Description:
Health Care Management Software
S.I.C.: 7372; 7371; 7373
N.A.I.C.S.: 511210; 541511; 541512
Advertising Expenditures: $37,000
Media: 10
Personnel:
Jay Dunlap *(Gen Mgr)*
Brands & Products:
E-MAXMC
LANDACORP
MAXMC
MAXSYS
MAXSYS II

LANGUAGE LINE SERVICES HOLDINGS, INC.
(Holding of Providence Equity Partners LLC)
1 Lowr Ragsdale Dr Bldg 2
Monterey, CA 93940
Tel.: (831) 648-5861
Toll Free: (877) 886-3885
E-mail: info@languageline.com
Web Site: www.languageline.com
E-Mail For Key Personnel:
Public Relations: pr@languageline.com
Approx. Rev.: $278,174,000
Approx. Number Employees: 4,634
Year Founded: 1982
Business Description:
Over-the-Phone Language Interpretation & Document Translation Services
S.I.C.: 7389
N.A.I.C.S.: 541930
Advertising Expenditures: $100,000
Media: 2-7-10
Personnel:
Dennis G. Dracup *(Chm)*
Louis F. Provenzano, Jr. *(Pres & CEO)*
Michael F. Schmidt *(CFO & Sr VP)*
Karen Gilhooly *(Sr VP-Sls & Mktg)*
Robert Koen *(VP & Gen Mgr-General Market Sls)*
Jeffrey M. Johnson *(Dir-Sls-Natl)*
Phil Speciale *(Dir-Sls)*
Jeanette Anders *(Mgr-Health Care & Pub Sector)*
Greg Holt *(Mgr-Govt Markets)*
Julie Metzger *(Mgr-Sls-Natl)*
Brands & Products:
LANGUAGE LINE
LANGUAGE LINE OVER THE PHONE
Advertising Agency:
rbb Public Relations
355 Alhambra Cir Ste 800
Miami, FL 33134
Tel.: (305) 448-7450
Fax: (305) 448-5027

LANIER WORLDWIDE, INC.
(Name Changed to Ricoh Americas Corp.)

LANTRONIX, INC.
167 Technology Dr
Irvine, CA 92618
Tel.: (949) 453-3990
Fax: (949) 450-7249
E-mail: sales@lantronix.com
Web Site: www.lantronix.com
E-Mail For Key Personnel:
Sales Director: sales@lantronix.com
Approx. Rev.: $46,375,000
Approx. Number Employees: 115
Year Founded: 1989
Business Description:
Designer, Developer & Marketer of Products that Enable Electronic Devices to be Connected to the Internet
S.I.C.: 3669; 3577; 3661
N.A.I.C.S.: 334290; 334119; 334210
Advertising Expenditures: $511,000
Media: 4-10
Personnel:
Lewis Solomon *(Chm)*
Kurt Busch *(Pres & CEO)*
Jeremy Whitaker *(CFO)*
Jeff Kost *(Sr VP-WW Sls & Outbound Mktg)*
Daryl Miller *(VP-Engrg)*
Robert Robinson *(VP-Worldwide Sls)*
Anthony Shimkin *(VP-Mktg)*
Tom Buckley *(Sr Dir-Sls)*

Key to Media (For complete agency information see *The Advertising Red Books-Agencies* edition):
1. Bus. Publs. 2. Cable T.V. 3. Catalogs & Directories. 4. Co-op Adv. 5. Consumer Mags. 6. D.M. to Bus. Estab.7. D.M. to Consumers 8. Daily Newsp. 9. Exhibits/Trade Shows 10. Foreign 11. Infomercial 12. Internet Adv.13. Multimedia 14. Network Radio 15. Network T.V. 16. Newsp. Distr. Mags. 17. Other 18. Outdoor (Posters, Transit) 19. Point of Purchase20. Premiums, Novelties 21. Product Samples 22. Special Events Mktg. 23. Spot Radio 24. Spot T.V. 25. Weekly Newsp. 26. Yellow Page Adv.

Jamie Messina *(Dir-Medical Indus Sls-Midwest US Reg)*
Colin Murphy *(Dir-Medical Indus Sls-Northeast US Reg)*

Brands & Products:
BOS-KIT
COBOX
COM PORT REDIRECTOR
CONNECT YOUR IMAGINATION TO THE NET
DEVICEINSTALLER
DSTNI
DVI-FIBERLYNX
EASY CONNECTION
EVOLUTION OS
EZWEBCON
INTELLIBOX
LANTRONIX
LIGHTWAVE
MATCHPORT
MATRIX-HUB
MICRO
MSS-VIA
MSSLITE
NETWORK ANYTHING. NETWORK EVERYTHING.
PC SERVERSWITCH
PCFIBERLYNX
RTEL
SECURE COM PORT REDIRECTOR
SECUREBOX
SECURELINX
SECURELINX SLK
SECURELINX SPIDER
SEVURE COM PORT REDIRECTOR
UBOX
USB SERVERSWITCH
WIBOX
WIMICRO
WIPORT
XCHIP
XCHIP DIRECT
XPORT
XPRESS

LAPLINK SOFTWARE, INC.
14335 NE 24th St Ste 201
Bellevue, WA 98007
Tel.: (425) 952-6000
Fax: (425) 952-6002
Toll Free: (800) LAPLINK
Web Site: www.laplink.com
E-Mail For Key Personnel:
Marketing Director: marketing@laplink.com
Public Relations: pr@laplink.com
Approx. Number Employees: 85
Year Founded: 1983
Business Description:
Software Mfr
S.I.C.: 7371
N.A.I.C.S.: 541511
Media: 1-2-4-6-7-10-11-13-22-26
Distr.: Natl.
Personnel:
Thomas Koll *(Chm & CEO)*
Randall L. Clark *(COO)*
Emir Aboulhosn *(VP-Global Mktg & Comm)*
Mike Oldham *(VP-OEM Sls & Mktg)*
Brands & Products:
CONNECT YOUR WORLD
CONTROLLER
EVERYWHERE
FILEMOVER
FILESENDER
FTP
GOLD
LAPLINK CONTROLLER
LAPLINK EVERYWHERE
LAPLINK GOLD 11.5
LAPLINK GOLD CORPORATE
LAPLINK V FOR DOS
PCDEFENSE
PCMOVER
PDASYNC
PDASYNC 3.0
SECURE VNC
SHAREDIRECT
SMARTXCHANGE
SPEEDSYNC

LAPWORKS, INC.
7955 Layton St
Rancho Cucamonga, CA 91730
Tel.: (909) 948-1828
Toll Free: (877) 527-9675
E-mail: sales@laptopdesk.net
Web Site: www.laptopdesk.net
E-Mail For Key Personnel:
President: jose@laptopdesk.net
Sales Director: sales@laptopdesk.net
Business Description:
Retailer of Laptop Computers
S.I.C.: 5734; 5045
N.A.I.C.S.: 443120; 423430
Media: 6-10-13
Personnel:
Jose Calero *(Owner)*
Brands & Products:
ACROBAT
COOLFAN
ENVOY
ERGO
FUTURA
KWIK FIND
LAPTOP LEGS
LAPWORKS
MACFEET
MOUZPAD
SWIV-ALL
SWIVLPAD
ULTRALITE
WIZARD
X-STAND
Z-LIFT
Advertising Agency:
Moody & Associates
2821 Stanford Ave
Dallas, TX 75225
Tel.: (214) 363-3460
Fax: (214) 363-3122
— Michelle Moody *(Acct Exec)*

LASERCARD CORPORATION
(Sub. of Assa Abloy AB)
1875 N Shoreline Blvd
Mountain View, CA 94043
Tel.: (650) 969-4428
Fax: (650) 969-3140
E-mail: investors@lasercard.com
Web Site: www.lasercard.com
E-Mail For Key Personnel:
Sales Director: sales@lasercard.com
Approx. Rev.: $58,611,000
Approx. Number Employees: 203
Year Founded: 1968
Business Description:
Holding Company; Optical Memory Cards & Drives Mfr
S.I.C.: 6719; 3572; 3695
N.A.I.C.S.: 551112; 334112; 334613
Import Export
Advertising Expenditures: $234,000
Personnel:
Robert T. Devincenzi *(Pres & CEO)*
Christopher J. Dyball *(COO)*
Steven G. Larson *(Treas & VP-Fin)*
Stephen D. Price-Francis *(VP-Mktg)*
Alex Giakoumis *(Sr Dir)*
Brands & Products:
CONCIERGECARD
EMBEDDED HOLOGRAMHD
LASER ENCODER 8
LASERBADGE
LASERCARD
LASERPASS
OPTICAL IDLOCK
OPTICALPROXIMITY
OPTICHIP
SMART/OPTICAL

LAWSON SOFTWARE, INC.
380 Saint Peter St
Saint Paul, MN 55102-1302
Tel.: (651) 767-7000
Fax: (651) 767-7141
Toll Free: (800) 477-1357
E-mail: info@lawson.com
Web Site: www.lawson.com
E-Mail For Key Personnel:
Public Relations: media@lawson.com
Approx. Rev.: $736,408,000
Approx. Number Employees: 3,900
Year Founded: 1975
Business Description:
Developer & Distr of Enterprise & Business Management Software
S.I.C.: 7372; 7371; 8748
N.A.I.C.S.: 334611; 511210; 541511; 541618
Export
Advertising Expenditures: $13,000,000
Media: 2-4-5-7-9-10-11-14
Distr.: Intl.
Budget Set: May
Personnel:
H. Richard Lawson *(Co-Chm)*
Romesh T. Wadhwani *(Co-Chm)*
Harry Debes *(Pres & CEO)*
Fady Sfeir *(VP-Channel Partners-EMEA)*
Bruce B. McPheeters *(Gen Counsel, Sec & Sr VP)*
Colin Balmforth *(Exec VP)*
Eduardo Sanchez *(Exec VP-Global Sls)*
Scott Swoish *(Exec VP-Global Svcs)*
Eric Verniaut *(Exec VP-M3 Industries)*
Frank Cohen *(Sr VP-EMEA Sls)*
Jeff Comport *(Sr VP-Product Mgmt)*
Larry Dunivan *(Sr VP-Human Capital Mgmt Products)*
Guenther Tolkmit *(Sr VP-Product Dev)*
Kristin E. Trecker *(Sr VP-HR)*
David Hope *(Mng Dir-Asia Pacific & Gen Mgr)*
Terrence Blake *(VP-Corp Comm)*
Nam D. Vo *(VP-Global Healthcare Strategy)*
Andrew Dalziel *(Dir-Mktg-Fashion)*
Tom Passe *(Sr Product Mgr-Tech)*
Joe Thornton *(Mgr-Media Rels)*
Brands & Products:
DRILL AROUND
LAWSON
LAWSON INSIGHT
LAWSON PORTAL
Advertising Agency:
Whitney Worldwide Inc.
553 Hayward Ave N Ste 250
Saint Paul, MN 55128
Tel.: (651) 748-5000
Fax: (651) 748-4000
Toll Free: (800) 597-0227

LEAP WIRELESS INTERNATIONAL, INC.
5887 Copley Dr
San Diego, CA 92111
Tel.: (858) 882-6000
Fax: (858) 882-6010
E-mail: ir@leapwireless.com
Web Site: www.leapwireless.com
Approx. Rev.: $2,697,203,000
Approx. Number Employees: 4,362
Business Description:
Wireless Telecommunications
S.I.C.: 4812
N.A.I.C.S.: 517212
Advertising Expenditures: $151,200,000
Media: 13-31
Personnel:
Stewart Douglas Hutcheson *(Pres & CEO)*
Walter Berger *(CFO & Exec VP)*
Raymond J. Roman *(COO & Exec VP)*
Dave P. Truzinski *(CIO & Sr VP)*
T. Scott Edwards *(CMO, Sr VP & Gen Mgr)*
Jeffrey E. Nachbor *(Chief Acctg Officer & Sr VP-Fin Ops)*
Robert J. Irving Jr. *(Gen Counsel, Sec & Sr VP)*
James Seines *(Treas & VP-Fin)*
Bob Young *(Exec VP-Field Ops)*
David A. Davis *(Sr VP-Strategic Initiatives)*
Michael Hahn *(Sr VP-Supply Chain Mgmt, Procurement & Real Estate)*
Colin Holland *(Sr VP-Engrg & Tech Ops)*
William D. Ingram *(Sr VP-Strategy)*
Greg Post *(Sr VP-Field Sls & Field Ops)*
Leonard C. Stephens *(Sr VP-HR)*
Linda Wokoun *(Sr VP-Mktg & Customer Care)*
Amy Wakeham *(Sr Dir-IR & Corp Comm)*
Brands & Products:
BREW
CRICKET
CRICKET BROADBAND
CRICKET PAYGO
CRICKET WIRELESS
JUMP
LEAP
Advertising Agency:
Mentus
6755 Mira Mesa Blvd Ste 123
San Diego, CA 92121-4311
Tel.: (858) 455-5500
Fax: (858) 455-6872

LENOVO GROUP LTD
(Sub. of Lenovo Group Limited)
1009 Think Pl
Morrisville, NC 27560
Toll Free: (866) 968-4465
Web Site: www.lenovo.com
Business Description:
Computer Hardware
S.I.C.: 3575

Lenovo Group Ltd — (Continued)

N.A.I.C.S.: 334113
Personnel:
Amy Boaz *(Mgr-Interactive Mktg)*
Advertising Agencies:
Clean Design, Inc.
10 Laboratory Dr Bldg 2 Ste 200
Research Triangle Park, NC 27709
Tel.: (919) 544-2193
Fax: (919) 473-2200

Saatchi & Saatchi
(Sub. of Publicis Groupe S.A.)
(Worldwide Headquarters)
375 Hudson St
New York, NY 10014-3660
Tel.: (212) 463-2000
Fax: (212) 463-9856

LEXMARK INTERNATIONAL, INC.
740 W New Cir Rd
Lexington, KY 40550
Tel.: (859) 232-2000
Fax: (859) 232-2403
Toll Free: (800) 539-6275
E-mail: privacy@lexmark.com
Web Site: www.lexmark.com
E-Mail For Key Personnel:
Public Relations: corpcomm@lexmark.com
Approx. Rev.: $4,199,700,000
Approx. Number Employees: 13,200
Year Founded: 1991
Business Description:
Laser, Inkjet & Dot Matrix Printers & Supplies Mfr, Developer & Retailer
S.I.C.: 5734; 3571; 3577
N.A.I.C.S.: 443120; 334111; 334119
Import Export
Advertising Expenditures: $51,500,000
Media: 2-4-7-10
Distr.: Natl.
Budget Set: Apr. -May
Personnel:
Paul A. Rooke *(Pres & CEO)*
John W. Gamble, Jr. *(CFO & Exec VP)*
Marty S. Canning *(Pres-Printing Solutions & Svcs Div & Exec VP)*
Robert J. Patton *(Gen Counsel, Sec & VP)*
Jeri Isbell *(VP-HR)*
Bill Summers *(Product Mgr)*
Brands & Products:
ACCUFEED
COLORSAVER
FONTVISION
LEXEXPRESS
LEXMARK
LEXONSITE
LINEA
MARKNET
MARKTRACK
MARKVISION
OPTRA
PASSION FOR PRINTING IDEAS
PERFECTFINISH
PRECISIONPHOTO
PRECISIONSENSE
PRINTCRYPTON
PRINTRIO
PROPRINTER
SELECTRIC
Advertising Agencies:
Lewis Global Public Relations
6080 Center Dr
Los Angeles, CA 90045
Tel.: (310) 407-5186
Fax: (310) 229-5799

Power Creative
11701 Commonwealth Dr
Louisville, KY 40299-2358
Tel.: (502) 267-0772
Fax: (502) 267-1727

LIME ENERGY CO.
1280 Landmeier Rd
Elk Grove Village, IL 60007-2410
Tel.: (847) 437-1666
Fax: (847) 437-4969
E-mail: info@lime-energy.com
Web Site: www.lime-energy.com
Approx. Rev.: $95,718,000
Approx. Number Employees: 270
Year Founded: 1998
Business Description:
Energy Saving Technology
S.I.C.: 4911; 3825; 4939
N.A.I.C.S.: 221122; 334515
Advertising Expenditures: $182,000
Media: 10
Personnel:
Daniel W. Parke *(Pres)*
David R. Asplund *(CEO)*
Jeffrey R. Mistarz *(CFO)*
John O'Rourke *(COO)*
David R. Krueger *(Pres-Comml & Indus Div)*
Richard P. Kiphart *(Principal & Head-Corp Fin)*
Robert Meier *(VP-Strategic Accounts)*
Pradeep Kapadia *(Dir-Bus Dev)*
Brands & Products:
ENERGYSAVER
LESS IS MORE
LIME ENERGY
VIRTUAL NEGAWATT POWER PLAN
VNPP

LINKSHARE CORPORATION
(Sub. of Rakuten USA, Inc.)
215 Park Ave S 9th Fl
New York, NY 10003
Tel.: (646) 654-6000
Fax: (646) 943-8204
E-mail: contact@linkshare.com
Web Site: www.linkshare.com
Approx. Sls.: $10,200,000
Approx. Number Employees: 98
Year Founded: 1996
Business Description:
Online Search, Lead Generation & Affiliate Marketing Services
S.I.C.: 5045; 7374
N.A.I.C.S.: 425110; 518210
Personnel:
Yasuhisa Iida *(Pres & CEO)*
Jonathan Levine *(COO)*
Mark Kirschner *(CMO)*
Reginald Rasch *(Gen Counsel)*
Joseph Sabatino *(VP-Sls)*
Brands & Products:
LINKSHARE
Advertising Agency:
Blanc & Otus Public Relations
20 Park Plz Ste 1120
Boston, MA 02116-4308
Tel.: (617) 451-6070
Fax: (617) 451-6113
— Elizabeth Yekhtikian *(Acct Exec)*

LINKSYS
(Div. of Cisco Systems, Inc.)
121 Theory Dr
Irvine, CA 92612
Tel.: (949) 261-1288
Fax: (949) 823-3002
Toll Free: (800) 326-7114
Web Site: www.linksys.com
Approx. Sls.: $430,400,000
Approx. Number Employees: 350
Year Founded: 1988
Business Description:
VoIP, Wireless & Ethernet Networking
S.I.C.: 5065
N.A.I.C.S.: 423690
Media: 6
Personnel:
Shelly McDowell *(CFO)*
Ned Hooper *(Sr VP-Corp Dev & Consumer/Small Bus)*
Greg Memo *(VP & Gen Mgr-Consumer Bus Org)*
Marna Bullard *(VP-World Wide Mktg)*
Tim Thornton *(Sr Dir-Eng Svs)*
Brands & Products:
DUAL-BAND WIRELESS-N GAMING ADAPTE
DUAL-BAND WIRELESS-N GIGABIT ROUTER
ETHERFAST CABLE/DSL ROUTER
LINKSYS
LINKSYS MEDIA CENTER EXTENDER
NAS200
RANGEPLUS WIRELESS ROUTER
SIMULTANEOUS DUAL-N BAND WIRELESS ROUTER
ULTRA RANGEPLUS WIRELESS-N BROADBAND ROUTER
WIRELESS-G BROADBAND ROUTER
WIRELESS-G BROADBAND ROUTER WITH SPEEDBOOSTER
WIRELESS-G CABLE GATEWAY
WIRELESS-G GAME ADAPTER
WIRELESS-G HOME ROUTER
WIRELESS-G INTERNET HOME MONITORING CAMERA
WIRELESS-G MUSIC BRIDGE
WIRELESS-G ROUTER FOR MOBILE BROADB
WIRELESS-N GIGABIT GAMING ROUTER
WIRELESS-N GIGABIT ROUTER
WIRELESS-N GIGABIT SECURITY ROUTER WITH VPN
WIRELESS-N HOME ROUTER

LIONBRIDGE TECHNOLOGIES INC.
1050 Winter St
Waltham, MA 02451-1460
Tel.: (781) 434-6000
Fax: (781) 434-6034
E-mail: pr@lionbridge.com
Web Site: www.lionbridge.com
Approx. Rev.: $405,238,000
Approx. Number Employees: 4,500
Year Founded: 1996
Business Description:
Software, User Manuals & Web Content Translation & Globalization Services
S.I.C.: 7379
N.A.I.C.S.: 541519
Advertising Expenditures: $92,000
Media: 2-10-13
Personnel:
Rory J. Cowan *(Chm, Pres & CEO)*
Donald M. Muir *(CFO)*
Paula Shannon *(Chief Sls Officer & Sr VP)*
Peggy Shukur *(Gen Counsel, Sec & Sr VP)*
Henri Broekmate *(Sr VP-Ops-Worldwide)*
Michele Erwin *(Sr VP-HR)*
Brands & Products:
ACCELERATING YOUR GLOBAL SUCCESS
FREEWAY
GLOBALIZATION-AT-SOURCE
LIONACCESS
LIONBRIDGE
LIONLINGUIST
LIONSTREAM
LOGOPORT
RAPID GLOBALIZATION METHODOLOGY
TRADOS
VERITEST

LIVE IN LOVE, INC.
(d/b/a Family Labels)
1931 Banks Rd
Margate, FL 33063
Tel.: (954) 791-9122
Fax: (954) 791-2526
E-mail: wmjberg@alo.com
Web Site: www.familylabels.com
Approx. Number Employees: 10
Year Founded: 1996
Business Description:
Retailer of Stationery Products
S.I.C.: 5943
N.A.I.C.S.: 453210
Media: 3-6-8-13
Personnel:
Bill Berg *(Owner)*
Brands & Products:
FAMILY LABELS
PUTTING SMILES ON FACES

LIVEWIRE MOBILE, INC.
1 Monarch Dr Ste 203
Littleton, MA 01460
Tel.: (978) 742-3100
Fax: (978) 742-6965
E-mail: info@livewiremobile.com
Web Site: www.livewiremobile.com
Approx. Rev.: $16,808,000
Approx. Number Employees: 168
Year Founded: 1984
Business Description:
Technology-Leading Systems & System Building Blocks Designer for Voice, Video & Data Services on Wireless & Wireline Networks
S.I.C.: 3669; 3661; 7373
N.A.I.C.S.: 334290; 334210; 541512
Media: 2-7-10
Personnel:
Robert M. Pons *(Chm)*
Matthew Stecker *(Pres & CEO)*
Todd D. Donahue *(CFO)*
Eugene J. DiDonato *(Gen Counsel & VP)*
Adam Thibault *(VP-Sls)*
Brands & Products:
ALLIANCE GENERATION
CONVERGENCE GENERATION
HMIC
LIVEWIRE MOBILE

Key to Media (For complete agency information see *The Advertising Red Books-Agencies* edition):
1. Bus. Publs. 2. Cable T.V. 3. Catalogs & Directories. 4. Co-op Adv. 5. Consumer Mags. 6. D.M. to Bus. Estab.7. D.M. to Consumers 8. Daily Newsp. 9. Exhibits/Trade Shows 10. Foreign 11. Infomercial 12. Internet Adv.13. Multimedia 14. Network Radio 15. Network T.V. 16. Newsp. Distr. Mags. 17. Other 18. Outdoor (Posters, Transit) 19. Point of Purchase20. Premiums, Novelties 21. Product Samples 22. Special Events Mktg. 23. Spot Radio 24. Spot T.V. 25. Weekly Newsp. 26. Yellow Page Adv.

MYCALLER
NMS HEARSAY
OPEN ACCESS
VISION
VISION VOICE SERVER

LML PAYMENT SYSTEMS INC.

1140 W Pender St Ste 1680
Vancouver, BC V6E 4G1, Canada
Tel.: (604) 689-4440
Fax: (604) 689-4413
E-mail: info@lmlpayment.com
Web Site: www.lmlpayment.com
Approx. Rev.: $47,160,490
Approx. Number Employees: 59
Year Founded: 1996
Business Description:
Electronic Check Processing Services
S.I.C.: 7374
N.A.I.C.S.: 518210
Media: 2-10
Personnel:
Patrick H. Gaines *(Chm & CEO)*
Craig Thomson *(Pres)*
Richard R. Schulz *(Chief Acctg Officer & Controller)*
Chris Koide *(Exec VP-Ops)*
Brands & Products:
LASR
LASR DATA
LASR DEBIT
LASR DIRECT
LML PAYMENT SYSTEMS
YOUR PARTNER IN PAYMENTS

LOCAL MATTERS, INC.

1221 Auraria Pkwy
Denver, CO 80204
Tel.: (303) 572-1122
Fax: (303) 572-1123
E-mail: info@localmatters.com
Web Site: www.localmatters.com
Sales Range: $1-9.9 Million
Approx. Number Employees: 193
Business Description:
Software & Media Services
S.I.C.: 7372
N.A.I.C.S.: 511210
Advertising Expenditures: $1,012,350
Personnel:
Greg Gruse *(Sr VP-Bus Dev)*

LOCKHEED MARTIN ASPEN SYSTEMS

(Unit of Lockheed Martin Information Technology - Enterprise Solutions & Services)
2277 Research Blvd
Rockville, MD 20850
Tel.: (301) 519-5000
Fax: (301) 330-8946
Web Site: www.lockheedmartin.com/isgs/index.html
Sales Range: $100-124.9 Million
Approx. Number Employees: 1,651
Year Founded: 1958
Business Description:
Information Management & Data Processing Services
S.I.C.: 7374; 7373
N.A.I.C.S.: 518210; 541512
Media: 2-7-9-10-13-25
Distr.: Natl.
Budget Set: Oct.
Brands & Products:
ASPEN SYSTEMS
ASPENANSWERS
ASPENCREATIVE
ASPENMED
ASPENVIEW
ICITE
OPUS POWER

LOFFLER BUSINESS SYSTEMS INC.

1101 E 78th St Ste 200
Bloomington, MN 55420
Tel.: (952) 925-6800
Fax: (952) 925-6801
E-mail: info@loffler.com
Web Site: www.loffler.com
Sales Range: $50-74.9 Million
Approx. Number Employees: 280
Year Founded: 1986
Business Description:
Distributor of Office Equipment
S.I.C.: 6512
N.A.I.C.S.: 531120
Personnel:
Neil Lee *(CFO)*
Don Tremblay *(VP & Gen Mgr)*
Advertising Agency:
Nemer Fieger
6250 Excelsior Blvd Ste 203
Minneapolis, MN 55416-2735
Tel.: (952) 925-4848
Fax: (952) 925-1907

LOGIC TRENDS, INC.

500 Colonial Ctr Pkwy Ste 150
Roswell, GA 30076
Tel.: (770) 551-5050
Fax: (770) 551-5055
E-mail: ltinfo@logictrends.com
Web Site: www.logictrends.com
Sales Range: $25-49.9 Million
Approx. Number Employees: 60
Business Description:
Data Access Management
S.I.C.: 7376
N.A.I.C.S.: 541513
Personnel:
Ken Stone *(CEO)*
Brands & Products:
IAM5
LOGIC TRENDS
Advertising Agency:
Carabiner Communications
4372 Misty Morning Ln
Lilburn, GA 30047
Tel.: (770) 923-8332
Fax: (888) 686-7688
Identity & Access Management Solutions

LOGILITY, INC.

(Sub. of American Software, Inc.)
470 E Paces Ferry Rd NE
Atlanta, GA 30305
Tel.: (404) 261-9777
Fax: (404) 264-5206
Toll Free: (800) 762-5207
E-mail: info@logility.com
Web Site: www.logility.com
Approx. Rev.: $44,908,000
Approx. Number Employees: 141
Year Founded: 1996
Business Description:
Business Application Software Providing Supply Chain Managment Solutions
S.I.C.: 7372; 7371
N.A.I.C.S.: 511210; 541511
Advertising Expenditures: $9,778,000
Media: 7-10-21-22
Personnel:
James C. Edenfield *(Chm)*
J. Michael Edenfield *(Pres & CEO)*
Vincent C. Klinges *(CFO)*
Herman L. Moncrief *(Principal Acctg Officer & Controller)*
James R. McGuone *(Gen Counsel)*
H. Allan Dow *(Exec VP-Worldwide Sls & Mktg)*
Karin L. Bursa *(VP-Mktg)*
Donald L. Thomas *(VP-Customer Svc)*
Brands & Products:
LOGILITY VOYAGER COLLABORATE
LOGILITY VOYAGER SOLUTIONS

LOGMEIN, INC.

500 Unicorn Pk Dr
Woburn, MA 01801-3345
Tel.: (781) 638-9050
Fax: (781) 998-7792
E-mail: info@logmein.com
Web Site: www.logmein.com
Approx. Rev.: $101,057,207
Approx. Number Employees: 415
Year Founded: 2003
Business Description:
Remote Computer Connectivity Products & Services
S.I.C.: 7379; 4812
N.A.I.C.S.: 541519; 517212
Advertising Expenditures: $11,717,000
Media: 2-7-10-13-14-18
Personnel:
Michael K. Simon *(CEO)*
James F. Kelliher *(CFO)*
Michael J. Donahue *(Gen Counsel & VP)*
Seth Shaw *(Sr VP-Sls)*
Brands & Products:
LOGMEIN
LOGMEIN BACKUP
LOGMEIN CENTRAL
LOGMEIN FREE
LOGMEIN GRAVITY
LOGMEIN HAMACHI
LOGMEIN IGNITION
LOGMEIN IT REACH
LOGMEIN PRO
LOGMEIN RESCUE
REMOTELYANYWHERE

LOWRY COMPUTER PRODUCTS, INC.

(Sub. of Lowry Holding Company Inc.)
9420 Maltby Rd
Brighton, MI 48116
Tel.: (810) 229-7200
Fax: (810) 229-5189
Toll Free: (800) 733-0210
E-mail: info@lowrycomputer.com
Web Site: www.lowrycomputer.com
Sales Range: $25-49.9 Million
Approx. Number Employees: 220
Year Founded: 1974
Business Description:
Mfr of Bar Code Solutions & Wireless Networking Software
S.I.C.: 5045
N.A.I.C.S.: 423430
Export
Media: 2-10
Distr.: Intl.
Personnel:
Michael Lowry *(Pres & CEO)*
Steve Lowry *(Exec VP)*
Brands & Products:
LOWRY
PASS

LSI CORPORATION

1621 Barber Ln
Milpitas, CA 95035
Tel.: (408) 433-8000
Fax: (408) 954-3220
Toll Free: (866) 574-5741
E-mail: customer.advocacy@lsil.com
Web Site: www.lsilogic.com
Approx. Rev.: $2,570,047,000
Approx. Number Employees: 5,718
Year Founded: 1981
Business Description:
Storage, Networking & Consumer Systems & Software Technologies
S.I.C.: 3674; 7371; 7389
N.A.I.C.S.: 334413; 541511; 561499
Import Export
Advertising Expenditures: $8,100,000
Media: 10
Personnel:
Gregorio Reyes *(Chm)*
Abhijit Y. Talwalkar *(Pres & CEO)*
Bryon Look *(CFO, Chief Admin Officer & Exec VP)*
Jeff Richardson *(COO & Exec VP)*
Jean F. Rankin *(Gen Counsel, Sec & Exec VP)*
Philip G. Brace *(Sr VP-Corp Plng & Mktg)*
Greg Huff *(Sr VP-Corp Strategy)*
Brands & Products:
AAMUX
AMBASSADOR
CELXPRES
COMCENTRIX
COREWARE
DATAMAPPER
DIMMER SWITCH
E-QOE
EASYMACRO
ENGENIO
EXTREMERAID
EYEFINDER
FESTINO
FLEX I/O
FLEXMAP
FLEXSTREAM
FUSION-MPT
GIGABLAZE
GIGX
GLOBAL ARRAY MANAGER
HOTSCALE
HY-SPAN
HYPERMAPPER
HYPERPHY
IMEGARAID
INSTANT USB
ITBBU
LINK MAPPER
LINKXPRESS
LSI
LUXWORKS
LYNX
MARS
MEGARAID
MEGARAID MANAGEMENT SUITE
MEGARAID STORAGE MANAGER
MEMOIR
MODERN-ART
MOLOTOF
MULTICOPY
MULTICORE DONE RIGHT
MULTIMIGRADE
MULTIMIRROR

Key to Media (For complete agency information see *The Advertising Red Books-Agencies* edition):
1. Bus. Publs. 2. Cable T.V. 3. Catalogs & Directories. 4. Co-op Adv. 5. Consumer Mags. 6. D.M. to Bus. Estab.7. D.M. to Consumers 8. Daily Newsp. 9. Exhibits/Trade Shows 10. Foreign 11. Infomercial 12. Internet Adv.13. Multimedia 14. Network Radio 15. Network T.V. 16. Newsp. Distr. Mags. 17. Other 18. Outdoor (Posters, Transit) 19. Point of Purchase20. Premiums, Novelties 21. Product Samples 22. Special Events Mktg. 23. Spot Radio 24. Spot T.V. 25. Weekly Newsp. 26. Yellow Page Adv.

LSI Corporation — (Continued)

MULTIVIEW
MYSTORAGE
PAYLOAD PLUS
POWER CONSOLE
POWERED BY E-QOE
REPLICATION EXPRESS
REX
SAFEPARK
SAFESTORE
SANARRAY
SANMAPPING
SANSHARE
SANTRICITY
SCORPIO
SCRIPTS
SDMS
SILICON QOS
SILICON STOR
SIMPLICITY
SMARTPATH
SOLVING THE SYSTEM CARD PUZZLE
SPA
SPEEDREACH
SSD GUARD
STARPRO
STATISTICAL POST PROCESSING
STORAGE PERFORMANCE ANALYSER
STOREAGE
STREAMPACK
SUPERMAPPER
SURELINK
SVM
SVM APP-PACK
SVM REPORT GENERATOR
SYSTEM COREWARE
TARASI
TAS
TRUEFIRE
TRUEPHY
TRUESTORE
ULTRAMAPPER
VIRTUAL PIPELINE
XBB
XML THREAT MANAGER
XOOM
XTM
ZEUS

LUXOR CORP.
(Div. of EBSCO Industries, Inc.)
2245 N Delaney Rd
Waukegan, IL 60087
Mailing Address:
PO Box 830
Waukegan, IL 60079-0830
Tel.: (847) 244-1800
Fax: (847) 244-1818
Fax: (800) 327-1698
Toll Free: (800) 323-4656
E-mail: luxorfurn@ameritech.net
Web Site: www.luxorfurn.com
E-Mail For Key Personnel:
Sales Director: sales@luxorfurn.com
Sales Range: $10-24.9 Million
Approx. Number Employees: 60
Year Founded: 1952
Business Description:
Furniture Mfr
S.I.C.: 2522; 2521
N.A.I.C.S.: 337214; 337211
Import Export
Media: 2-4-7
Distr.: Intl.; Natl.
Brands & Products:
DURAWELD
ENDURA
ENONOMOUNT
LUXOR
PRESTIGE SERIES
PROMOUNT
STUDIO SERIES

LYNUXWORKS, INC.
855 Embedded Way
San Jose, CA 95138-1018
Tel.: (408) 979-3900
Fax: (408) 979-3920
Toll Free: (800) 255-5969
E-mail: inside@lnxw.com
Web Site: www.lynuxworks.com
Approx. Number Employees: 75
Year Founded: 1986
Business Description:
Software & Operating System Technology Developer
S.I.C.: 7372
N.A.I.C.S.: 511210
Media: 10-13
Personnel:
Inder Singh *(Chm)*
Gurjot Singh *(Pres & CEO)*
Mark Baker *(VP-Sls)*
Robert Day *(VP-Mktg)*
Arun Subbarao *(VP-Engrg)*
Kirsten Long *(Dir-Mktg Comm)*
Brands & Products:
BLUECAT
CODEWARRIOR IDE
LINUX
LLYNXINSURE++
LYNUXWORKS
LYNXINSURE
LYNXOS
MESSENGER
POSIX
SPYKER
TOTALVIEW
UNIX
VISUALLYNUX
VISUALLYNUX IDE

LYRIS, INC.
6401 Hollis St Ste 125
Emeryville, CA 94608
Tel.: (510) 844-1600
Fax: (510) 844-1598
Toll Free: (800) 768-2929
Web Site: www.lyris.com
Approx. Rev.: $44,246,000
Approx. Number Employees: 272
Business Description:
Email Marketing Technology
S.I.C.: 7372; 7373; 8742
N.A.I.C.S.: 511210; 541512; 541613
Advertising Expenditures: $5,100,000
Media: 10-13
Personnel:
William T. Comfort, III *(Chm)*
Wolfgang Maasberg *(CEO)*
Keith D. Taylor *(CFO)*
Jim Lovelady *(Sr VP-Sls)*
Tina Stewart *(Sr VP-Mktg)*
V. J. Anand *(VP-Engrg)*
Andrea Scarnecchia *(VP-Mktg)*
Cindy Sherrett *(VP-Programs & Engrg)*
David Fowler *(Dir-Email Strategy, Deliverability & Privacy Compliance)*
Brands & Products:
LISTMANAGER
LYRIS
LYRIS HQ
LYRIS HQ AGENCY EDITION
SPARKLIST
Advertising Agency:
Blanc & Otus Public Relations
60 Green St
San Francisco, CA 94111
Tel.: (415) 856-5100
Fax: (415) 856-5193

MACH CIBERNET
(Sub. of MACH S.a.r.l.)
4600 East-West Hwy Ste 500
Bethesda, MD 20814-3491
Tel.: (301) 961-0810
Fax: (301) 961-0811
Sales Range: $10-24.9 Million
Approx. Number Employees: 130
Business Description:
Multi-Service Financial Settlement Solutions & Data Clearing Services for the Wireless Marketplace
S.I.C.: 7374
N.A.I.C.S.: 518210
Media: 10
Personnel:
Michael Muller *(VP & Gen Mgr-Product Mgmt)*
Mark Daley *(Mktg Dir-Cibernet)*
Michel Gontard *(Dir-Sls MEA)*
Alex James *(Dir-Sls WEU)*
Joseph Kammerer *(Dir-Sls LAM)*
George Lam *(Dir-Sls APAC)*
Gary Moore *(Mgr-Sls & Acct)*
Brands & Products:
CIBERNET

MAD CATZ INTERACTIVE INC.
7480 Mission Valley Rd Ste 101
San Diego, CA 92108
Tel.: (619) 683-9830
Fax: (619) 683-9839
Toll Free: (800) 831-1442
Web Site: www.madcatz.com
Approx. Sls.: $183,974,000
Approx. Number Employees: 257
Year Founded: 1989
Business Description:
Controllers & Accessories for Video Game Consoles & Personal Computers Mfr, Distr & Marketer
S.I.C.: 3577; 3679; 7379
N.A.I.C.S.: 334119; 334418; 541519
Advertising Expenditures: $4,405,000
Media: 10
Personnel:
Thomas R. Brown *(Chm)*
Darren Richardson *(Pres & CEO)*
Allyson Vanderford *(Interim CFO)*
Brian Andersen *(COO)*
Whitney Peterson *(Gen Counsel & VP-Corp Dev)*
Aaron Smith *(Product Mgr)*
Brands & Products:
AIRDRIVES
BLASTER
BLINGKIT
CONTROL PAD PRO
CYBORG
DUAL FORCE
DUAL FORCE 2
DUAL FORCE 2 CONTROLLER
DUAL FORCE PRO
ECLIPSE
GAMESHARK
JOYTECH
LUMICON
LYNX
MAD CATZ
MICROCON
PANTHER
PLAY HARDER PLAY TOGETHER
SAITEK
TRITTON

MADE2MANAGE SYSTEMS, INC.
(Joint Venture of Battery Ventures, L.P. & Thoma Bravo, LLC)
450 E 96th St Ste 300
Indianapolis, IN 46240
Tel.: (317) 249-1200
Fax: (317) 249-1999
Toll Free: (800) 626-0220
E-mail: info@made2manage.com
Web Site: www.made2manage.com
E-Mail For Key Personnel:
Public Relations: mstahley@made2manage.com
Year Founded: 1986
Business Description:
Enterprise Software for Small & Midsize Manufacturers
S.I.C.: 7372
N.A.I.C.S.: 511210
Multimedia: 10%; Bus. Publs.: 20%; Consumer Mags.: 10%; D.M. to Bus. Estab.: 20%; Exhibits/Trade Shows: 30%; Premiums, Novelties: 10%
Personnel:
Jeff Tognoni *(Pres & CEO)*
Tom Millay *(Gen Mgr)*
Brands & Products:
M2M
M2M BI
M2M CRM
M2M ERP
M2M LINK
M2M SCM
M2M VIP
MADE2MANAGE

MAGMA DESIGN AUTOMATION INC.
1650 Technology Dr
San Jose, CA 95110
Tel.: (408) 565-7500
Fax: (408) 565-7501
E-mail: info@magma-da.com
Web Site: www.magma-da.com
Approx. Rev.: $123,077,000
Approx. Number Employees: 677
Year Founded: 1997
Business Description:
Electronic Design Automation (EDA) Software Products & Related Services
S.I.C.: 7372; 7371
N.A.I.C.S.: 334611; 541511
Advertising Expenditures: $100,000
Media: 10-22
Personnel:
Rajeev Madhavan *(Chm & CEO)*
Roy E. Jewell *(Pres & COO)*
Peter S. Teshima *(CFO & Corp VP-Fin)*
Premal Buch *(Gen Mgr & Corp VP-Design Implementation Bus Unit)*
Anirudh Devgan *(Gen Mgr & Corp VP-Design Implementation Bus Unit)*
Carl Burrow *(VP-Sls, North America, Europe & India)*
Milan G. Lazich *(VP-Corp Mktg)*
Alok Mehrotra *(VP-Sls)*
Monica Marmie *(Dir-Mktg Comm)*
Brands & Products:
ARCHEVALUATOR
AUTOMATED CHIP CREATION

Key to Media (For complete agency information see *The Advertising Red Books-Agencies* edition):
1. Bus. Publs. 2. Cable T.V. 3. Catalogs & Directories. 4. Co-op Adv. 5. Consumer Mags. 6. D.M. to Bus. Estab.7. D.M. to Consumers 8. Daily Newsp. 9. Exhibits/Trade Shows 10. Foreign 11. Infomercial 12. Internet Adv.13. Multimedia 14. Network Radio 15. Network T.V. 16. Newsp. Distr. Mags. 17. Other 18. Outdoor (Posters, Transit) 19. Point of Purchase20. Premiums, Novelties 21. Product Samples 22. Special Events Mktg. 23. Spot Radio 24. Spot T.V. 25. Weekly Newsp. 26. Yellow Page Adv.

BLAST CREATE
BLAST DFT
BLAST FPGA
BLAST FUSION
BLAST FUSION APX
BLAST LOGIC
BLAST NOISE
BLAST PLAN
BLAST PLAN PRO
BLAST POWER
BLAST PROTOTYPE
BLAST RAIL
BLAST RTL
BLAST SA
BLAST VIEW
BLAST YIELD
CHARACTERIZATION-TO-SILICON
CORE
DESIGN AHEAD OF THE CURVE
DIAMOND SI
FASTEST PATH FROM RTL TO SILICON
FASTEST PATH TO SILICON
FINESIM
FINEWAVE
FIXEDTIMING
FLOW MANAGERGLASSBOX
HYDRA
HYPERCELL
MAGAMA
MAGMACAST
MEGALAB
MERLIN
MOLTEN
PALACE
PHYSICAL NETLIST
QUARTZ
QUARTZ FORMAL
QUARTZ RC
QUICKCAP
QUICKIND
RELATIVE FLOORPLANNING CONSTRAINTS
SIGN-OFF IN THE LOOP
SILICONSMART
SMART SAMPLING
SUPERSITE
TALUS
TITAN
VISUAL VOLCANO
VOLCANO

MAGNA VISUAL, INC.

9400 Watson Rd
Saint Louis, MO 63126-1596
Tel.: (314) 843-9000
Fax: (314) 843-0000
Toll Free: (800) 843-3399
E-mail: magna@magnavisual.com
Web Site: www.magnavisual.com
Approx. Number Employees: 50
Year Founded: 1961
Business Description:
Magnetic Boards & Accessories
S.I.C.: 3993
N.A.I.C.S.: 339950
Export
Advertising Expenditures: $250,000
Media: 2-4-7-10-21-26
Distr.: Intl.; Natl.
Budget Set: Nov.
Personnel:
William R. Cady *(Owner)*
Frank Venturella *(VP-Sls & Mktg)*
Brands & Products:
MAGNA KLEEN
MAGNA VISUAL
MAGNETIC E3 CERAMICSTEEL

MAGNAPLAN CORPORATION VISUAL PLANNING DIVISION

(Div. of Magnaplan Corporation)
1320 Rte 9
Champlain, NY 12919
Tel.: (518) 298-8404
Fax: (518) 298-2368
E-mail: info@visualplanning.com
Web Site: www.visualplanning.com
Approx. Number Employees: 10
Year Founded: 1967
Business Description:
Graphic Visual Controls, Layout Boards & Stationery Supplies Whslr
S.I.C.: 3499; 3993
N.A.I.C.S.: 332999; 339950
Import Export
Advertising Expenditures: $25,000
Media: 2-4-5-7-9-13-21-23-25-26
Distr.: Natl.
Budget Set: Monthly
Personnel:
Boris Polanski *(Mgr-Adv)*
Brands & Products:
ALL WAYS
KLING
LECTURER'S MARKER
LIQUID CHALK
MAGNAPLAN
MAGNETICALLY ALIGNED
OVERLAY/UNDERLAY
THE PLANNER
TRIPLE ERASABILITY SYSTEM
VISITINT
VISUTATE
VISUTYPE
Advertising Agency:
J. Pollack Josephson & Assoc.
1320 Rt. 9
Champlain, NY 12919
Tel.: (514) 738-8474
Fax: (514) 739-0085
(Scheduling Boards, Easels & Pads, Magnets)

MAGNECORP, INC.

1920 Annapolis Ln N
Minneapolis, MN 55441-3751
Tel.: (763) 383-1400
Fax: (763) 383-1500
Toll Free: (888) 330-6254
E-mail: info@magnecorp.com
Web Site: www.magnecorp.com
Sales Range: $25-49.9 Million
Approx. Number Employees: 5
Year Founded: 1977
Business Description:
Ladderless Systems for Hanging Signs Mfr
S.I.C.: 2519; 3993
N.A.I.C.S.: 337125; 339950
Import Export
Media: 2-4-10-21
Distr.: Natl.
Personnel:
A. Edward Maass *(Pres)*
John Maass *(Gen Mgr)*
Brands & Products:
HANG/EASE
MAGNACLAMP
MAGNECORP
SIGN-EEZ
SIMPLE SOLUTIONS FOR HANGING & HOLDING

MAIL BOXES ETC., INC.

(Sub. of United Parcel Service Co.)
6060 Cornerstone Ct W
San Diego, CA 92121-3795
Tel.: (858) 455-8800
Fax: (858) 546-7488
Toll Free: (800) 7894MBE
E-mail: mbe@mbe.com
Web Site: www.mbe.com
E-Mail For Key Personnel:
Public Relations: pr@mbe.com
Sales Range: $75-99.9 Million
Approx. Number Employees: 274
Year Founded: 1980
Business Description:
Franchisor Postal & Shipping, Business & Communications Services
S.I.C.: 7389; 6794
N.A.I.C.S.: 561431; 533110
Media: 3-7-13-14-15-18-19-23-24
Distr.: Intl.
Budget Set: Mar.
Personnel:
Stuart Mathis *(Pres)*
Mahasty Seradj *(Controller & Sr VP-Fin)*
Don Higginson *(Sr VP-Franchise Rels)*
Kevin Foley *(VP-HR)*
Michelle Van Slyke *(VP-Mktg)*
Brands & Products:
UPS STORE

MAJESCO ENTERTAINMENT COMPANY

160 Raritan Ctr Pkwy
Edison, NJ 08837
Tel.: (732) 225-8910
Fax: (732) 225-8408
E-mail: investorrelations@majescoentertainment.com
Web Site:
www.majescoentertainment.com
Approx. Rev.: $75,648,000
Approx. Number Employees: 71
Year Founded: 1986
Business Description:
Interactive Entertainment Products Mfr & Distr
S.I.C.: 7372
N.A.I.C.S.: 511210; 334611
Advertising Expenditures: $1,600,000
Media: 2-6-10-13-16-19-23-24
Personnel:
Allan I. Grafman *(Chm)*
Jesse Sutton *(CEO)*
Michael Vesey *(CFO)*
Christina Glorioso *(CMO)*
Adam Sultan *(Gen Counsel, Sec & Sr VP-Bus & Legal Affairs)*
Joseph Sutton *(Exec VP-R&D)*
Chris Gray *(Sr VP-Production)*
Tony Chien *(Sr Product Mgr)*
Advertising Agency:
Reverb Communications Inc.
18711 Tiffeni Dr Ste K
Twain Harte, CA 95383
Tel.: (209) 586-1495
Fax: (209) 586-1855

MANAGEMENT DYNAMICS, INC.

1 Meadowlands Plz
East Rutherford, NJ 07073
Tel.: (201) 935-8588
Fax: (201) 935-5187
E-mail: solutions@managementdynamics.com
Web Site:
www.managementdynamics.com
Sales Range: $10-24.9 Million
Approx. Number Employees: 160
Year Founded: 1990
Business Description:
Global Trade Management Solutions
S.I.C.: 8742
N.A.I.C.S.: 541614
Advertising Expenditures: $250,000
Media: 2-4-7-10-13
Personnel:
Barry M.V. Williams *(Chm)*
John Preuninger *(Pres & COO)*
James Preuninger *(CEO)*
Stephanie Miles *(Sr VP-Comml Svcs)*
Nathan Pieri *(Sr VP-Mktg & Product Mgmt)*
Al Cooke *(VP-Sls)*
Annika Helmrich *(Sr Mgr-Global Mktg)*

THE MANAGEMENT NETWORK GROUP, INC.

(d/b/a TMNG Global)
7300 College Blvd Ste 302
Overland Park, KS 66210
Tel.: (913) 345-9315
Fax: (913) 451-1845
Toll Free: (888) 480-8664
Web Site: www.tmng.com
Approx. Rev.: $67,243,000
Approx. Number Employees: 421
Business Description:
Management & Consulting Services to Communications Industry
S.I.C.: 8742; 8748
N.A.I.C.S.: 541611; 541690
Media: 10-13
Personnel:
Micky K. Woo *(Pres & COO)*
Donald E. Klumb *(CFO)*
Ronald Angner, Sr. *(Principal & Sr VP)*
Jonathan Bartholomew *(Principal & VP)*
Thurston Cromwell *(Gen Counsel)*
Nancy Morrow *(VP-HR)*
Hoon Heh *(Gen Mgr)*
Brands & Products:
ASCERTAIN
LEXICON
OPTIMIZING PERFORMANCE ... IN A CONVERGED WORLD
TMNG QBC
TMNG QSA
TMNGGLOBAL

MANAGEMENT RECRUITERS INTERNATIONAL, INC.

(Sub. of CDI Corp.)
(d/b/a MRINetwork)
1717 Arch St 36th Fl
Philadelphia, PA 19103
Tel.: (215) 569-2200
Fax: (215) 751-1757
Toll Free: (888) 836-9890
Web Site: www.mrinetwork.com
Sales Range: $500-549.9 Million
Approx. Number Employees: 2,500
Year Founded: 1965
Business Description:
Executive Search & Recruitment Services
S.I.C.: 7361
N.A.I.C.S.: 561310
Advertising Expenditures: $4,000,000
Media: 2-4-6-9-10-14-15-23-24-25-26

Key to Media (For complete agency information see *The Advertising Red Books-Agencies* edition):
1. Bus. Publs. 2. Cable T.V. 3. Catalogs & Directories. 4. Co-op Adv. 5. Consumer Mags. 6. D.M. to Bus. Estab.7. D.M. to Consumers
8. Daily Newsp. 9. Exhibits/Trade Shows 10. Foreign 11. Infomercial 12. Internet Adv.13. Multimedia 14. Network Radio
15. Network T.V. 16. Newsp. Distr. Mags. 17. Other 18. Outdoor (Posters, Transit) 19. Point of Purchase20. Premiums, Novelties
21. Product Samples 22. Special Events Mktg. 23. Spot Radio 24. Spot T.V. 25. Weekly Newsp. 26. Yellow Page Adv.

Management Recruiters International, Inc. — (Continued)

Distr.: Intl.
Personnel:
Robert Romaine *(Pres)*
Tom Verratti *(CFO)*
Evan Davis *(COO & Sr VP-Franchise Dev)*
Nancy Halverson *(Sr VP-Learning & Talent Dev)*
Gary Williams *(Sr VP-Franchise Rels)*
Seamus Kelleher *(VP-Mktg & Comm)*
Scott Bass *(Dir-Mktg)*
Ronni Nuzzi *(Dir-Field Svc)*
Tim Ozier *(Dir-Contract Staffing)*
Nancy Perry *(Dir-New Office Dev)*

MANATRON, INC.

(Holding of Thoma Bravo, LLC)
510 E Milham Ave
Portage, MI 49002
Tel.: (269) 567-2900
Fax: (269) 567-2930
Toll Free: (866) 471-2900
E-mail: info@manatron.com
Web Site: www.manatron.com
Approx. Number Employees: 334
Year Founded: 1969
Business Description:
Software Designer, Developer, Marketer & Supporter for Government Organizations
S.I.C.: 7372
N.A.I.C.S.: 511210
Media: 2-7-10
Distr.: Reg.
Personnel:
G. William McKinzie *(Pres & CEO)*
Early L. Stephens *(Exec VP-Corp Strategy)*
Marty A. Ulanski *(Exec VP-GRM Ops)*
Kurt J. Wagner *(Exec VP-Ops)*
Bob Brower *(Reg VP-Sls-South Central Reg)*
Woody Carter *(Reg VP-Sls-Northern Reg)*
John Walters *(Reg VP-Sls-Western Reg)*
Mary Nestell Gephart *(VP-HR & Admin)*
Rachel Bryant *(Dir-Mktg & PR)*
Diane Mickunas-Ries *(Mgr-Mktg)*
Brands & Products:
CAMA
EGOVERNMENT
GOVERNMENT REVENUE MANAGEMENT
MANATRON
MVP GIS
MVP TAX
PROVAL
PROVAL PLUS
Advertising Agency:
Hidalgo & De Vries, Inc.
560 5th St Ste 401
Grand Rapids, MI 49504
Tel.: (616) 493-5000
Fax: (616) 493-5001

MANHATTAN ASSOCIATES, INC.

2300 Windy Ridge Pkwy SE Ste 700
Atlanta, GA 30339-5665
Tel.: (770) 955-7070
Fax: (770) 955-0302
E-mail: info@manh.com
Web Site: www.manhattanassociates.com
Approx. Rev.: $297,117,000
Approx. Number Employees: 1,925
Year Founded: 1990
Business Description:
Supply Chain Management Products & Services
S.I.C.: 2541; 7372; 7373
N.A.I.C.S.: 337212; 511210; 541512
Advertising Expenditures: $10,000
Media: 10-22
Personnel:
John J. Huntz Jr. *(Chm)*
Peter F. Sinisgalli *(Pres & CEO)*
Dennis B. Story *(CFO & Exec VP)*
Eddie Capel *(COO & Exec VP)*
Terrie O'Hanlon *(CMO & Sr VP)*
Bruce Richards *(Chief Legal Officer & Sr VP)*
Jeffrey S. Mitchell *(Exec VP-Americas Ops)*
Jeff Baum *(Sr VP-Intl Ops)*
Jeff Cashman *(Sr VP-Bus Dev)*
Brands & Products:
INTEGRATED LOGISTICS SOLUTIONS
MANHATTAN ASSOCIATES
MANHATTAN FAST TRACK
MANHATTAN SCOPE
PKMS
RFID IN A BOX
SLOT-IT
SUPPLY CHAIN ITS ALL WE DO
THE SUPPLY CHAIN PEOPLE

MANPOWER INC.

100 Manpower Place
Milwaukee, WI 53212
Mailing Address:
PO Box 2053
Milwaukee, WI 53201-2053
Tel.: (414) 961-1000
Fax: (414) 961-7081
Fax: (414) 906-7985
E-mail: professional@na.manpower.com
Web Site: www.manpower.com
E-Mail For Key Personnel:
Public Relations: tracy.shilobrit@manpower.com
Approx. Rev.: $18,866,500,000
Approx. Number Employees: 30,000
Year Founded: 1948
Business Description:
Permanent, Temporary & Contract Employment & Workforce Management Solution Services
S.I.C.: 7363; 8299
N.A.I.C.S.: 561311; 561320; 561330; 611430
Advertising Expenditures: $29,400,000
Media: 2-3-6-7-8-9-10-13-18-19-20-22-23-24-25-26
Distr.: Intl.; Natl.
Personnel:
Jeffrey A. Joerres *(Chm, Pres & CEO)*
Michael J. Van Handel *(CFO & Exec VP)*
Emma van Rooyen *(CMO & Sr VP)*
Kenneth C. Hunt *(Sr VP & Chief Legal Officer)*
Barbara J. Beck *(Pres-Europe, Middle East & Africa & Exec VP)*
Darryl E. Green *(Pres-Asia Pacific/ Middle East & Exec VP)*
Francoise Gri *(Exec VP, Pres-Southern Europe)*
Jonas Prising *(Pres-Ops-North America & Exec VP)*
David Arkless *(Pres-Corp & Govt Affairs)*
Owen J. Sullivan *(CEO-Right Mgmt & Jefferson Wells & Exec VP)*
Mara Swan *(Exec VP-Global Strategy & Talent)*
Tammy Johns *(Sr VP-Innovation & Workforce Solutions)*
Jorge Perez *(Sr VP-North America)*
Brands & Products:
MANPOWER
SKILLWARE
ULTRADEX
ULTRASKILL

MANROLAND INC.

(Sub. of manroland AG)
800 E Oakhill Dr
Westmont, IL 60559
Tel.: (630) 920-2000
Fax: (630) 920-2457
Fax: (630) 920-9146
Toll Free: (800) 700-2344
E-mail: marketing@manroland.us
Web Site: www.manroland.us
Approx. Sls.: $350,000,000
Approx. Number Employees: 160
Year Founded: 1994
Business Description:
Printing Machinery Mfr
S.I.C.: 3555
N.A.I.C.S.: 333293
Import Export
Advertising Expenditures: $600,000
Bus. Publs.: $450,000; D.M. to Consumers: $60,000; Exhibits/Trade Shows: $90,000
Distr.: Intl.; Natl.
Budget Set: May
Personnel:
Vince Lapinski *(CEO)*
Brands & Products:
COLORMAN
CROMOMAN
GEOMAN
LITHOMAN
MAN ROLANDS
REGIOMAN
ROTOMAN
UNISET

MARATHON TECHNOLOGIES CORP.

295 Foster St
Littleton, MA 01460
Tel.: (978) 489-1100
Fax: (978) 489-1101
E-mail: info@marathontechnologies.com
Web Site: www.marathontechnologies.com
Approx. Number Employees: 100
Business Description:
Server Security Consulting, Training, Support, Maintenance, Installation, & Integration
S.I.C.: 7372
N.A.I.C.S.: 511210
Personnel:
Jim Welch *(Pres & CEO)*
George C. Tranos *(CEO)*
Thomas Goebels *(Mgr-Sls-Germany, Austria & Switzerland Reg)*
Advertising Agency:
Corey McPherson Nash
63 Pleasant St
Watertown, MA 02472
Tel.: (617) 924-6050
Fax: (616) 923-0857

MARCONI CORP.

(Sub. of Telent Limited)
3000 Marconi Dr
Warrendale, PA 15086-7502
Tel.: (724) 742-4444
Fax: (724) 742-7742
Toll Free: (888) 404-0444
Toll Free: (800) MARCONI
E-mail: ehs.inquiries@marconi.com
Web Site: www.marconi.com
Approx. Number Employees: 900
Year Founded: 1990
Business Description:
Broadband Routing & Switching Services
S.I.C.: 3577
N.A.I.C.S.: 334119
Media: 2-7-24
Personnel:
Paviter Binning *(CFO & Dir)*
Steve Grady *(VP-Mktg Officer)*
Mike Burgess *(Exec VP-Commun)*
Carla Feldman *(Exec VP-Sls-Mktg)*
Alex Marshall *(VP-Product Mktg)*
Michael Kent Atkinson *(Sr Dir)*
David Beck *(Dir-Commun)*
Brands & Products:
FORE SYSTEMS
FORERUNNER

MARKEM-IMAJE

(Sub. of Markem-Imaje S.A.)
150 Congress St
Keene, NH 03431
Mailing Address:
PO Box 2100
Keene, NH 03431-0467
Tel.: (603) 352-1130
Fax: (603) 357-5871
Toll Free: (800) 258-5356
E-mail: custsvc@markem-imaje.com
Web Site: www.markem-imaje.com
E-Mail For Key Personnel:
Sales Director: sales@markem.com
Sales Range: $200-249.9 Million
Approx. Number Employees: 500
Year Founded: 1911
Business Description:
Product Marking, Coding & Tracking Systems Equipment & Software Mfr
S.I.C.: 3555; 3651; 3663; 3679; 7372
N.A.I.C.S.: 333293; 334220; 334310; 334418; 334419; 334611; 511210
Import Export
Advertising Expenditures: $500,000
Media: 1-2-4-5-10-11-13-17-21
Distr.: Intl.; Natl.
Budget Set: Nov.
Brands & Products:
5000 SERIES
9820 TOUCH DRY
9840 TOUCH DRY
9880 TOUCH DRY
CIMCONTROL
CIMJET 311
CIMJET 342
CIMLINK
COMPOSER
OPTIMARK
SMARTDATE
SMARTDATE 2I

Key to Media (For complete agency information see *The Advertising Red Books-Agencies* edition):
1. Bus. Publs. 2. Cable T.V. 3. Catalogs & Directories. 4. Co-op Adv. 5. Consumer Mags. 6. D.M. to Bus. Estab.7. D.M. to Consumers 8. Daily Newsp. 9. Exhibits/Trade Shows 10. Foreign 11. Infomercial 12. Internet Adv.13. Multimedia 14. Network Radio 15. Network T.V. 16. Newsp. Distr. Mags. 17. Other 18. Outdoor (Posters, Transit) 19. Point of Purchase20. Premiums, Novelties 21. Product Samples 22. Special Events Mktg. 23. Spot Radio 24. Spot T.V. 25. Weekly Newsp. 26. Yellow Page Adv.

SMARTDATE 3I
SMARTLASE 100 SERIES
SMARTLASE 130
SMARTLASE 130S
SMARTLASE SL
SMARTTOUCH
TOUCH DRY
UPTIME

MARKET PLANNING SOLUTIONS INC.
4343 S 118th E Ave Ste C
Tulsa, OK 74146
Tel.: (918) 877-6774
Fax: (918) 877-6960
Toll Free: (800) 727-6774
E-mail: info@mpsisolutions.com
Web Site: www.mpsisolutions.com
Sales Range: $10-24.9 Million
Approx. Number Employees: 67
Year Founded: 1970
Business Description:
Decision Support Software & Information Databases Mfr; Consulting Services
S.I.C.: 7371; 7372; 7375
N.A.I.C.S.: 541511; 511210; 518111
Advertising Expenditures: $65,000
Media: 7-10-17
Personnel:
Ronald R. Harper *(Founder & Chm)*
Jim Auten *(CEO)*
Brands & Products:
DATA MANAGER
DATA METRIX
LOCATIONXPERT
MPSI
PRICE IT! PRO
PRICEIT PRO
PRICETRACKER
PVO
RETAIL EXPLORER
STREETBACK PRICING
STREETMETRIX
STREETMETRIX DISPLAY
STREETMETRIX PLUS
TRAFFICMETRIX

MARKETING INNOVATORS INTERNATIONAL, INC.
9701 W Higgins Rd
Rosemont, IL 60018
Tel.: (847) 696-1111
Fax: (847) 696-3194
Toll Free: (800) 543-7373
E-mail: info@marketinginnovators.com
Web Site:
www.marketinginnovators.com
Sales Range: $75-99.9 Million
Approx. Number Employees: 55
Year Founded: 1978
Business Description:
Management Incentive Products & Services
S.I.C.: 7361
N.A.I.C.S.: 541612
Media: 2-4-7-10-13
Personnel:
Lois M. LeMenager *(Founder, Chm & CEO)*
Richard A. Blabolil *(Pres)*
Sherry Blabolil-Das *(Exec VP)*
Brands & Products:
INSPIRING PEOPLE TO GREATER PERFORMANCE
MARKETING INNOVATORS
MIBANC
MICHOICE
MIPERC
MISTYLE
STORED VALUE

MARTIN DAWES ANALYTICS
(Sub. of Martin Dawes Systems)
321 Summer St 5th Fl
Boston, MA 02210
Tel.: (617) 345-5422
Fax: (617) 345-5475
Toll Free: (877) 650-5282
E-mail: info@mda-data.com
Web Site: www.mda-data.com
Approx. Number Employees: 25
Year Founded: 1994
Business Description:
Revenue Assurance & Cost Management Software
S.I.C.: 7371
N.A.I.C.S.: 541511
Media: 10
Personnel:
Andrew Rockwell *(CEO)*
Dewi Thomas *(Mng Dir)*
Rastislav Nukovic *(VP-Engrg)*
Bill Belcher *(Dir-Sls)*
Brands & Products:
ECHO
REVEL

MARTIN UNIVERSAL DESIGN, INC.
4444 Lawton St
Detroit, MI 48208
Tel.: (313) 895-0700
Fax: (313) 895-0709
Web Site: www.martinuniversal.com
Approx. Number Employees: 25
Year Founded: 1947
Business Description:
Artist & Drafting Supplies Importer & Distr
S.I.C.: 2521; 2522
N.A.I.C.S.: 337211; 337214
Import Export
Advertising Expenditures: $50,000
Media: 2-5-6-7-8-10-21
Distr.: Intl.; Natl.
Budget Set: Dec.
Personnel:
Dennis Kapp *(CEO)*
Joe Augustyne *(Dir-Pur)*
Brands & Products:
ARTWRIGHT

MARUDAS PRINT SERVICES & PROMOTIONAL PRODUCTS, INC.
20 Yorkton Ct
Saint Paul, MN 55117
Tel.: (651) 697-7820
Fax: (651) 697-7822
Toll Free: (800) 879-3879
E-mail: info@marudas.com
Web Site: www.marudas.com
Sales Range: $50-74.9 Million
Approx. Number Employees: 50
Year Founded: 1983
Business Description:
Custom Business Forms, Office Supplies & Promotional Products Mfr & Distr
S.I.C.: 5112; 7319
N.A.I.C.S.: 424120; 541890
Import Export
Media: 4
Personnel:
Alex Marudas *(Pres)*
Philip P. Marudas *(Pres)*

MASTEC, INC.
800 S Douglas Rd 12th Fl
Coral Gables, FL 33134
Tel.: (305) 599-1800
Fax: (305) 406-1960
E-mail: services@mastec.com
Web Site: www.mastec.com
Approx. Rev.: $2,308,031,000
Approx. Number Employees: 9,400
Year Founded: 1929
Business Description:
Telecommunications & Energy Infrastructure Construction Services
S.I.C.: 1623; 1629
N.A.I.C.S.: 237130; 237990
Media: 2-10-22
Personnel:
Jorge Mas *(Chm)*
Ray Harris *(Pres)*
Jose Ramon Mas *(CEO)*
C. Robert Campbell *(CFO & Exec VP)*
Robert E. Apple *(COO)*
Darrell Mays *(Pres-Wireless)*
Zach Mcguire *(Grp Pres-Satellite Svcs)*
Bryan Westerman *(Grp Pres-Comm)*
Alberto De Cardenas *(Gen Counsel & Exec VP)*

MATRIX INTEGRATION LLC
417 Main St
Jasper, IN 47546
Tel.: (812) 634-1550
Fax: (812) 634-2573
Toll Free: (800) 264-1550
E-mail: webmaster@matrixintegration.com
Web Site: www.matrixintegration.com
Sales Range: $25-49.9 Million
Approx. Number Employees: 85
Year Founded: 1971
Business Description:
IT Infrastructure, Personal Computing & Access Devices, Networking Services, Structured Cabling, Telephony, Printing, Imaging & After-Sale Services
S.I.C.: 7373; 2759; 3357; 4812; 7371; 7378; 7389
N.A.I.C.S.: 541512; 323115; 335921; 517212; 541511; 561499; 811212
Media: 10
Personnel:
Brenda Stallings *(Pres)*
Curt Trainer *(VP-Sls)*
Jason Bohnert *(Mgr-Inventory, Procurement & Transport)*
Angelin Stiles *(Mgr-HR)*
Amy Williams *(Mgr-Mktg & Bus Dev)*
Chad Williams *(Mgr-Pub Sector Div)*

MAXXESS SYSTEMS, INC.
(Sub. of Iteris, Inc.)
1515 S Manchester Ave
Anaheim, CA 92802-2907
Tel.: (714) 772-1000
Fax: (714) 780-7592
Toll Free: (800) 842-0221
Web Site: www.maxxesssystems.com
E-Mail For Key Personnel:
Sales Director: sales@maxxess-systems.com
Sales Range: $10-24.9 Million
Approx. Number Employees: 70
Year Founded: 1975
Business Description:
Access Technology Services
S.I.C.: 3699
N.A.I.C.S.: 335999
Export
Media: 1-2-4-7-10-11
Distr.: Intl.; Natl.
Budget Set: July
Personnel:
Lee Copland *(Mng Dir)*
Danielle Benvin *(Mgr-Customer Svc)*
Brands & Products:
AMBIT
AXXESS NS
BARLOCK
RAMM
VIDEOKEY

MC2
3 Alpine Ct
Chestnut Ridge, NY 10977
Tel.: (845) 578-1620
Fax: (845) 578-1625
Toll Free: (800) 537-8073
Web Site: www.mc-2.com
Approx. Number Employees: 350
Year Founded: 1980
Business Description:
Marketing Solutions Services, Exhibits, Events & Interactive Media Productions
S.I.C.: 8742
N.A.I.C.S.: 541613
Import Export
Media: 7-10
Personnel:
Rick Rubio *(Pres-Northeast Div)*

MCAFEE, INC.
(Sub. of Intel Corporation)
2821 Mission College Blvd
Santa Clara, CA 95054
Tel.: (408) 988-3832
Fax: (408) 720-8450
Toll Free: (800) 338-8754
E-mail: press@mcafee.com
Web Site: www.mcafee.com
Approx. Rev.: $2,064,807,000
Approx. Number Employees: 6,300
Year Founded: 1989
Business Description:
Computer Security Software, Products & Services
S.I.C.: 7372; 7379
N.A.I.C.S.: 511210; 541519
Export
Advertising Expenditures: $15,200,000
Media: 2-7-10-13
Personnel:
Michael P. DeCesare *(Co-Pres)*
Todd Gebhart *(Co-Pres)*
Mark Tonnesen *(CIO & Sr VP)*
David Milam *(CMO & Exec VP)*
Mark D. Cochran *(Chief Legal Officer, Gen Counsel & Exec VP)*
George Kurtz *(CTO-Worldwide & Exec VP)*
Jean-Claude Broido *(Pres-Japan)*
Steve Redman *(Pres-Asia Pacific Reg)*
Joseph Gabbert *(Exec VP-HR)*
Barry McPherson *(Exec VP-Worldwide Technical Support & Customer Svc)*
Joe Sexton *(Exec VP-Global Sls)*

Key to Media (For complete agency information see *The Advertising Red Books-Agencies* edition):
1. Bus. Publs. 2. Cable T.V. 3. Catalogs & Directories. 4. Co-op Adv. 5. Consumer Mags. 6. D.M. to Bus. Estab.7. D.M. to Consumers
8. Daily Newsp. 9. Exhibits/Trade Shows 10. Foreign 11. Infomercial 12. Internet Adv.13. Multimedia 14. Network Radio
15. Network T.V. 16. Newsp. Distr. Mags. 17. Other 18. Outdoor (Posters, Transit) 19. Point of Purchase20. Premiums, Novelties
21. Product Samples 22. Special Events Mktg. 23. Spot Radio 24. Spot T.V. 25. Weekly Newsp. 26. Yellow Page Adv.

McAfee, Inc. — (Continued)

Gerhard Watzinger *(Exec VP-Corp Strategy & Bus Dev)*
Stuart McClure *(Sr VP, Gen Mgr-Risk & Compliance)*
Marc Olesen *(Sr VP, Gen Mgr-Content & Cloud Security)*
Michael Busselen *(Sr VP-Global External Affairs)*
Alex Thurber *(Sr VP-WW Channels)*
Alva Purvis *(Sr Dir-Global Channels)*
Brandie Claborn *(Dir-Exec Comm)*
Hiep Dang *(Dir-Ops-McAfee Labs)*
Erica Coleman *(Sr Mgr-PR)*

Brands & Products:
INTERNET SECURITY
INTRUSHIELD
MCAFEE
MCAFEE SITEADVISOR
MCAFEE VIRUSSCAN
PERSONAL FIREWALL PLUS
Platinum Select
SPAMKILLER
VIRUSSCAN ENTERPRISE

Advertising Agencies:
OMD Worldwide
195 Broadway
New York, NY 10007
Tel.: (212) 590-7100
(Technology Security, Media Planning/ Buying)

Tribal DDB Worldwide
437 Madison Ave 8th Fl
New York, NY 10022
Tel.: (212) 515-8600
Fax: (212) 515-8660
(Technology Security)

Verve Communications Group
325 N Saint Paul St Ste 1360
Dallas, TX 75201
Tel.: (214) 965-9933
Fax: (214) 965-9889

MCBEE RAPID FORMS

(Sub. of Deluxe Small Business Services)
PO Box 1186
Lancaster, CA 93584-9961
Tel.: (661) 942-1144
Toll Free: (800) 610-2911
E-mail: info@mcbeeinc.com
Web Site: www.mcbeeinc.com
Sales Range: $150-199.9 Million
Approx. Number Employees: 839
Year Founded: 1906
Business Description:
Check & Related Business Form Mfr & Marketer
S.I.C.: 2782
N.A.I.C.S.: 323118
Import Export
Media: 2-4-7-10-13-20-26
Distr.: Natl.
Budget Set: Oct.
Brands & Products:
MCBEE

MCMILLION RESEARCH

1012 Kanawha Blvd E Ste 301
Charleston, WV 25301
Tel.: (304) 343-9650
Fax: (304) 343-6522
E-mail: jmace@mcmillionresearch.com
Web Site: www.mcmillionresearch.com
Sales Range: $100-124.9 Million
Approx. Number Employees: 150
Business Description:
National Data Collection & Market Research Services
S.I.C.: 2741
N.A.I.C.S.: 511140
Media: 13
Personnel:
Gary McMillion *(Pres)*

MEADWESTVACO CONSUMER & OFFICE PRODUCTS

(Div. of MeadWestvaco Corporation)
4751 Hempstead Sta Dr
Kettering, OH 45429
Tel.: (937) 495-6323
Fax: (937) 495-4553
Sales Range: $500-549.9 Million
Approx. Number Employees: 1,200
Business Description:
Office Supplies & Stationery Products Mfr
S.I.C.: 2678
N.A.I.C.S.: 322233
Media: 2-10-15-19-24
Distr.: Natl.
Budget Set: Sept. -Oct.
Personnel:
Neil A. McLachlan *(Pres)*
Lori Conley *(Dir-Mktg)*
Advertising Agency:
Landau Public Relations
700 W Saint Clair Ave Ste 414
Cleveland, OH 44113
Tel.: (216) 696-1686
Fax: (216) 771-5206

MEADWESTVACO CORPORATION - ENVELOPE DIVISION

(Div. of MeadWestvaco Corp. - Office Products Group)
2001 Roosevelt Ave
Springfield, MA 01104
Mailing Address:
PO Box 3300
Springfield, MA 01102-3300
Tel.: (413) 736-7211
Fax: (413) 787-9741
Fax: (413) 739-9648
E-mail: info@meadwestvacocorporation.com
Web Site: www.meadwestvaco.com/index.htm
Sales Range: $25-49.9 Million
Approx. Number Employees: 85
Year Founded: 1898
Business Description:
Envelopes Mfr
S.I.C.: 2679; 2677
N.A.I.C.S.: 322299; 322232
Export
Media: 2-4-7-10-19-20-21
Distr.: Natl.
Personnel:
Karl Unger *(Mgr-Mktg)*

MEADWESTVACO CORP. - OFFICE PRODUCTS GROUP

(Sub. of MeadWestvaco Corporation)
101 ONeil Rd
Sidney, NY 13838-1055
Tel.: (607) 563-9411
Fax: (607) 563-8811
Toll Free: (800) 323-0500
Sales Range: $75-99.9 Million
Approx. Number Employees: 1,000
Business Description:
Desk Calendars, Appointment & Recordkeeping Books Mfr
S.I.C.: 2782; 2752
N.A.I.C.S.: 323118; 323110
Export
Advertising Expenditures: $400,000
Media: 2-4-10-21-22
Distr.: Intl.; Natl.
Budget Set: Oct.
Personnel:
John A. Luke, Jr. *(Chm & CEO)*
David Williamson *(Exec VP & Gen Mgr-Office Products Grp)*

MEDECISION, INC.

(Sub. of Health Care Service Corporation)
601 Lee Rd Chesterbrook Corporate Center
Wayne, PA 19087
Tel.: (610) 540-0202
Fax: (610) 540-0270
E-mail: hrinfo@medecision.com
Web Site: www.medecision.com
E-Mail For Key Personnel:
Marketing Director: marketing@medecision.com
Approx. Rev.: $44,755,000
Approx. Number Employees: 249
Year Founded: 1988
Business Description:
Medical Decision & Support Management Software Designer & Mfr
S.I.C.: 7371
N.A.I.C.S.: 541511
Media: 2-7-10
Personnel:
David St. Clair *(Founder)*
Colleen Reitan *(Chm)*
Deborah M. Gage *(Pres & CEO)*
Carl E. Smith *(CFO & Exec VP)*
Carole Hodsdon *(COO & Exec VP)*
Eric Demers *(Chief Strategy Officer & Exec VP)*
Andrew P. Schuyler *(Chief Mdsg Officer)*
Tracey Costello *(Sr VP-Mktg)*
Brands & Products:
CAREPLANNER
CASEALERT
IEXCHANGE
MEDECISION

MEDIA 100

(Unit of Optibase Inc.)
260 Cedar Hill St
Marlborough, MA 01752-4710
Tel.: (703) 462-1640
Toll Free: (800) 773-1770
E-mail: customerservice@media100.com
Web Site: www.media100.com
Approx. Sls.: $19,081,000
Approx. Number Employees: 52
Year Founded: 1973
Business Description:
Advanced Media Systems Services
S.I.C.: 3577; 7389
N.A.I.C.S.: 334119; 541490
Export
Advertising Expenditures: $2,000,000
Media: 2-7-10-20
Distr.: Intl.; Natl.
Brands & Products:
844/X
IFINISH
MEDIA 100
MEDIA 100 HD
MEDIA 100 I
Advertising Agency:
Zazil Media Group
90 Hamilton St
Cambridge, MA 02139
Tel.: (617) 817-6595
Fax: (617) 812-7683

MEDIA NETWORKS INC.

(Sub. of Time Inc.)
1 Station Pl
Stamford, CT 06902
Tel.: (203) 967-3100
Fax: (203) 967-6472
Toll Free: (800) 225-3457
Web Site: www.mni.com
Sales Range: $25-49.9 Million
Approx. Number Employees: 180
Year Founded: 1980
Business Description:
Produce & Sell Ads for National Magazines For Distribution on Basis of Locale
S.I.C.: 7311
N.A.I.C.S.: 541810
Media: 2-4-7-10-18-20-26
Distr.: Natl.
Personnel:
Robert Reif *(Pres)*
Mark Hintsa *(VP-Mktg & IT)*
Matthew Fanelli *(Exec Dir-Digital Media Grp)*
David Mevorah *(Dir-Adv)*
Michael P. Nasif *(Dir-Bus Dev-Digital)*

MEDIA SCIENCES INTERNATIONAL, INC.

8 Allerman Rd
Oakland, NJ 07436-3324
Tel.: (201) 677-9311
Fax: (201) 677-1440
Toll Free: (888) 376-8348
E-mail: info@mediasciences.com
Web Site: www.mediasciences.com
Approx. Rev.: $21,941,931
Approx. Number Employees: 62
Year Founded: 1983
Business Description:
Printing Supplies Mfr
S.I.C.: 2893; 3955
N.A.I.C.S.: 325910; 339944
Advertising Expenditures: $673,000
Media: 7-8-10-20-21
Personnel:
Willem Van Rijn *(Chm)*
Marc D. Durand *(Pres & CEO)*
Denise Hawkins *(CFO & Sec)*
James W. Johnston *(Exec VP)*
Eric Tuvesson *(VP-Prod Dev & Engrg)*
William C. Besold *(Dir-Mktg Comm)*
Bradford J. Huntley *(Dir-Sls-Office Channel)*
Amaya Martinez Lalanne *(Country Mgr-France-Sls)*
Leo VanOrden *(Mgr-Plant)*
Brands & Products:
MEDIA SCIENCES
THE SCIENCE OF COLOR
Advertising Agency:
Shaw & Todd, Inc.
95 Mt Bethel Rd 1st Fl
Warren, NJ 07059

Key to Media (For complete agency information see *The Advertising Red Books-Agencies* edition):
1. Bus. Publs. 2. Cable T.V. 3. Catalogs & Directories. 4. Co-op Adv. 5. Consumer Mags. 6. D.M. to Bus. Estab.7. D.M. to Consumers
8. Daily Newsp. 9. Exhibits/Trade Shows 10. Foreign 11. Infomercial 12. Internet Adv.13. Multimedia 14. Network Radio
15. Network T.V. 16. Newsp. Distr. Mags. 17. Other 18. Outdoor (Posters, Transit) 19. Point of Purchase20. Premiums, Novelties
21. Product Samples 22. Special Events Mktg. 23. Spot Radio 24. Spot T.V. 25. Weekly Newsp. 26. Yellow Page Adv.

Tel.: (908) 668-1106
Fax: (908) 668-1107

MEDIABANK LLC

600 W Chicago Ave Ste 350
Chicago, IL 60654
Tel.: (312) 676-4646
Fax: (312) 870-1787
Web Site: www.mbxg.com
Approx. Number Employees: 200
Business Description:
Media Buying Technology & Services
S.I.C.: 7319
N.A.I.C.S.: 541890
Personnel:
John Bauschard *(Pres)*
Bill Wise *(CEO)*
Advertising Agency:
Doner
25900 Northwestern Hwy
Southfield, MI 48075
Tel.: (248) 354-9700
Fax: (248) 827-8440

MEDIAGRIF INTERACTIVE TECHNOLOGIES, INC.

1010 De Serigny St Ste 800
Longueuil, QC J4K 5G7, Canada
Tel.: (450) 677-8797
Fax: (450) 677-4612
E-mail: info@mediagrif.com
Web Site: www.mediagrif.com
Approx. Rev.: $44,750,546
Approx. Number Employees: 336
Year Founded: 1996
Business Description:
E-Business Networks & Solutions Whslr
S.I.C.: 5045
N.A.I.C.S.: 425110
Media: 10
Personnel:
Claude Roy *(Pres & CEO)*
Paul Bourque *(CFO)*
Helene Hallak *(Gen Counsel & Sr VP)*
Mark Eigenbauer *(Sr VP)*
Richard Lampron *(Sr VP)*
Paul Saunders *(Sr VP)*
Stephane Anglaret *(VP-Tech)*

MEDIALIVE INTERNATIONAL INC.

795 Folsom St 6th Fl
San Francisco, CA 94107
Tel.: (415) 905-2300
Fax: (415) 905-2329
Web Site: liveevents.techweb.com/
E-Mail For Key Personnel:
Public Relations: emily.swanson@mlii.com
Sales Range: $150-199.9 Million
Approx. Number Employees: 350
Business Description:
Organizer of Information Technology Trade Shows
S.I.C.: 7389
N.A.I.C.S.: 561990
Personnel:
Anne Miller *(Corp Sr VP-Sls)*
Kate Spellman *(Sr VP-Mktg Strategy-Bus)*
Scott Vaughan *(VP-Mktg)*
Sherbrooke Balser *(Mktg Dir)*
Tara Gibb *(Mktg Dir)*
Felicia Hamerman *(Mktg Dir)*
Jessica Marty *(Mktg Dir)*
Karen Tom *(Mktg Dir)*
Carolyn Herr *(Dir-Event Ops)*
Michael Whalen *(Dir-Intl Sls Dev)*
Brands & Products:
COMDEX
FS4TORONTO
GTEC
JAVAONE
NETWORLD+INTEROP
NEXT GENERATION NETWORKS
SEYBOLD SEMINARS
SOFTBANK FORUMS
VOICECON
Advertising Agency:
The Bivings Group
2201 Wisconsin Ave NW Ste 310
Washington, DC 20007
Tel.: (202) 741-1500
Fax: (202) 741-1501

MEDIASTREET, INC.

44 W Jefryn Blvd Unit Y
Deer Park, NY 11729
Tel.: (631) 242-5505
Fax: (631) 242-5515
Fax: (888) 329-5991
Toll Free: (888) 633-4295
E-mail: orderinfo@mediastreet.com
Web Site: www.mediastreet.com
Approx. Number Employees: 110
Business Description:
Inkjet Printer Ink & Paper Mfr & Distr
S.I.C.: 2865
N.A.I.C.S.: 325132
Personnel:
Norm Levy *(Pres)*
Advertising Agency:
Zapwater Communications
1165 N Clark St Ste 313
Chicago, IL 60610
Tel.: (312) 771-1271
Tel.: (312) 943-0333
Fax: (312) 943-0852

MEDICAL INFORMATION TECHNOLOGY, INC.

(d/b/a MEDITECH)
Meditech Cir
Westwood, MA 02090
Tel.: (781) 821-3000
Fax: (781) 821-2199
E-mail: info@meditech.com
Web Site: www.meditech.com
Approx. Rev.: $459,098,488
Approx. Number Employees: 3,295
Year Founded: 1969
Business Description:
Information System Software for Medical Industry
S.I.C.: 5045; 7371; 7372
N.A.I.C.S.: 423430; 511210; 541511
Import Export
Media: 10-13
Personnel:
A. Neil Pappalardo *(Chm & CEO)*
Lawrence A. Polimeno *(Vice Chm)*
Howard Messing *(Pres & COO)*
Barbara A. Manzolillo *(CFO & Treas)*
Robert G. Gale *(Sr VP-Product Dev)*
Joanne Wood *(Sr VP-Client Svcs)*
Stuart N. Lefthes *(VP-Sls)*
Michelle O'Connor *(VP-Product Dev)*
Hoda Sayed-Friel *(VP-Mktg)*
Brands & Products:
MEDITECH

MEDIDATA SOLUTIONS, INC.

79 Fifth Ave 8th Fl
New York, NY 10003
Tel.: (212) 918-1800
Fax: (212) 918-1818
Toll Free: (877) 511-4200
E-mail: info@mdsol.com
Web Site: www.mdsol.com
Approx. Rev.: $166,426,000
Approx. Number Employees: 598
Year Founded: 1999
Business Description:
Medical Technology Software
S.I.C.: 7373; 7372
N.A.I.C.S.: 541512; 511210
Advertising Expenditures: $104,336
Media: 17-22
Personnel:
Edward F. Ikeguchi *(Co-Founder & Chief Medical Officer)*
Tarek A. Sherif *(Chm & CEO)*
Glen M. de Vries *(Pres)*
Bruce D. Dalziel *(CFO & Exec VP-Compliance)*
Cory Douglas *(Chief Acctg Officer, VP & Controller)*
Michael I. Otner *(Gen Counsel)*
Steven I. Hirschfeld *(Exec VP-Sls & Alliances)*
Lineene N. Krasnow *(Exec VP-Product & Mktg)*
Bryan Spielman *(Exec VP-Strategy & Corp Dev)*
Keith Howells *(Sr VP-Dev)*
Earl Hulihan *(Sr VP-Regulatory Affairs)*
Arden Schneider *(Sr VP-HR)*
Vik Shah *(Sr VP-Svcs)*
Joe Tyers *(Sr VP-Strategic Accts)*
Daniel Mudgett *(VP)*
Brands & Products:
MEDIDATA
MEDIDATA CRO CONTRACTOR
MEDIDATA DESIGNER
MEDIDATA GRANTS MANAGER
MEDIDATA RAVE

MEDIWARE INFORMATION SYSTEMS, INC.

11711 W 79th St
Lenexa, KS 66214
Tel.: (913) 307-1000
Fax: (913) 307-1111
E-mail: info@mediware.com
Web Site: www.mediware.com
Approx. Rev.: $55,523,000
Approx. Number Employees: 292
Year Founded: 1980
Business Description:
Develops, Markets, Licenses, Implements & Supports Clinical Management Information Solutions
S.I.C.: 7372; 7373
N.A.I.C.S.: 511210; 541512
Advertising Expenditures: $685,000
Personnel:
Lawrence E. Auriana *(Chm)*
Thomas Kelly Mann *(Pres & CEO)*
Michael Martens *(CFO)*
John Damgaard *(COO)*
Robert C. Weber *(Chief Legal Officer)*
Michael Anania *(VP & Gen Mgr-Blood Center Technologies Product Grp)*
John Van Blaricum *(VP-Mktg & Comm)*
Mary Truvillion *(VP-HR)*
Brands & Products:
BIOLOGICARE
BLOODSAFE
DIGIMEDICS
HCLL
HEMOCARE
JAC
LIFELINE
LIFETRAK
MEDICOE
MEDICOETM
MEDIMAR
MEDIMARTM
MEDIWARE
PERIOPERATIVE SOLUTIONS
PHARMAKON
SAFE FOR THEM.SAFE FOR YOU
WORX
WORX UNIVERSAL
Advertising Agency:
Redington Inc.
49 Richmondville Ave Ste 108
Westport, CT 06880
Tel.: (203) 222-7399
Tel.: (212) 926-1733
Fax: (203) 222-1819

MEDQUIST HOLDINGS INC.

(Formerly CBaySystems Holdings Limited)
9009 Carothers Pkwy
Franklin, TN 37067
Tel.: (615) 261-1740
Toll Free: (866) 295-4600
Approx. Rev.: $417,326,000
Approx. Number Employees: 12,000
Year Founded: 1998
Business Description:
Holding Company; Medical Practice & Hospital Management Software
S.I.C.: 6719; 7372; 7373
N.A.I.C.S.: 551112; 511210; 541512
Advertising Expenditures: $1,909,000
Personnel:
Robert M. Aquilina *(Chm)*
Venu Raman Kumar *(Vice Chm)*
Peter Masanotti *(Pres & CEO)*
Anthony D. James *(CFO)*

MEDSTAFF, INC.

3805 W Chester Pike Ste 200
Newtown Square, PA 19073
Tel.: (610) 356-6337
Fax: (610) 353-7850
Fax: (610) 356-1480
Toll Free: (800) 732-9992
E-mail: eromanelli@medstaffinc.com
Web Site: www.medstaffinc.com
Approx. Number Employees: 130
Business Description:
Nurses' Registry
S.I.C.: 7361
N.A.I.C.S.: 561310
Media: 2-10
Personnel:
Tim Rodden *(COO)*

MEGAPATH, INC.

(Holding of Platinum Equity, LLC)
555 Anton Blvd Ste 200
Costa Mesa, CA 92626
Tel.: (714) 327-2000
Fax: (714) 327-2001
Toll Free: (877) 634-2728
Web Site: www.megapath.com
Approx. Number Employees: 400
Business Description:
Managed IP Data, Voice & Security Services
S.I.C.: 7373
N.A.I.C.S.: 541512
Media: 10
Personnel:
D. Craig Young *(Chm & CEO)*

Key to Media (For complete agency information see *The Advertising Red Books-Agencies* edition):
1. Bus. Publs. 2. Cable T.V. 3. Catalogs & Directories. 4. Co-op Adv. 5. Consumer Mags. 6. D.M. to Bus. Estab.7. D.M. to Consumers
8. Daily Newsp. 9. Exhibits/Trade Shows 10. Foreign 11. Infomercial 12. Internet Adv.13. Multimedia 14. Network Radio
15. Network T.V. 16. Newsp. Distr. Mags. 17. Other 18. Outdoor (Posters, Transit) 19. Point of Purchase20. Premiums, Novelties
21. Product Samples 22. Special Events Mktg. 23. Spot Radio 24. Spot T.V. 25. Weekly Newsp. 26. Yellow Page Adv.

MegaPath, Inc. — (Continued)

Paul Milley *(CFO)*
Brett Flinchum *(COO)*
Patrick Bennett *(Chief Strategy Officer & Head-Wholesale Markets)*
Bruce Chatterley *(Pres-Bus Markets)*
Doug Carlen *(Gen Counsel)*
Chris Gellos *(Sr VP-Sls)*

MELISSA DATA CORP.

22382 Avenida Empresa
Rancho Santa Margarita, CA 92688-2112
Tel.: (949) 589-5200
Fax: (949) 589-5211
Toll Free: (800) 800-6245
E-mail: info@melissadata.com
Web Site: www.melissadata.com
Approx. Number Employees: 105
Year Founded: 1985
Business Description:
Listing Sales & Services
S.I.C.: 7371; 5045
N.A.I.C.S.: 541511; 423430
Media: 2-4
Personnel:
Raymond F. Melissa *(Founder & Pres)*
Brands & Products:
ADDREESSOBJECT
ADDRESSDOCTOR
ADDRESSVALIDATOR
CANADIAN ADDRESSER
CONTACTZONE
DOUBLETAKE 2
EASYSTREET
ELOT
GEOCODER
IP2LOCATION
MAILERS
NAME OBJECT
NCOA LINK
PERSONATOR 3
PHONE OBJECT
QUICK LOCATE
RIGHTFIELDER 3
ZIP DATA
ZIP SELECT
ZIP USA

MENTOR GRAPHICS CORPORATION

8005 SW Boeckman Rd
Wilsonville, OR 97070-9733
Tel.: (503) 685-7000
Fax: (503) 685-7704
Toll Free: (800) 592-2210
E-mail: sales_info@mentor.com
Web Site: www.mentor.com
Approx. Rev.: $914,753,000
Approx. Number Employees: 4,700
Year Founded: 1981
Business Description:
Electronic Design Automation
Software Mfr, Designer & Marketer
S.I.C.: 7371; 7372
N.A.I.C.S.: 541511; 511210
Advertising Expenditures: $3,528,000
Media: 2-4-7-10-13-18-22
Distr.: Natl.
Budget Set: Nov.
Personnel:
Walden C. Rhines *(Chm & CEO)*
Gregory K. Hinckley *(Pres & COO)*
Ananthan Thandri *(CIO & VP)*
Dean Freed *(Gen Counsel & VP)*
L. Don Maulsby *(Sr VP-World Trade)*
Simon Bloch *(VP, Gen Mgr-Design & Synthesis Div)*
Robert Hum *(VP & Gen Mgr-Deep Submicron Div)*
Serge Leef *(VP-New Ventures & Gen Mgr-Sys Level Engrg Div)*
Henry Potts *(VP & Gen Mgr-Sys Design Div)*
Joseph Sawicki *(VP & Gen Mgr-Design-to-Silicon Div)*
Eric Selosse *(VP & Gen Mgr-Mentor Emulation Div)*
Marc Corbacho *(VP-Sls-America)*
Brian Derrick *(VP-Corp Mktg)*
Alan Friedman *(VP-HR)*
Guy Moshe *(Gen Mgr-Design Creation Bus-Design Creation Synthesis Div)*
Glenn Perry *(Gen Mgr)*
Joe Reinhart *(Dir-IR)*
Darrell Teegarden *(Dir-Sys Modeling & Analysis Bus Unit)*
Sonia Harrison *(Sr Mgr-PR)*
Brands & Products:
0-IN
3D DESIGN
A WORLD OF LEARNING
A-XGMAC
ABIST
ACCUPARTGEN
ACCUPARTNER
ACCUPARTS
ACCUSIM
ADAPTSIM
ADEPT
ADIT
ADVANCE
ADVANCE JED
ADVANCE MS
ADVANCE RFIC
ADVANCE VCB
ALGORITHMIC C
AMPLE
ANALOG ANALYST
ANALOG STATION
APPNOTES
APTIX
ARC4
ARCHER VERIFICATION
ARES
ARITHMETIC BIST
ARTGRID
ARTROUTER
ARTSHAPE
ASICPLAN
ASICVECTOR INTERFACES
ASPIRE
ASSESS2000
AUTHEXPRESS
AUTOACTIVE
AUTOCELLS
AUTODISSOLVE
AUTOFILTER
AUTOFLOW
AUTOLIB
AUTOLINEAR
AUTOLINK
AUTOLOGIC
AUTOLOGIC BLOCKS
AUTOLOGIC FPGA
AUTOLOGIC VHDL
AUTOMOTIVELIB
AUTOPAR
AUTOTHERM
AUTOTHERM DUO
AUTOTHERM MCM
AUTOVIEW
AUTOWIRE STATION
AXEL
AXEL SYMBOL GENIE
BIST COMPILER
BIST-IN-PLACE
BIST-READY
BISTARCHITECT
BLAST
BLAZE
BOARD ARCHITECT
BOARD DESIGNER
BOARD LAYOUT
BOARD PROCESS LIBRARY
BOARD STATION
BOARDSIM
BOLD ADMINISTRATOR
BOLD BROWSER
BOLD COMPOSER
BOM EXPLORER 6.0
BOUNDARYSCAN
BRIDGEPOINT
BSDARCHITECT
BSPBUILDER
BUY ON DEMAND
CABLE ANALYZER
CABLE STATION
CAECO DESIGNER
CAEFORM
CALIBRE
CALIBRE CB
CALIBRE DESIGNREV
CALIBRE DRC
CALIBRE DRC-H
CALIBRE FRACTUREH
CALIBRE FRACTUREJ
CALIBRE FRACTUREK
CALIBRE FRACTUREM
CALIBRE FRACTURET
CALIBRE FRACTUREV
CALIBRE INTERACTIVE
CALIBRE LFD
CALIBRE LITHOVIEW
CALIBRE LVS-H
CALIBRE MDP EMBEDDED SVRF
CALIBRE MDPMERGE
CALIBRE MDPSTAT
CALIBRE MDPVERIFY
CALIBRE MDPVIEW
CALIBRE MGC
CALIBRE MTFLEX
CALIBRE OPCPRO
CALIBRE OPCSBAR
CALIBRE OPCVERIFY
CALIBRE ORC
CALIBRE PRINTIMAGE
CALIBRE PSMCHECK
CALIBRE PSMGATE
CALIBRE RVE
CALIBRE TDOPC
CALIBRE VERIFICATION CENTER
CALIBRE WORKBENCH
CALIBRE XRC
CAMCAD
CAMCAD GRAPHIC 4.5
CAMCAD PCB TRANSLATOR 4.5
CAMCAD PROFESSIONAL 4.5
CAMCAD VISION 4.5
CAPITAL
CAPITAL ANALYSIS
CAPITAL ARCHIVE
CAPITAL BRIDGES
CAPITAL DOCUMENTS
CAPITAL H
CAPITAL H THE COMPLETE DESKTOP ENGINEER
CAPITAL HARNESS
CAPITAL HARNESSXC
CAPITAL INSIGHT
CAPITAL INTEGRATION
CAPITAL MANAGER
CAPITAL MANUFACTURE
CAPITAL SUPPORT
CAPITAL SYSTEMS
CAPTURE STATION
CAT/TRANSCABLE
CATAPULT
CEE-J
CELARO
CELL BUILDER
CELL STATION
CELLFLOOR
CELLGEN
CELLGRAPH
CELLPLACE
CELLPOWER
CELLROUTE
CENTRICITY
CEOC
CERTE
CHAMELEON ART
CHASEX
CHECKERWARE
CHECKMATE
CHEOS
CHIPGRAPH
CHIPLISTER
CIRCUIT PATHFINDER
CO-LSIM
CO-VERIFICATION ENVIRONMENT
CODE/LAB
COMMLIB
COMMLIB BMC
CONCURRENT BOARD PROCESSSM
CONCURRENT DESIGN ENVIRONMENT
CONNECTIVITY DATAPORT
CONSTRAINT EDITOR SYSTEM
CONTINUUM
CONTINUUM POWER ANALYST
CORE BUILDER
CORE FACTORY
COREALLIANCE
COREBIST
CRE8VENTURES
CTINTEGRATOR
DATA SOLVENT
DATACENTRIC MODEL
DATAFUSION
DATAPATH
DBUG
DC ANALYZER
DEBUG DETECTIVE
DELTANET 6.0
DELTAV
DESIGN ARCHITECT
DESIGN ARCHITECT ELITE
DESIGN ARCHITECT-IC
DESIGN CAPTURE
DESIGN EXCHANGE
DESIGN MANAGER
DESIGN STATION
DESIGNANALYST
DESIGNBOOK
DESIGNVIEW
DESKTOPASIC
DESTINATION PCB
DESTINY RE
DFTADVISOR
DFTARCHITECT
DFTINSIGHT
DIRECT SYSTEM VERIFICATION
DIRECTCONNECTSM
DMS
DMS XCHANGE

Key to Media (For complete agency information see *The Advertising Red Books-Agencies* edition):
1. Bus. Publs. 2. Cable T.V. 3. Catalogs & Directories. 4. Co-op Adv. 5. Consumer Mags. 6. D.M. to Bus. Estab.7. D.M. to Consumers 8. Daily Newsp. 9. Exhibits/Trade Shows 10. Foreign 11. Infomercial 12. Internet Adv.13. Multimedia 14. Network Radio 15. Network T.V. 16. Newsp. Distr. Mags. 17. Other 18. Outdoor (Posters, Transit) 19. Point of Purchase20. Premiums, Novelties 21. Product Samples 22. Special Events Mktg. 23. Spot Radio 24. Spot T.V. 25. Weekly Newsp. 26. Yellow Page Adv.

DOCUMENTATION STATION
DSS (DECISION SUPPORT SYSTEM)
DSV
DXANALOG
DXDATABOOK
DXDATAMANAGER
DXDESIGNER
DXENTERPRISE FOR AGILE
DXLIBRARYSTUDIO
DXMATRIX
DXPARTS
DXPDF
DXSIM
DXVARIANTMANAGER
DXVIEWDRAW
DXVIEWONLY
E3LCABLE
ECO IMMUNITYSM
EDA TECH FORUM
EDGE
EDGE DEBUGGER
EDGE PROFILER
EDT
ELDO
EMPOWERING SOLUTIONS
ENGINEER'S DESKTOP
ENGINEERVIEW
ENREAD
ENTERPRISE LIBRARIAN
ENWRITE
EPARTNERS
EPARTS
EPLANNER
EPRODUCT DESIGNER
EPRODUCT SERVICES
ESIGHT
ESIM
EXEMPLAR
EXEMPLARLOGIC
EXPEDITION
EXPEDITION SERIES
EXPERT2000SM
EXPLORER CAECO LAYOUT
EXPLORER CHECKMATE
EXPLORER DATAPATH
EXPLORER LSIM
EXPLORER LSIM-C
EXPLORER LSIM-S
EXPLORER LTIME
EXPLORER SCHEMATIC
EXPLORER VHDLSIM
EXPRESSI/O
EZWAVE
FABFACTORY
FABLINK
FALCON
FALCON FRAMEWORK
FASTEYE
FASTSCAN
FASTSTART
FASTTRACK CONSULTING
FDL (FLOW DEFINITION LANGUAGE)
FIRST-PASS DESIGN SUCCESS
FIRST-PASS SUCCESS
FLEXSIM
FLEXTEST
FLOEFD
FLOEFD MECHANICA BRIDGE
FLOEFD PATRAN BRIDGE
FLOEFDPRO
FLOEFDV5
FLOMCAD BRIDGE CATIA V5 READER
FLOTHERM
FLOTHERMPCB
FLOVENT
FLOVIZ
FLOWTABS
FLOWXPERT
FORMA
FORMALPRO
FPGA ADVANTAGE
FPGA BOARDLINK
FPGA BUILDER
FPGA STATION
FPGA XCHANGE
FPGADVISOR
FPGASIM
FRAMECONNECT
FUSION
GALILEO
GATE STATION
GATEGRAPH
GATEPLACE
GATEROUTE
GDT
GDT CORE
GDT DESIGNER
GDT DEVELOPER
GENIE
GENWARE
GEOM GENIE
HARDWARE MODELING LIBRARY
HDL ARCHITECT
HDL ARCHITECT STATION
HDL ASSISTANT
HDL AUTHOR
HDL DESIGNER
HDL DESIGNER SERIES
HDL DETECTIVE
HDL INVENTOR
HDL LINK
HDL PILOT
HDL PROCESSOR
HDL2GRAPHICS
HDLSCORE
HDLSIM
HDLWRITE
HIC RULES
HIERARCHIAL INJECTION
HIERARCHY INJECTION
HOTPLOT
HYBRID DESIGNER
HYBRID STATION
HYPERLYNX
HYPERSUITE
I/O DESIGNER
IB
IC DESIGN STATION
IC DESIGNER
IC LAYOUT STATION
IC STATION
ICANALYST
ICBASIC
ICBLOCKS
ICCHECK
ICCOMPACT
ICDEVICE
ICEXTRACT
ICGEN
ICGRAPH
ICLINK
ICLISTER
ICPLAN
ICRT CONTROLLER LCOMPILER
ICRULES
ICSTUDIO
ICTRACE
ICVERIFY
ICVIEW
ICX
ICX PRO
ICX PROJECT MODELING
ICX SENTRY
ICX STANDARD LIBRARY
ICX TAU
ICX VERIFY
ICX VISION
IDEA SERIES
IDEA STATION
IFX
IKOS
IN ALL THE RIGHT PLACES
INEXIA
INFACT
INFLEXION PLATFORM
INFORM
INNOVATE PCB
INNOVEDA
INTEGRA STATION
INTEGRATED PRODUCT DEVELOPMENT
INTEGRATION TOOL KIT
INTELLITEST
INTERACTIVE LAYOUT
INTERCONNECT TABLE
INTERFACE-BASED DESIGN
INTRASTEPSM
INVENTRA
IP ENGINE
IP EVALUATION KIT
IP FACTORY
IP-PCB
IP QUICKUSE
IPSIM
IS_ANALYZER
ISD CREATIONSM
IS_FLOORPLANNER
IS_MULTIBOARD
ISOLVE
IS_OPTIMIZER
IS_SYNTHESIZER
IT
IT'S MORE THAN JUST TOOLS
IV'LOCITY
JOBSPY
KNOWLEDGE CENTER
KNOWLEDGE-SOURCING
LANGUAGE NEUTRAL LICENSING
LATIUM
LAYOUT
LBIST
LBISTARCHITECT
LC
LCORE
LEAF CELL TOOLKIT
LED
LED LAYOUT
LEONARDO
LEONARDOINSIGHT
LEONARDOSPECTRUM
LIBRARIAN
LIBRARY BUILDER
LIBRARY MANAGER
LINESIM
LNL
LOGIC BUILDER
LOGICAL CABLE
LOGICBIST
LOGICLIB
LOGIO
LSIM
LSIM DSM
LSIM GATE
LSIM POWER ANALYST
LSIM REVIEW
LSIM SWITCH
LSIM XL
LSIMNET
MACH PA
MACH TA
MAJIC
MANUFACTUREVIEW
MANUFACTURING ADVISOR
MANUFACTURING CABLE
MASKCOMPOSE
MBIST
MBIST FLEX
MBIST FULL-SPEED
MBIST IN-PLACE
MBIST MANAGER
MBISTARCHITECT
MCM DESIGNER
MCM STATION
MCPIEXP
MDV
MECHANICAL INTERFACE
MEGAFUNCTION
MEGAMACRO
MEMORY BUILDER
MEMORY BUILDER CONDUCTOR
MEMORY BUILDER MOZART
MEMORY DESIGNER
MEMORY MODEL BUILDER
MEMORYBIST
MENTOR
MENTOR GRAPHICS
MICRED
MICROPLAN
MICROROUTE
MICROTEC
MIXED-SIGNAL PRO
MNEMOTEST
MODEL TECHNOLOGY
MODELEDITOR
MODELSIM
MODELSTATION
MODELVIEWER
MODELVIEWERPLUS
MODGEN
MONET
MPCIEXP
MS ANALYZER
MS ARCHITECT
MS-EXPRESS
MSIMON
MSLAB
MSVIEW
MTPI
NANOKERNAL
NETCHECK
NETED
NUCLEUS
NUCLEUS EDGE
OLYMPUS-SOC
OMNINET VERSION 6.0
ONLINE KNOWLEDGE CENTER
OPENDOOR
OPSIM
OUTNET
P&RINTEGRATOR
PACKAGE
PADS
PARADE
PATHLINK
PCB-GEN
PDLSIM
PINNACLE
PLATFORM EXPRESS
PLLTEST
POWERPCB
QUESTA
QUICKPART BUILDER
QUICKPART TABLES
QUICKVHDL
SCAP

Key to Media (For complete agency information see *The Advertising Red Books-Agencies* edition):
1. Bus. Publs. 2. Cable T.V. 3. Catalogs & Directories. 4. Co-op Adv. 5. Consumer Mags. 6. D.M. to Bus. Estab.7. D.M. to Consumers
8. Daily Newsp. 9. Exhibits/Trade Shows 10. Foreign 11. Infomercial 12. Internet Adv.13. Multimedia 14. Network Radio
15. Network T.V. 16. Newsp. Distr. Mags. 17. Other 18. Outdoor (Posters, Transit) 19. Point of Purchase20. Premiums, Novelties
21. Product Samples 22. Special Events Mktg. 23. Spot Radio 24. Spot T.V. 25. Weekly Newsp. 26. Yellow Page Adv.

Mentor Graphics Corporation — (Continued)

SDF
SERDESTEST
SILICONINSIGHT
SOCSCAN
STREAMVIEW
SUPPORTNET
TEAMPCB
TESSENT
TESTKOMPRESS
TIME-IT
TRANSACT
TRANSCABLE
TRANSLAYOUT
USER2USER
UTOPIA
VIEWBASE
VIEWSIM
WAVEFORM DATAPORT
WORKXPERT
XCALIBRE
XCONFIG
XRAY
XTREMEPCB
YIELDASSIST
YIELDINSIGHT
ZEELAN
ZLIBS

Advertising Agency:
Leopard
555 17th St Ste 300
Denver, CO 80202-3908
Tel.: (303) 527-2900
Fax: (303) 530-3480

MERCURY COMPUTER SYSTEMS, INC.

201 Riverneck Rd
Chelmsford, MA 01824-2820
Tel.: (978) 256-1300
Tel.: (978) 967-1401
Fax: (978) 256-3599
Toll Free: (866) 627-6951
E-mail: info@mc.com
Web Site: www.mc.com
Approx. Rev.: $228,710,000
Approx. Number Employees: 602
Year Founded: 1981
Business Description:
Realtime Multicomputer Systems Mfr
S.I.C.: 3571; 3679
N.A.I.C.S.: 334111; 334419
Export
Advertising Expenditures: $255,000
Media: 17
Personnel:
Vincent Vitto *(Chm)*
Mark Aslett *(Pres & CEO)*
Terrence M. Ryan *(Pres & Gen Mgr-Mercury Federal)*
Robert E. Hult *(CFO, Treas & Sr VP)*
Charles A. Speicher *(Chief Acctg Officer, VP & Controller)*
Alex A. Van Adzin *(Gen Counsel, Corporation Sec & VP)*
Didier M. C. Thibaud *(Sr VP & Gen Mgr-Advanced Computing Solutions)*
Gerald M. Haines, II *(Sr VP-Corp Dev)*
Craig A. Saline *(Sr VP-HR)*
Randy Dean *(VP & Gen Mgr-Integrated Solutions)*
Barry S. Isenstein *(VP & Gen Mgr)*
Brian Hoerl *(VP-Sls-Worldwide)*
Jose Freitas *(Dir-HR)*
Tom Roberts *(Product Mgr-Mktg)*
Laurent Coureau *(Mgr-WW Sale & Mkgt Oil & Gas market)*
Kathy Sniezek *(Project Leader-Mktg, Project Leader-Mktg & Mgr-PR)*
Brands & Products:
ADAPDEV
ALTIVEC
AMIRA
APPLICATION READY SYSTEM
ARS
BATTLE READY COTS
CHALLENGES DRIVE INNOVATION
CHECKMC
CONVERGED SENSOR NETWORK
CPI
CSN
ECHOCORE
ECHOTEK
EMBEDDED SMART PROCESSING
ENSEMBLE
ENSEMBLE2
ESP
EXACTPHASE
EXAMINERT
FREESCALE
GPEXPRESS
IMPACTRT
MC/OS
MC/OS CERTIFIED
MCEXEC
MCH6
MCH9
MCOE
MCV6
MCV9
MERCURY COMPUTER SYSTEMS
MOMENTUM
MRRCURY
MULTICORE PLUS
MULTIPORT
MYRIAD
OPENVPX
PARALLEL ACCELERATION SYSTEM
PAS
PIXL
POET
POWERBLOCK
POWERSTREAM
RACE
RACE CERTIFIED
RACE SERIES
RACE SERIES MULTIPORT
RACE SERIES MYRIAD
RACE++
RACETRACK
RACEWARE
RACEWAY READY
RIN-T
ROUT-T
TATL
VANTAGE RT
VANTAGERT
VISAGERT
VSIPL
WAVEFORM-READY

MERISEL, INC.

(Holding of Stonington Partners Inc.)
127 W 30th St 5th Fl
New York, NY 10001
Tel.: (212) 594-4800
Toll Free: (800) MERISEL
Web Site: www.merisel.com
Approx. Sls.: $71,946,000
Approx. Number Employees: 349
Year Founded: 1980
Business Description:
Visual Communications & Brand Solutions
S.I.C.: 7336; 2759
N.A.I.C.S.: 541430; 323115
Media: 1-2-4-7-10-20-21-22
Distr.: Intl.; Natl.
Budget Set: Oct.
Personnel:
Donald R. Uzzi *(Chm & CEO)*
Victor L. Cisario *(CFO, Exec VP-Fin & Asst Sec)*
John H. Peterson *(CFO & Exec VP)*
Guy Claudy *(Pres-Crush Creative LLC)*
John J. Sheehan *(Pres-ColorEdge Div)*
Michael A. Berman *(Chief Client Officer & Exec VP)*

MERU NETWORKS, INC.

894 Ross Dr
Sunnyvale, CA 94089
Tel.: (408) 215-5300
Web Site: www.merunetworks.com
Approx. Rev.: $85,004,000
Approx. Number Employees: 292
Year Founded: 2002
Business Description:
Virtualized Wireless LAN Solutions
S.I.C.: 4812
N.A.I.C.S.: 517212
Advertising Expenditures: $22,000
Media: 17
Personnel:
Vaduvur Bharghavan *(CTO & Founder-Meru Networks)*
Ihab Abu-Hakima *(Pres & CEO)*
Brett T. White *(CFO)*
Carl Gustin *(CMO)*
Richard Mosher *(Gen Counsel)*
Kamal Anand *(Sr VP-Corp Dev & Strategy)*
Philip Simmons *(Sr VP-Engrg)*
Larry Vaughn *(Sr VP-Worldwide Sls, Svcs & Support)*
David Kelly *(VP-Sls-Intl)*
Margie Kriebel *(Sr Dir-Corp Mktg & Comm)*
Patrick Crane *(Dir-Market Res & Bus Intelligence)*
Brands & Products:
SYSTEM DIRECTOR

METASOLV, INC.

(Sub. of Oracle Corporation)
(d/b/a Oracle Corporation)
5556 Tennyson Pkwy
Plano, TX 75024
Tel.: (214) 427-0500
Fax: (214) 427-0505
Toll Free: (800) 747-0791
Web Site: www.oracle.com
Sales Range: $75-99.9 Million
Approx. Number Employees: 438
Year Founded: 1992
Business Description:
Computers, Peripherals & Software Services
S.I.C.: 7371
N.A.I.C.S.: 541511
Import Export
Media: 10
Personnel:
T. Curtis Holmes *(Pres & CEO)*
Brands & Products:
METASOLV

METASTORM, INC.

(Sub. of Open Text Corporation)
500 E Pratt St Ste 1250
Baltimore, MD 21202-3167
Tel.: (443) 874-1300
Fax: (443) 874-1336
Toll Free: (877) 321-6382
E-mail: info@metastorm.com
Web Site: www.metastorm.com
Sales Range: $125-149.9 Million
Approx. Number Employees: 300
Year Founded: 1996
Business Description:
Computer Software Developer
S.I.C.: 7371; 7372
N.A.I.C.S.: 541511; 511210
Advertising Expenditures: $49,095
Media: 10-13-22
Personnel:
Christopher S. Desautelle *(CFO, Treas, VP-Fin & Asst Sec)*
Eileen M. Garry *(CMO & VP-Worldwide Mktg)*
Gregory A. Carter *(CTO & Exec VP-Product Dev)*
Swata J. Gandhi *(Gen Counsel, Sec, Exec VP & Asst Treas)*
Janet Halma *(Exec VP-Sls Ops-Americas)*
Mike Malaure *(VP-Sls-Intl)*
Legg Mason *(VP-Comm)*
Laura Mooney *(VP-Corp Comm)*
Paul Roth *(VP-Integration Sls)*
Neil Hudspeth *(Sr Dir-Mktg)*
Michael Cawsey *(Reg Dir-Australia & New Zealand)*
Brands & Products:
BUSINESS TO THE POWER OF 3
E-WORK
ENTERPRISE PROCESS ADVANTAGE
METASTORM
METASTORM BPM
METASTORM DISCOVERY
METASTORM DNA
POWERING ENTERPRISE PROCESS ADVANTAGE
PROCESS POD
PROVISION

MFV EXPOSITIONS, LLC

210 E Rte 4
Paramus, NJ 07652
Tel.: (201) 226-1130
Fax: (201) 226-1131
E-mail: info@franchiseexpo.com
Web Site: www.mfvexpo.com
Approx. Number Employees: 25
Business Description:
Trade Shows & Online Buyers Guides Producer
S.I.C.: 7389
N.A.I.C.S.: 561920
Media: 2-13
Advertising Agency:
Interexpo Communications
3309 Bennington Ct
Winter Park, FL 32792-6221
Tel.: (407) 310-4168
Fax: (321) 214-0011

MICRO 2000, INC.

600 N Central Ave
Glendale, CA 91203
Tel.: (818) 547-0125
Fax: (818) 502-0226
Toll Free: (800) 864-8008
E-mail: netsales@micro2000.com

Key to Media (For complete agency information see *The Advertising Red Books-Agencies* edition):
1. Bus. Publs. 2. Cable T.V. 3. Catalogs & Directories. 4. Co-op Adv. 5. Consumer Mags. 6. D.M. to Bus. Estab.7. D.M. to Consumers 8. Daily Newsp. 9. Exhibits/Trade Shows 10. Foreign 11. Infomercial 12. Internet Adv.13. Multimedia 14. Network Radio 15. Network T.V. 16. Newsp. Distr. Mags. 17. Other 18. Outdoor (Posters, Transit) 19. Point of Purchase20. Premiums, Novelties 21. Product Samples 22. Special Events Mktg. 23. Spot Radio 24. Spot T.V. 25. Weekly Newsp. 26. Yellow Page Adv.

Web Site: www.micro2000.com
Approx. Number Employees: 15
Year Founded: 1990
Business Description:
Computer Equipment Retailer
S.I.C.: 5045; 5734
N.A.I.C.S.: 423430; 443120
Media: 13
Personnel:
Rob McFarlane *(CEO)*
Brands & Products:
ERASERDISK
MICRO-SCOPE
MICRO-SCOPE SUITE
PC HARDWARE MADE EASY
POST-PROBE
REMOTESCOPE
UNIVERSAL DIAGNOSTIC
USB-SCOPE

MICROAGE, INC.

(Sub. of Frontier Technology LLC)
8160 S Hardy Dr Ste 101
Tempe, AZ 85284
Tel.: (480) 366-2000
Fax: (480) 366-2224
Toll Free: (800) 336-1800
E-mail: employment@microage.com
Web Site: www.microage.com
E-Mail For Key Personnel:
Sales Director: sales@microage.com
Approx. Number Employees: 80
Year Founded: 1976
Business Description:
Computers & Business Machines Retailer & Mfr
S.I.C.: 7373
N.A.I.C.S.: 541512
Advertising Expenditures: $2,500,000
Media: 1-2-4-5-8-10-13-22
Distr.: Intl.; Natl.
Personnel:
Jeffrey D. McKeever *(Chm)*
Roger W. Rouse *(CFO & VP)*
Mark T. McKeever *(COO & VP)*
Tracey M. Hayes *(VP-Sls)*
Brands & Products:
MICROAGE

MICROBOARDS TECHNOLOGY, LLC

8150 Mallory Ct
Chanhassen, MN 55317-0846
Tel.: (952) 556-1600
Fax: (952) 556-1620
E-mail: info@microboards.com
Web Site: www.microboards.com
E-Mail For Key Personnel:
Sales Director: sales@microboards.com
Sales Range: $25-49.9 Million
Approx. Number Employees: 45
Year Founded: 1996
Business Description:
Computer Storage Devices, DVD & CD Duplication Services
S.I.C.: 3572; 3577
N.A.I.C.S.: 334112; 334119
Import Export
Media: 6
Personnel:
Mitch Ackmann *(Pres)*
Yoshihito Kumakura *(CFO)*
Aaron Pratt *(Dir-Mktg)*
Brands & Products:
BRAVOPRO
ENDEAVOR
GEMINI
MICROBOARDS
ORBIT
PLAYWRITE
PRINT FACTORY
RIMAGE
SIGNATURE
TASCAM

MICRON TECHNOLOGY, INC.

8000 S Federal Way
Boise, ID 83716-9632
Mailing Address:
PO Box 6
Boise, ID 83707-0006
Tel.: (208) 368-4000
Fax: (208) 368-4435
E-mail: inverel@micron.com
Web Site: www.micron.com
E-Mail For Key Personnel:
Public Relations: inverel@micron.com
Approx. Sls.: $8,482,000,000
Approx. Number Employees: 25,900
Year Founded: 1978
Business Description:
Memory, Storage & Imaging Semiconductor Products Mfr
S.I.C.: 3674; 3679
N.A.I.C.S.: 334413; 334419
Export
Advertising Expenditures: $5,200,000
Media: 6-8-10-11-19-21-26
Distr.: Direct to Consumer; Intl.; Natl.
Budget Set: Aug.
Personnel:
Steven R. Appleton *(Chm & CEO)*
D. Mark Durcan *(Pres & COO)*
Ronald C. Foster *(CFO & VP-Fin)*
Roderic W. Lewis *(Gen Counsel, Corp Sec & VP-Legal Affairs)*
Mark Adams *(VP-Sls-Worldwide)*
James A. Mahoney *(VP-Info Sys)*
Pat T Otte *(VP-HR)*
Farshid Tabrizi *(Dir-Strategic Bus Dev-NAND OEM)*
Ivan Donaldson *(Mgr-IR)*
Jan R. Reimer *(Asst Sec)*
Brands & Products:
ASPEN MEMORY
BALLISTIX
BALLISTIX TRACER
BRILLIANT MEMORY SOLUTIONS
CELLULARRAM
CRUCIAL
CRUCIAL TECHNOLOGY
ENDUR-IC
GIZMO
MEMORY ADVISOR
THE MEMORY EXPERTS
MICRON
OSMIUM
Q-FLASH
REALSSD
RENDITION
SAMURAI
SPECTEK
SPECTEK SELECT
SYNCBURST
TWIN DIE
Advertising Agency:
LION New Media
20700 44th Ave W Ste 290
Lynnwood, WA 98026
Tel.: (425) 742-6828

MICROS SYSTEMS, INC.

7031 Columbia Gateway Dr
Columbia, MD 21046-2289
Tel.: (443) 285-6000
Fax: (443) 285-8000
Toll Free: (800) 638-0985
E-mail: info@micros.com
Web Site: www.micros.com
Approx. Rev.: $1,007,859,000
Approx. Number Employees: 4,953
Year Founded: 1977
Business Description:
Holding Company; Restaurant, Hospitality & Specialty Retail Equipment & Software Mfr, Distr & Support Services
S.I.C.: 6719; 5044; 5045; 7372; 8748
N.A.I.C.S.: 551112; 423420; 423430; 511210; 541690
Import Export
Advertising Expenditures: $4,200,000
Media: 2-10
Distr.: Intl.
Budget Set: June
Personnel:
A. L. Giannopoulos *(Chm, Pres & CEO)*
Cynthia A. Russo *(CFO & Exec VP)*
Jennifer M. Kurdle *(Chief Admin Officer & Exec VP)*
James T. Walsh *(Chief Info Security Officer)*
Thomas L. Patz *(Gen Counsel & Exec VP-Strategic Initiatives)*
Peter J. Rogers, Jr. *(Exec VP-IR & Bus Dev)*
Edgar J. Chapel *(Sr VP-Distr-North America)*
John E. Gularson *(Sr VP-Retail Sys)*
Daniel M. Jubb *(Sr VP-Hotels Bus Unit)*
Louise J. Casamento *(VP-Mktg)*
Brad S. Gilmore *(VP-Procurement & Logistics)*
Debra McIntyre *(VP-HR)*
Mike Snow *(Dir-eBus, Res & Dev)*
Brands & Products:
FIDELIO
GUEST CONNECTION
JTECH SOLUTIONS
MICROS
MICROS 3700
MICROS 9700
MICROS E7
OPERA
PATIENT SELECT
RES 4.0
SIMPHONY
STORE 21
TANGENTPOS
TRADEWIND
Advertising Agency:
Marriner Marketing Communications, Inc.
10221 Wincopin Cir Ste 300
Columbia, MD 21044-3419
Tel.: (410) 715-1500
Fax: (410) 995-3609
Toll Free: (800) 268-6475

MICROSEMI CORPORATION

2381 Morse Ave
Irvine, CA 92614
Tel.: (949) 221-7100
Fax: (949) 756-0308
Toll Free: (800) 713-4113
E-mail: dsonksen@microsemi.com
Web Site: www.microsemi.com
Approx. Sls.: $518,268,000
Approx. Number Employees: 2,250
Year Founded: 1960
Business Description:
Analog & Mixed Signal Integrated Circuits & Discrete Semiconductors Mfr
S.I.C.: 3674; 3679
N.A.I.C.S.: 334413; 334418; 334419
Import Export
Media: 2-4-10-21
Personnel:
Dennis R. Leibel *(Chm)*
James J. Peterson *(Pres & CEO)*
John W. Hohener *(CFO & VP)*
Ralph Brandi *(Chief Ops Officer & Exec VP)*
Steven Litchfield *(Exec VP & Chief Strategy Officer)*
Russell Garcia *(Exec VP-Mktg & Sls)*
Esmat Hamdy *(Sr VP-TD & Ops)*
John M. Holtrust *(Sr VP-HR)*
Esam Elashmawi *(VP & Gen Mgr)*
Paul Pickle *(VP & Gen Mgr)*
John Costello *(VP-Sls)*
Michael G. Sivetts, III *(VP-Distr Sls)*
Brands & Products:
ASPM
ISOTOP
MICROSEMI
POWER MOS 7
POWER MOS 8
POWER MOS IV
T-MAX
THUNDERBOLT IGBT

MICROSOFT CORPORATION

1 Microsoft Way
Redmond, WA 98052-6399
Tel.: (425) 882-8080
Fax: (425) 936-7329
Toll Free: (800) 642-7676
E-mail: msft@microsoft.com
Web Site: www.microsoft.com
Approx. Rev.: $69,943,000,000
Approx. Number Employees: 90,000
Year Founded: 1975
Business Description:
Software Publisher
S.I.C.: 7372
N.A.I.C.S.: 511210
Advertising Expenditures: $190,000,000
Media: 2-3-4-5-6-7-8-13-15-21-31
Distr.: Intl.; Natl.
Budget Set: Mar.
Personnel:
Bill Gates *(Chm)*
Steven A. Ballmer *(CEO)*
Tami Reller *(CFO & Corp VP-Windows & Windows Live)*
Peter Klein *(CFO)*
Brian Kevin Turner *(COO)*
Tony Scott *(CIO & Corp VP)*
Chris Capossela *(CMO & Sr VP-Consumer Channels & Central Mktg Grp)*
Gayle Troberman *(Chief Creative Officer)*
Frank H. Brod *(Chief Acctg Officer, VP-Fin & Admin)*
Craig Mundie *(Chief Res & Strategy Officer)*
Rick Rashid *(Chief Research Officer-Microsoft Research)*
Jean-Philippe Courtois *(Pres-Microsoft Intl)*

Key to Media (For complete agency information see *The Advertising Red Books-Agencies* edition):
1. Bus. Publs. 2. Cable T.V. 3. Catalogs & Directories. 4. Co-op Adv. 5. Consumer Mags. 6. D.M. to Bus. Estab.7. D.M. to Consumers 8. Daily Newsp. 9. Exhibits/Trade Shows 10. Foreign 11. Infomercial 12. Internet Adv.13. Multimedia 14. Network Radio 15. Network T.V. 16. Newsp. Distr. Mags. 17. Other 18. Outdoor (Posters, Transit) 19. Point of Purchase20. Premiums, Novelties 21. Product Samples 22. Special Events Mktg. 23. Spot Radio 24. Spot T.V. 25. Weekly Newsp. 26. Yellow Page Adv.

Microsoft Corporation — (Continued)

Andrew Lees *(Pres-Windows Phone Div)*
Qi Lu *(Pres-Online Svcs Div)*
Satya Nadella *(Pres-Server & Tools Bus)*
Steven Sinofsky *(Pres-Windows & Windows Live Div)*
Robert H. Youngjohns *(Pres-Sls & Mktg-North America)*
Alain Crozier *(CFO-Sls, Mktg & Svcs Grp & VP)*
Bradford L. Smith *(Gen Counsel, Sr VP-Legal & Corp Affairs)*
Lisa Brummel *(Sr VP-HR)*
Chris Jones *(Sr VP-Windows Live)*
Ted Kummert *(Sr VP-Bus Platform Div)*
Antoine Leblond *(Sr VP-Windows Web Svcs)*
Mich Mathews *(Sr VP-Central Mktg Grp)*
Yusuf Mehdi *(Sr VP-Online Audience Bus)*
Eric Rudder *(Sr VP-Tech Strategy)*
S. Somasegar *(Sr VP-Developer Div)*
Amitabh Srivastava *(Sr VP-Server & Cloud Div)*
Henry P. Vigil *(Sr VP-Strategy & Partnerships)*
Nancy J. Anderson *(VP & Deputy Gen Counsel-Legal & Corp Affairs-Litigation Grp)*
Tom Burt *(Corp VP & Deputy Gen Counsel-Litigation Grp)*
David Howard *(Corp VP & Deputy Gen Counsel-Litigation Grp)*
Pamela S. Passman *(VP & Deputy Gen Counsel-Global Corp Affairs)*
Mary E. Snapp *(VP & Deputy Gen Counsel-Law & Corp Affairs Dept)*
Michael Delman *(VP-Global Mktg-Interactive Entertainment Bus)*
Tom Gibbons *(VP-TV, Svc Bus & Interactive Entertainment Bus)*
Kathleen Hogan *(VP-Microsoft Services)*
Frank Holland *(Corp VP-Adv & Online Bus)*
Bob Kelly *(VP-Windows Azure Mktg)*
Mitchell L. Koch *(VP-Worldwide Retail Sls & Mktg Grp-Entertainment Devices)*
Lewis Levin *(VP-Office Bus Applications Strategy)*
Jim Minervino *(VP-Corp Mktg Strategy & Insights)*
Michael Park *(Corp VP-Sls, Mktg & Ops-Microsoft Bus Solutions)*
Frank Shaw *(Corp VP-Corp Comm)*
Allison Watson *(VP-Bus & Mktg Grp-North America)*
Blair Westlake *(VP-Media & Entertainment Grp)*
Kevin Peck *(Head-Global Brand Strategy-Central Mktg Grp)*
Matthew V. Booty *(Gen Mgr-Mobile Games)*
Aaron Easterly *(Gen Mgr)*
Nate McLemore *(Gen Mgr-Health Solutions Grp)*
David Webster *(Gen Mgr-Brand & Mktg Strategy)*
Mark Bolger *(Sr Dir-Mktg-Surface Computing)*
Ryan Mugford *(Sr Dir-Global Field Engagement)*
Adam Sohn *(Sr Dir-PR & Influencer Rels)*
Alison Lange Engel *(Dir-Mktg)*
Bill Capodanno *(Dir-Digital Marcom Plng & Effectiveness)*
Marc Adam *(Dir-Worldwide Online Mktg)*
Cynthia Bishop *(Dir-Pricing & Licensing-Desktop & Cloud Svcs-Global)*
Natalie Bowman *(Dir-Brand & Creative Strategy)*
Steve Brown *(Dir-Product Mgmt-Security & Access)*
Dean Carignan *(Dir-Adv Bus Strategy)*
Frank Cavaliere *(Dir-Federal Govt Affairs)*
Grete Faremo *(Dir-Corp Affairs)*
William J. Hankes *(Dir-Bing PR)*
Natasha Hritzuk *(Dir-Insights-Global)*
Sheryl Hudson *(Dir-Marcom Media Plng)*
Inese Kingsmill *(Dir-Mktg)*
Cyrus Krohn *(Dir & Exec Producer)*
Erika Nagy *(Dir-US Sourcing)*
Mari Kim Novak *(Dir-Indus Relations-MSN)*
Eric Picard *(Dir-Adv Tech Strategy)*
Jose Pinero *(Dir-Diversity & Multicultural Mktg)*
Scott Rockfeld *(Dir-Mobile Comm Bus)*
Jason Scott *(Dir-Global Agencies)*
Esco Strong *(Dir-Display Monetization & Yield Analytics)*
John Vassallo *(Dir-Bus Dev)*
Jim Watson *(Dir-Microsoft Media Network)*
Ryan Duguid *(Sr Product Mgr-Sharepoint)*
Wendi Dunlap *(Sr Mgr-MarCom Media Plng)*
Chris Kilkes *(Sr Mgr-Mktg & Media)*
Sherry Mendel *(Sr Mgr-Mktg)*
Leanne Notley *(Sr Mgr-HR)*
John Schuerenberg *(Sr Mgr-Mktg)*
Ashwin Kulkarni *(Sr Product Mgr-Windows Embedded)*
Aashish Dhamdhere *(Sr Product Mgr-Windows Azure)*
B. J. Haberkorn *(Product Mgr-Lync Grp)*
Philomena Lobo *(Product Mgr-Bing Maps & Bing Mobile)*
Todd Rutherford *(Product Mgr-Windows Entertainment)*
David Zipkin *(Product Mgr-Windows)*
Ted Backman *(Mgr-Principal Dev)*
Bill Bush *(Mgr-Mktg-Mobile Comm Bus)*
Lindsay Jurist-Rosner *(Mgr-Mktg)*
Irene Plenefisch *(Mgr-Govt Affairs)*
Julie Smith *(Mgr-Relationship Mktg)*
Surya Vanka *(Mgr-Principal UX)*

Brands & Products:
ACCESS
ACTIVE ACCESSIBILITY
ACTIVE DESKTOP
ACTIVEMOVIE
ACTIVESTORE
ACTIVESYNC
ACTIVEX
ADVISOR FYI
AERO
AGE OF EMPIRES
THE AGE OF KINGS
AGE OF MYTHOLOGY
AMALGA
ASK FOR GENUINE MICROSOFT SOFTWARE
ATLAS
AUTHENTICODE
AUTOROUTE
AUTOROUTE EXPRESS
AUTOROUTE PLUS
AZURIK
BACKOFFICE
BANKSHOT BILLIARDS
BATTLETECH
BING
BITLOCKER
BIZSPARK
BIZTALK
BLINX
BLOOD WAKE
BLUE DRAGON
BLUETOOTH NOTEBOOK MOUSE 5000
BOOKDINGS
BRUTE FORCE
BUGLIGHT
CALIBRI
CAMBRIA
CANDARA
CARBONATED GAMES
CARIADINGS
CLEARTYPE
THE CODE ROOM
CONSOLAS
CONSTANTIA
CONVECTION
CONVERGENCE
CORBEL
CORTANA
CRACKDOWN
CRIMSON SKIES
DATATIPS
DAUNPENH
DEXTERITY
DIGITAL ANVIL
DIRECT3D
DIRECTANIMATION
DIRECTBAND
DIRECTDRAW
DIRECTINPUT
DIRECTMUSIC
DIRECTPLAY
DIRECTSHOW
DIRECTSOUND
DIRECTX
DREAMSCENE
DREAMSPARK
DRIVATAR
DYNAMICS CRM ONLINE
ENSEMBLE STUDIOS
ENTOURAGE
ESP
EXCEL
EXHIBITION
EXPEDIA.COM
EXPRESSION
EXPRESSION BLEND
FASA STUDIO
FAST
FINTY FLUSH
FLEXGO
FLUENT
FOREFRONT
FORZA MOTORSPORT
FOXPRO
FREELANCER
FRINGER
FRONTPAGE
FRX
FUZION FRENZY
GAINSKEEPER
GAME WITH FAME
GAMESPRING
GEORGIA
GISHA
GREAT PLAINS
GROOVE
HABU
HALO
HALO 3
HALO WARS
HDCD
HEALTHVAULT
HEXIC
HIGH ROAD TO REVENGE
HOMEADVISOR
HOTMAIL
HOTSTART
HYPER-V
INFINITE UNDISCOVERY
INKSEINE
INTELLIMIRROR
INTELLIMORPH
INTELLISENSE
INTELLISHRINK
INTERNET EXPLORER
ISKOOLA POTA
ITS MR PANTS
JAWBREAKER
JSCRIPT
KINECT
KUNG FU CHAOS
LIFECHAT
LINEDRIVE
LIONHEAD
LIPS
LOST ODYSSEY
MAPPOINT
MARINE MANIA
MASTER CHIEF
MAXIMUM CHASE
MECHASSAULT
MECHCOMMANDER
MECHWARRIOR
MEDIAROOM
MEDVAULT
MICROSOFT
MICROSOFT ACTIVE DIRECTORY
MICROSOFT ADCENTER
MICROSOFT BOOKSHELF
MICROSOFT CARPOINT
MICROSOFT DYNAMICS ERP
MICROSOFT ENCARTA
MICROSOFT EXCHANGE
MICROSOFT HOME ESSENTIALS
MICROSOFT INTELLIMOUSE
MICROSOFT LYNC
MICROSOFT NATURAL KEYBOARD
MICROSOFT OFFICE 2010
MICROSOFT OFFICE OUTLOOK
MICROSOFT OFFICE WEB APPS
MICROSOFT PC
MICROSOFT PRESS
MICROSOFT SHAREPOINT
MICROSOFT SQL SERVER
MICROSOFT SURFACE
MICROSOFT VISUAL C++
MICROSOFT VISUAL J++
MICROSOFT VISUAL STUDIO
MIDTOWN MADNESS
MOBILE MEMORY MOUSE 8000
MONEYCENTRAL
MONSTER TRUCK MADNESS
MORPHX
MOTOCROSS MADNESS
MOZAKI
MS

Key to Media (For complete agency information see *The Advertising Red Books-Agencies* edition):
1. Bus. Publs. 2. Cable T.V. 3. Catalogs & Directories. 4. Co-op Adv. 5. Consumer Mags. 6. D.M. to Bus. Estab.7. D.M. to Consumers 8. Daily Newsp. 9. Exhibits/Trade Shows 10. Foreign 11. Infomercial 12. Internet Adv.13. Multimedia 14. Network Radio 15. Network T.V. 16. Newsp. Distr. Mags. 17. Other 18. Outdoor (Posters, Transit) 19. Point of Purchase20. Premiums, Novelties 21. Product Samples 22. Special Events Mktg. 23. Spot Radio 24. Spot T.V. 25. Weekly Newsp. 26. Yellow Page Adv.

MS-DOS
MSDN
MSN
MULTIPOINT
NAVISION
NAVREADY
NINA
NINETY-NINE NIGHTS
OFFICE
OFFICE 365
OFFICE INFOPATH
OFFICE ONENOTE
ONECARE
OPENTYPE
OPTIMATCH
OUTSMART
PEOPLE READY
PERFECT DARK ZERO
PERFORMANCEPOINT
PGR
PHANTOM DUST
PHOTOSYNTH
PINPOINT
PIVOTCHART
PIVOTTABLE
PLACEWARE
PLAYFX
PLAYREADY
POPFLY
POWERPOINT
PROCLARITY
PROJECT GOTHAM RACING
QUANTUM REDSHIFT
RALLY
RARE
READYBOOST
READYDRIVE
RECLUSA
RESPONSE POINT
RISE OF LEGENDS
RISE OF NATIONS
RISE OF PERATHIA
ROUNDTABLE
RP STYLIZED
SABRE WULF
SEADRAGON
SEGOE
SHADOWRUN
SHAPESHEET
SHAREPOINT
SIDEGUIDE
SIDESHOW
SIDEWINDER
SILVERLIGHT
SKYDRIVE
SMARTART
SMARTER HOSPITALITY
SMARTER RETAILING
SMARTSHAPES
SNEAKERS
SOFTGRID
SOFTRICITY
SONGSMITH
SPACES FOR OUR WORLD
SPORTSLOUNGE
SQL AZURE
SQL SERVER
STARLANCER
STARTS HERE
STEADYSTATE
SUDEKI
SUPERFETCH
SYSTEM CENTER
TAHOMA
TAO FENG
TERMINAL SERVICES REMOTEAPP
THE TIME SWEEPER
TRUESKILL
TURN 10
U-PROVE
UNIVERSAL EDITION
UTOPIA
VERDANA
VIRTUAL EARTH
VISIO
VISTA
VISUAL BASIC
VISUAL C#
VISUAL INTERDEV
VISUAL J#
VISUAL J++
VISUAL SOURCESAFE
VISUAL STUDIO
VIVA PINATA
VOODOO VINCE
WEBDINGS
WEBTV
WEBTV NETWORK
WHACKED!
WHERE DO YOU WANT TO GO TODAY?
WIN32
WINDOWS
WINDOWS 2000
WINDOWS 95
WINDOWS AZURE
WINDOWS CARDSPACE
WINDOWS EMBEDDED
WINDOWS INTUNE
WINDOWS LIVE
WINDOW'S LIVE HOTMAIL
WINDOWS MEDIA
WINDOWS MOBILE
WINDOWS NT
WINDOWS PHONE
WINDOWS POWERSHELL
WINDOWS SERVER
WINDOWS SERVER HYPER-V
WINDOWS SERVER SYSTEM
WINDOWS SEVER
WINDOWS VISTA
WINDOWS XP
WINFX
WINGDINGS
WIRELESS NOTEBOOK LASER MOUSE 7000
WONDERWALL
WORD
XBOX
XBOX 360
XBOX 360 ELITE
XBOX LIVE
XNA
XRANK
YOUR POTENTIAL. OUR PASSION
ZOO TYCOON
ZUNE

Advertising Agencies:

72andSunny
6300 Arizona Cir
Los Angeles, CA 90045
Tel.: (310) 215-9009
Fax: (310) 215-9012

agencytwofifteen
215 Leidesdorff St
San Francisco, CA 94111
Tel.: (415) 262-3500
Alan Wake
Bright Falls
Gears of War
Microsoft XBOX Halo Reach

AKQA, Inc.
175 Varick St 10th Fl
New York, NY 10014
Tel.: (212) 989-2572
Fax: (212) 989-2363
Xbox 360

AKQA, Inc.
118 King St 6th Fl
San Francisco, CA 94107
Tel.: (415) 645-9400
Fax: (415) 645-9420
Microsoft XBOX Halo Reach

Anvil Media, Inc.
310 NE Failing St.
Portland, OR 97212
Tel.: (503) 595-6050
Fax: (503) 223-1008

Atlas
315 5th Ave S Ste 500
Seattle, WA 98104
Tel.: (206) 816-8000

Bates 141 China
Room 2708 Tower A Tian Yuan Gang Center C2
Beijing, 100027, China
Tel.: (86) 10 8438 9999
Fax: (86) 10 8438 9888

Big Fuel Communications LLC
298 5th Ave 5th Fl
New York, NY 10001
Tel.: (212) 616-6300
Fax: (212) 658-9226

Blast Radius
285 Madison Ave 12th Fl
New York, NY 10017
Tel.: (212) 925-4900
Fax: (212) 925-5247
Office 2010
SharePoint 2010

Blockdot
8350 N Central Expressway Ste 400
Dallas, TX 75206
Tel.: (214) 890-4100
Fax: (214) 890-4155
Brand Identity Forum

The Bohle Company
1625 Stanford St
Santa Monica, CA 90404
Tel.: (310) 785-0515
Fax: (310) 277-2066

Bradley & Montgomery Advertising
342 E Saint Joseph St
Indianapolis, IN 46204
Tel.: (317) 423-1745
Internet Explorer 9
Microsoft Small Business
Office 2007

Brownstein Group
215 S Broad St 9th Fl
Philadelphia, PA 19107-5325
Tel.: (215) 735-3470
Fax: (215) 735-6298

CMD
1631 NW Thurman St
Portland, OR 97209-2558
Tel.: (503) 223-6794
Fax: (503) 223-2430

Cole & Weber United
221 Yale Ave N Ste 600
Seattle, WA 98109
Tel.: (206) 447-9595
Fax: (206) 233-0178

CP+B
3390 Mary St Ste 300
Coconut Grove, FL 33133
Tel.: (305) 859-2070
Fax: (305) 854-3419
(Zune)

CP+B Boulder
6450 Gunpark Dr
Boulder, CO 80301
Tel.: (303) 628-5100
Fax: (303) 516-0227
Epic Share
Internet Explorer 8
Windows 7
Windows Phone 7

Creative Artists Agency
2000 Ave of the Stars
Los Angeles, CA 90067
Tel.: (424) 288-2000
Fax: (424) 288-2900

Creature
1508 10th Ave
Seattle, WA 98122
Tel.: (206) 625-6994
Fax: (206) 625-6904
Windows Home Server

Deep Focus
345 Hudson St 5th Fl
New York, NY 10014
Tel.: (212) 792-6800
Fax: (212) 792-6899

Deutsch New York
111 8th Ave 14th Fl
New York, NY 10011
Tel.: (212) 605-8000
— Mike Shackle *(Sr VP & Grp Dir-Creative-Microso)*

Edelman
250 Hudson St
New York, NY 10013
Tel.: (212) 768-0550
Fax: (212) 704-0128
Games Console
Kinect For Xbox 360

Edelman
3rd Floor Toranomon 45 MT Bldg
Tokyo, 105-001, Japan
Tel.: (81) 3 6403 5200
Fax: (81) 3 6403 5201

Edelman
5900 Wilshire Blvd 24th & 25th Floors
Los Angeles, CA 90036
Tel.: (323) 857-9100
Fax: (323) 857-9117
Zune
— Ivette Zurita *(Acct Exec)*

EVB-Evolution Bureau
55 Union St
San Francisco, CA 94111
Tel.: (415) 281-3950
Fax: (415) 281-3957
Live Derby 2007

Key to Media (For complete agency information see *The Advertising Red Books-Agencies* edition):
1. Bus. Publs. 2. Cable T.V. 3. Catalogs & Directories. 4. Co-op Adv. 5. Consumer Mags. 6. D.M. to Bus. Estab.7. D.M. to Consumers
8. Daily Newsp. 9. Exhibits/Trade Shows 10. Foreign 11. Infomercial 12. Internet Adv.13. Multimedia 14. Network Radio
15. Network T.V. 16. Newsp. Distr. Mags. 17. Other 18. Outdoor (Posters, Transit) 19. Point of Purchase20. Premiums, Novelties
21. Product Samples 22. Special Events Mktg. 23. Spot Radio 24. Spot T.V. 25. Weekly Newsp. 26. Yellow Page Adv.

Microsoft Corporation — (Continued)

FD Americas Public Affairs
1101 K St NW 9th Fl
Washington, DC 20005
Tel.: (202) 346-8800
Fax: (202) 346-8804

Go Direct!
30A Kandahar Street
Singapore, 198890, Singapore
Tel.: (65) 6372 4177
Fax: (65) 6323 0139

Hydrogen Advertising
1520 4th Ave Ste 600
Seattle, WA 98101
Tel.: (206) 389-9500
Fax: (206) 389-4849
(B2B Campaign for Online Services)

J. Walter Thompson Company
(d/b/a JWT)
466 Lexington Ave
New York, NY 10017-3140
Tel.: (212) 210-7000
Fax: (212) 210-7299
People-Ready

Lopez Negrete Communications, Inc.
3336 Richmond Ave Ste 200
Houston, TX 77098
Tel.: (713) 877-8777
Fax: (713) 877-8796
— Randy Stockdale *(Exec Grp Acct Dir)*

McCann Erickson Worldwide
622 3rd Ave
New York, NY 10017-6707
Tel.: (646) 865-2000
Fax: (646) 487-9610
(X-Box Videogame Console)
Halo 3

PeraltaStrawberryFrog
Avenida Mofarrej 1200
Sao Paulo, 05311-000, Brazil
Tel.: (55) 11 3834 8344
Fax: (55) 11 3834 8344

Publicis Groupe S.A.
133 Ave des Champs-Elysee
75008
Paris, France
Tel.: (33) 1 44 43 70 00
Fax: (33) 1 44 43 75 25

Red Bricks Media
1062 Folsom St Ste 300
San Francisco, CA 94103
Tel.: (415) 255-0650
Fax: (415) 255-0660

Reprise Media
55 5th Ave 16th Fl
New York, NY 10003
Tel.: (212) 444-7474
Search Marketing

T3 (The Think Tank)
1806 Rio Grande
Austin, TX 78701
Tel.: (512) 499-8811
Fax: (512) 499-8552

Tribal DDB San Francisco
555 Market St Ste 500
San Francisco, CA 94105
Tel.: (415) 732-2200
Fax: (415) 732-2295

Waggener Edstrom
225 108th Ave NE Ste 700
Bellevue, WA 98004-5737
Tel.: (425) 638-7000
Fax: (425) 638-7001

Wexley School for Girls
2218 5th Ave
Seattle, WA 98121
Tel.: (206) 438-8900
Live Search Maps

Wikreate
145 Vallejo St Ste 6
San Francisco, CA 94111
Tel.: (415) 362-0440
Fax: (415) 362-0430

Wunderman
(Worldwide Headquarters)
285 Madison Ave
New York, NY 10017
Tel.: (212) 941-3000
Fax: (212) 210-5454
Computer Game
Global Direct Marketing Agency of Record
Motion Controlled Gaming System
Video Game

MICROSOFT CORP.

(Branch of Microsoft Business Division)
4700 S Syracuse St Ste 700
Denver, CO 80237
Tel.: (303) 741-8000
Fax: (303) 741-3335
Toll Free: (800) 379-8733
E-mail: info@microsoft.com
Web Site: www.microsoft.com
E-Mail For Key Personnel:
Marketing Director: branding@frxsoft.com
Sales Director: sales@frxsoft.com
Sales Range: $25-49.9 Million
Approx. Number Employees: 150
Year Founded: 1989
Business Description:
Financial Analytics Software Mfr
S.I.C.: 7372
N.A.I.C.S.: 511210
Media: 10
Personnel:
Abe Thomas *(Gen Mgr-Microsoft.com)*
Bonnie Chan *(Sr Dir-Media)*
Cari Johnson *(Sr Dir-Advertiser Solutions)*
Brett Dennis *(Dir-Windows Phone-Global)*
Jay Seideman *(Dir-Channel Sls-Microsoft Adv Exchange)*
Terry Ginley *(Mgr-Bus Intelligence Global)*
Craig Rutherford *(Mgr-Fin-Grp)*
Jeanne O'Kelley *(Strategist-Healthcare Svcs-The Americas)*
Brands & Products:
FORECASTER
FORECASTER ROI TOOL
FRX

MICROSYSTEMS

3025 Highland Pkwy Ste 450
Downers Grove, IL 60515
Tel.: (630) 598-1100
Fax: (630) 598-9520
E-mail: support@microsystems.com
Web Site: www.microsystems.com
Sales Range: $75-99.9 Million
Approx. Number Employees: 100
Business Description:
Document Lifecycle Software; Document Creation, Productivity & Control
S.I.C.: 7372
N.A.I.C.S.: 511210
Media: 10-13-22
Personnel:
Tom O'Sullivan *(CEO)*
John Rigas *(CFO)*
Sherry Kappel *(Sr VP & Chief Innovations Officer)*
Steve Brecia *(VP-Sls)*
Brian Hall *(VP-Client Rels & Mktg)*
Bonnie Reed *(Dir-Mktg)*
Brands & Products:
THE DOCUMENT EXPERTS
DOCXAMINE
DOCXCHANGE
DOCXTOOLS
LEGAL TEMPLATESPLUS
MICROSYSTEMS

MICROTUNE, INC.

(Sub. of Zoran Corporation)
2201 10th St
Plano, TX 75074
Tel.: (972) 673-1600
Fax: (972) 673-1602
Approx. Rev.: $74,570,000
Approx. Number Employees: 276
Business Description:
Radio Frequency Tuners & Transceivers Mfr
S.I.C.: 3679
N.A.I.C.S.: 334419
Media: 5-11-22
Personnel:
Justin M. Chapman *(CFO & VP)*
Robert S. Kirk *(VP-Sls)*

THE MILLARD GROUP

7301 N Cicero Ave
Lincolnwood, IL 60712
Tel.: (847) 674-4100
Fax: (847) 677-0790
Web Site: www.millardgroup.com
Sales Range: $700-749.9 Million
Approx. Number Employees: 3,000
Year Founded: 1958
Business Description:
Office Buildings & Institutional Janitorial Services & Personnel Supply Services
S.I.C.: 7349
N.A.I.C.S.: 561720
Media: 2
Distr.: Direct to Consumer; Natl.
Personnel:
Lawrence B. Kugler *(Pres)*
Brands & Products:
ADMIRAL
Advertising Agency:
Morris Advertising Inc.
16229 W 65th Pl
Arvada, CO 80007
Tel.: (303) 431-5087
Fax: (303) 380-9630

MILLER HEIMAN INC.

(Group of Sterling Investment Partners, L.P.)
10509 Professional Cir Ste 100
Reno, NV 89521
Tel.: (775) 827-4411
Fax: (775) 827-5517
Toll Free: (877) 678-3380
E-mail: info@millerheiman.com
Web Site: www.millerheiman.com
Approx. Number Employees: 35
Year Founded: 1980
Business Description:
Sales Performance Consulting Services
S.I.C.: 8742
N.A.I.C.S.: 541613
Media: 2-4-7-8-10-13-22
Personnel:
Sam Reese *(Pres & CEO)*
Calvin Quan *(CFO)*
Leonard Distaso *(Gen Counsel & Sr VP)*
Tim Call *(Exec VP)*
Leigh Hooker *(Exec VP-Sls Ops)*
Bethany Schultz *(Exec VP-Client Engagement & Strategy)*

MILLER, NASH, WIENER, HAGER & CARLSEN

111 SW Fifth Ave
Portland, OR 97204
Tel.: (503) 224-5858
Web Site: www.millernash.com
Personnel:
Elise Brickner Schulz *(Dir-Legal Support Svc)*
Advertising Agency:
Lane PR
905 SW 16th Ave
Portland, OR 97205
Tel.: (503) 221-0480
Fax: (503) 221-9765

MILTOPE GROUP, INC.

(Sub. of Vision Technologies Systems, Inc.)
(d/b/a VT Miltope)
500 Richardson Rd S
Hope Hull, AL 36043
Tel.: (334) 284-8665
Fax: (334) 613-6302
Toll Free: (800) MILTOPE
E-mail: info@miltope.com
Web Site: www.miltope.com
Sales Range: $25-49.9 Million
Approx. Number Employees: 200
Year Founded: 1975
Business Description:
Microcomputers & Computer Peripheral Equipment, Work Stations, Handheld, Portable & Laptop Computers, Printers, Mass Storage Devices, Terminals & Disk Drives Designer & Mfr
S.I.C.: 3572; 3577
N.A.I.C.S.: 334112; 334119
Import Export
Media: 2-5-7-10-13
Distr.: Intl.; Natl.
Budget Set: Oct.
Personnel:
Julie A. Briggs *(Pres & CEO)*
Tom B. Dake *(CFO & VP-Fin)*
Brands & Products:
MSD
MSD ICE
PONY PCU
TP-4429
TP-4840
VCU-1600

Key to Media (For complete agency information see *The Advertising Red Books-Agencies* edition):
1. Bus. Publs. 2. Cable T.V. 3. Catalogs & Directories. 4. Co-op Adv. 5. Consumer Mags. 6. D.M. to Bus. Estab.7. D.M. to Consumers
8. Daily Newsp. 9. Exhibits/Trade Shows 10. Foreign 11. Infomercial 12. Internet Adv.13. Multimedia 14. Network Radio
15. Network T.V. 16. Newsp. Distr. Mags. 17. Other 18. Outdoor (Posters, Transit) 19. Point of Purchase20. Premiums, Novelties
21. Product Samples 22. Special Events Mktg. 23. Spot Radio 24. Spot T.V. 25. Weekly Newsp. 26. Yellow Page Adv.

MINDMAKER, INC.

PO Box 506
Placerville, CA 95667
Tel.: (408) 467-9200
Fax: (408) 467-9202
E-mail: president@mindmaker.com
Web Site: www.mindmaker.com
E-Mail For Key Personnel:
Marketing Director: marketing@mindmaker.com
Approx. Number Employees: 150
Year Founded: 1996
Business Description:
Software Developer
S.I.C.: 8733; 7371
N.A.I.C.S.: 541710; 541511
Media: 13
Personnel:
Jozsef Kiraly *(Owner)*
Brands & Products:
ALM
ASSOCIATIVE LEARNING MEMORY
FLEXVOICE
FLEXVOICE TTS
GAME COMMANDER
HIGHLIGHTHOUND
MOUSEASSIST
MOUSEASSIST 2.0 PRO
PALM
QUERYHOOD
QUERYHOUND
REALM
TEXTASSIST
TISENTO
TISENTO ASR
TOPICHOUND
VOICEASSIST
WORDHOUND

MIPS TECHNOLOGIES, INC.

955 E Arques Ave
Sunnyvale, CA 94085
Tel.: (650) 567-5000
Fax: (650) 567-5150
E-mail: webteam-mips@mips.com
Web Site: www.mips.com
E-Mail For Key Personnel:
Sales Director: sales@mips.com
Approx. Rev.: $82,040,000
Approx. Number Employees: 162
Year Founded: 1984
Business Description:
Reduced-Instruction Set Computing Technology Mfr
S.I.C.: 3674; 7371
N.A.I.C.S.: 334413; 541511
Advertising Expenditures: $14,851,000
Media: 4-7-13-16
Personnel:
Kenneth L. Coleman *(Chm)*
Sandeep S. Vij *(Pres & CEO)*
Jose Epifanio da Franca *(Pres & Gen Mgr-Analog Bus Grp)*
Maury Austin *(CFO)*
Gail Shulman *(Gen Counsel, Sec & VP)*
Ravikrishna Cherukuri *(VP-Engrg)*
Brad Holtzinger *(VP-Sls-Worldwide)*
Mark Pittman *(VP-Sls-Asia Pacific Reg)*
Dave Singhal *(VP-Corp Dev & Strategy)*
Art Swift *(VP-Mktg & Bus Dev)*
Brands & Products:
1004K
1004KC
1004KF
1074K
1074KC
1074KF
20K
20KC
24K
24KC
24KE
24KEC
24KEF
24KF
25KF
34K
34KC
34KF
4K
4KC
4KE
4KEC
4KEM
4KEP
4KM
4KP
4KS
4KSC
4KSD
5K
5KC
5KF
74K
74KC
74KF
AT THE CORE OF THE USER EXPERIENCE
ATLAS
BUSBRIDGE
CLAM
CNMIPS
COREFPGA
CORELV
COREXTEND
EC
FASTMIPS
FPGAVIEW
FS2
FS2 NAVIGATOR
HYPERDEBUG
HYPERJTAG
JALGO
M14K
M14KC
M4K
MALTA
MDMX
MED
MGB
MICROMIPS
MIPS
MIPS-3D
MIPS-BASED
MIPS I
MIPS II
MIPS III
MIPS IV
MIPS TECHNOLOGIES
MIPS V
MIPS-VERIFIED
MIPS16
MIPS16E
MIPS32
MIPS64
MIPSPRO
MIPSSIM
OCI
PDTRACE
THE PIPELINE
PRO SERIES
QUICKMIPS
R10000
R12000
R12000A
R14000
R14000A
R16000
R3000
R4000
R5000
SAFE-SOC
SEAD
SEAD-2
SMARTMIPS
SOC-IT
YAMON

MITEK SYSTEMS, INC.

8911 Balboa Ave Ste B
San Diego, CA 92123-1507
Tel.: (858) 503-7810
Fax: (858) 503-7820
E-mail: info@miteksystems.com
Web Site: www.miteksystems.com
E-Mail For Key Personnel:
President: jthornton@miteksys.com
Sales Director: sales@miteksys.com
Approx. Sls.: $5,118,901
Approx. Number Employees: 19
Year Founded: 1986
Business Description:
Automatic Data Recognition Software Producer; Check Image Analytics Producer Used to Detect Check Fraud & Improve Customer Service
S.I.C.: 3577; 7371
N.A.I.C.S.: 334119; 541511
Export
Advertising Expenditures: $40,000
Media: 10-13
Distr.: Intl.; Natl.
Personnel:
John M. Thornton *(Chm)*
James B. DeBello *(Pres & CEO)*
Russell C. Clark *(CFO)*
Josh Roach *(Sr VP-Engrg & Product Mgmt)*
Louise Steller *(Dir-Bus Dev & Sls)*
Jan Charvat *(Product Mgr)*
Brands & Products:
DOCTUS
DYNAFIND
FRAUDPROTECT
IMAGENET
IMAGENET DATA CAPTURE
IMAGENET MOBILE DEPOSIT
IMAGENET PAYMENTS
IMAGENET PHOTO & VIDEO
IMAGENET PREP & ID
IMAGENET SIGNATURES
IMAGESCORE
MITEK SYSTEMS
QUICKFX
QUICKFX PRO
QUICKSTROKES

MKS INC.

410 Albert St
Waterloo, ON N2L 3V3, Canada
Tel.: (519) 884-2251
Fax: (519) 884-8861
Toll Free: (800) 265-2797
E-mail: info@mks.com
Web Site: www.mks.com
E-Mail For Key Personnel:
Marketing Director: ellyn@mks.com
Public Relations: ellyn@mks.com
Approx. Rev.: $61,584,418
Approx. Number Employees: 52
Year Founded: 1984
Business Description:
Software Configuration Management & UNIX to Windows Cross Platform Development Tools Services
S.I.C.: 7373
N.A.I.C.S.: 541512
Media: 1-4-8-10-13-20-22
Personnel:
M. Alex White *(Founder)*
Philip C. Deck *(Chm)*
Gerald S. Hurlow *(Vice Chm)*
Michael W. Harris *(CEO)*
Douglas M. Sawatzky *(CFO)*
R. Larry Wasylishyn *(Gen Counsel & Sec)*
John J. Cull *(VP-Mktg & Customer Solutions)*
Doug Akers *(Dir-Customer Requirements)*
Megan Hall *(Dir-HR)*
Brands & Products:
ALERTCENTRE
EXTRACTDB
IMPLEMENTER
MKS
MKS ALERTCENTRE
MKS INTEGRITY MANAGER
MKS SOURCE INTEGRITY
MKS SOURCE INTEGRITY ENTERPRISE
MKS TOOLKIT
MKS TOOLKIT FOR ENTERPRISE DEVELOPERS
NEWVERSION
OPENMAKE
PROJECTMASTER
SUPPORTCENTER

MKS SOFTWARE INC.

(Sub. of MKS Inc.)
12701 Fair Lakes Cir Ste 350
Fairfax, VA 22033-4910
Tel.: (703) 803-3343
Fax: (703) 803-3344
Toll Free: (800) 637-8034
E-mail: tk-info@mkssoftware.com
Web Site: www.mks.com
Approx. Number Employees: 30
Business Description:
Software Products & Consulting Services
S.I.C.: 7372
N.A.I.C.S.: 511210
Advertising Expenditures: $1,000,000
Media: 2-7-13
Distr.: Intl.; Natl.
Personnel:
Wendy Mades *(VP-Mktg Commun)*
Brands & Products:
NUTCRACKER TOOLS

MMRGLOBAL, INC.

4401 Wilshire Blvd Ste 200
Los Angeles, CA 90010
Tel.: (310) 476-7002
E-mail: info@mmrmail.com
Web Site: www.mymedicalrecords.com
Approx. Rev.: $972,988
Approx. Number Employees: 8
Year Founded: 2000
Business Description:
Computer Information Storage Products
S.I.C.: 3572

Key to Media (For complete agency information see *The Advertising Red Books-Agencies* edition):
1. Bus. Publs. 2. Cable T.V. 3. Catalogs & Directories. 4. Co-op Adv. 5. Consumer Mags. 6. D.M. to Bus. Estab.7. D.M. to Consumers 8. Daily Newsp. 9. Exhibits/Trade Shows 10. Foreign 11. Infomercial 12. Internet Adv.13. Multimedia 14. Network Radio 15. Network T.V. 16. Newsp. Distr. Mags. 17. Other 18. Outdoor (Posters, Transit) 19. Point of Purchase20. Premiums, Novelties 21. Product Samples 22. Special Events Mktg. 23. Spot Radio 24. Spot T.V. 25. Weekly Newsp. 26. Yellow Page Adv.

MMRGLOBAL, INC. — (Continued)

N.A.I.C.S.: 334112
Advertising Expenditures: $224,846
Personnel:
Robert H. Lorsch *(Chm, Pres & CEO)*
Ingrid Safranek *(CFO & VP-Fin)*
Sunil Singhal *(Exec VP-Technology & Product Dev)*
Rafael Salazar *(VP-Comm & Carrier Rels)*

MOBILE COMPUTING CORPORATION

6300 NW Dr Unit 1
Mississauga, ON L4V 1J7, Canada
Tel.: (905) 676-8900
Fax: (905) 676-9191
Toll Free: (800) 392-8651
E-mail: marketing@mobilecom.com
Web Site: www.mobilecom.com
Sales Range: $10-24.9 Million
Approx. Number Employees: 30
Year Founded: 1984
Business Description:
Workforce Automation Software Solutions
S.I.C.: 7372; 8748
N.A.I.C.S.: 334611; 541618
Media: 2-10
Personnel:
Jake Van Ginkel *(CEO)*
Advertising Agency:
Maverick Public Relations
37 Madison Ave
Toronto, ON M5R 2S2, Canada
Tel.: (416) 640-5525
Fax: (416) 640-5524

MOBILE SERVICES GROUP, INC.

700 N Brand Blvd St 1000
La Crescenta, CA 91203
Tel.: (818) 253-3200
Tel.: (818) 253-3291
Fax: (818) 253-3293
Toll Free: (800) 662-8810
E-mail: info@mobilestorage.com
Web Site: www.mobileservicesgroup.com
Sales Range: $200-249.9 Million
Approx. Number Employees: 990
Year Founded: 1987
Business Description:
Portable Storage Solutions
S.I.C.: 4225
N.A.I.C.S.: 493110
Advertising Expenditures: $3,650,000
Media: 1-2-10-22
Personnel:
Sanjay Swani *(Chm)*
Douglas A. Waugaman *(Pres & CEO)*
Jerry E. Vaughn *(Exec VP-Admin)*
Allan Villegas *(Dir-Fin)*

MODCOMP, INC.

(Sub. of CSP Inc.)
Ste A 1500 S Powerline Rd
Deerfield Beach, FL 33442-8185
Tel.: (954) 571-4600
Fax: (954) 571-4700
Toll Free: (800) 940-1111
Telex: 372 7837
E-mail: info@modcomp.com
Web Site: www.modcomp.com
Approx. Sls.: $50,000,000
Approx. Number Employees: 160
Year Founded: 1970
Business Description:
Process Control, Data Acquisition & System Integration Services
S.I.C.: 7373; 7378
N.A.I.C.S.: 541512; 811212
Advertising Expenditures: $200,000
Bus. Publs.: $100,000; D.M. to Bus. Estab.: $50,000; Exhibits/Trade Shows: $50,000
Distr.: Intl.; Natl.
Budget Set: Oct.
Personnel:
Victor Dellovo *(Pres)*
Ron Cook *(VP-Tech)*
Earl Clark *(Dir-Americas Svcs)*
Sandra Alvarez *(Mgr)*
Brands & Products:
CLASSIC
MAX IV, 32
PACE/32
REAL/IX
SCADABASE
VIEWMAX

MONROE SYSTEMS FOR BUSINESS

(Div. of Carolina Wholesale Office Machine Company, Inc.)
47 Runway Dr Ste G
Levittown, PA 19057-4738
Tel.: (267) 580-2600
Fax: (267) 580-2645
Toll Free: (888) 666-7631
E-mail: csr@monroe-systems.com
Web Site: www.monroe-systems.com
Approx. Number Employees: 100
Year Founded: 1912
Business Description:
Electronic Printing & Display Calculators Mfr
S.I.C.: 5044
N.A.I.C.S.: 423420
Import Export
Media: 2-4-5-7-8-10-13
Distr.: Intl.; Natl.
Budget Set: Oct.
Personnel:
Richard D. Roberts *(CEO)*
William Ault *(COO)*
Mary Robinson *(Office Mgr)*
Brands & Products:
MONROE

MOORE PUSH PIN CO.

1300 E Mermaid Ln
Wyndmoor, PA 19038-7664
Tel.: (215) 233-5700
Fax: (215) 233-0660
Toll Free: (877) 446-6673
E-mail: sales@push-pin.com
Web Site: www.push-pin.com
E-Mail For Key Personnel:
Sales Director: sales@push-pin.com
Approx. Number Employees: 47
Year Founded: 1900
Business Description:
Specialty Fastener Products Designer, Mfr & Marketer
S.I.C.: 3965
N.A.I.C.S.: 339993
Import Export
Media: 1-4-5-10-19-20-21
Distr.: Intl.; Natl.
Budget Set: Oct.
Brands & Products:
CLIP HANGERS
CLIP IT
CRYSTAL CLEAR TAPE
CRYSTAL CLEAR TAPE & DISPENSER
FOAMFAST
MOORE
PIC-SURE-STAY
SNUB-IT
THE STEEL BOXX
TACKY TAPE
THIN PIN

MOORE WALLACE NORTH AMERICA, INC.

(Sub. of R.R. Donnelley & Sons Company)
111 S Lacker Dr
Chicago, IL 60606
Tel.: (847) 607-6000
Fax: (847) 607-7099
E-mail: info@rrdonnelley.com
Web Site: www.rrdonnelley.com
Sales Range: $75-99.9 Million
Approx. Number Employees: 350
Business Description:
Direct Mail Printing Services
S.I.C.: 7331
N.A.I.C.S.: 541860
Media: 1-2-4-7-9-10-20-21
Personnel:
Matt Gresge *(Pres-Tops)*
Brands & Products:
CLEANTAC
COMPURITE
DRIBACK
MOORE BUSINESS COMMUNICATION SERVICES
MOORE CLEAN PRINT
MOOREGUARD
NOTE STIX
PROPAGE
REGENESIS
SEALERMATE
SPEEDISEALER
STRATEGIC CUSTOMER SERVICES

MOREDIRECT

(Sub. of PC Connection, Inc.)
4800 T-Rex Ave Ste 300
Boca Raton, FL 33431
Tel.: (561) 237-3300
Fax: (561) 237-3390
E-mail: customerservice@moredirect.com
Web Site: www.moredirect.com
E-Mail For Key Personnel:
Marketing Director: jgarrity@moredirect.com
Sales Director: sales@moredirect.com
Sales Range: $25-49.9 Million
Approx. Number Employees: 160
Year Founded: 1992
Business Description:
Information Technology Solutions
S.I.C.: 5045
N.A.I.C.S.: 423430
Media: 4-7-13
Personnel:
John Thomas *(Pres)*
Kerri Chiappone *(CFO)*
Jorge Legon *(Dir-IT Ops/Applications)*
Brands & Products:
TRAXX

MOTOROLA ENTERPRISE MOBILITY

(Div. of Motorola Solutions, Inc.)
1 Motorola Plz
Holtsville, NY 11742-1300
Tel.: (631) 738-2400
Fax: (631) 738-5990
Toll Free: (800) 927-9626
Toll Free: (800) 722-6234
Sales Range: $1-4.9 Billion
Approx. Number Employees: 5,200
Year Founded: 1975
Business Description:
Bar Code Laser Scanners Mfr
S.I.C.: 3577; 3663
N.A.I.C.S.: 334119; 334220
Import Export
Advertising Expenditures: $10,000,000
Media: 4-7-10-13-20
Distr.: Intl.; Natl.
Budget Set: Dec.
Personnel:
Anthony Bartolo *(VP & Gen Mgr-Wireless Infrastructure)*
Alan Melling *(Sr Dir-RFID Product & Program Mgmt)*
Frank Riso *(Sr Dir-Retail Industry Lead)*
Yangmin Shen *(Dir-Innovation Dev)*
Angelo Lamme *(Sr Mgr-Product Mktg)*
Chris Ciervo *(Sr Mgr-Product Mktg)*
Lorie Rosenbaum *(Sr Mgr-Product Naming)*
Brands & Products:
AIRBEAM
CAPTRA
COBRA
CYCLONE
THE ENTERPRISE MOBILITY COMPANY
LASERTOUCH
MINISCAN
MYSYMBOLCARE
NETVISION
OMNILINK
PHASER
SPECTRUM 24
SYMBOL
SYMOBILE
Advertising Agency:
ANEW Marketing Group
811 W Jericho Tpke Ste 109E
Smithtown, NY 11787
Tel.: (631) 982-4000
Fax: (631) 434-1129

MOTRICITY, INC.

601 108th Ave NE Ste 800
Bellevue, WA 98004
Tel.: (425) 957-6200
Fax: (425) 957-6201
E-mail: info@motricity.com
Web Site: www.motricity.com
Approx. Rev.: $133,379,000
Approx. Number Employees: 339
Business Description:
Mobile Information & Entertainment Content Software & Services
S.I.C.: 7372
N.A.I.C.S.: 511210; 517919
Advertising Expenditures: $492,000
Personnel:
James R. Smith, Jr. *(Interim CEO)*
Allyn P. Hebner *(CFO)*
John O'Rourke *(CMO)*
James Ryan *(Chief Strategy Officer)*
Richard E. Leigh, Jr. *(Gen Counsel, Corp Sec & VP)*
Abe Danzinger *(VP-Sls Engrg)*

Key to Media (For complete agency information see *The Advertising Red Books-Agencies* edition):
1. Bus. Publs. 2. Cable T.V. 3. Catalogs & Directories. 4. Co-op Adv. 5. Consumer Mags. 6. D.M. to Bus. Estab.7. D.M. to Consumers
8. Daily Newsp. 9. Exhibits/Trade Shows 10. Foreign 11. Infomercial 12. Internet Adv.13. Multimedia 14. Network Radio
15. Network T.V. 16. Newsp. Distr. Mags. 17. Other 18. Outdoor (Posters, Transit) 19. Point of Purchase20. Premiums, Novelties
21. Product Samples 22. Special Events Mktg. 23. Spot Radio 24. Spot T.V. 25. Weekly Newsp. 26. Yellow Page Adv.

Brands & Products:
MCORE
MOTRICITY
Advertising Agency:
PAN Communications
300 Brickstone Sq 7th Fl
Andover, MA 01810
Tel.: (978) 474-1900
Fax: (978) 474-1903

MOVEA, INC.

(Sub. of Movea SA)
680 N McCarthy Blvd Ste 120
Milpitas, CA 95035
Fax: (408) 255-9075
Toll Free: (800) 316-5432
E-mail: sales@gyration.com
Web Site: www.gyration.com
E-Mail For Key Personnel:
Sales Director: sales@gyration.com
Sales Range: $1-9.9 Million
Approx. Number Employees: 40
Year Founded: 1989
Business Description:
Hardware & Software Solutions Utilizing Motion Sensing Wireless Peripherals
S.I.C.: 3679; 3577
N.A.I.C.S.: 334419; 334119
Media: 10
Personnel:
Bryan Hoadley *(Exec VP & Gen Mgr)*
Brands & Products:
GYROPOINT TECHNOLOGY
GYROREMOTE
MICROGYRO 100
ULTRA

MPHASE TECHNOLOGIES, INC.

587 Connecticut Ave
Norwalk, CT 06854-1711
Tel.: (203) 838-2741
Toll Free: (877) 674-2738
E-mail: info@mphasetech.com
Web Site: www.mphasetech.com
Approx. Rev.: $354,157
Approx. Number Employees: 9
Year Founded: 1996
Business Description:
Broadcast Digital Television & High-Speed Data Services
S.I.C.: 3663; 3661; 5065
N.A.I.C.S.: 334220; 334210; 423690
Advertising Expenditures: $250,000
Media: 10
Personnel:
Ronald A. Durando *(Chm, Pres & CEO)*
Martin S. Smiley *(CFO & Gen Counsel)*
Gustave T. Dotoli *(COO)*
Brands & Products:
MPHASE
Advertising Agency:
Giles Communications, LLC
2975 Westchester Ave Ste 402
Purchase, NY 10577
Tel.: (914) 644-3500
Fax: (914) 696-4120

MRV COMMUNICATIONS, INC.

20415 Nordhoff St
Chatsworth, CA 91311
Tel.: (818) 773-0900
Fax: (818) 773-0906
E-mail: sales@mrv.com
Web Site: www.mrv.com
E-Mail For Key Personnel:
Sales Director: sales@mrv.com
Public Relations: pr@mrv.com
Approx. Rev.: $263,911,000
Approx. Number Employees: 743
Year Founded: 1988
Business Description:
Laser Components & Equipment & Computer Networking Products Mfr
S.I.C.: 3674; 3679; 5049
N.A.I.C.S.: 334413; 334419; 423490
Advertising Expenditures: $1,900,000
Media: 2-10-13
Personnel:
Near Margalit *(Pres)*
Dilip Singh *(CEO)*
Chris D. King *(CFO)*
Jennifer Hankes Painter *(Chief Compliance Officer, Gen Counsel, Sec & VP)*
Barry R. Gorsun *(Pres-Optical Comm Sys Div)*
David Stehlin *(Sr VP-Sls & Mktg-Optical Comm Sys)*
Chris Tenes *(VP-Sls)*
Blima Tuller *(VP-Fin)*

MSC SOFTWARE CORPORATION

(Sub. of Symphony Technology Group, LLC)
2 MacArthur Pl
Santa Ana, CA 92707
Tel.: (714) 540-8900
Fax: (714) 784-4056
Toll Free: (800) 328-4672
Telex: 472 0462 MSC
Web Site: www.mscsoftware.com
Sales Range: $200-249.9 Million
Approx. Number Employees: 1,006
Year Founded: 1963
Business Description:
Virtual Development Application Services
S.I.C.: 5734; 7372; 7373
N.A.I.C.S.: 443120; 334611; 511210; 541512
Advertising Expenditures: $813,000
Media: 2-4-5-7-10-11-13
Personnel:
Dominic Gallello *(Pres & CEO)*
Amir A. Mobayen *(Exec VP-Worldwide Sls & Svcs)*
Ken Welch *(VP-Strategy & Product Mgmt)*
Brands & Products:
ADAMS
CATCMM
CATIA
DYNAMIC DESIGNER
DYTRAN
EASY5
ENGINEERING-E.COM
ENGINEERING EXCHANGE
FLIGHTLOADS
INTERACTIVE PHYSICS
LAMINATE MODELER
MARC
MD.ADAMS
MD.NASTRAN
MENTAT
MSC
MSC.ACUMEN
MSC.ADAMS
MSC.AFEA
MSC.AKUSMOD
MSC.AMS FVA
MSC.ASTROS
MSC.CATCMM
MSC.CONSTRUCT
MSC.DROPTEST
MSC.DYNAMIC DESIGNER
MSC.DYTRAN
MSC.EASY5
MSC.ENTERPRISE MVISION
MSC.EXPLORE
MSC.FATIGUE
MSC.FEA
MSC.FLIGHTLOADS
MSC.GS-MESHER
MSC.MARC
MSC.MARC MENTAT
MSC.MASTERKEY
MSC.MVISION
MSC.NASTRAN
MSC.NVH MANAGER
MSC.PATRAN
MSC.PATRAN LAMINATE
MSC.ROBUST DESIGN
MSC.SIMMANAGER
MSC.SIMXPERT
MSC.SOFY
MSC.SUPERFORGE
MSC.SUPERFORM
MSC.SUPERMODEL
MSC.TFEA
MSC.THERMAL
MSC.ULTIMA
MSC.VISUALNASTRAN
MSC.VISUALNASTRAN 4D
MVISION DATABANKS
PATRAN
PRO ENGINEER
SIMDESIGNER
SIMOFFICE
SIMULATING REALITY
SIMULATION CENTER
SOFY
UNIGRAPHICS
WORKING MODEL

MSGI SECURITY SOLUTIONS, INC.

575 Madison Ave 10th Fl
New York, NY 10002
Tel.: (212) 605-0245
Fax: (212) 605-0222
E-mail: info@msgisecurity.com
Web Site: www.msgisecurity.com
Approx. Rev.: $2,423,330
Approx. Number Employees: 3
Business Description:
Security Software Products & Services; Encryption Technologies Developer for Surveillance, Intelligence Monitoring & Data Protection
S.I.C.: 7372; 7371; 7373; 7382
N.A.I.C.S.: 511210; 541511; 541512; 561621
Media: 2-13
Personnel:
J. Jeremy Barbera *(Chm & CEO)*
James A. Abrahamson *(Vice Chm)*
Joseph C. Peters *(Pres)*
Richard J. Mitchell III *(Chief Acctg Officer, Treas & Sec)*

MTI SYSTEMS INC.

59 Interstate Dr
West Springfield, MA 01089
Tel.: (413) 733-1972
Fax: (413) 739-9250
Toll Free: (800) 644-4318
E-mail: info@mtisystems.com
Web Site: www.mtisystems.com
E-Mail For Key Personnel:
Marketing Director: marketing@mtisystems.com
Sales Director: sales@mtisystems.com
Approx. Number Employees: 20
Year Founded: 1982
Business Description:
Cost Estimating Computer Software Publisher
S.I.C.: 7372; 7371
N.A.I.C.S.: 511210; 541511
Export
Media: 2-10
Distr.: Intl.; Natl.
Budget Set: Sept.
Personnel:
Rene Laviolette *(COO)*
Nancy Charkiewicz *(Mgr-Adv)*
Brands & Products:
COSTIMATOR
COSTIMATOR JS
COSTIMATOR OEM
MTI SYSTEMS

MTM TECHNOLOGIES, INC.

1200 High Ridge Rd
Stamford, CT 06905
Tel.: (203) 975-3700
Fax: (203) 975-3701
E-mail: info@mtm.com
Web Site: www.mtm.com
Sales Range: $150-199.9 Million
Approx. Number Employees: 416
Year Founded: 1986
Business Description:
Systems Consultants & Technical Specialists Services
S.I.C.: 7373; 8748
N.A.I.C.S.: 541512; 541690
Media: 2-4-10
Personnel:
Gerald A. Poch *(Chm)*
Steven Stringer *(Pres & CEO)*
J.W. Braukman *(CFO & Sr VP)*
Jed Ayres *(Sr VP-Partner Mgmt & Mktg)*
John Centinaro *(Sr VP-Natl Svcs)*
Yvonne Gluck *(Sr VP-Strategic Initiatives)*
Dave Shimp *(Sr VP-HR)*

MTS MEDICATION TECHNOLOGIES, INC.

(Holding of Excellere Partners)
2003 Gandy Blvd N
Saint Petersburg, FL 33702
Tel.: (727) 576-6311
Fax: (800) 671-0588
Toll Free: (800) 671-0508
E-mail: solutions@mts-mt.com
Web Site: www.mts-mt.com
Approx. Sls.: $76,275,000
Approx. Number Employees: 271
Year Founded: 1984
Business Description:
Medication Compliance Packaging Systems
S.I.C.: 2834; 5047
N.A.I.C.S.: 325412; 423450
Media: 2-10
Personnel:
John D. Stanton *(Vice Chm)*
William Shields *(Pres)*
Todd E. Siegel *(CEO)*

Key to Media (For complete agency information see *The Advertising Red Books-Agencies* edition):
1. Bus. Publs. 2. Cable T.V. 3. Catalogs & Directories. 4. Co-op Adv. 5. Consumer Mags. 6. D.M. to Bus. Estab.7. D.M. to Consumers 8. Daily Newsp. 9. Exhibits/Trade Shows 10. Foreign 11. Infomercial 12. Internet Adv.13. Multimedia 14. Network Radio 15. Network T.V. 16. Newsp. Distr. Mags. 17. Other 18. Outdoor (Posters, Transit) 19. Point of Purchase20. Premiums, Novelties 21. Product Samples 22. Special Events Mktg. 23. Spot Radio 24. Spot T.V. 25. Weekly Newsp. 26. Yellow Page Adv.

MTS Medication Technologies, Inc. — (Continued)

Michael D. Stevenson *(COO & VP)*
Dennis H. Ayo *(Sr VP-Sls & Mktg)*
Ronald M. Rosenbaum *(VP-Tech)*
Brands & Products:
AUTOGEN
DEBLISTER
GEMINI
MEDLOCKER
MTS-350
MTS-400
MTS-500
MTS MEDICATION TECHNOLOGIES
MULTI-DOSE
ONDEMAND ACCUFLEX
ONDEMAND EXCELL
ONDEMAND EXPRESS
ONDEMAND EXPRESS II
ONDEMAND MULTI-MED
OPTI-PAK
PLUSPAK
RXMAP
SELECT SEAL
SURESEAL
UNIT-DOSE

MTS SYSTEMS CORPORATION

14000 Technology Dr
Eden Prairie, MN 55344
Tel.: (952) 937-4000
Fax: (952) 937-4515
Toll Free: (800) 328-2255 (Sls)
Telex: 29-0521 MTSSYSTEM ENPE
Web Site: www.mts.com
Approx. Rev.: $374,053,000
Approx. Number Employees: 1,948
Year Founded: 1966
Business Description:
Testing & Sensing Solutions
S.I.C.: 3829; 3824; 8711
N.A.I.C.S.: 334519; 334514; 541330
Export
Advertising Expenditures: $1,000,000
Media: 2-4-7-10-11
Distr.: Intl.; Natl.
Budget Set: July
Personnel:
David J. Anderson *(Chm)*
William V. Murray *(Interim Pres & Interim CEO)*
Susan E. Knight *(CFO)*
Steven G. Mahon *(Chief Compliance Officer, Gen Counsel & Sr VP)*
Arthur R. Baker *(VP & Gen Mgr-Test Bus)*
David Meier *(VP-Worldwide Selling & Mktg)*
Kathleen M. Staby *(VP-HR & Strategy)*
Christoph Leser *(Product Mgr)*
Paul Nave *(Mgr-Market Dev)*
Marcia Lindberg *(Asst Sec)*
Brands & Products:
ACCUPHASE
ADVANTAGE
AERO-90
AEROPRO
ALLIANCE RT
BE CERTAIN
COMPONENT RPC
FIRST ROAD
FLAT-TRAC
FLEXTEST
FLEXTEST GT
FLEXTEST SE
FLEXTEST SE BASIC
FLEXTEST SE PLUS
I-DEAS PRO
LEVEL PLUS
MINI BIONIX II
MTS
MTS BIONIX
MTS INSIGHT
MTS LANDMARK
MTS TEST SUITE
MULTI-AXIAL SIMULATION TABLE
MULTIPURPOSE
NANO BIONIX
NANO INDENTER
POWERTEK
QTEST
REMOTE PARAMETER CONTROL
RENEW
ROADWHEEL
RPC PRO
SAFEDESIGN INSIGHT
SAFEPASS 201
SCHEMA
SILENTFLO
SWIFT
SYNERGIE
TEMPOSONICS
TESTLINE
TESTSTAR
TESTWARE
TESTWORKS
TYTRON
VIRTUAL ENGINE

MULTI-TECH SYSTEMS INC.

2205 Woodale Dr
Mounds View, MN 55112-4909
Tel.: (763) 785-3500
Fax: (763) 785-9874
Toll Free: (800) 328-9717
Toll Free: (888) 288-5470
E-mail: info@multitech.com
Web Site: www.multitech.com
Approx. Number Employees: 380
Year Founded: 1970
Business Description:
Telephony, Internet, Remote Access & Device Networking Products Mfr
S.I.C.: 3661; 3663
N.A.I.C.S.: 334210; 334220
Media: 10-13
Personnel:
Patricia Sharma *(Pres & CEO)*
Damian J. Luna *(COO)*
Carol Montour *(VP-Mktg & Comm)*
Paul Kraska *(Mgr-Mktg)*
Brands & Products:
CALLFINDER
COMMPLETE
FAXFINDER
INTELLIGENT SERIAL INTERFACE
MMCMODEM
MODEMMODULE
MULTIACCESS
MULTICONNECT
MULTIMOBILE
MULTIMODEM
MULTIMODEMDID
MULTIMODEMDSVD
MULTITECH SYSTEMS
MULTIVOIP
RASFINDER
RJMODEM
ROUTEFINDER
SMSFINDER
SOCKETETHERNET IP
SOCKETMODEM
SOCKETSLIC
SOCKETWIRELESS
TALKANYTIME
ZDXMODEMRACK

MULTIBAND CORPORATION

9449 Science Ctr Dr
Minneapolis, MN 55428
Tel.: (763) 504-3000
Fax: (763) 504-3060
Toll Free: (866) 577-6263
E-mail: info@multibandusa.com
Web Site: www.multibandusa.com
Approx. Rev.: $265,594,000
Approx. Number Employees: 3,202
Year Founded: 1975
Business Description:
Video, Data & Voice Systems Services
S.I.C.: 4813; 7629
N.A.I.C.S.: 517310; 517110; 811211
Advertising Expenditures: $28,000
Media: 2-7
Personnel:
Donald M. Miller *(Chm)*
James L. Mandel *(CEO)*
Steven M. Bell *(CFO)*
David Ekman *(CIO)*
Mitch Clarke *(Exec VP)*

MULTIMEDIA GAMES INC.

Bldg B Ste 400 206 Wild Basin Rd S
Austin, TX 78746
Tel.: (512) 334-7500
Fax: (512) 334-7695
E-mail: gameinfo@mm-games.com
Web Site: www.multimediagames.com
Approx. Rev.: $117,936,000
Approx. Number Employees: 397
Year Founded: 1991
Business Description:
Interactive Bingo & Video Lottery Games & Related Electronic Games Designer & Mfr
S.I.C.: 7373; 3999; 5092; 7379; 7999
N.A.I.C.S.: 541512; 339999; 423920; 541519; 713990
Import Export
Media: 1-10-13-19-20
Personnel:
Patrick J. Ramsey *(Pres & CEO)*
Adam D. Chibib *(CFO)*
Jerome R. Smith *(Chief Compliance Officer, Gen Counsel, Sec & Sr VP)*
Mick Roemer *(Sr VP-Sls)*
Joaquin Aviles *(VP-Tech)*
Randi Ingram *(VP-Sls-Casino Gaming)*
Phil Sherwood *(VP-Sls-Govt & Central Determinate)*
Ken Lynchard *(Dir-Sls)*
Lee Hoffman *(Mgr-Sls-Charity Gaming)*
Karen Wirkus *(Mgr-Sls-Charity Gaming)*
Brands & Products:
BAD MONKEY
BETTY BOOP'S ROARING 20'S
BIG CASH BINGO
BLACK & WHITE
BOOM
FILTHY RICH
FLASH 21
FRUIT STAND
GLORY 7'S
JACKPORT PARTY
JUNGLE JUICE
MAXIMUM LOCKDOWN
MEGA CASH
MEGA MELTDOWN
MEGABINGO
MEGABINGO SESSIONS
MEGACASH
MEGAMANIA
MEGAMILLIONS BINGO
MEGANANZA
MEGAPICK
MEGAREELS
MEGASKILL
MEGASWEEPS
MEGAWHEELS
MELT DOWN
MELTDOWN
MELTDOWN CORE REACTION
MGAME
MOONSTRUCK
MULTIMEDIA GAMES
PEOPLE'S CHOICE

MURATEC AMERICA, INC.

(Sub. of Murata Machinery USA Inc.)
3301 E Plano Pkwy Ste 100
Plano, TX 75074
Tel.: (469) 429-3300
Fax: (469) 429-3311
E-mail: webmaster@muratec.com
Web Site: www.muratec.com
Approx. Number Employees: 50
Year Founded: 1982
Business Description:
Facsimile Equipment & Cellular Telephones Mfr
S.I.C.: 5065; 3661
N.A.I.C.S.: 423690; 334210
Advertising Expenditures: $2,800,000
Media: 4-5-6-7-10-14-15-17-19-23-24-25
Distr.: Intl.; Natl.
Personnel:
James C. D'Emidio *(Pres)*
Jim Demidio *(Pres)*
Lou Stricklin *(Mgr-Mktg)*
Brands & Products:
CLIENTEXPRESS
MURATEC
OFFICEBRIDGE
ONEPRINT
UNIMESSAGE

MURPHY-BROWN LLC

(Sub. of Murphy-Brown Holdings LLC)
2822 Hwy 24 W
Warsaw, NC 28398
Mailing Address:
PO Box 856
Warsaw, NC 28398-0856
Tel.: (910) 293-3434
Fax: (910) 293-7551
Web Site: www.murphybrown.com
Sales Range: $1-4.9 Billion
Approx. Number Employees: 4,860
Year Founded: 1939
Business Description:
Producers of Hogs & Turkeys
S.I.C.: 0213
N.A.I.C.S.: 112210
Export
Personnel:
Jerry H. Godwin *(Pres)*
Brock McKloskey *(VP-HR)*
Brands & Products:
MURPHY-BROWN
Advertising Agency:
Charleston/Orwig, Inc.
515 W North Shore Dr
Hartland, WI 53029-8312
Tel.: (262) 563-5100
Fax: (262) 563-5101

Key to Media (For complete agency information see *The Advertising Red Books-Agencies* edition):
1. Bus. Publs. 2. Cable T.V. 3. Catalogs & Directories. 4. Co-op Adv. 5. Consumer Mags. 6. D.M. to Bus. Estab.7. D.M. to Consumers
8. Daily Newsp. 9. Exhibits/Trade Shows 10. Foreign 11. Infomercial 12. Internet Adv.13. Multimedia 14. Network Radio
15. Network T.V. 16. Newsp. Distr. Mags. 17. Other 18. Outdoor (Posters, Transit) 19. Point of Purchase20. Premiums, Novelties
21. Product Samples 22. Special Events Mktg. 23. Spot Radio 24. Spot T.V. 25. Weekly Newsp. 26. Yellow Page Adv.

MUTOH AMERICA INC.
(Sub. of Mutoh Holdings Co., Ltd.)
2602 S 47th St Ste 102
Phoenix, AZ 85034
Tel.: (480) 968-7772
Fax: (602) 414-4645
Fax: (480) 968-7990
Toll Free: (800) 99MUTOH
E-mail: webmaster@mutoh.com
Web Site: www.mutoh.com
Approx. Number Employees: 25
Year Founded: 1963
Business Description:
Large Format Graphic Printers Distr
S.I.C.: 5045
N.A.I.C.S.: 423430
Import Export
Advertising Expenditures: $839,000
Catalogs & Directories: $50,000; Co-op Adv.: $100,000; Consumer Mags.: $75,000; Exhibits/Trade Shows: $50,000; Foreign: $460,000; Other: $99,000; Premiums, Novelties: $5,000
Personnel:
Brian Phitts *(Dir-Sls)*
Gary Rudnick *(Dir-Sls)*
Crystal Baus *(Mgr-Mktg Comm)*
Brands & Products:
ECO-SOLVENT PLUS
FALCON II
FALCON II OUTDOOR
FALCON OUTDOOR
FALCON PLUS
TOUCAN
ULTIMA 1400
ULTIMA 850

MYBIZOFFICE, INC
13454 Sunrise Vly Dr 5th Fl
Herndon, VA 20171
Tel.: (703) 793-6000
Fax: (703) 793-6070
E-mail: info@mybizoffice.com
Web Site: www.mybizoffice.com
Approx. Sls.: $3,000,000
Approx. Number Employees: 450
Year Founded: 1986
Business Description:
Employment & Financial Services for Independent Professionals & Clients
S.I.C.: 7374
N.A.I.C.S.: 518210
Media: 2-7-13
Personnel:
Gene Zaino *(Pres & CEO)*
Kimberly Osgood *(VP-Fin & Acctg)*

NAPSTER, INC.
(Sub. of Best Buy Co., Inc.)
9044 Melrose Ave
Los Angeles, CA 90069
Tel.: (310) 281-5000
Toll Free: (866) 280-7694
Web Site: www.napster.com
Approx. Rev.: $127,452,000
Approx. Number Employees: 133
Year Founded: 2000
Business Description:
Interactive Digital Music Distr
S.I.C.: 7371; 2741; 7379
N.A.I.C.S.: 541511; 516110; 541519
Advertising Expenditures: $5,200,000
Media: 3-8-10-13-22
Personnel:
Glenn Kaino *(Chief Creative Officer)*
Aileen Atkins *(Gen Counsel& Sr VP-Bus Affairs)*
Christopher Allen *(Gen Mgr)*
Brands & Products:
NAPSTER

NATIONAL DATACOMPUTER, INC.
19B Crosby Dr Ste 310
Bedford, MA 01730
Tel.: (978) 663-7677
Fax: (978) 667-1869
E-mail: sales@ndcomputer.com
Web Site: www.ndcomputer.com
E-Mail For Key Personnel:
Sales Director: sales@ndcomputer.com
Approx. Rev.: $908,971
Approx. Number Employees: 6
Year Founded: 1967
Business Description:
Handheld Inventory Computer Mfr
S.I.C.: 3571; 7371
N.A.I.C.S.: 334111; 541511
Export
Advertising Expenditures: $529,790
Media: 2-4-7-10
Distr.: Intl.; Natl.
Brands & Products:
DATACOMPUTER
DC4CE
FINANCIAL AUDIT
NDI
WINTAKES

NATIONAL INSTRUMENTS CORPORATION
11500 N Mopac Expy Bldg B
Austin, TX 78759-3504
Tel.: (512) 794-0100
Fax: (512) 683-8411
E-mail: info@ni.com
Web Site: www.ni.com
Approx. Sls.: $873,220,000
Approx. Number Employees: 5,280
Year Founded: 1976
Business Description:
Supplier of Computer-Based Instrumentation Software & Hardware Products & Solutions
S.I.C.: 3823; 7372
N.A.I.C.S.: 334513; 334611; 511210
Advertising Expenditures: $13,200,000
Media: 2-10
Personnel:
James J. Truchard *(Founder, Chm, Pres & CEO)*
Alexander M. Davern *(CFO, COO, Treas & Exec VP)*
David Hugley *(Gen Counsel, Sec & VP)*
Phillip D. Hester *(Sr VP-R&D)*
Peter Zogas *(Sr VP-Sls & Mktg)*
Ray Almgren *(VP-Product Mktg-Core Platforms)*
Mark Finger *(VP-HR)*
Ajit Gokhale *(VP-Product Mktg)*
John Graff *(VP-Sls & Mktg-Americas)*
Francis Griffiths *(VP-Sls & Mktg-Europe)*
John Hanks *(VP-Life Science)*
Victor Mieres *(VP-Sls & Mktg-Asia/Pacific)*
John Pasquarette *(VP-eBus)*
John Roiko *(VP-Fin)*
Tony Vento *(VP-Sys & Applications Engrg)*
Matt Friedman *(Sr Product Mgr-PXI Platform)*
Julia Betts *(Mgr-Corp Comm)*

NATIONAL PERSONNEL ASSOCIATES COOPERATIVE, INC.
1680 Viewpond Dr SE
Grand Rapids, MI 49508-4907
Tel.: (616) 455-6555
Fax: (616) 455-8255
E-mail: npa@npaworldwide.com
Web Site: www.npaworldwide.com
Sales Range: $10-24.9 Million
Approx. Number Employees: 8
Business Description:
Network of Personnel Placement Professionals
S.I.C.: 7361
N.A.I.C.S.: 541612
Media: 2-5-10
Distr.: Natl.
Budget Set: Mar.
Personnel:
Dave Nerz *(Pres)*
Brands & Products:
COMPUTERNET
FINANCENET
MEDNET
OPSNET
PROCESSNET
QNET
SALESNET
TECHNET

NATIONAL RESEARCH CORPORATION
1245 Q St
Lincoln, NE 68508-3636
Tel.: (402) 475-2525
Fax: (402) 475-9061
E-mail: info@nationalresearch.com
Web Site: www.nationalresearch.com
E-Mail For Key Personnel:
President: mhays@nationalresearch.com
Approx. Rev.: $63,398,000
Approx. Number Employees: 253
Year Founded: 1981
Business Description:
Ongoing Survey-Based Performance Measurement,; Analysis & Tracking Services to the Healthcare Industry
S.I.C.: 8733; 8732
N.A.I.C.S.: 541710; 541910
Advertising Expenditures: $202,000
Media: 7
Personnel:
Michael D. Hays *(Pres & CEO)*
Patrick E. Beans *(VP, CFO, Treas & Sec)*

NAVTEQ CORP.
(Sub. of Nokia Inc.)
425 W Randolph St
Chicago, IL 60606
Tel.: (312) 894-7000
Fax: (312) 894-7050
Web Site: www.navteq.com
Approx. Rev.: $496,512,000
Approx. Number Employees: 3,349
Year Founded: 1985
Business Description:
Comprehensive Digital Map Information Services for Automotive Navigation Systems, Mobile Navigation Devices & Internet-Based Mapping Applications
S.I.C.: 8713; 7371
N.A.I.C.S.: 541360; 541370; 541511
Media: 2-7-8-10-13-17
Personnel:
Judson C. Green *(Pres, CEO & Exec Dir)*
Amreesh Modi *(CTO & Exec VP)*
Lawrence M. Kaplan *(Gen Counsel, Sec & Exec VP)*
Denise M. Doyle *(Exec VP-Strategy & Bus Plng)*
Clifford I. Fox *(Exec VP-NAVTEQ Map Div)*
John K. Macleod *(Exec VP)*
Jeffrey L. Mize *(Exec VP-Global Sls)*
Howard Hayes *(Sr VP-Trafic)*
Christine C. Moore *(Sr VP-HR)*
Richard E. Shuman *(Sr VP)*
Kelly A. Smith *(Sr VP-Corp Mktg)*
Lonnie Arima *(VP & Gen Mgr-Americas Personal Navigation Products)*
Christopher M. Rothey *(VP-Adv)*
Bob Basiewicz *(Dir-Digital Art)*
Jennifer Schuh *(Specialist-PR)*
Brands & Products:
NAVTEQ

NCR CORPORATION
3097 Satellite Blvd
Duluth, GA 30096
Tel.: (937) 445-5000
Fax: (937) 445-5541
Toll Free: (800) 225-5627
E-mail: investor.relations@ncr.com
Web Site: www.ncr.com
Approx. Rev.: $4,819,000,000
Approx. Number Employees: 21,000
Year Founded: 1884
Business Description:
Automated Teller Machines, Point-of-Sale Terminals & Bar Code Scanners Mfr; Data Warehousing Services
S.I.C.: 3572; 3555; 3577; 3581; 3827; 7374
N.A.I.C.S.: 334112; 333293; 333311; 333314; 334119; 518210
Import Export
Media: 2-5-7-10-11-13-17
Distr.: Intl.; Natl.
Personnel:
William R. Nuti *(Chm & CEO)*
Jim Calabrese *(CFO & COO)*
Robert Fishman *(CFO, Chief Acctg Officer & Sr VP)*
William Van Curen *(Interim CIO & VP-IT)*
Richard Bravman *(CMO & VP-Corp Dev)*
Alan Chow *(CTO & Sr VP-R & D)*
Jennifer Daniels *(Gen Counsel & Sec)*
John G. Bruno *(Exec VP)*
Daniel T. Bogan *(Sr VP & Gen Mgr-NCR Consumables)*
Scott Kingsfield *(Sr VP & Gen Mgr-Retail)*
Christopher J. Askew *(Sr VP-Svcs)*
Peter A. Dorsman *(Sr VP-Global Ops)*
Peter Leav *(Sr VP-Global Sls)*
Andrea L. Ledford *(Sr VP-HR)*
Justin Hotard *(VP & Gen Mgr-Entertainment)*
Mark Quinlan *(VP & Gen Mgr)*
Janet Brewer *(VP-Comm)*
Tushar Kothari *(VP-Sls)*
Brands & Products:
ADVANCED STORE
APTRA
CHEXPRESS
COMPATIBLE
DYNAKEY

Key to Media (For complete agency information see *The Advertising Red Books-Agencies* edition):
1. Bus. Publs. 2. Cable T.V. 3. Catalogs & Directories. 4. Co-op Adv. 5. Consumer Mags. 6. D.M. to Bus. Estab.7. D.M. to Consumers 8. Daily Newsp. 9. Exhibits/Trade Shows 10. Foreign 11. Infomercial 12. Internet Adv.13. Multimedia 14. Network Radio 15. Network T.V. 16. Newsp. Distr. Mags. 17. Other 18. Outdoor (Posters, Transit) 19. Point of Purchase20. Premiums, Novelties 21. Product Samples 22. Special Events Mktg. 23. Spot Radio 24. Spot T.V. 25. Weekly Newsp. 26. Yellow Page Adv.

NCR Corporation — (Continued)

EASYPOINT
EXPERIENCE A NEW WORLD OF INTERACTION
IMAGEMARK
ITRAN
LASERSELECT
NCR
NCR @ YOUR SERVICE
NCR FASTLANE
NCR REALPOS
NCR REALPRICE
NCR REALSCAN
NCR REALSOLUTIONS
NCR SELFSERV
PERSONAS
TERADATA

NEGAFILE SYSTEMS

(Sub. of Electron Microscopy Sciences, Inc.)
3069 Edison Furlong Rd
Furlong, PA 18925-1235
Mailing Address:
PO Box 78
Furlong, PA 18925-0078
Tel.: (215) 348-2356
Fax: (215) 348-8822
Toll Free: (888) 881-6435
E-mail: info@negafile.com
Web Site: www.negafile.com
Approx. Number Employees: 10
Year Founded: 1939
Business Description:
Files & Preservers Mfr for Negatives, Slides & Prints
S.I.C.: 3861; 5043
N.A.I.C.S.: 333315; 423410
Export
Media: 4-6-10-19-21
Distr.: Natl.
Budget Set: Dec.
Personnel:
Peter Goodman *(Pres)*
Christopher Goodman *(Comptroller)*
Brands & Products:
NEGAFILE

NER HOLDINGS INC.

307 S Delsea Dr
Glassboro, NJ 08028-2608
Tel.: (856) 881-5524
Fax: (856) 881-2393
Toll Free: (888) 637-3282
E-mail: admin@nerdata.com
Web Site: www.nerdata.com
Approx. Number Employees: 350
Year Founded: 1971
Business Description:
Holding Company; Computer Peripheral Equipment Mfr
S.I.C.: 6719; 3577
N.A.I.C.S.: 551112; 334119
Media: 2-5-10-25
Personnel:
Francis C. Oatway *(Chm & CEO)*
Stephen Oatway *(Pres & COO)*
Chris Oatway *(CFO & CIO)*
Dudley A. DeVore *(Exec VP-Sls)*
Scott Steele *(Sr VP-Bus Devel & Mktg)*
Greg Stover *(Sr VP-Sls)*
Rob Huttemann *(VP & Gen Mgr)*
Ron Celli *(Dir-Media Mgmt)*
Tom Bergamo *(Mgr-Credit & Collections)*
Brands & Products:
DSVIEW
FLEX-PAK
GLIDEAWAY
HOTSPOTR
IDENTITY
INNOVATION. LEADERSHIP. VALUE DRIVEN.
MEGAPRINT
MEGATONE
NER
PAC-TOTE
PARAGON
PRINT4
S.A.M.
SLOT ADDRESSABLE MANAGEMENT
SMRTSYSTEM
TURTLE

NET TALK.COM, INC.

1100 NW 163rd Dr
Miami, FL 33169
Tel.: (305) 621-1200
Fax: (305) 621-1201
E-mail: sales@nettalk.com
Web Site: www.nettalk.com
E-Mail For Key Personnel:
Sales Director: sales@nettalk.com
Approx. Rev.: $737,498
Approx. Number Employees: 35
Business Description:
Commercial & Residential Telecommunication Services
S.I.C.: 4812
N.A.I.C.S.: 517212
Advertising Expenditures: $357,413
Personnel:
Guillermo Rodriguez *(CFO)*
Kenneth A. Hosfeld *(Exec VP)*
Anastasios Kyriakides *(Dir-Mktg)*

NETAPP, INC.

495 E Java Dr
Sunnyvale, CA 94089
Tel.: (408) 822-6000
Fax: (408) 822-4501
E-mail: investor_relations@netapp.com
Web Site: www.netapp.com
Approx. Rev.: $5,122,600,000
Approx. Number Employees: 11,212
Year Founded: 1992
Business Description:
Computer Integrated Systems Design Services
S.I.C.: 3572; 7373
N.A.I.C.S.: 334112; 541512
Media: 2-4-7-13
Distr.: Intl.
Personnel:
David Hitz *(Co-Founder & Exec VP)*
James Lau *(Co-Founder & Exec VP)*
Daniel J. Warmenhoven *(Chm)*
Thomas Georgens *(Pres & CEO)*
Steven J. Gomo *(CFO & Exec VP)*
Christine Heckart *(CMO)*
Vic Mahadevan *(Chief Strategy Officer)*
Matthew Fawcett *(Gen Counsel, Sec & Sr VP)*
Ed Deenihan *(Exec VP-Customer Advocacy)*
Manish Goel *(Exec VP-Product Ops)*
Gwen Mcdonald *(Exec VP-HR)*
Bob Pearse *(Exec VP-Bus Dev & Mktg)*
Rob Salmon *(Exec VP-Field Ops)*
Rich Clifton *(Sr VP & Gen Mgr-Tech Enablement & Solutions Org)*
Mark Jon Bluth *(Sr VP-Ops)*
Tom Gerstenberger *(Sr VP-Field Strategy & Ops)*
Jay Kidd *(Sr VP-Product Strategy)*
Steve Kleiman *(Chief Scientist Officer & Sr VP)*
Julie Parrish *(Sr VP-Sls-Worldwide)*
Patrick Rogers *(VP-Corp Alliances)*
Jodi Baumann *(Sr Dir-Corp Comm)*
Tara Dhillon *(Sr Dir-IR)*
Kris Newton *(Sr Dir-Market Intelligence & Strategy)*
Kris C. Hansen *(Mgr-US Comml Sls-South Texas District)*
Brands & Products:
APPLIANCEWATCH
BROCADE ENCRYPTION
CIFS
DATA ONTAP
DATA ONTAP 7G
DATA ONTAP GX
DATA ONTAP GX SYSTEM
DATA ONTAP SNAPSHOT
DATAFABRIC
DATAFORT
DEDUPLICATION
FAS2000 SERIES SOFTWARE PACKS
FAS3100 SERIES
FAS6000 SERIES
FASERVER
FC HOST PLATFORMS
FC SAN
FC SWITCHES & DIRECTORS
FCOE
FILE STORAGE RESOURCE MANAGER
FILERVIEW
FLEXCACHE
FLEXCLONE
FLEXSHARE
FLEXVOL
HA SYSTEM CONFIGURATION
INFORMATION SERVER
IP SAN (ISCSI) SOLUTIONS
LIFETIME KEY MANAGEMENT
LOCKVAULT
METROCLUSTER
MULTISTORE
NAS
NEARSTORE
NETAPP
NETAPP ONCOMMAND
NETAPP VTL
NETWORK APPLIANCE
NFS
OPEN STANDARDS INTEGRATION
OPEN SYSTEMS SNAPVAULT
OPERATIONS MANAGER
PERFORMANCE ACCELERATION MODULE
PROTECTION MANAGER
PROVISIONING SOFTWARE
RAID-DP
SANSCREEN
SECURESHARE
SINGLE MAILBOX RECOVERY
SNAPDRIVE
SNAPLOCK
SNAPMANAGER
SNAPMIRROR
SNAPMOVER
SNAPRESTORE
SNAPSHOT
SNAPVALIDATOR
SNAPVAULT
STORAGE ACCELERATION APPLIANCE
STORAGEGRID
SYNCMIRROR
SYSTEM MANAGEMENT
V3100 SERIES
V6000 SERIES
VIRTUAL FILE MANAGER
WAFL
Advertising Agencies:
Catapult Direct
1700 Winchester Blvd
Campbell, CA 95008
Tel.: (408) 369-8111

Mediasmith
274 Brannan St Ste 601
San Francisco, CA 94107-2000
Tel.: (415) 252-9339
Fax: (415) 252-9854

NETDEPOSIT, INC.

(Sub. of Zions Bancorporation)
4141 Highland Dr
Salt Lake City, UT 84124
Tel.: (479) 273-6067
Fax: (479) 273-6064
E-mail: info@netdeposit.com
Web Site: www.net-deposit.com
Sales Range: $25-49.9 Million
Approx. Number Employees: 50
Business Description:
Electronic Check Software Whslr
S.I.C.: 5045
N.A.I.C.S.: 423430
Media: 7-10
Personnel:
Danne L. Buchanan *(CEO)*
Brands & Products:
NETCAPTURE
NETCONNECT
NETDEPOSIT

NETEZZA CORPORATION

(Sub. of International Business Machines Corporation)
26 Forest St
Marlborough, MA 01752
Tel.: (508) 382-8200
Fax: (508) 382-8300
Web Site: www.netezza.com
Approx. Rev.: $190,635,000
Approx. Number Employees: 425
Year Founded: 2000
Business Description:
Data Warehouse Appliances
S.I.C.: 3572
N.A.I.C.S.: 334112
Advertising Expenditures: $400,000
Media: 1-10-17-22
Personnel:
Patrick J. Scannell, Jr. *(CFO, Treas & Sr VP)*
Patricia Cotter *(Sr VP-Ops)*
David Flaxman *(Sr VP-Products & Tech)*
Prat Moghe *(Sr VP-Strategy & Mktg)*
Raymond Tacoma *(Sr VP-Worldwide Sls)*
Kelli-Ann Mccabe *(VP-HR)*
John Metzger *(VP-Product Strategy)*
Wendy Wheeler *(VP-Mktg-Corp & Field)*
Marty Woodford *(VP-Info Sys)*
Advertising Agency:
Schwartz Communications, Inc.
230 3rd Ave

Waltham, MA 02451
Tel.: (781) 684-0770
Fax: (781) 684-6500
— Ann McDonough *(Acct Exec)*
— Dawn Sullivan *(Acct Exec)*

NETGEAR, INC.
350 E Plumeria Dr
San Jose, CA 95134
Tel.: (408) 907-8000
Fax: (408) 907-8097
E-mail: netgear.rebateinfo@netgear.com
Web Site: www.netgear.com
Approx. Rev.: $902,052,000
Approx. Number Employees: 654
Business Description:
Network Solutions Products Mfr
S.I.C.: 3577; 3661; 3669
N.A.I.C.S.: 334119; 334210; 334290
Advertising Expenditures: $14,400,000
Media: 6-19
Personnel:
Patrick C.S. Lo *(Chm & CEO)*
Christine M. Gorjanc *(CFO)*
Michael F. Falcon *(Sr VP-Ops & Support)*
Charles T. Olson *(Sr VP-Engrg)*
David Soares *(Sr VP-Sls & SMB Bus-Worldwide)*
Michael A. Werdann *(VP-Sls-America)*
Jason Leung *(Sr Mgr-Product Mktg-Comml Security Solutions)*
Brands & Products:
CONNECT WITH INNOVATION
EVERYBODY'S CONNECTING
FRONTVIEW
GEAR GUY
NETGEAR
POWERSHIFT
PROSAFE
PROSECURE
RAIDAR
RAIDIATOR
RANGEMAX
READYNAS
SMART WIZARD
SUPER G
X-RAID
X-RAID2
Advertising Agencies:
Sterling Communications
750 University Ave Ste 100
Los Gatos, CA 95032
Tel.: (408) 395-5500
Fax: (408) 395-5533
Public Relations

Weber Shandwick-Sunnyvale
150 Mathilda Pl Ste 302
Sunnyvale, CA 94086
Tel.: (408) 530-8400
Fax: (408) 530-8474
US Agency of Record

NETLOGIC MICROSYSTEMS, INC.
3975 Freedom Cir
Santa Clara, CA 95054
Tel.: (408) 454-3000
E-mail: info@netlogicmicro.com
Web Site: www.netlogicmicro.com
Approx. Rev.: $381,745,000
Approx. Number Employees: 645
Year Founded: 1998
Business Description:
Fabless Semiconductor Computer Chips Designer & Mfr
S.I.C.: 3674
N.A.I.C.S.: 334413
Export
Media: 10-13
Personnel:
Leonard Charles Perham *(Chm)*
Ronald S. Jankov *(Pres & CEO)*
Michael T. Tate *(CFO & VP)*
Varadarajan Srinivasan *(CTO & VP-Product Dev)*
Roland Cortes *(Gen Counsel, Sec & VP)*
Behrooz Abdi *(Exec VP)*
Ibrahim Korgav *(Sr VP-Worldwide Bus Ops)*
Marcia Zander *(Sr VP-Worldwide Sls)*
Dimitrios Dimitrelis *(VP-Engrg)*
Chris O'Reilly *(VP-Mktg)*
Si Gutierrez *(Sr Dir-Supply Chain & Plng-Global)*
Brands & Products:
AELURUS
AYAMA
CYNAPSE
FASTLINK
INSPECTS EVERY BIT EVERY PACKET EVERY RULE
KEY CAPTURE
MINI-KEY
NETL7
NETLITE
NETLOGIC MICROSYSTEMS
PUTTING INTELLIGENCE IN THE NETWORK
SAHASRA INTELLIGENCE ELEVATED
SOFT PRIORITY
SYNCCAM
ZERO TABLE MANAGEMENT

NETMOTION WIRELESS, INC.
701 N 34th St Ste 250
Seattle, WA 98103
Tel.: (206) 691-5500
Fax: (206) 691-5501
Toll Free: (877) 818-7626
E-mail: marketing@nmwco.com
Web Site: www.netmotionwireless.com
Approx. Rev.: $21,487,000
Approx. Number Employees: 112
Year Founded: 2001
Business Description:
Mobile Productivity & Management Software Publisher
S.I.C.: 7372; 4812; 7379
N.A.I.C.S.: 511210; 517212; 541519
Media: 10
Personnel:
Gordon H. Smith *(Chm)*
Robert H. Hunsberger *(Pres & CEO)*
Brian Rice *(CFO & Sr VP)*
Andy Willett *(Sr VP-Sls & Mktg)*
Rob Mattson *(Reg VP-Sls)*
Pam Cory *(VP-Mktg)*
Paul Riebock *(VP-Federal Market)*

NETOPIA, INC.
(Sub. of Motorola Mobility Holdings, Inc.)
(d/b/a Motorola Broadband Solutions Group)
1101 Marina Village Pkwy Ste 200
Emeryville, CA 94501
Tel.: (510) 217-7451
Fax: (510) 217-7601
Toll Free: (800) 672-2946
Web Site: www.netopia.com
Approx. Rev.: $113,264,000
Approx. Number Employees: 297
Year Founded: 1986
Business Description:
Broadband Networking Equipment & Carrier-Class Software Mfr
S.I.C.: 3577; 3679; 7372
N.A.I.C.S.: 334119; 334418; 334611; 511210
Export
Advertising Expenditures: $400,000
Media: 2-4-6-7-10-11-13-19-26
Distr.: Intl.; Natl.
Personnel:
Alan B. Lefkof *(Corp VP & Gen Mgr)*
Brands & Products:
BROADBAND WITHOUT BOUNDARIES
BUSINESS VISIBILITY
CAYMAN
ECARE
HOME VISIBILITY
NETOCTOPUS
TIMBUKTU
TIMBUKTU PRO

NETSMART TECHNOLOGIES, INC.
(Joint Venture of Insight Venture Partners & Bessemer Venture Partners)
3500 Sunrise Hwy Ste D-122
Great River, NY 11739
Tel.: (631) 968-2000
Fax: (631) 968-2123
Toll Free: (800) 421-7503
E-mail: info@ntst.com
Web Site: www.ntst.com
Approx. Rev.: $59,049,683
Approx. Number Employees: 337
Year Founded: 1992
Business Description:
Health & Human Services Software Developer, Marketer & Technical Support Services; Owned by Insight Venture Partners & Bessemer Venture Partners
S.I.C.: 7372; 7374; 7389
N.A.I.C.S.: 511210; 518210; 541990; 561499
Advertising Expenditures: $395,476
Media: 1-2-5-9-10-13
Personnel:
James L. Conway *(CEO)*
Anthony F. Grisanti *(CFO & Exec VP)*
Timothy Donovan *(Gen Counsel)*
James H. Gargiulo *(Exec VP-Clients & Solutions)*
Joseph R. McGovern *(Exec VP-Strategic Initiatives)*
Kevin Scalia *(Exec VP-Corp Dev)*
Alan B. Tillinghast *(Exec VP-Ops)*

NETWORK EQUIPMENT TECHNOLOGIES, INC.
(d/b/a Net.com)
6900 Paseo Padre Pkwy
Fremont, CA 94555-3660
Tel.: (510) 713-7300
Fax: (510) 574-4000
Toll Free: (800) 234-4638
E-mail: info@net.com
Web Site: www.net.com
E-Mail For Key Personnel:
Public Relations: publicrelations@net.com
Approx. Rev.: $60,147,000
Approx. Number Employees: 234
Year Founded: 1983
Business Description:
Voice, ATM & IP Development Services
S.I.C.: 3661; 7629
N.A.I.C.S.: 334210; 811211
Export
Advertising Expenditures: $23,493,000
Media: 2-7-10-13
Personnel:
Dixon R. Doll *(Chm)*
Charles Nicholas Keating, Jr. *(Pres & CEO)*
David Wagenseller *(CFO & VP-Fin)*
Talbot A. Harty *(CTO & CMO)*
Frank Slattery *(Gen Counsel & VP)*
Matthew Krueger *(VP-Corp Mktg & Bus Dev)*
Caroline Strickler *(VP-HR)*
Brands & Products:
CELLXPRESS
FRAME RELAY EXCHANGE
FRAMEXPRESS
IDNX PRIMESWITCH
ISDNX
LAN/WAN EXCHANGE
NET
NETMS
NETOPEN
PANAVUE
PORTEXTENDER
PRIMEVOICE
PROMINA
SCREAM
SHOUT
SHOUTIP
SPX
STM
SWIFTCELL

NETWORK HARDWARE RESALE, LLC
Ste A 26 Castilian Dr
Goleta, CA 93117-5565
Tel.: (805) 964-9975
Fax: (805) 964-9405
Toll Free: (800) 451-3407
E-mail: cory@networkhardware.com
Web Site: www.networkhardware.com
Approx. Number Employees: 200
Year Founded: 1985
Business Description:
Used Networking Equipment Whslr
S.I.C.: 5045
N.A.I.C.S.: 423430
Media: 10-13
Personnel:
Chuck Sheldon *(Chm)*
Mike Sheldon *(Pres & CEO)*
Andrea Greene *(CFO)*
Mark V. Kelly *(VP-IT)*
Michael W. Lodato *(VP-Mktg & Bus Dev)*
Sara Harshbarger *(Dir-Svcs)*
Doron Halevi *(Mgr-Europe)*

NETWORK SYSTEMS INTERNATIONAL, INC.
3859 Battleground Ave Suite 301
Greensboro, NC 27401
Tel.: (336) 271-8400
Fax: (336) 273-3235
Toll Free: (800) 400-8949

Key to Media (For complete agency information see *The Advertising Red Books-Agencies* edition):
1. Bus. Publs. 2. Cable T.V. 3. Catalogs & Directories. 4. Co-op Adv. 5. Consumer Mags. 6. D.M. to Bus. Estab.7. D.M. to Consumers 8. Daily Newsp. 9. Exhibits/Trade Shows 10. Foreign 11. Infomercial 12. Internet Adv.13. Multimedia 14. Network Radio 15. Network T.V. 16. Newsp. Distr. Mags. 17. Other 18. Outdoor (Posters, Transit) 19. Point of Purchase20. Premiums, Novelties 21. Product Samples 22. Special Events Mktg. 23. Spot Radio 24. Spot T.V. 25. Weekly Newsp. 26. Yellow Page Adv.

Network Systems International, Inc.—(Continued)

E-mail: info@nesi.net
Web Site: www.nesi.net
Approx. Number Employees: 15
Year Founded: 1974
Business Description:
Develops & Markets Enterprise Resource Planning & Supply Chain Management Software Solutions
S.I.C.: 7372; 7371
N.A.I.C.S.: 511210; 541511
Media: 7-10
Personnel:
Robbie M. Efird *(CEO)*
Aitan Zacharin *(CMO & CIO)*
Brands & Products:
THE NET COLLECTION
NET EXEC
NETWORK SYSTEMS INTERNATIONAL
SOFTWARE THAT NEVER WEARS OUT
TRACKINGPORTAL.NET

NETWORKFLEET, INC.
(Sub. of HUGHES Telematics, Inc.)
6363 Greenwich Dr Ste 200
San Diego, CA 92122
Tel.: (858) 450-3245
Fax: (858) 450-3246
Toll Free: (866) 227-7323 (Sales)
E-mail: info@networkfleet.com
Web Site: www.networkcar.com
Sales Range: $1-9.9 Million
Approx. Number Employees: 110
Year Founded: 1999
Business Description:
Motor Vehicle Remote Monitoring & Data Communication Technologies Developer & Marketer
S.I.C.: 3714; 3663; 7372
N.A.I.C.S.: 336322; 334220; 511210
Media: 2-6
Personnel:
Diego A. Borrego *(Founder & VP-Product Engrg)*
Keith Schneider *(Pres & CEO)*
Tamara Chamberlin *(VP-Sls)*
Joshua Haims *(VP-Fin)*
Craig Whitney *(VP-Mktg)*
Chris Ransom *(Dir-Product Mgmt)*

NEW HORIZONS WORLDWIDE, INC.
1900 S State College Blvd Ste 450
Anaheim, CA 92806
Tel.: (484) 567-3000
Tel.: (484) 567-3039 (IR)
Fax: (714) 940-5807
Web Site: www.newhorizons.com
E-Mail For Key Personnel:
Public Relations: mark.tucker@newhorizons.com
Approx. Rev.: $33,977,000
Approx. Number Employees: 215
Year Founded: 1982
Business Description:
Computer Training Centers Owner & Franchisor
S.I.C.: 8243; 8299
N.A.I.C.S.: 611420; 611699; 611710
Advertising Expenditures: $338,000
Media: 1-2-4-8-9-10-11-13-14-15-18-19-20-21-22-23-24-25-26
Personnel:
David L. Warnock *(Chm)*
Mark A. Miller *(CEO)*
Howard H. Mark *(CIO & Exec VP)*
Gregory E. Marsella *(Gen Counsel, Sec & VP)*
Timothy Kleczka *(Sr VP-Ops)*
Heidi D. Rose *(Sr VP-Mktg)*
Mark Tucker *(VP-Mktg)*
Brands & Products:
COMPUTER LEARNING CENTERS
NEW HORIZONS
NEW HORIZONS COMPUTER LEARNING CENTERS

NEW ULM TELECOM, INC.
27 N Minnesota St
New Ulm, MN 56073
Tel.: (507) 354-4111
Fax: (507) 233-4241
E-mail: onlinecustomerservice@nutelecom.net
Web Site: www.nutelecom.net
Approx. Rev.: $31,919,163
Approx. Number Employees: 131
Business Description:
Telecommunication Services
S.I.C.: 4813; 4812
N.A.I.C.S.: 517110; 517212
Advertising Expenditures: $220,474
Personnel:
James P Jensen *(Chm)*
Bill Otis *(Pres & CEO)*
Curtis Owen Kawlewski *(CFO)*
Barbara Bornhoft *(COO, Sec & VP)*

NEWTECH INFOSYSTEMS, INC.
9999 Muirlands Blvd
Irvine, CA 92618
Tel.: (949) 421-0720
Fax: (949) 421-0750
E-mail: info@ntius.com
Web Site: www.ntius.com
Approx. Sls.: $5,600,000
Approx. Number Employees: 30
Business Description:
Software Products Developer & Distr
S.I.C.: 5734
N.A.I.C.S.: 443120
Media: 6
Personnel:
William Yao *(Pres)*
Chris Chen *(VP-Sls)*
Brands & Products:
BACKUP NOW
DRAGON BURN
DRIVEBACKUP
EASYSTEPS
FILECD
REALONE
RHAPSODY
Advertising Agency:
Marken Communications Inc.
3375 Scott Blvd Ste 236
Santa Clara, CA 95054-3113
Tel.: (408) 986-0100
Fax: (408) 986-0162
— Andy Marken *(Pres)*

NEXPRESS SOLUTIONS LLC
(Sub. of Eastman Kodak Company)
2600 Manitou Rd
Rochester, NY 14653
Fax: (585) 253-5525
Fax: (585) 253-1590
Toll Free: (800) 698-3324
Web Site: www.nexpress.com
Approx. Sls.: $70,000,000
Approx. Number Employees: 610
Year Founded: 1998
Business Description:
Toners & Prepared Photographic Mfr
S.I.C.: 3861
N.A.I.C.S.: 325992
Media: 10-13

NEXSAN CORPORATION
555 St Charles Dr Ste 202
Thousand Oaks, CA 91360
Tel.: (805) 418-2700
Fax: (805) 418-2799
Toll Free: (866) 463-9726
E-mail: sales@nexsan.com
Web Site: www.nexsan.com
E-Mail For Key Personnel:
Sales Director: sales@nexsan.com
Sales Range: $50-74.9 Million
Approx. Number Employees: 126
Year Founded: 2001
Business Description:
Computer Storage Devices
S.I.C.: 3572
N.A.I.C.S.: 334112
Advertising Expenditures: $109,000
Media: 5-10-13
Personnel:
Richard A. McGinn *(Co-Chm)*
George Weiss *(Co-Chm)*
Philip Black *(Pres & CEO)*
Eugene Spies *(CFO)*
Richard Mussman *(COO)*
James Molenda *(Co Founder, Exec VP-Global Sls Ops & Stragegic Accts)*
Gregg Pugmire *(Exec VP-Bus Dev)*
Victoria Grey *(Sr VP-Mktg)*

NEXTANCE, INC.
(Sub. of Versata Enterprises Inc.)
475 Broadway St
Redwood City, CA 94063
Tel.: (650) 716-2400
Fax: (650) 716-2399
E-mail: info@nextance.com
Web Site: www.nextance.com
Sales Range: $10-24.9 Million
Approx. Number Employees: 79
Year Founded: 2000
Business Description:
Management Software & Services
S.I.C.: 7371
N.A.I.C.S.: 541511
Media: 10

NEXTEST SYSTEMS CORP.
(Sub. of Teradyne Inc.)
875 Embedded Way
San Jose, CA 95138
Tel.: (408) 960-2400
Fax: (408) 960-7660
E-mail: sales@nextest.com
Web Site: www.nextest.com
E-Mail For Key Personnel:
Sales Director: sales@nextest.com
Approx. Rev.: $79,721,000
Approx. Number Employees: 229
Year Founded: 1997
Business Description:
Automated Test Equipment Designer Mfr
S.I.C.: 3825; 3674
N.A.I.C.S.: 334515; 334413
Advertising Expenditures: $947,000
Media: 10
Personnel:
Craig Foster *(VP-Engrg)*
Brands & Products:
DYNAMIC ANALOG
MAGNUM
MAVERICK
MAVERICK GT
MAVERICK HD
MAVERICK TESTER
MAVERICK VT

NEXTSYSSECURE, INC.
(d/b/a Interloci Network Management)
PO Box 295
Hudson, NH 03051
Tel.: (617) 532-1026
Fax: (603) 386-7200
E-mail: sales@nextsyssecure.com
Web Site: www.interloci.com
Approx. Sls.: $2,000,000
Approx. Number Employees: 30
Year Founded: 2000
Business Description:
Network Management Products & Services
S.I.C.: 8742
N.A.I.C.S.: 541611
Media: 10-13
Brands & Products:
NETWORKSAOK
USBMON

NIC INC.
25501 W Valley Parkway Ste 300
Olathe, KS 66061
Tel.: (877) 234-3468
Fax: (913) 498-3472
E-mail: cneff@nicusa.com
Web Site: www.nicusa.com
E-Mail For Key Personnel:
Marketing Director: cneff@nicusa.com
Approx. Rev.: $161,533,859
Approx. Number Employees: 596
Year Founded: 1997
Business Description:
Internet-Based, Electronic Government Services
S.I.C.: 7371; 8742
N.A.I.C.S.: 541614; 541511; 541611
Media: 10-13-22
Personnel:
Harry Herington *(Chm & CEO)*
Stephen M. Kovzan *(CFO)*
William F. Bradley, Jr. *(COO & Gen Counsel)*
Aimi Daughtery *(Chief Acctg Officer)*
Robert Knapp *(Exec VP)*
Christopher Neff *(VP-Mktg)*
Candy Irven *(Reg Mgr-Bus Dev & Dir-Programs & Alliances)*
Nancy Beaton *(Dir-Comm, IR & Mktg)*
Elizabeth Proudfit *(Dir-Bus Dev)*
Brands & Products:
THE PEOPLE BEHIND EGOVERNMENT
PUTTING GOVERNMENT AT YOUR FINGERTIPS

NIELSEN BUZZMETRICS
(Branch of Nielsen BuzzMetrics, Inc.)
1128 Main St 4th Fl
Cincinnati, OH 45212
Tel.: (513) 618-6700
Fax: (513) 618-6702
Web Site: www.nielsenbuzzmetrics.com
Year Founded: 1997

Key to Media (For complete agency information see *The Advertising Red Books-Agencies* edition):
1. Bus. Publs. 2. Cable T.V. 3. Catalogs & Directories. 4. Co-op Adv. 5. Consumer Mags. 6. D.M. to Bus. Estab.7. D.M. to Consumers 8. Daily Newsp. 9. Exhibits/Trade Shows 10. Foreign 11. Infomercial 12. Internet Adv.13. Multimedia 14. Network Radio 15. Network T.V. 16. Newsp. Distr. Mags. 17. Other 18. Outdoor (Posters, Transit) 19. Point of Purchase20. Premiums, Novelties 21. Product Samples 22. Special Events Mktg. 23. Spot Radio 24. Spot T.V. 25. Weekly Newsp. 26. Yellow Page Adv.

Business Description:
Online Consumer-Generated Media Analysis Services
S.I.C.: 8732
N.A.I.C.S.: 541910
Media: 2-4-7-10-13-17
Personnel:
Karthik Iyer *(COO)*
Jay Stockwell *(Sr VP & Chief Revenue Officer-Digital Media)*

NIGHTINGALE
(Sub. of Nightingale Informatix Corporation)
10670 White Rock Rd Ste 300
Rancho Cordova, CA 95670-6018
Tel.: (916) 638-4744
Tel.: (916) 231-4833
Fax: (916) 638-0504
Toll Free: (800) 343-5737
Toll Free: (877) 879-8633
E-mail: info@nightingale.md
Web Site: www.nightingale.md
Sales Range: $1-9.9 Million
Approx. Number Employees: 9
Year Founded: 1997
Business Description:
Healthcare Information Systems Software & Technology Mfr
S.I.C.: 7372; 7371; 7373; 7379
N.A.I.C.S.: 334611; 511210; 541511; 541512; 541519
Advertising Expenditures: $50,000
Media: 2-7-10-13
Personnel:
Sam Chebib *(Pres & CEO)*
Liesel Loesch *(VP-Fin & Admin)*
Jennifer Dosetti *(Mgr-Mktg)*
Brands & Products:
BILLADVANTAGE
CHARTKEEPER
CODEADVANTAGE
ENCOUNTERPRO
NORTHERN HEALTH
NORTHERN HEALTH ANESTHESIA
RIDGEMARK
SECURECONNECT
THERAPIST HELPER

NITROSECURITY, INC.
230 Commerce Way
Portsmouth, NH 03801
Tel.: (603) 766-8160
Fax: (603) 766-8169
Web Site: www.nitrosecurity.com
Approx. Rev.: $2,353,197
Approx. Number Employees: 51
Business Description:
Computer Network Security Monitoring, Analysis & Protection Hardware & Software
S.I.C.: 7373
N.A.I.C.S.: 541512
Advertising Expenditures: $53,633
Media: 7-10
Personnel:
Kenneth R. Levine *(Chm, Pres & CEO)*
Angiras Koorapaty *(CFO)*
Jerry Skurla *(Exec VP-Mktg)*
Howard D. Stewart *(Exec VP-Engrg)*
Advertising Agency:
SHIFT Communications LLC
20 Guest St Ste 200
Brighton, MA 02135
Tel.: (617) 779-1800
Fax: (617) 779-1899

NORTH AMERICAN CORP.
2101 Claire Ct
Glenview, IL 60025-7634
Tel.: (847) 832-4000
Fax: (847) 832-4010
E-mail: custcare@nacorporation.com
Web Site: www.na.com
Approx. Number Employees: 100
Business Description:
Janitorial & Office Supplies Mfr & Whslr
S.I.C.: 5122
N.A.I.C.S.: 446120
Advertising Expenditures: $500,000
Media: 1-4-6-10-20
Personnel:
John Miller *(Pres)*
Rosemarie Egan *(CFO)*
Linda Coplan *(Dir-HR)*
Mark Gaggiano *(Dir-IT)*

NORTHCORE TECHNOLOGIES INC.
302 The E Mall
Etobicoke, ON M9B 6C7, Canada
Tel.: (416) 640-0400
Fax: (416) 640-0412
Toll Free: (888) 287-7467
E-mail: info@northcore.com
Web Site: www.northcore.com
Approx. Rev.: $647,970
Approx. Number Employees: 16
Year Founded: 1988
Business Description:
Asset Management Services
S.I.C.: 7372; 7371
N.A.I.C.S.: 334611; 541511
Media: 10
Personnel:
Anthony DeCristofaro *(Chm)*
Amit Monga *(Pres & CEO)*
James Moskos *(COO)*
Don Clearwater *(Dir-Tech)*

NORTHSTAR MARINE ELECTRONICS
(Sub. of Navico Norway AS)
30 Sudbury Rd
Acton, MA 01720
Tel.: (978) 897-6600
Fax: (978) 897-8264
Toll Free: (800) 628-4487
E-mail: ns-support@navico.com
Web Site: www.northstarcmc.com
E-Mail For Key Personnel:
Sales Director: sales@bntmarine.com
Approx. Number Employees: 45
Year Founded: 1970
Business Description:
Electronic Navigation Equipment Mfr
S.I.C.: 3812
N.A.I.C.S.: 334511
Media: 2-4-6-7-8-10-13-26

NOVATION LLC
(Sub. of VHA Inc.)
125 E John Carpenter Freeway
Irving, TX 75062
Tel.: (972) 581-5000
Fax: (972) 581-5011
E-mail: info@novationco.com
Web Site: www.novationco.com
Approx. Number Employees: 400
Year Founded: 1998
Business Description:
Provider of Management Consulting Services
S.I.C.: 8742; 5047
N.A.I.C.S.: 541611; 423450
Personnel:
Jody Hatcher *(Pres & CEO)*
Jill Witter *(Gen Counsel, Ethics/ Compliance Officer & VP)*
Larry McComber *(Sr VP-Strategic Svcs)*
Eldon Petersen *(Sr VP)*
Dan Sweeney *(Sr VP-Info & Data Svcs)*
Jo Klein *(VP-Strategy, Plng & Res)*
Advertising Agency:
SKSW Advertising
1255 W 15th St Ste 800
Plano, TX 75075
Tel.: (972) 424-3000
Fax: (972) 424-3011

NOVELL INC.
(Joint Venture of Golden Gate Capital, Francisco Partners Management, LLC & Thoma Bravo, LLC)
404 Wyman St Ste 500
Waltham, MA 02451
Tel.: (781) 464-8000
Fax: (782) 464-8100
Toll Free: (888) 321-4272
E-mail: crc@novell.com
Web Site: www.novell.com
Approx. Rev.: $811,871,000
Approx. Number Employees: 3,400
Year Founded: 1983
Business Description:
Networking & E-Business Software & Services
S.I.C.: 7372
N.A.I.C.S.: 334611; 511210
Export
Advertising Expenditures: $3,900,000
Media: 2-6-9-13-15-18
Distr.: Intl.; Natl.
Budget Set: Apr.
Personnel:
Jose Almandoz *(CIO & VP)*
Maarten Koster *(Pres/Gen Mgr-Asia Pacific)*
Joseph H. Wagner *(Sr VP & Gen Mgr-Global Alliances)*
Javier Colado *(Sr VP-Global Sls)*
Russell C. Poole *(Sr VP-HR)*
Bill Smith *(VP-Fin)*
Shane D. Wall *(VP-Sls-Mktg)*
Ian Bruce *(Dir-Mktg-Analyst & Press Rels-Worldwide)*
Brands & Products:
ACCESS MANAGER
ACCESSAWARE
APPARMOR
APPNOTES
BANDIT
BANSHEE
BEAGLE
BORDERMANAGER
BORDERMANAGER FASTCACHE
BRAINSHARE
BUSINESSHARE
C-WORTHY
CDE
CLIENT32
CNE
CONSOLEONE
COOL SOLUTIONS
CRYPTOMARK
DEFRAME
DEVELOPERNET
DIGITALME
DIRXML
DR. CACHE
EDIRECTORY
EGUIDE
EVOLUTION
EXCELERATOR
EXTEND
FAN-OUT FAILOVER
FORMULA
FULL SERVICE DIRECTORY
GLOBAL MHS
GROUPWISE
HOT FIX
HOTLIST
ICECORE
ICHAIN
IFOLDER
IMMUNIX
IPX
JBROKER
JEDIT
LAN WORKGROUP
LAN WORKPLACE
LOCKON
LOGICSOURCE
MAKING IT WORK AS ONE
MCNE
MCNI
MOONLIGHT
MYCMDB
NCP
NEAP
NETDEVICE
NETMAIL
NETWARE
NICI
NOTP
NOVELL
NSURE
NTERPRISE
OPENSUSE
PLATESPIN FORGE
POWERCONVERT
QUICKFINDER
RED CARPET
SCHEMAX
SENTINEL
SHOPNOVELL
SITESCAPE
SUBDOMAIN
SUSE
VLM
VOLERA
WEBWORKZONE
WHEREAWARE
XAD
XIMIAN
ZENWORKS
ZON
Advertising Agencies:
PAN Communications
300 Brickstone Sq 7th Fl
Andover, MA 01810
Tel.: (978) 474-1900
Fax: (978) 474-1903

Philip Johnson Associates
12 Arrow St
Cambridge, MA 02138
Tel.: (617) 492-5899
Fax: (617) 661-1530
— Janet Carlisle *(Acct Exec)*

PJA
12 Arrow St
Cambridge, MA 02138-5105
Tel.: (617) 492-5899
Fax: (617) 661-1530

NUANCE COMMUNICATIONS, INC.

1 Wayside Rd
Burlington, MA 01803
Tel.: (781) 565-5000
Fax: (781) 565-5001
Web Site: www.nuance.com
Approx. Rev.: $1,118,948,000
Approx. Number Employees: 6,100
Year Founded: 1993
Business Description:
Document Management, Digital Imaging & Speech Recognition Software Developer
S.I.C.: 7372; 7371; 7389
N.A.I.C.S.: 334611; 511210; 541511; 561499
Export
Advertising Expenditures: $21,100,000
Media: 1-2-4-5-6-7-8-9-10-20-25
Distr.: Intl.; Natl.
Budget Set: Dec.
Personnel:
Paul A. Ricci *(Chm & CEO)*
Thomas L. Beaudoin *(CFO & Exec VP)*
Steven L. Horan *(CIO & Sr VP)*
Steven G. Chambers *(CMO)*
Vlad Sejnoha *(CTO & Sr VP)*
Gary Clayton *(Chief Creative Officer)*
Donald W. Hunt *(Pres-Worldwide Sls)*
Jo-Anne Sinclair *(Gen Counsel & Sr VP)*
Janet Dillione *(Exec VP & Gen Mgr-Healthcare Bus)*
Jeanne F. McCann *(Exec VP-Ops)*
Bill Nelson *(Exec VP-Worldwide Sls)*
Peter Mahoney *(Sr VP & Gen Mgr-Dragon Bus Unit)*
Michael Thompson *(Sr VP & Gen Mgr-Mobile)*
Thomas J. Chisholm *(Sr VP-Enterprise Products & Svcs)*
Dawn M. Howarth *(Sr VP-HR)*
Richard S. Palmer *(Sr VP-Corp Dev)*
Steven Hebert *(Sr Dir-Fin)*
Steven Steenhaut *(Dir-Mktg-Intl)*
Brands & Products:
DRAGON NATURALLY SPEAKING
ESCRIPTION
THE EXPERIENCE SPEAKS FOR ITSELF
EXSPEECH
GOMD
ICHART
NUANCE
OMNIPAGE PRO
OPENSPEECH
PAPERPORT
POWERSCRIBE
RADCUBE
RADPORT
REALSPEAK
SPEECHMAGIC
SPEECHSECURE
TEXTBRIDGE PRO
VERIPHY
VOCON
WALKABOUT
Advertising Agencies:
Aloft Group, Inc.
26 Parker St
Newburyport, MA 01950
Tel.: (978) 462-0002
Fax: (978) 462-4337

FORGE worldwide
142 Berkeley St
Boston, MA 02116
Tel.: (617) 262-4800

NUANCE DICTAPHONE HEALTHCARE SOLUTIONS

(Sub. of Nuance Communications, Inc.)
1 Wayside Rd
Burlington, MA 01803
Tel.: (203) 381-7000
Fax: (781) 565-5001
Toll Free: (800) 243-4405
E-mail: webmaster@nuance.com
Web Site: www.nuance.com
Approx. Sls.: $350,000,000
Approx. Number Employees: 500
Year Founded: 1881
Business Description:
Medical Voice Recognition & Documentation Software Developer & Mfr
S.I.C.: 7372; 7338; 7371
N.A.I.C.S.: 511210; 541511; 561410
Export
Advertising Expenditures: $3,000,000
Media: 2-4-6-7-8-9-10-11-16-20-23-25
Distr.: Intl.; Natl.
Budget Set: Dec.
Personnel:
Janet Dillione *(Exec VP & Gen Mgr-Healthcare Div)*
Peter Durlach *(Sr VP-Mktg & Product Strategy)*
Ed Rucinski *(Sr VP-Sls-North America)*

NUMARA SOFTWARE, INC.

(Sub. of TA Associates, Inc.)
2202 NW Shore Blvd Ste 650
Tampa, FL 33607
Tel.: (813) 227-4500
Fax: (813) 227-4501
Toll Free: (800) 557-6970
Web Site: www.numarasoftware.com
Approx. Number Employees: 200
Year Founded: 1991
Business Description:
Developer of Asset Management, Software Deployment & Network Monitoring Software
S.I.C.: 7372
N.A.I.C.S.: 511210
Media: 5-10
Personnel:
John Burton *(Chm)*
Dave Hansen *(CEO)*
Michael Branca *(CFO)*
Matt Dircks *(VP-Products)*
Elisabeth Granozio *(Product Mgr)*
Brands & Products:
TRACK IT!

NUVIEW WEST

(Sub. of NuView Systems Inc.)
855 SW Yates Dr Ste 201
Bend, OR 97702
Tel.: (541) 617-5100
Fax: (541) 617-5160
Toll Free: (800) 618-3880
E-mail: info@nuviewinc.com
Web Site: www.nuviewinc.com
Approx. Number Employees: 25
Year Founded: 1975
Business Description:
Human Resources & Payroll Applications Software Publisher
S.I.C.: 7372
N.A.I.C.S.: 511210
Media: 2-10-13-21
Personnel:
Shafiq Lokhandwala *(Pres & CEO)*
David W. Spring *(Mgr-Dev)*
Brands & Products:
CORT
CORT HCM

NVE CORPORATION

11409 Valley View Rd
Eden Prairie, MN 55344-3617
Tel.: (952) 829-9217
Fax: (952) 829-9189
Toll Free: (800) 467-7141
E-mail: iso-info@nve.com
Web Site: www.nve.com
Approx. Rev.: $31,197,063
Approx. Number Employees: 58
Year Founded: 1989
Business Description:
Spintronic Devices Developer, Mfr & Sales
S.I.C.: 3674
N.A.I.C.S.: 334413
Media: 7-10-13
Personnel:
Terrence W. Glarner *(Chm)*
Daniel A. Baker *(Pres & CEO)*
Curt A. Reynders *(CFO)*
Brands & Products:
AT-MRAM
GMR SWITCH
GT SENSOR
ISOLOOP
NVE

NVIDIA CORPORATION

2701 San Tomas Expy
Santa Clara, CA 95050-2519
Tel.: (408) 486-2000
Fax: (408) 486-2200
E-mail: info@nvidia.com
Web Site: www.nvidia.com
Approx. Rev.: $3,543,309,000
Approx. Number Employees: 6,029
Year Founded: 1993
Business Description:
Programmable Graphics Processors & Related Software Mfr
S.I.C.: 3674; 7371
N.A.I.C.S.: 334413; 541511
Advertising Expenditures: $9,500,000
Media: 6-10-13
Personnel:
Jen-Hsun Huang *(Co-Founder, Pres & CEO)*
Chris A. Malachowsky *(Co-Founder, NVIDIA Fellow & Sr VP-Res)*
Karen Burns *(CFO)*
Bill Dally *(Chief Scientist & VP-Res)*
Michael Byron *(Chief Acctg Officer & VP-Fin)*
David M. Shannon *(Gen Counsel, Sec & Exec VP)*
Ajay K. Puri *(Exec VP-Worldwide Sls)*
Debora Shoquist *(Exec VP-Ops)*
Jonah M. Alben *(Sr VP-Engrg)*
Philip J. Carmack *(Sr VP-Mobile Bus Unit)*
Dwight Diercks *(Sr VP-Software Engrg)*
Jeffrey D. Fisher *(Sr VP-GPU Bus Unit)*
Frank Fox *(Sr VP-Consumer Electronics Engrg)*
Joseph D. Greco *(Sr VP-VLSI Engrg)*
Michael W. Hara *(Sr VP-IR)*
Gary Hicok *(Sr VP-Mobile Bus Unit)*
Brian M. Kelleher *(Sr VP-GPU Engrg)*
Michael LaBianca *(Sr VP-HR)*
Tommy Lee *(Sr VP-Sys & Application Engrg)*
Tony Tamasi *(Sr VP-Content & Tech)*
Daniel F. Vivoli *(Sr VP-Mktg)*
Neil Trevett *(VP)*
Andrew Cresci *(Gen Mgr-Vertical Mktg)*
Phil Eisler *(Gen Mgr-3D Vision)*
Jim Vandegrift *(Sr Dir-Creative Svcs)*
Derek Perez *(Dir-PR)*
Shawn Worsell *(Mgr-Product Line)*
Andrew Fear *(Sr Product Mgr)*
Will Wade *(Sr Product Mgr-Quadro Virtualization & Remoting)*
William J. Miller *(Consultant)*
Brands & Products:
ACCUVIEW ANTIALIASING
ACTIVEARMOR
ANTIALIASING
BUSINESS PLATFORM
CINEFX
CUDA
DIGITAL VIBRANCE CONTROL
DIRECTX
DOLBY
DUALNET
FORCEWARE
GEFORCE
GEFORCE 6600
GEFORCE 6600 GT
GELATO
GOFORCE
HYPERTRANSPORT
INTELLISAMPLE
MEDIASHIELD
MEDIASQUEEZE
NFINITEFX
NFORCE
NTUNE
NVIDIA
NVIEW
NVKEYSTONE
NVROTATE
OPENGL
PCI EXPRESS
PERSONAL CINEMA
POWERMIZER
PUREVIDEO
QUADRO
SOUNDSTORM
TESLA
TIVOTOGO
TURBOCACHE
ULTRASHADOW
Advertising Agency:
Cutwater
55 Union St
San Francisco, CA 94111-1227
Tel.: (415) 315-4100
Fax: (415) 315-4200

OBSIDIAN ENTERTAINMENT, INC.

8105 Irvine Ctr Dr
Irvine, CA 92681
Tel.: (949) 379-3300
Fax: (714) 436-1007
E-mail: info@obsidianent.com
Web Site: www.obsidianent.com
Approx. Number Employees: 120
Business Description:
Entertainment Software Developer
S.I.C.: 7371

Key to Media (For complete agency information see *The Advertising Red Books-Agencies* edition):
1. Bus. Publs. 2. Cable T.V. 3. Catalogs & Directories. 4. Co-op Adv. 5. Consumer Mags. 6. D.M. to Bus. Estab.7. D.M. to Consumers 8. Daily Newsp. 9. Exhibits/Trade Shows 10. Foreign 11. Infomercial 12. Internet Adv.13. Multimedia 14. Network Radio 15. Network T.V. 16. Newsp. Distr. Mags. 17. Other 18. Outdoor (Posters, Transit) 19. Point of Purchase20. Premiums, Novelties 21. Product Samples 22. Special Events Mktg. 23. Spot Radio 24. Spot T.V. 25. Weekly Newsp. 26. Yellow Page Adv.

N.A.I.C.S.: 541511
Media: 6-8
Personnel:
Chris Avellone *(Co-Owner, Chief Creative Officer & Dir-Creative)*
Chris Jones *(Co-Owner & CTO)*
Feargus Urquhart *(CEO)*

OCCAM NETWORKS INC.

(Sub. of Calix Inc.)
6868 Cortona Dr
Santa Barbara, CA 93117
Tel.: (805) 692-2900
Fax: (805) 692-2999
E-mail: sales@occamnetworks.com
Web Site: www.occamnetworks.com
Approx. Rev.: $84,046,000
Approx. Number Employees: 186
Year Founded: 1999
Business Description:
Telecommunications Transmission Equipment Mfr
S.I.C.: 3661; 3571; 3577
N.A.I.C.S.: 334210; 334111; 334119
Advertising Expenditures: $55,000
Media: 2-7-8
Personnel:
Robert L. Howard-Anderson *(Pres & CEO)*
Mike Riedel *(Reg VP)*
Tom Gordon *(VP-Sls)*
David C. Mason *(VP-Engrg)*
Russell J. Sharer *(VP-Mktg)*
Brands & Products:
OCCAMVIEW

OCE DOCUMENT PRINTING SYSTEMS

(Sub. of Oce-USA Holding, Inc.)
100 Oakview Dr
Trumbull, CT 06611-4724
Tel.: (203) 365-7000
Toll Free: (800) 945-9708
Web Site: www.oceusa.com
Sales Range: $600-649.9 Million
Approx. Number Employees: 3,600
Business Description:
Faxes & Copiers Mfr & Sales
S.I.C.: 3661; 3861
N.A.I.C.S.: 334210; 333315
Media: 7-15-24
Personnel:
John R. Reilly *(Pres-Document Printing Sys)*
Anthony J. Marino *(Corp Counsel, Sec & VP)*
James A. Magrone *(Sr VP-Svc)*
William Midgley *(Sr VP-Admin & Logistics)*
George E. Clark *(VP & Gen Mgr-Bus Products Centers)*
Brands & Products:
IMAGISTICS

OCE NORTH AMERICA, INC.

(Sub. of Oce N.V.)
5450 N Cumberland Ave
Chicago, IL 60656-1484
Tel.: (773) 714-8500
Fax: (773) 714-4056
E-mail: info@oceusa.com
Web Site: www.oceusa.com
Approx. Number Employees: 20,000
Year Founded: 1963
Business Description:
Copiers, Printers, Plotters & Supplies Mfr
S.I.C.: 5044
N.A.I.C.S.: 423420
Import Export
Advertising Expenditures: $5,000,000
Media: 2-4-7-10-20
Distr.: Natl.
Budget Set: Sept.
Personnel:
Joseph D. Skrzypczak *(Pres & CEO)*
Eric Vandoninck *(CFO & Sr VP)*
Mal Baboyian *(Pres-Production Printing Sys)*
Patrick Chapuis *(Pres-Wide Format Printing Sys)*
John Reilly *(Pres-Document Printing Sys)*
Chris C. Dewart *(Sr VP-Sls & Mktg)*
Dan Krzesinski *(Sr VP-Svc)*
William Midgley *(Sr VP-Admin & Logistics)*
Gerrit Terlouw *(Sr VP-Tech & Software Support)*
Randy Wagner *(Sr VP-HR)*
James A. Magrone *(VP-Corp Comm)*
Mike Troy *(VP-Office Mktg)*
Advertising Agencies:
Jacobs Agency
308 W Erie 2nd Fl
Chicago, IL 60654
Tel.: (312) 664-5000
Fax: (312) 664-5080

Street Level Studio
250 Waukegan Ave
Highwood, IL 60040
Tel.: (847) 432-5150

OCZ TECHNOLOGY GROUP, INC.

6373 San Ignacio Ave
San Jose, CA 95119
Tel.: (408) 733-8400
Fax: (408) 733-5200
E-mail: pr@ocztechnology.com
Web Site: www.ocztechnology.com
Approx. Rev.: $190,116,000
Approx. Number Employees: 422
Year Founded: 2000
Business Description:
Computer Memory Components Developer
S.I.C.: 3572
N.A.I.C.S.: 334112
Advertising Expenditures: $3,000,000
Media: 5-10
Personnel:
Ryan Maurice Petersen *(Pres & CEO)*
Arthur Frederick Knapp *(CFO)*
Alex Mei *(CMO & Exec VP)*
Steve Lee *(Sr VP & Gen Mgr-Bus Unit-Power Mgmt)*
John Apps *(Sr VP-Ops)*
Eugene Chang *(VP-Pur)*
Jessica Luken *(Dir-Global Mktg)*
Bonnie Mott *(Mgr-IR)*

OFFICE DEPOT, INC.

6600 N Military Tr
Boca Raton, FL 33496
Tel.: (561) 438-4800
Fax: (561) 438-4001
Toll Free: (800) 937-3600
E-mail: Investor.Relations@officedepot.com
Web Site: www.officedepot.com
Approx. Sls.: $11,633,094,000
Approx. Number Employees: 40,000
Year Founded: 1986
Business Description:
Office Supply Stores Owner & Operator
S.I.C.: 5943; 5112; 7359
N.A.I.C.S.: 453210; 424120; 532420
Import
Advertising Expenditures: $469,500,000
Media: 2-3-4-5-6-7-8-9-10-11-13-14-15-18-22-23-24-25-26-31
Distr.: Reg.
Personnel:
Neil R. Austrian *(Interim Chm & Interim CEO)*
Michael D. Newman *(CFO)*
Bob Moore *(CMO & Exec VP)*
Charles E. Brown *(Pres-Intl)*
Kevin Peters *(Pres-North America)*
Elisa D.C. Garcia *(Gen Counsel & Exec VP)*
Michael Allison *(Exec VP-HR)*
Steven M. Schmidt *(Exec VP-Corp Strategy & New Bus Dev)*
Mark E. Hutchens *(Controller & Sr VP-Fin)*
Juan Guerrero *(Sr VP)*
Christine Buscarino *(VP-Direct & Customer Mktg)*
Brian Levine *(VP-Corp Comm)*
Barry Litwin *(VP-Global Ecommerce)*
Kristin Micalizo *(VP-Mktg)*
Randall W. Wick *(VP-Mdsg)*
Farla Efros *(Interim Head-Mdsg)*
Dan Depace *(Sr Dir)*
Mark Miller *(Sr Dir-Bus Process Improvement)*
John Nixon *(Sr Dir-Solutions)*
Nicole Fraley *(Dir-Online Adv)*
Jennifer Rodriguez *(Sr Mgr-Lease Admin)*
Kristina Corrales *(Mgr-Mktg-3M)*
Chris Pope *(Mgr-Dept)*
Advertising Agencies:
Newspaper Services of America, Inc.
3025 Highland Pkwy Ste 700
Downers Grove, IL 60515-5506
Tel.: (630) 729-7500
Fax: (630) 241-7223
(Print)

Prometheus
225 N Michigan Ave
Chicago, IL 60601
Tel.: (312) 324-7000
Tel.: (312) 419-5252
Fax: (312) 324-8204

Zimmerman Advertising
2200 W Commercial Blvd Ste 300
Fort Lauderdale, FL 33309-3064
Tel.: (954) 644-4000
Fax: (954) 731-2977
Toll Free: (800) 248-8522
Agency of Record
Office Supplies and Services

OFFICEMAX INCORPORATED

263 Shuman Blvd
Naperville, IL 60563
Mailing Address:
PO Box 228070
Shaker Heights, OH 44122-8070
Tel.: (630) 438-7800
Fax: (630) 438-2452
Toll Free: (800) 472-6473
Toll Free: (877) 633-4236
E-mail: info@officemax.com
Web Site: www.officemax.com
E-Mail For Key Personnel:
Public Relations: pr@officemax.com
Approx. Sls.: $7,150,007,000
Approx. Number Employees: 19,000
Year Founded: 1988
Business Description:
Office Supplies & Furniture Stores & Printing Services
S.I.C.: 5943; 2752; 5111; 5712
N.A.I.C.S.: 453210; 323114; 424110; 442110
Advertising Expenditures: $228,300,000
Media: 3-4-5-6-8-9-11-13-18-22-26
Distr.: Intl.; Natl.
Personnel:
Ravichandra K. Saligram *(Pres & CEO)*
Bruce H. Besanko *(CFO & Chief Admin Officer & Exec VP)*
Randy Burdick *(CIO & Exec VP)*
Steve Parsons *(Chief HR Officer & Exec VP)*
John Voytilla *(VP-Global Loss Prevention)*
Carolynn Brooks *(Chief Diversity Officer)*
Michael J. Lewis *(Pres-Retail & Exec VP)*
Matthew R. Broad *(Gen Counsel & Exec VP)*
Steve Embree *(Exec VP-Mdsg-Retail)*
Harold Mulet *(Exec VP)*
Reuben E. Slone *(Exec VP-Supply Chain)*
Ryan Vero *(Chief Mdsg Officer & Exec VP)*
David Kelly *(Mng Dir-Ops-Australia & Sr VP)*
John Bender *(Sr VP-Building Products)*
Bob Deiters *(Sr VP)*
Ben Groce *(Sr VP-Paper Solutions)*
Gary Marshall *(Sr VP)*
Bob Thacker *(Sr VP-Mktg)*
Vincent Hannity *(VP-Corp Comm)*
Michael Kitz *(VP-OfficeMax Brands, Product Dev & Imports)*
Frank Virella *(VP-Mdsg)*
William Bonner *(Sr Dir-External Rels)*
Jean Romer *(Mgr)*
Jennifer Rook *(Mgr-PR)*
Mike Steele *(Coord-IR)*
Brands & Products:
CHECKMAX PRICING
COPYMAX
FURNITUREMAX
MAX CALENDAR
MAX MEANS MORE
MAXASSURANCE
MAXBACKUP
MAXBRITE
MAXMAIL
MAXMAILBOX
MAXMEETING
MAXMEMORIES
MAXPERKS
MAXTRAVEL
OFFICE MAX IMPRESS
OFFICEMAX
OFFICEMAX CORPORATE DIRECT
OFFICEMAX EXPRESS
OFFICEMAX PDQ
OFFICEMAX TAKES YOUR SAVINGS TO THE MAX
OFFICEMAX.COM

Key to Media (For complete agency information see *The Advertising Red Books-Agencies* edition):
1. Bus. Publs. 2. Cable T.V. 3. Catalogs & Directories. 4. Co-op Adv. 5. Consumer Mags. 6. D.M. to Bus. Estab.7. D.M. to Consumers 8. Daily Newsp. 9. Exhibits/Trade Shows 10. Foreign 11. Infomercial 12. Internet Adv.13. Multimedia 14. Network Radio 15. Network T.V. 16. Newsp. Distr. Mags. 17. Other 18. Outdoor (Posters, Transit) 19. Point of Purchase20. Premiums, Novelties 21. Product Samples 22. Special Events Mktg. 23. Spot Radio 24. Spot T.V. 25. Weekly Newsp. 26. Yellow Page Adv.

OFFICEMAX INCORPORATED — (Continued)

OFFICEMAX.COM: WHERE SMART BUSINESS IS GOING
SAVINGS IS THE BOTTOM LINE
WHAT'S YOUR THING?

Advertising Agencies:
DDB Chicago
200 E Randolph St
Chicago, IL 60601
Tel.: (312) 552-6000
Fax: (312) 552-2370

The Direct Impact Company
99 Canal Center Plz Ste 450
Alexandria, VA 22314-1588
Tel.: (703) 684-1245
Fax: (703) 684-1249

Escape Pod
750 N Orleans Ste 403
Chicago, IL 60610
Tel.: (312) 274-1180
Fax: (312) 274-0996

EVB-Evolution Bureau
55 Union St
San Francisco, CA 94111
Tel.: (415) 281-3950
Fax: (415) 281-3957

Marketing Support, Inc.
200 E Randolph Dr Ste 5000
Chicago, IL 60601
Tel.: (312) 565-0044
Fax: (312) 946-6100

mono
(Partially Owned by MDC Partners)
3036 Hennepin Ave
Minneapolis, MN 55408
Tel.: (612) 822-4135
Fax: (612) 454-4950

PromoGroup
444 N Orleans St Ste 400
Chicago, IL 60610-4494
Tel.: (312) 467-1300
Fax: (312) 467-1311

OKI DATA AMERICAS, INC.

(Sub. of Oki Data Corporation)
2000 Bishops Gate Blvd
Mount Laurel, NJ 08054-4620
Tel.: (856) 235-2600
Fax: (856) 222-5320
Toll Free: (800) OKIDATA
E-mail: support@okidata.com
Web Site: www.okidata.com
Approx. Sls.: $30,000,000
Approx. Number Employees: 600
Year Founded: 1972
Business Description:
Printing & Imaging Equipment Mfr & Whslr
S.I.C.: 3555; 3577
N.A.I.C.S.: 333293; 334119
Advertising Expenditures: $4,000,000
Media: 2-4-5-7-10-13-14-20-22
Distr.: Distr. Natl.; Intl.
Personnel:
Takabumi Asahi *(Pres & CEO)*
James J. Hargadon *(CFO & Exec VP)*
Scott Becker *(Exec VP-Sls & Mktg-North America)*
Taka Nakano *(Sr VP-Latin America Ops)*
Mitsuaki Takahara *(Sr VP-Corp Plng & Ops & Strategic Tech Provider Bus Unit)*
Shinichi Katakura *(VP-Engrg)*
Gus Piccin *(VP-Solution Provider & BTA Sls-US)*
Greg Van Acker *(VP-Sls-US)*
Yoshimi Iioka *(Gen Mgr-Latin America Ops)*
Mario Pallotta *(Gen Mgr-Canada)*
Timothy O'Shea *(Dir-Managed Print Svcs Bus Dev)*
Carl Taylor *(Dir-Mktg)*
Doug August *(Sr Product Mgr-Software & Solutions)*
Michael Bozek *(Sr Mgr)*
Terry Cruikshank *(Sr Mgr-Industry Mktg)*
Mike Garofola *(Sr Mgr-Mktg-Color Products)*

Advertising Agencies:
Domus Inc.
123 S Broad St Ste 1980
Philadelphia, PA 19109
Tel.: (215) 772-2800
Fax: (215) 772-2819
Advertising & Marketing Communications Agency of Record
U.S. Public Relations Agency of Record

Impressions-A.B.A. Industries, Inc.
393 Jericho Tpk
Mineola, NY 11501
Tel.: (516) 739-3210
Fax: (516) 739-9246

OKI SEMICONDUCTOR AMERICA, INC.

(Sub. of Oki Semiconductor Co., Ltd.)
1173 Borregas Ave
Sunnyvale, CA 94089
Tel.: (408) 720-1900
Fax: (408) 720-1921
Toll Free: (800) TEAMOKI
Telex: 910-338-0508 OKI SUVL
Web Site: www2.okisemi.com
Sales Range: $200-249.9 Million
Approx. Number Employees: 10
Year Founded: 1977
Business Description:
Sales & Marketing of Semiconductor Products
S.I.C.: 5045; 5065
N.A.I.C.S.: 423430; 423690
Import
Advertising Expenditures: $1,500,000
Media: 1-2-4-7-10-11-13
Distr.: Intl.; Natl.
Budget Set: Oct.
Personnel:
Hiroshi Nagai *(CFO & VP-Fin)*
Nader Sadrzadeh *(CIO & VP-Admin)*
Brands & Products:
ARM
MICROPLATON

OMTOOL, LTD.

6 Riverside Dr
Andover, MA 01810
Tel.: (978) 327-5700
Fax: (978) 659-1300
Toll Free: (800) 886-7845
E-mail: kcummings@omtool.com
Web Site: www.omtool.com
Sales Range: $10-24.9 Million
Approx. Number Employees: 84
Year Founded: 1991
Business Description:
Business Document, Information & Communications Software Mfr
S.I.C.: 7372; 7338; 7371; 7389
N.A.I.C.S.: 511210; 541511; 561410; 561499
Advertising Expenditures: $195,925
Media: 2-7-10-13
Personnel:
Robert L. Voelk *(Chm, Pres & CEO)*
Daniel A. Coccoluto *(CFO, Treas & Sec)*
Karen Cummings *(Exec VP-Sls & Mktg)*
Eamonn Doyle *(VP-IT)*
Cara Fascione *(VP-Sls)*
Kelvyn Stirk *(VP-Strategic Acct Organization)*
Brands & Products:
ACCUROUTE
DRIVING YOUR INFORMATION ROUTE
GENIDOCS
GENIFAX
OMTOOL
SWIFTWRITER
Advertising Agency:
PAN Communications
300 Brickstone Sq 7th Fl
Andover, MA 01810
Tel.: (978) 474-1900
Fax: (978) 474-1903

ON ASSIGNMENT, INC.

26745 Malibu Hills Rd
Calabasas, CA 91301
Tel.: (818) 878-7900
Fax: (818) 878-7930
Toll Free: (800) 998-3413
E-mail: info@onassignment.com
Web Site: www.onassignment.com
Approx. Rev.: $438,065,000
Approx. Number Employees: 1,123
Year Founded: 1985
Business Description:
Scientific & Healthcare Employment Services
S.I.C.: 7363; 7361
N.A.I.C.S.: 561320; 561310
Advertising Expenditures: $3,100,000
Media: 2-10-13-25
Personnel:
Peter T. Dameris *(Pres & CEO)*
James L. Brill *(CFO & Sr VP-Fin)*
Michael C. Payne *(CIO & Sr VP-Shared Svcs)*
Mark S. Brouse *(Pres-VISTA Staffing Solutions)*
Michael J. Mcgowan *(Pres-Oxford Global Resources Inc)*
Emmett B. McGrath *(Pres-Life Sciences & Allied Healthcare)*
Christina Gibson *(Controller & VP-Fin)*
Angela Kolarek *(VP-HR)*
Scott Sampson *(Dir-Fin Reporting)*
Brands & Products:
DIAGNOSTIC IMAGING STAFF
LAB SUPPORT
ON ASSIGNMENT

ONFORCE, INC.

10 Maguire Rd Bldg 2 Ste 232
Lexington, MA 02421
Tel.: (781) 761-9100
Fax: (781) 862-2901
Toll Free: (888) 515-0100
E-mail: info@onforce.com
Web Site: www.onforce.com
Year Founded: 2004
Business Description:
Technology Services
S.I.C.: 7375
N.A.I.C.S.: 518111
Personnel:
Peter Cannone *(CEO)*
Bill Lucchini *(COO)*
Robert Andrews *(VP-Tech)*
Advertising Agency:
Airfoil Public Relations
1000 Town Ctr Dr Ste 600
Southfield, MI 48075
Tel.: (248) 304-1400
Fax: (248) 304-1401
Toll Free: (866) AIRFOIL

ONSTREAM MEDIA CORPORATION

1291 SW 29th Ave
Pompano Beach, FL 33069
Tel.: (954) 917-6655
Fax: (954) 917-6660
Toll Free: (866) 857-1960
Web Site: www.onstreammedia.com
Approx. Rev.: $16,694,106
Approx. Number Employees: 96
Year Founded: 1993
Business Description:
Webcasting & Networking Solutions for the Entertainment Industry & Marketing Solutions for the Travel Industry
S.I.C.: 7373
N.A.I.C.S.: 541512
Advertising Expenditures: $340,000
Personnel:
Randy S. Selman *(Chm, Pres & CEO)*
Robert Tomlinson *(CFO)*
Alan M. Saperstein *(COO & Exec VP)*
David Glassman *(CMO & Sr VP)*
Ari Kestin *(Pres-Infinite Conferencing, Exec VP & Gen Mgr-Webcasting Div)*
Clifford Friedland *(Sr VP-Bus Dev)*
Brands & Products:
AUCTION VIDEO
IENCODE
ONSTREAM
ONSTREAM MEDIA
STORE & STREAM
STREAMING PUBLISHER
Advertising Agency:
RedChip Companies, Inc.
500 Winderely Pl Ste 100
Maitland, FL 32751
Tel.: (407) 644-4256
Fax: (407) 644-0758
Toll Free: (800) 733-2447

ONYX SOFTWARE CORPORATION

(Joint Venture of Battery Ventures, L.P. & Thoma Bravo, LLC)
12131 113th Ave NE Ste 101
Kirkland, WA 98034
Tel.: (425) 250-5800
Fax: (425) 823-3075
Toll Free: (888) 275-6699
E-mail: info@onyx.com
Web Site: www.onyx.com

Key to Media (For complete agency information see *The Advertising Red Books-Agencies* edition):
1. Bus. Publs. 2. Cable T.V. 3. Catalogs & Directories. 4. Co-op Adv. 5. Consumer Mags. 6. D.M. to Bus. Estab.7. D.M. to Consumers
8. Daily Newsp. 9. Exhibits/Trade Shows 10. Foreign 11. Infomercial 12. Internet Adv.13. Multimedia 14. Network Radio
15. Network T.V. 16. Newsp. Distr. Mags. 17. Other 18. Outdoor (Posters, Transit) 19. Point of Purchase20. Premiums, Novelties
21. Product Samples 22. Special Events Mktg. 23. Spot Radio 24. Spot T.V. 25. Weekly Newsp. 26. Yellow Page Adv.

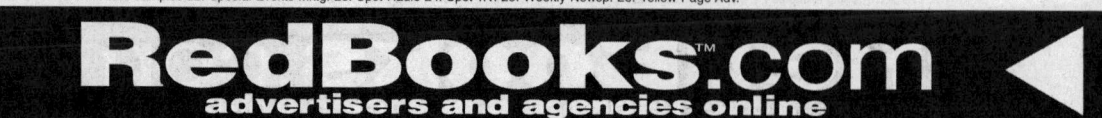

Sales Range: $50-74.9 Million
Approx. Number Employees: 245
Year Founded: 1994
Business Description:
Computer Software Mfr
S.I.C.: 7372
N.A.I.C.S.: 334611; 511210
Advertising Expenditures: $2,100,000
Media: 2-7-17
Personnel:
Thomas Milay *(VP-Mktg)*
Brands & Products:
ONYX
ONYX CUSTOMER PORTAL
ONYX EMPLOYEE PORTAL
ONYX PARTNER PORTAL

OPEN TEXT

(Sub. of Open Text Corporation)
700 King Farm Blvd Ste 600
Rockville, MD 20850-5749
Tel.: (301) 548-4000
Fax: (301) 548-4015
Web Site: www.opentext.com
E-Mail For Key Personnel:
Sales Director: sales@artesia.com
Public Relations: publicrelations@artesia.com
Approx. Number Employees: 100
Business Description:
Digital Asset Management & Internet Publishing Software Solutions
S.I.C.: 7371; 2741; 7372
N.A.I.C.S.: 541511; 511210; 516110
Advertising Expenditures: $100,000
Media: 10-13-22
Personnel:
D. Scott Bowen *(Pres)*
Richard Maganini *(Dir-Corp Comm)*
Brands & Products:
TEAMS

OPEN TEXT CORPORATION

275 Frank Tompa Dr
Waterloo, ON N2L 0A1, Canada
Tel.: (519) 888-7111
Fax: (519) 888-0677
Toll Free: (800) 499-6544
Toll Free: (800) 4996-5440 (International)
E-mail: sales@opentext.com
Web Site: www.opentext.com
Approx. Rev.: $1,033,303,000
Approx. Number Employees: 4,410
Year Founded: 1991
Business Description:
Enterprise Content Management Software Solutions
S.I.C.: 7372; 7371
N.A.I.C.S.: 511210; 541511
Media: 5-7-10-11-13
Personnel:
P. Thomas Jenkins *(Chm & Chief Strategy Officer)*
John Shackleton *(Pres & CEO)*
Paul McFeeters *(CFO)*
James Latham *(CMO)*
Gordon A. Davies *(Chief Legal Officer & Sec)*
Marten Den Haring *(Exec VP-Semantic Technologies)*
Kamran Kheirolomoom *(Sr VP & Gen Mgr-BPM Bus)*
Tony Preston *(Sr VP-Global HR)*
Louis Mousseau *(VP-Sls & Svcs-Canada)*
Paul O'Donnell *(Gen Mgr-Americas)*
David Wareham *(Gen Mgr-EMEA)*
Brands & Products:
CONNECTIVITY SECURE SERVER
DOMEA
EXCEED
EXCEED FREEDOM
EXCEED ONDEMAND
EXCEED POWERSUITE
EXCEED XDK
FIRSTCLASS
HOSTEXPLORER
OPEN TEXT
OPEN TEXT ECM

OPENCONNECT SYSTEMS, INC.

2711 Lyndon B Johnson Fwy Ste 700
Dallas, TX 75234-7323
Tel.: (972) 484-5200
Tel.: (972) 888-0470
Fax: (972) 484-6100
Toll Free: (800) 551-5881
E-mail: info@oc.com
Web Site: www.oc.com
Sales Range: $25-49.9 Million
Approx. Number Employees: 35
Year Founded: 1981
Business Description:
e-Business Services & Solutions
S.I.C.: 3577; 7373
N.A.I.C.S.: 334119; 541512
Media: 2-13-16-25
Personnel:
Stuart H. Burris, Jr. *(Pres & CTO)*
Edward M. Peters *(CEO)*
Charles Brockenbush *(CFO)*
Christopher R. Houck *(Sr VP-Product Mktg)*
Alex B. Moulas *(Sr VP-Bus Dev & Mktg)*
Brands & Products:
CDICONNECT
COMPREHEND
DISCOVERNOW
MANAGEMENT SERVER
SECURE CLIENTCONNECT
SLICONNECT
SNA ACCESS SERVER
SNA PRINT SERVER
SQLCONNECT
WEBCONNECT
WEBCONNECT SSO
XML CONNECT

OPENLINK FINANCIAL, INC.

(Holding of The Carlyle Group, LLC)
1502 RXR Plz 8h Fl W Tower
Uniondale, NY 11556
Tel.: (516) 227-6600
Fax: (516) 227-1799
Web Site: www.olf.com
Sales Range: $125-149.9 Million
Approx. Number Employees: 560
Year Founded: 1992
Business Description:
Cross-Asset Trading, Risk Management & Related Operational & Portfolio Management Software
S.I.C.: 7372
N.A.I.C.S.: 511210
Media: 7-17
Personnel:
Coleman Fung *(Founder & Chm)*
Kevin J. Hesselbirg *(CEO)*
Wolfgang Ferse *(Exec VP-Commodities & Energy Solutions)*
Kenneth A. Knowles, III *(Exec VP-Fin & Risk Solutions)*
Brian Rosengold *(Dir-Fin)*

OPENTABLE, INC.

799 Market St 4th Fl
San Francisco, CA 94103
Tel.: (415) 344-4200
Fax: (415) 267-0944
Toll Free: (800) 673-6822
Web Site: www.opentable.com
Approx. Rev.: $98,991,000
Approx. Number Employees: 493
Year Founded: 1998
Business Description:
Reservation, Table Management & Guest Management Software
S.I.C.: 7372
N.A.I.C.S.: 511210
Advertising Expenditures: $1,789,000
Media: 7-10-13-17
Personnel:
Jeffrey D. Jordan *(Chm)*
Matthew Roberts *(CEO)*
I. Duncan Robertson *(CFO)*
Joel Brown *(Sr VP-Ops)*
Michael Dodson *(Sr VP-Sls)*
Charlie McCullough *(Sr VP-Engrg)*
Jack Shay *(Dir-Product Mgmt)*
Brands & Products:
OPENTABLE
OPENTABLE DINERS CHOICE

OPENTV CORP.

(Sub. of Kudelski S.A.)
275 Sacramento St
San Francisco, CA 94111
Tel.: (415) 962-5000
Fax: (415) 962-5300
E-mail: info@opentv.com
Web Site: www.opentv.com
E-Mail For Key Personnel:
Public Relations: pr@opentv.com
Approx. Rev.: $120,012,000
Approx. Number Employees: 589
Year Founded: 1994
Business Description:
Technologies & Services Enabling the Delivery of Digital & Richer Interactive Television Experiences
S.I.C.: 7371; 5065; 7372
N.A.I.C.S.: 541511; 423690; 511210
Advertising Expenditures: $300,000
Media: 2-10-13-26
Personnel:
Andre Kudelski *(Chm)*
Mark Beariault *(Gen Counsel, Sec & Sr VP)*
Paul Woidke *(Sr VP & Gen Mgr-Advanced Adv)*
Joel Zdepski *(Chief Architect & Sr VP-Tech)*
David McLaren *(VP-Engrg)*
Brands & Products:
ITV
OPENTV
PLAYJAM

OPENWAVE SYSTEMS INC.

2100 Seaport Blvd
Redwood City, CA 94063-5546
Tel.: (650) 480-8000
Fax: (650) 480-8100
E-mail: info@openwave.com
Web Site: www.openwave.com
Approx. Rev.: $155,546,000
Approx. Number Employees: 536
Year Founded: 1994
Business Description:
Infrastructure Software & Applications Developer for the Convergence of Internet Usage with Wireless Telephones
S.I.C.: 7371; 7372
N.A.I.C.S.: 541511; 334611
Advertising Expenditures: $2,400,000
Media: 27
Personnel:
Peter Feld *(Chm)*
Mike Mulica *(CEO)*
Anne Brennan *(CFO)*
Bruce K. Posey *(Gen Counsel, Sec & Sr VP)*
John C. Charters *(Sr VP-Worldwide Sls)*
John Giere *(Sr VP-Products & Mktg)*
Sean MacNeil *(Sr VP-Engrg & Global Svcs)*
Eileen Nelson *(Sr VP-HR)*
Vikki Herrera *(Dir-Corp Mktg)*
Jan Lowdon *(Sr Mgr-Mktg Comm)*
Brands & Products:
DOWNLOAD MANAGER
EDGE GX
EDGE GX ANTI-ABUSE
EMAIL MX
GUARDIAN
INSTANT MESSAGING CLIENT
LOCATION STUDIO
MOBILE ACCESS GATEWAY
MOBILE BROWSER
MOBILE DEVICE MANAGER
MOBILE EMAIL
MULTIMEDIA MESSAGE
OPENMEDIA
OPENSTREAM
OPENWAVE
OPENWEB
OUTREACH EXPRESS
PASSPORT
PHONE SIMULATOR
POC EMBEDDED CLIENT
RICH MAIL
VIDEO PORTAL
VIDEO VOICEMAIL
VOICEMAIL
WAP PUSH LIBRARY
Advertising Agency:
The Blueshirt Group
456 Montgomery St 11th Fl
San Francisco, CA 94104
Tel.: (415) 217-7722
Fax: (415) 217-7721
Investor Relations

OPEX CORPORATION

305 Commerce Dr
Moorestown, NJ 08057-4215
Tel.: (856) 727-1100
Fax: (856) 727-1955
Web Site: www.opex.com
Approx. Number Employees: 550
Year Founded: 1973
Business Description:
Mailroom Automation Machines Mfr
S.I.C.: 3579
N.A.I.C.S.: 333313
Media: 2
Personnel:
David Stevens *(Pres & CEO)*
Brands & Products:
AS3600I
EV-2
EXACT SEQUENCE SORT
IQ SORT

Key to Media (For complete agency information see *The Advertising Red Books-Agencies* edition):
1. Bus. Publs. 2. Cable T.V. 3. Catalogs & Directories. 4. Co-op Adv. 5. Consumer Mags. 6. D.M. to Bus. Estab.7. D.M. to Consumers 8. Daily Newsp. 9. Exhibits/Trade Shows 10. Foreign 11. Infomercial 12. Internet Adv.13. Multimedia 14. Network Radio 15. Network T.V. 16. Newsp. Distr. Mags. 17. Other 18. Outdoor (Posters, Transit) 19. Point of Purchase20. Premiums, Novelties 21. Product Samples 22. Special Events Mktg. 23. Spot Radio 24. Spot T.V. 25. Weekly Newsp. 26. Yellow Page Adv.

Opex Corporation — (Continued)

MAXISORT
MINI MILL
MPE 7.5
MPS 17
MPS 40
MPS 7
NETWORKING SOLUTION
OPEX
PARASCRIPT
PUREVISION
RJ7
SYSTEM 150

OPNET TECHNOLOGIES, INC.

7255 Woodmont Ave
Bethesda, MD 20814
Tel.: (240) 497-3000
Fax: (240) 497-3001
E-mail: info@opnet.com
Web Site: www.opnet.com
Approx. Rev.: $147,986,000
Approx. Number Employees: 578
Year Founded: 1986
Business Description:
Network Management Software Solutions
S.I.C.: 7372; 7371
N.A.I.C.S.: 334611; 541511
Advertising Expenditures: $556,000
Personnel:
Marc A. Cohen *(Chm & CEO)*
Alain J. Cohen *(Pres & CTO)*
Melvin F. Wesley, III *(CFO & VP)*
Alberto Morales *(CIO)*
Dennis R. McCoy *(Gen Counsel & VP)*
Yevgeny Gurevich *(Sr VP-Engrg)*
Todd Kaloudis *(Sr VP-Bus Dev & Global Channels)*
Joseph J. Lenz *(Sr VP)*
Eric S. Nudelman *(Sr VP-Applications Engrg & Trng)*
Pradeep K. Singh *(Sr VP-Engrg)*
Brands & Products:
3D NETWORK VISUALIZER
ACE ANALYST
ACE LIVE
COMMANDER
IT GURU
IT GURU NETWORK PLANNER
IT GURU SYSTEMS PLANNER
IT SENTINEL
MAKING NETWORKS AND APPLICATIONS PERFORM
MODELER
NCOMPASS
NETDOCTOR
NETMAPPER
OPNET
OPNET NCOMPASS
PANORAMA
REPORT SERVER
SP GURU
SP GURU NETWORK PLANNER
SP GURU TRANSPORT PLANNER
SP SENTINEL
TIREM
TRANSCEIVER PIPELINE
VNESERVER

OPUS INTERNATIONAL, INC.

1191 E Newport Center Dr PH-E
Deerfield Beach, FL 33442
Tel.: (954) 428-3888
Fax: (954) 428-5470
E-mail: resumes@foodscience.com
Web Site: www.foodscience.com
Approx. Number Employees: 6
Business Description:
Executive Recruitment Services for the Food Science Industry
S.I.C.: 7361
N.A.I.C.S.: 541612
Media: 2-13
Personnel:
Moira McGrath *(Pres)*
Suzanne Scully *(Office Mgr)*

ORACLE AMERICA, INC.

(Formerly Sun Microsystems, Inc.)
(Sub. of Oracle Corporation)
4150 Network Cir
Santa Clara, CA 95054
Tel.: (650) 960-1300
Telex: 287815
Web Site: www.oracle.com/us/sun/index.htm
Sales Range: $5-14.9 Billion
Approx. Number Employees: 29,000
Year Founded: 1982
Business Description:
Computer Workstations, Servers, Programming & Productivity Software Mfr
S.I.C.: 3571; 7371; 7373
N.A.I.C.S.: 334111; 541511; 541512
Advertising Expenditures: $25,000,000
Media: 2-6-10-11-17
Distr.: Intl.; Natl.
Budget Set: Nov.
Personnel:
Jeffrey E. Epstein *(CFO & Exec VP)*
Robert Worrall *(CIO)*
Gregory M. Papadopoulos *(CTO & Exec VP-R & D)*
William N. MacGowan *(Chief HR Officer & Exec VP-People & Places)*
David Douglas *(Sr VP-Cloud Computing & Chief Sustainability Officer)*
Vengalil K. Chatterjee *(Chief Acctg Officer)*
Michelle Dennedy *(Chief Privacy Officer)*
Dorian E. Daley *(Gen Counsel, Sec & Sr VP)*
Keith Block *(Exec VP-Oracle North America)*
Anil P. Gadre *(Exec VP-Application Platform Software)*
Richard L. Green *(Exec VP-Software Grp)*
Eugene G. McCabe *(Exec VP-Worldwide Ops)*
Isabelle Roussin *(Exec VP-Mktg)*
Peter Ryan *(Exec VP-Global Sls & Svcs)*
Brian Sutphin *(Exec VP-Corp Dev & Alliances)*
Alain Andreoli *(Sr VP-Global Sls & Svc-European Reg)*
Jon Benson *(Sr VP-Storage)*
Christine Bucklin *(Sr VP-Corp Strategic Plng)*
Cheryl Cook *(Sr VP-North America)*
Denis Heraud *(Sr VP-Emerging Markets)*
Daniel Miller *(Sr VP-Global Sys Practice)*
Eva Sage-Gavin *(Sr VP-Global Talent Org)*
Craig D. Norris *(VP-Corp Law & Asst Sec)*
Subodh Bapat *(VP & Engr)*
Tan Kwang-Meng *(VP-Partners Sls Org)*
Noel Hartzell *(Dir-Exec Comm)*
Mauricio Leal *(Dir-Sun Developer Network Programs-Latin America)*
Larry Nelson *(Dir-Global Citizenship)*
Bruno Sousa *(Global Dir-OpenSource Communities)*
Paul Ziots *(Dir-IR)*
Gail Truman *(Sr Mgr-Product-StorageTek 5800 System)*
Brands & Products:
INFOBUS
JAVA
JAVA 2D
JAVA TV
JAVASCRIPT
JAVASOFT
JCERT
SOLARIS
SOLARIS OPERATING SYSTEM
SUN BLADE
SUN DATACENTER
SUN FIRE
SUN JAVA
SUN NETRA
SUN RAY SERVER
SUN STORAGE COMMON ARRAY MANAGER
Advertising Agencies:
Aerial Advertising Services
333 W Jack London Blvd Hangar 241
Livermore, CA 94551
Tel.: (925) 449-0210

BRC Marketing Inc.
7051 Corporate Way
Dayton, OH 45459
Tel.: (937) 384-0515
Fax: (937) 384-0522
Toll Free: (888) 905-0515

Butler, Shine, Stern & Partners
20 Liberty Ship Way
Sausalito, CA 94965-3312
Tel.: (415) 331-6049
Fax: (415) 331-3524

Gosh! Advertising Pte. Ltd.
10 Anson Road #11-21 International Plaza
Singapore, 079903, Singapore
Tel.: (65) 6323 9359
Fax: (65) 6223 2787
(Asian Advertising)

hawkeye
2828 Routh St Ste 300
Dallas, TX 75201
Tel.: (214) 659-5615
Fax: (214) 747-1897

hawkeye
325 Arlington Ave Ste 700
Charlotte, NC 28203
Tel.: (704) 344-7900
Fax: (704) 344-7920

Lois Paul & Partners
150 Presidential Way
Woburn, MA 01801
Tel.: (781) 782-5000
Fax: (781) 782-5999

NAVAJO Company
1164 Cadillac Ct
Milpitas, CA 95035
Tel.: (408) 957-3800
Fax: (408) 957-3809

PointRoll Inc.
951 E Hector St
Conshohocken, PA 19428
Tel.: (267) 558-1300
Fax: (267) 285-1141
Toll Free: (800) 203-6956

Starcom Adplus AG
Heinrichstrasse 225
8005
Zurich, Switzerland
Tel.: (41) 43 366 61 61
Fax: (41) 43 366 61 62

Traction Corporation
1349 Larkin St
San Francisco, CA 94109
Tel.: (415) 962-5823
Fax: (415) 962-5815

ORACLE CORPORATION

500 Oracle Pkwy
Redwood City, CA 94065
Tel.: (650) 506-7000
Fax: (650) 506-7200
Toll Free: (800) 392-2999
Web Site: www.oracle.com
Approx. Rev.: $35,622,000,000
Approx. Number Employees: 108,000
Year Founded: 1977
Business Description:
Database Management Software Developer & Whslr
S.I.C.: 7372; 7373
N.A.I.C.S.: 334611; 511210; 541512
Export
Advertising Expenditures: $88,000,000
Media: 2-6-7-9-10-11-15
Distr.: Intl.; Natl.
Personnel:
Jeffrey O. Henley *(Chm)*
Safra A. Catz *(Co-Pres & CFO)*
Mark V. Hurd *(Co-Pres)*
Lawrence J. Ellison *(CEO)*
Mark Sunday *(CIO & Sr VP)*
Judith Sim *(CMO)*
William Corey West *(Chief Acctg Officer, Sr VP & Controller)*
Mary Ann Davidson *(Chief Security Officer)*
Takao Endo *(Pres/CEO-Japan)*
Dorian E. Daley *(Gen Counsel, Sec & Sr VP)*
Steve Au Yeung *(Exec VP-Asia Pacific)*
Keith G. Block *(Exec VP-North America)*
John F. Fowler *(Exec VP-Sys)*
Thomas Kurian *(Exec VP-Product Dev)*
Loic le Guisquet *(Exec VP-Europe, Middle East & Africa)*
Luiz Meisler *(Exec VP-Latin America)*
Charles Rozwat *(Exec VP-Customer Svcs)*
Michael E. Splain *(Exec VP-Microelectronics Grp)*
Robert K. Weiler *(Exec VP-Global Bus Units)*
Derek H. Williams *(Exec VP)*
Frank Brienzi *(Sr VP & Gen Mgr-Fin Svcs Global Bus Unit)*
Neil de Crescenzo *(Sr VP & Gen Mgr-Health Sciences Global Bus Unit)*

Stephan Scholl *(Sr VP & Gen Mgr-Oracle Utilites)*
Michael R. Webster *(Sr VP & Gen Mgr-Retail)*
Judson Althoff *(Sr VP-Worldwide Alliances, Channels & Embedded Sls)*
Ted Bereswill *(Sr VP-North America Alliances & Channels)*
Cliff Godwin *(Sr VP-Applications Dev)*
Mark Johnson *(Sr VP-Pub Sector)*
Andrian Jones *(Sr VP-Hardware Sls-Asia Pacific & Japan)*
Juan C. Jones *(Sr VP-Support Svcs-North America)*
Douglas Kehring *(Sr VP-Corp Dev & Strategic Plng)*
Joanne Olsen *(Sr VP-Cloud Svcs)*
R. Ravisankar *(Sr VP)*
Cindy Reese *(Sr VP-Ops-Worldwide)*
Richard Sarwal *(Sr VP-Product Dev)*
Sonny Singh *(Sr VP-Industries Bus Unit)*
Ken Z. Volpe *(Sr VP-Commerce Product Dev)*
Joyce Westerdahl *(Sr VP-HR)*
Balaji Yelamanchili *(Sr VP)*
Amit Jasuja *(VP-Dev Identity Mgmt & Security Products)*
Maha Muzumdar *(VP-Supply Chain Mktg)*
Rick Schultz *(VP-Product Mktg)*
Robert Shimp *(Global VP-Product Mktg)*
Christian Smith *(VP-Sls)*
Martin Young *(VP-Strategy-Health Sciences GBU)*
Rich Buchheim *(Sr Dir)*
Brian Dayton *(Sr Dir)*
Rakesh Dhoopar *(Sr Dir-Product Mgmt)*
Stuart Dunsmore *(Sr Dir-Applications Dev)*
Moe Fardoost *(Sr Dir-Product Mktg)*
Deborah Lilienthal Hellinger *(Sr Dir-Corp Comm)*
Michael Lehmann *(Sr Dir-Product Mgmt-Java Platform Grp)*
Ashish Mohindroo *(Sr Dir-Product Mktg)*
Cassandra Moren *(Sr Dir-CG WSD Indus Mktg)*
John Brust *(Dir-Product Mktg)*
Marc Chanliau *(Dir-Product Mgmt)*
Rebecca Hahn *(Dir-PR)*
Dain Hansen *(Dir-Product Mktg)*
Arvind Jain *(Dir-Product Strategy)*
Eloy Ontiveros *(Dir)*
Susie Penner *(Dir-Corp Comm)*
Mark Scardina *(Dir-Application QoS Mgmt)*
Deborah Sutton *(Dir-Tech Mktg-Asia Pacific Reg)*
Michael Suttle *(Reg Mgr-CRM)*
Mark Kalstrand *(Sr Product Mgr)*
Kuassi Mensah *(Sr Mgr-Product Mgmt)*
Noel Moossa *(Sr Mgr-Global Adv)*
Jessica Stoecker *(Sr Mgr-Adv-Global)*
Teri Whitaker *(Sr Mgr-PR)*
Katarina Obradovic-Sarkic *(Sr Product Mgr-JDeveloper/Application Dev Tools)*
Blaise Ribet *(Product Mgr)*
Vinay Shukla *(Product Mgr-Oracle Platform Security Svcs)*
Tammy Bednar *(Product Mgr-Database Security)*
MaryBeth Pierantoni *(Product Mgr)*
Jinyu Wang *(Product Mgr-XML Product Mgmt)*
Danielle Cormier *(Mgr-PR)*
John Dolan *(Mgr-Consulting Sls)*

Brands & Products:
10 G ENTERPRISE EDITION
10 G JAVA EDITION
AUTOVUE
JD EDWARDS
ORACLE
PEOPLESOFT ENTERPRISE

Advertising Agencies:
Starcom Worldwide
5200 Lankershim Ste 600
North Hollywood, CA 91601
Tel.: (818) 753-7200
Fax: (818) 753-7350

ZENO Group
(An Affiliate of Daniel J. Edelman Company)
200 Park Ave S Ste 1603
New York, NY 10003
Tel.: (212) 299-8888
Fax: (212) 462-1026

ORACLE NUMETRIX CO.
(Sub. of Oracle Corporation)
145 King Street West Suite 500
Toronto, ON M5H 1J8, Canada
Tel.: (416) 642-9800
Fax: (416) 642-0315
Toll Free: (800) 633-0925
E-mail: contact.oracle@oracle.com
Web Site: www.oracle.com/global/ca-en/corporate/offices.html
Sales Range: $100-124.9 Million
Year Founded: 1984
Business Description:
Business Software Mfr
S.I.C.: 7372
N.A.I.C.S.: 334611
Media: 2-7-10

ORC WORLDWIDE
500 5th Ave 5th Fl
New York, NY 10110-8701
Tel.: (212) 719-3400
Fax: (212) 398-1358
E-mail: info@orcww.com
Web Site: www.orcworldwide.com
Sales Range: $25-49.9 Million
Approx. Number Employees: 100
Year Founded: 1953
Business Description:
Management Consulting Services
S.I.C.: 8742; 8748
N.A.I.C.S.: 541611; 541618
Personnel:
William C. Bruce *(Sr VP)*
Roger Herod *(Sr VP)*
Frank White *(Sr VP)*
Brands & Products:
ORC WORLDWIDE
SIRS
Advertising Agency:
Stern + Associates
11 Commerce Dr
Cranford, NJ 07016
Tel.: (908) 276-4344
Fax: (908) 276-7007

ORTRONICS/LEGRAND
(Sub. of Pass & Seymour/Legrand)
125 Eugene O'Neill Dr
New London, CT 06320-6417
Tel.: (860) 445-3800
Fax: (860) 405-2970
Fax: (888) 282-0043
Toll Free: (877) 599-5393
Toll Free: (800) 934-5432
E-mail: connect@ortronics.com
Web Site: www.ortronics,com
Approx. Number Employees: 275
Business Description:
Cabling Systems & Networking Equipment
S.I.C.: 3577; 3357
N.A.I.C.S.: 334119; 335921
Export
Media: 7-10-11-13
Distr.: Natl.
Budget Set: Mar.
Personnel:
Mark Panico *(Pres-Data comm Div)*
John Pezzetti *(Dir-Enterprise Solutions Program)*
Carolyn Venceslau *(Reg Mgr)*
Bernard Jouandin *(Commun Mgr-Euro)*
Marianela Ferrada *(Sls Mgr)*
Gustavo Demesa *(Mgr-Trainer & Tech)*
Advertising Agencies:
Godfrey Advertising
40 N Christian St
Lancaster, PA 17602
Tel.: (717) 393-3831
Fax: (717) 393-1403

MarketSense
7020 High Grove Blvd
Burr Ridge, IL 60527-7599
Tel.: (630) 654-0170
Fax: (630) 654-0302
Toll Free: (800) 827-0170

OTHER WORLD COMPUTING
2650 Bridge Ln
Woodstock, IL 60098
Tel.: (815) 333-5023
Fax: (815) 338-4332
E-mail: eileen@macsales.com
Web Site: www.macsales.com
Approx. Number Employees: 100
Business Description:
Computer Products Whslr
S.I.C.: 5045
N.A.I.C.S.: 423430
Advertising Agency:
Thomas Public Relations, Inc.
734 Walt Whitman Rd Ste 206
Melville, NY 11747
Tel.: (631) 549-7575
Fax: (613) 549-1129

OTTERBOX PRODUCTS LLC
209 S. Meldrum St
Fort Collins, CO 80524
Tel.: (970) 493-8446
Fax: (970) 493-1755
Toll Free: (888) 695-8820
E-mail: customer.service@otterbox.com
Web Site: www.otterbox.com
Sales Range: $25-49.9 Million
Approx. Number Employees: 123
Year Founded: 1996
Business Description:
Handheld Device Protective Cover Mfr
S.I.C.: 5099; 3999
N.A.I.C.S.: 423990; 339999
Media: 29
Personnel:
Curt Richardson *(Founder & CEO)*
Brian Thomas *(Pres)*
Kristin Goliher *(Mgr-PR)*
Kelly Richardson *(Specialist-PR)*

OVERLAND STORAGE, INC.
9112 Spectrum Center Blvd
San Diego, CA 92123
Tel.: (858) 571-5555
Fax: (858) 571-0982
Fax: (858) 571-3664
Toll Free: (800) 729-8725
Web Site: www.overlandstorage.com
E-Mail For Key Personnel:
President: VLoforti@overlandstorage.com
Approx. Rev.: $70,197,000
Approx. Number Employees: 195
Year Founded: 1980
Business Description:
Data Storage, Backup & Recovery Technologies Developer & Mfr
S.I.C.: 3572; 3577
N.A.I.C.S.: 334112; 334119
Advertising Expenditures: $500,000
Media: 2-7-8-10-13-22
Personnel:
Scott McClendon *(Chm)*
Eric L. Kelly *(Pres & CEO)*
Kurt L. Kalbfleisch *(CFO & VP-Fin)*
Geoff Barrall *(CTO & VP-Engrg)*
Jillian Mansolf *(VP-Sls & Mktg)*
Peri Grover *(Dir-Product Mgmt)*
Brands & Products:
ARCVAUL 24
ARCVAULT
ARCVAULT 12
ARVAULT 48
BACKBONE NETVAULT
CA ETRUST ANTIVIRUS
DYNAMIC VIRTUAL TAPE
ENTERPRISEXPRESS
GUARDIANOS
GUTS
ISCSI
LIBRARYPRO
LIBRARYXPRESS
LOADERXPRESS
MINILIBRARYXPRESS
NEO
NEO 2000
NEO 4100
NEO 4200
NEO 8000
OVERLAND STORAGE
POWERLOADER
PROTECTIONPAC
REO
REO 1550
REO 4500
REO 4500C
REO 9100
REO 9100C
REO 9500D
REO MULTISITEPAC
REO PROTECTION OS
SANPIPER
SNAP EDR EXPRESS
SNAP EDR STANDARD
SNAP ENTERPRISE DATA REPLICATOR
SNAP EXPANSION S50
SNAP SERVER
SNAP SERVER 110
SNAP SERVER 210
SNAP SERVER 410
SNAP SERVER 520
SNAP SERVER 620
SNAP SERVER 650

Key to Media (For complete agency information see *The Advertising Red Books-Agencies* edition):
1. Bus. Publs. 2. Cable T.V. 3. Catalogs & Directories. 4. Co-op Adv. 5. Consumer Mags. 6. D.M. to Bus. Estab.7. D.M. to Consumers
8. Daily Newsp. 9. Exhibits/Trade Shows 10. Foreign 11. Infomercial 12. Internet Adv.13. Multimedia 14. Network Radio
15. Network T.V. 16. Newsp. Distr. Mags. 17. Other 18. Outdoor (Posters, Transit) 19. Point of Purchase20. Premiums, Novelties
21. Product Samples 22. Special Events Mktg. 23. Spot Radio 24. Spot T.V. 25. Weekly Newsp. 26. Yellow Page Adv.

Overland Storage, Inc. — (Continued)

SNAP SERVER MANAGER
SNAPSHOT
STORASSURE
ULTAMUS RAID
ULTAMUS RAID 1200
ULTAMUS RAID 4800
VARS
VR2
WEB TLC
XCHANGENOW

PALM, INC.

(Sub. of Hewlett-Packard Company)
950 W Maude Ave
Sunnyvale, CA 94085
Tel.: (408) 617-7000
Fax: (408) 617-0100
Web Site: www.palm.com/us
Approx. Rev.: $735,872,000
Approx. Number Employees: 939
Year Founded: 1992
Business Description:
Handheld Computing Products & Industry Standard Platforms Mfr
S.I.C.: 3575; 3571
N.A.I.C.S.: 334113; 334111
Advertising Expenditures: $89,000,000
Media: 2-5-6-13-19-24
Personnel:
Jeffrey C. Hawkins *(Founder)*
Jonathan J. Rubinstein *(Chm, Pres & CEO)*
Mary E. Doyle *(Gen Counsel, Sec & Sr VP)*
Rena Lane *(Sr VP-HR)*
Kathleen C. Mitic *(Sr VP-Product Mktg)*
Frankie Liow *(Mgr-Mktg)*
Brands & Products:
ADD IT
ADDIT
BLAZER
CENTRO
FOLEO
HANDMAIL
LIFEDRIVE
MY PALM
PALM
PALM CENTRO
PALM OS
PALM PILOT
PALM POWERED
PALM PRE
PALM WEB OS
PALMGEAR
PALMGLOVE
PALMPACL
PALMPIX
TOUCHSTONE
TREO
TUNGSTEN
VERSAMAIL
WESYNC
ZIRE
Advertising Agencies:
iCrossing, Inc.
15169 N Scottsdale Rd Ste C400
Scottsdale, AZ 85254
Tel.: (480) 505-5800
Fax: (480) 505-5801
Toll Free: (866) 620-3780

Marden-Kane, Inc.
11 N Skokie Hwy Ste 109
Lake Bluff, IL 60044
Tel.: (847) 283-0441
Fax: (847) 283-0442

PAR TECHNOLOGY CORPORATION

PAR Technology Park 8383 Seneca Tpke
New Hartford, NY 13413-4991
Tel.: (315) 738-0600
Fax: (315) 738-0411
Toll Free: (800) 448-6505
E-mail: askpar@partech.com
Web Site: www.partech.com
Approx. Rev.: $239,939,000
Approx. Number Employees: 1,538
Year Founded: 1968
Business Description:
Professional Services & Enterprise Business Intelligence Software Mfr
S.I.C.: 3873; 3582; 3952; 7373
N.A.I.C.S.: 334518; 333312; 339942; 541512
Import Export
Media: 2-4-7-8-13
Personnel:
Paul B. Domorski *(Chm, Pres & CEO)*
Ronald J. Casciano *(CFO, Chief Acctg Officer, Treas & VP)*
Charles A. Constantino *(Exec VP)*
Gregory T. Cortese *(Exec VP)*
Brands & Products:
KNOW YOUR BUSINESS BETTER
PAR

PARADIGM GEOPHYSICAL CORP.

(Sub. of Paradigm B.V.)
2 Memorial Plz 820 Gessner Rd Ste 400
Houston, TX 77024
Tel.: (713) 393-4800
Fax: (713) 393-4802
Toll Free: (888) 223-6631
E-mail: supportus@pdgm.com
Approx. Number Employees: 100
Business Description:
Oil & Natural Gas Software Systems
S.I.C.: 7372; 8748
N.A.I.C.S.: 511210; 541690
Brands & Products:
A VISION OF ENERGY
PARADIGM SOFTWARE
Advertising Agency:
Koroberi
1506 E Franklin St Ste 300
Chapel Hill, NC 27514
Tel.: (919) 960-9794
Fax: (919) 960-8570

PARAMETRIC TECHNOLOGY CORPORATION

140 Kendrick St
Needham, MA 02494-2714
Tel.: (781) 370-5000
Fax: (781) 370-6000
Toll Free: (800) 782-3776
E-mail: sales@ptc.com
Web Site: www.ptc.com
Approx. Rev.: $1,010,049,000
Approx. Number Employees: 5,317
Year Founded: 1985
Business Description:
Software Publisher
S.I.C.: 7373; 7372
N.A.I.C.S.: 511210; 334611; 541512
Export
Advertising Expenditures: $2,400,000
Media: 1-4-7-11-13-22
Distr.: Intl.; Natl.
Personnel:
C. Richard Harrison *(Chm)*
James E. Heppelmann *(Pres & CEO)*
Jeffrey D. Glidden *(CFO & Exec VP)*
Aaron C. Von Staats *(Gen Counsel, Sec & Corp VP)*
Trenton H. Brown *(Exec VP-Intl Sls)*
Barry F. Cohen *(Exec VP-Strategy)*
Anthony Paul DiBona *(Exec VP-Maintence Support-Global)*
Robert Ranaldi *(Exec VP-Worldwide Sls & Distr)*
William S. Berutti *(VP & Gen Mgr)*
Nicole Rowe *(Dir-Comm)*
Beth Ambaruch *(Sr Mgr-Corp Comm)*
Anita Berryman *(Sr Mgr-Corp Comm)*
Marilyn Cohodas *(Program Mgr-Mktg)*
Brands & Products:
ARBORTEXT
CADDS 5I
COCREATE
DIVISION
GRANITE
GRANITE ONE
HARMONY
ICEM
INTERCOMM
MATHCAD
PRO/DESKTOP
PRO/ENGINEER
PRO/MECHANIC
PRODUCTVIEW
PROENGINEER WILDFIRE
PTC
WINDCHILL

PARAMETRIC TECHNOLOGY CORP.

(Formerly CoCreate Software, Inc.)
(Sub. of Parametric Technology GmbH)
(d/b/a PTC)
3801 Automation Way Ste 110
Fort Collins, CO 80525-3434
Tel.: (970) 267-8000
Fax: (970) 267-8001
Toll Free: (866) 267-8311
E-mail: Info-AM@CoCreate.com
Web Site: www.ptc.com
Sales Range: $75-99.9 Million
Year Founded: 1984
Business Description:
Flexible CAD & Collaborative PLM Applications Developer
S.I.C.: 7371; 7372
N.A.I.C.S.: 541511; 511210
Media: 2-4
Personnel:
William M. Gascoigne *(CEO)*
Hansjoerg Plaggemars *(COO)*
Ulrich Mahle *(VP-Worldwide Mktg & Product Devel)*
Craig Rode *(VP-US Sls Opers)*
Todd Black *(Mgr-Mktg Communications)*

PARK CITY GROUP, INC.

3160 Pinebrook Rd
Park City, UT 84098
Tel.: (435) 645-2000
Fax: (435) 645-2010
E-mail: info@parkcitygroup.com
Web Site: www.parkcitygroup.com
Approx. Rev.: $10,874,560
Approx. Number Employees: 52
Business Description:
Operation Management Software
S.I.C.: 7372; 7373
N.A.I.C.S.: 511210; 541512
Media: 2-7-10-17
Personnel:
Randall K. Fields *(Chm & CEO)*
David Colbert *(CFO)*
Brands & Products:
ACTIONMANAGER

PATNI AMERICAS, INC.

(Sub. of Patni Computer Systems Limited)
1 Broadway 15th fl
Cambridge, MA 02142
Tel.: (617) 914-8000
Fax: (617) 914-8200
E-mail: patni-usa@patni.com
Web Site: www.patni.com
Approx. Number Employees: 50
Business Description:
Computer Systems Design
S.I.C.: 7373; 7371
N.A.I.C.S.: 541512; 541511
Personnel:
Frank Khoshnoud *(Sr VP, Global Head Mfg-Retail & Distr)*
Robert Rando *(VP-Sls)*
Advertising Agency:
PAN Communications
300 Brickstone Sq 7th Fl
Andover, MA 01810
Tel.: (978) 474-1900
Fax: (978) 474-1903

PAVILION TECHNOLOGIES

(Div. of Rockwell Automation, Inc.)
10415 Morado Cir Bldg III Ste 100
Austin, TX 78759-5877
Tel.: (512) 438-1400
Fax: (512) 438-1401
Toll Free: (800) 880-5432
Web Site: www.pavtech.com
Approx. Sls.: $18,000,000
Approx. Number Employees: 120
Year Founded: 1991
Business Description:
Manufacturing Process Software
S.I.C.: 7371; 7372
N.A.I.C.S.: 541511; 511210
Media: 2-10-13
Personnel:
Greg Jackson *(Pres)*
James Dornes *(VP-Sls-North America)*
Colin Masson *(Dir-Res)*

PC CONNECTION, INC.

Rte 101 A 730 Milford Rd
Merrimack, NH 03054
Tel.: (603) 683-2000
Fax: (603) 423-5748
Toll Free: (888) 213-0607
E-mail: ir@pcconnection.com
Web Site: www.pcconnection.com
E-Mail For Key Personnel:
Public Relations:
corporatecommunications@pcconnection.com
Approx. Sls.: $1,974,198,000
Approx. Number Employees: 1,556
Year Founded: 1982
Business Description:
Direct Marketer of Computer Products
S.I.C.: 5045; 5961
N.A.I.C.S.: 423430; 454111; 454113
Advertising Expenditures: $17,887,000
Media: 2-4-7-8-11-13

Key to Media (For complete agency information see *The Advertising Red Books-Agencies* edition):
1. Bus. Publs. 2. Cable T.V. 3. Catalogs & Directories. 4. Co-op Adv. 5. Consumer Mags. 6. D.M. to Bus. Estab.7. D.M. to Consumers
8. Daily Newsp. 9. Exhibits/Trade Shows 10. Foreign 11. Infomercial 12. Internet Adv.13. Multimedia 14. Network Radio
15. Network T.V. 16. Newsp. Distr. Mags. 17. Other 18. Outdoor (Posters, Transit) 19. Point of Purchase20. Premiums, Novelties
21. Product Samples 22. Special Events Mktg. 23. Spot Radio 24. Spot T.V. 25. Weekly Newsp. 26. Yellow Page Adv.

Personnel:
Patricia Gallup *(Founder, Chm & Chief Admin Officer)*
Timothy J. McGrath *(CEO)*
Jack Ferguson *(CFO, Treas & Exec VP)*
Stephen Baldridge *(Controller & Sr VP-Fin)*
Brands & Products:
PC CONNECTION
WE HAVE YOUR BRAND
Advertising Agency:
Lodico & Company
60 McAllister Dr
Carlisle, MA 01741
Tel.: (978) 369-6556
Fax: (978) 369-6284

PC MALL, INC.
2555 W 190th St
Torrance, CA 90504-6002
Tel.: (310) 354-5600
Fax: (310) 225-4030
Toll Free: (800) 555-6255
Web Site: www.pcmall.com
Approx. Sls.: $1,368,314,000
Approx. Number Employees: 2,562
Year Founded: 1987
Business Description:
Direct Marketer of Computers & Accessories
S.I.C.: 5961; 5045; 5734
N.A.I.C.S.:* 454111; 423430; 443120; 454113
Advertising Expenditures: $5,400,000
Media: 4-5-6-7-8-10-13
Personnel:
Frank F. Khulusi *(Chm, Pres & CEO)*
Brandon H. LaVerne *(CFO)*
Daniel J. DeVries *(Pres-MacMall)*
Robert I. Newton *(Gen Counsel)*
Joseph B. Hayek *(Exec VP-Corp Dev & IR)*
Kristin M. Rogers *(Exec VP-Sls & Mktg)*

PC POWER & COOLING, INC.
(Sub. of OCZ TECHNOLOGY GROUP, INC.)
5995 Avenida Encinas
Carlsbad, CA 92008
Tel.: (760) 931-5700
Fax: (760) 931-6988
Toll Free: (800) 722-6555
E-mail: sales@pcpower.com
Web Site: www.pcpower.com
E-Mail For Key Personnel:
Sales Director: sales@pcpower.com
Sales Range: $25-49.9 Million
Approx. Number Employees: 40
Year Founded: 1985
Business Description:
Computer Power Supplies
S.I.C.: 3575; 5045
N.A.I.C.S.: 334113; 423430
Media: 6
Brands & Products:
PC POWER AND COOLING INC.
SILENCER
TURBO-COOL

PCTEL, INC.
471 Brighton Dr
Bloomingdale, IL 60108
Tel.: (630) 372-6800
Fax: (630) 372-8077
E-mail: investorrelations@pctel.com
Web Site: www.pctel.com
E-Mail For Key Personnel:
Public Relations: jack.seller@pctel.com
Approx. Rev.: $69,254,000
Approx. Number Employees: 345
Year Founded: 1994
Business Description:
Wireless Propagation & Optimization Products & Solutions
S.I.C.: 4812; 3669; 5045; 7371; 7372; 7373
N.A.I.C.S.: 517212; 334290; 423430; 511210; 541511; 541512
Advertising Expenditures: $200,000
Media: 2-10-17-22
Personnel:
Martin H. Singer *(Chm & CEO)*
John W. Schoen *(CFO & VP)*
Varda Goldman *(Gen Counsel & VP)*
Jeffrey A. Miller *(Sr VP-Sls & Mktg)*
Tony Kobrinetz *(VP-Tech & Ops)*
Jack Seller *(Dir-Mktg & PR)*
Brands & Products:
ANTENNA SPECIALISTS
BLUEWAVE
CLARIFY
HARD HAT
INSITE
LINEBACKER
MAXRAD
MEDALLION
MICROPULSE
MOSAIC
ON-GLASS
PCTEL
SEEGULL
SIGMA
SIMPLIFYING MOBILITY
WI-SYS
Advertising Agency:
Calysto Communications
861 Sapphire Ln Sugar Hill
Atlanta, GA 30518
Tel.: (404) 266-2060
Fax: (404) 266-2041

PEGASUS SOLUTIONS, INC.
(Holding of Prides Capital, LLC)
8350 N Central Expwy Ste 1900
Dallas, TX 75206
Tel.: (214) 234-4000
Fax: (214) 234-4040
E-mail: sales@pegs.com
Web Site: www.pegs.com
E-Mail For Key Personnel:
Sales Director: sales@pegs.com
Sales Range: $150-199.9 Million
Approx. Number Employees: 150
Year Founded: 1989
Business Description:
Reservation, Electronic Distribution, Financial & Representation Services to the Hotel & Travel Industries
S.I.C.: 7374; 7371
N.A.I.C.S.: 518210; 541511
Advertising Expenditures: $2,400,000
Media: 2-4-7-10-13-18-21-22-26
Personnel:
Mike Kistner *(CEO)*
Marcie Hyder *(CFO)*
Ric Leutwyler *(COO & Pres-Utell)*
Chris Klimko *(Gen Counsel & Sr VP)*
Steve Lapekas *(Exec VP-Corp Bus Dev)*
John D. Owens *(Sr VP-Global Sls)*
Connie Rheams *(Sr VP-Strategic Sls)*
Andrew Stringer *(Sr VP-HR)*
Mark Southlind *(VP-Corp Mktg & Comm)*
Hubert Tupay *(VP-Distr Sls)*
Brands & Products:
PEGASUS
UTELL

PEGASYSTEMS INC.
101 Main St
Cambridge, MA 02142-1590
Tel.: (617) 374-9600
Fax: (617) 374-9620
E-mail: info@pega.com
Web Site: www.pega.com
Approx. Rev.: $336,599,000
Approx. Number Employees: 1,509
Business Description:
Business Process Management Software Solutions
S.I.C.: 7372; 7371; 7373; 7374
N.A.I.C.S.: 511210; 518210; 541511; 541512
Export
Personnel:
Alan Trefler *(Founder, Chm & CEO)*
Richard H. Jones *(Pres & COO)*
Craig A. Dynes *(CFO & Sr VP)*
Grant Johnson *(CMO)*
Gary W. Kirkham *(Principal-Insurance Indus Solutions)*
Shawn Hoyt *(Gen Counsel & VP)*
Douglas Kra *(Sr VP-Global Svcs)*
Max Mayer *(Sr VP-Corp Dev)*
Michael Pyle *(Sr VP-Engrg & Product Dev)*
Brands & Products:
BUILD FOR CHANGE
CHANGE AWARE
PEGA
PEGA CUSTOMER PROCESS MANAGER
PEGABANKING SMART ADJUST
PEGABANKING SMART MONITOR
PEGACARD
PEGACSP
PEGAHEALTH
PEGAIMAGE MANAGER
PEGAINDEX
PEGAREACH
PEGAREELAY
PEGARESEARCH MANAGER
PEGARULES
PEGARULES PROCESS COMMANDER
PEGAVIEW
PEGAWEB
PEGAWORKBENCH
PEGAWORKS
PEGAWORLD
SIMPLY SMART DISPUTE
SMART ADJUST
SMART BPM
SMART DIALOG
SMART INVESTIGATE
SMART VIEWS
SMARTBPM
SMARTBPO
SWIFTNET
WORKSTATION+
Advertising Agency:
Lois Paul & Partners
150 Presidential Way
Woburn, MA 01801
Tel.: (781) 782-5000
Fax: (781) 782-5999

PEGASYSTEMS INC.
(Formerly Chordiant Software, Inc.)
(Sub. of Pegasystems Inc.)
20400 Stevens Creek Blvd Ste 400
Cupertino, CA 95014
Tel.: (408) 517-6100
Fax: (408) 517-0270
Toll Free: (888) 246-7342
Web Site: www.pega.com
E-Mail For Key Personnel:
Sales Director: sales@chordiant.com
Approx. Rev.: $77,462,000
Approx. Number Employees: 222
Year Founded: 1997
Business Description:
Customer Relationship Management Solutions Developer for Business-to-Consumer Enterprises
S.I.C.: 7372
N.A.I.C.S.: 334611; 511210
Advertising Expenditures: $200,000
Media: 1-4-7-13-23
Personnel:
Peter S. Norman *(CFO & Sr VP)*
Frank J. Florence *(CMO & VP)*
Shawn Hoyt *(Gen Counsel & VP)*
Simon Gates *(VP-Sls-Western Europe)*
Brands & Products:
CHORDIANT FOUNDATION SERVER
CX TECHNOLOGY
OPTIMIZING THE CUSTOMER EXPERIENCE

PENTEL OF AMERICA, LTD.
(Sub. of Pentel Co., Ltd.)
2715 Columbia St
Torrance, CA 90503
Tel.: (310) 320-3831
Fax: (310) 533-0697
Toll Free: (800) 421-1419
Web Site: www.pentel.com
E-Mail For Key Personnel:
Marketing Director: mktg@pentel.com
Public Relations: pr@pentel.com
Approx. Number Employees: 270
Year Founded: 1965
Business Description:
Mfr. of Pens, Liquid Ink Ball Pens, Porous Point Pens, Plastic Point Pens, Mechanical Pencils, Markers, Art Materials, Sliding Sleeve Automatic Pencils & Leads
S.I.C.: 5112; 3951
N.A.I.C.S.: 424120; 339941
Import Export
Advertising Expenditures: $2,500,000
Media: 2-5-6-7-8-10-19-20-23
Distr.: Natl.
Budget Set: Apr.
Personnel:
I. Nakayama *(CEO)*
Ilene Albert-Nelson *(Dir-Mktg)*
Wendy Vickery *(Mgr-Mktg)*
Brands & Products:
A125 SHARPLET-2
ENCORE GRIP
EXCALIBUR
FABRIC FUN
FORTE
FOUNTAIN PENTEL
GIZMO
HI-POLYMER
HYBRID-2
HYBRID GEL GRIP

Key to Media (For complete agency information see *The Advertising Red Books-Agencies* edition):
1. Bus. Publs. 2. Cable T.V. 3. Catalogs & Directories. 4. Co-op Adv. 5. Consumer Mags. 6. D.M. to Bus. Estab.7. D.M. to Consumers
8. Daily Newsp. 9. Exhibits/Trade Shows 10. Foreign 11. Infomercial 12. Internet Adv.13. Multimedia 14. Network Radio
15. Network T.V. 16. Newsp. Distr. Mags. 17. Other 18. Outdoor (Posters, Transit) 19. Point of Purchase20. Premiums, Novelties
21. Product Samples 22. Special Events Mktg. 23. Spot Radio 24. Spot T.V. 25. Weekly Newsp. 26. Yellow Page Adv.

Pentel of America, Ltd. — (Continued)

HYBRID GEL ROLLER
HYPER-G
LANCELOT
MARKATHON
MECHANICA
METALLIC GEL ROLLER
MILKY GEL ROLLER
PENTEL R.S.V.P.
PRO AM
QUICKER CLICKER
R204 MICRO FINE SUPERBALL
R206 SUPERBALL
ROLL N' GLUE
ROLLING WRITER
SHARP
SHARPLET-2
SIGN PENS
SLIM
SUPER FINE PENTEL
SUPER HI-POLYMER
TECHNICA-X
TECHNICLICK
TRADIO

Advertising Agencies:
Alloy Media + Marketing
10 Abeel Rd
Cranbury, NJ 08512
Tel.: (609) 655-8878
Fax: (609) 395-0737
(Hyper-G)

RiechesBaird, Inc.
1 Wrigley
Irvine, CA 92618
Tel.: (949) 586-1200
Fax: (949) 586-1201
(Hyper-G)

PEOPLECLICK, INC.

(Sub. of Peopleclick Authoria)
(d/b/a Peopleclick Authoria - Raleigh)
2 Hannover Sq 7th Fl
Raleigh, NC 27601
Tel.: (919) 645-2800
Fax: (919) 645-2801
Web Site: www.peopleclick.com
Sales Range: $25-49.9 Million
Approx. Number Employees: 172
Year Founded: 1997
Business Description:
Talent Acquisition & Workforce Compliance Software & Consulting Services
S.I.C.: 7372; 5045; 7361
N.A.I.C.S.: 511210; 423430; 541612
Media: 10
Personnel:
Timothy Beaumont *(Sr VP-Sls)*
Brands & Products:
AAPLANNER
CLICKAAP
CLICKEM
CLICKXG RMS
CLICKXG VMS
MONITOR
PAYSTAT
PEOPLECLICK

PEPPERBALL TECHNOLOGIES, INC.

6142 Nancy Rdg Dr Ste 101
San Diego, CA 92121
Tel.: (858) 638-0236
Fax: (858) 638-0781
Toll Free: (877) 887-3773
E-mail: info@pepperball.com
Web Site: www.pepperball.com
Sales Range: $10-24.9 Million
Approx. Number Employees: 19
Year Founded: 1999
Business Description:
High-Tech Security Products Mfr
S.I.C.: 7382; 3695; 3812
N.A.I.C.S.: 561621; 334511; 334613
Advertising Expenditures: $953,000
Personnel:
Eric P. Wenaas *(Chm & Pres)*
John Stiska *(CEO)*
Christin Lewis *(CFO & Asst Sec)*
Conrad Sun *(COO)*
Ed Vasel *(VP-Engrg & Product Dev)*
Brands & Products:
CHEM-NETICS
SHIFTWATCH
SHIFTWATCH TVS

PEPPERWEED CONSULTING LLC

Blaymore II 1603 Carmody Ct
Sewickley, PA 15143
Toll Free: (888) 229-0145
E-mail: info@pepperweed.com
Web Site: www.pepperweed.com
Sales Range: $25-49.9 Million
Approx. Number Employees: 50
Year Founded: 1996
Business Description:
IT Infrastructure, Management & Consulting Services
S.I.C.: 7373; 7379; 8748
N.A.I.C.S.: 541512; 541519; 541690
Media: 10

PERLE SYSTEMS LIMITED

60 Renfrew Dr
Markham, ON L3R 0E1, Canada
Tel.: (905) 475-6070
Fax: (905) 475-2377
Toll Free: (800) 467-3753
E-mail: info@perle.com
Web Site: www.perle.com
Sales Range: $25-49.9 Million
Approx. Number Employees: 100
Year Founded: 1976
Business Description:
Internet Protocol Networking Product Developer, Vendor & Mfr
S.I.C.: 3577
N.A.I.C.S.: 334119
Media: 2
Personnel:
Joseph E. Perle *(CEO)*
Derrick Barnett *(CFO)*
John Feeney *(COO)*
Julie McDaniel *(VP-Mktg)*
Al Davies *(Dir-Product Mktg)*
Brands & Products:
PERLE
TRUESERIAL

PERRYGRAF

25 W 550 Geneva Rd
Carol Stream, IL 60118
Tel.: (630) 784-0100
Fax: (630) 784-6690
Toll Free: (800) 423-5329
E-mail: sales@perrygraf.com
Web Site: www.perrygraf.com
E-Mail For Key Personnel:
Sales Director: sales@perrygraf.com
Approx. Sls.: $5,000,000
Approx. Number Employees: 65
Year Founded: 1934
Business Description:
Mfr. & Sales of Slide-Charts, Wheel-Charts & Pop-Ups
S.I.C.: 3829; 3579
N.A.I.C.S.: 334519; 333313
Export
Advertising Expenditures: $500,000
Media: 7-10
Distr.: Natl.
Budget Set: Nov.
Personnel:
Julie Johnson *(Pres)*
Don Hoff *(Dir-Sls & Mktg)*
Brands & Products:
PERRYGRAF
PERRYGRAF POP-UPS
WE PUT YOUR MESSAGE IN MOTION!

PERVASIVE SOFTWARE INC.

12365 Riata Trace Pkwy Bldg B
Austin, TX 78727-6418
Tel.: (512) 231-6000
Fax: (512) 231-6010
Toll Free: (800) 287-4383
E-mail: info@pervasive.com
Web Site: www.pervasive.com
E-Mail For Key Personnel:
Sales Director: salessupport@pervasive.com
Public Relations: pr@pervasive.com
Approx. Rev.: $48,393,000
Approx. Number Employees: 252
Year Founded: 1994
Business Description:
Software Developer
S.I.C.: 7372; 5045; 7371
N.A.I.C.S.: 511210; 334611; 423430; 541511
Advertising Expenditures: $1,400,000
Media: 2-6-7-10-22
Personnel:
John E. Farr *(Pres & CEO)*
Randall G. Jonkers *(CFO)*
Michael E. Hoskins *(CTO, Exec VP-Pervasive Software & Gen Mgr-Integration Products)*
Stephen Padgett *(VP-IT)*
Lance Speck *(Gen Mgr-Integration Products)*
Gilbert Van Cutsem *(Gen Mgr-Database Products)*
Brands & Products:
BTRIEVE
BUILT ON PERVASIVE SOFTWARE
DATA JUNCTION
DATACLOUD
METADATA STUDIO
PERVASIVE
PERVASIVE AUDITMASTER
PERVASIVE BACKUP AGENT
PERVASIVE BUSINESS INTEGRATOR
PERVASIVE DATA INTEGRATOR
PERVASIVE DATA PROFILER
PERVASIVE DATAEXCHANGE
PERVASIVE DATARUSH
PERVASIVE DATATOOLS
PERVASIVE INTEGRATION MANAGER
PERVASIVE MESSAGESTORE
PERVASIVE PSQL
PERVASIVE PSQL V9
PERVASIVE SAAS BUSINESS INTEGRATOR
PERVASIVE SAAS DATA INTEGRATOR
PERVASIVE SOFTWARE
PERVASIVE.SQL
PERVASIVE.SQL SDK
POSTGRES
SCALABLE SQL
Advertising Agency:
Horn Group Inc.
612 Howard St Ste 100
San Francisco, CA 94105
Tel.: (415) 905-4000
Fax: (415) 905-4001
Social Media, PR, Interactive Design Services
— Erin Zehr *(VP)*

PHASE FORWARD INCORPORATED

(Sub. of Oracle Corporation)
77 Fourth Ave
Waltham, MA 02451
Tel.: (781) 890-7878
Fax: (781) 890-4848
Toll Free: (888) 703-1122
E-mail: info@phaseforward.com
Web Site: www.phaseforward.com
Approx. Rev.: $213,257,000
Approx. Number Employees: 939
Year Founded: 1997
Business Description:
Integrated Data Management Solutions for Clinical Trials & Drug Safety
S.I.C.: 7371; 7372; 7374; 7389
N.A.I.C.S.: 541511; 511210; 518210; 541990
Advertising Expenditures: $22,000
Media: 17
Personnel:
Robert K. Weiler *(CEO)*
Michael Owings *(Chief Privacy Officer, VP-Quality & Regulatory Compliance)*
D. Ari Buchler *(Sr VP-Legal & Regulatory Svcs)*
Brands & Products:
CLINTRIAL
EMPIRICA
INFORM
INPHASE
LABPAS CT
LABPAS EM
LABPAS SR
LIMS LABPAS
OUTCOMELOGIX
PHASE FORWARD
SLEEPLOGIX
WEBSDM

PHILIPS DICTATION SYSTEMS

(Div. of Philips Electronics North America)
66 Perimeter Ctr E 8th Fl
Atlanta, GA 30346
Tel.: (770) 821-3680
Fax: (770) 821-3922
Toll Free: (888) 260-6261
E-mail: dawn.nye@philips.com
Web Site: www.dictation.philips.com
Approx. Number Employees: 6
Year Founded: 1957
Business Description:
Marketer of Digital & Analog Dictation Equipment; Pocket Size Recorders & Remote Microphone Dictation Systems
S.I.C.: 5044
N.A.I.C.S.: 423420
Media: 2-7-10-21
Distr.: Natl.

Key to Media (For complete agency information see *The Advertising Red Books-Agencies* edition):
1. Bus. Publs. 2. Cable T.V. 3. Catalogs & Directories. 4. Co-op Adv. 5. Consumer Mags. 6. D.M. to Bus. Estab.7. D.M. to Consumers 8. Daily Newsp. 9. Exhibits/Trade Shows 10. Foreign 11. Infomercial 12. Internet Adv.13. Multimedia 14. Network Radio 15. Network T.V. 16. Newsp. Distr. Mags. 17. Other 18. Outdoor (Posters, Transit) 19. Point of Purchase20. Premiums, Novelties 21. Product Samples 22. Special Events Mktg. 23. Spot Radio 24. Spot T.V. 25. Weekly Newsp. 26. Yellow Page Adv.

Budget Set: Nov. -Dec.
Personnel:
Dawn Nye *(Mgr-Sls Support)*
Brands & Products:
POCKET MEMO
SPEECHMIKE CLASSIC
SPEECHMIKE PRO

PHOENIX AMERICAN SALESFOCUS SOLUTIONS, INC.
(Sub. of Phoenix American Incorporated)
2401 Kerner Blvd
San Rafael, CA 94901-5529
Tel.: (415) 485-4500
Fax: (415) 485-4891
Toll Free: (888) 325-6277
E-mail: sfsinfo@phxa.com
Web Site: www.salesfocussolutions.com
Approx. Number Employees: 25
Business Description:
Sales Force Automation, CRM Solutions & Computer Programming Related Services
S.I.C.: 7371
N.A.I.C.S.: 541511
Media: 10

PHOENIX TECHNOLOGIES LTD.
(Holding of Marlin Equity Partners, LLC)
915 Murphy Ranch Rd
Milpitas, CA 95035
Tel.: (408) 570-1000
Fax: (408) 570-1001
Toll Free: (800) 677-7305
E-mail: americas_sales@phoenix.com
Web Site: www.phoenix.com
Sales Range: $50-74.9 Million
Approx. Number Employees: 400
Year Founded: 1979
Business Description:
Systems Software for Personal Computers & Peripherals
S.I.C.: 7372
N.A.I.C.S.: 511210; 334611
Export
Advertising Expenditures: $700,000
Personnel:
Rich Geruson *(Pres & CEO)*
David A. Everett *(Sr VP-Field Ops)*
Surendra Arora *(VP-Mktg & Product Dev)*
Srinivas Raman *(VP-Engrg)*
Brands & Products:
ACPI ARCHITECT
ADVANCED ACPI
AWARDBIOS
BIOS AGENT
BIOS ENHANCEMENTS & MODULES
BIOSAGENTPLUS
COREARCHITECT
DEVICECONNECT
DRIVERAGENT
FIRSTBIOS
FIRSTWARE
FLASHPRO
HYPERSPACE
MULTIKEY
NOTEBIOS
NOTEDOCK
PHLASH
PHOENIX
PHOENIX ALWAYS SDK
PHOENIX AWARD
PHOENIX FAILSAFE
PHOENIX FREEZE
PHOENIX SECURECORE
PHOENIX SECURITY SDK
PHOENIXBIOS
REGISTRY WIZARD
SERVERBIOS
TRUSTCONNECTOR
TRUSTEDCORE
UNDELETEPLUS
WINPHLASH

PICIS, INC.
100 Quannapowitt Pkwy Ste 405
Wakefield, MA 01880
Tel.: (781) 557-3000
Fax: (781) 557-3140
Web Site: www.picis.com
Sales Range: $50-74.9 Million
Approx. Number Employees: 500
Year Founded: 1993
Business Description:
Information Systems for High-Acuity Care
S.I.C.: 7373
N.A.I.C.S.: 541512
Media: 10
Personnel:
Richard M. Johnston *(Chm)*
Christine M. Cournoyer *(Pres & COO)*
Todd C. Cozzens *(CEO)*
Melissa Cruz *(CFO, Exec VP-Fin & Admin)*
Michael Mitsock *(CMO & Sr VP-Mktg-Global)*
Mark D. Crockett *(Pres-Emergency Care Div)*
Joseph M. Smith *(Pres-Perioperative Care Div)*
Elizabeth A. Popovich *(Exec VP-Ops-Intl)*
Samuel H. Adams *(Sr VP-Sls-North America)*
Scott Iverson *(Sr VP-Prof Svcs)*
Jo Ann Ploen *(VP-Sls-Midwest)*

PICKTURETALK
3180 Crow Canyon Pl Ste 135
San Ramon, CA 94583-1339
Tel.: (925) 328-1500
Fax: (925) 355-1591
Web Site: www.picturetalk.com
Approx. Number Employees: 15
Year Founded: 1995
Business Description:
Client-Services & Client Web Conferencing Services
S.I.C.: 7376
N.A.I.C.S.: 541513
Media: 2-7
Personnel:
Mitch Diamond *(Pres)*
Jody Whitsett *(Dir-Bus Dev)*

THE PILOT CORPORATION OF AMERICA
(Sub. of Pilot Corporation)
60 Commerce Dr
Trumbull, CT 06611-5403
Tel.: (203) 377-8800
Fax: (203) 377-4024
E-mail: service@pilotpen.com
Web Site: www.pilotpen.com
Approx. Number Employees: 306
Year Founded: 1970
Business Description:
Mfr. of Writing Instruments
S.I.C.: 5112; 3951
N.A.I.C.S.: 424120; 339941
Import Export
Media: 2-3-4-5-6-7-8-10-11-13-15-19-20-22
Distr.: Natl.
Budget Set: Sept.
Personnel:
Robert Silberman *(Dir-Mktg)*

PINNACLE DATA SYSTEMS, INC.
6600 Port Rd Ste 100
Groveport, OH 43125
Tel.: (614) 748-1150
Fax: (614) 409-1269
Toll Free: (800) 882-8282
E-mail: info@pinnacle.com
Web Site: www.pinnacle.com
E-Mail For Key Personnel:
Sales Director: info.sales@pinnacle.com
Approx. Sls.: $29,445,000
Approx. Number Employees: 148
Business Description:
Made-to-Order UNIX-Based Servers Mfr
S.I.C.: 3571; 7379
N.A.I.C.S.: 334111; 541519
Advertising Expenditures: $63,000
Media: 17
Personnel:
John D. Bair *(Chm, CEO & CTO)*
Nicholas J. Tomashot *(CFO, Treas & Sec)*
Timothy J. Harper *(COO)*
Brands & Products:
ADVANCEDMC
ADVANCEDTCA
COMPACTPCI

PINNACLE SYSTEMS, INC.
(Sub. of Avid Technology, Inc.)
280 N Bernardo Ave
Mountain View, CA 94043-5238
Tel.: (650) 526-1600
Fax: (650) 526-1601
E-mail: sales@pinnaclesys.com
Web Site: www.pinnaclesys.com
E-Mail For Key Personnel:
Sales Director: sales@pinnaclesys.com
Public Relations: pr@pinnaclesys.com
Sales Range: $300-349.9 Million
Approx. Number Employees: 185
Year Founded: 1986
Business Description:
Designer, Mfr & Marketer of Digital Video Post Production Tools
S.I.C.: 3663; 3577
N.A.I.C.S.: 334220; 334119
Advertising Expenditures: $9,200,000
Media: 2-5-6-7-10-13
Brands & Products:
CINEWAVE
DAZZLE
DEKO
DEKOCAST
HOLLYWOOD
INSTANT
INSTANT VIDEOALBUM
LIQUID EDITION
MEDIASTREAM
MYMP3PRO
PALLADIUM EXCHANGE
PALLADIUM STORE
PCTV
PINNACLE
POSTDEKO
PRO-ONE
SHOWCENTER
STREAMGENIE
STUDIO
STUDIO DC10PLUS
TARGA
THUNDER
TILEDEKO PRO
VORTEX
Advertising Agency:
Marken Communications Inc.
3375 Scott Blvd Ste 236
Santa Clara, CA 95054-3113
Tel.: (408) 986-0100
Fax: (408) 986-0162

PITNEY BOWES INC.
1 Elmcroft Rd
Stamford, CT 06926-0700
Tel.: (203) 356-5000
Fax: (203) 351-7336
E-mail: investorrelations@pb.com
Web Site: www.pb.com
Approx. Rev.: $5,425,254,000
Approx. Number Employees: 30,700
Year Founded: 1920
Business Description:
Mailing, Shipping, Copying, Communications Recording & Facsimile Systems; Item Identification & Tracking Systems & Supplies; Mailroom, Reprographics & Related Management Services
S.I.C.: 3873; 3952; 7359
N.A.I.C.S.: 334518; 339942; 532210; 532299; 532310; 532420; 532490
Export
Media: 2-4-5-6-7-8-9-10-11-13-16-18-19-20-21-22-23-24-25-26
Distr.: Direct to Consumer; Natl.
Budget Set: Dec.
Personnel:
Murray D. Martin *(Chm, Pres & CEO)*
Michael Monahan *(CFO & Exec VP)*
Gregory E. Buoncontri *(CIO & Exec VP)*
Johnna G. Torsone *(Chief HR Officer & Exec VP & Interim Chief Legal/ Compliance Offic)*
Daniel J. Goldstein *(Chief Legal Officer, Chief Compliance Officer & Exec VP)*
Joseph H. Timko *(Chief Strategy & Innovation Officer & Exec VP)*
Steven J. Green *(Chief Acctg Officer & VP-Fin)*
Leslie R. Abi-Karam *(Pres-Mailing Solutions Mgmt & Exec VP)*
Elise R. DeBois *(Pres-Global Fin Svcs & Exec VP)*
Vicki A. O'Meara *(Pres-Mgmt Svcs & Exec VP)*
Patrick M. Brand *(Pres-Mailing-US & VP)*
John O'Hara *(Pres-Bus Insight & VP)*
Chuck Cordray *(Pres-Volly Platform)*
Ramesh A. Lakshmi Ratan *(Pres-Pitney Bowes Document Messaging Technologies)*
Elizabeth Lee *(Dir-Mktg-Volly)*
Brands & Products:
ACCUTRAC
ACCUTRAC SA
ADDRESSRIGHT
APS

Key to Media (For complete agency information see *The Advertising Red Books-Agencies* edition):
1. Bus. Publs. 2. Cable T.V. 3. Catalogs & Directories. 4. Co-op Adv. 5. Consumer Mags. 6. D.M. to Bus. Estab.7. D.M. to Consumers
8. Daily Newsp. 9. Exhibits/Trade Shows 10. Foreign 11. Infomercial 12. Internet Adv.13. Multimedia 14. Network Radio
15. Network T.V. 16. Newsp. Distr. Mags. 17. Other 18. Outdoor (Posters, Transit) 19. Point of Purchase20. Premiums, Novelties
21. Product Samples 22. Special Events Mktg. 23. Spot Radio 24. Spot T.V. 25. Weekly Newsp. 26. Yellow Page Adv.

Pitney Bowes Inc. — (Continued)

ARRIVAL
AUTOMATED DOCUMENT FACTORIES
AUTOMATIC ELECTRONIC MAIL OPENERS
BUDGET MANAGER
BUSINESS MANAGER
CASS
COVERBIND
CUSTOMER SATISFACTION GUARANTEE
D3
DELIVERABILITY
DESKTOP EXPRESS
DESKTOP PUBLISHING
DFWORKS
DM 1100
DM 200
DM 300
DM 400
DM 525
DM 575
DM 875
DM 925
DM INFINITY SERIES
DMAIL
DOC1 SUITE
DOCUMATCH
ENGINEERING THE FLOW OF COMMUNICATION
EPS
FASTPAC
FINALIST
FINETUNE DATA
FLOWMASTER
FORWARDTRAK
FORWARDTRAK NET
FPS
GALAXY
H5LP
IMAGEALERT
INSITE
INTEGRA SERIES
INTELLIGENT MAIL
LISTANALYST
LOBBYGUARD
MAILER'S CHOICE
MAILSTATION
OFFICERIGHT
OLYMPUS
OLYMPUS II
ON ROUTE
PB FIRST
PB TMS
PBC
PERSONAL POST
PITNEY BOWES ENVIRONMENTAL LAB
POSTAGE BY PHONE
POSTPERFECT
SHIPREQUEST
SHIPSTREAM
SHIPSTREAM MANAGER
SMARTMAILER
SMARTMAILER 7
STATEMENT CREATION
STREAMWEAVER
VARISORT
VERIMOVE

Advertising Agencies:
OgilvyOne Worldwide
636 11th Ave
New York, NY 10036
Tel.: (212) 237-4000
Fax: (212) 237-5123

Yeck Brothers Company
2222 Arbor Blvd
Dayton, OH 45439-1522
Tel.: (937) 294-4000
Fax: (937) 294-6985
Toll Free: (800) 417-2767

PITNEY BOWES SOFTWARE INC.

(Sub. of Pitney Bowes Inc.)
(d/b/a Pitney Bowes Business Insight)
1 Global View
Troy, NY 12180-8399
Tel.: (518) 285-6000
Fax: (518) 285-6070
Toll Free: (800) 327-8627
E-mail: pbbi.sales@pb.com
Web Site: www.mapinfo.com
E-Mail For Key Personnel:
Sales Director: sales@mapinfo.com
Approx. Rev.: $165,495,008
Approx. Number Employees: 900
Year Founded: 1986
Business Description:
Geographical Data Products & Location-Based Analysis Services
S.I.C.: 7372; 7374
N.A.I.C.S.: 511210; 518210
Export
Media: 2-6-8-10-13-20-22
Distr.: Intl.
Budget Set: Oct.
Personnel:
John O'Hara *(Pres)*
Ben Semmes *(Grp Operating Officer)*
Brands & Products:
AREACODEINFO
CALLINGAREAINFO
CLECINFO
EXCHANGEINFO
IMAGEPRO
LATAINFO
LECINFO
MAP XTEND
MAPBASIC
MAPINFO MAP X
MAPINFO MAPXTREME
MAPINFO PROFESSIONAL
MAPINFO PROVIEWER
MAPINFO SPATIALWARE
MAPMARKER
MAPSHOP
MAPX
MAPXTEND
MAPXTREME
MARKETMATH
MEDIAPRINTS
MIAWARE
MICALLPLAN
MILISTS
MOBILEMARKETINFO
OBSTACLEINFO
POPINFO
POSTCODES
POSTMAP
POSTPOINT
PROFESSIONAL
PROVIEWER
PSAP PRO
PSYTE
RATECENTERINFO
RISKDATAINFO
SPATIALWARE
STREETPRO
STREETPRO BASIC
TARGET PRO
TOPOLOGY MANAGER
TOPOMAP 250K
TRANSAMERICA FLOODMAP
VERTICAL MAPPER
WIRELESSINFO
WORLDINFO
ZIP+4 MAPINFO MAPMARKER
Advertising Agency:
Wanderlust
297 River St
Troy, NY 12180
Tel.: (518) 272-2500
Fax: (518) 272-2500

PIVOTAL RESOURCES, INC.

1646 N California Blvd Ste 520
Walnut Creek, CA 94596
Tel.: (925) 975-0500
Fax: (925) 975-0501
Toll Free: (800) 699-6220
Web Site: www.pivotalresources.com
Approx. Number Employees: 10
Year Founded: 1993
Business Description:
Organizational Improvement Consulting Services
S.I.C.: 7389
N.A.I.C.S.: 561499
Media: 2-7
Personnel:
Peter Pande *(Pres)*
Brands & Products:
NLIGHTEN
OAKTREE
SIGMA STATION
THE SIX SIGMA WAY
THE SIX SIGMA WAY TEAM FIELDBOOK
WHAT IS SIX SIGMA

PLANAR SYSTEMS, INC.

1195 NW Compton Dr
Beaverton, OR 97006-1992
Tel.: (503) 748-1100
Fax: (503) 748-1493
Toll Free: (866) 475-2627
E-mail: public_relations@planar.com
Web Site: www.planar.com
Approx. Sls.: $175,668,000
Approx. Number Employees: 429
Year Founded: 1983
Business Description:
Flat-Panel Display Technologies Mfr & Sales
S.I.C.: 3679; 1311; 3575; 3663; 3823
N.A.I.C.S.: 334419; 211111; 334113; 334220; 334513
Import Export
Advertising Expenditures: $1,895,000
Media: 7-10
Personnel:
Gregory H. Turnbull *(Chm)*
Gerald K. Perkel *(Pres & CEO)*
Scott Hildebrandt *(CFO & VP)*
Stephen Going *(Gen Counsel, Sec & VP)*
Douglas K. Barnes *(VP & Gen Mgr)*
Mark A. Ceciliani *(VP & Gen Mgr-Comml Bus Unit)*
Benjamin Clifton *(VP-Tech)*
Pippa Edelen *(Dir-WW Mktg Runco)*
Steve Seminario *(Product Mgr)*
Cindy McCullough *(Mgr-Touch Product Mktg)*
Terry Trover *(Mgr-Global Sls-3D Stereoscopic Displays)*
Brands & Products:
BRILLIANTCOLOR
THE DEFINITION OF QUALITY
DOME CXTRA QX EDITION
DOME DASHBOARD
INDUSTRY LEADING CUSTOMER FIRST
INVITIUM
PLANAR
PLANAR DLP
RUNCO
STEREO MIRROR
THIN-BEZEL
VIDIKRON
VITALSCREEN
WHEN IMAGE EXPERIENCE MATTERS.
Advertising Agency:
Anvil Media, Inc.
310 NE Failing St.
Portland, OR 97212
Tel.: (503) 595-6050
Fax: (503) 223-1008

THE PLANET

(Name Changed to Softlayer Technologies Inc)

PLATO LEARNING, INC.

(Holding of Thoma Bravo, LLC)
5600 W 83rd St Ste 300 8200 Twr
Bloomington, MN 55437
Tel.: (952) 832-1000
Fax: (952) 832-1200
Toll Free: (800) 869-2000
Toll Free: (800) 447-5286
E-mail: marketing@plato.com
Web Site: www.plato.com
Approx. Rev.: $65,183,000
Approx. Number Employees: 300
Year Founded: 1989
Business Description:
Educational Software Publishers
S.I.C.: 7372; 2721; 8299
N.A.I.C.S.: 511210; 511120; 611710
Import Export
Advertising Expenditures: $298,000
Personnel:
Vincent P. Riera *(Pres & CEO)*
Robert J. Rueckl *(CFO)*
Ian Kees *(Corp Counsel & VP)*
Jamie Candee *(VP-Product & Mktg)*
Stacey Herteux *(Dir-HR)*
Mary Schneider *(Dir-Mktg)*
Brands & Products:
ACADEMIC SYSTEMS
INSPIRED SOLUTIONS FOR TEACHING & LEARNING
PLATO
PLATO LEARNING
PLATO VOCABULARY BUILDER
STRAIGHT CURVE

PLEXUS CORP.

1 Plexus Way
Neenah, WI 54956
Tel.: (920) 722-3451
Fax: (920) 751-5395
Web Site: www.plexus.com
Approx. Sls.: $2,013,393,000
Approx. Number Employees: 8,700
Year Founded: 1980
Business Description:
Mfr of Electronic Products for Medical, Telecommunications, Industrial & Computer Markets
S.I.C.: 3672; 3679
N.A.I.C.S.: 334412; 334419
Media: 7-10
Personnel:
John L. Nussbaum *(Chm)*

Key to Media (For complete agency information see *The Advertising Red Books-Agencies* edition):
1. Bus. Publs. 2. Cable T.V. 3. Catalogs & Directories. 4. Co-op Adv. 5. Consumer Mags. 6. D.M. to Bus. Estab.7. D.M. to Consumers 8. Daily Newsp. 9. Exhibits/Trade Shows 10. Foreign 11. Infomercial 12. Internet Adv.13. Multimedia 14. Network Radio 15. Network T.V. 16. Newsp. Distr. Mags. 17. Other 18. Outdoor (Posters, Transit) 19. Point of Purchase20. Premiums, Novelties 21. Product Samples 22. Special Events Mktg. 23. Spot Radio 24. Spot T.V. 25. Weekly Newsp. 26. Yellow Page Adv.

Dean A. Foate *(Pres & CEO)*
Ginger M. Jones *(CFO & Sr VP)*
Angelo M. Ninivaggi *(Gen Counsel, Sec & Sr VP)*
Mike D. Buseman *(Exec VP-Global Mfg Ops)*
Todd Kelsey *(Exec VP-Global Customer Svcs)*
Joseph E. Mauthe *(Sr VP-HR-Global)*
Michael T. Verstegen *(Sr VP-Global Market Dev)*
Amy Salisbury *(Dir-Customer)*
Mark Wolfgram *(Mgr-Sls Support)*
Brands & Products:
PLEXUS
WHERE IDEAS BECOME REALITY

PLX TECHNOLOGY, INC.

870 W Maude Ave
Sunnyvale, CA 94085-2910
Tel.: (408) 774-9060
Fax: (408) 774-2169
E-mail: investor-relations@plxtech.com
Web Site: www.plxtech.com
Approx. Rev.: $116,560,000
Approx. Number Employees: 260
Year Founded: 1994
Business Description:
Semiconductor Devices & Software Developer & Supplier
S.I.C.: 3674
N.A.I.C.S.: 334413
Media: 7-10-11
Personnel:
D. James Guzy *(Chm)*
Ralph H. Schmitt *(Pres & CEO)*
Arthur O. Whipple *(CFO, Sec & VP)*
Lawrence Chisvin *(COO)*
Ron Cates *(VP-Mktg & Networking Products)*
Vijay Meduri *(VP-Engrg)*
Ken Murray *(VP-HR)*
David K. Raun *(VP-Mktg & Bus Dev)*
Gene Schaeffer *(VP-Sls-Worldwide)*
James Tout *(VP-Engrg-Storage)*
Shin Kobayashi *(Reg Mgr-Sls)*
Kevin Lee *(Reg Mgr-Sls)*
Jerry Steach *(Mgr-Pub Rel)*
Brands & Products:
ADVANCEDMC
DATA PIPE ARCHITECTURE
EXPRESSLANE
FASTLANE
HYPERTRANSPORT
NET2272
NET2282
NETCHIP
OX12OCL840
OX16C950B
OX16C954B
OX16PCL954
OX16PCL958
OXCB950
OXCF950B
OXCFU950
OXE810DSE
OXE810SE
OXFORD
OXMPCL952
OXMPCL954
OXPCLE200
OXPCLE840
OXPCLE952
OXPCLE954
OXPCLE958
OXU210HP
OXU931DS
OXU931S
OXU931SF
OXUF934DSA
OXUF934DSB
OXUF934SSA
OXUFFS936QSE
OXUFS936DS
OXUFS936DSE
OXUPCL952
OXUPCL954
OXUS931SE
PCL 9030
PCL 9052
PCL 9054
PCL 9056
PCL 9060
PCL 9080
PCL 9656
PCL EXPRESS
PCL6140
PCL6150
PCL6152
PCL6154
PCL6156
PCL6254
PCL6350
PCL6466
PCL6520
PCL6540
PEX 8111
PEX 8112
PEX 8114
PEX 83113
PEX 8505
PEX 8508
PEX 8509
PEX 8512
PEX 8516
PEX 8517
PEX 8518
PEX 8524
PEX 8525
PEX 8532
PEX 8533
PEX 8547
PEX 8548
PEX 8604
PEX 8606
PEX 8608
PEX 8609
PEX 8612
PEX 8614
PEX 8615
PEX 8616
PEX 8618
PEX 8619
PEX 8624
PEX 8632
PEX 8647
PEX 8648
PEX 8649
PEX 8664
PEX 8680
PEX 8696
PLX
PLX TECHNOLOGY
POWERDRIVE

PNY TECHNOLOGIES, INC.

299 Webro Rd
Parsippany, NJ 07054-0218
Tel.: (973) 515-9700
Fax: (973) 560-5590
Web Site: www.pny.com
Sales Range: $300-349.9 Million
Approx. Number Employees: 450
Business Description:
Computer Memory Upgrades Mfr & Distributor
S.I.C.: 3674
N.A.I.C.S.: 334413
Advertising Expenditures: $4,000,000
Media: 2-4-6-7-8-9-10-11-13-14-18-23-25-26
Personnel:
Gadi Cohen *(Pres)*
Robert J. Stone *(Sr VP-Opers)*
John P. Hughes *(Sr VP)*
Mark J. Ciano *(VP-Fin & Admin Svcs)*
Anthony Gomez *(VP-Sls & Mktg)*
Ed Tomasi *(Dir-Mktg)*
Jeff Medeiros *(Dir-Mktg)*
Nicholas Mauro *(Sr Mgr-Mktg)*
Margaret Salleroli *(Sr Mgr-Mktg Comm)*
Carl Flygare *(Product Mktg Mgr-Quadro)*
Laurie Hill *(Mgr-Product Line)*
Laure Lapgue *(Mgr-Flash Media-Europe)*
John Orzepowski *(Mgr-Mktg)*
Brands & Products:
A SOLUTION FOR EVERY LIFESTYLE
COLLEGIATE ATTACHE
COMPACTFLASH
LADY ATTACHE
MAXFILE ATTACHE
MEMORY MASTER
MICROSD
MINI ATTACHE
MULTIMEDIA
NVIDIA
NVIDIA QUADRO
NVIDIA QUADRO PLEX
OPTIMA
OPTIMA COMPACTFLASH
OPTIMA SECURE DIGITAL
PNY
QUADRO
SECURE DIGITAL
SMARTMEDIA
VERTO
XD-PICTURE CARD
XLR8
Advertising Agency:
More2 Ltd.
10 Henrietta Street
London, WC2E 8PS, United Kingdom
Tel.: (44) 0 207 420 5050
Fax: (44) 0 207 420 5099
— Denora Langley Wright *(Acct Mgr)*
— Marcia Butterfield *(Sr Acct Exec)*

POLYCOM, INC.

(Formerly SpectraLink Corporation)
(Sub. of Polycom, Inc.)
5755 Central Ave
Boulder, CO 80301-2848
Tel.: (303) 440-5330
Fax: (303) 440-5331
Toll Free: (800) 676-5465
E-mail: michelle.chessler@polycom.com
Web Site: www.polycom.com
Approx. Sls.: $144,772,000
Approx. Number Employees: 419
Business Description:
Wireless Telephone Systems Designer, Mfr & Marketer for the Workplace
S.I.C.: 3663; 4813
N.A.I.C.S.: 334220; 517110
Advertising Expenditures: $590,000
Media: 10
Personnel:
Michelle Greene Chessler *(Dir-Demand Generation)*
Carolyn Smyth *(Dir-Fin)*
Chris Thorson *(Dir-Mktg)*
Brands & Products:
LINK WIRELESS TELEPHONE SYSTEM

POLYWELL COMPUTERS, INC.

1461 San Mateo Ave
South San Francisco, CA 94080-6505
Tel.: (650) 583-7222
Fax: (650) 583-1974
Toll Free: (800) 999-1278
E-mail: info@polywell.com
Web Site: www.polywell.com
Approx. Sls.: $8,000,000
Approx. Number Employees: 60
Year Founded: 1987
Business Description:
Mfr. & Marketer of Computers & Components
S.I.C.: 3571; 5734
N.A.I.C.S.: 334111; 443120
Media: 2
Personnel:
Chin Lo *(Pres)*
Brands & Products:
NETDISK
POLY TABLET
POLYALPHA
POLYCENTER
POLYCLUSTERING
POLYDUAL
POLYNETRA
POLYNOTE
POLYRACK
POLYRAXX
POLYSERVER
POLYSTATION
POLYULTRA
SUMA
ULTRASPARC

POMEROY IT SOLUTIONS, INC.

(Holding of Platinum Equity, LLC)
1020 Petersburg Rd
Hebron, KY 41048-8222
Tel.: (859) 586-0600
Fax: (859) 586-4414
Toll Free: (800) 846-8727
Web Site: www.pomeroy.com
E-Mail For Key Personnel:
Public Relations: JMcKenzie@pomeroy.com
Approx. Rev.: $565,830,000
Approx. Number Employees: 2,013
Year Founded: 1982
Business Description:
Hardware, Software, Technical Staffing, Computer Infrastructure & Lifecycle Services
S.I.C.: 7373; 7376; 7379
N.A.I.C.S.: 541512; 541513; 541519
Advertising Expenditures: $410,000
Media: 5-10-22
Personnel:
Christopher C. Froman *(Pres & CEO)*
Craig Propst *(CFO, Treas & Sr VP)*
Keith M. Blachowiak *(CIO & Sr VP-Ops)*
Kristi P. Nelson *(Gen Counsel & Sr VP-HR)*
John F. McKenna *(Sr VP-Corp Dev & Svcs)*

Key to Media (For complete agency information see *The Advertising Red Books-Agencies* edition):
1. Bus. Publs. 2. Cable T.V. 3. Catalogs & Directories. 4. Co-op Adv. 5. Consumer Mags. 6. D.M. to Bus. Estab.7. D.M. to Consumers
8. Daily Newsp. 9. Exhibits/Trade Shows 10. Foreign 11. Infomercial 12. Internet Adv.13. Multimedia 14. Network Radio
15. Network T.V. 16. Newsp. Distr. Mags. 17. Other 18. Outdoor (Posters, Transit) 19. Point of Purchase20. Premiums, Novelties
21. Product Samples 22. Special Events Mktg. 23. Spot Radio 24. Spot T.V. 25. Weekly Newsp. 26. Yellow Page Adv.

Pomeroy IT Solutions, Inc. — (Continued)

Peter Thelen *(Sr VP-Pub Sector, Comml & Enterprise Markets)*
Greg G. Lorenzen *(Mgr-Ops & Product Svcs)*

POSTNET INTERNATIONAL FRANCHISE CORPORATION
1819 Wazee St
Denver, CO 80202
Tel.: (303) 771-7100
Fax: (303) 771-7133
Toll Free: (800) 841-7171
E-mail: info@postnet.com
Web Site: www.postnet.com
Approx. Sls.: $5,000,000
Approx. Number Employees: 25
Year Founded: 1993
Business Description:
Postal & Business Services
S.I.C.: 4311
N.A.I.C.S.: 491110
Export
Media: 2-7-8
Personnel:
Steven J. Greenbaum *(Founder)*
Brian Spindel *(Founder)*
Brands & Products:
POSTNET

POWER QUOTIENT INTERNATIONAL USA, INC.
(d/b/a PQI Corporation)
46539 Fremont Blvd
Fremont, CA 94538
Tel.: (510) 651-7281
Fax: (510) 651-7240
E-mail: sales@pqimemory.com
Web Site: www.pqigroup.com
E-Mail For Key Personnel:
Sales Director: sales@pqimemory.com
Approx. Number Employees: 12
Year Founded: 1997
Business Description:
Mfr., Designer & Marketer of Flash Memory Storage Devices & Peripherals
S.I.C.: 3823
N.A.I.C.S.: 334513
Media: 6
Personnel:
Jacky Lai *(Pres-Computer Memory)*
Brands & Products:
COMPACTFLASH
DISKONMODULE
DUAL VOLTAGE
INTELLIGENT FRAME
INTELLIGENT STICK
JOYTONE
MINI SD
MPACK
MR FLASH
MTRIX
MULTIMEDIACARD
SECURE DIGITAL CARD
WIDE-TEMP
YOUR WAY. YOUR STYLE.

PRECISION DATA PRODUCTS, INC.
5036 Falcon View Ave SE
Kentwood, MI 49512
Tel.: (616) 698-2242
Fax: (616) 698-9047
E-mail: sales@precision.com
Web Site: www.precision.com
E-Mail For Key Personnel:
Sales Director: sales@precision.com
Sales Range: $10-24.9 Million
Approx. Number Employees: 30
Year Founded: 1979
Business Description:
Computer Products Distr
S.I.C.: 5045
N.A.I.C.S.: 423430
Media: 4-5-7-22-26
Personnel:
Gail A. Huff *(Pres)*

PREFERRED HEALTHCARE STAFFING INC.
(Sub. of AMN Healthcare Services, Inc.)
100 W Cypress Creek Rd Ste 750
Fort Lauderdale, FL 33309
Tel.: (954) 492-8772
Fax: (888) 329-2411
Toll Free: (800) 735-4774
E-mail: travel@preferredhealthcare.com
Web Site:
www.preferredhealthcare.com
Approx. Sls.: $2,000,000
Approx. Number Employees: 40
Business Description:
Healthcare Staffing Services
S.I.C.: 7361
N.A.I.C.S.: 561310
Media: 2

PRESCIENT APPLIED INTELLIGENCE, INC.
(Sub. of Park City Group, Inc.)
1247 Ward Ave Ste 200
West Chester, PA 19380
Tel.: (610) 719-1600
Fax: (610) 719-8575
E-mail: info@prescient.com
Web Site: www.prescient.com
Sales Range: $1-9.9 Million
Approx. Number Employees: 40
Year Founded: 1999
Business Description:
Retail Supply Chain & Replenishment Services
S.I.C.: 5045; 7389
N.A.I.C.S.: 425110; 541990
Media: 2-10
Personnel:
Randall Field *(Chm & CEO)*
Kent Rice *(Dir-Advanced Commerce Dev)*
Brands & Products:
PRESCIENT
PRESCIENT APPLIED INTELLIGENCE
VISIBILITY & ANALYTICS

PRESILIENT, LLC
(Formerly Incentra LLC)
12303 Airport Way Ste 250
Broomfield, CO 80021
Toll Free: (800) 397-1719
E-mail: info@presilient.com
Web Site: www.presilient.com
Sales Range: $125-149.9 Million
Approx. Number Employees: 265
Business Description:
IT Support Services
S.I.C.: 3572; 7373
N.A.I.C.S.: 334112; 541512
Advertising Expenditures: $60,586
Media: 5-7-10-22
Personnel:
Mike Parsons *(Pres)*
Frank DiTirro *(CFO)*
Jim Intoccio *(Sr VP-Sls & Mktg)*
C. J. Herman *(VP-Product Dev)*
Bill Golon *(Dir-Customer Svc)*
Brands & Products:
DIVACOMPLETE
DIVADIRECTOR
DIVAMONITOR
DIVARCHIVE
DIVAWORKS
FRONT PORCH

PRESSTEK, INC.
(Sub. of Presstek, Inc.)
201 W Oakton St
Des Plaines, IL 60018-1855
Tel.: (847) 759-2400
Fax: (800) 447-1231
Toll Free: (800) 752-5139
Telex: 724356 A B DICK NILE B
Web Site: www.presstek.com
Sales Range: $550-599.9 Million
Approx. Number Employees: 1,445
Year Founded: 1884
Business Description:
Offset Duplicating, Digital Pre-Press Equipment & Supplies Mfr
S.I.C.: 3555; 3873; 3952; 5045; 5046
N.A.I.C.S.: 333293; 334518; 339942; 423440; 425110
Import Export
Advertising Expenditures: $1,525,000
Media: 1-2-4-5-6-7-8-10-11-13-20-22-26
Distr.: Intl.
Personnel:
Ron Cardone *(CIO)*
Mark Sullivan *(Product Dir-Digital Printing)*
Brands & Products:
A.B. DICK
ITEK GRAPHIX
MULTIGRAPHICS

PRINCETON DISKETTE CO., INC.
Monmouth Shores Corp Pk 1324 Wyckoff Rd
Wall Township, NJ 07753-6800
Tel.: (732) 892-6136
Fax: (732) 892-6186
Toll Free: (800) 426-0247 (sales)
E-mail: Sales@princetoncd.com
Web Site: www.princetondisc.com
E-Mail For Key Personnel:
Sales Director: Sales@princetoncd.com
Approx. Sls.: $3,200,000
Approx. Number Employees: 20
Year Founded: 1986
Business Description:
Diskette & Software Duplication Whslr
S.I.C.: 5065; 7371
N.A.I.C.S.: 423690; 541511
Media: 4-6
Personnel:
Lisa Conti *(Pres)*

PRINTEGRA CORPORATION
(Sub. of Cenveo Inc.)
403 Westpark Ct Ste A
Peachtree City, GA 30269
Tel.: (770) 631-6070
Fax: (770) 631-6188
Toll Free: (800) 422-6070
E-mail: southga@printegra.com
Web Site: www.printegra.com
E-Mail For Key Personnel:
President: ccampbell@printegra.com
Approx. Sls.: $90,000,000
Approx. Number Employees: 780
Business Description:
Office Products, Business Forms & Software
S.I.C.: 2761; 2782; 5112
N.A.I.C.S.: 323116; 323118; 424120
Export
Media: 4-7-10-11
Personnel:
Bob Saunders *(Sr VP-Sls & Mktg)*
Steve Wakefield *(VP-IT)*
Brands & Products:
COPY ALERT
EPRINTLINE
FORMSOURCE
FOUR51
PRINTEGRA
TOPFORM

PRINTINGFORLESS.COM, INC.
100 PFL Way
Livingston, MT 59047
Tel.: (406) 222-2689
Fax: (406) 222-4990
E-mail: info@printingforless.com
Web Site: www.printingforless.com
Sales Range: $1-9.9 Million
Approx. Number Employees: 100
Year Founded: 1996
Business Description:
Online Commercial Printing Services
S.I.C.: 2752; 2791
N.A.I.C.S.: 323110; 323122
Advertising Expenditures: $2,000,000
Media: 2-6-9-13-21-26
Personnel:
Andrew S. Field *(Pres & CEO)*
Marne Reed *(VP-HR, Strategy & Dev)*
Brands & Products:
AMERICA'S PRINT SHOP
INSTAPRICE
PRINTINGFORLESS.COM

PRINTRONIX, INC.
(Holding of Vector Capital Corp.)
14600 Myford Rd
Irvine, CA 92606-1005
Mailing Address:
PO Box 19559
Irvine, CA 92623-9559
Tel.: (714) 368-2300
Fax: (714) 368-2600
Toll Free: (800) 665-6210
E-mail: info@printronix.com
Web Site: www.printronix.com
Approx. Rev.: $128,416,000
Approx. Number Employees: 673
Year Founded: 1974
Business Description:
Line Matrix Printers, Page Printers & Continuous Form Laser Printers & Thermal Transfer Printers Mfr
S.I.C.: 3577; 2759; 3555
N.A.I.C.S.: 334119; 323115; 333293
Import Export
Advertising Expenditures: $1,800,000
Media: 1-2-4-5-7-10-11-13
Distr.: Intl.; Natl.
Budget Set: Dec.
Personnel:
Randy Eisenbach *(CEO)*
Rhonda Longmore-Grund *(CFO)*
C. Victor Fitzsimmons *(Sr VP-Ops)*

Key to Media (For complete agency information see *The Advertising Red Books-Agencies* edition):
1. Bus. Publs. 2. Cable T.V. 3. Catalogs & Directories. 4. Co-op Adv. 5. Consumer Mags. 6. D.M. to Bus. Estab.7. D.M. to Consumers
8. Daily Newsp. 9. Exhibits/Trade Shows 10. Foreign 11. Infomercial 12. Internet Adv.13. Multimedia 14. Network Radio
15. Network T.V. 16. Newsp. Distr. Mags. 17. Other 18. Outdoor (Posters, Transit) 19. Point of Purchase20. Premiums, Novelties
21. Product Samples 22. Special Events Mktg. 23. Spot Radio 24. Spot T.V. 25. Weekly Newsp. 26. Yellow Page Adv.

Albert Ching *(VP-Asia Pacific Sls & Mktg)*
Claus Hinge *(VP-Sls & Mktg-EMEA)*
Juli A. Mathews *(VP-HR)*
Brands & Products:
DURAFUSION
LINE PRINTER PLUS
PRINTNET
PRINTRONIX
PSA

PROCESS ACADEMY, INC.
(d/b/a Xpertdoc)
1160 Levis Street Ste 102
Lachine, QC J6W 5S6, Canada
Tel.: (450) 961-9111
Fax: (450) 961-9113
Toll Free: (866) 961-9111
E-mail: info@xpertdoc.com
Web Site: www.xpertdoc.com
Business Description:
Automated Business Document Production Solutions
S.I.C.: 7338
N.A.I.C.S.: 561410
Media: 10-13
Personnel:
Francis Dion *(Founder & Pres)*
Brands & Products:
REPORTING MADE EASY
XPERTDOC
XPERTDOC CONTACT GADGET
XPERTDOC DATA GADGET
XPERTDOC STUDIO 2006
XPERTDOC STUDIO 2007

PROFESSIONAL CONTROL CORPORATION
N11 4W 18770 Clinton Dr
Germantown, WI 53022-3118
Tel.: (262) 251-3000
Fax: (262) 251-7334
Web Site: www.pccweb.com
Approx. Number Employees: 70
Year Founded: 1980
Business Description:
Software Programs Integrator for Offices & Factories
S.I.C.: 5045
N.A.I.C.S.: 423430
Import Export
Media: 2-4-7-10
Distr.: Natl.
Personnel:
Robert D. Dumke *(Pres)*
Jack Dumke *(CFO)*

PROFESSIONAL EDUCATION INSTITUTE
7020 High Grove Blvd
Burr Ridge, IL 60527
Tel.: (630) 382-1000
Fax: (630) 325-0825
E-mail: charwig@thepei.com
Web Site: www.thepei.com
Approx. Number Employees: 500
Year Founded: 1983
Business Description:
Personal Finance, Educational & Other Products Retailer
S.I.C.: 7313
N.A.I.C.S.: 541840
Advertising Expenditures: $200,000
Media: 3-8-15-24
Distr.: Natl.
Personnel:
Donald Strumillo *(Owner)*
Mark Holecek *(Chm)*
Michael E. Hussey *(Pres)*
Christine Harwig *(CFO)*
Roger Sinnes *(CMO)*
Les Matsunura *(VP-Info Sys)*
Rodney Miller *(VP-HR)*
Lou Storiale *(Sr Product Mgr)*
Brands & Products:
CARLETON H. SHEETS
EDUCATION FOR REAL LIFE
NO DOWN PAYMENT
PEI
REAL PROFIT$

PROGRESS SOFTWARE CORPORATION
14 Oak Park Dr
Bedford, MA 01730-1414
Tel.: (781) 280-4000
Fax: (781) 280-4095
Toll Free: (800) 477-6473
Web Site: www.progress.com
Approx. Rev.: $529,120,000
Approx. Number Employees: 1,576
Year Founded: 1981
Business Description:
Business Application Infrastructure Software Developer, Marketer & Distr
S.I.C.: 7372; 5045; 7371
N.A.I.C.S.: 511210; 423430; 541511
Media: 7-10-13
Personnel:
Barry N. Bycoff *(Chm)*
Richard D. Reidy *(Pres & CEO)*
Charles F. Wagner, Jr. *(CFO & Exec VP-Fin & Admin)*
David A. Benson *(CIO & Exec VP)*
Gary Conway *(CMO & Exec VP)*
James D. Freedman *(Gen Counsel & Sr VP)*
David G. Ireland *(Exec VP & Gen Mgr-Application Dev Platforms)*
Christopher Larsen *(Exec VP-Field Ops-Global)*
Joseph A. Andrews *(Sr VP & Head-HR)*
John Goodson *(Sr VP-Products)*
Graeme Clark *(VP-Fin Svcs-EMEA Reg)*
Frank Sacco *(VP-Fin Svcs)*
Rob Steward *(VP-Engrg)*
Brands & Products:
ACTIONAL
APPSERVER
ARTIX
BUSINESS EMPOWERMENT
BUSINESS MAKING PROGRESS
CACHE-FORWARD
CONNECT EVERYTHING. ACHIEVE ANYTHING.
DATADIRECT CONNECT64
DATADIRECT OPENACCESS
DATADIRECT SEQUELINK
DATADIRECT SHADOW
DATADIRECT SHADOW INTERFACE
DATADIRECT TECHNOLOGIES
DATADIRECT XML CONVERTERS
DATADIRECT XQUERY
DATAXTEND
DYNAMIC ROUTING ARCHITECTURE
EASYASK
FATHOM
FUSE
IF OBJECTS COULD TALK.
IONA
OBJECTSTORE
OPENEDGE
ORBACUS
ORBIX STANDARD
PERFORMANCE. NOT PROMISES.
PERSISTENCE EDGEXTEND
PERSISTENCE POWERTIER
POWERED BY PROGRESS
PRGORESS APAMA
PROGRESS
PROGRESS ACTIONAL
PROGRESS ACTIONAL FLEX POINT FOR SONIC
PROGRESS APAMA
PROGRESS APPSALIVE
PROGRESS ASPEN
PROGRESS BUSINESSEDGE
PROGRESS DATAXTEND
PROGRESS EMPOWERMENT CENTER
PROGRESS INTELLISTREAM
PROGRESS OBJECTSTORE
PROGRESS OPENEDGE
PROGRESS POSSE
PROGRESS POSSENET
PROGRESS PRO VISION
PROGRESS PS SELECT
PROGRESS RESULTS
PROGRESS SOFTWARE BUSINESS MAKING PROGRESS
PROGRESS SOFTWARE DEVELOPERS NETWORK
PROGRESS SONICMQ CLIENT BRIDGE
PROGRESS SONICMQ CLIENT PLUS
PROGRESS SONICMQ .NET CLIENT
PROGRESS SONICMQ RESOURCE ADAPTERS
PROGRESS SPEEDSCRIPT
PROGRESS STORMGLASS
PROGRESS WEBSPEED
SHADOW
SONIC
STYLUS STUDIO XML
VOICE OF EXPERIENCE
WEBCLIENT
WEBSPEED
WHO MAKES PROGRESS
YOUR WORLD. YOUR SOA.
Advertising Agencies:
Overdrive
38 Everett St 2nd Fl
Boston, MA 02134
Tel.: (617) 254-5000
Fax: (617) 254-5003

Schwartz Communications, Inc.
230 3rd Ave
Waltham, MA 02451
Tel.: (781) 684-0770
Fax: (781) 684-6500

PROGRESSIVE NURSING STAFFERS INC.
5531 B Hempstead Way
Springfield, VA 22151
Tel.: (703) 750-1010
Fax: (703) 750-1087
Toll Free: (888) 750-1012
Web Site:
www.progressivenursing.com
Approx. Sls.: $45,800,000
Approx. Number Employees: 102
Year Founded: 1987
Business Description:
Temporary Nursing Staffing Services
S.I.C.: 7363
N.A.I.C.S.: 561320
Media: 2
Personnel:
Gary Hughes *(Pres)*
Jim Narron *(CFO)*

PROMISE TECHNOLOGY, INC.
580 Cottonwood Dr
Milpitas, CA 95035
Tel.: (408) 228-1400
Fax: (408) 228-1100
Web Site: www.promise.com
Business Description:
Computer Storage Technology
S.I.C.: 3572
N.A.I.C.S.: 334112
Media: 7-10
Personnel:
James Lee *(CEO)*
Ray Bahar *(VP-Sls & Mktg)*

PROSTAR COMPUTER, INC.
837 S Lawson St
City of Industry, CA 91748
Tel.: (626) 839-6472
Fax: (626) 854-3438
Toll Free: (888) 576-4742
Web Site: www.pro-star.com
Approx. Number Employees: 25
Year Founded: 1992
Business Description:
Retailer of Computers
S.I.C.: 5045; 5734
N.A.I.C.S.: 423430; 443120
Media: 6-8-10
Personnel:
Terry Wang *(Pres)*

PROTEXT MOBILITY, INC.
(Formerly Echo Metrix, Inc.)
6800 Jericho Turnpike Ste 208E
Syosset, NY 11791
Tel.: (516) 802-0223
Fax: (516) 802-0228
E-mail: info@protextmobility.com
Web Site: www.protextmobility.com
Approx. Rev.: $30,853
Approx. Number Employees: 5
Year Founded: 2001
Business Description:
Protection & Family Safety Mobile Applications Software
S.I.C.: 7372; 4812
N.A.I.C.S.: 511210; 517212; 519130
Advertising Expenditures: $176,000
Media: 17
Personnel:
Erica Zalbert *(Interim Co-CEO & CFO)*
Peter Charles *(Interim Co-CEO & COO)*
Kyle Crawford *(VP-Bus Dev & Product Mktg)*
Robert B. Mumford *(VP-Sls & Strategic Partnerships)*

PROTOCOL SOLUTIONS GROUP
(Sub. of LeCroy Corporation)
(d/b/a CATC)
3385 Scott Blvd
Santa Clara, CA 95054
Tel.: (408) 727-6600
Fax: (408) 727-6622
Toll Free: (800) 553-2769
E-mail: sales@catc.com
Web Site: www.catc.com
E-Mail For Key Personnel:
Sales Director: sales@catc.com

Key to Media (For complete agency information see *The Advertising Red Books-Agencies* edition):
1. Bus. Publs. 2. Cable T.V. 3. Catalogs & Directories. 4. Co-op Adv. 5. Consumer Mags. 6. D.M. to Bus. Estab.7. D.M. to Consumers
8. Daily Newsp. 9. Exhibits/Trade Shows 10. Foreign 11. Infomercial 12. Internet Adv.13. Multimedia 14. Network Radio
15. Network T.V. 16. Newsp. Distr. Mags. 17. Other 18. Outdoor (Posters, Transit) 19. Point of Purchase20. Premiums, Novelties
21. Product Samples 22. Special Events Mktg. 23. Spot Radio 24. Spot T.V. 25. Weekly Newsp. 26. Yellow Page Adv.

Protocol Solutions Group — (Continued)

Sales Range: $10-24.9 Million
Approx. Number Employees: 72
Year Founded: 1992
Business Description:
Oscilloscopes, Protocol Analyzers & Related Test & Measurement Solutions
S.I.C.: 3829; 3571; 7371
N.A.I.C.S.: 334519; 334111; 541511
Media: 10
Personnel:
Jason LeBeck *(COO)*
Brands & Products:
ADVISOR
AUDITOR
BTTRACER AND TRAINER
BUSENGINE
CATC BUSENGINE
CATC TRACE
CHIEF
DISK DRIVE
FCTRACER
FIREINSPECTOR
FIRELNSPECTOR
FIREWIRE
HCITRACER
IBTRACER
I.LINK
INFINIBAND
LECROY ADVISOR
LECROY CHIEF
MERLIN
PETRACER
PETRAINER
SAS INFUSION
SASTRACER
SASTRACER AND TRAINER
SATA INFUSION
SATRACER
SERIAL DATA
TRACE
TRAINER
USB INSPECTOR
USBMOBILE
USBMOBLIE
UWBTRACER
WAVEEXPERT
WAVEMASTER
WAVEPRO
WAVERUNNER
WAVESURFER
WIMEDIA
X-STREAM

PROVIEW TECHNOLOGY INC.

(Branch of Proview International Holdings Limited)
7373 Hunt Dr
Garden Grove, CA 92841
Tel.: (714) 230-8626
Fax: (714) 379-6291
Web Site: www.proview.net
Approx. Number Employees: 100
Business Description:
LCD Computer Monitor Retailer & Marketer
S.I.C.: 5045
N.A.I.C.S.: 423430
Media: 2-5-6-10
Brands & Products:
KDS USA

PUBCO CORPORATION

3830 Kelley Ave
Cleveland, OH 44114
Tel.: (216) 881-5300
Fax: (216) 881-8380
Approx. Number Employees: 260
Year Founded: 1958
Business Description:
Holding Company
S.I.C.: 6719
N.A.I.C.S.: 551112
Import Export
Media: 7-8
Distr.: Natl.
Personnel:
Robert H. Kanner *(Chm, Pres & CEO)*
Leo L. Matthews *(Pres-Construction Prods)*
Stephen R. Kalette *(Gen Counsel, Sec & VP-Admin)*
Jay A. Goldblatt *(Asst Sec)*
Brands & Products:
ASPEN IMAGING INTERNATIONAL

PURPLE COMMUNICATIONS, INC.

433 Hackensack Ave 3rd Fl
Hackensack, NJ 07601
Tel.: (916) 435-3320
Tel.: (201) 527-1520 (tty)
Fax: (201) 996-1772
E-mail: support@purple.us
Web Site: www.goamerica.com
Approx. Rev.: $109,166,000
Approx. Number Employees: 428
Year Founded: 1996
Business Description:
Relay & Wireless Communications & Professional Interpreter Services for Deaf, Hard-of-Hearing & Speech-Impaired Consumers
S.I.C.: 4812
N.A.I.C.S.: 517212
Advertising Expenditures: $253,000
Media: 10
Personnel:
Behdad Eghbali *(Chm)*
Ronald E. Obray *(Vice Chm)*
Daniel R. Luis *(Pres)*
Donald G. Barnhart *(CFO, Sec & Sr VP)*
Ahmet Corapcioglu *(Interim CIO)*
John R. Ferron *(Pres/CFO-Video & Community Svcs)*
Janet L Bailey *(Sr VP-Community Interpreting)*
Joshua Rochlin *(Sr VP-Bus Devel)*
Andrea Wilson *(Sr VP-Talent Mgmt)*
Rick Personette *(VP-Sls)*
George Sutcliffe *(VP-Product Strategy)*
Brands & Products:
CLEAR MOBILE
GOAMERICA
GO.WEB
I711.COM
WYNDTELL

QLIK TECHNOLOGIES INC.

150 Radnor Chester Rd Ste #220
Radnor, PA 19087
Fax: (610) 975-5987
Toll Free: (888) 828-9768
E-mail: infous@qliktech.com
Web Site: www.qlikview.com
Approx. Rev.: $226,521,000
Approx. Number Employees: 780
Year Founded: 1993
Business Description:
Software Developer & Publisher
S.I.C.: 7372
N.A.I.C.S.: 511210
Advertising Expenditures: $15,300,000
Personnel:
Bruce Golden *(Chm)*
Lars Bjork *(CEO)*
William G. Sorenson *(CFO)*
Leslie Bonney *(COO)*
Anthony Deighton *(CTO & Sr VP-Products)*
Jonas Nachmanson *(Chief Product Strategy Officer)*
Dennis Johnson *(VP-Fin)*
Douglas Laird *(VP-Mktg)*
Brands & Products:
QLIKVIEW

QNX SOFTWARE SYSTEMS LTD

(Sub. of Research In Motion Ltd.)
175 Terence Matthews Crescent
Ottawa, ON K2M 1W8, Canada
Tel.: (613) 591-0931
Fax: (631) 591-3579
Toll Free: (800) 676-0566
E-mail: info@qnx.com
Web Site: www.qnx.com
Sales Range: $50-74.9 Million
Approx. Number Employees: 200
Year Founded: 1980
Business Description:
Operating System Software
S.I.C.: 7372
N.A.I.C.S.: 334611
Media: 10-13
Personnel:
Dan Dodge *(Founder & CEO)*
Jennifer Camelon *(CFO & VP-Fin)*
Mike Michalyshyn *(Gen Counsel & VP-HR)*
Derek Kuhn *(VP-Sls & Mktg)*
Sebastien Marineau-Mes *(VP-Engrg)*
Linda Campbell *(Dir-Strategic Alliances)*
Kerry Johnson *(Dir-Product Mgmt)*
Andrew Poliak *(Dir-Automotive Bus Dev)*
Leo Forget *(Product Mgr)*
Paul Leroux *(Mgr-PR)*
Brands & Products:
QNX
QNX MOMENTICS
QNX NEUTRINO
QNX PHOTON MICROGUI
Advertising Agency:
Schwartz Communications, Inc.
230 3rd Ave
Waltham, MA 02451
Tel.: (781) 684-0770
Fax: (781) 684-6500

QUALSTAR CORPORATION

3990-B Heritage Oak Ct
Simi Valley, CA 93063-6711
Tel.: (805) 583-7744
Fax: (805) 583-7749
E-mail: sales@qualstar.com
Web Site: www.qualstar.com
E-Mail For Key Personnel:
Sales Director: sales@qualstar.com
Approx. Rev.: $18,302,000
Approx. Number Employees: 70
Business Description:
Automated Magnetic Tape Libraries Used to Store, Retrieve & Manage Electronic Data Designer, Developer, Mfr & Distr
S.I.C.: 3572; 3695; 5044
N.A.I.C.S.: 334112; 334613; 423420
Advertising Expenditures: $342,000
Media: 10
Personnel:
William J. Gervais *(Pres & CEO)*
Nidhi H. Andalon *(CFO & VP)*
Richard A. Nelson *(Sec & VP-Engrg)*
Randy Johnson *(VP & Gen Mgr-N2Power)*
Robert Covey *(VP-Mktg)*
Brands & Products:
N2POWER
Q-LINK
QUALSTAR
SANSMART
TERALOADER

QUANTUM CORPORATION

1650 Technology Dr Ste 800
San Jose, CA 95110
Tel.: (408) 894-4000
Fax: (408) 944-4040
Toll Free: (800) 677-6268
E-mail: ir@quantum.com
Web Site: www.quantum.com
Approx. Rev.: $672,720,000
Approx. Number Employees: 1,830
Year Founded: 1980
Business Description:
Data Storage Systems
S.I.C.: 3572
N.A.I.C.S.: 334112
Import Export
Advertising Expenditures: $5,000,000
Media: 2-4-5-6-7-10-11-20
Distr.: Intl.
Personnel:
Richard E. Belluzzo *(Chm)*
Jonathan W. Gacek *(Pres & CEO)*
Linda M. Breard *(CFO)*
Shawn D. Hall *(Gen Counsel, Sec & Sr VP)*
William C. Britts *(Exec VP-Worldwide Mktg, Svc & Bus Dev)*
Barbara Barrett *(Sr VP-HR)*
Rob Clark *(Sr VP-Disk & Tape Backup Product Grp)*
Janae Stow Lee *(Sr VP-File Sys & Archive Product Grp)*
Don Martella *(Sr VP-Engrg)*
Jim Mudd *(Sr VP-Ops)*
Ted Stinson *(Sr VP-Worldwide Sls)*
Brands & Products:
AMASS
BACKUP EXEC
DAT DDS
DLT
DLT VS
DLTICE
DLTSAGE
DLTTAPE
DX-SERIES
DXI-SERIES
DYNAMIC POWERDOWN
FASTSENSE
FLEXLINK
GOVAULT
LTO
MEDIASHIELD
OPTYON
PX-SERIES
QUANTUM
QUANTUM VISION
RACKMOUNT
RADICAL SIMPLICITY
SCALAR
SMARTSHIELD
SMARTVERIFY
SNAP APPLIANCE

Key to Media (For complete agency information see *The Advertising Red Books-Agencies* edition):
1. Bus. Publs. 2. Cable T.V. 3. Catalogs & Directories. 4. Co-op Adv. 5. Consumer Mags. 6. D.M. to Bus. Estab.7. D.M. to Consumers
8. Daily Newsp. 9. Exhibits/Trade Shows 10. Foreign 11. Infomercial 12. Internet Adv.13. Multimedia 14. Network Radio
15. Network T.V. 16. Newsp. Distr. Mags. 17. Other 18. Outdoor (Posters, Transit) 19. Point of Purchase20. Premiums, Novelties
21. Product Samples 22. Special Events Mktg. 23. Spot Radio 24. Spot T.V. 25. Weekly Newsp. 26. Yellow Page Adv.

SPEED TRANSFER
STACKLINK
STORAGECARE
STORNEXT
SUPERLOADER
TAPESHIELD
TAPEWARE
TRAVAN
VALUELOADER
VALUSMART

QUARK, INC.

1800 Grant St
Denver, CO 80203
Tel.: (303) 894-8888
Fax: (303) 894-3399
E-mail: employment@quark.com
Web Site: www.quark.com
Approx. Number Employees: 1,000
Year Founded: 1981
Business Description:
Developer of Electronic Publishing & Communication Software
S.I.C.: 7372; 7371
N.A.I.C.S.: 511210; 541511
Media: 2-7-10-13
Personnel:
Raymond Schiavone *(Pres & CEO)*
Kevin Mammel *(CFO)*
Jim Haggarty *(CIO)*
Peter Jensen *(Gen Counsel)*
P.G. Bartlett *(Sr VP-Product Mgmt)*
Matthew Wallis *(Sr VP-Sls-EMEA & Asia)*
Gyan Prakash *(VP-Sls-Asia, Middle East & Africa)*
Tim Banister *(Gen Mgr-Desktop Technologies)*
Dan Logan *(Sr Product Mgr-QuarkXPress)*
Brands & Products:
DYNAMIC DOCUMENT SERVER
QUARK
QUARK DIGITAL MEDIA SYSTEM
QUARK PUBLISHING SYSTEM
QUARKALLIANCE
QUARKCOMMERCE
QUARKCONNECT
QUARKCOPYDESK
QUARKCOPYDESK PASSPORT
QUARKCOPYDESK SPECIAL EDITION
QUARKDISPATCH
QUARKDMS
QUARKLIBRARIES
QUARKTECH
QUARKWRAPTURE
QUARKXPRESS
QUARKXPRESS PASSPORT
QUARKXTENSIONS
SERVICEPLUS
XTENSIONS

QUEST SOFTWARE, INC.

5 Polaris Way
Aliso Viejo, CA 92656-5356
Tel.: (949) 754-8000
Fax: (949) 754-8999
E-mail: info@quest.com
Web Site: www.quest.com
Approx. Rev.: $767,097,000
Approx. Number Employees: 3,460
Year Founded: 1987
Business Description:
Prepackaged Software
S.I.C.: 7372; 7373
N.A.I.C.S.: 511210; 334611; 541512
Import Export
Advertising Expenditures: $5,900,000
Media: 5-10-21
Personnel:
Raymond J. Lane *(Chm)*
Douglas F. Garn *(Pres & CEO)*
Joe Signorelli *(Pres & Dir-Rep)*
Scott J. Davidson *(CFO & Sr VP)*
Alan Fudge *(Sr VP-Worldwide Sls)*
Kevin Norlin *(VP & Gen Mgr-Sls-EMEA)*
Steve Kahan *(VP-Mktg)*
Daphne Kent *(Sr Mgr-Analyst Rels)*
John Whittaker *(Sr Product Mgr)*
Jerry Elmquist *(Mgr-Pub Sector Channels & Alliances)*
Brands & Products:
ACCESS MANAGER
ACTIVE ADMINISTRATOR
ACTIVEGROUPS
ACTIVEROLES DIRECT
ACTIVEROLES SERVER
ADMC
APPLICATION ASSURANCE SUITE
APPLICATION PERFORMANCE MANAGEMENT SUITE
ARCHIVE MANAGEMENT SUITE
ARCHIVE MANAGER
AUTHENTICATION SERVICES
AVAILABILITY MANAGER
BENCHMARK FACTORY
BIG BROTHER
BUSINESS INSIGHT
CAPACITY MANAGER FOR SQL SERVER
CENTRAL
CHANGE DIRECTOR FOR SQL SERVER
CHANGEAUDITOR FOR ACTIVE DIRECTORY
CHANGEAUDITOR FOR EXCHANGE
CHANGEAUDITOR FOR FILE SYSTEMS
CODE TESTER FOR ORACLE
COEFFICIENT
COLLABORATION SERVICES
COMPAREROCKET
COMPLIANCE SUITE
DATAFACTORY
DEFENDER
DEPLOYDIRECTOR
DESKTOP AUTHORITY
DIRECTORYANALYZER
DIRECTORYTROUBLESHOOTER
DISCOVERY WIZARD FOR SHAREPOINT
DISCOVERY WIZARD FOR SQL SERVER
DOMAIN MIGRATION WIZARD
DOMAIN STATISTICS WIZARD
DS EXPERT
E-DISCOVERY MANAGER
ENTERPRISE SECURITY REPORTER
ENTERPRISE SINGLE SIGN-ON
ERDISK
EXCHANGE MIGRATION WIZARD
FILE MIGRATOR FOR SHAREPOINT
FILE SYSTEM AUDITOR
FOGLIGHT
FOGLIGHT PERFORMANCE ANALYSIS FOR SQL SERVER
GPOADMIN
GROUP POLICY EXTENSIONS
GROUP POLICY MANAGER
GROUPWISE MIGRATOR
INSYNC
INTRUST
INTRUST PLUG-IN FOR ACTIVE DIRECTORY
INTRUST PLUG-IN FOR EXCHANGE
INTRUST PLUG-IN FOR FILE ACCESS
JCLASS
JCLASS SERVERVIEWS
JPROBE
KNOWLEDGE PORTAL
KNOWLEDGE XPERT
KNOWLEDGE XPERT FOR DB2 Z/OS
KNOWLEDGE XPERT FOR MYSQL
KNOWLEDGE XPERT FOR ORACLE ADMINISTRATION
KNOWLEDGE XPERT FOR PL/SQL
LITESPEED
LITESPEED FOR SQL SERVER
MANAGEMENT CONSOLE
MANAGEMENT PACK FOR AS400
MANAGEMENT PACK FOR .NET
MANAGEMENT SUITE
MANAGEMENT XTENSIONS - CONFIGURATION MANAGER 2007
MANAGEMENT XTENSIONS FOR SMS
MANAGEMENT XTENSIONS - OPERATIONS MANAGER 2007
MESSAGESTATS
MIGRATION MANAGER
MIGRATION MANAGER FOR EXCHANGE
MIGRATION MANAGER FOR SHAREPOINT
MIGRATION SUITE
MIGRATION SUITE FOR ACTIVE DIRECTORY
MIGRATOR FOR SAMETIME
MISSIONCONTROL
MOVE MAILBOX MANAGER
MPE SOLUTIONS
MSI STUDIO FOR CONFIGURATION MANAGER
NDS MIGRATOR
NOTES MIGRATOR
NOTES MIGRATOR FOR SHAREPOINT
OBJECT RESTORE
OFFLINE FOLDER WIZARD
PASSWORD MANAGER
PASSWORD RESET MANAGER
PATCH MANAGEMENT
PERFORMANCE MANAGEMENT SUITE
PERFORMANCE SUITE
PERFORMASURE
POLICY AUTHORITY FOR UNIFIED COMMUNICATIONS
POWERGUI
PRIVILEGE MANAGER FOR UNIX
PUBLIC FOLDER MIGRATOR FOR SHAREPOINT
QDESIGNER
QUEST CENTRAL
QUEST CENTRAL FOR DB2
QUEST CENTRAL FOR ORACLE
QUEST COEXISTENCE MANAGER FOR NOTES
QUEST PERFORMANCE TUNING SUITE FOR SYBASE ASE
QUEST SOFTWARE
QUEST SQL OPTIMIZER SUITE FOR SYBASE ASE
QUEST WEB PARTS FOR SHAREPOINT
RECOVERY MANAGER
RECOVERY MANAGER FOR EXCHANGE
RECOVERY MANAGER FOR SHAREPOINT
REPORTADMIN FOR ACS
REPORTER
REPORTER EXPRESS
SCHEMA MANAGER
SECURE COPY
SECURITY EXPLORER
SECURITY EXPLORER FOR EXCHANGE
SECURITY EXPLORER FOR FILE SERVERS
SECURITY EXPLORER FOR SQL SERVER
SECURITY EXPLORER FOR WORKSTATIONS
SECURITYMANAGER
SELECTDL
SELF-SERVICE WEB PORTAL
SHAREPLEX
SINGLE SIGN-ON FOR JAVA
SINGLE SIGN-ON FOR NETWEAVER
SITE ADMINISTRATOR FOR SHAREPOINT
SPACE MANAGEMENT WITH LIVEREORG
SPOTLIGHT
SPOTLIGHT ON DB2 LUW
SPOTLIGHT ON MESSAGING
SPOTLIGHT ON MYSQL
SPOTLIGHT ON ORACLE
SPOTLIGHT ON SQL SERVER ENTERPRISE
SPOTLIGHT ON SYBASE ASE
SPOTLIGHT ON UNIX/LINUX
SQL NAVIGATOR
SQL OPTIMIZER
SQL OPTIMIZER FOR ORACLE
SQL OPTIMIZER FOR SYBASE
SQL TURBO
SQL WATCH
STAT
STAT ACM
STAT ACM FOR PEOPLESOFT
STORAGE ASSESSMENT TOOL
STORAGE CONSOLIDATOR
STORAGE HORIZON
STORAGE SUITE
STORAGE SUITE FOR WINDOWS
TOAD
TOAD DBA SUITE FOR IBM DB2
TOAD DBA SUITE FOR ORACLE
TOAD DEVELOPMENT SUITE FOR ORACLE
TOAD FOR DATA ANALYSTS
TOAD FOR IBM DB2 LUW
TOAD FOR IBM DB2 Z/OS
TOAD FOR MYSQL
TOAD FOR ORACLE
TOAD FOR SQL SERVER
UPDATE UTILITY
USER EXPERIENCE MONITOR
VINTELA
VISTA PLUS
VWORKSPACE
WEB PARTS FOR SHAREPOINT
WEBTHORITY
XRT
Advertising Agencies:
Greenough Communications
9 Harcourt St
Boston, MA 02116
Tel.: (617) 275-6500
Fax: (617) 275-6501

Key to Media (For complete agency information see *The Advertising Red Books-Agencies* edition):
1. Bus. Publs. 2. Cable T.V. 3. Catalogs & Directories. 4. Co-op Adv. 5. Consumer Mags. 6. D.M. to Bus. Estab.7. D.M. to Consumers
8. Daily Newsp. 9. Exhibits/Trade Shows 10. Foreign 11. Infomercial 12. Internet Adv.13. Multimedia 14. Network Radio
15. Network T.V. 16. Newsp. Distr. Mags. 17. Other 18. Outdoor (Posters, Transit) 19. Point of Purchase20. Premiums, Novelties
21. Product Samples 22. Special Events Mktg. 23. Spot Radio 24. Spot T.V. 25. Weekly Newsp. 26. Yellow Page Adv.

Quest Software, Inc. — (Continued)

McKinney Chicago
430 W Erie Ste 400
Chicago, IL 60610
Tel.: (312) 944-6784
Fax: (312) 944-6789

QUILOGY, INC.
(Sub. of Aspect Software, Inc.)
117 S Main St
Saint Charles, MO 63301
Tel.: (636) 947-9393
Fax: (636) 947-7474
E-mail: accounting@quilogy.com
Web Site: www.quilogy.com
Approx. Number Employees: 300
Business Description:
Custom Computer Programming Services
S.I.C.: 7371
N.A.I.C.S.: 541511
Media: 10
Brands & Products:
THE ART & SCIENCE OF BUSINESS
QUILOGY

QUORUM INFORMATION TECHNOLOGIES INC.
10655 Southport Road Southwest
Suite 300
Calgary, AB T2W 4Y1, Canada
Tel.: (403) 777-0036
Fax: (403) 777-0039
Toll Free: (888) 267-6180
E-mail: investors@quorumdms.com
Web Site: www.quorumdms.com
Approx. Rev.: $7,840,607
Approx. Number Employees: 50
Year Founded: 2000
Business Description:
Automobile Computer Systems Design & Related Services
S.I.C.: 7371
N.A.I.C.S.: 541511
Advertising Expenditures: $52,352
Media: 7-10-13
Personnel:
John Carmichael *(Chm)*
Maury Marks *(Pres & CEO)*
Jeff Sharpe *(CFO & VP)*
Mark Allen *(VP-Sls, Mktg & Svcs)*
Paul Elert *(Mgr-Program-Strategic Accts)*
Darren Hawthorne *(Mgr-Network Svcs)*
Scott Maroni *(Mgr-Svcs Delivery)*
Yvette Martin *(Mgr-Support Svcs)*
Tim Spracklin *(Mgr-Reg Dev)*
Brands & Products:
QUORUM
XSELLERATOR

QVIDIAN
(Formerly Kadient, Inc.)
175 Cabot St Ste 210
Lowell, MA 01854
Tel.: (978) 703-7605
Fax: (978) 703-7631
Toll Free: (877) 523-4368
Web Site: www.qvidian.com
Sales Range: $10-24.9 Million
Approx. Number Employees: 36
Year Founded: 1994
Business Description:
Sales Support Software Developer
S.I.C.: 7372
N.A.I.C.S.: 511210
Media: 2
Personnel:
Lewis Miller *(Pres)*
Jim Eliason *(CFO)*
Michael Po *(Exec VP-Ops)*
Marty Siewert *(Sr VP-Sls)*
Larry DiLoreto *(VP-Global Sls)*
Brian Vass *(VP-Mktg)*
Brands & Products:
E-PROPOSALS
HYPERASSEMBLY
PRAGMATECH SOFTWARE
PRESENTATION EXPRESS
PROPOSAL AUTOMATION SUITE
PROPOSALEXPRESS
RFP MACHINE
RFP TRACKING SYSTEM
WEB PUBLISHER

RADIANT SYSTEMS, INC.
3925 Brookside Pkwy
Alpharetta, GA 30022-4429
Tel.: (770) 576-6000
Fax: (770) 754-7790
Toll Free: (800) 229-0991
E-mail: inquiries@radiantsystems.com
Web Site: www.radiantsystems.com
Approx. Rev.: $346,414,000
Approx. Number Employees: 1,377
Business Description:
Technology Solutions for Product & Employee Profitability & Customer Service
S.I.C.: 7373
N.A.I.C.S.: 541512
Advertising Expenditures: $1,500,000
Media: 10-22
Personnel:
Alon Goren *(Chm & CTO)*
John H. Heyman *(CEO)*
Mark E. Haidet *(CFO)*
Andrew S. Heyman *(COO)*
Paul Langenbahn *(Pres-Hospitality Div)*
Mark Schoen *(Pres-Intl Div)*
Carlyle Taylor *(Pres-Hardware Div)*
Keith Hicks *(Exec VP-HR)*
Chris Lybeer *(Exec VP)*
Brands & Products:
ALWAYS EASY. ALWAYS ON.
ORDERPOINT!
RADIANT
WEBSCHEDULING

RADISYS CORPORATION
5445 NE Dawson Creek Dr
Hillsboro, OR 97124
Tel.: (503) 615-1100
Fax: (503) 615-1115
Toll Free: (800) 950-0044
E-mail: info@radisys.com
Web Site: www.radisys.com
Approx. Rev.: $284,311,000
Approx. Number Employees: 567
Year Founded: 1987
Business Description:
Embedded Computer Systems Mfr
S.I.C.: 3577; 3571; 7379
N.A.I.C.S.: 334119; 334111; 541519
Advertising Expenditures: $2,100,000
Media: 2-7-10-13
Distr.: Intl.
Personnel:
Scott C. Grout *(Pres & CEO)*
Brian Bronson *(CFO)*
Christian Anthony Lepiane *(VP-Global Sls, Svc & Corp Mktg)*
Brands & Products:
ARTIC
ENDURA
MICROWARE
THE POWER OF WE
PROCELERANT
PROMENTUM
RADISYS

RADISYS CORPORATION
(Sub. of RadiSys Corporation)
5445 NE Dawson Creek Dr
Hillsboro, OR 97124
Tel.: (503) 615-1100
Fax: (503) 615-1115
Toll Free: (800) 475-9000
E-mail: info@radisys.com
Web Site: www.radisys.com
Sales Range: $25-49.9 Million
Approx. Number Employees: 300
Year Founded: 1977
Business Description:
Develops & Markets Real-Time Operating System Software & Development Tools to Embedded Systems, Communications & Consumer Products Markets
S.I.C.: 7373; 7371
N.A.I.C.S.: 541512; 541511
Advertising Expenditures: $200,000
Media: 7-10-13
Brands & Products:
ATCA-1000
CP50
ENDURA BG845G
ENDURA CH815C
ENDURA GL815E
ENDURA LS855
ENDURA PW810
ENP-3504
ENP-3511
EPC-3311
EPC-3412
ESM-3100
THE POWER OF WE
SYS50

RADIX CORPORATION
(Sub. of Elecsys Corporation)
4855 Wiley Post Way
Salt Lake City, UT 84116-2875
Tel.: (801) 537-1717
Fax: (801) 328-3401
Toll Free: (800) 367-9256
Web Site: www.radix-corp.com
E-Mail For Key Personnel:
Sales Director: sales@radix-intl.com
Sales Range: $75-99.9 Million
Approx. Number Employees: 150
Year Founded: 1969
Business Description:
Handheld Computers & Portable Printers Mfr
S.I.C.: 3571; 3555
N.A.I.C.S.: 334111; 333293
Export
Media: 2-10
Brands & Products:
FP40
FW 700
FW230
FW300
FW500
RADIX

RAINMAKER SYSTEMS INC.
900 E Hamilton Ave Ste 400
Campbell, CA 95008-0670
Tel.: (408) 626-3800
Fax: (408) 369-0910
Toll Free: (800) 631-1545
E-mail: inquiries@rmkr.com
Web Site: www.rmkr.com
Approx. Rev.: $42,768,000
Approx. Number Employees: 950
Business Description:
Outsourced Marketing Services & Software
S.I.C.: 7372; 7389; 8741; 8742
N.A.I.C.S.: 511210; 541613; 561110; 561422
Advertising Expenditures: $2,838,000
Media: 8
Personnel:
Alok Mohan *(Chm)*
Michael Silton *(CEO)*
Thomas Venable *(Sr VP-Sls & Mktg)*
Phil Johnson *(VP-HR)*
David Lechler *(VP-Sector Sls)*
Fatima Madha *(Dir-Sls)*
Pamela Sziebert *(Dir-Mktg)*
Andy Wamstad *(Dir-Sls)*
Kevin Domino *(Mgr-Sls Ops)*
Brands & Products:
CONTRACT RENEWALS PLUS
EDUCATION SALES PLUS
RAINMAKER
RAINMAKER SYSTEM

RALLY SOFTWARE DEVELOPMENT CORP.
4001 Discovery Dr Ste 220
Boulder, CO 80303
Tel.: (303) 565-2800
Fax: (303) 226-1179
Toll Free: (866) 348-1552
E-mail: info@rallydev.com
Web Site: www.rallydev.com
Sales Range: $25-49.9 Million
Approx. Number Employees: 75
Year Founded: 2001
Business Description:
Software Developer
S.I.C.: 7372
N.A.I.C.S.: 511210
Personnel:
Ryan Martens *(Founder & CTO)*
Timothy Miller *(CEO)*
Jim Lejeal *(CFO)*
Don Hazell *(Exec VP-Worldwide Sls & Field Ops)*
Richard Leavitt *(Exec VP-Worldwide Mktg)*
Advertising Agency:
GroundFloor Media, Inc.
1923 Market St
Denver, CO 80202
Tel.: (303) 865-8110
Fax: (303) 253-9763

RAMBUS INC.
1050 Enterprise Way Ste 700
Sunnyvale, CA 94089
Tel.: (408) 462-8000
Fax: (408) 462-8001
E-mail: info@rambus.com
Web Site: www.rambus.com
E-Mail For Key Personnel:
Public Relations: pr@rambus.com
Approx. Rev.: $323,390,000
Approx. Number Employees: 390
Year Founded: 1990
Business Description:
High-Speed Chip Interface Inventor & Designer
S.I.C.: 3674

Key to Media (For complete agency information see *The Advertising Red Books-Agencies* edition):
1. Bus. Publs. 2. Cable T.V. 3. Catalogs & Directories. 4. Co-op Adv. 5. Consumer Mags. 6. D.M. to Bus. Estab.7. D.M. to Consumers 8. Daily Newsp. 9. Exhibits/Trade Shows 10. Foreign 11. Infomercial 12. Internet Adv.13. Multimedia 14. Network Radio 15. Network T.V. 16. Newsp. Distr. Mags. 17. Other 18. Outdoor (Posters, Transit) 19. Point of Purchase20. Premiums, Novelties 21. Product Samples 22. Special Events Mktg. 23. Spot Radio 24. Spot T.V. 25. Weekly Newsp. 26. Yellow Page Adv.

N.A.I.C.S.: 334413
Advertising Expenditures: $1,600,000
Media: 6-10
Personnel:
Bruce Dunlevie *(Chm)*
Harold E. Hughes, Jr. *(Pres & CEO)*
Satish Rishi *(CFO & Sr VP-Fin)*
Thomas R. Lavelle *(Gen Counsel & Sr VP)*
Sharon E. Holt *(Sr VP & Gen Mgr-Semiconductor Bus Grp)*
Martin Scott *(Sr VP & Gen Mgr-New Bus Grp)*
Kevin S. Donnelly *(Sr VP-IP Strategy)*
Jeffery Robert Parker *(Sr VP-Lighting & Display Tech)*
Christopher M. Pickett *(Sr VP-Licensing)*
Michael Schroeder *(Sr VP-HR)*
Laura S. Stark *(Sr VP-Corp Dev)*
Brands & Products:
DDR
FLEXCLOCKING
FLEXIO
FLEXLINK
FLEXPHASE
FLY-BY
THE FUTURE OF MEMORY
MOBILE XDR
PCIEXPRESS
QRSL
RAMBUS
RASER
RDRAM
RIMM
SO-RIMM
XDR
XDR 2
YOUR LICENSE TO SPEED
Advertising Agencies:
Connecting Point Communications
665 3rd St Ste 100
San Francisco, CA 94107
Tel.: (415) 442-2400
Fax: (415) 442-0288

Grady Britton
808 SW 3rd Ave #700
Portland, OR 97204
Tel.: (503) 222-0626
Fax: (503) 222-0154

The Hoffman Agency
70 N 2nd St
San Jose, CA 95113-1204
Tel.: (408) 286-2611
Fax: (408) 286-0133

The1stMovement
1010 E Union St Ste 120
Pasadena, CA 91106
Tel.: (626) 689-4993
Fax: (626) 628-1991

RAMTRON INTERNATIONAL CORPORATION
1850 Ramtron Dr
Colorado Springs, CO 80921-3620
Tel.: (719) 481-7000
Fax: (719) 481-9294
E-mail: info@ramtron.com
Web Site: www.ramtron.com
Approx. Rev.: $70,204,000
Approx. Number Employees: 123
Year Founded: 1984
Business Description:
Communications, Electronics & Memory Chips Devices
S.I.C.: 3674
N.A.I.C.S.: 334413
Advertising Expenditures: $95,000
Media: 4-7-11-13
Personnel:
William G. Howard, Jr. *(Chm)*
Eric A. Balzer *(CEO)*
Mark R. Kent *(CFO)*
Michael D. Hollabaugh *(CMO)*
Pete Zimmer *(VP-Sls)*
Jamie Gauld *(Mgr-Customer Svc & Sls Support)*
Hee-Jun Lee *(Mgr-Sls)*
Christopher Wray *(Mgr-Mktg Comm)*
Brands & Products:
FRAM
RAMTRON

RAND A TECHNOLOGY CORPORATION
(Holding of Ampersand Venture Management 2003 LLC)
(d/b/a Rand Worldwide)
151 Courtney Park Dr W
Mississauga, ON L5W 1Y5, Canada
Tel.: (905) 625-2000
Fax: (905) 625-8535
E-mail: info@rand.com
Web Site: www.rand.com
Approx. Rev.: $100,093,006
Approx. Number Employees: 447
Year Founded: 1986
Business Description:
Engineering & Information Technology
S.I.C.: 7373
N.A.I.C.S.: 541512
Media: 2-4-7-8-10-11-17-26
Personnel:
Mark Dulude *(CEO)*
Robert F. Heeg *(Exec VP-IMAGINIT Worldwide Opers)*
Brands & Products:
BOEING
CETOL
IMAGINIT
Q CHECKER
RAND

RAND WORLDWIDE, INC.
(Formerly Avatech Solutions, Inc.)
161 Worcester Rd Ste 401
Framingham, MA 01701
Tel.: (508) 663-1400
Fax: (508) 663-1401
Toll Free: (877) 726-3243
Web Site: www.rand.com
Approx. Rev.: $31,326,000
Approx. Number Employees: 146
Year Founded: 1997
Business Description:
Design Automation & Product Lifecycle Management Solutions
S.I.C.: 5045; 5063; 7372
N.A.I.C.S.: 423430; 334611; 423610
Advertising Expenditures: $1,352,000
Media: 10
Personnel:
Lawrence Rychlak *(Pres, CFO & Sec)*
Marc L. Dulude *(CEO)*
Bruce White *(Sr VP-Sls)*
Chantale Marchand *(VP-Mktg)*
Brands & Products:
AUTODESK
AUTODESK INVENTOR

RAXCO SOFTWARE, INC.
6 Montgomery Vlg Ave Ste 500
Gaithersburg, MD 20879
Tel.: (301) 527-0803
Fax: (301) 519-7711
Toll Free: (800) 546-9728
E-mail: sales@raxco.com
Web Site: www.raxco.com
E-Mail For Key Personnel:
Sales Director: sales@raxco.com
Approx. Sls.: $4,000,000
Approx. Number Employees: 40
Business Description:
Developer & Marketer of High-Performance Systems Administration Software & Resource Management Solutions
S.I.C.: 7371; 7372
N.A.I.C.S.: 541511; 511210
Media: 6
Personnel:
Arthur Frischman *(Pres)*
Robert E. Nolan *(CEO)*
Timothy J. Larkin *(CFO)*
Victoria A. Baylin *(Corp Counsel)*
Joe Abusamra *(VP-Mktg & Ops)*
Richard Moskowitz *(VP-Sls)*
Brands & Products:
DISKSTATE
FIRSTDEFENSE-ISR
PERFECTDISK
PERFECTSPEED
REPAIRDISK MANAGER
THE SMARTER WAY TO DEFRAG

RCM TECHNOLOGIES, INC.
2500 McClellan Ave Ste 350
Pennsauken, NJ 08109-4613
Tel.: (856) 486-1777
Fax: (856) 488-8833
Toll Free: (877) RCM-0007
E-mail: info@rcmt.com
Web Site: www.rcmt.com
Approx. Rev.: $162,022,000
Approx. Number Employees: 1,590
Year Founded: 1971
Business Description:
Information Technology & Engineering Services
S.I.C.: 7372; 7373
N.A.I.C.S.: 511210; 541512
Advertising Expenditures: $632,000
Media: 1-2-4-7-10-20
Personnel:
Leon Kopyt *(Chm & CEO)*
Kevin D. Miller *(CFO & Sr VP)*
Rocco Campanelli *(Exec VP-Engrg Svcs)*
Tim Brandt *(Grp Sr VP-IT)*
Glenn Bubb *(Dir-IT)*
Sue Casola *(Dir-HR)*
Art Dell *(Mgr-Corp Svcs)*
Brands & Products:
RCM
SMART SHORE
THE SOURCE OF SMART SOLUTIONS

REALNETWORKS, INC.
2601 Elliott Ave Ste 1000
Seattle, WA 98121-3306
Mailing Address:
PO Box 91123
Seattle, WA 98111-9223
Tel.: (206) 674-2700
Fax: (206) 674-2695
E-mail: privacy@real.com
Web Site: www.realnetworks.com
Approx. Rev.: $401,733,000
Approx. Number Employees: 1,319
Year Founded: 1994
Business Description:
Developer of Digital Media Services & Software
S.I.C.: 7371; 7372; 7373
N.A.I.C.S.: 541511; 511210; 541512
Advertising Expenditures: $75,800,000
Media: 2-6-10-13
Personnel:
Robert Glaser *(Founder& Chm)*
Michael C. Lunsford *(Interim CEO)*
Dan Sheeran *(Sr VP-Corp Partnerships & Bus Dev)*
Michael Eggers *(CFO & Sr VP)*
Judith Bitterli *(CMO & Sr VP-Unifi Product Div)*
Savino R. Ferrales *(Sr VP-HR)*
Matt Hulett *(Sr VP-Games Div)*
Philip W. O'Neil *(Sr VP-Music)*
Michael Schutzler *(Sr VP-Games Div & Adv Ops)*
Carla Stratfold *(Sr VP-Sls-Integration Program Office)*
Scott Uomoto *(Sr VP)*
William J. Hankes *(VP-Corp Comm)*
Bob Riccitelli *(VP-Tech, Products & Solutions-EMEA)*
Jackie Lang *(Gen Mgr-Consumer Mktg)*
Julie Pitt *(Gen Mgr-Game Mktg-Worldwide)*
Matt Graves *(Dir-Pub Rels-Real Music)*
Brands & Products:
HELIX
LIVEPAUSE
OSPREY
PERFECT PLAY
PRESENTERPRO
RADIOPASS
REAL
REAL BUBBLE
REAL GUIDE
REALARCADE
REALAUDIO
REALJUKEBOX
REALMEDIA
REALNETWORKS
REALONE
REALONE PLAYER
REALONE SUPERPASS
REALPIX
REALPLAYER
REALPLAYER PLUS
REALPRESENTER
REALPRODUCER
REALRHAPSODY
REALSLIDESHOW
REALVIDEO
RHAPSODY
SURESTREAM
TURBOPLAY
VISUAL COMMUNICATOR PRO
Advertising Agencies:
droga5
400 Lafayette 5th Fl
New York, NY 10003
Tel.: (917) 237-8888
Fax: (917) 237-8889
Rhapsody

Publicis West
424 2nd Ave W
Seattle, WA 98119-4013
Tel.: (206) 285-2222

Key to Media (For complete agency information see *The Advertising Red Books-Agencies* edition):
1. Bus. Publs. 2. Cable T.V. 3. Catalogs & Directories. 4. Co-op Adv. 5. Consumer Mags. 6. D.M. to Bus. Estab.7. D.M. to Consumers
8. Daily Newsp. 9. Exhibits/Trade Shows 10. Foreign 11. Infomercial 12. Internet Adv.13. Multimedia 14. Network Radio
15. Network T.V. 16. Newsp. Distr. Mags. 17. Other 18. Outdoor (Posters, Transit) 19. Point of Purchase20. Premiums, Novelties
21. Product Samples 22. Special Events Mktg. 23. Spot Radio 24. Spot T.V. 25. Weekly Newsp. 26. Yellow Page Adv.

RealNetworks, Inc. — (Continued)

Fax: (206) 273-4219

SHIFT Communications
260 California St 9th Fl
San Francisco, CA 94111
Tel.: (415) 591-8402
Tel.: (415) 591-8400
Fax: (415) 591-8450

REALNETWORKS, INC.

(Formerly WiderThan Americas, Inc.)
(Sub. of RealNetworks, Inc.)
11600 Sunrise Valley Dr Ste 200
Reston, VA 20191
Tel.: (703) 437-4422
Fax: (703) 437-6515
Sales Range: $25-49.9 Million
Approx. Number Employees: 70
Year Founded: 2000
Business Description:
Mobile Internet Applications & Services
S.I.C.: 4899
N.A.I.C.S.: 517910
Media: 22
Personnel:
Lawrence W. Moores *(Sr VP-ASP Solutions & Mktg)*
Vern Poyner *(Sr VP-Tech Products & Solutions)*
Brands & Products:
COLORING
METCALF

RECURSION SOFTWARE, INC.

2591 N Dallas Pkwy Ste 200
Frisco, TX 75034
Tel.: (972) 731-8800
Fax: (972) 731-8881
E-mail: info@recursionsw.com
Web Site: www.recursionsw.com
Sales Range: $75-99.9 Million
Approx. Number Employees: 20
Year Founded: 2001
Business Description:
Provider of Java, C++ & Csharp Development Solutions
S.I.C.: 5734
N.A.I.C.S.: 443120
Media: 2-13
Personnel:
Paul A. Lipari *(Pres & CEO)*
John Patoskie *(VP-Ops & Engrg)*
Brands & Products:
C# TOOLKIT
C++ TOOLKIT
CINERGI
JGL TOOLKIT
PERVASIVE SOFTWARE FOR A CONNECTED WORLD
RECURSION SOFTWARE
VOYAGER

RED HAT, INC.

1801 Varsity Dr
Raleigh, NC 27606-2072
Tel.: (919) 754-3700
Fax: (919) 754-3701
Toll Free: (888) 733-4281
E-mail: customerservice@redhat.com
Web Site: www.redhat.com
Approx. Rev.: $909,277,000
Approx. Number Employees: 3,700
Year Founded: 1994
Business Description:
Developer of Open Source Internet Infrastructure Solutions
S.I.C.: 7372; 7371
N.A.I.C.S.: 511210; 541511
Advertising Expenditures: $25,500,000

Media: 5-9-10-13-17

Personnel:
Henry Hugh Shelton *(Chm)*
James M. Whitehurst *(Pres & CEO)*
Charles E. Peters *(CFO & Exec VP)*
Lee Congdon *(CIO)*
Brian Stevens *(CTO & VP-Engrg-Worldwide)*
Paul J. Cormier *(Pres-Products & Tech & Exec VP)*
Alex Pinchev *(Pres-Global Sls, Svcs & Field Mktg & Exec VP)*
Michael R. Cunningham *(Gen Counsel & Exec VP)*
Robert Tiller *(VP & Asst Gen Counsel-IP)*
DeLisa Alexander *(Exec VP-People & Brand)*
Tom Rabon *(Exec VP-Corp Affairs)*
Jackie Yeaney *(Exec VP-Strategy & Corp Mktg)*
Mark E. Cook *(VP-Fin & Controller)*
Robert Shimp *(VP-Mktg & Tech)*
Leigh Day *(Sr Dir-Corp Comm)*
Mike Ferris *(Dir-Cloud Computing Ecosystem)*
Juan Noceda *(Product Mgr-OpenShift)*
Teresa Wilkerson *(Mktg Mgr)*
Tobias Crawley *(Software Engr)*

Advertising Agencies:
Center Line
310 S Harrington St
Raleigh, NC 27603
Tel.: (919) 821-2921
Fax: (919) 821-2922

SpeakerBox Communications
7900 Westpark Dr Ste T410
McLean, VA 22102
Tel.: (703) 287-7800

REDPRAIRIE HOLDING, INC.

(Holding of New Mountain Capital, LLC)
20700 Swenson Dr
Waukesha, WI 53186
Tel.: (262) 317-2000
Toll Free: (877) 733-7724
E-mail: info@redprairie.com
Web Site: www.redprairie.com

Approx. Rev.: $292,860,000
Approx. Number Employees: 1,051
Year Founded: 2005

Business Description:
Holding Company; Software Products Mfr
S.I.C.: 6719; 7372
N.A.I.C.S.: 551112; 511210
Advertising Expenditures: $4,500,000

Personnel:
R. Michael Mayoras *(CEO)*
Paul J. Ilse *(CFO)*
Carol O'Kelley *(CMO)*
John Kopcke *(CTO & Exec VP-Product Dev)*
Laura L. Fese *(Chief Legal Officer)*
Doug Braun *(Pres-Global Ops)*
Martin Hiscox *(Pres-Intl)*
Joe Juliano *(Pres-Americas)*
Chris Hickey *(Exec VP-Sls-Americas)*
Steve Stanislaus *(Exec VP-HR)*

REED EXHIBITIONS - AMERICAS

(Joint Venture of Reed Elsevier NV & Reed Elsevier plc)
383 Main Ave
Norwalk, CT 06851
Tel.: (203) 840-4800
Fax: (203) 840-8505
E-mail: inquiry@reedexpo.com
Web Site: www.reedexpo.com
Approx. Number Employees: 300
Business Description:
Business & Consumer Exhibitions Organizer
S.I.C.: 7389
N.A.I.C.S.: 561920
Media: 10
Personnel:
Chet W. Burchett *(Reg Pres-Americas)*
Nancy Walsh *(Exec VP-Exhibitions-North America)*
Joanne Bottoni-Jepsen *(Sr VP-HR)*
Dennis MacDonald *(Sr VP)*
Ted Rawson *(Sr VP-Knowledge Mgmt)*
Gregory M. Topalian *(Sr VP)*
Gregg Vautrin *(Sr VP-Fin & Bus Devlp)*
David J. Bonaparte *(Grp VP)*
Eileen Ainsworth *(VP-Fin)*
Maryann T. Cavino *(VP-HR)*
John Denke *(VP-Intl Sls)*
Denise Halter *(VP-Mktg Svcs)*
Courtney C. Muller *(VP-Sls)*
Kimberlie Leon *(Dir-Mktg)*
Andrea M. Tencza *(Dir-Mktg)*
Thomas J. Loughran *(Event Dir)*
Marco Labbate *(Mgr-Intl Sls)*

RELAX TECHNOLOGY, INC.

(d/b/a Granite Digital)
3101 Whipple Rd
Union City, CA 94587
Tel.: (510) 471-6442
Fax: (510) 471-6267
E-mail: info@granitedigital.com
Web Site: www.granitedigital.com
Approx. Sls.: $2,500,000
Approx. Number Employees: 20
Year Founded: 1980
Business Description:
Storage Systems & Peripherals Mfr
S.I.C.: 3577
N.A.I.C.S.: 334119
Media: 6-13
Personnel:
Frank Gabrielli *(Pres)*
Brands & Products:
FIREVUE
GRANITE DIGITAL

REPLOGLE GLOBES, INC.

2801 S 25th Ave
Broadview, IL 60155-4531
Tel.: (708) 343-0900
Fax: (708) 343-0923
Toll Free: (800) 275-4452
Toll Free: (800) 445-6237
E-mail: info@replogleglobes.com
Web Site: www.replogleglobes.com
Approx. Number Employees: 150
Year Founded: 1930
Business Description:
Mfr of World Globes
S.I.C.: 3999; 2741
N.A.I.C.S.: 339999; 511199
Import Export
Media: 2-4-5-6-7-8-9-13-14-15-17-19-20-24-25-26
Distr.: Intl.; Natl.
Budget Set: Oct.
Personnel:
Ed Dieschbourg *(Co-Pres)*
Daniel W. Dillon *(Co-Pres)*
Bob Mitchell *(Mgr-Sls-North America)*
Brands & Products:
GLOBEMASTER
SCANGLOBE
STARLIGHT GLOBE
Advertising Agency:
Straight North, LLC.
700 Commerce Dr Ste 140
Oak Brook, IL 60523
Tel.: (630) 366-8150
Fax: (630) 366-8151

RESILENT, LLC

(Sub. of Gabriel Technologies Corporation)
(d/b/a Digital Defense Group)
Millennium Plz 15858 W Dodge Rd
Omaha, NE 68118
Tel.: (402) 397-2273
Fax: (402) 861-9455
Web Site: www.mydigitaldefense.com
Sales Range: $10-24.9 Million
Approx. Number Employees: 15
Business Description:
Developer & Supplier of Biometric Security Products
S.I.C.: 7382
N.A.I.C.S.: 561621
Media: 10
Personnel:
Mark Mongar *(COO & CIO)*
Mike Weaver *(Chief Legal Officer)*

RESOURCES CONNECTION, INC.

17101 Armstrong Ave
Irvine, CA 92614
Tel.: (714) 430-6400
Fax: (714) 428-6090
E-mail: investorinfo@resources-us.com
Web Site: www.resourcesglobal.com
Approx. Rev.: $498,998,000
Approx. Number Employees: 2,783
Business Description:
Employment Services
S.I.C.: 8742; 7361
N.A.I.C.S.: 561310; 541611; 541612
Media: 2-6-7
Personnel:
Anthony Cherbak *(Pres & COO)*
Donald B. Murray *(Exec Chm & CEO)*
Nathan W. Franke *(CFO & Exec VP)*
Brands & Products:
RESOURCES

RETURN PATH, INC.

304 Park Ave S 7th Fl
New York, NY 10010-4311
Tel.: (212) 905-5500
Fax: (212) 905-5501
Toll Free: (866) 362-4577
E-mail: info@returnpath.net
Web Site: www.returnpath.net
Approx. Rev.: $23,000,000
Approx. Number Employees: 111
Year Founded: 1999
Business Description:
E-Mail Address Update Service
S.I.C.: 4813
N.A.I.C.S.: 517110
Media: 2

Key to Media (For complete agency information see *The Advertising Red Books-Agencies* edition):
1. Bus. Publs. 2. Cable T.V. 3. Catalogs & Directories. 4. Co-op Adv. 5. Consumer Mags. 6. D.M. to Bus. Estab.7. D.M. to Consumers 8. Daily Newsp. 9. Exhibits/Trade Shows 10. Foreign 11. Infomercial 12. Internet Adv.13. Multimedia 14. Network Radio 15. Network T.V. 16. Newsp. Distr. Mags. 17. Other 18. Outdoor (Posters, Transit) 19. Point of Purchase20. Premiums, Novelties 21. Product Samples 22. Special Events Mktg. 23. Spot Radio 24. Spot T.V. 25. Weekly Newsp. 26. Yellow Page Adv.

Personnel:
Matt Blumberg *(Co-Founder, Chm & CEO)*
George Bilbrey *(Co-Founder & Pres)*
Jack Sinclair *(Co-Founder, COO & CFO)*
Tom Bartel *(Chief Privacy Officer, CIPP)*
Anita Absey *(Sr VP-Global Sls & Svc)*
Angela Baldonero *(Sr VP-People)*
Jeff Mattes *(VP & Gen Mgr-Authentic Response)*
Mike Billingsley *(VP-Sls-Authentic Response Div)*
Dennis Malaspina *(VP-Sls)*
Margaret Farmakis *(Sr Dir-Response Consulting)*
Larry Karipides *(Dir-Sls & Client Dev)*

THE REYNOLDS & REYNOLDS COMPANY
1 Reynolds Way
Kettering, OH 45430
Tel.: (937) 485-2000
Fax: (937) 485-8971
Toll Free: (877) 462-5723
E-mail: info@reyrey.com
Web Site: www.reyrey.com
Sales Range: $1-4.9 Billion
Approx. Number Employees: 6,000
Business Description:
Computer Software & Services for Automotive Retailers
S.I.C.: 7373; 7372; 7379; 8748
N.A.I.C.S.: 541512; 511210; 541519; 541690
Media: 2-13
Distr.: Natl.
Budget Set: July -Aug.
Personnel:
Robert T. Brockman *(Chm & CEO)*
Rob Nalley *(Vice Chm)*
Dan Agan *(Exec VP)*
Jerry Kirwan *(Sr VP & Gen Mgr)*
Trey Hiers *(VP-Mktg)*
Terry Jones *(Dir-Player Rels)*
Advertising Agency:
BRC Marketing Inc.
7051 Corporate Way
Dayton, OH 45459
Tel.: (937) 384-0515
Fax: (937) 384-0522
Toll Free: (888) 905-0515

RF INDUSTRIES, LTD.
7610 Miramar Rd Bldg 6000
San Diego, CA 92126-4202
Tel.: (858) 549-6340
Fax: (858) 549-6345
Toll Free: (800) 233-1728
E-mail: rfi@rfindustries.com
Web Site: www.rfindustries.com
Approx. Sls.: $16,322,178
Approx. Number Employees: 110
Business Description:
Wired & Wireless Solutions for the Telecom & Biomedical Markets
S.I.C.: 3678; 3643; 3663
N.A.I.C.S.: 334417; 334220; 335931
Advertising Expenditures: $215,000
Media: 10
Personnel:
Howard F. Hill *(Founder, Pres & CEO)*
James S. Doss *(CFO)*
Manny Gutsche *(VP-Sls & Mktg)*
Brands & Products:
ANDREW
BLUEWAVE
EUPEN
RF INDUSTRIES
RF NEULINK
TELEDESIGN
UNICABLE
UNIDAPT

RICHARDSON GROUP INC.
1818 Market St Ste 2800
Philadelphia, PA 19103
Tel.: (215) 940-9255
Fax: (215) 940-3510
E-mail: info@richardson.com
Web Site: www.richardson.com
Sales Range: $25-49.9 Million
Approx. Number Employees: 110
Business Description:
Global Sales Training & Consulting Services
S.I.C.: 8748
N.A.I.C.S.: 541618
Media: 2-10-22
Personnel:
David J. DiStefano *(Pres & CEO)*
Bill Zarrilli *(CFO & Sr VP)*
Joseph Jacobs *(CTO & Sr VP)*
Deborah Antonelli *(Exec VP-Global Sls)*
James A. Brodo *(Sr VP-Mktg)*

RICOH AMERICAS CORPORATION
(Sub. of Ricoh Company, Ltd.)
5 Dedrick Pl
West Caldwell, NJ 07006-6304
Tel.: (973) 882-2000
Fax: (973) 882-5840
Toll Free: (800) 63RICOH
E-mail: magio.support@ricoh-usa.com
Web Site: www.ricoh-usa.com
E-Mail For Key Personnel:
Public Relations: russell.marchetta@ricoh-usa.com
Sales Range: $15-24.9 Billion
Approx. Number Employees: 3,000
Year Founded: 1962
Business Description:
Digital Imaging & Document Solutions
S.I.C.: 5044; 5065
N.A.I.C.S.: 423420; 423690
Import Export
Advertising Expenditures: $19,000,000
Media: 2-4-5-6-7-9-10-12-13-14-20-21-22-23-26
Distr.: Intl.; Natl.
Budget Set: Various
Personnel:
Martin Brodigan *(Pres & CEO)*
Tracey Rothenberger *(CIO & Sr VP)*
Mark Hershey *(Gen Counsel & Sr VP)*
Ann Moser *(Sr VP)*
Hede Nonaka *(Exec VP)*
Shun Sato *(Sr VP-Mktg)*
Donna Venable *(Sr VP-HR)*
Mike Dane *(VP-Mktg)*
David Greene *(VP-Sls)*
Brands & Products:
AOE
AQUA PRO
ARCADIA
CL3000
CROWWW
DOCUMENTMALL
DOCUMENTSERVER PRO
GLOBALSCAN
IMAGEDIRECTOR
JUST LINK
LS3000
OUR EARTH, OUR TOMORROW
PXP
RAMDRIVE
RDC-1
RDC-300
REQ
RICOH DEVELOPER SUPPORT PROGRAM
RICOH NC 5006
RPCS
RSCRIPT
RXP-10
SAF-PAK
WDSM
Advertising Agencies:
The Coakley Heagerty Advertising & Public Relations Co.
1155 N 1st St Ste 201
San Jose, CA 95112-4925
Tel.: (408) 275-9400
Fax: (408) 995-0600

Gigante Vaz Partners Advertising, Inc.
295 Lafayette St Fl 7
New York, NY 10012
Tel.: (212) 343-0004
Fax: (212) 343-0776

Mason & Kichar Recruitment Advertising
260 Amity Rd
Woodbridge, CT 06525
Tel.: (203) 392-0252
Fax: (203) 392-0255

Peppercom
470 Park Ave S 5th Fl
New York, NY 10016
Tel.: (212) 931-6100
Fax: (212) 931-6159

RICOH AMERICAS CORP.
(Formerly Lanier Worldwide, Inc.)
(Sub. of Ricoh Americas Corporation)
2300 Parklake Dr NE
Atlanta, GA 30345-2902
Tel.: (770) 496-9500
Fax: (770) 563-8436
Toll Free: (800) 708-7088
Web Site: www.ricoh-usa.com
Approx. Number Employees: 4,000
Year Founded: 1934
Business Description:
Office Products Marketer, Sales & Servicer Including Copying Systems, Facsimile Units, Dictation Equipment, Document Systems, Information Management Systems & PC Based Recording Systems
S.I.C.: 3555; 5044
N.A.I.C.S.: 333293; 423420
Media: 2-3-5-6-7-10-18
Distr.: Direct to Consumer; Intl.; Natl.
Budget Set: July
Personnel:
Vera Arthur *(VP-HR)*
Ann Franks *(VP-IT)*
Dominic Pontrelli *(Gen Mgr)*

RICOH PRINTING SYSTEMS AMERICA, INC.
(Sub. of Ricoh Printing Systems, Ltd.)
2635-A Park Center Dr
Simi Valley, CA 93065
Tel.: (805) 578-4000
Fax: (805) 578-4001
Web Site: www.rpsa.ricoh.com
Approx. Number Employees: 1,200
Year Founded: 1962
Business Description:
Computer Printers, Printer Supplies, Digital Communications Equipment Mfr & Sales
S.I.C.: 3575; 3577; 3661; 3679
N.A.I.C.S.: 334113; 334119; 334210; 334418
Import Export
Advertising Expenditures: $50,000
Media: 1-2-4-5-7-10-11-20
Distr.: Intl.; Natl.
Budget Set: Apr.
Brands & Products:
8000 SERIES
9000 SERIES
B P SERIES
B SERIES
DATARIBBON
DOTS IN MOTION
JET PACK
JOLT
LB SERIES
LM SERIES
LZR 1200 SERIES
LZR 2600 SERIES
M SERIES
PRINTWATCH
SI SERIES
SURESEAL
TYPHOON
VPT

RIDG-U-RAK, INC.
120 S Lake St
North East, PA 16428-1232
Tel.: (814) 725-8751
Fax: (814) 725-5659
E-mail: info@ridgurak.com
Web Site: www.ridgurak.com
Approx. Sls.: $75,000,000
Approx. Number Employees: 360
Year Founded: 1942
Business Description:
Complete Storage Systems & Pallet Storage Racks Designer & Distr
S.I.C.: 2519
N.A.I.C.S.: 337125
Media: 2-4-7-10-13-17-21-24-26
Distr.: Natl.
Budget Set: Nov.
Personnel:
John B. Pellegrino *(Pres & CEO)*
Brands & Products:
COLUMN SENTRY
EXTENDO-MAX
PUSH PAK
RIDG U RAK
RIDG-U-SPAN
RIDG-U-TIER
STACK-U-RAK
SYSTEM 2000
Advertising Agency:
Altman-Hall Associates
235 W 7th St
Erie, PA 16501-1601
Tel.: (814) 454-0158
Fax: (814) 454-3266
(Ridg-U-Rak Steel Storage Racks)

RIGHTNOW TECHNOLOGIES, INC.
136 Enterprise Blvd
Bozeman, MT 59718

Key to Media (For complete agency information see *The Advertising Red Books-Agencies* edition):
1. Bus. Publs. 2. Cable T.V. 3. Catalogs & Directories. 4. Co-op Adv. 5. Consumer Mags. 6. D.M. to Bus. Estab.7. D.M. to Consumers 8. Daily Newsp. 9. Exhibits/Trade Shows 10. Foreign 11. Infomercial 12. Internet Adv.13. Multimedia 14. Network Radio 15. Network T.V. 16. Newsp. Distr. Mags. 17. Other 18. Outdoor (Posters, Transit) 19. Point of Purchase20. Premiums, Novelties 21. Product Samples 22. Special Events Mktg. 23. Spot Radio 24. Spot T.V. 25. Weekly Newsp. 26. Yellow Page Adv.

RightNow Technologies, Inc. — (Continued)

Tel.: (406) 522-4200
Fax: (406) 522-4227
Toll Free: (877) 363-5678
E-mail: ir@rightnow.com
Web Site: www.rightnow.com
Approx. Rev.: $185,522,000
Approx. Number Employees: 920
Year Founded: 1995
Business Description:
Business Oriented Computer Software
S.I.C.: 7372; 7371
N.A.I.C.S.: 334611; 511210; 541511
Export
Advertising Expenditures: $3,500,000
Media: 10-22
Personnel:
Greg R. Gianforte *(Founder & CEO)*
Wayne E. Huyard *(Pres & COO)*
Jeff C. Davison *(CFO)*
Pete Stoneberg *(Deputy CIO-Govt Cloud & VP-Cloud Delivery)*
Laef Olson *(CIO)*
Jason Mittelstaedt *(CMO)*
Alan Rassaby *(Gen Counsel, Sr VP & Corp Sec)*
Susan J. Carstensen *(Sr VP-Customer Experience & Asst Sec)*
Marcus Bragg *(Sr VP-Global Sls)*
Joseph Brown *(VP & Gen Mgr-EMEA)*
Steve Daines *(VP & Gen Mgr)*
Ted Bray *(VP-Indirect Sls-Singapore)*
Christine Randle *(Mgr-Pub Sector Influencer Rels)*
Brands & Products:
RIGHTNOW
RIGHTNOW ANALYTICS
RIGHTNOW ANSWER MANAGEMENT
RIGHTNOW CHAT
RIGHTNOW CO-BROWSE
RIGHTNOW CONNECT
RIGHTNOW CONTACT CENTER
RIGHTNOW CONTACT MANAGEMENT
RIGHTNOW CORE
RIGHTNOW CRM
RIGHTNOW CRM SUITE
RIGHTNOW CUSTOMER SEGMENTATION
RIGHTNOW EMAIL MARKETING
RIGHTNOW EMAIL RESPONSE MANAGEMENT
RIGHTNOW ESERVICE
RIGHTNOW FEEDBACK
RIGHTNOW FORUMS
RIGHTNOW INCIDENT MANAGEMENT
RIGHTNOW KNOWLEDGE MANAGEMENT
RIGHTNOW LIVE
RIGHTNOW LOCATOR
RIGHTNOW MARKETING
RIGHTNOW METRICS
RIGHTNOW OPPORTUNITY MANAGEMENT
RIGHTNOW SALES
RIGHTNOW SERVICE
RIGHTNOW TASK MANAGEMENT
RIGHTNOW VOICE
RIGHTNOW WEB SELF-SERVICE

RISK SCIENCES GROUP, INC.

(Sub. of Crawford & Company)
1900 E Golf Rd Ste 700
Schaumburg, IL 60173-5032
Tel.: (847) 619-7475
Fax: (847) 619-0534
Toll Free: (800) 619-0224
E-mail: rsgsales@us.crawco.com
Web Site: www.risksciencesgroup.com
Sales Range: $50-74.9 Million
Approx. Number Employees: 100
Year Founded: 1978
Business Description:
Computer Software Applications; Builder & Maintenance Solutions for Large Corporate Database Operations Primarily in the Insured & Self-Insured Industries
S.I.C.: 7376
N.A.I.C.S.: 541513
Media: 2-7-10-13
Brands & Products:
CRAWFORD NOTES
SIGMA ENCORE

RIVERDEEP, INC.

(Div. of Houghton Mifflin Harcourt Publishing Company)
100 Pine St Fl 19
San Francisco, CA 94111-5102
Tel.: (415) 659-2000
Toll Free: (800) 395-0277
Web Site: www.riverdeep.net
Approx. Number Employees: 700
Business Description:
Education & Training Software
S.I.C.: 7372
N.A.I.C.S.: 511210
Media: 2-4-5-6-7-8-10-19-20-21-23-25
Distr.: Natl.
Budget Set: Feb.

ROBERT HALF INTERNATIONAL INC.

2884 Sand Hill Rd
Menlo Park, CA 94025-7072
Tel.: (650) 234-6000
Fax: (650) 234-6999
Web Site: www.rhi.com
Approx. Rev.: $3,175,093,000
Approx. Number Employees: 10,400
Year Founded: 1948
Business Description:
Specialized Staffing Services & Administrative Support Personnel
S.I.C.: 7363; 7361
N.A.I.C.S.: 561320; 561310
Advertising Expenditures: $37,900,000
Media: 2-6-7-8-9-10-13-14-25-26
Personnel:
Harold Max Messmer, Jr. *(Chm & CEO)*
M. Keith Waddell *(Vice Chm, Pres & CFO)*
Michael C. Buckley *(Chief Admin Officer, Treas & Exec VP)*
Paul F. Gentzkow *(Pres/COO-Staffing Svcs)*
Steven Karel *(Gen Counsel, Sec & Sr VP)*
Robert W. Glass *(Exec VP-Corp Dev)*
Evelyn Crane-Oliver *(Sr VP & Assoc Gen Counsel)*
Reesa Staten *(Sr VP-Corp Comm)*
Paula Streit *(Sr VP-Operational Fin & Acctg)*
Elena West *(Sr VP-Mktg)*
Amanda Leach-Rouvi *(Sr Dir-Product Mktg & Staffing Brands)*
Brands & Products:
ACCOUNTEMPS
THE CREATIVE GROUP
OFFICETEAM
PROTIVITI
RESUMANIA
RHI
ROBERT HALF
TALENT MATCH
Advertising Agency:
Red Bricks Media
1062 Folsom St Ste 300
San Francisco, CA 94103
Tel.: (415) 255-0650
Fax: (415) 255-0660

ROCKWELL SOFTWARE, INC.

(Sub. of Rockwell Automation, Inc.)
1201 S 2nd St
Milwaukee, WI 53204
Tel.: (414) 382-8300
Fax: (414) 382-8153
E-mail: info@software.rockwell.com
Web Site: www.software.rockwell.com
Sales Range: $150-199.9 Million
Approx. Number Employees: 600
Business Description:
Industrial Automated Software
S.I.C.: 7372
N.A.I.C.S.: 334611; 511210
Advertising Expenditures: $300,000
Media: 7-10
Distr.: Intl.
Personnel:
Dave Cooper *(CTO & Dir-Tech)*
Brands & Products:
RS BIZWARE
RS LOGICS
RS VIEW
Advertising Agency:
Wyse
668 Euclid Ave
Cleveland, OH 44114
Tel.: (216) 696-2424
Fax: (216) 736-4425

ROGUE WAVE SOFTWARE, INC.

(Holding of Battery Ventures, L.P.)
5500 Flatiron Pkwy Ste 200
Boulder, CO 80301
Tel.: (303) 473-9118
Fax: (303) 473-9137
Toll Free: (800) 487-3217
E-mail: sales@roguewave.com
Web Site: www.roguewave.com
E-Mail For Key Personnel:
Sales Director: sales@roguewave.com
Sales Range: $10-24.9 Million
Approx. Number Employees: 100
Year Founded: 1989
Business Description:
Software for Creating & Managing Enterprise Systems
S.I.C.: 7372; 7371
N.A.I.C.S.: 511210; 541511
Advertising Expenditures: $471,000
Media: 2-7-10-13-22
Personnel:
Brian Pierce *(CEO)*
Sean FitzGerald *(CTO & Sr VP-Engrg)*
Tom Gaunt *(Sr VP-Sls)*
Adam Schauer *(VP-Fin)*
Brands & Products:
ROGUE WAVE
ROGUE WAVE SOURCEPRO C ++
ROGUE WAVE STINGRAY STUDIO

ROSETTA STONE INC.

1919 N Lynn St 7th Floor
Arlington, VA 22209
Tel.: (540) 432-6166
Fax: (540) 432-0953
Toll Free: (800) 788-0822
E-mail: cmartin@rosettastone.com
Web Site: www.rosettastone.com
E-Mail For Key Personnel:
Public Relations: rbrennan@rosettastone.com
Approx. Rev.: $258,868,000
Approx. Number Employees: 1,084
Year Founded: 1992
Business Description:
Language Learning Solutions Including Software, Online Services & Audio Practice Tools
S.I.C.: 7372; 2741; 8299
N.A.I.C.S.: 511210; 516110; 611710
Advertising Expenditures: $33,900,000
Media: 6-8-10-13-17-18-23-24
Personnel:
Tom P. H. Adams *(CEO)*
Stephen M. Swad *(CFO)*
Matthew C. Sysak *(VP & Controller)*
Helena Wong *(Pres-Intl)*
Michael C. Wu *(Gen Counsel & Corp Sec)*
Jay Topper *(Sr VP-Customer Success)*
Gregory W. Long *(Sr VP-Corp Dev)*
Pamela Mulder *(Sr VP-Intl Dev)*
Reilly Brennan *(Dir-PR)*
Philip Dunne *(Dir-Mktg)*
Marion Bettinger *(Sr Mgr-Project)*
Megan Richter *(Mgr-PR)*
Brands & Products:
ADAPTIVE RECALL
AUDIO COMPANION
CONTEXTUAL FORMATION
DYNAMIC IMMERSION
ROSETTA STONE
ROSETTA STONE LANGUAGE LEARNING SUCCESS
ROSETTA WORLD
ROSETTASTONE.COM
ROSETTAWORLD.COM
Advertising Agencies:
GolinHarris
Fox Court
London, WC1X 8WS, United Kingdom
Tel.: (44) 20 7067 0600
Fax: (44) 870 990 5447
Language-Learning Software

GolinHarris
2200 Clarendon Blvd Ste 1100
Arlington, VA 22201
Tel.: (703) 741-7500
Fax: (703) 741-7501
Language-Learning Software

ROSS SYSTEMS, INC.

(Sub. of CDC Software, Inc.)
2 Concourse Pkwy Northeast Ste 800
Atlanta, GA 30328-5588
Tel.: (770) 351-9600
Fax: (770) 351-0036
Toll Free: (877) 767-7462
Sales Range: $25-49.9 Million
Approx. Number Employees: 260
Year Founded: 1972

Key to Media (For complete agency information see *The Advertising Red Books-Agencies* edition):
1. Bus. Publs. 2. Cable T.V. 3. Catalogs & Directories. 4. Co-op Adv. 5. Consumer Mags. 6. D.M. to Bus. Estab.7. D.M. to Consumers
8. Daily Newsp. 9. Exhibits/Trade Shows 10. Foreign 11. Infomercial 12. Internet Adv.13. Multimedia 14. Network Radio
15. Network T.V. 16. Newsp. Distr. Mags. 17. Other 18. Outdoor (Posters, Transit) 19. Point of Purchase20. Premiums, Novelties
21. Product Samples 22. Special Events Mktg. 23. Spot Radio 24. Spot T.V. 25. Weekly Newsp. 26. Yellow Page Adv.

Business Description:
Industry Improvement ERP Software for the Process Manufacturing Industry; Focus on Food & Beverage, Life Sciences, Chemicals, Metals & Natural Products
S.I.C.: 7372; 7373
N.A.I.C.S.: 511210; 541512
Advertising Expenditures: $574,000
Media: 2-5-7-8-9-10-11-25-26
Distr.: Intl.
Personnel:
Gary Nowacki *(Sr VP-North America)*
Brands & Products:
IRENAISSANCE

ROUSSEAU METAL, INC.
105 W De Gaspe Ave
Saint-Jean-Port-Joli, QC G0R 3G0, Canada
Tel.: (418) 598-3381
Fax: (418) 598-6776
Toll Free: (800) 463-4271
E-mail: rousseau@rousseaumetal.com
Web Site: www.rousseaumetal.com
E-Mail For Key Personnel:
President: simon-pierre.pare@rousseaumetal.com
Approx. Number Employees: 350
Year Founded: 1950
Business Description:
Storage Systems, Shelving Cabinets & Workstations Mfr
S.I.C.: 3429
N.A.I.C.S.: 332510
Export
Media: 2-4-5-10-13
Distr.: Natl.
Budget Set: Sept.
Personnel:
Simon Pierre Pare *(Pres & Gen Mgr)*
Charles Pare *(Mktg Dir & Sls Dir)*
Sebastien Lavoie *(Dir-Acctg & Mgr-Fin)*
Melissa Barrette *(Mgr-Mktg)*
Brands & Products:
ROUSSEAU
SPIDER
YOUR STORAGE SOLUTION

ROYAL CONSUMER INFORMATION PRODUCTS INC.
2 Riverview Dr 3rd Fl
Somerset, NJ 08873
Tel.: (732) 627-9977
Fax: (732) 627-9928
E-mail: hotline@royal.com
Web Site: www.royal.com
Approx. Number Employees: 100
Business Description:
Personal Electronic Organizers, Calculators, Cash Registers & Electronic Desk Accessories, Electric Adding Machines, Electronic Printing Calculators, Office Supplies & Printers Mfr
S.I.C.: 5044; 5065
N.A.I.C.S.: 423420; 423690
Import
Media: 2-4-6-7-10-13-16-19-23-24
Distr.: Direct to Retailer
Personnel:
Salomon Suwalsky *(Pres)*
David Fraser *(CFO)*
Todd Althoff *(VP-Mktg)*
Brands & Products:
ROYAL
ROYTYPE
Advertising Agency:
HWH Public Relations
1414 Ave of the Americas Fl 12
New York, NY 10019
Tel.: (212) 355-5049
Fax: (212) 593-0065

RSA SECURITY INC.
(Sub. of EMC Corporation)
(d/b/a RSA, The Security Division of EMC)
174 Middlesex Tpke
Bedford, MA 01730-1408
Tel.: (781) 515-5000
Fax: (781) 515-5010
Toll Free: (877) RSA-4900
E-mail: webmaster@rsasecurity.com
Web Site: www.rsasecurity.com
Sales Range: $300-349.9 Million
Approx. Number Employees: 1,282
Year Founded: 1984
Business Description:
Computer Security Services & Technologies Mfr
S.I.C.: 3577; 7371; 7372; 7379
N.A.I.C.S.: 334119; 511210; 541511; 541519
Advertising Expenditures: $869,000
Media: 5-7-10
Personnel:
Thomas P. Heiser *(Pres)*
Arthur W. Coviello Jr. *(CEO)*
Mark Quigley *(Sr VP-Ops)*
Brands & Products:
RSA ACCESS MANAGER
RSA BSAFE
RSA ENVISION
RSA SECURID
Advertising Agency:
The Other Agency Inc.
36 Jaconnet St
Newton, MA 02461
Tel.: (617) 244-4042

RTN STEALTH SOFTWARE INC.
200 8338 120th Street
Surrey, BC V3W 3N4, Canada
Tel.: (604) 687-0879
Fax: (604) 408-9301
E-mail: info@rtnstealth.com
Web Site: www.rtnstealth.com
Business Description:
Securities Trading Software Publisher
S.I.C.: 7372
N.A.I.C.S.: 511210
Advertising Expenditures: $51,672
Media: 17
Personnel:
Michael Boulter *(Pres & COO)*
Lucky Janda *(CEO)*
Larry Tsang *(CFO)*
Rana Vig *(Exec VP-Corp Ops)*
Brands & Products:
STEALTH

RUGGEDCOM INC.
300 Applewood Crescent, Concord
Woodbridge, ON L4k 5c7, Canada
Tel.: (905) 856-5288
Fax: (905) 856-1995
Toll Free: (888) 264-0006
E-mail: enquries@ruggedcom.com
Web Site: www.ruggedcom.com
Approx. Rev.: $71,188,205
Business Description:
Communications Networking Solutions
S.I.C.: 7373
N.A.I.C.S.: 541512
Media: 10-11-22
Personnel:
Peter Crombie *(Chm)*
Marzio P. Pozzuoli *(Pres & CEO)*
Roy Dalton *(CFO)*
Clive Dias *(COO & VP-Ops)*
Rudi Carolsfeld *(VP-Sls-Asia Pacific Reg)*
Joe Gould *(VP-Sls-Americas)*
Emiliano Marquesini *(VP-Sls-EMEA)*
Rene Midence *(VP-Mktg)*
Jim Slinowsky *(Dir-Mktg)*

RUSSELL & MILLER, INC.
(Sub. of Deluxe Small Business Services)
12342 Bell Ranch Dr
Santa Fe Springs, CA 90670
Mailing Address:
PO Box 2152
Santa Fe Springs, CA 90670-0017
Tel.: (562) 946-6900
Toll Free: (800) 231-9600
Web Site: www.russellandmiller.com
E-Mail For Key Personnel:
President: president@russellandmiller.com
Marketing Director: marketing@russellandmiller.com
Sales Director: sales@russellandmiller.com
Sales Range: $25-49.9 Million
Approx. Number Employees: 109
Year Founded: 1948
Business Description:
Merchandising & Display Products & Services
S.I.C.: 3993; 5961
N.A.I.C.S.: 339950; 454113
Media: 4-13-17

RUSSELL REYNOLDS ASSOCIATES INC.
200 Park Ave 23rd Fl
New York, NY 10166-2399
Tel.: (212) 351-2000
Fax: (212) 370-0896
E-mail: info@russellreynolds.com
Web Site: www.russellreynolds.com
Approx. Number Employees: 300
Year Founded: 1969
Business Description:
Executive Search Services
S.I.C.: 7361
N.A.I.C.S.: 541612
Personnel:
Matthew Wright *(Pres & CEO)*
Kathleen Fitzpatrick *(Mng Dir & CIO)*
Sarah Eames *(Mng Dir)*
Clarke Murphy *(Mng Dir)*
Laurie Nash *(Mng Dir)*
Albert H. Morris *(Chief Admin Officer)*
Sandra Galvin *(Dir-Mktg & Comm-Americas)*
Peter Drummond-Hay *(Area Mgr)*
Advertising Agency:
Makovsky & Company, Inc.
16 E 34th St 15th Fl
New York, NY 10016
Tel.: (212) 508-9600
Fax: (212) 751-9710
Agency of Record

RWD TECHNOLOGIES LLC
5521 Research Pk Dr
Baltimore, MD 21228
Tel.: (410) 869-1000
Fax: (410) 869-3001
Toll Free: (888) 793-8324
E-mail: jobs@rwd.com
Web Site: www.rwd.com
Sales Range: $100-124.9 Million
Approx. Number Employees: 1,200
Year Founded: 1988
Business Description:
Integrated Services to Companies in Complex Operating & High-Technology Environments
S.I.C.: 7373; 8742
N.A.I.C.S.: 541512; 541611
Advertising Expenditures: $609,000
Media: 9-10-25
Personnel:
Robert Deutsch *(Founder & Chm)*
Laurens MacLure, Jr. *(Pres & CEO)*
Nancy Williams *(Sr Mgr-Mktg)*
Brands & Products:
RWD
RWD INFO PAK
RWD INFOVISION
RWD LEANVISION
RWD PBA
RWD PERFORMANCEVISION
RWD PROVISION
RWD TECHNOLOGIES
RWD UPERFORM
RWD USER PERFORMANCE PAK
SOLUTIONS THAT PERFORM
WE BRING PEOPLE AND TECHNOLOGY TOGETHER

S. GRAHAM & ASSOCIATES
455 N Cityfront Plz Ste 1420
Chicago, IL 60611
Tel.: (312) 755-0234
Fax: (312) 467-9425
E-mail: lstraughter@stedmangraham.com
Web Site: www.stedmangraham.com
Sales Range: $100-124.9 Million
Approx. Number Employees: 10
Year Founded: 1988
Business Description:
Business, Marketing & Corporate Training & Personnel Development Services
S.I.C.: 8742
N.A.I.C.S.: 541613
Media: 10-13-22
Personnel:
Stedman Graham *(Chm & CEO)*

SABA SOFTWARE, INC.
2400 Bridge Pkwy
Redwood City, CA 94065
Tel.: (650) 581-2500
Fax: (650) 581-2581
E-mail: info@saba.com
Web Site: www.saba.com
Approx. Rev.: $109,570,000
Approx. Number Employees: 598
Business Description:
People Management Software Products & Services
S.I.C.: 7372
N.A.I.C.S.: 334611; 511210
Advertising Expenditures: $200,000
Personnel:
Bobby Yazdani *(Chm & CEO)*
William Slater *(CFO & Exec VP)*

Key to Media (For complete agency information see *The Advertising Red Books-Agencies* edition):
1. Bus. Publs. 2. Cable T.V. 3. Catalogs & Directories. 4. Co-op Adv. 5. Consumer Mags. 6. D.M. to Bus. Estab.7. D.M. to Consumers
8. Daily Newsp. 9. Exhibits/Trade Shows 10. Foreign 11. Infomercial 12. Internet Adv.13. Multimedia 14. Network Radio
15. Network T.V. 16. Newsp. Distr. Mags. 17. Other 18. Outdoor (Posters, Transit) 19. Point of Purchase20. Premiums, Novelties
21. Product Samples 22. Special Events Mktg. 23. Spot Radio 24. Spot T.V. 25. Weekly Newsp. 26. Yellow Page Adv.

Saba Software, Inc. — (Continued)

Joan Cronin *(Chief People Officer & Sr VP)*
Jeff Carr *(Pres-Global Field Ops)*
Peter Williams *(Exec VP-Corp Dev)*
Don Bosworth *(Sr VP & Gen Mgr-North America)*
Laurent Pacalin *(Sr VP & Gen Mgr-Saba Learning)*
Amar Dhaliwal *(Sr VP-Product Ops Grp)*
Olivier Ghezi *(Sr VP-Global Channels)*
Madhukar Govindaraju *(Sr VP-Global Engring)*
Karen Steele *(Sr VP-Corp Mktg)*
Yvette Cameron *(VP & Gen Mgr-People Performance)*
Jim Lundy *(VP & Gen Mgr-Collaboration)*

Brands & Products:
CENTRA
SABA ANALYTICS
SABA CENTRA
SABA CERTIFICATION MANAGEMENT
SABA COLLABORATION
SABA CONTENT
SABA LEARNING
SABA LEARNING COMMERCE
SABA LEARNING NETWORK
SABA LEARNING PROVIDER NETWORK
SABA LN
SABA LPN
SABA PERFORMANCE
SABA PERFORMANCE REVIEWS
SABA PUBLISHER
SABA UNIVERSITY
SABA.THE PEOPLE MANAGEMENT SOLUTION.

SAFEGUARD BUSINESS SYSTEMS, INC.

(Sub. of Deluxe Small Business Services)
8585 N Stemmons Fwy Ste 600N
Dallas, TX 75247
Tel.: (214) 905-3935
Fax: (214) 905-3832
Toll Free: (800) 338-0636
E-mail: info@gosafeguard.com
Web Site: www.gosafeguard.com
E-Mail For Key Personnel:
Marketing Director: david.millheiser@gosafeguard.com
Sales Range: $150-199.9 Million
Approx. Number Employees: 850
Year Founded: 1956
Business Description:
Check, Check-Writing System & Business Form Mfr & Marketer
S.I.C.: 2761; 7374
N.A.I.C.S.: 323116; 518210
Export
Media: 2-4-5-7-10-20-26
Distr.: Natl.
Budget Set: Oct.
Personnel:
J. J. Sorrenti *(Pres)*
Michael Dunlap *(Gen Counsel)*
Mark Roggenkamp *(Sr VP-Mktg)*
Kellye Santos *(VP-Customer Service)*
Terry Robison *(Dir-Application Dev)*

Brands & Products:
BUSINESS VISION
COLOR ACCESS
COLOR MASTER
COLOR SENTRY
SAFEGUARD
SAFETRAK

SAFEGUARD SCIENTIFICS, INC.

435 Devon Park Dr Bldg 800
Wayne, PA 19087-1945
Tel.: (610) 293-0600
Fax: (610) 293-0601
Toll Free: (877) 506-7371
E-mail: ir@safeguard.com
Web Site: www.safeguard.com
Approx. Int. Income: $718,000
Approx. Number Employees: 28
Year Founded: 1953
Business Description:
Holding Company; Investment Services Focused on Growth-Stage Life Sciences & Technology Businesses
S.I.C.: 6719; 6282; 7379; 7389
N.A.I.C.S.: 551112; 523930; 541519; 541990
Media: 1-7-14-15
Distr.: Intl.; Natl.
Personnel:
Andrew E. Lietz *(Chm)*
Peter J. Boni *(Pres & CEO)*
Stephen T. Zarrilli *(CFO & Sr VP)*
John E. Shave *(Gen Counsel & Sr VP)*
Brian J. Sisko *(Gen Counsel & Sr VP)*
Deirdre Blackburn *(Sec & Mgr-Legal Sys)*
James A. Datin *(Mng Dir-Life Sciences Grp & Exec VP)*
Kevin L. Kemmerer *(Exec VP & Mng Dir-Tech Group)*

Brands & Products:
SAFEGUARD

SAFENET, INC.

(Sub. of SAFENET HOLDING CORPORATION)
4690 Millennium Dr Ste 400
Belcamp, MD 21017-1526
Tel.: (410) 931-7500
Fax: (410) 931-7524
Toll Free: (800) 533-3958
E-mail: humanresources@safenet-inc.com
Web Site: www.safenet-inc.com
Year Founded: 1983
Business Description:
Network Security Products
S.I.C.: 7373
N.A.I.C.S.: 541512
Advertising Expenditures: $2,802,000
Media: 5-7-8-10-13-16-17
Personnel:
Chris Fedde *(Pres & CEO)*
Charles J. Neral *(CFO & Sr VP)*
Jan Manning *(CIO & VP)*
Phil Saunders *(Chief Revenue Officer & Exec VP)*
Kevin Hicks *(Gen Counsel & Sec)*
Jim Summers *(Sr VP & Gen Mgr-Data Protection)*
Prakash Panjwani *(Sr VP & Gen Mgr-Rights Mgmt)*
Steve Messick *(Sr VP-Worldwide Sls)*
Tsion Gonen *(Corp VP-Products & Mktg)*
Diane Smith *(VP-HR)*

Brands & Products:
AXIS
HIGHASSURANCE
IKEY
LUNA
QUICKSEC
SAFENET
SAFENET SECUREIP TECHNOLOGY
SAFEXCEL
SAFEZONE
SENTINEL
SOFTREMOTE

Advertising Agency:
Qorvis Communications
1201 Connecticut Ave NW Ste 500
Washington, DC 20036
Tel.: (202) 496-1000
Fax: (202) 496-1300

SAFENET, INC.

(Sub. of SafeNet, Inc.)
6 Venture Ste 315
Irvine, CA 92618
Tel.: (949) 450-7300
Fax: (949) 753-9510
Web Site: www.safenet-inc.com
Approx. Number Employees: 472
Year Founded: 1984
Business Description:
Computer Hardware & Software Piracy Security Products Marketer
S.I.C.: 3577
N.A.I.C.S.: 334119
Import Export
Media: 2-6-7-8-10-13-17-20
Distr.: Intl.; Natl.
Budget Set: Nov.

SAGE SOFTWARE, INC.

(Sub. of The Sage Group plc)
56 Technology Dr
Irvine, CA 92618
Tel.: (949) 753-1222
Fax: (949) 753-0374
Toll Free: (800) 854-3415
Web Site: www.sagesoftware.com
Sales Range: $1-4.9 Billion
Approx. Number Employees: 400
Year Founded: 1985
Business Description:
Supplier of Business Management Software & Services
S.I.C.: 7372; 7389
N.A.I.C.S.: 511210; 561499
Media: 2-4-5-6-7-8-10-13-16-17-19-25-26
Distr.: Intl.; Natl.
Budget Set: July -Aug.
Personnel:
Pascal Houillon *(Pres)*
Marc Loupe *(CFO)*
Juan Rodriguez *(CIO)*
Greg Hammermaster *(Pres-Payment Solutions Div)*
Melody Williams Dapp *(Gen Counsel & Exec VP)*
Himanshu Palsule *(Exec VP-Product Strategy & Mktg)*
Becky Krause *(Dir-HR)*

Brands & Products:
ABRA SUITE
PEACHTREE ACCOUNTING 2004
PEACHTREE COMPLETE ACCOUNTING 2004
PEACHTREE FIRST ACCOUNTING 2004
PLATINUM FOR WINDOWS
SALESLOGIX
TIMESLIPS
VISUAL 1040 TAX
VISUAL ACCOUNTS PAYABLE
VISUAL ACCOUNTS RECEIVABLE
VISUAL DEPRECIATION

Advertising Agencies:
Dentsu America, Inc.
32 Ave of the Americas 16th Fl
New York, NY 10013
Tel.: (212) 397-3333
Fax: (212) 397-3322

Doremus (San Francisco)
555 Market St 19th Fl
San Francisco, CA 94105
Tel.: (415) 273-7817
Tel.: (415) 273-7840
Fax: (415) 398-0854

Porter Novelli
3500 Lenox Rd Alliance Ctr Ste 1400
Atlanta, GA 30326
Tel.: (404) 995-4500
Fax: (404) 995-4501

SAIC, INC.

1710 SAIC Dr
McLean, VA 22102
Tel.: (703) 676-4300
Toll Free: (800) 430-7629
E-mail: zollarsr@saic.com
Web Site: www.saic.com
Approx. Rev.: $11,117,000,000
Approx. Number Employees: 43,400
Year Founded: 1969
Business Description:
High-Tech Products & Services, Research & Development; Systems Integration & Information Technology Services
S.I.C.: 7371; 7373; 8733
N.A.I.C.S.: 541511; 541512; 541710
Import Export
Media: 4-10-20
Personnel:
A. Thomas Young *(Chm)*
Walter P. Havenstein *(CEO)*
Mark W. Sopp *(CFO & Exec VP)*
Deborah H. Alderson *(Pres-Defense Solutions Grp)*
Joseph W. Craver, III *(Pres-Health, Energy & Civil Solutions Grp)*
K. Stuart Shea *(Pres-Intelligence, Surveillance & Reconnaissance Grp)*
David Heimbrook *(CEO-SAIC-Frederick, Inc.)*
Vincent A. Maffeo *(Exec VP & Gen Counsel-Audit)*
James E. Cuff *(Exec VP-Bus Dev, Strategy, M&A)*
Debbie Lee James *(Exec VP-Comm & Govt Affairs)*
Brian F. Keenan *(Exec VP-HR)*
Anthony J. Moraco *(Exec VP-Ops & Performance Excellence)*
Robert S. Zitz *(Sr VP & Chief Architect-Sys-ISR Grp)*
John R. Hartley *(Sr VP & Controller)*
Rex Ballard *(Sr VP & Gen Mgr)*
John Fratamico *(Sr VP & Gen Mgr-Bus Unit)*
Greg W. Henson *(Sr VP & Dir-New Bus Dev)*
Kevin E. Murphy *(Sr VP & Dir-Mergers & Acq)*
William Arthur Decker *(Chief Engr-Intelligence & Security Grp & Sr VP)*

Key to Media (For complete agency information see *The Advertising Red Books-Agencies* edition):
1. Bus. Publs. 2. Cable T.V. 3. Catalogs & Directories. 4. Co-op Adv. 5. Consumer Mags. 6. D.M. to Bus. Estab.7. D.M. to Consumers
8. Daily Newsp. 9. Exhibits/Trade Shows 10. Foreign 11. Infomercial 12. Internet Adv.13. Multimedia 14. Network Radio
15. Network T.V. 16. Newsp. Distr. Mags. 17. Other 18. Outdoor (Posters, Transit) 19. Point of Purchase20. Premiums, Novelties
21. Product Samples 22. Special Events Mktg. 23. Spot Radio 24. Spot T.V. 25. Weekly Newsp. 26. Yellow Page Adv.

Sarah Allen *(Sr VP-HR)*
Clement Chen *(Sr VP-Strategic Dev-ILPSG)*
Gene Colabatistto *(Sr VP)*
Lucy Reilly Fitch *(Sr VP-Corp Comm)*
Steven K. Galson *(Sr VP-Civilian Health Ops)*
James B. Idell *(Sr VP-Corp Dev)*
Andrew Jazwick *(Sr VP-Aviation Security)*
Paul E. Levi *(Sr VP-IR)*
Don Bradshaw *(VP & Sr Dir-Defense Health Ops-Health Solutions Bus Unit)*
Ron Zollars *(VP & Dir-Pub Affairs)*
Laura Luke *(VP-Media Rels)*
Stephen J. Comber *(Gen Mgr-Health Solutions Bus Unit)*
Larry D. Cox *(Gen Mgr-Cyber & Info Solutions Bus Unit)*
Martin J. Howle *(Dir-Special Projects-Corp Real Estate)*

Advertising Agencies:
ENC Marketing & Communications
1430 Spring Hill Rd Ste 575
McLean, VA 22102
Tel.: (703) 288-1620
Fax: (703) 288-1637

The Richards Group, Inc.
8750 N Central Expy Ste 100
Dallas, TX 75231-6430
Tel.: (214) 891-5700
Fax: (214) 265-2933

SALES PERFORMANCE INTERNATIONAL, INC.

4720 Piedmont Rd Dr Ste 400
Charlotte, NC 28210
Tel.: (704) 364-9298
Fax: (704) 364-8114
E-mail: info@spisales.com
Web Site: www.solutionselling.com
Approx. Number Employees: 40
Business Description:
Sales Process Consulting Services
S.I.C.: 7361
N.A.I.C.S.: 541612
Media: 2
Personnel:
Keith M. Eades *(Founder & CEO)*
Robert Kear *(CMO & Partner)*
Douglas L. Handy *(CFO)*
Sean R. DesNoyer *(COO)*
Timothy P. Sullivan *(Dir-Dev)*
James Touchstone *(Dir-Learning Programs)*
Brands & Products:
SALES PERFORMANCE INTERNATIONAL
SOLUTION SELLING
VALUE MAPPING

SALSBURY INDUSTRIES

1010 E 62nd St
Los Angeles, CA 90001-1598
Tel.: (323) 846-6700
Fax: (323) 846-6800
Fax: (800) 660-1966
Toll Free: (800) 624-5269
E-mail: salsbury@mailboxes.com
Web Site: www.mailboxes.com
Approx. Number Employees: 150
Year Founded: 1936
Business Description:
Postal Lock Boxes, Cubicle Tracks, Cubicle Curtains & Mailboxes Mfr & Distr
S.I.C.: 3469
N.A.I.C.S.: 332116
Import Export
Advertising Expenditures: $300,000
Media: 4-6-7-10-13-18-21-26
Distr.: Natl.
Budget Set: Sept.
Personnel:
Dennis Fraher *(Owner)*
John Fraher *(Chm)*
Michael Lobosso *(CFO)*
Steve Gov *(Dir-Ops)*
Brands & Products:
LOCKERS.COM
MAILBOXES.COM
SALSBURY
SALSBURY INDUSTRIES

SAMSYS TECHNOLOGIES, INC.

44 E Beaver Creek Rd Unit 11
Richmond Hill, ON L4B 1G8, Canada
Tel.: (905) 707-0404
Fax: (905) 707-9944
Toll Free: (888) 483-6646
E-mail: samsys@samsys.com
Web Site: www.samsys.com
Sales Range: $1-9.9 Million
Approx. Number Employees: 10
Business Description:
Radio Frequency Identification Hardware Solutions
S.I.C.: 4832
N.A.I.C.S.: 515111
Media: 2-7-10

SAND TECHNOLOGY, INC.

215 Redfern Ste 410
Westmount, QC H3Z 3L5, Canada
Tel.: (514) 939-3477
Fax: (514) 939-2042
Toll Free: (877) 468-2538
E-mail: info@sand.com
Web Site: www.sand.com
Approx. Rev.: $6,422,500
Approx. Number Employees: 40
Year Founded: 1983
Business Description:
Data Management Software & Storage, Accessing & Analyzing of Data On-Demand Solutions
S.I.C.: 7372
N.A.I.C.S.: 511210; 334611
Import
Advertising Expenditures: $5,220,443
Personnel:
Arthur G. Ritchie *(Founder & Chm)*
Mike Pilcher *(Pres & COO)*
Thomas M. O'Donnell *(CEO)*
Tony J. Guiliano *(CFO, VP-Fin)*
Brian Schwartz *(VP-Sls)*
Brands & Products:
MPSO
SAND
SAND ANALYTIC SERVER
SAND/DNA
SAND/DNA ACCESS
SAND/DNA ACRM
SAND/DNA ADVISE
SAND/DNA ANALYTICS
SAND EXTENSIBLE WAREHOUSE
SAND SEARCHABLE ARCHIVE
SAND TECHNOLOGY
TIME TRAVEL

SANDISK CORPORATION

601 McCarthy Blvd
Milpitas, CA 95035-7932
Tel.: (408) 801-1000
Fax: (408) 801-8657
E-mail: ir@sandisk.com
Web Site: www.sandisk.com
E-Mail For Key Personnel:
Public Relations: sandiskPR@sandisk.com
Approx. Rev.: $4,826,807,000
Approx. Number Employees: 3,469
Year Founded: 1988
Business Description:
Flash Memory Data Storage Products Designer, Developer & Marketer
S.I.C.: 3572; 8733
N.A.I.C.S.: 334112; 541710
Advertising Expenditures: $4,000,000
Media: 2-8-10-11-24
Personnel:
Sanjay Mehrotra *(CEO)*
Judy Bruner *(CFO & Exec VP-Admin)*
Yoram Cedar *(CTO & Exec VP)*
Jim Brelsford *(Chief Legal Officer & Sr VP)*
Sumit Sadana *(Chief Strategy Officer & Sr VP)*
Juha Raisanen *(Sr VP)*
Mike Morganstern *(Sr Dir-Product Mgmt)*
Steven Koch *(Dir-Sls-Latin America)*
Pablo De Simone *(Mgr-Territory)*
Brands & Products:
CONNECT
CONNECT PLUS
CONTOUR
CROSSPASS
CRUZER
CRUZER CONTOUR
CRUZER CROSSFIRE
CRUZER FLEUR
CRUZER FREEDOM
CRUZER SPECTRUM
CRUZERLOCK
CRUZERLOGIN
CRUZERSYNC
FANFARE
FLASHCP
GRUVI
IMAGEMATE
INAND
MEGASIM
MEMORY STICK DUO
MEMORY STICK PRO
MEMORY STICK PRO DUO
MI CROSDHC
MICROMATE
MICROSD
MINI SD
MINISDHC
MMCMOBILE
PASSION FOR PERFORMANCE
RAPIDGX
RESCUEPRO
RS-MMC
SANDISK
SANDISK CRUZER
SANDISK EXTREME
SANDISK FLASHBACK
SANDISK GRUVI
SANDISK IMAGEMATE
SANDISK MOBILE ULTRA
SANDISK MOBILEMATE
SANDISK PSSD
SANDISK SANSA
SANDISK SD
SANDISK ULTRA
SANDISK USSD
SANDISK VIDEO HD
SANGO
SANSA
SANSA CONNECT
SANSA EXPRESS
SANSA FUZE
SANSA SHAKER
SD
SDHC
SHOOT AND STORE
SLOT MUSIC
SLOT SPOT
SMARTHDHC
STORE YOUR WORLD IN OURS
TAKE TV
TRANSFERMATE
TRANSFLASH
TRIFLASH
TRUEFFS
TRUSTEDFLASH
TRUSTEDSIGNINS
TRUSTWATCH
V-MATE
XD-PICTURE CARD
Advertising Agencies:
Euro RSCG Worldwide - San Francisco
1355 Sansome St
San Francisco, CA 94111
Tel.: (415) 345-7700
Fax: (415) 345-7705

Grey San Francisco
303 2nd St Ste 300 N Tower
San Francisco, CA 94107
Tel.: (415) 403-8000
Fax: (415) 403-8204

Nolin BBDO
3575 Boulevard St-Laurent Suite 300
Montreal, QC H2X 2T7, Canada
Tel.: (514) 939-4100
Fax: (514) 939-4006

Publicis & Hal Riney
2001 The Embarcadero
San Francisco, CA 94133-5200
Tel.: (415) 293-2001
Fax: (415) 293-2620
Agency of Record

Red Bricks Media
1062 Folsom St Ste 300
San Francisco, CA 94103
Tel.: (415) 255-0650
Fax: (415) 255-0660

SANFORD L.P.

(Sub. of Newell Rubbermaid Inc.)
2707 Butterfield Rd
Oak Brook, IL 60523
Tel.: (630) 481-2000
Fax: (630) 481-2099
Toll Free: (800) 323-0749
E-mail: info@sanfordcorp.com
Web Site: www.sanfordcorp.com
Sales Range: $900-999.9 Million
Approx. Number Employees: 2,500
Year Founded: 1857
Business Description:
Felt-Tip Markers, Specialty Marking Instruments, Paper Adhesives, Stamp Pads & Inks, Custom & Pre-Inked Stamps, Marking Inks, Porous Tip Pens, Woodcase Pencils, Colored Pencils & Art Products Mfr
S.I.C.: 3951; 3953
N.A.I.C.S.: 339941; 339943
Import Export

Key to Media (For complete agency information see *The Advertising Red Books-Agencies* edition):
1. Bus. Publs. 2. Cable T.V. 3. Catalogs & Directories. 4. Co-op Adv. 5. Consumer Mags. 6. D.M. to Bus. Estab.7. D.M. to Consumers
8. Daily Newsp. 9. Exhibits/Trade Shows 10. Foreign 11. Infomercial 12. Internet Adv.13. Multimedia 14. Network Radio
15. Network T.V. 16. Newsp. Distr. Mags. 17. Other 18. Outdoor (Posters, Transit) 19. Point of Purchase20. Premiums, Novelties
21. Product Samples 22. Special Events Mktg. 23. Spot Radio 24. Spot T.V. 25. Weekly Newsp. 26. Yellow Page Adv.

Sanford L.P. — (Continued)

Advertising Expenditures: $3,500,000
Media: 1-2-4-5-6-10-19-20-21
Distr.: Intl.; Natl.
Budget Set: Jan.
Personnel:
Ben Gadbois *(Pres)*
Mark Radoha *(Dir-Integrated Mktg Comm)*
Brands & Products:
ACCENT
AROMA ACCENT
AUTOGRAPH PENN
CALLIGRAPHIC
CARPENTER PENCIL
CLICKSTER
CLICKSTER GRIP
COLORIFIC
DISKRIBE
ELEMENTS
EXPO
EXPO 2 CARIBBEAN COLORS
EXPO II
EXPRESSO
EXTEND
GRUMBACHER
HANDHUGGERS
KING SIZE
LABEL PEN
LIQUID ACCENT
LOGO
LOGO II
LOGO III
LOGO IV
MAJOR ACCENT
MARK AWAY
MARKETTE
MEAN STREAK
PENGUIN
POCKET ACCENT
POWER MARKER
POWER MARKER PLUS
PRISMACOLOR
ROTRING
RUB-A-DUB
SANFORD
SANFORD OIL PASTELS
SANFORD RUBBER CEMENT
SANFORD STAMP PADS
SENSA
SHARPIE
SHARPIE INDUSTRIAL MARKER
SHARPIE TWIN-TIP
SUPERSHARPIE
TEXT ACCENT
TEXTLITER
TITANIUM
TRI-GRIP
TRIGRIP COLORS
UNI-BALL
UNI-BLAZER
UNIBALL GEL METALLICS
UNIBALL GEL SCENTS
VIS-A-VIS
WATERMAN
ZEZE
Advertising Agencies:
BrandBuzz
285 Madison Ave 22nd Fl
New York, NY 10017
Tel.: (212) 210-3879
Fax: (212) 210-3878
Sharpie

Draftfcb
101 E Erie St
Chicago, IL 60611
Tel.: (312) 425-5000
Fax: (312) 425-5010

Empower MediaMarketing
(MEDIA THAT WORKS)
1111 Saint Gregory St
Cincinnati, OH 45202
Tel.: (513) 871-9454
Fax: (513) 871-1804
Media Planning & Buying

SAP AMERICA, INC.
(Sub. of SAP AG)
3999 W Chester Pke
Newtown Square, PA 19073
Tel.: (610) 661-1000
Fax: (610) 355-3106
E-mail: info.saphosting@sap.com
Web Site: www.sap.com/usa/index.epx
Sales Range: $1-4.9 Billion
Approx. Number Employees: 5,097
Business Description:
Business Software Developer, Publisher & Whslr
S.I.C.: 7372; 5045
N.A.I.C.S.: 511210; 423430
Media: 2-6
Personnel:
Mark R. White *(Exec Officer-Inside Sls)*
Robert Courteau *(Pres-North America Reg)*
Brad C. Brubaker *(Sr VP & Gen Counsel-Global Field Ops)*
Jeff Harvey *(Chief Customer Officer, Sr VP & Gen Counsel)*
Ross Wainwright *(Exec VP-North America Field Svcs)*
Patrick Bakey *(Sr VP & Gen Mgr-Strategic Industries)*
Paul Carreiro *(Sr VP & Gen Mgr-Central Region)*
Gregory McStravick *(Sr VP & Gen Mgr-East Reg)*
Glenn Wada *(Sr VP & Gen Mgr)*
Chakib Boudary *(Sr VP-Value Engrg)*
Kevin Gilroy *(Sr VP-Ecosystem & Channels)*
James Hughes *(Sr VP-Fin Svcs)*
Terry W. Laudal *(Sr VP-HR)*
Steve Lucas *(Gen Mgr-Global, Sr Exec-SAP Bus Analytics & Tech)*
James Dever *(Dir-Corp Reputation Mgmt)*
Evan Welsh *(Dir-Global PR)*
Bhuvan Wadhwa *(Mgr-Mktg)*
Scott Pruitt *(Sr Acct Exec-Large Enterprise)*

SAPORITO FINISHING COMPANY
3119 South Austin Blvd
Cicero, IL 60804
Tel.: (708) 222-5300
Fax: (708) 780-0741
Web Site: www.saporitofinishing.com
Approx. Number Employees: 4
Business Description:
Anodizing (Plating) Of Metals Or Formed Products
S.I.C.: 3471
N.A.I.C.S.: 332813
Personnel:
Charles Saporito, Sr. *(Pres)*

Advertising Agency:
NM Marketing Communications, Inc.
706 Waukegan Rd
Glenview, IL 60025
Tel.: (847) 657-6011
Fax: (847) 657-8425

SARCOM
(Formerly Wareforce)
(Sub. of PC Mall, Inc.)
111 North Canal St Suite 1551
Chicago, IL 60606
Fax: (224) 625-8796
Toll Free: (800) 555-6255
Toll Free: (800) 700-1000
Sales Range: $25-49.9 Million
Approx. Number Employees: 30
Year Founded: 1997
Business Description:
Computer and Software Stores, Personal and Home Entertainment Computers & Accessories, Computer and Peripheral Equipment & Mail Order Computer Software
S.I.C.: 5045
N.A.I.C.S.: 423430
Import
Advertising Expenditures: $3,000,000
Catalogs & Directories: $2,100,000;
Consumer Mags.: $600,000; Exhibits/Trade Shows: $300,000
Distr.: Direct to Consumer; Reg.
Personnel:
Rich Lepow *(Pres)*

SAS INSTITUTE (CANADA), INC.
(Sub. of SAS Institute Inc.)
280 King St E Ste 500
PO Box 819
Toronto, ON M5A 1K7, Canada
Tel.: (416) 363-4424
Fax: (416) 363-5399
Web Site: www.sas.com/ca
Approx. Number Employees: 200
Business Description:
Software Sales
S.I.C.: 7372
N.A.I.C.S.: 334611
Personnel:
Carl Farrell *(Pres)*

Advertising Agency:
Environics Communications
33 Bloor Street E Suite 900
Toronto, ON M4W 3H1, Canada
Tel.: (416) 920-9000
Fax: (416) 920-1822

SAS INSTITUTE INC.
(d/b/a SAS)
SAS Campus Dr
Cary, NC 27513-2414
Tel.: (919) 677-8000
Fax: (919) 677-4444
Toll Free: (800) 727-0025
E-mail: software@sas.com
Web Site: www.sas.com
Approx. Number Employees: 9,921
Year Founded: 1976
Business Description:
Software & Related Services Developers
S.I.C.: 7372; 8243
N.A.I.C.S.: 511210; 611420
Media: 1-2-3-4-7-8-9-10-13-14-15-16-17-18-21-23-24-25
Distr.: Intl.; Natl.
Personnel:
John Sall *(Co-Founder & Exec VP)*
James Goodnight *(CEO)*
Don Parker *(CFO & Sr VP)*
Suzanne Gordon *(CIO & VP-IT)*
Jim Davis *(CMO & Sr VP)*
John Boswell *(Chief Legal Officer, Corp Sec & Sr VP)*
Keith Collins *(CTO & Sr VP)*
David Davis *(VP & Chief Acctg Officer)*
Carl Farrell *(Exec VP-SAS Americas)*
Russ Cobb *(VP-Alliances & Product Mktg)*
Jennifer Mann *(VP-HR)*
Brands & Products:
APPDEV STUDIO
AUTHOR SERVICE
BEYOND BI
CFO VISION
COMPENSATION VISION
CREATE
EDUMATION
EDUPASS
EMULUS
ENTERPRISE GUIDE
ENTERPRISE MINER
ENTERPRISE REPORTER
EVAAS
EXEC SOLUTIONS
GESCAN
HR VISION
IML
INFOTAP
INSIGHT
INTELLIVISOR
IT CHARGE MANAGER
IT SERVICE VISION
JMPER CABLE
MEA
METADATA
NEOVISUALS
OBSERVATIONS
OLAP
OMNIMARKET
THE POWER TO KNOW
PROCUREMENT VISION
QUEX
SAS
SAS/AF
SAS/ASSIST
SAS/CPE
SAS/DMI
SAS/ETS
SAS/GRAPH
SAS/IMS
SAS INSCHOOL
SAS INSTITUTE
SAS ONLINE TUTOR
SAS/QC
SAS/RTERM
SAS/SHARE
SAS/SPECTRAVIEW
SAS/STAT
SASWARE BALLOT
SCALE
SELECTEXT
SOLUTIONS@WORK
STAT
THE STATISTICAL DISCOVERY SOFTWARE
STATVIEW
SYSTEM 2000
TEXT MINER
WEBAF
WEBEIS
WEBHOUND

Key to Media (For complete agency information see *The Advertising Red Books-Agencies* edition):
1. Bus. Publs. 2. Cable T.V. 3. Catalogs & Directories. 4. Co-op Adv. 5. Consumer Mags. 6. D.M. to Bus. Estab.7. D.M. to Consumers
8. Daily Newsp. 9. Exhibits/Trade Shows 10. Foreign 11. Infomercial 12. Internet Adv.13. Multimedia 14. Network Radio
15. Network T.V. 16. Newsp. Distr. Mags. 17. Other 18. Outdoor (Posters, Transit) 19. Point of Purchase20. Premiums, Novelties
21. Product Samples 22. Special Events Mktg. 23. Spot Radio 24. Spot T.V. 25. Weekly Newsp. 26. Yellow Page Adv.

SAVIN CORPORATION
(Sub. of Ricoh Company, Ltd.)
93 Lake Ave
Danbury, CT 06810
Mailing Address:
5 Dedrick Pl
West Caldwell, NJ 07006-6304
Tel.: (203) 448-2960
Fax: (203) 967-5014
E-mail: sales@savin.com
Web Site: www.savin.com
Approx. Number Employees: 200
Year Founded: 1959
Business Description:
Black & White & Full Color Digital Imaging Systems, Laser Printers, Digital Duplicators & Facsimile Systems Parts, Supplies & Services Marketer & Distr
S.I.C.: 5044; 5065
N.A.I.C.S.: 423420; 423690
Import
Media: 1-2-3-5-6-7-8-9-10-13-18-20-23-26
Distr.: Natl.
Personnel:
Jim Ivy *(Chm & CEO)*
Brands & Products:
SAVIN
SAVINFAX
SHREDMAN
Advertising Agencies:
Genova & Partners, Inc.
487 E Main St Ste 324
Mount Kisco, NY 10549
Tel.: (914) 666-3982
Fax: (914) 666-3986

Wahlstrom Group
(Corporate Headquarters)
800 Connecticut Ave
Norwalk, CT 06854
Tel.: (203) 299-4200
Fax: (203) 299-4299
Toll Free: (800) 348-7347

SAVVIS, INC
1 SAVVIS Pkwy
Town and Country, MO 63017
Tel.: (314) 628-7000
Toll Free: (800) 728-8471
Toll Free: (888) 638-6771
E-mail: info@savvis.net
Web Site: www.savvis.net
Approx. Rev.: $932,984,000
Approx. Number Employees: 2,440
Year Founded: 1995
Business Description:
Information Technology Services
S.I.C.: 7371; 7375
N.A.I.C.S.: 541511; 518111
Advertising Expenditures: $3,900,000
Personnel:
James E. Ousley *(Chm & CEO)*
William D. Fathers *(Pres)*
Jeffrey H. Von Deylen *(Sr VP-Global Ops & Client Svcs)*
James D. Mori *(Mng Dir-Sls-US)*
Varghese Thomas *(Head-Fin Svcs-Global)*
Justin Lopinot *(Mgr-PR)*
David Mills *(Mgr-Technical Ops)*
Brands & Products:
SAAS
SAVVIS
TRANSFORMING INFORMATION TECHNOLOGY

Advertising Agency:
Ogilvy Public Relations Worldwide
636 11th Ave
New York, NY 10036
Tel.: (212) 880-5200
Fax: (212) 370-4636

SCALABLE SOFTWARE, INC.
11044 Research Blvd Ste D 300
Austin, TX 78753
Tel.: (713) 316-4900
Fax: (713) 583-9266
E-mail: info@scalable.com
Web Site: www.scalable.com
E-Mail For Key Personnel:
Sales Director: sales@scalable.com
Sales Range: $75-99.9 Million
Approx. Number Employees: 50
Year Founded: 1998
Business Description:
Information Security Products & Services
S.I.C.: 8733
N.A.I.C.S.: 541710
Media: 10
Personnel:
Mark Cresswell *(Pres)*
Kristin D'Alessio *(Dir-Fin & Admin)*
Brands & Products:
SCALABLE

SCAN-OPTICS, LLC
(Holding of Patriarch Partners, LLC)
169 Progress Dr
Manchester, CT 06042
Tel.: (860) 645-7878
Fax: (860) 645-7995
Toll Free: (800) 745-6001
E-mail: info@scanoptics.com
Web Site: www.scanoptics.com
Approx. Number Employees: 183
Year Founded: 1968
Business Description:
Document Processing; Imaging Solutions & Technologies & Services
S.I.C.: 3577; 7373
N.A.I.C.S.: 334119; 541512
Export
Media: 2-10
Budget Set: Nov.
Personnel:
Richard Lieberfarb *(COO & Sr VP)*
Raymond Parker *(Exec VP-Sls & Bus Dev)*
Gary Desmarais *(VP-Engrg)*
John Casanova *(Dir-Bus Dev-Document Process Outsourcing)*
Penny Riordan *(Dir-Quality)*
Brands & Products:
ACCUSCORE
ACCUTEST
ADDRESSBUILDER
DOCWISE
FREEDOM
IMAGE EMC++
KEYENTRY
ORDEREXPRESS
PAYWISE
PROOFEXPRESS
SCAN-OPTICS
SO CAPTURE
SO DESIGNER
SO SERIES SCANNERS
TAXEXPRESS
VISTACAPTURE

SCANTRON CORPORATION
(Sub. of Harland Clarke Holdings Corp.)
1251 East Dyer Rd Ste 200
Santa Ana, CA 92705
Tel.: (949) 639-7500
Fax: (714) 437-4210
Toll Free: (800) 722-6876
E-mail: customer_service@scantron.com
Web Site: www.scantron.com
E-Mail For Key Personnel:
Sales Director: sales@scantron.com
Sales Range: $100-124.9 Million
Approx. Number Employees: 50
Year Founded: 1972
Business Description:
Automated Data Entry & Collection Equipment & Related Supplies Designer, Developer, Mfr & Marketer
S.I.C.: 3589; 2752; 2761; 3555; 3577; 7372; 7374; 7378; 7379
N.A.I.C.S.: 333319; 323114; 323116; 333293; 334119; 511210; 518210; 541519; 811212
Export
Media: 1-2-4-6-7-10-11-13-17-22-26
Distr.: Intl.; Natl.
Budget Set: Nov.
Personnel:
Bill Hansen *(Pres)*
Bruce Kraft *(CFO & COO)*
John O'Hair *(CTO & Sr VP)*
Larry Ganzell *(Sr VP-HR)*
Sean Ryan *(Sr VP & Gen Mgr-K-12)*
Jacky McIntosh *(Sr VP-Client Svcs)*
Sal Rahman *(VP-Sls & Strategic Partnerships)*
Eric Rohy *(VP-Product Mgmt & Corp Mktg)*
Brands & Products:
ASSESSMENT CONNECTION
CLASSROOM WIZARD
CURRICULUM DESIGNER
ELISTEN
FLIPS
LIQUIDOFFICE
PARSYSTEM
PERFORMANCE SERIES
QUICKSCORE II
SCANBOOK
SCANMARK
SCANTRON
SKILLS CONNECTION
SLUGGER
TELEFORM
Advertising Agency:
RiechesBaird, Inc.
1 Wrigley
Irvine, CA 92618
Tel.: (949) 586-1200
Fax: (949) 586-1201

SCHER GROUP
6401 Davies Industrial Pkwy Ste B
Solon, OH 44139
Tel.: (440) 542-2780
Fax: (440) 542-2795
Toll Free: (800) 745-7219
Toll Free: (877) 745-2745
E-mail: sales@schergroup.com
Web Site: www.schergroup.com
E-Mail For Key Personnel:
Sales Director: sales@schergroup.com
Approx. Number Employees: 70
Year Founded: 1994
Business Description:
Provider of Management Consulting Services
S.I.C.: 8748; 7514
N.A.I.C.S.: 541618; 532111
Media: 2
Personnel:
Rob Scher *(Pres)*
Jen Benroth *(CFO & Dir-Admin)*
Jennifer H. Waldeck *(Dir-Curriculum Dev)*

SCHOOL SPECIALTY, INC.
W6316 Design Dr
Greenville, WI 54942-8404
Mailing Address:
PO Box 1579
Appleton, WI 54912-1579
Tel.: (920) 734-5712
Fax: (920) 882-5863
Toll Free: (888) 388-3224
E-mail: info@schoolspecialty.com
Web Site: www.schoolspecialty.com
Approx. Rev.: $762,078,000
Approx. Number Employees: 1,919
Year Founded: 1959
Business Description:
Non-Textbook Educational Supplies & Furniture Distr
S.I.C.: 5112; 5021; 5049; 5113
N.A.I.C.S.: 424120; 423210; 423490; 424130
Import
Media: 2-4-22
Personnel:
Terry L. Lay *(Chm)*
David J. Vander Zanden *(Pres & CEO)*
David N. Vander Ploeg *(CFO & Exec VP)*
Rachel McKinney *(Chief HR Officer & Exec VP)*
Joseph E. Elliott *(Pres-School Specialty Science)*
Richmond Y. Holden, Jr. *(Exec VP-Educational Resources)*
Stephen F. Korte *(Exec VP-Accelerated Learning)*
John Thoreson *(Exec VP)*
Brands & Products:
ABC
ABILITATIONS
AMERICAN EDUCATION PUBLISHING
BRIGHTER CHILD
BRODHEAD GARRET
CALIFONE
CHILDCRAFT
CLASSROOM SELECT
CPO SCIENCE
DELTA EDUCATION
DELTA SCIENCE MODULES
EDUCATION ESSENTIALS
EPS
FAST FOOD MATH
FOSS
FRANK SCHAFFER
FREY SCIENTIFIC
HAMMOND & STEPHENS
IDEAL
INSTRUCTIONAL FAIR
INTEGRATIONS
JUDY INSTRUCTO
MATH IN A NUTSHELL
NEO/SCI
THE POWER OF TEACHING. THE WONDERS OF LEARNING
PREMIER
PROJECTS BY DESIGN

Key to Media (For complete agency information see *The Advertising Red Books-Agencies* edition):
1. Bus. Publs. 2. Cable T.V. 3. Catalogs & Directories. 4. Co-op Adv. 5. Consumer Mags. 6. D.M. to Bus. Estab.7. D.M. to Consumers
8. Daily Newsp. 9. Exhibits/Trade Shows 10. Foreign 11. Infomercial 12. Internet Adv.13. Multimedia 14. Network Radio
15. Network T.V. 16. Newsp. Distr. Mags. 17. Other 18. Outdoor (Posters, Transit) 19. Point of Purchase20. Premiums, Novelties
21. Product Samples 22. Special Events Mktg. 23. Spot Radio 24. Spot T.V. 25. Weekly Newsp. 26. Yellow Page Adv.

School Specialty, Inc. — (Continued)

SAX
SAX ARTS & CRAFTS
SAX FAMILY & CONSUMER SCIENCES
SCHOOL SMART
SCHOOL SPECIALTY
SCHOOL SPECIALTY PUBLISHING
SPARK
SPECTRUM
SPORTIME
THINKMATH!

SCHWAB CORPORATION
(Sub. of Sentry Group, Inc.)
110 Profesional Ct
Lafayette, IN 47905-5088
Tel.: (765) 447-9470
Fax: (765) 447-8278
Toll Free: (800) 447-7233
E-mail: cs@schwabcorp.com
Web Site: www.schwabcorp.com
Approx. Number Employees: 105
Year Founded: 1872
Business Description:
Safes & Insulated Filing Cabinets Mfr
S.I.C.: 2522; 3499
N.A.I.C.S.: 337214; 332999
Export
Advertising Expenditures: $200,500
Distr.: Intl.; Natl.
Budget Set: Oct.
Personnel:
Gideon Sasson *(CIO)*
Ronald Lashbrook *(VP-Sls & Mktg)*
Tony Lucido *(Gen Mgr)*
Brands & Products:
FIRE GUARD
HERO
SCHWAB
SCHWABCORP
SERIES 2500 FIRE FILES
SERIES 5000 2HR
SERIES 5000 VERTICAL FILES
TRIDENT

SCIENCE APPLICATIONS INTERNATIONAL CORPORATION
(Sub. of SAIC, Inc.)
155 Passaic Ave
Fairfield, NJ 07004
Tel.: (973) 575-6620
Fax: (973) 575-5467
Web Site: www.saic.com
Approx. Rev.: $250,000,000
Approx. Number Employees: 175
Year Founded: 1940
Business Description:
Electronic Procurement, Logistics & Supply Chain Management Services
S.I.C.: 8742; 7389
N.A.I.C.S.: 541614; 541990
Import Export
Media: 4-13
Personnel:
Mike McGovern *(VP-Bus Devel & Mktg)*
Brands & Products:
PROCURENET
PURCHASEPLACE

SCIENTIFIC GAMES CORPORATION
750 Lexington Ave 25th Fl
New York, NY 10022-1200
Tel.: (212) 754-2233
Fax: (212) 754-2372
Web Site: www.scientificgames.com
Approx. Rev.: $882,499,000
Approx. Number Employees: 3,200
Year Founded: 1984
Business Description:
Computerized Wagering Systems Mfr & Retailer for Horse & Greyhound Racetracks, Jai Alai Frontons & Off-Track Wagering Facilities
S.I.C.: 7371; 7373; 7999
N.A.I.C.S.: 541511; 541512; 713290; 713990
Media: 2
Personnel:
A. Lorne Weil *(Chm & CEO)*
David L. Kennedy *(Vice Chm)*
Brooks Pierce *(Pres)*
Steven M. Saferin *(Chief Creative Officer, Pres-Properties Group & VP)*
Steve W. Beason *(CTO-Enterprise & Sr VP)*
Larry A. Potts *(Chief Compliance Officer, VP & Dir-Security)*
Michael R. Chambrello *(CEO-Asia Pacific Reg)*
Ian Timmis *(CEO-Global Draw Ltd & Games Media)*
Grier C. Raclin *(Gen Counsel & Sr VP)*
Robert Kowalczyk *(Sr VP-Internet Svcs)*
Advertising Agency:
Spector & Associates, Inc.
65 Broadway Ste 899
New York, NY 10006
Tel.: (212) 943-5858
Fax: (212) 430-3849

SCIENTIGO, INC.
6701 Carmel Rd Ste 205
Charlotte, NC 28226
Tel.: (704) 837-0500
Sales Range: Less than $1 Million
Approx. Number Employees: 21
Year Founded: 2003
Business Description:
Software Solutions & Media Services
S.I.C.: 7372; 7373
N.A.I.C.S.: 334611; 541512
Media: 1-10-22
Personnel:
Stuart J. Yarbrough *(Chm)*
Paul S. Odom *(Sr VP & Chief Scientist)*
Advertising Agency:
Elite Financial Communications Group, LLC
605 Crescent Executive Ct Ste 124
Lake Mary, FL 32746
Tel.: (407) 585-1080
Fax: (407) 585-1081

SCIQUEST, INC.
(Holding of Trinity Ventures)
6501 Weston Pkwy Ste 200
Cary, NC 27513
Tel.: (919) 659-2100
Fax: (919) 659-2199
Toll Free: (877) 710-0413
E-mail: sales@sciquest.com
Web Site: www.sciquest.com
E-Mail For Key Personnel:
Marketing Director: marketing@sciquest.com
Approx. Rev.: $42,477,000
Approx. Number Employees: 192
Year Founded: 1995
Business Description:
Technology & Services to Optimize Procurement & Materials Management for the Life Sciences, Higher Education & Industrial Research Markets
S.I.C.: 7372; 7373; 7389
N.A.I.C.S.: 511210; 541512; 561499
Advertising Expenditures: $635,000
Media: 6-7-10
Personnel:
Noel J. Fenton *(Chm)*
Stephen J. Wiehe *(Pres & CEO)*
Rudy C. Howard *(CFO)*
James B. Duke *(COO)*
Jeffrey A. Martini *(Sr VP-Worldwide Sls)*
C. Gamble Heffernan *(VP-Mktg & Strategy)*
Jennifer G. Kaelin *(VP-Fin)*
Ann Thomas *(VP-HR)*
David Buffaloe *(Dir-Mktg)*
David Rimmington *(Dir-Sls-EMEA)*
Brands & Products:
SCIQUEST

THE SCO GROUP, INC.
333 S 520 W Ste 170
Lindon, UT 84042-1911
Tel.: (801) 765-4999
Fax: (801) 765-1313
Web Site: www.thescogroup.com
Approx. Rev.: $15,568,000
Approx. Number Employees: 63
Year Founded: 1994
Business Description:
Linux-Based Software Developer & Marketer & Related Services
S.I.C.: 7372; 7371
N.A.I.C.S.: 334611; 541511
Advertising Expenditures: $136,000
Media: 5-10
Personnel:
Ken R. Nielsen *(CFO)*
Chris Sontag *(Sr VP & Gen Mgr-Market Dev)*
Brands & Products:
OPENSERVER
SCO
SCO OPENSERVER
SCO UNIXWARE
SCOOFFICE SERVER
SCOX WEB SERVICES SUBSTRATE
SMALLFOOT
TEAMSCO

SCRIPTO-TOKAI CORP.
2055 S Haven Ave
Ontario, CA 91761-0736
Tel.: (909) 476-4600
Fax: (909) 390-3900
Fax: (909) 476-4642
Toll Free: (800) 241-8552
Web Site: www.tokai-corporation.com/index2.html
Sales Range: $100-124.9 Million
Approx. Number Employees: 75
Year Founded: 1923
Business Description:
Mfr. & Distr of Writing Instruments, Lighters, & Other Packaged Consumer Products
S.I.C.: 3499; 3951
N.A.I.C.S.: 332999; 339941
Import Export
Advertising Expenditures: $600,000
Bus. Publs.: $150,000; Consumer Mags.: $450,000
Distr.: Natl.
Budget Set: Apr.
Brands & Products:
AIM N FLAME
AUTO LOC
DECO LITE
EDIT
ELECTRA
ELITE
GEO
GIGA
MEGA GRIP
MIGHTY MATCH
OPTIMA
PRO21
SCRIPTO
THE SCRIPTO ERASABLE PEN
SKIN-SKRIBE
SKINS
SPARE TIME
STREAMLINE
SUPER STIC
TINY LITE
TOKAI
TURBO
ULTIMA
VESTA
VIEWS
WILDPRINTS

SEAMLESS CORPORATION
(Name Changed to GDT TEK, Inc.)

SED INTERNATIONAL HOLDINGS, INC.
4916 N Royal Atlanta Dr
Tucker, GA 30084-3031
Tel.: (770) 491-8962
Fax: (800) 745-7700
Toll Free: (800) 444-8962
E-mail: sales@sedintl.com
Web Site: www.sedonline.com
E-Mail For Key Personnel:
Sales Director: sales@sedintl.com
Approx. Sls.: $606,983,000
Approx. Number Employees: 402
Year Founded: 1980
Business Description:
Microcomputers, Computer Peripheral Equipment & Cellular Phones Distr
S.I.C.: 5045; 5065
N.A.I.C.S.: 423430; 423690
Export
Media: 2-4-6-7-8-10-13-16-20-22-26
Personnel:
Samuel A. Kidston *(Chm)*
Jonathan Elster *(Pres & CEO)*
John Stanley Baumgartner, Jr. *(CFO & Sr VP)*
Lyle Dickler *(Treas, Sec & VP-Fin)*
Eddie Lageyre *(Sr VP-Pur)*
Ronell Rivera *(Sr VP-Latin America)*
Dave Burroughs *(VP-Sls-US)*
Daniel Greenlee *(VP-Domestic Sls)*
Rob Kalman *(VP-US & Corp Mktg)*

SEGA ENTERTAINMENT USA INC
(Sub. of Sega Corporation)
350 Rhode Island St Ste 400
San Francisco, CA 94103
Tel.: (818) 254-4263
Fax: (818) 254-4313
Web Site: www.sega.com
Approx. Sls.: $71,400,000
Approx. Number Employees: 1,700
Year Founded: 1996

Key to Media (For complete agency information see *The Advertising Red Books-Agencies* edition):
1. Bus. Publs. 2. Cable T.V. 3. Catalogs & Directories. 4. Co-op Adv. 5. Consumer Mags. 6. D.M. to Bus. Estab.7. D.M. to Consumers 8. Daily Newsp. 9. Exhibits/Trade Shows 10. Foreign 11. Infomercial 12. Internet Adv.13. Multimedia 14. Network Radio 15. Network T.V. 16. Newsp. Distr. Mags. 17. Other 18. Outdoor (Posters, Transit) 19. Point of Purchase20. Premiums, Novelties 21. Product Samples 22. Special Events Mktg. 23. Spot Radio 24. Spot T.V. 25. Weekly Newsp. 26. Yellow Page Adv.

Business Description:
Coin-Operated Amusement Devices
S.I.C.: 7993
N.A.I.C.S.: 713120
Import Export
Personnel:
Cory Haynes *(Pres & COO)*
Advertising Agency:
Mass Transmit
453 W17th St
New York, NY 10011
Tel.: (704) 706-2670
Fax: (704) 447-7262

SELECT STAFFING
(Holding of Koosharem Corporation)
Park Central Bldg 410 Ware Blvd Ste 205
Tampa, FL 33619
Tel.: (813) 830-7700
Fax: (813) 830-7029
E-mail: tampa2@selectstaffing.com
Web Site: www.selectremedy.com
Sales Range: $125-149.9 Million
Approx. Number Employees: 100
Year Founded: 1978
Business Description:
Staffing Services
S.I.C.: 7363; 7361
N.A.I.C.S.: 561320; 561310
Advertising Expenditures: $257,000
Media: 7-16
Personnel:
Shawn Levisky *(Gen Mgr & Dir-IT)*
Heidi Grew *(Dir-Sls & Mktg)*

SELECTICA, INC.
1740 Technology Dr Ste 450
San Jose, CA 95110
Tel.: (408) 570-9700
Fax: (408) 570-9705
Toll Free: (877) 712-9560
E-mail: info@selectica.com
Web Site: www.selectica.com
Approx. Rev.: $14,523,000
Approx. Number Employees: 51
Year Founded: 1996
Business Description:
Software Publishing & Internet Related Services
S.I.C.: 7371; 7372; 8742
N.A.I.C.S.: 511210; 334611; 541511; 541611
Advertising Expenditures: $19,000
Media: 1-10-13
Personnel:
Alan B. Howe *(Chm)*
Jason Stern *(Pres & CEO)*
Todd A. Spartz *(CFO)*
Leonard Rainow *(COO)*
Kamal Ahluwalia *(Chief Strategy Officer)*
Jim Bleakley *(VP-Worldwide Channel Sls & Alliances)*
Jennifer Bomze *(VP-Mktg)*
Rajesh Kamat *(VP-Pro Svcs Tech Ops)*
Leo Sigal *(VP-Engrg)*
Rob Milks *(Dir-Sls)*
Brands & Products:
SELECTICA
SELECTICA COMPOSER SUITE
SELECTICA CONFIGURATION PLATFORM
SELECTICA CONFIGURATOR
SELECTICA CONTRACT LIFECYCLE MANAGEMENT
SELECTICA CONTRACT PERFORMANCE MANAGEMENT
SELECTICA ENTERPRISE PRODUCTIVITY SUITE
SELECTICA KNOWLEDGEBASE DEVELOPMENT ENVIRONMENT
SELECTICA PRICER
SELECTICA QUOTER
SELECTICA REPOSITORY
SELECTICA SOLUTION ADVISOR
SELECTICA STUDIO

SELECTREMEDY
(Sub. of SelectRemedy)
(d/b/a Remedy Intelligent Staffing)
3820 State St
Santa Barbara, CA 93105-2610
Tel.: (949) 425-7600
Fax: (800) 307-3633
Toll Free: (800) 828-3726
Web Site: www.selectremedy.com
Sales Range: $500-549.9 Million
Approx. Number Employees: 100
Year Founded: 1965
Business Description:
Temporary Staffing Services
S.I.C.: 7363; 7361
N.A.I.C.S.: 561320; 561310; 561330
Advertising Expenditures: $1,199,000
Media: 2-7-10-13-26
Personnel:
Gunnar Gooding *(Sr VP-Ops & Sls)*
Brands & Products:
EDGE
HPT
I/SEARCH
INTELLIGENT STAFFING. EXTRA-MILE SERVICE.
MAPS

SENTO CORPORATION
600 E Timpanogos Cir Bldg H
Orem, UT 84097
Tel.: (801) 431-9200
Fax: (801) 532-2173
Toll Free: (800) 868-8448
E-mail: corporate@sento.com
Web Site: www.sento.com
Sales Range: $50-74.9 Million
Approx. Number Employees: 1,840
Year Founded: 1986
Business Description:
Information Technology, Outsourcing Services, Technical Support Services, Help-Desk Functions, Technical Training & Education
S.I.C.: 7373; 5045; 7376; 7379
N.A.I.C.S.: 541512; 423430; 541513; 541519
Advertising Expenditures: $365,856
Personnel:
Dan McReynolds *(Interim Pres & CEO)*
Stanley J. Cutler *(Sr VP-Fin)*
Heather Doman *(Mgr-HR)*
Brands & Products:
ASSIST
CUSTOMER CHOICE PLATFORM
CXP
THE POWER TO CHOOSE
RECITE
RIGHT CHANNELING
SENTO
SENTO BUSINESS INTELLIGENCE
SERVICE INTERVENTION
SITEMANAGER

SENTRY GROUP, INC.
(d/b/a/ SentrySafe)
900 Linden Ave
Rochester, NY 14625-2700
Tel.: (585) 381-4900
Fax: (585) 381-8559
Toll Free: (800) 828-1438
E-mail: consumerinfo@sentrysafe.com
Web Site: www.sentrysafe.com
Approx. Number Employees: 400
Year Founded: 1930
Business Description:
Fire & Theft Resistant Safes, Chests & Files Mfr
S.I.C.: 3499; 3089
N.A.I.C.S.: 332999; 326199
Export
Media: 2-4-6-10-19-23-24
Distr.: Intl.; Natl.
Budget Set: Oct.
Personnel:
James Brush *(CEO)*
Michael Norris *(Gen Counsel & VP-HR)*
Douglas Wolk *(VP-Sls)*
Greg Bonsib *(Dir-Mktg)*
Robin Crawford *(Brand Mgr-Packaging & Mdsg)*
Brands & Products:
FIRE-SAFE
KEEP/SAFE
SENTRY
SENTRY FIRE SAFE SECURITY CHEST
SENTRY SAFE
Advertising Agencies:
Chase Communications Corporation
1400 E. Genesee St.
Skaneateles, NY 13152
Tel.: (315) 685-3409

Dixon Schwabl Advertising
1595 Moseley Rd
Victor, NY 14564
Tel.: (585) 383-0380
Fax: (585) 383-1661

SERENA SOFTWARE, INC.
(Holding of Silver Lake Partners, L.P.)
1900 Seaport Blvd 2nd Fl
Redwood City, CA 94063-5587
Tel.: (650) 481-3400
Fax: (650) 481-3700
Toll Free: (800) 457-3736
E-mail: info@serena.com
Web Site: www.serena.com
Approx. Rev.: $214,386,000
Approx. Number Employees: 579
Business Description:
Computer Software Mfr
S.I.C.: 7372
N.A.I.C.S.: 511210
Advertising Expenditures: $3,100,000
Media: 7-10
Personnel:
John A.C. Swainson *(Chm)*
John Nugent *(Pres & CEO)*
Robert I. Pender Jr. *(CFO, Sr VP-Fin & Admin)*
Edward F. Malysz *(Gen Counsel & Sr VP)*
David Hurwitz *(Sr VP-Worldwide Mktg)*
Mike deFisser *(VP-Sls & Svc-North America)*
Ashley Owen *(Dir-Product Mgmt)*
Brands & Products:
CHANGE GOVERNANCE
CHANGEMAN
COLLAGE
COMPAREX
MERITAGE
PROCESS VIEW
PROCESSVIEW COMPOSER
RTM
SAFE
SERENA
SERENA CHANGEMAN
SERENA COLLAGE
SERENA DIMENSIONS
SERENA PROFESSIONAL
SERENA STARTOOL
SERENA TEAMTRACK
STARTOOL
TEAM TRACK
TEAMTRACK
VERSION MANAGER

SERIOUS MAGIC, INC.
101 Parkshore Dr Ste 250
Folsom, CA 95630
Tel.: (916) 985-8000
Fax: (916) 985-8095
Web Site: www.seriousmagic.com
Year Founded: 2001
Business Description:
Visual Communication Tools Developer
S.I.C.: 7372
N.A.I.C.S.: 511210
Media: 2
Brands & Products:
DV RACK
ULTRA
VISUAL COMMUNICATOR

SEWARD & KISSEL LLP
One Battery Park Plz
New York, NY 10004
Tel.: (212) 574-1200
Fax: (212) 480-8421
Web Site: www.sewkis.com
Personnel:
John Tavss *(Partner)*
Advertising Agency:
Gibbs & Soell, Inc.
60 E 42nd St
New York, NY 10165
Tel.: (212) 697-2600
Fax: (212) 697-2646

SFN GROUP, INC.
2050 Spectrum Blvd
Fort Lauderdale, FL 33309-3008
Tel.: (954) 308-7600
Fax: (954) 308-6056
Toll Free: (800) 422-3819
Web Site: www.sfngroup.com/
Approx. Rev.: $2,053,376,000
Approx. Number Employees: 171,000
Year Founded: 1946
Business Description:
Temporary & Permanent Placement Staffing & Management Services
S.I.C.: 7363; 7361; 8742; 8748
N.A.I.C.S.: 561330; 541611; 541612; 541618; 561310; 561320
Media: 2-3-6-9-10-13-15-25-26
Distr.: Natl.
Budget Set: Dec.
Personnel:
James J. Forese *(Chm)*
Roy G. Krause *(Pres & CEO)*
Mark W. Smith *(CFO & Exec VP)*

SFN Group, Inc. — (Continued)
William J. Grubbs *(COO & Exec VP)*
Richard Harris *(CIO & VP-IT Svcs)*
John D. Heins *(Chief HR Officer & Sr VP)*
Loretta A. Penn *(Pres-Staffing Svcs & Sr VP)*
Rebecca Callahan *(Pres-SourceRight Solutions)*
Thad Florence *(Gen Counsel & Sr VP)*
Teri L. Miller *(VP-Fin)*
Daniel Oakes *(Dir-Solutions Design)*
Brands & Products:
PERSONNEL POOL
SPHERION
TODAYS STAFFING
YOUR BRIDGE FOR THE BEST HIRE

SHEAFFER PEN CORPORATION
(Sub. of BIC Corporation)
One BIC Way
Shelton, CT 06484-6299
Tel.: (203) 783-2313
Web Site: www.sheaffer.com
Approx. Number Employees: 150
Year Founded: 1913
Business Description:
Fountain Pens, Ballpoint Pens, Writing Instruments, Cartridge Pens, Mechanical Pencils, Desk Sets & Calligraphy Pens Mfr
S.I.C.: 3951; 5112
N.A.I.C.S.: 339941; 424120
Export
Media: 2-6-10-11-19
Distr.: Intl.; Natl.
Budget Set: Jan. -Feb.
Personnel:
Gretchen L. Dickenson *(Brand Mgr)*
Brands & Products:
AGIO
AWARD
BALANCE
CONNOISSEUR
DELTAGRIP
THE INTRIGUE
JAVELIN
NONONSENSE
PRELUDE
REACKTOR
SENTINEL
SHEAFFER
SKRIP
TARGA BY SHEAFFER
TRIUMPH IMPERIAL
WHITE DOT

SHORETEL, INC.
960 Stewart Dr
Sunnyvale, CA 94085
Tel.: (408) 331-3300
Fax: (408) 331-3333
Toll Free: (800) 425-9385
Web Site: www.shoretel.com
Approx. Rev.: $148,464,000
Approx. Number Employees: 479
Year Founded: 1996
Business Description:
IP Telecommunications Systems
S.I.C.: 3661; 3669; 4812
N.A.I.C.S.: 334210; 334290; 517212
Media: 10-17
Personnel:
Gary J. Daichendt *(Chm)*
Peter Blackmore *(CEO)*
Michael E. Healy *(CFO & Sr VP)*
Rick Parkinson *(CIO)*
Kevin Gavin *(CMO)*
Pedro E. Rump *(Sr VP-Engrg & Ops)*
Dale Tonogai *(VP-Engrg)*
Tonya Chin *(Dir-IR)*

SHRED-TECH INC.
295 Pinebush Rd
Cambridge, ON N1T 1B2, Canada
Tel.: (519) 621-3560
Fax: (519) 621-4288
Toll Free: (800) 465-3214
E-mail: shred@shred-tech.com
Web Site: www.shred-tech.com
Sales Range: $50-74.9 Million
Approx. Number Employees: 120
Year Founded: 1978
Business Description:
Shredding Equipment & Reduction Systems
S.I.C.: 3579; 4953
N.A.I.C.S.: 333313; 562219
Personnel:
Rob Glass *(Pres & CEO)*
David Harburn *(COO)*
Brands & Products:
FEED HOPPER
GRIPPER TIPPER
PLUS 1
SHRED TECH
Advertising Agency:
Airfoil Public Relations
1000 Town Ctr Dr Ste 600
Southfield, MI 48075
Tel.: (248) 304-1400
Fax: (248) 304-1401
Toll Free: (866) AIRFOIL
Mobile & Plant-Based Document Destruction & Recycling Systems

SIEMENS MEDICAL SOLUTIONS USA, INC.
(Sub. of Siemens Medical Solutions GmbH)
51 Valley Stream Pkwy
Malvern, PA 19355
Tel.: (610) 219-6300
Toll Free: (888) 826-9702
E-mail: e.health@sms.siemens.com
Web Site: www.siemensmedical.com
Approx. Number Employees: 8,000
Business Description:
Diagnostic & Therapeutic Systems & Devices Mfr, Developer & Marketer
S.I.C.: 3841; 3845
N.A.I.C.S.: 339112; 334510
Media: 1-2-4-7-10-20
Distr.: Intl.; Natl.
Personnel:
Heinrich Kolem *(Pres & CEO)*
Amanda Naiman *(Mgr-Media Rels)*

SIEMENS PLM SOFTWARE
(Div. of Siemens Automation & Drives Group)
5800 Granite Pkwy Ste 600
Plano, TX 75024
Tel.: (972) 987-3000
Fax: (972) 987-3299
Toll Free: (800) 498-5351
Toll Free: (800) 848-7372
E-mail: info.plm@siemens.com
Web Site: www.plm.automation.siemens.com/en_us/index.shtml
Sales Range: $1-4.9 Billion
Approx. Number Employees: 7,400
Year Founded: 1967
Business Description:
Product Lifecycle Management (PLM) Software & Services
S.I.C.: 7373; 7371
N.A.I.C.S.: 541512; 541511
Export
Advertising Expenditures: $6,600,000
Media: 2-4-10
Distr.: Natl.
Personnel:
Anthony J. Affuso *(Chm & CEO)*
Charles C. Grindstaff *(Pres & CTO)*
Peter Bichara *(CFO & Exec VP)*
Craig J. Berry *(CIO & Sr VP)*
Rose Marie E. Glazer *(Gen Counsel & Sec)*
Dave Shirk *(Exec VP-Global Mktg)*
Paul Vogel *(Exec VP-Global Sls & Svcs)*
Hans-Kurt Lubberstedt *(Sr VP & Mng Dir-Asia Pacific)*
Dave Shook *(Mng Dir-Americas & Sr VP)*
Tony Hemmelgarn *(Sr VP & Country Mgr- US)*
Ed Arlin *(Sr VP-Gen Motors)*
Dan Malliet *(Sr VP-HR)*
Mike Sayen *(VP-Strategy)*
Advertising Agency:
Chletcos/Gallagher Inc.
63 Greene St Ste 602
New York, NY 10012
Tel.: (212) 334-2455
Fax: (212) 334-2463

SIEMENS POWER TECHNOLOGIES INTERNATIONAL
(Div. of Siemens Energy)
400 State St
Schenectady, NY 12301-1058
Mailing Address:
PO Box 1058
Schenectady, NY 12301-1058
Tel.: (518) 395-5000
Fax: (518) 346-2777
Web Site: www.pti-us.com
Approx. Number Employees: 70
Year Founded: 1969
Business Description:
Engineering Consulting Services, Software & Education Courses for the Electric Utility Industry
S.I.C.: 8711; 7371
N.A.I.C.S.: 541330; 541511
Media: 10
Personnel:
James Feltes *(Asst VP)*

SIGHTLINE SYSTEMS CORPORATION
11130 Fairfax Blvd Ste 200
Fairfax, VA 22030
Tel.: (703) 563-3000
Fax: (703) 563-4000
Toll Free: (877) 744-4854
E-mail: support@sightlinesystems.com
Web Site: www.sightlinesystems.com
Sales Range: $10-24.9 Million
Year Founded: 1979
Business Description:
Automated Performance Analysis & Correlation Software
S.I.C.: 7389
N.A.I.C.S.: 519190
Export
Media: 7-10
Distr.: Direct to Consumer; Natl.
Budget Set: June
Personnel:
Brandon Witte *(Pres & CEO)*
John Checklick *(Dir-Prof Svcs)*
Debra Ray *(Dir-Customer Svc)*

SIGMA DESIGNS, INC.
1778 McCarthy Blvd
Milpitas, CA 95035
Tel.: (408) 262-9003
Fax: (408) 957-9740
Toll Free: (800) 845-8086
E-mail: marketing@sdesigns.com
Web Site: www.sigmadesigns.com
Approx. Rev.: $286,915,000
Approx. Number Employees: 592
Year Founded: 1982
Business Description:
Enhancement Products Mfr & Marketer for Personal Computers, Including Desktop Video, High-Resolution & Video Graphics, Boards & Chipsets, Video Conferencing & Desktop Notebook PC's
S.I.C.: 3674; 3577
N.A.I.C.S.: 334413; 334119
Import Export
Advertising Expenditures: $5,076,000
Media: 1-2-4-5-7-8-10-11-17-21-22
Distr.: Intl.; Natl.
Budget Set: Jan.
Personnel:
Thinh Q. Tran *(Chm & CEO)*
Thomas E. Gay, III *(CFO)*
Gabi Hilevitz *(VP & Gen Mgr-Home Connectivity Grp)*
David L. Lynch *(VP & Gen Mgr-Media Processor Grp)*
Jacques Martinella *(VP-Engrg)*
Keith Jack *(Sr Dir-Product Mktg, Media Processor Bus Grp)*
Brands & Products:
COAIR
MAXIMA
MAXIMA PRO
NETSTREAM
POWERING THE DIGITAL MEDIA GENERATION
REALMAGIC
SIGMA DESIGNS
ULTRA
VXP
WINDEO
Z-WAVE
Advertising Agency:
Atomic Public Relations
735 Market St 4th Fl
San Francisco, CA 94103
Tel.: (415) 402-0230
Fax: (415) 402-0237
— Allyson Stinchfield *(Acct Exec)*

SILICON GRAPHICS INTERNATIONAL CORP
46600 Landing Pkwy
Fremont, CA 94538
Tel.: (510) 933-8300
Fax: (408) 321-0293
Web Site: www.sgi.com
Approx. Rev.: $403,717,000
Approx. Number Employees: 1,264
Year Founded: 1999

Key to Media (For complete agency information see *The Advertising Red Books-Agencies* edition):
1. Bus. Publs. 2. Cable T.V. 3. Catalogs & Directories. 4. Co-op Adv. 5. Consumer Mags. 6. D.M. to Bus. Estab.7. D.M. to Consumers 8. Daily Newsp. 9. Exhibits/Trade Shows 10. Foreign 11. Infomercial 12. Internet Adv.13. Multimedia 14. Network Radio 15. Network T.V. 16. Newsp. Distr. Mags. 17. Other 18. Outdoor (Posters, Transit) 19. Point of Purchase20. Premiums, Novelties 21. Product Samples 22. Special Events Mktg. 23. Spot Radio 24. Spot T.V. 25. Weekly Newsp. 26. Yellow Page Adv.

Business Description:
Highly Scalable Computer Servers & High Capacity Storage Systems Designer & Mfr
S.I.C.: 3571; 3669; 3679; 3699; 7373; 8711
N.A.I.C.S.: 334111; 334290; 334419; 335999; 541330; 541512
Export
Advertising Expenditures: $389,000
Personnel:
Ronald D. Verdoorn *(Chm)*
Mark J. Barrenechea *(CEO)*
James D. Wheat *(CFO & Sr VP)*
Dominic Martinelli *(CIO)*
Franz Aman *(CMO)*
Eng Lim Goh *(CTO & Sr VP)*
Timothy Pebworth *(Chief Acctg Officer & VP)*
Jennifer Pileggi *(Gen Counsel, Sec & Sr VP)*
Tony Carrozza *(Sr VP-Worldwide Sls)*
Dick Harkness *(Sr VP-Mfg)*
Praveen K. Mandal *(Sr VP-Engrg)*
Jennifer Pratt *(Sr VP-HR)*
Rick Rinehart *(Sr VP-Svcs)*
Brands & Products:
OMNISTOR
RACKABLE
STORVIEW
Advertising Agency:
Ogilvy PR
111 Sutter St 11th Fl
San Francisco, CA 94104-4541
Tel.: (415) 677-2700
Fax: (415) 677-2770
Agency of Record
Brand Awareness

SILICON MOUNTAIN HOLDINGS, INC.

2300 Central Ave Unit D
Boulder, CO 80301
Tel.: (303) 938-1155
Fax: (303) 938-1166
E-mail: info@smmdirect.com
Web Site: www.smmdirect.com
Sales Range: $25-49.9 Million
Approx. Number Employees: 31
Year Founded: 1983
Business Description:
Holding Company; Branded Computer Memory Products, Servers & Storage Devices Marketer & Whslr
S.I.C.: 6719; 3572; 5045; 7379
N.A.I.C.S.: 551112; 334112; 423430; 541519
Advertising Expenditures: $739,261
Personnel:
Rudolph A. Cates, III *(Pres & CEO)*
Brands & Products:
RULE THE PLAYGROUND
SILICON MOUNTAIN MEMORY
SILICON MOUNTAIN TECHNOLOGIES
SMMDIRECT
VISIONMAN

SILVON SOFTWARE INC.

900 Oakmont Ln Ste 400
Westmont, IL 60559
Tel.: (630) 655-3313
Fax: (630) 655-3377
Toll Free: (800) 874-5866
E-mail: info@silvon.com
Web Site: www.silvon.com
Approx. Number Employees: 50
Year Founded: 1987
Business Description:
Computer Software Development
S.I.C.: 7371
N.A.I.C.S.: 541511
Personnel:
Mike Hennel *(Pres & CEO)*
John Hughes *(Sr VP-Sls & Mktg)*
Steve Morgan *(Gen Mgr-Devel)*
Brands & Products:
DATATRACKER
SALESTRACKER
SILVON
SIMPLIFYING THE VIEW OF BUSINESS
STRATUM
Advertising Agency:
WH2P, Inc.
3704 Kennett Pike Ste 400
Wilmington, DE 19807
Tel.: (302) 479-8330
Fax: (866) 480-9518
Toll Free: (866) 480-9518

SIMULATIONS PLUS, INC.

42505 10th St W Ste 109
Lancaster, CA 93534-7059
Tel.: (661) 723-7723
Fax: (661) 723-5524
Toll Free: (888) 266-9294
E-mail: info@simulations-plus.com
Web Site: www.simulations-plus.com
Approx. Sls.: $10,711,829
Approx. Number Employees: 39
Business Description:
Drug Absorption Rates Modeling Software Developer
S.I.C.: 7373; 2834; 7372
N.A.I.C.S.: 541512; 325412; 511210
Advertising Expenditures: $40,000
Media: 17
Personnel:
Walter S. Woltosz *(Chm, Pres & CEO)*
Momoko A. Beran *(CFO & VP-Ops)*
John DiBella *(Dir-Mktg & Sls)*
Brands & Products:
ADME PARTNERS
ADMET MODELER
ADMET PREDICTOR
CLASSPHARMER
DDDPLUS
GASTROPLUS
INTEGRATING SCIENCE AND SOFTWARE
SIMULATIONSPLUS

SIRSIDYNIX CORPORATION

101 Washington St SE
Huntsville, AL 35801-4827
Tel.: (256) 704-7000
Fax: (256) 704-7007
Toll Free: (800) 917-4774
E-mail: sales@sirsidynix.com
Web Site: www.sirsidynix.com
E-Mail For Key Personnel:
Sales Director: sales@sirsidynix.com
Approx. Number Employees: 400
Business Description:
Library Systems Vendor
S.I.C.: 7371; 7373; 7379
N.A.I.C.S.: 541511; 541512; 541519
Media: 10-13
Personnel:
Bill Davison *(CEO)*
John Gardiner *(CFO & Chief Strategy Officer)*
Bill Kennedy *(Sr VP-Fin)*
John Dickson *(VP-Engrg)*
Kate Duval *(VP-Strategic Initiatives)*
Thomas Gates *(VP-Mktg)*
Nancy Giamone *(VP-HR)*
Sheridan Richey *(VP-Product Dev)*
Darren Wallace *(Dir-Sls & Mktg-Asia Pac)*
Ranny Lacanienta *(Dir-Product Mgmt)*

SIRSIDYNIX CORPORATION

(Sub. of SirsiDynix Corporation)
1276 N Warson Rd
Saint Louis, MO 63132
Tel.: (314) 432-1100
Fax: (314) 993-8927
Toll Free: (800) 325-0888
Web Site: www.sirsidynix.com/Company/regions.php
Approx. Number Employees: 205
Year Founded: 1975
Business Description:
Application Software Developer & Marketer
S.I.C.: 7373
N.A.I.C.S.: 541512
Media: 2-7-10

SITEL CORPORATION

(Sub. of Onex Corporation)
2 American Center 3102 W End Ave Ste 1000
Nashville, TN 37203-1324
Tel.: (615) 301-7100
Fax: (615) 301-7150
E-mail: info@sitel.com
Web Site: www.sitel.com
Approx. Rev.: $1,863,919,000
Approx. Number Employees: 42,000
Business Description:
Business Outsourcing Services
S.I.C.: 7389
N.A.I.C.S.: 561499
Media: 2-7
Personnel:
David Garner *(Chm)*
Dagoberto Quintana *(Pres & CEO)*
Mandy Edwards *(CIO)*
David Beckman *(Chief Legal Officer & Sec)*
Michael Wellman *(Chief HR Officer)*
Donald B. Berryman *(Gen Mgr-Americas)*

SKILLSOFT PLC

(Holding of Berkshire Partners LLC)
107 Northeastern Blvd
Nashua, NH 03062
Tel.: (603) 324-3000
Fax: (603) 324-3009
Toll Free: (877) 545-5763
E-mail: information@skillsoft.com
Web Site: www.skillsoft.com
Approx. Rev.: $328,494,000
Approx. Number Employees: 1,124
Business Description:
Interactive Software Developer
S.I.C.: 7372; 8299
N.A.I.C.S.: 511210; 334611; 611430
Advertising Expenditures: $781,000
Media: 2-7-8-10-13
Personnel:
Charles Moran *(Chm, Pres & CEO)*
Thomas J. McDonald *(CFO & Exec VP-Ops)*
Jerald A. Nine *(COO)*
Anthony P. Amato *(Chief Acctg Officer & VP-Fin & Treasury)*
Colm Darcy *(Exec VP-Content Dev)*
Mark A. Townsend *(Exec VP-Tech)*
John Ambrose *(Sr VP-Strategy & Corp Dev & Emerging Bus)*
Lee Ritze *(Sr VP-Mktg)*
Brands & Products:
ANALYSTPERSPECTIVES
BOOKS24X7
BUSINESSPRO
ELEMENTSESSENTIELSFRANCAIS
ENGINEERINGPRO
EXECBLUEPRINTS
EXECSUITE
EXECSUMMARIES
EXPRESS GUIDE
FINANCEPRO
GOVESSENTIALS
HOSPITALITYPRO
ITIL
ITPRO
MANAGERSUITE
OFFICEESSENTIALS
REFERENCEWARE
ROLEPLAY
SEARCH-AND-LEARN
SKILLCHOICE
SKILLPORT
SKILLSOFT
SKILLSOFT DIALOGUE
SKILLVIEW
Advertising Agency:
Lois Paul & Partners
150 Presidential Way
Woburn, MA 01801
Tel.: (781) 782-5000
Fax: (781) 782-5999

SM&A CORPORATION

4695 MacArthur Ct 8th Fl
Newport Beach, CA 92660-1882
Tel.: (949) 975-1550
Fax: (949) 975-1624
E-mail: info@smawins.com.
Web Site: www.smawins.com
Sales Range: $75-99.9 Million
Approx. Number Employees: 400
Year Founded: 1982
Business Description:
Proposal Management & High-End Contract Support Services
S.I.C.: 7361; 8742
N.A.I.C.S.: 541612; 541611
Media: 2-10-17
Personnel:
James R. Eckstaedt *(CFO & Exec VP)*
Daniel R. Hart *(CFO & Sr VP)*
Kevin L. Reiners *(COO)*

SMART ONLINE, INC.

4505 Emperor Blvd Ste 320
Durham, NC 27703
Tel.: (919) 765-5000
Fax: (919) 765-5020
Toll Free: (800) 791-1000
E-mail: corporate@smartonline.com
Web Site: www.smartonline.com
Approx. Rev.: $1,028,879
Approx. Number Employees: 22
Business Description:
Software Development Services
S.I.C.: 7372
N.A.I.C.S.: 511210
Advertising Expenditures: $114,586
Media: 17
Personnel:
Dror Zoreff *(Chm, Interim Pres & CEO)*
Thaddeus J. Shalek *(Interim CFO)*
Bob Dieterle *(Sr VP & Gen Mgr)*

Key to Media (For complete agency information see *The Advertising Red Books-Agencies* edition):
1. Bus. Publs. 2. Cable T.V. 3. Catalogs & Directories. 4. Co-op Adv. 5. Consumer Mags. 6. D.M. to Bus. Estab.7. D.M. to Consumers 8. Daily Newsp. 9. Exhibits/Trade Shows 10. Foreign 11. Infomercial 12. Internet Adv.13. Multimedia 14. Network Radio 15. Network T.V. 16. Newsp. Distr. Mags. 17. Other 18. Outdoor (Posters, Transit) 19. Point of Purchase20. Premiums, Novelties 21. Product Samples 22. Special Events Mktg. 23. Spot Radio 24. Spot T.V. 25. Weekly Newsp. 26. Yellow Page Adv.

SMART SOFTWARE, INC.
4 Hill Rd
Belmont, MA 02478-4303
Tel.: (617) 489-2743
Fax: (617) 489-2748
Toll Free: (800) SMART-99
Toll Free: (800) 762-7899
E-mail: info@smartcorp.com
Web Site: www.smartcorp.com
Approx. Number Employees: 10
Year Founded: 1984
Business Description:
Business Planning & Forecasting Software Developer
S.I.C.: 7372; 8249
N.A.I.C.S.: 511210; 611519
Export
Media: 1-2-4-5-7-10-17-19-21-26
Distr.: Intl.; Natl.
Personnel:
Charles Smart *(Pres)*
Greg Hartunian *(Dir-Sls)*
Brands & Products:
SEE WHAT'S NEXT
SMART SOFTWARE
SMARTCOLLABORATOR
SMARTFORECASTS
SMARTFORECASTS ENTERPRISE
SMARTWEB COLLABORATOR
Advertising Agency:
NeedhamGroup
Needham, MA 02492
Tel.: (781) 559-8061

SMARTDB CORPORATION
4600 Bohannon Dr Suite 230
Menlo Park, CA 94025
Tel.: (650) 328-9798
Fax: (650) 571-9774
Toll Free: (888) 243-8762
E-mail: info@smartdbcorp.com
Web Site: www.smartdbcorp.com
Sales Range: $1-9.9 Million
Approx. Number Employees: 30
Year Founded: 1996
Business Description:
Enterprise Application Integration Technology & Automated Adapter Development
S.I.C.: 7372; 7371; 7373; 7379
N.A.I.C.S.: 511210; 541511; 541512; 541519
Media: 2-6-10-13
Personnel:
George Langan *(Dir)*
Brands & Products:
INTELLIGENT ADAPTERS
SMARTDB WORKBENCH

SMEAD MANUFACTURING COMPANY
600 Smead Blvd
Hastings, MN 55033-2200
Tel.: (651) 437-4111
Fax: (800) 959-9134
Fax: (651) 437-9134
E-mail: customer@smead.com
Web Site: www.smead.com
Sales Range: $550-599.9 Million
Approx. Number Employees: 2,600
Year Founded: 1906
Business Description:
Paper Filing Supplies & Records Management Software Mfr & Distr
S.I.C.: 2679; 7372
N.A.I.C.S.: 322299; 511210
Import Export
Media: 1-2-4-5-6-7-8-10-13-19-21
Distr.: Natl.
Personnel:
Sharon Hoffman Avent *(Pres & CEO)*
Robert Karrick *(COO & Exec VP)*
David J. Fasbender *(Sr VP-Sls & Mktg)*
Walter Glashan *(Sr VP-Ops)*
Dale Olson *(VP-Fin)*
Dean Schwanke *(VP-HR)*
Thomas Sullivan *(VP-Sls)*
Garland Cook *(Gen Mgr)*
Steve Black *(Sr Mgr-Product)*
Michelle Hanson *(Mgr-Mktg Comm)*
Brands & Products:
ALPHA-Z
CELL-U-WELD
COLORBAR
COPY CLAW
FLEX-I-VISION
IMAGETRAX
INNDURA
KEEPING YOU ORGANIZED
OFFICE DATA
SEAL & VIEW
SHELF-MASTER
SMARTSTRIP
SMEAD
T-D-I
TELL-I-VISION
TREVEALL
TUFF POCKET
TYVEK
ULTRACOLOR
VIEWABLES
Advertising Agency:
Strother Communications
222 S 9th St Fl 41
Minneapolis, MN 55402
Tel.: (612) 288-2400
Fax: (612) 288-0504
— Jenny Silgen *(Acct Exec)*

SMITH CORONA CORPORATION
(Sub. of Pubco Corporation)
3830 Kelley Ave
Cleveland, OH 44114
Tel.: (216) 881-5300
Fax: (800) 523-2881
Toll Free: (800) 448-1018
Web Site: www.smithcorona.com
Approx. Number Employees: 95
Business Description:
Printer Products & Accessories Mfr
S.I.C.: 5943
N.A.I.C.S.: 453210
Import Export
Advertising Expenditures: $4,000,000
Media: 1-2-5-6-9-18-19-26
Distr.: Intl.; Natl.
Budget Set: June
Personnel:
Martin D. Wilson *(Pres & CEO)*
Barrie Hamilton *(Mng Dir)*
Brands & Products:
SMITH CORONA
THE WAY YOU WANT TO WORK

SMITH MICRO SOFTWARE, INC.
51 Columbia Ste 200
Aliso Viejo, CA 92656-1456
Tel.: (949) 362-5800
Fax: (949) 362-2300
Toll Free: (800) 964-7674
E-mail: cs@smithmicro.com
Web Site: www.smithmicro.com
E-Mail For Key Personnel:
Sales Director: sales@smithmicro.com
Approx. Rev.: $130,501,000
Approx. Number Employees: 549
Year Founded: 1982
Business Description:
Wireless Communication, Internet & eBusiness Software Products Developer & Marketer
S.I.C.: 7372
N.A.I.C.S.: 334611; 511210
Export
Advertising Expenditures: $900,000
Media: 10-22
Personnel:
William W. Smith, Jr. *(Chm, Pres & CEO)*
Andrew C. Schmidt *(CFO)*
Robert Elliott *(CMO)*
Thomas P. Matthews *(Chief Strategy Officer)*
Von Cameron *(Exec VP-World Wide Sls)*
David Polzine *(Dir-Utilities & Productivity Solutions Grp)*
Steve Cooper *(Sr Product Mgr-Productivity & Graphics)*
Pauline Shumake *(Product Mgr)*
Brands & Products:
AQUAZONE
BOOSTXP
CHECKIT
DROPSTUFF
DROPTAR
DROPZIP
FAXSTF
GOBAR
HOTFAX
HOTTIME
ICLEAN
ICSPYWARE
INSTALLERMAKER
INTELLINEWS
INTERNET CLEANUP
ISUPPORT
PRIVATE FILE
QUICKLINK
SECUREDELETE
SHRINKWRAP
SMITH MICRO SOFTWARE
STUFFIT DELUXE
STUFFIT ENGINE
STUFFIT EXPANDER
STUFFIT EXPRESS
STUFFIT LITE
VIDEOLINK
WEBDNA
ZIPMAGIC
Advertising Agency:
Lewis PR
535 Boylston St Ste 603
Boston, MA 02116
Tel.: (617) 226-8840
Fax: (617) 421-8619

SNELLING STAFFING SERVICES
(Holding of Patriarch Partners, LLC)
(d/b/a Snelling Personnel Services)
12801 N Central Expy Ste 600
Dallas, TX 75243-1726
Tel.: (972) 239-7575
Fax: (972) 239-6879
Toll Free: (800) 756-7500
Toll Free: (800) 475-4550
E-mail: info@snelling.com
Web Site: www.snelling.com
Sales Range: $350-399.9 Million
Approx. Number Employees: 450
Year Founded: 1951
Business Description:
Staffing Services
S.I.C.: 7363
N.A.I.C.S.: 561320
Advertising Expenditures: $1,200,000
Media: 1-2-3-4-5-6-7-8-9-10-15-18-19-20-21-23-25-26
Distr.: Direct to Consumer; Natl.
Budget Set: May
Personnel:
Tim Fielding *(Pres & CEO)*
Bill Roberts *(CFO & Sr VP)*
Barbara McAninch *(Chief Legal Officer)*
Brands & Products:
SNELLING & SNELLING
SNELLING PERSONNEL SERVICES

SOA SOFTWARE, INC.
12100 Wilshire Blvd Ste 1800
Los Angeles, CA 90025
Tel.: (310) 826-1317
Fax: (310) 820-8601
E-mail: info@soa.com
Web Site: www.soasoftware.com
E-Mail For Key Personnel:
Marketing Director: dknight@digev.com
Approx. Number Employees: 30
Year Founded: 1998
Business Description:
Web Services Management & Security Solutions
S.I.C.: 6799
N.A.I.C.S.: 519130
Media: 10
Personnel:
Eric Pulier *(Founder & Chm)*
Paul Gigg *(Pres & CEO)*
Roberto Medrano *(Exec VP)*
Frank Martinez *(Exec VP-Product Strategy)*
Brent Carlson *(Sr VP-Tech)*
Alex Lazar *(Sr VP-Sls)*
Jim Mackay *(Sr VP-Bus Dev)*
Corey Scobie *(VP-Tech)*
Brands & Products:
DIGITAL EVOLUTION
DIGITAL EVOLUTION ALERT MANAGER
DIGITAL EVOLUTION CONSOLE
DIGITAL EVOLUTION GATEWAY
DIGITAL EVOLUTION MANAGEMENT POINT
DIGITAL EVOLUTION POLICY MANAGER
DIGITAL EVOLUTION REGISTRY
DIGITAL EVOLUTION SERVICE MANAGER
DIGITAL EVOLUTION XML VPN
THE DIGITAL EVOLUTION XML VPN

SOCKET MOBILE, INC.
39700 Eureka Dr
Newark, CA 94560-4808
Tel.: (510) 933-3000
Tel.: (510) 744-2700
Fax: (510) 933-3030
Fax: (510) 744-2727
Toll Free: (800) 552-3300
E-mail: info@socketmobile.com
Web Site: www.socketcom.com
E-Mail For Key Personnel:

Key to Media (For complete agency information see *The Advertising Red Books-Agencies* edition):
1. Bus. Publs. 2. Cable T.V. 3. Catalogs & Directories. 4. Co-op Adv. 5. Consumer Mags. 6. D.M. to Bus. Estab.7. D.M. to Consumers 8. Daily Newsp. 9. Exhibits/Trade Shows 10. Foreign 11. Infomercial 12. Internet Adv.13. Multimedia 14. Network Radio 15. Network T.V. 16. Newsp. Distr. Mags. 17. Other 18. Outdoor (Posters, Transit) 19. Point of Purchase20. Premiums, Novelties 21. Product Samples 22. Special Events Mktg. 23. Spot Radio 24. Spot T.V. 25. Weekly Newsp. 26. Yellow Page Adv.

Sales Director: sales@socketcom.com
Approx. Rev.: $13,498,196
Approx. Number Employees: 64
Year Founded: 1992
Business Description:
Connection Solutions Developer & Retailer for Handheld Mobile Devices
S.I.C.: 3571; 3577
N.A.I.C.S.: 334111; 334119
Advertising Expenditures: $188,600
Media: 2-10-11-13-26
Personnel:
Michael L. Gifford *(Founder, Exec VP, Gen Mgr-OEM Bus Unit & VP-Mktg)*
Charlie Bass *(Chm)*
Kevin J. Mills *(Pres & CEO)*
David W. Dunlap *(CFO & Sec)*
Tim I. Miller *(VP-Worldwide Ops & Engrg)*
Samantha Chu *(Product Mgr-Data Collection)*
Brands & Products:
BUSINESS MOBILITY NOW!
IN-HAND SCAN CARD
MOBILITY FRIENDLY
ORGANIZEIT
SOCKET
SOCKETSCAN
SOMO
WI-FI

SOFTBRANDS, INC.
(Holding of Golden Gate Capital)
800 LaSalle Ave Ste 2100
Minneapolis, MN 55402
Tel.: (612) 851-1500
Fax: (612) 851-1560
Toll Free: (800) 342-5675
E-mail: info@softbrands.com
Web Site: www.infor.com/softbrands
Sales Range: $75-99.9 Million
Approx. Number Employees: 770
Business Description:
Manufacturing & Hospitality Industries Enterprise Management Software Publisher & Distr; Owned by Golden Gate Capital & by Infor Global Solutions, Inc.
S.I.C.: 7372; 5045; 7371
N.A.I.C.S.: 511210; 423430; 541511
Advertising Expenditures: $200,000
Media: 5-8-16
Personnel:
Gregg A. Waldon *(CFO)*
Patricia A. Elias *(Gen Counsel)*
Renee Conklin *(VP-HR)*
Jo-Ann Masters *(Dir)*
Brands & Products:
DEMANDSTREAM
ENABLING GROWTH
EVOLUTION
FOURTH SHIFT
SOFTBRANDS
VISIBAR
VISIWATCH

SOFTCHOICE CORPORATION
173 Dufferin St Ste 200
Toronto, ON M6K 3H7, Canada
Tel.: (416) 588-9000
Fax: (416) 588-9001
Toll Free: (800) 268-7638
E-mail: info@softchoice.com
Web Site: www.softchoice.com
Approx. Rev.: $1,000,248,000
Approx. Number Employees: 900
Year Founded: 1989
Business Description:
Technology Products & Solutions
S.I.C.: 7373
N.A.I.C.S.: 541512
Media: 2-4-10
Personnel:
Bill Linton *(Chm)*
David L. MacDonald *(Pres & CEO)*
David .A Long *(CFO & Sr VP-Fin)*
Kevin Wright *(CIO & Sr VP)*
Nick Foster *(Sr VP-Bus Dev)*
Steve Johnson *(Sr VP-Solution Sls & Professional Svcs)*
Steve Leslie *(Sr VP-Sls)*
Sergio Vettese *(VP-Fin)*
Nicole Wengle *(VP-Sls-Canada)*
Eric Gardiner *(Mgr-Corp Mktg)*

SOFTLAYER TECHNOLOGIES INC
(Formerly The Planet)
(Sub. of SoftLayer Technologies Inc.)
315 Capital
Houston, TX 77020
Tel.: (214) 782-7800
Fax: (214) 782-7898
Toll Free: (800) 377-6103
Toll Free: (800) 504-7873
Sales Range: $25-49.9 Million
Approx. Number Employees: 500
Year Founded: 1998
Business Description:
Internet Hosting Services
S.I.C.: 7375
N.A.I.C.S.: 518111
Personnel:
Douglas J. Erwin *(Chm & CEO)*
Joseph E. Horzepa *(Gen Counsel)*
James P. Picone *(VP-Customer Care)*
Robert Walters *(Gen Mgr-Data Protection Bus Unit)*
Yvonne Donaldson *(Dir-PR)*
Brands & Products:
READY TO GO SERVERS
Advertising Agency:
Globalfluency
4151 Middlefield Rd
Palo Alto, CA 94303
Tel.: (650) 328-5555
Fax: (650) 328-5016
— Catherine Leahy *(Acct Exec)*

SOFTWARE AG, INC.
(Sub. of Software AG)
11700 Plaza America Dr Ste 700
Reston, VA 20191-5453
Tel.: (703) 860-5050
Fax: (703) 391-6975
Toll Free: (888) 724-2394
E-mail: sales@softwareuse.com
Web Site: www.softwareagusa.com
E-Mail For Key Personnel:
Sales Director: sales@softwareusa.com
Approx. Number Employees: 300
Year Founded: 1979
Business Description:
Database Management Systems Software, Enterprise Integration Software, Applications Development & Information Center Tools Retailer
S.I.C.: 7372
N.A.I.C.S.: 511210
Advertising Expenditures: $2,000,000
Media: 2-7-10
Distr.: Intl.; Natl.
Personnel:
Mark Moscato *(Sr VP-HR)*
Advertising Agency:
Fleishman-Hillard Inc.
855 Boylston St 5th Fl
Boston, MA 02116
Tel.: (617) 267-8223
Fax: (617) 267-5905

SOFTWARE HOUSE INTERNATIONAL, INC. (SHI)
33 Knightsbridge Rd
Piscataway, NJ 08854-3925
Tel.: (732) 764-8888
Fax: (732) 764-8889
Toll Free: (888) 764-8888
Web Site: www.shi.com
Approx. Rev.: $2,300,000,000
Approx. Number Employees: 1,000
Year Founded: 1982
Business Description:
Global Computer Products Distr
S.I.C.: 5045; 7372
N.A.I.C.S.: 423430; 511210
Export
Media: 10-13
Personnel:
Leo Koguan *(Chm & Co-CEO)*
Thai Lee *(Pres & Co-CEO)*
Paul Ng *(VP-Fin)*

SOGETI USA LLC
(Sub. of Sogeti)
7735 Paragon Rd Ste A
Dayton, OH 45459
Tel.: (937) 433-3334
Fax: (937) 433-4048
Web Site: www.us.sogeti.com
Sales Range: $400-449.9 Million
Approx. Number Employees: 2,000
Business Description:
IT & Other Professional Technical Services
S.I.C.: 7373; 7374
N.A.I.C.S.: 541512; 518210
Personnel:
Jeff Neville *(CFO)*
Mike Pleiman *(Exec VP)*
Kelly Maroney *(Dir-Mktg)*
Brands & Products:
SOGETI
Advertising Agency:
Impressions-A.B.A. Industries, Inc.
393 Jericho Tpk
Mineola, NY 11501
Tel.: (516) 739-3210
Fax: (516) 739-9246

SOLARWINDS, INC.
3711 S MoPac Expressway
Austin, TX 78746
Tel.: (512) 682-9300
Fax: (512) 682-9301
Toll Free: (866) 530-8100
E-mail: pr@solarwinds.com
Web Site: www.solarwinds.com
Approx. Rev.: $152,393,000
Approx. Number Employees: 458
Year Founded: 1999
Business Description:
Corporate IT & Network Infrastructure Services
S.I.C.: 7379; 7372; 8748
N.A.I.C.S.: 541519; 511210; 541690
Advertising Expenditures: $1,600,000
Media: 8-17
Personnel:
Kevin B. Thompson *(Pres & CEO)*
Michael J. Berry *(CFO & Sr VP)*
Bryan A. Sims *(Gen Counsel, Sec & VP)*
Douglas G. Hibberd *(Sr VP-Engrg & Gen Mgr-APAC)*
Kenny L. Van Zant *(Sr VP & Chief Product Strategist)*
Paul Strelzick *(Sr VP-Worldwide Sls)*
J. Barton Kalsu *(VP-Fin)*
Garry D. Strop *(VP-HR & Corp Infrastructure)*
Brands & Products:
ENGINEER'S TOOLSET
IPMONITOR
LANSURVEYOR
ORION
SOLARWINDS
THWACK

SOLIDWORKS CORPORATION
(Sub. of Dassault Systemes S.A.)
300 Baker Ave
Concord, MA 01742
Tel.: (978) 371-5011
Fax: (978) 371-7303
Toll Free: (800) 693-9000
E-mail: info@solidworks.com
Web Site: www.solidworks.com
Business Description:
Provider of Software
S.I.C.: 7371
N.A.I.C.S.: 541511
Personnel:
Bertrand Sicot *(CEO)*
Robert Kudrle *(Dir-Art & Designer-UX)*
Advertising Agency:
Beaupre & Co. Public Relations Inc.
1 Harbour Pl Ste 230
Portsmouth, NH 03801-3837
Tel.: (603) 436-6690
Fax: (603) 436-8054

SONIC FOUNDRY, INC.
222 W Washington Ave Ste 775
Madison, WI 53703
Tel.: (608) 443-1600
Fax: (608) 443-1601
Toll Free: (877) 783-7987
E-mail: customerservice@sonicfoundry.com
Web Site: www.sonicfoundry.com
Approx. Rev.: $20,476,000
Approx. Number Employees: 90
Year Founded: 1991
Business Description:
Digital Media & Internet Software Tools Services
S.I.C.: 3663; 7371; 8732
N.A.I.C.S.: 334220; 541511; 541910
Advertising Expenditures: $156,000
Media: 17
Personnel:
Mark Burish *(Chm)*
Gary R. Weis *(CEO)*
Kenneth A. Minor *(CFO & Asst Sec)*
Robert M. Lipps *(Exec VP-Sls)*
Dharmesh K. Sampat *(VP-Engrg)*
Erica St. Angel *(VP-Mktg)*
John Pollard *(Mgr-Technical Product)*
Brands & Products:
MEDIASITE
SONIC FOUNDRY
WEBCASTING & KNOWLEDGE MANAGEMENT

SONICWALL, INC.
(Holding of Thoma Bravo, LLC)
2001 Logic Dr

Key to Media (For complete agency information see *The Advertising Red Books-Agencies* edition):
1. Bus. Publs. 2. Cable T.V. 3. Catalogs & Directories. 4. Co-op Adv. 5. Consumer Mags. 6. D.M. to Bus. Estab.7. D.M. to Consumers 8. Daily Newsp. 9. Exhibits/Trade Shows 10. Foreign 11. Infomercial 12. Internet Adv.13. Multimedia 14. Network Radio 15. Network T.V. 16. Newsp. Distr. Mags. 17. Other 18. Outdoor (Posters, Transit) 19. Point of Purchase20. Premiums, Novelties 21. Product Samples 22. Special Events Mktg. 23. Spot Radio 24. Spot T.V. 25. Weekly Newsp. 26. Yellow Page Adv.

SonicWALL, Inc. — (Continued)

San Jose, CA 95124
Tel.: (408) 745-9600
Fax: (408) 745-9300
Toll Free: (888) 557-6642
E-mail: sales@sonicwall.com
Web Site: www.sonicwall.com
Approx. Rev.: $200,575,000
Approx. Number Employees: 819
Year Founded: 1991
Business Description:
Integrated Network Security, Identity, Mobility & Productivity Solutions
S.I.C.: 3577; 7372; 7379; 7382
N.A.I.C.S.: 334119; 511210; 541519; 561621
Advertising Expenditures: $1,200,000
Media: 2-7-8-10
Personnel:
John C. Shoemaker *(Chm)*
Matthew T. Medeiros *(Pres & CEO)*
Robert D. Selvi *(CFO)*
John Gmuender *(CTO & VP-Engrg)*
Robert B. Knauff *(Chief Acctg Officer)*
Patrick Sweeney *(VP-Product Mgmt & Corp Mktg)*
Jock Breitwieser *(Dir-Global PR)*
Brands & Products:
BAKE-OFF
COMPREHENSIVE INTERNET SECURITY
CONTENT FILTERING SERVICE
CONTINUOUS DATA PROTECTION
GLOBAL MANAGEMENT SYSTEM
GLOBAL VPN CLIENT
PRO
PROTECTION AT THE SPEED OF BUSINESS
SONICWALL
SONICWALL ANTI-SPAM / EMAIL SECURITY
SONICWALL CONTENT SECURITY MANAGEMENT
SONICWALL EMAIL SECURITY
SONICWALL ENDPOINT SECURITY
SONICWALL GLOBAL MANAGEMENT SYSTEM
SONICWALL NSA 240
SONICWALL PRO
SONICWALL SONICOS ENHANCED FIRMWARE
SONICWALL SONICOS STANDARD FIRMWARE
SONICWALL SSL VPN SECURE REMOTE ACCESS
SONICWALL TZ 210 WIRELESS-N
SONICWALL UNIFIED THREAT MANAGEMENT
SONICWALL VIRTUAL ASSIST SECURE REMOTE SUPPORT
TZ
TZW
VIEWPOINT

SOTHEBY'S INC.

(Sub. of Sotheby's)
1334 York Ave
New York, NY 10021
Tel.: (212) 606-7000
Fax: (212) 606-7107
Toll Free: (888) 752-0002
E-mail: onlineprivacy@sothebys.com
Web Site: www.sothebys.com
Sales Range: $200-249.9 Million
Approx. Number Employees: 2,000
Year Founded: 1744
Business Description:
Auctioneer of Art
S.I.C.: 5961
N.A.I.C.S.: 454112
Advertising Expenditures: $1,000,000
Media: 2-4-6-8-9-11-17-22-25-26
Distr.: Reg.
Budget Set: Dec.
Personnel:
Michael I. Sovern *(Chm)*
William F. Ruprecht *(Pres & CEO)*
George Bailey *(Mng Dir-Sothebys Europe)*
Daryl Wickstrom *(Mng Dir-Global Auction Division)*
Richard Buckley *(Mng Dir)*
William S. Sheridan *(CFO & Exec VP)*
Donaldson Pillsbury *(Exec VP & Worldwide Gen Counsel)*
Karl Hermanns *(Dir-Mktg-Europe)*
Amy Todd Middleton *(Dir-Global Mktg)*
Brands & Products:
SOTHEBY'S

SOURCEFIRE, INC.

9770 Patuxent Woods Dr
Columbia, MD 21046
Tel.: (410) 290-1616
Fax: (410) 290-0024
Toll Free: (800) 917-4134
Web Site: www.sourcefire.com
Approx. Rev.: $130,572,000
Approx. Number Employees: 351
Year Founded: 2001
Business Description:
Network Security Services
S.I.C.: 7382; 7371; 7372
N.A.I.C.S.: 561621; 511210; 541511
Advertising Expenditures: $73,000
Media: 7-10-11-13-17
Personnel:
Steven R. Polk *(Chm)*
Tom M. McDonough *(Pres & COO)*
John C. Burris *(CEO)*
Todd P. Headley *(CFO)*
Michele M. Perry-Boucher *(CMO)*
Nicholas G. Margarites *(Chief Acctg Officer & VP-Fin)*
Douglas W. Mcnitt *(Gen Counsel)*
Tom D. Ashoff *(Sr VP-Engrg)*
John T. Czupak *(Sr VP-Corp & Bus Dev)*
Gregory S. Fitzgerald *(Sr VP-Mktg)*
John G. Negron *(Sr VP-Sls-Worldwide)*
Kimberly Childers *(Mgr-Mktg Comm)*
Brands & Products:
KNOW MORE SECURITY RISKS NO MORE GUESSING
SNORT
SOURCEFIRE
SOURCEFIRE 3D
SOURCEFIRE DEFENSE CENTER
SOURCEFIRE IPS
SOURCEFIRE RNA
SOURCEFIRE RUA
SOURCEFIRE VRT
Advertising Agency:
Welz & Weisel Communications
9990 Lee Hwy Ste 500
Fairfax, VA 22030
Tel.: (703) 218-3555
— Tony Welz *(Principal)*

SOVRAN SELF STORAGE, INC.

6467 Main St
Buffalo, NY 14221
Tel.: (716) 633-1850
Fax: (716) 633-1860
E-mail: info@sovranss.com
Web Site: www.sovranss.com
Approx. Rev.: $192,072,000
Approx. Number Employees: 1,027
Year Founded: 1995
Business Description:
Real Estate Investment Trust that Owns, Aquires, Develops & Manages Self-Storage Facilities
S.I.C.: 6798; 4225
N.A.I.C.S.: 525930; 531130
Advertising Expenditures: $1,900,000
Personnel:
Robert J. Attea *(Chm & CEO)*
Kenneth F. Myszka *(Pres & COO)*
David L. Rogers *(CFO)*
Edward Killeen *(Exec VP-Sls & Ops)*
Paul T. Powell *(Exec VP-Real Estate)*
Randy Hillman *(Reg VP-Ops)*
John Manes *(Reg VP)*
Jeffrey Myszka *(Reg VP)*
Andrew Gregoire *(VP-Fin)*
Diane Piegza *(VP-Corp Comm)*
Joan Brickell *(Dir-Audits)*
Jennifer Kozub *(Dir-HR)*
Charlotte Weber *(Sr Mgr-Project)*
Diane Steger *(Mgr-Acctg)*

SPANSION INC.

915 DeGuigne Dr PO Box 3453
Sunnyvale, CA 94088
Tel.: (408) 962-2500
Toll Free: (866) 772-6746
Web Site: www.spansion.com
Approx. Sls.: $764,687,000
Approx. Number Employees: 3,400
Year Founded: 1993
Business Description:
Computer Flash Memory Mfr
S.I.C.: 3577; 3572; 3674; 7373; 7389
N.A.I.C.S.: 334119; 334112; 334413; 541490; 541512
Advertising Expenditures: $1,000,000
Personnel:
H. Raymond Bingham *(Chm)*
John H. Kispert *(Pres, CEO, CFO & COO)*
Masao Taguchi *(Pres, Chief Scientist & Exec VP)*
Randy Furr *(CFO & Exec VP)*
John Brincko *(Chief Restructuring Officer)*
Scot A. Griffin *(Gen Counsel & Sr VP)*
Carla Golla *(Exec VP)*
Ahmed Nawaz *(Exec VP-Wireless Solutions Grp)*
Hans Wildenberg *(Exec VP)*
Jay Legenhausen *(Sr VP-Worldwide Sls)*
Joseph Rauschmayer *(Sr VP-Wafer Fabrication Ops, Corp Quality & Product Engrg)*
Saied Tehrani *(Sr VP-R & D)*
Carroll Jacoby *(VP-HR)*
Robert Fan *(Dir-Segment Mktg)*
Advertising Agency:
The Hoffman Agency
70 N 2nd St
San Jose, CA 95113-1204
Tel.: (408) 286-2611
Fax: (408) 286-0133

SPARK NETWORKS, INC.

8383 Wilshire Blvd Ste 800
Beverly Hills, CA 90211
Tel.: (323) 658-3000
Fax: (323) 658-3001
E-mail: info@spark.net
Web Site: www.spark.net
Approx. Rev.: $40,851,000
Approx. Number Employees: 144
Year Founded: 1998
Business Description:
Internet Dating Service
S.I.C.: 4311; 2741; 7299
N.A.I.C.S.: 491110; 516110; 812990
Advertising Expenditures: $15,000,000
Media: 3-6-8-13-18-22
Personnel:
Greg Liberman *(Pres & CEO)*
Brett Zane *(CFO)*
Greg Franchina *(CIO)*
Josh Kreinberg *(Gen Counsel & Corp Sec)*
Brands & Products:
AMERICANSINGLES
BLACKSINGLES.COM
CATHOLICMINGLE.COM
CHRISTIANMINGLE
DATE.CA
FACELINK.COM
HURRYDATE.COM
INTERRACIALSINGLES.NET
JDATE
LDS MINGLE
PRIMESINGLES.NET
SINGLEPARENTSMINGLE.COM
SPARK NETWORKS
WHERE PEOPLE CONNECT

SPARKS MARKETING GROUP, INC.

2828 Charter Rd
Philadelphia, PA 19154-2111
Tel.: (215) 676-1100
Fax: (215) 676-1991
Toll Free: (800) 925-7727
E-mail: info@sparksonline.com
Web Site: www.sparksonline.com
Sales Range: $75-99.9 Million
Approx. Number Employees: 313
Year Founded: 1966
Business Description:
Exhibits, Displays & Store Fixtures Designer & Mgr
S.I.C.: 7319; 7389
N.A.I.C.S.: 561920; 541850; 561990
Media: 2-10-22
Personnel:
Jeffrey K. Harrow *(Chm)*
Robert Ginsburg *(CEO & CFO)*
Brands & Products:
DMS
DRIVING BRAND PERFORMANCE.
S-FORM
SPARKS
SPARKSLINK
SPARKSPORT

SPECIALTY PROFESSIONAL SERVICES CORP.

21814 Northern Blvd Ste 205
Bayside, NY 11361
Tel.: (718) 428-3600
Fax: (718) 225-9421
Toll Free: (800) 863-3666
E-mail: info@thespecialty.com
Web Site: www.thespecialty.com
Approx. Number Employees: 15
Business Description:
Temporary Nursing Employment Services

Key to Media (For complete agency information see *The Advertising Red Books-Agencies* edition):
1. Bus. Publs. 2. Cable T.V. 3. Catalogs & Directories. 4. Co-op Adv. 5. Consumer Mags. 6. D.M. to Bus. Estab.7. D.M. to Consumers 8. Daily Newsp. 9. Exhibits/Trade Shows 10. Foreign 11. Infomercial 12. Internet Adv.13. Multimedia 14. Network Radio 15. Network T.V. 16. Newsp. Distr. Mags. 17. Other 18. Outdoor (Posters, Transit) 19. Point of Purchase20. Premiums, Novelties 21. Product Samples 22. Special Events Mktg. 23. Spot Radio 24. Spot T.V. 25. Weekly Newsp. 26. Yellow Page Adv.

S.I.C.: 7361
N.A.I.C.S.: 561310
Media: 2
Personnel:
Matthew Scherr *(Pres)*

SPECTRUM GROUP INTERNATIONAL, INC.
18061 Fitch
Irvine, CA 92614
Tel.: (949) 955-1250
Fax: (949) 955-1824
Web Site: www.spectrumgpi.com
Approx. Rev.: $7,202,171,000
Approx. Number Employees: 169
Business Description:
Auction Services
S.I.C.: 5999; 7389
N.A.I.C.S.: 453998; 561499
Advertising Expenditures: $3,886,000
Media: 4
Personnel:
Antonio Arenas *(Chm)*
Gregory N. Roberts *(Pres & CEO)*
Paul Soth *(CFO & Exec VP)*
Carol Meltzer *(Chief Admin Officer, Gen Counsel & Exec VP)*
Arthur Hamilton *(Chief Acctg Officer & Exec VP)*
Kenn Frantz *(Dir-Internal Controls)*
Advertising Agency:
BVK
250 W Coventry Ct #300
Milwaukee, WI 53217-3972
Tel.: (414) 228-1990
Fax: (414) 228-7561
Toll Free: (888) 347-3212

THE SPERRY & HUTCHINSON COMPANY, INC.
1625 S Congress Ave Ste 200
Delray Beach, FL 33445
Tel.: (561) 454-7600
Fax: (561) 265-2493
E-mail: customerservice@shsolutions.com
Approx. Number Employees: 150
Year Founded: 1896
Business Description:
Premium & Marketing Incentive Services
S.I.C.: 5963
N.A.I.C.S.: 454390
Advertising Expenditures: $1,500,000
Media: 2-4-6-7-8-9-10-13-18-19-20-23-24-25
Distr.: Natl.
Budget Set: Dec.
Personnel:
Joel R. Carpenter *(Chm)*
Estella Santiago *(VP-Fin)*
Al Smith *(VP-Sales)*
Brands & Products:
GREEN STAMPS
GREENPOINTS
S & H GREEN STAMPS
S & H GREENPOINTS

SPOKE SOFTWARE, INC.
1670 S Amphlett Blvd Ste 530
San Mateo, CA 94402
Tel.: (650) 403-5900
Fax: (650) 525-0791
Web Site: www.spoke.com
Year Founded: 2002
Business Description:
Provider of Enterprise-Class Professional Relationship Applications
S.I.C.: 7371
N.A.I.C.S.: 541511
Media: 2
Brands & Products:
SPOKE

SPP PROCESS TECHNOLOGY SYSTEMS LIMITED-THERMAL DIVISION
(Div. of Surface Technology Systems plc)
440 Kings Village Rd
Scotts Valley, CA 95066
Tel.: (831) 438-2100
Fax: (831) 439-6223
Web Site: www.spp-pts.com
Business Description:
Semiconductor Production Equipment Mfr
S.I.C.: 3559; 3674
N.A.I.C.S.: 333295; 334413
Advertising Expenditures: $45,000
Media: 17
Personnel:
Vivek Rao *(VP & Gen Mgr-Thermal Products Div)*

SPS COMMERCE, INC.
333 S Seventh St Ste 1000
Minneapolis, MN 55402
Tel.: (612) 435-9400
Fax: (612) 435-9402
Toll Free: (866) 245-8100
E-mail: info@spscommerce.com
Web Site: www.spscommerce.com
Approx. Rev.: $44,597,000
Approx. Number Employees: 353
Business Description:
On-Demand Supply Chain Management Solutions, Integration, Collaboration, Connectivity, Visibility & Data Analytics
S.I.C.: 7373; 5045; 7372; 7379
N.A.I.C.S.: 541512; 425110; 511210; 541519
Advertising Expenditures: $94,000
Media: 17
Personnel:
Archie C. Black *(Pres & CEO)*
David Verette *(VP-Partner Sls)*
Kimberly K. Nelson *(CFO, Chief Acctg Officer & Exec VP)*
Michael J. Gray *(COO & Exec VP-Ops)*
James J. Frome *(Exec VP & Chief Strategy Officer)*
David J. Novak, Jr. *(Exec VP-Sls & Bus Dev)*
Anne Knapp *(VP-Tech)*
Deb Ratelle *(VP-HR & Admin Svcs)*

SPSS INC.
(Sub. of IBM Software Group)
(d/b/a IBM SPSS)
233 S Wacker Dr 11th Fl
Chicago, IL 60606-6412
Tel.: (312) 651-3000
Fax: (312) 651-3668
Toll Free: (800) 543-2185
E-mail: ir2@spss.com
Web Site: www.spss.com
Sales Range: $300-349.9 Million
Approx. Number Employees: 1,100
Year Founded: 1968
Business Description:
Predictive Analytics Software & Data Mining Solutions
S.I.C.: 7372
N.A.I.C.S.: 511210
Export
Advertising Expenditures: $1,600,000
Media: 2-4-6-7-8-10-13
Distr.: Direct to Consumer; Natl.
Budget Set: Nov.
Personnel:
Deepak Advani *(CEO & VP-Predictive Analytics)*
Robert C. Weber *(Gen Counsel & Sr VP-Legal, Regulatory Affairs)*
Dr. John E. Kelly, III *(Sr VP & Dir-IBM Res)*
Rodney C. Adkins *(Sr VP-IBM Sys & Tech Grp)*
Michael E. Daniels *(Sr VP & Grp Exec-Svcs)*
Jon C. Iwata *(Sr VP-Mktg & Comm)*
Frank Kern *(Sr VP-IBM Global Bus Svcs)*
Alex Kormushoff *(Sr VP-Worldwide Ops)*
J. Randall MacDonald *(Sr VP-HR)*
Virginia M Rometty *(Sr VP, Grp Exec-Sls, Mktg & Startegy)*
Linda S. Sanford *(Sr VP-Enterprise On Demand Transformation & IT)*
Colin Shearer *(Sr VP-Strategic Analytics)*
Janine Warell *(Sr Dir-Corp Comm)*
Brands & Products:
ALLCLEAR
AMOS
ANALYSIS & REPORTING SOLUTION
ANALYZER
ANALYZER FOR THE WEB
ANSWERTREE
ASP
BUDGETING TEMPLATE
CAPI SOLUTION
CAPRI
CATI SOLUTION
CFO SUITE
CLEMENTINE
CLEMENTINE FOR ISERIES
CLEMENTINE GRADUATE PACK
CLEO
CLEVERCONTENT BY ALCHEMEDIA
COMPONENTS
CUSTOMECENTRIC DATA CENTER
CUSTOMER FOCUS SUITE
CUSTOMERCENTRIC
DATA ENTRY ENTERPRISE SERVER
DATA SERVER AGENT
DATA VISUALIZATION COMPONENTS & ENGINES
DBMS/COPY PLUS
DECISION TREES
DELTAGRAPH
DEPLOYMENT ACCELERATOR FOR INFINIUM
DEPLOYMENT ACCELERATOR FOR J.D. EDWARD
DEPLOYMENT ACCELERATOR FOR SSA BPC
DESKTOP AUTHOR
DESKTOP REPORTER
DEVELOPER LIBRARY
DIMENSION DEVELOPMENT LIBRARY
DIMENSIONNET
DIMENSIONS ASP
DIMENSIONS COMPONENT PACK
DIMENSIONS DATA MODEL
DIMENSIONS DEVELOPMENT LIBRARY
DIMENSIONS REPORTER
DIMENSIONS SERVICE BUREAU
DISCOVERLT FOR CRM
DISCOVERLT FOR HEALTHCARE
DISCOVERLT FOR RETAIL
DISCOVERLT FOR TELECOMMUNICAITONS
DISCOVERLT FOR UNIFIED CHANNEL MANAGEMENT IN BANKI
DISCOVERLT FRAMEWORK
DISCOVERLT REPOSITORY
DISCOVERLT SOLUTIONS
DISCOVERLT WEB
ENTERPRISE REPORTING
ENTRYWARE BY TECHNEOS
ESSBASE
FINANCIAL REPORTING TEMPLATE FORMS
GOLDIMINER 2.0
GRAPHEXPRESS
IN2FORM DESIGNER
IN2QUEST CAPI
INTERLINK FOR J.D. EDWARDS
INTERVIEW PLAYER
INTERVIEW REPORTER
ISMS
ITRACKS ONLINE QUALITATIVE RESEARCH
JDE INTERLINK
JOBFLOW AGENT
KPI DASHBOARD
LEXIQUEST
MAPINFO
MRDIALER
MRINTERVIEW
MRINTERVIEW CATI
MRPAPER
MRSCAN
MRSTUDIO
MRTABLES
MRTRANSLATE
NETGENESIS
NEURAL CONNECTION
NVIZN
OPINION PLACE INTERNET SMAPLE
PAPER SURVEY SOLUTION
PASW ADVANCED STATISTICS
PASW CATEGORIES
PASW COLLABORATION & DEPLOYMENT SERVICES
PASW COMPLEX SAMPLES
PASW CONJOINT
PASW CUSTOM TABLES
PASW DATA COLLECTION AUTHOR
PASW DATA COLLECTION AUTHOR PROFESSIONAL
PASW DATA COLLECTION DATA MODEL
PASW DATA COLLECTION INTERVIEWER
PASW DATA COLLECTION INTERVIEWER PHONE
PASW DATA COLLECTION INTERVIEWER SERVER
PASW DATA COLLECTION INTERVIEWER WEB
PASW DATA COLLECTION PAPER
PASW DATA COLLECTION REMOTE ADMINISTRATOR
PASW DATA COLLECTION REPORTS FOR SURVEYS
PASW DATA COLLECTION SCAN
PASW DATA COLLECTION WEB REPORTS FOR SURVEYS
PASW DATA PREPARATION

Key to Media (For complete agency information see *The Advertising Red Books-Agencies* edition):
1. Bus. Publs. 2. Cable T.V. 3. Catalogs & Directories. 4. Co-op Adv. 5. Consumer Mags. 6. D.M. to Bus. Estab.7. D.M. to Consumers 8. Daily Newsp. 9. Exhibits/Trade Shows 10. Foreign 11. Infomercial 12. Internet Adv.13. Multimedia 14. Network Radio 15. Network T.V. 16. Newsp. Distr. Mags. 17. Other 18. Outdoor (Posters, Transit) 19. Point of Purchase20. Premiums, Novelties 21. Product Samples 22. Special Events Mktg. 23. Spot Radio 24. Spot T.V. 25. Weekly Newsp. 26. Yellow Page Adv.

SPSS Inc. — (Continued)

PASW DECISION TREES
PASW EXACT TESTS
PASW EZ RFM
PASW FORECASTING
PASW MISSING VALUES
PASW MODELER SERVER
PASW MODELER SOLUTION PUBLISHER
PASW NEURAL NETWORKS
PASW REGRESSION
PASW STATISTICS
PASW STATISTICS BASE
PASW STATISTICS PROGRAMMABILITY EXTENSION
PASW STATISTICS SERVER
PASW TEXT ANALYTICS
PASW TEXT ANALYTICS FOR SURVEYS
PASW VIZ DESIGNER
PORTAL SOLUTION
PREDICTIVE ANALYTIC COMPONENTS
PREDICTIVE WEB ANALYTICS
PREDICTIVECLAIMS
PREDICTIVEMARKETING
QUANCEPT CATI
QUANCEPT TELEPHONY SYSTEM
QUANCEPT WEB
QUANQUEST
QUANTUM
QUANVERT
QUERY
QUINPUT
RECOMMENDATION ENGINE
REGRESSION MODELS
REMOTE MANAGER
REPORT WRITER
RESEARCH AUTOMATION
SAMPLEPOWER
SHOWCASE
SHOWCASE DEPLOYMENT ACCELERATORS
SHOWCASE ENTERPRISE REPORTING
SHOWCASE ESSBASE FOR SYSTEM I5
SHOWCASE INTERLINK
SHOWCASE SUITE FROM SPSS
SHOWCASE WAREHOUSE BUILDER
SHOWCASE WAREHOUSE MANAGER
SIGMAGEL
SIGMAPLOT
SIGMASCAN PRO
SIGMASTAT
SMART VIEWER
SMARTSCORE
SMARTVIEWER FOR WINDOWS
SMARTVIEWER WEB SERVER
SPSS
SPSS ADAPTER FOR PREDICTIVE ENTERPRISE SERVICES
SPSS ADVANCED MODELS
SPSS ADVANTAGE
SPSS ADVANTAGE FOR EXCEL 2007
SPSS CAREER STARTER
SPSS CATEGORIES
SPSS CONJOINT
SPSS DATA ENTRY
SPSS DATA ENTRY BUILDER
SPSS DATA ENTRY ENTERPRISE SERVER
SPSS DATA ENTRY STATION
SPSS DATA MINING CERTIFICATE PROGRAM
SPSS DIAMOND
SPSS EXACT TESTS
SPSS FOR OEM PARTNERS
SPSS GRADUATE PACK
SPSS INC. SOFTWARE FOR INSTRUCTION
SPSS MAPS
SPSS MISSING VALUE ANALYSIS
SPSS MR DATA MODEL
SPSS MR EXCEL VIEWER
SPSS MR ONLINE
SPSS ONLINE SERVICES
SPSS PREDICTIVE ENTERPRISE SERVICES
SPSS REGRESSION MODELS
SPSS REPORT WRITER
SPSS STUDENT VERSIONS
SPSS TABLES
SPSS TEXT ANALYSIS FOR SURVEYS
SPSS TRENDS
SPSS WEBAPP FRAMEWORK
SSA BPC DEPLOYMENT ACCELERATOR
STRATEGY SUITE
SURVEYCRAFT
SVWS KPI SYSTEM
SYSTAT
TEXTSMART
TIMECAST MODELER/TIMECAST SCENARIO ANALYZER
VERBASTAT
WEB RESEARCH SOLUTION
XPEDIO

SPYRUS, INC.

1860 Hartog Dr
San Jose, CA 95131
Tel.: (408) 392-9131
Fax: (408) 392-0319
E-mail: info@spyrus.com
Web Site: www.spyrus.com
Approx. Number Employees: 40
Business Description:
Computer Peripheral Equipment
S.I.C.: 3577; 7371
N.A.I.C.S.: 334119; 541511
Personnel:
Tom Dickens *(COO)*
Brands & Products:
EN-SIGN
FORTEZZA
HYDRA PC
LYNKS
MYSAFEID
ROSETTA
SECURITY-IN-A-BOX
SECURITY TO THE EDGE
SIGNAL IDENTITY MANAGER
SPYRUS
TALISMAN/DS
Advertising Agency:
Madison Alexander PR
19 Wedgwood
Irvine, CA 92620
Tel.: (714) 832-8716
Fax: (714) 832-8916
— Dan Chmielewski *(Principal)*

SRA INTERNATIONAL, INC.

4300 Fair Lakes Ct
Fairfax, VA 22033-4232
Tel.: (703) 803-1500
Fax: (703) 803-1509
E-mail: investor@sra.com
Web Site: www.sra.com
Approx. Rev.: $1,666,629,000
Approx. Number Employees: 7,100
Year Founded: 1978
Business Description:
Information Technology Services & Solutions
S.I.C.: 7371; 5045; 8748
N.A.I.C.S.: 541511; 423430; 541690
Media: 9-10-17-25
Personnel:
Ernst Volgenau *(Founder & Chm)*
Stanton D. Sloane *(Pres)*
William L. Ballhaus *(CEO)*
Richard Nadeau *(CFO & Exec VP)*
Timothy J. Atkin *(COO & Exec VP)*
Brian Michl *(CIO & VP)*
James G. McClave *(Pres-SRA-EMEA)*
Susan Hideko Pearson *(Sr Principal-Enterprise Logistics)*
Mark D. Schultz *(Gen Counsel)*
Sheila Blackwell *(Sr VP-Comm & Pub Affairs)*
Joseph Patrick Burke *(Sr VP)*
Mary Good *(Sr VP-HR)*
Scott F. Large *(Sr VP-Intelligence & Space)*
Kevin W Layton *(Sr VP-Technical Ops)*
David L. Matthews *(Sr VP-Quality & Tech Ops)*
Jeffrey Rydant *(Sr VP-Natl Security Sector)*
Stephen M. Tolbert *(Sr VP-Health & Civil Svcs Sector)*
George Batsakis *(VP & Dir-Defense Bus Solutions)*
William H. Bell *(VP & Dir-Info Assurance & Privacy Solutions)*
Timothy A. Campen *(VP, Dir-Special Ops & JIEDDO Support)*
Michael D. D'Andrea *(VP & Dir-Homeland Security & Law Enforcement)*
Ben Gieseman *(VP & Dir-Corp Pricing)*
Anna M. Hogan *(VP & Dir-Command & Control)*
John M. Luongo *(Dir & VP-Mktg & Sls)*
Carl B. Rosenblatt *(VP & Dir-Proposal Dev)*
David Schneeman *(VP & Dir-Fin-Intl Ops)*
Pat Sidhu *(VP & Dir-Spectrum Solutions Grp)*
Brands & Products:
CAL/GANG
DOCMATCHER
ELITE
ELITE SECURE
GANGNET
GEOLLECT
GISTIT
HONESTY & SERVICE
NETOWL
NORTHSTAR LEARNING
ORION NETLEADS
ORIONLEADS
ORIONLINK
ORIONMAGIC
ORIONSEARCH
ORIONVIA
OWL LOGO
PILLAR
RAMBLE
SCL
SRA
TASKFORCE
Advertising Agency:
DPR Group, Inc.
12850 Middlebrook Rd Ste 107
Germantown, MD 20874
Tel.: (240) 686-1000
Fax: (240) 686-0600

SRS LABS, INC.

2909 Daimler St
Santa Ana, CA 92705
Tel.: (949) 442-1070
Fax: (949) 852-1099
Toll Free: (800) 243-2733
E-mail: ir@srslabs.com
Web Site: www.srslabs.com
Approx. Rev.: $31,220,389
Approx. Number Employees: 106
Business Description:
Audio Enhancement, Voice Processing & Surround Sound Technology Products Mfr & Distr
S.I.C.: 3674; 3651
N.A.I.C.S.: 334413; 334310
Import Export
Advertising Expenditures: $85,992
Media: 10
Personnel:
Thomas C.K. Yuen *(Chm & CEO)*
Ulrich Gottschling *(CFO)*
Alan D. Kraemer *(CTO & Exec VP)*
Allen H. Gharapetian *(Sr VP-Mktg)*
John Kellogg *(Exec Dir-Corp Strategy)*
Cyndee Pelino *(Dir-Mktg Comm)*
Brands & Products:
CIRCLE SURROUND
CIRCLE SURROUND AUTOMOTIVE
CIRCLE SURROUND II
DIALOG CLARITY
FOCUS
MOBILE EQ
MOBILE HD
NOISE REDUCTION
SRS
SRS 3D
SRS 3D POSITIONAL
SRS AUTOMOTIVE
SRS HEADPHONE
TRUBASS
TRUMEDIA
TRUSURROUND
TRUSURROUND HD
TRUSURROUND HD4
TRUSURROUND XT
TRUSURROUND XT HEADPHONE
TRUVOLUME
VIP
WOW
WOW HD
WOW XT
Advertising Agency:
Blue C
3183-C Airway Ave
Costa Mesa, CA 92626
Tel.: (949) 723-9202
Fax: (714) 540-5800

SS&C TECHNOLOGIES HOLDINGS, INC.

(Holding of The Carlyle Group, LLC)
80 Lamberton Rd
Windsor, CT 06095
Tel.: (860) 298-4500
Fax: (860) 298-4900
Toll Free: (800) 234-0556
E-mail: investorrelations@sscinc.com
Web Site: www.ssctech.com

Key to Media (For complete agency information see *The Advertising Red Books-Agencies* edition):
1. Bus. Publs. 2. Cable T.V. 3. Catalogs & Directories. 4. Co-op Adv. 5. Consumer Mags. 6. D.M. to Bus. Estab.7. D.M. to Consumers 8. Daily Newsp. 9. Exhibits/Trade Shows 10. Foreign 11. Infomercial 12. Internet Adv.13. Multimedia 14. Network Radio 15. Network T.V. 16. Newsp. Distr. Mags. 17. Other 18. Outdoor (Posters, Transit) 19. Point of Purchase20. Premiums, Novelties 21. Product Samples 22. Special Events Mktg. 23. Spot Radio 24. Spot T.V. 25. Weekly Newsp. 26. Yellow Page Adv.

Approx. Rev.: $328,905,000
Approx. Number Employees: 1,399
Year Founded: 1986
Business Description:
Investment & Financial Management Software & Related Services
S.I.C.: 7372; 7371
N.A.I.C.S.: 511210; 541511
Media: 2-7-10-13
Personnel:
William C. Stone *(Chm & CEO)*
Normand A. Boulanger *(Pres & COO)*
Richard Shalowitz *(Mng Dir & Sr VP)*
Patrick J. Pedonti *(Sr VP & CFO)*
John R. Sharpe *(CIO & Sr VP)*
Steve H. Kremidas *(Chief Dev Officer & Sr VP)*
Sean Egan *(Sr VP-Real Estate & Gen Mgr)*
Alex Marasco *(Sr VP & Gen Mgr)*
Thomas McMackin *(Sr VP & Gen Mgr)*
Colleen Nelsen *(Sr VP & Gen Mgr)*
Suresh Thekkenmar *(Sr VP & Gen Mgr)*
James Ramenda *(Sr VP-Enterprise Risk)*
Doug Benedetto *(VP-Strategic Accounts)*
Chris Ullman *(Dir-Commun)*
Brands & Products:
ADVISORWARE
ADVISORWARE ENTERPRISE
ALTAIR
ANTARES
BANC MALL
BLOCKTALK
BLOCKTALKPLUS
CAMRA
CAMRA D CLASS
DBC CAPS
DBC DEBT MANAGER
DBC FINANCE
DBC FINLITE
DBC HOUSING
DBC MULTI-FAMILY
DBC MULTI-FAMILY/HEALTH CARE
DBC PORTOPT
DBC STUDENT LOAN
DEBT AND DERIVATIVES
FINESSE HD
FMCNET
FUNDRUNNER
FUNDRUNNER INVESTORSITE
FUNDRUNNER MARATHON
GLOBAL DEBT MANAGER
GWP ADVISOR
GWP MODEL
GWP TRADE
HEATMAPS
INFORMATION MANAGER
LIGHTNING
LIGHTNING TRADEDESK
LMS
LMS LOAN SUITE
LMS ORIGINATOR
LMS SERVICER
MABEL
MARGINMAN
MARKETLOOK
MONEY MARKET MANAGER
PACER
PAGES
PALMS
PORTPRO
PORTPRO MALL
PRO-JECT
PTS
RECON
SAMTRAK
SKYLINE
SKYLINE PROPERTY MANAGEMENT
SKYLINE II
SS&C
SYLVAN
TOTAL RECONCILIATION
TOTAL RETURN
TRADEDESK
TRADETHRU
ZOOLOGIC

THE SSI GROUP, INC.
4721 Morrison Dr
Mobile, AL 36609-3350
Mailing Address:
PO Box 991835
Mobile, AL 36691-8835
Tel.: (251) 345-0000
Fax: (251) 345-0123
Toll Free: (800) 880-3032
E-mail: info@ssigroup.com
Web Site: www.thessigroup.com
Approx. Number Employees: 335
Year Founded: 1988
Business Description:
Information Technology Services
S.I.C.: 7371; 7372
N.A.I.C.S.: 541511; 511210
Media: 2-10
Personnel:
Bobby Smith *(Pres & CEO)*
James M. Lyons *(CFO & VP)*
Douglas J. Bilbrey *(Exec VP-Sls & Mktg)*
Scott O'Neill *(VP-Sls)*
Raymond M. Payne *(VP-Sls)*
Mary R. Hyland *(Asst VP-Regulatory Affairs)*
Robert Totty *(Asst VP)*
Betsy Herp *(Dir-Mktg)*
Brands & Products:
CLICKON
CLICKON ALLNET
CLICKON PREVENT
MORE THAN YOU THOUGHT
ONEPOINT
SSI
WE MAKE EVERYTHING CLICK

ST. BERNARD SOFTWARE INC.
15333 Ave of Science
San Diego, CA 92128
Tel.: (858) 676-2277
Fax: (858) 676-2299
Toll Free: (800) 782-3762
Web Site: www.stbernard.com
Approx. Rev.: $18,071,000
Approx. Number Employees: 127
Year Founded: 1995
Business Description:
Internet Management Software Mfr & Designer
S.I.C.: 7372
N.A.I.C.S.: 334611; 511210
Advertising Expenditures: $1,100,000
Media: 2-4-7-10-13-26
Personnel:
Louis E. Ryan *(Chm, Pres & CEO)*
David Smith *(Sr VP-Worldwide Comml Sls)*
Thalia R. Gietzen *(VP-Fin)*
Tom Bennett *(VP-Mktg & Corp Dev)*
Ed Hubler *(Dir-Intl Sls)*
Brands & Products:
EPRISM
IPRISM
OPEN FILE MANAGER
ST. BERNARD
UPDATEEXPERT

STAEDTLER, INC.
(Sub. of STAEDTLER MARS GmbH & Co KG)
21900 Plummer St
Chatsworth, CA 91311-4001
Mailing Address:
PO Box 2196
Chatsworth, CA 91311-2196
Tel.: (818) 882-6000
Fax: (818) 882-3767
Toll Free: (800) 776-5544
E-mail: info@staedtler-usa.com
Web Site: www.staedtler-usa.com
Sales Range: $10-24.9 Million
Approx. Number Employees: 45
Year Founded: 1922
Business Description:
Pens, Pencils & Other Stationery Products Mfr & Distr
S.I.C.: 5112; 5049
N.A.I.C.S.: 424120; 423490
Import Export
Advertising Expenditures: $200,000
Media: 2-4-5-6-7-8-10-19-20-21
Distr.: Natl.
Budget Set: Nov.
Personnel:
Michael Wiesmann *(Pres & CEO)*
Mui Sel Ko *(CFO)*
Kathy Luis *(Mgr-Creative Design)*
Brands & Products:
AURA
CARVE
ERGOSOFT
GLIMMER GELS
GXL GEL
INTEGRITY
KARAT
LIQUID POINT
LUMOCOLOR
MARS DATA 3
MARS-LUMOGRAPH
MARS-PLASTIC
MARS-SUPERBOW
MARSGRAPHIC
MARSMATIC-700
MASTERCARD
MULTI 3
MULTI 4
NORIS CLUB
PHOTO DECO
REMEDY
TEXTSURFER
TEXTSURFER CLASSIC
TRIGON
TRIPLUS

STAFFING REMEDIES
295 Madison Ave 8th Fl
New York, NY 10017
Tel.: (212) 683-0680
Fax: (212) 697-3007
Toll Free: (800) 383-9065
E-mail: remcure@staffingremedies.com
Web Site: www.staffingremedies.com
Approx. Number Employees: 25
Year Founded: 1999
Business Description:
Medical Staffing Services
S.I.C.: 7299
N.A.I.C.S.: 812199
Media: 2-13
Personnel:
Taulette Morant *(Mgr-Staffing)*

STANDARD DUPLICATING MACHINES CORPORATION
10 Connector Rd
Andover, MA 01810-5927
Tel.: (978) 470-1920
Fax: (978) 470-0819
Toll Free: (800) 526-4774
Web Site: www.sdmc.com
Approx. Number Employees: 65
Year Founded: 1910
Business Description:
Duplicating Machines, Collators, Binders, Bookletmakers, Cutters, Folders, Numberers, Joggers, Staplers & Associated Supplies Mfr
S.I.C.: 5044; 2782
N.A.I.C.S.: 423420; 323118
Import Export
Advertising Expenditures: $1,500,000
Media: 1-2-4-5-7-10-13-18-26
Distr.: Natl.
Budget Set: Oct. -Nov.
Personnel:
Steven Reny *(Pres)*
Douglas E. Reny *(VP & Dir-Mktg-Standard Bus Sys)*
Mark Hunt *(Dir-Mktg-Standard Finishing Sys)*
Brands & Products:
ACCUBINDPRO2
AUTOCREASER
BIND-FAST
DOCUCREASE
DOCUFOLD
EASYCREASEPRO
HORIZON
HUNKLER
JOG-FAST
MAILMASTER
MAILWRAP
ROLL TO ROLL
STANDARD
STITCHLINER
VARIWEB
VEA 520

THE STANDARD REGISTER COMPANY
600 Albany St
Dayton, OH 45401
Mailing Address:
PO Box 1167
Dayton, OH 45401-1167
Tel.: (937) 221-1000
Fax: (937) 221-1239
Toll Free: (800) 755-6405
E-mail: webmaster@standardregister.com
Web Site: www.standardregister.com
Approx. Rev.: $668,377,000
Approx. Number Employees: 2,600
Year Founded: 1912
Business Description:
Document & Print Management Services
S.I.C.: 2752; 2672; 2761
N.A.I.C.S.: 323110; 322222; 323116
Import
Media: 1-2-7-9-10-17-20-21
Distr.: Natl.
Budget Set: Sept.
Personnel:
F. David Clarke, III *(Chm)*

Key to Media (For complete agency information see *The Advertising Red Books-Agencies* edition):
1. Bus. Publs. 2. Cable T.V. 3. Catalogs & Directories. 4. Co-op Adv. 5. Consumer Mags. 6. D.M. to Bus. Estab.7. D.M. to Consumers
8. Daily Newsp. 9. Exhibits/Trade Shows 10. Foreign 11. Infomercial 12. Internet Adv.13. Multimedia 14. Network Radio
15. Network T.V. 16. Newsp. Distr. Mags. 17. Other 18. Outdoor (Posters, Transit) 19. Point of Purchase20. Premiums, Novelties
21. Product Samples 22. Special Events Mktg. 23. Spot Radio 24. Spot T.V. 25. Weekly Newsp. 26. Yellow Page Adv.

The Standard Register Company —
(Continued)

Joseph P. Morgan, Jr. *(Pres & CEO)*
Robert M. Ginnan *(CFO, Treas & VP)*
Donna L. Beladi *(Chief Strategy Officer)*
Jerrold A. Beigel *(Pres-Comml Bus)*
Brad Cates *(Pres-Healthcare Bus Unit)*
Tom Furey *(Pres-Indus Bus Unit)*
Gerard D. Sowar *(Gen Counsel, Sec & VP)*
Scott Wallace *(VP-Strategic Dev, Healthcaret)*
Laura Bates *(Dir-Internal Audit)*
Ann B. Scales *(Dir-Healthcare Mktg & Product Mgmt-Document & Info Mgmt Solutions)*
Brian Yavorsky *(Product Mgr-Customer Comm)*

Brands & Products:
CLEAN RELEASE
EXPEDATA
FOMADS
FORMFLOW
FORMIC
FORMOL
HAT PUNCH
IMPROVING THE WAY BUSINESS GETS DONE
KANT-SLIP
MACHINE MATED
MANAGING THE DOCUMENTS YOU CAN'T LIVE WITHOUT
PS
REGISTRATOR
RSVP
SOURCE RECORD PUNCH
STANBOOK
STANCUT
STANDARD REGISTER
STANFAST
STANFLEX
STANGUARD
STANSET
STATUSQUE
THERMOBOND
TOTAL SCRIPTS
UARCO
V-FLEX
ZIPCARD
ZIPMAILER
ZIPPAK
ZIPSET

Advertising Agencies:
Impressions-A.B.A. Industries, Inc.
393 Jericho Tpk
Mineola, NY 11501
Tel.: (516) 739-3210
Fax: (516) 739-9246

Interval
111 Washington Ave N Ste 250
Minneapolis, MN 55401
Tel.: (612) 672-9842
Fax: (612) 376-7976

STAPLES, INC.

500 Staples Dr
Framingham, MA 01702
Tel.: (508) 253-5000
Toll Free: (800) 3STAPLE
Web Site: www.staples.com
Approx. Sls.: $24,545,113,000
Approx. Number Employees: 52,919
Year Founded: 1986
Business Description:
Office Supplies & Office Products
S.I.C.: 5943; 3596; 5044; 5112
N.A.I.C.S.: 453210; 333997; 423420; 424120
Import Export
Advertising Expenditures: $553,500,000
Media: 2-3-4-5-6-7-9-10-11-13-14-15-16-18-19-22-23-24-25-26-31
Distr.: Reg.
Personnel:
Ronald L. Sargent *(Chm & CEO)*
John J. Mahoney *(Vice Chm & CFO)*
Michael A. Miles, Jr. *(Pres & COO)*
Joseph G. Doody *(Pres-North American Delivery)*
Steve E. Matyas *(Pres-Staples Bus Depot)*
Demos Parneros *(Pres-US Stores)*
Rob Vale *(Pres-Staples Europe)*
Jay G. Baitler *(Exec VP-Staples Contract)*
John K. Barton *(Exec VP-Intl Dev)*
Jevin S. Eagle *(Exec VP-Mdsg & Mktg)*
Shira D. Goodman *(Exec VP-HR)*
David N. Perron *(Exec VP-Mdsg & Supply Chain)*
Christine T. Komola *(Sr VP & Controller)*
Mark Mettler *(Sr VP & Gen Mgr-Mdsg)*
Elaine Bruzios *(Sr VP-Fin-North American Delivery)*
John F. Burke *(Sr VP-Bus Svcs)*
Steven Bussberg *(Sr VP-Bus Delivery)*
Amee Chande *(Sr VP-Strategy)*
David D'Angelo *(Sr VP-Staples Brands Grp)*
Michael DeSanto, Jr. *(Sr VP)*
Steven Fund *(Sr VP-Global Brand Mktg)*
Nicholas P. Hotchkins *(Sr VP-Fin-US Retail Bus)*
Pete S. Howard *(Sr VP-Southern Europe)*
Carole E. Johnson *(Sr VP-Adv)*
Donald LeBlanc *(Sr VP-Retail Mktg)*
John M. Lynch *(Sr VP)*
Steve F. Mastrogiacomo *(Sr VP-Plng & Inventory Mgmt)*
Carole McFarland *(Sr VP-Adv)*
Otis Pannell *(Sr VP)*
Donald Ralph *(Sr VP-Logistics)*
Donna S. Rosenberg *(Sr VP-Pricing)*
Bernard I. Schachter *(Sr VP-Real Estate)*
Rob Peters *(VP-Fin-Staples Europe)*
Rachel Trueblood *(VP-Corp Branding & Adv)*
Tom McCann *(Dir-Retail Usability Res)*
Carrie McElwee *(Dir-PR)*
Amy Shanley *(Dir-Commun Rels)*
Marjorie Shaw *(Dir-Media Svcs)*
Tom Tobin *(Dir-Creative-Interactive)*

Brands & Products:
EASY BUTTON
STAPLES
STAPLES 365 SAVINGS
STAPLES NATIONAL ADVANTAGE
STAPLES REWARDS
STAPLES TEACHER REWARDS
STAPLES THE OFFICE SUPERSTORE
THAT WAS EASY

Advertising Agencies:
Digitas Inc.
33 Arch St
Boston, MA 02110
Tel.: (617) 867-1000
Fax: (617) 867-1111

Duffy & Shanley, Inc.
10 Charles St
Providence, RI 02904
Tel.: (401) 274-0001
Fax: (401) 274-3535
Public Relations

Kelley Chunn & Assoc.
Hibernian Hall 184 Dudley St Ste 106
Boston, MA 02119
Tel.: (617) 427-0997
Fax: (617) 427-3997
Toll Free: (866) 427-0997

McCann Erickson Advertising Ltd.
(Sub. of the Interpublic Group of Companies)
7-11 Herbrand Street
London, WC1N 1EX, United Kingdom
Tel.: (44) 20 7837 3737
Fax: (44) 20 7837 3773
Office Supplies

McCann Erickson/New York
622 3rd Ave
New York, NY 10017
Tel.: (646) 865-2000
Fax: (646) 487-9610

MediaCom
498 7th Ave
New York, NY 10018
Tel.: (212) 912-4200
Fax: (212) 508-4386
(Media Buying & Planning)

National Retail Services
51 Sugar Hollow Rd
Danbury, CT 06810
Tel.: (203) 790-1744
Fax: (203) 798-1644

Nova Marketing
300 Crown Colony Dr
Quincy, MA 02169
Tel.: (617) 770-0304
Fax: (617) 770-1821

PlattForm Advertising
708 3rd Ave 12th Fl
New York, NY 10017
Tel.: (212) 684-4800
Fax: (212) 576-1129
Toll Free: (866) 671-4429

PointRoll Inc.
951 E Hector St
Conshohocken, PA 19428
Tel.: (267) 558-1300
Fax: (267) 285-1141
Toll Free: (800) 203-6956

Tilson PR
1001 Yamato Rd Ste 400
Boca Raton, FL 33431
Tel.: (561) 998-1995
Fax: (561) 998-1790
Toll Free: (888) 397-7878
2008 Back-to-School Campaign

THE STAPLEX COMPANY, INC.

777 5th Ave
Brooklyn, NY 11232
Tel.: (718) 768-3333
Fax: (718) 965-0750
Toll Free: (800) 221-0822
E-mail: info@staplex.com
Web Site: www.staplex.com
Approx. Number Employees: 20
Year Founded: 1949
Business Description:
Automatic Electric Stapling Machines & Electric Mail Openers Mfr
S.I.C.: 3952; 3821
N.A.I.C.S.: 339942; 339111
Export
Media: 2-4-5-13-20-26
Distr.: Natl.
Budget Set: May -Nov.
Personnel:
R. Powers *(VP-Sls)*
Greg Pauls *(Mgr-Mktg & Adv)*

Brands & Products:
ACCUSLITTER
STAPL-A-MATIC
STAPLEX
TABSTER

STAT-A-MATRIX, INC.

(Holding of The SAM Group)
1 Quality Pl
Edison, NJ 08820-1073
Tel.: (732) 548-0600
Fax: (732) 548-4085
Toll Free: (800) 472-6477
E-mail: info@statamatrix.com
Web Site: www.statamatrix.com
Approx. Number Employees: 180
Year Founded: 1968
Business Description:
Management Consulting & Training Services
S.I.C.: 8742; 8299
N.A.I.C.S.: 541611; 611430
Media: 2-4-7-10-11-13-20
Distr.: Intl.
Budget Set: Sept.
Personnel:
Alan Marash *(CEO)*
I. Robert Marash *(Exec VP)*

STEC, INC.

(d/b/a Simple Tech)
3001 Daimler St
Santa Ana, CA 92705-5812
Tel.: (949) 476-1180
Fax: (949) 476-1209
Toll Free: (800) 367-7330
E-mail: oeminfo@stec-inc.com
Web Site: www.stec-inc.com
Approx. Rev.: $280,149,000
Approx. Number Employees: 809
Year Founded: 1990
Business Description:
Memory & Storage Products Mfr
S.I.C.: 3572
N.A.I.C.S.: 334112
Import Export
Advertising Expenditures: $58,000
Media: 10
Personnel:
Mark Moshayedi *(Pres, COO, CTO & Sec)*
Manouch Moshayedi *(CEO)*
Raymond D. Cook *(CFO)*
Michael Nilsson *(VP-Sls)*

Brands & Products:
ATA PC CARD
BONZAI
COMPACTFLASH
DRIVELINK
FLASHLINK
IC TOWER

Key to Media (For complete agency information see *The Advertising Red Books-Agencies* edition):
1. Bus. Publs. 2. Cable T.V. 3. Catalogs & Directories. 4. Co-op Adv. 5. Consumer Mags. 6. D.M. to Bus. Estab.7. D.M. to Consumers
8. Daily Newsp. 9. Exhibits/Trade Shows 10. Foreign 11. Infomercial 12. Internet Adv.13. Multimedia 14. Network Radio
15. Network T.V. 16. Newsp. Distr. Mags. 17. Other 18. Outdoor (Posters, Transit) 19. Point of Purchase20. Premiums, Novelties
21. Product Samples 22. Special Events Mktg. 23. Spot Radio 24. Spot T.V. 25. Weekly Newsp. 26. Yellow Page Adv.

IDE FLASH MODULE
IDE FLD
INT64Y8W128M8L-A15LTU
INT64Y8W256M8L-A15LTU
ISCD
MACH4
MACH4 CF
MACH4 SSD
MACH8
MACH8 SSD
MACH8IOPS SSD
MACH8MLC SSD
MICROSD
MINISD
MULTIMEDIACARD
NA72Z4W512M8M-A18JTG
SECUREDIGITAL
SIMPLESHARE
SIMPLETRANSFER
SL64F8W128M8L-A15LTG
SL64F8W128M8L-A18JTG
SL64F8W256M8L-A15LTG
SL64Y8W128M8L-A15LTU
SL64Y8W128M8L-A18JTU
SL64Y8W256M8L-A15LTU
SL64Y8W256M8L-A18JTU
SL72Y8W128M8M-A15LTU
SL72Y8W128M8M-A18JTU
SL72Y8W256M8M-A15LTU
SL72Y8W256M8M-A18JTU
SL72Z4W256M8M-A15LTU
SL72Z4W256M8M-A18JTU
SL72Z4W512M8M-A15LTG
SL72Z4W512M8M-A15LTU
SL72Z4W512M8M-A18JTU
SL72Z8W128M8M-A15LTU
SL72Z8W128M8M-A18JTU
SL72Z8W128M8M-B15LTU
SL72Z8W128M8M-B18JTU
SL72Z8W128M8M-B25GTU
SL72Z8W256M8M-A15LTG
SL72Z8W256M8M-A15LTU
SL72Z8W256M8M-B25GTU
SLATA128MM1U(I)
SLATA16GM1U(I)
SLATA1GM1U(I)
SLATA256MM1U(I)
SLATA2GM1U(I)
SLATA4GM1U(I)
SLATA512MM1U(I)
SLATA8GM1U(I)
SLCF128MM1U(I)
SLCF16GM1T2U(I)
SLCF16GM4U(I)
SLCF1GM1U(I)
SLCF256MM1U(I)
SLCF2GM1U(I)
SLCF4GM1U(I)
SLCF512MM1U(I)
SLCF8GM1U(I)
SLCF8GM4U(I)
SLCFAD(I)U
SLFDM(40/44)H-8GM1U(I)
SLFDM(40/44)(V/H)-128MM1U(I)
SLFDM(40/44)(V/H)-1GM1U(I)
SLFDM(40/44)(V/H)-256MM1U(I)
SLFDM(40/44)(V/H)-2GM1U(I)
SLFDM(40/44)(V/H)-4GM1U(I)
SLFDM(40/44)(V/H)-512MM1U(I)
SLFLD25-1 28MM 1 U(I)
SLFLD25-1 6GM 1 U(I)
SLFLD25-16GM1U(I)
SLFLD25-1GM1U(I)
SLFLD25-256MM1U(I)
SLFLD25-2GM1U(I)
SLFLD25-4GM1U(I)
SLFLD25-512MM1U(I)
SLFLD25-8GM 1 U(I)
SLMPCI16GM4U-M
SLMPCI32GM4U-M
SLMPCI4GM4U-M
SLMPCI8GM4U-M
SLMSD128BS(I)U
SLMSD1GBBS(I)U
SLMSD256BS(I)U
SLMSD2GBBS(I)U
SLMSD512BS(I)U
SLSD128BS(I)U
SLSD1GBBS(I)U
SLSD256BS(I)U
SLSD2GBBS(I)U
SLSD512BS(I)U
SLUFD128MU1U(I)-Y
SLUFD1GU1U(I)-Y
SLUFD256MU1U(I)-Y
SLUFD2GU1U(I)-Y
SLUFD4GU1U(I)-Y
SLUFD512MU1U(I)-Y
SLUFDM128MU1U(I)-Y
SLUFDM1GU1U(I)-Y
SLUFDM256MU1U(I)-Y
SLUFDM2GU1U(I)-Y
SLUFDM4GU1U(I)-Y
SLUFDM512MU1U(I)-Y
SLUFDM8GU1U(I)-Y
SLUSCD128MU1U(I)-Y
SLUSCD1GU1U(I)-Y
SLUSCD256MU1U(I)-Y
SLUSCD2GU1U(I)-Y
SLUSCD4GU1U(I)-Y
SLUSCD512MU1U(I)-y
STEC
UFD
UM-SSD
USB FLASH MODULE
USCD
ZEUSIOPS
ZEUSIOPS SSD

STEELCASE INC.

901 44th St SE
Grand Rapids, MI 49508
Mailing Address:
PO Box 1967
Grand Rapids, MI 49501-1967
Tel.: (616) 247-2710
Fax: (616) 475-2270
E-mail: ir@steelcase.com
Web Site: www.steelcase.com
Approx. Rev.: $2,437,100,000
Approx. Number Employees: 10,000
Year Founded: 1912
Business Description:
Office Furnishings Mfr & Office Design Services
S.I.C.: 2522; 2521
N.A.I.C.S.: 337214; 337211
Import Export
Media: 1-2-3-4-7-8-9-10-13-15-20-22-26
Distr.: Natl.
Budget Set: Oct.
Personnel:
Robert C. Pew, III *(Chm)*
James P. Hackett *(Pres & CEO)*
David C. Sylvester *(CFO & VP)*
Lizbeth S. O'Shaughnessy *(Chief Legal Officer, Sec & VP)*
Nancy W. Hickey *(Chief Admin Officer & Sr VP)*
Mark T. Mossing *(Chief Acctg Officer & Controller)*
James P. Keane *(Pres-Steelcase Grp)*
Frank H. Merlotti, Jr. *(Pres-Coalesse)*
Mark A. Baker *(Sr VP & Global Ops Officer)*
Mark T. Greiner *(Sr VP-WorkSpace Futures)*
Ruth Howard *(Dir-Mktg & Sls)*
Brands & Products:
19 PLATFORM
319 EXECUTIVE
4 O'CLOCK
470 PARADE
472 MAX STACKER
A LA CARTE
A SMARTER WAY TO WORK
ABACUS
ABOUT FACE
ACADIA
ACRES
AGILI-T
AIRTOUCH
AKIRA
ALCOVE
ALERION
ALERON
ALIGHT
ALINA
ALISO
ALLY
AMARIS
AMERICAN ELECT
AMIA
AMIRANTE
ANSWER
ARBOR
ARCHIPELAGO
ARRIVA
ARRONDI
ASANA
ASCOT
ASHANTI
ASPEKT
ASSISA
ASTOR
AU LAIT TABLE
AVENIR
AVON
AWAIT
BALLET
BARIOLAGE
BARRYMORE
BELLAROSE
BIX
BIX SIDE TABLE
BLUMENTHAL
BOB GUEST
BOB LOUNGE
BOB TABLES
BOCCIE
BOOTHE
BOTTOMLINE
BRACKEN
BRADBURY
BRAYTON
BRETON
BROADMOOR
BROOK
BRUNSWICK
BURTON
CABLE KEEPER
CABLE MANAGER
CABLE RINGS
CABLE SPOOL
CACHET
CACHET STACK
CALCULITE
CALLA
CALM TABLES
CANECREEK
CANOPY
CANTO
CAPA
CATCHET
CHANCELLOR
CHESTER
CHORD
CHORD EXECUTIVE
CIRCA
CLASSIC RECTANGULAR
CLUB
CLUB GRANDE
CLUB MOBILE
COACH
COBI
COLLABORATION
COLLEGIUM
COMPANY
CONFAIR
CONFIDANTE
CONTEXT
CONVENE
CONVENE TABLE
COPPICE
COPYCAM
CORNICE
COUPE
COUPE GRANDE
COUPE GRANDE MOBILE
COUPE WOOD
CPU TROLLEY
CREW
CREW GUEST
CRITERION
CRITERION PLUS
CROQUET
CRUSHED CAN
C:SCAPE
CURA
CURRENCY
DEARBORN
DECK
DECORUM
DENSKA
DERBY
DESIGNTEX
DETAILS
DETOUR
DIEKMAN
DIVA
DO WHAT YOU DO BETTER
DOMINO
DONOVAN
DOUBLE X-TENZ
DRIVE
DUNE
DUO
E-TABLE
ELECTIVE ELEMENTS
ELLA
ELLIPSE
ELSA
EMBER CHROME
EMBRASURE
EMERGE
ENEA
ENEA BARSTOOL
ENEA CAFE TABLE
ENGLAND
ENSEMBLE
EQUILIBRIUM
ESCAPADE
ETUDE
EVANEAU
EXAM STOOL
EXCHANGE
FIRENZE

Steelcase Inc. — (Continued)

FIRST FILE
FLAT TOP
FLIPCHART
FLUTE
FOOTREST
FOXTROT
FREESTANDING PALM REST
FRESCO
FURROWS
FYI
GALILEI
GARLAND
GENTRY
GINGER
GINKGO BILOBA
GRIP
GROOVE
GROUPWORK
HALLMARK
HARBOR
HARDWEAR
HERREN
I2I
IMPACT
IN LINE DOC SUPPORT
INCOGNITO
INDY
INTELLUME
INTERNODE
IOS
JACK
JACKET
JENNY
JENNY CLUB
JERSEY
JM LYNNE
JULES
KAMI
KART
KART STACK
KAST
KATHRYN
KICK
KICK FREESTANDING
LA COSTA
LANDMARK
LATTITUDE EXECUTIVE
LAZLO
LEAP
LET'S B
LINCOLN
LIVEBACK
LORIA
LOW-PROFILE
LYRA
LYRIC
MAESTRO
MALIBU
MALIBU TOO
MANSFIELD
MARTINIQUE
MASON
MASQUE
MAX-STACKER
MEADOW
MEANDER
MEDIA:SCAPE
MERINGUE
METALLICS
MIGRATIONS
MIGRATIONS ROUND
MIGRATIONS TABLE
MILANO
MINERAL
MINGLE
MISTIC
MITRA
MITRA RECLINER
MONTAGE
MONTEZUMA
MOVE
NEIGHBOR
NESSO
NICHE
NOLITA
NOMAD
NORFOLK
THE OFFICE ENVIRONMENT COMPANY
OPERA
OPUS
ORCHID
ORIANA
OUTLOOK EMPRESS
OUTLOOK HAWTHORNE
OUTLOOK JARRAH
OUTLOOK LINDEN
OUTLOOK NIKKO
OUTLOOK SEQUOIA
PALERMO
PAPERFLO
PARADE
PARADIGM
PASIO
PASSERELLE
PASSERELLE BENCH
PASSIVE
PATHWAYS
PAYBACK
PCT
PEEK
PEEK BARSTOOL
PENDALYTE
PERFLYTE
PERMISO
PERSONAL UNDERLINE
PISA
PLAYER
POST & BEAM
POWER PINCHER
POWERARC
PROGENY
PROTEGE
R2
RAF SYSTEM
RALLY
RAPPORT
RAVE
RAVE TANDEM
REGATTA
RELEVANT
REPLY
REUNION
REUNION NOMAD
REVEST
RIPPLE
RISER
RIZZI ARC
ROCCO
ROCKY
ROOMWIZARD
ROSA
ROUGH AND READY
ROVER
RUNNER
SAWYER
SCOOP STOOL
SECANT
SENECAL
SENSOR
SERENE
SERIES 9000
SHELF LIGHT-ADVANCED
SHELF LIGHT-STANDARD
SHELF LIGHT-UTILITY
SHIMMY
SIDEWALK
SIDEWALK MOBILE
SIDEWALK OTTOMAN/BENCHES
SIENTO
SIESTE
SINE
SIX PACK
SKYLAR
SLATWALL/SLATRAIL
SLUMBER
SMOKE
SNODGRASS
SOFTLEAF
SONATA
SORA
SORREL
SPINZ
SPRINGBOARD
ST. CLAIR
STEELCASE
STILETTO
STOW DAVIS
SUMO
SURPRISE
SWATHMORE
SWATHMORE GRAND MOBILE
SWEEPER
SWITCH
SWITCH EXECUTIVE
SYNC
TEAMWORK
TECHNIQUE
TEMPLATE
TERRAZZO
THEOREM
THINK
THOUGHTFUL LOUNGE
THUNDER
TOPAZ
TOPO
TOUCHDOWN
TOWER TOO
TRADITIONAL LOUNGE
TRAIN
TRANSFORMING THE WAYS PEOPLE WORK
TRANSLITE
TREES
TRILLIUM
TRILOGY
TURNSTONE
TX2
U-FREE
UNDERLINE
UNISON
UNIVERSAL WORKSURFACES
UNO
VALENCIA
VECTA
VECTAFLEX
VERGE
VIBE
VIRIDIAN
WALDEN
WALK-AND-TALK
WALKSTATION
WERNDL
WERNDL COMMUNICATOR
WERNDL CONFERENCE
WERNDL EMERGE
WERNDL FLIP TOP
WERNDL FREEWALL
WERNDL INFOTAINER
WERNDL MOBY
WERNDL TOUCHDOWN
WILSHIRE
WIZARD
WOBBLE
WORKFLOW
X-STACK
X-TENZ

Advertising Agency:
Peppercom
470 Park Ave S 5th Fl
New York, NY 10016
Tel.: (212) 931-6100
Fax: (212) 931-6159

STEELCLOUD, INC.

14040 Park Center Rd Ste 210
Herndon, VA 20171-3246
Tel.: (703) 674-5500
Fax: (703) 674-5506
E-mail: salescenter@steelcloud.com
Web Site: www.steelcloud.com
Approx. Rev.: $1,519,899
Approx. Number Employees: 10
Year Founded: 1987
Business Description:
Engineering & Manufacturing Software Integrator & Server Product Mfr
S.I.C.: 7371; 3577; 5045; 5734; 7379
N.A.I.C.S.: 541511; 334119; 423430; 443120; 541519
Import Export
Advertising Expenditures: $122,000
Media: 10-13
Personnel:
Kenneth A. Merlau *(Chm)*
Brian H. Hajost *(Pres & CEO)*
Steven Snyder *(CFO)*
Brands & Products:
STEELCLOUD
STEELWORKS
SURE AUDIT
TRANSFORMING TECHNOLOGY INTO RESULTS

STEFANINI TECHTEAM GLOBAL, INC.

(Formerly TechTeam Global, Inc.)
(Sub. of Stefanini International Corp.)
27335 W 11 Mile Rd
Southfield, MI 48033
Tel.: (248) 357-2866
Fax: (248) 357-2570
Toll Free: (800) 522-4451
E-mail: info@techteam.com
Web Site: www.techteam.com
E-Mail For Key Personnel:
Sales Director: sales@techteam.com
Sales Range: $200-249.9 Million
Business Description:
Outsourced Computer Help Desk Support, Systems Integration & Technical Staffing & Training Services
S.I.C.: 7373; 7371; 7389
N.A.I.C.S.: 541512; 541511; 561499
Media: 10-13
Personnel:
Antonio Moreira *(CEO)*
Heidi K. Hagle *(VP-HR)*
Jeffrey J. Ruffini *(VP-Svc Delivery)*

STELEX

(Sub. of Vital Signs, Inc.)
3331 St Rd Ste 300
Bensalem, PA 19020
Tel.: (215) 638-9700
Fax: (215) 638-9333
E-mail: info@stelex.com

Key to Media (For complete agency information see *The Advertising Red Books-Agencies* edition):
1. Bus. Publs. 2. Cable T.V. 3. Catalogs & Directories. 4. Co-op Adv. 5. Consumer Mags. 6. D.M. to Bus. Estab.7. D.M. to Consumers 8. Daily Newsp. 9. Exhibits/Trade Shows 10. Foreign 11. Infomercial 12. Internet Adv.13. Multimedia 14. Network Radio 15. Network T.V. 16. Newsp. Distr. Mags. 17. Other 18. Outdoor (Posters, Transit) 19. Point of Purchase20. Premiums, Novelties 21. Product Samples 22. Special Events Mktg. 23. Spot Radio 24. Spot T.V. 25. Weekly Newsp. 26. Yellow Page Adv.

Web Site: www.stelex.com
Sales Range: $25-49.9 Million
Approx. Number Employees: 135
Business Description:
Compliance Solutions Consulting Services
S.I.C.: 8748; 8742
N.A.I.C.S.: 541690; 541611
Media: 10
Personnel:
Tony Kashani *(Pres)*
David Chiaramonte *(Mng Dir)*
Maria Alvarez *(Dir-Sls & Mktg)*
Vamsee Dasaka *(Dir-Laboratory & Mfg Compliance)*
Brian Nace *(Dir-Enterprise Sys Solutions)*
Brands & Products:
STELEX

STELLENT, INC.
(Sub. of Oracle Corporation)
(d/b/a Oracle Corporation)
7500 Flying Cloud Dr Ste 500
Eden Prairie, MN 55344-3703
Tel.: (952) 564-2200
Fax: (952) 564-2088
Web Site: www.oracle.com
Sales Range: $100-124.9 Million
Approx. Number Employees: 560
Year Founded: 1989
Business Description:
Content Management Solutions
S.I.C.: 7372
N.A.I.C.S.: 334611; 511210
Advertising Agency:
Chlopak, Leonard, Schechter & Associates
1850 M St NW Ste 800
Washington, DC 20036-5803
Tel.: (202) 289-5900
Fax: (202) 289-4141

STERLING COMMERCE, INC.
(Sub. of International Business Machines Corporation)
4600 Lakehurst Ct
Dublin, OH 43016-3255
Mailing Address:
PO Box 8000
Dublin, OH 43016-2000
Tel.: (614) 793-7000
Fax: (614) 793-4040
Toll Free: (800) 876-9772
E-mail: info@sterlingcommerce.com
Web Site:
www.sterlingcommerce.com
Sales Range: $450-499.9 Million
Approx. Number Employees: 2,400
Year Founded: 1975
Business Description:
Holding Company; Business Integration Software Publisher, Whslr & Value-Added Network Services
S.I.C.: 6719; 5045; 7372
N.A.I.C.S.: 551112; 423430; 511210
Media: 2-7-10-11-13-20-22
Personnel:
Donna Angiulo *(CFO)*
Steven Aulds *(Sr VP-Tech)*
Phil Galati *(Sr VP-Global Svcs)*
Joel Reed *(Sr VP-Product Mgmt & Mktg)*
Dave Robinson *(Sr VP-European Field Ops)*
Deborah Surrette *(Sr VP-Field Ops-America)*
Joe Horine *(Dir-Corp Comm)*
George Middlebrook *(Dir-B2B)*
Advertising Agencies:
DMW Worldwide LLC
1325 Morris Dr Ste 100
Wayne, PA 19087-5521
Tel.: (610) 407-0407
Fax: (610) 407-0410

Emerging Marketing
29 W 3rd Ave
Columbus, OH 43201
Tel.: (614) 923-6000
Fax: (614) 424-6200

Fleishman-Hillard Inc.
4745 Alla Rd
Marina Del Rey, CA 90292-6311
Tel.: (310) 482-4270
Fax: (310) 482-4271
— Michael Paige *(Acct Exec)*

STEVENS & STEVENS BUSINESS RECORDS MANAGEMENT, INC.
(Private-Parent-Single Location)
11515 53rd St N
Clearwater, FL 33760
Tel.: (727) 573-3900
Web Site: www.ssbrm.com
Approx. Rev.: $1,200,000
Approx. Number Employees: 20
Year Founded: 1994
Business Description:
Storage & Retrieval Of Inactive Business Records
S.I.C.: 4226
N.A.I.C.S.: 493190
Media: 10-13-22-26
Personnel:
Marshall Stevens *(Pres)*

STINGER MEDICAL LLC
1152 Park Ave
Murfreesboro, TN 37129-4912
Tel.: (615) 896-1652
Fax: (615) 896-8906
Web Site: www.stingermedical.com
Sales Range: $1-9.9 Million
Approx. Number Employees: 50
Year Founded: 1994
Business Description:
Integrated Computer Workstations, Power Systems & Custom Accessories Mfr
S.I.C.: 3441
N.A.I.C.S.: 332312
Media: 10
Personnel:
Gary Coonan *(Pres & CEO)*
Brands & Products:
FUSION
INTEGRITI VITALS
LEVITATOR
NURSEADVOCATE
NURSESENSOR
RHINOGUARD
SLIMLINE
STINGER MEDICAL

STM NETWORKS
(Holding of Sloan Capital Partners LLC)
2 Faraday
Irvine, CA 92618-2737
Tel.: (949) 753-7864
Fax: (949) 273-6020
E-mail: investorinfo@stmi.com
Web Site: www.stmi.com
Sales Range: $25-49.9 Million
Approx. Number Employees: 100
Year Founded: 1982
Business Description:
Satellite Communications Networks Mfr
S.I.C.: 3663
N.A.I.C.S.: 334220
Export
Media: 2
Personnel:
Emil Youssefzadeh *(CEO)*
Umar Javed *(Exec VP)*
Anthony Naff *(VP-Fin)*

STRATASYS, INC.
7665 Commerce Way
Eden Prairie, MN 55344-2020
Tel.: (952) 937-3000
Fax: (952) 937-0070
Toll Free: (888) 480-3548
E-mail: info@stratasys.com
Web Site: www.stratasys.com
Approx. Rev.: $117,099,282
Approx. Number Employees: 414
Year Founded: 1989
Business Description:
Rapid Prototyping Devices Designer & Mfr for Creation of Physical Models from Computerized Designs
S.I.C.: 7379; 3577
N.A.I.C.S.: 541519; 334119
Advertising Expenditures: $2,800,000
Media: 2-7-10-13
Personnel:
S. Scott Crump *(Chm, Pres, CEO & Treas)*
Robert F. Gallagher *(CFO)*
Larry Doerr *(Sr VP-R&D Ops)*
Jonathan Lee Cobb *(VP & Gen Mgr)*
Woodrow J. Frost *(VP-Sls)*
Fred Fischer *(Dir-Materials Bus Dev)*
Shane M. Glenn *(Dir-IR)*
Mary Stanley *(Product Mgr)*
Cary Feik *(Mgr-HR)*
Joe Hiemenz *(Mgr-PR)*
Brands & Products:
ABSPLUS
CATALYST EX
CONTROL CENTER
DIMENSION
EDEN333
FDM
FDM MAXUM
FDM PROCESS
FDM TEAM
FDM TITAN
FDM VANTAGE
FORTUS
FORTUS 200MC
FORTUS 360MC
FORTUS 400MC
FORTUS 900MC
INSIGHT
MAKE IT REAL
MAXUM
REAL PARTS
REDEYE
REDEYE RPM
STRATASYS
TITAN
UPRINT
VANTAGE
WATERWORKS

STRATOS GLOBAL CORPORATION
(Sub. of Inmarsat plc)
6550 Rock Spring Dr Ste 650
Bethesda, MD 20817
Tel.: (301) 214-8800
Fax: (301) 214-8801
E-mail: info@stratosglobal.com
Web Site: www.stratosglobal.com
Approx. Rev.: $638,994,000
Approx. Number Employees: 600
Year Founded: 1985
Business Description:
Mobile & Fixed Satellite Communications Services
S.I.C.: 4899; 4812
N.A.I.C.S.: 517410; 517212
Media: 7-10
Personnel:
James J. Parm *(Pres & CEO)*
Paula M. McDonald *(CFO & Exec VP)*
John M. Mackey *(CTO & Sr VP)*
Bruce Henoch *(Gen Counsel & VP)*
John D. Prentice *(Sr VP-Broadband Svcs)*
Ronald Spithout *(Sr VP-MSS Sls-Worldwide)*
Carla Riggs *(Dir-Mktg Comm)*
Brands & Products:
BEYOND THE HORIZON
DATASAT II
FLEETBROADBAND
INMARSAT
IRIDIUM
STRATOS
STRATOSITEK

STRATUS TECHNOLOGIES, INC.
(Sub. of Stratus Technologies International S.a.r.l.)
111 Powdermill Rd
Maynard, MA 01754-3409
Tel.: (978) 461-7000
Fax: (978) 461-5210
Toll Free: (800) 458-0042
E-mail: webmaster@stratus.com
Web Site: www.stratus.com
E-Mail For Key Personnel:
Public Relations: ken.donoghue@stratus.com
Sales Range: $250-299.9 Million
Year Founded: 1980
Business Description:
Computer Systems Mfr; Computer System Design & Support Services
S.I.C.: 3571; 7371; 7373; 7389
N.A.I.C.S.: 334111; 541511; 541512; 561499
Export
Advertising Expenditures: $750,000
Media: 2-7-10-13
Distr.: Intl.; Natl.
Personnel:
David C. Laurello *(Chm, Pres & CEO)*
Robert C. Laufer *(CFO & Sr VP)*
Roy Sanford *(CMO)*
Fred Prifty *(Gen Counsel & VP)*
Allan L. Jennings *(Sr VP-Product & Solutions Dev)*
William Lowe *(Sr VP-Customer Care)*
Peter Flynn *(VP-Customer Svcs-Worldwide)*
Delfi L. Nieto *(VP-HR)*
Tim Wegner *(VP-Software Engrg)*

Key to Media (For complete agency information see *The Advertising Red Books-Agencies* edition):
1. Bus. Publs. 2. Cable T.V. 3. Catalogs & Directories. 4. Co-op Adv. 5. Consumer Mags. 6. D.M. to Bus. Estab.7. D.M. to Consumers 8. Daily Newsp. 9. Exhibits/Trade Shows 10. Foreign 11. Infomercial 12. Internet Adv.13. Multimedia 14. Network Radio 15. Network T.V. 16. Newsp. Distr. Mags. 17. Other 18. Outdoor (Posters, Transit) 19. Point of Purchase20. Premiums, Novelties 21. Product Samples 22. Special Events Mktg. 23. Spot Radio 24. Spot T.V. 25. Weekly Newsp. 26. Yellow Page Adv.

Stratus Technologies, Inc. — (Continued)

Brands & Products:
ACTIVESERVICE
CONTINUOUS PROCESSING
CONTINUUM
FTSERVER

STREAMCORE INC.

425 Market St Ste 2200
San Francisco, CA 94105
Tel.: (415) 955-0594
Fax: (415) 397-6309
E-mail: support@streamcore.com
Web Site: www.streamcore.com
Year Founded: 2003
Business Description:
Computer Application Traffic Management Systems
S.I.C.: 7373
N.A.I.C.S.: 541512
Media: 17
Personnel:
Diaa Elyaacoubi *(Pres & CEO)*
Raphaelle Colson *(CFO)*
Maurice Abecassis *(VP-Sls)*
Eric Jeux *(Co-Director)*

STREAMWARE CORPORATION

(Div. of Crane Merchandising Systems)
55 Providence Hwy
Norwood, MA 02062
Tel.: (781) 551-0010
Fax: (781) 551-0515
Web Site: www.streamware.com
Sales Range: $10-24.9 Million
Approx. Number Employees: 19
Business Description:
Vending & Delivery Software Publisher
S.I.C.: 7372
N.A.I.C.S.: 511210
Personnel:
Damien Moroney *(VP-Sls & Mktg)*
Brands & Products:
DELIVERYMAX
VENDMAX
Advertising Agency:
Fruitt Communications, Inc.
594 Marrett Rd Ste 10
Lexington, MA 02421
Tel.: (781) 274-0330
Fax: (781) 674-9192

STRUCTURED COMMUNICATION SYSTEMS, INC.

12901 se 97 Ave Ste 400
Clackamas, OR 97015
Tel.: (503) 513-9979
Fax: (503) 513-4600
Toll Free: (800) 881-0962
Web Site: www.structured.com
Sales Range: $25-49.9 Million
Approx. Number Employees: 60
Year Founded: 1992
Business Description:
IT Services
S.I.C.: 7373; 3572; 7371; 8748
N.A.I.C.S.: 541512; 334112; 541511; 541690
Media: 10
Personnel:
Ronald L. Fowler *(Pres & CEO)*

SUCCESSFACTORS, INC.

1500 Fashion Island Blvd Ste 300
San Mateo, CA 94404
Tel.: (650) 645-2000
Fax: (650) 645-2099
Toll Free: (800) 809-9920
E-mail: info@successfactors.com
Web Site: www.successfactors.com
Approx. Rev.: $205,926,000
Approx. Number Employees: 1,047
Year Founded: 2001
Business Description:
Performance & Talent Management Software Solutions
S.I.C.: 7372; 7373; 7389
N.A.I.C.S.: 511210; 541512; 561499
Advertising Expenditures: $2,300,000
Personnel:
Lars Dalgaard *(Founder & CEO)*
Douglas J. Burgum *(Chm)*
Doug Dennerline *(Pres)*
Bruce C. Felt, Jr. *(CFO)*
Tom Fisher *(CIO)*
Kara Wilson *(CMO)*
Karie Willyerd *(Chief Learning Officer)*
Jeremy Bauer *(VP-IT)*
Philip H. Carty *(VP-Sls-Eastern Area)*
William Harmer, III *(VP-Security)*
Jay Larson *(VP-Field Ops)*
Peter Riccio *(VP-Sls)*
Murray Sargent *(VP-Sls-Asia Pacific)*

SUMTOTAL SYSTEMS, INC.

(Holding of Vista Equity Partners LLC)
2850 NW 43rd St Ste 200
Gainesville, FL 32606
Tel.: (352) 264-2800
Fax: (352) 374-2257
E-mail: sales@sumtotalsystems.com
Web Site: www.sumtotalsystems.com
E-Mail For Key Personnel:
Sales Director: sales@sumtotalsystems.com
Approx. Rev.: $126,646,000
Approx. Number Employees: 832
Year Founded: 2004
Business Description:
Infrastructure Software Products & Services
S.I.C.: 7389; 7371; 7372; 8742
N.A.I.C.S.: 511210; 334611; 541511; 541611; 541990; 561499
Advertising Expenditures: $800,000
Media: 2-7-10-13
Personnel:
John Borgerding *(CEO)*
Betty Hung *(CFO)*
Nadeem Syed *(COO)*
Gregg Monastiero *(Exec VP-Sls & Mktg)*
Bobby Slaton *(Exec VP-Pro Svcs & Support)*
Richard Watkins *(Sr VP-Product Dev)*
Brands & Products:
ACCELERATE PERFORMANCE. ACCELERATE PROFITS.
ASPEN
ASPEN VIRTUAL CLASSROOM SERVER
CLICK2LEARN
PREFERENCE
RESULTSONDEMAND-COMPENSATION
RESULTSONDEMAND-LEARNING
RESULTSONDEMAND-PERFORMANCE
SUMTOTAL
SUMTOTAL ENTERPRISE SUITE
TOOLBOOK
TOTALACCESS
TOTALCOLLABORATION
TOTALDASHBOARD
TOTALINFORMATION
TOTALLCMS
TOTALLMS
TOTALPERFORMANCE
TOTALVCS

SUN MICROSYSTEMS, INC.

(Name Changed to Oracle America, Inc.)

SUNGARD DATA SYSTEMS INC.

(Sub. of SunGard Capital Corp.)
680 E Swedesford Rd
Wayne, PA 19087
Tel.: (484) 582-2000
Fax: (610) 225-1120
Toll Free: (800) 825-2518
E-mail: getinfo@sungard.com
Web Site: www.sungard.com
Approx. Number Employees: 20,000
Year Founded: 1982
Business Description:
Integrated IT Solutions & e-Processing Services for Financial Industry
S.I.C.: 7374; 7372; 7379
N.A.I.C.S.: 518210; 511210; 541519
Export
Advertising Expenditures: $2,013,000
Media: 2-4-7-10-13
Distr.: Natl.
Personnel:
Glenn H. Hutchins *(Chm)*
Cristobal Conde *(Pres & CEO)*
John E. McArdle *(Grp CEO)*
Robert F. Woods *(CFO)*
Brian Robins *(CMO & Sr VP)*
Kathleen Asser Weslock *(Chief HR Officer & Sr VP-HR)*
Harold C. Finders *(CEO-Fin Systems)*
Ronald M. Lang *(CEO-Higher Education)*
Gilbert O. Santos *(CEO-Public Sector)*
Victoria E. Silbey *(Gen Counsel & Sr VP-Legal)*
Josie Palazzolo *(Sr VP & Product Mgr)*
Richard C. Tarbox *(Sr VP-Corp Dev)*
Brands & Products:
ADAPTIV
ADAPTIVE
ADDVANTAGE
ADMINISTAR
ADVANCE
ALLOCATIONMASTER
AMARTA
APSYS
AVANTGARD
BANCWARE
BONDMASTER
BRASS
BROKERAUDIT
CADEXTAN
CERTMASTER
CHARLOTTE
COLLEGIS
COMPASS
CSSII
DATA CENTER OUTSOURCING
DECALOG
DEGREEWORKS
DEVON
ENERGYSCOPE
ENERGYSERVER
ENFORM CONSULTING
ENTEGRATE
FAME
FORMWORK
FRONT ARENA
FRONTIER INSURANCE
GLOBAL ONE
GLOBAL PLUS
GLOBAL PORTFOLIO II
IFAS
IMPOWER
INTAS
INTRADER
INVESTAR
INVESTIER
INVESTONE
INVESTONE ENTERPRISE
INVESTRAN
IWORKS
KIODEX
LOANET
MACESS
MARTINI
MICROHEDGE
MINT
MONIS
OCTANE8
OMNI
OPTAS
OSSI
OUTPUT SOLUTIONS
OVERLAY MANAGER
PAL SYSTEM
PHASE
PHASE 3
PLANNING STATION
POWERDATA
POWERIMAGE
PROTEGENT
REECH
REFERENCEPOINT
RELIUS
SMARTCALL
STEP
STUDENTPLUS
SUNGARD
SUNSTAR
SYNAPSE
VIVISTA
WEALTHSTATION
XAMIN
ZAINET

SUNGARD EMPLOYEE BENEFIT SYSTEMS

(Sub. of SunGard Financial Systems, Inc.)
(d/b/a SunGard EBSi)
104 Inverness Ctr Pl
Birmingham, AL 35242
Tel.: (205) 437-7500
Fax: (205) 437-7991
E-mail: ebs.marketing@sungardebs.com
Web Site: www.sungard.com
Approx. Number Employees: 300
Year Founded: 1964
Business Description:
Employee Benefit Software Solutions
S.I.C.: 7372
N.A.I.C.S.: 511210
Advertising Expenditures: $60,000
Media: 2-4-10-17
Distr.: Natl.
Personnel:
Tom Makeever *(Sr VP-Sls)*
Alan Gross *(Dir-Mktg Commun)*
Shelli Adamson *(Mgr-Mktg)*

Key to Media (For complete agency information see *The Advertising Red Books-Agencies* edition):
1. Bus. Publs. 2. Cable T.V. 3. Catalogs & Directories. 4. Co-op Adv. 5. Consumer Mags. 6. D.M. to Bus. Estab.7. D.M. to Consumers 8. Daily Newsp. 9. Exhibits/Trade Shows 10. Foreign 11. Infomercial 12. Internet Adv.13. Multimedia 14. Network Radio 15. Network T.V. 16. Newsp. Distr. Mags. 17. Other 18. Outdoor (Posters, Transit) 19. Point of Purchase20. Premiums, Novelties 21. Product Samples 22. Special Events Mktg. 23. Spot Radio 24. Spot T.V. 25. Weekly Newsp. 26. Yellow Page Adv.

SUNGARD FINANCIAL SYSTEMS-RELIUS-JACKSONVILLE
(Branch of SunGard Financial Systems, Inc.)
1660 Prudential Dr
Jacksonville, FL 32207-8197
Mailing Address:
PO Box 47470
Jacksonville, FL 32247-7470
Tel.: (904) 399-5888
Fax: (904) 399-5551
Toll Free: (800) 326-7235
Web Site: www.relius.net
Sales Range: $10-24.9 Million
Approx. Number Employees: 192
Year Founded: 1974
Business Description:
Employee Benefits Computer Software & Services
S.I.C.: 7372; 7361; 7371
N.A.I.C.S.: 511210; 541511; 541612
Media: 10-13
Personnel:
Ken Simons *(Sr VP)*
Leslie Harlow *(VP-Info Sys & Tech)*

SUNGARD HIGHER EDUCATION INC.
(Div. of SunGard Data Systems Inc.)
4 Country View Rd
Malvern, PA 19355-1408
Tel.: (610) 647-5930
Fax: (610) 578-5102
Toll Free: (800) 223-7036
E-mail: hrsc@sungardhe.com
Web Site: www.sungardhe.com
Approx. Number Employees: 1,600
Year Founded: 1968
Business Description:
Learning Software, Support & Consultation Systems
S.I.C.: 7373; 7372; 7376
N.A.I.C.S.: 541512; 511210; 541513
Media: 2-7-8-10-13
Personnel:
Ron Lang *(CEO)*
Amy Turner LaDow *(CIO)*
Jeff Cottle *(Sr VP-HR)*
William H. Graves *(Sr VP-Academic Strategy)*
Jack Kramer *(Sr VP-Customer Satisfaction)*

SUPER MICRO COMPUTER, INC.
980 Rock Ave
San Jose, CA 95131
Tel.: (408) 503-8000
Fax: (408) 503-8008
E-mail: marketing@supermicro.com
Web Site: www.supermicro.com
Approx. Sls.: $721,438,000
Approx. Number Employees: 1,012
Year Founded: 1993
Business Description:
Computer Hardware Mfr
S.I.C.: 3577
N.A.I.C.S.: 334119
Advertising Expenditures: $2,038,000
Media: 1-2-5-9-10-17-24-25
Personnel:
Charles Liang *(Founder, Chm, Pres & CEO)*
Howard Hideshima *(CFO)*
Yih-Shyan Liaw *(Sec & VP-Intl Sls)*
Tau Leng *(Dir-Mktg & Sys Integration)*

SUPPLEMENTAL HEALTH CARE SERVICES, INC.
1640 Redstone Ctr Dr Ste 200
Park City, UT 84098
Tel.: (435) 645-0788
Fax: (435) 645-0792
Toll Free: (866) 474-6677
E-mail: info@supplementalhealthcare.com
Web Site: www.supplementalhealthcare.com
Approx. Number Employees: 3,000
Business Description:
Nurse Staffing Services
S.I.C.: 8399; 7361
N.A.I.C.S.: 813212; 561310
Media: 2
Personnel:
Janet Elkin *(Pres & CEO)*

SUPPORTSAVE SOLUTIONS, INC.
11132 Ventura Blvd Ste 420
Studio City, CA 91604
Tel.: (925) 304-4400
E-mail: sales@supportsave.com
Web Site: www.supportsave.com
Approx. Rev.: $2,866,822
Approx. Number Employees: 290
Year Founded: 2007
Business Description:
Offshore Business Process Outsourcing Services
S.I.C.: 7389
N.A.I.C.S.: 561499
Advertising Expenditures: $104,389
Media: 13
Personnel:
Aina Mae Dumlao-Johns *(Co-Founder & Treas)*
Christopher Johns *(Pres & CEO)*
Michael Palasick *(CFO)*
Prateek Hastir *(VP-Strategy & Bus Dev)*
Gavin Kesten *(VP-Sls)*
David Foot *(Dir-IT)*
Teresa Fernandez *(Mgr-HR)*
Beatrice White *(Mgr-Ops)*

SURADO SOLUTIONS, INC.
588 Technology Ct Ste 200
Riverside, CA 92507
Tel.: (951) 682-4895
Fax: (951) 686-8503
Toll Free: (800) 478-7236
E-mail: information@suradocrm.com
Web Site: www.suradocrm.com
Approx. Number Employees: 28
Year Founded: 1995
Business Description:
Customer Relationship Management & E-Business Software Solutions
S.I.C.: 7371
N.A.I.C.S.: 541511
Media: 6-10
Personnel:
Sundip Doshi *(Chm & CEO)*
Brands & Products:
ALWAYS IN SYNC
SURADO
SURADO ENTERPRISE CRM
SURADO SMART BUSINESS MANAGER
SURADO SMART CONTACT MANAGER PRO

SYBASE, INC.
(Sub. of SAP America, Inc.)
1 Sybase Dr
Dublin, CA 94568-7902
Tel.: (925) 236-5000
Fax: (925) 236-4321
Toll Free: (800) 792-2735
E-mail: investor_relations@sybase.com
Web Site: www.sybase.com
E-Mail For Key Personnel:
President: John.Chen@sybase.com
Approx. Rev.: $1,170,569,000
Approx. Number Employees: 3,819
Year Founded: 1979
Business Description:
Enterprise Software Development, Marketing & Support
S.I.C.: 7371; 7372; 7373
N.A.I.C.S.: 541511; 334611; 511210; 541512
Export
Advertising Expenditures: $6,600,000
Media: 2-3-5-6-7-9-11-13-14-15-18-19-22-23-24-26
Personnel:
John S. Chen *(Chm & CEO)*
Jeffrey G. Ross *(CFO & Sr VP)*
Raj Nathan *(CMO-Worldwide Mktg & Bus Solutions Ops & Sr VP)*
Steven M. Capelli *(Pres-Worldwide Field Ops)*
Dan R. Carl *(Gen Counsel, Sec & VP)*
Billy Ho *(Sr VP-Product & Tech Ops)*
Brands & Products:
ADAPTIVE SERVER ENTERPRISE
ADVANTAGE DATABASE SERVER
AFARIA
AVANTGO
DATAWINDOW
FINANCIAL FUSION
IANYWHERE
IANYWHERE SOLUTIONS
MBANKING 365
MIRROR ACTIVATOR
POWERBUILDER
POWERDESIGNER
RAP
REMOTEWARE
REPLICATION
SQL ANYWHERE
SYBASE
XTNDCONNECT PC
Advertising Agency:
bite communications
345 Spear St Ste 750
San Francisco, CA 94105
Tel.: (415) 365-0222
Fax: (415) 365-0223

SYKES ENTERPRISES, INCORPORATED
400 N Ashley Dr Ste 2800
Tampa, FL 33602
Tel.: (813) 274-1000
Fax: (813) 273-0148
Toll Free: (800) 867-9537
E-mail: info.america@corp.skyes.com
Web Site: www.sykes.com
Approx. Rev.: $1,158,718,000
Approx. Number Employees: 43,400
Year Founded: 1977
Business Description:
Outsourced Customer Contact Management Solutions & Services in the Business Process Outsourcing (BPO) Arena
S.I.C.: 7373; 7371
N.A.I.C.S.: 541512; 541511
Media: 2-7-8-10-13-16-17-22-26
Distr.: Intl.
Personnel:
Charles E. Sykes *(Pres & CEO)*
W. Michael Kipphut *(CFO & Exec VP)*
David L. Pearson *(CIO & Exec VP)*
James T. Holder *(Gen Counsel, Corp Sec & Exec VP)*
Daniel L. Hernandez *(Exec VP-Global Strategy)*
James C. Hobby *(Exec VP-Global Ops)*
Jenna R. Nelson *(Exec VP-HR)*
Lawrence R. Zingale *(Exec VP-Global Sls & Client Mgmt)*
Brands & Products:
REAL PEOPLE REAL SOLUTIONS
SYKES
Advertising Agency:
Bayshore Solutions Inc
600 N West Shore Blvd Ste 700
Tampa, FL 33609
Tel.: (813) 902-0141
Fax: (813) 839-9022

SYMANTEC CORPORATION
350 Ellis St
Mountain View, CA 94043
Tel.: (650) 527-8000
Toll Free: (800) 441-7234
E-mail: investor-relations@symantec.com
Web Site: www.symantec.com
Approx. Rev.: $6,190,000,000
Approx. Number Employees: 18,600
Year Founded: 1982
Business Description:
Client, Gateway & Server Security Solutions for Virus Protection, Firewall, Virtual Private Network, Vulnerability Management, Intrusion Detection, Internet Content & E-Mail Filtering; Remote Management Technologies & Security Services to Individuals, Enterprises & Service Providers
S.I.C.: 7372; 7371
N.A.I.C.S.: 334611; 511210; 541511
Advertising Expenditures: $668,000,000
Media: 2-4-6-7-8-9-10-11-23
Distr.: Intl.; Natl.
Personnel:
John W. Thompson *(Chm)*
Enrique T. Salem *(Pres & CEO)*
James A. Beer *(CFO & Exec VP)*
David Thompson *(Grp Pres & CIO-Symantec Svcs Grp)*
Carine Clark *(CMO & Sr VP)*
Stephen Trilling *(CTO & Sr VP)*
Angela T. Tucci *(Chief Strategy Officer & Sr VP)*
Phillip A. Bullock *(Chief Acctg Officer & Sr VP-Fin)*
Rebecca Ranninger *(Chief HR Officer & Exec VP)*
Janice D. Chaffin *(Grp Pres-Consumer Bus Unit)*
Francis deSouza *(Grp Pres-Enterprise Products & Svcs)*

Key to Media (For complete agency information see *The Advertising Red Books-Agencies* edition):
1. Bus. Publs. 2. Cable T.V. 3. Catalogs & Directories. 4. Co-op Adv. 5. Consumer Mags. 6. D.M. to Bus. Estab.7. D.M. to Consumers 8. Daily Newsp. 9. Exhibits/Trade Shows 10. Foreign 11. Infomercial 12. Internet Adv.13. Multimedia 14. Network Radio 15. Network T.V. 16. Newsp. Distr. Mags. 17. Other 18. Outdoor (Posters, Transit) 19. Point of Purchase20. Premiums, Novelties 21. Product Samples 22. Special Events Mktg. 23. Spot Radio 24. Spot T.V. 25. Weekly Newsp. 26. Yellow Page Adv.

Symantec Corporation — (Continued)

Rowan Trollope *(Grp Pres-SMB & Symantec.cloud)*
Scott C. Taylor *(Gen Counsel, Sec & Exec VP)*
Bill Robbins *(Exec VP-Worldwide Sls & Svcs)*
John Brigden *(Sr VP-Europe, Middle East & Africa Geography)*
Anil Chakravarthy *(Sr VP-Storage & Availability Mgmt Grp)*
Chirantan Desai *(Sr VP-Endpoint & Mobility Grp)*
Art Gilliland *(Sr VP-Info Security Grp)*
Bernard Kwok *(Sr VP-Asia Pacific & Japan Geography)*
Deepak Mohan *(Sr VP-Info Mgmt Grp)*
Rich Spring *(Sr VP-Americas)*
Marco Puebla *(Dir-Svcs Online Sls-Global)*
Hormazd Romer *(Dir-Product Mktg)*
Deborah Clark *(Sr Mgr-Category Mktg-Norton Mobile)*

Brands & Products:
ACTIONABLE INFRASTRUCTURE
ACTIVE EXTENSIONS
ACTIVEADMIN
ALTIRIS
ANTI-FREEZE
APPLICATION SAVER
BACKUP EXEC
BARE METAL RESTORE
BINDVIEW
BLOODHOUND
BOOTGUARD
BRIGHTMAIL
BV-ADMIN
BV-CONTROL
CARBON COPY
CARRIERSCAN
CLEANSWEEP
COLORSCALE
COMMANDCENTRAL
CONFIDENCE IN A CONNECTED WORLD.
CONFIDENCE ONLINE
DAY-END SYNC
DIGITAL IMMUNE SYSTEM
DISKDOUBLER
DISKLOCK
DRIVE IMAGE
ENTERPRISE SECURITY MANAGER
ENTERPRISE VAULT
FLASHSNAP
FLOWCHASER
GHOST
GHOST WALKER
GOBACK
HEALTHY PC
I-GEAR
I3
ICOMMAND
INDEPTH
INFORMATION FOUNDATION
INFORMATION INTEGRITY
INFOVAULT
INTELLICRYPT
INTRUDER ALERT
LIVESTATE
LIVEUPDATE
MAIL-GEAR
MANAGEFUSION
MICROMEASURE
NETBACKUP
NORTON
NORTON 360
NORTON ANTIVIRUS
NORTON SYSTEMWORKS
NORTON UTILITIES
NORTON WINDOCTOR
OMNIGUARD
OPFORCE
PARTITIONMAGIC
PC ANYWHERE
POWERQUEST
POWERVPN
PROCOMM
PROCOMM PLUS
PUREDISK
QUICKLOG
RAPTOR
RECOURSE TECHNOLOGIES
RELICORE
REPLICATION EXEC
SAFETYSWEEP
SANPOINT
SANPOINT CONTROL
SECUREEXCHANGE
SERVERMAGIC
SESA
SITESTOR
SMARTSECTOR
SMARTUNE
SONAR
SPEED DISK
SPEEDSEND
STORAGE EXEC
STORAGECENTRAL
SYGATE
SYMANTEC
SYMANTEC DEPLOYCENTER
SYMANTEC ENTERPRISE SECURITY ARCHITECTURE
SYMANTEC INFORM
SYMANTEC INSIGHT
SYMANTEC INTRUDER ALERT
SYMANTEC MAIL-GEAR
SYMANTEC MOBILE ESSENTIALS
SYMANTEC ON COMMAND DISCOVERY
SYMANTEC ON ICOMMAND
SYMANTEC ON IPATCH
TALKWORKS
TRUSCAN
TRUSTOR
TURN IT ON. KEEP IT ON
UNERASE
UPSCALE
V2I
V2I BUILDER
V2I OBSERVER
V2I PROTECTOR
VERITAS
VERITAS DATA CENTER FOUNDATION
VERITAS SERVER FOUNDATION
VERITAS STORAGE FOUNDATION
VIRTUALLY ANYWHERE
VISION360
VONTU
WINFAX
WIPEDISK
WIPEFILE
WISE
WISE PACKAGE STUDIO
WISE SOLUTIONS
WORK VIRTUALLY ANYWHERE

Advertising Agencies:
Arc Worldwide
(Sub. of Publicis Groupe S.A.)
35 W Wacker Dr 15th Fl
Chicago, IL 60601
Tel.: (312) 220-3200
Fax: (312) 220-1995
Internet Security

Arc Worldwide
2001 The Embarcadero
San Francisco, CA 94133
Tel.: (312) 220-1177
Norton

DDB South Africa
Silverpoint Office Park Bldg 1 22 Ealing Crescent
Johannesburg, South Africa
Tel.: (27) 11 267 2800
Fax: (27) 86 632 6270

Gage
10000 Hwy 55
Minneapolis, MN 55441-6300
Tel.: (763) 595-3800
Fax: (763) 595-3871
Toll Free: (877) TRY-GAGE

Grey San Francisco
303 2nd St Ste 300 N Tower
San Francisco, CA 94107
Tel.: (415) 403-8000
Fax: (415) 403-8204
Norton

Leo Burnett USA
35 W Wacker Dr
Chicago, IL 60601-1723
Tel.: (312) 220-5959
Fax: (312) 220-3299
Norton

SYMANTEC CORPORATION

(Div. of Symantec Corporation)
1359 N Research Way Bldg K
Orem, UT 84059
Mailing Address:
PO Box 1911
Orem, UT 84059
Tel.: (801) 437-8900
Fax: (801) 226-8941
Toll Free: (800) 379-2566
Web Site: www.symantec.com
Approx. Rev.: $64,000,000
Approx. Number Employees: 309
Year Founded: 1993
Business Description:
Storage Lifecycle Automation Solutions
S.I.C.: 7372; 7371
N.A.I.C.S.: 511210; 541511
Media: 6
Personnel:
Hugo Parra *(Product Mgr)*
Brands & Products:
DEEPSIGHT
DISCOVERY
GHOST
LIVESTATE
PARTITIONMAGIC
PCANYWHERE
VOLUMEMANAGER

SYMMETRY CORP

420 S Hillview Dr
Milpitas, CA 95035
Tel.: (408) 942-7700
Fax: (408) 942-7711
E-mail: sdinfo@symmcorp.com
Web Site: www.symmetrydirect.com
Approx. Number Employees: 52
Business Description:
Direct Selling Establishments
S.I.C.: 5963; 8011
N.A.I.C.S.: 454390; 621111
Personnel:
Rudy Revak *(Founder & Pres)*
Steven Kole *(CFO & Sr VP)*
Mark Crapo *(Sr VP-Product Dev & Trng)*
Mary Julich *(Sr VP-Mktg)*
Willie Larkin *(Sr VP-Distributor Trng & Dev)*
Brands & Products:
ADVANCED OMEGA
ALOE PLUS
APHRODISIA 136
BIO-INFINITY
BOGO BLASTER FOAMER
BOTANA C
BOTANA E
BOTANA G
BOTANACLEANSE
BOTANACLEANSEPLUS
BOTANALAX
BOTANIC GOLD
CALCIUM COVERAGE
CARBLESS
CARDIO ESSENTIALS
CLARITY
CLEANSE BUNDLE
COLDRX
COUNTERTOP
DREAM LOTION
EASEGM
EXTREME FUEL
EXTREME IGNITION
EXTREME RECOVERY
FEMALE BALANCE
FRUIT-A-MINS
FUTURE STAR
GENESIS
GLUCOSAMINE FORMULA
IMMUNITY
JOINT SUPPORT BUNDLE
LIPO-SORB
MALE BALANCE
MEGA JUICE
NATURALS
NEUROCALM
NEW ATTITUDE
NIGHTLITE
NUTRAPACK
NUTRITIONAL PRODUCTS
OPTIBREATHE
PARACLEANSE
PREMIUM PLUS
PROTECTION 4 LIFE
SIMPLYSLYM
SKIN RENEWAL
SLYMPACK
STRESS BUNDLE
SYMMETRY 4 PETS
SYMMETRY DIRECT
THERMOBALANCE
TRANQUILITY
ULTRA SLYMPACK
ULTRA VITALITY
VITALITY SYSTEM
WINTER BUNDLE
WOW PACK
WOW SMOOTHIE
Advertising Agency:
Red Brown Kle
840 N Old World Third St Ste 401
Milwaukee, WI 53203
Tel.: (414) 272-2600
Fax: (414) 272-2690
Toll Free: (888) 725-2041

Key to Media (For complete agency information see *The Advertising Red Books-Agencies* edition):
1. Bus. Publs. 2. Cable T.V. 3. Catalogs & Directories. 4. Co-op Adv. 5. Consumer Mags. 6. D.M. to Bus. Estab.7. D.M. to Consumers 8. Daily Newsp. 9. Exhibits/Trade Shows 10. Foreign 11. Infomercial 12. Internet Adv.13. Multimedia 14. Network Radio 15. Network T.V. 16. Newsp. Distr. Mags. 17. Other 18. Outdoor (Posters, Transit) 19. Point of Purchase20. Premiums, Novelties 21. Product Samples 22. Special Events Mktg. 23. Spot Radio 24. Spot T.V. 25. Weekly Newsp. 26. Yellow Page Adv.

SYNCHRONOSS TECHNOLOGIES, INC.
750 Route 202 S Ste 600
Bridgewater, NJ 08807
Tel.: (908) 547-1250
Fax: (908) 547-1285
Toll Free: (866) 620-3940
E-mail: investor@synchronoss.com
Web Site: www.synchronoss.com
Approx. Rev.: $165,969,000
Approx. Number Employees: 758
Year Founded: 2000
Business Description:
Electronic Commerce Transaction Management Solutions
S.I.C.: 8748
N.A.I.C.S.: 541618
Advertising Expenditures: $40,000
Media: 4-7-10
Personnel:
Stephen G. Waldis *(Chm, Pres & CEO)*
Michael Mulica *(Pres & Head-Strategy & Corp Dev)*
Lawrence R. Irving *(CFO, Treas & Exec VP)*
Robert E. Garcia *(COO & Exec VP)*
S. Andrew Cox *(CIO & VP)*
Patrick J. Doran *(CTO & Exec VP)*
Christopher S. Putnam *(Exec VP-Sls)*
Daniel W. Rizer *(Exec VP-Bus Dev)*
Ronald J. Prague *(Sr VP)*
Mike Arnold *(VP & Gen Mgr)*
Brands & Products:
ACTIVATIONNOW
CONVERGENCENOW
PEFORMANCEPARTNER
SYNCHRONOSS

SYNGENCE CORPORATION
5151 Belt Line Rd Ste 1100
Dallas, TX 75254
Tel.: (214) 269-2900
Fax: (214) 269-2901
Toll Free: (800) 796-4362
E-mail: info@syngence.com
Web Site: www.syngence.com
Approx. Rev.: $2,703,000
Approx. Number Employees: 21
Business Description:
Software Tools & Applications That Enable the Automated Search of Large Document Collections Such As Legal Documents
S.I.C.: 7372; 7373
N.A.I.C.S.: 511210; 541512
Advertising Expenditures: $198,481
Media: 7
Personnel:
Johan Liedgren *(Chm)*
Randall D. Miles *(Pres & CEO)*
Chris V. Johnson *(CFO)*

SYNIVERSE HOLDINGS, INC.
(Holding of The Carlyle Group, LLC)
(d/b/a Syniverse Technologies)
8125 Highwoods Palm Way
Tampa, FL 33647
Mailing Address:
PO Box 2924
Tampa, FL 33601-2924
Tel.: (813) 637-5000
Fax: (813) 273-4818
Toll Free: (888) 724-3579
E-mail: hotline@syniverse.com
Web Site: www.syniverse.com
Approx. Rev.: $482,991,000
Approx. Number Employees: 1,289
Year Founded: 1986
Business Description:
Wireless Telephone Services
S.I.C.: 7299; 4899; 7373
N.A.I.C.S.: 812990; 517910; 541512
Advertising Expenditures: $612,000
Media: 2-10
Personnel:
Robert J. Marino *(Chm)*
Tony G. Holcombe *(Pres & CEO)*
Janet Roberts *(CMO)*
Martin A. Picciano *(Chief Acctg Officer & Sr VP)*
Laura E. Binion *(Gen Counsel & Sr VP)*
Michael J. O'Brien *(Sr VP-Bus Dev)*
Barry Derrick *(Sr Engr-Application Sys & Incident Mgmt)*
Brands & Products:
ACCESS
ACCESSIBILITY
FOLLOW ME ROAMING PLUS
FRAUDINTERCEPTOR
FRAUDMANAGER
FRAUDX
INLINK
INPACK
INPORT
INPOSITION
LATALINKS
SIMPLIFYING COMPLEXITY, DELIVERING POSSIBILITIES.
STREAMLINER
SYNIVERSE
SYNIVERSE NEXT
UNIROAM
VISIBILITY
VISWISE
Advertising Agency:
Stein Rogan + Partners
432 Park Ave S
New York, NY 10016-8013
Tel.: (212) 213-1112
Fax: (212) 779-7305

SYNNEX CORPORATION
44201 Nobel Dr
Fremont, CA 94538-3178
Tel.: (510) 656-3333
Fax: (510) 668-3777
Toll Free: (800) 756-9888
E-mail: support@synnex.com
Web Site: www.synnex.com
Approx. Rev.: $8,614,141,000
Approx. Number Employees: 7,454
Year Founded: 1980
Business Description:
Computer Hardware, Peripheral & Software Distr
S.I.C.: 7379; 5045
N.A.I.C.S.: 541519; 423430
Export
Media: 7-11
Personnel:
Kevin M. Murai *(Pres & CEO)*
Thomas C. Alsborg *(CFO)*
Dennis Polk *(COO)*
Gary Gulmon *(CIO & Sr VP)*
Peter Larocque *(Pres-US Distr)*
Simon Leung *(Gen Counsel, Corp Sec & Sr VP)*
Mike Vaishnav *(Sr VP & Controller)*
Christopher Caldwell *(Sr VP & Gen Mgr-Global Bus Dev)*
Stephen Ichinaga *(Sr VP & Gen Mgr-Sys)*
Charlotte Chou *(Sr VP-Mfg Ops)*
Peter J. Coleman *(Sr VP-HP Enterprise Tech Soluti)*
David Dennis *(Sr VP-Product Mgmt)*
Steve Jow *(Sr VP-Sls)*
Pradip Madan *(Sr VP-Corp Strategy & Dev)*
Gary Palenbaum *(Sr VP-Product Mgmt)*
Timothy Rush *(Sr VP-Ops)*
Robert L. Stegner *(Sr VP-Mktg-North America)*
Michael R. Thomson *(Sr VP-Partner Advocacy)*
T. J. Trojan *(Sr VP-Product Mgmt)*
Michael P. Van Gieson *(Sr VP-Product Mgmt)*
Lori Barker *(Sr Dir-IR)*
Laura Crowley *(Dir-IR & PR)*

SYNOPSYS, INC.
700 E Middlefield Rd
Mountain View, CA 94043-4033
Tel.: (650) 584-5000
Fax: (650) 584-4249
Toll Free: (800) 541-7737
E-mail: invest-info@synopsys.com
Web Site: www.synopsys.com
Approx. Rev.: $1,380,661,000
Approx. Number Employees: 6,707
Year Founded: 1986
Business Description:
Semiconductor Design & Verification Software Developer
S.I.C.: 7373; 7371; 7372
N.A.I.C.S.: 541512; 334611; 541511
Media: 2-10
Distr.: Natl.
Personnel:
Aart J. de Geus *(Chm & CEO)*
Chi-Foon Chan *(Pres & COO)*
Brian M. Beattie *(CFO)*
Brian E. Cabrera *(Gen Counsel, Sec & VP)*
Antun Domic *(Sr VP & Gen Mgr-Implementation Grp)*
Manoj Gandhi *(Sr VP & Gen Mgr-Verification Grp)*
Fu-Hwa Ko *(Sr VP & Gen Mgr-Silicon Engrg Grp)*
Sheng-Chun Lo *(Sr VP & Gen Mgr-Analog Mixed Signal Grp)*
John Chilton *(Sr VP-Mktg & Strategic Dev)*
Deirdre Hanford *(Sr VP-Global Tech Svcs)*
Joseph W. Logan *(Sr VP-Sls-Worldwide)*
Brands & Products:
AFGEN
AMPS
APOLLO
ASTRO
ASTRO-RAIL
ASTRO-XTALK
AURORA
AVANWAVES
BEHAVIOR EXTRACTING SYNTHESIS TECHNOLOGY
BEST
CADABRA
CATS
CERTIFY
CHIPIT
COLUMBIA
COLUMBIA-CE
CONFIRMA
COSMOS
COSMOSLE
COSMOSSCOPE
CRITIC
CUSTOMSIM
DC EXPERT
DC PROFESSIONAL
DC ULTRA
DESIGN ANALYZER
DESIGN COMPILER
DESIGN VISION
DESIGNERHDL
DESIGNPOWER
DESIGNWARE
DFTMAX
DIRECT SILICON ACCESS
DISCOVERY
ECLYPSE
ENCORE
EPIC
FORMALITY
GALAXY
GALAXY CUSTOM DESIGNER
HANEX
HAPS
HAPSTRAK
HDL ANALYST
HDL COMPILER
HERCULES
HIERARCHICAL OPTIMIZATION TECHNOLOGY
HIGH-PERFORMANCE ASIC PROTOTYPING SYSTEM
HSIM
HSIMPLUS
HSPICE
I-VIRTUAL STEPPER
IDENTIFY
IICE
IN-PHASE
IN-SYNC
IN-TANDEM
JUPITER
JUPITER-DP
JUPITERXT
JUPITERXT-ASIC
LEDA
LIBERTY
LIBRA-PASSPORT
LIBRARY COMPILER
MAGELLAN
MAP-IN
MARS
MARS-RAIL
MARS-XTALK
MAST
MILKYWAY
MODELSOURCE
MODELTOOLS
MODULE COMPILER
MULTIPOINT
NANOSIM
OPENVERA
PATHMILL
PHILIPS COOLFLUX
PHYSICAL ANALYST
PHYSICAL COMPILER
PLANET
PLANET-PL
POLARIS
POWER COMPILER
PREDICTABLE SUCCESS
PRIME TIME
PRIMETIME
RAPHAEL
SATURN
SCIROCCO
SCIROCCO-I
SCOPE

Key to Media (For complete agency information see *The Advertising Red Books-Agencies* edition):
1. Bus. Publs. 2. Cable T.V. 3. Catalogs & Directories. 4. Co-op Adv. 5. Consumer Mags. 6. D.M. to Bus. Estab.7. D.M. to Consumers 8. Daily Newsp. 9. Exhibits/Trade Shows 10. Foreign 11. Infomercial 12. Internet Adv.13. Multimedia 14. Network Radio 15. Network T.V. 16. Newsp. Distr. Mags. 17. Other 18. Outdoor (Posters, Transit) 19. Point of Purchase20. Premiums, Novelties 21. Product Samples 22. Special Events Mktg. 23. Spot Radio 24. Spot T.V. 25. Weekly Newsp. 26. Yellow Page Adv.

Synopsys, Inc. — (Continued)

SIMPLY BETTER RESULTS
SIVL
SNUG
SOLVNET
STAR-RCXT
STAR-SIMXT
SVP CAFE
SYNDICATED
SYNOPSYS
SYNPLICITY
THE SYNPLICITY LOGO
SYNPLIFY
SYNPLIFY PRO
SYNTHESIS CONSTRAINTS
OPTIMIZATION ENVIRONMENT
SYSTEM COMPILER
SYSTEM DESIGNER
TAP-IN
TAURUS
TETRAMAX
TOTALRECALL
TSUPREM-4
UMRBUS
VCS
VCS EXPRESS
VCSI
VERA
VHDL COMPILER
VIRSIM
VMC
YIELDIRECTOR

Advertising Agencies:
DMNA
97 S Second St Ste 300
San Jose, CA 95113-2512
Tel.: (408) 512-2110
Fax: (408) 297-8020

MCA Public Relations
2119 Landings Dr
Mountain View, CA 94043
Tel.: (650) 968-8900

SYNOPSYS, INC.-SYNPLICITY BUSINESS GROUP

(Group of Synopsys, Inc.)
600 W California Ave
Sunnyvale, CA 94086
Tel.: (408) 215-6000
Fax: (408) 222-0268
Approx. Rev.: $71,166,000
Approx. Number Employees: 328
Year Founded: 1994
Business Description:
Semiconductor Design & Verification Software Developer
S.I.C.: 7372; 7371
N.A.I.C.S.: 334611; 511210; 541511
Advertising Expenditures: $143,000
Personnel:
Andrew Haines, Sr. *(Sr VP-Mktg)*
Andrew Dauman *(VP-Engrg, Solutions Grp)*
James Lovas *(VP-Worldwide Sls)*
Advertising Agency:
Tsantes Consulting Group
1825 Constitution Ct
San Jose, CA 95124
Tel.: (408) 309-9926

SYNTEGRA (USA) INC.

(Sub. of British Telecommunications plc)
4201 Lexington Ave N
Saint Paul, MN 55126-6161
Tel.: (651) 415-4401
Fax: (651) 415-4891
Toll Free: (888) 742-5864
E-mail: info@syntegra.com
Web Site: www.syntegra.com
Approx. Number Employees: 600
Year Founded: 1957
Business Description:
Global Systems Integrator, Architecture Implementation & Lifetime Support of Electronic Commerce, Product Data Management, Computer Aided Design & Client Server Solutions Mfr
S.I.C.: 7373
N.A.I.C.S.: 541512
Advertising Expenditures: $200,000
Media: 2-17

SYNTEL, INC.

525 E Big Beaver Rd Ste 300
Troy, MI 48083-1364
Tel.: (248) 619-2800
Fax: (248) 619-2888
E-mail: info@syntelinc.com
Web Site: www.syntelinc.com
Approx. Rev.: $532,133,000
Approx. Number Employees: 11,710
Year Founded: 1980
Business Description:
Computer Software & Services; IT Outsourcing
S.I.C.: 7371
N.A.I.C.S.: 541511
Media: 2-7-8-10-13
Personnel:
Bharat Desai *(Co-Founder & Chm)*
Neerja Sethi *(Co-Founder & VP)*
Prashant Ranade *(Pres & CEO)*
Arvind S. Godbole *(CFO & Chief Info Security Officer)*
Daniel M. Moore *(Chief Admin Officer, Gen Counsel & Sec)*
Rakesh Khanna *(Pres-Bus Unit Banking & Fin)*
Anil Jain *(Sr VP-Insurance Vertical & Head-Bus Unit)*
R. S. Ramdas *(Sr VP-Corp Svcs & Head-Global Procurement)*
Marlin Mackey *(Sr VP-Customer Relationships)*
Lakshmanan Chidambaram *(Head-Sls & Member-Leadership Team)*
Brands & Products:
CONSIDER IT DONE
IDENTEON
INTELLISOURCING
INTELLITRANSFER
LATEST-TO-LEGACY
NEW2USA.COM
SKILLBAY
SYNAPPTEST
SYNAPPTOOL
TEAMSOURCING

SYNTELLECT, INC.

(Sub. of Enghouse Systems Limited)
2095 W Pinnaple Peak Rd Ste 110
Phoenix, AZ 85027
Tel.: (602) 789-2800
Fax: (602) 789-2768
Toll Free: (800) 788-9733
E-mail: info@syntellect.com
Web Site: www.syntellect.com
Approx. Number Employees: 120
Year Founded: 1984
Business Description:
Speech-Enabled Customer, Employee & Supply-Chain Self-Service Software Solutions & Hosted Services
S.I.C.: 3571; 3661
N.A.I.C.S.: 334111; 334210
Export
Media: 2-10-13
Personnel:
Steve Dodenhoff *(Pres)*
John Sloan *(VP-Product Mgmt & Mktg)*
Bruce Petillo *(Dir-Mktg)*
Bruce Sherman *(Product Mgr-Voiyager)*
Brands & Products:
CONTINUUM
VISTA

SYNYGY, INC.

2501 Seaport Dr Ste 100
Chester, PA 19013-2249
Tel.: (610) 494-3300
Fax: (610) 494-3301
E-mail: info@synygy.com
Web Site: www.synygy.com
E-Mail For Key Personnel:
Sales Director: sales@synygy.com
Approx. Number Employees: 450
Year Founded: 1991
Business Description:
Enterprise Incentive Management, Software & Services
S.I.C.: 8742; 7371
N.A.I.C.S.: 541611; 541511
Export
Media: 2-7-10-13-22
Personnel:
Mark A. Stiffler *(Founder, Pres & CEO)*
Karen Tulis *(Mng Dir)*
Chetan J. Shah *(COO)*
Walt E. Montague *(Gen Counsel & VP)*
Scott Cawood *(Exec VP-Global Ops)*
Kenneth Bjorkelo *(Reg VP)*
Jeff Evernham *(Reg VP)*
Amit Gupta *(Reg VP)*
Brands & Products:
PERFORMANCE DEFINED
RESULTS DELIVERED
SYNYGY
SYNYGY EIM
Advertising Agency:
Brodeur Partners
855 Boylston St 2nd Fl
Boston, MA 02116-2622
Tel.: (617) 587-2800
Fax: (617) 587-2828
Public Relations

SYS TECHNOLOGIES, INC.

(Sub. of Kratos Defense & Security Solutions, Inc.)
5050 Murphy Canyon Rd Ste 200
San Diego, CA 92123-4399
Tel.: (858) 715-5500
Fax: (858) 715-5510
Toll Free: (888) 600-9797
Web Site: www.systechnologies.com
Approx. Rev.: $75,927,000
Approx. Number Employees: 404
Business Description:
Technical Professional Services To Government Agencies
S.I.C.: 7373; 7372; 8711; 8742
N.A.I.C.S.: 541512; 334611; 541330; 541611
Media: 2-10-18-26
Personnel:
Ben Goodwin *(Sr VP-Mktg, VP-Sls & Security & Indus Sys Grp)*
Linda E. Gagnon *(Sr VP-Sys Engrg & Mgmt Div)*

SYSTEMAX, INC.

11 Harbor Park Dr
Port Washington, NY 11050-4650
Tel.: (516) 608-7000
Fax: (516) 608-7001
Web Site: www.systemax.com
Approx. Sls.: $3,589,989,000
Approx. Number Employees: 5,600
Year Founded: 1951
Business Description:
Computers, Peripherals & Software
S.I.C.: 3575; 5046; 5961
N.A.I.C.S.: 334113; 423440; 454111
Import Export
Advertising Expenditures: $31,700,000
Media: 4-5-13-23
Personnel:
Richard Leeds *(Chm & CEO)*
Robert Leeds *(Vice Chm)*
Lawrence P. Reinhold *(CFO & Exec VP)*
David Sprosty *(CEO-Tech Products Grp-North America)*
Curt S. Rush *(Gen Counsel & Sec)*
Brands & Products:
CIRCUITCITY.COM
SYSTEMAX
TIGER
ULTRA

TAB PRODUCTS CO. LLC

(Sub. of H.S. Morgan Limited Partnership)
605 Fourth St
Mayville, WI 53050
Tel.: (920) 387-3131
Fax: (920) 387-1805
Toll Free: (888) 822-9777
E-mail: info@tab.com
Web Site: www.tab.com
Sales Range: $100-124.9 Million
Approx. Number Employees: 550
Year Founded: 1947
Business Description:
Filing Equipment, Computer Accessory Products, Forms Handling Machines, Mobile Storage Systems, Labels, Folders & Filing Supplies, Office Furniture, File Services, Records Management Software
S.I.C.: 5943; 2678
N.A.I.C.S.: 453210; 322233
Export
Advertising Expenditures: $710,000
Media: 2-4-7-10-11-13-26
Distr.: Intl.; Natl.
Budget Set: June
Personnel:
William Graham *(Pres)*
Thaddeus Jaroszewicz *(CEO)*
John Palmer *(CFO)*
Charles Stilwill *(Sr VP-Sls)*
Carol Ann Hartnagle *(VP-Sls)*
Mark Mandelberg *(VP-Sls-Eastern Reg)*
Terry Dilter *(Dir-IT)*
Dana Noel *(Dir-HR)*
Lori Lockwood *(Sr Mgr-Mktg)*
Jim Hepp *(Mgr-Mfg)*

Key to Media (For complete agency information see *The Advertising Red Books-Agencies* edition):
1. Bus. Publs. 2. Cable T.V. 3. Catalogs & Directories. 4. Co-op Adv. 5. Consumer Mags. 6. D.M. to Bus. Estab.7. D.M. to Consumers 8. Daily Newsp. 9. Exhibits/Trade Shows 10. Foreign 11. Infomercial 12. Internet Adv.13. Multimedia 14. Network Radio 15. Network T.V. 16. Newsp. Distr. Mags. 17. Other 18. Outdoor (Posters, Transit) 19. Point of Purchase20. Premiums, Novelties 21. Product Samples 22. Special Events Mktg. 23. Spot Radio 24. Spot T.V. 25. Weekly Newsp. 26. Yellow Page Adv.

Brands & Products:
2TAB
COMPUCOLOR
DATA MEDIA
DATAFILE
DESIGNER SERIES
FILE TRACKER
FILEPAK
FORTIFILE
HANDLE-IT
PRESTIGE
SIDE-TRAC
SPACEFINDER
TAB-TRAC
TABQUIK
TAPE-ID
TWINFILE
UNI-TRAC

TAKE-TWO INTERACTIVE SOFTWARE, INC.
622 Broadway
New York, NY 10012-3230
Tel.: (646) 536-2842
Fax: (212) 334-6644
E-mail: ir@take2games.com
Web Site: www.take2games.com
Approx. Rev.: $1,136,876,000
Approx. Number Employees: 2,118
Business Description:
Interactive Entertainment Software, Hardware & Accessories Developer, Publisher & Distr
S.I.C.: 7372; 7371
N.A.I.C.S.: 511210; 334611; 541511
Advertising Expenditures: $115,089,000
Media: 5-8-10-13-18-19-23-24
Personnel:
Strauss H. Zelnick *(Chm & CEO)*
Lainie Goldstein *(CFO)*
Karl Slatoff *(COO)*
Sam Houser *(Pres-Rockstar Games Div)*
Seth Krauss *(Gen Counsel & Exec VP)*
Jason Argent *(VP-Mktg, 2K Sports)*
Chris Snyder *(Dir-Mktg)*
Brands & Products:
T2
TAKE-TWO INTERACTIVE

TALARIS INC.
(Sub. of Talaris Ltd.)
2441 Warrenville Rd
Lisle, IL 60532-3664
Tel.: (630) 577-1000
Fax: (630) 577-1217
Web Site: www.talaris.com
Sales Range: $75-99.9 Million
Approx. Number Employees: 30
Year Founded: 1821
Business Description:
Cash Handling Equipment Mfr
S.I.C.: 3579; 3577
N.A.I.C.S.: 333313; 334119
Import Export
Advertising Expenditures: $3,000,000
Media: 2-4-7-10
Distr.: Natl.
Personnel:
Chris Regan *(Pres)*
Diane Schreiner *(Dir-Mktg)*
Brands & Products:
ACCUCHANGE
BRANDT
CASHIER
COUNTESS
CVM 4000
NO-MOIST
SALEM

TALEO CORPORATION
4140 Dublin Blvd Ste 400
Dublin, CA 94568
Tel.: (925) 452-3000
Fax: (925) 452-3001
Toll Free: (888) 836-3669
Web Site: www.taleo.com
Approx. Rev.: $237,275,000
Approx. Number Employees: 1,164
Year Founded: 1998
Business Description:
Human Resource Management Software Publisher
S.I.C.: 7372
N.A.I.C.S.: 511210
Advertising Expenditures: $700,000
Personnel:
Michael Gregoire *(Chm & CEO)*
Douglas C. Jeffries *(CFO & Exec VP)*
Heidi M. Melin *(CMO & Exec VP)*
Jonathan Faddis *(Gen Counsel, Corp Sec & Sr VP)*
Guy Gauvin *(Exec VP-Global Svcs)*
Neil Hudspith *(Chief Customer Officer & Exec VP-Worldwide Field Ops)*
Jason Blessing *(Sr VP-Products & Tech)*
Michael Boese *(Sr VP-TBE & Talent Grid)*
Hans Lidforss *(Sr VP-Strategy & Corp Dev)*
Paul Pronsati *(Sr VP-Ops)*
Adam Brenner *(Grp VP-Europe, Middle East & Africa)*
Chris Lee *(Grp VP-People & Talent)*
Brands & Products:
TALENT DRIVES PERFORMANCE
TALEO
TALEO AGENCY
TALEO ASSESSMENT
TALEO BUSINESS EDITION
TALEO CAMPUS
TALEO COMPLIANCE
TALEO CONTINGENT
TALEO ENTERPRISE EDITION
TALEO HOURLY
TALEO ONBOARDING
TALEO PASSPORT
TALEO PROFESSIONAL
TALEO SCHEDULING CENTER
TALEO TALENTREACH

TALK-A-PHONE CO.
7530 N Natchez Ave
Niles, IL 60714
Tel.: (773) 539-1100
Fax: (773) 539-1241
E-mail: info@talkaphone.com
Web Site: www.talkaphone.com
E-Mail For Key Personnel:
Sales Director: rshanes@talkaphone.com
Approx. Number Employees: 50
Year Founded: 1937
Business Description:
Intercom Systems Mfr for Office, Industrial Use, Fast Food Drive Thru Systems, Self-Service Gas Station Systems & Americans with Disabilities Act Complaint Communication Systems & Hands-Free Emergency Phones (ADA Compliant)
S.I.C.: 3669
N.A.I.C.S.: 334290
Export
Media: 2-4-10
Distr.: Natl.
Personnel:
Samuel Shanes *(Owner)*
Zvie Liberman *(Pres)*
Robert Shanes *(VP-Sls)*
Brands & Products:
CREATING COMMUNICATIONS SOLUTIONS
TALK-A-PHONE

TALX CORPORATION
(Div. of Equifax Inc.)
11432 Lackland
Saint Louis, MO 63146
Tel.: (314) 214-7000
Fax: (314) 214-7588
E-mail: moreinfo@talx.com
Web Site: www.talx.com
Approx. Rev.: $207,427,008
Approx. Number Employees: 1,751
Year Founded: 1973
Business Description:
Outsource Services for Human Resources & Payroll Applications
S.I.C.: 7373
N.A.I.C.S.: 541512
Media: 7-10-13-26
Personnel:
William W. Canfield *(Pres & CEO)*
Lee Adrean *(CFO)*
John F. Williamson *(Sr VP-Ops & IT)*
Robert Bell *(VP-Sls)*
Brands & Products:
EPAYROLL
FASTIME
HIREXPRESS
UC EXPRESS
W-2 EXPRESS
THE WORK NUMBER
THE WORK NUMBER EPAYROLL SERVICES

TANDBERG DATA
(Sub. of Tandberg Data GmbH)
2108 55th St
Boulder, CO 80301-2601
Tel.: (303) 442-4333
Fax: (303) 417-7170
Toll Free: (800) 392-2983
E-mail: salesUS@tandbergdata.com
Web Site: www.tandbergdata.com
Sales Range: $75-99.9 Million
Approx. Number Employees: 318
Year Founded: 1987
Business Description:
Business Data Storage & Protection Solutions
S.I.C.: 7372
N.A.I.C.S.: 511210
Import Export
Advertising Expenditures: $186,000
Media: 2-7-10-13-21
Personnel:
Scott Petersen *(Sr VP)*
James Jackson *(Product Mgr-Tape Drives)*
Brands & Products:
EXABYTE
VXA

TANGENT COMPUTER INC.
197 Airport Blvd
Burlingame, CA 94010-2006
Tel.: (650) 342-9388
Fax: (650) 342-9380
Toll Free: (800) 342-9388
E-mail: 1sales1@tangent.com
Web Site: www.tangent.com
E-Mail For Key Personnel:
Sales Director: sales@tangent.com
Approx. Number Employees: 90
Year Founded: 1989
Business Description:
Computer Mfr
S.I.C.: 3571; 5734
N.A.I.C.S.: 334111; 443120
Import Export
Media: 8-10
Personnel:
Doug Monsour *(Pres & CEO)*
Brands & Products:
DATACOVE
MEDALLION
PENDANT
PILLAR
SHUTTLE
TANGENT
TANGENTSTOR
VALERA
Advertising Agency:
5W Public Relations
888 7th Ave 12th Fl
New York, NY 10106
Tel.: (212) 999-5585
Fax: (646) 328-1711
(DataCove)

TANGOE, INC.
35 Executive Blvd
Orange, CT 06477
Tel.: (203) 859-9300
Fax: (203) 859-9427
E-mail: info@tangoe.com
Web Site: www.tangoe.com
Approx. Rev.: $56,916,722
Approx. Number Employees: 439
Year Founded: 2000
Business Description:
Communications Software & Services
S.I.C.: 7372; 3669; 7371
N.A.I.C.S.: 511210; 334290; 541511
Personnel:
Charles D. Gamble *(Founder & Sr VP-Fixed Solutions)*
Albert R. Subbloie, Jr. *(Chm, Pres & CEO)*
Gary R. Martino *(CFO)*
Craig Gosselin *(CMO)*
Albert M. Rossini *(Exec VP-Global Sls)*
Chris Mezzatesta *(Sr VP)*
Paul Schmidt *(Sr VP-Mktg)*
Scott E. Snyder *(Sr VP-Mobile Solutions)*
Robert Whitmore *(Sr VP-Prof Svcs)*
Jacques Wagemaker *(VP-Mktg)*
Advertising Agency:
PAN Communications
300 Brickstone Sq 7th Fl
Andover, MA 01810
Tel.: (978) 474-1900
Fax: (978) 474-1903

TARGUS GROUP INTERNATIONAL, INC.
(Holding of Fenway Partners, Inc.)
1211 N Miller St
Anaheim, CA 92806-1933
Tel.: (714) 765-5555
Fax: (714) 765-5599
Toll Free: (877) 482-7487
E-mail: publicrelations@targus.com
Web Site: www.targus.com

Key to Media (For complete agency information see *The Advertising Red Books-Agencies* edition):
1. Bus. Publs. 2. Cable T.V. 3. Catalogs & Directories. 4. Co-op Adv. 5. Consumer Mags. 6. D.M. to Bus. Estab.7. D.M. to Consumers 8. Daily Newsp. 9. Exhibits/Trade Shows 10. Foreign 11. Infomercial 12. Internet Adv.13. Multimedia 14. Network Radio 15. Network T.V. 16. Newsp. Distr. Mags. 17. Other 18. Outdoor (Posters, Transit) 19. Point of Purchase20. Premiums, Novelties 21. Product Samples 22. Special Events Mktg. 23. Spot Radio 24. Spot T.V. 25. Weekly Newsp. 26. Yellow Page Adv.

Targus Group International, Inc. — (Continued)

Approx. Number Employees: 250
Year Founded: 1982
Business Description:
Portable Solutions & Mobile Computing Accessories Mfr
S.I.C.: 5099
N.A.I.C.S.: 423990
Media: 6-10
Personnel:
Robert L. Davis *(Gen Counsel & Sr VP)*
Theresa Hope-Reese *(Sr VP-HR)*
Al Giazzon *(Mgr-Mktg)*
Henry Watanabe *(Mgr-Product Mktg)*
Brands & Products:
PORT
TARGUS
Advertising Agency:
KLR Communications, Inc.
575 Anton Blvd 3rd Fl
Costa Mesa, CA 92626
Tel.: (949) 509-1888

TEAM HEALTH, INC.
(Sub. of Team Health Holdings, Inc.)
(d/b/a TeamHealth)
1900 Winston Rd Ste 300
Knoxville, TN 37919-3606
Mailing Address:
PO Box 30698
Knoxville, TN 37919
Tel.: (865) 693-1000
Fax: (865) 539-8003
Toll Free: (800) 342-2898
Web Site: www.teamhealth.com
Sales Range: $350-399.9 Million
Approx. Number Employees: 5,800
Business Description:
Health Care Staffing & Management Services
S.I.C.: 8742
N.A.I.C.S.: 541611
Media: 2-7-10-13
Personnel:
Lynn Massingale *(Chm)*
Greg Roth *(Pres & CEO)*
David P. Jones *(CFO)*
Joseph B. Carman *(Chief Admin Officer)*
George Tracy *(Pres-Mary Anne Koines & Sr VP)*
Robert Joyner *(Gen Counsel & Exec VP)*
Matthew M. Rice *(Sr VP-Northwest Emergency Physicians)*
Robert J. Abramowski *(Exec VP-Fin & Admin)*
Kent Bristow *(Sr VP-Ops)*
John Craig *(Sr VP)*
Michael Shea *(Sr VP-Bus Dev & Mktg)*
Robert Stiefel *(Sr VP)*
Tracy Young *(VP-Mktg)*

TECH DATA CORPORATION
5350 Tech Data Dr
Clearwater, FL 33760-3122
Mailing Address:
PO Box 6260
Clearwater, FL 33758-6260
Tel.: (727) 539-7429
Fax: (727) 538-7803
E-mail: ir@techdata.com
Web Site: www.techdata.com
Approx. Sls.: $24,375,973,000
Approx. Number Employees: 8,700
Year Founded: 1974
Business Description:
Information Technology Hardware & Software Mfr & Distr
S.I.C.: 5045; 3577; 7372
N.A.I.C.S.: 423430; 334119; 511210
Import Export
Media: 2-5
Distr.: Intl.
Budget Set: July
Personnel:
Steven A. Raymund *(Chm)*
Robert M. Dutkowsky *(CEO)*
Jeffery P. Howells *(CFO & Exec VP)*
John M. Tonnison *(CIO & Exec VP)*
Nestor Cano *(Pres-Europe)*
Murray Wright *(Pres-Americas)*
David R. Vetter *(Gen Counsel, Sec & Sr VP)*
Charles V. Dannewitz *(Treas & Sr VP-Tax)*
Joseph B. Trepani *(Sr VP & Controller)*
Darryl Branch *(Sr VP-Logistics & Integration Svcs)*
Benjamin Godwin *(Sr VP-Real Estate & Corp Svcs)*
Pete Peterson *(Sr VP-Sls)*
Brooke D. Powers *(Sr VP-Pur & Supply Chain Mgmt-America)*
Joseph Quaglia *(Sr VP-US Mktg)*
William K. Todd Jr. *(Sr VP)*
Gregory S. Banning *(VP-Small to Medium Sized Bus Sls & Gen Mgr-Ops-Costa Rica)*
Chuck Bartlett *(VP-Mktg)*
Marty Bauerlein *(VP-Sls)*
Terry Hagerty *(VP-Natl Acct Sls)*
Mark Livings *(VP-eBusiness Sys)*
Caryl N. Lucarelli *(VP-HR)*
John O'Shea *(VP-Product Mktg)*
Jackie Baron *(Dir-Sls)*
Brands & Products:
THE DIFFERENCE IN DISTRIBUTION
TECH DATA

TECHDEPOT
(Div. of 4SURE.com, Inc.)
6 Cambridge Dr
Trumbull, CT 06611
Tel.: (203) 615-7000
Fax: (203) 615-7006
Toll Free: (800) 721-8344
Web Site: www.techdepot.com
Sales Range: $150-199.9 Million
Business Description:
Computer & Technology Products Direct Marketer
S.I.C.: 5045
N.A.I.C.S.: 423430
Media: 7-8-13
Personnel:
Bruce Martin *(Pres)*
Candy Murphy *(VP-Mdsg & Mktg)*

TECHNISOURCE, INC.
(Sub. of SFN Group, Inc.)
425 W Capitol Ave
Little Rock, AR 72201-3401
Tel.: (501) 664-1100
Fax: (501) 537-4518
Toll Free: (877) 664-1101
E-mail: info@technisource.com
Web Site: www.technisource.com
Approx. Rev.: $279,000,000
Approx. Number Employees: 3,000
Year Founded: 1987
Business Description:
Information Technology Staffing & Consulting Services
S.I.C.: 7363; 5045
N.A.I.C.S.: 561320; 423430
Advertising Expenditures: $1,300,000
Media: 7-13
Personnel:
Stephen R. Bova *(Chm & CEO)*
Michael Winwood *(Pres)*
John Baschab *(Sr VP-Mgmt Svcs)*
Brands & Products:
TECHNISOURCE

TECHNOLOGY EXECUTIVES CLUB, LTD.
1580 S Milwaukee Ave Ste 305
Libertyville, IL 60048
Tel.: (847) 837-3900
Fax: (847) 837-3901
Web Site: www.technologyexecutivesclub.com
Approx. Number Employees: 5
Year Founded: 2000
Business Description:
Promoter of Internet Business to Business
S.I.C.: 6411
N.A.I.C.S.: 524210
Media: 2-9-10-13
Personnel:
Alex Jarett *(Pres)*
Maria Tuthill *(Dir-Member Svcs)*
Brands & Products:
COLLABORATION CHALLENGES & STRATEGIES
TECHNOLOGY EXECUTIVES CLUB
VIRTUALIZATION & GREEN IT

TECHTARGET, INC.
275 Grove St
Newton, MA 02466
Tel.: (617) 431-9200
Toll Free: (888) 274-4111
E-mail: info@techtarget.com
Web Site: www.techtarget.com
Approx. Rev.: $95,009,000
Approx. Number Employees: 577
Year Founded: 1999
Business Description:
Information Services & Solutions for IT Industry
S.I.C.: 2741; 5045; 5961; 7379
N.A.I.C.S.: 516110; 425110; 454111; 541519
Advertising Expenditures: $30,000
Media: 2-13
Personnel:
Don Hawk *(Co-Founder & Pres)*
Greg Strakosch *(Co-Founder & CEO)*
Jeffrey R. Wakely *(CFO)*
Mike Bolduc *(Publr-TechTarget Bus Applications & Analytics Media)*
Marc Laplante *(Publr-Techtarget Data Center & Virtualization Media)*
Brian McGovern *(Publr-TechTarget Application Dev Media)*
Michael Cotoia *(Exec VP)*
Marilou Barsam *(Sr VP-Client Svcs & Corp Mktg)*
Jeff Ramminger *(Sr VP-Product Mgmt)*
Sean Tierney *(Sr VP-Product Dev & Tech)*
Maureen Donnelly *(VP-Fin)*
Arden Port *(VP-HR)*
Susan Fogarty *(Editorial Dir-Networking Media)*
Kerry Glance *(Editorial Dir- Enterprise Applications)*
Tom Click *(Sr Dir-Sls)*
Brands & Products:
LABMICE.NET
MYITFORUM.COM
SEARCH390.COM
SEARCH400.COM
SEARCHCIO-MIDMARKET.COM
SEARCHCIO.COM
SEARCHCOMPLIANCE.COM
SEARCHCRM.COM
SEARCHDATABACKUP.COM
SEARCHDATABASE.COM
SEARCHDATAMANAGEMENT.COM
SEARCHDISASTERRECOVERY.COM
SEARCHDOMINO.COM
SEARCHENTERPRISEDESKTOP.COM
SEARCHENTERPRISELINUX.COM
SEARCHENTERPRISEWAN.COM
SEARCHEXCHANGE.COM
SEARCHFINANCIALSECURITY.COM
SEARCHMANUFACTURINGERP.COM
SEARCHMIDMARKETSECURITY.COM
SEARCHMOBILECOMPUTING.COM
SEARCHNETWORKING.COM
SEARCHORACLE.COM
SEARCHSAP.COM
SEARCHSECURITYCHANNEL.COM
SEARCHSECURITY.COM
SEARCHSECURITY.CO.UK
SEARCHSMALLBIZ.COM
SEARCHSMBSTORAGE.COM
SEARCHSQLSERVER.COM
SEARCHSTORAGE.COM
SEARCHSTORAGE.CO.UK
SEARCHTELECOM.COM
SEARCHUNIFIEDCOMMUNICATIONS.COM
SEARCHVB.COM
SEARCHWEBSERVICES.COM
SEARCHWIN2000.COM
SEARCHWINDOWSSERVER.COM
SEARCHWINIT.COM
SEARCHWINSYSTEMS.COM
STORAGE MAGAZINE
TECH TARGET.COM NETWORK OF IT WEBSITES
TECHTARGET
WHATIS.COM

TECHTRACKER, INC.
55 SW Yamhill St 3rd Fl
Portland, OR 97204-3312
Tel.: (503) 227-2571
Fax: (503) 227-2573
E-mail: email@techtracker.com
Web Site: www.techtracker.com
Approx. Number Employees: 25
Year Founded: 1999
Business Description:
Software Information & Services
S.I.C.: 7372
N.A.I.C.S.: 511210
Media: 4-10-13-19-23
Brands & Products:
MACFIXIT PRO
MACFIXIT.COM
TECHTRACKER
TECHTRACKER PRO
VERSIONTRACKER PLUS
VERSIONTRACKER PRO
VERSIONTRACKER.COM

TECSYS, INC.
No-1 Pl Alexis Nihon Ste 800
Montreal, QC H3Z 3B8, Canada

Key to Media (For complete agency information see *The Advertising Red Books-Agencies* edition):
1. Bus. Publs. 2. Cable T.V. 3. Catalogs & Directories. 4. Co-op Adv. 5. Consumer Mags. 6. D.M. to Bus. Estab.7. D.M. to Consumers 8. Daily Newsp. 9. Exhibits/Trade Shows 10. Foreign 11. Infomercial 12. Internet Adv.13. Multimedia 14. Network Radio 15. Network T.V. 16. Newsp. Distr. Mags. 17. Other 18. Outdoor (Posters, Transit) 19. Point of Purchase20. Premiums, Novelties 21. Product Samples 22. Special Events Mktg. 23. Spot Radio 24. Spot T.V. 25. Weekly Newsp. 26. Yellow Page Adv.

Tel.: (514) 866-0001
Fax: (514) 866-1805
Toll Free: (800) 922-8649
E-mail: info@tecsys.com
Web Site: www.tecsys.com
Approx. Rev.: $13,048,740
Approx. Number Employees: 242
Business Description:
Developer, Marketer & Seller of Wide-Chain Management Software
S.I.C.: 3577
N.A.I.C.S.: 334119
Media: 10
Personnel:
David Brereton *(Exec Chm)*
Peter Brereton *(Pres & CEO)*
Berty Ho-Wo-Cheong *(CFO, Sec, VP-Fin & Admin)*
Greg MacNeill *(Sr VP)*
Mike Kalika *(VP & Gen Mgr-TLM Grp)*
Tom Wilson *(VP & Gen Mgr-SMB & IDM Grp)*
Patricia Barry *(VP-HR)*
Robert Colosino *(VP-Mktg & Bus Dev)*
John Reichert *(Mgr-WMS Product & Dir-Client Solutions)*
Brands & Products:
ELITE
ENABLING SUPPLY CHAIN EXCELLENCE
THE ITOPIA ADVANTAGE
TECSYS

TEKSYSTEMS, INC.
(Sub. of Allegis Group Inc.)
7437 Race Rd
Hanover, MD 21076
Tel.: (410) 540-7100
Fax: (410) 570-3437
Toll Free: (888) 519-0776
E-mail: webmaster@teksystems.com
Web Site: www.teksystems.com
Sales Range: $1-4.9 Billion
Approx. Number Employees: 4,000
Business Description:
Provider of Strategic Staffing & Managed Services for Information Technology & Communications
S.I.C.: 7373; 7376
N.A.I.C.S.: 541512; 541513
Media: 2
Personnel:
John T. Carey *(Chm)*

TELANETIX, INC.
11201 SE 8th St Ste 200
Bellevue, WA 98004
Tel.: (206) 621-3500
Fax: (425) 646-9078
E-mail: info@telanetix.com
Web Site: www.telanetix.com
Approx. Rev.: $28,520,084
Approx. Number Employees: 86
Year Founded: 2002
Business Description:
VoIP Products & Services
S.I.C.: 3663; 4812
N.A.I.C.S.: 334220; 517212
Advertising Expenditures: $2,400,000
Personnel:
Douglas N. Johnson *(Chm & CEO)*
J. Paul Quinn *(CFO)*

TELCORDIA TECHNOLOGIES, INC.
(Joint Venture of Providence Equity Partners LLC & Warburg Pincus LLC)
1 Telcordia Dr
Piscataway, NJ 08854-4157
Tel.: (732) 699-2000
Fax: (732) 336-2320
Toll Free: (800) 521-2673
Web Site: www.telcordia.com
Sales Range: $800-899.9 Million
Approx. Number Employees: 2,500
Year Founded: 1984
Business Description:
Telecommunications Networking & Operations Software
S.I.C.: 7371; 7373
N.A.I.C.S.: 541511; 541512
Media: 2-7-9-10-11-13-17-20-22
Distr.: Natl.
Budget Set: Dec.
Personnel:
Mark Greenquist *(Pres & CEO)*
Carol Skurkay *(CIO & VP)*
Linda DeLukey *(Exec VP-HR & Security)*
Krista Wald *(Exec Dir-Corp Comm)*
Nicole Gagnan *(Mgr-Internet Adv)*
Advertising Agency:
Rare Method Interactive Corp.
165 S Main St Ste 300
Salt Lake City, UT 84101
Tel.: (801) 539-1818
Fax: (801) 539-8484

TELEBYTE, INC.
355 Marcus Blvd
Hauppauge, NY 11788
Tel.: (631) 423-3232
Fax: (631) 385-8184
Toll Free: (800) 835-3298
E-mail: sales@telebyteusa.com
Web Site: www.telebyte.biz
E-Mail For Key Personnel:
Sales Director: sales@telebyteusa.com
Sales Range: $1-9.9 Million
Approx. Number Employees: 40
Year Founded: 1983
Business Description:
Fiber & Copper Connectivity Products Mfr
S.I.C.: 3669; 3661
N.A.I.C.S.: 334290; 334210
Media: 4-7-10
Personnel:
Kenneth Schneider *(Owner)*
Michael Breneisen *(Pres)*

TELECOMMUNICATION SYSTEMS INC.
275 W St
Annapolis, MD 21401-3466
Tel.: (410) 263-7616
Fax: (410) 263-7617
E-mail: tcsupport@telecomsys.com
Web Site: www1.telecomsys.com
Approx. Rev.: $388,803,000
Approx. Number Employees: 1,189
Year Founded: 1987
Business Description:
Computer Integrated Systems Design Services
S.I.C.: 7373; 4899; 7372
N.A.I.C.S.: 541512; 334611; 517910
Advertising Expenditures: $54,000
Media: 2-7-10-13-23-24
Personnel:
Maurice B. Tose *(Chm, Pres & CEO)*
Thomas M. Brandt, Jr. *(CFO & Sr VP)*
Richard A. Young *(COO & Exec VP)*
Timothy Lorello *(CMO)*
Drew Morin *(CTO & Sr VP)*
Michael D. Bristol, Sr. *(Sr VP & Gen Mgr-Govt Solutions Grp)*
Brian McNealy *(Sr VP-Global Comml Sls)*
Chris Nabinger *(Sr VP-Svc Bureau Ops)*
Jay F. Whitehurst *(Sr VP-Comml Software Grp)*
Patrick Brant *(VP-Sls & Mktg-Govt Solutions Grp)*
Allen Green *(VP-Govt Strategic Programs)*
Kim Robert Scovill *(Sr Dir-Legal & Regulatory Affairs)*
Brands & Products:
ALERTS
CONNECTIONS THAT MATTER
ENABLING CONVERGENT TECHNOLOGIES
GALILEO
LIVEWIRE911
MYCOOP
RAVE911
SWIFTLINK
TCS
TCS SNAPTRACK
TELECONTINUITY SERVICE
VOICE ENABLED MARKETPLACE
WIRELESS INTELLIGENT GATEWAY
XYFORCE
XYPAGES
XYPOINT
Advertising Agencies:
Adler Display
7140 Windsor Blvd
Baltimore, MD 21244
Tel.: (410) 281-1200
Fax: (410) 281-2187
Toll Free: (888) 578-7443
Exhibit Booth Fabrication & Graphics

G&G Outfitters Inc.
4901 Forbes Blvd
Lanham, MD 20706
Tel.: (301) 731-2099
Fax: (301) 731-5199

Welz & Weisel Communications
9990 Lee Hwy Ste 500
Fairfax, VA 22030
Tel.: (703) 218-3555
Pub Rels
— Evan W. Weisel *(Acct Exec)*

TELEDATA INFORMATICS LTD.
(Sub. of Teledata Informatics Ltd.)
245 Main St Ste 390
White Plains, NY 10601-2425
Tel.: (914) 686-2100
Fax: (914) 686-7900
E-mail: info@teledata-usa.com
Web Site: www.teledata-usa.com
Business Description:
Software Products & Services
S.I.C.: 7372; 7373; 7379
N.A.I.C.S.: 334611; 511210; 541512; 541519
Media: 10
Personnel:
Anush Ramachandran *(Owner)*

TELETOUCH COMMUNICATIONS, INC.
5718 Airport Freeway
Fort Worth, TX 76117
Mailing Address:
PO Box 6540
Tyler, TX 75711-6540
Tel.: (817) 654-6225
Toll Free: (800) 232-3888
E-mail: information@teletouch.com
Web Site: www.teletouch.com
Approx. Rev.: $51,959,000
Approx. Number Employees: 199
Year Founded: 1977
Business Description:
Pager Communication Services
S.I.C.: 7629; 4812
N.A.I.C.S.: 517211; 517212; 811211
Advertising Expenditures: $582,000
Media: 10
Personnel:
Robert M. McMurrey *(Chm)*
Thomas A. Hyde, Jr. *(Pres & COO)*
Douglas E. Sloan *(CFO)*

TELEVIDEO, INC.
2342 Harris Way
San Jose, CA 95131-1413
Tel.: (408) 954-8333
Fax: (408) 954-0622
E-mail: info@televideo.com
Web Site: www.televideo.com
Sales Range: $1-9.9 Million
Approx. Number Employees: 20
Year Founded: 1975
Business Description:
Designs, Manufactures & Markets High Performance Video Display Terminals
S.I.C.: 3575; 3679
N.A.I.C.S.: 334113; 334419
Export
Advertising Expenditures: $38,000
Media: 2-5-7-10-13-26
Distr.: Direct to Consumer; Intl.; Natl.; Reg.
Budget Set: Quarterly
Personnel:
K. Philip Hwang *(Chm & CEO)*
Brands & Products:
PIONEERS IN NETWORK COMPUTING
TELECLIENT
TELECLIENT 7000
TELECLIENT TC7010
TELECLIENT TC7020
TELECLIENT TC7370
TELECLIENT TC7380
TELEMANAGER
TELESMART
TELEVIDEO

TELOS CORPORATION
19886 Ashburn Rd
Ashburn, VA 20147-2358
Tel.: (703) 724-3800
Fax: (703) 724-3855
Toll Free: (800) 444-9628
E-mail: info@telos.com
Web Site: www.telos.com
Approx. Rev.: $225,797,000
Approx. Number Employees: 630
Year Founded: 1967
Business Description:
IT Solutions
S.I.C.: 7373
N.A.I.C.S.: 541512
Export
Media: 2-4-10-20
Distr.: Natl.
Budget Set: Jan.
Personnel:
John B. Wood *(Chm & CEO)*
Michele Nakazawa *(CFO & Exec VP)*

Key to Media (For complete agency information see *The Advertising Red Books-Agencies* edition):
1. Bus. Publs. 2. Cable T.V. 3. Catalogs & Directories. 4. Co-op Adv. 5. Consumer Mags. 6. D.M. to Bus. Estab.7. D.M. to Consumers
8. Daily Newsp. 9. Exhibits/Trade Shows 10. Foreign 11. Infomercial 12. Internet Adv.13. Multimedia 14. Network Radio
15. Network T.V. 16. Newsp. Distr. Mags. 17. Other 18. Outdoor (Posters, Transit) 19. Point of Purchase20. Premiums, Novelties
21. Product Samples 22. Special Events Mktg. 23. Spot Radio 24. Spot T.V. 25. Weekly Newsp. 26. Yellow Page Adv.

Telos Corporation — (Continued)

Edward L. Williams *(COO & Exec VP)*
Michael P. Flaherty *(Chief Admin Officer, Gen Counsel & Exec VP)*
Richard P. Tracy *(CTO, Chief Security Officer & Sr VP)*
Robert J. Marino *(Exec VP-Special Projects)*
Brendan D. Malloy *(Sr VP & Gen Mgr-Secure Networks Div)*
Robert J. Brandewie *(Sr VP-Identity & Security Solutions)*
Emmett Wood *(VP-Mktg)*
Anthony Faughn *(Dir-Bus Dev-Special Programs-Secure Networks Grp)*
Renate Neely *(Dir-Mktg)*

Brands & Products:
TELOS
XACTA
XACTA COMMERCE TRUST
XACTA IA MANAGER
XACTA WEBC&A

TELTRONICS, INC.

2511 Corporate Way
Palmetto, FL 34221
Tel.: (941) 753-5000
Fax: (941) 751-7724
E-mail: srq@teltronics.com
Web Site: www.teltronics.com
E-Mail For Key Personnel:
President: ecameron@teltronics.com
Approx. Sls.: $43,092,000
Approx. Number Employees: 186
Year Founded: 1969
Business Description:
Equipment & Application Software Developer, Mfr & Marketer for the Telecommunications Industry
S.I.C.: 3679; 3661; 3669
N.A.I.C.S.: 334418; 334210; 334290
Export
Advertising Expenditures: $100,000
Media: 2-7-8-10-13-18-20-21-22-26
Personnel:
Ewen R. Cameron *(Pres & CEO)*
Angela L. Marvin *(CFO & VP-Fin)*
Norman R. Dobiesz *(Exec VP-Bus Dev)*
Richard W. Begando *(Sr VP-Intl Sls)*
Robert B. Ramey *(Sr VP-Mfg Ops)*
Kevin Wilson *(Sr VP-Engrg)*
Christopher Doyle *(VP-Mktg)*
Blair O'Keefe *(VP-Legal Affairs)*

Brands & Products:
20-20
20-20 IXP
CALL QUEST
CERATO
CERATO IP
CERATO ME/LE
CERATO SE
CERATO VISION IP
CYPREON
IDEAS THAT COMMUNICATE
IRISNGEN
IXP
NET-PATH
NET-PATH PLUS
NET-PATHM
OMNIWORKS
SEBEA
SITE EVENT BUFFER II
TELTRONICS
TELTRONICS IRISNGEN
VISION
VISION I PHONE
VISION LS
VISION PATH
VISIONWORKS
VOICE FORUM
VOICE FORUM MANAGER

THE TELX GROUP, INC.

1 State St 21st Fl
New York, NY 10004
Tel.: (212) 480-3300
Fax: (212) 480-8384
Web Site: www.telx.com
Approx. Rev.: $98,335,000
Approx. Number Employees: 175
Year Founded: 2000
Business Description:
Network Neutral, Global Interconnection & Colocation Solutions
S.I.C.: 3663
N.A.I.C.S.: 334220
Advertising Expenditures: $161,000
Media: 10-17-22
Personnel:
Christopher W. Downie *(Pres & CFO)*
Eric Shepcaro *(CEO)*
Clayton Mynard *(Gen Counsel, Sec & Sr VP)*
William Kolman *(Exec VP-Sls)*
Michael Terlizzi *(Exec VP-Ops)*
J. Todd Raymond *(Sr VP-Facility Acq)*
Michael Cattell *(VP-Vertical Markets)*

TENSION ENVELOPE CORPORATION

819 E 19th St
Kansas City, MO 64108-1703
Tel.: (816) 471-3800
Fax: (816) 283-1498
E-mail: inform@tension.com
Web Site: www.tension.com
E-Mail For Key Personnel:
President: wsberkley@tension.com
Public Relations: dimler@tension.com
Approx. Rev.: $200,000,000
Approx. Number Employees: 1,000
Year Founded: 1886
Business Description:
Custom Envelopes Mfr
S.I.C.: 2677; 5112
N.A.I.C.S.: 322232; 424120
Advertising Expenditures: $250,000
Media: 1-2-7-10-13-26
Distr.: Direct to Consumer; Natl.
Budget Set: Oct.
Personnel:
Bill Berkley *(Founder, Pres & CEO)*
E. Bertram Berkley *(Chm)*
Dan Imler *(Dir-Adv)*

Brands & Products:
ADDRESS SAVER
BOXVELOPE
CARBONLESS-RECEIPT
FORMVELOPE
HOT POTATO
KARD-KARRIER
KARDVELOPE
LEATHERETTE
PANEL-LOK
PHOTO WALLET ENVELOPES
PULL-OPE
QUICK-OPE
RIP-OPE
ROUND TRIP
SEAL'N RESEAL
SEND 'N RETURN
SIM-PULL
SPECIAL WINDOWS
STRIP-N-SEAL
TEN-TUF ENVELOPES
TENSION GROOVED ENVELOPES
TOUCH 'N SEAL

Advertising Agency:
Walz Tetrick Advertising
6299 Nall Ave Ste 300
Mission, KS 66202-3547
Tel.: (913) 789-8778
Fax: (913) 789-8493
(Envelopes)
— Charles M. Tetrick *(Pres.)*

TERADATA CORPORATION

10000 Innovation Dr
Dayton, OH 45342
Toll Free: (866) 548-8348
Web Site: www.teradata.com
Approx. Rev.: $1,936,000,000
Approx. Number Employees: 7,400
Business Description:
Data Warehousing & Analytic Technology Products & Services
S.I.C.: 7374
N.A.I.C.S.: 518210
Export
Media: 10-13-22
Personnel:
James M. Ringler *(Chm)*
Michael F. Koehler *(Pres & CEO)*
Stephen M. Scheppmann *(CFO)*
Bruce A. Langos *(COO)*
Darryl D. Mcdonald *(CMO, Exec VP-Applications & Bus Dev)*
Todd B Carver *(Deputy Gen Counsel & Chief Ethics/Compliance Officer)*
Alan Chow *(Chief Customer Officer)*
Rocky J. Blanton *(Pres-Americas Reg)*
Peter Hand *(Pres-Asia Pacific)*
Hermann Wimmer *(Pres-EMEA Reg)*
Laura Nyquist *(Gen Counsel & Sec)*
Robert E. Fair, Jr. *(Exec VP-Global Field Ops)*
Dan Harrington *(Exec VP-Tech & Support Svcs)*
Saundra Davis *(VP-HR)*

Advertising Agency:
BRC Marketing Inc.
7051 Corporate Way
Dayton, OH 45459
Tel.: (937) 384-0515
Fax: (937) 384-0522
Toll Free: (888) 905-0515

THOMAS GROUP, INC.

5221 N O'Connor Blvd Ste 500
Irving, TX 75039
Tel.: (972) 869-3400
Fax: (972) 443-1742
Toll Free: (800) 826-2057
E-mail: info@thomasgroup.com
Web Site: www.thomasgroup.com
Approx. Rev.: $3,514,000
Approx. Number Employees: 28
Year Founded: 1978
Business Description:
Operations & Process Improvement Management Consulting Services
S.I.C.: 8742
N.A.I.C.S.: 541614; 541611
Advertising Expenditures: $20,000
Media: 10
Personnel:
Michael E. McGrath *(Chm)*
Mike Romeri *(Pres & CEO)*
Frank W. Tilley *(CFO & VP)*
Tom Zych *(Pres-Govt Ops)*

THOMSON COMPUMARK

(Sub. of Thomson Legal)
500 Victory Rd
North Quincy, MA 02171-3132
Tel.: (617) 479-1600
Fax: (617) 786-8273
Fax: (800) 543-1983
Toll Free: (800) 692-8833
E-mail: support@t-t.com
Web Site: www.compumark.thomson.com
Approx. Number Employees: 350
Year Founded: 1932
Business Description:
Trademark Search Services; Intellectual Property Research
S.I.C.: 7375
N.A.I.C.S.: 518111
Media: 2-4-7-10-21
Personnel:
Carla Murphy *(Exec Asst , CTO-IP Solutions & VP-Product Dev)*
Ronda Majure *(VP-Sls & Mktg-Americas)*
Brian Baker *(Sls Mgr-Central US)*
Chris Tangang *(Mgr-Sls)*

Brands & Products:
SAEGIS
TRADEMARKSCAN

THOMSON ELITE

(Sub. of Thomson Legal)
5100 W Goldleaf Cir Ste 100
Los Angeles, CA 90056-1271
Tel.: (323) 642-5200
Fax: (323) 642-5400
E-mail: webmaster@elite.com
Web Site: www.elite.com
Approx. Number Employees: 600
Year Founded: 1981
Business Description:
Financial & Practice Management Software & Services
S.I.C.: 7389; 2741
N.A.I.C.S.: 519190; 516110
Media: 2-7-13
Distr.: Intl.
Personnel:
Steven M. Buege *(Pres & CEO)*
Dan Tacone *(Sr VP)*
Marlowe Lichtenfeld *(VP-HR)*
Salim Sunderji *(VP-Fin)*
Steve Todd *(VP-Legal)*

Brands & Products:
ELITE APEX
ENCOMPASS
TIMESOLV
TIMETRAX

THOMSON REUTERS

(Formerly Micromedex, Inc.)
(Sub. of Thomson Healthcare)
6200 S Syracuse Way Ste 300
Greenwood Village, CO 80111-4740
Tel.: (303) 486-6400
Fax: (303) 486-6464
Toll Free: (800) 525-9083
Sales Range: $75-99.9 Million
Approx. Number Employees: 450
Year Founded: 1974
Business Description:
Computerized & Printed Information for Professionals
S.I.C.: 7375
N.A.I.C.S.: 518111
Media: 2-4-7-13

Key to Media (For complete agency information see *The Advertising Red Books-Agencies* edition):
1. Bus. Publs. 2. Cable T.V. 3. Catalogs & Directories. 4. Co-op Adv. 5. Consumer Mags. 6. D.M. to Bus. Estab.7. D.M. to Consumers 8. Daily Newsp. 9. Exhibits/Trade Shows 10. Foreign 11. Infomercial 12. Internet Adv.13. Multimedia 14. Network Radio 15. Network T.V. 16. Newsp. Distr. Mags. 17. Other 18. Outdoor (Posters, Transit) 19. Point of Purchase20. Premiums, Novelties 21. Product Samples 22. Special Events Mktg. 23. Spot Radio 24. Spot T.V. 25. Weekly Newsp. 26. Yellow Page Adv.

Personnel:
Scott Kinney *(Pres-West Education Grp)*
Pete Dorogoff *(VP & Head-Digital & Social Media-Global)*
Rick Plaut *(Editor-Web)*
Ivan Oransky *(Exec Dir-Reuters Health)*

Brands & Products:
DRUGDEX
HEALTHCARE SERIES
POISINDEX
RIGHT DECISION. RIGHT NOW
USPDI

THOMSON RIA
(Sub. of Thomson Reuters Tax & Accounting)
2395 Midway Rd
Carrollton, TX 75006-2575
Tel.: (972) 250-7000
Fax: (972) 250-8847
Toll Free: (800) FASTTAX
Web Site: www.thomsonreuters.com
Approx. Number Employees: 600
Year Founded: 1998
Business Description:
Computerized Tax Processing Service
S.I.C.: 7371; 2721
N.A.I.C.S.: 541511; 511120
Export
Advertising Expenditures: $500,000
Media: 2-4-7-8-10-13
Distr.: Natl.
Budget Set: Dec.
Brands & Products:
FAST-TAX
GOSYSTEM
INSOURCE
SMART BRIDGE
TRUST EASE

THOTWAVE TECHNOLOGIES
2054 Kildaire Farm Rd #322
Cary, NC 27511
Tel.: (919) 931-4736
Toll Free: (800) 591-THOT
E-mail: info@thotwave.com
Web Site: www.thotwave.com
Business Description:
Data Storage & Management & Computer System Design
S.I.C.: 7374; 7371
N.A.I.C.S.: 518210; 541511
Personnel:
Greg Nelson *(Founder & CEO)*
Advertising Agency:
Hummingbird Creative Group
160 NE Maynard Rd Ste 205
Cary, NC 27513
Tel.: (919) 854-9100
Fax: (919) 854-9101

TIBCO SOFTWARE INC.
3303 Hillview Ave
Palo Alto, CA 94304
Tel.: (650) 846-1000
Fax: (650) 846-1005
Toll Free: (800) 420-8450
E-mail: corp-pr@tibco.com
Web Site: www.tibco.com
Approx. Rev.: $754,007,000
Approx. Number Employees: 2,540
Year Founded: 1997
Business Description:
Service-Oriented Architecture, Business Process Management & Business Optimization Software; Computer System Design, Integration & Installation Services
S.I.C.: 7373; 7371; 7372
N.A.I.C.S.: 511210; 334611; 541511; 541512
Advertising Expenditures: $2,500,000
Media: 2-8-10
Personnel:
Vivek Y. Ranadive *(Chm & CEO)*
Sydney L. Carey *(CFO & Exec VP)*
Murray D. Rode *(COO)*
William Hughes *(Gen Counsel, Sec & Exec VP)*
Tom Laffey *(Exec VP-Products & Tech)*
Ram Menon *(Exec VP-Worldwide Mktg)*
Murat Sonmez *(Exec VP-Global Field Ops)*
Brands & Products:
BUSINESSFACTOR
BUSINESSWORKS
HAWK
INCONCERT
INFORMATION BUS
PORTALBUILDER
THE POWER OF NOW
THE POWER TO PREDICT
PREDICTIVE BUSINESS
RENDEZVOUS
TIBCO
TIBCO ACTIVEMATRIX BUSINESSWORKS
TIBCO SILVER
TUCON
Advertising Agencies:
The Bateman Group
1550 Bryant St Ste 770
San Francisco, CA 94103
Tel.: (415) 503-1818
Fax: (415) 503-1880

Horn Group Inc.
612 Howard St Ste 100
San Francisco, CA 94105
Tel.: (415) 905-4000
Fax: (415) 905-4001

WorldWalk Media
417A E Washington Blvd
San Francisco, CA 94129-1145
Tel.: (415) 933-8450

TIDAL SOFTWARE INC.
(Sub. of Cisco Systems, Inc.)
Ste 201 2100 Geng Rd
Palo Alto, CA 94303-3307
Tel.: (650) 475-4600
Fax: (650) 475-4700
E-mail: info@tidalsoftware.com
Web Site: www.tidalsoftware.com
Sales Range: $25-49.9 Million
Approx. Number Employees: 100
Year Founded: 1978
Business Description:
Job Scheduling & Automation Solutions for the IT Industry
S.I.C.: 7371; 7389
N.A.I.C.S.: 541511; 561499
Media: 10
Personnel:
Flint Brenton *(Pres & CEO)*
Charlie Velasquez *(VP-Fin)*
Brands & Products:
ENTERPRISE SCHEDULER
HORIZON
REPORTSAFE
TIDAL
TIDAL ENTERPRISE SCHEDULER
TIDAL EVENT MANAGER
TIDAL NEXTGEN
TIDAL PROCESS MANAGER
TRANSPORTER

TIER TECHNOLOGIES INC.
11130 Sunrise Valley Dr Ste 300
Reston, VA 20191
Tel.: (571) 382-1000
Fax: (571) 382-1002
E-mail: info@tier.com
Web Site: www.tier.com
Approx. Rev.: $130,224,000
Approx. Number Employees: 220
Year Founded: 1991
Business Description:
Information Technology Consulting, Application Development, Software Engineering, Training & Business Outsourcing Services to Large Companies & Government Agencies
S.I.C.: 7373
N.A.I.C.S.: 541512
Advertising Expenditures: $700,000
Media: 5-10-17-22
Personnel:
Alex P. Hart *(Pres & CEO)*
John Guszak *(Interim CFO, Interim Chief Acctg Officer & Interim Treas)*
Keith S. Omsberg *(Gen Counsel, Sec & VP)*
Atul Garg *(Sr VP-Product Mgmt)*
Keith S. Kendrick *(Sr VP-Strategic Mktg)*
Brands & Products:
1-800-2PAY-TAX
FUND FINDER
KIDS1ST
OFFICIAL PAYMENTS CORP.
TIER
TIER ELECTRONIC PAYMENT SOLUTIONS

TIGERLOGIC CORPORATION
25 A Technology Dr
Irvine, CA 92618-2382
Tel.: (949) 442-4400
Fax: (949) 250-8187
Web Site: www.rainingdata.com
Approx. Rev.: $13,670,000
Approx. Number Employees: 87
Year Founded: 2000
Business Description:
Computer Software Development Services
S.I.C.: 7372; 7371
N.A.I.C.S.: 511210; 541511
Advertising Expenditures: $5,129,000
Media: 10
Personnel:
Richard W. Koe *(Chm, Interim Pres & CEO)*
Thomas G. Lim *(CFO, Sec & VP-Fin)*
John H. Bramley *(VP-Product Dev)*
Cliff Torng *(VP-Mktg)*
Brands & Products:
ADVANCED PICK
D3
EPHARMA
FLASHCONNECT
MAKING DATA USEFUL
MVBASE
MVDESIGNER
MVENTERPRISE
OMNIS STUDIO
PICK
PICKDBI
TIGERLOGIC
YOLINK

TIMBERLINE SOFTWARE CORPORATION
(Sub. of Sage Software, Inc.)
15195 NW Greenbrier Pkwy
Beaverton, OR 97006-5701
Tel.: (503) 690-6775
Tel.: (949) 450-3891 (Integrated Mktg)
Fax: (503) 439-5700
Toll Free: (800) 628-6583
E-mail: webmaster@sage.com
Web Site: www.timberline.com
Approx. Number Employees: 315
Year Founded: 1971
Business Description:
Vertical Software Developer, Publisher & Marketer for the Construction, Architectural/Engineering & Real Estate Industries
S.I.C.: 7372; 7373
N.A.I.C.S.: 511210; 541512
Export
Media: 2-7-10-13
Personnel:
Robert Deshaies *(Gen Mgr)*
Brands & Products:
TIMBERLINE
TIMBERLINE ACCOUNTING
TIMBERLINE ESTIMATING
TIMBERLINE PROPERTY MANAGEMENT
TIMBERLINE SERVICE MANAGEMENT

TMG HEALTH, INC.
(Sub. of Health Care Service Corporation)
455 S Gulph Rd Ste 307
King of Prussia, PA 19406
Tel.: (610) 878-9111
Fax: (610) 878-5525
Toll Free: (888) 776-4662
Web Site: www.tmghealth.com
Sales Range: $50-74.9 Million
Approx. Number Employees: 879
Year Founded: 1998
Business Description:
Technology Enabled Business Process Outsourcing (BOP) Services for Insurers, Employers, Health Plans, Medicare, Medicaid & Group Retiree Health Plans
S.I.C.: 7389; 7379
N.A.I.C.S.: 561499; 541519
Personnel:
John T. Tighe, III *(Founder, Pres & CEO)*
Alan N. Vinick *(CFO)*
Robert Masterson *(CIO)*
Robert Dunn *(Chief Dev Officer & Exec VP)*
Olga Thornton *(Chief Comml Officer & Sr VP)*
Vincent M. Dadamo *(Gen Counsel & Sr VP)*
Kimberly Line Courtois *(VP-HR)*
Advertising Agency:
Holton Sentivan and Gury
7 E Skippack Pike
Ambler, PA 19002
Tel.: (215) 619-7600
Fax: (215) 619-7621
(Website)

Key to Media (For complete agency information see *The Advertising Red Books-Agencies* edition):
1. Bus. Publs. 2. Cable T.V. 3. Catalogs & Directories. 4. Co-op Adv. 5. Consumer Mags. 6. D.M. to Bus. Estab.7. D.M. to Consumers 8. Daily Newsp. 9. Exhibits/Trade Shows 10. Foreign 11. Infomercial 12. Internet Adv.13. Multimedia 14. Network Radio 15. Network T.V. 16. Newsp. Distr. Mags. 17. Other 18. Outdoor (Posters, Transit) 19. Point of Purchase20. Premiums, Novelties 21. Product Samples 22. Special Events Mktg. 23. Spot Radio 24. Spot T.V. 25. Weekly Newsp. 26. Yellow Page Adv.

TOTAL SYSTEM SERVICES, INC.

(d/b/a TSYS)
1 TSYS Way
Columbus, GA 31901
Tel.: (706) 649-2310
Fax: (706) 644-8065
E-mail: info@tsys.com
Web Site: www.tsys.com
Approx. Rev.: $1,717,577,000
Approx. Number Employees: 7,788
Business Description:
Electronic Payment Processing Services
S.I.C.: 6099
N.A.I.C.S.: 522320
Advertising Expenditures: $327,000
Media: 2-10-11-22
Personnel:
M. Troy Woods *(Pres & COO)*
Virginia A. Holman *(Grp CEO-Global Mktg & Corp Comm)*
James B. Lipham *(CFO & Sr Exec VP)*
Kenneth L. Tye *(CIO & Sr Exec VP)*
Stephen W. Humber *(CTO & Exec VP)*
Ryland L. Harrelson *(Chief HR Officer & Exec VP)*
Dorenda K. Weaver *(Chief Acctg Officer & Exec VP)*
William A. Pruett *(Sr Exec VP & Pres-North America Svcs)*
Robert J. Philbin *(Exec VP)*
Gracie H. Allmond *(Pres-Columbus Productions)*
G. Sanders Griffith, III *(Gen Counsel, Sec & Sr Exec VP)*
Kathleen Moates *(Gen Counsel)*
James Cosgrove *(Treas & Grp Exec-Fin)*
Connie C. Dudley *(Exec VP-Product & Client Dev)*
Gaylon Jowers, Jr. *(Exec VP-Sls & Strategy & Emerging Markets)*
Kelley C. Knutson *(Exec VP-Global Svcs)*
Colleen W. Kynard *(Exec VP-Customer Care)*
Allen Pettis *(Exec VP-Major Acct Relationship Mgmt)*
Peggy Bekavac Olson *(VP-Mktg)*
Cyle Mims *(Coord-Media & External Comm)*
Shawn Roberts *(Coord-IR)*
Suzanne Kump *(Grp Exec-HR)*
Brands & Products:
TSYS

TRADEONE

11149 Research Blvd Ste 400
Austin, TX 78759
Tel.: (512) 343-2002
Fax: (512) 343-1717
Toll Free: (866) 4TRADE1
E-mail: sales@tradeonemktg.com
Web Site: www.tradeone.com
E-Mail For Key Personnel:
Sales Director: sales@tradeonemktg.com
Approx. Number Employees: 100
Year Founded: 1997
Business Description:
Marketing & Promotional Services
S.I.C.: 8742; 8732
N.A.I.C.S.: 541611; 541613; 541910
Media: 7-10-13-17-22
Distr.: Natl.
Personnel:
John T. Atkinson *(Chm)*
Dan Hickox *(Pres)*
Evelyn Nugent *(Exec VP)*
Advertising Agency:
Maloney Strategic Communications
11520 N Central Expwy Ste 236
Dallas, TX 75243
Tel.: (214) 342-8385
Fax: (214) 342-8386

TRANSACT TECHNOLOGIES INCORPORATED

2319 Whitney Ave Ste 3B
Hamden, CT 06518-3534
Tel.: (203) 859-6800
Fax: (203) 949-9048
E-mail: corporate@transact-tech.com
Web Site: www.transact-tech.com
Approx. Sls.: $63,194,000
Approx. Number Employees: 123
Business Description:
Printers & Related Products for Recording Financial Transactions
S.I.C.: 3569
N.A.I.C.S.: 333999
Advertising Expenditures: $824,000
Media: 10
Personnel:
Bart C. Shuldman *(Chm & CEO)*
Steven A. DeMartino *(CFO)*
Christopher Galletta *(Chief Acctg Officer & Controller)*
Tracey S. Chernay *(Exec VP-Sls & Mktg)*
Michael S. Kumpf *(Exec VP-Engrg)*
Andrew John Hoffman *(Sr VP-Ops)*
Brands & Products:
BANKJET
EPIC
IMPORT
INSTALOAD
ITHACA
ITHACOLOR
ITHERM
KITCHENJET
MADE TO ORDER. BUILT TO LAST
POSJET
POWER POCKET
POWEROLL
QDT
SERVERPORT
TICKETBURST
TRANSACT

TRANSCORE HOLDINGS INC.

(Sub. of Roper Industries, Inc.)
8158 Adams Dr
Hummelstown, PA 17036
Tel.: (717) 561-2400
Fax: (717) 564-8439
Web Site: www.transcore.com
Sales Range: $300-349.9 Million
Approx. Number Employees: 1,800
Business Description:
Computer Software, Supplies & Services
S.I.C.: 7372; 5045
N.A.I.C.S.: 511210; 423430
Media: 2-6-10
Personnel:
Joseph Grabias *(CFO & Exec VP)*
Kelly Gravelle *(CTO & Exec VP)*
John Simler *(Pres-Intelligent Transportation Sys Grp)*
John Worthington *(Pres-Comml Tech Grp)*
Tim Bickmore *(Exec VP)*
George McGraw *(Exec VP-Ops)*
David Sparks *(Exec VP-Transportation Sys & Svcs)*
Barbara Caitlin *(Mgr-Media Rels)*
Brands & Products:
AMTECH
EGO
GLOBALWAVE
TRANSCORE
Advertising Agency:
Blanchard Schaefer Advertising & Public Relations
1521 N Cooper St Ste 600
Arlington, TX 76011
Tel.: (817) 226-4332
Fax: (817) 860-2004

TRANSEND CORPORATION

225 Emerson St
Palo Alto, CA 94301-1026
Tel.: (650) 324-5370
Fax: (650) 324-5377
E-mail: sales.info@transend.com
Web Site: www.transend.com
E-Mail For Key Personnel:
President: krefetz@transend.com
Sales Director: sales.info@transend.com
Sales Range: Less than $1 Million
Approx. Number Employees: 10
Year Founded: 1974
Business Description:
E-Mail Migration & Coexistence Software Mfr
S.I.C.: 7371
N.A.I.C.S.: 541511
Export
Media: 2-7-13-18
Distr.: Intl.; Natl.
Budget Set: Apr.
Personnel:
Fred Krefetz *(Pres & CEO)*
Rob Shurtleff *(Gen Mgr-Microsoft Workgroup Solutions Product Unit)*
Audrey Augun *(Mgr-Mktg)*
Brands & Products:
CONNECTORWARE
TRANSEND
TRANSEND ADMINISTRATOR
TRANSEND MIGRATOR

TRANSLATIONS.COM

3 Park Ave
New York, NY 10016-5902
Tel.: (212) 689-1616
Fax: (212) 685-9797
E-mail: newyork@translations.com
Web Site: www.translations.com
Sales Range: $1-9.9 Million
Approx. Number Employees: 85
Business Description:
Globalization Technology & Services
S.I.C.: 7389
N.A.I.C.S.: 541930
Media: 2-13-22
Personnel:
Phil Shawe *(Co-CEO)*
Roy B. Trujillo *(COO)*
Mark Hjerpe *(Dir-Sls)*
Mike McPherson *(Dir-Client Svcs)*
Joachim Zink *(Dir-Fin-TransPerfect Translations)*

TRANSNET CORPORATION

45 Columbia Rd
Somerville, NJ 08876
Tel.: (908) 253-0500
Fax: (908) 253-0601
Toll Free: (800) 526-4965
E-mail: contact_us@transnet.com
Web Site: www.transnet.com
Approx. Rev.: $20,943,304
Approx. Number Employees: 85
Year Founded: 1969
Business Description:
Markets & Leases Computer Terminals, Personal & Business Computers & Related Equipment; Computer Supplies, Service & Maintenance
S.I.C.: 5045; 5734
N.A.I.C.S.: 423430; 443120
Media: 2-5-7-8-20-25-26
Distr.: Natl.
Budget Set: June
Personnel:
John J. Wilk *(Chm & CFO)*
Steven J. Wilk *(Pres & CEO)*

TRIPWIRE, INC.

101 SW Main St Ste 1500
Portland, OR 97204
Tel.: (503) 276-7500
Fax: (503) 223-0182
Toll Free: (800) 874-7947
E-mail: sales@tripwire.com
Web Site: www.tripwire.com
E-Mail For Key Personnel:
Sales Director: sales@tripwire.com
Approx. Rev.: $74,006,000
Approx. Number Employees: 314
Year Founded: 1997
Business Description:
IT Security & Compliance Automation Software Solutions
S.I.C.: 7372; 7371
N.A.I.C.S.: 511210; 541511
Advertising Expenditures: $3,700,000
Media: 1-10-13-22
Personnel:
William W. Lattin *(Chm)*
Jim B. Johnson *(Pres & CEO)*
Kelly E. Lang *(CFO & VP)*
Robert C. McCarthy *(Treas & VP-Fin)*
Mark Bradley *(VP-Sls-EMEA)*
Aaron Lerner *(VP-Engrg)*
Aliza Scott *(VP-HR & Organizational Dev)*
Rekha Shenoy *(VP-Mktg)*
Brands & Products:
TRIPWIRE VIA
VWIRE

THE TRIZETTO GROUP, INC.

(Holding of Apax Partners LLP)
6061 S Willow Dr Ste 310
Greenwood Village, CO 80111
Tel.: (303) 495-7000
Fax: (303) 495-7001
E-mail: salesinfo@trizetto.com
Web Site: www.trizetto.com
Sales Range: $450-499.9 Million
Approx. Number Employees: 2,000
Year Founded: 1997
Business Description:
Healthcare Technology Services
S.I.C.: 7374; 7372; 8721
N.A.I.C.S.: 518210; 511210; 541219
Advertising Expenditures: $1,200,000
Media: 2
Personnel:
Jeffrey H. Margolis *(Founder & Chm)*
Tony Bellomo *(Pres)*
Alan Ross *(Mng Dir)*
Regina Paolillo *(CFO & Exec VP-Enterprise Svcs)*

Key to Media (For complete agency information see *The Advertising Red Books-Agencies* edition):
1. Bus. Publs. 2. Cable T.V. 3. Catalogs & Directories. 4. Co-op Adv. 5. Consumer Mags. 6. D.M. to Bus. Estab.7. D.M. to Consumers 8. Daily Newsp. 9. Exhibits/Trade Shows 10. Foreign 11. Infomercial 12. Internet Adv.13. Multimedia 14. Network Radio 15. Network T.V. 16. Newsp. Distr. Mags. 17. Other 18. Outdoor (Posters, Transit) 19. Point of Purchase20. Premiums, Novelties 21. Product Samples 22. Special Events Mktg. 23. Spot Radio 24. Spot T.V. 25. Weekly Newsp. 26. Yellow Page Adv.

Alan Cullop *(CIO & Sr VP)*
Dan Spirek *(CMO, Chief Strategy Officer, Exec VP-Enterprise Strategy & Comm)*
Jeffrey Rideout *(Chief Medical Officer & Sr VP-Care/Cost Mgmt)*
Larry Bridge *(Pres-Govt & Intl Markets)*
John Jordan *(Pres-Healthcare Market)*
Joseph Manheim *(Pres-Benefits Admin)*
Tim Hascall *(Exec VP)*
Rick M. Fitzgerald *(Sr VP)*
Harish Mysore *(Sr VP-Corp Dev & Strategic Alliances)*
Jay Sultan *(Assoc VP & Product Mgr-Value Based Reimbursement)*
Denise Giacoia *(Dir-Mktg Tech Product Mktg Ops)*

Brands & Products:
CAREADVANCE
CLAIMFACTS
CLAIMSEXCHANGE
CLAIMSLINK
CLINICAL CAREADVANCE
CLINICALOGIC
DECIPHER
DIRECTLINK
FACETS
FACETS EXTENDED ENTERPRISE
GROUPFACTS
HEALTHEWARE
HEALTHWEB
HIPAA GATEWAY
HIPAASUCCESS
NCVO
NETWORX
NETWORXMODELER
PERSONAL CAREADVANCE
QICLINK
TRIZETTO

Advertising Agencies:
PJA
12 Arrow St
Cambridge, MA 02138-5105
Tel.: (617) 492-5899
Fax: (617) 661-1530
— Kristina Talevi *(Acct Mgr)*

Schwartz Communications, Inc.
230 3rd Ave
Waltham, MA 02451
Tel.: (781) 684-0770
Fax: (781) 684-6500

TROWBRIDGE ENTERPRISES

(d/b/a Palace Art & Office Supply)
2606 Chanticleer Ave
Santa Cruz, CA 95065
Tel.: (831) 476-3815
Fax: (831) 476-4036
Fax: (888) 637-0246
Toll Free: (888) 637-5373
E-mail: sales@gopalace.com
Web Site: www.gopalace.com
E-Mail For Key Personnel:
Sales Director: sales@gopalace.com
Approx. Sls.: $11,784,032
Approx. Number Employees: 45
Year Founded: 1949
Business Description:
Stationery & Office Supplies Distr & Retailer
S.I.C.: 5112; 5943
N.A.I.C.S.: 424120; 453210
Media: 4-8-13
Personnel:
Frank H. Trowbridge, III *(Owner)*
Gary Trowbridge *(Owner)*
Roy Trowbridge *(Owner)*
Peggy Paylow *(Mgr-Comml Sls-Mktg)*

TROY GROUP INC.

940 S Coast Dr Ste 200
Costa Mesa, CA 92626
Tel.: (714) 241-4760
Fax: (714) 241-4761
E-mail: inquire@troygroup.com
Web Site: www.troygroup.com
Approx. Sls.: $47,679,000
Approx. Number Employees: 215
Year Founded: 1982
Business Description:
Computer Peripheral Equipment; Printer Electronic Internet Business to Business
S.I.C.: 7373; 3577
N.A.I.C.S.: 541512; 334119
Import Export
Advertising Expenditures: $333,000
Media: 7-10-13
Personnel:
Patrick J. Dirk *(Chm & CEO)*
Brian P. Dirk *(Vice Chm, Pres & COO)*
Dennis C. Fairchild *(CFO)*
John Hodgson *(VP-Mktg & Inside Sls)*
Brands & Products:
CHECKWRITING
ECHECKSECURE
ETHERSYNC
ETHERWIND
POCKETPRO
SECURE CHECKFLOW ENTERPRISE
STARACH
TOEM5XX
TROY
TROY CHECKWRITING SOFTWARE
TROY FORTRESS CHECK PAPER
TROY IRD PAPER
TROY MICR
TROY SECUREFLOW OUTPUT MANAGER
TROY SECURITY CHECK PAPER
TROY SECURITY PLUS CHECK PAPER
TROY200
WINDCONNECT
WINDCONNECT II
WINDPORT

TRUEBLUE, INC.

1015 A St
Tacoma, WA 98402
Mailing Address:
PO Box 2910
Tacoma, WA 98401-2910
Tel.: (253) 383-9101
Fax: (877) 733-0399
Toll Free: (800) 610-8920
Web Site: www.trueblueinc.com
Approx. Rev.: $1,149,367,000
Approx. Number Employees: 2,600
Year Founded: 1989
Business Description:
Temporary Staffing Services
S.I.C.: 7363; 7361
N.A.I.C.S.: 561320; 561310
Advertising Expenditures: $3,300,000
Media: 7-10-18-20-22-23-26
Personnel:
Joseph P. Sambataro, Jr. *(Chm)*
Steven C. Cooper *(Pres & CEO)*
Derrek L. Gafford *(CFO & Exec VP)*
Billie R. Otto *(CIO & Sr VP)*
Wayne W. Larkin *(Pres-Labor Ready)*
Jim Defebaugh, IV *(Gen Counsel, Sec & Exec VP)*
Robert Breen *(Sr VP-Strategic Plng & Fin Analysis)*
Stacey Burke *(VP-Corp Comm)*
Brands & Products:
CLP
LABOR READY
THE LEADER IN BLUE-COLLAR STAFFING
PLANETECHS
SPARTAN STAFFING
TRUEBLUE

TTC MARKETING SOLUTIONS

3945 N Neenah Ave
Chicago, IL 60634
Tel.: (773) 545-0407
Fax: (773) 545-4034
E-mail: sales@ttcmarketingsolutions.com
Web Site:
www.ttcmarketingsolutions.com
E-Mail For Key Personnel:
Sales Director: sales@ttcmarketingsolutions.com
Approx. Number Employees: 300
Year Founded: 1984
Business Description:
Inbound & Outbound Telemarketing
S.I.C.: 8742; 7389
N.A.I.C.S.: 561422; 541611; 541990
Advertising Expenditures: $100,000
Media: 2-4-7-10-13
Personnel:
Mary Shanley *(Pres)*
Bob Aloisio *(VP-Sls & Mktg)*

TWELVE TONE SYSTEMS, INC.

(d/b/a Cakewalk)
268 Summer St
Boston, MA 02210
Tel.: (617) 423-9004
Fax: (617) 423-9007
Toll Free: (888) CAKEWALK
Web Site: www.cakewalk.com
Approx. Sls.: $10,000,000
Approx. Number Employees: 60
Year Founded: 1987
Business Description:
Music Software
S.I.C.: 5045
N.A.I.C.S.: 423430
Media: 8-10-13
Personnel:
Greg Hendershott *(CEO)*
Anthony Conte *(VP-Sls)*
Michael Hoover *(Dir-Product Mgmt)*
Zac Kenney *(Accts Mgr)*
Brands & Products:
CAKEWALK
CAKEWALK MUSIC CREATOR
HOME STUDIO
KINETIC
SONAR

TWG INNOVATIVE SOLUTIONS, INC.

(Sub. of The Warranty Group, Inc.)
13922 Denver W Pkwy Bldg 54
Golden, CO 80401
Tel.: (303) 279-2900
Fax: (303) 216-1732
Web Site: www.thewarrantygroup.com
Approx. Number Employees: 500
Business Description:
Solutions for Extended Service Plan Programs to Customer Relationship Management Services, Direct Mail, Financial & Insurance Administration & Telemarketing Services
S.I.C.: 8742; 7389
N.A.I.C.S.: 541611; 561499
Media: 2-7-13
Personnel:
David L. Cole *(Chm & CEO)*
Mike F. Frosch *(Pres & COO)*
Brands & Products:
REPEVALUATOR

TYLER TECHNOLOGIES, INC.

5949 Sherry Ln Ste 1400
Dallas, TX 75225-8010
Tel.: (972) 713-3700
Fax: (972) 713-3741
Web Site: www.tylertech.com
Approx. Rev.: $288,628,000
Approx. Number Employees: 2,054
Year Founded: 1966
Business Description:
Technology, Software, Data Warehousing & Electronic Document Management Systems & Services
S.I.C.: 7373; 7372
N.A.I.C.S.: 541512; 334611
Media: 4-10
Distr.: Natl.
Personnel:
John M. Yeaman *(Chm)*
John S. Marr, Jr. *(Pres & CEO)*
Brian K. Miller *(CFO, Treas & Sr VP)*
W. Michael Smith *(Chief Acctg Officer & VP)*
Brett Kate *(Pres-Local Govt Div)*
Dustin R. Womble *(Exec VP & CEO-Courts & Justice & Local Govt Div)*
H. Lynn Moore, Jr. *(Gen Counsel & Exec VP)*

UBICS, INC.

(Div. of United Breweries (Holdings) Ltd.)
333 Technology Dr Ste 210
Canonsburg, PA 15317-9513
Tel.: (724) 746-6001
Fax: (724) 746-9597
Toll Free: (800) 441-0077
E-mail: ubics@ubics.com
Web Site: www.ubics.com
Sales Range: $25-49.9 Million
Approx. Number Employees: 200
Year Founded: 1993
Business Description:
Information Technology Services
S.I.C.: 7371
N.A.I.C.S.: 541511
Media: 10-13
Personnel:
Vijay Mallya *(Chm & CEO)*
Sameer Walvalkar *(COO)*
Bruce Thompson *(VP-Sls)*

THE ULTIMATE SOFTWARE GROUP, INC.

2000 Ultimate Way
Weston, FL 33326-3643
Tel.: (954) 331-7000
Fax: (954) 331-7300
Toll Free: (800) 432-1729
E-mail: ir@ultimatesoftware.com
Web Site: www.ultimatesoftware.com

Key to Media (For complete agency information see *The Advertising Red Books-Agencies* edition):
1. Bus. Publs. 2. Cable T.V. 3. Catalogs & Directories. 4. Co-op Adv. 5. Consumer Mags. 6. D.M. to Bus. Estab.7. D.M. to Consumers 8. Daily Newsp. 9. Exhibits/Trade Shows 10. Foreign 11. Infomercial 12. Internet Adv.13. Multimedia 14. Network Radio 15. Network T.V. 16. Newsp. Distr. Mags. 17. Other 18. Outdoor (Posters, Transit) 19. Point of Purchase20. Premiums, Novelties 21. Product Samples 22. Special Events Mktg. 23. Spot Radio 24. Spot T.V. 25. Weekly Newsp. 26. Yellow Page Adv.

The Ultimate Software Group, Inc. — (Continued)

Approx. Rev.: $227,811,000
Approx. Number Employees: 1,134
Year Founded: 1990
Business Description:
Web Based Payroll & Employee Management Solutions
S.I.C.: 7372; 8742
N.A.I.C.S.: 334611; 511210; 541611
Media: 7-10-13
Personnel:
Scott S. Scherr *(Founder, Chm, Pres & CEO)*
Marc D. Scherr *(Vice Chm & COO)*
Mitchell K. Dauerman *(CFO & Exec VP)*
Vivian Maza *(Sec & Sr VP)*
Linda Miller *(Sr VP-Mktg)*
Darlene Marcroft *(Dir-PR)*
Brands & Products:
INTERSOURCING
ULTIMATE SOFTWARE
ULTIPRO
Advertising Agency:
SBC Advertising
333 W Nationwide Blvd
Columbus, OH 43215
Tel.: (614) 891-7070
Fax: (614) 255-2600
Toll Free: (866) 891-7001

ULTIMATE TECHNOLOGY CORPORATION

100 Rawson Rd
Victor, NY 14564-1170
Tel.: (585) 924-9500
Fax: (585) 924-1434
Toll Free: (800) 349-0546
E-mail: info@utcretail.com
Web Site: www.utcretail.com
Approx. Number Employees: 200
Year Founded: 1988
Business Description:
Point of Sale Displays, Terminals, Keyboards & Peripheral Devices Mfr
S.I.C.: 3577; 7389
N.A.I.C.S.: 334119; 541990
Import Export
Advertising Expenditures: $500,000
Media: 2-4-5-7-8-10-13-20-21-22-26
Distr.: Intl.
Budget Set: Dec.
Personnel:
Samuel J. Villanti *(Pres & CEO)*
Karen L.F. Palmer *(CFO & VP)*
Randy Hems *(VP-Engrng)*
Patrick Barr *(Product Mgr-UTC RETAIL)*
Brands & Products:
ULTIMANET
ULTIMATOUCH 1800 SERIES
UTC PD 1100
UTC PD 1200
UTC PD 220
UTC RETAIL
UTC SERIES 500 COMPACT POS KEYBOARD
UTC SERIES 600 ENHANCED POS KEYBOARD

UNICA CORPORATION

(Sub. of International Business Machines Corporation)
Reservoir Pl N 170 Tracer Ln
Waltham, MA 02451
Tel.: (781) 259-5900
Tel.: (781) 839-8000
Fax: (781) 890-0012
Toll Free: (877) 864-2261
E-mail: unica@unica.com
Web Site: www.unica.com
Approx. Rev.: $100,618,000
Approx. Number Employees: 440
Year Founded: 1992
Business Description:
Customer Relationship Management & Enterprise Marketing Management Software & Services
S.I.C.: 7372; 8732; 8742
N.A.I.C.S.: 511210; 541613; 541910
Advertising Expenditures: $344,000
Media: 7-10-13-22
Personnel:
David Cheung *(Co-Founder)*
Ruby Kennedy *(Co-Founder)*
Yuchun Lee *(Chm & CEO)*
Paul McNulty *(CMO & Sr VP)*
Chris Manton-Jones *(Sr VP-Worldwide Sls)*
David Sweet *(Sr VP-Corp Devel)*
Vivian Vitale *(Sr VP-HR)*
Brands & Products:
AFFINIUM CAMPAIGN
AFFINIUM DETECT
AFFINIUM LEADS
AFFINIUM MODEL
AFFINIUM NETINSIGHT
AFFINIUM PLAN
UNICA
UNICA NETTRACKER

UNICCO SERVICE COMPANY

(Sub. of UGL Limited)
275 Grove St
Auburndale, MA 02466-2272
Tel.: (617) 527-5222
Fax: (617) 969-2210
Toll Free: (800) 283-9222
E-mail: webmaster@unicco.com
Web Site: www.unicco.com
E-Mail For Key Personnel:
Marketing Director: marketing@unicco.com
Approx. Rev.: $721,000,000
Year Founded: 1949
Business Description:
Building, Maintenance, Janitorial, Office, Electrical & Integrated Facility Services
S.I.C.: 7349
N.A.I.C.S.: 561720
Media: 10
Personnel:
George A. Keches *(Pres)*
James E. Lawlor *(CFO & VP)*
Jeffrey Peterson *(CIO)*
Walter W. Crow *(Gen Counsel & VP)*
George R. Lohnes *(VP-Mktg)*
Arthur Mushkin *(VP-HR)*
Heidi Anderson-Rhodes *(Sr Dir-Program Dev)*
Brands & Products:
UNICCO
Advertising Agency:
Soucy Communications Group
465 Pine St
Lowell, MA 01851
Tel.: (781) 898-7305
— Sandy McLaughlin *(Acct Exec)*

UNIFY CORPORATION

1420 Rocky Ridge Dr Ste 380
Roseville, CA 95661
Tel.: (916) 928-6400
Fax: (916) 928-6404
Toll Free: (800) 248-6439
E-mail: info@unify.com
Web Site: www.unify.com
E-Mail For Key Personnel:
Public Relations: press@unify.com
Approx. Rev.: $46,993,000
Approx. Number Employees: 204
Year Founded: 1980
Business Description:
Application Solutions
S.I.C.: 7372; 7371; 7373; 7376
N.A.I.C.S.: 334611; 541511; 541512; 541513
Advertising Expenditures: $800,000
Media: 7-10-13
Distr.: Intl.
Personnel:
Steven D. Whiteman *(Chm)*
Todd E. Wille *(Pres & CEO)*
Steven D. Bonham *(CFO & VP-Fin & Admin)*
Kurt A. Jensen *(COO & Exec VP)*
Duane v. George *(CTO & Sr VP-Product Dev)*
Mark T. Bygraves *(Sr VP-Sls-Europe, Middle East & Africa)*
Frank Verardi *(VP-Sls-Americas & Asia Pacific)*
Deb Thornton *(Sr Dir-Mktg)*
Brands & Products:
ACCELL
ACCELL/IDS
ACCELL/SQL
ACCELL/WEB
COMPOSER SABERTOOTH
DATASERVER ELS
NXJ DEVELOPER
NXJ ENTERPRISE
REPORT BUILDER
SQLBASE
SQLBASE TREASURY
TEAM DEVELOPER
UNIFY
UNIFY DATASERVER
UNIFY NXJ
UNIFY VISION
VISION

THE UNION GROUP

649 Alden St
Fall River, MA 02722-3160
Tel.: (508) 675-4545
Fax: (508) 677-0130
Toll Free: (800) 289-3523
E-mail: info@theuniongroup.com
Web Site: www.theuniongroup.com
Sales Range: $25-49.9 Million
Approx. Number Employees: 200
Year Founded: 1909
Business Description:
Custom Loose-leaf Binders, Business Forms, Software Packaging & Indexes Mfr & Sale
S.I.C.: 2782; 2631
N.A.I.C.S.: 323118; 322130
Import
Media: 2-4-7-8-10
Distr.: Natl.
Personnel:
Elliot Comenitz *(Pres)*

UNION PEN COMPANY

PO Box 220
Hagaman, NY 12086
Fax: (518) 770-7018
Toll Free: (800) 846-6600
E-mail: orders@imprintsonline.com
Web Site: www.imprintsonline.com
Approx. Number Employees: 140
Year Founded: 1904
Business Description:
Imprinted Promotional Products
S.I.C.: 7389
N.A.I.C.S.: 561990
Import Export
Advertising Expenditures: $3,500,000
Media: 2-4-5-7-11-13-20-21-25
Distr.: Intl.
Brands & Products:
CASTLETON PEN
CELEBRATE. COMMEMORATE. RECOGNIZE
CONTESSA PEN
DUPREE PEN
ELLISTON PEN
HEWITT PEN
LASER-TWIST
REDFIELD PEN
REVERE PEN
SUMMITT
UNION PEN COMPANY

UNISYS CORPORATION

801 Lakeview Dr Ste 100
Blue Bell, PA 19422
Tel.: (215) 986-4011
Fax: (215) 986-2312
E-mail: investor@unisys.com
Web Site: www.unisys.com
Approx. Rev.: $4,019,600,000
Approx. Number Employees: 22,900
Year Founded: 1986
Business Description:
Information Technology Consulting Services
S.I.C.: 8748; 7373; 7379; 7389
N.A.I.C.S.: 541618; 541512; 541519; 541690; 561499
Import Export
Advertising Expenditures: $600,000
Media: 2-7-9-10-13-15-18-22
Distr.: Intl.
Budget Set: Jan. -Dec.
Personnel:
J. Edward Coleman *(Chm & CEO)*
Janet B. Haugen *(CFO & Sr VP)*
Suresh Mathews *(CIO & Sr VP)*
Dominick Cavuoto *(Pres-TCIS & Worldwide Strategic Svcs & Sr VP)*
Ted Davies *(Pres-Federal Sys & Sr VP)*
Ron Frankenfield *(Pres-Global Outsourcing & Infrastructure Svcs)*
Nancy S. Sundheim *(Gen Counsel, Sec & Sr VP)*
Patricia A. Bradford *(Sr VP-Worldwide HR)*
M. Lazane Smith *(Sr VP-Corp Dev)*
Scott Whyman *(VP/Gen Mgr-Global Outsourcing & Infrastructure-Asia Pacific)*
John Strain *(VP & Dir-Mktg & Global Transportation)*
Jim Kerr *(VP-Global PR & Reg Comm)*
Elizabeth Smith *(VP-Sls-Federal Sys)*
William L. Bancroft *(Global VP & Gen Mgr-IT Outsourcing Global Ops)*
Brands & Products:
UNISYS
Advertising Agencies:
Gregory FCA
27 W Athens Ave Ste 200
Ardmore, PA 19003
Tel.: (610) 642-8253
Fax: (610) 642-1258

Fax: (610) 649-9029
Toll Free: (800) 499-4734

Lewis PR
575 Market St Ste 2550
San Francisco, CA 94105
Tel.: (415) 992-4400
Creative
Public Relations
Traditional & New Media
US Agency of Record

O'Keeffe & Co.
921 King St
Alexandria, VA 22314
Tel.: (703) 883-9000
Fax: (703) 883-9007

PHD New York
220 E 42nd St 7th Fl
New York, NY 10017-5806
Tel.: (212) 894-6600
Fax: (212) 894-4100
Media Planning & Buying

StrawberryFrog
60 Madison Ave Ph
New York, NY 10010
Tel.: (212) 366-0500

Weber Shandwick
(Sub. of The Interpublic Group of Companies)
919 3rd Ave
New York, NY 10022
Tel.: (212) 445-8000
Fax: (212) 445-8001
(North American Public Relations, Services Division)

UPEK, INC.

5900 Christie Ave
Emeryville, CA 94608
Tel.: (510) 420-2600
Fax: (510) 420-2699
Web Site: www.upek.com
Sales Range: $50-74.9 Million
Approx. Number Employees: 121
Year Founded: 2007
Business Description:
Security Products & Solutions For the Fingerprint Authentication Market
S.I.C.: 7382
N.A.I.C.S.: 561621
Media: 13-17
Personnel:
Alan Kramer *(Founder, Pres & COO)*
Robert H. Bond *(VP-Dev)*
Patrick Bouju *(VP-Worldwide Sls)*
Carl Temme *(VP-Bus Dev & Strategic Mktg)*
Brian DeGonia *(Product Mgr-Software)*
Brands & Products:
DIGITAL IDENTITY
EIKON
PROTECTOR SUITE
SECURITY MADE SIMPLE
UPEK
Advertising Agency:
Connecting Point Communications
665 3rd St Ste 100
San Francisco, CA 94107
Tel.: (415) 442-2400
Fax: (415) 442-0288

USERS INCORPORATED

(Sub. of Fiserv, Inc.)
455 S Gulth Rd
King of Prussia, PA 19406
Tel.: (610) 687-9400
Fax: (610) 293-4480
Toll Free: (800) 523-7282
E-mail: info@users.com
Web Site: www.users.com
Sales Range: $100-124.9 Million
Approx. Number Employees: 250
Year Founded: 1963
Business Description:
Technology Solutions & Services to Credit Unions
S.I.C.: 5045
N.A.I.C.S.: 423430
Media: 2-10
Personnel:
P. Sano *(CFO)*
Terry Murphy *(Sr VP-Project Mgmt)*
Dianne Rothenberger *(VP-HR)*
Brands & Products:
DATASAFE

VALIANCE PARTNERS, INC.

75 Claremont Rd Ste 206
Bernardsville, NJ 07924
Tel.: (908) 334-2300
Fax: (908) 845-0423
Toll Free: (800) 880-4540
E-mail: info@valiancepartners.com
Web Site: www.valiancepartners.com
Sales Range: $1-9.9 Million
Approx. Number Employees: 30
Business Description:
Software & Technical Services for Data Migration
S.I.C.: 7372; 7373; 7379
N.A.I.C.S.: 511210; 541512; 541519
Personnel:
Richard Higger *(Founder & Pres)*
David Katzoff *(Mng Dir)*
Nagesh Sarma *(Mng Dir)*
Brands & Products:
TRUCOMPARE
TRUMIGRATE
VALIANCE PARTNERS
Advertising Agency:
Affect Strategies
989 Ave of the Americas 6th Fl
New York, NY 10018
Tel.: (212) 398-9680
Fax: (212) 504-8211

VALLEY BUSINESS MACHINES

2712 S 3600 W Ste G
West Valley City, UT 84119
Tel.: (801) 969-6303
Fax: (801) 969-4013
Toll Free: (800) 462-2019
Web Site: www.valleybusinessmachines.com
Business Description:
Office Supplies Retailer & Whslr
N.A.I.C.S.: 453210; 424120
Media: 5
Personnel:
Richard Hanson *(Pres)*

VALVE CORPORATION

PO Box 1688
Bellevue, WA 98009
Tel.: (425) 889-9642
Fax: (425) 827-4843
E-mail: contact@valvesoftware.com
Web Site: www.valvesoftware.com
Approx. Number Employees: 120
Year Founded: 1996
Business Description:
Entertainment Software & Technology Developer
S.I.C.: 7372; 3577
N.A.I.C.S.: 511210; 334119
Media: 5-10-13-20
Personnel:
Gabe Newell *(Founder & Mng Dir)*
Scott Lynch *(COO)*
Doug Lombardi *(VP-Mktg)*
Jason Holtman *(Dir-Bus Devel & Legal Affairs)*
Katie Engel *(Office Mgr)*
Erik Johnson *(Mgr-Project)*
Jakob Jungels *(Artist-3D, Animator & Designer-Game)*

VAN SON HOLLAND INK CORPORATION OF AMERICA

185 Oval Dr
Islandia, NY 11749
Tel.: (631) 715-7000
Fax: (631) 715-7020
Toll Free: (800) 645-4182
E-mail: info@vansonink.com
Web Site: www.vansonink.com
Approx. Sls.: $35,000,000
Approx. Number Employees: 100
Year Founded: 1872
Business Description:
Printing Inks Importer Mfr & Distr
S.I.C.: 5085
N.A.I.C.S.: 423840
Import Export
Media: 2-4-5-7-8-10-11-17-21
Distr.: Intl.
Budget Set: Nov.
Brands & Products:
AQUA BASE PLUS
ARTCOLOUR
CML-OIL BASE PLUS
COMMERCIAL PRESS INKS
DIGI-INK
DIGITAL DUPLICATE INKS
EASYPRINT
INFINITY
INKJET INKS
OFFSET PRINTING INKS
PRESSROOM SUPPLIES
QUICKSON MULTIFRESH
QUICKSON PLUS
QUICKSON PRO
ROTASON
RUBBER BASE PLUS
SIGNATURE
SONADRY
SONAGLOSS
SONAPRINT
TOUGH TEX
TOUGH TEX LR
UNIPAK
Advertising Agency:
Harrison Leifer DiMarco, Inc.
100 Merrick Rd
Rockville Centre, NY 11570-4800
Tel.: (516) 536-2020
Fax: (516) 536-2641
Toll Free: (888) 571-2500
(Printing Inks & Related Supplies)

VANGENT, INC.

(Holding of Veritas Capital Fund, L.P.)
4250 N Fairfax Dr Ste 1200
Arlington, VA 22203
Tel.: (703) 284-5600
Fax: (703) 284-5628
Toll Free: (800) 359-1440
Web Site: www.vangent.com
Approx. Rev.: $761,841,000
Approx. Number Employees: 7,008
Business Description:
Information Management & Business Process Outsourcing Services for Government, Commercial, Education & Healthcare Organizations
S.I.C.: 7389; 8748
N.A.I.C.S.: 561499; 519190; 541690; 561990
Personnel:
Robert B. McKeon *(Chm)*
John McNamara Curtis *(Pres & CEO)*
James C. Reagan *(CFO & Sr VP)*
John George *(CIO & Sr VP)*
Kevin T. Boyle *(Gen Counsel, Sec & Sr VP)*
Jeff Bohling *(Sr VP & Gen Mgr-Civilian & Natl Security Div)*
David J. Fabianski *(Sr VP & Gen Mgr-Human Capital & Intl)*
Kerry Weems *(Sr VP & Gen Mgr)*
Gerald Calhoun *(Sr VP-HR)*
Giovanna S. Patterson *(Sr VP-Mktg & Sls)*
Advertising Agency:
O'Keeffe & Co.
921 King St
Alexandria, VA 22314
Tel.: (703) 883-9000
Fax: (703) 883-9007

VENTYX, INC.

(Holding of Vista Equity Partners LLC)
3301 Windy Ridge Pkwy
Atlanta, GA 30339
Tel.: (770) 952-8444
Fax: (770) 989-4231
Toll Free: (800) 650-8444
E-mail: sales@ventyx.com
Web Site: www.ventyx.com
E-Mail For Key Personnel:
Sales Director: sales@ventyx.com
Approx. Number Employees: 1,200
Year Founded: 1976
Business Description:
Asset Management Software & Services
S.I.C.: 7372
N.A.I.C.S.: 511210
Advertising Expenditures: $425,000
Media: 2-7-8-10-13
Personnel:
Vince Burkett *(Exec Chm & CEO)*
Steve Carpenter *(COO)*
Charles Goodman *(COO)*
Andy Bane *(Exec VP-Product & Mktg)*
Will Dailey *(Exec VP)*
Gary Frazier *(Dir-Corp Comm)*

VERAMARK TECHNOLOGIES, INC.

1565 Jefferson Rd Ste 120
Rochester, NY 14623
Tel.: (585) 381-6000
Fax: (585) 383-6800
E-mail: info@veramark.com
Web Site: www.veramark.com
Approx. Sls.: $13,165,209
Approx. Number Employees: 78
Year Founded: 1983
Business Description:
Telecommunications Design, Production & Servicing; Call Accounting; Web Based Telemanagement Software
S.I.C.: 7372; 7371
N.A.I.C.S.: 511210; 334611; 541511

Key to Media (For complete agency information see *The Advertising Red Books-Agencies* edition):
1. Bus. Publs. 2. Cable T.V. 3. Catalogs & Directories. 4. Co-op Adv. 5. Consumer Mags. 6. D.M. to Bus. Estab.7. D.M. to Consumers 8. Daily Newsp. 9. Exhibits/Trade Shows 10. Foreign 11. Infomercial 12. Internet Adv.13. Multimedia 14. Network Radio 15. Network T.V. 16. Newsp. Distr. Mags. 17. Other 18. Outdoor (Posters, Transit) 19. Point of Purchase20. Premiums, Novelties 21. Product Samples 22. Special Events Mktg. 23. Spot Radio 24. Spot T.V. 25. Weekly Newsp. 26. Yellow Page Adv.

Veramark Technologies, Inc. — (Continued)
Import Export
Media: 2-7-8-10
Personnel:
Anthony C. Mazzullo *(Chm, Pres & CEO)*
Ronald C. Lundy *(CFO, & VP-Fin)*
Joshua Bouk *(Sr VP-Strategic Svcs)*
Thomas McAlees *(Sr VP-Engrg & Ops)*
Denise Chapman *(VP-Mktg)*
Brands & Products:
ECAS
TEM
VERASMART

VERIFONE SYSTEMS, INC.
(Formerly VeriFone Holdings, Inc.)
2099 Gateway Pl Ste 600
San Jose, CA 95110
Tel.: (408) 232-7800
Fax: (408) 232-7811
Toll Free: (800) 837-4366
E-mail: info-emea@verifone.com
Web Site: www.verifone.com
Approx. Rev.: $1,001,537,000
Approx. Number Employees: 2,565
Year Founded: 1981
Business Description:
Holding Company; Point-of-Sale Software & Technologies Mfr & Distr
S.I.C.: 6719; 3575; 3577; 7372
N.A.I.C.S.: 551112; 334113; 334119; 511210
Import Export
Advertising Expenditures: $1,300,000
Media: 4-5-7-8-9-10-11-13-25
Distr.: Intl.
Budget Set: Dec.
Personnel:
Charles R. Rinehart *(Chm)*
Douglas G. Bergeron *(CEO)*
Robert Dykes *(CFO & Sr VP)*
Albert Liu *(Gen Counsel & Sr VP)*
Isaac Angel *(Exec VP-Global Ops)*
Jeffrey C. Dumbrell *(Exec VP)*
Elmore Waller *(Exec VP-Software, Petroleum, Taxi & Media Solutions)*
Fernando Lopez *(Sr VP & Gen Mgr-Latin America & The Caribbean)*
Robbie Lopez *(Sr VP & Gen Mgr-Software Solutions)*
Patrick McGivern *(Sr VP-Global Supply Chain & Ops)*
Jennifer Miles *(Sr VP-Retail, Global Security & Vertical Solutions)*
Paul Rasori *(Sr VP-Mktg)*
David Turnbull *(Sr VP-R&D)*
Shaun Burger *(VP & Gen Mgr-Northern Europe, Middle East & Africa)*
Soner Casur *(VP & Gen Mgr-South East Europe)*
Dawn LaPlante *(VP-HR)*
Chris Polos *(VP-Adv Sls)*
Brands & Products:
CODE CENTER
DEVNET
EVERESTPLUS
JCHARGE
MX
NURIT
OMNI 3750
PAYWARE
PCCHARGE
PINPAD
QX
RITA SERVER
SAPPHIRE
SECURA INTEGRATED
SOFTPAY
TOPAZ XL
VERICENTRE
VERISHIELD
VERIX
VISUALPAYMENTS
THE WAY TO PAY
Advertising Agency:
Merge Agency, LLC
550 Pharr Rd Ste 630
Atlanta, GA 30305
Tel.: (404) 724-4942
Fax: (404) 724-0141

VERINT SYSTEMS INC.
(Sub. of Comverse Technology, Inc.)
330 S Service Rd
Melville, NY 11747
Tel.: (631) 962-9600
Fax: (631) 962-9300
E-mail: marketing.americas@verint.com
Web Site: www.verint.com
Approx. Rev.: $726,799,000
Approx. Number Employees: 2,800
Business Description:
Security & Business Intelligence Software
S.I.C.: 7372; 3669; 7373
N.A.I.C.S.: 511210; 334290; 541512
Media: 1-4-7-10
Personnel:
Dan Bodner *(Pres & CEO)*
Elan Moriah *(Pres & Corp Officer-Verint Witness Actionable Solutions)*
Douglas Robinson *(CFO & Corp Officer)*
Peter Fante *(Chief Legal Officer & Sec)*
Meir Sperling *(Pres-APAC)*
Debjit Das *(VP-Mktg)*
Brands & Products:
RELIANT
STAR-GATE
ULTRA
Advertising Agency:
Merritt Group
11600 Sunrise Valley Dr Ste 320
Reston, VA 20191-1416
Tel.: (703) 390-1500
Fax: (703) 860-2080

VERINT WITNESS ACTIONABLE SOLUTIONS
(Sub. of VERINT SYSTEMS INC.)
300 Colonial Ctr Pkwy Ste 600
Roswell, GA 30076
Tel.: (770) 754-1900
Fax: (770) 754-1873
Toll Free: (888) 3-WITNESS
E-mail: info@verint.com
Web Site: www.verint.com
Sales Range: $150-199.9 Million
Approx. Number Employees: 619
Year Founded: 1988
Business Description:
Computer Software Developer
S.I.C.: 7372
N.A.I.C.S.: 334611; 511210
Advertising Expenditures: $500,000
Media: 7-10-13-17
Personnel:
Dan Bodner *(Pres, CEO, Dir & Corp Officer)*
Doug Robinson *(CFO & Corp Officer)*
Elan Moriah *(Pres-Americas)*
Nancy Treaster *(Sr VP & Gen Mgr)*
John Bourne *(Sr VP-Global Channels & Alliances)*
Ryan Hollenbeck *(Sr VP-Mktg)*
Kathy Miller *(Sr VP-Global Fin & Acctg)*
Brands & Products:
EQUALITY
EQUALITY ANALYSIS
EQUALITY BALANCE
EQUALITY CALLMINER
EQUALITY CONTACTSTORE
EQUALITY COURSEWARE
EQUALITY EVALUATION
EQUALITY FOCUS
EQUALITY NOW
EQUALITY OFFICE
EQUALITY PRODUCER
EQUALITY VISION

VERIPACK.COM, INC.
(Name Changed to Bags & Bows)

VERISIGN, INC.
21355 Ridgetop Circle
Dulles, VA 20166
Tel.: (650) 961-7500
Fax: (650) 961-7300
Toll Free: (877) 438-8776
E-mail: ir@verisign.com
Web Site: www.verisign.com
Approx. Rev.: $1,028,953,000
Approx. Number Employees: 1,048
Year Founded: 1995
Business Description:
Digital Commerce & Telecommunications Products & Services
S.I.C.: 7371; 2741; 4812; 4899; 7372; 7374; 8748
N.A.I.C.S.: 541511; 511210; 516110; 517212; 517910; 518210; 541690
Advertising Expenditures: $33,200,000
Media: 2-6-8-9-10-13-14-15-23-24
Personnel:
D. James Bidzos *(Chm, Pres & CEO)*
Grant L. Clark *(Chief Admin Officer)*
Richard H. Goshorn *(Gen Counsel, Sec & Sr VP)*
John Talbot *(VP-Corp Mktg)*
Chris Klein *(Product Mgr)*
Brands & Products:
ATLAS
CHECKMARK CIRCLE DESIGN
DEVICE CERTIFICATE SERVICES
DIGITAL CERTIFICATE
DIGITAL ID
ECA CERTIFICATE
MANAGED PKI
METCALF
MY CREDENTIAL FOR ADOBE
NETDISCOVERY
NETSURE
NON-FEDERAL SHARED SERVICE PROVIDER PKI
PREPAYIN
PROCESSING CENTER PKI
SECURE SITE
SECURE SITE PRO
SECURE SITE PRO WITH EV
SECURE SITE WITH EV
SHARED SERVICE PROVIDER PKI
SMARTPAY
SPEEDSUITE
SSL FOR ENTERPRISE
TRUE CREDENTIALS FOR ADOBE
TRUST NETWORK
UNIFIED AUTHENTIFICATION OTP
UNIFIED AUTHENTICATION PKI FOR WINDOWS
VERISIGN
VERISIGN & DESIGN
VERISIGN DESIGN
VERISIGN IDEFENSE SECURITY
VERISIGN IDENTITY PROTECTION
VERISIGN SECURED DESIGN
VERISIGN SECURED SEAL
VERISIGN SSL CETIFICATES
VERTICAL SERVICE PROVIDER
VIP AUTHENTICATION
VIP CREDENTIAL
VIP FRAUD DETECTION
XOOMERANG
Advertising Agencies:
Butler, Shine, Stern & Partners
20 Liberty Ship Way
Sausalito, CA 94965-3312
Tel.: (415) 331-6049
Fax: (415) 331-3524

Catapult Direct
1700 Winchester Blvd
Campbell, CA 95008
Tel.: (408) 369-8111

FD Americas Public Affairs
1101 K St NW 9th Fl
Washington, DC 20005
Tel.: (202) 346-8800
Fax: (202) 346-8804

McCann Erickson Worldwide
622 3rd Ave
New York, NY 10017-6707
Tel.: (646) 865-2000
Fax: (646) 487-9610

SKOW
690 Texas St
San Francisco, CA 94107
Tel.: (888) 983-0880
Toll Free: (888) 983-0880, ext. 804

Weber Shandwick
(Sub. of The Interpublic Group of Companies)
919 3rd Ave
New York, NY 10022
Tel.: (212) 445-8000
Fax: (212) 445-8001

THE VERNON COMPANY
1 Promotional Pl
Newton, IA 50208
Tel.: (641) 792-9000
Fax: (641) 792-6901
E-mail: sharlae@vernoncompany.com
Web Site: www.vernoncompany.com
E-Mail For Key Personnel:
Marketing Director: jeffb@vernoncompany.com
Sales Director: daver@vernoncompany.com
Public Relations: vickip@vernoncompany.com
Approx. Number Employees: 700
Year Founded: 1902
Business Description:
Promotional Products, Ad Specialties, & Specific Incentives & Premiums Mfr & Distr
S.I.C.: 7319; 3993
N.A.I.C.S.: 541890; 339950
Import
Media: 3-7-8-10-13-16-20-21-26

Key to Media (For complete agency information see *The Advertising Red Books-Agencies* edition):
1. Bus. Publs. 2. Cable T.V. 3. Catalogs & Directories. 4. Co-op Adv. 5. Consumer Mags. 6. D.M. to Bus. Estab.7. D.M. to Consumers
8. Daily Newsp. 9. Exhibits/Trade Shows 10. Foreign 11. Infomercial 12. Internet Adv.13. Multimedia 14. Network Radio
15. Network T.V. 16. Newsp. Distr. Mags. 17. Other 18. Outdoor (Posters, Transit) 19. Point of Purchase20. Premiums, Novelties
21. Product Samples 22. Special Events Mktg. 23. Spot Radio 24. Spot T.V. 25. Weekly Newsp. 26. Yellow Page Adv.

Distr.: Direct to Consumer; Natl.
Budget Set: Mar.
Personnel:
William F. Vernon *(Chm & CEO)*
Chris Vernon *(Pres & COO)*
Brad Lundquist *(CFO & VP)*
Dan Stevenson *(Exec VP)*
Jeff Burnett *(VP-Mktg)*
Dave Regan *(VP-Sls)*
Vicki Palm *(Mgr-Comm)*
Andrea Smith *(Mgr-Sls-Natl)*

VERSO TECHNOLOGIES, INC.
(Filed Chapter 11 Bankruptcy 4/30/2008)
400 Galleria Pkwy SE Ste 200
Atlanta, GA 30339-3182
Tel.: (678) 589-3500
Fax: (678) 589-3750
Toll Free: (866) 829-8776
E-mail: info@verso.com
Sales Range: $25-49.9 Million
Approx. Number Employees: 261
Year Founded: 1992
Business Description:
Networking Hardware, Software & Services to Telecom Companies
S.I.C.: 7373; 3661
N.A.I.C.S.: 541512; 334210
Advertising Expenditures: $1,400,000
Media: 2-4-7-10-13-17-20-21-22
Personnel:
Mark H. Dunaway *(Pres)*
Martin D. Kidder *(CFO)*
Brands & Products:
CLARENT
EXTENDER
I-MASTER
NACT
NETAUDITOR
NETPERFORMER
NETSPECTIVE
SKYPERFORMER
TELEMATE
VERSO

VERTICAL COMMUNICATIONS, INC.
3979 Freedom Cir Ste 400
Santa Clara, CA 95054
Tel.: (408) 404-1600
Fax: (408) 969-9601
Web Site: www.vertical.com
Sales Range: $50-74.9 Million
Approx. Number Employees: 243
Year Founded: 1982
Business Description:
Computer Telephony Solutions for Small & Medium Businesses
S.I.C.: 7372
N.A.I.C.S.: 511210; 334611
Export
Advertising Expenditures: $83,000
Media: 2-7-10-13
Distr.: Intl.
Budget Set: June
Personnel:
William Y. Tauscher *(Chm & CEO)*
Peter H. Bailey *(Pres & COO)*
Dick Anderson *(Exec VP-Large Enterprise Sls)*
David Ridder *(Sr VP-Channel Sls)*
Christopher H. Brookins *(VP-Engrg)*
Ken Kark *(Product Mgr)*
Brands & Products:
COMDIAL DX-120
COMDIAL DX-120FX II
COMDIAL MP5000
INSTANT OFFICE
SBX IP 320
TELEVANTAGE
VERTICAL
VODAVI
VODAVI STAR PLUS
VODAVI TELENIUM IP
VODAVI XTS IP
WAVE IP
XCELERATOR IP

VERTICAL SEARCH WORKS INC.
1919 Gallows Rd Ste 1050
Vienna, VA 22182-3900
Tel.: (703) 761-3700
Fax: (703) 761-1990
Toll Free: (800) 755-7005
E-mail: invest@verticalsearchworks.com
Web Site: www.verticalsearchworks.com
Approx. Rev.: $800,000
Approx. Number Employees: 30
Year Founded: 1980
Business Description:
Search & Categorization Software Solutions Designer, Developer, Marketer, Implementer & Supporter
S.I.C.: 7373; 7371; 7372
N.A.I.C.S.: 511210; 334611; 541511; 541512
Export
Advertising Expenditures: $55,000
Media: 1-4-5-7-10-20-22
Distr.: Direct to Consumer; Intl.; Natl.
Personnel:
Patrick C. Condo *(Co-Chm & Founder)*
Keith Young *(Founder & Co-Chm)*
Colin Jeavons *(CEO)*
Matthew G. Jones *(CFO)*
Michael Tuohy *(Dir & Publr-Sls)*
Mark MacDonald *(VP-Sls & Adv)*
Brands & Products:
CONVERA
RETRIEVALWARE
SCREENING ROOM
Advertising Agency:
G.S. Schwartz & Co. Inc.
470 Park Ave S 10th Fl S
New York, NY 10016-6819
Tel.: (212) 725-4500
Fax: (212) 725-9188

VERTICALRESPONSE, INC.
501 2nd St Ste 700
San Francisco, CA 94107
Tel.: (415) 905-6880
Fax: (415) 808-2480
Toll Free: (866) 6VERTICAL
Web Site: www.verticalresponse.com
Sales Range: $10-24.9 Million
Approx. Number Employees: 100
Year Founded: 2001
Business Description:
Internet-Based Business Support Services
S.I.C.: 7371; 7331; 7389
N.A.I.C.S.: 541511; 519190; 541860
Personnel:
Janine Popick *(Founder, Pres & CEO)*
David Shiba *(COO)*
Alf Brand *(Dir-Mktg Comm)*
Advertising Agency:
Atomic Public Relations
735 Market St 4th Fl
San Francisco, CA 94103
Tel.: (415) 402-0230
Fax: (415) 402-0237
— Martha Shaughnessy *(Acct Exec)*

VERUTEK TECHNOLOGIES, INC.
65 W Dudley Town Rd Ste 100
Bloomfield, CT 06002
Tel.: (860) 242-9800
Fax: (860) 242-9899
E-mail: jcollins@verutek.com
Web Site: www.verutek.com
Sales Range: $1-9.9 Million
Approx. Number Employees: 21
Year Founded: 2006
Business Description:
Green Nanotechnology Solutions
S.I.C.: 8999; 7389
N.A.I.C.S.: 541620; 541990
Advertising Expenditures: $2,813
Media: 17
Personnel:
John Collins *(Founder)*
Douglas K. Anderson *(Chm)*
Dan Socci *(CEO)*
George Hoag *(Sr VP & Dir-R & D)*
Brands & Products:
COELUENT TECHNOLOGIES
S-ISCO
VERUSOL
VERUTEK

VIASAT, INC.
6155 El Camino Real
Carlsbad, CA 92009-1602
Tel.: (760) 476-2200
Fax: (760) 929-3941
E-mail: investorrelations@viasat.com
Web Site: www.viasat.com
Approx. Rev.: $802,206,000
Approx. Number Employees: 2,200
Year Founded: 1986
Business Description:
Advanced Digital Satellite Telecommunications & Wireless Signal Processing Equipment Mfr
S.I.C.: 3663
N.A.I.C.S.: 334220
Export
Advertising Expenditures: $200,000
Media: 2-10-18
Personnel:
Mark D. Dankberg *(Co-Founder, Chm & CEO)*
Steven R. Hart *(Co-Founder, Co-CTO & VP)*
Mark J. Miller *(Co-Founder, Co-CTO & VP)*
Richard A. Baldridge *(Pres & COO)*
Ronald G. Wangerin *(CFO & VP)*
Keven K. Lippert *(Gen Counsel, Sec & VP)*
Kevin J. Harkenrider *(Sr VP-Infrastructure Ops)*
Gregory D. Monahan *(Sr VP)*
Tomas E. Moore *(Sr VP)*
H. Stephen Estes *(VP-HR)*
Rich Lindstrom *(VP-Engrg)*
Brands & Products:
ACCELENET
ALTASEC
ARCLIGHT
BLUE FORCE TRACKING
COMSAT LABORATORIES
HAIPE
KIV-21
LINKSTAR
LINKWAY
POCKET DTS
SKYLINX
STARWIRE
SURFBEAM
VIASAT
VIASAT-1
WILDBLUE

VIATECH PUBLISHING SOLUTIONS
1440 5th Ave
Bay Shore, NY 11706
Tel.: (631) 968-8500
Fax: (631) 968-0830
Toll Free: (800) 865-8558
E-mail: salescorp@viatechpub.com
Web Site: www.viatechpub.com
E-Mail For Key Personnel:
Sales Director: salescorp@viatechpub.com
Sales Range: $25-49.9 Million
Approx. Number Employees: 450
Year Founded: 1928
Business Description:
Advertising Aids; Presentations; Sales Manuals; Loose Leaf Binders; Laser Printing & Fulfillment Services
S.I.C.: 2782; 2789
N.A.I.C.S.: 323118; 323121
Advertising Expenditures: $370,000
Media: 1-2-4-8-10-21-26
Distr.: Intl.; Natl.
Budget Set: July
Personnel:
Michael Bertuch *(Pres)*
Tom Ginocchio *(CFO)*
Ron Simmons *(COO)*
Brands & Products:
ON-DEMAND DESTINATION PRINTING
VIATECH

VICTOR TECHNOLOGY
175 E Crossrods Pkwy
Bolingbrook, IL 60440
Tel.: (630) 754-4400
Fax: (630) 972-3902
Toll Free: (800) 628-2420
E-mail: webmaster@victortech.com
Web Site: www.victortech.com
Approx. Number Employees: 30
Year Founded: 1981
Business Description:
Calculators Mfr & Distr
S.I.C.: 5044; 5045
N.A.I.C.S.: 423420; 423430
Media: 2-4-5-7-10-20
Distr.: Intl.; Natl.
Budget Set: Sept.
Personnel:
Jordan Feiger *(Pres)*
Brands & Products:
VICTOR

VIDEO PROFESSOR INC.
12055 W 2nd Pl
Lakewood, CO 80228-1526
Tel.: (303) 232-1244
Toll Free: (800) 525-7763
E-mail: info@videoprofessor.com
Web Site: www.videoprofessor.com
Approx. Sls.: $50,000,000
Approx. Number Employees: 200
Year Founded: 1987
Business Description:
Training Software Services
S.I.C.: 8243; 7372
N.A.I.C.S.: 611420; 511210

Key to Media (For complete agency information see *The Advertising Red Books-Agencies* edition):
1. Bus. Publs. 2. Cable T.V. 3. Catalogs & Directories. 4. Co-op Adv. 5. Consumer Mags. 6. D.M. to Bus. Estab.7. D.M. to Consumers
8. Daily Newsp. 9. Exhibits/Trade Shows 10. Foreign 11. Infomercial 12. Internet Adv.13. Multimedia 14. Network Radio
15. Network T.V. 16. Newsp. Distr. Mags. 17. Other 18. Outdoor (Posters, Transit) 19. Point of Purchase20. Premiums, Novelties
21. Product Samples 22. Special Events Mktg. 23. Spot Radio 24. Spot T.V. 25. Weekly Newsp. 26. Yellow Page Adv.

Video Professor Inc. — (Continued)

Media: 3-6-12-13
Personnel:
John W. Scherer *(Owner)*
Brands & Products:
KNOWLEDGE AT THE SPEED OF LIFE
TRY MY PRODUCT
VIDEO PROFESSOR

VIDEOJET TECHNOLOGIES INC.

(Sub. of Danaher Corporation)
1500 Mittel Blvd
Wood Dale, IL 60191-1073
Tel.: (630) 860-7300
Fax: (630) 616-3657
Fax: (630) 616-3623
Toll Free: (800) 843-3610
Web Site: www.videojet.com
Sales Range: $400-449.9 Million
Approx. Number Employees: 1,500
Year Founded: 1980
Business Description:
Large & Small Character Ink Jet Printers, Laser Coding Systems, Thermal Transfer Printers, RFID Solutions, High Speed Imaging, Addressing & Mailing Equipment, In-Line Graphic Control Systems & Postal Coding Systems Mfr & Distr
S.I.C.: 3579
N.A.I.C.S.: 333313
Export
Advertising Expenditures: $500,000
Media: 2-4-7-8-9-10-11-13-16-23-25-26
Distr.: Intl.; Natl.
Personnel:
Matt Trerotola *(Pres)*
Brands & Products:
ALLPRINT
ALLTEC
BLUEPRINT
CHESHIRE
CONNECTOR
DATAFLEX
EXCEL 2100
INKSOURCE
MARSH
MARSH ENCORE
MARSH OVERTURE
MARSH PATRIONPLUS
MARSH UNICORN
POSTNET
PRINTMANAGER 2000
TOTALSOURCE
VIDEOJET
VIDEOJET BROADCAST SYSTEM
VIDEOJET EXCEL
VIDEOJET FOCUS
VIDEOJET IPRO
WILLETT
Advertising Agency:
Bader Rutter & Associates, Inc.
13845 Bishops Dr
Brookfield, WI 53005
Tel.: (262) 784-7200
Fax: (262) 938-5595
Toll Free: (888) 742-2337

VIDEX, INC.

1105 NE Cir Blvd
Corvallis, OR 97330
Tel.: (541) 758-0521
Fax: (541) 752-5285
E-mail: sales@videx.com
Web Site: www.videx.com
E-Mail For Key Personnel:
Sales Director: sales@videx.com
Approx. Number Employees: 56
Year Founded: 1979
Business Description:
Data Collection & Access Control Products Designer & Mfr
S.I.C.: 3577; 7372
N.A.I.C.S.: 334119; 511210
Media: 4-10
Personnel:
Paul Davis *(Pres)*
Kathleen Childs *(Mgr-Media)*
Brands & Products:
AUDITLINK
AUTHORIZER
BARCODE LABELER
CYBERKEY
CYBERLOCK
CYBERPOINT
DURATRAX
DURAWAND
ICLOCK
LASERLITE
LASERLITE PRO
OMNIWAND
PULSESTAR
SCHLAGE
TIMEWAND
TOUCH PROBE
TOUCHACCESS
TOUCHPROBE

VIEW SYSTEMS, INC.

1550 Caton Center Dr Ste E
Baltimore, MD 21227
Tel.: (410) 242-8439
Fax: (410) 242-0765
Toll Free: (877) 843-9462
E-mail: info@viewsystems.com
Web Site: www.viewsystems.com
Approx. Rev.: $768,026
Approx. Number Employees: 7
Year Founded: 1989
Business Description:
Software & Hardware Systems for Security & Surveillance Applications
S.I.C.: 7372; 3577; 7382
N.A.I.C.S.: 511210; 334119; 561621
Advertising Expenditures: $25,862
Media: 17
Personnel:
Gunther Than *(CEO & Treas)*

VIEWSONIC CORPORATION

381 Brea Cyn Rd
Walnut, CA 91789
Tel.: (909) 444-8800
Fax: (909) 468-1202
Toll Free: (800) 888-8593
E-mail: info@viewsonic.com
Web Site: www.viewsonic.com
E-Mail For Key Personnel:
Marketing Director: bredna.roth@viewsonic.com
Sales Range: $1-4.9 Billion
Approx. Number Employees: 786
Year Founded: 1987
Business Description:
Computer Displays, LCD & Plasma Television Sets, Wireless Networking Equipment, LCD Projectors & Handheld Computer Mfr
S.I.C.: 3577; 3663
N.A.I.C.S.: 334119; 334220
Advertising Expenditures: $27,944,000
Media: 6-10-11
Personnel:
James Chu *(Chm & CEO)*
H. C. Ho *(Pres-Global Products Grp)*
Adam Hanin *(VP-Mktg)*
Brian Igoe *(VP-Sls & ViewSonic Americas)*
Jeff Volpe *(VP-Mktg-Americas)*
Roger Chien *(Product Mgr-Projectors)*
Brands & Products:
ARAG
AUTO TUNE
CLEARMOTIV
CLEARPICTURE
COLLIGO
CYBERCLEAR
CYBERVISION
DIGITAL CONFERENCE
DIGITAL DISPLAY
E SQUARED
E2
EXPRESS EXCHANGE
FAXSONIC
GOTOMYPC
JOURNEY OF HOPE
KENSINGTON
LUCID
MEGABASE
MEGAMONITOR
MINDJET
NEOSAT
NEXTVISION
NOW ON DISPLAY
OFFICE THEATER
ONVIEW
OPTI-GREEN
OPTI-UPS
OPTIQUEST
OPTISYNC
PERFECTFLAT
PERFECTPORTRAIT
PERFECTSOUND
PERFECTVIEW
POWERONE
PROSERIES
SKETCHBOOK PRO
STAR
SUPERCLEAR
SUPERCONTRAST
SUPERPRESS
THINEDGE
ULTRABRITE
VESA
VIDITALK
VIEWBOOK
VIEWCARE
VIEWDOCK
VIEWMATCH
VIEWMATE
VIEWMETER
VIEWPANEL
VIEWSONIC
VISIONBANK
WI-FI
XTREME MONITOR
XTREMEVIEW
ZINIO
Advertising Agency:
NYCA
1010 S Coast Hwy Ste 101
Encinitas, CA 92024
Tel.: (760) 436-7033
Fax: (760) 436-7047

VIQ SOLUTIONS INC.

Bankers Hall 888 3rd St SW Ste 1031
Calgary, AB T2P 5C5, Canada
Tel.: (403) 444-6777
Fax: (403) 444-6778
E-mail: info@viqsolutions.com
Web Site: www.viqsolutions.com
Approx. Sls.: $12,450,854
Year Founded: 1984
Business Description:
Computer-Based Digital Audio Capture & Management Software Mfr & Marketer
S.I.C.: 7372
N.A.I.C.S.: 334611; 511210
Media: 6-10-13
Personnel:
Norman Inkster *(Chm)*
David Outhwaite *(Pres & CEO)*
Karen Hersh *(CFO)*
Brands & Products:
ACCESSPOINT
CFPLAYER
CONTINUUM
COURTABLE
COURTFLOW
ENCOMPASS PRO
MURF
NETSCRIBE
RECORDABLE
RECORDIAB
VFTRANSPORT
VIQ
VIQ SHUTTLE DRA

VIRTUSA CORPORATION

2000 W Park Dr
Westborough, MA 01581
Tel.: (508) 389-7300
Fax: (508) 366-9901
Web Site: www.virtusa.com
Approx. Rev.: $217,979,000
Approx. Number Employees: 5,056
Business Description:
IT Consulting Services
S.I.C.: 8748; 7379
N.A.I.C.S.: 541690; 541519
Advertising Expenditures: $243,000
Personnel:
Kris A. Canekeratne *(Chm & CEO)*
Stefan Fraas *(Mng Dir & Sr VP)*
Ranjan Kalia *(CFO, Treas, Sec & Sr VP)*
Roger Keith Modder *(COO & Exec VP)*
Thomas R. Holler *(Chief Strategy Officer & Exec VP)*
Paul Tutun *(Gen Counsel, Asst Sec & Sr VP)*
John Gillis *(Exec VP-Client Svcs & Bus Dev)*
Raj Rajgopal *(Exec VP-Bus Dev & Client Svcs)*
Samir Dhir *(Sr VP & Head-Global Delivery & Ops-India)*
Jim Francis *(Sr VP-Worldwide Sls)*
Bob Graham *(VP-Banking & Fin Svcs)*
Advertising Agency:
Greenough Communications
9 Harcourt St
Boston, MA 02116
Tel.: (617) 275-6500
Fax: (617) 275-6501

VISIRECORD SYSTEMS, INC.

145 Grassy Plain St
Bethel, CT 06801
Tel.: (203) 743-5700
Fax: (203) 743-6463
Toll Free: (800) 992-9925
Approx. Number Employees: 4

Key to Media (For complete agency information see *The Advertising Red Books-Agencies* edition):
1. Bus. Publs. 2. Cable T.V. 3. Catalogs & Directories. 4. Co-op Adv. 5. Consumer Mags. 6. D.M. to Bus. Estab.7. D.M. to Consumers 8. Daily Newsp. 9. Exhibits/Trade Shows 10. Foreign 11. Infomercial 12. Internet Adv.13. Multimedia 14. Network Radio 15. Network T.V. 16. Newsp. Distr. Mags. 17. Other 18. Outdoor (Posters, Transit) 19. Point of Purchase20. Premiums, Novelties 21. Product Samples 22. Special Events Mktg. 23. Spot Radio 24. Spot T.V. 25. Weekly Newsp. 26. Yellow Page Adv.

Year Founded: 1987
Business Description:
Commercial & Professional Recordkeeping Systems Developer & Mfr
S.I.C.: 7389
N.A.I.C.S.: 561499
Media: 2-7-8-10
Distr.: Direct to Consumer; Natl.
Budget Set: Oct.
Personnel:
Robert Stumpf *(Pres & Gen Mgr)*
Brands & Products:
CODAFILE
MEDICON

VITRIA TECHNOLOGY, INC.
(Sub. of Innovation Technology Group)
945 Stewart Dr
Sunnyvale, CA 94085
Tel.: (408) 212-2700
Fax: (408) 212-2757
E-mail: info@vitria.com
Web Site: www.vitria.com
Sales Range: $50-74.9 Million
Approx. Number Employees: 247
Year Founded: 1994
Business Description:
Prepackaged Software Mfr
S.I.C.: 7372
N.A.I.C.S.: 334611; 511210
Advertising Expenditures: $75,000
Media: 8-10
Personnel:
JoMei Chang *(Co-Founder & CEO)*
Dale Skeen *(Co-Founder & CTO)*
Kevin Thompson *(CFO)*
Kevin Thomson *(CFO)*
Bob Meindl *(Sr VP-Sls-Worldwide)*
Brands & Products:
BUSINESSWARE
CLEANORDER
EXCEPTION MANAGER
M3O
ORDER ACCELERATOR
RESOLUTION ACCELERATOR
SMART CLAIMS
SMART GATEWAY
SMARTCARE
SMARTCLAIMS
SMARTRESPONSE
SWIFTCOMPLETE
VITRIA

VMWARE, INC.
(Sub. of EMC Corporation)
3401 Hillview Ave
Palo Alto, CA 94304
Tel.: (650) 475-5000
Fax: (650) 475-5001
Toll Free: (877) 486-9273
Web Site: www.vmware.com
Approx. Rev.: $2,857,343,000
Approx. Number Employees: 9,000
Business Description:
Virtualization Solutions
S.I.C.: 7372; 7379
N.A.I.C.S.: 511210; 541519
Advertising Expenditures: $13,700,000
Personnel:
Joseph M. Tucci *(Chm)*
Paul A. Maritz *(CEO)*
Mark S. Peek *(CFO & Pres-Bus Ops)*
Mark Egan *(CIO)*
Rick Jackson *(CMO)*
Richard J. McAniff *(Chief Dev Officer & Pres-Products)*
S. Dawn Smith *(Chief Compliance Officer, Gen Counsel, Sec & Sr VP)*
Stephen Herrod *(CTO & Sr VP-R & D)*
Carl M. Eschenbach *(Pres-Customer Ops)*
T. Tod Nielsen *(Pres-Applications Platform)*
Jeff Casale *(Sr VP & Gen Mgr-Bus Ops-Americas Reg)*
Raghu Raghuram *(Sr VP & Gen Mgr-Server Bus Unit)*
Scott Bajtos *(Sr VP-Global Support Svcs)*
Betsy Sutter *(Sr VP-HR)*
Brian Byun *(Gen Mgr & VP-Cloud Applications & Services)*
Israel David *(VP-IT Bus Mgmt)*
Michael Haase *(VP-IR & Treasury)*
Steven Hallett *(VP-IT)*
Robert M. Juncker *(Sr Dir-R&D)*
Andrew Goodlace *(Dir-Comml Sls-Australia & New Zealand)*
Sheryl Sage *(Dir-Alliance Programs)*
Rajeev Kutty *(Mgr-Technical Partner)*
Scott Devine *(Engr)*
Brands & Products:
VMWARE ACE
VMWARE ESXI
VMWARE PLAYER
VMWARE THINAPP
VMWARE VCLOUD
VMWARE VIEW 4
VMWARE VSPHERE 4
Advertising Agencies:
O'Keeffe & Co.
921 King St
Alexandria, VA 22314
Tel.: (703) 883-9000
Fax: (703) 883-9007

OutCast Communications
123 Townsend St Ste 500
San Francisco, CA 94107
Tel.: (415) 392-8282
Fax: (415) 392-8281

VOCUS, INC.
4296 Forbes Blvd
Lanham, MD 20706
Tel.: (301) 459-2590
Fax: (301) 459-2827
Toll Free: (800) 345-5572
E-mail: info@vocus.com
Web Site: www.vocus.com
Approx. Rev.: $96,760,000
Approx. Number Employees: 687
Year Founded: 1988
Business Description:
Software Solutions for Public Relations Management
S.I.C.: 7372; 7371
N.A.I.C.S.: 511210; 334611; 541511
Advertising Expenditures: $5,219,000
Personnel:
Richard Rudman *(Pres & CEO)*
Stephen Vintz *(CFO & Exec VP)*
William Wagner *(COO & Exec VP)*
James Bruno *(Sr VP-Corp Dev)*
Darren Stewart *(Sr VP-Global Svcs)*
Norman Weissberg *(Sr VP-Sls-Global)*
Brands & Products:
ON DEMAND SOFTWARE FOR PUBLIC RELATIONS MANAGEMENT
VOCUS
VOCUS PUBLIC RELATIONS 3.0

VOLT INFORMATION SCIENCES, INC.
560 Lexington Ave 15th Fl
New York, NY 10022-6828
Tel.: (212) 704-2400
Fax: (212) 704-2417
Web Site: www.volt.com
Sales Range: $1-4.9 Billion
Approx. Number Employees: 5,000
Year Founded: 1950
Business Description:
Electronic Publishing Systems, Staffing, Data Management & Telephone Directory Services
S.I.C.: 7363; 3571; 7371; 7373; 7376; 7379
N.A.I.C.S.: 561320; 334111; 541511; 541512; 541513; 541519
Import Export
Media: 2-4-9-10-25-26
Distr.: Natl.
Budget Set: Oct.
Personnel:
Steven A. Shaw *(Pres & CEO)*
James Whitney Mayhew *(Interim CFO)*
Howard B. Weinreich *(Gen Counsel & Sr VP)*
Ludwig M. Guarino *(Treas & Sr VP)*
Jerome Shaw *(Sec & Exec VP)*
Jack Egan *(Sr VP-Global Plng & Budgeting)*
Louise Ross *(VP-HR)*

VR INTERACTIVE CORPORATION
86 Nelsons Landing Boulevard Suite 103
Bedford, NS B4A 4C6, Canada
Tel.: (902) 446-4020
Fax: (902) 446-6345
Toll Free: (888) 848-1908
E-mail: info@vri.ca
Web Site: www.vri.ca
Approx. Rev.:
Year Founded: 2000
Business Description:
Internet Image Capturing Products Developer
S.I.C.: 7373
N.A.I.C.S.: 541512
Media: 10
Personnel:
Donald M. Sheehan *(Pres & CEO)*
Clarence H. Loveless *(CFO)*
Brands & Products:
IMAGING THE WORLD AROUND YOU
IWRAP360
SURROUNDPHOTO
VR INTERACTIVE

VULCAN INFORMATION PACKAGING
(Div. of EBSCO Industries, Inc.)
1 Looseleaf Ln
Vincent, AL 35178
Mailing Address:
PO Box 29
Vincent, AL 35178-0029
Tel.: (205) 672-2241
Fax: (800) 344-8939
Toll Free: (800) 633-4526
E-mail: sales@vip.ebsco.com
Web Site: www.vulcan-online.com
E-Mail For Key Personnel:
Sales Director: sales@vip.ebsco.com
Approx. Number Employees: 200
Year Founded: 1947
Business Description:
Loose Leaf Binders, Audio-Visual Packaging, Index Tabs, Plastic Tab Indexes, Convention Packages; Advertising Specialty Items, Software Packaging, Complete Line of Stock Loose Leaf Binders; Custom & Stock Corrugated Boxes for Packaging Services
S.I.C.: 2782
N.A.I.C.S.: 323118
Media: 2-4-7-10-13
Distr.: Natl.
Personnel:
J.T. Stephens *(Owner)*
Brands & Products:
VULCAN

THE WACKENHUT CORPORATION
(Name Changed to G4S Secure Solutions USA)

WALL STREET SYSTEMS INC.
1290 Avenue of the Americas 22nd Fl
New York, NY 10004
Tel.: (212) 809-7200
Fax: (212) 809-7578
E-mail: webmaster@wallstreetsystems.com
Web Site: www.wallstreetsystems.com
Sales Range: $10-24.9 Million
Approx. Number Employees: 250
Business Description:
Computer Software Development
S.I.C.: 7371
N.A.I.C.S.: 541511
Brands & Products:
ALERI
EMPOWERING TREASURY, TRADING AND SETTLEMENT
WALL STREET SYSTEMS
WALLSTREET BACKOFFICE
WALLSTREET FX
WALLSTREET SUITE
WALLSTREET TREASURY
Advertising Agencies:
Fishburn Hedges
77 Kingsway
London, WC2B 6SR, United Kingdom
Tel.: (44) 20 7839 4321
Fax: (44) 20 7242 4202

Intermarket Communications
425 Madison Ave Ste 600
New York, NY 10017-1110
Tel.: (212) 888-6115
Fax: (212) 888-6157

WAREFORCE
(Name Changed to SARCOM)

WARNER BROS. WORLDWIDE CONSUMER PRODUCTS
(Sub. of Warner Bros. Entertainment Inc.)
4000 Warner Blvd
Burbank, CA 91522-0001
Tel.: (818) 954-6000
Fax: (818) 954-6102
Web Site: www.warnerbrothers.com
Sales Range: $100-124.9 Million
Approx. Number Employees: 150
Year Founded: 1960

Key to Media (For complete agency information see *The Advertising Red Books-Agencies* edition):
1. Bus. Publs. 2. Cable T.V. 3. Catalogs & Directories. 4. Co-op Adv. 5. Consumer Mags. 6. D.M. to Bus. Estab.7. D.M. to Consumers
8. Daily Newsp. 9. Exhibits/Trade Shows 10. Foreign 11. Infomercial 12. Internet Adv.13. Multimedia 14. Network Radio
15. Network T.V. 16. Newsp. Distr. Mags. 17. Other 18. Outdoor (Posters, Transit) 19. Point of Purchase20. Premiums, Novelties
21. Product Samples 22. Special Events Mktg. 23. Spot Radio 24. Spot T.V. 25. Weekly Newsp. 26. Yellow Page Adv.

Warner Bros. Worldwide Consumer Products — (Continued)

Business Description:
Entertainment Product Licensing Services
S.I.C.: 5199
N.A.I.C.S.: 424990
Export
Media: 1-2-4-7-10-11-19
Distr.: Intl.; Natl.
Budget Set: Sept.
Personnel:
Brad Globe *(Pres)*
Karen McTier *(Exec VP-Domestic Licensing & Worldwide Mktg)*

WARRANTECH CORPORATION
(Sub. of AmTrust Financial Services, Inc.)
2200 Hwy 121
Bedford, TX 76021
Tel.: (817) 785-6601
Fax: (817) 436-6151
Toll Free: (800) 833-8801
E-mail: info@warrantech.com
Web Site: www.warrantech.com
Sales Range: $100-124.9 Million
Approx. Number Employees: 349
Year Founded: 1986
Business Description:
Extended Service Contracts & Administrative Services
S.I.C.: 7389; 6399
N.A.I.C.S.: 561499; 524128
Advertising Expenditures: $301,849
Media: 7-17
Personnel:
Joel San Antonio *(Founder, Chm & CEO)*
Laurence Tutt *(COO & Sr VP-IT)*
Shaun Hickson *(Pres-Consumer Product Svcs)*
Thomas J. Fontanetta *(Sr VP-Sys Dev)*
Jeanine M. Folz *(Sr VP)*
Advertising Agency:
Michael A. Burns & Associates, Inc.
3333 Lee Pkwy Ste 450
Dallas, TX 75219-5139
Tel.: (214) 521-8596
Fax: (214) 521-8599
(Public Relations)

WATCHGUARD TECHNOLOGIES, INC.
(Holding of Francisco Partners Management, LLC)
505 5th Ave S Ste 500
Seattle, WA 98104-3892
Tel.: (206) 613-6600
Fax: (206) 521-8342
E-mail: information@watchguard.com
Web Site: www.watchguard.com
Sales Range: $75-99.9 Million
Approx. Number Employees: 370
Year Founded: 1996
Business Description:
Specialized Internet Security Services
S.I.C.: 7372; 7373
N.A.I.C.S.: 511210; 541512
Advertising Expenditures: $122,000
Media: 7-10
Personnel:
Joe Wang *(CEO)*
Eric Aarrestad *(VP-Mktg)*
Terry Haas *(VP-Sls-Intl)*
Bill Smith *(VP-Sls-America)*
Sin-Yaw Wang *(VP-Engrg)*
Mark Romano *(Dir-Global Channel & Field Mktg)*
Karen Bogel *(Mgr-HR)*
Brands & Products:
APPLOCK
AUDITSCAN
DESIGNING PEACE OF MIND
FIREBOX
FIREBOX EDGE
FIREBOX X
LIVESECURITY
SERVERLOCK
SOHO
VCLASS
WATCHGUARD
X CORE
X PEAK
XCORE
XPEAK
Advertising Agency:
Lewis Public Relations
678 N Glenville Dr
Richardson, TX 75081
Tel.: (214) 635-3050
Fax: (214) 635-3030

WAYSIDE TECHNOLOGY GROUP, INC.
1157 Shrewsbury Ave
Shrewsbury, NJ 07702-4321
Tel.: (732) 389-0932
Fax: (732) 389-1207
E-mail: investors@waysidetechnology.com
Web Site: www.waysidetechnology.com
Approx. Sls.: $206,730,000
Approx. Number Employees: 102
Year Founded: 1982
Business Description:
Software Distr & Reseller
S.I.C.: 5045; 5961
N.A.I.C.S.: 423430; 454111; 454113
Advertising Expenditures: $2,400,000
Media: 4-7-10-17
Personnel:
Simon F. Nynens *(Chm, Pres & CEO)*
Kevin T. Scull *(Chief Acctg Officer & VP)*
Daniel T. Jamieson *(VP & Gen Mgr-Lifeboat Distr)*
Richard J. Bevis *(VP-Mktg)*
Brands & Products:
PROGRAMMER'S PARADISE
WAYSIDE TECHNOLOGY GROUP

W.B. MASON COMPANY
59 Centre St
Brockton, MA 02303
Tel.: (508) 586-3434
Fax: (800) 773-4488
Toll Free: (888) WBMASON
Web Site: www.wbmason.com
Approx. Rev.: $265,000,000
Approx. Number Employees: 1,000
Year Founded: 1898
Business Description:
Office Furniture & Supplies & Printing Supplies Whslr
S.I.C.: 5712; 5943
N.A.I.C.S.: 442110; 453210
Media: 2-3-4-5-6-7-8-9-13-15-18-20-24-25-26
Distr.: Direct to Consumer; Natl.
Budget Set: Nov.
Personnel:
Steven Greene *(Chm)*
Leo J. Meehan, III *(Pres & CEO)*
Tony DiPippa *(CFO)*
John Greene *(Exec VP)*
Thomas Golden *(Sr VP)*
Dean Orr *(VP-Mktg)*
Laura McNeil *(Dir-Pur)*
Peter Manning *(Branch Mgr)*

WEBCRAFTERS INC.
2211 Fordem Ave
Madison, WI 53704-4611
Tel.: (608) 244-3561
Fax: (608) 244-5120
E-mail: info@webcrafters-inc.com
Web Site: www.webcrafters-inc.com
Sales Range: $50-74.9 Million
Approx. Number Employees: 560
Year Founded: 1921
Business Description:
Provider of Book Printing Services
S.I.C.: 2732; 2752
N.A.I.C.S.: 323117; 323110
Personnel:
John J Frautschi *(Chm)*
Jack Gardner *(Pres)*
Bob Malinowski *(CEO)*
Advertising Agency:
Glowac, Harris, Madison Inc.
330 S Whitney Way Ste 300
Madison, WI 53705
Tel.: (608) 232-9696
Fax: (608) 232-9636

WEBER MARKING SYSTEMS, INC.
711 W Algonquin Rd
Arlington Heights, IL 60005-4415
Tel.: (847) 364-8500
Fax: (847) 364-8575
Toll Free: (800) 843-4242
E-mail: info@webermarking.com
Web Site: www.webermarking.com
E-Mail For Key Personnel:
Sales Director: rcampbell@webermarking.com
Sales Range: $100-124.9 Million
Approx. Number Employees: 700
Year Founded: 1932
Business Description:
Labeling & Coding Equipment & Pressure Sensitive Labels Mfr
S.I.C.: 3555; 2672
N.A.I.C.S.: 333293; 322222
Export
Media: 2-4-7-10-11-13
Distr.: Intl.
Budget Set: Jan.
Personnel:
Joseph Weber, Jr. *(Chm)*
Glenn C. Gilly *(Pres & CEO)*
Shirley Hurley *(VP-HR)*
Tom Michalsen *(Dir-Mktg)*
Mark Parker *(Sls Mgr-Reg)*
Paul King *(Mgr-Svcs)*
Randall J. Stake *(Mgr-Mktg Comm)*
Marilynn Wagner *(Mgr-Prime Bus Team)*
Chris Erbach *(Webmaster)*
Brands & Products:
ECLIPSE
FASTAGGER
FLEXTUFF
LEGIJET
LEGITRONIC
SMARTTRAK
WEBER

WEBEX COMMUNICATIONS, INC.
(Sub. of Cisco Systems, Inc.)
3979 Freedom Cir
Santa Clara, CA 95054
Tel.: (408) 435-7000
Fax: (408) 435-7004
Toll Free: (877) 509-3239
E-mail: info@webex.com
Web Site: www.webex.com
Approx. Rev.: $380,012,000
Approx. Number Employees: 2,189
Year Founded: 1996
Business Description:
Real Time, Interactive Multimedia Communications Services For Websites
S.I.C.: 7372; 7373
N.A.I.C.S.: 511210; 541512
Advertising Expenditures: $28,500,000
Media: 10-13-23-24
Personnel:
Subrah S. Iyar *(Chm & CEO)*
Dan Russo *(Mgr-Online Grp Product Mktg)*
Brands & Products:
EVENT CENTER
MEDIATONE
MEETING CENTER
SMARTTECH
WEBEX
WEBEX EVENT CENTER
WEBEX MEETING CENTER
WEBEX SMARTTECH

WEBSENSE, INC.
10240 Sorrento Valley Rd
San Diego, CA 92121
Tel.: (858) 320-8000
Fax: (858) 458-2950
Toll Free: (800) 723-1166
E-mail: info@websense.com
Web Site: www.websense.com
E-Mail For Key Personnel:
Sales Director: sales@websense.com
Approx. Rev.: $332,762,000
Approx. Number Employees: 1,442
Year Founded: 1994
Business Description:
Employee Internet Management Software Technology Designer
S.I.C.: 7373; 7372; 7375
N.A.I.C.S.: 541512; 511210; 518111
Advertising Expenditures: $6,000,000
Media: 2-5-7-10-13
Personnel:
John B. Carrington *(Chm)*
John R. McCormack *(Pres)*
Vernon Eugene Hodges *(CEO)*
Arthur S. Locke *(CFO & Sr VP)*
Didier Guibal *(Exec VP-Worldwide Sls)*
Susan Brown *(VP-HR & Admin)*
Kate Patterson *(VP-Corp Comm & IR)*
Brands & Products:
APPCATCHER
APPLICATION LOCKDOWN
BANDWIDTH OPTIMIZER
BANDWIDTH PG
BLACKSPIDER
BRANDWATCHER
CHANNEL CONNECT
CLIENT APPLICATION MANAGER
CLIENT POLICY MANAGER

Key to Media (For complete agency information see *The Advertising Red Books-Agencies* edition):
1. Bus. Publs. 2. Cable T.V. 3. Catalogs & Directories. 4. Co-op Adv. 5. Consumer Mags. 6. D.M. to Bus. Estab.7. D.M. to Consumers
8. Daily Newsp. 9. Exhibits/Trade Shows 10. Foreign 11. Infomercial 12. Internet Adv.13. Multimedia 14. Network Radio
15. Network T.V. 16. Newsp. Distr. Mags. 17. Other 18. Outdoor (Posters, Transit) 19. Point of Purchase20. Premiums, Novelties
21. Product Samples 22. Special Events Mktg. 23. Spot Radio 24. Spot T.V. 25. Weekly Newsp. 26. Yellow Page Adv.

CONTENT AUDITOR
CONTENT ENFORCER
DEEP CONTENT CONTROL
DYNAMIC PROTOCOL MANAGEMENT
ESSENTIAL INFORMATION PROTECTION
EXPRESS LOCKDOWN
IM ATTACHMENT MANAGER
IM CONTROL
INTELLIGENT CONTENT PROTECTION
INTERNET HONEYGRID
LOCKDOWN EDITION
NETWORK ACCESS LOCKDOWN
PRECISEID
PREMIUM GROUPS
PRIORITY ONE
PRODUCTIVITY PG
PROTOCOLCATCHER
REAL-TIME ANALYZER
REAL-TIME SECURITY UPDATES
REMOVABLE MEDIA LOCKDOWN
SECURING PRODUCTIVITY
SECURITY FILTERING
SECURITY LABS
SECURITY PG
SITEWATCHER
THREATSEEKER
THREATSEEKER NETWORK
THREATWATCHER
WE FIND THEM BEFORE THEY FIND YOU
WEB DEFENCE
WEB PROTECTION SERVICES
WEB SECURITY
WEB SECURITY ECOSYSTEM
WEBBLAZER
WEBCATCHER
WEBSENSE
WEBSENSE CONTENT GATEWAY
WEBSENSE ENTERPRISE
WEBSENSE EXPRESS
WEMSENSE WEB SECURITY ECOSYSTEM
WSE
WSX

WEST CORPORATION

(Joint Venture of Thomas H. Lee Partners, L.P. & Quadrangle Group LLC)
11808 Miracle Hills Dr
Omaha, NE 68154
Tel.: (402) 963-1200
Fax: (402) 963-1602
Toll Free: (800) 232-0900
Web Site: www.west.com
Approx. Rev.: $2,388,211,000
Approx. Number Employees: 33,400
Year Founded: 1986
Business Description:
Audio, Web & Video Conferencing Products Mfr
S.I.C.: 3651; 4899
N.A.I.C.S.: 334310; 517910
Export
Media: 10
Personnel:
Nancee R. Berger *(Pres & COO)*
Paul M. Mendlik *(CFO, Treas & Exec VP-Fin)*
Mark Lavin *(Chief Admin Officer & Exec VP-Corp Svcs)*
R. Patrick Shields *(Chief Acctg Officer & Sr VP)*
Skip Hanson *(Pres-Consumer Svcs)*
Mick Mazour *(Pres-Bus Svcs)*
Steven M. Stangl *(Pres-Comm Svcs)*
Todd B. Strubbe *(Pres-Unified Communications)*
David C. Mussman *(Gen Counsel, Sec & Exec VP)*
Michael M. Sturgeon *(Exec VP-Sls & Mktg)*
David J. Treinen *(Exec VP-Corp Dev & Plng)*
Brands & Products:
WEST
Advertising Agency:
American Consulting Group, Inc.
1329 Taughannock Blvd
Ithaca, NY 14850
Tel.: (607) 272-9111
Fax: (607) 272-5588

WESTCON GROUP, INC.

(Sub. of Datatec Limited)
520 White Plains Rd, 2 Fl
Tarrytown, NY 10591-5116
Tel.: (914) 829-7000
Fax: (914) 829-7897
Web Site: www.westcongroup.com
Approx. Number Employees: 1,000
Year Founded: 1985
Business Description:
Networking Equipment Resale Services
S.I.C.: 5045; 4899
N.A.I.C.S.: 423430; 517910
Import Export
Advertising Expenditures: $414,000
Media: 2-7
Personnel:
Thomas Dolan *(Chm)*
Dean Douglas *(Pres & CEO)*
Leigh Howard *(Mng Dir-Westcon Grp Australia)*
John P. O'Malley, III *(CFO & Exec VP-Fin)*
William Hurley *(CTO & Exec VP)*
Nancy Saltzman *(Gen Counsel, Sec & VP)*
Bill Corbin *(Exec VP-Global Vendor Relationships)*
Wendy O'Keeffe *(Exec VP-Asia Pacific)*
David Grant *(Sr VP-Europe & Westcon Grp)*
Lynn Smurthwaite-Murphy *(Sr VP-US & Canada)*
Andy Banks *(VP-North America-Cisco Sls)*
Otavio Barbosa *(Gen Mgr-Westcon Latin America)*
Kevin Cooney *(Dir-Fin Plng & Analysis)*
Richard Hodgetts *(Dir-Fin-Europe)*
Richard Roux *(Dir-Avaya Product Mgmt)*
Jeffrey Touzeau *(Dir-Corp Comm)*
Joe Nicoletti *(Mgr-Security Product)*
Brands & Products:
NETWORKING TOGETHER
USPTO
Advertising Agency:
Horn Group
55 Broad St Fl 29
New York, NY 10004
Tel.: (646) 202-9750
Fax: (646) 826-0022

WESTERN DIGITAL CORPORATION

3355 Michelson Dr Ste 100
Irvine, CA 92612
Tel.: (949) 672-7000
Fax: (949) 672-5408
Toll Free: (800) 695-6399
E-mail: selectretail@wdc.com
Web Site: www.westerndigital.com
Approx. Rev.: $9,526,000,000
Approx. Number Employees: 65,431
Year Founded: 1970
Business Description:
Hard Drives Designer & Mfr for the Mainstream Personal Computer & Consumer Electronics Markets
S.I.C.: 3572
N.A.I.C.S.: 334112
Import Export
Advertising Expenditures: $7,000,000
Media: 2-4-5-6-7-8-10-13-20
Distr.: Natl.
Personnel:
Thomas E. Pardun *(Chm)*
John F. Coyne *(Pres & CEO)*
Wolfgang U. Nickl *(CFO & Sr VP)*
Timothy M. Leyden *(COO)*
James D. Morris *(Exec VP & Gen Mgr-Storage Products)*
James K. Welsh, III *(Exec VP & Gen Mgr-Branded Products)*
James J. Murphy *(Exec VP-Sls & Sls Ops-Worldwide)*
Scott Davis *(VP-Sls)*
Peter Edinger *(VP-Sls-EMEA)*
Dale Pistilli *(VP-Mktg-Branded Products Grp)*
Steve Shattuck *(Dir-PR)*
Brands & Products:
ACTIVE POWER SAVE
CAVIAR
DATA LIFEGUARD
DATA LIFEGUARD TOOLS
DATA ONHAND
DUAL-OPTION
DURASTEP RAMP
EASYLINK
ESSENTIAL
FIT LAB
FLEXPOWER
THE FUTURE OF STORAGE ...TODAY
ICEPACK
INTELLIPARK
INTELLIPOWER
INTELLISEEK
LIFEEST
MIONET
MIONET DRIVEACCESS
MY BOOK
MY BOOK ESSENTIAL EDITION
MY BOOK HOME EDITION
MY BOOK MIRROR EDITION
MY BOOK OFFICE EDITION
MY BOOK STUDIO EDITION
MY BOOK WORLD EDITION
MY DVR EXPANDER
MY PASSPORT
MY PASSPORT ELITE
MY PASSPORT ESSENTIAL
MY PASSPORT STUDIO
NETCENTER
NOTOUCH
OPTIPLAY
OPTIZONE
PASSPORT
THE POWER OF DESIGN
POWERARMOR
PREMIUM EDITION
PREMIUM ES EDITION
PRO EDITION
PUT YOUR LIFE ON IT
RAFF
RAPTOR
REDUCED POWER SPINUP
SAFE SHUTDOWN
SCORPIO
SECURECONNECT
SECUREPARK
SHOCK GUARD
SHOCKSHIELD
SIDESTROY
SIERASE
SIKEY
SILICONBLADE
SILICONDRIVE
SILICONDRIVE SECURE
SILKSTREAM
SIPROTECT
SIPURGE
SISCRUB
SISECURE
SISMART
SISTOR
SISWEEP
SIZONE
SMARTPOWER
SOFTSEEK
SOLIDSTOR
STABLETRAC
SURECONNECT
WD
WD ANYWHERE ACCESS
WD BACKUP
WD CAVIAR
WD CAVIAR BLACK
WD CAVIAR BLUE
WD CAVIAR GREEN
WD DUAL-OPTION
WD ELEMENTS
WD GREENPOWER TECHNOLOGY
WD LIVEWIRE
WD PERFORMER
WD RAPTOR
WD SCORPIO
WD SCORPIO BLACK
WD SCORPIO BLUE
WD SHARESPACE
WD SILCONDRIVE
WD SYNC
WD TV
WD VELOCIRAPTOR
WHISPERDRIVE
Advertising Agency:
Lexicon Communications Corp.
520 Bellmore Way
Pasadena, CA 91103
Tel.: (626) 683-9200
Fax: (622) 628-1960

WESTERN STATES ENVELOPE & LABEL

4480 N 132nd St
Butler, WI 53007-2004
Tel.: (262) 781-5540
Fax: (262) 781-5791
Fax: (800) 753-2329
Toll Free: (800) 558-0514
E-mail: customerservice.wi@westernstatesenvelope.com
Web Site: www.westernstatesenvelope.com
Approx. Number Employees: 750
Year Founded: 1908
Business Description:
Envelope & Label Mfr
S.I.C.: 2677; 2672
N.A.I.C.S.: 322232; 322222

Key to Media (For complete agency information see *The Advertising Red Books-Agencies* edition):
1. Bus. Publs. 2. Cable T.V. 3. Catalogs & Directories. 4. Co-op Adv. 5. Consumer Mags. 6. D.M. to Bus. Estab.7. D.M. to Consumers
8. Daily Newsp. 9. Exhibits/Trade Shows 10. Foreign 11. Infomercial 12. Internet Adv.13. Multimedia 14. Network Radio
15. Network T.V. 16. Newsp. Distr. Mags. 17. Other 18. Outdoor (Posters, Transit) 19. Point of Purchase20. Premiums, Novelties
21. Product Samples 22. Special Events Mktg. 23. Spot Radio 24. Spot T.V. 25. Weekly Newsp. 26. Yellow Page Adv.

Western States Envelope & Label — (Continued)

Advertising Expenditures: $200,000
Media: 1-2-4-7-10-13-18-20-21-26
Distr.: Reg.
Budget Set: Apr.
Personnel:
George F. Moss *(Chm & CEO)*
Mark S. Lemberger *(Pres)*
Thomas J. Rewolinski *(Sr VP-Fin Ops)*
Stephen Brocker *(VP-Sls & Mktg)*
Rus Schallert *(Dir-HR)*
Brands & Products:
BASTIAN MICRA DOCUMENTS

WESTMONT STAFFING & PERSONNEL, INC.

(Sub. of 123 Payroll Services, Inc.)
123 Main St
Dallas, TX 75226
Tel.: (214) 555-1212
Approx. Billings:
Business Description:
Staffing Services
S.I.C.: 7361
N.A.I.C.S.: 541612
Personnel:
Cassandra Burns *(Gen Mgr)*
Advertising Agency:
Browning Advertising, Inc.
121 Chanlon Rd
New Providence, NJ 07974
Tel.: (908) 464-0000
Fax: (908) 790-5405
— Henry Gifford *(Acct Exec)*

WHITE GLOVE PLACEMENT INC.

85 Bartlett St
Brooklyn, NY 11206
Tel.: (718) 387-8163
Fax: (718) 387-8359
E-mail: whiteglove.nurses@verizon.net
Web Site: www.whiteglovecare.com
Approx. Number Employees: 500
Business Description:
Nursing Placement Agency
S.I.C.: 7361
N.A.I.C.S.: 561310
Media: 2-6-13-22
Personnel:
Meir Lefkowitz *(Pres)*

WHITE SKY, INC.

825 S Grant St Ste 250
San Mateo, CA 94402
Tel.: (650) 286-9440
Fax: (650) 286-9273
E-mail: info@whitesky.com
Web Site: www.whitesky.com
Approx. Number Employees: 18
Year Founded: 2005
Business Description:
Designer, Developer & Marketer of Authentication Systems for the Prevention of Online Identity Theft
S.I.C.: 7373
N.A.I.C.S.: 541512
Media: 17
Personnel:
Jerry Thompson *(Founder)*
V. David Watkins *(Pres & CEO)*
Ira Scharfglass, Sr. *(Sr VP-Dev)*
Pankaj Srivastava, Sr. *(Sr VP-Mktg)*
Brands & Products:
ID VAULT

WIND RIVER SYSTEMS, INC.

(Sub. of Intel Corporation)
500 Wind River Way
Alameda, CA 94501-1171
Tel.: (510) 748-4100
Fax: (510) 749-2010
Toll Free: (800) 545-9463
E-mail: support@windriver.com
Web Site: www.windriver.com
Approx. Rev.: $359,664,000
Approx. Number Employees: 1,673
Year Founded: 1981
Business Description:
Integrated Embedded Software Services
S.I.C.: 7372; 7371; 7373
N.A.I.C.S.: 511210; 541511; 541512
Export
Advertising Expenditures: $4,900,000
Media: 2-10-13
Personnel:
Kenneth R. Klein *(Pres)*
Ian R. Halifax *(CFO, Sec, Sr VP-Fin & Admin)*
Barry Mainz *(COO)*
Tomas Evensen *(CTO, VP, Gen Mgr-Wind River Tools & Common Tech Products Div)*
Jane E. Bone *(Chief Acctg Officer)*
Vincent Rerolle *(Chief Strategic Officer)*
Scot K. Morrison *(Sr VP-Products)*
Jerry Ashford *(VP & Gen Mgr-Mobile Solutions)*
Amit Ronen *(VP & Gen Mgr-Device Mgmt Product Div)*
Jeff Loehr *(VP-HR)*
Bryan Thomas *(Sr Dir-Global Comm)*
Brands & Products:
ALCHEMY
ATTACHE PLUS
BACKPLANE
BETTERSTATE
BLUE THUNDER
BLUETHUNDER
BOOT LOADER
BSD
BSD/OS INTERNET SERVER EDITION
BSDI
CODETEST FOR TORNADO
COURIER
CROSSCODE
CROSSWIND
D-C++
D-CC
DDI
DECORUM
DIAB-C/C++ COMPILER
DIAB RTA SUITE
DOCTOR DESIGN
DRIVERS
EMBEDDED DESKTOP
EMBEDDED TIMES
ENVOY
ENVOY SNMP AGENT
ESP & DESIGN
THE EXPERT'S CHOICE
FRAME RELAY
FUZZY PARSER
HARDWARE REFERENCE DESIGNS
HOW SMART THINGS THINK
HTML WORKS
HYPERBUILD
ICESTORM
ISDN
ISI
IVASION
JAVA TECHNOLOGIES
JEXPRESS
JEXTREME
JWORKS
LIASON
LOOK! FOR TORNADO
MACPOET
MEGACO
MGCP
MIBWAY FOR RAPIDCONTROL
NETWORK ACCESS CLIENTS
NUKEPOET
ONE-SOLUTION
OPEN
OPTIC
OSEKWORKS
OSEKWORKS, PERFORMANCEPAK
PERSONAL JWORKS
PHILE+
PLUG&SIM
PNA+
POET GATEWAY
POSEK
POWER COMPILING SOLUTIONS
POWERPC 8260 TRAINING
PREPC+
PRISM+ 2
PRISM+ 3
PROBE+
PRPC+
PSET
PSOS+
PSOS+M
PSOSIM
PSOSYSTEM 2.5
PSOSYSTEM 3
PX11+
R2 SIGNALING
RAPID CONTROL FOR APPLETS
RAPID CONTROL FOR CLI
RAPID LOGIC
RAPIDCONTROL
RAPIDCONTROL FOR WEB
RBS
REAL-TIME TRACE
RIP
ROUTER ENGINES
RTA SUITE
SCOPEPAK
SINGLESTEP DEBUGGER
SINGLESTEP FOR TORNADO 2 AND POWERPC TARGETS
SINGLESTEP WITH VISION
SIP
SNIFF+
SNMP
SNMP SOLUTIONS
SS7
STORMPAD
SURROUNDVIEW
TAKEFIVE
TORNADO
TORNADO AE
TORNADO BSP DEVELOPER'S KIT
TORNADO FOR DO-178B
TORNADO FOR HOME GATEWAYS
TORNADO FOR INDUSTRIAL AUTOMATION
TORNADO FOR INTELLIGENT I/O
TORNADO FOR INTELLIGENT NETWORK ACCELERATION
TORNADO FOR MANAGED SWITCHES
TORNADO FOR OSEKWORKS
TORNADO II FOR VXWORKS
TORNADO TOOLS 3 FOR VXWORKS AE
TOUCHSTONE
TRUEFFS FOR TORNADO
TURBOJ
URGE TO CONVERGE
USB
USB DEVELOPER'S KIT
VANTAGEISI
VISIONICE II
VISIONPROBE II
VISIONWARE
VISIONXD
VISUAL SLICKEDIT - TORNADO EDITION
VSPWORKS
VX WORKS
VXDCOM
VXFUSION
VXGDB
VXGNU
VXMP
VXOPC
VXSIM
VXVMI
VXWORKS AE
VXWORKS NETWORK STACK
WEBPDA
WEBPLUS
WEBTEL
WIND FOUNDATION CLASSES
WIND ML
WIND WEB SERVER
WINDCONFIG
WINDLINK
WINDMANAGE
WINDML
WINDNET
WINDNET 802.11B
WINDNET ATM
WINDNET BGP
WINDNET IPSEC
WINDNET L2TP
WINDNET MPLS
WINDNET MULTILINK
WINDNET NAT
WINDNET OSPF
WINDNET PPOE
WINDNET PPP
WINDNET RADIUS CLIENT
WINDNET ROUTER STACK
WINDNET SIGTRAN
WINDNET SNMP
WINDNET STREAMS
WINDPOWER
WINDSH
WINDSTORM
WINDSURF
WINDVIEW
WINDVIEW 2.0
WINNAT
WINPOET
WINPOET SDK
WINVPN
WISP
X.25
ZEROCOPY
ZINC
ZINC 6.0 FOR VXWORKS
ZINC FOR DESKTOP

WIRELESS MATRIX CORPORATION

12369 B Sunrise Valley Dr
Reston, VA 20191
Tel.: (703) 262-0500
Fax: (703) 262-0380
Toll Free: (888) 843-8554

Key to Media (For complete agency information see *The Advertising Red Books-Agencies* edition):
1. Bus. Publs. 2. Cable T.V. 3. Catalogs & Directories. 4. Co-op Adv. 5. Consumer Mags. 6. D.M. to Bus. Estab.7. D.M. to Consumers
8. Daily Newsp. 9. Exhibits/Trade Shows 10. Foreign 11. Infomercial 12. Internet Adv.13. Multimedia 14. Network Radio
15. Network T.V. 16. Newsp. Distr. Mags. 17. Other 18. Outdoor (Posters, Transit) 19. Point of Purchase20. Premiums, Novelties
21. Product Samples 22. Special Events Mktg. 23. Spot Radio 24. Spot T.V. 25. Weekly Newsp. 26. Yellow Page Adv.

E-mail: customercare@wirelessmatrix.com
Web Site: www.wirelessmatrixcorp.com
Approx. Sls.: $42,371,000
Approx. Number Employees: 100
Business Description:
Fax, Data & Voice Communication Hardware, Software & Services
S.I.C.: 4812
N.A.I.C.S.: 517212
Media: 2-4-7-10-13
Personnel:
J. Richard Carlson *(Pres & CEO)*
Maria C. Izurieta *(CFO)*
Al Milligan *(COO)*
Terry Prime *(Sr VP-Engrg)*
Mary Foltz *(VP-Products & Mktg)*
Michael Jakab *(VP-Sls)*
Doug Lane *(Mgr-Mktg Project)*
Brands & Products:
BUSINESS WITHOUT BOUNDARIES
Advertising Agency:
Strategic Communications Group
1400 Spring St Ste 330
Silver Spring, MD 20910
Tel.: (301) 408-4500
Fax: (301) 408-4506
Pub Rels

WIS INTERNATIONAL
(Holding of AMERICAN CAPITAL, LTD.)
9265 Sky Park Ct
San Diego, CA 92123-4375
Tel.: (858) 565-8111
Fax: (858) 565-8406
E-mail: feedback@wisusa.com
Web Site: www.wisusa.com
E-Mail For Key Personnel:
Public Relations: rkendis@wisusa.com
Sales Range: $1-4.9 Billion
Approx. Number Employees: 15,000
Year Founded: 1953
Business Description:
Retail Inventory Services
S.I.C.: 7389
N.A.I.C.S.: 561499
Media: 2-10-20-22
Distr.: Natl.
Personnel:
David Haller *(VP-Sls, Acct Mgmt & Mktg)*
Advertising Agency:
Woodend, Nessel & Friends
12526 High Bluff Dr Ste 300
San Diego, CA 92103
Tel.: (858) 792-3624
Fax: (858) 792-3625
(Inventory Services)

WIZZARD SOFTWARE CORPORATION
5001 Baum Blvd Ste 770
Pittsburgh, PA 15213
Tel.: (412) 621-0902
Fax: (412) 621-2625
E-mail: contact@wizzardsoftware.com
Web Site: www.wizzardsoftware.com
Approx. Rev.: $5,540,122
Approx. Number Employees: 50
Year Founded: 1995
Business Description:
Speech Recognition & Text-To-Speech Software & Hardware Products & Services
S.I.C.: 3577; 7372
N.A.I.C.S.: 334119; 511210
Advertising Expenditures: $293,546
Media: 1
Personnel:
Christopher J. Spencer *(Chm, Pres & CEO)*
John Busshaus *(CFO)*

WORKPLACE OPTIONS
3020 Highwood Blvd
Raleigh, NC 27604
Tel.: (919) 834-6506
Fax: (919) 833-9888
E-mail: info@workplaceoptions.com
Web Site: www.workplaceoptions.com
Sales Range: $1-9.9 Million
Approx. Number Employees: 100
Business Description:
Work-Life Employee Benefits Services
S.I.C.: 7363
N.A.I.C.S.: 561320
Media: 22
Personnel:
Alan King *(Pres & Mng Dir)*
Dean Debnam *(CEO)*
Mary Ellen Gornick *(Sr VP-Global Products)*

WORKSTREAM INC.
485 N Keller Rd Ste 500
Maitland, FL 32751
Tel.: (407) 475-5500
Fax: (407) 475-5517
Toll Free: (866) 953-8800
E-mail: info@workstreaminc.com
Web Site: www.workstreaminc.com
Approx. Rev.: $16,524,765
Approx. Number Employees: 86
Year Founded: 1996
Business Description:
Human Resources Management Software Developer
S.I.C.: 7372
N.A.I.C.S.: 511210
Advertising Expenditures: $409,000
Media: 9-13
Personnel:
Jeffrey Moss *(Chm)*
John Long *(CEO)*
Brands & Products:
TALENT MANAGEMENT
TALENTCENTER

WORLD WIDE TECHNOLOGY HOLDING CO., INC.
(d/b/a World Wide Technology, Inc.)
60 Weldon Pkwy
Maryland Heights, MO 63043-3202
Tel.: (314) 569-7000
Fax: (314) 569-8300
Toll Free: (800) 432-7008
Web Site: www.wwt.com
Approx. Sls.: $2,500,000,000
Approx. Number Employees: 1,008
Year Founded: 1990
Business Description:
Computers, Peripherals & Software Mfr
S.I.C.: 5045; 5065
N.A.I.C.S.: 423430; 423690
Import Export
Media: 10
Personnel:
David L. Steward *(Chm)*
Joseph G. Koenig *(Pres)*
James P. Kavanaugh *(CEO)*
Thomas W. Strunk *(CFO)*
Mark J. Catalano *(Pres-Comml Sls)*
Ann W. Marr *(VP-HR)*
Robert M. Olwig *(VP-Corp Bus Dev)*

WORTH DATA INC.
623 Swift St
Santa Cruz, CA 95060
Tel.: (831) 458-9938
Fax: (831) 458-9964
Toll Free: (800) 345-4220
E-mail: wds@barcodehq.com
Web Site: www.barcodehq.com
Approx. Number Employees: 15
Year Founded: 1986
Business Description:
Bar Code Scanners & Bar Code Software Mfr
S.I.C.: 3577
N.A.I.C.S.: 334119
Export
Media: 4-8-13
Brands & Products:
BARFONT
LABELLRIGHT
TRICODER
USB WEDGE SAVER
WORTH DATA

WRIGHT EXPRESS CORPORATION
97 Darling Ave
South Portland, ME 04106
Tel.: (207) 773-8171
Fax: (207) 874-1766
Fax: (207) 791-1687
Toll Free: (866) 230-1633
E-mail: investors@wrightexpress.com
Web Site: www.wrightexpress.com
Approx. Rev.: $390,406,000
Approx. Number Employees: 881
Business Description:
Payment Processing & Information Management Services
S.I.C.: 6099; 7389
N.A.I.C.S.: 522320; 519190
Advertising Expenditures: $4,974,000
Personnel:
Michael E. Dubyak *(Chm, Pres & CEO)*
Rowland T. Moriarty *(Vice Chm)*
Steve Elder *(CFO)*
George Hogan *(CIO & Sr VP)*
Gregory D. Iverson *(Pres-Pacific Pride Svcs)*
Melissa D. Smith *(Pres-North America)*
Hilary A. Rapkin *(Gen Counsel, Sec & Sr VP)*
Gareth Gumbley *(Exec VP-Wright Express Intl)*
David D. Maxsimic *(Exec VP-Sls & Mktg)*
Robert C. Cornett *(Sr VP-HR)*
Ken Janosick *(Sr VP-Small Bus Solutions)*
Jamie Morin *(Sr VP-Client Svc Ops)*
Greg Strzegowski *(Sr VP-Corp Dev)*
Brands & Products:
THE FLEET CARD THAT'S DRIVING AMERICA'S BUSINESS
HEAVY TRUCK CARD
UNIVERSAL FLEET CARD
WEXINDEX
WEXONLINE
WEXSMART
WRIGHT EXPRESS

XATA CORPORATION
965 Prairie Center Dr
Eden Prairie, MN 55344
Tel.: (952) 707-5600
Fax: (952) 894-2463
Toll Free: (800) 745-9282
E-mail: info@xata.com
Web Site: www.xata.com
Approx. Rev.: $70,651,000
Approx. Number Employees: 200
Year Founded: 1985
Business Description:
Supplier of Onboard Information Technology for the Transportation Industry
S.I.C.: 7372; 7373
N.A.I.C.S.: 511210; 541512
Advertising Expenditures: $1,100,000
Personnel:
John J. Coughlan *(Chm, Pres & CEO)*
Scott G. Christian *(CFO)*
David A. Gagne *(COO)*
Wes Fredenburg *(Gen Counsel)*
Diane Hendricks *(Specialist-HR)*
Brands & Products:
OPCENTER
SMART CHECKS
SMARTCOM
TREQ-L
XATANET

XENTRIS WIRELESS, LLC
1250A Greenbriar Dr
Addison, IL 60101
Fax: (630) 693-9800
Toll Free: (800) 458-2820
E-mail: customerservice@xentriswireless.com
Web Site: www.xentriswireless.com
Business Description:
Wireless Accessories Mfr & Distr
N.A.I.C.S.: 334220
Media: 4
Personnel:
Bill Christy *(Pres & CEO)*

XEROX CANADA INC.
(Sub. of Xerox Corporation)
5650 Yonge Street
North York, ON M2M 4G7, Canada
Tel.: (416) 229-3769
Fax: (416) 733-6498
Toll Free: (800) ASK-XEROX
Web Site: www.xerox.ca
Sales Range: $1-4.9 Billion
Approx. Number Employees: 3,000
Year Founded: 1953
Business Description:
Copiers, Fax Machines, Scan Devices & Laser Printers Mfr
S.I.C.: 5112
N.A.I.C.S.: 424120
Media: 1-2-3-4-5-6-7-8-9-10-12-13-15-17-18-19-20-22-23-24-25-26
Distr.: Natl.
Personnel:
Mandy Shapanski *(Pres & CEO)*
Christa Carone *(CMO & Corp VP-Xerox Corp)*
Simon Matow *(Pres-Western Ops)*
Shay Code *(VP & Gen Mgr-Western Market Centre)*
Jim Muzyka *(VP & Gen Mgr-Global Svcs)*
Al Varney *(VP-Mktg)*

Key to Media (For complete agency information see *The Advertising Red Books-Agencies* edition):
1. Bus. Publs. 2. Cable T.V. 3. Catalogs & Directories. 4. Co-op Adv. 5. Consumer Mags. 6. D.M. to Bus. Estab.7. D.M. to Consumers
8. Daily Newsp. 9. Exhibits/Trade Shows 10. Foreign 11. Infomercial 12. Internet Adv.13. Multimedia 14. Network Radio
15. Network T.V. 16. Newsp. Distr. Mags. 17. Other 18. Outdoor (Posters, Transit) 19. Point of Purchase20. Premiums, Novelties
21. Product Samples 22. Special Events Mktg. 23. Spot Radio 24. Spot T.V. 25. Weekly Newsp. 26. Yellow Page Adv.

Xerox Canada Inc. — (Continued)

Margaret Zanel *(VP-Strategy & Bus Transformation)*
Janet Aitken *(Mgr-Adv)*

Advertising Agencies:
Environics Communications
33 Bloor Street E Suite 900
Toronto, ON M4W 3H1, Canada
Tel.: (416) 920-9000
Fax: (416) 920-1822

Y&R, Ltd.
60 Bloor Street West
Toronto, ON M4W 1J2, Canada
Tel.: (416) 961-5111
Fax: (416) 961-7890

XEROX CORPORATION

45 Glover Ave
Norwalk, CT 06856
Mailing Address:
PO Box 4505
Stamford, CT 06856-4505
Tel.: (203) 968-3000
Fax: (203) 968-3384
Fax: (203) 968-3218
Toll Free: (800) 334-6200
E-mail: webmaster@xerox.com
Web Site: www.xerox.com
Approx. Rev.: $21,633,000,000
Approx. Number Employees: 136,500
Year Founded: 1906
Business Description:
Document Solutions, Services & Systems Including Color & Black & White Printers, Digital Presses, Multifunction Devices, Digital Copiers Designed for Offices & Production Printing Environments; Offers Associated Supplies, Software, & Support Services
S.I.C.: 7389; 3861
N.A.I.C.S.: 561439; 333315
Import Export
Media: 1-2-3-4-5-6-7-8-9-10-11-13-14-15-18-20-22-26
Distr.: Intl.; Natl.
Personnel:
Ursula M. Burns *(Chm & CEO)*
Lawrence A. Zimmerman *(Vice Chm)*
Luca Maestri *(CFO & Exec VP)*
John E. McDermott *(CIO & VP)*
Christa Carone *(CMO & VP-Mktg & Comm)*
Sophie V. Vandebroek *(CTO, Pres-Innovation Grp & Corp VP)*
Uta Werner *(Chief Strategy Officer & VP)*
Carol Ann McFate *(Chief Investment Officer)*
Gary R. Kabureck *(Chief Acctg Officer & VP)*
Phil Harlow *(Chief Diversity & Indus Rels Officer)*
Patricia M. Nazemetz *(Chief HR & Ethics Officer)*
Armando Zagalo de Lima *(Pres-Europe/Global Customer Ops & Exec VP)*
James A. Firestone *(Pres-Corp Ops & Exec VP)*
Eric Armour *(Corp VP & Pres-Graphic Comm Bus)*
Rick Dastin *(Corp VP & Pres-Enterprise Bus Grp)*
Jacques Guers *(Corp VP & Pres-Xerox Europe)*
John M. Kelly *(Corp VP & Pres-Global Svcs Grp-North America)*
Jule E. Limoli *(Pres-Agent Ops-North America & Corp VP)*
Herve Tessler *(Pres-Developing Markets Ops & VP)*
Kevin M. Warren *(Pres-US Customer Ops & VP)*
Willem T. Appelo *(Pres-Xerox Global Bus & Svcs Grp & Corp Sr VP)*
Russell M. Peacock *(Pres-Xerox North America & Corp Sr VP)*
Don H. Liu *(Gen Counsel, Sec & Sr VP)*
Lynn R. Blodgett *(Exec VP)*
D. Cameron Hyde *(Sr VP-Global Accts Ops)*
Jean-Noel Machon *(Sr VP)*
Brian Walsh *(Reg VP)*
Leslie F. Varon *(Controller & VP-Fin)*
Shaun W. Pantling *(VP, Dir & Gen Mgr-Xerox Global Svcs Europe)*
Michael R. Steinharter *(VP & Gen Mgr-Fin Svcs Sector)*
Anthony M Federico *(Corp VP, Chief Engr & Graphic Comm Exec)*
Barbara Basney *(VP-Global Adv)*
Fred Debolt *(VP-USSG Mktg Ops)*
Mike Festa *(VP-Bus Transformation, Fin, Mergers & Acq)*
Carl Langsenkamp *(VP-Pub Rel)*
Tom Maddison *(VP-HR)*
Joe Mancini *(VP-Fin-Xerox North America)*
Leah Queseda *(VP-Mktg-Enterprise Bus Grp)*
Bonnie Jaeckel *(Sr Mgr-Adv)*
Chris Auclair *(Sr Brand Mgr)*
Chris Acocella *(Coord-IR)*

Brands & Products:
2-PHASE EXTRACTION
4595
4635
4700
470CX
4850
4890
495
5009
5011
5012
5014
5018
5021
5028
5034
5052
5053
5065
5080
5090
5100
5114
5201
5203
5205
5210
5220
5240
5260
5280
5305
5306
5309
5310
5313
5318
5320
5322
5328
5335
5337
5340
5343C
5350
5352C
5365
5380
5388
5390
555
5614
5624
5626
5680
575
5818
5820
5837
5845C
5855C
5885
5890
5895
7009
7033
7041
7085
722 SOLUTION
7346
7356
7399
765
785
8142
8160
8254E
8264E
8265
8290
8365
8390
8825 DDS
8830
92C LPS
92C NPS
ACCXES
ACCXES & DESIGN
ADMISSIONS XPRESS
ALPHAAVE 35
ASST
ASTORIA
BIG I, LITTLE T
BILLXCHANGE
BLACK CATHODE
BOOK IN TIME
BOOKMARK35
BOUND TO IMPRESS
C20
C32 COLOR
C35
C40 COLOR
C45
C55
C65
C75
C90
CARBONCONX
CENTREDIRECT
CENTREWARE
CHANNEL FLASH
CHRYSTAL
COLOR XPRESSIONS
COLORCOAT
COLORGRAFX TONER
COLORLINK PUBLISHING SYSTEM
COLORS OF EXCELLENCE
COLORSTIX
COMPASS PROSPECT TRACKING
COMPUSET
CONCOURSE PROSPECT DIALOGS
CONSENSUS MATRIX
CONTENTGUARD
CONTROLCENTRE
COPIER ASSISTANT
COPYCENTRE
CUSTOMER SERVICE PLATFORM
DEVICE-CENTRIC-SERVICES
DIABLO
DIAGNOSTIC NAVIGATOR
DIGIFINISH
DIGIPATH
DIGITAL BOOKMARK
DIGITAL COLOR ELITE SILK
DIGITAL COLOR GLOSS
DIGITAL LASER OPAQUE
DIGITAL VISIONS
DOCUCARD
DOCUGLOSSCARD
DOCUIMAGE
DOCUJOB
DOCULAN
DOCULIFE
DOCULINK
DOCULOCK
DOCUMATE
DOCUMENT ADVISOR OFFICE
DOCUMENT APPLIANCE
DOCUMENT CENTRE IMAGE RETRIEVER
DOCUMENT CHANNEL
THE DOCUMENT COMPANY
DOCUMENT HOME CENTRE
DOCUMENT INTENSIVE BUSINESS PROCESSES
DOCUMENT SOULS
THE DOCUMENT SOURCE
DOCUMENT WORKCENTRE
DOCUMENTING DREAMS
DOCUMENTING DREAMS WRITING WEEK
DOCUMENTS DIRECT
DOCUMENTS ON DEMAND
DOCUPAC
DOCUPATH
DOCUPM
DOCUPRINT 6135
DOCUPRINT NC60
DOCUPRINT P12
DOCUPRINT P8
DOCUPRINTSERVER
DOCURIGHT
DOCUSHARE
DOCUSP
DOCUSTAMP
DOCUTECH
DOCUTECH NETWORK PUBLISHER
DOCXPRESS
DP 1011
DURAPAPER
E-KITS DIRECT
EASY STREET
EASY-VI
ECLICK
ECOWORX
ECOWORX DESIGN
EDUCATORS EDGE
EMAIL AND DESIGN
EMAIL DESIGN
EOMS AND DESIGN
EVENTSPOTTER

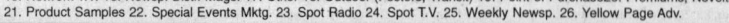

Key to Media (For complete agency information see *The Advertising Red Books-Agencies* edition):
1. Bus. Publs. 2. Cable T.V. 3. Catalogs & Directories. 4. Co-op Adv. 5. Consumer Mags. 6. D.M. to Bus. Estab.7. D.M. to Consumers
8. Daily Newsp. 9. Exhibits/Trade Shows 10. Foreign 11. Infomercial 12. Internet Adv.13. Multimedia 14. Network Radio
15. Network T.V. 16. Newsp. Distr. Mags. 17. Other 18. Outdoor (Posters, Transit) 19. Point of Purchase20. Premiums, Novelties
21. Product Samples 22. Special Events Mktg. 23. Spot Radio 24. Spot T.V. 25. Weekly Newsp. 26. Yellow Page Adv.

EVERFLAT
EVERFLAT IMAGE SOLUTIONS PAPER
EXP6000
EXPERT
EXPRESS MODE DESIGN
EXPRESS YOURSELF
EXTREME SERVICE
FACTSPOTTER
FAXCENTRE
FF DESIGN
FINEPOINT
FLOWPORT
FREEDOM OF CHOICE
FREEFLOW
FREEFLOW MAKEREADY
FREEFLOW OFFICE
FREEFLOW OUTPUT MANAGER
FREEFLOW PREPRESS SUITE
FREEFLOW PROCESS MANAGER
FREEFLOW PRODUCTION HUB
FUNFLIP
GLOBAL PRINT DRIVER
GLOSSMARK
GREEN WORLD ALLIANCE
GYRICON
HARLEQUIN
HEALTHCARE DOCUMENT CHECKUP & DESIGN
HI-WHITE
HORIZON PROPHECY POLLS
IGEN3
IGEN4
IMAGE FIX
IMAGE RETRIEVER
IMAGESITE
IMAGING KIOST SOLUTION
INFOSCENT
INFOSMART
INISHKEA
INK STICK CONFIGURATION(340/350/360-C)
INK STICK CONFIGURATION(340/350/360-K
INK STICK CONFIGURATION(340/350/360-M)
INK STICK CONFIGURATION(340/350/360-Y)
INK STICK DESIGN(340/350/360-C)
INK STICK DESIGN(340/350/360-K)
INK STICK DESIGN(340/350/360-M)
INK STICK DESIGN(340/350/360-Y)
INK STICK DESIGN(SWIFT-C)
INKLOGIC
INNOVATION CHANGES EVERYTHING
INTELLIGENT LOAN FOLDER
INXIGHT
IT'S COMPATIBLE
IT'S SO SIMPLE IT'S BRILLIANT
KNOWLEDGE PUMP
KNOWLEDGE SHARING CENTRE
KNOWLEDGE STREET
KNOWLEDGE TRAIN
KNOWLEDGE WORKER
KNOWLEDGESHARE
LDP LEAN DOCUMENT PRODUCTION & DESIGN
LET'S SAY THANKS
LOFT
M15
M20
M35
M45
M55
MADE FOR EACH OTHER
MAJESTIK COLOR SERIES
MAJESTIK COLOR SERIES DESIGN
MAPS BRAND CHARTING
MDOC
MEETINGRIGHT
METERASSISTANT
MOBILE EXPRESS DRIVER
MOBILEDOC
N2025
N2125
N2825
N32
N3225
N40
N4025
NEUE CLASSIC
NEUE MODERN FAMILY
THE NEW BUSINESS OF PRINTING
NEW BUSINESS OF PRINTING, THE
NSPLUS
NUVERA
OMNIFAX
ONE WORLD CAMPAIGN
OPTIMIZED FOR XEROX FREEFLOW
ORDERQUIX
ORIAS
P1202
P1210
PAGE PLUS PROGRAM
PAGECAM
PAGETRAK
PAPER THAT KNOWS WHERE IT IS GOING
PAPER WARE
PARC
PARC & DESIGN
PARC-CERTIFIED FIELDWORKER
PEARLIZED ELEGANCE
PERSONAL ATTENTION POWERFUL RESULTS
PHASER
PHASERCAL
PHASERMATCH
PHASERSHARE
PHASERSMART
PIXOGRAPHY
POPOUT PRISM
THE POWER BEHIND PRODUCTION
POWERED BY XEROX
PRIMARY IMAGE
PRINT FOR SUCCESS
PRINTERACT
PRINTERMAP
PRINTING INNOVATION WITH XEROX IMAGING AWARDS
PRINTINGSCOUT
PRINTXCHANGE
PROACTIVE CONSUMABLES MANAGEME
PROFILER TARGET IDENTIFICATION
PROFITACCELERATOR
PROFITQUICK
QUICKSTART
REBEE
REDIGLYPH
REQDIRECT
REQDIRECT PLUS AND DESIGN
RING TUFF
RISKSPOTTER
ROOMS
SCAN TO PC DESKTOP
SEARCH FOR HEROES
SEE THE DIFFERENCE QUALITY MAKES
SENTINEL CUSTOMER SATISFACTION
SENTINEL NET EXPERIENCE SCORE
SENTINEL SATISFACTION ASSURANCE SYSTEM
SERVEWARE
SERVICES & SOLUTIONS IMPLEMENTATION PROCESS
SGML VALIDATION STUDIO
SIGNSYNC DESIGN
SILX
SIXTH SENSE
SMART KIT
SMARTDOCUMENT TRAVEL
SMARTER DOCUMENT MANAGEMENT
SMARTPAPER
SMARTPRESS
SMARTPRESS PRODUCTION CONSULTA
SMARTPRESS SERVICES
SMARTPRESS TECHNOLOGY
SMARTSEND
SMARTSIZE
SNAPCOLOR
SOLAR FLARE
SOLVINGRIGHT
SPARROW WEB
SPORTSPIX
SQUAREFOLD
STRESSEDMETAL
STYLIZED X DESIGN
STYLIZED X DESIGN, PIXELATED PORTION
SUPPLIES DEVELOPMENT CENTRE & DESIGN
SUPPLIESASSISTANT
SX3000
SX3000T
SYNCROSIGN
SYNERGIX
TELECOPIER
THERE'S A NEW WAY TO LOOK AT IT
THINK WIDER
TOTAL SATISFACTION SERVICES
UPUBLISHER
VALUE ASSURANCE PROCESS
VALUEQUIX
VALUPERFCARD
VIA XEROX
VIPP
VISUAL RECALL
VP
WALK-UP
WORKCENTRE
X-TREME FILLING
XC1255
XC1875
XC33
XC540
XC580
XC820
XC830
XC865
XCOUNTER
XEROX
XEROX CAPITAL SERVICES AND DESIGN
THE XEROX COMPANY STORE
XEROX CONNECT AND DESIGN
XEROX INTELLIGENT BARCODE UTILITY
XEROX MAKES YOUR WORK. .FLOW
XEROX PROFESSIONAL DOCUMENT SERVICES
XEROX SCAN MANAGER
XEROX VALUE ASSURANCE PROCESS
XIP-LIGHT
XPRESSO
XPRINT
XPS
YOUR WORDS, YOUR PICTURES
ZERO LANDFILL

Advertising Agencies:

GoConvergence
4545 36th St
Orlando, FL 32811
Tel.: (407) 235-3210
Fax: (407) 299-9907

MEC, Global HQ, New York
825 7th Ave
New York, NY 10019-6014
Tel.: (212) 474-0000
Fax: (212) 474-0020
Fax: (212) 474-0003

Rainey Kelly Campbell Roalfe/Y&R
Greater London House Hampstead Rd
London, NW1 7QP, United Kingdom
Tel.: (44) 207 611 6568
Fax: (44) 207 611 6011
Color Multifunction Products

Text 100 Rochester Corp.
4 Commercial St Ste 500
Rochester, NY 14614
Tel.: (585) 697-7723
Fax: (585) 697-7817

VML-New York
285 Madison Ave
New York, NY 10017
Tel.: (212) 210-3653
Fax: (212) 880-7543

Y&R
285 Madison Ave
New York, NY 10017-6401
Tel.: (212) 210-3000
Fax: (212) 490-9073
Fax: (212) 370-3796
Fax: (212) 210-5169
(Copiers, Duplicators, Multifunctional Engineering Products, Fax Machines, Publishing Systems, Printers & Printing Systems, Scanners, Software Networks, Work Station Supplies)

XETA TECHNOLOGIES, INC.

1814 W Tacoma St
Broken Arrow, OK 74012
Tel.: (918) 664-8200
Fax: (918) 664-6876
Toll Free: (800) 845-9145
E-mail: cheryl.moll@xeta.com
Web Site: www.xeta.com
Approx. Rev.: $85,678,283
Approx. Number Employees: 467
Year Founded: 1981
Business Description:
Voice & Data Integration, PBX Systems & Call Accounting Systems
S.I.C.: 3661; 4899
N.A.I.C.S.: 334210; 517910
Media: 2-10
Personnel:
Ronald L. Siegenthaler *(Chm)*
Gregory D. Forrest *(Pres & CEO)*
Robert B. Wagner *(CFO)*

XETA Technologies, Inc. — (Continued)

Paul R. Comeau *(COO)*
Scott Davis *(Exec Dir)*
Thomas Luce *(Exec Dir-Strategic Relships & Managed Svcs)*

Brands & Products:
VIRTUAL XL
VIRTUAL XL II
XETA
XETA TECHNOLOGIES
XL
XPERT
XTRAMILE

XILINX, INC.
2100 Logic Dr
San Jose, CA 95154-3400
Tel.: (408) 559-7778
Fax: (408) 559-7114
Toll Free: (800) 494-5469
E-mail: publicrelations@xilinx.com
Web Site: www.xilinx.com
Approx. Rev.: $2,369,445,000
Approx. Number Employees: 3,099
Year Founded: 1984
Business Description:
Custom Software Designer; User-Programmable Logic Integrated Circuits Mfr
S.I.C.: 3674; 7371; 7372
N.A.I.C.S.: 334413; 511210; 541511
Import Export
Advertising Expenditures: $2,445,000
Media: 2-5-10-11-13-20
Distr.: Intl.
Personnel:
Philip T. Gianos *(Chm)*
Moshe N. Gavrielov *(Pres & CEO)*
Jon A. Olson *(CFO & Sr VP)*
Ivo Bolsens *(CTO & Sr VP)*
Scott R. Hover-Smoot *(Gen Counsel, Sec & VP)*
Victor Peng *(Sr VP-Programmable Platforms Dev)*
Vincent F. Ratford *(Sr VP-Mktg-Worldwide)*
Vincent L. Tong *(Sr VP-Worldwide Quality & New Product Introductions)*
Frank A. Tornaghi *(Sr VP-Worldwide Sls)*
Krishna Rangasayee *(Corp VP & Gen Mgr-Comm Bus Unit)*
Suresh Menon *(VP-Engrg)*
Harvey Steele, Jr. *(VP-Segment Mktg & Bus Ops)*
Brands & Products:
ACCELDSP
ALTERA CYCLONE
ALTERA STRATIX
AMBA
ARTIX
ASMBL
CHIPSCOPE
CHIPSYNC
COOLRUNNER
EASY PATH
ISE
KINTEX
LOGIC CELL ARRAYS
LOGICORE
MICROBLAZE
PICOBLAZE
ROCKETCHIPS
ROCKETIO
ROCKETPHY
SPARTAN
SPARTAN-3
SPARTAN-3A
SPARTAN-3E
SPARTAN-II
VIRTEX
VIRTEX-4
VIRTEX-5
VIRTEX-6
VIRTEX-E
VIRTEX-II
VIRTEX II EASYPATH
WEBFITTER
WEBPACK
XACT
XC4000
XC9500
XCHECKER
XILINX
XILINX SPARTAN-IIE
XILINX VIRTEX-II
XST
ZYNQ

XIUM CORPORATION
106 E Old Settlers Blvd
Round Rock, TX 78664
Tel.: (512) 218-4100
Fax: (512) 218-0983
E-mail: info@goxium.com
Web Site: www.goxium.com
Approx. Number Employees: 25
Business Description:
Wireless Antenna Technologies
S.I.C.: 3651; 5731
N.A.I.C.S.: 334310; 443112
Media: 10

XO COMMUNICATIONS
(Sub. of XO Holdings, Inc.)
13865 Sunrise Vly Rd
Herndon, VA 20171
Tel.: (703) 547-2000
Fax: (703) 547-2881
Web Site: www.xo.com/about/news/Pages/129.aspx
Sales Range: $200-249.9 Million
Business Description:
Telecommunications Services for Business & Telecom Carriers
S.I.C.: 4899
N.A.I.C.S.: 517910
Personnel:
Carl Icahn *(Chm)*
Laura W. Thomas *(Interim CEO & CFO)*
Mike Toplisek *(CMO & Sr VP-Bus Svcs)*
Debbie Pollock-Berry *(Sr VP-HR)*
Shane McNamara *(VP-Indirect Sls)*
Patrick Thompson *(Dir-Legislative Affairs)*
Sheri McKenna *(Mgr-Reg Sls Ops)*
Advertising Agencies:
Brodeur Partners
855 Boylston St 2nd Fl
Boston, MA 02116-2622
Tel.: (617) 587-2800
Fax: (617) 587-2828

Reputation Partners
105 W Adams St Ste 2220
Chicago, IL 60603
Tel.: (312) 222-9887
Fax: (312) 222-9755

XPLANE CORP.
(Sub. of Dachis Corporation, Inc.)
926 NW 13th Ave Ste 220
Portland, OR 97209
Mailing Address:
PO Box 3068
Portland, OR 97208-3068
Tel.: (503) 224-5228
Fax: (503) 292-5561
Web Site: www.xplane.com
Approx. Sls.: $2,000,000
Approx. Number Employees: 10
Year Founded: 1993
Business Description:
Graphic Design Services
S.I.C.: 7336
N.A.I.C.S.: 541430
Media: 2-10-13
Personnel:
Dave Gray *(Founder & Chm)*
Aric Wood *(CEO)*
Judd Knight *(Mng Dir-South Africa)*
Brian Cross *(Sr VP-Svcs)*
Scott Matthews *(Dir-Design)*
Bill Keaggy *(Brand Mgr)*
Brands & Products:
THE VISUAL THINKING COMPANY
XPLANATIONS
XPLANE
XPRESS

XPLORE TECHNOLOGIES CORP.
14000 Summit Dr Ste 900
Austin, TX 78728
Tel.: (512) 336-7797
Fax: (512) 336-7791
E-mail: info@xploretech.com
Web Site: www.xploretech.com
Approx. Rev.: $17,759,000
Approx. Number Employees: 38
Year Founded: 1996
Business Description:
Mobile & Wireless Engineering, Manufacturing, Marketing & Supporting Services
S.I.C.: 7373; 3663
N.A.I.C.S.: 541512; 334220
Advertising Expenditures: $66,000
Personnel:
Philip S. Sassower *(Chm & CEO)*
Mark Holleran *(Pres & COO)*
Michael J. Rapisand *(CFO & Sec)*
Bryan J. Bell *(VP-Engrg)*
John R. Osborne *(VP-Mktg)*
Brands & Products:
ALLVUE
IX
Advertising Agency:
Martin E. Janis & Company, Inc.
401 N Michigan Ave Ste 2920
Chicago, IL 60611
Tel.: (312) 943-1100
Fax: (312) 943-3583

THE YANKEE GROUP
(Holding of Monitor Clipper Partners, Inc.)
31 St James Ave
Boston, MA 02116
Tel.: (617) 956-5000
Fax: (617) 956-5005
E-mail: info@yankeegroup.com
Web Site: www.yankeegroup.com
Approx. Number Employees: 180
Business Description:
Information Technology Market Research & Analytical Report Services
S.I.C.: 8732; 8748
N.A.I.C.S.: 541910; 541690
Personnel:
Emily Nagle Green *(Chm)*
Terry Waters *(Pres & CEO)*
Jason Shore *(COO)*
Gigi Wang *(Chief Res Officer)*
Zeus Kerravala *(Sr VP & Distinguished Res Fellow)*
Shirley MacBeth *(VP-Mktg & Product Dev)*
Advertising Agency:
Waggener Edstrom
225 108th Ave NE Ste 700
Bellevue, WA 98004-5737
Tel.: (425) 638-7000
Fax: (425) 638-7001

YASUTOMO & CO.
490 Eccles Ave
South San Francisco, CA 94080-1901
Tel.: (650) 737-8888
Fax: (650) 737-8877
Toll Free: (800) 262-6454
E-mail: info@yasutomo.com
Web Site: www.yasutomo.com
Approx. Sls.: $9,275,000
Approx. Number Employees: 22
Year Founded: 1954
Business Description:
Stationery Supplies, Art Material, Paper Products & Writing Instruments Whslr
S.I.C.: 5199; 5112
N.A.I.C.S.: 424990; 424120
Import Export
Advertising Expenditures: $355,000
Media: 2-4-5-10-21-26
Distr.: Natl.
Budget Set: Oct.
Personnel:
Daniel H. Egusa *(Owner, Pres & CEO)*
Glen Egusa *(COO)*
Clarissa Pollock *(Coord-Mktg)*
Brands & Products:
CERA BALL
FABRIC MATE
GRIP
LIHIT
MIZUHIKI
NIJI
STYLIST
Y&C

YOTTAMARK
1400 Bridge Pkwy Ste 101
Redwood City, CA 94065
Tel.: (650) 264-6200
Fax: (650) 264-6220
Toll Free: (866) 768-7878
E-mail: info@yottamark.com
Web Site: www.yottamark.com
Business Description:
Unit-Level Brand Security Solutions
S.I.C.: 7382
N.A.I.C.S.: 561621
Media: 10
Personnel:
J. Scott Carr *(Pres & CEO)*
Elliott Grant *(CMO)*
Mark Belinsky *(Sr VP-Corp & Bus Dev)*
Sean Calhoon *(VP-Product Dev)*
William Hoover *(VP-Fin & Ops)*
Todd Laurence *(VP-Sls)*
Peter Townsend *(Sr Dir-Customer Ops)*

Key to Media (For complete agency information see *The Advertising Red Books-Agencies* edition):
1. Bus. Publs. 2. Cable T.V. 3. Catalogs & Directories. 4. Co-op Adv. 5. Consumer Mags. 6. D.M. to Bus. Estab.7. D.M. to Consumers
8. Daily Newsp. 9. Exhibits/Trade Shows 10. Foreign 11. Infomercial 12. Internet Adv.13. Multimedia 14. Network Radio
15. Network T.V. 16. Newsp. Distr. Mags. 17. Other 18. Outdoor (Posters, Transit) 19. Point of Purchase20. Premiums, Novelties
21. Product Samples 22. Special Events Mktg. 23. Spot Radio 24. Spot T.V. 25. Weekly Newsp. 26. Yellow Page Adv.

ZANTAZ INC.
(Name Changed to Autonomy Pleasanton)

ZILLIANT, INC.
3815 S Capital Texas Hwy Ste 300
Austin, TX 78704
Tel.: (512) 531-8500
Fax: (512) 531-8599
Toll Free: (877) 893-1085
E-mail: info@zilliant.com
Web Site: www.zilliant.com
Approx. Number Employees: 100
Year Founded: 1998
Business Description:
Software Systems Analysis
S.I.C.: 7375; 8742
N.A.I.C.S.: 518111; 541611
Media: 10-13
Personnel:
Greg Peters *(Chm, Pres & CEO)*
John Thornton *(Gen Partner)*
Tim Hamilton *(COO)*
Beth Weeks *(VP-Engrg)*

ZILOG INC.
(Sub. of IXYS Corporation)
(d/b/a Zilog an IXYS Company)
6800 Santa Teresa Blvd
San Jose, CA 95119
Tel.: (408) 513-1500
Fax: (408) 365-8535
Toll Free: (866) 469-4564
Web Site: www.zilog.com
Approx. Sls.: $36,157,000
Approx. Number Employees: 174
Year Founded: 1974
Business Description:
Semiconductor Product Mfr
S.I.C.: 3674
N.A.I.C.S.: 334413
Advertising Expenditures: $500,000
Media: 5-10
Personnel:
Uzi Sasson *(Pres)*
Mike Glynn *(Dir-IT)*
Brands & Products:
BLASTER
BULLET
CRIMZON
CRIMZON RC EXPRESS
EMBEDDED IN LIFE
ENCORE!
ENCORE! XP
EPIR
EZ80
EZ80ACCLAIM
EZ80ACCLAIMPLUS!
ICEBOX
IRDA
Z16F
Z8 ENCORE! MC
Z8 GP
ZDOTS
ZILOG
ZNEO

ZIX CORPORATION
2711 N Haskell Ave Ste 2300
Dallas, TX 75204-2911
Tel.: (214) 370-2000
Fax: (214) 370-2070
Toll Free: (888) 771-4049
E-mail: info@zixit.com
Web Site: www.zixcorp.com
Approx. Rev.: $33,066,000
Approx. Number Employees: 123
Year Founded: 1984
Business Description:
Digital Signature & Encryption Technology Developer
S.I.C.: 7374; 2741; 7372; 7382
N.A.I.C.S.: 518210; 511210; 516110; 561621
Export
Advertising Expenditures: $361,000
Media: 10
Personnel:
Richard D. Spurr *(Chm, Pres, CEO & COO)*
Michael W. English *(Chief Acctg Officer)*
Geoff R. Bibby *(VP-Corp Mktg)*
Jim J. Lesniak *(VP-Sls & Mktg)*
David J. Robertson *(VP-Engrg)*
Brands & Products:
POCKETSCRIPT
ZIX CORPORATION
ZIXAUDITOR
ZIXCONNECT
ZIXCORP
ZIXDIRECT
ZIXDIRECTORY
ZIXIT
ZIXMAIL
ZIXMESSAGE
ZIXPORT
ZIXRESEARCH CENTER
ZIXSECURE CENTER
ZIXVPM
ZIXWORKS
Advertising Agency:
PAN Communications
300 Brickstone Sq 7th Fl
Andover, MA 01810
Tel.: (978) 474-1900
Fax: (978) 474-1903
Pub Rels

ZONE LABS LLC
(Sub. of Check Point Software Technologies, Inc.)
800 Bridge Pkwy
Redwood City, CA 94065
Tel.: (650) 628-2000
Fax: (650) 628-2180
E-mail: info@zonelabs.com
Web Site: www.zonelabs.com
Approx. Number Employees: 160
Year Founded: 1997
Business Description:
Security Software Mfr
S.I.C.: 7371
N.A.I.C.S.: 541511
Media: 13
Brands & Products:
IMSECURE
SMARTER SECURITY
TRUE VECTOR
ZONE LABS
ZONEALARM

ZOO ENTERTAINMENT, INC.
3805 Edwards Rd Ste 605
Cincinnati, OH 45209
Tel.: (513) 824-8297
Fax: (513) 278-0111
E-mail: customerservice@zoogamesinc.com
Web Site: www.zoogamesinc.com
Approx. Rev.: $63,446,000
Approx. Number Employees: 32
Business Description:
Games Software Publisher & Distr
S.I.C.: 7372; 5045; 7829
N.A.I.C.S.: 511210; 423430; 512199
Advertising Expenditures: $828,000
Personnel:
Jay A. Wolf *(Chm & Sec)*
Mark Seremet *(Pres & CEO)*
David J. Fremed *(CFO)*
Steven Buchanan *(COO-Zoo Publ)*

ZOOM TECHNOLOGIES, INC.
150 E 42nd St
New York, NY 10017
Tel.: (917) 609-0333
E-mail: investor@zoom.com
Web Site: www.zoom.com
E-Mail For Key Personnel:
President: frankm@zoomtel.com
Public Relations: terrym@zoomtel.com
Approx. Rev.: $252,589,072
Approx. Number Employees: 1,800
Year Founded: 1977
Business Description:
Communications & Internet Device Mfr
S.I.C.: 3679; 3577; 3661; 3669
N.A.I.C.S.: 334418; 334119; 334210; 334290
Export
Media: 2-5-10-17
Personnel:
Lei Gu *(Chm & CEO)*
Anthony K. Chan *(CFO)*
Brands & Products:
ACCURA
AWARD TECHNOLOGY
COMSTAR
GLOBAL VILLAGE
HAYES
HOTSHOT
IHIFI
OPTIMA
PRACTICAL PERIPHERALS
STERLING
TELEPORT
ZOOM
ZOOMAIR
ZOOMCAM
ZOOMGUARD
ZOOMTEL

ZT GROUP INT'L INC.
350 Meadowlands Pkwy
Secaucus, NJ 70941-1810
Tel.: (201) 559-1000
Fax: (201) 559-1004
Toll Free: (866) 984-7687
E-mail: corpsales@ztsystems.com
Web Site: www.ztsystems.com
E-Mail For Key Personnel:
Sales Director: sales@ztgroup.com
Sales Range: $100-124.9 Million
Approx. Number Employees: 150
Business Description:
Systems Integration, Networking & Storage Solutions
S.I.C.: 5045
N.A.I.C.S.: 423430
Media: 6-10-13-22
Personnel:
Frank Chang *(Pres)*

Key to Media (For complete agency information see *The Advertising Red Books-Agencies* edition):
1. Bus. Publs. 2. Cable T.V. 3. Catalogs & Directories. 4. Co-op Adv. 5. Consumer Mags. 6. D.M. to Bus. Estab.7. D.M. to Consumers 8. Daily Newsp. 9. Exhibits/Trade Shows 10. Foreign 11. Infomercial 12. Internet Adv.13. Multimedia 14. Network Radio 15. Network T.V. 16. Newsp. Distr. Mags. 17. Other 18. Outdoor (Posters, Transit) 19. Point of Purchase20. Premiums, Novelties 21. Product Samples 22. Special Events Mktg. 23. Spot Radio 24. Spot T.V. 25. Weekly Newsp. 26. Yellow Page Adv.

Cosmetics & Toiletries

Cosmetics — Dental Care Products — Fragrances — Hair Care Products — Shaving Aids — Skin Care Products

ACTIVE ORGANICS, INC.
1097 Yates St
Lewisville, TX 75057
Tel.: (972) 221-7500
Fax: (972) 221-3324
E-mail: info@activeorganics.com
Web Site: www.activeorganics.com
Approx. Number Employees: 70
Year Founded: 1981
Business Description:
Specialty Cosmetic Ingredients & Botanical Extracts Mfr
S.I.C.: 5149; 2844
N.A.I.C.S.: 424490; 325620
Media: 2-4-10
Personnel:
Michael Bishop *(Pres)*
Janice Varvel *(Controller & Mgr-Acctg)*
John Thayer *(Dir-Ops)*
Brands & Products:
ACTICEL
ACTIFIRM
ACTIGEN
ACTIGLIDE
ACTIGLOW
ACTILAC
ACTIMOIST
ACTIPHYTE
ACTIPLEX
ACTISEA
ACTISLIM
ANTIQUENCH

ADVANCED BEAUTY SYSTEMS INC.
5720 LBJ Freeway Ste 400
Dallas, TX 75240
Tel.: (972) 934-9888
Fax: (972) 934-9886
E-mail: info@bodycology.com
Web Site: www.bodycology.com
Approx. Number Employees: 30
Business Description:
Marketer & Distr of Skin, Hair & Bath Products
S.I.C.: 5999
N.A.I.C.S.: 446199
Media: 21
Personnel:
Chris McClain *(Pres)*
Worth Anne Herrell *(Dir-Mktg)*
Jordan Morrow *(Mgr-Product Dev)*
Brands & Products:
BODYCOLOGY
DR. TEAL'S

AJAX COMB COMPANY
(Div. of Antonio's Manufacturing Inc.)
800 2nd St
Cresson, PA 16630-1142
Tel.: (814) 886-8171
Fax: (814) 886-5103
Toll Free: (800) 327-5181
E-mail: info@antoniosmfg.com
Web Site: www.antoniosmfg.com
Approx. Sls.: $1,000,000
Approx. Number Employees: 32
Year Founded: 1882
Business Description:
Comb Mfr
S.I.C.: 3089
N.A.I.C.S.: 326199
Export
Media: 4-6-7-8-10-19-21
Distr.: Natl.
Budget Set: Dec.
Personnel:
Anthony R. Romani II *(Pres & CEO)*
Brands & Products:
AJAX
BESTEVER
DURLON
LOVE
SURREY

ALBERTO-CULVER COMPANY
2525 Armitage Ave
Melrose Park, IL 60160-1125
Tel.: (708) 450-3000
Fax: (708) 450-3354
Web Site: www.alberto.com
E-Mail For Key Personnel:
Public Relations: dstone@alberto.com
Approx. Sls.: $1,597,233,000
Approx. Number Employees: 2,600
Year Founded: 1955
Business Description:
Toiletries, Food Specialties & Household Products Mfr & Whslr
S.I.C.: 2841; 2034; 2844
N.A.I.C.S.: 325611; 311423; 325620
Export
Advertising Expenditures: $265,000,000
Media: 2-3-6-9-10-13-14-15-16-18-22
Distr.: Intl.; Natl.
Personnel:
Carol Lavin Bernick *(Chm)*
Vincent James Marino *(Pres & CEO)*
Gina R. Boswell *(Pres-Global Brands)*
Kenneth Keller *(Pres-US)*
Gary P. Schmidt *(Gen Counsel, Sec & Sr VP)*
Brent Shakeshaft *(VP-Mktg-Global)*
Daniel B. Stone *(VP-Corp Comm)*
Rob Keen *(Sr Dir-Mktg-Global Tresemme)*
Brandy Ruff *(Dir-Integrated Mktg Comm)*
Randy Schueller *(Dir-R & D)*
Stephen Strong *(Dir-Interactive-Global)*
Keith Ford *(Mgr-Interactive Project)*
Brands & Products:
ALBERTO VO5
BAKER'S JOY
BOTANICALS
D.P.T.
FDS
JUST FOR ME
LAVISH
MOISTURE PLUS
MOLLY MCBUTTER
MOTIONS
MRS. DASH
NEXXUS
NOURISH
NOXZEMA
SOFT & BEAUTIFUL
ST. IVES
STATIC GUARD
SUGARTWIN
TEXTURE SOFTNER
TRESEMME
Advertising Agencies:
ArnoldNYC
110 5th Ave
New York, NY 10011
Tel.: (212) 463-1000
Fax: (212) 463-1080
Nexxus
Noxzema
St. Ives

Deforest Creative Group
300 W Lake St
Elmhurst, IL 60126
Tel.: (630) 834-7200
Fax: (630) 279-8410

Element 79
(Part of the Omincom Group)
200 E Randolph St 33rd Fl
Chicago, IL 60601
Tel.: (312) 233-8100
Fax: (312) 233-8298

Mullen
101 N Cherry St Ste 600
Winston Salem, NC 27101-4035
Tel.: (336) 765-3630
Fax: (336) 774-9550
Tresemme

ALBERTO-CULVER CONSUMER PRODUCTS WORLDWIDE
(Sub. of Alberto-Culver Company)
2525 Armitage Ave
Melrose Park, IL 60160-1125
Tel.: (708) 450-3000
Fax: (708) 450-3435
Web Site: www.alberto.com
Sales Range: $1-4.9 Billion
Approx. Number Employees: 11,000
Year Founded: 1955
Business Description:
Toiletries, Food Specialties & Household Products Mfr & Whslr
S.I.C.: 2844; 2869
N.A.I.C.S.: 325620; 325199
Media: 2-3-6-8-9-10-13-15-16-18-19-23-24
Personnel:
James Marino *(Pres & CEO)*
Kirstin B. Muntean *(VP-Corp Strategy & Global Bus Dev)*
Brands & Products:
ALBERTO VO5

ALLEGHANY PHARMACAL CORP.
277 Northern Blvd
Great Neck, NY 11021-4703
Tel.: (516) 466-0660
Fax: (516) 482-1525
Toll Free: (800) 645-6190
E-mail: allepharm@aol.com
Web Site: www.alleghanypharmacal.com
Sales Range: $10-24.9 Million
Approx. Number Employees: 25
Year Founded: 1979

Key to Media (For complete agency information see *The Advertising Red Books-Agencies* edition):
1. Bus. Publs. 2. Cable T.V. 3. Catalogs & Directories. 4. Co-op Adv. 5. Consumer Mags. 6. D.M. to Bus. Estab.7. D.M. to Consumers 8. Daily Newsp. 9. Exhibits/Trade Shows 10. Foreign 11. Infomercial 12. Internet Adv.13. Multimedia 14. Network Radio 15. Network T.V. 16. Newsp. Distr. Mags. 17. Other 18. Outdoor (Posters, Transit) 19. Point of Purchase20. Premiums, Novelties 21. Product Samples 22. Special Events Mktg. 23. Spot Radio 24. Spot T.V. 25. Weekly Newsp. 26. Yellow Page Adv.

Business Description:
Shampoo, Hair Spray, Conditioner, Gels, Mousse, Relaxers & Other Hair Care Products Mfr
S.I.C.: 5122; 2844
N.A.I.C.S.: 424210; 325620
Import Export
Media: 2-3-6-7-8-11-15-18-19-23-24-25
Distr.: Natl.
Personnel:
Sheldon Finkle *(CFO)*
Brands & Products:
HASK
LUSTRASILK
MOISTURE MAX
PURE SHINE
RIGHT-ON
SALON STYLE
VIGOROL
WILLOWLAKE

ALOE CREME LABORATORIES, INC.

160 Meister Ave
North Branch, NJ 08876
Tel.: (908) 231-8888
Fax: (908) 238-8060
Web Site: www.aloecreme.com
Approx. Number Employees: 10
Year Founded: 1955
Business Description:
Skin Care Products Mfr
S.I.C.: 2844
N.A.I.C.S.: 325620
Advertising Expenditures: $8,730,000
Media: 2-3-5-6-7-8-9-10-11-14-15-16-18-19-20-21-23-24-25-26
Distr.: Natl.
Personnel:
Douglas Siegel *(Founder, Pres & CEO)*
Richard Keller *(VP-Mktg)*
Brands & Products:
ALOE-RELIEF
ALOE SUN
ALOE SUN AFTER TAN
ALOEDERM
CUREDERMA
MOISTURE PLUS

ALOETTE COSMETICS, INC.

3715 Northside Pkwy Bldg 200 Ste 200
Atlanta, GA 30327
Tel.: (678) 444-2563
Fax: (678) 444-2564
Toll Free: (800) ALOETTE
E-mail: customerservice@aloette.com
Web Site: www.aloettecosmetics.com
Sales Range: $25-49.9 Million
Approx. Number Employees: 180
Year Founded: 1978
Business Description:
Skin Care Products & Cosmetics Mfr & Whslr
S.I.C.: 5122; 8741
N.A.I.C.S.: 424210; 561110
Import Export
Media: 4-8-10-15-21-22-23-24
Distr.: Natl.
Personnel:
Christie Cohen *(Chm)*
Robert Cohen *(Co-CEO)*
Brands & Products:
ALOEPURE
ALOESPA
ALOETTE
IMAGINE

AMERICAN INTERNATIONAL INDUSTRIES COMPANY

2220 Gaspar Ave
Los Angeles, CA 90040-1516
Tel.: (323) 728-2999
Fax: (323) 728-1823
E-mail: customer_service@aiibeauty.com
Web Site: www.aiibeauty.com
Approx. Number Employees: 22
Year Founded: 1971
Business Description:
Health & Beauty Aids Mfr
S.I.C.: 5122; 2844
N.A.I.C.S.: 424210; 325620
Import Export
Advertising Expenditures: $500,000
Media: 2-5-6-10-13-15-19-21
Distr.: Natl.
Personnel:
Zvi Ryzman *(Pres & CEO)*
Terri Cooper *(Exec VP)*
David Woolf *(Exec VP)*
Anne Moratto *(Dir-PR & Adv)*
Brands & Products:
5 SECOND
5 SECOUND NAIL
AMERICAN INTERNATIONAL INDUSTRIES
ANDREA
ARDELL
BODY DRENCH
BYE BYE BLEMISH
CHECI
CHINA GLAZE
CLEAN + EASY
CLUBMAN
CLUBMAN-PINAUD
CLUBMAN USA
CORRECTIONIST
DELORE
EGYPTIAN HENNA
ESN
EUROPEAN SECRETS
EZ-FLOW
FRIGHT NIGHT
GENA
GIGI
GYPSY
L'ORBETTE
'N RAGE
NATURESSENCE
NO-TWEEZE
ONE TOUCH
PROLINC
PURIST NATURALS
RAW
SECHE
SUPERNAIL
SURGI-CARE
WATER WORKS
WOLTRA
YOUTHAIR

AMERICAN SAFETY RAZOR COMPANY

(Sub. of Lion Capital LLP)
(Filed Ch 11 Bankruptcy #10-12351 on 07/29/2010 in U.S. Bankruptcy Ct, Dist of DE, Wilmington)
240 Cedar Knolls Rd
Cedar Knolls, NJ 07927
Tel.: (973) 753-3000
Fax: (973) 326-9004
E-mail: asr@asrco.com
Web Site: www.asrco.com
Approx. Number Employees: 1,800
Year Founded: 1875
Business Description:
Shaving, Industrial & Surgical Blades, Knives, Soap & Shampoo Mfr
S.I.C.: 3842; 2841
N.A.I.C.S.: 339113; 325611
Import Export
Media: 2-4-5-6-8-9-10-14-15-19-20-23-24
Distr.: Intl.; Natl.
Budget Set: Nov. -Dec.
Brands & Products:
ACTI-FLEXX
AMERICAN LINE
AMERICAN WHITE CROSS
ARDELL
BUMP FIGHTER
BURMA SHAVE
CRYSTAL
DERMABLADE
DERMASEAL
EVER-READY
FACE-GUARD
FLICKER
GEM
HEWITT
MBC
MEGAS
MICRO MATRIX
PAL
PAREX
PARSON
PERSONNA
PERSONNA PLUS
SHOWER SHAVER
SMARTEDGE
TOUCH-UP
TREET
TRI-FLEXXX
WHISPER

ANDIS COMPANY

1800 Renaissance Blvd
Sturtevant, WI 53177-1743
Tel.: (262) 884-2600
Fax: (262) 884-1100
Toll Free: (800) 558-9441
E-mail: info@andisco.com
Web Site: www.andis.com
E-Mail For Key Personnel:
Public Relations: fkoeller@andisco.com
Approx. Number Employees: 450
Year Founded: 1922
Business Description:
Clippers, Blow Driers & Hair Care Products Mfr
S.I.C.: 3999; 5064
N.A.I.C.S.: 339999; 423620
Import Export
Advertising Expenditures: $343,000
Bus. Publs.: $180,000; Catalogs & Directories: $15,000; Co-op Adv.: $100,000; Exhibits/Trade Shows: $40,000; Point of Purchase: $5,000; Product Samples: $3,000
Distr.: Intl.; Natl.
Budget Set: Oct.
Personnel:
Matt L. Andis *(Pres)*
Marcia Andis *(Sr VP-Market Dev)*
Fred Koeller *(VP-Mktg)*
Mary L. Kosch *(VP-HR)*
Gary Stanczyk *(VP-Sls)*
Brands & Products:
AGCL LIGHT SPEED
AGR
ALL-IN-ONE
ANDIS
BEAUTE MASTER
BEAUTY MASTER
BGR
CLIPPET
COLORWAVES
COOL CARE PLUS
DETACHABLE PLUS
ELEVATE
EUROMASTER
FADE BLADE
GETTA HAIRCUT
GOLD MEDAL
HANG-UP
HEADLINER
LIFELINE
LIGHTSPEED
LOLA
MASTER
MICRO TURBO
OUTLINER II
PHAT MASTER CLIPPER
PICK OF THE PROFESSIONALS
POWER GROOM
POWER TRIM
PRETTY QUICK
PROMOTOR
PROSTYLE
RUBY
SAFE-T-LIGHT
SELECT CUT
SELECTAIRE
SLIMLINE
SOFT SET
SPEEDMASTER
STYLINER
SUPER SELECT
T-EDJER
T-LIGHT
T-OUTLINER
TACK-MATE
TRENDSETTER
ULTRA
ULTRAEDGE
Advertising Agency:
Andis Advertising
1800 Renaissance Blvd
Sturtevant, WI 53177
Tel.: (262) 884-2600
Fax: (262) 884-1100
Toll Free: (800) 558-9441
(Andis)

ANNIE OAKLEY ENTERPRISES, INC.

300 Johnson St
Ligonier, IN 46767
Mailing Address:
PO Box 203
Ligonier, IN 46767
Tel.: (260) 894-7219
Fax: (260) 894-7104
Web Site: www.annieoakley.com
Approx. Number Employees: 12
Year Founded: 1980
Business Description:
Essential Oils, Perfumes & Accessories Mfr & Whslr
S.I.C.: 2844; 5122
N.A.I.C.S.: 325620; 446120
Media: 4-10-13
Personnel:
Renee A. Gabet *(Founder)*

Key to Media (For complete agency information see *The Advertising Red Books-Agencies* edition):
1. Bus. Publs. 2. Cable T.V. 3. Catalogs & Directories. 4. Co-op Adv. 5. Consumer Mags. 6. D.M. to Bus. Estab.7. D.M. to Consumers
8. Daily Newsp. 9. Exhibits/Trade Shows 10. Foreign 11. Infomercial 12. Internet Adv.13. Multimedia 14. Network Radio
15. Network T.V. 16. Newsp. Distr. Mags. 17. Other 18. Outdoor (Posters, Transit) 19. Point of Purchase20. Premiums, Novelties
21. Product Samples 22. Special Events Mktg. 23. Spot Radio 24. Spot T.V. 25. Weekly Newsp. 26. Yellow Page Adv.

Annie Oakley Enterprises, Inc. — (Continued)

Brands & Products:
ANNIE OAKLEY
ECLECTIC REMEDIES
EVENING LAVENDER
INDIAN MUSK
MORNING DEW
SAGE BRUSH
STAMPEDE FOR MEN
SUNSET

ANTONIO'S MANUFACTURING INC.
800 2nd St
Cresson, PA 16630
Tel.: (814) 886-8171
Fax: (814) 886-5103
Toll Free: (800) 327-5181
E-mail: antajax@antoniosmfg.com
Web Site: www.antoniosmfg.com
Approx. Number Employees: 13
Year Founded: 1971
Business Description:
Hair Products Mfr
S.I.C.: 3089; 3082; 3084
N.A.I.C.S.: 326199; 326121; 326122
Media: 4-6-7-8-10-19-21
Personnel:
Anthony R. Romani, II *(Pres & CEO)*

AQUAMINT LABORATORIES, INC.
6874 Hawthorn Park Dr
Indianapolis, IN 46220-3909
Tel.: (317) 595-0730
Fax: (317) 595-0770
Approx. Number Employees: 3
Year Founded: 1959
Business Description:
Cosmetics Mfr
S.I.C.: 2844
N.A.I.C.S.: 325620
Export
Media: 6-8
Distr.: Natl.
Personnel:
Eugene Allen, Jr. *(Pres & CEO)*
Brands & Products:
CARPAL THERAPY
WORKMAN'S HAND CLEANER
YOUNGER THAN SPRINGTIME

AR-EX LTD.
1282 Old Skokie Valley Rd
Highland Park, IL 60035-3016
Tel.: (847) 579-1408
Fax: (847) 579-1437
Web Site: www.ar-ex.com
Sales Range: $1-9.9 Million
Approx. Number Employees: 40
Year Founded: 1938
Business Description:
Hypo-Allergenic Cosmetics & Personal Care Products Whslr
S.I.C.: 5122
N.A.I.C.S.: 424210
Export
Media: 7-9-10-18-19-20-21-25-26
Distr.: Intl.; Natl.
Personnel:
Perry Blatt *(Pres)*
Brands & Products:
AR-EX

AROMALAND INC.
1326 Rufina Cir
Santa Fe, NM 87507
Tel.: (505) 438-0402
Fax: (505) 438-7223
Toll Free: (800) 933-5267
E-mail: info@aromaland.com
Web Site: www.aromaland.com
Approx. Number Employees: 25
Year Founded: 1986
Business Description:
Aromatherapy Products Mfr & Whslr
S.I.C.: 2899
N.A.I.C.S.: 325998
Advertising Expenditures: $100,000
Media: 8-13
Personnel:
Ralf Moller *(Founder)*
Elizabeth Bezzerides *(Pres)*
Mark Martinez *(CFO)*
Brands & Products:
AROMAFREE
AROMALAND
THE ESSENCE OF WELL-BEING

AROMATIQUE INC.
3421 Hwy 25 N
Heber Springs, AR 72543
Tel.: (501) 362-7511
Fax: (501) 362-5361
E-mail: info@aromatique.com
Web Site: www.aromatique.com
Approx. Sls.: $30,000,000
Approx. Number Employees: 300
Year Founded: 1983
Business Description:
Fragrances, Oils, Room Sprays, Candles, Bath Products & Decorative Containers & Accessories Mfr
S.I.C.: 3999; 2841
N.A.I.C.S.: 339999; 325611
Import Export
Media: 13
Personnel:
Patricia P. Upton *(Pres & CEO)*
Steve Lawrence *(Chief Admin Officer & VP)*
Chad E. Evans *(VP & Dir-Production)*
Judy Balderree *(VP-Customer Svc)*
Carlton Collier *(VP-Sls & Mktg)*
Peggy Harris *(Dir-Publicity)*
Brands & Products:
AMARETTO NOG
AROMATIQUE
BERRIES
CINNAMON CIDER
CITRUS PLUM BERRY
FRAGRANCE
FRESH AIR
GARDENIA
KIWI PEAR
MANGO MELON
MYSTIC WOODS
ORCHID
PEPPERCORN
POMEGRANATE
SMALL OF SPRING
SPLENDOR
SUMMER SORBET
WHISPERS OF THE FOREST

AT LAST NATURALS, INC.
401 Columbus Ave
Valhalla, NY 10595
Tel.: (914) 747-3599
Fax: (914) 747-3791
Toll Free: (800) 527-8123
E-mail: info@atlastnaturals.com
Web Site: www.atlastnaturals.com
E-Mail For Key Personnel:
President: bruce@alast.com
Sales Director: bruce@alast.com
Approx. Number Employees: 50
Year Founded: 1967
Business Description:
Cosmetics & Pharmaceuticals Mfr
S.I.C.: 2844; 2834
N.A.I.C.S.: 325620; 325412
Export
Advertising Expenditures: $450,000
Media: 2-4-6-10-21
Distr.: Intl.; Natl.
Personnel:
Fred Rosen *(Gen Counsel & Exec VP)*
Brands & Products:
AT LAST
AT LAST NATURALS
EQUIGEST
MENO-HERBS
MSM
SUL-RAY

AUBREY ORGANICS INC.
4419 N Manhattan Ave
Tampa, FL 33614
Tel.: (813) 877-4186
Fax: (813) 876-8166
Toll Free: (800) 282-7394
E-mail: advertising@aubrey-organics.com
Web Site: www.aubrey-organics.com
Sales Range: $10-24.9 Million
Approx. Number Employees: 50
Year Founded: 1967
Business Description:
Toilet Preparations & Cosmetics Mfr
S.I.C.: 2844; 7231
N.A.I.C.S.: 325620; 812112
Media: 4-6-8
Personnel:
Aubrey W. Hampton *(Founder & CEO)*
Patricia Basin *(Dir-Ops & Mktg Svcs)*
Brands & Products:
AFTER SUN
ALOE ESSENCE
ANGELICA
ANTI-ITCH
AUBREY ORGANICS
B-5 DESIGN
BGA PROTEIN
BLUE CYPRESS
BLUE GREEN ALGAE
BRONZER
CALAGUALA
CALAL
CALENDULA
CAMOMILE
CLEAN UP!
COLLAGEN AND ALMOND
COLOR ME NATURAL
E PLUS HIGH C
EARTH AWARE
ELYSIAN FIELDS
EQYPTAIN HENNA
EVENING PRIMROSE
FACE FLOWERS
FEET RELIEF
GINSENG
GONE
GREEN TEA
HERBAL LIQUID
HERBESSENCE
HONEYSUCKLE ROSE
ISLAND NATURALS
JASMINE SHINE
JOJOBA AND ALOE
LEMON BLOSSOM
LIQUID SPARKLE
LUMESSENCE
MANDARIN MAGIC
MEALS AND HERB
MEN'S STOCK
MUSK SPLASH
NATURAL BABY
NATURAL BODY HIGHLIGHTER
NATURAL HERBAL
NATURAL LIPS
NATURAL MINT
NATURAL MISSST
NATURAL SPA
NATURE'S BALANCE
NEAT FEET
NYAANZA NATURALS
ORGANIMALS
ORGANOWAFERS
OVERNIGHT PASSPORT
PRIMROSE AND LAVENDER
PRIMROSE TANGLE-GO
RELAX-R-BATH
ROSA MOSQUETA
SEA BUCKTHORN
SEA SPA
SEA WONDERS
SEAWARE
SELENIUM NATURAL
SUN SHADE
SWIMMER'S
TITANIA
ULTIMATE MOIST
VEGECELL
VEGECOL
WHITE CAMELLIA
WILD WIND
WINTERIZER

AVALON NATURAL PRODUCTS, INC.
(Sub. of The Hain Celestial Group, Inc.)
1105 Industrial Ave
Petaluma, CA 94952
Tel.: (707) 769-5120
Fax: (707) 769-0868
E-mail: info@avalonnaturalproducts.com
Web Site:
www.avalonnaturalproducts.com
Sales Range: $25-49.9 Million
Approx. Number Employees: 54
Year Founded: 1989
Business Description:
Organic Personal Care Products Mfr
S.I.C.: 2844; 2841
N.A.I.C.S.: 325620; 325611
Media: 6
Brands & Products:
ALBA BOTANICA
AVALON ORGANICS
UN-PETROLEUM
Advertising Agency:
Harrison & Shriftman
8523 Sunset Blvd
Los Angeles, CA 90069
Tel.: (310) 855-1600
Fax: (310) 855-7510

AVEDA CORPORATION
(Sub. of The Estee Lauder Companies Inc.)
4000 Pheasant Ridge Dr NE
Blaine, MN 55449-7106
Tel.: (763) 783-4000
Fax: (763) 783-4110
Toll Free: (800) 644-4831
Web Site: www.aveda.com

Key to Media (For complete agency information see *The Advertising Red Books-Agencies* edition):
1. Bus. Publs. 2. Cable T.V. 3. Catalogs & Directories. 4. Co-op Adv. 5. Consumer Mags. 6. D.M. to Bus. Estab.7. D.M. to Consumers
8. Daily Newsp. 9. Exhibits/Trade Shows 10. Foreign 11. Infomercial 12. Internet Adv.13. Multimedia 14. Network Radio
15. Network T.V. 16. Newsp. Distr. Mags. 17. Other 18. Outdoor (Posters, Transit) 19. Point of Purchase20. Premiums, Novelties
21. Product Samples 22. Special Events Mktg. 23. Spot Radio 24. Spot T.V. 25. Weekly Newsp. 26. Yellow Page Adv.

Sales Range: $900-999.9 Million
Approx. Number Employees: 1,500
Business Description:
Cosmetics Mfr
S.I.C.: 2844; 7231
N.A.I.C.S.: 325620; 611511
Media: 4-6-8-10-13-19
Personnel:
Dominique Conseil *(Pres)*
Holly Johnson *(VP-HR)*
Antoinette Beenders *(Dir-Global Creative)*
Gigi Abbadie *(Dir-Global Mktg)*
Brands & Products:
AVEDA
AVEDA LOVE
BLUSH MINUS MINERAL OIL
CHAKRA
COLOR PLUS DEFINE
COLOR PLUS SHIMMER
COLORWASH SHADOW PLUS VITAMINS
CONCEAL PLUS PROTECT
COOLING CALMING COLOR
COOLING CALMING COVER
DUAL BASE MINUS OIL
EYE LINE MINUS PETRO WAXES
INSPIRITU
LOOSE POWDER PLUS REPLENISH
MASCARA PLUS ROSE
MOISTURE PLUS TINT
MOSSCARA
ONECOLOR PLUS TWO
PRESSED POWDER PLUS ANTI-OXIDANTS
PURE-FUME
SHADOW PLUS VITAMINS
URUKU
Advertising Agency:
Ultra 16
36 Cooper Sq 4F
New York, NY 10003
Tel.: (212) 260-6454
Fax: (212) 260-6552

AVON PRODUCTS, INC.

1345 Ave of the Americas
New York, NY 10105-0302
Tel.: (212) 282-5000
Fax: (212) 282-6049
Telex: ITT: 42-38-94
E-mail: investor.relations@avon.com
Web Site: www.avon.com
Approx. Rev.: $10,862,800,000
Approx. Number Employees: 42,000
Year Founded: 1886
Business Description:
Holding Company; Cosmetics Mfr & Distr
S.I.C.: 6719; 2844
N.A.I.C.S.: 551112; 325620
Import Export
Advertising Expenditures: $400,400,000
Media: 2-3-4-6-8-11-13-15-21-30
Distr.: Direct to Consumer; Natl.
Budget Set: Oct.
Personnel:
Andrea Jung *(Chm & CEO)*
Charles W. Cramb *(Vice Chm-Developed Market Grp & Interim CFO)*
Charles M. Herington *(Exec VP-Developing Market Grp)*
Lucien Alziari *(Sr VP-HR & Corp Responsibility)*
Geralyn R. Breig *(Sr VP)*
Nancy Glaser *(Sr VP-Global Comm)*
John Higson *(Sr VP-Comml Ops-Global)*
John F. Owen *(Sr VP-Global Supply Chain)*
James C. Wei *(Sr VP-Asia Pacific)*
Richard S. Foggio *(Grp VP-Fin)*
Victor Beaudet *(VP-Corp Comm)*
Paulo Moledo *(Gen Mgr-South Latin American Markets)*
Donna M. Campanella *(Exec Dir-Global Media)*
Susan Arnot Heaney *(Dir-Corp Responsibility)*
Jillian Dempsey *(Dir-Creative Color-Global)*
Nadine Defoe *(Sr Mgr-Acct Svcs)*
Dwana Scantlebury *(Mktg Mgr)*
Stephanie Bobb *(Mgr-Sls-Mid Willamette Valley District)*
Brands & Products:
ADVANCED TECHNIQUES
AGELESS RESULTS
ANEW
ASTONISHING LENGTHS
AVON
AVON BASICS
AVON COLOR
AVON SOLUTIONS
BECOMING
BEYOND COLOR
BLACK SUEDE
BLUE RUSH
BUST-SCULPT
CELADRIN
CELLU-SCULPT
CHRISTIAN LACROIX ROUGE
CLEARSKIN
COLOR TREND
THE COMPANY FOR WOMEN
COOL CONFIDENCE
CRYSTAL LAURA
DAILY MOISTURE
DEREK JETER DRIVEN
DREAMLIFE
EXTRAORDINARY
EXTREME VOLUME
EYESHADOW TRIO
FAR AWAY
FEELIN FRESH
FOOT WORKS
FRESH & SMOOTH
GLAZEWEAR
GLIMMERSTICKS
GODDESS
HAIKU
HEALTHY BOOST
IMARI
INSTINCT
LASH PROFESSIONAL
LIGHTEN UP
LITTLE BLACK DRESS
MARK.
MESMERIZE
MISTAKE PROOF
MOISTURE THERAPY
MULTI-BOOST
NAIL EXPERTS
NAILWEAR
NASCAR
NATURALS
NURTURA
ON DUTY
PERCEIVE
PERFECT WEAR
PERSONAL MATCH
PINK SUEDE
PLANET SPA
PRO-TO-GO
PROEXTREME
PROSPORT
RARE GOLD
RARE PEARLS
RENEW & REFRESH
SHEER ROSE
SKIN-SO-SOFT
SLICK TINT
SLIM AND SLEEK
SLIMWELL
SOFT & FIRM
SOFT & GLOW
SPEED DRY
STERLING SILVER
SUN
SUPERSHOCK
SWEET HONESTY
TODAY, TOMORROW, ALWAYS
TRESELLE
TRUE COLOR
TRUE PORE-FECTION
U BY UNGARO
ULTRA COLOR
ULTRA LUXURY
VISUAL PREFECTION
VITADVANCE
WILD COUNTRY
WOMEN OF EARTH
Advertising Agencies:
MediaVest USA
1675 Broadway
New York, NY 10019
Tel.: (212) 468-4000
Fax: (212) 468-4110
(Media)

Northlich
Sawyer Point Bldg 720 Pete Rose Way
Cincinnati, OH 45202
Tel.: (513) 421-8840
Fax: (513) 455-4749

Soho Square
636 11th Ave
New York, NY 10036
Tel.: (212) 237-7646

BARE ESCENTUALS, INC.

(Sub. of Shiseido Americas Corporation)
71 Stevenson St 22nd Flr
San Francisco, CA 94105
Tel.: (415) 489-5000
Fax: (415) 288-3590
Toll Free: (888) 795-4747
E-mail: be-pr@bareescentuals.com
Web Site: www.bareescentuals.com
Approx. Sls.: $557,502,000
Approx. Number Employees: 2,200
Year Founded: 1976
Business Description:
Toiletries, Cosmetics & Hair Care Products Whslr & Mfr
S.I.C.: 2844; 5122
N.A.I.C.S.: 325620; 446120
Advertising Expenditures: $5,192,000
Media: 6-12-13
Personnel:
Leslie A. Blodgett *(CEO)*
Myles B. McCormick *(CFO, COO & Exec VP)*
Simon Cowell *(CMO)*
Laurie Beja Miller *(Sr VP & Gen Mgr-North America)*
Nathan Pence *(VP-Creative)*
Brands & Products:
BARE ESCENTUALS
CUSH
Advertising Agencies:
Mindshare
303 2nd St S Tower 9th Fl
San Francisco, CA 94107
Tel.: (415) 856-5260
Fax: (415) 856-5298
Media

TBWA Chiat Day Los Angeles
5353 Grosvenor Blvd
Los Angeles, CA 90066
Tel.: (310) 305-5000
Fax: (310) 305-6000
Agency of Record
Public Relations
Social Media
Traditional & Digital Advertising

BATH & BODY WORKS, LLC

(Sub. of Limited Brands, Inc.)
7 Limited Pkwy E
Reynoldsburg, OH 43068-5300
Tel.: (614) 856-6000
Fax: (614) 856-6613
Toll Free: (800) 395-1001
E-mail: ameslow@bbw.com
Web Site: www.bathandbodyworks.com
Sales Range: $1-4.9 Billion
Approx. Number Employees: 2,000
Business Description:
Cosmetics & Personal Care Products Sales
S.I.C.: 5122; 2844
N.A.I.C.S.: 446120; 325620
Personnel:
Diane L. Neal *(CEO)*
Andrew Meslow *(Chief Admin Officer)*
Camille McDonald *(Pres-Brand Mdsg)*
George Arenschield *(VP-Mdse Plng & Allocation)*
Advertising Agency:
Resource Interactive
343 N Front St
Columbus, OH 43215-2219
Tel.: (614) 621-2888
Fax: (614) 621-2873
Toll Free: (800) 550-5815

BEAUTICONTROL COSMETICS, INC.

(Sub. of Tupperware Brands Corporation)
2121 Midway Rd
Carrollton, TX 75006-5039
Mailing Address:
PO Box 815189
Dallas, TX 75381-5189
Tel.: (972) 458-0601
Fax: (972) 233-4724
Toll Free: (800) BEAUTI-1
E-mail: clientservices@beauticontrol.com
Web Site: www.beauticontrol.com
Sales Range: $75-99.9 Million
Approx. Number Employees: 300
Year Founded: 1982
Business Description:
Health & Beauty Aids Whslr
S.I.C.: 2844; 7299
N.A.I.C.S.: 325620; 812199
Advertising Expenditures: $3,500,000
Multimedia: $500,000; D.M. to Consumers: $2,000,000; Special Events Mktg.: $1,000,000

Key to Media (For complete agency information see *The Advertising Red Books-Agencies* edition):
1. Bus. Publs. 2. Cable T.V. 3. Catalogs & Directories. 4. Co-op Adv. 5. Consumer Mags. 6. D.M. to Bus. Estab.7. D.M. to Consumers
8. Daily Newsp. 9. Exhibits/Trade Shows 10. Foreign 11. Infomercial 12. Internet Adv.13. Multimedia 14. Network Radio
15. Network T.V. 16. Newsp. Distr. Mags. 17. Other 18. Outdoor (Posters, Transit) 19. Point of Purchase20. Premiums, Novelties
21. Product Samples 22. Special Events Mktg. 23. Spot Radio 24. Spot T.V. 25. Weekly Newsp. 26. Yellow Page Adv.

BeautiControl Cosmetics, Inc. — (Continued)

Distr.: Direct to Consumer; Natl.
Budget Set: Oct.
Personnel:
Daisy Chin-Lor *(Pres)*
Gary Jones *(VP-Product Dev, R&D)*
Brands & Products:
BEAUTICONTROL

BEIERSDORF NORTH AMERICA INC.
(Sub. of Beiersdorf AG)
Wilson Corp Ctr 187 Danbury Rd
Wilton, CT 06897
Tel.: (203) 563-5800
Fax: (203) 563-5895
Web Site: www.bdfusa.com
Approx. Number Employees: 2,025
Business Description:
Holding Company
S.I.C.: 2844; 5122
N.A.I.C.S.: 325620; 424210
Personnel:
Robert Hughes *(Pres-North America & Canada)*
Magnus Jonsson *(VP-Mktg)*
Amy Nenner *(VP-HR & Admin)*
Advertising Agencies:
Carat
150 E 42nd St
New York, NY 10017
Tel.: (212) 689-6800
Fax: (212) 689-6005
Media Planning & Buying

Draftfcb
101 E Erie St
Chicago, IL 60611
Tel.: (312) 425-5000
Fax: (312) 425-5010

Mason & Kichar Recruitment Advertising
260 Amity Rd
Woodbridge, CT 06525
Tel.: (203) 392-0252
Fax: (203) 392-0255

TBWA Chiat Day New York
488 Madison Ave
New York, NY 10022
Tel.: (212) 804-1000
Fax: (212) 804-1200
(Nivea)

BELL FLAVORS & FRAGRANCES, INC.
500 Academy Dr
Northbrook, IL 60062-2419
Tel.: (847) 291-8300
Fax: (847) 291-1217
E-mail: info@bellff.com
Web Site: www.bell-europe.com
Sales Range: $10-24.9 Million
Approx. Number Employees: 120
Business Description:
Flavors, Fragrances & Aromatics Mfr
S.I.C.: 2869; 2844
N.A.I.C.S.: 325199; 325620
Export
Media: 2-4-7-10
Distr.: Intl.; Natl.
Budget Set: Annually
Personnel:
James H. Heinz *(Pres)*
Katie Gutierrez *(Mgr-Mktg)*
Brands & Products:
BELL
YOUR COMPETITIVE ADVANTAGE!

BENEFIT COSMETICS LLC
(Sub. of LVMH Moet Hennessy Louis Vuitton SA)
685 Market St 7th Fl
San Francisco, CA 94105
Tel.: (415) 781-8153
Fax: (415) 781-3930
Toll Free: (800) 781-2336
E-mail: customer@benefitcosmetics.com
Web Site: www.benefitcosmetics.com
Approx. Number Employees: 72
Year Founded: 1990
Business Description:
Perfumes & Cosmetics Mfr & Whslr
S.I.C.: 5122
N.A.I.C.S.: 446120; 424210
Media: 4-6-8
Personnel:
Julie Bell *(VP-Mktg)*
Lindsey Rollin *(Dir-Product Mktg Copy)*
Brands & Products:
BENEFIT COSMETICS
Advertising Agency:
MediaCom
498 7th Ave
New York, NY 10018
Tel.: (212) 912-4200
Fax: (212) 508-4386

BLISSWORLD LLC
(Sub. of Starwood Hotels & Resorts Worldwide, Inc.)
75 Varick St
New York, NY 10013
Tel.: (212) 931-6383
Fax: (212) 931-6376
E-mail: info@blissworld.com
Web Site: www.blissworld.com
Sales Range: $100-124.9 Million
Approx. Number Employees: 150
Business Description:
Spa & Beauty Products Services
S.I.C.: 5122
N.A.I.C.S.: 424210
Media: 4-11-13
Personnel:
Michael Indursky *(Pres)*
Thea Kocher *(Brand Mgr)*
Brands & Products:
BLISS
REMEDE

BLISTEX, INC.
1800 Swift Dr
Oak Brook, IL 60523-1577
Tel.: (630) 571-2870
Fax: (630) 571-3437
Toll Free: (800) 837-1800
Web Site: www.blistex.com
Sales Range: $125-149.9 Million
Approx. Number Employees: 200
Year Founded: 1947
Business Description:
Oral Care & Skin Care Products Mfr
S.I.C.: 2844; 2834
N.A.I.C.S.: 325620; 325412
Import Export
Media: 2-3-4-6-13-15-19-20-21-24
Distr.: Intl.; Natl.
Personnel:
D. C. Arch *(Chm & CEO)*
Michael J. Donnantuono *(Pres & COO)*
Kevin Brunory *(VP-Sls)*
Brian Satre *(VP-Mktg)*
Mike Wojcik *(VP-Tech)*
Brands & Products:
BLISTEX
BLISTEX CLEAR ADVANCE
BLISTEX COMPLETE MOISTURE
BLISTEX FRUIT SMOOTHIES
BLISTEX HERBAL ANSWER
BLISTEX LIP BALM
BLISTEX LIP MEDEX
BLISTEX LIP OINTMENT
BLISTEX LIP REVITALIZER
BLISTEX LIP TONE
BLISTEX MEDICATED SKIN CARE
BLISTEX PRO CARE
BLISTEX PRO RELIEF
BLISTEX SILK & SHINE
BLISTEX ULTRA PROTECTION
CHERRY SPLASH
CLEAR ADVANCE
DCT
DEEP RENEWAL
DISCOVER WHAT YOUR LIPS ARE MISSING.
FOILLE
FRUIT SMOOTHIES
GENTLE SENSE
GLYSOMED
HERBAL ANSWER
IVAREST
KANK-A
LIP MEDEX
LIP REVITALIZER
LIP TONE
MOISTURE SPLASH
RASPBERRY LEMONADE BLAST
SOOTHING SPLASH
STRI-DEX
Advertising Agency:
ML Rogers
102 Madison Ave 10th Fl
New York, NY 10016
Tel.: (212) 213-3833
Oral Care & Skin Care Products
Stri-Dex

BLYTH, INC.
1 E Weaver St
Greenwich, CT 06831
Tel.: (203) 661-1926
Fax: (203) 661-1969
E-mail: blyth@blythinc.com
Web Site: www.blyth.com
Approx. Sls.: $900,927,000
Approx. Number Employees: 2,300
Year Founded: 1977
Business Description:
Candles, Candle Accessories & Home Fragrance Products Mfr
S.I.C.: 3999; 2844; 5947
N.A.I.C.S.: 339999; 325620; 453220
Import Export
Advertising Expenditures: $5,000,000
Media: 4-8-11-13-19
Personnel:
Robert B. Goergen *(Chm & CEO)*
Tyler P. Schuessler *(Pres)*
Robert H. Barghaus *(CFO & VP)*
Anne M. Butler *(Pres-PartyLite-Worldwide & VP)*
Robert B. Goergen, Jr. *(Pres-Multichannel Grp & VP)*
Edward J. Scannell *(Dir-Internal Audit)*
Brands & Products:
AMBRIA
CAROLINA
CBK
COLONIAL
COLONIAL CANDLE OF CAPE COD
HANDY FUEL
LILJEHOLMENS
PARTYLITE
STERNO

THE BONNE BELL COMPANY
1006 Crocker Rd
Westlake, OH 44145
Tel.: (440) 835-2440
Fax: (216) 221-6256
Toll Free: (800) 321-1006
E-mail: customerservice@bonnebell.com
Web Site: www.bonnebell.com
Sales Range: $100-124.9 Million
Approx. Number Employees: 750
Year Founded: 1927
Business Description:
Lotion, Cosmetics & Fragrances Mfr
S.I.C.: 2844
N.A.I.C.S.: 325620
Export
Advertising Expenditures: $300,000
Media: 2-5-6-19-21
Distr.: Distr.; Natl.
Personnel:
Jess Bell, Jr. *(Chm & CEO)*
Robert Evans *(COO)*
Joyce Laing *(Mgr-Sls Ops)*
Brands & Products:
A BEAUTIFUL IDEA
BLEND N GLOW
BONNEBELL
CLIC IT
ENTICEMINT
EYE STYLE
EYESTYLE SHADOW BOX
FASHION PASSION BAGS
GEL BRONZE
GLIMMER BRONZE
GLIMMER LIGHTS
HONEYKISS
JEWELL SMACKERS
KISS THIS GLOSS
LASH GLOSS
LIP D'VOTION
LIP D'VOTION SHIMMERS
LIP GLAM
LIP LITES
LIP SHAKE
LIP SMACKER
LIPBURST
LIPLITES
LIPSHAKE
MAKE YOUR OWN JELLY GLOSS
MOON & STARS BAG
POWDER BRONZE
PRINCESS POWER BAG
ROLL-ON GLITTER
SMACKER
SMOOTH
SOUR SMACKERS
SPARKLE COLORGLAZE
SUN SMACKERS
SUNBLUSH BRONZE
Advertising Agency:
Ocean Bridge Group
1714 16th St
Santa Monica, CA 90404
Tel.: (310) 392-3200

BORGHESE, INC.
10 E 34th St Fl 3
New York, NY 10016-4327
Tel.: (212) 659-5300
Fax: (212) 659-5301

Key to Media (For complete agency information see *The Advertising Red Books-Agencies* edition):
1. Bus. Publs. 2. Cable T.V. 3. Catalogs & Directories. 4. Co-op Adv. 5. Consumer Mags. 6. D.M. to Bus. Estab.7. D.M. to Consumers
8. Daily Newsp. 9. Exhibits/Trade Shows 10. Foreign 11. Infomercial 12. Internet Adv.13. Multimedia 14. Network Radio
15. Network T.V. 16. Newsp. Distr. Mags. 17. Other 18. Outdoor (Posters, Transit) 19. Point of Purchase20. Premiums, Novelties
21. Product Samples 22. Special Events Mktg. 23. Spot Radio 24. Spot T.V. 25. Weekly Newsp. 26. Yellow Page Adv.

E-mail: info@borghese.com
Web Site: www.borghese.com
Sales Range: $50-74.9 Million
Approx. Number Employees: 140
Business Description:
Cosmetics & Fragrances Mfr
S.I.C.: 5122
N.A.I.C.S.: 424210
Media: 10-11-13
Distr.: Intl.; Natl.
Personnel:
Georgette Mosbacher *(Pres & CEO)*
Neal Petrocelli *(VP-Mktg)*
Brands & Products:
CREMA OCCHI INTENSIVA
CURA-C
THE ELEMENTS OF LIFE
IL BACIO
SIERO INTENSIVO
SUPERIORE
Advertising Agency:
Agency212, LLC
(The Tucker Partnership, Inc. (Parent Company))
112 W 20th St 7th Fl
New York, NY 10011
Tel.: (212) 994-6700
Fax: (212) 994-6699
— Evan Ziccardi *(Acct Exec)*

BRISTOL-MYERS SQUIBB COMPANY

345 Park Ave
New York, NY 10154-0004
Tel.: (212) 546-4000
Fax: (212) 546-4020
E-mail: customer.relations@bms.com
Web Site: www.bms.com
Approx. Sls.: $19,484,000,000
Approx. Number Employees: 27,000
Year Founded: 1933
Business Description:
Beauty, Health, Nutritional, Pharmaceutical, Household Products & Medical Devices Mfr & Whslr
S.I.C.: 2834; 2023; 2844; 3841; 5047
N.A.I.C.S.: 325412; 311514; 325620; 339112; 423450
Import Export
Advertising Expenditures: $1,136,000,000
Media: 2-3-6-8-9-11-13-14-15-16-17-18-21-22-23-24
Distr.: Intl.; Natl.
Budget Set: Oct.
Personnel:
James M. Cornelius *(Chm)*
Lamberto Andreotti *(Pres & CEO)*
Charles Bancroft *(CFO)*
Jonathan K. Sprole *(VP & Chief Compliance Officer & Deputy Gen Counsel)*
Elliott Sigal *(Chief Scientific Officer, Pres-R&D & Exec VP)*
David Johnson *(Pres-AB Volvo & CEO-The Volvo Grp)*
Beatrice Cazala *(Pres-Europe/Global Commercialization & Sr VP-Comml Ops)*
Anthony C. Hooper *(Pres-Americas & Sr VP-Comml Ops)*
Carlo de Notaristefani *(Pres-Tech Ops & Global Support Functions)*
Sandra Leung *(Gen Counsel, Sec & Sr VP)*
Joseph C. Caldarella *(Sr VP & Controller)*
Giovanni Caforio *(Sr VP-Oncology)*
John E. Celentano *(Sr VP-HR, Publis Affairs & Philanthropy)*
Brian Daniels *(Sr VP-Global Dev & Medical Affairs)*
Jeremy M. Levin *(Sr VP-External Science, Tech & Licensing)*
Frank C. Pasqualone *(Sr VP-Southern Europe)*
Quentin Roach *(Chief Procurement Officer & Sr VP)*
Richard L. Wolgemuth *(Sr VP)*
Paul Aronsohn *(Dir-Exec Comm)*
Dan Maurer *(Dir-eMktg)*
Cheryl Borne *(Mgr-eMktg)*
Brands & Products:
ABILIFY
ATRIPLA
AVALIDE
AVAPRO
BARACLUDE
BICNU
BLENOXANE
BRISTOL-MYERS SQUIBB
BUSPAR
CARDIOLITE
CEENU
CEFZIL
COUMADIN
DEFINITY
DESYREL
DOVONEX
DROXIA
EMSAM
ENFAMIL
ERBITUX
ETOPOPHOS
GLUCOPHAGE XR
GLUCOVANCE
HYDREA
IFEX
IXEMPRA
KENALOG-10
LAC-HYDRIN
LIPIL
LODOSYN
LYSODREN
MEGACE
METAGLIP
MIRALUMA
MONOPRIL
MONOPRIL-HCT
MUTAMYCIN
MYCOSTATIN
ORENCIA
PARAPLATIN
PLATINOL
PLAVIX
PRAVACHOL
REYATAX
REYATAZ
RUBEX
SECURE THE FUTURE
SERZONE
SPRYCEL
STADOL NS
SUSTIVA
TAXOL
TEQUIN
TESLAC
TOGETHER WE CAN PREVAIL
VEPESID
VIDEX
VIDEX EC
VUMON
WESTCORT
ZERIT
Advertising Agencies:
AM/PM Advertising Inc.
345 Claremont Ave Ste 26
Montclair, NJ 07042
Tel.: (973) 824-8600
Fax: (646) 366-1168

Cramp & Associates, Inc.
1327 Grenox Rd
Wynnewood, PA 19096-2402
Tel.: (610) 649-6002
Fax: (610) 649-6005

Draftfcb
101 E Erie St
Chicago, IL 60611
Tel.: (312) 425-5000
Fax: (312) 425-5010

H4B Chelsea
75 9th Ave 2R
New York, NY 10011
Tel.: (212) 299-5000
Fax: (212) 299-5050
Toll Free: (800) 358-6420
(Pravachol)

metzgerlehner worldwide partners AG
Bahnhofstrasse 44
CH-8703
Erlenbach, Zurich Switzerland
Tel.: (41) 1 913 77 77
Fax: (41) 1 913 77 00

Photosound Communications
1000 Wyckoff Ave
Mahwah, NJ 08536
Tel.: (609) 514-5366
Fax: (609) 514-5377

PointRoll Inc.
951 E Hector St
Conshohocken, PA 19428
Tel.: (267) 558-1300
Fax: (267) 285-1141
Toll Free: (800) 203-6956

Shirley/Hutchinson Creative Works
707 N Franklin Ste 100
Tampa, FL 33602
Tel.: (813) 229-6162
Fax: (813) 229-6262
Toll Free: (866) 479-1548

Starcom MediaVest Group
35 W Wacker Dr
Chicago, IL 60601-1723
Tel.: (312) 220-3535
Fax: (312) 220-6530

Unit 7
30 Irving Pl 11th Fl
New York, NY 10003
Tel.: (212) 209-1600
Fax: (212) 209-1800

Wishbone
245 5th Ave 12th Fl
New York, NY 10016
Tel.: (646) 486-9700
Tel.: (646) 486-9701
Fax: (212) 213-0659

CALIFORNIA PACIFIC RESEARCH, INC.

(d/b/a New Generation)
300 Brinkby Ave Ste 200
Reno, NV 89509-4359
Tel.: (775) 829-5600
Fax: (775) 829-5619
Toll Free: (800) 745-5642
E-mail: sales@newgen2000.com
Web Site: www.newgen2000.com
E-Mail For Key Personnel:
Sales Director: sales@newgen2000.com
Approx. Number Employees: 10
Business Description:
Hair Care Products Mfr & Whslr
S.I.C.: 5999
N.A.I.C.S.: 446199
Media: 8-13-19-23-24
Distr.: Natl.
Budget Set: Apr.
Personnel:
Lori Cigler *(Mgr)*
Brands & Products:
NEW GENERATION

CAMEO, INC.

995 E 3rd St
Perrysburg, OH 43551-4355
Mailing Address:
PO Box 535
Toledo, OH 43697-0535
Tel.: (419) 661-9611
Fax: (419) 661-9607
Approx. Sls.: $4,000,000
Approx. Number Employees: 75
Year Founded: 1987
Business Description:
Cosmetics & Lotions Mfr
S.I.C.: 2844
N.A.I.C.S.: 325620
Export
Media: 2-5-7-10-21
Distr.: Intl.; Natl.
Budget Set: Jan.
Personnel:
Brandon Ison *(Exec VP)*
Robert Fedynich *(VP-Mktg)*

CAROLINA HERRERA LTD

(Affil. of Puig Beauty Fashion Group, S.L.)
501 7th Ave
New York, NY 10018-5911
Tel.: (212) 944-5757
Fax: (212) 944-7996
E-mail: info@carolinaherrera.com
Web Site: www.carolinaherrera.com
Approx. Number Employees: 125
Year Founded: 1914
Business Description:
Clothing Designer & Mfr & Cologne & Fragrance Distr
S.I.C.: 2335; 2339; 2844
N.A.I.C.S.: 315233; 315239; 325620
Advertising Expenditures: $3,000,000
Media: 4-5-6-7-16-19
Distr.: Intl.; Natl.
Personnel:
Mario Grauso *(Pres & CEO)*
Robert McCormick *(CFO)*
Brands & Products:
212
212 FOR MEN
HERRERA FOR MEN
Advertising Agency:
Bailey Gardiner Inc.
444 W. Beech St Ste 400
San Diego, CA 92101
Tel.: (619) 295-8232
Fax: (619) 295-8234

Key to Media (For complete agency information see *The Advertising Red Books-Agencies* edition):
1. Bus. Publs. 2. Cable T.V. 3. Catalogs & Directories. 4. Co-op Adv. 5. Consumer Mags. 6. D.M. to Bus. Estab.7. D.M. to Consumers
8. Daily Newsp. 9. Exhibits/Trade Shows 10. Foreign 11. Infomercial 12. Internet Adv.13. Multimedia 14. Network Radio
15. Network T.V. 16. Newsp. Distr. Mags. 17. Other 18. Outdoor (Posters, Transit) 19. Point of Purchase20. Premiums, Novelties
21. Product Samples 22. Special Events Mktg. 23. Spot Radio 24. Spot T.V. 25. Weekly Newsp. 26. Yellow Page Adv.

CASWELL-MASSEY CO. LTD.
(Holding of The Equitium Group, LLC)
121 Fieldcrest Ave
Edison, NJ 08837
Tel.: (732) 225-2181
Fax: (732) 225-2385
Toll Free: (800) 326-0500
E-mail: info@caswellmasseyltd.com
Web Site: www.caswell-massey.com
Approx. Number Employees: 80
Year Founded: 1752
Business Description:
Fragrance Stores & Catalog
S.I.C.: 5122
N.A.I.C.S.: 446120; 424210
Import Export
Advertising Expenditures: $1,000,000
Media: 2-4-5-6-7-8-9-10-16-17-19-22-23-25-26
Distr.: Direct to Consumer; Natl.
Budget Set: Dec.
Personnel:
Amir R. Amir *(CEO)*
Brands & Products:
AURA OF PATCHOULI
BAY RUMS
CASWELL/MASSEY
DAMASK
DOMESTIC BLISS
DR. HUNTERS CASTILE MINI SOAP BAR
ELIXIR OF LOVE NO. 1
ENGLISH LAVENDER
FREESIA
GARDENIA
GIFT OF THE SEA
GREENBRIAR
HONEYSUCKLE
HONEYSUCKLE COLLECTION
JOCKEY CLUB
LIFT OF THE VALLEY
LILAC
MUSGO REAL
NEWPORT
NUMBER SIX
ROGER AND GALLET
SENSUAL
TRICORN
VERBENA
WASH AWAY YOUR SINS SOAP

CCA INDUSTRIES, INC.
200 Murray Hill Pkwy
East Rutherford, NJ 07073-2144
Mailing Address:
PO Box 7486
East Rutherford, NJ 07073-7486
Tel.: (201) 330-1400
Fax: (201) 842-6014
Toll Free: (800) 524-2720
E-mail: amberyoung@ccaindustries.com
Web Site: www.ccaindustries.com
E-Mail For Key Personnel:
President: davidedell@ccaindustries.com
Public Relations: iberman@ccaindustries.com
Approx. Rev.: $50,811,642
Approx. Number Employees: 153
Year Founded: 1983
Business Description:
Health & Beauty Aids Mfr & Distr
S.I.C.: 2844; 2023; 2841
N.A.I.C.S.: 325620; 311514; 325611
Import Export
Advertising Expenditures: $7,493,282
Media: 1-5-6-14-15-19-23-24
Distr.: Natl.
Personnel:
Ira W. Berman *(Chm, Sec & Exec VP)*
Dunnan Edell *(Pres & COO)*
David Edell *(CEO)*
Stephen Heit *(CFO & Exec VP)*
Elias Ciudad *(Exec VP-IT)*
Drew Edell *(Exec VP-Product Dev & Production)*
Jim Gonedes *(Exec VP-Mktg)*
Brands & Products:
BIKINI ZONE
CCA INDUSTRIES, INC.
CHERRY VANILLA
HAIR OFF
IPR-3
MEGA-G
MEGA-T
MEGA-T PLUS
MEGATRIM CLA
NUTRA NAIL
PARFUM DE VANILLE
PLUS WHITE
POUND-X
PRO-PERM
SCARZONE
SHAVEZONE
SOLAR SENSE
SUDDEN CHANGE
WASH 'N CURL
WASH 'N TINT
Advertising Agencies:
Chestnut Communications, Inc.
15 E Putnam Ave
Greenwich, CT 06830-7242
Tel.: (203) 629-9098
Fax: (203) 869-0416

The In-House Agency, Inc.
55 Madison Ave Ste 400
Morristown, NJ 07960
Tel.: (973) 285-3259
Fax: (908) 996-3593

CHANEL, INC.
(Sub. of Chanel S.A.)
9 W 57th St Fl 44
New York, NY 10019-2701
Tel.: (212) 688-5055
Fax: (212) 752-1851
Toll Free: (800) 550-0005
E-mail: info@chanel.com
Web Site: www.chanel.com
Sales Range: $200-249.9 Million
Approx. Number Employees: 300
Business Description:
Fragrances, Cosmetics & Mens & Womens Accessories Mfr
S.I.C.: 2844; 2339
N.A.I.C.S.: 325620; 315239
Media: 1-4-5-6-9-10-19-24-25-30
Distr.: Intl.; Natl.
Personnel:
Alain Wertheimer *(Chm)*
Michael Rena *(Exec VP)*
Lyle Saunders *(VP-Creative Svcs)*
Lynn Kopper *(Dir-Mktg)*
Advertising Agency:
Eve Seco Display Inc.
209 Waters Edge
Valley Cottage, NY 10989
Tel.: (845) 268-5111
Fax: (845) 268-5115

CHURCH & DWIGHT CANADA CORP.
(Sub. of Church & Dwight International Consumer Products)
6600 Kitimat Road
Mississauga, ON L5N 1L9, Canada
Tel.: (905) 696-6570
Fax: (905) 826-0389
E-mail: information-canada@churchdwight.ca
Web Site: www.churchdwight.ca
Sales Range: $50-74.9 Million
Approx. Number Employees: 200
Year Founded: 1904
Business Description:
Toiletries & Consumer Products Mfr
S.I.C.: 2844
N.A.I.C.S.: 325620
Import Export
Media: 1-5-6-9-11-15-18-19-21-23-24-25
Distr.: Natl.
Budget Set: Nov. -Dec.
Personnel:
Gregory J. Drohan *(Pres)*
Veronique Hamel *(Dir-Mktg CPG, OTC & Pharmaceutical Dev Laboratory)*
Brands & Products:
ARM & HAMMER
ATASOL
BENTASIL
BIONET
DIOVOL
FERMENTOL
GRAVOL
INFANTOL
MALTEVOL 12
OVOL
RUB A535
Advertising Agency:
kirshenbaum bond senecal + partners Toronto
2 Bloor Street E 26th Fl
Toronto, ON M4W 3J4, Canada
Tel.: (416) 260-7000
Fax: (416) 260-7100

CLINIQUE LABORATORIES, INC.
(Sub. of The Estee Lauder Companies Inc.)
767 5th Ave
New York, NY 10153
Tel.: (212) 572-3800
Web Site: www.clinique.com
Sales Range: $150-199.9 Million
Year Founded: 1968
Business Description:
Skin Care, Makeup & Fragrance Products Mfr & Distr
S.I.C.: 2844
N.A.I.C.S.: 325620
Media: 6-21
Personnel:
Ronald S. Lauder *(Chm)*
CeCe Coffin *(Sr VP-Global Comm)*
Agnes Landau *(Sr VP-Global Mktg)*
Jessica Magaro *(Exec Dir-Clinique Online)*
Advertising Agencies:
J. Walter Thompson Company (d/b/a JWT)
466 Lexington Ave
New York, NY 10017-3140
Tel.: (212) 210-7000
Fax: (212) 210-7299
Agency of Record

MSLGROUP
1675 Broadway 9th Floor
New York, NY 10019-5865
Tel.: (212) 468-4200
Fax: (212) 468-3007

COLGATE-PALMOLIVE CANADA INC.
(Sub. of Colgate-Palmolive Company)
895 Don Mills Rd Morneau Sbeco Ctr Bldg 2
Toronto, ON M3C 1W3, Canada
Tel.: (416) 421-6000
Fax: (416) 421-6913
Web Site: www.colgate.com
Sales Range: $25-49.9 Million
Approx. Number Employees: 130
Year Founded: 1920
Business Description:
Household Products & Toiletries Mfr
S.I.C.: 2844
N.A.I.C.S.: 325620
Media: 6-8-9-15-18-19-20-21-24
Distr.: Natl.
Budget Set: Aug. -Sept.
Personnel:
Scott Jeffery *(Pres)*
Advertising Agency:
Y&R, Ltd.
60 Bloor Street West
Toronto, ON M4W 1J2, Canada
Tel.: (416) 961-5111
Fax: (416) 961-7890
(Colgate Toothpaste, Rinse & Toothbrushes, Palmolive Dishwashing Liquid, Menen Speed Stick, Lady Speed Stick & Javex Bleach)

COLGATE-PALMOLIVE COMPANY
300 Park Ave
New York, NY 10022-7499
Tel.: (212) 310-2000
Fax: (212) 310-2475
Toll Free: (800) 221-4607
E-mail: investor_relations@colpal.com
Web Site: www.colgate.com
Approx. Sls.: $15,564,000,000
Approx. Number Employees: 39,200
Year Founded: 1806
Business Description:
Household & Personal Care Products, Pet Care Products, Specialty Hostess & Decorator Accessories Mfr & Distr
S.I.C.: 2841; 3991
N.A.I.C.S.: 325611; 339994
Import Export
Advertising Expenditures: $1,534,000,000
Media: 1-2-3-6-8-9-11-14-15-16-18-19-21-22-25
Distr.: Intl.; Natl.
Personnel:
Ian M. Cook *(Chm, Pres & CEO)*
Roger D. Calmeyer *(Mng Dir)*
Mukul Deoras *(Mng Dir)*
Dennis J. Hickey *(CFO)*
Fabian T. Garcia *(COO)*
Tom Greene *(CIO & VP)*
Gregory P. Woodson *(Chief Ethics/Compliance Officer & VP)*
Neil Thompson *(Pres/CEO-Hills Pet Nutrition)*
Nigel B. Burton *(Pres-Global Oral Care-Consumer Insights & Adv)*
Antonio Caro *(Pres-Global Customer Dev)*

Key to Media (For complete agency information see *The Advertising Red Books-Agencies* edition):
1. Bus. Publs. 2. Cable T.V. 3. Catalogs & Directories. 4. Co-op Adv. 5. Consumer Mags. 6. D.M. to Bus. Estab.7. D.M. to Consumers
8. Daily Newsp. 9. Exhibits/Trade Shows 10. Foreign 11. Infomercial 12. Internet Adv.13. Multimedia 14. Network Radio
15. Network T.V. 16. Newsp. Distr. Mags. 17. Other 18. Outdoor (Posters, Transit) 19. Point of Purchase20. Premiums, Novelties
21. Product Samples 22. Special Events Mktg. 23. Spot Radio 24. Spot T.V. 25. Weekly Newsp. 26. Yellow Page Adv.

Alexandre De Guillenchmidt *(Pres-Colgate-Europe)*
Suzan F. Harrison *(Pres-Comml Bus Analytics)*
Scott W. Jeffrey, Jr. *(Pres-Colgate-Canada)*
Richard Mener *(Pres-Colgate-Africa & Middle East)*
Derrick E.M. Samuel *(Pres-Greater Asia)*
Paul Stoneham *(Pres-Bus Dev-Global)*
Noel R. Wallace *(Pres-Colgate North America & Global Sustainability)*
Andrew D. Hendry *(Gen Counsel, Sec & Sr VP)*
Daniel B. Marsili *(Sr VP-Global HR)*
Bina H. Thompson *(Sr VP-IR)*
Bradley Farr *(VP & Gen Mgr-South Africa)*
Peter Brons-Poulsen *(VP & Gen Mgr-GABA Intl)*
Joergen Erichsen *(VP & Gen Mgr-Hills Pet Nutrition-Europe)*
Jean-Luc Fischer *(VP & Gen Mgr-Southern Cone & Latin America)*
Peggy Gerichter *(VP & Gen Mgr-Colgate-Central American Reg)*
Luis Gutierrez *(VP & Gen Mgr-West Andean Reg & Latin America)*
Sheila A. Hopkins *(VP & Gen Mgr-Prof Oral Care)*
Wojciech Krol *(VP & Gen Mgr-Central European Reg)*
Andrea Lagioia *(VP & Gen Mgr-Colgate France)*
Maria Fernanda Mejia *(VP & Gen Mgr-Global Personal Care)*
Chris E. Pedersen *(VP & Gen Mgr-Colgate South Pacific)*
Francisco Munoz Ramirez *(VP & Gen Mgr-Colgate-Russia)*
Ricardo Ramos *(VP & Gen Mgr-Brazil)*
Louis Ruggiere *(VP & Gen Mgr-Hawley & Hazel-Taiwan)*
Bernal Saborio *(VP & Gen Mgr-Caribbean Reg)*
Scott Sherwood *(VP & Gen Mgr-Colgate UK & Ireland)*
James H. Shoultz *(VP & Gen Mgr-Mexico)*
Panagiotis Tsourapas *(VP & Gen Mgr-Global Toothbrush Div)*
Juan Pablo Zamorano *(VP & Gen Mgr-Home Care-Global)*
Katherine Hargrove Ramundo *(VP, Asst Sec & Deputy Gen Counsel)*
Nina Gillman *(Asst Sec & VP-Global Legal)*
Rosemary Nelson *(Deputy Gen Counsel & VP-Ops)*
Joseph M. Bertolini *(VP-Fin-Global)*
Stephen J. Fogarty *(VP-Shopper Mktg-Global)*
Robert E. Frazier *(VP-Customer Svc)*
Jan Guifarro *(VP-Corp Comm)*
Malcolm Jones *(VP-Fin-Global)*
Hans L. Pohlschroeder *(VP-Treasury)*
Phil Shotts *(VP-Fin-Global)*
Katherine S. Weida *(VP-Org Dev Legal)*
Julie A. Zerbe *(VP-HR-Global)*
Carla Kelly *(Gen Mgr-Multicultural Mktg)*
Mindel Klein-Lepore *(Dir-Digital Mktg-North America)*
Donna Richardsen *(Dir-Online Mktg-Global)*

Brands & Products:
AJAX
AXION
CARIBBEAN COOL
CLEAN BLAST
CLEAN GLIDE
COLGATE
COLGATE 360
COLGATE ACTIVE SALT
COLGATE ADVANCED WHITENING
COLGATE BAKING SODA TOOTHPASTE
COLGATE BUBBLE FRUITE
COLGATE CIBACA FAMILY PROTECTION
COLGATE DENTAL FLOSS
COLGATE DURAPHAT
COLGATE EXTRA-CLEAN
COLGATE FRESH CONFIDENCE
COLGATE FRESH ENERGY GEL
COLGATE GEL-KAM
COLGATE HERBAL
COLGATE KIDS TOOTHPASTE
COLGATE MASSAGER
COLGATE MAXFRESH
COLGATE MOTION
COLGATE NAVIGATOR
COLGATE PHOS-FLUR
COLGATE PLATINUM
COLGATE PLUS
COLGATE SENSITIVE
COLGATE SIMPLY WHITE
COLGATE TARTAR CONTROL
COLGATE TOOTHPOWDER
COLGATE TOTAL
COLGATE TOTAL PROFESSIONAL
COLGATE VISIBLE WHITE
COLGATE WAVE
COLGATE WHITENING GEL
COLGATE ZIGZAG JUNIOR
COLGATE ZIGZAG PLUS
COOL FOREST
COOL FUSION
CRYSTAL CLEAN
FOAM WORKS
FRESH FUSION
FRESH RUSH
FRESH STRIPE
HALO SHAMPOO
ICY BLAST
ICY SURGE
INVISIBLE DRY
IRISH SPRING
LADY SPEED STICK
MENNEN
MY FIRST COLGATE
ORAGARD-B
PALMOLIVE
PALMOLIVE AROMA LIQUID HAND WASH - RELAX
PALMOLIVE AROMA SHOWER GEL - RELAX
PALMOLIVE AROMA SHOWER GEL - VITALITY
PALMOLIVE CHARMIS CREAM
PALMOLIVE NATURALS LIQUID HAND WASH - MILK & OLIVE
PALMOLIVE NATURALS MOISTURIZING BODY WASH
PALMOLIVE SHAVE CREAM
PALMOLIVE THERMAL SPA - FIRMING & MASSAGE
PLAX
POWDER BURST
POWDER SOFT
POWER OF NATURE
SATIN PEAR
SKIN BRACER
SOFTSOAP
SPEED STICK
SPORT
SUAVITEL
TEEN SPIRIT
WATERFALL
WILD FREESIA
WORLD OF CARE

Advertising Agencies:
Big Fuel Communications LLC
298 5th Ave 5th Fl
New York, NY 10001
Tel.: (212) 616-6300
Fax: (212) 658-9226

Cohn & Wolfe
200 Fifth Ave
New York, NY 10010
Tel.: (212) 798-9700
Fax: (212) 329-9900
Irish Spring Body Wash

SiboneyUSA/New York
729 7th Ave 9th Fl
New York, NY 10019
Tel.: (212) 337-8956
Fax: (212) 337-8901
Agency of Record
Baby Magic
Baking Soda
Cavity Protection
Fab Color Plus Laundry Detergent
Hispanic Bfands
Irish Spring Waterfall
Mennen Speed Stick & Speed Stick Gel Deodorants
Peroxide
Plus & Total Toothbrushs
Sports Bar Soaps
Tartar Control Toothpastes
Ultra Palmolive Original Dishwashing Liquid

Young & Rubicam Inc.
285 Madison Ave
New York, NY 10017-6401
Tel.: (212) 210-3000
Fax: (212) 490-9073
Octopus

COLOMER USA, INC.

(Div. of The Colomer Group)
5344 Overmyer Dr
Jacksonville, FL 32254
Mailing Address:
PO Box 37557
Jacksonville, FL 32236
Tel.: (904) 693-1200
Fax: (904) 693-5365
Web Site: www.colomerusa.com
Approx. Number Employees: 2,000
Business Description:
Professional Cosmetic & Hair Care Products Mfr & Distr
S.I.C.: 2844
N.A.I.C.S.: 325620
Media: 6
Personnel:
John Mulgrew *(Sr VP-Sls)*

Brands & Products:
ABBA
ALPHA
APOLLO
BIO BALANCE
BLOWAVE
BUSY BEAUTY
CREME RELAXER
CUSTOM
FAB-SILK
FABULAXER
FINAL ONE
FINISHEEN
FLEX
FORMULA ZP II
FUTURA II
GLIS'N
GREAT FEELINGS
GUYS AND DOLLS
HAIR PROTEIN BUILDER
HERBAL DEEP CLEAN
HOLD TIGHT
LIQUID TEX
LIVELY SET
MAXIMUM TREATMENT
MILK PLUS 6
MOISTCURE
MONA
MP 200
NATURAL HONEY
PC-2000
PERM LIFE
PROTINA
ROUX
SALON NO-LYE
SENSOR PERM
SHAPINGS
SNAPPY SET
SONATURAL HAIR SPRAY
TEXTURE SILK
THERMAL TEX
TONE UP
YOUNG CURL
YOUNG HAIR

THE COLOR FACTORY, INC.

8430 Tujunga Ave
Sun Valley, CA 91352-3108
Tel.: (818) 767-2889
Fax: (818) 767-4062
Web Site: www.colorfactoryla.com
Approx. Number Employees: 100
Year Founded: 1984
Business Description:
Cosmetics Mfr
S.I.C.: 2844
N.A.I.C.S.: 325620
Media: 2-4-5-10-12-13-19-21
Personnel:
Al Booth *(Pres & CEO)*
Judy Zegarelli *(Sr VP)*
Brian Smith *(Dir-HR)*

COLOR ME BEAUTIFUL, INC.

7000 Infantry Ridge Rd Ste 400
Manassas, VA 20109
Tel.: (703) 471-6400
Fax: (703) 471-0127
Toll Free: (800) 533-5503
Web Site: www.colormebeautiful.com
Sales Range: $350-399.9 Million
Approx. Number Employees: 60
Year Founded: 1974
Business Description:
Cosmetics Mfr & Distr
S.I.C.: 5122
N.A.I.C.S.: 424210
Media: 4-6-8-10-11-13-20

Color Me Beautiful, Inc. — (Continued)

Budget Set: Dec.
Personnel:
Steve DiAntonio *(Owner)*
Yvonne McGee *(Pres & COO)*
David Meehan *(Pres-Retail)*
Sharon Boone *(VP-Mktg & Adv)*
Lucinda Law *(VP-Sls & Mktg)*
Brands & Products:
ADRIEN ARPEL
COLOR ME BEAUTIFUL
FLORI ROBERTS
GALE HAYMAN
IMAN
PATTI LABELLE

CONAIR CORPORATION

150 Milford Rd
East Windsor, NJ 08520
Tel.: (609) 426-1300
Fax: (609) 426-9475
Toll Free: (800) 366-5391
Web Site: www.conair.com
Approx. Rev.: $1,490,000,000
Approx. Number Employees: 3,459
Year Founded: 1959
Business Description:
Personal Care, Dental & Beauty Aid Products, Consumer Electronic & Kitchen Appliances Mfr & Developer
S.I.C.: 3634
N.A.I.C.S.: 335211
Import
Media: 2-3-5-6-9-10-12-14-15-19-20-23-24
Distr.: Natl.
Budget Set: Nov.
Personnel:
Ronald T. Diamond *(Pres)*
Barry Haber *(Co-Pres)*
Pat Yonnotta *(CFO)*
Ricard Margulies *(Gen Counsel)*
John Mayorek *(Sr VP-Ops)*
Robert Dixon *(VP-Adv)*
Andrew J. Klein *(Dir-Mktg)*
Stacey DeFelice *(Coord-PR)*
Brands & Products:
BABYLISS
BODY SOOTHER
CLASSIQUE
CLEANHEAD
COMBO CUT
COMFORT TOUCH
CONAIR
CONAIR FOR GREAT HAIR...SALON RESULTS AT HOME
CONAIR PRO STYLE
CUISINART
CUSTOM CUT
DRY 'N STRAIGHT
EASY START
ECODRY
EURO STYLE
FRIZZ DEFENSE
GEL GRIPS
HYPE HAIR
ILLUMINA
IMPRESSIONS
INFINITI
INFINITI CORD-KEEPER
INFINITI NANO SILVER
INTERPLAK
ION SHINE
ION SHINE CLEARPOWER
IONIC CORD-KEEPER
JHERI REDDING
OPTICLEAN
PICTURE PERFECT
POLLENEX
THE POWER OF PINK
PRO STYLER
PROCOLOR ACCENTS
PROSHINE
QUICK BRAID
SHINE EFFECTS
SHINY STYLES
SIMPLE CUT
SQWEEZ
STRAIGHT STYLES
STYLER DRYER
SUPER CLIPS
THERMACELL
TOUCH 'N TONE
TOURMALINE CERAMIC
TRAVEL SMART
ULTRA CUT
ULTRA-SLIM
WARING
Advertising Agencies:
The Lanmark Group Inc.
527 Industrial Way W
Eatontown, NJ 07724-2211
Tel.: (732) 389-4500
Fax: (732) 389-4998

Roher Public Relations
24007 Ventura Blvd Ste 290
Calabasas, CA 91364
Tel.: (818) 887-8838
Fax: (818) 591-1477

CONOPCO

(Div. of Conopco, Inc.)
(d/b/a Unilever Home & Personal Care USA)
205 N Michigan Ave Ste 3200
Chicago, IL 60601-5933
Tel.: (312) 661-0222
Fax: (312) 661-2250
E-mail: info@unilever.com
Web Site: www.unilever.com
Approx. Number Employees: 350
Year Founded: 1927
Business Description:
Personal Care Products Mfr
S.I.C.: 2844; 2841
N.A.I.C.S.: 325620; 325611
Export
Media: 4-6-8-10-11-13-21
Distr.: Natl.
Budget Set: Oct.
Personnel:
Fernando Acosta *(VP-Dove Brand Devel-Global)*
Pablo Gazzera *(Dir-Dove Personal Wash Brand)*
Jennifer Healy *(Mgr-Axe Brand)*
Gaston Vaneri *(Mgr-Dove Personal Wash Brand)*
Advertising Agency:
Ogilvy & Mather
350 W Mart Ctr Dr Ste 1100
Chicago, IL 60654-1866
Tel.: (312) 856-8200
Fax: (312) 856-8207

COSMETIC IMPORTS MARKETING GROUP, INC.

2330 State Rte 11
Mooers, NY 12958-0219
Fax: (800) 317-6711
Toll Free: (800) 322-3507
E-mail: info@facosmetics.com
Web Site: www.facosmetics.com
Approx. Sls.: $2,000,000
Approx. Number Employees: 6
Year Founded: 1984
Business Description:
Cosmetics Distr
S.I.C.: 5122
N.A.I.C.S.: 424210
Import
Media: 3-6-8-10-15-18-19-21
Distr.: Intl.
Budget Set: Nov.
Personnel:
Hiro Kotchounian *(Pres & CEO)*
Jerri Alpin *(Mgr-Mktg)*
Brands & Products:
ALGEMARIN
FA

COSMOPRO WEST, INC.

15773 Gateway Cir
Tustin, CA 92780-6470
Tel.: (714) 258-8301
Fax: (714) 258-8302
Toll Free: (800) 446-3751
E-mail: sales@cosmoproshop.com
Web Site: www.cosmoproshop.com
E-Mail For Key Personnel:
Sales Director: sales@cosmoproshop.com
Approx. Number Employees: 25
Year Founded: 1988
Business Description:
Skincare, Beauty & Healthcare Products Distr & Spa Care Equipment Mfr
S.I.C.: 2844; 2834; 2841; 5999
N.A.I.C.S.: 325620; 325412; 325611; 446199
Media: 6-7-8-13
Personnel:
Phillippe Hennessy *(Pres)*

COTY, INC.

2 Park Ave
New York, NY 10016
Tel.: (212) 479-4300
Web Site: www.coty.com
Sales Range: $1-4.9 Billion
Approx. Number Employees: 6,500
Year Founded: 1996
Business Description:
Cosmetics & Fragrances Distr
S.I.C.: 2844
N.A.I.C.S.: 325620
Media: 2-4-5-6-7-8-9-10-11-14-15-16-18-19-20-21-23-24-25
Distr.: Natl.
Budget Set: Oct.
Personnel:
Peter Harf *(Chm)*
Michele Scannavini *(Pres)*
Bernd Beetz *(CEO)*
Renato Semerari *(Pres-Coty Beauty)*
Kevin Monaco *(Treas & Sr VP-Tax)*
Geraud-Marie Lacassagne *(Sr VP-HR)*
Steve Mormoris *(Sr VP-Global Mktg-Coty Beauty)*
Catherine Walsh *(Sr VP-American Fragrances-Coty Prestige)*
Jason Bell *(Mgr-Customer Mktg)*
Brands & Products:
AMERICAN ORIGINAL
ASPEN
COTY PRESTIGE
DARK VANILLA
EXCLAMATION
GRAVITY
ICI
JOVAN MUSK
LONGING
NIKOS SCULPTURE DELICATE FLEUR
PREFERRED STOCK
SAND & SABLE
STETSON
VANILLA FIELDS
VANILLA MUSK
Advertising Agencies:
Della Femina Rothschild Jeary & Partners
902 Broadway 15th Fl
New York, NY 10010
Tel.: (212) 506-0700
Fax: (212) 506-0751

G2 Tokyo
Ebisu Square 1-23-23 Ebisu
Tokyo, 150-0013, Japan
Tel.: (81) 3 5423 1727
Fax: (81) 3 5423 1747

Laird+Partners
475 10th Ave 7th Fl
New York, NY 10018
Tel.: (212) 478-8181
Fax: (212) 478-8210
Global Creative Duties-Sally Hansen, La Crosse & NYC Color

OMD Worldwide
195 Broadway
New York, NY 10007
Tel.: (212) 590-7100
Media Buying & Planning-U.S., Canada, Ireland & United Kingdom

Quaker City Mercantile
114-120 S 13th St
Philadelphia, PA 19107
Tel.: (215) 922-5220
Fax: (215) 922-5228

RAPP
437 Madison Ave 3rd Fl
New York, NY 10022
Tel.: (212) 817-6800
Fax: (212) 590-8400
Analytics
CRM
Display
E-Mail
Global Digital Agency of Record-Sally Hansen & licensed Guess, Halle Berry, Beckham & Playboy
Social Media
Website Design

VML-New York
285 Madison Ave
New York, NY 10017
Tel.: (212) 210-3653
Fax: (212) 880-7543

COVER GIRL COSMETICS

(Sub. of The Procter & Gamble Company)
11050 York Rd
Hunt Valley, MD 21030-2005
Tel.: (410) 785-7300
Fax: (410) 785-8623
Web Site: www.covergirl.com
Sales Range: $1-4.9 Billion
Approx. Number Employees: 2,000
Year Founded: 1885

Key to Media (For complete agency information see *The Advertising Red Books-Agencies* edition):
1. Bus. Publs. 2. Cable T.V. 3. Catalogs & Directories. 4. Co-op Adv. 5. Consumer Mags. 6. D.M. to Bus. Estab.7. D.M. to Consumers 8. Daily Newsp. 9. Exhibits/Trade Shows 10. Foreign 11. Infomercial 12. Internet Adv.13. Multimedia 14. Network Radio 15. Network T.V. 16. Newsp. Distr. Mags. 17. Other 18. Outdoor (Posters, Transit) 19. Point of Purchase20. Premiums, Novelties 21. Product Samples 22. Special Events Mktg. 23. Spot Radio 24. Spot T.V. 25. Weekly Newsp. 26. Yellow Page Adv.

Business Description:
Cosmetics Mfr
S.I.C.: 2844
N.A.I.C.S.: 325620
Media: 5-6-9-10-11-17-19-23-24-25
Distr.: Natl.
Personnel:
Vince Hudson *(Gen Mgr)*
Cathy Laporte *(Dir-Mkt)*
Michelle Froah *(Brand Mgr)*
Luna Ravenna *(Asst Brand Mgr)*
Brands & Products:
ALL-DAY
BRUSH-ON-BLUSH
CHEEKERS
CLEAN LASH
CONTINUOUS COLOR
COVER GIRL
COVER GIRL POWDER
EXTREMELY GENTLE SOFTLINER
EYEBROW & LINER PENCIL
FOUR KIT
GALLERY EIGHT KIT
INCOGNITO
THE INVISIBLE CONCEALER
LASTING PERFORMANCE
LONG 'N LUSH
LUMINESSE
LUMINESSE SATIN FINISH
MAKEUPMATE
MARATHON
MOISTUREWEAR
NAILSLICKS
PERFECT BLEND
PROFESSIONAL
SHAPE 'N BLUSH
SINGLE KIT
SOFTLINE
TEN TERRIFIC NAILS
THICK LASH 2
THICK 'N THIN
THREE KIT
ULTRA PRECISE
Advertising Agencies:
Grey Geneva
1 rue Lugardon
1211
Geneva, Switzerland
Tel.: (41) 22906 4949
Fax: (41) 22906 4940

Marina Maher Communications
830 3rd Ave
New York, NY 10022
Tel.: (212) 485-6800
Fax: (212) 355-6318

CREATIVE NAIL DESIGN, INC.
(Sub. of Colomer USA, Inc.)
1125 Joshua Way
Vista, CA 92081
Tel.: (760) 599-2900
Fax: (760) 599-4005
Toll Free: (877) 263-6245
E-mail: hotline@cnd.com
Web Site: www.cnd.com
Approx. Number Employees: 100
Year Founded: 1979
Business Description:
Nail Care & Beauty Products Mfr
S.I.C.: 2844; 2841
N.A.I.C.S.: 325620; 325611
Media: 6-22
Personnel:
Jan Arnold *(Co-Founder)*
Stuart Nordstrom *(Co-Founder)*
John Heffner *(Pres & CEO)*
Kim Natale *(VP-Mktg)*
Tony Nemer *(VP-Intl Sls)*
Brands & Products:
RAW EARTH
SCENTSATIONS
SOLAROIL
SPAMANICURE
SPAPEDICURE

C.S. DENT & CO.
(Div. of Grandpa Brands Company)
1820 Airport Exchange Blvd
Erlanger, KY 41018-3192
Tel.: (859) 647-0777
Fax: (859) 647-0778
Toll Free: (800) 684-1468
E-mail: gbc@grandpabrands.com
Web Site: www.grandpabrands.com
Approx. Number Employees: 30
Year Founded: 1888
Business Description:
Over-the-Counter Toothache & Other Health & Beauty Preparations Mfr
S.I.C.: 2834; 2841
N.A.I.C.S.: 325412; 325611
Export
Media: 2-4-10
Personnel:
Richard D. Oliver *(Chm, Pres & CEO)*
Brands & Products:
DENT'S

DANA CLASSIC FRAGRANCES, INC.
(Holding of Dimeling, Schreiber & Park)
400 Yester Ave
Saddle Brook, NJ 07663
Tel.: (201) 881-8550
Fax: (973) 416-0499
Web Site: www.danaclassics.com/
Approx. Number Employees: 120
Year Founded: 1999
Business Description:
Nail Care Products & Fragrances Mfr
S.I.C.: 2844
N.A.I.C.S.: 325620
Media: 1-2-3-4-6-9-10-15-16-18-19-20-21-22-23-24
Personnel:
Joseph Seinkiewicz *(CFO)*
Brands & Products:
CANOE
CHANTILLY
ENGLISH LEATHER
HEAVEN SENT
LOVE'S BABY SOFT
NAVY
TABU

DHC USA INC.
(Sub. of DHC Corporation)
115 Sansome St Ste 400
San Francisco, CA 94104
Tel.: (415) 908-1400
Fax: (888) 650-7118
Fax: (415) 908-1408
Toll Free: (800) 342-2273
E-mail: help@dhccare.com
Web Site: www.dhccare.com
Approx. Number Employees: 30
Business Description:
Skincare Product Whslr
S.I.C.: 5961; 2844; 5122
N.A.I.C.S.: 454113; 325620; 446120
Media: 4-6-8-21
Personnel:
Gary Gauntt *(Pres)*
Miles Perdiguerra *(Dir-Mktg)*

THE DIAL CORPORATION
(Sub. of Henkel AG & Co. KGaA)
19001 N Rd
Scottsdale, AZ 85255
Tel.: (480) 754-3425
Fax: (480) 754-1098
E-mail: corprel@dialcorp.com
Web Site: www.henkelna.com
Sales Range: $1-4.9 Billion
Approx. Number Employees: 822
Year Founded: 1996
Business Description:
Consumer Products Mfr
S.I.C.: 2841; 2844
N.A.I.C.S.: 325611; 325620
Advertising Expenditures: $33,629,000
Media: 2-3-6-8-10-11-15-19-21-23-24
Distr.: Natl.
Budget Set: Oct. -Nov.
Personnel:
Stefan Sudhoff *(Pres-Henkel Consumer Goods)*
Richard F. Theiler *(Sr VP-Res & Devel)*
Tracy VanBibber *(Chief Customer Solutions Officier & Sr VP-Sls)*
Toby Gubitz *(VP-Mktg-APDO)*
Kiem Ho *(Dir-Bus Dev & Innovation)*
Chris Sommer *(Dir-Mktg)*
Ann M. Toca *(Dir-Adv & Consumer Promo)*
Steven Koven *(Brand Mgr-RGX)*
Sami Myohanen *(Brand Mgr-Pure & Natural)*
Derek Schwendinger *(Brand Mgr-Purex)*
Mike Cecil *(Sr Brand Mgr-Innovation)*
Erick Dickens *(Brand Mgr-Renuzit)*
Brands & Products:
APPIAN WAY
AREN'T YOU GLAD YOU USE DIAL?
ARMOUR
AROMASENSE
BORATEEM
COAST
COMBAT
CREAM
DIAL
DIAL ANTIOXIDANT BODY WASH
DIAL FOR MEN BLUE GRIT
DIAL YOGURT
GENTLE SOFT
HERBAL SPRINGS
HIGH IMPACT
NEVER GET CAUGHT OFF GUARD
ONE TOUCH
PURE & NATURAL
PUREX
PUREX BABY
RENUZIT
RGX
RIGHT GUARD
RIGHT GUARD SPORT
RIGHT GUARD XTREME
SOFT & DRI
SOFT SCRUB
STA-FLO
SUPER ODOR NEUTRALIZER
TONE
TREND
TRI SCENTS
TROPICAL ESCAPE
ZOUT
Advertising Agencies:
Energy BBDO
410 N Michigan Ave
Chicago, IL 60611-4213
Tel.: (312) 337-7860
Fax: (312) 337-6871

Kaleidoscope Marketing and Communications Incorporated
346 Fairlawn Avenue
Toronto, ON M5M 1T6, Canada
Tel.: (416) 785-8558

Lime Public Relations & Promotion
160 Varick St 4th Fl
New York, NY 10013
Tel.: (212) 633-0080
Fax: (212) 633-1711
Soft & Dri

Night Agency
307 Canal St Fl 2
New York, NY 10013
Tel.: (212) 431-1945
Fax: (917) 677-8327

OMD-USA
195 Broadway
New York, NY 10007
Tel.: (212) 590-7100

DIVINE SKIN, INC.
(d/b/a DS Laboratories)
1680 Meridian Ave Ste 301
Miami, FL 33139
Toll Free: (888) 404-7770
Web Site: www.divineskin.com
Approx. Rev.: $5,452,523
Approx. Number Employees: 11
Year Founded: 2007
Business Description:
Skin Care & Personal Care Products Mfr & Marketer
S.I.C.: 2844; 5122
N.A.I.C.S.: 325620; 424210
Advertising Expenditures: $364,566
Media: 4-8-13-17
Personnel:
Daniel Khesin *(Chm, CEO & Chief Acctg Officer)*
Robin Powell *(Pres)*
Michael Paul Strong *(VP-Sls)*

EB5 CORPORATION
2711 NW St Helen Rd
Portland, OR 97210
Tel.: (503) 230-8008
Fax: (503) 230-0321
Toll Free: (800) 683-2325
E-mail: info@eb5.com
Web Site: www.eb5.com
Approx. Number Employees: 20
Business Description:
Cosmetics Retailer
S.I.C.: 2844; 5961
N.A.I.C.S.: 325620; 454113
Advertising Expenditures: $3,000,000
Media: 5-9-25
Distr.: Natl.
Budget Set: May
Personnel:
Robert C. Heldfond *(Founder)*
Shay Tyroler *(Head-Strategy)*
Brands & Products:
CLARIFYING FACIAL BAR
CLARIFYING TONER
EB5

Key to Media (For complete agency information see *The Advertising Red Books-Agencies* edition):
1. Bus. Publs. 2. Cable T.V. 3. Catalogs & Directories. 4. Co-op Adv. 5. Consumer Mags. 6. D.M. to Bus. Estab.7. D.M. to Consumers
8. Daily Newsp. 9. Exhibits/Trade Shows 10. Foreign 11. Infomercial 12. Internet Adv.13. Multimedia 14. Network Radio
15. Network T.V. 16. Newsp. Distr. Mags. 17. Other 18. Outdoor (Posters, Transit) 19. Point of Purchase20. Premiums, Novelties
21. Product Samples 22. Special Events Mktg. 23. Spot Radio 24. Spot T.V. 25. Weekly Newsp. 26. Yellow Page Adv.

EB5 Corporation — (Continued)

FORMULAS FOR YOUNGER LOOKING SKIN
VIBRANT EYES

ELIZABETH ARDEN, INC.
2400 SW 145th Ave 2nd Fl
Miramar, FL 33027-4145
Tel.: (954) 364-6900
Fax: (954) 364-6910
Toll Free: (800) 227-2445
E-mail: publicrelations@elizabetharden.com
Web Site: www.elizabetharden.com
Approx. Sls.: $1,175,500,000
Approx. Number Employees: 2,260
Year Founded: 1960
Business Description:
Fragrances & Cosmetics Mfr & Marketer
S.I.C.: 2844; 5122
N.A.I.C.S.: 325620; 446120
Export
Advertising Expenditures: $324,100,000
Media: 4-5-6-15-18-19-23
Personnel:
E. Scott Beattie *(Chm, Pres & CEO)*
Stephen J. Smith *(CFO & Exec VP)*
L. Hoy Heise *(CIO & Exec VP)*
Kathy Widmer *(CMO & Exec VP)*
Chih-Hsin Chen *(Pres-Elizabeth Arden-China)*
Oscar E. Marina *(Gen Counsel, Sec & Exec VP)*
Elizabeth Park *(Exec VP-Global Mktg & Gen Mgr-USA)*
Joel B. Ronkin *(Exec VP & Gen Mgr-North America)*
Jacobus A.J. Steffens *(Exec VP & Gen Mgr-Intl)*
Dirk Trappmann *(Exec VP & Gen Mgr-Intl)*
Gretchen Goslin *(Exec VP-Bus Dev)*
Michael H. Lombardi *(Exec VP-Package Design & Innovation)*
Pierre Pirard *(Exec VP-Product Innovation & Global Supply Chain)*
Ronald L. Rolleston *(Exec VP)*
Art Spiro *(Exec VP-Mktg)*
Jeffrey M. Arnold *(Sr VP-Mass Selling Bus Unit)*
Marcey Becker *(Sr VP-Fin, Treasury & Corp Dev)*
Lita Cunningham *(Sr VP-Global HR)*
William Dubose *(Sr VP-Global Wal-Mart & Sams Club)*
Eli Khouri *(Sr VP-Bus Dev)*
Mark Newberry *(Sr VP-Global Logistics)*
Heide Rand *(Sr VP)*
Michael Shin *(Sr VP-Europe)*
Tamara Steele *(Sr VP-Global Fragrance Mktg)*
David Rattner *(VP-Fin & Controller)*
Sebastian Clifton-Welker *(Dir-Mktg-APO Reg)*
Jim Barlow *(Dir-Global Bus Intelligence)*
David A. Lathan *(Dir-InfoTech-Infrastructure & Web Dev)*
Ana Chavez *(Mgr-Legal Admin)*
Brands & Products:
5TH AVENUE
5TH AVENUE AFTER FIVE
ALBERTA FERRETTI
ALFRED SUNG
ARDENBEAUTY
BLUE GRASS
BOB MACKIE
BRITNEY SPEARS
CERAMIDES
COLOR INTRIGUE
CURVE
DESIGN
EAU FRAICHE
EIGHT HOUR CREAM
ELIZABETH ARDEN
ELIZABETH ARDEN 5TH AVENUE
ELIZABETH ARDEN GREEN TEA
ELIZABETH ARDEN'S PROVOCATIVE WOMAN
ELIZABETH ARDEN'S RED DOOR
ELIZABETH TAYLOR'S WHITE DIAMONDS
EXCEPTIONAL
FLAWLESS FINISH
FOREVER ELIZABETH
GARDENIA
GEOFFREY BEENE
GIORGIO BEVERLY HILLS
GREEN TEA
GREEN TEA REVITALIZE
GREY FLANNEL
HALSTON
INTERVENE
JOHN VARVATOS
JUICY COUTURE
KATE SPADE NEW YORK
LUCKY
MARIAH CAREY
MEDITERRANEAN
MILLENNIUM
OVERNIGHT SUCCESS
PASSION
PLUMP PERFECT
PRETTY ELIZABETH ARDEN
PREVAGE
PROVOCATIVE
PS FINE COLOGNE FOR MEN
RED DOOR REVEALED
RED DOOR VELVET
ROCAWEAR
SHEER HALSTON
SUNFLOWERS
TAYLOR SWIFT
UNBOUND
USHER
WHITE DIAMONDS
WHITE SHOULDERS
WINGS
Z-14
Advertising Agencies:
PHD China
Rm 1101 Tower 2
Shanghai, 200030, China
Tel.: (86) 21 6407 8080
Fax: (86) 21 6447 1059
Digital Media Planning & Buying
Fragrance
Makeup
Skincare
Traditional Media Planning & Buying

PHD Media UK
The Telephone Exchange 5 N Crescent
London, WC1E 7PH, United Kingdom
Tel.: (44) 20 7446 0555
Fax: (44) 20 7446 7100
Digital Media Planning & Buying
Fragrance
Makeup
Skincare
Traditional Media Planning & Buying

PHD Singapore
3 Anson Rd 31-02 Springleaf Tower
Singapore, 0799090, Singapore
Tel.: (65) 6877 8770
Digital Media Planning & Buying
Fragrance
Makeup
Skincare
Traditional Media Planning & Buying

PHD Thailand
10 Floor Amarin Plaza
Bangkok, 10330, Thailand
Tel.: (66) 2 256 9360
Fax: (66) 22569366
Digital Media Planning & Buying
Fragrance
Makeup
Skincare
Traditional Media Planning & Buying

THE ELTRON COMPANY
3611 Cahuenga Blvd W
Hollywood, CA 90068
Tel.: (323) 876-5454
Fax: (323) 876-5634
Toll Free: (800) 276-4405
E-mail: parksproducts@earthlink.net
Web Site: www.parksproducts.com
E-Mail For Key Personnel:
President: john@parksproducts.com
Sales Director: gary@parksproducts.com
Approx. Number Employees: 25
Year Founded: 1957
Business Description:
Electric Shavers & Shaving Accessories Mfr
S.I.C.: 7311
N.A.I.C.S.: 541810
Import Export
Media: 4-6-7-10-13-19-20-21-23-26
Distr.: Natl.
Personnel:
John R. Parks *(Pres)*
David Weisenberg *(Mgr-Natl Sls)*
Brands & Products:
ELTRON
THE ELTRON COMPANY
GO-GIRL
PRE/AFT
PREP
S-BLADE
SHAVE EASE
SHAVE STICK
SHAVE'R CORD

EMINENCE ORGANIC SKIN CARE INC.
Denman Pl
PO Box 47029
Vancouver, BC Canada
Tel.: (604) 602-4787
Fax: (604) 602-4731
Toll Free: (888) 747-6342
E-mail: info@eminenceorganics.com
Web Site: www.eminenceorganics.com
Approx. Number Employees: 150
Year Founded: 1958
Business Description:
Beauty Products Mfr
S.I.C.: 2844
N.A.I.C.S.: 325620
Media: 4-6-10-22
Personnel:
Boldijarre Koronczay *(Founder)*

ER'GO CANDLES INC.
10830 Composite Dr
Dallas, TX 75220
Tel.: (214) 905-9050
Fax: (214) 905-9075
E-mail: ergo@ergocandle.com
Web Site: www.ergocandle.com
Approx. Number Employees: 15
Year Founded: 1999
Business Description:
Candles & Fragrances Mfr
S.I.C.: 2844; 2841
N.A.I.C.S.: 325620; 325611
Media: 6-10
Personnel:
Kathy Vassallo *(Pres)*
Ardene Flahavin *(VP-Sls & Mktg)*

ESSCENTUAL BRANDS, LLC
4835 E Cactus Rd Ste 245
Scottsdale, AZ 85254
Tel.: (602) 889-4800
Fax: (602) 889-4830
E-mail: info@esscentualbrands.com
Web Site: www.belae.com
Approx. Number Employees: 27
Year Founded: 1998
Business Description:
Home Fragrances, Bath & Body Soaps & Lotions Mfr
S.I.C.: 2844
N.A.I.C.S.: 325620
Media: 4-7-8-10-18-19-21
Personnel:
Paul Hansen *(CFO)*
Brands & Products:
ARRAN AROMATICS
CLAIRE BURKE
VITABATH
VITABATH EXPRESSIVE

THE ESTEE LAUDER COMPANIES INC.
767 5th Ave
New York, NY 10153-0023
Tel.: (212) 572-4200
Fax: (212) 572-6633
E-mail: irdept@estee.com
Web Site: www.elcompanies.com
Approx. Sls.: $8,810,000,000
Approx. Number Employees: 32,300
Year Founded: 1946
Business Description:
Cosmetics & Fragrances Mfr & Whslr
S.I.C.: 5122; 2841; 2844
N.A.I.C.S.: 446120; 325611; 325620
Advertising Expenditures: $2,458,000,000
Media: 3-4-6-8-9-13-15-16-18-19-20-21-22-23-24-25
Distr.: Intl.; Natl.
Budget Set: July
Personnel:
William P. Lauder *(Chm)*
Fabrizio Freda *(Co-Pres & CEO)*
Jane Lauder *(Global Pres & Gen Mgr-Origins & Ojon)*
John Demsey *(Co-Pres)*
Richard W. Kunes *(CFO & Exec VP)*
Olivier Bottrie *(Pres-Travel Retailing)*
Caroline Geerlings *(Pres-Tom Ford Beauty & New Bus)*
Lynne Greene *(Pres-Clinique, Origins & Ojon-Global)*

Key to Media (For complete agency information see *The Advertising Red Books-Agencies* edition):
1. Bus. Publs. 2. Cable T.V. 3. Catalogs & Directories. 4. Co-op Adv. 5. Consumer Mags. 6. D.M. to Bus. Estab.7. D.M. to Consumers 8. Daily Newsp. 9. Exhibits/Trade Shows 10. Foreign 11. Infomercial 12. Internet Adv.13. Multimedia 14. Network Radio 15. Network T.V. 16. Newsp. Distr. Mags. 17. Other 18. Outdoor (Posters, Transit) 19. Point of Purchase20. Premiums, Novelties 21. Product Samples 22. Special Events Mktg. 23. Spot Radio 24. Spot T.V. 25. Weekly Newsp. 26. Yellow Page Adv.

Jane Hertzmark Hudis *(Pres-Global Brand)*
Cedric Prouve *(Pres-Intl Grp)*
Sara E. Moss *(Gen Counsel & Exec VP)*
Amy Digeso *(Exec VP-Global HR)*
Harvey Gedeon *(Exec VP-R&D, Product Innovation & Brand Product Dev)*
Gregory F. Polcer *(Exec VP-Global Supply Chain)*
Alexandra C. Trower *(Exec VP-Global Comm)*
Daniel M. Annese *(Sr VP & Gen Mgr-Intl)*
Richard Ferretti *(Sr VP & Global Dir-Creative)*
Aerin Lauder *(Sr VP & Dir-Global Creative)*
Susan Akkad *(Sr VP-Corp Diversity Mktg)*
Jennifer Balbier *(Sr VP-Global Prod Dev)*
Marianne Diorio *(Sr VP-Global Brand Comm)*
Georgia Garinois-Melenikiotou *(Sr VP-Corp Mktg)*
Evelyn H. Lauder *(Sr VP)*
Christopher Wood *(Sr VP-Global Strategic Modernization Initiative)*
Bari D. Seiden *(VP-Comm-Global)*
Marisa Thalberg *(VP-Digital Mktg-Global)*
Nancy Mahon *(Exec Dir)*
Eleanor F. Powell *(Exec Dir-IR)*
Colleen Scanlon *(Dir-Mktg)*

Brands & Products:
AMERICAN BEAUTY
ARAMIS
AVEDA
BOBBI BROWN
BRINGING THE BEST TO EVERYONE WE TOUCH.
BUMBLE AND BUMBLE
CLINIQUE
COACH
DAISY FUENTES
DARPHIN
DONNA KARAN
ESTEE LAUDER
EYES BY DESIGN
FLIRT!
GOOD SKIN
GRASSROOTS
JO MALONE
LA MER
LAB SERIES
M-A-C
MICHEAL KORS
OJON
ORIGINS
PRESCRIPTIVES
SEAN JOHN
TOMMY HILFIGER

Advertising Agencies:
Anthem Worldwide
77 Maiden Ln 4th Fl
San Francisco, CA 94108
Tel.: (415) 896-9399
Fax: (415) 896-9387

Badalato Ginsberg
445 Park Ave
New York, NY 10022
Tel.: (646) 225-6654
Fax: (646) 225-6664

Mindshare
498 7th Ave
New York, NY 10018
Tel.: (212) 297-7000
Fax: (212) 297-7001

OMD Worldwide
195 Broadway
New York, NY 10007
Tel.: (212) 590-7100

ESTEE LAUDER COSMETICS LTD.

(Sub. of The Estee Lauder Companies Inc.)
161 Commander Blvd
Toronto, ON M1S 3K9, Canada
Tel.: (416) 292-1111
Fax: (416) 292-3495
Toll Free: (800) 387-6707
E-mail: info@esteelauder.com
Web Site: www.esteelauder.com
Sales Range: $10-24.9 Million
Approx. Number Employees: 300
Year Founded: 1960
Business Description:
Perfumes & Cosmetics Mfr
S.I.C.: 2844
N.A.I.C.S.: 325620
Media: 8-10-13
Personnel:
John Demsey *(Pres)*

E.T. BROWNE DRUG COMPANY, INC.

440 Sylvan Ave
Englewood Cliffs, NJ 07632
Mailing Address:
PO Box 1613
Englewood Cliffs, NJ 07632
Tel.: (201) 894-9020
Fax: (201) 894-5152
Toll Free: (877) 725-6377
E-mail: info@etbrowne.com
Web Site: www.etbrowne.com
E-Mail For Key Personnel:
President: rneis@etbrown.com
Marketing Director: dnichols@etbrowne.com
Approx. Number Employees: 250
Year Founded: 1840
Business Description:
Perfumes, Skin Care, Lotions, Toiletries & Hair Care Products Mfr
S.I.C.: 2844
N.A.I.C.S.: 325620
Export
Media: 4-5-6-7-8-9-10-11-19-20-21-25
Distr.: Natl.
Personnel:
Robert Neis *(Pres)*
Rebecca Brown *(VP-Mktg)*
Debra Nichols *(VP-Mktg)*

Brands & Products:
BLACK & BEAUTIFUL
COCONUT BRONZE
COCONUT BUTTER FORMULA
COCONUT OIL FORMULA
NO BLADE
PALMER'S
PALMER'S COCOA BUTTER FORMULA
PALMER'S COCONUT OIL FORMULA
PALMER'S HAIR CARE
PALMER'S HAIR SUCCESS
PALMER'S NO BLADE
PALMER'S SKIN SOFTENING CREAM
PALMER'S SKIN SUCCESS
SHEA BUTTER FORMULA
SKIN SOFTENING CREAM
SKINSUCCESS

ETON DERMA LABORATORIES, INC.

(d/b/a Acne-Statin)
4300 Promanede Way Ste 319
Marina Del Rey, CA 90292-5426
Tel.: (310) 827-5757
Fax: (310) 827-6220
Toll Free: (800) 762-2263
E-mail: acne@acne-statin.com
Web Site: acnestatin.com
Sales Range: $25-49.9 Million
Approx. Number Employees: 15
Business Description:
Skin Care Products Mfr
S.I.C.: 2844; 5122
N.A.I.C.S.: 325620; 446120
Media: 3-6-8-12-13-24
Distr.: Natl.
Personnel:
Atida Karr *(Pres & CEO)*

Brands & Products:
ACNE-STATIN
SOPSTITUTE
SUN STATIN

FAIRMOUNT MINERALS, INC.

11833 Ravenna Rd
Chardon, OH 44024-7006
Tel.: (440) 285-3132
Fax: (440) 285-0707
Web Site: www.fairmountminerals.com
E-Mail For Key Personnel:
President: chuck.fowler@fairmountminerals.com
Marketing Director: mo.lynn@fairmountminerals.com
Approx. Number Employees: 450
Year Founded: 1986
Business Description:
Industrial Sand Production
S.I.C.: 1446
N.A.I.C.S.: 212322
Import Export
Personnel:
William E. Conway *(Chm)*
Charles D. Fowler *(Pres & CEO)*
Jennifer D. Deckard *(CFO)*
Lori Krieger *(Mgr-Customer Svc)*
Tim McMillin *(Mgr-Mktg)*

Brands & Products:
AQUAQUARTZ
BLACK MAGNUM
DIVOT FIX
FLEXSAND
NITAMIN
PREVENT
SPECTRAQUARTZ
TOP PRO
TOUR BLEND
TOUR GRADE

Advertising Agency:
Alexander Marketing Services
801 Broadway NW Ste 300
Grand Rapids, MI 49504
Tel.: (616) 957-2000

FANCL INTERNATIONAL, INC.

(Sub. of Fancl Corporation)
17138 Pullman St Ste 100
Irvine, CA 92614
Tel.: (949) 476-8167
Fax: (949) 476-8168
E-mail: contact@fancl.com
Web Site: www.fancl.com
Approx. Number Employees: 20
Year Founded: 1997
Business Description:
Cosmetics & Toiletries Sales
S.I.C.: 5961
N.A.I.C.S.: 454113
Media: 6
Personnel:
Gen Inomata *(Pres)*
Meri Baregamian *(Gen Mgr-Sls & Mktg)*

Brands & Products:
BOSCIA

FASHION FAIR COSMETICS, LLC

(Sub. of Johnson Publishing Company, Inc.)
820 S Michigan Ave
Chicago, IL 60605-2103
Tel.: (312) 322-9444
Fax: (312) 322-0918
Web Site: www.fashionfair.com
Approx. Number Employees: 150
Year Founded: 1973
Business Description:
Cosmetics Mfr
S.I.C.: 5122
N.A.I.C.S.: 446120
Media: 8-9-19
Distr.: Intl.; Natl.
Personnel:
Linda Johnson Rice *(Chm & CEO)*
Clarisa Wilson *(Pres)*
Anne Sempowski Ward *(COO)*
J. Lance Clarke *(Sr VP)*
Sheila Jinkins *(VP-HR)*

Brands & Products:
EBONE

FIRMENICH INCORPORATED

(Sub. of Firmenich S.A.)
250 Plainsboro Rd
Plainsboro, NJ 08536
Mailing Address:
PO Box 5880
Princeton, NJ 08543-5880
Tel.: (609) 452-1000
Fax: (609) 452-6077
Toll Free: (800) 257-9591
Web Site: www.firmenich.com
Approx. Number Employees: 700
Year Founded: 1894
Business Description:
Fragrances, Aromatic Chemicals, Artificial & Natural Flavors Mfr
S.I.C.: 2869; 2899
N.A.I.C.S.: 325199; 325998
Media: 2-7-13
Distr.: Intl.; Natl.
Personnel:
Bob Weinstein *(Pres-Ingredients Div-Global)*

FIRMENICH INTERNATIONAL FINE FRAGRANCE CENTER

(Sub. of Firmenich S.A.)
625 Madison Ave 17th Fl
New York, NY 10022-3213
Tel.: (212) 489-4800
Fax: (212) 980-4312
Web Site: www.firmenich.com
Approx. Number Employees: 80
Year Founded: 1895

Key to Media (For complete agency information see *The Advertising Red Books-Agencies* edition):
1. Bus. Publs. 2. Cable T.V. 3. Catalogs & Directories. 4. Co-op Adv. 5. Consumer Mags. 6. D.M. to Bus. Estab.7. D.M. to Consumers 8. Daily Newsp. 9. Exhibits/Trade Shows 10. Foreign 11. Infomercial 12. Internet Adv.13. Multimedia 14. Network Radio 15. Network T.V. 16. Newsp. Distr. Mags. 17. Other 18. Outdoor (Posters, Transit) 19. Point of Purchase20. Premiums, Novelties 21. Product Samples 22. Special Events Mktg. 23. Spot Radio 24. Spot T.V. 25. Weekly Newsp. 26. Yellow Page Adv.

Firmenich International Fine Fragrance Center — (Continued)

Business Description:
Perfumes & Fragrances Mfr
S.I.C.: 5169; 2844
N.A.I.C.S.: 424690; 325620
Media: 2-4

Brands & Products:
FLOWER

FRAGRANCE RESOURCES, INC.
620 Rte 3 W PO Box 4277
Clifton, NJ 07014
Tel.: (973) 777-2979
Fax: (973) 458-5239
Web Site: www.fragrancer.com
Approx. Number Employees: 110
Year Founded: 1987
Business Description:
Oils & Essential Oils Mfr
S.I.C.: 2899
N.A.I.C.S.: 325998
Import Export
Media: 2
Budget Set: Dec.
Personnel:
Kristof Gerberding *(Pres & CEO)*
Robert A. Palumbo *(Exec VP-Fin & HR)*
Larry Zakreski *(Sr VP-Ops)*
Michael Simpson *(VP-Mktg)*
Dominick Firetto *(Dir Acctg)*

FRAGRANT ESSENCE
5612-162 A Ave
Edmonton, AB Canada
Tel.: (780) 903-3130
Fax: (780) 472-2827
E-mail: valents@fragrantessence.com
Web Site: www.fragrantessence.com
Approx. Number Employees: 1
Business Description:
Essential Oils & Natural Body Products Sales
S.I.C.: 2844; 2841
N.A.I.C.S.: 325620; 325611
Media: 4-8-13

Brands & Products:
FRAGRANT ESSENCE

FRAMESI USA, INC.
(Affil. of Framesi S.p.A.)
400 Chess St
Coraopolis, PA 15108-3927
Tel.: (412) 269-2950
Fax: (412) 264-5696
Toll Free: (800) 321-9648
Sales Range: $25-49.9 Million
Year Founded: 1990
Business Description:
Hair Care Products Distr
S.I.C.: 5122
N.A.I.C.S.: 424210
Import Export
Media: 5-6-10-19-21
Distr.: Natl.
Budget Set: Mar.
Personnel:
Dennis Katawczik *(Pres)*
Terri Volkanas *(Mgr-Mktg)*

FRONTIER NATURAL PRODUCTS CO-OP
3021 78th St
Norway, IA 52318
Tel.: (319) 227-7996
Fax: (319) 227-7966
E-mail: customercare@frontiercoop.com
Web Site: www.frontiercoop.com
Approx. Sls.: $39,287,738
Approx. Number Employees: 200
Business Description:
Herbs & Spices, Aromatherapy
S.I.C.: 2099; 5122
N.A.I.C.S.: 311942; 424210
Media: 6
Personnel:
Tony Bedard *(CEO)*
Bill Kooistra *(CFO)*
Clint Landis *(CMO)*
Kory Kazimour *(Brand Mgr)*

Brands & Products:
AURA CACIA
FRONTIER
QUALITY PRODUCTS FOR NATURAL LIVING
SIMPLY ORGANIC

THE GILLETTE COMPANY
(Group of The Procter & Gamble Company)
(aka Global Gillette)
1 Gillette Pk
Boston, MA 02127
Tel.: (617) 421-7000
Telex: 6817060
Web Site: www.gillette.com
Sales Range: $5-14.9 Billion
Approx. Number Employees: 28,700
Year Founded: 1901
Business Description:
Consumer Products Mfr
S.I.C.: 2844; 2841; 3421; 3423; 3433
N.A.I.C.S.: 325620; 325611; 332211; 332212; 333414
Import Export
Advertising Expenditures: $966,000,000
Media: 3-6-8-9-14-15-16-17-18-21-23-24
Distr.: Intl.; Natl.
Personnel:
Kathy Lane *(CIO & Sr VP)*
Mary Ann Pesce *(Pres-Personal Care)*
James Moorhead *(Dir-Mktg Assoc)*
David Palmer *(Brand Mgr-Gillette Clinical Strength)*

Brands & Products:
AAPRI
AGILITY
ANSWER
ARISTA
ARRAY
ATRA
ATRA PLUS
BARE ELEGANCE
BEHAVE
BIG BODY
BOBBI
BODY FLOWERS
BRAUN
BRAUN HAND BLENDER
BRAUN SYNCRO
BRUSH PLUS
BRUSH UP
CLC
CLEAR BENEFIT
CLEAR DIFFERENCE
COMPLTE SKINCARE
CONTOURPLUS
CROSSACTION
CURL FREE
CURL-OIL MOISTURE BALANCER
CURVE'N BODY
CUSTOM PLUS
DAISY
DAISY PLUS
DEEP MAGIC
DENTAL CENTER
DRIVE
DUNE
DURACELL
DURACELL ULTRA
EARTH BORN
EPIC
EXTREME SPORT
FEEL FREE
FINGER PINKIES
FLEX CONTROL
FLEXISOFT
FOAMY
FOHO FOR OILY HAIR ONLY
FOOT GUARD
FREE 'N EASY
FUSION CHROME COLLECTION
GILLETTE
GILLETTE AGILITY
GILLETTE ANTI-PERSPIRANT
GILLETTE BLUE BLADES
GILLETTE FOR WOMEN
GILLETTE SENSOR
GILLETTE SERIES
GILLETTE SERIES COOL WAVE
GILLETTE SERIES WILD RAIN
GILLETTE SUPER BLUE BLADES
GILLETTE SUPER-SPEED
GOOD NEWS
GOOD NEWS PIVOT PLUS
GYRO
HAPPY FACE
HEADS UP
HEART
HOLD & CLEAN
THE HOT ONE
HUMMING BIRD
INTERSPACE
JUST WHISTLE
THE KNACK
LEMON UP
LOOK OF NATURE
LUSTRA COLORS
M 3 POWER
MACH 3 TURBO
MACH3
MARINER'S
MICROTRAC
MY ISLANDS
MYOKO
NO-SHA
OFF-HAND
ORAL-B
PAPERCREME
PC-123
PLAQUE REMOVER
PLATINUM-PLUS
POR EQUAL
PRESTOBARBAMAX PLUS
PRISMATICS
PROBAK
PROBAK JR.
PROM
THE REAL CURL
RIGHT-ON
RIGHT-ON CURL
RIGHT-ON RIGHT BACK
ROLLER PERM
SATIN CARE
SENSOR
SENSOR EXCEL
SENSOR FOR WOMEN
SENSOR3
SILK-EPIL
SILKIENCE
SILVER CURL
SOFT TOUCH
SPIN
STATIC
SWIVEL
TAG
TECH-RAZOR
TIP TONI
TONETTE
TONI LIGHTWAVES
TONI SILKWAVE
TRAC II
TRINITY
VALET AUTO-STROP
VENUS
VENUS DIVINE
VENUS EMBRACE
VITALIZER
WIDGET
WILD RAIN
X-HYDRA

Advertising Agencies:
BBDO New York
1285 Ave of the Americas 7th Fl
New York, NY 10019-6028
Tel.: (212) 459-5000
(Non-Electric Shaving Supplies for Men & Women, Oral Care Products & Duracell Batteries)
Rembrandt
Venus Embrace
— Peter Geary *(Exec VP & Sr Acct Dir)*

Ketchum
(Part of Omnicom)
1285 Ave of the Americas
New York, NY 10019
Tel.: (646) 935-3900
Fax: (646) 935-4482
External Relations Agency of Record
PR

Saatchi & Saatchi X
375 Hudson St
New York, NY 10014-3660
Tel.: (212) 463-2000
Fax: (212) 463-2438
Fusion

GLAXOSMITHKLINE CONSUMER HEALTHCARE
(Sub. of GlaxoSmithKline Plc)
1000 GSK Dr
Moon Township, PA 15108
Mailing Address:
PO Box 1467
Moon Township, PA 15108
Tel.: (412) 200-4000
Fax: (412) 249-4521
Toll Free: (800) 456-6670
Telex: 506468
Web Site: www.gsk.com
Approx. Number Employees: 2,000
Business Description:
Consumer Healthcare Product Mfr
S.I.C.: 2834; 2841; 2844
N.A.I.C.S.: 325412; 325611; 325620
Export
Media: 6-8-9-10-13-14-15-18-19-20-21-23-24
Distr.: Natl.

Key to Media (For complete agency information see *The Advertising Red Books-Agencies* edition):
1. Bus. Publs. 2. Cable T.V. 3. Catalogs & Directories. 4. Co-op Adv. 5. Consumer Mags. 6. D.M. to Bus. Estab.7. D.M. to Consumers
8. Daily Newsp. 9. Exhibits/Trade Shows 10. Foreign 11. Infomercial 12. Internet Adv.13. Multimedia 14. Network Radio
15. Network T.V. 16. Newsp. Distr. Mags. 17. Other 18. Outdoor (Posters, Transit) 19. Point of Purchase20. Premiums, Novelties
21. Product Samples 22. Special Events Mktg. 23. Spot Radio 24. Spot T.V. 25. Weekly Newsp. 26. Yellow Page Adv.

Budget Set: Dec.
Personnel:
John Graham *(CMO-North America)*
Roger Scarlett-Smith *(Pres-Consumer Healthcare-North America)*
Emma Walmsley *(Pres-Europe)*
Christopher Rich *(Sr VP-Wellness Bus Unit-Global)*
Karen Scollick *(VP-Behavioral Sciences)*
Joe Cadle *(Dir-Mktg-Weight Control Products)*
Amardeep Kahlon *(Dir-Mktg-Behavioral Sciences)*
Debbie Weis *(Dir-Bus Dev)*
Michele Klingensmith *(Sr Brand Mgr-Aquafresh White Trays)*
Karen L. Schade *(Sr Mgr)*
Chris Saltmar *(Mgr-Brand Innovation-Nicorette)*
Patrick Seiffert *(Sr Brand Mgr)*
Stacey Harris *(Mgr-Mktg)*
Advertising Agencies:
Arnold Worldwide
101 Huntington Ave
Boston, MA 02199-7603
Tel.: (617) 587-8000
Fax: (617) 587-8004
Alli
Nicorette
Commit
NicoDerm CQ

MediaCom
498 7th Ave
New York, NY 10018
Tel.: (212) 912-4200
Fax: (212) 508-4386
(Media)

GOLD MEDAL HAIR PRODUCTS, INC.
1 Bennington Ave
Freeport, NY 11520-3953
Tel.: (516) 378-6900
Fax: (516) 378-0168
Toll Free: (800) 324-7136
E-mail: customerservice@goldmedalhair.com
Web Site: www.goldmedalhair.com
Approx. Number Employees: 10
Year Founded: 1942
Business Description:
Hair-Care Products, Curling Irons & Skin-Care Products Mfr & Mail Order Catalog Retailer
S.I.C.: 5961; 2844
N.A.I.C.S.: 454113; 325620
Import Export
Media: 4-6-8-13
Distr.: Intl.; Natl.
Budget Set: Monthly
Personnel:
Richard Laban *(Pres)*
Rhonda Friedman *(Dir-Adv)*
Brands & Products:
ALL SWEPT UP
ALL WOMEN
BLEND
BODY SHAPER
CARBONOEL
CELLU SOLVE
CURLS & PAGE BOY
DOUBLE CURL
EASY WAVE
ELEGANT
FANNI BRA
FIESTA
GOLD MEDAL HAIR
HAIR A WAY
INSTANT HAIR
JERRI FALL
LAN-O-TRESS
MARKHIDE
MEDALO
N-K PEACHES & CREAM FACIAL
POWER GRO
SECRET HIPS
SECRET PADS
SHIM SKIN
SMOKE ODOR KLEEN
SUPER NAIL GRO
TOP SECRET-SHAPER
TRIM DOWN
WAIST NIPPER

GOODY PRODUCTS, INC.
(Sub. of Newell Rubbermaid Inc.)
400 Galleria Pkwy Ste 1100
Atlanta, GA 30339
Tel.: (770) 418-7300
Fax: (770) 615-4740
Toll Free: (800) 631-8832
E-mail: feedback@goody.com
Web Site: www.goody.com
Sales Range: $800-899.9 Million
Approx. Number Employees: 800
Year Founded: 1907
Business Description:
Hair Rollers, Barrettes, Headbands, Combs, Brushes, Clips, Pins, Shower Caps & Mirrors Mfr
S.I.C.: 5499; 5122; 5912
N.A.I.C.S.: 446191; 446110; 446120
Import Export
Media: 2-4-5-6-10-19-22
Distr.: Intl.; Natl.
Budget Set: Nov.
Personnel:
Steve Jennings *(VP-Sls)*
Amy Cullen *(Mgr-Channel Mktg)*
Brands & Products:
ACE
GOODY
GOODY TRAVEL
Advertising Agencies:
Ashworth Associates, Inc.
745 danforth avenue Suite 303
Toronto, ON M4J 1L4, Canada
Tel.: (416) 603-6005
Fax: (416) 603-9272
Canadian Pub Rels

Creative Media Marketing
594 Broadway Ste 500
New York, NY 10012
Tel.: (212) 979-8884
Fax: (212) 979-8577
Toll Free: (888) 826-6477
Pub Rels

GREAT CLIPS, INC.
7700 France Ave S Ste 425
Minneapolis, MN 55435
Tel.: (952) 893-9088
Fax: (952) 844-3444
Toll Free: (800) 999-5959
Web Site: www.greatclips.com
Approx. Number Employees: 200
Year Founded: 1982
Business Description:
Hair Salons Franchiser
S.I.C.: 7231
N.A.I.C.S.: 812112
Media: 1-3-5-7-8-9-10-16-18-21-23-24-25-26
Distr.: Natl.
Budget Set: Oct.
Personnel:
Ray Barton *(Chm)*
Charlie Simpson *(Pres)*
Rhoda Olsen *(CEO)*
Steve Overholzer *(CFO)*
Dean Wieber *(Exec VP-New Bus Dev)*
Stephen Hockett *(Sr VP-Ops)*
Terry Miller *(VP-Mktg & Comm)*
Nancy Uden *(VP-Franchise Svcs & HR)*
Brands & Products:
DETOUR
GREAT CLIPS
TEA TREE
Advertising Agencies:
Campbell Mithun, Inc.
Campbell Mithun Tower 222 S 9th St
Minneapolis, MN 55402-3389
Tel.: (612) 347-1000
Fax: (612) 347-1515

Compass Point Media
222 S 9th St
Minneapolis, MN 55402-3362
Tel.: (612) 347-6900
Fax: (612) 347-6969

LaBreche
500 Washington Ave S Ste 2020
Minneapolis, MN 55415
Tel.: (612) 338-0901
Fax: (612) 338-0921

GREEN ENDEAVORS, INC.
(Sub. of Nexia Holdings, Inc.)
59 W 100 S 2nd Fl
Salt Lake City, UT 84101
Tel.: (801) 575-8073
Fax: (801) 575-8092
Web Site: www.green-endeavors.com
Approx. Rev.: $2,250,998
Approx. Number Employees: 78
Business Description:
Salon Owner & Operator
S.I.C.: 7231
N.A.I.C.S.: 812112
Advertising Expenditures: $106,207
Media: 17
Personnel:
Richard D. Surber *(Pres & CEO)*
Richard G. Clegg *(CFO)*

GURWITCH PRODUCTS, LLC
(Sub. of Alticor Inc.)
13259 N Promenade Blvd
Stafford, TX 77477
Tel.: (281) 275-7000
Fax: (281) 275-7070
Toll Free: (888) MERCIER
Web Site: www.lauramercier.com
Sales Range: $125-149.9 Million
Approx. Number Employees: 220
Business Description:
Cosmetic Products Developer, Mfr & Marketer
S.I.C.: 2844
N.A.I.C.S.: 325620
Personnel:
Claudia Poccia *(Pres & CEO)*
Ellen Greenwald *(CMO-Global)*
Advertising Agency:
Indelible Media, Corp.
535 8th Ave Fl 16
New York, NY 10018
Tel.: (212) 629-0802
Fax: (212) 629-6476
Laura Mercier Cosmetics

H2O PLUS, LLC
(Joint Venture of The Goldman Sachs Group, Inc. & The Williams Capital Group, L.P.)
845 W Madison St
Chicago, IL 60607
Tel.: (312) 850-9283
Fax: (312) 633-1470
Web Site: www.h2oplus.com
Sales Range: $75-99.9 Million
Approx. Number Employees: 150
Year Founded: 1989
Business Description:
Water-Based Skincare Products Mfr & Distr; Owned by The Goldman Sachs Group, Inc. & by The Williams Capital Group, L.P.
S.I.C.: 2844
N.A.I.C.S.: 325620
Personnel:
Bryan Butler *(CFO)*
Scott Oats *(Sr VP-Strategic Initiatives)*
Brands & Products:
OASIS
Advertising Agency:
Siren Public Relations Inc.
594 Broadway Ste 1202
New York, NY 10012
Tel.: (212) 625-3500
Fax: (212) 625-3596

HAIR CLUB FOR MEN, LTD., INC.
(Sub. of Regis Corporation)
(d/b/a Hair Club for Men and Women)
1515 S Federal Hwy Ste 401
Boca Raton, FL 33432-7450
Tel.: (561) 361-7600
Fax: (561) 361-7680
Toll Free: (888) 888-8986
Web Site: www.hairclub.com
Sales Range: $125-149.9 Million
Approx. Number Employees: 500
Year Founded: 1976
Business Description:
Hair Restoration Centers Owner & Operator
S.I.C.: 7299
N.A.I.C.S.: 812199
Media: 3-6-8-12-13-15
Personnel:
Darryll Porter *(Pres & CEO)*
Brands & Products:
BIO-FUSE
BIO-MATRIX
EXT-EXTREME HAIR THERAPY
HAIR CLUB
HAIR CLUB FOR KIDS
HAIR CLUB FOR MEN
HAIR CLUB FOR WOMEN
MAKING YOU LOOK GOOD IS WHAT WE DO BEST
MAXXAM
POLYFUSE
STRAND-BY-STRAND
THE TIME IS RIGHT
Advertising Agency:
HCA (Hair Club Advertising)
1515 S Federal Hwy Ste 401
Boca Raton, FL 33432
Tel.: (561) 361-7600
Fax: (561) 361-7685

Key to Media (For complete agency information see *The Advertising Red Books-Agencies* edition):
1. Bus. Publs. 2. Cable T.V. 3. Catalogs & Directories. 4. Co-op Adv. 5. Consumer Mags. 6. D.M. to Bus. Estab.7. D.M. to Consumers
8. Daily Newsp. 9. Exhibits/Trade Shows 10. Foreign 11. Infomercial 12. Internet Adv.13. Multimedia 14. Network Radio
15. Network T.V. 16. Newsp. Distr. Mags. 17. Other 18. Outdoor (Posters, Transit) 19. Point of Purchase20. Premiums, Novelties
21. Product Samples 22. Special Events Mktg. 23. Spot Radio 24. Spot T.V. 25. Weekly Newsp. 26. Yellow Page Adv.

THE HAIR CUTTERY
(Div. of The Ratner Companies)
1577 Spring Hill Rd Ste 500
Vienna, VA 22182
Tel.: (703) 698-7090
Fax: (703) 269-5390
Web Site: www.haircuttery.com
Approx. Number Employees: 8
Year Founded: 1974
Business Description:
Beauty Shops
S.I.C.: 7231
N.A.I.C.S.: 812112
Advertising Agency:
TBC Inc.
900 S Wolfe St
Baltimore, MD 21231
Tel.: (410) 347-7500
Fax: (410) 986-1299

HELEN OF TROY LIMITED
1 Helen of Troy Plz
El Paso, TX 79912-1148
Tel.: (915) 225-8000
Fax: (915) 225-8004
Web Site: www.hotus.com
Approx. Rev.: $777,043,000
Approx. Number Employees: 1,317
Year Founded: 1968
Business Description:
Hair Care Appliances Designer, Developer & Marketer
S.I.C.: 3634; 3999
N.A.I.C.S.: 335211; 339999
Import Export
Advertising Expenditures: $34,990,000
Media: 2-4-5-6-8-9-10-15-19-24-25
Distr.: Natl.
Budget Set: Oct.
Personnel:
Gerald J. Rubin *(Chm, Pres & CEO)*
Gary B. Abromovitz *(Deputy Chm)*
Thomas Benson *(CFO & Sr VP)*
Brian L. Grass *(Asst CFO & VP)*
Robert D. Spear *(CIO & Sr VP)*
Arthur A. August *(Pres-Prof Div)*
Alex Lee *(Pres-OXO)*
Vincent D. Carson *(Gen Counsel, Sec & Sr VP)*
Michael Cafaro *(Exec VP-New Product Dev & Mfg)*
Richard R. Dwyer *(Exec VP-Bus Ops)*
Tom Gebhart *(Sr VP & Gen Mgr-Belson Products)*
Alan Ames *(Sr VP-Sls-Accessories)*
John Boomer *(Sr VP-Intl)*
Pedro T. Contreras *(Sr VP-Global IT)*
Jack Jancin *(Sr VP-Idelle Labs)*
Larry Witt *(Sr VP-Mktg OXO)*
Bob Ballard *(VP-Mktg Retail-Personal Care Appliances)*
Debra Curry *(VP-HR)*
Scott Hagstrom *(VP-Sls-Prof Div)*
John Hunnicutt *(VP-Mktg-Idelle Labs)*
Melinda Jordan *(VP-HR)*
Mary Esther Minjares *(VP-Sls Ops & Customer Svc)*
Ricardo Placenia *(VP-Engrg & New Product Dev)*
Perry Sansone *(VP-Sls-Idelle Labs)*
Tracy Scheuerman *(VP-Fin-OXO)*
Theressa Taricco *(VP-Mktg-Pro Div)*
Scott Viola *(VP-Sls)*
Chris Weist *(VP-Fin & Strategic Plng-Retail Personal Care)*
Richard J. Oppenheim *(Controller-Fin)*
Mark Conroy *(Gen Mgr-UK, EMEA & Asia Pacific)*
Brands & Products:
AMMENS
BED HEAD
BELSON
BELSON PRO
BRAUN
BRUT
BRUT REVOLUTION
CANDELA
CAREL
CARUSO
COMARE
CONDITION 3-IN-1
CURIMASTER
DAZEY
DCNL
DR. SCHOLL?S
DURACRAFT
ECSTASY
EPIL-STOP
FINAL NET
FUSION TOOLS
GALLERY
GALLERY SERIES
GOLD N'HOT
GOLD 'N HOT
GOOD GRIPS
HEALTH O METER
HELEN OF TROY
HONEYWELL
HOT SPA
HOT TOOLS
INFUSIUM 23
ISOBEL
KARINA
MEGA HOT
NANDI
NOSQUITO
OGILVIE
OXO
OXO STEEL
OXO TOT OXO TOT
PERT PLUS
PREMIERE
PRO BEAUTY TOOLS
PROFILES
PROTEC
REVLON
SALON EDITION
SCHOLL
SEA BREEZE
SHEAR TECHNOLOGY
SKINMILK
SMART TEMP
SOFTHEAT
SOFTWORKS
STINGER
STRAIGHT TO THE MAXX
SURE
TIMEBLOCK
TONI&GUY
VEET
VICKS
VIDAL SASSOON
VITALIS
WAVE RAGE
WIGO

HILLHOUSE NATURALS FARM, LTD.
1917 Hughes Rd
Wickliffe, KY 42087
Tel.: (270) 335-3585
Fax: (270) 335-5054
Toll Free: (800) 993-2767
E-mail: joycehillhouse@aol.com
Web Site: www.hillhousenaturals.com
Sales Range: $1-9.9 Million
Approx. Number Employees: 32
Year Founded: 1986
Business Description:
Home Fragrance Products Including Potpourri, Candles, Sachets, Oils, Fragrance Mist & Pillar Candles Mfr & Retailer
S.I.C.: 2844; 5122
N.A.I.C.S.: 325620; 446120
Media: 6
Personnel:
Shelly Batts *(Pres)*

HOLLYWOOD TANNING SYSTEMS, INC.
11 Enterprise Ct
Sewell, NJ 08080-4112
Tel.: (856) 914-9090
Fax: (856) 914-9099
E-mail: info@hollywoodtan.com
Web Site: www.hollywoodtan.com
Approx. Number Employees: 50
Business Description:
Tanning Salons
S.I.C.: 6794; 7299
N.A.I.C.S.: 533110; 812199
Media: 3-8
Brands & Products:
HOLLYWOOD TANS
TANETICS

HOMESTYLE PRODUCTS LLC
147 Mill Ridge Rd
Lynchburg, VA 24502-8008
Tel.: (434) 832-8008
Fax: (434) 832-8008
Web Site:
www.homestyleproducts.net
Business Description:
Home Furnishing Products
S.I.C.: 5023
N.A.I.C.S.: 423220
Media: 4-6-8
Brands & Products:
BLAIR
FRIENDSHIP FAVORITES
HOME SHOWCASE

INFUSION BRANDS INTERNATIONAL, INC.
(Formerly OmniReliant Holdings, Inc.)
14375 Myer Lake Cir
Clearwater, FL 33760
Tel.: (727) 230-1031
Fax: (813) 885-5911
Web Site: www.infusionbrands.com
Approx. Sls.: $24,828,417
Approx. Number Employees: 19
Year Founded: 2006
Business Description:
Beauty Care Products & Fragrances Creator, Designer, Distr & Sales
S.I.C.: 2844; 3961; 5099; 5122
N.A.I.C.S.: 325620; 339914; 423990; 446120
Advertising Expenditures: $6,150,505
Media: 12-13
Personnel:
Greg Sarnow *(Pres & COO)*
Bill Barlow *(Exec VP)*
Travis Berger *(VP-Retail Sls)*
Lisa Martinez *(Dir-HR)*

INSTANTRON CO., INC.
3712 Pawtucket Ave
Riverside, RI 02915-5105
Tel.: (401) 433-6800
Fax: (401) 433-4235
Toll Free: (800) 886-6141
E-mail: sales@instantron.com
Web Site: www.instantron.com
E-Mail For Key Personnel:
Sales Director: sales@instantron.com
Approx. Sls.: $1,800,000
Approx. Number Employees: 5
Year Founded: 1880
Business Description:
Electrolysis Epilators for Permanent Hair Removal Mfr & Retailer
S.I.C.: 3634; 5999
N.A.I.C.S.: 335211; 453998
Import Export
Media: 2-4-7-10-20-26
Distr.: Intl.
Personnel:
Harold C. Mahler, Jr. *(Pres)*
Brands & Products:
CUSHMAN
IMPERIAL
INSTANTRON
LAUREN
PRO-TEC
SPECTRUM
SPRINT
SS-99

INTELLIGENT BEAUTY, LLC
2301 Rosecrans Ave Ste 4100
El Segundo, CA 90245
Tel.: (310) 683-0940
Fax: (310) 643-0776
E-mail: employment@ibinc.com
Web Site: www.ibinc.com
Approx. Number Employees: 175
Business Description:
Marketing & Brand Management
S.I.C.: 8742
N.A.I.C.S.: 541613
Media: 2-6-10-13-24
Personnel:
Bob Johnson *(Co-Founder)*
Adam Goldenberg *(Co-CEO)*
Elizabeth Francis *(CMO)*
Don Ressler *(Mgr-Warehouse)*
Brands & Products:
INTELLIGENT BEAUTY
IQ DERMA
RAWNATURALBEAUTY.COM
REDPOINT COSMETICS

INTER PARFUMS, INC.
551 5th Ave Ste 1500
New York, NY 10176
Tel.: (212) 983-2640
Fax: (212) 983-4197
Toll Free: (800) 533-6010
E-mail: bcampbell@interparfumsinc.com
Web Site: www.interparfumsinc.com
Approx. Sls.: $460,411,000
Approx. Number Employees: 271
Year Founded: 1983
Business Description:
Alternative Designer Fragrances & Cosmetics Distr
S.I.C.: 5122; 2841; 2844
N.A.I.C.S.: 446120; 325611; 325620
Import Export
Advertising Expenditures: $69,200,000

Key to Media (For complete agency information see *The Advertising Red Books-Agencies* edition):
1. Bus. Publs. 2. Cable T.V. 3. Catalogs & Directories. 4. Co-op Adv. 5. Consumer Mags. 6. D.M. to Bus. Estab.7. D.M. to Consumers
8. Daily Newsp. 9. Exhibits/Trade Shows 10. Foreign 11. Infomercial 12. Internet Adv.13. Multimedia 14. Network Radio
15. Network T.V. 16. Newsp. Distr. Mags. 17. Other 18. Outdoor (Posters, Transit) 19. Point of Purchase20. Premiums, Novelties
21. Product Samples 22. Special Events Mktg. 23. Spot Radio 24. Spot T.V. 25. Weekly Newsp. 26. Yellow Page Adv.

Media: 1-3-5-6-8-10
Distr.: Intl.; Natl.
Personnel:
Jean Madar *(Chm & CEO)*
Philippe Benacin *(Pres)*
Russell Greenberg *(CFO & Exec VP)*
Michel Bes *(Pres-Sls)*
Andy Clarke *(Pres-Specialty Retail Div)*
Brands & Products:
APPLE
AZIZA
CAPTAIN
EURO COLLECTIONS
INTER PARFUMS, INC.
INTIMATE
JEAN PHILIPPE
LANVIN
LORD
NICKEL
PARFUMS MOLYNEUX
QUARTZ
REGAL COLLECTIONS
ROYAL SELECTIONS
Advertising Agency:
Brandimage Desgrippes & Laga
990 Skokie Blvd
Northbrook, IL 60062
Tel.: (847) 291-0500
Fax: (847) 291-0516

INTERNATIONAL FLAVORS & FRAGRANCES INC.

521 W 57th St
New York, NY 10019-2901
Tel.: (212) 765-5500
Fax: (212) 708-7132
E-mail: corporate.communications@iff.com
Web Site: www.iff.com
Approx. Sls.: $2,622,862,000
Approx. Number Employees: 5,500
Year Founded: 1909
Business Description:
Flavors, Fragrances & Aroma Chemicals Developer & Producer
S.I.C.: 2819; 2869; 2899
N.A.I.C.S.: 325188; 325199; 325998
Import Export
Media: 2-6-9-10-11-21
Distr.: Intl.; Natl.
Budget Set: Dec.
Personnel:
Douglas Tough *(Chm & CEO)*
Kevin Berryman *(CFO & Exec VP)*
Nicolas Mirzayantz *(Pres-Fragrances)*
Hernan Vaisman *(Pres-Flavors Grp)*
Anne Chwat *(Gen Counsel, Sec & Sr VP)*
Beth E. Ford *(Exec VP & Head-Supply Chain)*
Ahmet Baydar *(Sr VP-R&D)*
Matt Frost *(Global Mktg Dir)*
Judith Gross *(Dir-Global Fragrance Innovation)*
Amanda Anastasiou *(Sr Mgr-Mktg-Global Personal Wash)*
P. Ramesh Babu *(Mgr-R & D-Chemicals)*
Brands & Products:
AURA OF AROMA
BACDANOL
BORNAFIX
CASHMERAN
CASSIFIX
CEDRAMBER
CITRALVA
COCAL
COOLTEK
CYCLACET
CYCLAPROP
CYCLOGALBANIFF
DULCINYL
FLEXIMINT
FRAGRANCES OF LIFE
GALAXOLIDE
GENERESSENCE
HELIONAL
IFF
IPLOT
ISO E SUPER
JESSEMAL
KHARISMAL
KOAVONE
KOHINOOL
KUMARONE
LIFFAROME
LINDENOL
LIVING FLOWER
LIVING FRUIT
LYRAL
MEIJIFF
MONTAVERDI
PAMPLEFLEUR
PARADIFF
PHENAFLEUR
PHENOXANOL
POLYIFF
ROBUSTONE
ROMANCE OF FLOWERS
SANTALIFF
STRAWBERIFF
TETRAHYDRO MUGUOL
TRIMOFIX
TRIPLAL
UNIPINE
VANDOR
VERDOX
VERTENEX
VERTOFIX
Advertising Agency:
Redscope
619 W 54th St 7th Fl
New York, NY 10010
Tel.: (212) 505-3100
Fax: (212) 582-2152

INVERNESS CORPORATION

(Sub. of Cookson Precious Metals)
PO Box 2973 6 Hazel St
Attleboro, MA 02703
Tel.: (774) 203-1130
Toll Free: (800) 255-8556
Toll Free: (800) 423-2060
Web Site: www.invernesscorp.com
Approx. Number Employees: 17,000
Year Founded: 1974
Business Description:
Jewelry & Hair Removal Products; Ear-piercing Systems; Jewelry Cleaners & Personal Care Jewelry Products; Professional Waxing Systems Mfr & Marketer
S.I.C.: 7299; 3841
N.A.I.C.S.: 812199; 339112
Import Export
Advertising Expenditures: $1,000,000
Media: 1-2-4-5-6-10-15-16-19-24-25
Distr.: Direct to Consumer; Intl.; Natl.
Budget Set: Mar.
Personnel:
Judi Toczylowski *(VP-Sls & Mktg)*
Mike Fitzgerald *(Dir-Mktg)*
Brands & Products:
BABY PIERCER
EAR CARE ANTISEPTIC
GIFT OF EAR PIERCING
INVERNESS 1000
INVERNESS 2000
KLIKXX
PERSONAL PIERCER

IREDALE MINERAL COSMETICS LTD.

28 Church St
Great Barrington, MA 01230
Tel.: (413) 644-9900
Fax: (413) 644-9105
Toll Free: (800) 817-5665
E-mail: info@janeiredale.com
Web Site: www.janeiredale.com
Approx. Number Employees: 60
Year Founded: 1994
Business Description:
Cosmetics Mfr & Retailer
S.I.C.: 2844; 2841; 5122
N.A.I.C.S.: 325620; 325611; 446120
Media: 6-10
Personnel:
Jane Iredale *(Founder, Pres & CEO)*
Theresa Robison *(VP-Sls & Mktg)*
Brands & Products:
AMAZING BASE
BALANCE
CIRCLE/DELETE
COVERCARE
HOLIDAY PUREGLOSS
LIP DRINK
LIQUID MINERALS
MAGIC MITT
PUREBROW
PUREGLOSS
PURELASH
PUREMATTE
PUREMOIST
PUREPRESSED
THE SKIN CARE MAKEUP
Advertising Agency:
Lippe Taylor
215 Park Ave S 16th Fl
New York, NY 10003
Tel.: (212) 598-4400
Fax: (212) 598-0620

J. STRICKLAND & COMPANY

10420 Desoto Rd
Olive Branch, MS 38654-5301
Tel.: (662) 890-2306
Fax: (662) 890-1154
Toll Free: (800) 366-7853
E-mail: info@jstrickland.net
Web Site: www.jstrickland.net
Approx. Number Employees: 125
Year Founded: 1936
Business Description:
Hair & Skin Care Products & Cosmetics Mfr
S.I.C.: 2844; 5122
N.A.I.C.S.: 325620; 446120
Export
Media: 1-3-4-5-6-7-8-10-11-13-18-19-20-21-23-24-25
Distr.: Intl.; Natl.
Budget Set: Oct.
Personnel:
Linda Clifton *(Pres)*
James E. McKelroy *(Exec VP & VP-Fin)*
N. G. Tercy *(Dir-PR & Personnel)*
Donald Baldock *(Coord-Adv)*
Brands & Products:
AFRICAN GOLD
ARTRA
BLUE MAGIC
GLOVER'S
HOYT
JUST SO
NADINOLA
OTHINE
ROYAL CROWN
SULFUR-8
WORLDS OF CURLS
ZURI

JAMES GRIFFITH SALON

257 Tamiami Trl S
Venice, FL 34285
Tel.: (941) 484-2665
Tel.: (941) 486-0915
Fax: (941) 484-5436
E-mail: info@jamesgriffithsalon.com
Approx. Number Employees: 22
Business Description:
Beauty Salons
S.I.C.: 7231
N.A.I.C.S.: 812112
Media: 3-6-9-13-25
Personnel:
James Griffith *(Owner)*

JASON NATURAL PRODUCTS INC.

(Sub. of The Hain Celestial Group, Inc.)
(d/b/a Jason Natural Cosmetics)
8468 Warner Dr
Culver City, CA 90232
Tel.: (310) 838-7543
Fax: (310) 353-9580
Toll Free: (877) 527-6601
E-mail: jmp@jason-natrual.com
Web Site: www.jason-natural.com
Sales Range: $25-49.9 Million
Approx. Number Employees: 100
Business Description:
All Natural Health & Beauty Products Mfr & Distr
S.I.C.: 2844
N.A.I.C.S.: 325620
Import Export
Media: 6-10-20-21-22
Brands & Products:
A-PLEX
A-PLEX3
APRICOT SCRUBBLE
BALANCING ASTRINGENT
BEAUTIFUL LEGS & FABULOUS FEET
BURP BUSTER
C-LIGHT
"C" MY LIPS
CAP-MAX
CAP-MAX6
CITRUS 6-IN-1
D-CLOG
DANDRUFF RELIEF
DEEP-C
DUAL FUSION
ESTER-C
FABULOUS FEET
FEELIN' WONDERFUL
FOREST ESSENCE
FRESH FACE
HEALTHY MOUTH
HEMP
HI-SHINE MENDS ENDS
HYPER-C SERUM
IN BALANCE WITH NATURE

Key to Media (For complete agency information see *The Advertising Red Books-Agencies* edition):
1. Bus. Publs. 2. Cable T.V. 3. Catalogs & Directories. 4. Co-op Adv. 5. Consumer Mags. 6. D.M. to Bus. Estab.7. D.M. to Consumers 8. Daily Newsp. 9. Exhibits/Trade Shows 10. Foreign 11. Infomercial 12. Internet Adv.13. Multimedia 14. Network Radio 15. Network T.V. 16. Newsp. Distr. Mags. 17. Other 18. Outdoor (Posters, Transit) 19. Point of Purchase20. Premiums, Novelties 21. Product Samples 22. Special Events Mktg. 23. Spot Radio 24. Spot T.V. 25. Weekly Newsp. 26. Yellow Page Adv.

Jason Natural Products Inc. — (Continued)

JASON NATURAL
JOJOBA
KIDS ONLY
NATURAL THIGH RX
NATURAL THIGH THERAPY
NEW CELL EYE AREA THERAPY
NEW CELL THERAPY
NUTRISMILE
ORAL COMFORT
POWER PRIMER
POWERSMILE
PRO SOY MAX
PRO-VITAMIN THIN-TO-THICK
QUICK CLEAN
QUICKIES
RE-HYDRATING FRESHENER
REFRESHING CLEANSER
REHAB
SEA FRESH
SEA RESULTS
SEXYFRESH
SHAVING LOTION FOR BEAUTIFUL LEGS
SKIN-AMINS
SOY MAX
STUCK-UP
SUNBRELLAS
SUPER-C
SUPER-C CLEANSER
SUPER-C TONER
SWIMMERS & SPORTS
TALL GRASS
TEA TREE
THERAPY
THIN TO THICK
TWO-NIGHT WATCH
ULTRA-C
VEGE WAX FLOSS
VITA-C MAX
WILD YAM
WOMEN WISE

JINNY BEAUTY SUPPLY CO. INC.
3505 N Kimball Ave
Chicago, IL 60618
Tel.: (773) 588-7200
Fax: (773) 588-5600
Toll Free: (800) 535-6110
E-mail: sales@jinny.com
Web Site: www.jinny.com
E-Mail For Key Personnel:
Sales Director: sales@jinny.com
Approx. Number Employees: 35
Business Description:
Ethnic Beauty Supply Whslr & Distr
S.I.C.: 5122
N.A.I.C.S.: 424210
Media: 10-26
Personnel:
Eddie Jhin *(Pres)*

JOHN PAUL MITCHELL SYSTEMS
9701 Wilshire Blvd Ste 1205
Beverly Hills, CA 90212
Tel.: (310) 248-3888
Fax: (310) 248-2780
E-mail: bhreception@jpms.com
Web Site: www.paulmitchell.com
Sales Range: $800-899.9 Million
Approx. Number Employees: 100
Year Founded: 1980
Business Description:
Hair Preparations Mfr & Distr
S.I.C.: 5122
N.A.I.C.S.: 424210
Import Export
Media: 6-15-19
Personnel:
John DeJoria *(Chm & CEO)*
Luke Jacobellis *(Pres)*
Rick Battaglini *(VP-Fin)*
Nikola Cline *(Dir-Mktg)*
Brands & Products:
AWAPUHI
AWAPUHI MOISTURE MIST
BABY DON'T CRY
COLOR PROTECT
COLOR SHAMPOO
THE CONDITIONER
THE CREAM
DEFINING POMADE
THE DETANGLER
DRY WAX
ENHANCING FOAM
ESP
EXPRESS STYLE
EXTRA BODY
FAST DRYING SCULPTING SPRAY
FINISHING SPRAY
FIRM FINISHING SPRAY
FOAMING POMMADE
FREEZE AND SHINE
FREEZE AND SHINE SUPER SPRAY
FRIZZ CALMPLEX
GLOSS DROPS
HAIR REPAIR TREATMENT
HAIR SCULPTING
HAIR SCULPTING LOTION
HEAT SEAL
ILLUMINATING SHINE SPRAY
INKWORKS
INSTANT MOISTURE
LAB
LITE DETANGLER
THE MASQUE
MODERN ELIXIRS
PAUL MITCHELL
PAUL MITCHELL LAB
PM SHINES
QUICK SLIP
RE-WORKS
REFINING CONDITIONER
REFINING SHAMPOO
THE RELAXER
THE RINSE
ROUND TRIP
SCULPTING FOAM
SEAL AND SHINE
THE SHINE
SHINES
SLICK WORKS
SOFT SCULPTING SPRAY GEL
SOFT SPRAY
SPRAY WAX
STRAIGHT WORKS
STYLING CREME
STYLING SERUM
SUPER-CHARGED MOISTURIZER
SUPER CLEAN
SUPER CLEAN EXTRA
SUPER CLEAN LIGHT
SUPER CLEAN SCULPTING GEL
SUPER CLEAN SPRAY
SUPER SCULPT
SUPER SKINNY
THE SUPER STRENGTHENER
SUPER STRONG
TAMING SPRAY
TEA TREE
TEA TREE SPECIAL
TEXTURIZING BALM
VOLUMIZING SPRAY
THE WASH
WAX WORKS
XTG

JOICO LABORATORIES INC.
(Sub. of Zotos International, Inc.)
488 E Santa Clara Ste 301
Arcadia, CA 91006
Mailing Address:
PO Box 42308
Los Angeles, CA 90042-0308
Tel.: (626) 321-4100
Toll Free: (800) 44-JOICO
Toll Free: (800) 805-6426
E-mail: info@joico.com
Web Site: www.joico.com
Approx. Number Employees: 200
Year Founded: 1975
Business Description:
Salon Products & Services
S.I.C.: 2844
N.A.I.C.S.: 325620
Import Export
Media: 6-8-13-19-21-22
Personnel:
Sid Cook *(Global VP-Sls & Education)*

JOLEN CREME BLEACH CORP.
25 Walls Dr Ste 1
Fairfield, CT 06824
Mailing Address:
PO Box 458
Fairfield, CT 06824-0458
Tel.: (203) 259-8779
Fax: (203) 259-2389
E-mail: jolen.creme.bleach@snet.net
Approx. Number Employees: 15
Year Founded: 1965
Business Description:
Cream Bleach for Superfluous Hair Mfr & Whslr
S.I.C.: 5122
N.A.I.C.S.: 424210
Export
Media: 5-6
Distr.: Direct to Consumer; Intl.; Natl.
Personnel:
Evelyn K. Kossak *(Pres)*
Herman Kranes *(Mgr-Production)*
Brands & Products:
JOLEN
Advertising Agency:
K&K Advertising Associates
PO Box 458
Fairfield, CT 06824-0458
Tel.: (203) 255-4449
Fax: (203) 259-2389

KAO BRANDS CO. INC.
(Sub. of Kao Corporation)
2535 Spring Grove Ave
Cincinnati, OH 45214-1773
Mailing Address:
PO Box 145444
Cincinnati, OH 45250-5444
Tel.: (513) 421-1400
Fax: (513) 455-5499
Toll Free: (800) 742-8798
Web Site: www.kaobrands.com
Sales Range: $50-74.9 Million
Approx. Number Employees: 560
Year Founded: 1882
Business Description:
Lotions & Soaps Mfr
S.I.C.: 2841
N.A.I.C.S.: 325611
Import Export
Advertising Expenditures: $15,000,000
Media: 3-6-9-13-15-18-19-23-24
Distr.: Natl.
Budget Set: Bi-annually
Personnel:
William J. Gentner *(Pres & CEO)*
David Stern *(Global CMO & Sr VP)*
Joseph Workman *(Sr VP-Fin & Ops)*
Judy Beaudry *(VP-Global Mktg Svcs)*
Paul Tutt *(Sr Dir-Mktg & Bus Dev)*
Brands & Products:
ATTACK
BAN
BIO BEEDS
BIORE
BLAUNE
BUB
CLEAR CLEAN
CURED
CUREL
ESSENTIAL
FAMILY
GENTLE TOUCH
GLASS QUICKLE
HAITER
HUMMING 1/3
JENNE
JERGENS
JUST
LAVENUS
LIESE
MAGICLEAN
MERIT
MORE
NEW BEADS
QUICKLE
QUICKLE WIPER
SOFINA
SOFINA AUBE
SOFT SENSE
TOUCH
TSUYADASHI MYPET
ZAV
Advertising Agencies:
Enlighten
3027 Miller Rd
Ann Arbor, MI 48103
Tel.: (734) 668-6678
Fax: (734) 668-1883

Holland Advertising:Interactive
700 Walnut St Ste 205
Cincinnati, OH 45202-2011
Tel.: (513) 744-3000
Fax: (513) 721-1269

Initiative Worldwide
(Part of The Interpublic Group of Companies, Inc.)
1 Dag Hammerskjold Plz 5th Fl
New York, NY 10017
Tel.: (212) 605-7000
Fax: (212) 605-7200

KARINA INC.
(Sub. of Helen of Troy Limited)
1 Helen of Troy Plz
El Paso, TX 79912
Tel.: (915) 834-2500
Fax: (915) 845-1652
Toll Free: (800) 654-3548
Sales Range: $75-99.9 Million
Approx. Number Employees: 100
Year Founded: 1972

Key to Media (For complete agency information see *The Advertising Red Books-Agencies* edition):
1. Bus. Publs. 2. Cable T.V. 3. Catalogs & Directories. 4. Co-op Adv. 5. Consumer Mags. 6. D.M. to Bus. Estab.7. D.M. to Consumers 8. Daily Newsp. 9. Exhibits/Trade Shows 10. Foreign 11. Infomercial 12. Internet Adv.13. Multimedia 14. Network Radio 15. Network T.V. 16. Newsp. Distr. Mags. 17. Other 18. Outdoor (Posters, Transit) 19. Point of Purchase20. Premiums, Novelties 21. Product Samples 22. Special Events Mktg. 23. Spot Radio 24. Spot T.V. 25. Weekly Newsp. 26. Yellow Page Adv.

Business Description:
Distr of Decorative Hair Accessories
S.I.C.: 5131; 5199
N.A.I.C.S.: 424310; 424990
Advertising Expenditures:
$15,000,000
Media: 4-6-9-19
Distr.: Natl.
Budget Set: Feb.
Personnel:
Gerald J. Rubin *(Pres & CEO)*
Brands & Products:
KARINA GIRL

KERSTIN FLORIAN, INC.
20492 Crescent Bay Dr Ste 100
Lake Forest, CA 92630
Tel.: (949) 595-4300
Fax: (949) 206-4557
Toll Free: (800) 233-6629
Toll Free: (888) KERSTIN
Web Site: www.kerstinflorian.com
Approx. Number Employees: 23
Business Description:
Skin Care Products
S.I.C.: 2844; 2841
N.A.I.C.S.: 325620; 325611
Media: 6-10
Personnel:
Kerstin Florian *(Owner)*
Julie Andrews *(Dir-Mktg & PR)*
Kellie Lambert *(Dir-Mktg & Adv)*

KEYSTONE LABORATORIES, INC.
1103 Kansas St
Memphis, TN 38106
Mailing Address:
PO Box 2026
Memphis, TN 38101-2026
Tel.: (901) 774-8860
Fax: (901) 774-0675
Toll Free: (800) 772-8860
E-mail: customerservice@keystone-labs.com
Web Site: www.keystone-labs.com
Sales Range: $450-499.9 Million
Approx. Number Employees: 20
Year Founded: 1923
Business Description:
Hair Care Products & Toiletries Mfr
S.I.C.: 2844
N.A.I.C.S.: 325620
Export
Media: 4-5-6-10-19-20-21-23-24
Distr.: Intl.; Natl.
Budget Set: Nov.
Personnel:
Melinda Burns *(Owner)*
David Delbrocco *(Pres)*
Brands & Products:
BETTER BRAIDS
BETTER BRAIDS HERBAL
BETTER LOCKS
LA
LONG AID
LONG AID K7
ULTRA GLOW

KOKEN MANUFACTURING COMPANY, INC.
(Sub. of Takara Belmont Corporation)
1631 Martin Luther King Dr
Saint Louis, MO 63106
Mailing Address:
PO Box 265
Saint Louis, MO 63166-0265
Tel.: (314) 231-7383
Fax: (314) 241-7255
Toll Free: (800) 325-7373
Web Site: www.takarabelmont.com
Approx. Number Employees: 92
Business Description:
Barber & Beauty Shop Equipment Mfr
S.I.C.: 2531
N.A.I.C.S.: 337127
Import Export
Media: 2-4-8-10
Distr.: Natl.
Budget Set: Jan.
Personnel:
Larry Handle *(VP & Gen Mgr)*

KOLMAR LABS GROUP
50 Tice Blvd
Woodcliff Lake, NJ 07677
Tel.: (201) 782-0404
Fax: (201) 782-0246
E-mail: info@kolmar.com
Web Site: www.kolmarlabsgroup.com
Approx. Number Employees: 1,000
Business Description:
Mfr of Cosmetics, Personal Care Products, Dissolvable Film Packettes & Dry-Coated Non-Wovens
S.I.C.: 2844
N.A.I.C.S.: 325620
Media: 2-13
Personnel:
Joseph M. Healy *(Chm)*
Robert E. Blanchard *(Vice Chm & CEO)*
Robert E. Theroux *(CEO)*
Nancy Strojny *(Sr VP-Sls & Mktg)*

KRONOS LLC
2301 Rosecrans Ave Ste 4100
Manhattan Beach, CA 90245-4967
Toll Free: (866) 548-2906
E-mail: hello@kronoshair.com
Web Site: www.kronoshair.com
Business Description:
Age Corrective Hair Care Products
S.I.C.: 7231
N.A.I.C.S.: 812112
Media: 13
Personnel:
Courtney Kretchman *(Mgr-PR)*
Kimberly Tobman *(Dir-PR)*

LA FEMME PERFUMERY INC.
351 12th Ave S
Naples, FL 34102
Tel.: (239) 434-7444
Web Site:
www.lafemmeperfumerynaples.com
Approx. Number Employees: 10
Year Founded: 1984
Business Description:
Perfume & Cosmetics
S.I.C.: 5122; 7231
N.A.I.C.S.: 446120; 812112
Media: 6-8
Personnel:
Michael Elden *(Pres)*

LADY PRIMROSE'S, INC.
3631 W Davis Ste C
Dallas, TX 75211-3145
Tel.: (214) 747-7673
Fax: (214) 747-8335
Toll Free: (888) 382-7673
Toll Free: (888) 809-7673
E-mail: info@ladyprimrose.com
Web Site: www.ladyprimrose.com
Approx. Number Employees: 18
Business Description:
Bathing & Skin Products
S.I.C.: 2844; 2841
N.A.I.C.S.: 325620; 325611
Media: 6
Personnel:
Deby Fowler *(Co-Founder)*
Carolin Rose Hunter *(Co-Founder)*
Shirley Pieratt *(Pres)*

LANCASTER COSMETICS INTERNATIONAL
(Sub. of Lancaster Group US LLC)
350 5th Ave
New York, NY 10118
Tel.: (212) 389-7300
Fax: (212) 223-8064
Web Site: www.lancasterus.com
Approx. Number Employees: 800
Year Founded: 1979
Business Description:
Cosmetics Distr
S.I.C.: 5122
N.A.I.C.S.: 446120
Export
Advertising Expenditures:
$22,000,000
Media: 2-4-5-6-7-9-11-13-18-22-23-24
Distr.: Intl.; Natl.
Personnel:
Harish Manwani *(Pres)*
Brands & Products:
CALVIN
CK ONE
ESCAPE
ESCAPE FOR MEN
ETERNITY
ETERNITY FOR MEN
OBSESSION
OBSESSION FOR MEN

LANCASTER GROUP US LLC
(Div. of Coty, Inc.)
1 Park Ave 4th Fl
New York, NY 10016
Tel.: (212) 389-7000
Fax: (212) 655-3650
Web Site: www.coty.com
Approx. Number Employees: 212
Business Description:
Cosmetics & Fragrances Marketer
S.I.C.: 2844
N.A.I.C.S.: 325620
Media: 6
Personnel:
Bob Cankes *(Pres)*
Brands & Products:
LANCASTER

LANMAN & KEMP-BARCLAY CO., INC.
25 Woodland Ave
Westwood, NJ 07675
Tel.: (201) 666-4990
Fax: (201) 666-5836
Toll Free: (800) 848-5047
Telex: 642807
E-mail: sales@lanman-and-kemp.com
Web Site: www.lanman-and-kemp.com
E-Mail For Key Personnel:
Sales Director: sales@lanman-and-kemp.com
Sales Range: $10-24.9 Million
Approx. Number Employees: 15
Year Founded: 1808
Business Description:
Cologne, Soap & Hair Tonic Mfr
S.I.C.: 2841; 2844
N.A.I.C.S.: 325611; 325620
Export
Media: 7-9-10-11-19-23-24
Distr.: Intl.; Natl.
Budget Set: Oct.
Personnel:
George Miller *(Pres)*
Daisy Villegas *(Gen Mgr)*
Brands & Products:
BARRYS TRICOPHEROUS
BARRYS TRICOPHEROUS TRADITIONAL
FLORIDA WATER
FLORIDA WATER AEROSOL
JACKPOT AEROSOL
KANANGA WATER
MONEY JACKPOT SOAP
REUTER SOAP
TOUCH OF LOVE

LEVLAD, LLC
(Holding of Harvest Partners LLC)
(d/b/a Nature's Gate)
9200 Mason Ave
Chatsworth, CA 91311-6005
Tel.: (818) 882-2951
Fax: (818) 341-3840
Toll Free: (800) 327-2012
E-mail: naturesgate@worldpantry.com
Web Site: www.levlad.com
Approx. Number Employees: 270
Year Founded: 1974
Business Description:
Cosmetics & Promotional Products Mfr
S.I.C.: 2844
N.A.I.C.S.: 325620
Import Export
Advertising Expenditures: $500,000
Media: 2-4-5-6-7-10-19-20-21-23
Distr.: Intl.; Natl.
Budget Set: Monthly
Personnel:
Stephen A. Biroczky *(CEO & Mgr-Ops)*
Casi Hudson *(Dir-Mktg)*
Brands & Products:
ALOEGEN
NATURE'S GATE
ORGANICS
PETAL FRESH NATURALS

LIZ CLAIBORNE COSMETICS, INC.
(Div. of Liz Claiborne, Inc.)
1441 Broadway
New York, NY 10018
Tel.: (212) 354-4900
Fax: (212) 626-1789
Web Site: www.lizclaiborne.com
Sales Range: $75-99.9 Million
Approx. Number Employees: 240
Business Description:
Cosmetics Mfr & Retailer
S.I.C.: 2844
N.A.I.C.S.: 325620
Advertising Expenditures: $5,000,000
Media: 3-5-6-8-9-10-13-19-21-22-23-24
Distr.: Natl.
Personnel:
David Hirschler *(VP-Mktg)*
Carl Zeitz *(Dir-Mktg)*

Liz Claiborne Cosmetics, Inc. — (Continued)

Brands & Products:
BORA BORA
CURVE
LUCKY YOU
MAMBO
SPARK

L'OREAL USA, DESIGNER FRAGRANCE DIVISION

(Div. of L'Oreal USA, Inc.)
575 5th Ave
New York, NY 10017-2422
Tel.: (212) 984-4000
Fax: (212) 984-5321
Web Site: www.loreal.com
Business Description:
Mfr. of Fragrances
S.I.C.: 5122
N.A.I.C.S.: 446120
Export
Advertising Expenditures: $14,000,000
Media: 6-8-9-14-15-19-23-24
Distr.: Natl.
Budget Set: Oct.

L'OREAL USA, INC.

(Sub. of L'Oreal S.A.)
575 5th Ave
New York, NY 10017-2422
Tel.: (212) 818-1500
Tel.: (212) 984-4414 (Press Office)
Fax: (212) 984-4999
E-mail: media@us.loreal.com
Web Site: www.lorealusa.com
Sales Range: $1-4.9 Billion
Approx. Number Employees: 1,000
Year Founded: 1953
Business Description:
Hair Preparations, Cosmetics & Fragrances Mfr
S.I.C.: 2844
N.A.I.C.S.: 325620
Import Export
Advertising Expenditures: $120,000,000
Media: 2-6-7-9-14-15-16-18-19-23-24
Distr.: Natl.
Budget Set: Jan. -Dec.
Personnel:
Frederic Roze *(Pres & CEO)*
Joseph Campinell *(Pres-Consumer Products)*
Carol J. Hamilton *(Pres-Luxury Products Div)*
Rebecca A. Caruso *(Exec VP-Corp Comm)*
Roger Dolden *(Exec VP-Bus Dev & External Fin Rels)*
Pamela Gill Alabaster *(Sr VP-Corp Comm & External Affairs)*
Suzie Davidowitz *(Sr VP-Corp Comm)*
Sarah Hibberson *(Sr VP-HR)*
Richard Jones *(Sr VP-Ops-Luxury & Active Cosmetics Divisions)*
Vince Serpico *(Sr VP-Ops-North America)*
Antonis Spiliotopoulos *(Sr VP-Consumer Products Div)*
Richard Getler *(VP-Interactive & eBusiness Strategy)*
Lisa Carvalho *(VP-PR)*
Diane Lewis *(VP-HR & Talent Recruitment)*
Paul Schiraldi *(VP-Mktg)*
Patrice Blanot *(Asst VP-Ecommerce/CRM/Social Media-Armani/Yves Saint Laurent)*
Rachel Weiss *(Asst VP-Digital Strategy & Interactive Mktg)*
Henric Sark *(Gen Mgr-Active Cosmetics)*
Dian Abbey *(Dir-Pur)*
Brands & Products:
DERMABLEND
L'OREAL CLASSIC SALON PRODUCTS
L'OREAL PROFESSIONAL
L'OREAL TECHNIQUE
MIZANI
SKINCEUTICALS
SOFTSHEEN CARSON
VICHY
Advertising Agencies:
ECommerce Partners
59 Franklin St Ste 6B
New York, NY 10013
Tel.: (212) 334-3390
Fax: (503) 218-5585
Toll Free: (866) 431-6669

Moxie Interactive Inc.
The Northyards 384 Northyards Blvd NW Ste 290
Atlanta, GA 30313-2440
Tel.: (404) 601-4500
Fax: (404) 601-4505
Digital Agency of Record

Publicis USA
(Sub. of Publicis, S.A., Paris, France)
4 Herald Sq 950 6th Ave
New York, NY 10001
Tel.: (212) 279-5550
Fax: (212) 279-5560

R/GA
350 W 39th St
New York, NY 10018-1402
Tel.: (212) 946-4000
Fax: (212) 946-4010
Website

Rokkan
176 Grand St 2nd Fl
New York, NY 10012-4003
Tel.: (212) 835-9300
Fax: (212) 251-9393
Kiehl's

Universal McCann
100 33rd St 8th Fl
New York, NY 10001
Tel.: (212) 883-4700
Media Buying Assignment

ZenithOptimedia
299 W Houston St 11th Fl
New York, NY 10014
Tel.: (212) 859-5100
Fax: (212) 727-9495
Garnier
Maybelline New York
Media Planning

LUSTER PRODUCTS INC.

1104 W 43rd St
Chicago, IL 60609
Tel.: (773) 579-1800
Fax: (773) 579-1912
E-mail: lusterprod@msn.com
Web Site: www.lusterproducts.com
Approx. Number Employees: 400
Year Founded: 1957
Business Description:
Beauty Aids Mfr
S.I.C.: 2844
N.A.I.C.S.: 325620
Export
Advertising Expenditures: $1,000,000
Media: 3-4-6-10-11-19-20-21-22-23-24
Distr.: Intl.; Natl.
Budget Set: Sept.
Personnel:
Jory Luster *(Pres)*
Reginald Maynor *(Dir-Sls-Intl)*
Brenda Turner *(Dir-Mktg)*
Brands & Products:
ARTEFFEX
DESIGNER TOUCH
EARTH SECRETS
GEL'N
PCJ
PCJ PRETTY-N-SILKY
PINK
S-CURL
SASSAFRAZ
SHORT LOOKS
STRAIGHTFX
STRAIT SHADES
Advertising Agency:
Owensmorris Communications, Inc.
(d/b/a Owens Morris Communications)
29 S Lasalle St Ste 1000
Chicago, IL 60603-1502
Tel.: (312) 701-0388
Fax: (312) 701-0389

LUZIER PERSONALIZED COSMETICS, INC.

7910-7912 Troost Ave
Kansas City, MO 64131-1920
Tel.: (816) 531-8338
Fax: (816) 531-6979
Toll Free: (800) 821-6632
E-mail: customerservice@luzier.com
Web Site: www.luzier.com
Approx. Number Employees: 20
Year Founded: 1923
Business Description:
Skin Care & Cosmetics Mfr & Whslr
S.I.C.: 2844
N.A.I.C.S.: 325620
Media: 4-6-7-8-23-25-26
Distr.: Direct to Consumer; Natl.
Budget Set: Nov.
Personnel:
Kathy Grissom *(Chm & CEO)*
Kari Johnson *(Pres)*
Grant Grissom *(Chief Ops Officer)*
Brands & Products:
GRACE COLLECTION
HELLO BETTY
IMPACT FOR MEN
LUMAR
LUZIER
MIRACLE STONE
PASSIONATE PLUMERIA
SOFT 'N PERFECT
SPECIAL CARE

M.A.C. COSMETICS

(Sub. of The Estee Lauder Companies Inc.)
100 Alden Rd
Markham, ON L3R 4C1, Canada
Tel.: (905) 470-7877
Fax: (905) 470-8646
Toll Free: (800) 387-6707
Web Site: www.maccosmetics.com
Sales Range: $200-249.9 Million
Approx. Number Employees: 400
Business Description:
Cosmetics Mfr
S.I.C.: 2844
N.A.I.C.S.: 325620
Media: 6
Personnel:
Karen Buglisi *(Pres-Global Brand)*
Nancy Mahon *(Sr VP)*
Bob Dunham *(VP-Global Fin & Forecasting)*

MAJESTIC DRUG COMPANY, INC.

4996 Main St
South Fallsburg, NY 12779
Tel.: (845) 436-0011
Fax: (845) 436-0022
Toll Free: (800) 238-0220
E-mail: custserv@majesticdrug.com
Web Site: www.majesticdrug.com
E-Mail For Key Personnel:
President: larry@majesticdrug.com
Approx. Number Employees: 8
Year Founded: 1950
Business Description:
Health & Beauty Aids Mfr
S.I.C.: 5122
N.A.I.C.S.: 424210
Export
Media: 2-3-4-5-6-7-9-10-15-17
Distr.: Natl.
Personnel:
Larry Fishman *(Pres)*
Brands & Products:
DENTEMP
DENTEMP OS
DENTOOL
DENTOOL JR.
D.O.C.
FEMYSTIQUE
KUTKIT
MAJESTIC
MANDELAY
NEEDS MET
RECAPIT
RED FOX
REFILIT
SWORD FLOSS
SWORD FLOSS PROXI-PLUS
Advertising Agency:
Zodiac Advertising
PO Box 490
South Fallsburg, NY 12779
Tel.: (845) 436-0011
Fax: (845) 436-0022

MARIANNA IMPORTS INC.

11222 I St
Omaha, NE 68137
Tel.: (402) 593-0211
Fax: (402) 593-0614
Toll Free: (800) 228-9060
E-mail: marianna@mariannaind.com
Web Site: www.mariannaind.com
Approx. Sls.: $12,186,583
Approx. Number Employees: 220
Year Founded: 1964
Business Description:
Beauty Products Mfr & Distr
S.I.C.: 5122
N.A.I.C.S.: 424210
Import Export
Media: 4-10

Key to Media (For complete agency information see *The Advertising Red Books-Agencies* edition):
1. Bus. Publs. 2. Cable T.V. 3. Catalogs & Directories. 4. Co-op Adv. 5. Consumer Mags. 6. D.M. to Bus. Estab.7. D.M. to Consumers
8. Daily Newsp. 9. Exhibits/Trade Shows 10. Foreign 11. Infomercial 12. Internet Adv.13. Multimedia 14. Network Radio
15. Network T.V. 16. Newsp. Distr. Mags. 17. Other 18. Outdoor (Posters, Transit) 19. Point of Purchase20. Premiums, Novelties
21. Product Samples 22. Special Events Mktg. 23. Spot Radio 24. Spot T.V. 25. Weekly Newsp. 26. Yellow Page Adv.

Personnel:
Michael Cosentino *(Pres)*
Brands & Products:
MARIANNA

MARILYN MIGLIN, L.P.
1230 W Washington Blvd Ste100
Chicago, IL 60607
Tel.: (312) 266-4600
Fax: (312) 266-9170
Toll Free: (800) 662-1120
E-mail: mail@marilynmiglin.com
Web Site: www.marilynmiglin.com
Sales Range: $50-74.9 Million
Approx. Number Employees: 50
Year Founded: 1963
Business Description:
Cosmetics, Fragrances & Skin Care Products Mfr
S.I.C.: 5122
N.A.I.C.S.: 446120
Import Export
Advertising Expenditures: $600,000
Media: 4-6-8-10-13-19-21-22
Distr.: Direct to Consumer; Intl.; Natl.
Personnel:
Marilyn Miglin *(Partner)*
Marlena Miglin *(COO & Gen Mgr)*
Brands & Products:
DESTINY
MAGIC
MARILYN MIGLIN
MYSTIC
PERFECT BALANCE
PHEROMONE
PHEROMONE FOR MEN

MARY KAY HOLDING CORPORATION
16251 Dallas Pkwy
Addison, TX 75001-6801
Tel.: (972) 687-6300
Fax: (972) 687-1609
Toll Free: (800) 627-9529
Web Site: www.marykay.com
Approx. Number Employees: 4,000
Year Founded: 1963
Business Description:
Cosmetics & Toiletries Holding Company
S.I.C.: 2844; 5122; 6719
N.A.I.C.S.: 325620; 446120; 551112
Media: 4-6-8-10-13
Personnel:
Richard R. Rogers *(Chm)*
David B. Holl *(Pres & CEO)*
Brands & Products:
MARY KAY

MARY KAY INC.
(Sub. of Mary Kay Holding Corporation)
16251 Dallas Pkwy
Addison, TX 75001
Mailing Address:
PO Box 799045
Dallas, TX 75379-9045
Tel.: (972) 687-6300
Fax: (972) 687-1611
Toll Free: (800) MARY-KAY
Web Site: www.marykay.com
Approx. Number Employees: 1,250
Year Founded: 1963
Business Description:
Cosmetics & Toiletries Mfr & Retailer
S.I.C.: 2844; 3961
N.A.I.C.S.: 325620; 339914
Media: 6-7-8-10-21
Distr.: Intl.; Natl.
Budget Set: Sept. -Oct.
Personnel:
Richard R. Rogers *(Co-Founder & Chm)*
David B. Holl *(Pres & CEO)*
Rhonda Shasteen *(CMO)*
Nathan Moore *(Chief Legal Officer & Sec)*
Darrel Overcash *(Pres-Opers-US & Canada)*
Terry Smith *(Sr VP-Fin)*
Shannon Summers *(Dir-Mktg Commun)*
Krystal Williams *(Dir-Sls)*

MATRIX ESSENTIALS, INC.
(Sub. of L'Oreal USA, Inc.)
575 5th Ave
New York, NY 10017-2422
Tel.: (212) 818-1500
Fax: (212) 973-5321
Toll Free: (800) 282-2822
E-mail: info@matrixessentials.com
Web Site: www.matrix.com
Approx. Number Employees: 1,000
Year Founded: 1980
Business Description:
Hair Care Products Mfr
S.I.C.: 2844; 5122
N.A.I.C.S.: 325620; 446120
Export
Advertising Expenditures: $2,500,000
Media: 1-2-4-5-6-7-10-21
Distr.: Natl.
Personnel:
Pat Parenty *(Pres)*
Colin Walsh *(VP & Gen Mgr-Matrix US)*
Brands & Products:
AMPLIFY
BIOLAGE
MATRIX ESSENTIALS COSMETICS
SLEEK.LOOK
VAVOOM

MAYBELLINE, INC.
(Sub. of L'Oreal USA, Inc.)
575 5th Ave
New York, NY 10017-2422
Tel.: (212) 818-1500
E-mail: webmaster@maybelline.com
Web Site: www.maybelline.com
Approx. Number Employees: 2,000
Business Description:
Cosmetics & Cosmetic Accessories Mfr
S.I.C.: 5122; 2844
N.A.I.C.S.: 446120; 325620
Import Export
Media: 3-6-8-10-11-13-14-15-18-19-21-22
Distr.: Intl.; Natl.
Budget Set: Monthly
Personnel:
Robert B. McKeon *(Chm)*
David Greenberg *(Pres)*
Ed Trapani *(VP, Mgr-Natl Sls & Maybelline Cosmetics-NY)*
Deborah Marquardt *(VP-Media & Integrated Mktg)*
Stephanie Rinaldi *(VP-Customer Mktg, Sls Ops & Garnier)*
Lynne Addeo *(Asst VP-Sls Ops)*
Deborah Curtis *(Asst VP-Mktg)*
Denise Quattrochi *(Asst VP-Consumer Promos-Maybelline-Garnier)*
Kristen Yraola *(Asst VP-Digital Media & Internet)*
Malena Higuera *(Dir-Global Mktg)*
Brooke Reutter *(Dir-Retail Image)*
Amy Whang *(Sr Mgr-Mktg)*
Brands & Products:
BRUSH BLUSH BRONZER
COLOR DELIGHTS
COLOR SENSATIONAL
COOL EFFECT
COVER STICK
DREAM MOUSSE
DREAM SMOOTH
EVERFRESH
EXPERT EYES
EXPRESS
EYE DUETS
EYE EXPRESS
EYE STUDIO
FOREVER
GREAT WEAR
ILLEGAL LENGTHS
LASH DISCOVERY
LASH EXPANSION
LINEWORKS
LIP EXPRESS
LIQUID EYES
MAYBELLINE
MINERAL POWER
MOISTURE WHIP
PURE STAY
ROLLER COLOR
SHINE FREE
SKY HIGH CURVES
SMOOTH RESULT
TRUE ILLUSION
ULTIMATE WEAR
ULTRA-BROW
VOLUME EXPRESS
WEAR 'N GO
WET SHINE
WONDER CURL
WONDER FINISH
Advertising Agencies:
Gotham Incorporated
150 E 42nd St 12th Fl
New York, NY 10017
Tel.: (212) 414-7000
Fax: (212) 414-7095
(Maybelline Cosmetics)

MRM China
1045 Huaihai Zhong Rd
200031
Shanghai, China
Tel.: (86) 21 2411 1111
Fax: (86) 21 2411 1222
Digital Agency of Record

MCT HOLDING CORPORATION
3884 E North Little Cottonwood Rd
Salt Lake City, UT 84092
Tel.: (801) 580-4555
Approx. Rev.: $35,783
Year Founded: 2004
Business Description:
Indoor Tanning Salon Owner & Operator
S.I.C.: 7231
N.A.I.C.S.: 812112
Media: 8-9-18-25-26
Personnel:
David C. Merrell *(Pres)*
Brands & Products:
MALIBU CLUB TAN

ME SALON
11328 Montgomery Rd
Cincinnati, OH 45249
Tel.: (513) 489-9283
Web Site: www.mesalonbycara.com
Business Description:
Hair Salon
S.I.C.: 7231
N.A.I.C.S.: 812112
Media: 8
Personnel:
Cara d'Ambrosio *(Owner)*

MERLE NORMAN COSMETICS, INC.
9130 Bellanca Ave
Los Angeles, CA 90045-4710
Tel.: (310) 641-3000
Fax: (310) 216-0693
Fax: (310) 641-7144
Toll Free: (800) 421-6648
Web Site: www.merlenorman.com
Sales Range: $75-99.9 Million
Approx. Number Employees: 640
Year Founded: 1931
Business Description:
Cosmetics Mfr
S.I.C.: 2844; 5122
N.A.I.C.S.: 325620; 446120
Advertising Expenditures: $5,000,000
Media: 2-6-9-23-24-25
Distr.: Intl.; Natl.
Budget Set: Mar. -Apr.
Personnel:
Arthur O. Armstrong *(CEO)*
Mark Grimmet *(CFO)*
Rosanna McCollough *(COO)*
Dean Melnick *(VP-Personnel)*
Brands & Products:
AQUA BASE
AQUA-LUBE
AUTOMATIC DEFINITIVE
AUTOMATIC EYELINER
AUTOMATIC SHADOW BASE
BLUSH ROUGE
BROW SEALER
COMPLEX
COVER UP
CREAMY FLO-MATIC
DECOLLETE
DEFINITIVE
DUAL SPECTRUM
DUSKGLO
FLO-MATIC
FRESH 'N FAIR
HC-12
HEX
INSPIRATIONS
LIQUID MAKEUP SPF 16
LUXIVA
MEGALUSTER
MERLE NORMAN
MERLE NORMAN SHIMMERSTICK
MIRACOL
MN FOR MEN
MOIST LIP COLOR
NATURE'S CRYSTAL
ONLY NATURAL
POWDER BASE
PREVENTAGE
PROTECTIVE VEIL
REGENCY
REMARKABLE FINISH
RETOUCH COVER CREME
SALON FORMULA
SHEER FACE POWDER
SHIMMERSTICK

Key to Media (For complete agency information see *The Advertising Red Books-Agencies* edition):
1. Bus. Publs. 2. Cable T.V. 3. Catalogs & Directories. 4. Co-op Adv. 5. Consumer Mags. 6. D.M. to Bus. Estab.7. D.M. to Consumers
8. Daily Newsp. 9. Exhibits/Trade Shows 10. Foreign 11. Infomercial 12. Internet Adv.13. Multimedia 14. Network Radio
15. Network T.V. 16. Newsp. Distr. Mags. 17. Other 18. Outdoor (Posters, Transit) 19. Point of Purchase20. Premiums, Novelties
21. Product Samples 22. Special Events Mktg. 23. Spot Radio 24. Spot T.V. 25. Weekly Newsp. 26. Yellow Page Adv.

Merle Norman Cosmetics, Inc. — (Continued)

SUPER-LUBE
TOTAL FINISH
TRY BEFORE YOU BUY
ULTRA LIP SHINE
WARM BLUSH
WATERPROOF
WATERPROOF MASCARA

Advertising Agency:
Twelve Creative
1906 Highland Ave
Cincinnati, OH 45219-3161
Tel.: (513) 763-5416

MURRAY'S WORLDWIDE, INC.

21841 Wyoming St
Oak Park, MI 48237-3126
Tel.: (248) 691-9156
Fax: (248) 691-9158
Toll Free: (800) 448-6548
Web Site: www.murrayspomade.com
Approx. Number Employees: 15
Year Founded: 1925
Business Description:
Hair Care Product Mfr
S.I.C.: 2844
N.A.I.C.S.: 325620
Advertising Expenditures: $250,000
Media: 2-6-7-10
Distr.: Natl.
Personnel:
James Berlin *(Dir-Mktg)*
Brands & Products:
COCOSOFT
EXELENTO
HAIR GLO
LOC-LOCK
MURRAY'S
MURRAY'S BEESWAX
MURRAY'S BLACK BEESWAX
MURRAY'S ORIGINAL
MURRAY'S SUPER LIGHT
NU NILE
UNLOCK

NATURAL ESSENTIALS, INC.

(d/b/a Natural Essentials/Fashion220)
1800 Miller Pkwy
Streetsboro, OH 44241
Tel.: (330) 562-8022
Fax: (330) 562-7618
Toll Free: (888) YOUR220
E-mail: info@fashion220.net
Web Site: www.fashion220.net
Approx. Sls.: $1,200,000
Approx. Number Employees: 20
Year Founded: 1962
Business Description:
Cosmetics, Baby Care Products, Hair Care Products & Car Fresheners Mfr
S.I.C.: 2844
N.A.I.C.S.: 325620
Import Export
Media: 2-4-7-10-11-13
Distr.: Intl.; Natl.
Personnel:
Gary Pellegrino *(Pres)*

NATUROPATHICA LTD.

Red Horse Plz 74 Montauk Hwy Ste 1
East Hampton, NY 11937
Tel.: (631) 329-8792
Fax: (631) 329-2196
Toll Free: (800) 669-7618
E-mail: service@naturopathica.com
Web Site: www.naturopathica.com
Approx. Number Employees: 20
Year Founded: 1995
Business Description:
Skin & Body Care Products
S.I.C.: 2844; 2841
N.A.I.C.S.: 325620; 325611
Media: 6
Personnel:
Barbara Close *(Pres)*
Brands & Products:
NATUROPATHICA
PURE INGREDIENTS. PURE RESULTS

NEUTROGENA CORPORATION

(Sub. of Johnson & Johnson)
5760 W 96th St
Los Angeles, CA 90045
Tel.: (310) 642-1150
Fax: (310) 337-5556
Toll Free: (800) 421-6857
Web Site: www.neutrogena.com
Sales Range: $500-549.9 Million
Approx. Number Employees: 700
Year Founded: 1962
Business Description:
Skin & Hair Care Products Mfr
S.I.C.: 2844; 2841
N.A.I.C.S.: 325620; 325611
Import Export
Media: 1-2-5-6-8-9-10-11-19-20-21-23-24
Distr.: Intl.; Natl.
Budget Set: Oct. -Nov.
Personnel:
Mitch Reback *(CFO)*
Yohini Appa *(Exec Dir-Scientific Affairs)*
Cindy Zielinski *(Dir-Mktg)*
Brands & Products:
BODY CLEAR
FULL VOLUME
HEALTHY DEFENSE
INSTANT BRONZE
MOISTURESHINE
NEUTROGENA
NEW HANDS
NORWEGIAN FORMULA
ON-THE-SPOT
SUMMER GLOW
T/GEL
T/SAL
UNDER COVER
VISIBLY EVEN
WEIGHTLESS VOLUME
Advertising Agencies:
Roberts + Langer DDB
437 Madison Ave 8th Fl
New York, NY 10022
Tel.: (646) 289-7300
Fax: (212) 593-1286

Tribal DDB Worldwide
437 Madison Ave 8th Fl
New York, NY 10022
Tel.: (212) 515-8600
Fax: (212) 515-8660
Skin Cancer Awareness

NIOXIN RESEARCH LABORATORIES, INC.

(Sub. of The Procter & Gamble Company)
2124 Skyview Dr
Lithia Springs, GA 30122
Tel.: (770) 944-1308
Fax: (678) 229-3403
E-mail: customer_service@nioxin.com
Web Site: www.nioxin.com
Sales Range: $50-74.9 Million
Approx. Number Employees: 150
Business Description:
Hair Care Product Mfr
S.I.C.: 2844; 5122
N.A.I.C.S.: 325620; 446120
Media: 10-19
Personnel:
Eva Graham *(Founder & owner)*
Brian Graham *(CEO)*
Brands & Products:
BLISS
FOLLICLE BOOSTER
LIFT VOLUMIZING MIST
LIQUID FOAM
LIQUID GEL
MOISTURE AND STRENGTH
NIOGEL
NIOSPRAY
RECHARGING COMPLEX
SCALP THERAPY
SEMODEX HAIR & SCALP SYSTEM
SEMODEX SCALP SERUM
SEMODEX SEBOLYTIC CLEANSER
SMOOTHLY DEFINED
STRUCTURE AND STRENGTH

NORTHERN LABS, INC.

5800 W Dr
Manitowoc, WI 54220-4168
Tel.: (920) 684-7137
Fax: (920) 684-4957
E-mail: Info@northernlabs.com
Web Site: www.northernlabs.com
Approx. Number Employees: 200
Year Founded: 1946
Business Description:
Hair Care & Bath Products, Automotive Care Products, Household Products, Silver, Jewelry, Metal, Fabric, Leather & Furniture Care Products & Car Polishes, Waxes & Cleaners Mfr
S.I.C.: 2842; 2844
N.A.I.C.S.: 325612; 325620
Export
Advertising Expenditures: $200,000
Media: 3-5-6-9-10-15-19-21
Distr.: Natl.
Budget Set: Sept.
Personnel:
J.D. Culea *(Pres & CEO)*
Kim Ryan *(Mgr-HR)*
Brands & Products:
CAPRI
FORMULA 1
MR. METAL
NORTHERN LABS
PAN CLEAN

NU SKIN ENTERPRISES, INC.

1 Nu Skin Plz 75 W Center St
Provo, UT 84601-4432
Tel.: (801) 345-1000
Fax: (801) 345-2799
E-mail: contact@nuskin.com
Web Site: www.nuskin.com/en_US/corporate/company.html
Approx. Rev.: $1,537,259,000
Approx. Number Employees: 3,400
Year Founded: 1984
Business Description:
Cosmetics, Vitamins, Hair Care Products, Personal Care Products & Over-the-Counter Products Mfr & Distr
S.I.C.: 5122; 2844
N.A.I.C.S.: 424210; 325620
Advertising Expenditures: $2,100,000
Media: 10-21-22
Personnel:
Blake M. Roney *(Chm)*
Steven J. Lund *(Vice Chm)*
M. Truman Hunt *(Pres & CEO)*
Luke Yoo *(VP-North Asia Reg, Pres & Gen Mgr)*
Ritch N. Wood *(CFO)*
Ashok Pahwa *(CMO)*
Joseph Y. Chang *(Exec VP-Product Dev & Chief Scientific Officer)*
Daniel R. Chard *(Pres-Global Sls & Ops)*
Andrew Fan *(Pres-Greater China Reg)*
Brett Nelson *(Pres-North Asia Region & Japan)*
Melisa Tantoco Quijano *(Pres-Southeast Asia Reg)*
Scott E. Schwerdt *(Pres-Americas, Europe & South Pacific)*
D. Matthew Dorny *(Gen Counsel, Sec & VP)*
Sandra N. Tillotson *(Sr VP)*
Antonia Chang *(VP-Global Distributor Success)*
John F. Fralick *(VP-IT)*
Brian R. Lords *(VP-Fin)*
Jack Petersen *(VP-Corp Strategy & Dev)*
Elizabeth Thibaudeau *(VP-Mktg)*
Kara Schneck *(Sr Dir-PR)*
Scott Pond *(Dir-IR)*
Brands & Products:
AP-24
AROMA SIGN
AVA PUHI MONI
BIG PLANET
BIO ST. JOHN'S
BIOGINKGO
BP HEALTHCARD
BP INTERNET SECURITY
BP SECURITY ANALYZER
BP TELECOM
CALMING TOUCH
CELLTREX
CHOLESTIN
CITRISOMES
CORDYMAX
CORTITROL
CRAVE EASE
CREAMY HYDRATING MASQUE
CUSTOM COLOR
DAILYKIND
DEFINING EFFECTS
DERMATIC EFFECTS
DESERT BREEZE
DESIRED EFFECTS
DIENE-O-LEAN
THE DIFFERENCE, DEMONSTRATED
DIVIDENDS
DUOLEAN
EPOCH
EPOCH BABY
ESTERA
EVERGLIDE
FACE LIFT
FIBRENET
FIREWALKER
FLEXCREME
FREEFALL
G3
GALVANIC SPA
GLACIAL MARINE MUD

Key to Media (For complete agency information see *The Advertising Red Books-Agencies* edition):
1. Bus. Publs. 2. Cable T.V. 3. Catalogs & Directories. 4. Co-op Adv. 5. Consumer Mags. 6. D.M. to Bus. Estab.7. D.M. to Consumers
8. Daily Newsp. 9. Exhibits/Trade Shows 10. Foreign 11. Infomercial 12. Internet Adv.13. Multimedia 14. Network Radio
15. Network T.V. 16. Newsp. Distr. Mags. 17. Other 18. Outdoor (Posters, Transit) 19. Point of Purchase20. Premiums, Novelties
21. Product Samples 22. Special Events Mktg. 23. Spot Radio 24. Spot T.V. 25. Weekly Newsp. 26. Yellow Page Adv.

GOWEAR
HOLDINGPATTERN
HPX HYDRATING GEL
HTP COMPLEX
HYDRAKIND
ICEDANCER
IDEALEYES
IGG BOOST
JUNGAMALS
LIFE ESSENTIALS
LIFEPAK
LIPIDOL
MAKEAMENDS
MARINEOMEGA
MAXCAST
MAXVAULT
METABOTRIM
MOISTURE RESTORE
MOISTURSHADE
MOVIE MAGIC
NIGHT SUPPLY
NU COLOUR
NU SKIN
NU SKIN 180
NU SKIN CLEAR ACTION
NUTRICENTIALS
NUTRIFI
NUTRIMMUNE CHEWS
NUTRIOL
OVERDRIVE
PERENNIAL
PHARMANEX
PHOTOMAX
POLISHING PEEL
PROBIO PCC
PRODERM
RARE EARTHS
REISHIMAX
SEALASTIN
SHINNING EFFECTS
SKIN BENEFICIAL
SOLE SOLUTION
STRONGHOLD
STYLINFOAM
STYLINGEL
SUBTLE EFFECTS
SUNRIGHT
TEGREEN
TRA
TRI-PHASIC WHITE
TRICALGOXYL
TRIMPAK
TRIMSHAKE
TRIMSTIK
TRU FACE
VENIX
VITOX
VOLUMEKIND
XOI BAR

OPI PRODUCTS INC.

13034 Saticoy St
North Hollywood, CA 91605-3510
Tel.: (818) 759-2400
Fax: (818) 759-5770
Toll Free: (800) 341-9999
Web Site: www.opi.com
Approx. Number Employees: 450
Year Founded: 1981
Business Description:
Cosmetics & Nail Products Preparations
S.I.C.: 2844; 5087
N.A.I.C.S.: 325620; 423850
Import Export
Media: 2-4-5-6-11-13-18-19-20-22
Personnel:
George Schaeffer *(Pres & CEO)*
Dena Hagan *(CFO)*
Eric Schwartz *(COO)*
Suzi Weiss-Fishmann *(Exec VP & Dir-Artistic)*
William Halfacre *(Exec VP-Sls & Mktg)*
Brands & Products:
A-ROSE AT DAWN
ALL THAT RAZZ-BERRY
APHRODITE'S PINK NIGHTIE
ARGENTEENY PINKINI
AVOJUICE
AVOPLEX NAIL
BELIZE IT OR NOT
BIG APPLE RED
BLACK ONYX
BLUSHINGHAM PALACE
BOGOTA BLACKBERRY
CAJUN SHRIMP
CALIFORNIA RASPBERRY
CANDLES ON MY CAKE
CARA MIA CRIMSON
CHA-CHING CHERRY
CHAPEL OF LOVE
CHEYENNE PEPPER
CHICAGO CHAMPAGNE TOAST
CHICAGO GET A MANICURE
CHICK FLICK CHERRY
CHIPSKIP
CHOCOLATE MOOSE
CHOCOLATE SHAKE-SPEARE
COLOR OF THE ZEN-TURY
DANCING IN THE ISLES
DEER VALLEY SPICE
DON'T BE KOI WITH ME
DON'T SOCRA-TEASE ME
DON'T WIN YUKON DO IT
DOUBLE DECKER RED
DRESS TO EMPRESS
DRIPDRY
DULCE DE LECHE
DUSK OVER CAIRO
DUTCH TULIPS
EDIN BURGUNDY
FIJI WEEJEE FAWN
FRIAR FRIAR PANTS ON FIRE
GOT THE BLUES FOR RED
GRAND CANYON SUNSET
GRAND CENTRAL CARNATION
THE GRAPE LAKES
HAVE A TEMPURA TAN-TRUM
HOLY PINK PAGODA
HONG KONG SUNRISE
HOODOO VOODOO
I'M NOT REALLY A WAITRESS
INNSBRUCK BRONZE
ITALIAN LOVE AFFAIR
IT'S ALL GREEK TO ME
IT'S SHEER LUCK
JAPANESE ROSE GARDEN
JAVA MAUVE-A
JEWEL OF INDIA
KENNEBUNK-PORT
LA PAZ-ITIVELY HOT
LET THEM EAT RICE CAKE
LINCOLN PARK AFTER DARK
MAINE-IAC MAUVE
MALAGA WINE
MALAYSIAN MIST
MAROONED ON THE MAGNIFICENT MILE
MARQUIS D'MAUVE
MAUVING TO MANITOBA
MELON OF TROY
MISO HAPPY WITH THIS COLOR
MOST HONORABLE RED
MOTHER ROAD ROSE
MRS. O'LEARY'S BBQ
MY KIND OF BROWN
NAIL ENVY
NANTUCKET MIST
NIAGARA FALLS
NICE COLOR EH
NOMAD'S DREAM
NOT SO BORA-BORA-ING PIN
O'HARE & NAILS LOOK GREAT
OPI
OPI RED
OPI TOP COAT
PAINT YOUR TORON-TOES ROSE
PERU-B-RUBY
PISTOL PACKIN' PINK
POLAR BARE
POMPEII PURPLE
RAPIDRY
RED RED RHINE
REDIPUS-OEDIPUS
ROMEO AND JOLIET
ROYAL FLUSH BLUSH
SENORITA ROSE-ALITA
SHANGHAI SHIMMER
SILENT MAUVIE
SKINNY DIP'N LAKE MICHG'N
SMOK'N IN HAVANA
SOHO NICE TO MEET YOU
SONORA SUNSET
START-TO-FINISH
SUZY SELL SUSHI BY THE SEASHORE
THAT'S AN "EL" OF A COLOR
THE THRILL OF BRAZIL
TO EROS IS HUMAN
TROPICAL PUNCH
VAN-COUVERED IN SNOW
WINDY CITY PRETTY
YOU'RE A PISA WORK
YOU'RE SUCH A KABUKI QUEEN
YOURVILLAORMINE
YUCATAN IF U WANT

ORLY INTERNATIONAL, INC.

7710 Haskell Ave
Los Angeles, CA 91406
Tel.: (818) 994-1001
Fax: (818) 994-1144
Toll Free: (800) 275-1111
Web Site: www.orlybeauty.com
Sales Range: $50-74.9 Million
Approx. Number Employees: 85
Year Founded: 1975
Business Description:
Nail Care & Hand, Foot & Body Products Mfr
S.I.C.: 2844
N.A.I.C.S.: 325620
Export
Bus. Publs.: 90%; Catalogs & Directories: 10%
Distr.: Intl.; Natl.
Personnel:
Jeff Pink *(Founder & Chm)*
Carina Breda *(Sr VP-Mktg)*
Veronica Reyes *(VP-Fin, IT & HR)*
Brands & Products:
BONDER
CALCIUM SHIELD
CLEAN PREP
CUTICLE CARE COMPLEX
CUTIQUE
DOUBLE-TIME SHINE
FUNGUS MD
GLOSSER
IN A SNAP
MAGNIFIQUE
NAIL ARMOR
NAIL DEFENSE
NAIL RESCUE
NAIL WHITENER
NAILS FOR MALES
NO BITE
ORIGINAL FRENCH MANICURE
ORLY
ORLY PEDICURE SPA
RICH RENEWAL
SEC N DRY
SHEER RADIANCE
SMUDGE FIXER
SPRITZ DRY
SUGARFIX
SUNSCREEN FOR NAILS
TIKI TIME
TOP 2 BOTTOM
TOUGH COOKIE
WONT CHIP

P&G-CLAIROL, INC.

(Sub. of The Procter & Gamble Company)
(d/b/a Clairol)
1 Blachley Rd
Stamford, CT 06922-0002
Tel.: (203) 357-5000
Fax: (212) 261-2022
Toll Free: (800) 252-4765
Web Site: www.clairol.com
Sales Range: $25-49.9 Million
Approx. Number Employees: 100
Business Description:
Hair Coloring & Hair Care Products Mfr & Marketer
S.I.C.: 2841; 2844
N.A.I.C.S.: 325611; 325620
Media: 2-5-6-8-9-11-13-15-16-18-23-24-25-26
Distr.: Natl.
Personnel:
Eileen Sawyers *(Dir-Mktg)*
Mark Jeffreys *(Brand Mgr-Nice & Easy)*
Brands & Products:
BALSAM COLOR
BORN BLONDE
FROST & TIP
HAIRPAINTING
HERBAL ESSENCES
HYDRIENCE
LOVING CARE
NATURAL DIMENSIONS
NATURAL INSTINCTS
NATURAL INSTINCTS FOR MEN
NICE 'N EASY
SUMMER BLONDE
TEXTURES & TONES
TOUCH OF SUN
ULTRESS
Advertising Agency:
Abstract Edge
455 Broadway 4th Fl
New York, NY 10013
Tel.: (212) 352-9311
Fax: (212) 952-9498

PARFUMS CHRISTIAN DIOR, INC

(Sub. of LVMH Moet Hennessy Louis Vuitton SA)
19 E 57th St
New York, NY 10022-2508
Tel.: (212) 931-2200
Fax: (212) 751-7478
Web Site: www.dior.com
Approx. Number Employees: 40
Year Founded: 1947
Business Description:
Perfumes, Eau de Cologne, Eau de

Key to Media (For complete agency information see *The Advertising Red Books-Agencies* edition):
1. Bus. Publs. 2. Cable T.V. 3. Catalogs & Directories. 4. Co-op Adv. 5. Consumer Mags. 6. D.M. to Bus. Estab.7. D.M. to Consumers
8. Daily Newsp. 9. Exhibits/Trade Shows 10. Foreign 11. Infomercial 12. Internet Adv.13. Multimedia 14. Network Radio
15. Network T.V. 16. Newsp. Distr. Mags. 17. Other 18. Outdoor (Posters, Transit) 19. Point of Purchase20. Premiums, Novelties
21. Product Samples 22. Special Events Mktg. 23. Spot Radio 24. Spot T.V. 25. Weekly Newsp. 26. Yellow Page Adv.

Parfums Christian Dior, Inc — (Continued)

Toilette, Dusting Powder, Bath Items, Lipstick, Nail Enamel, Men's Toiletries, Nail Conditioners, Makeup, Skin Care
S.I.C.: 5122
N.A.I.C.S.: 446120
Advertising Expenditures: $4,000,000
Media: 5-6-9-21-23-24-30
Distr.: Natl.
Budget Set: Nov.
Personnel:
Claude Martinez *(Pres & CEO)*
Joanna Grillo *(VP-HR)*
Stephanie Lacasse *(Mgr-Mktg Retail Svcs)*
Brands & Products:
CAPTURE
DIOR
DIOR ADDICT EDITION LIMITEE
DIOR ADDICT PERFUMED BODY LINE
DIOR RALEXANDTE
DIORELLA
DIORESSENCE
DIORISSIMO
DUNE
DUNE MEN
DUNE SUN
EAU DE DIOR ENERGISANTE
EAU DE DIOR RALEXANTE
EAU DE DOLCE VITA
EAU FRAICHE
EAU SAUVAGE
EAU SAUVAGE EXTREME
EQUITE
FAHRENHEIT
FAHRENHEIT 0 DEGREE
HIGHER FACE & BODY COLLECTION
HYDRA DIOR
HYPNOTIC POISON
ICONE
J'ADORE EAU DE PARFUM
J'ADORE EAU DE TOLIETTE
J'ADORE PERFUMED BODY LINE
J'ADORE SUMMER
L'OR J'ADORE
POISON
RESULTANTE
TENDRE POISON

PARFUMS DE COEUR LTD.
85 Old Kings Hwy N
Darien, CT 06820-4724
Tel.: (203) 655-8807
Fax: (203) 656-2121
Toll Free: (800) 887-2738
E-mail: custservice@parfumsdecoeur.com
Web Site: www.parfumsdecoeur.com
Approx. Number Employees: 95
Year Founded: 1981
Business Description:
Perfume & Body Spray Mfr
S.I.C.: 2844
N.A.I.C.S.: 325620
Export
Advertising Expenditures: $14,200,000
Media: 3-5-6-8-15-19-23-24
Distr.: Natl.
Personnel:
Mark A. Laracy *(Pres & CEO)*
Edward J. Kaminski *(CFO, VP-Fin & Admin)*
Roy Slowers *(VP-Sls)*
Eileen Syla *(VP-Customer Service)*
Marissa Palmer *(Dir-Mktg)*
Brands & Products:
A LITTLE SEXY
ACQUA DI GIO
APPLE FANTASY
APRICOT HONEY
AVIANCE NIGHT MUSK
BABE
BEING TOGETHER
BOD
BODY FANTASIES
CACHET
COLD WATER
CONFESS
COTTON CANDY
CUCUMBER MELON
DESIGNER IMPOSTERS
DESIGNER QUALITY FRAGRANCES, NOT DESIGNER PRICES
FAIRCHILD
FLY WITH ME
FREESIA FANTASY
FRESH BLUE MUSK
FRESH WHITE MUSK
FRESH WHITE MUSK FANTASY
FRESH XTREME
GINGER LOTUS
GREAT LIFE
GUMMI BEARS
HAPPY
JUICE BAR
LONE STAR
MALIBU MUSK
MASCOLINO
NEW MUSK
NEW MUSK FOR MEN
NEW MUSK FOR WOMEN
NEW YORK NIGHTS
NINJA
PAJAMA PARTY
PARFUMS DE COEUR
PEAR FANTASY
PLEASURES
PLUMERIA FANTASY
PRIMO
PRINCE MATCHABELLI
RASPBERRY FANTASY
REALLY RIPPED ABS
ROCK HARD
SENSUALE
SKIN MUSK
SUGAR VANILLA
TAHOE
TEDDY BEAR
TEKNO
TUBEROSE MUSK
U-TWO
U-YOU
UNSCENTED
UPROAR
VANILLA FANTASY
WANNA PLAY?
WARM SUGAR VANILLA
WHITE GINGER
WIND SONG
X

PARLUX FRAGRANCES, INC.
5900 N Andrews Ave Ste 500
Fort Lauderdale, FL 33309
Tel.: (954) 316-9008
Fax: (954) 491-1187
E-mail: info@parlux.com
Web Site: www.parlux.com
Approx. Sls.: $123,006,000
Approx. Number Employees: 135
Year Founded: 1984
Business Description:
Fragrances & Related Products Designer, Mfr, Distr & Marketer
S.I.C.: 2844; 2841; 5122
N.A.I.C.S.: 325620; 325611; 424210
Export
Advertising Expenditures: $32,652,000
Media: 4-5-6-11-15-19-21
Distr.: Intl.; Natl.
Personnel:
Frederick E. Purches *(Chm & CEO)*
Raymond J. Balsys *(CFO & Sr VP)*
Frank A. Buttacavoli *(COO & Exec VP)*
Kathleen Galvin *(VP-Mktg)*
Brands & Products:
LIMOUSINE
PARLUX
Advertising Agency:
LSZ Communications
400 E 57th St
New York, NY 10022
Tel.: (212) 486-9260
Public Relations

PERFUMANIA HOLDINGS, INC.
35 Sawgrass Dr Ste 2
Bellport, NY 11713
Tel.: (631) 866-4100
E-mail: business@perfumania.com
Web Site: www.perfumania.com
Approx. Sls.: $484,800,000
Approx. Number Employees: 1,996
Year Founded: 1999
Business Description:
Holding Company; Discount Retail Fragrances
S.I.C.: 5999; 5122
N.A.I.C.S.: 446120; 424210; 453998
Advertising Expenditures: $2,900,000
Personnel:
Stephen L. Nussdorf *(Chm)*
Michael W. Katz *(Pres & CEO)*
Donna Dellomo *(CFO & Sec)*

PERFUMANIA, INC.
(Sub. of Perfumania Holdings, Inc.)
251 International Pkwy
Sunrise, FL 33325
Tel.: (954) 335-9100
Fax: (954) 335-9166
E-mail: business@perfumania.com
Web Site: www.perfumania.com
Sales Range: $100-124.9 Million
Approx. Number Employees: 200
Year Founded: 1987
Business Description:
Fragrances & Related Products Retailer
S.I.C.: 5122
N.A.I.C.S.: 424210; 446120
Advertising Expenditures: $1,650,000
Media: 4-6-8-23-24
Personnel:
Michael W. Katz *(Pres & CEO)*
Donovan Chin *(CFO)*
Jessica Plumital *(Dir-Mktg)*
Bonnie Nelson *(Dir-Mktg)*

PERSONAL PRODUCTS COMPANY
(Div. of McNEIL-PPC, Inc.)
199 Grandview Rd
Skillman, NJ 08558-9418
Tel.: (908) 874-1000
Fax: (908) 874-1231
Sales Range: $300-349.9 Million
Business Description:
Women's Products Mfr
S.I.C.: 2676
N.A.I.C.S.: 322291
Media: 6-15-23-24
Distr.: Natl.
Personnel:
Michael Sneed *(Pres)*
Robert Laschiazza *(VP-Fin)*
Brands & Products:
CAREFREE PANTY SHIELDS
MODESS
O.B.
SERENITY GUARDS
STAYFREE SILHOUETTES
SURE & NATURAL
Advertising Agency:
Deutsch New York
111 8th Ave 14th Fl
New York, NY 10011
Tel.: (212) 605-8000

PETER THOMAS ROTH LABS LLC
460 Park Ave 16th Fl
New York, NY 10022-1829
Tel.: (212) 581-5800
Fax: (212) 581-5810
E-mail: info@peterthomasroth.com
Web Site: www.peterthomasroth.com
Approx. Sls.: $15,000,000
Approx. Number Employees: 25
Business Description:
Cosmetic Preparations Mfr
S.I.C.: 2844
N.A.I.C.S.: 325620
Media: 6-15
Personnel:
Peter Thomas Roth *(Mng Dir)*
Sarah Klug *(Pres-Mktg)*
Brands & Products:
PETER THOMAS ROTH

PEVONIA INTERNATIONAL, INC.
300 Fentress Blvd
Daytona Beach, FL 32114
Tel.: (386) 254-1967
Fax: (386) 254-0641
Toll Free: (800) 351-3516
E-mail: pevonia@pevonia.com
Web Site: www.pevonia.com
Sales Range: $10-24.9 Million
Approx. Number Employees: 50
Business Description:
Skin Care Products Mfr & Retailer
S.I.C.: 2844
N.A.I.C.S.: 325620
Media: 6-10-11-22
Personnel:
Philippe Hennessy *(Pres)*
Brands & Products:
ENZYMO-SPHERIDES
PEEL-O-ZYM
PEVONIA BOTANICA
PEVOVITALE
POWER REPAIR
SABAI
SPALASIUM
Advertising Agency:
Creative Media Marketing
594 Broadway Ste 500
New York, NY 10012
Tel.: (212) 979-8884
Fax: (212) 979-8577

Key to Media (For complete agency information see *The Advertising Red Books-Agencies* edition):
1. Bus. Publs. 2. Cable T.V. 3. Catalogs & Directories. 4. Co-op Adv. 5. Consumer Mags. 6. D.M. to Bus. Estab.7. D.M. to Consumers 8. Daily Newsp. 9. Exhibits/Trade Shows 10. Foreign 11. Infomercial 12. Internet Adv.13. Multimedia 14. Network Radio 15. Network T.V. 16. Newsp. Distr. Mags. 17. Other 18. Outdoor (Posters, Transit) 19. Point of Purchase20. Premiums, Novelties 21. Product Samples 22. Special Events Mktg. 23. Spot Radio 24. Spot T.V. 25. Weekly Newsp. 26. Yellow Page Adv.

Toll Free: (888) 826-6477
Pevonia Botanica

PIVOT POINT INTERNATIONAL, INC.

1560 Sherman Ave Ste 700
Evanston, IL 60201-4813
Tel.: (773) 973-0500
Tel.: (773) 594-9200
Fax: (847) 866-7040
Toll Free: (800) 886-4247
E-mail: info@pivot-point.com
Web Site: www.pivot-point.com
Sales Range: $75-99.9 Million
Approx. Number Employees: 110
Year Founded: 1962
Business Description:
Beauty School
S.I.C.: 9411; 2731
N.A.I.C.S.: 923110; 511130
Media: 10-22
Personnel:
Leo Passage *(Founder)*
Karen Wilkins Donache *(CEO)*
Robert Sieh *(Sr VP-Fin & Internal Ops)*
Mamie Bohn *(Product Mgr)*
Brands & Products:
MINDFUL TEACHING
PIVOT POINT
SALON FUNDAMENTALS
SNAP CAP

PLANET BEACH FRANCHISING CORPORATION

5145 Taravella Rd
Marrero, LA 70072
Tel.: (504) 361-5550
Fax: (504) 361-5540
Toll Free: (888) 290-8266
E-mail: information@planetbeach.com
Web Site: www.planetbeach.com
Approx. Rev.: $13,269,120
Approx. Number Employees: 42
Year Founded: 1996
Business Description:
Tanning & Day Spa Franchisor
S.I.C.: 7231; 6794
N.A.I.C.S.: 812112; 533110
Advertising Expenditures: $63,179
Media: 6-17-22-23-24
Personnel:
Tiffany Lassiegne *(Pres)*
Stephen P. Smith *(CEO)*
Craig M. Berner *(CFO)*
Richard L. Juka *(COO & Sr VP)*
David Mesa, Jr. *(Sr VP)*
Nancy M. Price *(Sr VP-Sls)*
Brands & Products:
THE PLANET BEACH
PLANET BEACH CONTEMPO SPA

PLAYTEX PRODUCTS, INC.

(Sub. of Energizer Holdings, Inc.)
(d/b/a Energizer Personal Care Division)
6 Research Dr
Shelton, CT 06484
Tel.: (203) 944-5500
Fax: (203) 341-4260
Toll Free: (800) 310-4290
E-mail: invrel@playtexproductsinc.com
Web Site: www.playtexproductsinc.com
Approx. Sls.: $636,147,968
Approx. Number Employees: 1,250
Year Founded: 1932
Business Description:
Lotions, Latex Gloves, Infant & Feminine Care Products Mfr
S.I.C.: 3999; 2676; 2822; 2899; 3069
N.A.I.C.S.: 339999; 322291; 325212; 325998; 326299
Advertising Expenditures: $97,000,000
Media: 3-4-5-6-7-8-9-10-14-15-18-19-20-21-22-23-24-25
Distr.: Intl.; Natl.
Budget Set: Sept.
Personnel:
David P. Hatfield *(Pres & CEO)*
Jeffrey Wolf *(Sr Brand Mgr-Edge Shave Gel)*
Brands & Products:
BANANA BOAT
BINKY
BUBBLE
COMFORT FLEX
DIAPER GENIE
DRINKUP
DRIP-CATCH
DROP-INS
EMBRACE
FIRST SIPSTER
GENTLE GLIDE
INSTANT PROTECTION
INSULATOR
INSULATOR SPORT
KINDER-GRIP
MOST LIKE MOTHER
NATURAL ACTION
NATURAL SHAPE
NATURALATCH
ORTHO-PRO
QUICKSTRAW
SAFE 'N SURE
SIPEASE
SIPSTER
SOFT COMFORT
TIP 'N SIP
ULTRA-FRESH
VENTAIRE
WET ONES
Advertising Agency:
MEC - NA HQ, New York
825 7th Ave
New York, NY 10019-5818
Tel.: (212) 474-0000
Fax: (212) 474-0003
Banana Boat Suncreen
Infant & Feminine Care Products

PRESTIGE BRANDS HOLDINGS, INC.

(Holding of GTCR Golder Rauner, LLC)
(d/b/a Prestige Brands International, Inc.)
90 N Broadway
Irvington, NY 10533
Tel.: (914) 524-6810
Tel.: (914) 524-6800
Fax: (914) 524-6815
Web Site: www.prestigebrands.com
Approx. Rev.: $336,510,000
Approx. Number Employees: 100
Business Description:
Over-the-Counter Drugs, Household Cleaning & Personal Care Products
S.I.C.: 2834; 8742
N.A.I.C.S.: 325412; 541613
Advertising Expenditures: $42,897,000
Media: 1-3-4-6-7-8-9-12-13-14-15-16-18-19-21-23-24-25
Personnel:
Matthew M. Mannelly *(Pres & CEO)*
Ronald M. Lombardi *(CFO)*
Timothy J. Connors *(CMO)*
Eric S. Klee *(Gen Counsel & Sec)*
Jean Boyko *(Sr VP-Science & Tech)*
John Parkinson *(Sr VP-Intl)*
Kristina Skeffington *(Sr Brand Mgr-Little Remedies)*
Brands & Products:
CHLORASEPTIC
CHORE BOY
CINCH
CLEAR EYES
CLOVERINE
COMET
COMPUND W
DERMOPLAST
THE DOCTOR'S BRUSHPICK
THE DOCTOR'S NITE GUARD
DRAMAMINE
EFFERDENT
EFFERGRIP
LITTLE REMEDIES
LUDEN'S
MURINE
NASALCROM
NEW-SKIN
PEDIACARE
PRELL
SPIC AND SPAN
WARTNER
Advertising Agencies:
RJ Palmer LLC
156 W 56th St 5th Fl
New York, NY 10019-3800
Tel.: (212) 541-6770
Fax: (212) 541-6769
Local & National Media Buying

Robin Leedy & Associates
118 N Bedford Rd Ste 302
Mount Kisco, NY 10549
Tel.: (914) 241-0086
Fax: (914) 242-2061

PRO-CUTS, INC.

(Sub. of Regis Corporation)
7201 Metro Blvd
Minneapolis, MN 55439
Tel.: (952) 947-7777
Web Site: www.procuts.com
Sales Range: $50-74.9 Million
Business Description:
Hair Salon Franchisor
S.I.C.: 7231
N.A.I.C.S.: 812112
Media: 13-20
Personnel:
Paul Finkelstein *(Pres & CEO)*
Advertising Agency:
Southwest Media Group
2100 Ross Ave Ste 3200
Dallas, TX 75201
Tel.: (214) 561-5543
Fax: (214) 744-1086

PRO-LINE INTERNATIONAL

(Sub. of Alberto-Culver Company)
2525 Armitage Ave
Melrose Park, IL 60160
Tel.: (708) 450-3000
Toll Free: (800) 527-5879
Web Site: www.albertmulticultural.com
E-Mail For Key Personnel:
President: eric.brown@prolinecorp.com
Sales Range: $150-199.9 Million
Approx. Number Employees: 268
Year Founded: 1970
Business Description:
Hair Products Mfr
S.I.C.: 5122; 2844
N.A.I.C.S.: 446120; 325620
Import Export
Advertising Expenditures: $3,500,000
Media: 1-2-3-4-5-6-8-9-10-11-14-15-18-19-20-21-22-23-24-25
Distr.: Intl.; Natl.
Budget Set: Oct.

RANIR LLC

4701 E Paris Rd SE
Grand Rapids, MI 49512
Tel.: (616) 698-8880
Fax: (616) 222-0710
E-mail: contact@ranir.com
Web Site: www.ranir.com
Approx. Number Employees: 450
Year Founded: 1972
Business Description:
Mfr & Marketer of Oral Care Products; Owned by Kayak Holdings LLC, an Investment Group Led by Richard P. Kiphart
S.I.C.: 3843
N.A.I.C.S.: 339114
Import Export
Media: 2-5-10-19
Distr.: Intl.; Natl.
Personnel:
Christine Henisee *(Pres & CEO)*
Joe Townsend *(CFO)*
James Peliotes *(VP-Mktg)*
Marvin Coopersmith *(Mgr-Sls)*
Brands & Products:
ADVANCED WHITENING WRAPS
ALL-PRO
ANGLE EDGE+
AURORA
CLARIDENT
EASEBETWEEN
EASYFLEX
ELITE
FLAVOR ACTION
GEM GRIP
GRANDE DENTURE
HI-TECH
INTERDENTAL FLOSSUPS
KIDS WILDLIFE FLOSSUPS
MICROTEX
MULTIFIT CONTOUR
ORBIT
POLARIS
PREMIER
PREMIER TRAVEL TOOTHBRUSH
RANIR
REPLACE-ME
SMARTGRIP
SQUEEZABLE
SUPER SLIP
SURF
WHITENING GEL
WHITENING GEL NIGHT
WHITENING WRAPS
XTREME
XTREME MASSAGE

Key to Media (For complete agency information see *The Advertising Red Books-Agencies* edition):
1. Bus. Publs. 2. Cable T.V. 3. Catalogs & Directories. 4. Co-op Adv. 5. Consumer Mags. 6. D.M. to Bus. Estab.7. D.M. to Consumers
8. Daily Newsp. 9. Exhibits/Trade Shows 10. Foreign 11. Infomercial 12. Internet Adv.13. Multimedia 14. Network Radio
15. Network T.V. 16. Newsp. Distr. Mags. 17. Other 18. Outdoor (Posters, Transit) 19. Point of Purchase20. Premiums, Novelties
21. Product Samples 22. Special Events Mktg. 23. Spot Radio 24. Spot T.V. 25. Weekly Newsp. 26. Yellow Page Adv.

THE RATNER COMPANIES
(d/b/a Creative Hairdressers)
1577 Spring Hill Rd Ste 500
Vienna, VA 22182-2223
Tel.: (703) 269-5400
Fax: (703) 876-2897
Toll Free: (800) 874-6288
Web Site: www.ratnerco.com
Sales Range: $200-249.9 Million
Approx. Number Employees: 10,000
Year Founded: 1974
Business Description:
Hair Salon Chain Owner & Operator
S.I.C.: 7231
N.A.I.C.S.: 812112
Media: 1-5-6-8-9-10-20-22-23-24-25-26
Distr.: Direct to Consumer; Reg.
Personnel:
Dennis Ratner *(Founder, CEO & Stylist)*
Ben Tyser *(CFO)*
Les Mardiks *(Gen Counsel & Sr VP)*
Warren Ratner *(Exec VP)*
Brands & Products:
BUBBLES
COLORWORKS
HAIR CUTTERY
MORE IS LESS
SALON CIELO & SPA
SALON PLAZA

REDKEN LABORATORIES LLC
(Sub. of L'Oreal USA, Inc.)
575 5th Ave
New York, NY 10017-2422
Tel.: (212) 818-1500
Fax: (212) 984-5321
Web Site: www.redken.com
Approx. Number Employees: 4,000
Year Founded: 1960
Business Description:
Hair Care Products Mfr & Distr
S.I.C.: 2844; 5122
N.A.I.C.S.: 325620; 446120
Export
Media: 6-8-10-11-13-19
Personnel:
Pat Parenty *(Pres)*
Rachel Weiss *(Sr Dir-Interactive Mktg)*
Advertising Agency:
Digital Pulp
220 E 23rd St Ste 900
New York, NY 10010
Tel.: (212) 679-0676
Fax: (212) 679-6217
Urban Experiment Hair Products

REGIS CORPORATION
7201 Metro Blvd
Minneapolis, MN 55439-2130
Tel.: (952) 947-7777
Fax: (952) 947-7600
Web Site: www.regiscorp.com
Approx. Rev.: $2,325,869,000
Approx. Number Employees: 55,000
Year Founded: 1954
Business Description:
Salons, Beauty Schools & Hair Restoration Centers Owner & Operator
S.I.C.: 7231; 5122; 9411
N.A.I.C.S.: 812112; 446120; 923110
Advertising Expenditures: $61,400,000
Media: 2-6-8-9-10-13-14-15-18-23-24-25-26
Personnel:
Paul D. Finkelstein *(Chm & CEO)*
Randy L. Pearce *(Pres)*
Brent Moen *(CFO & Sr VP)*
David Bortnem *(COO & Exec VP)*
Andrew Cohen *(Pres-Salon Div)*
John Exline *(Pres-SmartStyle Family Hair Salons)*
Eric A. Bakken *(Gen Counsel & Exec VP-Bus Dev)*
Norma Knudsen *(Exec VP-Mdsg)*
Gordon B. Nelson *(Exec VP-Fashion & Education)*
Jackie Lang *(Sr VP & Mng Dir-UK)*
David W. Foley *(Sr VP-Real Estate)*
Mark Fosland *(Sr VP-Fin & IR)*
Mary Kiley *(Sr VP-Intl Mktg)*
Brands & Products:
BEAUTY SUPPLY OUTLET
BEST CUTS
BIOLAGE
BORICS
CARLTON HAIR
CITY LOOKS
COIFF & CO.
COOL CUTS 4 KIDS
COST CUTTERS
FAMOUS HAIR
FIESTA HAIR
FIRST CHOICE HAIRCUTTERS
GREAT EXPECTATIONS
HAIR CLUB FOR MEN AND WOMEN
HAIR EXCITEMENT
HAIR EXPRESS
HAIRCRAFTERS
HAIRMASTERS
HEAD START
HOLIDAY HAIR
INTERMEDE
IT'S A 10
JEAN LOUIS DAVID
KENRA
MAGICUTS
MASTERCUTS
MIA & MAXX
MITCHELL'S
MITCHELL'S HAIR STYLING
NIOXIN
PANOPOULOS
PAUL MITCHELL
PRO-CUTS
PROGRESSIONS
RAZE
REDKEN
REGIS
REGIS DESIGNLINE
REGIS SALONS
RENEE BEAUTY
SAINT ALGUE
THE SALON
SATURDAY'S
SEBASTIAN
SEXY HAIR CONCEPTS
SMARTSTYLE
STYLE AMERICA
SUPERCUTS
TGF
TIGI BEDHEAD
TRADE SECRET
WE CARE HAIR
Advertising Agency:
JSML Media, LLC
11200 86th Ave N
Minneapolis, MN 55369
Tel.: (763) 657-2263
Fax: (763) 657-2261
Toll Free: (800) 657-3100

REVLON CONSUMER PRODUCTS CORPORATION
(Sub. of Revlon, Inc.)
237 Park Ave
New York, NY 10017
Tel.: (212) 527-4000
Web Site: www.revlon.com
Approx. Sls.: $1,321,400,000
Approx. Number Employees: 4,900
Year Founded: 1992
Business Description:
Perfumes, Cosmetics & Other Toilet Preparations
S.I.C.: 2844; 2841
N.A.I.C.S.: 325620; 325611
Advertising Expenditures: $265,200,000
Personnel:
Ronald O. Perelman *(Chm)*
David L. Kennedy *(Vice Chm & Sr Exec VP)*
Alan T. Ennis *(Pres & CEO)*
Graeme Howard *(Mng Dir-Asia Pacific & Sr VP)*
Simon Worraker *(Mng Dir-Canada & Sr VP)*
Steven Berns *(CFO, Treas & Exec VP)*
Chris Elshaw *(COO & Exec VP)*
Robert K. Kretzman *(Chief Legal Officer, Gen Counsel & Exec VP-HR)*
Gina Mastantuono *(Chief Acctg Officer, Sr VP & Controller)*
Neil Scancarella *(Chief Science Officer & Exec VP)*
Manuel Blanco *(Mng Dir-Latin America & Sr VP)*
Arthur Franson *(Sr VP-Mfg)*
Mark M. Sexton *(Sr VP-Taxes)*
Martine Williamson *(VP-Mktg)*
Advertising Agency:
MediaCom US
777 3rd Ave
New York, NY 10017-1401
Tel.: (212) 912-4200
Fax: (212) 508-4386

REVLON, INC.
(Sub. of MacAndrews & Forbes Holdings Inc.)
237 Park Ave
New York, NY 10017
Tel.: (212) 527-4000
Fax: (212) 527-4995
Toll Free: (800) 473-8566
Web Site: www.revloninc.com
Approx. Sls.: $1,321,400,000
Approx. Number Employees: 4,900
Year Founded: 1932
Business Description:
Holding Company; Cosmetics, Beauty Products & Fragrances Mfr & Distr
S.I.C.: 6719; 2841; 2844
N.A.I.C.S.: 551112; 325611; 325620
Advertising Expenditures: $265,200,000
Media: 3-6-13-15-16-18-24
Distr.: Intl.
Budget Set: June
Personnel:
Ronald O. Perelman *(Chm)*
David L. Kennedy *(Vice Chm)*
Alan T. Ennis *(Pres & CEO)*
Angie Justice *(Sr Lead Exec Asst to Vice Chm, CEO & COO)*
Steven Berns *(CFO & Exec VP)*
Chris Elshaw *(COO & Exec VP)*
Julia Goldin *(Sr VP & Global CMO)*
Robert K. Kretzman *(Chief Legal Officer, Gen Counsel & Exec VP-HR)*
Neil Scancarella *(Exec VP & Chief Science Officer)*
Gina Mastantuono *(Chief Acctg Officer & Sr VP)*
Mark M. Sexton *(Gen Counsel-Tax & Sr VP)*
Elise Garofalo *(Sr VP-Treas & IR)*
Carl Kooyoomjian *(Exec VP-Tech Affairs & Worldwide Ops)*
Karl Obrecht *(Exec VP-Sls)*
Manuel Blanco *(Mng Dir-Latin America & Sr VP)*
Graeme Howard *(Sr VP, Mng Dir-Asia Pacific, Africa & Worldwide Travel Retail)*
Arthur Franson *(Sr VP-Worldwide Mfg)*
Kiki Rees *(Sr VP-Media & Comm)*
Brands & Products:
ABSOLUTELY FABULOUS
ALMAY
CHARLIE
COLORSTAY
CUSTOM CREATIONS
FIRE & ICE
FROST & GLOW
GERMAINE MONTEIL
HIGH DIMENSION
JEANNE GATINEAU
LASH FANTASY
MITCHUM
NEW COMPLEXION
NINES
NO SWEAT
REVLON
SCAASI
SKINLIGHTS
SUPER LUSTROUS
SUPER TOP SPEED
ULTIMA II
UNFORGETTABLE
VISAGE
VITAL RADIANCE
VITAMIN C ABSOLUTE
Advertising Agencies:
Euro RSCG Worldwide Latin America
Gorriti 5995
C1414BKK
Buenos Aires, 1414, Argentina
Tel.: (54) 11 5288 6000
Fax: (54) 11 5288 6099

The Kaplan Thaler Group
825 8th Ave 34th Fl
New York, NY 10019
Tel.: (212) 474-5000
Fax: (212) 474-5702

MediaCom US
777 3rd Ave
New York, NY 10017-1401
Tel.: (212) 912-4200
Fax: (212) 508-4386

TAXI New York
455 Broadway 3rd Fl
New York, NY 10013
Tel.: (212) 414-8294
Fax: (212) 414-8444
Creative

ROBERTET, INC.
(Sub. of Robertet S.A.)
125 Bauer Dr

Key to Media (For complete agency information see *The Advertising Red Books-Agencies* edition):
1. Bus. Publs. 2. Cable T.V. 3. Catalogs & Directories. 4. Co-op Adv. 5. Consumer Mags. 6. D.M. to Bus. Estab.7. D.M. to Consumers 8. Daily Newsp. 9. Exhibits/Trade Shows 10. Foreign 11. Infomercial 12. Internet Adv.13. Multimedia 14. Network Radio 15. Network T.V. 16. Newsp. Distr. Mags. 17. Other 18. Outdoor (Posters, Transit) 19. Point of Purchase20. Premiums, Novelties 21. Product Samples 22. Special Events Mktg. 23. Spot Radio 24. Spot T.V. 25. Weekly Newsp. 26. Yellow Page Adv.

Oakland, NJ 07436-3123
Mailing Address:
PO Box 60
Oakland, NJ 07436-0660
Tel.: (201) 337-7100
Fax: (201) 337-0070
Web Site: www.robertet.com
Approx. Number Employees: 45
Year Founded: 1958
Business Description:
Produces Essential Aromatic & Specialty Oils, Perfume Compounds
S.I.C.: 5149; 2844
N.A.I.C.S.: 424490; 325620
Import Export
Advertising Expenditures: $700,000
Media: 2-4-11-20-21
Distr.: Intl.; Natl.
Budget Set: Apr.
Brands & Products:
ROBERTET

SALLY BEAUTY HOLDINGS, INC.
3001 Colorado Blvd
Denton, TX 76210
Mailing Address:
PO Box 490
Denton, TX 76202-0490
Tel.: (940) 898-7500
Fax: (940) 383-8143
E-mail: sbhinquiries@sallybeautyholdings.com
Web Site: www.sallybeautyholdings.com
Approx. Sls.: $2,916,090,000
Approx. Number Employees: 11,400
Year Founded: 1964
Business Description:
Professional Beauty Supplies Distr
S.I.C.: 5122; 5999
N.A.I.C.S.: 446120; 453998
Import
Advertising Expenditures: $64,600,000
Media: 1-3-4-5-6-7-8-9-16-17-18-19-20-21-22-23-24-25-26
Distr.: Direct to Consumer; Reg.; Wholesale to Trade
Personnel:
James G. Berges *(Chm)*
John R. Golliher *(Pres-BSG)*
Gary G. Winterhalter *(CEO)*
Mark J. Flaherty *(CFO & Sr VP)*
Cathy Witt *(CIO & Sr VP-Distr)*
Neil B. Riemer *(Pres-Armstrong McCall)*
Michael G. Spinozzi *(Pres-Sally Beauty Supply)*
Rahl H. Roos *(Gen Counsel, Sec & Sr VP)*
Bennie L. Lowery *(Sr VP & Gen Mgr-Mdsg-Beauty Sys Grp)*
Matt Haltom *(VP & Deputy Gen Counsel)*
Jim Biggerstaff *(VP-HR)*
Susan Walker *(VP-Mktg)*
Jan Roberts *(Dir-Corp Comm)*
Advertising Agency:
The King Group
1801 Northhampton Ste 410
Desoto, TX 75115
Tel.: (214) 720-9046
Fax: (214) 720-1435
(Ethnic Advertising)

SCHWARZKOPF & DEP, INC.
(Sub. of Henkel AG & Co. KGaA)
1063 McGaw Ave Ste 100
Irvine, CA 92614-5506
Tel.: (949) 794-5500
Fax: (949) 794-5501
E-mail: info@henkelna.com
Web Site: www.henkelna.com
Approx. Number Employees: 40
Year Founded: 1958
Business Description:
Personal Care Products Mfr, Marketer & Distr
S.I.C.: 2844; 5122
N.A.I.C.S.: 325620; 424210
Import Export
Media: 2-3-5-6-9-10-15-18-19-20-21-23-24
Distr.: Intl.; Natl.
Budget Set: Apr.
Personnel:
Lorrie Manning *(VP-Sls)*
Evangeline Bumagat *(Mgr-Brand Mktg, Schwarzkopf Professional)*
Brands & Products:
AGREE
DEP
FA
L. A. LOOKS
LAVORIS
LILT
NATURES FAMILY
PORCELANA
THEORIE
TOPOL
Advertising Agencies:
DDB Los Angeles
340 Main St
Venice, CA 90291
Tel.: (310) 907-1500
Fax: (310) 907-1571

MEC
2nd Fl Corner, Augustus Terr & Parnell Rise
Priv Bag 93234
Auckland, New Zealand
Tel.: (64) 9 308 5335
Fax: (64) 9 308 5405
Media

MEC
Level 14 65 Berry Street
Sydney, NSW 2060, Australia
Tel.: (61) 2 8356 0600
Fax: (61) 2 8356 0604
Media

SCOLDING LOCKS CORP.
1520 W Rogers Ave
Appleton, WI 54914-5007
Tel.: (920) 733-5561
Fax: (920) 733-8800
E-mail: info@scoldinglocks.com
Web Site: www.scoldinglocks.com
Approx. Sls.: $5,000,000
Approx. Number Employees: 85
Business Description:
Hair Rollers & Pins & Other Hair-Care Products Mfr
S.I.C.: 3965; 5131
N.A.I.C.S.: 339993; 424310
Media: 2-4-6-10-21
Distr.: Natl.
Budget Set: Nov.
Personnel:
Ted Skaer *(Pres)*

Brands & Products:
BEAUTY MAID
HOLLYWOOD
LA FEMME
LADY LORA
MAJORETTE
SALON SET

SEPHORA USA INC
(Sub. of Sephora)
525 Market St 11th Fl
San Francisco, CA 94105-2708
Tel.: (415) 284-3300
Fax: (415) 284-3434
Toll Free: (877) 737-4672
E-mail: customerservice@cs.sephora.com
Web Site: www.sephora.com
Approx. Number Employees: 220
Business Description:
Perfumes & Cosmetics Retailer
S.I.C.: 5122
N.A.I.C.S.: 446120
Media: 1-6-10-12-20-21-24
Personnel:
David Suliteanu *(Pres & CEO)*
Patrick J. Murray, Jr. *(CFO & Sr VP)*
Pauline Roothman *(Sr VP-HR)*
Sharon Rothstein *(Sr VP-Mktg)*
Kelly Coller *(Dir-Mktg-Sephora Originals)*

SHISEIDO COSMETICS AMERICA OF SAC
(Unit of Shiseido Americas Corporation)
900 3rd Ave Fl 15
New York, NY 10022-4795
Tel.: (212) 805-2300
Fax: (212) 688-0109
E-mail: info@sca.shiseido.com
Web Site: www.sca.shiseido.com
Approx. Sls.: $200,000,000
Approx. Number Employees: 1,128
Year Founded: 1965
Business Description:
Cosmetics Whslr
S.I.C.: 5122
N.A.I.C.S.: 424210
Import
Media: 2-5-6-8-9-19-20-21-22-23-24-25
Distr.: Natl.
Budget Set: Sept.
Personnel:
Heidi Manheimer *(Pres & CEO)*
Toshitada Hori *(COO)*
Linda Ten Eyck *(Sr VP-Sls Ops)*
Jadzia Tirch *(Sr VP-Adv & PR)*
Gisela Ballard *(Exec Dir Mktg)*
Nicole Cardillo *(Dir-PR)*
Elana McElrath *(Mgr-HR)*
Brands & Products:
ADVANCED ESSENTIAL ENERGY
BIO-PERFORMANCE
ENERGIZING FRAGRANCE
PURENESS
SHISEIDO THE SKINCARE
SUNCARE
VITAL-PERFECTION
VOCALISE
ZEN
Advertising Agency:
AdAsia Communications, Inc.
85 Fifth Ave 7th Fl
New York, NY 10003
Tel.: (212) 871-6886
Fax: (212) 871-6883

SOFT SHEEN/CARSON PRODUCTS, INC.
(Div. of L'Oreal USA, Inc.)
575 Fifth Ave 19th Fl
New York, NY 10017
Tel.: (212) 818-1500
Toll Free: (800) 442-4643
Web Site: www.softsheen-carson.com
Approx. Number Employees: 150
Year Founded: 1964
Business Description:
Hair Care Products Mfr
S.I.C.: 2844
N.A.I.C.S.: 325620
Media: 2-4-5-6-7-8-16-17-18-19-22-23-24-26
Distr.: Natl.

ST. IVES LABORATORIES, INC.
(Sub. of Alberto-Culver Company)
20355 Corisco St
Chatsworth, CA 91311-6520
Tel.: (818) 998-3511
Fax: (818) 349-9749
Approx. Rev.: $59,000,000
Approx. Number Employees: 150
Year Founded: 1996
Business Description:
Perfumes Cosmetics & Other Toilet Preparations
S.I.C.: 2844
N.A.I.C.S.: 325620
Media: 6
Personnel:
Howard B. Bernick *(Chm)*
Oscar Saldarriaga *(Gen Mgr)*
Advertising Agency:
EVB-Evolution Bureau
55 Union St
San Francisco, CA 94111
Tel.: (415) 281-3950
Fax: (415) 281-3957
Facial Cleansers

STA-RITE GINNIE LOU, INC.
245 E S 1st St
Shelbyville, IL 62565-2332
Mailing Address:
PO Box 435
Shelbyville, IL 62565-0435
Tel.: (217) 774-3921
Fax: (217) 774-5234
Toll Free: (800) STARITE
Toll Free: (800) 782-7483
E-mail: sales@sta-riteginnielou.com
Web Site: www.sta-riteginnielou.com
E-Mail For Key Personnel:
Sales Director: sales@sta-riteginnielou.com
Approx. Number Employees: 15
Year Founded: 1917
Business Description:
Bobby Pins, Hair Pins, Roller Clips, Rubber Bands, Metal-Free Ponytail Holders, Hair Brushes, Combs, Lifts, Piks, Trimmers, Barrettes, Clamps, Side Combs, Hair Ornaments, Hair Nets, Wave Nets, Caps, Bonnets, Rollers & Rods Mfr & Distr
S.I.C.: 3965
N.A.I.C.S.: 339993
Import Export
Media: 4-7-10-21
Distr.: Intl.; Natl.
Personnel:
Robert N. Bolinger *(Chm)*
Noel Bolinger *(Pres)*

Key to Media (For complete agency information see *The Advertising Red Books-Agencies* edition):
1. Bus. Publs. 2. Cable T.V. 3. Catalogs & Directories. 4. Co-op Adv. 5. Consumer Mags. 6. D.M. to Bus. Estab.7. D.M. to Consumers 8. Daily Newsp. 9. Exhibits/Trade Shows 10. Foreign 11. Infomercial 12. Internet Adv.13. Multimedia 14. Network Radio 15. Network T.V. 16. Newsp. Distr. Mags. 17. Other 18. Outdoor (Posters, Transit) 19. Point of Purchase20. Premiums, Novelties 21. Product Samples 22. Special Events Mktg. 23. Spot Radio 24. Spot T.V. 25. Weekly Newsp. 26. Yellow Page Adv.

Sta-Rite Ginnie Lou, Inc. — (Continued)

Brands & Products:
FAS-PIK
PONY OH'S
SNAP-EZE
STA-RITE
TINY TWEEZ

STEARNS PRODUCTS INC.
(d/b/a Derma e)
4485 Runway St
Simi Valley, CA 93063
Tel.: (805) 582-2710
Fax: (805) 582-2730
Toll Free: (800) 521-3342
Web Site: www.dermae.net
Sales Range: $1-9.9 Million
Approx. Number Employees: 10
Business Description:
Beauty Care Products
S.I.C.: 2844
N.A.I.C.S.: 325620
Media: 6-13
Personnel:
David Stearn *(Pres)*
Susan Morehart *(Dir-Sls & Mktg)*
Brands & Products:
DERMA E

STILA CORP.
(Holding of Patriarch Partners, LLC)
2801 Hyperion Ave Ste 102
Los Angeles, CA 90027
Tel.: (866) 784-5201
Fax: (323) 913-1493
E-mail: custcare@stilacosmetics.com
Web Site: www.stilacosmetics.com
Approx. Number Employees: 24
Business Description:
Cosmetics
S.I.C.: 2844
N.A.I.C.S.: 325620
Media: 2-6
Personnel:
Deanna Kangas *(CEO)*
Kaci Harabedian *(Dir-Sls & Mktg)*
Lindsey Kracum *(Online Mktg Mgr)*

STRAIGHT ARROW PRODUCTS, INC.
2020 Highland Ave
Bethlehem, PA 18020
Tel.: (610) 882-9606
Fax: (610) 882-9688
Web Site: www.manentail.com
Sales Range: $1-9.9 Million
Approx. Number Employees: 35
Business Description:
Hair Care & Skin Care Products Mfr
S.I.C.: 2834; 2844
N.A.I.C.S.: 325412; 325620
Media: 2-3-4-6-10-13-21
Personnel:
Devon Katzev *(Pres)*
Ed Kline *(VP-Sls & Mktg)*
Brands & Products:
BARRIER
FOOT MIRACLE
HOOFMAKER
MANE 'N TAIL
MINERAL ICE
THE ORIGINAL MANE'N TAIL
PRO-TECT
RECONSTRUCTOR
SHINE-ON
SKIN MIRACLE
STRAIGHT ARROW

SUPERCUTS, INC.
(Sub. of Regis Corporation)
7201 Metro Blvd
Minneapolis, MN 55439
Tel.: (952) 947-7777
Fax: (952) 947-7600
Toll Free: (888) 888-7778
Web Site: www.supercuts.com
Sales Range: $300-349.9 Million
Approx. Number Employees: 4,000
Year Founded: 1975
Business Description:
Haircare Retailer & Franchisor
S.I.C.: 7231
N.A.I.C.S.: 812112
Media: 15
Personnel:
Diane Calta *(COO)*
Advertising Agencies:
Element 79
(Part of the Omincom Group)
200 E Randolph St 33rd Fl
Chicago, IL 60601
Tel.: (312) 233-8100
Fax: (312) 233-8298

Hill Holliday
53 State St
Boston, MA 02109
Tel.: (617) 366-4000
Media Agency of Record
Media Strategy, Planning & Buying

TANNING RESEARCH LABORATORIES, INC.
(Sub. of Playtex Products, Inc.)
(d/b/a Hawaiian Tropic)
1190 N US Hwy 1
Ormond Beach, FL 32174-2997
Tel.: (386) 677-9559
Fax: (386) 677-9595
Toll Free: (800) 874-4844
Web Site: www.hawaiiantropic.com
Sales Range: $50-74.9 Million
Approx. Number Employees: 200
Year Founded: 1969
Business Description:
Skin Care Product Mfr
S.I.C.: 2844
N.A.I.C.S.: 325620
Advertising Expenditures: $3,500,000
Media: 2-4-5-6-7-8-10-11-13-14-18-19-20-21-22-23-25
Distr.: Intl.; Natl.
Budget Set: Apr. -June

TOM'S OF MAINE, INC.
(Div. of Colgate-Palmolive Company)
302 Lafayette Ctr
Kennebunk, ME 04043-0710
Tel.: (207) 985-2944
Fax: (207) 985-2196
Toll Free: (800) 367-8667
E-mail: info@tomsofmaine.com
Web Site: www.tomsofmaine.com
Sales Range: $25-49.9 Million
Approx. Number Employees: 175
Year Founded: 1970
Business Description:
Natural Toothpaste, Deodorant, Mouthwash, Shaving Cream, Cough & Cold Wellness Products, Glycerin Bars, Liquid Soap & Dental Ribbon Mfr
S.I.C.: 2841; 2844
N.A.I.C.S.: 325611; 325620
Personnel:
Tom O'Brien *(CEO)*

Brands & Products:
NATURALLY, IT WORKS.
Advertising Agencies:
PGR Media, LLC.
34 Farnsworth St 2nd Fl
Boston, MA 02210
Tel.: (617) 502-8400
Fax: (617) 451-0451

ZAAZ
414 Olive Way Ste 500
Seattle, WA 98101
Tel.: (206) 341-9885
Fax: (206) 749-9868

TONI & GUY USA, INC.
2311 Midway Rd
Dallas, TX 75006
Tel.: (972) 931-1567
Fax: (972) 248-0798
Toll Free: (800) 236-9391
Web Site: www.toniguy.com
Sales Range: $200-249.9 Million
Approx. Number Employees: 450
Business Description:
Haircare Products; Hair Salons
S.I.C.: 7231; 5087
N.A.I.C.S.: 812112; 423850
Media: 6-10
Personnel:
Bruno Mascolo *(Pres)*
Kyara Mascolo *(VP-Mktg)*
Brands & Products:
BED HEAD
CATWALK
CURLS ROCK
TIGI
TONI & GUY

TRANS-INDIA PRODUCTS, INC.
(d/b/a SHIKAI Products)
3354 Coffey Ln Ste A
Santa Rosa, CA 95403
Tel.: (707) 544-0298
Fax: (707) 544-0266
E-mail: info@shikai.com
Web Site: www.shikai.com
Sales Range: $1-9.9 Million
Approx. Number Employees: 15
Business Description:
Cosmetics Mfr
S.I.C.: 2844
N.A.I.C.S.: 325620
Media: 6
Personnel:
Jason Sepp *(Dir-Mktg)*

TRI-K INDUSTRIES, INC.
(Sub. of Galaxy Surfactants Limited)
151 Veterans Dr
Northvale, NJ 07647
Mailing Address:
PO Box 128
Northvale, NJ 07647-0128
Tel.: (201) 750-1055
Fax: (201) 750-9785
Toll Free: (800) 526-0372
E-mail: info@tri-k.com
Web Site: www.tri-k.com
E-Mail For Key Personnel:
President: renod@tri-k.com
Sales Range: $10-24.9 Million
Approx. Number Employees: 50
Year Founded: 1973
Business Description:
Cosmetic Ingredients Supplier
S.I.C.: 5122; 5169
N.A.I.C.S.: 424210; 424690
Import Export
Media: 4-10
Distr.: Natl.
Budget Set: Jan.
Personnel:
Reno Del Dotto *(Pres)*
John Carratura *(Acct Mgr-Inside Sls)*
Doug Krysiak *(Mgr-Product Bus)*
Brands & Products:
BIOBASE
GLOSSAMER
SOLASHIELD

TWEEZERMAN INTERNATIONAL
(Sub. of Henkel AG & Co. KGaA)
2 Tri Harbor Ct
Port Washington, NY 11050
Tel.: (516) 676-7772
Fax: (516) 676-8788
Toll Free: (800) 645-3340
E-mail: info@tweezerman.com
Web Site: www.tweezerman.com
Approx. Number Employees: 175
Year Founded: 1980
Business Description:
Grooming & Beauty Products
S.I.C.: 5087; 5122
N.A.I.C.S.: 423850; 446120
Media: 2-4-6-10-22
Personnel:
Cornelia Wittke *(Pres & CEO)*
Art Malen *(Exec VP-Sls-Global)*
Jerry Agostisi *(VP-IT)*
Danielle Rosen *(Dir-Mktg)*
Brands & Products:
BROWMOUSSE
GERMBUSTER
MASCARA PROTECTOR
PEDI-SOX
SLANT
TWEEZERMAN

ULTA SALON, COSMETICS & FRAGRANCE, INC.
1000 Remington Blvd Ste 120
Bolingbrook, IL 60440
Tel.: (630) 410-4800
Toll Free: (866) 340-3704
E-mail: investorrelations@ulta.com
Web Site: www.ulta.com
Approx. Sls.: $1,454,838,000
Approx. Number Employees: 4,000
Year Founded: 1990
Business Description:
Cosmetics, Beauty Supplies, Perfumes & Accessories Retailer
S.I.C.: 5122; 7231
N.A.I.C.S.: 446120; 812112
Import
Advertising Expenditures: $84,796,000
Media: 1-4-5-6-8-9-13-16-22-25
Distr.: Reg.
Personnel:
Gregg R. Bodnar *(CFO)*
Robert S. Guttman *(Gen Counsel, Sec & Sr VP)*
Joe Addante *(VP-Fin)*
Allan Frostman *(Dir-Merchandise & Mktg Finance)*
Brands & Products:
BASICALLY U
FORMATIV
ULTA BEAUTY
ULTA PROFESSIONAL
ULTA.COM

Key to Media (For complete agency information see *The Advertising Red Books-Agencies* edition):
1. Bus. Publs. 2. Cable T.V. 3. Catalogs & Directories. 4. Co-op Adv. 5. Consumer Mags. 6. D.M. to Bus. Estab.7. D.M. to Consumers 8. Daily Newsp. 9. Exhibits/Trade Shows 10. Foreign 11. Infomercial 12. Internet Adv.13. Multimedia 14. Network Radio 15. Network T.V. 16. Newsp. Distr. Mags. 17. Other 18. Outdoor (Posters, Transit) 19. Point of Purchase20. Premiums, Novelties 21. Product Samples 22. Special Events Mktg. 23. Spot Radio 24. Spot T.V. 25. Weekly Newsp. 26. Yellow Page Adv.

Advertising Agencies:
DKC
386 Park Ave S 10th Fl
New York, NY 10016
Tel.: (212) 685-4300
Fax: (212) 685-9024
Agency of Record
Consumer Publicity

The Richards Group, Inc.
8750 N Central Expy Ste 100
Dallas, TX 75231-6430
Tel.: (214) 891-5700
Fax: (214) 265-2933
Strategic Marketing

Schawk Retail Marketing
1 N Dearborn Ste 700
Chicago, IL 60602
Tel.: (312) 666-9200
Fax: (312) 260-1970
Toll Free: (888) AMBROSI

UNGERER & COMPANY

4 Bridgewater Ln
Lincoln Park, NJ 07035-1439
Mailing Address:
PO Box U
Lincoln Park, NJ 07035-0900
Tel.: (973) 628-0600
Fax: (973) 628-0251
Telex: 4754267
E-mail: aking@ungerer.org
Web Site:
www.ungererandcompany.com
Approx. Number Employees: 125
Year Founded: 1893
Business Description:
Essential Oils, Aromatic Chemicals, Fragrance Bases, Perfume Specialties, Imitation & Genuine Fruit Flavors Mfr, Developer & Marketer
S.I.C.: 2087; 2844
N.A.I.C.S.: 311930; 325620
Media: 4-7-13-21
Distr.: Intl.; Natl.
Budget Set: Oct.
Personnel:
Kenneth G. Voorhees *(Pres)*
Rick Dambres *(CFO)*
Tom Volckening *(Pres-Flavor Div)*
John Olsen *(VP-Sls)*

VIDAL SASSOON CO.

(Sub. of The Procter & Gamble Company)
PO Box 599
Cincinnati, OH 45201-0599
Tel.: (513) 983-1100
Fax: (513) 983-2230
Toll Free: (888) 855-8987
Web Site: www.pg.com/company/who_we_are/worldwide_operations.shtml
Sales Range: $1-4.9 Billion
Year Founded: 1885
Business Description:
Professional & Retail Hair Care Mfr & Marketer; Beauty Salons Licensor; Hair Care Appliances Mfr
S.I.C.: 2844; 3589; 5122; 7231
N.A.I.C.S.: 325620; 333319; 446120; 812112
Media: 6-9-10-11-15-19-24
Distr.: Natl.
Budget Set: Jan.
Personnel:
Jim Stengel *(Global Mktg Officer)*

Brands & Products:
VIDAL SASSOON

Advertising Agency:
Leo Burnett Worldwide, Inc.
35 W Wacker Dr
Chicago, IL 60601-1723
Tel.: (312) 220-5959
Fax: (312) 220-3299

WAHL CLIPPER CORPORATION

2900 Locust St
Sterling, IL 61081-0578
Tel.: (815) 625-6525
Fax: (815) 625-0091
Web Site: www.wahlclipper.com
Approx. Number Employees: 2,000
Year Founded: 1919
Business Description:
Hair Clippers, Beard & Mustache Trimmers, Cordless Soldering Irons, Shavers & Massagers Mfr
S.I.C.: 3999; 3634
N.A.I.C.S.: 339999; 335211
Import Export
Media: 3-5-6-10-12
Distr.: Natl.
Budget Set: Oct. -Nov.
Personnel:
Gregory S. Wahl *(Chm & CEO)*
Bruce Kramer *(VP-Sls & Mktg)*
Pat Anello *(Dir-Mktg)*

Brands & Products:
5 STAR SERIES
BALDFADER
CHROMEPRO
CLIP 'N TRIM
COMB 'N CUT
GROOMSMAN
HOMECUT
HOMEPRO
ISO-TIP
LADY WAHL
LIFT 'N WASH
MASSAGE MASTER
METRO
STERLING
STUBBLE DEVICE
TRIM
TRIM 'N VAC
TRUEGUARD
WAHL
WAHL CUSTOM SHAVE SYSTEM
WAHL PROFESSIONAL
WAHL TRIM N VAC

Advertising Agency:
Marketing Support, Inc.
200 E Randolph Dr Ste 5000
Chicago, IL 60601
Tel.: (312) 565-0044
Fax: (312) 946-6100

THE W.E. BASSETT COMPANY

100 Trap Falls Rd
Shelton, CT 06484
Tel.: (203) 929-8483
Fax: (203) 929-8963
E-mail: rsalkowski@trim.com
Web Site: www.trim.com
E-Mail For Key Personnel:
Marketing Director: lperry@trim.com
Approx. Number Employees: 150
Year Founded: 1939
Business Description:
Mfr. of Manicure Implements, Gift Sets & Personal Care Products
S.I.C.: 3421; 2844
N.A.I.C.S.: 332211; 325620
Import Export
Media: 2-4-5-10-16-19-21
Distr.: Intl.; Natl.
Budget Set: Dec.
Personnel:
William C. Bassett *(Chm)*
V. C. Finney *(Pres)*
Paul Jones *(VP-Fin)*
Hugh Scollins *(VP-Sls & Mktg)*
Amanda Kmetz *(Mgr-Mktg)*

Brands & Products:
DIAMON DEB
EASY HOLD
GEM
KURLASH
KURLASH/DIAMON DEB
NEAT FEET
TOOLS FOR THE PROS
TOTALLY TOGETHER
TRIM
TRIM FOR TOTS

THE WELLA CORPORATION

(Sub. of Wella AG)
6109 DeSoto Ave
Woodland Hills, CA 91367
Tel.: (818) 999-5112
Fax: (818) 712-7770
Toll Free: (800) 526-4657
E-mail: hotline@wellasebastian.com
Web Site: www.wellausa.com
Sales Range: $800-899.9 Million
Approx. Number Employees: 1,045
Year Founded: 1931
Business Description:
Hair Care Products Mfr
S.I.C.: 2844; 2841
N.A.I.C.S.: 325620; 325611
Import Export
Media: 2-3-6-9-10-15-19-20-21-22-24
Distr.: Natl.
Budget Set: Sept.
Personnel:
Ruben Carranza *(Mng Dir)*

Brands & Products:
KOLESTRAL
LIQUID HAIR

WHITE RAIN CORPORATION

(Div. of Diamond Products Company)
PO Box 1777
Mango, FL 33550
Tel.: (813) 622-8895
Fax: (813) 630-0234
Toll Free: (800) 575-7960
E-mail: comments@whiterain.com
Web Site: www.whiterain.com
Approx. Number Employees: 300
Business Description:
Beauty Products Mfr
S.I.C.: 5122; 2844
N.A.I.C.S.: 424210; 325620
Export
Media: 2-3-6-7-8-10-13-15-18-20-22
Personnel:
Thayer Smith *(Pres & CEO)*

Brands & Products:
ADORN
DIPPITY-DO SPORT
DIPPITY-DO TECHNO
THE DRY LOOK
MINK DIFFERENCE
TAME
TE-TAO
TONI
WHITE RAIN

YSL BEAUTE, INC.

(Sub. of Gucci Group N.V.)
3 E 57th St
New York, NY 10022
Tel.: (212) 980-2970
Fax: (212) 715-7379
Telex: 62843457
Web Site: www.ysl.com
Sales Range: $900-999.9 Million
Approx. Number Employees: 125
Year Founded: 1973
Business Description:
Perfumes & Fragrances Mfr & Distr
S.I.C.: 5122; 5311
N.A.I.C.S.: 446120; 452111
Advertising Expenditures: $250,000
Media: 6-7-8-9-10-11-13-19-23-24-25
Distr.: Intl.; Natl.
Personnel:
Laura Lendrun *(Pres)*

Brands & Products:
FIRST
STENDHAL
VOLUPTE

ZKIN

The Miami Institute Four Seasons Hotel 1441 Brickle Ave
Miami, FL 33131
Tel.: (305) 651-9903
Fax: (305) 651-4278
Toll Free: (877) 428-FACE
E-mail: info@zkin.net
Web Site: www.zkin.net
Business Description:
Skin Care Products
S.I.C.: 5122
N.A.I.C.S.: 446120
Media: 8-13
Personnel:
Stephen A. Watson *(CEO)*
Julio F. Gallo *(Dir-Medical)*

Brands & Products:
ZKIN

ZOTOS INTERNATIONAL, INC.

(Sub. of Shiseido Company Ltd. - Pharmaceutical, Salon & Food Products Division)
100 Tokeneke Rd
Darien, CT 06820-4825
Tel.: (203) 655-8911
Toll Free: (800) 242-9283
E-mail: info@zotos.com
Web Site: www.zotos.com
Approx. Number Employees: 120
Year Founded: 1929
Business Description:
Beauty Aid Products Mfr & Distr
S.I.C.: 2844
N.A.I.C.S.: 325620
Advertising Expenditures: $4,000,000
Media: 2-5-6-7-8-10-11-16-19-20-21-22
Distr.: Intl.
Personnel:
Bruce Selan *(VP)*

Brands & Products:
7TH DIMENSION
ACCLAIM
BAIN DE TERRE
BLONDIE
C'BONTE
DESIGN FREEDOM
DUO CLEAN
DUO-THERM
FEELS SO LIVELY

Key to Media (For complete agency information see *The Advertising Red Books-Agencies* edition):
1. Bus. Publs. 2. Cable T.V. 3. Catalogs & Directories. 4. Co-op Adv. 5. Consumer Mags. 6. D.M. to Bus. Estab.7. D.M. to Consumers 8. Daily Newsp. 9. Exhibits/Trade Shows 10. Foreign 11. Infomercial 12. Internet Adv.13. Multimedia 14. Network Radio 15. Network T.V. 16. Newsp. Distr. Mags. 17. Other 18. Outdoor (Posters, Transit) 19. Point of Purchase20. Premiums, Novelties 21. Product Samples 22. Special Events Mktg. 23. Spot Radio 24. Spot T.V. 25. Weekly Newsp. 26. Yellow Page Adv.

Zotos International, Inc. — (Continued)

FORECAST
GENTLE PURSUASION
GLOSSTONES
LIKE NATURAL
LUSTRE FINISH
MIRACLE FINISH
MOISTURE WAVE
NATURELLE
NUTRI-OX SYSTEM
PERFECT COMB-OUT
POST IMPRESSIONS
TEXTURE CARE
THEATRICS
THERM-A-SENTIALS
THERMODYNAMICS
ULTRABOND
VARIATIONS
VOLUMAX CURL REDUCER
WARM & GENTLE
WAVE LENGTHS
Z FORCE
ZOTOS

Advertising Agency:
Pierce Mattie Public Relations
62 W 45th St Fl 3
New York, NY 10036
Tel.: (212) 243-1431
Fax: (212) 243-7795
Beauty Products

Key to Media (For complete agency information see *The Advertising Red Books-Agencies* edition):
1. Bus. Publs. 2. Cable T.V. 3. Catalogs & Directories. 4. Co-op Adv. 5. Consumer Mags. 6. D.M. to Bus. Estab.7. D.M. to Consumers
8. Daily Newsp. 9. Exhibits/Trade Shows 10. Foreign 11. Infomercial 12. Internet Adv.13. Multimedia 14. Network Radio
15. Network T.V. 16. Newsp. Distr. Mags. 17. Other 18. Outdoor (Posters, Transit) 19. Point of Purchase20. Premiums, Novelties
21. Product Samples 22. Special Events Mktg. 23. Spot Radio 24. Spot T.V. 25. Weekly Newsp. 26. Yellow Page Adv.

Cultural & Recreational Entertainment

Amusement Parks — Entertainment Facilities — Museums — Musical Instruments — Professional Sports Clubs

24 HOUR FITNESS WORLDWIDE INC.
(Holding of Forstmann Little & Co.)
12647 Alcosta Blvd 5th Fl
San Ramon, CA 94583
Mailing Address:
PO Box 2689
San Ramon, CA 92018
Tel.: (925) 543-3100
Fax: (925) 543-3200
Toll Free: (800) 432-6348
Web Site: www.24hourfitness.com
Approx. Number Employees: 20,000
Year Founded: 1983
Business Description:
Fitness Centers Owner & Operator
S.I.C.: 7991
N.A.I.C.S.: 713940
Media: 4-8-26
Personnel:
C. Lieberg *(CEO)*
Tony Wells *(CMO & Exec VP)*
Bill Quinn *(Sr VP-Mdsg)*
Franck Ardourel *(Sr Dir-Online Mktg)*
Brands & Products:
24 HOUR FITNESS
HART'S ATHLETIC CLUBS
Q CLUBS
Advertising Agency:
Barkley
1740 Main St
Kansas City, MO 64108
Tel.: (816) 842-1500

3ALITY DIGITAL, LLC
55 E Orange Grove Ave
Burbank, CA 91502
Tel.: (818) 333-3000
Fax: (818) 333-3001
E-mail: info@3alitydigital.com
Web Site: www.3alitydigital.com
Approx. Number Employees: 55
Year Founded: 2006
Business Description:
Live-Action 3D Feature Films & Commercials Producer
S.I.C.: 7812
N.A.I.C.S.: 512110
Media: 18
Personnel:
Steve Schklair *(Founder & CEO)*
David Modell *(Chm)*
Gari Ann Douglass *(CFO & COO)*

A N D MUSIC CORP.
(Sub. of Young Chang Akki Co. Ltd.)
(d/b/a Young Chang)
19060 S Dominguez Hill Dr
Rancho Dominguez, CA 90220
Tel.: (310) 637-2000
Fax: (310) 637-2025
Toll Free: (866) 798-6979
E-mail: info@youngchang.com
Web Site: www.youngchang.com
Sales Range: $50-74.9 Million
Approx. Number Employees: 35
Year Founded: 1984
Business Description:
Piano Mfr
S.I.C.: 3931
N.A.I.C.S.: 339992
Import
Advertising Expenditures: $500,000
Media: 6
Distr.: Natl.
Budget Set: Dec.
Personnel:
Vincent Choi *(Exec VP)*
Brands & Products:
BERGMANN
KURZWEIL
PRAINBERGER
YOUNG CHANG

ABILENE PHILHARMONIC ASSOCIATION
402 Cypress St Ste 130
Abilene, TX 79601
Tel.: (325) 677-6710
Fax: (325) 677-6710
Toll Free: (800) 460-0610
E-mail: philharmonic@abilene.com
Web Site:
www.abilenephilharmonic.org
Sales Range: Less than $1 Million
Approx. Number Employees: 4
Business Description:
Symphony Orchestra
S.I.C.: 7929
N.A.I.C.S.: 711130
Media: 9-13-18-20-22-23-24-25
Personnel:
Leanne Baldwin *(Exec Dir)*
David Itkin *(Dir-Music)*

ACADEMY OF MOTION PICTURE ARTS & SCIENCES
8949 Wilshire Blvd
Beverly Hills, CA 90211-1907
Tel.: (310) 247-3000
Fax: (310) 285-9619
E-mail: ampas@oscars.org
Web Site: www.oscars.org
Approx. Number Employees: 175
Year Founded: 1927
Business Description:
Organization for the Promotion of Motion Pictures
S.I.C.: 7829; 8621
N.A.I.C.S.: 512199; 813920
Media: 6-10-15-22
Personnel:
Tom Sherak *(Pres)*
Bruce Davis *(Exec Dir)*
Richard Miller *(Dir-Awards Admin)*
Leslie Unger *(Dir-Comm)*
Janet Weiss *(Dir-Mktg)*
Brands & Products:
ACADEMY AWARDS
A.M.P.A.S.
NICHOLL FELLOWSHIPS
OSCAR
OSCAR NIGHT
OSCARS
SCI-TECH AWARDS
STUDENT ACADEMY AWARDS
Advertising Agencies:
Carlsson & Company Inc.
29710 Whitley Collins Dr
Rancho Palos Verdes, CA 90275
Tel.: (310) 377-7582
Fax: (888) 415-2101

TBWA Chiat Day Los Angeles
5353 Grosvenor Blvd
Los Angeles, CA 90066
Tel.: (310) 305-5000
Fax: (310) 305-6000

ACADIANA SYMPHONY ASSOCIATION
412 Travis St
Lafayette, LA 70505
Mailing Address:
PO Box 53632
Lafayette, LA 70505
Tel.: (337) 232-4277
Fax: (337) 237-4712
Web Site:
www.acadianasymphony.org
Sales Range: Less than $1 Million
Approx. Number Employees: 5
Business Description:
Symphony Orchestra
S.I.C.: 7929
N.A.I.C.S.: 711130
Media: 9-20-23-24-25
Personnel:
Mona Burris *(Exec Dir)*
Taryn Marceaux *(Dir-Education)*
Mariusz Smolij *(Dir-Music & Conductor)*
Ivan Antonov *(Mgr-Personnel & Librarian)*
Tonio Cutrera *(Mgr-Ops)*

THE ADLER PLANETARIUM & ASTRONOMY MUSEUM
1300 S Lk Shore Dr
Chicago, IL 60605-2403
Tel.: (312) 922-7827
Fax: (312) 322-2257
E-mail: pr@adlerplanetarium.org
Web Site: www.adlerplanetarium.org
E-Mail For Key Personnel:
Public Relations: pr@adlernet.org
Approx. Number Employees: 200
Year Founded: 1930
Business Description:
Planetarium, History & Science Museum
S.I.C.: 8412
N.A.I.C.S.: 712110
Import Export
Media: 1-4-6-8-9-10-15-21-22-23
Distr.: Direct to Consumer; Reg.
Personnel:
Brian C. Cressey *(Chm)*
Paul H. Knappenberger *(Pres)*
Marge Marek *(COO & Exec VP)*

ADVENTURE ISLAND
(Unit of SeaWorld Parks & Entertainment LLC)
4500 E Bougainvillea Ave
Tampa, FL 33617-3443
Tel.: (813) 987-5600
Fax: (813) 987-5654
Web Site: www.adventureisland.com
Sales Range: $75-99.9 Million
Approx. Number Employees: 450
Business Description:
Water Theme Park
S.I.C.: 7996
N.A.I.C.S.: 713110
Media: 9
Personnel:
Jim Dean *(Pres)*
Tonia Mercado *(Office Mgr)*

Key to Media (For complete agency information see *The Advertising Red Books-Agencies* edition):
1. Bus. Publs. 2. Cable T.V. 3. Catalogs & Directories. 4. Co-op Adv. 5. Consumer Mags. 6. D.M. to Bus. Estab.7. D.M. to Consumers
8. Daily Newsp. 9. Exhibits/Trade Shows 10. Foreign 11. Infomercial 12. Internet Adv.13. Multimedia 14. Network Radio
15. Network T.V. 16. Newsp. Distr. Mags. 17. Other 18. Outdoor (Posters, Transit) 19. Point of Purchase20. Premiums, Novelties
21. Product Samples 22. Special Events Mktg. 23. Spot Radio 24. Spot T.V. 25. Weekly Newsp. 26. Yellow Page Adv.

ADVENTURE LANDS OF AMERICA, INC.
305 34th Ave NW
Altoona, IA 50009
Tel.: (515) 266-2121
Fax: (515) 266-9831
Toll Free: (800) 532-1286
E-mail: info@adventurelandpark.com
Web Site: www.adventurelandpark.com
Approx. Number Employees: 1,000
Year Founded: 1972
Business Description:
Amusement Park
S.I.C.: 7996; 7011
N.A.I.C.S.: 713110; 721110
Media: 2-3-5-6-7-8-9-13-18-22-23-24-25
Distr.: Direct to Consumer; Reg.
Budget Set: Nov.
Personnel:
John F. Krantz *(Chm, CEO & Chief Imaginer)*
Dan A. Bohner *(CFO)*
Doug Cornwell *(COO)*
Bill Fisher *(Dir-Mktg)*
Brands & Products:
ADVENTURELAND
Advertising Agency:
Main Street Enterprises (House Agency)
PO Box 3355
Des Moines, IA 50316
Tel.: (515) 266-2121
(Adventureland Park, Adventureland Inn & Adventureland Campground)

AKRON SYMPHONY ORCHESTRA
17 N Broadway
Akron, OH 44308
Tel.: (330) 535-8131
Fax: (330) 535-7302
Web Site: www.akronsymphony.org
Approx. Number Employees: 85
Business Description:
Symphony Orchestra
S.I.C.: 7929
N.A.I.C.S.: 711130
Media: 1-4-5-6-8-9-13-20-23-24-25-26
Personnel:
Cory Smith *(Principal-Librarian)*
Philip Wallz *(Exec Dir)*
Renee Dee *(Dir-Artistic Plng)*
Hugh Floid *(Dir-Chorus)*
Jason Swank *(Dir-Mktg & PR)*
Christopher Wilkins *(Dir-Music)*

ALABAMA SYMPHONY ORCHESTRA
3621 6th Ave S
Birmingham, AL 35222
Tel.: (205) 251-6929
Fax: (205) 251-6840
E-mail: orchestra@alabamasymphony.com
Web Site: www.alabamasymphony.org
Approx. Number Employees: 72
Business Description:
Symphony Orchestra
S.I.C.: 7929
N.A.I.C.S.: 711130
Media: 6-8-9-13-18-20-22-23-24-25
Personnel:
Justin Brown *(Dir-Music)*
Mark Patrick *(Interim Dir-Ops)*
Advertising Agency:
DavisDenny Advertising & Related Services, Inc.
2545 Highland Ave
Birmingham, AL 35205
Tel.: (205) 933-0355
Fax: (205) 933-1450

ALACHUA COUNTY VISITORS & CONVENTION BUREAU
30 E University Ave
Gainesville, FL 32601
Tel.: (352) 374-5260
Fax: (352) 338-3213
Web Site: www.visitgainesville.com
Business Description:
Tourism Promoter
S.I.C.: 7389
N.A.I.C.S.: 561591
Advertising Expenditures: $200,000
Media: 6
Personnel:
Nancy Fischer *(Dir-Sls)*
Roland Loog *(Dir-Tourism Dev)*
Tamara Herchel *(Mgr)*
Marcheta Keefer *(Mgr-Tourism & Media Mktg)*

ALBANY SYMPHONY ORCHESTRA
308 Flint Ave
Albany, GA 31701
Mailing Address:
PO Box 70065
Albany, GA 31708-0065
Tel.: (229) 317-6799
Fax: (229) 430-6798
E-mail: albanysymphony@yahoo.com
Web Site: www.albanysymphony.org
Year Founded: 1965
Business Description:
Symphony Orchestra
S.I.C.: 7929
N.A.I.C.S.: 711130
Media: 9-23-24-25
Personnel:
Diane Kern Cunningham *(Pres)*
Paula Fay *(Exec Dir)*
Claire Fox Hillard *(Dir-Music & Conductor)*
Edward J. Trammell *(Mgr-Ops & PR)*

ALBANY SYMPHONY ORCHESTRA
19 Clinton Ave
Albany, NY 12207
Tel.: (518) 465-4755
Fax: (518) 465-3711
E-mail: info@albanysymphony.com
Web Site: www.albanysymphony.com
Approx. Number Employees: 10
Business Description:
Symphony Orchestra
S.I.C.: 7389
N.A.I.C.S.: 711320
Media: 9-22-23-24-25
Personnel:
Scott Alan *(Dir-Fin)*

ALEXANDRIA SYMPHONY ORCHESTRA
2121 Eisenhower Ave Ste 608
Alexandria, VA 22314
Tel.: (703) 548-0885
Fax: (703) 548-0985
E-mail: alex@alexsym.org
Web Site: www.alexsym.org
Approx. Number Employees: 7
Business Description:
Symphony Orchestra
S.I.C.: 7929
N.A.I.C.S.: 711130
Media: 4-8-9-20-23-24-25
Personnel:
Grady C. Frank *(Pres)*
Adrian Finlay *(Exec Dir)*
Kim Allen Kluge *(Dir-Music)*

ALL-AMERICAN SPORTPARK, INC.
6730 Las Vegas Blvd S
Las Vegas, NV 89119-3311
Tel.: (702) 798-7777
Fax: (702) 739-9509
Approx. Rev.: $1,802,276
Approx. Number Employees: 6
Year Founded: 1984
Business Description:
Theme Park Operator
S.I.C.: 7996; 7997
N.A.I.C.S.: 713110; 713910
Advertising Expenditures: $250,000
Media: 2-6-17
Personnel:
Vaso Boreta *(Chm)*
Ronald S. Boreta *(Pres, CEO, CFO, Treas & Sec)*
Cara Brunette *(Controller & Dir)*

ALLEN ORGAN COMPANY
150 Locust St
Macungie, PA 18062-1165
Mailing Address:
PO Box 36
Macungie, PA 18062-0036
Tel.: (610) 966-2200
Tel.: (610) 966-2202
Fax: (610) 965-3098
Web Site: www.allenorgan.com
Sales Range: $75-99.9 Million
Approx. Number Employees: 270
Year Founded: 1945
Business Description:
Mfr of Electronic Keyboards, Digital Organs & Accessories for Churches
S.I.C.: 3931; 2741
N.A.I.C.S.: 339992; 512230
Import Export
Advertising Expenditures: $278,327
Media: 2-4-6-7-8-9-10
Distr.: Intl.; Natl.
Personnel:
Steven A. Markowitz *(Pres)*
Barry Holben *(VP-Sls)*
Aram Basmadjian *(Mgr-Special Projects)*
Jerry O'Brien *(Mgr-Adv)*
Brands & Products:
ACOUSTIC PORTRAIT
ALLEN ELITE
ALLEN ENSEMBLE
ALLEN ORGAN COMPANY
CHAPEL
DIANE BISH SERIES
DIANE BISH SIGNATURE SERIES
EAC
ENSEMBLE
GEORGE WRIGHT
HERALD
HERITAGE
LEGACY AUDIO
LUMITECH
LYN LARSEN
MIDI ASSISTANT
PIPE
PROTEGE
QUANTUM
RENAISSANCE
RENAISSANCE CLASSIC
RENAISSANCE PIPE
RENAISSANCE QUANTUM
RENAISSANCE THEATRE
SIGNATURE
SMART RECORDER
SOUNDMATRIX TECHNOLOGY

ALLEY THEATRE
615 Texas Ave
Houston, TX 77002
Tel.: (713) 228-9341
Fax: (713) 222-6542
E-mail: webmaster@alleytheatre.org
Web Site: www.alleytheatre.org
Approx. Rev.: $13,000,000
Approx. Number Employees: 135
Year Founded: 1947
Business Description:
Theatre Production
S.I.C.: 7389
N.A.I.C.S.: 711310
Media: 3-7-8-9-13-18-20-22-23-24-25
Personnel:
Dean R. Gladden *(Mng Dir)*
Kenneth Swackhamer *(Gen Mgr)*
Gregory Boyd *(Dir-Artistic)*
Dennis Draper *(Dir-Ops & Events)*
Rodi Franco *(Dir-Mktg & Comm)*
Nancy Giles *(Dir-Dev)*
Tom O'Dell *(Dir-Audience Svcs)*
Don Poole *(Dir-Fin)*
James Black *(Assoc Dir)*
Kevin Rigdon *(Assoc Dir-Design)*
Jennifer Maki *(Designer-Mktg)*
Brands & Products:
ALLEY THEATRE
SUMMER CHILLS

AMC ENTERTAINMENT HOLDINGS, INC.
920 Main St
Kansas City, MO 64105
Tel.: (816) 221-4000
Web Site: www.amctheatres.com
Approx. Rev.: $2,417,739,000
Approx. Number Employees: 1,100
Year Founded: 2007
Business Description:
Holding Company; Motion Picture Theaters Owner & Operator
S.I.C.: 6719; 7832
N.A.I.C.S.: 551112; 512131
Advertising Expenditures: $78,499,000
Personnel:
Aaron J. Stone *(Chm)*
Gerardo I. Lopez *(Pres & CEO)*
Craig R. Ramsey *(CFO & Exec VP)*
Chris A. Cox *(Chief Acctg Officer & Sr VP)*
Kevin M. Connor *(Gen Counsel, Sec & Sr VP)*
Terry W. Crawford *(Treas & Sr VP)*
Michael W. Zwonitzer *(Sr VP-Fin)*
Justin Scott *(Dir-PR)*
Advertising Agencies:
RAPP
437 Madison Ave 3rd Fl
New York, NY 10022
Tel.: (212) 817-6800
Fax: (212) 590-8400
Agency of Record-Direct Marketing & CRM

Key to Media (For complete agency information see *The Advertising Red Books-Agencies* edition):
1. Bus. Publs. 2. Cable T.V. 3. Catalogs & Directories. 4. Co-op Adv. 5. Consumer Mags. 6. D.M. to Bus. Estab.7. D.M. to Consumers 8. Daily Newsp. 9. Exhibits/Trade Shows 10. Foreign 11. Infomercial 12. Internet Adv.13. Multimedia 14. Network Radio 15. Network T.V. 16. Newsp. Distr. Mags. 17. Other 18. Outdoor (Posters, Transit) 19. Point of Purchase20. Premiums, Novelties 21. Product Samples 22. Special Events Mktg. 23. Spot Radio 24. Spot T.V. 25. Weekly Newsp. 26. Yellow Page Adv.

Signal to Noise
55 Union St 3rd Fl
San Francisco, CA 94111
Tel.: (415) 817-3800
Fax: (415) 817-3801
Agency of Record-Digital Marketing

AMC ENTERTAINMENT INC.
(Holding of Marquee Holdings, Inc.)
920 Main St
Kansas City, MO 64105
Mailing Address:
PO Box 219615
Kansas City, MO 64121-9615
Tel.: (816) 221-4000
Fax: (816) 480-4617
Web Site: www.amctheatres.com
Approx. Number Employees: 800
Year Founded: 1920
Business Description:
Motion Picture Theaters Owner & Operator
S.I.C.: 7832
N.A.I.C.S.: 512131
Advertising Expenditures: $6,723,000
Personnel:
Aaron J. Stone *(Chm)*
Gerardo I. Lopez *(Pres & CEO)*
Craig R. Ramsey *(CFO & Exec VP)*
Mike Czinege *(CIO)*
Stephen A. Colanero *(CMO & Exec VP)*
Chris A. Cox *(Chief Acctg Officer & Sr VP)*
Keith Wiedenkeller *(Chief People Officer & Sr VP)*
Robert J. Lenihan *(Pres-Programming)*
Kevin M. Connor *(Gen Counsel, Sec & Sr VP)*
John D. McDonald *(Exec VP-United States Ops)*
Mark A. McDonald *(Exec VP-Global Dev)*
George Patterson *(Sr VP)*
Michael W. Zwonitzer *(Sr VP-Fin)*
Jason Norris *(Dir-Digital Mktg)*
Chad Novak *(Dir-Hosted Svcs-Tech & Sys Dept)*
Justin Scott *(Dir-Corp Comm)*
Andy Traub *(Dir-Recruitment)*
Brands & Products:
AMC
AMC THEATRES
EXPERIENCE THE DIFFERENCE
MOVIEWATCHER
Advertising Agencies:
RAPP
437 Madison Ave 3rd Fl
New York, NY 10022
Tel.: (212) 817-6800
Fax: (212) 590-8400
Direct & Customer Relationship Marketing

Signal to Noise
55 Union St 3rd Fl
San Francisco, CA 94111
Tel.: (415) 817-3800
Fax: (415) 817-3801
Digital Marketing

AMERICAN ASSOCIATION OF COMMUNITY THEATRE
8402 Briarwood Cir
Lago Vista, TX 78645
Tel.: (512) 267-0711
Fax: (512) 267-0712
Toll Free: (800) 687-2228
E-mail: info@aact.org
Web Site: www.aact.org
Approx. Number Employees: 4
Year Founded: 1958
Business Description:
Theatrical Association
S.I.C.: 7389
N.A.I.C.S.: 711310
Media: 10-22

AMERICAN CASINO & ENTERTAINMENT PROPERTIES LLC
2000 Las Vegas Blvd S
Las Vegas, NV 89104
Tel.: (702) 380-7777
Fax: (702) 380-7732
Web Site: www.acepllc.com
Approx. Rev.: $336,838,000
Approx. Number Employees: 4,300
Business Description:
Casino Hotel Owner & Operator
S.I.C.: 7011
N.A.I.C.S.: 721120
Advertising Expenditures: $9,500,000
Personnel:
Frank V. Riolo *(CEO)*
Edward W. Martin, III *(CFO & Treas)*
Phyllis A. Gilland *(Gen Counsel, Sec & VP)*
Ronald P. Lurie *(Exec VP & Gen Mgr-Arizona Charlies Decatur)*
Paul Hobson *(Sr VP & Gen Mgr-Aquarius Casino Resort)*
Mark Majetich *(Sr VP & Gen Mgr-Arizona Charlies Boulder)*

AMERICAN CONSERVATORY THEATRE
(d/b/a A.C.T.)
30 Grant Ave FL 6
San Francisco, CA 94108
Tel.: (415) 834-3200
Fax: (415) 834-2711
E-mail: rtaradash@act-sf.org
Web Site: www.act-sfbay.org
Sales Range: $10-24.9 Million
Approx. Number Employees: 300
Year Founded: 1965
Business Description:
Theatrical Productions
S.I.C.: 7922; 6512
N.A.I.C.S.: 711110; 531120
Media: 9-10-18-20-23-24-25
Personnel:
Ellen Richard *(Exec Dir)*
Janette Andrawes *(Dir-Mktg & PR)*
Carey Perloff *(Dir-Artistic)*
Melissa Smith *(Dir-Conservatory)*
Randy Taradash *(Assoc Dir-Mktg & Promos)*
Dianne Prichard *(Mgr-Company)*
Kate Stewart *(Mgr-HR)*

AMERICAN FILM INSTITUTE
2021 N Western Ave
Los Angeles, CA 90027-1657
Tel.: (323) 856-7600
Fax: (323) 467-4578
E-mail: info@afi.com
Web Site: www.afi.com
Sales Range: $25-49.9 Million
Approx. Number Employees: 120
Year Founded: 1967
Business Description:
Motion Picture Industry Support & Education Services
S.I.C.: 8699
N.A.I.C.S.: 813990
Media: 2-4-10-13-20
Personnel:
Bob Gazzale *(Pres & CEO)*
Bruce Neiner *(CFO & Treas)*
Nancy Harris *(COO)*
Paul Jacques *(Chief Info & Infrastructure Officer)*
Tess Csiszar *(Dir-Special Events)*

AMERICAN GOLF CORPORATION
(Joint Venture of Starwood Capital Group Global LLC)
2951 28th St
Santa Monica, CA 90405-2961
Tel.: (310) 664-4000
Fax: (310) 664-4000
Toll Free: (888) 345-4259
Web Site: www.americangolf.com
Sales Range: $700-749.9 Million
Approx. Number Employees: 10,000
Year Founded: 1968
Business Description:
Golf Course Operation
S.I.C.: 7997
N.A.I.C.S.: 713910
Advertising Expenditures: $200,000
Media: 2-6-10-18
Personnel:
Paul Major *(Pres & CEO)*
Keith Brown *(Chief Ops Officer & Sr VP)*
Craig Kniffen *(Sr VP-Maintenance)*
Ryan Kimberling *(Dir-Revenue Mgmt & Product Mgr-Golfzing)*
Advertising Agency:
McMurry
1010 E Missouri Ave
Phoenix, AZ 85014
Tel.: (602) 395-5850
Fax: (602) 248-2925
Toll Free: (888) MCMURRY
Toll Free: (888) 626-8779

THE AMERICAN STAGE COMPANY INC.
163 3rd St N
Saint Petersburg, FL 33701
Mailing Address:
PO Box 1560
Saint Petersburg, FL 33731
Tel.: (727) 823-1600
Tel.: (727) 823-7529
Fax: (727) 821-2444
E-mail: info@americanstage.org
Web Site: www.americanstage.org
Approx. Number Employees: 12
Year Founded: 1977
Business Description:
Theatrical Plays Producer
S.I.C.: 7922
N.A.I.C.S.: 711110
Media: 7-8-9-18-20-22-23-24-25-26
Personnel:
Todd Olson *(Dir-Producing Artistic)*
Andy Orrell *(Dir-Mktg)*
Leyla Prior *(Dir-Fin)*
Tom Block *(Mgr-Opers)*

AMERICAN SYMPHONY ORCHESTRA LEAGUE
33 W 60th St 5th Fl
New York, NY 10023-7905
Tel.: (212) 262-5161
Fax: (212) 262-5198
E-mail: league@americanorchestra.org
Web Site:
www.americanorchestra.org
Approx. Number Employees: 50
Business Description:
Promoter of Symphonic & Orchestral Music
S.I.C.: 7929
N.A.I.C.S.: 711130
Media: 7-10-13
Personnel:
Jesse Rosen *(Pres & CEO)*
Russell Jones *(VP-Mktg & Membership Dev)*
Glens Falls *(Exec Dir)*
Stephen Alter *(Mgr-Adv & Meetings)*
Robert Sandoa *(Mgr-Symphony)*
Brands & Products:
OLIS
SYMPHONY

AMERICAN WAGERING, INC.
675 Grier Dr
Las Vegas, NV 89119-3738
Tel.: (702) 735-0101
Fax: (702) 735-0142
E-mail: info@americanwagering.com
Web Site:
www.americanwagering.com
Approx. Rev.: $11,645,709
Approx. Number Employees: 168
Year Founded: 1976
Business Description:
Holding Company; Sports Wagering Systems; Gambling Establishments & Operations
S.I.C.: 6719; 7011; 7999
N.A.I.C.S.: 713290; 551112; 713990; 721120
Advertising Expenditures: $99,252
Media: 17
Personnel:
Victor J. Salerno *(Chm, Pres & CEO)*
Robert Kocienski *(CFO & COO)*
John English *(Sr VP-Bus Dev & Pub Affairs)*

AMERISTAR CASINOS, INC.
3773 Howard Hughes Pkwy Ste 490 S
Las Vegas, NV 89109
Tel.: (702) 567-7000
Fax: (702) 369-8860
Web Site: www.ameristarcasinos.com
Approx. Rev.: $1,491,850,000
Approx. Number Employees: 4,950
Business Description:
Casinos & Related Hotel, Food & Beverage, Entertainment & Other Facilities Owner & Operator
S.I.C.: 7999; 5812; 7011
N.A.I.C.S.: 713210; 721120; 722110
Advertising Expenditures: $26,100,000
Media: 6-8-13-14-15-16-18
Personnel:
Gordon R. Kanofsky *(Vice Chm & CEO)*
Lawrence A. Hodges *(Pres & COO)*
Thomas M. Steinbauer *(CFO, Treas, Sec & Sr VP-Fin)*
Peter C. Walsh *(Chief Admin Officer, Gen Counsel & Sr VP)*
Heather A. Rollo *(Chief Acctg Officer)*
Sheleen Quish *(Sr VP-IT & HR)*
Michelle Shriver *(Sr VP-Ops)*
Troy Stremming *(Sr VP-Govt Relations & Pub Affairs)*

Key to Media (For complete agency information see *The Advertising Red Books-Agencies* edition):
1. Bus. Publs. 2. Cable T.V. 3. Catalogs & Directories. 4. Co-op Adv. 5. Consumer Mags. 6. D.M. to Bus. Estab.7. D.M. to Consumers 8. Daily Newsp. 9. Exhibits/Trade Shows 10. Foreign 11. Infomercial 12. Internet Adv.13. Multimedia 14. Network Radio 15. Network T.V. 16. Newsp. Distr. Mags. 17. Other 18. Outdoor (Posters, Transit) 19. Point of Purchase20. Premiums, Novelties 21. Product Samples 22. Special Events Mktg. 23. Spot Radio 24. Spot T.V. 25. Weekly Newsp. 26. Yellow Page Adv.

Ameristar Casinos, Inc. — (Continued)

Kim Carpenter *(Dir-Hotel, Catering Sls, Player Dev & Sls)*
Roxann M. Kinkade *(Dir-Comm)*
Advertising Agency:
Haworth Marketing & Media Company
TCF Tower 10th Fl 121 S 8th St
Minneapolis, MN 55402
Tel.: (612) 677-8900
Fax: (612) 677-8901

AMF BOWLING CENTERS, INC.

(Sub. of AMF Bowling Worldwide, Inc.)
7313 Bell Creek Rd
Mechanicsville, VA 23111
Tel.: (804) 730-4000
Fax: (804) 559-6222
Web Site: www.amf.com
Approx. Number Employees: 200
Business Description:
Bowling Lanes & Bowling Centers Operator
S.I.C.: 7999
N.A.I.C.S.: 713990
Advertising Expenditures: $4,000,000
Media: 3-8-9-18-22-23-24-25
Personnel:
Fred Hipp *(CEO)*
Merrell Wreden *(VP-Mktg)*
Joan Phares *(Dir-Field Mktg)*
Advertising Agencies:
93 Octane
23 W Broad St Ste 302
Richmond, VA 23220
Tel.: (804) 643-8800
Fax: (804) 643-8900

circle S studio
201 W 7th St
Richmond, VA 23224
Tel.: (804) 232-2908
Fax: (804) 232-2094

Elevation
9 W Main St
Richmond, VA 23220
Tel.: (804) 780-2300
Fax: (804) 780-2323

ANAHEIM DUCKS HOCKEY CLUB, LLC

Honda Ctr 2695 E Katella Ave
Anaheim, CA 92806
Tel.: (714) 940-2900
Fax: (714) 704-2443
Web Site: ducks.nhl.com
Approx. Number Employees: 200
Year Founded: 1992
Business Description:
Professional Hockey Club
S.I.C.: 7941
N.A.I.C.S.: 711211
Media: 9-13-18-23-24-25
Distr.: Natl.
Personnel:
Henry Samueli *(Owner)*
Susan Samueli *(Owner)*
Michael Schulman *(CEO)*
Doug Heller *(CFO & VP-Fin)*
Bob Murray *(Exec VP & Gen Mgr)*
David McNab *(Sr VP-Hockey Ops)*
Jay Scott *(VP-HR)*
Aaron Teats *(VP-Multi-Media & Community Dev)*
Adam Brady *(Dir-Publ & New Media)*
Alain Chainey *(Dir-Player Dev)*
Alex Evezich *(Dir-Corp Relations & Res)*
Alex Gilchrist *(Dir-Media & Comm)*
Wendy Grover *(Dir-Corp Partnerships)*
Tracie Jones *(Dir-Mktg)*
Martin Madden *(Dir-Amateur Scouting)*
Jim Panetta *(Dir-Premium Sls & Svc)*
Rick Paterson *(Dir-Professional Scouting)*
Matt Savant *(Dir-Fan Dev)*
Wendy Yamagishi *(Dir-Community Rels & Pub Affairs)*
Tim Ryan *(Mgr-Hockey Ops)*
Doug Shearer *(Mgr-Equipment)*
Lisa Johnson *(Coord-Mktg)*

ANCHORAGE SYMPHONY ORCHESTRA

400 D St Ste 230
Anchorage, AK 99501
Tel.: (907) 274-8668
Fax: (907) 272-7916
E-mail: afo@yourafo.org
Web Site:
www.anchoragesymphony.org
Approx. Number Employees: 50
Business Description:
Symphony Orchestra Services
S.I.C.: 7929
N.A.I.C.S.: 711130
Media: 9-20-23-25
Personnel:
Sherri Burkhart Reddick *(Exec Dir)*
Kristin Cosgrove *(Dir-Mktg & PR)*
Jean Lenoir *(Mgr-Personnel)*
Lauren MacKenzie Miller *(Mgr-Production)*

ANDERSON SYMPHONY ORCHESTRA

1124 Meridian St
Anderson, IN 46016
Tel.: (765) 644-2111
Fax: (765) 644-7703
Toll Free: (888) 644-9490
E-mail: aso@andersonsymphony.org
Web Site:
www.andersonsymphony.org
Approx. Number Employees: 2
Business Description:
Symphony Orchestra
S.I.C.: 7389
N.A.I.C.S.: 711320
Media: 8-9-20-23-24-25
Personnel:
Richard L. Sowers *(Dir-Music)*

ANDREAS ENTERPRISES, INC.

2547 Halfway Rd
Middleburg, VA 20118
Tel.: (540) 687-8282
E-mail: andreasstudio@aol.com
Web Site: www.andreasstudio.com
Approx. Number Employees: 20
Year Founded: 1979
Business Description:
Fine Arts Gallery
S.I.C.: 8412
N.A.I.C.S.: 712110; 712120
Media: 4-10-22-25
Personnel:
George C. Andreas *(Chm & Pres)*
Christopher M. Andreas *(Exec VP)*
Ursula E. Andreas *(Exec VP)*

THE ANDY WARHOL MUSEUM

117 Sandusky St
Pittsburgh, PA 15212-5890
Tel.: (412) 237-8300
Fax: (412) 237-8340
E-mail: information@warhol.org
Web Site: www.warhol.org
Approx. Number Employees: 55
Business Description:
Art Museum Services
S.I.C.: 8412
N.A.I.C.S.: 712110
Media: 5-8-9-10-13-20-22-23-24-25
Personnel:
Tresa Barner *(Coord-Youth Programs)*
Thomas Sokolowski *(Exec Dir)*
Rachel Baron-Horn *(Dir-Fin & Ops)*
Rick Armstrong *(Comm Mgr)*
Greg Burchard *(Mgr-Rights, Photography, Reproductions Svcs)*
Jesse Kowalski *(Coord-Exhibitions)*
Advertising Agency:
Beanstalk
220 E 42nd St 15th Fl
New York, NY 10017
Tel.: (212) 421-6060
Fax: (212) 421-6388

ANGELS BASEBALL, L.P.

(d/b/a Los Angeles Angels of Anaheim)
2000 Gene Autry Way
Anaheim, CA 92806-6100
Tel.: (714) 940-2000
Fax: (714) 940-2001
E-mail: info@angelsbaseball.com
Web Site: www.angelsbaseball.com
Approx. Number Employees: 100
Year Founded: 1961
Business Description:
Professional Baseball Club
S.I.C.: 7941
N.A.I.C.S.: 711211
Media: 3-4-9-13-18-19-20-22-23-24-25
Personnel:
Arturo Moreno *(Owner)*
Dennis Kuhl *(Chm)*
John Carpino *(Pres)*
Bill Beverage *(CFO)*
Robert Alvarado *(VP-Ticket Sls & Mktg)*
Richard McClemmy *(VP-Corp Sls)*
Tim Mead *(VP-Comm)*
Molly Taylor *(VP-Fin & Admin)*
Tony Reagins *(Gen Mgr)*
Ken Forsch *(Asst Gen Mgr)*
Eddie Bane *(Dir-Scouting)*
David Cohen *(Dir-Legal Affairs & Risk Mgmt)*
Abe Flores *(Dir-Player Dev)*
Lewis Yocum *(Dir-Medical)*
Matt Bennett *(Mgr-Commity Rels)*
Brands & Products:
ANGELS
ANGELS BASEBALL FOUNDATION
ANGELS SCHOLARS
LOS ANGELES ANGELS
Advertising Agencies:
LatinoLandia
17595 Harvard Ave Ste C5000
Irvine, CA 92614
Tel.: (949) 502-8822
Fax: (949) 502-8855

MLB Advanced Media, L.P.
75 9th Ave 5th Fl
New York, NY 10011
Tel.: (212) 485-3444
Fax: (212) 485-3456

ANN ARBOR SYMPHONY ORCHESTRA

220 E Huron St
Ann Arbor, MI 48104
Tel.: (734) 994-4801
Fax: (734) 994-3949
E-mail: a2so@a2so.com
Web Site: www.a2so.com
Sales Range: Less than $1 Million
Approx. Number Employees: 80
Year Founded: 1928
Business Description:
Symphony Orchestra
S.I.C.: 7929
N.A.I.C.S.: 711130
Media: 9-20-22-23-24-25
Personnel:
Kim A. Eagle *(Pres)*
Mary Steffek Blaske *(Exec Dir)*
Gregg Emerson Powell *(Mgr-Personnel)*
Brands & Products:
ANN ARBOR SYMPHONY ORCHESTRA
MUSIC IN THE KEY OF A2

ANNAPOLIS SYMPHONY ORCHESTRA ASSOCIATION INC.

801 Chase St
Annapolis, MD 21401
Tel.: (410) 269-1132
Fax: (410) 263-0616
E-mail: info@annapolissymphony.org
Web Site:
www.annapolissymphony.org
Approx. Number Employees: 5
Year Founded: 1965
Business Description:
Symphony Orchestra
S.I.C.: 7929
N.A.I.C.S.: 711130
Media: 10-20-23-24-25
Personnel:
Anne S. Porter *(Vice Chm)*
Jose-Luis Novo *(Dir-Music)*
Sharon Dickerson *(Bus Mgr)*

ARCADIA ALL-FLORIDA CHAMPIONSHIP RODEO

124 Heard St
Arcadia, FL 34266
Toll Free: (800) 749-7633
Web Site: www.arcadiarodeo.com
Business Description:
Rodeo
S.I.C.: 7389
N.A.I.C.S.: 711310
Media: 9-13-22-23-24-25
Personnel:
Don T. Hall *(Pres)*
James S. Parker *(First VP)*
Walter M. Brown *(2nd VP)*

ARENA STAGE

1101 6th St SW
Washington, DC 20024
Tel.: (202) 554-9066
Fax: (202) 488-4056
E-mail: info@arenastage.org
Web Site: www.arena-stage.org
Approx. Sls.: $11,187,957
Approx. Number Employees: 150
Business Description:
Performing Arts Center
S.I.C.: 7389
N.A.I.C.S.: 711310
Media: 7-8-9-20-22-23-24-25

Key to Media (For complete agency information see *The Advertising Red Books-Agencies* edition):
1. Bus. Publs. 2. Cable T.V. 3. Catalogs & Directories. 4. Co-op Adv. 5. Consumer Mags. 6. D.M. to Bus. Estab.7. D.M. to Consumers
8. Daily Newsp. 9. Exhibits/Trade Shows 10. Foreign 11. Infomercial 12. Internet Adv.13. Multimedia 14. Network Radio
15. Network T.V. 16. Newsp. Distr. Mags. 17. Other 18. Outdoor (Posters; Transit) 19. Point of Purchase20. Premiums, Novelties
21. Product Samples 22. Special Events Mktg. 23. Spot Radio 24. Spot T.V. 25. Weekly Newsp. 26. Yellow Page Adv.

Personnel:
Guy Bergquist *(Dir-Facility Project)*
Molly Smith *(Dir-Artistic)*
Nick Pietras *(Mgr-Mktg)*
Neal Racioppo *(Mgr-Mktg)*

ARGOSY GAMING COMPANY
(Sub. of Penn National Gaming, Inc.)
219 Piasa St
Alton, IL 62002
Tel.: (618) 474-7500
Fax: (618) 474-7636
E-mail: webmaster@argosycasinos.com
Web Site: www.argosy.com
Sales Range: $200-249.9 Million
Approx. Number Employees: 6,193
Year Founded: 1996
Business Description:
Casinos Owner & Operator
S.I.C.: 7999
N.A.I.C.S.: 713210
Advertising Expenditures: $15,213,000
Brands & Products:
ARGOSY
Advertising Agency:
MMG Worldwide
4601 Madison Ave
Kansas City, MO 64112
Tel.: (816) 472-5988
Fax: (816) 471-5395

ARGOSY LAWRENCEBURG
(Div. of Argosy Gaming Company)
777 Argosy Pkwy
Lawrenceburg, IN 47025
Tel.: (812) 539-8000
Fax: (812) 539-8283
Web Site: www.pngaming.com
Sales Range: $250-299.9 Million
Approx. Number Employees: 2,400
Business Description:
Casino Services
S.I.C.: 7999
N.A.I.C.S.: 713210
Advertising Agency:
Jaffoni & Collins
116 E 16th St 11th Fl
New York, NY 10003-2112
Tel.: (212) 835-8500
Fax: (212) 835-8525

ARIZONA CARDINALS FOOTBALL CLUB, INC.
8701 S Hardy Dr
Tempe, AZ 85284
Mailing Address:
PO Box 888
Phoenix, AZ 85001-0888
Tel.: (602) 379-0101
Fax: (602) 379-1819
E-mail: info@azcardinals.com
Web Site: www.azcardinals.com
E-Mail For Key Personnel:
President: wvbidwill@cardinals.nfl.com
Marketing Director: rminegar@cardinals.nfl.com
Approx. Number Employees: 200
Year Founded: 1920
Business Description:
Professional Football Franchise
S.I.C.: 7941
N.A.I.C.S.: 711211
Advertising Expenditures: $1,000,000
Media: 9-18-22-23-24
Distr.: Natl.
Personnel:
William V. Bidwill *(Owner & Chm)*
Michael J. Bidwill *(Pres)*
Adrian Bracy *(CFO)*
Ron Minegar *(Chief Bus Officer & Exec VP)*
Mark Dalton *(VP-Media Rels)*
Mark Feller *(VP-Tech)*
Rick Knight *(VP-Security)*
Lisa Manning *(VP-Mktg)*
Rod Graves *(Gen Mgr)*
Steve Bomar *(Sr Dir-Ticketing)*
Anthony Edwards *(Sr Dir-Player Dev)*
Luis Zendejas *(Sr Dir-Community Rels)*
Rob Brakel *(Dir-Video)*
Miriam Carlson *(Dir-Fin Plng & Analysis)*
Scott Coleman *(Dir-Partner Svc & Activation)*
Steve Keim *(Dir-Player Personnel)*
Patrick Tankersley *(Dir-Cardinals Charities)*
Reggie Terry *(Dir-Football Admin)*
Erica Anderson *(Sr Mgr-Corp Svcs)*
Cari Belanger-Maas *(Sr Mgr-Suite & Guest Rels)*
Mark Ahlemeier *(Mgr-Equipment)*
Orlando Avila *(Mgr-Mktg & Brdcst Svcs)*
Scott Bull *(Mgr-Tempe Box Office)*
Rolando Cantu *(Mgr-Intl Bus Ventures)*
Michael Conner *(Mgr-Video & Score Board Ops)*
Ryan Funk *(Mgr-Glendale Box Office)*
Bill Lewis *(Mgr-Alumni Rels)*
Chris Melvin *(Mgr-Media Rels)*
Percy Silva *(Mgr-Mdse)*
Richard Tomey *(Mgr-Bus Dev)*
Darren Urban *(Mgr-Website)*
Brands & Products:
ARIZONA CARDINALS

ARIZONA DIAMONDBACKS
401 E Jefferson St
Phoenix, AZ 85004
Mailing Address:
PO Box 2095
Phoenix, AZ 85001-2095
Tel.: (602) 462-6000
Fax: (602) 462-6599
E-mail: fanfeedback@diamondbacks.mlb.com
Web Site:
arizona.diamondbacks.mlb.com
Approx. Number Employees: 200
Year Founded: 1995
Business Description:
Professional Baseball Club
S.I.C.: 7941
N.A.I.C.S.: 711211
Media: 5-9-18-19-20-22-23-24
Personnel:
Earl G. Kendrick *(Mng Gen Partner)*
Derrick Hall *(Pres & CEO)*
Mike Chipman *(Gen Partner)*
Jeff Royer *(Gen Partner)*
Thomas Harris *(CFO & Exec VP)*
Robert Zweig *(CIO & VP)*
Nona Lee *(Gen Counsel & Sr VP)*
Cullen Maxey *(Exec VP-Bus Ops)*
Jerry Dipoto *(Sr VP-Scouting & Player Dev)*
John Fisher *(Sr VP-Ticket Sls & Mktg)*
Josh Rawitch *(Sr VP-Comm)*
Peter Woodfork *(VP & Asst Gen Mgr)*
Craig Bradley *(VP-Fin)*
Shaun Rachau *(VP-Comm)*
Marian Rhodes *(VP-HR)*
Billy Ryan *(Asst Gen Mgr)*
Karina Bohn *(Sr Dir-Mktg)*
Steve Mullins *(Sr Dir-Corp Partnerships)*
Roger Riley *(Sr Dir-Team Travel)*
Graham Rossini *(Sr Dir-Special Projects & Fan Experience)*
Doug Alkire *(Brand Dir)*
Kristi Haas *(Dir-Travel Svcs)*
Tom Allison *(Dir-Scouting)*
Kenny Farrell *(Dir-Ticket Dev & Ops)*
Jim Hawkins *(Dir-Building Svcs)*
Jeff Jacobs *(Dir-Fin Mgmt)*
Chris James *(Dir-Acctg)*
Chad MacDonald *(Dir-Scouting-Intl)*
Sean Maguire *(Dir-Security)*
Shiraz Rehman *(Dir-Player Personnel)*
Jeff Rodin *(Dir-Baseball Outreach & Dev)*
Julie Romero *(Dir-Hispanic Sls & Mktg)*
Greg Salvatore *(Dir-Publ)*
Bryan White *(Dir-Event Svcs)*
Jim White *(Dir-Facilities Engrg)*
Scott Worden *(Dir-Grp & Suite Sls)*
Luis Calderon *(Sr Mgr-Ticket Ops)*
Marshall Cheever *(Sr Mgr-Facilities Engrg)*
Tim Emory *(Sr Mgr-Acct-Corp Partnerships)*
Josie Deininger *(Mgr-Benefits)*
Gregory Green *(Mgr-Security)*
Diney Ransford *(Mgr-Suite & Premium Svcs)*
Casey Wilcox *(Mgr-Player & Media Rels)*
Tim Martin *(Acct Exec & Team Lead-Suite Sls)*
Brands & Products:
A
ARIZONA DIAMONDBACKS
EL PASO DIABLOS
TUCSON SIDEWINDERS
Advertising Agency:
MLB Advanced Media, L.P.
75 9th Ave 5th Fl
New York, NY 10011
Tel.: (212) 485-3444
Fax: (212) 485-3456

THE ARMED FORCES MILITARY MUSEUM
2050 34th Way N
Largo, FL 33771
Tel.: (727) 539-8371
Fax: (727) 524-4967
E-mail: info@armedforcesmuseum.com
Web Site:
www.armedforcesmuseum.com
Approx. Number Employees: 15
Business Description:
Military Museum
S.I.C.: 8412
N.A.I.C.S.: 712110
Media: 2-4-6-7-8-9-10-18-20-22-23-24-25-27-29
Personnel:
John J. Piazza, Sr. *(Founder & Pres)*
Enos Burks *(Dir-Plant Ops)*
Dave Marino *(Dir-Creative)*
Nadine Piazza *(Dir-Ops)*
Michelle Simoneau *(Dir-Bus Dev)*

THE ART INSTITUTE OF CHICAGO
111 S Michigan Ave
Chicago, IL 60603-6492
Tel.: (312) 443-3600
Fax: (312) 443-0849
E-mail: aic.publicaffairs@artic.edu
Web Site: www.artic.edu
Sales Estimate: $40-59 Million
Approx. Number Employees: 1,600
Year Founded: 1879
Business Description:
Art Museum
S.I.C.: 8412; 7911
N.A.I.C.S.: 712110; 611610
Media: 6-8-9-18-23-24
Distr.: Direct to Consumer; Reg.
Personnel:
James Cuno *(Pres & Dir)*
David A. Thurm *(COO)*
Advertising Agency:
Mindshare
350 W Mart Center Dr Ste 1270
Chicago, IL 60654-1270
Tel.: (312) 242-1100
Fax: (312) 242-1350

THE ART INSTITUTES
(Sub. of Education Management Corporation)
420 Blvd of the Allies
Pittsburgh, PA 15222
Fax: (412) 263-6667
Toll Free: (800) 275-2470
Web Site: www.artinstitutes.edu
Business Description:
Art Schools
S.I.C.: 8221
N.A.I.C.S.: 611310
Personnel:
George Fry *(Pres)*
Laurie Barkman *(VP-Mktg & Adv)*
Advertising Agency:
Cellit
213 W Institute Pl Ste 603
Chicago, IL 60610
Tel.: (312) 492-4128
Fax: (866) 856-3936
Toll Free: (800) 790-6597

ARTHUR MURRAY INTERNATIONAL, INC.
1077 Ponce De Leon Blvd
Coral Gables, FL 33134-3319
Tel.: (305) 445-9645
Fax: (305) 445-0451
E-mail: amurray@arthurmurray.com
Web Site: www.arthurmurray.com
Approx. Number Employees: 15
Year Founded: 1912
Business Description:
American, Latin, Social & Ballroom Dance Instruction
S.I.C.: 6794
N.A.I.C.S.: 533110
Advertising Expenditures: $4,000,000
Media: 3-9-10-12-13-14-15-22-25-26
Distr.: Intl.; Natl.
Personnel:
Philip S. Masters *(Chm)*
John Kimmins *(Pres)*
George B. Theiss *(CEO)*
Carlos Borras *(COO)*
Thomas D. Murdock *(VP-Mktg & Promos)*
Brands & Products:
ARTHUR MURRAY
Advertising Agency:
Poller & Jordan Advertising Agency, Inc.

Key to Media (For complete agency information see *The Advertising Red Books-Agencies* edition):
1. Bus. Publs. 2. Cable T.V. 3. Catalogs & Directories. 4. Co-op Adv. 5. Consumer Mags. 6. D.M. to Bus. Estab.7. D.M. to Consumers 8. Daily Newsp. 9. Exhibits/Trade Shows 10. Foreign 11. Infomercial 12. Internet Adv.13. Multimedia 14. Network Radio 15. Network T.V. 16. Newsp. Distr. Mags. 17. Other 18. Outdoor (Posters, Transit) 19. Point of Purchase20. Premiums, Novelties 21. Product Samples 22. Special Events Mktg. 23. Spot Radio 24. Spot T.V. 25. Weekly Newsp. 26. Yellow Page Adv.

Arthur Murray International, Inc. — (Continued)

373 NW Shore View Dr
Port Saint Lucie, FL 34986
Tel.: (305) 470-8005
Fax: (305) 598-9078

ASHEVILLE SYMPHONY SOCIETY INC.
PO Box 2852
Asheville, NC 28802
Tel.: (828) 254-7046
Fax: (828) 254-1761
E-mail: info@ashevillesymphony.org
Web Site:
www.ashevillesymphony.org
Approx. Number Employees: 4
Year Founded: 1962
Business Description:
Symphony Orchestra
S.I.C.: 7929; 7991
N.A.I.C.S.: 711130; 713940
Media: 9-20-23-24-25
Personnel:
Larry Modlin *(VP-Fin)*
Steven R. Hageman *(Exec Dir)*
Carol McCollum *(Dir)*

ASHLAND SYMPHONY ORCHESTRA
401 College Ave
Ashland, OH 44805
Tel.: (419) 289-5115
Fax: (419) 289-5329
Web Site: www.ashlandsymphony.org
Approx. Number Employees: 4
Business Description:
Symphony Orchestra
S.I.C.: 7929
N.A.I.C.S.: 711130
Media: 9-20-23-24-25
Personnel:
Arie Lipsky *(Dir-Music & Conductor)*

ATLANTA FALCONS FOOTBALL CLUB, LLC
4400 Falcon Pkwy
Flowery Branch, GA 30542-3176
Tel.: (770) 965-3115
Fax: (770) 965-3185
Web Site: www.atlantafalcons.com
Approx. Number Employees: 115
Business Description:
Professional Football Franchise
S.I.C.: 7941
N.A.I.C.S.: 711211
Media: 9-13-20-22-23-24
Distr.: Reg.
Budget Set: Dec.
Personnel:
Arthur M. Blank *(Owner & CEO)*
Rich McKay *(Pres)*
Greg Beadles *(CFO & VP)*
Jim Smith *(CMO)*
Kim Shreckengost *(Chief-Staff-AMB Grp, LLC & Exec VP)*
Danny Branch *(VP-IT)*
Dave Cohen *(VP-Sls)*
Thomas Dimitroff *(Gen Mgr)*
Frank Kleha *(Sr Dir-Media Rels)*
Kevin Winston *(Sr Dir-Player Dev)*
David Caldwell *(Dir-College Scouting)*
Mike Crews *(Dir-Video)*
Jeff Fish *(Dir-Athletic Performance)*
Mike Gilfanan *(Dir-Ticket Ops)*
Mike Gilsenan *(Dir-Ticket Ops)*
Dan Levak *(Dir-New Media)*
Kendyl Moss *(Dir-Community Rels)*
Karl Pierburg *(Dir-Football Sys)*
Nick Polk *(Dir-Football Admin)*
Don Rovak *(Dir-Ticket Sls & Svcs)*
Les Snead *(Dir-Player Personnel)*
Spencer Treadwell *(Dir-Logistics & Facilities)*
Karen Walters *(Dir-HR)*
Roddy White *(Dir-Event Mktg & Client Services)*
Lionel Vital *(Asst Dir-Player Personnel)*
Michael Benford *(Mgr-Creative Svcs)*
Brian Boigner *(Mgr-Equipment)*
Connie Bonner *(Mgr-Ticket Acctg)*
Wallace Norman *(Mgr-Payroll & Benefits)*
Warren Parr *(Mgr-Grp Ticket Sls)*
Travis Pelleymounter *(Mgr-Premium Sls)*
Sarah Smith *(Mgr-Client Svcs)*
Hamzah Ahmad *(Coord-Event Mktg)*
Brands & Products:
ATLANTA FALCONS
Advertising Agencies:
Click Here, Inc.
8750 N Central Expy Ste 100
Dallas, TX 75231-6430
Tel.: (214) 891-5325
Fax: (214) 346-4870

The Richards Group, Inc.
8750 N Central Expy Ste 100
Dallas, TX 75231-6430
Tel.: (214) 891-5700
Fax: (214) 265-2933

ATLANTA MOTOR SPEEDWAY, INC.
(Sub. of Speedway Motorsports, Inc.)
1500 Tara Pl
Hampton, GA 30228-1884
Mailing Address:
PO Box 500
Hampton, GA 30228-0500
Tel.: (770) 946-4211
Fax: (770) 946-3945
E-mail: amstix@atlantamotorspeedway.com
Web Site:
www.atlantamotorspeedway.com
E-Mail For Key Personnel:
Sales Director: gregw@atlantarace.com
Sales Range: $10-24.9 Million
Approx. Number Employees: 75
Year Founded: 1959
Business Description:
Motorsports Facility & Motorsports Promotion & Entertainment Events
S.I.C.: 7948
N.A.I.C.S.: 711212
Media: 5-8-9-18-22-23-24-25
Distr.: Natl.
Budget Set: Mar. -Nov.
Personnel:
Ed Clark *(Pres & Gen Mgr)*
Mike Bruner *(VP-Fin)*
Greg Walter *(VP-Sls)*
Dave Heckman *(Dir-IT)*
Marcy Scott *(Dir-Mktg & Promo)*
Dennis Shubert *(Dir-Ops)*
Sheila Summey *(Asst Controller)*
Advertising Agency:
The Tombras Group
630 Concord St
Knoxville, TN 37919-3305
Tel.: (865) 524-5376
Fax: (865) 524-5667

ATLANTA NATIONAL LEAGUE BASEBALL CLUB, INC.
(Sub. of Liberty Media LLC)
(d/b/a Atlanta Braves)
755 Hank Aaron Dr
Atlanta, GA 30315
Mailing Address:
PO Box 4064
Atlanta, GA 30302-4064
Tel.: (404) 522-7630
Fax: (404) 885-4318
E-mail: braves@atlantabraves.com
Web Site:
atlanta.braves.mlb.com/index.jsp?c_id=atl
Sales Range: $50-74.9 Million
Approx. Number Employees: 190
Year Founded: 1966
Business Description:
Professional Baseball Club
S.I.C.: 7941
N.A.I.C.S.: 711211
Media: 2-3-6-7-8-9-13-14-15-18-20-22-23-24-25-26
Distr.: Natl.
Budget Set: Sept.
Personnel:
John Schuerholz *(Pres)*
Terence F. McGuirk *(CEO)*
Chip Moore *(CFO-Atlanta Braves & Sr VP)*
Greg Heller *(Gen Counsel & Sr VP)*
Frank Wren *(Exec VP & Gen Mgr)*
Mike Plant *(Exec VP-Bus Ops)*
Derek L. Schiller *(Exec VP-Sls & Mktg)*
Henry L. Aaron *(Sr VP)*
Advertising Agencies:
Blue Sky Agency
950 Lowery Blvd Ste 30
Atlanta, GA 30318
Tel.: (404) 876-0202
Fax: (404) 876-0212

MLB Advanced Media, L.P.
75 9th Ave 5th Fl
New York, NY 10011
Tel.: (212) 485-3444
Fax: (212) 485-3456

ATLANTA SYMPHONY ORCHESTRA
1280 Peachtree St
Atlanta, GA 30309-3552
Tel.: (404) 733-4900
Fax: (404) 733-4999
E-mail: info@atlantasymphony.org
Web Site: www.atlantasymphony.org
Sales Range: $75-99.9 Million
Approx. Number Employees: 500
Business Description:
Symphony Orchestra
S.I.C.: 8699; 7929
N.A.I.C.S.: 813990; 711130
Media: 9-18-20-22-23-24-25
Personnel:
Donald F. Fox *(Exec VP-Bus Ops)*
John Sparrow *(VP & Gen Mgr)*
Paul Barrett *(Sr Mgr-Production)*
Melanie Kite *(Office Mgr)*
Russell Williamson *(Mgr-Orchestra Personnel)*

ATLANTA THRASHERS HOCKEY CLUB
(Holding of Atlanta Spirit LLC)
Centennial Tower 101 Marietta St Northwest Ste 1900
Atlanta, GA 30303
Tel.: (404) 828-3800
Tel.: (404) 878-3300
Fax: (404) 828-3224
E-mail: atlanta.thrashers@atlantaspirit.com
Web Site: www.atlantathrashers.com
Sales Range: $50-74.9 Million
Approx. Number Employees: 50
Year Founded: 1997
Business Description:
National Hockey League Team
S.I.C.: 7941
N.A.I.C.S.: 711211
Advertising Expenditures: $1,000,000
Media: 2-3-4-6-7-8-9-10-13-14-15-18-22-23-24-25
Personnel:
William Daly *(COO)*
Advertising Agency:
Blue Sky Agency
950 Lowery Blvd Ste 30
Atlanta, GA 30318
Tel.: (404) 876-0202
Fax: (404) 876-0212

ATRINSIC, INC.
469 7th Ave 10th Fl
New York, NY 10018
Tel.: (212) 273-1141
E-mail: ir@atrinsic.com
Web Site: www.atrinsic.com
Approx. Rev.: $40,026,000
Approx. Number Employees: 41
Year Founded: 2005
Business Description:
Digital Entertainment Products & Services
S.I.C.: 2741; 4899
N.A.I.C.S.: 516110; 517910
Media: 13
Personnel:
Jerome A. Chazen *(Chm)*
Stuart Goldfarb *(Pres & CEO)*
Nathan Fong *(CFO)*
Aaron Baker *(Exec VP-Interactive)*
Raymond Musci *(Exec VP-Corp Dev)*
Kevin Vye *(Sr VP-Tech)*
Brands & Products:
WWW.IMATCHUP.COM
Advertising Agency:
Hill & Knowlton, Inc.
1601 Cloverfield Blvd Ste 3000N
Santa Monica, CA 90404
Tel.: (310) 633-9400
Fax: (310) 633-9401

ATTITASH
(Sub. of Peak Resorts, Inc.)
Rte 302 PO Box 308
Bartlett, NH 03812-0308
Tel.: (603) 374-2368
Fax: (603) 374-1960
E-mail: info@attitash.com
Web Site: www.attitash.com
Approx. Number Employees: 600
Business Description:
Ski Resort Services
S.I.C.: 5812
N.A.I.C.S.: 722110
Media: 1-8-10-13-20-22
Personnel:
Tom Chasse *(Pres & Mng Dir)*
Frank Guerriero *(Dir-Mktg)*
John Lowell *(Mgr-Lodging)*

Key to Media (For complete agency information see *The Advertising Red Books-Agencies* edition):
1. Bus. Publs. 2. Cable T.V. 3. Catalogs & Directories. 4. Co-op Adv. 5. Consumer Mags. 6. D.M. to Bus. Estab.7. D.M. to Consumers 8. Daily Newsp. 9. Exhibits/Trade Shows 10. Foreign 11. Infomercial 12. Internet Adv.13. Multimedia 14. Network Radio 15. Network T.V. 16. Newsp. Distr. Mags. 17. Other 18. Outdoor (Posters, Transit) 19. Point of Purchase20. Premiums, Novelties 21. Product Samples 22. Special Events Mktg. 23. Spot Radio 24. Spot T.V. 25. Weekly Newsp. 26. Yellow Page Adv.

AUDUBON NATURE INSTITUTE
6500 Magazine St
New Orleans, LA 70118
Mailing Address:
PO Box 4327
New Orleans, LA 70178
Tel.: (504) 861-2537
Fax: (504) 212-5157
E-mail: air@auduboninstitute.org
Web Site: www.auduboninstitute.org
Sales Range: $10-24.9 Million
Approx. Number Employees: 700
Business Description:
Zoological Gardens & Nature Preserve
S.I.C.: 8422
N.A.I.C.S.: 712130
Advertising Expenditures: $2,000,000
Media: 8-9-10-13-23-24-25
Personnel:
L. Ronald Forman *(CEO)*
Brands & Products:
AUDUBON NATURE INSTITUTE
ENTERGY IMAX THEATRE

AUGUSTA SYMPHONY INC.
1301 Greene St Ste 200
Augusta, GA 30901
Mailing Address:
PO Box 579
Augusta, GA 30903-0579
Tel.: (706) 826-4705
Fax: (706) 826-4735
E-mail: office@augustasymphony.org
Web Site: www.augustasymphony.org
E-Mail For Key Personnel:
Marketing Director: marketing@augustasymphony.org
Sales Range: $1-9.9 Million
Approx. Number Employees: 90
Business Description:
Symphony Orchestra
S.I.C.: 7929
N.A.I.C.S.: 711130
Media: 6-9-13-20-22-23-24-25
Personnel:
Sandra Self *(Exec Dir)*
Shizuo Kuwahara *(Dir-Music)*
Martha Robinson *(Dir-Ops)*
Arthur Ross *(Mgr-Special Svcs & Orchestra Personnel)*

AUSTIN SYMPHONY ORCHESTRA
1101 Red River
Austin, TX 78701
Tel.: (512) 476-6064
Fax: (512) 476-6242
Fax: (512) 473-8743
Toll Free: (888) 4MAESTRO
E-mail: contact@austinsymphony.org
Web Site: www.austinsymphony.org
Year Founded: 1911
Business Description:
Symphony Orchestra
S.I.C.: 7929
N.A.I.C.S.: 711130
Media: 9-20-22-23-24-25
Personnel:
D. J. Sibley *(Chm)*
Joe R. Long *(Pres)*
Edward Z. Safady *(Exec VP)*
Daniel B. Powell, III *(VP-Budget & Fin)*
George Gibbs *(Asst VP-Orchestra Hospitality)*
Joe E. Holt *(Asst VP-Concert Hospitality)*
Steve A. Wilson *(Asst VP-Budget & Fin)*
Anthony Corroa *(Exec Dir)*
Peter Bay *(Dir-Music)*
Pat Cherico *(Dir-Volunteer Ushers)*
Diana Eblen *(Dir-Education)*
Peggy Gunn *(Dir-Dev)*
Craig Hahn *(Dir-Ops & Production)*
Jason Nicholson *(Dir-Mktg)*
Denice Yeagin *(Dir-Info Sys)*

AVEDIS ZILDJIAN COMPANY
22 Longwater Dr
Norwell, MA 02061-1612
Tel.: (781) 871-2200
Fax: (781) 878-6202
Web Site: www.zildjian.com
Sales Range: $75-99.9 Million
Approx. Number Employees: 170
Business Description:
Mfr. of Cymbals & Drumsticks
S.I.C.: 3931
N.A.I.C.S.: 339992
Export
Advertising Expenditures: $620,000
Media: 2-4-6-7-8-10-11-19-20
Distr.: Intl.; Natl.
Budget Set: Nov.
Personnel:
Craigie Zildjian *(CEO)*
Brad Baker *(CMO & VP-Mktg)*
Jerry Donegan *(VP-Sls)*
Debbie Zildjian *(VP-HR)*
Brands & Products:
THE AMERICAN DRUMMERS ACHIEVEMENT AWARDS
AVEDIS ZILDJIAN
EDGE
ESSENTIAL SERIES
ZBT
ZIL-BEL
ZILCO NEW BEAT
ZILDJIAN

AWARE RECORDS
624 Davis St 2nd Fl
Evanston, IL 60201
Tel.: (847) 424-2000
Fax: (847) 424-2001
E-mail: awareinfo@awaremusic.com
Web Site: www.awarerecords.com
Approx. Number Employees: 5
Year Founded: 1993
Business Description:
Record Promotions
S.I.C.: 2741
N.A.I.C.S.: 512230
Media: 8-10-11
Personnel:
Gregg Latterman *(Founder & CEO)*
Mark Cunningham *(VP-Mktg & Mgr)*

AXL MUSICAL INSTRUMENTS CO., LTD., CORP.
PO Box 808
Millbrae, CA 94030-9998
Tel.: (415) 508-1398
Fax: (415) 508-1396
E-mail: mail@axlusa.com
Web Site: www.axlusa.com
Sales Range: $10-24.9 Million
Approx. Number Employees: 300
Business Description:
Musical Instruments Mfr
S.I.C.: 3931
N.A.I.C.S.: 339992
Media: 10-11
Personnel:
Alan Liu *(Chm)*
Brad Townsend *(Sr VP-Intl Sls & Mktg)*

BAKERSFIELD SYMPHONY ORCHESTRA
1328 34th St Ste A
Bakersfield, CA 93301
Tel.: (661) 323-7928
Fax: (661) 323-7331
E-mail: music@bakersfieldsymphony.org
Web Site:
www.bakersfieldsymphony.org
Sales Range: Less than $1 Million
Approx. Number Employees: 75
Business Description:
Symphony Orchestra
S.I.C.: 7929
N.A.I.C.S.: 711130
Media: 3-8-9-23-24-25
Personnel:
Marci Maynard *(Pres)*
Mike Chertok *(Dir-Devel)*
John Farrer *(Dir-Music)*
Mary Moore *(Mgr-Ops)*
Jim Mueller *(Engr)*

BALDWIN PIANO, INC.
(Sub. of Gibson Guitar Corp.)
309 Plus Pk Blvd
Nashville, TN 37217
Tel.: (615) 871-4500
Tel.: (615) 277-2190
Fax: (615) 889-5509
Toll Free: (800) 876-2976
Web Site: www2.gibson.com/Products/Pianos/Search.aspx
Approx. Number Employees: 1,500
Year Founded: 1862
Business Description:
Organs & Pianos Mfr & Sales
S.I.C.: 3931; 5736
N.A.I.C.S.: 339992; 451140
Import Export
Media: 6-10-13-19-20-22
Personnel:
Henry Juszkiewicz *(Chm & CEO)*
Karen Robb *(Dir-Mktg)*
Brands & Products:
BALDWIN ARTIST GRANDS
BALDWIN CUSTOM GRANDS
BALDWIN PRO SERIES
CHICKERING GRANDS
D.H. BALDWIN VERTICALS

BALLET THEATRE FOUNDATION, INC.
(d/b/a American Ballet Theatre)
890 Broadway
New York, NY 10003
Tel.: (212) 477-3030
Fax: (212) 254-5938
E-mail: info@abt.org
Web Site: www.abt.org
Approx. Rev.: $35,000,000
Approx. Number Employees: 165
Business Description:
Ballet Production Services
S.I.C.: 7922
N.A.I.C.S.: 711120
Media: 7-8-9-10-18-20-22-23-24-25
Personnel:
Lewis S. Ranieri *(Chm)*
Mildred C. Brinn *(Vice Chm)*
David G. Lansky *(Gen Mgr)*
James Timm *(Dir-Mktg & Brand Mgmt)*
Brad Fields *(Dir-Lighting)*
Wendy Fisher *(Dir-Special Events)*
Kevin McKenzie *(Dir-Artistic)*
N. James Whitehill *(Dir-Production)*
Mary Jo Ziesel *(Dir-Education & Trng)*
Victor Barbee *(Assoc Dir-Artistic)*
Roseanne Forni *(Office Mgr)*
Catherine Brown *(Mgr-Payroll & Benefits)*
Vince Lingner *(Mgr-IT)*
Dathan Manning *(Mgr-Principal Stage)*
Danielle Ventimiglia *(Mgr-Stage)*
Brands & Products:
ABT
AMERICAN BALLET THEATRE

BALLY TECHNOLOGIES, INC.
6601 S Bermuda Rd
Las Vegas, NV 89119-3605
Tel.: (702) 584-7600
Fax: (702) 584-7710
E-mail: sales@ballytech.com
Web Site: www.ballytech.com
Approx. Rev.: $758,155,000
Approx. Number Employees: 2,827
Year Founded: 1968
Business Description:
Casino Game Machines Mfr & Operator
S.I.C.: 7999
N.A.I.C.S.: 713290; 713990
Advertising Expenditures: $8,200,000
Media: 6-7-8-10-11-13-14-25
Personnel:
Kevin Verner *(Chm)*
Ramesh Srinivasan *(Pres & COO)*
Richard M. Haddrill *(CEO)*
Neil P. Davidson *(CFO & Treas)*
Mark Lerner *(Gen Counsel, Sec & Sr VP-Law & Govt)*
Bryan Kelly *(Sr VP-Tech)*
Derik Mooberry *(Sr VP-Products & Ops)*
Dan Savage *(VP-Mktg)*
Jean Venneman *(VP-Product Mgmt)*
Rick Meitzler *(Dir-Sls-Illinois VLT)*
Keith Michel *(Dir-Mobile Tech)*
Laura Olson-Reyes *(Dir-Corp Comm)*
Mark J. Wiedemer *(Dir-Sys Sls)*
Riley Meredith *(Mgr-Social Media)*
Brands & Products:
1,000,000 DEGREES
99 BOTTLES OF BEER
ALPHA
BALLY
BALLY COOL SIGN
BALLY LIVE REWARDS
BALLY ONE SYSTEM
BALLY SMS
BLAZING 7S
BLAZING 7S DOUBLE
BLUE SPOT BINGO
BONUS FRENZY
BOXCAR BONUS
CASINO CHALLENGE
CASTLE CRASHER
CMS
DIAMOND LINE 775
DIAMONDS & DEVILS
DOWNLOAD CONFIGURATION MANAGER
DUAL VISION
FIVE & DIME
THE HEIST
HOT SHOT PROGRESSIVE
I LOVE JACKPOTS
IVIEW DM
LONE STAR

Key to Media (For complete agency information see *The Advertising Red Books-Agencies* edition):
1. Bus. Publs. 2. Cable T.V. 3. Catalogs & Directories. 4. Co-op Adv. 5. Consumer Mags. 6. D.M. to Bus. Estab.7. D.M. to Consumers
8. Daily Newsp. 9. Exhibits/Trade Shows 10. Foreign 11. Infomercial 12. Internet Adv.13. Multimedia 14. Network Radio
15. Network T.V. 16. Newsp. Distr. Mags. 17. Other 18. Outdoor (Posters, Transit) 19. Point of Purchase20. Premiums, Novelties
21. Product Samples 22. Special Events Mktg. 23. Spot Radio 24. Spot T.V. 25. Weekly Newsp. 26. Yellow Page Adv.

Bally Technologies, Inc. — (Continued)

MCC
MILLIONAIRE SEVENS
MULTICONNECT
NETWORK FLOOR OF THE FUTURE
OPEN CASINO MANAGER
PAYDAY POKER
PIRATES GOLD
QUARTER MILLION
QUICK HIT
RAPID DOUBLE JACKPOT
REEL MONEY
ROARING 20S
SUPER BLAZING 7S
TABLE VIEW
TMS
WILD BONUS SEVENS
YOU DRIVE OUR INNOVATION

Advertising Agency:
The Firm Public Relations & Marketing
6157 S Rainbow Blvd
Las Vegas, NV 89118
Tel.: (702) 739-9933
Fax: (702) 739-9779
75th Anniversary Events

BALLY TOTAL FITNESS HOLDINGS CORPORATION

(Holding of Harbert Management Corporation)
8700 W Bryn Mawr Ave 3rd Fl
Chicago, IL 60631-3512
Tel.: (773) 380-3000
Fax: (773) 693-2982
Toll Free: (800) 515-CLUB
Web Site: www.ballyfitness.com
Sales Range: $1-4.9 Billion
Approx. Number Employees: 8,800
Business Description:
Holding Company; Physical Fitness Facilities
S.I.C.: 7991
N.A.I.C.S.: 713940
Advertising Expenditures: $57,154,000
Media: 8-9-13-14-15-18-22-23-24-26
Personnel:
Michael Sheehan *(CEO)*
Steven D. Barnhart *(CFO & Sr VP)*
Guy Ghier *(CIO & Sr VP)*
Dennis Cary *(CMO & Sr VP)*
Thomas S. Massimino *(Sr VP-Ops)*
Brands & Products:
BALLETONE
BALLY SPORTS CLUBS
BALLY TOTAL FITNESS
BODY GEM
BOSU
CRUNCH FITNESS
FITNESS FORMULA
GORILLA SPORTS
KWANDO
OREGON SCIENTIFIC
PINNACLE FITNESS
POWERFLEX
RAPID RESULTS
RAPID REWARDS
REACTION CYCLING
RESIST-A-BALL
ROPESPORT
SONICARE ELITE
SPORTS CLUBS OF CANADA
TOTAL FITNESS
URBAN REBOUNDING
WAI LANA
ZUMBA

Advertising Agencies:
EastWest Marketing Group
401 5th Ave 4th Fl
New York, NY 10016
Tel.: (212) 951-7220
Fax: (212) 951-7201

Grupo Gallegos
401 E Ocean Blvd Ste 600
Long Beach, CA 90802
Tel.: (562) 256-3600
Fax: (562) 256-3620

LH Advertising Agency Inc.
200 N Central Ave Ste 220
Hartsdale, NY 10530
Tel.: (914) 285-3456
Fax: (914) 285-3450

Tom, Dick & Harry Advertising
350 W Erie 2nd Fl
Chicago, IL 60654
Tel.: (312) 327-9500
Fax: (312) 327-9501

BALTIMORE ORIOLES, L.P.

333 W Camden St
Baltimore, MD 21201
Tel.: (410) 685-9800
Fax: (410) 547-6277
E-mail: birdmail@oriolepark.com
Web Site: baltimore.orioles.mlb.com/bal/ballpark/index.jsp
Approx. Number Employees: 200
Year Founded: 1954
Business Description:
Professional Baseball Club
S.I.C.: 7941
N.A.I.C.S.: 711211
Import
Media: 3-4-8-9-10-13-18-20-22-23-24-25
Distr.: Natl.
Budget Set: Jan.
Personnel:
Peter G. Angelos *(Chm & CEO)*
Thomas L. Clancy, Jr. *(Vice Chm-Community Projects & Pub Affairs)*
George P. Stamas *(Partner)*
Robert A. Ames *(CFO & VP)*
John P. Angelos *(Exec VP)*
Joe Jordan *(Dir-Scouting)*
Matt Klentak *(Dir-Baseball Ops)*
David Stockstill *(Dir-Intl Scouting)*
John Stockstill *(Dir-Player Dev)*
Bill Wilkes *(Dir-Baseball Admin)*
Brands & Products:
ORIOLES
Advertising Agency:
MLB Advanced Media, L.P.
75 9th Ave 5th Fl
New York, NY 10011
Tel.: (212) 485-3444
Fax: (212) 485-3456

BALTIMORE RAVENS LIMITED PARTNERSHIP

1101 Russell St
Baltimore, MD 21230
Tel.: (410) 547-8100
Fax: (410) 654-6239
E-mail: inquiries@baltimoreravens.com
Web Site: www.baltimoreravens.com
Approx. Number Employees: 130
Year Founded: 1946
Business Description:
Professional Football Franchise
S.I.C.: 7941
N.A.I.C.S.: 711211
Advertising Expenditures: $1,000,000
Media: 1-2-4-8-9-17-18-22-23-24-25
Distr.: Direct to Consumer; Reg.
Budget Set: Jan.
Personnel:
Stephen J. Bisciotti *(Co-Owner)*
Arthur B. Modell *(Owner)*
Richard W. Cass *(Pres)*
Jeff Goering *(CFO & VP)*
Ozzie Newsome *(Exec VP & Gen Mgr)*
Kevin Byrne *(Sr VP-Pub & Community Rels)*
Ed Burchell *(VP-Reg Partnerships & Sls)*
Mark Burdett *(VP-Corp Sls & Dev)*
Gabrielle Valdez Dow *(VP-Mktg)*
Bill Jankowski *(VP-IT)*
Kevin Rochlitz *(VP-Natl Partnerships & Sls)*
Sarah Ellison *(Digital Media-Editor & Writer)*
O. J. Brigance *(Dir-Player Dev)*
Eric DeCosta *(Dir-Player Personnel)*
John Dube *(Dir-Football Video Ops)*
Nick Fusee *(Dir-IT)*
Elizabeth Jackson *(Dir-HR)*
Vincent Newsome *(Dir-Pro Personnel)*
Darren Sanders *(Dir-Security)*
Chad Steele *(Dir-Media Rels)*
Mark Bienvenu *(Asst Dir-Football Video Ops)*
Harry Swayne *(Asst Dir-Player Programs)*
Mike Burke *(Mgr-Ticket Sls & Hospitality)*
John Cline *(Mgr-Event & Guest Svcs)*
Megan Collins *(Mgr-Events & Entertainment)*
Andi Goodwin *(Mgr-Comm Rels)*
Josh Hartman *(Mgr-Premium Svcs & Suites)*
Patti Holtery *(Mgr-Payroll)*
Kate Kaiser *(Mgr-Corp Sls Admin)*
Jessica Markison *(Mgr-Footbal Admin)*
Adam Mazalewski *(Mgr-Ticket Ops)*
Jay O'Brien *(Mgr-Brdcst)*
Jobie Waldt *(Mgr-Stadium Ops)*
Brands & Products:
BALTIMORE RAVENS

BALTIMORE SYMPHONY ORCHESTRA

1212 Cathedral St
Baltimore, MD 21201
Tel.: (410) 783-8000
Tel.: (410) 783-8024
Fax: (410) 783-8131
E-mail: orderhelp@bsomusic.org
Web Site: www.bsomusic.org
Approx. Number Employees: 200
Business Description:
Symphony Orchestra
S.I.C.: 6512; 7929
N.A.I.C.S.: 531120; 711130
Media: 6-8-9-13-18-20-23-24-25
Personnel:
Paul Meecham *(Pres & CEO)*
Deborah Goetz *(Dir-Mktg)*
Alicia Lin *(Dir-Ops & Facilities)*
Alana Morrall *(Dir-Individual Giving)*
Marilyn Rife *(Dir-Orchestra Personnel & HR)*
Joanne Rosenthal *(Dir-Major Gifts & Planned Giving)*
Lisa Sheppley *(Assoc Dir-Education)*
Toby Blumenthal *(Mgr-Facility Sls)*
Tiffany Bryan *(Mgr-Front-House)*
Curtis Jones *(Mgr-Building Svcs)*
Peter Murphy *(Mgr-Ticket Svcs)*
Brands & Products:
BSO
SYMPHONY WITH A TWIST
Advertising Agency:
MGH, Inc.
100 Painters Mill Rd Ste 600
Owings Mills, MD 21117-7305
Tel.: (410) 902-5000
Fax: (410) 902-8712

BANGOR SYMPHONY ORCHESTRA

51A Main St
Bangor, ME 04402
Tel.: (207) 942-5555
Fax: (207) 990-1272
Toll Free: (800) 639-3221
E-mail: symphony@bangorsymphony.com
Web Site: www.bangorsymphony.com
Approx. Number Employees: 5
Business Description:
Symphony Orchestra
S.I.C.: 7929
N.A.I.C.S.: 711130
Media: 8-9-20-23-24-25
Personnel:
Scott Burditt *(Principal)*
David Whitehill *(Exec Dir)*
Xiao-Lu Li *(Dir-Music & Conductor)*
Sarah S. P. McCarthy *(Dir-Dev & Mktg)*

BARBARA B. MANN PERFORMING ARTS HALL

8099 College Pkwy SW
Fort Myers, FL 33919
Tel.: (239) 481-4849
Tel.: (239) 489-3033
Fax: (239) 489-0326
Toll Free: (800) 440-7469
Web Site: www.bbmannpah.com
Approx. Number Employees: 30
Business Description:
Theatrical Production
S.I.C.: 7389
N.A.I.C.S.: 711310
Media: 6-7-8-9-20-25
Personnel:
Peg Welty *(Dir-Mktg)*
Chris Senell *(Mgr-Box Office)*

THE BASEBALL CLUB OF SEATTLE, L.P.

(d/b/a Seattle Mariners)
1250 1st Ave S
Seattle, WA 98134-1216
Tel.: (206) 346-4000
Fax: (206) 346-4450
E-mail: fanfeedback@mariners.com
Web Site: www.mariners.com
Sales Range: $150-199.9 Million
Approx. Number Employees: 200
Year Founded: 1977
Business Description:
Professional Baseball Club
S.I.C.: 7941
N.A.I.C.S.: 711211
Advertising Expenditures: $2,000,000
Media: 1-2-3-6-7-8-9-10-11-13-18-19-20-22-23-24
Distr.: Reg.
Budget Set: Sept. -Oct.

Key to Media (For complete agency information see *The Advertising Red Books-Agencies* edition):
1. Bus. Publs. 2. Cable T.V. 3. Catalogs & Directories. 4. Co-op Adv. 5. Consumer Mags. 6. D.M. to Bus. Estab.7. D.M. to Consumers
8. Daily Newsp. 9. Exhibits/Trade Shows 10. Foreign 11. Infomercial 12. Internet Adv.13. Multimedia 14. Network Radio
15. Network T.V. 16. Newsp. Distr. Mags. 17. Other 18. Outdoor (Posters, Transit) 19. Point of Purchase20. Premiums, Novelties
21. Product Samples 22. Special Events Mktg. 23. Spot Radio 24. Spot T.V. 25. Weekly Newsp. 26. Yellow Page Adv.

Personnel:
Howard A. Lincoln *(Chm & CEO)*
Chuck Armstrong *(Pres & COO)*
Jack Zduriencik *(Exec VP & Gen Mgr-Baseball Ops)*
Bob Aylward *(Exec VP-Bus Ops)*
Kevin Mather *(Exec VP-Fin & Ballpark Opers)*
Bart Waldman *(Exec VP-Legal & Govt Affairs)*
Randy Adamack *(VP-Comm)*
Joe Chard *(VP-Community Rels & Corp Bus)*
Tim Kornegay *(VP-Fin)*
Kevin Martinez *(VP-Mktg)*
Marianne Short *(VP-HR)*
Frances Traisman *(VP-Sls)*

Brands & Products:
SEATTLE MARINERS

Advertising Agencies:
Copacino + Fujikado, LLC
101 Yesler Way Ste 500
Seattle, WA 98104
Tel.: (206) 467-6610
Fax: (206) 467-6604

MLB Advanced Media, L.P.
75 9th Ave 5th Fl
New York, NY 10011
Tel.: (212) 485-3444
Fax: (212) 485-3456

BATANGA, INC.
2121 Ponce De Leon Blvd
Coral Gables, FL 33134
Tel.: (305) 476-2974
Fax: (305) 476-8280
E-mail: feedback@batanga.com
Web Site: www.batanga.com
Approx. Number Employees: 150
Business Description:
Media & Entertainment Services for the US Hispanic Community
S.I.C.: 7313
N.A.I.C.S.: 541840
Advertising Expenditures: $5,000,000
Media: 1-2-10-13-22
Personnel:
Rafael Urbina *(Chm & CEO)*
Hector Santaella *(CFO)*
Margie Bonomo *(Sr VP-Sls)*

Advertising Agency:
KFM Advertising
3119 Ponce de Leon Blvd Ste A
Coral Gables, FL 33134
Tel.: (305) 443-3136
Fax: (305) 443-3419

BELLE OF ORLEANS, LLC
(Sub. of TROPICANA ENTERTAINMENT INC.)
(d/b/a Amelia Belle Casino)
500 Lake Palourde Rd
Amelia, LA 70340
Tel.: (985) 631-1777
Fax: (985) 631-1778
E-mail: info@ameliabellecasino.com
Web Site:
www.ameliabellecasino.com
Approx. Number Employees: 800
Business Description:
Riverboat Casino Operator
S.I.C.: 7999
N.A.I.C.S.: 713210
Media: 8-9-13-20-22-23-24-25

BELLEVUE PHILHARMONIC ORCHESTRA INC.
10900 NE 4th St #2300
Bellevue, WA 98004
Tel.: (425) 455-4171
Fax: (425) 455-9170
E-mail: info@bellevuephil.org
Web Site: www.bellevuephil.org
Sales Range: $1-9.9 Million
Approx. Number Employees: 65
Year Founded: 1967
Business Description:
Symphony Orchestra
S.I.C.: 7929
N.A.I.C.S.: 711130
Media: 9-20-22-23-24-25
Personnel:
Kirsten G. James *(Principal)*
Fusao Kajima *(Dir-Music)*

BERKELEY SYMPHONY ORCHESTRA
1942 University Ave Ste 207
Berkeley, CA 94704
Tel.: (510) 841-2800
Fax: (510) 841-5422
E-mail: mail@berkeleysymphony.org
Web Site:
www.berkeleysymphony.org
Sales Range: $10-24.9 Million
Approx. Number Employees: 45
Business Description:
Symphony Orchestra
S.I.C.: 7929
N.A.I.C.S.: 711130
Media: 9-20-23-24-25
Personnel:
Kathleen Henschel *(Pres)*
James A. Kleinmann *(Exec Dir)*
Joana Carneiro *(Dir-Music)*
Ming Luke *(Assoc Conductor & Dir-Music Education)*
Jenny Lee *(Mgr-Mktg)*

BIG APPLE CIRCUS LTD.
505 8th Ave FL 19
New York, NY 10018
Tel.: (212) 268-2500
Fax: (212) 268-3163
Web Site: www.bigapplecircus.org
Approx. Number Employees: 40
Business Description:
Circus
S.I.C.: 7389
N.A.I.C.S.: 711310
Media: 1-3-6-13-18-20-22-24
Personnel:
Michael Christensen *(Co-Founder & Dir-Creative)*
Leslie Alpert Schuldenfrei *(Sr Dir-Mktg)*
Joel W. Dein *(Dir-Comm)*
Guillaume Dufresnoy *(Dir-Artistic)*
Jim Roper *(Dir-Concessions)*
Tanya M. Santiago *(Dir-Admin)*
Karen McCarty *(Assoc Dir-Creative of Community Programs)*

BILLINGS SYMPHONY SOCIETY INC.
2721 2nd Ave N Ste 350
Billings, MT 59101
Tel.: (406) 252-3610
Fax: (406) 252-3353
E-mail: symphony@billingssymphony.org
Web Site: www.billingssymphony.org
Approx. Number Employees: 9
Year Founded: 1950
Business Description:
Symphony Orchestra
S.I.C.: 7929
N.A.I.C.S.: 711130
Media: 8-9-18-20-23-24-25
Personnel:
Sandra Culhane *(Exec Dir)*

BINGHAMTON PHILHARMONIC INC.
31 Front St
Binghamton, NY 13905
Tel.: (607) 722-6717
Fax: (607) 722-6526
E-mail: info@binghamtonphilharmonic.org
Web Site:
www.binghamtonphilharmonic.org
Sales Range: Less than $1 Million
Approx. Number Employees: 5
Business Description:
Symphony Orchestra Services
S.I.C.: 7929
N.A.I.C.S.: 711130
Media: 9-20-23-24-25
Personnel:
June Christensen *(Dir-Admin & Patron Svcs)*
Sandra J. Griffiths *(Dir-Dev)*
Ubaldo Valli *(Mgr-Personnel)*

BIRMINGHAM JEFFERSON CONVENTION COMPLEX
2100 Richard Arrington Jr Blvd
Birmingham, AL 35203
Tel.: (205) 458-8400
Fax: (205) 458-8530
E-mail: info@bjcc.org
Web Site: www.bjcc.org
Sales Range: $50-74.9 Million
Approx. Number Employees: 130
Year Founded: 1965
Business Description:
Convention Center
S.I.C.: 7011; 5813
N.A.I.C.S.: 721110; 722410
Media: 10-22

BLUE MAN PRODUCTIONS, INC.
599 Broadway Fl 5
New York, NY 10012
Tel.: (212) 226-6366
Fax: (212) 226-6609
Toll Free: (800) BLUEMAN
E-mail: management@blueman.com
Web Site: www.blueman.com
Approx. Number Employees: 40
Business Description:
Musical Theatre Producer
S.I.C.: 7922; 2741; 7929; 8999
N.A.I.C.S.: 711110; 512210; 512230; 711130
Media: 8-13-20-22-23
Personnel:
Matt Goldman *(Co-Founder)*
Phil Stanton *(Co-Founder)*
Christopher Wink *(Founder)*

Advertising Agency:
Yellin/McCarron, Inc.
280 Summer St 4th Fl
Boston, MA 02210
Tel.: (617) 426-9211
Fax: (617) 426-7443

BMG/MUSIC
(Sub. of BMG Music Publishing)
1540 Broadway
New York, NY 10036-4039
Tel.: (212) 930-4939
Fax: (212) 930-4011
E-mail: info@bmg.com
Web Site: www.bmg.com
Sales Estimate: $5-9.9 Million
Approx. Number Employees: 4,500
Business Description:
International Manufacturing & Marketing of Records & Tapes, Record & Tape Club
S.I.C.: 3652; 5099
N.A.I.C.S.: 334612; 423990
Advertising Expenditures: $200,000
Media: 6-13
Personnel:
Hartwig Masuch *(CEO)*
Steven Moran *(COO)*
Laurent Hubert *(Exec VP)*
Lou Robinson *(Sr VP-Video Promotion/Artist Dev)*

Brands & Products:
ARISTA

BOCA RESORTS, INC.
(Sub. of Celanese AG)
501 E Camino Real
Boca Raton, FL 33432-6127
Tel.: (561) 447-5300
Fax: (561) 394-3961
E-mail: investor@bocaresortsinc.com
Web Site: www.luxuryresorts.com
Sales Range: $300-349.9 Million
Approx. Number Employees: 1,000
Year Founded: 1926
Business Description:
Holding Company; Operator of Leisure, Recreation, Entertainment & Sports Businesses
S.I.C.: 7011
N.A.I.C.S.: 721110
Advertising Expenditures: $3,700,000
Media: 1-4-5-6-7-8-9-19-20-22-23-24-25
Distr.: Reg.
Budget Set: June -July
Personnel:
Richard C. Rochon *(Vice Chm)*
Stephen Aft *(Pres & COO)*
Victoria Jones *(Dir-Mktg)*
Sandra Tagoia *(Dir-HR)*

BOISE PHILHARMONIC ASSOCIATION, INC.
516 S 9th St
Boise, ID 83702
Tel.: (208) 344-7849
Fax: (208) 336-9078
Toll Free: (888) 300-7849
E-mail: info@boisephilharmonic.org
Web Site: www.boisephilharmonic.org
Sales Range: $50-74.9 Million
Approx. Number Employees: 90
Business Description:
Orchestra
S.I.C.: 7929
N.A.I.C.S.: 711130
Media: 9-20-22-23-24-25
Personnel:
John Stedman *(Pres)*
Tony Boatman *(Exec Dir)*
Tina Kierce *(Dir-Mktg & Sls)*
Marilyn Goerrich *(Mgr-Orchestra Personnel)*
Forrest Hartviggsen *(Mgr-Stage)*
Lindsey Leslie *(Mgr-Patron Svcs)*

Key to Media (For complete agency information see *The Advertising Red Books-Agencies* edition):
1. Bus. Publs. 2. Cable T.V. 3. Catalogs & Directories. 4. Co-op Adv. 5. Consumer Mags. 6. D.M. to Bus. Estab.7. D.M. to Consumers 8. Daily Newsp. 9. Exhibits/Trade Shows 10. Foreign 11. Infomercial 12. Internet Adv.13. Multimedia 14. Network Radio 15. Network T.V. 16. Newsp. Distr. Mags. 17. Other 18. Outdoor (Posters, Transit) 19. Point of Purchase20. Premiums, Novelties 21. Product Samples 22. Special Events Mktg. 23. Spot Radio 24. Spot T.V. 25. Weekly Newsp. 26. Yellow Page Adv.

BOSTON BALLET INC.
19 Clarendon St
Boston, MA 02116
Tel.: (617) 695-6950
Fax: (617) 695-6995
Web Site: www.bostonballet.org
Approx. Number Employees: 115
Year Founded: 1963
Business Description:
Ballet Production
S.I.C.: 7922
N.A.I.C.S.: 711120
Media: 8-9-20-23-24-25
Personnel:
Valerie Wilder *(Exec Dir)*
Leslie Cardill *(Dir-Mktg)*
Benjamin J. Phillips *(Dir-Tech & Mgr-Production)*
Amy Holland *(Dir-Adv & Mktg Programs)*
Jonathan McPhee *(Dir-Music & Principal Conductor)*
Mikko Nissinen *(Dir-Artistic)*
Rachel Yurman *(Dir-Foundation Rels)*
Charles K. Heightchew *(Mgr-Costumes & Wardrobe)*
Craig Margolis *(Mgr-Production Stage)*

BOSTON CELTICS LIMITED PARTNERSHIP
(Sub. of Boston Basketball Partners LLC)
226 Causeway St
Boston, MA 02114
Tel.: (617) 523-6050
Fax: (617) 523-5949
E-mail: contact@celtics.com
Web Site: www.celtics.com
Approx. Number Employees: 100
Year Founded: 1986
Business Description:
Owner & Operator of the Boston Celtics Professional Basketball Franchise
S.I.C.: 7941
N.A.I.C.S.: 711211
Media: 3-9-18-19-23-24
Distr.: Direct to Consumer
Personnel:
Robert Epstein *(Mng Partner & Alternate Governor)*
H. Irving Grousbeck *(Mng Partner & Alternate Governor)*
Stephen G. Pagliuca *(Mng Partner & Alternate Governor)*
Wycliffe Grousbeck *(Mng Partner)*
Sean Barror *(Sr VP-Corp Partnerships & Bus Dev)*
Bill Reissfelder *(CFO & Sr VP)*
Shawn Sullivan *(CMO)*
Danny Ainge *(Pres-Basketball Ops)*
Daryl Morey *(Mng Dir-Basketball Ops & Gen Mgr)*
Jay Wessel *(VP-Tech)*
Patrick Lynch *(Sr Dir-Acctg & Ops)*
Mackenzie Silverio *(Sr Dir-Ticket Sls & Mktg)*
Bill Bonsiewicz *(Dir-Media Relations)*
Duane Johnson *(Dir-Ticket Admin)*
Keith Sliney *(Dir-Creative)*
Peter Stringer *(Dir-Interactive Media)*
Nicole Federico *(Sr Mgr-Bus Dev)*
Rob Billings *(Mgr-Risk)*
Brands & Products:
BOSTON CELTICS

BOSTON PROFESSIONAL HOCKEY ASSOCIATION, INC.
(d/b/a Boston Bruins)
100 Legends Way
Boston, MA 02114-1390
Tel.: (617) 624-1900
Fax: (617) 624-1754
Fax: (617) 523-7184
Web Site: www.bostonbruins.com
Approx. Number Employees: 100
Year Founded: 1924
Business Description:
Professional Hockey Franchise
S.I.C.: 7941
N.A.I.C.S.: 711211
Media: 9-10-18-22-23-25
Distr.: Natl.
Personnel:
Jeremy M. Jacobs, Sr. *(Owner & Governor)*
Cam Neely *(Pres & Alternate Governor)*
Charles Jacobs *(Principal & Alternate Governor)*
Amy Latimer *(Sr VP-Sls & Mktg)*
Jim Bednarek *(VP-Fin)*
Peter Chiarelli *(Gen Mgr)*
Jim Benning *(Asst Gen Mgr)*
Don Sweeney *(Asst Gen Mgr)*
Scott Bradley *(Dir-Player Personnel)*
Brands & Products:
BOSTON BRUINS
BRUINS STREET BRIGADE
Advertising Agencies:
Arnold Worldwide
101 Huntington Ave
Boston, MA 02199-7603
Tel.: (617) 587-8000
Fax: (617) 587-8004
Agency of Record
Digital
Integrated Marketing Campaign
OOH
Print
TV

FUSE/ideas
255 Elm St Ste 201
Somerville, MA 02144
Tel.: (617) 776-5800
Fax: (617) 776-5821

BOSTON RED SOX BASEBALL CLUB LIMITED PARTNERSHIP
(Sub. of New England Sports Ventures, LLC)
4 Yawkey Way Fenway Park
Boston, MA 02215
Tel.: (617) 226-6000
Tel.: (617) 267-9440
Fax: (617) 375-0944
E-mail: info@redsox.com
Web Site: www.redsox.com
Approx. Number Employees: 120
Year Founded: 1901
Business Description:
Professional Baseball Club
S.I.C.: 7941
N.A.I.C.S.: 711211
Media: 3-6-8-9-10-13-15-18-19-20-23-24
Distr.: Natl.
Budget Set: Jan.
Personnel:
John W. Henry *(Owner)*
Thomas C. Werner *(Chm)*
David Ginsberg *(Vice Chm)*
Phillip H. Morse *(Vice Chm)*
Larry Lucchino *(Pres & CEO)*
Samuel H. Kennedy *(COO & Exec VP)*
Theo N. Epstein *(Exec VP & Gen Mgr)*
Jonathan Gilula *(Exec VP-Bus Affairs)*
Ben Cherington *(Sr VP & Asst Gen Mgr)*
Meg Vaillancourt *(Sr VP & Exec Dir-Red Sox Foundation)*
Jennifer Flynn *(Sr VP & Asst Gen Counsel)*
Ron Bumgarner *(Sr VP-Ticketing)*
Lawrence Cancro *(Sr VP-Fenway Affairs)*
Susan Goodenow *(Sr VP-Pub Affairs & Mktg)*
Troup Parkinson *(Sr VP-Corp Partnerships)*
Craig Shipley *(Sr VP-Player Personnel & InterNatl Scouting)*
Janet Marie Smith *(Sr VP-Plng & Design)*
Mary Sprong *(Sr VP-HR & Admin)*
Dick Bresciani *(VP-Emeritus & Team Historian)*
Marcell M. Bhangoo *(Dir-Client Svcs)*
Ethan Faggett *(Asst Dir-Florida Baseball Ops)*
Cathy Fahy *(Sr Mgr-Acctg)*
Sean P. Carragher *(Mgr-Ticket Acctg & Admin)*
J. Joseph Cochran *(Mgr-Clubhouse & Equipment)*
Advertising Agencies:
Conover Tuttle Pace
77 N Washington St
Boston, MA 02114
Tel.: (617) 412-4000
Fax: (617) 412-4411

Conventures, Inc.
1 Design Ctr Pl Ste 718
Boston, MA 02210-2335
Tel.: (617) 439-7700
Fax: (617) 439-7701

MLB Advanced Media, L.P.
75 9th Ave 5th Fl
New York, NY 10011
Tel.: (212) 485-3444
Fax: (212) 485-3456

BOSTON SYMPHONY ORCHESTRA INC.
301 Massachusetts Ave
Boston, MA 02115
Tel.: (617) 266-1492
Fax: (617) 638-9367
E-mail: rbradway@bso.org
Web Site: www.bso.org
Approx. Sls.: $37,319,000
Approx. Number Employees: 249
Business Description:
Symphony Orchestra
S.I.C.: 7929
N.A.I.C.S.: 711130
Media: 8-9-13-18-20-22-23-24-25
Personnel:
Thomas D. May *(CFO)*
Kim Noltemy *(Chief Mktg & Comm Officer)*
Sarah L. Manoog *(Dir-Mktg)*
Rich Bradway *(Assoc Dir-E-Commerce & New Media)*
Kathleen Drohan *(Assoc Dir-PR)*
Mary E. Thomson *(Assoc Dir-Dev Corp Events)*
John Demick *(Mgr-Stage)*
Sid Guidicianne *(Mgr-Front of House)*
Doreen Reis *(Mgr-Adv & Events)*
Brands & Products:
BOSTON POPS
BOSTON POPS ESPLANADE ORCHESTRA
THE BOSTON POPS ORCHESTRA
BOSTON SYMPHONY ORCHESTRA
RED SOX
TANGLEWOOD

BOULDER PHILHARMONIC ORCHESTRA
2590 Walnut St
Boulder, CO 80302
Tel.: (303) 449-1343
Fax: (303) 443-9203
E-mail: info@boulderphil.org
Web Site: www.boulderphil.org
Sales Range: Less than $1 Million
Approx. Number Employees: 150
Year Founded: 1958
Business Description:
Orchestra
S.I.C.: 7929; 7922
N.A.I.C.S.: 711130; 711120
Media: 8-9-13-20-23-24-25
Personnel:
Kevin Shuck *(Exec Dir)*
Michael Butterman *(Dir-Music)*
Kim Peoria *(Mgr-Orchestra Personnel)*
Glenn Ross *(Mgr-Concert)*

BOWL AMERICA INCORPORATED
6446 Edsall Rd
Alexandria, VA 22312
Mailing Address:
PO Box 1288
Springfield, VA 22151-0288
Tel.: (703) 941-6300
Fax: (703) 256-2430
E-mail: administrator@bowl-america.com
Web Site: www.bowl-america.com
Approx. Rev.: $26,517,850
Approx. Number Employees: 250
Year Founded: 1958
Business Description:
Bowling Centers Operator; Food & Beverage Services, Game Rooms, Rental Lockers & Playroom Facilities
S.I.C.: 7933
N.A.I.C.S.: 713950
Advertising Expenditures: $849,095
Personnel:
Leslie H. Goldberg *(Pres, CEO & COO)*
Cheryl A. Dragoo *(Chief Acctg Officer & Sr VP)*
Ruth E. Macklin *(Treas, Sec & Sr VP)*

BRADENTON MOTORSPORTS PARK
21000 SR 64
Bradenton, FL 34212
Tel.: (941) 748-1320
Fax: (941) 741-8534
E-mail: info@bradentonmotorsports.com
Web Site:
www.bradentonmotorsports.com
Business Description:
Motor Strip for Drag Racing
S.I.C.: 7948

Key to Media (For complete agency information see *The Advertising Red Books-Agencies* edition):
1. Bus. Publs. 2. Cable T.V. 3. Catalogs & Directories. 4. Co-op Adv. 5. Consumer Mags. 6. D.M. to Bus. Estab.7. D.M. to Consumers 8. Daily Newsp. 9. Exhibits/Trade Shows 10. Foreign 11. Infomercial 12. Internet Adv.13. Multimedia 14. Network Radio 15. Network T.V. 16. Newsp. Distr. Mags. 17. Other 18. Outdoor (Posters, Transit) 19. Point of Purchase20. Premiums, Novelties 21. Product Samples 22. Special Events Mktg. 23. Spot Radio 24. Spot T.V. 25. Weekly Newsp. 26. Yellow Page Adv.

N.A.I.C.S.: 711212
Media: 13-22-23-24
Personnel:
Alan Chervitz *(owner)*
Todd Dickinson *(Owner)*

BREEDLOVE GUITAR CO.
2843 NW Lolo
Bend, OR 97701-9042
Tel.: (541) 385-8339
Fax: (541) 385-8183
E-mail: info@breedloveguitars.com
Web Site: www.breedloveguitars.com
E-Mail For Key Personnel:
Sales Director: pnewport@breedloveguitars.com
Approx. Number Employees: 40
Year Founded: 1990
Business Description:
Guitars & Mandolins
S.I.C.: 3931; 5099
N.A.I.C.S.: 339992; 423990
Advertising Expenditures: $200,000
Media: 6-10-13-19-22
Distr.: Intl.; Natl.
Personnel:
Tom Bedell *(Pres)*
Brands & Products:
ALPINE
ATLAS
BLACK GOLD
BREEDLOVE
CASCADE
CLASSIC XII
CM CLASSIC
COLUMBIA
DIAMOND
ED GERHARD EXOTIC
ED GERHARD SIGNATURE
EXOTIC VI
KING KOA
MARK I
MARK II
MARK IV
MCKENZIE
NORTHWEST
NYLON NOUVEAU
OLYMPIC
ORCA
OREGON
PACIFIC
PASSPORT
PASSPORT PLUS
PERFORMANCE BALANCE
PERFORMANCE BOSSA NOVA
PERFORMANCE BREEDLOVE FOCUS
PERFORMANCE FOCUS
PERFORMANCE FOCUS DREADNOUGHT
PERFORMANCE FUSION
PHOENIX
QUARTZ
QUARTZ FF
QUARTZ KF
QUARTZ KO
QUARTZ OF
QUARTZ OO
RETRO
REVIVAL
REVIVAL TENOR
ROGUE
ROOTS
SPIRIT

BRISTOL BAY PRODUCTIONS, LLC
(Sub. of Anschutz Film Group, LLC)
1888 Century Park E 14th Fl
Los Angeles, CA 90067
Tel.: (310) 887-1000
Fax: (310) 887-1001
E-mail: info@bristolbayproduction.com
Approx. Number Employees: 80
Business Description:
Movie Production
S.I.C.: 7812
N.A.I.C.S.: 512110
Media: 13-17
Personnel:
David Weil *(CEO)*

BROOKLYN CHILDREN'S MUSEUM INC.
145 Brooklyn Ave
Brooklyn, NY 11213
Tel.: (718) 735-4400
Fax: (718) 604-7442
Web Site: www.brooklynkids.org
Approx. Number Employees: 100
Year Founded: 1899
Business Description:
Children's Museum
S.I.C.: 8412; 9111
N.A.I.C.S.: 712110; 921110
Media: 9-10-20-23-24-25
Personnel:
William D. Rifkin *(Chm)*

BROOKLYN PHILHARMONIC
55 Washington St Ste 656
Brooklyn, NY 11201
Tel.: (718) 488-5700
Fax: (718) 488-5901
E-mail: info@brooklynphilharmonic.org
Web Site:
www.brooklynphilharmonic.org
Sales Range: Less than $1 Million
Approx. Number Employees: 6
Business Description:
Symphony Orchestra
S.I.C.: 7929
N.A.I.C.S.: 711130
Media: 8-9-13-20-22-23
Personnel:
J. Barclay Collins *(Chm)*
Greg Pierson *(COO)*
Michael Christie *(Dir-Music)*
Christopher Shannon *(Mgr-Special Events)*
Jon Taylor *(Mgr-Personnel)*

BUCCANEERS LIMITED PARTNERSHIP
(d/b/a Tampa Bay Buccaneers)
1 Buccaneer Pl
Tampa, FL 33607
Tel.: (813) 870-2700
Fax: (813) 554-1399
Toll Free: (800) 282-0683
Web Site: www.buccaneers.com
Approx. Number Employees: 175
Year Founded: 1973
Business Description:
Professional Football Franchise
S.I.C.: 7941
N.A.I.C.S.: 711211
Media: 3-4-5-9-18-22-23-24-25
Distr.: Natl.
Personnel:
Malcolm Glazer *(Owner & Pres)*
Bryan Glazer *(Co-Chm)*
Edward Glazer *(Co-Chm)*
Joel Glazer *(Co-Chm)*
Mark Dominik *(Gen Mgr)*
Jonathan Grella *(Dir-Comm)*
Dennis Hickey *(Dir-College Scouting)*
Dave Levy *(Dir-Video)*
Chris Bryan *(Asst Dir-Video)*
James Sorenson *(Mgr-Equipment)*
Brands & Products:
BARRETT'S BACKERS
BRYANT'S BUCAROOS
CADILLAC'S KIDS
CLAYTON'S NEXT GENERATION FOUNDATION
DAVIN'S DREAM TEAM
FLIP'S SQUAD
GAINES' GANG
HOVAN'S HEROES
ONE BUC CLUB
TAMPA BAY BUCCANEERS

BUFFALO BILLS, INC.
1 Bills Dr
Orchard Park, NY 14127-2237
Tel.: (716) 648-1800
Fax: (716) 649-6446
Toll Free: (877) BBTICKS
E-mail: info@buffalobills.com
Web Site: www.buffalobills.com
Approx. Number Employees: 300
Year Founded: 1960
Business Description:
Professional Football Franchise
S.I.C.: 7941
N.A.I.C.S.: 711211
Advertising Expenditures: $6,000,000
Media: 9-23-25
Distr.: Local
Personnel:
Ralph C. Wilson, Jr. *(Pres)*
Russ Brandon *(CEO)*
Mary Owen *(Exec VP-Strategic Plng)*
Pete Guelli *(Sr VP-Bus Ventures)*
Marc Honan *(Sr VP-Mktg & Brdcst)*
Jim Overdorf *(Sr VP-Football Admin)*
David Wheat *(Sr VP-Bus Ops)*
Scott Berchtold *(VP-Comm)*
Gretchen Geitter *(VP-Community Rels)*
Dan Evans *(Exec Dir-IT)*
Andy Major *(Exec Dir-Mktg)*
Stephen Asposto *(Dir & Engr-Video Production)*
Mike Ciechoski *(Dir-Ticket Sls)*
Christopher Clark *(Dir-Security)*
Chris Colleary *(Dir-Ticket Ops & Customer Svc)*
Chris Costanzo *(Dir-Premium Seating)*
Debbi Cummins *(Dir-Ticket Sys)*
Perry Dix *(Dir-Stadium Ops)*
Greg Estes *(Dir-Video)*
Chris Jenkins *(Dir-Media Rels)*
Tim Kehoe *(Dir-Mdse)*
Henry Kunttu *(Dir-Video)*
Paul Lancaster *(Dir-Player Programs)*
Elisabeth Malstrom *(Dir-HR)*
John Marzo *(Dir-Medical)*
Neal McMullen *(Dir-Sls)*
Gregg Pastore *(Dir-New Media)*
Don Purdy *(Dir-Football Admin)*
Chris Voigt *(Dir-Ops & Event Svcs)*
Bob Schatz *(Asst Dir-Stadium Ops)*
Chris Holland *(Sr Mgr-Ticket Sls)*
Pat Mathews *(Sr Mgr-Customer Rels)*
Karen Renzi *(Sr Mgr-Suite Svcs)*
Donna Andreef *(Mgr-Season Ticket Svc)*
Chris Brown *(Mgr-New Media & Publications)*
Sharon Hart *(Mgr-Premium Seat Svc)*
Dave Hojnowski *(Mgr-Equipment)*
Julie Lantaff *(Mgr-Bus Ops)*
Marty McLaughlin *(Coord-Security)*
Brands & Products:
BUFFALO BILLS
Advertising Agency:
Martino Flynn LLC
175 Sully's Trl Ste 100
Pittsford, NY 14534
Tel.: (585) 421-0100
Fax: (585) 421-0121

BUFFALO PHILHARMONIC ORCHESTRA SOCIETY INC.
499 Franklin St
Buffalo, NY 14202
Tel.: (716) 885-0331
Fax: (716) 885-9372
Web Site: www.bpo.org
Approx. Rev.: $10,000,000
Approx. Number Employees: 150
Business Description:
Symphony Orchestra
S.I.C.: 7929; 8742
N.A.I.C.S.: 711130; 541611
Media: 9-10-13-18-20-22-23-24-25
Personnel:
Stephen M. Baker *(Exec Dir)*
Jennifer Barbee *(Dir-Dev)*
Lisa J. Gallo *(Dir-Orchestra-Artistic Ops)*
Margaret Phillips *(Dir-Dev)*
Jennifer N. Comisso *(Mgr-Personnel)*
Barbara McCulloch *(Mgr-Info Resources)*

BUSCH GARDENS TAMPA BAY
(Unit of SeaWorld Parks & Entertainment LLC)
3605 E Bougainvillea Ave
Tampa, FL 33612-6433
Tel.: (813) 987-5000
Fax: (813) 987-5447
Web Site: www.buschgardens.com
Sales Range: $400-449.9 Million
Business Description:
Theme Park
S.I.C.: 7996; 8422
N.A.I.C.S.: 713110; 712130
Media: 3-8-9-13-18-22-23-24-25
Personnel:
Donnie Mills *(Exec VP & Gen Mgr)*
Advertising Agency:
OMD Chicago
225 N Michigan Ave 19th Fl
Chicago, IL 60601-7757
Tel.: (312) 324-7000
Fax: (312) 324-8201
— Lori Thompson *(Acct Exec)*

CABELA'S INC.
1 Cabela Dr
Sidney, NE 69160-1001
Tel.: (308) 254-5505
Fax: (308) 254-4800
E-mail: recruitment@cabelas.com
Web Site: www.cabelas.com
Approx. Rev.: $2,663,242,000
Approx. Number Employees: 6,100
Year Founded: 1961
Business Description:
Catalog & In-Store Sales of Sporting Goods
S.I.C.: 5941; 5961
N.A.I.C.S.: 451110; 454113

Key to Media (For complete agency information see *The Advertising Red Books-Agencies* edition):
1. Bus. Publs. 2. Cable T.V. 3. Catalogs & Directories. 4. Co-op Adv. 5. Consumer Mags. 6. D.M. to Bus. Estab.7. D.M. to Consumers 8. Daily Newsp. 9. Exhibits/Trade Shows 10. Foreign 11. Infomercial 12. Internet Adv.13. Multimedia 14. Network Radio 15. Network T.V. 16. Newsp. Distr. Mags. 17. Other 18. Outdoor (Posters, Transit) 19. Point of Purchase20. Premiums, Novelties 21. Product Samples 22. Special Events Mktg. 23. Spot Radio 24. Spot T.V. 25. Weekly Newsp. 26. Yellow Page Adv.

Cabela's Inc. — (Continued)

Import Export
Advertising Expenditures: $188,312,000
Media: 3-4-8-10-13-19-22
Personnel:
James W. Cabela *(Co-Founder & Vice Chm)*
Richard N. Cabela *(Chm)*
Dennis Highby *(Vice Chm)*
Thomas L. Millner *(Pres & CEO)*
Joseph M. Friebe *(Exec VP, Pres & CEO- Worlds Foremost Bank)*
Ralph W. Castner *(CFO & Exec VP)*
Michael Copeland *(COO & Exec VP)*
Charles Baldwin *(Chief Admin Officer & Exec VP)*
Chris Gay *(Dir-IR & Treas)*
Brian J. Linneman *(Exec VP & Chief Mdsg Officer)*
Douglas R. Means *(Exec VP & Chief Supply Chain Officer)*
Scott K. Williams *(Chief Mktg & ECommerce Officer & Exec VP)*
Scott Frnka *(VP-Mdsg-General Outdoors)*
Brands & Products:
ALASKAN GUIDE
ALASKAN OUTFITTER
BARGAIN CAVE
BOUNDARY WATERS
BOWHUNTER XTREME
CABELA'S
CABELA'S CLUB
DEPTHMASTER
DRY-PLUS
DRY-PLUS PRO SERIES
ES1 RAIN SYSTEM
EXV
FISH EAGLE
GHIL-LEAF
GOLD LABEL
GORE-TEX
GRAND RIVER LODGE
GUIDEWEAR
KING KAT
LATE SEASON
MAG TOUCH
MASTER GUIDE
MICRODOWN
MOUNTAIN HIKERS
MT050
PACLITE
PINE RIDGE
PRESTIGE
PRO-GUIDE
PRODIGY
RAINY RIVER
REALIMAGE
REVOLUTION
RIVER GUIDE
SALT STRIKER
SCENT-LOK
SCENT SEAL
SCENT SKINZ
SCENT X-TERMINATOR
SECLUSION 3D
SECLUSION 3D OUTFITTER
SILENT STALK
SILENT SUEDE
SILENT-TECH
STILLHUNTER
SUPER SLAM
T.A.G.S
TCS
TOURNEY TRAIL
TRIPLETAKE
ULTIMATE SUEDE
WEATHER-BLOCK
WHITETAIL EXTREME
WHUPPIN' STICK
WILD WINGS
WORLD'S FOREMOST BANK
WORLD'S FOREMOST OUTFITTER
XPG
Advertising Agencies:
Black Diamond Media
574 Heritage Rd Ste 201A
Southbury, CT 06488
Tel.: (203) 262-0588
Fax: (203) 262-0589

Thunder Factory New York
59 W 19th St Ste 4B
New York, NY 10011
Tel.: (212) 537-4020
Fax: (212) 965-8363

THE CABLE CENTER

2000 Buchtel Blvd
Denver, CO 80210
Tel.: (303) 871-4885
Fax: (303) 871-4514
Web Site: www.cablecenter.org
Sales Range: $1-9.9 Million
Approx. Number Employees: 25
Business Description:
Education & Information Services about the Cable Television Industry
S.I.C.: 4841
N.A.I.C.S.: 515210
Media: 2-7-10-22
Personnel:
Larry Satkowiak *(Pres & COO)*
Peter Derschang *(Sr VP)*
Diane Schieman-Christman *(Sr VP-Mktg & Dev)*
Jennifer Pellegrino *(Mgr-Mktg)*

CALGARY FLAMES LIMITED PARTNERSHIP

555 Saddledome Rise SE Station M
PO Box 1540
Calgary, AB T2G 2W1, Canada
Tel.: (403) 777-2177
Fax: (403) 777-2171
E-mail: customerservice@calgaryflames.com
Web Site: www.calgaryflames.com
Approx. Number Employees: 950
Year Founded: 1980
Business Description:
Professional Hockey Team & Multi-Purpose Entertainment Facility
S.I.C.: 7941
N.A.I.C.S.: 711211
Media: 9-13-15-18-20-22
Distr.: Reg.
Budget Set: May -June
Personnel:
Alvin G. Libin *(Owner & Dir)*
Allan P. Markin *(Owner)*
Jeffrey J. McCaig *(Co-Owner)*
Byron J. Seaman *(Owner)*
Daryl K. Seaman *(Co-Owner)*
Ken King *(Pres & CEO)*
Peter Hanlon *(VP-Comm)*
Jim Bagshaw *(VP-Adv, Sponsorship & Mktg)*
Rollie Cyr *(VP-Sls)*
Jay Feaster *(Gen Mgr-Acting)*
Pat Halls *(Sr Dir-Adv)*
Mike Burke *(Dir-Hockey Admin)*
Tod Button *(Dir-Scouting)*
Kevin Gross *(Dir-Corp Sponsership)*
Art Hernandez *(Dir-Food Svcs)*
Clayton H. Riddell *(Dir)*
Mike Sands *(Dir-Amateur Scouting)*
Bob White *(Dir-Exec Suites)*
Gus Thorson *(Mgr-Equipment)*

CALGARY PHILHARMONIC ORCHESTRA

205 8th Ave SE
Calgary, AB Canada
Tel.: (403) 571-0270
Tel.: (403) 571-0849 (Box Office)
Fax: (403) 294-7424
E-mail: info@cpo-live.com
Web Site: www.cpo-live.com
Approx. Number Employees: 25
Year Founded: 1955
Business Description:
Symphony Orchestra
S.I.C.: 7929
N.A.I.C.S.: 711190

Media: 7-8-9-20-22-23-24-25

Personnel:
Ann Lewis-Luppino *(Pres & CEO)*
Marylou Bennetts *(Dir-Sls & Mktg)*
Allison Geskin *(Dir-Dev)*
Christina Mattern *(Mgr-Mktg & Comm)*
Tim Rawlings *(Mgr-Orchestra Personnel)*

CALGARY STAMPEDE

1410 Olympic Way SE
Calgary, AB T2G 2W1, Canada
Tel.: (403) 261-0101
Fax: (403) 265-7197
Web Site: calgarystampede.com
Business Description:
Volunteer-Supported, Not-for-Profit Community Organization that Preserves & Promotes Western Heritage & Values
S.I.C.: 7999
N.A.I.C.S.: 713990

Personnel:
David Chalack *(Chm & Pres)*
Vern Kimball *(CEO)*
Paul Harrison *(CFO, VP-Support Svcs)*

Advertising Agency:
LPi Communications Group Inc.
101 253 62nd Ave SE
Calgary, AB T2H 0R5, Canada
Tel.: (403) 735-0655
Fax: (403) 735-0530
Toll Free: (888) 835-0655

CALIFORNIA MUSICAL THEATRE CORPORATION

1510 J St Ste 200
Sacramento, CA 95814
Tel.: (916) 446-5880
Fax: (916) 446-1370
E-mail: contact@calmt.com
Web Site: www.californiamusicaltheatre.com
Approx. Number Employees: 20
Year Founded: 1949
Business Description:
Musical Theatrical Production
S.I.C.: 7922; 7929
N.A.I.C.S.: 711110; 711130

Media: 4-8-9-13-18-20-23-24-25

Personnel:
Richard Lewis *(Exec Dir)*
Christopher Bower *(Dir-Mktg & PR)*
Laura Mattice Hunter *(Mgr-Box Office)*
Brands & Products:
THE BROADWAY SERIES
CALIFORNIA MUSICAL THEATRE
COSMOPOLITAN CABARET
MUSIC CIRCUS

CALIFORNIA PHILHARMONIC ORCHESTRA

1120 Huntington Dr
San Marino, CA 91108
Tel.: (626) 300-8200
Fax: (626) 300-8010
E-mail: info@calphil.org
Web Site: www.calphil.org
Sales Range: $1-9.9 Million
Approx. Number Employees: 3
Business Description:
Orchestra
S.I.C.: 7929
N.A.I.C.S.: 711130
Media: 9-20-23-24-25
Personnel:
Melina Kernc *(Dir-Music)*
Victor Vener *(Dir-Music)*
Advertising Agency:
The Artime Group
65 N Raymond Ave Ste 205
Pasadena, CA 91103-3947
Tel.: (626) 583-1855
Fax: (626) 583-1861

CALIFORNIA SPORTS, INC.

(d/b/a Los Angeles Lakers)
555 N Nash St
El Segundo, CA 90245
Tel.: (310) 426-6000
Fax: (310) 426-6115
Web Site: www.nba.com
Sales Range: $125-149.9 Million
Approx. Number Employees: 60
Year Founded: 1975
Business Description:
Professional Sports Franchise
S.I.C.: 7389
N.A.I.C.S.: 711320
Media: 9-13-23-24
Personnel:
Jerry Buss *(Pres)*
Mitch Kupchak *(Exec VP-Basketball Opers & Gen Mgr)*
Keith Harris *(VP-Mktg)*
Ronnie Lester *(Asst Gen Mgr)*
Brands & Products:
LOS ANGELES LAKERS
LOS ANGELES SPARKS
Advertising Agency:
One Eighteen Advertising
12400 Wilshire Blvd Ste 540
Los Angeles, CA 90025
Tel.: (310) 442-0118
Fax: (310) 442-0141

CAMPGROUP LLC

3 New King St
White Plains, NY 10604
Tel.: (914) 997-2177
Fax: (914) 422-3635
E-mail: info@campgroup.com
Web Site: www.campgroup.com
Approx. Number Employees: 60
Year Founded: 1998
Business Description:
Summer Camp Owner & Operator
S.I.C.: 7032
N.A.I.C.S.: 721214

Key to Media (For complete agency information see *The Advertising Red Books-Agencies* edition):
1. Bus. Publs. 2. Cable T.V. 3. Catalogs & Directories. 4. Co-op Adv. 5. Consumer Mags. 6. D.M. to Bus. Estab.7. D.M. to Consumers
8. Daily Newsp. 9. Exhibits/Trade Shows 10. Foreign 11. Infomercial 12. Internet Adv.13. Multimedia 14. Network Radio
15. Network T.V. 16. Newsp. Distr. Mags. 17. Other 18. Outdoor (Posters, Transit) 19. Point of Purchase20. Premiums, Novelties
21. Product Samples 22. Special Events Mktg. 23. Spot Radio 24. Spot T.V. 25. Weekly Newsp. 26. Yellow Page Adv.

Media: 20-23-24
Personnel:
Mark Benerofe *(Pres)*
Andy Benerofe *(CEO)*
Jeffrey Bershad *(CFO)*

CANADA'S WONDERLAND COMPANY
(Sub. of Cedar Fair, L.P.)
9580 Jane Street
Vaughan, ON L6A 1S6, Canada
Tel.: (905) 832-7000
Fax: (905) 832-7419
Web Site:
www.canadaswonderland.com
Sales Range: $25-49.9 Million
Approx. Number Employees: 160
Year Founded: 1981
Business Description:
Amusement Park Services
S.I.C.: 7996
N.A.I.C.S.: 713110
Media: 4-6-8-9-13-14-15-19-22-23-24-26
Budget Set: Sept. -Oct.
Personnel:
Raffy Kaprefyan *(Exec VP & Gen Mgr)*
Dave Phillips *(VP-Mktg & Sls)*
Ganesh Prasad *(Dir-Fin & IT)*
Brands & Products:
CLIFFHANGER
DRAGON FIRE
DROP ZONE
SLEDGE HAMMER
SPONGEBOB SQUAREPANTS 3D
TOP GUN
VORTEX

CANLAN ICE SPORTS CORPORATION
6501 Sprott Street
Burnaby, BC V5B 3B8, Canada
Tel.: (604) 736-9152
Fax: (604) 736-9170
E-mail: info@icesports.com
Web Site: www.icesports.com
Approx. Rev.: $71,163,558
Approx. Number Employees: 963
Year Founded: 1956
Business Description:
Ice Rinks Development Services
S.I.C.: 7991
N.A.I.C.S.: 713940
Media: 2-4-7-8-10-18-23
Personnel:
W. Grant Ballantyne *(Chm)*
Joey St-Aubin *(Pres & CEO)*
Michael F. Gellard *(CFO & Sr VP)*
Mark E. Reynolds *(Chief Privacy Officer & VP-HR)*
Mark Faubert *(Sr VP-Ops)*
Ivan C. Wu *(Controller & VP-Fin)*
Paul Dillion *(VP-Sls & Mktg & Svc)*
Sarah Leckie *(Dir-Mktg-Natl)*
Brands & Products:
3 ON 3
ASHL (ADULT SAFE HOCKEY LEAGUE)
ASHN
CANLAN CLASSIC TOURNAMENTS
CANLAN HOCKEY CAMPS
CANLAN ICE SPORTS HOCKEY ACADEMY
CANLAN ICE SPORTS SKATING ACADEMY
CANLAN SPORTS CAMPS
THIRSTY PENGUIN
WHERE THE EXPERIENCE IS EVERYTHING
YHL (YOUTH HOCKEY LEAGUE)

CANTERBURY PARK HOLDING CORPORATION
1100 Canterbury Rd
Shakopee, MN 55379-1867
Tel.: (952) 445-7223
Fax: (952) 496-6400
Toll Free: (800) 340-6361
Web Site: www.canterburypark.com
Approx. Rev.: $40,103,277
Approx. Number Employees: 256
Year Founded: 1994
Business Description:
Racetrack Operator & Betting Services
S.I.C.: 7948; 7999
N.A.I.C.S.: 711212; 713290
Advertising Expenditures: $1,330,485
Media: 8-9-13-18-23-24-25
Personnel:
Curtis A. Sampson *(Chm)*
Dale H. Schenian *(Vice Chm)*
Randall D. Sampson *(Pres & CEO)*
David C. Hansen *(CFO, Sec & VP-Fin)*
Michael J. Garin *(VP-Hospitality & Asst Sec)*
Brands & Products:
CANTERBURY PARK

CANUCKS SPORTS & ENTERTAINMENT
(Holding of Aquilini Investment Group)
800 Griffiths Way
Vancouver, BC V6B 6G1, Canada
Tel.: (604) 899-7400
Fax: (604) 899-7401
Web Site: canucks.nhl.com
Sales Range: $10-24.9 Million
Approx. Number Employees: 200
Year Founded: 1995
Business Description:
Holding Company; Professional Hockey Franchise & Sports Arena Owner & Operator
S.I.C.: 6719; 7389; 7941
N.A.I.C.S.: 551112; 711211; 711310
Advertising Expenditures: $300,000
Media: 3-7-8-9-14-15-22-23-24-25
Distr.: Natl.
Personnel:
Francesco Aquilini *(Chm & Governor)*
Mike Gillis *(Pres & Gen Mgr-Vancouver Canucks)*
Todd Kobus *(CFO & VP-Fin)*
Victor P. de Bonis *(COO & Alternate Governor)*
Harvey Jones *(VP & Gen Mgr-Arena Ops)*
Brands & Products:
VANCOUVER CANUCKS

CARMEL SYMPHONY ORCHESTRA, INC.
11 1st Ave NE
Carmel, IN 46032
Tel.: (317) 844-9717
Fax: (317) 844-9916
E-mail: info@carmelsymphony.org
Web Site: www.carmelsymphony.org
Business Description:
Symphony Orchestra
S.I.C.: 7929
N.A.I.C.S.: 711130
Media: 9-20-23-24-25
Personnel:
Alan Davis *(Pres & CEO)*
Jason Spangler *(Principal)*
David Bowden *(Dir-Music)*
Denise Ryan *(Office Mgr)*

CAROLINA HURRICANES HOCKEY CLUB
(Sub. of Gale Force Holdings LP)
1400 Edwards Mill Rd
Raleigh, NC 27607-3624
Tel.: (919) 467-7825
Fax: (919) 462-7030
E-mail: media@carolinehurricanes.com
Web Site: www.caneshockey.com
Approx. Number Employees: 100
Year Founded: 1971
Business Description:
Professional Hockey Franchise
S.I.C.: 7941; 7389
N.A.I.C.S.: 711211; 711410
Media: 2-3-4-6-8-9-13-18-23-24-25
Distr.: Natl.
Personnel:
Peter Karmanos, Jr. *(Owner, CEO & Governor)*
Jim Rutherford *(Pres & Gen Mgr)*
Mike Amendola *(CFO & Alternate Governor)*
Davin Olsen *(VP & Gen Mgr)*
Jason Karmanos *(VP & Asst Gen Mgr)*
Brian Tatum *(Sr Dir-Team Ops)*
Mike Sundheim *(Dir-Media Rels)*
Kyle Hanlin *(Mgr-Media Rels & Brdcst Coord)*
Skip Cunningham *(Mgr-Equipment)*
Bob Gorman *(Mgr-Equipment)*
Wally Tatomir *(Mgr-Equipment)*
Brands & Products:
CAROLINA HURRICANES

CAROWINDS
(Sub. of Cedar Fair, L.P.)
14523 Carowinds Blvd
Charlotte, NC 28273
Mailing Address:
PO Box 410289
Charlotte, NC 28241
Tel.: (704) 588-2600
Fax: (704) 587-9034
Toll Free: (800) 888-4386
Web Site: www.carowinds.com
Sales Range: $25-49.9 Million
Approx. Number Employees: 125
Year Founded: 1973
Business Description:
Amusement Park Services
S.I.C.: 7996
N.A.I.C.S.: 713110
Media: 4-6-7-8-9-13-22-23-24-25
Distr.: Reg.
Budget Set: Nov.
Personnel:
Dale Kaetzel *(VP-Mktg & Asst Gen Mgr)*
Scott Anderson *(Mgr-Mktg & PR)*
Dany Swords *(Mgr-Pub Rels)*
Brands & Products:
THE HURLER
RICOCHET
SCAROWINDS
TAXI JAM
TOP GUN: THE JET COASTER

CASINO NOVA SCOTIA
(Sub. of Great Canadian Gaming Corporation)
1983 Upper Water Street
Halifax, NS B3J 3Y5, Canada
Tel.: (902) 425-7777
Fax: (902) 428-7846
E-mail: contactus@casinonovascotia.com
Web Site: www.casinonovascotia.com
Approx. Number Employees: 800
Business Description:
Casino
S.I.C.: 7999; 7011
N.A.I.C.S.: 721120; 611620; 713990; 721110; 721199
Media: 8-9-13-20-22-23-24-25
Personnel:
Roxanne Bentley *(Mgr-Catering & Banquet)*

CASINO PLAYERS, INC.
700 W Hillsboro Blvd Bldg 2 Ste 104
Deerfield, FL 33441
Tel.: (954) 684-8288
Web Site:
www.casinoratedplayers.com
Approx. Sls.: $77,591
Year Founded: 2005
Business Description:
Casino Representative Companies Acquirer, Gambler Database Marketer & Free Room Supplier
S.I.C.: 7999
N.A.I.C.S.: 713290
Advertising Expenditures: $341,000
Media: 3-7-8-9-13-25
Personnel:
Joseph Fahoome *(Pres)*
William G. Forhan *(CEO)*

CASINO QUEEN, INC.
200 S Front St
East Saint Louis, IL 62201-1222
Tel.: (618) 874-5000
Fax: (618) 874-5081
Toll Free: (800) 777-0777
E-mail: queen@casinoqueen.com
Web Site: www.casinoqueen.com
Sales Range: $200-249.9 Million
Approx. Number Employees: 1,100
Year Founded: 1993
Business Description:
Hotel & Casino Owner & Operator
S.I.C.: 7011
N.A.I.C.S.: 721120
Advertising Expenditures: $4,000,000
Media: 2-3-5-7-8-9-13-18-20-22-23-24-25-26
Distr.: Reg.
Budget Set: Dec.
Personnel:
James G. Koman *(Pres)*
Bob Barrows *(CFO)*
Todd Ribick *(Dir-Mktg)*
Advertising Agency:
Turec Advertising Associates, Inc.
(Private-Parent-Single Location)
9272 Olive Blvd
Saint Louis, MO 63132
Tel.: (314) 993-1190

CEDAR FAIR, L.P.
1 Cedar Point Dr
Sandusky, OH 44870-5259
Tel.: (419) 626-0830
Fax: (419) 627-2260
E-mail: investing@cedarfair.com
Web Site: www.cedarfair.com
Approx. Rev.: $977,592,000
Approx. Number Employees: 1,500
Year Founded: 1987

Key to Media (For complete agency information see *The Advertising Red Books-Agencies* edition):
1. Bus. Publs. 2. Cable T.V. 3. Catalogs & Directories. 4. Co-op Adv. 5. Consumer Mags. 6. D.M. to Bus. Estab.7. D.M. to Consumers
8. Daily Newsp. 9. Exhibits/Trade Shows 10. Foreign 11. Infomercial 12. Internet Adv.13. Multimedia 14. Network Radio
15. Network T.V. 16. Newsp. Distr. Mags. 17. Other 18. Outdoor (Posters, Transit) 19. Point of Purchase20. Premiums, Novelties
21. Product Samples 22. Special Events Mktg. 23. Spot Radio 24. Spot T.V. 25. Weekly Newsp. 26. Yellow Page Adv.

Cedar Fair, L.P. — (Continued)

Business Description:
Owner & Operator of Amusement Parks & Resorts
S.I.C.: 7389; 7011; 7996; 7997; 7999
N.A.I.C.S.: 711320; 713110; 713910; 713990; 721110
Import
Advertising Expenditures: $52,000,000
Media: 3-6-7-8-9-10-18-19-23-24-25-26
Distr.: Reg.
Budget Set: Jan.
Personnel:
Matt Ouimet *(Pres)*
Richard L. Kinzel *(CEO)*
Peter J. Crage *(CFO & Exec VP)*
Richard A. Zimmerman *(COO)*
Duffield E. Milkie *(Gen Counsel & Corp VP)*
H. Philip Bender *(Exec VP)*
H. John Hildebrandt *(VP & Gen Mgr)*
Scott Tanner *(Corp VP-Sls)*
Bob Wagner *(Corp VP-Strategic Alliances)*
Stacy Frole *(Dir-IR)*
Brands & Products:
THE AMAZEMENT PARK
CALIFORNIA'S GREAT AMERICA
CANADA'S WONDERLAND
CAROWINDS
CASTAWAY BAY
CEDAR FAIR
CEDAR POINT
COASTER QUEST
COL. JOHN PHILLIPS OHOOMPAPA
DORNEY PARK
DORNEY PARK & WILDWATER KINGDOM
FURY OF THE NILE
GEAUGA LAKE
GHOSTRIDER
HALLOWEEKENDS
HERCULES
KINGS DOMINION
KINGS ISLAND
KNOTT'S BERRY FARM
MAMBA
MANTIS
MICHIGAN'S ADVENTURE
MILLENNIUM FORCE
OCEANS OF FUN
ORIENT EXPRESS
RAPTOR
SHIVERING TIMBERS
SOAK CITY
STEEL FORCE
TALON
THUNDERHAWK
TIMBER WOLF
TOP THRILL DRAGSTER
VALLEYFAIR!
WILD THING
WILDWATER ADVENTURE
WILDWATER KINGDOM
WORLDS OF FUN
Advertising Agencies:
Fahlgren Mortine
4030 Easton Station Ste 300
Columbus, OH 43219
Tel.: (614) 383-1500
Fax: (614) 383-1501

Fahlgren Mortine Public Relations
4030 Easton Sta Ste 300
Columbus, OH 43219
Tel.: (614) 383-1500
Fax: (614) 383-1501

MARCA Miami
3390 Mary St Ste 254
Coconut Grove, FL 33133
Tel.: (305) 665-5410
Tel.: (305) 423-8301
Fax: (305) 665-3533

CEDAR POINT
(Sub. of Cedar Fair, L.P.)
1 Cedar Point Dr
Sandusky, OH 44870-5259
Tel.: (419) 626-0830
Fax: (419) 627-2200
E-mail: dwyrick@cedarpoint.com
Web Site: www.cedarpoint.com
E-Mail For Key Personnel:
Public Relations: robini@cedarpoint.com
Sales Range: $75-99.9 Million
Approx. Number Employees: 300
Year Founded: 1870
Business Description:
Amusement Park
S.I.C.: 7996; 7011
N.A.I.C.S.: 713110; 721110
Import
Media: 3-5-6-8-9-13-18-19-22-23-24-26
Personnel:
H. John Hildebrandt *(VP & Gen Mgr)*
Lee Alexakos *(Corp VP-Mktg & Adv)*
Robin Innes *(Dir-PR)*
Bryan Edwards *(Mgr-Sls Promos)*

CEDAR RAPIDS SYMPHONY
119 3rd Ave SE
Cedar Rapids, IA 52401
Tel.: (319) 366-8203
Fax: (319) 366-5206
Toll Free: (800) 369-TUNE
E-mail: webmaster@crsymphony.org
Web Site: www.crsymphony.org
Approx. Number Employees: 90
Year Founded: 1921
Business Description:
Symphony Orchestra
S.I.C.: 7911
N.A.I.C.S.: 611610
Media: 8-9-13-16-18-20-22-23-24-25-26
Personnel:
Tim Charles *(Pres)*
Ken Dekock *(Mng Dir)*
Darcy Bemus *(Dir-Bus Dev)*
Nancy Duncan *(Dir-Fin)*
Ciara Roos *(Dir-Mktg)*
Christian Tiemeyer *(Dir-Music)*
Karen Liegl *(Mgr-School)*

CENTER THEATRE GROUP OF LOS ANGELES, INC.
601 W Temple St
Los Angeles, CA 90012
Tel.: (213) 628-2772
Fax: (213) 972-8062
Web Site:
www.centertheatregroup.com
Sales Range: $25-49.9 Million
Approx. Number Employees: 100
Year Founded: 1967
Business Description:
Theatrical Services
S.I.C.: 7922
N.A.I.C.S.: 711110
Media: 4-9-18-20-22-23-24-25
Personnel:
Martin Massman *(Chm)*
Jim Royce *(Dir-Mktg & Commun)*
Michael Ritchie *(Dir-Art)*

CENTRAL WISCONSIN SYMPHONY ORCHESTRA INC.
1128 Main St PO Box 65
Stevens Point, WI 54481
Tel.: (715) 345-2976
Toll Free: (800) 838-3378
E-mail: cwso@cwso.org
Web Site: www.cwso.org
Approx. Number Employees: 4
Year Founded: 1947
Business Description:
Symphony Orchestra
S.I.C.: 7929
N.A.I.C.S.: 711130
Media: 8-9-20-23-24-25
Personnel:
Dan Dogherty *(Pres)*
Ann Huntoon *(Mng Dir)*
Patrick Miles *(Dir-Music)*
Andrea Van Natta *(Dir-Fin)*
Jodi Engum Kryshak *(Mgr-Orchestra)*
Sarah Belcher *(Librarian-Music)*

CENTURY CASINOS INC.
2860 S Circle Dr Ste 350
Colorado Springs, CO 80906
Tel.: (719) 527-8300
Fax: (719) 527-8301
E-mail: investor@cnty.com
Web Site: www.cnty.com
Approx. Rev.: $68,054,000
Approx. Number Employees: 876
Year Founded: 1992
Business Description:
Gaming Casinos Management
S.I.C.: 7999; 5813; 7997
N.A.I.C.S.: 713210; 713290; 713910; 713990; 722410
Advertising Expenditures: $1,600,000
Media: 2-3-6-14-15-18
Personnel:
Erwin Haitzmann *(Chm & Co-CEO)*
Peter Hoetzinger *(Vice Chm, Pres & Co-CEO)*
Margaret Stapleton *(CFO & Exec VP)*
Al Wilson *(Gen Mgr-Calgary)*

CHAMBER ORCHESTRA OF PHILADELPHIA
1520 Locust St Ste 500
Philadelphia, PA 19102
Tel.: (215) 545-5451
Fax: (215) 545-3868
E-mail: info@chamberorchestra.org
Web Site: www.chamberorchestra.org
Approx. Rev.: $2,000,000
Approx. Number Employees: 40
Year Founded: 1964
Business Description:
Chamber Orchestra
S.I.C.: 7929
N.A.I.C.S.: 711130
Media: 8-9-18-23-24-25
Personnel:
Kenneth M. Jarin *(Chm)*
William H. Roberts *(Pres)*
Linda Freidman *(Comptroller)*
Ignat Solzhenitsyn *(Dir-Music)*
Carolann Atene *(Mgr-Subscriptions & Box Office)*

CHANCE RIDES MANUFACTURING CO.
4219 Irving St
Wichita, KS 67209-2613
Mailing Address:
PO Box 12328
Wichita, KS 67277-2328
Tel.: (316) 942-7411
Fax: (316) 942-7416
Toll Free: (800) CHANCE-1
E-mail: rides@rides.com
Web Site: www.rides.com
Approx. Number Employees: 150
Year Founded: 1985
Business Description:
Carnival & Amusement Park Rides, Machines & Equipment Mfr
S.I.C.: 7999
N.A.I.C.S.: 713990
Export
Media: 2-7-10
Personnel:
Richard G. Chance *(Pres & CEO)*
Jeff A. Roth *(Legal Advisor)*

CHANEY ENTERTAINMENT, INC.
PO Box 4550
Palm Springs, CA 92263
Tel.: (760) 324-8322
E-mail: info@lonchaney.com
Web Site: www.lonchaney.com
Year Founded: 1992
Business Description:
Patent Owner
S.I.C.: 7929
N.A.I.C.S.: 711190
Media: 4-10
Personnel:
Ron Chaney *(Pres & CEO)*

CHARLOTTE CIVIC ORCHESTRA
PO Box 11334
Charlotte, NC 28220-1334
Tel.: (704) 344-0098
Web Site:
www.charlottecivicorchestra.org
Approx. Number Employees: 1
Business Description:
Symphony Orchestra
S.I.C.: 7389
N.A.I.C.S.: 711310
Media: 9-20-23-24-25
Personnel:
Reese Manceaux *(Librarian)*

CHARLOTTE SYMPHONY ORCHESTRA
301 S Tryon St Ste 1700
Charlotte, NC 28282
Tel.: (704) 972-2003
Fax: (704) 972-2012
Web Site:
www.charlottesymphony.org
Approx. Number Employees: 30
Business Description:
Symphony Orchestra
S.I.C.: 7929
N.A.I.C.S.: 711130
Media: 5-7-8-9-10-13-20-23-24-25
Personnel:
Margaret Dreher *(Vice Chm-Dev)*
M. Scott Belford *(Dir-Mktg)*
Bud Simmons *(Dir-Ops)*
Meg Whalen *(Dir-PR & Community Engagement)*

Key to Media (For complete agency information see *The Advertising Red Books-Agencies* edition):
1. Bus. Publs. 2. Cable T.V. 3. Catalogs & Directories. 4. Co-op Adv. 5. Consumer Mags. 6. D.M. to Bus. Estab.7. D.M. to Consumers
8. Daily Newsp. 9. Exhibits/Trade Shows 10. Foreign 11. Infomercial 12. Internet Adv.13. Multimedia 14. Network Radio
15. Network T.V. 16. Newsp. Distr. Mags. 17. Other 18. Outdoor (Posters, Transit) 19. Point of Purchase20. Premiums, Novelties
21. Product Samples 22. Special Events Mktg. 23. Spot Radio 24. Spot T.V. 25. Weekly Newsp. 26. Yellow Page Adv.

Celia Jelley *(Mgr-Orchestra Personnel)*
Stephanie Stenglein *(Mgr-Annual Fund)*

CHATTANOOGA SYMPHONY & OPERA ASSOCIATION

630 Chestnut St
Chattanooga, TN 37402
Tel.: (423) 267-8583
Fax: (423) 265-6520
E-mail: info@chattanoogasymphony.org
Web Site: www.chattanoogasymphony.org
Approx. Number Employees: 50
Business Description:
Symphony Orchestra
S.I.C.: 7929
N.A.I.C.S.: 711130
Media: 9-20-22-23-24-25
Personnel:
Molly Sasse *(Exec Dir)*
Kayoko Dan *(Dir-Music)*
Darrin Hassevoort *(Dir-CSO Choruses)*
Katie Wilson *(Dir-Mktg & Dev)*
Kathy Allison *(Mgr-Ops)*
Eric Anderson *(Mgr-Orchestra Personnel)*
Martha Sellman *(Mgr-Customer Svc & Sls)*
Steve Tonkinson *(Mgr-Education & Outreach)*

CHEYENNE SYMPHONY SOCIETY, INC.

1904 Thomes Ave
Cheyenne, WY 82001
Tel.: (307) 778-8561
Fax: (307) 634-7512
E-mail: email@cheyennesymphony.org
Web Site: www.cheyennesymphony.org
Approx. Number Employees: 83
Year Founded: 1954
Business Description:
Symphony Orchestra
S.I.C.: 7929
N.A.I.C.S.: 711130
Media: 9-20-23-24-25
Personnel:
William Intriligagor *(Dir-Music & Conductor)*
Chloe Illoway *(Exec Dir)*
Kim Lovett *(Exec Dir)*

CHICAGO BEARS FOOTBALL CLUB, INC.

Halas Hall 1000 Football Dr
Lake Forest, IL 60045
Tel.: (847) 295-6600
Fax: (847) 295-8986
E-mail: info@chicagobears.com
Web Site: www.chicagobears.com
Approx. Number Employees: 150
Year Founded: 1920
Business Description:
Professional Football Franchise
S.I.C.: 7941
N.A.I.C.S.: 711211
Media: 3-9-23-24
Distr.: Natl.
Budget Set: Dec.
Personnel:
Michael B. McCaskey *(Chm)*
Ted Phillips *(Pres & CEO)*
Jerry Angelo *(Gen Mgr)*
Chris Hibbs *(Sr Dir-Sls & Mktg)*
Bobby DePaul *(Dir-Pro Personnel)*
Greg Gabriel *(Dir-College Scouting)*
Dean Pope *(Asst Dir-Video)*
Kevin Turks *(Asst Dir-Pro Personnel)*
Tony Medlin *(Mgr-Equipment)*
Brands & Products:
CHICAGO BEARS

CHICAGO BLACKHAWK HOCKEY TEAM, INC.

(Sub. of Wirtz Corporation)
(d/b/a Chicago Blackhawks)
1901 W Madison St
Chicago, IL 60612
Tel.: (312) 455-7000
Fax: (312) 455-7041
E-mail: general@chicagoblackhawks.com
Web Site: blackhawks.nhl.com
Sales Range: $75-99.9 Million
Approx. Number Employees: 150
Year Founded: 1926
Business Description:
Professional Hockey Team
S.I.C.: 7941
N.A.I.C.S.: 711211
Import
Media: 1-9-22-23-24-25
Distr.: Direct to Consumer; Reg.
Budget Set: Monthly
Personnel:
William Rockwell Wirtz *(Chm)*
John F. McDonough *(Pres & CEO)*
Jay Blowman *(Exec VP)*
Stan Bowman *(VP & Gen Mgr)*
James K. Bare *(Exec Dir-Ticket Ops)*
Dave Knickerbocker *(Sr Dir-Mktg & Bus Dev)*
Pete Hassen *(Sr Dir-Market Dev & Community Affairs)*
Tony Ommen *(Sr Dir-Team Svcs)*
Steve Waight *(Sr Dir-Corp Sponsorships)*
Marc Bergevin *(Dir-Player Personnel)*
Brandon Faber *(Dir-Media Rels)*
Adam Kempenaar *(Dir-New Media & Creative Svcs)*
Adam Rogowin *(Dir-PR)*
Dan Rozenblat *(Dir, Ticket Sales & Svc)*
T. J. Skattum *(Dir-Fin)*
Marie Sutera *(Dir-HR)*
Julie Lovins *(Sr Mgr-Customer Svc)*
Steve DiLenardi *(Mgr-Grp Sls & Special Projects)*
Michael Dorsch *(Mgr-Acctg)*
Kelly Bednarchuk Smith *(Mgr-Client Svcs)*
Advertising Agencies:
Coudal Partners
400 N May St Ste 301
Chicago, IL 60622
Tel.: (312) 243-1107
Fax: (312) 243-1108
(Hockey Team)

Ogilvy & Mather
350 W Mart Ctr Dr Ste 1100
Chicago, IL 60654-1866
Tel.: (312) 856-8200
Fax: (312) 856-8207

CHICAGO NATIONAL LEAGUE BALL CLUB, LLC

(d/b/a Chicago Cubs)
1060 W Addison St
Chicago, IL 60613-4397
Tel.: (773) 404-2827
Fax: (773) 404-4129
Web Site: chicago.cubs.mlb.com
Approx. Number Employees: 300
Business Description:
Professional Baseball Club
S.I.C.: 7941
N.A.I.C.S.: 711211
Media: 3-7-8-20-23-26
Distr.: Natl.
Budget Set: Oct. -Nov.
Personnel:
Thomas S. Ricketts *(Owner & Chm)*
Crane H. Kenney *(Pres)*
John Greifenkamp *(CFO & VP)*
Wally Hayward *(Chief Mktg Officer & Exec VP)*
Michael Lufrano *(Gen Counsel & Sr VP-Community Affairs)*
Mark McGuire *(Exec VP-Bus Ops)*
Jim Hendry *(VP & Gen Mgr)*
Julian Green *(VP-Comm & Community Affairs)*
Randy Bush *(Asst Gen Mgr)*
Carl Rice *(Sr Dir-Info Sys & Special Projects)*
Jennifer Surma *(Sr Dir-HR)*
Peter Chase *(Dir-Media Relations)*
Frank Maloney *(Dir-Ticket Ops)*
Lena McDonagh *(Dir-Publ & Creative Svcs)*
Scott Nelson *(Dir-Baseball Admin)*
Mark O'Neal *(Dir-Athletic Trng)*
Jodi Reischl *(Co-Dir-Fin)*
Tim Wilken *(Dir-Amateur & Prof Scouting)*
Jason Carr *(Asst Dir-Media Relations)*
Brian Garza *(Asst Dir-Ticket Sls)*
Joe Kirchen *(Asst Dir-Ticket Svcs)*
Louis Artiaga *(Mgr-Mezzanine Suites)*
Michael Hill *(Mgr-Event Ops & Security)*
Jamie Norton *(Mgr-Fin)*
Joseph Rios *(Mgr-Special Events, Player Rels & Entertainment)*
Mike Van Poucke *(Mgr-Acctg & Fin)*
Lydia Wahlke *(Asst Gen Counsel)*
Brands & Products:
CHICAGO CUBS
Advertising Agencies:
J. Herman Sitrick Advertising, Inc.
8340 Lincoln Ave Ste 202
Skokie, IL 60077-2466
Tel.: (847) 677-3511
Fax: (847) 677-3546

MLB Advanced Media, L.P.
75 9th Ave 5th Fl
New York, NY 10011
Tel.: (212) 485-3444
Fax: (212) 485-3456

CHICAGO PROFESSIONAL SPORTS LIMITED PARTNERSHIP

(d/b/a Chicago Bulls)
1901 W Madison St
Chicago, IL 60612-2459
Tel.: (312) 455-4000
Web Site: www.nba.com/bulls
Approx. Number Employees: 100
Year Founded: 1966
Business Description:
Professional Basketball Team
S.I.C.: 7941
N.A.I.C.S.: 711211
Media: 3-8-9-10-13-15-18-20-22-23-24-25
Distr.: Natl.
Personnel:
Jerry Reinsdorf *(Chm & Alternate NBA Governor)*
John Paxson *(Exec VP-Basketball Ops)*
Steve Schanwald *(Exec VP-Bus Ops & Alternate Governor-NBA)*
Irwin Mandel *(Sr VP-Fin & Legal)*
Gar Forman *(Gen Mgr)*
David Dowd *(Sr Dir-Ticket Sls)*
Tim Hallam *(Sr Dir-Media & PR)*
Greg Hanrahan *(Sr Dir-Premium Seating)*
David Kurland *(Sr Dir-Community Rels)*
Joe O'Neil *(Sr Dir-Ticket Ops)*
Scott Sonnenberg *(Sr Dir-Corp Partnerships)*
John Viola *(Sr Dir-Corp Partnerships-Scott Sonnenberg)*
Jeff Wohlschlaeger *(Sr Dir-Game Ops)*
Curtis Baddeley *(Dir-Rental Suites)*
Jay Hillock *(Dir-Pro Personnel)*
Tom Holbert *(Dir-Team Security)*
Steve Julius *(Dir-Player Programs)*
Matt Lloyd *(Dir-College Scouting)*
Bob Love *(Dir-Community Affairs)*
Jon Shoemaker *(Dir-Creative Svcs)*
Karen Stack-Umlauf *(Dir-Basketball Admin)*
Jeremy Thum *(Dir-Interactive Mktg)*
Sebrina Brewster *(Sr Mgr-Media & PR)*
Jill Gayton *(Sr Mgr-Guest Svcs)*
Tony Hyde *(Sr Mgr-Publ)*
Tony Rokita *(Sr Mgr-Community Events)*
Pam Sher *(Sr Mgr-Ticket Ops)*
Jason Siok *(Sr Mgr-E-Commerce Mktg)*
Whitney Smith *(Sr Mgr-Corp Partner Activation)*
Ben Adair *(Mgr-Pur)*
Christine Cronin *(Mgr-Corp Comm)*
Nancy DeFauw *(Mgr-Ticket Ops)*
Adam Fluck *(Mgr-Internet Svcs)*
John Ligmanowski *(Mgr-Equipment)*
Jeff Pitcock *(Mgr-Creative Svcs)*
Kristine Simantirakis *(Mgr-Database Mktg)*
Valerie Toth *(Mgr-Premium Seating)*
De Borah Wells *(Mgr-Game Ops)*
Matt Yob *(Mgr-Media & PR)*
Michele Chambers *(Asst Controller)*
Brands & Products:
CHICAGO BULLS

CHICAGO SYMPHONY ORCHESTRA

220 S Michigan Ave
Chicago, IL 60604
Tel.: (312) 294-3333
Fax: (312) 294-3329
Toll Free: (800) 223-7114
Web Site: www.cso.org
Sales Range: $25-49.9 Million
Approx. Number Employees: 1,410
Year Founded: 1890
Business Description:
Symphony Orchestra
S.I.C.: 7929
N.A.I.C.S.: 711130
Media: 7-8-9-18-20-23-24-25
Personnel:
Richard B. Kapnick *(Vice Chm)*

Key to Media (For complete agency information see *The Advertising Red Books-Agencies* edition):
1. Bus. Publs. 2. Cable T.V. 3. Catalogs & Directories. 4. Co-op Adv. 5. Consumer Mags. 6. D.M. to Bus. Estab.7. D.M. to Consumers 8. Daily Newsp. 9. Exhibits/Trade Shows 10. Foreign 11. Infomercial 12. Internet Adv.13. Multimedia 14. Network Radio 15. Network T.V. 16. Newsp. Distr. Mags. 17. Other 18. Outdoor (Posters, Transit) 19. Point of Purchase20. Premiums, Novelties 21. Product Samples 22. Special Events Mktg. 23. Spot Radio 24. Spot T.V. 25. Weekly Newsp. 26. Yellow Page Adv.

Chicago Symphony Orchestra — (Continued)

Deborah Card *(Pres)*
Isabelle C. Goossen *(VP-Fin & Admin & Asst Treas)*
Kevin Giglinto *(VP-Sls & Mktg)*
Paulette Jean Volf *(Asst Controller)*
Lisa McDaniel *(Dir-Programs)*
Kimberly Duffy *(Project Mgr)*
Penelope Johnson *(Project Mgr)*
Kelly Kerins *(Mgr-Stage)*
Brands & Products:
ECHO
LIVE AT SYMPHONY CENTER
MEOWZART
MUSICORPS
WOOFGANG

CHICAGO THEATRE GROUP INC.

(d/b/a The Goodman Theatre)
170 N Dearborn St
Chicago, IL 60601
Tel.: (312) 443-3811
Fax: (312) 443-3821
E-mail: info@goodmantheatre.org
Web Site: www.goodmantheatre.org
Approx. Number Employees: 100
Year Founded: 1925
Business Description:
Theatrical Producers & Services
S.I.C.: 7922
N.A.I.C.S.: 711110
Media: 9-18-20-23-24-25
Personnel:
Shawn M. Donnelley *(Chm)*
Peter I. Mason *(Pres)*
Melissa Hard *(Sr Advancement Officer-Major Gifts)*
Peter Calibraro *(Gen Mgr)*
Jeff M. Ciaramita *(Sr Dir-Admin & Stewardship)*
Lori Kleinerman *(Dir-Mktg & PR)*
Jay Corsi *(Dir-Adv & Sls)*
Robert Falls *(Dir-Artistic)*
Mark J. Kozy *(Dir-Ops)*
Dorlisa Martin *(Dir-Dev)*
Chris Tiffany *(Dir-Foundation-Govt Support)*
Jenny Brennan *(Mgr-Campaign)*
Jodi J. Brown *(Mgr-HR & Bus Office)*
Scott Conn *(Mgr-Production)*

CHICAGO WHITE SOX LTD.

333 W 35th St
Chicago, IL 60616-3651
Tel.: (312) 674-1000
Fax: (312) 674-5104
E-mail: fanfeedback@chisox.com
Web Site: www.whitesox.com
Approx. Number Employees: 4,000
Year Founded: 1900
Business Description:
Professional Baseball Club
S.I.C.: 7941
N.A.I.C.S.: 711211
Media: 3-7-8-9-10-13-15-18-20-22-23-24-25
Distr.: Natl.
Budget Set: Sept.
Personnel:
Jerry M. Reinsdorf *(Chm)*
Edward M. Einhorn *(Vice Chm)*
John Corvino *(Gen Counsel)*
Howard Pizer *(Exec VP)*
Ken Williams *(Sr VP & Gen Mgr)*
Brooks Boyer *(Sr VP-Sls & Mktg)*
Tim Buzard *(Sr VP-Admin)*
Scott Reifert *(Sr VP-Comm)*
Terry Savarise *(Sr VP-Stadium Ops)*
Rick Hahn *(VP & Asst Gen Mgr)*
Grace Guerrero Zwit *(Sr Dir-Minor League Ops)*
Bob Beghtol *(Dir-Media Rels)*
Buddy Bell *(Dir-Player Dev)*
Dan Fabian *(Dir-Baseball Ops)*
Lou Hernandez *(Dir-Pub Rel)*
Doug Laumann *(Dir-Amateur Scouting)*
Mike Mazza *(Dir-Ticket Ops)*
Tom Sheridan *(Dir-Ticket Sls)*
Sam Lawson *(Mgr-Corp Dev/Ticket Sls)*
Pat O'Connell *(Mgr-Media Rels)*
Chris Taylor *(Mgr-Acctg)*
Ken Wisz *(Mgr-Ticket Acctg Admin)*
Stephanie Johnson *(Coord-Baseball Video)*
Brands & Products:
AMATEUR CITY ELITE
CHICAGO WHITE SOX
SOX SPLIT RAFFLE
SPEAKERS BUREAU
VOLUNTEER CORPS
Advertising Agencies:
Energy BBDO
410 N Michigan Ave
Chicago, IL 60611-4213
Tel.: (312) 337-7860
Fax: (312) 337-6871

Madre
Petrona Eyle 450 DTO C1107
Buenos Aires, Argentina
Tel.: (54) 11 5787 0500

MLB Advanced Media, L.P.
75 9th Ave 5th Fl
New York, NY 10011
Tel.: (212) 485-3444
Fax: (212) 485-3456

The San Jose Group
233 N Michigan Ave 24 Fl
Chicago, IL 60601
Tel.: (312) 565-7000
Fax: (312) 565-7500
Hispanic Market

CHICAGO ZOOLOGICAL SOCIETY, INC.

(d/b/a Brookfield Zoo)
3300 Golf Rd
Brookfield, IL 60513-1060
Tel.: (708) 485-0263
Fax: (708) 485-5419
Toll Free: (800) 201-0784
E-mail: member.questions@brookfieldzoo.org
Web Site: www.brookfieldzoo.org
Approx. Rev.: $50,000,000
Approx. Number Employees: 450
Year Founded: 1934
Business Description:
Zoological Park
S.I.C.: 8422
N.A.I.C.S.: 712130
Import
Advertising Expenditures: $800,000
Media: 3-6-8-9-18-20-22-23-24-25
Distr.: Reg.
Budget Set: Nov.
Personnel:
Stuart Strahl *(Pres & CEO)*
Ann Clark *(Sr VP-Mktg)*
Dan Wharton *(Sr VP-Animal Programs)*
Sondi Katzen *(Dir-Pub Rels)*
Ursula Bender *(Mgr-Off Site Channel Mktg)*
Advertising Agency:
DesignKitchen
1140 W Fulton Market
Chicago, IL 60607-1219
Tel.: (312) 455-0388
Fax: (312) 455-0285

THE CHILDREN'S MUSEUM AT SARATOGA

69 Caroline St
Saratoga Springs, NY 12866
Tel.: (518) 584-5540
E-mail: info@cmssny.org
Web Site: www.childrensmuseumatsaratoga.org
Approx. Number Employees: 15
Business Description:
Children's Museum
S.I.C.: 8412
N.A.I.C.S.: 712110
Media: 8-9-10-20-22-23-24-25
Personnel:
Michelle Smith *(Exec Dir)*

CHILDREN'S MUSEUM OF DENVER, INC.

2121 Children's Museum Dr
Denver, CO 80211
Tel.: (303) 433-7444
Fax: (303) 433-9520
E-mail: information@cmdenver.org
Web Site: www.cmdenver.org
Approx. Rev.: $2,248,680
Approx. Number Employees: 35
Year Founded: 1973
Business Description:
Non-Profit Children's Museum
S.I.C.: 8412; 7999
N.A.I.C.S.: 712110; 713990
Advertising Expenditures: $45,000
Media: 6-8-9-10-18-23-26
Personnel:
Tom Downey *(Pres)*
Doug Elenowitz *(Partner-Brownfield Partners, LLC)*
Gretchen Kerr *(Chief Museum Officer)*

CHURCHILL DOWNS, INC.

700 Central Ave
Louisville, KY 40208-1212
Tel.: (502) 636-4400
E-mail: customerservice@kyderby.com
Web Site: www.churchilldownsincorporated.com
Approx. Rev.: $585,345,000
Approx. Number Employees: 2,000
Year Founded: 1874
Business Description:
Horse Racing, Casino, & Online Gambling
S.I.C.: 7948; 7999
N.A.I.C.S.: 711212; 711219
Advertising Expenditures: $8,000,000
Media: 2-3-5-7-8-9-13-15-18-20-22-23-24-25-26
Distr.: Direct to Consumer; Reg.
Budget Set: Aug.
Personnel:
Carl F. Pollard *(Chm)*
William C. Carstanjen *(Pres & COO)*
Robert L. Evans *(Chm-Elect & CEO)*
William E. Mudd *(CFO & Exec VP)*
Rebecca C. Reed *(Chief Compliance Officer, Sec & Sr VP-Legal Affairs)*
Rohit Thukral *(Pres-TwinSpirescom & Exec VP-Tech Initiatives)*
Alan K. Tse *(Gen Counsel & Exec VP)*
Michael W. Anderson *(Treas & VP-Fin)*
Tim Bryant *(Sr VP)*
T. Kevin Flanery *(Sr VP-Churchill Downs Racetrack Pres)*
James E. Gay *(Sr VP-Bus Dev)*
Donald R. Richardson *(Sr VP-Racing)*
Julie Koenig *(VP-Corp Comm)*
Brands & Products:
ARLINGTON PARK
CALDER RACE COURSE
CHURCHILL DOWNS
CHURCHILL DOWNS INCORPORATED
KENTUCKY DERBY
Advertising Agencies:
Hoffman York
1000 N Water St Ste 1600
Milwaukee, WI 53202-6667
Tel.: (414) 289-9700
Fax: (414) 289-0417
Toll Free: (800) 842-3020

Red7e
637 W Main St
Louisville, KY 40202-2987
Tel.: (502) 585-3403
Fax: (502) 582-2043
Toll Free: (800) 656-7272

CINCINNATI ART MUSEUM

953 Eden Park Dr
Cincinnati, OH 45202
Tel.: (513) 639-2995
Fax: (513) 721-0129
Web Site: www.cincinnatiartmuseum.org
Approx. Number Employees: 150
Business Description:
Museum of Twentieth Century & Contemporary Art & Design
S.I.C.: 8412
N.A.I.C.S.: 712110
Advertising Expenditures: $400,532
Media: 2-13-14-25
Personnel:
Aaron Betsky *(Dir)*

CINCINNATI BENGALS, INC.

1 Paul Brown Stadium
Cincinnati, OH 45202-3418
Tel.: (513) 621-3550
Fax: (513) 621-3570
E-mail: cincinnatibengals@nfl.com
Web Site: www.bengals.com
Approx. Number Employees: 130
Year Founded: 1968
Business Description:
Professional Football Franchise
S.I.C.: 7941
N.A.I.C.S.: 711211
Media: 2-3-7-8-10-13-14-15-18-23-24
Distr.: Natl.
Personnel:
Mike Brown *(Pres)*
Bill Scanlon *(CFO)*
Katie Blackburn *(Exec VP)*
Pete Brown *(Sr VP-Player Personnel)*
Eric Ball *(Dir-Player Relations)*
Bob Bedinghaus *(Dir-Bus Dev)*
Jeff Berding *(Dir-Sls & Pub Affairs)*

Key to Media (For complete agency information see *The Advertising Red Books-Agencies* edition):
1. Bus. Publs. 2. Cable T.V. 3. Catalogs & Directories. 4. Co-op Adv. 5. Consumer Mags. 6. D.M. to Bus. Estab.7. D.M. to Consumers 8. Daily Newsp. 9. Exhibits/Trade Shows 10. Foreign 11. Infomercial 12. Internet Adv.13. Multimedia 14. Network Radio 15. Network T.V. 16. Newsp. Distr. Mags. 17. Other 18. Outdoor (Posters, Transit) 19. Point of Purchase20. Premiums, Novelties 21. Product Samples 22. Special Events Mktg. 23. Spot Radio 24. Spot T.V. 25. Weekly Newsp. 26. Yellow Page Adv.

Travis Brammer *(Dir-Video)*
Jack Brennan *(Dir-PR)*
Vince Cicero *(Dir-Corp Sls & Mktg)*
Rusty Guy *(Dir-Security)*
Michael Kayes *(Dir-Tech)*
Jim Lippincott *(Dir-Football Ops)*
Jo Ann Ralstin *(Dir-Tech)*
Duke Tobin *(Dir-Player Personnel)*
P. J. Combs *(Asst Dir-PR)*
Brian Sells *(Asst Dir-Corp Sls & Mktg)*
Kent Stearman *(Asst Dir-Video)*
Wade Martin *(Sr Mgr-Corp Sls)*
Bill Connelly *(Bus Mgr)*
Jeff Brickner *(Mgr-Equipment)*
Tim Kelly *(Mgr-Tickets)*
Monty Montague *(Mgr-Mdsg)*
Andy Ware *(Mgr-Website & New Media)*
Alex Simons *(Coord-Events)*
Brands & Products:
BENGALS

CINCINNATI MUSEUM CENTER INC.

1301 Western Ave
Cincinnati, OH 45203-1130
Tel.: (513) 287-7000
Fax: (513) 287-7002
Toll Free: (800) 733-2077
E-mail: webmaster@cincymuseum.org
Web Site: www.cincymuseum.org
Sales Range: $10-24.9 Million
Approx. Number Employees: 200
Year Founded: 1990
Business Description:
Museum
S.I.C.: 8742; 7389
N.A.I.C.S.: 541611; 711310
Media: 8-9-10-13-18-20-23-24-25
Personnel:
Douglass W. McDonald *(Pres & CEO)*
R. Keith Harrison *(Global Product Supply Officer)*
Jane Garvey *(VP-Mktg & Comm)*
Holly Greaves *(Dir-Adv & Mktg)*

CINCINNATI SYMPHONY ORCHESTRA

1241 Elm St
Cincinnati, OH 45202
Tel.: (513) 621-1919
Fax: (513) 744-3535
E-mail: info@cincinnatisymphony.org
Web Site: www.cincinnatisymphony.org
Approx. Sls.: $34,471,189
Approx. Number Employees: 150
Year Founded: 1895
Business Description:
Symphony Orchestra
S.I.C.: 7929
N.A.I.C.S.: 711130
Media: 4-8-9-10-13-18-20-23-24-25
Personnel:
Janell Weinstock *(VP & Gen Mgr-Production)*
M. Todd Bezold *(Dir-Mktg & Subscriptions)*
Patricia Carmichael *(Dir-Art)*
Amy Finch *(Dir-Sls)*
Sharon D. Grayton *(Dir-Data Standards)*
Kathy Jorgensen-Finley *(Dir-Community Engagement & Diversity)*
Heather L. Stengle *(Dir-Ops)*
Elise Hyder *(Mgr-Sls)*
Advertising Agency:
Music & Event Management, Inc.
1241 Elm St
Cincinnati, OH 45202
Tel.: (513) 721-3555

CINEMARK HOLDINGS, INC.

3900 Dallas Pkwy Ste 500
Plano, TX 75093-7865
Tel.: (972) 665-1000
Tel.: (972) 665-1500 (Investor Rels)
Toll Free: (800) 246-3627
E-mail: investors@cinemark.com
Web Site: www.cinemark.com
Approx. Rev.: $2,141,144,000
Approx. Number Employees: 14,600
Year Founded: 2006
Business Description:
Holding Company; Motion Picture Theaters Owner
S.I.C.: 7832; 6719
N.A.I.C.S.: 512131; 551112
Advertising Expenditures: $7,279,000
Personnel:
Lee Roy Mitchell *(Chm)*
Timothy Warner *(Pres & COO)*
Alan W. Stock *(CEO)*
Robert Copple *(CFO, Treas, Exec VP & Asst Sec)*
Michael D. Cavalier *(Gen Counsel, Sec & Sr VP)*
Robert Carmony *(Sr VP-New Tech & Trng)*
Walter Hebert, III *(Sr VP-Pur)*
Tom Owens *(Sr VP-Real Estate)*
Steve Zuehlke *(VP & Dir-Theatre Ops)*
James Meredith *(VP-Mktg & Comm)*
Advertising Agency:
Jaffoni & Collins
116 E 16th St 11th Fl
New York, NY 10003-2112
Tel.: (212) 835-8500
Fax: (212) 835-8525

CIRQUE DU SOLEIL INC.

8400 2nd Ave
Montreal, QC H1Z 4M6, Canada
Tel.: (514) 722-2324
Fax: (514) 722-3692
E-mail: mediainfo@cirquedusoleil.com
Web Site: www.cirquedusoleil.com
Approx. Number Employees: 4,000
Year Founded: 1984
Business Description:
Theatrical & Music Producer
S.I.C.: 7922; 2741; 7389; 7929
N.A.I.C.S.: 711110; 512230; 711130; 711310
Media: 3-6-10-11-13-15-18-20
Personnel:
Guy Laliberte *(Founder)*
Daniel Lamarre *(Pres & CEO)*
Gilles Ste-Croix *(Sr VP-Creation Content)*
Mario D'Amico *(VP-Mktg)*
Maria Bonzanigo *(Dir-Musical)*
Guy Caron *(Dir-Creation)*
Renee Claude Menard *(Dir-Pub Rels)*
Serge Roy *(Dir-Creation)*
Sophie Lemieux *(Assoc Dir-Sls & Mktg Touring Shows)*
Marie-Eve Lafreniere *(Mgr-Mktg Svcs)*
Brands & Products:
ALEGRIA
CIRQUE DU SOLEIL
DRALION
KA
LA NOUBA
MYSTERE
O
QUIDAM
SALTIMBANCO
SOLSTROM
VAREKAI
ZUMANITY
Advertising Agency:
SID LEE
75 Queen Street Ofc 1400
Montreal, QC H3C 2N6, Canada
Tel.: (514) 282-2200
Fax: (514) 282-0499

CLEARPLAY

2385 S 300 W
Salt Lake City, UT 84115
Tel.: (801) 463-4899
Web Site: www.clearplay.com
Business Description:
DVD Filter System; Parental Control System which Filters Objectionable Content from a DVD
S.I.C.: 3651
N.A.I.C.S.: 334310
Media: 3
Personnel:
Matt Jarman *(Co-Founder)*
Bill Aho *(CEO)*
Advertising Agency:
INK, Inc.
511 Delaware St Ste 200
Kansas City, MO 64105
Tel.: (816) 753-6222
Fax: (816) 753-8188
Toll Free: (866) 753-6222
Pub Rels

CLEVELAND BROWNS FOOTBALL COMPANY LLC

76 Lou Groza Blvd
Berea, OH 44017-1238
Tel.: (440) 824-6284
Fax: (440) 891-5009
E-mail: tickets@clevelandbrowns.com
Web Site: www.clevelandbrowns.com
Sales Range: $150-199.9 Million
Approx. Number Employees: 200
Business Description:
Professional Football Franchise
S.I.C.: 7941
N.A.I.C.S.: 711211
Media: 9-13-22-23-24
Personnel:
Randolph D. Lerner *(Owner)*
Mike G. Holmgren *(Pres)*
David A. Jenkins *(Sr VP-Fin & Admin)*
Lewis C. Merletti *(Sr VP-Security)*
Bill Bonsiewicz *(VP-Comm)*
Carl Meyer *(VP-Security)*
John Penhollow *(VP-Corp Sls & Svc)*
Brett Reynolds *(VP-Mktg)*
George Muller *(Dir-Creative Svcs)*
Todd Argust *(Dir-Stadium Ops)*
Reagan Berube *(Dir-Content & Production)*
Jerry Butler *(Dir-Player Dev)*
Brandon Covert *(Dir-IT)*
Renee Harvey *(Dir-Community Outreach)*
Michael Nikolaus *(Dir-Admin)*
Nicole Peters *(Dir-Client Svcs)*
Gregory Rush *(Dir-Fin)*
Steve Sabo *(Dir-Pro Personnel)*
John Schulze *(Dir-Ticket Ops)*
David Lee *(Sr Mgr-Ticket Ops)*
Mike Patton *(Sr Mgr-Season Ticketing)*
Sean Reilly *(Sr Mgr-Mktg Comm)*
Bill Baron *(Mgr-Custodial Svcs)*
Ross Benjamin *(Mgr-Stadium Security)*
Seamus Carr *(Mgr-Corp Sls)*
Paul Corto *(Mgr-Bus Dev)*
Steve Eyerman *(Mgr-Stadium Ops)*
Ken Rundle *(Mgr-Training Facility Security)*
Matthew Srodek *(Mgr-Berea Facilities)*
Jermel Wilkerson *(Mgr-Web)*
Pam Smith *(Asst Controller)*
Brands & Products:
CLEVELAND BROWNS
HATS OFF TO OUR HEROES
PLAY 60
VISION FIRST

CLEVELAND CAVALIERS/ QUICKEN LOANS ARENA

(Unit of Cavaliers Operating Company, LLC)
1 Center Ct
Cleveland, OH 44115-4001
Tel.: (216) 420-2000
Fax: (216) 420-2101
Toll Free: (800) 332-2287
Web Site: www.nba.com/cavaliers
Year Founded: 1970
Business Description:
Professional Basketball Team
S.I.C.: 7941
N.A.I.C.S.: 711211
Media: 3-8-9-12-18-20-22-23-24-25
Distr.: Reg.
Budget Set: July
Personnel:
Dan Gilbert *(Founder & Chm)*
Len Komoroski *(Pres)*
David Katzman *(Mng Partner)*
Tad Carper *(Sr VP-Commun)*
Tracy Marek *(Sr VP-Mktg)*
Chris Grant *(Gen Mgr)*
Christine Lesko *(Dir-Adv)*
Nathaniel Ferrall *(Mgr-Mktg)*
Brands & Products:
CLEVELAND BARONS
CLEVELAND CAVALIERS
Advertising Agencies:
Cenergy Communications, LLC (d/b/a Cenergy Sports)
728 Main St
East Aurora, NY 14052
Tel.: (716) 652-7400
Fax: (716) 652-7161
(Branding, Sales Activation)

Stern Advertising, Inc.
29125 Chagrin Blvd
Cleveland, OH 44122-4622
Tel.: (216) 464-4850
Fax: (216) 464-7859

CLEVELAND INDIANS BASEBALL COMPANY, INC.

2401 Ontario St
Cleveland, OH 44115
Tel.: (216) 420-4200
Fax: (216) 420-4799
E-mail: info@indians.com
Web Site: www.indians.com
Approx. Number Employees: 150
Year Founded: 1901
Business Description:
Professional Baseball Club
S.I.C.: 7941

Key to Media (For complete agency information see *The Advertising Red Books-Agencies* edition):
1. Bus. Publs. 2. Cable T.V. 3. Catalogs & Directories. 4. Co-op Adv. 5. Consumer Mags. 6. D.M. to Bus. Estab.7. D.M. to Consumers 8. Daily Newsp. 9. Exhibits/Trade Shows 10. Foreign 11. Infomercial 12. Internet Adv.13. Multimedia 14. Network Radio 15. Network T.V. 16. Newsp. Distr. Mags. 17. Other 18. Outdoor (Posters, Transit) 19. Point of Purchase20. Premiums, Novelties 21. Product Samples 22. Special Events Mktg. 23. Spot Radio 24. Spot T.V. 25. Weekly Newsp. 26. Yellow Page Adv.

Cleveland Indians Baseball Company, Inc. — (Continued)

N.A.I.C.S.: 711211
Advertising Expenditures: $793,000
Media: 3-7-8-9-10-13-14-18-20-22-23-24-25
Distr.: Natl.
Budget Set: Oct.
Personnel:
Lawrence J. Dolan *(Owner & CEO)*
Paul J. Dolan *(Pres)*
Ken Stefanov *(CFO & Sr VP-Fin)*
Sara Lehrke *(Chief Diversity Officer & Sr Dir-HR)*
Joe Znidarsic *(Gen Counsel & VP)*
Mark Shapiro *(Exec VP & Gen Mgr)*
Dennis Lehman *(Exec VP-Bus Affairs)*
Victor Gregovits *(Sr VP-Sls & Mktg)*
Chris Antonetti *(VP-Baseball Ops & Asst Gen Mgr)*
Bob DiBiasio *(VP-PR)*
John Mirabelli *(Asst Gen Mgr)*
Sanaa Julien *(Dir-Mktg)*
Brands & Products:
INDIANS
NCC
Advertising Agency:
MLB Advanced Media, L.P.
75 9th Ave 5th Fl
New York, NY 10011
Tel.: (212) 485-3444
Fax: (212) 485-3456

THE CLOSE COMBAT COMPANY, LLC

1000C Lake St
Ramsey, NJ 07446
Fax: (973) 863-7475
Toll Free: (888) 765-3731
Web Site:
www.closecombattraining.com
Business Description:
Self-Defense Training Services
S.I.C.: 7999
N.A.I.C.S.: 611620
Personnel:
Chris Pizzo *(Pres & Chief Instructor)*
Advertising Agency:
Rosica Strategic Public Relations
95 Rt 17 S Ste 109
Paramus, NJ 07652
Tel.: (201) 843-5600
Fax: (201) 843-5680

CLUB DE HOCKEY CANADIEN, INC.

(d/b/a Montreal Canadiens)
Bell Centre 1260 De la Gauchetiere Street West
Montreal, QC H3B 5E8, Canada
Mailing Address:
1275 Saint Antoine Street West
Montreal, QC H3C 5L2, Canada
Tel.: (514) 932-2582
Fax: (514) 932-8736
E-mail: cec@centrebell.ca
Web Site: www.canadiens.nhl.com
Sales Range: $75-99.9 Million
Approx. Number Employees: 150
Year Founded: 1909
Business Description:
Professional Hockey Franchise
S.I.C.: 7941
N.A.I.C.S.: 711211
Media: 9-13-14-15-18-23-24
Distr.: Natl.
Personnel:
Geoff Molson *(Chm, CEO & Mng Partner)*
Pierre Boivin *(Pres)*
Andrew Molson *(Gen Partner)*
Justin Molson *(Gen Partner)*
Michael Andlauer *(Partner)*
Luc Bertrand *(Partner)*
Fred Steer *(CFO)*
Rejean Houle *(Pres-Canadiens Alumni Association)*
Pierre Gauthier *(Exec VP & Gen Mgr)*
Donald Beauchamp *(VP-Comm & Community Relations)*
Ray Lalonde *(VP-Mktg & Sls)*
Dominick Saillant *(Dir-Media Rels)*
Trevor Timmins *(Dir-Player Recruitment & Dev)*
Claudine Crepin *(Mgr-Team Svcs & Hockey Admin)*
Brands & Products:
MONTREAL CANADIENS

COLLEGE FOOTBALL HALL OF FAME

111 S Saint Joseph St
South Bend, IN 46601
Tel.: (574) 235-9999
Fax: (574) 235-5720
Toll Free: (800) 440-FAME
Web Site: www.collegefootball.org
Approx. Number Employees: 20
Business Description:
College Football Museum
S.I.C.: 8412
N.A.I.C.S.: 712110
Advertising Expenditures: $200,000
Media: 13-15
Personnel:
Lisa Malin *(Exec Dir)*
Katie Berrettini *(Asst Dir-Mktg & Dev)*
Richard Allen *(Mgr-Multimedia & IT)*
Patti Glascoe *(Mgr-Fin Svcs)*
Advertising Agencies:
Pathfinders Advertising & Marketing Group
3830 Edison Lakes Pkwy
Mishawaka, IN 46545-3400
Tel.: (574) 259-5908
Fax: (574) 259-5978

Villing & Company, Inc.
5909 Nimtz Pkwy
South Bend, IN 46628
Tel.: (574) 277-0215
Fax: (574) 277-5513

COLONIAL WILLIAMSBURG FOUNDATION

134 N Henry St
Williamsburg, VA 23187
Mailing Address:
PO Box 1776
Williamsburg, VA 23187-1776
Tel.: (757) 229-1000
Fax: (757) 220-7702
Web Site: www.history.org
Approx. Rev.: $141,500,000
Approx. Number Employees: 3,000
Year Founded: 1926
Business Description:
Tourism Information
S.I.C.: 5947; 8412
N.A.I.C.S.: 453220; 712110
Media: 3-4-5-6-8-9-13-18-22-24-26
Distr.: Natl.; Reg.
Budget Set: Dec.
Personnel:
Colin G. Campbell *(Chm)*
John S. Bacon *(Gen Counsel, Sec & VP)*
Richard J. Hadley, Jr. *(Dir-Museum Design)*
Sally McConnell *(Dir-Brand Strategy & Mktg Comm)*
Christine Nord *(Dir-Accounts-Natl)*
Richard G. Tilghman *(Dir)*
Brands & Products:
AMERICA. CHAPTER I.
COLONIAL WILLIAMSBURG
THAT THE FUTURE MAY LEARN FORM THE PAST
WILLIAMSBURG
WILLIAMSBURG PURE SIMPLE TODAY
WILLIAMSBURG RESERVE

COLORADO AVALANCHE, LLC

(Sub. of Kroenke Sports Enterprises LLC)
Pepsi Ctr 1000 Chopper Cir
Denver, CO 80204
Tel.: (303) 405-1100
Fax: (303) 575-1920
Web Site: avalanche.nhl.com
Sales Range: $75-99.9 Million
Approx. Number Employees: 600
Year Founded: 1979
Business Description:
Professional Hockey Club
S.I.C.: 7941
N.A.I.C.S.: 711211
Advertising Expenditures: $200,000
Media: 9-13-14-15-23-24
Personnel:
E. Stanley Kroenke *(Owner)*
Pierre Lacroix *(Pres & Alternate Governor)*
Michael Benson *(Treas & Sr VP-Bus Affairs)*
Greg Sherman *(Gen Mgr, Exec VP & Alternate Governor)*
Jean Martineau *(Sr VP-Comm & Bus Ops)*
Mark Waggoner *(Sr VP-Fin)*
Brian Kitts *(Sr Dir-Mktg & Pub Rel)*
Brendan McNicholas *(Sr Dir-Media Svcs & Internet)*
Brad Smith *(Dir-Player Personnel)*
Brands & Products:
COLORADO AVALANCHE

COLORADO CASINO RESORTS, INC.

1 S Nevada Ave Sky Box 2
Colorado Springs, CO 80903-1809
Tel.: (719) 635-7047
Fax: (719) 577-4908
Approx. Number Employees: 330
Year Founded: 1995
Business Description:
Owner & Operator of Gaming Facilities
S.I.C.: 7011
N.A.I.C.S.: 721120
Advertising Expenditures: $600,000

COLORADO ROCKIES BASEBALL CLUB, LTD.

Coors Field 2001 Blake St
Denver, CO 80205-2000
Tel.: (303) 292-0200
Fax: (303) 312-2216
Toll Free: (800) 388-7625
E-mail: fanfeedback@rockies.mlb.com
Web Site:
www.colorado.rockies.mlb.com
Sales Range: $25-49.9 Million
Approx. Number Employees: 120
Year Founded: 1993
Business Description:
Professional Baseball Club
S.I.C.: 7941
N.A.I.C.S.: 711211
Media: 3-6-9-13-18-22-23-24-25
Distr.: Reg.
Personnel:
Richard L. Monfort *(Owner, Chm & CEO)*
Charles K. Monfort *(Owner & Gen Partner)*
Harold R. Roth *(CFO, Exec VP & Legal Counsel)*
Gregory D. Feasel *(COO & Exec VP)*
Kevin H. Kahn *(Chief Customer Officer & VP-Ballpark Ops)*
Daniel J. O'Dowd *(Chief Baseball Officer, Exec VP & Gen Mgr)*
William P. Geivett *(Asst Gen Mgr & Sr VP-Scouting & Player Dev)*
Jay E. Alves *(VP-Comm & PR)*
Marcy English Glasser *(VP-Corp Sls)*
Michael J. Kent *(VP-Fin)*
Sue Ann McClaren *(VP-Ticket Svcs, Ops & Sls)*
Elizabeth E. Stecklein *(VP-HR)*
Jeff Bridich *(Sr Dir-Baseball Ops)*
Steven Burke *(Sr Dir-Guest Svcs)*
Jill Roberts Campbell *(Sr Dir-Adv, Mktg & Publ)*
Kevin G. Fenton *(Sr Dir-Ticket Svcs, Ops & Sls)*
Marc Gustafson *(Sr Dir-Player Dev)*
Gary Lawrence *(Sr Dir-Pur)*
Tom Probst *(Sr Dir-Medical Ops & Special Projects)*
James Wiener *(Sr Dir-Engrg & Facilities)*
Jeff Benner *(Dir-Season Tickets & Sls Grp)*
Randy Carlill *(Dir-Engrg)*
Paul Egins *(Dir-Major League Ops)*
Phil Emerson *(Dir-Acctg)*
Brendan Falvey *(Dir-New Partner Dev)*
Jason Fleming *(Dir-Promos & Special Events)*
Kent Hakes *(Dir-Ticket Ops & Fin)*
Aaron Heinrich *(Dir-Retail Ops)*
Don Lyon *(Dir-Security & Safety)*
Dan Olsen *(Dir-Facilities)*
Keith Schulz *(Dir-Clubhouse Ops)*
Bill Stephani *(Dir-Info Sys)*
Scott Donaldson *(Asst Dir-Ticket Ops)*
Mary Beth Benner *(Mgr-Ballpark Svcs)*
Alan Bossart *(Mgr-Visiting Clubhouse)*
Kevin Flood *(Mgr-Ticket Ops)*
Charlie Hepp *(Mgr-Comm & PR)*
Farrah Magee *(Mgr-Season Tickets)*
Brands & Products:
COLORADO ROCKIES
Advertising Agency:
MLB Advanced Media, L.P.
75 9th Ave 5th Fl
New York, NY 10011
Tel.: (212) 485-3444
Fax: (212) 485-3456

Key to Media (For complete agency information see *The Advertising Red Books-Agencies* edition):
1. Bus. Publs. 2. Cable T.V. 3. Catalogs & Directories. 4. Co-op Adv. 5. Consumer Mags. 6. D.M. to Bus. Estab.7. D.M. to Consumers 8. Daily Newsp. 9. Exhibits/Trade Shows 10. Foreign 11. Infomercial 12. Internet Adv.13. Multimedia 14. Network Radio 15. Network T.V. 16. Newsp. Distr. Mags. 17. Other 18. Outdoor (Posters, Transit) 19. Point of Purchase20. Premiums, Novelties 21. Product Samples 22. Special Events Mktg. 23. Spot Radio 24. Spot T.V. 25. Weekly Newsp. 26. Yellow Page Adv.

COLORADO SYMPHONY ASSOCIATION INC.
Boettcher Concert Hall Denver Performing Arts Complex 1000 14th St #15
Denver, CO 80202-2333
Tel.: (303) 292-5566
Fax: (303) 293-2649
E-mail: admin@coloradosymphony.org
Web Site: www.coloradosymphony.org
Approx. Rev.: $9,000,000
Approx. Number Employees: 110
Business Description:
Symphony Orchestra
S.I.C.: 7929
N.A.I.C.S.: 711130
Advertising Expenditures: $425,000
Media: 6-8-9-13-18-20-22-23-24-25-26
Personnel:
Rebecca Grabler *(Dir-Dev Ops)*
Jeffrey Kahane *(Dir-Music)*
Christine Kechter *(Dir-Mktg-Pub Rels)*
Samantha Teter *(Dir-Mktg & Sls)*
Doug Yost *(Dir-Info Svcs)*
Larry Brezicka *(Mgr-Orchestra Personnel)*

THE COLUMBIA ORCHESTRA
8510 High Ridge Rd
Ellicott City, MD 21043-3308
Tel.: (410) 465-8777
Fax: (410) 465-8778
E-mail: execdir@columbiaorchestra.org
Web Site: www.columbiaorchestra.org
Sales Range: Less than $1 Million
Approx. Number Employees: 3
Business Description:
Symphony Orchestra
S.I.C.: 7929
N.A.I.C.S.: 711130
Media: 8-9-20-23-24-25
Personnel:
Bruce Kuehne *(Pres)*
Tedd Griepentrog *(Exec Dir)*
Jason Love *(Dir-Music)*

COLUMBUS ASSOCIATION FOR THE PERFORMING ARTS CORPORATION
55 E State St
Columbus, OH 43215
Tel.: (614) 469-1045
Fax: (614) 469-0429
Web Site: www.capa.com
Sales Range: $10-24.9 Million
Approx. Number Employees: 705
Business Description:
Theater Building, Ownership & Operation
S.I.C.: 6512
N.A.I.C.S.: 531120
Media: 9-18-20-23-24-25
Personnel:
William Conner *(Pres & CEO)*
Brands & Products:
CAPA

COLUMBUS BLUE JACKETS
Nationwide Arena 200 W Nationwide Blvd 3rd Fl
Columbus, OH 43215
Tel.: (614) 246-4625
Fax: (614) 246-4007
E-mail: contact@bluejackets.com
Web Site: www.bluejackets.com
Approx. Number Employees: 150
Year Founded: 1997
Business Description:
Professional Hockey Team
S.I.C.: 7991
N.A.I.C.S.: 713940
Advertising Expenditures: $500,000
Media: 9-13-18-22-23-24-25
Personnel:
Mike Priest *(Pres)*
T. J. LaMendola *(CFO)*
Greg Kirstein *(Gen Counsel & Sr VP)*
Scott Howson *(Exec VP-Hockey Ops & Gen Mgr)*
Larry Hoepfner *(Exec VP-Bus Ops)*
Cameron Scholvin *(Sr VP-Corp Dev)*
Marc Gregory *(VP-Mktg)*
Todd Sharrock *(VP-PR)*
Don Boyd *(Asst Gen Mgr)*
Chris MacFarland *(Asst Gen Mgr)*
Paul Castron *(Dir-Amateur Scouting)*
Jim Connolly *(Dir-IT)*
Karen Davis *(Dir-Community Rels)*
Bob Strumm *(Dir-Professional Scouting)*
John Williams *(Asst Dir-Amateur Scouting)*
Kate Furman *(Mgr-Community Dev)*
John Gruber *(Mgr-IT)*
Ryan Holtmann *(Mgr-Comm)*
Jason LaPlace *(Asst Controller)*
Brands & Products:
BLUEJACKETS.COM
COLUMBUS BLUE JACKETS
Advertising Agency:
DigiKnow
3615 Superior Ave Bldg 44 4th Fl
Cleveland, OH 44114
Tel.: (216) 325-1800
Fax: (216) 325-1801

COLUMBUS PRO MUSICA INC.
(d/b/a Columbus Indiana Philharmonic)
315 Franklin St
Columbus, IN 47201
Tel.: (812) 376-2638
Fax: (812) 376-2567
E-mail: info@thecip.org
Web Site: www.thecip.org
Approx. Number Employees: 11
Year Founded: 1987
Business Description:
Symphony Orchestra
S.I.C.: 7929
N.A.I.C.S.: 711130
Media: 7-8-9-13-20-22-23-24-25
Personnel:
Judy Summerville *(Pres)*
Robert Williamson *(Treas)*
Alice O. Curry *(Exec Dir)*
David Bowden *(Dir-Music)*
Ruth E. Dwyer *(Dir-Artistic & Choral)*
Charles Latshaw *(Dir-Philharmonic Youth Orchestra & Youth Ensemble Music)*
Joyce Wire *(Admin Mgr)*

COMMONWEALTH ZOOLOGICAL CORP.
(d/b/a Franklin Park Zoo)
(d/b/a Zoo New England)
1 Franklin Pk Rd
Boston, MA 02121
Tel.: (617) 989-2000
Tel.: (617) 541-5466
Fax: (617) 989-2025
E-mail: info@zoonewengland.com
Web Site: www.zoonewengland.org
Approx. Number Employees: 175
Business Description:
Zoo
S.I.C.: 8422
N.A.I.C.S.: 712130
Media: 8-9-10-20-23-24-25
Personnel:
Grace Fey *(Chm)*
John Linehan *(Pres & CEO)*
Brooke Waldrop *(Mgr-Pub Rels)*

COMMUNITY THEATRE
100 S St
Morristown, NJ 07960
Tel.: (973) 539-0345
Tel.: (973) 539-8008
Fax: (973) 455-1607
E-mail: info@mayart.org
Web Site: www.mayarts.org
E-Mail For Key Personnel:
Marketing Director: dgrossman@communitytheatrenj.com
Approx. Number Employees: 50
Year Founded: 1937
Business Description:
Theater Company
S.I.C.: 7922; 7389
N.A.I.C.S.: 711110; 711410
Media: 7-8-9-18-23-25
Personnel:
A. Dale Mayo *(Chm)*
Allison Larena *(Exec Dir)*
Ed Kirchdoerffer *(Dir-Mktg)*

CONN-SELMER, INC.
(Sub. of Steinway Musical Instruments, Inc.)
600 Industrial Pkwy
Elkhart, IN 46516-5414
Mailing Address:
PO Box 310
Elkhart, IN 46515-0310
Tel.: (574) 522-1675
Fax: (574) 295-5405
Web Site: www.selmer.com
Sales Range: $350-399.9 Million
Approx. Number Employees: 1,000
Business Description:
Mfr. of Musical Woodwind Instruments
S.I.C.: 3931; 5736
N.A.I.C.S.: 339992; 451140
Advertising Expenditures: $600,000
Media: 2-4-6-7-10-11-19-22
Distr.: Natl.
Personnel:
John M. Stoner, Jr. *(Pres)*
Mary Anne Irwin *(VP-Fin & Controller)*
Tim Matterson *(Product Mgr-String Instruments)*
Brands & Products:
CONN SELMER UNIVERSITY
SELMER

CONTOURS EXPRESS, INC.
156 Imperial Way
Nicholasville, KY 40356
Tel.: (877) 227-2282
Tel.: (859) 885-6441
Fax: (859) 242-2240
Toll Free: (877) 227-2282
Web Site: www.contoursexpress.com
Sales Range: $1-9.9 Million
Approx. Number Employees: 8
Year Founded: 1998
Business Description:
Franchised Chain of Women-Only Fitness Facilities
S.I.C.: 7991
N.A.I.C.S.: 713940
Media: 3
Personnel:
Bill Helton *(Pres)*
Advertising Agency:
Spot Runner
3600 Wilshire Blvd
Los Angeles, CA 90048
Tel.: (310) 430-7900
Fax: (310) 430-7999

COYOTES HOCKEY, LLC
(Holding of National Hockey League)
(d/b/a Phoenix Coyotes)
(Filed for Ch. 11 Bankruptcy on 5/5/2009)
6751 N Sunset Blvd Ste 200
Glendale, AZ 85305
Tel.: (623) 772-3200
Fax: (623) 463-8810
E-mail: webmaster@phoenixcoyotes.com
Web Site: www.coyotes.nhl.com
E-Mail For Key Personnel:
Marketing Director: brogers@nhl.com
Sales Range: $50-74.9 Million
Approx. Number Employees: 150
Year Founded: 1996
Business Description:
Professional Hockey Team
S.I.C.: 7941
N.A.I.C.S.: 711211
Media: 8-9-10-18-20-22-23-24
Distr.: Natl.
Personnel:
Mike Nealy *(Alternate Governor & COO)*
Michael Bucek *(CMO & Exec VP)*
Don Maloney *(Exec VP, Gen Mgr & Alternate Governor)*
Jim Foss *(Sr VP & Gen Mgr-Arena Mgmt Grp)*
Joe Leibfried *(VP-Fin & Controller)*
Brad Treliving *(VP-Hockey Ops & Asst Gen Mgr)*
Julie Atherton *(VP-HR)*
Stacey Cohen *(VP-Mktg)*
Jay Gaskin *(Sr Dir-IT)*
Dave Vest *(Sr Dir-News Content)*
Sean Burke *(Dir-Prospect Dev)*
Sarah Finecey *(Dir-Community Relations & Fan Dev)*
Jeff Jones *(Dir-Parking & Traffic-Arena Mgmt Grp)*
Sean Langer *(Dir-Facility Ops-Arena Mgmt Grp)*
Chris O'Hearn *(Dir-Hockey Admin)*
Jim O'Neal *(Dir-Security)*
Kyle Olsen *(Dir-Events-Arena Mgmt Grp)*
Ted Santiago *(Dir-Adv & Media)*
Paul Serbic *(Dir-Guest Svcs-Arena Mgmt Grp)*
Douglas Vanderheyden *(Dir-Ticket Ops)*
Julie Atheton *(Mgr)*
John Dickey *(Mgr-Pur)*
Burlenti Shaban *(Asst Controller)*
Brands & Products:
COYOTES CAUSES
GOING GREEN
PHOENIX COYOTES
Advertising Agencies:
Contact Designs LLC
8960 E Raintree Dr Ste 400

Key to Media (For complete agency information see *The Advertising Red Books-Agencies* edition):
1. Bus. Publs. 2. Cable T.V. 3. Catalogs & Directories. 4. Co-op Adv. 5. Consumer Mags. 6. D.M. to Bus. Estab.7. D.M. to Consumers 8. Daily Newsp. 9. Exhibits/Trade Shows 10. Foreign 11. Infomercial 12. Internet Adv.13. Multimedia 14. Network Radio 15. Network T.V. 16. Newsp. Distr. Mags. 17. Other 18. Outdoor (Posters, Transit) 19. Point of Purchase20. Premiums, Novelties 21. Product Samples 22. Special Events Mktg. 23. Spot Radio 24. Spot T.V. 25. Weekly Newsp. 26. Yellow Page Adv.

Coyotes Hockey, LLC — (Continued)

Scottsdale, AZ 85260
Tel.: (480) 921-1732

Fallon Worldwide
901 Marquette Ave Ste 2400
Minneapolis, MN 55402
Tel.: (612) 758-2345
Fax: (612) 758-2346
Agency of Record
Coyotes 2011-12
Promotional Marketing Events

CURVES INTERNATIONAL INC.

100 Ritchie Rd
Waco, TX 76712
Tel.: (254) 399-9285
Fax: (254) 741-9249
Toll Free: (800) 848-1096
E-mail: marketing@curves.com
Web Site: www.curves.com
Sales Range: $25-49.9 Million
Approx. Number Employees: 80
Year Founded: 1995
Business Description:
Women's Fitness & Weight Loss Centers Franchiser
S.I.C.: 7299; 7991
N.A.I.C.S.: 812191; 713940
Media: 3-6-8-9-15-21-22
Personnel:
Gary Heavin *(Founder & CEO)*
Mike Raymond *(Pres & Head-Mktg)*
Ronnie Glaesmann *(CFO)*
Brands & Products:
CURVACEOUS
CURVES
CURVESSMART
DIANE
THE POWER TO AMAZE YOURSELF
YOUR CURVES WILL AMAZE YOU.
Advertising Agencies:
Apollo Interactive, Inc.
8556 Hayden Pl
Culver City, CA 90232
Tel.: (310) 836-9777
Fax: (310) 836-6261
Toll Free: (800) 599-7499

Kori Lee & Associates
15333 Culver Dr Ste 340
Irvine, CA 92604-3078
Tel.: (949) 552-6368

Publicis Dallas
7300 Lonestar Dr
Plano, TX 75024
Tel.: (972) 628-7500
Fax: (972) 628-7864

Publicis USA
(Sub. of Publicis, S.A., Paris, France)
4 Herald Sq 950 6th Ave
New York, NY 10001
Tel.: (212) 279-5550
Fax: (212) 279-5560

DALLAS COWBOYS FOOTBALL CLUB, LTD.

Cowboys Ctr 1 Cowboys Pkwy
Irving, TX 75063
Tel.: (972) 556-9900
Fax: (972) 556-9304
E-mail: contact@dallascowboys.com
Web Site: www.dallascowboys.com
Approx. Number Employees: 300
Year Founded: 1960
Business Description:
Professional Football Franchise
S.I.C.: 7941
N.A.I.C.S.: 711211
Media: 3-6-9-13-15-18-20-22-23-24-25
Distr.: Direct to Consumer; Natl.
Personnel:
George Mitchell *(CFO)*
Charlotte Jones Anderson *(Pres-Charities & Exec VP-Brand Mgmt)*
Dave Frey *(Controller)*
Robin Woith *(Sr Dir-Sls & Mktg)*
Rich Dalrymple *(Dir-Pub Rel)*
Brands & Products:
DALLAS COWBOYS
DALLAS COWBOYS OFFICIAL WEEKLY

DALLAS MAVERICKS

The Pavilion 2909 Taylor St
Dallas, TX 75226
Tel.: (214) 747-6287
Fax: (214) 752-3860
Web Site: www.dallasmavericks.com
Sales Range: $100-124.9 Million
Approx. Number Employees: 100
Year Founded: 1980
Business Description:
Professional Basketball Team
S.I.C.: 7941
N.A.I.C.S.: 711211
Advertising Expenditures: $400,000
Consumer Mags.: $25,000; Daily Newsp.: $375,000
Distr.: Reg.
Budget Set: July
Personnel:
Mark Cuban *(Owner)*
Terdema L. Ussery, II *(Pres & CEO)*
Floyd Jahner *(CFO & VP)*
Donn Nelson *(Pres-Basketball Ops & Gen Mgr)*
George Killebrew *(Sr VP-Corp Sponsorships)*
Buddy Pittman *(Sr VP-HR)*
Paul Monroe *(VP-Mktg & Comm)*
Keith Grant *(Asst Gen Mgr)*
Ken Bonzon *(Dir-Tech & Info Sys)*
Derek Earls *(Dir-Security)*
Mary Jean Gaines *(Dir-Ticket Admin)*
Sarah Melton *(Dir-Comm-Basketball)*
Tom Ward *(Dir-Production)*
Gina Calvert *(Mgr-Corp Comm & Community Rels)*
Scott Tomlin *(Mgr-Basketball Comm)*
Brands & Products:
DALLAS MAVERICKS

THE DALLAS OPERA

8350 N Central Expy Ste 210
Dallas, TX 75206
Tel.: (214) 443-1043
Fax: (214) 443-1060
E-mail: virginia@dallasopera.org
Web Site: www.dallasopera.org
Approx. Number Employees: 35
Business Description:
Opera Company
S.I.C.: 7922
N.A.I.C.S.: 711110
Advertising Expenditures: $500,000
Media: 1-8-9-10-13-18-20-22-23-24-25
Personnel:
T. Peter Townsend *(VP-Fin)*
Jennifer Schuder *(Dir-Mktg)*

DALLAS STARS L.P.

(Sub. of Hicks Sports Group, LLC)
2601 Ave Of The Stars
Frisco, TX 75034
Tel.: (214) 387-5500
Fax: (214) 387-5503
Toll Free: (800) GO-SKATE
E-mail: starsfeedback@dallasstars.com
Web Site: www.dallasstars.com
Sales Range: $50-74.9 Million
Approx. Number Employees: 200
Year Founded: 1993
Business Description:
Professional Hockey Team
S.I.C.: 7941
N.A.I.C.S.: 711211
Media: 3-8-9-13-18-22-23-24
Distr.: Reg.
Budget Set: Apr.
Personnel:
Thomas O. Hicks *(Owner & Chm)*
Tony Tavares *(Pres)*
Robert Hutson *(CFO & Exec VP-Fin)*
Randy Locey *(Exec VP-Bus Ops)*
Geoff Moore *(Exec VP-Sls-Mktg)*
Joe Nieu Dwendyk *(Gen Mgr)*
Rob Scichili *(Sr Dir-Comm)*
Mark Janko *(Dir-PR)*
Jason Rademan *(Dir-Media Rels)*
Brands & Products:
DALLAS STARS
STARCENTER
STREETSTARS
Advertising Agency:
Door Number 3
1050 E 11th St Ste 250
Austin, TX 78702
Tel.: (512) 391-1773
Fax: (512) 391-1926
Hockey Team

DALLAS SYMPHONY ASSOCIATION INC.

(d/b/a Dallas Symphony Orchestra)
2301 Flora St
Dallas, TX 75201
Tel.: (214) 692-0203
Web Site: www.dallassymphony.com
Sales Range: $25-49.9 Million
Approx. Number Employees: 68
Business Description:
Symphony Orchestra
S.I.C.: 7929
N.A.I.C.S.: 711130
Media: 9-18-20-23-24-25
Personnel:
Nancy McThompson *(Dir-Volunteer Svcs)*
Michael Coren *(Mgr-Orchestra Personnel)*
Lilian E. Godsey *(Mgr-Donor Stewardship)*
Carl Wong *(Mgr-Stage)*
Brands & Products:
AMAZING MUSIC
LISTEN AND LEARN FAMILY CONCERTS

DAYTON PHILHARMONIC ORCHESTRA ASSOCIATION, INC.

109 N Main St Ste 200
Dayton, OH 45402
Tel.: (937) 224-3521
Fax: (937) 223-9189
E-mail: info@daytonphilharmonic.com
Web Site: www.daytonphilharmonic.com
Sales Range: $1-9.9 Million
Approx. Number Employees: 17
Year Founded: 1933
Business Description:
Symphony Orchestra
S.I.C.: 7929
N.A.I.C.S.: 711130
Media: 1-7-8-9-20-22-23-24-25-26
Personnel:
Paul Helfrich *(Pres)*
Matthew Borger *(Dir-Ops)*
David Bukvic *(Dir-Mktg & Comm)*
Pete Klosterman *(Dir-Fin)*
Gloria Pugh *(Dir-Education)*
Jan Clarke *(Mgr-Events)*
Erika Niemi *(Mgr-Production)*
Jane Varella *(Mgr-Orchestra Personnel)*

DEAN MARKLEY STRINGS, INC.

3350 Scott Blvd Ste 45
Santa Clara, CA 95054
Tel.: (408) 988-2456
Fax: (408) 988-0441
Toll Free: (800) 800-1008
Web Site: www.deanmarkley.com
Sales Range: $10-24.9 Million
Approx. Number Employees: 20
Year Founded: 1971
Business Description:
Musical Instrument Mfr
S.I.C.: 3931
N.A.I.C.S.: 339992
Media: 2-4-10
Personnel:
Dean Markley *(Owner & Pres)*
Bari Wilson *(Exec VP)*

DEARBORN SYMPHONY ORCHESTRA

PO Box 2063
Dearborn, MI 48123
Tel.: (313) 565-2424
Fax: (313) 565-2411
E-mail: info@dearbornsymphony.org
Web Site: www.dearbornsymphony.org
Sales Range: Less than $1 Million
Approx. Number Employees: 1
Business Description:
Symphony Orchestra
S.I.C.: 7922
N.A.I.C.S.: 711110
Media: 8-9-20-23-24-25
Personnel:
Sandra Butler *(Pres)*
Robert Kuhlman *(Dir-Dev)*

DEBARTOLO CORPORATION

7620 Market Street
Youngstown, OH 44512
Tel.: (330) 965-2000
Fax: (330) 965-2077
Approx. Number Employees: 12
Year Founded: 1944
Business Description:
Holding Company
S.I.C.: 6719; 7941; 7999
N.A.I.C.S.: 551112; 711211; 711219
Media: 1-2-10-18
Distr.: Direct to Consumer; Reg.

Key to Media (For complete agency information see *The Advertising Red Books-Agencies* edition):
1. Bus. Publs. 2. Cable T.V. 3. Catalogs & Directories. 4. Co-op Adv. 5. Consumer Mags. 6. D.M. to Bus. Estab.7. D.M. to Consumers 8. Daily Newsp. 9. Exhibits/Trade Shows 10. Foreign 11. Infomercial 12. Internet Adv.13. Multimedia 14. Network Radio 15. Network T.V. 16. Newsp. Distr. Mags. 17. Other 18. Outdoor (Posters, Transit) 19. Point of Purchase20. Premiums, Novelties 21. Product Samples 22. Special Events Mktg. 23. Spot Radio 24. Spot T.V. 25. Weekly Newsp. 26. Yellow Page Adv.

Personnel:
Marie Denise DeBartolo York *(Co-Owner)*
John C. York, II *(Co-Owner)*

DELAWARE ART MUSEUM
2301 Kentmere Pkwy
Wilmington, DE 19806
Tel.: (302) 571-9590
Fax: (302) 428-1049
Web Site: www.delart.org
Approx. Number Employees: 50
Business Description:
Art Museum
S.I.C.: 8412
N.A.I.C.S.: 712110
Media: 7-8-9-10-13-20-22-23-24-25
Personnel:
Danielle Rice *(Exec Dir)*
Bruce Canter *(Dir-Ops)*
Susan M. Stalnecker *(Dir-Dev)*
Courtney Waring *(Dir-Education)*
Connie Cordeiro *(Mgr-Museum Store & Mgr-VSR)*
Stacey Hartnett *(Mgr-Fin)*
Jim Plummer *(Mgr-Tech Ops)*
Heather Campbell Coyle *(Assoc Curator)*

DELAWARE MUSEUM OF NATURAL HISTORY
4840 Kennett Pike
Wilmington, DE 19807
Tel.: (302) 658-9111
Fax: (302) 658-2610
Web Site: www.delmnh.org
Sales Range: $10-24.9 Million
Approx. Number Employees: 20
Business Description:
Museum Services
S.I.C.: 8412
N.A.I.C.S.: 712110
Media: 5-8-9-10-13-22-23-24-25
Personnel:
Jean Woods *(Dir-Collections)*
Leslie Skibinski *(Mgr-Mollusks Collections)*

DELAWARE SYMPHONY ASSOCIATION
818 N Market St
Wilmington, DE 19801
Tel.: (302) 656-7442
Fax: (302) 656-7754
E-mail: info@desymphony.org
Web Site: www.desymphony.org
Approx. Number Employees: 15
Business Description:
Symphony Orchestra
S.I.C.: 7929
N.A.I.C.S.: 711130
Media: 8-9-20-22-23-25
Personnel:
David Amado *(Dir-Music)*

DENVER BRONCOS FOOTBALL CLUB
(Holding of Bowlen Sports, Inc.)
13655 Broncos Pkwy
Englewood, CO 80112-4150
Tel.: (303) 649-9000
Tel.: (720) 258-3100 (Marketing)
Fax: (303) 649-9354
E-mail: info@denverbroncos.com
Web Site: www.denverbroncos.com
Approx. Number Employees: 200
Year Founded: 1959
Business Description:
Professional Football Franchise
S.I.C.: 7941
N.A.I.C.S.: 711211
Media: 7-8-9-13-18-20-22-23-24
Distr.: Natl.
Personnel:
Pat D. Bowlen *(CEO)*
Joe Ellis *(Pres)*
Rich Slivka *(Gen Counsel & Exec VP-Admin)*
John Elway *(Exec VP-Football Ops)*
Mac Freeman *(Sr VP-Bus Dev)*
Dave Abrams *(VP-Security)*
Dennis Moore *(VP-Mktg & Sls)*
Jim Saccomano *(VP-Corp Comm)*
Justin Webster *(VP-Fin)*
Andy Gorchov *(Gen Mgr-Stadium Ops)*
Brain Xanders *(Gen Mgr)*
Kirk Dyer *(Exec Dir-Ticket Ops & Admin)*
Brady Kellogg *(Sr Dir-Corp Partnerships)*
Mike Bluem *(Dir-Football Admin)*
Katie Delay *(Dir-Ticket Ops)*
Fred Fleming *(Dir-Special Svcs-Pro Scouting)*
Tony Lazzaro *(Dir-Football Info Sys)*
Amy Marolf *(Dir-Corp Partnership Svcs)*
Sheila Thomas *(Dir-HR)*
Billy Thompson *(Dir-Community Outreach)*
Kelly Woodward *(Dir-Community Dev)*
Sandy Bretzlauf Young *(Sr Mgr-Mktg)*
Rick Seifert *(Comm Mgr)*
Kelly Trimble *(Mgr-Travel Svcs)*
Scott Bliek *(Mgr-Event Svcs & Security)*
Fred Krebs *(Mgr-Cash Mgmt & Treasury)*
Bobby Mestas *(Mgr-Special Events & Fan Dev)*
Chris Newman *(Mgr-IT Network)*
Derek Thomas *(Mgr-Mktg Partnerships)*
Chris Valenti *(Mgr-Equipment)*
Clark Wray *(Mgr-Ticket Ops & Database)*
Brands & Products:
DENVER BRONCOS

DENVER CENTER FOR THE PERFORMING ARTS INC.
1101 13th St
Denver, CO 80204-2154
Tel.: (303) 893-4000
Fax: (303) 893-3206
Web Site: www.denvercenter.org
Approx. Number Employees: 285
Year Founded: 1972
Business Description:
Theatrical Producers & Services
S.I.C.: 7389
N.A.I.C.S.: 711310
Import Export
Media: 2-3-8-9-10-13-18-20-22-23-24-25
Personnel:
Donald R. Seawell *(Founder & Chm)*
Randall Weeks *(Pres & COO)*
Dorothy Denny *(Exec VP & Dir-Dev)*
Jeff Hovorka *(Dir-Media & Mktg)*
Kent Thompson *(Dir-Artistic)*
Brands & Products:
DENVER CENTER THEATRE COMPANY'S WORKING STAGES
DRAMATIC LEARNING
E-SHAKESPEARE

THE DENVER NUGGETS LIMITED PARTNERSHIP
(Sub. of Kroenke Sports Enterprises LLC)
1000 Chopper Cir
Denver, CO 80204-5809
Tel.: (303) 405-1100
Fax: (303) 575-1920
E-mail: nuggetsmail@pepsicenter.com
Web Site: www.nba.com/nuggets
Sales Range: $75-99.9 Million
Approx. Number Employees: 500
Year Founded: 1967
Business Description:
Professional Basketball Team
S.I.C.: 7941
N.A.I.C.S.: 711211
Advertising Expenditures: $200,000
Media: 1-2-3-4-5-6-7-8-9-10-13-14-15-18-20-22-23-24-25
Distr.: Reg.
Budget Set: June
Personnel:
E. Stanley Kroenke *(Owner)*
David Ehrlich *(Pres)*
Masai Ujiri *(Exec VP-Basketball Ops)*
Mark Waggoner *(Sr VP-Fin & Kroenke Sports)*
Rex Chapman *(VP-Player Personnel)*
David Fredman *(Asst Gen Mgr)*
Jeff Weltman *(Asst Gen Mgr)*
Lisa Johnson *(Exec Dir-Basketball Admin)*
Tim Gelt *(Dir-Media Rels)*
Sparky Gonzales *(Mgr-Equipment)*
Mark Randall *(Mgr-Player Devel)*
Ryan Woodcock *(Coord-Media Rels & Website)*
Brands & Products:
DENVER NUGGETS

DES MOINES SYMPHONY ASSOCIATION
221 Walnut St
Des Moines, IA 50309
Tel.: (515) 280-4000
Fax: (515) 280-4005
E-mail: info@dmsymphony.org
Web Site: www.dmsymphony.org
Approx. Number Employees: 100
Business Description:
Symphony Orchestra
S.I.C.: 7929; 7389
N.A.I.C.S.: 711130; 561990
Media: 9-19-20-22-23-24-25
Personnel:
Jim Sandager *(Pres)*
Jeffrey Cannon *(Treas)*
Ann Hartz *(Controller)*
Richard L. Early *(Exec Dir)*
Joseph Giunta *(Dir-Music)*
Gene Wibben *(Mgr-Orchestra Personnel)*

THE DETROIT LIONS, INC.
222 Republic Dr
Allen Park, MI 48101
Tel.: (313) 216-4000
Fax: (313) 216-4226
Toll Free: (800) 616-ROAR
Web Site: www.detroitlions.com
Approx. Number Employees: 200
Year Founded: 1934
Business Description:
Professional Football Franchise
S.I.C.: 7941
N.A.I.C.S.: 711211
Media: 10-18-22
Distr.: Natl.
Personnel:
Tom Lewand *(Pres)*
Tom Lesnau *(CFO & Sr VP-Fin)*
Bill Keenist *(Sr VP-Comm)*
Allison Maki *(VP-Fin & Admin)*
Martin Mayhew *(Gen Mgr)*
Galen Duncan *(Sr Dir-Player Dev)*
Bob Gardner *(Sr Dir-Facility Mgmt)*
Tim Pendell *(Sr Dir-Community Affairs)*
Matt Barnhart *(Dir-Media Rels)*
Bryan Bender *(Dir-Brdcst Production)*
Al Brooks *(Dir-Security-Ford Field)*
Chris Fritzsching *(Dir-Youth Football Programs)*
Mark Graham *(Dir-Ticket Ops & Customer Svc)*
Dan Jaroshewich *(Dir-Sports Events)*
Mike Mazurek *(Dir-Suite Sls)*
Scott McEwen *(Dir-College Scouting)*
Terri McKay *(Dir-IT)*
Elton Moore *(Dir-Security)*
Iain Nelson *(Dir-Football Admin)*
Joe Schmit *(Dir-Mktg-Pub Rel)*
Joel Scott *(Dir-Mktg)*
Beth Smiley *(Dir-HR-Ford Field)*
Dan Sylvester *(Dir-Ticket Sls)*
Robert Yanagi *(Dir-Video Ops)*
Mark Cheklich *(Asst Dir-Sponsorship & Suite Sls)*
Kim Doverspike *(Asst Dir-Community Affairs)*
Ben Manges *(Asst Dir-Media Rels)*
Bill McCall *(Asst Dir-Ticket Ops)*
Michael Richardson *(Asst Dir-Video)*
Charlie Sanders *(Asst Dir-Pro Personnel)*
Deanna Caldwell *(Mgr-Creative Svcs)*
Anne Campbell *(Mgr-Sponsorship & Suite Sls Svc)*
Mark Glenn *(Mgr-Facilities)*
Judy Kowalkowski *(Mgr-Acctg Ops)*
Tim O'Neill *(Mgr-Equipment)*
Brands & Products:
DETROIT LIONS
DETROIT LIONS L.E.A.D.ERS FOR LIFE
DETROIT LIONS SKILL DEVELOPMENT SESSIONS
DETROIT LIONS YOUTH FOOTBALL
DETROIT LIONS YOUTH FOOTBALL FORUM

DETROIT PISTONS BASKETBALL COMPANY
(Holding of Palace Sports & Entertainment, Inc.)
6 Championship Dr
Auburn Hills, MI 48326-1753
Tel.: (248) 377-0100
Fax: (248) 377-3260
Web Site: www.detroit.com
Approx. Number Employees: 300
Year Founded: 1941
Business Description:
Professional Basketball Franchise
S.I.C.: 7941
N.A.I.C.S.: 711211
Media: 3-9-10-13-14-15-18-20-22-23-24-25
Distr.: Natl.
Personnel:
Alan Ostfield *(Pres & CEO)*
John O'Reilly *(CFO & Sr VP)*

Key to Media (For complete agency information see *The Advertising Red Books-Agencies* edition):
1. Bus. Publs. 2. Cable T.V. 3. Catalogs & Directories. 4. Co-op Adv. 5. Consumer Mags. 6. D.M. to Bus. Estab.7. D.M. to Consumers 8. Daily Newsp. 9. Exhibits/Trade Shows 10. Foreign 11. Infomercial 12. Internet Adv.13. Multimedia 14. Network Radio 15. Network T.V. 16. Newsp. Distr. Mags. 17. Other 18. Outdoor (Posters, Transit) 19. Point of Purchase20. Premiums, Novelties 21. Product Samples 22. Special Events Mktg. 23. Spot Radio 24. Spot T.V. 25. Weekly Newsp. 26. Yellow Page Adv.

Detroit Pistons Basketball Company — (Continued)

Susan Greenfield *(Gen Counsel)*
Marilyn Hauser *(Exec VP)*
Dan Hauser *(VP-Corp Mktg)*

Brands & Products:
DETROIT PISTONS

Advertising Agency:
OLSON
1625 Hennepin Ave
Minneapolis, MN 55403
Tel.: (612) 215-9800
Fax: (612) 215-9801

DETROIT RED WINGS, INC.

(Sub. of Ilitch Holdings, Inc.)
Joe Louis Arena 600 Civic Ctr Dr
Detroit, MI 48226
Tel.: (313) 396-7000
Fax: (313) 396-7998
E-mail: wingsinfo@detroitredwings.com
Web Site: www.detroitredwings.com
Approx. Number Employees: 1,000
Year Founded: 1926

Business Description:
Professional Hockey Team
S.I.C.: 3949
N.A.I.C.S.: 339920
Advertising Expenditures: $500,000
Media: 9-13-23-24

Personnel:
Michael Ilitch *(Co-Owner & Governor)*
Marian Ilitch *(Co-Owner & Treas/ Sec)*
Robert E. Carr *(Gen Counsel & Alternate Governor)*
Jim Devellano *(Sr VP)*
Ken Holland *(VP & Gen Mgr)*
Jim Nill *(VP & Asst Gen Mgr)*
Paul MacDonald *(VP-Fin)*
John Hahn *(Sr Dir-Comm)*
Mike Bayoff *(Dir-Publ/New Media/ Alumni Relations)*
James Bullo *(Dir-Opers)*
Ryan Martin *(Dir-Hockey Admin)*
Kimberly Reckley *(Dir-Corp Partnership Svcs)*

Brands & Products:
DETROIT RED WINGS CLOTHING

Advertising Agency:
Simons Michelson Zieve, Inc.
900 Wilshire Dr Ste 102
Troy, MI 48084-1634
Tel.: (248) 362-4242
Fax: (248) 362-2014

DETROIT SYMPHONY ORCHESTRA, INC.

3711 Woodward
Detroit, MI 48201
Tel.: (313) 576-5100
Fax: (313) 576-5101
E-mail: info@dso.org
Web Site: www.detroitsymphony.com
Sales Range: $10-24.9 Million
Approx. Number Employees: 250

Business Description:
Symphony Orchestra
S.I.C.: 7929
N.A.I.C.S.: 711130
Media: 8-9-18-20-23-24-25-26

Personnel:
Stanley Frankel *(Chm)*
Patricia Walker *(COO)*
Paul W. Hogle *(Exec VP)*

Brands & Products:
DETROIT SYMPHONY ORCHESTRA
THE MAX
MAX M. FISHER MUSIC CENTER

Advertising Agency:
Solomon Friedman Advertising
40900 Woodward Ave Ste 300
Bloomfield Hills, MI 48304-2256
Tel.: (248) 540-0660
Fax: (248) 540-2124

DETROIT TIGERS BASEBALL CLUB, INC.

(Sub. of Ilitch Holdings, Inc.)
2100 Woodward Ave
Detroit, MI 48201-3474
Tel.: (313) 471-2000
Fax: (313) 471-2010
E-mail: tigers@detroittigers.com
Web Site: www.tigers.mlb.com
Approx. Number Employees: 320
Year Founded: 1901

Business Description:
Professional Baseball Club
S.I.C.: 7941
N.A.I.C.S.: 711211
Media: 3-6-7-8-9-18-23-24-26
Distr.: Natl.
Budget Set: Oct.

Personnel:
David Dombrowski *(Pres, CEO & Gen Mgr)*
Stephen Quinn *(CFO & VP-Fin & Admin)*
Jim Devellano *(Sr VP)*
Duane McLean *(Sr VP-Bus Ops)*
Al Avila *(VP & Asst Gen Mgr)*
Ron Colangelo *(VP-Comm)*
Scot Pett *(VP-Suite Sls & Svcs)*
John Westhoff *(VP & Baseball Legal Counsel)*
Ellen Hill Zeringue *(VP-Mktg)*
Karen Gruca *(Sr Dir-HR)*
Kelli Kollman *(Sr Dir-Fin)*
Eli Bayless *(Dir-Promos & In-Game Entertainment)*
DeAndre Berry *(Dir-Pur & Supplier Diversity)*
Molly Betensley *(Dir-Brdcst)*
Brian Britten *(Dir-Baseball Media Rels)*
Cheryl Evans *(Dir-Minor League & Scouting Admin)*
Jordan Field *(Dir-Detroit Tigers Foundation)*
Steve Fox *(Dir-Ticket Sls)*
Maureen Kraatz *(Dir-Payroll)*
Dwain Lewis *(Dir-Grp Sls)*
Dan Lunetta *(Dir-Minor League Ops)*
Tom Moore *(Dir-Intl Ops)*
Kevin Rand *(Dir-Medical & Head Trainer-Athletic)*
Mike Smith *(Dir-Baseball Ops)*
Ron Wade *(Dir-Mktg)*
Zach Wagner *(Dir-Corp Sls)*
Scott Wruble *(Dir-IT)*
Jeff Lutz *(Asst Dir-Ticket Sls)*
Ed Goward *(Sr Mgr-Park Ops)*
Sam Abrams *(Mgr-Player Relations & Youth Sports Programs)*
Jill Baran *(Mgr-Event & Guest Svcs)*
Allan Carisse *(Mgr-Park Ops)*
Sheila Robine *(Mgr-Acctg)*
Alexandrea Thrubis *(Mgr-Community Affairs)*
Jeremy Hostetter *(Sr Acct Exec)*
Michael Ilitch *(Sr Acct Exec)*
Corey Bell *(Acct Exec-Fundraising Program Liason)*

Brands & Products:
DETROIT TIGERS STADIUM

Advertising Agencies:
MLB Advanced Media, L.P.
75 9th Ave 5th Fl
New York, NY 10011
Tel.: (212) 485-3444
Fax: (212) 485-3456

Simons Michelson Zieve, Inc.
900 Wilshire Dr Ste 102
Troy, MI 48084-1634
Tel.: (248) 362-4242
Fax: (248) 362-2014

DISCOVERY CENTER OF IDAHO

131 Myrtle St
Boise, ID 83702
Tel.: (208) 343-9895
Fax: (208) 343-0105
E-mail: d.lambuth@scidaho.org
Web Site: www.scidaho.org
Approx. Number Employees: 20

Business Description:
Museum
S.I.C.: 8412
N.A.I.C.S.: 712110
Media: 8-9-10-20-23-24-25

Personnel:
Doug Lambuth *(Dir-Mktg)*
Bill Molina *(Dir-Exhibit)*
T. Woody Sobey *(Dir-Education)*

DISCOVERY GATEWAY CHILDREN'S MUSEUM

444 W 100 S
Salt Lake City, UT 84101
Tel.: (801) 456-5437
Tel.: (801) 328-3383
Fax: (801) 456-5440
E-mail: lsmith@discoverygateway.org
Web Site: www.discoverygateway.org
E-Mail For Key Personnel:
Public Relations: sbellomy@childmuseum.org
Approx. Number Employees: 15

Business Description:
Children's Museum Services
S.I.C.: 8412
N.A.I.C.S.: 712110
Media: 5-9-10-20-23-24-25

Personnel:
Joe Gonzales *(Office Mgr)*
Ada Butler *(Mgr-Admin)*

DISNEY THEATRICAL PRODUCTIONS

(Sub. of The Walt Disney Company)
890 Broadway
New York, NY 10036
Tel.: (212) 353-5057
Web Site: disney.go.com/theatre/index.html#/home/
Sales Range: $25-49.9 Million

Business Description:
Theatrical Production
S.I.C.: 7922
N.A.I.C.S.: 711110

Personnel:
Thomas Schumacher *(Pres)*
Andrew Flatt *(VP-Mktg)*

Advertising Agencies:
DeWynters Limited
48 Leicester Sq
London, WC2H 7QD, United Kingdom
Tel.: (44) 20 7321 0488
Fax: (44) 20 7321 0104

DVA Media & Marketing
4515 Van Nuys Blvd Ste 402
Sherman Oaks, CA 91403
Tel.: (818) 995-0050
Fax: (818) 995-0250

Serino Coyne LLC
(Sub. of Omnicom Group Inc.)
1515 Broadway 36th Fl
New York, NY 10036-8901
Tel.: (212) 626-2700
Fax: (212) 626-2799

Starcom MediaVest Group
35 W Wacker Dr
Chicago, IL 60601-1723
Tel.: (312) 220-3535
Fax: (312) 220-6530
Disney Productions
— Ashley Huggett *(Media Assoc-Lego Brand)*
— Grisselle Mojica *(Media Assoc-Disney)*

DISNEYLAND RESORTS

(Div. of Walt Disney Resorts)
1313 S Harbor Blvd
Anaheim, CA 92802-8023
Tel.: (714) 781-4000
Fax: (714) 781-1940
Web Site: www.disney.com
Sales Range: $75-99.9 Million

Business Description:
Vacation Services
S.I.C.: 7389; 7996
N.A.I.C.S.: 541990; 713110
Media: 8-9-13-18-23-24
Distr.: Direct to Consumer; Reg.

Personnel:
George Kalogridis *(Pres)*
Kristin Nolt Wingard *(Exec VP-Public Affairs)*
Claire Bilby *(Sr VP-Sls & Distr Mktg)*
Rob Doughty *(VP-Comm)*
Duncan Wardle *(VP)*

Advertising Agencies:
Mering & Associates
1700 I St Ste 210
Sacramento, CA 95811
Tel.: (916) 441-0571
Fax: (916) 441-1370

Starcom MediaVest Group
35 W Wacker Dr
Chicago, IL 60601-1723
Tel.: (312) 220-3535
Fax: (312) 220-6530

DOVER DOWNS GAMING & ENTERTAINMENT, INC.

1131 N DuPont Hwy
Dover, DE 19901
Tel.: (302) 674-4600
Fax: (302) 857-3253
Toll Free: (800) 711-5882
Web Site: www.doverdowns.com
Approx. Rev.: $238,149,000
Approx. Number Employees: 1,081

Business Description:
Hotel, Casino & Harness Horse Racing Track Operator

Key to Media (For complete agency information see *The Advertising Red Books-Agencies* edition):
1. Bus. Publs. 2. Cable T.V. 3. Catalogs & Directories. 4. Co-op Adv. 5. Consumer Mags. 6. D.M. to Bus. Estab.7. D.M. to Consumers 8. Daily Newsp. 9. Exhibits/Trade Shows 10. Foreign 11. Infomercial 12. Internet Adv.13. Multimedia 14. Network Radio 15. Network T.V. 16. Newsp. Distr. Mags. 17. Other 18. Outdoor (Posters, Transit) 19. Point of Purchase20. Premiums, Novelties 21. Product Samples 22. Special Events Mktg. 23. Spot Radio 24. Spot T.V. 25. Weekly Newsp. 26. Yellow Page Adv.

S.I.C.: 7999; 7011; 7948
N.A.I.C.S.: 713290; 711212; 711219; 721120
Media: 22
Personnel:
Henry B. Tippie *(Chm)*
Edward J. Sutor *(Pres & CEO)*
Timothy R. Horne *(CFO, Treas & Sr VP)*
Klaus M. Belohoubek *(Gen Counsel, Sec & Sr VP)*
Janie Libby *(VP-HR)*
Gloria Hammelef *(Sr Dir-Mktg)*
Ann Stack *(Mgr-Adv)*
Brands & Products:
1 MILLION JACKPOT SLOT
CAPITAL CLUB
CAPITAL GOLD
CAPITAL PLATINUM
COME PLAY!
DOVER DOWNS
DOVER DOWNS RACEWAY
DOVER DOWNS SLOTS
SWEET PERKS TOO

DOVER MOTORSPORTS, INC.
1131 N Dupont Hwy
Dover, DE 19901
Mailing Address:
PO Box 843
Dover, DE 19903
Tel.: (302) 883-6500
Fax: (302) 672-0100
E-mail: info@dovermotorsports.com
Web Site: www.dovermotorsports.com
Approx. Rev.: $62,960,000
Approx. Number Employees: 68
Year Founded: 1966
Business Description:
Promoter of Motorsports Events & Operator of Motorsports Tracks
S.I.C.: 7948; 7999
N.A.I.C.S.: 711212; 713290; 713990
Advertising Expenditures: $2,192,000
Media: 3-8-10-14-15-18-20-22-23-24-26
Personnel:
Henry B. Tippie *(Chm)*
Denis L. McGlynn *(Pres & CEO)*
Klaus M. Belohoubek *(Gen Counsel, Sec & Sr VP)*
Thomas Wintermantel *(Treas & Asst Sec)*
Michael A. Tatoian *(Exec VP)*
Mark Rossi *(VP-Sls & Mktg)*
Monica Weber *(Asst VP-Mktg)*
Gary Camp *(Dir-PR)*
Brands & Products:
DOVER
DOVER INTERNATIONAL SPEEDWAY
DOVER MOTORSPORTS
GATEWAY GUY
GATEWAY INTERNATIONAL RACEWAY
GATEWAY MOTORSPORTS CLUB
GRAND PRIX OF ST PETERSBURG
MEMPHIS MOTORSPORTS PARK
MILES THE MONSTER
MONSTER BRIDGE
MONSTER MILE
THE MOST EXCITING SEAT IN SPORTS!
NASHVILLE SUPERSPEEDWAY
TAKE A KID TO THE RACES
VELOCITY

Advertising Agency:
StarShipley
135 S West St
Wilmington, DE 19801
Tel.: (302) 434-8700
Fax: (302) 434-8701

DREAMS, INC.
2 S University Dr Ste 325
Plantation, FL 33324
Tel.: (954) 377-0002
Fax: (954) 475-8785
Web Site: www.dreamscorp.com
Approx. Rev.: $111,363,000
Approx. Number Employees: 405
Year Founded: 1980
Business Description:
Holding Company; Sports Apparel & Memorabilia Mfr, Distr & Retailer
S.I.C.: 6719; 2389; 5699; 5941; 5947; 5961
N.A.I.C.S.: 551112; 315299; 448190; 451110; 453220; 454111
Advertising Expenditures: $5,806,000
Personnel:
Sam D. Battistone *(Chm)*
Ross Tannenbaum *(Pres & CEO)*
Manoharan Sivashanmugam *(CIO)*
Mitch Adelstein *(Pres-Mfg)*
Kevin Bates *(Pres-Retail)*
David M. Greene *(Sec & Sr VP-Fin & Strategic Plng)*

DUBUQUE SYMPHONY ORCHESTRA
2728 Asbury Rd Ste 900
Dubuque, IA 52001
Tel.: (563) 557-1677
Fax: (563) 557-9841
Toll Free: (866) 803-9280
E-mail: info@dubuquesymphony.org
Web Site: www.dubuquesymphony.org
Approx. Number Employees: 10
Business Description:
Symphony Orchestra Services
S.I.C.: 7929
N.A.I.C.S.: 711130
Media: 9-20-23-24-25

DULUTH SUPERIOR SYMPHONY ORCHESTRA
331 W Superior St Ste 100
Duluth, MN 55802
Tel.: (218) 623-3776
Fax: (218) 623-3789
E-mail: tickets@dsso.com
Web Site: www.dsso.com
Approx. Number Employees: 6
Business Description:
Symphony Orchestra
S.I.C.: 7929
N.A.I.C.S.: 711130
Media: 9-20-23-24-25
Personnel:
Michael Beery *(Dir-Fin)*
Nathan Carlsgaard *(Dir-Ops & Personnel)*
Barb Darland *(Dir-Mktg)*
Markand Thakar *(Dir-Music)*

EAST TEXAS SYMPHONY ORCHESTRA
522 S Broadway Ave Ste 101
Tyler, TX 75702-8111
Tel.: (903) 526-3876
Fax: (903) 592-7649
E-mail: info@etso.org
Web Site: www.etso.org
Approx. Sls.: $500,000
Approx. Number Employees: 4
Year Founded: 1936
Business Description:
Symphony Orchestra
S.I.C.: 7929
N.A.I.C.S.: 711130
Media: 9-20-23-24-25
Personnel:
Robert Mabry *(Chm & Pres)*
Nancy B. Wrenn *(Exec Dir)*
Rise Jones *(Dir-Fin)*

EDMONTON OILERS HOCKEY CLUB
11230 110th St
Edmonton, AB Canada
Tel.: (780) 414-4000
Fax: (780) 409-5890
Toll Free: (866) 414-4625
E-mail: contact@edmontonoilers.com
Web Site: www.edmontonoilers.com
E-Mail For Key Personnel:
Marketing Director: nminckler@edmontonoilers.com
Approx. Number Employees: 80
Year Founded: 1972
Business Description:
Professional Hockey Franchise
S.I.C.: 7941
N.A.I.C.S.: 711211
Media: 7-8-9-13-18-23-24-26
Distr.: Natl.
Personnel:
Cal Nichols *(Chm)*
Patrick LaForge *(Pres & CEO)*
Darryl Boessenkool *(CFO & VP-Fin)*
Kevin Lowe *(Pres-Hockey Ops & Alternate Governor)*
Stew MacDonald *(Exec VP-Commerical Ops)*
Allan Watt *(VP-Comm, Brdcst & Publicity)*
Rick Olczyk *(Asst Gen Mgr, Dir-Hockey Ops & Legal Affairs)*
Natalie Minckler *(Exec Dir)*
Tandy Kustiak *(Dir-HR)*
Brands & Products:
EDMONTON OILERS
ICE SCHOOL
RAISE A READER

EL PASO SYMPHONY ORCHESTRA
PO Box 180
El Paso, TX 79942
Tel.: (915) 532-3776
Fax: (915) 533-8162
E-mail: epsoorg@epso.org
Web Site: www.epso.org
Approx. Number Employees: 5
Business Description:
Symphony Orchestra
S.I.C.: 7929
N.A.I.C.S.: 711130
Media: 7-8-9-13-20-22-23-24-25
Personnel:
Ruth Ellen Jacobson *(Exec Dir)*
Diana de la Torre *(Mgr-Ticket)*
Linda Fischer *(Mgr-Bus Dev)*
Rosemary Flores *(Mgr-Ops)*
Advertising Agency:
Lara & Company
1317 Montana Ave
El Paso, TX 79902-5530
Tel.: (915) 544-9800
Fax: (915) 544-9200

THE EMPIRE SPORTS & ENTERTAINMENT HOLDINGS CO.
(Formerly Excel Global, Inc.)
110 Green St Ste 403
New York, NY 10012
Tel.: (212) 810-6193
Fax: (646) 370-4283
Web Site: www.theempirese.com
Approx. Rev.: $906,639
Approx. Number Employees: 5
Year Founded: 2007
Business Description:
Sports & Music Promoter & Producer
S.I.C.: 7389
N.A.I.C.S.: 711310
Advertising Expenditures: $41,003
Media: 17
Personnel:
Sheldon Finkel *(Co-Chm & CEO)*
Barry Honig *(Co-Chm)*
Adam C. Wasserman *(CFO)*
Peter Levy *(Exec VP)*

EMPIRE STATE BUILDING COMPANY LLC
(Sub. of Empire State Building Associates LLC)
60 E 42nd St 48th Fl
New York, NY 10165-0006
Tel.: (212) 736-3100
Fax: (212) 850-2780
E-mail: info@esbnyc.com
Web Site: www.esbnyc.com
Approx. Rev.: $138,501,100
Approx. Number Employees: 200
Business Description:
Nonresidential Building Operator
S.I.C.: 6512
N.A.I.C.S.: 531120
Import Export
Advertising Expenditures: $792,588
Personnel:
Anthony E. Malkin *(Owner)*
Jon Peahl *(Dir-Sls, ESB Observatory)*
Brands & Products:
EMPIRE STATE BUILDING

ENTERTAINMENT ONE LTD.
175 Bloor St E Ste 1400 N Tower
Toronto, ON M4W 3R8, Canada
Tel.: (905) 624-7337
Fax: (905) 624-7310
E-mail: info@entertainmentone.ca
Web Site: www.entertainmentone.ca
Approx. Rev.: $766,146,458
Approx. Number Employees: 1,104
Business Description:
Retail Entertainment Distr
S.I.C.: 3652
N.A.I.C.S.: 512220
Media: 16-18-19-21-23-24
Personnel:
Darren D. Throop *(CEO)*
Giles Willits *(CFO)*
Patrice Theroux *(Pres-Filmed Entertainment)*
Benedict Carver *(Sr VP-Filmed Entertainment-Los Angeles)*

EQUINOX FITNESS CLUBS
895 Broadway
New York, NY 10003
Tel.: (212) 774-6363
Fax: (212) 777-9510
E-mail: ms@equinox.com

Key to Media (For complete agency information see *The Advertising Red Books-Agencies* edition):
1. Bus. Publs. 2. Cable T.V. 3. Catalogs & Directories. 4. Co-op Adv. 5. Consumer Mags. 6. D.M. to Bus. Estab.7. D.M. to Consumers 8. Daily Newsp. 9. Exhibits/Trade Shows 10. Foreign 11. Infomercial 12. Internet Adv.13. Multimedia 14. Network Radio 15. Network T.V. 16. Newsp. Distr. Mags. 17. Other 18. Outdoor (Posters, Transit) 19. Point of Purchase20. Premiums, Novelties 21. Product Samples 22. Special Events Mktg. 23. Spot Radio 24. Spot T.V. 25. Weekly Newsp. 26. Yellow Page Adv.

Equinox Fitness Clubs — (Continued)

Web Site: www.equinox.com
Year Founded: 1991
Business Description:
Fitness Services
S.I.C.: 7991
N.A.I.C.S.: 713940
Personnel:
Harvey Spevak *(Pres & CEO)*
Larry Segall *(CFO & Exec VP)*
Scott Rosen *(COO)*
Cynthia S. Nicholson *(CMO & Exec VP)*
Bianca Kosoy *(Sr Dir-Creative)*
Advertising Agencies:
Gotham Direct
353 Lexington Ave 14th Fl
New York, NY 10016
Tel.: (212) 279-1474
Fax: (212) 279-1475

iCrossing, Inc.
15169 N Scottsdale Rd Ste C400
Scottsdale, AZ 85254
Tel.: (480) 505-5800
Fax: (480) 505-5801
Toll Free: (866) 620-3780
Digital Media Agency of Record
Display Media Campaigns
Lifestyle Branding
Online Member Acquisition
Paid Search (SEM)

ERIE PHILHARMONIC
609 Walnut St
Erie, PA 16502-1852
Tel.: (814) 455-1375
Fax: (814) 455-1377
E-mail: info@eriephil.org
Web Site: www.eriephil.org
Sales Range: Less than $1 Million
Approx. Number Employees: 10
Business Description:
Symphony Orchestra
S.I.C.: 7929
N.A.I.C.S.: 711130
Media: 7-8-9-13-20-22-23-24-25
Personnel:
Murthy Murthy Deborah *(Pres)*
Russell S. Warner *(Gen Counsel & VP)*
Eric Borenstein *(Exec Dir)*
Karen Beardsley-Petit *(Dir-Mktg & PR)*
Robert Dolwick *(Dir & Conductor)*
Eric Marshall *(Office Mgr & Mgr-Box Office)*

ESSIE COSMETICS, LTD.
19 19 37th St
Astoria, NY 11105
Tel.: (718) 726-5000
Fax: (718) 726-7680
Toll Free: (800) 232-1155
E-mail: info@essie.com
Web Site: www.essie.com
Sales Range: $25-49.9 Million
Approx. Number Employees: 35
Year Founded: 1981
Business Description:
Cosmetics & Fragrances Mfr
S.I.C.: 2844
N.A.I.C.S.: 325620
Advertising Expenditures: $4,000,000
Media: 6-10-13-15-19-22
Personnel:
Essie Weingarten *(Founder & Pres)*
Brands & Products:
BEACH PARTY
BILLIONAILS
CASTAWAY
CLAM BAKE
ESSIE
ESSIESPA
EXPOSURE
MILLIONAILS
MODA
NATURALLY CLEAN
NUDE BEACH
QUICK-E
SHINE-E
TRILLIONAILS
VINYL BIKINI

EVANSTON SYMPHONY ORCHESTRA ASSOCIATION
PO Box 778
Evanston, IL 60204
Tel.: (847) 864-8804
E-mail: esomusic@evanstonsymphony.org
Web Site:
www.evanstonsymphony.org
Business Description:
Symphony Orchestra
S.I.C.: 7929
N.A.I.C.S.: 711130
Media: 9-20-23-24-25
Personnel:
Cheryl Haack *(Pres)*
Lawrence Eckerling *(Dir-Music)*

EVANSVILLE PHILHARMONIC ORCHESTRA CORP.
530 Main St
Evansville, IN 47701
Tel.: (812) 425-5050
Fax: (812) 426-7008
E-mail: evphil@evansvillephilharmonic.org
Web Site:
www.evansvillephilharmonic.org
Approx. Number Employees: 95
Business Description:
Orchestra
S.I.C.: 7929
N.A.I.C.S.: 711190
Media: 9-20-23-24-25
Personnel:
Glenn Roberts *(Exec Dir)*
Kimberly Bredemeier *(Dir-Ops)*
Betsy Heiger *(Dir-Publ)*
Carrie Marrept *(Dir-Mktg)*
Tim Smith *(Mgr-Personnel & Librarian)*

EVERETT SYMPHONY ASSOCIATION
2710 Colby Ave
Everett, WA 98201-3511
Tel.: (425) 258-1605
Fax: (425) 258-1693
E-mail: info@everettsymphony.org
Web Site: www.everettsymphony.org
Approx. Number Employees: 60
Year Founded: 1935
Business Description:
Symphony Orchestra
S.I.C.: 8699; 7929
N.A.I.C.S.: 813990; 711130
Media: 7-8-9-20-23-24-25
Personnel:
Paul-Elliott Cobbs *(Dir-Music)*

EXCEL GLOBAL, INC.
(Name Changed to THE EMPIRE SPORTS & ENTERTAINMENT HOLDINGS CO.)

EXODUS FILM GROUP
1201 Electric Ave
Venice, CA 90291
Tel.: (310) 392-7778
Web Site: www.exodusfilmgroup.com
Approx. Number Employees: 35
Business Description:
Feature Length Film Producer
S.I.C.: 7812
N.A.I.C.S.: 512110
Media: 6-17-18
Personnel:
Max Howard *(Pres)*
Delbert Whetter *(COO)*
Jerome Williams *(Sr VP-Bus Affairs)*

EXPLORA SCIENCE CENTER & CHILDREN'S MUSEUM OF ALBUQUERQUE
1701 Mountain Rd NW
Albuquerque, NM 87104
Tel.: (505) 224-8300
Fax: (505) 224-8325
E-mail: explora@esccma.org
Web Site: www.explora.us
Approx. Number Employees: 80
Business Description:
Children's Museum
S.I.C.: 8412
N.A.I.C.S.: 712110
Media: 8-9-10-20-23-24-25
Personnel:
Patrick Lopez *(Exec Dir)*
Betsy Adamson *(Dir-Exhibits)*
Kristin Leigh *(Dir-Educational Svcs)*
Joan Moulson *(Mgr-Retail)*
Ellen Welker *(Mgr-External Rels)*
Liz Ernst *(Coord-Admissions & Reservations)*
Isabel Gonvales *(Coord-Office)*

FACETS MULTI-MEDIA, INC.
1517 W Fullerton Ave
Chicago, IL 60614-2096
Tel.: (773) 281-9075
Fax: (773) 929-5437
Toll Free: (800) 331-6197
E-mail: sales@facets.org
Web Site: www.facetsdbd.com
E-Mail For Key Personnel:
Sales Director: sales@facets.org
Sales Range: Less than $1 Million
Approx. Number Employees: 50
Year Founded: 1975
Business Description:
Artistic Film Screener & Video Retailer
S.I.C.: 5961
N.A.I.C.S.: 454113
Media: 2-4-7-8-10-13-25
Personnel:
Eric Holst *(Mgr-Ops)*

FAIR GROUNDS CORPORATION
(Sub. of Churchill Downs, Inc.)
1751 Gentilly Blvd
New Orleans, LA 70119
Tel.: (504) 944-5515
Fax: (504) 944-2511
E-mail: webmaster@fgno.com
Web Site: www.fgno.com
E-Mail For Key Personnel:
Marketing Director: lennyv@accesscom.net
Sales Director: groups@accesscom.net
Sales Range: $25-49.9 Million
Approx. Number Employees: 805
Year Founded: 1872
Business Description:
Thoroughbred Horse Racing Tracks Owner & Operator
S.I.C.: 7948
N.A.I.C.S.: 711212
Advertising Expenditures: $500,000
Media: 3-6-9-18-23-24
Distr.: Reg.
Personnel:
Tim Bryant *(Pres & Sr VP)*
Brands & Products:
FAIR GROUNDS RACE COURSE
NEW ORLEANS JAZZ AND HERITAGE FESTIVAL
ROCKIN' HORSE GAME ROOM
Advertising Agency:
Continental Advertising
(House Agency)
1751 Gentilly Blvd.
New Orleans, LA 70119
Tel.: (504) 944-5515
Fax: (504) 944-2511
Fair Grounds & The Finish Line

FAIRBANKS SYMPHONY ASSOCIATION
234 Fine Arts Complex 312 Tanana Dr
Fairbanks, AK 99775
Tel.: (907) 474-5733
Fax: (907) 474-5147
E-mail: symphony@fairbankssymphony.org
Web Site:
www.fairbankssymphony.org
Sales Range: $50-74.9 Million
Approx. Number Employees: 4
Year Founded: 1958
Business Description:
Symphony Orchestra
S.I.C.: 7929
N.A.I.C.S.: 711130
Media: 8-9-20-22-23-24-25
Personnel:
Chuck Lemke *(Pres)*
Laura Bergh *(Exec Dir)*
George Rydlinski *(Dir-Mktg)*
James Spontak *(Librarian)*

FARGO-MOORHEAD SYMPHONY
810 4th Ave S
Moorhead, MN 56560
Tel.: (218) 233-8397
Fax: (218) 236-1845
E-mail: fmsymphony@i29.net
Web Site: www.fmsymphony.org
Sales Range: Less than $1 Million
Approx. Number Employees: 4
Business Description:
Symphony Orchestra
S.I.C.: 7929
N.A.I.C.S.: 711130
Advertising Expenditures: $25,000
Media: 8-9-20-23-24-25-26
Personnel:
Bernard Rubenstein *(Dir-Music)*

FELD ENTERTAINMENT, INC.
8607 Westwood Ctr Dr
Vienna, VA 22182-7506

Key to Media (For complete agency information see *The Advertising Red Books-Agencies* edition):
1. Bus. Publs. 2. Cable T.V. 3. Catalogs & Directories. 4. Co-op Adv. 5. Consumer Mags. 6. D.M. to Bus. Estab.7. D.M. to Consumers
8. Daily Newsp. 9. Exhibits/Trade Shows 10. Foreign 11. Infomercial 12. Internet Adv.13. Multimedia 14. Network Radio
15. Network T.V. 16. Newsp. Distr. Mags. 17. Other 18. Outdoor (Posters, Transit) 19. Point of Purchase20. Premiums, Novelties
21. Product Samples 22. Special Events Mktg. 23. Spot Radio 24. Spot T.V. 25. Weekly Newsp. 26. Yellow Page Adv.

Tel.: (703) 448-4093
Fax: (703) 448-4100
Fax: (703) 448-4156
Toll Free: (888) 435-3939
E-mail: info@feldentertainment.com
Web Site: www.feldentertainment.com
E-Mail For Key Personnel:
Marketing Director: webmarketing@feldinc.com
Sales Range: $1-4.9 Billion
Approx. Number Employees: 2,500
Year Founded: 1967
Business Description:
Circus, Ice Show & Motor Sports Producer & Promoter
S.I.C.: 7929; 7389
N.A.I.C.S.: 711110; 711310; 711320
Media: 3-7-8-9-10-13-18-22-25
Distr.: Intl.
Personnel:
Kenneth Feld *(CEO)*
Neil Gurnsey *(CIO)*
Jerome Sowalsky *(Gen Counsel & Exec VP)*
Alana Feld *(Exec VP)*
Nicole Feld *(Exec VP)*
Graham Burman *(VP-Mdsg)*
Kirk McCoy *(VP-HR)*
Keat Senclaub *(VP-Fin)*
James Chakedis *(Dir-Intl Transportation)*
Brands & Products:
BARNUM'S KALEIDOSCAPE
DISNEY ON ICE
FELD ENTERTAINMENT
GEORGE LUCAS' SUPER LIVE ADVERNTURE
GOOSEBUMPS
GREATEST SHOW ON EARTH
ICE FOLLIES
RINGLING BROS. & BARNUM & BAILEY
Advertising Agencies:
Abrials & Partners
805 King St 2nd Fl
Alexandria, VA 22314
Tel.: (703) 548-2570
Fax: (703) 548-3788

Franco Public Relations Group
400 Renaissance Ctr Ste 1000
Detroit, MI 48243
Tel.: (313) 567-2300
Fax: (313) 567-4486
(Family Entertainment)

Specialized Media Services, Inc.
741 Kenilworth Ave Ste 204
Charlotte, NC 28204
Tel.: (704) 333-3111
Fax: (704) 332-7466

FENDER MUSICAL INSTRUMENTS CORPORATION

8860 E Chaparral Rd Ste 100
Scottsdale, AZ 85250-2618
Tel.: (480) 596-9690
Fax: (480) 596-1384
E-mail: consumerrelations@fender.com
Web Site: www.fender.com
Sales Range: $250-299.9 Million
Approx. Number Employees: 1,800
Year Founded: 1946
Business Description:
Musical Instruments Mfr & Sales
S.I.C.: 3931; 5736
N.A.I.C.S.: 339992; 451140
Import Export
Advertising Expenditures: $4,500,000
Media: 5-6-8-10-13-16-19-20-22
Distr.: Intl.
Budget Set: Sept. -Oct.
Personnel:
Mark Fukunaga *(Co-Chm)*
Michael Lazarus *(Co-Chm)*
Larry Thomas *(CEO)*
Jim Broenen *(CFO)*
Richard McDonald *(Sr VP-Global Mktg)*
Jason Padgett *(VP-PR & Corp Comm)*
Rich Siegle *(Dir-Branding)*
Brands & Products:
ACOUSTASONIC
ACOUSTASONIC STRAT
AMP CAN
BASSMAN
BENEDETTO
BRAND X
BUDDY GUY POLKA DOT STRATOCASTER
BUDDY GUY STRATOCASTER
BULLET
CHAMPION
CHARVEL
CYBER-CHAMP
CYBER-DELUXE
CYBER FOOT CONTROLLER
CYBER-TWIN SE
CYCLONE
CYCLONE HH
CYCLONE II
DELUXE 900
DELUXE ACTIVE JAZZ BASS
DELUXE ACTIVE JAZZ BASS V
DELUXE PLAYERS STRAT
DELUXE STRAT HSS
DELUXE ZONE BASS
DIMENSION BASS
DYNA-TOUCH
ERIC CLAPTON STRATOCASTER
FENDER
FENDER BASSMAN
FRONTMAN AMP
GOLDEN STRATOCASTER
GRETSCH
GUILD
HIGHWAY 1
JACKSON
JAG-STANG
JAGUAR BARITONE CUSTOM
JAMES BURTON TELECASTER
JEFF BECK STRATOCASTER
JIMMIE VAUGHAN TEX-MEX STRAT
JOHN 5 TELECASTER
KXR
LITE ASH STRATOCASTER
LITE ASH TELECASTER
MARK KNOPFLER STRATOCASTER
MUDDY WATERS TELECASTER
NASHVILLE B-BENDER TELE
NASHVILLE TELE
POWERHOUSE STRAT
PRINCETON
ROBERT CRAY STRATOCASTER
RODRIGUEZ
SHOWMASTER
SHOWMASTER FAT HH
SHOWMASTER FAT SSS
SHOWMASTER QBT HH
SHOWMASTER QBT SSS
SQUIER
STAGE 1000
STAGE 1600
STEVIE RAY VAUGHAN STRATOCASTER
STRAT HH
STRAT HSS
STRATOCASTER
STRATOCASTER HARD TAIL
STRATOCASTER LEFT HAND
SWR
TC-90 THINLINE
TELECASTER
TELECASTER ASH
TELECASTER BLACKOUT
TELECASTER CUSTOM
TELECASTER DELUXE
TELECASTER LEFT HAND
TELECASTER THINLINE
TIE-DYE STRATOCASTER
TIME MACHINE
TORONADO
ULTIMATE CHORUS
YNGWIE MALMSTEEN STRATOCASTER
Advertising Agency:
Moses Anshell, Inc.
20 W Jackson St
Phoenix, AZ 85003
Tel.: (602) 254-7312
Fax: (602) 324-1222

THE FIELD MUSEUM

1400 S Lk Shore Dr
Chicago, IL 60605-2496
Tel.: (312) 922-9410
Fax: (312) 665-7932
Toll Free: (800) FIELD54
E-mail: webmaster@fieldmuseum.org
Web Site: www.fieldmuseum.org
Approx. Number Employees: 490
Year Founded: 1893
Business Description:
Natural History Museum
S.I.C.: 8412
N.A.I.C.S.: 712110
Media: 1-2-3-4-6-7-8-9-10-13-15-18-20-22-23-24-25-26
Distr.: Reg.
Budget Set: Aug.
Personnel:
John Bates *(Chm)*
Linda S. Wolf *(Vice Chm-Mktg)*
John W. McCarter, Jr. *(Pres & CEO)*
Joseph Brennan *(Gen Counsel & VP-External Affairs)*
James Croft *(Exec VP)*
Lance Grande *(Sr VP, Head-Collections, Res & Curator)*
Debra Moskovits *(Sr VP-Environment, Culture & Conservation)*
Jennifer Hirsch *(Dir-Res & Ops-Cultural Understanding)*
Laurel Ross *(Dir-Conservation)*
Madeleine Tudor *(Ops Mgr)*
Clinton Nichols *(Mgr-Community Dev)*
James H. Boone *(Mgr-Insects Dept-Zoology)*
Jochen Gerber *(Mgr-Invertebrates Dept-Zoology)*
Thomas Gnoske *(Mgr-Birds Dept-Zoology)*
John Phelps *(Mgr-Mammals Dept-Zoology)*
Alan Resetar *(Mgr-Amphibians)*
Mary Anne Rogers *(Mgr-Fishes Dept-Zoology)*
David Willard *(Mgr-Birds Dept-Zoology)*
Philip Willink *(Mgr-Fishes Dept-Zoology)*
Brands & Products:
THE FIELD MUSEUM
T. REX SUE
Advertising Agencies:
DDB Chicago
200 E Randolph St
Chicago, IL 60601
Tel.: (312) 552-6000
Fax: (312) 552-2370

OMD Chicago
225 N Michigan Ave 19th Fl
Chicago, IL 60601-7757
Tel.: (312) 324-7000
Fax: (312) 324-8201

RPM Advertising
222 S Morgan St
Chicago, IL 60610
Tel.: (312) 455-8600
Fax: (312) 455-8617
Toll Free: (800) 475-2000

FIESTA TEXAS, INC.

(Sub. of Six Flags Theme Parks Inc.)
17000 IH-10 W
San Antonio, TX 78257
Tel.: (210) 697-5000
Fax: (210) 697-5444
Web Site: www.sixflags.com/parks/fiestatexas
Sales Range: $50-74.9 Million
Approx. Number Employees: 200
Year Founded: 1992
Business Description:
Owner & Operator of Theme Parks
S.I.C.: 7996
N.A.I.C.S.: 713110
Media: 3-9-18-19-22-23-24
Personnel:
Martin Bozer *(Pres)*
Sandra Jones *(Dir-Mktg)*
Brands & Products:
SIX FLAGS FIESTA

FINGER LAKES RACING ASSOCIATION INC.

(Sub. of Delaware North Companies, Inc.)
5857 Rte 96
Farmington, NY 14425
Mailing Address:
PO Box 25250
Farmington, NY 14425-0250
Tel.: (585) 924-3232
Fax: (585) 924-3967
E-mail: publicity@fingerlakesracetrack.com
Web Site:
www.fingerlakesracetrack.com
E-Mail For Key Personnel:
Marketing Director: smartin@fingerlakesracetrack.com
Public Relations: smartin@fingerlakesracetrack.com
Approx. Number Employees: 425
Year Founded: 1962
Business Description:
Thoroughbred Race Track
S.I.C.: 7948
N.A.I.C.S.: 711212
Advertising Expenditures: $334,000
D.M. to Consumers: $38,000; Daily Newsp.: $120,000; Exhibits/Trade Shows: $6,000; Premiums, Novelties: $15,000; Spot Radio: $110,000; Spot T.V.: $45,000
Distr.: Reg.

Key to Media (For complete agency information see *The Advertising Red Books-Agencies* edition):
1. Bus. Publs. 2. Cable T.V. 3. Catalogs & Directories. 4. Co-op Adv. 5. Consumer Mags. 6. D.M. to Bus. Estab.7. D.M. to Consumers
8. Daily Newsp. 9. Exhibits/Trade Shows 10. Foreign 11. Infomercial 12. Internet Adv.13. Multimedia 14. Network Radio
15. Network T.V. 16. Newsp. Distr. Mags. 17. Other 18. Outdoor (Posters, Transit) 19. Point of Purchase20. Premiums, Novelties
21. Product Samples 22. Special Events Mktg. 23. Spot Radio 24. Spot T.V. 25. Weekly Newsp. 26. Yellow Page Adv.

Finger Lakes Racing Association Inc. — (Continued)

Budget Set: Jan.
Personnel:
Chris Riegle *(Pres & Gen Mgr)*
Steven Martin *(Dir-Mktg & Gaming)*
Brands & Products:
YOU BET IT'S FUN

FLAGSTAFF SYMPHONY ASSOCIATION

113 E Aspen Ave Ste A
Flagstaff, AZ 86001
Tel.: (928) 774-5107
Fax: (928) 774-5109
E-mail: info@flagstaffsymphony.org
Web Site: www.flagstaffsymphony.org
Approx. Number Employees: 5
Business Description:
Symphony Orchestra
S.I.C.: 7929
N.A.I.C.S.: 711130
Advertising Expenditures: $35,000
Media: 9-18-20-23-24-25

FLAMINGO-LAUGHLIN, INC.

(Holding of Icahn Enterprises L.P.)
1900 S Casino Dr
Laughlin, NV 89029
Tel.: (702) 298-5111
Fax: (702) 298-5182
Web Site: www.caesars.com/flamingo/laughlin
Sales Range: $350-399.9 Million
Approx. Number Employees: 1,800
Business Description:
Hotel & Casino
S.I.C.: 7999; 7011
N.A.I.C.S.: 721120; 611620; 713990; 721110; 721199
Media: 8-9-13-20-22-23-24-25

FLORIDA GAMING CORPORATION

3500 NW 37th Ave
Miami, FL 33142-4923
Tel.: (305) 633-6400
Fax: (305) 634-1712
E-mail: miajaili@bellsouth.net
Web Site: www.fla-gaming.com
Approx. Rev.: $9,323,417
Approx. Number Employees: 86
Year Founded: 1976
Business Description:
Gaming Venues Operator
S.I.C.: 7999
N.A.I.C.S.: 713990; 713290
Advertising Expenditures: $213,293
Media: 2-3-7-8-9-18-19-20-22-23-24-25
Distr.: Natl.
Personnel:
W. Bennett Collett *(Chm & CEO)*
W. Bennett Collett Jr. *(Pres & COO)*
Brands & Products:
FT.PIERCE JAI-ALAI
MIAMI JAI-ALAI
Advertising Agency:
Idea Garden Advertising, Inc.
865 16th Pl
Vero Beach, FL 32960
Tel.: (772) 778-2832

FLORIDA HOLOCAUST MUSEUM, INC.

55 5th St S
Saint Petersburg, FL 33701
Tel.: (727) 820-0100
Fax: (727) 821-8435
Toll Free: (800) 960-7448
E-mail: admin@flholocaustmuseum.org
Web Site: www.flholocaustmuseum.org
Approx. Sls.: $2,403,000
Approx. Number Employees: 50
Year Founded: 1990
Business Description:
Holocaust History Museum
S.I.C.: 8412
N.A.I.C.S.: 712110
Media: 3-6-9-10-18-20-23-24-25

FLORIDA INTERNATIONAL MUSEUM AT ST. PETERSBURG COLLEGE

244 2nd Ave N
Saint Petersburg, FL 33701
Tel.: (727) 341-7900
Fax: (727) 341-7908
Web Site: www.spcollege.edu/fimuseum/index.html
Approx. Number Employees: 20
Year Founded: 1995
Business Description:
Museum
S.I.C.: 8412
N.A.I.C.S.: 712110
Media: 3-6-9-10-18-20-23-24-25
Personnel:
David R. Punzak *(Chm)*
William B. Hoyt *(Associate VP)*
Diana Dillon *(Controller)*
Kathy Oathout *(Exec Dir)*
Windy Crowder *(Dir-Volunteers)*
Christine Kathan *(Dir-Education)*
Advertising Agency:
The Carter Group
551 3rd Ave S
Saint Petersburg, FL 33701
Tel.: (727) 898-3008
— Bob Carter *(Principal)*

FLORIDA MARLINS, L.P.

Sun Life Stadium 2267 Dan Marino Blvd
Miami, FL 33056
Tel.: (305) 626-7400
Fax: (305) 626-7428
E-mail: ticketsales@marlins.com
Web Site: www.marlins.com
Approx. Rev.: $76,000,000
Approx. Number Employees: 135
Year Founded: 1993
Business Description:
Professional Baseball Club
S.I.C.: 7941
N.A.I.C.S.: 711211
Media: 8-18-20-22-23-24
Distr.: Reg.
Budget Set: Nov.
Personnel:
Jeffrey H. Loria *(Owner & CEO)*
Joel A. Mael *(Vice Chm)*
David P. Samson *(Pres)*
Michel Bussiere *(CFO & Exec VP)*
Larry Beinfest *(Pres-Baseball Ops)*
Derek Jackson *(Gen Counsel)*
Claude Delorme *(Sr VP-Stadium Dev)*
Sean Flynn *(Sr VP-Mktg)*
Susan Jaison *(Sr VP-Fin)*
P. J. Loyello *(Sr VP)*
Michael Hill *(VP & Gen Mgr)*
Jim Fleming *(VP-Player Dev/Scouting & Asst Gen Mgr)*
Dan Jennings *(VP-Player Personnel & Asst Gen Mgr)*
Brendan Cunningham *(VP-Sls)*
Bill Beck *(Sr Dir-Team Travel)*
Ana Hernandez *(Sr Dir-HR)*
Larry Blocker *(Dir-Game Presentaion & Events)*
Brian Chattin *(Dir-Player Dev)*
J. David Enriquez *(Dir-IT)*
Albert Gonzalez *(Dir-Intl Ops)*
Alfred Hernandez *(Dir-Creative Svcs)*
Spencer Linden *(Dir-Ticket Ops)*
William Makris *(Dir-Ticket Sls)*
Juan Martinez *(Dir-Multicultural Mktg)*
Stan Meek *(Dir-Scouting)*
Matthew Roebuck *(Dir-Media Rels)*
Angela Smith *(Dir-Community Outreach)*
Anthony Tome *(Dir-Corp Sls)*
Gregg Leonard *(Asst Dir-Scouting)*
David Kuan *(Mgr-Tech Support)*
Sam Mora *(Mgr-Telecom)*
Marty Sewell *(Mgr-Media Rels)*
John Silverman *(Mgr-Equipment)*
Robert Vigon *(Mgr-Creative Svcs Photography)*
Brands & Products:
MARLINS
Advertising Agencies:
MLB Advanced Media, L.P.
75 9th Ave 5th Fl
New York, NY 10011
Tel.: (212) 485-3444
Fax: (212) 485-3456

Zimmerman Advertising
2200 W Commercial Blvd Ste 300
Fort Lauderdale, FL 33309-3064
Tel.: (954) 644-4000
Fax: (954) 731-2977
Toll Free: (800) 248-8522

THE FLORIDA ORCHESTRA

244 Second Ave N Stw 420
Saint Petersburg, FL 33701
Tel.: (813) 286-1170
Fax: (737) 892-3338
E-mail: admin@floridaorchestra.org
Web Site: www.floridaorchestra.org
Approx. Number Employees: 90
Business Description:
Orchestral Music
S.I.C.: 7929
N.A.I.C.S.: 711130
Media: 6-8-9-13-18-23-24-25
Personnel:
Thomas Sarquhar *(Chm)*
Sherry Powell *(Dir-Mktg & Comm)*
Art Molinaro *(Dir-Tech & Sr Mgr-Stage)*
Stefan Sanderling *(Dir-Music)*
Henry Adams *(Assoc Dir-Mktg & Comm)*
William Abbey *(Mgr-Grp Svcs)*
Deanna Fulgoni-Johnston *(Mgr-Artisitic Admin & Logistics)*
Carrie Olin *(Mgr-Mktg & Comm)*

FLORIDA PANTHERS HOCKEY CLUB, LTD.

(Sub. of Sunrise Sports & Entertainment)
One Panther Pkwy
Sunrise, FL 33323-5315
Tel.: (954) 835-7000
Fax: (954) 835-7200
E-mail: jobs@floridapanthers.com
Web Site: www.floridapanthers.com
Approx. Number Employees: 80
Year Founded: 1993
Business Description:
Professional Hockey Team
S.I.C.: 7941; 7991
N.A.I.C.S.: 711211; 713940
Media: 9-13-18-19-23-24
Personnel:
Alan Cohen *(Chm, CEO & Gen Partner)*
Michael Yormark *(Pres & COO)*
Dennis Docil *(Dir-Arena Experience)*
Evelyn Lopez *(CFO)*
Pedro Goncalves *(Sr VP-Bus Rels & Strategic Partnerships)*
Chad Johnson *(Sr VP-Sls & Mktg)*
Carol Duncanson *(VP-HR)*
Steve Ziff *(Sr Dir-Brand Activation)*
Justin Copertino *(Mgr-Comm)*
Brands & Products:
FLORIDA PANTHERS
Advertising Agencies:
Lipof Advertising
830 Peters Rd Ste D100
Plantation, FL 33324
Tel.: (954) 472-9999
Fax: (954) 472-1222

Zimmerman Advertising
2200 W Commercial Blvd Ste 300
Fort Lauderdale, FL 33309-3064
Tel.: (954) 644-4000
Fax: (954) 731-2977
Toll Free: (800) 248-8522

FLORIDA STATE FAIR AUTHORITY

4800 US Hwy 301 N
Tampa, FL 33610
Tel.: (813) 621-7821
Fax: (813) 740-3505
Web Site: www.floridastatefair.com
Approx. Number Employees: 65
Business Description:
Amusement Services
S.I.C.: 7996
N.A.I.C.S.: 713110
Media: 3-5-9-18-22-23-25
Personnel:
Charles C. Pesano *(Exec Dir)*
Fred Brown *(Dir-Ops)*
Dennis McDermott *(Dir-Event Svcs)*
Jeff Shreaves *(Dir-IT)*
Bruce Scheuerman *(Mgr-Fin & Billing)*
Phyllis Bridges *(Mgr-Pur)*
Bill Bullock *(Mgr-Facilities Opers & Safety)*
Joyce Covington *(Mgr-Special Events)*
Advertising Agencies:
HarmonTampa, Inc.
405 S Dale Mabry Hwy Ste 138
Tampa, FL 33609-2244
Tel.: (813) 288-6909
Fax: (813) 489-2581
Toll Free: (800) 952-0068

Nuevo Advertising Group, Inc.
677 N Washington Blvd
Sarasota, FL 34236
Tel.: (941) 752-4433
Fax: (941) 752-1114

FORD'S THEATRE SOCIETY INC.

511 10th St NW
Washington, DC 20004
Tel.: (202) 638-2941

Key to Media (For complete agency information see *The Advertising Red Books-Agencies* edition):
1. Bus. Publs. 2. Cable T.V. 3. Catalogs & Directories. 4. Co-op Adv. 5. Consumer Mags. 6. D.M. to Bus. Estab.7. D.M. to Consumers
8. Daily Newsp. 9. Exhibits/Trade Shows 10. Foreign 11. Infomercial 12. Internet Adv.13. Multimedia 14. Network Radio
15. Network T.V. 16. Newsp. Distr. Mags. 17. Other 18. Outdoor (Posters, Transit) 19. Point of Purchase20. Premiums, Novelties
21. Product Samples 22. Special Events Mktg. 23. Spot Radio 24. Spot T.V. 25. Weekly Newsp. 26. Yellow Page Adv.

Fax: (202) 347-3858
E-mail: onstage@fordstheatre.org
Web Site: www.fords.org
Approx. Rev.: $9,000,000
Approx. Number Employees: 25
Business Description:
Producer of Theatrical Plays
S.I.C.: 7922
N.A.I.C.S.: 711110
Media: 9-10-13-18-20-22-23-24-25
Personnel:
Steve Hudgins *(Dir-Technical)*
Liza Lorenz *(Dir-Comm & Mktg)*
Paul Tetreault *(Dir-Producing)*
Jennifer Kiefer *(Assoc Dir-Devel)*
Ken Wright *(Office Mgr)*
Advertising Agency:
CDR Fundraising Group
16900 Science Dr Ste 210
Bowie, MD 20715
Tel.: (301) 858-1500
Fax: (301) 858-0107

FORT WAYNE PHILHARMONIC ORCHESTRA

4901 Fuller Dr
Fort Wayne, IN 46835
Tel.: (260) 481-0770
Fax: (260) 481-0769
Toll Free: (888) 402-2224
E-mail: info@fwphil.org
Web Site: www.fwphil.ogr
Sales Range: $10-24.9 Million
Approx. Number Employees: 25
Year Founded: 1944
Business Description:
Symphony Orchestra
S.I.C.: 7929
N.A.I.C.S.: 711130
Media: 7-8-9-20-22-23-24-25
Personnel:
Christy Sandmeyer *(Vice Chm-Dev)*
J. L. Nave, III *(Pres & CEO)*
Matt Kelley *(Dir)*
Gregory Stieber *(Mgr-Artistic Production)*
Ryan Trinkofsky *(Mgr-Stage)*

FORT WORTH SYMPHONY ASSOCIATION

330 E 4th St Ste 200
Fort Worth, TX 76102
Tel.: (817) 665-6500
Fax: (817) 665-6600
E-mail: administration@fwsymphony.org
Web Site: www.fwsymphony.org
Approx. Number Employees: 20
Business Description:
Symphony Orchestra
S.I.C.: 7922
N.A.I.C.S.: 711110
Media: 9-18-20-23-24-25
Personnel:
Ann Koonsman *(Pres)*
Melinda Hayden *(CFO & VP-Fin)*
Amy Adkins *(Pres-Elect)*
David Hadlock *(VP-Mktg)*
Ryan Bonifas *(Mgr-Production)*
Trish Ciaravino *(Mgr)*
Kimberly Denena *(Mgr-Fin)*
Scott Griffitts *(Mgr-Info Svcs)*
Andrea Helm *(Mgr-Patron Dev)*
Chris Munoz *(Mgr-Ops)*
Kristen Stevenson *(Mgr-Ticket Svcs)*
Brenda J. Tullos *(Mgr-Orchestra Personnel)*

FOX ASSOCIATES, LLC

(d/b/a Fox Theatre)
527 N Grand Blvd
Saint Louis, MO 63103
Tel.: (314) 534-1678
Fax: (314) 534-8415
E-mail: webmaster@fabulousfox.com
Web Site: www.fabulousfox.com
Approx. Number Employees: 40
Business Description:
Entertainers & Entertainment Groups
S.I.C.: 7389
N.A.I.C.S.: 711320
Media: 9-20-22-23-24-25
Personnel:
Richard Baker *(Pres)*
Jana Scharnhorst *(VP-Mktg)*

FOX VALLEY SYMPHONY ASSOCIATION INC.

111 W College Ave Ste 550
Appleton, WI 54911-5706
Tel.: (920) 968-0300
Fax: (920) 968-0303
E-mail: info@foxvalleysymphony.com
Web Site:
www.foxvalleysymphony.com
Approx. Number Employees: 50
Business Description:
Symphony Orchestra
S.I.C.: 7389
N.A.I.C.S.: 711320
Media: 9-20-23-25
Personnel:
William Harke *(VP-Mktg)*
Marta Weldon *(Exec Dir)*
Brian Groner *(Dir-Music)*
Kim Hughes *(Mgr-Annual Fund)*
Brian Sas *(Mgr-Box Office)*

FOXWOODS RESORT CASINO

(Sub. of Mashantucket Pequot Gaming Enterprise Inc.)
39 Norwich Westerly Rd
Ledyard, CT 06338
Mailing Address:
Rt 2 PO Box 3777
Mashantucket, CT 06338
Tel.: (860) 312-3000
Fax: (860) 396-3599
Toll Free: (800) FOXWOODS
E-mail: information@foxwoods.com
Web Site: www.foxwoods.com
Sales Range: $75-99.9 Million
Approx. Number Employees: 15,000
Business Description:
Casino
S.I.C.: 7011
N.A.I.C.S.: 721120
Media: 3-6-13-14-15-16-18-22-23-24-25
Personnel:
Scott Butera *(Pres & CEO)*
Todd Greenberg *(COO)*
Barry Cregan *(Sr VP-Dev)*
Tara Gregson *(VP-Brand Strategy)*
Brands & Products:
FOXWOODS
Advertising Agencies:
Dolabany Communications Group
57 Providence Hwy
Norwood, MA 02062
Tel.: (781) 769-6800
Fax: (781) 769-8228

Horizon Media, Inc.
75 Varick St
New York, NY 10013
Tel.: (212) 220-5000
Toll Free: (800) 633-4201
MGM Grand at Foxwoods

Mullen
40 Broad St
Boston, MA 02109
Tel.: (617) 226-9000
Fax: (617) 226-9100

Zeta Interactive
99 Pk Ave 23rd Fl
New York, NY 10016
Tel.: (646) 834-9400
Fax: (646) 834-9390

THE FRANKLIN INSTITUTE

222 N 20th St
Philadelphia, PA 19103-1115
Tel.: (215) 448-1200
Fax: (215) 448-1235
E-mail: webteam@fi.edu
Web Site: www.fi.edu
E-Mail For Key Personnel:
President: dwint@fi.edu
Public Relations: jeffg@fi.edu
Approx. Number Employees: 150
Year Founded: 1824
Business Description:
Hands-On Science Museum & Benjamin Franklin National Memorial; International Awards for Science & Technology; Educational Web-Site; Local & National Science Education Progams
S.I.C.: 8412; 8299
N.A.I.C.S.: 712110; 611699
Advertising Expenditures: $500,000
Media: 2-3-7-8-9-10-18-19-20-22-23-24-25-26
Distr.: Reg.
Personnel:
Dennis M. Wint *(Pres & CEO)*
Karen Corbin *(Sr VP-Programs, Mktg & Bus Dev)*
Carol A. Parssinen *(Sr VP-Innovation Ctr)*
Reid L. Styles *(VP-HR)*
Hillary Olson *(Dir-Integrated Programming)*
Kat Stein *(Dir-PR & Comm)*
Stefanie Cerulli *(Commun Mgr)*
Advertising Agency:
The Archer Group
233 N King St
Wilmington, DE 19801
Tel.: (302) 429-9120
Fax: (302) 429-8720
Sci-Store Online

FREMONT SYMPHONY ORCHESTRA

PO Box 104
Fremont, CA 94537
Tel.: (510) 794-1659
Fax: (510) 794-1658
Web Site: www.fremontsymphony.org
Approx. Number Employees: 75
Year Founded: 1964
Business Description:
Symphony Orchestra
S.I.C.: 7929
N.A.I.C.S.: 711130
Media: 8-9-18-20-23-24-25
Personnel:
Susan L. Rose *(Gen Mgr)*
Ann Millican *(Dir-Dev)*
David Sloss *(Dir-Music)*
Carole Klein *(Mgr-Personnel)*
Laurien Jones *(Librarian)*

GAME SHOW PLACEMENTS LTD.

7011 Willoughby Ave
Los Angeles, CA 90038-2332
Tel.: (323) 874-7818
Fax: (323) 874-0643
E-mail: gsp@ix.netcom.com
Web Site: www.gspltd.com
Approx. Number Employees: 3
Year Founded: 1970
Business Description:
Promotional Product Placement Services on Gameshows
S.I.C.: 8742; 7311
N.A.I.C.S.: 541613; 541810
Advertising Expenditures: $250,000
Media: 2-7-17-20-22
Distr.: Natl.
Budget Set: Jan.
Personnel:
Benjamin D. Robertson *(Pres)*
Samuel Robertson *(CEO)*
Advertising Agency:
The Robertson Co./GSP Ltd.
7011 Willoughby Ave
Los Angeles, CA 90038-2332
Tel.: (323) 874-7867
Tel.: (323) 874-7818
Fax: (323) 874-0643

GARDEN STATE PHILHARMONIC

1 College Dr Po BOX 2001
Toms River, NJ 08754
Tel.: (732) 255-0460
Fax: (732) 255-0478
E-mail: gspmusic@earthlink.net
Web Site:
www.gardenstatephilharmonic.org
Business Description:
Symphony Orchestra
S.I.C.: 7929
N.A.I.C.S.: 711130
Media: 9-20-23-24-25
Personnel:
Anthony LaGruth *(Dir-Artistic)*

GEAUGA LAKE & WILDWATER KINGDOM

(Sub. of Cedar Fair, L.P.)
1100 Squires Rd
Aurora, OH 44202-8749
Tel.: (330) 562-8303
Web Site: www.wildwaterfun.com
Sales Range: $50-74.9 Million
Approx. Number Employees: 220
Year Founded: 1970
Business Description:
Amusement Park, Arcade & Attractions
S.I.C.: 7996
N.A.I.C.S.: 713110
Media: 8-15-18
Distr.: Direct to Consumer; Reg.

GENERAL SPORTS & ENTERTAINMENT, LLC

400 Water St Ste 250
Rochester, MI 48307
Tel.: (248) 601-2200
Fax: (248) 601-2400
Web Site: www.generalsports.com
E-Mail For Key Personnel:
President: aappleby@generalsports.com
Approx. Number Employees: 95

General Sports & Entertainment, LLC — (Continued)

Business Description:
Sports & Entertainment Services
S.I.C.: 7941
N.A.I.C.S.: 711211
Media: 1-3-9-13-18-23-24
Personnel:
Andrew D. Appleby *(Chm & CEO-Gen)*

GIBSON GUITAR CORP.
(d/b/a Gibson Musical Instruments)
309 Plus Pk Blvd
Nashville, TN 37217
Tel.: (615) 871-4500
Fax: (615) 889-5509
Toll Free: (800) 444-2766
E-mail: relations@gibson.com
Web Site: www.gibson.com
Sales Range: $250-299.9 Million
Approx. Number Employees: 3,000
Year Founded: 1894
Business Description:
Musical Instruments & Accessories Mfr & Marketer
S.I.C.: 3931; 5736
N.A.I.C.S.: 339992; 451140
Media: 22
Personnel:
Henry Juszkiewicz *(Chm & CEO)*
David H. Berryman *(Pres)*
Keith Brawley *(Pres-North America)*
Cory Moore *(Dir-Mktg)*
Brands & Products:
'57 CLASSIC
ACCU-VOICE
AEOLIAN
AJ
AMERICANA
AVANTE
BALDWIN
BANJOS
BASS
BLUES HAWK
BUMBLE BEE
BURSTBUCKER
CHET ATKINS
CHICKERING
CLASSIC MODE
CUSTOM DIRECT
CUSTOM L-5
DOBRO
DOUBLE BALL
DOVE
DRUMMER
DUAL-RAIL
DV DEMON
EAR PLUG
ECHOPLEX
EL CAPITAN
ELECTAR
EPIPHONE
EPOCH
ES
EXPLORER
FADED
FLATIRON
FV
GIBSON
GIBSON PURE
GOLDTONE
HAMILTON
HAWK
THE HOME DIGITAL JUKEBOX
HOWARD
HUMMINGBIRD
J-45
J-50
KRAMER
LEGRAND
LES PAUL
LPX
MAESTRO
MANDOLINS
MASTERBILT
MO' BABY
MODERNE
MUSICSHOP
MUSICYO GEAR
MUSICYO.COM
NIGHTHAWK
OB-MX
OBERHEIM
OBL
ORIGINAL HOUND DOG
ORVILLE
PURE
QUAD-RAIL
RADIO KING
ROCK HIS WORLD
SAVANT
SHADOW
SIGNATURE
SJ
SLINGERLAND
SPIRIT
STEINBERGER
STUDIO KING
SWINGMASTER
TALENT
TOBIAS
V-FACTOR
VALLEY ARTS
VICTORY
VINTAGE RE-ISSUE
VOODOO
WES MONTGOMERY
WURLITZER
X-FACTOR
X-PLORER

GLENS FALLS SYMPHONY ORCHESTRA, INC.
PO Box 2036
Glens Falls, NY 12801-2036
Tel.: (518) 793-1348
Fax: (518) 798-9122
E-mail: info@gfso.org
Web Site: www.gfso.org
E-Mail For Key Personnel:
President: pres@glensfallssymphony.org
Approx. Number Employees: 2
Business Description:
Symphony Orchestra Services
S.I.C.: 7929
N.A.I.C.S.: 711130
Media: 9-20-23-24-25
Personnel:
Robert B. Rosoff *(Exec Dir)*
Charles Peltz *(Dir-Music)*

GODWIN'S GATORLAND, INC.
14501 S Orange Blossom Trl
Orlando, FL 32837
Tel.: (407) 855-5496
Fax: (407) 855-3381
Toll Free: (800) 393-JAWS
E-mail: customerservice@gatorland.com
Web Site: www.gatorland.com
Approx. Number Employees: 90
Year Founded: 1949
Business Description:
Theme Park
S.I.C.: 7996; 7999
N.A.I.C.S.: 713110; 712190
Media: 6-10-13-19
Personnel:
Mark McHugh *(Pres & CEO)*
Michelle Harris *(Mgr-Mktg)*
Brands & Products:
ALLIGATOR CAPITAL OF THE WORLD
GATORLAND

GOLDEN NUGGET HOTEL
(Sub. of Landry's Restaurants Inc.)
129 E Fremont St
Las Vegas, NV 89101-5603
Tel.: (702) 385-7111
Fax: (702) 382-9092
Toll Free: (800) 846-5336
E-mail: info@goldennugget.com
Web Site: www.goldennugget.com
Sales Range: $50-74.9 Million
Approx. Number Employees: 3,145
Business Description:
Hotel & Casino Operator
S.I.C.: 7011; 5812
N.A.I.C.S.: 721120; 722110
Advertising Expenditures: $940,000
Personnel:
Brett Kellerman *(COO)*
William Sylvester *(Sr VP-Fin)*
Amy Chasey *(VP-Mktg)*

GOLDEN STATE WARRIORS, LLC
1011 Broadway
Oakland, CA 94607-4019
Tel.: (510) 986-2200
Fax: (510) 452-0132
Web Site: www.nba.com
Approx. Number Employees: 100
Year Founded: 1946
Business Description:
Professional Basketball Team
S.I.C.: 7941
N.A.I.C.S.: 711211
Media: 9-13-18-20-22-23-24-25
Personnel:
Rick Welts *(Pres & COO)*
Larry Riley *(Exec VP & Gen Mgr)*
Travis Stanley *(Exec VP-Team Mktg)*
Xavier Cobos *(Mgr-Partnership Dev)*
Brands & Products:
GOLDEN STATE WARRIORS

GOLD'S GYM INTERNATIONAL INC.
(Sub. of TRT Holdings Inc.)
Ste 1300 125 E John Carpenter Fwy
Irving, TX 75062-2366
Tel.: (214) 574-4653
Fax: (214) 296-5000
Toll Free: (800) 457-5375
E-mail: info@goldsgym.com
Web Site: www.goldsgym.com
Approx. Sls.: $25,989,000
Approx. Number Employees: 100
Business Description:
Fitness Center Owner, Operator & Franchisor
S.I.C.: 7991
N.A.I.C.S.: 713940
Personnel:
Lisa Zoellner *(CMO)*
Keith Albright *(Sr VP-Franchising)*
Joel Tallman *(Sr VP-Franchising & Global Ops)*
Cody Pierce *(Dir-Franchise Mktg)*
Dave Reiseman *(Dir-Comm)*
Advertising Agencies:
Camelot Communications, Inc.
8140 Walnut Hill Ln Ste 700
Dallas, TX 75231
Tel.: (214) 373-6999
Fax: (214) 373-6854

McKinney
(d/b/a McKinney Silver)
318 Blackwell St
Durham, NC 27701
Tel.: (919) 313-0802
Fax: (919) 313-0805

The MWW Group
1 Meadowlands Plz 6th Fl
East Rutherford, NJ 07073
Tel.: (201) 507-9500
Fax: (201) 507-0092
(Consumer Awareness)

Riester
802 N 3rd Ave
Phoenix, AZ 85003
Tel.: (602) 462-2200
Fax: (602) 307-5811

GRAND RAPIDS SYMPHONY SOCIETY
300 Ottawa Ave NW Ste 100
Grand Rapids, MI 49503
Tel.: (616) 454-9451
Fax: (616) 454-7477
E-mail: info@grsymphony.org
Web Site: www.grsymphony.org
Approx. Number Employees: 100
Year Founded: 1930
Business Description:
Symphony Orchestra
S.I.C.: 7929
N.A.I.C.S.: 711130
Media: 9-20-23-24-25
Personnel:
James Keane *(Vice Chm)*
Stephanie L. Leonardos *(Vice Chm)*
Roger D. Nelson *(VP & Gen Mgr-Ops)*
Daniel S. Jonkman *(VP-HR & Fin)*
Karen L. Mueller *(VP-Mktg & PR)*
David Lockington *(Dir-Music)*
Kathy Rohlman *(Dir-Ops)*
Celeste Stefaneck Dyehouse *(Dir-Ticketing Ops)*
Claire Van Brandeghen *(Dir-Education)*
Nathan Parnell *(Office Mgr & Receptionist)*

GREAT AMERICA
(Sub. of Cedar Fair, L.P.)
2401 Agnew Rd
Santa Clara, CA 95054-1201
Mailing Address:
PO Box 1776
Santa Clara, CA 95052-1776
Tel.: (408) 988-1776
Fax: (408) 986-5863
Web Site: www.cagreatamerica.com
Sales Range: $25-49.9 Million
Approx. Number Employees: 150
Year Founded: 1976
Business Description:
Amusement Park Services
S.I.C.: 7996
N.A.I.C.S.: 713110

Key to Media (For complete agency information see *The Advertising Red Books-Agencies* edition):
1. Bus. Publs. 2. Cable T.V. 3. Catalogs & Directories. 4. Co-op Adv. 5. Consumer Mags. 6. D.M. to Bus. Estab.7. D.M. to Consumers
8. Daily Newsp. 9. Exhibits/Trade Shows 10. Foreign 11. Infomercial 12. Internet Adv.13. Multimedia 14. Network Radio
15. Network T.V. 16. Newsp. Distr. Mags. 17. Other 18. Outdoor (Posters, Transit) 19. Point of Purchase20. Premiums, Novelties
21. Product Samples 22. Special Events Mktg. 23. Spot Radio 24. Spot T.V. 25. Weekly Newsp. 26. Yellow Page Adv.

Media: 2-3-5-6-7-8-9-10-13-19-22-23-24-25-26
Distr.: Direct to Consumer
Budget Set: Aug.
Personnel:
Raul Rehndorg *(Gen Mgr)*
Jim Stellmack *(Dir)*

GREAT EXPLORATIONS, INC.
1925 4th St N
Saint Petersburg, FL 33704
Tel.: (727) 821-8992
Fax: (727) 823-7287
E-mail: mail@greatexplorations.org
Web Site: www.greatexplorations.org
Approx. Number Employees: 32
Business Description:
Hands-On Children's Museum
S.I.C.: 8412
N.A.I.C.S.: 712110
Media: 9-10-20-23-24-25
Personnel:
Colleen Terry *(Dir-Mktg)*

GREEN BAY PACKERS, INC.
1265 Lombardi Ave
Green Bay, WI 54304-3927
Tel.: (920) 569-7500
Fax: (920) 569-7301
Web Site: www.packers.com
Sales Range: $150-199.9 Million
Approx. Number Employees: 500
Year Founded: 1919
Business Description:
Professional Football Franchise
S.I.C.: 7941
N.A.I.C.S.: 711211
Media: 3-8-9-13-15-18-19-20-22-23-24-25
Personnel:
Mark H. Murphy *(Pres & CEO)*
Ted Thompson *(Exec VP, Gen Mgr & Dir-Football Ops)*
Jennifer Ark *(Dir-Premium Sls & Guest Svcs)*
Craig Benzel *(Dir-Mktg & Corp Sls)*
Doug Collins *(Dir-Corporate Security & Risk Mgmt)*
Rob Davis *(Dir-Player Dev)*
John Dorsey *(Dir-College Scouting)*
Mike Eayrs *(Dir-R&D)*
Bob Eckberg *(Dir-Video)*
Ted Eisenreich *(Dir-Facility Ops)*
Kate Hogan *(Dir-Retail Ops)*
Reggie McKenzie *(Dir-Football Ops)*
Mark Wagner *(Dir-Ticket Ops)*
Jason Wahlers *(Dir-PR)*
Wayne Wichlacz *(Dir-IT)*
Chris Kirby *(Asst Dir-Video)*
Cathy Dworak *(Mgr-Community Outreach)*
Todd Edlebeck *(Mgr-Facilities)*
Kandi Goltz *(Mgr-Game & Fan Dev)*
Allen Johnson *(Mgr-Fields)*
Nicole Ledvina *(Mgr-HR)*
Michelle Palubicki *(Mgr-Mktg)*
John Wurzer *(Mgr-Electrical)*
Brands & Products:
G
GREEN BAY PACKERS
LAMBEAU FIELD

GREEN BAY SYMPHONY ORCHESTRA INC.
1240 Main St
Green Bay, WI 54302
Tel.: (920) 435-3465
Fax: (920) 435-1427
E-mail: info@greenbaysymphony.org
Web Site: www.greenbaysymphony.org
Approx. Number Employees: 10
Year Founded: 1914
Business Description:
Symphony Orchestra
S.I.C.: 7929
N.A.I.C.S.: 711130
Media: 7-8-9-20-23-24-25
Personnel:
Bridget-Michaele Reischl *(Dir-Music)*

GREENWICH SYMPHONY ORCHESTRA INC.
PO Box 35
Greenwich, CT 06836
Tel.: (203) 869-2664
Fax: (203) 869-2664
Web Site: www.greenwichsym.org
Business Description:
Symphony Orchestra
S.I.C.: 7929; 8611
N.A.I.C.S.: 711130; 813910
Media: 8-9-20-23-24-25
Personnel:
Mary J. Radcliffe *(Pres)*
David Gilbert *(Dir-Music)*

GREENWICH VILLAGE ORCHESTRA
PO Box 910
New York, NY 10113
Tel.: (212) 932-0372
E-mail: info@gvo.org
Web Site: www.gvo.org
Year Founded: 1986
Business Description:
Symphony Orchestra
S.I.C.: 5411
N.A.I.C.S.: 445110
Media: 9-20-23-24-25
Personnel:
Sunita de Souza *(Pres)*
Susie Dylan *(Co-Pres)*
Joanna Spencer *(Co-Pres)*
Advertising Agency:
The Cementworks, LLC
(d/b/a The CementBloc)
641 Sixth Ave 5th Fl
New York, NY 10011
Tel.: (212) 524-6200
Fax: (212) 524-6299

GUITAR CENTER, INC.
(Sub. of Guitar Center Holdings, Inc.)
5795 Lindero Canyon Rd
Westlake Village, CA 91362
Tel.: (818) 735-8800
Fax: (818) 735-4923
E-mail: midi@guitarcenter.com
Web Site: www.guitarcenter.com
Approx. Sls.: $2,029,966,000
Approx. Number Employees: 9,540
Year Founded: 1959
Business Description:
Retail Stores Selling Musical Instruments & Recording Equipment
S.I.C.: 5736; 5013; 5099
N.A.I.C.S.: 451140; 423990; 441310
Advertising Expenditures: $3,660,000
Media: 5-8-13-19-22-23-24
Personnel:
Gregory A. Trojan *(Pres & COO)*
Norman Hajjar *(CFO & Exec VP)*
Erick Mason *(CFO & Exec VP)*
John Zavada *(CIO & Exec VP)*
Robert Fort *(VP-IT & CIO-Divisional)*
Leland Smith *(Gen Counsel, Sec & Exec VP-Corp Dev)*
David Angress *(Exec VP-Intl Dev & Proprietary Brands)*
Maxx Galster *(Exec VP-Stores)*
Gene Joly *(Exec VP-Stores)*
Dennis Haffeman *(Sr VP-HR)*
Glen Peiser *(VP-Adv)*
Dustin Hinz *(Dir-Music & Entertainment Mktg)*
Glenn Noyes *(Dir-Category Mgmt-Drums & Percussion Div)*
Greg Riggs *(Product Mgr-Tech)*
Brands & Products:
GUITAR CENTER
Advertising Agency:
Creative Civilization An Aguilar/Girard Agency
106 Auditorium Cir 2nd Fl
San Antonio, TX 78205-1310
Tel.: (210) 227-1999
Fax: (210) 227-5999

GUTHRIE THEATER FOUNDATION
818 S Seconds St
Minneapolis, MN 55415
Tel.: (612) 347-1100
Fax: (612) 225-6004
Web Site: www.guthrietheater.org
Year Founded: 1963
Business Description:
Theatrical Association
S.I.C.: 8611
N.A.I.C.S.: 813910
Media: 7-8-10-13-18-20-23-24-25-26
Personnel:
Melodie Bahan *(Dir-Comm-PR)*
Trisha Kirk *(Dir-Mktg)*

G.WHIZ - THE HANDS-ON SCIENCE MUSEUM
1001 Blvd of the Arts
Sarasota, FL 34236
Tel.: (941) 309-4949
Fax: (941) 906-7292
E-mail: info@gwiz.org
Web Site: www.gwiz.org
Approx. Number Employees: 35
Business Description:
Hands-On Science Museum
S.I.C.: 8412
N.A.I.C.S.: 712110
Media: 8-9-10-20-22-23-24-25
Personnel:
Cheryl Burstein *(Dir-Mktg)*
Aleks Spalvins *(Dir-Education)*

HAMMELL MUSIC INC.
2700 E W Maple Rd
Commerce Township, MI 48390-3838
Tel.: (734) 762-1760
Fax: (734) 427-6525
E-mail: info@hammell.com
Web Site: www.hammell.com
Approx. Number Employees: 40
Business Description:
Pianos
S.I.C.: 5736
N.A.I.C.S.: 451140
Media: 6-22-24-25
Personnel:
Tim Hoy *(Owner-Hammell Music)*

HARRAH'S LOUISIANA DOWNS CASINO & RACETRACK
(Joint Venture of Apollo Advisors, L.P. & TPG Capital, L.P.)
8000 E Texas St
Bossier City, LA 71111
Tel.: (318) 742-5555
Toll Free: (800) 551-7223
Web Site: www.harrahslouisianadowns.com
Approx. Number Employees: 1,000
Year Founded: 1974
Business Description:
Horse Racetrack, Casino, Hotel, Bar & Restaurant Operator
S.I.C.: 7948; 7011; 7999
N.A.I.C.S.: 711212; 713290; 721120
Media: 3-9-18-23-24-25
Personnel:
Geno Iafrace *(Pres)*
Shannon McKellar *(VP-Mktg)*
Brands & Products:
LOUISIANA DOWNS

HARTFORD SYMPHONY ORCHESTRA INC.
99 Pett St Ste 500
Hartford, CT 06103
Tel.: (860) 246-8742
Fax: (860) 247-1720
E-mail: info@hartfordsymphony.org
Web Site: www.hartfordsymphony.org
Sales Range: $75-99.9 Million
Approx. Number Employees: 101
Business Description:
Symphony Orchestra
S.I.C.: 7929
N.A.I.C.S.: 711130
Media: 9-18-20-23-24-25
Personnel:
Kristen Phillips *(Pres & CEO)*
Cheryl Anderson *(Dir-Fin & HR)*

HAWKS BASKETBALL, INC.
(Sub. of Turner Broadcasting System, Inc.)
(d/b/a Atlanta Hawks)
Centennial Tower 101 Marietta St NW Ste 1900
Atlanta, GA 30303
Tel.: (404) 878-3800
Fax: (404) 878-3765
Web Site: www.nba.com/hawks/?tmd=1
Sales Range: $75-99.9 Million
Approx. Number Employees: 300
Year Founded: 1949
Business Description:
Professional Basketball Team
S.I.C.: 7941
N.A.I.C.S.: 711211
Advertising Expenditures: $5,000,000
Media: 8-13
Personnel:
Rick Sund *(Exec VP & Gen Mgr)*
Jim Pfeifer *(VP-Mktg & Adv & Branding)*
Jon Steinberg *(Dir-Media Rels)*

HELENA SYMPHONY SOCIETY INC.
48 Hibbard Way
Helena, MT 59624
Tel.: (406) 442-1860
Fax: (406) 442-2411
E-mail: office@helenasymphony.org
Web Site: www.helenasymphony.org

Helena Symphony Society Inc. — (Continued)

Approx. Number Employees: 4
Business Description:
Symphony Orchestra
S.I.C.: 7929
N.A.I.C.S.: 711130
Media: 9-20-23-24-25
Personnel:
Allan R. Scott *(Dir-Music & Conductor)*

HENRY FORD MUSEUM AND GREENFIELD VILLAGE

20900 Oakwood Blvd
Dearborn, MI 48124-5029
Tel.: (313) 982-6001
Tel.: (313) 982-6125 (Pub Rels)
Tel.: (313) 982-6126 (Pub Rels)
Fax: (313) 982-6230
E-mail: info@thehenryford.org
Web Site: www.thehenryford.org
Sales Range: $400-449.9 Million
Approx. Number Employees: 1,000
Year Founded: 1929
Business Description:
Indoor/Outdoor Museum Complex
S.I.C.: 8412
N.A.I.C.S.: 712110
Media: 1-3-4-5-6-7-8-9-10-13-16-18-22-23-24-25
Distr.: Direct to Consumer; Reg.
Budget Set: Oct.
Personnel:
Patricia E. Mooradian *(Pres & Sec)*
Christian Overland *(Exec VP)*
Wendy Metros *(Dir-PR)*
Advertising Agency:
Solomon Friedman Advertising
40900 Woodward Ave Ste 300
Bloomfield Hills, MI 48304-2256
Tel.: (248) 540-0660
Fax: (248) 540-2124

HERBST GAMING, LLC

3440 W Russell Rd
Las Vegas, NV 89118
Tel.: (702) 889-7695
Fax: (702) 740-4630
E-mail: ir@herbstgaming.com
Web Site: www.herbstgaming.com
Approx. Rev.: $701,101,000
Approx. Number Employees: 3,839
Year Founded: 1997
Business Description:
Slot Machine & Casino Operator
S.I.C.: 7999
N.A.I.C.S.: 713990; 713210; 713290
Media: 17-22
Personnel:
Ferenc B. Szony *(Pres)*
John Christopher Krabiel *(CFO & Treas)*
Sean T. Higgins *(Gen Counsel)*
Donna Lehmann *(Sr VP-Fin)*
David Ross *(Dir)*

HERSCHEND FAMILY ENTERTAINMENT CORP.

399 Silver Dollar City Pkwy
Branson, MO 65616-6172
Tel.: (417) 338-2611
Fax: (417) 338-8080
E-mail: employment@silverdollarcity.com
Web Site: www.hfecorp.com
Sales Range: $250-299.9 Million
Approx. Number Employees: 4,000
Year Founded: 1957
Business Description:
Themed Amusement Parks, Water Parks & Campgrounds
S.I.C.: 7996
N.A.I.C.S.: 713110
Import
Advertising Expenditures: $2,950,000
Media: 6-7-8-9-13-18-23-24
Distr.: Direct to Consumer; Reg.
Budget Set: Oct.
Personnel:
Jack Herschend *(Co-Founder)*
Peter Herschend *(Co-Founder)*
Joel K. Manby *(Pres & CEO)*
Andrew Wexler *(CFO & Sr VP-Fin)*
Rick Baker *(Sr VP-Mktg)*
Sonny Horton *(VP-Sls & Mktg)*
Michael Hutcherson *(VP-Retail)*
Jason Blain *(Dir-Patnership & Brand Alliances)*
Brands & Products:
CELEBRATION CITY
DIXIE STAMPEDE
THE GRAND VILLAGE
RIDE THE DUCKS
SDC CAMPGROUND
SHOWBOAT BRANSON BELLE
SILVER DOLLAR CITY
WHITE WATER
THE WILDERNESS

HOB ENTERTAINMENT, INC.

(Sub. of Live Nation Entertainment, Inc.)
(d/b/a House of Blues)
6255 W Sunset Blvd 16th Fl
Los Angeles, CA 90028
Tel.: (323) 769-4600
Fax: (323) 769-4780
Web Site: www.hob.com
Approx. Sls.: $43,400,000
Approx. Number Employees: 125
Year Founded: 1992
Business Description:
Holding Company; Live Entertainment & Restaurant Properties Operator; Concert Promotion Services
S.I.C.: 6719; 5812; 5813; 7389
N.A.I.C.S.: 551112; 711310; 722110; 722410
Media: 9-18-20-22-25
Personnel:
Michael Rapino *(Pres & CEO)*
Brands & Products:
HOB

HOB-LOB LIMITED PARTNERSHIP

7707 SW 44th St
Oklahoma City, OK 73179-4808
Tel.: (405) 745-1100
Fax: (405) 745-1547 1721
Web Site: www.hobbylobby.com
Approx. Number Employees: 13,000
Business Description:
Hobbies, Arts & Crafts Supplies Retailer
S.I.C.: 5945; 5949; 5961; 6719
N.A.I.C.S.: 451120; 451130; 454111; 454113; 551112
Media: 4
Personnel:
David Green *(Founder & CEO)*
Steve Green *(Pres)*
Jon Cargill *(CFO)*
John Graham *(Asst Gen Counsel)*
Brands & Products:
HOBBY LOBBY.COM
PROJECT:INSPIRATION

HOCKEY WESTERN NEW YORK, LLC

(d/b/a Buffalo Sabres)
HSBC Arena 1 Seymour Knox III Plz
Buffalo, NY 14203
Tel.: (716) 855-4100
Fax: (716) 855-4110
Toll Free: (888) 467-22737
E-mail: webmaster@sabres.com
Web Site: www.sabres.com
Approx. Number Employees: 120
Year Founded: 1970
Business Description:
Professional Hockey Team
S.I.C.: 7941
N.A.I.C.S.: 711211
Advertising Expenditures: $250,000
Media: 1-3-8-9-13-18-22-23-24
Distr.: Natl.
Budget Set: July
Personnel:
B. Thomas Golisano *(Owner)*
Lawrence Quinn *(Mng Partner)*
Dan DiPofi *(COO)*
Ron Bertovich *(Exec VP-Admin)*
Kevin Billet *(Sr VP)*
John Livsey *(VP-Bus Dev & Sls)*
Darcy Reiger *(Gen Mgr)*
Christine Adamczyk *(Dir-R & D)*
Frank Cravotta *(Dir-Creative Svcs)*
Mike Gilbert *(Dir-Pub Rel)*
Mike Kaminska *(Dir-Mdsg)*
Rob Kopacz *(Dir-Mktg)*
Chuck LaMattina *(Dir-Fin & Admin)*
Stan Makowski *(Dir)*
Richard Mugel *(Dir-HR & Legal Affairs)*
Gary Muxworthy *(Dir-Sls & Mktg)*
John Sinclair *(Dir-Sls, Admin, Ops, R&D)*
Brigid Haensel *(Mgr-HR)*
Christine Ivansitz *(Mgr-Acctg)*
Tom Matheny *(Mgr-Mktg)*
Jeff Smith *(Mgr-Sales)*
Kevin Snow *(Mgr-R & D)*
Brian Wheeler *(Mgr-R & D)*
Brands & Products:
BUFFALO SABRES

HOHNER, INC./HSS

(Sub. of Hohner Musikinstrumente GmbH & Co. KG)
1000 Technology Park Dr
Glen Allen, VA 23059-4500
Mailing Address:
PO Box 15035
Richmond, VA 23227-0435
Tel.: (804) 515-1900
Fax: (804) 515-0189
E-mail: info@hohnerusa.com
Web Site: www.hohnerusa.com
E-Mail For Key Personnel:
Sales Director: bgreen@hohnerusa.com
Sales Range: $25-49.9 Million
Approx. Number Employees: 40
Year Founded: 1857
Business Description:
Distr of Harmonicas, Melodicas, Diatonic & Piano Accordions, Recorders, Instruments for Music Education, Percussion Instruments, Musical Accessories, Electric & Acoustic Guitars, Cymbals & Drums
S.I.C.: 3931
N.A.I.C.S.: 339992
Import Export
Advertising Expenditures: $800,000
Media: 2-4-5-6-7-8-10-17-19-20
Distr.: Natl.
Budget Set: Apr. -Mar.
Brands & Products:
HOHNER
LANIKAI
PLAYFUL HARMONIES
ROCKWOOD
SONOR

HOLLAND SYMPHONY ORCHESTRA

PO Box 2685
Holland, MI 49422-8084
Tel.: (616) 296-6780
Fax: (616) 396-6298
E-mail: hso@hollandsymphony.org
Web Site: www.hollandsymphony.org
Approx. Number Employees: 3
Year Founded: 1989
Business Description:
Symphony Orchestra
S.I.C.: 7929
N.A.I.C.S.: 711130
Media: 9-20-23-24-25

HOUSTON ASTROS BASEBALL CLUB

(Sub. of Houston McLane Company Inc.)
501 Crawford St Ste 400 PO Box 288
Houston, TX 77002-2113
Mailing Address:
PO Box 288
Houston, TX 77001-0288
Tel.: (713) 259-8000
Fax: (713) 259-8025
Toll Free: (800) ASTROS2
E-mail: fanfeedback@astros.mlb.com
Web Site:
www.houston.astros.mlb.com
Approx. Number Employees: 200
Year Founded: 1962
Business Description:
Professional Baseball Club
S.I.C.: 7941
N.A.I.C.S.: 711211
Media: 2-3-6-7-8-9-10-11-13-15-18-20-22-23-24-25
Distr.: Natl.
Budget Set: Dec.
Personnel:
Drayton McLane, Jr. *(Chm & CEO)*
Pam Gardner *(Pres-Bus Ops)*
Tal Smith *(Pres-Baseball Ops)*
Jaime Hildreth *(Sr VP-Premium Sponsorships)*
Jay Lucas *(Sr VP-Comm)*
Marty Price *(Sr VP-Events & Guest Svcs)*
Jackie Traywick *(Sr VP-Fin & Admin)*
Jennifer Germer *(VP-Mktg & Ticket Sls)*
John Sorrentino *(VP-Sls & Premium Seating)*
Larry Stokes *(VP-HR & Stadium Security)*
Ed Wade *(Gen Mgr)*
David Gottfried *(Asst Gen Mgr-Baseball Ops)*
Ricky Bennett *(Dir-Pro Scouting)*
Brands & Products:
HOUSTON ASTROS

Key to Media (For complete agency information see *The Advertising Red Books-Agencies* edition):
1. Bus. Publs. 2. Cable T.V. 3. Catalogs & Directories. 4. Co-op Adv. 5. Consumer Mags. 6. D.M. to Bus. Estab.7. D.M. to Consumers
8. Daily Newsp. 9. Exhibits/Trade Shows 10. Foreign 11. Infomercial 12. Internet Adv.13. Multimedia 14. Network Radio
15. Network T.V. 16. Newsp. Distr. Mags. 17. Other 18. Outdoor (Posters, Transit) 19. Point of Purchase20. Premiums, Novelties
21. Product Samples 22. Special Events Mktg. 23. Spot Radio 24. Spot T.V. 25. Weekly Newsp. 26. Yellow Page Adv.

Advertising Agency:
MLB Advanced Media, L.P.
75 9th Ave 5th Fl
New York, NY 10011
Tel.: (212) 485-3444
Fax: (212) 485-3456

HOUSTON GRAND OPERA ASSOCIATION
510 Preston
Houston, TX 77002
Tel.: (713) 546-0200
Fax: (713) 225-2574
Web Site:
www.houstongrandopera.org
Approx. Sls.: $17,844,042
Approx. Number Employees: 100
Business Description:
Opera Company
S.I.C.: 7922
N.A.I.C.S.: 711110
Media: 9-10-18-23-24-25
Personnel:
Beth Madison *(Chm)*
Anthony Freud *(CEO & Gen Dir)*
Rauli Garcia *(CFO)*
Greg Robertson *(Chief Advancement Officer)*
Deborah Hirsch *(Sr Dir-Devel)*
Elizabeth Baisley *(Dir-Comm)*
David Chambers *(Dir-Institutional Gifts)*
Kathleen Kelly *(Music Dir-HGO Studio)*
Melissa Kiesel *(Dir-HR)*
Guyla Pircher *(Dir-Special Events)*
Patrick Summers *(Dir-Music)*
Ken Vaughn *(Dir-Info Sys)*
Lee Whatley *(Dir-Bus Analytics)*
Richard Wong *(Dir-Customer Care & Audience Dev)*
Timothy Gibbs *(Mgr-Acctg)*
M. Jane Orosco *(Mgr-Mktg Data)*

HOUSTON ROCKETS
1510 Polk St
Houston, TX 77002
Tel.: (713) 758-7200
Fax: (713) 963-7358
Web Site: www.nba.com/rockets
Approx. Number Employees: 160
Year Founded: 1967
Business Description:
Professional Basketball Teams
S.I.C.: 7941
N.A.I.C.S.: 711211
Advertising Expenditures: $700,000
Media: 3-6-8-9-10-13-14-15-18-20-22-23-24-25
Distr.: Natl.
Personnel:
Les Alexander *(Owner)*
Thaddeus B. Brown *(CEO)*
Marcus Jolibois *(CFO)*
Chris Dacey *(Chief Strategy Officer)*
Mark Norelli *(VP-Ticket Sls)*
Terri Glenn *(Mgr-Office)*
Brands & Products:
HOUSTON COMETS
HOUSTON ROCKETS
SIGNED, SEALED, DELIVERED
TOYOTA CENTER

HOUSTON SYMPHONY SOCIETY
615 Louisiana St Ste 102
Houston, TX 77002
Tel.: (713) 224-4240
Fax: (713) 224-6129
Web Site: www.houstonsymphony.org
Business Description:
Symphony Orchestra
S.I.C.: 7929
N.A.I.C.S.: 711130
Media: 7-8-9-13-20-22-23-24-25
Personnel:
Ed Wulfe *(Chm)*
Bobby Tudor *(Pres)*
Matthew VanBesien *(CEO & Exec Dir)*
Michael D. Pawson *(CFO)*
Stephen G. Tipps *(Gen Counsel)*
Aurelie Desmarais *(Sr Dir-Artistic Plng)*
Merle N. Bratlie *(Dir-Artist Svcs)*
Roger Daily *(Dir-Music Matters)*
Philip Gulla *(Dir-Tech)*
Heather Fails *(Mgr-Ticketing Database)*
Janis Pease LaRocque *(Mgr-Patron Database)*
Chris Westerfelt *(Mgr-Accts Payable & Special Projects)*
Carol Wilson *(Mgr-Music Matters)*

HOUSTON TEXANS, L.P.
2 Reliant Pk
Houston, TX 77054
Tel.: (832) 667-2000
Fax: (832) 667-2100
Web Site: www.houstontexans.com
Approx. Number Employees: 130
Year Founded: 1999
Business Description:
Professional Football Franchise
S.I.C.: 7941
N.A.I.C.S.: 711211
Media: 8-13-15-18-20-22-23-24
Personnel:
Robert C. McNair *(Founder, Chm & CEO)*
Philip J. Burguieres *(Vice Chm)*
D. Cal McNair *(Vice Chm)*
Jamey Rootes *(Pres)*
Kirbyjon H. Caldwell *(Partner)*
Charles W. Duncan, Jr. *(Partner)*
Harry Gee, Jr. *(Partner)*
Javier Loya *(Partner)*
Kay Onstead *(Partner)*
Fayez Sarofim *(Partner)*
Joseph W. Sutton *(Partner)*
Chuck Watson *(Partner)*
Scott E. Schwinger *(CFO, Treas & Sr VP)*
Suzie Thomas *(Chief Admin Officer, Gen Counsel & Sr VP)*
Greg Kondritz *(Gen Counsel)*
Ryan Reichert *(VP-Security)*
John Vidalin *(VP-Corp Sls & Mktg)*
Greg Watson *(VP-Fin)*
Tony Wyllie *(VP-Comm)*
Rick Smith *(Gen Mgr)*
Jay Brunetti *(Dir-Equipment Svcs)*
Kevin Cooper *(Dir-Comm)*
Jennifer Davenport *(Dir-Community Dev)*
Brian Gardner *(Dir-Pro Personnel)*
Greg Grissom *(Dir-Corp Dev)*
Joe Malota *(Dir-Video Ops)*
Glenda Morrison *(Dir-HR)*
Diane Ozzolek *(Dir-Event Svcs)*
Nick Schenck *(Dir-Digital Media & Publ)*
Jeff Schmitz *(Dir-IT)*
Dale Strahm *(Dir-College Scouting)*
Brian Varnadoe *(Dir-Premium Seating)*
Sean Washington *(Dir-Player Dev)*

HUNTINGTON SYMPHONY ORCHESTRA
PO Box 2434
Huntington, WV 25725-2434
Tel.: (304) 781-8343
Fax: (304) 781-0670
E-mail: huntingtonsymphony@gmail.com
Web Site:
www.huntingtonsymphony.org
Approx. Number Employees: 4
Year Founded: 1930
Business Description:
Symphony Orchestra
S.I.C.: 7922
N.A.I.C.S.: 711110
Media: 9-23-24-25
Personnel:
Kimo Furumoto *(Dir-Music)*
Sandy White *(Mgr-Personnel)*

HUNTSVILLE SYMPHONY ORCHESTRA
Von Braun Ctr 700 Monroe St
Huntsville, AL 35801
Mailing Address:
PO Box 2400
Huntsville, AL 35804
Tel.: (256) 539-4818
Fax: (256) 539-4819
E-mail: hso@hiwaay.net
Web Site: www.hso.org
Approx. Number Employees: 8
Business Description:
Symphony Orchestra
S.I.C.: 7389
N.A.I.C.S.: 711320
Media: 9-13-18-20-23-24-25
Personnel:
Dianne Halcomb *(Pres & CEO)*
Jeff Linholm *(Dir-Mktg & PR)*
Hunter Thomas *(Mgr-Orchestra Personnel & Librarian)*
Advertising Agency:
Inergi
3414A Governors Dr
Huntsville, AL 35805
Tel.: (256) 704-7700
Fax: (256) 704-7704

ILIKE, INC.
1605 Boylston Ave Ste 202
Seattle, WA 98122
Tel.: (415) 704-3432
Fax: (415) 704-3232
E-mail: pr@iLike-inc.com
Web Site: www.ilike.com
Year Founded: 2002
Business Description:
Music-Based Social Networking Services
S.I.C.: 2741
N.A.I.C.S.: 516110; 511140; 512230
Advertising Agency:
Brew Media Relations
3015 Main St Ste 350
Santa Monica, CA 90405
Tel.: (310) 526-8576
— Brooke Hammerling *(Acct Exec)*

ILLINOIS PHILHARMONIC ORCHESTRA
377 Artists Walk
Park Forest, IL 60466
Tel.: (708) 481-7774
Fax: (708) 481-7998
Web Site: www.ipomusic.org
Approx. Number Employees: 80
Business Description:
Orchestra
S.I.C.: 7929
N.A.I.C.S.: 711130
Media: 9-13-20-23-24-25
Personnel:
Mario Carlasare *(Dir-Mktg & Educational Outreach)*

ILLINOIS SYMPHONY ORCHESTRA
524 1/2 Capitol Ave
Springfield, IL 62701
Tel.: (217) 522-2838
Fax: (217) 522-7374
Toll Free: (800) 401-7222
E-mail: info@ilsymphony.org
Web Site: www.ilsymphony.org
Sales Range: Less than $1 Million
Approx. Number Employees: 4
Business Description:
Symphony Orchestra
S.I.C.: 7389
N.A.I.C.S.: 711320
Media: 9-20-23-24-25
Personnel:
Trevor Orthmann *(Exec Dir)*
Karen Lynne Deal *(Dir-Music)*
Dawn Lolar *(Office Mgr)*

INDIANAPOLIS COLTS, INC.
7001 W 56th St
Indianapolis, IN 46254-9725
Tel.: (317) 297-2658
Fax: (317) 297-8971
Toll Free: (800) 805-2658
E-mail: info@colts.nfl.net
Web Site: www.colts.com
Approx. Number Employees: 100
Year Founded: 1953
Business Description:
Professional Football Franchise
S.I.C.: 7941
N.A.I.C.S.: 711211
Media: 2-3-6-7-8-9-10-12-13-14-15-17-18-20-22-23-24-25
Distr.: Natl.
Budget Set: Feb.
Personnel:
James Irsay *(Owner & CEO)*
Bill Polian *(Vice Chm)*
Pete Ward *(COO)*
Dan Emerson *(Gen Counsel)*
Bob Terpening *(Exec VP)*
Tom Zupancic *(Sr VP-Sls & Mktg)*
Chris Polian *(VP & Gen Mgr-Football Ops)*
Kurt Humphrey *(VP-Fin)*
Craig Kelley *(VP-PR)*
Chuck O'Hara *(Sr Dir-Mktg)*
Natalie Palmer *(Sr Dir-Visitor Svcs & Special Events)*
Bill Brooks *(Dir-Admin)*
Kip Brownfield *(Dir-Ticket Sls)*
Steve Champlin *(Dir-Football Admin)*
Ryan Fannin *(Dir-Football Info Sys)*
Matt Godbout *(Dir-Sponsorship Sls)*
Marty Heckscher *(Dir-Video)*
A. J. Macht *(Dir-Internet Svcs)*
Bob Parenteau *(Dir-Ticket Ops)*
Clyde Powers *(Dir-Pro Player Personnel)*
Tom Telesco *(Dir-Player Personnel)*
Brian Woodrum *(Dir-Production)*
Vernon Cheek *(Asst Dir-PR)*
Jamil Stafford *(Asst Dir-Ticket Ops)*
John Starliper *(Asst Dir-Video)*

Key to Media (For complete agency information see *The Advertising Red Books-Agencies* edition):
1. Bus. Publs. 2. Cable T.V. 3. Catalogs & Directories. 4. Co-op Adv. 5. Consumer Mags. 6. D.M. to Bus. Estab.7. D.M. to Consumers
8. Daily Newsp. 9. Exhibits/Trade Shows 10. Foreign 11. Infomercial 12. Internet Adv.13. Multimedia 14. Network Radio
15. Network T.V. 16. Newsp. Distr. Mags. 17. Other 18. Outdoor (Posters, Transit) 19. Point of Purchase20. Premiums, Novelties
21. Product Samples 22. Special Events Mktg. 23. Spot Radio 24. Spot T.V. 25. Weekly Newsp. 26. Yellow Page Adv.

Indianapolis Colts, Inc. — (Continued)

Dave Atkins *(Mgr-Facility)*
Scott Davis *(Mgr-Colts Pavilion)*
Justin Dickens *(Mgr-Publicity)*
Jeffrey Gorman *(Mgr-Brdcst Svcs)*
Jerry Harbin *(Mgr-Team Partnerships)*
Jon Scott *(Mgr-Equipment)*

Brands & Products:
COLTS.COM
INDIANAPOLIS COLTS

Advertising Agency:
Borshoff
47 S Pennsylvania St Ste 500
Indianapolis, IN 46204
Tel.: (317) 631-6400
Fax: (317) 631-6499

INDIANAPOLIS SYMPHONY ORCHESTRA

32 E Washington St Ste 600
Indianapolis, IN 46204-2919
Tel.: (317) 262-1100
Fax: (317) 262-1159
E-mail: bxoffice@indianapolissymphony.org
Web Site: www.indianapolissymphony.org
Approx. Number Employees: 80

Business Description:
Symphony Orchestra
S.I.C.: 7929
N.A.I.C.S.: 711130
Media: 8-9-18-20-23-24-25

Personnel:
Simon Crookall *(Pres & CEO)*
Jane Shriner *(CFO, VP-Fin & Strategic Plng)*
Thomas R. Ramsey *(VP & Gen Mgr)*
Mark Newman *(VP-Mktg & Comm)*
Ty A. Johnson *(Sr Dir-Pops Programming)*
Tom Atkins *(Dir-Archives)*
Joanne Bennett *(Dir-Facilities & Audience Svcs)*
Rita Steinberg *(Dir-Dev)*
Toby Tokolan *(Dir-Artistic Plng)*
Mario Venzago *(Dir-Music)*
Meg Williams *(Dir-Community Partnerships)*
Linda Noble *(Assoc Dir-Education)*
Timothy Northcutt *(Assoc Dir-Comm)*
Michael Runyan *(Mgr-Library)*
K. Blake Schlabach *(Mgr-Orchestra Personnel)*
Ryan Singer *(Mgr-Info Svcs)*

Advertising Agency:
360 Group
36 S Pennsylvania St Ste 190
Indianapolis, IN 46204
Tel.: (317) 633-1456
Fax: (317) 633-1461

INTERNATIONAL SPEEDWAY CORPORATION

1 Daytona Blvd
Daytona Beach, FL 32114
Tel.: (386) 254-2700
Web Site: www.iscmotorsports.com
Approx. Rev.: $645,357,000
Approx. Number Employees: 850
Year Founded: 1953

Business Description:
Holding Company; Motorsports Racetrack Owner, Operator & Events Promoter
S.I.C.: 6719; 7389; 7948; 7999
N.A.I.C.S.: 551112; 711212; 711310; 713990
Advertising Expenditures: $18,400,000
Media: 5-6-14-15-18-22-23-24

Personnel:
James C. France *(Chm)*
Lesa France Kennedy *(Vice Chm & CEO)*
John R. Saunders *(Pres)*
Daniel W. Houser *(CFO, Treas & Sr VP)*
Craig A. Neeb *(CIO & VP-Multi-Channel Mktg)*
Daryl Q. Wolfe *(CMO & VP)*
Brett Scharback *(Chief Compliance Officer, VP, Deputy Gen Counsel & Asst Sec)*
W. Garrett Crotty *(Gen Counsel, Sec & Sr VP)*
Laura Jackson *(VP-HR)*

Brands & Products:
24 HOURS OF DAYTONA
ACCELERATION ALLEY
THE ACTION TRACK
AMERICROWN
CALIFORNIA SPEEDWAY
CHICAGOLAND SPEEDWAY
DARLINGTON RACEWAY
DAYTONA 500
DAYTONA 500 EXPERIENCE
DAYTONA DREAM LAPS
DAYTONA INTERNATIONAL SPEEDWAY
DAYTONA USA
THE GLEN
THE GREAT AMERICAN RACE
HOMESTEAD-MIAMI SPEEDWAY
ISC
KANSAS SPEEDWAY
MARTINSVILLE SPEEDWAY
MICHIGAN INTERNATIONAL SPEEDWAY
MOTOR RACING NETWORK
MRN RADIO
PHOENIX INTERNATIONAL RACEWAY
RACETICKETS.COM
RICHMOND INTERNATIONAL RACEWAY
ROUTE 66 RACEWAY
SOUTHERN 500
SPEEDWEEKS
TALLADEGA SUPERSPEEDWAY
TOO TOUGH TO TAME
WATKINS GLEN INTERNATIONAL
WORLD CENTER OF RACING

Advertising Agency:
deutschMedia
111 8th Ave 14th Fl
New York, NY 10011-5201
Tel.: (212) 981-7600
Fax: (212) 981-7525

ISLE OF CAPRI CASINOS, INC.

600 Emerson Rd Ste 300
Saint Louis, MO 63141
Tel.: (228) 396-7000
Fax: (228) 396-2634
Toll Free: (800) -THE-ISLE
Web Site: www.islecorp.com
Approx. Rev.: $1,211,534,000
Approx. Number Employees: 8,600
Year Founded: 1992

Business Description:
Branded Gaming Facilities & Related Lodging & Entertainment Facilities Developer, Owner & Operator; Riverboat, Dockside & Land-Based Casinos Owner & Operator
S.I.C.: 7999; 7011; 7948
N.A.I.C.S.: 713290; 711212; 713990; 721120
Advertising Expenditures: $36,404,000

Personnel:
James B. Perry *(Chm)*
Robert S. Goldstein *(Vice Chm)*
Virginia M. McDowell *(Pres & CEO)*
Dale R. Black *(CFO & Sr VP)*
Arnold Block *(COO)*
Jeanne-Marie Wilkins *(CIO & Sr VP)*
D. Douglas Burkhalter *(CMO & Sr VP)*
Donn R. Mitchell, II *(Chief Admin Officer)*
Edmund L. Quatmann, Jr. *(Chief Legal Officer)*
Eric Hausler *(Chief Strategic Officer)*
Sarah Jackson *(Sr VP-HR)*
Richard Weber *(Sr VP-Acctg)*
Doug Shipley *(VP & Gen Mgr)*
Jill Haynes *(Sr Dir-Corp Comm)*
Elissa Plastino *(Brand Mgr)*

Brands & Products:
ISLE
ISLE OF CAPRI CASINOS
LADY LUCK

Advertising Agencies:
All Star Incentive Marketing, Inc.
660 Main St
Fiskdale, MA 01518
Tel.: (508) 347-7672
Fax: (508) 347-5404
Toll Free: (800) 526-8629

Godwin Advertising Agency, Inc. (d/b/a GodwinGroup)
1 Jackson Pl 188 E Capitol St Ste 800
Jackson, MS 39201
Tel.: (601) 354-5711
Fax: (601) 960-5869

J&R MUSIC WORLD

23 Pk Row
New York, NY 10038-2302
Tel.: (212) 732-8600
Fax: (212) 238-9191
E-mail: corporate@jr.com
Web Site: www.jr.com
Approx. Number Employees: 100

Business Description:
Music Stores
S.I.C.: 5731; 5735
N.A.I.C.S.: 443112; 451220

Personnel:
Rachelle Friedman *(Pres)*
Joe Friedman *(CEO)*

Advertising Agency:
Concrete Media
43 E Moonachie Rd
Hackensack, NJ 07601
Tel.: (201) 440-2626
Fax: (201) 440-3433

JACKSON SYMPHONY ASSOCIATION INC.

1903 N Highland Ave
Jackson, TN 38301
Mailing Address:
PO Box 3429
Jackson, TN 38303-3429
Tel.: (731) 427-6440
Fax: (731) 427-6417
Web Site: www.thejacksonsymphonycompany.org
Sales Range: Less than $1 Million
Approx. Number Employees: 5
Year Founded: 1961

Business Description:
Symphony Orchestra
S.I.C.: 7389
N.A.I.C.S.: 711320
Media: 8-9-20-23-24-25

Personnel:
Jordan Tang *(Dir-Music)*
Lynn White *(Coord-Education)*

JACKSONVILLE JAGUARS, LTD.

1 Everbank Fields Dr
Jacksonville, FL 32202
Tel.: (904) 633-6000
Fax: (904) 633-6050
E-mail: info@jaguars.com
Web Site: www.jaguars.com
Approx. Number Employees: 150
Year Founded: 1993

Business Description:
Professional Football Franchise
S.I.C.: 7941
N.A.I.C.S.: 711211
Media: 9-13-23-24

Personnel:
J. Wayne Weaver *(Owner, Chm & CEO)*
Bill Prescott *(CFO & Sr VP-Stadium Ops)*
Paul Vance *(Gen Counsel & Sr VP-Football Ops)*
Dan Edwards *(Sr VP-Comm & Media)*
Gene Smith *(Gen Mgr)*
Skip Richardson *(Exec Dir-Football Ops & Facilities)*
Bruce Swindell *(Exec Dir-Info Tech)*
Macky Weaver *(Exec Dir-Corp Sponsorship)*
Tim Bishko *(Dir-Ticket Ops)*
Devin Bonik *(Dir-Football Dev)*
Terry McDonough *(Dir-Player Personnel)*
Mike Perkins *(Dir-Video)*
Tim Walsh *(Dir-Football Admin)*
Louis Clark *(Asst Dir-Pro Personnel)*
Tim Mingey *(Asst Dir-College Personnel)*
Drew Hampton *(Mgr-Equipment)*
Sashi Brown *(Asst Gen Counsel)*

Advertising Agency:
Dalton Agency
140 W Monroe St
Jacksonville, FL 32202
Tel.: (904) 398-5222
Fax: (904) 398-5220
Toll Free: (888) 409-2691

JACKSONVILLE SYMPHONY ASSOCIATION

300 W Water St Ste 200
Jacksonville, FL 32202
Tel.: (904) 354-5547
Fax: (904) 354-9238
Toll Free: (877) 662-6731
Web Site: www.jaxsymphony.org
Approx. Number Employees: 95

Business Description:
Symphony Orchestra
S.I.C.: 7929
N.A.I.C.S.: 711130
Media: 1-4-8-9-10-13-20-22-23-24-25

Personnel:
Merryn Corsat *(Principal)*

Key to Media (For complete agency information see *The Advertising Red Books-Agencies* edition):
1. Bus. Publs. 2. Cable T.V. 3. Catalogs & Directories. 4. Co-op Adv. 5. Consumer Mags. 6. D.M. to Bus. Estab.7. D.M. to Consumers
8. Daily Newsp. 9. Exhibits/Trade Shows 10. Foreign 11. Infomercial 12. Internet Adv.13. Multimedia 14. Network Radio
15. Network T.V. 16. Newsp. Distr. Mags. 17. Other 18. Outdoor (Posters, Transit) 19. Point of Purchase20. Premiums, Novelties
21. Product Samples 22. Special Events Mktg. 23. Spot Radio 24. Spot T.V. 25. Weekly Newsp. 26. Yellow Page Adv.

Holly Bryan *(Dir-Fin)*
Lynn Evans *(Dir-Devel)*
Fabio Mechetti *(Dir-Music)*
Sally Pettegrew *(Dir-Admin)*
Josh Schwerdtfeger *(Dir-Sls)*
Phyllis Benzenberg *(Mgr-Patron Svcs)*

JACUZZI BRANDS CORPORATION
(Holding of Apollo Management, L.P.)
14525 Montevista Ave
Chino, CA 91710
Tel.: (909) 606-7733
Tel.: (909) 606-1416 (Spa Div)
Tel.: (909) 548-7732 (Bath Div)
Fax: (909) 606-0195
Web Site: www.jacuzzibrands.com
Approx. Sls.: $1,202,400,000
Approx. Number Employees: 4,907
Year Founded: 1995
Business Description:
Plumbing Products
S.I.C.: 3432; 3261
N.A.I.C.S.: 332913; 327111
Advertising Expenditures: $31,900,000
Media: 6-10-12-13-18
Personnel:
Thomas D. Koos *(Pres & CEO)*
Moris Smith *(Sr VP-Sls-Bath Div)*
Drew Meng *(VP-Mktg)*
William Smelley *(Mgr-Mktg)*
Brands & Products:
ACCUPRO
ALLUSION
AMIGA
AQUALIBRIUM
AQUASOUND
AURA
BELLAVISTA
BIANCA
BONAIRE
CAMBIA
CAPELLA
CETRA
CIPREA
CORTINA
DONNIELI
DUETTA
ELARA
FIORE
FONTANA
FRESCO
GALLERY
JACUZZI
LAMORINDA
LUMINOSA
LUNA
LUXURA
MAJORA
MILANO
MITO
MORPHOSIS
NEO
NOVA
OPALIA
OPTICA
OPTIONAL RAPIDHEAT
POWERPRO
PURE AIR
REAL
RENDITIONS
RIVA
SABELLA
SEDONA
SIGNA
STEAMPRO
SUMMER RAIN
TARA
THERAPRO
TORRETTA
TRU-LEVEL
VANTAGE
VENICIA
VIZION
WATER RAINBOW
WATER THAT MOVES YOU

JAZZ BASKETBALL INVESTORS, INC.
(Sub. of Larry H. Miller Sports & Entertainment Group of Companies)
(d/b/a Utah Jazz)
301 W S Temple
Salt Lake City, UT 84101-1216
Tel.: (801) 325-2500
Fax: (801) 325-2578
Web Site: www.nba.com/jazz
Approx. Number Employees: 500
Year Founded: 1979
Business Description:
Professional Basketball Team
S.I.C.: 7941
N.A.I.C.S.: 711211
Media: 2-3-4-6-7-8-9-14-15-18-22-23-24-25-26
Distr.: Natl.
Budget Set: Sept.
Personnel:
Randy Rigby *(Pres)*
Robert Hyde *(CFO & Pres-Fanzz, Exec VP & Asst Gen Mgr)*
Kevin O'Connor *(Gen Mgr & Exec VP-Basketball Ops)*
Chris Baum *(Sr VP-Brdcst)*
Jim Olson *(Sr VP-Sls & Mktg)*
Scott Williams *(Sr VP-Facilities)*
John Larson *(VP-Fin)*
Linda Luchetti *(VP-Comm)*
Eric Schulz *(VP-Mktg)*
Patti Balli *(Dir-Community Rels)*
Brendan Burke *(Dir-Mktg & New Media)*
Mike Chidsey *(Dir-Video)*
Chantay Davies *(Dir-Promos & Game Ops)*
Brian Devir *(Dir-Corp Partnerships-Local)*
Justin Durfey *(Dir-Ticket Ops)*
BeLinda Emerson *(Dir-Adv)*
Dan Knight *(Dir-Ops)*
Meikle LaHue *(Dir-Promotions & Game Ops)*
Craig Meyer *(Dir-Event Security)*
Rich Muirbrook *(Dir-Fan Rels & Youth Programs)*
Jonathan Rinehart *(Dir-Comm)*
Ted Roberts *(Dir-Corp Partnerships-Natl)*
Richard Smith *(Dir-Basketball Ops)*
Bobbie Walker *(Dir-Ticket Sls)*
Shawn Waters *(Dir-Info Sys)*
Paul Welsh *(Dir-HR)*
Derek Garduno *(Sr Mgr-Comm)*
Amy Gunn *(Mgr-Payroll)*
Brands & Products:
UTAH JAZZ
Advertising Agency:
Saxton Horne Advertising
9350 S 150 E Ste 950
Sandy, UT 84070
Tel.: (801) 304-1000
Fax: (801) 304-1008
(NBA Basketball Team)

THE JOHN AND MABLE RINGLING MUSEUM OF ART
5401 Bay Shore Rd
Sarasota, FL 34243
Tel.: (941) 359-5700
Fax: (941) 359-5745
E-mail: info@ringling.org
Web Site: www.ringling.org
Year Founded: 1927
Business Description:
Museum
S.I.C.: 8412
N.A.I.C.S.: 712110
Advertising Expenditures: $320,000
Media: 4-6-9-10-18-20-23-24-25
Personnel:
Chip Willis *(COO)*
Pam Fendt *(Dir-Mktg)*

JOHN F. KENNEDY CENTER FOR THE PERFORMING ARTS
2700 F St NW
Washington, DC 20566
Tel.: (202) 416-8000
Fax: (202) 416-8205
Toll Free: (800) 444-1324
Web Site: www.kennedy-center.org
Approx. Number Employees: 1,100
Year Founded: 1976
Business Description:
Performing Arts Services
S.I.C.: 7389
N.A.I.C.S.: 711310; 711320
Advertising Expenditures: $500,000
Media: 3-5-6-7-8-9-10-13-22-23-24-25
Distr.: Natl.
Personnel:
Stephen Allen Schwarzman *(Chm)*
Michael M. Kaiser *(Pres)*
Lynn Pratt *(CFO)*
Maria Kersten *(Gen Counsel)*
David Kitto *(VP-Mktg & Sls)*
Scott Bushnell *(Dir-Creative-Adv)*
John Dow *(Mgr-Press Office)*
Suanne Hall *(Mgr-Adv Svcs)*
Ann Stock *(Asst Sec)*
Brands & Products:
A CAPITAL FOURTH
ARTSEDGE
THE COLOR PURPLE
EXPLORE THE ARTS
IMAGINATION CELEBRATON
THE KENNEDY CENTER
MILLENNIUM STAGE
SPRING AWAKENING

JOHN G. SHEDD AQUARIUM
1200 S Lk Shore Dr
Chicago, IL 60605
Tel.: (312) 939-2435
Fax: (312) 939-8069
E-mail: contactus@sheddaquarium.org
Web Site: www.sheddaquarium.org
Approx. Number Employees: 300
Year Founded: 1929
Business Description:
Public Aquarium
S.I.C.: 8422
N.A.I.C.S.: 712130
Media: 2-5-6-8-9-10-13-17-18-22-23-26
Distr.: Direct to Consumer; Reg.
Budget Set: Oct.
Personnel:
Ted A. Beattie *(Pres & CEO)*
Joyce Simon *(CFO, Treas, Sec & Exec VP)*
Debra Kerr-Fassnacht *(Exec VP)*
Meghan Curran *(Dir-Mktg)*

JOHNSTOWN SYMPHONY ORCHESTRA
227 Franklin St Ste 304
Johnstown, PA 15901
Tel.: (814) 535-6738
Fax: (814) 535-6739
E-mail: info@johnstowmsymphony.org
Web Site: www.johnstownsymphony.org
Approx. Number Employees: 3
Business Description:
Symphony Orchestra
S.I.C.: 7929
N.A.I.C.S.: 711190
Advertising Expenditures: $30,000
Media: 2-7-8-9-23-24
Personnel:
Patricia Hofscher *(Exec Dir)*
Istvan Jaray *(Dir-Music)*

JUNEAU SYMPHONY
522 W 10th St Basement
Juneau, AK 99801
Mailing Address:
PO Box 21236
Juneau, AK 99802-1236
Tel.: (907) 586-4676
Fax: (907) 463-2555
E-mail: info@juneausymphony.org
Web Site: www.juneausymphony.org
Approx. Number Employees: 2
Year Founded: 1962
Business Description:
Symphony Orchestra
S.I.C.: 7929
N.A.I.C.S.: 711130
Media: 9-18-20-23-24-25
Personnel:
Susan Burke *(Pres)*
Kyle Wiley Pickett *(Dir-Music)*
Elizabeth Agnew *(Exec Dir)*

KALAMAZOO SYMPHONY ORCHESTRA
359 S Kalamazoo Mall Ste 100
Kalamazoo, MI 49007
Tel.: (269) 349-7759
Fax: (269) 349-9229
Web Site: www.kalamazoosymphony.com
Sales Range: $75-99.9 Million
Approx. Number Employees: 10
Business Description:
Symphony Orchestra
S.I.C.: 7929
N.A.I.C.S.: 711130
Media: 9-20-23-24-25
Personnel:
Thomas Andrews *(Dir-Mktg & PR)*
Frank Silva *(Mgr-Personnel)*

KAMAN MUSIC CORPORATION
(Sub. of Fender Musical Instruments Corporation)
55 Griffin Rd S
Bloomfield, CT 06002
Mailing Address:
PO Box 507
Bloomfield, CT 06002-0507
Tel.: (860) 509-8888
Fax: (860) 509-8890
E-mail: info@kamanmusic.com
Web Site: www.kamanmusic.com
E-Mail For Key Personnel:

Key to Media (For complete agency information see *The Advertising Red Books-Agencies* edition):
1. Bus. Publs. 2. Cable T.V. 3. Catalogs & Directories. 4. Co-op Adv. 5. Consumer Mags. 6. D.M. to Bus. Estab.7. D.M. to Consumers 8. Daily Newsp. 9. Exhibits/Trade Shows 10. Foreign 11. Infomercial 12. Internet Adv.13. Multimedia 14. Network Radio 15. Network T.V. 16. Newsp. Distr. Mags. 17. Other 18. Outdoor (Posters, Transit) 19. Point of Purchase20. Premiums, Novelties 21. Product Samples 22. Special Events Mktg. 23. Spot Radio 24. Spot T.V. 25. Weekly Newsp. 26. Yellow Page Adv.

Kaman Music Corporation — (Continued)

Sales Director: sales@kamanmusic.com
Approx. Number Employees: 120
Year Founded: 1966
Business Description:
Musical Instrument & Musical Products Distr & Whslr
S.I.C.: 5736
N.A.I.C.S.: 451140
Media: 2-4-6-7-10-11-13-20-23-24-26
Distr.: Intl.; Natl.
Budget Set: Sept.
Personnel:
Larry Dunn *(CFO & Sr VP)*
Edward G. Miller *(COO)*
Nicole Nearing *(Mgr-Comm & Media Rels)*

KAMPGROUNDS OF AMERICA, INC.

(Sub. of KOA Holdings Inc.)
550 N 31st St
Billings, MT 59101
Mailing Address:
PO Box 30558
Billings, MT 59114-0558
Tel.: (406) 248-7444
Fax: (406) 248-7414
E-mail: info@koa.com
Web Site: www.koa.com
Sales Range: $25-49.9 Million
Approx. Number Employees: 333
Year Founded: 1962
Business Description:
Campground Franchisor
S.I.C.: 7032; 6794
N.A.I.C.S.: 721214; 533110
Advertising Expenditures: $3,000,000
Media: 1-2-3-4-5-6-8-10-11-13-18-19-21-22
Distr.: Direct to Consumer; Intl.; Natl.
Budget Set: Sept.
Personnel:
Jim Rogers *(Chm & CEO)*
Pat Hittmeier *(Pres)*
John Burke *(CFO, Treas & VP)*
Carol Preble *(VP-Franchise Sls)*
Jef Sutherland *(VP-Franchise Ops)*
Randy Howell *(Asst VP)*
Brands & Products:
KAMPING KABINS
KAMPING KOTTAGES
KAMPING LODGES
KOA VALUE KARD
Advertising Agency:
JMPR, Inc.
5850 Canoga Ave Ste 300
Woodland Hills, CA 91367
Tel.: (818) 992-4353
Fax: (818) 992-0543

KANSAS CITY CHIEFS FOOTBALL CLUB, INC.

1 Arrowhead Dr
Kansas City, MO 64129-1651
Tel.: (816) 920-9300
Fax: (816) 923-4719
E-mail: info@kcchiefs.com
Web Site: www.kcchiefs.com
Sales Range: $50-74.9 Million
Approx. Number Employees: 150
Year Founded: 1960
Business Description:
Professional Football Franchise
S.I.C.: 7941
N.A.I.C.S.: 711211
Media: 3-6-10-15-18-20-22-23-24
Distr.: Reg.
Budget Set: Jan.
Personnel:
Clark Hunt *(Chm & CEO)*
Denny Thum *(Pres)*
Dale Young *(Treas & Dir-Fin)*
Woodie Dixon *(Gen Counsel & VP-Bus Affairs)*
Rob Alberino *(VP-Media & Mktg)*
Tammy Fruits *(VP-Sls & Mktg)*
Scott Pioli *(Gen Mgr)*
Lamonte Winston *(Exec Dir-Player Dev)*
Brenda Sniezek *(Dir-Community Rels & Assoc Dir-PR)*
Ken Blume *(Dir-Dev)*
Pat Brazil *(Dir-Video Ops)*
Chuck Cook *(Dir-College Scouting)*
Ray Farmer *(Dir-Pro Personnel)*
Doug Hopkins *(Dir-Ticket Ops)*
Richard McOsker *(Dir-Info Sys)*
Bob Moore *(Dir-PR)*
Gary Spani *(Dir-Special Events)*
David Steffano *(Dir-Sls & Mktg)*
Bob Stirton *(Dir-IT)*
Ken Radino *(Asst Dir-Video Ops)*
Pete Moris *(Assoc Dir-Pub Rel)*
Chuck Castellano *(Mgr-Community Rels)*
Ron Bachtel *(Mgr-Stadium Sys)*
Gene Barr *(Mgr-Security)*
Lance Brown *(Mgr-Internet & Digital Media)*
Andre Bruce *(Mgr-Sports Field)*
Mike Davidson *(Mgr-Equipment)*
Howie Erenberg *(Mgr-Game)*
Brad Kuhbander *(Mgr-Football Info)*
Jim Loges *(Mgr-Construction & Repair)*
Brad MacLachlan *(Mgr-Ticket Ops)*
Jayne Martin *(Mgr-Customer Rls & Premium Svcs)*
Jeremy Slavens *(Mgr-Mktg)*
Tom Stephens *(Mgr-Creative Svcs)*
Sondra Taylor *(Mgr-HR)*
Brands & Products:
KANSAS CITY CHIEFS
Advertising Agencies:
Bernstein-Rein Advertising, Inc.
4600 Madison Ave Ste 1500
Kansas City, MO 64112-3016
Tel.: (816) 756-0640
Fax: (816) 399-6000
Toll Free: (800) 571-6246

Trozzolo Communications Group
802 Broadway Ste 300
Kansas City, MO 64105
Tel.: (816) 842-8111
Fax: (816) 842-8188

VML, Inc.
250 Richards Rd
Kansas City, MO 64116-4279
Tel.: (816) 283-0700
Fax: (816) 283-0954
Toll Free: (800) 990-2468

KANSAS CITY ROYALS BASEBALL CORPORATION

1 Royal Way
Kansas City, MO 64129
Mailing Address:
PO Box 419969
Kansas City, MO 64141-6969
Tel.: (816) 921-8000
Fax: (816) 921-1366
Web Site: www.royals.com
E-Mail For Key Personnel:
Marketing Director: marketing@royals.mlb.com
Sales Range: $75-99.9 Million
Approx. Number Employees: 75
Year Founded: 1969
Business Description:
Professional Baseball Club
S.I.C.: 7941
N.A.I.C.S.: 711211
Import
Media: 1-3-5-7-8-9-13-18-20-21-22-23-24-25-26
Distr.: Natl.
Budget Set: Oct.
Personnel:
David D. Glass *(Owner, Chm & CEO)*
Dan Glass *(Pres)*
Dan Crabtree *(Gen Counsel)*
Dayton Moore *(Gen Mgr & Sr VP-Baseball Ops)*
Kevin Uhlich *(Sr VP-Bus Ops)*
Dean Taylor *(VP-Baseball Ops & Asst Gen Mgr)*
David Laverentz *(VP-Fin & Admin)*
Dale Rohr *(VP-Fin & Admin)*
Michael Swanson *(VP-Comm & Brdcst Production)*
JJ Picollo *(Asst Gen Mgr-Scouting & Player Dev)*
Ben Aken *(Sr Dir-Community Rels)*
Jeff Davenport *(Sr Dir-Team Travel & Clubhouse Ops)*
Wes Engram *(Sr Dir-Corp Partnerships)*
Deric Ladnier *(Sr Dir-Scouting)*
Steve Shiffman *(Sr Dir-Ticket Sls & Customer Svc)*
Chris Darr *(Dir-Ticket Ops)*
Patrick Fleischmann *(Dir-Renovation Acctg & Risk Mgmt)*
David Holtzman *(Dir-Media Rels)*
Curt Nelson *(Dir-Royals HOF)*
Scott Sharp *(Dir-Minor League Ops)*
Sean Ritchie *(Mgr-Acctg)*
Brands & Products:
KANSAS CITY ROYALS
ROYAL LANCERS
SLUGGERRR
Advertising Agency:
MLB Advanced Media, L.P.
75 9th Ave 5th Fl
New York, NY 10011
Tel.: (212) 485-3444
Fax: (212) 485-3456

KANSAS CITY SYMPHONY

1703 Wyandotte St Ste 200
Kansas City, MO 64108-1672
Tel.: (816) 471-1100
Fax: (816) 471-0976
E-mail: info@kcsymphony.org
Web Site: www.kcsymphony.org
Approx. Number Employees: 30
Business Description:
Symphony Orchestra
S.I.C.: 7929; 7389
N.A.I.C.S.: 711130; 711310
Media: 8-9-13-20-22-23-25
Personnel:
R. Crosby Kemper, Jr. *(Founder)*
Shirley Bush Helzberg *(Pres)*
Andrew Birgensmith *(Gen Mgr)*
Frank Byrne *(Exec Dir)*
Jeff Barker *(Dir-Mktg)*
Ron Fredman *(Dir-Dev)*
Michael Stern *(Dir-Music)*
Barbara Tate *(Dir-Bus Ops)*
Christy Roberts *(Assoc Mktg Mgr)*
Amy Best *(Mgr-Opers)*
Andrew Fogel *(Mgr-Ticketing Svcs)*
Ande Gogel *(Customer Svc Center Mgr)*
Kathy Houston *(Mgr-Acctg)*
Stephen Murray *(Mgr-Education)*

THE KAUFMAN CENTER

129 W 67th St
New York, NY 10023
Tel.: (212) 501-3303
Fax: (212) 874-7865
E-mail: info@kaufman-center.org
Web Site: www.kaufman-center.org
Approx. Number Employees: 50
Business Description:
Performing Arts Center
S.I.C.: 7389
N.A.I.C.S.: 711310
Media: 7-8-9-20-22-23-24-25
Personnel:
Lydia Kontos *(Exec Dir)*
Kathy Hubbard *(Dir-Admin)*
Brands & Products:
LUCY MOSES SCHOOL
MERKIN CONCERT HALL
SPECIAL MUSIC SCHOOL

KAWAI AMERICA CORPORATION

(Sub. of Kawai Musical Instruments Mfg. Co., Ltd.)
2055 E University Dr
Compton, CA 90220-6411
Mailing Address:
PO Box 9045
Rancho Dominguez, CA 90224-9045
Tel.: (310) 631-1771
Fax: (310) 604-6913
Web Site: www.kawaius.com
Approx. Number Employees: 30
Year Founded: 1963
Business Description:
Musical Instrument Importer & Distr
S.I.C.: 5099
N.A.I.C.S.: 423990
Import
Media: 2-4-8-10-18-19-20-21
Distr.: Natl.
Budget Set: Apr.
Personnel:
Joe Deleski *(Dir-Adv)*

KCS INTERNATIONAL, INC.

804 Pecor St
Oconto, WI 54153
Tel.: (920) 834-2211
Fax: (920) 834-2797
Fax: (920) 834-2105
Sales Range: $100-124.9 Million
Approx. Number Employees: 1,100
Year Founded: 1993
Business Description:
Boat Building & Repairing
S.I.C.: 3732
N.A.I.C.S.: 336612
Import Export
Media: 10
Distr.: Boats
Personnel:
Kenneth C. Stock *(Chm & CEO)*
Mark Pederson *(Pres)*
Brands & Products:
CRUISERS
RAMPAGE

Key to Media (For complete agency information see *The Advertising Red Books-Agencies* edition):
1. Bus. Publs. 2. Cable T.V. 3. Catalogs & Directories. 4. Co-op Adv. 5. Consumer Mags. 6. D.M. to Bus. Estab.7. D.M. to Consumers 8. Daily Newsp. 9. Exhibits/Trade Shows 10. Foreign 11. Infomercial 12. Internet Adv.13. Multimedia 14. Network Radio 15. Network T.V. 16. Newsp. Distr. Mags. 17. Other 18. Outdoor (Posters, Transit) 19. Point of Purchase20. Premiums, Novelties 21. Product Samples 22. Special Events Mktg. 23. Spot Radio 24. Spot T.V. 25. Weekly Newsp. 26. Yellow Page Adv.

Advertising Agency:
BVK
250 W Coventry Ct #300
Milwaukee, WI 53217-3972
Tel.: (414) 228-1990
Fax: (414) 228-7561
Toll Free: (888) 347-3212

KENTUCKY DERBY FESTIVAL, INC.

1001 S 3rd St
Louisville, KY 40203
Tel.: (502) 584-6383
Fax: (502) 589-4674
E-mail: info@kdf.org
Web Site: www.kdf.org
Approx. Number Employees: 23
Year Founded: 1956
Business Description:
Kentucky Derby Promotion
S.I.C.: 8641; 8611
N.A.I.C.S.: 813410; 813910
Advertising Expenditures: $150,000
Media: 8-9-10-17-18-19-22-23-24-25
Distr.: Reg.
Personnel:
Ja Hillebrand *(Chm)*
Michael E. Berry *(Pres & CEO)*
Pat Armstrong *(Sr VP)*
Stacey Robinson *(Sr VP-Ops)*
Aimee Boyd *(VP-Comm)*
Bridget Sherrill *(VP-Mdse)*
Dodie L. Holderfield *(Mgr-Adv & Promos)*
Jennifer Morgan Keesaer *(Mgr-Mdsg)*
Mark Shallcross *(Mgr-Comm)*
Brands & Products:
CHOW WAGON
KENTUCKY DERBY FESTIVAL
MINIMARATHON
NIGHT OF THE FUTURE STARS
PEGASUS
RUN FOR THE ROSE
THEY'RE OFF
THOROBRED

KEY WEST SYMPHONY ORCHESTRA

PO Box 774
Key West, FL 33041
Tel.: (305) 292-1774
Fax: (305) 292-5623
Web Site:
www.keywestsymphony.com
Approx. Number Employees: 90
Business Description:
Symphony Orchestra
S.I.C.: 7929
N.A.I.C.S.: 711130
Media: 9-22-23-24-25
Personnel:
Susan Collins *(Gen Mgr)*
Sebrina Maria Alfonso *(Dir-Music)*

KNOTT'S BERRY FARM

(Sub. of Cedar Fair, L.P.)
8039 Beach Blvd
Buena Park, CA 90620
Tel.: (714) 220-5200
Fax: (714) 220-5124
E-mail: info@knotts.com
Web Site: www.knotts.com
E-Mail For Key Personnel:
Public Relations: pr@knotts.com
Sales Range: $400-449.9 Million
Approx. Number Employees: 2,000
Year Founded: 1922
Business Description:
Amusement Park Operator
S.I.C.: 7996; 2033
N.A.I.C.S.: 713110; 311421
Import Export
Media: 1-2-3-5-6-8-9-10-11-13-18-19-20-22-23-24-25-26
Distr.: Natl.
Budget Set: Nov. -Dec.
Personnel:
Carolyn Kehler *(Sr VP-Mktg & Sls-W Coast Opers)*
Jack T. Falfas *(VP & Gen Mgr)*
Lupita Suda *(Mgr-Adv, Promotions & Special Events)*
Brands & Products:
BIGFOOT RAPIDS
BOOMERANG
CALIFORNIA MARKETPLACE
INDEPENDENCE HALL
JAGUAR!
KINGDOM OF THE DINOSAURS
RIP TIDE
SKY CABIN

KNOXVILLE SYMPHONY SOCIETY INC.

100 Southgate St Ste 302
Knoxville, TN 37902
Tel.: (865) 523-1178
Fax: (865) 546-3766
E-mail: ksopix@knoxvillesymphony.com
Web Site:
www.knoxvillesymphony.com
Approx. Sls.: $3,500,000
Approx. Number Employees: 14
Year Founded: 1910
Business Description:
Symphony Orchestra
S.I.C.: 8699
N.A.I.C.S.: 813990
Media: 7-8-9-13-20-23-24-25
Personnel:
Chuck Kocal *(Dir-Mktg)*
Mike Greiner *(Dir-Fin)*
Lucas Richman *(Dir-Music)*
Stacy Taylor *(Dir-Ops)*
Lisa Cosse *(Mgr-Annual Fund)*
Kathy Hart-Reilly *(Mgr-Youth Orchestra)*

KORG USA, INC.

(Sub. of Korg Inc.)
316 S Service Rd
Melville, NY 11747
Tel.: (631) 390-6800
Tel.: (631) 390-6500
Fax: (631) 390-6501
Toll Free: (800) 645-3188
Telex: 291407 KORG OR
Web Site: www.korg.com
Sales Range: $100-124.9 Million
Approx. Number Employees: 115
Year Founded: 1963
Business Description:
Musical Instruments; Synthesizers; Sound Modules; Digital Pianos; Tuners; Hyperperformance Processors
S.I.C.: 2741; 5736
N.A.I.C.S.: 512230; 451140
Import Export
Media: 2-4-5-6-8-10-19-20-22
Budget Set: Mar.
Personnel:
Joseph Castronovo *(Pres-Soundtree)*
Joe Gilmartin *(Product Mgr-Korg Tuners & Metronomes)*
Brands & Products:
AMPWORKS B
AMPWORKS G
BX-3
C-6500
CX-3
D16XD
D32XD
DT3
DT7
DTR-1000
DTR-2000
ELECTRIBE A
ELECTRIBE AMKII
ELECTRIBE M
ELECTRIBE MX
ELECTRIBE S
ELETCTRIBE MKII
GT3
KAOSS MIXER
KAOSS PAD ENTRANCER
KP2 KAOSS PAD
MARSHALL
MICROKONTROL
MICROKORG
MS2000B
MS2000BR
NC-300
NC-500
PA1X
PA50
PA60
PA80
SP-200
SP-300
SP-500
TONEWORKS
TRITON EXTREME
TRITON LE
TRITON RACK
TRITON STUDIO
TRITONPRO
VOX
X5D
Advertising Agency:
Eve Seco Display Inc.
209 Waters Edge
Valley Cottage, NY 10989
Tel.: (845) 268-5111
Fax: (845) 268-5115

LA CROSSE SYMPHONY ORCHESTRA, INC.

3217 Commerce St
La Crosse, WI 54603
Tel.: (608) 783-2121
Fax: (608) 783-3121
E-mail: lacrossesymphony@lacrossesymphony.org
Web Site: www.lacrossesymphony.org
Approx. Number Employees: 3
Year Founded: 1898
Business Description:
Symphony Orchestra
S.I.C.: 7929
N.A.I.C.S.: 711130
Media: 9-20-23-24-25
Personnel:
Tracy Fell *(Exec Dir)*
Connie Smith *(Exec Dir)*

LAKE SHORE SYMPHONY ORCHESTRA

PO Box 11973
Chicago, IL 60611-0973
Tel.: (312) 409-5670
E-mail: info@lsso.org
Web Site: www.lsso.org
Approx. Number Employees: 25
Year Founded: 1973
Business Description:
Not-for-Profit Symphony Orchestra
S.I.C.: 7929
N.A.I.C.S.: 711130
Media: 7-8-9-20-23-24-25
Personnel:
Richard Peck *(Pres)*
Seymour Horowitz *(Treas)*
Jeremy Young *(VP & Dir-Concert Admin)*
Jerry Ragusa *(Dir-Fundraising)*
Ruth Swislow *(Dir-Individual Sponsorships)*
Russell Vinick *(Dir-Music)*

LAKE TAHOE CRUISES, INC.

(Sub. of ARAMARK Harrison Lodging)
900 Ski Run Blvd Ste 2
South Lake Tahoe, CA 96150-3364
Tel.: (775) 589-4906
Fax: (530) 541-8685
Toll Free: (800) 238-2463
E-mail: info@zephyrcove.com
Web Site: www.laketahoecruises.com
Business Description:
Cruise Services
S.I.C.: 4482
N.A.I.C.S.: 483114
Media: 6-7-10

LANCASTER SYMPHONY ORCHESTRA

226 N Arch St
Lancaster, PA 17603
Mailing Address:
PO Box 1281
Lancaster, PA 17608-1281
Tel.: (717) 291-6440
Fax: (717) 291-6441
Web Site:
www.lancastersymphony.org
Approx. Sls.: $1,000,000
Approx. Number Employees: 12
Year Founded: 1947
Business Description:
Symphony Orchestra
S.I.C.: 7929
N.A.I.C.S.: 711130
Media: 8-9-23-24-25
Personnel:
M. Scott Robinson *(Pres & CEO)*
Nancy LeVasseur *(Mgr-Web Content, Dir-Community Engagement & Grants)*
Shelley Cohen Hershey *(Dir-Dev)*
Heather Colosi *(Dir-Mktg & Special Events)*
Stephen Gunzenhauser *(Conductor & Dir-Music)*
Thomas Blanchard *(Mgr-Orchestra Personnel)*
Barb McConnell *(Mgr-Subscription & Bus)*

LANSING SYMPHONY ORCHESTRA

501 S Capitol Ave Ste 400
Lansing, MI 48933
Tel.: (517) 487-5001
Fax: (517) 487-0210

Key to Media (For complete agency information see *The Advertising Red Books-Agencies* edition):
1. Bus. Publs. 2. Cable T.V. 3. Catalogs & Directories. 4. Co-op Adv. 5. Consumer Mags. 6. D.M. to Bus. Estab.7. D.M. to Consumers
8. Daily Newsp. 9. Exhibits/Trade Shows 10. Foreign 11. Infomercial 12. Internet Adv.13. Multimedia 14. Network Radio
15. Network T.V. 16. Newsp. Distr. Mags. 17. Other 18. Outdoor (Posters, Transit) 19. Point of Purchase20. Premiums, Novelties
21. Product Samples 22. Special Events Mktg. 23. Spot Radio 24. Spot T.V. 25. Weekly Newsp. 26. Yellow Page Adv.

Lansing Symphony Orchestra — (Continued)

E-mail: info@lansingsymphony.org
Web Site: www.lansingsymphony.org
Approx. Number Employees: 6
Year Founded: 1929
Business Description:
Symphony Orchestra
S.I.C.: 7929
N.A.I.C.S.: 711130
Media: 9-20-23-24-25
Personnel:
R. Samuel Holland *(Pres-Elect)*
Karen Cutshaw *(Dir-Fin & Ops)*
Timothy Muffitt *(Music Dir)*

LAPORTE COUNTY SYMPHONY ORCHESTRA

PO Box 563
La Porte, IN 46352
Tel.: (219) 362-9020
Fax: (219) 362-9020
E-mail: executive@lcso.net
Web Site: www.lcso.net
Sales Range: Less than $1 Million
Approx. Number Employees: 1
Business Description:
Symphony Orchestra
S.I.C.: 7929
N.A.I.C.S.: 711130
Media: 8-9-20-23-24-25
Personnel:
Marcia Morres *(Pres)*
Lee Bauman *(Exec Dir)*
Philip J. Bauman *(Dir-Music)*
Diana Ford *(Dir-Education)*

LAS COLINAS SYMPHONY ORCHESTRA ASSOCIATION INC.

4322 N Beltline Rd Ste B114
Irving, TX 75038
Mailing Address:
PO Box 141446
Irving, TX 75014
Tel.: (972) 252-4800
Fax: (972) 550-7954
Web Site:
www.lascolinassymphony.org
Year Founded: 1991
Business Description:
Symphony Orchestra
S.I.C.: 7929
N.A.I.C.S.: 711130
Media: 9-20-23-24-25
Personnel:
David Hawkins *(Co-Pres)*
Deborah Hawkins *(Exec Dir)*
Robert Carter Austin *(Dir-Musical & Conductor)*

LEGOLAND CALIFORNIA LLC

(Sub. of Merlin Entertainments Group Ltd.)
1 Legoland Dr
Carlsbad, CA 92008
Tel.: (760) 918-5346
Fax: (760) 918-5375
Web Site: www.legoland.com
Sales Range: $50-74.9 Million
Approx. Number Employees: 400
Business Description:
Theme Park Operations
S.I.C.: 7996
N.A.I.C.S.: 713110
Media: 6-9-23-24-25
Personnel:
Peter Kock *(Dir-Mktg & Sls)*
Lynn Crockett *(Mgr-Education)*
Advertising Agencies:
Dailey & Associates
(Sub. of The Interpublic Group of Cos., Inc.)
8687 Melrose Ave Ste G300
West Hollywood, CA 90069-5701
Tel.: (310) 360-3100
Fax: (310) 360-0810

Pereira & O'Dell
215 2nd St
San Francisco, CA 94105
Tel.: (415) 284-9916
Fax: (415) 284-9926

LEXINGTON PHILHARMONIC SOCIETY

161 N Mill St
Lexington, KY 40507
Tel.: (859) 233-4226
Fax: (859) 233-7896
Toll Free: (888) 494-4226
E-mail: office@lexphil.org
Web Site: www.lexphil.org
Sales Range: $10-24.9 Million
Approx. Number Employees: 100
Business Description:
Symphony Orchestra
S.I.C.: 7389
N.A.I.C.S.: 711320
Media: 9-20-23-24-25
Personnel:
Alison Kaiser *(Gen Mgr)*

LIBERTY SCIENCE CENTER, INC.

222 Jersey City Blvd
Jersey City, NJ 07305
Tel.: (201) 451-0006
Fax: (201) 451-5931
E-mail: guestcomments@lsc.org
Web Site: www.lsc.org
Sales Range: $10-24.9 Million
Approx. Number Employees: 280
Year Founded: 1993
Business Description:
Science Exhibits, Hands-on Children's Displays & IMAX Theatre Attractions
S.I.C.: 8412
N.A.I.C.S.: 712110
Media: 8-9-10-13-23-24-25
Personnel:
Emlyn Koster *(Pres & CEO)*
Lawrence Bathgate *(Partner)*
Connie Claman *(CFO & VP-Resource Admin)*
Barry Zubrow *(Chief Admin Officer)*
Elizabeth Stoner *(Sr VP-Clinical Devel)*
Mark Mattia *(VP-Mktg & Comm)*

LIGHTNING HOCKEY LP

(Holding of Tampa Bay Sports & Entertainment LLC)
(d/b/a Tampa Bay Lightning Hockey Club)
401 Channelside Dr
Tampa, FL 33602-5400
Tel.: (813) 301-6600
Fax: (813) 301-1482
Web Site: lightning.nhl.com
Approx. Number Employees: 100
Year Founded: 1992
Business Description:
Professional Hockey Club
S.I.C.: 7941
N.A.I.C.S.: 711211
Advertising Expenditures: $200,000
Media: 3-7-8-9-10-14-15-18-22-23-24-25
Distr.: Natl.
Personnel:
Jeff Vinik *(Owner, Chm & Governor)*
Tod Leiweke *(CEO & Alternate Governor)*
Paul Davis *(Gen Counsel & Sr VP)*
Brad Lott *(Exec VP-Sls & Mktg)*
Bill Wickett *(Exec VP-Comm)*
Patrick Duffy *(Sr VP-Corp Sls)*
Keith Harris *(Sr VP-HR)*
Steve Yzerman *(VP & Gen Mgr)*
Tom Kurvers *(Asst Gen Mgr)*
Ryan Bringger *(Sr Dir-New Bus Dev)*
Paul Wallace *(Sr Dir-Client Sls & Retention)*
Ryan West *(Sr Dir-Ticket Sls)*
Ryan Belec *(Dir-Team Svcs)*
Amanda Graul *(Dir-Client Svcs)*
Ira Guttentag *(Dir-Medical)*
Jim Hammett *(Dir-Player Personnel)*
Ian Steele *(Dir-IT)*
Nashira Babooram *(Sr Mgr-Mktg)*
Liz Sylvia *(Mgr-Hockey Admin)*
Ray Thill *(Mgr-Equipment)*

Brands & Products:
TAMPA BAY LIGHTNING

Advertising Agencies:
Ad Gals of Tampa
1517 7th Ave., Ste. D
Tampa, FL 33605
Tel.: (813) 258-3668

FKQ Advertising + Marketing
15351 Roosevelt Blvd
Clearwater, FL 33760-3534
Tel.: (727) 539-8800
Fax: (866) 707-6648

LINCOLN CENTER FOR THE PERFORMING ARTS, INC.

70 Lincoln Ctr Plz
New York, NY 10023
Tel.: (212) 875-5000
Fax: (212) 875-5011
E-mail: webmaster@lincolncenter.org
Web Site: www.lincolncenter.org
Sales Range: $75-99.9 Million
Approx. Number Employees: 511
Business Description:
Theatrical Producers & Services
S.I.C.: 7922
N.A.I.C.S.: 711110
Media: 9-18-20-23-24-25
Personnel:
Reynold Levy *(Pres)*
Lesley Friedman Rosenthal *(Gen Counsel, Sec & VP)*
Liza Parker *(Sr VP-HR & Lincoln Center Opns)*
Tamar C. Podell *(Sr VP-Plng & Dev)*
Erica Zielinski *(Gen Mgr)*
Rosemarie Garipoli *(Exec Dir-Bravo Lincoln Center Campaign)*
Scott Noppe-Brandon *(Exec Dir)*
Farang Azari *(Dir-Planning)*
Christine Donato *(Dir-Dev Ops)*
Arlene Graime *(Dir)*
Thomas Lollar *(Dir-Visual Art)*
Nigel Redden *(Dir-Festival)*
Hanako Yamaguchi *(Dir-Music Programming)*
Daniel A. Fletcher *(Assoc Dir)*
Mara Forbes *(Assoc Dir-Mktg)*
Richard Greene *(Assoc Dir)*
Terry Larsen *(Assoc Dir-Concert Halls/ Production)*
Stacey Tunks *(Mgr-HR)*
John Goberman *(Exec Producer-Television)*
Brands & Products:
AMERICAN SONGBOOK
CENTERCHARGE
JAZZ AT LINCOLN CENTER
LINCOLN CENTER
LIVE FROM LINCOLN CENTER
MIDSUMMER NIGHT SWING
MOSTLY MOZART
Advertising Agencies:
A.D. Lubow, LLC
1 Penn Plz Ste 5312
New York, NY 10119-5312
Tel.: (212) 564-3250
Fax: (212) 564-2866

Beekman Marketing, Inc.
35 E 21st St Seventh Fl
New York, NY 10010
Tel.: (212) 387-8500
Fax: (212) 387-7875

Planit
500 E Pratt St 10th Fl
Baltimore, MD 21202
Tel.: (410) 962-8500
Fax: (410) 962-8508

LINCOLN PARK ZOO

2001 N Clark St
Chicago, IL 60614
Mailing Address:
PO Box 14903
Chicago, IL 60614
Tel.: (312) 742-2000
Fax: (312) 742-2306
E-mail: questions@lpzoo.com
Web Site: www.lpzoo.com
Approx. Number Employees: 160
Year Founded: 1868
Business Description:
Zoo Operator
S.I.C.: 8422
N.A.I.C.S.: 712130
Advertising Expenditures: $100,000
Media: 7-8-9-10-13-18-20-22-23-25
Distr.: Direct to Consumer; Reg.
Personnel:
Kevin J. Bell *(Pres & CEO)*
Troy Baresel *(CFO)*
Peggy Martin *(Dir-Design & Comm)*

LINCOLN SYMPHONY ORCHESTRA

233 S 13th St Ste 1702
Lincoln, NE 68508
Tel.: (402) 476-2211
E-mail: info@lincolnsymphony.com
Web Site: www.lincolnsymphony.com
Sales Range: $10-24.9 Million
Approx. Number Employees: 6
Year Founded: 1927
Business Description:
Symphony Orchestra
S.I.C.: 7929
N.A.I.C.S.: 711130
Media: 9-20-23-24-25
Personnel:
Barbara Zach *(Exec Dir)*
Edward Polochick *(Dir-Music)*
Susan Larson Rodenburg *(Dir-Mktg)*
Tricia Coulton *(Mgr-Acctg)*
Amanda Sambiso *(Mgr-Acctg)*

Key to Media (For complete agency information see *The Advertising Red Books-Agencies* edition):
1. Bus. Publs. 2. Cable T.V. 3. Catalogs & Directories. 4. Co-op Adv. 5. Consumer Mags. 6. D.M. to Bus. Estab.7. D.M. to Consumers
8. Daily Newsp. 9. Exhibits/Trade Shows 10. Foreign 11. Infomercial 12. Internet Adv.13. Multimedia 14. Network Radio
15. Network T.V. 16. Newsp. Distr. Mags. 17. Other 18. Outdoor (Posters, Transit) 19. Point of Purchase20. Premiums, Novelties
21. Product Samples 22. Special Events Mktg. 23. Spot Radio 24. Spot T.V. 25. Weekly Newsp. 26. Yellow Page Adv.

LITTLEFIELD CORPORATION
2501 N Lamar Blvd
Austin, TX 78705
Tel.: (512) 476-5141
Fax: (512) 476-5680
E-mail: customerservice@littlefield.com
Web Site: www.littlefield.com
Approx. Rev.: $9,635,310
Approx. Number Employees: 20
Year Founded: 1994
Business Description:
Developer, Owner & Operator of Charitable Bingo Halls, Gaming & Amusement Arcades; Owner & Developer of Party Rental & Catering Companies.
S.I.C.: 7999; 7997
N.A.I.C.S.: 713990; 713910
Advertising Expenditures: $47,000
Media: 20-22
Personnel:
Carlton R. Williams, Jr. *(Chm)*
Jeffrey L. Minch *(Pres & CEO)*
Richard S. Chilinski *(CFO & Exec VP)*
Michael J. Lindley *(Sr VP)*
Brands & Products:
ADVENTURELESS CAPITAL
URGENT EXCELLENCE

LITTLETON SYMPHONY ORCHESTRA
5894 S Datura
Littleton, CO 80120
Mailing Address:
PO Box 1208
Littleton, CO 80160-1208
Tel.: (303) 933-6824
E-mail: info@littletonsymphony.org
Web Site: www.littletonsymphony.org
Year Founded: 1984
Business Description:
Symphony Orchestra
S.I.C.: 7929
N.A.I.C.S.: 711130
Media: 9-20-23-24-25
Personnel:
Rich Spritz *(Pres)*
Jurgen de Lemos *(Dir-Music & Conductor)*

LIVE NATION ENTERTAINMENT, INC.
9348 Civic Center Dr
Beverly Hills, CA 90210
Tel.: (310) 867-7000
Fax: (310) 867-7001
Web Site: www.livenation.com
Approx. Rev.: $5,063,748,000
Approx. Number Employees: 6,500
Business Description:
Live Entertainment Producer & Promoter
S.I.C.: 7389; 7313; 7812; 7819; 7999
N.A.I.C.S.: 711310; 512110; 512191; 541840; 711320; 711410; 713990
Advertising Expenditures: $178,700,000
Personnel:
Irving L. Azoff *(Chm)*
Russell Wallach *(Pres)*
Michael Rapino *(CEO)*
Kathy Willard *(CFO & Exec VP)*
Brian Capo *(Chief Acctg Officer)*
Arthur Fogel *(Chm-Global Music & CEO-Global Touring)*
Jodi Goodman *(Pres-Northern California)*
Eric Pirritt *(Pres-Colorado & Rocky Mountain Reg)*
Bob Roux *(Pres-Live Nation Concerts)*
Nathan Hubbard *(CEO-Ticketing)*
Alan Ridgeway *(CEO-Intl Music)*
Michael G. Rowles *(Gen Counsel & Exec VP)*
John Hopmans *(Exec VP-Mergers & Acq & Strategic Fin)*
Django Bayless *(Sr VP)*
Scott Amerman *(Dir-Premium Seat Sls)*
David Beck *(Dir-Sls-Premium Seat Sls-North East)*
Tammy LeMelle *(Dir-Mktg)*
Advertising Agencies:
1 Trick Pony
251 Bellevue Ave 2nd Fl
Hammonton, NJ 08037
Tel.: (609) 704-2660
Fax: (646) 619-4095

Genesis-Vizeum
22 St Claire Ave E Ste 500
Toronto, ON M4T 2S5, Canada
Tel.: (416) 967-7282
Fax: (416) 967-1395

InnoVision Media Group
3301 E Hill St Ste 401
Signal Hill, CA 90755
Tel.: (562) 961-3610
Fax: (562) 961-3616
Toll Free: (888) 843-9255

Serino Coyne LLC
(Sub. of Omnicom Group Inc.)
1515 Broadway 36th Fl
New York, NY 10036-8901
Tel.: (212) 626-2700
Fax: (212) 626-2799

Vice Squad
1407 Main St Ste 904
Dallas, TX 75202
Tel.: (214) 682-1545
Fax: (214) 889-3100

Worx Branding & Advertising
18 Waterbury Rd
Prospect, CT 06712-1215
Tel.: (203) 758-3311
Fax: (203) 758-6847

LIVE NATION WORLDWIDE - TIMES SQUARE OFFICE
(Branch of Live Nation Entertainment, Inc.)
220 W 42nd St
New York, NY 10036-7202
Tel.: (917) 421-4000
Tel.: (917) 421-5100
Sales Range: $100-124.9 Million
Year Founded: 1998
Business Description:
Producer & Promoter of Live Entertainment Events
S.I.C.: 7389
N.A.I.C.S.: 711320
Media: 2-13
Personnel:
Bruce Eskowitz *(CEO-NA Music)*
Brands & Products:
IT'S BETTER LIVE

LONG BEACH SYMPHONY ORCHESTRA
110 W Ocean Blvd Ste 22
Long Beach, CA 90802
Tel.: (562) 436-3203
Fax: (562) 491-3599
E-mail: lbso@lbso.org
Web Site: www.lbso.org
Sales Range: $10-24.9 Million
Approx. Number Employees: 300
Business Description:
Symphony Orchestra
S.I.C.: 7929
N.A.I.C.S.: 711130
Media: 8-9-13-20-23-24-25
Personnel:
Janet Nyquist *(Gen Mgr)*
Enrique Arturo Diemecke *(Dir-Music)*
Donna Thrall *(Dir-Fin & Admin)*
Kari Regan *(Mgr-Special Events & Ops)*

LONG ISLAND CHILDREN'S MUSEUM
11 Davis Ave
Garden City, NY 11530
Tel.: (516) 224-5800
Fax: (516) 302-8188
Web Site: www.licm.org
Approx. Number Employees: 100
Business Description:
Children's Museum
S.I.C.: 8412
N.A.I.C.S.: 712110
Media: 8-9-10-20-23-24-25
Personnel:
Maureen P. Mangan *(Dir-Comm)*
Erik Schurink *(Dir-Exec)*

LONG ISLAND PHILHARMONIC
1 Huntington Quadrangle
Melville, NY 11747
Tel.: (631) 293-2223
Fax: (631) 293-2655
E-mail: info@liphilharmonic.org
Web Site: www.liphilharmonic.org
Approx. Number Employees: 8
Business Description:
Symphony Orchestra
S.I.C.: 7929
N.A.I.C.S.: 711130
Media: 9-20-23-24-25
Personnel:
Larry Austin *(Chm)*
John J. Russell *(Pres)*
Linda M. Morrisey *(Gen Mgr)*
David Carp *(Librarian)*

LOS ANGELES CLIPPERS
1111 S Figueroa St Ste 1100
Los Angeles, CA 90015
Tel.: (213) 742-7500
Fax: (213) 742-7550
Web Site: www.clippers.com
E-Mail For Key Personnel:
President: aroeser@clippers.com
Marketing Director: cfl@clippers.com
Sales Range: $10-24.9 Million
Approx. Number Employees: 80
Year Founded: 1970
Business Description:
Professional Basketball Franchise Owner & Operator
S.I.C.: 7941
N.A.I.C.S.: 711211
Media: 2-3-6-7-8-9-10-13-18-23-24-25
Distr.: Reg.
Budget Set: May -June
Personnel:
Donald T. Sterling *(Owner & Chm)*
Bob Platt *(Gen Counsel)*
Andy Roeser *(Exec VP)*
Carl Lahr *(Sr VP-Mktg & Sls)*
Ed Lamb *(VP-Fin & Controller)*
Christian Howard *(VP-Mktg & Brdcst)*
Joe Safety *(VP-Comm)*
Neil Olshey *(Gen Mgr)*
Chris Beyer *(Sr Dir-Sponsorship Sls)*
Greg Flaherty *(Sr Dir-Corp Sls)*
Denise Booth *(Dir-Community Rels & Player Programs)*
Rob Raichlen *(Dir-Comm)*
Gary Sacks *(Dir-Scouting)*
Advertising Agency:
HEILBrice
9840 Irvine Center Dr
Irvine, CA 92618
Tel.: (949) 336-8800
Fax: (949) 336-8819

LOS ANGELES COUNTY FAIR ASSOCIATION
1101 W McKinley Ave
Pomona, CA 91768
Mailing Address:
PO Box 2250
Pomona, CA 91769
Tel.: (909) 623-3111
Fax: (909) 865-3602
E-mail: info@fairplex.com
Web Site: www.lacountyfair.com
Approx. Number Employees: 300
Year Founded: 1922
Business Description:
Convention Center
S.I.C.: 7999; 8412
N.A.I.C.S.: 713990; 712110
Media: 10-18-24-25
Personnel:
Richard P. Crean *(Chm)*
Reginald Webb *(Vice Chm)*
Jim Henwood *(Pres & CEO)*
Dale Coleman *(VP-Sls & Mktg)*
Kathy Wadham *(Dir-Creative Devel)*
Renee Mendoza *(Dir-HR)*

LOS ANGELES DODGERS INC.
1000 Elysian Park Ave
Los Angeles, CA 90012-1199
Tel.: (323) 224-1500
Tel.: (323) 224-1309
Tel.: (323) 224-1400
Fax: (323) 224-2617
Fax: (323) 224-1269
Web Site:
losangeles.dodgers.mlb.com
Approx. Number Employees: 1,200
Year Founded: 1884
Business Description:
Professional Baseball Club
S.I.C.: 7941
N.A.I.C.S.: 711211
Media: 3-4-7-8-9-11-18-19-20-22-23-24-25-26
Distr.: Direct to Customer; Natl.
Personnel:
Frank McCourt *(Owner & Chm)*
Don Newcombe *(Chm & Special Advisor)*
Steve Soboroff *(Vice Chm)*
Peter Wilhelm *(CFO)*
Charles Steinberg *(CMO & Exec VP)*
Sam Fernandez *(Gen Counsel & Sr VP)*
Marlo Vandemore *(VP-Fin)*

Key to Media (For complete agency information see *The Advertising Red Books-Agencies* edition):
1. Bus. Publs. 2. Cable T.V. 3. Catalogs & Directories. 4. Co-op Adv. 5. Consumer Mags. 6. D.M. to Bus. Estab.7. D.M. to Consumers 8. Daily Newsp. 9. Exhibits/Trade Shows 10. Foreign 11. Infomercial 12. Internet Adv.13. Multimedia 14. Network Radio 15. Network T.V. 16. Newsp. Distr. Mags. 17. Other 18. Outdoor (Posters, Transit) 19. Point of Purchase20. Premiums, Novelties 21. Product Samples 22. Special Events Mktg. 23. Spot Radio 24. Spot T.V. 25. Weekly Newsp. 26. Yellow Page Adv.

Los Angeles Dodgers Inc. — (Continued)

Marco White *(VP-IT)*
De Jon Watson *(Asst Gen Mgr - Player Dev)*
Ned Colletti *(Gen Mgr)*
Logan White *(Asst Gen Mgr-Amateur & Intl Scouting)*
Warren Leonard *(Sr Dir-HR & Deputy Gen Counsel)*
Tim Hallgren *(Dir-Scouting)*
Ellen Harrigan *(Dir-Baseball Admin)*
Vanessa Leyvas *(Dir-Admin & Mktg & Pub Rel)*
Jorge Martin *(Dir-Publ)*
Jenny Oh *(Dir-Partnership Admin)*
Rebecca Aguilar *(Sr Mgr-Payroll & Accts Payable)*
Roxanne Adams *(Mgr-Ticket Admin)*
Jennifer Harris *(Mgr-Payroll)*
Jorge Jarrin *(Mgr-Radio Brdcst Sls & Hispanic Initiatives)*
Desiree Sanchez *(Mgr-Ticket Ops)*

Brands & Products:
DODGERS
LA
LOS ANGELES DODGERS
THINKCURE

Advertising Agencies:
Alternative & Innovative Marketing, LLC
8120 Engineer Rd
San Diego, CA 92111
Tel.: (760) 747-0444
Fax: (760) 747-0477

MLB Advanced Media, L.P.
75 9th Ave 5th Fl
New York, NY 10011
Tel.: (212) 485-3444
Fax: (212) 485-3456

LOS ANGELES KINGS HOCKEY CLUB L.P.

1111 S Figueroa St
Los Angeles, CA 90015
Tel.: (213) 742-7100
Fax: (213) 742-7296
Toll Free: (888) KINGSLA
E-mail: feedback@lakings.com
Web Site: www.lakings.com
Sales Range: $75-99.9 Million
Approx. Number Employees: 120
Year Founded: 1967
Business Description:
Professional Hockey Team Owner & Operator
S.I.C.: 7941
N.A.I.C.S.: 711211
Media: 3-5-9-10-13-18-22-23-24
Distr.: Natl.
Personnel:
Dean Lombardi *(Pres & Gen Mgr-Alternate Governor)*
Shelby Russell *(Dir-Partnership Activation)*
Dan Beckerman *(CFO)*
Michael Altieri *(VP-Comm & Content)*
Jeff Moeller *(Sr Dir-Comm)*

LOS ANGELES PHILHARMONIC ASSOCIATION

111 S Grand Ave
Los Angeles, CA 90012
Tel.: (323) 850-2000
Fax: (213) 972-7397
E-mail: info@laphil.com
Web Site: www.laphil.com
Approx. Sls.: $54,037,000
Approx. Number Employees: 195
Year Founded: 1919
Business Description:
Entertainers & Entertainment Groups
S.I.C.: 7389
N.A.I.C.S.: 711320
Media: 9-18-20-23-24-25
Personnel:
David Bohnett *(Chm)*
Deborah Borda *(Pres)*
Advertising Agencies:
Davidson & Choy Publicity
4311 Wilshire Blvd Ste 202
Los Angeles, CA 90010
Tel.: (323) 954-7510
Fax: (323) 954-7520

Palisades Media Group, Inc.
1620 26th St Ste 200 S
Santa Monica, CA 90404-4013
Tel.: (310) 828-9100
Fax: (310) 828-9117

The Ruder Finn Group
301 E 57th St
New York, NY 10022-2900
Tel.: (212) 593-6400
Fax: (212) 593-6397

LOS ANGELES TURF CLUB, INCORPORATED

(Holding of The Santa Anita Companies, Inc.)
(d/b/a Santa Anita Park)
285 W Huntington Dr
Arcadia, CA 91007
Mailing Address:
PO Box 60014
Arcadia, CA 91066-6014
Tel.: (626) 574-7223
Fax: (626) 574-5074
E-mail: info@santaanita.com
Web Site: www.santaanita.com
Sales Range: $75-99.9 Million
Approx. Number Employees: 300
Year Founded: 1934
Business Description:
Horse Racetrack Operator
S.I.C.: 7948
N.A.I.C.S.: 711212
Media: 8-9-10-23-24-25
Distr.: Reg.
Budget Set: Oct.
Personnel:
George Haines *(Interim Pres)*
Allen Gutterman *(VP-Mktg)*

LOTO-QUEBEC

500 Sherbrooke St W Ste 2100
Montreal, QC H3A 3G6, Canada
Tel.: (514) 282-8000
Fax: (514) 873-9258
Fax: (514) 499-8660
Toll Free: (800) 350-9033
Web Site: www.loto-quebec.com
Sales Range: $1-4.9 Billion
Approx. Number Employees: 7,000
Year Founded: 1969
Business Description:
Operates Numbers Games, Television Lotteries, Sport Betting, Video Lottery, Casinos, Network Bingo & Multimedia Games
S.I.C.: 7999
N.A.I.C.S.: 713290
Personnel:
Alain Cousineau *(Chm, Pres & CEO)*
Simon Patenaude *(Mng Dir-Mktg)*
Victor Devito *(Mng Dir-Sls & Bus Rels)*
Jean Royer *(COO & Sr VP)*
Robert Ayotte *(Pres-Ops-Lotteries)*
Lynne Roiter *(Corp Sec & VP-Legal Affairs)*
Pierre Bibeau *(Sr VP-Corp Comm & Pub Affairs)*
Marcel Croux *(Sr VP-Corp Affairs)*
Gille Dufour *(Sr VP-Fin Affairs)*
Andre Dumouchel *(VP-HR)*
Johanne Rock *(VP-Fin & Admin)*
Francois Huot *(Dir-Corp Strategies & Risks)*
Martin Larose *(Dir-Internal Auditing)*
Jean-Pierre Roy *(Dir-Media Rels & Publications)*
Lynda Zuliani *(Dir-Adv & Bus Comm)*
Advertising Agency:
Bos Advertising
3970 Saint-Ambroise street
Montreal, QC H4C 2C7, Canada
Tel.: (514) 848-0010
Fax: (514) 373-2992

LOUISIANA PHILHARMONIC ORCHESTRA

1010 Common St Ste 2120
New Orleans, LA 70112-2465
Tel.: (504) 523-6530
Fax: (504) 595-8468
E-mail: info@lpomusic.com
Web Site: www.lpomusic.com
Approx. Number Employees: 75
Business Description:
Symphony Orchestra
S.I.C.: 7389
N.A.I.C.S.: 711320
Media: 9-20-22-23-24-25
Personnel:
Babs Mollere *(Mng Dir)*
Sharon Litwin *(Sr VP-External Affairs)*

LOUISVILLE ORCHESTRA, INC.

323 W Broadway Ste 700
Louisville, KY 40202
Tel.: (502) 587-8681
Fax: (502) 589-7870
E-mail: info@louisvilleorchestra.org
Web Site: www.louisvilleorchestra.org
Approx. Number Employees: 100
Year Founded: 1937
Business Description:
Symphony Orchestra
S.I.C.: 7929
N.A.I.C.S.: 711130
Advertising Expenditures: $300,000
Media: 3-6-7-8-9-13-18-20-22-23-24-25-26
Personnel:
Tonya McSorley *(CFO)*
Patrick J. Welsh *(Gen Counsel)*
Bill Lamb *(Co-VP-Comm)*
Jorge Mester *(Music Dir)*
Carla Givan Motes *(Dir-Patron Svcs-Ticket Ops)*
Ed Schadt *(Dir-Dev)*
Deborah Sunya Moore *(Dir-Education & Community Engagement)*
Callie Chapman *(Mgr-Design)*
Adrienne Hinkebein *(Mgr-Personnel)*
Bill Polk *(Mgr-Stage)*

LOWRY PARK ZOOLOGICAL SOCIETY OF TAMPA INC.

(d/b/a Lowry Park Zoo)
1101 W Sligh Ave
Tampa, FL 33604
Tel.: (813) 935-8552
Fax: (813) 935-9486
E-mail: information@lowryparkzoo.com
Web Site: www.lowryparkzoo.com
Approx. Number Employees: 300
Business Description:
Zoo
S.I.C.: 8422
N.A.I.C.S.: 712130
Media: 6-8-9-10-18-20-23-24-25
Personnel:
Susan Lykes Mueller *(Chm)*
Craig Pugh *(Pres & CEO)*
David Zimmerman *(COO & Exec VP)*
Trisha Rothman *(VP-Mktg & Sls)*
Rachel Nelson *(Dir-Pub Rel)*

LUBBOCK SYMPHONY ORCHESTRA

601 Ave K
Lubbock, TX 79401
Tel.: (806) 762-1688
Fax: (806) 762-1824
Web Site: www.lubbocksymphony.org
E-Mail For Key Personnel:
President: pparkman@lubbocksymphony.org
Sales Range: Less than $1 Million
Approx. Number Employees: 10
Year Founded: 1946
Business Description:
Symphony Orchestra Services
S.I.C.: 7929
N.A.I.C.S.: 711130
Media: 9-20-23-24-25
Personnel:
Brad Green *(Chm)*
Mary Saathoff *(Pres & CEO)*

LYNCHBURG SYMPHONY ORCHESTRA

621 Court St
Lynchburg, VA 24504
Tel.: (434) 845-6604
Fax: (434) 845-0768
E-mail: info@lynchburgsymphony.com
Web Site:
www.lynchburgsymphony.com
Approx. Number Employees: 3
Year Founded: 1983
Business Description:
Symphony Orchestra
S.I.C.: 7929
N.A.I.C.S.: 711130
Media: 4-8-9-13-20-22-23-24-25
Personnel:
Rick Piester *(Exec Dir)*
Bruce Habitzruther *(Dir-Music & Conductor)*
Rick Edwards *(Coord-Dev)*

MADAME WALKER THEATRE CENTER

617 Indiana Ave
Indianapolis, IN 46202
Tel.: (317) 236-2099
Fax: (317) 236-2097
E-mail: mwtcevents@aol.com
Web Site: www.walkertheatre.com
E-Mail For Key Personnel:
Public Relations: brucemwtc@aol.com
Approx. Number Employees: 10
Year Founded: 1979

Key to Media (For complete agency information see *The Advertising Red Books-Agencies* edition):
1. Bus. Publs. 2. Cable T.V. 3. Catalogs & Directories. 4. Co-op Adv. 5. Consumer Mags. 6. D.M. to Bus. Estab.7. D.M. to Consumers
8. Daily Newsp. 9. Exhibits/Trade Shows 10. Foreign 11. Infomercial 12. Internet Adv.13. Multimedia 14. Network Radio
15. Network T.V. 16. Newsp. Distr. Mags. 17. Other 18. Outdoor (Posters, Transit) 19. Point of Purchase20. Premiums, Novelties
21. Product Samples 22. Special Events Mktg. 23. Spot Radio 24. Spot T.V. 25. Weekly Newsp. 26. Yellow Page Adv.

Business Description:
Cultural Arts & Theater Venue
S.I.C.: 8322
N.A.I.C.S.: 624190
Media: 1-2-4-5-6-7-8-9-10-11-13-16-18-19-20-21-22-23-24-25-26
Distr.: Intl.; Natl.
Budget Set: June -July
Personnel:
Terry Whitt Bailey *(Pres & CEO)*

MAHAFFEY THEATER FOUNDATION
400 1st St S
Saint Petersburg, FL 33701-4341
Tel.: (727) 892-5798
Fax: (727) 892-5897
E-mail: info@mahaffeytheater.com
Web Site: www.mahaffeytheater.com
Approx. Number Employees: 35
Business Description:
Theatrical Producer
S.I.C.: 7389
N.A.I.C.S.: 711310
Media: 3-8-13-22
Personnel:
David Rovine *(Gen Mgr)*

THE MAJESTIC STAR CASINO, LLC
(Filed Ch 11 Bankruptcy #914136 on 11/23/09 in U.S. Bankruptcy Ct, Dist of DE, Wilmington)
301 Fremont St
Las Vegas, NV 89101
Tel.: (702) 388-2400
Fax: (702) 382-5562
Web Site: www.majesticstar.com
Sales Range: $350-399.9 Million
Approx. Number Employees: 2,700
Year Founded: 1993
Business Description:
Holding Company; Casino Hotel Owner & Operator
S.I.C.: 6719; 7011
N.A.I.C.S.: 551112; 721120
Advertising Expenditures: $22,689,392
Media: 1-6-9-18-22-23-24-25
Personnel:
Don H. Barden *(Chm, Pres & CEO)*
John S. Bennett *(CFO, Treas & VP)*

MAJOR LEAGUE BASEBALL
245 Park Ave
New York, NY 10167
Tel.: (212) 931-7800
Fax: (212) 949-8636
E-mail: info@mlb.com
Web Site: www.mlb.com
Year Founded: 1903
Business Description:
Professional Baseball Organization
S.I.C.: 8699
N.A.I.C.S.: 813990
Media: 3-5-13-14-15-18-19-20-22-23-24
Distr.: Natl.
Budget Set: Nov.
Personnel:
Allan H. Selig *(Commissioner)*
Jonathan D. Mariner *(CFO & Exec VP)*
John McHale, Jr. *(CIO, Exec VP-Admin & Interim Exec VP-Baseball Ops)*
Jacqueline Parkes *(CMO)*
Tony Petitti *(Pres/CEO-MLB Network)*
Thomas Ostertag *(Gen Counsel & Sr VP)*
Tim Brosnan *(Exec VP-Bus)*
Rob Manfred *(Exec VP-HR & Labor Rels)*
Jimmie L. Solomon *(Exec VP-Baseball Ops)*
Mary Abrams Beck *(Sr VP-Mktg & Promos)*
Jim Gallagher *(Sr VP-Corp Comm)*
Josh Lukin *(Dir-Club Initiatives)*
Advertising Agencies:
Hill Holliday
53 State St
Boston, MA 02109
Tel.: (617) 366-4000

Media Storm LLC
99 Washington St
South Norwalk, CT 06854
Tel.: (203) 852-8001
Fax: (203) 852-5592
(MLB Network, Media Buying)

MAJOR LEAGUE SOCCER LLC
420 5th Ave
New York, NY 10018
Tel.: (212) 450-1200
Fax: (212) 450-1305
E-mail: feedback@mlsnet.com
Web Site: www.mlsnet.com
Sales Range: $50-74.9 Million
Approx. Number Employees: 110
Year Founded: 1995
Business Description:
Professional Soccer League
S.I.C.: 7999
N.A.I.C.S.: 713990
Import Export
Media: 20-22
Personnel:
Sean Prendergast *(CFO)*
J. Russell Findlay *(CMO-MLS & Soccer United)*
Kathy Carter *(Pres-Mktg-Soccer United)*
Dan Courtemanche *(Exec VP-Comm)*
Joshua Neier *(Dir-Fin)*
Advertising Agency:
Dentsu America, Inc.
32 Ave of the Americas 16th Fl
New York, NY 10013
Tel.: (212) 397-3333
Fax: (212) 397-3322
"It only takes 90 minutes for your world to change"
Print
TV

MAKEMUSIC, INC.
7615 Golden Triangle Dr Ste M
Eden Prairie, MN 55344-3848
Tel.: (952) 937-9611
Fax: (952) 937-9760
Toll Free: (800) 843-2066
E-mail: investorrelations@makemusic.com
Web Site: www.makemusic.com
Approx. Rev.: $17,148,000
Approx. Number Employees: 100
Business Description:
Music Technology Products Mfr & Marketer
S.I.C.: 2741
N.A.I.C.S.: 512230
Advertising Expenditures: $905,000
Media: 2-4-7-8-10-13
Personnel:
Robert B. Morrison *(Chm)*
Karen van Lith *(CEO)*
Karen L. Vanderbosch *(CFO & COO)*
Rick Hammond *(VP-Mktg & Solutions Mgmt)*
Brands & Products:
ALLEGRO
FINALE
FINALE ALLEGRO
FINALE GUITAR
FINALE NOTEPAD
FINALE PRINTMUSIC
FINALE SHOWCASE
FINALE SONGWRITER
FINALE VIEWER
FINALEMUSIC.COM
INTELLIGENT ACCOMPANIMENT
MAKEMUSIC
NOTEPAD PLUS
PRINTMUSIC
SMARTMUSIC

MAPLE LEAF SPORTS & ENTERTAINMENT LTD.
(Holding of Teachers' Private Capital)
50 Bay St Ste 400
Toronto, ON M5J 2L2, Canada
Tel.: (416) 815-5400
Fax: (416) 359-9205
Web Site: www.mlse.com
Approx. Number Employees: 500
Business Description:
Owner & Operator of Professional Sports Teams, Television Networks & Sports & Entertainment Facilities
S.I.C.: 7941
N.A.I.C.S.: 711211
Media: 7-8-9-13-18-20-22
Distr.: Natl.
Personnel:
Larry Tanenbaum *(Chm)*
Richard A. Peddie *(Pres & CEO)*
Ian Clarke *(CFO & Exec VP)*
Tom Anselmi *(COO & Exec VP)*
Robin Brudner *(Gen Counsel, Sec & Exec VP)*
Robert Hunter *(Exec VP & Gen Mgr-Air Canada Centre)*
Chris Hebb *(Sr VP-Brdcst & Content)*
David Hopkinson *(Sr VP-Bus Partnerships)*
Kevin Nonomura *(Sr VP-Fin)*
Beth Robertson *(Sr VP-Ticket Sls & Svc)*
Mardi Walker *(Sr VP-People)*
Chris Shewfelt *(Dir-Corp Partnerships)*
Jordan Vade *(Dir-Sls)*
Matt Godin *(Mgr-Corp Partnership Mktg)*
Alexandra Ashton *(Acct Exec-Corp Mktg Partnership)*
Stephanie Hill *(Acct Exec-Corp Mktg Partnership)*
Bryce Eldridge *(Analyst-Sls)*
Brands & Products:
AIR CANADA CENTRE
LEAFS TV
RAPTORS NBA TV
TORONTO MAPLE LEAFS
TORONTO RAPTORS
WWW.MAPLELEAFS.COM
WWW.RAPTORS.COM

MARINE PRODUCTS CORPORATION
2801 Buford Hwy Ste 520
Atlanta, GA 30329
Tel.: (404) 321-7910
Fax: (404) 321-5483
Web Site: www.marineproductscorp.com
Approx. Sls.: $101,011,000
Approx. Number Employees: 360
Business Description:
Fiberglass Boat Building & Repairing
S.I.C.: 3732; 3731
N.A.I.C.S.: 336612; 336611
Advertising Expenditures: $1,206,000
Media: 5-22
Personnel:
R. Randall Rollins *(Chm)*
Richard A. Hubbell *(Pres & CEO)*
Ben M. Palmer *(CFO)*
James A. Lane, Jr. *(Exec VP)*
James C. Landers *(VP-Corp Fin)*
Brands & Products:
CHAPARRAL
MARINE PRODUCTS
ROBALO

MARINELAND OF FLORIDA
9600 Ocean Shore Blvd
Saint Augustine, FL 32080-8613
Tel.: (904) 471-1111
Fax: (904) 460-1330
Toll Free: (888) 279-9194
Web Site: www.marineland.net
Approx. Number Employees: 50
Business Description:
Marine Park
S.I.C.: 7999; 5941
N.A.I.C.S.: 712190; 451110
Media: 6-9-20-25
Personnel:
Curt Allen *(Gen Mgr)*

MARQUEE HOLDINGS, INC.
(Holding of AMC ENTERTAINMENT HOLDINGS, INC.)
920 Main St
Kansas City, MO 64105
Tel.: (816) 221-4000
Web Site: www.amctheatres.com/
Approx. Number Employees: 800
Year Founded: 2004
Business Description:
Holding Company; Motion Picture Theaters Owner & Operator
S.I.C.: 6719; 7832
N.A.I.C.S.: 551112; 512131
Advertising Expenditures: $18,112,000
Personnel:
Gerardo I. Lopez *(Pres & CEO)*
Craig R. Ramsey *(CFO & Exec VP)*
Chris A. Cox *(Chief Acctg Officer & Sr VP)*
Kevin M. Connor *(Gen Counsel, Sec & Sr VP)*
Terry W. Crawford *(Treas & Sr VP)*
John D. McDonald *(Exec VP & Dir-US & Canada Ops)*
Mark A. McDonald *(Exec VP-Intl Ops)*
Michael W. Zwonitzer *(VP-Fin)*
Richard Thomas *(Dir-Mktg & Promotional)*

MARYLAND SYMPHONY ORCHESTRA
30 W Washington St
Hagerstown, MD 21740
Tel.: (301) 797-4000
Fax: (301) 797-2314
E-mail: info@marylandsymphony.org
Web Site:
www.marylandsymphony.org

Key to Media (For complete agency information see *The Advertising Red Books-Agencies* edition):
1. Bus. Publs. 2. Cable T.V. 3. Catalogs & Directories. 4. Co-op Adv. 5. Consumer Mags. 6. D.M. to Bus. Estab.7. D.M. to Consumers 8. Daily Newsp. 9. Exhibits/Trade Shows 10. Foreign 11. Infomercial 12. Internet Adv.13. Multimedia 14. Network Radio 15. Network T.V. 16. Newsp. Distr. Mags. 17. Other 18. Outdoor (Posters, Transit) 19. Point of Purchase20. Premiums, Novelties 21. Product Samples 22. Special Events Mktg. 23. Spot Radio 24. Spot T.V. 25. Weekly Newsp. 26. Yellow Page Adv.

Maryland Symphony Orchestra — (Continued)

Approx. Number Employees: 6
Business Description:
Symphony Orchestra
S.I.C.: 7929
N.A.I.C.S.: 711130
Media: 9-20-23-24-25
Personnel:
Elizabeth Schulze *(Dir-Music & Conductor)*

MARYLAND ZOOLOGICAL SOCIETY, INC.

(d/b/a Maryland Zoo)
Druid Hill Park
Baltimore, MD 21217
Tel.: (443) 552-5250
Web Site: www.marylandzoo.org
Approx. Number Employees: 200
Year Founded: 1876
Business Description:
Zoo & Animal Research & Conservation Operator
S.I.C.: 8422
N.A.I.C.S.: 712130
Media: 6-9-18-23-24-25-26
Personnel:
Elizabeth Grieb *(Pres & CEO)*
Jane Ballentine *(Dir-Mktg & PR)*
Jennifer Ludwig *(Dir-Bd Rels, Compliance & Quality Assurance)*
Advertising Agency:
Weber Shandwick-Baltimore
2809 Boston St Ste 8
Baltimore, MD 21224
Tel.: (410) 558-2100
Fax: (410) 558-2188

MASSACHUSETTS CONVENTION CENTER AUTHORITY

415 Summer St
Boston, MA 02210-1719
Tel.: (617) 954-2000
Fax: (617) 954-2299
E-mail: info@massconvention.com
Web Site: www.massconvention.com
Sales Range: $10-24.9 Million
Approx. Number Employees: 91
Year Founded: 1982
Business Description:
Auditorium & Hall Operation
S.I.C.: 6512; 7521
N.A.I.C.S.: 531120; 812930
Media: 9-20-22-23-24-25
Budget Set: Dec.
Personnel:
William J. Smith *(Gen Counsel)*
Bob Mollica *(Dir-Sports Mktg-Trade Show Sls)*
Susan Byrnes *(Exec Asst & Office Mgr)*

MAYWOOD PARK TROTTING ASSOCIATION, INC.

8600 W N Ave
Maywood, IL 60160
Tel.: (708) 343-4800
Fax: (708) 343-2564
E-mail: info@maywoodpark.com
Web Site: www.maywoodpark.com
E-Mail For Key Personnel:
President: duke@maywoodpark.com
Marketing Director: marketing@maywoodpark.com
Sales Range: $100-124.9 Million
Approx. Number Employees: 250
Year Founded: 1946
Business Description:
Horse Race Track Operator
S.I.C.: 7948
N.A.I.C.S.: 711212
Media: 3-8-9-13-23-25
Personnel:
Duke Johnston *(Pres)*
Paul Svendsen *(VP-Fin)*
Jim Hannon *(Dir-Simulcast Ops)*
Brands & Products:
MAYWOOD PARK

MEDIEVAL DINNER & TOURNAMENT, INC.

7662 Beach Blvd
Buena Park, CA 90620-1838
Tel.: (714) 562-0221
Fax: (714) 670-2721
Toll Free: (800) 899-6600
E-mail: comments@medievaltimes.com
Web Site: www.medievaltimes.com
Approx. Number Employees: 500
Year Founded: 1986
Business Description:
Restaurants & Entertainment with a Medieval Theme
S.I.C.: 7922
N.A.I.C.S.: 711110
Import
Media: 2-3-6-9-10-17-18-22-23-24-25
Distr.: Direct to Consumer; Natl.
Personnel:
Kenneth H. Kim *(Pres, CEO, Treas & Sec)*
Ricko Montaner *(Sr VP)*
David Manuel *(Mgr-Mktg & Sls)*
Brands & Products:
MEDIEVAL TIMES
Advertising Agency:
Mediaspot, Inc.
1550 Bayside Dr
Corona Del Mar, CA 92625-1711
Tel.: (949) 721-0500
Fax: (949) 721-0555

MEMPHIS GRIZZLIES

191 Beale St
Memphis, TN 38103-3715
Tel.: (901) 888-4667
Fax: (901) 205-1444
Web Site: www.nba.com/grizzlies
Approx. Number Employees: 117
Business Description:
Professional Basketball Team
S.I.C.: 7941
N.A.I.C.S.: 711211
Media: 8-10-13-18-20-22-23-24
Personnel:
Kenny Williamson *(Asst Gen Mgr)*
John Pugliese *(Sr Dir-Mktg Comm)*
Mat Warner *(Sr Dir-Premium Sls & Svcs)*
Chris Bork *(Dir-Corp Partnerships)*
Lamont Nelson *(Dir-Grp Sls)*
Jason Potter *(Dir-Promos & Event Presentation)*
David Thompson *(Dir-Creative Svcs)*
Lesley Torrell *(Dir-Internet Mktg & Web Dev)*
Hark Athwal *(Sr Acct Exec-Sls)*
LaTonya Lane *(Sr Acct Exec-Ticket Sls)*
Brands & Products:
GRIZZLIES AUCTIONS
MEMPHIS GRIZZLIES
Advertising Agency:
The Brand Squad
6000 Poplar Ave Ste 250
Memphis, TN 38119
Tel.: (901) 866-9402
Fax: (901) 261-5411

MEMPHIS SYMPHONY ORCHESTRA

585 S Mendenhall Rd
Memphis, TN 38117
Tel.: (901) 537-2525
Fax: (901) 537-2550
E-mail: information@memphissymphony.org
Web Site: www.memphissymphony.org
Approx. Number Employees: 25
Year Founded: 1952
Business Description:
Symphony Orchestra
S.I.C.: 7929
N.A.I.C.S.: 711130
Media: 4-7-8-9-13-20-22-23-24-25
Personnel:
Diane Poag *(Chm)*
Ryan Fleur *(Pres & CEO)*
Anita Reddan *(Bus Mgr)*

THE MENNELLO MUSEUM OF MODERN ART

900 E Princeton St
Orlando, FL 32803
Tel.: (407) 246-4278
Fax: (407) 246-4329
E-mail: menello.museum@cityoforlando.net
Web Site: www.mennellomuseum.org
Approx. Number Employees: 2
Business Description:
Art Museum
S.I.C.: 8412
N.A.I.C.S.: 712110
Media: 6
Personnel:
Michael A. Mennello *(Founder)*
Frank Holt *(Exec Dir)*
Kim Robinson *(Office Mgr)*

THE METROPOLITAN MUSEUM OF ART

1000 5th Ave
New York, NY 10028-0198
Tel.: (212) 879-5500
Fax: (212) 570-3879
E-mail: communication@metmuseum.org
Web Site: www.metmuseum.org
Approx. Number Employees: 2,500
Year Founded: 1870
Business Description:
Art Museum
S.I.C.: 8412; 5999
N.A.I.C.S.: 712110; 453998
Media: 4-8-9-22-23-24
Distr.: Direct to Consumer; Reg.
Personnel:
James R. Houghton *(Chm)*
Emily K. Rafferty *(Pres)*
Philippe De Montebello *(CEO)*
Suzanne Brenner *(Chief Investment Officer)*
Sharon Cott *(Gen Counsel)*
Harold Holzer *(Sr VP-External Affairs)*
Jennifer Oetting *(Sr Mgr-Adv & Mktg)*
Advertising Agency:
LaPlaca Cohen
43 W 24th St Tenth Fl
New York, NY 10010-3205
Tel.: (212) 675-4106
Fax: (212) 675-4763
(Media Buyer)

THE METROPOLITAN OPERA

Lincoln Ctr
New York, NY 10023
Tel.: (212) 362-6000
Web Site: www.metopera.org
Approx. Number Employees: 1,500
Business Description:
Opera Producers
S.I.C.: 8641
N.A.I.C.S.: 813410
Media: 8-20-23-24-25
Personnel:
Peter Gelb *(Gen Mgr)*
James Levine *(Dir-Music)*
Thomas Mygatt *(Deputy Dir-Mktg & Adv)*
Advertising Agencies:
Serino Coyne LLC
(Sub. of Omnicom Group Inc.)
1515 Broadway 36th Fl
New York, NY 10036-8901
Tel.: (212) 626-2700
Fax: (212) 626-2799

Tag Online Inc.
6 Prospect Village Plz 1st Fl
Clifton, NJ 07013
Tel.: (973) 783-5583
Fax: (973) 783-5334

METROPOLITAN PIER & EXPOSITION AUTHORITY

301 E Cermak Rd
Chicago, IL 60616
Tel.: (312) 791-7500
Fax: (312) 791-6227
E-mail: mcpgenlinfo@mpea.com
Web Site: www.mpea.com
Sales Range: $150-199.9 Million
Approx. Number Employees: 500
Business Description:
Convention & Show Services
S.I.C.: 7389; 7999
N.A.I.C.S.: 561920; 713990
Media: 4-7-9-10-13-20-22-23-24-25
Personnel:
Theodore R. Tetzlaff *(Chm)*
Bruce R. Meckler *(Vice Chm)*

METROPOLITAN THEATRES CORPORATION

8727 W Third St
Los Angeles, CA 90048-3843
Tel.: (310) 858-2800
Fax: (310) 858-2860
E-mail: info@metrotheatres.com
Web Site: www.metrotheatres.com
Approx. Number Employees: 900
Year Founded: 1936
Business Description:
Motion Picture Viewing Services
S.I.C.: 7832
N.A.I.C.S.: 512131
Advertising Expenditures: $1,000,000
Media: 1-10-13-22-26
Personnel:
Bruce Corwin *(Chm & CEO)*
David Corwin *(Pres)*
Allen Gilbert *(Exec VP)*
Alan Stokes *(VP-Film Mktg & Adv)*

Key to Media (For complete agency information see *The Advertising Red Books-Agencies* edition):
1. Bus. Publs. 2. Cable T.V. 3. Catalogs & Directories. 4. Co-op Adv. 5. Consumer Mags. 6. D.M. to Bus. Estab.7. D.M. to Consumers 8. Daily Newsp. 9. Exhibits/Trade Shows 10. Foreign 11. Infomercial 12. Internet Adv.13. Multimedia 14. Network Radio 15. Network T.V. 16. Newsp. Distr. Mags. 17. Other 18. Outdoor (Posters, Transit) 19. Point of Purchase20. Premiums, Novelties 21. Product Samples 22. Special Events Mktg. 23. Spot Radio 24. Spot T.V. 25. Weekly Newsp. 26. Yellow Page Adv.

MIAMI CITY BALLET, INC.
2200 Liberty Ave
Miami Beach, FL 33139
Tel.: (305) 929-7000
Fax: (305) 929-7002
E-mail: admin@miamicityballet.org
Web Site: www.miamicityballet.org
Approx. Number Employees: 136
Year Founded: 1985
Business Description:
Ballet Production Services
S.I.C.: 7922; 7911
N.A.I.C.S.: 711120; 611610
Media: 9-20-23-24-25
Personnel:
Edward Villella *(CEO & Dir-Founding Artistic)*
Nora Weinreich *(Officer-Gifts)*
Mark Cole *(Gen Mgr)*
Pamela Gardiner *(Exec Dir & In-House Counsel)*
Bill Miller *(Dir-Mktg & Comm)*
Ricardo Montealegre *(Dir-School Admin)*
Caroline Murray *(Asst Dir-Mktg)*
Donna Lenchuk *(Office Mgr & Sr Exec Asst to Artistic Dir)*
Abram Best *(Mgr)*
Richard Dotson *(Mgr-Box Office)*
Viena Howe *(Mgr-Foundations & Govt Rels)*
Nicole M. Mitchell *(Mgr-Production Stage)*
Roberto Santiago *(Mgr-PR)*
Orene Tross-Harris *(Mgr-Gifts)*

MIAMI DOLPHINS, LTD.
(Holding of Dolphins Enterprises, LLC)
7500 SW 30th St
Davie, FL 33314-1020
Tel.: (954) 452-7000
Fax: (954) 452-7027
Web Site: www.miamidolphins.com
Approx. Number Employees: 200
Year Founded: 1967
Business Description:
Professional Football Franchise
S.I.C.: 7941
N.A.I.C.S.: 711211
Media: 3-9-10-14-15-18-20-22-23
Distr.: Natl.
Personnel:
Jorge M. Perez *(Vice Chm & Partner)*
Donald F. Shula *(Vice Chm)*
Michael Dee *(CEO)*
Marc Anthony *(Partner)*
Emilio Estefan *(Partner)*
Gloria Estefan *(Partner)*
Stacy Ann Ferguson *(Partner)*
H. Wayne Huizenga *(Partner)*
Serena Williams *(Partner)*
Venus Williams *(Partner)*
Tery Howard *(CTO & Sr VP)*
Harold Talisman *(Chief Admin Officer)*
Dawn Aponte *(Sr VP-Football Ops)*
Bill Galante *(Sr VP-Ops-Davie)*
Harvey Greene *(Sr VP-Media Rels)*
Adam Grossman *(Sr VP-Pub Affairs)*
Jim Rushton *(Sr VP-Corp Partnerships & Integrated Media)*
Jill R. Strafaci *(Sr VP-Fin & Admin)*
Mark Tilson *(Sr VP-Sls & Ticket Ops)*
Scott Loft *(VP-Ticket Sls & Svc)*
Jeff Ireland *(Gen Mgr)*
Yolanda Barreto *(Sr Dir-HR)*
Betsy Reuther Christy *(Sr Dir-Fin)*
Jeff Griffith *(Sr Dir-Programming & Production)*
Richard Lassiter *(Sr Dir-Premium Seating)*
Wayne Partello *(Sr Dir-Content & Creative)*
David Saifman *(Sr Dir-Ticket Svcs & Ops)*
Danielle Sergeant *(Sr Dir-Client Svcs)*
Scott Stone *(Sr Dir-Internet & Publ)*
George Torres *(Sr Dir-Mktg & Corp Comm)*
Ilona Wolpin *(Sr Dir-Community Rels)*
Scott Baynes *(Dir-Customer Svc)*
Joe Curbelo *(Dir-Server & Infrastructure Support Svcs)*
Chris Grier *(Dir-College Scouting)*
Bob Hack *(Dir-Video)*
David Murphey *(Dir-Media Sls)*
Ron Summers *(Dir-Engrg & Maintenance)*
Kaleb Thornhill *(Dir-Player Dev)*
Brian Gaine *(Asst Dir-Player Personnel)*
Joe Cimino *(Mgr-Equipment)*
Brands & Products:
MIAMI DOLPHINS
Advertising Agencies:
Luna Creative Design
15829 N 51st Pl
Scottsdale, AZ 85254
Tel.: (602) 494-4048
Fax: (602) 765-7955

Republica
2153 Coral Way
Miami, FL 33145
Tel.: (305) 442-0977
Fax: (305) 443-1631
Advertising
Agency of Record
Bilingual (English and Spanish)
Campaigns
Interactive
Miami Dolphins Special Teams
Public Relations

MIAMI HEAT LIMITED PARTNERSHIP
(Holding of FBA II, Inc.)
601 Biscayne Blvd
Miami, FL 33132-1801
Tel.: (786) 777-1000
Fax: (786) 777-1608
Web Site: www.nba.com/heat
Approx. Number Employees: 180
Year Founded: 1987
Business Description:
Professional Basketball Team
S.I.C.: 7941
N.A.I.C.S.: 711211
Media: 2-3-6-7-8-9-13-14-15-18-19-20-22-23-24-25-26
Distr.: Local
Budget Set: July -Aug.
Personnel:
Pat Riley *(Pres)*
Nick Arison *(CEO)*
Sammy Schulman *(CFO & Exec VP)*
Tony Coba *(CIO & Sr VP)*
Michael McCullough *(CMO & Exec VP)*
Eric Woolworth *(Pres-Bus Ops)*
Raquel Libman *(Gen Counsel & Exec VP)*
Kim Stone *(Exec VP & Gen Mgr)*
Stephen Weber *(Exec VP-Sls)*
Andy Elisburg *(Sr VP & Asst Gen Mgr)*
Jeff Craney *(VP-Mktg Div)*
Brands & Products:
MIAMI HEAT

MID-STATE RACEWAY, INC.
14 Ruth St
Vernon, NY 13476
Mailing Address:
PO Box 860
Vernon, NY 13476
Tel.: (315) 829-2201
Fax: (315) 829-4384
Toll Free: (877) 777-8559
E-mail: vdowns@nytds.net
Web Site: www.vernondowns.com
Approx. Sls.: $8,000,000
Approx. Number Employees: 75
Year Founded: 1953
Business Description:
Thoroughbred Horse Racing
S.I.C.: 7999
N.A.I.C.S.: 711219
Media: 3-9-15-18-22-23-24-25
Distr.: Reg.
Personnel:
James Guay *(Dir-Mktg)*

THE MID-TEXAS SYMPHONY SOCIETY
PO Box 3216
Seguin, TX 78155
Tel.: (830) 372-8089
Tel.: (830) 629-0336
Fax: (830) 372-8112
E-mail: mts@tlu.edu
Web Site: www.mtsymphony.org
Approx. Number Employees: 1
Year Founded: 1978
Business Description:
Symphony Orchestra
S.I.C.: 7929
N.A.I.C.S.: 711130
Media: 7-8-9-13-20-22-23-24-25
Personnel:
Anita Windecker *(Founder)*
Cathy Talcott *(VP-Mktg)*
David Mairs *(Dir-Music)*

MILWAUKEE BREWERS BASEBALL CLUB, INC.
1 Brewers Way
Milwaukee, WI 53214-3651
Tel.: (414) 902-4400
Fax: (414) 902-4058
E-mail: tix@milwaukeebrewers.com
Web Site: www.brewers.com
Approx. Number Employees: 100
Year Founded: 1970
Business Description:
Professional Baseball Club
S.I.C.: 7941
N.A.I.C.S.: 711211
Advertising Expenditures: $300,000
Media: 2-8-9-13-18-22-23-24-25
Distr.: Natl.
Budget Set: Oct.
Personnel:
Mark Attanasio *(Chm & Principal Owner)*
Rick Schlesinger *(COO)*
Martin Wronski *(Gen Counsel & VP)*
Doug Melvin *(Exec VP & Gen Mgr)*
Jack Zduriencik *(Exec VP & Gen Mgr-Baseball Ops)*
Gord Ash *(VP & Asst Gen Mgr)*
Sally Andrist *(VP-HR & Office Mgmt)*
Tylor Barnes *(VP-Comm)*
Tom Hecht *(VP-Corp Mktg)*
Jill Aronoff *(Sr Dir-Mdse Branding)*
Bob Hallas *(Sr Dir-Stadium Ops)*
Matt Kenny *(Sr Dir-Event Svcs)*
Andrew Pauls *(Sr Dir-Corp Mktg)*
Kathy Schwab *(Sr Dir-Mktg)*
Teddy Werner *(Sr Dir-Bus Ops)*
Tony Migliaccio *(Dir-Clubhouse Ops & Mgr-Equipment)*
Deron Anderson *(Dir-Audio & Video Production)*
Regis Bane *(Dir-Ticket Ops)*
Tom Flanagan *(Dir-Baseball Ops)*
Tim Hewes *(Dir-Employee Assistance Program)*
Dan Larrea *(Dir-Team Travel)*
Karl Mueller *(Dir-Video Scouting & Baseball Res)*
Dave Tamburrino *(Dir-Corp Mktg)*
Gary Vanden Berg *(Dir-Grounds)*
Mike Vassallo *(Dir-Media Rels)*
Tony Diggs *(Asst Dir-Player Dev & Trng Center)*
Caitlin Moyer *(Sr Mgr-Adv & Mktg)*
Scott Martens *(Bus Mgr-Player Dev & Minor League Ops)*
Katina Shaw *(Mgr-Community Relations)*
Vicki Wise *(Mgr-Acctg)*
Brands & Products:
MILWAUKEE BREWERS
RACING SAUSAGE
Advertising Agency:
MLB Advanced Media, L.P.
75 9th Ave 5th Fl
New York, NY 10011
Tel.: (212) 485-3444
Fax: (212) 485-3456

MILWAUKEE BUCKS, INC.
1001 N 4th St
Milwaukee, WI 53203-1314
Tel.: (414) 227-0500
Fax: (414) 227-0543
Web Site: www.nba.com
E-Mail For Key Personnel:
Marketing Director: jsteinmiller@milwaukeebucks.com
Sales Director: jgrayson@milwaukeebucks.com
Public Relations: chanson@milwaukeebucks.com
Approx. Number Employees: 75
Year Founded: 1968
Business Description:
Professional Basketball Team
S.I.C.: 7941
N.A.I.C.S.: 711211
Media: 3-8-9-10-13-18-19-20-22-23-24-25
Distr.: Reg.
Budget Set: May
Personnel:
Herb Kohl *(President)*
Michael Burr *(CFO)*
Dave Babcock *(Dir-Player Personnel)*
Jim Grayson *(Dir-Ticket Sls)*
Clark Hillery *(Dir-Team Svcs)*
Skip Robinson *(Dir-CR & Player Dev)*
Dan Smyczek *(Dir-PR)*
Jim Woloszyk *(Dir-Fin)*
David Trattner *(Asst Dir-Sales)*
Kareeda Chones *(Mgr-Corp Partership Svcs)*
Ron Kiepert *(Mgr-IT)*
Steve Tarachow *(Mgr-Grp Ticket Sls)*

Key to Media (For complete agency information see *The Advertising Red Books-Agencies* edition):
1. Bus. Publs. 2. Cable T.V. 3. Catalogs & Directories. 4. Co-op Adv. 5. Consumer Mags. 6. D.M. to Bus. Estab.7. D.M. to Consumers
8. Daily Newsp. 9. Exhibits/Trade Shows 10. Foreign 11. Infomercial 12. Internet Adv.13. Multimedia 14. Network Radio
15. Network T.V. 16. Newsp. Distr. Mags. 17. Other 18. Outdoor (Posters, Transit) 19. Point of Purchase20. Premiums, Novelties
21. Product Samples 22. Special Events Mktg. 23. Spot Radio 24. Spot T.V. 25. Weekly Newsp. 26. Yellow Page Adv.

Milwaukee Bucks, Inc. — (Continued)
Sue Thompson *(Mgr-Ticket Ops)*
Rick Wermager *(Mgr-Svcs Ticket Grp)*
Brands & Products:
MILWAUKEE BUCKS

MILWAUKEE SYMPHONY ORCHESTRA INC.
700 N Water St Ste 700
Milwaukee, WI 53202
Tel.: (414) 291-6010
Fax: (414) 291-7610
E-mail: info@milwaukeesymphony.org
Web Site: www.mso.org
Approx. Number Employees: 120
Business Description:
Symphony Orchestra
S.I.C.: 7922
N.A.I.C.S.: 711110
Media: 8-9-18-20-23-24-25
Personnel:
Maryellen H. Gleason *(Pres)*
Renee Logee *(Gen Mgr)*
Christine Burgener *(Dir-Ops)*
Edo Dewaart *(Dir-Music)*
Sarah Hogan *(Dir-Mktg)*
Luther Gray *(Mgr-Patron Svcs)*
Mason Langfitt *(Mgr-Education Concert)*
Paul Moody *(Mgr-Info Sys & Tech)*
Mary Novak *(Mgr-HR)*
Linda Unkefer *(Mgr-Orchestra Personnel)*
Karen Ann Falkowski *(Coord-Adv & Production)*
Brands & Products:
MSO

MINNESOTA ORCHESTRA
1111 Nicollet Mall
Minneapolis, MN 55403
Tel.: (612) 371-5600
Fax: (612) 371-7170
E-mail: info@mnorch.org
Web Site: www.minnesotaorchestra.org
Approx. Rev.: $78,000,000
Approx. Number Employees: 850
Year Founded: 1903
Business Description:
Symphony Orchestra
S.I.C.: 7929
N.A.I.C.S.: 711190
Media: 6-7-8-9-18-20-22-23-24-25
Personnel:
Michael Henson *(Pres & CEO)*
Robert Neu *(VP & Gen Mgr-Artistic)*
Cynthia Grzanowski *(Dir-Mktg, Single Ticket Sls & Audience Dev)*
David Sailer *(Dir-Mktg, Subscription Sls & Audience Svcs)*
Jim Bartsch *(Dir-Education)*
Dan Kupfer *(Dir-Facilities)*
Esther Saarela *(Dir-HR)*
Casandra A. Swan *(Dir-Ticket & House Svcs)*
Michael Black *(Mgr-Devel Ops & Corp Donor Benefits)*
Timothy Eickholt *(Mgr-Stage)*
Ron Foster Smith *(Mgr-Mktg)*
Ronald J. Fostersmith *(Mgr-Mktg)*
Mark Georgesen *(Mgr-Concert Enhancements & Concessions)*
Julie Haight-Curran *(Mgr-Orchestra Personnel)*
Beth Kellar-Long *(Mgr-Orchestra Ops)*
Mele Willis *(Mgr-Outreach & Educational Partnerships)*

MINNESOTA TIMBERWOLVES BASKETBALL LIMITED PARTNERSHIP
600 1st Ave N
Minneapolis, MN 55403-1400
Tel.: (612) 673-1600
Fax: (612) 673-1699
Web Site: www.nba.com/timberwolves
Approx. Sls.: $40,000,000
Approx. Number Employees: 100
Year Founded: 1989
Business Description:
Professional Basketball Team
S.I.C.: 7941
N.A.I.C.S.: 711211
Advertising Expenditures: $600,000
Media: 9-13-23-24
Personnel:
Glen A. Taylor *(Owner)*
Chris Wright *(Pres)*
Rob Moor *(CEO)*
Rob Babcock *(Asst Gen Mgr)*
Tony Ronzone *(Asst Gen Mgr)*
Zarko Durisic *(Dir-Player Personnel)*
Brands & Products:
MINNESOTA TIMBERWOLVES

MINNESOTA TWINS, LLC
(Holding of Twins Sports Inc.)
1 Twins Way
Minneapolis, MN 55403
Tel.: (612) 659-3400
Fax: (612) 375-7480
E-mail: twins@twinsbaseball.com
Web Site: minnesota.twins.mlb.com
Approx. Number Employees: 600
Year Founded: 1901
Business Description:
Professional Baseball Club
S.I.C.: 7941
N.A.I.C.S.: 711211
Media: 3-7-8-9-13-19-20-22-23-24-25
Distr.: Natl.
Budget Set: Oct.
Personnel:
Dave St. Peter *(Pres)*
Bill Smith *(Sr VP & Gen Mgr)*
Kevin Smith *(Sr VP & Gen Mgr)*
Laura Day *(Sr VP-Bus Dev)*
Kip Elliott *(Sr VP-Bus Admin)*
John Avenson *(VP-Tech)*
Raenell Dorn *(VP-HR & Diversity)*
Patrick Klinger *(VP-Mktg)*
Rob Antony *(Asst Gen Mgr)*
Nancy O'Brien *(Sr Dir-Adv)*
Andy Price *(Sr Dir-Broadcasting & Game Presentation)*
Bryan Donaldson *(Dir-Community Affairs)*
Mike Herman *(Dir-Baseball Comm)*
Heidi Sammon *(Dir-Event Mktg)*
Eric Hudson *(Sr Mgr-Season Ticket Sls & Svc)*
Jerry McLaughlin *(Sr Mgr-Ticket Acctg)*
Bodie Forsling *(Mgr-Client Svcs)*
Molly Gallatin *(Mgr-Publ & Media Svcs)*
Ron Gardenhire *(Mgr-Field)*
Deron Johnson *(Mgr-Database Mktg)*
Brands & Products:
MINNESOTA TWINS
Advertising Agencies:
MLB Advanced Media, L.P.
75 9th Ave 5th Fl
New York, NY 10011
Tel.: (212) 485-3444
Fax: (212) 485-3456

Periscope
921 Washington Ave S
Minneapolis, MN 55415
Tel.: (612) 399-0500
Fax: (612) 399-0600
Toll Free: (800) 339-2103

MINNESOTA VIKINGS FOOTBALL CLUB, INC.
9520 Viking Dr
Eden Prairie, MN 55344
Tel.: (952) 828-6500
Fax: (952) 828-6540
Web Site: www.vikings.com
Approx. Number Employees: 200
Year Founded: 1961
Business Description:
Professional Football Franchise
S.I.C.: 7941
N.A.I.C.S.: 711211
Media: 9-10-13-14-15-18-20-22-25
Distr.: Natl.
Personnel:
Zygi Wilf *(Co-Owner & Chm)*
Leonard Wilf *(Co-Owner & Vice Chm)*
Mark Wilf *(Co-Owner & Pres)*
Reggie Fowler *(Co-Owner & Partner)*
Alan Landis *(Co-Owner & Partner)*
David Mandelbaum *(Co-Owner & Partner)*
Jeffrey Wilf *(Co-Owner & Partner)*
Steve Poppen *(CFO & VP-Fin)*
Steve LaCroix *(CMO & VP-Sls & Mktg)*
Kevin Warren *(Chief Admin Officer & VP-Legal Affairs)*
Jeff Anderson *(Dir-Corp Comm)*
Dannon Hulskotter *(Dir-Mktg & Bus Dev)*
Bryan Harper *(Sr Mgr-Mktg-Brdcst Production/Entertainment)*
Erin Swartz *(Mgr-Mktg-Branding & Promos)*
Nathan Fix *(Mgr-Mktg Partnerships)*
Brands & Products:
VIKINGS
Advertising Agencies:
BBDO Minneapolis
150 S 5th St Ste 3500
Minneapolis, MN 55402-4200
Tel.: (612) 338-8401
Fax: (612) 656-0602

Creative Consumer Concepts
10955 Granada Ln
Overland Park, KS 66211
Tel.: (913) 491-6444
Viktor the Viking

MINNESOTA WILD HOCKEY CLUB, LP
(Sub. of Minnesota Hockey Ventures Group, LP)
317 Washington St
Saint Paul, MN 55102-1609
Tel.: (651) 602-6000
Fax: (651) 222-1055
E-mail: info@wild.com
Web Site: www.wild.nhl.com
Approx. Number Employees: 300
Year Founded: 1997
Business Description:
Professional Hockey Club
S.I.C.: 7941
N.A.I.C.S.: 711211
Media: 3-9-20-22-23-24
Personnel:
Craig Leipold *(Owner & Governor)*
Jac Sperling *(Vice Chm)*
Jeffrey Pellegrom *(CFO)*
Matt Majka *(COO)*
Jim Ibister *(VP-Facility Admin & Gen Mgr-Saint Paul RiverCentre)*
Jack Larson *(VP & Gen Mgr-Xcel Energy Center)*
Bill Robertson *(VP-Comm & Brdcst Production)*
Chuck Fletcher *(Gen Mgr)*
Tom Lynn *(Gen Mgr)*
Sheldon Burns *(Dir-Medical)*
Blair Mackasey *(Dir-Player Personnel)*
Brands & Products:
MINNESOTA WILD
XCEL ENERGY CENTER

MISSISSIPPI MUSEUM OF ART
380 S Lamar St
Jackson, MS 39201
Tel.: (601) 960-1515
Fax: (601) 960-1505
Toll Free: (866) VIEW-ART
E-mail: aharkins@msmuseumart.org
Web Site: www.msmuseumart.org
Approx. Number Employees: 40
Business Description:
Museum
S.I.C.: 8699; 8412
N.A.I.C.S.: 813990; 712110
Media: 4-8-9-10-13-20-23-24-25
Personnel:
Betsy Bradley *(Dir)*
Maggie Lacey *(Dir-Mktg)*
Nina Moss *(Dir-Comm)*

MISSISSIPPI SYMPHONY ORCHESTRA
201 E Pascagoula St
Jackson, MS 39201
Mailing Address:
PO Box 2052
Jackson, MS 39225-2052
Tel.: (601) 960-1565
Fax: (601) 960-1564
Web Site: www.msorchestra.com
Approx. Number Employees: 65
Year Founded: 1944
Business Description:
Symphony Orchestra
S.I.C.: 7929
N.A.I.C.S.: 711130
Advertising Expenditures: $40,000
Media: 8-9-23-24-25
Personnel:
Michael Beattie *(Pres & Exec Dir)*

MOBILE SYMPHONY, INC.
257 Dolphin
Mobile, AL 36652-3127
Tel.: (251) 432-2010
Fax: (251) 432-6618
E-mail: info@mobilesymphony.org
Web Site: www.mobilesymphony.org
Approx. Sls.: $1,000,000
Approx. Number Employees: 27
Year Founded: 1970
Business Description:
Symphony Orchestra
S.I.C.: 7929
N.A.I.C.S.: 711130
Advertising Expenditures: $100,000
Media: 9-18-20-23-24-25
Personnel:
Christina L. Littleton *(CEO)*
Greg Gordon *(COO)*

Key to Media (For complete agency information see *The Advertising Red Books-Agencies* edition):
1. Bus. Publs. 2. Cable T.V. 3. Catalogs & Directories. 4. Co-op Adv. 5. Consumer Mags. 6. D.M. to Bus. Estab.7. D.M. to Consumers
8. Daily Newsp. 9. Exhibits/Trade Shows 10. Foreign 11. Infomercial 12. Internet Adv.13. Multimedia 14. Network Radio
15. Network T.V. 16. Newsp. Distr. Mags. 17. Other 18. Outdoor (Posters, Transit) 19. Point of Purchase20. Premiums, Novelties
21. Product Samples 22. Special Events Mktg. 23. Spot Radio 24. Spot T.V. 25. Weekly Newsp. 26. Yellow Page Adv.

Stephen Hedrick *(Exec Dir)*
Heather Arnott *(Dir-Mktg)*
Scott Speck *(Dir-Music & Conductor)*
Sarah Wright *(Dir-Education)*

MODESTO SYMPHONY ORCHESTRA
911 13th St
Modesto, CA 95354
Tel.: (209) 523-4156
Fax: (209) 523-0201
E-mail: krossi@modestosymphony.org
Web Site:
www.modestosymphony.org
Approx. Number Employees: 10
Year Founded: 1931
Business Description:
Symphony Orchestra
S.I.C.: 7929
N.A.I.C.S.: 711130
Media: 9-20-23-24-25
Personnel:
Lori A. Terra *(Dir-Fin)*
Donelle Page *(Principal)*
Lisa Desfaugeres *(Dir-Mktg)*
David Lockington *(Dir-Music)*
Matthew Buckman *(Mgr-Devel)*

MOHEGAN TRIBAL GAMING AUTHORITY
(d/b/a Mohegan Sun Casino)
1 Mohegan Sun Blvd
Uncasville, CT 06382-1355
Tel.: (860) 862-8000
Toll Free: (888) 226-7711
E-mail: webmaster@mohegansun.com
Web Site: www.mtga.com
Approx. Rev.: $1,539,626,000
Approx. Number Employees: 8,350
Year Founded: 1996
Business Description:
Gambling Resort & Casino Services
S.I.C.: 7011; 7999
N.A.I.C.S.: 721120; 713290
Advertising Expenditures: $29,600,000
Media: 2-3-6-7-8-9-10-13-14-15-18-20-22-23-24-25-26
Personnel:
Bruce S. Bozsum *(Chm)*
Ralph James Gessner, Jr. *(Vice Chm)*
Jeffrey E. Hartmann *(Pres & CEO-Mohegan Sun)*
Mitchell Grossinger Etess *(CEO)*
Mario Kontomerkos *(CFO)*
Paul Wright *(CMO)*
Robert Soper *(Pres-Pocono Downs)*
Gary S. Crowder *(Sr VP-Resort Ops)*
Ann Beinert *(VP-HR)*
Kara Fox-LaRose *(VP-Mktg-Pocono Downs)*
George Galinsky *(VP-Adv & Public Rels)*
Peter J. Roberti *(VP-Corp Fin)*
Candace Engdall *(Dir-Internet Mktg)*
Brands & Products:
MOHEGAN SUN
MOHEGAN TRIBAL GAMING AUTHORITY
Advertising Agencies:
Horizon Media, Inc.
75 Varick St
New York, NY 10013
Tel.: (212) 220-5000
Toll Free: (800) 633-4201
Media Agency

Naked Communications New York
96 Greene St Ste 3
New York, NY 10012
Tel.: (212) 625-3082
Fax: (212) 625-3087
Marketing & Channel Integration

Profero
Centro 3 19 Mandela St
London, NW1 0DU, United Kingdom
Tel.: (44) 20 7387 2000
Fax: (44) 20 7529 8700
Digital/Social Media

Visions Advertising Media, LLC
426 Shore Rd Ste B
Atlantic City, NJ 08401
Tel.: (609) 926-6358
Fax: (609) 926-6358

MONARCH CASINO & RESORT, INC.
3800 S Virginia St
Reno, NV 89502
Tel.: (775) 335-4600
Fax: (775) 332-9171
E-mail: info@monarchcasino.com
Web Site: www.monarchcasino.com
Approx. Rev.: $170,468,282
Approx. Number Employees: 1,815
Year Founded: 1993
Business Description:
Holding Company; Casino Hotels Owner & Operator
S.I.C.: 7011; 6289; 6719
N.A.I.C.S.: 721120; 523999; 551112
Advertising Expenditures: $3,883,958
Media: 1-4-10-20-21-22
Personnel:
Bob Farahi *(Co-Chm & Pres)*
John Farahi *(Co-Chm & CEO)*
Ronald Rowan *(CFO)*
Debra Robinson *(Gen Counsel)*
Brands & Products:
ATLANTIS

MOREAN ARTS CENTER
719 Central Ave
Saint Petersburg, FL 33701
Tel.: (727) 822-7872
Fax: (727) 821-0516
E-mail: info@moreanartscenter.org
Web Site: moreanartscenter.org
Approx. Number Employees: 24
Year Founded: 1917
Business Description:
Museum & Art Exhibitions
S.I.C.: 7911; 8412
N.A.I.C.S.: 611610; 712110
Media: 5-9-10-18-20-23-24-25
Personnel:
Richard Jacobs *(Chm)*
Evelyn Craft *(Exec Dir)*
Beth Reynolds *(Dir-Photography & Digital Imaging Program)*
Lara Shelton *(Dir-Devel)*
Mich Sullivan *(Mgr-Ops)*

MORRIS MUSEUM INC.
6 Normandy Heights Rd
Morristown, NJ 07960
Tel.: (973) 971-3700
Fax: (973) 538-0154
E-mail: information@morrismuseum.org
Web Site: www.morrismuseum.org
Approx. Number Employees: 31
Year Founded: 1913
Business Description:
Museum
S.I.C.: 8412
N.A.I.C.S.: 712110
Media: 4-6-7-8-9-10-13-20-22-23-24-25
Personnel:
Mary M. Chandor *(Chm)*
Steven H. Miller *(Exec Dir)*
Eric Hafen *(Dir-Artistic-Bickford Theatre)*
Lewis Perlmutter *(Dir-Technical-Bickford Theatre)*
Bridget Meyer *(Mgr-Earned Income)*
Laurel Smith *(Mgr-Bickford Theatre)*
Ann Aptaker *(Curator-Exhibitions)*

MOSI (MUSEUM OF SCIENCE & INDUSTRY)
4801 E Fowler Ave
Tampa, FL 33617
Tel.: (813) 987-6000
Fax: (813) 987-6310
Toll Free: (800) 995-MOSI
Web Site: www.mosi.org
Approx. Number Employees: 70
Business Description:
Science Museum & Attraction
S.I.C.: 8412
N.A.I.C.S.: 712110
Media: 5-6-8-9-10-13-20-22-23-24-25
Personnel:
Witt Ostrenko *(Pres & CEO)*
Vicki W. Ahrens *(Sr VP-Ops)*
Tanya Vomacka *(VP-Mktg & Corp Rels)*

MOTE MARINE LABORATORY, INC.
1600 Ken Thompson Pkwy
Sarasota, FL 34236
Tel.: (941) 388-4441
Fax: (941) 388-4312
E-mail: info@mote.org
Web Site: www.mote.org
Approx. Number Employees: 250
Business Description:
Marine Laboratory & Aquarium
S.I.C.: 8733
N.A.I.C.S.: 541710
Media: 8-9-10-19-20-23-24-25
Personnel:
Vernon Buchanan *(Vice Chm)*
Kumar Mahadevan *(Pres & CEO)*
Dena Smith *(CFO & VP-Admin)*
Ernest D. Estevez *(Dir-Center-Coastal Ecology & Mgr-Coastal Resources Program)*
Kenneth M. Leber *(Dir-Center for Fisheries Enhancement)*
Kevan Main *(Dir-Center for Aquaculture Res & Devel)*
Richard H. Pierce *(Dir-Center for Ecotoxicology & Sr Scientist)*
Susan Stover *(Dir-Library)*
Jim K. Culter *(Mgr-Program-Benthic Ecology)*
Kellie Dixon *(Program Mgr-Environ Chemistry)*
Randall S. Wells *(Mgr-Program-Center for Marine Mammal & Sea Turtle Res)*

MOTOR TREND AUTO SHOWS, LLC
6375 Flank Dr
Harrisburg, PA 17112
Tel.: (717) 671-4300
Fax: (717) 671-4303
Web Site:
www.motortrendautoshows.com
Business Description:
Auto Show Producer
S.I.C.: 7389
N.A.I.C.S.: 561920
Media: 10-28
Personnel:
John W. Marriott, III *(Sr VP & Gen Mgr)*
Lisa Gelb *(VP-Sls & Mktg)*
Lauren Holzman *(VP-PR)*

MOTORSPORTS AUTHENTICS LLC
(Holding of International Speedway Corporation)
6301 Performance Dr
Concord, NC 28027
Tel.: (704) 454-4000
Toll Free: (888) 332-5823
E-mail: webmaster@action-performance.com
Web Site: www.action-performance.com
Sales Range: $300-349.9 Million
Approx. Number Employees: 590
Business Description:
Licensed Motorsports Collectibles & Consumer Merchandise Designer, Marketer & Distr
S.I.C.: 2392
N.A.I.C.S.: 314129
Media: 4-5
Personnel:
Herbert M. Baum *(Chm)*
Brands & Products:
ACTION RACING
BROOKFIELD
CASTAWAY
ELITE
JEFF HAMILTON
MCARTHUR
MINICHAMPS
MUSCLE MACHINES
RACING COLLECTABLES CLUB
WINNER'S CIRCLE

MOUNT CRANMORE SKI RESORT, INC.
(Sub. of Booth Creek Ski Holdings, Inc.)
(d/b/a Cranmore Mountain Resort)
1 Skimobile Rd
North Conway, NH 03860-5364
Mailing Address:
PO Box 1640
North Conway, NH 03860-1640
Tel.: (603) 356-8500
Fax: (603) 356-8526
E-mail: info@cranmore.com
Web Site: www.cranmore.com
Approx. Number Employees: 100
Year Founded: 1937
Business Description:
Skiing & Snowboarding Resort
S.I.C.: 7999
N.A.I.C.S.: 713920
Media: 18-23-25
Personnel:
Ben Wilcox *(Pres & Gen Mgr)*
Kathy Bennett *(Dir-Mktg)*

MOUNT SNOW LTD.
(Sub. of Greenspring at Mt. Snow Homeowner's Association, Inc.)
Coldbrook Rd

Key to Media (For complete agency information see *The Advertising Red Books-Agencies* edition):
1. Bus. Publs. 2. Cable T.V. 3. Catalogs & Directories. 4. Co-op Adv. 5. Consumer Mags. 6. D.M. to Bus. Estab.7. D.M. to Consumers
8. Daily Newsp. 9. Exhibits/Trade Shows 10. Foreign 11. Infomercial 12. Internet Adv.13. Multimedia 14. Network Radio
15. Network T.V. 16. Newsp. Distr. Mags. 17. Other 18. Outdoor (Posters, Transit) 19. Point of Purchase20. Premiums, Novelties
21. Product Samples 22. Special Events Mktg. 23. Spot Radio 24. Spot T.V. 25. Weekly Newsp. 26. Yellow Page Adv.

Mount Snow Ltd. — (Continued)

Wilmington, VT 05363
Tel.: (802) 464-3333
Fax: (802) 464-4141
Sales Range: $100-124.9 Million
Approx. Number Employees: 1,000
Year Founded: 1949
Business Description:
Ski Resort
S.I.C.: 7999
N.A.I.C.S.: 713920
Media: 8-18-22

MOUNT SNOW LTD.
(Sub. of Peak Resorts, Inc.)
39 Pisgah Rd
West Dover, VT 05356
Tel.: (802) 464-2151
Fax: (802) 464-4135
Toll Free: (800) 245-SNOW
E-mail: info@mountsnow.com
Web Site: www.mountsnow.com
Approx. Number Employees: 1,200
Year Founded: 1954
Business Description:
Ski Resorts
S.I.C.: 7011
N.A.I.C.S.: 721199; 721110
Media: 1-10-18-20
Distr.: Direct to Consumer; Intl.; Reg.

MTR GAMING GROUP, INC.
State Rte 2 S
Chester, WV 26034
Mailing Address:
PO Box 356
Chester, WV 26034-0356
Tel.: (304) 387-5712
Fax: (304) 387-2167
E-mail: info@mtrgaming.com
Web Site: www.mtrgaming.com
Approx. Rev.: $434,697,000
Approx. Number Employees: 2,500
Year Founded: 1988
Business Description:
Owner & Operator of Racetracks & Casinos
S.I.C.: 7948; 7011; 7999
N.A.I.C.S.: 711212; 711219; 713290; 713990; 721120
Advertising Expenditures: $12,800,000
Media: 2-6-8-9-10-13-15-18-20-22-23-24-25-26
Personnel:
Steven M. Billick *(Chm)*
Robert A. Blatt *(Vice Chm)*
Jeffrey J. Dahl *(Pres & CEO)*
John W. Bittner, Jr. *(CFO & Exec VP)*
Joseph L. Billhimer, Jr. *(Sr VP-Ops & Dev)*
Brands & Products:
MOUNTAINEER RACETRACK & GAMING RESORT
MTR

MUSEUM OF AMERICAN FINANCE
48 Wall St
New York, NY 10005
Tel.: (212) 908-4110
Fax: (212) 908-4601
E-mail: info@financialhistory.org
Web Site: www.moaf.org
Approx. Number Employees: 50
Business Description:
Finance History Museum
S.I.C.: 8412
N.A.I.C.S.: 712110
Personnel:
David Cowen *(Pres)*
Kristin Aguilera *(Dir-Comm)*
Jeanne Baker Driscoll *(Dir-Dev)*
Advertising Agency:
Makovsky & Company, Inc.
16 E 34th St 15th Fl
New York, NY 10016
Tel.: (212) 508-9600
Fax: (212) 751-9710

MUSEUM OF DISCOVERY & SCIENCE, INC.
401 SW 2nd St
Fort Lauderdale, FL 33312
Tel.: (954) 467-6637
Fax: (945) 467-0046
Web Site: www.mods.org
Approx. Rev.: $5,000,000
Approx. Number Employees: 75
Year Founded: 1977
Business Description:
Science Museum
S.I.C.: 8412
N.A.I.C.S.: 712110
Media: 5-6-7-8-9-10-20-22-23-24-25
Personnel:
Terry W. Stiles *(Chm)*
Kim L. Cavendish *(Pres)*
Patty Ackerman *(CFO & VP-Fin)*
Marlene Janetos *(VP-Visitor Svcs, Mktg & Comm)*
Susan Kenneth *(Creative Dir)*
Theresa Waldron *(Dir-Visitor Svcs & Mktg)*

MUSEUM OF FINE ARTS, HOUSTON
1001 Bissonnet St
Houston, TX 77005
Tel.: (713) 639-7300
Tel.: (713) 639-7540 (Pub Rels)
Fax: (713) 639-7311
E-mail: pr@mfah.org
Web Site: www.mfah.org
Approx. Rev.: $55,000,000
Approx. Number Employees: 600
Business Description:
Art Museum
S.I.C.: 8412
N.A.I.C.S.: 712110; 712120
Media: 6-10
Personnel:
Isabel B. Wilson *(Chm)*

MUSEUM OF FINE ARTS OF ST. PETERSBURG FLORIDA INC.
255 Beach Dr NE
Saint Petersburg, FL 33701
Tel.: (727) 896-2667
Fax: (727) 894-4638
E-mail: webmonkey@fine-arts.org
Web Site: www.fine-arts.org
Sales Range: $10-24.9 Million
Approx. Number Employees: 25
Business Description:
Art Museum
S.I.C.: 8412
N.A.I.C.S.: 712110
Media: 6-9-10-18-20-23-24
Personnel:
Diana Dillon *(Fin Officer)*
David Connelly *(Dir-PR)*
Kent Lydecker *(Dir-Museum)*
Roger W. Zeh *(Asst Dir-Museum)*
Jordana S. Weiss *(Librarian)*

THE MUSEUM OF MODERN ART
11 W 53rd St
New York, NY 10019
Tel.: (212) 708-9400
Fax: (212) 708-9889
E-mail: info@moma.org
Web Site: www.moma.org
E-Mail For Key Personnel:
Public Relations: pressoffice@moma.org
Approx. Number Employees: 700
Year Founded: 1929
Business Description:
Museum of Twentieth Century & Contemporary Art & Design
S.I.C.: 8412
N.A.I.C.S.: 712110
Media: 2-6-9-13-14-18-23
Personnel:
Steve Peltzman *(CIO)*
Allegra Burnette *(Dir-Creative & Digital Media)*
Glenn D. Lowery *(Dir-Museum)*
Pamela Shaw *(Product Mgr)*
Victor Samra *(Mgr-Digital Media Mktg)*
James Gara *(Asst Treas)*
Brands & Products:
MOMA
Advertising Agency:
Big Spaceship
45 Main St Ste 716
Brooklyn, NY 11201
Tel.: (718) 222-0281
Fax: (718) 971-1062

MUSEUM OF SCIENCE AND INDUSTRY
57th St and Lk Shore Dr
Chicago, IL 60637
Tel.: (773) 684-1414
Fax: (773) 684-7141
Toll Free: (800) GOTOMSI
E-mail: human.resources@msichicago.org
Web Site: www.msichicago.org
Approx. Number Employees: 400
Year Founded: 1933
Business Description:
Science & Technology Museum
S.I.C.: 8412
N.A.I.C.S.: 712110
Media: 6-8-9-10-13-17-18-19-22-23-25
Distr.: Direct to Consumer; Reg.
Personnel:
David Mosena *(Pres & CEO)*
Bob Fisher *(CFO & VP-Fin & Admin)*
David J. Vitale *(Chief Admin Officer)*
E. R. Medina *(VP & Gen Mgr)*
Marva Anderson *(Dir-Corp)*
Maureen Sak *(Dir-Mktg)*
Brands & Products:
ACTION! AN ADVENTURE IN MOVIE MAKING
ANTARCTICA
THE BIG IDEA
BRAIN FOOD
ESCAPE FROM ZIRCON
EXPLORE: BLUE PLANET RED PLANET
FAST FORWARD INVENTING THE FUTURE
LIVE FROM THE HEART
MUSEUM OF SCIENCE AND INDUSTRY
SCIENCE CHICAGO LIFE'S A LAB
SCIENCE STORMS
SMART HOME: GREEN + WIRED
SOLAR MAX
TOYMAKER 3000
U-505 SUBMARINE
WE'VE GOT FUN DOWN TO A SCIENCE
YOU! THE EXPERIENCE
Advertising Agencies:
Hoffman York
142 E Ontario St Ste 13
Chicago, IL 60611-2818
Tel.: (312) 787-2330
Fax: (312) 787-2320
(Museum)

Leo Burnett USA
35 W Wacker Dr
Chicago, IL 60601-1723
Tel.: (312) 220-5959
Fax: (312) 220-3299

MUSICAL ARTS ASSOCIATION
(d/b/a Cleveland Orchestra)
11001 Euclid Ave
Cleveland, OH 44106
Tel.: (216) 231-7300
Fax: (216) 231-4038
E-mail: info@clevelandorchestra.com
Web Site: www.clevelandorch.com
Sales Range: $10-24.9 Million
Approx. Number Employees: 200
Year Founded: 1915
Business Description:
Symphony Orchestra
S.I.C.: 7929; 6512
N.A.I.C.S.: 711130; 531120
Media: 9-18-20-23-24-25
Personnel:
Dennis W. Labarre *(Pres)*
Binne Ross *(CMO)*
Gary Hanson *(Exec Dir)*
Sandi M.A. Macdonald *(Dir-Residency-Miami)*
Joe Short *(Mgr-Stage)*

MUVICO THEATERS INC.
3101 N Federal Hwy 6th Fl
Fort Lauderdale, FL 33306
Tel.: (954) 564-6550
Fax: (954) 564-6553
E-mail: development@muvico.com
Web Site: www.muvico.com
Sales Range: $25-49.9 Million
Approx. Number Employees: 25
Year Founded: 1984
Business Description:
Motion Picture Theaters
S.I.C.: 7832; 7812
N.A.I.C.S.: 512131; 512110
Media: 8-10-13
Personnel:
Neil F. Bretan *(Pres & CEO)*
Brands & Products:
MUVICO THEATERS
Advertising Agency:
Kaye Communications Inc.
555 S Federal Hwy Ste 370
Boca Raton, FL 33432
Tel.: (561) 392-5166
Fax: (561) 392-5842

Key to Media (For complete agency information see *The Advertising Red Books-Agencies* edition):
1. Bus. Publs. 2. Cable T.V. 3. Catalogs & Directories. 4. Co-op Adv. 5. Consumer Mags. 6. D.M. to Bus. Estab.7. D.M. to Consumers
8. Daily Newsp. 9. Exhibits/Trade Shows 10. Foreign 11. Infomercial 12. Internet Adv.13. Multimedia 14. Network Radio
15. Network T.V. 16. Newsp. Distr. Mags. 17. Other 18. Outdoor (Posters, Transit) 19. Point of Purchase20. Premiums, Novelties
21. Product Samples 22. Special Events Mktg. 23. Spot Radio 24. Spot T.V. 25. Weekly Newsp. 26. Yellow Page Adv.

NAPA VALLEY SYMPHONY
1100 Lincoln Ave Ste 108
Napa, CA 94558
Tel.: (707) 944-9910
E-mail: info@napavalleysymphony.org
Web Site:
www.napavalleysymphony.org
Approx. Number Employees: 10
Business Description:
Symphony Orchestra
S.I.C.: 7929
N.A.I.C.S.: 711130
Media: 8-9-20-22-23
Personnel:
Lonne Carr *(Pres)*
Richard Aldag *(Exec Dir)*
Karen Frost *(Dir-Ops)*
Jeanette Isenberg *(Mgr-Orchestra Personnel)*
Advertising Agency:
Fuller & Associates
PO Box 329
Napa, CA 94559
Tel.: (707) 253-0868
Fax: (707) 253-0959

NAPLES ZOO INC.
1590 Goodlette-Frank Rd
Naples, FL 34102
Tel.: (239) 262-5409
Fax: (239) 262-6866
Toll Free: (888) 520-3756
E-mail: info@napleszoo.com
Web Site: www.napleszoo.com
Approx. Number Employees: 60
Year Founded: 1919
Business Description:
Zoo
S.I.C.: 8422; 5947
N.A.I.C.S.: 712130; 453220
Media: 8-9-13-20-22-23-25
Personnel:
Denise Rendina *(Dir-Pub Rels & Mktg)*
Douglas Rickenbach *(Dir-Ops)*
David Tetzlaff *(Dir-Zoo)*
Tim L. Tetzlaff *(Dir-Conservation & Comm)*

NASHVILLE PREDATORS, LLC
501 Broadway
Nashville, TN 37203-3932
Tel.: (615) 770-2300
Fax: (615) 770-2309
E-mail: jobs@nashvillepredators.com
Web Site:
www.nashvillepredators.com
Approx. Number Employees: 510
Year Founded: 1998
Business Description:
Professional Hockey Franchise
S.I.C.: 6719; 7941
N.A.I.C.S.: 551112; 711211
Media: 3-8-9-13-18-20-21-22-23-24-25-26
Personnel:
Sean Henry *(Pres & COO)*
Jeff Cogen *(CEO & Governor-Alternate)*
Gerry Helper *(Sr VP-Hockey Comm & PR)*
Chris Junghans *(Sr VP-Corp Dev)*
Blake Grant *(Sr Dir-Event Presentation)*
Brands & Products:
NASHVILLE PREDATORS

Advertising Agency:
Gish, Sherwood & Friends, Inc.
(d/b/a GS&F)
4235 Hillsboro Pike
Nashville, TN 37215-3344
Tel.: (615) 385-1100
Fax: (615) 783-0500

NASHVILLE SYMPHONY ASSOCIATION
1 Symphony Pl
Nashville, TN 37201
Tel.: (615) 687-6500
Fax: (615) 687-6505
Web Site:
www.nashvillesymphony.org
Approx. Number Employees: 180
Year Founded: 1920
Business Description:
Symphony Orchestra
S.I.C.: 7929
N.A.I.C.S.: 711130
Media: 7-8-9-13-20-22-23-24-25
Personnel:
Alan D. Valentine *(Pres & CEO)*
Michael Kirby *(CFO, VP-Fin & Admin)*
Mark A. Blakeman *(VP-Orchestra & Building Ops & Gen Mgr)*
Kimberly Darlington *(Dir-Ticket Svcs)*
Jonathan Marx *(Dir-Comm)*
Rodney Irvin *(Asst Dir-Ticket Svcs)*
Anne Dickson *(Mgr-Orchestra Personnel)*
Brands & Products:
AMERICAN ENCORES
NASHVILLE SYMPHONY

NATIONAL AQUARIUM IN BALTIMORE INC.
501 E Pratt St
Baltimore, MD 21202
Tel.: (410) 576-3800
Tel.: (410) 576-3874 (Media Rels)
Fax: (410) 659-8641
E-mail: media@aqua.org
Web Site: www.aqua.org
Sales Range: $25-49.9 Million
Approx. Number Employees: 400
Business Description:
Aquarium
S.I.C.: 8422
N.A.I.C.S.: 712130
Media: 9-10-18-20-23-24
Personnel:
Joseph Hoffberger *(CFO & Deputy Exec Dir-Admin)*
Paula Schaedlich *(COO)*
David M. Pittenger *(Exec Dir)*
Mark Yost, Jr. *(Dir-Govt Affairs)*
Advertising Agencies:
MGH, Inc.
100 Painters Mill Rd Ste 600
Owings Mills, MD 21117-7305
Tel.: (410) 902-5000
Fax: (410) 902-8712

Proforma Stewart & Associates
PO Box 220
Simpsonville, MD 21150
Tel.: (410) 312-5050
Fax: (410) 312-9011

NATIONAL ARTS CENTRE CORPORATION
53 Elgin Street at Conference Square
Ottawa, ON K1P 5W1, Canada
Tel.: (613) 947-7000
Fax: (613) 996-2828
Toll Free: (866) 850-ARTS
E-mail: info@nac-cna.ca
Web Site: www.nac-cna.ca
Sales Range: $25-49.9 Million
Approx. Number Employees: 925
Business Description:
Performing Arts
S.I.C.: 7389
N.A.I.C.S.: 711310
Media: 9-10-13-14-15-18-20-22-23-24-25
Personnel:
Adrian L. Burns *(Vice Chm)*
Peter Herrndorf *(Pres & CEO)*
Daniel Senyk *(CFO & Dir-Fin)*
Helene Nadeau *(CMO-French Theatre)*
Jane Moore *(Chief Advancement Officer)*
Guy Warin *(Comm & Media Rels Officer)*
Genevieve Cimon *(Dir-Music Education & Community Engagement)*
Debbie Collins *(Dir-HR)*
Alex Gazale *(Dir-Production)*
Paul Hennig *(Dir-Production Ops)*
Diane Landry *(Dir-Mktg)*
Wajdi Mouawad *(Dir-Artistic-French Theatre)*
Daphne Burt *(Mgr-Artistic Plng)*
Anna Calvesbert *(Mgr-ArtsAliveca)*
Nelson McDougall *(Mgr-Personnel)*
Natalie Peachy *(Mgr-Sls & Mktg)*
Cecily Quinn *(Mgr-Box Office)*
Marnie Richardson *(Mgr-New Media)*
Gaston Roussy *(Mgr-House)*
Louise Rowe *(Mgr-Fin & Admin)*
Shannon Whidden *(Mgr-Orchestra)*

NATIONAL ASSOCIATION FOR STOCK CAR AUTO RACING
(d/b/a NASCAR)
1801 W International Speedway Blvd
Daytona Beach, FL 32114-1215
Tel.: (386) 253-0611
Fax: (386) 947-6712
Web Site: www.nascar.com
Approx. Sls.: $323,400,000
Approx. Number Employees: 850
Year Founded: 1947
Business Description:
Professional Stock Car Racing Organization
S.I.C.: 8699
N.A.I.C.S.: 813990
Advertising Expenditures: $1,000,000
Consumer Mags.: $600,000; Other: $200,000; Point of Purchase: $200,000
Personnel:
Brian France *(Chm & CEO)*
Mark Dyer *(Pres & CEO)*
Steve Phelps *(CMO)*
W. Garrett Crotty *(Gen Counsel & Sec)*
Paul B. Brooks *(Sr VP)*
Jim Hunter *(Sr VP)*
Jim O'Connell *(VP-Corp Mktg)*
Doris I. Rumery *(VP-Fin)*
Christine DeMichael *(Sr Mgr-Consumer Mktg)*
Advertising Agencies:
Asphalt Media
114 W 17th St
New York, NY 10011
Tel.: (212) 924-5332
Fax: (212) 989-3783

Harris, Baio & McCullough Inc.
520 S Frnt St
Philadelphia, PA 19147-1723
Tel.: (215) 440-9800
Fax: (215) 440-9812

The Martin Agency
One Shockoe Plz
Richmond, VA 23219-4132
Tel.: (804) 698-8000
Fax: (804) 698-8001

Therapy
2010 S Westgate Ave
Los Angeles, CA 90025
Tel.: (310) 917-1507
Fax: (310) 917-1562

NATIONAL ASSOCIATION OF PROFESSIONAL BASEBALL LEAGUES, INC.
(d/b/a Minor League Baseball)
9550 16th St N
Saint Petersburg, FL 33716
Mailing Address:
PO Box A
Saint Petersburg, FL 33731
Tel.: (727) 822-6937
Fax: (727) 821-5819
E-mail: admin@minorleaguebaseball.com
Web Site:
www.minorleaguebaseball.com
Approx. Sls.: $2,500,000
Approx. Number Employees: 40
Year Founded: 1901
Business Description:
Governing Body of Minor League Baseball Teams
S.I.C.: 8699
N.A.I.C.S.: 813990
Media: 8-10-13-20-22
Personnel:
Eric Krupa *(Pres-South Atlantic League)*
Scott Poley *(Sr VP-Legal Affairs)*
Brian Earle *(Exec Dir-Branded Properties)*
Mike Fitzpatrick *(Exec Dir-PBUC)*
Rod Meadows *(Exec Dir-Sls & Mktg)*
Tim Brunswick *(Dir-Baseball Ops)*
Rob Colamarino *(Dir-IT)*
Steve Densa *(Dir-Media Relations)*
Heather Raburn *(Asst Dir-Sls)*
Melissa Keilen *(Sr Mgr-Sls & Mktg)*
Noreen Brantner *(Mgr-Exhibition Svcs)*
Jeff Carrier *(Acctg Mgr)*
Mary Marandi *(Mgr-Team Relations)*

NATIONAL BASEBALL HALL OF FAME & MUSEUM, INC.
25 Main St
Cooperstown, NY 13326
Tel.: (607) 547-7200
Fax: (607) 547-2044
Toll Free: (888) 425-5633
E-mail: info@baseballhalloffame.org
Web Site:
www.baseballhalloffame.org
Approx. Number Employees: 73
Year Founded: 1936
Business Description:
Baseball Museum
S.I.C.: 8412; 5947
N.A.I.C.S.: 712110; 453220
Media: 1-3-4-8-10-13-15-18-20-22-23-24-25
Distr.: Natl.

Key to Media (For complete agency information see *The Advertising Red Books-Agencies* edition):
1. Bus. Publs. 2. Cable T.V. 3. Catalogs & Directories. 4. Co-op Adv. 5. Consumer Mags. 6. D.M. to Bus. Estab.7. D.M. to Consumers
8. Daily Newsp. 9. Exhibits/Trade Shows 10. Foreign 11. Infomercial 12. Internet Adv.13. Multimedia 14. Network Radio
15. Network T.V. 16. Newsp. Distr. Mags. 17. Other 18. Outdoor (Posters, Transit) 19. Point of Purchase20. Premiums, Novelties
21. Product Samples 22. Special Events Mktg. 23. Spot Radio 24. Spot T.V. 25. Weekly Newsp. 26. Yellow Page Adv.

National Baseball Hall of Fame & Museum, Inc. — (Continued)

Personnel:
Jane Forbes Clark *(Chm)*
Jeffrey Idelson *(Pres)*
Bill Haase *(Sr VP)*

Brands & Products:
NATIONAL BASEBALL

NATIONAL BASKETBALL ASSOCIATION

(d/b/a NBA)
Olympic Twr 645 5th Ave
New York, NY 10022
Tel.: (212) 407-8000
Fax: (212) 754-6414
E-mail: fanrelations@nba.com
Web Site: www.nba.com
Approx. Number Employees: 800
Year Founded: 1946
Business Description:
Professional Basketball Organization
S.I.C.: 8699
N.A.I.C.S.: 813990
Advertising Expenditures:
$25,000,000
Personnel:
David J. Stern *(Commissioner)*
Adam Silver *(COO & Deputy Commissioner)*
Michael Gliedman *(CIO & Sr VP)*
Kim A. Berger *(Sr VP & Chief Compliance Officer)*
Robert Criqui *(Pres-Admin)*
Joel M. Litvin *(Pres-League Ops & Natl Basketball Association)*
Heidi Ueberroth *(Pres-NBA-Intl)*
Ski Austin *(Exec VP-Events & Attractions)*
Kathleen Behrens *(Exec VP-Social Responsibility & Player Programs)*
Kerry D. Chandler *(Exec VP-HR)*
Christopher Granger *(Exec VP-Team Mktg & Bus Ops)*
Daniel Meiseles *(Exec VP, Exec Producer-Production, Programming & Brdcst)*
Mark A. Tatum *(Exec VP-Mktg Partnerships)*
Bryan Perez *(Sr VP & Gen Mgr-NBA Digital)*
Steven M. Angel *(Sr VP-League Ops & Officiating)*
Michael Bass *(Sr VP-Mktg Comm)*
Chris Brennan *(Sr VP-Retail Dev)*
Thomas A. Carelli *(Sr VP-Brdcst)*
Linda Choong *(Sr VP-Retail Grp)*
Peter Farnsworth *(Sr VP-Bus Dev)*
Paul Hirschheimer *(Sr VP-Multimedia Production)*
Sal Larocca *(Sr VP-Global Mdsg Grp)*
Kenny Payne *(Sr VP-Events & Attractions)*
Vicky Picca *(Sr VP-Licensing & Bus Affairs)*
Christopher J. Russo *(Sr VP-Facilities & Admin)*
Jon Hammond *(Sr Dir-Mktg Comm)*
Darrell McLennan-Fordyce *(Sr Dir-Mktg Comm)*

Brands & Products:
NBA

Advertising Agencies:
Dentsu America, Inc.
32 Ave of the Americas 16th Fl
New York, NY 10013
Tel.: (212) 397-3333
Fax: (212) 397-3322

Goodby, Silverstein & Partners, Inc.
(Part of Omnicom Group, Inc.)
720 California St
San Francisco, CA 94108-2404
Tel.: (415) 392-0669
Fax: (415) 788-4303

NATIONAL CINEMEDIA, INC.

9110 E Nichols Ave Ste 200
Centennial, CO 80112-3405
Tel.: (303) 792-3600
Fax: (303) 792-8800
Toll Free: (800) 828-2828
E-mail: investors@ncm.com
Web Site: www.ncm.com
Approx. Rev.: $427,500,000
Approx. Number Employees: 609
Year Founded: 1985
Business Description:
In-Theater Advertising Services
S.I.C.: 7319; 7999
N.A.I.C.S.: 541890; 713990
Advertising Expenditures:
$20,000,000
Personnel:
Kurt C. Hall *(Chm & CEO)*
Gary W. Ferrera *(CFO, Chief Risk Officer & Exec VP)*
Earl B. Weihe *(COO & Exec VP)*
Clifford E. Marks *(Pres-Sls & Mktg)*
Ralph E. Hardy *(Gen Counsel & Exec VP)*
Pam Biederman *(Sr VP)*
Doug Gellerman *(Sr VP-West Coast Sls)*
Lauren Leff *(Sr VP-PR & Comm)*
David Murray *(VP-Integrated Sls & Mktg)*
Brands & Products:
CINEBAGS
CINEBUCKETS
CINEKIOSKS
CINEPROMOTIONS
CINESAMPLING
CINETICKETS
DTDS
MOVIE TUNES
ON-SCREEN ENTERTAINMENT
PRE-SHOW COUNTDOWN
SUPER CINESIGNS

NATIONAL COLLEGIATE ATHLETIC ASSOCIATION

(d/b/a NCAA)
1802 Alonzo Watford Sr Dr
Indianapolis, IN 46202
Tel.: (317) 917-6222
Fax: (317) 917-6888
Web Site: www.ncaa.org
Approx. Number Employees: 400
Business Description:
Collegiate Athletic Program Governing Organization
S.I.C.: 7941; 7999
N.A.I.C.S.: 711211; 711219
Personnel:
Bob Williams *(Mng Dir-Pub & Media Rels)*
Erik Christianson *(Dir-PR & Media Rels)*
Gail Dent *(Assoc Dir)*
Stacey Osburn *(Assoc Dir-Pub & Media)*
Durenka Robie *(Coord-Corp Brdcst & Alliances)*
Brands & Products:
3-MINUTE DRILL
65 TEAMS...ONE DREAM
ALL DAY EVERY DAY. OUR GAME.
AND THEN THERE WERE FOUR
THE BIG DANCE
CHAMPIONS PLAY HERE
CHAMPIONSHIP CITY
COLLEGE CUP
COLLEGE WORLD SERIES
CWS
DOUBLE-A ZONE
EIGHT AT THE PLATE
ELITE EIGHT
ELITE8
F4
FINAL 4
FINAL FOUR
FINAL FOUR FRIDAY
FROZEN FOUR
HALL OF CHAMPIONS
HOOP CITY
IT'S MORE THAN A GAME
IT'S THE JOURNEY
JJ JUMPER
MEN'S COLLEGE CUP
MEN'S ELITE EIGHT
MEN'S FINAL 4
MEN'S FINAL FOUR
MEN'S FROZEN FOUR
MIDDLE SCHOOL MADNESS
MIDNIGHT MADNESS
NATIONAL CHAMPION OF CHAMPIONS
NATIONAL COLLEGIATE ATHLETIC ASSOCIATION
NATIONAL COLLEGIATE CHAMPIONSHIPS
NCAA
NCAA BASKETBALL
NCAA CHAMIONSHIPS
NCAA CHAMPIONSHIPS
NCAA COLLEGE CUP
THE NCAA EXPERIENCE
NCAA HALL OF CHAMPIONS
NCAA INTERNATIONAL
NCAA KIDS
NCAA NEWS
NCAA PHOTOS
NCAA SWEET 16
THE PINNACLE AWAITS
PINNACLE OF FITNESS
THE ROAD ENDS HERE
THE ROAD TO ATLANTA
THE ROAD TO CARY
THE ROAD TO CLEVELAND
THE ROAD TO DETROIT
THE ROAD TO INDIANAPOLIS
THE ROAD TO MINNEAPOLIS
THE ROAD TO NEW ORLEANS
THE ROAD TO OMAHA
THE ROAD TO SAN ANTONIO
THE ROAD TO SAN DIEGO
THE ROAD TO ST. LOUIS
ROAD TO THE FINAL FOUR
THE ROAD TO THE FINAL FOUR
SELECTION SUNDAY
STAGG BOWL
WE ARE THE GAME
WOMEN'S COLLEGE CUP
WOMEN'S COLLEGE WORLD SERIES
WOMEN'S ELITE EIGHT
WOMEN'S FINAL 4
WOMEN'S FINAL FOUR
WOMEN'S FROZEN FOUR
YES
Advertising Agencies:
Burson-Marsteller
(Part of Young & Rubicam Brands, a Sub. of WPP Group plc)
230 Park Ave S
New York, NY 10003-1566
Tel.: (212) 614-4000
Fax: (212) 598-5407

Young & Rubicam Inc.
285 Madison Ave
New York, NY 10017-6401
Tel.: (212) 210-3000
Fax: (212) 490-9073

NATIONAL FOOTBALL LEAGUE

280 Park Ave
New York, NY 10017-1216
Tel.: (212) 450-2000
Fax: (212) 681-7599
Web Site: www.nfl.com
Sales Range: $1-4.9 Billion
Approx. Number Employees: 450
Year Founded: 1920
Business Description:
Professional Football Organization
S.I.C.: 8699
N.A.I.C.S.: 813990
Media: 1-2-3-5-6-8-10-11-13-14-15-16-18-19-20-23-24
Distr.: Intl.; Natl.
Personnel:
Mark Waller *(CMO)*
Eric P. Grubman *(Pres-Bus Ventures & Exec VP)*
Ray Anderson *(Exec VP-Football Ops)*
Paul B. Hicks, III *(Exec VP-Comm & Govt Affairs)*
Keith Turner *(Sr VP-Sls & Sponsorship)*
Peter O'Reilly *(VP-Fan Strategy & Mktg)*
Rob Stecklow *(Dir-Adv & Media)*
Advertising Agencies:
BBDO New York
1285 Ave of the Americas 7th Fl
New York, NY 10019-6028
Tel.: (212) 459-5000
(NFL Fantasy Football, NFLShop.com)

Grey New York
777 3rd Ave
New York, NY 10017-1401
Tel.: (212) 546-2000
Fax: (212) 546-1495

Harris Marketing Group
102 Pierce St
Birmingham, MI 48009-6018
Tel.: (248) 723-6300
Fax: (248) 723-6301

The Vidal Partnership
228 E 45th St 11th Fl
New York, NY 10017-3303
Tel.: (646) 356-6600
Fax: (212) 661-7650

NATIONAL FOOTBALL MUSEUM, INC.

(d/b/a Professional Football Hall of Fame)
2121 George Halas Dr NW
Canton, OH 44708-2630
Tel.: (330) 456-8207
Fax: (330) 456-8175
Web Site: www.profootballhof.com

Key to Media (For complete agency information see *The Advertising Red Books-Agencies* edition):
1. Bus. Publs. 2. Cable T.V. 3. Catalogs & Directories. 4. Co-op Adv. 5. Consumer Mags. 6. D.M. to Bus. Estab.7. D.M. to Consumers
8. Daily Newsp. 9. Exhibits/Trade Shows 10. Foreign 11. Infomercial 12. Internet Adv.13. Multimedia 14. Network Radio
15. Network T.V. 16. Newsp. Distr. Mags. 17. Other 18. Outdoor (Posters, Transit) 19. Point of Purchase20. Premiums, Novelties
21. Product Samples 22. Special Events Mktg. 23. Spot Radio 24. Spot T.V. 25. Weekly Newsp. 26. Yellow Page Adv.

Sales Range: $1-9.9 Million
Approx. Number Employees: 60
Year Founded: 1963
Business Description:
Professional Sports Museum
S.I.C.: 8412
N.A.I.C.S.: 712110
Media: 1-8-10-18-22-24
Distr.: Natl.
Personnel:
Thomas W. Schervish *(Chm)*
Theodore V. Boyd *(Vice Chm)*
Stephen A. Perry *(Pres)*
Joe Horrigan *(VP-Comm & Exhibits)*
Dave Motts *(VP-Mktg & Ops)*
Nichole Cardinale *(Mgr-Admissions & Special Events)*
Pete Fierle *(Mgr-Info Svcs)*
Kevin Shiplett *(Mgr-Ops)*
Gary R. Smith *(Asst Treas)*

NATIONAL HOCKEY LEAGUE
1185 Ave of the Americas 15th Fl
New York, NY 10036-1104
Tel.: (212) 789-2000
Fax: (212) 789-2020
E-mail: info@nhl.com
Web Site: www.nhl.com
Approx. Number Employees: 300
Year Founded: 1900
Business Description:
Professional Hockey Organization
S.I.C.: 8699
N.A.I.C.S.: 813990
Advertising Expenditures: $200,000
Media: 9-13-25
Distr.: Natl.
Budget Set: July
Personnel:
Craig Harnett *(CFO, Sr Exec VP & Treas)*
John Collins *(COO)*
Colin Campbell *(Exec VP & Dir-Hockey Ops)*
Brian Jennings *(Exec VP-Mktg)*
Bill Daly *(VP & Dir-Hockey Ops)*
Casey Rovinelli *(Dir-Digital Mktg)*
Brands & Products:
IS THIS THE YEAR?
NHL
NHL CENTER ICE
NHL FACE OFF
NHL GAMECENTER
NHL GAMECENTER LIVE
NHL NETWORK
NHL WINTER CLASSIC
NHL.COM
Advertising Agencies:
Prospectus Associates
90 Sparks St Ste 400
Ottawa, ON K1P 5B4, Canada
Tel.: (613) 569-3200
Fax: (613) 722-0025

Young & Rubicam Inc.
285 Madison Ave
New York, NY 10017-6401
Tel.: (212) 210-3000
Fax: (212) 490-9073

NATIONAL PHILHARMONIC
5301 Tuckerman Ln
Bethesda, MD 20852-3385
Tel.: (301) 762-8580
Tel.: (301) 493-9283
Fax: (301) 493-9284
E-mail: office@nationalphilharmonic.org
Web Site:
www.nationalphilharmonic.org
Approx. Number Employees: 50
Business Description:
Symphony Orchestra
S.I.C.: 7929
N.A.I.C.S.: 711130
Advertising Expenditures: $140,000
Media: 8-9-23-25
Personnel:
Kenneth A. Oldham, Jr. *(Pres)*
Stanley Engebretson *(Chorale Artistic Dir)*
Piotr Gajewski *(Dir-Music & Conductor)*

NATIONAL SYMPHONY ORCHESTRA
(Affil. of John F. Kennedy Center for the Performing Arts)
2700 F St
Washington, DC 20566
Mailing Address:
PO Box 10808
Arlington, VA 22210
Tel.: (202) 416-8000
Fax: (202) 416-8105
Web Site: www.nationalsymphony.org
Approx. Number Employees: 25
Business Description:
Symphony Orchestra
S.I.C.: 7929
N.A.I.C.S.: 711130
Media: 10-18-20-23-24-25
Personnel:
Leonard Slatkin *(Dir-Music)*
Carole Wysocki *(Dir-NSO Education)*
Brands & Products:
NSO

THE NATIONAL THEATRE CORPORATION
1321 Pennsylvania Ave
Washington, DC 20004
Tel.: (202) 783-6854
Fax: (202) 638-4830
Toll Free: (800) 447-7400
E-mail: dbm@nationaltheater.org
Web Site: www.nationaltheatre.org
Sales Range: $10-24.9 Million
Approx. Number Employees: 50
Year Founded: 1835
Business Description:
Theatrical Producer
S.I.C.: 7922
N.A.I.C.S.: 711110
Media: 7-8-9-13-18-20-23-24-25
Brands & Products:
THE NATIONAL THEATRE
THE THEATRE OF PRESIDENTS

NATIONAL THOROUGHBRED RACING ASSOCIATION
2525 Harrodsburg Rd Ste 400
Lexington, KY 40504-3359
Tel.: (859) 245-6872
Fax: (859) 223-3945
E-mail: ntra@ntra.com
Web Site: www.ntra.com
Approx. Number Employees: 25
Year Founded: 1998
Business Description:
Governing Body of Thoroughbred Horse Racing
S.I.C.: 7999
N.A.I.C.S.: 711219
Advertising Expenditures: $3,500,000
Media: 2-3-7-8-9-13-14-15-18-20-21-22-23-24
Personnel:
Vicki L. Baumgardner *(CFO)*
Keith Chamblin *(Sr VP-Mktg & Indus Rels)*
Susan Parks *(Sr Dir-Sls)*
Fred Vickers *(Mgr-Art)*
Advertising Agency:
Conover Tuttle Pace
77 N Washington St
Boston, MA 02114
Tel.: (617) 412-4000
Fax: (617) 412-4411

NBA PROPERTIES, INC.
(Sub. of National Basketball Association)
100 Plz Dr
Secaucus, NJ 07094-3766
Tel.: (201) 865-1500
Fax: (201) 865-2626
E-mail: info@nba.com
Web Site: www.nba.com
Approx. Number Employees: 25
Year Founded: 1982
Business Description:
Marketing & Licensing for the NBA
S.I.C.: 7389
N.A.I.C.S.: 711320
Media: 13
Personnel:
Alaya Deutsch *(Sr VP & Chief Intellectual Property Counsel)*

NEW BOSTON GARDEN CORP.
(Sub. of Delaware North Companies, Inc.)
1 Fleetcenter Pl Ste 200
Boston, MA 02114-1303
Tel.: (617) 624-1050
Fax: (617) 624-1818
E-mail: jobs@fleetcenter.com
Web Site: www.fleetcenter.com
Approx. Number Employees: 250
Year Founded: 1928
Business Description:
Operator of a Sports & Entertainment Arena
S.I.C.: 5812; 5994
N.A.I.C.S.: 722110; 451212
Media: 4-7-8-9-18-23-24
Distr.: Reg.
Personnel:
Jeremy Jacobs *(Chm & CEO)*
Charles E. Moran, Jr. *(Pres & COO)*
John A. Wentzell *(Pres)*
Michael Wall *(Chief Legal Officer)*
Charles Jacobs *(Principal)*
Lou Jacobs *(Principal)*
Fran Allen *(Exec VP-Sls)*
Larry Cancro *(Sr VP)*
James K. Bednarek *(VP-Fin Admin)*
Stephen H. Nazro *(VP-Customer Svc & Events)*
Lorraine Spadaro *(VP-Technology)*
Catherine Dionne *(Controller & Dir)*
Advertising Agency:
Regan Communications Group
106 Union Wharf
Boston, MA 02109
Tel.: (617) 488-2800
Fax: (617) 488-2830

THE NEW DETROIT SCIENCE CENTER
5020 John R St
Detroit, MI 48202
Tel.: (313) 577-8400
Fax: (313) 832-1623
E-mail: info@sciencedetroit.org
Web Site:
www.detroitsciencecenter.org
Approx. Number Employees: 100
Year Founded: 1965
Business Description:
Science Museum
S.I.C.: 8412
N.A.I.C.S.: 712110
Advertising Expenditures: $400,000
Media: 8-9-10-20-23-24-25
Personnel:
Francois J. Castaing *(Chm)*
Kevin Prihod *(Pres & CEO)*
Kerri Budde *(Dir-Traveling Exhibits)*
Kelly Fulford *(Dir-Pub Rel & Mktg)*

NEW ENGLAND PATRIOTS FOOTBALL CLUB, INC.
(Sub. of The Kraft Group LLC)
1 Patriot Pl
Foxboro, MA 02035
Tel.: (508) 543-8200
Fax: (508) 543-0285
E-mail: webmaster@patriots.com
Web Site: www.patriots.com
Approx. Number Employees: 150
Year Founded: 1959
Business Description:
Professional Football Franchise
S.I.C.: 7941
N.A.I.C.S.: 711211
Media: 6-7-8-9-10-13-14-18-20-22-23-24
Distr.: Natl.
Personnel:
Robert K. Kraft *(Chm & CEO)*
Jonathan A. Kraft *(Pres)*
Mark Briggs *(COO)*
Jennifer Ferron *(VP-Mktg Ops)*
Jim Hausmann *(VP-Fin)*
Nick Caserio *(Dir-Player Personnel)*
Brands & Products:
PATRIOTS

NEW ENGLAND PHILHARMONIC
1906 Massachusetts Ave
Cambridge, MA 02140
Tel.: (617) 868-1222
Web Site: www.nephilharmonic.org
Business Description:
Symphony Orchestra
S.I.C.: 7929
N.A.I.C.S.: 711130
Media: 8-9-20-23-24-25
Personnel:
John Guthrie *(Pres)*
Richard Pittman *(Dir-Music)*
Katherine McWilliams *(Mgr-Personnel)*

THE NEW HAMPSHIRE PHILHARMONIC
83 Hanover St
Manchester, NH 03101
Tel.: (603) 647-6476
E-mail: info@nhphil.org
Web Site: www.nhphilharmonic.org
Year Founded: 1905
Business Description:
Symphony Orchestra
S.I.C.: 7929
N.A.I.C.S.: 711130
Media: 7-8-9-13-20-23-24-25

Key to Media (For complete agency information see *The Advertising Red Books-Agencies* edition):
1. Bus. Publs. 2. Cable T.V. 3. Catalogs & Directories. 4. Co-op Adv. 5. Consumer Mags. 6. D.M. to Bus. Estab.7. D.M. to Consumers 8. Daily Newsp. 9. Exhibits/Trade Shows 10. Foreign 11. Infomercial 12. Internet Adv.13. Multimedia 14. Network Radio 15. Network T.V. 16. Newsp. Distr. Mags. 17. Other 18. Outdoor (Posters, Transit) 19. Point of Purchase20. Premiums, Novelties 21. Product Samples 22. Special Events Mktg. 23. Spot Radio 24. Spot T.V. 25. Weekly Newsp. 26. Yellow Page Adv.

The New Hampshire Philharmonic — (Continued)

Personnel:
Paul Hoffman *(VP & Exec Dir)*
Anthony Princiotti *(Dir-Music)*

NEW HAVEN SYMPHONY ORCHESTRA

PO Box 9718
New Haven, CT 06536
Tel.: (203) 865-0831
Fax: (203) 865-0845
E-mail: nforbes@newhavensymphony.org
Web Site: www.newhavensymphony.org
Approx. Number Employees: 100
Year Founded: 1894
Business Description:
Symphony Orchestra
S.I.C.: 7929
N.A.I.C.S.: 711130
Media: 8-9-13-20-23-24-25
Personnel:
Natalie Forbes *(Exec Dir)*
Alex Morr *(Dir-Opers)*

NEW JERSEY DEVILS LLC

Prudential Ctr 165 Mulberry St
Newark, NJ 07102
Tel.: (973) 757-6100
E-mail: mgmt@newjerseydevils.com
Web Site: devils.nhl.com
Approx. Number Employees: 35
Year Founded: 1974
Business Description:
Professional Hockey Franchise
S.I.C.: 7941
N.A.I.C.S.: 711211
Media: 3-4-9-18-20-22-23-24
Distr.: Natl.
Personnel:
Jeffrey Vanderbeek *(Chm & Mng Partner)*
Louis Lamoriello *(Pres, CEO & Gen Mgr)*
Scott Struble *(CFO & Exec VP)*
Chris Modrzynski *(COO & Sr Exec VP)*
Joseph C. Benedetti *(Gen Counsel & Sr VP)*
David Conte *(Exec VP-Hockey Ops & Dir-Scouting)*
Gordon Lavalette *(Exec VP-Admin)*
Peter S. McMullen *(Exec VP)*
Terry Farmer *(Sr VP-Ticket Ops)*
Mark A. Gheduzzi *(Sr VP-Facilities)*
Mike Levine *(Sr VP-Comm)*
Brands & Products:
NEW JERSEY DEVILS

NEW JERSEY NETS

(Holding of Onexim Group)
390 Murray Hill Pkwy
East Rutherford, NJ 07073-2109
Tel.: (201) 935-8888
Fax: (201) 939-1088
Web Site: www.nba.com/nets
Sales Range: $75-99.9 Million
Approx. Number Employees: 150
Year Founded: 1967
Business Description:
Professional Basketball Team
S.I.C.: 7941
N.A.I.C.S.: 711211
Media: 8-9-10-11-13-20-22-23-24
Distr.: Reg.
Budget Set: July
Personnel:
Brett Yormark *(CEO)*
Charlie Mierswa *(CFO & Exec VP-Bus Ops)*
Fred Mangione *(CMO & Sr VP)*
Leo Ehrline *(Chief Admin Officer, Chief Relationship Officer & Exec VP)*
Jeff Gewirtz *(Chief Legal Officer & Exec VP)*
John Sparks *(Sr VP & Gen Mgr-Arena Ops)*
Chris Brahe *(Sr VP-Partnership Sls & Mktg)*
Petra Pope *(Sr VP-Event Mktg & Community Rels)*
Gary Sussman *(VP-PR)*
Billy King *(Gen Mgr)*
Bobby Marks *(Asst Gen Mgr)*
Chris Carrino *(Exec Dir-Brdcst Production)*
Marie Chindamo *(Exec Dir-HR)*
J.M. Caparro *(Sr Dir-Ticket Sls & Svc)*
Jeff Gamble *(Sr Dir-Creative & Interactive Mktg)*
Aaron Harris *(Sr Dir-PR)*
Joseph Stetson *(Sr Dir-Mktg)*
Frank Sullivan *(Sr Dir-Grp Sls)*
John Alfano *(Dir-Partnership Mktg)*
Michelle Alongi *(Dir-Community Rels)*
Lewis Gibbons *(Dir-Ops)*
Daniel Harris *(Dir-Ticket Ops)*
Paul Kamras *(Dir-Game Presentation & Event Mktg)*
Mitch Kaufman *(Dir-Video Ops)*
Randy Lewis *(Dir-Mktg)*
Jason Oddo *(Dir-Fin)*
Elisa Padilla *(Dir-Res & Strategic Mktg)*
Josh Peikon *(Dir-Sls-Suite)*
Gregg Polinsky *(Dir-Player Personnel)*
Abner Neufeld *(Asst Dir-Grp Sls)*
Michael Winkler *(Asst Dir-Ticket Sls)*
Ben Couch *(Mgr-Interactive Mktg)*
Nathaniel Gelman *(Mgr-Premium Seating Acct)*

NEW JERSEY SPORTS & EXPOSITION AUTHORITY

50 State Rte 120
East Rutherford, NJ 07073
Tel.: (201) 935-8500
Fax: (201) 842-4050
E-mail: info@njsea.com
Web Site: www.meadowlands.com
Sales Range: $100-124.9 Million
Approx. Number Employees: 2,700
Business Description:
Horse Race Track Operation
S.I.C.: 7948; 7389
N.A.I.C.S.: 711212; 711310
Media: 3-8-9-13-18-22-23-24-25
Personnel:
Dennis R. Robinson *(Pres & CEO)*

NEW MEXICO SYMPHONY ORCHESTRA

4407 Menaul Blvd NE
Albuquerque, NM 87190-0208
Tel.: (505) 881-9590
Fax: (505) 881-9456
Web Site: www.nmso.org
Approx. Number Employees: 18
Business Description:
Symphony Orchestra
S.I.C.: 7929
N.A.I.C.S.: 711130
Media: 7-8-9-13-20-22-23-24-25
Personnel:
Guillermo Figueroa *(Dir-Music)*
Roger Melone *(Dir-Choral)*
Robin Rupe *(Mgr-Production)*
Advertising Agency:
Wayne Scheiner & Co
PO Box 8254
Albuquerque, NM 87198
Tel.: (505) 256-9224

NEW ORLEANS HORNETS NBA LIMITED PARTNERSHIP

1250 Poydras St 19th Fl
New Orleans, LA 70113
Tel.: (504) 593-4700
Fax: (504) 593-4702
E-mail: hugo@hornets.com
Web Site: www.hornets.com
Approx. Number Employees: 200
Year Founded: 1988
Business Description:
Professional Basketball Team
S.I.C.: 7941
N.A.I.C.S.: 711211
Advertising Expenditures: $500,000
Media: 8-9-13-18-20-23-24
Personnel:
Hugh Weber *(Pres)*
Gary Chouest *(Partner)*
Ed Lang *(CFO)*
Pat McKinney *(VP-HR)*
Dell Demps *(Gen Mgr)*
Brands & Products:
NEW ORLEANS HORNETS

NEW ORLEANS SAINTS L.P.

5800 Airline Dr
Metairie, LA 70003-3876
Tel.: (504) 733-0255
Fax: (504) 731-1810
E-mail: info@neworleanssaints.com
Web Site: www.neworleanssaints.com
Approx. Number Employees: 130
Year Founded: 1966
Business Description:
Professional Football Franchise
S.I.C.: 7941
N.A.I.C.S.: 711211
Advertising Expenditures: $500,000
Media: 3-9-13-15-18-20-22-23-24-25
Personnel:
Tom Benson *(Owner)*
Rita Benson LeBlanc *(Co-Owner & Exec VP)*
Dennis Lauscha *(CFO & Exec VP)*
Mickey Loomis *(Exec VP & Gen Mgr)*
Greg Bensel *(VP-Comm)*
Ben Hales *(VP-Mktg & Bus Dev)*
Charleen Sharpe *(Comptroller)*
Doug Miller *(Sr Dir-PR)*
Jean-Paul Dardenne *(Dir-Corp Partnerships)*
Dave Desposito *(Dir-Video)*
Khai Harley *(Dir-Football Admin)*
Cindy Hart *(Dir-Suite Sls, Svcs & Special Events)*
Michael C. Hebert *(Dir-Photography)*
Fred McAfee *(Dir-Player Dev)*
James Nagaoka *(Dir-Ops)*
Ryan Pace *(Dir-Pro Scouting)*
Rick Reiprish *(Dir-College Scouting)*
Ian Tigchelaar *(Dir-Bus & Mktg Ops)*
Jason Trosclair *(Dir-Youth Programs)*
Elicia Broussard *(Asst Dir-Community Rels)*
Jeff Jacobs *(Asst Dir-Video)*
Travis Burkett *(Sr Mgr-Sls)*
Terry Ashburn *(Mgr-Facilities)*
Jody Barbier *(Mgr-Application Support-IT)*
Danny Callahan *(Mgr-Applications Dev-IT)*
Keira Durrette *(Mgr-Corp Partnerships Svc)*
Jeff Huffman *(Mgr-IT/Network)*
Justin Macione *(Mgr-Comm)*
Dan Simmons *(Mgr-Equipment)*
Brands & Products:
NEW ORLEANS SAINTS
Advertising Agency:
Calzone & Associates
1011 Lee Ave
Lafayette, LA 70502
Tel.: (337) 235-2924
Fax: (337) 237-0556

NEW YORK CITY BALLET

20 Lincoln Ctr Plz
New York, NY 10023
Tel.: (212) 870-5677
Fax: (212) 870-7791
E-mail: nycb@nycballet.com
Web Site: www.nycballet.com
Approx. Number Employees: 400
Business Description:
Ballet Producer
S.I.C.: 7922; 7911
N.A.I.C.S.: 711110; 611610
Media: 8-23-24
Personnel:
Edward Villella *(CEO)*
Katherine E. Brown *(Exec Dir)*
Brooks Parsons *(Sr Dir-Ops)*
Karen Girgy *(Dir-Mktg)*
Advertising Agency:
AKQA, Inc.
175 Varick St 10th Fl
New York, NY 10014
Tel.: (212) 989-2572
Fax: (212) 989-2363
(Web Site)

NEW YORK CITY OFF-TRACK BETTING CORPORATION

1501 Broadway Times Sq
New York, NY 10036-5601
Tel.: (212) 221-5200
Fax: (212) 704-5176
Web Site: www.nycotb.com
Approx. Number Employees: 2,700
Year Founded: 1970
Business Description:
Horse Racing Services
S.I.C.: 7999
N.A.I.C.S.: 713290
Advertising Expenditures: $2,325,000
Media: 3-9-20-22-23-24-25-26
Distr.: Reg.
Budget Set: June
Personnel:
Ray Casey *(Pres)*
Ron Ceisler *(Sr VP-Mktg)*
Brands & Products:
NYCOTB
Advertising Agency:
Ventura Associates International LLC
1040 Ave of the Americas Fl 20
New York, NY 10018-3730
Tel.: (212) 302-8277
Fax: (212) 302-2587
— Lisa Manhart *(Acct. Exec.)*

NEW YORK CITY OPERA INC.

20 Lincoln Ctr Plz
New York, NY 10023

Key to Media (For complete agency information see *The Advertising Red Books-Agencies* edition):
1. Bus. Publs. 2. Cable T.V. 3. Catalogs & Directories. 4. Co-op Adv. 5. Consumer Mags. 6. D.M. to Bus. Estab.7. D.M. to Consumers
8. Daily Newsp. 9. Exhibits/Trade Shows 10. Foreign 11. Infomercial 12. Internet Adv.13. Multimedia 14. Network Radio
15. Network T.V. 16. Newsp. Distr. Mags. 17. Other 18. Outdoor (Posters, Transit) 19. Point of Purchase20. Premiums, Novelties
21. Product Samples 22. Special Events Mktg. 23. Spot Radio 24. Spot T.V. 25. Weekly Newsp. 26. Yellow Page Adv.

Tel.: (212) 870-5600
Tel.: (212) 870-6582 (Mktg)
Fax: (212) 724-1120
E-mail: marketing@nycopera.com
Web Site: www.nycopera.com
Sales Range: $25-49.9 Million
Approx. Number Employees: 600
Business Description:
Producer of Opera
S.I.C.: 7922
N.A.I.C.S.: 711110
Media: 4-8-9-10-13-18-20-23-24-25
Personnel:
George Manahan *(Dir-Music)*
Tom Trayer *(Dir-Mktg)*
Sharon Marmora *(Asst Dir-Mktg)*

NEW YORK FOOTBALL GIANTS
Timex Performance Ctr 1925 Giant Dr
East Rutherford, NJ 07073
Tel.: (201) 935-8111
Fax: (201) 939-5447
E-mail: feedback@fans.giants.com
Web Site: www.giants.com
Sales Range: $125-149.9 Million
Approx. Number Employees: 140
Year Founded: 1925
Business Description:
Professional Football Franchise
S.I.C.: 7941
N.A.I.C.S.: 711211
Media: 10-13-18-20-22
Distr.: Natl.
Personnel:
Jonathan M. Tisch *(Co-Chm & Treas)*
Steve Tisch *(Chm & Exec VP)*
John K. Mara *(Pres & CEO)*
Christine Procops *(CFO & VP)*
Mike Stevens *(CMO & Sr VP)*
Jerry Reese *(Sr VP & Gen Mgr)*
Pat Hanlon *(VP-Comm)*
Rusty Hawley *(VP-Mktg)*
Dan Lynch *(VP-Media & Partnerships)*
Beth Roche *(Dir-Mktg Svcs & Youth Programs-Giants)*
David Gettleman *(Dir-Pro Personnel)*
E. Peter John-Baptiste *(Dir-PR)*
Francis X. Mara *(Dir-Promos)*
Doug Murphy *(Dir-Creative Svcs)*
Jim Phelan *(Dir-Admin)*
Marc Ross *(Dir-College Scouting)*
Charles Way *(Dir-Player Dev)*
Brands & Products:
GIANTS
NY

NEW YORK HALL OF SCIENCE
4701 11th St
Corona, NY 11368
Tel.: (718) 699-0005
Fax: (718) 699-1341
E-mail: info@nyhallsci.org
Web Site: www.nyhallsci.org
Approx. Number Employees: 150
Business Description:
Science Museum
S.I.C.: 8412
N.A.I.C.S.: 712110
Media: 7-8-9-10-20-22-23-24-25
Personnel:
Margaret Honey *(Pres & CEO)*
Paul Konigstein *(Fin Dir-Grants Mgmt)*
Preeti Gupta *(Sr VP-Education & Family Programs)*
Tara Keblish *(Dir-Membership & Strategic Mktg)*
Mary Record *(Dir-Comm)*
Eric Siegel *(Chief Content Officer & Dir)*
Ravi Baldeo *(Supvr-Interpretations & Demonstrations)*

NEW YORK ISLANDERS HOCKEY CLUB, L.P.
1255 Hempstead Tpke
Uniondale, NY 11553
Tel.: (516) 501-6700
Fax: (516) 501-6762
E-mail: customerservice@newyorkislanders.com
Web Site: www.newyorkislanders.com
Approx. Number Employees: 100
Year Founded: 1972
Business Description:
Professional Hockey Franchise
S.I.C.: 7941
N.A.I.C.S.: 711211
Advertising Expenditures: $3,000,000
Media: 1-3-6-7-8-9-10-16-18-19-20-22-23-24-25
Distr.: Natl.
Budget Set: May -June
Personnel:
Charles B. Wang *(Owner & Governor)*
Arthur Maccarthy *(CFO & Sr VP)*
Garth Snow *(Gen Mgr)*
Ken Morrow *(Dir-Pro Scouting)*
Brands & Products:
NY ISLANDERS
Advertising Agency:
Wilen Group
5 Wellwood Ave
Farmingdale, NY 11735-1213
Tel.: (631) 439-5000
Fax: (631) 439-4536
Toll Free: (800) 809-4536

NEW YORK JETS FOOTBALL CLUB, INC.
1000 Fulton Ave
Hempstead, NY 11550
Tel.: (516) 560-8100
Fax: (516) 560-8198
E-mail: eyewear@hlbouton.com
Web Site: www.newyorkjets.com
Approx. Number Employees: 130
Year Founded: 1963
Business Description:
Professional Football Franchise
S.I.C.: 7941
N.A.I.C.S.: 711211
Media: 3-7-8-9-10-13-14-15-20-22-25
Distr.: Reg.
Personnel:
Woody Johnson *(Chm & CEO)*
Mike Gerstle *(Pres-Fin)*
Matt Higgins *(Exec VP-Bus Ops)*
Thad Sheely *(Exec VP-Fin & Stadium Dev)*
Robert Parente *(VP)*
Joey Clinkscales *(VP-College Scouting)*
Marc Riccio *(VP-Corp Sls & Mktg)*
Scott Cohen *(Asst Gen Mgr)*
Mike Tannenbaum *(Gen Mgr)*
Rich Gentile *(Sr Dir-merchandising)*
Clay Hampton *(Sr Dir-Ops)*
Victoria Vitarelli *(Dir-Mktg)*
Dave Szott *(Dir-Player Dev)*
Tim Tubito *(Dir-Video)*
Jennifer Fitzpatrick *(Mgr-Mktg)*
Brands & Products:
GENERATION JETS
JETS TRAINING CAMP
NEW YORK JETS
Advertising Agency:
Fly Communications
40 W 25th St
New York, NY 10010
Tel.: (212) 675-8484
Fax: (212) 675-3677
(New Stadium Promotion)

NEW YORK KNICKERBOCKERS
(Sub. of Madison Square Garden, L.P.)
(d/b/a New York Knicks)
Madison Sq Garden 2 Pennsylvania Plz
New York, NY 10121-0091
Tel.: (212) 465-6000
Tel.: (212) 465-6471
Fax: (212) 465-6498
Web Site: www.nyknicks.com
Sales Range: $350-399.9 Million
Approx. Number Employees: 2,000
Year Founded: 1946
Business Description:
Professional Basketball Team
S.I.C.: 7941
N.A.I.C.S.: 711211
Advertising Expenditures: $3,000,000
Media: 4-6-8-9-10-18-19-20-22-23
Distr.: Natl.
Personnel:
Frank Murphy *(Sr VP-Basketball Affairs)*
Nicole Jeter West *(Dir-Mktg)*
Brands & Products:
NY KNICKERBOCKERS
Advertising Agencies:
Merkley + Partners
(Sub. of Omnicom Group, Inc.)
200 Varick St
New York, NY 10014-4810
Tel.: (212) 366-3500
Fax: (212) 805-7445

o2kl
10 W 18th St 6th Fl
New York, NY 10011
Tel.: (646) 829-6239
Fax: (646) 839-6254

NEW YORK RACING ASSOCIATION, INC.
PO Box 90
Ozone Park, NY 11417
Tel.: (718) 641-4700
Fax: (718) 835-5246
Toll Free: (800) 522-5554
E-mail: nyrapress@nyrainc.com
Web Site: www.nyra.com
Approx. Number Employees: 1,800
Year Founded: 1955
Business Description:
Owner & Operator of Racetracks
S.I.C.: 4813; 7389; 7948
N.A.I.C.S.: 517110; 561990; 711212
Advertising Expenditures: $3,000,000
Media: 8-9-13-20-22-23-24-26
Distr.: Reg.
Budget Set: Nov. -Dec.
Personnel:
Charles Hayward *(Pres & CEO)*
Brands & Products:
AQUEDUCT
BELMONT PARK
NYRA
SARATOGA

NEW YORK RANGERS HOCKEY CLUB
(Sub. of Madison Square Garden, L.P.)
2 Pennsylvania Plz
New York, NY 10121
Tel.: (212) 465-6000
Fax: (212) 465-6438
Web Site: www.newyorkrangers.com
Sales Range: $1-9.9 Million
Year Founded: 1926
Business Description:
Professional Hockey Team
S.I.C.: 7941; 7389
N.A.I.C.S.: 711211; 711310
Media: 4-6-8-9-10-18-19-20-22-23
Personnel:
Hank J. Ratner *(Vice Chm)*
Glen Sather *(Pres & Gen Mgr)*
Robert M. Pollichino *(CFO & Exec VP)*
John Cudmore *(Sr VP-Fin & Controller)*
Marc Schoenfeld *(Deputy Gen Counsel & Sr VP-Teams)*
Mark Piazza *(Sr VP-Ops)*
Don Maloney *(VP & Asst Gen Mgr)*
Joanecy Kagalingan *(Dir-Design)*
Tziona Katz *(Mgr-Interactive Mktg)*
Advertising Agency:
The Brooklyn Brothers
18 E 17th St 6th Fl
New York, NY 10003
Tel.: (212) 242-0200
Fax: (212) 242-0217

NEW YORK YANKEES
(Holding of New York Yankees Partnership)
Yankee Stadium 1 E 161st St & River Ave
Bronx, NY 10451
Tel.: (718) 293-6000
Fax: (718) 293-8431
Web Site: newyork.yankees.mlb.com
Sales Range: $300-349.9 Million
Approx. Number Employees: 120
Year Founded: 1903
Business Description:
Professional Baseball Club
S.I.C.: 7941
N.A.I.C.S.: 711211
Advertising Expenditures: $500,000
Media: 3-7-8-9-18-20-22-23-24-25
Distr.: Natl.
Personnel:
Henry G. Steinbrenner *(Co-Chm & Gen Partner)*
Harold Z. Steinbrenner *(Co-Chm)*
Joan Steinbrenner *(Principal Owner & Chm)*
Jessica Steinbrenner *(Vice Chm & Gen Partner)*
Jennifer Steinbrenner Swindal *(Vice Chm & Gen Partner)*
Randy Levine *(Pres)*
Anthony Bruno *(CFO & Sr VP)*
Robert Brown *(Co-CFO & VP-Acctg)*
Scott Krug *(CFO & VP-Fin Ops)*
Lonn A. Trost *(COO)*
Sonny Hight *(Chief Strategy Officer & Sr VP)*
Brian Cashman *(Sr VP & Gen Mgr)*

Key to Media (For complete agency information see *The Advertising Red Books-Agencies* edition):
1. Bus. Publs. 2. Cable T.V. 3. Catalogs & Directories. 4. Co-op Adv. 5. Consumer Mags. 6. D.M. to Bus. Estab.7. D.M. to Consumers
8. Daily Newsp. 9. Exhibits/Trade Shows 10. Foreign 11. Infomercial 12. Internet Adv.13. Multimedia 14. Network Radio
15. Network T.V. 16. Newsp. Distr. Mags. 17. Other 18. Outdoor (Posters, Transit) 19. Point of Purchase20. Premiums, Novelties
21. Product Samples 22. Special Events Mktg. 23. Spot Radio 24. Spot T.V. 25. Weekly Newsp. 26. Yellow Page Adv.

New York Yankees — (Continued)

Marty Greenspun *(Sr VP-Strategic Ventures)*
Felix M. Lopez *(Sr VP)*
Mark Newman *(Sr VP-Baseball Ops)*
Brian Smith *(Sr VP-Corp & Community Rels)*
Michael J. Tusiani *(Sr VP-Corp Sls & Sponsorships)*
Deborah A. Tymon *(Sr VP-Mktg)*
Jean Afterman *(VP & Asst Gen Mgr)*
Alan Chang *(VP-Legal Affairs & Deputy Gen Counsel)*
Kevin Dart *(Exec Dir-Ticket Ops)*
Jeff Kline *(Exec Dir-Ticket Ops)*
Doug Behar *(Sr Dir-Stadium Ops)*
Michael Bonner *(Sr Dir-Scoreboard & Brdcst Production)*
Irfan Kirimca *(Sr Dir-Ticket Ops)*
Mike Lane *(Sr Dir-Tech)*
David Bernstein *(Dir-Hospitality)*
Bryan Calka *(Dir-Corp Sls & Sponsorships)*
Billy Eppler *(Dir-Prof Scouting)*
Manuel Garcia *(Dir-Latino Affairs)*
Stanley Kay *(Dir-Entertainment)*
Kara Mooney *(Dir-Creative Svcs)*
Tony Morante *(Dir-Stadium Tours)*
Alfred Santasiere, III *(Dir-Publ)*
Jason Zillo *(Dir-Media Rels)*

Brands & Products:
NEW YORK YANKEES
YANKEES MAGAZINE
YANKEES YEARBOOK
YES NETWORK

Advertising Agencies:
Concrete Media
43 E Moonachie Rd
Hackensack, NJ 07601
Tel.: (201) 440-2626
Fax: (201) 440-3433

MLB Advanced Media, L.P.
75 9th Ave 5th Fl
New York, NY 10011
Tel.: (212) 485-3444
Fax: (212) 485-3456

Rubenstein Associates, Inc.
1345 Ave of the Americas Fl 30
New York, NY 10105-0109
Tel.: (212) 843-8000
Fax: (212) 843-9200
Pub Rels

NEWPORT AQUARIUM

One Aquarium Way
Newport, KY 41071
Tel.: (859) 261-7444
Fax: (859) 261-5888
Web Site: www.newportaquarium.com
Business Description:
Aquarium
S.I.C.: 8422
N.A.I.C.S.: 712130
Media: 3-9-13-14-15-25
Personnel:
Lynn Margason *(Dir-Mktg)*

NEWPORT ART MUSEUM

76 Bellevue Ave
Newport, RI 02840
Tel.: (401) 848-8200
Fax: (401) 848-8205
E-mail: info@newportartmuseum.org
Web Site:
www.newportartmuseum.org
Approx. Number Employees: 20
Business Description:
Art Museum
S.I.C.: 8412; 7911
N.A.I.C.S.: 712110; 611610
Media: 7-8-9-10-13-20-22-23-24-25
Personnel:
Shawn Parker *(Dir-Education)*

NEWTON SYMPHONY ORCHESTRA

230 Central St
Auburndale, MA 02466-2333
Tel.: (617) 965-2555
Fax: (617) 965-0450
E-mail: office@newtonsymphony.org
Web Site: www.newtonsymphony.org
Approx. Number Employees: 1
Business Description:
Symphony Orchestra
S.I.C.: 7929
N.A.I.C.S.: 711130
Media: 9-20-22-23-25
Personnel:
Letitia Stevens *(Exec Dir)*
Susan Porr *(Mgr-Personnel)*

NORTH CAROLINA SYMPHONY

4350 Lassiter at North Hills Ave Ste 50
Raleigh, NC 27609
Tel.: (919) 733-2750
Fax: (919) 733-2720
E-mail: info@ncsymphony.org
Web Site: www.ncsymphony.org
Sales Range: $10-24.9 Million
Approx. Number Employees: 85
Business Description:
Symphony Orchestra
S.I.C.: 7929; 9199
N.A.I.C.S.: 711130; 921190
Media: 9-20-22-23-24-25
Personnel:
Don K. Davis *(Pres & CEO - Interim)*
Scott Freck *(VP-Artistic Ops & Gen Mgr)*
Suzanne McKeon *(VP-Mktg & Audience Dev)*
Grant Llewellyn *(Dir)*
Allyn Love *(Dir-Ops)*
Rob Maddrey *(Dir-Statewide Dev)*
Jeannie Mellinger *(Dir-Comm)*
Brenda Knight *(Mgr-Fin)*

Advertising Agency:
ClickCulture
3739 National Dr Ste 210
Raleigh, NC 27612
Tel.: (919) 420-7736
Fax: (919) 420-7758
(Web Site)

NORTH SHORE PHILHARMONIC ORCHESTRA

PO Box 461
Danvers, MA 01923-0761
Tel.: (781) 286-0024
E-mail: nsphil@hotmail.com
Web Site: www.nspo.org
Business Description:
Symphony Orchestra
S.I.C.: 6512; 6552
N.A.I.C.S.: 531120; 237210
Media: 9-20-23-24-25
Personnel:
Robert A. Marra, Jr. *(Pres)*
Robert Lehmann *(Dir-Music)*
Lisa McDonough *(Librarian)*

NORTHBROOK SYMPHONY ORCHESTRA INC.

899 Skokie Blvd Ste LL12
Northbrook, IL 60062
Tel.: (847) 272-0755
E-mail: information@northbrooksymphony.org
Web Site:
www.northbrooksymphony.org
Approx. Number Employees: 30
Business Description:
Symphony Orchestra
S.I.C.: 7389
N.A.I.C.S.: 711320
Media: 9-20-23-24-25
Personnel:
Susan Laing *(Pres)*
Lawrence Rapchak *(Dir-Music & Conductor)*

NORTHWEST BUSINESS FOR CULTURE AND THE ARTS

522 SW 5th Ave Ste 1285
Portland, OR 97204
Tel.: (503) 228-2977
Fax: (503) 248-1808
E-mail: info@nwbca.org
Web Site: www.nwbca.org
Sales Range: Less than $1 Million
Sales Estimate: $100-119 Million
Approx. Number Employees: 4
Business Description:
Non-Profitable Organization
S.I.C.: 8999
N.A.I.C.S.: 711510
Media: 7-17
Personnel:
Virginia Willard *(Exec Dir)*
Susan Myers *(Assoc Dir)*

NORTHWEST IOWA SYMPHONY ORCHESTRA

498 4th Ave NW
Sioux Center, IA 51250
Tel.: (712) 722-6230
Fax: (712) 722-6035
E-mail: niso@dordt.edu
Web Site: www.niso.dordt.edu
Sales Range: Less than $1 Million
Approx. Number Employees: 50
Business Description:
Symphony Orchestra
S.I.C.: 8699
N.A.I.C.S.: 813990
Media: 9-20-23-24-25
Personnel:
Bernie Weitenaar *(Pres)*
James Koldenhoven *(Interim Gen Mgr)*

OAKLAND ATHLETICS LIMITED PARTNERSHIP

(Sub. of Athletics Investment Group, LLC)
(d/b/a Oakland A's)
7000 Coliseum Way
Oakland, CA 94621
Tel.: (510) 638-4900
Fax: (510) 563-2376
E-mail: fanfeedback@athletics.mlb.com
Web Site:
www.oakland.athletics.mlb.com
Sales Range: $75-99.9 Million
Approx. Number Employees: 200
Year Founded: 1901
Business Description:
Professional Baseball Club
S.I.C.: 7941
N.A.I.C.S.: 711211
Media: 9-10-18-20-22-23-24
Distr.: Natl.
Personnel:
Lewis N. Wolff *(Mng Partner)*
Michael Crowley *(Pres)*
Billy Beane *(VP & Gen Mgr)*
Jim Leahey *(VP-Sls & Mktg)*
Ken Pries *(VP-Commun & Broadcasting)*
Paul Wong *(VP-Fin)*
David Forst *(Asst Gen Mgr)*
Steve Fanelli *(Exec Dir-Ticket Sls & Ops)*
David Don *(Sr Dir-Multimedia Svcs)*
Eric Kubota *(Dir-Scouting)*
Keith Lieppman *(Dir-Player Dev)*
Billy Owens *(Dir-Player Personnel)*
Pamela Pitts *(Dir-Baseball Admin)*
Bob Rose *(Dir-PR)*
Farhan Zaidi *(Dir-Baseball Ops)*
Kristy Fick *(Mgr-Player & Media Relations)*
Debbie Gallas *(Mgr-Media Svcs)*
Zachary Glare *(Mgr-Mktg)*
Mike Ono *(Mgr-Creative Svcs)*
Detra Paige *(Mgr-Community Rels)*
Heather Rajeski *(Mgr-Promos & Special Events)*
Steve Vucinich *(Mgr-Equipment)*

Brands & Products:
A'S AMIGOS
COMMUNITY DAYS
HOME RUN READERS
LITTLE A'S
MATHLETICS
OAKLAND ATHLETICS
RACE AROUND THE BASES
SENIOR DAYS
TAKE THE FIELD WITH THE A'S

Advertising Agencies:
Eleven Inc.
445 Bush St 8th Fl
San Francisco, CA 94108
Tel.: (415) 707-1111
Fax: (415) 707-1100

Hub Strategy and Communication
39 Mesa St Ste 212
San Francisco, CA 94129
Tel.: (415) 561-4345
Fax: (415) 771-5965
Creative Agency of Record

McCann Worldgroup
600 Battery St
San Francisco, CA 94111
Tel.: (415) 262-5600
Fax: (415) 262-5400

MLB Advanced Media, L.P.
75 9th Ave 5th Fl
New York, NY 10011
Tel.: (212) 485-3444
Fax: (212) 485-3456

THE OAKLAND RAIDERS, L.P.

1220 Harbor Bay Pkwy
Alameda, CA 94502-6501
Tel.: (510) 864-5000
Fax: (510) 864-5134
E-mail: feedback@raiders.com
Web Site: www.raiders.com
Approx. Number Employees: 100
Year Founded: 1960

Key to Media (For complete agency information see *The Advertising Red Books-Agencies* edition):
1. Bus. Publs. 2. Cable T.V. 3. Catalogs & Directories. 4. Co-op Adv. 5. Consumer Mags. 6. D.M. to Bus. Estab.7. D.M. to Consumers
8. Daily Newsp. 9. Exhibits/Trade Shows 10. Foreign 11. Infomercial 12. Internet Adv.13. Multimedia 14. Network Radio
15. Network T.V. 16. Newsp. Distr. Mags. 17. Other 18. Outdoor (Posters, Transit) 19. Point of Purchase20. Premiums, Novelties
21. Product Samples 22. Special Events Mktg. 23. Spot Radio 24. Spot T.V. 25. Weekly Newsp. 26. Yellow Page Adv.

Business Description:
Professional Football Franchise
S.I.C.: 7941
N.A.I.C.S.: 711211
Media: 9-18-23-24-25
Distr.: Natl.
Budget Set: July
Personnel:
Allen Davis *(Owner)*
Amy Trask *(CEO)*
Jeff Birren *(Gen Counsel)*
Marc Badain *(Dir-Fin)*
Mike Taylor *(Dir-PR)*
Brands & Products:
RAIDERS
Advertising Agency:
Baker Street Partners
2410 Baker St
San Francisco, CA 94123
Tel.: (415) 659-3900
Fax: (415) 659-3903

OAKLAWN JOCKEY CLUB, INC.
2705 Central Ave
Hot Springs, AR 71902
Tel.: (501) 623-4411
Fax: (501) 701-1399
Toll Free: (800) OAKLAWN
E-mail: winning@oaklawn.com
Web Site: www.oaklawn.com
Approx. Rev.: $15,000,000
Approx. Number Employees: 450
Year Founded: 1904
Business Description:
Horse Racetrack & Casino Owner & Operator
S.I.C.: 7948; 7999
N.A.I.C.S.: 711212; 713210
Advertising Expenditures: $1,000,000
Media: 9-10-13-23-24-25
Distr.: Reg.
Personnel:
Charles J. Cella *(Pres)*
Eric Jackson *(Gen Mgr)*
Kim Burge-Baron *(Dir-Mktg)*
Bobby Geiger *(Dir-Wagering)*
Terry Wallace *(Dir-Media Rels)*
Brands & Products:
OAKLAWN

OKLAHOMA CITY PHILHARMONIC ORCHESTRA SOCIETY, INC.
428 W California Ste 210
Oklahoma City, OK 73102
Tel.: (405) 232-7575
Fax: (405) 232-4353
E-mail: info@okcphilharmonic.org
Web Site: www.okcphilharmonic.org
Approx. Number Employees: 75
Business Description:
Symphony Orchestra
S.I.C.: 7929
N.A.I.C.S.: 711130
Media: 1-8-9-20-22-23-24-25
Personnel:
kris markes *(Gen Mgr)*
Edward Walker *(Exec Dir)*
Joel Levine *(Dir-Music)*
Michelle Winters *(Dir-Mktg/PR/Sls)*
Michael Helt *(Mgr-Personnel)*

OKLAHOMA CITY THUNDER
(Sub. of The Professional Basketball Club, LLC)
2 Leadership Sq 211 N Robinson Ave Ste 300
Oklahoma City, OK 73102
Tel.: (405) 208-4800
Fax: (405) 429-7900
E-mail: sans@thunder.nba.com
Web Site: www.nba.com/thunder
Approx. Number Employees: 100
Year Founded: 1967
Business Description:
Professional Basketball Team
S.I.C.: 7941
N.A.I.C.S.: 711211
Media: 3-4-7-8-9-14-15-18-22-23-24-25-26
Distr.: Reg.
Budget Set: Sept. -Oct.
Personnel:
Clayton I. Bennett *(Chm)*
Danny Barth *(Chief Admin Officer & Exec VP)*
Sam Presti *(Exec VP & Gen Mgr)*
Terry McLaughlin *(Exec VP-Admin)*
Jeff Jacobson *(Sr Dir-Bus Dev)*
Karen Bryant *(Sr VP-Commun & Community Dev)*
Brian M. Byrnes *(Sr VP-Sls & Mktg)*
Pete Winemiller *(Sr VP-Guest Rels)*
Troy Weaver *(Asst Gen Mgr)*
Bill Branch *(Dir-Pro Player Personnel)*
Dwight Daub *(Dir-Athletic Performance)*
Brian Facchini *(Dir-Basketball Comm)*
Wayne Guymon *(Dir-Bus Dev)*
Rob Hennigan *(Dir-College & Intl Player Personnel)*
Abby Morgan *(Dir-Account Svcs)*
Paul Rivers *(Dir-Minor League Ops & Basketball Tech)*
Frank Ross *(Dir-Scouting-East Coast)*
Tom Savage *(Dir-Corp Comm)*
Marc St. Yves *(Dir-Team Ops)*
Donnie Strack *(Dir-Medical Svcs)*
Ayana Clinton *(Mgr-Player Svcs & Appearances)*
Vin Bhavnani *(Coord-Video)*
Brands & Products:
SUPERSONICS

OKLAHOMA CITY ZOOLOGICAL PARK
2101 NE 50th St
Oklahoma City, OK 73111-7106
Tel.: (405) 424-3344
Fax: (405) 425-0297
E-mail: guestrelations@okczoo.com
Web Site: www.okczoo.com
Approx. Number Employees: 130
Year Founded: 1904
Business Description:
Botanical Gardens
S.I.C.: 8422
N.A.I.C.S.: 712130
Advertising Expenditures: $300,000
Media: 3-6-9-10-13-16-18-20-22-23-24-25-26
Distr.: Direct to Consumer; Reg.
Budget Set: Jan.
Personnel:
Julie Hall *(Vice Chm)*
Diuse Scott *(Exec Dir)*
Mark Campbell *(Dir-Bus Svcs)*
Gicki Flores *(Dir-HR)*
Tara Henson *(Dir-Mktg-Pub Rels)*
Karen Jones *(Dir-Visitor Svcs)*
Marce Lester *(Mgr-Graphics)*

OLD SALEM, INCORPORATED
600 S Main St
Winston Salem, NC 27101
Tel.: (336) 721-7300
Fax: (336) 721-7335
E-mail: webmaster@oldsalem.org
Web Site: www.oldsalem.org
Sales Range: $10-24.9 Million
Approx. Number Employees: 200
Year Founded: 1950
Business Description:
Owner & Operator of Gift Shop, Retail Bakery, Book Store & Museums; Tourist Attraction
S.I.C.: 5947; 5461
N.A.I.C.S.: 453220; 311811
Media: 8-9-10-20-23-24-25
Personnel:
Lauren Werner *(Dir-Mktg)*
Brands & Products:
HERR KATER
J. BLUM: PRINTER & MERCHANT
MAGGIE-BESSIE
MESDA, THE OLD SALEM TOY MUSEUM
MUSEUM OF EARLY SOUTHERN DECORATIVE ARTS
OLD SALEM
THE OLD SALEM CHILDREN'S MUSEUM
T. BAGGE: MERCHANT
WINKLER BAKERY
WWW.MESDA.ORG
WWW.OLDSALEM.ORG

OMAHA COMMUNITY PLAYHOUSE
6915 Cass St
Omaha, NE 68132
Tel.: (402) 553-4890
Fax: (402) 553-6288
E-mail: info@omahaplayhouse.org
Web Site: www.omahaplayhouse.org
Approx. Number Employees: 50
Business Description:
Theatre Production
S.I.C.: 7389
N.A.I.C.S.: 711310
Media: 8-9-13-20-23-24-25
Personnel:
Timothy Schmad *(Pres)*
Betsye Paragas *(Dir-Mktg & PR)*
Susan Baer Collins *(Assoc Dir-Artistic)*
Carl Beck *(Dir-Artistic)*
James Boggess *(Dir-Music)*
Alena Furlong *(Dir-Dev)*
Donn Hook *(Dir-Technical)*
Melanie Walters *(Dir-Education)*
Matthew Bross *(Mgr-House)*
Lanelle Poole *(Mgr-Box Office)*

OMAHA SYMPHONY ASSOCIATION
1605 Howard St
Omaha, NE 68102-2705
Tel.: (402) 342-3836
Fax: (402) 342-3819
E-mail: info@omahasymphony.org
Web Site: www.omahasymphony.org
Approx. Number Employees: 25
Year Founded: 1921
Business Description:
Symphony Orchestra
S.I.C.: 7929
N.A.I.C.S.: 711130
Media: 8-9-13-20-22-23-24-25
Personnel:
Kenneth E. Stinson *(Chm)*
Pamela Cleary *(Interim Pres & CEO-Omaha Symphony)*
Eric C. Swenson *(Office Mgr & Mgr-IT/IS)*
Ricardo Amador *(Mgr-Orchestra Personnel)*
Howard Coffin *(Mgr-Box Office)*
Gregory Clinton *(Librarian)*

OMAHA ZOOLOGICAL SOCIETY
(d/b/a Henry Doorly Zoo)
3701 S 10th St
Omaha, NE 68107
Tel.: (402) 733-8401
Fax: (402) 733-7868
E-mail: promotions@omahazoo.com
Web Site: www.omahazoo.com
E-Mail For Key Personnel:
Marketing Director: marketing@omahazoo.com
Approx. Number Employees: 300
Year Founded: 1952
Business Description:
Zoological Garden
S.I.C.: 8422
N.A.I.C.S.: 712130
Media: 9-10-20-22-23-24-25
Personnel:
Lee Simmons *(Owner)*
Jeremy Eddie *(CFO)*
Brands & Products:
LOZIER IMAX
OMAHA'S HENRY DOORLY ZOO

ONTARIO PLACE CORPORATION
955 Lakeshore Blvd W
Toronto, ON Canada
Tel.: (416) 314-9900
Fax: (416) 314-9992
Toll Free: (866) 663-4386
E-mail: info@ontarioplace.com
Web Site: www.ontarioplace.com
E-Mail For Key Personnel:
Sales Director: janet.burley@ontarioplace.com
Approx. Number Employees: 70
Year Founded: 1971
Business Description:
Amusement Parks Owner & Operater
S.I.C.: 7996
N.A.I.C.S.: 713110
Advertising Expenditures: $1,000,000
Media: 6-9-23-24-25
Distr.: Natl.
Budget Set: Jan.
Personnel:
Sharon Beaman *(Head-Corp & Grp Sls)*
Jonathan Daley *(Dir-Guest Svcs & Corp Affairs)*
Mike Dwyer *(Mgr-Marina)*
Glenn Harden *(Mgr-Loss Prevention & Security)*
Jennifer Kerr *(Mgr-Media Rels)*
Nick Kondrat *(Mgr-Media Relations)*
Alto White *(Mgr-Pur & Office Svcs)*
Brands & Products:
CINESPHERE
FROSTER SOAKCITY
ONTARIO PLACE
SOUTH BEACH

OPERA AMERICA
Ste 1600 330 7th Ave
New York, NY 10001-5248
Tel.: (202) 293-4466
Fax: (202) 393-0735
E-mail: frontdesk@operaamerica.org

Key to Media (For complete agency information see *The Advertising Red Books-Agencies* edition):
1. Bus. Publs. 2. Cable T.V. 3. Catalogs & Directories. 4. Co-op Adv. 5. Consumer Mags. 6. D.M. to Bus. Estab.7. D.M. to Consumers 8. Daily Newsp. 9. Exhibits/Trade Shows 10. Foreign 11. Infomercial 12. Internet Adv.13. Multimedia 14. Network Radio 15. Network T.V. 16. Newsp. Distr. Mags. 17. Other 18. Outdoor (Posters, Transit) 19. Point of Purchase20. Premiums, Novelties 21. Product Samples 22. Special Events Mktg. 23. Spot Radio 24. Spot T.V. 25. Weekly Newsp. 26. Yellow Page Adv.

OPERA America — (Continued)

Web Site: www.operaamerica.org
Business Description:
Information, Technical & Administrative Services to the Opera Community
S.I.C.: 7389; 8742
N.A.I.C.S.: 561499; 541611
Media: 6-10
Personnel:
Marc A. Scorca *(Pres & CEO)*
Kelley Rourke *(Editor, Opera America Magazine)*
Katherine Ehle *(Art Dir)*
Susan Schultz *(Mgr-Acctg)*

OPERA OMAHA INC.
1625 Farnam Ste 100
Omaha, NE 68102
Tel.: (402) 346-7372
Fax: (402) 346-7323
Toll Free: (877) 34-OPERA
E-mail: info@operaomaha.org
Web Site: www.operaomaha.org
Approx. Number Employees: 15
Business Description:
Opera
S.I.C.: 7922
N.A.I.C.S.: 711110
Media: 9-10-13-18-20-22-23-24-25
Personnel:
Richard D. Holland *(Vice Chm)*
Frederick Simon *(Exec VP)*
Rudy Thomas *(Exec VP)*

THE OPIUM GROUP
690 Lincoln Rd
Miami Beach, FL 33139
Tel.: (305) 695-8411
Fax: (786) 507-3424
Web Site: www.theopiumgroup.com
Business Description:
Nightclubs Owner & Operator
S.I.C.: 8699
N.A.I.C.S.: 813990
Media: 13-16-22-23
Personnel:
Hassan Benjelloum *(COO)*
Vanessa Menkes *(VP-Comm)*
Carlos Correal *(Dir-Mktg)*

THE ORCHARD ENTERPRISES, INC.
(Sub. of Dimensional Associates, LLC)
23 E 4th St 3rd Fl
New York, NY 10003
Tel.: (212) 201-9280
Fax: (212) 201-9203
Web Site: www.theorchard.com
Approx. Rev.: $62,271,481
Approx. Number Employees: 88
Business Description:
Music, Video & Game Licensing
S.I.C.: 2741; 7822; 7829
N.A.I.C.S.: 512230; 512120; 512199
Advertising Expenditures: $84,448
Media: 2-10
Personnel:
Richard Gottehrer *(Founder & Chief Creative Officer)*
Scott Cohen *(VP-Intl & Co-Founder)*
Bradley Peter Navin *(CEO)*
Alexis H. Shapiro *(Gen Counsel & Sr VP)*
Steve Haase *(Exec VP-Bus Dev)*
Jeff Nimerofsky *(Sr VP-Fin Grp)*
Prashant Bahadur *(VP & Gen Mgr)*
Scott Bergman *(VP-Sls & Mktg)*
Josh Builder *(VP-Product Dev & Ops)*
Tom Lorenc *(VP-Engrg)*

ORCHESTRE SYMPHONIQUE DE MONTREAL
260 De Maisonneuve W Blvd
Montreal, QC Canada
Tel.: (514) 842-3402
Tel.: (514) 842-9951
Fax: (514) 842-0728
E-mail: general@osm.ca
Web Site: www.osm.ca
Approx. Number Employees: 150
Business Description:
Symphony Orchestra
S.I.C.: 7929
N.A.I.C.S.: 711190
Media: 4-7-8-9-22-23-24-25
Personnel:
Lucien Bouchard *(Chm)*
Helene Desmarais *(Deputy Chm)*
Marie-Jose Nadeau *(Vice Chm)*
Norman M. Steinberg *(Vice Chm)*
Madeleine Careau *(CEO)*
Melanie La Couture *(COO)*
Daniele Lavoie *(Gen Mgr-Fondation-IOSM & Dir-OSM Fundraising)*
Marie-Josee Desrochers *(Sr Dir-Mktg & Comm)*
Gilbert Brault *(Dir-Sls & Customer Svc)*
Michael Carpenter *(Dir-Personnel-Musicians)*
Paul Fortin *(Dir-Programming)*
Rachel Laplante *(Dir-Sponsorship Dev & Strategic Alliances)*
Amalie Hamilton *(Coord-Sponsorship Mgmt)*

ORDWAY CENTER FOR THE PERFORMING ARTS
345 Washington St
Saint Paul, MN 55102
Tel.: (651) 282-3000
Fax: (651) 224-5319
Web Site: www.ordway.org
Approx. Sls.: $19,704,300
Approx. Number Employees: 250
Year Founded: 1980
Business Description:
Theatrical Production Services
S.I.C.: 7922
N.A.I.C.S.: 711110
Media: 7-8-9-10-13-20-22-23-24-25
Personnel:
Patricia Mitchell *(Pres & CEO)*

ORLANDO MAGIC
(Sub. of RDV Sports)
8701 Maitland Summit Blvd
Orlando, FL 32810-5915
Tel.: (407) 916-2400
Fax: (407) 916-2830
Web Site: www.orlandomagic.com
Approx. Number Employees: 100
Year Founded: 1989
Business Description:
Professional Basketball Franchise
S.I.C.: 7941
N.A.I.C.S.: 711211
Media: 1-6-9-10-13-14-15-18-20-22-23-24
Personnel:
Bob Vander Weide *(Pres & CEO)*
Jason Coleman *(VP-IT)*
Chris D'Orso *(VP-Sls)*
Lucas Daniel Boyce *(Dir-Multicultural Insights & Cause Mktg)*
Michael Forde *(Dir-Corp Partnership)*
Deborah Rios-Barnes *(Asst Dir-Multicultural Affairs)*
Darrell Harbin *(Sr Mgr-Partnership Dev)*
Jennifer Farrell *(Mgr-Tourism)*
Melissa Miller *(Mgr-Creative Svcs)*
Brands & Products:
MAGIC RADIO
ORLANDO MAGIC
Advertising Agency:
GoConvergence
4545 36th St
Orlando, FL 32811
Tel.: (407) 235-3210
Fax: (407) 299-9907

ORLANDO PHILHARMONIC ORCHESTRA INC.
812 E Rollins St Ste 300
Orlando, FL 32803
Tel.: (407) 896-6700
Fax: (407) 896-5512
Web Site: www.orlandophil.org
Approx. Number Employees: 10
Year Founded: 1991
Business Description:
Symphony Orchestra
S.I.C.: 7929
N.A.I.C.S.: 711130
Media: 2-3-6-8-9-13-18-20-22-23-24-25-26
Personnel:
Candice Crawford *(Pres)*
Mark Fischer *(Gen Mgr)*
David Schillhammer *(Exec Dir)*
Gretchen Miller *(Dir-PR & Publ)*
Sandy Rendek *(Dir-Mktg)*
David Whitfield *(Dir-Fin)*
James Ault *(Mgr-Personnel)*
Diane Bishop *(Mgr-Box Office)*
Carl Rendek *(Mgr-Production)*

OTTAWA SENATORS HOCKEY CLUB
(Sub. of Capital Sports Group of Companies)
Scociabank Pl Centre 1000 Palladium Dr
Kanata, ON K2V 1A5, Canada
Tel.: (613) 599-0250
Fax: (613) 599-0358
E-mail: info@ottawasenators.com
Web Site: www.ottawasenators.com
Year Founded: 1883
Business Description:
Professional Hockey Franchise
S.I.C.: 7941; 7389
N.A.I.C.S.: 711211; 711310
Media: 9-18-20-22-23-24
Distr.: Natl.
Personnel:
Eugene Melnyk *(Owner, Chm & Governor)*
Cyril M. Leeder *(Pres & Alternate Governor)*
Erin Crowe *(CFO, Exec VP & Alternate Governor)*
Dave Ready *(Pres-Ottawa Senators Foundation)*
Mark Bonneau *(Sr VP)*
Jeff Kyle *(VP-Mktg)*
Phil Legault *(VP-Comm)*
John Muckler *(Gen Mgr)*
Anders Hedberg *(Dir-Player Personnel)*
Scott Allegrino *(Mgr-Equipment)*
Brands & Products:
OTTAWA SENATORS

PACERS BASKETBALL, LLC
(d/b/a Indiana Pacers)
125 S Pennsylvania St
Indianapolis, IN 46204-3610
Tel.: (317) 917-2500
Fax: (317) 917-2599
E-mail: pacersinsider@pacers.com
Web Site: www.nba.com
Approx. Number Employees: 250
Business Description:
Professional Basketball Team
S.I.C.: 7941
N.A.I.C.S.: 711211
Media: 3-6-7-8-9-10-14-15-18-20-22-23-24-25-26
Distr.: Natl.
Personnel:
Herbert Simon *(Co-Owner)*
Melvin J. Simon *(Co-Owner)*
Kevin Bower *(CFO & Exec VP)*
Rick Fuson *(COO)*
Larry Joe Bird *(Pres-Basketball Opers)*
Larry Mago *(VP-Mktg)*
Kelly Krauskopf *(Gen Mgr)*
David Morway *(Gen Mgr)*
Conrad Brunner *(Dir-Internet Mktg)*
Wendy Sommers *(Dir-Creative Svcs)*
Brands & Products:
INDIANA PACERS
PASSION. PRIDE. PACERS
Advertising Agency:
Publicis in Mid America
200 S Meridian St Ste 500
Indianapolis, IN 46225-1076
Tel.: (317) 639-5135
Fax: (317) 639-5134

PADI AMERICAS
(Sub. of Capital Investments & Ventures Corp.)
30151 Tomas St
Rancho Santa Margarita, CA 92688-2125
Tel.: (949) 858-7234
Fax: (949) 267-1267
Toll Free: (800) 729-7234
E-mail: webmaster@padi.com
Web Site: www.padi.com
Approx. Sls.: $30,000,000
Approx. Number Employees: 180
Year Founded: 1983
Business Description:
Diving Training Organization
S.I.C.: 8621; 8299
N.A.I.C.S.: 813920; 611430
Import Export
Media: 6
Personnel:
Drew Richardson *(Pres & COO)*
Kristin Valette *(Dir-Mktg)*

PADRES L.P.
(d/b/a San Diego Padres)
PETCO Park 100 Pk Blvd
San Diego, CA 92101
Mailing Address:
PO Box 122000
San Diego, CA 92112-2000
Tel.: (619) 795-5000
Fax: (619) 795-5035
Web Site: www.padres.com
Sales Range: $50-74.9 Million
Approx. Number Employees: 150
Year Founded: 1968

Key to Media (For complete agency information see *The Advertising Red Books-Agencies* edition):
1. Bus. Publs. 2. Cable T.V. 3. Catalogs & Directories. 4. Co-op Adv. 5. Consumer Mags. 6. D.M. to Bus. Estab.7. D.M. to Consumers 8. Daily Newsp. 9. Exhibits/Trade Shows 10. Foreign 11. Infomercial 12. Internet Adv.13. Multimedia 14. Network Radio 15. Network T.V. 16. Newsp. Distr. Mags. 17. Other 18. Outdoor (Posters, Transit) 19. Point of Purchase20. Premiums, Novelties 21. Product Samples 22. Special Events Mktg. 23. Spot Radio 24. Spot T.V. 25. Weekly Newsp. 26. Yellow Page Adv.

Business Description:
Professional Baseball Club
S.I.C.: 7941
N.A.I.C.S.: 711211
Advertising Expenditures: $250,000
Media: 3-7-8-9-10-12-13-18-20-23-24-25
Distr.: Natl.
Budget Set: Sept.
Personnel:
John Moores *(Chm)*
Jeff Moorad *(Vice Chm & CEO)*
Tom Garfinkel *(Pres & COO)*
Fred M. Gerson *(CFO & Exec VP)*
Paul DePodesta *(Exec VP)*
David M. Winfield *(Exec VP & Sr Advisor)*
Laura Broderick *(Sr VP-Brand Dev)*
Josh Byrnes *(Sr VP-Baseball Ops)*
Sarah Farnsworth *(Sr VP-Pub Affairs)*
Fred Uhlman, Jr. *(VP & Asst Gen Mgr)*
Jed Hoyer *(Gen Mgr)*
Michael Babida *(Exec Dir-Pur & Mdsg)*
Tamara Furman *(Exec Dir-HR)*
Jim Kiersnowski *(Exec Dir-Ticket Ops)*
Kameron Durham *(Dir-Guest Svcs)*
Jack Ensch *(Dir-Military Affairs)*
Laura Evans *(Dir-Ticket Customer Svcs)*
Ken Kawachi *(Dir-Event Ops)*
Erik Meyer *(Dir-Entertainment & Production)*
Warren Miller *(Dir-Communications)*
Randy Smith *(Dir-Player Dev & Intl Scouting)*
Mike Wickham *(Dir-Minor League Ops)*
Claire Abernethy *(Asst Dir-Payroll & Risk Mgmt)*
Jeff Brown *(Asst Dir-Ticket Dist)*
Brigid Ryan Cranmer *(Mgr-Military Programs)*
Alicia Davis *(Mgr-HR)*
Gabriel Kunde *(Mgr-Ticket Distr)*
Ellen LoPresti *(Mgr-Ticket Sys)*
Brian Prilaman *(Mgr-Equipment)*
Ben Roller *(Mgr-Ticket Ops)*
Nhu Tran *(Mgr-Community Affairs & Padres Foundation)*
Brands & Products:
SAN DIEGO PADRES
Advertising Agencies:
Baker Street Partners
2410 Baker St
San Francisco, CA 94123
Tel.: (415) 659-3900
Fax: (415) 659-3903

MLB Advanced Media, L.P.
75 9th Ave 5th Fl
New York, NY 10011
Tel.: (212) 485-3444
Fax: (212) 485-3456

PADUCAH SYMPHONY ORCHESTRA
201 Broadway
Paducah, KY 42001
Tel.: (270) 444-0065
Fax: (270) 444-0456
Toll Free: (800) 738-3727
Web Site:
www.paducahsymphony.org
Approx. Number Employees: 200
Business Description:
Symphony Orchestra
S.I.C.: 7929
N.A.I.C.S.: 711130
Media: 9-20-23-24-25
Personnel:
John Williams, Jr. *(Pres)*
Richard Roof *(VP-Admin)*
Daniel Sene *(Exec Dir)*
Bradley Almquist *(Dir-Choruses)*

THE PALEY CENTER FOR MEDIA
25 W 52nd St
New York, NY 10019
Tel.: (212) 621-6600
Tel.: (212) 621-6800
Fax: (212) 621-6737
Web Site: www.paleycenter.org
Approx. Number Employees: 150
Year Founded: 1976
Business Description:
Museum Chronicling the History of Television & Radio
S.I.C.: 8412; 7999
N.A.I.C.S.: 712110; 713990
Media: 4-8-9-10-20-22-23-24-25
Personnel:
Frank A. Bennack, Jr. *(Chm)*
Gordon Crawford *(Co-Vice Chm)*
Gustave M. Hauser *(Co-Vice Chm)*
Mel Karmazin *(Co-Vice Chm)*
Patricia E. Mitchell *(Pres & CEO)*
John Wolters *(CFO & VP)*
J. Max Robins *(VP & Exec Dir)*

PALLADIUM THEATER, INC.
253 5th Ave N
Saint Petersburg, FL 33701
Tel.: (727) 822-3590
Fax: (727) 822-3584
Web Site: www.mypalladium.org
Business Description:
Theatrical Producer
S.I.C.: 7389
N.A.I.C.S.: 711310
Media: 8-9-13-22-25
Personnel:
Ken Casebier *(Mgr-Mktg)*

PANTHERS FOOTBALL, LLC
(d/b/a Carolina Panthers)
800 S Mint St
Charlotte, NC 28202
Tel.: (704) 358-7000
Fax: (704) 358-7675
E-mail: feedback@panthers.com
Web Site: www.panthers.com
Sales Range: $25-49.9 Million
Approx. Number Employees: 130
Year Founded: 1993
Business Description:
Professional Football Franchise
S.I.C.: 7941
N.A.I.C.S.: 711211
Advertising Expenditures: $600,000
Media: 9-18-22-23-24-26
Distr.: Natl.
Personnel:
Jerome J. Richardson *(Founder & Owner)*
Dave Olsen *(CFO)*
Danny Morrison *(Pres-Panthers Stadium)*
Richard M. Thigpen *(Gen Counsel)*
Marty Hurney *(Gen Mgr)*
Brandon Beane *(Dir-Football Ops)*
Gene Brown *(Dir-Security)*
Jon Credit *(Dir-IT)*
Charlie Dayton *(Dir-Comm)*
Riley Fields *(Dir-Community Rels, Cheerleader & Mascot Programs)*
Don Gregory *(Dir-College Scouting)*
Mark Hobbs *(Dir-Video)*
Jackie Jeffries *(Dir-HR)*
Mark Koncz *(Dir-Pro Scouting)*
Kyle Ritchie *(Dir-Entertainment & PantherVision)*
Rob Rogers *(Dir-Team Admin)*
Henry Thomas *(Dir-Brdcst & New Media)*
Phil Youtsey *(Dir-Ticket Sls & Ops)*
Matthew Getz *(Mgr-Facility)*
Jackie Miles *(Mgr-Equipment)*
Scott Paul *(Mgr-Ops)*
Brands & Products:
CAROLINA PANTHERS
Advertising Agency:
Luquire George Andrews, Inc. (dba LGA)
4201 Congress St Ste 400
Charlotte, NC 28209
Tel.: (704) 552-6565
Fax: (704) 552-1972

PASADENA PLAYHOUSE
39 S El Molino Ave
Pasadena, CA 91101
Tel.: (626) 792-8672
Fax: (626) 351-0291
E-mail: vwatson@pasadenaplayhouse.org
Web Site:
www.pasadenaplayhouse.org
Sales Range: $10-24.9 Million
Approx. Number Employees: 50
Business Description:
Theatrical Productions
S.I.C.: 7922
N.A.I.C.S.: 711110
Media: 8-23-24
Personnel:
Michele Engemann *(Chm)*
Vivienne Dipeolu *(Mng Dir)*
Stephen Eich *(Exec Dir)*
John Alexander *(Dir-Commun)*
Jennifer Berger *(Dir-Dev)*
Sheldon Epps *(Dir-Art)*
Tom Ware *(Producing Dir)*
Michael Prichard *(Mgr-Acctg)*

PASADENA SYMPHONY ASSOCIATION
117 E Colorado Blvd Ste 200
Pasadena, CA 91105
Tel.: (626) 793-7172
Fax: (626) 793-7180
E-mail: info@pasadenasymphony-pops.org
Web Site: www.pasadenasymphony-pops.org
Approx. Sls.: $336,000
Approx. Number Employees: 25
Year Founded: 1928
Business Description:
Symphony Orchestra
S.I.C.: 8641; 7929
N.A.I.C.S.: 813410; 711130
Media: 9-20-22-23-24-25
Personnel:
Diane C. Rankin *(Pres)*
Richard L. Barr *(Dir)*
Jorge Mester *(Dir-Music)*

PAUL REED SMITH GUITARS
(d/b/a PRS Guitars)
380 Log Canoe Cir
Stevensville, MD 21666-2166
Tel.: (410) 643-9970
Fax: (410) 643-9980
E-mail: custserv@prsguitars.com
Web Site: www.prsguitars.com
Sales Range: $25-49.9 Million
Approx. Number Employees: 140
Business Description:
Guitars Mfr
S.I.C.: 3931
N.A.I.C.S.: 339992
Advertising Expenditures: $200,000
Media: 6-10-19-22
Distr.: Intl.; Natl.
Personnel:
Paul Smith *(Owner)*
Jack Higginbotham *(Pres)*
Larry Urier *(Mgr-Sls & Mktg)*
Brands & Products:
BILLY MARTIN
CE MAHOGANY
CUSTOM
HOLLOWBODY
MCCARTY
MCCARTY HOLLOWBODY
MCCARTY SOAPBAR
MODERN EAGLE
PAUL REED SMITH
PRS
ROSEWOOD
SANTANA
SE SOAPBAR
SINGLECUT
SWAMP ASH
SWAMP ASH SPECIAL
TREMONTI SE

PEAK RESORTS, INC.
17409 Hidden Valley Dr
Wildwood, MO 63025-2213
Tel.: (636) 938-7474
Fax: (636) 549-0064
Web Site: www.peakresorts.com
Approx. Rev.: $89,845,800
Approx. Number Employees: 400
Year Founded: 1997
Business Description:
Ski Resorts Operator
S.I.C.: 7011; 7999
N.A.I.C.S.: 721110; 713990
Advertising Expenditures: $1,384,800
Personnel:
Timothy D. Boyd *(Pres & CEO)*
Steven J. Mueller *(CFO, VP & Sec)*

PEDRO LAND INC.
(Sub. of The Schafer Company Inc.)
(d/b/a South of the Border)
I-95 Hwy 301-501
Hamer, SC 29547
Tel.: (843) 774-2411
Fax: (843) 774-0904
Toll Free: (800) 845-6011
Web Site: www.pedroland.com
Approx. Sls.: $48,200,000
Approx. Number Employees: 300
Year Founded: 1961
Business Description:
Amusement Services
S.I.C.: 7996; 5947
N.A.I.C.S.: 713110; 453220
Media: 18
Personnel:
Jim Holiday *(Gen Mgr)*

PENN NATIONAL GAMING, INC.
Wyomissing Professional Ctr 825
Berkshire Blvd Ste 200
Wyomissing, PA 19610
Tel.: (610) 373-2400

Key to Media (For complete agency information see *The Advertising Red Books-Agencies* edition):
1. Bus. Publs. 2. Cable T.V. 3. Catalogs & Directories. 4. Co-op Adv. 5. Consumer Mags. 6. D.M. to Bus. Estab.7. D.M. to Consumers
8. Daily Newsp. 9. Exhibits/Trade Shows 10. Foreign 11. Infomercial 12. Internet Adv.13. Multimedia 14. Network Radio
15. Network T.V. 16. Newsp. Distr. Mags. 17. Other 18. Outdoor (Posters, Transit) 19. Point of Purchase20. Premiums, Novelties
21. Product Samples 22. Special Events Mktg. 23. Spot Radio 24. Spot T.V. 25. Weekly Newsp. 26. Yellow Page Adv.

Penn National Gaming, Inc. — (Continued)

Fax: (610) 373-4966
E-mail: corporate@pngaming.com
Web Site: www.pngaming.com
Approx. Rev.: $2,459,111,000
Approx. Number Employees: 15,636
Year Founded: 1972
Business Description:
Horse Racing & Casino Faclities Owner & Operator
S.I.C.: 7999; 7011; 7948; 7993; 7997
N.A.I.C.S.: 713290; 711212; 713120; 713210; 713910; 721120
Media: 9-18-23-24-25
Distr.: Reg.
Personnel:
Peter M. Carlino *(Chm & CEO)*
Timothy J. Wilmott *(Pres & COO)*
William J. Clifford *(CFO)*
Tom Beauchamp *(CIO)*
Thomas N. Auriemma *(VP & Chief Compliance Officer)*
Desiree A. Burke *(Chief Acctg Officer & VP)*
Jordan B. Savitch *(Gen Counsel & Sr VP)*
James Baum *(Sr VP-Project Dev)*
Eugene P. Clark *(Sr VP-HR)*
John V. Finamore *(Sr VP-Reg Ops)*
Steven T. Snyder *(Sr VP-Corp Dev)*
Brands & Products:
ADVENTURE SLOTS
ALTON BELLE
BELLE OF SIOUX CITY
BELLES & BEAUS
BELLES & BEAUS THE 50 & BETTER SENIOR CLUB
THE BEST GAME IN TOWN
BET ON THE ROUGE
BIENVILLE BAY BUFFET
BRIDGING THE BAY
BULLPEN CASINO
CASINO ROUGE
CHARLES TOWN RACES
DIFFERENT BY DESIGN
EBET USA
EYE, HI & GOODBYE!
EYE, HI & GOODBYE ARGOSY & DESIGN
FAIRBANKS
FASTDRAW
FOUNTAINS OF CASH & DESIGN
GET TO THE ROUGE
GOT FUN FEVER
THE GREAT ESCAPE
HIT IT AT THE BELLE!
HOLIDAY HYSTERIA
IT PAYS TO BE PREFERRED
IT'S THE BEST GAME IN TOWN
JACKPOT JAVA
JOURDAN RIVER GRILLE
LET YOURSELF GO
LUCK HAPPENS HERE
LUCKY FOR YOU
MAGIC MONEY
MILLION DOLLAR MANIA & DESIGN
MUGS SHOP TIL YOU DROP
NOW CARD
NOW CLUB
PENN NATIONAL GAMING, INC.
PENN NATIONAL RACE COURSE
PLAYERS CHOICE
PRIZEFECTA
QUICK PAY
QUICKTIX
RESERVATION BLACKJACK
RESERVATION BLACKJACK&DESIGN
SILVER SCREEN GAMING
SLOTPLAY
SPA AT THE BAY
SUMMER OF LUCK
SUNDANCE CAFE
SUPER PAY ROYALS
TELEBET
THERE'S A NEW GAME IN TOWN
TUSCANY STEAKS & SEAFOOD
VIDEO POKER PARLOUR & DESIGN
WE'VE GOT A YOU ATTITUDE!
WHEN YOU'RE READY TO PLAY
WHY PLAY ANYWHERE ELSE?
WOMAN WITH EXTENDED HAIR DESIGN
THE WORLD SERIES OF HANDICAPPING
YOUR LUCKY PLACE
Advertising Agency:
MMG Worldwide
4601 Madison Ave
Kansas City, MO 64112
Tel.: (816) 472-5988
Fax: (816) 471-5395

PETER NERO & THE PHILLY POPS

(Sub. of The Philadelphia Orchestra Association)
260 S Broad St 16th Fl
Philadelphia, PA 19102
Tel.: (215) 893-1900
Fax: (215) 893-3139
E-mail: info@phillypops.com
Web Site: www.phillypops.com
Approx. Number Employees: 5
Year Founded: 1981
Business Description:
Symphony Orchestra
S.I.C.: 7929
N.A.I.C.S.: 711130
Media: 7-8-9-10-13-22-23-24-25
Personnel:
Earnest Toplis *(Gen Mgr)*

PGA TOUR, INC.

112 PGA Tour Blvd
Ponte Vedra Beach, FL 32082
Tel.: (904) 285-3700
Fax: (904) 285-7913
Web Site: www.pgatour.com
Sales Range: $650-699.9 Million
Approx. Number Employees: 700
Business Description:
Golf Tournament Organizer
S.I.C.: 7999; 7997
N.A.I.C.S.: 713990; 713910
Media: 5-15-20-22
Personnel:
Richard J. Farris *(Chm & Pres)*
Henry T. Hughes *(CEO)*
Ronald E. Price *(CFO & Exec VP)*
Edward L. Moorhouse *(Co-COO)*
Charles L. Zink *(Co-COO)*
Thomas Wade *(CMO)*
Robert J. Combs *(Sr VP-Comm, Res & Pub Affairs)*
Ty Votaw *(Exec VP-Intl Affairs)*
W. William Calfee *(Sr VP)*
Ric Clarson *(Sr VP-Brand Mktg)*
Raymond T. Harm *(Sr VP-Sls)*
Advertising Agencies:
Caffeine
438 Forbes Ave
New Haven, CT 06512-1932
Tel.: (203) 468-6396
Fax: (203) 468-7608

Doner
25900 Northwestern Hwy
Southfield, MI 48075
Tel.: (248) 354-9700
Fax: (248) 827-8440

GSD&M
828 W 6th St
Austin, TX 78703-5420
Tel.: (512) 242-4736
Fax: (512) 242-4700

PHILADELPHIA 76ERS, L.P.

(Sub. of Comcast Spectacor, L.P.)
3601 S Broad St
Philadelphia, PA 19148
Tel.: (215) 339-7676
Fax: (215) 339-7618
Web Site: www.nba.com/sixers
Sales Range: $10-24.9 Million
Approx. Number Employees: 55
Year Founded: 1963
Business Description:
Professional Basketball Team
S.I.C.: 7941; 7999
N.A.I.C.S.: 711211; 611620
Media: 2-3-4-6-7-8-9-10-13-14-15-18-20-22-23-24-25-26
Distr.: Direct to Consumer; Reg.
Personnel:
Russ Chandler *(CFO & Exec VP)*
Phil Weinberg *(Gen Counsel & Exec VP)*
Tony Dileo *(Sr VP & Asst Gen Mgr)*
Lara Price *(Sr VP-Bus Ops)*
Andy Speiser *(Sr VP-Fin)*
Shawn Anderson *(VP-Ticket Sls)*
Larry Meli *(VP-Box Office & Customer Svc)*
Ed Stefanski *(Gen Mgr)*
Nick Gesacion *(Dir-New Media)*
Allen Lumpkin *(Dir-Admin-Basketball)*
Brad McCleary *(Dir-Ticket Sls)*
Tom McGinnis *(Dir-Radio Brdcst)*
Harvey Pollack *(Dir-Statistical Info)*
Michael Preston *(Dir-PR)*
Courtney Witte *(Dir-Player Personnel)*
Shana Booker *(Mktg Mgr)*
Pete Sousa *(Mgr-PR)*
Brands & Products:
76ERS

PHILADELPHIA EAGLES FOOTBALL CLUB, INC.

1 Novacare Way
Philadelphia, PA 19145-5900
Tel.: (215) 463-2500
Fax: (215) 339-5464
E-mail: webmaster@philadelphiaeagles.com
Web Site:
www.philadelphiaeagles.com
Sales Range: $75-99.9 Million
Approx. Number Employees: 100
Year Founded: 1933
Business Description:
Professional Football Franchise
S.I.C.: 7941
N.A.I.C.S.: 711211
Media: 5-9-14-15-22-23-24-25
Distr.: Natl.
Personnel:
Jeffrey Lurie *(Chm & CEO)*
Joseph Banner *(Pres)*
Don Smolenski *(COO)*
Aileen Daly *(Gen Counsel)*
Andy Reid *(Exec VP-Football Ops & Head Coach)*
Pamela Browner Crawley *(Sr VP-Pub Affairs & Govt Rels)*
Mark Donovan *(Sr VP-Bus Ops)*
Frank Gumienny *(VP-Fin)*
Howie Roseman *(Gen Mgr)*
Maggie Arganbright *(Dir-Digital Mktg & Brand Activation)*
Leonard Bonacci *(Dir-Event Ops)*
Derek Boyko *(Dir-Football Media Svcs)*
Leo Carlin *(Dir-Ticket Client Svc)*
Harold Carmichael *(Dir-Player Programs)*
Laini DeLawter *(Dir-Ticket Office Ops)*
Mike Dougherty *(Dir-Video)*
Tracy Foster *(Dir-Client Svcs)*
Ryan Grigson *(Dir-Player Personnel)*
Brendan McQuillan *(Dir-Mdsg)*
Jason Miller *(Dir-Facility Mgmt)*
Kristie Pappal *(Dir-HR)*
John Pawling *(Dir-IT)*
John Hatfield *(Mgr-Equipment)*
Julie Hirshey *(Mgr-Community Rels)*
Katie Holhan *(Mgr-Corp Partnerships)*
Joe Malatesta *(Mgr-Premium Sls)*
Brands & Products:
NFL
Advertising Agency:
RealTime Media, Inc.
1060 1st Ave Ste 201
King of Prussia, PA 19406
Tel.: (610) 337-3600
Fax: (610) 337-2300

PHILADELPHIA FLYERS, L.P.

(Sub. of Comcast Spectacor, L.P.)
3601 S Broad St
Philadelphia, PA 19148
Tel.: (215) 465-4500
Fax: (215) 952-5210
Web Site: flyers.nhl.com
Sales Range: $10-24.9 Million
Approx. Number Employees: 45
Year Founded: 1966
Business Description:
Professional Hockey Team
S.I.C.: 7941
N.A.I.C.S.: 711211
Advertising Expenditures: $5,000,000
Bus. Publs.: $2,000,000; Exhibits/Trade Shows: $1,500,000; Other: $1,500,000
Distr.: Natl.
Personnel:
Edward M. Snider *(Chm)*
Keith Allen *(Exec VP)*
Bob Clarke *(Sr VP)*
Shawn Tilger *(Sr VP-Bus Ops)*
Jim Willits *(VP-Sls)*
Doreen Holmgren *(Gen Mgr)*
Paul Holmgren *(Gen Mgr)*
Barry Hanrahan *(Asst Gen Mgr)*
Zack Hill *(Sr Dir-Comm)*
Bo Koelle *(Sr Dir-Sls)*
Lindsey Domers *(Mktg Dir)*
Bryan Anton *(Dir-Ticket Sls)*
Dave Brown *(Dir-Player Personnel)*
Jimmy Dunk *(Dir-Premium Seating)*
Anthony Gioia *(Dir-Game Presentation)*
Bryan Hardenbergh *(Dir-Team Svcs)*
Missy Keeler *(Dir-Customer Svc)*
Don Luce *(Dir-Player Dev)*
Linda Mantai *(Dir-Community Rels & Fan Dev)*
Chris Pryor *(Dir-Hockey Ops)*

Key to Media (For complete agency information see *The Advertising Red Books-Agencies* edition):
1. Bus. Publs. 2. Cable T.V. 3. Catalogs & Directories. 4. Co-op Adv. 5. Consumer Mags. 6. D.M. to Bus. Estab.7. D.M. to Consumers
8. Daily Newsp. 9. Exhibits/Trade Shows 10. Foreign 11. Infomercial 12. Internet Adv.13. Multimedia 14. Network Radio
15. Network T.V. 16. Newsp. Distr. Mags. 17. Other 18. Outdoor (Posters, Transit) 19. Point of Purchase20. Premiums, Novelties
21. Product Samples 22. Special Events Mktg. 23. Spot Radio 24. Spot T.V. 25. Weekly Newsp. 26. Yellow Page Adv.

Graig Selgrath *(Dir-Premium Svcs)*
Mike Garrity *(Sls Mgr-Sponsorship)*
Rob Johnson *(Mktg Mgr)*
Rob Baer *(Mgr-Fan Dev)*
Jeremy Bland *(Mgr-Bus Dev)*
Michelle Diago *(Mgr-Ticket Ops)*
Louis Harmelin *(Mgr-Natl Sls)*
Travis Kraus *(Mgr-Client Dev)*
Eric Stiles *(Mgr-Premium Svcs)*
Andrew Humphreys *(Sr Acct Exec)*
Michael O'connor *(Sr Acct Exec)*
Joe Watson *(Sr Acct Exec-Adv Sls)*
Bryan Collins *(Acct Exec)*
Kim Chuba *(Accountant)*

Brands & Products:
FLYERS

PHILADELPHIA MUSEUM OF ART

26th Benjamin Franklin Pkwy
Philadelphia, PA 19130
Tel.: (215) 763-8100
Fax: (215) 236-4465
E-mail: visitoservices@philamuseum.org
Web Site: www.philamuseum.org
Approx. Number Employees: 350
Year Founded: 1876
Business Description:
Art Gallery, Commercial
S.I.C.: 8412
N.A.I.C.S.: 712110
Media: 10-20-23-24-25
Personnel:
Charles Croce *(Exec Dir & CEO)*
Timothy Rub *(CEO)*
Robert Rambo *(CFO & Sec)*
Norman Keyes *(Dir-Comm, Mktg & PR)*
Conna Clark *(Mgr-Production)*

THE PHILADELPHIA ORCHESTRA ASSOCIATION

The Atlantic Bldg 260 S Broad St 16th Fl
Philadelphia, PA 19102
Tel.: (215) 893-1900
Fax: (215) 875-7649
E-mail: philadelphia_orchestra@philorch.org
Web Site: www.philorch.org
Approx. Number Employees: 110
Business Description:
Music Producer
S.I.C.: 7929; 6512
N.A.I.C.S.: 711130; 531120
Media: 1-8-9-13-18-20-23-24-25
Personnel:
Richard B. Worley *(Chm)*
Allison Vulgamore *(Pres & CEO)*
Mario Mestichelli *(CFO & VP)*
Craig Hamilton *(VP & Gen Mgr)*
Katherine Blodgett *(VP-Comm & Pub Rel)*
Ruth Kasow *(Controller)*
Ari Solotoff *(Chief of Staff & Dir-Plng)*
Michelle Guim *(Asst Database Mgr)*
Karen Tomlinson *(Mgr-HR)*

Brands & Products:
ACADEMY OF MUSIC

PHILADELPHIA PHANTOMS, INC.

(Div. of Philadelphia Flyers, L.P.)
1 Civic Ctr Dr
Glens Falls, NY 12801
Tel.: (518) 480-3355
Fax: (518) 480-3357
E-mail: info@phantomshockey.com
Web Site: www.phantomshockey.com
Sales Range: $1-9.9 Million
Approx. Number Employees: 15
Year Founded: 1996
Business Description:
Professional Hockey Team
S.I.C.: 7941
N.A.I.C.S.: 711211
Media: 1-3-4-5-6-7-8-9-13-14-15-18-19-20-22-23-24-25

PHILHARMONIA BAROQUE ORCHESTRA

180 Redwood St Ste 200
San Francisco, CA 94102
Tel.: (415) 252-1288
Fax: (415) 252-1488
E-mail: info@philharmonia.org
Web Site: www.philharmonia.org
Sales Range: $10-24.9 Million
Approx. Number Employees: 10
Business Description:
Orchestra
S.I.C.: 7929
N.A.I.C.S.: 711130
Media: 8-9-13-18-20-22-23-25
Personnel:
David Challinor *(Mgr-Subscription & Patron Svcs)*
David Wilson *(Coord-Education & Production)*

PHILHARMONIC SOCIETY OF NORTHEASTERN PENNSYLVANIA

(d/b/a The Northeastern Pennsylvania Philharmonic)
4101 Bimey Ave
Moosic, PA 18507
Tel.: (570) 341-1568
Fax: (570) 941-0318
E-mail: info@nepaphil.org
Web Site: www.nepaphil.org
Approx. Number Employees: 7
Business Description:
Symphony Orchestra
S.I.C.: 7389
N.A.I.C.S.: 711310
Media: 9-20-23-24-25
Personnel:
Nancy Schmidtt Farkas *(Exec Dir)*
Steve Parulski *(Dir-Mktg & PR)*
Lawrence Loh *(Dir-Music)*

PHILHARMONIC SYMPHONY SOCIETY OF NEW YORK INC.

(d/b/a New York Philharmonic)
Avery Fisher Hall 10 Lincoln Ctr Plz
New York, NY 10023-6990
Tel.: (212) 875-5900
Fax: (212) 875-5717
E-mail: nypfeedback@nyphil.org
Web Site: www.nyphil.org
Approx. Rev.: $21,000,000
Approx. Number Employees: 200
Year Founded: 1842
Business Description:
Symphony Orchestra
S.I.C.: 7389
N.A.I.C.S.: 711320
Media: 4-9-10-18-20-22-23-24-25
Personnel:
Zarin Mehta *(Pres & Exec Dir)*
David Snead *(VP-Mktg)*
Lucy Kraus *(Editor-Publ)*
Marion Cotrone *(Dir-Special Events & Volunteer Svcs)*
Ann Hilton *(Dir-Sls)*
Pamela Katz *(Dir-Fin)*
Amy Mugavero *(Dir-Major & Planned Gifts)*
Julii Oh *(Dir-Mktg)*
Monica Parks *(Dir-Publ)*
Lawrence Rock *(Dir-Audio)*
Catherine Williams *(Dir-HR)*
John May *(Mgr-Subscriptions)*
Carl R. Schiebler *(Mgr-Orchestra Personnel)*
Barbara Shear *(Mgr-Res)*

Brands & Products:
NEW YORK PHILHARMONIC
YOUNG PEOPLE'S CONCERTS

Advertising Agencies:
Chemistry Communications Inc.
535 Smithfield St Ste 230
Pittsburgh, PA 15222
Tel.: (412) 642-0642
Fax: (412) 642-0650

Munn Rabot LLC
33 W 17th St Fl 3
New York, NY 10011-5511
Tel.: (212) 727-3900
Fax: (212) 604-9804
Toll Free: (888) 847-0290

THE PHILLIES, L.P.

(d/b/a Philadelphia Phillies)
Citizens Bank Park 1 Citizens Bank Way
Philadelphia, PA 19148
Tel.: (215) 463-6000
Fax: (215) 463-6025
E-mail: fanfeedback@phillies.mlb.com
Web Site:
www.philadelphia.phillies.mlb.com
Approx. Number Employees: 200
Year Founded: 1893
Business Description:
Professional Baseball Club
S.I.C.: 7941
N.A.I.C.S.: 711211
Import
Media: 1-3-4-5-6-7-8-9-10-13-18-19-20-21-22-23-24
Distr.: Natl.
Budget Set: Nov.
Personnel:
Bill Giles *(Chm)*
David Montgomery *(Pres, CEO & Gen Partner)*
John Nickolas *(CFO & VP)*
Bill Webb *(Gen Counsel & Sr VP)*
Ruben Amaro, Jr. *(Sr VP & Gen Mgr)*
David Buck *(Sr VP-Mktg & Adv Sls)*
Jerry Clothier *(Sr VP-Bus & Fin)*
Michael Stiles *(Sr VP-Admin & Ops)*
Bonnie D. Clark *(VP-Comm)*
Larry Shenk *(VP-Alumni)*
Chuck LaMar *(Asst Gen Mgr-Player Dev & Scouting)*
Kevin Beale *(Dir-Suite Sls & Client Svcs)*
Scott Brandreth *(Dir-Mdsg)*
John Brazer *(Dir-Publicity)*
Greg Casterioto *(Dir-Baseball Comm)*
Frank Coppenbarger *(Dir-Team Travel & Clubhouse Svcs)*
Mike DiMuzio *(Dir-Ballpark Ops)*
Mark DiNardo *(Dir-Brdcst & Video Svcs)*
Meghan Leary Essman *(Dir-Fan Dev & Educational Programs)*
Kurt Funk *(Dir-Mktg Programs & Events)*
Joe Giles *(Dir-Ballpark Enterprises & Bus Dev)*
Dan Goroff *(Dir-Ticket Dept)*
Joe Jordan *(Dir-Player Dev)*
Brian Lamoreaux *(Dir-Info Sys)*
Chris Long *(Dir-Entertainment)*
Rob MacPherson *(Dir-Corp Partnerships)*
Brian Mahoney *(Dir-Adv Sls)*
JoAnn Marano *(Dir-HR & Benefits)*
Susan Ingersoll Papaneri *(Dir-Baseball Admin)*
Christopher Pohl *(Dir-Ticket Tech & Dev)*
Derek Schuster *(Dir-Season Ticket Sls)*
Eric Tobin *(Dir-Event Ops)*
Tina Urban *(Dir-Print & Creative Svcs)*
Karen Wright *(Dir-Payroll Svcs)*
Steve Noworyta *(Asst Dir-Minor League Ops)*
Rob Brooks *(Mgr-Brdcst Production)*
Sal DeAngelis *(Mgr-Ops & Security)*
Ken Duffy *(Mgr-Ticket Ops)*
Phil Feather *(Mgr-Ticket Svcs & Intern Program)*
Leila Graham-Willis *(Mgr-Special Events)*
Jo-Anne Levy-Lamoreaux *(Mgr-Adv & Internet Svcs)*
Lori Loughlin *(Mgr-Ticket Vault Svcs)*
Tom Mashek *(Mgr-Suite Sls & Svcs)*
Sharon Nelson *(Mgr-Box Office Ops)*
Debbie Nocito *(Mgr-Client Svcs & Alumni Rels)*
Dan Stephenson *(Mgr-Video Production)*
Tom Sullivan *(Mgr-Adv Sls)*

Brands & Products:
BASEBALL ACADEMY
BASWEBALL 101 CLINIC
CARPENTER CUP
HOME RUN DERBY
PHANTASY CAMP
PHILADELPHIA PHILLIES
PHILLIES BALLGIRLS
PHILLIES PHESTIVAL
PHILLIES PHUNDAMENTALS
RED GOES GREEN
ROOKIE LEAGUE

Advertising Agencies:
MayoSeitz Media
532 E. Township Line Rd
Blue Bell, PA 19422
Tel.: (215) 641-8700
Fax: (215) 641-8712
— Jon Seitz *(Mgr.-Plng.)*

MLB Advanced Media, L.P.
75 9th Ave 5th Fl
New York, NY 10011
Tel.: (212) 485-3444
Fax: (212) 485-3456

PHILLIPS DE PURY & COMPANY

450 W 15th St
New York, NY 10011
Tel.: (212) 940-1200
Fax: (212) 924-5403
Toll Free: (800) 825ART1
E-mail: info@phillipsdepury.com
Web Site: www.phillipsdepury.com
Approx. Number Employees: 200
Year Founded: 1796

Key to Media (For complete agency information see *The Advertising Red Books-Agencies* edition):
1. Bus. Publs. 2. Cable T.V. 3. Catalogs & Directories. 4. Co-op Adv. 5. Consumer Mags. 6. D.M. to Bus. Estab.7. D.M. to Consumers
8. Daily Newsp. 9. Exhibits/Trade Shows 10. Foreign 11. Infomercial 12. Internet Adv.13. Multimedia 14. Network Radio
15. Network T.V. 16. Newsp. Distr. Mags. 17. Other 18. Outdoor (Posters, Transit) 19. Point of Purchase20. Premiums, Novelties
21. Product Samples 22. Special Events Mktg. 23. Spot Radio 24. Spot T.V. 25. Weekly Newsp. 26. Yellow Page Adv.

Phillips de Pury & Company — (Continued)

Business Description:
Fine Art Auctioneers & Appraisers
S.I.C.: 5961
N.A.I.C.S.: 454112
Import Export
Media: 4-6-8-9-18-25
Distr.: Intl.; Natl.

Personnel:
Simon de Pury *(Chm & Chief Auctioneer)*
Sean Cleary *(Mng Dir)*

Brands & Products:
PHILLIPS

PHOENIX SUNS

(Unit of Suns Legacy Partners, LLC)
201 E Jefferson St
Phoenix, AZ 85004-2412
Tel.: (602) 379-7900
Fax: (602) 379-7922
Web Site: www.nba.com/suns
Approx. Number Employees: 300
Year Founded: 1968

Business Description:
Professional Basketball Franchise
S.I.C.: 7941
N.A.I.C.S.: 711211
Media: 3-4-8-9-13-18-19-20-22-23-24-25
Distr.: Natl.

Personnel:
Robert G. Sarver *(Owner)*
Gerald J. Colangelo *(Chm)*
Sam Garvin *(Vice Chm)*
Jahm Najafi *(Vice Chm)*
Jason Rowley *(COO)*
Lon Babby *(Pres-Basketball Ops)*
Brad Casper *(Pres-Bus & Non-Basketball Ops)*
Jim Pitman *(Exec VP-Fin & Admin)*
Ralph Marchetta *(Sr VP & Gen Mgr)*
Lynn Agnello *(Sr VP-Mktg Partnerships)*
Al McCoy *(Sr VP-Brdcst)*
Jay Parry *(Sr VP-Brand & Bus Dev)*
Jeff Ianello *(VP-Sls)*
Jeramie McPeek *(VP-Digital)*
Jon Phillips *(VP-Fin)*
Peter Wong *(VP-HR)*
Lance Blanks *(Gen Mgr)*
Niki Adams *(Sr Dir-Mktg)*
Jamie Morris LeVine *(Sr Dir-PR & Community Rels)*
Nick Forro *(Dir-New Bus Dev)*
Sheila Guy *(Dir-Payroll Svcs)*
Karen Rausch *(Dir-HR)*
Dan Siekmann *(Dir-Mktg)*
John Trailor *(Dir-Player Personnel)*
Bridget Black *(Asst Controller)*

Brands & Products:
ARIZONA RATTLERS
PHOENIX ARENA SPORTS
PHOENIX MERCURY
PHOENIX SUNS
SIXTHMAN

Advertising Agency:
The Lavidge Company
2777 E Camelback Rd Ste 300
Phoenix, AZ 85016
Tel.: (480) 998-2600
Fax: (480) 998-5525

PHOENIX SYMPHONY ASSOCIATION

1 N 1st St Ste 200
Phoenix, AZ 85004
Tel.: (602) 495-1117
Fax: (602) 253-1772
E-mail: info@phoenixsymphony.org
Web Site: www.phoenixsymphony.org
Sales Range: $25-49.9 Million
Approx. Number Employees: 30

Business Description:
Symphony Orchestra
S.I.C.: 7929
N.A.I.C.S.: 711130
Media: 8-10-18-20-22-23-24-25

Personnel:
Bill Wanser *(Principal)*
Michael Christie *(Dir-Music)*
James Cerracchio *(Office Mgr)*
Andrea Galyean *(Office Mgr)*
Jennifer Bellman *(Mgr-Opers)*
Kim Davis *(Mgr-Education)*
Mark Dix *(Mgr-Arts)*
Kellan Meko *(Mgr-Mktg)*
Jenny Sanford *(Mgr-Ops)*
Brandon Walls *(Mgr-Audience Dev)*
James Way *(Mgr-Production)*

PINNACLE ENTERTAINMENT, INC.

8918 Spanish Ridge Ave
Las Vegas, NV 89148
Tel.: (702) 541-7777
E-mail: contactus@pnkmail.com
Web Site: www.pnkinc.com
Approx. Rev.: $1,093,800,000
Approx. Number Employees: 7,533
Year Founded: 1938

Business Description:
Casinos & Hotels Owner & Operator
S.I.C.: 7011; 7999
N.A.I.C.S.: 721120; 713290; 721110
Advertising Expenditures: $22,700,000
Media: 6-9-18-20-23-24
Distr.: Reg.
Budget Set: Dec.

Personnel:
Anthony M. Sanfilippo *(Pres & CEO)*
Carlos A. Ruisanchez *(CFO, Chief Acctg Officer & Exec VP)*
Virginia E. Shanks *(CMO & Exec VP)*
Clifford D. Kortman *(Pres-Pinnacle Design & Construction, Exec VP-Construction, Dev)*
John A. Godfrey *(Gen Counsel & Exec VP-Strategy)*
Jeff Babinski *(VP & Gen Mgr)*

Brands & Products:
BELTERRA
BOOMTOWN
CASINO MAGIC
L'AUBERGE
LUMIERE PLACE
MYCHOICE
PINNACLE

Advertising Agencies:
Euro RSCG Worldwide Latin America
Gorriti 5995
C1414BKK
Buenos Aires, 1414, Argentina
Tel.: (54) 11 5288 6000
Fax: (54) 11 5288 6099

SK+G Advertising
8912 Spanish Ridge Ave
Las Vegas, NV 89148
Tel.: (702) 478-4000
Fax: (702) 478-4001

PITTSBURGH BASEBALL, INC.

(Sub. of Pittsburgh Baseball Holdings, Inc.)
(d/b/a Pittsburgh Pirates)
PNC Pk 115 Federal St
Pittsburgh, PA 15212
Tel.: (412) 323-5000
Fax: (412) 325-4479
Web Site: www.pittsburgh.pirates.com
Approx. Number Employees: 100
Year Founded: 1891

Business Description:
Professional Baseball Club
S.I.C.: 7941
N.A.I.C.S.: 711211
Media: 3-5-6-7-8-9-10-18-19-20-22-23-24
Distr.: Natl.
Budget Set: Oct.

Personnel:
Robert Nutting *(Chm)*
Frank Coonelly *(Pres)*
James D. Plake *(CFO & Exec VP)*
Larry Silverman *(Gen Counsel & Sr VP)*
Dennis DaPra *(Sr VP & Gen Mgr-PNC Park)*
Neal Huntington *(Gen Mgr-Pirates)*
Brian Chiera *(Sr Dir-Mktg & Ticket Sls)*
Brian Warecki *(Sr Dir-Comm)*
Patrick DeMeo *(Dir-Medical)*
Kyle Stark *(Dir-Player Dev)*
Jim Trdinich *(Dir-Media Relations)*
Kiley Cauvel *(Mgr-Mktg)*
Mark Oresic *(Mgr-Acctg)*

Brands & Products:
PITTSBURGH PIRATES

Advertising Agency:
MLB Advanced Media, L.P.
75 9th Ave 5th Fl
New York, NY 10011
Tel.: (212) 485-3444
Fax: (212) 485-3456

PITTSBURGH PENGUINS LLC

(Sub. of Lemieux Group L.P.)
1001 5th Ave
Pittsburgh, PA 15219
Tel.: (412) 642-1300
Fax: (412) 255-1980
Web Site: penguins.nhl.com
Approx. Number Employees: 200
Year Founded: 1967

Business Description:
Professional Hockey Club
S.I.C.: 7941
N.A.I.C.S.: 711211
Media: 3-6-7-8-9-10-13-14-15-18-20-22-23-24-25-26
Distr.: Natl.

Personnel:
Mario Lemieux *(Chm)*
David Morehouse *(Pres & CEO)*
Dave Soltesz *(Pres)*
Ray Shero *(Exec VP & Gen Mgr)*
Jason Botterill *(Asst Gen Mgr)*
Kim Bogesdorfer *(Sr Dir-Corp Sls)*
Frank Buonomo *(Sr Dir-Team Ops)*
Rod Murray *(Sr Dir-Event Presentation & Production Ops)*
Jennifer Bullano *(Dir-Comm)*
Ross Miller *(Dir-Mktg)*
Mark Turley *(Dir-Media-Corp Sls)*

Brands & Products:
PITTSBURGH PENGUINS

Advertising Agency:
Vibes Media
205 W Wacker Dr Ste 2300
Chicago, IL 60606
Tel.: (312) 753-6330
Fax: (312) 753-6332

PITTSBURGH STEELERS SPORTS INC.

3400 S Water St
Pittsburgh, PA 15203
Tel.: (412) 432-7800
Fax: (412) 432-7876
E-mail: feedback@fans.steelers.com
Web Site: www.steelers.com
Approx. Number Employees: 130
Year Founded: 1933

Business Description:
Professional Football Franchise
S.I.C.: 7941
N.A.I.C.S.: 711211
Advertising Expenditures: $550,000
Media: 5-8-14-15-18-20-22-23-24
Distr.: Natl.

Personnel:
Arthur J. Rooney, II *(Pres)*
Kevin Colbert *(Dir-Football Ops)*
Tony Quatrini *(Dir-Mktg)*
Bob Tyler *(Dir-Fin)*
John Wodarek *(Mgr-Entertainment & Mktg)*
Burt Lauten *(Mgr-PR & Media)*
Jodie Spagnolli *(Asst Controller)*
Rick Giugliano *(Coord-Mktg)*
David Lockett *(Coord-Comm)*

Brands & Products:
STEELERS

PITTSBURGH SYMPHONY INC.

600 Penn Ave
Pittsburgh, PA 15222
Tel.: (412) 392-4900
Fax: (412) 392-3311
E-mail: questions@pittsburghsymphony.org
Web Site:
www.pittsburghsymphony.org

Business Description:
Symphony Orchestra
S.I.C.: 7929
N.A.I.C.S.: 711130
Media: 9-18-20-23-24-25

Personnel:
Richard Simmons *(Chm)*
Lisa Donnermeyer *(Pres)*
Mary Schrempp *(Sr VP & Gen Mgr)*
Marcie Solomon *(Gen Mgr)*
Aleta King *(Sr Dir-Patron Dev)*
Allison Hill *(Sls Dir)*
Yu-Ling Cheng *(Dir-Mktg)*
Jodi Weisfield *(Dir-Major Campaign)*
Kevin DeLuca *(Mgr-IT)*
Marianne Haffey *(Mgr-Sls Grp)*
Kelvin Hill *(Mgr-Orchestra Personnel)*
Mark Cieslewicz *(Chief Engr)*

PLAINFIELD SYMPHONY SOCIETY INC.

PO Box 5093
Plainfield, NJ 07061
Tel.: (908) 561-5140
E-mail: info@plainfieldsymphony.org
Web Site:
www.plainfieldsymphony.org

Business Description:
Symphony Orchestra
S.I.C.: 7929
N.A.I.C.S.: 711130

Key to Media (For complete agency information see *The Advertising Red Books-Agencies* edition):
1. Bus. Publs. 2. Cable T.V. 3. Catalogs & Directories. 4. Co-op Adv. 5. Consumer Mags. 6. D.M. to Bus. Estab. 7. D.M. to Consumers 8. Daily Newsp. 9. Exhibits/Trade Shows 10. Foreign 11. Infomercial 12. Internet Adv. 13. Multimedia 14. Network Radio 15. Network T.V. 16. Newsp. Distr. Mags. 17. Other 18. Outdoor (Posters, Transit) 19. Point of Purchase 20. Premiums, Novelties 21. Product Samples 22. Special Events Mktg. 23. Spot Radio 24. Spot T.V. 25. Weekly Newsp. 26. Yellow Page Adv.

Media: 4-8-9-20-23-24-25
Personnel:
Wendy Dore Burney *(Pres)*
Sabin Pautza *(Dir-Music)*

PLAYHOUSE SQUARE FOUNDATION
(d/b/a Playhouse Square Center)
1501 Euclid Ave Ste 200
Cleveland, OH 44115
Tel.: (216) 771-4444
Fax: (216) 771-0217
Web Site: www.playhousesquare.org
Approx. Rev.: $40,000,000
Approx. Number Employees: 300
Business Description:
Theatrical Production
S.I.C.: 7922
N.A.I.C.S.: 711110
Media: 8-23-24
Personnel:
Art J. Falco *(Pres & CEO)*
Advertising Agency:
Dix & Eaton Incorporated
200 Public Sq Ste 1400
Cleveland, OH 44114
Tel.: (216) 241-0405
Fax: (216) 241-3070

PLAYNETWORK, INC.
8727 148th Ave NE
Redmond, WA 98052
Tel.: (425) 497-8100
Fax: (425) 497-8181
Toll Free: (888) 567-7529
E-mail: info@playnetwork.com
Web Site: www.playnetwork.com
Approx. Number Employees: 61
Year Founded: 1996
Business Description:
Customized Audio, Music & Video Programming
S.I.C.: 3651
N.A.I.C.S.: 334310
Personnel:
Lon Troxel *(Chm & CEO)*
Sue Hoover *(CFO, VP-Fin & Admin)*
Darrell Champagne *(Exec VP-Ops)*
Craig Hubbell *(Exec VP-Media Svcs)*
Brian Hirsh *(Sr VP-Mktg, Licensing & New Media)*
Walt Tatum *(Sr VP-Sls-North America)*
Advertising Agency:
PAN Communications
300 Brickstone Sq 7th Fl
Andover, MA 01810
Tel.: (978) 474-1900
Fax: (978) 474-1903

PLYMOUTH CANTON SYMPHONY SOCIETY
774 N Sheldon Rd
Plymouth, MI 48170
Tel.: (734) 451-2112
Fax: (734) 451-3458
E-mail: info@plymouthcantonsymphony.org
Web Site:
www.plymouthsymphony.org
Year Founded: 1945
Business Description:
Symphony Orchestra
S.I.C.: 7929
N.A.I.C.S.: 711130
Media: 9-20-23-24-25
Personnel:
Nan Harrison Washburn *(Dir-Music & Conductor)*
Faith Demorest *(Mgr-Personnel, Production & Music Librarian)*

POLYNESIAN CULTURAL CENTER
55-220 Kam Hwy
Laie, HI 96762
Tel.: (808) 293-3000
Fax: (808) 293-3339
Toll Free: (800) 367-7060
E-mail: info@polynesia.com
Web Site: www.polynesia.com
Approx. Sls.: $36,000,000
Approx. Number Employees: 1,100
Business Description:
Tourist Attraction
S.I.C.: 7999; 5812
N.A.I.C.S.: 712190; 722110
Media: 9-20-23-24-25
Personnel:
Von D. Orgill *(Pres)*
Advertising Agency:
Richter7
280 S 400 W Ste 200
Salt Lake City, UT 84101
Tel.: (801) 521-2903
Fax: (801) 359-2420

PORTLAND CHILDREN'S MUSEUM 2ND GENERATION
4015 SW Canyon Rd
Portland, OR 97221
Tel.: (503) 223-6500
Fax: (503) 223-6600
E-mail: info@portlandcm.org
Web Site: www.portlandcm.org
Sales Range: $10-24.9 Million
Approx. Number Employees: 60
Business Description:
Hands-On Children's Museum
S.I.C.: 8412
N.A.I.C.S.: 712110
Media: 9-10-23-24-25
Personnel:
Shannon Grosswiler *(Dir-Comm & Mktg)*

PORTLAND SYMPHONY ORCHESTRA
50 Monument Sq 2nd Fl
Portland, ME 04101
Tel.: (207) 773-6128
Fax: (207) 773-6089
E-mail: psobox@portlandsymphony.com
Web Site:
www.portlandsymphony.com
Sales Range: Less than $1 Million
Approx. Number Employees: 12
Year Founded: 1923
Business Description:
Symphony Orchestra
S.I.C.: 7929
N.A.I.C.S.: 711130
Media: 9-20-22-23-24-25
Personnel:
Alice Kornhauser *(Dir-Mktg & Comm)*
Carolyn Nishon *(Dir-Artistic Ops)*
Allison W. Earnhart *(Mgr-Sls & Corp Rels)*
Gary Massey *(Engr)*

PORTLAND TRAIL BLAZERS
(Holding of Vulcan Sports & Entertainment LLC)
1 Center Ct Ste 200
Portland, OR 97227-2103
Tel.: (503) 234-9291
Fax: (503) 736-2187
E-mail: fanmail@blazers.com
Web Site: www.trailblazers.com
Sales Range: $75-99.9 Million
Approx. Number Employees: 125
Year Founded: 1970
Business Description:
National Basketball Team
S.I.C.: 7941
N.A.I.C.S.: 711211
Media: 1-3-4-7-10-14-15-18-20-22-23-24-25
Distr.: Natl.
Personnel:
Paul G. Allen *(Owner)*
Larry Miller *(Pres)*
Gregg Olson *(CFO & Sr VP)*
Chris Dill *(CIO & VP)*
Michael Fennell *(Gen Counsel & Sr VP)*
J. E. Isaac *(Sr VP-Bus Affairs)*
Sarah Mensah-Wohlford *(Sr VP & Operating Officer)*
Michelle Daterman *(VP-Tickets & Mktg)*
Traci Rose *(VP-Comm & Community Rels)*
Rich Cho *(Gen Mgr)*
Mike Janes *(Dir-Engrg & Tech Ops)*
Lori Spencer *(Dir-Internal Ticketing)*
Kim Koenig *(Asst Dir-Mktg)*
Brands & Products:
PORTLAND TRAIL BLAZERS

PREMIER EXHIBITIONS, INC.
3340 Peachtree Rd NE Ste 2250
Atlanta, GA 30326
Tel.: (404) 842-2600
Fax: (404) 842-2626
E-mail: kmorgenstern@prxi.com
Web Site: www.prxi.com
Approx. Rev.: $44,751,000
Approx. Number Employees: 77
Business Description:
Unique, Museum Quality Special Exhibition Operator
S.I.C.: 7999
N.A.I.C.S.: 713990
Advertising Expenditures: $5,951,000
Personnel:
Mark A. Sellers, III *(Chm)*
Christopher J. Davino *(Pres & CEO)*
Michael J. Little *(CFO)*
Kris Hart *(CMO & VP)*
Robert A. Brandon *(Gen Counsel, Sec & VP-Bus Affairs)*
Katherine Morgenstern *(Dir-Pub Rel)*

PRESIDENT CASINOS, INC.
800 N 1st St
Saint Louis, MO 63102-2529
Tel.: (314) 622-3000
Fax: (314) 622-3029
Toll Free: (800) 772-3647
Web Site: www.presidentinc.com
Sales Range: $75-99.9 Million
Approx. Number Employees: 5
Year Founded: 1992
Business Description:
Dockside Gaming Facilities Owner & Operator
S.I.C.: 7999
N.A.I.C.S.: 713290
Media: 8-18-23-24-25
Personnel:
Ralph J. Vaclavik *(CFO & Sr VP)*

PRINCE WILLIAM SYMPHONY ORCHESTRA INC.
8665 Sudley Rd Ste 305
Manassas, VA 20110
Tel.: (703) 659-0103
E-mail: dm.pwso@pwso.org
Web Site: www.pwso.org
Approx. Number Employees: 40
Year Founded: 1972
Business Description:
Symphony Orchestra
S.I.C.: 7929
N.A.I.C.S.: 711130
Media: 8-9-20-24-25

PRINCETON SYMPHONY ORCHESTRA
PO Box 250
Princeton, NJ 08542
Tel.: (609) 497-0020
Fax: (609) 497-0904
E-mail: info@princetonsymphony.org
Web Site:
www.princetonsymphony.org
Approx. Number Employees: 3
Year Founded: 1980
Business Description:
Symphony Orchestra
S.I.C.: 7929
N.A.I.C.S.: 711130
Media: 9-23-24-25
Personnel:
David Tierno *(Pres)*
Kiri Murakami *(Gen Mgr)*
Karen Klaverkamp *(Mgr-Mktg & Dev)*

PROMUSICA CHAMBER ORCHESTRA
243 N 5th St Ste 202
Columbus, OH 43215
Tel.: (614) 464-0066
Fax: (614) 464-4141
E-mail: info@promusicacolumbus.org
Web Site:
www.promusicacolumbus.org
Approx. Number Employees: 5
Business Description:
Symphony Orchestra
S.I.C.: 7929
N.A.I.C.S.: 711130
Media: 9-20-23-24-25
Personnel:
Janet Chen *(Exec Dir)*
Timothy Russell *(Dir-Music)*
Thomas Battenberg *(Mgr-Personnel & Music Librarian)*
Yvette Boyer *(Mgr-Fin)*

PROVIDENCE PERFORMING ARTS CENTER
220 Weybosset St
Providence, RI 02903
Tel.: (401) 421-2997
Fax: (401) 421-5767
Web Site: www.ppacri.org
Approx. Sls.: $14,086,849
Approx. Number Employees: 50
Business Description:
Performing Arts Center Production
S.I.C.: 7389
N.A.I.C.S.: 711310
Media: 9-18-20-23-24-25
Personnel:
James Lynn Singleton *(Pres & CEO)*
Alan J. Chille *(Gen Mgr)*
David Luongo *(Dir-Security)*
Christopher J. Myers *(Dir-Info Sys)*
P. J. Prokop *(Dir-Mktg)*

Key to Media (For complete agency information see *The Advertising Red Books-Agencies* edition):
1. Bus. Publs. 2. Cable T.V. 3. Catalogs & Directories. 4. Co-op Adv. 5. Consumer Mags. 6. D.M. to Bus. Estab.7. D.M. to Consumers 8. Daily Newsp. 9. Exhibits/Trade Shows 10. Foreign 11. Infomercial 12. Internet Adv.13. Multimedia 14. Network Radio 15. Network T.V. 16. Newsp. Distr. Mags. 17. Other 18. Outdoor (Posters, Transit) 19. Point of Purchase20. Premiums, Novelties 21. Product Samples 22. Special Events Mktg. 23. Spot Radio 24. Spot T.V. 25. Weekly Newsp. 26. Yellow Page Adv.

Providence Performing Arts Center — (Continued)

Rosemary A. Sienko-Koehler *(Office Mgr)*
Nick Berardinelli *(Mgr-Opers)*

THE PUBLIC THEATER

425 Lafayette St
New York, NY 10003
Tel.: (212) 539-8500
Fax: (212) 539-8505
Web Site: www.publictheater.org
Approx. Sls.: $12,918,251
Approx. Number Employees: 100
Year Founded: 1962
Business Description:
Theatrical Production Services
S.I.C.: 7922
N.A.I.C.S.: 711110
Media: 3-6-8-9-10-13-18-23-25
Personnel:
Gail Merrifield Papp *(Founder)*
Paul J. Fribourg *(Chm & CEO)*
Andrew Hamingson *(Exec Dir)*
Nella Vera *(Dir-Mktg)*

QUEENS SYMPHONY ORCHESTRA

70-31 84th St Bldg 38
Glendale, NY 11385
Tel.: (718) 326-4455
Fax: (718) 326-4499
E-mail: qso@queenssymphony.org
Web Site: www.queenssymphony.org
Sales Range: Less than $1 Million
Approx. Number Employees: 5
Business Description:
Symphony Orchestra
S.I.C.: 7929
N.A.I.C.S.: 711130
Media: 9-20-23-24-25
Personnel:
Herbert M. Chain *(Pres)*
Elsi Levy *(Exec VP)*
Lynda Herndon *(Exec Dir)*
Constantine Kitsopoulos *(Dir-Music)*
Abba Bogin *(Mgr-Personnel)*
Kate Oberjat *(Mgr-Mktg & Comm)*
Dale Turk *(Librarian)*

QUINCY SYMPHONY ORCHESTRA ASSOCIATION

428 Maine St Ste 270
Quincy, IL 62301
Tel.: (217) 222-2856
Fax: (217) 222-2869
E-mail: qsoa@adams.net
Web Site: www.qsoa.org
Sales Range: Less than $1 Million
Approx. Number Employees: 5
Year Founded: 1947
Business Description:
Symphony Orchestra
S.I.C.: 7389
N.A.I.C.S.: 711320
Media: 9-20-23-24-25
Personnel:
Jane Polett *(Gen Mgr)*

RACINE SYMPHONY ORCHESTRA ASSOCIATION INC.

PO Box 1874
Racine, WI 53401-1874
Tel.: (262) 636-9285
E-mail: mail@racinesymphony.org
Web Site: www.racinesymphony.org
Sales Range: Less than $1 Million
Approx. Number Employees: 2
Business Description:
Symphony Orchestra
S.I.C.: 7929
N.A.I.C.S.: 711130
Media: 9-20-23-24-25
Personnel:
Nancy DeKraay *(Pres)*
Andrew Massey *(Dir-Music)*
Robb Seftar *(Mgr-Personnel)*

RAINIER SYMPHONY

PO Box 58182
Seattle, WA 98138
Tel.: (206) 781-5618
E-mail: questions@rainiersymphony.org
Web Site: www.rainiersymphony.org
Approx. Number Employees: 100
Year Founded: 1981
Business Description:
Symphony Orchestra
S.I.C.: 7929
N.A.I.C.S.: 711130
Media: 8-9-20-23-24-25
Personnel:
Tom Metcalf *(Pres)*
David Wayne Waltman *(Dir-Music)*
Marisa Hartman *(Mgr-Orchestra)*

RANGERS BASEBALL LLC

(Formerly Texas Rangers Inc.)
(Sub. of Rangers Baseball Express LLC)
(d/b/a Texas Rangers)
1000 Ballpark Way Ste 400
Arlington, TX 76011-5170
Mailing Address:
PO Box 90111
Arlington, TX 76004
Tel.: (817) 273-5222
Fax: (817) 273-5256
E-mail: team@texasrangers.com
Web Site: texas.rangers.mlb.com
Approx. Number Employees: 200
Year Founded: 1960
Business Description:
Professional Baseball Club
S.I.C.: 7941
N.A.I.C.S.: 711211
Advertising Expenditures: $500,000
Media: 3-7-8-9-14-15-18-22-23-24-25
Distr.: Natl.
Personnel:
Lynn Nolan Ryan, Jr. *(Pres & CEO)*
Kellie Fischer *(CFO & Exec VP)*
Rick George *(COO)*
John Blake *(Exec VP-Comm)*
Joe Januszewski *(Exec VP-Partnerships & Dev)*
Rob Matwick *(Exec VP-Ballpark Ops)*
Todd Taylor *(Exec VP-Ticket Sls & Mktg)*
Jay Miller *(Sr VP)*
Jim Cochrane *(VP-Corp Sls)*
Paige Jackson Farragut *(VP-Suite Sls & Svc)*
John Hardin *(VP-Event Ops & Security)*
Grady Raskin *(VP-Sponsorship Sls)*
Terry Turner *(VP-HR)*
Starr Pritchard *(Controller & Asst VP)*
Diane Atkinson *(Asst VP-Mdsg)*
Mike Bullock *(Asst VP-IT)*
Kelly Calvert *(Asst VP-Mktg)*
Taunee Paur Taylor *(Asst VP-Player/Community Rels)*
Jon Daniels *(Gen Mgr)*
Thad Levine *(Asst Gen Mgr)*
Karin Morris *(Exec Dir-Foundation & Dir-Hispanic Mktg)*
Rainer Uhlir *(Sr Creative Dir-Graphic Design)*
Breon Dennis *(Sr Dir-Baseball Programs, Youth Ballpark & Corp Clinics)*
Sherry Flow *(Sr Dir-Promos & Special Events)*
Donnie Pordash *(Sr Dir-Customer Svc)*
A. J. Preller *(Sr Dir-Player Personnel)*
Rich Rice *(Sr Dir-Media Rels)*
Scott Servais *(Sr Dir-Player Dev)*
Rush Olson *(Creative Dir-Media)*
Chris Lyngos *(Dir-Travel)*
Josh Boyd *(Dir-Pro Scouting)*
Danielle Cornwell *(Dir-Event Ops)*
Ron Hopkins *(Dir-Scouting)*
Mike Lentz *(Dir-Ticket Svcs)*
Stephen Moore *(Dir-Mdse)*
Angie Swint *(Dir-Brdcst)*
Kaylan Eastepp *(Mgr-Mktg)*
Donna Blaylock Ebersole *(Mgr-Payroll)*
Bill Edevane *(Mgr-Application Sys)*
Heather Hansen King *(Mgr-Sls-Nightly Rental Suites)*
Fred Phillips *(Mgr-IT Sys & Customer Svc)*
Richard Price *(Mgr-Equipment & Home Clubhouse)*
Delia Willms *(Mgr-Sls-Long Term Suites)*
Patrick Harvey *(Sr Acct Exec-Grp Sls)*
Troy King *(Sr Acct Exec-Season Tickets)*

Brands & Products:
TEXAS RANGERS
YOU COULD USE SOME BASEBALL

Advertising Agencies:
Core Group Advertising, Inc.
4141 Office Pkwy
Dallas, TX 75204
Tel.: (214) 821-5888
Fax: (214) 827-1223
— Pete Northway *(Acct. Exec.)*

Door Number 3
1050 E 11th St Ste 250
Austin, TX 78702
Tel.: (512) 391-1773
Fax: (512) 391-1926

MLB Advanced Media, L.P.
75 9th Ave 5th Fl
New York, NY 10011
Tel.: (212) 485-3444
Fax: (212) 485-3456

RAZORGATOR, INC.

11150 Santa Monica Blvd Ste 500
Los Angeles, CA 90025
Tel.: (310) 289-3000
Fax: (310) 289-3010
Toll Free: (800) 852-7771
Web Site: www.razorgator.com
Sales Range: $25-49.9 Million
Approx. Number Employees: 20
Business Description:
Entertainment Ticket Sales
S.I.C.: 4729; 7389
N.A.I.C.S.: 561599; 711310
Media: 5-13
Personnel:
Brendan Ross *(CEO)*

READING INTERNATIONAL, INC.

500 Citadel Dr Ste 300
Commerce, CA 90040-1572
Tel.: (213) 235-2240
Fax: (213) 239-2229
Web Site: www.readingrdi.com
E-Mail For Key Personnel:
Public Relations: ajmatyezynski@crgcorporation.com
Approx. Rev.: $229,817,000
Approx. Number Employees: 2,056
Year Founded: 1999
Business Description:
Holding Company; Movie Theater Owner
S.I.C.: 6719; 6531; 7832
N.A.I.C.S.: 551112; 512131; 531210
Advertising Expenditures: $2,600,000
Personnel:
James J. Cotter *(Chm & CEO)*
Andrzej Matyczynski *(CFO)*
John Hunter *(COO)*
Robert F. Smerling *(Pres-Domestic Cinemas)*
Wayne Smith *(Exec Dir-Ops-Australia & New Zealand)*
Ian Sands *(Dir-Cinema Ops-Australia & New Zealand)*
John Willey *(Dir-Real Estate Dev-Australia & New Zealand)*

READING SYMPHONY ORCHESTRA ASSOCIATION

147 N 5th St
Reading, PA 19601-3401
Tel.: (610) 373-7557
Fax: (601) 373-5446
E-mail: info@readingsymphony.org
Web Site: www.readingsymphony.org
Sales Range: Less than $1 Million
Approx. Number Employees: 6
Year Founded: 1913
Business Description:
Symphony Orchestra
S.I.C.: 7929
N.A.I.C.S.: 711130
Media: 9-20-23-24-25
Personnel:
Andrew Constantine *(Dir-Music)*
Donna Kline *(Mgr-Orchestra)*
Barry Long *(Mgr-Production)*
Doug McNames *(Mgr-Personnel)*

REDS BASEBALL PARTNERS, LLC

(d/b/a Cincinnati Reds)
Great American Ball Park 100 Main St
Cincinnati, OH 45202
Tel.: (513) 765-7000
Fax: (513) 765-7342
Web Site: cincinnati.reds.mlb.com
E-Mail For Key Personnel:
Marketing Director: marketing@reds.mlb.com
Sales Range: $100-124.9 Million
Approx. Number Employees: 40
Year Founded: 1869
Business Description:
Professional Baseball Club
S.I.C.: 7941
N.A.I.C.S.: 711211
Media: 9-10-18-20-22-23-24
Distr.: Natl.

Key to Media (For complete agency information see *The Advertising Red Books-Agencies* edition):
1. Bus. Publs. 2. Cable T.V. 3. Catalogs & Directories. 4. Co-op Adv. 5. Consumer Mags. 6. D.M. to Bus. Estab.7. D.M. to Consumers 8. Daily Newsp. 9. Exhibits/Trade Shows 10. Foreign 11. Infomercial 12. Internet Adv.13. Multimedia 14. Network Radio 15. Network T.V. 16. Newsp. Distr. Mags. 17. Other 18. Outdoor (Posters, Transit) 19. Point of Purchase20. Premiums, Novelties 21. Product Samples 22. Special Events Mktg. 23. Spot Radio 24. Spot T.V. 25. Weekly Newsp. 26. Yellow Page Adv.

Personnel:
W. Joseph Williams, Jr. *(Chm)*
Thomas L. Williams *(Vice Chm & Treas)*
Robert H. Castellini *(Pres & CEO)*
Doug Healy *(CFO & VP-Fin)*
Phillip J. Castellini *(COO)*
Walt Jocketty *(Pres-Baseball Ops & Gen Mgr)*
James A. Marx *(Gen Counsel & VP)*
Karen Forgus *(Sr VP-Bus Ops)*
Bob Miller *(VP & Asst Gen Mgr)*
Ralph Mitchell *(VP-Comm & Mktg)*
Bill Reinberger *(VP-Corp Sls)*
Scott Nethery *(Asst Gen Mgr & Sr Dir-Pro Scouting)*
Jennifer Berger *(Sr Dir)*
Chris Buckley *(Sr Dir-Amateur Scouting)*
Terry Reynolds *(Sr Dir-Pro & Global Scouting)*
Rob Butcher *(Dir-Media Rels)*
Timothy Kremchek *(Dir-Medical)*
Lorrie Platt *(Dir-Community Rels)*
Craig Warman *(Dir-Ticket Client Svcs)*
Larry Herms *(Asst Dir-Media Rels)*
Jamie Ramsey *(Asst Dir-Media Rels)*
Bernie Stowe *(Sr Mgr-Clubhouse & Equipment)*
Lisa Braun *(Mgr-Mktg)*
Jill Niemeyer *(Mgr-Acctg)*
Rick Stowe *(Mgr-Reds Clubhouse & Equipment)*
Brands & Products:
CINCINNATI REDS
Advertising Agency:
MLB Advanced Media, L.P.
75 9th Ave 5th Fl
New York, NY 10011
Tel.: (212) 485-3444
Fax: (212) 485-3456

REGAL ENTERTAINMENT GROUP
(Sub. of The Anschutz Corporation)
7132 Regal Ln
Knoxville, TN 37918
Tel.: (865) 922-1123
Fax: (865) 922-3188
Web Site: www.regmovies.com
Approx. Rev.: $2,807,900,000
Approx. Number Employees: 22,061
Year Founded: 2002
Business Description:
Holding Company; Motion Picture Theater Owner & Operator
S.I.C.: 6719; 7832
N.A.I.C.S.: 551112; 512131
Advertising Expenditures: $1,026,700,000
Media: 9-13-14-22-23-25
Personnel:
Michael L. Campbell *(Chm)*
Gregory W. Dunn *(Pres & COO)*
Amy E. Miles *(CEO)*
David H. Ownby *(CFO, Treas & Exec VP)*
Dick Westerling *(Pres-Mktg & Sls)*
Peter B. Brandow *(Gen Counsel, Sec & Exec VP)*
Brands & Products:
CINEMA ART
REGAL CINEMEETINGS AND EVENTS
REGAL CROWN CLUB
REGAL EXPRESS
WE DO ENTERTAINMENT BIG

RENAISSANCE ENTERTAINMENT CORP.
(Sub. of Ellora Entertainment, LLC)
275 Century Cir Ste 102
Louisville, CO 80027
Tel.: (303) 664-0300
Fax: (303) 664-0303
E-mail: stan@renfair.com
Web Site: www.renfair.com
Sales Range: $10-24.9 Million
Approx. Number Employees: 200
Business Description:
Renaissance Fair Operator
S.I.C.: 7999; 7389
N.A.I.C.S.: 713990; 561920
Advertising Expenditures: $1,590,999
Media: 7-8-10-18-23-24-25
Personnel:
Charles Leavell *(Chm, CEO & CFO)*
J. Stanley Gilbert *(Pres & COO)*

RHODE ISLAND PHILHARMONIC ORCHESTRA INC.
667 Waterman Ave
East Providence, RI 02914
Tel.: (401) 831-3123
Fax: (401) 248-7071
E-mail: information@riphil.org
Web Site: www.riphil.org
Approx. Number Employees: 145
Business Description:
Symphony Orchestra
S.I.C.: 7929
N.A.I.C.S.: 711130
Media: 9-20-23-24-25
Personnel:
Pamela Kennedy *(Dir-Mktg & PR)*
Robert Schlesinger *(Mgr-Sls)*

RICHARDSON SYMPHONY ORCHESTRA
2100 N Collins Ste 310
Richardson, TX 75080
Tel.: (972) 234-4195
Fax: (972) 238-7514
E-mail: info@richardsonsymphony.org
Web Site:
www.richardsonsymphony.org
Approx. Number Employees: 3
Year Founded: 1962
Business Description:
Symphony Orchestra
S.I.C.: 7929
N.A.I.C.S.: 711130
Media: 7-8-9-20-22-23-24-25
Personnel:
George Landis *(Pres)*
Stot Wilkinson *(Exec VP-Dev)*
Anshel Brusilow *(Dir-Music & Conductor)*

RICHMOND PHILHARMONIC INC.
8100 Three Chopt Rd Ste 238
Richmond, VA 23229
Tel.: (804) 673-7400
Fax: (804) 673-7470
E-mail: rpo@richmondphilharmonic.org
Web Site:
www.richmondphilharmonic.org
Approx. Rev.: $40,000
Approx. Number Employees: 75
Year Founded: 1972
Business Description:
Symphony Orchestra
S.I.C.: 3931
N.A.I.C.S.: 339992
Media: 8-9-20-23-24-25
Personnel:
Durwood Felton *(Pres & Dir)*

RICHMOND SYMPHONY
300 W Franklin St
Richmond, VA 23220
Tel.: (804) 788-4717
Fax: (804) 788-1541
Web Site:
www.richmondsymphony.com
Approx. Number Employees: 65
Year Founded: 1957
Business Description:
Symphony Orchestra
S.I.C.: 7929; 2721
N.A.I.C.S.: 711130; 511120
Media: 8-9-13-20-22-23-24-25
Personnel:
David Fisk *(Exec Dir)*
Aimee Halbruner *(Dir-Education & Community Engagement)*
Mark Russell Smith *(Dir-Music)*
Shelby Murphy *(Mgr-Youth Orchestras & Assistant Dir-Education)*
Katie Freeman *(Asst Dir-Patron Svcs)*
Keishawna Gilliam *(Office Mgr)*
Barbara Baker *(Mgr-Chorus)*
Jimmy Carroll *(Mgr-Production)*

RIVIERA HOLDINGS CORP.
(Filed Ch 11 Bankruptcy #10-22910 on 07/13/2010 in U.S. Bankruptcy Ct, Dist of NV, Las Vegas)
2901 Las Vegas Blvd S
Las Vegas, NV 89109-1933
Tel.: (702) 794-9527
Tel.: (702) 734-5110
Fax: (702) 794-9442
E-mail: psimons@theriviera.com
Web Site: www.rivierahotel.com
Approx. Rev.: $135,719,000
Approx. Number Employees: 947
Year Founded: 1993
Business Description:
Hotel & Casino Owner & Operator
S.I.C.: 7011
N.A.I.C.S.: 721120; 721110
Advertising Expenditures: $2,246,000
Media: 6-8-10-22-23-24
Personnel:
Vincent L. DiVito *(Chm)*
Andy Choy *(CEO)*
Larry King *(CFO, Treas & VP-Fin)*
Robert A. Vannucci *(Pres/COO-Riviera Operating Corp)*
Tim Wilbur *(CIO & VP-Riviera Oper Corp)*
Tullio J. Marchionne *(Gen Counsel & Sec)*
Brands & Products:
RIVIERA HOTEL & CASINO

ROANOKE SYMPHONY SOCIETY
541 Luck Ave SW Ste 200
Roanoke, VA 24016
Tel.: (540) 343-6221
Fax: (540) 343-0065
Toll Free: (866) 277-9127
E-mail: music@rso.com
Web Site: www.rso.com
Sales Range: Less than $1 Million
Approx. Number Employees: 15
Business Description:
Symphony Orchestra
S.I.C.: 7929
N.A.I.C.S.: 711130
Media: 7-8-9-20-22-23-24-25
Personnel:
Richard Maxwell *(Pres)*
Anastasia Jellison *(Principal-Harp)*
Jack Hans *(Treas)*
Grant Ellis *(Dir-Ops)*
Liz Lochdrunner *(Dir-Education)*
JoAnn Steele *(Dir-Junior Strings)*
David Stewart Wiley *(Dir-Music & Conductor)*

ROBERT W. WOODRUFF ARTS CENTER
1280 Peachtree St NE
Atlanta, GA 30309
Tel.: (404) 733-4200
Fax: (404) 733-4281
E-mail: info@woodruffcenter.org
Web Site: www.woodruffcenter.org
Approx. Number Employees: 1,600
Year Founded: 1968
Business Description:
Symphony Orchestra
S.I.C.: 7389
N.A.I.C.S.: 711310
Media: 9-10-18-20-22-23-24-25
Personnel:
Joseph R. Bankoff *(Pres & CEO)*
Beauchamp C. Carr *(Exec VP)*
Kathleen Smith *(VP-Comm & Center Initiatives)*
Charlie Wade *(VP-Mktg)*
Susan Booth *(Artistic Dir-Alliance Theatre Company)*
Robert Spano *(Dir-Atlanta Symphony Orchestra)*

ROCHESTER BROADWAY THEATRE LEAGUE
(d/b/a Ticket Express)
885 E Main St
Rochester, NY 14605
Tel.: (585) 325-7760
Fax: (585) 325-6742
E-mail: info@rbtl.org
Web Site: www.rbtl.org
Approx. Number Employees: 15
Business Description:
Entertainment Service
S.I.C.: 7929
N.A.I.C.S.: 711190
Media: 9-18-20-23-24-25
Personnel:
Don Jeffries *(Pres & CEO)*
John C. Parkhurst *(Exec VP)*
Francine N. Brokaw *(VP-Fin)*
Aimee Frank *(Mktg Mgr)*
Jessica Karlsen *(Mktg-Coord)*

ROCHESTER PHILHARMONIC ORCHESTRA INC.
108 E Ave
Rochester, NY 14604
Tel.: (585) 454-7311
Fax: (585) 423-2256
Web Site: www.rpo.org
Approx. Rev.: $8,000,000
Approx. Number Employees: 25
Business Description:
Symphony Orchestra
S.I.C.: 8641; 7389
N.A.I.C.S.: 813410; 711320
Media: 9-18-20-22-23-24-25
Personnel:
Susan Welch *(Chm)*
Keith M. Wilson *(Vice Chm)*

Key to Media (For complete agency information see *The Advertising Red Books-Agencies* edition):
1. Bus. Publs. 2. Cable T.V. 3. Catalogs & Directories. 4. Co-op Adv. 5. Consumer Mags. 6. D.M. to Bus. Estab.7. D.M. to Consumers
8. Daily Newsp. 9. Exhibits/Trade Shows 10. Foreign 11. Infomercial 12. Internet Adv.13. Multimedia 14. Network Radio
15. Network T.V. 16. Newsp. Distr. Mags. 17. Other 18. Outdoor (Posters, Transit) 19. Point of Purchase20. Premiums, Novelties
21. Product Samples 22. Special Events Mktg. 23. Spot Radio 24. Spot T.V. 25. Weekly Newsp. 26. Yellow Page Adv.

Rochester Philharmonic Orchestra Inc. — (Continued)

Charles H. Owens *(Pres & CEO)*
Janice Hanson *(Mgr-Mktg & Electronic Comm)*
Barbara Larson *(Mgr-Education & Community Programs)*
Marilyn Merrigan *(Mgr-Volunteers & Special Events)*
Irene Shaffer *(Mgr-HR)*
Joseph Werner *(Mgr-Personnel)*

ROCKFORD SYMPHONY ORCHESTRA

711 N Main St
Rockford, IL 61103
Tel.: (815) 965-0049
Fax: (815) 965-0642
E-mail: info@rockfordsymphony.com
Web Site: www.rockfordsymphony.com
Approx. Number Employees: 7
Business Description:
Symphony Orchestra
S.I.C.: 7929
N.A.I.C.S.: 711130
Media: 9-20-23-24-25
Personnel:
Jim Gingrich *(Pres)*
Julie Schaper *(Exec Dir)*
Lorie Langan *(Dir-Education & Community Engagement)*
Steven Larsen *(Dir-Music)*

ROUNDABOUT THEATRE COMPANY

231 W 39th St
New York, NY 10018
Tel.: (212) 719-9393
Fax: (212) 869-8817
E-mail: info@roundabouttheatre.org
Web Site: www.roundabouttheatre.org
Approx. Rev.: $75,000,000
Approx. Number Employees: 250
Business Description:
Theatrical Production
S.I.C.: 7389
N.A.I.C.S.: 711310
Advertising Expenditures: $5,534,000
Media: 7-8-9-10-13-20-23-24-25
Personnel:
Harold Wolpert *(Mng Dir)*
Julia Levy *(Exec Dir)*
Lynne Gugenheim Gregory *(Dir-Dev)*
Todd Haimes *(Dir-Artistic)*
David B. Steffen *(Dir-Mktg & Sls Promo)*

SACRAMENTO KINGS

(Sub. of Maloof Sports & Entertainment)
Arco Arena 1 Sports Pkwy
Sacramento, CA 95834-2300
Tel.: (916) 928-0000
Fax: (916) 928-0727
E-mail: gmaloof@arcoarena.com
Web Site: www.kings.com
Business Description:
Professional Basketball Franchise
S.I.C.: 7389; 5812
N.A.I.C.S.: 711310; 722310
Media: 4-7-8-9-10-14-15-23-24
Distr.: Reg.
Budget Set: Aug.
Personnel:
Gavin Maloof *(Co-Owner & Vice Chm)*
Joe Maloof *(Co-Owner & Pres)*
Geoff Petrie *(Pres-Basketball Ops)*
John Thomas *(Pres-Bus Ops)*
Ruth Hill *(VP-Fin)*
Brands & Products:
SACRAMENTO KINGS

SACRAMENTO PHILHARMONIC ORCHESTRA

3418 3rd Ave
Sacramento, CA 95817
Tel.: (916) 732-9045
Fax: (916) 732-9049
E-mail: info@sacphil.org
Web Site: www.sacphil.org
Sales Range: $25-49.9 Million
Approx. Number Employees: 7
Business Description:
Orchestra
S.I.C.: 7929
N.A.I.C.S.: 711130
Media: 5-9-20-23-24-25
Personnel:
Ken Raskin *(Dir-Ops-Orchestra Personnel/Orchestra Librarian)*
Larry Murdock *(Mgr-Stage)*

SAINT LOUIS CARDINALS, L.P.

Busch Stadium 700 Clark St
Saint Louis, MO 63102-1722
Tel.: (314) 345-9600
Fax: (314) 345-9521
E-mail: ticketinfo@cardinals.com
Web Site: www.cardinals.com
Approx. Number Employees: 100
Year Founded: 1900
Business Description:
Professional Baseball Club
S.I.C.: 7941
N.A.I.C.S.: 711211
Media: 6-9-13-18-20-22-23-24
Distr.: Direct to Consumer; Reg.
Personnel:
William O. DeWitt, Jr. *(Chm & CEO)*
William DeWitt, III *(Pres)*
Brad Wood *(CFO & Sr VP)*
Mark Whittle *(Gen Counsel, VP & Asst Sec)*
Dan Farrell *(Sr VP-Sls & Mktg)*
John Mozeliak *(VP & Gen Mgr)*
Vicki Bryant *(VP-Event Svcs & Mdsg)*
Jeff Luhnow *(VP-Amateur Scouting & Player Dev)*
Thane van Breusegen *(VP-Corp Mktg & Stadium Entertainment)*
John Abbamondi *(Asst Gen Mgr)*
Brands & Products:
ST. LOUIS CARDINALS
Advertising Agencies:
Barkley
304 N Broadway
Saint Louis, MO 63102
Tel.: (314) 727-9500
Fax: (314) 727-0561
Toll Free: (800) 886-0561

MLB Advanced Media, L.P.
75 9th Ave 5th Fl
New York, NY 10011
Tel.: (212) 485-3444
Fax: (212) 485-3456

SAINT LOUIS RAMS FOOTBALL COMPANY

1 Rams Way
Saint Louis, MO 63045-1523
Tel.: (314) 982-7267
Fax: (314) 770-0392
E-mail: sales@stlouisrams.com
Web Site: www.stlouisrams.com
E-Mail For Key Personnel:
Sales Director: sales@stlouisrams.com
Sales Range: $100-124.9 Million
Approx. Number Employees: 150
Year Founded: 1937
Business Description:
Professional Football Franchise
S.I.C.: 7941
N.A.I.C.S.: 711211
Media: 10-20-22
Distr.: Natl.
Personnel:
E. Stanley Kroenke *(Owner & Chm)*
Kevin Demoss *(COO & Exec VP-Football Ops)*
Bob Reif *(Chief Mktg Officer & Exec VP-Mktg & Sls)*
Molly Higgins *(VP-Corp Comm & Civic Affairs)*
Michael T. Naughton *(VP-Fin)*
Rick Smith *(VP-Pub Rel)*
Tony Softli *(VP-Player Personnel)*
Billy Devaney *(Gen Mgr)*
Ted Crews *(Sr Dir-Comm)*
Jake Bye *(Dir-Ticket Sls & Premium Seating)*
Larry Clerico *(Dir-Video Ops)*
Bill Consoli *(Dir-Info Sys)*
Keely Fimbres *(Dir-Special Events)*
Tom Guthrie *(Dir-Entertainment)*
Keith Harris *(Dir-nternet Svcs & Bus Dev)*
Lawrence McCutcheon *(Dir-Player Personnel)*
Susan Slemmer *(Dir-Partnership Support & Dev)*
Artis Twyman *(Dir-Media Rels)*
Chad Watson *(Dir-Corp Sls)*
Shad Watson *(Dir-Corp Sls)*
Kanyon West *(Dir-Ticket Ops)*
Michael Yarbrough *(Dir-Community Outreach)*
Matt Cady *(Asst Dir-Ticket Sls & Svc)*
Pam Benoist *(Mgr-Suite Svcs)*
Kim Kohler *(Mgr-Payroll)*
Brands & Products:
SAINT LOUIS RAMS
Advertising Agency:
Rodgers Townsend, LLC
1000 Clark Ave 5th Fl
Saint Louis, MO 63102
Tel.: (314) 436-9960
Fax: (314) 436-9961

THE SAINT PAUL CHAMBER ORCHESTRA

3rd Fl The Hamm Bldg 408 Saint Peter St
Saint Paul, MN 55102-1497
Tel.: (651) 292-3248
Fax: (651) 292-3281
E-mail: info@spcomail.org
Web Site: www.thespco.org
Sales Range: $50-74.9 Million
Approx. Number Employees: 75
Year Founded: 1959
Business Description:
Symphony Orchestra
S.I.C.: 7929
N.A.I.C.S.: 711130
Media: 7-8-9-10-13-20-22-23-25
Personnel:
Jon Limbacher *(COO & VP)*
Christine Dahl *(Editor-Prelude)*
Jessica Etten *(Dir-Mktg & Comm)*
Theresa Gienapp *(Dir-Dev)*
Melissa Spencer *(Asst Dir-Devel-Institutional Support)*
Jim Belich *(Mgr-Ticket Office & Database Administrator)*
Aimee Johnson *(Mgr-Creative)*
Jon Kjarum *(Mgr-Tech)*
Kelly MacLennan *(Mgr-Orchestra Personnel)*
Mark Niehaus *(Mgr-Acctg)*
Jason Piehl *(Mgr-Production)*

SALT LAKE BEES

(Affil. of Angels Baseball, L.P.)
77 W 1300 S
Salt Lake City, UT 84115-5326
Tel.: (801) 325-2273
Tel.: (801) 350-6900
Fax: (801) 485-6818
E-mail: info@stingersbaseball.com
Web Site: www.slbees.com
Year Founded: 1915
Business Description:
Baseball Team
S.I.C.: 7941
N.A.I.C.S.: 711211
Media: 9-13-18-19-20-22-23-24-25-26
Personnel:
Larry H. Miller *(Owner)*
Robert Hyde *(CFO & Exec VP)*
Eric Shulz *(CMO)*
Linda Luchetti *(Sr VP-Comm)*
Jim Olson *(Sr VP-Salt Lake Bees)*
Mike Snarr *(Sr VP-LHMSE Strategic Partnerships)*
Marc Amicone *(VP & Gen Mgr)*
John Larson *(VP-Fin)*
Brad Tammen *(Asst Gen Mgr)*

SALVADOR DALI MUSEUM

1000 Third St S
Saint Petersburg, FL 33701
Tel.: (727) 823-3767
Fax: (727) 894-6068
E-mail: info@thedali.org
Web Site: www.thedali.org
Sales Range: $10-24.9 Million
Approx. Number Employees: 30
Business Description:
Museum & Art Gallery
S.I.C.: 8412
N.A.I.C.S.: 712110
Media: 3-6-9-10-17-18-20-25-26
Personnel:
Hank Hine *(Exec Dir)*
Kathy White *(Dir-Mktg)*
Marcia Crawley *(Dir-Dev)*

SAN ANTONIO SPURS LLC

(Holding of Spurs Sports & Entertainment)
1 At AT&T Center Pkwy
San Antonio, TX 78219
Tel.: (210) 224-8557
Fax: (210) 444-5100
E-mail: fanrelat@mail.spurs.com
Web Site: www.nba.com/spurs
Approx. Number Employees: 200
Year Founded: 1967
Business Description:
Professional Basketball Franchise
S.I.C.: 7941
N.A.I.C.S.: 711211
Advertising Expenditures: $1,000,000

Key to Media (For complete agency information see *The Advertising Red Books-Agencies* edition):
1. Bus. Publs. 2. Cable T.V. 3. Catalogs & Directories. 4. Co-op Adv. 5. Consumer Mags. 6. D.M. to Bus. Estab.7. D.M. to Consumers
8. Daily Newsp. 9. Exhibits/Trade Shows 10. Foreign 11. Infomercial 12. Internet Adv.13. Multimedia 14. Network Radio
15. Network T.V. 16. Newsp. Distr. Mags. 17. Other 18. Outdoor (Posters, Transit) 19. Point of Purchase20. Premiums, Novelties
21. Product Samples 22. Special Events Mktg. 23. Spot Radio 24. Spot T.V. 25. Weekly Newsp. 26. Yellow Page Adv.

Media: 3-13-14-15-18-22-23-24
Distr.: Natl.
Budget Set: June
Personnel:
Pete Holt *(Owner, Chm & CEO)*
Gregg Popovich *(Exec VP-Basketball Opers & Head Coach)*
Rick A. Pych *(Exec VP)*
Bruce Guthrie *(VP-Mktg)*
Paula Winslow *(Dir-HR)*
Pam Benavides *(Mgr-Adv)*
Brands & Products:
SAN ANTONIO SPURS
SPURS FOUNDATION
Advertising Agency:
Dublin & Associates, Inc.
3015 San Pedro
San Antonio, TX 78212-4721
Tel.: (210) 227-0221
Fax: (210) 227-6634
(Public Relations)

SAN DIEGO CHARGERS FOOTBALL CO.

4020 Murphy Canyon Rd
San Diego, CA 92123
Mailing Address:
PO Box 609609
San Diego, CA 92160-9609
Tel.: (858) 874-4500
Fax: (858) 292-2760
Toll Free: (877) CHARGERS
Web Site: www.chargers.com
Sales Range: $125-149.9 Million
Approx. Number Employees: 135
Year Founded: 1960
Business Description:
Professional Football Franchise
S.I.C.: 7941
N.A.I.C.S.: 711211
Advertising Expenditures: $700,000
Media: 1-2-3-4-5-6-7-8-9-10-12-13-18-19-20-22-23-24-25
Distr.: Direct to Consumer; Reg.
Budget Set: Jan.
Personnel:
Alex G. Spanos *(Owner)*
Dean A. Spanos *(Pres & CEO)*
Jeanne M. Bonk *(CFO & Exec VP)*
Ken Derrett *(CMO & Sr VP)*
A. J. Smith *(Exec VP & Gen Mgr)*
Ed McGuire *(Exec VP-Football Ops & Asst Gen Mgr)*
Jeremiah T. Murphy *(Exec VP)*
A. G. Spanos *(Exec VP & Exec Officer)*
Michael A. Spanos *(Exec VP)*
Dennis O'Leary *(Sr Dir-Mktg Partnerships)*
Todd Poulsen *(Sr Dir-Ticket Sls & Svc)*
Shirley Aboyme *(Dir-Guest Svcs)*
Dennis Abraham *(Dir-Pro Scouting)*
Michael L. Dougherty *(Dir-Ticket Ops)*
Brian Duddy *(Dir-Video Ops)*
Arthur Hightower *(Dir-Player Dev)*
John Hinek *(Dir-Bus Ops)*
Bill Johnston *(Dir-PR)*
Kimberley Layton *(Dir-Pub Affairs, Corp & Community Rels)*
Dick Lewis *(Dir-Security & Player Outreach)*
Sean O'Connor *(Dir-Stadium/Game Ops & Special Events)*
Jimmy Raye *(Dir-Player Personnel)*
John Spanos *(Dir-College Scouting)*
Mike Biehl *(Asst Dir-College Scouting)*
Scott Yoffe *(Asst Dir-Pub Rel)*
S. Brandon Ward *(Sr Mgr-Mktg Partnerships & Brdcst Production)*
Doug Carnahan *(Mgr-Corp Sls)*
Tom Carson *(Mgr-Stadium Ops)*
Kevin Daly *(Mgr-Creative Svcs)*
Chris Lee *(Mgr-Acctg)*
Chrystal Lee *(Mgr-Acctg)*
Joel Price *(Mgr-Internet Svcs)*
Bob Wick *(Mgr-Equipment)*
Brands & Products:
CHARGERS

SAN DIEGO SOCIETY OF NATURAL HISTORY

(d/b/a San Diego Natural History Museum)
1788 El Prado
San Diego, CA 92101
Tel.: (619) 232-3821
Fax: (619) 255-0171
E-mail: administration@sdnhm.org
Web Site: www.sdnhm.org
Sales Range: $10-24.9 Million
Approx. Number Employees: 100
Year Founded: 1984
Business Description:
Natural History Museum
S.I.C.: 8412
N.A.I.C.S.: 712110
Advertising Expenditures: $737,977
Media: 3-6-8-9-10-13-14-15-18-20-22-23-24-25-26
Personnel:
Michael W. Hager *(Pres & CEO)*
George H. Brooks-Gonyer *(CFO, COO & VP)*
Eowyn Bates *(Dir-Annual Fund)*
Doretta Winkelman *(Dir-Natl)*

SAN DIEGO SYMPHONY ORCHESTRA ASSOCIATION

1245 7th Ave
San Diego, CA 92101
Tel.: (619) 235-0800
Fax: (619) 235-0005
Web Site:
www.sandiegosymphony.com
Approx. Number Employees: 110
Business Description:
Symphony Orchestra
S.I.C.: 7929
N.A.I.C.S.: 711130
Media: 8-9-20-23-24-25
Personnel:
Seth Goldman *(CFO & Chief Admin Officer)*
Robert H. Wilkins *(COO)*
Greg Parry *(Dir-Mktg)*
Edward B. Gill *(Dir-Foundation Board)*
Stephen Kougias *(Dir-PR)*
Megan Pogue *(Dir)*
Mitchell R. Woodbury *(Dir-Foundation Board)*
Lisa Baker *(Assoc Dir-Mktg-Ticket Svcs)*
LeAnna Zevely *(Office Mgr)*
Mariellen Oliver *(Asst Controller & Mgr-HR)*
Nancy Fisch *(Mgr-Library)*
Gerry Gagliardi *(Mgr-Direct Sls)*
Douglas Hall *(Mgr-Orchestra Personnel)*
Jennifer Ringle *(Mgr-Production)*

SAN FRANCISCO FORTY NINERS, LTD.

(Sub. of DeBartolo Corporation)
(d/b/a San Francisco 49ers)
4949 Centennial Blvd
Santa Clara, CA 95054-1229
Tel.: (408) 562-4949
Fax: (408) 727-4937
E-mail: info@sf49ers.com
Web Site: www.sf49ers.com
Sales Range: $50-74.9 Million
Approx. Number Employees: 200
Business Description:
Professional Football Franchise
S.I.C.: 7941
N.A.I.C.S.: 711211
Media: 10-18-22
Distr.: Natl.
Personnel:
Denise DeBartolo York *(Co-Chm)*
John C. York *(Co-Chm)*
Jed York *(Pres & CEO)*
Larry MacNeil *(CFO)*
Andy Dolich *(COO)*
Paraag Marathe *(COO)*
Gideon Yu *(Chief Strategy Officer)*
Lal Heneghan *(Exec VP-Football Admin)*
Patty Inglis *(Exec VP-Stadium Project)*
Lisa Lang *(VP-Comm)*
Jim Mercurio *(VP-Stadium Ops & Security)*
Michael P. Williams *(VP-Mktg)*
Trent Baalke *(Gen Mgr)*
Fred Formosa *(Dir-Security)*
Tom Gamble *(Dir-Player Personnel)*
Alexander Ignacio *(Dir-IT)*
Guy McIntyre *(Dir-Alumni Rels)*
Joanne Pasternack *(Dir-Community Rels)*
Joel Patten *(Dir-College Scouting)*
Bob Sargent *(Dir-Brdcst & Corp Sls)*
Lynn Carrozzi *(Sr Mgr-Ticket Ops)*
Dan Henderson *(Sr Mgr-Stadium Ops)*
Esther Chi *(Mgr-Acctg)*
Anthony Lozano *(Mgr-Facilities)*
Joan Pires *(Mgr-Payroll)*
Steve Risser *(Mgr-Team Logistics)*
Steve Urbaniak *(Mgr-Equipment)*
Keith Yanagi *(Mgr-Video Ops)*
Willie McHargue *(Sr Acct Exec)*
Brands & Products:
49ERS

SAN FRANCISCO GIANTS BASEBALL CLUB

(Holding of San Francisco Baseball Associates, L.P.)
AT&T Park 24 Willie Mays Plz
San Francisco, CA 94107
Tel.: (415) 972-2000
Fax: (415) 947-3399
Web Site:
sanfrancisco.giants.mlb.com
Approx. Number Employees: 130
Year Founded: 1883
Business Description:
Professional Baseball Club
S.I.C.: 7941
N.A.I.C.S.: 711211
Advertising Expenditures: $750,000
Media: 9-13-18-19-20-22-23-24
Distr.: Natl.
Personnel:
Laurence M. Baer *(Pres)*
William H. Neukom *(CEO)*
John F. Yee *(CFO)*
Bill Schlough *(CIO & Sr VP)*
Jack F. Bair *(Gen Counsel & Sr VP)*
Brian R. Sabean *(Sr VP & Gen Mgr-Team)*
Mario Alioto *(Sr VP-Corp Mktg)*
Jorge Costa *(Sr VP-Ballpark Ops)*
Tom McDonald *(Sr VP-Consumer Mktg)*
Staci A. Slaughter *(Sr VP-Comm)*
Elizabeth R. Murphy *(VP & Deputy Gen Counsel)*
Nancy Donati *(VP-Publ & Creative Svcs)*
Annemarie Hastings *(VP-Client Relations)*
Lisa Pantages *(VP-Fin)*
Russ Stanley *(VP-Ticket Svcs & Client Relations)*
Joyce Thomas *(VP-HR)*
Dick Tidrow *(VP-Player Personnel)*
Jeff Tucker *(VP-Sls)*
Chris Gargano *(Sr Dir-Mktg & Entertainment)*
Jim Moorehead *(Sr Dir-Media Relations)*
Jerry Drobny *(Dir-Interactive Mktg)*
Valerie McGuire *(Dir-Special Events Mktg)*
Fred Stanley *(Dir-Player Dev)*
Keith T. Scheeler *(Mgr-Acctg)*
Brands & Products:
PACIFIC BELL PARK
SAN FRANCISCO GIANTS
Advertising Agencies:
Gumas Advertising
99 Shotwell St
San Francisco, CA 94103-3625
Tel.: (415) 621-7575
Fax: (415) 255-8804

MLB Advanced Media, L.P.
75 9th Ave 5th Fl
New York, NY 10011
Tel.: (212) 485-3444
Fax: (212) 485-3456

Swirl Advertising
1620 Montgomery St Ste 140
San Francisco, CA 94111
Tel.: (415) 276-8300
Fax: (415) 276-8301

SAN FRANCISCO OPERA ASSOCIATION

301 Van Ness Ave
San Francisco, CA 94102
Tel.: (415) 861-4008
Fax: (415) 621-7508
Web Site: www.sfopera.com
Approx. Sls.: $30,040,788
Approx. Number Employees: 60
Business Description:
Opera Company
S.I.C.: 7922
N.A.I.C.S.: 711110
Advertising Expenditures: $1,000,000
Media: 8-9-10-11-13-18-20-22-23-24-25
Personnel:
Keith Cerny *(CFO & Exec Dir)*
Advertising Agencies:
Mission Minded
4441 19th St
San Francisco, CA 94114
Tel.: (415) 552-9360
Fax: (415) 276-1873

Shuman & Associates
120 W 58th St
New York, NY 10019
Tel.: (212) 315-1300

Key to Media (For complete agency information see *The Advertising Red Books-Agencies* edition):
1. Bus. Publs. 2. Cable T.V. 3. Catalogs & Directories. 4. Co-op Adv. 5. Consumer Mags. 6. D.M. to Bus. Estab.7. D.M. to Consumers
8. Daily Newsp. 9. Exhibits/Trade Shows 10. Foreign 11. Infomercial 12. Internet Adv.13. Multimedia 14. Network Radio
15. Network T.V. 16. Newsp. Distr. Mags. 17. Other 18. Outdoor (Posters, Transit) 19. Point of Purchase20. Premiums, Novelties
21. Product Samples 22. Special Events Mktg. 23. Spot Radio 24. Spot T.V. 25. Weekly Newsp. 26. Yellow Page Adv.

SAN FRANCISCO SYMPHONY
201 Van Ness Ave
San Francisco, CA 94102
Tel.: (415) 552-8000
Fax: (415) 431-6857
E-mail: bassink@sfsymphony.org
Web Site: www.sfsymphony.org
Sales Range: $50-74.9 Million
Approx. Number Employees: 200
Business Description:
Symphony Orchestra
S.I.C.: 7929
N.A.I.C.S.: 711130
Media: 9-18-20-23-24-25
Personnel:
Michacel Lawrence *(Sr Major Gifts Officer)*
John Kieser *(Gen Mgr)*
Brent Assink *(Exec Dir)*
Julie Ambrose *(Dir-Major Gifts)*
Caroline Colburn *(Dir-Proposal Dev)*
Ronald Gallman *(Dir-Education & Youth Orchestra)*
Robert W. Lasher *(Dir-Dev)*
Sammi Madison *(Dir-Education Programs)*
Stephen Steiner *(Dir-Gift Plng)*
Michael Tilson Thomas *(Dir-Music)*
Lisa Zadek *(Dir-Plng)*
Michelle Consunji *(Mgr-Staffing & Employee Rels)*
Paul Delucchi *(Mgr-Repeat Performance)*
Jeannette Garbarini-Walters *(Mgr-Retail-Ops)*
Emily Limon *(Mgr-Iteractive Mktg)*
Joyce Cron Wessling *(Mgr-Tours & Media Production)*
Andrea Yannone *(Mgr-Programs)*
Rob Levin *(Webmaster)*
Brands & Products:
AMERICAN MAVERICKS
THE BLACK AND WHITE BALL

SAN FRANCISCO ZOOLOGICAL SOCIETY
1 Zoo Rd
San Francisco, CA 94132-1027
Tel.: (415) 753-7080
Tel.: (415) 753-8141
Fax: (415) 681-2039
E-mail: animals@sfzoo.org
Web Site: www.sfzoo.org
Approx. Number Employees: 200
Year Founded: 1954
Business Description:
Zoo & Zoological Research
S.I.C.: 8422
N.A.I.C.S.: 712130
Media: 18-22-23-24
Personnel:
Tanya Peterson *(Pres)*
Advertising Agencies:
BBDO West
555 Market St 17th Fl
San Francisco, CA 94105
Tel.: (415) 808-6200
Fax: (415) 808-6221

Grey San Francisco
303 2nd St Ste 300 N Tower
San Francisco, CA 94107
Tel.: (415) 403-8000
Fax: (415) 403-8204

SAN JOSE SHARKS, LLC
525 W Santa Clara St
San Jose, CA 95113-1520
Tel.: (408) 287-7070
Fax: (408) 999-5797
Web Site: www.sjsharks.com
Sales Range: $50-74.9 Million
Approx. Number Employees: 100
Year Founded: 1990
Business Description:
Professional Hockey Team
S.I.C.: 7941
N.A.I.C.S.: 711211
Import Export
Advertising Expenditures: $500,000
Media: 3-4-5-7-8-9-13-18-20-22-23-24-25
Distr.: Reg.
Budget Set: July
Personnel:
Charlie Faas *(CFO & Exec VP)*
Jim Goddard *(Exec VP & Gen Mgr-San Jose Arena)*
Malcolm Bordelon *(Exec VP-Bus Ops)*
Kent Russell *(VP-Sls & Mktg)*
Doug Bentz *(Dir-Mktg)*
Brands & Products:
SAN JOSE SHARKS

SANTA BARBARA SYMPHONY
1330 State St Ste 102
Santa Barbara, CA 93101
Tel.: (805) 898-9626
Fax: (805) 898-9326
E-mail: info@thesymphony.org
Web Site: www.thesymphony.org
Approx. Number Employees: 10
Business Description:
Symphony Orchestra
S.I.C.: 7929
N.A.I.C.S.: 711130
Media: 8-9-13-19-20-23-24-25
Personnel:
Barbara H. Burger *(Dir-Mktg)*

SANTA FE OPERA
17053 US Hwy 84/285
Santa Fe, NM 87506
Tel.: (505) 986-5955
Fax: (505) 986-5999
Web Site: www.santafeopera.org
Approx. Sls.: $12,455,384
Approx. Number Employees: 58
Business Description:
Opera Company
S.I.C.: 7922
N.A.I.C.S.: 711110
Media: 9-10-18-20-23-24-25
Personnel:
Paul Hoffmann *(Chm)*

SARASOTA OPERA
61 N Pineapple Ave
Sarasota, FL 34236
Tel.: (941) 366-8450
Fax: (941) 955-5571
Web Site: www.sarasotaopera.org
Business Description:
Opera House
S.I.C.: 7929
N.A.I.C.S.: 711190
Media: 6-9-18-20-23-24-25
Personnel:
Susan Danis *(Exec Dir)*
Darcy Ballew *(Dir-Mkg & PR)*
Victor DeRenzi *(Dir-Artistic)*
Ken Tarasi *(Dir-Fin)*
Samuel Lowry *(Mktg Comm)*
Chris Burtless *(Mgr-Facilities & Theater)*

SARATOGA HARNESS RACING INC.
(d/b/a Saratoga Equine Sports Center)
342 Jefferson St
Saratoga Springs, NY 12866
Mailing Address:
PO Box 356
Saratoga Springs, NY 12866-0356
Tel.: (518) 584-2110
Fax: (518) 580-0126
E-mail: info@saratogagamingandraceway.com
Web Site:
www.saratogagamingandraceway.com
Sales Range: $200-249.9 Million
Approx. Number Employees: 400
Year Founded: 1941
Business Description:
Live Harness Racing & Simulcast Wagering
S.I.C.: 7948
N.A.I.C.S.: 711212
Advertising Expenditures: $365,000
Media: 6-9-10-13-18-20-22-23-24-26
Distr.: Natl.; Reg.
Budget Set: Dec.
Personnel:
Daniel Gerrity *(Pres)*
James Hartman *(COO & Exec VP)*
George Wiley *(Treas)*
Rita Cox *(Sr VP-Mktg & External Affairs)*
Brands & Products:
DISCOVER SOMETHING SARATOGA

SARATOGA PERFORMING ARTS CENTER, INC.
108 Ave of the Pines
Saratoga Springs, NY 12866
Tel.: (518) 584-9330
Fax: (518) 584-0809
E-mail: media@spac.org
Web Site: www.spac.org
Approx. Number Employees: 15
Year Founded: 1966
Business Description:
Performing Arts Center Production
S.I.C.: 7389
N.A.I.C.S.: 711310
Media: 8-9-18-23-24-25
Personnel:
Marcia J. White *(Pres & Exec Dir)*
Richard Geary *(CFO & COO)*
Linda Deschenes *(Dir-Youth Arts Programs)*
Lisa Hill *(Specialist-PR & Dev)*
Brands & Products:
SPAC

THE SCIENCE CENTER
3711 Market St Ste 800
Philadelphia, PA 19104
Tel.: (215) 966-6000
Fax: (215) 966-6002
E-mail: info@sciencecenter.org
Web Site: www.sciencecenter.org
Approx. Number Employees: 45
Business Description:
Children's Science Museum
S.I.C.: 8412
N.A.I.C.S.: 712110
Media: 9-10-20-22-23-24-25
Personnel:
Mark Carvlin *(Founder & Mng Dir)*
Richard P. Jaffe *(Chm)*
Steven Tang *(Pres & CEO)*
Curt Hess *(Sr VP-Real Estate Ops)*

SCIENCE CENTER OF PINELLAS COUNTY, INC.
7701 22nd Ave N
Saint Petersburg, FL 33710
Tel.: (727) 384-0027
Fax: (727) 343-5729
E-mail: scenter5@tampabay.rr.com
Web Site:
www.sciencecenterofpinellas.org
Approx. Number Employees: 25
Year Founded: 1959
Business Description:
Science Museum
S.I.C.: 8412
N.A.I.C.S.: 712110
Media: 3-7-9-10-25

SCORES HOLDING COMPANY, INC.
533-535 W 27th St
New York, NY 10001
Tel.: (212) 868-4900
Fax: (212) 868-4414
E-mail: info@scoresholding.com
Web Site: www.scoresholding.com
Approx. Rev.: $514,155
Approx. Number Employees: 2
Business Description:
Holding Company; Gentleman's Clubs
S.I.C.: 7999; 5813
N.A.I.C.S.: 713990; 722410
Advertising Expenditures: $31,846
Media: 18
Personnel:
Robert M. Gans *(Pres & CEO)*

SCREENVISION CINEMA NETWORK LLC
(Joint Venture of Shamrock Holdings, Inc. & Technicolor S.A.)
1411 Broadway
New York, NY 10018
Tel.: (212) 497-0400
Tel.: (212) 497-0412
Fax: (212) 497-0500
Web Site: www.screenvision.com
Approx. Number Employees: 105
Business Description:
Cinema Advertising Services; Joint Venture of Technicolor S.A. (50%) & Shamrock Holdings, Inc. (50%)
S.I.C.: 7319
N.A.I.C.S.: 541890
Media: 17
Personnel:
Travis Reid *(Pres & CEO)*
Kevin J. Neary *(CFO)*
Alan Burge *(COO)*
Mark Mitchell *(Chief Revenue Officer)*
Andy Blacker *(Sr VP-Mktg & Res)*
Darryl Schaffer *(Exec VP-Ops & Exhibitor Rels)*
Alan Brittain *(Sr VP-Local Sls)*
Geroge Najarin *(Sr VP-HR & Admin)*
Al Connor *(VP-Sls-Central Reg)*
Eric McCarthy *(VP-Sls-Western Region)*
Tony McIlwain *(VP-Sls-Western Reg)*
Detroit Sakin *(VP-Natl Western-Midwestern Sls)*
Drew Driscoll *(Dir-Sls)*
Teresa Heberling *(Dir-Sls)*
Gene Sanderfield *(Dir-Sls)*

Key to Media (For complete agency information see *The Advertising Red Books-Agencies* edition):
1. Bus. Publs. 2. Cable T.V. 3. Catalogs & Directories. 4. Co-op Adv. 5. Consumer Mags. 6. D.M. to Bus. Estab.7. D.M. to Consumers
8. Daily Newsp. 9. Exhibits/Trade Shows 10. Foreign 11. Infomercial 12. Internet Adv.13. Multimedia 14. Network Radio
15. Network T.V. 16. Newsp. Distr. Mags. 17. Other 18. Outdoor (Posters, Transit) 19. Point of Purchase20. Premiums, Novelties
21. Product Samples 22. Special Events Mktg. 23. Spot Radio 24. Spot T.V. 25. Weekly Newsp. 26. Yellow Page Adv.

Advertising Agency:
Dan Klores Communications
(d/b/a dkc)
386 Park Ave S 10th Fl
New York, NY 10016
Tel.: (212) 685-4300
Fax: (212) 685-9024

SEATTLE PHILHARMONIC ORCHESTRA
PO Box 177
Seattle, WA 98111
Tel.: (206) 528-6878
Web Site: www.seattlephil.com
Year Founded: 1944
Business Description:
Symphony Orchestra
S.I.C.: 7929
N.A.I.C.S.: 711130
Media: 8-9-20-23-24-25
Personnel:
Joseph Gallagher *(Pres)*
Adam Stern *(Dir-Music)*
Dick Griffith *(Mgr-Personnel)*

SEATTLE SEAHAWKS
(Holding of Vulcan Sports & Entertainment LLC)
12 Seahawks Way
Renton, WA 98056
Tel.: (425) 203-8000
Toll Free: (888) 635-4295
E-mail: sales@seahawks.com
Web Site: www.seahawks.com
E-Mail For Key Personnel:
Sales Director: sales@seahawks.com
Sales Range: $100-124.9 Million
Approx. Number Employees: 200
Year Founded: 1976
Business Description:
Professional Football Franchise
S.I.C.: 7941
N.A.I.C.S.: 711211
Media: 3-8-9-10-18-20-22-23-24-25-26
Distr.: Natl.
Personnel:
Paul G. Allen *(Chm)*
Peter McLoughlin *(Pres)*
Karen Harrison *(CFO & VP-Fin)*
John Rizzardini *(COO)*
Lance Lopes *(Sr VP, Gen Counsel-Seahawks, FGI & Sounders FC)*
Ruston Webster *(VP-Player Personnel)*
Dave Pearson *(VP-Comm & Brdcst)*
Maurice Kelly *(Sr Dir-Player Dev)*
Dave Auckland *(Dir-Fin)*
Bill Chapin *(Dir-Mktg & Partnership Dev)*
Rick Crawford *(Dir-Brdcst Production Svcs & Game Presentation)*
Thom Fermstad *(Dir-Video)*
Scott Fitterer *(Dir-College Scouting)*
Lane Gammel *(Dir-Comm)*
Sandy Gregory *(Dir-Community Outreach)*
Kevin Griffin *(Dir-Community Rels)*
Sue Harris *(Dir-Retail Ops)*
Brian Jones *(Dir-Partnership Dev)*
Cindy Kelley *(Dir-HR)*
Suzanne Lavender *(Dir-Corp Comm)*
Rick Ninomiyo *(Dir-Security)*
Kenton Olson *(Dir-Digital Media & Emerging Media)*
Amy Sprangers *(Dir-Suite Sls/Svc & Corp Hospitality)*
John Wright *(Dir-Facilities & Fields)*
Mike Yowarsky *(Dir-College Scouting-Eastern Reg)*
Brad Campbell *(Asst Dir-Video)*
Sarita Carter *(Asst Dir-HR)*
Paul Johns *(Asst Dir-Community Outreach)*
Brian O'Connell *(Asst Dir-Brdcst)*
Kristina Howell Culmer *(Bus Mgr-Corp Partnerships)*
Dale Cramer *(Mgr-Facilities)*
Eric Engberg *(Mgr-Suite Sls)*
Rich Gonzales *(Mgr-Comm)*
Christy Grady *(Mgr-Partnership Dev)*
Stephanie Gray *(Mgr-Mktg)*
Erik Kennedy *(Mgr-Equipment)*
Vikki Knopf *(Mgr-Retail Ops)*
William Saguilla *(Mgr-Acctg)*
Stacey Terry *(Mgr-Database Mktg)*
Sarah Tompkins *(Mgr-Corp Hospitality)*
John Weaver *(Mgr-Graphic Design)*
Brands & Products:
SEATTLE SEAHAWKS
Advertising Agencies:
Cypress Consulting
100 S King St Ste 300
Seattle, WA 98104
Tel.: (206) 281-8240
Fax: (206) 281-8266

Edelman
2301 5th Ave Ste 500
Seattle, WA 98121-1678
Tel.: (206) 223-1606
Fax: (206) 467-7978

SEATTLE STORM
(Holding of Force 10 Hoops LLC)
3421 Thorn Dyke Ave W
Seattle, WA 98119-4153
Tel.: (206) 281-5800
Fax: (206) 281-5828
E-mail: fans@sonics-storm.com
Web Site: www.wnba.com
Year Founded: 1999
Business Description:
Professional Basketball Team
S.I.C.: 7941
N.A.I.C.S.: 711211
Media: 1-3-4-6-8-9-10-13-14-15-18-19-20-22-23-24-26
Distr.: Natl.
Personnel:
Karen Bryant *(CEO)*
Shannon Burley *(VP-Mktg)*
Brian Agler *(Head-Coach & Dir-Player Personnel)*
Missy Bequette *(Dir-Basketball Ops)*
Tricia McLean *(Dir-Fin & HR)*
Teresa Wippel *(Dir-Comm & Community Rels)*
Laura Sgrecci *(Sr Mgr-Mktg & Promotions)*
Brands & Products:
SEATTLE STORM
STORM WATCH

SEATTLE SYMPHONY ORCHESTRA
200 University St
Seattle, WA 98111-3906
Tel.: (206) 215-4700
Fax: (206) 215-4701
E-mail: info@seattlesymphony.org
Web Site: www.seattlesymphony.org
Approx. Number Employees: 150
Year Founded: 1903
Business Description:
Symphony Orchestra
S.I.C.: 7929
N.A.I.C.S.: 711130
Media: 8-9-18-20-22-23-25
Personnel:
Christie Wood *(Dir-Mktg)*
Brands & Products:
BENAROYA HALL
DISCOVER MUSIC!
S
SEATTLE POPS
SEATTLE SYMPHONY
SOUNDBRIDGE
SYMPHONEVE
SYMPHONY ON WHEELS
WOLFGANG

SEATTLE THEATRE GROUP
911 Pine St
Seattle, WA 98101
Tel.: (206) 467-5510
Fax: (206) 682-4837
E-mail: info@stgpresents.org
Web Site: www.stgpresents.org
Sales Range: $10-24.9 Million
Approx. Number Employees: 100
Business Description:
Performing Arts Organization
S.I.C.: 6512
N.A.I.C.S.: 531120
Media: 8-9-13-17-18-23-24-25
Personnel:
Clark Van Bogart *(CFO)*
David Allen *(COO)*
Josh LaBelle *(Exec Dir)*
Jason Ferguson *(Dir-Programming)*
Brian Layton *(Dir-Venues)*
Ginny Matheson *(Dir-HR)*
Mike Miles *(Dir-Tech)*
Danielle Olson *(Dir-Corp Rels)*
Ken Potts *(Dir-Mktg-Season & Major Programs)*
Jeff J. Beauvoir *(Mgr-Box Office)*
Amanda Bedeoo *(Mgr-PR)*

SEAWORLD CALIFORNIA
(Unit of SeaWorld Parks & Entertainment LLC)
500 Sea World Dr
San Diego, CA 92109-7904
Tel.: (619) 226-3682
Tel.: (619) 226-3982
Fax: (619) 226-3996
Telex: 910 335 1184
Web Site: www.seaworld.com
Approx. Sls.: $12,000,000
Approx. Number Employees: 4,000
Year Founded: 1964
Business Description:
Theme Park & Zoo
S.I.C.: 7996; 0273; 8422
N.A.I.C.S.: 713110; 112519; 712130
Import
Media: 2-4-5-6-7-8-9-10-18-19-20-24-25-26
Distr.: Direct to Consumer; Reg.
Budget Set: Nov.

SEAWORLD FLORIDA
(Unit of SeaWorld Parks & Entertainment LLC)
7007 SeaWorld Dr
Orlando, FL 32821-8009
Tel.: (407) 351-3600
Tel.: (407) 370-1562
Fax: (407) 363-2256
Toll Free: (888) 800-5447
Web Site: www.seaworld.com
Sales Range: $350-399.9 Million
Approx. Number Employees: 3,000
Year Founded: 1973
Business Description:
Theme Park & Zoo
S.I.C.: 7996; 8422
N.A.I.C.S.: 713110; 712130
Media: 2-3-4-5-6-7-8-9-10-11-17-18-19-23-24-25-26
Distr.: Direct to Consumer; Reg.
Budget Set: Aug.
Advertising Agency:
DDB Chicago
200 E Randolph St
Chicago, IL 60601
Tel.: (312) 552-6000
Fax: (312) 552-2370
(Sea World Theme Park)

SEAWORLD PARKS & ENTERTAINMENT LLC
(Holding of The Blackstone Group L.P.)
9205 S Park Ctr Loop Ste 400
Orlando, FL 32819
Tel.: (407) 226-5210
Fax: (407) 226-5019
Web Site: www.seaworld.com
E-Mail For Key Personnel:
Public Relations: fred.jacobs@anheuser-busch.com
Sales Range: $1-4.9 Billion
Approx. Number Employees: 25,000
Year Founded: 1979
Business Description:
Theme Parks Operator
S.I.C.: 7996
N.A.I.C.S.: 713110
Media: 3-5-6-9-11-12-13-15-18-22-23-24-25
Distr.: Natl.
Personnel:
Jim Atchison *(Pres & CEO)*
Joseph A. Couceiro *(CMO)*
Bradley F. Andrews *(Pres-Zoological Ops)*
John T. Reilly *(Exec VP & Gen Mgr)*
David L. Hammer *(Exec VP-HR)*
James B. Dean *(VP-Retail)*
Steven L. Glashower *(VP-Engrg & Creative Dept)*
Fred Jacobs *(VP-Comm)*
Daniel J. Decker *(Gen Mgr)*
Andrew P. Fichthorn *(Gen Mgr)*
Advertising Agencies:
BFG Communications
6 Anolyn Ct
Bluffton, SC 29910
Tel.: (843) 837-9115
Fax: (843) 837-9225

DDB Chicago
200 E Randolph St
Chicago, IL 60601
Tel.: (312) 552-6000
Fax: (312) 552-2370
(Adventure Island, Busch Gardens Tampa & Williamsburg, Cypress Gardens, Sea World of Florida & Ohio, Sesame Place, Water Country U.S.A., National Sales)

SEAWORLD TEXAS
(Unit of SeaWorld Parks & Entertainment LLC)
10500 SeaWorld Dr
San Antonio, TX 78251-3001

Key to Media (For complete agency information see *The Advertising Red Books-Agencies* edition):
1. Bus. Publs. 2. Cable T.V. 3. Catalogs & Directories. 4. Co-op Adv. 5. Consumer Mags. 6. D.M. to Bus. Estab.7. D.M. to Consumers
8. Daily Newsp. 9. Exhibits/Trade Shows 10. Foreign 11. Infomercial 12. Internet Adv.13. Multimedia 14. Network Radio
15. Network T.V. 16. Newsp. Distr. Mags. 17. Other 18. Outdoor (Posters, Transit) 19. Point of Purchase20. Premiums, Novelties
21. Product Samples 22. Special Events Mktg. 23. Spot Radio 24. Spot T.V. 25. Weekly Newsp. 26. Yellow Page Adv.

SeaWorld Texas — (Continued)

Tel.: (210) 523-3600
Tel.: (210) 523-3198
Fax: (210) 523-3130
Sales Range: $400-449.9 Million
Approx. Number Employees: 2,300
Year Founded: 1988
Business Description:
Theme Park & Zoo
S.I.C.: 7996; 0273; 8422
N.A.I.C.S.: 713110; 112519; 712130
Advertising Expenditures: $5,000,000
Media: 2-4-5-6-7-8-9-17-18-19-23-24-25-26
Distr.: Direct to Consumer; Reg.
Personnel:
Daniel J. Decker *(Pres-Park)*
Bob Wetesnik *(VP-Fin)*

SENECA PARK ZOOLOGICAL SOCIETY
2222 Saint Paul St
Rochester, NY 14621-1097
Tel.: (585) 336-7200
Fax: (585) 342-1477
Web Site: www.senecaparkzoo.org
Approx. Number Employees: 50
Business Description:
Zoo
S.I.C.: 8422
N.A.I.C.S.: 712130
Media: 9-10-20-23-24-25
Personnel:
David Riedman *(Pres)*
Rachel Baker August *(Exec Dir)*
Larry Sorel *(Dir-Seneca Park Zoo)*

SESAME PLACE
(Unit of SeaWorld Parks & Entertainment LLC)
100 Sesame Rd
Langhorne, PA 19047-1821
Mailing Address:
PO Box L979
Langhorne, PA 19047-1821
Tel.: (215) 752-7070
Fax: (215) 741-5307
E-mail: guestcomments@sesameplace.com
Web Site: www.sesameplace.com
Sales Range: $10-24.9 Million
Approx. Number Employees: 70
Business Description:
Theme Park
S.I.C.: 7996
N.A.I.C.S.: 713110
Media: 6-18-22-23-24
Personnel:
Donnie Mills *(COO)*
Robert J. Caruso *(Exec VP & Gen Mgr)*

SGE GAMING
5125 W Oquendo Rd Ste 6
Las Vegas, NV 89118
Tel.: (702) 914-9900
Fax: (702) 914-9911
E-mail: info@sgti.com
Web Site: www.sgti.com
Approx. Number Employees: 12
Business Description:
Toys & Games Developer & Sales
S.I.C.: 5092
N.A.I.C.S.: 423920
Media: 4-17
Personnel:
Allen Legator *(Pres)*

THE SHAKESPEARE THEATRE, INC.
516 8th St SE
Washington, DC 20003-2834
Tel.: (202) 547-3230
Fax: (202) 547-0226
Toll Free: (877) 487-8849
E-mail: webadmin@shakespeartheatre.org
Web Site:
www.shakespearetheatre.org
Approx. Sls.: $13,954,558
Approx. Number Employees: 140
Business Description:
Theatrical Companies
S.I.C.: 7922
N.A.I.C.S.: 711110
Media: 8-9-10-18-23-24-25
Personnel:
Robert E. Falb *(Vice Chm)*
Chris Jennings *(Mng Dir)*
Michael Kahn *(Dir-Artistic)*
Darby Lunceford *(Dir-Mktg & Comm)*
Mark Prey *(Dir-Technical)*
James Roemer *(Dir-Admin)*
Samantha Wyer *(Dir-Education)*
Genevieve Cooper *(Assoc Dir-Production)*
Kimberley Mauldin *(Mgr-HR)*

SHEBOYGAN SYMPHONY ORCHESTRA INC.
921 N 8th St Ste 208
Sheboygan, WI 53081
Tel.: (920) 452-1985
Fax: (920) 452-0165
E-mail: shebsym@sheboygansymphony.org
Web Site:
www.sheboygansymphony.org
Sales Range: Less than $1 Million
Approx. Number Employees: 2
Year Founded: 1918
Business Description:
Symphony Orchestra
S.I.C.: 8641; 7929
N.A.I.C.S.: 813410; 711130
Media: 9-13-18-23-25
Personnel:
eric johnson *(Mng Dir)*

SHREVEPORT SYMPHONY ORCHESTRA
619 Louisiana Ave Ste 400
Shreveport, LA 71101
Tel.: (318) 222-7496
Fax: (318) 222-7490
E-mail: info@shreveportsymphony.com
Web Site:
www.shreveportsymphony.com
Approx. Number Employees: 40
Business Description:
Symphony Orchestra
S.I.C.: 7929
N.A.I.C.S.: 711130
Media: 9-20-22-23-24-25
Personnel:
Susan R. Perry *(Dir-Fin)*
Scott Green *(Exec Dir)*
Shirley Handler *(Reg Dir)*
Michael Butterman *(Dir-Music & Conductor)*
Janice Nelson *(Dir-Ops & Education)*
Kermit Poling *(Dir-Music)*
Lester Senter Wilson *(Dir)*
Daphne Cates *(Mgr-Box Office)*
Susan W. Rogers *(Mgr-Personnel)*
Jenifer Akers *(Coord-Dev)*

SIGNATURES NETWORK, INC.
(Sub. of Live Nation Entertainment, Inc.)
2 Bryant St Ste 300
San Francisco, CA 94105
Tel.: (415) 247-7400
E-mail: info@signaturenetworks.com
Web Site:
www.signaturesnetwork.com
Sales Range: $25-49.9 Million
Approx. Number Employees: 70
Year Founded: 1999
Business Description:
Music Merchandise Licensing Services
S.I.C.: 6794
N.A.I.C.S.: 533110
Media: 22
Personnel:
Phil Cussen *(Pres & COO)*
Dell Furano *(CEO)*
Myles Silton *(Gen Counsel & Sr VP-Bus Affairs)*
Rick Fish *(Exec VP-Artist Rels)*
Pete Weber *(Sr VP-Tour & Event Ops)*

SILVER SPRINGS, INC.
(Sub. of Palace Entertainment Holdings, Inc.)
5656 E Silver Springs Blvd
Silver Springs, FL 34488
Tel.: (352) 236-2121
Fax: (352) 236-1732
E-mail: ssinfo@silversprings.com
Web Site: www.silversprings.com
Approx. Number Employees: 550
Year Founded: 1878
Business Description:
Family Entertainment Parks
S.I.C.: 7996; 7999
N.A.I.C.S.: 713110; 713990
Advertising Expenditures: $2,177,000
Media: 2-3-4-7-8-9-10-13-18-19-20-22-23-24-25
Distr.: Natl.
Budget Set: Sept.
Personnel:
Terry Turner *(Gen Mgr)*

SIOUX CITY SYMPHONY ORCHESTRA
520 Pierce St Ste 375
Sioux City, IA 51101
Tel.: (712) 277-2111
Fax: (712) 252-0224
E-mail: info@siouxcitysymphony.org
Web Site:
www.siouxcitysymphony.org
Approx. Number Employees: 4
Business Description:
Symphony Orchestra
S.I.C.: 7929
N.A.I.C.S.: 711130
Media: 9-20-23-24-25
Personnel:
Trinette Patterson *(Office Mgr & Mgr-Box Office)*
Dick Bogenrief *(Mgr-Ops)*

SIX FLAGS ENTERTAINMENT CORP.
924 Ave J E
Grand Prairie, TX 75050
Tel.: (972) 595-5000
E-mail: investors@sftp.com
Web Site: www.sixflags.com
Approx. Rev.: $975,889,000
Approx. Number Employees: 1,900
Year Founded: 1961
Business Description:
Theme Parks Owner & Operator
S.I.C.: 7996
N.A.I.C.S.: 713110
Advertising Expenditures: $91,456,000
Media: 3-5-6-7-8-9-11-13-14-15-18-19-20-22-23-24-25
Distr.: Reg.
Personnel:
James W.P. Reid-Anderson *(Chm, Pres & CEO)*
John M. Duffey *(CFO)*
Alexander Weber, Jr. *(COO)*
Michael S. Israel *(CIO & Sr VP)*
Leonard A. Russ *(Chief Acctg Officer & VP)*
Lance C. Balk *(Gen Counsel)*
Thomas Iven *(Sr VP-Park Ops-West Coast)*
John Odum *(Sr VP-Park Ops-East Coast)*
John E. Bement *(Sr VP-In-Park Svcs)*
Walter S. Hawrylak *(Sr VP-Admin)*
Nancy A. Krejsa *(Sr VP-IR & Corp Comm)*
David McKillips *(Sr VP-Corp Alliances)*
Brett Petit *(Sr VP-Mktg)*
Brands & Products:
FRONTIER CITY
GREAT ESCAPE
SIX FLAGS
SIX FLAGS AMERICA
SIX FLAGS ASTROWORLD
SIX FLAGS DARIEN LAKE
SIX FLAGS DISCOVERY KINGDOM
SIX FLAGS DUBAILAND
SIX FLAGS ELITCH GARDENS
SIX FLAGS FIESTA TEXAS
SIX FLAGS GREAT ADVENTURE
SIX FLAGS GREAT AMERICA
SIX FLAGS HURRICANE HARBOR
SIX FLAGS KENTUCKY KINGDOM
SIX FLAGS MAGIC MOUNTAIN
SIX FLAGS MARINE WORLD
SIX FLAGS NEW ENGLAND
SIX FLAGS NEW ORLEANS
SIX FLAGS OVER GEORGIA
SIX FLAGS OVER TEXAS
SIX FLAGS ST. LOUIS
SIX FLAGS WHITE WATER
SIX FLAGS WILD SAFARI
SPLASHTOWN - HOUSTON
WATERWORLD CONCORD
WATERWORLD SACRAMENTO
WHITE WATER - ATLANTA
WHITE WATER BAY
WYANDOT LAKE
Advertising Agencies:
Bennett Kuhn Varner, Inc.
3390 Peachtree Rd 10th Fl
Atlanta, GA 30326
Tel.: (404) 233-0332
Fax: (404) 233-0302

Don Jagoda Associates, Inc.
100 Marcus Dr
Melville, NY 11747-4229
Tel.: (631) 454-1800
Fax: (631) 454-1834

Key to Media (For complete agency information see *The Advertising Red Books-Agencies* edition):
1. Bus. Publs. 2. Cable T.V. 3. Catalogs & Directories. 4. Co-op Adv. 5. Consumer Mags. 6. D.M. to Bus. Estab.7. D.M. to Consumers
8. Daily Newsp. 9. Exhibits/Trade Shows 10. Foreign 11. Infomercial 12. Internet Adv.13. Multimedia 14. Network Radio
15. Network T.V. 16. Newsp. Distr. Mags. 17. Other 18. Outdoor (Posters, Transit) 19. Point of Purchase20. Premiums, Novelties
21. Product Samples 22. Special Events Mktg. 23. Spot Radio 24. Spot T.V. 25. Weekly Newsp. 26. Yellow Page Adv.

SIX FLAGS GREAT ADVENTURE LLC
(Sub. of Six Flags Theme Parks Inc.)
Rte 537
Jackson, NJ 08527
Mailing Address:
PO Box 120
Jackson, NJ 08527-0120
Tel.: (732) 928-1821
Fax: (732) 928-2092
E-mail: info@sixflags.com
Web Site: www.sixflags.com/parks/greatadventure
Sales Range: $50-74.9 Million
Approx. Number Employees: 375
Year Founded: 1977
Business Description:
Theme Park
S.I.C.: 7996
N.A.I.C.S.: 713110
Import
Advertising Expenditures: $500,000
Media: 3-4-5-7-8-9-10-13-19-22-23-24-25
Distr.: Reg.
Budget Set: Nov.

SIX FLAGS GREAT AMERICA, INC.
(Sub. of Six Flags Theme Parks Inc.)
1 Great American Pkwy 542 N Route 21
Gurnee, IL 60031-0776
Tel.: (847) 249-4636
Tel.: (847) 249-1776
Fax: (847) 249-9166
Web Site: www.sixflags.com/parks/greatamerica
Sales Range: $50-74.9 Million
Approx. Number Employees: 250
Business Description:
Amusement Theme Park
S.I.C.: 7996
N.A.I.C.S.: 713110
Media: 2-3-4-7-8-9-10-11-13-16-18-20-22-23-24-25
Distr.: Direct to Consumer; Reg.
Budget Set: Mar.
Advertising Agency:
Zimmerman Advertising
2 Mid America Plz Ste 510
Oakbrook Terrace, IL 60181-1937
Tel.: (630) 574-1059
Fax: (630) 472-3148
— Ralph Carey *(Acct Exec)*

SIX FLAGS MAGIC MOUNTAIN & HURRICANE HARBOR
(Sub. of Six Flags Theme Parks Inc.)
26101 Magic Mountain Pkwy
Valencia, CA 91355-1052
Mailing Address:
PO Box 5500
Valencia, CA 91385-5500
Tel.: (661) 255-4111
Fax: (661) 255-4815
Fax: (661) 255-4701
Web Site: www.sixflags.com/magicmountain
Sales Range: $400-449.9 Million
Approx. Number Employees: 3,000
Year Founded: 1971
Business Description:
Family Theme Park
S.I.C.: 7996; 7389
N.A.I.C.S.: 713110; 711320
Media: 3-5-6-7-8-9-10-13-18-20-23-24
Distr.: Reg.
Budget Set: Nov. -Aug.

SIX FLAGS OVER GEORGIA, INC.
(Sub. of Six Flags Theme Parks Inc.)
275 Riverside Pkwy SW
Austell, GA 30168
Tel.: (770) 948-9290
Tel.: (770) 739-3400 (Administrative)
Tel.: (770) 739-3410 (Employment)
Fax: (770) 819-8256
E-mail: info@sixflags.com
Web Site: www.sixflags.com
Sales Range: $25-49.9 Million
Approx. Number Employees: 100
Business Description:
Theme Park
S.I.C.: 7996
N.A.I.C.S.: 713110
Advertising Expenditures: $500,000
Media: 7-8-9-23-24
Distr.: Intl.; Natl.
Budget Set: Dec.
Personnel:
Melinda Ashcraft *(Pres)*
Stephen Heard *(Dir-Sls)*
Trvor Leonard *(Dir-White Water-American Adventures)*
Jehan Gliksman *(Mgr-Adv & Promotions)*
Advertising Agency:
BKV Inc.
10561 Barkley St Ste 200
Overland Park, KS 66212
Tel.: (913) 648-8333
Fax: (913) 648-5024

SIX FLAGS OVER TEXAS, INC.
(Sub. of Six Flags Theme Parks Inc.)
2201 Road To Six Flags
Arlington, TX 76011-5157
Mailing Address:
PO Box 90191
Arlington, TX 76004-3191
Tel.: (817) 640-8900
Fax: (817) 607-6144
Web Site: www.sixflags.com
Sales Range: $50-74.9 Million
Approx. Number Employees: 270
Year Founded: 1961
Business Description:
Theme Park
S.I.C.: 7996; 7999
N.A.I.C.S.: 713110; 713990
Media: 3-6-7-8-9-13-18-23-24-25
Distr.: Reg.
Budget Set: Oct.
Personnel:
Steve Martindale *(Pres-Park)*
Jim Brothers *(Dir-Mktg)*
Jonette Daggs *(Dir-Sls)*
Jan Weenick *(Mgr-Adv & Promos)*
Brands & Products:
SIX FLAGS

SIX FLAGS SAINT LOUIS LLC
(Sub. of Six Flags Theme Parks Inc.)
4900 6 Flags Rd
Eureka, MO 63025
Mailing Address:
PO Box 60
Eureka, MO 63025-0060
Tel.: (636) 938-5300
Fax: (636) 587-3617
E-mail: info@sixflags.com
Web Site: www.sixflags.com/parks/stlouis
Sales Range: $25-49.9 Million
Approx. Number Employees: 125
Year Founded: 1971
Business Description:
Family Entertainment Theme Park
S.I.C.: 7996; 7999
N.A.I.C.S.: 713110; 713990
Media: 3-5-8-9-13-18-19-20-23-24-25-26
Distr.: Reg.
Budget Set: Oct.
Personnel:
Dave Roemer *(Pres)*
Advertising Agency:
Zimmerman Advertising
2 Mid America Plz Ste 510
Oakbrook Terrace, IL 60181-1937
Tel.: (630) 574-1059
Fax: (630) 472-3148

SIX FLAGS THEME PARKS INC.
(Sub. of Six Flags Entertainment Corp.)
924 E Ave J
Grand Prairie, TX 75050-2622
Tel.: (972) 595-5000
Fax: (972) 641-0323
E-mail: info@sixflags.com
Web Site: www.sixflags.com
Sales Range: $25-49.9 Million
Approx. Number Employees: 100
Year Founded: 1961
Business Description:
Operator of Amusement Parks & Water Parks
S.I.C.: 7996
N.A.I.C.S.: 713110
Media: 3-5-6-7-8-9-10-13-15-18-20
Distr.: Natl.
Personnel:
Michael S. Israel *(CIO & Sr VP)*
Advertising Agency:
Zimmerman Advertising
2 Mid America Plz Ste 510
Oakbrook Terrace, IL 60181-1937
Tel.: (630) 574-1059
Fax: (630) 472-3148

SKYLINE GROUP, INC.
(d/b/a Skyline Caverns)
10344 Stonewall Jackson Hwy
Front Royal, VA 22630-5110
Tel.: (540) 635-4545
Fax: (540) 636-8059
Toll Free: (800) 296-4545
E-mail: info@skylinecaverns.com
Web Site: www.skylinecaverns.com
Approx. Number Employees: 25
Year Founded: 1937
Business Description:
Tourist Attraction
S.I.C.: 7999; 5947
N.A.I.C.S.: 712190; 453220
Advertising Expenditures: $100,000
Media: 4-5-8-10-15-18
Distr.: Direct to Consumer; Reg.
Budget Set: Nov.
Personnel:
Lowell B. Baughan *(Pres)*
Brands & Products:
EPIC ADVENTURE
SKYLINE CAVERNS

SMSC ENTERPRISES
(d/b/a Mystic Lake Casino Hotel)
2400 Mystic Lake Blvd
Prior Lake, MN 55372
Tel.: (952) 445-9000
Fax: (952) 496-7199
Toll Free: (800) 262-7799
E-mail: marketing@mysticlake.com
Web Site: www.mysticlake.com
Sales Range: $350-399.9 Million
Approx. Number Employees: 4,000
Year Founded: 1981
Business Description:
Casino Operator
S.I.C.: 7999; 7011
N.A.I.C.S.: 713290; 721120
Media: 8-9-18-22-23-24
Distr.: Natl.
Personnel:
Stan Crooks *(Chm)*
Kelley Thomas-Reis *(Dir-Mktg)*

THE SOUND SYMPHONY
20 Nevinwood Pl
Huntington Station, NY 11746
Tel.: (631) 549-3881
Fax: (631) 271-5742
E-mail: mail@soundsymphony.org
Web Site: www.soundsymphony.org
Approx. Number Employees: 4
Business Description:
Symphony Orchestra
S.I.C.: 7929
N.A.I.C.S.: 711130
Media: 9-20-23-24-25
Personnel:
Daniel F. Millheiser *(Chm)*
John DeWitt *(Principal)*
Dorothy Savitch *(Dir-Music)*
Jennifer Haley *(Mgr-Personnel)*

SOUTH CAROLINA PHILHARMONIC ASSOCIATION INC.
721 Lady St Ste B
Columbia, SC 29201
Tel.: (803) 771-7937
Fax: (803) 771-0268
E-mail: info@scphilharmonic.com
Web Site: www.scphilharmonic.com
E-Mail For Key Personnel:
Public Relations: jasonrapp@scphilharmonic.com
Approx. Number Employees: 100
Business Description:
Symphony Orchestra Services
S.I.C.: 7929
N.A.I.C.S.: 711130
Media: 8-9-13-20-23-24-25
Personnel:
Thomas R. Gottshall *(Pres)*
Rhonda P. Hunsinger *(Exec Dir)*
Jason Rapp *(Dir-Comm & Mgr-Box Office)*
Maurice Hood *(Mgr-Personnel)*
John L. Hunsinger, II *(Mgr-Production & Stage)*
Judith Lawrence *(Mgr-Youth Orchestra)*

SOUTH DAKOTA SYMPHONY ORCHESTRA
315 N Main Ave Ste 204
Sioux Falls, SD 57104
Tel.: (605) 335-7933
Fax: (605) 335-1958
Toll Free: (866) 681-7376
E-mail: sdsymphony@sdsymphony.org
Web Site: www.sdsymphony.org
Sales Range: $50-74.9 Million
Approx. Number Employees: 45

Key to Media (For complete agency information see *The Advertising Red Books-Agencies* edition):
1. Bus. Publs. 2. Cable T.V. 3. Catalogs & Directories. 4. Co-op Adv. 5. Consumer Mags. 6. D.M. to Bus. Estab.7. D.M. to Consumers 8. Daily Newsp. 9. Exhibits/Trade Shows 10. Foreign 11. Infomercial 12. Internet Adv.13. Multimedia 14. Network Radio 15. Network T.V. 16. Newsp. Distr. Mags. 17. Other 18. Outdoor (Posters, Transit) 19. Point of Purchase20. Premiums, Novelties 21. Product Samples 22. Special Events Mktg. 23. Spot Radio 24. Spot T.V. 25. Weekly Newsp. 26. Yellow Page Adv.

South Dakota Symphony Orchestra — (Continued)

Business Description:
Symphony Orchestra
S.I.C.: 7389
N.A.I.C.S.: 711320
Media: 9-20-22-23-24-25
Personnel:
Tom Bennett *(CEO)*
Linda Clement *(Dir-Dev)*
Delta David Gier *(Dir-Music & Conductor)*
Sue Sidoti *(Mgr-Personnel)*

SOUTH FLORIDA MUSEUM

201 10th St W
Bradenton, FL 34205
Tel.: (941) 746-4131
Fax: (941) 747-2556
E-mail: info@southfloridamuseum.org
Web Site:
www.southfloridamuseum.org
Approx. Number Employees: 30
Business Description:
Museum
S.I.C.: 8412; 8422
N.A.I.C.S.: 712110; 712130
Media: 8-9-20-23-24-25
Personnel:
Brynne Anne Besio *(Exec Dir)*
Kelly Foster *(Dir-Mktg)*

SOUTHWEST FLORIDA SYMPHONY

12651 McGregor Blvd Bldg 4-403
Fort Myers, FL 33919
Tel.: (239) 418-0996
Fax: (239) 418-0725
E-mail: info@swflso.org
Web Site: www.swflso.org
Approx. Number Employees: 10
Year Founded: 1961
Business Description:
Symphony Orchestra
S.I.C.: 7929
N.A.I.C.S.: 711130
Media: 9-20-23-24-25
Personnel:
Christine Lacroix *(Pres)*
Francis H. Goldman *(Exec Dir)*
Tiffany Heck *(Dir-Devel)*
Heidi Kelley *(Dir-Mktg)*
Alex Albanese *(Mgr-Opers & Personnel)*

SPEEDWAY MOTORSPORTS, INC.

5555 Concord Pkwy S
Concord, NC 28027
Tel.: (704) 455-3239
Fax: (704) 455-2168
E-mail: invrelations@lowesmotorspeedway.com
Web Site:
www.speedwaymotorsports.com
Approx. Rev.: $502,243,000
Approx. Number Employees: 791
Year Founded: 1994
Business Description:
Holding Company; Motorsports Racetrack Owner & Operator
S.I.C.: 6719; 7948
N.A.I.C.S.: 551112; 711212
Advertising Expenditures: $18,790,000
Media: 22
Personnel:
O. Bruton Smith *(Chm & CEO)*
William R. Brooks *(Vice Chm, CFO, Treas & Exec VP)*
Marcus G. Smith *(Pres & COO)*
Brands & Products:
ATLANTA MOTOR SPEEDWAY
ATOMIC OIL
AUTOFAIR
AVBLEND
BANDOLERO
BLUEGRASS CLUB
BRISTOL MOTOR SPEEDWAY
CHARLOTTE MOTOR SPEEDWAY
DIESEL 40- THE ENGINE CONDITIONER
FANS FIRST
INFINEON RACEWAY
IT SOAKS INTO METAL
KENTUCKY CLUB
KENTUCKY SPEEDWAY
LAS VEGAS MOTOR SPEEDWAY
LEGENDS CARE
LENCKITE
LINKITE
LUG NUT
MICRO-LUBRICANT
MOTORSPORTS BY MAIL
NEW HAMPSHIRE MOTOR SPEEDWAY
PERFORMANCE RACING NETWORK
POUR A NEW ENGINE INTO YOUR CAR
SEARS POINT RACEWAY
SPARKY
THE SPEEDWAY CLUB
TEXAS MOTOR SPEEDWAY
TMS
TOP OF THE COP
WBL
WILD MAN
ZMAX
Advertising Agency:
The Tombras Group
630 Concord St
Knoxville, TN 37919-3305
Tel.: (865) 524-5376
Fax: (865) 524-5667

SPOKANE SYMPHONY ORCHESTRA

1001 W Sprague Ave
Spokane, WA 99201
Tel.: (509) 624-1200
Web Site:
www.spokanesymphony.org
Approx. Number Employees: 100
Year Founded: 1945
Business Description:
Symphony Orchestra
S.I.C.: 7929
N.A.I.C.S.: 711130
Advertising Expenditures: $50,000
Media: 7-8-9-13-20-22-23-24-25
Personnel:
Ronald P. Stanley *(Pres)*
Dori Clark *(VP-Pub Rels)*
Donald Nelson *(Gen Mgr)*
Brenda Nienhouse *(Exec Dir)*
Annie Matlow *(Dir-Mktg & PR)*
Eckart Preu *(Dir-Music)*
Clint Burgess *(Mgr-Comm)*
Gale Coffee *(Mgr-Personnel)*
Charles Karschney *(Mgr-Production)*
Brands & Products:
SPOKANE SYMPHONY
SYMFUNNIES

SPOLETO FESTIVAL USA

14 George St
Charleston, SC 29401
Tel.: (843) 722-2764
Fax: (843) 723-6383
Web Site: www.spoletousa.org
Approx. Number Employees: 16
Year Founded: 1977
Business Description:
Festival Operation
S.I.C.: 7999
N.A.I.C.S.: 713990
Media: 13-20-22
Personnel:
Martha R. Ingram *(Chm)*
Paula Edwards *(Dir-Media-PR)*
Joseph Flummerfelt *(Dir-Artistic)*
Julia Forster *(Dir-Devel)*
Tasha Gandy *(Dir-Fin)*
J. R. English *(Mgr-Acctg)*
Katie Kinard *(Mgr-Box Office)*
Stephanie Steele *(Mgr-Writing & Res)*
Rhys Williams *(Mgr-Production)*
Susie Prueter *(Asst Mgr-Production)*
David Graham *(Volunteer Coord)*
Nunally Kersh *(Producer)*

THE SPORTS CLUB COMPANY, INC.

1835 Sepulveda Blvd
Los Angeles, CA 90025
Tel.: (310) 473-1447
Web Site: www.thesportsclubla.com/site/showpage.php?id=11
Sales Range: $50-74.9 Million
Approx. Number Employees: 2,619
Year Founded: 1989
Business Description:
Sports & Fitness Clubs Developer & Operator
S.I.C.: 7991
N.A.I.C.S.: 713940
Advertising Expenditures: $733,000
Media: 3-6-8-14-15-22-23-24
Personnel:
Nanette Pattee Francini *(Founder & Pres)*
D. Michael Talla *(Chm)*
Rex A. Licklider *(CEO)*
Brands & Products:
THE SPORTS CLUB/LA

SPORTSNET NEW YORK, LLC

(Joint Venture of Comcast Corporation, Sterling Equities, Inc. & Time Warner Cable Inc.)
75 Rockefeller Plz
New York, NY 10019
Tel.: (212) 485-4800
Fax: (212) 485-4803
E-mail: info@sny.tv
Web Site: www.sny.tv
Sales Range: $25-49.9 Million
Approx. Number Employees: 50
Year Founded: 2006
Business Description:
Regional Sports Television Network; Owned by Sterling Entertainment Enterprises, LLC, Comcast Corp. & Time Warner Cable Inc.
S.I.C.: 4833; 4841
N.A.I.C.S.: 515120; 515210
Personnel:
Gary Morgenstern *(Sr VP-Programming)*
Steve Raab *(VP-Mktg & Bus Dev)*
Scott Weinfeld *(VP-Fin & Admin)*
Advertising Agency:
Cornerstone Promotion, Inc.
71 W 23rd St Fl 13
New York, NY 10010
Tel.: (212) 741-7100
Fax: (212) 741-4747
SNY Invitational

SPRINGFIELD SYMPHONY ASSOCIATION, INC.

411 N Sherman Pkwy
Springfield, MO 65802
Tel.: (417) 864-6683
Fax: (417) 864-8967
E-mail: info@springfieldmosymphony.org
Web Site:
www.springfieldmosymphony.org
Approx. Number Employees: 25
Business Description:
Symphony Orchestra
S.I.C.: 8399
N.A.I.C.S.: 813319
Media: 9-20-23-24-25
Personnel:
Janice Bennett *(Exec Dir)*
Ron Spigelman *(Dir-Music & Conductor)*

SPRINGFIELD SYMPHONY ORCHESTRA

300 S Fountain Ave
Springfield, OH 45506
Tel.: (937) 325-8100
Fax: (937) 325-2299
E-mail: info@springfieldsym.org
Web Site: www.springfieldsym.org
Sales Range: Less than $1 Million
Approx. Number Employees: 70
Business Description:
Symphony Orchestra
S.I.C.: 7929
N.A.I.C.S.: 711130
Media: 9-20-23-24-25
Personnel:
David Deitrick *(Exec Dir)*
Peter Stafford Wilson *(Dir-Music)*
Robyn Zimmann *(SSO Asst Principal-Hornist & Dir-SSO Ops & Education)*

ST. LOUIS BLUES HOCKEY CLUB, LLC

(Holding of SCP Worldwide)
1401 Clark Ave
Saint Louis, MO 63103-2700
Tel.: (314) 622-2500
Fax: (314) 622-2582
E-mail: Info@stlblues.com
Web Site: www.blues.nhl.com
Approx. Number Employees: 100
Year Founded: 1967
Business Description:
Professional Hockey Franchise
S.I.C.: 7941
N.A.I.C.S.: 711211
Media: 8-9-13-19-20-22-23-24
Distr.: Natl.
Budget Set: July
Personnel:
David W. Checketts *(Chm & Governor)*
David Bullock *(CMO & Exec VP)*
John Davidson *(Pres-Hockey Ops & Alternate Governor)*

Key to Media (For complete agency information see *The Advertising Red Books-Agencies* edition):
1. Bus. Publs. 2. Cable T.V. 3. Catalogs & Directories. 4. Co-op Adv. 5. Consumer Mags. 6. D.M. to Bus. Estab.7. D.M. to Consumers 8. Daily Newsp. 9. Exhibits/Trade Shows 10. Foreign 11. Infomercial 12. Internet Adv.13. Multimedia 14. Network Radio 15. Network T.V. 16. Newsp. Distr. Mags. 17. Other 18. Outdoor (Posters, Transit) 19. Point of Purchase20. Premiums, Novelties 21. Product Samples 22. Special Events Mktg. 23. Spot Radio 24. Spot T.V. 25. Weekly Newsp. 26. Yellow Page Adv.

Doug Armstrong *(Exec VP & Gen Mgr)*
Mark Toffolo *(Exec VP-Corp & Sponsorship Sls)*
Todd Lambert *(Sr VP-Sls)*
Michael McCarthy *(Sr VP-Bus Dev-SCP-Worldwide)*
Phil Siddle *(Sr VP-Fin & Admin)*
Eric Stisser *(Sr VP-Bus Dev)*
Karrie Yager *(Sr VP-Mktg)*
Michael Caruso *(VP-PR)*
Jarmo Kekalainen *(Asst Gen Mgr & Dir-Amateur Scouting)*
Jennifer Nevins *(Sr Dir-Grp Sls)*
Chris Frome *(Dir-Event Presentation)*
Don Newman *(Dir-Event Ops)*
George Pavlik *(Dir-Retail)*
Jessica Reid Bateman *(Asst Dir-Guest Svcs)*

Brands & Products:
SAINT LOUIS BLUES

Advertising Agency:
Schupp Company, Inc.
401 Pine St
Saint Louis, MO 63102-2731
Tel.: (314) 421-5200
Fax: (314) 421-5554

ST. LOUIS PHILHARMONIC ORCHESTRA

PO Box 220537
Saint Louis, MO 63122
Tel.: (314) 421-3600
E-mail: info@stphilharmonic.org
Web Site: www.stlphilharmonic.org
Business Description:
Symphony Orchestra
S.I.C.: 7929
N.A.I.C.S.: 711130
Media: 9-20-23-24-25
Personnel:
Marilyn K. Humiston *(Pres)*
David Lyon *(Treas)*

ST. LOUIS SYMPHONY ORCHESTRA

718 N Grand Blvd
Saint Louis, MO 63103
Tel.: (314) 533-2500
Fax: (314) 286-4142
Web Site: www.slso.org
Sales Range: $25-49.9 Million
Approx. Number Employees: 77
Business Description:
Symphony Orchestra
S.I.C.: 7929
N.A.I.C.S.: 711130
Media: 9-18-20-23-24-25
Personnel:
Ned O. Lemkemeier *(Chm)*
James Garrone *(CFO)*
Joanna Robertson *(VP-Mktg)*
Dale Fisher *(Mgr-Web & Multimedia)*

Brands & Products:
IN UNISON

ST. PETE TIMES FORUM

(Unit of Lightning Hockey LP)
401 Channelside Dr
Tampa, FL 33602
Tel.: (813) 276-7300
Fax: (813) 301-1480
Web Site: www.sptimesforum.com
Year Founded: 1995
Business Description:
Sports & Entertainment Arena Operator
S.I.C.: 7389
N.A.I.C.S.: 711310
Media: 9-18-22-23-24
Personnel:
Bruce Ground *(Gen Mgr)*
Tony Castillo *(Mgr-Facility Patrol)*
Ricardo Collado *(Mgr-Bus Ops)*
Amy Ford *(Mgr-Facility Svcs)*
Jenna Lemons *(Mgr-Platinum Svcs)*
Tripp Turbiville *(Mgr-Front of House)*

ST. PETERSBURG FESTIVAL OF STATES

147 2nd S Ste 306
Saint Petersburg, FL 33701
Tel.: (727) 821-9888
Fax: (727) 821-9880
E-mail: info@festivalofstates.com
Web Site: www.festivalofstates.com
Approx. Number Employees: 3
Business Description:
Festival
S.I.C.: 7999
N.A.I.C.S.: 713990
Media: 3-9-20-23-25
Personnel:
Pat Erett *(Mgr-Fin)*

ST. PETERSBURG MUSEUM OF HISTORY

335 2nd Ave NE
Saint Petersburg, FL 33701
Tel.: (727) 894-1052
Fax: (727) 823-7276
E-mail: office@spmoh.org
Web Site: www.spmoh.org
Approx. Number Employees: 10
Year Founded: 1920
Business Description:
Museum
S.I.C.: 8412
N.A.I.C.S.: 712120
Media: 3-6-9-10-18-20-22-23-24-25
Personnel:
Connie Kone *(Pres)*
Ann Wikoff *(Archivist)*

STAGES PRODUCTIONS, INC.

7906 Bayshore Dr
Seminole, FL 33776
Tel.: (727) 399-1020
Fax: (727) 399-1027
E-mail: stagesprd@aol.com
Web Site:
www.stagesproductions.com
Year Founded: 1988
Business Description:
Musical Theater Producer
S.I.C.: 7922; 7929
N.A.I.C.S.: 711110; 711130
Media: 8-10

THE STAMFORD SYMPHONY ORCHESTRA

263 Tresser Blvd
Stamford, CT 06901-3532
Tel.: (203) 325-1407
Fax: (203) 325-8762
E-mail: office@stamfordsymphony.org
Web Site:
www.stamfordsymphony.org
Approx. Number Employees: 40
Year Founded: 1919
Business Description:
Symphony Orchestra
S.I.C.: 7929
N.A.I.C.S.: 711130
Media: 9-20-23-24-25
Personnel:
Steven C. Parrish *(Chm)*
Barbara J. Smith-Soroca *(Pres & CEO)*
Nicholas Rudd *(Principal-Anderson Rudd Company, Inc)*
Adria Benjamin *(Mgr-Personnel)*

THE STATE THEATRE

11 Livingston Ave
New Brunswick, NJ 08901-1903
Tel.: (732) 247-7200
Fax: (732) 247-4005
E-mail: info@statetheatrenj.org
Web Site: www.statetheatrenj.org
Approx. Number Employees: 45
Business Description:
Theatre Producer
S.I.C.: 7922
N.A.I.C.S.: 711110
Media: 8-9-13-18-19-20-22-23-24-25
Personnel:
Wesley O. Brustad *(Pres & CEO)*
Jerry Campagna *(CFO)*
Marion F. Combs *(Sr VP-Dev)*
Daniel B. Grossman *(VP-Mktg)*
Tracy Furr *(Dir-Art)*
Dave Hartkern *(Dir-Ops)*
Kelly Skenner *(Dir-Pub Rels)*

STATION CASINOS, INC.

(Holding of Colony Capital, LLC)
1505 S Pavilion Center Dr
Las Vegas, NV 89135
Tel.: (702) 495-3000
Fax: (702) 495-3404
E-mail: investors@stationcasinos.com
Web Site: www.stationcasinos.com
Approx. Rev.: $1,017,550,000
Approx. Number Employees: 12,224
Year Founded: 1983
Business Description:
Casinos & Hotels
S.I.C.: 7999; 7011; 7997
N.A.I.C.S.: 713290; 713910; 721120
Advertising Expenditures: $1,800,000
Media: 2-3-4-7-8-9-10-13-14-15-18-20-22-23-24-25-26
Personnel:
Frank J. Fertitta III *(Chm, Pres & CEO)*
Kevin L. Kelley *(COO & Exec VP)*
Scott M. Nielson *(Chief Dev Officer & Exec VP)*
Thomas M. Friel *(Chief Acctg Officer, Treas & Exec VP)*
Richard J. Haskins *(Gen Counsel, Sec & Exec VP)*
Ray Gambardella *(Dir-Player Dev)*
Sean P. McKay *(Dir-Shared Svcs)*
Lori Nelson *(Dir-Corp Commun)*

Brands & Products:
BARLEYS CASINO AND BREWERY
BOULDER STATION HOTEL AND CASINO
FIESTA HENDERSON HOTEL & CASINO
FIESTA RANCHO CASINO & HOTEL
PALACE STATION HOTEL AND CASINO
SANTA FE STATION HOTEL & CASINO
STATION CASINOS
SUNSET STATION HOTEL AND CASINO
TEXAS STATION GAMBLING HALL AND HOTEL
WILD WILD WEST GAMBLING HALL AND HOTEL

STEINWAY & SONS

(Sub. of Steinway Musical Instruments, Inc.)
1 Steinway Pl
Long Island City, NY 11105
Tel.: (718) 721-2600
Fax: (718) 932-4332
E-mail: info@steinway.com
Web Site: www.steinway.com
Sales Range: $150-199.9 Million
Approx. Number Employees: 500
Year Founded: 1853
Business Description:
Mfr. & Retailer of Pianos
S.I.C.: 3931; 5736
N.A.I.C.S.: 339992; 451140
Export
Advertising Expenditures: $1,500,000
Media: 1-3-4-6-8-9-10-11-13-19-22-23-24-26
Distr.: Intl.; Natl.
Personnel:
Leo Spellman *(Sr Dir-Comm)*

Brands & Products:
BOSTON
ESSEX
STEINWAY & SONS

Advertising Agency:
Wallwork Curry McKenna
10 City Sq 5th Fl
Charlestown, MA 02129
Tel.: (617) 266-8200
Fax: (617) 266-8270

STEINWAY MUSICAL INSTRUMENTS, INC.

800 South St Ste 305
Waltham, MA 02453-1480
Tel.: (781) 894-9770
Fax: (781) 894-9803
E-mail: corporate@steinwaymusical.com
Web Site: www.steinwaymusical.com
Approx. Sls.: $318,121,000
Approx. Number Employees: 1,680
Business Description:
Musical Instruments Mfr & Distr
S.I.C.: 3931; 5736
N.A.I.C.S.: 339992; 451140
Advertising Expenditures: $5,200,000
Media: 4-8-9-10-13-25
Personnel:
Kyle R. Kirkland *(Chm)*
Dana D. Messina *(CEO)*
Thomas Kurrer *(Pres-Steinway, Sons Worldwide)*
Ronald Losby *(Pres-Steinway & Sons-Americas)*

Brands & Products:
BUESCHER
SELMER
STEINWAY
STEINWAY MUSICAL INSTRUMENT
WILLIAM LEWIS & SON

STERLING METS, L.P.

(Holding of Sterling Equities, Inc.)
(d/b/a The New York Mets)
Citi Field 126th St & Roosevelt Ave
Flushing, NY 11368-1699
Tel.: (718) 507-8499
Fax: (718) 507-6395
E-mail: ticketoffice@nymets.com
Web Site: www.mets.com

Key to Media (For complete agency information see *The Advertising Red Books-Agencies* edition):
1. Bus. Publs. 2. Cable T.V. 3. Catalogs & Directories. 4. Co-op Adv. 5. Consumer Mags. 6. D.M. to Bus. Estab.7. D.M. to Consumers 8. Daily Newsp. 9. Exhibits/Trade Shows 10. Foreign 11. Infomercial 12. Internet Adv.13. Multimedia 14. Network Radio 15. Network T.V. 16. Newsp. Distr. Mags. 17. Other 18. Outdoor (Posters, Transit) 19. Point of Purchase20. Premiums, Novelties 21. Product Samples 22. Special Events Mktg. 23. Spot Radio 24. Spot T.V. 25. Weekly Newsp. 26. Yellow Page Adv.

Sterling Mets, L.P. — (Continued)

Sales Range: $200-249.9 Million
Business Description:
Professional Baseball Club
S.I.C.: 7941
N.A.I.C.S.: 711211
Personnel:
Fred Wilpon *(Chm, CEO & Partner)*
Saul B. Katz *(Pres & Partner)*
Jeff Wilpon *(COO & Partner)*
Arthur Friedman *(Partner)*
David M. Katz *(Partner)*
Michael Katz *(Partner)*
Tom Osterman *(Partner)*
Marvin Tepper *(Partner)*
Richard A. Wilpon *(Partner)*
Mark Peskin *(CFO)*
Dave Howard *(Exec VP-Bus Ops)*
Paul Asencio *(Sr VP-Corp Sls & Svcs)*
David Newman *(Sr VP-Mktg & Comm)*
John Ricco *(VP & Asst Gen Mgr & Interim Gen Mgr)*
Jay Horwitz *(VP-Media Rels)*
Bill Ianniciello *(VP-Ticket Sls & Svcs)*
Robert Kasdon *(VP-Security)*
Advertising Agency:
MLB Advanced Media, L.P.
75 9th Ave 5th Fl
New York, NY 10011
Tel.: (212) 485-3444
Fax: (212) 485-3456

STUBHUB, INC.
(Sub. of eBay Inc.)
199 Fremont St Ste 300
San Francisco, CA 94105
Tel.: (415) 222-8400
Fax: (415) 222-8552
Toll Free: (866) STUBHUB
E-mail: custmerservice@stubhub.com
Web Site: www.stubhub.com
Sales Range: $150-199.9 Million
Approx. Number Employees: 230
Year Founded: 2000
Business Description:
Online Ticket Buying & Selling Marketplace
S.I.C.: 5961; 2741
N.A.I.C.S.: 454111; 516110
Personnel:
Chris Tsakalakis *(Pres)*
Noah Goldberg *(Sr Dir-Bus Ops)*
Brands & Products:
STUBHUB!
Advertising Agency:
Finn Partners
388 Market St Ste 1400
San Francisco, CA 94111-5316
Tel.: (415) 541-0750
Fax: (415) 541-0720

SUGARLOAF/USA
(Div. of Boyne USA Resorts Inc.)
5092 Access Rd
Carrabassett Valley, ME 04947-9799
Tel.: (207) 237-2000
Fax: (207) 237-3768
E-mail: info@sugarloaf.com
Web Site: www.sugarloaf.com
Approx. Number Employees: 200
Business Description:
Operators of Sugarloaf Mountain Ski Resort
S.I.C.: 7999; 7011
N.A.I.C.S.: 713920; 721199
Media: 1-6-10-18
Personnel:
John Diller *(Mng Dir)*
Cathy Witherspoon *(VP-Skier Svcs & HR)*
Brad Larsen *(Dir-Sls & Mktg)*
Nancy Peabbles *(Dir-Skier Svcs & Guest Svc)*
Ethan Austin *(Mgr-Comm)*

SUNDAY RIVER SKIWAY CORP.
(Div. of Boyne USA Resorts Inc.)
15 S Rdg Rd PO Box 450
Bethel, ME 04217-0450
Tel.: (207) 824-3000
Fax: (207) 824-5110
E-mail: info@sundayriver.com
Web Site: www.sundayriver.com
Approx. Number Employees: 1,500
Business Description:
Resort & Ski Area Operator
S.I.C.: 7999; 5812; 7011
N.A.I.C.S.: 713920; 721110; 722110
Media: 8-10-13-18-23
Personnel:
Nick Lambert *(VP-Sls & Mktg)*

SYMPHONY IN C
One Market St Ste 1C
Camden, NJ 08102
Tel.: (856) 963-6683
Fax: (856) 963-9612
Web Site: www.symphonyinc.org
Sales Range: Less than $1 Million
Approx. Number Employees: 5
Business Description:
Symphony Orchestra
S.I.C.: 7929
N.A.I.C.S.: 711130
Media: 8-9-18-20-22-23-24-25
Personnel:
Pamela Brant *(VP-Mktg & Pub Rel)*
Rossen Milanov *(Dir-Music)*
Michael Volpert *(Dir-Artistic Opers & Education)*
Advertising Agency:
Keiler & Company
304 Main St
Farmington, CT 06032-2985
Tel.: (860) 677-8821
Fax: (860) 676-8164

SYMPHONY OF THE SOUTHWEST
56 S Ctr
Mesa, AZ 85211
Tel.: (480) 827-2143
Fax: (480) 827-2070
Web Site: symphonyofthesouthwest.org
Approx. Sls.: $56,000
Approx. Number Employees: 3
Year Founded: 1992
Business Description:
Symphony Orchestra
S.I.C.: 8641; 7929
N.A.I.C.S.: 813410; 711190
Media: 9-13-18-20-23-24-25
Personnel:
Guillaume G. Marmet *(Exec Dir)*
Cal Stuart Kellog *(Dir-Music)*

SYRACUSE SYMPHONY ORCHESTRA
411 Montgomery St Ste 40
Syracuse, NY 13202
Tel.: (315) 424-8222
Fax: (315) 424-1131
E-mail: info@syracusesymphony.org
Web Site: www.syracusesymphony.org
Approx. Number Employees: 100
Business Description:
Symphony Orchestra
S.I.C.: 7929
N.A.I.C.S.: 711130
Media: 5-9-20-22-23-24-25
Personnel:
Rocco Mangano *(Chm)*
David A.A. Ridings *(Vice Chm)*
Peter H. Soderberg *(Vice Chm)*
Richard Decker *(VP & Gen Mgr)*
Daniel Hege *(Dir-Music)*
Edward Kochian *(Interim Dir)*
Jon Mosbo *(Mgr-Orchestra)*

TALLAHASSEE SYMPHONY ORCHESTRA
1345 Thomasville Rd
Tallahassee, FL 32303
Tel.: (850) 224-0461
Fax: (850) 222-9092
E-mail: operations@tallahasseesymphony.org
Web Site: www.tallahasseesymphony.org
Approx. Number Employees: 50
Year Founded: 1979
Business Description:
Symphony Orchestra Services
S.I.C.: 7929
N.A.I.C.S.: 711130
Media: 5-9-10-20-23-24-25
Personnel:
Amanda Sauer *(Exec Dir)*

TAMPA BAY PERFORMING ARTS CENTER INC.
1010 N WC MacInnes Pl
Tampa, FL 33602
Tel.: (813) 222-1000
Fax: (813) 222-1057
E-mail: info@tbpac.org
Web Site: www.tbpac.org
Approx. Rev.: $28,000,000
Approx. Number Employees: 350
Business Description:
Theatrical Productions & Entertainment Venues
S.I.C.: 7922
N.A.I.C.S.: 711110
Media: 6-9-10-18-20-22-23-24-25
Personnel:
Judith Lisi *(CEO)*
Michael Kilgore *(VP-Mktg)*
Carla Armstrong *(Dir-Corp Giving & Sponsorship)*
Paul B. Bilyeu *(Dir-PR)*
Summer Bohnenkamp *(Dir-Mktg)*
Michael Chamoun *(Dir-Production Svcs)*
Bill Fogarty *(Dir-Patron & Volunteer Svcs)*
Brad Hudson *(Dir-Video & Documentary Projects)*
Richard Brown *(Mgr-Retail Ops)*
Angela Brugger *(Mgr-Mktg)*
Rick Criswell *(Mgr-Jaeb Theater)*
Christen Petitt *(Svcs Mgr)*
Donald Moyer *(Asst Mgr-Production)*
Gloria Heath *(Coord-Volunteer)*
Brands & Products:
CENTER BILL

TAMPA BAY RAYS BASEBALL, LTD.
Tropicana Field 1 Tropicana Dr
Saint Petersburg, FL 33705
Tel.: (727) 825-3137
Fax: (727) 825-3111
Toll Free: (888) FANRAYS
E-mail: fanfeedback@raysbaseball.com
Web Site: www.raysbaseball.com
Approx. Number Employees: 300
Year Founded: 1995
Business Description:
Professional Baseball Club
S.I.C.: 7941
N.A.I.C.S.: 711211
Media: 3-6-8-9-13-18-20-22-23-24-25
Personnel:
Stuart Sternberg *(Owner)*
Matthew P. Silverman *(Pres)*
John P. Higgins *(Gen Counsel & Sr VP-Admin)*
Andrew Friedman *(Exec VP-Baseball Ops)*
Brian Auld *(Sr VP-Bus Ops)*
Mark Fernandez *(Sr VP)*
Gerry Hunsicker *(Sr VP-Baseball Ops)*
Michael Kalt *(Sr VP-Dev & Bus Affairs)*
Rob Gagliardi *(VP-Fin)*
Tom Hoof *(VP-Mktg & Community Rels)*
Brian Richeson *(VP-Sls & Svc)*
Rick Vaughn *(VP-Comm)*
Brian Killingsworth *(Sr Dir-Mktg)*
Clark Beacom *(Sr Dir-Grp & Suite Sls)*
Aaron Cohn *(Sr Dir-Corp Partnerships)*
Scott Kelyman *(Sr Dir-Building Ops)*
Larry McCabe *(Sr Dir-Brdcst)*
Suzanne Murchland *(Sr Dir-Community Rels)*
Juan Ramirez *(Sr Dir-IT)*
William Walsh *(Sr Dir-Dev)*
Bill Wiener, Jr. *(Sr Dir-Procurement & Bus Svcs)*
Carlos Alfonso *(Dir-Intl Ops)*
Robert Bennett *(Dir-Ticket Ops)*
Lou Costanza *(Dir-In-Game Entertainment)*
Sandy Dengler *(Dir-Major League Admin)*
Dan Feinstein *(Dir-Baseball Ops)*
Ron Golick *(Dir-Audio/Visual Svcs)*
Cass Halpin *(Dir-Partner/VIP Rels)*
R.J. Harrison *(Dir-Scouting)*
Rich Herrera *(Dir-Radio Ops/Brdcst Production)*
Tom Karac *(Dir-Event Ops)*
Mitch Lukevics *(Dir-Minor League Ops)*
Chris Raineri *(Dir-Building Ops)*
Jeff Tanzer *(Dir-Season Ticket Sls & Svc)*
Jennifer Lyn Tran *(Dir-HR)*
Eric Weisberg *(Dir-Customer Svc & Stadium Experience)*
Jason Wilmoth *(Dir-Corp Partnership Svcs)*
Jeff Ziegler *(Dir-Team Travel)*
Leslie Tieszen *(Sr Mgr-Community Rels)*
Carmen Molina *(Mgr-Comm)*
Debbie Brooks *(Mgr-Mdse)*
Carey Cox *(Mgr-Adv)*
Michael Griffith *(Mgr-Security)*
Todd Hardy *(Mgr-Events)*

Key to Media (For complete agency information see *The Advertising Red Books-Agencies* edition):
1. Bus. Publs. 2. Cable T.V. 3. Catalogs & Directories. 4. Co-op Adv. 5. Consumer Mags. 6. D.M. to Bus. Estab.7. D.M. to Consumers
8. Daily Newsp. 9. Exhibits/Trade Shows 10. Foreign 11. Infomercial 12. Internet Adv.13. Multimedia 14. Network Radio
15. Network T.V. 16. Newsp. Distr. Mags. 17. Other 18. Outdoor (Posters, Transit) 19. Point of Purchase20. Premiums, Novelties
21. Product Samples 22. Special Events Mktg. 23. Spot Radio 24. Spot T.V. 25. Weekly Newsp. 26. Yellow Page Adv.

Chris Westmoreland *(Mgr-Equipment & Home Clubhouse)*
Brands & Products:
TAMPA BAY DEVIL RAYS
Advertising Agencies:
MLB Advanced Media, L.P.
75 9th Ave 5th Fl
New York, NY 10011
Tel.: (212) 485-3444
Fax: (212) 485-3456

Pyper Paul + Kenney, Inc.
1102 N Florida Ave
Tampa, FL 33602
Tel.: (813) 496-7000
Fax: (813) 496-7003

TAMPA BAY STORM
401 Channelside Dr
Tampa, FL 33602-5400
Tel.: (813) 276-7300
Fax: (813) 276-7301
E-mail: coach@tampastorm.com
Web Site: www.tampabaystorm.com
Approx. Number Employees: 45
Year Founded: 1991
Business Description:
Professional Arena Football Team
S.I.C.: 7941
N.A.I.C.S.: 711211
Advertising Expenditures: $200,000
Media: 2-3-4-9-16-20-22-23-24-25-26
Distr.: Reg.
Budget Set: Sept.
Personnel:
Derrick Brooks *(Pres)*
Joe Fada *(CFO)*
Paul Davis *(Gen Counsel & VP)*
Jim Ciotoli *(Dir-Broadcast Production & Game Ops)*
Dave Ewart *(Dir-Player Personnel)*
Kindra Stocher *(Dir-Storm Dancers)*
Brian Breseman *(Mgr-Media Rels)*
Brands & Products:
TAMPA BAY STORM
Advertising Agency:
Nuevo Advertising Group, Inc.
677 N Washington Blvd
Sarasota, FL 34236
Tel.: (941) 752-4433
Fax: (941) 752-1114

TAYLOR-LISTUG INC.
1980 Gillespie Way
El Cajon, CA 92020
Tel.: (619) 258-1207
Fax: (619) 258-1623
Toll Free: (800) 943-6782
Web Site: www.taylorguitars.com
Approx. Number Employees: 370
Year Founded: 1968
Business Description:
Guitar & Guitar Parts Mfr
S.I.C.: 3931
N.A.I.C.S.: 339992
Media: 4-22
Personnel:
Kurt Listug *(Co-Founder & CEO)*
Robert Taylor *(Pres)*

TELLURIDE SKI & GOLF COMPANY LLP
565 Mtn Vlg Blvd
Telluride, CO 81435-9521
Tel.: (970) 728-6900
Fax: (970) 728-6228
E-mail: lmartin@tellurideskiresort.com
Web Site: www.tellurideskiresort.com
Approx. Number Employees: 371
Year Founded: 1972
Business Description:
Recreation Services
S.I.C.: 7999; 7997
N.A.I.C.S.: 487990; 713910
Export
Media: 4-7-8-10-13
Personnel:
Chuck Horning *(Owner)*
Matt Skinner *(VP-Sls & Mktg)*
Patrick Rothe *(Dir-Sls)*
Brands & Products:
THE MOST BEAUTIFUL PLACE YOU'LL EVER SKI

TENNESSEE FOOTBALL, INC.
(d/b/a Tennessee Titans)
Baptist Sports Park 460 Great Cir Rd
Nashville, TN 37228
Tel.: (615) 565-4000
Fax: (615) 565-4105
Web Site: www.titansonline.com
Approx. Number Employees: 80
Year Founded: 1959
Business Description:
Professional Football Franchise
S.I.C.: 7941
N.A.I.C.S.: 711211
Advertising Expenditures: $200,000
Media: 3-9-22-23-24-25-26
Distr.: Natl.
Budget Set: Apr.
Personnel:
K. S. Adams, Jr. *(Founder, Co-Owner, Chm, Pres & CEO)*
Jenneen Kaufman *(CFO & VP)*
Steve Underwood *(Gen Counsel, Sr Exec VP & Exec Asst to Chm)*
Mike Reinfeldt *(Exec VP & Gen Mgr)*
Don MacLachlan *(Exec VP-Admin & Facilities)*
Elza Bullock *(VP & Asst Gen Counsel)*
Bob Hyde *(VP-Community Rels)*
Ralph Ockenfels *(VP-Mktg)*
Stuart Spears *(VP-Bus Ops & Sls)*
Marty Collins *(Sr Dir-Ticket Ops)*
Steve Berk *(Dir-Security)*
Robbie Bohren *(Dir-Media Rels)*
Gary Glenn *(Dir-Internet Ops & Publ)*
Russ Hudson *(Dir-Info Sys)*
Mike Keith *(Dir-Brdcst Production)*
Anthony Pastrana *(Dir-Video)*
Tina Tuggle *(Dir-Player Dev)*
Bill Wainwright *(Dir-Suite Sales & Svcs)*
Craig Pelat *(Asst Dir-Info Sys)*
Dwight Spradlin *(Asst Dir-Media Rels)*
Tim Zenner *(Asst Dir-Ticket Ops)*
Brent Akers *(Mgr-Ops)*
Tresa Halbrooks *(Mgr-Community Rels)*
Anthony Hall *(Mgr-Ticketing-Hospitality Club Members)*
Dempsey Henderson *(Mgr-Facilities)*
Brad McClanahan *(Mgr-Mktg)*
Paul Noska *(Mgr-Equipment)*
Blu Whipple *(Asst Gen Counsel)*
Brands & Products:
TENNESSEE TITANS
Advertising Agency:
Gish, Sherwood & Friends, Inc.
(d/b/a GS&F)
4235 Hillsboro Pike
Nashville, TN 37215-3344
Tel.: (615) 385-1100
Fax: (615) 783-0500

TENNESSEE PHILHARMONIC SYMPHONY ORCHESTRA ASSOCIATION
PO Box 36
Murfreesboro, TN 37133-0036
Tel.: (615) 898-1862
Fax: (615) 898-0810
E-mail: symphony@murfreesboro.com
Web Site: www.murfreesborosymphony.com
Approx. Number Employees: 3
Business Description:
Symphony Orchestra
S.I.C.: 7929
N.A.I.C.S.: 711130
Media: 9-13-20-23-24-25-26

TGC, INC.
(Sub. of Comcast Corporation)
7580 Commerce Ctr Dr
Orlando, FL 32819-8947
Tel.: (407) 363-4653
Fax: (407) 363-7976
E-mail: info@thegolfchannel.com
Web Site: www.thegolfchannel.com
Sales Range: $100-124.9 Million
Approx. Number Employees: 350
Year Founded: 1995
Business Description:
Twenty-Four Hour Golf Network Featuring Worldwide Tournament Coverage & Instructional Shows
S.I.C.: 4841; 4833
N.A.I.C.S.: 515210; 515120
Media: 2-3-6-9-10-13-14-15-16-19-20-22-23-24-25
Distr.: Natl.
Personnel:
Ta-Wei Chien *(CEO)*
Jack Lascar *(Partner)*
Jeff Dilley *(CFO)*
Gene Pizzolato *(CMO, COO-New Media Ventures & Chief Revenue Officer)*
Kevin Byrnes *(Sr VP-Sponsorship Sls)*
Virginia O'Brien *(Sr VP-Mktg)*
Theresa McCann *(VP-Sls, Mktg & GDIS)*
Michelle Walden *(VP-Information Systems)*
David Desmond *(Dir-Sls-Golf Sponsorship)*
Nicci Fry *(Dir-Consumer Mktg)*
Michael Lee *(Area Mgr-Western USA)*
Tom Pierce *(Mktg Mgr)*
Tim Brooks *(Mgr-Houston)*
Mike Hendrix *(Mgr-Reg Sls)*
Susie Sipe *(Mgr-Adv)*

THANKSGIVING POINT
3003 N Thanksgiving Way
Lehi, UT 84043
Tel.: (801) 768-2300
Fax: (801) 768-4941
Toll Free: (888) 672-6040
E-mail: info@thanksgivingpoint.com
Web Site: www.thanksgivingpoint.org
Approx. Number Employees: 100
Business Description:
Entertainment Services; Museum, Golf, Botanical Garden, Shopping, Dining & Children's Zoo
S.I.C.: 7999
N.A.I.C.S.: 713990
Media: 8-9-10-13-20-22-23-24-25
Personnel:
Mike Washburn *(CEO)*
Allen Ash *(CFO)*
Tracy Erdmann *(Dir-Thanksgiving Gardens)*
Molina Welcker *(Dir-Catering)*
Kendall Wimmer *(Dir-Food Svcs & Retail)*
Wendy Herzog *(Mgr-HR)*
David Shane Johnson *(Mgr-Dev)*
Advertising Agency:
Rare Method Interactive Corp.
165 S Main St Ste 300
Salt Lake City, UT 84101
Tel.: (801) 539-1818
Fax: (801) 539-8484

THEATER & ARTS FOUNDATION
(d/b/a La Jolla Playhouse)
PO Box 12039
La Jolla, CA 92039
Tel.: (858) 550-1070
Fax: (858) 550-1075
Web Site: www.lajollaplayhouse.com
Approx. Number Employees: 40
Business Description:
Theatrical Production
S.I.C.: 8641; 7922
N.A.I.C.S.: 813410; 711110
Media: 8-23-24
Personnel:
Michael Rosenberg *(Mng Dir)*
Christofer Ashley *(Dir-Artistic)*

THEATER LEAGUE INC.
8900 Stateline Rd Ste 350
Leawood, KS 66206
Tel.: (913) 652-7400
Fax: (913) 652-7479
E-mail: info@theatreleague.com
Web Site: www.theaterleague.com
Approx. Number Employees: 16
Business Description:
Theatrical Production & Promotion Services
S.I.C.: 7389
N.A.I.C.S.: 711320
Media: 8-23-24
Personnel:
Mark Edelman *(Pres)*
Amy Hamm *(Sr Dir-Mktg)*
Catherine Cone *(Dir-Ticketing & Admin)*
Debbie Davis *(Dir-Bus Affairs)*
Reida York *(Dir-Adv, Promotions & PR)*
Karen Yuhasz *(Dir-Production)*

THEATRE COMMUNICATIONS GROUP, INC.
520 8th Ave 24th Fl
New York, NY 10018-4156
Tel.: (212) 609-5900
Fax: (212) 609-5901
E-mail: tcg@tcg.org
Web Site: www.tcg.org
Approx. Number Employees: 50
Business Description:
American Theatre Promoter; Books Publisher
S.I.C.: 8621; 2731
N.A.I.C.S.: 813920; 511130
Media: 2-7-10-13-22
Personnel:
Abel Lopez *(Pres)*

Key to Media (For complete agency information see *The Advertising Red Books-Agencies* edition):
1. Bus. Publs. 2. Cable T.V. 3. Catalogs & Directories. 4. Co-op Adv. 5. Consumer Mags. 6. D.M. to Bus. Estab.7. D.M. to Consumers
8. Daily Newsp. 9. Exhibits/Trade Shows 10. Foreign 11. Infomercial 12. Internet Adv.13. Multimedia 14. Network Radio
15. Network T.V. 16. Newsp. Distr. Mags. 17. Other 18. Outdoor (Posters, Transit) 19. Point of Purchase20. Premiums, Novelties
21. Product Samples 22. Special Events Mktg. 23. Spot Radio 24. Spot T.V. 25. Weekly Newsp. 26. Yellow Page Adv.

Theatre Communications Group, Inc. — (Continued)

Kevin E. Moore *(Mng Dir)*
Kathy Sova *(Editorial Dir-TCG Books , Playscript & Dir-American Theatre)*
Teresa Eyring *(Exec Dir)*
Anthony Barilla *(Associate Dir-Production)*
Laurie Baskin *(Dir-Govt & Education Programs)*
Emilya Cachapero *(Dir-Artistic Programs & Dir-Intl Theatre Institute/ US)*
Jennifer Cleary *(Dir-Membership)*
Phillip Matthews *(Dir-Audience Programs)*
Kitty Suen *(Dir-Creative)*
Carol Van Keuren *(Dir-Adv)*
Jenni Werner *(Dir-Programming)*
Leigh A. Zona *(Dir-Mktg)*
Demosthenes Chrysan *(Office Mgr)*
Michael Shatara *(Assoc Office Mgr)*
Ana Torres *(Assoc Office Mgr)*
Janelle Bernard *(Associate Customer Service Mgr)*

Brands & Products:
AMERICAN THEATRE
ARTSEARCH
TCG
THEATRE PROFILES

THEATRE FOR A NEW AUDIENCE

154 Christopher St Ste 3D
New York, NY 10014
Tel.: (212) 229-2819
Fax: (212) 229-2911
E-mail: info@tfana.org
Web Site: www.tfana.org
Sales Range: $25-49.9 Million
Approx. Number Employees: 15
Year Founded: 1979
Business Description:
Theatre Production
S.I.C.: 7922
N.A.I.C.S.: 711110
Media: 7-8-9-20-25
Personnel:
Theodore C. Rogers *(Chm)*
Jeffrey Horowitz *(Pres)*
James Lynes *(Dir-Dev)*
Advertising Agency:
The Bruce Cohen Group, Ltd.
PO Box 534
Water Mill, NY 11976-0534
Tel.: (212) 580-9548
Fax: (212) 580-9895
Public Relations

THEATREWORKSUSA

151 W 26th St FL 7
New York, NY 10001
Tel.: (212) 647-1100
Fax: (212) 924-5377
Toll Free: (800) 497-5007
E-mail: info@theatreworksusa.org
Web Site: www.theatreworksusa.org
Approx. Number Employees: 30
Year Founded: 1961
Business Description:
Non-Profit Theatrical Company
S.I.C.: 7922
N.A.I.C.S.: 711110
Media: 8
Personnel:
Charles Hull *(Founder)*
Ken Arthur *(Dir-Producing)*
Steven A. Lattanzi *(Dir-Plng)*
Barbara Pasternack *(Dir-Artistic)*
Beth Prather *(Dir-Education)*
Barbara Sandek *(Dir-Mktg)*
Steve Cochran *(Assoc Dir-Mktg)*
Bob Daley *(Mgr-Production)*
Sean Hagerty *(Mgr-Box Office)*
Patrick Dwyer *(Coord-Mktg)*

TIHATI PRODUCTIONS LTD., INC.

3615 Harding Ave Ste 509
Honolulu, HI 96816-3757
Tel.: (808) 735-0292
Fax: (808) 735-9479
E-mail: jeanne@tihati.com
Web Site: www.tihati.com
Sales Range: $900-999.9 Million
Approx. Number Employees: 825
Year Founded: 1971
Business Description:
Entertainers & Entertainment Groups
S.I.C.: 7929
N.A.I.C.S.: 711190
Media: 22
Personnel:
Cha Thompson *(Owner)*
Jack E. Thompson *(Pres)*

TIX CORPORATION

12001 Ventura Pl Ste 340
Studio City, CA 91604
Tel.: (818) 761-1002
Fax: (818) 761-1072
Web Site: www.tixcorp.com
Approx. Rev.: $81,791,000
Approx. Number Employees: 172
Year Founded: 1993
Business Description:
Ticketing, Event Merchandising & Live Entertainment Production & Promotion Services
S.I.C.: 7389
N.A.I.C.S.: 711310
Advertising Expenditures: $1,800,000
Personnel:
Mitchell J. Francis *(CEO)*
Steve Handy *(CFO)*
Kimberly Simon *(COO)*

TM STUDIOS, INC.

(Sub. of Triton Media, LLC)
2002 Academy Ln Ste 110
Dallas, TX 75234
Tel.: (972) 406-6800
Fax: (972) 406-6890
E-mail: info@tmstudios.com
Web Site: www.tmstudios.com
Approx. Number Employees: 40
Business Description:
Music-Based Products & Services for Broadcast Media Use
S.I.C.: 7389
N.A.I.C.S.: 512290
Media: 2-10
Personnel:
Chris Corcoran *(VP-Sls)*
Rob Kowald *(Dir-IT)*
Ryan Lambert *(Dir-Mktg & Web Dev)*
Chris Stevens *(Sr Mgr-Sls-Reg)*
Janet Cailloux *(Mgr-Acctg)*

TOLEDO SYMPHONY

1838 Parkwood Ave Ste 310
Toledo, OH 43604
Tel.: (419) 246-8000
Fax: (419) 321-6890
Web Site: www.toledosymphony.com
Sales Range: $25-49.9 Million
Approx. Number Employees: 20
Business Description:
Symphony Orchestra
S.I.C.: 7929
N.A.I.C.S.: 711130
Media: 8-9-13-20-22-23-24-25
Personnel:
Kathleen Carroll *(Pres & CEO)*
Randi Dier *(VP-Fin)*
Keith McWatters *(Gen Mgr)*
Ashley Mirakina *(Dir-Mktg & PR)*
Sandra Clark *(Sls Mgr)*
Raymond Clark *(Mgr-Production)*
Julie Heigel *(Mgr-Annual Funds)*
Tim Lake *(Mgr-Stage)*
Ashley Mirakian *(Mgr-Mktg)*

TOMMY BARTLETT, INC.

560 Wisconsin Dells Pkwy
Wisconsin Dells, WI 53965
Tel.: (608) 254-2525
Fax: (608) 254-6103
E-mail: bartlett@tommybartlett.com
Web Site: www.tommybartlett.com
Approx. Number Employees: 150
Year Founded: 1948
Business Description:
Operator of Water Show
S.I.C.: 7999
N.A.I.C.S.: 713990
Advertising Expenditures: $700,000
Media: 2-3-5-6-8-9-10-14-15-16-18-20-23-24
Distr.: Direct to Consumer; Reg.
Budget Set: Dec.
Personnel:
Thomas M. Diehl *(Co-Owner, Pres & Gen Mgr)*
Margaret Diehl *(Exec VP)*
Jill C. Diehl *(VP-Adv & Promo)*
Joey Lincicum *(VP-Production)*

TOPEKA SYMPHONY SOCIETY INC.

PO Box 2206
Topeka, KS 66601
Tel.: (785) 232-2032
Fax: (785) 232-6204
E-mail: tso@topekasymphony.org
Web Site: www.topekasymphony.org
Approx. Number Employees: 5
Business Description:
Symphony Orchestra
S.I.C.: 7929
N.A.I.C.S.: 711130
Media: 7-8-9-13-20-23-24-25
Personnel:
Kathy Maag *(Gen Mgr)*
Sarah Bailey *(Dir)*
John Wesley Strickler *(Dir-Music & Conductor)*

THE TOPPS COMPANY, INC.

(Holding of Madison Dearborn Partners, LLC)
1 Whitehall St
New York, NY 10004-2109
Tel.: (212) 376-0300
Fax: (212) 376-0573
E-mail: info@topps.com
Web Site: www.topps.com
Approx. Sls.: $326,668,992
Approx. Number Employees: 422
Year Founded: 1938
Business Description:
International Marketer of Collectible Trading Cards, Confections, Sticker Collections, Collectible Strategy Games & Comic Books
S.I.C.: 2759; 2099; 2741
N.A.I.C.S.: 323119; 311340; 511199
Import Export
Advertising Expenditures: $3,659,000
Media: 4-7-8-10-19-20-21-22-24
Distr.: Natl.
Personnel:
Ryan O'Hara *(Pres & CEO)*
John S. Budd *(VP-Mktg)*
John C. Buscaglia *(VP-Sls)*
Ira Friedman *(VP-Publ & New Product Dev)*
Clay Luraschi *(Brand Mgr-Baseball)*
Brands & Products:
BABY BOTTLE POP
BAZOOKA
BLASTS
BUBBLE GUM BOOSTER
ETOPPS
HALF CHOCOLATELY, HALF CANDY, HALF CRAZY
JUICY DROP POP
MEGA MOUTH CANDY SPRAY
PUSH POP LOLLIPOPS
RING POP LOLLIPOPS
STADIUM CLUB SPORTS CARDS
THUMB FUN LOLLIPOPS
TOPPS
TOPPS ARCHIVES
TOPPS FINEST
TOPPS GALLERY
TOPPS SPORTS CARDS
TOPPS VAULT
TRIPLE BLASTS
VERTIGO
Advertising Agency:
Spike/DDB
55 Washington St Ste 650
Brooklyn, NY 11201
Tel.: (718) 596-5400
Fax: (212) 415-3101
Baseball Cards

TORONTO BLUE JAYS BASEBALL CLUB

(Sub. of Rogers Media Inc.)
1 Blue Jays Way Ste 3200
Toronto, ON M5V 1J1, Canada
Tel.: (416) 341-1000
Fax: (416) 341-1250
Toll Free: (888) 892-4564
E-mail: info@bluejays.com
Web Site: www.bluejays.com
Sales Range: $75-99.9 Million
Approx. Number Employees: 300
Year Founded: 1977
Business Description:
Professional Baseball Club
S.I.C.: 7941
N.A.I.C.S.: 711211
Media: 7-8-9-10-13-18-22-23-24
Personnel:
Paul Beeston *(Pres & CEO)*
Alex Anthopoulos *(Sr VP-Baseball Ops & Gen Mgr)*
Richard Wong *(Sr VP-Stadium Ops)*
Tony LaCava *(VP-Baseball Ops & Asst Gen Mgr)*
Mario Coutinho *(VP-Stadium Ops & Security)*
Silvio D'addario *(VP-Events)*
Anthony Partipilo *(VP-Mktg & Mdsg)*
Jay Stenhouse *(VP-Comm)*
Danielle Silverstein *(Exec Dir)*
Doug Barr *(Dir-Ticket Ops)*

Key to Media (For complete agency information see *The Advertising Red Books-Agencies* edition):
1. Bus. Publs. 2. Cable T.V. 3. Catalogs & Directories. 4. Co-op Adv. 5. Consumer Mags. 6. D.M. to Bus. Estab.7. D.M. to Consumers 8. Daily Newsp. 9. Exhibits/Trade Shows 10. Foreign 11. Infomercial 12. Internet Adv.13. Multimedia 14. Network Radio 15. Network T.V. 16. Newsp. Distr. Mags. 17. Other 18. Outdoor (Posters, Transit) 19. Point of Purchase20. Premiums, Novelties 21. Product Samples 22. Special Events Mktg. 23. Spot Radio 24. Spot T.V. 25. Weekly Newsp. 26. Yellow Page Adv.

John Griffin *(Dir-Bus Dev)*
Jon Lalonde *(Dir-Scouting)*
Franc Rota *(Dir-Ticket Sls & Svc)*
Dick Scott *(Dir-Player Dev)*
Krista Semotiuk *(Dir-Strategic Mktg Partnerships)*
Mike Shaw *(Dir)*
Sheila Stella *(Dir-Ticket Svcs)*
Charlie Wilson *(Dir-Minor League Ops)*
Nadia Flaim *(Mgr-Comm)*
Holly Purdon *(Mgr-Community Mktg & Player Rels)*
Jeff Ross *(Mgr-Equipment)*

Brands & Products:
TORONTO BLUE JAYS

Advertising Agency:
MLB Advanced Media, L.P.
75 9th Ave 5th Fl
New York, NY 10011
Tel.: (212) 485-3444
Fax: (212) 485-3456

TORONTO MAPLE LEAF HOCKEY CLUB

(Sub. of Maple Leaf Sports & Entertainment Ltd.)
40 Bay St Ste 400
Toronto, ON M5J 2X2, Canada
Tel.: (416) 815-5700
Fax: (416) 359-9331
Web Site: www.mapleleafs.com
Approx. Number Employees: 900
Year Founded: 1927
Business Description:
Professional Hockey Franchise
S.I.C.: 7941
N.A.I.C.S.: 711211
Media: 3-5-9-10-13-18-20-22-23-24

Personnel:
Brian Burke *(Pres & Gen Mgr)*
Mike Penny *(Asst Gen Mgr & Dir-Player Personnel)*
Cloude Loiselle *(Asst Gen Mgr)*
Reid Mitchell *(Dir-Hockey & Scouting Admin)*
Dave Griffiths *(Mgr-Team Svcs)*
Brian Pappineau *(Mgr-Equipment)*

Advertising Agency:
Field Day Inc.
171 E Liberty St Ste 320
Toronto, ON M6K 3P6, Canada
Tel.: (416) 408-4446
Fax: (416) 408-4447

TORONTO RAPTORS BASKETBALL CLUB INC.

(Sub. of Maple Leaf Sports & Entertainment Ltd.)
40 Bay St Ste 400
Toronto, ON M5J 2X2, Canada
Tel.: (416) 815-5500
Fax: (416) 359-9332
Web Site: www.raptors.com
Approx. Number Employees: 50
Year Founded: 1995
Business Description:
Professional Basketball Franchise
S.I.C.: 7941
N.A.I.C.S.: 711211
Media: 3-6-9-13-18-20-22-23-24

Personnel:
Bryan Colangelo *(Pres & Gen Mgr-Alternate NBA Governor)*
Shannon Hosford *(Sr Dir-Mktg)*
Jim Kelly *(Sr Dir-Scouting)*
Alex McKechnie *(Dir-Sports Science)*
Kevin DiPietro *(Mgr-Equipment & Coord-Travel)*

Advertising Agency:
Field Day Inc.
171 E Liberty St Ste 320
Toronto, ON M6K 3P6, Canada
Tel.: (416) 408-4446
Fax: (416) 408-4447

TORONTO SYMPHONY ORCHESTRA

212 King St W Ste 550
Toronto, ON Canada
Tel.: (416) 593-7769
Fax: (416) 977-2912
E-mail: info@tso.ca
Web Site: www.tso.ca
Approx. Number Employees: 150
Business Description:
Symphony Orchestra
S.I.C.: 7929
N.A.I.C.S.: 711190
Media: 8-9-18-20-23-24-25
Personnel:
Allan S. Kimberley *(Chm)*
Ana P. Lopes *(Co-Chm)*
Robert W. Corcoran *(Vice Chm)*
Gary Corrin *(Principal)*
Bob Rae *(Principal)*
Mike Forrester *(VP-Mktg & Bus Dev)*
Pema Lektsog *(Sr Dir-Corp Partnerships & Foundations)*
Fiona Buttars *(Dir-Mktg Ops)*
Loie Fallis *(Dir-Artistic Plng)*
Lisa Hamel *(Dir-Bus Admin & Fin)*
Lisa Mackay *(Dir-Sls & Promos)*
Roberta Smith *(Dir-Orchestra Ops & Education Programmes)*
Scott Wilson *(Dir-Ops)*
Heather Slater *(Assoc Dir-Artistic Admin & Programming)*
Brian Columbus *(Sr Mgr-Dev Ops)*
Peter Madgett *(Asst Mgr-Orchestra Personnel)*
Kevin Devaux *(Mgr-Customer Svc)*
Matthew Jones *(Mgr-Info Sys)*
David Kent *(Mgr-Orchestra Personnel)*
Liz Parker *(Mgr-Publicity)*
Chris Walroth *(Mgr-Production)*
Suzy Yin *(Mgr-Acctg)*
Karen Turner *(Asst Mgr-Customer Svc)*
Christine King *(Coord-Ticketing Svcs)*

TOWN SPORTS INTERNATIONAL HOLDINGS, INC.

(d/b/a New York Sports Clubs)
5 Penn Plz 4th Fl
New York, NY 10001
Tel.: (212) 246-6700
Fax: (212) 246-8422
Web Site: www.mysportsclubs.com
Approx. Rev.: $462,387,000
Approx. Number Employees: 2,200
Year Founded: 2004
Business Description:
Holding Company; Fitness & Recreational Sports Centers Owner & Operator
S.I.C.: 6719; 7991; 7999
N.A.I.C.S.: 551112; 611620; 713940
Advertising Expenditures: $6,690,000
Media: 8-13-19-23-24
Personnel:
Thomas J. Galligan, III *(Chm)*
Robert J. Giardina *(Pres & CEO)*
Daniel Gallagher *(CFO)*
Martin Annese *(COO)*
Paul Barron *(CIO)*
David M. Kastin *(Gen Counsel, Sec & Sr VP)*
Margaret Houren *(Sr VP-Info Svcs)*
Brands & Products:
BOSTON SPORTS CLUBS
NEW YORK SPORTS CLUBS
PHILADELPHIA SPORTS CLUBS
TOWN SPORTS
WASHINGTON SPORTS CLUBS

TRANS CONTINENTAL ENTERTAINMENT GROUP, INC.

127 W Church St Ste 300
Orlando, FL 32801
Tel.: (407) 244-3400
Fax: (407) 244-3335
Toll Free: (866) 582-4201
E-mail: info@talentrock.com
Web Site: www.talentrock.com
Approx. Number Employees: 350
Business Description:
Talent Scout
S.I.C.: 7389
N.A.I.C.S.: 711410
Media: 13-20-22
Personnel:
Lou Pearlman *(Founder & Chm)*
Brands & Products:
FASHION ROCK

TUCSON SYMPHONY ORCHESTRA

2175 N 6th Ave
Tucson, AZ 85705-5606
Tel.: (520) 792-9155
Fax: (520) 792-9314
Web Site: www.tucsonsymphony.org
Approx. Number Employees: 110
Business Description:
Symphony Orchestra
S.I.C.: 7929
N.A.I.C.S.: 711130
Media: 7-8-9-13-18-20-22-23-24-25
Personnel:
Barbara Heineman *(Dir-Fin)*
Susan Franano *(Exec Dir)*
Sue DeBenedette *(Dir-Mktg & PR)*
Shawn A. Campbell *(Dir-Education & Community Engagement)*
George Hanson *(Dir-Music)*
Wanda L. Kay *(Dir-Dev)*
Eric Holtan *(Asst Dir-TSO Chorus)*
G. Mark Sandberg *(Mgr-Production Stage)*
John Campbell *(Asst Mgr-Box Office)*
Mary Lindley *(Mgr-Education Programs)*

UBISOFT INC.

(Sub. of Ubisoft Entertainment S.A.)
625 Third St
San Francisco, CA 94107
Tel.: (415) 547-4000
Fax: (415) 547-4001
Web Site: www.ubi.com
Business Description:
Interactive Entertainment Products Developer, Publisher & Distr
S.I.C.: 7372; 3944; 5045
N.A.I.C.S.: 511210; 339932; 423430
Personnel:
Laurent Detoc *(Pres)*
Jaime Borasi *(Dir-PR)*
Jeffrey Dickstein *(Dir-Sls-Digital Adv)*
Justin Landskron *(Dir-Digital Mktg)*
Adam Novickas *(Dir-Mktg)*
Carrie Feigel *(Sr Brand Mgr-Nintendo)*

Advertising Agencies:
Cutwater
55 Union St
San Francisco, CA 94111-1227
Tel.: (415) 315-4100
Fax: (415) 315-4200

Zenith Media
2049 Century Park E Ste 1300
Los Angeles, CA 90067
Tel.: (310) 551-3500
Fax: (310) 551-4119
(Media Buying & Planning)

UNITED STATES OLYMPIC COMMITTEE

(d/b/a USOC)
One Olympic Plz
Colorado Springs, CO 80909-5766
Tel.: (719) 632-5551
Fax: (719) 632-0250
E-mail: media@usoc.org
Web Site: www.teamusa.org
Year Founded: 1978
Business Description:
U.S. Arm of the International Olympic Committee
S.I.C.: 8699
N.A.I.C.S.: 813990
Media: 6-8-13-15-18-20-22
Personnel:
Larry Probst *(Chm)*
Scott Blackmun *(CEO)*
Norman Bellingham *(COO)*
Lisa Baird *(CMO)*
Advertising Agencies:
McGarry Bowen, LLC
601 W 26th St Ste 1150
New York, NY 10001
Tel.: (212) 598-2900
Fax: (212) 598-2996

Merkle Inc.
7001 Columbia Gateway Dr
Columbia, MD 21046
Tel.: (443) 542-4000
Fax: (443) 542-4001
Direct Mail Fundraising

VML, Inc.
250 Richards Rd
Kansas City, MO 64116-4279
Tel.: (816) 283-0700
Fax: (816) 283-0954
Toll Free: (800) 990-2468
Brand Communications
Digital
Marketing
Print
Social Media

Y&R
285 Madison Ave
New York, NY 10017-6401
Tel.: (212) 210-3000
Fax: (212) 490-9073
Fax: (212) 370-3796
Fax: (212) 210-5169
Brand Communications
Digital
Marketing
Print
Social Media

Key to Media (For complete agency information see *The Advertising Red Books-Agencies* edition):
1. Bus. Publs. 2. Cable T.V. 3. Catalogs & Directories. 4. Co-op Adv. 5. Consumer Mags. 6. D.M. to Bus. Estab.7. D.M. to Consumers 8. Daily Newsp. 9. Exhibits/Trade Shows 10. Foreign 11. Infomercial 12. Internet Adv.13. Multimedia 14. Network Radio 15. Network T.V. 16. Newsp. Distr. Mags. 17. Other 18. Outdoor (Posters, Transit) 19. Point of Purchase20. Premiums, Novelties 21. Product Samples 22. Special Events Mktg. 23. Spot Radio 24. Spot T.V. 25. Weekly Newsp. 26. Yellow Page Adv.

UNIVERSAL ORLANDO
(Joint Venture of Rank America Inc.)
1000 Universal Studios Plz
Orlando, FL 32819-7601
Tel.: (407) 363-8000
Fax: (407) 363-8090
Web Site: www.usf.com
Business Description:
Television Film Studio & Motion Picture Theme Park Operator
S.I.C.: 7996
N.A.I.C.S.: 713110
Media: 3-6-8-9-13-18-20-22-23-24-25
Personnel:
Tom Roditus *(Mng Dir)*
Kurt Kostur *(Sr VP-Mktg)*
Fred Lounsberry *(VP-Sls)*
Tom Schroder *(VP-Corp Comm)*
Diane Petit *(Gen Mgr-Loews Portofino Bay Hotel)*
Advertising Agency:
David & Goliath
909 N Sepulveda Blvd Ste 700
El Segundo, CA 90245
Tel.: (310) 445-5200
Fax: (310) 445-5201
(18th Annual Halloween Horror Nights)

UTAH SYMPHONY & OPERA
Abavenel Hall 123 W S Temple
Salt Lake City, UT 84101-1496
Tel.: (801) 533-5626
Fax: (801) 869-9026
E-mail: info@utahsymphony.org
Web Site:
www.utahsymphonyopera.org
Approx. Rev.: $11,000,000
Approx. Number Employees: 130
Year Founded: 1940
Business Description:
Symphony Orchestra & Opera Producer
S.I.C.: 7922; 7929
N.A.I.C.S.: 711110; 711130
Media: 7-8-9-20-23-24-25
Personnel:
Steve Hogan *(CFO & VP-Fin)*
David S. Green *(COO & Sr VP)*
Shelley Gillespie *(Coord-Dev)*
Rose Brown *(Dir-Opera Costume)*
Paula Fowler *(Dir-Education & Community Outreach)*
Keith Lockhart *(Dir-Music)*
Lisa Hagan Bruemmer *(Asst Mgr-Personnel)*
Devon Schwartz *(Asst Mgr-Stage)*
Llewellyn Humphreys *(Mgr-Personnel)*
Michelle Peterson *(Mgr)*

THE UTICA SYMPHONY ORCHESTRA
261 Genesee St
Utica, NY 13501
Tel.: (315) 732-5146
Fax: (315) 732-5147
E-mail: executivedirector@uticasymphony.net
Web Site: www.uticasymphony.net
Sales Range: Less than $1 Million
Approx. Number Employees: 75
Business Description:
Symphony Orchestra
S.I.C.: 7389
N.A.I.C.S.: 711320
Media: 8-9-20-23-24-25
Personnel:
Carol Gilberti *(Pres)*
Adam Kelly *(Exec VP)*
Charles Schneider *(Dir-Music)*

VANCOUVER SYMPHONY ORCHESTRA
601 Smithe St
Vancouver, BC Canada
Tel.: (604) 876-3434
Fax: (604) 684-9264
E-mail: customerservice@vancouversymphony.ca
Web Site:
www.vancouversymphony.ca
Approx. Number Employees: 100
Year Founded: 1919
Business Description:
Symphony Orchestra
S.I.C.: 7929
N.A.I.C.S.: 711190
Media: 2-3-7-8-9-13-20-22-23-24-25
Personnel:
Alan Pyatt *(Vice-Chm)*
Arthur H. Willms *(Chm)*
Jeff Alexander *(Pres & CEO)*
Alan Gove *(VP-Mktg & Sls)*
Mary Ann Moir *(VP-Fin & Admin)*
Debra Marcus *(Dir-IT & HR)*
Jennifer Polci *(Dir-Corp & Major Gifts)*
Cameron Rowe *(Dir-Ticketing & Audience Svcs)*
Bramwell Tovey *(Dir-Music)*
Shirley Bidewell *(Mgr-Gift Shop & Volunteer Resources)*
Lawrence Blackman *(Mgr-Orchestra Personnel)*
Stephanie Fung *(Mgr-Mktg Projects)*
Kenn Livingstone *(Mgr-Database)*

VCG HOLDING CORP.
390 Union Blvd Ste 540
Lakewood, CO 80228
Tel.: (303) 934-2424
Web Site: www.vcgh.com
Approx. Rev.: $55,269,961
Approx. Number Employees: 868
Year Founded: 2002
Business Description:
Adult Night Club & Sports Bar Owner & Operator
S.I.C.: 7999; 5812; 5813
N.A.I.C.S.: 713990; 722110; 722410
Advertising Expenditures: $2,805,260
Media: 6-9-18-22-25
Personnel:
Troy H. Lowrie *(Chm & CEO)*
Michael L. Ocello *(Pres & COO)*

VERMONT SYMPHONY ORCHESTRA
2 Church St Ste 19
Burlington, VT 05401-4457
Tel.: (802) 864-5741
Fax: (802) 864-5109
Toll Free: (800) VSO-9293
E-mail: info@vso.org
Web Site: www.vso.org
Sales Range: $10-24.9 Million
Approx. Number Employees: 57
Business Description:
Symphony Orchestra
S.I.C.: 7929
N.A.I.C.S.: 711130
Media: 7-8-9-20-22-23-24-25
Personnel:
Kenley Squier *(Chm)*
Rebecca Stone *(Dir-Mktg)*
Samantha Talbot *(Office Mgr)*
Eleanor Long *(Mgr-Orchestra)*

VICTORIA SYMPHONY SOCIETY
620 View St Ste 610
Victoria, BC V8W 1J6, Canada
Tel.: (250) 385-9771
Fax: (250) 385-7767
E-mail: administration@victoriasymphony.ca
Web Site: www.victoriasymphony.ca
Approx. Number Employees: 11
Business Description:
Symphony Orchestra
S.I.C.: 7929
N.A.I.C.S.: 711190
Media: 9-20-22-23-24-25
Personnel:
Marsha Hanen *(Pres)*
Tania Miller *(Dir-Music)*
Pat Taylor *(Dir-Fin)*
Lynn Mesher *(Office Mgr)*

VIRGIN ENTERTAINMENT GROUP, INC.
(Sub. of Virgin Group Ltd.)
5757 Wilshire Blvd Ste 300
Los Angeles, CA 90036
Tel.: (323) 935-1500
Web Site: www.virginmega.com
Approx. Number Employees: 1,000
Year Founded: 1992
Business Description:
Music, Movies & Other Media Products Mail Ordering Services & Retail Store Operator
S.I.C.: 5735; 5731; 5961
N.A.I.C.S.: 451220; 443112; 454111; 454113
Advertising Agencies:
Ashba Media
700 San Vicente Ste G410
West Hollywood, CA 90069
Tel.: (310) 385-4716
Fax: (818) 991-4399
Toll Free: (888) 882-0432

SJ Communications
25251 Paseo De Alicia Ste 200
Los Angeles, CA 92653
Tel.: (818) 881-3889
Fax: (818) 332-4212

VIRGINIA BEACH SYMPHONY ORCHESTRA LEAGUE
PO Box 2544
Virginia Beach, VA 23450-2544
Tel.: (757) 671-8611
E-mail: vbsoed@aol.com
Web Site: www.vbso.org
Year Founded: 1981
Business Description:
Symphony Orchestra
S.I.C.: 7929
N.A.I.C.S.: 711130
Media: 9-20-23-24-25
Personnel:
David S. Kunkel *(Dir-Music)*

VIRGINIA SYMPHONY ORCHESTRA
861 Glenroock Rd Ste 200
Norfolk, VA 23502
Tel.: (757) 466-3060
Fax: (757) 466-3046
Web Site: www.virginiasymphony.org
Approx. Number Employees: 125
Year Founded: 1920
Business Description:
Symphony Orchestra
S.I.C.: 7929
N.A.I.C.S.: 711130
Media: 7-8-9-13-20-22-23-24-25
Personnel:
Lana Sadowski *(Assoc Dir-Mktg)*
Susan Colpitts *(Dir)*
JoAnn Falletta *(Dir-Music)*
Donna Hudgins *(Dir-PR)*
Kaitlin Padden Robb *(Asst Dir-Dev)*
Sylvia Stewart *(Mgr-House & Coord-Volunteer)*
Terrie Carpenter *(Mgr-Box Office)*
Kevin Genus *(Mgr-Production)*
Ray Landon *(Mgr-Chorus)*

VISION GAMING & TECHNOLOGY INC.
2055 Boggs Rd
Duluth, GA 30096-4690
Tel.: (770) 923-9900
Fax: (770) 923-0097
Fax: (678) 226-0226
E-mail: info@visiongamingtech.com
Web Site: www.vision-gaming.com
Approx. Rev.: $15,566,000
Approx. Number Employees: 49
Year Founded: 1993
Business Description:
Amusement & Recreational Services
S.I.C.: 7999; 7371
N.A.I.C.S.: 713990; 541511
Import Export
Media: 6-10
Brands & Products:
54 CARD POKER
8 BALL POKER
AMERICAN STAR KENO
B-BALL KENO
BAYOU MAGIC
BEST GUESS BONUS
BLACK GOLD 21
BLACKGOLD 21
BOUNTIFUL BONUS
BUSH BUCKS
COUNTERTOP CHAMPION
DEUCES WILD
DOUBLE-UP KENO
DRAGONS LAIR
GOLD ROW BONUS
GOOFY GOPHERS!
JACKS OR BETTER
JOKER POKER
KING OF THE RING
LIGHTNING KENO
MYSTIC WILD CARD
PIGGIES WILD
POKER PLUS
POT O' GOLD
POT O' GOLD A K $1000 BLACKJACK
POTLUCK BINGO
PROGRESSIVE BLACKJACK PROCESS
RACE MASTER
ROAMING SUITS
SHAMROCK 7'S
SHAMROCK POKER
SLOT PLUS
SNAKE EYES
SPINBALL BONUS
SPOILS OF WAR
SUPER DOUBLE-UP KENO
SUPERBALL KENO
SUPERGOLD BINGO
SUPERPICK LOTTO

Key to Media (For complete agency information see *The Advertising Red Books-Agencies* edition):
1. Bus. Publs. 2. Cable T.V. 3. Catalogs & Directories. 4. Co-op Adv. 5. Consumer Mags. 6. D.M. to Bus. Estab.7. D.M. to Consumers 8. Daily Newsp. 9. Exhibits/Trade Shows 10. Foreign 11. Infomercial 12. Internet Adv.13. Multimedia 14. Network Radio 15. Network T.V. 16. Newsp. Distr. Mags. 17. Other 18. Outdoor (Posters, Transit) 19. Point of Purchase20. Premiums, Novelties 21. Product Samples 22. Special Events Mktg. 23. Spot Radio 24. Spot T.V. 25. Weekly Newsp. 26. Yellow Page Adv.

TALISMAN POKER
TOUCH 6 LOTTO
TOUCHEASY KENO
TRIPLE 7'S
VISION GAMING & TECHNOLOGY INC
WILD JOKER

WALLA WALLA SYMPHONY SOCIETY

PO Box 92
Walla Walla, WA 99362
Tel.: (509) 529-8020
Fax: (509) 529-1353
E-mail: info@wwsymphony.org
Web Site: www.wwsymphony.org
Year Founded: 1907
Business Description:
Symphony Orchestra
S.I.C.: 7929
N.A.I.C.S.: 711190
Media: 7-8-9-13-20-23-24-25
Personnel:
Michael Wenberg *(CEO)*
Yaacov Bergman *(Dir-Music & Conductor)*

WALT DISNEY WORLD CO.

(Sub. of Walt Disney Parks & Resorts)
PO Box 10000
Lake Buena Vista, FL 32830-1000
Tel.: (407) 824-2222
Fax: (407) 566-5700
Fax: (407) 828-8174
E-mail: wdw.guest.communications@disneyworld.com
Web Site: www.disneyworld.com
Approx. Number Employees: 55,000
Year Founded: 1971
Business Description:
Operator of Resort
S.I.C.: 2389
N.A.I.C.S.: 315299
Media: 1-2-3-4-6-8-9-10-11-13-15-18-19-20-22-23-24-25-26
Distr.: Natl.
Budget Set: Oct.
Personnel:
Robert A. Iger *(Pres & CEO)*
Jayne Parker *(Chief HR Officer & Exec VP)*
Alan Braverman *(Gen Counsel, Sec & Sr Exec VP)*
Christine M. Mccarthy *(Treas & Exec VP-Corp Real Estate, Sourcing & Alliances)*
Kevin Mayer *(Exec VP-Corp Strategy & Bus Dev)*
Zenia Mucha *(Exec VP-Corp Comm-The Walt Disney Co)*
Brian Besanceney *(Sr VP-Pub Affairs, Worldwide Govt & Indus Rels)*
Ronald L. Iden *(Sr VP-Global Security)*
Brent Woodford *(Sr VP-Plng & Control)*
Jeff Larson *(VP-Adv)*
Leanne Jakubowski *(Dir-Social Media)*
Jacquee Polak *(Dir-Pub Affairs)*
Brands & Products:
DISNEY'S ANIMAL KINGDOM
EPCOT
MAGIC KINGDOM
WALT DISNEY WORLD
Advertising Agencies:
Leo Burnett Worldwide, Inc.
35 W Wacker Dr
Chicago, IL 60601-1723
Tel.: (312) 220-5959
Fax: (312) 220-3299

McGarry Bowen, LLC
601 W 26th St Ste 1150
New York, NY 10001
Tel.: (212) 598-2900
Fax: (212) 598-2996

Starcom MediaVest Group
35 W Wacker Dr
Chicago, IL 60601-1723
Tel.: (312) 220-3535
Fax: (312) 220-6530

WARNER MUSIC GROUP CORP.

75 Rockefeller Plz
New York, NY 10019
Tel.: (212) 275-2000
Fax: (212) 757-3985
Web Site: www.wmg.com
Approx. Rev.: $2,984,000,000
Approx. Number Employees: 3,700
Year Founded: 1929
Business Description:
Records, Tapes & Music Publisher
S.I.C.: 2741; 3652; 7999
N.A.I.C.S.: 512230; 334612; 713990
Advertising Expenditures: $106,000,000
Media: 1-2-3-4-6-8-9-12-13-14-15-17-23-24-25
Personnel:
Edgar M. Bronfman, Jr. *(Chm)*
John Reid *(Vice Chm-Warner Music Intl & CEO-Warner Music Europe)*
Michael D. Fleisher *(Vice Chm-Strategy & Ops)*
Stephen F. Cooper *(CEO)*
Ron Wilcox *(Exec Counsel-Bus Affairs, Strategic & Digital Initiatives)*
Lyor Cohen *(Chm/CEO-Recorded Music-Americas & UK)*
Kevin Gore *(Pres/CEO-Rhino Entertainment)*
Cameron Strang *(CEO-Warner Chappell Music Inc)*
Paul M. Robinson *(Gen Counsel & Exec VP)*
Chris Ancliff *(Gen Counsel)*
William Tanous *(Exec VP-Comm & Mktg)*
Stephen Bryan *(Sr VP-Digital Strategy & Bus Dev)*
David Marcus *(Sr VP-Artist Svcs-Worldwide)*
Jim Reid *(Sr VP-Synchronisation-Europe)*
Susan Mazo *(VP-Corp Comm)*
David Orleans *(Gen Mgr-Alternative Distr Alliance)*
Raoul Chatterjee *(Dir-Comml Innovation)*
Brands & Products:
ATLANTIC
BAD BOY
CORDLESS
ELEKTRA
LAVA
MAVERICK
NONESUCH
REPRISE
RHINO
ROADRUNNER
RYKODISC
SIRE
WARNER BROS.
WARNER MUSIC GROUP
WORD
Advertising Agency:
The Geary Company
3136 E Russell Rd
Las Vegas, NV 89120-3463
Tel.: (702) 382-9610
Fax: (702) 382-0920

WASHINGTON CAPITALS

(Holding of Lincoln Holdings, LLC)
627 N Glebe Rd Ste 850
Arlington, VA 22203
Tel.: (202) 266-2200
Fax: (202) 266-2360
E-mail: info@washcaps.com
Web Site: www.washingtoncaps.com
E-Mail For Key Personnel:
Sales Director: groupsales@washcaps.com
Approx. Number Employees: 35
Year Founded: 1974
Business Description:
Professional Hockey Franchise
S.I.C.: 7941
N.A.I.C.S.: 711211
Media: 5-9-13-14-15-20-22-23-24
Personnel:
Theodore J. Leonsis *(Owner, Chm & CEO)*
Richard M. Patrick *(Vice Chm, Team Pres & COO)*
Joseph Dupriest *(CMO & VP)*
Kurt Kehl *(Chief Comm Officer & VP-Comm)*
James Van Stone *(Sr VP-Ticket Sls)*
George McPhee *(VP & Gen Mgr)*
Keith Burrows *(VP-Fin)*
Don Fishman *(Asst Gen Mgr & Dir-Legal Affairs)*
Brian MacLellan *(Asst Gen Mgr & Dir-Player Personnel)*
Anthony Aspaas *(Sr Dir-Ticket Sls)*
John Greeley *(Sr Dir-Corp Sls)*
Brian McPartland *(Sr Dir-IT)*
Tim Bronaugh *(Dir-Amateur Hockey Sls)*
Nate Ewell *(Dir-Media Relations)*
Kim Frank *(Dir-Fan Dev & Promos)*
Greg Monares *(Dir-Guest Svcs)*
Sean Parker *(Dir-Digital Media)*
Steve Richmond *(Dir-Player Dev)*
Jill Ruehle *(Dir-Acctg)*
Christopher Sheap *(Dir-Ticket Ops)*
Kris Wagner *(Dir-Scouting Ops)*
Elizabeth Wodatch *(Dir-Community Rels)*
Letitia Petrillo *(Reg Mgr-Sls)*
David Boettinger *(Sr Mgr-Sls Reg)*
Brands & Products:
CAPSCARE
WASHINGTON CAPITALS
Advertising Agency:
Alexander & Tom
3500 Boston St Ste 225
Baltimore, MD 21224-5275
Tel.: (410) 327-7400
Fax: (410) 327-7403

WASHINGTON FOOTBALL, INC.

(d/b/a Washington Redskins)
21300 Redskin Park Dr
Ashburn, VA 20147
Tel.: (703) 726-7411
Fax: (703) 726-7086
Web Site: www.redskins.com
Approx. Number Employees: 750
Year Founded: 1932
Business Description:
Professional Football Franchise
S.I.C.: 7941
N.A.I.C.S.: 711211
Media: 10-13-20-22
Distr.: Natl.
Personnel:
Daniel M. Snyder *(Owner & Chm)*
Mitch Gershman *(CMO)*
Dennis Greene *(Pres-Bus Ops)*
Mike Shanahan *(Exec VP-Football Ops & Head Coach-Redskins)*
Bruce Allen *(Exec VP & Gen Mgr)*
Ken Harvey *(Dir-Responsibility)*
Brands & Products:
WASHINGTON REDSKINS

WASHINGTON NATIONAL OPERA

2600 Virginia Ave NW
Washington, DC 20037-3301
Tel.: (202) 295-2420
Fax: (202) 295-2479
E-mail: info@dc-opera.org
Web Site: www.dc-opera.org
Sales Range: $25-49.9 Million
Approx. Number Employees: 75
Business Description:
Opera Music & Theatre Production Services
S.I.C.: 7922
N.A.I.C.S.: 711110
Media: 8-9-18-20-23-24-25
Personnel:
Kenneth R. Feinberg *(Pres)*
Placido Domingo *(Gen Dir)*
Philippe Auguin *(Dir-Music)*

WASHINGTON NATIONALS, L.P.

1500 S Capitol St SE
Washington, DC 20003-1507
Tel.: (202) 675-6287
Fax: (202) 640-7107
E-mail: tanya.johnson@nationals.com
Web Site: www.nationals.com
Approx. Number Employees: 200
Business Description:
Professional Baseball Club
S.I.C.: 7941
N.A.I.C.S.: 711211
Media: 1-18-20-22-23-24
Personnel:
Stan Kasten *(Pres)*
Squire Galbreath *(Partner)*
Lori Creasy *(CFO)*
Tom Ward *(CMO & Sr VP)*
Alphonso Maldon, Jr. *(Pres-Washington Natls Dream Foundation)*
Damon T. Jones *(Gen Counsel & VP)*
Mike Rizzo *(Exec VP-Baseball Ops & Gen Mgr)*
Bob Wolfe *(Exec VP)*
Bob Boone *(VP-Player Dev & Asst Gen Mgr)*
John Guagliano *(VP-Mktg & Brdcst)*
John Dever *(Sr Dir-Baseball Media Rels)*
Dana Brown *(Dir-Scouting)*
Mike Gazda *(Dir-Baseball Media Rels)*
Kelly Pitchford *(Dir-Acctg)*
Mark Scialabba *(Dir-Minor League Ops)*

Key to Media (For complete agency information see *The Advertising Red Books-Agencies* edition):
1. Bus. Publs. 2. Cable T.V. 3. Catalogs & Directories. 4. Co-op Adv. 5. Consumer Mags. 6. D.M. to Bus. Estab.7. D.M. to Consumers
8. Daily Newsp. 9. Exhibits/Trade Shows 10. Foreign 11. Infomercial 12. Internet Adv.13. Multimedia 14. Network Radio
15. Network T.V. 16. Newsp. Distr. Mags. 17. Other 18. Outdoor (Posters, Transit) 19. Point of Purchase20. Premiums, Novelties
21. Product Samples 22. Special Events Mktg. 23. Spot Radio 24. Spot T.V. 25. Weekly Newsp. 26. Yellow Page Adv.

Washington Nationals, L.P. — (Continued)

Advertising Agencies:
MLB Advanced Media, L.P.
75 9th Ave 5th Fl
New York, NY 10011
Tel.: (212) 485-3444
Fax: (212) 485-3456

OLSON
1625 Hennepin Ave
Minneapolis, MN 55403
Tel.: (612) 215-9800
Fax: (612) 215-9801

White & Partners
13665 Dulles Technology Dr Ste 150
Herndon, VA 20171-4607
Tel.: (703) 793-3000
Fax: (703) 793-1495
Toll Free: (800) 211-0874

WASHINGTON WIZARDS

(Unit of Washington Sports & Entertainment, L.P.)
601 F St NW
Washington, DC 20004-1605
Tel.: (202) 661-5000
Fax: (202) 661-5101
E-mail: wizardsfan@washsports.com
Web Site: www.nba.com/wizards
E-Mail For Key Personnel:
Marketing Director: anicolaides@washsports.com
Approx. Number Employees: 100
Year Founded: 1961
Business Description:
Professional Basketball Franchise
S.I.C.: 7941
N.A.I.C.S.: 711211
Advertising Expenditures: $750,000
Media: 3-7-8-9-10-14-15-22-23-24
Distr.: Local
Personnel:
Ernie Grunfeld *(Pres)*
Judy Holland *(Sr VP-Washington Sports & Entertainment)*
Rick Moreland *(Sr VP-Sls & Corp Mktg)*
Ann Nicolaides *(VP-Mktg)*
Missy Rentz *(VP-Mktg)*
Bill Hanni *(Sr Dir-Ticket Sls)*

Brands & Products:
WIZARDS

WATERLOO-CEDAR FALLS SYMPHONY ORCHESTRA

Gallagher-Bluedorn Performing Arts Ctr
Cedar Falls, IA 50614-0803
Tel.: (319) 273-3373
Fax: (319) 273-3363
E-mail: information@wcfsymphony.org
Web Site: www.wcfsymphony.org
Sales Range: Less than $1 Million
Approx. Number Employees: 80
Year Founded: 1929
Business Description:
Symphony Orchestra
S.I.C.: 8641
N.A.I.C.S.: 813410
Media: 8-9-20-22-23-24-25
Personnel:
Jason Weinberger *(Dir-Music)*

WCCO-TV

(Unit of CBS Television Stations Inc.)
90 S 11th St
Minneapolis, MN 55403-2414
Tel.: (612) 339-4444
Fax: (612) 330-2767
E-mail: wcconewstips@wcco.com
Web Site: www.wcco.com
Business Description:
Television Broadcasting Services
S.I.C.: 4833
N.A.I.C.S.: 515120
Media: 9-18-24
Personnel:
Brien Kennedy *(VP & Gen Mgr)*
Mike Caputa *(Dir-News)*
Mark Rosen *(Dir-Sports)*

WEEKI WACHEE SPRINGS, LLC

(d/b/a Weeki Wachee Springs State Park)
6131 Commercial Way
Weeki Wachee, FL 34606-1121
Tel.: (352) 592-5656
Fax: (352) 592-5689
E-mail: info@weekiwachee.com
Web Site: www.weekiwachee.com
Approx. Number Employees: 100
Year Founded: 1946
Business Description:
Natural Spring & Theme Park
S.I.C.: 7999; 7996
N.A.I.C.S.: 712190; 713110
Media: 4-6-8-10-17-18-19-23-24-25-26
Distr.: Direct to Consumer
Budget Set: Aug.
Personnel:
Robyn Anderson *(Gen Mgr)*
Tolby Brewer *(Gen Mgr)*
John Athanason *(Dir-Mktg & Pub Rel)*

WENATCHEE VALLEY SYMPHONY

20 N Cleveland Ave
Wenatchee, WA 98801-2649
Mailing Address:
PO Box 3423
Wenatchee, WA 98807
Tel.: (509) 667-2640
Tel.: (509) 667-0904
E-mail: wensymphony@aol.com
Web Site:
www.wenatcheesymphony.com
Year Founded: 1947
Business Description:
Symphony Orchestra
S.I.C.: 7929
N.A.I.C.S.: 711130
Media: 9-20-23-24-25
Personnel:
Beth Jensen *(Exec Dir)*
Marty Zyskowski *(Dir-Music & Conductor)*

WEST VIRGINIA SYMPHONY ORCHESTRA INC.

1 Clay Sq
Charleston, WV 25301
Tel.: (304) 561-3551
Tel.: (304) 561-3504 (Mktg)
Fax: (304) 561-3598
E-mail: info@wvsymphony.org
Web Site: www.wvsymphony.org
Approx. Number Employees: 10
Year Founded: 1939
Business Description:
Symphony Orchestra
S.I.C.: 7929
N.A.I.C.S.: 711130
Media: 9-20-23-24-25
Personnel:
Daniel S. Foster *(Chm)*
David Gross *(Pres)*
Marcia Grazes *(Office Mgr)*
Bob Turizziani *(Mgr-Personnel)*

WESTCHESTER PHILHARMONIC

123 Main St Lbby Level
White Plains, NY 10601
Tel.: (914) 682-3707
Fax: (914) 682-3716
E-mail: info@westchesterphil.org
Web Site: www.westchesterphil.org
Approx. Number Employees: 75
Business Description:
Symphony Orchestra
S.I.C.: 7929
N.A.I.C.S.: 711130
Media: 8-9-13-18-20-23-24-25
Personnel:
Neil Aaron *(Pres)*
Joshua Worby *(Exec Dir)*
Lenore Eggleston *(Dir-Mktg)*
Itzhak Perlman *(Artistic Dir)*
Jonathan Taylor *(Mgr-Personnel & Artistic Administrator)*

WESTERN PIEDMONT SYMPHONY

243 3rd Ave NE Ste 1-N
Hickory, NC 28601
Tel.: (828) 324-8603
Fax: (828) 324-1301
E-mail: info@wpsymphony.org
Web Site: www.wpsymphony.org
Approx. Number Employees: 125
Business Description:
Symphony Orchestra
S.I.C.: 7929
N.A.I.C.S.: 711130
Media: 9-20-23-24-25
Personnel:
Brian Adair *(Pres)*
Chris Brown *(Exec Dir)*
Paulette Miller *(Dir-Mktg)*
John Gordon Ross *(Dir-Music & Conductor)*
R.J. Wohlman *(Librarian)*

WESTERN REGIONAL OFF-TRACK BETTING CORPORATION

700 Ellicott St
Batavia, NY 14020-3744
Tel.: (585) 343-1423
Fax: (585) 343-6873
Toll Free: (800) 724-2000
E-mail: info@westernotb.com
Web Site: www.batavia-downs.com
Approx. Number Employees: 514
Year Founded: 1973
Business Description:
Pari-Mutual Off-Track Wagering
S.I.C.: 1623; 7999
N.A.I.C.S.: 237110; 713290
Media: 3-8-9-18-20-22-23-24-25
Distr.: Reg.
Personnel:
Martin C. Basinait *(Pres, CEO & Gen Mgr)*
Michael Kane *(Pres & CEO-Batavia Downs Gen Mgr)*
Timothy McCarthy *(Gen Counsel)*
Patrick Murphy *(Exec VP)*
James Haas *(Mgr-Mutuels & Comm)*

WESTERVILLE SYMPHONY ORCHESTRA

167 S State St
Westerville, OH 43086
Mailing Address:
PO Box 478
Westerville, OH 43086-0478
Tel.: (614) 899-9000
E-mail: info@westervillesymphony.org
Web Site:
www.westervillesymphony.org
Business Description:
Symphony Orchestra
S.I.C.: 7929
N.A.I.C.S.: 711130
Media: 8-9-20-23-24-25
Personnel:
Peter Stafford Wilson *(Dir-Music)*
Claire Brock *(Mgr-Ops)*

WESTMORELAND SYMPHONY ORCHESTRA

Ste 1 951 Old Salem Rd
Greensburg, PA 15601-1386
Tel.: (724) 837-1850
Fax: (724) 837-1342
E-mail: info@westmorelandsymphony.org
Web Site:
www.westmorelandsymphony.org
Approx. Rev.: $450,000
Approx. Number Employees: 3
Year Founded: 1969
Business Description:
Symphony Orchestra
S.I.C.: 8641
N.A.I.C.S.: 813410
Media: 9-20-22-23-24-25
Personnel:
Morrie Brand *(Exec Dir)*
Cheryl Cirelli *(Mgr-Office)*
Ramona Coppage *(Mgr-WYSO)*

WET 'N WILD, INC.

(Joint Venture of Comcast Corporation & General Electric Company)
6200 International Dr
Orlando, FL 32819
Tel.: (407) 351-1800
Fax: (407) 363-1147
Toll Free: (800) 992-WILD
E-mail: info@wetnwildorf.com
Web Site: www.wetnwildorlando.com
E-Mail For Key Personnel:
Public Relations: pr@wetnwildorf.com
Sales Range: $50-74.9 Million
Approx. Number Employees: 400
Year Founded: 1977
Business Description:
Amusement Park Services
S.I.C.: 7996
N.A.I.C.S.: 713110
Media: 4-8-13
Distr.: Reg.
Budget Set: Oct.
Personnel:
Mike Black *(Gen Mgr)*
Dave Wright *(Dir-Sls & Mktg)*

Brands & Products:
THE BLAST
THE STORM
WET 'N WILD

WF CINEMA HOLDINGS, L.P.

(d/b/a Mann Theatres)
16530 Ventura Blvd Ste 500

Key to Media (For complete agency information see *The Advertising Red Books-Agencies* edition):
1. Bus. Publs. 2. Cable T.V. 3. Catalogs & Directories. 4. Co-op Adv. 5. Consumer Mags. 6. D.M. to Bus. Estab.7. D.M. to Consumers
8. Daily Newsp. 9. Exhibits/Trade Shows 10. Foreign 11. Infomercial 12. Internet Adv.13. Multimedia 14. Network Radio
15. Network T.V. 16. Newsp. Distr. Mags. 17. Other 18. Outdoor (Posters, Transit) 19. Point of Purchase20. Premiums, Novelties
21. Product Samples 22. Special Events Mktg. 23. Spot Radio 24. Spot T.V. 25. Weekly Newsp. 26. Yellow Page Adv.

Encino, CA 91436
Mailing Address:
PO Box 20077
Encino, CA 91416-0077
Tel.: (818) 784-6266
Fax: (818) 784-6749
E-mail: talk2mann@manntheatres.com
Web Site: wf.manntheatres.com
Sales Range: $10-24.9 Million
Approx. Number Employees: 20
Year Founded: 2000
Business Description:
Movie Theater Owner & Operator
S.I.C.: 7832
N.A.I.C.S.: 512131
Media: 5-7-8-9-17-22-25
Personnel:
Peter Dobson *(Co-CEO)*
Sandy Rodriguez *(Dir-Mktg)*
Brands & Products:
BRUIN THEATRE
CRITERION 6
GRAUMAN'S CHINESE THEATRE
MANN CHINESE 6
MANN THEATRES
VILLAGE THEATRE

WHATCOM SYMPHONY ORCHESTRA

2915 Newmarket St Ste 104
Bellingham, WA 98228
Mailing Address:
PO Box 28895
Bellingham, WA 98228
Tel.: (360) 756-6752
Fax: (360) 756-6455
E-mail: info@whatcomsymphony.com
Web Site:
www.whatcomsymphony.com
Business Description:
Symphony Orchestra Services
S.I.C.: 7929
N.A.I.C.S.: 711130
Media: 9-20-23-24-25
Personnel:
Dave Bargelt *(Pres)*
Roger Briggs *(Dir)*

WICHITA SYMPHONY SOCIETY INC.

225 W Douglas Ste 207
Wichita, KS 67202
Tel.: (316) 267-5259
Fax: (316) 267-1937
E-mail: symphony@wso.org
Web Site: www.wso.org
Approx. Number Employees: 120
Business Description:
Symphony Orchestra
S.I.C.: 7929
N.A.I.C.S.: 711130
Media: 9-20-23-24-25
Personnel:
Cecil J. Riney *(Dir-Symphony Chorus)*
Andrew Sewell *(Dir-Music)*
Linda Marshall *(Bus Mgr)*
Michelle Wheeler *(Office Mgr)*
Anne Marie C. Brown *(Mgr-Ops)*

WILD ADVENTURES, INC.

3766 Old Clyattville Rd
Valdosta, GA 31601
Tel.: (229) 219-7080
Fax: (229) 559-1485
E-mail: humanresource@wildadventures.com
Web Site: www.wildadventures.com
Approx. Number Employees: 600
Business Description:
Provider of Amusement Rides, Shows, Animal Safaris, Concerts
S.I.C.: 7996
N.A.I.C.S.: 713110
Media: 10-18-23-24

WILDLIFE CONSERVATION SOCIETY

Bronx Zoo 2300 Southern Blvd
Bronx, NY 10460
Tel.: (718) 220-5100
Fax: (718) 220-5525
Fax: (718) 220-6890
E-mail: membership@wcs.org
Web Site: www.wcs.org
Approx. Number Employees: 110
Year Founded: 1895
Business Description:
Administration of Zoos & Wildlife Educational Programs
S.I.C.: 8422; 8299
N.A.I.C.S.: 712130; 611710
Advertising Expenditures: $500,000
Media: 8-10-13-20-22
Personnel:
Steven Sanderson *(Pres & CEO)*
Patricia Calabrese *(CFO & Exec VP-Admin)*
John R. Robinson *(Chief Conservation Officer & Exec VP)*
Robert Cook *(Exec VP & Gen Dir-Living Institutions)*
W. B. McKeown *(Gen Counsel & Sr VP)*
John Calvelli *(Exec VP-Pub Affairs)*
Kent Redford *(VP-Strategy)*
James Deutsch *(Dir-WCS-Africa)*
Michelle Levengood *(Mgr-Sls Grp-New York Zoos & Aquarium)*
Advertising Agency:
Deutsch, Inc.
(A Lowe & Partners Company)
111 8th Ave 14th Fl
New York, NY 10011-5201
Tel.: (212) 981-7600
Fax: (212) 981-7525

WILLIAMSPORT SYMPHONY ORCHESTRA

220 W Fourth St
Williamsport, PA 17701-6102
Tel.: (570) 322-0227
E-mail: info@willimsportsymphony.com
Web Site:
www.williamsportsymphony.com
Approx. Number Employees: 70
Business Description:
Symphony Orchestra
S.I.C.: 8641; 7389
N.A.I.C.S.: 813410; 711320
Media: 8-9-18-20-23-24-25
Personnel:
Miki Rebeck *(Pres)*
John J. Blair *(Dir-Mktg)*

WILMINGTON SYMPHONY ORCHESTRA

4608 Cedar Ave Ste 105
Wilmington, NC 28403
Tel.: (910) 791-9262
Fax: (910) 791-8970
E-mail: info@wilmingtonsymphony.org
Web Site:
www.wilmingtonsymphony.org
Approx. Rev.: $300,000
Business Description:
Symphony Orchestra
S.I.C.: 7929
N.A.I.C.S.: 711130
Media: 9-20-23-24-25
Personnel:
Robert Roer *(Pres)*
Reed Wallace *(Exec Dir)*
Steven Errante *(Dir-Musical & Conductor)*

WIND-UP RECORDS

(Sub. of Wind-up Entertainment, Inc.)
79 Madison Ave
New York, NY 10016
Tel.: (212) 895-3100
Fax: (212) 895-3285
Web Site: www.winduprecords.com
Business Description:
Music Company
S.I.C.: 2741
N.A.I.C.S.: 512230
Media: 10-13

WINDSOR SYMPHONY SOCIETY

487 Ouellette Ave
Windsor, ON Canada
Tel.: (519) 973-1238
Fax: (519) 973-0764
Toll Free: (888) 327-8327
Web Site:
www.windsorsymphony.com
Approx. Number Employees: 15
Year Founded: 1949
Business Description:
Symphony Orchestra
S.I.C.: 7929
N.A.I.C.S.: 711190
Media: 6-8-9-18-20-23-24-25
Personnel:
Vicky Kyriaco-Wilson *(Pres)*
Barbara Kuker *(1st VP)*
Jeth Mill *(Exec Dir)*
Susan McKee *(Dir-Mktg)*
Carolyne Daley *(Dir-Fin & Admin)*
Mina Grossman-Ianni *(Dir-Devel)*
John Morris Russell *(Dir-Music)*
Corey Fitzpatrick *(Mgr-Personnel & Asst Mgr-Ops)*

WINSTON-SALEM SYMPHONY ASSOCIATION INC.

680 W 4th St Ste 101
Winston Salem, NC 27101
Tel.: (336) 725-1035
Fax: (336) 725-3924
E-mail: mvale@wssymphony.org
Web Site: www.wssymphony.org
Approx. Number Employees: 12
Business Description:
Symphony Orchestra
S.I.C.: 7929
N.A.I.C.S.: 711130
Media: 8-9-20-23-24-25
Personnel:
Merritt Vale *(Pres & CEO)*
Selina Carter *(Dir-Fin)*
John Horsman *(Mgr-Ops & Stage)*

WISCONSIN CHAMBER ORCHESTRA

321 E Main St
Madison, WI 53703
Tel.: (608) 257-0638
Fax: (608) 257-0611
E-mail: wco@wcoconcerts.org
Web Site: www.wcoconcerts.org
Approx. Number Employees: 10
Year Founded: 1961
Business Description:
Symphony Orchestra
S.I.C.: 7929
N.A.I.C.S.: 711130
Advertising Expenditures: $10,000,000
Media: 4-7-8-9-10-13-20-22-23-24-25
Personnel:
Martha Scales *(Gen Mgr)*

WMS GAMING CHICAGO

(Branch of WMS Industries Inc.)
3401 N California Ave
Chicago, IL 60618
Tel.: (773) 961-1620
Fax: (773) 961-1234
E-mail: info@wmsgaming.com
Web Site: www.wmsgaming.com
Sales Range: $150-199.9 Million
Approx. Number Employees: 800
Year Founded: 1991
Business Description:
Mfr., Designer & Marketer of Slot Machines
S.I.C.: 3999
N.A.I.C.S.: 339999
Export
Personnel:
Brian R. Gamache *(Chm & CEO)*
Orrin J. Edidin *(Pres)*
Scott D. Schweinfurth *(CFO, Treas & Exec VP)*
Advertising Agency:
Ypartnership
423 S Keller Rd Ste 100
Orlando, FL 32810-6121
Tel.: (407) 875-1111
Fax: (407) 875-1115

WMS INDUSTRIES INC.

800 S Northpoint Blvd
Waukegan, IL 60085
Tel.: (847) 785-3000
Fax: (847) 785-3058
E-mail: webmaster@wmsgaming.com
Web Site: www.wms.com
Approx. Rev.: $783,300,000
Approx. Number Employees: 1,880
Year Founded: 1944
Business Description:
Mfr. & Designer of Coin-Operated Amusement Games & Video Lottery Terminals; Engineering, Manufacturing & Testing of Electronic & Electromechanical Products for Third Parties; Video Home Game Cartridges
S.I.C.: 2531; 2499; 3575; 3589; 3999; 5045; 5084; 7389; 7999
N.A.I.C.S.: 713290; 321999; 333319; 334113; 337127; 339999; 423830; 425110; 425120; 611620; 713990
Export
Advertising Expenditures: $800,000
Media: 1-2-4-6-7-10-11
Distr.: Intl.
Personnel:
Brian R. Gamache *(Chm & CEO)*
Orrin J. Edidin *(Pres)*
Scott D. Schweinfurth *(CFO, Treas & Exec VP)*
Kenneth Lochiatto *(COO & Exec VP)*
John P. McNicholas, Jr. *(Chief Acctg Officer, Controller & VP)*

Key to Media (For complete agency information see *The Advertising Red Books-Agencies* edition):
1. Bus. Publs. 2. Cable T.V. 3. Catalogs & Directories. 4. Co-op Adv. 5. Consumer Mags. 6. D.M. to Bus. Estab.7. D.M. to Consumers
8. Daily Newsp. 9. Exhibits/Trade Shows 10. Foreign 11. Infomercial 12. Internet Adv.13. Multimedia 14. Network Radio
15. Network T.V. 16. Newsp. Distr. Mags. 17. Other 18. Outdoor (Posters, Transit) 19. Point of Purchase20. Premiums, Novelties
21. Product Samples 22. Special Events Mktg. 23. Spot Radio 24. Spot T.V. 25. Weekly Newsp. 26. Yellow Page Adv.

WMS Industries Inc. — (Continued)

Larry J. Pacey *(Chief Innovation Officer & Exec VP-Global Products)*
Kathleen J. McJohn *(Gen Counsel, Sec & VP)*
Fred M. Gabbard *(Sr VP-Product Dev Ops)*
Michael P. Rutz *(Sr VP-Global Supply Chain)*
Rob Bone *(VP, Gen Mgr-Western Sls & Ops)*
Amy J. Lipton *(VP-Mktg)*
Louis J. Nicastro *(Dir-Founding)*
Edward W. Rabin, Jr. *(Dir-Lead)*

Brands & Products:
10 CARAT WINS
2X SHERIFF'S STARS
2X WILD & CRAZY
3 ALARM FIRE
3RV
3RV DESIGN
3X HOT HOT 777
5 LEVEL DEUCES WILD PLUS
5 LEVEL TENS OR BETTER
5X RAILROAD
9 SUNS
ADAPTIVE GAMING
ALL IN THE CARDS
ALL THAT GLITTERS
ALLAN QUATERMAIN
ALPINE ADVENTURE
AMAZING SEVENS
AMERICAN 7'S
AMERICAN 7'S PLUS
AMERICAN REELS
AMERICAN SPIRIT
ARMADA
AWESOME 8'S
AY CARAMBA
AZTEC ADVENTURE
BAMBOOZLED
BAND OF VIKINGS
BATTLESHIP
BEE BUCKS
THE BEST THINGS IN LIFE
BET THE FARM
BIG BAND PIGGY BANKIN
BIG BANG
BIG EVENT
BIG MONEY BOARD
BIG MONEY CHEESE CAPER
BIG MONEY SHOT
BIG TIPPERS
BIG X WILD
BIRTHDAY CASH
BLACK KNIGHT
BLAST FROM THE PAST
BLUE DIAMONDS
BLUE LAGOON
BLUE MOON
BLUEBIRD
BLUEBIRD 2 DESIGN
BLUEBIRD XD
BONKIN' BUCKS
BONUS BOOSTER
BONUS JACKS POKER
BOTTOM LINE
BOUNCING BUCKS
BRAZILIAN BEAUTY
BRIGHT DIAMONDS
BUCK 'N WIN
BURNING REELS
CAFE MULA
CAJUN FIRE
CAN'T LOSE
CAPTAIN'S COVE
CARNIVAL OF CASH
CASCADE MOUNTAIN
CASH CROP
CAST FOR CASH
CAT'S MEOW
CENTER STAR WILD
CHAIRMAN OF THE BOARD
CHARMING CHERRIES
CHERRY BLAST
CHERRY BOMB
CHIEFTAINS
CHILI PEPPER PARTY
CHINA MOON
CLASSIC TV GAME SHOW
CLUE
COLOR DOTMATION
COLOSSAL JACKPOTS
COMMUNITY GAMING
COMPETE TO WIN
COOL CAT CASH
CORNER THE MARKET
CORONADO GOLD
COUNT MONEY
COW TIPPING
CPU NXT
CPU NXT2
CRAZY DIAMONDS
CROCODILE CASH
CRYSTAL FOREST
DANCING DOLPHINS
DEJA VU DIAMONDS
DIAMOND HUNT
DIAMOND RIDGE
DIAMOND RING
DIAMONDS IN THE ROUGH
DIAMONDS OF DUBLIN
DIGGING FOR GOLD
DOLPHIN BAY
DOTMATION
DOUBLE EASY MONEY
DOUBLE KENO BLASTER
DOUBLE LIFE OF LUXURY
DOUBLE STAMPEDE DELUXE
DR. JACKPOT & MR. WILD
DRAGON FIRE
DRAGON WORLD
EASY HOLD
EGYPT
EGYPTIAN RICHES
EMERALD EYES
EMERALD RING
ENCHANTED KINGDOM
EXPLORE NEW WORLDS
EXTRA EXTRA LUCK
EXTRA POINT
THE EYE OF HORUS
EYE OF THE DRAGON
FAIRY'S FORTUNE
FAR EAST FORTUNES
FIERY SEVENS
FIRE ISLAND
FLUSH FORTUNE POKER
FOREVER SEVENS
FORTUNE SEEKER
FORTUNES OF THE CARIBBEAN
FREE PARKING
FREE SPIN BONANZA
FREE SPIN FRENZY
FREE SPIN MAXIMUS
FREE SPIN PLUNDER
FREEDOMPORT
FUN HOUSE
G+
GALACTIC PAYBACK
GAME OF DRAGONS
GAMING ZONE
GAZE OF STONE
GEM HUNTER
GEMS, GEMS, GEMS
GENIE & THE SULTAN'S JEWELS
GET HOOKED
GETTIN' LUCKY
THE GODFATHER
GOLD FISH
GOLD GOLD GOLD
GOLD TAG 7S
GOLDEN CHARIOTS
GOLDEN CHERRIES
GOLDEN EMPEROR
GOLDEN HAMMER
GOLDEN MOAI
GOLDEN PEARL
GOOSIN' AROUND
GRAND HOTEL
GREAT EAGLE
GREAT SCOT!
GREAT WALL
GRECIAN GOLD
GRIFFIN'S GATE
GUSHER
HAPPY DAYS
HEART & SOUL
HEARTS OF VENICE
HEAT WAVE
HELIOS
HIDDEN HAVEN
HIGH DOLLAR 7S
HIGH SPEED
HOG WILD
HOPPIN' WILD
HOT HOT 777
HOT HOT ACTION
HOT HOT JACKPOTS
HOT HOT PENNY
HOT HOT PENNY DESIGN
HOT HOT SUPER JACKPOT
HOT HOT SUPER RESPIN
HOT HOT TOURNAMENT POWER
HOT PICKS
HOT PROPERTIES
HOT TO TROT
HOT TOPPINGS
HOUDINI REELS OF MYSTERY
HUMMINGBIRD
INSTANT WINNER
INSTANT WINNER & DESIGN
INVADERS FROM THE PLANET MOOLAH
INVASION WILD
ISLAND FORTUNE
IT PAID FROM OUTER SPACE
JACKPOT BLOCK PARTY
JACKPOT CANYON
JACKPOT COMET
JACKPOT EXPLOSION
JACKPOT PARTY
JACKPOT PARTY PROGRESSIVE
JACKPOT STAMPEDE
JACKPOT STATION
THE JADE ELEPHANT
THE JADE MONKEY
JADE PALACE
JEWELS OF AFRICA
JEWELS OF ISIS
JEWELS OF THE NIGHT
JEWELS OF THE PHARAOH
JUMP JIVE & WIN
JUNGLE CATS
JUNGLE MAJESTY
JUNGLE WILD
KABOOM
KAHUNA KASH
KALEIDOSCOPE
KEEPIN' UP WITH THE JONESES
KENO BOOSTER
KENO BURST
KILAUEA FREE SPIN ERUPTION
KING MIDAS
KING OF AFRICA
KING OF THE WILD
KINGDOM OF THE TITANS
KNIGHTS & DRAGONS
KRAKATOA EAST OF JAVA
LADY OF SPAIN
LANCELOT
LEARNING EDGE
LEMON LIME TWIST
LEPRECHAUN'S GOLD
LIFE OF LUXURY
LIGHTHOUSE LOOT
LIGHTNING STRIKE
LIVE LOBSTERS DANCE PARTY
LIVE LOBSTERS DANCING NIGHTLY
LOOSE DIAMONDS
THE LORD OF THE RINGS
LOS AZTECAS
LOVE TO WIN
LUAU LOOT
LUCKY LEMMINGS
LUCKY LIZARD
LUCKY MEERKATS
LUCKY MONEY STACKS
LUCKY SEALS
MADAME X
MAGIC CRYSTAL
MAGIC LAMP
MAGIC TIME
MAGNETIC 7'S
MAH JONG LIGHTNING
MAJESTIC WOLF
MAORI RICHES
MARDI GRAS MADNESS
MAX YOUR EDGE
MAYAN SUN
MEGA MULTIPLIER
MEGA MULTIPLIER 125X
MERMAID'S GOLD
MERMAID'S WONDERS
MIDWAY
MILK MONEY
MONEY BELT
MONEY BURST
MONEY FEVER
MONEY GRAB
MONEY GROOVE
MONEY HIVE
MONEY MONEY MONEY
MONEY ON THE MOVE
MONEY TO BURN
MONEYLINE
MONOPOLY
MOOLAH ROUGE
MOON RISING
MOUNTAIN KING
MOVERS & SHAKERS
MULTI MAGIC
MULTI-PAY PLUS
MULTI-PAY PLUS POKER
MULTI-PAY POKER
MULTIPLIER BOOST
MULTIPLYING PROGRESSIVE
MYSTICAL DRAGON
MYSTICAL FORTUNES
MYSTICAL LOTUS
NEPTUNE'S KINGDOM
NINJA SPIRIT
OCEAN'S DEEP
OFF THE CHARTS
ONCE AROUND
ONCE AROUND DELUXE
ONE FOR THE FANS

Key to Media (For complete agency information see *The Advertising Red Books-Agencies* edition):
1. Bus. Publs. 2. Cable T.V. 3. Catalogs & Directories. 4. Co-op Adv. 5. Consumer Mags. 6. D.M. to Bus. Estab.7. D.M. to Consumers 8. Daily Newsp. 9. Exhibits/Trade Shows 10. Foreign 11. Infomercial 12. Internet Adv.13. Multimedia 14. Network Radio 15. Network T.V. 16. Newsp. Distr. Mags. 17. Other 18. Outdoor (Posters, Transit) 19. Point of Purchase20. Premiums, Novelties 21. Product Samples 22. Special Events Mktg. 23. Spot Radio 24. Spot T.V. 25. Weekly Newsp. 26. Yellow Page Adv.

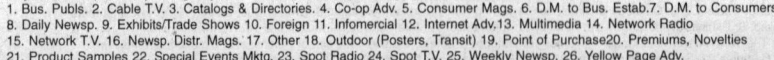

OPAL RING
OPEN THE VAULT
ORION
OWN IT ALL
PALACE OF RICHES
PANDA RICHES
PANDA'S JADE
PARTNERS IN CASH
PARTY TRAIN
PEGASUS
PERFECT GAME
PERFECT MATCH
PHARAOH'S PYRAMID
PICK-N-SPIN
PICK YOUR FORTUNE
PIGGY BANKIN
PIRATE'S GETAWAY
PLANET LOOT
POLYNESIAN PRINCESS
POWER SEAT
POWER SEVENS
PREMIER NIGHT
PRESS YOUR LUCK
THE PRICE IS RIGHT
PRIZE SPIN
PYRAMID OF THE KINGS
QUACKERS
QUEEN'S KNIGHT
RACE FOR THE GOLD
RAKIN' IT IN
RAPID PLAY
RA'S RICHES
REBEL 777
RECORD JACKPOTS
REEL ADVENTURE
REEL 'EM IN BIG BASS BUCKS
REEL 'EM IN CAST FOR CASH
REEL 'EM IN CATCH THAT BIG ONE
REEL 'EM IN POKER
REEL ESTATE
REEL ESTATE TYCOON
REEL HEROES
REEL HOT WINS
REEL LEGENDS
REEL RICH DEVIL
REEL RICHES
REELS O'DUBLIN
RESPIN PLUNDER
RETURN OF THE TITANS
RETURN TO PLANET LOOT
RICH LITTLE PIGGIES
RICHES OF ROME
RICHES OF THE AMAZON
RICHES OF THE PHARAOH
RICHES OF THE UNIVERSE
RING OF FIRE
RING QUEST
RISING FORTUNES
RIVER BELLE 21
ROAD TO RICHES
ROBIN HOOD'S SHERWOOD TREASURE
ROCKET RICHES
ROLL & WIN
ROLL CREDITS
ROMAN DYNASTY
ROME & EGYPT
ROPE 'EM IN
ROSE OF CAIRO
ROTATING WILD
ROYAL FAMILY
ROYAL TREASURES
ROYAL UNICORN
RUBY RING
SABERTOOTH
SAMURAI MASTER
SAVE THE WORLD
SCATTERTAINMENT
SCRATCH A WILD
SCROLL TOP
SEEING STARS
SERGEANT WINBIG
SEVEN STREAK
SHAKIN' BACON
SHEEPLOAD OF CASH
SHIMMER
SILK KIMONO
SILVER SWORD
SILVERBACK
SLOT MACHINE UNIVERSITY
SLOTSKY
SOMETHING FOR NOTHING
SPANISH PARADISE
SPINNING STREAK
ST. PETERSBURG
STAGE OF RICHES
STAR OF INDIA
STAR TREK
STEER CRAZY
STROKE OF LUCK
SUMMER SOLSTICE
SUPER CREDITS
SUPER EASY MONEY
SUPER HUGE
SUPER HUGE 7S DESIGN
SUPER JACKPOT PARTY
SUPER MULTI-PAY
SUPER SCATTER
SUPER SHOT SEVENS DESIGN
SWINGIN' & SPINNIN'
SWINGIN' IN THE GREEN
SWORDS OF HONOR
THAI TREASURES
THEY'RE OFF
THUNDERHAWK
TIGER'S REALM
TIKI GOLD
TIME MACHINE
TOAST OF THE TOWN
TOP BANANA
TOUR OF STARS
TOWER POKER
TRANSMISSIVE REELS
TREASURE CEREMONY
TREASURE DIVER
TREASURE SEEKER
TREASURE TALES
TREASURE TOUR USA
TREASURES OF MACAU
TREASURES OF MACHU PICCHU
TREASURES OF SPARTA
TRIPLE CHARMS
TRIPLE GOLDEN CHERRIES
TRIPLE LUNKER
TRIPLE LUXURY
TRIPLE TREAT
TWICE THE ICE
TWINSTAR
TWINSTAR2
ULTRA HIT PROGRESSIVE
UNLOCK THE TREASURE
UP UP & AWAY
UP YOUR KILT
VALIANT KNIGHT
VENICE RICHES
VIVA MAMBO
WAGE-NET
WHAT PLAYERS WANT
WHIPPING WILD
WHO DUNNIT?
THE WHOLE ENCHILADA
WICKED RICHES
WILD & LOOSE
WILD & WILDER
WILD AVALANCHE
WILD CHANCE
WILD COUNTRY
WILD DEVILS
WILD FRONTIER
WILD LIGHTNING
WILD SAFARI
WILD SHOT
WILD STREAK
WILD WILD SAFARI
WILD WILDERNESS
WILD WIZARD
WILD ZONE
WILLIAMS
WINNERS NETWORK
WINNING BID
WINNING STREAK
WISH YOU WERE HERE
WITCHES BREW
THE WIZARD OF OZ
WIZARD SPINS
WMS
WMS AUDIO CHIME
WMS BLADE
WMS GAMING
WOLF SPIRIT
WOLVERTON
WRAP AROUND PAYS
X MARKS THE SPOT
X-TRA HOT 777 DESIGN
X-TREME REELS
XERXES
XFACTOR
YAHTZEE
YIN & YANG
YUKON GOLD

Advertising Agency:
Access Communications, LLC
101 Howard St 2nd Fl
San Francisco, CA 94105
Tel.: (415) 904-7070
Fax: (415) 904-7055

WNBA ENTERPRISES, LLC
(Sub. of National Basketball Association)
645 5th Ave
New York, NY 10022-5910
Tel.: (212) 688-9622
Fax: (212) 750-9622
E-mail: brandon@meierwnba.com
Web Site: www.wnba.com
Sales Range: $10-24.9 Million
Approx. Number Employees: 25
Year Founded: 1996
Business Description:
Administrators for the Women's National Basketball Association
S.I.C.: 7941
N.A.I.C.S.: 711211
Media: 13-15
Personnel:
Laurel Richie *(Pres)*
Christine Godleski *(COO)*
Jamin S. Dershowitz *(Gen Counsel)*
Mike Behrman *(Sr VP-Bus Affairs)*
Thaddeus Brown *(Sr VP-Sls)*
Renee Brown *(VP-Player Personnel)*
Kelley Hardwick *(Dir-Security)*
Mike Bellerive *(Mgr-Interactive Mktg)*
Aaron Bryan *(Mgr-Mktg)*
Brandon Meier *(Mgr-Mktg)*

Brands & Products:
WNBA

Advertising Agency:
Harris Marketing Group
102 Pierce St
Birmingham, MI 48009-6018
Tel.: (248) 723-6300
Fax: (248) 723-6301

WOLFTRAP FOUNDATION FOR THE PERFORMING ARTS
1645 Trap Rd
Vienna, VA 22182
Tel.: (703) 255-1900
Fax: (703) 255-1905
E-mail: wolftrap@wolftrap.org
Web Site: www.wolftrap.org
Approx. Sls.: $23,100,000
Approx. Number Employees: 80
Year Founded: 1966
Business Description:
Theater Building Owner & Operator
S.I.C.: 7389
N.A.I.C.S.: 711320
Media: 9-18-20-23-24-25
Personnel:
Terrence D. Jones *(Pres & CEO)*
Malisa Chotiner *(Dir-PR)*
Graham Binder *(Asst Dir-PR)*

WORLD GOLF HALL OF FAME
1 World Golf Pl
Saint Augustine, FL 32092
Tel.: (904) 940-4000
Tel.: (904) 940-4123
Fax: (904) 940-4394
Web Site:
www.worldgolfhalloffame.com
Sales Range: $1-9.9 Million
Approx. Number Employees: 100
Business Description:
Museum
S.I.C.: 8412
N.A.I.C.S.: 712110
Media: 6
Personnel:
Jack Peter *(COO & Sr VP)*

WORLD SERIES OF GOLF, INC.
10161 Park Run Dr Ste 150
Las Vegas, NV 89145
Tel.: (702) 740-1740
E-mail: info@worldseriesofgolf.com
Web Site: www.worldseriesofgolf.com
Approx. Rev.: $25,000
Approx. Number Employees: 2
Business Description:
Golf Tournaments & Events; Website Publisher
S.I.C.: 7389; 7999
N.A.I.C.S.: 711320; 519130; 713990
Media: 3-6-13-17-18
Personnel:
Patrick Brown *(CEO & Treas)*
James D. Tilton, Jr. *(CFO)*

WORLD WRESTLING ENTERTAINMENT, INC.
1241 E Main St
Stamford, CT 06902-3521
Tel.: (203) 352-8600
Fax: (203) 359-5151
E-mail: fanservices@wwecorp.com
Web Site: www.corporate.wwe.com
Approx. Rev.: $477,655,000
Approx. Number Employees: 585
Business Description:
Sports Entertainment
S.I.C.: 7812; 7389; 7929; 7999
N.A.I.C.S.: 512110; 711190; 711320; 713990
Advertising Expenditures: $4,100,000
Media: 2-3-4-6-8-10-11-13-14-15-18-19-20-22-23-24

World Wrestling Entertainment, Inc. — (Continued)

Personnel:
Vincent K. McMahon *(Chm & CEO)*
George A. Barrios *(CFO)*
Michael Lake *(Pres-WWE Films)*
Michael Luisi *(Gen Counsel, Sec & Exec VP-Bus Dev)*
Kevin Dunn *(Exec VP-Television Production)*
Brian Kalinowski *(Exec VP-Digital Media)*
John Laurinaitis *(Exec VP-Talent Rels)*
Stephanie Mcmahon Levesque *(Exec VP-Creative Dev & Ops)*
Mike Pavone *(Exec VP-WWE Studios)*
James Ross *(Exec VP-Bus Strategies)*
Andrew Whitaker *(Exec VP-Intl)*
Michelle Wilson *(Exec VP-Mktg)*
Jim Connelly *(Sr VP-Consumer Products)*
Eddie Hill *(Sr VP-Mktg)*
Gary Davis *(VP-Corp Comm)*
Robert Zimmerman *(VP-PR & Corp Comm)*
Neil Lawi *(Gen Mgr-WWE Music Grp)*
Brands & Products:
WORLD CHAMPIONSHIP WRESTLING
WORLD WRESTLING ENTERTAINMENT
WRESTLEMANIA
WWE
WWE NEW YORK
WWE RACING
WWE RAW
WWE SMACKDOWN
WWE SUPERSTARS
XFL
Advertising Agencies:
Conover Tuttle Pace
77 N Washington St
Boston, MA 02114
Tel.: (617) 412-4000
Fax: (617) 412-4411

Horizon Media, Inc.
75 Varick St
New York, NY 10013
Tel.: (212) 220-5000
Toll Free: (800) 633-4201

Specialized Media Services, Inc.
741 Kenilworth Ave Ste 204
Charlotte, NC 28204
Tel.: (704) 333-3111
Fax: (704) 332-7466

WOW! WORLD OF WONDER CHILDREN'S MUSEUM

110 N Harrison Ave
Lafayette, CO 80026
Tel.: (303) 604-2424
Fax: (303) 666-8376
E-mail: webmaster@wowmuseum.com
Web Site: www.wowmuseum.com
Approx. Number Employees: 10
Business Description:
Children's Museum
S.I.C.: 8412
N.A.I.C.S.: 712110
Media: 8-9-10-20-23-24-25
Personnel:
Lisa Atallah *(Co-Founder & Exec Dir)*
Dario Atallah *(Co-Founder, Board Treas & Sr Product Mgr)*
Katie McDonald *(Dir-Mktg)*
Susan Rasmussen *(Dir-Ops)*

WQXR FM

(Sub. of New York Public Radio)
122 5th Ave
New York, NY 10011-5605
Tel.: (212) 633-7600
Fax: (212) 633-7666
Fax: (212) 633-7677 (Accounting)
Fax: (212) 633-7666 (Marketing)
Web Site: www.wqxr.com
Approx. Number Employees: 20
Year Founded: 1936
Business Description:
Classical Music Radio Station
S.I.C.: 4832
N.A.I.C.S.: 515112
Media: 9-13-18-22-23
Personnel:
Thomas Bartunek *(Pres & Gen Mgr)*

WYOMING SYMPHONY ORCHESTRA

2257 David St Ste1B
Casper, WY 82601
Tel.: (307) 266-1478
Fax: (307) 266-4522
E-mail: office@wyomingsymphony.org
Web Site:
www.wyomingsymphony.org
Sales Range: Less than $1 Million
Approx. Number Employees: 6
Business Description:
Symphony Orchestra
S.I.C.: 7929
N.A.I.C.S.: 711130
Media: 7-8-9-13-19-20-22-23-24-25
Personnel:
Tir Nan *(Exec Dir)*

YACHTING PROMOTIONS, INC.

(Sub. of Active Interest Media, Inc.)
1115 NE 9th Ave
Fort Lauderdale, FL 33304-2110
Tel.: (954) 764-7642
Fax: (954) 462-4140
Toll Free: (800) 940-7642
E-mail: info@showmanagement.com
Web Site:
www.showmanagement.com
Approx. Number Employees: 20
Year Founded: 1976
Business Description:
Boatshow Producer
S.I.C.: 7389
N.A.I.C.S.: 561920
Advertising Expenditures: $200,000
Media: 2-3-4-6-7-8-9-10-13-16-18-22-23-24-25-26
Distr.: Intl.; Natl.
Budget Set: Apr.
Personnel:
Efram Zimbalist, Jr. *(Pres & CEO)*
Dane Graziano *(COO & VP)*
Steve Sheer *(Dir-Mktg)*
Brands & Products:
FORT LAUDERDALE INTERNATIONAL BOAT SHOW
SHOW MANAGEMENT
YACHTING PROMOTIONS
Advertising Agency:
Show Management Advertising
1115 NE 9th Ave
Fort Lauderdale, FL 33304-2110
Tel.: (954) 764-7642
Fax: (954) 462-4140
Toll Free: (800) 940-7642
(Boats & Boat Shows)

YAMAHA CORPORATION OF AMERICA

(Affil. of Yamaha Corporation)
6600 Orangethorpe Ave
Buena Park, CA 90620
Tel.: (714) 522-9011
Fax: (714) 522-9814
E-mail: infostation@yamaha.com
Web Site: www.yamaha.com
Approx. Number Employees: 450
Year Founded: 1960
Business Description:
Musical Instruments Mfr
S.I.C.: 3931; 5065
N.A.I.C.S.: 339992; 423690
Import Export
Media: 2-6-8-10-11-18-19-20
Distr.: Intl.; Natl.
Budget Set: Apr.
Personnel:
Takuya Nakata *(Pres)*
Katsuhiko Kishida *(Sr Mng Dir)*
Brian Jemelion *(Sr VP-Fin & Admin)*
Rick Young *(Sr VP-Yamaha Corp-America)*
Karren Salter *(VP & Gen Mgr-Customer Fin Svcs)*
Yasuhiro Kira *(Gen Mgr-The Product Design Laboratory)*
Mark Anderson *(Dir-Mktg)*
Paul Furtkamp *(Mgr-Sls-Natl-Comm Audio Systems Div)*
Cameron Shearer *(Product Mgr)*
Yoshiyuki Aiba *(Mgr-Plng-Keyboard Div)*
Kazunari Fukaya *(Mgr-Mktg)*
Brands & Products:
ELECTONE
MAGICSTOMP
MUSICSOFT
PM1D
THREE TUNING FORKS IN A CIRCLE
Advertising Agencies:
Giles Communications, LLC
2975 Westchester Ave Ste 402
Purchase, NY 10577
Tel.: (914) 644-3500
Fax: (914) 696-4120

Hoffman York
1000 N Water St Ste 1600
Milwaukee, WI 53202-6667
Tel.: (414) 289-9700
Fax: (414) 289-0417
Toll Free: (800) 842-3020

MGM Gold Communications
12 W 31st St 7th Fl
New York, NY 10001
Tel.: (212) 869-7323
Fax: (212) 869-7249

RMI Marketing & Advertising
436 Old Hook Rd 2nd Fl
Emerson, NJ 07631
Tel.: (201) 261-7000
Fax: (201) 261-4970

YORK SYMPHONY ORCHESTRA

10 N Beaver St
York, PA 17401
Tel.: (717) 812-0717
Fax: (717) 812-0689
E-mail: ysoisgreat@comcast.org
Web Site: www.yorksymphony.org
Sales Range: Less than $1 Million
Approx. Number Employees: 5
Business Description:
Symphony Orchestra Services
S.I.C.: 7929
N.A.I.C.S.: 711130
Media: 9-20-23-24-25
Personnel:
Wayne Umland *(Pres)*
Henry Nixon *(Exec Dir)*
Phyllis LoPresti *(Office Mgr)*

YOUNG BROADCASTING OF GREEN BAY, INC.

(Sub. of Young Broadcasting, LLC)
(d/b/a WBAY-TV)
115 S Jefferson St
Green Bay, WI 54301-4534
Tel.: (920) 432-3331
Fax: (920) 438-3355
E-mail: wbay@wbay.com
Web Site: www.wbay.com
Sales Range: $25-49.9 Million
Approx. Number Employees: 115
Year Founded: 1953
Business Description:
Television Broadcasting Station
S.I.C.: 4833
N.A.I.C.S.: 515120
Media: 22-24
Personnel:
Debora McCermott *(Pres)*
Don Carmichael *(Gen Mgr)*
Tom McCarey *(Dir-News)*
Dick Millhiser *(Mgr-Program & Ops)*

YOUNG BROADCASTING OF NASHVILLE, INC.

(Sub. of Young Broadcasting, LLC)
(d/b/a WKRN-TV)
441 Murfreesboro Rd
Nashville, TN 37210-2842
Tel.: (615) 369-7222
Fax: (615) 369-7329
E-mail: news@wkrn.com
Web Site: www.wkrn.com
Sales Range: $25-49.9 Million
Approx. Number Employees: 125
Year Founded: 1953
Business Description:
Television Broadcasting Station
S.I.C.: 4833
N.A.I.C.S.: 515120
Media: 4-8-10-13-18-22-24-26
Personnel:
Steve Watt *(Gen Mgr-Sls)*
Mike Tarrolly *(Dir-Mktg)*

ZOOLOGICAL SOCIETY OF SAN DIEGO

2920 Zoo Dr
San Diego, CA 92101-1646
Mailing Address:
PO Box 120551
San Diego, CA 92112-0551
Tel.: (619) 231-1515
Tel.: (619) 685-3291 (Mktg)
Fax: (619) 685-3290
E-mail: membership@sandiegozoo.org
Web Site: www.sandiegozoo.org
Sales Range: $125-149.9 Million
Approx. Number Employees: 2,300
Year Founded: 1916
Business Description:
Owner & Operator of Zoo
S.I.C.: 8422; 5947

Key to Media (For complete agency information see *The Advertising Red Books-Agencies* edition):
1. Bus. Publs. 2. Cable T.V. 3. Catalogs & Directories. 4. Co-op Adv. 5. Consumer Mags. 6. D.M. to Bus. Estab.7. D.M. to Consumers 8. Daily Newsp. 9. Exhibits/Trade Shows 10. Foreign 11. Infomercial 12. Internet Adv.13. Multimedia 14. Network Radio 15. Network T.V. 16. Newsp. Distr. Mags. 17. Other 18. Outdoor (Posters, Transit) 19. Point of Purchase20. Premiums, Novelties 21. Product Samples 22. Special Events Mktg. 23. Spot Radio 24. Spot T.V. 25. Weekly Newsp. 26. Yellow Page Adv.

N.A.I.C.S.: 712130; 453220
Advertising Expenditures: $5,600,000
Media: 1-3-4-5-6-8-9-10-11-12-13-14-15-18-19-20-21-22-23-24-25
Distr.: Direct to Consumer; Reg.
Budget Set: July

Personnel:
Doug Mayers *(Pres)*
Paula Brock *(CFO)*
Douglas G. Myers *(Exec Dir)*
Ted Molter *(Dir-Mktg)*

Brands & Products:
CONSERVATION AND RESEARCH FOR ENDANGERED SPECIES
SAN DIEGO ZOO
SAN DIEGO ZOO'S WILD ANIMAL PARK
THE ZOOLOGICAL SOCIETY OF SAN DIEGO

Advertising Agencies:
M&C Saatchi
2032 Broadway
Santa Monica, CA 90404
Tel.: (310) 401-6070
Fax: (310) 264-1910

Round2 Communications, LLC
10866 Wilshire Blvd Ste 900
Los Angeles, CA 90024
Tel.: (310) 481-8040
Fax: (310) 571-1827

Key to Media (For complete agency information see *The Advertising Red Books-Agencies* edition):
1. Bus. Publs. 2. Cable T.V. 3. Catalogs & Directories. 4. Co-op Adv. 5. Consumer Mags. 6. D.M. to Bus. Estab.7. D.M. to Consumers 8. Daily Newsp. 9. Exhibits/Trade Shows 10. Foreign 11. Infomercial 12. Internet Adv.13. Multimedia 14. Network Radio 15. Network T.V. 16. Newsp. Distr. Mags. 17. Other 18. Outdoor (Posters, Transit) 19. Point of Purchase20. Premiums, Novelties 21. Product Samples 22. Special Events Mktg. 23. Spot Radio 24. Spot T.V. 25. Weekly Newsp. 26. Yellow Page Adv.

Department Stores & Mail Order Houses

Catalog Stores — Direct Order Companies — General Merchandise Stores — Specialty Stores — Variety Stores

1-877-SPIRITS.COM, INC.
99 Powerhouse Rd Ste 200
Roslyn Heights, NY 11577
Tel.: (516) 626-4150
Fax: (516) 626-4164
Toll Free: (877) 774-7487
E-mail: info@877spirits.com
Web Site: www.877spirits.com
Business Description:
Champagne, Spirits, Wine, Gourmet Gift Baskets, Cigars & Chocolates Delivery Services
S.I.C.: 5961
N.A.I.C.S.: 454113
Media: 4-6-7-8-13

1.800.VENDING, INC.
1284 W Flint Meadow Dr
Kaysville, UT 84037
Tel.: (801) 593-0084
Fax: (801) 593-6449
Toll Free: (800) 836-3464
Web Site: www.1800vending.com
Sales Range: $1-9.9 Million
Approx. Number Employees: 12
Business Description:
Vending Machine Mfr, Operator & Franchisor
S.I.C.: 5962; 3581
N.A.I.C.S.: 454210; 333311
Media: 6
Personnel:
Michael Burnett *(Pres)*

99 CENTS ONLY STORES
4000 Union Pacific Ave
Los Angeles, CA 90023-3202
Tel.: (323) 980-8145
Fax: (323) 980-8160
E-mail: IR@99only.com
Web Site: www.99only.com
Approx. Sls.: $1,423,878,000
Approx. Number Employees: 12,000
Year Founded: 1982
Business Description:
Single-Price Retail Chain
S.I.C.: 5399; 5199
N.A.I.C.S.: 452990; 424990
Advertising Expenditures: $5,500,000
Media: 9-18-22-23-25
Personnel:
David Gold *(Chm)*
Jeff Gold *(Pres & COO)*
Eric J. Schiffer *(CEO)*
Robert F. Kautz *(CFO & Exec VP)*
Robert Adams *(CTO & Sr VP)*
Russell Wolpert *(Chief Legal Officer & Sr VP)*
Howard Gold *(Exec VP-Special Projects)*
James G. Parros *(Sr VP-Logistics)*
Helen Pipkin *(VP-Whole Sls)*
Henry Miller *(Mgr-Office Svcs)*

AARDVARK SWIM & SPORT, INC.
14221-A Willard Rd Ste 1050
Chantilly, VA 20151
Tel.: (703) 631-6045
Toll Free: (800) 729-1577
E-mail: info@aardvarkswim.com
Web Site: www.aardvarkswim.com
Sales Range: $25-49.9 Million
Approx. Number Employees: 30
Year Founded: 1985
Business Description:
Swim Wear, Swim Equipment & Related Accessories Mail Order
S.I.C.: 5137
N.A.I.C.S.: 424330
Media: 4-8-13
Personnel:
Robert York *(Pres)*
Brands & Products:
AARDVARK

ACADEMIC SUPERSTORE, LP
(Sub. of Journey Education Marketing, Inc.)
2101 E Saint Elmo Rd Ste 360
Austin, TX 78744
Tel.: (512) 450-1199
Fax: (866) 947-4525
Toll Free: (800) 817-2347
E-mail: contact@academicsuperstore.com
Web Site: www.academicsuperstore.com
Sales Range: $25-49.9 Million
Approx. Number Employees: 30
Year Founded: 1998
Business Description:
Educational Software Retailer
S.I.C.: 5045; 5961
N.A.I.C.S.: 423430; 454111; 454113
Media: 4-6
Brands & Products:
ACADEMIC SUPERSTORE
SAVINGS, SERVICE, AND SELECTION

AIRCRAFT SPRUCE & SPECIALTY CO.
225 Airport Cir
Corona, CA 92880
Tel.: (951) 372-9555
Fax: (951) 372-0555
Toll Free: (877) 4SPRUCE
E-mail: info@aircraftspruce.com
Web Site: www.aircraftspruce.com
Sales Range: $75-99.9 Million
Approx. Number Employees: 140
Business Description:
Mail Order of Aircraft & Automotive Parts
S.I.C.: 5599; 5088
N.A.I.C.S.: 441229; 423860
Media: 4-11-13
Personnel:
Jim Irwin *(Pres)*

A.K.A. GOURMET
(Sub. of Wine.com, Inc.)
1414 Harbour Way S
Richmond, CA 94804-3625
Tel.: (510) 903-7700
Fax: (510) 903-7722
Toll Free: (800) 900-0252
E-mail: customerservice@akagourmet.com
Web Site: www.akagourmet.com
Approx. Number Employees: 35
Year Founded: 1987
Business Description:
Online Food & Gift Catalog
S.I.C.: 5961
N.A.I.C.S.: 454111
Media: 4-5-13
Brands & Products:
A.K.A. GOURMET

ALIBRIS, INC.
(Holding of Oak Hill Capital Partners, L.P.)
1250 45th St Ste 100
Emeryville, CA 94608
Tel.: (510) 594-4500
Fax: (510) 652-2403
E-mail: pr@alibris.com
Web Site: www.alibris.com
Sales Range: $25-49.9 Million
Year Founded: 1998
Business Description:
Online Books, Movies, Music Services
S.I.C.: 5961; 5192
N.A.I.C.S.: 454111; 424920; 454113
Advertising Expenditures: $1,008,000
Media: 6-8-13-25
Personnel:
Richard M. Weatherford *(Founder)*
Richard Hewitt *(CFO)*
Liz Derr *(COO)*
Mariah DeLeon *(VP-Employee, HR & Community Rels)*
Jeanie Bunker *(Gen Mgr)*
Brands & Products:
ALIBRIS

ALLEGRO CORPORATION
20048 NE San Rafel St
Portland, OR 97230
Tel.: (503) 491-8480
Fax: (503) 491-8488
E-mail: info@allegro-music.com
Web Site: www.allegro-music.com
Approx. Sls.: $17,000,000
Approx. Number Employees: 120
Business Description:
Music & DVD Distr
S.I.C.: 5099; 5961
N.A.I.C.S.: 423990; 454113
Media: 4-13
Personnel:
Joseph Micallef *(Chm & CEO)*
John Schman *(Product Mgr-NewSound-Allegro Media Grp)*
Bill Tennant *(Product Mgr)*
Bryan Huitt *(Mgr-Allegro Classical Product)*
Brands & Products:
ALLEGRO

AMC, INC.
(d/b/a AmericasMart Atlanta)
240 Peachtree St NW Ste 2200
Atlanta, GA 30303-1327
Tel.: (404) 220-3000
Fax: (404) 220-3030
E-mail: info@americasmart.com
Web Site: www.americasmart.com
Approx. Number Employees: 300
Year Founded: 1961
Business Description:
Trade Show Center Manager
S.I.C.: 6512
N.A.I.C.S.: 531120
Advertising Expenditures: $3,000,000
Media: 1-2-5-6-7-9-10-11-20-25
Distr.: Natl.
Budget Set: Oct.

Key to Media (For complete agency information see *The Advertising Red Books-Agencies* edition):
1. Bus. Publs. 2. Cable T.V. 3. Catalogs & Directories. 4. Co-op Adv. 5. Consumer Mags. 6. D.M. to Bus. Estab.7. D.M. to Consumers
8. Daily Newsp. 9. Exhibits/Trade Shows 10. Foreign 11. Infomercial 12. Internet Adv.13. Multimedia 14. Network Radio
15. Network T.V. 16. Newsp. Distr. Mags. 17. Other 18. Outdoor (Posters, Transit) 19. Point of Purchase20. Premiums, Novelties
21. Product Samples 22. Special Events Mktg. 23. Spot Radio 24. Spot T.V. 25. Weekly Newsp. 26. Yellow Page Adv.

Personnel:
John C. Portman, Jr. *(Chm & CEO)*
Jeffrey L. Portman *(Pres & COO)*
Kevin Albrechtson *(Chief Quality Officer)*
Neal Patton *(Gen Counsel & Corp Sec)*
Henry G. Almquist *(Exec VP)*
Virginia Gorday *(Sr VP-Ops)*
Jo Ann Miller *(Sr VP-Trade Show)*
Mike Turnbull *(Sr VP-Mktg)*
Kaye Davis *(Exec Dir-Fashion & Apparel Tradeshows)*
Julie Auton *(Dir-Mktg)*
Tara Tuschinski *(Dir-PR)*
Brands & Products:
AMC TRADE SHOWS, LTD.
AMERICASMART
AMERICASMART ALPHA
AMERICASMART FIRSTLOOK
AMERICASMART PREMIER
ATLANTA APPAREL MART
ATLANTA DECORATIVE ARTS CENTER
ATLANTA FASHION PREVIEW
ATLANTA MARKET DIRECTORY
ATLANTA MARKET PREVIEW
ATLANTA MERCHANDISE MART
E-FACTOR
FLORIDA GIFT SHOW
INFORUM

AMERICAN ART CLAY CO., INC.

6060 Guion Rd
Indianapolis, IN 46254-1222
Tel.: (317) 244-6871
Fax: (317) 248-9300
Toll Free: (800) 374-1600
E-mail: catalog@amaco.com
Web Site: www.amaco.com
Approx. Sls.: $21,500,000
Approx. Number Employees: 130
Year Founded: 1919
Business Description:
Ceramic Clay & Accessories
S.I.C.: 3295; 3559
N.A.I.C.S.: 327992; 333298
Media: 4-13
Personnel:
Lester B. Sandoe, Jr. *(Chm)*
Bill Berry *(Pres & COO)*
Diana Faris *(Dir-Sls)*
Brands & Products:
AMACO

AMERICAN BLIND AND WALLPAPER FACTORY, INC.

31557 School Craft Rd
Livonia, MI 48150
Tel.: (734) 207-5800
Fax: (734) 207-0947
E-mail: info@americanblind.com
Web Site: www.americanblind.com
Approx. Number Employees: 100
Business Description:
Mail Order of Window Furnishings, Wall Coverings & Carpet
S.I.C.: 5961
N.A.I.C.S.: 454113
Media: 3-4-6-17
Personnel:
Joel Levine *(Chm, Pres & CEO)*

AMERIMARK DIRECT, LLC

(Sub. of JH Partners LLC)
6864 Engle Rd
Cleveland, OH 44130
Tel.: (440) 325-2000
Fax: (440) 234-8925
Toll Free: (877) 268-9594
Web Site: www.amerimark.com
Approx. Number Employees: 600
Year Founded: 1969
Business Description:
Direct Marketing; Women's Apparel; Cosmetics & Fragrances; Jewelry, Watches & Accessories; Health Related Merchandise
S.I.C.: 5961; 7331
N.A.I.C.S.: 454113; 541860
Media: 4-6-8-13
Personnel:
Gareth Giesler *(Chm & CEO)*
Louis Giesler *(Pres)*
Diane Huzar *(Exec VP)*
Brands & Products:
AMERIMARK

AMSCAN HOLDINGS, INC.

(Joint Venture of Advent International Corporation, Berkshire Partners LLC & Weston Presidio Capital)
80 Grasslands Rd
Elmsford, NY 10523
Tel.: (914) 345-2020
Fax: (914) 345-3884
Web Site: www.amscan.com
Approx. Rev.: $1,599,094,000
Approx. Number Employees: 5,470
Business Description:
Holding Company
S.I.C.: 6719
N.A.I.C.S.: 551112
Advertising Expenditures: $53,256,000
Personnel:
Robert J. Small *(Chm)*
James M. Harrison *(Pres & COO)*
Gerald C. Rittenberg *(CEO)*
Michael A. Correale *(CFO)*
Sheldon Babyatsky *(Sr VP-Sls)*
Brent Schlosser *(Sr VP-New Bus Dev)*
Brands & Products:
AMSCAN
THE PARTY PEOPLE

ANNA'S LINEN COMPANY INC.

3550 Hyland Ave
Costa Mesa, CA 92626-1438
Tel.: (714) 850-0504
Fax: (714) 850-9170
Toll Free: (800) 326-6279
E-mail: info@annaslinens.com
Web Site: www.annaslinens.com
Sales Range: $200-249.9 Million
Approx. Number Employees: 2,000
Year Founded: 1988
Business Description:
Home Furnishing Services
S.I.C.: 5719
N.A.I.C.S.: 442299
Media: 4-16
Personnel:
Alan Gladstone *(Founder, Chm, Pres, CEO & Sec)*
Neil T. Watanabe *(CFO & Exec VP)*
Scott Gladstone *(COO)*
Carie Doll *(Sr VP-Mktg & Mdsg)*
Abby Areinoff *(VP-HR)*
Jim Stonehill *(Dir-Real Estate)*
Advertising Agency:
Kovel/Fuller
9925 Jefferson Blvd
Culver City, CA 90232-3505
Tel.: (310) 841-4444
Fax: (310) 841-4599

ANNIE'S INC.

1610 Fifth St
Berkeley, CA 94710
Tel.: (510) 558-7500
Toll Free: (800) 288-1089
E-mail: bernie@annies.com
Web Site: www.annies.com
Approx. Number Employees: 26
Business Description:
Organic Foods Mfr & Wholesaler
S.I.C.: 2099
N.A.I.C.S.: 311999
Media: 4-8
Personnel:
Annie Withey *(Co-Founder)*
John Foraker *(CEO)*
Sarah Bird *(Sr VP-Mktg)*
Aimee Sands *(Dir-Equity Mktg)*
Robyn Young *(Sr Brand Mgr)*
Brands & Products:
ALL STARS
ANNIE'S
ARTHUR
ARTHUR LOOPS
BERNIEOS
CHEESY RAVIOLI
CURLY FETTUCCINE
GEMELLI
HERB CHICKEN
MILD MEXICAN
P'SGHETTI LOOPS
RADIATORE
SIMPLY ORGANIC
TUNA SPIRALS
YUMMY CHEESE
Advertising Agency:
TDA Advertising & Design
1500 Pearl St Ste 300
Boulder, CO 80302
Tel.: (303) 247-1180
Fax: (303) 247-1214
Organic & Natural Foods

APPLESEED'S, INC.

(Holding of Orchard Brands Corporation)
30 Tozer Rd Ste 4
Beverly, MA 01915-5500
Tel.: (978) 922-2040
Fax: (800) 755-7557
Fax: (978) 922-7001
Toll Free: (800) 767-6666
Web Site: www.appleseeds.com
Year Founded: 1946
Business Description:
Women's Apparel Retailer
S.I.C.: 5961; 5621
N.A.I.C.S.: 454113; 448120
Media: 4-6-8-13
Distr.: Direct to Consumer; Natl.
Budget Set: Jan.
Personnel:
Neale Attenborough *(CEO)*
Brands & Products:
APPLESEED'S

B. SHACKMAN & COMPANY, INC.

9964 W Miller Dr
Galesburg, MI 49053
Tel.: (269) 484-1000
Fax: (269) 484-1010
Toll Free: (800) 221-7656
E-mail: info@shackman.com
Web Site: www.shackman.com
Approx. Sls.: $2,000,000
Approx. Number Employees: 15
Year Founded: 1898
Business Description:
Paper Goods, Toys & Novelties Mfr
S.I.C.: 5399
N.A.I.C.S.: 452990
Import Export
Advertising Expenditures: $50,000
Media: 4-10-13
Distr.: Intl.
Personnel:
Julianna Castro *(VP-Mktg)*
Brands & Products:
B. SHACKMAN COMPANY
KITTY CUCUMBER

BANANA REPUBLIC

(Div. of The Gap, Inc.)
2 Folsom St
San Francisco, CA 94105
Tel.: (650) 952-4400
Fax: (415) 427-2553
Toll Free: (800) 333-7899
Web Site: www.bananarepublic.com
Sales Range: $100-124.9 Million
Year Founded: 1978
Business Description:
Specialty Apparel Retailer
S.I.C.: 5611; 5621
N.A.I.C.S.: 448110; 448120
Media: 4-6-8-9-13-19-22-24-25
Distr.: Direct to Consumer; Natl.
Personnel:
Jack Calhoun *(Pres)*
Catherine Sadler *(CMO & Sr VP)*
Simon Kneen *(Dir-Creative & Exec VP-Design)*
Karyn Hillman *(Sr VP-Mdsg-Gap Adult-Gap Inc)*
Chris Nicklo *(VP-Mktg)*
Brands & Products:
BANANA REPUBLIC
Advertising Agencies:
LaForce & Stevens
132 W 21st St
New York, NY 10011
Tel.: (212) 242-9353
Fax: (212) 242-9565

MG&G Advertising, Inc.
69 5th Ave 5th Fl
New York, NY 10003
Tel.: (646) 638-1447
Fax: (646) 638-1455

BARGAIN SUPPLY COMPANY

844 E Jefferson St
Louisville, KY 40206-1618
Tel.: (502) 562-5000
Fax: (502) 562-5051
Toll Free: (800) 322-5226
E-mail: sales@bargainsupply.com
Web Site: www.bargainsupply.com
E-Mail For Key Personnel:
Sales Director: sales@bargainsupply.com
Approx. Number Employees: 45
Year Founded: 1929
Business Description:
Retailer of General Merchandise
S.I.C.: 5072; 5399
N.A.I.C.S.: 423710; 452990
Consumer Mags.: 60%; Exhibits/Trade Shows: 40%
Distr.: Reg.
Budget Set: Dec.

Key to Media (For complete agency information see *The Advertising Red Books-Agencies* edition):
1. Bus. Publs. 2. Cable T.V. 3. Catalogs & Directories. 4. Co-op Adv. 5. Consumer Mags. 6. D.M. to Bus. Estab.7. D.M. to Consumers 8. Daily Newsp. 9. Exhibits/Trade Shows 10. Foreign 11. Infomercial 12. Internet Adv.13. Multimedia 14. Network Radio 15. Network T.V. 16. Newsp. Distr. Mags. 17. Other 18. Outdoor (Posters, Transit) 19. Point of Purchase20. Premiums, Novelties 21. Product Samples 22. Special Events Mktg. 23. Spot Radio 24. Spot T.V. 25. Weekly Newsp. 26. Yellow Page Adv.

Bargain Supply Company — (Continued)

Personnel:
Brad Ogden *(Pres)*
John A. Ogden *(Pres)*

BASELINE SPORTS, INC.
5257 Cleveland St
Virginia Beach, VA 23452
Tel.: (757) 626-1520
Fax: (757) 626-1522
E-mail: info@blsports.com
E-Mail For Key Personnel:
Sales Director: sales@blsports.com
Sales Range: $1-9.9 Million
Approx. Number Employees: 8
Business Description:
Furniture Mfr
S.I.C.: 2512; 5712
N.A.I.C.S.: 337121; 442110
Media: 4-10
Personnel:
Red Barnes *(Owner)*

BEALL'S, INC.
1806 38th Ave E
Bradenton, FL 34208-4708
Mailing Address:
PO Box 25207
Bradenton, FL 34206-5207
Tel.: (941) 747-2355
Fax: (941) 746-1171
E-mail: jobsbds@beallsinc.com
Web Site: www.beallsinc.com
Approx. Number Employees: 10,000
Year Founded: 1920
Business Description:
Operator of Department Stores
S.I.C.: 5651; 5719
N.A.I.C.S.: 448140; 442299
Media: 3-4-5-8-9-13-18-19-20-22-23-24-25
Distr.: Direct to Consumer; Reg.
Budget Set: June
Personnel:
Robert M. Beall, II *(Owner)*
Dan Love *(Pres)*
Stephen M. Knopik *(CEO)*
Dick Judd *(COO & Exec VP)*
Ray Gordon *(Sr VP-Distr & Transportation)*
Gwen Bennett *(VP-Ecommerce)*
Dan Doyle *(VP-HR & Loss Prevention)*
Brands & Products:
BEALL'S
Advertising Agencies:
Dalton Agency
140 W Monroe St
Jacksonville, FL 32202
Tel.: (904) 398-5222
Fax: (904) 398-5220
Toll Free: (888) 409-2691

Nuevo Advertising Group, Inc.
677 N Washington Blvd
Sarasota, FL 34236
Tel.: (941) 752-4433
Fax: (941) 752-1114

Phids, Inc.
(D/B/A Acquirgy)
877 Executive Ctr Dr W Ste 300
Saint Petersburg, FL 33702-2474
Tel.: (727) 576-6630
Fax: (727) 576-4864

BELK, INC.
2801 W Tyvola Rd
Charlotte, NC 28217-4500
Tel.: (704) 357-1000
Fax: (704) 357-1788
Toll Free: (866) 235-5443
Web Site: www.belk.com
Approx. Rev.: $3,513,275,000
Approx. Number Employees: 24,000
Year Founded: 1888
Business Description:
Department Store Operator
S.I.C.: 5311
N.A.I.C.S.: 452111
Advertising Expenditures: $143,200,000
Media: 8-9-13-16-18-22-23-24-25
Personnel:
Thomas M. Belk, Jr. *(Chm & CEO)*
John R. Belk *(Pres & COO)*
Kathryn Bufano *(Co-Pres & Chief Mdsg Officer)*
H. W. McKay Belk *(Pres & Chief Mdsg Officer)*
Brian T. Marley *(CFO & Exec VP)*
Michael Laurenti *(CIO & Exec VP)*
Rodney F. Samples *(Principal Acctg Officer, VP & Controller)*
Ralph A. Pitts *(Gen Counsel, Sec & Exec VP)*
David Neri *(Exec VP & Gen Mgr-Mdse)*
Jon Pollack *(Exec VP-E-Commerce Bus, Mktg & Sls Promotion)*
Ron Shealy *(Exec VP-Ops)*
Adam M. Orvos *(Sr VP-Fin & Controller)*
Ivy Chin *(Sr VP-E-Commerce)*
Betty Buchanan *(Mgr-Stockholder Rels)*
Cheri Hawkes *(Mgr-Online Mktg)*
Darryl Williams *(Mgr-Exec Comm)*
Brands & Products:
ALL FOR YOU
BELK
Advertising Agencies:
Mindshare
3340 Peachtree Rd NE Ste 300
Atlanta, GA 30326
Tel.: (404) 832-3400
Fax: (404) 832-3430
Media Agency of Record

Ologie
447 E Main St
Columbus, OH 43215
Tel.: (614) 221-1107
Fax: (614) 221-1108
Toll Free: (800) 962-1107

Panorama Public Relations
1500 1st Ave N Ste B106
Birmingham, AL 35233
Tel.: (205) 328-9334
Fax: (205) 323-0897

BERGDORF GOODMAN, INC.
(Joint Venture of Leonard Green & Partners, L.P., Warburg Pincus LLC & TPG Capital, L.P.)
754 Fifth Ave
New York, NY 10019-2503
Tel.: (212) 753-7300
Toll Free: (800) 558-1855
Web Site:
www.bergdorfgoodman.com
Approx. Number Employees: 1,300
Business Description:
Retail Specialty Stores
S.I.C.: 5621
N.A.I.C.S.: 448120
Advertising Expenditures: $500,000
Media: 4-5-6-8-9-22
Distr.: Direct to Consumer; Natl.
Budget Set: Sept. -Mar.
Personnel:
Ginny Hershey-Lambert *(Exec VP-Mdsg)*
Mallory Andrews *(VP-Sls Promo & Mktg & PR)*

BEST IMPRESSIONS CATALOG COMPANY
(Sub. of Malcolm Group Inc.)
345 N Lewis Ave
Oglesby, IL 61348
Tel.: (815) 883-3532
Fax: (815) 883-8346
Toll Free: (800) 635-2378
E-mail: feedback@bestimpressions.com
Web Site: www.bestimpressions.com
Approx. Rev.: $16,459,224
Approx. Number Employees: 30
Business Description:
Promotional Products Mail Order Catalog Sales
S.I.C.: 5961
N.A.I.C.S.: 454113
Media: 4-8-20
Personnel:
Cindy Kurkowski *(Pres & CEO)*
Brands & Products:
PRIORITY PLUS PROGRAM

BEVAN MANUFACTURING CORP.
(d/b/a Costume Gallery)
4451 Rte 130
Burlington, NJ 08016
Tel.: (609) 386-6501
Fax: (609) 386-6503
Toll Free: (800) 222-8125
E-mail: info@costumegallery.net
Web Site: www.costumegallery.net
Approx. Number Employees: 75
Business Description:
Dance Costumes Mfr
S.I.C.: 2389; 2329; 2339; 2341; 5961
N.A.I.C.S.: 315999; 315211; 315212; 315231; 454113
Media: 4-6-7
Personnel:
Ellen Ferreira *(Pres)*

BIG LOTS, INC.
300 Phillipi Rd
Columbus, OH 43228
Mailing Address:
PO Box 28512
Columbus, OH 43228-0512
Tel.: (614) 278-6800
Fax: (614) 278-6666
Toll Free: (800) 877-1253
E-mail: investor_relations@biglots.com
Web Site: www.biglots.com
Approx. Sls.: $4,952,244,000
Approx. Number Employees: 13,000
Year Founded: 1967
Business Description:
Holding Company; Specialty Retail Stores, Wholesale Housewares, Electronics, Hardware, Automotive Equipment, Accessories, Food Items, Health & Beauty Aids, Sports Goods, Toys & Jewelry
S.I.C.: 5399; 5023; 5311
N.A.I.C.S.: 452990; 423220; 452112
Import Export
Advertising Expenditures: $92,000,000
Media: 3-9-14-15-18-19-23-24-25
Distr.: Natl.; Reg.
Budget Set: Nov.
Personnel:
Steven S. Fishman *(Chm, Pres & CEO)*
Joe R. Cooper *(CFO)*
Lisa M. Bachmann *(CIO & Exec VP-Supply Chain Mgmt)*
Charles W. Haubiel, II *(Sr VP-Legal & Real Estate, Gen Counsel, Corp Sec)*
John C. Martin *(Exec VP-Admin)*
Brad A. Waite *(Exec VP)*
Douglas N. Wurl *(Exec VP-Mdsg)*
Robert Samuel Segal *(Sr VP & Gen Mgr-Mdse)*
Steven R. Smart *(Sr VP & Gen Mgr-Mdse)*
Christopher T. Chapin *(Sr VP-Store Ops)*
Robert C. Claxton *(Sr VP-Mktg)*
Norman John Rankin *(Sr VP-Capital & Wholesale)*
Harold Allan Wilson *(Sr VP-Distr & Transportation Svcs)*
Gary E. Huber *(Reg VP)*
Thomas R. Myron *(Reg VP)*
Kim K. Horner *(VP-Mdsg)*
Karen L. Lutz-Iento *(VP-Mdsg)*
Jo L. Roney *(VP-HR Svcs)*
Shelley L. Rubin *(VP-Adv)*
Sharon A. Smith *(VP-Mdse Allocation)*
Brands & Products:
BIG LOTS
BUZZ CLUB
Advertising Agencies:
Amalgamated Advertising LLC
145 W 30th St 7th Fl
New York, NY 10001
Tel.: (646) 878-1700
Fax: (646) 878-1787

Initiative
1 Dag Hammarskjold Plz
New York, NY 10017
Tel.: (212) 605-7000
Fax: (917) 305-4003

BIG LOTS STORES, INC.
(Sub. of Big Lots, Inc.)
300 Phillipi Rd
Columbus, OH 43228
Tel.: (614) 278-6800
Fax: (614) 278-6676
Sales Range: $250-299.9 Million
Approx. Number Employees: 7,325
Year Founded: 1953
Business Description:
Retail Department Stores
S.I.C.: 5399; 5199
N.A.I.C.S.: 452990; 424990
Import
Advertising Expenditures: $500,000
Media: 8-15-18-23-24-25
Distr.: Direct to Consumer; Natl.
Budget Set: Sept. -Oct.
Personnel:
Steven S. Fishman *(Chm, Pres & CEO)*

BIGG'S HYPER SHOPPES, INC.
(Sub. of SUPERVALU, Inc.)
25 Whitney Dr Ste 122
Milford, OH 45150-8400

Key to Media (For complete agency information see *The Advertising Red Books-Agencies* edition):
1. Bus. Publs. 2. Cable T.V. 3. Catalogs & Directories. 4. Co-op Adv. 5. Consumer Mags. 6. D.M. to Bus. Estab.7. D.M. to Consumers 8. Daily Newsp. 9. Exhibits/Trade Shows 10. Foreign 11. Infomercial 12. Internet Adv.13. Multimedia 14. Network Radio 15. Network T.V. 16. Newsp. Distr. Mags. 17. Other 18. Outdoor (Posters, Transit) 19. Point of Purchase20. Premiums, Novelties 21. Product Samples 22. Special Events Mktg. 23. Spot Radio 24. Spot T.V. 25. Weekly Newsp. 26. Yellow Page Adv.

Tel.: (513) 248-9300
Fax: (513) 248-9731
Web Site: www.biggs.com
E-Mail For Key Personnel:
Sales Director: sales@biggs.com
Approx. Sls.: $450,000,000
Approx. Number Employees: 80
Year Founded: 1984
Business Description:
General Merchandise & Food Retailing
S.I.C.: 5411; 5311; 5399
N.A.I.C.S.: 445110; 445120; 452112; 452910
Personnel:
Jimmy Nichols *(Pres)*
Shirley Cornetet *(Asst Mgr-Acctg)*
Advertising Agency:
OLSON
1625 Hennepin Ave
Minneapolis, MN 55403
Tel.: (612) 215-9800
Fax: (612) 215-9801

BLAIR CORPORATION

(Holding of Orchard Brands Corporation)
220 Hickory St
Warren, PA 16366-0001
Tel.: (814) 723-3600
Fax: (814) 726-6123
Toll Free: (800) 821-5744
Web Site: www.blair.com
Sales Range: $400-449.9 Million
Approx. Number Employees: 1,760
Year Founded: 1910
Business Description:
Mail Order Retailer of a Broad Range of Home Products & Apparel for Men & Women
S.I.C.: 5961
N.A.I.C.S.: 454113; 454111
Advertising Expenditures: $119,300,000
Media: 1-4-5-6-8-13
Distr.: Direct to Consumer; Natl.
Personnel:
Michael R. Delprince *(VP-Fin)*
Dave Walde *(Mgr-Property & Asst VP)*
Brands & Products:
BLAIR
Advertising Agency:
G.S. Schwartz & Co. Inc.
470 Park Ave S 10th Fl S
New York, NY 10016-6819
Tel.: (212) 725-4500
Fax: (212) 725-9188
(Investor Relations Services)

BLOOMINGDALE'S, INC.

(Sub. of Macy's, Inc.)
1000 3rd Ave
New York, NY 10022-1231
Tel.: (212) 705-2000
Fax: (212) 705-2805
Web Site: www.bloomingdales.com
Sales Range: $1-4.9 Billion
Approx. Number Employees: 10,500
Year Founded: 1872
Business Description:
Department Stores & Mail Order Catalog Sales
S.I.C.: 5311
N.A.I.C.S.: 452111
Advertising Expenditures: $105,000,000
Media: 1-3-4-5-6-7-8-9-10-11-13-16-17-18-19-20-21-22-23-24-25
Distr.: Direct to Consumer; Natl.
Personnel:
Michael Gould *(Chm & CEO)*
Tony Spring *(Pres)*
Bruce Berman *(CFO)*
Frank Doroff *(Sr Exec VP & Gen Mgr-Mdse-Ready to Wear & The Fashion Office)*
David Fisher *(Exec VP & Gen Mgr Mdse)*
Frank Berman *(Sr VP-Mktg)*
Charlie Silver *(VP-Mktg)*
Hollie Lamport *(Dir-Media)*
Kristen Orr *(Acct Exec-Mktg)*
Brands & Products:
B MAGAZINE
EAST ISLAND
METROPOLITAN VIEW
STUDIO B
SUTTON
YOUNG EASTSIDER
Advertising Agencies:
Brierley & Partners
8401 N Central Expy Ste 1000 LB-37
Dallas, TX 75225-4403
Tel.: (214) 760-8700
Fax: (214) 743-5511

Organic, Inc.
555 Market St 4th Fl
San Francisco, CA 94105
Tel.: (415) 581-5300
Fax: (415) 581-5400

BOB'S DISCOUNT FURNITURE INC.

428 Tolland Tpke
Manchester, CT 06040-1765
Tel.: (860) 645-3200
Fax: (860) 645-3211
Web Site: www.mybobs.com
Sales Range: $200-249.9 Million
Approx. Number Employees: 1,000
Year Founded: 1991
Business Description:
Furniture Stores
S.I.C.: 5712
N.A.I.C.S.: 442110
Import Export
Personnel:
Robert Kaufman *(Pres)*
Edmond J. English *(CEO)*
Cathy Poulin *(Dir-PR)*
Advertising Agency:
Dennis PR Group
41 Crossroads Ste 228
West Hartford, CT 06117
Tel.: (860) 523-7500
Fax: (720) 533-7501
Toll Free: (800) 990-6685

THE BON TON STORES, INC.

2801 E Market St
York, PA 17402
Mailing Address:
PO Box 2821
York, PA 17405-2821
Tel.: (717) 757-7660
Fax: (717) 751-3108
E-mail: ir@bonton.com
Web Site: www.bonton.com
E-Mail For Key Personnel:
Public Relations: mkarr@bonton.com
Approx. Rev.: $3,046,485,000
Approx. Number Employees: 26,500
Year Founded: 1898
Business Description:
Department Store Chain
S.I.C.: 5311
N.A.I.C.S.: 452112; 452111
Import
Advertising Expenditures: $138,805,000
Personnel:
Tim Grumbacher *(Chm)*
Anthony J. Buccina *(Vice Chm & Pres-Mdsg)*
Byron L. Bergren *(Pres & CEO)*
Keith E. Plowman *(CFO, Principal Acctg Officer & Exec VP)*
Barbara Schrantz *(COO & VP-Mktg)*
Dennis R. Clouser *(Exec VP-HR, Procurement, Ops & Info Svcs)*
Joyce Armeli *(Sr VP & Gen Mdse Mgr-Center Core & Children's)*
Mary Kerr *(VP-IR & PR)*
Advertising Agency:
Starcom USA
35 W Wacker Dr
Chicago, IL 60601
Tel.: (312) 220-3535
Fax: (312) 220-6530
Media Buying & Planning

BORDERS GROUP, INC.

(Filed Chapter 11 Bankruptcy #11-10614 on 02/16/2011 in U.S. Bankruptcy Ct, Dist of NY, Manhattan)
100 Phoenix Dr
Ann Arbor, MI 48108-2202
Tel.: (734) 477-1100
Fax: (734) 477-1285
E-mail: pempie@bordersgroupinc.com
Web Site: www.bordersgroupinc.com
Approx. Sls.: $2,274,900,000
Approx. Number Employees: 5,700
Business Description:
Holding Company; Book Superstores & Mall-Based Bookstores; Books, Music & DVD Retailer
S.I.C.: 5942; 5735; 5999; 6719
N.A.I.C.S.: 451211; 451220; 453998; 551112
Advertising Expenditures: $35,000,000
Media: 2-5-6-8-9-13-14-19-23-25-31
Personnel:
Bennett LeBow *(Chm & CEO)*
Michael J. Edwards *(Pres)*
Scott D. Henry *(CFO & Exec VP)*
Glen Tomaszewski *(Chief Acctg Officer, VP & Controller)*
Michele M. Delahunty-Cloutier *(Chief Mdsg Officer & Exec VP)*
Rosalind Thompson *(Sr VP-HR)*
Eric Kovats *(VP-Southeast Reg)*
Mike Ferrari *(Dir-Mdsg)*
Brands & Products:
BORDERS
BORDERS BOOKS & MUSIC
BORDERS BOOKSHOP
BORDERS MUSIC CAFE
Advertising Agency:
KSL Media, Inc.
367 Park Ave S 4th Fl
New York, NY 10016
Tel.: (212) 352-5800
Fax: (212) 352-5935

BOSCOV'S DEPARTMENT STORE, LLC

(Sub. of Boscov's Inc.)
4500 Perkiomen Ave
Reading, PA 19606-3202
Tel.: (610) 779-2000
Fax: (610) 370-3799
E-mail: info@boscovs.com
Web Site: www.boscovs.com
Approx. Sls.: $1,100,000,000
Approx. Number Employees: 12,000
Year Founded: 1911
Business Description:
Department Store
S.I.C.: 5311
N.A.I.C.S.: 452111
Advertising Expenditures: $50,000,000
Media: 3-9-13-16-23-24-25
Personnel:
Albert Boscov *(Chm & CEO)*
Jim Boscov *(Vice Chm)*
Sam Flamholz *(Co-Pres & Chief Admin Officer)*
Burton Krieger *(Co-Pres & Chief Mdsg Officer)*
Toni Miller *(CFO & Exec VP)*
Harry Roberts *(CIO & Sr VP)*
Russell C. Diehm *(Chief Acctg Officer & Sr VP-Fin)*
Edward McKeaney *(Chief Mdsg Officer-Home Store)*
Larry Bergman *(Sr VP & Dir-Supply Chain Ops)*
Gary Boyer *(Sr VP & Dir-Stores)*
Joe McGrath *(Sr VP & Gen Mdsg Mgr-Major Appliances, TV, Electronics, Audio)*
Brian Nugent *(Sr VP & Gen Mdsg Mgr-Mens)*
Ed Elko *(Sr VP-HR)*
John Hlis *(Sr VP-Real Estate & Dev)*
T.J. Javier *(Sr VP, Gen Mdsg Mgr-Ladies Ready to Wear, Shoes & Lingerie)*
Derek Luppino *(Sr VP-GMM, Jewelry, Cosmetics & Juniors, Girls & Infants)*
Dean Sheaffer *(Sr VP-Credit & Customer Rels Mgmt)*
John Young *(Sr VP & Gen Mdsg Mgr-Home)*
Kenneth S. Lakin *(Dir-Ops)*
Advertising Agencies:
Harmelin Media
525 Righters Ferry Rd
Bala Cynwyd, PA 19004-1315
Tel.: (610) 668-7900
Fax: (610) 668-9548

The MWW Group
1 Meadowlands Plz 6th Fl
East Rutherford, NJ 07073
Tel.: (201) 507-9500
Fax: (201) 507-0092
(Public Relations)

THE BRADFORD GROUP

9333 N Milwaukee Ave
Niles, IL 60714-1381
Tel.: (847) 966-2770
Fax: (847) 966-3121
Toll Free: (877) 268-6638
Toll Free: (800) 545-2077
Web Site: www.collectiblestoday.com
Sales Range: $100-124.9 Million
Approx. Number Employees: 600
Year Founded: 1973

Key to Media (For complete agency information see *The Advertising Red Books-Agencies* edition):
1. Bus. Publs. 2. Cable T.V. 3. Catalogs & Directories. 4. Co-op Adv. 5. Consumer Mags. 6. D.M. to Bus. Estab.7. D.M. to Consumers 8. Daily Newsp. 9. Exhibits/Trade Shows 10. Foreign 11. Infomercial 12. Internet Adv.13. Multimedia 14. Network Radio 15. Network T.V. 16. Newsp. Distr. Mags. 17. Other 18. Outdoor (Posters, Transit) 19. Point of Purchase20. Premiums, Novelties 21. Product Samples 22. Special Events Mktg. 23. Spot Radio 24. Spot T.V. 25. Weekly Newsp. 26. Yellow Page Adv.

The Bradford Group — (Continued)

Business Description:
Direct Mail Retail Marketing of Collectors Items
S.I.C.: 5961; 5199
N.A.I.C.S.: 454113; 424990
Import Export
Advertising Expenditures: $40,000,000
Media: 3-4-5-6-8-9-13-24-25
Distr.: Natl.

Personnel:
Richard W. Tinberg *(Chm, Pres & CEO)*
Shay Gallagher *(Sr VP & Gen Mgr-Mktg)*
Karen Cox *(Dir-Mktg Svcs)*

Brands & Products:
ASHTON DRAKE
BRADFORD EXCHANGE

Advertising Agency:
Midwest List & Media
(d/b/a The Bradford Group Marketing Services Department)
9333 N Milwaukee Ave
Niles, IL 60714
Tel.: (847) 966-2485
Fax: (847) 581-8630
(Collectibles)

BROOKSTONE, INC.

(Sub. of OSIM International Ltd)
1 Innovation Way
Merrimack, NH 03054-4873
Tel.: (603) 880-9500
Fax: (603) 577-8001
Toll Free: (800) 846-3000
E-mail: customerservice@brookstone.com
Web Site: www.brookstone.com
Sales Range: $450-499.9 Million
Approx. Number Employees: 1,484
Year Founded: 1965

Business Description:
Specialty Products Retailer
S.I.C.: 5947; 5712; 5961; 5999
N.A.I.C.S.: 453220; 442110; 446199; 453998; 454113
Import
Advertising Expenditures: $30,300,000
Media: 4-6-17-19

Personnel:
Jackson Peter Tai *(Chm)*
Ronald D. Boire *(Pres & CEO)*
M. Rufus Woodard *(VP-Product Dev, Wholesale & Licensing)*
John Lucey *(Dir-Internet Mktg)*

THE BUCKLE, INC.

2407 W 24th St
Kearney, NE 68845-4915
Mailing Address:
PO Box 1480
Kearney, NE 68848-1480
Tel.: (308) 236-8491
Fax: (308) 236-4493
Toll Free: (800) 626-1255
E-mail: webmaster@buckle.com
Web Site: www.buckle.com
E-Mail For Key Personnel:
President: dennis.nelson@buckle.com
Public Relations: karen.rhoads@buckle.com
Approx. Sls.: $949,832,000
Approx. Number Employees: 7,600
Year Founded: 1948

Business Description:
Casual Apparel, Footwear & Accessories Retailer
S.I.C.: 5651; 5661
N.A.I.C.S.: 448140; 448210
Import
Advertising Expenditures: $8,521,000
Media: 6-9-13-19-22-25

Personnel:
Daniel J. Hirschfeld *(Chm)*
Dennis H. Nelson *(Pres & CEO)*
Karen B. Rhoads *(CFO, Treas & VP-Fin)*
Kyle L. Hanson *(Gen Counsel & Corp Sec)*
James E. Shada *(Exec VP-Sls)*
Robert M. Carlberg *(VP-Mens Mdsg)*
Kari G. Smith *(VP-Sls)*
Patricia K. Whisler *(VP-Womens Mdsg)*
Lori Cody *(Dir-Mktg)*
Cody Kevan *(Dir-Music & Entertainment Promos)*
Justin Gill *(Mgr-Store-Coronado Mall Store)*
Dane Henricksen *(Mgr-Woodland Mall)*

Brands & Products:
BKE
BUCKLE
RECLAIM

BURLINGTON COAT FACTORY WAREHOUSE CORPORATION

(Holding of Bain Capital, LLC)
1830 Rte 130 N
Burlington, NJ 08016
Tel.: (609) 387-7800
Fax: (609) 387-7071
Toll Free: (800) 444-COATS
Web Site: www.burlingtoncoatfactory.com
Approx. Rev.: $3,701,100,000
Approx. Number Employees: 31,399
Year Founded: 1972

Business Description:
Retailer of Apparel, Shoes & Accessories for Men, Women & Children; Home Furnishings, Linens & Juvenile Furniture
S.I.C.: 5311; 5651; 5699
N.A.I.C.S.: 452111; 448140; 448190
Advertising Expenditures: $600,000
Distr.: Natl.

Personnel:
Thomas A. Kingsbury *(Pres & CEO)*
Todd Weyhrich *(CFO & Exec VP)*
Dennis P. Hodgson *(CIO & Sr VP)*
Garry Graham *(CMO & Exec VP)*
John Crimmins *(Chief Acctg Officer & Sr VP)*
Paul C. Tang *(Gen Counsel & Exec VP)*
Fred Hand *(Exec VP-Stores)*
Marc Katz *(Exec VP-Mdse Support & IT)*
Joyce Manning Magrini *(Exec VP-HR)*
Peter M. Cupps *(Sr VP-Construction & Procurement)*
Michael J. Metheny *(Sr VP)*

Advertising Agencies:
Cramer-Krasselt
225 N Michigan Ave
Chicago, IL 60601-7601
Tel.: (312) 616-9600
Fax: (312) 616-3839

Initiative Worldwide
(Part of The Interpublic Group of Companies, Inc.)
1 Dag Hammerskjold Plz 5th Fl
New York, NY 10017
Tel.: (212) 605-7000
Fax: (212) 605-7200

Norman Stevens
76 S. Orange
South Orange, NJ 07079
Tel.: (973) 762-8100
Fax: (973) 762-7968
(Display-Retail)

CAPALBO'S GIFT BASKETS

25 Ann St
Clifton, NJ 07013
Tel.: (973) 667-6262
Fax: (973) 450-1199
Toll Free: (800) 252-6262
E-mail: info@capalbosgiftbaskets.com
Web Site: www.capalbosgiftbaskets.com
Approx. Number Employees: 50
Year Founded: 1906

Business Description:
Fruit & Gourmet Gift Baskets Distr
S.I.C.: 5961
N.A.I.C.S.: 454113
Media: 4-7-8-13-26
Distr.: Natl.

CARIBOU COFFEE COMPANY, INC.

(Holding of Arcapita, Inc.)
3900 Lakebreeze Ave N
Minneapolis, MN 55429
Tel.: (763) 592-2200
Fax: (763) 592-2300
Toll Free: (888) 227-4268
E-mail: webmaster@cariboucoffee.com
Web Site: www.cariboucoffee.com
Approx. Sls.: $283,997,000
Approx. Number Employees: 1,642
Year Founded: 1992

Business Description:
Coffeehouse Operator
S.I.C.: 5812
N.A.I.C.S.: 722213
Advertising Expenditures: $7,800,000
Media: 4-13-20

Personnel:
Gary A. Graves *(Chm)*
Michael J. Tattersfield *(Pres & CEO)*
Timothy J. Hennessy *(CFO)*
Daniel E. Lee *(Gen Counsel)*
Daniel J. Hurdle *(Sr VP-Retail)*
Alfredo Martel *(Sr VP-Mktg & Product Mgmt)*
Henry Suerth *(Sr VP-Comml Bus)*
Karen E. McBride *(VP-HR)*
Chad Trewick *(Sr Dir-Coffee & Tea Ops)*

Brands & Products:
CARIBOU COFFEE
CARIBOU ICED COFFEE
ETHIOPIA SIDAMO
ETHIOPIAN ORGANIC YIRGACHEFFE

Advertising Agency:
Colle+McVoy
400 1st Ave N Ste 700
Minneapolis, MN 55401-1954
Tel.: (612) 305-6000
Fax: (612) 305-6500
Agency of Record
Bou-isim Taglines
Logo

CARSON PIRIE SCOTT & CO.

(Sub. of The Bon Ton Stores, Inc.)
2801 E Market St
York, PA 17402
Tel.: (717) 757-7660
Fax: (717) 751-3037
Toll Free: (800) 233-7626
Web Site: www.carsons.com
Approx. Number Employees: 62,000
Year Founded: 1854

Business Description:
Department Store
S.I.C.: 5311
N.A.I.C.S.: 452111
Advertising Expenditures: $500,000
Media: 3-4-5-6-8-9-16-18-19-20-22-23-24-25
Distr.: Direct to Consumer; Reg.

Personnel:
Byron L. Bergren *(Pres)*
Michael N. Nemoir *(Sr VP & Gen Mgr-Mdse-Men's & Home)*
Kiki Lockwood *(Sr VP & Gen Mgr-Mdse-Ready to Wear)*

Brands & Products:
BOSTON STORE
CARSON PIRIE SCOTT & CO.

CARVIN CORP.

12340 World Trade Dr
San Diego, CA 92128
Tel.: (858) 487-1600
Fax: (858) 487-7620
E-mail: info@carvin.com
Web Site: www.carvin.com
Sales Range: $10-24.9 Million
Approx. Number Employees: 105

Business Description:
Musical Instruments
S.I.C.: 3931; 5736
N.A.I.C.S.: 339992; 451140
Media: 4-8-13

CD BABY, INC.

5925 NE 80th Ave
Portland, OR 97218-2891
Tel.: (503) 595-3000
Fax: (503) 296-2370
E-mail: cdbaby@cdbaby.com
Web Site: www.cdbaby.com
Approx. Number Employees: 85
Year Founded: 1998

Business Description:
Sales of CDs
S.I.C.: 5735
N.A.I.C.S.: 451220
Media: 13

Personnel:
Brian Felson *(Pres)*

CELEBRATE EXPRESS, INC.

(Sub. of BUYSEASONS, Inc.)
5915 S Moorland Rd
New Berlin, WI 53151
Tel.: (262) 901-2324
Toll Free: (800) BIRTHDAY
Toll Free: (800) 424-7843
Web Site: www.celebrateexpress.com

Key to Media (For complete agency information see *The Advertising Red Books-Agencies* edition):
1. Bus. Publs. 2. Cable T.V. 3. Catalogs & Directories. 4. Co-op Adv. 5. Consumer Mags. 6. D.M. to Bus. Estab.7. D.M. to Consumers 8. Daily Newsp. 9. Exhibits/Trade Shows 10. Foreign 11. Infomercial 12. Internet Adv.13. Multimedia 14. Network Radio 15. Network T.V. 16. Newsp. Distr. Mags. 17. Other 18. Outdoor (Posters, Transit) 19. Point of Purchase20. Premiums, Novelties 21. Product Samples 22. Special Events Mktg. 23. Spot Radio 24. Spot T.V. 25. Weekly Newsp. 26. Yellow Page Adv.

Approx. Sls.: $85,243,093
Approx. Number Employees: 332
Year Founded: 1994
Business Description:
Party Supplies & Costume Retailer
S.I.C.: 5961; 5947
N.A.I.C.S.: 454111; 453220; 454113
Advertising Expenditures: $19,835,000
Media: 4-8-13
Personnel:
David Karst *(VP-HR)*
Neil McCafferty *(VP-Fin)*
Brands & Products:
BIRTHDAY EXPRESS
BIRTHDAY EXPRESS.COM
COSTUME EXPRESS
COSTUME EXPRESS.COM
STORYBOOK HEIRLOOMS
STORYBOOK.COM

CERAMIC DEVELOPMENT CORP.
(d/b/a Aftosa)
1776 Wright Ave
Richmond, CA 94804
Tel.: (510) 233-0334
Fax: (510) 233-3569
Toll Free: (800) 231-0397
E-mail: customerservice@aftosa.com
Web Site: www.aftosa.com
Approx. Number Employees: 6
Business Description:
Ceramic Accessories Whslr
S.I.C.: 5023
N.A.I.C.S.: 423220
Media: 4-13
Personnel:
Arnie Bernstein *(Owner)*

CHELSEA & SCOTT, LTD.
75 Albrecht Dr
Lake Bluff, IL 60044
Tel.: (847) 615-2110
Fax: (847) 615-7326
Toll Free: (800) 274-8440
Web Site: www.onestepahead.com
Approx. Sls.: $65,000,000
Approx. Number Employees: 140
Business Description:
Direct Sales of Children's & Baby Products
S.I.C.: 5961
N.A.I.C.S.: 454113
Media: 4-8-13
Personnel:
Karen B. Scott *(Owner)*
Brands & Products:
ONESTEPAHEAD

CHERYL & CO. INCORPORATED
(Sub. of 1-800-Flowers.com, Inc.)
646 McCorkle Blvd
Westerville, OH 43082
Tel.: (614) 776-1529
Fax: (614) 891-8699
Toll Free: (800) 433-1787
Web Site: www.cherylandco.com
Approx. Sls.: $24,106,368
Approx. Number Employees: 300
Business Description:
Cookies, Desserts & Gift Baskets Retailer & Catalog Sales
S.I.C.: 2052; 5961
N.A.I.C.S.: 311821; 454113
Media: 4-7-8-13
Personnel:
Steve Druckman *(Pres)*
Denise Graham *(VP-Mktg)*
Advertising Agency:
The Ruder Finn Group
301 E 57th St
New York, NY 10022-2900
Tel.: (212) 593-6400
Fax: (212) 593-6397

CKX, INC.
650 Madison Ave
New York, NY 10022
Tel.: (212) 838-3100
Web Site: ir.ckx.com
Approx. Rev.: $273,724,000
Approx. Number Employees: 310
Year Founded: 1974
Business Description:
Entertainment Holding Company
S.I.C.: 7812; 6289; 7999
N.A.I.C.S.: 512110; 523999; 713990
Advertising Expenditures: $1,600,000
Personnel:
Michael G. Ferrel *(CEO)*
Thomas P. Benson *(CFO, Treas & Exec VP)*
Kraig G. Fox *(COO)*
Chris Gannett *(CMO)*
Howard J. Tytel *(Sr Exec VP & Dir-Legal & Governmental Affairs)*

CLAIRE'S STORES, INC.
(Holding of Apollo Management, L.P.)
2400 W Central Rd
Hoffman Estates, IL 60192
Tel.: (847) 765-1100
E-mail: customerservice@claires.com
Web Site: www.clairestores.com
Approx. Sls.: $1,426,397,000
Approx. Number Employees: 6,992
Year Founded: 1961
Business Description:
Women's Fashion Accessories & Apparel Retailer
S.I.C.: 5699
N.A.I.C.S.: 448190; 448150
Import Export
Advertising Expenditures: $12,800,000
Media: 4-6-7-8-9-10-13-17-21
Distr.: Direct to Consumer; Reg.
Personnel:
Peter P. Copses *(Chm)*
James G. Conroy *(Pres)*
Eugene S. Kahn *(CEO)*
J. Per Brodin *(CFO & Exec VP)*
Jay Friedman *(Pres-North America)*
Beatrice Lafon *(Pres-Europe)*
Rebecca Orand *(Gen Counsel & Sr VP-Quality Assurance)*
Joseph A. DeFalco *(Sr VP-HR)*
Dan Mollerus *(VP-Mktg Intl)*
David Ovis *(VP-Global Taxation)*
Brands & Products:
BOW BANGLES
CLAIRE'S
CLAIRE'S BOUTIQUES
DARA MICHELLE
ICING

COLDWATER CREEK, INC.
1 Coldwater Creek Dr
Sandpoint, ID 83864
Tel.: (208) 263-2266
Fax: (208) 263-1582
Toll Free: (800) 510-2808
E-mail: customerservice@thecreek.com
Web Site: www.coldwater-creek.com
Approx. Sls.: $981,101,000
Approx. Number Employees: 2,832
Year Founded: 1984
Business Description:
Specialty Direct Mail Retailer of Apparel, Gifts & Jewelry
S.I.C.: 5621; 5699; 5961
N.A.I.C.S.: 448120; 448150; 454113
Advertising Expenditures: $47,700,000
Media: 4-8-13
Personnel:
Dennis C. Pence *(Chm & CEO)*
Jerome Jessup *(Co-Pres & Chief Creative Officer)*
Jill Brown Dean *(Co-Pres & Chief Mdsg Officer)*
James A. Bell *(CFO & Sr VP)*
Dan Moen *(CIO & Sr VP-Mktg)*
Jeffrey Parisian *(Chief Strategy Officer & Sr VP)*
Gerard El Chaar *(Pres-Div & Sr VP)*
John E. Hayes, III *(Gen Counsel, Sec & Sr VP)*
Kathy McConnell *(Sr VP-Product Dev)*
Claudia Runkel *(Sr VP-Sourcing)*
Tim Dilworth *(VP-Mktg & Ecommerce)*
Joe Gravitt *(VP-Retail)*
Robert Jansen *(VP-Inventory Plng)*
Marie Hirsch *(Dir-IR)*
Brands & Products:
COLDWATER CREEK
COLDWATER CREEK THE SPA
INVISIBLE COMFORT
PALE JADE
WATERSILK
WINDFLOWER COLDWATER CREEK
Advertising Agency:
DeVito/Verdi
100 5th Ave 16th Fl
New York, NY 10011
Tel.: (212) 431-4694
Fax: (212) 431-4940
Agency of Record
Branding
Creative
Design Consulting
National Advertising

COLORTYME, INC.
(Sub. of Rent-A-Center, Inc.)
5700 Tennyson Pkwy Ste 180
Plano, TX 75024-3585
Tel.: (972) 403-4900
Tel.: (972) 608-5376
Fax: (972) 403-4935
Toll Free: (800) 411-8963
Web Site: www.colortyme.com
Sales Range: $25-49.9 Million
Approx. Number Employees: 20
Business Description:
Franchiser of Rent-to-Own Stores
S.I.C.: 5064; 5021
N.A.I.C.S.: 423620; 423210
Media: 1-3-8-15-19-21-26
Distr.: Natl.
Budget Set: Jan.
Personnel:
Robert F. Bloom *(Pres & CEO)*
Amy Woods *(Dir-Mktg)*
Brands & Products:
COLORTYME

COLUMBIA HOUSE
(Sub. of Direct Brands, Inc.)
1 Penn Plz 250 W 34th St 5th Fl
New York, NY 10119
Tel.: (212) 596-2000
Fax: (212) 596-2213
Web Site: www.columbiahouse.com
Approx. Number Employees: 4,000
Year Founded: 1955
Business Description:
Mail Order Retailer of CDs, Tapes & Books
S.I.C.: 5961
N.A.I.C.S.: 454113
Advertising Expenditures: $100,000,000
Media: 2-5-6-7-8-9-10-14-15-16-23-24-25-26
Distr.: Natl.
Personnel:
Michael Chauliac *(Dir-Online Mktg)*
Advertising Agency:
Dehart and Darr Associates, Inc.
1360 Beverly Rd
McLean, VA 22101
Tel.: (703) 448-1000
Fax: (703) 790-3460

CONCORD MUSIC GROUP, INC.
(Joint Venture of Village Roadshow Limited & Clarity Partners, L.P.)
900 N. Rohlwing R
Itasca, IL 60143
Tel.: (310) 385-4455
Fax: (310) 385-4466
Toll Free: (800) 551-5299
E-mail: customerservice@concordmusicgroup.com
Web Site: www.concordmusicgroup.com
Approx. Sls.: $6,400,000
Approx. Number Employees: 35
Year Founded: 2004
Business Description:
Pre-Recorded Music & Related Products Mfr
S.I.C.: 5099; 6794
N.A.I.C.S.: 423990; 533110
Media: 6
Personnel:
Norman Lear *(Chm)*
Glen Barros *(CEO)*
Jeffrey Spector *(Product Mgr)*

CONROYS FLOWERS INC.
(Sub. of 1-800-Flowers.com, Inc.)
6055 E Washington Blvd #235
Commerce, CA 90040
Tel.: (323) 888-8795
Fax: (818) 843-6362
Toll Free: (800) 266-7697
Web Site: www.1800conroys.com
Sales Range: Less than $1 Million
Approx. Number Employees: 25
Year Founded: 1961
Business Description:
Retailers of Flower Shops
S.I.C.: 7389
N.A.I.C.S.: 561499
Advertising Expenditures: $1,000,000
Media: 4-9-10-17-18-19-26
Distr.: Direct to Consumer; Reg.
Brands & Products:
CONROYS FLOWERS

COSMETIQUE, INC.
200 Corporate Woods Pkwy
Vernon Hills, IL 60061-3171

Key to Media (For complete agency information see *The Advertising Red Books-Agencies* edition):
1. Bus. Publs. 2. Cable T.V. 3. Catalogs & Directories. 4. Co-op Adv. 5. Consumer Mags. 6. D.M. to Bus. Estab.7. D.M. to Consumers
8. Daily Newsp. 9. Exhibits/Trade Shows 10. Foreign 11. Infomercial 12. Internet Adv.13. Multimedia 14. Network Radio
15. Network T.V. 16. Newsp. Distr. Mags. 17. Other 18. Outdoor (Posters, Transit) 19. Point of Purchase20. Premiums, Novelties
21. Product Samples 22. Special Events Mktg. 23. Spot Radio 24. Spot T.V. 25. Weekly Newsp. 26. Yellow Page Adv.

Cosmetique, Inc. — (Continued)

Tel.: (847) 913-9099
Fax: (847) 913-9496
E-mail: customerservice@cosmetique.com
Web Site: www.cosmetique.com
Sales Range: $25-49.9 Million
Approx. Number Employees: 40
Year Founded: 1974
Business Description:
Mail Order Cosmetics
S.I.C.: 5961; 5122
N.A.I.C.S.: 454113; 424210
Import Export
Media: 2-4-5-6-8-9
Distr.: Natl.
Budget Set: Sept.
Personnel:
June Giugni *(Pres)*
Chuck Campbell *(Exec VP)*
Brands & Products:
ARABELLA STUART
CADETTE
DIANDRA
JEAN-MICHELLE
MADELINE MONO
PRINCESS LIVIA
RUBIGO
SARA ST. JAMES
SISTINA

COSTCO WHOLESALE CORPORATION

999 Lake Dr
Issaquah, WA 98027-8990
Tel.: (425) 313-8100
Fax: (425) 313-8103
E-mail: customerservice@costco.com
Web Site: www.costco.com
E-Mail For Key Personnel:
President: jsinegal@costco.com
Marketing Director: groeglin@costco.com
Public Relations: bnelson@costco.com
Approx. Rev.: $77,946,000,000
Approx. Number Employees: 82,000
Year Founded: 1976
Business Description:
Consumer Goods Sales
S.I.C.: 5399
N.A.I.C.S.: 452910; 452990
Import
Media: 7-8-17-19
Distr.: Natl.
Personnel:
Jeffrey H. Brotman *(Chm)*
W. Craig Jelinek *(Pres & COO)*
James D. Sinegal *(CEO)*
Richard A. Galanti *(CFO & Exec VP)*
Dennis R. Zook *(COO-Southwest & Mexico Div, Exec VP)*
Joel Benoliel *(Chief Legal Officer & Sr VP-Admin)*
John D. McKay *(COO-Northern Div & Exec VP)*
Joseph P. Portera *(COO-Eastern & Canadian Div & Exec VP)*
Douglas W. Schutt *(COO-Mdse & Exec VP)*
Paul G. Moulton *(Exec VP-Info Sys)*
David S. Petterson *(Sr VP & Controller)*
Roger A. Campbell *(Sr VP & Gen Mgr-Southeast Region)*
John B. Gaherty *(Sr VP & Gen Mgr-Midwest Region)*
Jaime Gonzalez *(Sr VP & Gen Mgr-Mexico)*
Bruce A. Greenwood *(Sr VP & Gen Mgr-Los Angeles Region)*
Robert D. Hicok *(Sr VP & Gen Mgr-San Diego Region)*
Dennis A. Hoover *(Sr VP & Gen Mgr-Bay Area Region)*
Jeffrey R. Long *(Sr VP & Gen Mgr-Northeast Region)*
Russ Miller *(Sr VP & Gen Mgr-Western Canada Region)*
Pierre Riel *(Sr VP & Gen Mgr-Eastern Canada Region)*
Louise Wendling *(Sr VP & Country Mgr-Canada)*
Don Burdick *(Sr VP-Info Sys)*
Charles V. Burnett *(Sr VP-Pharmacy)*
Richard C. Chavez *(Sr VP-Wholesale Industries & Bus Dev)*
Dennis Knapp *(Sr VP & Gen Mdse Mgr-Non-Foods)*
Franz Lazarus *(Sr VP-Admin-Global Ops)*
Jeffrey Lyons *(Sr VP-Mdsg-Fresh Foods)*
John Matthews *(Sr VP-HR & Risk Mgmt)*
Ali Moayeri *(Sr VP-Construction)*
James P. Murphy *(Sr VP-InterNatl Ops)*
Ginnie M. Roeglin *(Sr VP-E-Commerce & Publ)*
John Thelan *(Sr VP-Depot Ops)*
Paul Latham *(VP-Membership & Mktg)*
Robert E. Nelson *(VP-Fin Plng & IR)*
Jeff Elliott *(Asst VP-Fin & IR)*
Brands & Products:
BALLANTRAE WINE MERCHANTS
CANINE CLUB
CHOCOLATES OF THE WORLD
COSTCO
COSTCO BUSINESS CENTER
THE COSTCO CONNECTION
COSTCO HOME
COSTCO ONLINE
COSTCO WHOLESALE CASH
COURT CLASSIC
EXECUTIVE MEMBER
FUNHOUSE TREATS
GOLD STAR
KIRKLAND SIGNATURE
NO LINES ONLINE
PRICE CLUB
SEATTLE MOUNTAIN
Advertising Agency:
TFC, Inc.
690 Airpark Rd
Napa, CA 94558
Tel.: (707) 224-6161
Fax: (707) 224-6161

COUNTRY HOME PRODUCTS INC.

75 Meigs Rd
Vergennes, VT 05491
Mailing Address:
PO Box 25
Vergennes, VT 05491
Tel.: (802) 877-1200
Fax: (802) 877-1212
Toll Free: (800) 687-6575
Toll Free: (800) 446-8746
E-mail: info@countryhomeproducts.com
Web Site:
www.countryhomeproducts.com
Approx. Number Employees: 250
Year Founded: 1985
Business Description:
Supplier of Nursery & Garden Equipment; Mail Order Sales of Lawn Equipment
S.I.C.: 5961; 8743
N.A.I.C.S.: 454113; 541820
Import Export
Media: 1-4-6-11-12-23-24-25
Distr.: Intl.; Natl.
Brands & Products:
COUNTRY HOME PRODUCTS
DR CHIPPER
DR FIELD BRUSH MOWER
DR POWERWAGON
DR TRIMMER/MOWER
DR WHISPERLITE
NEUTON

CREATIVE CATALOGS CORPORATION

(d/ba/a Personal Creations)
19W661 101st St
Lemont, IL 60439-9668
Tel.: (630) 655-3200
Fax: (630) 655-3299
Toll Free: (888) 527-1404
Toll Free: (866) 834-7695
Web Site: www.personalize.com
Approx. Sls.: $23,649,000
Approx. Number Employees: 100
Business Description:
Mail Order
S.I.C.: 5961; 7299
N.A.I.C.S.: 454113; 812990
Media: 4-5-8
Personnel:
Judy Nelson *(VP-Sls & Mktg)*

CRITICS' CHOICE VIDEO, INC.

(Div. of Infinity Resources, Inc.)
900 N Rohlwing Rd PO Box 749
Itasca, IL 60143
Tel.: (630) 775-3300
Fax: (630) 775-0260
Toll Free: (800) 993-6357
E-mail: vcatalog@ccvideo.com
Web Site: www.ccvideo.com
Approx. Number Employees: 150
Business Description:
Movies Online Catalog Whslr
S.I.C.: 5961
N.A.I.C.S.: 454113
Media: 4-8-13
Personnel:
Dennis E. Abboud *(Pres)*

CURRENT USA, INC.

(Sub. of Taylor Corporation)
1005 E Woodman Rd
Colorado Springs, CO 80920
Tel.: (719) 594-4100
Fax: (719) 531-2820
Fax: (800) 993-3232
Toll Free: (877) 665-4458
Web Site: www.currentcatalog.com
Approx. Number Employees: 1,200
Year Founded: 1950
Business Description:
Mail Order Stationery & Greeting Cards
S.I.C.: 5961; 5947
N.A.I.C.S.: 454113; 453220
Media: 6-8-13-16
Brands & Products:
CURRENT
WHERE STAYING IN TOUCH IS AFFORDABLE & FUN

CVS CAREMARK CORPORATION

1 CVS Dr
Woonsocket, RI 02895-6146
Tel.: (401) 765-1500
Fax: (401) 766-2917
E-mail: customercare@cvs.com
Web Site: www.cvs.com
Approx. Rev.: $96,413,000,000
Approx. Number Employees: 201,000
Year Founded: 1963
Business Description:
Pharmacy Chain Owner & Operator
S.I.C.: 5912
N.A.I.C.S.: 446110
Import
Advertising Expenditures: $234,000,000
Media: 2-4-5-6-8-13-15-16-24
Personnel:
Larry J. Merlo *(Pres & CEO)*
David M. Denton *(CFO & Exec VP)*
Stuart M. McGuigan *(CIO & Sr VP)*
Rob Price *(CMO)*
Douglas A. Sgarro *(Chief Legal Officer-CVS Caremark & Exec VP)*
Troyen A. Brennan *(Chief Medical Officer & Exec VP)*
Laird Daniels *(Chief Acctg Officer, Sr VP & Controller)*
Lisa G. Bisaccia *(Chief HR Officer & Sr VP)*
Jonathan C. Roberts *(COO-PBM & Exec VP)*
Chris W. Bodine *(Exec VP)*
Jack E. Bruner *(Exec VP-Strategic Dev)*
Per G. H. Lofberg *(Exec VP)*
Mike Bloom *(Sr VP-Mdsg & Supply Chain)*
Nancy R. Christal *(Sr VP-IR)*
Len Greer *(Sr VP-Mktg)*
Eileen Howard-Dunn *(Sr VP-Corp Comm & Community Rels)*
Carolyn Castel *(VP-Corp Comm)*
Michael P. McGuire *(Sr Dir-IR)*
Ron Austerlade *(Dir-Market Intelligence)*
Christine Cramer *(Dir-PR)*
Mike DeAngelis *(Dir-PR)*
Paula Harries *(Dir-Client & Member Svcs Res)*
Erin Pensa *(Sr Mgr-PR)*
Joanne Dwyer *(Mgr-PR)*
Matt Thorsen *(Mgr-Production Svcs)*
Brands & Products:
ACCORDANT
CAREPLUS
CVS
CVS.COM
EXPECT SOMETHING EXTRA
EXTRA BUCKS
EXTRACARE
FREE EXTRAS
PROACTIVE PHARMACY CARE
UPROMISE
Advertising Agencies:
Arnold Worldwide
101 Huntington Ave
Boston, MA 02199-7603
Tel.: (617) 587-8000
Fax: (617) 587-8004
Creative

Key to Media (For complete agency information see *The Advertising Red Books-Agencies* edition):
1. Bus. Publs. 2. Cable T.V. 3. Catalogs & Directories. 4. Co-op Adv. 5. Consumer Mags. 6. D.M. to Bus. Estab.7. D.M. to Consumers 8. Daily Newsp. 9. Exhibits/Trade Shows 10. Foreign 11. Infomercial 12. Internet Adv.13. Multimedia 14. Network Radio 15. Network T.V. 16. Newsp. Distr. Mags. 17. Other 18. Outdoor (Posters, Transit) 19. Point of Purchase20. Premiums, Novelties 21. Product Samples 22. Special Events Mktg. 23. Spot Radio 24. Spot T.V. 25. Weekly Newsp. 26. Yellow Page Adv.

Mindshare
498 7th Ave
New York, NY 10018
Tel.: (212) 297-7000
Fax: (212) 297-7001
Media Buying & Planning

DANBURY MINT
(Div. of MBI Inc.)
(d/b/a Danbury Mint Sports)
47 Richards Ave
Norwalk, CT 06857-0001
Tel.: (203) 853-2000
Fax: (203) 831-9661
Toll Free: (800) 243-4664
E-mail: customerservice@danburymint.com
Web Site: www.danburymintsports.com
Approx. Number Employees: 250
Business Description:
Sports Collectibles Direct Mailer
S.I.C.: 5961
N.A.I.C.S.: 454113
Advertising Expenditures: $500,000
Media: 6-8-16
Distr.: Direct to Consumer; Natl.
Personnel:
Theodore R. Stanley *(Pres)*
Advertising Agencies:
MBI Inc.
47 Richards Ave
Norwalk, CT 06857
Tel.: (203) 853-2000
Fax: (203) 831-9661

OgilvyAction
350 W Mart Center Dr Ste 1100
Chicago, IL 60654-1866
Tel.: (312) 527-3900
Fax: (312) 527-3327

DANIEL SMITH INC.
4150 1st Ave S
Seattle, WA 98134
Tel.: (206) 223-9599
Fax: (206) 224-3567
E-mail: customer.service@danielsmith.com
Web Site: www.danielsmith.com
Approx. Sls.: $18,700,000
Approx. Number Employees: 87
Business Description:
Arts & Crafts Equipment & Supplies, Mail Order
S.I.C.: 5961; 5945
N.A.I.C.S.: 454113; 451120
Media: 4-8-13-16
Personnel:
John Cogley *(Owner)*
Brands & Products:
ART MASKOID
ARTBIN
BLACK GOLD
DA VINCI
EXTRA-FINE
GRUMBACHER
MASQUEPEN
ORIGINAL
ULTIMATE

DAY-TIMERS, INC.
(Sub. of ACCO Brands Corporation)
1 Willow Ln
East Texas, PA 18046
Tel.: (610) 398-1151
Fax: (610) 398-5520
Fax: (800) 452-7398
Toll Free: (800) 457-5702
Web Site: www.daytimer.com
Sales Range: $75-99.9 Million
Approx. Number Employees: 500
Year Founded: 1947
Business Description:
Time Management & Organizational Solutions
S.I.C.: 2752; 5961
N.A.I.C.S.: 323110; 454113
Media: 4-7-8-13
Distr.: Natl.
Personnel:
Kelli Holzman *(Controller & VP-Fin)*
Martha A. Curren *(VP & Gen Mgr)*
Bob Keppel *(Dir-Consumer Direct Mktg)*

DEP DISTRIBUTION EXCLUSIVE LTEE
(Sub. of Pindoff Record Sales Limited)
6255 rue Hutchison Suite 103
Montreal, QC H2V 4C7, Canada
Tel.: (514) 274-2040
Fax: (514) 274-2045
E-mail: info@dep.ca
Web Site: www.dep.ca
Business Description:
Compact Discs, Cassettes, Videos & DVDs Retailer
S.I.C.: 5735
N.A.I.C.S.: 451220
Media: 2-4-8-13-14-15-18-23-24
Personnel:
Maurice Courtois *(Pres)*
Georges Tremblay *(Sr VP)*
Luc Duchaine *(Sr Dir-Sls)*
Dave Ingrouville *(Sr Dir-Ops)*
France Carle *(Mgr-Acctg)*
Tara Lalonde *(Mgr-Data)*
Andre Ramsay *(Supvr-Sls Video)*
Advertising Agency:
Beat Media
6255 rue Hutchison Ste 103
Montreal, QC H2V 4C7, Canada
Tel.: (514) 274-2040

DICK BLICK COMPANY
(Sub. of Dick Blick Holdings Inc.)
(d/b/a Dick Blick Art Materials)
1849 Green Bay Rd Ste 310
Highland Park, IL 60035
Mailing Address:
PO Box 1267
Galesburg, IL 61402-1267
Tel.: (847) 681-6800
Fax: (847) 266-8803
Fax: (800) 621-8293
Toll Free: (800) 933-2542
E-mail: info@dickblick.com
Web Site: www.dickblick.com
Approx. Number Employees: 50
Year Founded: 1911
Business Description:
Art Supplies Mail Order & Retail Store Operator
S.I.C.: 5961; 5999
N.A.I.C.S.: 454113; 453998
Export
Media: 6-8-10-11-13
Personnel:
Robert Buchsbaum *(CEO)*

DILLARD'S INC.
1600 Cantrell Rd
Little Rock, AR 72201-1110
Mailing Address:
PO Box 486
Little Rock, AR 72203-0486
Tel.: (501) 376-5200
Fax: (501) 399-7831
Telex: 910-722-7322
Web Site: www.dillards.com
Approx. Sls.: $6,120,961,000
Approx. Number Employees: 29,564
Year Founded: 1938
Business Description:
Department Stores
S.I.C.: 5311
N.A.I.C.S.: 452111
Import
Advertising Expenditures: $106,000,000
Media: 4-6-8-9-23-24
Distr.: Reg.
Budget Set: Feb. -Aug.
Personnel:
William T. Dillard, II *(Owner & Chm)*
Alexander F. Dillard, Jr. *(Pres)*
James I. Freeman *(CFO, Principal Acctg Officer, Sr VP & Asst Sec)*
Paul J. Schroeder, Jr. *(Gen Counsel & VP)*
Drue Matheny *(Exec VP)*
Joseph P. Brennan *(VP-Mdsg)*
Mike Hodapp *(Dir-Mktg Digital)*
Julie J. Bull *(Dir-IR)*
Advertising Agencies:
Southwest Media Group
2100 Ross Ave Ste 3200
Dallas, TX 75201
Tel.: (214) 561-5543
Fax: (214) 744-1086

Stone Ward
225 E Markham St Ste 450
Little Rock, AR 72201-1629
Tel.: (501) 375-3003
Fax: (501) 375-8314

DIRECTBUY, INC.
(Sub. of Trivest Partners, LP)
8450 Broadway
Merrillville, IN 46410-6221
Tel.: (219) 736-1100
Fax: (219) 755-6279
Web Site: www.directbuy.com
Approx. Number Employees: 400
Year Founded: 1971
Business Description:
Discount Home Furnishings Retailer
S.I.C.: 5399; 5021; 5064; 5961
N.A.I.C.S.: 452910; 423210; 423620; 454111; 454113
Import Export
Personnel:
Scott M. Powell *(Pres)*
Geoff Kehoe *(CMO)*
Advertising Agency:
Fleishman-Hillard Inc.
John Hancock Ctr Ste 3300 875 N Michigan Ave
Chicago, IL 60611-1901
Tel.: (312) 751-8878
Fax: (312) 751-8191

DIVERSIFIED PROMOTIONS INC.
(d/b/a Diabetic Promotions)
31132 Vine St
Willowick, OH 44095
Tel.: (440) 943-6185
Fax: (440) 943-2187
Toll Free: (800) 433-1477
E-mail: info@diabeticpromotions.com
Web Site: www.diabeticpromotions.com
Approx. Sls.: $3,500,000
Approx. Number Employees: 5
Year Founded: 1986
Business Description:
Mail-Order Diabetic Care Products
S.I.C.: 5961
N.A.I.C.S.: 454113
Media: 4-6-13
Personnel:
David J. Snyder *(Pres)*
Advertising Agency:
Dynamics Online, Inc.
23230 Chagrin Blvd Ste 210
Beachwood, OH 44122-5495
Tel.: (216) 292-4410
Fax: (216) 292-4420

DOLLAR GENERAL CORPORATION
(Holding of KKR & CO. L.P.)
100 Mission Ridge Dr
Goodlettsville, TN 37072-2171
Tel.: (615) 855-4000
Fax: (615) 855-5252
Web Site: www.dollargeneral.com
Approx. Sls.: $13,035,000,000
Approx. Number Employees: 85,900
Year Founded: 1955
Business Description:
General Merchandise Retailer
S.I.C.: 5399
N.A.I.C.S.: 452990
Import
Advertising Expenditures: $46,900,000
Media: 7-8
Distr.: Direct to Consumer; Reg.
Budget Set: Sept.
Personnel:
Richard W. Dreiling *(Chm & CEO)*
David M. Tehle *(CFO & Exec VP)*
Bob Ravener *(Chief People Officer & Exec VP)*
Todd J. Vasos *(Div Pres & Chief Mdsg Officer)*
Kathleen R. Guion *(Pres-Store Ops & Store Dev)*
Susan S. Lanigan *(Gen Counsel & Exec VP)*
John W. Flanigan *(Exec VP-Global Supply Chain)*
Anita C. Elliott *(Sr VP & Controller)*
Bryan Wheeler *(VP & Mdse Mgr)*
Angela Martin *(Dir-Mktg)*
Colby Swann *(Dir-Mktg)*
Brands & Products:
DOLLAR GENERAL
DOLLAR GENERAL STORES
Advertising Agency:
JWT U.S.A., Inc.
(d/b/a JWT-Team Detroit)
550 Town Ctr Dr
Dearborn, MI 48126
Tel.: (313) 615-3100
Tel.: (313) 615-2000 (Team Detroit)
Fax: (313) 964-3191
Fax: (212) 615-4600

DOLLAR TREE, INC.
500 Volvo Pkwy
Chesapeake, VA 23320-1604
Tel.: (757) 321-5000
Fax: (757) 321-5292
Fax: (757) 321-5111
E-mail: info@dollartree.com

Key to Media (For complete agency information see *The Advertising Red Books-Agencies* edition):
1. Bus. Publs. 2. Cable T.V. 3. Catalogs & Directories. 4. Co-op Adv. 5. Consumer Mags. 6. D.M. to Bus. Estab.7. D.M. to Consumers
8. Daily Newsp. 9. Exhibits/Trade Shows 10. Foreign 11. Infomercial 12. Internet Adv.13. Multimedia 14. Network Radio
15. Network T.V. 16. Newsp. Distr. Mags. 17. Other 18. Outdoor (Posters, Transit) 19. Point of Purchase20. Premiums, Novelties
21. Product Samples 22. Special Events Mktg. 23. Spot Radio 24. Spot T.V. 25. Weekly Newsp. 26. Yellow Page Adv.

Dollar Tree, Inc. — (Continued)

Web Site: www.dollartree.com
Approx. Sls.: $5,882,400,000
Approx. Number Employees: 13,060
Year Founded: 1986
Business Description:
Holding Company: Discount Retail Store Chain
S.I.C.: 6719
N.A.I.C.S.: 551112
Import
Advertising Expenditures: $11,100,000
Media: 13
Personnel:
Bob Sasser *(Pres & CEO)*
Kevin S. Wampler *(CFO)*
Gary M. Philbin *(COO)*
Robert H. Rudman *(Chief Mdsg Officer)*
James A. Gorry, III *(Gen Counsel & Sec)*
Mike Witynski *(Sr VP-Stores)*
Advertising Agencies:
Adam Friedman Associates
11 E 44 St 5th Fl
New York, NY 10017
Tel.: (212) 981-2529
Fax: (212) 981-8174

Rockett Interactive
111 Centrewest Ct
Cary, NC 27513
Tel.: (919) 678-8994
Fax: (919) 678-8910

DOLLARAMA INC.
5805 Royalmount Avenue
Montreal, QC H4P 0A1, Canada
Tel.: (514) 737-1006
Fax: (514) 940-6169
Web Site: www.dollarama.com
Approx. Rev.: $1,226,976,988
Approx. Number Employees: 12,371
Business Description:
General Merchandise Stores
S.I.C.: 5399; 5311
N.A.I.C.S.: 452990; 452112
Personnel:
Larry Rossy *(Chm & CEO)*
Michael Ross *(CFO & Sec)*
Stephane Gonthier *(COO)*
Neil Rossy *(Chief Mdsg Officer)*
Leonard Assaly *(Sr VP-IT & Logistics)*
Geoffrey Robillard *(Sr VP-Import)*
Advertising Agency:
Bos Advertising
3970 Saint-Ambroise street
Montreal, QC H4C 2C7, Canada
Tel.: (514) 848-0010
Fax: (514) 373-2992

DOMO RECORDS, INC.
11340 W Olympic Blvd Ste 270
Los Angeles, CA 90064
Tel.: (310) 966-4414
Web Site: www.domo.com
Sales Range: $1-9.9 Million
Approx. Number Employees: 7
Year Founded: 1993
Business Description:
New Age & World Music Producer & Distr
S.I.C.: 8999; 3652
N.A.I.C.S.: 512210; 512220
Media: 4-6-8-13-20
Personnel:
Eiichi Naito *(Founder)*
Brands & Products:
DOMO

DR. LEONARD HEALTH CARE CATALOG
100 Nixon Ln
Edison, NJ 08837
Tel.: (732) 225-0100
Fax: (732) 225-0302
Fax: (732) 572-3029
Web Site: www.drleonards.com
Sales Range: $250-299.9 Million
Approx. Number Employees: 600
Business Description:
Catalog Sales
S.I.C.: 5961
N.A.I.C.S.: 454113
Media: 4-8
Personnel:
Joe Albanese *(CFO & Exec VP)*
Brands & Products:
DR. LEONARD'S
SHOPNOW PAY PLAN

THE DRESS BARN, INC.
30 Dunnigan Dr
Suffern, NY 10901-4101
Tel.: (845) 369-4500
Fax: (845) 369-4829
E-mail: customerservice@dressbarn.com
Web Site: www.dressbarn.com
Approx. Sls.: $2,374,571,000
Approx. Number Employees: 9,000
Year Founded: 1962
Business Description:
Women's Clothing & Accessories Retailer
S.I.C.: 5621; 5699
N.A.I.C.S.: 448120; 448150
Advertising Expenditures: $24,500,000
Media: 4-8-9-10-16-18-22-25
Distr.: Natl.
Budget Set: June
Personnel:
Elliot S. Jaffe *(Chm)*
David R. Jaffe *(Pres & CEO)*
Armand Correia *(CFO & Exec VP)*
Vivian Behrens *(CMO & Sr VP)*
Wexler Gene *(Gen Counsel, Sr VP & Asst Sec)*
Jeffrey C. Gerstel *(Sr VP)*
Elise Jaffe *(Sr VP)*
Brands & Products:
DRESS BARN

DRG RECORDS INCORPORATED
740 Broadway Fl 7
New York, NY 10003
Tel.: (212) 614-2800
Fax: (212) 614-2153
Toll Free: (866) 293-2854
E-mail: info@drgrecords.com
Web Site: www.drgrecords.com
Approx. Number Employees: 20
Year Founded: 1976
Business Description:
Music CDs Focusing on Broadway Musicals, Film Soundtracks, Jazz, Cabaret & World Music Mail Order
S.I.C.: 3652; 5961
N.A.I.C.S.: 334612; 454113
Media: 4-8-10-13-23
Personnel:
Hugh Fordin *(Pres & CEO)*

DRYSDALES INC.
3220 S Memorial Dr
Tulsa, OK 74145
Tel.: (918) 664-6481
Fax: (918) 664-1431
Toll Free: (800) 444-6481
E-mail: customerservice@drysdales.com
Web Site: www.drysdales.com
Approx. Number Employees: 125
Year Founded: 1981
Business Description:
Western Apparel Retailer
S.I.C.: 5699; 5611
N.A.I.C.S.: 448190; 448110
Advertising Expenditures: $1,000,000
Media: 4-8-13-23-24-25-26
Personnel:
Jim McClure *(Pres)*
Brands & Products:
DRYSDALES

DUCKWALL-ALCO STORES INC
401 Cottage Ave
Abilene, KS 67410-2849
Tel.: (785) 263-3350
Fax: (785) 263-7531
E-mail: webmaster@duckwall.com
Web Site: www.duckwall.com
E-Mail For Key Personnel:
Marketing Director: BStreit@duckwall.com
Approx. Sls.: $465,199,000
Approx. Number Employees: 3,460
Year Founded: 1901
Business Description:
Discount Retail Chain
S.I.C.: 5311; 5399
N.A.I.C.S.: 452112; 452990
Import
Advertising Expenditures: $9,700,000
Media: 5-8-9-19-23-25
Distr.: Reg.
Budget Set: Oct. -Nov.
Personnel:
Royce Winsten *(Chm)*
Richard E. Wilson *(Pres & CEO)*
Wayne S. Peterson *(CFO & Sr VP)*
Jane Gilmartin *(COO & Exec VP)*
Edmond C. Beaith *(CIO & Sr VP)*
Tom L. Canfield Jr. *(Sr VP-Logistics & Admin)*
Brent A. Streit *(VP-Supply Chain & Mktg)*

E. MISHAN & SONS, INC.
230 5th Ave Ste 800
New York, NY 10001-7704
Tel.: (212) 689-9094
Fax: (212) 213-1518
Web Site: www.emsoninc.com
Approx. Number Employees: 45
Year Founded: 1945
Business Description:
"As Seen on TV" Products Mfr, Marketer & Distr
S.I.C.: 5199
N.A.I.C.S.: 424990
Advertising Expenditures: $8,000,000
Media: 3-4-7-8-12-13-15-17-24
Distr.: Intl.
Personnel:
Ike Mishan *(Pres)*
Eddie Mishan *(Partner)*
Jeff Mishan *(Dir-Adv)*
Brands & Products:
EMSON

EBY-BROWN CO.
280 W Shuman Blvd Ste 280
Naperville, IL 60563-2578
Mailing Address:
PO Box 3067
Naperville, IL 60566-7067
Tel.: (630) 778-2800
Fax: (630) 778-2830
Toll Free: (800) 553-8249
E-mail: sales@eby-brown.com
Web Site: www.eby-brown.com
E-Mail For Key Personnel:
Sales Director: sales@eby-brown.com
Approx. Sls.: $3,670,000,000
Approx. Number Employees: 2,150
Year Founded: 1887
Business Description:
Candy, Tobacco, Food, Snacks & General Merchandise Distr
S.I.C.: 5141; 5122; 5145; 5194
N.A.I.C.S.: 424410; 424210; 424450; 424940
Media: 2-4
Personnel:
Richard Wake *(Co-Pres)*
Tom Wake *(Co-Pres)*
Mark Smetana *(CFO)*
Bob Burkholder *(CIO)*
Jode Bunce *(Exec VP)*
Brett Fender *(Exec VP-Mdsg)*
Al Palma *(Exec VP-Sls)*
Chris Timmons *(Exec VP-Ops)*
Ron Coppel *(Sr VP-Bus Dev)*
Ralph Kallman *(VP-Adv Promo)*
Sharon Kuncl *(VP-Mdsg)*
Rick Thorgensen *(VP-HR)*
Mike Wierzbicki *(VP-Mdsg)*
Sharon Beetham *(Mgr-Corp Clerical)*
Bruce Cantor *(Mgr-Strategic Insights)*
Joan Nauman *(Mgr-HR)*

EDEN COMPANY
80 Triangle Blvd
Carlstadt, NJ 07072-2701
Tel.: (201) 438-2250
Fax: (201) 438-5353
E-mail: rschuman@edenco.org
Sales Range: Less than $1 Million
Approx. Number Employees: 5
Year Founded: 1940
Business Description:
General Merchandise Distr
S.I.C.: 5122
N.A.I.C.S.: 424210
Media: 2-25
Personnel:
Robert Schuman *(Pres)*

EDIBLE ARRANGEMENTS INTERNATIONAL, INC.
95 Barnes Rd
Wallingford, CT 06492
Tel.: (203) 774-8000
Fax: (203) 774-0531
Toll Free: (866) 363-7848
E-mail: info@ediblearrangements.com
Web Site:
www.ediblearrangements.com
Sales Range: $100-124.9 Million
Approx. Number Employees: 100
Year Founded: 1999
Business Description:
Fresh Fruit, Specialty Foods & Gifts

Key to Media (For complete agency information see *The Advertising Red Books-Agencies* edition):
1. Bus. Publs. 2. Cable T.V. 3. Catalogs & Directories. 4. Co-op Adv. 5. Consumer Mags. 6. D.M. to Bus. Estab.7. D.M. to Consumers
8. Daily Newsp. 9. Exhibits/Trade Shows 10. Foreign 11. Infomercial 12. Internet Adv.13. Multimedia 14. Network Radio
15. Network T.V. 16. Newsp. Distr. Mags. 17. Other 18. Outdoor (Posters, Transit) 19. Point of Purchase20. Premiums, Novelties
21. Product Samples 22. Special Events Mktg. 23. Spot Radio 24. Spot T.V. 25. Weekly Newsp. 26. Yellow Page Adv.

S.I.C.: 5992; 5499; 5961
N.A.I.C.S.: 453110; 445299; 454111; 454113
Media: 4-6-8-13-15-16
Personnel:
Tariq Farid *(Pres & CEO)*
Kamran Farid *(COO)*
Kristi Ferguson *(Exec VP)*
Steve Thomas *(VP-Mktg)*
Brands & Products:
APPLE BLOSSOM
BABY'S FIRST BOUQUET
BERRY BEST
BERRY CHOCLATE BOUQUET
BLOOMING DAISIES
BUNDLE OF JOY
DELICIOUS CELEBRATION
DELICIOUS FRUIT DESIGN
DELICIOUS PARTY
DELIVERY DELIGHT
THE DIPPED FRUIT BOUQUET
EDIBLE ARRANGEMENTS
FRUIT FIESTA
FRUTATION
GET FRESH
HEARTS AND BERRIES
HEARTS AND KISSES
JUICY WISHES
MANGO KIWI BLOSSOM
MANGO KIWI FESTIVAL
MELON DELIGHT
MOON DELIGHT
NUTS FOR BERRIES
ORANGE BLOSSOM
ROCK A BYE BOUQUET
SIMPLY DAISIES
SWEET CELEBRATION
SWEETHEART BOUQUET
TOP OF THE CLASS CELEBRATION
TRIPLE PLAY BOUQUET
WATERMELON DAISY
WATERMELON FESTIVAL
YOU'RE BERRY SPECIAL
Advertising Agency:
Hot Dish Advertising
800 Washington Ave N Ste 200
Minneapolis, MN 55401
Tel.: (612) 341-3100
Fax: (612) 341-0555

THE ELDER-BEERMAN STORES CORP.
(Sub. of The Bon Ton Stores, Inc.)
2801 E Market St
York, PA 17402
Mailing Address:
PO Box 2821
York, PA 17402
Tel.: (717) 757-7660
Fax: (717) 751-3108
Web Site: www.elder-beerman.com
Sales Range: $1-4.9 Billion
Approx. Number Employees: 15,000
Year Founded: 1883
Business Description:
Department & Furniture Stores
S.I.C.: 5712
N.A.I.C.S.: 442110
Import
Media: 1-2
Personnel:
Byron L. Bergren *(Pres & CEO)*
Keith Blowman *(CFO, Treas, Sec & Exec VP)*
Jeff Miller *(Sr VP & Controller)*
Dennis R. Clouser *(Sr VP-HR)*
Brands & Products:
ELDER-BEERMAN

THE ELYSIAN FIELDS, INC.
(d/b/a Elysian Fields)
1273 S Tamiami Trl
Sarasota, FL 34239
Tel.: (941) 361-3006
Fax: (941) 366-4982
E-mail: info@elysianfieldsonline.com
Web Site:
www.elysianfieldsonline.com
Approx. Rev.: $1,500,000
Approx. Number Employees: 18
Year Founded: 1992
Business Description:
Specialty Retail Books & Gifts
S.I.C.: 5942
N.A.I.C.S.: 451211
Media: 3-6-9-13-15-22-24-25
Personnel:
Lea Semple *(Owner)*
Kimberly Perkins *(Pres)*

ERNIE BALL INC.
53973 Polk St
Coachella, CA 92236
Tel.: (760) 775-4222
Fax: (800) 577-3225
Toll Free: (800) 543-2255
E-mail: info@ernieball.com
Web Site: www.ernieball.com
Approx. Number Employees: 311
Business Description:
Guitars & Musical Instrument Accessories Mfr & Sales
S.I.C.: 3931; 5736
N.A.I.C.S.: 339992; 451140
Media: 6-13
Personnel:
Brian Ball *(Mgr-Mktg)*
Brands & Products:
3+1
4+2
AXIS
CUSTOM GAUGE
EARTHWOOD
ERNIE BALL
MUSIC MAN
SILHOUETTE
SLINKY
STERLING
STINGRAY

EXCELLIGENCE LEARNING CORP.
(Holding of Thoma Bravo, LLC)
(d/b/a Learning Star Corp)
2 Lower Ragsdale Dr Ste 200
Monterey, CA 93940
Tel.: (831) 333-2000
Web Site:
www.excelligencelearning.com
Sales Range: $125-149.9 Million
Approx. Number Employees: 398
Year Founded: 2000
Business Description:
Educational Products Developer, Mfr & Retailer
S.I.C.: 5961; 2741; 8299
N.A.I.C.S.: 454111; 454113; 516110; 611710
Media: 4-10
Personnel:
Ronald Elliott *(Chm)*
Judith McGuinn *(Pres)*
Kelly Crampton *(CEO)*
Mike Gaitley *(VP-Legal)*
Brands & Products:
EXCELLIGENCE

FAMILY DOLLAR STORES, INC.
10401 Monroe Rd
Matthews, NC 28105
Mailing Address:
PO Box 1017
Charlotte, NC 28201-1017
Tel.: (704) 847-6961
Fax: (704) 847-0189
E-mail: employment@familydollar.com
Web Site: www.familydollar.com
Approx. Sls.: $7,866,971,000
Approx. Number Employees: 30,000
Year Founded: 1959
Business Description:
Discount Store Retailer
S.I.C.: 5399
N.A.I.C.S.: 452910
Import
Advertising Expenditures: $12,400,000
Media: 8-16
Distr.: Reg.
Personnel:
Howard R. Levine *(Chm & CEO)*
Dorlisa K. Flur *(Vice Chm & Chief Admin Officer)*
Michael K. Bloom *(Pres & COO)*
Kenneth T. Smith *(CFO, Chief Acctg Officer & Sr VP)*
Joshua R. Jewett *(CIO & Sr VP-IT)*
James C. Snyder, Jr. *(Gen Counsel, Sec & Sr VP)*
Charles S. Gibson Jr. *(Exec VP-Supply Chain)*
Barry W. Sullivan *(Exec VP-Store Ops)*
Kevin Boyanowski *(Sr VP-Sourcing-Global)*
Bryan P. Causey *(Sr VP-Space Mgmt & Inventory Optimization)*
Keith M. Gehl *(Sr VP-Real Estate & Facilities)*
Don Hamblen *(Sr VP-Customer Mktg)*
Trey Johnson *(Sr VP-Food)*
Thomas M. Nash *(Sr VP-New Stores)*
John J. Scanlon *(Sr VP-Mdsg)*
Bryan Venberg *(Sr VP-HR)*
Paul White *(Sr VP-Apparel, Home & Seasonal)*
Stephen F. Phillips *(Reg VP)*
Donna Barker *(VP-Mdsg & Mgr-Gen Mdse)*
Richard P. Siliakus *(VP)*
Mark S. Chidester *(VP-HR & Team Rels)*
James Hayes *(VP-Internal Audit)*
Timothy A. Matz *(VP-Div)*
Colin McGinnis *(VP-Store Ops Support & Procurement)*
Donald G. Smith *(VP-Mktg)*
David R. Styka *(VP-Fin)*
Jacob J. Modla *(Deputy Gen Counsel)*
Brands & Products:
FAMILY DOLLAR
FAMILY DOLLAR STORES
Advertising Agency:
Bernstein-Rein Advertising, Inc.
4600 Madison Ave Ste 1500
Kansas City, MO 64112-3016
Tel.: (816) 756-0640
Fax: (816) 399-6000
Toll Free: (800) 571-6246
Agency of Record

FILENE'S BASEMENT, INC.
(Sub. of Syms Corporation)
25 Corporate Dr Ste 400
Burlington, MA 01803
Tel.: (617) 348-7000
Fax: (617) 348-7130
Toll Free: (888) 843-8474
Web Site: www.filenesbasement.com
Approx. Sls.: $466,300,000
Year Founded: 1908
Business Description:
Discount Department Store Operator
S.I.C.: 5311
N.A.I.C.S.: 452112
Media: 6-8-9-13-14-16-17-22-23-24-25
Distr.: Direct to Consumer; Reg.
Advertising Agency:
Night Agency
307 Canal St Fl 2
New York, NY 10013
Tel.: (212) 431-1945
Fax: (917) 677-8327

FIRST FEDERAL COIN CORP.
14101 Southcross Dr W
Burnsville, MN 55337
Toll Free: (800) 721-0346
E-mail: customerservice@firstfederalcoin.com
Web Site: www.firstfederalcoin.com
Business Description:
Coin & Medallic Collectibles
S.I.C.: 5092
N.A.I.C.S.: 423920
Media: 2-8-10-13-23-26
Personnel:
Nicholas J. Bruyer *(CEO)*

FLAX ARTIST'S MATERIALS
1699 Market St
Brisbane, CA 94103
Tel.: (415) 552-2355
Fax: (415) 552-2743
E-mail: info@flaxart.com
Web Site: www.flaxart.com
Sales Range: $10-24.9 Million
Approx. Number Employees: 40
Year Founded: 1938
Business Description:
Art Supplies Retailer
S.I.C.: 5999; 5199
N.A.I.C.S.: 453998; 424990
Media: 4-8-13
Personnel:
Philip Flax *(Pres)*
Howard Flax *(CEO)*

FLOWERS TODAY, INC.
(d/b/a Blooms Today)
15405 John Marshall Hwy
Haymarket, VA 20169
Toll Free: (800) 520-0573
Web Site: www.bloomstoday.com
Business Description:
Florist
S.I.C.: 5992
N.A.I.C.S.: 453110
Media: 5-13
Personnel:
Cindy Estep *(Exec VP)*

FLYNN & O'HARA UNIFORMS INC.
10905 Dutton Rd
Philadelphia, PA 19154
Tel.: (215) 637-4600
Fax: (215) 637-6392

Key to Media (For complete agency information see *The Advertising Red Books-Agencies* edition):
1. Bus. Publs. 2. Cable T.V. 3. Catalogs & Directories. 4. Co-op Adv. 5. Consumer Mags. 6. D.M. to Bus. Estab.7. D.M. to Consumers 8. Daily Newsp. 9. Exhibits/Trade Shows 10. Foreign 11. Infomercial 12. Internet Adv.13. Multimedia 14. Network Radio 15. Network T.V. 16. Newsp. Distr. Mags. 17. Other 18. Outdoor (Posters, Transit) 19. Point of Purchase20. Premiums, Novelties 21. Product Samples 22. Special Events Mktg. 23. Spot Radio 24. Spot T.V. 25. Weekly Newsp. 26. Yellow Page Adv.

Flynn & O'Hara Uniforms Inc. — (Continued)

Toll Free: (800) 441-4122
E-mail: customerservice@flynnohara.com
Web Site: www.flynnohara.com
Approx. Number Employees: 200
Year Founded: 1972
Business Description:
Uniforms Mfr
S.I.C.: 5699
N.A.I.C.S.: 448190
Media: 4-7
Personnel:
Sean Flynn *(Owner)*

FOLLETT HIGHER EDUCATION GROUP

(Sub. of Follett Corporation)
1818 Swift Dr
Oak Brook, IL 60523-1576
Tel.: (630) 279-2330
Fax: (630) 279-2569
Toll Free: (800) 323-4506
Web Site: www.fheg.follett.com
Approx. Number Employees: 300
Business Description:
College Bookstores Contract Management
S.I.C.: 5942; 5943
N.A.I.C.S.: 451211; 453210
Media: 2-3-4-5-8-9-10-13-18-19-20-21-22-23-24-25-26
Personnel:
Tom Christopher *(Pres)*
Jay Amond *(CFO & Sr VP)*
Doug Thompson *(CIO & Sr VP)*
Steve Pribyl *(Sr VP, Dir-Retail Ops & Sales)*
David Hainline *(Sr VP-Ecommerce & Bus Dev)*
Fred Weber *(Sr VP-Wholesale & Distr Svcs)*
Carol Winter *(Sr VP-Gen Mdse)*
Advertising Agencies:
Tom, Dick & Harry Advertising
350 W Erie 2nd Fl
Chicago, IL 60654
Tel.: (312) 327-9500
Fax: (312) 327-9501

Torque
167 N Racine
Chicago, IL 60607
Tel.: (312) 421-7858
Fax: (312) 421-7866

FOOTLIGHT RECORDS INC.

PO Box 496
Georgetown, CT 06829
Tel.: (203) 544-8288
Fax: (203) 544-8288
Toll Free: (888) 627-3993
E-mail: originalcatse@aol.com
Web Site: www.footlight.com
Approx. Number Employees: 2
Year Founded: 1977
Business Description:
Record Store
S.I.C.: 5735; 5961
N.A.I.C.S.: 451220; 454111; 454113
Media: 4-6-8
Personnel:
Bruce Yeko *(Owner)*

FOREIGN TRADERS, INC.

2873 Cox Rd
Santa Fe, NM 87507
Tel.: (505) 983-6441
Fax: (505) 989-8917
Web Site: www.foreigntraders.com
E-Mail For Key Personnel:
President: alex@foreigntraders.com
Sales Director: laura@foreigntraders.com
Sales Range: $10-24.9 Million
Approx. Number Employees: 3
Year Founded: 1927
Business Description:
Household Wares, Furnishings, Rugs, Gifts & Artwares Retailer
S.I.C.: 2541; 5021
N.A.I.C.S.: 337212; 423210
Export
Advertising Expenditures: $50,000
Media: 4-6-25
Distr.: Direct to Consumer; Natl.
Budget Set: Oct. -May
Personnel:
Alex Tschursin *(Owner)*
Brands & Products:
FOREIGN TRADERS

FORMULA ONE IMPRESSIONS INC.

(d/b/a Crusin' USA)
6262 Olive Blvd
Saint Louis, MO 63130
Tel.: (314) 426-4886
Fax: (314) 426-1713
Toll Free: (800) 444-1685
E-mail: sales@cruisinusa.com
Web Site: www.cruisinusa.com
E-Mail For Key Personnel:
Sales Director: sales@cruisinusa.com
Sales Range: $10-24.9 Million
Approx. Number Employees: 25
Business Description:
General Merchandise Store
S.I.C.: 2261
N.A.I.C.S.: 313311
Media: 4-13
Personnel:
Helene Spetner *(Pres)*
Alan Spetner *(Chief Cruisin Officer)*
Tim Coggeshall *(VP-Sls)*
Marcia Gilson *(Mgr-Office & Orders)*
Susan Ryan *(Mgr-Art & Production)*
Brands & Products:
CRUISIN

FRANCHISE CONCEPTS, INC.

221 First Executive Ave
Saint Peters, MO 63376
Fax: (877) 832-6694
Toll Free: (866) 719-8200
E-mail: information@fcibiz.com
Web Site:
www.franchiseconceptsinc.com
Approx. Number Employees: 20
Year Founded: 1979
Business Description:
Print, Poster & Custom Framing Retailer
S.I.C.: 5999; 5947
N.A.I.C.S.: 453998; 453220
Media: 1-3-4-6-7-8-9-10-13-14-15-16-17-18-19-20-22-23-24-25-26
Distr.: Natl.
Personnel:
Joe Lynch *(CFO)*
Brands & Products:
DECK THE WALLS
FCI
FRAMING & ART CENTER
THE GREAT FRAME UP

FRANKLIN MILLS LLC

(Sub. of The Mills Properties)
1455 Franklin Mills Cir
Philadelphia, PA 19154
Tel.: (215) 632-1500
Fax: (215) 632-7888
Web Site: www.franklinmills.com
Sales Range: $25-49.9 Million
Approx. Number Employees: 60
Business Description:
Shopping & Entertainment Center Operators
S.I.C.: 6552
N.A.I.C.S.: 237210
Personnel:
Joseph Binger *(Gen Mgr)*
Advertising Agency:
Furia Rubel Communications
2 Hidden Ln Bldg 2
Doylestown, PA 18901
Tel.: (215) 340-0480
Fax: (215) 340-0580

THE FRANKLIN MINT, LLC

801 Springdale Dr Ste 200
Exton, PA 19341-2897
Tel.: (610) 884-4800
Fax: (610) 884-4756
Toll Free: (800) 843-6468
Web Site: www.franklinmint.com
Sales Range: $150-199.9 Million
Approx. Number Employees: 300
Year Founded: 1964
Business Description:
Mfr & Direct Marketing of Heirloom Quality Collectibles
S.I.C.: 5094; 5947; 5961; 5963
N.A.I.C.S.: 423940; 453220; 454111; 454113; 454390
Media: 2-4-6-10-13
Distr.: Direct to Consumer; Intl.; Natl.
Budget Set: Nov.
Personnel:
M. Moshe Malamud *(Owner)*
Steven J. Sisskind *(CEO)*
Noah Becker *(CFO)*
Gwynne Gorr *(VP-Mktg & Product Dev)*
Nathan Brimmer *(Dir-IT)*
Monica Brogan *(Dir-Telemarketing & Customer Svc)*
Lewis Checchia *(Dir-Licensing & New Bus Dev)*
Walter Kole *(Dir-Mktg)*
Chris Lyons *(Dir-Wholesale Sls)*
Karen Vitale *(Dir-Concept Dev)*
Brands & Products:
THE FRANKLIN MINT
Advertising Agency:
Franklin Adv. Services (House Agency)
U. S. Rte. 1
Franklin Center, PA 19091
Tel.: (610) 459-6000

FRED MEYER STORES, INC.

(Sub. of Fred Meyer, Inc.)
3800 SE 22nd Ave
Portland, OR 97202-2918
Mailing Address:
PO Box 42121
Portland, OR 97242-0121
Tel.: (503) 232-8844
Fax: (503) 797-3469
Toll Free: (888) 247-4439
Telex: 360415
E-mail: advertising@fredmeyer.com
Web Site: www.fredmeyer.com
Sales Range: $400-449.9 Million
Approx. Number Employees: 1,500
Year Founded: 1922
Business Description:
Department Store
S.I.C.: 5311
N.A.I.C.S.: 452111
Import
Advertising Expenditures: $3,500,000
Media: 1-3-4-5-7-8-9-10-13-16-18-19-21-23-24-25
Distr.: Reg.
Personnel:
David B. Dillon *(CEO)*
David W. Deatherage *(CFO & VP)*
Carl Wojciechowski *(Grp VP-HR)*
Greg Johnson *(VP-Health & Beauty Care Products)*
Ross Thomas *(VP-Sls & Mktg)*
Pamela Crane *(Asst VP-Property Mgmt)*
Tom Gibbons *(Dir-Real Estate Dev)*
Jim Coombes *(Sr Mgr-Entitlements)*
Don Forrest *(Sr Mgr-Site Acq)*
Gail Penney *(Sr Mgr-Leasing)*
Advertising Agency:
CB&S Advertising
3800 SE 22nd Ave
Portland, OR 97202
Tel.: (503) 797-3200
(TV & Radio)

FREDERICK'S OF HOLLYWOOD, INC.

6255 Sunset Blvd
Hollywood, CA 90028
Tel.: (323) 466-5151
Fax: (323) 464-5149
E-mail: custserv@fredericks.com
Web Site: www.fredericks.com
Sales Range: $50-74.9 Million
Approx. Number Employees: 1,000
Year Founded: 1946
Business Description:
Retailer of Women's Apparel Merchandise Through Mail Order Catalogs & Boutique Specialty Stores
S.I.C.: 5621; 5699
N.A.I.C.S.: 448120; 448150
Advertising Expenditures: $12,600,000
Media: 4-6-8-9-13-19
Distr.: Direct to Consumer; Natl.
Budget Set: July
Personnel:
Thomas Lynch *(Chm & CEO)*
Don Jones *(Pres & COO)*
Thomas Rende *(CFO)*
Brands & Products:
FREDERICK'S OF HOLLYWOOD
FREDERICKS.COM
STAR CLUB

FRED'S INC.

4300 New Getwell Rd
Memphis, TN 38118-6801
Tel.: (901) 365-8880
Fax: (901) 328-0354
Toll Free: (800) 374-7417
E-mail: fredsonlinesupport@fredsinc.com
Web Site: www.fredsinc.com
Approx. Sls.: $1,841,755,000
Approx. Number Employees: 4,873
Year Founded: 1947

Key to Media (For complete agency information see *The Advertising Red Books-Agencies* edition):
1. Bus. Publs. 2. Cable T.V. 3. Catalogs & Directories. 4. Co-op Adv. 5. Consumer Mags. 6. D.M. to Bus. Estab.7. D.M. to Consumers 8. Daily Newsp. 9. Exhibits/Trade Shows 10. Foreign 11. Infomercial 12. Internet Adv.13. Multimedia 14. Network Radio 15. Network T.V. 16. Newsp. Distr. Mags. 17. Other 18. Outdoor (Posters, Transit) 19. Point of Purchase20. Premiums, Novelties 21. Product Samples 22. Special Events Mktg. 23. Spot Radio 24. Spot T.V. 25. Weekly Newsp. 26. Yellow Page Adv.

Business Description:
Discount General Merchandise Stores
S.I.C.: 5399; 5912
N.A.I.C.S.: 452990; 446110
Import
Advertising Expenditures:
$24,500,000
Media: 5-8-9-13-14-19-23-24-25
Distr.: Reg.
Budget Set: Nov. -Dec.
Personnel:
Michael J. Hayes *(Chm)*
Bruce A. Efird *(Pres & CEO)*
Jerry A. Shore *(CFO, Chief Admin Officer & Exec VP)*
John A. Casey *(Exec VP-Pharmacy Acq)*
Rick A. Chambers *(Exec VP-Pharmacy Ops)*
Dennis K. Curtis *(Exec VP & Gen Mdse Mgr)*
James R. Fennema *(Sr VP)*
David Gagne *(Reg VP-Store Ops)*
Jamie Naughcon *(VP-HR)*
Eddie Marshall *(Dir-Media)*
Ursula Roman *(Dir-Mktg)*
Brands & Products:
FRED'S
FRED'S KIDS
SOUTHERN EXPRESSIONS

FREETHOUGHT ENTERPRISES, INC.
(d/b/a AnimeNation)
13814 Wright Cir
Tampa, FL 33626
Tel.: (813) 925-1116
Fax: (813) 925-1247
Toll Free: (888) MY-ANIME
E-mail: webmaster@animenation.com
Web Site: www.animenation.com
Sales Range: Less than $1 Million
Approx. Number Employees: 19
Year Founded: 1995
Business Description:
Online Anime & Related Products Whslr
S.I.C.: 5961
N.A.I.C.S.: 454113
Media: 4-6-8-10-13
Personnel:
Gene Field *(Founder & Pres)*
Brands & Products:
ANIMENATION
LIFE. DEATH. ANIME IN BETWEEN.

FTD.COM INC.
(Sub. of Florists' Transworld Delivery, Inc.)
3113 Woodcreek Dr
Downers Grove, IL 60515
Tel.: (630) 719-7800
Fax: (630) 719-4859
Toll Free: (800) 788-9000
Web Site: www.ftdi.com
Sales Range: $75-99.9 Million
Approx. Number Employees: 300
Business Description:
Internet & Telephone Marketer of Flowers & Specialty Gifts
S.I.C.: 5992; 5961
N.A.I.C.S.: 453110; 454113
Media: 4-8-13-23

GALLERY OF HISTORY, INC.
3601 W Sahara Ave
Las Vegas, NV 89102-5379
Tel.: (702) 364-1000
Fax: (702) 364-1285
Toll Free: (800) 425-5379
Toll Free: (800) GALLERY
E-mail: sales@galleryofhistory.com
Web Site: www.galleryofhistory.com
E-Mail For Key Personnel:
Sales Director: sales@galleryofhistory.com
Sales Range: Less than $1 Million
Approx. Number Employees: 7
Year Founded: 1981
Business Description:
Historical Memorabilia Marketer & Auctions
S.I.C.: 5961; 5999
N.A.I.C.S.: 454112; 453998
Advertising Expenditures: $40,292
Media: 13
Personnel:
Todd M. Axelrod *(Chm, Pres & CEO)*
Rod R. Lynam *(CFO, Treas & Asst Sec)*

THE GAP, INC.
2 Folsom St
San Francisco, CA 94105
Tel.: (650) 952-4400
Fax: (415) 427-2553
Toll Free: (800) 333-7899
E-mail: investor_relations@gap.com
Web Site: www.gap.com
Approx. Sls.: $14,664,000,000
Approx. Number Employees: 134,000
Year Founded: 1969
Business Description:
Specialty Apparel Retailer
S.I.C.: 5651; 5611; 5621; 5641; 5699
N.A.I.C.S.: 448140; 448110; 448120; 448130; 448150
Import Export
Advertising Expenditures:
$516,000,000
Media: 3-4-6-8-9-10-11-13-14-15-16-17-18-19-23-24-25
Distr.: Intl.; Natl.
Personnel:
Glenn K. Murphy *(Chm & CEO)*
Sabrina Simmons *(CFO & Exec VP)*
Tom Keiser *(CIO & Exec VP)*
Seth Farbman *(CMO)*
Michelle Banks *(Chief Compliance Officer, Gen Counsel, Corp Sec & Exec VP)*
Art Peck *(Pres-Gap North America)*
Pamela B. Wallack *(Head-Global Creative Center)*
Jack Calhoun *(Pres-Banana Republic)*
Toby Lenk *(Pres-Direct)*
Stephen Sunnucks *(Pres-Europe & Intl Strategic Alliances)*
Stan P. Raggio *(Exec VP-Global Supply Chain)*
Eva Sage-Gavin *(Exec VP-Global HR & Corp Affairs)*
David Zoba *(SVP-Global Real Estate)*
Jacquie Lenart *(VP-Mktg)*
Kari Shellhorn *(Brand Dir-Comm)*
Olivia Doyne *(Dir-PR & Engagement Mktg)*
Mark Fiske *(Dir-Bus Dev)*
Brands & Products:
ATHLETA
BANANA REPUBLIC
GAP
GAP DESIGN EDITIONS
OLD NAVY
PIPERLIME
Advertising Agencies:
Acxiom Digital
1051 Hillsdale Blvd Ste 400
Foster City, CA 94404
Tel.: (650) 356-3400
Fax: (650) 356-3410

AKQA, Inc.
118 King St 6th Fl
San Francisco, CA 94107
Tel.: (415) 645-9400
Fax: (415) 645-9420

Baker Creative
386 Main St
Groveport, OH 43125
Tel.: (614) 836-3845
Toll Free: (877) BAKER03

CP+B
3390 Mary St Ste 300
Coconut Grove, FL 33133
Tel.: (305) 859-2070
Fax: (305) 854-3419

Kitcatt Nohr Alexander Shaw, Ltd.
48-50 Saint John St
London, EC1 4DG, United Kingdom
Tel.: (44) 207 012 3950
Fax: (44) 207 253 6709

Mekanism, Inc.
640 Second St 3rd Fl
San Francisco, CA 94107
Tel.: (415) 908-4000
Fax: (415) 908-3993

Ogilvy & Mather
(Sub. of WPP Group plc)
636 11th Ave
New York, NY 10036
Tel.: (212) 237-4000
Fax: (212) 237-5123
Global Agency of Record

PHD
(An Omnicom Company)
220 E 42nd 7th Fl
New York, NY 10017
Tel.: (212) 894-6600
Fax: (212) 894-4100

GARDEN RIDGE CORPORATION
(Holding of Three Cities Research, Inc.)
19411 Atrium Pl Ste 170
Houston, TX 77084-6024
Tel.: (281) 579-7901
Tel.: (281) 578-2334
Fax: (281) 578-0999
Web Site: www.gardenridge.com
Approx. Sls.: $460,000,000
Approx. Number Employees: 300
Year Founded: 1979
Business Description:
Home Furniture, Accessories, Crafts & Seasonal Products Retailer
S.I.C.: 5999; 5719
N.A.I.C.S.: 453998; 442299
Media: 6-18-23-24
Distr.: Natl.
Personnel:
Tom Kibarian *(CEO)*
Brands & Products:
GARDEN RIDGE

GARNET HILL
(Sub. of Cornerstone Brands, Inc.)
231 Main St
Franconia, NH 03580
Tel.: (603) 823-5545
Fax: (603) 823-7034
Toll Free: (800) 870-3513
E-mail: sclark@garnethill.com
Web Site: www.garnethill.com
Approx. Sls.: $35,000,000
Approx. Number Employees: 220
Year Founded: 1976
Business Description:
Women's Clothing & Bedding Mail Order Retailer
S.I.C.: 5961; 5621
N.A.I.C.S.: 454113; 448120
Media: 4-6-8-13
Personnel:
Russ Gaitskill *(Pres & CEO)*
Mark DiMarzio *(VP-Mktg & Bus Dev)*

GEBO DISTRIBUTING CO., INC.
3109 Olton Rd
Plainview, TX 79072-6763
Mailing Address:
PO Box 850
Plainview, TX 79073-0850
Tel.: (806) 293-4212
Fax: (806) 293-3992
Web Site: www.gebos.com/contact.asp
Approx. Number Employees: 150
Year Founded: 1958
Business Description:
Retail Farm & Home Supplies; Clothing; Automotive Supplies Including Tires & Batteries
S.I.C.: 5999; 5261
N.A.I.C.S.: 453998; 444220
Advertising Expenditures: $1,500,000
Media: 8-9-17-18-19-23-24
Distr.: Direct to Consumer; Reg.
Personnel:
Mike McCarthy *(Pres)*
Dick Crigger *(Dir-Pur)*
Advertising Agency:
N. Armstrong Advertising
2103 64th St
Lubbock, TX 79412
Tel.: (806) 745-9004
Fax: (806) 745-9004
(Farm Supplies; Auto Supplies; Dog Food; Clothing)

GEORGETOWN TOBACCO & PIPE STORES INC.
3144 M St NW
Washington, DC 20007
Tel.: (202) 338-5100
Fax: (202) 338-0008
Toll Free: (800) 345-1459
E-mail: info@gttobacco.com
Web Site: www.gttobacco.com
Approx. Sls.: $2,000,000
Approx. Number Employees: 10
Business Description:
Tobacco Pipes & Cigars Retailer
S.I.C.: 5993
N.A.I.C.S.: 453991
Media: 4-8
Personnel:
David Berkebile *(Owner)*

THE GIVING BASKET INC.
44 Main St
Chester, NJ 07930
Tel.: (908) 879-4483

Key to Media (For complete agency information see *The Advertising Red Books-Agencies* edition):
1. Bus. Publs. 2. Cable T.V. 3. Catalogs & Directories. 4. Co-op Adv. 5. Consumer Mags. 6. D.M. to Bus. Estab.7. D.M. to Consumers
8. Daily Newsp. 9. Exhibits/Trade Shows 10. Foreign 11. Infomercial 12. Internet Adv.13. Multimedia 14. Network Radio
15. Network T.V. 16. Newsp. Distr. Mags. 17. Other 18. Outdoor (Posters, Transit) 19. Point of Purchase20. Premiums, Novelties
21. Product Samples 22. Special Events Mktg. 23. Spot Radio 24. Spot T.V. 25. Weekly Newsp. 26. Yellow Page Adv.

The Giving Basket Inc. — (Continued)

Fax: (908) 879-4168
Toll Free: (800) 344-8464
E-mail: info@thegivingbasket.com
Web Site: www.thegivingbasket.com
Year Founded: 1989
Business Description:
Sales of Gift Baskets & Gifts
S.I.C.: 5947; 5992
N.A.I.C.S.: 453220; 453110
Media: 7-8-13-26
Personnel:
Michelle Kotarski *(Owner)*

THE GLIK COMPANY

3248 Nameoki Rd
Granite City, IL 62040-5014
Tel.: (618) 876-6717
Fax: (618) 876-7819
E-mail: info@gliks.com
Web Site: www.gliks.com
Approx. Number Employees: 400
Year Founded: 1897
Business Description:
Men's & Ladies' Apparel Stores
S.I.C.: 5651; 5311
N.A.I.C.S.: 448140; 452111
Media: 4-8-9-13-19-22
Distr.: Direct to Consumer
Personnel:
Jeff Glik *(Pres & CEO)*
Darryl Gerstenecker *(CFO & CIO)*
Kristi Ham *(Dir-Mktg)*
Brands & Products:
GLIK'S

GLOBAL FRANCHISE MANAGEMENT LLC

(Sub. of Levine Leichtman Capital Partners Inc.)
1346 Oakbrook Dr Ste 170
Norcross, GA 30093
Tel.: (770) 514-4500
Fax: (770) 514-4903
Toll Free: (800) 524-6444
Web Site: www.globalfranchise.com/
Sales Range: $1-4.9 Billion
Business Description:
Brand Management Services
S.I.C.: 6282; 6794
N.A.I.C.S.: 523920; 533110
Advertising Expenditures: $1,300,000
Media: 2-13
Personnel:
M. Christopher Dull *(Pres & CEO)*
Jenn Johnston *(CMO & COO)*
Gerald Brouillette *(VP-IT)*
Jerry Slover *(VP-Retail)*
Samantha Reid *(Mgr-Customer Rels)*

GNP/CRESCENDO RECORD COMPANY INC.

1405 N Avon St
Burbank, CA 91505
Tel.: (818) 566-8900
Fax: (818) 566-8901
Toll Free: (800) 654-7029
E-mail: gnp@pacificnet.net
Web Site: www.gnpcrescendo.com
Approx. Number Employees: 8
Year Founded: 1954
Business Description:
Distributor of Recorded Music
S.I.C.: 5735; 5961
N.A.I.C.S.: 451220; 454111; 454113
Media: 4-6-8-13

GOODWILL INDUSTRIES INTERNATIONAL, INC.

15810 Indianola Dr
Rockville, MD 20855
Tel.: (301) 530-6500
Fax: (301) 530-1516
Toll Free: (800) 664-6577
E-mail: contactus@goodwill.org
Web Site: www.goodwill.org
Sales Range: $1-4.9 Billion
Approx. Number Employees: 82,300
Year Founded: 1902
Business Description:
Used Merchandise Retailer; Vocational Rehabilitation Services
S.I.C.: 5399; 8331
N.A.I.C.S.: 452990; 624310
Media: 2-3-5-6-7-8-9-10-17-18-23-24-26
Distr.: Intl.
Personnel:
Jim Gibbons *(Pres & CEO)*
Marla Jackson *(COO)*
Rebecca Helterbrand *(Chief Brand Officer)*
Lauretta Cunningham *(Sr VP-Retail Ops)*
Advertising Agencies:
BradfordLawton, LLC
1020 Townsend Ave
San Antonio, TX 78209
Tel.: (210) 832-0555
Fax: (210) 732-8555
Donate Truck Wrap

The Phelps Group
901 Wilshire Blvd
Santa Monica, CA 90401-1854
Tel.: (310) 752-4400
Fax: (310) 752-4444

GORDMANS STORES INC.

(Holding of Sun Capital Partners, Inc.)
12100 W Ctr Rd
Omaha, NE 68144-3969
Tel.: (402) 691-4000
Fax: (402) 691-4269
Web Site: www.gordmans.com
Approx. Sls.: $517,001,000
Approx. Number Employees: 1,200
Year Founded: 1982
Business Description:
Discount Department Store Operator
S.I.C.: 5311; 5611; 5621; 5641; 5651; 5699; 5719
N.A.I.C.S.: 452112; 442299; 448110; 448120; 448130; 448140; 448150; 448190
Advertising Expenditures: $14,600,000
Media: 9-16-24-25
Personnel:
Thomas V. Taylor, Jr. *(Chm)*
Jeffrey J. Gordman *(Pres & CEO)*
Mike James *(CFO, Treas & VP)*
Richard H. Heyman *(CIO & VP)*
Brands & Products:
SOMETHING UNEXPECTED

GOTTSCHALKS INC.

(Filed for Chapter 11 Bankruptcy 1/14/09)
7 River Park Pl E
Fresno, CA 93720-1501
Tel.: (559) 434-4800
Fax: (559) 434-4666
Toll Free: (800) 843-6206
Sales Range: $400-449.9 Million
Year Founded: 1904
Business Description:
Department Stores & Specialty Stores Operator
S.I.C.: 5311; 5621
N.A.I.C.S.: 452111; 448120
Advertising Expenditures: $30,015,000
Media: 4-5-8-9-14-15-22
Personnel:
James R. Famalette *(Chm, Pres & CEO)*
J. Gregory Ambro *(COO & Exec VP, Acting Principal Fin Officer)*
Patricia Bowlby *(VP-Mktg)*

GUMP'S CORP.

(Affil. of Walden Venture Capital)
(d/b/a Gump's of San Francisco)
135 Post St
San Francisco, CA 94108-4701
Tel.: (415) 982-1616
Fax: (415) 984-9379
Toll Free: (800) 882-8055
E-mail: info@gumps.com
Web Site: www.gumps.com
Approx. Number Employees: 100
Year Founded: 1861
Business Description:
Modern & Antique Gifts, Art Objects, Jewelry, Home Furnishings & Decorations Specialty Store Operator
S.I.C.: 5947; 5712; 5719; 5944
N.A.I.C.S.: 453220; 442110; 442299; 448310
Import
Media: 4-8-9-10-13-14-16-22
Distr.: Direct to Consumer; Natl.
Budget Set: Varies
Personnel:
Carmen Roberson *(Dir-Retail Mktg)*
Brands & Products:
GUMP'S

GUYETTE & SCHMIDT, INC.

24718 Beverly Rd
Saint Michaels, MD 21663
Tel.: (410) 745-0485
Fax: (410) 745-0487
E-mail: decoys@guyetteandschmidt.com
Web Site:
www.guyetteandschmidt.com
Sales Range: $10-24.9 Million
Approx. Number Employees: 7
Year Founded: 1984
Business Description:
Auctions
S.I.C.: 7389
N.A.I.C.S.: 561990
Media: 2-4-6-9-10-13-22-25
Personnel:
Gary Guyette *(Co-Owner)*
Frank Schmidt *(Co-Owner)*
Jaime Sayers *(Office Mgr)*
Kendall Guyette *(Mgr-Auction Floor)*

HABAND COMPANY, INC.

(Holding of Orchard Brands Corporation)
110 Bauer Dr
Oakland, NJ 07436-3105
Tel.: (201) 651-1000
Fax: (201) 405-7774
Web Site: www.haband.com
Approx. Number Employees: 350
Year Founded: 1925
Business Description:
Mail Order Sales of Clothing
S.I.C.: 5961; 5611; 5621
N.A.I.C.S.: 454113; 448110; 448120; 454111
Media: 2-4-6-8-9-13-16
Distr.: Natl.
Personnel:
Max Habernickel *(Co-Founder & CEO)*
James McClane *(Pres)*
Anthony Del Gaudio *(CFO)*
Joan Heinrichs *(Dir-Adv Space)*
Brands & Products:
1-STITCH
A SHORTS STORY
ACTIVE JOE
ADRIAN DELAFIELD
ALOHA BREEZE
THE AMAZING EXTEND-O-TOTE
AMAZING STRETCH LACE
AMERICAN SWEETHEART
AT EASE
AUTOMAGIC
BARRACUDA
BEND OVER
BLUE STARBURST
BOTANY 500
BOWS & BLOOMS
BREEZY BLOOMS
CAMBRIDGE
CAN GO
CASCADING HEARTS
CASHMIRACLE
CASUAL COMFORT
CASUAL JOE
CHANTAL
CHANTILLY
CHECKMATES
CHECKULATOR
CLASSIQUE SPORT
CLOUD FLEECE
COMFORT LITES
COMFORT WITH CACHE
COOL WEAVE!
COTTAGE GARDEN
COTTON CARESS
COZEE-CORD
CROSS CHECK
DAINTY DAISIES
DATE NIGHT
DEER STAGS
DIAGONAL DASH
DIGISCALE
DOTS WITH DASH
DOUBLE DEAL!
DOUBLE DELIGHT
DOUBLE TAKE!
DR. SCHOLL'S
DREAM PUFFS
DRESS TO IMPRESS
DUKE 301
THE EASY SNAP
EGGGENIE
FIT-FOREVER
FLAME KING
FLIRTATION
FLORENTINA
FOREVER ORGANIZED
FRONT & CENTER
FUN & SUN
FUN ON THE RUN
GET SET, GO
GLACIER BAY
GLAMA
GO-TO-IT
GOLD TOE
GREAT OUTDOORSMAN

Key to Media (For complete agency information see *The Advertising Red Books-Agencies* edition):
1. Bus. Publs. 2. Cable T.V. 3. Catalogs & Directories. 4. Co-op Adv. 5. Consumer Mags. 6. D.M. to Bus. Estab.7. D.M. to Consumers
8. Daily Newsp. 9. Exhibits/Trade Shows 10. Foreign 11. Infomercial 12. Internet Adv.13. Multimedia 14. Network Radio
15. Network T.V. 16. Newsp. Distr. Mags. 17. Other 18. Outdoor (Posters, Transit) 19. Point of Purchase20. Premiums, Novelties
21. Product Samples 22. Special Events Mktg. 23. Spot Radio 24. Spot T.V. 25. Weekly Newsp. 26. Yellow Page Adv.

GREEN EASE
H SALON
HABAND
HABAND TRAVELERS
HABARDINE
HANDY BULB
HAPPILY EVER ACCURATE
HEALTHRITE
HOLD IT ALL
I FEEL PRETTY
IBU-RELIEF 12
INFINITEYE
IONIC WHISPER
IONOMATIC 3000
IONOMATIC PLUS
ISLAND STAGS
JUMBO SHAMSORB
JUST BEGAUZE
JUST RIGHT
KAREENA
KNIT TO BE TRIED
LACE WITH GRAC
LADYFAIRE
LARGO BAY
LEATHER LIFECASE
LEATHER ZIP & GO!
LET'S PARTY!
LINENEASE
LOVE IN BLOOM
LOVELADIES
LUCERNE
MACRO-SORB
MAGIC CHOPPER
MAGIC CLASPS
MAGICSLIM
MAIDENFORM
MARILYN MONROE
MISTY MEADOW
MIX 'N' FIX
THE MONTCLAIR
MOONBEAMS
MUSHROOMS
NANTUCKET SOUND
NEW BALANCE
NEWPORT
NONYX
NORTHPORT
NOVELLA
OMEGA
OOH LA LA!
OPTI-FLEX
PARK AVE
PARTY PERFECT
PEEL IT
PERFECT PERFORMANCE
PERFECTLY SUITED
PET-I-CURE
PLAY FAVORITES
PLAYFULLY PLUSH
POSHMINA
PREP-O-MATIC
PRETTY & PRACTICAL
PROPET
QUICKLAWN
RAIN OR SHINE
RED CROSS SHOES
RIBBONS & ROSEBUDS
SAFETY TOUCH
SALON STUDIO
SARA MORGAN
SET OF 4 TRAVEL BRIGHT
SILKY & SLEEK
SIMPLE ELEGANCE
SLIM WEAR
SMART & SNAPPY
SNAP-IT-UP
SNUGGIE
SNUGGLEWEAR
SOFTKINS
SOMETHING SPECIAL
SPEEDY PASTA
SUMMER COOLERS
SUMMER GARDEN
SWEET INSPIRATION
SWEET SWEATERS
SWIRLS OF PEARLS
TEA TIME
THERMAFLEECE
TOTES
TRAVEL-READY
TUDOR COURT
TWEEZE
TWICE AS NICE
TWO-IN-ONE
ULTRALUXE
UNDERWAIR
VALLEY LANE
WARMTH & BRAWN
WORSTERWARM
ZIP 'N GO
ZIP 'N VAC
ZIPPING ALONG

Advertising Agency:
Fairview Advertising
112 Bauer Dr
Oakland, NJ 07436-3105
Tel.: (201) 651-9784
Fax: (201) 405-7774
(Ladies' & Mens' Apparel)
— Christine Silvestri *(Dir-Print Media)*

HANNA ANDERSSON CORPORATION

(Sub. of Kellwood Company)
1010 NW Flanders St
Portland, OR 97209-3119
Tel.: (503) 242-0920
Fax: (503) 222-0544
Fax: (503) 321-5289 (Orders)
Toll Free: (800) 222-0544
E-mail: customerservice@hannaandersson.com
Web Site: www.hannaandersson.com
Approx. Number Employees: 203
Year Founded: 1983
Business Description:
Apparel & Accessories Mfr
S.I.C.: 5699; 5611; 5621; 5641; 5651
N.A.I.C.S.: 448190; 448110; 448120; 448130; 448140; 448150
Media: 4-6-13
Personnel:
Adam Stone *(Pres & COO)*
Philip Iosca *(CEO)*
Rod Rice *(CFO)*
Jackie Ardrey *(Sr VP-Mdsg & Design)*
Jim Davis *(Sr VP-Supply Chain)*
Steve Dunn *(VP-Info Sys)*
Gretchen Peterson *(VP-HR)*
Alison Polenz *(VP-Mktg)*
Jessica Polonsky *(VP-Retail)*
Brands & Products:
HANNA ANDERSSON

HANOVER DIRECT, INC.

(Holding of Chelsey Direct, LLC)
1500 Harbor Blvd
Weehawken, NJ 07087
Tel.: (201) 863-7300
Fax: (201) 272-3280
E-mail: information@hanoverdirect.com
Web Site: www.hanoverdirect.com
Sales Range: $400-449.9 Million
Approx. Number Employees: 1,840
Year Founded: 1911
Business Description:
Catalog Publisher & Direct Marketer
S.I.C.: 5961; 5947
N.A.I.C.S.: 454113; 453220; 454111
Import
Media: 2-4-5-6-8-9-13-15-16-17-18-19-20-22-23-24-25
Distr.: Natl.
Budget Set: Jan.
Personnel:
William Watchtel *(Chm)*
Don Kelly *(Pres & CEO)*
Peter Wallman *(COO)*
Dennis Werner *(Sr VP-Sls & Mktg)*
Robin Baskin *(VP-Ecommerce)*
Brands & Products:
CLEARANCE WORLD
THE COMPANY STORE
DOMESTICATIONS
INTERNATIONAL MALE
SILHOUETTES
UNDERGEAR
Advertising Agencies:
NetPlus Marketing, Inc.
625 Ridge Pike Bldg E Ste 200
Conshohocken, PA 19428
Tel.: (610) 897-2380
Fax: (610) 897-2381

Pluzynski/Associates, Inc.
26 W 17th St 10th Fl
New York, NY 10011
Tel.: (212) 645-1414
Fax: (212) 645-2013

HAROLD'S STORES, INC.

(Filed Ch 11 Bankruptcy #815032 on 11/07/08 in U.S. Bankruptcy Ct, Western Dist of OK, Oklahoma City)
5919 Maple Ave
Dallas, TX 75235
Tel.: (214) 366-0600
Fax: (214) 366-1061
Web Site: www.harolds.com
Sales Range: $75-99.9 Million
Approx. Number Employees: 362
Business Description:
Women's & Men's Clothing Sales
S.I.C.: 5651; 5611; 5621
N.A.I.C.S.: 448140; 448110; 448120
Import Export
Advertising Expenditures: $5,237,000
Media: 4-8-13
Personnel:
William E. Haslam *(Chm)*
Cheryl Sergeant *(Chief Mdsg Officer & Exec VP)*
Brands & Products:
HAROLD POWELL
HAROLD'S
OLD SCHOOL
OLD SCHOOL CLOTHING COMPANY

HARRIET CARTER GIFTS, INC.

425 Stump Rd
Montgomeryville, PA 18936-9631
Tel.: (215) 361-5100
Fax: (215) 368-8670
Toll Free: (800) 377-7878
Web Site: www.harrietcarter.com
Approx. Sls.: $40,000,000
Approx. Number Employees: 140
Year Founded: 1958
Business Description:
Mail Order Household Accessories & Gifts
S.I.C.: 5961
N.A.I.C.S.: 454113
Advertising Expenditures: $250,000
Media: 4-6-8-12-13
Distr.: Direct to Consumer
Budget Set: Oct.
Personnel:
William Garbose *(Pres & CEO)*
Brands & Products:
HARRIET CARTER

HARRINGTONS OF VERMONT, INC.

210 E Main St
Richmond, VT 05477-7721
Tel.: (802) 434-7560
Tel.: (802) 434-4444 (Orders)
Fax: (802) 434-3166
E-mail: info@harringtonham.com
Web Site: www.harringtonham.com
Approx. Number Employees: 30
Year Founded: 1873
Business Description:
Mail Order of Gourmet Foods
S.I.C.: 5147; 5947
N.A.I.C.S.: 311612; 453220
Advertising Expenditures: $250,000
Media: 4-6-7-8-9-13-21-25
Distr.: Natl.
Budget Set: May -Nov.
Personnel:
Peter Klinkenberg *(Owner & Pres)*
Michael Barb *(Controller)*
Brands & Products:
HARRINGTONS OF VERMONT
Advertising Agency:
Harrington's Ad Direct
(House Agency)
210 E. Main St.
Richmond, VT 05477
Tel.: (802) 434-7500
Fax: (802) 434-3166
(Smoked Meats & Specialty Foods)

HART STORES INC.

900 Pl Paul-Kane
Laval, QC H7C 2T2, Canada
Tel.: (450) 661-4155
Fax: (450) 661-4731
E-mail: hartstoresinfo@hartstores.com
Web Site: www.hartstores.com
Approx. Sls.: $175,635,870
Approx. Number Employees: 1,700
Business Description:
Department Stores
S.I.C.: 5311
N.A.I.C.S.: 452111
Media: 8-13-16
Personnel:
Harry Hart *(Chm & CEO)*
Robert Harritt *(CFO & VP-Fin)*
Robert A. Farah *(COO)*
Michael Lussier *(VP-IT)*
Howard Michaels *(VP-Mdsg)*
Salvatore Pugliese *(VP-IT & Sys)*
Marc-Andre Boyer *(Dir-Logistic & Distr)*
Stephane Gibeau *(Dir-Store Ops)*
Tina Ruggiero *(Dir-Bus Solutions & Ops)*
Howard Urtick *(Mgr-Adv & Promos)*

Key to Media (For complete agency information see *The Advertising Red Books-Agencies* edition):
1. Bus. Publs. 2. Cable T.V. 3. Catalogs & Directories. 4. Co-op Adv. 5. Consumer Mags. 6. D.M. to Bus. Estab.7. D.M. to Consumers 8. Daily Newsp. 9. Exhibits/Trade Shows 10. Foreign 11. Infomercial 12. Internet Adv.13. Multimedia 14. Network Radio 15. Network T.V. 16. Newsp. Distr. Mags. 17. Other 18. Outdoor (Posters, Transit) 19. Point of Purchase20. Premiums, Novelties 21. Product Samples 22. Special Events Mktg. 23. Spot Radio 24. Spot T.V. 25. Weekly Newsp. 26. Yellow Page Adv.

HASTINGS ENTERTAINMENT, INC.
3601 Plains Blvd
Amarillo, TX 79102-1019
Tel.: (806) 351-2300
Fax: (806) 351-2424
E-mail: webmaster@hastings-ent.com
Web Site: www.gohastings.com
Approx. Rev.: $521,055,000
Approx. Number Employees: 1,889
Year Founded: 1968
Business Description:
Multimedia Entertainment Retailer
S.I.C.: 5735; 5942; 5961
N.A.I.C.S.: 451220; 451211; 454111; 454113
Advertising Expenditures: $7,700,000
Media: 5-9-15-24-25
Personnel:
John H. Marmaduke *(Pres & CEO)*
Dan Crow *(CFO & VP-Fin)*
Alan van Ongevalle *(Sr VP-Mdsg)*
Kevin J. Ball *(VP-Mktg)*
Victor Fuentes *(VP & Div Mgr-Mdse)*
John Hintz *(VP-IT)*
Phil McConnell *(VP & Div Mgr-Mdse)*

HEARST BUSINESS MEDIA
(Div. of The Hearst Corporation)
50 Charles Lindbergh Blvd Ste 100
Uniondale, NY 11553
Tel.: (516) 227-1300
Fax: (516) 227-1901
E-mail: hearstbusinessmedia@hearst.com
Web Site: www.hearst.com
Approx. Number Employees: 55
Business Description:
Catalog of Electronic Products, Equipment & Services
S.I.C.: 7311
N.A.I.C.S.: 541810
Media: 4-13
Personnel:
Richard P. Malloch *(Pres)*
James M. Asher *(Chief Legal Officer, Sr VP & Chief Dev Officer)*
Charles Tuchinda *(Chief Innovation Officer-Healthcare)*
Frank A. Bennack, Jr. *(CEO-Hearst Corp & VP)*
Eve Burton *(VP & Gen Counsel-Hearst Corp)*
Steven A. Hobbs *(Exec VP & Deputy Grp Head)*
Ronald J. Doerfler *(Sr VP-Fin & Admin)*
Brands & Products:
FLOOR COVERING WEEKLY
Advertising Agency:
SiiTE Interactive
419 Park Ave S Ste 907
New York, NY 10016
Tel.: (212) 481-9070
Fax: (212) 481-9074

HEATHKIT COMPANY, INC.
(d/b/a Heathkit Educational Systems)
2024 Hawthorne Ave
Saint Joseph, MI 49085
Tel.: (269) 925-6000
Fax: (269) 925-2898
Toll Free: (800) 253-0570
E-mail: info@heathkit.com
Web Site: www.heathkit.com
Approx. Sls.: $20,000,000
Approx. Number Employees: 24
Year Founded: 1926
Business Description:
Direct Mail Services, Electronics & Servicing Courses for Classroom & Individual Learning Courses
S.I.C.: 3999
N.A.I.C.S.: 339999
Media: 2-4-6-8-10-11-20-22
Distr.: Intl.; Natl.
Personnel:
Lori Marciniak *(Pres & CEO)*
Ernie Wake *(Dir-Mktg & Sls)*
Brands & Products:
DIGICALL
HE-ROBOT
HEATHKIT EDUCATIONAL SYSTEMS

HICE SEWING INC.
14630 Section Line Rd
Elkmont, AL 35620
Tel.: (256) 232-0140
Fax: (256) 232-0910
Toll Free: (800) 752-4927
E-mail: info@hicesewing.com
Web Site: www.hicesewing.com
Approx. Number Employees: 35
Business Description:
Medical & General Apparel Mfr; Embroidery & Screen Printing Services
S.I.C.: 2389
N.A.I.C.S.: 315299
Media: 2-4-8-10
Personnel:
Shirley Hice *(Pres)*
Brands & Products:
HICE

HOME DECOR PRODUCTS, INC.
47 Brunswick Ave
Edison, NJ 08817
Tel.: (732) 593-1200
Fax: (732) 512-0691
E-mail: info@homedecorproducts.com
Web Site: www.hdpi.com
Sales Range: $75-99.9 Million
Approx. Number Employees: 130
Year Founded: 2000
Business Description:
Online Home Improvement Products Retailer
S.I.C.: 5961; 5719
N.A.I.C.S.: 454111; 442299
Media: 4-13
Personnel:
Jonathan C. Bernstein *(CEO)*
Pamela Graham *(Sr VP-Adv Partnerships)*
Brands & Products:
BARBECUES.COM
CHEFSCORNER.COM
CHRISTMASCATALOG.COM
CLIQUIDATE.COM
HECHINGER.COM
HOMECLICK.COM
KNOBSANDTHINGS.COM
POOLCLICK.COM

HOUSE OF WESLEY, INC.
1704 Morrissey Dr
Bloomington, IL 61704
Tel.: (309) 664-7334
Fax: (309) 663-6691
E-mail: customercare@houseofwesley.com
Web Site: www.houseofwesley.com
Sales Range: $75-99.9 Million
Approx. Number Employees: 75
Year Founded: 1954
Business Description:
Mail Order & Web-Based Garden & Nursery Products
S.I.C.: 5961
N.A.I.C.S.: 454113
Media: 2-8-9-10-18
Distr.: Natl.
Budget Set: Monthly
Personnel:
Richard B. Owen *(Pres)*
Brands & Products:
HOUSE OF WESLEY
Advertising Agency:
Adtron, Inc.
4415 E Cotton Center Blvd
Phoenix, AZ 85040
Tel.: (309) 662-1221
Fax: (602) 735-0349

HUDSON'S BAY COMPANY
(Joint Venture of Apollo Advisors, L.P. & National Realty & Development Corp.)
(d/b/a Hbc)
401 Bay St Ste 500
Toronto, ON M5H 2Y4, Canada
Tel.: (416) 861-6112
Tel.: (416) 861-6691 (Pub Rel)
Fax: (416) 861-4720
E-mail: firstnamelastname@hbc.com
Web Site: www.hbc.com
Approx. Rev.: $6,282,098,060
Approx. Number Employees: 62,394
Year Founded: 1670
Business Description:
Specialty Retail & Department Stores Operator
S.I.C.: 5311; 5719
N.A.I.C.S.: 452111; 442299
Import
Media: 9-15-23-25
Distr.: Natl.
Budget Set: Oct. -Dec.
Personnel:
Darlene Goren *(CIO)*
Mark Foote *(Pres/CEO-Zellers Discount Div)*
Robert M. Kolida *(Exec VP-HR)*
Kerry Mader *(Sr VP-Specialty)*
Nicholas Padovano *(Sr VP-Store Ops)*
Melvin R. Mitzel *(VP-Shared Svcs-Fin)*
Brands & Products:
THE BAY
GREAT THINGS FOR CANADA
HBC.COM
HOME OUTFITTERS
ZELLERS

THE INCREDIBLE CHRISTMAS PLACE
2470 Pkwy
Pigeon Forge, TN 37863
Tel.: (865) 453-0415
Fax: (865) 453-3318
Toll Free: (800) 445-3396
E-mail: santa@christmasplace.com
Web Site: www.christmasplace.com
Approx. Number Employees: 250
Year Founded: 1986
Business Description:
Christmas Items, Gifts & Collectibles Retailer
S.I.C.: 5999
N.A.I.C.S.: 453998
Media: 2-4-13
Personnel:
Marion Biggs *(Pres & CEO)*
Carolyn Fairbank *(COO)*
Janet Donaldson *(Mgr-Adv)*
Brands & Products:
CHRISTMASPLACE.COM
IT'S WORTH A CLICK

INTERNATIONAL PLAZA & BAY STREET
(Div. of Taubman Centers, Inc.)
2223 NW Shore Blvd
Tampa, FL 33607
Tel.: (813) 342-3790
Tel.: (813) 342-3780 (Pub Rels)
Fax: (813) 342-3788
E-mail: mmaldonada@taubman.com
Web Site: www.shopinternationalplaza.com
Sales Range: $150-199.9 Million
Approx. Number Employees: 300
Business Description:
Shopping Complex
S.I.C.: 5999; 5731
N.A.I.C.S.: 453910; 443112
Media: 8-9-13-22
Personnel:
Nina Mahoney *(Dir-Mktg & Sponsorship)*
Nina Polm *(Dir-Mktg)*

INTRADA INC.
2220 Mountain Blvd Ste 220
Oakland, CA 94611
Tel.: (510) 338-0310
Fax: (510) 336-1615
E-mail: intrada@intrada.com
Web Site: www.intrada.com
Year Founded: 1980
Business Description:
Motion Picture Soundtracks
S.I.C.: 3652; 5735; 5961
N.A.I.C.S.: 334612; 451220; 454111; 454113
Media: 2-4-6-10-13
Personnel:
Douglass Fake *(Owner & Pres)*
Roger Feigelson *(Dir-Mktg)*
Joe Sikoryak *(Dir-Design)*
Jeff Johnson *(Mgr-Store)*
Brands & Products:
EXCALIBUR COLLECTION
INTRADA

J. CREW GROUP, INC.
(Holding of TPG Capital, L.P.)
770 Broadway
New York, NY 10003
Tel.: (212) 209-2500
Fax: (212) 209-2666
Toll Free: (800) 562-0258
E-mail: inquiries@jcrew.com
Web Site: www.jcrew.com
Approx. Rev.: $1,683,470,000
Approx. Number Employees: 3,800
Year Founded: 1983
Business Description:
Clothing Retailer
S.I.C.: 5961; 5611; 5621; 5699
N.A.I.C.S.: 454113; 448110; 448120; 448150; 448190
Import
Advertising Expenditures: $18,802,000
Media: 4-5-6-8-9-11-13-19-20-25-26
Distr.: Natl.; Reg.

Key to Media (For complete agency information see *The Advertising Red Books-Agencies* edition):
1. Bus. Publs. 2. Cable T.V. 3. Catalogs & Directories. 4. Co-op Adv. 5. Consumer Mags. 6. D.M. to Bus. Estab.7. D.M. to Consumers
8. Daily Newsp. 9. Exhibits/Trade Shows 10. Foreign 11. Infomercial 12. Internet Adv.13. Multimedia 14. Network Radio
15. Network T.V. 16. Newsp. Distr. Mags. 17. Other 18. Outdoor (Posters, Transit) 19. Point of Purchase20. Premiums, Novelties
21. Product Samples 22. Special Events Mktg. 23. Spot Radio 24. Spot T.V. 25. Weekly Newsp. 26. Yellow Page Adv.

Budget Set: May -Nov.
Personnel:
Millard S. Drexler *(Chm & CEO)*
Jenna Lyons *(Pres & Exec Dir-Creative)*
James Scully *(CFO & Chief Admin Officer)*
Jennifer Carr-Smith *(COO-Direct & Sr VP)*
Trish Donnelly *(Exec VP-Direct Channel)*
Linda Markoe *(Exec VP-HR)*
Libby Wadle *(Exec VP-Retail & Factory)*
Scott D. Hyatt *(Sr VP-Mfg)*
Ashley Sargent *(Sr VP-Brand Creative)*
Laura Willensky *(Sr VP-Madewell Retail Channel)*
Kelley Hall *(Mgr-Recruiting & Field)*
Brands & Products:
CREWCUTS
J CREW
MADEWELL
Advertising Agencies:
Buddy Media, Inc.
1845 Broadway 3rd Fl
New York, NY 10023
Tel.: (646) 786-1400

Westover Media
11578 SW Riverwood Rd
Portland, OR 97219
Tel.: (503) 675-2580
Fax: (503) 675-2581

THE J. JILL GROUP, INC.
(Holding of Golden Gate Capital)
4 Batterymarch Park
Quincy, MA 02169
Tel.: (617) 376-4300
Fax: (617) 769-0177
Web Site: www.jjill.com
Sales Range: $400-449.9 Million
Approx. Number Employees: 3,400
Year Founded: 1987
Business Description:
Classic Women's Apparel & Accessories Mail Order Catalog Whslr & Store Retailer
S.I.C.: 5621; 5961
N.A.I.C.S.: 448120; 454113
Advertising Expenditures: $8,833,000
Media: 2-4-6
Personnel:
Paula J. Bennett *(Pres & CEO)*
Hilary Chasin *(CMO & Sr VP)*
Avra Myers *(Sr VP & Gen Mgr-Mdsg)*
Sue Walsh *(Sr VP-Stores)*

JACK FROST SHOPS
95 Main St
Jackson, NH 03846
Mailing Address:
PO Box F
Jackson, NH 03846-0805
Tel.: (603) 383-4391
Fax: (603) 383-4331
E-mail: info@jackfrostshop.com
Web Site: www.jackfrostshop.com/
Year Founded: 1945
Business Description:
Retailer Ski Fashions & Equipment
S.I.C.: 5699; 7999
N.A.I.C.S.: 448190; 532292
Media: 9-13-23
Distr.: Reg.
Budget Set: Apr.
Personnel:
William Tinkham *(Co-Owner)*
Brands & Products:
AMERICA'S BEST BOOTFITTERS

THE JAZZ STORE
(Div. of Musical Heritage Society Inc.)
1710 Hwy 35
Oakhurst, NJ 07755
Mailing Address:
PO Box 3009
Oakhurst, NJ 07755
Tel.: (732) 531-7000
Fax: (732) 517-0438
Toll Free: (800) 558-9513
Web Site: www.jazzstore.com
Approx. Number Employees: 70
Business Description:
Direct Marketing Services for Jazz Merchandise
S.I.C.: 5961; 5947
N.A.I.C.S.: 454113; 453220
Media: 4-8-13
Personnel:
Jeffrey Nissim *(Pres)*

J.C. PENNEY COMPANY, INC.
6501 Legacy Dr
Plano, TX 75024-3612
Tel.: (972) 431-1000
Fax: (972) 431-1362
Web Site: www.jcpenney.net
Approx. Sls.: $17,759,000,000
Approx. Number Employees: 156,000
Year Founded: 2002
Business Description:
Holding Company; Department Stores & Catalog Sales
S.I.C.: 5311; 5961; 6719
N.A.I.C.S.: 452111; 454113; 551112
Advertising Expenditures: $1,172,000,000
Media: 3-4-5-6-9-14-15-23-24-25
Personnel:
Myron E. Ullman, III *(Chm)*
Michael R. Francis *(Pres)*
Ron Johnson *(CEO)*
Michael P. Dastugue *(CFO & Exec VP)*
Ed Robben *(Sr VP & CIO)*
Michael J. Boylson *(CMO & Exec VP)*
Michael T. Theilmann *(Chief Admin Officer, Chief HR & Exec VP)*
Janet L. Dhillon *(Gen Counsel, Sec & Exec VP)*
Michael W. Taxter *(Exec VP & Dir-JCPenney Stores)*
Clarence Kelley *(Exec VP-Plng & Allocation)*
Steven Lawrence *(Exec VP & Sr Gen Mdse Mgr-Mens Apparel)*
Ken Mangone *(Exec VP-Product Dev & Sourcing)*
Thomas M. Nealon *(Exec VP)*
Elizabeth H. Sweney *(Exec VP & Sr Gen Mdse Mgr-Womens Apparel)*
Dennis Miller *(Sr VP & Controller)*
Ruby Anik *(Sr VP & Dir-Brand Mktg)*
Marie Lacertosa *(Sr VP & Dir-Supply Chain)*
Thomas A. Clerkin *(Sr VP-Property Dev)*
Pam Mortensen *(Sr VP & Gen Mdse Mgr-Fine Jewelry)*
Bruce Kilkowsk *(VP & Dir-Procurement)*
Kristin Hays *(VP-Fin-Supply Chain)*
Angelika Torres *(Dir-IR)*
Laura Carros *(Mgr-Customer Loyalty & Res)*
Brands & Products:
A.N.A.
EVERY DAY MATTERS
JCPENNY
Advertising Agencies:
Conill Advertising, Inc.
800 Brickell Ave Ste 400
Miami, FL 33131
Tel.: (305) 351-2901
Fax: (305) 351-2509
Creative & Account
Hispanic

Dieste
1999 Bryan St Ste 2700
Dallas, TX 75201
Tel.: (214) 259-8000
Fax: (214) 259-8040

EVB-Evolution Bureau
55 Union St
San Francisco, CA 94111
Tel.: (415) 281-3950
Fax: (415) 281-3957

interTrend Communications, Inc.
555 E Ocean Blvd
Long Beach, CA 90802-5003
Tel.: (562) 733-1888
Fax: (562) 733-1889

OMD Worldwide
195 Broadway
New York, NY 10007
Tel.: (212) 590-7100
Hispanic
Media Buying

Razorfish
821 2nd Ave Ste 1800
Seattle, WA 98104-2343
Tel.: (206) 816-8800
Fax: (206) 816-8808

Saatchi & Saatchi
(Sub. of Publicis Groupe S.A.)
(Worldwide Headquarters)
375 Hudson St
New York, NY 10014-3660
Tel.: (212) 463-2000
Fax: (212) 463-9856
(Jewelry)

Saatchi & Saatchi New York
375 Hudson St
New York, NY 10014-3660
Tel.: (212) 463-2000
Fax: (212) 463-9855

J.L. TODD AUCTION CO.
531 Broad St
Rome, GA 30162-0553
Tel.: (706) 291-7007
Fax: (706) 291-0335
Toll Free: (800) 241-7591
E-mail: info@jltodd.com
Web Site: www.jltodd.com
E-Mail For Key Personnel:
President: tjtarpley@jltodd.com
Approx. Number Employees: 10
Year Founded: 1917
Business Description:
Auctioneer
S.I.C.: 5961; 6531
N.A.I.C.S.: 454112; 531210
Media: 2-3-8-9-13-18-23-25
Distr.: Natl.
Personnel:
Randy Land *(Exec VP)*
John Todd *(Exec VP)*
Advertising Agency:
Todd Advertising Agency, Inc.
PO Box 553
Rome, GA 30162-0553
Tel.: (706) 291-7007
Fax: (706) 291-0335
Toll Free: (800) 241-7591
(Real Estate)
— Linda Fletcher *(Adv. Mgr.)*

JOHNSON SMITH COMPANY
4514 19th St Ct E
Bradenton, FL 34203
Tel.: (941) 747-5566
Fax: (941) 748-5385
Toll Free: (800) 558-1142
E-mail: info@johnsonsmith.com
Web Site: www.johnsonsmith.com
Approx. Number Employees: 100
Year Founded: 1914
Business Description:
Mail Order Novelties & Gifts
S.I.C.: 3674; 5961
N.A.I.C.S.: 334413; 454113
Import Export
Advertising Expenditures: $12,000,000
Media: 2-3-4-6-8-9-14-16-20-25-26
Distr.: Natl.
Budget Set: Monthly
Personnel:
Kim Boyd *(VP-Mktg)*
Linda Jacobs *(Mgr-Mdsg)*
Brands & Products:
BETTYS ATTIC
CLEVER GEAR & OTHER SMART INNOVATIONS
FULL OF LIFE
HALLOWEENONLY.COM
JOHNSON SMITH CO
THE LIGHTER SIDE
THINGS YOU NEVER KNEW EXISTED
Advertising Agency:
Globe Advertising Service
4514 19th St Ct E
Bradenton, FL 34203
Tel.: (941) 747-5566
Fax: (941) 746-7962

JOURNEY EDUCATION MARKETING, INC.
(Sub. of Digital River, Inc.)
13755 Hutton Dr Ste 500
Dallas, TX 75234
Tel.: (972) 481-2000
Fax: (972) 481-2150
Toll Free: (800) 874-9001
E-mail: marketing@journeyed.com
Web Site: www.journeyed.com
Sales Range: $10-24.9 Million
Business Description:
Educational Software Distr
S.I.C.: 5734
N.A.I.C.S.: 443120
Media: 4
Personnel:
Nathan Jones *(Pres)*

Key to Media (For complete agency information see *The Advertising Red Books-Agencies* edition):
1. Bus. Publs. 2. Cable T.V. 3. Catalogs & Directories. 4. Co-op Adv. 5. Consumer Mags. 6. D.M. to Bus. Estab.7. D.M. to Consumers 8. Daily Newsp. 9. Exhibits/Trade Shows 10. Foreign 11. Infomercial 12. Internet Adv.13. Multimedia 14. Network Radio 15. Network T.V. 16. Newsp. Distr. Mags. 17. Other 18. Outdoor (Posters, Transit) 19. Point of Purchase20. Premiums, Novelties 21. Product Samples 22. Special Events Mktg. 23. Spot Radio 24. Spot T.V. 25. Weekly Newsp. 26. Yellow Page Adv.

Journey Education Marketing, Inc. — (Continued)

Michael Fischler *(CEO)*
Greg Lamkin *(Dir-Sls-North America)*
Tim Lilly *(Mgr-Natl Consortia)*

JS&A GROUP, INC.

(d/b/a Blublocker)
3350 Palm Ctr Dr
Las Vegas, NV 89103
Tel.: (702) 597-2000
Fax: (702) 597-2002
Toll Free: (800) 323-6400
E-mail: info@blublocker.com
Web Site: www.blublocker.com
Approx. Number Employees: 10
Year Founded: 1971
Business Description:
Marketing & Mail Order Services
S.I.C.: 5961; 7311
N.A.I.C.S.: 454113; 541810
Media: 6-8-9-13
Distr.: Intl.; Natl.
Budget Set: June -Oct.
Personnel:
Joseph Sugarman *(Founder & CEO)*
Mary Stanke *(Pres)*
George Gerstman *(Gen Counsel)*

JUSTFLOWERS.COM

2127 Westwood Blvd Ste 200
Los Angeles, CA 90028
Fax: (310) 626-8473
Toll Free: (800) 777-1911
E-mail: john@justflowersinc.com
Web Site: www.justflowers.com
Business Description:
Florist
S.I.C.: 5992
N.A.I.C.S.: 453110
Media: 13-17-20
Personnel:
Nelson Garrett *(Pres)*

KMART CORPORATION

(Sub. of Sears Holdings Corporation)
3333 Beverly Rd
Hoffman Estates, IL 60179
Tel.: (847) 286-2500
Fax: (847) 286-5500
Web Site: www.kmartcorp.com
Sales Range: $15-24.9 Billion
Approx. Number Employees: 133,000
Business Description:
General Merchandising Services
S.I.C.: 5311
N.A.I.C.S.: 452111
Advertising Expenditures:
$446,000,000
Media: 2-3-4-8-9-13-14-15-17-23-24-25
Personnel:
Lisa Schultz *(Sr VP & Chief Creative Officer)*
John D. Goodman *(Exec VP-Apparel & Home)*
James P. Mixon *(Sr VP)*
Linda Gawura *(Adv Dev Mgr)*
Brands & Products:
ABBEY HILL
BIG KMART
JACLYN SMITH HOME COLLECTION
KMART
LIMON Y SAL
SUPER KMART
Advertising Agencies:
Draftfcb
101 E Erie St
Chicago, IL 60611
Tel.: (312) 425-5000
Fax: (312) 425-5010
Creative

Mindshare
498 7th Ave
New York, NY 10018
Tel.: (212) 297-7000
Fax: (212) 297-7001

MPG
(Div. of HAVAS)
195 Broadway 12th Fl
New York, NY 10007
Tel.: (646) 587-5000
Fax: (646) 587-5005
Media Buying

Peterson Milla Hooks
1315 Harmon Pl
Minneapolis, MN 55403-1926
Tel.: (612) 349-9116
Fax: (612) 349-9141
Money Can't Buy Style

KOHL'S CORPORATION

N56 W17000 Ridgewood Dr
Menomonee Falls, WI 53051
Tel.: (262) 703-7000
Fax: (262) 703-6143
E-mail: investor.relations@kohls.com
Web Site: www.kohls.com
Approx. Sls.: $18,391,000,000
Approx. Number Employees: 29,000
Year Founded: 1962
Business Description:
Department Store Owner & Operator
S.I.C.: 5311; 5651
N.A.I.C.S.: 452112; 448140; 452111
Import
Advertising Expenditures:
$869,000,000
Media: 3-5-8-9-14-16-18-19-23-24-25
Distr.: Reg.
Budget Set: Mar. -Sept.
Personnel:
Kevin Mansell *(Chm, Pres & CEO)*
Wesley S. McDonald *(CFO & Sr Exec VP)*
Julie Gardner *(CMO & Exec VP)*
John M. Worthington *(Chief Admin Officer)*
Donald A. Brennan *(Chief Mdsg Officer)*
Richard D. Schepp *(Gen Counsel)*
Jack H. Boyle *(Exec VP, Gen Mdse Mgr-Womens Apparel & Accessories)*
Jeff Manby *(Gen Mdse Mgr-Mens & Children & Exec VP)*
Jon Grosso *(Exec VP & Dir-Stores)*
Kenneth Bonning *(Exec VP-Logistics & Store Plng)*
Janelle Havner *(Exec VP-Mdse Presentation)*
Telvin Jeffries *(Exec VP)*
Jon K. Nordeen *(Exec VP-Admin)*
Paige Thomas *(Exec VP & Gen Mdse Mgr-Juniors' & Jewelry)*
Brian F. Miller *(Sr VP-Corp Governance)*
Vicki Shamion *(VP-PR & Community Rels)*
Tim Payne *(Mgr-IS Resource)*
Rick Seeger *(Mgr-Data Warehouse)*
Andrea Glatfelter *(Coord-PR-Consumer Brands)*
Brands & Products:
EXPECT GREAT THINGS
KOHL'S
Advertising Agencies:
Casanova Pendrill, LLC
275-A McCormick Ave Ste 100
Costa Mesa, CA 92626-3369
Tel.: (714) 918-8200
Fax: (714) 918-8295

McCann Erickson/New York
622 3rd Ave
New York, NY 10017
Tel.: (646) 865-2000
Fax: (646) 487-9610

KUM & GO

(Sub. of Krause Gentle Corporation)
6400 Westown Pkwy
West Des Moines, IA 50266-7709
Tel.: (515) 226-0128
Fax: (515) 226-1595
E-mail: info@kumandgo.com
Web Site: www.kumandgo.com
Approx. Rev.: $1,430,000,000
Approx. Number Employees: 3,663
Business Description:
Convenience Stores
S.I.C.: 5541; 5411
N.A.I.C.S.: 447190; 445120
Personnel:
W. A. Krause *(Founder & Chm)*
Kyle J. Krause *(Pres)*
Advertising Agency:
Cranford Johnson Robinson Woods
303 W Capitol Ave
Little Rock, AR 72201-3531
Tel.: (501) 975-6251
Fax: (501) 975-4241
Toll Free: (888) 383-2579

LANDS' END, INC.

(Sub. of Sears, Roebuck & Co.)
Lands' End Ln
Dodgeville, WI 53595
Tel.: (608) 935-9341
Fax: (608) 935-4260
Fax: (800) 332-0103
Toll Free: (800) 356-4444
E-mail: mailbox@landsend.com
Web Site: www.landsend.com
Sales Range: $1-4.9 Billion
Approx. Number Employees: 7,400
Year Founded: 1963
Business Description:
Apparel & Housewares Mfr & Whslr
S.I.C.: 5961; 5611; 5699
N.A.I.C.S.: 454113; 448110; 448150
Media: 2-3-4-6-8-9-11-13-18-25
Distr.: Natl.
Budget Set: Dec.
Personnel:
Edgar Huber *(Pres & CEO)*
Tim Martin *(CFO & COO)*
Chris Kolbe *(Pres-Brand)*
Robert McElroy *(Sr VP-Intl)*
Todd Peletta *(Sr VP-Inventory Mgmt)*
Kelly A. Ritchie *(Sr VP-Employee Svcs)*
Susan Sachatello *(Sr VP-Mktg)*
Michele Casper *(Dir-Pub Rels)*
Brands & Products:
LANDS' END
THE WORLD'S CLOTHING STORE
Advertising Agencies:
Arena Red
247 Tottenham Court Road
London, W1T 7QX, United Kingdom
Tel.: (44) 20 7434 0813
Fax: (44) 20 7287 5056
Fax: (44) 20 7439 3954

Waldbillig & Besteman, Inc.
8001 Excelsior Dr Ste 110
Madison, WI 53717-1956
Tel.: (608) 829-0900
Fax: (608) 829-0901
Toll Free: (800) 395-4767

LANE BRYANT

(Div. of CHARMING SHOPPES, INC.)
3344 Morse Crossing
Columbus, OH 43219
Tel.: (215) 633-2497
Fax: (614) 463-5242
Toll Free: (800) 248-2000
Web Site: www.lanebryant.com
Sales Range: $200-249.9 Million
Approx. Number Employees: 250
Business Description:
Women's Special-Size Apparel Mfr & Retailer
S.I.C.: 5621
N.A.I.C.S.: 448120
Media: 4-6-8-9-10-13-16-18-19-24-25
Distr.: Natl.
Budget Set: Nov.
Personnel:
Brian P. Woolf *(Pres)*
Marla C. Anderson *(Pres-Outlet Bus)*
Carrie Klein *(Sr VP & Gen Mgr)*
Debbie Martin *(Sr VP)*
Roland Medrano *(Sr VP-Global Sourcing)*
Sandra Tillett *(Sr VP)*
Kathy Quickert *(Dir-Mktg)*
Brands & Products:
CACIQUE
COTTON SENSUAL CURVES
FIGURE
FLAUNT
HOUSTON
LAFAYETTE
LEXINGTON
MADISON
METROLINE
SATIN SENSUAL CURVES
SENSUAL CURVES
SHEERWARE
SMOOTH PERFORMANCE
Advertising Agency:
Zimmerman Advertising
2200 W Commercial Blvd Ste 300
Fort Lauderdale, FL 33309-3064
Tel.: (954) 644-4000
Fax: (954) 731-2977
Toll Free: (800) 248-8522
(Creative, Media)

LEVENGER COMPANY

420 S Congress Ave
Delray Beach, FL 33445
Tel.: (561) 276-2436
Fax: (561) 272-1553
E-mail: contact@levenger.com
Web Site: www.levenger.com
Sales Range: $75-99.9 Million
Approx. Number Employees: 120
Year Founded: 1987
Business Description:
Retail Mail Order
S.I.C.: 5961
N.A.I.C.S.: 454113
Advertising Expenditures:
$16,000,000

Key to Media (For complete agency information see *The Advertising Red Books-Agencies* edition):
1. Bus. Publs. 2. Cable T.V. 3. Catalogs & Directories. 4. Co-op Adv. 5. Consumer Mags. 6. D.M. to Bus. Estab.7. D.M. to Consumers
8. Daily Newsp. 9. Exhibits/Trade Shows 10. Foreign 11. Infomercial 12. Internet Adv.13. Multimedia 14. Network Radio
15. Network T.V. 16. Newsp. Distr. Mags. 17. Other 18. Outdoor (Posters, Transit) 19. Point of Purchase20. Premiums, Novelties
21. Product Samples 22. Special Events Mktg. 23. Spot Radio 24. Spot T.V. 25. Weekly Newsp. 26. Yellow Page Adv.

Media: 4-13
Personnel:
Lori Leveen *(Founder)*
Steven Leveen *(Founder)*
Brands & Products:
CAREZZA
LEVENGER
LIVINGSTONE
WELL-READ LIFE

LILLIAN VERNON CORPORATION
(Sub. of Current USA, Inc.)
2600 International Parkwa
Virginia Beach, VA 23452
Tel.: (757) 427-7700
Fax: (800) 852-2365
Toll Free: (800) 907-9291
E-mail: custserv@lillianvernon.com
Web Site: www.lillianvernon.com
E-Mail For Key Personnel:
Sales Director: corpsales@lillianvernon.com
Public Relations: dch@lillianvernon.com
Sales Range: $200-249.9 Million
Approx. Number Employees: 1,200
Year Founded: 1951
Business Description:
Catalog & Online Retailer of Assorted Gifts & Products
S.I.C.: 5961; 5399; 5947
N.A.I.C.S.: 454113; 452990; 453220
Media: 4-8-13
Distr.: Intl.; Natl.
Budget Set: Dec.
Personnel:
Richard Mather *(Gen Mgr)*
Brands & Products:
FAVORITES
LILLIAN VERNON
LILLY'S KIDS
PERSONALIZED GIFTS

LIMITED BRANDS, INC.
3 Limited Pkwy
Columbus, OH 43230-1467
Mailing Address:
PO Box 16000
Columbus, OH 43216-1600
Tel.: (614) 415-7000
Fax: (614) 415-7440
E-mail: InvestorRelations@LimitedBrands.com
Web Site: www.limitedbrands.com
Approx. Sls.: $9,613,000,000
Approx. Number Employees: 17,500
Year Founded: 1963
Business Description:
Specialty Store Owner & Operator
S.I.C.: 5621; 5699
N.A.I.C.S.: 448120; 448190
Advertising Expenditures: $473,000,000
Media: 4-8-9-10-11-15-23-25
Distr.: Natl.
Budget Set: June
Personnel:
Leslie H. Wexner *(Chm & CEO)*
Martin Waters *(Pres)*
Stuart B. Burgdoerfer *(CFO & Exec VP)*
Martyn R. Redgrave *(Chief Admin Officer & Exec VP)*
Jane L. Ramsey *(Exec VP-HR)*
Jeanette Cantone *(Sr VP-Lingerie Projects-Limited Design Svcs)*
Lucy Spencer *(Mgr-Mktg-Intl Export Grp)*
Advertising Agencies:
The Media Kitchen
160 Varick St
New York, NY 10013
Tel.: (212) 633-0080
Fax: (212) 633-0080

Ologie
447 E Main St
Columbus, OH 43215
Tel.: (614) 221-1107
Fax: (614) 221-1108
Toll Free: (800) 962-1107

LITTLE SCOTLAND
95 Akerley Boulevard
Dartmouth, NS B3B 1R7, Canada
Tel.: (902) 468-9084
Fax: (902) 468-2178
Toll Free: (877) 670-2737
E-mail: sales@littlescotland.com
Web Site: www.littlescotland.com
Approx. Number Employees: 9
Business Description:
Scottish, Irish & Welsh Music, Clothing & Gift Items Retailer & Direct Marketer
S.I.C.: 5961; 5399; 5947
N.A.I.C.S.: 454113; 452990; 453220
Media: 4-8-11-13
Personnel:
Innis Campbell *(Pres)*

LITTLETON COIN CO., INC.
1309 Mt Eustis Rd
Littleton, NH 03561
Tel.: (603) 444-5386
Fax: (603) 444-0121
Toll Free: (800) 645-3122
E-mail: info@littletoncoin.com
Web Site: www.littletoncoin.com
Approx. Number Employees: 330
Year Founded: 1945
Business Description:
Mail Order Collector Coins
S.I.C.: 5961
N.A.I.C.S.: 454113
Advertising Expenditures: $3,000,000
Media: 2-3-4-5-6-7-8-9-10-16-21-22-25
Distr.: Natl.
Budget Set: May
Personnel:
Maynard Sundman *(Founder)*
David M. Sundman *(Pres)*
Edward Timothy *(CEO)*
Michael Morelli *(COO)*
Samantha Dube *(Mgr-Web Mktg)*
Madline Fraz *(Mgr-Creative Svcs)*
Brands & Products:
LITTLETON
LITTLETON COIN COMPANY
LITTLETON'S CUSTOM COIN FOLDERS

L.L. BEAN, INC.
15 Casco St
Freeport, ME 04033
Tel.: (207) 865-4761
Fax: (207) 552-2802
Toll Free: (800) 441-5713
E-mail: business@llbean.com
Web Site: www.llbean.com
Approx. Sls.: $1,500,000,000
Approx. Number Employees: 3,900
Year Founded: 1912
Business Description:
Apparel, Housewares, Outerwear & Sports Equipment Sales
S.I.C.: 2389
N.A.I.C.S.: 315999
Media: 3-4-6-8-9-10-13-15-16-24
Distr.: Intl.; Natl.
Budget Set: Bi-annually
Personnel:
Leon A. Gorman *(Chm)*
Chris McCormick *(Pres & CEO)*
Mark Fasold *(CFO)*
Steve Fuller *(CMO)*
Andy Beahm *(Asst Treas)*
Nancy Fischman *(Dir-Creative Ops)*
Brands & Products:
ACADIA CRUISER
ALLAGASH
BEAN'S
FLYING TIGER
GUARANTEED YOU HAVE OUR WORD
L.L. BEAN
MAINE GUIDE
MICRO MESH
NORTHWOODS
QUICKEXCHANGE
SIGMA
STOWAWAY RAINWEAR
SUNSMART
SWIFT RIVER
TRAILBLAZER
TURBO TRANSIT
WELLIE
WICKED GOOD
WINTER WALKER
WOODLANDS
Advertising Agencies:
Championship Group, Inc.
1954 Airport Rd Ste 200
Atlanta, GA 30341
Tel.: (770) 457-5777
Fax: (770) 457-1248

GSD&M
828 W 6th St
Austin, TX 78703-5420
Tel.: (512) 242-4736
Fax: (512) 242-4700
Creative
Media Planning & Buying

McCabe Duval + Associates
10 Moulton St
Portland, ME 04101
Tel.: (207) 773-4538
Fax: (207) 773-7245
Toll Free: (800) 603-6069

PointRoll Inc.
951 E Hector St
Conshohocken, PA 19428
Tel.: (267) 558-1300
Fax: (267) 285-1141
Toll Free: (800) 203-6956

LORD & TAYLOR LLC
(Joint Venture of Apollo Advisors, L.P. & National Realty & Development Corp.)
424 5th Ave
New York, NY 10018-2703
Tel.: (212) 391-3344
Fax: (212) 768-0743
Web Site: www.lordandtaylor.com
Approx. Number Employees: 5,000
Year Founded: 1826
Business Description:
Clothing & Clothing Accessories Department Stores Operator
S.I.C.: 5311; 5122; 5611; 5621; 5661; 5699; 5944
N.A.I.C.S.: 452111; 446120; 448110; 448120; 448150; 448210; 448310
Media: 4-8-9-10-22-25
Personnel:
Brendan L. Hoffman *(Pres & CEO)*
Michael Culhane *(Exec VP-Fin & Admin)*
Marybeth Sheridan *(Sr VP & Gen Mgr-Mdse)*
Amy Avitabile *(Sr VP Mktg)*
Jarrod Johanns *(Sr VP-Plng & Allocation)*
Brands & Products:
BLACK BROWN 1826

MACY'S CENTRAL
(Sub. of Macy's, Inc.)
223 Perimeter Center Pkwy
Atlanta, GA 30346-1301
Tel.: (770) 913-4000
Fax: (770) 913-5114
Web Site: www.macys.com
Sales Range: $1-4.9 Billion
Approx. Number Employees: 15,500
Year Founded: 1830
Business Description:
Department Store Operator
S.I.C.: 5311
N.A.I.C.S.: 452111
Import
Media: 3-4-5-8-9-19-22-23-24-25-26
Distr.: Reg.
Budget Set: Nov. -May
Personnel:
Diane Mahood *(Exec VP-Mktg)*
Sue Gardner *(Sr VP & Gen Mdse Mgr-Home)*

MACY'S EAST
(Sub. of Macy's, Inc.)
151 W 34th St 17th Fl
New York, NY 10001
Tel.: (212) 695-4400
Fax: (212) 494-1517
E-mail: info@macys.com
Web Site: www.macys.com
Sales Range: $50-74.9 Million
Approx. Number Employees: 200
Year Founded: 1858
Business Description:
Department Stores Operator
S.I.C.: 5311
N.A.I.C.S.: 452111
Advertising Expenditures: $289,400,000
Consumer Mags.: $3,700,000; Daily Newsp.: $139,175,000; Newsp. Distr. Mags.: $1,029,000; Other: $100,700,000; Outdoor (Posters, Transit): $295,000; Spot Radio: $89,000; Spot T.V.: $44,412,000
Distr.: Natl.; Reg.
Personnel:
Ronald Klein *(Chief Stores Officer)*
Amy Kule *(VP-Mktg-Macys Annual Events)*
Avis Scott *(Dir-Product)*

MACY'S FLORIDA
(Sub. of Macy's, Inc.)
22 E Flagler St

Key to Media (For complete agency information see *The Advertising Red Books-Agencies* edition):
1. Bus. Publs. 2. Cable T.V. 3. Catalogs & Directories. 4. Co-op Adv. 5. Consumer Mags. 6. D.M. to Bus. Estab.7. D.M. to Consumers
8. Daily Newsp. 9. Exhibits/Trade Shows 10. Foreign 11. Infomercial 12. Internet Adv.13. Multimedia 14. Network Radio
15. Network T.V. 16. Newsp. Distr. Mags. 17. Other 18. Outdoor (Posters, Transit) 19. Point of Purchase20. Premiums, Novelties
21. Product Samples 22. Special Events Mktg. 23. Spot Radio 24. Spot T.V. 25. Weekly Newsp. 26. Yellow Page Adv.

Macy's Florida — (Continued)

Miami, FL 33131-1004
Tel.: (305) 835-5151
Tel.: (305) 577-1858
Fax: (305) 577-2003
Web Site: www.macys.com
Sales Range: $800-899.9 Million
Approx. Number Employees: 10,000
Year Founded: 1898
Business Description:
Department Stores
S.I.C.: 5311; 5651
N.A.I.C.S.: 452111; 448140
Import Export
Media: 3-4-5-6-7-8-9-10-11-13-14-15-16-18-19-20-21-22-23-24-25-26
Distr.: Direct to Consumer; Reg.
Personnel:
Julie Greiner *(Chm & CEO)*
J. David Scheiner *(Pres & COO)*
Molly Langenstein *(Sr VP & Gen Mgr-Mdsg)*
Gilbert Lorenzo *(VP-Mktg)*
Advertising Agency:
Starcom USA
35 W Wacker Dr
Chicago, IL 60601
Tel.: (312) 220-3535
Fax: (312) 220-6530

MACY'S, INC.

7 W 7th St
Cincinnati, OH 45202-2424
Tel.: (513) 579-7000
Fax: (513) 579-7555
Toll Free: (800) 261-5385
Web Site: www.macysinc.com/
Approx. Sls.: $25,003,000,000
Approx. Number Employees: 166,000
Year Founded: 1929
Business Description:
Department Stores Operator
S.I.C.: 5311; 5961
N.A.I.C.S.: 452111; 454113
Import
Advertising Expenditures: $1,072,000,000
Media: 4-5-8-15-19-22
Personnel:
Terry J. Lundgren *(Chm, Pres & CEO)*
Janet E. Grove *(Vice Chm)*
Karen M. Hoguet *(CFO)*
Peter R. Sachse *(CMO)*
Thomas L. Cole *(Chief Admin Officer)*
Jeffrey Gennette *(Chief Mdsg Officer)*
Dennis J. Broderick *(Gen Counsel & Sec)*
William L. Hawthorne, III *(Sr VP-Diversity Strategies & Legal Affairs)*
Martine Reardon *(Exec VP)*
Michael Zorn *(Sr VP-Assoc & Labor Rels)*
Corliss Fong *(VP-Diversity Strategies)*
James A. Sluzewski *(VP-Corp Comm & External Affairs)*
Felicia Williams *(VP-Treasury & Risk Mgmt)*
Colleen Sherry *(Mgr-Online Media)*
Brands & Products:
ALFANI
CHARTER CLUB
MACY'S
MACY'S INC
STYLE & CO.
Advertising Agencies:
DunnHumby Associates Ltd.
Aurora House 71 - 75 Uxbridge Rd
London, W5 5SL, United Kingdom
Tel.: (44) 20 8832 9222
Fax: (44) 20 8832 9333

J. Walter Thompson Company (d/b/a JWT)
466 Lexington Ave
New York, NY 10017-3140
Tel.: (212) 210-7000
Fax: (212) 210-7299
Believe Campaign (Benefits Make-A-Wish Foundation)
Macy's

MEC Interaction
825 7th Ave
New York, NY 10019
Tel.: (212) 474-0000
Fax: (212) 474-0003

Northlich
Sawyer Point Bldg 720 Pete Rose Way
Cincinnati, OH 45202
Tel.: (513) 421-8840
Fax: (513) 455-4749

MAGELLAN'S INTERNATIONAL TRAVEL CORP.

3317 Number A State St
Santa Barbara, CA 93101
Tel.: (805) 568-5402
Fax: (805) 568-5406
Fax: (800) 962-4940
Toll Free: (800) 962-4943
E-mail: cservice@magellans.com
Web Site: www.magellans.com
Approx. Number Employees: 80
Year Founded: 1989
Business Description:
Travel Supplies Mail Order & Sales
S.I.C.: 5961
N.A.I.C.S.: 454113
Media: 4-8-13
Personnel:
Mark Gallow *(CEO)*
Brands & Products:
MAGELLAN'S

MARKETING CONCEPTS OF MINNESOTA, INC.

130 Lk Ave
Spicer, MN 56288
Tel.: (320) 796-6245
Fax: (320) 796-6036
E-mail: info@marketingconcepts.com
Web Site: www.marketingconcepts.com
Approx. Sls.: $17,200,000
Approx. Number Employees: 101
Business Description:
Mail Order Services
S.I.C.: 5961; 7336
N.A.I.C.S.: 454113; 541430
Media: 7-13
Personnel:
Diane Buzzeo *(CEO)*

MARSHALLS OF MA, INC.

(Sub. of Marmaxx Operating Corp.)
770 Cochituate Rd
Framingham, MA 01701
Tel.: (508) 390-1000
Tel.: (508) 390-6258
Toll Free: (888) MARSHALLS
Web Site: www.marshallsonline.com
Sales Range: $600-649.9 Million
Approx. Number Employees: 2,000
Year Founded: 1956
Business Description:
Off-Price Family Apparel Retailer
S.I.C.: 5311
N.A.I.C.S.: 452112
Media: 3-6-8-9-13-18-19-22-23-24-25
Distr.: Natl.
Personnel:
Karen Coppola *(Sr VP-Mktg)*
Emily Trent *(VP-Mktg)*
Rebecca Leonard *(Assoc VP-PR)*
Amy Cafazzo *(Supvr-Media Rels)*
Advertising Agencies:
GSD&M
828 W 6th St
Austin, TX 78703-5420
Tel.: (512) 242-4736
Fax: (512) 242-4700
Digital Creative

LatinWorks Marketing, Inc.
206 E 9th St Capital Tower Fl 13
Austin, TX 78701
Tel.: (512) 479-6200
Fax: (512) 479-6024

MASTERS, INC.

111 Hempstead Tpke 2nd Fl
West Hempstead, NY 11552
Tel.: (516) 292-3710
Fax: (516) 292-3837
Approx. Rev.: $10,000,000
Approx. Number Employees: 75
Year Founded: 1937
Business Description:
Operator Department Stores
S.I.C.: 5641; 5621
N.A.I.C.S.: 448130; 448120
Media: 16
Distr.: Reg.
Budget Set: Jan.
Personnel:
Steven Greenspan *(Owner & Buyer)*
Richard Greenspan *(Pres)*
Brands & Products:
LADY ROSE
LORD BIBB
MASTERS

MBI INC.

47 Richards Ave
Norwalk, CT 06857
Tel.: (203) 853-2000
Fax: (203) 831-9661
E-mail: webmail@mbi-inc.com
Web Site: www.mbi-inc.com
Sales Range: $100-124.9 Million
Approx. Number Employees: 600
Business Description:
Direct Marketer Collectibles
S.I.C.: 5961
N.A.I.C.S.: 454113
Import
Media: 4-6-8-9-25
Distr.: Natl.
Personnel:
Theodore R. Stanley *(Chm)*
Peter Maglathlin *(Pres)*
Brands & Products:
DANBURY MINT
MBI
Advertising Agency:
MBI Inc.
47 Richards Ave
Norwalk, CT 06857
Tel.: (203) 853-2000
Fax: (203) 831-9661

MEIJER, INC.

2929 Walker Rd NW
Grand Rapids, MI 49544-9424
Tel.: (616) 453-6711
Fax: (616) 791-2572
E-mail: help@meijer.com
Web Site: www.meijer.com
Sales Range: $5-14.9 Billion
Approx. Number Employees: 65,000
Year Founded: 1962
Business Description:
General Merchandise Stores, Department Stores & Supermarkets Owner & Operator
S.I.C.: 5411; 5311; 5399
N.A.I.C.S.: 445110; 452112; 452910
Import
Advertising Expenditures: $10,000,000
Media: 7-9-18-19-22-23-24-25
Distr.: Reg.
Personnel:
Hendrik G. Meijer *(Co-Chm & CEO)*
Doug Meijer *(Co-Chm)*
Paul Boyer *(Vice Chm)*
Mark A. Murray *(Pres)*
Ruben Alcaraz *(Dir-Consumer Insights)*
Brands & Products:
MEIJER
Advertising Agencies:
DeVito/Verdi
100 5th Ave 16th Fl
New York, NY 10011
Tel.: (212) 431-4694
Fax: (212) 431-4940

Empower MediaMarketing (MEDIA THAT WORKS)
1111 Saint Gregory St
Cincinnati, OH 45202
Tel.: (513) 871-9454
Fax: (513) 871-1804
(Media Strategy, Planning & Buying)

JohnsonRauhoff
2525 Lake Pines Dr
Saint Joseph, MI 49085
Tel.: (269) 428-9212
Fax: (269) 428-3312
Toll Free: (800) 572-3996

Molecular
The Arsenal of the Charles 343 Arsenal St
Watertown, MA 02472
Tel.: (617) 218-6500
Fax: (617) 218-6700

PromoGroup
444 N Orleans St Ste 400
Chicago, IL 60610-4494
Tel.: (312) 467-1300
Fax: (312) 467-1311

MERVYN'S, LLC

(Joint Venture of Cerberus Capital Management, L.P., Sun Capital Partners, Inc., Lubert-Adler Management, Inc. & Klaff Realty, L.P.)
22301 Foothill Blvd MS 2115

Key to Media (For complete agency information see *The Advertising Red Books-Agencies* edition):
1. Bus. Publs. 2. Cable T.V. 3. Catalogs & Directories. 4. Co-op Adv. 5. Consumer Mags. 6. D.M. to Bus. Estab.7. D.M. to Consumers 8. Daily Newsp. 9. Exhibits/Trade Shows 10. Foreign 11. Infomercial 12. Internet Adv.13. Multimedia 14. Network Radio 15. Network T.V. 16. Newsp. Distr. Mags. 17. Other 18. Outdoor (Posters, Transit) 19. Point of Purchase20. Premiums, Novelties 21. Product Samples 22. Special Events Mktg. 23. Spot Radio 24. Spot T.V. 25. Weekly Newsp. 26. Yellow Page Adv.

Hayward, CA 94541-2709
Tel.: (510) 727-3000
Fax: (510) 727-5666
E-mail: customer.service@mervyns.com
Web Site: www.mervyns.com
Sales Range: $1-4.9 Billion
Approx. Number Employees: 23,000
Year Founded: 1949
Business Description:
Department Store Operator; Owned by Sun Capital Partners, Inc., Cerberus Capital Management, L.P., Lubert-Adler Management, Inc. & Klaff Realty, L.P.
S.I.C.: 5311; 5611; 5621
N.A.I.C.S.: 452111; 448110; 448120
Media: 8-9-17-23-24
Distr.: Direct to Consumer; Reg.
Personnel:
Kurt Streitz *(CIO & Sr VP)*
Ed Beck *(Gen Counsel, Sec & Sr VP)*
John Serino *(Exec VP-Opers)*
Michael Wallen *(Sr VP & Mgr-Gen Mdse)*
Bob Crosslin *(Sr VP-Supply Chain)*
Kari Heerdt *(Sr VP-HR)*
Susan Mesec *(Sr VP-Mktg)*
David Kranz *(VP & Mdse Mgr-Misses Apparel)*
Gary Schettino *(VP & Mdse Mgr-Men's)*
Brands & Products:
MERVYN'S
Advertising Agency:
Cervera International Corporation
10800 Ventura Blvd
Studio City, CA 91604
Tel.: (818) 508-9892
Fax: (818) 508-1520
(Hispanic)

MIDWEST DIRECT
2222 W 110th St
Cleveland, OH 44102
Tel.: (216) 472-4922
Fax: (216) 251-2577
Toll Free: (800) 686-6666
E-mail: info@mw-direct.com
Web Site: www.mw-direct.com
Sales Range: $125-149.9 Million
Approx. Number Employees: 250
Business Description:
Printing & Mailing Services
S.I.C.: 5961
N.A.I.C.S.: 454113
Advertising Agency:
Crowl, Montgomery & Clark, Inc.
123 Wilbur Dr NE
North Canton, OH 44720-8691
Tel.: (330) 494-6999
Fax: (330) 494-6242
Toll Free: (888) 649-8745

MILES KIMBALL COMPANY
(Sub. of Blyth, Inc.)
250 City Ctr
Oshkosh, WI 54906
Tel.: (920) 231-3800
Fax: (920) 231-4804
E-mail: csr@mileskimball.com
Web Site: www.mileskimball.com
Sales Range: $350-399.9 Million
Approx. Number Employees: 750
Year Founded: 1935
Business Description:
Mail-Order Catalogs for Gift Wares, Housewares, Toys & Greeting Cards
S.I.C.: 5961; 2771
N.A.I.C.S.: 454113; 511191
Advertising Expenditures: $30,700,000
Catalogs & Directories: $100,000; D.M. to Consumers: $30,000,000; Premiums, Novelties: $500,000; Spot Radio: $100,000
Distr.: Direct to Consumer; Natl.
Personnel:
Vicki Updike *(Pres)*
Margie Harvie *(VP-HR)*
Charlene Mirkiani *(Brand Mgr-As We Change & Easy Comforts)*
Brands & Products:
CHRISTMAS CARDS BY MILES KIMBALL OF OSHKOSH
EXPOSURES
HOME MARKETPLACE
MILES KIMBALL
QUIBBLE-FREE GUARANTEE
Advertising Agency:
Phids, Inc.
(D/B/A Acquirgy)
877 Executive Ctr Dr W Ste 300
Saint Petersburg, FL 33702-2474
Tel.: (727) 576-6630
Fax: (727) 576-4864

MOVIES UNLIMITED INC.
3015 Darnell Rd
Philadelphia, PA 19154-3201
Tel.: (215) 637-4444
Fax: (215) 637-2350
E-mail: movies@moviesunlimited.com
Web Site: www.moviesunlimited.com
Approx. Number Employees: 40
Year Founded: 1978
Business Description:
Video Tapes & DVDs Mail Order, Retailer & Rental Services
S.I.C.: 5735; 5961; 7841
N.A.I.C.S.: 451220; 454113; 532230
Media: 4-5-6-13-26
Personnel:
Jerry Frebowitz *(Pres)*
Ed Weiss *(Gen Mgr)*
Brands & Products:
THE MOVIE COLLECTOR'S WEBSITE
MOVIES UNLIMITED
WE'RE THE MOVIEST!

MUSICAL HERITAGE SOCIETY INC.
1710 State Route 35
Oakhurst, NJ 07755-2910
Tel.: (732) 531-7000
Fax: (732) 517-0438
E-mail: memberservices@musicalheritage.org
Web Site: www.musicalheritage.org
Approx. Number Employees: 60
Year Founded: 1989
Business Description:
Music Mail Order
S.I.C.: 5961
N.A.I.C.S.: 454113
Media: 4-8-13

NASCO INTERNATIONAL, INC.
(Sub. of The Aristotle Corporation)
901 Janesville Ave
Fort Atkinson, WI 53538-2402
Tel.: (920) 563-2446
Fax: (920) 563-8296
Toll Free: (800) 558-9595
E-mail: info@enasco.com
Web Site: www.enasco.com
Approx. Number Employees: 1,000
Year Founded: 1941
Business Description:
Agricultural, Home Economics & Educational Supplies Mfr
S.I.C.: 5961; 5083
N.A.I.C.S.: 454113; 423820
Advertising Expenditures: $800,000
Media: 2-4-6-8-10-17-21
Distr.: Direct to Consumer; Natl.
Budget Set: Sept.
Personnel:
Dean Johnson *(Pres)*
Jack Marshall *(Dir-Pur)*

NASCO MODESTO
(Sub. of Nasco International, Inc.)
4825 Stoddard Rd
Modesto, CA 95356-9318
Mailing Address:
PO Box 3837
Modesto, CA 95352-3837
Tel.: (209) 545-1600
Fax: (209) 545-1669
Toll Free: (800) 558-9595
E-mail: custserv@enasco.com
Web Site: www.enasco.com
Sales Range: $1-9.9 Million
Approx. Number Employees: 80
Year Founded: 1941
Business Description:
Educational Products for Various Organizations
S.I.C.: 8299; 5961
N.A.I.C.S.: 611710; 454113
Advertising Expenditures: $250,000
Media: 2-4-7-10-13
Distr.: Natl.
Budget Set: Oct.
Brands & Products:
ELASTRATOR
JOURGENSEN
LIFE/FORM
NASCO
NASCO-GUARD
SECATEUR
WHIRL-PAK

NATIONAL CONSUMER MARKETING
470 Pk Ave S 8th Fl S
New York, NY 10016
Tel.: (212) 686-8680
Web Site: www.publisherschoice.com
Approx. Number Employees: 30
Year Founded: 1984
Business Description:
Direct Mail Products
S.I.C.: 5961
N.A.I.C.S.: 454113
Media: 1-4-8-13-16-24-25
Distr.: Natl.
Personnel:
Bud Bironti *(Pres)*
Brands & Products:
PUBLISHERS CHOICE

NAXOS OF AMERICA INC.
(Sub. of HNH International Ltd.)
416 Mary Lindsay Polk Dr Ste 509
Franklin, TN 37067
Tel.: (615) 771-9393
Fax: (615) 771-6747
E-mail: naxos@naxosusa.com
Web Site: www.naxos.com
Approx. Number Employees: 35
Business Description:
Classical Music Distr
S.I.C.: 3652
N.A.I.C.S.: 334612
Media: 4-8-13-25
Personnel:
Jim Selby *(CEO)*
Reijo Kiilunen *(Pres-Ondine Records)*
Jonathan Eby *(Dir-Ops)*
Collin J. Rae *(Sr Mgr-Digital Mktg)*
Matt Whittier *(Sr Mgr-Mktg)*

NBC ACQUISITION CORP.
4700 S 19th St
Lincoln, NE 68512-1216
Tel.: (402) 421-7300
Fax: (402) 421-0507
E-mail: info@nebook.com
Web Site: www.nebook.com
Approx. Rev.: $605,493,613
Approx. Number Employees: 1,300
Business Description:
Holding Company; Book Stores
S.I.C.: 6719; 5942
N.A.I.C.S.: 551112; 451211
Advertising Expenditures: $7,300,000
Personnel:
Barry S. Major *(Pres & COO)*
Mark W. Oppegard *(CEO)*
Alan G. Siemek *(CFO)*

NEIMAN MARCUS STORES
(Joint Venture of Leonard Green & Partners, L.P., Warburg Pincus LLC & TPG Capital, L.P.)
1618 Main St
Dallas, TX 75201
Tel.: (214) 743-7600
Fax: (214) 573-5992
Toll Free: (800) 937-9146
Web Site: www.neimanmarcus.com
Approx. Number Employees: 14,700
Year Founded: 1907
Business Description:
Speciality Retailing Men's, Women's & Children's Clothing & Accessories
S.I.C.: 5311; 5961
N.A.I.C.S.: 452111; 454113
Import
Advertising Expenditures: $500,000
Media: 4-5-6-7-8-9-13-18-23-25
Distr.: Natl.
Personnel:
James E. Skinner *(CFO)*
Wanda Gierhart *(CMO)*
Shelle Bagot *(VP & Gen Mgr)*
Ken Downing *(Dir-Fashion)*
Brands & Products:
NEIMAN MARCUS
Advertising Agency:
Neiman Marcus Advertising
1618 Main St
Dallas, TX 75201
Tel.: (214) 743-7600
Fax: (214) 573-5992
(NM Merchandise & Services)

NEW YORK & COMPANY, INC.
(Holding of Irving Place Capital Management, L.P.)
450 W 33rd St 5th Fl
New York, NY 10001-2606
Tel.: (212) 884-2000
Fax: (212) 629-2396
Web Site: www.nyandcompany.com
Approx. Sls.: $1,021,699,000
Approx. Number Employees: 2,236
Year Founded: 1963

Key to Media (For complete agency information see *The Advertising Red Books-Agencies* edition):
1. Bus. Publs. 2. Cable T.V. 3. Catalogs & Directories. 4. Co-op Adv. 5. Consumer Mags. 6. D.M. to Bus. Estab.7. D.M. to Consumers 8. Daily Newsp. 9. Exhibits/Trade Shows 10. Foreign 11. Infomercial 12. Internet Adv.13. Multimedia 14. Network Radio 15. Network T.V. 16. Newsp. Distr. Mags. 17. Other 18. Outdoor (Posters, Transit) 19. Point of Purchase20. Premiums, Novelties 21. Product Samples 22. Special Events Mktg. 23. Spot Radio 24. Spot T.V. 25. Weekly Newsp. 26. Yellow Page Adv.

New York & Company, Inc. — (Continued)

Business Description:
Women's Clothing Stores
S.I.C.: 5621
N.A.I.C.S.: 448120
Advertising Expenditures: $33,546,000
Media: 8-19
Distr.: Natl.
Personnel:
Eran Cohen *(CMO & Exec VP)*
Michele Parsons *(Exec VP-Mdsg)*
David Witkewicz *(Exec VP-Design)*
Katie McCormick *(Dir-ECommerce Mktg)*
Advertising Agency:
Toth Brand Imaging
215 First St
Cambridge, MA 02142
Tel.: (617) 252-0787
Fax: (617) 252-0838

NORDSTROM, INC.
1617 6th Ave Ste 700
Seattle, WA 98101-1707
Tel.: (206) 628-2111
Fax: (206) 628-1795
Toll Free: (888) 282-6060
E-mail: invrelations@nordstrom.com
Web Site: www.nordstrom.com
Approx. Rev.: $9,700,000,000
Approx. Number Employees: 52,000
Year Founded: 1901
Business Description:
Apparel, Shoes & Accessories for Men, Women, & Children Retailer
S.I.C.: 5621; 5651; 5661
N.A.I.C.S.: 448120; 448140; 448210
Advertising Expenditures: $114,000,000
Media: 4-6-8-9-13-14-15-16-18-19-22-23-24
Distr.: Direct to Consumer; Natl.
Personnel:
Enrique Hernandez, Jr. *(Chm)*
Blake W. Nordstrom *(Pres)*
Michael G. Koppel *(CFO & Exec VP)*
Daniel F. Little *(Chief Admin Officer & Exec VP)*
Kevin Knight *(Pres-Nordstrom Credit & Exec VP)*
Erik B. Nordstrom *(Pres-Stores & Exec VP)*
James Nordstrom *(Pres-Nordstrom Direct & Exec VP)*
Peter E. Nordstrom *(Pres-Mdsg & Exec VP)*
James Thomas *(Pres-Nordstrom Rack & Exec VP)*
Mark Tritton *(Pres-Nordstrom Product Group & Exec VP)*
Jack H. Minuk *(Exec VP & Gen Mdse Mgr-Shoe Div)*
Margaret Myers *(Exec VP & Gen Mdse Mgr-Accessories & Womens Specialized Div)*
Scott A. Meden *(Exec VP & Gen Mgr-Mdse-Shoe Div)*
Laurie M. Black *(Exec VP & Gen Mdse Mgr-Cosmetic Div)*
James H. Bromley *(Exec VP)*
Linda Toschi Finn *(Exec VP-Mktg)*
Jeffrey S. Kalinsky *(Exec VP-Designer Mdsg)*
Loretta Soffe *(Exec VP & Gen Mdse Mgr-Womens Apparel Div)*
Delena M. Sunday *(Exec VP-HR & Diversity Affairs)*
David Witman *(Exec VP & Gen Mdse Mgr-Menswear & Kidswear Div)*
Amelia Letcher *(VP & Dir-Corp Diversity Affairs)*
James A. Howell *(VP-Fin)*
Terri Rose *(VP-Mktg)*
Leslie Aoyama *(Reg Dir-Northern California Hawaii)*
Rodney Friend *(Reg Dir-Los Angeles Orange County)*
Sandra Loza *(Reg Dir-MidWest)*
Kelly Mason *(Reg Dir-Northwest)*
Jerzy Romanowski *(Reg Dir-East Coast)*
Chris Holloway *(Dir-IR & Corp Dev)*
Mary Ann Lucchesi *(Dir-Adv-FLS)*
Sandy Fabre *(Mgr-IR)*
Brands & Products:
CASLON
CLASSIQUES
FRENCHI
HALOGEN
JOHN W. NORDSTROM
NORDSTROM
NORDSTROM 1901
NORDSTROM BABY
NORDSTROM BUTTERFLY DESIGN
NORDSTROM CRYSTAL COLLECTION
NORDSTROM HORSE & CROWN DESIGN
NORDSTROM LAYETTE
NORDSTROM RACK
Advertising Agencies:
Copacino + Fujikado, LLC
101 Yesler Way Ste 500
Seattle, WA 98104
Tel.: (206) 467-6610
Fax: (206) 467-6604

Fallon Worldwide
901 Marquette Ave Ste 2400
Minneapolis, MN 55402
Tel.: (612) 758-2345
Fax: (612) 758-2346

JWT Inside
2425 Olympic Blvd
Santa Monica, CA 90404
Tel.: (310) 309-8282
Fax: (310) 309-8283

Marke Communications
45 W 45th St 16th Fl
New York, NY 10036
Tel.: (212) 201-0600
Fax: (212) 213-0785

NORM THOMPSON OUTFITTERS INC.
(Holding of Orchard Brands Corporation)
3188 NW Aloclek Dr
Hillsboro, OR 97124-7134
Tel.: (503) 614-4600
Fax: (503) 614-4601
Toll Free: (877) 718-7899
Web Site: www.normthompson.com
Approx. Number Employees: 250
Year Founded: 1949
Business Description:
Catalog & Mail-Order Services
S.I.C.: 5961; 5136; 5137; 5947
N.A.I.C.S.: 454113; 424320; 424330; 453220
Media: 4-13
Personnel:
John Difrancesco *(CEO)*
Julie Rood *(VP-Mdsg)*
Brands & Products:
ESCAPE FROM THE ORDINARY
GETTING OFF THE BEATEN PATH
NORM THOMPSON
PRODUCTS THAT MAKE LIFE EASIER
SAHALIE
SOLUTIONS

OLLIE'S BARGAIN OUTLET INC.
6295 Allentown Blvd Ste A
Harrisburg, PA 17112-2606
Tel.: (717) 657-2300
Fax: (717) 901-3064
E-mail: olliesmark@olliesbargainoutlet.com
Web Site: www.olliesbargainoutlet.com
Approx. Number Employees: 1,300
Year Founded: 1982
Business Description:
Miscellaneous General Merchandise Stores
S.I.C.: 5399; 5199
N.A.I.C.S.: 452990; 424990
Import Export
Personnel:
Mark Butler *(Pres & CEO)*
John Swygert *(CFO)*
Advertising Agency:
Neiman Group
614 N Frnt St
Harrisburg, PA 17101-1057
Tel.: (717) 232-5554
Fax: (717) 232-7998
25th Anniversary

OLYMPIA SALES, INC.
215 Moody Rd
Enfield, CT 06082
Tel.: (860) 749-0751
Fax: (860) 763-4861
E-mail: info@olympiasales.net
Web Site: www.olympiasales.net
Approx. Sls.: $21,000,000
Approx. Number Employees: 10
Year Founded: 1966
Business Description:
Wholesaler Greeting Cards, Stationery & Labels; Catalog Sales of Paper Products & Domestic & Imported Gift Items
S.I.C.: 5112; 5961
N.A.I.C.S.: 424120; 454113
Import
Media: 4-7-8-13
Personnel:
Tom O'Hara *(Pres)*
Arthur P. O'Hara *(Dir-Art)*
Brands & Products:
HOLD-A-NOTES
OLYMPIA SALES

OMAHA STEAKS INTERNATIONAL, INC.
10909 John Galt Blvd
Omaha, NE 68137
Tel.: (402) 331-1010
Fax: (402) 597-8125
Toll Free: (800) 960-8400
E-mail: custserv@omahasteaks.com
Web Site: www.omahasteaks.com
Sales Range: $300-349.9 Million
Approx. Number Employees: 1,800
Year Founded: 1917
Business Description:
Steaks, Red Meats & Other Gourmet Foods Marketer, Distr & Retailer
S.I.C.: 5147
N.A.I.C.S.: 311612; 424470
Export
Media: 4-5-6-7-8-9-13-19
Distr.: Direct to Consumer; Direct to Retailer; Natl.
Budget Set: Mar.
Personnel:
Todd D. Simon *(Owner & Sr VP)*
Alan D. Simon *(Chm & CEO)*
Bruce A. Simon *(Pres)*
Dave Hershiser *(CFO)*
Frederick Simon *(Exec VP)*
Vickie Hagen *(VP & Gen Mgr-Mktg)*
Robert J. Bezousek *(VP-Production)*
Jim Bohan *(Dir-Benefits & Compensation)*
Brands & Products:
ENTERTAIN WITH PIZAZZ FROM OMAHA STEAKS
FROM THE HEART OF BEEF COUNTRY, U.S.A.
GIVE. SAVOR. CELEBRATE
GOLDEN PLAINS FOODS
OMAHA STEAKHOUSE
OMAHA STEAKS
OMAHA STEAKS WINE CLUB
OMASTEAK
PREMIUM HEARTLAND QUALITY
PRIDE OF NEBRASKA
PRIVATE RESERVE
THE STEAK LOVER'S COMPANION
TABLESTAR CUSTOM MEATS
THEBESTCHOICE
TODAY'S MENU
TRY A LITTLE TENDERNESS
WE WROTE THE BOOK ON RED MEAT
WE WROTE THE BOOK ON STEAK
Advertising Agency:
Omaha Creative Group
11030 O St
Omaha, NE 68137-2346
Tel.: (402) 597-3000
Fax: (402) 597-8222
Toll Free: (800) 228-2778
(Aged Midwestern Beef, Hand Cut & Frozen; Other Meats, Poultry, Seafood, Appetizers & Desserts; For Home Dining, Personal & Business Gifts & Incentive Programs)

ONLY NEW AGE MUSIC, INC.
8033 Sunset Blvd Ste 472
West Hollywood, CA 90046
Tel.: (323) 851-3355
Fax: (323) 851-7981
E-mail: info@newagemusic.com
Web Site: www.newagemusic.com
Approx. Number Employees: 3
Business Description:
Provider of Products & Services for New Age Music
S.I.C.: 5735
N.A.I.C.S.: 451220
Media: 2-4-8-10-13-23
Brands & Products:
GNOMUSY
GRUNDMAN
NEW AGE MUSIC
NON PROFIT MUSIC

Key to Media (For complete agency information see *The Advertising Red Books-Agencies* edition):
1. Bus. Publs. 2. Cable T.V. 3. Catalogs & Directories. 4. Co-op Adv. 5. Consumer Mags. 6. D.M. to Bus. Estab.7. D.M. to Consumers
8. Daily Newsp. 9. Exhibits/Trade Shows 10. Foreign 11. Infomercial 12. Internet Adv.13. Multimedia 14. Network Radio
15. Network T.V. 16. Newsp. Distr. Mags. 17. Other 18. Outdoor (Posters, Transit) 19. Point of Purchase20. Premiums, Novelties
21. Product Samples 22. Special Events Mktg. 23. Spot Radio 24. Spot T.V. 25. Weekly Newsp. 26. Yellow Page Adv.

SOUNDS OF NATURE SERIES
TRANQUILITY SERIES

THE ORVIS COMPANY, INC.
178 Conservation Way
Sunderland, VT 05250
Tel.: (802) 362-3622
Fax: (802) 362-3525
Toll Free: (888) 235-9763
E-mail: customer_service@orvis.com
Web Site: www.orvis.com
Approx. Sls.: $270,000,000
Approx. Number Employees: 1,500
Year Founded: 1856
Business Description:
Mail Order of Sporting Goods, Gifts & Sportswear
S.I.C.: 5961; 5941
N.A.I.C.S.: 454113; 451110
Import Export
Media: 2-3-4-6-8-9-10-13-15-18-19-20-21-22-23
Distr.: Direct to Consumer; Natl.
Budget Set: Oct.
Personnel:
Leigh H. Perkins, Sr. *(Chm)*
Ray McCready *(Pres)*
Leigh H. Perkins, Jr. *(CEO)*
Michael Dowd *(VP-Mktg, Multichannel)*
Bill Eyre *(Dir-Brand & Corp Mktg)*
Ryan Shadrin *(Dir-Mdsg)*
James Hathaway *(Mgr-Comm)*
Brands & Products:
BARBOUR
BUZZ OFF
GOKEY
INSECT SHIELD
ORVIS
ORVIS DOG'S NEST
ORVIS MYLAR
TOUGHCHEW

OVERTON'S INC.
(Sub. of Gander Mountain Company)
111 Red Bank Rd
Greenville, NC 27858
Tel.: (252) 355-7600
Fax: (252) 355-2923
Toll Free: (800) 334-6541
E-mail: service@overtons.com
Web Site: www.overtons.com
Sales Range: $75-99.9 Million
Approx. Number Employees: 255
Year Founded: 1970
Business Description:
Boating & Water Sports Equipment Retailer
S.I.C.: 5961; 5941
N.A.I.C.S.: 454111; 451110; 454113
Import Export
Media: 4-5-6-7-8-13-23-24
Personnel:
Mark Metcalfe *(Pres & CEO)*
John Daigle *(CFO)*
Brands & Products:
OVERTON'S

PACIFIC SUNWEAR OF CALIFORNIA INC
(d/b/a PacSun)
3450 E Miraloma Ave
Anaheim, CA 92806-2101
Tel.: (714) 414-4000
Fax: (714) 414-4251
Toll Free: (877) 372-2786
E-mail: info@pacsun.com
Web Site: www.pacsun.com
Approx. Sls.: $929,506,000
Approx. Number Employees: 2,750
Year Founded: 1980
Business Description:
Casual Apparel, Accessories & Footwear Store & On-Line Retailer for Teenagers & Young Adults
S.I.C.: 5611; 5621; 5661; 5699
N.A.I.C.S.: 448110; 448120; 448150; 448190; 448210
Advertising Expenditures: $17,000,000
Media: 8-10-13-22
Personnel:
Gary H. Schoenfeld *(Pres & CEO)*
Michael Kaplan *(CFO & Sr VP)*
Jon Brewer *(Sr VP-Product Dev & Supply Chain)*
John Fontana *(Sr VP-Inventory Mgmt)*
Christine Lee *(Sr VP & Gen Mdse Mgr-Juniors)*
Charlie Mescher *(Sr VP-Mens Mdsg)*
Kelly Bladow *(VP & Gen Mgr-Juniors & Outlet)*
Wayne Bowman *(VP-Store Design, Pur & Construction)*
Brands & Products:
PACIFIC SUNWEAR
PACIFIC SUNWEAR OF CALIFORNIA
PACSUN

PARKE-BELL LTD., INC.
709 W 12th St
Huntingburg, IN 47542-9589
Tel.: (812) 683-3707
Fax: (812) 683-5921
Toll Free: (800) 457-7456
E-mail: toc@touchofclass.com
Web Site: www.touchofclass.com
Approx. Number Employees: 250
Year Founded: 1978
Business Description:
Catalog & Mail-Order Houses
S.I.C.: 5961
N.A.I.C.S.: 454113
Import Export
Media: 4-8
Personnel:
Fred Bell *(Pres)*

PARTY CITY CORPORATION
(Joint Venture of Advent International Corporation, Berkshire Partners LLC & Weston Presidio Capital)
25 Green Pond Rd Ste 1
Rockaway, NJ 07866
Tel.: (973) 983-0888
Fax: (973) 983-6310
E-mail: talktous@partycity.com
Web Site: www.partycity.com
Approx. Number Employees: 1,500
Year Founded: 1986
Business Description:
Retailer of Party Supplies
S.I.C.: 5947; 5999
N.A.I.C.S.: 453220; 453998
Advertising Expenditures: $25,200,000
Media: 8-16-18-23-24-25
Distr.: Natl.
Personnel:
Lisa G. Laube *(Pres)*
Steven Skiba *(CIO)*
Gregg A. Melnick *(Pres-Party City Retail Grp)*
Brands & Products:
PARTY CITY

PAUL STUART, INC.
Madison Ave and 45th St
New York, NY 10017
Tel.: (212) 682-0320
Fax: (212) 983-2742
Toll Free: (866) 278-8278
E-mail: paulstuart@paulstuart.com
Web Site: www.paulstuart.com
Sales Range: $100-124.9 Million
Approx. Number Employees: 200
Year Founded: 1938
Business Description:
Retail Apparel Specialty Store
S.I.C.: 5611; 5621
N.A.I.C.S.: 448110; 448120
Advertising Expenditures: $1,000,000
Media: 4-6-9-23-25-26
Distr.: Direct to Consumer; Intl.; Natl.
Personnel:
Michael Ostrover *(Pres & CEO)*
Jack Donahue *(CFO)*
Mona Reilly *(Dir-Pub Rels)*
Shahriar Shahandeh *(Mgr-Mktg)*
Brands & Products:
CARLO
DANTE
DEVON
HARPER
MADE-TO-MEASURE
MATTEO
PAUL STUART
PEMBROKE
RICHARDSON
SEVILLE
SIERRA
WYATT

PERFORMANCE DIRECT, INC.
(Holding of North Castle Partners, L.L.C.)
(d/b/a Performance Bicycle)
144 Old Lystra Rd PO Box 2741
Chapel Hill, NC 27515-2741
Tel.: (919) 933-9113
Fax: (919) 942-5431
Toll Free: (800) 727-2433
Web Site: www.performancebike.com
Approx. Number Employees: 250
Year Founded: 1982
Business Description:
Mail Order Bicycle Retailer
S.I.C.: 5961; 5941
N.A.I.C.S.: 454113; 451110
Import Export
Media: 4-5-13
Personnel:
Garry Snook *(Founder, Chm & Co-CEO)*
James Thompson *(Co-CEO)*
Mike Starkey *(VP-IT)*
Mary Tanner *(Dir-Acctg)*
Brands & Products:
PERFORMANACE BICYCLE

PETMED EXPRESS, INC.
(d/b/a 1-800-PetMeds)
1441 SW 29th Ave
Pompano Beach, FL 33069
Tel.: (954) 979-5995
Fax: (954) 971-0544
Toll Free: (800) PETMEDS
E-mail: customerservice@1800petmeds.com
Web Site: www.1888petmeds.com
Approx. Sls.: $231,642,000
Approx. Number Employees: 240
Business Description:
Pet Pharmacy
S.I.C.: 0742; 5961
N.A.I.C.S.: 541940; 454111; 454113
Advertising Expenditures: $27,400,000
Media: 3-4-5-8-13-15
Personnel:
Robert C. Schweitzer *(Chm)*
Menderes Akdag *(Pres & CEO)*
Bruce S. Rosenbloom *(CFO & Treas)*
Alison Berges *(Gen Counsel)*
Brands & Products:
1-800-PETMEDS
ADVANTAGE
DERAMAXX
FRONTLINE PLUS
HEARTGARD PLUS
INTERCEPTOR
K9 ADVANTIX
PROGRAM TABLETS
REVOLUTION
RIMADYL
SENTINEL

PINE STATE TRADING COMPANY
8 Ellis Ave
Augusta, ME 04330-7199
Tel.: (207) 622-3741
Fax: (207) 626-0150
Toll Free: (800) 451-5500
E-mail: info@pinestatetrading.com
Web Site: www.pinestatetrading.com
Approx. Number Employees: 350
Year Founded: 1940
Business Description:
Wholesale Tobacco, Confectionery, Beer & Wine; Operators of Vending Machines
S.I.C.: 5194; 5181
N.A.I.C.S.: 424940; 424810
Media: 4-13-16-17-23-24-26
Personnel:
Paul Cottrell *(Pres)*
Gary Pelletier *(CFO)*

POPULAR CLUB PLAN, INC.
(Holding of York Management Services, Inc.)
22 Lincoln Pl
Garfield, NJ 07026-1904
Tel.: (973) 471-4300
Fax: (973) 472-3249
Toll Free: (800) POPCLUB
E-mail: webmaster@popularclub.com
Web Site: www.popularclub.com
Approx. Number Employees: 900
Business Description:
Mail Order Catalog Sales & Marketer
S.I.C.: 5961
N.A.I.C.S.: 454113
Media: 4-8-13-24
Personnel:
Gene Pepi *(Pres)*
Brands & Products:
POPULAR CLUB
POPULAR SHOPPING CLUB

POSTERITATI
239 Center St
New York, NY 10013
Tel.: (212) 226-2207
Fax: (212) 226-2102
E-mail: mail@posteritati.com
Web Site: www.posteritati.com
Approx. Number Employees: 3
Business Description:
Posters
S.I.C.: 5399

Key to Media (For complete agency information see *The Advertising Red Books-Agencies* edition):
1. Bus. Publs. 2. Cable T.V. 3. Catalogs & Directories. 4. Co-op Adv. 5. Consumer Mags. 6. D.M. to Bus. Estab.7. D.M. to Consumers
8. Daily Newsp. 9. Exhibits/Trade Shows 10. Foreign 11. Infomercial 12. Internet Adv.13. Multimedia 14. Network Radio
15. Network T.V. 16. Newsp. Distr. Mags. 17. Other 18. Outdoor (Posters, Transit) 19. Point of Purchase20. Premiums, Novelties
21. Product Samples 22. Special Events Mktg. 23. Spot Radio 24. Spot T.V. 25. Weekly Newsp. 26. Yellow Page Adv.

Posteritati — (Continued)

N.A.I.C.S.: 452910
Media: 6-10
Personnel:
Sam Sarowitz *(Owner)*

PRESCRIPTIONS PLUS, INC.
(Private-Parent-Single Location)
3381 Fairlane Farms Rd
West Palm Beach, FL 33414
Tel.: (561) 795-1636
Fax: (561) 795-1207
Toll Free: (800) 990-9826
Approx. Rev.: $2,900,000
Approx. Number Employees: 25
Year Founded: 1997
Business Description:
Mail Order Diabetic Supply Company
S.I.C.: 5961
N.A.I.C.S.: 454113
Media: 8-13-20
Personnel:
Frank Suess *(Pres)*
Susan Amsler *(Supvr-Graphic Design Mktg)*

PRO GROUP, INC.
6300 S Syracuse Way Ste 500
Centennial, CO 80155
Tel.: (303) 792-3000
Fax: (303) 792-5589
E-mail: contact@pro-group.com
Web Site: www.pro-group.com
Approx. Number Employees: 25
Year Founded: 1956
Business Description:
Hardware Distribution & Merchandising Consultation
S.I.C.: 5072
N.A.I.C.S.: 423710
Advertising Expenditures: $3,375,000
Distr.: Intl.; Natl.
Budget Set: Sept.
Personnel:
Steve Synnott *(Pres & CEO)*
Shari Kalbach *(Mng Dir-PRO Hardware)*
Michele Simes *(Dir-Events)*
Brands & Products:
DEZIGNRITE
FARM MART
GARDEN MASTER
NPD
PRIDE MASTERCRAFT
PRO HARDWARE
PROVEN BRANDS
PROVEN MARKETING GROUP

PROVELL, INC.
11100 Wayzata Blvd Ste 680
Minneapolis, MN 55305
Tel.: (952) 258-2000
Fax: (952) 258-2100
Toll Free: (800) 729-9000
E-mail: webmaster@provell.com
Web Site: www.provell.com
Sales Range: $125-149.9 Million
Approx. Number Employees: 34
Year Founded: 1986
Business Description:
Direct Response Marketer
S.I.C.: 5961
N.A.I.C.S.: 454113
Import
Advertising Expenditures: $500,000
Media: 4
Personnel:
George S. Richards *(Chm, Pres & CEO)*
Rod Merry *(CIO & Sr VP)*
Michael McGowan *(CMO & Sr VP-Mktg)*
Brands & Products:
BUYERS PLUS
EXPLORE USA
HOMEPLAY
PREFERRED BUYERS' CLUB
PROVELL

PUBLISHERS CLEARING HOUSE
382 Channel Dr
Port Washington, NY 11050-2219
Tel.: (516) 883-5432
Fax: (516) 883-5769
Toll Free: (800) 645-9242
Web Site: www.pch.com
Approx. Number Employees: 500
Year Founded: 1953
Business Description:
Catalog, Mail Order & Television Sales
S.I.C.: 5961; 5963
N.A.I.C.S.: 454113; 454390
Import Export
Advertising Expenditures: $25,000,000
Media: 15-24
Distr.: Natl.
Personnel:
Andy Goldberg *(Pres & CEO)*
Rick Busch *(CFO & SVP-Publishers)*
Andrew Zucker *(Chief Revenue Officer-PCH Online)*
Harold W. Low *(Gen Counsel & VP)*
Deborah Holland *(Exec VP-Creative Strategy, Comm & Consumer Affairs)*
Craig Anderson *(Sr VP-Ops & Mktg Svcs)*
Todd Sloane *(Sr VP)*
Josh Glantz *(VP & Gen Mgr)*
Sal Tripi *(Sr Dir-Ops & Compliance)*
Vicky Hsu *(Dir-Online Mktg)*
Brands & Products:
PCH
PUBLISHERS CLEARING HOUSE
Advertising Agency:
KSL Media, Inc.
367 Park Ave S 4th Fl
New York, NY 10016
Tel.: (212) 352-5800
Fax: (212) 352-5935

PURITAN'S PRIDE, INC.
(Sub. of NBTY, Inc.)
90 Orville Dr
Bohemia, NY 11716-2521
Tel.: (631) 567-9500
Fax: (631) 471-5693
Toll Free: (800) 645-1030
E-mail: info@puritanspride.com
Web Site: www.puritanspride.com
Approx. Sls.: $5,300,000
Year Founded: 1973
Business Description:
Vitamin Mfr; Catalog & Mail-Order Houses
S.I.C.: 2833; 2844; 5961
N.A.I.C.S.: 325411; 325620; 454113
Import Export
Media: 4-6-8
Personnel:
Timothy Connor *(VP-Fin & Admin)*
Brands & Products:
PURITAN'S PRIDE

RAINBOW APPAREL COMPANIES INC.
(Sub. of AIJJ Enterprises Inc.)
1000 Pennsylvania Ave
Brooklyn, NY 11207-8417
Tel.: (718) 485-3000
Fax: (718) 485-3807
Web Site: www.rainbowshops.com
Approx. Sls.: $200,000,000
Approx. Number Employees: 1,000
Year Founded: 1935
Business Description:
Apparel Sales
S.I.C.: 5621
N.A.I.C.S.: 448120
Advertising Expenditures: $500,000
Media: 9-23-24
Distr.: Direct to Consumer; Natl.
Budget Set: June-Nov.
Personnel:
Joseph Chehebar *(Dir-E-Commerce)*
Brands & Products:
RAINBOW APPAREL

REDCATS USA, L.P.
(Sub. of Redcats USA, Inc.)
(d/b/a Bargain Catalog Outlet (BCO))
463 7th Ave
New York, NY 10018-7604
Mailing Address:
PO Box 4407
Taunton, MA 02780-0432
Tel.: (212) 613-9500
Fax: (212) 613-9590
Web Site: www.bcoutlet.com
Approx. Number Employees: 300
Business Description:
Women's & Men's Special-Size Apparel Catalog Retailer
S.I.C.: 5961
N.A.I.C.S.: 454111; 454113
Media: 4-6-8-13
Personnel:
Eric Courteille *(CFO)*
Brands & Products:
BRYLANE
CHADWICK'S OF BOSTON
JESSICA LONDON
KINGSIZE
LA REDOUTE
LERNER
ROAMAN'S

ROSCO LABORATORIES, INC.
52 Harbor View Ave
Stamford, CT 06902-5914
Tel.: (203) 708-8900
Fax: (203) 708-8919
E-mail: info@rosco.com
Web Site: www.rosco.com
Approx. Number Employees: 190
Year Founded: 1910
Business Description:
Mfr. of Products Used by Theater, TV & Film Industries
S.I.C.: 3861
N.A.I.C.S.: 333315
Media: 4
Personnel:
Stan Miller *(Chm)*
Mark Engel *(Pres)*
Ian Baseby *(Mng Dir)*
Stan Schwartz *(Exec VP)*
Donna Nicol *(Dir-Mktg & Creative)*
Maria Szots *(Office Mgr)*
Huey Davis *(Mgr-Traffic)*
Andreas Dessloch *(Mgr-Bus Dev)*
Rowena Landini *(Export Mgr)*
Joanna Shapley *(Mgr-Bus Dev)*
Stephen Spendiff *(Mgr-Product, Mktg & Ops)*
Joel Svendsen *(Mgr-Sls Initiatives)*
Brands & Products:
ADAGIO
ADAGIO TOUR
ALPHA
APPRENTICE
ARABESQUE
CABRIOLE
CALCOLOR
CHROMA KEY
CINEDICHRO
CINEGEL
CINELUX
CLEARCOLOUR
COLDFLOW
COLORCOAT
COLORINE
COLORIZER
COLORIZERS
COLORLINE
COLORWAVES
CRYSTALGEL
CYSTALGEL
DELTA
DIFFRACTIONS
DIGICOMP
E-COLOUR
EVEREST 3D
FLEXBOND
FLEXCOAT
FLUORESCENT
FOAMCOAT
GLAM
GLAME
HAZEMAKER
HORIZON
I-CUE
IDDINGS
IMAGE GLASS
IMAGEPRO
INFINITY
KEYSTROKE
LAY-IN
MATTE BLACK CINEFOIL
METALIX
MULTI-LENS
OFF BROADWAY
PERMACOLOR
POLARIZING
PORTABARRE
PRISMATIC
PRISMATICS
ROSCO COOKIES
ROSCOFLAMEX
ROSCOGLO
ROSCOLENE
ROSCOLEUM
ROSCOLUX
ROSCOTILES
ROYALE
RUN POWERPOINT
SHIMMER SCRIM
SHOWCLOTH
SMOOTHS
SPARKLENE
SPECTRUMGOBOS
STORARO
SUPERGEL
TOUGH PRIME
TV PAINT
ULTIMATTE

Key to Media (For complete agency information see *The Advertising Red Books-Agencies* edition):
1. Bus. Publs. 2. Cable T.V. 3. Catalogs & Directories. 4. Co-op Adv. 5. Consumer Mags. 6. D.M. to Bus. Estab.7. D.M. to Consumers 8. Daily Newsp. 9. Exhibits/Trade Shows 10. Foreign 11. Infomercial 12. Internet Adv.13. Multimedia 14. Network Radio 15. Network T.V. 16. Newsp. Distr. Mags. 17. Other 18. Outdoor (Posters, Transit) 19. Point of Purchase20. Premiums, Novelties 21. Product Samples 22. Special Events Mktg. 23. Spot Radio 24. Spot T.V. 25. Weekly Newsp. 26. Yellow Page Adv.

VIVIDFX
VORTEX
WALLHUGGER

ROSS-SIMONS INC.
9 Ross Simons Dr
Cranston, RI 02920-4475
Tel.: (401) 463-3100
Fax: (401) 463-8599
E-mail: customerservice@ross-simons.com
Web Site: www.ross-simons.com
Approx. Number Employees: 400
Year Founded: 1952
Business Description:
Catalog & Mail-Order Services
S.I.C.: 5944; 5947
N.A.I.C.S.: 448310; 453220
Import Export
Media: 4-6-9-23-24
Personnel:
Darrell S. Ross *(CEO)*
Jeanne Desmarais Cox *(Mgr-Mktg-e-Commerce)*
Advertising Agency:
RDW Group Inc.
125 Holden St
Providence, RI 02908-4919
Tel.: (401) 521-2700
Fax: (401) 521-0014

ROSS STORES, INC.
(d/b/a Ross Dress for Less)
4440 Rosewood Dr
Pleasanton, CA 94588
Tel.: (925) 965-4400
E-mail: investor.relations@ros.com
Web Site: www.rossstores.com
Approx. Sls.: $7,866,100,000
Approx. Number Employees: 14,000
Year Founded: 1957
Business Description:
Retailer of Clothing, Shoes, Home Accents, Luggage & Cosmetics
S.I.C.: 5651; 5311
N.A.I.C.S.: 448140; 452112
Advertising Expenditures: $54,300,000
Media: 4-8-9-14-15-17-18-23-24
Personnel:
Michael Balmuth *(Vice Chm & CEO)*
Michael B. O'Sullivan *(Co-Pres & COO)*
James S. Fassio *(Co-Pres & Chief Dev Officer)*
Douglas Baker *(Pres/Chief Mdse Officer-DISCOUNTS)*
John G. Call *(CFO & Sr VP)*
Michael K. Kobayashi *(CIO & Exec VP-Supply Chain & Allocation)*
Barbara Rentler *(Pres/Chief Mdsg Officer-Ross Dress for Less)*
Mark LeHocky *(Gen Counsel, Corp Sec & Sr VP)*
Bernie Brautigan *(Exec VP-Mdsg)*
Ken Caruana *(Exec VP-Strategy, Mktg & HR)*
Gary L. Cribb *(Exec VP-Stores & Loss Prevention)*
Lisa Panattoni *(Exec VP-Mdsg)*
Jennifer Vecchio *(Exec VP-Mdsg)*
Angela Culhane *(Sr VP & Gen Mgr-Mdse-Housewares, Cosmetics & Fragrances)*
Susanne DeMarco *(Sr VP & Gen Mgr-Mdse-Shoes)*
Joyce Pearson *(Sr VP & Gen Mgr-Mdse-Dresses)*
Carl Matteo *(Sr VP & Gen Mdse Mgr)*
Gregg McGillis *(Sr VP-Property Dev)*
Art Roth *(Sr VP-Mdse Control)*
Mary Walter *(Sr VP-Stores)*
Michael L. Wilson *(Sr VP-Supply Chain)*
Brands & Products:
DD'S DISCOUNTS
ROSS
ROSS DRESS FOR LESS
ROSS STORES
Advertising Agency:
Seidel Advertising
562 Grant Ave.
San Francisco, CA 94108
Tel.: (415) 955-9110
(Print & Outdoor)

RUSH INDUSTRIES, INC.
263 Harden Hwy
Mineola, NY 11501
Tel.: (516) 741-0346
Fax: (516) 741-0348
Fax: (516) 741-0358
Web Site: www.rushindustries.com
Approx. Number Employees: 11
Business Description:
Mail Order Services
S.I.C.: 5961
N.A.I.C.S.: 454113
Media: 4
Personnel:
Linda Harrison *(Co-Pres)*
Esra Sheena *(Co-Pres)*

SAKS FIFTH AVENUE, INC.
(Sub. of Saks Incorporated)
12 E 49th St
New York, NY 10017
Tel.: (212) 940-5305
Fax: (212) 940-4299
Web Site: www.saksfifthavenue.com
Sales Range: $1-4.9 Billion
Approx. Number Employees: 500
Year Founded: 1924
Business Description:
Department Stores
S.I.C.: 5311
N.A.I.C.S.: 452111
Advertising Expenditures: $550,000
Media: 4-5-6-8-9-23
Distr.: Direct to Consumer
Budget Set: Jan. -July
Personnel:
Ron Frasch *(Pres & Chief Mdsg Officer)*
Denise Incandela *(CMO)*
Terron Schaefer *(Chief Creative Officer & Exec VP)*
Cody Kondo *(Sr VP & Gen Mdsg Mgr-Men's)*
Eric Jennings *(VP & Dir-Fashion-Mens, Home, Gifts)*
Marta Nowakowski *(VP & Mgr-Mdse-Jewelry)*
Jennifer DeWinter *(Gen Mgr-Mdsg)*
Deborah Walters *(Gen Mgr-Mdsg)*
Molly Leis *(Dir-Mktg)*
Staci Mack *(Mgr-Cosmetic Fragrance Selling)*
Advertising Agency:
iris ny
588 Broadway Ste 505
New York, NY 10012
Tel.: (212) 966-1529
Fax: (212) 966-1671

SAKS INCORPORATED
12 E 49th St
New York, NY 10017
Tel.: (212) 940-5305
E-mail: Julia_Bentley@saksinc.com
Web Site: www.saksincorporated.com
Approx. Sls.: $2,785,745,000
Approx. Number Employees: 9,804
Year Founded: 1919
Business Description:
Department Store Operator
S.I.C.: 5311; 5961
N.A.I.C.S.: 452111; 454113
Import
Advertising Expenditures: $45,465,000
Media: 3-4-5-7-8-9-10-18-19-22-23-24-25-26
Distr.: Reg.
Personnel:
Stephen I. Sadove *(Chm & CEO)*
Ronald L. Frasch *(Pres & Chief Mdsg Officer)*
Kevin G. Wills *(CFO & Exec VP)*
Michael Rodgers *(CIO & Exec VP-Svc Ops)*
Denise Incandela *(Pres-Saks Direct)*
Robert T. Wallstrom *(Pres-OFF 5th & Grp Sr VP)*
Michael Brizel *(Gen Counsel & Exec VP)*
Christine A. Morena *(Exec VP-HR)*
Vince Corno *(Sr VP-Real Estate)*
Kimberly Grabel *(Sr VP-Mktg)*
Brands & Products:
CLUB LIBBY LU
OFF 5TH
SAKS FIFTH AVENUE
Advertising Agency:
iris ny
588 Broadway Ste 505
New York, NY 10012
Tel.: (212) 966-1529
Fax: (212) 966-1671

SAM'S CLUB
(Div. of Wal-Mart Stores, Inc.)
608 SW 8th St
Bentonville, AR 72716-0001
Tel.: (479) 277-7000
Web Site: www.samsclub.com
Sales Range: $1-4.9 Billion
Approx. Number Employees: 3,500
Year Founded: 1983
Business Description:
Wholesale Club
S.I.C.: 5311
N.A.I.C.S.: 452112
Advertising Expenditures: $15,000,000
Media: 2-3-4-5-6-8-9-10-11-13-14-15-16-18-19-20-21-22-23-24-25
Personnel:
Brian C. Cornell *(Pres & CEO)*
Linda P. Hefner *(Chief Mdsg Officer & Exec VP)*
Whitney Head *(Gen Counsel)*
Cindy Davis *(Exec VP-Membership, E-Commerce & Mktg)*
Ignacio Perez Lizaur *(Exec VP-Ops)*
Gregory E. Spragg *(Exec VP-Mdsg & Replenishment)*
Celia Swanson *(Exec VP)*
Patty Warwick *(Sr VP & Gen Mgr-Mdsg)*
Charles Redfield *(Sr VP-Food & Beverages)*
Mike Turner *(Sr VP-Membership)*
Dex McCreary *(Sr Dir-Mdsg & Wine, Beer & Spirits)*
Advertising Agencies:
Marketing Support, Inc.
200 E Randolph Dr Ste 5000
Chicago, IL 60601
Tel.: (312) 565-0044
Fax: (312) 946-6100

Saatchi & Saatchi X
605 Lakeview Dr
Springdale, AR 72764
Tel.: (479) 575-0200
Fax: (479) 725-1136

SCHOTTENSTEIN STORES CORPORATION
4300 East 5th Ave
Columbus, OH 43207-1680
Tel.: (614) 221-9200
Fax: (614) 449-4377
Fax: (614) 449-0403
Sales Range: $650-699.9 Million
Approx. Number Employees: 5,300
Year Founded: 1917
Business Description:
Holding Company
S.I.C.: 6719; 5311; 5661; 5712
N.A.I.C.S.: 551112; 442110; 448210; 452112
Media: 3-8-9-16-23-24-25-26
Distr.: Reg.
Personnel:
Irwin A. Bain *(Gen Counsel & VP)*

SEARS CANADA INC.
(Sub. of Sears, Roebuck & Co.)
290 Young St Ste 700
Toronto, ON M5B 2C3, Canada
Mailing Address:
123 Mutual St
Toronto, ON M5B 2B2, Canada
Tel.: (416) 362-1711
Fax: (416) 941-2501
E-mail: home@sears.ca
Web Site: www.sears.ca
Approx. Rev.: $5,200,600,000
Approx. Number Employees: 37,000
Year Founded: 1953
Business Description:
General Merchandising Services
S.I.C.: 5399
N.A.I.C.S.: 452990
Media: 4-6-7-8-9-10-13-14-15-17-18-22-23-24-25-26
Distr.: Natl.
Budget Set: Sept.
Personnel:
William C. Crowley *(Chm)*
Dene L. Rogers *(Pres & CEO)*
Allen Ravas *(CFO)*
Scott Silver *(Exec VP-Mdsg-Home & Hardlines)*
Richard A. Brown *(Sr VP-Mdsg & Mktg)*
Ismat Mirza *(VP-Bus Capability & HR)*
Brands & Products:
SEARS
SEARS FLOOR COVERINGS
Advertising Agency:
A. Eicoff & Co.
(Div. of Ogilvy & Mather Worldwide)
401 N Michigan Ave 4th Fl
Chicago, IL 60611-4212
Tel.: (312) 527-7183

Key to Media (For complete agency information see *The Advertising Red Books-Agencies* edition):
1. Bus. Publs. 2. Cable T.V. 3. Catalogs & Directories. 4. Co-op Adv. 5. Consumer Mags. 6. D.M. to Bus. Estab.7. D.M. to Consumers 8. Daily Newsp. 9. Exhibits/Trade Shows 10. Foreign 11. Infomercial 12. Internet Adv.13. Multimedia 14. Network Radio 15. Network T.V. 16. Newsp. Distr. Mags. 17. Other 18. Outdoor (Posters, Transit) 19. Point of Purchase20. Premiums, Novelties 21. Product Samples 22. Special Events Mktg. 23. Spot Radio 24. Spot T.V. 25. Weekly Newsp. 26. Yellow Page Adv.

Sears Canada Inc. — (Continued)

Fax: (312) 527-7188
Toll Free: (800) 333-6605

SEARS HOLDINGS CORPORATION

3333 Beverly Rd
Hoffman Estates, IL 60179
Tel.: (847) 286-2500
Fax: (847) 286-7829
Toll Free: (800) 732-7780
Web Site: www.searshc.com
Approx. Rev.: $43,326,000,000
Approx. Number Employees: 312,000
Business Description:
Holding Company; General Merchandising Services
S.I.C.: 5311; 5013
N.A.I.C.S.: 452111; 441310; 452112
Advertising Expenditures: $2,000,000,000
Media: 1-3-4-5-6-8-9-12-13-14-15-16-17-18-19-20-22-23-24-25-26
Distr.: Natl.
Personnel:
Edward S. Lampert *(Chm)*
Louis J. D'Ambrosio *(Pres & CEO)*
Robert A. Schriesheim *(CFO & Exec VP)*
Timothy Kasbe *(CIO)*
Monica Woo *(CMO & VP)*
William K. Phelan *(Chief Acctg Officer, Treas, Sr VP & Controller)*
David Friedman *(Pres-Mktg & Sr VP)*
Lana Cain Krauter *(Pres-Apparel & Sr VP)*
Raj Penkar *(Pres-Supply Chain & Sr VP)*
Stuart C. Reed *(Pres-Home Svcs)*
Scott J. Freidheim *(Exec VP)*
John D. Goodman *(Exec VP-Apparel & Home Bus)*
W. Bruce Johnson *(Exec VP)*
Lisa Schultz *(Exec VP-Design)*
Michael D. Collins *(Sr VP-Fin)*
William R. Harker *(Sr VP)*
James P. Mixon *(Sr VP-Supply Chain)*
Louis Ramery *(Sr VP-Customer Relationship Mktg)*
Ron Brunette *(VP)*
Bill Guise *(VP-IT Mktg & Info Analytics)*
Robert Raible *(VP-Integrated Mktg Commun)*
Sue W. Elseewi *(Dir-Consumer Res)*
Kimberly Freely *(Dir-Comm)*
Gary Lalla *(Product Mgr-Craftsman Lawn & Garden)*
Steve Cook *(Mgr-Automotive)*
Teresa Jordan *(Mgr-Search Mktg)*
Gina Radke *(Mgr-Digital Strategy & Analytics-Sears Kmart Footwear)*
William White *(Mgr-Tech)*
Michael Woolf *(Mgr-Social Media & Loyalty Mktg)*
Daran Redenbaugh *(Sr Web Designer)*
Brands & Products:
1-800-4MY-HOME
APOSTROPHE
CANYON RIVER BLUES
COVINGTON
CRAFTSMAN
CRAFTSMAN CLUB
CRAFTSMAN PROFESSIONAL
CRB
CRB KHAKIS
DIEHARD
EASY LIVING
EVENWAVE
FUNTRONICS
THE GOOD LIFE AT A GREAT PRICE. GUARANTEED.
THE GREAT INDOORS
HOMELIFE
KENMORE
KENMORE ELITE
KIDVANTAGE
KIDVANTAGE CLUB
LIFE WELL SPENT
MOSAIC
MOSAIC WOMAN
NTB
NTB NATIONAL TIRE & BATTERY
NUESTRA GENTE
ORCHARD HARDWARE & GARDEN
ORCHARD SUPPLY & HARDWARE
PARTSDIRECT
POWER SNIP
PULSE
QUICKWRENCH
REDI DRILL
SEARS
SEARS AUTO CENTERS
SEARS BEST CUSTOMER
SEARS CANADA
SEARS CARD
SEARS DIRECT PURCHASE STOCK PLAN
SEARS FAMILY ENRICHMENT FUND
SEARS HARDWARE
SEARS HOLDINGS CORPORTION
SEARS HOME SERVICES
SEARS HOMECENTRAL
SEARS MEXICO
SEARS PREMIER CARD
SEARS UNIVERSITY
SEARS.COM
SHOWPLACE
SMARTREACH
THE SOFTER SIDE OF SEARS
STRUCTURE
TODO PARA TI
TOOL TERRITORY
ULTRAWASH
WEATHERBEATER
WISH BOOK
WORKWEAR
Advertising Agencies:
ARS Advertising Inc.
1001 Reads Lake Rd
Chattanooga, TN 37415-2056
Tel.: (423) 875-3743
Fax: (423) 875-5346

Bozell
1022 Leavenworth St
Omaha, NE 68102
Tel.: (402) 965-4434
Fax: (402) 965-4399

DesignKitchen
1140 W Fulton Market
Chicago, IL 60607-1219
Tel.: (312) 455-0388
Fax: (312) 455-0285
Blue Crew HQ Digital Platform
Interactive

Digitas Inc.
33 Arch St
Boston, MA 02110
Tel.: (617) 867-1000
Fax: (617) 867-1111
K-Mart
Sears

Euro RSCG Worldwide PR
(Corporate Headquarters)
200 Madison Ave
New York, NY 10016
Tel.: (212) 367-6800
Fax: (212) 367-7154
Public Relations

Hydra Group, Inc.
8800 Wilshire Blvd 2nd Fl
Beverly Hills, CA 90211
Tel.: (310) 659-5755
Fax: (310) 659-5855

Marketing Support, Inc.
200 E Randolph Dr Ste 5000
Chicago, IL 60601
Tel.: (312) 565-0044
Fax: (312) 946-6100

McGarry Bowen, LLC
601 W 26th St Ste 1150
New York, NY 10001
Tel.: (212) 598-2900
Fax: (212) 598-2996
Creative
Marketing

MPG
(Div. of HAVAS)
195 Broadway 12th Fl
New York, NY 10007
Tel.: (646) 587-5000
Fax: (646) 587-5005
Kmart
Media Buying
Sears

MPG Chicago
36 E Grand Ave 5th Fl
Chicago, IL 60611
Tel.: (312) 640-4700
Fax: (312) 337-3898
Media

OgilvyOne Worldwide
636 11th Ave
New York, NY 10036
Tel.: (212) 237-4000
Fax: (212) 237-5123
Sears
Kmart

Radix Communications, Inc.
3399 S Lakeshore Dr
Saint Joseph, MI 49085
Tel.: (269) 982-7400
Fax: (269) 982-7405

Response Media, Inc.
3155 Medlock Bridge Rd
Norcross, GA 30071-1423
Tel.: (770) 451-5478
Fax: (770) 451-4929

Unicom Marketing Group
2875 S 25th Ave
Broadview, IL 60155
Tel.: (312) 738-1404
Fax: (708) 410-4501

WHITTMANHART
1717 Arch St Ste 2800
Philadelphia, PA 19103
Tel.: (215) 636-9500
Fax: (267) 765-4801

Young & Rubicam Chicago
233 N Michigan Ave 16th Fl
Chicago, IL 60601-5519
Tel.: (312) 596-3000
Fax: (312) 596-3130
Craftsman
Die Hard
Kenmore

SEARS, ROEBUCK & CO.

(Sub. of Sears Holdings Corporation)
3333 Beverly Rd
Hoffman Estates, IL 60179
Tel.: (847) 286-7292
Fax: (847) 286-7829
Toll Free: (800) 732-7780
Web Site: www.sears.com
Approx. Number Employees: 247,000
Year Founded: 1886
Business Description:
General Merchandising Services
S.I.C.: 5399
N.A.I.C.S.: 452990
Advertising Expenditures: $1,700,000,000
Media: 1-3-4-5-6-8-9-12-13-14-15-16-17-18-19-20-22-23-24-25-26
Personnel:
Edward S. Lampert *(Chm)*
Craig Israel *(Pres-Apparel & Sr VP)*
Imran Jooma *(Pres-Ecommerce & Sr VP)*
Sharon M. Brady *(VP-HR)*
Becky Case *(VP-Adv & Creative Svcs)*
Dana Fowler *(Dir-Interactive Mktg)*
Mike Cassar *(Brand Mgr-Craftsman)*
George Kurkowski *(Brand Mgr-DieHard)*
Advertising Agencies:
NFM Group Inc.
320 Fort Duquesne Blvd 26 H
Pittsburgh, PA 15222
Tel.: (412) 394-6400
Fax: (412) 394-6411
Sports Marketing & Special Events

Young & Rubicam Chicago
233 N Michigan Ave 16th Fl
Chicago, IL 60601-5519
Tel.: (312) 596-3000
Fax: (312) 596-3130

SHARPE DRY GOODS CO., INC.

200 N Broadway St
Checotah, OK 74426-2432
Tel.: (918) 473-2233
Fax: (918) 473-0346
Toll Free: (800) 238-6491
E-mail: questions@sharpeclothing.com
Web Site: www.sharpeclothing.com
Approx. Number Employees: 400
Year Founded: 1920
Business Description:
Clothing Retailer
S.I.C.: 5311
N.A.I.C.S.: 452111
Advertising Expenditures: $610,000
Cable T.V.: $60,000; D.M. to Consumers: $450,000; Daily Newsp.: $10,000; Outdoor (Posters, Transit): $10,000; Spot Radio: $5,000; Spot T.V.: $30,000; Weekly Newsp.: $25,000; Yellow Page Adv.: $20,000
Distr.: Reg.
Budget Set: Dec.-Jan.

Key to Media (For complete agency information see *The Advertising Red Books-Agencies* edition):
1. Bus. Publs. 2. Cable T.V. 3. Catalogs & Directories. 4. Co-op Adv. 5. Consumer Mags. 6. D.M. to Bus. Estab.7. D.M. to Consumers 8. Daily Newsp. 9. Exhibits/Trade Shows 10. Foreign 11. Infomercial 12. Internet Adv.13. Multimedia 14. Network Radio 15. Network T.V. 16. Newsp. Distr. Mags. 17. Other 18. Outdoor (Posters, Transit) 19. Point of Purchase20. Premiums, Novelties 21. Product Samples 22. Special Events Mktg. 23. Spot Radio 24. Spot T.V. 25. Weekly Newsp. 26. Yellow Page Adv.

Personnel:
Louis K. Sharpe, IV *(Chm, Pres, CEO & Dir-Adv)*
Thomas A. Sharpe *(Gen Counsel)*

Brands & Products:
SHARPE'S

SHEPLERS, INC.
(Holding of Gryphon Investors, LLC)
6501 W Kellogg Dr
Wichita, KS 67209-2211
Tel.: (316) 946-3838
Fax: (316) 946-3729
Toll Free: (800) 833-7007
E-mail: service@sheplers.com
Web Site: www.sheplers.com
Approx. Number Employees: 1,000
Year Founded: 1946

Business Description:
Department Store & Mail Order Sales
S.I.C.: 5699; 5661
N.A.I.C.S.: 448190; 448210
Advertising Expenditures: $4,500,000
Media: 2-3-4-5-6-8-9-10-13-18-19-23-24-26
Distr.: Intl.; Natl.
Budget Set: Feb.

Personnel:
Bob Myers *(Pres & CEO)*
John Wilcox *(VP-Sls)*

SHOPKO
(Holding of Sun Capital Partners, Inc.)
700 Pilgrim Way
Green Bay, WI 54307-5263
Mailing Address:
PO Box 19060
Green Bay, WI 54307-9060
Tel.: (920) 429-2211
Fax: (920) 429-4799
Toll Free: (800) 791-7333
E-mail: webmaster@shopko.com
Web Site: www.shopko.com
Sales Range: $1-4.9 Billion
Approx. Number Employees: 22,800
Year Founded: 1962

Business Description:
Discount Retail Services
S.I.C.: 5399; 5311; 5912
N.A.I.C.S.: 452990; 446110; 452112
Import
Advertising Expenditures: $42,000,000
Media: 4-5-8-9-13-19-23-24-26
Distr.: Reg.
Budget Set: Sept.

Personnel:
W. Paul Jones *(Chm, Pres & CEO)*
Mary Meixelsperger *(CFO & Sr VP)*
Tammy Hermann *(CIO & Sr VP)*
Raymond Petersen *(CTO & VP-Ecommerce)*
Jill Soltau *(Exec VP & Chief Mdsg Officer)*
Michael Bettiga *(Sr VP)*
Jeff Csuy *(Sr VP & Gen Mdse Mgr-Apparel & Accessories)*
Chad Frazell *(Sr VP-HR)*
Jack Ingersoll *(Sr VP-Supply Chain & Inventory Mgmt)*
Jack Mullen *(Sr VP-Mktg)*
Jim DePaul *(VP-Fin-Facilities & Construction)*
Kathy Friedland *(VP-Adv)*
Michael Sidders *(VP-Ecommerce)*
Susan Nelson-McNerney *(Dir-Photo Studio & Digital Production)*
Dave Wong *(Dir-Employee Rels & Recruiting)*

SHORELINE IMAGE WORKS LLC
331 Sailfish Dr
Tarpon Springs, FL 34688
Tel.: (727) 786-4078
Fax: (727) 230-4839
E-mail: shorelineimageworks@tampabay.rr.com
Web Site: www.shorelineimageworks.com

Business Description:
Advertising Specialty & Graphic Design Services
S.I.C.: 7319
N.A.I.C.S.: 541890
Media: 4-10-13-16-29

Personnel:
Lynne Wilson *(Owner)*

SINISTER CINEMA
PO Box 4369
Medford, OR 97501-0168
Tel.: (541) 773-6860
Fax: (541) 779-8650
E-mail: scinema@qwestoffice.net
Web Site: www.sinistercinema.com
Approx. Number Employees: 3

Business Description:
Specialty Videos & DVDs Mail Order
S.I.C.: 5961; 7822
N.A.I.C.S.: 454113; 512120
Media: 4-6-8-13

Personnel:
Greg Luce *(Owner & Pres)*

Brands & Products:
SINISTER CINEMA.COM

SMITH & HAWKEN, LTD.
(Sub. of Scotts Miracle-Gro Company)
4 Hamilton Landing ste 100
Novato, CA 94949
Tel.: (415) 506-3700
Fax: (415) 506-3900
Toll Free: (800) 940-1170
E-mail: smithandhawkencustomerservice@innotrac.com
Web Site: www.smithandhawken.com
Sales Range: $75-99.9 Million
Approx. Number Employees: 100

Business Description:
Gardening Tools & Accessories Retailer
S.I.C.: 5961; 5261
N.A.I.C.S.: 454113; 444220
Media: 4-6-7-8-9-10-22-23-25
Distr.: Natl.

Personnel:
Gordon M. Erickson *(CEO)*

Brands & Products:
HEIRLOOM TOOL
PREMIUM TEAK

SMOKY MOUNTAIN KNIFE WORKS INC.
2320 Winfield Dunn Pkwy
Sevierville, TN 37876-0557
Tel.: (865) 453-5871
Fax: (865) 428-5991
Toll Free: (800) 251-9306
E-mail: info@smkw.com
Web Site: www.eknifeworks.com
Approx. Number Employees: 200
Year Founded: 1974

Business Description:
Catalog & Mail-Order Houses
S.I.C.: 5961; 5719
N.A.I.C.S.: 454113; 442299
Import Export
Media: 4-12-13-17-20

Personnel:
Kevin G. Pipes *(Pres)*
Travis Fergersen *(CFO)*

SNOWBOARD CONNECTION
263 Yale Ave
Seattle, WA 98109
Tel.: (206) 467-8545
Fax: (206) 467-9468
E-mail: info@snowboardconnection.com
Web Site: www.snowboardconnection.com
Approx. Number Employees: 7

Business Description:
Retailer of Ski Equipment, Clothing & Accessories
S.I.C.: 5699
N.A.I.C.S.: 448150
Export
Advertising Expenditures: $90,000
Media: 4-6-8-10-11-13

Personnel:
John Logic *(Pres & Dir-Adv-Mktg)*

Advertising Agency:
PuredesignGroup
7717 California Ave SW
Seattle, WA 98136
Tel.: (206) 935-9325
Fax: (206) 935-9325

SPECIALTY CATALOG CORPORATION
(Sub. of EdgeStone Capital Partners Inc.)
400 Manley St
West Bridgewater, MA 02379
Tel.: (508) 638-7000
Web Site: www.scdirect.com
Sales Range: $10-24.9 Million
Approx. Number Employees: 300
Year Founded: 1978

Business Description:
Catalogs & Mail Order Services
S.I.C.: 5961; 8299
N.A.I.C.S.: 454113; 611699
Import Export
Media: 4-6-8-13

Personnel:
Jon Bernstein *(Pres, CEO)*
Peter Tulp *(CFO & COO)*

Brands & Products:
DAXBOURNE INTERNATIONAL
ESPECIALLY YOURS
HEART OF GOLD
PAULA YOUNG
SALON SILHOUETTES
WESTERN SCHOOLS
WIGSHOP.COM

SPECIALTY MERCHANDISE CORPORATION
996 Flower Glen St
Simi Valley, CA 93065
Tel.: (805) 578-5500
Fax: (805) 584-8267
Toll Free: (800) 382-6868
Web Site: www.smcorp.com
Sales Range: $25-49.9 Million
Approx. Number Employees: 500
Year Founded: 1948

Business Description:
Consumer Goods Mail Order Services
S.I.C.: 5961
N.A.I.C.S.: 454113
Media: 6-8-12

Personnel:
Mark Schwartz *(Pres & CEO)*

SPENCER GIFTS LLC
(Holding of ACON Investments, LLC)
6826 Black Horse Pike
Egg Harbor Township, NJ 08234
Tel.: (609) 645-3300
Fax: (609) 645-5633
Web Site: www.spencersonline.com
Sales Range: $500-549.9 Million
Approx. Number Employees: 4,200
Year Founded: 1947

Business Description:
Novelty Store Operator
S.I.C.: 5947
N.A.I.C.S.: 453220
Media: 6-8-23-24-25
Distr.: Natl.
Budget Set: July

Personnel:
Steven Silverstein *(Owner)*
Michelle Molton *(CFO)*
Debbie De Rosa *(Sr Mgr-Mktg)*

Brands & Products:
SPENCER GIFTS
SPIRIT HALLOWEEN SUPERSTORE

STAR STRUCK/PROTEAM, INC.
(Sub. of Dreams, Inc.)
2 Turnage Ln
Bethel, CT 06801
Mailing Address:
PO Box 308
Bethel, CT 06801
Tel.: (203) 794-1655
Fax: (914) 833-1068
Toll Free: (877) 843-4263
E-mail: webmaster@starstruck.com
Web Site: www.starstruck.com
Sales Range: $50-74.9 Million
Approx. Number Employees: 100
Year Founded: 1996

Business Description:
Sports Apparel & Jewelry Distr & Retailer
S.I.C.: 5091
N.A.I.C.S.: 423910
Media: 4-13

Personnel:
Kenneth Karlan *(Owner)*
Jason Scheets *(COO)*

Brands & Products:
THE GAME STARTS HERE!
SAHARA
STAR STRUCK
TOWN & COUNTRY

STARCREST PRODUCTS OF CALIFORNIA
3660 Brennan Ave
Perris, CA 92571
Tel.: (951) 943-2011
Fax: (951) 943-2971
E-mail: starcrest@starcalis.com
Web Site: www.talkpointcommunications.com
Approx. Number Employees: 1,700
Year Founded: 1971

Business Description:
Mail Order House
S.I.C.: 5961
N.A.I.C.S.: 454113

Key to Media (For complete agency information see *The Advertising Red Books-Agencies* edition):
1. Bus. Publs. 2. Cable T.V. 3. Catalogs & Directories. 4. Co-op Adv. 5. Consumer Mags. 6. D.M. to Bus. Estab.7. D.M. to Consumers 8. Daily Newsp. 9. Exhibits/Trade Shows 10. Foreign 11. Infomercial 12. Internet Adv.13. Multimedia 14. Network Radio 15. Network T.V. 16. Newsp. Distr. Mags. 17. Other 18. Outdoor (Posters, Transit) 19. Point of Purchase20. Premiums, Novelties 21. Product Samples 22. Special Events Mktg. 23. Spot Radio 24. Spot T.V. 25. Weekly Newsp. 26. Yellow Page Adv.

Starcrest Products of California — (Continued)

Media: 8
Personnel:
T. M. Calandra *(Owner & CEO)*
Michael E. Donnelly *(Pres)*
Brands & Products:
MAKE LIFE EASIER
STARCREST
STARCREST PRODUCTS OF CALIFORNIA

STEIN MART, INC.
1200 Riverplace Blvd
Jacksonville, FL 32207
Tel.: (904) 346-1500
Fax: (904) 398-4341
E-mail: smrt@steinmart.com
Web Site: www.steinmart.com
Approx. Sls.: $1,181,510,000
Approx. Number Employees: 6,000
Year Founded: 1908
Business Description:
Department Stores
S.I.C.: 5651; 5311
N.A.I.C.S.: 448140; 452111
Advertising Expenditures: $53,800,000
Media: 5-9-18-19-22-24-25
Distr.: Natl.
Budget Set: Jan. -Dec.
Personnel:
Jay Stein *(Chm & Interim CEO)*
John H. Williams, Jr. *(Vice Chm)*
Gregory W. Kleffner *(CFO & Exec VP-Fin)*
D. Hunt Hawkins *(Chief Admin Officer & Exec VP)*
Brian R. Morrow *(Chief Mdsg Officer & Exec VP)*
Clayton E. Roberson Jr. *(Sr VP & Controller)*
Gary L. Pierce *(Sr VP & Dir-Stores)*
Michael D. Ray *(Sr VP & Dir-Stores)*
Glori Katz *(Sr VP-Mktg & Adv)*
Brands & Products:
ONCE YOU GO YOU GET IT
STEIN MART
Advertising Agency:
ArnoldNYC
110 5th Ave
New York, NY 10011
Tel.: (212) 463-1000
Fax: (212) 463-1080
Agency of Record

STORK AVENUE, INC.
2441 Bellevue Avenue
Daytona Beach, FL 32114
Tel.: (305) 669-4878
Fax: (386) 271-3147
Toll Free: (888) 677-3029
E-mail: customerservice@storkavenue.com
Web Site: www.storkavenue.com
Sales Range: $1-9.9 Million
Approx. Number Employees: 35
Business Description:
Mail Order of Birth Announcements & Invitations
S.I.C.: 5961
N.A.I.C.S.: 454113
Media: 4-5-6-8-13-21
Personnel:
Robert J. Hunter, Jr. *(Pres)*
Rita Valdes *(CFO)*
Brands & Products:
IT ALL STARTS HERE
STORK AVENUE

SUNBELT RENTALS
(Sub. of Sunbelt Rentals, Inc.)
2341 Deerfield Dr
Fort Mill, SC 29715
Tel.: (803) 578-5811
Fax: (954) 760-6565
Web Site: www.sunbeltrentals.com
Sales Range: $650-699.9 Million
Approx. Number Employees: 3,500
Year Founded: 1997
Business Description:
Equipment Rental Services
S.I.C.: 7359
N.A.I.C.S.: 532490
Advertising Expenditures: $5,101,000
Media: 1-5-7-16-19-23-26
Personnel:
Nat Brookhouse *(Dir-Sls Support & Mktg)*
Brands & Products:
NATIONSRENT
NO SWEAT

SUNDANCE CATALOG CO., LTD.
3865 W 2400 S
Salt Lake City, UT 84120-7212
Tel.: (800) 422-2770
Fax: (801) 973-4989
Fax: (800) 843-9445
Toll Free: (800) 422-2770
E-mail: info@sundancecatalog.com
Web Site: www.sundancecatalog.com
Sales Range: $75-99.9 Million
Approx. Number Employees: 250
Year Founded: 1989
Business Description:
Catalog & Mail-Order Houses
S.I.C.: 5961
N.A.I.C.S.: 454113
Import Export
Media: 4-8
Personnel:
Matdy Erdos *(Pres & Dir)*
Meil Hynes *(CFO)*

SVM, LP
200 E Howard Ave ste 220
Des Plaines, IL 60018
Tel.: (847) 553-9100
Fax: (847) 553-9222
E-mail: info@svmcards.com
Web Site: www.svmcards.com
Approx. Number Employees: 30
Year Founded: 1997
Business Description:
Prepaid Gift Cards Distr
S.I.C.: 8742
N.A.I.C.S.: 541611
Media: 2-5-7-10-13-19
Personnel:
Jim Leroux *(Pres)*
Marshall Reavis *(CEO)*
Paul Eno *(CIO)*
Pamela Gerhardt *(Sr Dir-Mktg)*
Jim Speir *(Dir-Sls)*
Brands & Products:
SVM

TARGET CORPORATION
1000 Nicollet Mall
Minneapolis, MN 55403-2467
Tel.: (612) 304-6073
Fax: (612) 696-3731
Web Site: www.target.com
Approx. Rev.: $65,786,000,000
Approx. Number Employees: 355,000
Year Founded: 1902
Business Description:
Holding Company; Discount Department & Grocery Stores Operator
S.I.C.: 6719; 5311; 5411
N.A.I.C.S.: 551112; 445110; 452112
Import
Advertising Expenditures: $1,292,000,000
Media: 3-6-9-15-16-18-22-23-24-31
Distr.: Direct to Consumer; Natl.
Personnel:
Gregg W. Steinhafel *(Chm, Pres & CEO)*
Douglas A. Scovanner *(CFO & Exec VP)*
Beth M. Jacob *(CIO & Exec VP-Target Tech Svcs)*
Lalit Ahuja *(Pres/Mng Dir-Target India)*
Tony Fisher *(Pres-Canada)*
Timothy A. Mantel *(Pres-Target Sourcing Svcs)*
Terrence J. Scully *(Pres-Target Fin Svcs)*
Laysha Ward *(Pres-Community Rels & Target Foundation)*
Timothy R. Baer *(Gen Counsel, Sec & Exec VP)*
John D. Griffith *(Exec VP-Property Dev)*
Jodeen A. Kozlak *(Exec VP-HR)*
Tina M. Schiel *(Exec VP-Stores)*
Kathryn A. Tesija *(Exec VP-Mdsg)*
Janna Adair-Potts *(Sr VP-Store Ops)*
Patricia Adams *(Sr VP-Mdsg-Apparel & Accessories)*
Stacia J. Andersen *(Sr VP-Mdsg-Home)*
Carmela Batacchi *(Sr VP-Sourcing Svcs)*
Bryan Berg *(Sr VP-Stores)*
Leonard Chapman *(Sr VP-Stores)*
Barbara Dugan *(Sr VP-Target Sourcing Svcs)*
Corey L. Haaland *(Sr VP-Fin Plng, Analysis & Tax)*
Cynthia Ho *(Sr VP-Target Sourcing Svcs)*
Derek L. Jenkins *(Sr VP-Stores)*
Keri Jones *(Sr VP-Health & Beauty Mdsg)*
Susan D. Kahn *(Sr VP-Comm & Publicity)*
Sid Keswani *(Sr VP-Stores)*
Richard N. Maguire *(Sr VP-Mdse Plng)*
Annette Miller *(Sr VP-Mdsg-Grocery)*
John Mulligan *(Sr VP-Treasury & Acctg)*
Scott Nelson *(Sr VP-Real Estate)*
Mark Schindele *(Sr VP-Mdsg-Hardlines)*
Rich Varda *(Sr VP-Store Design)*
Jane P. Windmeier *(Sr VP-Fin Ops & Tech)*
Victoria Lozano *(VP-Portfolio Mktg)*
John Lick *(Sr Mgr-Exec Producer Brdcst Adv)*
Brent Rosso *(Sr Mgr-Digital Media)*
Greg Cunningham *(Mgr-Brand Mktg)*
Dianne Gerber *(Mgr-Digital Media)*
Angela Jarvis *(Mgr-Digital Media)*
Jen Klise *(Mgr-Corp Innovation)*
Anna Kruse *(Mgr-Planner & Digital Vendor Mktg)*
Chris Campion *(Analyst-Mktg)*
Adam Dieruf *(Analyst-Mktg-Digital Media)*
Nathan Jokinen *(Analyst-Mktg-Digital Media)*
Andrew Pierce *(Analyst-Mktg-Digital Media)*
Allison Schwartz *(Analyst-Mktg-Digital Media)*
Brands & Products:
ARCHER FARMS
BULLSEYE DESIGN
BULLSEYE DOG
CHOXIE
EXPECT MORE, PAY LESS
MARKET PANTRY
MERONA
MINI WINE CUBE
MOSSIMO
SUPERTARGET
SUTTON & DODGE
TARGET
TARGET CORPORATION
UP & UP
WINE CUBE
Advertising Agencies:
ARS Advertising Inc.
1001 Reads Lake Rd
Chattanooga, TN 37415-2056
Tel.: (423) 875-3743
Fax: (423) 875-5346

Atmosphere Proximity
1285 Ave of the Americas 5th Fl
New York, NY 10019
Tel.: (212) 827-2500
Fax: (212) 827-2525

BBDO North America
1285 Ave of the Americas
New York, NY 10019-6028
Tel.: (212) 459-5000
Fax: (212) 459-6814

Euro RSCG London
Cupola House 15 Alfred Place
London, WC1E 7EB, United Kingdom
Tel.: (44) 207 240 4111
Fax: (44) 207 467 9210

FAME
60 S Sixth St Ste 2600
Minneapolis, MN 55402
Tel.: (612) 746-3263
Fax: (612) 746-3333

Grupo Gallegos
401 E Ocean Blvd Ste 600
Long Beach, CA 90802
Tel.: (562) 256-3600
Fax: (562) 256-3620

Haworth Marketing & Media Company
10900 Wilshire Blvd Ste 2050
Los Angeles, CA 90024-6530
Tel.: (310) 824-7777
Fax: (310) 824-7778
Media Buying Services

Huge
45 Main St Ste 220
Brooklyn, NY 11201
Tel.: (718) 625-4843
Fax: (718) 625-5157

Key to Media (For complete agency information see *The Advertising Red Books-Agencies* edition):
1. Bus. Publs. 2. Cable T.V. 3. Catalogs & Directories. 4. Co-op Adv. 5. Consumer Mags. 6. D.M. to Bus. Estab.7. D.M. to Consumers
8. Daily Newsp. 9. Exhibits/Trade Shows 10. Foreign 11. Infomercial 12. Internet Adv.13. Multimedia 14. Network Radio
15. Network T.V. 16. Newsp. Distr. Mags. 17. Other 18. Outdoor (Posters, Transit) 19. Point of Purchase20. Premiums, Novelties
21. Product Samples 22. Special Events Mktg. 23. Spot Radio 24. Spot T.V. 25. Weekly Newsp. 26. Yellow Page Adv.

Mother New York
595 11th Ave
New York, NY 10036
Tel.: (212) 254-2800
Fax: (212) 254-6121
Kaleidoscopic Fashion Spectacular

OLSON
1625 Hennepin Ave
Minneapolis, MN 55403
Tel.: (612) 215-9800
Fax: (612) 215-9801
Target Kaleidoscopic Fashion Spectacular

Peterson Milla Hooks
1315 Harmon Pl
Minneapolis, MN 55403-1926
Tel.: (612) 349-9116
Fax: (612) 349-9141

Ron Foth Advertising
8100 N High St
Columbus, OH 43235-6400
Tel.: (614) 888-7771
Fax: (614) 888-5933

Wieden + Kennedy, Inc.
224 NW 13th Ave
Portland, OR 97209-2953
Tel.: (503) 937-7000
Fax: (503) 937-8000

Wink, Incorporated
126 N 3rd St #100
Minneapolis, MN 55401
Tel.: (612) 455-2642
Fax: (612) 455-2645

TBC GLOBAL NEWS NETWORK, INC.

130 W Kentucky Ave
Franklin, KY 42134
Tel.: (270) 586-0280
Web Site: www.tbcglobalnews.com/
Business Description:
Business News Broadcasting Services
S.I.C.: 4833
N.A.I.C.S.: 515120
Advertising Expenditures: $10,400
Media: 1-8-12-13-23-25
Personnel:
Glenn W. McMachen, Sr. *(Pres, CEO, Treas & Sec)*

TECHNOBRANDS, INC.

(d/b/a firstStreet)
1998 Ruffin Mill Rd
Colonial Heights, VA 23834-5913
Tel.: (804) 524-9888
Fax: (804) 524-9889
Toll Free: (800) 992-2966
Toll Free: (800) 704-1210
Web Site: www.firststreetonline.com
Sales Range: $25-49.9 Million
Approx. Number Employees: 200
Year Founded: 1984
Business Description:
Retailer & Mail Order of Electronics, Computers, Home & Garden Products, Fitness Products, Personal Care Products, Lighting, Automotive Products, Office Products, Bedding & Watches & Clocks
S.I.C.: 5961; 7375
N.A.I.C.S.: 454113; 518111
Import
Advertising Expenditures: $18,000,000
Media: 4-5-6-9-13-23-24-25
Distr.: Natl.
Personnel:
Mark Gordon *(Pres & CEO)*
Hunter Donaldson *(VP-Sales & Customer Svc)*
John Fleming *(VP-Media)*
Kevin Miller *(VP-Fin)*
Dave Modena *(VP-Mdsg)*
Brands & Products:
FIRSTSTREET
FOR BOOMERS AND BEYOND
JITTERBUG

THE TERRITORY AHEAD

(Sub. of Cornerstone Brands, Inc.)
419 State St
Santa Barbara, CA 93101-2304
Tel.: (805) 962-5558
Fax: (800) 232-9882
Toll Free: (800) 882-4323
E-mail: customerservice@territoryahead.com
Web Site: www.territoryahead.com
Sales Range: $250-299.9 Million
Approx. Number Employees: 185
Year Founded: 1988
Business Description:
Men's & Women's Casual Clothing Store & Catalog Retailer
S.I.C.: 5699; 5611; 5621; 5961
N.A.I.C.S.: 454111; 448110; 448120; 448150; 454113
Media: 4-13
Brands & Products:
A-LIST T'S
ACTIVE DUTY HENLEY
ADAPTABLE SUEDE
ADORNOS
ADVENTURESS LINEN
AFFLUENT DOBBY
AFTER HOURS
AFTER-HOURS SWEAT
AFTERNOON TEA
AIRMAN'S
AIRMEN'S BASEBALL
ALBORADA T
ALISAL SILK
ALL-PURPOSE
ALL SEASONS
ALPAMAYO HENLEY
ALTER-EGO
AMBIDEXTROUS
AMBROSIA
AMONTILLADO
ANDANTE SILK
ANDEAN
ANTARA
ANTI-AGITATION
ANTI-TRIBULATION WORK
ANTIGUO
ARMCHAIR HUNTER'S
ARRIVAL
ARROWTOWN
ARROYO SUEDED
ARROYO SUEDED POLO
ARTISAN DOBBY
ARTISTIC LICENSE
ATYPICAL TROPICAL
AVENIDA
AVIATRIX
BACK BEAT
BAJA MALIBU
BAJIO RANCH
BALANCING ACT DOBBY
BAND OF OUTSIDERS
BANDANNA IN PARADISE
BAR DOBBY
BARITONE TENCEL
BASIC AND BEYOND V-NECK
BATIK
BATIK CAMPESINA
BEACH HOUSE
BELLA COOLA
BELLA COOLA SILK
BENCHMARK
BEST BET BEDFORD
BIG SKY LOAFERS
BIG WAFFLE
BIG WAFFLE POLO
BONITA
BOTANICA
BRAZEN
BREAKAWAY PLAID
BUCKSTOP
CAFE POLO
CAFFE' SUEDE
CANNON BEACH
CANYON SUEDE
CARAMELO
CARAVAN
CIBOLO CREEK
CLASS-ACT
CLOUD FOREST CREPE
CLOUD HOUSE
COCONUT
COLORS OF DIEGO
COMFORT
COMFORT WASH
CONSEQUENTIAL
CONTEXT TEE
CONVERTIBLE
CONVERTIBLE TOP
COUPE' DOBBY
COVERT TWILL
CRAZE IKAT
CREME DE LA CORD
CRISSCROSS CORD
CROCHETED-EDGE
CROSSOVER
CROSSOVER LOUNGER
CUBATAS DOBBY
CUEVAS LINEN
CURVY CABLE
CUZCO
DAYDREAM
DEEP INDIGO
DEER CREEK
DIEGO
DOS MUNDOS
DOWN-TIME
DRAGONFLY DOBBY
DRESSED-DOWN
DUET SILK
DUPLICITY DOBBY
DUPLICITY KNIT
EASY SILK-LINEN
EASYGOING
EL MERCADO
ELLE
EMBROIDERED SUPPORTING
EUREKA! SUEDE
EVERYDAY DOVE WRAP
FADE TWILL
FIFTH WORLD
FIORI
FIORI WASHABLE
FIRST NATURE
FLOATING ISLANDS
FLORAL
FORMERLY FORMAL OXFORD
FRENCH TERRY
FRESCO TUNIC
FRESH-BREWED
FRESH-BREWED T
FRINGE
FULL COVERAGE TANK
GEMINI REVERSIBLE
GLOBETROTTER
GO-TO
GO-TO DENIM
GOOD SPORT CORDUROY
GRAN VIA
HABANERO WASHABLE
HAPPY SERAPE
HARMONY
HAVE STRETCH TRAVEL
HAYES DOBBY
HEISHI
HIDALGO HENLEY
HIDALGO LINEN
HIDDEN CARGO
HIGH ALTITUDE
HOSSMAN
HUASCA PUEBLO
INCA TRAIL
INSTANT UPGRADE
IRONWOOD
ISABELLA BIRD
ISLAND RANCH
JEANEOLOGY
KALAMKARI
KEEP YOUR COOL
KILOMETER 88
LA BAJADA
LA DOLCE VITA
LA FEMME
LA GRANJA
LA PLAZA
LA VIE
LAS BRISAS
LAS RAMBLAS
LAST BEST WEST
LATTICE
LIFE OF RILEY
LIGHT FLIGHT
LINEN SAGEBRUSH
LINEN-SILK
LINEN STROLLERS
LIVE AND LET LIVE
LIVE-IN
LOGAN PASS
THE LONG
LONG HAUL
LOST WORLD DOBBY
LOUNGING LIZARD
LUNA
MANANA COMPADRE
MANANA LINEN TROUSERS
MANITOTO
MARIPOSA
MATAURA
MAVERICK
MELLOWED LINEN TUNIC
MEMOIR
MIDRANGE
MIDRANGE LINEN-SILK
MILANESE
MINI CHECKER PATCHWORK
MINIMALIST PLAID
MIRADOR
MOCK MOCS
MODERN MASTER
MODERNE MANDARIN
MOJAVE SILK
MOTOCLUB
NAZCA
NEW CONFECTIONER'S
NEW OLD FAVORITE

Key to Media (For complete agency information see *The Advertising Red Books-Agencies* edition):
1. Bus. Publs. 2. Cable T.V. 3. Catalogs & Directories. 4. Co-op Adv. 5. Consumer Mags. 6. D.M. to Bus. Estab.7. D.M. to Consumers 8. Daily Newsp. 9. Exhibits/Trade Shows 10. Foreign 11. Infomercial 12. Internet Adv.13. Multimedia 14. Network Radio 15. Network T.V. 16. Newsp. Distr. Mags. 17. Other 18. Outdoor (Posters, Transit) 19. Point of Purchase20. Premiums, Novelties 21. Product Samples 22. Special Events Mktg. 23. Spot Radio 24. Spot T.V. 25. Weekly Newsp. 26. Yellow Page Adv.

The Territory Ahead — (Continued)

NOUVEAU
OASIS TOP
OCEANO
OPEN-MINDED
OUTPOST
OWN BOSS
OXFORD PICANTE
PACHUCA DOBBY
PACIFIC LINEN
PACIFIC RIM INDIGO
PAJARO DUNES
PALAPA
PALETA
PANAMERICANA
PEACHAM
PENCIL SKETCH
PERENNIAL
PERFECTLY PAISLEY
PERUVIAN
PERUVIAN ARTISAN
PIN-STRIPED DENIM
PIRAMIDE DEL SOL
POCITAS BEACH
POINT BREAKER
QUEENSTOWN
QUID PRO THROW-ON
RANCH HAND
RAQUETTE
RAQUETTE LAKE CRUISER
RARE BLUE DENIM
RAYADA
REFINED RENEGADE
REGULAR JOE
REGULATION CHINOS PLAIN-FRONT
REGULATION CHINOS PLEATED
RELAXED
REMOLINO DENIM
REQUIRED TASTE
REQUIRED TASTE BLAZER
RESTORATIVE
REVIVE
THE RIGHT WHITE
RISE & SHINE
RIVERSTONE TWILL
ROAD-RALLY LOAFERS
ROCK 'N' STROLL TREKKERS
ROSARITA
ROXFORDS
SAGRADO
SALSA
SAN MIGUEL
SAN NICOLAS SHIRT
SANTA ANNAPURNA
SAVANNAH
SEA BREEZE
SECRET OF RELAXATION
SERENADE
SERENDIPITY TENCEL
SERENE
SERENIDAD
SILK NOIL
SILK REDEMPTION BLAZER
SILVER ROUTE
SIMPATICO
SLOGS
SMOOTH-SEASON
SOL SEEKER
SOUTH COAST POPOVER
SOUTH PACIFIC
SPINDRIFT
SPORTING LIFE
STARGAZER BATIK
STEADFAST SILK
STEALTH STRETCH
STRIKE IT RICH
SUMMERTIME BLUE
SUN SEEKER
SUNSET DREAM
SURFACE CHARACTER
TABOOSE
TABOOSE PULL-ON
TAQUILE ISLAND
TERRA-COTTA
TERRACE SUNSET
THE TERRITORY AHEAD
TERRITORY ISLE
TULA
TULIPAN
TUMBLEBUCK
THE TWILL IS GONE
TWILL LANDSMAN
TWO-WAY
UNCOMMONLY
UNPLUGGED
UNPLUGGED KNIT
UPLIFTING
UPLIFTING CAMISOLE
URBAN RANGE
VACANCES
VAGUELY ATHLETIC
VAGUELY ATHLETIC T
VERANDA TUNIC
VERANO RIBBED
VINTAGE
VINTAGE MODERNE
VOYAGER
WALK THE WALK
WALLOWA
WASHABLE SUEDE HOODIE
WEAREVER
WELL-HEELED
WESTERN STRETCH
WINE COUNTRY
WOODSMAN PULLOVER
WORK RELEASE
YOUR BASIC
ZENITH
ZENITH TWILLS
ZEPHYR
ZEPHYR PULL-ONS

THINGS REMEMBERED, INC.

(Holding of GB Merchant Partners, LLC)
5500 Avion Park Dr
Highland Heights, OH 44143
Tel.: (440) 473-2000
Fax: (440) 473-2018
Toll Free: (800) 274-7367
E-mail: customerservice@thingsremembered.com
Web Site: www.thingsremembered.com
Approx. Sls.: $300,000,000
Approx. Number Employees: 4,000
Business Description:
Engraved & Personalized Gifts Retailer
S.I.C.: 5947
N.A.I.C.S.: 453220
Import
Media: 5-6-7-8-9-14-15-23-24-25
Distr.: Natl.
Budget Set: July
Personnel:
Michael Anthony *(CEO)*
Frank Rowan *(CFO)*
Linda Postell *(Sr VP-Mdsg, E-Commerce & Mktg)*
Alice Guiney *(VP-HR)*
Brands & Products:
THINGS ENGRAVED ARE THINGS REMEMBERED
THINGS REMEMBERED
Advertising Agencies:
Doner
25900 Northwestern Hwy
Southfield, MI 48075
Tel.: (248) 354-9700
Fax: (248) 827-8440

Landau Public Relations
700 W Saint Clair Ave Ste 414
Cleveland, OH 44113
Tel.: (216) 696-1686
Fax: (216) 771-5206

Stern Advertising, Inc.
29125 Chagrin Blvd
Cleveland, OH 44122-4622
Tel.: (216) 464-4850
Fax: (216) 464-7859

T.J. MAXX

(Sub. of Marmaxx Operating Corp.)
770 Cochituate Rd
Framingham, MA 01701
Tel.: (508) 390-1000
Fax: (508) 390-2366
Fax: (508) 390-2828
Web Site: www.tjmaxx.com
Approx. Sls.: $1,517,116,032
Approx. Number Employees: 35,000
Year Founded: 1976
Business Description:
Retailer of Off-Price Apparel & Other Domestic Products
S.I.C.: 5311; 5651
N.A.I.C.S.: 452112; 448140
Import
Media: 3-6-8-9-10-13-15-18-19-22-23-24-25
Distr.: Natl.
Personnel:
Karen Coppola *(Sr VP-Mktg)*
Rebecca Leonard *(Assoc VP-PR)*
Andy Maercklein *(Dir-Mktg)*
Brands & Products:
MAXXMAIL
T.J. MAXX

THE TJX COMPANIES, INC.

770 Cochituate Rd
Framingham, MA 01701
Tel.: (508) 390-1000
Fax: (508) 390-2828
Web Site: www.tjx.com
Approx. Sls.: $21,942,193,000
Approx. Number Employees: 166,000
Year Founded: 1987
Business Description:
Off-Price Apparel & Home Fashions Retailer
S.I.C.: 5651; 5311
N.A.I.C.S.: 448140; 452111; 452112
Import
Advertising Expenditures: $249,800,000
Media: 3-6-8-9-13-14-15-18-22-23-24-25
Distr.: Reg.
Personnel:
Bernard Cammarata *(Chm)*
Ernie L. Herrman *(Pres)*
Carol M. Meyrowitz *(CEO)*
Jeffrey G. Naylor *(CFO, Chief Admin Officer & Sr Exec VP)*
Paul Kangas *(Sr VP-HR)*
Sherry Lang *(Sr VP-IR & PR)*
Stacey Lane *(VP-Mktg)*
Melanie Campbell *(Mgr-Interactive Mktg)*
Eileen Cavicchi *(Mgr-Consumer Insights)*
Brands & Products:
TJX
Advertising Agencies:
GSD&M
828 W 6th St
Austin, TX 78703-5420
Tel.: (512) 242-4736
Fax: (512) 242-4700
National TV Spots
T.J. Maxx
Marshalls

Mullen
101 N Cherry St Ste 600
Winston Salem, NC 27101-4035
Tel.: (336) 765-3630
Fax: (336) 774-9550
Marshalls

VML, Inc.
250 Richards Rd
Kansas City, MO 64116-4279
Tel.: (816) 283-0700
Fax: (816) 283-0954
Toll Free: (800) 990-2468

THE TOG SHOP

(Holding of Orchard Brands Corporation)
30 Tozer Rd
Beverly, MA 01915
Tel.: (978) 922-2040
Fax: (978) 922-7001
Toll Free: (800) 367-8647
E-mail: custserv@togshop.com
Web Site: www.togshop.com
Approx. Number Employees: 225
Year Founded: 1953
Business Description:
Women's Apparel Catalog & On-Line Retailer
S.I.C.: 5961; 5621
N.A.I.C.S.: 454113; 448120
Advertising Expenditures: $8,000,000
Media: 4-6-13
Distr.: Natl.
Personnel:
Neale Attenborough *(CEO)*
Brands & Products:
HAYMAKER
TOG
TOG SHOP
VERA

TOTAL FULFILLMENT SERVICES LLC

126 Monroe Tpke
Trumbull, CT 06611
Tel.: (203) 261-7088
Fax: (203) 261-0778
Toll Free: (888) 454-9552
Approx. Number Employees: 60
Year Founded: 1995
Business Description:
Provider of Call Center & Mail Order Fulfillment Services
S.I.C.: 5961
N.A.I.C.S.: 454113
Media: 2
Personnel:
Steve Gordon *(Pres)*
Arthur Pliner *(Dir-Sls)*
Trish Slavin *(Mgr-Mktg)*

Key to Media (For complete agency information see *The Advertising Red Books-Agencies* edition):
1. Bus. Publs. 2. Cable T.V. 3. Catalogs & Directories. 4. Co-op Adv. 5. Consumer Mags. 6. D.M. to Bus. Estab.7. D.M. to Consumers 8. Daily Newsp. 9. Exhibits/Trade Shows 10. Foreign 11. Infomercial 12. Internet Adv.13. Multimedia 14. Network Radio 15. Network T.V. 16. Newsp. Distr. Mags. 17. Other 18. Outdoor (Posters, Transit) 19. Point of Purchase20. Premiums, Novelties 21. Product Samples 22. Special Events Mktg. 23. Spot Radio 24. Spot T.V. 25. Weekly Newsp. 26. Yellow Page Adv.

TOWNSEND ENTERPRISES, INC.
(d/b/a Sinclair Institute)
PO Box 8865
Chapel Hill, NC 27515
Tel.: (919) 929-5703
Sales Range: $10-24.9 Million
Approx. Number Employees: 45
Business Description:
Video Producer & Mail Order
S.I.C.: 7812; 5961
N.A.I.C.S.: 512110; 454111; 454113
Media: 4-6-8-13

TRADER JOE'S CO.
(Sub. of TACT Holding)
604 W Huntington Dr
Monrovia, CA 91016-6346
Tel.: (626) 358-8884
Web Site: www.traderjoes.com
Approx. Rev.: $8,000,000,000
Approx. Number Employees: 3,500
Year Founded: 1958
Business Description:
Specialty Market
S.I.C.: 5411; 5921
N.A.I.C.S.: 445110; 445310
Advertising Expenditures: $300,000
Media: 8-13-18-19
Personnel:
Dan T. Bane *(Chm & CEO)*
Thomas English *(CIO & VP)*
Jon Basalone *(Sr VP-Mktg)*
Charles J. Pilliter *(Sr VP-Ops)*
Christy Hughes *(Reg VP)*
Laurie Mead *(VP-HR)*

TRIAD MARKETING INC.
(d/b/a Haverhills)
16911 Grays Bay Blvd
Wayzata, MN 55391-2922
Tel.: (952) 476-2006
Fax: (952) 942-7999
Toll Free: (800) 797-7367
E-mail: information@haverhills.com
Web Site: www.haverhills.com
Sales Range: Less than $1 Million
Approx. Number Employees: 2
Year Founded: 1967
Business Description:
Retail Mail Order
S.I.C.: 5961
N.A.I.C.S.: 454113
Media: 4-8-13
Personnel:
Paul Harris *(Pres)*

TUESDAY MORNING CORPORATION
(Holding of Madison Dearborn Partners, LLC)
6250 LBJ Fwy
Dallas, TX 75240
Tel.: (972) 387-3562
Fax: (972) 387-1974
E-mail: custserv@tuesdaymorning.com
Web Site: www.sportsupplygroup.com
Approx. Sls.: $821,150,000
Approx. Number Employees: 1,900
Year Founded: 1974
Business Description:
Deep Discount Retail, Gift Wares, Housewares, Linens, Toys & Seasonal Stores
S.I.C.: 5719; 5399; 5947; 5948
N.A.I.C.S.: 442299; 448320; 452990; 453220
Import
Advertising Expenditures: $26,963,000
Media: 8-9-23-24-25
Distr.: Natl.
Budget Set: June
Personnel:
Bruce A. Quinnell *(Chm)*
Kathleen Mason *(Pres & CEO)*
Stephanie Bowman *(CFO & Exec VP)*
Michael Marchetti *(COO & Exec VP)*
Ross Manning *(Sr Mktg Officer & Sr VP)*
Melinda Page *(Sr VP & Gen Mgr-Mdse)*
Grant Anderson *(VP-IT Mdsg Sys)*
Brands & Products:
TUESDAY MORNING
Advertising Agencies:
Laurey Peat & Associates
2001 Ross Ave Ste 3170
Dallas, TX 75201
Tel.: (214) 871-8787
Fax: (214) 953-1871

National Newspaper Placement Services
766 N Sun Dr Ste 2090
Lake Mary, FL 32746-2553
Tel.: (850) 521-1195
Fax: (850) 577-3646
Toll Free: (800) 742-1373

ULLA POPKEN LTD.
12201 Long Green Pk
Glen Arm, MD 21057
Tel.: (410) 592-9190
Fax: (410) 592-9380
Toll Free: (800) 245-ULLA
E-mail: support@ullapopken.com
Web Site: www.ullapopken.com
Approx. Number Employees: 50
Business Description:
Women's Clothing Retailer
S.I.C.: 5621; 5699
N.A.I.C.S.: 448120; 448150
Media: 4-5-8-13
Personnel:
Thomas Schneider *(CEO)*
Brands & Products:
ULLA POPKEN

UMSI INCORPORATED
125 Lincoln Blvd
Middlesex, NJ 08846-1060
Tel.: (732) 805-0200
Fax: (206) 202-7663
E-mail: wholesale@umsiinc.com
Web Site: www.umsiinc.com
Sales Range: $1-9.9 Million
Approx. Number Employees: 3
Year Founded: 1966
Business Description:
Magic Supplies Mail Order
S.I.C.: 5961
N.A.I.C.S.: 454113
Media: 4-8-13
Personnel:
Robert Bokor *(Pres)*
Brands & Products:
ABRACADABRA MAGIC

UNIVERSAL COIN & BULLION LTD.
7410 Phelan Blvd
Beaumont, TX 77706
Tel.: (409) 835-1192
Fax: (409) 866-2022
Toll Free: (800) 459-2646
Toll Free: (800) 459COIN
E-mail: info@universalcoin.com
Web Site: www.universalcoin.com
Sales Range: $250-299.9 Million
Approx. Number Employees: 30
Business Description:
Coin Dealer
S.I.C.: 5999; 5094
N.A.I.C.S.: 453998; 423940
Media: 6
Personnel:
Michael Fuljenz *(Pres)*

URBAN OUTFITTERS, INC.
5000 S Broad St
Philadelphia, PA 19112
Tel.: (215) 454-5500
Fax: (215) 568-1549
E-mail: robert.ross@urbanout.com
Web Site: www.urbanoutfittersinc.com
Approx. Sls.: $2,274,102,000
Approx. Number Employees: 6,432
Year Founded: 1976
Business Description:
Women's & Men's Clothing & Accessories Retail Sales
S.I.C.: 5621; 5611; 5651
N.A.I.C.S.: 448120; 448110; 448140
Import Export
Advertising Expenditures: $58,336,000
Media: 4-8-10-19-22
Personnel:
Richard A. Hayne *(Chm & Pres)*
Glen T. Senk *(CEO)*
Eric Artz *(CFO)*
Freeman M. Zausner *(Chief Admin Officer)*
Glen A. Bodzy *(Gen Counsel & Sec)*
Oona McCullough *(Dir-IR)*
Joe Stratter *(Dir-Mktg & Store Technologies)*
Mike Isabella *(Assoc Dir-Mktg & Bus Dev)*
Brands & Products:
ANTHROPOLOGIE
CO-OPERATIVE
ECOTE
FREE PEOPLE
IDRA
LEIFSDOTTIR
LUCKY PENNY
NAP TIME
SLANT
STAPLEFORD
TERRAIN
URBAN OUTFITTERS
URBN

VALUEVISION MEDIA, INC.
6740 Shady Oak Rd
Eden Prairie, MN 55344-3433
Tel.: (952) 943-6000
Fax: (952) 943-6711
E-mail: investorrelations@vvtv.com
Web Site: www.valuevisionmedia.com
Approx. Sls.: $562,273,000
Approx. Number Employees: 905
Year Founded: 1990
Business Description:
Direct Market Retailer of Specialty & Gift Products
S.I.C.: 5961
N.A.I.C.S.: 454111; 454113
Advertising Expenditures: $18,099,000
Media: 8-13
Personnel:
Randy Steven Ronning *(Chm)*
G. Robert Ayd *(Pres)*
Keith R. Stewart *(CEO)*
William J. McGrath *(CFO & Sr VP)*
Annette Repasch *(Chief Mdsg Officer)*
Nancy Kunkle *(Sr VP-Customer Experience)*
Brands & Products:
SHOPNBC

VARESE SARABANDE RECORDS, INC.
11846 Ventura Blvd Ste 130
Studio City, CA 91604-2620
Tel.: (818) 753-4143
Fax: (818) 753-7596
Toll Free: (800) 827-3734
E-mail: info@varesesarabande.com
Web Site: www.varesesarabande.com
Approx. Number Employees: 10
Year Founded: 1978
Business Description:
Cinema Soundtracks & Music Recordings Reissues Distr
S.I.C.: 7389; 2741; 8999
N.A.I.C.S.: 512290; 512210; 512230
Media: 4-5-6-8-9-13-20-23-25
Personnel:
Chris Kuchler *(Pres)*
Steve Knapp *(Exec VP-Bus & Legal Affairs)*
Brian Davis *(Dir-Sls & Mktg-Natl)*
Brands & Products:
ALONG THE BLUES HIGHWAY
VARESE SARABANDE
VARESE VINTAGE
WILDCAT RECORDS

VERMONT COUNTRY STORE, INC.
5650 Main St PO Box 1108
Manchester Center, VT 05255-1108
Tel.: (802) 362-8460
Fax: (802) 362-8288
Fax: (802) 362-0285
E-mail: customerservice@vermontcountrystore.com
Web Site:
www.vermontcountrystore.com
Sales Range: $450-499.9 Million
Approx. Number Employees: 400
Year Founded: 1945
Business Description:
Mail-Order Services
S.I.C.: 5961; 5399
N.A.I.C.S.: 454113; 452990
Import Export
Media: 4-8-13
Personnel:
Lyman Orton *(Owner)*
Bill Shouldice *(Pres & CEO)*
Brands & Products:
PURVEYORS OF THE PRACTICAL & HARD-TO-FIND
SOCK MONKEY
THE VERMONT COUNTRY STORE

VICTORIAN PAPER COMPANY
(d/b/a Victorian Trading Company)
15600 W 99th St
Lenexa, KS 66219
Tel.: (913) 438-3995
Fax: (913) 438-5255

Key to Media (For complete agency information see *The Advertising Red Books-Agencies* edition):
1. Bus. Publs. 2. Cable T.V. 3. Catalogs & Directories. 4. Co-op Adv. 5. Consumer Mags. 6. D.M. to Bus. Estab.7. D.M. to Consumers
8. Daily Newsp. 9. Exhibits/Trade Shows 10. Foreign 11. Infomercial 12. Internet Adv.13. Multimedia 14. Network Radio
15. Network T.V. 16. Newsp. Distr. Mags. 17. Other 18. Outdoor (Posters, Transit) 19. Point of Purchase20. Premiums, Novelties
21. Product Samples 22. Special Events Mktg. 23. Spot Radio 24. Spot T.V. 25. Weekly Newsp. 26. Yellow Page Adv.

Victorian Paper Company — (Continued)

Toll Free: (800) 700-2035
E-mail: sales@victoriantrading.com
Web Site: www.victoriantrading.com
E-Mail For Key Personnel:
Sales Director: sales@victoriantrading.com
Approx. Number Employees: 60
Year Founded: 1987
Business Description:
Mail Order Sales of Paper Products
S.I.C.: 5961; 5112
N.A.I.C.S.: 454113; 424120
Media: 4-8-13
Personnel:
Melissa Rolston *(Owner & Founder)*
Randy Rolston *(Pres)*

VICTORIA'S SECRET STORES, LLC

(Sub. of Limited Brands, Inc.)
4 Limited Pkwy E
Reynoldsburg, OH 43068-5302
Tel.: (614) 577-7111
Fax: (614) 577-7088
Toll Free: (800) 411-5116
Web Site: www.victoriasecret.com
Sales Range: $1-4.9 Billion
Business Description:
Lingerie Sales
S.I.C.: 5699; 5621
N.A.I.C.S.: 448150; 448120
Import
Advertising Expenditures: $34,000,000
Media: 3-4-6-9-13-15-16-19-22
Distr.: Natl.
Personnel:
Sharen Jester Turney *(Pres & CEO)*
Bill E May, Jr *(COO)*
Lori Greeley *(CEO-Stores)*
Monica Mitro *(Exec VP-PR)*
Dein Boyle *(Sr VP-Mdse Plng)*
Steve Silbaugh *(VP-Mktg)*
Brands & Products:
ANGELS BY VICTORIA'S SECRET
IPEX
SECOND SKIN SATIN
VICTORIA'S SECRET

VIVRE, INC.

11 E 26th St 15th Fl
New York, NY 10010
Tel.: (212) 739-6205
Fax: (212) 739-1736
Toll Free: (800) 411-6515
E-mail: customercare@vivre.com
Web Site: www.vivre.com
Approx. Number Employees: 30
Year Founded: 1996
Business Description:
Direct Marketer of European Luxury Items
S.I.C.: 5719
N.A.I.C.S.: 442299
Media: 4-8-13
Personnel:
Eva Jeanbart-Lorenzotti *(Founder & CEO)*
Brands & Products:
CORAL-TRIMMED LINEN TUNIC
DIAMOND PATTERN BANGLE
HAIRCALF JOURNALS
LARGE CROC STAMPED ENVELOPE
LEATHER ALLEGRA
LOTUS ARTS DE VIVRE
PATENT POUCH
STAMPED CROC JOURNALS
STERLING AND MAHOGANY ICECREAM PINT BUCKET
SUEDE JACQUELINE BAG
SUEDE LIZARD ALLEGRA
SUEDE TRAVEL BACKGAMMON ROLL
VIVRE
VOYAGE. DISCOVER. COLLECT. SHOP

WAL-MART CANADA CORP.

(Sub. of Wal-Mart Stores, Inc.)
1940 Argentia Rd
Mississauga, ON L5N 1P9, Canada
Tel.: (905) 821-2111
Fax: (905) 821-6393
Web Site: www.walmartcanada.ca
Approx. Number Employees: 77,000
Year Founded: 1994
Business Description:
Discount Department Store Operator
S.I.C.: 5311
N.A.I.C.S.: 452112
Personnel:
David Cheesewright *(Pres & CEO)*
Trudy Fahie *(Pres & CEO-Walmart Canada Bank)*
Bob Hakeem *(Sr VP-People Div)*
Sylvain Prudhomme *(Sr VP-Mdse)*
Jim Thompson *(Sr VP-Ops)*
Sean Coutts *(Gen Mgr-Ecommerce)*
Kevin Groh *(Dir-Corp Affairs)*
John Lawrence *(Dir-Corp Social Responsibility)*
Advertising Agency:
JWT Company Ltd.
160 Bloor St E
Toronto, ON M4W 3P7, Canada
Tel.: (416) 926-7300
Fax: (416) 926-7389

WAL-MART STORES, INC.

702 SW 8th St
Bentonville, AR 72716-8611
Tel.: (479) 273-4000
Web Site: www.walmartstores.com
Approx. Rev.: $421,849,000,000
Approx. Number Employees: 2,100,000
Year Founded: 1984
Business Description:
Discount & General Merchandise Department Stores
S.I.C.: 5311; 5399; 5411; 5812; 5912
N.A.I.C.S.: 452990; 445110; 446110; 452111; 452910; 722110
Import Export
Advertising Expenditures: $2,500,000,000
Media: 1-2-3-4-5-6-8-9-11-13-14-15-16-17-18-19-20-21-22-23-24-25-26
Distr.: Intl.; Natl.; Reg.
Budget Set: Jan. -Jan.
Personnel:
S. Robson Walton *(Chm)*
Eduardo Castro-Wright *(Vice Chm)*
Michael T. Duke *(Pres & CEO)*
Charles M. Holley, Jr. *(CFO, Treas & Exec VP)*
Rollin L. Ford *(CIO & Exec VP)*
Stephen F. Quinn *(CMO & Exec VP-Walmart US)*
Thomas A. Mars *(Chief Admin Officer-Walmart US & Exec VP)*
Duncan C. Mac Naughton *(Chief Mdsg Officer & Exec VP-Walmart US)*
Scott Price *(Exec VP & Pres/CEO-Walmart Asia)*
Brian C. Cornell *(Pres/CEO-Sams Club)*
C. Douglas McMillon *(Pres/CEO-Walmart Intl)*
William S. Simon *(Pres/CEO-Walmart US)*
Michael S. Moore *(Pres-Walmart Central & Exec VP)*
Eric S. Zorn *(Pres-Wal-Mart Realty & Walmart US & Exec VP)*
John O. Agwunobi *(Pres-Health & Wellness & Sr VP)*
Michael J. Bender *(Pres-Walmart West)*
Rosalind G. Brewer *(Pres-Walmart East & Walmart US)*
Stephan Fanderl *(Pres-Emerging Markets-East)*
Jane J. Thompson *(Pres-Fin Svcs)*
Jeffrey J. Gearhart *(Gen Counsel, Corp Sec & Exec VP)*
Jeffrey A. Davis *(Treas & Sr VP)*
Andy Barron *(Exec VP-Softlines & Walmart US)*
Leslie A. Dach *(Exec VP-Corp Affairs)*
Cindy Davis *(Exec VP-Global Consumer Insights)*
Johnnie C. Dobbs, Jr. *(Exec VP-Logistics, Supply Chain & Walmart US)*
Ed Kolodzieski *(Exec VP-Global Sourcing)*
Gisel Ruiz *(Exec VP-People & Walmart US)*
Jack L. Sinclair *(Exec VP-Food & Walmart US)*
John T. Westling *(Exec VP-Gen Mdse, Replenishment & Walmart U.S.)*
Steven P. Whaley *(Sr VP & Controller)*
Pam Kohn *(Sr VP & Gen Mgr-Mdsg)*
Dottie Mattison *(Sr VP & Gen Mgr-Apparel)*
Paul Beahm *(Sr VP-Pharmacy Health & Wellness)*
Ray Bracy *(Sr VP-Govt Rels)*
Steve Bratspies *(Sr VP-Mktg)*
Steve Breen *(Sr VP-Snacks & Drinks)*
Don Frieson *(Sr VP-Supply Chain)*
Michael Fung *(Sr VP-Fin)*
Lev Khasis *(Sr VP)*
Matt Kistler *(Sr VP-Mktg Ops)*
Jeff Macho *(Sr VP-Global Procurement)*
Seong Ohm *(Sr VP-Gen Mdse Global Mdsg Center)*
Laura Phillips *(Sr VP-Toys & Seasonal Mdse)*
Santiago Roces *(Sr VP-Small Formats)*
Tony Rogers *(Sr VP-Mktg)*
Andrea Thomas *(Sr VP-Sustainability)*
Michael A. Cook *(VP & Asst Treas)*
Janet Bareis *(VP-Mdsg)*
Andy Ruben *(VP-Multi Channel Global Commerce)*
Carol Schumacher *(VP-HR)*
Wanda Young *(Sr Dir-Digital strategy)*
Kim Brandner *(Sr Dir-Sourcing, Dry & Frozen Grocery)*
Rand Waddoups *(Sr Dir-Brand Mdsg-Electronics)*
Rex Conklin *(Media Dir)*
Gwen Kelly *(Sr Mgr-Mktg)*
Chinissa White *(Sr Mgr-Media Svcs)*
L. Mecole Brown *(Mgr-Ops)*
Don R. Kerr *(Mgr-Market-Northern California)*
Brands & Products:
ATHLETIC WORKS
CANOPY
EQUATE
FADED GLORY
GEORGE
GREAT VALUE
MAINSTAYS
NO BOUNDARIES
OL' ROY
ONE SOURCE
OZARK TRAIL
PARENT'S CHOICE
PURITAN
SAM'S AMERICAN CHOICE
SPRING VALLEY
SUPERMERCADO DE WALMART
WAL-MART
WAL-MART SUPERCENTER
Advertising Agencies:
Arnold Worldwide
101 Huntington Ave
Boston, MA 02199-7603
Tel.: (617) 587-8000
Fax: (617) 587-8004

Blue Worldwide
1875 Eye St NW Ste 900
Washington, DC 20006
Tel.: (202) 326-1721
Fax: (202) 371-2858
Corporate Identity, Creative & Public Relations

Capita Technologies, Inc.
17600 Gillette Ave
Irvine, CA 92614
Tel.: (949) 260-3000
Fax: (949) 851-9875

Cohn & Wolfe
8730 W Sunset Blvd 5th Fl
Los Angeles, CA 90069-2210
Tel.: (310) 967-2900
Fax: (310) 967-2910

Cohn & Wolfe
200 Fifth Ave
New York, NY 10010
Tel.: (212) 798-9700
Fax: (212) 329-9900

Daniel J. Edelman, Inc.
(d/b/a Edelman)
200 E Randolph St Fl 63
Chicago, IL 60601-6705
Tel.: (312) 240-3000
Fax: (312) 240-2900
Public Relations

E. Morris Communications, Inc.
820 N Orleans St Ste 402
Chicago, IL 60610
Tel.: (312) 943-2900
Fax: (312) 943-5856
Toll Free: (877) 916-0007
Multicultural Creative

E.B. Lane
733 W McDowell Rd
Phoenix, AZ 85007-1727
Tel.: (602) 258-5263
Fax: (602) 257-8128

Key to Media (For complete agency information see *The Advertising Red Books-Agencies* edition):
1. Bus. Publs. 2. Cable T.V. 3. Catalogs & Directories. 4. Co-op Adv. 5. Consumer Mags. 6. D.M. to Bus. Estab.7. D.M. to Consumers 8. Daily Newsp. 9. Exhibits/Trade Shows 10. Foreign 11. Infomercial 12. Internet Adv.13. Multimedia 14. Network Radio 15. Network T.V. 16. Newsp. Distr. Mags. 17. Other 18. Outdoor (Posters, Transit) 19. Point of Purchase20. Premiums, Novelties 21. Product Samples 22. Special Events Mktg. 23. Spot Radio 24. Spot T.V. 25. Weekly Newsp. 26. Yellow Page Adv.

Public Relations & Marketing in Arizona

The Geppetto Group
95 Morton St 8th Fl
New York, NY 10014-3336
Tel.: (212) 462-8140
Fax: (212) 462-8197

GlobalHue
Ste 1600 4000 Town Ctr
Southfield, MI 48076
Tel.: (248) 223-8900
Fax: (248) 304-8877
African American Market

GolinHarris
(Part of the Interpublic Group of Companies)
111 E Wacker Dr 11th Fl
Chicago, IL 60601-4306
Tel.: (312) 729-4000
Fax: (312) 729-4010

Grey Puerto Rico
PO Box 367
San Juan, PR 00918
Tel.: (787) 999-9000
Fax: (787) 999-6711

Idex Creative Marketing
1655 Wynne Rd Ste 101
Cordova, TN 38016-4905
Tel.: (901) 373-7500
Fax: (901) 373-7171
Wal-Mart Foundation

IW Group, Inc.
(An IPG Co.)
8687 Melrose Ave Ste G540
West Hollywood, CA 90069
Tel.: (310) 289-5500
Fax: (310) 289-5501
Asian American Market

JohnsonRauhoff
2525 Lake Pines Dr
Saint Joseph, MI 49085
Tel.: (269) 428-9212
Fax: (269) 428-3312
Toll Free: (800) 572-3996
General Merchandise (Photography)

JWT Canada
160 Bloor St E Ste 800
Toronto, ON M4W 3P7, Canada
Tel.: (416) 926-7300
Fax: (416) 967-2859

Lopez Negrete Communications, Inc.
3336 Richmond Ave Ste 200
Houston, TX 77098
Tel.: (713) 877-8777
Fax: (713) 877-8796
Hispanic Market

The Marketing Store-Promotional Marketing
1 Lincoln Centre, 18 W 140 Butterfield, Ste 1600
Oakbrook Terrace, IL 60181
Tel.: (630) 693-1400

The Martin Agency
One Shockoe Plz
Richmond, VA 23219-4132
Tel.: (804) 698-8000
Fax: (804) 698-8001
Creative

Mindshare
8F Development Center 3 Lin Jiang Rd
Guangzhou, 510623, China
Tel.: (86) 20 2881 8288
Fax: (86) 20 3785 1070
(Media Planning/Buying)

NATIONAL Public Relations
2001 McGill College Ave Ste 800
Montreal, QC H3A 1G1, Canada
Tel.: (514) 843-7171
Fax: (514) 843-6976
Public Relations in Canada

Pocket Billboards
4804 Laurel Canyon Blvd Ste 105
Studio City, CA 91607
Tel.: (818) 505-1005
Fax: (818) 505-1105
Outdoor, Billboards

Porter Novelli
(Sub. of Omnicom Group, Inc.)
75 Varick St 6th Fl
New York, NY 10013
Tel.: (212) 601-8000
Fax: (212) 601-8101

Prime Policy Group
1110 Vermont Ave NW Ste 1200
Washington, DC 20005-3554
Tel.: (202) 530-0500
Fax: (202) 530-4500

Publicis & Hal Riney
2001 The Embarcadero
San Francisco, CA 94133-5200
Tel.: (415) 293-2001
Fax: (415) 293-2620
Great Value Brand

R/GA
350 W 39th St
New York, NY 10018-1402
Tel.: (212) 946-4000
Fax: (212) 946-4010
Online

Runyon Saltzman & Einhorn
1 Capitol Mall 4th Fl Ste 400
Sacramento, CA 95814
Tel.: (916) 446-9900
Fax: (916) 446-3619

Saatchi & Saatchi X
605 Lakeview Dr
Springdale, AR 72764
Tel.: (479) 575-0200
Fax: (479) 725-1136
In-Store, Shopper & Associate Communications

Starcom MediaVest
222 Merchandise Mart Plz Ste 550
Chicago, IL 60654
Tel.: (312) 970-8400
Fax: (312) 970-8464
Media Buying

StratMar Retail Services
109 Willett Ave
Port Chester, NY 10573-4232
Toll Free: (800) 866-2399
In-Store Advertising

TPN Inc.
9400 N Central Expwy Ste 1500
Dallas, TX 75231-5044
Tel.: (214) 692-1522
Fax: (214) 692-8316

Watt International, Inc.
300 Bayview Ave
Toronto, ON M5A 3R7, Canada
Tel.: (416) 364-9384
Fax: (416) 364-1098
Design

Yeck Brothers Company
2222 Arbor Blvd
Dayton, OH 45439-1522
Tel.: (937) 294-4000
Fax: (937) 294-6985
Toll Free: (800) 417-2767
Direct Mail

WALGREEN CO.

200 Wilmot Rd
Deerfield, IL 60015-4620
Tel.: (847) 914-2500
Fax: (847) 914-2804
E-mail: investor.relations@walgreens.com
Web Site: www.walgreens.com
Approx. Sls.: $67,420,000,000
Approx. Number Employees: 177,000
Year Founded: 1901
Business Description:
Drug Stores
S.I.C.: 5912
N.A.I.C.S.: 446110
Import
Advertising Expenditures: $271,000,000
Media: 1-3-9-13-15-16-18-19-22-23-24-25
Distr.: Direct to Consumer; Natl.
Budget Set: May
Personnel:
Alan G. McNally *(Chm)*
Gregory D. Wasson *(Pres & CEO)*
Wade D. Miquelon *(CFO & Exec VP)*
Tim Theriault *(CIO & Sr VP)*
April Marbury *(CIO-Clinical Solutions)*
Robert G. Zimmerman *(Chief Strategy Officer)*
Kathleen Wilson-Thompson *(Chief HR Officer & Sr VP)*
Laura K. Merten *(Chief Compliance & Privacy Officer & VP-Loss Prevention & Profit)*
Graham Atkinson *(Chief Customer Experience Officer)*
Peter Hotz *(Pres-Take Care Health Employer Solutions Grp & VP)*
Sona Chawla *(Pres-E-Commerce)*
Kermit R. Crawford *(Pres-Pharmacy Svcs)*
Joseph C. Magnacca *(Pres-Daily Living Products & Solutions)*
Bryan Pugh *(Pres-Daily Living Products & Solutions)*
Hal F. Rosenbluth *(Pres-Walgreens Health & Wellness)*
Mark A. Wagner *(Pres-Community Mgmt)*
Thomas J. Sabatino, Jr. *(Gen Counsel, Sec & Exec VP)*
Michael Nameth *(Exec VP)*
Mia M. Scholz *(Sr VP-Acctg & Controller)*
Jeffrey Berkowitz *(Sr VP-Pharmaceutical Dev & Market Access)*
Donald C. Huonker *(Sr VP)*
J. Randolph Lewis *(Sr VP-Supply Chain Mgmt)*
Steve Broughton *(Gen Mgr-Mdse & VP-Consumables)*
Steven L. Lubin *(Gen Mgr-Mktg-NonMainland Ops & Div VP)*
W. Michael Arnoult, Jr. *(VP-Customer Centric Retailing)*
Cindy Donohoe *(VP-Pharmacy Healthcare Mktg)*
Charles V. Greener *(VP-Corp Affairs & Comm)*
Rick J. Hans *(VP-IR & Fin)*
Catherine Lindner *(VP-Retail Mktg)*
Deborah Sabo *(VP-Mktg Svcs)*
Todd Vang *(VP-Mktg Insights & Loyalty Div)*
Jabir Patel *(Dir & Gen Mdse Mgr-Online Photo)*
Robert Thompkins *(Gen Mgr-Mdse-The Health & Wellness Pur Grp)*
Shannon Petree *(Gen Mgr-Mdse-Beauty & Personal Care)*
Mark Cordes *(Sr Dir-Mktg Ops & Plng)*
Debra B. Garza *(Dir-Govt & Community Rels)*
John Gremer *(Dir-Community Affairs)*
Lisa Guidice *(Dir-Adv & Promos)*
Jude Pierre-Louis *(Dir-Diabetes Svcs)*
Carlo Baldan *(Mgr-Mdse, Personal Care, Beauty & Fashion)*
Bob Cinq-Mars *(Div Mgr-Mdse-Over-The-Counter Products)*
Scott Minger *(Mgr-Vitamins Category)*
Brands & Products:
ADVANTAGE90
ALLER-MELTS
ARCTIC FROST
CASUAL GEAR
COMFORT ASSURED
COMFORT-SMOOTH
EASYSAVER
FAST READ
FRESH BREATH
W
WALGREEN
WALGREENS
WALGREENS.COM
Advertising Agencies:
Arc Worldwide
(Sub. of Publicis Groupe S.A.)
35 W Wacker Dr 15th Fl
Chicago, IL 60601
Tel.: (312) 220-3200
Fax: (312) 220-1995

Butler, Shine, Stern & Partners
20 Liberty Ship Way
Sausalito, CA 94965-3312
Tel.: (415) 331-6049
Fax: (415) 331-3524
In-Store Healthcare Clinic

Digitas, Inc.
111 E Wacker Dr Ste 1500
Chicago, IL 60601-4501
Tel.: (312) 729-0100
Fax: (312) 729-0111

Downtown Partners Chicago
200 E Randolph St 34th Fl
Chicago, IL 60601
Tel.: (312) 552-5800
Tel.: (312) 552-5804

Key to Media (For complete agency information see *The Advertising Red Books-Agencies* edition):
1. Bus. Publs. 2. Cable T.V. 3. Catalogs & Directories. 4. Co-op Adv. 5. Consumer Mags. 6. D.M. to Bus. Estab.7. D.M. to Consumers
8. Daily Newsp. 9. Exhibits/Trade Shows 10. Foreign 11. Infomercial 12. Internet Adv.13. Multimedia 14. Network Radio
15. Network T.V. 16. Newsp. Distr. Mags. 17. Other 18. Outdoor (Posters, Transit) 19. Point of Purchase20. Premiums, Novelties
21. Product Samples 22. Special Events Mktg. 23. Spot Radio 24. Spot T.V. 25. Weekly Newsp. 26. Yellow Page Adv.

Walgreen Co. — (Continued)

Fax: (312) 552-2330

Starcom USA
35 W Wacker Dr
Chicago, IL 60601
Tel.: (312) 220-3535
Fax: (312) 220-6530
Media Agency of Record

WALLPAPERS-TO-GO, INC.

PO Box 1677
Marble Falls, TX 78654
Tel.: (830) 693-1056
Fax: (830) 693-1057
Toll Free: (800) 843-7094
E-mail: info@wallpaperstogo.com
Web Site: www.wallpaperstogo.com
Approx. Number Employees: 80
Year Founded: 1977
Business Description:
Wallpaper Sales
S.I.C.: 5231; 6794
N.A.I.C.S.: 444120; 533110
Advertising Expenditures: $200,000
Media: 5-8-9-17-18-19-23-24-25-26
Distr.: Natl.
Personnel:
Harold Otto *(Pres)*

WALTER DRAKE, INC.

(Sub. of Blyth, Inc.)
4630 Forge Rd Ste A
Colorado Springs, CO 80907
Tel.: (719) 638-3000
Fax: (888) 252-8462
Toll Free: (877) 925-8373
Toll Free: (800) 525-9291
E-mail: help@wdrake.com
Web Site: www.wdrake.com
Sales Range: $25-49.9 Million
Approx. Number Employees: 22
Year Founded: 1947
Business Description:
Mail Order Services
S.I.C.: 5961
N.A.I.C.S.: 454113
Import
Media: 4-5-8-13-23-24-25-26
Distr.: Direct to Consumer; Natl.
Budget Set: Jan. -Dec.
Brands & Products:
WALTER DRAKE
Advertising Agency:
Miles Kimball Company
250 City Ctr
Oshkosh, WI 54906
Tel.: (920) 231-3800
Fax: (920) 231-4804

WARNER BROS. RECORDS, INC.

(Sub. of Warner Music Group Corp.)
3300 Warner Blvd
Burbank, CA 91505
Tel.: (818) 846-9090
Fax: (818) 846-8474
Web Site:
www.warnerbrosrecords.com
Sales Range: $75-99.9 Million
Approx. Number Employees: 300
Business Description:
Records, Tapes & Music Publisher
S.I.C.: 7389
N.A.I.C.S.: 512290
Media: 2-6-7-8-9-13-22
Distr.: Natl.
Budget Set: Jan.
Personnel:
Rob Cavallo *(Chm)*
Todd Moscowitz *(Co-Pres & CEO)*
Livia Tortella *(Co-Pres & COO)*
Mark Bright *(Pres & CEO-Word Entertainment)*
J. Scavo *(Sr VP-Digital Mktg)*

WILD WINGS INC.

2101 S Hwy 61
Lake City, MN 55041
Tel.: (651) 345-5355
Fax: (651) 345-2981
Toll Free: (800) 445-4833
E-mail: info@wildwings.com
Web Site: www.wildwings.com
Approx. Sls.: $20,000,000
Approx. Number Employees: 70
Business Description:
Mail Order House
S.I.C.: 5961; 2741
N.A.I.C.S.: 454113; 511199
Media: 4-8
Personnel:
Randy Eggenberger *(CEO)*
Brands & Products:
WILD WINGS

WINMARK CORPORATION

605 Highway 169 N Ste 400
Minneapolis, MN 55441
Tel.: (763) 520-8500
Fax: (763) 520-8410
Toll Free: (800) 567-6600
E-mail: winmark.information@winmarkcorporation.com
Web Site:
www.winmarkcorporation.com
Approx. Rev.: $41,203,600
Approx. Number Employees: 100
Year Founded: 1988
Business Description:
Value Oriented Retail Concepts Developer, Franchiser & Operater for Stores that Buy, Sell, Trade & Consign Quality Used & New Merchandise
S.I.C.: 5399; 5651; 5736; 5932; 5941; 5945
N.A.I.C.S.: 452990; 448140; 451110; 451120; 451140; 453310
Advertising Expenditures: $116,500
Media: 5-8
Personnel:
John L. Morgan *(Chm & CEO)*
Brett D. Heffes *(Pres)*
Anthony D. Ishaug *(CFO & Treas)*
Steven A. Murphy *(Pres-Franchising)*
Leah A. Goff *(VP-HR)*
Merry Beth Hovey *(VP-Mktg)*
Brands & Products:
CREATE SUPPORT FINANCE BUSINESS
LEASEMANAGER
MUSIC GO ROUND
ONCE UPON A CHILD
PLAT IT AGAIN SPORTS
PLATO'S CLOSET
WINMARK
WINMARK BUSINESS SOLUTIONS
WINMARK CAPITAL
WIRTH BUSINESS CREDIT

WM. F. COMLY & SON, INC.

1825 E Boston St
Philadelphia, PA 19125-1201
Tel.: (215) 634-2500
Fax: (215) 634-0496
Toll Free: (800) 883-2665
E-mail: auctions@comly.com
Web Site: www.comly.com
Approx. Number Employees: 30
Year Founded: 1834
Business Description:
Auction Services
S.I.C.: 5961
N.A.I.C.S.: 454112
Media: 2-7-9-13-25-26
Distr.: Reg.
Budget Set: Dec. -Jan.
Personnel:
Andrew J. Comly *(Owner, Auctioneer & Appraiser)*
Stephen E. Comly *(Pres)*
Miriam Solter *(Mgr-Adv)*
Brands & Products:
COMLY
WM. F. COMLY & SON

XS CARGO INCOME FUND

15435 131 Avenue
Edmonton, AB T5V 0A4, Canada
Tel.: (780) 413-4296
Fax: (780) 413-4297
E-mail: custservice@xscargo.com
Web Site: www.shopxscargo.com
Approx. Sls.: $103,774,606
Approx. Number Employees: 113
Year Founded: 2005
Business Description:
Discount Merchandise Retailer
S.I.C.: 5311; 5961
N.A.I.C.S.: 452111; 454111
Media: 9
Personnel:
William M. Gray *(Chm & Sec)*
Michael J. McKenna *(Pres & CEO)*

THE YANKEE CANDLE COMPANY, INC.

(Holding of Madison Dearborn Partners, LLC)
16 Yankee Candle Way
South Deerfield, MA 01373
Mailing Address:
PO Box 110
South Deerfield, MA 01373-0110
Tel.: (413) 665-8306
Fax: (413) 665-4815
Toll Free: (800) 839-6038
E-mail: info@yankeecandle.com
Web Site: www.yankeecandle.com
Approx. Sls.: $687,600,000
Approx. Number Employees: 2,100
Year Founded: 1969
Business Description:
Designer, Mfr, Whslr & Retailer of Scented Candles
S.I.C.: 3999; 5999
N.A.I.C.S.: 339999; 453998
Advertising Expenditures: $13,057,000
Media: 4-6-8-10-16-19-23
Personnel:
Craig W. Rydin *(Chm)*
Harlan M. Kent *(Pres & CEO)*
Martha S. LaCroix *(Chief HR Officer & Exec VP)*
James A. Perley *(Pres-Intl Div, Exec VP & Gen Counsel)*
Stephen Farley *(Pres-Retail Div)*
Bruce L. Hartman *(Sr VP-Fin)*
Art Rubeck *(Sr VP-Supply Chain)*
Deborah Norris *(VP & Grp Mgr-Consumer Direct, Fundraising & Outlets)*
Heidi Partain *(Dir-Consumer Insights)*
Brands & Products:
AMBER SUNSET
BALSAM AND CEDAR HOUSEWARMER
BUTTERCREAM
CHRISTMAS EVA
CHRISTMAS WISH
CHRISTMAS WREATH
CLEAN COTTON
FRESH COMFORT
HARVEST
HOLIDAY SAGE
HOUSEWARMER
ILLUMINATIONS
ISLAND MANGO
JACK FROST
MIDSUMMERS NIGHT
MISTLETOE
SPLASH OF RAIN
SUGARED PLUMS
SUMMER FRESH
SUNWASHED LINEN
SWEET HOME
TART
YANKEE CANDLE

ZENVESCO, INC.

(d/b/a Kidstuff.com)
7090 Whipple Ave
North Canton, OH 44720
Tel.: (330) 244-9518
Fax: (330) 244-9518
E-mail: info@kidstuff.com
Web Site: www.kidstuff.com
Approx. Number Employees: 20
Business Description:
Children's Products Retailer
S.I.C.: 3944
N.A.I.C.S.: 339932
Media: 4-8-10-13
Personnel:
William L. Miller *(Pres)*
Brands & Products:
JEANNIE'S KIDS CLUB
KID STUFF
THE NATURAL BABY CATALOG
PERFECTLY SAFE

Key to Media (For complete agency information see *The Advertising Red Books-Agencies* edition):
1. Bus. Publs. 2. Cable T.V. 3. Catalogs & Directories. 4. Co-op Adv. 5. Consumer Mags. 6. D.M. to Bus. Estab.7. D.M. to Consumers 8. Daily Newsp. 9. Exhibits/Trade Shows 10. Foreign 11. Infomercial 12. Internet Adv.13. Multimedia 14. Network Radio 15. Network T.V. 16. Newsp. Distr. Mags. 17. Other 18. Outdoor (Posters, Transit) 19. Point of Purchase20. Premiums, Novelties 21. Product Samples 22. Special Events Mktg. 23. Spot Radio 24. Spot T.V. 25. Weekly Newsp. 26. Yellow Page Adv.

Electronics, Radio & Television

Audio Equipment — Electronic Detection Systems — Electronic Parts — Video Equipment

AAVID THERMALLOY, LLC
(Sub. of Aavid Thermal Technologies, Inc.)
70 Commercial St
Concord, NH 03301
Tel.: (603) 224-9988
Fax: (603) 223-1790
E-mail: info@aavid.com
Web Site: www.aavidthermalloy.com
Sales Range: $100-124.9 Million
Approx. Number Employees: 1,000
Year Founded: 1964
Business Description:
Thermal Engineering & Thermal Management Solutions to Semiconductor Industry
S.I.C.: 3679
N.A.I.C.S.: 334419
Media: 2-4-7-10
Distr.: Intl.; Natl.
Budget Set: Dec.
Personnel:
Bhartan R. Patel *(Pres & CEO)*
Brian Byrne *(CFO, Treas & VP)*

ABT ELECTRONICS, INC.
1200 Milwaukee Ave
Glenview, IL 60025
Tel.: (847) 967-8830
Fax: (847) 544-2270
E-mail: abtmarketing@abt.com
Web Site: www.abt.com
Sales Range: $400-449.9 Million
Approx. Number Employees: 1,000
Year Founded: 1936
Business Description:
Electronics Retailer
S.I.C.: 5731; 5961
N.A.I.C.S.: 443112; 454111; 454113
Media: 13
Personnel:
Robert Abt *(CEO)*
Steve Tazic *(Mgr-Mktg)*

ACOPIAN TECHNICAL COMPANY
131 Loomis St
Easton, PA 18045
Mailing Address:
PO Box 638
Easton, PA 18044
Tel.: (610) 258-5441
Fax: (610) 258-2842
E-mail: atcsales@acopian.com
Web Site: www.acopian.com
Approx. Number Employees: 130
Year Founded: 1960
Business Description:
Electronic Power Supply Mfr
S.I.C.: 3679
N.A.I.C.S.: 334419
Export
Advertising Expenditures: $200,000
Media: 2-4-7
Distr.: Intl.; Natl.
Personnel:
G. Acopian *(Pres)*
Thomas Skopal *(VP-Mktg)*

ACR ELECTRONICS, INC.
(Sub. of Cobham Mission Systems)
5757 Ravenswood Rd
Fort Lauderdale, FL 33312-6603
Tel.: (954) 981-3333
Fax: (954) 983-5087
Toll Free: (800) 432-0227
E-mail: info@acrelectronics.com
Web Site: www.acrelectronics.com
E-Mail For Key Personnel:
President: pfrank@acrelectronics.com
Sales Director: rcrowder@acrelectronics.com
Approx. Number Employees: 225
Year Founded: 1956
Business Description:
Electronic Rescue & Survival Equipment Mfr
S.I.C.: 3648
N.A.I.C.S.: 335129
Media: 4-5-6-8-10-19
Distr.: Intl.; Natl.
Budget Set: Oct. -Nov.
Personnel:
Ron Crowder *(Dir-Sls)*
Dennis London *(Dir-Sls Europe)*
Scott Morgan *(Dir-Bus Dev-Satellite Comm)*
Chris Wahler *(Dir-Mktg)*
Brands & Products:
406 PLB
ACR
C-LIGHT
C-STROBE
DISTRESS O.S
DOUBLEFLY
FIREFLY
FIREFLY 2
FIREFLY PLUS
GLOBALFIX
GYPSI
GYPSI 406 PLB
HEMILIGHT
HOT SHOT
L-20(A)
L8-1(A)
L8-3
MINI B
MS-2000 (M)
RAPIDDITCH
RAPIDDITCH EXPRESS BAG
RAPIDFIRE LIGHT
RAPIDFIX 406
SEA SHELTER
THERMABLANKET
UNIVERSAL LOWPRO
VECTA 2
Advertising Agency:
Seitz, Inc.
1350 S Powerline Rd Ste 111
Pompano Beach, FL 33069
Tel.: (954) 970-3394
Fax: (954) 970-3396

ACTIVE ELECTRICAL SUPPLY COMPANY
4240 W Lawrence Ave
Chicago, IL 60630-2730
Tel.: (773) 282-6300
Fax: (773) 282-5206
E-mail: info@active-elec.com
Web Site: www.active-elec.com
Approx. Number Employees: 120
Year Founded: 1953
Business Description:
Wholesale Electrical Distr
S.I.C.: 5063; 5719
N.A.I.C.S.: 423610; 442299
Advertising Expenditures: $350,000
Media: 2-4-5-6-7-10-11-14-18-19-20-22-23-25-26
Distr.: Reg.
Budget Set: Aug.
Personnel:
Ray Fox *(Pres)*
James Swan *(VP & Gen Mgr)*
Linda Fox *(VP & Mgr-Credit)*

ACTIVE POWER, INC.
2128 W Braker Ln Bldg 12
Austin, TX 78758
Tel.: (512) 836-6464
Fax: (512) 836-4511
E-mail: info@activepower.com
Web Site: www.activepower.com
Approx. Rev.: $64,955,000
Approx. Number Employees: 181
Year Founded: 1996
Business Description:
Mfr. of Energy Storage Products
S.I.C.: 4939; 3679
N.A.I.C.S.: 221111; 334419
Advertising Expenditures: $33,000
Media: 2-7-10
Personnel:
Benjamin L. Scott *(Chm)*
James A. Clishem *(Pres & CEO)*
John K. Penver *(CFO, Sec & VP-Fin)*
Uwe Schrader-Hausmann *(CTO & VP-Engrg)*
Martin T. Olsen *(VP & Gen Mgr-Global Sls & Bus Dev)*
Lisa M. Brown *(VP-Mktg & Sls Ops)*
Lee Higgins *(Mgr-PR)*
Brands & Products:
ACTIVE POWER
CLEANSOURCE
CLEANSOURCE2
GENSTART
QUALITY POWER FOR A DIGITAL WORLD

ADDVANTAGE TECHNOLOGIES GROUP, INC.
1221 E Houston
Broken Arrow, OK 74012
Tel.: (918) 251-9121
Fax: (918) 251-0792
Web Site: www.addvantagetech.com
Approx. Rev.: $47,306,130
Approx. Number Employees: 129
Year Founded: 1985
Business Description:
New & Used Cable TV Equipment Sales
S.I.C.: 5046; 3663; 5063; 5065
N.A.I.C.S.: 423440; 334220; 423610; 423690
Advertising Expenditures: $200,000
Media: 2-7
Personnel:
David E. Chymiak *(Chm)*
Kenneth A. Chymiak *(Pres & CEO)*
Scott A. Francis *(CFO)*

ADT SECURITY SERVICES, INC.
(Sub. of Tyco Fire & Security)
1 Town Ctr Rd
Boca Raton, FL 33486-1010

Key to Media (For complete agency information see *The Advertising Red Books-Agencies* edition):
1. Bus. Publs. 2. Cable T.V. 3. Catalogs & Directories. 4. Co-op Adv. 5. Consumer Mags. 6. D.M. to Bus. Estab.7. D.M. to Consumers 8. Daily Newsp. 9. Exhibits/Trade Shows 10. Foreign 11. Infomercial 12. Internet Adv.13. Multimedia 14. Network Radio 15. Network T.V. 16. Newsp. Distr. Mags. 17. Other 18. Outdoor (Posters, Transit) 19. Point of Purchase20. Premiums, Novelties 21. Product Samples 22. Special Events Mktg. 23. Spot Radio 24. Spot T.V. 25. Weekly Newsp. 26. Yellow Page Adv.

ADT Security Services, Inc. — (Continued)

Mailing Address:
PO Box 5035
Boca Raton, FL 33431
Tel.: (561) 988-3600
Fax: (561) 988-3601
Web Site: www.adt.com
Approx. Number Employees: 700
Year Founded: 1874
Business Description:
Homer Monitoring Services & Electric Security System Mfr
S.I.C.: 7382; 3699
N.A.I.C.S.: 561621; 335999
Media: 1-2-3-4-5-6-7-8-9-10-13-18-19-20-22-23-24-25-26
Distr.: Intl.; Natl.
Budget Set: Nov.
Personnel:
John C. Kenning *(Pres-Comml)*
John B. Koch *(Pres-ADT North America)*
Mike Hanley *(VP-Installation & Svc)*
Lee Pernice *(Dir-Retail Mktg)*
Brands & Products:
ADT
ADT ALWAYS THERE
ASSETPRO
DOUBLECHECK
MOBILESAFETY
PREMISEPRO
RANGER AMERICAN
SAFESHIELD
SAFEWATCH
SENSORMATIC
STILL THE FIRST
VIDEOPOINT
Advertising Agency:
Doner
25900 Northwestern Hwy.
Southfield, MI 48075
Tel.: (248) 354-9700
Fax: (248) 827-8440

ADVANCED ANALOGIC TECHNOLOGIES INCORPORATED
(d/b/a AnalogicTech)
3230 Scott Blvd
Santa Clara, CA 95054-3011
Tel.: (408) 737-4600
Fax: (408) 767-4611
E-mail: info@analogictech.com
Web Site: www.analogictech.com
Approx. Rev.: $94,061,000
Approx. Number Employees: 281
Business Description:
Power Management Semiconductor Designer, Marketer & Supplier for Consumer Electronics
S.I.C.: 3699; 3674
N.A.I.C.S.: 335999; 334413
Advertising Expenditures: $500,000
Media: 2-10-22
Personnel:
Samuel J. Anderson *(Chm)*
Richard K. Williams *(Pres, CEO & CTO)*
Ashok Chandran *(Interim CFO)*
Jun-Wei Chen *(VP-Tech)*
Brands & Products:
ANALOGIC
CHARGEPUMP
WE MANAGE YOUR POWER

ADVANCED ENERGY INDUSTRIES, INC.
1625 Sharp Point Dr
Fort Collins, CO 80525-4423
Tel.: (970) 221-4670
Fax: (970) 221-5583
Toll Free: (800) 446-9167
E-mail: ir@aei.com
Web Site: www.advanced-energy.com
Approx. Sls.: $459,414,000
Approx. Number Employees: 1,788
Year Founded: 1981
Business Description:
Mfr of Electronic Power Supplies & Controls
S.I.C.: 3679; 3663; 3699
N.A.I.C.S.: 334418; 334220; 334419; 335999
Export
Advertising Expenditures: $600,000
Personnel:
Yuval Wasserman *(Pres & COO)*
Garry Rogerson *(CEO)*
Danny C. Herron *(CFO & Exec VP)*
James Guilmart *(Sr VP)*
Brands & Products:
ACTIVE MATCHING NETWORK
ADVANCED ENERGY
AE
AERA
APEX
ASTRAL
CESAR
CRYSTAL
DIAMOND
DRESSLER
EMCO
EWAVE
FIXEDMATCH
FLAT PANEL FOCUS
GENCAL
HFV
HILIGHT
HPG
IDS
IKOR
INTEGRO
LINEUP
LITMAS
MACH ONE
NAVIGATOR
NEURALSTEP
OVATION
PARAMOUNT
PDX
PI-980
PINNACLE
POWERVIEW
PV SUN TIMES
RPT
SAFEGUARD
SEKIDENKO
SOLARON
SPUTTER SPOTLIGHT
SUMMIT
TRANSFORMER
VARIOMATCH
XSTREAM
Z'SCAN
Z'WARE

ADVANCED MEDIA TECHNOLOGIES, INC.
(Sub. of ITOCHU Corporation)
3150 SW 15th Street
Deerfield Beach, FL 33442
Tel.: (954) 427-5711
Fax: (954) 427-9688
Toll Free: (888) 293-5856
E-mail: sales@goamt.com
Web Site: www.amt.com
E-Mail For Key Personnel:
Sales Director: sales@goamt.com
Approx. Number Employees: 50
Business Description:
Importation & Distribution of Satellite Receivers
S.I.C.: 4841
N.A.I.C.S.: 515210
Advertising Expenditures: $600,000
Media: 2-6-8-9-10
Distr.: Natl.
Budget Set: Dec.
Personnel:
Ken Mosca *(CEO)*

ADVANCED MICRO DEVICES, INC.
1 AMD Pl
Sunnyvale, CA 94085-3905
Mailing Address:
PO Box 3453
Sunnyvale, CA 94088-3453
Tel.: (408) 749-4000
Fax: (408) 749-4291
Toll Free: (800) 538-8450
E-mail: tech.support@amd.com
Web Site: www.amd.com
Approx. Rev.: $6,494,000,000
Approx. Number Employees: 11,100
Year Founded: 1969
Business Description:
Complex Integrated Circuits Mfr; Microprocessors & Related Peripherals, Memories, Programmable Logic Devices; Circuits for Telecommunications, Office Automation & Networking Applications
S.I.C.: 3674; 3572
N.A.I.C.S.: 334413; 334112
Import Export
Advertising Expenditures: $313,000,000
Media: 2-3-4-5-6-7-8-9-10-11-13-15-18-22-24-25
Distr.: Intl.
Budget Set: Nov.
Personnel:
Bruce L. Claflin *(Chm)*
Rory P. Read *(Pres & CEO)*
Thomas J. Seifert *(CFO & Sr VP)*
Mike Wolfe *(CIO)*
Nigel Dessau *(CMO & Sr VP)*
Emilio Ghilardi *(Chief Sls Officer & Sr VP)*
Karen Guo *(Pres-Greater China & Sr VP)*
Harry A. Wolin *(Gen Counsel, Sr VP & Sec)*
Richard Bergman *(Sr VP & Gen Mgr-Products Grp)*
Allen Sockwell *(Chief Talent Officer & Sr VP-HR)*
Bernard Biolchinias *(VP-Sls & Gen Mgr-Middle East, Turkey & Africa Reg)*
Chris Cloran *(Corp VP & Gen Mgr-Client Div)*
Ronaldo Miranda *(VP & Gen Mgr-Latin America)*
Ben Williams *(Corp VP & Gen Mgr-Asia Pacific)*
Patrick Moorhead *(Corp VP, Fellow-Corp Mktg & Member-Office of Strategy)*
Daryl Sartain *(Dir-Tech Enabling Grp)*
Erik Salo *(Dir-Mktg-Geode Products)*
Charlie Boswell *(Dir-Digital Media & Entertainment)*
Kevin Knox *(Dir-Enterprise Segment Mktg & Bus Dev)*
Georgeanna Liu *(Dir-Market Res-Global)*
Allen Reichard *(Dir-Event Mktg)*
Brent Kerby *(Sr Mgr-Product -Opteron-Mktg)*
Susan Kimmel-Lines *(Sr Mgr-Integrated Mktg-Outbound Mktg & Creative Svcs)*
Craig Lakey *(Sr Mgr-Product Mktg & Pro Graphics)*
Simon Solotko *(Sr Mgr-Advanced Mktg)*
Rami Al Saleh *(Mgr-Sls-MEA)*
John Crank *(Mgr-Worldwide Channel & Distr Bus)*
Pushpita Prasad *(Mgr-Corp Comm)*
Kishna Weaver *(Mgr-Product Mktg)*
Brands & Products:
3DC
3DNOW!
50X15
ADVANCED MICRO DEVICES
AGESA
ALERTIT
ALL-IN-WONDER
AM186
AM188
AM486
AMD
AMD-750
AMD-751
AMD-756
AMD-760
AMD-761
AMD-762
AMD-766
AMD-768
AMD-8000
AMD-8100
AMD-8111
AMD-8113
AMD-8114
AMD-8115
AMD-8131
AMD-8132
AMD-8151
AMD-8152
AMD-8161
AMD ATHLON
AMD COOLCORE
AMD DIGITAL MEDIA XPRESS
AMD DURON
AMD EFFICEON
AMD GEODE
AMD IMAGEON
AMD-K6
AMD-K7
AMD-K8
AMD LIVE!
AMD OPTERON
AMD OVERDRIVE
AMD PHENOM
AMD POWERNOW!
AMD SEMPRON
AMD TURION
AMD VIRTUALIZATION
AMD XILLEON
AMD XPRESS
AMD XPRESSNOW!
AMDEBUG
AMDIRECT
ASK AMD

Key to Media (For complete agency information see *The Advertising Red Books-Agencies* edition):
1. Bus. Publs. 2. Cable T.V. 3. Catalogs & Directories. 4. Co-op Adv. 5. Consumer Mags. 6. D.M. to Bus. Estab.7. D.M. to Consumers 8. Daily Newsp. 9. Exhibits/Trade Shows 10. Foreign 11. Infomercial 12. Internet Adv.13. Multimedia 14. Network Radio 15. Network T.V. 16. Newsp. Distr. Mags. 17. Other 18. Outdoor (Posters, Transit) 19. Point of Purchase20. Premiums, Novelties 21. Product Samples 22. Special Events Mktg. 23. Spot Radio 24. Spot T.V. 25. Weekly Newsp. 26. Yellow Page Adv.

ASPECT
ATI
ATI & DESIGN
ATI AVIVO
ATI CATALYST
ATI FIREMV
ATI FIREPRO
ATI HYPERMEMORY
ATI MOBILITY RADEON
ATI MULTIMEDIA CENTER
ATI RADEON
ATI TV WONDER
AU1000
AU1100
AU1500
AWESIM
CATALYST
CATALYST MEDIA CENTER
CLOSE TO METAL
CROSSFIRE
CTM
E-HOME WONDER
E86
E86MON
EAZYCONNECT
EAZYLAUNCH
EAZYLOOK
ELAN
ES1000
FIREGL
FLEXFIT
FM-ON-DEMAND
FULLSTREAM
THE FUTURE IS FUSION
GEODE ORIGAMI
GEODELINK
HDTV WONDER
HOMEPHY
HTX
HYDRAVISION
HYPERTRANSPORT
HYPERZ
M-LINK
MAGIC PACKET
MEDIADSP
MIRRORBIT
MOBILE AMD ATHLON
MOBILE AMD SEMPRON
MULTVIEW
NETPHY
PCNET
PCNET-FAST
PCNET-PRO
PERMANET
PIXEL TAPESTRY
POWERPLAY
POWERSHIFT
Q-PACK
QUANTISPEED
REMOTE WONDER
SIMNOW
SMARTDMA
SMARTGART
SMARTSHADER
SMOOTHVISION
SPANSION
SURROUNDVIEW
THRUVIEW
TRUFORM
TV-ON-CHIP
TV-ON-DEMAND
THE ULTIMATE VISUAL EXPERIENCE
VARI-BRIGHT
VERSAVISION
VIDEO IMMERSION
VIDEOSHADER
VIDEOSOAP
WEBPAD
WONDER
XCLAIM
XILLEON
XPRESSAUDIO
XPRESSGRAPHICS
XPRESSHUB
XPRESSRAM

Advertising Agencies:
The Bivings Group
2201 Wisconsin Ave NW Ste 310
Washington, DC 20007
Tel.: (202) 741-1500
Fax: (202) 741-1501

Daniel J. Edelman, Inc.
(d/b/a Edelman)
200 E Randolph St Fl 63
Chicago, IL 60601-6705
Tel.: (312) 240-3000
Fax: (312) 240-2900
US Agency of Record

George P. Johnson Company, Inc.
11301 Burnet Rd 2nd Fl
Austin, TX 78758
Tel.: (512) 286-2066
Fax: (512) 286-3300
Global Events

SicolaMartin
206 E 9th Ste 1800
Austin, TX 78701
Tel.: (512) 343-0264
Fax: (512) 343-0659

AEROFLEX INCORPORATED

(Sub. of Aeroflex Holding Corp.)
35 S Service Rd
Plainview, NY 11803
Mailing Address:
PO Box 6022
Plainview, NY 11803-0622
Tel.: (516) 694-6700
Fax: (516) 694-0658
Toll Free: (800) 843-1553
E-mail: info-test@aeroflex.com
Web Site: www.aeroflex.com
E-Mail For Key Personnel:
President: LBorow@aeroflex.com
Approx. Sls.: $655,048,000
Approx. Number Employees: 2,850
Year Founded: 1937
Business Description:
Microelectronics, Test & Measurement Equipment Mfr
S.I.C.: 3674; 3621; 3812; 3823
N.A.I.C.S.: 334413; 334511; 334513; 335312
Import Export
Advertising Expenditures: $300,000
Media: 2-4-8-10-20
Distr.: Natl.
Budget Set: May
Personnel:
Robert B. McKeon *(Chm)*
Leonard Borow *(Pres & CEO)*
John Adamovich, Jr. *(CFO, Sec & Sr VP)*
John E. Buyko *(Exec VP, Pres-AMS)*
Charles Badlato *(Treas, VP & Asst Sec)*
Luis F. Riano *(Mgr-Latin America-Area Sls)*
Brands & Products:
ACTAIR
AEROFLEX
AMPLICOMM
COMSTRON
KORFUND DYNAMICS
LINTEK
MIAMI
MIC TECHNOLOGY
RDL
STAR BAG
TATRA
TRI LINK
UTMC
Advertising Agency:
KZS Advertising
811 W Jericho Tpke Ste 109E
Smithtown, NY 11787
Tel.: (631) 348-1440
Fax: (631) 348-1449

AEROJET-GENERAL CORPORATION

(Div. of GenCorp Inc.)
Hwy 50 Aerojet Rd
Rancho Cordova, CA 95742
Mailing Address:
PO Box 13222
Sacramento, CA 95813
Tel.: (916) 355-4000
Fax: (916) 351-8667
E-mail: comments@aerojet.com
Web Site: www.aerojet.com
Sales Range: $450-499.9 Million
Approx. Number Employees: 3,000
Year Founded: 1942
Business Description:
Provider of Aerospace & Defence Services
S.I.C.: 3764
N.A.I.C.S.: 336415
Media: 2-4-10
Distr.: Intl.; Natl.
Budget Set: Aug.
Personnel:
Scott J. Seymour *(Pres)*
Craig Halterman *(CIO & VP)*
Elizabeth Zacharias *(VP-HR)*
James A. Drakes *(Exec Dir-Advanced Programs-Bus Dev Dept)*
Tim Murphy *(Dir-Pub Affairs-Realty Investments)*

AGILENT TECHNOLOGIES, INC.

5301 Stevens Creek Blvd
Santa Clara, CA 95051
Tel.: (408) 345-8886
Fax: (408) 345-8474
Toll Free: (877) 424-4536
E-mail: contact_us@agilent.com
Web Site: www.agilent.com
Approx. Rev.: $5,444,000,000
Approx. Number Employees: 18,500
Year Founded: 1939
Business Description:
Communications Components, Electronic & Optical Test Measuring & Monitoring Instruments Mfr
S.I.C.: 3674; 3824; 3825
N.A.I.C.S.: 334413; 334514; 334515
Import Export
Advertising Expenditures: $45,000,000
Media: 2-3-6-9-13-14-15-23-24
Personnel:
William P. Sullivan *(Pres & CEO)*
Didier Hirsch *(CFO & Sr VP)*
Michael McMullen *(Sr VP-Agilent & Pres-Chemical Analysis Grp)*
Ron Nersesian *(Sr VP-Agilent & Pres-Electronic Measurement Grp)*
Marie Oh Huber *(Gen Counsel, Sec & Sr VP)*
Jean M. Halloran *(Sr VP-HR)*
Nicolas Roelofs *(Sr VP)*
Gooi Soon Chai *(VP & Gen Mgr-Electronic Instruments Bus Unit Electronic Measure)*
Saleem N. Odeh *(VP & Gen Mgr-Sls, Svc & Support-Electronic Measurement Grp)*
Neil Cook *(VP-R&D, Dir-Molecular Tech Laboratories)*
Sheila Robertson *(VP-Dev & Strategy)*
Frank Ditore *(Product Mgr-SystemVue)*
Linda Lloyd *(Product Mgr-Biocolumns)*
Amy Flores *(Mgr-Corp Media Rels)*
Peter Schweiger *(Corp Acct Mgr & Mgr-Mktg Dev-Americas)*
Brands & Products:
ACCUBOND
AGILENT TECHNOLOGIES
AWARETEST
COMPACT
MEDALIST
OMNIBER
OMNINET
PARBERT
ZORBAX
Advertising Agencies:
Beattie Communications Group
4 Great James St
London, WC1N 3DB, United Kingdom
Tel.: (44) 207 053 6000
Fax: (44) 207 053 6001

Euro RSCG 4D
Burg A Colijnweg 2
P O BOX 9149
1182 AL
Amstelveen, 1180 MC, Netherlands
Tel.: (31) 20 456 5000
Fax: (31) 20 456 5100

Euro RSCG Life
New Otani Garden Court 8F 4-1
Kioicho
Tokyo, 102-8578, Japan
Tel.: (81) 3 5403 7600
Fax: (81) 3 5403 7603

hawkeye
325 Arlington Ave Ste 700
Charlotte, NC 28203
Tel.: (704) 344-7900
Fax: (704) 344-7920

MPG Minneapolis
8500 Normandale Lk Blvd Ste 1960
Minneapolis, MN 55437
Tel.: (952) 832-9510
Fax: (952) 832-9505

PARTNERS+simons
25 Drydock Ave 8th Fl
Boston, MA 02210
Tel.: (617) 330-9393
Fax: (617) 330-9394

PMG Asia Pacific Pte Ltd.
71 Neil Road
Singapore, 088900, Singapore
Tel.: (65) 6324 7955

Key to Media (For complete agency information see *The Advertising Red Books-Agencies* edition):
1. Bus. Publs. 2. Cable T.V. 3. Catalogs & Directories. 4. Co-op Adv. 5. Consumer Mags. 6. D.M. to Bus. Estab.7. D.M. to Consumers 8. Daily Newsp. 9. Exhibits/Trade Shows 10. Foreign 11. Infomercial 12. Internet Adv.13. Multimedia 14. Network Radio 15. Network T.V. 16. Newsp. Distr. Mags. 17. Other 18. Outdoor (Posters, Transit) 19. Point of Purchase20. Premiums, Novelties 21. Product Samples 22. Special Events Mktg. 23. Spot Radio 24. Spot T.V. 25. Weekly Newsp. 26. Yellow Page Adv.

Agilent Technologies, Inc. — (Continued)

Fax: (65) 6324 8284

PMG China - Beijing
Unit #819 Tower A Full Link Plz
Beijing, 100020, China
Tel.: (86) 10 6588 3399

Sharpe Blackmore Euro RSCG
473 Adelaide St W Ste 300
Toronto, ON M5V 1T1, Canada
Tel.: (416) 920-6864
Fax: (416) 920-5043

SS PR
2700 Patriot Blvd Ste 430
Lincolnshire, IL 60026
Tel.: (847) 955-0700
Fax: (847) 955-7720
Toll Free: (800) 287-7720

AGILENT TECHNOLOGIES, INC

(Sub. of Agilent Technologies, Inc.)
234 Cromwell Hill Rd
Monroe, NY 10950
Tel.: (845) 782-6544
Fax: (845) 782-4745
E-mail: info_us@acqiris.com
Sales Range: $100-124.9 Million
Business Description:
Communications Components & Electronic & Optical Test Measuring & Monitoring Instruments Mfr
S.I.C.: 3824; 3825
N.A.I.C.S.: 334514; 334515
Advertising Agency:
The Simon Group, Inc.
1506 Old Bethlehem Pike
Sellersville, PA 18960-1427
Tel.: (215) 453-8700
Fax: (215) 453-1670

AGILYSYS, INC.

28925 Fountain Parkway
Solon, OH 44139
Tel.: (440) 519-8700
Toll Free: (800) 262-3600
E-mail: investors@agilysys.com
Web Site: www.agilysys.com
Approx. Sls.: $675,470,000
Approx. Number Employees: 1,179
Year Founded: 1963
Business Description:
IT Solutions for Corporate & Public Sector Customers
S.I.C.: 5065; 5045
N.A.I.C.S.: 423690; 423430
Import
Media: 2-4-6-7-10-17
Distr.: Natl.
Personnel:
James H. Dennedy *(Pres & CEO)*
Henry R. Bond *(CFO & Sr VP)*
Tina Stehle *(COO & Sr VP)*
Kathleen A. Weigand *(Gen Counsel & Sr VP-HR)*
Paul Civils *(Sr VP & Gen Mgr-Retail Solutions)*
Tony Mellina *(Sr VP & Gen Mgr-Tech Solutions)*
Tony Ross *(VP-Sls-Hospitality Solutions Grp)*
Brands & Products:
CUSTOMERCENTRIC
FIRSTOP
KEYNOTES
Advertising Agency:
Dix & Eaton Incorporated
200 Public Sq Ste 1400
Cleveland, OH 44114
Tel.: (216) 241-0405
Fax: (216) 241-3070

AL & ED'S CORPORATION

(d/b/a Al & Ed's Autosound)
6855 Havenhurst Hwy
Van Nuys, CA 91406
Tel.: (818) 908-5700
Fax: (818) 908-5701
Toll Free: (888) 900-8800
E-mail: customerservice@al-eds.com
Web Site: www.al-eds.com
Approx. Number Employees: 275
Year Founded: 1954
Business Description:
Retailer of Mobile Electronics; Cellular Phones, Car Radios, Stereos, Navigation Systems, Paging, Vehicle, Multimedia & Car Alarms
S.I.C.: 5999; 5013
N.A.I.C.S.: 453998; 441310
Media: 9-14-16-25
Distr.: Natl.
Personnel:
Gabi Mashal *(Pres)*
Barry Hodis *(Mgr-Ops)*
Advertising Agency:
The Pollack PR Marketing Group
1901 Ave of the Stars Ste 1040
Los Angeles, CA 90067
Tel.: (310) 556-4443
Fax: (310) 286-2350
Pub Rels

ALCATEL-LUCENT

(Sub. of ALCATEL LUCENT)
600-700 Mountain Ave
New Providence, NJ 07974
Tel.: (908) 508-8080
Web Site: www.alcatel-lucent.com/wps/portal/contactus
Approx. Rev.: $7,940,000,000
Approx. Number Employees: 21,946
Year Founded: 1996
Business Description:
Wireline & Mobile Telecommunications Infrastructure Design Services
S.I.C.: 4899; 3661
N.A.I.C.S.: 517910; 334210
Media: 2-9-11
Distr.: Direct to Consumer
Budget Set: Dec.
Personnel:
Mark G. Gibbens *(Chief Investment Officer & Head-Corp Fin)*
Sandip Mukerjee *(Pres-IMS Solutions)*
Janet Davidson *(Exec VP)*
Patty Wong *(Mgr-Corp Strategic Mktg)*
Brands & Products:
5ESS
5EXC
APX
CBX 3500
CBX 500
CDMA2000
CELLPIPE
GX 550
JUNIPER NETWORKS E-SERIES
JUNIPER NETWORKS M-SERIES
JUNIPER NETWORKS T-SERIES
LAMBDAUNITE
LAMBDAXTREME
LUCENT
MAX TNT
MESSAGING LINK
THE METROPOLIS
MXOS
MYVIEW TV
NAVIS
NAVISACCESS
NAVISCORE
NAVISRADIUS
NAVISXTEND
NETMINDER
NOVATEL MERLIN
ONELINK
PACKETIN
PACKETSTAR
PIPELINE
QVPN BUILDER
SABLIME
STINGER
SUPERCONNECT
SUPERLINE
SUPERPIPE
SUREPAY
TELESERVICES CALLMANAGER
TRUE ACCESS
V16
VITALACCESS
VITALAPPS
VITALEVENT
VITALNET
VITALQIP
VITALSQM
VITALSUITE
VPN FIREWALL BRICK
WAVESTAR
WINCONSOLE
Advertising Agencies:
Alexander & Richardson
161 Washington Valley Rd Ste 205
Warren, NJ 07059-7121
Tel.: (732) 302-1223
Fax: (732) 356-9574

Alexander & Tom
3500 Boston St Ste 225
Baltimore, MD 21224-5275
Tel.: (410) 327-7400
Fax: (410) 327-7403

DeCarolis Design & Marketing
476 S 1st St
San Jose, CA 95113
Tel.: (408) 947-1411
Fax: (408) 947-1570

FaceTime Strategy
430 W Roosevelt Rd
Wheaton, IL 60187-5056
Tel.: (312) 324-3198

K2 Communications
PO Box 1641
Doylestown, PA 18901-9838
Tel.: (215) 230-7671
Fax: (215) 230-8385

ALCATEL-LUCENT

(Div. of Alcatel-Lucent)
1701 Harbor Bay Pkwy Ste 1
Alameda, CA 94502
Tel.: (510) 769-6001
Fax: (510) 814-2300
Toll Free: (800) 621-9578
E-mail: execoffice@alcatel-lucent.com
Web Site: www.alcatel-lucent.com
Approx. Sls.: $1,478,682,000
Approx. Number Employees: 721
Year Founded: 1989
Business Description:
Develops, Manufactures, Markets, Sells & Supports a Broad Range of High-Speed Digital Remote Networking Products Covering ISPS, WANS, Telecommunication Carriers
S.I.C.: 3572; 3661
N.A.I.C.S.: 334112; 334210
Advertising Expenditures: $2,500,000
Media: 7-11-13
Personnel:
Tony Costa *(Dir-Strategy)*
Mike Maney *(Dir-Influencer Mgmt)*
Brands & Products:
ACCELERATE
APX 8000
IGEN
LAMBDAUNITE
NAVIS
WAVESTAR ADM 16/1

ALCATEL-LUCENT USA, INC.

(Sub. of Alcatel-Lucent)
3400 W Plano Pkwy
Plano, TX 75075
Tel.: (972) 519-3000
Fax: (972) 477-6878
Toll Free: (800) ALCATEL
Web Site: www.alcatel-lucent.com
Sales Range: $600-649.9 Million
Approx. Number Employees: 6,753
Year Founded: 1976
Business Description:
Mfr., Designer, Developer & Marketer of Digital Switching, Transmission, Access & Private Network System Products
S.I.C.: 3661; 1731
N.A.I.C.S.: 334210; 238210
Import Export
Advertising Expenditures: $1,000,000
Media: 2-3-7-9-10-18-24-26
Distr.: Intl.; Natl.
Budget Set: Oct.
Personnel:
Kenneth Frank *(Pres-Solutions, Exec VP & Mktg)*
Brands & Products:
ACCUDACS
BASIS
CP1000S
CP2000
CP3000
CP4000
DSC NEXOS
DYNAMIC OFFICE BALANCER
IBSS
IMTN
LITESPAN
MEGAHUB
PAIRSPAN
SCANCOM
STARSPAN
TERAHUB
TIMESPAN
VGDF
WRAP-A-DAX

ALION SCIENCE AND TECHNOLOGY CORPORATION

1750 Tysons Blvd Ste 1300
McLean, VA 22102
Tel.: (703) 918-4480
Fax: (703) 506-1813
Toll Free: (877) 771-6252
E-mail: contact@alionscience.com
Web Site: www.alionscience.com

Key to Media (For complete agency information see *The Advertising Red Books-Agencies* edition):
1. Bus. Publs. 2. Cable T.V. 3. Catalogs & Directories. 4. Co-op Adv. 5. Consumer Mags. 6. D.M. to Bus. Estab.7. D.M. to Consumers
8. Daily Newsp. 9. Exhibits/Trade Shows 10. Foreign 11. Infomercial 12. Internet Adv.13. Multimedia 14. Network Radio
15. Network T.V. 16. Newsp. Distr. Mags. 17. Other 18. Outdoor (Posters, Transit) 19. Point of Purchase20. Premiums, Novelties
21. Product Samples 22. Special Events Mktg. 23. Spot Radio 24. Spot T.V. 25. Weekly Newsp. 26. Yellow Page Adv.

Approx. Rev.: $833,988,000
Approx. Number Employees: 2,886
Year Founded: 2001
Business Description:
Defense Analysis Products, Wireless Telecommunication Networks, Industrial Facilities, Weapon Analysis & Support Products & Modeling & Simulation Technologies Primarily for Military Use
S.I.C.: 8733; 3731; 4812; 8299; 8711; 9711
N.A.I.C.S.: 541710; 336611; 517212; 541330; 611512; 928110
Media: 10
Personnel:
Bahman Atefi *(Chm & CEO)*
Michael J. Alber *(CFO)*
Stacy Mendler *(COO)*
Patricia A. Weaver *(Chief Admin Officer)*
Thomas McCabe *(Gen Counsel & Sec)*
Charles Fletcher, Jr. *(Sr VP & Mgr-Strategic Ops Grp)*
Stephen Miller *(VP & Mgr-Mgmt & Decision Support Ops)*
Tim Cook *(Dir-Govt Rels)*
Damon Griggs *(Dir-Strategic Initiatives)*
Steve Kimmel *(Dir-Strategic Customers Rels)*
Christopher Amos *(Mgr-Tech Solutions Grp)*
Susan Archer *(Mgr-Operational Solutions Grp)*
Richard E. Brooks *(Mgr-Distributed Simulation Grp)*
Greg Bryant *(Mgr-Integration Solutions Grp)*
Scott Fry *(Mgr-Engrg & Integration Solutions Sector)*
David H. Ohle *(Mgr-Defense Ops & Integrations Sector)*
Rod Riddick *(Deputy Mgr-Engrg & Integration Solutions Sector)*
John Waikwicz *(Mgr-Design & Engrg & Tech Grp)*
Brands & Products:
3D IMANUAL
ACAT
ATACT
THE BUDDY SYSTEM
FACET
IMANUAL
MOBSIM
RF ANALYST
SIMVIEWER
SMART
SVS

ALLIED MOTION TECHNOLOGIES INC.

23 Inverness Way E Ste 150
Englewood, CO 80112-5711
Tel.: (303) 799-8520
Fax: (303) 799-8521
E-mail: corpinfo@alliedmotion.com
Web Site: www.alliedmotion.com
Approx. Rev.: $80,591,000
Approx. Number Employees: 456
Year Founded: 1962
Business Description:
Motion Application Solutions & Services
S.I.C.: 3829; 3621; 3625; 3643
N.A.I.C.S.: 334519; 335312; 335314; 335931
Import Export
Media: 2-7-10-21
Distr.: Natl.
Budget Set: Dec.
Personnel:
Richard D. Smith *(Chm & CFO)*
Richard S. Warzala *(Pres & CEO)*
Kenneth R. Wyman *(CIO & VP-Mktg)*

ALLIEDBARTON SECURITY SERVICES

(Holding of The Blackstone Group L.P.)
161 Washington St Ste 600
Conshohocken, PA 19428
Tel.: (484) 351-1300
Fax: (610) 239-1107
Toll Free: (888) 239-1104
E-mail: info@alliedbarton.com
Web Site: www.alliedbarton.com
E-Mail For Key Personnel:
Public Relations: mediarelations@alliedbarton.com
Sales Range: $800-899.9 Million
Approx. Number Employees: 38,000
Year Founded: 1957
Business Description:
Asset Protection & Security Services
S.I.C.: 7381
N.A.I.C.S.: 561613; 561611; 561612
Media: 1-2-4-7-9-10
Distr.: Natl.
Budget Set: May
Personnel:
William C. Whitmore, Jr. *(Chm, Pres & CEO)*
William A. Torzolini *(CFO)*
Jim Gillece *(Chief People Officer & Sr VP-Human Capital Mgmt)*
Carol Johnson *(Sr VP-Client Experience)*

ALPINE ELECTRONICS OF AMERICA, INC.

(Sub. of Alps Electric Co., Ltd.)
19145 Gramercy Pl
Torrance, CA 90501-1128
Mailing Address:
PO Box 2859
Torrance, CA 90509-2859
Tel.: (310) 326-8000
Fax: (310) 533-0369
Fax: (310) 782-0726 (Mktg)
Toll Free: (800) ALPINE1
Web Site: www.alpine.com
Approx. Number Employees: 356
Year Founded: 1978
Business Description:
Mfr & Importer of Mobile Electronics
S.I.C.: 5064; 3651
N.A.I.C.S.: 423620; 334310
Import Export
Advertising Expenditures: $1,000,000
Media: 6-19
Distr.: Natl.
Budget Set: Oct.
Personnel:
Kaz Watanabe *(Pres)*
Koichi Endo *(CTO-Product Dev & Dir)*
Jim O'Neill *(Exec VP-Sls & Mktg)*
Toshinori Kobayashi *(Dir-Sls & Mktg Plng)*
Satoshi Soma *(Dir-Corp Planning & Admin)*
Brands & Products:
ALPINE
Advertising Agency:
Wong, Doody, Crandall, Wiener
8500 Steller Dr Ste 5
Culver City, CA 90232-2427
Tel.: (310) 280-7800
Fax: (310) 280-7780
(Retail & Trade Advertising & Multimedia Promotion of New Products)

AMATEUR ELECTRONIC SUPPLY LLC

5710 W Good Hope Rd
Milwaukee, WI 53223-4736
Tel.: (414) 358-4088
Tel.: (414) 358-0333
Fax: (414) 358-3337
Toll Free: (800) 558-0411
E-mail: milwaukee@aesham.com
Web Site: www.aesham.com
Approx. Number Employees: 25
Year Founded: 1998
Business Description:
Radios & Electronic Supplies Distr
S.I.C.: 5731; 5065
N.A.I.C.S.: 443112; 423690
Import Export
Media: 4-8-13
Personnel:
Phil M. Majerus *(Owner)*
Brands & Products:
AES

AMERICAN SHIZUKI CORPORATION

(Sub. of Shizuki Electric Company, Inc.)
(d/b/a ASC Capacitors)
301 W O St
Ogallala, NE 69153
Tel.: (308) 284-3611
Fax: (308) 284-8324
E-mail: sales@ascapacitor.com
Web Site: www.ascapacitor.com
E-Mail For Key Personnel:
Sales Director: sales@ascapacitor.com
Approx. Number Employees: 150
Business Description:
Electronic Components Mfr
S.I.C.: 3675
N.A.I.C.S.: 334414
Import Export
Media: 2-4-7-10-21
Distr.: Intl.; Natl.
Budget Set: Apr.
Personnel:
Steve Zimmerman *(Pres)*
Stacey Bauer *(Dir-Bus Dev)*
Ron Hollmann *(Mgr-Mktg & Sls)*
Bill Reutzel *(Mgr-QA/QC)*
Brands & Products:
ASC

AMERICAN TECHNICAL CERAMICS CORP.

(Sub. of AVX Corporation)
1 Norden Ln
Huntington Station, NY 11746
Tel.: (631) 622-4700
Fax: (631) 622-4748
E-mail: sales@atceramics.com
Web Site: www.atceramics.com
E-Mail For Key Personnel:
Sales Director: sales@atceramics.com
Approx. Sls.: $93,763,000
Approx. Number Employees: 782
Year Founded: 1966
Business Description:
RF/Microwave/Millimeter Wave Ceramic & Porcelain Capacitors & Thin Film Products Mf., Designer, Developer & Marketer
S.I.C.: 3675; 3679
N.A.I.C.S.: 334414; 334419
Export
Advertising Expenditures: $200,000
Media: 2-4-10-21
Distr.: Intl.; Natl.
Budget Set: July
Personnel:
Victor Insetta *(Pres & CEO)*
David Ott *(Sr VP-Ops-NY)*
Brands & Products:
MICROCAP
QUIK-CALC
QUIK PICK 48 HOUR SHIPMENT SYSTEM
SUPERCHIPS
TECH-SELECT

AMERICAN TECHNOLOGY CORPORATION

(Name Changed to LRAD Corporation)

AMETEK FLOORCARE SPECIALTY MOTORS DIVISION

(Div. of AMETEK Electromechanical Group)
627 Lake St
Kent, OH 44240
Tel.: (330) 673-3451
Fax: (330) 677-3736
Web Site: www.gselectric.com
Sales Range: $250-299.9 Million
Approx. Number Employees: 820
Year Founded: 1968
Business Description:
Specialty Motor Mfr
S.I.C.: 3621; 5063
N.A.I.C.S.: 335312; 423610
Import Export
Bus. Publs.: 45%; Co-op Adv.: 50%; Exhibits/Trade Shows: 5%
Brands & Products:
B-PAK

AMETEK PANALARM PRODUCTS

(Unit of AMETEK Electronic Instruments Group)
1725 Western Dr
West Chicago, IL 60185-1880
Tel.: (630) 231-5900
Fax: (630) 621-3154
Web Site: www.panalarm.com
Sales Range: $75-99.9 Million
Approx. Number Employees: 9
Business Description:
Monitoring Products Mfr
S.I.C.: 5065; 5063
N.A.I.C.S.: 423690; 423610
Import Export
Media: 2-3-10-26
Distr.: Natl.
Budget Set: Sept.
Brands & Products:
PANALARM
Advertising Agency:
Lefton Company
100 Independence Mall W

Key to Media (For complete agency information see *The Advertising Red Books-Agencies* edition):
1. Bus. Publs. 2. Cable T.V. 3. Catalogs & Directories. 4. Co-op Adv. 5. Consumer Mags. 6. D.M. to Bus. Estab.7. D.M. to Consumers 8. Daily Newsp. 9. Exhibits/Trade Shows 10. Foreign 11. Infomercial 12. Internet Adv.13. Multimedia 14. Network Radio 15. Network T.V. 16. Newsp. Distr. Mags. 17. Other 18. Outdoor (Posters, Transit) 19. Point of Purchase20. Premiums, Novelties 21. Product Samples 22. Special Events Mktg. 23. Spot Radio 24. Spot T.V. 25. Weekly Newsp. 26. Yellow Page Adv.

AMETEK Panalarm Products — (Continued)

Philadelphia, PA 19106-2399
Tel.: (215) 923-9600
Fax: (215) 351-4298

AMETEK PROGRAMMABLE POWER, INC.

(Sub. of AMETEK Electronic Instruments Group)
9250 Brown Deer Rd
San Diego, CA 92121-2267
Tel.: (858) 450-0085
Fax: (858) 458-0267
Toll Free: (800) 733-5427
Web Site: www.elgar.com
Sales Range: $50-74.9 Million
Approx. Number Employees: 400
Year Founded: 1965
Business Description:
Programmable Power Supply System Developer & Mfr
S.I.C.: 3663; 3651; 3679; 4911; 4924; 4931; 4939
N.A.I.C.S.: 334220; 221119; 221121; 221122; 221210; 334310; 334418; 334419
Import Export
Media: 2-4-10
Distr.: Intl.; Natl.
Budget Set: Oct.
Personnel:
Tim Croal *(VP & Gen Mgr-Programmable Power Div)*
William Ruff *(Dir-Mktg)*
Brands & Products:
CONTINUOUSWAVE
SMARTWAVE
SWAE
TRUEWAVE
Advertising Agency:
760 Media, Inc.
6965 El Camino Real Ste 105-543
Carlsbad, CA 92011
Tel.: (760) 603-8133
Fax: (760) 603-8138
Toll Free: (888) 760-4332

AMPHENOL CANADA CORP. AEROSPACE & INDUSTRIAL

(Sub. of Amphenol Aerospace & Industrial Operations)
605 Milner Avenue
Toronto, ON M1B 5X6, Canada
Tel.: (416) 291-4401
Fax: (416) 292-0647
E-mail: sales@amphenolcanada.com
Web Site: www.amphenolcanada.com
E-Mail For Key Personnel:
Sales Director: sales@amphenolcanada.com
Sales Range: $25-49.9 Million
Approx. Number Employees: 150
Business Description:
Filtered Connectors & Specialty Interconnect Devices
S.I.C.: 3669
N.A.I.C.S.: 334290
Media: 4

AMPHENOL CORPORATION

358 Hall Ave
Wallingford, CT 06492-3574
Tel.: (203) 265-8900
Fax: (203) 265-8516
Toll Free: (877) 267-4366
Web Site: www.amphenol.com
Approx. Sls.: $3,554,101,000
Approx. Number Employees: 39,100
Year Founded: 1932
Business Description:
Cable & Connector Mfr
S.I.C.: 3678; 3643
N.A.I.C.S.: 334417; 335931
Advertising Expenditures: $250,000
Media: 2-4-7-10-17
Distr.: Natl.
Personnel:
Richard Adam Norwitt *(Co-Pres & CEO)*
Zachary W. Raley *(Co-Pres & Sr VP)*
Diana G. Reardon *(CFO & Sr VP)*
Edward C. Wetmore *(Gen Counsel, Sec & VP)*
Richard E. Schneider *(Sr VP & Grp Gen Mgr)*
Luc Walter *(Sr VP & Grp Gen Mgr-Intl Military & Aerospace Ops)*
Jerome F. Monteith *(VP-HR)*
Udo Naujoks *(Gen Mgr-Amphenol-Tuchel Electronics GmbH)*
Sherry Madsen *(Coord-Trade Show)*
Brands & Products:
THE ADVANTAGE LINE
AIRMAX VS
APTERA
APTERA STACKER
ARMORLITE
C-BYTE
CLGA
CONTROLBOSS
CROSSBOW
CSTACK
EHSD
FLEXTILT
GBX
HD-OPTX
HDM
HDM PLUS
MOTIONGRADE
NEXLEV
NOVONIC
POWERBOSS
POWERBOSSLITE
PULSE-LOK
PULSE-NET
PULSE-PLUS
RADSOK
SIMLOCK
SOCAPEX
SPECTRA-STRIP
STAR-LINE
STAR-LINE EX
TEXLMATE
TIMES FIBER
TUCHEL
VENTURA
VHDM
VHDM-HSD
XCEDE

AMTEL SECURITY SYSTEMS, INC.

1 Amtel Plz 1691 NW 107th Ave
Miami, FL 33172-2707
Tel.: (305) 591-8200
Fax: (305) 470-2683
Toll Free: (800) 222-6835
E-mail: sales@amtelsecurity.com
Web Site: www.amtelasps.com
E-Mail For Key Personnel:
Sales Director: sales@amtelsecurity.com
Approx. Number Employees: 25
Year Founded: 1982
Business Description:
Mfr. of Pre-Entry Telephonic Security Systems, Alarm Panels & Parking Barrier Gates
S.I.C.: 3699; 7382
N.A.I.C.S.: 335999; 561621
Media: 2-4-7-8-10-13-25-26
Distr.: Natl.
Budget Set: Dec.
Personnel:
Suresh Gajwani *(Pres)*
Brands & Products:
AMGATE 880
UNEX
VOIDEX

AMUNEAL MANUFACTURING CORPORATION

4737 Darrah St
Philadelphia, PA 19124
Tel.: (215) 535-3000
Fax: (215) 743-1715
Toll Free: (800) 755-9843
E-mail: info@amuneal.com
Web Site: www.amuneal.com
Sales Range: $1-9.9 Million
Approx. Number Employees: 60
Year Founded: 1965
Business Description:
Magnetic Shield Mfr
S.I.C.: 3444; 3553
N.A.I.C.S.: 332322; 333210
Export
Media: 2-4-8-10-20-21
Distr.: Intl.; Natl.
Budget Set: Dec.
Personnel:
Larry Maltin *(Pres)*
Adam Kamens *(CEO)*
Symond Brain *(VP-Fin & Admin)*
Brands & Products:
AMUMETAL
AMUNEAL
AMUNEAL MANUFACTURING CORP
AMUNICKEL
CRYOPERM 10

ANADIGICS, INC.

141 Mount Bethel Rd
Warren, NJ 07059-5148
Tel.: (908) 668-5000
Fax: (908) 668-5068
E-mail: sales@anadigics.com
Web Site: www.anadigics.com
E-Mail For Key Personnel:
President: bbastani@anadigics.com
Sales Director: sales@anadigics.com
Approx. Sls.: $216,714,000
Approx. Number Employees: 590
Year Founded: 1985
Business Description:
Radio Frequency & Microwave Integrated Circuits
S.I.C.: 3674
N.A.I.C.S.: 334413
Export
Advertising Expenditures: $21,300,000
Media: 2-4-7-10-16-18-20-22
Personnel:
Lewis Solomon *(Chm)*
Ronald Michels *(CEO)*
Tom DeNigris *(COO)*
Thomas C. Shields *(COO)*
Charles Huang *(Exec VP)*
John van Saders *(Sr VP-RF Products)*
John E. Warren, III *(Sr VP)*
Jennifer Palella *(Sr Dir-Mktg)*
Kristina Panek *(Mgr-IR & Stock Plan Admin)*

ANALOG DEVICES, INC.

1 Technology Way PO Box 9106
Norwood, MA 02062-9106
Tel.: (781) 329-4700
Toll Free: (800) 262-5643
E-mail: corp.pr@analog.com
Web Site: www.analog.com
Approx. Rev.: $2,761,503,000
Approx. Number Employees: 8,500
Year Founded: 1965
Business Description:
Designing, Manufacturing & Marketing of High-Performance Analog, Mixed-Signal & Digital Signal Processing Integrated Circuits
S.I.C.: 3674
N.A.I.C.S.: 334413
Import Export
Advertising Expenditures: $3,700,000
Media: 2-4-5-7-10-11
Distr.: Intl.; Natl.
Budget Set: Sept.
Personnel:
Ray Stata *(Chm)*
Jerald G. Fishman *(Pres & CEO)*
David A. Zinsner *(CFO & VP-Fin)*
Seamus Brennan *(Chief Acctg Officer, VP & Controller)*
Margaret K. Seif *(Gen Counsel, Sec & VP)*
William A. Martin *(Treas & Dir-Mergers & Acq)*
Dennis Dempsey *(VP & Gen Mgr-Limerick Mfg)*
Mark Martin *(VP & Gen Mgr-Micromachined Products Div)*
Lon Bott *(VP-Sls-Americas)*
William Matson *(VP-HR)*
Mindy Kohl *(Dir-IR)*
Brands & Products:
ADC ANALYZER
ADISIMADC
ADISIMPOWER
ADVANTIV
ANYCAP
BLACKFIN
CAPTOUCH
DECDRIVER
ICOUPLER
IMEMS
ISENSOR
MACSYM
MICROCONVERTER
OTHELLO
PULSAR
RTI
SALEM
SHARC
SIGMA DSP
SIMPLE SEQUENCER
SOFTCELL
SOFTFONE
TIGERSHARC
TRUPWR
VISUALFONE
X-STREAM
Advertising Agencies:
F&H Porter Novelli
Brabanter Str 4
80805
Munich, Germany
Tel.: (49) 89 121 750

Key to Media (For complete agency information see *The Advertising Red Books-Agencies* edition):
1. Bus. Publs. 2. Cable T.V. 3. Catalogs & Directories. 4. Co-op Adv. 5. Consumer Mags. 6. D.M. to Bus. Estab.7. D.M. to Consumers
8. Daily Newsp. 9. Exhibits/Trade Shows 10. Foreign 11. Infomercial 12. Internet Adv.13. Multimedia 14. Network Radio
15. Network T.V. 16. Newsp. Distr. Mags. 17. Other 18. Outdoor (Posters, Transit) 19. Point of Purchase20. Premiums, Novelties
21. Product Samples 22. Special Events Mktg. 23. Spot Radio 24. Spot T.V. 25. Weekly Newsp. 26. Yellow Page Adv.

Fax: (49) 89 121 751 97

K&L Inc.
Hakuyo Building 3-10 Nibancho
Tokyo, 102-0084, Japan
Tel.: (81) 3 3263 2996
Fax: (81) 3 5211 8134

Media & More, Inc.
17 New England Exec Park
Burlington, MA 01803
Tel.: (781) 272-0440
Fax: (781) 272-4660

Polese Clancy Inc.
300 Summer St
Boston, MA 02210
Tel.: (617) 423-3800
Fax: (617) 423-3802

Porter Novelli
(Sub. of Omnicom Group, Inc.)
75 Varick St 6th Fl
New York, NY 10013
Tel.: (212) 601-8000
Fax: (212) 601-8101

Porter Novelli-Boston
2 Seaport Ln Ste 900
Boston, MA 02110
Tel.: (617) 897-8200
Fax: (617) 897-8203

Porter Novelli-Paris
28 Rue Broca
75005
Paris, France
Tel.: (33) 1 449 49 797
Fax: (33) 1 449 49 798

ST Associates, Inc.
1 Teal Rd
Wakefield, MA 01880
Tel.: (781) 246-4700
Fax: (781) 246-4218

ANAREN, INC.

6635 Kirkville Rd
East Syracuse, NY 13057
Tel.: (315) 432-8909
Fax: (315) 432-9121
Toll Free: (800) 544-2414
E-mail: sales@anaren.com
Web Site: www.anaren.com
Approx. Sls.: $179,170,000
Approx. Number Employees: 1,032
Year Founded: 1967
Business Description:
Mfr, Engineer & Supplier of RF Microwave Components & Subassemblies
S.I.C.: 3663; 3679
N.A.I.C.S.: 334220; 334419
Import Export
Advertising Expenditures: $400,000
Media: 2-5-7-10-22
Distr.: Intl.; Natl.
Budget Set: July
Personnel:
Lawrence A. Sala *(Chm, Pres & CEO)*
Carl W. Gerst, Jr. *(Vice Chm & CTO)*
George A. Blanton *(CFO, Treas & Sr VP)*
David M. Ferrara *(Gen Counsel)*
Mark P. Burdick *(Sr VP & Gen Mgr)*
Timothy P. Ross *(Sr VP-Bus Dev)*
Amy B. Tewksbury *(Sr VP-HR)*
Gert R. Thygesen *(Sr VP-Tech)*
Bill Barrett *(Reg Mgr-Sls)*
Yong Chen *(Reg Mgr-Sls)*
Rob Orford *(Reg Mgr-Sls)*
Brands & Products:
ANAREN
ANDRENALINE
RF POWER
WHAT'LL WE THINK OF NEXT?
XINGER
Advertising Agency:
Latorra, Paul & McCann
120 E Washington St
Syracuse, NY 13202-4000
Tel.: (315) 476-1646
Fax: (315) 476-1611
Media Buying

ANDREA ELECTRONICS CORPORATION

65 Orville Dr
Bohemia, NY 11716
Tel.: (631) 719-1800
Fax: (631) 719-1998
Toll Free: (800) 442-7787
E-mail: support@andreaelectronics.com
Web Site:
www.andreaelectronics.com
E-Mail For Key Personnel:
Public Relations: JohnL@andreaelectronics.com
Approx. Rev.: $4,915,513
Approx. Number Employees: 20
Year Founded: 1934
Business Description:
Hardware & Software Microphone Technologies Developer
S.I.C.: 3663; 3577
N.A.I.C.S.: 334220; 334119
Import Export
Advertising Expenditures: $20,677
Media: 2-4-10
Personnel:
Douglas J. Andrea *(Pres, CEO & Chm)*
Corisa L. Guiffre *(CFO & VP)*
Brands & Products:
ANC-300
ANC-700
ANC-750
ANDREA
APS-100
AUDIOCOMMANDER
BLINX
CA-910
CS-900
CS-950
DFTA
DSDA
ECHOSTOP
HS-75
MC-100
NC-11
NC-61
NC-65
NC-7100
P-100
PCTI
PCTI II
PUREAUDIO
S-100
SOUNDMAX
SUPERBEAM
T-100
TRS1
USBD-2A
VOICECENTER

ANDREW WIRELESS SOLUTIONS

(Sub. of CommScope Wireless Network Solutions)
3 Westbrook Corporate Ctr Ste 900
Westchester, IL 60154
Tel.: (708) 236-6600
Toll Free: (800) 255-1479
Web Site: www.andrew.com
Sales Range: $1-4.9 Billion
Year Founded: 1937
Business Description:
Communications Equipment Systems Mfr
S.I.C.: 3669; 3357; 3663
N.A.I.C.S.: 334290; 334220; 335929
Export
Advertising Expenditures: $4,800,000
Media: 2-4-5-6-7-10-21-22
Distr.: Intl.; Natl.
Budget Set: Sept.
Personnel:
Ben Cardwell *(Pres-Sls-Worldwide)*
Julie Nielson *(VP-Product Mgmt & Engrg)*
Chinnee Tong *(VP-Sls-China)*
Brands & Products:
POSITIVESTOP
RADIAX
TELETILT
VALULINE

ANRITSU COMPANY

(Sub. of Anritsu Corporation)
490 Jarvis Dr
Morgan Hill, CA 95037-2809
Tel.: (408) 778-2000
E-mail: infor@us.anritsu.com
Web Site: www.us.anritsu.com
Approx. Number Employees: 450
Year Founded: 1960
Business Description:
Communication & Network Devices Mfr
S.I.C.: 5065; 3825
N.A.I.C.S.: 423690; 334515
Export
Advertising Expenditures: $1,250,000
Media: 2-4-10
Distr.: Direct to Consumer; Intl.; Natl.
Budget Set: Oct.
Personnel:
Frank Tiernan *(Pres)*
Wade Hulon *(VP & Gen Mgr-Anritsu Co)*
Donn Mulder *(VP & Gen Mgr)*
Katherine Van Diepen *(Dir-Mktg Comm)*
Brands & Products:
K CONNECTORS
SITE MASTER
V CONNECTORS
Advertising Agency:
Loomis Group
345 Spear St Ste 110
San Francisco, CA 94105
Tel.: (415) 882-9494
Fax: (415) 882-7209

ANSALDO STS

(Formerly Union Switch & Signal Inc.)
(Sub. of Ansaldo STS S.p.A.)
1000 Technology Dr
Pittsburgh, PA 15219-3120
Mailing Address:
PO Box 420
Pittsburgh, PA 15219
Tel.: (412) 688-2400
Fax: (412) 688-2399
Toll Free: (800) 351-1520
Web Site: www.ansaldo-sts.com/en/index.html
Sales Range: $200-249.9 Million
Approx. Number Employees: 950
Year Founded: 1881
Business Description:
Railway Signaling & Automation Equipment Mfr
S.I.C.: 3743
N.A.I.C.S.: 336510
Media: 1-2-4-6-7-10-11-20-23
Distr.: Intl.; Natl.
Budget Set: Sept. -Oct.
Personnel:
Sergio De Luce *(CEO)*
Jack Wilson *(Dir-Component Sls-Kansas)*
Russell Glorioso *(Mgr-Mktg Comm)*
Brands & Products:
ASES
DIGITAIR
DIGITRAC
GENISYS
MICROCAB
MICROLOK
MICROTRAX
Advertising Agency:
Planit
500 E Pratt St 10th Fl
Baltimore, MD 21202
Tel.: (410) 962-8500
Fax: (410) 962-8508

API TECHNOLOGIES CORP.

2300 Yonge Street Ste 1710
Toronto, ON M4P 1E4, Canada
Tel.: (631) 981-2400
Toll Free: (877) 274-0274
E-mail: investors@apinanotronics.com
Web Site: www.apinanotronics.com/
E-Mail For Key Personnel:
Sales Director: sales@api-electronics.com
Approx. Rev.: $68,550,030
Approx. Number Employees: 597
Year Founded: 1981
Business Description:
Electronic Components & Microelectronic Circuits Mfr
S.I.C.: 3679; 3674
N.A.I.C.S.: 334419; 334413
Advertising Expenditures: $292,416
Personnel:
Brian Randall Kahn *(Chm & CEO)*
Bel Lazar, Sr. *(Pres & COO)*
Claudio A. Mannarino *(CFO)*
Jonathan Pollack *(Exec VP)*

APPLIED MATERIALS, INC.

3050 Bowers Ave
Santa Clara, CA 95054-3201
Mailing Address:
PO Box 58039
Santa Clara, CA 95054
Tel.: (408) 727-5555
Fax: (408) 748-9943
Toll Free: (800) 882-0373
Telex: 6719476 AMTUW
E-mail: Info_FS@appliedmaterials.com
Web Site: www.appliedmaterials.com
Approx. Sls.: $9,548,667,000
Approx. Number Employees: 13,000
Year Founded: 1967

Key to Media (For complete agency information see *The Advertising Red Books-Agencies* edition):
1. Bus. Publs. 2. Cable T.V. 3. Catalogs & Directories. 4. Co-op Adv. 5. Consumer Mags. 6. D.M. to Bus. Estab.7. D.M. to Consumers 8. Daily Newsp. 9. Exhibits/Trade Shows 10. Foreign 11. Infomercial 12. Internet Adv.13. Multimedia 14. Network Radio 15. Network T.V. 16. Newsp. Distr. Mags. 17. Other 18. Outdoor (Posters, Transit) 19. Point of Purchase20. Premiums, Novelties 21. Product Samples 22. Special Events Mktg. 23. Spot Radio 24. Spot T.V. 25. Weekly Newsp. 26. Yellow Page Adv.

Applied Materials, Inc. — (Continued)

Business Description:
Supplier of Wafer Fabrication Systems & Services to the Global Semiconductor Industries; Plasma Etch Systems & Chemical Vapor Deposition (CVD) Systems
S.I.C.: 3559; 3674
N.A.I.C.S.: 333295; 334413
Import Export
Advertising Expenditures: $708,952
Media: 2-10-25
Distr.: Intl.; Natl.
Budget Set: Oct.
Personnel:
Michael R. Splinter *(Chm, Pres & CEO)*
George S. Davis *(CFO & Exec VP)*
Ron Kifer *(CIO & Grp VP)*
Thomas S. Timko *(Chief Acctg Officer, VP & Controller)*
Charlie Gay *(Pres-Applied Solar Bus)*
Aninda Moitra *(Pres-India)*
Joseph J. Sweeney *(Gen Counsel, Sec & Sr VP)*
Mark R. Pinto *(Exec VP & Gen Mgr-Energy & Environmental Solutions & Display Grp)*
Randhir Thakur *(Exec VP & Gen Mgr-Silicon Sys Grp)*
Gilad Almogy *(Sr VP & Gen Mgr-Display & Thin-Film Solar Bus Grp)*
Joseph G. Flanagan *(Sr VP-Ops & Supply Chain-Worldwide)*
Manfred Kerschbaum *(Sr VP)*
Chris Bowers *(Grp VP-Corp Initiatives)*
Mary Humiston *(Grp VP-Global HR)*
Mike Rice *(VP & Gen Mgr-Foundation Engrg)*
Avi Tepman *(VP-Engrg)*
Dana Tribula *(VP-Mktg-Applied Global Svcs)*
Ajith Kota *(Product Mgr-Global)*
Brands & Products:
AERA2
APPLIED MATERIALS
CENTURA
CHARGER
COMPLUS
ENDURA
OPUS
PRODUCER
PRODUCER GT
REFLEXION
TETRA
THINK IT. APPLY IT.
UVISION
VANTAGE
VANTAGE RADIANCE
VERASEM
VERITYSEM
WORKSTREAM
Advertising Agency:
The Phelps Group
901 Wilshire Blvd
Santa Monica, CA 90401-1854
Tel.: (310) 752-4400
Fax: (310) 752-4444

APPLIED MATERIALS, INC

(Formerly Semitool, Inc.)
(Sub. of Applied Materials, Inc.)
655 W Reserve Dr
Kalispell, MT 59901-2127
Tel.: (406) 752-2107
Fax: (406) 752-5522
Toll Free: (800) 548-8495
Web Site: www.appliedmaterials.com
Approx. Sls.: $139,040,000
Approx. Number Employees: 826
Business Description:
Semiconductor Fabrication Equipment Mfr
S.I.C.: 3559
N.A.I.C.S.: 333295
Import Export
Media: 2-4-7-10-13-22-26
Personnel:
Herbert Oetzlinger *(VP-Sls)*
Brands & Products:
CAPSULE
ECD TECHNOLOGY
EQUINOX
HYDROZONE
P4 TECHNOLOGY
RAIDER
SCEPTER
SEMITOOL
SIRIUS
SPECTRUM
STORM

APPLIED MICRO CIRCUITS CORPORATION

215 Moffett Park Dr
Sunnyvale, CA 94089
Tel.: (408) 542-8600
Toll Free: (800) 935-2622
E-mail: support@amcc.com
Web Site: www.amcc.com
Approx. Rev.: $247,710,000
Approx. Number Employees: 672
Year Founded: 1979
Business Description:
Designer, Developer, Mfr & Marketer of High-Performance, High-Bandwith Silicon Connectivity for the Telecommunications Industry
S.I.C.: 3674
N.A.I.C.S.: 334413
Advertising Expenditures: $1,200,000
Personnel:
Cesar Cesaratto *(Chm)*
Paramesh Gopi *(Pres & CEO)*
Robert G. Gargus *(CFO & Sr VP)*
Shiva K. Natarajan *(Chief Acctg Officer, VP & Corp Controller)*
Robert Fanfelle *(Sr VP-Mktg & Strategy & VP-Mktg-Comm Grp)*
Michael Major *(VP-HR)*

APPLIED SIGNAL TECHNOLOGY, INC.

(Sub. of Raytheon Space & Airborne Systems)
460 W California Ave
Sunnyvale, CA 94086-5151
Tel.: (408) 749-1888
Fax: (408) 738-1928
Toll Free: (800) 374-3560
E-mail: amr@appsig.com
Web Site: www.appsig.com
Approx. Rev.: $225,229,000
Approx. Number Employees: 856
Year Founded: 1984
Business Description:
Signal Processing Equipment Designer, Developer, Mfr & Marketer
S.I.C.: 3669; 3663
N.A.I.C.S.: 334290; 334220
Export
Media: 2-4-6-7-8-10
Personnel:
John R. Treichler *(Founder & CTO)*
William B. Van Vleet, III *(Pres)*
Mark M Andersson *(COO)*
David A. Baciocco *(VP-Strategy & Bus Dev)*
James E. Doyle *(VP-Fin)*
Stephen Ruddy *(Dir-Mktg)*
Anthony J. Santino, Jr. *(Dir-Strategic Programs)*
Brands & Products:
APPLIED SIGNAL TECHNOLOGY
COASTAL WATCH
DEEPSEE
DISCOVER-IE
DOUBLETALK
DUGOUT
ELVIRA
MINESCOUT
NEU-VISION
PROSAS
REACT

ARIA INTERNATIONAL HOLDINGS, INC.

4821 29th St N
Arlington, VA 22207
Tel.: (703) 232-1435
Fax: (888) 657-0434
Toll Free: (888) 802-2742 (Investor Rels)
E-mail: invstor@aria-int.com
Web Site: www.aria-int.com
Sales Range: $10-24.9 Million
Approx. Number Employees: 10
Business Description:
Surveillance & Communications Solutions
S.I.C.: 7382; 3679
N.A.I.C.S.: 561621; 334419
Advertising Expenditures: $118,182
Media: 17
Personnel:
Michael A. Crosby *(Founder)*
Scott Miller *(Gen Counsel & Sec)*
Jamie Suzanne Engels *(Dir-Ops)*
Lindsay Giacobazzi *(Dir-Fin)*

ARIES ELECTRONICS INC.

2609 Bartram Rd
Bristol, PA 19007
Tel.: (215) 781-9956
Fax: (215) 781-9845
E-mail: info@arieselec.com
Web Site: www.arieselec.com
E-Mail For Key Personnel:
Sales Director: frankf@arieselec.com
Approx. Number Employees: 50
Year Founded: 1972
Business Description:
Sockets, Electronic Tube
S.I.C.: 3679; 5065
N.A.I.C.S.: 334419; 423690
Personnel:
William Sinclair *(Pres & CEO)*
Frank Folmsbee *(Mgr-Sls)*
Brands & Products:
ARIES
BALLNEST
CORRECT-A-CHIP
DECI-CENTER
DIP-ER
DIP-R-SIZER
EDGE-GRIP
EJECT-A-DIP
LO-PRO
MICROSTRIP CONTACTS
MINI-LINK
PIN-LINE
PINBALL
STRIP-LINE
TOUCHSPRING
VERTISOCKET
Advertising Agency:
The Simon Group, Inc.
1506 Old Bethlehem Pike
Sellersville, PA 18960-1427
Tel.: (215) 453-8700
Fax: (215) 453-1670

ARROW ELECTRONICS, INC.

50 Marcus Dr
Melville, NY 11747-4210
Tel.: (631) 847-2000
Fax: (631) 847-2222
Toll Free: (800) 777-2776
E-mail: investor@arrow.com
Web Site: www.arrow.com
Approx. Sls.: $18,744,676,000
Approx. Number Employees: 12,700
Year Founded: 1935
Business Description:
Electronic Components & Computer Products Mfr & Distr
S.I.C.: 5065; 5064; 5734
N.A.I.C.S.: 423690; 423620; 443120
Export
Advertising Expenditures: $20,800,000
Media: 4
Distr.: Natl.
Budget Set: Dec.
Personnel:
Michael J. Long *(Chm, Pres & CEO)*
John C. Waddell *(Vice Chm)*
Paul J. Reilly *(CFO & Exec VP-Fin & Ops)*
Vincent T. Melvin *(CIO & VP)*
Andrew S. Bryant *(Pres-Global Enterprise Computing Solutions Bus)*
Peter T. Kong *(Pres-Global Components)*
Peter S. Brown *(Gen Counsel, Sec & Sr VP)*
John P. McMahon *(Sr VP-HR)*
Andy King *(VP-EMEA Mktg & Engrg)*
John Hourigan *(Dir-Corp Comm)*
Chris Maio *(Comm Mgr-External)*
Dawn Small *(Comm Mgr, Enterprise Computing Solutions)*
Brands & Products:
ARROW
ARROW ACES
ARROW ALERT
ARROW ASIC
ARROW COLLABORATOR
ARROW RISK MANAGER
ARROWEDGE
CONNECTIVITY DASHBOARD
Advertising Agencies:
KZS Advertising
811 W Jericho Tpke Ste 109E
Smithtown, NY 11787
Tel.: (631) 348-1440
Fax: (631) 348-1449

Sterling Rice Group
1801 13th St Ste 400
Boulder, CO 80302
Tel.: (303) 381-6400
Fax: (303) 444-6637

ASANTE TECHNOLOGIES, INC.

2223 Oakland Rd
San Jose, CA 95131-1402
Tel.: (408) 435-8388
Fax: (408) 432-7511
Toll Free: (800) 662-9686
E-mail: webmaster@asante.com

Key to Media (For complete agency information see *The Advertising Red Books-Agencies* edition):
1. Bus. Publs. 2. Cable T.V. 3. Catalogs & Directories. 4. Co-op Adv. 5. Consumer Mags. 6. D.M. to Bus. Estab.7. D.M. to Consumers 8. Daily Newsp. 9. Exhibits/Trade Shows 10. Foreign 11. Infomercial 12. Internet Adv.13. Multimedia 14. Network Radio 15. Network T.V. 16. Newsp. Distr. Mags. 17. Other 18. Outdoor (Posters, Transit) 19. Point of Purchase20. Premiums, Novelties 21. Product Samples 22. Special Events Mktg. 23. Spot Radio 24. Spot T.V. 25. Weekly Newsp. 26. Yellow Page Adv.

Web Site: www.asante.com
E-Mail For Key Personnel:
Sales Director: sales@asante.com
Approx. Number Employees: 45
Year Founded: 1988
Business Description:
High-Performance Networking Solutions for the Digital Graphics Communications & Education Markets
S.I.C.: 3577
N.A.I.C.S.: 334119
Media: 4-10-13-19-22
Personnel:
Beverly Jedynak *(Exec VP-Pub Rels)*
Bina Patel *(Dir-Channel Sls)*
Elko Prinz *(Mgr-Reg Sls)*
Mike Tobin *(Mgr-Sls-EMEA)*
Brands & Products:
ALL THE RIGHT CONNECTIONS
ASANTE
FRIENDLYNET
INTRACORE

ASCO VALVE CANADA
(Sub. of ASCO Valve, Inc.)
17 Airport Rd
PO Box 160
Brantford, ON N3T 5M8, Canada
Tel.: (519) 758-2700
Fax: (519) 758-5540
E-mail: info@ascovalve.com
Web Site: www.ascovalve.com
Sales Range: $25-49.9 Million
Approx. Number Employees: 140
Year Founded: 1965
Business Description:
Automatic Switches, Solenoid Valves, Electric Power Control Products & Rodless Cylinders Mfr
S.I.C.: 3613
N.A.I.C.S.: 335313
Export
Media: 1-2-4-10-17-20-22
Distr.: Natl.
Budget Set: Aug.
Personnel:
Joe Lacko *(Mng Dir)*
Bob Cadwel *(Mgr-Mktg)*
George Laubenstein *(Product Mgr-ASCO)*
Brands & Products:
GENERAL CONTROLS
JOUCOMATIC
RED HAT
RED HAT II
TRI-POINT

ASTRO-MED, INC.
600 E Greenwich Ave
West Warwick, RI 02893-7526
Tel.: (401) 828-4000
Fax: (401) 822-2430
Toll Free: (800) 343-4039
E-mail: investorrelations@astromed.com
Web Site: www.astro-medinc.com
Approx. Sls.: $71,016,111
Approx. Number Employees: 423
Year Founded: 1969
Business Description:
Developer, Mfr & Supplier of Hardware & Software Systems for Processing Data
S.I.C.: 3577; 3679; 7372
N.A.I.C.S.: 334119; 334418; 334611; 511210
Advertising Expenditures: $1,187,000
Media: 2-4-5-7-8-10-11-13
Distr.: Natl.
Budget Set: Dec.
Personnel:
Albert W. Ondis *(Chm & CEO)*
Everett V. Pizzuti *(Pres & COO)*
Joseph P. O'Connell *(CFO & Sr VP)*
Thomas W. Carll *(VP & Dir-Worldwide Sls-Test, Measurement & Ruggedized Products)*
Eric E. Pizzuti *(VP-QuickLabel Sys & Dir-Worldwide Sls)*
Gordon W. Bentley *(VP-IT)*
Elias G. Deeb *(VP-Media Sls & Mktg)*
April Ondis *(Mktg Dir-QuickLabel Sys-Worldwide)*
Kevin Brisson *(Product Manager-QuickLabel Systems Product Group)*
Peter Nadeau *(Product Mgr-Test & Measurement Product Grp)*
Tina Pollard *(Mktg Mgr-Grass Technologies)*
Brands & Products:
ASTRO-GRAPH
ASTRO-MED
ASTRODAQ
DASH
FASS
FIELD RECORDER
GRASS TELEFACTOR
MICROCELL
MT-95K2
QUICKLABEL
VIRTUAL CHART
VIVO!
ZEO!
Advertising Agency:
Steven London Associates
70-01 Austin St., Ste. 201A
Forest Hills, NY 11375
Tel.: (718) 261-3892

AT&T ALASCOM
(Sub. of AT&T Government Solutions)
505 E Bluff Dr
Anchorage, AK 99501-1107
Tel.: (907) 264-7000
Fax: (907) 264-7169
Web Site: www.attalascom.com
Sales Range: $150-199.9 Million
Approx. Number Employees: 300
Year Founded: 1900
Business Description:
Telecommunications, Cable Television & Internet Services
S.I.C.: 4899; 4833; 7375
N.A.I.C.S.: 517410; 515120; 518111
Media: 8-10-22-23-24-26
Distr.: Reg.
Personnel:
Mike Felix *(Pres)*
Cathy Opinsky *(Assoc Dir-Mktg Comm)*

AT&T MOBILITY LLC
(Div. of AT&T Inc.)
5344 Buford Hwy Ste B
Atlanta, GA 30342
Toll Free: (866) 246-4827
Web Site: www.wireless.att.com
Sales Range: $25-49.9 Billion
Approx. Number Employees: 69,876
Year Founded: 2000
Business Description:
Wireless Voice & Data Communications Services
S.I.C.: 4813; 4812
N.A.I.C.S.: 517110; 517212
Advertising Expenditures: $1,249,000,000
Media: 3-6-7-8-9-10-13-15-18-19-20-22-24
Personnel:
Ralph de la Vega *(Pres & CEO)*
Peter A. Ritcher *(CFO)*
F. Thaddeus Arroyo *(CIO)*
David Christopher *(CMO)*
Glenn Lurie *(Pres-Emerging Devices Resale & Partnerships)*
Kent Mathy *(Pres-Bus Markets Grp)*
Edgar L. Reynolds *(Pres-Network Ops)*
Paul R. Roth *(Pres-Sls & Mktg)*
Steve Sitton *(Pres-Southeast Reg)*
Joaquin R. Carbonell, III *(Gen Counsel & Sr VP)*
Rickford D. Bradley *(Exec VP-HR-Wireless)*
Phil Bienert *(Sr VP-Digital Experience)*
Kathleen L. Dowling *(Sr VP-Customer Svc)*
Stephen A. McGaw *(Sr VP-Corp Strategy)*
Pam Parisian *(Sr VP-IT-Wireless)*
Kristin S. Rinne *(Sr VP-Architecture & Plng)*
Daryl Evans *(VP-Consumer Adv & Marcom)*
Kent Evans *(Exec Dir-IR)*
Dave Garver *(Exec Dir-Bus Dev & Mobile Content)*
Chad Harris *(Exec Dir-Wireless Adv)*
Mark Siegel *(Exec Dir-Media Rels)*
Rochelle Cohen *(Sr Dir-Media Rels)*
Dawn Benton *(Dir-Corp Comm)*
Regina Exum *(Sr Mgr-Online Mktg)*
Roberto Garcia *(Mgr-Field Ops)*
Brands & Products:
ALLOVER
CINGULAR
FAMILYTALK
GOPHONE
MEDIA NET
MORE BARS IN MORE PLACES
RAISING THE BAR
ROLLOVER
Advertising Agencies:
BBDO Atlanta
3500 Lenox Rd NE Ste 1900
Atlanta, GA 30326-4232
Tel.: (404) 231-1700
Fax: (404) 841-1893
GoPhone

BBDO New York
1285 Ave of the Americas 7th Fl
New York, NY 10019-6028
Tel.: (212) 459-5000
GoPhone

Bennett Kuhn Varner, Inc.
3390 Peachtree Rd 10th Fl
Atlanta, GA 30326
Tel.: (404) 233-0332
Fax: (404) 233-0302

The Bravo Group HQ
285 Madison Ave 12th Fl
New York, NY 10017
Tel.: (212) 780-5800
AT&T Wireless

Nurun/Ant Farm Interactive
75 Fifth St NW Ste 600
Atlanta, GA 30308
Tel.: (404) 876-7281
Fax: (404) 876-7226
(Online Customer Relationship Management)

AT&T MOBILITY LLC
(Branch of AT&T Mobility LLC)
Appletree Business Park 2875 Union Rd Ste 35U
Cheektowaga, NY 14227
Tel.: (716) 435-2000
Fax: (716) 435-2673
E-mail: kate.mackinnon@cingular.com
Web Site: www.wireless.att.com
Sales Range: $50-74.9 Million
Approx. Number Employees: 170
Year Founded: 1983
Business Description:
Wireless Telecommunications Services
S.I.C.: 4812
N.A.I.C.S.: 517212
Advertising Expenditures: $600,000
Media: 23-24
Distr.: Natl.
Personnel:
Hal Lenox *(Pres)*
Mike Palmieri *(Asst VP-Mergers & Integrations)*
Jake Moskowitz *(Sr Mgr-Consumer Mktg)*

AT&T MOBILITY LLC
(Sub. of AT&T Mobility LLC)
7277 164th Ave NE
Redmond, WA 98052
Mailing Address:
PO Box 97061
Redmond, WA 98073
Tel.: (425) 580-6000
Fax: (425) 580-8505
Toll Free: (888) 288-3511
Web Site: www.wireless.att.com
Sales Range: $1-4.9 Billion
Approx. Number Employees: 5,000
Year Founded: 1987
Business Description:
Wireless Telecommunications Services
S.I.C.: 4812
N.A.I.C.S.: 517212
Media: 8-9-13-15-19
Distr.: Natl.

ATEK MANUFACTURING, LLC
(Sub. of ATEK Companies, Inc.)
210 NE 10th Ave
Brainerd, MN 56401
Tel.: (218) 829-1481
Fax: (218) 825-2299
Toll Free: (866) 879-2835
Web Site:
www.atekmanufacturing.com
Year Founded: 1982
Business Description:
Contract Manufacturing & Assembly Services
S.I.C.: 3599; 3679
N.A.I.C.S.: 332710; 334419
Personnel:
Kay Phillips *(Owner)*
Advertising Agency:
Risdall Marketing Group
550 Main St
New Brighton, MN 55112-3271
Tel.: (651) 286-6700
Fax: (651) 631-2561

Key to Media (For complete agency information see *The Advertising Red Books-Agencies* edition):
1. Bus. Publs. 2. Cable T.V. 3. Catalogs & Directories. 4. Co-op Adv. 5. Consumer Mags. 6. D.M. to Bus. Estab.7. D.M. to Consumers 8. Daily Newsp. 9. Exhibits/Trade Shows 10. Foreign 11. Infomercial 12. Internet Adv.13. Multimedia 14. Network Radio 15. Network T.V. 16. Newsp. Distr. Mags. 17. Other 18. Outdoor (Posters, Transit) 19. Point of Purchase20. Premiums, Novelties 21. Product Samples 22. Special Events Mktg. 23. Spot Radio 24. Spot T.V. 25. Weekly Newsp. 26. Yellow Page Adv.

ATEK Manufacturing, LLC — (Continued)

Toll Free: (888) RISDALL
Public Relations

ATLANTIC TELE-NETWORK, INC.

600 Cummings Ctr
Beverly, MA 01915
Tel.: (978) 619-1300
Web Site: www.atni.com
Approx. Rev.: $619,145,000
Approx. Number Employees: 1,765
Year Founded: 1987
Business Description:
Telecommunications Services
S.I.C.: 4812; 4813; 7374
N.A.I.C.S.: 517212; 517110; 518210
Media: 3-17-18-20-22-23-24
Personnel:
Cornelius B. Prior, Jr. *(Chm)*
Michael T. Prior *(Pres & CEO)*
Justin D. Benincasa *(CFO & Treas)*
Paul R. Bowersock *(Pres-Intl Ops)*
Leonard Q. Slap *(Gen Counsel & Sr VP)*
Douglas J. Minster *(Gen Counsel & VP)*
Karl D. Noone *(Sr VP & Controller)*
William F. Kreisher *(Sr VP-Corp Dev)*

ATLAS SOUND

(Sub. of MiTek Corporation)
1601 Jack McKay Blvd
Ennis, TX 75119-6507
Tel.: (972) 875-8413
Fax: (972) 875-8416
Toll Free: (800) 876-7337
Telex: 910-760-1650
E-mail: info@atlassound.com
Web Site: www.atlassound.com
Approx. Number Employees: 140
Year Founded: 1934
Business Description:
Mfr. of Loudspeakers, Emergency Communication Systems, Intercom & Telecom Products
S.I.C.: 3651
N.A.I.C.S.: 334310
Export
Media: 2-4-7-10-11-21
Distr.: Intl.; Natl.
Budget Set: Sept.
Personnel:
Loyd Ivey *(CEO)*
Bruce Marlin *(Sr VP-Engrg)*
Brands & Products:
ATLAS/SOUNDOLIER
KAPTON
OMNI-PURPOSE
PAGEKOM
SOUNDOLIER
STRATEGY SERIES
VARI-TAP
VARIZONE
VISIKOM
VOICE CONTROL
VOICE/TONE
WHISPERTOUCH

ATMEL CORPORATION

2325 Orchard Pkwy
San Jose, CA 95131-1034
Tel.: (408) 441-0311
Fax: (408) 436-4200
E-mail: northwest@atmel.com
Web Site: www.atmel.com/
Approx. Rev.: $1,644,060,000
Approx. Number Employees: 5,200
Year Founded: 1984
Business Description:
Advanced Semiconductors Designer, Marketer & Mfr
S.I.C.: 3674
N.A.I.C.S.: 334413
Import Export
Media: 2-10-11
Personnel:
Steven A. Laub *(Pres & CEO)*
Stephen Cumming *(CFO & VP-Fin)*
Walter T. Lifsey *(COO & Exec VP)*
Tom Wasilczyk *(CIO & VP-IT)*
Alf-Egil Bogen *(CMO & VP-Corp Mktg)*
Tsung-Ching Wu *(Exec VP-Pres Office)*
Ken Kwong *(VP-Corp Mktg)*
Jing Liao *(VP-HR-Global)*
Robert Valiton *(VP-Sls)*
Yang Chiah Yee *(VP-Sls-Asia Pacific & Japan)*
Bassam Khoury *(Gen Mgr & Sr Dir)*
Clive Over *(Dir-Global Mktg Comm)*
Peter Schuman *(Dir-IR)*
Jacko Wilbrink *(Dir-Product Mktg)*
Michele Casetta *(Mgr-Mktg)*
Benoit Makowka *(Mgr-Mktg)*
Bard Pedersen *(Mgr-AVR Product Line)*
Agnes Toan *(Mgr-PR)*
Brands & Products:
ADJACENT KEY SUPPRESSION
ADVX
AKS
ANTARIS
ATMEL
ATV
AVR
AVR DRAGON
AVR FREAKS
AVR STUDIO
BATTERY-VOLTAGE
CACHE LOGIC
CAN AVR
CAP
CRYPTOAUTHENTICATION
CRYPTOCOMPANION
CRYPTOCONTROLLER
CRYPTOMEMORY
CRYPTORF
DATAFLASH
DIOPSIS
DREAM
DUAL TOUCH
EVERYWHERE YOU ARE
FINGERCHIP
FLAMINGO
FPSLIC
IDIC
LOGIC DOUBLING
MAGIC DSP
MAXTOUCH
MEGAAVR
PHILIPP SPRING
PICOPOWER
PROCHIP DESIGNER
QFIELD
QNAV
QPROX
QRG
QSLIDE
QTOUCH
QTWO
QUANTUM RESEARCH GROUP
QWHEEL
RAPIDS
SAM-BA
SAM-ICE
SAM-PROG
SECURCORE
SECUREAVR
SIAP
SILICONCITY
STK
TINYAVR
TWINAVR
TWO TOUCH
VOYAGER
XMEGA
Z-LINK
ZIGBIT

AUDIO COMMAND SYSTEMS, INC.

694 Main St
Westbury, NY 11590
Tel.: (516) 997-5800
Fax: (516) 997-2195
Toll Free: (800) 382-2939
Web Site: www.audiocommand.com
Approx. Number Employees: 50
Year Founded: 1976
Business Description:
Custom Designs, Manufactures & Markets Remote Control Multiple Room Audio/Video Systems in Custom-Built Homes & Executive Offices
S.I.C.: 1731; 3571
N.A.I.C.S.: 238210; 334111
Media: 6
Personnel:
Jonathan Flamm *(Pres)*
Robert A. Kaufman *(CEO)*

AUDIO DESIGN ASSOCIATES, INC.

602 Mamaroneck Ave Ste 610
White Plains, NY 10605
Tel.: (914) 946-9565
Web Site: www.ada-usa.com
Business Description:
Audio & Video Electronics Systems Mfr & Installer
S.I.C.: 8711; 3651
N.A.I.C.S.: 541330; 334310
Media: 4-6
Personnel:
Albert Langella *(Pres, CEO & Chief Design Engineer)*
Brands & Products:
AUDIO DESIGN ASSOCIATES
THE BRAND OF EXCELLENCE
IBASE EXTENDER KIT IPOD

AUDIO RESEARCH CORPORATION

3900 Annapolis Ln N
Plymouth, MN 55447-5447
Tel.: (763) 577-9700
Fax: (763) 577-0323
E-mail: kfiebiger@audioresearch.com
Web Site: www.audioresearch.com
Approx. Number Employees: 40
Year Founded: 1970
Business Description:
Mfr. of Amplifiers, Electronic Crossovers & Audio Related Products
S.I.C.: 3651
N.A.I.C.S.: 334310
Export
Advertising Expenditures: $200,000
Media: 4-6-8-10-11
Distr.: Intl.; Natl.
Budget Set: June
Personnel:
Terry Dorn *(Pres)*
David Onan *(CFO)*
David Gordon *(Mng Dir-Sls)*
Brands & Products:
AUDIO RESEARCH
HIGH DEFINITION
NICHICON

AUDIO RESOURCE

7635 Jefferson Hwy
Baton Rouge, LA 70809-1102
Tel.: (504) 885-6988
Fax: (504) 885-6996
E-mail: jayval@audioresource.com
Web Site: www.audioresource.com
Approx. Number Employees: 6
Business Description:
Electronics Retailer
S.I.C.: 5731
N.A.I.C.S.: 443112
Media: 4-13
Personnel:
Jay Valentino *(Owner)*

AUDIO VISUAL INNOVATIONS, INC.

(d/b/a AVI-SPL, Inc.)
6301 Benjamin Rd Ste 101
Tampa, FL 33634-5181
Tel.: (813) 884-7168
Fax: (813) 882-9508
Toll Free: (800) 282-6733
E-mail: avisales@avispl.com
Web Site: www.avispl.com
Approx. Number Employees: 1,200
Year Founded: 1979
Business Description:
Audio Visual Equipment Support Services
S.I.C.: 7389
N.A.I.C.S.: 541990; 561990
Import Export
Media: 2-7-10-22
Personnel:
Martin Schaffel *(Owner, Pres & Exec Chm)*
Chad Gillenwater *(Vice Chm)*
Stephenie Scanlon *(Pres)*
John Zettel *(CEO)*
Peter C. Grabowski, Jr. *(CFO)*
Don LaNeve *(COO)*
Steve Benjamin *(Exec VP)*
Chris Bianchet *(Sr VP-Sys Integration)*
Jennifer Blomberg *(Sr VP-Sls)*
Randy Bonham *(VP-Strategic Accounts & Fin Svcs)*
Kelly Bousom *(VP-Internet Dev & Mktg)*
Brands & Products:
AUDIO VISUAL

AUDIOSEARS CORPORATION

2 S St
Stamford, NY 12167-1211
Tel.: (607) 652-7305
Fax: (607) 652-3653
Toll Free: (800) 533-7863
E-mail: sales@audiosears.com
Web Site: www.audiosears.com
E-Mail For Key Personnel:
Sales Director: sales@audiosears.com
Approx. Sls.: $8,000,000
Approx. Number Employees: 80
Year Founded: 1956

Key to Media (For complete agency information see *The Advertising Red Books-Agencies* edition):
1. Bus. Publs. 2. Cable T.V. 3. Catalogs & Directories. 4. Co-op Adv. 5. Consumer Mags. 6. D.M. to Bus. Estab.7. D.M. to Consumers
8. Daily Newsp. 9. Exhibits/Trade Shows 10. Foreign 11. Infomercial 12. Internet Adv.13. Multimedia 14. Network Radio
15. Network T.V. 16. Newsp. Distr. Mags. 17. Other 18. Outdoor (Posters, Transit) 19. Point of Purchase20. Premiums, Novelties
21. Product Samples 22. Special Events Mktg. 23. Spot Radio 24. Spot T.V. 25. Weekly Newsp. 26. Yellow Page Adv.

Business Description:
Mfr. of Telephone & Telegraph Apparatus; Handsets, Headsets, Microphones & Receivers
S.I.C.: 3661
N.A.I.C.S.: 334210
Export
Media: 2-4-7-10
Distr.: Intl.; Natl.
Personnel:
David Hartwell *(Pres)*
Brands & Products:
AS2100
AUDIOSEARS
ELIMINATOR

AUDIOVOX CORPORATION
180 Marcus Blvd
Hauppauge, NY 11788
Tel.: (631) 231-7750
Fax: (631) 434-3995
Web Site: www.audiovox.com
Approx. Sls.: $561,672,000
Approx. Number Employees: 1,020
Year Founded: 1965
Business Description:
Automotive Entertainment, Consumer Electronics & Vehicle Security Products Mfr
S.I.C.: 5065; 5064
N.A.I.C.S.: 423690; 423620
Import Export
Advertising Expenditures: $6,076,000
Media: 2-4-6-10-19
Distr.: Intl.; Natl.
Budget Set: Oct.
Personnel:
John J. Shalam *(Chm)*
Patrick M. Lavelle *(Pres & CEO)*
Charles M. Stoehr *(CFO & Sr VP)*
Ann Boutcher *(CMO & VP)*
C. David Geise *(Sr VP)*
Richard A. Maddia *(Sr VP)*
Thomas C. Malone *(Sr VP)*
Loriann Shelton *(Sr VP-Acctg & Credit)*
Brands & Products:
ACOUSTIC RESEARCH
ADVENT
AMBICO
AUDIOVOX
CAR LINK
CHAPMAN
CODE-ALARM
DISCWASHER
ENERGIZER
HECO
INCAAR
INVISION
JENSEN
MAC AUDIO
MAGNATE
MOVIES2GO
OEHLBACH
OMEGA
PHASE LINEAR
PRESTIGE
PURSUIT
RAMPAGE
RCA
RCA ACCESSORIES
RECOTON
ROAD GEAR
SCHWAIGER
SPIKEMASTER
TERK
Advertising Agency:
KZS Advertising
811 W Jericho Tpke Ste 109E
Smithtown, NY 11787
Tel.: (631) 348-1440
Fax: (631) 348-1449

AURORA CORP. OF AMERICA
(Sub. of Aurora Corporation)
3500 Challenger St
Torrance, CA 90503-1640
Tel.: (310) 793-5650
Fax: (310) 793-5658
Toll Free: (800) 327-8508
E-mail: info@auroracorp.com
Web Site: www.auroracorp.com
Approx. Number Employees: 35
Year Founded: 1955
Business Description:
Consumer Electronics Mfr
S.I.C.: 5044; 5712
N.A.I.C.S.: 423420; 442110
Media: 4-10
Distr.: Intl.; Natl.
Budget Set: Sept.
Personnel:
George Chang *(Gen Mgr)*
Brands & Products:
AURORA LUGGAGE
GEL 'N ROLL
JAMFREE

AUTHENTEC, INC.
100 Rialto Pl Ste 100
Melbourne, FL 32901
Tel.: (321) 308-1300
Fax: (321) 308-1430
E-mail: info@authentec.com
Web Site: www.authentec.com
E-Mail For Key Personnel:
Public Relations: brent.dietz@authentec.com
Approx. Rev.: $44,667,000
Approx. Number Employees: 242
Year Founded: 1998
Business Description:
Mixed-Signal Semiconductor Fingerprint Authentication Sensors Mfr
S.I.C.: 3674; 7382
N.A.I.C.S.: 334413; 561621
Advertising Expenditures: $147,000
Media: 10-17
Personnel:
Dale R. Setlak *(co-Founder)*
Lawrence J. Ciaccia, Jr. *(CEO)*
Philip L. Calamia *(CFO)*
Frederick R. Jorgenson *(Gen Counsel, Sec & VP)*
Anthony Iantosca *(Sr VP-Worldwide Ops & Quality)*
Mike Chaudoin *(Dir-Mktg-Govt & Access Control)*
Brent Dietz *(Dir-Comm)*
Advertising Agency:
Shelton Group
12400 Coit Rd Ste 650
Dallas, TX 75251
Tel.: (972) 239-5119
Fax: (972) 239-2292
Investor Relations Agency of Record

AVAYA INC.
(Joint Venture of Silver Lake Group, LLC & TPG Capital, L.P.)
211 Mount Airy Rd
Basking Ridge, NJ 07920
Tel.: (908) 953-6000
Toll Free: (866) GO-AVAYA
Web Site: www.avaya.com
Approx. Rev.: $5,060,000,000
Approx. Number Employees: 18,700
Year Founded: 2000
Business Description:
Business Communications Systems; Owned by Silver Lake Partners & TPG Capital L.P.
S.I.C.: 3661; 7372
N.A.I.C.S.: 334210; 511210
Media: 1-2-6-7-9-10-11-13-18-22-26
Personnel:
Kevin J. Kennedy *(Pres & CEO)*
Nidal Abu-Ltaif *(Mng Dir & VP-Emerging Markets)*
Mohammed Areff *(Mng Dir)*
Anthony Massetti *(CFO & Sr VP)*
Stephen J. Gold *(CIO & Sr VP)*
Pamela F. Craven *(Chief Admin Officer, Chief Compliance Officer & Gen Counsel)*
Kevin MacKay *(Chief Acctg Officer, VP & Controller)*
Mohamad Ali *(Pres-Avaya Global Svcs & Sr VP)*
Alan E. Baratz *(Pres-Global Comm Solutions & Sr VP)*
J. Joel Hackney, Jr. *(Pres-Field Ops, Sr VP-Global Sls & Mktg)*
James M. Chirico, Jr. *(Exec VP-Bus Ops)*
Roger Gaston *(Sr VP-HR)*
Brett Shockley *(Sr VP-Corp Dev & Strategy)*
Steve Bandrowczak *(VP & Gen Mgr, Data Solutions)*
Anthony Bartolo *(Gen Mgr & VP-Unified Comm Bus Unit)*
John DiLullo *(VP-Sls)*
Laura Misdom *(Dir-Global Brand Mgmt)*
Kimberly DeWolfe *(Sr Mgr-Mktg-Global)*
Brands & Products:
AUDIX
CALLMASTER
DEFINITY
INTUITY
MERLIN MAGIX
MULTIVANTAGE
OCTEL
PARTNER
VPNMANAGER
Advertising Agency:
Hodgson/Meyers
10210 NE Points Dr Ste 220
Kirkland, WA 98033-7872
Tel.: (425) 827-2506
Fax: (425) 822-0155

AVID TECHNOLOGY, INC.
75 Network Dr
Burlington, MA 01803
Tel.: (978) 640-6789
Fax: (978) 640-3366
E-mail: investor_relations@avid.com
Web Site: www.avid.com
Approx. Rev.: $678,522,000
Approx. Number Employees: 1,960
Year Founded: 1987
Business Description:
Nonlinear Film, Video, Audio & 3D Solutions Developer
S.I.C.: 3861; 3577; 7372
N.A.I.C.S.: 333315; 325992; 334119; 511210
Advertising Expenditures: $3,500,000
Media: 2-5-7-8-10-13-18-21
Personnel:
Gary G. Greenfield *(Pres & CEO)*
Kenneth Sexton *(CFO, Chief Admin Officer & Exec VP)*
Kirk E. Arnold *(COO & Exec VP)*
Jerry Kelly *(CIO & VP)*
Paige Parisi *(Gen Counsel, Sec & VP)*
Christopher C. Gahagan *(Sr VP-Products)*
Ron Greenberg *(Sr VP-Worldwide Mktg)*
Martin Vann *(Sr VP-Sls & Prof Svcs-Worlwide)*
Jason G. Burke *(VP-Fin)*
Paul Hennessey *(VP-Sls-EMEA)*
Ed Raine *(VP-HR)*
Paul Senechal *(VP-Supply & Tech)*
Tom Fitzsimmons *(Dir-IR)*
Rich Nevens *(Dir-Pro Audio Sls-Worldwide)*
Michele Perry *(Dir-Corp Comm)*
Brands & Products:
ANIMATTE
AVID
AVID 3D
AVID ACTIVE CONTENTMANAGER FOR BROADCAST
AVID ACTIVE CONTENTMANAGER SDK
AVID ADRENALINE
AVID AIRSPACE
AVID AIRSPEED
AVID CAPTURE MANAGER
AVID DNA FAMILY
AVID DNXCHANGE
AVID DS
AVID DS ASSIST STATION
AVID DS NITRIS
AVID DS NITRIS EDITOR
AVID DVD BY SONIC
AVID FX
AVID INEWS
AVID INEWS CONTROLAIR
AVID INEWS FAMILY
AVID INEWS MULTIBYTE
AVID INTERPLAY
AVID LEADERPLUS
AVID MEDIA BROWSE
AVID MEDIA COMPOSER
AVID MEDIA COMPOSER ADRENALINE
AVID MEDIA STATION XL
AVID MEDIADOCK ULTRA320
AVID MEDIARRAY ZX
AVID MOJO
AVID NEARCHIVE
AVID NEWSCUTTER
AVID NEWSCUTTER ADRENALINE FX
AVID NEWSCUTTER EFFECTS
AVID NEWSCUTTER FAMILY
AVID PRO TOOLS LE
AVID UNITY FOR NEWS
AVID UNITY LANSHARE EX
AVID UNITY LANSHARE FOR NEWS
AVID UNITY MEDIAMANAGER
AVID UNITY MEDIAMANAGER SELECT
AVID UNITY MEDIANETWORK
AVID UNITY PROENCODE
AVID UNITY TRANSFERMANAGER
AVID XDECK
AVID XPRESS
AVID XPRESS DV

Key to Media (For complete agency information see *The Advertising Red Books-Agencies* edition):
1. Bus. Publs. 2. Cable T.V. 3. Catalogs & Directories. 4. Co-op Adv. 5. Consumer Mags. 6. D.M. to Bus. Estab.7. D.M. to Consumers 8. Daily Newsp. 9. Exhibits/Trade Shows 10. Foreign 11. Infomercial 12. Internet Adv.13. Multimedia 14. Network Radio 15. Network T.V. 16. Newsp. Distr. Mags. 17. Other 18. Outdoor (Posters, Transit) 19. Point of Purchase20. Premiums, Novelties 21. Product Samples 22. Special Events Mktg. 23. Spot Radio 24. Spot T.V. 25. Weekly Newsp. 26. Yellow Page Adv.

Avid Technology, Inc. — (Continued)

AVID XPRESS PRO
AVID XPRESS STUDIO
AVOPTION
BEAUTY WITHOUT THE BANDWIDTH
COUNTDOWN
DIGIDESIGN PRO TOOLS
FILM COMPOSER
FLUIDFILM
FLUIDMOTION
FRAME CHASE
GOVERNMENT SOLUTIONS
HYPERCLIP
LAUNCH PAD
MAKE MANAGE MOVE
MEDIA ARRAY LP
MEDIA ARRAY XT
MEDIADOCK 2+
MEDIADRIVE RS 320/RVD
MEDIADRIVE RS FIREWIRE
MEDIARRAY II
METAFUZE
METASYNC
MISSION CONTROL
PATENTED STEADYGUIDE
SOFTIMAGE XSI
SPACESHIFT
SPECTRAGRAPH
SPECTRAMATTE
SYMPHONY

AVNET ELECTRONICS MARKETING

(Div. of Avnet, Inc.)
2211 S 47th St
Phoenix, AZ 85034
Tel.: (480) 643-5600
Toll Free: (800) 332-8638
Web Site: www.em.avnet.com
Sales Range: $150-199.9 Million
Business Description:
Electronics Sales & Distr
S.I.C.: 5065
N.A.I.C.S.: 423690
Media: 10
Personnel:
Harley M. Feldberg *(Pres)*
Richard Hamada *(CEO & COO)*
Tim Barber *(Sr VP-Global Bus Dev)*
Greg Frazier *(Exec VP, Sr VP-Bus Dev & Innovation)*
Steve Boysen *(Sr VP)*
Chuck Delph *(Sr VP-Sls-Americas)*
Sean Fanning *(Sr VP-Mktg & Comm-Worldwide)*
Alex Iuorio *(Sr VP-Supplier Mgmt-America)*
Ravi Kichloo *(Sr VP-Global Semiconductor Bus Dev)*
Chuck Kostalnick *(Sr VP-Avnet Embedded)*
Tom McCartney *(Sr VP-Bus Dev-Global)*
Advertising Agency:
Brodeur Partners
2201 E Camelback Rd Ste 370
Phoenix, AZ 85016-4771
Tel.: (602) 224-4055
Fax: (602) 956-1689

AVNET, INC.

2211 S 47th St
Phoenix, AZ 85034-6403
Tel.: (480) 643-2000
Fax: (480) 643-7370
Toll Free: (888) 822-8638
E-mail: investorrelations@avnet.com
Web Site: www.avnet.com
Approx. Sls.: $26,534,413,000
Approx. Number Employees: 17,600
Year Founded: 1921
Business Description:
Electronic Components, Enterprise Network, Computer Equipment & Embedded Subsystems Distr
S.I.C.: 5065; 5045
N.A.I.C.S.: 423690; 423430
Import Export
Advertising Expenditures: $3,000,000
Media: 2-9-10-13
Distr.: Natl.
Budget Set: Sept. -Oct.
Personnel:
Roy A. Vallee *(Chm)*
Richard Hamada *(Chm-Exec Bd & CEO)*
Raymond J. Sadowski *(CFO)*
Gerry Fay *(COO & Chief Global Logistics Officer)*
Steve Phillips *(CIO)*
Steve Church *(Chief Bus Dev Officer & Chief Process Officer)*
Tom McCartney *(Pres-Japan & Sr VP-Global Bus Dev)*
David Birk *(Gen Counsel & Sr VP)*
Gregory A. Frazier *(Exec VP-Bus Innovation Worldwide & VP)*
David Ashworth *(Sr VP-Global Semiconductors)*
Philip Gallagher *(Sr VP)*
Jeff Ittel *(Sr VP-Embedded Mktg & Asset Mgmt)*
John T. Clark *(VP & Dir-Global Fin Ops)*
Michael Costigan *(Dir-Mktg & Bus Innovation)*
Mike Despotes *(Reg Mgr-Sls)*
Brands & Products:
ACCELERATING YOUR SUCESS
AV
AVNET
AVNETDIRECT
CILICON
DEDICATED TO YOUR SUCCESS
ELECTRO AIR
EXTENSURE
FACT
GLOBAL SUPPLY CHAIN
HALL-MARK GLOBAL SOLUTIONS
LIAISON
PARTBUILDER
POURS
POURS REMOTE
PROMIERE
STATS ON-LINE
TECENTER
TMMS
Advertising Agencies:
Brodeur Partners
855 Boylston St 2nd Fl
Boston, MA 02116-2622
Tel.: (617) 587-2800
Fax: (617) 587-2828
(Public Relations)

Spark Design
414 S Mill Ave Ste 210
Tempe, AZ 85281
Tel.: (480) 929-0455
Fax: (480) 929-0039

Webemercial Interactive
33685 N 71st Way
Scottsdale, AZ 85262
Tel.: (602) 571-1700
Fax: (602) 744-2577
Toll Free: (888) 797-8700

AVO MULTI-AMP CORP

(Div. of TBG Holdings NV)
(d/b/a Megger)
4271 Bronze Way
Dallas, TX 75237
Tel.: (214) 333-3201
Fax: (214) 331-7399
Toll Free: (800) 723-2861
Telex: 163548 MULAM DL
E-mail: work@megger.com
Web Site: www.megger.com
Approx. Rev.: $60,000,000
Approx. Number Employees: 169
Year Founded: 1951
Business Description:
Electrical Test Equipment, Precision Electrical Instruments Field Testing Services, Education & Electric Meter Test Equipment & Accessories
S.I.C.: 3825
N.A.I.C.S.: 334515
Import Export
Media: 1-2-4-5-7-10-20-21-22
Distr.: Intl.; Natl.
Budget Set: Oct.
Personnel:
Rick Lawrence *(Mktg Dir)*
Brands & Products:
MEGGER
THE STATES

AVON WESCO

(Div. of WESCO International Inc.)
60 Hoffman Ave
Hauppauge, NY 11788
Tel.: (631) 582-4770
Tel.: (718) 657-1600
Fax: (631) 582-4237
E-mail: info@avonelec.com
Web Site: www.avonelec.com
Sales Range: $10-24.9 Million
Approx. Number Employees: 100
Business Description:
Electrical Supply Mfr
S.I.C.: 5063
N.A.I.C.S.: 423610
Media: 13

AVX CORPORATION

(Sub. of Kyocera Corporation)
1 AVX Blvd
Fountain Inn, SC 29644
Tel.: (864) 967-2150
E-mail: gib@avxcorp.com
Web Site: www.avxcorp.com
Approx. Sls.: $1,653,176,000
Approx. Number Employees: 11,200
Year Founded: 1972
Business Description:
Multilayer Ceramic Capacitors Mfr
S.I.C.: 3679; 3675; 5065
N.A.I.C.S.: 334419; 334414; 423690
Import Export
Media: 2-4-5-10-17
Distr.: Intl
Personnel:
John S. Gilbertson *(Chm, Pres & CEO)*
Kurt P. Cummings *(CFO, Treas, Sec & VP)*
Keith Thomas *(Pres-Kyocera Electronic Devices & VP)*
C. Marshall Jackson *(Exec VP-Sls & Mktg)*
Kathleen Kelly *(VP-HR)*
Peter Venuto *(VP-Sls)*
Steve Rabe *(Dir-Sls & Mktg)*
Gayle Smith *(Dir-MIS)*
Sonja Brown *(Global Product Mgr-Circuit Protection)*
Larry Eisenberger *(Product Mgr)*
Tim Piver *(Product Mgr)*
Carol Bourkue *(Mgr-Pur)*
Advertising Agency:
Business-to-Business Marketing Communications
900 Ridgefield Dr Ste 270
Raleigh, NC 27609-8524
Tel.: (919) 872-8172
Fax: (919) 872-8875

AWR CORPORATION

1960 E Grand Ave Ste 430
El Segundo, CA 90245
Tel.: (310) 726-3000
Fax: (310) 726-3005
E-mail: info@awrcorp.com
Web Site: www.awrcorp.com
Approx. Number Employees: 50
Business Description:
High-Frequency Electronic Design Automation Products
S.I.C.: 3679
N.A.I.C.S.: 334419
Media: 10
Personnel:
Joseph Pekarek *(Founder & CTO)*
Dane Collins *(CEO)*
Rick Bottomley *(CFO)*
Ted A. Miracco *(Exec VP-Sls & Mktg)*
Sherry Hess *(VP-Mktg)*
John DeFord *(Dir-Engrg)*
Stephen A. Maas *(Dir-Tech)*
Chris Paris *(Dir-European Ops)*
Heikki Rekonen *(Dir-AWR-APLAC)*
Brands & Products:
ANALOG OFFICE
APLAC
AWR
AXIEM
MICROWAVE OFFICE
VISUAL SYSTEM SIMULATOR

AXIA NETMEDIA CORPORATION

3300 450 1st Street Southwest
Calgary, AB T2P 5H1, Canada
Tel.: (403) 538-4000
Fax: (040) 353-84100
E-mail: info@axia.com
Web Site: www.axia.com
Approx. Rev.: $67,050,345
Business Description:
Communications Products
S.I.C.: 3663
N.A.I.C.S.: 334220
Advertising Expenditures: $933,922
Personnel:
Arthur R. Price *(Chm & CEO)*
Alan Hartslief *(CFO)*
Murray Sigler *(Pres-Axia North America)*
Jean-Michel Soulier *(Pres-Axia Networks-France)*
Nicole Springer *(Gen Counsel & VP)*
Corinne Hua *(VP-Fin & Controller)*
Jim Lindberg *(VP-Ops & Fin-Alberta)*
Dawn Tinling *(VP-IR & Comm)*

AXSYS TECHNOLOGIES, INC.

(Div. of General Dynamics Advanced Information Systems, Inc.)

Key to Media (For complete agency information see *The Advertising Red Books-Agencies* edition):
1. Bus. Publs. 2. Cable T.V. 3. Catalogs & Directories. 4. Co-op Adv. 5. Consumer Mags. 6. D.M. to Bus. Estab.7. D.M. to Consumers
8. Daily Newsp. 9. Exhibits/Trade Shows 10. Foreign 11. Infomercial 12. Internet Adv.13. Multimedia 14. Network Radio
15. Network T.V. 16. Newsp. Distr. Mags. 17. Other 18. Outdoor (Posters, Transit) 19. Point of Purchase20. Premiums, Novelties
21. Product Samples 22. Special Events Mktg. 23. Spot Radio 24. Spot T.V. 25. Weekly Newsp. 26. Yellow Page Adv.

175 Capitol Blvd Ste 103
Rocky Hill, CT 06067-3914
Tel.: (603) 864-6300
Fax: (860) 594-5750
E-mail: inquire@axsys.com
Web Site: www.axsys.com
Approx. Sls.: $245,484,000
Approx. Number Employees: 991
Year Founded: 1959
Business Description:
Optics, Motion Control Products & Precision Machining Designer & Mfr
S.I.C.: 3827; 3621; 3625
N.A.I.C.S.: 333314; 335312; 335314
Import Export
Advertising Expenditures: $500,000
Media: 2-4-6-9-10-25
Distr.: Intl.; Natl.
Budget Set: Oct.-Nov.
Personnel:
Keith Haney *(Dir-Law Enforcement Sls)*
Bart Kent *(Dir-Bus Dev)*
Brands & Products:
AXSYS
AXSYS TECHNOLOGIES
FAST
LASERTRAC
PRECISION TO THE NTH DEGREE
TELETRAC

AXXCELERA BROADBAND WIRELESS INC.
(Sub. of Moseley Associates, Inc.)
82 Coromar Dr
Santa Barbara, CA 93117
Tel.: (408) 894-7045
Fax: (805) 968-0791
E-mail: info@axxcelera.com
Web Site: www.axxcelera.com
Approx. Number Employees: 50
Year Founded: 1968
Business Description:
Supplier of Telecommunications Equipment, Earth Stations & Microwave Radios Used in Wireless Communications
S.I.C.: 3663
N.A.I.C.S.: 334220
Media: 2-10-13-17
Distr.: Natl.
Budget Set: June
Personnel:
Jamal N. Hamdani *(Pres & CEO)*
Bruce Tarr *(CFO)*
Tony Masters *(CTO & Sr VP)*
Jerry Kollman *(Sr VP-Sls, Mktg & Customer Support-Worldwide)*
Philip Rushton *(Sr VP-Ops)*
Brands & Products:
AB-100
AB-ACCESS
AB-E1/T1
AB-EXTENDER
AB-FULL ACCESS
AB-MUX
EXCELAIR

AZ ELECTRONIC MATERIALS USA CORP.
(Div. of AZ Electronic Materials Sarl)
70 Meister Ave
Somerville, NJ 08876-3440
Tel.: (908) 429-3500
Fax: (908) 429-3635
E-mail: az-info@az-em.com
Web Site: www.az-em.com
Approx. Number Employees: 800
Business Description:
Electronic Materials Mfr
S.I.C.: 3663; 3651; 3679
N.A.I.C.S.: 334220; 334310; 334418; 334419
Media: 10-11
Personnel:
Thomas W. von Krannichfeldt *(CEO)*
Ken Greatbatch *(CFO)*
Lisa Altland *(Mgr-Mktg)*
Brands & Products:
AZ

B&K COMPONENTS LTD.
2100 Old Union Rd
Buffalo, NY 14227
Tel.: (716) 656-0026
Fax: (716) 656-1291
Toll Free: (800) 543-5252
Web Site: www.bkcomp.com
Approx. Number Employees: 34
Year Founded: 1981
Business Description:
Audio Electronic Systems Mfr
S.I.C.: 3651
N.A.I.C.S.: 334310
Media: 6-10
Personnel:
John L. Beyer, III *(Pres)*
Brands & Products:
DIGITALDNA
DOLBY DIGITAL
DOLBY DIGITAL EX
DOLBY DIGITAL LOGIC
DTS-ES
DTS NEO
Advertising Agency:
Prime Source
8420 Main St
Williamsville, NY 14221
Tel.: (716) 634-4693
Fax: (716) 634-8617
Toll Free: (800) 498-5016

BADGER MAGNETICS INC.
(Formerly Mag-Con Engineering, Inc.)
(Div. of Badger Transformer Company, Inc.)
501 Apollo Dr
Lino Lakes, MN 55014
Tel.: (651) 784-8888
Fax: (651) 784-8100
Web Site: www.badgermagnetics.com
Approx. Number Employees: 30
Year Founded: 1960
Business Description:
Custom Transformers Designer & Mfr
S.I.C.: 3612; 3625
N.A.I.C.S.: 335311; 335314
Export
Media: 2-4-7-10-26
Distr.: Natl.
Budget Set: Feb.
Personnel:
Cliff Evans *(Pres)*

BAE SYSTEMS-INFORMATION WARFARE
(Div. of BAE Systems-Electronics & Integrated Solutions)
144 Daniel Webster Hwy N
Merrimack, NH 03054
Tel.: (603) 885-4321
Fax: (603) 885-3655
Web Site: www.baesystems.com
Approx. Number Employees: 4,500
Year Founded: 1951
Business Description:
Developer of Signal Management & Electronic Attack Systems
S.I.C.: 3812
N.A.I.C.S.: 334511
Media: 2-4-6-7-10-21
Distr.: Intl.; Natl.
Personnel:
Michael A. Heffron *(Pres)*
Kevin M. Perkins *(Gen Counsel & VP)*
Dan Gobel *(Dir-Program)*
Charlotte Lambkin *(Dir-Commun)*
Brands & Products:
ASE
CASTE
CETS
CMS
EDNA
IEWS
MCC
THAAD
USM-406
USM-458/NEWTS
USM-464
USM-638
USM-639
VHM

BAIRNCO CORPORATION
(Sub. of Handy & Harman Ltd.)
1133 Westchester Ave Ste N222
White Plains, NY 10604
Tel.: (914) 461-1300
E-mail: info@bairnco.com
Web Site: www.whxcorp.com/home.php
Approx. Sls.: $178,828,000
Approx. Number Employees: 1,020
Year Founded: 1981
Business Description:
Mfr of Cutting Products & Services, Laminated & Coated Products & Materials for Printed Circuit Boards & for Microwave Applications
S.I.C.: 2821; 3081; 3425
N.A.I.C.S.: 325211; 326113; 332213
Import Export
Media: 2-4-7-10
Distr.: Natl.
Budget Set: Oct.
Personnel:
Jim McCabe *(Sr VP, CFO, Pres-Shared Svcs)*
Brands & Products:
ARLON
CALON
KASCO
MII
SIGNTECH

BALLANTYNE STRONG, INC.
4350 McKinley St
Omaha, NE 68112-1643
Tel.: (402) 453-4444
Fax: (402) 453-7238
Toll Free: (800) 424-1215
Web Site: www.ballantyne-omaha.com
Approx. Rev.: $136,334,617
Approx. Number Employees: 289
Year Founded: 1932
Business Description:
Commercial Motion Picture Equipment & Lighting Systems Mfr., Designer & Distr
S.I.C.: 3861; 3648
N.A.I.C.S.: 333315; 325992; 335129
Advertising Expenditures: $800,000
Media: 2-10
Personnel:
William F. Welsh, II *(Chm)*
Gary L. Cavey *(Pres & CEO)*
Mary A. Carstens *(CFO)*
Christopher Stark *(COO & Sr VP)*
Ray F. Boegner *(Sr VP)*
Rick Sanjurjo *(VP-Engrg)*
Brian Hendricks *(Gen Mgr-Design & Mfg)*
P.L. Wong *(Gen Mgr-Strong Westrex)*
Brands & Products:
BALLANTYNE
BRITELIGHT
CANTO
CENTURY
FLAVOR-CRISP
THE FUTURE POWERED BY STRONG
GLADIATOR
MINITRACKER
NOCTURN
RIMA
SIMPLEX
SKYSWEEP
SKYTRACKER
SLX
STRONG
STX1
SUFIO
SUONO
SUPER TROUPE
THE SUPER TROUPER
TECHNOBEAM
TEMPO
TROUPERETTE
TRUSS TROUPER
XENON
XENOTECH
XPRESS
Advertising Agency:
Tom Mayar Graphics
5523 Pacific St
Omaha, NE 68106
Tel.: (402) 558-2222

BAND PRO FILM & DIGITAL INC.
3403 W Pacific Ave
Burbank, CA 91505
Tel.: (818) 841-9655
Fax: (818) 841-7649
E-mail: info@bandpro.com
Web Site: www.bandprodigital.com
Approx. Number Employees: 30
Business Description:
Retailer & Wholesaler of Video Equipment
S.I.C.: 5731; 5065
N.A.I.C.S.: 443112; 423690
Media: 6
Personnel:
Amnon H. Band *(Pres & CEO)*
Vincent Barton *(Mgr-Svcs)*

BASLER ELECTRIC COMPANY
Rte 143
Highland, IL 62249
Tel.: (618) 654-2341
Fax: (618) 654-2351
E-mail: info@basler.com
Web Site: www.basler.com
Approx. Number Employees: 1,090
Year Founded: 1942

Key to Media (For complete agency information see *The Advertising Red Books-Agencies* edition):
1. Bus. Publs. 2. Cable T.V. 3. Catalogs & Directories. 4. Co-op Adv. 5. Consumer Mags. 6. D.M. to Bus. Estab.7. D.M. to Consumers 8. Daily Newsp. 9. Exhibits/Trade Shows 10. Foreign 11. Infomercial 12. Internet Adv.13. Multimedia 14. Network Radio 15. Network T.V. 16. Newsp. Distr. Mags. 17. Other 18. Outdoor (Posters, Transit) 19. Point of Purchase20. Premiums, Novelties 21. Product Samples 22. Special Events Mktg. 23. Spot Radio 24. Spot T.V. 25. Weekly Newsp. 26. Yellow Page Adv.

Basler Electric Company — (Continued)

Business Description:
Custom Transformers & Electric Power Control Systems, Double Sided Printed Circuit Boards Mfr
S.I.C.: 3612; 3679
N.A.I.C.S.: 335311; 334419
Export
Advertising Expenditures: $400,000
Media: 2-4-7-10
Distr.: Natl.
Personnel:
William L. Basler *(Chm, CEO & Treas)*
Gary D. Dolbeare *(Pres & COO)*
Marilyn Frey *(VP-HR)*
Larry Perez *(Mgr-Product Mktg)*
Jake Hinterser *(Coord-Promos)*
Brands & Products:
ALTERREX
BASLER ELECTRIC

BEL FUSE INC.

206 Van Vorst St
Jersey City, NJ 07302-4421
Tel.: (201) 432-0463
Fax: (201) 432-9542
E-mail: belfuse@belfuse.com
Web Site: www.belfuse.com
Approx. Sls.: $302,539,000
Approx. Number Employees: 4,161
Year Founded: 1949
Business Description:
Network Electronic Components Mfr & Distr
S.I.C.: 3677; 3613; 3679
N.A.I.C.S.: 334416; 334419; 335313
Import
Advertising Expenditures: $230,000
Bus. Publs.: $25,000; Catalogs & Directories: $100,000; D.M. to Bus. Estab.: $10,000; Exhibits/Trade Shows: $35,000; Foreign: $50,000; Other: $10,000
Distr.: Natl.; Reg.
Personnel:
Daniel Bernstein *(Pres & CEO)*
Colin Dunn *(Sec & VP-Fin)*
Bob McBrien *(Prod Mgr-Fuses)*
Donna Marganella *(Mgr-Mktg & Comm)*
Brands & Products:
BEL
BELCOMBO
BELFUSE
BELMAG
BELSTACK
BELSTICK
COMPONENTS FOR A CONNECTED PLANET
HOMEPLUG
MAG JACK
Advertising Agency:
A.D. Adams Advertising, Inc.
560 Sylvan Ave
Englewood Cliffs, NJ 07632
Tel.: (201) 541-3111
Fax: (201) 266-0086
(Electronic Components, Fuses, Delay Lines, LAN & Telecom Magnetics & Hybrid/Value Added)

BELDEN, INC.

7733 Forsyth Blvd Ste 800
Saint Louis, MO 63105
Tel.: (314) 854-8000
Fax: (314) 854-8001
E-mail: info@belden.com
Web Site: www.belden.com
Approx. Rev.: $1,617,090,000
Approx. Number Employees: 6,600
Year Founded: 1902
Business Description:
Wire & Cable Products; Insulated Copper Wires, Cables & Cords; Fiber Optics Mfr
S.I.C.: 3356; 3357; 3496; 5063
N.A.I.C.S.: 331491; 331422; 332618; 335921; 423610
Export
Advertising Expenditures: $15,600,000
Media: 5-10-20-21-26
Distr.: Natl.
Budget Set: Dec.
Personnel:
Bryan C. Cressey *(Chm)*
John S. Stroup *(Pres & CEO)*
Gray G. Benoist *(CFO)*
Kevin L. Bloomfield *(Gen Counsel, Sec & VP)*
Cathy O. Staples *(Sr VP-HR)*
Steven R. Biegacki *(VP-Global Sls & Mktg)*
Frank Milano *(Dir-IR)*
Hans-Werner Eich *(Mgr-Mktg)*
Frank Stone *(Mgr-Mktg Comm & Resource)*
Brands & Products:
ALPHA
BANANA PEEL
BELDEN
BELDENCABLE
BELDFOIL
BRILLIANCE
CONFORMABLE
DATATWIST
DUOBOND
FLAMARREST
HOMECHOICE
INDUSTRIALTUFF
MEDIATWIST
NEW GENERATION
SENDING ALL THE RIGHT SIGNALS
UNREEL
XTRA-GUARD
Advertising Agency:
Adventive Marketing, Inc.
417 S Arlington Hts Rd
Arlington Heights, IL 60005-1932
Tel.: (847) 590-1110
Fax: (847) 590-1222

BELL INDUSTRIES, INC.

8888 Keystone Crossing Ste 1700
Indianapolis, IN 90245-5060
Tel.: (317) 704-6000
Fax: (317) 575-9401
Toll Free: (866) 782-2355
Web Site: www.bellind.com
Approx. Rev.: $100,577,000
Approx. Number Employees: 615
Year Founded: 1952
Business Description:
Specialty Electronic Components
S.I.C.: 5065; 5013; 7373
N.A.I.C.S.: 423690; 423120; 541512
Import Export
Advertising Expenditures: $154,000
Media: 17
Personnel:
Mark E. Schwarz *(Chm)*
Clinton J. Coleman *(CEO)*
Bob M. Berwanger *(Exec VP-Ops)*
Brent Schoolcraft *(Sr VP-HR)*
Brands & Products:
BELL INDUSTRIES
BUILD BELIEVE ACHIEVE

BENCHMARK ELECTRONICS, INC.

3000 Technology Dr
Angleton, TX 77515-2524
Tel.: (979) 849-6550
Fax: (979) 848-5270
E-mail: ellen.sykora@bench.com
Web Site: www.bench.com
Approx. Sls.: $2,402,143,000
Approx. Number Employees: 9,990
Year Founded: 1986
Business Description:
Printed Circuit Boards Mfr
S.I.C.: 3672; 3679
N.A.I.C.S.: 334412; 334418
Media: 10
Personnel:
Cary T. Fu *(Chm & CEO)*
Gayla J. Delly *(Pres)*
Donald F. Adam *(CFO)*
Steven A. Barton *(Exec VP)*
Ted Hirsch *(Mgr-Corp Assets)*
Loning Richardson *(Mgr-Bus Unit & Site Gen Mgr)*

BENMAR MARINE ELECTRONICS, INC.

PO Box 4007
Idyllwild, CA 92549
Tel.: (714) 540-5120
Fax: (714) 641-2614
E-mail: benmarmarine@aol.com
Web Site: www.benmarmarine.com
Sales Range: $25-49.9 Million
Approx. Number Employees: 35
Year Founded: 1959
Business Description:
Marine Autopilot Systems & Marine Fuel Management Systems
S.I.C.: 3812
N.A.I.C.S.: 334511
Export
Advertising Expenditures: $375,000
Media: 6
Distr.: Intl.; Natl.
Budget Set: Jan.
Personnel:
Robert Edwards *(Owner)*
Brands & Products:
COMPU-COURSE 220
COURSE SETTER 21
FMS 300

BEST BUY CO., INC.

7601 Penn Ave S
Richfield, MN 55423
Mailing Address:
PO Box 9312
Minneapolis, MN 55440-9312
Tel.: (612) 291-1000
Fax: (612) 292-4001
Toll Free: (888) 237-8289
E-mail: biz@bestbuy.com
Web Site: www.bestbuy.com
Approx. Rev.: $50,272,000,000
Approx. Number Employees: 180,000
Year Founded: 1966
Business Description:
Consumer Electronics, Home Office Products, Entertainment Software & Appliances Retailer
S.I.C.: 5722; 5731; 5999
N.A.I.C.S.: 443111; 443112; 453998
Advertising Expenditures: $901,000,000
Media: 3-5-8-9-13-18-22-23-24-25-26
Distr.: Direct to Consumer; Reg.
Personnel:
Richard M. Schulze *(Chm)*
Brian J. Dunn *(CEO)*
Ryan D. Robinson *(CFO-US Strategic Bus Unit & Sr VP)*
James L. Muehlbauer *(CFO & Exec VP-Fin)*
Neville Roberts *(CIO & Sr VP-Enterprise)*
Barry K. Judge *(CMO & Exec VP)*
Marise Kumar *(CMO, Chief Customer Experience Officer-Intl)*
Tim Sheehan *(Chief Admin Officer & Exec VP-Enterprise)*
Susan S. Grafton *(Chief Acctg Officer, VP & Controller)*
Carol A. Surface *(Chief HR Officer & Exec VP)*
Aura Oslapas *(Chief Design Officer & Sr VP)*
Kalendu Patel *(Pres-Asia & Exec VP-Enterprise)*
Shari L. Ballard *(Pres-Americas & Enterprise Exec VP)*
Sean Skelley *(Pres-Intl Retail Ops)*
Michael A. Vitelli *(Pres-Americas & Enterprise Exec VP)*
Chris Haskett *(Principal-Corp Dev)*
Joseph M. Joyce *(Gen Counsel & Sr VP)*
Neil McPhail *(Sr VP & Gen Mgr)*
Bill Hoffman *(Sr VP-Consumer Insights)*
Sean Connolly *(Sr Dir-Mktg-Computing)*
Julie Beth McFall Vipperman *(Sr Dir-Consumer & Brand Res)*
Paige Fitzgibbons *(Sr Mgr-Media Network)*
Mark Kudla *(Sr Product Mgr)*
Brands & Products:
BEST BUY
BEST BUY MOBILE
DYNEX
GEEK SQUAD
INSIGNIA
REWARD ZONE
ROCKETFISH
YELLOW TAG
Advertising Agencies:
BBDO New York
1285 Ave of the Americas 7th Fl
New York, NY 10019-6028
Tel.: (212) 459-5000

BBDO Worldwide Inc.
(Sub. of Omnicom Group, Inc.)
1285 Ave of the Americas
New York, NY 10019-6028
Tel.: (212) 459-5000
Fax: (212) 459-6645

Ketchum Directory Advertising/Kansas City
7015 College Blvd Ste 700
Overland Park, KS 66211-1524
Tel.: (913) 344-1900
Fax: (913) 344-1960
Toll Free: (800) 922-6977

La Comunidad
6400 Biscayne Blvd
Miami, FL 33138

Key to Media (For complete agency information see *The Advertising Red Books-Agencies* edition):
1. Bus. Publs. 2. Cable T.V. 3. Catalogs & Directories. 4. Co-op Adv. 5. Consumer Mags. 6. D.M. to Bus. Estab.7. D.M. to Consumers
8. Daily Newsp. 9. Exhibits/Trade Shows 10. Foreign 11. Infomercial 12. Internet Adv.13. Multimedia 14. Network Radio
15. Network T.V. 16. Newsp. Distr. Mags. 17. Other 18. Outdoor (Posters, Transit) 19. Point of Purchase20. Premiums, Novelties
21. Product Samples 22. Special Events Mktg. 23. Spot Radio 24. Spot T.V. 25. Weekly Newsp. 26. Yellow Page Adv.

Tel.: (305) 993-5700
Tel.: (305) 865-9600
Fax: (305) 865-9609

Manning Selvage & Lee
1170 Peachtree St NE Ste 400
Atlanta, GA 30309-7677
Tel.: (404) 875-1444
Fax: (404) 892-1274

Marketing Support, Inc.
200 E Randolph Dr Ste 5000
Chicago, IL 60601
Tel.: (312) 565-0044
Fax: (312) 946-6100

Moxie Interactive Inc.
The Northyards 384 Northyards Blvd
NW Ste 290
Atlanta, GA 30313-2440
Tel.: (404) 601-4500
Fax: (404) 601-4505

Starcom MediaVest Group
35 W Wacker Dr
Chicago, IL 60601-1723
Tel.: (312) 220-3535
Fax: (312) 220-6530
Media Buying & Planning

Tapestry Partners
35 W Wacker Dr
Chicago, IL 60601
Tel.: (312) 220-3535
Fax: (312) 220-6561

BEXEL CORPORATION

(Sub. of Vitec Group PLC)
2701 N Ontario St
Burbank, CA 91504
Tel.: (818) 841-5051
Fax: (818) 841-1572
Toll Free: (800) 225-6185
E-mail: burbank@bexel.com
Web Site: www.bexel.com
Approx. Number Employees: 80
Year Founded: 1981
Business Description:
Video Equipment & Ancillary Support Gear
S.I.C.: 5731
N.A.I.C.S.: 443112
Media: 6
Personnel:
Jerry Gepmer *(CEO)*
Craig Schiller *(Sr VP-Engrg & Technical Svcs)*
Bob Brcini *(VP & Gen Mgr)*
Oyette Auary *(Controller)*
Johnny Pastor *(Dir-Tech Ops)*

BLONDER TONGUE LABORATORIES, INC.

1 Jake Brown Rd
Old Bridge, NJ 08857
Mailing Address:
PO Box 1000
Old Bridge, NJ 08857
Tel.: (732) 679-4000
Fax: (732) 679-4353
Toll Free: (800) 523-6049
E-mail: information@blondertongue.com
Web Site: www.blondertongue.com
E-Mail For Key Personnel:
Sales Director: sales@blondertongue.com
Approx. Sls.: $30,508,000
Approx. Number Employees: 162
Year Founded: 1950
Business Description:
Electronics & Systems Equipment
Mfr, Designer & Supplier for the Cable Television Industry
S.I.C.: 3663; 3699
N.A.I.C.S.: 334220; 335999
Import Export
Advertising Expenditures: $50,000
Media: 2-4-7-10-13-18-21-26
Distr.: Natl.
Budget Set: Sept. -Oct.
Personnel:
Robert J. Palle, Jr. *(Pres, COO & Sec)*
James A. Luksch *(CEO)*
Emily Nikoo *(Sr VP)*
Eric S. Skolnik *(Sr VP)*
Norman A. Westcott *(Sr VP-Ops Svcs)*
Kant Mistry *(VP-Engrg)*
Lynn Russo *(Dir-Mktg & Admin)*
Lauren Yefler *(Mgr-Mktg Commun)*
Brands & Products:
BLONDER TONGUE
GALAXY III
LINCXPRESS SYSTEM
MASTERLINE
MEGAPORT
RETRO-LINX
TRAILBLAZER
TWIN STAR
VIDEOMASK
YOUR BROADBAND EQUIPMENT SOURCE VOICE.VIDEO.DATA

BOGEN COMMUNICATIONS INTERNATIONAL INC.

50 Spring St
Ramsey, NJ 07446
Tel.: (201) 934-8500
Fax: (201) 934-9832
Toll Free: (800) 999-2809
E-mail: info@bogen.com
Web Site: www.bogen.com
Approx. Rev.: $44,854,000
Approx. Number Employees: 150
Year Founded: 1932
Business Description:
Audio & Communications Equipment
Mfr, Designer & Marketer
S.I.C.: 3661; 3651; 3663
N.A.I.C.S.: 334210; 334220; 334310
Media: 1-2-4
Personnel:
Michael P. Fleischer *(Pres)*
Jonathan Guss *(CEO)*
Maureen A. Flotard *(CFO & VP-Fin)*
Anna Pansini *(Mgr-Mktg Comm)*
Brands & Products:
BOGEN
EASY DESIGN

BOINGO WIRELESS, INC.

10960 Wilshire Blvd Ste 800
Los Angeles, CA 90024
Tel.: (310) 586-5180
Fax: (310) 586-4060
E-mail: support@boingo.com
Web Site: www.boingo.com
Approx. Rev.: $65,715,000
Approx. Number Employees: 135
Year Founded: 2001
Business Description:
WiFi Software & Services
S.I.C.: 4812; 7372
N.A.I.C.S.: 517212; 511210
Advertising Expenditures: $1,296,000
Personnel:
Sky D. Dayton *(Chm)*
David Hagan *(Pres & CEO)*
Edward Zinser *(CFO)*
Colby Goff *(Sr VP-Network Strategy & Bus Dev)*
Peter Hovenier *(Sr VP-Fin)*
Alan Lang *(VP-Engrg)*
Brands & Products:
BOINGO
BOINGO WIRELESS
Advertising Agency:
Weber Shandwick-Los Angeles
8687 Melrose Ave 7th Fl
Los Angeles, CA 90069
Tel.: (310) 854-8200
Fax: (310) 854-8201
Agency of Record
Marketing
Strategic PR Counsel

BOSCH COMMUNICATIONS INC.

(Formerly Telex Communications, Inc.)
(Sub. of Bosch Security Systems, Inc.)
12000 Portland Ave
Burnsville, MN 55337-1522
Tel.: (952) 884-4051
Web Site: www.boschcommunications.com
Sales Range: $300-349.9 Million
Approx. Number Employees: 1,800
Year Founded: 1936
Business Description:
Electronic Audio Communication Devices Mfr
S.I.C.: 3669; 3663
N.A.I.C.S.: 334290; 334220
Export
Media: 2-4-5-6-7-10-11-22
Distr.: Intl.; Natl.
Budget Set: Dec. -Feb.
Personnel:
Thomas Hansen *(VP-Sls)*
Leigh P. Hart *(VP-Fin)*
Brands & Products:
AUDIOCOM
TELEX
TELEX LEGACY

BOSCH SECURITY SYSTEMS, INC.

(Sub. of Bosch Sicherheitssysteme Gmbh)
130 Perinton Pkwy
Fairport, NY 14450-9107
Tel.: (585) 223-4060
Fax: (585) 223-9180
Toll Free: (800) 289-0096
E-mail: security.sales@us.bosch.com
Web Site: www.boschsecurity.us
E-Mail For Key Personnel:
Marketing Director: DGundlach@detectionsys.com
Approx. Number Employees: 350
Year Founded: 1968
Business Description:
Commercial & Residential Security & Surveillance System Mfr
S.I.C.: 7382; 3669; 3861
N.A.I.C.S.: 561621; 333315; 334290
Import Export
Advertising Expenditures: $3,000,000
Media: 1-2-4-7-10-13
Distr.: Intl.; Natl.
Budget Set: Sept.
Personnel:
Daniel Gundlach *(VP-Mktg)*
Brands & Products:
AQC-21
AUTODOME INDOOR SYSTEMS
BILINX TECHNOLOGY
CM-15A
D1601
D1640
D1640-32
D2071A Series
D256A
D257A
D263
D265AW
D273
D281A
D282A
D282A-DH
D283A
D284
D285
D286
D296
D297
D300A
D300A-HV
D341P/D341I
D342P/D342I
D601
D602
D7014
D7015
D7022
D7024
D7025
D7030X
D7031
D7032
D7033 LCD
D7034
D7035
D7035B
D7036
D7038
D9068
D9133TTL-E
D9142F
D9142LC
D9142M
DS230
DS230F
DS233F
DS240
DS241
DS250
DS260
DS280
DS9484
EAZEO DVR1B1161
EAZEO OBSERVATION SYSTEM
ENVIRODOME CAMERA SYSTEMS
F220
F220-P
F220-PTH
F220-PTHC
FCP-500
FLEXIDOME I
FLEXIDOME II
FLEXIDOMEXT LTC 136X
FLEXIDOMEXTLTC 146X
GD2A
LTC 1261/22DN
LTC 1271
LTC 4600
LTC 4700
LTC 5231/90

Bosch Security Systems, Inc. — (Continued)

LTC 5234/90
MULTIPLEXER VS8394
MX250
MX280
SWITCHER VS7390
VC7D1305T
VIDEOJET 10
VIDEOJET 1000
VIDEOJET 8000
VIDEOJET XPRO
VIDOS-NVR
VIDOS VIDEO MANAGEMENT SYSTEM
VIP 10
VIP 1000
VIP X1
VIP X2
VIP XD
VMD01-M60

Advertising Agencies:
Eclipse Media Group Inc
20 Fowler Farm Rd
Scarborough, ME 04074
Tel.: (207) 510-0029
Tel.: (207) 319-7372

Stoner Bunting Advertising
210 W Grant St
Lancaster, PA 17603-3707
Tel.: (717) 291-1491
Fax: (717) 399-8197

BOSE CORPORATION

PO Box 9168
Framingham, MA 01701-9168
Tel.: (508) 879-7330
Fax: (508) 766-7543
Toll Free: (800) 999-2673
Web Site: www.bose.com
Approx. Rev.: $2,000,000,000
Approx. Number Employees: 8,000
Year Founded: 1964
Business Description:
Stereo Speaker Equipment, Professional Sound Systems & Home Theater Systems
S.I.C.: 3651
N.A.I.C.S.: 334310
Import Export
Media: 1-2-3-4-5-6-7-8-9-10-13-14-16-19-23-24
Distr.: Intl.; Natl.
Budget Set: Feb.
Personnel:
Bob Maresca *(Pres)*
Amar G. Bose *(CEO)*
Daniel A. Grady *(CFO & VP-Fin)*
Rob Ramrath *(CIO)*
Kenneth D. Jacob *(Chief Engr & Dir-Live Music Tech)*
Mark E. Sullivan *(Gen Counsel & Sec)*
Herbert W. Batchelder *(VP-Fin & Asst Treas)*
Rick Martino *(VP-HR-Global)*
Michael Mangione *(Dir-Consumer Mktg)*
Carolyn Cinotti *(Dir-Pub Rel)*
Phil Hess *(Dir-Product Mktg)*
Todd Kinsman *(Dir-Analytics)*
Liz Schaller *(Dir-Online Mktg)*
Terry Braga *(Mgr-Online Mktg)*
Alyssa Chong *(Mgr-Online Mktg Programs)*
Kevin Levine *(Mgr-Ops)*
Kristin Mallory *(Mgr-Digital Mktg-US Wholesale Grp)*
Brands & Products:
ACCOUSTIMASS
ACOUSTIC NOISE CANCELLING
ACOUSTIC WAVE
ACOUSTIMASS
BOSE
CINEMATE
COMPANION
DIRECT/REFLECTING
ELECTROFORCE
FREE SPACE
LIFESTYLE
MEDIAMATE
QUIETCOMFORT
ROOMMATE
SOUNDDOCK
SYNCOM
TRIPORT
VIRTUALLY INVISIBLE
WAVE
Advertising Agencies:
Captains of Industry
21 Union St
Boston, MA 02108
Tel.: (617) 725-1959
Fax: (617) 725-0089

Euro RSCG Singapore
3 Anson Road
Singapore, Singapore
Tel.: (65) 6317 6600
Fax: (65) 6317 6700

Garfield Group
60 Blacksmith Rd
Newtown, PA 18940
Tel.: (215) 867-8600
Fax: (215) 867-8610

Marketing Matters
2700 N 29th Ave Ste 101
Hollywood, FL 33020
Tel.: (954) 925-1511
Fax: (954) 925-1549

Mediacom London
124 Theobalds Road
London, WC1X 8RX, United Kingdom
Tel.: (44) 207 158 5500
Fax: (44) 207 158 5999

Resource Interactive
343 N Front St
Columbus, OH 43215-2219
Tel.: (614) 621-2888
Fax: (614) 621-2873
Toll Free: (800) 550-5815

Sarkissian Mason
135 W 26th St 5 Fl
New York, NY 10001
Tel.: (212) 625-8212
Fax: (212) 625-8211

Viewpoint Creative
254 Second Ave
Needham, MA 02494
Tel.: (781) 449-5858
Fax: (781) 449-7272

BOSTON ACOUSTICS, INC.

(Sub. of D&M Holdings Inc.)
300 Jubilee Dr
Peabody, MA 01960-4030
Mailing Address:
PO Box 6015
Peabody, MA 01961-6015
Tel.: (978) 538-5000
Fax: (978) 538-5199
E-mail: feedback@bostona.com
Web Site: www.bostonacoustics.com
Sales Range: $50-74.9 Million
Approx. Number Employees: 192
Year Founded: 1979
Business Description:
High Quality Loudspeaker Systems Mfr for Home, Automotive, Business & Professional Use
S.I.C.: 3651; 5064
N.A.I.C.S.: 334310; 423620
Import Export
Advertising Expenditures: $405,652
Media: 6-10-17-19
Distr.: Intl.; Natl.
Budget Set: Mar.
Personnel:
Eli Harary *(Sr VP & Gen Mgr)*
Phil Cohn *(Sr VP-Sls & Mktg)*
Debra A. Ricker *(VP-Fin)*
Steve Chilinski *(Gen Mgr)*
Colleen Anderson *(Mgr-Mktg Comm)*
Sanjay Sharma *(Mgr-Natl Sls-Mobile Audio)*
Brands & Products:
ACTIVE BASS CONTOUR
AMD
AVIDEA
BA
BASS TRAC
BOSTON
BOSTON ACOUSTICS
BOSTON ACOUSTICS RADIO
BOSTON ACOUSTICS.COM
BOSTON EVERYWHERE
BOSTON FS
BOSTON FX
BOSTON GT
BOSTON RALLY
THE BOSTON SOUND
BOSTON USB AUDIO SOFTWARE
BRAVO
CR
DCD
DESIGNER
DIGITAL BA
DIRECTVENT
DPS
DSI
DYNAMIC POWER SYSTEM
HIDDEN THEATER
KORTEC
LIVE TO LISTEN
MAGNAGUARD
MEDIATHEATER
MICROMEDIA
NEO 3R
NEO 5T
PERSONAL DESKTOP AUDIO
POWERVENT
PROSERIES
PV RECEPTER
RADIALVENT
RECEPTER RADIO
RUNABOUT
SLIMLINE SPEAKER TECHNOLOGY
SOUNDBAR
TUNABLERADIATORS
USB
VOYAGER
VR-M
YOUR SOUND SOLUTION
Z

BOURNS, INC.

1200 Columbia Ave
Riverside, CA 92507-2114
Tel.: (951) 781-5690
Fax: (951) 781-5273
E-mail: info@bourns.com
Web Site: www.bourns.com
Sales Range: $300-349.9 Million
Approx. Number Employees: 5,400
Year Founded: 1947
Business Description:
Electronic Components Mfr
S.I.C.: 3825; 3677
N.A.I.C.S.: 334515; 334416
Media: 2-4-5-7-9-10-11-21
Distr.: Intl.
Personnel:
Gordon L. Bourns *(CEO)*
William P. McKenna *(CFO & Treas)*
Mikelyn Bridges *(Mgr-Marcom)*
Brands & Products:
ACE
BOURNS
HYBRITRON
KNOBPOT
MULTIFUSE
TELEFUSE
TISP
TRIGARD
TRIMPOT

BOXLIGHT CORPORATION

NE 151 Hwy 300 Ste A
Belfair, WA 98528
Tel.: (360) 464-2119
Fax: (360) 282-6141
Toll Free: (800) 884-6464
Web Site: www.boxlight.com
E-Mail For Key Personnel:
Sales Director: sales@boxlight.com
Sales Range: $50-74.9 Million
Approx. Number Employees: 15
Year Founded: 1985
Business Description:
Audio-Visual Equipment & Supplies
S.I.C.: 5999; 5044
N.A.I.C.S.: 453998; 423420
Media: 2-8-13
Personnel:
Hank Nance *(Pres)*
Sunshine Nance *(Dir-Mktg)*
Brands & Products:
BOXLIGHT
PRESENTING A BETTER WAY

BRANDSMART USA

3200 SW 42nd St
Hollywood, FL 33312-6813
Tel.: (954) 797-4000
Fax: (954) 797-4061
Web Site: www.brandsmartusa.com
Sales Range: $200-249.9 Million
Approx. Number Employees: 1,000
Year Founded: 1977
Business Description:
Radio & Television & Electronic Products Retailer
S.I.C.: 5731; 5722
N.A.I.C.S.: 443112; 443111
Import Export
Media: 8-9-22

Key to Media (For complete agency information see *The Advertising Red Books-Agencies* edition):
1. Bus. Publs. 2. Cable T.V. 3. Catalogs & Directories. 4. Co-op Adv. 5. Consumer Mags. 6. D.M. to Bus. Estab.7. D.M. to Consumers
8. Daily Newsp. 9. Exhibits/Trade Shows 10. Foreign 11. Infomercial 12. Internet Adv.13. Multimedia 14. Network Radio
15. Network T.V. 16. Newsp. Distr. Mags. 17. Other 18. Outdoor (Posters, Transit) 19. Point of Purchase20. Premiums, Novelties
21. Product Samples 22. Special Events Mktg. 23. Spot Radio 24. Spot T.V. 25. Weekly Newsp. 26. Yellow Page Adv.

Personnel:
Robert Perlman *(Chm)*
Michael Perlman *(Pres)*
Eric Beazley *(CFO)*
Larry Sinewitz *(Exec VP)*
Ellen Stevens *(VP-Mktg)*
Janet Witczak *(VP-HR)*
Brands & Products:
BRANDSMART USA

BRIGHTSTAR CORPORATION
9725 NW 117th Ave #300
Miami, FL 33178
Tel.: (305) 421-6000
E-mail: communications@brightstarcorp.com
Web Site: www.brightstarcorp.com
Approx. Rev.: $4,612,863,000
Approx. Number Employees: 3,500
Year Founded: 1997
Business Description:
Wireless Distribution & Supply Chain Management Services
S.I.C.: 8742; 4812
N.A.I.C.S.: 541614; 517212
Media: 10
Personnel:
R. Marcelo Claure *(Chm & CEO)*
Dennis Strand *(CFO & Exec VP)*
Michael J. Cost *(Global COO)*
Oscar J. Fumagali *(Chief Corp Treas & Cash Conversion Cycle Officer)*
Denise Gibson *(Pres-Brightstar US & Canada)*
Sally J. Lange *(Pres-Retail Svcs)*
Rod Millar *(Pres-Europe)*
Arturo A. Osorio *(Pres-Asia Pacific)*
Oscar A. Rojas *(Pres-Latin America)*
Mark Shockley *(Pres-US & Canada)*
Celine Astuvillo *(Sr VP & Controller)*
Toby Mannheimer *(Sr VP-Global HR)*
Giampaolo Guarino *(VP-LATAM SOUTH & Gen Mgr-Argentina)*
Rafael M. de Guzman, III *(VP-Strategy)*
Diego G. Lopez Carbajal *(Dir-Product Mgmt)*
Advertising Agency:
Green Dot Advertising & Marketing
1819 W Ave Ste 5
Miami Beach, FL 33139
Tel.: (305) 674-8406
Fax: (305) 674-7898

THE BRIX GROUP INC.
541 Division St
Campbell, CA 95008-6905
Tel.: (408) 374-7900
Fax: (408) 374-5410
E-mail: info@brixcom.com
Web Site: www.brixcom.com
Sales Range: $125-149.9 Million
Approx. Number Employees: 180
Year Founded: 1971
Business Description:
Electronic Parts & Equipment
S.I.C.: 5065; 5013
N.A.I.C.S.: 423690; 423120
Import Export
Personnel:
David Shapiro *(Pres & CEO)*
Advertising Agency:
Walt & Company
2105 S Bascom Ave Ste 240
Campbell, CA 95008
Tel.: (408) 369-7200
Fax: (408) 369-7201
Agency of Record
Public Relations
Social Media Communications
Sprint 4G

BRK BRANDS, INC.
(Sub. of Jarden Branded Consumables)
3901 Liberty St Rd
Aurora, IL 60504-8122
Tel.: (630) 851-7330
Fax: (630) 851-9309
Web Site: www.firstalert.com
Approx. Sls.: $186,940,992
Approx. Number Employees: 200
Year Founded: 1969
Business Description:
Smoke & Carbon Monoxide Alarms, Home Safety Products & Health Products Mfr
S.I.C.: 3669; 3829
N.A.I.C.S.: 334290; 334519
Media: 3-5-6-9-14-15-17-18-25
Distr.: Intl.; Natl.
Personnel:
Tom Russo *(Pres)*
Mark Devine *(VP-Mktg)*
Jim Dockstader *(VP-Sls & Mktg)*
Deborah Hanson *(Dir-External Affairs)*
Brands & Products:
BE SAFE REPLACE
BRK
DOUBLE SENSOR
ESCAPE LIGHT
FAMILY GARD
FIRST ALERT

BROADCAST ELECTRONICS, INC.
(Holding of Audax Management Company, LLC)
4100 N 24th St
Quincy, IL 62305-3606
Mailing Address:
PO Box 3606
Quincy, IL 62305-3606
Tel.: (217) 224-9600
Fax: (217) 224-9607
E-mail: bdcast@bdcast.com
Web Site: www.bdcast.com
E-Mail For Key Personnel:
President: JRoark@bdcast.com
Approx. Sls.: $40,000,000
Approx. Number Employees: 100
Year Founded: 1959
Business Description:
AM, FM & Internet Radio Broadcasting Transmitter & Software Mfr
S.I.C.: 3663; 7372
N.A.I.C.S.: 334220; 511210
Export
Advertising Expenditures: $450,000
Bus. Publs.: $100,000; Catalogs & Directories: $80,000; D.M. to Bus. Estab.: $50,000; Exhibits/Trade Shows: $200,000; Other: $20,000
Distr.: Intl.; Natl.
Budget Set: Jan.
Personnel:
Joseph W. Roark *(CEO)*
Elizabeth K. Keck *(CFO)*
Tim Bealor *(VP-Sls)*
Richard Hinkle *(VP-Engrg)*
Chris Onan *(Reg Mgr-Sls)*
Jim Thomason *(Reg Mgr-Sls-Southeast)*
Jim Roberts *(Product Mgr-Datacasting)*
Hector Brown *(Mgr-Studio Technical Svcs)*
Kathy Ellerbrock *(Mgr-HR)*
Kevin Haider *(Mgr-Govt Sls)*
Kim Winking *(Mgr-Mktg Svcs)*
Brands & Products:
AUDIO VAULT
LYNX
SONIXSTREAM
VOXPRO

BSM TECHNOLOGIES INC.
5875 Highway 7 Suite 200
Woodbridge, ON L4L 1T9, Canada
Tel.: (905) 265-1200
Fax: (905) 265-1288
Toll Free: (866) 578-4315
E-mail: ir@bsmtechnologies.com
Web Site: www.bsmtechnologies.com
Approx. Rev.: $13,760,881
Approx. Number Employees: 40
Year Founded: 1996
Business Description:
After-Market, Wireless, High Security Vehicle Surveillance Products & Monitoring Services
S.I.C.: 4812; 3714; 7382
N.A.I.C.S.: 517212; 336322; 561621
Advertising Expenditures: $1,413,604
Personnel:
John K. Bell *(Chm)*
Aly Rahemtulla *(CEO)*
Jenny Stranges *(CFO)*
Eric Moran *(COO)*
Gabriel Bardas *(Chief Software Architect)*

BUD INDUSTRIES, INC.
4605 E 355th St
Willoughby, OH 44094-4629
Tel.: (440) 946-3200
Fax: (440) 951-4015
E-mail: saleseast@budind.com
Web Site: www.budind.com
E-Mail For Key Personnel:
President: bhaas@budind.com
Sales Director: saleseast@budind.com
Approx. Number Employees: 120
Year Founded: 1928
Business Description:
Electronic Enclosures & Accessories Mfr
S.I.C.: 3469; 3672
N.A.I.C.S.: 332116; 334412
Import Export
Media: 2-4-5-7-8-10-13-21
Distr.: Natl.
Budget Set: Jan.
Personnel:
Blair K. Haas *(Pres)*
Steve Haas *(Exec VP)*
Josiah Haas *(Dir-Sls)*
Brands & Products:
BUD
Advertising Agency:
Goldstein Group Communications
6000 Freedom Square Dr., Ste. 165
Cleveland, OH 44131
Tel.: (216) 573-2300
Fax: (216) 573-9964

BULOVA TECHNOLOGIES LLC
(Sub. of BULOVA TECHNOLOGIES GROUP, INC.)
101 N Queen St
Lancaster, PA 17603-3850
Mailing Address:
PO Box 4787
Lancaster, PA 17604-4787
Tel.: (717) 299-2581
Fax: (717) 397-3608 (Administration)
E-mail: bulovatech@bulovatech.com
Web Site: www.bulovatech.com
Sales Range: $25-49.9 Million
Approx. Number Employees: 300
Year Founded: 1995
Business Description:
Electronics & Electro-Mechanical Systems Contract Mfr
S.I.C.: 3679; 3672; 3674
N.A.I.C.S.: 334419; 334412; 334413
Personnel:
Stephen J. Gurba *(Pres & CEO)*
Craig Schnee *(Gen Counsel & VP)*
William E. Shrum *(VP-HR)*
Advertising Agency:
Ted Barkus Company, Inc.
8017 Anderson St
Philadelphia, PA 19118
Tel.: (215) 545-0616

BURLE INDUSTRIES, INC.
(Sub. of PHOTONIS Technologies S.A.S.)
1000 New Holland Ave
Lancaster, PA 17601-5606
Tel.: (717) 295-6000
Fax: (717) 295-6096
Toll Free: (800) 366-2875
E-mail: burlesls@burle.com
Web Site: www.burle.com
Sales Range: $75-99.9 Million
Approx. Number Employees: 400
Year Founded: 1942
Business Description:
Electron Tubes & Electro-Optical Devices Mfr
S.I.C.: 3671; 3812; 3827
N.A.I.C.S.: 334411; 333314; 334511
Import Export
Media: 2-7-10-13
Personnel:
Ronald L. Minnier *(Pres & CEO)*
Luis Vera *(VP-Sls & Mktg)*
Brands & Products:
BURLE
CHANNELTRON
CHEVRON
ELECTROGEN
EXTENDED DYNAMIC RANGE
FIELDMASTER
LONG-LIFE
MAGNUM
MICROTRON
PLANACON
QUANTACON
QUANTUM
QUICK-FIT
SPIRALTRON

C&D TECHNOLOGIES, INC.
1400 Union Meeting Rd
Blue Bell, PA 19422-0858
Tel.: (215) 619-2700
Fax: (215) 619-7840
Toll Free: (800) 543-8630
E-mail: custsvc@cdtechno.com
Web Site: www.cdtechno.com
Approx. Sls.: $354,831,000
Approx. Number Employees: 1,500
Year Founded: 1985

Key to Media (For complete agency information see *The Advertising Red Books-Agencies* edition):
1. Bus. Publs. 2. Cable T.V. 3. Catalogs & Directories. 4. Co-op Adv. 5. Consumer Mags. 6. D.M. to Bus. Estab.7. D.M. to Consumers 8. Daily Newsp. 9. Exhibits/Trade Shows 10. Foreign 11. Infomercial 12. Internet Adv.13. Multimedia 14. Network Radio 15. Network T.V. 16. Newsp. Distr. Mags. 17. Other 18. Outdoor (Posters, Transit) 19. Point of Purchase20. Premiums, Novelties 21. Product Samples 22. Special Events Mktg. 23. Spot Radio 24. Spot T.V. 25. Weekly Newsp. 26. Yellow Page Adv.

C&D Technologies, Inc. — (Continued)

Business Description:
Producer of Integrated Reserve Power Systems for Telecommunications, Electronic Information & Industrial Applications
S.I.C.: 3699; 3612; 3691; 5064; 5084
N.A.I.C.S.: 335999; 335311; 335911; 423620; 423830
Import Export
Advertising Expenditures: $385,000
Personnel:
David Treadwell *(Chm)*
Jeffrey A. Graves *(Pres & CEO)*
Ian J. Harvie *(CFO & Sr VP)*
Michael C. Crowley *(CIO & VP)*
Stan S. Wreford *(CTO & VP-Tech)*
David J. Anderson *(Gen Counsel, Sec & VP)*
John H. Brawner *(Treas & Dir-Shared Svcs)*
William Bachrach *(VP & Gen Mgr-Power Electronics Div)*
Kevin D. Burgess *(VP-HR)*
Margaret Sofio *(VP-HR)*
Brands & Products:
C&D
C&D TECHNOLOGIES
C-LINE
COMPUCHARGE
FERRO FIVE
LIBERTY
LIBERTY 2000 MAX
LIBERTY SERIES 1000
MAXRATE
MSENDUR
RANGER
SAGEON
SCOUT
SMARTBATTERY
VR SOLAR

CADDOCK ELECTRONICS, INC.
1717 Chicago Ave
Riverside, CA 92507-2364
Tel.: (951) 788-1700
Fax: (951) 369-1151
E-mail: caddock@caddock.com
Web Site: www.caddock.com
Sales Range: $10-24.9 Million
Approx. Number Employees: 234
Year Founded: 1962
Business Description:
Precision Resistors & Resistor Networks Mfr
S.I.C.: 3676
N.A.I.C.S.: 334415
Import Export
Media: 4-10
Brands & Products:
CADDOCK
KOOL PAK
KOOL-TAB
MICROMET
MICRONOX
TETRINOX

CALIFORNIA MICRO DEVICES CORPORATION
(Sub. of ON Semiconductor Corporation)
490 N McCarthy Blvd Ste 100
Milpitas, CA 95035-5118
Tel.: (408) 263-3214
Fax: (408) 263-7846
Toll Free: (800) 325-4966
E-mail: ir@calmicro.com
Web Site: www.calmicro.com
E-Mail For Key Personnel:
Marketing Director: marketing@calmicro.com
Sales Director: sales@calmicro.com
Approx. Sls.: $49,273,000
Approx. Number Employees: 103
Year Founded: 1980
Business Description:
Semiconductor Products & Digital Consumer Electronics Mfr
S.I.C.: 3674; 3676
N.A.I.C.S.: 334413; 334415
Advertising Expenditures: $400,000
Media: 2-5-10-20-21
Distr.: Intl.
Budget Set: Nov.
Personnel:
Robert V. Dickinson *(Pres & CEO)*
Kyle D. Baker *(VP-Mktg)*
Brands & Products:
ASIP
CENTURION
CMD
MEDIGUARD
OPTIGUARD
PHOTONIC
PICOGUARD
PICOGUARD XP
PICOGUARD XS
PRAETORIAN
SMARTOR

CALTROL
(Div. of Caltrol, Inc.)
7150 Koll Center Pkwy
Pleasanton, CA 94566-3100
Tel.: (925) 846-9000
Fax: (925) 846-0396
Toll Free: (800) 245-6695
Web Site: www.caltrol.com
Approx. Number Employees: 36
Year Founded: 1962
Business Description:
Process Instrumentation & Controls Distr
S.I.C.: 5084
N.A.I.C.S.: 423830
Export
Advertising Expenditures: $250,000
Media: 2-4-10-26
Distr.: Natl.
Budget Set: Dec.

CARMANAH TECHNOLOGIES CORPORATION
Building 4 203 Harbour Road
Victoria, BC V9A 3S2, Canada
Tel.: (250) 380-0052
Fax: (250) 380-0062
Toll Free: (877) 722-8877
E-mail: info@carmanah.com
Web Site: www.carmanah.com
Approx. Sls.: $33,921,000
Approx. Number Employees: 67
Year Founded: 1996
Business Description:
Renewable & Energy-Efficient Technology Solutions Integrator Focusing on Solar-Powered LED Lighting, Solar Power Systems (Off Grid & Grid Tie) & LED Illuminated Signage
S.I.C.: 3674; 3612; 3648; 3993
N.A.I.C.S.: 334413; 335129; 335311; 339950
Media: 10
Personnel:
Robert G. Cruickshank *(Chm)*
Bruce Cousins *(CEO)*
Roland Sartorius *(CFO)*
Brands & Products:
CARMANAH
DURAGEN
EVENLIT
EVERGEN
I-SHELTER
I-STOP
MICROSOURCE
WE PUT SOLAR TO WORK

CASCO PRODUCTS CORPORATION
(Sub. of Sequa Corporation)
855 Main St 10th Fl
Bridgeport, CT 06604
Tel.: (203) 922-3200
Fax: (203) 922-3201
E-mail: sales@cascoproducts.com
Web Site: www.cascoglobal.com
Approx. Number Employees: 1,000
Year Founded: 1921
Business Description:
Mfr. of Auto Cigarette Lighters & Electronic Sensor Component Parts
S.I.C.: 3714
N.A.I.C.S.: 336322
Import Export
Media: 2-4-10
Distr.: Natl.
Budget Set: Jan.
Personnel:
Ollie El-Haj *(Pres & Gen Mgr)*

CELLULAR SOUTH INC.
(Sub. of Telapex Inc.)
1018 Highland Colony Pkwy
Ridgeland, MS 39157-3301
Tel.: (601) 355-1522
Fax: (601) 353-0950
Toll Free: (877) 276-8841
E-mail: info@telapex.com
Web Site: www.telapex.com
Approx. Number Employees: 300
Year Founded: 1988
Business Description:
Radiotelephone Communication
S.I.C.: 4812
N.A.I.C.S.: 517212
Import Export
Media: 1-4-6-7-9-10-13-18-19-22-23-24-25-26
Personnel:
Wade Creekmore *(Pres)*
Suzy Hays *(Sr VP-Mktg)*
Advertising Agencies:
Spark Communications
222 Merchandise Mart Plz Ste 550
Chicago, IL 60654-1032
Tel.: (312) 970-8400
Fax: (312) 970-8464
Fax: (312) 970-8409

Thompson & Company Marketing Communications
50 Peabody Pl
Memphis, TN 38103-3667
Tel.: (901) 527-8000
Fax: (901) 527-3697

Young & Rubicam Inc.
285 Madison Ave
New York, NY 10017-6401
Tel.: (212) 210-3000
Fax: (212) 490-9073

CEPHAS HOLDING CORP.
2942 N 24th St Ste 114-508
Phoenix, AZ 85016
Tel.: (734) 274-5845
E-mail: investors@legendm.com
Web Site: www.legendm.com
Approx. Rev.: $921
Approx. Number Employees: 1
Year Founded: 1997
Business Description:
Branded Mobile Phone Products Developer & Marketer
S.I.C.: 3669; 5731; 7371
N.A.I.C.S.: 334290; 443112; 541511
Media: 5-13-20-22
Personnel:
Peter Klamka *(Chm, Pres, CEO, Treas & Sec)*

CERAMTEC NORTH AMERICA ELECTRONIC APPLICATIONS, INC.
(Sub. of CeramTec AG Innovative Ceramic Engineering)
1 Technology Pl
Laurens, SC 29360
Tel.: (864) 682-3215
Fax: (864) 682-1140
E-mail: sales@ceramtec.com
Web Site: www2.ceramtec.com
E-Mail For Key Personnel:
Sales Director: sales@ceramtec.com
Sales Range: $350-399.9 Million
Approx. Number Employees: 1,900
Year Founded: 1985
Business Description:
Advanced Technical Ceramics, Including Substrates, Packages & Seals Laser Facility
S.I.C.: 3299; 3479
N.A.I.C.S.: 327999; 332812
Media: 2-4-8-10-20-21
Personnel:
Roberto Vigo *(Mgr-Mktg)*
Brands & Products:
RUBALIT

CES INTERNATIONAL INC.
5905 Johns Rd
Tampa, FL 33634
Tel.: (813) 249-3399
Fax: (813) 249-3363
Toll Free: (800) 334-8378
E-mail: info@cesinternational.com
Web Site: www.cesinternational.com
Approx. Sls.: $13,816,277
Approx. Number Employees: 9
Business Description:
Telephone Equipment Mfr
S.I.C.: 5065
N.A.I.C.S.: 423690
Media: 10
Personnel:
Thomas Brunette *(Pres & CEO)*

CEVA, INC.
(Sub. of DSP Group, Inc.)
1943 Landings Dr
Mountain View, CA 94043
Tel.: (650) 417-7900
Fax: (650) 417-7995
E-mail: info@ceva-dsp.com
Web Site: www.ceva-dsp.com
Approx. Rev.: $44,911,000
Approx. Number Employees: 181
Year Founded: 1993

Key to Media (For complete agency information see *The Advertising Red Books-Agencies* edition):
1. Bus. Publs. 2. Cable T.V. 3. Catalogs & Directories. 4. Co-op Adv. 5. Consumer Mags. 6. D.M. to Bus. Estab.7. D.M. to Consumers 8. Daily Newsp. 9. Exhibits/Trade Shows 10. Foreign 11. Infomercial 12. Internet Adv.13. Multimedia 14. Network Radio 15. Network T.V. 16. Newsp. Distr. Mags. 17. Other 18. Outdoor (Posters, Transit) 19. Point of Purchase20. Premiums, Novelties 21. Product Samples 22. Special Events Mktg. 23. Spot Radio 24. Spot T.V. 25. Weekly Newsp. 26. Yellow Page Adv.

Business Description:
Intellectual Property Solutions for Mobile Internet Devices Designer & Developer
S.I.C.: 3674; 7371
N.A.I.C.S.: 334413; 541511
Advertising Expenditures: $489,000
Media: 10-13
Personnel:
Peter Mcmanamon *(Chm)*
Gideon Wertheizer *(CEO)*
Yaniv Arieli *(CFO)*
Issachar Ohana *(Exec VP-Sls-Worldwide)*
Eran Briman *(VP-Mktg)*
Richard Kingston *(Dir-Mktg & IR)*
Advertising Agencies:
Techworks Asia Ltd.
Unit A 7th Fl World Trust Tower
Central, China (Hong Kong)
Tel.: (852) 2524 4956
Tel.: (852) 2525 8038
Fax: (852) 2525 1893
Pub Rels-Asia Pacific
— Claire Walker *(Acct Exec)*

Wired Island Ltd.
PO Box 661
Providenciales, Turks & Caicos Islands
British WI
Tel.: (649) 941 4218
Fax: (649) 941 4219
Pub Rels-North America
— Mike Sottak *(Acct Exec)*

CHECKPOINT SYSTEMS, INC.

1 Commerce Sq 2005 Market St Ste 2410
Philadelphia, PA 19103
Tel.: (856) 848-1800
Fax: (856) 848-0937
Toll Free: (800) 257-5540
E-mail: craig.burns@checkpt.com
Web Site: www.checkpointsystems.com
Approx. Rev.: $834,498,000
Approx. Number Employees: 5,814
Year Founded: 1969
Business Description:
Integrated Electronic Security Systems Mfr
S.I.C.: 3669; 3699; 3812
N.A.I.C.S.: 334290; 334511; 335999
Export
Advertising Expenditures: $400,000
Media: 4-5-6-7-9-10-25-26
Distr.: Intl.; Natl.
Personnel:
Robert P. van der Merwe *(Chm, Pres & CEO)*
Raymond D. Andrews *(CFO & Sr VP)*
Robert Wiley *(Chief HR Officer & Sr VP)*
Farrokh Abadi *(Pres-Shrink Mgmt Solutions)*
Steven Davidson *(Pres-Global Apparel Labeling Solutions)*
Per H. Levin *(Pres-Mdse Visibility Solutions)*
James Wrigley *(Grp Pres-Global Customer Mgmt)*
John R. Van Zile *(Gen Counsel, Sec & Sr VP)*
Brands & Products:
CHECK-NET
CHECKCOUNT
CHECKPOINT
CHECKPRO AUDITOR
CHECKPRO MANAGER
CLARITY
CLARITY CONCEPT
COUNTERPOINT
FOX
GEN3
LIBERTY
LIBRARY SYSTEM
NEW LIBERTY
PERFORMA
PINNACLE
PROXIMITY PLUS
RAPIDCIRC
SECURE RINGS
SELL MORE. LOSE LESS.
SIGNATURE
STORECOUNT
SUPER TUFF TAG
THRESHOLDENTERPRISE
TURN-O-MATIC
UNI-F.I.T
UNIQUELY YOURS
VISIPLUS
WASHAWAY
YOUNIQUELY 4 U
Advertising Agencies:
Hollyrock/Miller Marketing Communications
117 Rockingham Row
Princeton, NJ 08540
Tel.: (609) 919-9292
Fax: (609) 919-9299

Teague Communication
28005 Smyth Dr Ste 112
Valencia, CA 91355
Tel.: (661) 297-5292
Fax: (661) 702-9705

CHINA TEL GROUP, INC.

12526 High Bluff Dr Ste 155
San Diego, CA 92130
Tel.: (760) 230-8986
Toll Free: (877) 260-9170
E-mail: investors@chinatelgroup.com
Web Site: www.chinatelgroup.com
Approx. Rev.: $955,311
Approx. Number Employees: 19
Year Founded: 2005
Business Description:
Holding Company; Wireless Telecommunications Carriers
S.I.C.: 4813; 3663; 6719
N.A.I.C.S.: 517210; 334220; 551112
Personnel:
Colin Yong Lee Tay *(Co-Founder & Pres)*
George Alvarez *(CEO)*
Carlos A. Trujillo *(CFO)*
Mario Alvarez *(COO)*
Isidoro Gutierrez *(Chief Admin Officer)*
Kenneth L. Waggoner *(Gen Counsel, Exec VP-Legal & Sec)*
Oliver Schwarz *(Exec VP-IR)*
Ryan Alvarez *(VP-Strategic Plng)*
Advertising Agency:
KCSA Strategic Communications (Kanan, Corbin, Schupak & Aronow, Inc.)
880 3rd Ave 6th Fl
New York, NY 10022
Tel.: (212) 682-6300
Fax: (212) 697-0910

CIENA CORPORATION

1201 Winterson Rd
Linthicum Heights, MD 21090-2203
Tel.: (410) 694-5700
Fax: (410) 694-5750
Toll Free: (800) 921-1144
E-mail: pr@ciena.com
Web Site: www.ciena.com
Approx. Rev.: $1,236,636,000
Approx. Number Employees: 4,201
Year Founded: 1992
Business Description:
Network Platforms, Software & Services
S.I.C.: 7373; 7372
N.A.I.C.S.: 541512; 511210
Advertising Expenditures: $110,618,000
Media: 10
Personnel:
Patrick H. Nettles *(Chm)*
Gary B. Smith *(Pres & CEO)*
James E. Moylan, Jr. *(CFO & Sr VP-Fin)*
John M. Crowther *(CIO & VP)*
Stephen B. Alexander *(CTO & Sr VP-Products & Tech)*
James Frodsham *(Chief Strategy Officer & Sr VP-Corp Dev)*
David M. Rothenstein *(Gen Counsel, Sec & Sr VP)*
Mike Aquino *(Sr VP-Global Field Ops)*
Rick Dodd *(Sr VP-Global Mktg)*
Randall Harris *(Sr VP-Global HR)*
Thomas Mock *(Sr VP-Comm)*
Philippe Morin *(Sr VP-Global Products Grp)*
Francois Locoh-Donou *(VP-Sls & Gen Mgr)*
Nicole Anderson *(Sr Dir-External Comm)*
Guillermo Corea *(Dir-Web & Community Mktg)*
Brands & Products:
CIENA
COREDIRECTOR
COREDIRECTOR CI
CORESTREAM
FASTMESH
FLEXIBLE CONCATENATION
FLEXSELECT
LIGHTWORKS
LIGHTWORKS EOS
LIGHTWORKS IOS
LIGHTWORKS ON-CENTER
LIGHTWORKS OS
LIGHTWORKS TOOLKIT
LUCENT SLC
METRODIRECTOR K2
MULTIWAVE
MULTIWAVE METRO
MULTIWAVE METRO ONE
MULTIWAVE SENTRY
THE NETWORK SPECIALIST
ON-CENTER
ONLINE
ONLINE METRO
ONWAVE
OPTX
OSRP
SIMPLY SMARTER LIGHT
SMARTSPAN
SMARTSUPPORT
SMARTTOOLS
VIRTUALWIRE
VLSR
WAVEDIRECTOR
WAVELOCK
WAVELOGIC
WAVEWATCHER
Advertising Agencies:
Davies Murphy Group
200 Wheeler Rd N Tower
Burlington, MA 01803
Tel.: (781) 418-2400
Fax: (781) 418-2480

Sloane & Company LLC (d/b/a Sloane & Company)
7 Times Sq Tower 17th Fl
New York, NY 10036
Tel.: (212) 486-9500
Fax: (212) 486-9094

CINEQUIPT INC.

2601 49th Ave N
Minneapolis, MN 55430
Tel.: (612) 627-9080
Fax: (612) 627-9789
Toll Free: (800) 809-9080
Toll Free: (888) 809-3080
Web Site: www.cinequipt.com
Sales Range: $25-49.9 Million
Approx. Number Employees: 18
Business Description:
Rental & Leasing of Video Equipment
S.I.C.: 7359; 5043
N.A.I.C.S.: 532299; 423410
Advertising Expenditures: $80,000
Media: 6
Personnel:
Dawn Mans *(Pres)*
Kellie Kreller *(CFO)*
Bryan Heiber *(Mgr-Sls)*
Brands & Products:
CINEQUIPT
OUR GEAR. YOUR VISION.
Advertising Agency:
Geoffrey Carlson Gage, LLC (d/b/a Geoffrey Carlson Gage Brand Solutions)
500 Lake St Ste 100
Excelsior, MN 55331-2010
Tel.: (952) 401-7658
Fax: (952) 401-7662

CIRRUS LOGIC, INC.

2901 Via Fortuna
Austin, TX 78746
Tel.: (512) 851-4000
Fax: (512) 851-4977
Toll Free: (800) 888-5016
E-mail: InvestorRelations@cirrus.com
Web Site: www.cirrus.com
Approx. Sls.: $369,571,000
Approx. Number Employees: 570
Year Founded: 1984
Business Description:
Developer of High-Precision Analog & Mixed-Signal Integrated Circuits
S.I.C.: 3674
N.A.I.C.S.: 334413
Advertising Expenditures: $1,300,000
Media: 2-7-10-13
Personnel:
Michael L. Hackworth *(Co-Founder & Chm)*
Jason P. Rhode *(Pres & CEO)*
Thurman K. Case *(CFO, Treas & VP-Fin)*
Gregory Scott Thomas *(Gen Counsel, Sec & VP)*
Scott Anderson *(Sr VP & Gen Mgr-Mixed-Signal Audio Div)*
Tom Stein *(VP & Gen Mgr-Apex Precision Power Bus)*

Cirrus Logic, Inc. — (Continued)

Jo-Dee M. Benson *(VP-Corp Comm & HR)*
Carl Alberty *(Dir-Mktg)*
Bill Schnell *(Mgr-PR)*

Brands & Products:
APEX PRECISION POWER
BLU-RAY
CIRRUS LOGIC
COBRANET
CRYSTAL
CRYSTAL LAN
LEADING THE DIGITAL ENTERTAINMENT REVOLUTION
TOTAL-E

Advertising Agency:
Curran & Connors, Inc.
3455 Peachtree Rd NE 5th Fl
Atlanta, GA 30326-3236
Tel.: (404) 239-3979
Toll Free: (800) 435-.0406

CLARION CORPORATION OF AMERICA

(Sub. of Clarion Co., Ltd.)
661 W Redondo Beach Blvd
Gardena, CA 90247
Tel.: (310) 327-9100
Fax: (310) 327-1999
Toll Free: (800) GO-CLARION
Web Site: www.clarion.com
Approx. Sls.: $4,100,000
Approx. Number Employees: 250
Year Founded: 1963

Business Description:
Mfr. of Car Stereos, Radios, Citizens Band Radios, Accessories, Cellular Phones & Video Monitors for Vehicles
S.I.C.: 5064; 3651
N.A.I.C.S.: 423620; 334310
Import
Advertising Expenditures: $2,000,000
Media: 1-2-3-4-6-9-10-14-15-16-19-22-23-24-25-26
Distr.: Natl.
Budget Set: June

Personnel:
Tom Hayashi *(Pres)*
Neil Carande *(VP-Retail Sls)*

Brands & Products:
MAGI-TUNE FM
PHAZE 1

CLEARONE COMMUNICATIONS, INC.

5225 Wiley Post Way Ste 500
Salt Lake City, UT 84116
Tel.: (801) 975-7200
Fax: (801) 977-0087
Toll Free: (800) 945-7730
E-mail: investor_relations@clearone.com
Web Site: www.clearone.com
E-Mail For Key Personnel:
Sales Director: sales@clearone.com
Approx. Rev.: $41,284,000
Approx. Number Employees: 122

Business Description:
Video Conferencing Products & Services
S.I.C.: 3661; 3663
N.A.I.C.S.: 334210; 334220
Advertising Expenditures: $750,000

Personnel:
Zeynep Hakimoglu *(Chm, Pres & CEO)*
Tracy Bathurst *(Chief Strategy Officer)*
Narsi Narayanan *(VP-Fin & Corp Sec)*

Brands & Products:
ACCUMIC
AP-WARE
AUDIO PERFECT
CANCELLATION
CEILING DOCCAM
CLEARONE
CONVERGE
D.A.R.E.
DEMOLETTER
DOCCAM
DOCCAM PRO
FLEXCAM
G-WARE
GENTNER
HDCONFERENCE
IDCAM
MAX
MAX WIRELESS PHONE
MAXATTACH
PERFECT
PTZCAM
RAV-WARE
STUDENTCAM
TEACHCAM
TITAN
XAP
YOU'RE VIRTUALLY THERE

CLEARWIRE CORPORATION

4400 Carillon Pt
Kirkland, WA 98033
Tel.: (425) 216-7600
Fax: (425) 216-7900
E-mail: support@clearwire.com
Web Site: www.clearwire.com
Approx. Rev.: $556,826,000
Approx. Number Employees: 3,600

Business Description:
Wireless Broadband Services
S.I.C.: 4812
N.A.I.C.S.: 517212
Advertising Expenditures: $213,900,000

Personnel:
John W. Stanton *(Chm)*
Erik E. Prusch *(Pres & CEO)*
Hope F. Cochran *(CFO)*
David D. Maquera *(Chief Strategy Officer & Sr VP)*
John Saw *(CTO & Sr VP)*
Broady R. Hodder *(Gen Counsel & Sr VP)*
R. Gerard Salemme *(Exec VP-Strategy, Policy & External Affairs)*
Thomas Enraght-Moony *(Sr VP-Mktg & Gen Mgr-Clear Online)*

Advertising Agencies:
al Punto Advertising, Inc.
730 El Camino Way Ste 200
Tustin, CA 92780-7733
Tel.: (714) 544-0888
Fax: (714) 544-0830

DDB Los Angeles
340 Main St
Venice, CA 90291
Tel.: (310) 907-1500
Fax: (310) 907-1571

Horizon Media, Inc.
1940 Century Park E 3rd Fl
Los Angeles, CA 90067-1700
Tel.: (310) 282-0909
Fax: (310) 229-8104
Toll Free: (800) 282-0901
Agency of Record
Media Planning & Buying

JLM Partners
1001 4th Ave Ste 2100
Seattle, WA 98154
Tel.: (206) 381-3600
Fax: (206) 381-3607
Broadband Services

Venables, Bell & Partners
201 Post St Ste 200
San Francisco, CA 94108
Tel.: (415) 288-3300
Fax: (415) 421-3683
(Agency of Record)

COBHAM DEFENSE ELECTRONIC SYSTEMS-M/A-COM INC.

(Sub. of Cobham Defence Systems Division)
1011 Pawtucket Blvd
Lowell, MA 01853
Tel.: (978) 442-4000
Fax: (978) 442-4001
Toll Free: (800) 366-2266
Web Site: www.macom.com
Sales Range: $200-249.9 Million
Approx. Number Employees: 600
Year Founded: 1950

Business Description:
Microwave & Radio Communications Systems Developer & Mfr
S.I.C.: 3669
N.A.I.C.S.: 334290
Media: 2-4-5-10-11-13-20-22
Distr.: Intl.; Natl.

Personnel:
Joe Thomas *(Pres & CEO)*
Victoria Dillon *(VP-Comm)*

Brands & Products:
EDACS
NETWORKFIRST
OPENSKY
P25IP

COBRA ELECTRONICS CORPORATION

6500 W Cortland St
Chicago, IL 60707-4000
Tel.: (773) 889-8870
Fax: (773) 794-1930
E-mail: productinfo@cobra.com
Web Site: www.cobra.com
Approx. Sls.: $110,520,000
Approx. Number Employees: 152
Year Founded: 1961

Business Description:
Consumer Electronic Products Designer & Marketer, Including CB Radios, Safety/Radar Detection Systems & Safety Alert Receivers & Transmitters & Family Radio Service Products
S.I.C.: 3663; 3651
N.A.I.C.S.: 334220; 334310
Import Export
Advertising Expenditures: $5,400,000
Media: 1-2-4-6-10-13-19-20-21
Distr.: Intl.; Natl.
Budget Set: Oct.

Personnel:
James R. Bazet *(Chm, Pres & CEO)*
Robert E. Ben *(VP, Controller & Interim CFO)*
Sally A. Washlow *(Sr VP-Mktg & Sls)*
William Chamberlain *(VP-Engrng & Quality)*
Gerald M. Laures *(VP-Fin)*
Dean Marino *(Sr Dir-IT)*

Brands & Products:
12 BAND
15-BAND
6 BAND
AURA
COBRA
COBRAMARINE
DIGIVIEW
DYNAMIKE
EASYSET
EXTRA SENSORY DETECTION
EXTREME BRIGHT DATAGRAFIX
HI GEAR
IASAP
INTELLIMUTE
INTELLISHIELD
LASEREYE
MICROTALK
NAV ONE
NIGHTWATCH
NOTHING COMES CLOSE TO A COBRA
PENTAGON PROTECTION
REVOLUTION
ROADREADY
S-XRS
SAFETY ALERT
SMARTPOWER
SOUNDTRACKER
SPECTRE ALERT
STREETFINDER
TRAFFIC WARNING SYSTEM
ULTRABRIGHT
VG-2 ALERT
VOICE ALERT
XTREME RANGE SUPERHETERODYNE

Advertising Agency:
GolinHarris
(Part of the Interpublic Group of Companies)
111 E Wacker Dr 11th Fl
Chicago, IL 60601-4306
Tel.: (312) 729-4000
Fax: (312) 729-4010

CODA OCTOPUS GROUP, INC.

164 W 25th St 6R
New York, NY 10001
Tel.: (212) 924-3442
Fax: (212) 924-3447
Web Site: www.codaoctopusgroup.com
Approx. Rev.: $13,224,435
Approx. Number Employees: 88

Business Description:
Underwater Technologies For Imaging, Mapping, Defence & Survey; Geosurvey Solutions
S.I.C.: 3674; 3679; 3812; 3861; 8713
N.A.I.C.S.: 334413; 333315; 334419; 334511; 541360
Advertising Expenditures: $1,237,175

Personnel:
Geoff Turner *(CEO)*

COMMUNICATIONS SYSTEMS, INC.

10900 Red Circle Dr
Minnetonka, MN 55343
Tel.: (952) 996-1562

Key to Media (For complete agency information see *The Advertising Red Books-Agencies* edition):
1. Bus. Publs. 2. Cable T.V. 3. Catalogs & Directories. 4. Co-op Adv. 5. Consumer Mags. 6. D.M. to Bus. Estab.7. D.M. to Consumers 8. Daily Newsp. 9. Exhibits/Trade Shows 10. Foreign 11. Infomercial 12. Internet Adv.13. Multimedia 14. Network Radio 15. Network T.V. 16. Newsp. Distr. Mags. 17. Other 18. Outdoor (Posters, Transit) 19. Point of Purchase20. Premiums, Novelties 21. Product Samples 22. Special Events Mktg. 23. Spot Radio 24. Spot T.V. 25. Weekly Newsp. 26. Yellow Page Adv.

Fax: (952) 996-1693
E-mail: colleenm@commsysinc.com
Web Site: www.commsystems.com
Approx. Sls.: $120,072,310
Approx. Number Employees: 458
Year Founded: 1969
Business Description:
Mfr & Marketer of Telecommunications Equipment
S.I.C.: 3679; 3661; 4899
N.A.I.C.S.: 334418; 334210; 517910
Export
Advertising Expenditures: $500,000
Media: 2-4-7-10-17-21
Distr.: Intl.; Natl.
Budget Set: Oct.
Personnel:
Curtis A. Sampson *(Chm)*
Jeffrey K. Berg *(Pres & CEO)*
David T. McGraw *(CFO & VP)*
William G. Schultz *(Exec VP-Ops)*
Bruce Blackwood *(VP & Gen Mgr-Suttle)*
Karen Nesburg Bleick *(VP-HR)*

COMPLIANCE SYSTEMS CORPORATION
50 Glen St Ste 308
Glen Cove, NY 11542
Tel.: (516) 674-4545
Approx. Number Employees: 1
Business Description:
Telecommunication Products Mfr
S.I.C.: 3669
N.A.I.C.S.: 334290
Advertising Expenditures: $216,991
Personnel:
Barry M. Brookstein *(Interim CEO & CFO)*
Stephan Dunigan *(Pres/CEO-Call Compliance Inc)*
Jim Robinson *(Pres/CEO-Execuserve Corp)*

COMTECH AHA CORPORATION
(Sub. of Comtech Telecommunications Corp.)
(d/b/a AHA)
1126 Alturas Dr
Moscow, ID 83843
Tel.: (208) 892-5600
Fax: (208) 892-5601
Web Site: www.comtechtel.com
Approx. Sls.: $10,000,000
Approx. Number Employees: 25
Business Description:
Semiconductors & Related Devices
S.I.C.: 3674
N.A.I.C.S.: 334413
Personnel:
Dan Wood *(Pres-Comtech Mobile Datacom Corp & Sr VP)*
Jerome Kapelus *(Sr VP-Corp Dev)*
William Thomson *(Gen Mgr-Comtech AHA Grp)*
Advertising Agency:
Shelton Group
12400 Coit Rd Ste 650
Dallas, TX 75251
Tel.: (972) 239-5119
Fax: (972) 239-2292

COMVERSE, INC.
(Sub. of Comverse Technology, Inc.)
100 Quannapowitt Pkwy
Wakefield, MA 01880-1315
Tel.: (781) 224-8888
Fax: (781) 224-8143
E-mail: training@comverse.com
Web Site: www.comverse.com
Sales Range: $25-49.9 Million
Approx. Number Employees: 100
Year Founded: 1984
Business Description:
Network-Based Messaging, Converged Billing & IP Communications Services
S.I.C.: 7373
N.A.I.C.S.: 541512
Export
Advertising Expenditures: $50,000,000
Media: 1-2-4-5-7-9-10-11-13-16-17-20-22-25
Distr.: Intl.; Natl.
Personnel:
Ziv Leitman *(CFO & Exec VP)*
Dror Bin *(Pres-Global Sls & Exec VP)*
Eitan Achlow *(Pres-APAC)*
Ramesh Barasia *(Pres-Comverse Americas)*
William Sorin *(Sec & Dir-Sls)*
Hezi Basok *(Sr VP-Ops)*
Lionel Chmilewsky *(Sr VP-Customer Facing Grp)*
Christopher Cyr *(VP & Gen Mgr)*
Rani Hagag *(VP-Product Mktg)*
Shlomo Weitz *(VP-Corp Customer Svc)*
Stacy Fassberg *(Assoc VP-Mktg)*
Cecilia Panozzo *(Dir-Mktg)*
Gustavo Paissan *(Mgr-Mktg)*
Brands & Products:
ACCESS NP
ACCESSMAX
CO ACCESS

CON-SPACE COMMUNICATIONS LTD.
5600 Parkwood Way Suite 505
Richmond, BC V6V 2M2, Canada
Tel.: (604) 244-9323
Fax: (604) 270-2138
Toll Free: (800) 546-3405
E-mail: info@con-space.com
Web Site: www.con-space.com
Sales Range: $1-9.9 Million
Year Founded: 1991
Business Description:
Communications Equipment Mfr
S.I.C.: 4812; 3669; 4813
N.A.I.C.S.: 517212; 334290; 517211; 517310
Advertising Expenditures: $149,113
Media: 10
Personnel:
Andrew Ibbetson *(Pres)*
Alan Jakobsen *(VP-Intl Sls)*
Gary Kent *(VP-Fin & Admin)*
Don Clarke *(Dir-Quality)*
Edwin Poppert *(Dir-Ops-US)*
Lauren Girdler *(Mgr-Customer Experience)*
Michael Leung *(Mgr-Mfg)*
Joseph Liang *(Mgr-Pur)*
Matt Wannop *(Mgr-Special Projects)*
Jorge Menyhart *(Chief Engr)*
Brands & Products:
CON-SPACE COMMUNICATIONS
SAFETY IN COMMUNICATION

CONKLIN CORPORATION
(Sub. of Intracom Holdings S.A.)
11360 Atlanta Development Center
Duluth, GA 30097
Tel.: (770) 295-2500
Fax: (770) 295-2600
E-mail: info@ga.conklincorp.com
Web Site: www.conklin-intracom.com
Sales Range: $25-49.9 Million
Approx. Number Employees: 100
Year Founded: 1957
Business Description:
Telecommunications
S.I.C.: 4899
N.A.I.C.S.: 517910
Import Export
Media: 2-4-7-10
Distr.: Natl.
Personnel:
Ian Meletios *(CEO)*
Christina Holland *(Mgr-Mktg)*

CONN'S, INC.
3295 College St
Beaumont, TX 77701
Tel.: (409) 832-1696
Fax: (409) 832-4344
Toll Free: (877) 472-5422
E-mail: customerservice@conns.com
Web Site: www.conns.com
Approx. Rev.: $790,524,000
Approx. Number Employees: 2,600
Year Founded: 1890
Business Description:
Home Appliances, Consumer Electronics, Home Computers, Computer Peripherals & Accessories, Lawn & Garden Products & Mattresses Retailer
S.I.C.: 5013; 5023; 5083; 5722; 5731
N.A.I.C.S.: 441310; 423220; 423820; 443111; 443112
Advertising Expenditures: $30,273,000
Personnel:
Theodore M. Wright *(Chm, Interim Pres & Interim CEO)*
Michael J. Poppe *(CFO)*
David W. Trahan *(Exec VP-Retail)*
Clinton W. Harwood *(Sr VP-IT)*

CONRAC, INC.
5124 Commerce Dr
Baldwin Park, CA 91706
Tel.: (626) 480-0095
Fax: (626) 480-0077
E-mail: monitors@conrac.com
Web Site: www.conrac.com
Approx. Number Employees: 9
Year Founded: 1939
Business Description:
Mfr. of CRT & Flat Panel Displays
S.I.C.: 3651; 3663
N.A.I.C.S.: 334310; 334220
Advertising Expenditures: $2,500,000
Media: 2-4-5-7-10-19-26
Distr.: Intl.; Natl.
Budget Set: Nov.
Personnel:
William Moeller *(Pres)*
Ray Allen *(CFO)*
Brands & Products:
AUTOTRAK
CONRAC

CONSOLIDATED COMMUNICATIONS HOLDINGS, INC.
121 S 17th St
Mattoon, IL 61938-3987
Tel.: (217) 235-3311
Fax: (217) 258-7883
E-mail: investor.relations@consolidated.com
Web Site: www.consolidated.com
Approx. Rev.: $383,366,000
Approx. Number Employees: 970
Year Founded: 1894
Business Description:
Holding Company; Voice & Data Telecommunications & Directory Services
S.I.C.: 4813; 2741; 4812; 4899; 6719
N.A.I.C.S.: 517110; 511140; 517212; 517910; 551112
Advertising Expenditures: $2,500,000
Media: 5-7-8-9-10-13-16-18-19-22-23-24-25-26
Personnel:
Richard A. Lumpkin *(Chm)*
Robert J. Currey *(Pres & CEO)*
Steven L. Childers *(CFO)*
Christopher A. Young *(CIO)*
C. Robert Udell, Jr. *(Pres-Telephone Ops-Texas)*
Steve J. Shirar *(Sr VP)*
Stephen Jones *(VP-HR)*

CONTINENTAL ELECTRONICS CORPORATION
(Holding of Lone Star Investment Advisors, LLC)
4212 S Buckner Blvd
Dallas, TX 75227
Tel.: (214) 381-7161
Fax: (214) 275-2397
E-mail: info@drs-bt.com
Web Site: www.contelec.com
E-Mail For Key Personnel:
Marketing Director: amina@contelec.com
Approx. Number Employees: 150
Year Founded: 1946
Business Description:
Radio Broadcast Transmission Equipment Mfr
S.I.C.: 3663
N.A.I.C.S.: 334220
Export
Media: 2-7-10

CONTROL CHIEF HOLDINGS, INC.
200 Williams St
Bradford, PA 16701-1411
Mailing Address:
PO Box 141
Bradford, PA 16701-0141
Tel.: (814) 362-6811
Fax: (814) 368-4133
E-mail: sales@controlchief.com
Web Site: www.controlchief.com
E-Mail For Key Personnel:
Sales Director: sales@controlchief.com
Sales Range: $1-9.9 Million
Approx. Number Employees: 43
Year Founded: 1959
Business Description:
Mfr. of Remote Controls for Industrial Machines
S.I.C.: 3625
N.A.I.C.S.: 335314
Media: 10
Personnel:
Douglas S. Bell *(Pres & CEO)*
Allison Ambrose *(Coord-Mktg & Graphics)*

Key to Media (For complete agency information see *The Advertising Red Books-Agencies* edition):
1. Bus. Publs. 2. Cable T.V. 3. Catalogs & Directories. 4. Co-op Adv. 5. Consumer Mags. 6. D.M. to Bus. Estab.7. D.M. to Consumers
8. Daily Newsp. 9. Exhibits/Trade Shows 10. Foreign 11. Infomercial 12. Internet Adv.13. Multimedia 14. Network Radio
15. Network T.V. 16. Newsp. Distr. Mags. 17. Other 18. Outdoor (Posters, Transit) 19. Point of Purchase20. Premiums, Novelties
21. Product Samples 22. Special Events Mktg. 23. Spot Radio 24. Spot T.V. 25. Weekly Newsp. 26. Yellow Page Adv.

Control Chief Holdings, Inc. — (Continued)

Brands & Products:
AKERSTROMS
COMMAND CHIEF
COMMUNICATOR
COMMUNICATORE
CONTROL CHF
CONTROL CHIEF
MU AND GO
PLUG AND GO
PLUG N GO
RAYMOTE
SCOUT
SUMMIT
TELECHIEF
TK6
TRAIN CHIEF

COOPER INTERCONNECT
(Unit of Cooper Crouse-Hinds, LLC)
23 Front St
Salem, NJ 08079
Tel.: (856) 935-7560
Fax: (856) 935-7694
E-mail: info@cooperinterconnect.com
Web Site:
www.cooperinterconnect.com
Sales Range: $250-299.9 Million
Approx. Number Employees: 450
Year Founded: 1971
Business Description:
Military & Industrial Cable & Connector Mfr
S.I.C.: 3357; 3679
N.A.I.C.S.: 335929; 334419
Import Export
Advertising Expenditures: $200,000
Media: 4-10
Personnel:
Dorothy Matchett *(Dir-Military Sls-Global)*
Steve Mcqueen *(Dir-Global Indus & Comml Sls)*
Greg Baugher *(Reg Mgr-Acct)*
Scott Blaine *(Reg Mgr-Sls-West)*
Jon Cheek *(Reg Mgr-Sls-Eastern)*
Mike Everson *(Reg Mgr-Indus & Comml Sls)*
Chuck Frederking *(Reg Mgr-Indus & Comml Sls)*
Van Murphy *(Reg Mgr-Indus & Comml Sls)*
Russ Simmons *(Reg Mgr-Sls-Midwest)*
William Barbera *(Natl Sls & Mktg Mgr)*
Ron Raines *(Sls Mgr)*
Patricia DuBois *(Mgr-Mktg & Product Support)*
Brands & Products:
GARRY ELECTRONICS
GENERAL CONNECTOR
MIGHTY MITE
POKE HOME
TINY TIM
VIKING ELECTRONICS
WIRE-PRO
WPI CABLE SYSTEMS
WPI SARASOTA

COOPER INTERCONNECT
(Branch of Cooper Interconnect)
5455 Endeavour Ct
Moorpark, CA 93021-1712
Mailing Address:
PO Box 8009
Moorpark, CA 93021-8009
Tel.: (805) 553-9633
Fax: (805) 553-9655
E-mail: info@cooperinterconnect.com
Web Site:
www.cooperinterconnect.com
E-Mail For Key Personnel:
Sales Director: sales@vikcon.com
Approx. Sls.: $15,000,000
Approx. Number Employees: 100
Year Founded: 1955
Business Description:
Military & Industrial Wire & Connector Mfr
S.I.C.: 3678; 3643
N.A.I.C.S.: 334417; 335931
Import Export
Media: 4-10-21-22
Distr.: Intl.; Natl.
Budget Set: Jan.
Personnel:
Doug Sims *(Reg Mgr)*
Cathryn Reynolds *(Mgr-Reg Sls-Maryland & Virginia)*

COOPER WHEELOCK
(Div. of Cooper Safety)
273 Branchport Ave
Long Branch, NJ 07740-6830
Tel.: (732) 222-6880
Fax: (732) 222-8707
Toll Free: (800) 631-2148
Web Site: www.cooperwheelock.com
Approx. Sls.: $30,000,000
Approx. Number Employees: 350
Business Description:
Fire Safety & Emergency Incident Communications Systems & Devices Designer & Mfr
S.I.C.: 3669; 9224
N.A.I.C.S.: 334290; 922160
Media: 2-5-7-10-20-21
Personnel:
Scott Hearn *(Pres)*
June A. Ballew *(VP-Sls)*
Jerry Johnston *(Mgr-Sys Sls-West Region)*
Todd Pelland *(Mgr-Sls-Eastern Reg)*
Chris Weaver *(Mgr-Sls-Eastern System)*
Brands & Products:
NACEVAC
NACTOOL
POWERPATH
SAFEPATH
STROBETOOL
WHEELOCK

CORNELL DUBILIER ELECTRONICS
(Sub. of Cornell Dubilier Electronics, Inc.)
140 Technology Pl
Liberty, SC 29657-3300
Tel.: (864) 843-2277
Fax: (864) 843-3800
E-mail: support@cde.com
Web Site: www.cde.com
Year Founded: 1933
Business Description:
Mfr. of Electronic Capacitors
S.I.C.: 3675; 3677
N.A.I.C.S.: 334414; 334416
Media: 1-2-4-5-7-10-17-20-21
Distr.: Intl.; Natl.
Budget Set: Apr. -June
Personnel:
James P. Kaplan *(Pres)*
Victor Whitworth *(CFO)*
Rex Easterly *(Prod Mgr)*
Ken Thompson *(Product Mgr-Film Capacitors & IGBT Snubbers)*
Laird Macomber *(Mgr-Tech)*
Mike McGeachie *(Engr-Application)*
Brands & Products:
CDE
MALLORY

CORRPRO COMPANIES, INC.
(Div. of Insituform Technologies Inc)
1055 W smith Rd
Medina, OH 44256-1328
Tel.: (330) 723-5082
Fax: (330) 723-0694
E-mail: investorrelations@corrpro.com
Web Site: www.corrpro.com
Approx. Rev.: $170,515,000
Approx. Number Employees: 716
Year Founded: 1984
Business Description:
Cathodic Protection Systems; Engineering Services; Corrosion Protection Services Relating to Coatings; Non-Destructive Testing; Pipeline Integrity & Reinforced Concrete Structures
S.I.C.: 8711; 8734
N.A.I.C.S.: 541330; 541380
Import Export
Advertising Expenditures: $300,000
Media: 2-4-8-10-13-20-22-26
Distr.: Direct to Consumer; Intl.; Natl.
Budget Set: Jan.
Personnel:
Jeff Rock *(Exec VP)*
Brands & Products:
CCI
CENTAP
CONCORDER
CORRPRO
CPL
HIRDA
PASS
PERMACELL
PERMANODE
SPIRA-PAK
TASC
Advertising Agency:
Marketects, Incorporated
1525 Lakeville Ste 221
Kingwood, TX 77339
Tel.: (281) 348-0888

CORTELCO SYSTEMS PUERTO RICO, INC.
Parque Ind Caguas Oeste Rd 156 km 58.2
Caguas, PR 00727-0137
Tel.: (787) 704-0000
Fax: (787) 704-3200
Web Site: www.cortelcopr.com
Sales Range: $10-24.9 Million
Approx. Number Employees: 63
Business Description:
Third-Party Reseller of Voice & Data Communication Systems
S.I.C.: 4812; 4813; 4899
N.A.I.C.S.: 517212; 517310; 517910
Advertising Expenditures: $4,161,000
Personnel:
Sergio Moren *(Chm)*
Juan Carlos Ramos *(Pres & CEO)*
Francisco Sanchez *(CFO & VP-Fin/Admin)*

CPI INTERNATIONAL, INC.
(Holding of Veritas Capital Fund, L.P.)
811 Hansen Way
Palo Alto, CA 94303
Tel.: (650) 846-2900
Fax: (650) 846-3276
E-mail: amanda.mogin@cpii.com
Web Site: www.cpii.com
Approx. Sls.: $360,434,000
Approx. Number Employees: 1,580
Business Description:
Microwave & Radio Frequency Solutions
S.I.C.: 5064; 3663
N.A.I.C.S.: 423620; 334220
Advertising Expenditures: $18,547,000
Media: 5-7
Personnel:
Michael B. Targoff *(Chm)*
Jarrett Wendt *(Pres & CEO)*
Joel A. Littman *(CFO)*
Don C. Coleman *(Pres-Beverly Microwave Div & VP)*
O. Joe Caldarelli *(Pres-Comm & Medical Products Div)*
Amanda Mogin *(Dir-IR)*

CRANE AEROSPACE & ELECTRONICS, KELTEC OPERATION
(Unit of Crane Aerospace Group)
84 Hill Ave NW
Fort Walton Beach, FL 32548-3858
Tel.: (850) 244-0043
Fax: (850) 664-0546
Web Site: www.crane.com
Sales Range: $75-99.9 Million
Approx. Number Employees: 250
Year Founded: 1965
Business Description:
Power Supply, Amplifier & Transmitter Designer & Mfr
S.I.C.: 3679
N.A.I.C.S.: 334419
Media: 10
Personnel:
Gregory A. Ward *(Pres-Aerospace Crane)*
David E. Bender *(Pres-Electronics Grp)*

CREE INC.
4600 Silicon Dr
Durham, NC 27703-8475
Tel.: (919) 313-5300
Fax: (919) 313-5558
E-mail: investorrelations@cree.com
Web Site: www.cree.com
Approx. Rev.: $987,615,000
Approx. Number Employees: 4,753
Year Founded: 1987
Business Description:
Semiconductors Mfr
S.I.C.: 3674
N.A.I.C.S.: 334413
Advertising Expenditures: $4,200,000
Personnel:
Charles M. Swoboda *(Chm, Pres & CEO)*
Alan J. Ruud *(Vice Chm-Lighting)*
John T. Kurtzweil *(CFO, Treas & Exec VP)*
Steve Kelley *(COO)*
Adam H. Broome *(Gen Counsel, Sec & VP-Legal)*
Robert Pollock *(Sr VP-Sls-Worldwide)*

Key to Media (For complete agency information see *The Advertising Red Books-Agencies* edition):
1. Bus. Publs. 2. Cable T.V. 3. Catalogs & Directories. 4. Co-op Adv. 5. Consumer Mags. 6. D.M. to Bus. Estab.7. D.M. to Consumers
8. Daily Newsp. 9. Exhibits/Trade Shows 10. Foreign 11. Infomercial 12. Internet Adv.13. Multimedia 14. Network Radio
15. Network T.V. 16. Newsp. Distr. Mags. 17. Other 18. Outdoor (Posters, Transit) 19. Point of Purchase20. Premiums, Novelties
21. Product Samples 22. Special Events Mktg. 23. Spot Radio 24. Spot T.V. 25. Weekly Newsp. 26. Yellow Page Adv.

Bruce Renouard *(Sr VP-Sls & Bus Dev)*
Robert C. Glass *(VP-Tech)*
Christopher M. James *(VP-Corp Mktg)*
Gary Barbari *(Dir-Mfg)*
Raiford Garrabrant *(Dir-IR)*
Anthony Grieco *(Dir-Sls)*
Michelle Murray *(Mgr-Corp Comm)*
Brands & Products:
CI
COLORWAVE
COTCO
CREATING TECHNOLOGY THAT CREATES SOLUTIONS
CREE
CREE LED LIGHT
CREE LED LIGHTING SOLUTIONS
CREE LED SOLUTION PROVIDER
CREE LEDS
CREE LIGHTING
DOWNLIGHT REINVENTED
ETC
EZ
EZ-12
EZ-16
EZ-18
EZ-21
EZ-24
EZ-7
EZ-8.5
EZ290
EZBRIGHT
EZBRIGHT1000
EZBRIGHT290
EZPC
EZR
GSIC
ICEFET
LED CITY
LED HOME
LED UNIVERSITY
LED WORKPLACE
LLF
LLS
MB
MB MAX
MB PLUS
MEGABRIGHT
MEGABRIGHT PLUS
RAZERTHIN
RETURN ON ENERGY
SUPERBLUE
SUPERBRIGHT
UB
ULTRABRIGHT
ULTRATHIN
UT
UT230
XB
XB PLUS
XB500
XB900
XBRIGHT
XBRIGHTPLUS
XLAMP
XT
XT-12
XT-16
XT-18
XT-21
XT-24
XT-27
XTHIN
ZERO RECOVERY
ZMP

Advertising Agency:
Business-to-Business Marketing Communications
900 Ridgefield Dr Ste 270
Raleigh, NC 27609-8524
Tel.: (919) 872-8172
Fax: (919) 872-8875

CRESTRON ELECTRONICS INC.

15 Volvo Dr
Rockleigh, NJ 07647-2507
Tel.: (201) 767-3400
Fax: (201) 767-7576
Toll Free: (800) 237-2041
Web Site: www.crestron.com
Approx. Number Employees: 2,000
Year Founded: 1971
Business Description:
Provider of Electronic Controlled & Audio Visual Integration Solutions
S.I.C.: 3571; 3651
N.A.I.C.S.: 334111; 334310
Import Export
Media: 6
Personnel:
George Feldstein *(Pres & CEO)*
Randy Klein *(Exec VP)*
Fred Bargetzi *(VP-Tech)*
Phil Breitschadel *(Mgr-Sls-Cobham)*
Derrick Hammett *(Mgr-Regional Sls)*
Justin Kennington *(Mgr-Digital Media Product Line)*
Brands & Products:
ADAGIO
APPLICATION BUILDER
BRITETOUCH
CAMEO
COLORTOUCH
CRESCAT
CRESNET
CRESNET-TO-LUTRON
CRESTON
CRESTON HOME
CRESTRON ENGRAVER
CRESTRON HOME
CRESTRON ROOMVIEW
CRESTRON SYSTEMBUILDER
D3 PRO
DECORE
DUALTOUCH
E-CONTROL
E-DATALOG
E-DIAL
E-MEDIA PLAYER
E-OUTLOOK
E-POWERPOINT
E-SCRIPT
E-START
E-VALET
GRAFIK EYE
HOLOVISION
ILUX
IMEDIA
INFINET
IPOD
ISYS
ISYS I/O
MEDIAMANAGER
MEDIAMARKER
MINILCD
MINITOUCH
QUCIKMEDIA
ROOMVIEW
SHOMY
SIMPL
SMARTOUCH
SMARTPRESENTER
SYNAPSE
TEST MANAGER
TOUCH-THE-PC
VIEWPORT
VISIONTOOLS
XPANEL
ZIGBEE

CRICKET COMMUNICATIONS, INC.

(Sub. of LEAP WIRELESS INTERNATIONAL, INC.)
5887 Copley Dr
San Diego, CA 92111
Tel.: (858) 882-6000
Fax: (858) 882-6010
E-mail: mediarelations@cricketcommunications.com
Web Site: www.mycricket.com
Sales Range: $200-249.9 Million
Business Description:
Wireless Telecommunications
S.I.C.: 4812
N.A.I.C.S.: 517212
Personnel:
Stewart D. Hutcheson *(Pres & CEO)*
Jaime Vasquez *(VP-Consumer Mktg)*
Susan Chandler *(Sr Product Mgr)*
Advertising Agency:
Red Door Interactive, Inc.
350 10th Ave Set 1100
San Diego, CA 92101
Tel.: (619) 398-2670
Fax: (619) 398-2671

CROWN AUDIO, INC.

(Sub. of Harman International Industries, Incorporated)
1718 W Mishawaka Rd
Elkhart, IN 46517-9439
Tel.: (574) 294-8000
Fax: (574) 294-8250
Toll Free: (800) 294-8000
E-mail: info@crownintl.com
Web Site: www.crownaudio.com
Sales Range: $50-74.9 Million
Approx. Number Employees: 500
Year Founded: 1947
Business Description:
Mfr. of Power Amplifiers; Pressure Zone & Hand-Held Microphones
S.I.C.: 3651; 3663
N.A.I.C.S.: 334310; 334220
Import Export
Media: 2-4-6-8-10-11-13-19-22
Distr.: Intl.; Natl.
Budget Set: Oct.
Personnel:
Gerald Stanley *(Sr VP-Res)*
Andy Stump *(Sr VP-Mfg)*
Scott Robbins *(VP-Sls)*
Brands & Products:
CROWN

CTS CORPORATION

905 West Blvd N
Elkhart, IN 46514-1875
Tel.: (574) 293-7511
Fax: (574) 293-6146
E-mail: customerservices@ctsfc.com
Web Site: www.ctscorp.com
E-Mail For Key Personnel:
President: Vkhilnani@ctscorp.com
Approx. Sls.: $552,641,000
Approx. Number Employees: 4,369
Year Founded: 1896
Business Description:
Electronic Components Designer, Mfr & Distr
S.I.C.: 3671; 3613; 3678; 3679
N.A.I.C.S.: 334411; 334417; 334419; 335313
Import Export
Media: 2-4-5-10-20-21
Distr.: Natl.
Budget Set: Nov.
Personnel:
Vinod M. Khilnani *(Chm, Pres & CEO)*
Thomas A. Kroll *(CFO & VP)*
Donald R. Schroeder *(Exec VP)*
Donna L. Belusar *(Sr VP-HR & IT)*
Mitchell J. Walorski *(Dir-Plng & IR)*
Brands & Products:
ACTIPLEX
CLEARONE
CTS
EMSWORLDWIDE
EVERY WHERE EVERY DAY
NWAVE
PIEZOPOWER

CTS ELECTRONIC COMPONENTS

(Div. of CTS Corporation)
171 Covington Dr
Bloomingdale, IL 60108
Tel.: (630) 577-8800
Fax: (630) 295-6601
Toll Free: (800) 757-6686
Web Site: www.ctscorp.com
E-Mail For Key Personnel:
Sales Director: sales@ctsfcp.com
Sales Range: $10-24.9 Million
Approx. Number Employees: 53
Year Founded: 1942
Business Description:
Quartz Crystals & Crystal Oscillators Clocks Mfr
S.I.C.: 4812; 4813
N.A.I.C.S.: 517212; 517211; 517310
Import Export
Media: 2-4-10
Distr.:
Budget Set: Oct.
Personnel:
Donald Schroader *(CEO)*
Brands & Products:
CTS
EMXO

CTS ELECTRONICS MANUFACTURING SOLUTIONS

(Sub. of CTS Corporation)
200 Science Dr
Moorpark, CA 93021-2003
Mailing Address:
PO Box 711
Rancho Cucamonga, CA 91729-0711
Tel.: (805) 532-2800
Fax: (805) 532-1769
Toll Free: (877) 376-2595
Web Site: www.ctscorp.com
Sales Range: $150-199.9 Million
Approx. Number Employees: 550
Year Founded: 1959
Business Description:
Electronics Manufacturing Services
S.I.C.: 3672
N.A.I.C.S.: 334412
Media: 4-8-10-13-26
Personnel:
Donald R. Schroeder *(Pres)*

Key to Media (For complete agency information see *The Advertising Red Books-Agencies* edition):
1. Bus. Publs. 2. Cable T.V. 3. Catalogs & Directories. 4. Co-op Adv. 5. Consumer Mags. 6. D.M. to Bus. Estab.7. D.M. to Consumers 8. Daily Newsp. 9. Exhibits/Trade Shows 10. Foreign 11. Infomercial 12. Internet Adv.13. Multimedia 14. Network Radio 15. Network T.V. 16. Newsp. Distr. Mags. 17. Other 18. Outdoor (Posters, Transit) 19. Point of Purchase20. Premiums, Novelties 21. Product Samples 22. Special Events Mktg. 23. Spot Radio 24. Spot T.V. 25. Weekly Newsp. 26. Yellow Page Adv.

CTS Electronics Manufacturing Solutions — (Continued)

Brands & Products:
SMTEK

CUBIC CORPORATION
9333 Balboa Ave
San Diego, CA 92123-1515
Mailing Address:
PO Box 85587
San Diego, CA 92186-5587
Tel.: (858) 277-6780
Fax: (858) 277-1878
Toll Free: (800) 818-8303
E-mail: cubicinfo@cubic.com
Web Site: www.cubic.com
Approx. Sls.: $1,194,189,000
Approx. Number Employees: 7,700
Year Founded: 1951
Business Description:
Combat Simulation Training Products & Mfr of Automatic Fare-Collection Systems for Public Transit
S.I.C.: 7379; 3589
N.A.I.C.S.: 541519; 333319
Import Export
Media: 2-10-11-20
Distr.: Intl.; Natl.
Personnel:
Walter J. Zable *(Chm, Pres & CEO)*
Walter C. Zable *(Vice Chm & VP)*
William W. Boyle *(CFO)*
Jimmie L. Balentine *(Pres-Mission Support Svcs)*
William L. Hoese *(Sec & Asst Gen Counsel)*
Jack W. Liddle *(Sr VP-Legislative Affairs)*
Bernard A. Kulchin *(Corp VP-HR)*
John A. Minteer *(VP-IT)*
John D. Thomas *(VP-Engrg)*
David W. Liddle *(Dir-Corp Comm)*
Diane L. Dyer *(Mgr-IR)*
Jan Stevens *(Mgr-Corp Comm)*
Brands & Products:
CUBIC
DSTAR
EST 2000
GO CARD
MILES 2000
Advertising Agency:
Anthology Marketing Group
1003 Bishop St Pauahi Tower 9th Fl
Honolulu, HI 96813
Tel.: (808) 544-3000

CURTIS INDUSTRIES INC.
(Div. of Powers Holdings, Inc.)
2400 S 43rd Str
Milwaukee, WI 53219
Tel.: (414) 649-4200
Fax: (414) 649-4279
Toll Free: (800) 657-0853
Web Site: www.curtisind.com
Approx. Number Employees: 100
Business Description:
Current Carrying Devices
S.I.C.: 5063
N.A.I.C.S.: 423610
Media: 4
Personnel:
Steven Power *(Pres)*

CVD EQUIPMENT CORPORATION
1860 Smithtown Ave
Ronkonkoma, NY 11779
Tel.: (631) 981-7081
Fax: (845) 981-7095
E-mail: info@cvdequipment.com
Web Site: www.cvdequipment.com
Approx. Rev.: $16,257,587
Approx. Number Employees: 128
Year Founded: 1982
Business Description:
Designs, Develops & Manufactures Customized Equipment & Solutions in Solar, Nano & Advanced Electronic Components
S.I.C.: 3678; 3559
N.A.I.C.S.: 334417; 332410; 333295
Advertising Expenditures: $56,696
Media: 17
Personnel:
Leonard A. Rosenbaum *(Chm, Pres & CEO)*
Glen R. Charles *(CFO & Sec)*
Martin J. Teitelbaum *(Asst Sec)*

THE CW TELEVISION NETWORK
(Joint Venture of Time Warner Inc. & National Amusements, Inc.)
3300 W Olive
Burbank, CA 91505
Tel.: (818) 977-2500
Fax: (818) 954-7667
E-mail: feedback@cwtv.com
Web Site: www.cwtv.com
Sales Range: $25-49.9 Million
Approx. Number Employees: 50
Business Description:
Television Network; Owned by National Amusement's, Inc. & Time Warner Inc.
S.I.C.: 4833
N.A.I.C.S.: 515120
Media: 13-15
Personnel:
Mark Pedowitz *(Pres)*
John Maata *(COO)*
Rick Haskin *(CMO)*
Thom Sherman *(Exec VP-Dev)*
Paul Hewitt *(Sr VP-Network Comm)*
Alison Tarrant *(Sr VP-Integrated Sls & Mktg)*
Advertising Agency:
OMD Los Angeles
5353 Grosvenor Blvd
Los Angeles, CA 90066
Tel.: (310) 301-3600
Fax: (646) 278-8000

CXR LARUS CORPORATION
(Sub. of EMRISE Corporation)
894 Faulstich Ct
San Jose, CA 95112
Tel.: (510) 657-8810
Fax: (510) 657-1158
Toll Free: (800) 537-5762
E-mail: info@cxrtelcom.com
Web Site: www.cxrtelcom.com
Sales Range: $10-24.9 Million
Approx. Number Employees: 50
Year Founded: 1984
Business Description:
Mfr. of Data Communications Test and Measurement Equipment and Telephone Test Equipment
S.I.C.: 3825
N.A.I.C.S.: 334515
Media: 2-4-7-9-10-16-20-25
Distr.: Intl.; Natl.
Budget Set: June
Personnel:
Larry Taillie *(Pres)*
Jim Shieh *(VP-Engrg)*
Chris Bailey *(Dir-Channel & Intl Sls)*
David Cole *(Dir-Corp Quality Assurance)*
Robert Nelson *(Dir-Mfg)*
Michael Ritz *(Dir-Product Mktg)*
Dan Burch *(Sls Mgr-Natl)*
Brands & Products:
HALCYON

DA-LITE SCREEN COMPANY
3100 N Detroit St
Warsaw, IN 46581
Tel.: (574) 267-8101
Fax: (574) 267-7804
Fax: (877) 325-4832
Toll Free: (800) 622-3737
E-mail: info@da-lite.com
Web Site: www.da-lite.com
Approx. Sls.: $131,900,000
Approx. Number Employees: 540
Year Founded: 1909
Business Description:
Projection Screens & Accessories Mfr
S.I.C.: 3861
N.A.I.C.S.: 325992; 333315
Import Export
Advertising Expenditures: $800,000
Media: 2-4-7-10-13
Distr.: Intl.; Natl.
Personnel:
Judith D. Loughran *(Owner)*
Richard E. Lundin *(Chm, Pres & CEO)*
Mike Powers *(CIO)*
Blake Brubaker *(VP-Sls)*
Wendy Long *(VP-Mktg)*
Jerry C. Young *(VP-Fin)*
Alisa Leek *(Coord-Bids & Quotations)*
Brands & Products:
ADVANCE PRODUCTS
ADVANCE QUICK LINK
ADVANTAGE DELUXE ELECTROL
ADVANTAGE ELECTROL
ADVANTAGE MANUAL
ASCENDER ELECTROL
BOARDROOM
BOARDROOM ELECTROL
CAMBRIDGE
CINEMA CONTOUR
CONCORD
CONTOUR
CONTOUR ELECTROL
COSMOPOLITAN
COSMOPOLITAN ELECTROL
DA-CURVE
DA-LIFT
DA-LITE
DA-LITE/ORAVISUAL
DA-LITE/WELT
DA-MAT
DA-SNAP
DA-TEX
DA-VIEW
DELUXE ELECTROL
DELUXE INSTA-THEATER
DELUXE MODEL B
DESIGNER CONTOUR
DESIGNER DA-TAB ELECTROL
DESIGNER ELECTROL
DESIGNER MANUAL
DESIGNER MODEL B
DIRECTOR ELECTROL
DUAL MASKING ELECTROL
ELECTROL
ELECTROLET
EXECUTIVE
EXECUTIVE ELECTROL
FAST-FOLD
FAST-FOLD DELUXE
FAST-FOLD TRUSS
FLOOR MODEL C
HORIZON ELECTROL
IMAGER
LACE AND GROMMET
MODEL B
MODEL C
MOTORIZED SCENIC ROLLER
ORAVISUAL
PERM-WALL
PICTURE KING
POLACOAT
PRE-ASSEMBLED PIXMOBILE
PRO IMAGER
PROCOLOR
PROFESSIONAL ELECTROL
PROJECT-O-STAND
PROJECTA
QUICK LINK
SCENIC ROLLER
SENIOR
SENIOR ELECTROL
SLIMLINE ELECTROL
STANDARD FAST-FOLD
TENSIONED COSMOPOLITAN
ULTRA
VENEER MODEL B
VERSATOL

DAGE-MTI OF MICHIGAN CITY, INC.
701 N Roeske Ave
Michigan City, IN 46360
Tel.: (219) 872-5514
Fax: (219) 872-5559
Telex: 532521
Web Site: www.dagemti.com
Approx. Number Employees: 15
Year Founded: 1952
Business Description:
Closed Circuit TV & Video Cameras; Monitors & Signal Processors Mfr
S.I.C.: 3569
N.A.I.C.S.: 333999
Media: 2-4-10
Distr.: Intl.; Natl.
Budget Set: Jan.
Personnel:
John B. Moore *(Pres & CEO)*
Peggy Moore *(Dir-Mktg)*
Brands & Products:
DAGE-MTI
EXCEL
EXPONENT
FIREWIRE

DAKTRONICS, INC.
201 Daktronics Dr
Brookings, SD 57006
Mailing Address:
PO Box 5128
Brookings, SD 57006-5128
Tel.: (605) 697-4000
Fax: (605) 697-4700
Toll Free: (800) 843-5843
E-mail: sales@daktronics.com
Web Site: www.daktronics.com
E-Mail For Key Personnel:
Sales Director: sales@daktronics.com
Approx. Sls.: $441,676,000
Approx. Number Employees: 2,100
Year Founded: 1968

Key to Media (For complete agency information see *The Advertising Red Books-Agencies* edition):
1. Bus. Publs. 2. Cable T.V. 3. Catalogs & Directories. 4. Co-op Adv. 5. Consumer Mags. 6. D.M. to Bus. Estab.7. D.M. to Consumers 8. Daily Newsp. 9. Exhibits/Trade Shows 10. Foreign 11. Infomercial 12. Internet Adv.13. Multimedia 14. Network Radio 15. Network T.V. 16. Newsp. Distr. Mags. 17. Other 18. Outdoor (Posters, Transit) 19. Point of Purchase20. Premiums, Novelties 21. Product Samples 22. Special Events Mktg. 23. Spot Radio 24. Spot T.V. 25. Weekly Newsp. 26. Yellow Page Adv.

Business Description:
Electronic Display Systems Designer & Mfr
S.I.C.: 3993; 3669
N.A.I.C.S.: 339950; 334290
Export
Advertising Expenditures: $1,895,000
Media: 2-4-7-8-10-13
Distr.: Natl.
Personnel:
Aelred J. Kurtenbach *(Founder & Chm)*
James B. Morgan *(Pres & CEO)*
William R. Retterath *(CFO & Treas)*
Carla S. Gatzke *(VP-HR)*
Seth T. Hansen *(VP-IT)*
Frank J. Kurtenbach *(VP-Sls)*
Jennifer Miller *(Reg Dir-Creative)*
Val Ellens *(Dir-Creative)*
Mark Steinkamp *(Dir-Mktg)*
Chris Bates *(Sr Mgr-Product)*
Angela Hatton *(Mgr-Mktg-Schools & Theatres BU)*
Brands & Products:
ACTIVE INPUT
ALL SPORT
DAKSTATS
DAKTENNIS
DAKTICKER
DAKTRONICS
DATAMASTER
DATASTREAMER
DATATIME
DATATRAC
DISTAVIEW
FINISH LYNX
FUELCAST
FUELIGHT
FUELINK
GALAXY
GALAXYPRO
GLOW CUBE
GOLD
GOLD PLUS
HY-TEK
IMAGI-PRINT
INFONET
KEYFRAME
MATSIDE
NET
OMEGA
OMNISPORT
ON THE ROAD
PANAVIEW
PLATINUM
PLATINUM ELITE
PLATINUM PLUS
POSITIONAL PIXELING
PRICEPLUS
PROAD
PROCAST
PRODASHER
PROFENCE
PROPIXEL
PRORAIL
PROSTAR
PROTABLE
PROTOUR
PURE PIXEL
REPLAY
SCAN'O'VISION
SPORTS WIRE
SPORTSLINK
SPORTSOUND
SPORTSTAR
STAR CIRCUITS
STARBURST
STAT CREW
STATVISION
SUNSPOT
TRUE PIXEL
TRUTIME
TUFF SPORT
UNIVIEW
V-LINK
V-NET
V-PLAY
V-TOUR
VALO
VANGUARD
VENUS
VISICONN
VORTEK
WEB-SYNC
WINDOWS

DALLAS SEMICONDUCTOR CORPORATION
(Sub. of Maxim Integrated Products, Inc.)
4401 S Beltwood Pkwy
Dallas, TX 75244
Tel.: (972) 371-4000
Fax: (972) 371-3715
E-mail: sales@dalsemi.com
Web Site: www.dalsemi.com
E-Mail For Key Personnel:
Sales Director: sales@Maxim-ic.com
Sales Range: $400-449.9 Million
Approx. Number Employees: 1,200
Year Founded: 1984
Business Description:
Semiconductor Mfr
S.I.C.: 3674
N.A.I.C.S.: 334413
Import Export
Media: 7-17
Distr.: Intl.; Natl.
Brands & Products:
1-WIRE
IBUTTON

DAVEL COMMUNICATIONS, INC.
(Sub. of Mobilepro Corp.)
200 Public Sq Ste 700
Cleveland, OH 44114-1158
Tel.: (216) 241-2555
Fax: (216) 875-4349
Toll Free: (800) 333-9920
E-mail: sales@davelcomm.com
Web Site: www.davelgroup.com
Sales Range: $75-99.9 Million
Approx. Number Employees: 293
Year Founded: 1979
Business Description:
Pay Telephone Services
S.I.C.: 4899; 3661; 4813; 9631
N.A.I.C.S.: 517910; 334210; 517310; 926130
Media: 7-10-20-26

DAVID CLARK COMPANY INCORPORATED
360 Franklin St
Worcester, MA 01615-0054
Tel.: (508) 751-5800
Fax: (508) 753-5827
E-mail: sales@davidclark.com
Web Site: www.davidclark.com
E-Mail For Key Personnel:
President: rvincent@davidclark.com
Sales Director: sales@davidclark.com
Public Relations: jfarr@davidclark.com
Approx. Number Employees: 300
Year Founded: 1935
Business Description:
Communication Equipment for High Noise Environments; Mfr. of High Altitude Pressure Suits
S.I.C.: 3663; 3842
N.A.I.C.S.: 334220; 339113
Import Export
Media: 2-10
Personnel:
Robert A Vincent *(Pres)*
Jack Bassick *(Exec VP)*
Richard Urella *(VP-Mktg & Sls)*
Bob Daigle *(Product Mgr)*
John Tasi *(Product Mgr)*
Dennis Buzzell *(Mgr-Aviation Market)*
John E. Farr *(Mgr-Natl Sls)*

DCI, INC.
(Sub. of Elecsys Corporation)
846 N Mart Way Crt
Olathe, KS 66061
Tel.: (913) 647-0158
Fax: (913) 982-5766
Web Site: www.elecsys.corp.com
Sales Range: $25-49.9 Million
Approx. Number Employees: 100
Year Founded: 2000
Business Description:
Electronic Assemblies & Displays Mfr
S.I.C.: 3625; 3679
N.A.I.C.S.: 335314; 334419
Import Export
Media: 2-4-10-13-26
Personnel:
Karl B. Gemperli *(Pres & CEO)*
Mike Morgan *(COO)*
Chris Thomas *(VP-Engrg)*
Brands & Products:
CRYSTALOID

DEI HOLDINGS, INC.
1 Viper Way
Vista, CA 92081-7853
Tel.: (760) 598-6200
Fax: (760) 598-6400
E-mail: investors@deiholdings.com
Web Site: www.deiholdings.com
E-Mail For Key Personnel:
Public Relations: pr@directed.com
Sales Range: $250-299.9 Million
Approx. Number Employees: 581
Year Founded: 1982
Business Description:
Home Theater Speakers, Automobile Audio & Video Equipment, Vehicle Security Systems, Remote Starters & Satellite Radio Receivers Mfr & Distr
S.I.C.: 3651; 3663; 5064
N.A.I.C.S.: 334310; 334220; 423620
Import Export
Advertising Expenditures: $2,218,000
Media: 2-5-6-10-17-19-22
Personnel:
Troy D. Templeton *(Chm)*
James E. Minarik *(Pres & CEO)*
Kevin P. Duffy *(CFO & Exec VP)*
Richard J. Hirshberg *(Treas & Sr VP-Fin)*
Mike Simmons *(Exec VP)*
Glenn R. Busse *(Sr VP-Sls & Customer Care)*
J. Steven Wood *(VP-Sls-Western)*
Brands & Products:
ASTROFLEX
AUTOMATE
AUTOSTART
AVITAL
CLIFFORD
COBALT
DEFINITIVE TECHNOLOGY
DIRECTED
HORNET
I-SONIC
ORION
POLK AUDIO
PRECISION POWER
PYTHON
READY REMOTE
RESPONDER
VALET
VIPER

DEL GLOBAL TECHNOLOGIES CORP.
100 Pine Aire Dr
Bay Shore, NY 11706
Tel.: (631) 231-6400
Toll Free: (800) 643-5270
E-mail: info@delglobaltech.com
Web Site: www.delglobal.com
Approx. Sls.: $67,921,000
Approx. Number Employees: 212
Year Founded: 1954
Business Description:
Medical Imaging & Diagnostic Systems Mfr
S.I.C.: 3679; 3845
N.A.I.C.S.: 334419; 334510
Export
Media: 2-4-7-10-11
Distr.: Direct to Consumer; Reg.
Budget Set: May
Personnel:
James R. Henderson *(Chm)*
John J. Quicke *(Pres & CEO)*
Mark A. Zorko *(CFO)*
Brands & Products:
BERTAN HIGH VOLTAGE
DEL
DEL HIGH VOLTAGE
DEL MEDICAL
DYNARAD
FILTRON
RFI
SPRAGUE
STANLEY
UNIVERSAL
VILLA

DELPHI ELECTRONICS & SAFETY
(Div. of Delphi Holdings L.L.P.)
2151 E Lincoln Rd
Kokomo, IN 46902-9005
Mailing Address:
PO Box 9005
Kokomo, IN 46904
Tel.: (765) 451-5011
Fax: (765) 451-0210
Web Site: www.delphi.com
Sales Range: $1-4.9 Billion
Approx. Number Employees: 7,000
Business Description:
Automotive Control Electronics & Hybrid Circuits Mfr
S.I.C.: 3714
N.A.I.C.S.: 336322
Media: 2-6-10
Distr.: Intl.; Natl.
Budget Set: Mar. -July
Personnel:
Jeffrey J. Owens *(Pres & VP)*

Key to Media (For complete agency information see *The Advertising Red Books-Agencies* edition):
1. Bus. Publs. 2. Cable T.V. 3. Catalogs & Directories. 4. Co-op Adv. 5. Consumer Mags. 6. D.M. to Bus. Estab.7. D.M. to Consumers
8. Daily Newsp. 9. Exhibits/Trade Shows 10. Foreign 11. Infomercial 12. Internet Adv.13. Multimedia 14. Network Radio
15. Network T.V. 16. Newsp. Distr. Mags. 17. Other 18. Outdoor (Posters, Transit) 19. Point of Purchase20. Premiums, Novelties
21. Product Samples 22. Special Events Mktg. 23. Spot Radio 24. Spot T.V. 25. Weekly Newsp. 26. Yellow Page Adv.

Delphi Electronics & Safety — (Continued)

Brands & Products:
DELCO/BOSE
DELCO ETR
DELCO LOC
PASS KEY

Advertising Agency:
Chletcos/Gallagher Inc.
63 Greene St Ste 602
New York, NY 10012
Tel.: (212) 334-2455
Fax: (212) 334-2463

DENON ELECTRONICS USA LLC

(Sub. of Denon Corporation)
100 Corporate Dr
Mahwah, NJ 07430-2041
Tel.: (973) 396-0810
Fax: (201) 762-6670
E-mail: info@usa.denon.com
Web Site: www.usa.denon.com
Sales Range: $25-49.9 Million
Year Founded: 1910
Business Description:
Mfr. of Audio & Video Equipment & Software Products
S.I.C.: 5099
N.A.I.C.S.: 423990
Import
Media: 2-6-7-8-10-13-19-20-21-22
Personnel:
Tomoki Akiyamo *(Treas)*
Nanette Casselli *(Mgr-Mktg & Events)*
Gloria Costigan *(Asst Controller)*
Brands & Products:
DENON STEREO EQUIPMENT

DESIGNATRONICS, INC.

2101 Jericho Tpke
New Hyde Park, NY 11042-5416
Tel.: (516) 328-3300
Fax: (516) 326-8827
E-mail: sdp-sisupport@sdp-si.com
Web Site: www.sdp-si.com
Approx. Number Employees: 350
Year Founded: 1960
Business Description:
Mechanical & Electro-Mechanical Components Mfr
S.I.C.: 3824; 3559
N.A.I.C.S.: 334514; 333298
Media: 2-10-13
Distr.: Intl.; Natl.
Budget Set: Aug.
Personnel:
Martin Hoffman *(Pres & CEO)*
Hitoshi Tanaka *(Sr VP)*
Herbert R. Arum *(Mgr-Mktg)*
Brands & Products:
DESIGNATRONICS
TECHNO

DETEX CORPORATION

302 Detex Dr
New Braunfels, TX 78130-3045
Tel.: (830) 629-2900
Fax: (830) 620-6711
Toll Free: (800) 729-3839
E-mail: detex@detex.com
Web Site: www.detex.com
Sales Range: $10-24.9 Million
Approx. Number Employees: 120
Year Founded: 1923
Business Description:
Clocks, Exit Control Locks, Alarms & Access Panels Mfr
S.I.C.: 3699
N.A.I.C.S.: 335999
Import Export
Advertising Expenditures: $200,000
Media: 1-2-4-7-10-11-21-22
Distr.: Intl.; Natl.
Budget Set: Oct. -Nov.
Personnel:
John Blodgett *(Pres)*
Philip N. Haselton *(CEO)*
David Alexander *(Mgr-Sls)*
Karen Morin *(Mgr-Customer Svcs)*
Brands & Products:
ADVANTER
ADVANTEX
DETEX
GUARDSMAN
NEWMAN
NEWMAN QUARTZ
SAFE-T-CHEK
WATCHCLOCK
WINDAU

DEVAR, INC.

706 Bostwick Ave
Bridgeport, CT 06605-2396
Tel.: (203) 368-6751
Fax: (203) 368-3747
Toll Free: (800) 566-6822
E-mail: info@devarinc.com
Web Site: www.devarinc.com
Approx. Number Employees: 120
Year Founded: 1961
Business Description:
Process Instruments, Temperature Transmitters, Data Loggers & Telemetry Mfr
S.I.C.: 3625; 5084
N.A.I.C.S.: 335314; 423830
Import Export
Advertising Expenditures: $500,000
Media: 2-4-7-10-25
Distr.: Intl.; Natl.
Personnel:
Anthony J. Ruscito *(Chm, Pres & CEO)*
Diane Billings *(VP-Acctg)*
Brands & Products:
DEVAR
SMART CHART
SMART CHART II

DEXTER MAGNETIC TECHNOLOGIES, INC.

(Sub. of Levine Leichtman Capital Partners Inc.)
1050 Morse Ave
Elk Grove Village, IL 60007-5110
Tel.: (847) 956-1140
Fax: (847) 956-8205
Toll Free: (800) 566-4517
E-mail: info@dextermag.com
Web Site: www.dextermag.com
Approx. Rev.: $60,000,000
Approx. Number Employees: 150
Business Description:
Magnets & Magnetic Products Mfr
S.I.C.: 3695; 3677
N.A.I.C.S.: 334613; 334416
Media: 10
Personnel:
Harley Kaplan *(Pres)*
Courtney Stone *(Mgr-Mktg)*
Brands & Products:
LIFESEP
NEOFORM

DIALIGHT CORPORATION

(Sub. of Dialight plc)
1501 Route 34 S
Farmingdale, NJ 07727
Tel.: (732) 919-3119
Fax: (732) 751-5778
Toll Free: (800) 835-2870
E-mail: info@dialight.com
Web Site: www.dialight.com
Approx. Number Employees: 100
Year Founded: 1938
Business Description:
Mfr of LED Products
S.I.C.: 3679; 3674
N.A.I.C.S.: 334419; 334413
Import Export
Media: 2-4-5-10-11-16-20-21
Distr.: Intl.; Natl.
Budget Set: Nov.
Brands & Products:
CBI
DATALITE
DIALCO
DIODE-LITE
MICRO LED
OPTOPIPE
PRISM

DIGITAL LIGHTWAVE, INC.

5775 Rio Vista Dr
Clearwater, FL 33760-3137
Tel.: (727) 442-6677
Fax: (727) 536-3541
Toll Free: (800) 548-9283
E-mail: info@lightwave.com
Web Site: www.lightwave.com
Sales Range: $10-24.9 Million
Approx. Number Employees: 39
Year Founded: 1991
Business Description:
Design, Develop, Market & Support Diagnostic Products for Monitoring, Maintaining & Managing Fiber Optic Networks
S.I.C.: 3663; 3661; 3829
N.A.I.C.S.: 334220; 334210; 334519
Advertising Expenditures: $500,000
Media: 2-4-7-10-13
Personnel:
Bryan J. Zwan *(Chm)*
Thomas L. Newhart *(VP-Sls)*
Tony Goodchild *(Dir-Product Mgmt & Mktg)*
Mo Karimi *(Dir-Ops)*
Sharon Bayly *(Mgr-Bus Dev)*
Brands & Products:
DIGITAL LIGHTWAVE
NIC
OPTICAL TEST SYSTEM
OPTICAL WAVELENGTH MANAGER

DIGITAL VIDEO SYSTEMS, INC.

357 Castro St Ste 5
Mountain View, CA 94041-1258
Tel.: (650) 938-8815
Fax: (650) 322-8109
Fax: (650) 938-8829
E-mail: ir@dvsystems.com
Web Site: www.dvsystems.com
Sales Range: $75-99.9 Million
Approx. Number Employees: 225
Year Founded: 1992
Business Description:
Developer of Digital Video Technologies
S.I.C.: 3651
N.A.I.C.S.: 334310
Advertising Expenditures: $300,000
Personnel:
Douglas T. Watson *(COO)*
Brands & Products:
DVS

DIODES INCORPORATED

15660 N Dallas Pkwy Ste 850
Dallas, TX 75248
Tel.: (972) 385-2810
E-mail: diodes-fin@diodes.com
Web Site: www.diodes.com
Approx. Sls.: $612,886,000
Approx. Number Employees: 3,986
Year Founded: 1959
Business Description:
Discrete Semiconductors Mfr, Whslr & Distr
S.I.C.: 3674; 9131
N.A.I.C.S.: 334413; 921140
Import Export
Media: 2-4-7
Distr.: Intl.; Natl.
Personnel:
Raymond Soong *(Chm)*
Keh-Shew Lu *(Pres & CEO)*
Richard D. White *(CFO, Sec & Treas)*
Collin Greene *(Pres-Europe & VP-Europe Sls & Mktg)*
Mark A. King *(Sr VP-Sls & Mktg)*
Joseph Liu *(Sr VP-Ops)*
Hans Rohrer *(Sr VP-Bus Dev)*
Julie Holland *(VP-Analog Products-Worldwide)*
Brands & Products:
DIODES
POWERDI
SBR
Advertising Agency:
Shelton Group
12400 Coit Rd Ste 650
Dallas, TX 75251
Tel.: (972) 239-5119
Fax: (972) 239-2292

DIT-MCO INTERNATIONAL CORPORATION

(Sub. of Xebec Corporation)
5612 Brighton Ter
Kansas City, MO 64130-4530
Tel.: (816) 444-9700
Fax: (816) 444-9737
Toll Free: (800) 821-3487
Web Site: www.ditmco.com
Sales Range: $10-24.9 Million
Approx. Number Employees: 100
Year Founded: 1948
Business Description:
Electronic Test Equipment Mfr
S.I.C.: 3825; 3829
N.A.I.C.S.: 334515; 334519
Export
Advertising Expenditures: $50,000
Media: 2-4-7-10
Distr.: Direct to Consumer; Intl.; Natl.
Budget Set: Dec.
Personnel:
Rick Thompson *(Pres & CEO)*
Gary Mullins *(VP-Sls, Mktg & Svc)*
Karl Sweers *(Mgr-Technical Mktg)*
Brands & Products:
DIT MCO ANALYSER

DIVX, INC.

(Sub. of Sonic Solutions)
4780 Eastgate Mall
San Diego, CA 92121
Tel.: (858) 882-0600

Key to Media (For complete agency information see *The Advertising Red Books-Agencies* edition):
1. Bus. Publs. 2. Cable T.V. 3. Catalogs & Directories. 4. Co-op Adv. 5. Consumer Mags. 6. D.M. to Bus. Estab.7. D.M. to Consumers 8. Daily Newsp. 9. Exhibits/Trade Shows 10. Foreign 11. Infomercial 12. Internet Adv.13. Multimedia 14. Network Radio 15. Network T.V. 16. Newsp. Distr. Mags. 17. Other 18. Outdoor (Posters, Transit) 19. Point of Purchase20. Premiums, Novelties 21. Product Samples 22. Special Events Mktg. 23. Spot Radio 24. Spot T.V. 25. Weekly Newsp. 26. Yellow Page Adv.

Tel.: (858) 882-0633
Fax: (858) 882-0601
Web Site: www.divx.com
Approx. Rev.: $70,606,000
Approx. Number Employees: 343
Year Founded: 2000
Business Description:
Media & Entertainment Software & Data Management Services
S.I.C.: 7371; 3577; 7373; 7376; 7379
N.A.I.C.S.: 541511; 334119; 541512; 541513; 541519
Advertising Expenditures: $200,000
Media: 5-8-9
Personnel:
David J. Richter *(Exec VP-Corp Dev & Legal Div)*
Brands & Products:
DIVX
DIVX CERTIFIED
DIVX CONNECTED
DIVX PLUS
DIVX QUALIFIED
DIVX ULTRA
OPENDIVX
STAGE 6

DOORGUARD SYSTEMS, INC.

8970 State Rte 108 Ste D
Columbia, MD 21045-2145
Tel.: (410) 992-5600
Fax: (410) 992-5694
Toll Free: (800) 442-6247
E-mail: info@doorguardsystems.com
Web Site: www.doorguardsystems.com
Approx. Sls.: $3,000,000
Approx. Number Employees: 10
Year Founded: 1978
Business Description:
Commercial, Industrial & Institutional Security Systems Mfr
S.I.C.: 7382; 1731
N.A.I.C.S.: 561621; 238210
Advertising Expenditures: $150,000
Media: 2-4-7-8-10-13-19-21
Distr.: Natl.
Personnel:
Sonny Croson *(Pres)*
Brands & Products:
DOORGUARD
DOORMAG
SENTRY
SENTRY 1000
TIMELOCK

DRAGONWAVE INC.

600 411 Legget Dr
Ottawa, ON K2K 3C9, Canada
Tel.: (613) 599-9991
Fax: (613) 599-4265
E-mail: info@dragonwaveinc.com
Web Site: www.dragonwaveinc.com
Approx. Rev.: $118,010,000
Approx. Number Employees: 278
Year Founded: 2000
Business Description:
Broadband Wireless Carrier-Grade Microwave Equipment Designer, Developer, Marketer & Sales
S.I.C.: 3663; 3669; 4812
N.A.I.C.S.: 334220; 334290; 517212
Personnel:
Erik Boch *(Founder, CTO & VP-Engrg)*
Dave Farrar *(Founder & VP-Ops)*
Gerard Vincent Spencer *(Chm)*
Peter Allen *(Pres & CEO)*
Russell James Frederick *(VP-Fin & CFO)*
Brian McCormack *(VP-Sls)*
Nadine Kittle *(Mgr-Mktg Comm)*
Advertising Agency:
Interprose Inc.
2635 Steeplechase Dr
Reston, VA 20191
Tel.: (703) 860-0577
Fax: (703) 860-1623

DRANETZ-BMI

(Sub. of Global Power Technology Inc.)
1000 New Durham Rd
Edison, NJ 08818
Mailing Address:
PO Box 4019
Edison, NJ 08818-4019
Tel.: (732) 287-3680
Fax: (732) 248-1834
Toll Free: (800) 372-6832
Telex: 499-7808
E-mail: sales@dranetz-bmi.com
Web Site: www.dranetz-bmi.com
E-Mail For Key Personnel:
Sales Director: sales@dranetz-bmi.com
Approx. Number Employees: 50
Year Founded: 1962
Business Description:
Mfr of Power Monitoring Equipment
S.I.C.: 3825
N.A.I.C.S.: 334515
Export
Advertising Expenditures: $200,000
Media: 1-2-4-5-7-10-11
Distr.: Intl.; Natl.
Budget Set: Apr.
Personnel:
Bob Hart *(Pres)*
Jay Litus *(VP-Sls)*
Brands & Products:
DRAN-LOGGER
DRAN-SCAN
DRAN-VIEW
DRANETZ
PES
POWER GUIDE
POWER PLATFORM PPI
POWEREXPLORER
SIGNATURE SYSTEM
TASKCARD

DRI CORPORATION

13760 Noel Rd Ste 830
Dallas, TX 75240
Tel.: (214) 378-8992
Fax: (214) 378-8437
E-mail: ir@digrec.com
Web Site: www.digrec.com
Approx. Sls.: $87,301,000
Approx. Number Employees: 275
Year Founded: 1983
Business Description:
Transportation & Law-Enforcement Digital Communication
S.I.C.: 3669; 3661; 3663; 3695
N.A.I.C.S.: 334290; 334210; 334220; 334613
Advertising Expenditures: $719,000
Personnel:
David L. Turney *(Chm & CEO)*
Oliver Wels *(Pres & COO-Ops-Global)*
Kathleen B. Oher *(CFO, Treas, Sec & VP)*
Stephen P. Slay *(Chief Acctg Officer & VP)*
Veronica B. Marks *(VP-Corp Comm, Asst Sec & Admin)*
Brands & Products:
DRI CORPORATION
MOBITEC
TALKING BUS
TWINVISION

DSI PONEMAH

(Sub. of Data Sciences International)
5525 CloverLeaf Pkwy
Valley View, OH 44125
Tel.: (216) 328-7000
Fax: (216) 328-7466
Fax: (216) 328-7400
Toll Free: (800) 468-5365
E-mail: info@datasci.com
Web Site: www.datasci.com
Approx. Number Employees: 25
Year Founded: 1928
Business Description:
Medical Research Equipment
S.I.C.: 3825; 3841
N.A.I.C.S.: 334515; 339112
Import Export
Advertising Expenditures: $300,000
Bus. Publs.: $60,000; D.M. to Bus. Estab.: $60,000; Exhibits/Trade Shows: $120,000; Other: $60,000
Distr.: Intl.; Natl.
Budget Set: Jan.
Personnel:
Dave Johnson *(Dir-Mktg)*
Michael Burch *(Mgr-Mktg)*
Brands & Products:
ACCUCHART
BRUSH
DATAGRAF
METRISITE
WINDOGRAF

DTS, INC.

5220 Las Virgenes Rd
Calabasas, CA 91302
Tel.: (818) 436-1000
Tel.: (818) 436-1080 (Pub Rel)
E-mail: david.blasucci@dts.com
Web Site: www.dts.com
Approx. Rev.: $87,096,000
Approx. Number Employees: 228
Year Founded: 1990
Business Description:
Digital Sound Systems Mfr
S.I.C.: 3651
N.A.I.C.S.: 334310
Advertising Expenditures: $2,744,000
Media: 6-10-11
Personnel:
Jon E. Kirchner *(Chm & CEO)*
Melvin L. Flanigan *(CFO & Exec VP-Fin)*
Brian D. Towne *(COO & Exec VP)*
Frederick Kitson *(CTO & Exec VP)*
Blake Welcher *(Legal Gen Counsel, Corp Sec & Exec VP)*
Sharon Kong Faltemier *(Sr VP-HR)*
Patrick J. Watson *(Sr VP-Strategy & Bus Dev)*
Alan Cohen *(VP-Mktg)*
David Blasucci *(Dir-Mktg Comm)*
Brands & Products:
DTS
DTS-HD ENCODER
DTS-HD HIGH RESOLUTION AUDIO
DTS-HD MASTER AUDIO SUITE
DTS-HD STREAMPLAYER
DTS-HD STREAMTOOLS
DTS MASTER AUDIO
DTS SURROUND SENSATION ULTRAPAC
DTS SURROUND SENSATION ULTRAPC
ULTRAPC
Advertising Agencies:
The Blueshirt Group
456 Montgomery St 11th Fl
San Francisco, CA 94104
Tel.: (415) 217-7722
Fax: (415) 217-7721

Formula PR
810 Parkview Dr N
El Segundo, CA 90245
Tel.: (310) 578-7050
Fax: (310) 578-7077
Agency of Record
Public Relations

DUCOMMUN TECHNOLOGIES, INC.

(Div. of Ducommun Incorporated)
23301 Wilmington Ave
Carson, CA 90745-6209
Tel.: (310) 513-7200
Fax: (310) 573-7298
E-mail: info@ductech.com
Web Site: www.ductech.com
E-Mail For Key Personnel:
Sales Director: sales@ductech.com
Sales Range: $75-99.9 Million
Approx. Number Employees: 200
Year Founded: 1945
Business Description:
Aircraft Engine Mfr
S.I.C.: 3728; 5065
N.A.I.C.S.: 336413; 423690
Media: 2-4-7-8
Distr.: Natl.
Budget Set: Oct.
Personnel:
Clair Lane *(Dir-Quality Assurance)*
Carol Trotter *(Dir-Sls-Admin)*
Brands & Products:
AMERICAN ELECTRONICS

DUKANE CORPORATION

2900 Dukane Dr
Saint Charles, IL 60174
Tel.: (630) 584-2300
Fax: (630) 584-5156
Toll Free: (800) 676-2485
E-mail: corporate@dukane.com
Web Site: www.dukcorp.com
Sales Range: $25-49.9 Million
Approx. Number Employees: 225
Year Founded: 1922
Business Description:
Mfr & Marketer of Advanced Technology Products
S.I.C.: 3663; 3861
N.A.I.C.S.: 334220; 333315
Import Export
Media: 2-4-5-7-10-11-20-26
Personnel:
Michael W. Ritschdorff *(Pres & CEO)*
Brad Johnson *(CFO & VP)*
Mike Johnston *(Mgr-Mktg & Sls-Natl)*
Brands & Products:
CAMERA 101
CONVA
DPC III
DUKANE
DYNAMIC PROCESS CONTROLLER

Key to Media (For complete agency information see *The Advertising Red Books-Agencies* edition):
1. Bus. Publs. 2. Cable T.V. 3. Catalogs & Directories. 4. Co-op Adv. 5. Consumer Mags. 6. D.M. to Bus. Estab.7. D.M. to Consumers 8. Daily Newsp. 9. Exhibits/Trade Shows 10. Foreign 11. Infomercial 12. Internet Adv.13. Multimedia 14. Network Radio 15. Network T.V. 16. Newsp. Distr. Mags. 17. Other 18. Outdoor (Posters, Transit) 19. Point of Purchase20. Premiums, Novelties 21. Product Samples 22. Special Events Mktg. 23. Spot Radio 24. Spot T.V. 25. Weekly Newsp. 26. Yellow Page Adv.

Dukane Corporation — (Continued)

INTELLIGENT PROCESS CONTROL
IPC
MAGNIVIEW 800
MAGNIVIEW 807
MAGNIVIEW 822
MAGNIVIEW 840
MAGNIVIEW 860
MAGNIVIEW SERIES
MAGNUM
NETMARK
PROLOGUE SUNDAYPLUS
SEACOM
SERVOWELD
STARFIRE
SUNSPLASH
ULTRA-COM

DURACELL

(Sub. of The Gillette Company)
14 Research Dr Berkshire Corporate Pk
Bethel, CT 06801
Tel.: (203) 796-4000
Fax: (203) 796-4269
Fax: (203) 207-7145
Fax: (203) 796-4745
E-mail: info@duracell.com
Web Site: www.duracell.com
Sales Range: $1-4.9 Billion
Approx. Number Employees: 5,500
Year Founded: 1944
Business Description:
Alkaline, Lithium & Zinc Air Batteries Mfr
S.I.C.: 3691; 3692
N.A.I.C.S.: 335911; 335912
Export
Media: 3-6-8-15-24
Distr.: Intl.; Natl.
Personnel:
Dan McCarthy *(Head-Global Brand Franchise)*
Brands & Products:
COPPERTOP
DURABEAM
DURACELL
DURACELL ULTRA
DYNACHARGE
PROCELL
Advertising Agencies:
Acme Idea Company
1 Marshall St
Norwalk, CT 06854-2262
Tel.: (203) 299-5490
Fax: (203) 299-5495
— Carol Herman *(Acct Exec)*

PainePR
415 Madison Ave 2nd Fl
New York, NY 10017
Tel.: (212) 613-4900
Fax: (212) 868-7206
— Chris Hayes *(Acct Exec)*

DYNATEX INTERNATIONAL

5577 Skylane Blvd
Santa Rosa, CA 95403-1048
Tel.: (707) 542-4227
Fax: (707) 579-8590
E-mail: sales@dynatex.com
Web Site: www.dynatex.com
E-Mail For Key Personnel:
Sales Director: sales@dynatex.com
Sales Range: $10-24.9 Million
Approx. Number Employees: 12
Year Founded: 1958
Business Description:
Semiconductor Dicing Equipment Mfr
S.I.C.: 3545; 8733
N.A.I.C.S.: 333515; 541710
Export
Media: 2-3-4-7-10-20-22
Distr.: Intl.; Natl.
Budget Set: Dec.
Personnel:
Kate Henry *(CEO)*
Leanne Sarcy *(CFO)*
Leanne Schmidt *(VP-Mktg)*
John Tyler *(VP-Mktg)*
Brands & Products:
BREAKER
C BLADES
DRY PROCESS DICING
DXB
DXE
DXL
DYNATEX
G-BLADES
GST 100 MM SCRIBER BREAKER
GST 150 MM SCRIBER BREAKER
GST SCRIBER BREAKER
KERF-AID
S BLADES
STRIPAID
WAFERGRIP

DYNAVOX INC.

(Sub. of Sunrise Medical Inc.)
2100 Wharton St Ste 400
Pittsburgh, PA 15203-1942
Tel.: (412) 381-4883
Fax: (412) 381-5241
Web Site: www.dynavoxtech.com
Approx. Sls.: $108,103,000
Approx. Number Employees: 437
Year Founded: 1983
Business Description:
Digitized Speech Devices Mfr
S.I.C.: 3679
N.A.I.C.S.: 334419
Advertising Expenditures: $1,386,000
Personnel:
Roger C. Holstein *(Chm)*
Michelle L. Heying *(Pres & COO)*
Edward L. Donnelly, Jr. *(CEO)*
Kenneth D. Misch *(CFO)*
Craig Balbassare *(CIO)*
Robert F. Cunningham *(CTO & Sr VP)*
Marcy Smorey-Giger *(Chief Legal Officer)*
Richard Ellenson *(Chief Vision Officer)*
Dave Colson *(Mgr-Digital Engagement)*
Brands & Products:
DYNAMO
DYNAVOX
DYNAWRITE
MIGHTYMO
MINIMO

ECESSA CORPORATION

2800 Campus Dr Ste 140
Plymouth, MN 55441-3674
Tel.: (763) 694-9949
Fax: (763) 551-0664
Toll Free: (800) 669-6242
Web Site: www.ecessa.com
E-Mail For Key Personnel:
President: r.thomas@ecessa.com
Sales Director: sales@ecessa.com
Sales Range: $10-24.9 Million
Approx. Number Employees: 25
Year Founded: 1968
Business Description:
Data Communication Products Mfr
S.I.C.: 3663
N.A.I.C.S.: 334220
Export
Media: 2-4-7-10
Distr.: Natl.
Budget Set: Feb.
Personnel:
Ronald L. Thomas *(Pres & CEO)*
Jason Breyer *(VP-Sls & Mktg)*
Brands & Products:
ASTROCOM
ASTROCOM NX1
ASTROCOM SP-100
ASTROCOM SP1000
ASTROCOM T-1000
POWERLINK
POWERLINK-IPLUS
POWERLINK-IV
POWERLINK-IVPLUS

EDO ARTISAN INC.

(Sub. of ITT Defense)
88 Ford Rd
Denville, NJ 07834
Tel.: (973) 361-1400
Fax: (973) 361-3112
E-mail: cmurat@artisan-usa.com
Sales Range: $25-49.9 Million
Approx. Number Employees: 80
Year Founded: 1950
Business Description:
Defense Contracting Solution & Manufacturing Services
S.I.C.: 3674; 3357
N.A.I.C.S.: 334413; 335929
Media: 2-8
Distr.: Natl.

ELANDIA INTERNATIONAL INC.

8200 NW 52nd Terrace Ste 102
Miami, FL 33166
Tel.: (305) 415-8830
Fax: (786) 413-1913
E-mail: ir@elandiagroup.com
Web Site: www.elandiagroup.com
Approx. Rev.: $150,921,716
Approx. Number Employees: 800
Business Description:
Information & Communications Technology
S.I.C.: 3663
N.A.I.C.S.: 334220
Advertising Expenditures: $889,000
Personnel:
Pete R. Pizarro *(Chm & CEO)*
Harley L. Rollins, III *(CFO, Treas & Sec)*

ELECSYS CORPORATION

846 N Market-Way Ct
Olathe, KS 66061
Tel.: (913) 647-0158
Fax: (913) 647-0132
E-mail: investorrelations@elecsyscorp.com
Web Site: www.elecsyscorp.com
Approx. Sls.: $17,028,000
Approx. Number Employees: 119
Year Founded: 1991
Business Description:
Holding Company
S.I.C.: 6719; 3663; 3812; 3993
N.A.I.C.S.: 551112; 334220; 334511; 339950
Export
Advertising Expenditures: $29,000
Media: 2-13
Personnel:
Robert D. Taylor *(Chm, Pres & CEO-Exec Airshare Corp)*
Karl B. Gemperli *(Pres & CEO)*
Todd A. Daniels *(CFO)*

ELECTROCUBE INCORPORATED

3366 Pomona Blvd
Pomona, CA 91768
Tel.: (909) 595-4037
Fax: (909) 595-0186
Toll Free: (800) 515-1112
E-mail: sales@electrocube.com
Web Site: www.electrocube.com
E-Mail For Key Personnel:
Sales Director: sales@electrocube.com
Approx. Number Employees: 65
Year Founded: 1964
Business Description:
Capacitors, Filters & Transformers Mfr
S.I.C.: 3679; 3675
N.A.I.C.S.: 334419; 334414
Export
Advertising Expenditures: $100,000
Media: 2-4-10-11-13-21
Distr.: Natl.
Budget Set: Oct.
Personnel:
Clay Parrill *(Pres & CEO)*
Brands & Products:
ELECTROCUBE

ELECTRONIC FILM CAPACITORS

(d/b/a EFC/Wesco)
41 Interstate Ln
Waterbury, CT 06705-2639
Tel.: (203) 755-3101
Fax: (203) 755-0659
E-mail: sales@wescocap.com
Web Site: www.wescocap.com
E-Mail For Key Personnel:
Sales Director: sales@wescocap.com
Approx. Sls.: $4,000,000
Approx. Number Employees: 40
Year Founded: 1958
Business Description:
Electrical Components
S.I.C.: 3699
N.A.I.C.S.: 335999
Import Export
Media: 2-4-7-10-13
Distr.: Intl.; Natl.
Budget Set: July
Personnel:
Bob Fountain *(Mgr-Inside Sls)*

ELECTROSONIC SYSTEMS, INC.

(Sub. of Helvar Merca Oy AB)
10320 Bren Rd E
Minnetonka, MN 55343
Tel.: (952) 931-7500
Fax: (952) 938-9311
E-mail: information@electrosonic.com
Web Site: www.electrosonic.com
E-Mail For Key Personnel:
President: kyle.carpenter@electrosonic.com
Approx. Number Employees: 28
Year Founded: 1964

Key to Media (For complete agency information see *The Advertising Red Books-Agencies* edition):
1. Bus. Publs. 2. Cable T.V. 3. Catalogs & Directories. 4. Co-op Adv. 5. Consumer Mags. 6. D.M. to Bus. Estab.7. D.M. to Consumers
8. Daily Newsp. 9. Exhibits/Trade Shows 10. Foreign 11. Infomercial 12. Internet Adv.13. Multimedia 14. Network Radio
15. Network T.V. 16. Newsp. Distr. Mags. 17. Other 18. Outdoor (Posters, Transit) 19. Point of Purchase20. Premiums, Novelties
21. Product Samples 22. Special Events Mktg. 23. Spot Radio 24. Spot T.V. 25. Weekly Newsp. 26. Yellow Page Adv.

Business Description:
Large Screen Image Processing Equipment Mfr
S.I.C.: 7373
N.A.I.C.S.: 541512
Media: 2-4-7-10
Personnel:
Jim Bowie *(CEO)*
Brands & Products:
C-THROUGH
ESCAN
ESLINX
IMAGE STAR
IMAGEMAG
VECTOR

ELO TOUCHSYSTEMS, INC.
(Sub. of TE Connectivity Ltd.)
301 Constitution Dr
Menlo Park, CA 94025
Tel.: (650) 361-4800
Fax: (650) 361-4722
Toll Free: (800) 557-1458
E-mail: eloinfo@elotouch.com
Web Site: www.elotouch.com
Approx. Number Employees: 500
Year Founded: 1971
Business Description:
Touch Screens & Touch Monitors Mfr
S.I.C.: 3577; 3679
N.A.I.C.S.: 334119; 334418
Import Export
Media: 2-4-7-8-10-13-22
Distr.: Natl.; Reg.
Budget Set: May
Personnel:
Mark Mendenhall *(Pres, VP & Gen Mgr)*
Steven Abramovich *(VP-Sls-North America & ANZ)*
Marianne Baker *(Dir-HR)*
Ken North *(Dir-Product & Tech)*
Frank Lung *(Product Mgr)*
Bob DeRenzi *(Mgr-Ops)*
Mike Sigona *(Mgr-Sys)*
Brands & Products:
ACCUTOUCH
CARROLTOUCH
INTELLITOUCH
ITOUCH
SECURE TOUCH

EMCORE CORPORATION
10420 Research Rd SE
Albuquerque, NM 87123
Tel.: (505) 332-5000
Fax: (505) 332-5100
E-mail: eodinfo@emcore.com
Web Site: www.emcore.com
Approx. Rev.: $191,278,000
Approx. Number Employees: 900
Year Founded: 1984
Business Description:
Compound Semiconductor Solutions Mfr
S.I.C.: 3674; 3559
N.A.I.C.S.: 334413; 333295
Media: 10-17
Personnel:
Reuben F. Richards, Jr. *(Chm)*
Mark Weinswig *(CFO)*
Christopher Larocca *(COO)*
Monica Van Berkel *(Chief Admin Officer)*
Hong Q. Hou *(VP & Gen Mgr)*
Charlie Wang *(VP & Gen Mgr-Emcore China)*
Brian Gibson *(Dir-Bus Dev)*
Brands & Products:
10221
10347A
10357A
10381
10382
10383
10384
10447A
10457A
10481
10482
10483
10484
10501
10901G
10990
10G 17-PIN
10G ROSA
10GB CX4
10GB LX4
155MBITS S APD-TIA T0-46
1612A DFB
1612B DFB
1614W DFB
1622 DFB
2801 PRO
2802 PRO
2804 CATV
2805 CATV
2806 CATV
2807 CATV
2808 CATV
2809 CATV
2860E
2860F
2990 PRO
2991R
2991T
3000
3000C
3000UB
3000UC
3005
3010
3015
3020
3030
3035
3058
3091 ODU
3091 PS-24 ODU
3091A
3112A
3120A
35XA
3641 DFB
3688A
3688D
3688M
3688U
3988
4112A
4120A
5016 RF
5017
6925 CWDM
7810
8603A
8604A
8710A
8720A
8810
8820
8850A
8860A
8910
8920
9936F
9937D
ARRAY VCSELS
ATJ
ATJM
BTJ
BTJM
DS-105TR
DS-108TR
DS-109TR
DS-120MDR
DS-150
DS-726/T3/E3
ECX-7700-XEN
ECX-7700-XFP
ELX-7100-X2M
ELX-7100-XEN
EMCORE
EMCORE MICROWAVE DLS
EMPOWER WITH LIGHT
EOS-6000
FA-2000
FABRY PEROT LRM TOSA
FDV Series
FMV-100K
FMV-563
FMV-564
FMV-567
FMV-574
FMV-574D2
FMV-586
FMV-593
FMV-595
FMV-603
FORC-404
GAN FETS
GEB-4800-IC
GELCORE
GEPON APD TIA IN TO-CAN
GEPON DFB LASERS IN TO-CAN
GPON APD TIA IN TO-CAN
GPON DFB
GPON DFB LASERS IN TO-CAN
LASER MOUSE VCSELS
LINXVIEW
LRM TOSA
MDA-7000
MDM-7000
MMV-110 MICRO
MMV-110 MINI
MMV-110 STANDARD
MMV-120 A-C
MMV-120A3C3
MTX9509 / MRX9509 TX/RX
MTX9516 / MRX9516 TX/RX
MTX9552 / MRX9552 TX/RX
MULTIVERSE CHASSIS
MULTIVERSE DTCR
NMOA8100
NMOA8200
OPTILINX
OPTILINX OLX-1000
OPTILINX OLX-3000
OPTILINX X-6000
OPTIVA
OPTIVA 1RU
OPTIVA 3RU CHASSIS
OPTIVA AUDIO
OPTIVA RS232/422/485
OPTIVA S-VIDEO
OPTIVA SDI
OPTIVAVIEW
OPTOCUBE
ORTEL
OSP-201
OT-HD-TRLSC-IC
OTP-1HD
OTS-128DTR
OTS-16A
OTS-16ATR
OTS-16DA
OTS-16DTR
OTS-1DVI2A
OTS-1DVI2A1D1KM
OTS-1ETR
OTS-1HD1ETR
OTS-1HD2DA
OTS-1HD2DTR
OTS-1LT
OTS-1REF
OTS-1SD
OTS-1SD1ETR
OTS-1SD2A
OTS-1SD2DA
OTS-1SD2DTR
OTS-1V
OTS-1V1DTR
OTS-1V1ETR
OTS-1V2A
OTS-1V2ATR1DTR
OTS-1V2ATR1DTR1ETR
OTS-1VTR2ATR
OTS-1VTR2ATR4DTR
OTS-1VTR2DTR
OTS-2DA
OTS-2DATR
OTS-2V4A
OTS-2V4ATR1ETR
OTS-2V4DTR
OTS-32DTR
OTS-3SD
OTS-3V
OTS-4A
OTS-4ATR
OTS-4DA
OTS-4DATR
OTS-4V8A
OTS-4VT
OTS-6SD
OTS-6V
OTS-8A
OTS-8ATR
OTS-8DA
OTS-8DTR
OTS-8V
PB 7000
PB 7100
PHEMTS
PIG TAILS
PONA 2100
PONA 3000
PS-100
PS-1205
QTR3400
QTR3432
QTR3500
QTR3600
R197A
R198A
R198P
RGB-4004 A/B/C
RGB-4006 A/B/C
SFP Modules
SFPB-4800-IC
SFPB-800-IC
SINGLET VCSELS
SMARTLINK
SYSTEM 10K
TURBODISC
USB-511
USB-520
VCSEL TOSA
WIBA

Key to Media (For complete agency information see *The Advertising Red Books-Agencies* edition):
1. Bus. Publs. 2. Cable T.V. 3. Catalogs & Directories. 4. Co-op Adv. 5. Consumer Mags. 6. D.M. to Bus. Estab.7. D.M. to Consumers 8. Daily Newsp. 9. Exhibits/Trade Shows 10. Foreign 11. Infomercial 12. Internet Adv.13. Multimedia 14. Network Radio 15. Network T.V. 16. Newsp. Distr. Mags. 17. Other 18. Outdoor (Posters, Transit) 19. Point of Purchase20. Premiums, Novelties 21. Product Samples 22. Special Events Mktg. 23. Spot Radio 24. Spot T.V. 25. Weekly Newsp. 26. Yellow Page Adv.

EMCORE Corporation — (Continued)

XEMT2100 / 3980
XENPAK
XLR-12-3-PP
ZTJ
ZTJM

EMERSON NETWORK POWER-EMBEDDED COMPUTING

(Div. of Emerson Network Power Embedded Computing)
8310 Excelsior Dr
Madison, WI 53717-1911
Tel.: (608) 831-5500
Fax: (608) 831-8844
Toll Free: (800) 356-9602
E-mail: info@artesyncp.com
Sales Range: $125-149.9 Million
Approx. Number Employees: 250
Year Founded: 1972
Business Description:
Power Conversion & Embedded Board Products Mfr
S.I.C.: 3669; 3677; 3679
N.A.I.C.S.: 334290; 334416; 334419
Export
Media: 2-4-7-10
Distr.: Direct to Bus.; Intl.; Natl.
Budget Set: Dec.
Personnel:
Bruce Dittmer *(Controller)*
Brands & Products:
ADVANCED TCA
BAJAPPC
KATANA
PMPPC7447
POWERPC
SPIDER DSF
SPIDER FRAME-RELAY
SPIDER STREAMS
SPIDERSS7
SPIDERWARE
WAN

EMERSON RADIO CORP.

85 Oxford Dr
Moonachie, NJ 07074
Tel.: (973) 428-2000
Fax: (973) 428-2067
E-mail: internet@emersonradio.com
Web Site: www.emersonradio.com
Approx. Rev.: $200,841,000
Approx. Number Employees: 98
Year Founded: 1948
Business Description:
Consumer Electronics Importer, Designer, Marketer & Distr
S.I.C.: 3651; 5064; 6794
N.A.I.C.S.: 334310; 423620; 533110
Import
Advertising Expenditures: $1,143,000
Personnel:
Christopher W. Ho *(Chm)*
Eduard Rudolf Helmuth *(Vice Chm)*
Duncan T. K. Hon *(CEO)*
Andrew L. Davis *(CFO, Treas, Sec & Exec VP)*
Barry Smith *(Asst Sec)*
Brands & Products:
BARBIE BLOOM BOX
BARBIE BLOOM TUBE
BARBIE BLOSSOM PLAYER
BARBIE TRUE BLOSSOM
EMERSON
H.H. SCOTT
IPOD SYSTEMS
OLEVIA
SMART SET

EMG, INC.

3165 Coffey Ln
Santa Rosa, CA 95403
Mailing Address:
PO Box 4394
Santa Rosa, CA 95402
Tel.: (707) 525-9941
Fax: (707) 575-7046
E-mail: sales@emgpickups.com
Web Site: www.emginc.com
E-Mail For Key Personnel:
Sales Director: sales@emgpickups.com
Approx. Sls.: $4,000,000
Approx. Number Employees: 80
Year Founded: 1974
Business Description:
Guitar Pick-Ups & Electronic Accessories Mfr
S.I.C.: 3679; 3931
N.A.I.C.S.: 334419; 339992
Advertising Expenditures: $400,000
Media: 10-13-22
Distr.: Intl.; Natl.
Personnel:
Rob Turner *(Pres)*
Brands & Products:
EMG
QUIKCONNECT
STRAT
ULTRAJAK

EMPOWER RF SYSTEMS, INC.

316 W Florence Ave
Inglewood, CA 90301
Tel.: (310) 412-8100
Fax: (310) 412-9232
E-mail: sales@empowerrf.com
Web Site: www.empowerrf.com
E-Mail For Key Personnel:
Sales Director: sales@empowerrf.com
Sales Range: $25-49.9 Million
Approx. Number Employees: 70
Year Founded: 2000
Business Description:
Radio Frequency Amplifiers Designer & Mfr
S.I.C.: 3679; 5065
N.A.I.C.S.: 334419; 423690
Media: 2-4-10
Personnel:
Barry Phelps *(Pres)*

EMRISE CORPORATION

2530 Meridian Pkwy
Durham, NC 27713
Tel.: (408) 200-3040
Fax: (408) 550-8340
E-mail: info@emrise.com
Web Site: www.emrise.com
Approx. Sls.: $30,561,000
Approx. Number Employees: 201
Year Founded: 1986
Business Description:
Holding Company; Electronic Aerospace, Defense & Telecommunications Systems & Components Mfr
S.I.C.: 6719; 3679; 3812; 3823; 5065
N.A.I.C.S.: 551112; 334419; 334511; 334513; 423690
Export
Media: 10
Personnel:
Carmine T. Oliva *(Chm & CEO)*
Graham Jefferies *(Pres)*
Brandi L. Festa *(Dir-Fin & Admin)*

ENCORE WIRE CORPORATION

1329 Millwood Rd
McKinney, TX 75069-7158
Tel.: (972) 562-9473
Fax: (972) 562-4744
E-mail: encorewire@encorewire.com
Web Site: www.encorewire.com
Approx. Sls.: $910,222,000
Approx. Number Employees: 737
Year Founded: 1990
Business Description:
Copper Electrical Building Wire & Cable Mfr
S.I.C.: 3351; 3339; 3357
N.A.I.C.S.: 331421; 331419; 331422; 335929
Export
Advertising Expenditures: $30,000
Media: 2-4-10-16-21
Personnel:
Donald E. Courtney *(Vice Chm)*
Daniel L. Jones *(Pres & CEO)*
Frank J. Bilban *(CFO, Treas, Sec & VP-Fin)*
Janet Sandler *(VP & Dir-Pur)*
Kevin Kieffer *(VP-Sls & Mktg)*
Brands & Products:
ENCORE WIRE
HANDY MAN'S CHOICE
NONLEDEX
SEOPRENE

ENDWAVE CORPORATION

130 Baytech Drive
San Jose, CA 95134
Tel.: (408) 522-3100
Fax: (408) 522-3102
Fax: (408) 522-3197
Web Site: www.endwave.com
Approx. Rev.: $16,716,000
Approx. Number Employees: 51
Business Description:
Radio Frequency Modules Designer, Mfr & Marketer
S.I.C.: 3663; 3679
N.A.I.C.S.: 334220; 334419
Media: 10
Personnel:
John J. Mikulsky *(Pres & CEO)*
Wade F. Meyercord *(Pres)*
Curt P. Sacks *(CFO & Sr VP)*
Daniel P. Teuthorn *(Sr VP-Tech)*
Brands & Products:
ALLEGRA
ARIA
ENDWAVE
EPSILON
JCA AMPLIFIER
MLMS

ENERGIZER HOLDINGS, INC.

533 Maryville University Dr
Saint Louis, MO 63141-5801
Tel.: (314) 985-2000
Fax: (314) 985-2205
Web Site: www.energizer.com
Approx. Sls.: $4,248,300,000
Approx. Number Employees: 16,700
Year Founded: 1999
Business Description:
Holding Company; Batteries, Flashlights, Razor Systems, Latex Gloves, Lotions, Feminine & Infant Care Products Mfr
S.I.C.: 6719; 2676; 2899; 3692; 3699; 3999; 5063; 5099
N.A.I.C.S.: 551112; 322291; 325998; 335912; 335999; 339999; 423610; 423990
Export
Advertising Expenditures: $461,300,000
Media: 2-3-4-6-10-14-15-16-19-20-22-23-24-26
Distr.: Intl.; Natl.
Personnel:
J. Patrick Mulcahy *(Chm)*
Ward M. Klein *(CEO)*
Daniel J. Sescleifer *(CFO & Exec VP)*
Joseph W. McClanathan *(Pres/CEO-Energizer Household Products)*
David P. Hatfield *(CEO-Energizer Personal Care)*
Gayle G. Stratmann *(Gen Counsel & VP)*
Peter J. Conrad *(VP-HR)*
Anne Bannister *(Gen Mgr-Strategic Lighting Ventures)*
David Woltz *(Global Brand Leader)*
Chit Itchon *(Sr Brand Mgr-Schick Intuition)*
Brands & Products:
ANYPLACE LIGHT
BANANA BOAT
BINKY
COMFORT GRIP
CONTRACTOR
DIAPER GENIE
DOUBLE BARREL
DOUBLE BRIGHT
DOUBLE DUTY
DROP-INS
EDGE
ENERGIZER
ENERGIZER ADVANCED FORMULA
ENERGIZER BUNNY
ENERGIZER E2
ENERGIZER MAX
ENERGIZER ULTRAPLUS
EVEREADY
EXACTA
EZ CHANGE
FIND ME
FOLDING LED
FULL ACCESS
HANDSAVER
HARDCASE
HAWAIIAN TROPIC
INSULATOR SPORT
INTUITION
K-BEAM
KEEP GOING
LIGHT CRAWLER
LIZARD LIGHT
MAX
NATURAL SHAPE
NATURALATCH
ORTHO PRO
OUTFITTER
PEN PRO
PLAYTEX
POCKET BASS
POCKET LED
POCKET SPOT
PROTECTOR
QUATTRO
RECHARGEABLE
SCHICK
SEA BEAM
SILK EFFECTS
SIPSTER

Key to Media (For complete agency information see *The Advertising Red Books-Agencies* edition):
1. Bus. Publs. 2. Cable T.V. 3. Catalogs & Directories. 4. Co-op Adv. 5. Consumer Mags. 6. D.M. to Bus. Estab.7. D.M. to Consumers
8. Daily Newsp. 9. Exhibits/Trade Shows 10. Foreign 11. Infomercial 12. Internet Adv.13. Multimedia 14. Network Radio
15. Network T.V. 16. Newsp. Distr. Mags. 17. Other 18. Outdoor (Posters, Transit) 19. Point of Purchase20. Premiums, Novelties
21. Product Samples 22. Special Events Mktg. 23. Spot Radio 24. Spot T.V. 25. Weekly Newsp. 26. Yellow Page Adv.

SKINTIMATE
ST SLIM TWIN
SUPER CHARGE
TITANIUM TECHNOLOGY
TRAILFINDER
VENTAIRE
WET ONES
WILD ANIMALS
WILKINSON SWORD
XTREME 3
Advertising Agencies:
Draftfcb Shimoni Finkelstein
57 Rothschild Blvd
65785
Tel Aviv, Israel
Tel.: (972) 74 717 777
Fax: (972) 74 717 7700

Grupo Gallegos
401 E Ocean Blvd Ste 600
Long Beach, CA 90802
Tel.: (562) 256-3600
Fax: (562) 256-3620

MEC, Global HQ, New York
825 7th Ave
New York, NY 10019-6014
Tel.: (212) 474-0000
Fax: (212) 474-0020
Fax: (212) 474-0003

Reach
111 Chertsey Rd
Woking, Surrey GU21 5BW, United Kingdom
Tel.: (44) 1483 711 300
Fax: (44) 1483 711 444

Rodgers Townsend, LLC
1000 Clark Ave 5th Fl
Saint Louis, MO 63102
Tel.: (314) 436-9960
Fax: (314) 436-9961

TBWA Chiat Day Los Angeles
5353 Grosvenor Blvd
Los Angeles, CA 90066
Tel.: (310) 305-5000
Fax: (310) 305-6000

TBWA Toronto
10 Lower Spadina Ave
Toronto, ON M5V 2Z2, Canada
Tel.: (416) 260-6600
Fax: (416) 260-8088

ENTERTAINMENT DISTRIBUTION COMPANY, INC.
(Sub. of EDCI Holdings, Inc.)
825 8th Ave 29th Fl
New York, NY 10019
Tel.: (212) 333-8400
Toll Free: (800) 543-2382
Web Site: www.edcllc.com
Sales Range: $550-599.9 Million
Approx. Number Employees: 2,000
Year Founded: 1945
Business Description:
Pre-Recorded CD's & DVD's Mfr & Distr
S.I.C.: 3663; 3652
N.A.I.C.S.: 334220; 334612
Export
Advertising Expenditures: $214,000
Personnel:
Thomas Costabile *(Pres & COO)*
Clarke H. Bailey *(Interim CEO)*
Matthew K. Behrent *(Exec VP-Corp Dev)*
Roger Morgan *(Exec VP-Intl Ops)*
Brands & Products:
GLENAYRE
VERSERA ICE
VESERA

ENTORIAN TECHNOLOGIES INC.
(Holding of Austin Ventures, LP)
4030 W Braker Ln
Austin, TX 78759
Tel.: (512) 334-0111
Fax: (512) 454-9409
Web Site: www.entorian.com
Approx. Rev.: $45,058,000
Approx. Number Employees: 47
Year Founded: 2002
Business Description:
Computer Equipment Mfr
S.I.C.: 3674; 3577; 3679
N.A.I.C.S.: 334413; 334119; 334418
Media: 1-2-4
Personnel:
Joseph A. Marengi *(Chm)*
Stephan B. Godevais *(Pres & CEO)*
W. Kirk Patterson *(CFO & Sr VP)*
Stephanie A. Lucie *(Gen Counsel, Sec & Sr VP)*
Brands & Products:
ARCTICORE
STAKTEK
VALUE FLASHSTAK
VALUE STAKPAK

THE ENTWISTLE CO.
Bigelow St
Hudson, MA 01749-2697
Tel.: (508) 481-4000
Fax: (508) 481-4004
E-mail: info@entwistleco.com
Web Site: www.entwistleco.com
E-Mail For Key Personnel:
President: trobinson@entwistle.com
Sales Range: $25-49.9 Million
Approx. Number Employees: 200
Year Founded: 1918
Business Description:
Electro-Mechanical Equipment for the Government; Machinery for Insulated Wire & Cable & Engineered Mobile Equipment
S.I.C.: 3489; 3569
N.A.I.C.S.: 332995; 333999
Import Export
Media: 2-4-7-10-13-17-20
Distr.: Natl.
Personnel:
Herbert I. Corkin *(Chm & CEO)*
C. Corkin *(Pres)*
Anthony Celozzi *(CFO & VP-Fin)*
Bruce Baldwin *(Mgr-Mktg)*
Jay S. Field *(Mgr-Sls Products)*
John Rodericks *(Engr-Sls)*
Brands & Products:
DIETZCO
DRAGNET
ENTWISTLE
KENETT
RITE-SIZE

EPSON ELECTRONICS AMERICA
(Sub. of Epson Toyocom Corporation)
1827 Walden Office Sq
Schaumburg, IL 60173
Tel.: (847) 925-8350
Fax: (847) 925-9054
Toll Free: (800) TOYOCOM
Web Site: www.eeaepson.com
Approx. Number Employees: 4
Year Founded: 1981
Business Description:
Mfr. of Electronic Components
S.I.C.: 5065
N.A.I.C.S.: 423690
Import Export
Media: 7
Distr.: Intl.; Natl.
Personnel:
Toshio Akahane *(Pres & CEO)*
Bob Porooshani *(Gen Mgr)*

ERICSSON, INC.
(Sub. of Telefonaktiebolaget LM Ericsson)
6300 Legacy Dr
Plano, TX 75024-3607
Tel.: (972) 583-0000
Fax: (972) 669-8860
E-mail: info@ericsson.com
Web Site: www.ericsson.com
Approx. Number Employees: 7,000
Business Description:
Mobile Telephone & Personal Paging Systems Engineer & Marketer
S.I.C.: 3663
N.A.I.C.S.: 334220
Advertising Expenditures: $3,000,000
Media: 2-7-8-9-25
Distr.: Natl.
Personnel:
Melissa Bakhtari *(Mgr-Bus Dev-IPX)*

E.S.C. ELECTRONICS CORP.
77-18 Windsor Pl
Central Islip, NY 11722
Tel.: (631) 467-5328
Fax: (631) 467-5066
E-mail: sales@custompowersystem.com
Web Site: www.custompowersystem.com
E-Mail For Key Personnel:
Sales Director: sales@custompowersystem.com
Sales Range: $25-49.9 Million
Approx. Number Employees: 100
Year Founded: 1953
Business Description:
Miniature Delay Lines, Networks & Radio Frequency Interference Filters Mfr
S.I.C.: 3679; 3677
N.A.I.C.S.: 334419; 334416
Import Export
Media: 2-4-7-20
Distr.: Natl.
Personnel:
Paul Alessandrini *(Pres)*

ESSEX GROUP, INC.
(Sub. of Superior Essex, Inc.)
1601 Wall St
Fort Wayne, IN 46802-4352
Mailing Address:
PO Box 1601
Fort Wayne, IN 46801-1601
Tel.: (260) 461-4000
Fax: (260) 461-4690
E-mail: magnetwire@superioressex.com
Web Site: www.superioressex.com
Approx. Number Employees: 200
Year Founded: 1930
Business Description:
Magnet Wire Mfr
S.I.C.: 3496; 3357
N.A.I.C.S.: 331422; 332618; 335929
Export
Media: 1-2-4-5-7-10-13-19-20
Distr.: Intl.; Natl.
Budget Set: Oct.
Personnel:
J. David Reed *(Pres)*
Victoria Thompson *(VP-IT)*
Brands & Products:
HANDIWIRE
ROYAL
SUPERIOR ESSEX

EVANS & SUTHERLAND COMPUTER CORPORATION
770 Komas Dr
Salt Lake City, UT 84108
Mailing Address:
PO Box 58700
Salt Lake City, UT 84158-0700
Tel.: (801) 588-1000
Fax: (801) 588-4500
E-mail: info@es.com
Web Site: www.es.com
E-Mail For Key Personnel:
Public Relations: JBjernfalk@es.com
Approx. Sls.: $27,481,000
Approx. Number Employees: 97
Year Founded: 1968
Business Description:
Simulation, Training & Engineering Hardware & Software Mfr
S.I.C.: 5734; 3577; 8243; 8299
N.A.I.C.S.: 443120; 334119; 611420; 611430; 611512
Export
Media: 7-10
Personnel:
David J. Coghlan *(Chm)*
David H. Bateman *(Pres & CEO)*
Paul L. Dailey *(CFO)*
Bob Morishita *(VP-HR)*
Brands & Products:
CHANLOCK
CONTINUOUSTEXTURE
DIGISTAR
E&S
EASIEST
ECT
ENSEMBLE
ENVIRONMENT CREATION TOOL
ENVIRONMENT PROCESSOR
EP
EPLOCK
EPX
ESCP
ESIG
ESLP
GLOBAL TEXTURE
HARMONY
INTEGRATOR
LASERWIDE
MELODY
MISSION COMMAND TRAINER
PIXEL ENGINE
RAPIDSCENE
RENDER BEAST
SENSORTEXTURE
SIMFUSION
SPX
SUPERTEXTURE
TARGETVIEW

Key to Media (For complete agency information see *The Advertising Red Books-Agencies* edition):
1. Bus. Publs. 2. Cable T.V. 3. Catalogs & Directories. 4. Co-op Adv. 5. Consumer Mags. 6. D.M. to Bus. Estab.7. D.M. to Consumers 8. Daily Newsp. 9. Exhibits/Trade Shows 10. Foreign 11. Infomercial 12. Internet Adv.13. Multimedia 14. Network Radio 15. Network T.V. 16. Newsp. Distr. Mags. 17. Other 18. Outdoor (Posters, Transit) 19. Point of Purchase20. Premiums, Novelties 21. Product Samples 22. Special Events Mktg. 23. Spot Radio 24. Spot T.V. 25. Weekly Newsp. 26. Yellow Page Adv.

Evans & Sutherland Computer Corporation — (Continued)

VISTA VIEW

EVERETT CHARLES TECHNOLOGIES

(Sub. of Dover Electronic Technologies, Inc.)
700 E Harrison Ave
Pomona, CA 91767
Mailing Address:
PO Box 2632
Pomona, CA 91769-2632
Tel.: (909) 625-5551
Fax: (909) 624-9746
E-mail: info@ectinfo.com
Web Site: www.ectinfo.com
Sales Range: $25-49.9 Million
Approx. Number Employees: 100
Year Founded: 1965
Business Description:
Production Assemblies & Test Equipment Mfr
S.I.C.: 3825; 3678
N.A.I.C.S.: 334515; 334417
Media: 1-2-4-7-10-11-21-22
Distr.: Intl.; Natl.
Budget Set: Sept.
Personnel:
Bud Fabian *(Pres)*
Mandy Spencer *(Dir-Customer Svc)*
Tom Merline *(Mgr-Sls-West Reg)*
Randy Phua *(Mgr-Sls-South Asia)*
Bob Chartrand *(Engr-Sls)*
Brands & Products:
DIP/LOC
ELIMINATOR
POGO

EVERGREEN SOLAR, INC.

138 Bartlett St
Marlborough, MA 01752-3004
Tel.: (508) 357-2221
Fax: (508) 229-0747
E-mail: info@evergreensolar.com
Web Site: www.evergreensolar.com
Approx. Rev.: $338,785,000
Approx. Number Employees: 1,034
Year Founded: 1994
Business Description:
Solar Power Cells, Panels & Systems Developer & Mfr
S.I.C.: 3674; 8733
N.A.I.C.S.: 334413; 541710
Media: 7-10-13-22
Personnel:
Edward C. Grady *(Chm)*
Michael El-Hillow *(Pres & CEO, COO & Sec)*
Donald W. Reilly *(CFO)*
Richard G. Chleboski *(VP-Strategy & Bus Dev)*
Gary T. Pollard *(VP-HR)*
Peter Rusch *(VP-Sls-Global)*
Thomas Hofmann *(Dir-Sls-Europe)*
Michael W. McCarthy *(Dir-IR & Govt Affairs)*
Brands & Products:
CEDAR LINE
ES-A
EVERGREEN SOLAR
STRING RIBBON
TEDLAR
THINK BEYOND

FAIRCHILD SEMICONDUCTOR CORPORATION

(Sub. of Fairchild Semiconductor International, Inc.)
3001 Orchard Pkwy
San Jose, CA 95134-2017
Tel.: (207) 775-8100
Fax: (207) 761-6139
Web Site: www.fairchildsemi.com
Sales Range: $1-4.9 Billion
Approx. Number Employees: 9,000
Year Founded: 1969
Business Description:
Semiconductor Products Mfr
S.I.C.: 3559; 3674
N.A.I.C.S.: 333295; 334413
Media: 2-4-5-10
Distr.: Natl.
Budget Set: Jan.
Personnel:
Justin Chiang *(Exec VP, Gen Mgr-Power Conversion, Indus & Automotive Products)*
Gerald Johnston *(Product Mgr)*

FAIRCHILD SEMICONDUCTOR INTERNATIONAL, INC.

3030 Orchard Pkwy
San Jose, CA 95134
Tel.: (408) 822-2000
Toll Free: (800) 341-0392
Web Site: www.fairchildsemi.com
Approx. Rev.: $1,599,700,000
Approx. Number Employees: 8,977
Business Description:
Semiconductor Technology Services
S.I.C.: 3674
N.A.I.C.S.: 334413
Personnel:
Mark S. Thompson *(Chm, Pres & CEO)*
Mark S. Frey *(CFO, Treas & Exec VP)*
Dan Kinzer *(CTO & Sr VP-Tech)*
Paul D. Delva *(Gen Counsel, Sec & Sr VP)*
Justin Chiang *(Exec VP & Gen Mgr-Power Conversion, Indus & Automotive Products)*
Robert J. Conrad *(Exec VP & Gen Mgr-Mobile, Computing, Consumer & Comm Products Grp)*
Robin G. Goodwin *(Exec VP-Mfg & Supply Chain)*
Allan Lam *(Exec VP-Worldwide Sls & Mktg)*
Dan A. Chandler *(Sr VP-Quality Assurance & Ops Excellence)*
Kevin B. London *(Sr VP-HR & Admin)*
Ole-Petter Brusdal *(VP-Sls-Europe)*
Brands & Products:
FAIRCHILD SEMICONDUCTOR
FPS
INTELLIMAX
THE POWER FRANCHISE
SAVING OUR WORLD 1MW AT A TIME
SPM
TINYLOGIC
VCX
Advertising Agency:
WelComm, Inc.
7975 Raytheon Rd Ste 340
San Diego, CA 92111-1622
Tel.: (858) 279-2100
Fax: (858) 279-5400
Toll Free: (888) WELCOMM
— Marsha Lisak *(Sr Acct Exec)*

FARADAY

(Sub. of Siemens Fire Safety)
8 Fernwood Rd
Florham Park, NJ 07932
Tel.: (973) 593-2600
Fax: (973) 593-6674
Toll Free: (877) 872-3301
E-mail: info@faradayllc.com
Web Site: www.faradayfirealarms.com
E-Mail For Key Personnel:
Sales Director: sales@faradayllc.com
Approx. Number Employees: 4
Year Founded: 1875
Business Description:
Mfr. of Fire Alarms, Annunciators, Signals, Faraday Fire Alarm Systems, Fire Alarm Devices, FOS Signaling Devices, Clock Programming Systems, Standard Electric Time
S.I.C.: 3669; 3873
N.A.I.C.S.: 334290; 334518
Export
Advertising Expenditures: $500,000
Media: 2-4-10-13-21
Distr.: Natl.
Budget Set: Jan.
Brands & Products:
FARADAY
FIRE SMART
FIRE WATCH
LIFE WATCH
MPC 1000
MPC 1500
STANDARD ELECTRIC TIME

FAROUDJA INC.

(Sub. of STMicroelectronics, Inc.)
180 Baytech Dr Ste 110
San Jose, CA 95134
Tel.: (408) 919-8700
Tel.: (408) 635-4200
Fax: (408) 957-0364
E-mail: info@faroudja.com
Web Site: www.faroudja.com
Approx. Number Employees: 35
Year Founded: 1971
Business Description:
Video Technology Services
S.I.C.: 8733; 3663
N.A.I.C.S.: 541710; 334220
Media: 6-10-22

FEDERAL SIGNAL CORPORATION

1415 W 22nd St Ste 1100
Oak Brook, IL 60523-2074
Tel.: (630) 954-2000
Fax: (630) 954-2030
E-mail: info@federalsignal.com
Web Site: www.federalsignal.com
Approx. Rev.: $726,500,000
Approx. Number Employees: 2,800
Year Founded: 1901
Business Description:
Fire Rescue Vehicles, Sweepers, Vacuum Trucks, Waterblasters, Parking Systems, Mining Equipment, Industrial Signaling & Lighting, Warning & Security Systems, & Interoperable Communications Equipment Designer & Mfr
S.I.C.: 3669; 3532; 3594; 3646; 3647; 3648; 3711; 3799; 7382
N.A.I.C.S.: 334290; 333131; 333996; 335122; 335129; 336111; 336120; 336321; 336999; 561621
Import Export
Media: 2-4-10
Distr.: Natl.
Budget Set: Sept.
Personnel:
James E. Goodwin *(Chm)*
Dennis J. Martin *(Pres & CEO)*
William G. Barker, III *(CFO & Sr VP)*
Jennifer L. Sherman *(Chief Admin Officer, Gen Counsel, Sec & Sr VP)*
Fred H. Lietz *(VP & Chief Procurement Officer)*
Manfred A. Rietsch *(Pres-Federal Signal Technologies Grp)*
Charles F. Avery, Jr. *(VP-IT & Controller)*
Leo T. Mahon *(VP-Strategy, Bus Dev & IR)*
Chad Pisha *(Interim Controller)*
Daniel J. Hickey *(Dir-Govt Rels)*
Brands & Products:
ADVANCING SECURITY & WELL BEING
BRONTO SKYLIFT
DAYTON
E-ONE
ELGIN
FEDERAL APD
FEDERAL SIGNAL
GUZZLER
JETSTREAM
NRL
PAULUHN
PCS
RAVO
SAULSBURY
SOLARIS
STINGER SPIKE
SUPERIOR
TARGET TECH
VACTOR
VACTOR HXX
VAMA
VICTOR
Advertising Agency:
Deforest Creative Group
300 W Lake St
Elmhurst, IL 60126
Tel.: (630) 834-7200
Fax: (630) 279-8410

FEDERAL SIGNAL SAFETY & SECURITY SYSTEMS GROUP

(Div. of Federal Signal Corporation)
2645 Federal Signal Dr
University Park, IL 60484-3167
Tel.: (708) 534-3400
Fax: (708) 534-4774
E-mail: info@fedsig.com
Web Site: www.federalsignal.com
Sales Range: $75-99.9 Million
Approx. Number Employees: 250
Year Founded: 1901
Business Description:
Emergency Equipment Mfr
S.I.C.: 3643
N.A.I.C.S.: 335931
Import Export
Media: 6-13-17
Distr.: Intl.; Natl.
Budget Set: Sept. -Oct.
Personnel:
David E. Janek *(Pres)*
Jean Bentley *(Mgr-Database Mktg)*

Key to Media (For complete agency information see *The Advertising Red Books-Agencies* edition):
1. Bus. Publs. 2. Cable T.V. 3. Catalogs & Directories. 4. Co-op Adv. 5. Consumer Mags. 6. D.M. to Bus. Estab.7. D.M. to Consumers 8. Daily Newsp. 9. Exhibits/Trade Shows 10. Foreign 11. Infomercial 12. Internet Adv.13. Multimedia 14. Network Radio 15. Network T.V. 16. Newsp. Distr. Mags. 17. Other 18. Outdoor (Posters, Transit) 19. Point of Purchase20. Premiums, Novelties 21. Product Samples 22. Special Events Mktg. 23. Spot Radio 24. Spot T.V. 25. Weekly Newsp. 26. Yellow Page Adv.

Brands & Products:
AUDIOMASTER
COMMANDER
COMMCENTER
ELECTRAFLASH
ELECTRARAY
FIREBALL
LITESTAK
MICROSTAT
PIONEER
SELECTONE
STARFIRE
STREAMLINE
TELCOM
VISALERT
VITALITE
VOICE GUN

FIBER SYSTEMS INTERNATIONAL, INC.
(Sub. of Amphenol International Military Aerospace & Industrial Operations)
1300 Central Expwy N Ste 100
Allen, TX 75013
Tel.: (214) 547-2400
Fax: (214) 547-9344
E-mail: info@fibersystems.com
Web Site: www.fibersystems.com
Sales Range: $150-199.9 Million
Business Description:
Fiber Optic Systems
S.I.C.: 3357
N.A.I.C.S.: 335921
Media: 10
Personnel:
Mark Curran *(VP-Sls & Mktg)*
William Reid *(VP-Product Dev)*
William A. Guernsey *(Gen Mgr)*
Brands & Products:
TFOCA-II

FIDELITY TECHNOLOGIES CORP.
2501 Kutztown Rd
Reading, PA 19605
Tel.: (610) 929-3330
Fax: (610) 929-1969
E-mail: ftcinfo@fidelitytech.com
Web Site: www.fidelitytech.com
Sales Range: $10-24.9 Million
Approx. Number Employees: 250
Year Founded: 1987
Business Description:
Mfr. of Radio & TV Communications Equipment
S.I.C.: 3663; 7629
N.A.I.C.S.: 334220; 811219
Personnel:
David Gulati *(Pres)*
Albert Jodzio *(VP-Mktg)*
Joseph Russell *(Gen Mgr)*
Paul Patterson *(Sr Mgr-Program-COMS)*
Advertising Agency:
Jaffe Communications, Inc.
200 N Ave E
Westfield, NJ 07090
Tel.: (908) 789-0700
Fax: (908) 292-1177

FILEMAKER, INC.
(Sub. of Apple Inc.)
5201 Patrick Henry Dr
Santa Clara, CA 95054
Tel.: (408) 987-7000
Fax: (408) 987-7460
Fax: (408) 987-3931
Toll Free: (800) 325-2747
E-mail: filemakerpr@filemaker.com
Web Site: www.filemaker.com
Sales Range: $75-99.9 Million
Approx. Number Employees: 285
Year Founded: 1998
Business Description:
Database Software Development Services
S.I.C.: 7372; 7373
N.A.I.C.S.: 511210; 541512
Export
Advertising Expenditures: $4,500,000
Bus. Publs.: $4,000,000; Foreign: $500,000
Distr.: Intl.; Natl.
Personnel:
Dominique Goupil *(Pres)*
John Pinheiro *(Gen Counsel & VP-Legal & HR)*
Bill Epling *(Sr VP-Fin & Ops)*
Keith Harris *(VP-Sls-EMEA)*
Scott Lewis *(VP-Ops & Info Sys)*
Keith Robinson *(VP-Sls-Americas & Asia-Pacific)*
Ryan Rosenberg *(VP-Mktg & Svcs)*
Simon Thornhill *(VP-Engrg)*
Dave Williams *(VP-Fin)*
Steven Ruddock *(Dir-Comm)*
Kevin Mallon *(Sr Mgr-PR)*
Ed Staton *(Sr Mgr-Mktg Programs)*
Brands & Products:
BENTO
FILEMAKER
FILEMAKER PRO
FILEMAKER SERVER

FILM EMPORIUM INC.
274 Madison Ave Ste 404
New York, NY 10016
Tel.: (212) 683-2433
Fax: (212) 683-2740
Toll Free: (800) 371-2555
E-mail: info@filmemporium.com
Web Site: www.filmemporium.com
Approx. Number Employees: 4
Year Founded: 1995
Business Description:
Motion Picture Film & Video Stock Distr
S.I.C.: 5043
N.A.I.C.S.: 423410
Media: 3-6-13
Personnel:
C. Criner *(Owner)*
L. Criner *(Owner)*

FINISAR CORPORATION
1389 Moffett Park Dr
Sunnyvale, CA 94089-1134
Tel.: (408) 548-1000
Fax: (408) 745-6097
E-mail: sales@finisar.com
Web Site: www.finisar.com
Approx. Rev.: $948,787,000
Approx. Number Employees: 8,065
Year Founded: 1988
Business Description:
Telecommunication Optical Subsystems & Components Designer & Mfr
S.I.C.: 3669; 3663; 3674; 3679; 8734
N.A.I.C.S.: 334290; 334220; 334413; 334419; 541380
Import Export
Advertising Expenditures: $31,000
Media: 5-10-13
Personnel:
Jerry S. Rawls *(Chm)*
Eitan Gertel *(CEO)*
Kurt Adzema *(CFO & Exec VP)*
Christopher Brown *(Exec VP)*
John H. Clark *(Exec VP-Tech & Global R&D)*
Todd Swanson *(Exec VP-Global Sls & Mktg)*
Joseph Young *(Exec VP-Global Ops)*
Mark Colyar *(Sr VP & Gen Mgr)*
John Drury *(VP-Fin)*
Brands & Products:
300 PIN
BUS DOCTOR
FINISAR
GBIC
NETWISDOM
PACKETMAKER
PON
ROADM
SATELLITE
SFF
SFP
SFP+
SURVEYOR
X2
XENPAK
XFP
XGIG
XPAK
Advertising Agency:
Voce Communications
298 S Sunnyvale Ave Ste 101
Sunnyvale, CA 94301
Tel.: (408) 738-7840
Fax: (408) 738-7858

FIREFLY MOBILE, INC.
119 Washington Ave Ste 401
Miami Beach, FL 33139
Tel.: (305) 538-2008
E-mail: busdev@fireflymobile.com
Web Site: www.fireflymobile.com
Year Founded: 2003
Business Description:
Mobile Telephones for Tweens & Parents
S.I.C.: 3661; 3663; 4812
N.A.I.C.S.: 334210; 334220; 517212
Media: 1-5-6-8-10-13-15-20-22-24
Personnel:
Donald L. Deubler *(Founder & Chief)*
Jim Hanson *(VP-Sls-Worldwide)*
Brands & Products:
FIREFLY
FIREFLY MINUTES
FLYKICKS
THE MOBILE PHONE FOR MOBILE KIDS
Advertising Agency:
Grow Marketing
1606 Union St
San Francisco, CA 94123
Tel.: (415) 440-4769
Fax: (415) 440-4779

FIRST SOLAR, INC.
350 W Washington St Ste 600
Tempe, AZ 85281-1244
Tel.: (602) 414-9300
Fax: (602) 414-9400
E-mail: info@firstsolar.com
Web Site: www.firstsolar.com
Approx. Sls.: $2,563,515,000
Approx. Number Employees: 6,100
Business Description:
Thin Film Semiconductor Solar Modules Designer & Mfr
S.I.C.: 3674
N.A.I.C.S.: 334413
Advertising Expenditures: $1,100,000
Personnel:
Michael J. Ahearn *(Chm)*
Robert J. Gillette *(CEO)*
Mark R. Widmar *(CFO)*
James Zhu *(Chief Acctg Officer)*
T. K. Kallenbach *(Pres-Components Bus Grp)*
Jens Meyerhoff *(Pres-Utility Sys Bus)*
Mary Beth Gustafsson *(Gen Counsel, Sec & Exec VP)*
Carol Campbell *(Exec VP-HR)*
James R. Miller *(Exec VP)*
Mike Koralewski *(VP-Site Ops, Plant Mgr & Gen Mgr-Perrysburg)*
Todd Spangler *(Gen Mgr & Dir-Site-Mesa)*
Brands & Products:
FIRST SOLAR
FIRST SOLAR & DESIGN
FIRST SOLAR PV
Advertising Agency:
Webemercial Interactive
33685 N 71st Way
Scottsdale, AZ 85262
Tel.: (602) 571-1700
Fax: (602) 744-2577
Toll Free: (888) 797-8700

FLOWTRON OUTDOOR PRODUCTS
(Div. of Armatron International, Inc.)
15 Highland Ave
Malden, MA 02148
Tel.: (781) 321-2300
Fax: (781) 324-8403
Toll Free: (800) 343-3280
E-mail: service@flowtron.com
Web Site: www.flowtron.com
E-Mail For Key Personnel:
Sales Director: sales@flowtron.com
Approx. Number Employees: 55
Year Founded: 1920
Business Description:
Electronic Pesticide Mfr; Lawn & Garden Power Equipment Mfr
S.I.C.: 3714; 3423; 3524; 3711
N.A.I.C.S.: 336340; 332212; 333112; 336211; 336312; 336322; 336350; 336399
Media: 2
Distr.: Natl.
Personnel:
Sal DeYoreo *(Pres)*
Jerry Casselano *(VP-Sls & Mktg)*
Brands & Products:
HANDY HAULER
LEAF EATER
STOREMORE

FORTUNE INDUSTRIES INC.
6402 Corporate Dr
Indianapolis, IN 46278
Tel.: (317) 532-1374
Fax: (317) 532-1011
E-mail: info@ffi.net
Web Site: www.ffi.net
Approx. Rev.: $60,694,000
Approx. Number Employees: 93

Key to Media (For complete agency information see *The Advertising Red Books-Agencies* edition):
1. Bus. Publs. 2. Cable T.V. 3. Catalogs & Directories. 4. Co-op Adv. 5. Consumer Mags. 6. D.M. to Bus. Estab.7. D.M. to Consumers 8. Daily Newsp. 9. Exhibits/Trade Shows 10. Foreign 11. Infomercial 12. Internet Adv.13. Multimedia 14. Network Radio 15. Network T.V. 16. Newsp. Distr. Mags. 17. Other 18. Outdoor (Posters, Transit) 19. Point of Purchase20. Premiums, Novelties 21. Product Samples 22. Special Events Mktg. 23. Spot Radio 24. Spot T.V. 25. Weekly Newsp. 26. Yellow Page Adv.

Fortune Industries Inc. — (Continued)

Business Description:
Wireless Infrastructure, Electronic Integration, Ultraviolet Technology & Human Resource Services
S.I.C.: 4119; 3663; 7361; 7629
N.A.I.C.S.: 485991; 334220; 541612; 811213
Import Export
Advertising Expenditures: $99,000
Media: 17
Personnel:
Carter M. Fortune *(Chm)*
Tena Mayberry *(Pres & CEO)*
Randy Butler *(CFO)*

FOX ELECTRONICS
5570 Enterprise Pkwy
Fort Myers, FL 33905
Tel.: (239) 693-0099
Fax: (239) 693-1554
Toll Free: (888) GET-2-FOX
E-mail: sales@foxonline.com
Web Site: www.foxonline.com
E-Mail For Key Personnel:
Sales Director: sales@foxonline.com
Sales Range: $25-49.9 Million
Approx. Number Employees: 75
Business Description:
Quartz Crystals, For Electronic Application
S.I.C.: 3679
N.A.I.C.S.: 334419
Personnel:
Edward Fox, Jr. *(Pres)*
Gene Trefethen *(CEO)*
Brands & Products:
FOX CRYSTALS AND OSCILLATORS
Advertising Agency:
The Simon Group, Inc.
1506 Old Bethlehem Pike
Sellersville, PA 18960-1427
Tel.: (215) 453-8700
Fax: (215) 453-1670

FREQUENCY ELECTRONICS, INC.
55 Charles Lindbergh Blvd
Mitchel Field, NY 11553-3682
Tel.: (516) 794-4500
Fax: (516) 794-4340
E-mail: ir@freqelec.com
Web Site: www.freqelec.com
Approx. Rev.: $53,223,000
Approx. Number Employees: 350
Year Founded: 1962
Business Description:
Precision Time & Frequency Products for Ground, Seaborne, Airborn & Space Terminal Platforms
S.I.C.: 3829; 3825
N.A.I.C.S.: 334519; 334515
Import Export
Media: 2-4
Distr.: Natl.
Budget Set: Dec.
Personnel:
Joseph P. Franklin *(Chm)*
Martin B. Bloch *(Pres & CEO)*
Alan L. Miller *(CFO & Treas)*
Markus Hechler *(Exec VP)*
Leonard Martire *(VP-Mktg)*
Robert Klomp *(Dir-HR & Asst Sec)*
Brands & Products:
FE
FEI
LYNX

FRY'S ELECTRONICS, INC.
600 E Brokaw Rd
San Jose, CA 95112-1006
Tel.: (408) 487-4500
Tel.: (480) 350-1484
Fax: (408) 487-4700
E-mail: info@frys.com
Web Site: www.frys.com
Sales Range: $1-4.9 Billion
Approx. Number Employees: 1,200
Year Founded: 1985
Business Description:
Consumer Electronics Retailer
S.I.C.: 5731; 5734
N.A.I.C.S.: 443112; 443120
Advertising Expenditures: $76,274,600
Media: 9-16-22-25
Personnel:
William R. Fry *(Pres)*
John Fry *(CEO)*
David Fry *(CIO)*
Kathryn Kolder *(Exec VP)*
Vanjie Moniz *(Mgr-Adv)*

FUJI ELECTRIC CORPORATION OF AMERICA
(Sub. of Fuji Electric Holdings Co., Ltd.)
Park 80 W Plz II
Saddle Brook, NJ 07663
Tel.: (201) 712-0555
Fax: (201) 368-8258
E-mail: contact@fecoa.fujielectric.com
Web Site: www.fujielectric.com
Sales Range: $10-24.9 Million
Approx. Number Employees: 50
Year Founded: 1970
Business Description:
Marketing of Semiconductors & Power Distributors & Control Equipment & Ring Blowers
S.I.C.: 5063
N.A.I.C.S.: 423610
Advertising Expenditures: $250,000
Media: 2-7-13
Distr.: Natl.

FUJITSU TEN CORP. OF AMERICA
(Sub. of Fujitsu America, Inc.)
19600 S Vermont Ave
Torrance, CA 90502
Tel.: (310) 327-2151
Fax: (310) 767-4375
Toll Free: (800) 233-2216
Web Site: www.eclipse-web.com
Sales Range: $150-199.9 Million
Approx. Number Employees: 120
Year Founded: 1975
Business Description:
Automotive Audio, Video, Navigation & Control Systems
S.I.C.: 5064; 7539
N.A.I.C.S.: 423620; 811118
Import Export
Media: 2-6-10-11-13
Distr.: Natl.
Budget Set: Apr.
Personnel:
Mike Odle *(VP-Sls & Mktg)*
Brands & Products:
37601
CD3413
CD5433
CD8053
CD8443
CH3083
ECLIPSE
ECLIPSE COMMANDER
ECLIPSE COMMANDER ADVANCE
FUJITSU TEN
STARTUNER

FUNMOBILITY, INC.
5568 Gibraltar Dr
Pleasanton, CA 94588
Tel.: (925) 598-9700
Fax: (925) 598-9770
E-mail: info@funmobility.com
Web Site: www.funmobility.com
Sales Range: $10-24.9 Million
Approx. Number Employees: 90
Year Founded: 1999
Business Description:
Mobile Phone Application Developer
S.I.C.: 7372; 4812
N.A.I.C.S.: 511210; 517212
Media: 10
Personnel:
Adam Lavine *(Founder & CEO)*
Dennis Chen *(Founder & CTO)*
Arvind Narain *(Pres & COO)*
Andy Baldocchi *(Sr VP-Sls)*
Eric Allen *(VP-Product & Strategy-FunMobility)*
Aimen Minhas *(VP-Mktg)*

FURUNO USA, INC.
(Sub. of Furuno Electric Co. Ltd.)
4400 NW Pacific Rim Blvd
Camas, WA 98607-9408
Tel.: (360) 834-9300
Fax: (360) 834-9400
Web Site: www.furuno.com
Approx. Number Employees: 100
Year Founded: 1978
Business Description:
Marine Electronics, Radar Systems, Fish Finders, Autopilots, Radios, Transceivers & Sonar & Sounder Systems Distribution & Repair
S.I.C.: 5088; 5065
N.A.I.C.S.: 423860; 423690
Import
Media: 6-10
Distr.: Intl.; Natl.
Personnel:
James Atteridge *(Pres)*
Jeff Kauzlaric *(Mgr-Adv & Comm)*
Dean Kurutz *(Mgr-Mktg)*
Brands & Products:
FURUNO

FUSION UV SYSTEMS, INC.
(Sub. of Spectris Plc)
910 Clopper Rd
Gaithersburg, MD 20878-1361
Tel.: (301) 527-2660
Fax: (301) 527-2661
E-mail: info@fusionuv.com
Web Site: www.fusionuv.com
Approx. Number Employees: 150
Business Description:
Ultra Violet Light Drying Systems Mfr
S.I.C.: 3679
N.A.I.C.S.: 334419
Media: 10-11
Personnel:
David Harbourne *(CEO)*
Chris Brandl *(Mgr-Regional Sls)*
John Guarniere *(Mgr-Market Support-Optical Fiber Curing)*

GENBAND, INC.
3605 E Plano Pkwy Ste 100
Plano, TX 75074
Tel.: (972) 521-5800
Fax: (972) 521-5801
Toll Free: (866) GENBAND
Web Site: www.genband.com
Sales Range: $25-49.9 Million
Approx. Number Employees: 300
Year Founded: 1999
Business Description:
IP Multimedia Application & Infrastructure Products & Solutions Supplier
S.I.C.: 4899
N.A.I.C.S.: 517910
Media: 10
Personnel:
Jon W. Bayless *(Chm)*
Charles D. Vogt *(Pres & CEO)*
Daryl Raiford *(CFO)*
Mehmet Balos *(CMO)*
Jan Gaulding *(Chief Admin Officer)*
Keith Landau *(Chief Product Officer)*
B. G. Kumar *(Pres-Networking & Applications-Frisco)*
Shauna Martin *(Gen Counsel & Exec VP)*
Pat Dolan *(Sr VP-EMEA & Asia Pacific)*
Daniel Lakey *(Sr VP-Americas Sls)*
John Mcnamara *(Sr VP-Global Channel Sls)*
Joe Uhr *(Sr Dir-Quality Sys)*
Advertising Agency:
Ketchum
Harwood Ctr 1999 Bryan St Ste 2500
Dallas, TX 75201
Tel.: (214) 259-3400
Fax: (214) 259-3450

GENNUM CORPORATION
4281 Harvester Rd
Burlington, ON L7L 5M4, Canada
Mailing Address:
PO Box 489 Station A
Burlington, ON L7R 3Y3, Canada
Tel.: (905) 632-2996
Fax: (905) 632-2055
E-mail: corporate@gennum.com
Web Site: www.gennum.com
Approx. Rev.: $128,893,000
Approx. Number Employees: 384
Year Founded: 1973
Business Description:
Silicon Integrated Circuits & Modules Designer, Mfr & Marketer
S.I.C.: 3825
N.A.I.C.S.: 334515
Media: 2-4-8-10-13
Personnel:
Robert S. Weiss *(Chm)*
Franz J. Fink *(Pres & CEO)*
R. Gregory Miller *(CFO & Sr VP-Fin & Admin)*
D. Chad Hutchison *(Gen Counsel, Sec & Sr VP)*
Gary M. Beauchamp *(Sr VP-Mixed Signal & Optical Products)*
Bruce W. Hannah *(Sr VP-HR)*
Klaus Mueller *(Sr VP-Global Sls)*
Robin Vaitonis *(Dir-Corp Comm)*
Nelly Marlowe *(Mgr-Corp Svcs)*
Brands & Products:
ACTIVECONNECT
ARKONLINE
AVIIA
CHIPCENTER

Key to Media (For complete agency information see *The Advertising Red Books-Agencies* edition):
1. Bus. Publs. 2. Cable T.V. 3. Catalogs & Directories. 4. Co-op Adv. 5. Consumer Mags. 6. D.M. to Bus. Estab.7. D.M. to Consumers 8. Daily Newsp. 9. Exhibits/Trade Shows 10. Foreign 11. Infomercial 12. Internet Adv.13. Multimedia 14. Network Radio 15. Network T.V. 16. Newsp. Distr. Mags. 17. Other 18. Outdoor (Posters, Transit) 19. Point of Purchase20. Premiums, Novelties 21. Product Samples 22. Special Events Mktg. 23. Spot Radio 24. Spot T.V. 25. Weekly Newsp. 26. Yellow Page Adv.

DUET
FIDELITYENGINE
FINEEDGE
FOUNDATION
FROGPAD
FRONTWAVE
GENBLUE
GENNUM
PARAGON
PCI EXPRESS
REALITYEXPANSION
TRUMOTIONHD
VENTURE
VISUAL EXCELLENCE PROCESSING
VOYAGEUR

GHENT MANUFACTURING, INC.

2999 Henkle Dr
Lebanon, OH 45036-9260
Tel.: (513) 932-3445
Fax: (513) 932-9252
Toll Free: (800) 543-0550
E-mail: info@ghent.com
Web Site: www.ghent.com
Approx. Number Employees: 190
Year Founded: 1976
Business Description:
Visual Communication & Presentation Aids Mfr
S.I.C.: 2531; 2493
N.A.I.C.S.: 337127; 321219
Import Export
Media: 2-4-7-10-13-17-19-21
Distr.: Intl.; Natl.
Brands & Products:
ATTIVO
CENTURION
CINTRA
CORNERSTONE
CREATE-A-SIGN DIRECTOR
DECOAURORA
DECOVUE
DUO-TRACK
DUROSLATE
GEMINI
GHENT
INDOOR/OUTDOOR DIRECTOR
OPEN FACE
PDQ
PHANTOM
PORTABLE DIRECTOR
PREMATAK
PROMA
SPECTRA
TITAN
TOWER
TRAPEASE
TREND
TRIUMPH
VERONA
VISUALL PC
WEATHER-ALL DIRECTOR
X-CEL

GIGA-TRONICS INCORPORATED

4650 Norris Canyon Rd
San Ramon, CA 94583-1320
Tel.: (925) 328-4650
Fax: (925) 328-4700
Toll Free: (800) 726-4442
E-mail: info@gigatronics.com
Web Site: www.gigatronics.com/
Approx. Sls.: $21,029,000
Approx. Number Employees: 94
Year Founded: 1980
Business Description:
Components, Subsystems & Support Equipment for the Wireless Telecommunications Industry Addressing Broadband Wireless Data Communications, Internet Telephony, Mobile Cellular Systems & Satellite Earth Station Uplinks Mfr
S.I.C.: 3825; 3679
N.A.I.C.S.: 334515; 334419
Export
Advertising Expenditures: $98,000
Media: 2-4-7-10-13
Distr.: Direct to Consumer; Intl.; Natl.
Personnel:
Garrett A. Garrettson *(Chm)*
John R. Regazzi *(Pres & CEO)*
Patrick J. Lawlor *(CFO, Sec & VP-Fin)*
Malcolm E. Levy *(Exec VP-Sls)*
Mark Elo *(VP-Mktg)*
Leonard Dixtine *(Mgr-Bus Dev & Sls)*
Brands & Products:
ASCOR
AUTOMATION XPRESS
GIGA-TRONICS
MEASUREMENT XPRESS
WAVEMAKER

GLOBAL TRAFFIC NETWORK, INC.

880 3rd Ave 6th Fl
New York, NY 10022
Tel.: (212) 896-1255
Fax: (212) 986-3380
E-mail: webmaster@globaltrafficnetwork.com
Web Site: www.globaltrafficnetwork.com
Approx. Rev.: $93,335,000
Approx. Number Employees: 152
Business Description:
News & Traffic Reporting Services to Radio & Television Stations
S.I.C.: 4832; 7383
N.A.I.C.S.: 515111; 519110
Personnel:
William L. Yde, III *(Chm, Pres & CEO)*
Scott E. Cody *(COO, CFO & Treas)*
Ivan N. Shulman *(Pres-Canada)*
William Pezzimenti *(Mng Dir-Australia, Dir-Sls & Trng-Intl)*
Advertising Agency:
KCSA Strategic Communications (Kanan, Corbin, Schupak & Aronow, Inc.)
880 3rd Ave 6th Fl
New York, NY 10022
Tel.: (212) 682-6300
Fax: (212) 697-0910

GLOBALIVE COMMUNICATIONS INC.

48 Young St 12th Fl
Toronto, ON M5E 1G6, Canada
Tel.: (416) 640-1088
Fax: (416) 640-1089
Toll Free: (877) 445-8606
E-mail: info@globalive.com
Web Site: www.globalive.com
Sales Range: $25-49.9 Million
Approx. Number Employees: 120
Year Founded: 1998
Business Description:
Telecommunications Services
S.I.C.: 4812
N.A.I.C.S.: 517212
Personnel:
Anthony Lacavera *(Chm)*
Ezio D'Onofrio *(Pres & COO)*
Brice Scheschuk *(CFO)*
Simon Lockie *(Chief Legal Officer)*
Andre Cote *(VP-Sls-Canopco)*
Nisha Amin *(Dir-Globalive Mktg)*
Rishi Bahall *(Dir-Network Engrg)*
Anthony Cozzi *(Dir-Data Tech)*
Ninon Laforce *(Dir-New Product Dev)*
Scott Melvin *(Dir-Ops)*
Pierre Methe *(Dir-Ops)*
Advertising Agency:
Narrative Advocacy Media
Toronto, ON Canada
Tel.: (416) 644-4122

GLOBECOMM SYSTEMS INC.

45 Oser Ave
Hauppauge, NY 11788-3816
Tel.: (631) 231-9800
Fax: (631) 231-1557
E-mail: info@globecommsystems.com
Web Site: www.globecommsystems.com
Approx. Rev.: $274,191,000
Approx. Number Employees: 475
Year Founded: 1994
Business Description:
Designs, Assembles & Installs Satellite Ground Systems & Networks
S.I.C.: 3663; 4899
N.A.I.C.S.: 334220; 517910
Media: 2-5-7-10-13
Personnel:
David E. Hershberg *(Chm & CEO)*
Keith A. Hall *(Pres & COO)*
Andrew C. Melfi *(CFO, Treas & Sr VP)*
Stephen C. Yablonski *(CTO & Sr VP-R&D-Expert Teams)*
Thomas C. Coyle *(Sr VP & Gen Mgr)*
Matthew Byron *(Sr VP-Corp Office)*
Paul J. Johnson *(Sr VP-Customer Rels & Contracts)*
Tom Parish *(Sr VP-Broadcast Tech)*
Andrew Silberstein *(VP & Gen Mgr)*
Paul Eterno *(VP-HR)*
Paul Scardino *(VP-Sls & Mktg)*
Walter Scharpf *(VP-Intl Mktg)*
Fred DuGourd *(Dir-Mktg)*
Brands & Products:
A LITTLE BIT OF SATELLITE GOES A LONG WAY
AXXSYS ORION
EXPLORER
GLOBECOMM
GSI
SKYBORNE
SPYGLASS CARRIER MONITORING SYSTEM
SUMMIT

GRANITE STATE MANUFACTURING

(Div. of Allard Nazarian Group Inc.)
124 Joliette St
Manchester, NH 03102-3017
Tel.: (603) 668-1900
Fax: (603) 668-1905
Toll Free: (800) GO-GSM-GO
E-mail: gsmsales@gsmai.com
Web Site: www.gsmai.com
Approx. Number Employees: 120
Year Founded: 1938
Business Description:
Electrical Instruments Mfr
S.I.C.: 3812; 3829
N.A.I.C.S.: 334511; 334519
Export
Media: 2-10
Brands & Products:
GRANITE STATE

GRASS VALLEY, INC.

(Sub. of Grass Valley France S.A.)
400 Providence Mine Rd
Nevada City, CA 95959-2953
Mailing Address:
PO Box 599000
Nevada City, CA 95959-7900
Tel.: (530) 478-3000
Fax: (530) 478-3755
Toll Free: (800) 547-8949
Telex: TRT 160432
E-mail: info@thomsongrassvalley.com
Web Site: www.thomsongrassvalley.com
Approx. Number Employees: 650
Year Founded: 1959
Business Description:
Broadcast, Media & Entertainment Equipment Mfr & Distr
S.I.C.: 3663
N.A.I.C.S.: 334220
Export
Advertising Expenditures: $2,670,000
Multimedia: $250,000; Bus. Publs.: $200,000; Catalogs & Directories: $150,000; Exhibits/Trade Shows: $2,000,000; Foreign: $50,000; Premiums, Novelties: $20,000
Distr.: Intl.; Natl.
Budget Set: Mar.
Personnel:
Alain Andreoli *(Pres & CEO)*
Charlie Dunn *(Exec VP-Products & Gen Mgr-Editing, Servers & Storage Product Grp)*
Harold Vermeulen *(VP-Media Playout Solutions)*
Nigel Stoddart *(Sls Mgr-South America)*
Denise R. Williams *(Mgr-PR)*
Brands & Products:
ACAPPELLA
APEX
CONCERTO
ENCORE
FEEDCLIP
GECKO
GVEOUS
IGNITE
INFINITY
INGESTATION
JUPITER
JUPITER ACCUSWITCH
K2
KALYPSO
KAMELEON
KAYAK
KURL
MAESTRO
NENNOS
NETCENTRAL
NEWSBROWSE
NEWSEDIT
NEWSQ
PERFORMER
PRELUDE
REVPRO
SATURN
SMARTTOUCH

Key to Media (For complete agency information see *The Advertising Red Books-Agencies* edition):
1. Bus. Publs. 2. Cable T.V. 3. Catalogs & Directories. 4. Co-op Adv. 5. Consumer Mags. 6. D.M. to Bus. Estab.7. D.M. to Consumers 8. Daily Newsp. 9. Exhibits/Trade Shows 10. Foreign 11. Infomercial 12. Internet Adv.13. Multimedia 14. Network Radio 15. Network T.V. 16. Newsp. Distr. Mags. 17. Other 18. Outdoor (Posters, Transit) 19. Point of Purchase20. Premiums, Novelties 21. Product Samples 22. Special Events Mktg. 23. Spot Radio 24. Spot T.V. 25. Weekly Newsp. 26. Yellow Page Adv.

Grass Valley, Inc. — (Continued)

TRINIX
TRITON
VENUS
ZODIAK

Advertising Agency:
Nonbox
319 SW Washington St Mezzanine Level
Portland, OR 97204
Tel.: (503) 227-1638
Fax: (503) 417-8613
— Dave Parmley *(Acct Supvr)*

GRIFFON CORPORATION

712 5th Ave 18th Fl
New York, NY 10019
Tel.: (212) 957-5000
E-mail: info@amstock.com
Web Site: www.griffoncorp.com
Approx. Rev.: $1,293,996,000
Approx. Number Employees: 5,700
Year Founded: 1970
Business Description:
Plastics Products Mfr
S.I.C.: 3089
N.A.I.C.S.: 326199
Advertising Expenditures: $14,700,000
Media: 2-3-5-9-10-16-17-25
Distr.: Intl.; Natl.
Budget Set: Oct.
Personnel:
Ronald J. Kramer *(Pres & CEO)*
Douglas J. Wetmore *(CFO & Exec VP)*
Patrick L. Alesia *(Chief Admin Officer & Sr VP)*
Brian G. Harris *(Chief Acctg Officer)*
Gary A Abyad *(Pres-Clopay Plastic Products)*
Eugene C Colleran *(Pres-Clopay)*
Steve Lynch *(Pres-Clopay Building Products)*
Brands & Products:
GRIFFON CORPORATION
Advertising Agency:
ICR
20 Custom House St Ste 930
Boston, MA 02110
Tel.: (617) 956-6725
Fax: (617) 956-6726

GUARDIAN ALARM COMPANY

(d/b/a Guardian Security Services)
20800 Southfield Rd
Southfield, MI 48075-4238
Tel.: (248) 423-1000
Tel.: (248) 423-3000 (HR)
Fax: (248) 423-3009
E-mail: webmaster@guardianalarm.com
Web Site: www.guardianalarm.com
Approx. Number Employees: 2,000
Year Founded: 1930
Business Description:
Security Systems Services
S.I.C.: 7382
N.A.I.C.S.: 561621
Media: 7-8-14-15-26
Personnel:
Milton Pierce *(Founder)*
Douglas Pierce *(Co-Owner)*
Richard Pierce *(Co-Owner)*
Karen Majeske *(Gen Mgr)*

GUARDIAN ELECTRIC MANUFACTURING COMPANY

(Sub. of Kelco Industries Inc.)
1425 Lk Ave
Woodstock, IL 60098-7419
Tel.: (815) 334-3600
Fax: (815) 337-0377
Toll Free: (800) 762-0369
E-mail: infoge@kelcomail.com
Web Site: www.guardian-electric.com
Sales Range: $1-9.9 Million
Approx. Number Employees: 80
Year Founded: 1976
Business Description:
Relays, Solenoids, Switches, Steppers & Controls, Aero Products, Grips, Military Relays Mfr
S.I.C.: 3679; 3625
N.A.I.C.S.: 334419; 335314
Import Export
Advertising Expenditures: $500,000
Media: 2-4-7-10
Distr.: Intl.; Natl.
Budget Set: Dec.
Personnel:
Michael Kelly *(Chm)*
Kevin Kelly *(Pres)*
Brands & Products:
GUARDIAN

HANDLEMAN COMPANY

500 Kirts Blvd
Troy, MI 48084-5225
Tel.: (248) 362-4400
Fax: (248) 362-3615
E-mail: corporate.info@handleman.com
Web Site: www.handleman.com
E-Mail For Key Personnel:
Public Relations: investors@handleman.com
Sales Range: $1-4.9 Billion
Approx. Number Employees: 4
Year Founded: 1934
Business Description:
Business Services
S.I.C.: 5099
N.A.I.C.S.: 423990
Media: 2-5-6-7-10-19-22
Personnel:
James B. Nicholson *(Chm)*
Albert A. Koch *(CEO)*
Rozanne Kokko *(CFO & SVP)*
Advertising Agency:
Marx Layne & Company
31420 Northwestern Hwy Ste 100
Farmington Hills, MI 48334
Tel.: (248) 855-6777
Fax: (248) 855-6719
Public Relations

HAPP CONTROLS INC.

(Holding of Pfingsten Partners, LLC)
106 Garlisch Dr
Elk Grove Village, IL 60007-1316
Tel.: (847) 593-6130
Fax: (847) 593-6137
Fax: (800) 593-4277
Toll Free: (888) 289-4277
E-mail: info@happcontrols.com
Web Site: www.happ.com
Approx. Number Employees: 204
Year Founded: 1986
Business Description:
Amusement, Gaming & Vending Parts Mfr & Distr
S.I.C.: 3581; 3679
N.A.I.C.S.: 333311; 334419
Media: 10-11
Personnel:
Son Tom *(VP-Mktg)*
Rich Santercola *(Dir-Mktg)*
Jay Pollitt *(Sls Mgr-Product)*
Laura Sadowski *(Mgr-Inside Sls & Mktg)*
Brands & Products:
HAPP

HARMAN CONSUMER, INC.

(Sub. of Harman International Industries, Incorporated)
(d/b/a Harman Consumer Group)
250 Crossways Pk Dr
Woodbury, NY 11797
Tel.: (516) 496-3400
Fax: (516) 682-3510
Web Site: www.harman.com
Sales Range: $50-74.9 Million
Approx. Number Employees: 200
Business Description:
Mfr. & Sales of High Fidelity Components
S.I.C.: 3651
N.A.I.C.S.: 334310
Advertising Expenditures: $1,900,000
Media: 3-4-5-6-7-10-19-20
Distr.: Intl.; Natl.
Budget Set: July
Personnel:
Richard S. Sorota *(Pres)*
Christopher M. Dragon *(Dir-Consumer & Field Mktg)*
Bob Hessler *(Mgr-CRM)*
Brands & Products:
AUDIO ACCESS
HARMAN KARDON
JBL

HARMAN INTERNATIONAL INDUSTRIES, INCORPORATED

400 Atlantic St 15th Fl
Stamford, CT 06901
Tel.: (203) 328-3500
Web Site: www.harman.com
Approx. Sls.: $3,772,345,000
Approx. Number Employees: 10,103
Year Founded: 1980
Business Description:
Video & Audio Systems Mfr
S.I.C.: 3651
N.A.I.C.S.: 334310
Import Export
Media: 2-4-6-7-10-11-13-19-22
Distr.: Intl.; Natl.
Personnel:
Dinesh C. Paliwal *(Chm, Pres & CEO)*
Sachin Lawande *(CTO, Co-Pres-Automotive Div & Exec VP)*
Michael Mauser *(Co-Pres-Infotainment & Lifestyle & Exec VP)*
Herbert K. Parker *(CFO & Exec VP)*
John Stacey *(Chief HR Officer & Exec VP)*
Jennifer Peter *(Chief Acctg Officer & VP)*
Blake Augsburger *(Pres-Prof Div & Exec VP)*
Todd A. Suko *(Gen Counsel, Sec & Exec VP)*
David Slump *(Exec VP-Corp Dev)*
Brad A. Hoffman *(VP-Corp Comm)*
Floyd E. Toole *(VP-Acoustical Engrg)*
Rob Lewis *(Dir-Sls-US-Studer Pro Audio)*
Stephanie Sauter *(Dir-Global Comm & Mktg-Europe)*
Darrin Shewchuk *(Dir-Corp Comm)*
Brands & Products:
AKG
AUDIOACCESS
BASS OPTIMIZATION SYSTEM
BECKER
BSS
CROWN
DBX
DIGITECH
DOD
HARMAN INTERNATIONAL
HARMAN/KARDON
HIQNET
INFINITY
JBL
LEXICON
LOGIC 7
MARGI
MARK LEVINSON
QNX
R.A.B.O.S.
REVEL
RIGITEX
ROOM ADAPTIVE BASS OPTIMIZATION SYSTEM
ROOM-FRIENDLY ACOUSTICAL DESIGN
SCREENARRAY
SELENIUM
SIGNATURE SERIES
SIGNATURE SOUND
SIMPLY CINEMA
SMART SUBWOOFER, THE
SOUNDCRAFT
SOUNDEFFECTS
SOUNDGEAR
SOUNDPOINT
SOUNDSTICKS
SPEAKERSHOP
SPIRIT
STARFISH
STRAIGHT-LINE SIGNAL PATH
STUDER
SYMMETRICAL FIELD GEOMETRY
SYNTHESIS
SYNTHESIS BOARDROOM
TIK SERIES
TLH
TLH II
TLH2
TOTAL SOLUTIONS
TRAFFICPRO
UNIPIVOT
UNIPLANE
UNIPOINT
Advertising Agency:
Isobar US
200 Clarendon St 23rd Fl
Boston, MA 02116
Tel.: (617) 449-4100
Fax: (617) 449-4200
Global Digital Agency of Record

HARRIS CORPORATION

1025 W NASA Blvd
Melbourne, FL 32919-0001
Tel.: (321) 727-9100
Fax: (321) 674-4740
Toll Free: (800) 442-7747
E-mail: webmaster@harris.com
Web Site: www.harris.com
E-Mail For Key Personnel:
Public Relations: jbroo@harris.com

Key to Media (For complete agency information see *The Advertising Red Books-Agencies* edition):
1. Bus. Publs. 2. Cable T.V. 3. Catalogs & Directories. 4. Co-op Adv. 5. Consumer Mags. 6. D.M. to Bus. Estab.7. D.M. to Consumers 8. Daily Newsp. 9. Exhibits/Trade Shows 10. Foreign 11. Infomercial 12. Internet Adv.13. Multimedia 14. Network Radio 15. Network T.V. 16. Newsp. Distr. Mags. 17. Other 18. Outdoor (Posters, Transit) 19. Point of Purchase20. Premiums, Novelties 21. Product Samples 22. Special Events Mktg. 23. Spot Radio 24. Spot T.V. 25. Weekly Newsp. 26. Yellow Page Adv.

Approx. Rev.: $5,924,600,000
Approx. Number Employees: 16,900
Year Founded: 1926
Business Description:
Holding Company; Electronic Systems & Communications Products Mfr
S.I.C.: 6719; 3663; 3669
N.A.I.C.S.: 551112; 334220; 334290
Import Export
Media: 2-7-10
Distr.: Intl.; Natl.
Personnel:
Howard L. Lance *(Chm)*
William M. Brown *(Pres & CEO)*
Gary L. McArthur *(CFO & Sr VP)*
Daniel R. Pearson *(COO & Exec VP)*
Ted Hengst *(CIO & Corp VP)*
Jeffrey S. Shuman *(Chief Admin Officer, Chief HR officer & Sr VP)*
R. Kent Buchanan *(CTO & VP-Engrg)*
Sheldon J. Fox *(Pres-Govt Comm Sys Div)*
John E. Heller *(Pres-IT Svcs)*
Dana A. Mehnert *(Pres-RF Comm Div)*
Harris P. Morris, Jr. *(Pres-Brdcst Comm Bus Div)*
Andy Start *(Pres-Intl Tactical Radio Comm)*
Scott T. Mikuen *(Gen Counsel, Sec & VP)*
Dale Meyerrose *(VP & Gen Mgr-Cyber Integrated Solutions)*
Jim Traficant *(VP & Gen Mgr-Harris Healthcare Solutions)*
Anthony Deglomine *(VP & Deputy Gen Counsel)*
Wesley B. Covell *(Chief Growth Officer & VP-Strategy)*
David Cunningham *(VP-HR & Comm Div)*
John L. Draheim *(VP-Fin Svcs)*
Walt Paskowski *(VP-Sls-North America-Pub Safety & Pro Comm Bus)*
Geno Viviano *(Dir-Indirect Channels-Pub Safety & Pro Comm Bus)*
Brands & Products:
ANYTIME. ANYWHERE
ASSURED COMMUNICATIONS
HARRIS
SECNET 11
Advertising Agency:
Matter Communications
50 Water St, Mill #3, The Tannery
Newburyport, MA 01950
Tel.: (978) 499-9250
Fax: (978) 499-9253

HARRIS CORP. BROADCAST COMMUNICATIONS DIVISION

(Div. of HARRIS CORPORATION)
(d/b/a Harris Broadcast Communications Division)
4393 Digital Way
Mason, OH 45040-7604
Tel.: (513) 459-3400
Fax: (513) 701-5302
E-mail: webmaster@harris.com
Web Site: www.broadcast.harris.com
Sales Range: $75-99.9 Million
Approx. Number Employees: 200
Year Founded: 1966
Business Description:
Broadcast Communications Equipment & Software Mfr & Distr
S.I.C.: 3663
N.A.I.C.S.: 334220
Import Export
Advertising Expenditures: $500,000
Media: 2-6-10
Distr.: Natl.
Budget Set: Apr.
Personnel:
Harris P. Morris, Jr. *(Pres)*
Richard Scott *(Sr VP-Sls & Svcs-Global)*
Bob Duncan *(VP & Gen Mgr-Media)*
Doug Means *(VP & Gen Mgr-Workflow, Infrastructure & Networking)*
John A. Scarcella *(VP & Gen Mgr-Consumer Bus-New York)*
Philip Argyris *(VP-Transmission Sys)*
David Cunningham *(VP-HR)*
Brad Turner *(VP-Strategy & Mktg)*
Brands & Products:
AUDIOMETRICS
TELEMIX

HARRIS CORP. RF COMMUNICATIONS DIVISION

(Div. of HARRIS CORPORATION)
(d/b/a Harris RF Communications Division)
1680 University Ave
Rochester, NY 14610-1839
Tel.: (585) 244-5830
Fax: (585) 242-4755
E-mail: rfcomm@harris.com
Web Site: www.rfcomm.harris.com
Sales Range: $500-549.9 Million
Approx. Number Employees: 2,000
Business Description:
Turnkey Communication Systems Involving Satellite, Microwave, HF, VHF, UHF & Fiber-Optic Technologies
S.I.C.: 3663
N.A.I.C.S.: 334220
Export
Advertising Expenditures: $1,200,000
Media: 1-2-4-7-10-11
Distr.: Intl.; Natl.
Budget Set: June
Personnel:
Dana A. Mehnert *(Pres)*
Stephen Marschilok *(Pres-Pub Safety & Pro Comm)*
Brendan O'Connell *(Pres-DoD Tactical Radio Comm)*
Andy Start *(Pres-Intl Bus)*
George Helm *(VP & Gen Mgr-Pub Safety & Pro Comm)*
Hal McDougall *(Acting VP & Gen Mgr-Intl Bus Unit)*
Kevin Aman *(Sr Mgr-Mktg Comm)*
Brands & Products:
AUTOLINK
HICOM

HCC AEGIS INC.

(Sub. of HCC Industries)
50 Welby Rd
New Bedford, MA 02745
Tel.: (508) 998-3141
Fax: (508) 995-7315
Web Site: www.hccindustries.com
Sales Range: $75-99.9 Million
Approx. Number Employees: 250
Year Founded: 1985
Business Description:
Custom & Semi-Custom Metal & Electronic Packages
S.I.C.: 3679
N.A.I.C.S.: 334419
Media: 10

HEI, INC.

1495 Steiger Lake Ln
Victoria, MN 55386
Mailing Address:
PO Box 5000
Victoria, MN 55386-5000
Tel.: (952) 443-2500
Fax: (952) 443-2668
E-mail: headqtrs@heii.com
Web Site: www.heii.com
Approx. Sls.: $31,530,000
Approx. Number Employees: 250
Year Founded: 1968
Business Description:
Microelectronic Subsystems & Components Designer & Mfr
S.I.C.: 3674
N.A.I.C.S.: 334413
Import Export
Advertising Expenditures: $517,000
Media: 2-7-10
Distr.: Intl.; Natl.
Budget Set: July
Personnel:
Thomas F. Leahy *(Chm)*
Mark B. Thomas *(CEO)*
Brands & Products:
HEI
LINK-IT
MICROELECTRONICS FOR LIFE SIZED SOLUTIONS

HELLERMANNTYTON

(Sub. of HellermannTyton Ltd.)
7930 N Faulkner Rd
Milwaukee, WI 53224-3423
Mailing Address:
PO Box 245017
Milwaukee, WI 53224-9517
Tel.: (414) 355-1130
Fax: (414) 355-7341
Toll Free: (800) 537-1512
Telex: 910-262-3094
E-mail: info@htamericas.com
Web Site: www.hellermann.tyton.com
Approx. Number Employees: 300
Business Description:
Cable Care Products Mfr
S.I.C.: 3089; 2891
N.A.I.C.S.: 326199; 325520
Media: 4-6-9-25-26
Distr.: Natl.
Budget Set: Oct.
Personnel:
Jim Campion *(Mng Dir)*
Terri Tuttle *(VP-Sls & Mktg)*
Brands & Products:
PRO-DUCT
SNAPPER HOSE CLAMP
TAG PRINT PRO

HEMISPHERE GPS INC.

4110 9th St SE
Calgary, AB T2G 3C4, Canada
Tel.: (403) 259-3311
Fax: (403) 259-8866
Toll Free: (877) 657-5276
E-mail: info@hemispheregps.com
Web Site: www.hemispheregps.com
Approx. Sls.: $55,998,250
Approx. Number Employees: 229
Year Founded: 1990
Business Description:
Satellite Communication Products Designer & Mfr
S.I.C.: 4899; 3669; 3812
N.A.I.C.S.: 517410; 334290; 334511
Media: 7-8-10-13-22
Personnel:
Michael J. Lang *(Chm)*
Steven L. Koles *(Pres & CEO)*
Cameron Olson *(CFO & Sr VP)*
Philip W. Gabriel *(VP & Gen Mgr-Precision Products Grp)*
Kip Pendleton *(VP & Gen Mgr-Agriculture)*
Jim Chinnick *(VP-Engrg)*
John Pohlake *(VP-Mktg, Product Mgmt)*
Michael Whitehead *(VP-Tech)*
John Bohlke *(Gen Mgr-Earthworks)*
Helen Pozsonyi *(Dir-HR)*
Brands & Products:
A100
AERIALACE
AIR FLITETRAC
AIR FLYING FLAGMAN
AIR INTELLIFLOW
AIR INTELLIGATE
AIR LITESTAR II
AIR M3
AIR MAPSTAR
AIR R100
AIRSTAR
ASSET-LINK
CLAAS
CORNERPOST
CRESCENT OEM BOARD
DGPS MAX
E-DIF
ECLIPSE OEM BOARD
ETURNS
FLEET-LINK
FREETRAC
GPSTEER
HEMISPHERE GPS
LV100 OEM BOARD
LX-1
MAPSTAR
MBX-4
MINIMAX
POCKETMAX
POWERMAX
PRECISION COMMERCIAL GPS TECHNOLOGY
R100
SATLOC
SATLOC M3
SBX-4
SERES
SPEED DRIVEX
SWATHSTAR
SWATHSTAR M3
VECTOR

HENRY BROS. ELECTRONICS, INC.

(Sub. of Kratos Defense & Security Solutions, Inc.)
17-01 Pollitt Dr
Fair Lawn, NJ 07410
Tel.: (201) 794-6500
Fax: (201) 794-8341
E-mail: breach@hbe-inc.com
Web Site: www.hbe-inc.com
Approx. Rev.: $55,105,469
Approx. Number Employees: 205
Year Founded: 1950
Business Description:
Security Systems
S.I.C.: 7382; 3669; 3679; 7373
N.A.I.C.S.: 561621; 334290; 334419; 541512
Export
Advertising Expenditures: $106,669

Key to Media (For complete agency information see *The Advertising Red Books-Agencies* edition):
1. Bus. Publs. 2. Cable T.V. 3. Catalogs & Directories. 4. Co-op Adv. 5. Consumer Mags. 6. D.M. to Bus. Estab.7. D.M. to Consumers 8. Daily Newsp. 9. Exhibits/Trade Shows 10. Foreign 11. Infomercial 12. Internet Adv.13. Multimedia 14. Network Radio 15. Network T.V. 16. Newsp. Distr. Mags. 17. Other 18. Outdoor (Posters, Transit) 19. Point of Purchase20. Premiums, Novelties 21. Product Samples 22. Special Events Mktg. 23. Spot Radio 24. Spot T.V. 25. Weekly Newsp. 26. Yellow Page Adv.

Henry Bros. Electronics, Inc. — (Continued)

Media: 4-7-10
Personnel:
James E. Henry *(Founder, Chm & CEO)*
John P. Hopkins *(CFO)*
John A. Batsch *(VP & Gen Mgr)*
John Noble *(VP & Gen Mgr-HBE Texas)*
Robert Hodgson *(VP-HR)*
Bruce DeBon *(Dir-Bus Dev-DSSI)*
Advertising Agency:
K.C.S.A. Holdings (Pty.) Ltd.
8 Leicester Rd
Bedfordview, Johannesburg 2007, South Africa
Tel.: (27) 0114565700
Fax: (27) 114565798

HERLEY FARMINGDALE
(Div. of Herley Industries, Inc.)
425 Smith St
Farmingdale, NY 11735-1106
Tel.: (516) 802-0900
Fax: (631) 630-2066
Telex: 310-287780
Web Site: www.herley.com
Sales Range: $25-49.9 Million
Approx. Number Employees: 110
Year Founded: 1960
Business Description:
Mfr. of Microwave Components & Integrated Circuits
S.I.C.: 3679; 5065
N.A.I.C.S.: 334419; 423690
Export
Media: 2-4
Distr.: Intl.; Natl.
Budget Set: Feb.
Brands & Products:
GENERAL MICROWAVE

HICKORY TECH CORPORATION
221 E Hickory St
Mankato, MN 56001-3610
Mailing Address:
PO Box 3248
Mankato, MN 56002-3248
Tel.: (507) 387-1151
Fax: (507) 625-9191
Toll Free: (800) 326-5789
E-mail: infosolutions@hickorytech.com
Web Site: www.hickorytech.com
Approx. Rev.: $162,247,000
Approx. Number Employees: 463
Year Founded: 1898
Business Description:
Telephone, Billing & Data Services, Equipment Sales & Telecommunications Products
S.I.C.: 4813; 4812
N.A.I.C.S.: 517110; 517212; 517310
Advertising Expenditures: $1,043,000
Media: 4-10-22
Personnel:
Dale E. Parker *(Chm)*
Diane L. Dewbrey *(Vice Chm)*
John W. Finke *(Pres & CEO)*
David A. Christensen *(CFO & Sr VP)*
Carol Wirsbinski *(COO & VP)*
Lane C. Nordquist *(CIO, Pres-Info Solutions & Corp VP)*
Damon D. Dutz *(Pres-Consumer & Network Solutions & Corp VP)*
Walter A. Prahl *(Pres-Bus, Wholesale Solutions & Corp VP)*
Mary T. Jacobs *(VP-HR)*
Scott Grill *(Dir-Sls & Mktg)*
Jennifer M. Spaude *(Dir-IR & Mktg)*
Sandra Gibbs *(Mgr-Mktg)*
Paavo Pyykkonen *(Mgr-Bus Dev)*

HITACHI AMERICA, LTD.
(Sub. of Hitachi, Ltd.)
1000 Marino Blvd
Brisbane, CA 94005
Tel.: (650) 589-8300
Fax: (650) 244-7920
Toll Free: (800) HITACHI
Telex: 234553
Web Site: www.hitachi.us
Approx. Number Employees: 100
Year Founded: 1959
Business Description:
Sales of Computers, Electronic & Industrial Components & Automotive Parts
S.I.C.: 5045; 5065
N.A.I.C.S.: 423430; 423690
Import Export
Media: 2-3-4-6-8-9-10-13-15-18-22-23-24-25
Budget Set: Apr.
Personnel:
Chiaki Fujiwara *(Pres & CEO)*
Tadahiko Ishigaki *(Sr VP & Exec Officer)*
Elizabeth King *(VP & Gen Mgr)*
Daniel Lee *(VP-Mktg-Ubiquitous Platforms Systems Div)*
Lauren Garvey *(Dir-Branding & Corp Comm)*
Bill Whalen *(Dir)*
Edgar Jimenez *(Mgr-Sls-Western Zone)*
Thomas Morris *(Mgr-Sls-PC Channel)*
Andrew Mulazzi *(Mgr-Bus Dev)*
Advertising Agencies:
Gotham Incorporated
150 E 42nd St 12th Fl
New York, NY 10017
Tel.: (212) 414-7000
Fax: (212) 414-7095

VML, Inc.
250 Richards Rd
Kansas City, MO 64116-4279
Tel.: (816) 283-0700
Fax: (816) 283-0954
Toll Free: (800) 990-2468

Weber Shandwick-San Francisco
600 Battery St
San Francisco, CA 94111
Tel.: (415) 262-5950
Fax: (415) 262-5982

HITTITE MICROWAVE CORPORATION
2 Elizabeth Dr
Chelmsford, MA 01824
Tel.: (978) 250-3343
Fax: (978) 250-3373
E-mail: sales@hittite.com
Web Site: www.hittite.com
Approx. Rev.: $244,256,000
Approx. Number Employees: 402
Year Founded: 1985
Business Description:
Communication Chip Mfr
S.I.C.: 3674; 3669; 3679
N.A.I.C.S.: 334413; 334290; 334419
Media: 2-4-7-10
Personnel:
Stephen G. Daly *(Pres & CEO)*
William W. Boecke *(CFO, Treas & VP)*
Norman G. Hildreth, Jr. *(VP-Sls & Mktg)*
Michael A. Olson *(VP-Engrg)*
Volker Schulz *(Sls Mgr-Germany)*

HOUSTON WIRE & CABLE COMPANY
10201 N Loop E
Houston, TX 77029-1415
Mailing Address:
PO Box 23221
Houston, TX 77228-3221
Tel.: (713) 609-2100
Fax: (713) 609-2101
Toll Free: (800) 468-9473
E-mail: gschwab@houwire.com
Web Site: www.houwire.com
E-Mail For Key Personnel:
President: csorrentino@houwire.com
Approx. Sls.: $308,522,000
Approx. Number Employees: 380
Year Founded: 1975
Business Description:
Distr of Specialty Wire & Cable
S.I.C.: 5063; 3496
N.A.I.C.S.: 423610; 332618
Export
Advertising Expenditures: $163,000
Media: 17
Personnel:
James L. Pokluda, III *(Pres)*
Charles A. Sorrentino *(CEO)*
Nicol G. Graham *(CFO, Treas & Sec)*
Christopher R. McLeod *(Sr VP-Ops)*
Eric S. Blankenship *(Reg VP)*
Marcus L. Jones *(Reg VP)*
Larry Scott *(Reg Mgr-Distr Center)*
Brands & Products:
DATAGUARD
HOUWIRE
LIFEGUARD

HTC AMERICA, INC.
(Sub. of HTC Corporation)
13920 SE Eastgate Way Ste 400
Bellevue, WA 98005
Tel.: (425) 861-9174
Fax: (425) 861-1715
Web Site: www.htc.com
Business Description:
Mobile Information & Communications Devices Designer & Mfr
S.I.C.: 3663
N.A.I.C.S.: 334220
Personnel:
Jason B. MacKenzie *(Pres-Global Sls & Mktg)*
Advertising Agencies:
Deutsch, Inc.
(A Lowe & Partners Company)
111 8th Ave 14th Fl
New York, NY 10011-5201
Tel.: (212) 981-7600
Fax: (212) 981-7525

Deutsch LA
5454 Beethoven St
Los Angeles, CA 90066-7017
Tel.: (310) 862-3000
Fax: (310) 862-3100

HUGHES NETWORK SYSTEMS LLC
(Sub. of Hughes Communications, Inc.)
11717 Exploration Ln
Germantown, MD 20876
Tel.: (301) 428-5500
Fax: (301) 428-1868
Web Site: www.hughes.com
Approx. Rev.: $1,037,743,000
Approx. Number Employees: 1,897
Year Founded: 1983
Business Description:
Satellite-Based Broadband Products & Services
S.I.C.: 4899
N.A.I.C.S.: 517410
Media: 10
Personnel:
Pradman P. Kaul *(Pres & CEO)*
Grant A. Barber *(CFO & Exec VP)*
Thomas J. McElroy *(Chief Acctg Officer)*
Dean A. Manson *(Gen Counsel, Sec & Sr VP)*
John McEwan *(Sr VP-Ops & Mfg)*
T. Paul Gaske *(Exec VP)*
Adrian Morris *(Exec VP)*
Bahram Pourmand *(Exec VP)*
Bob Buschman *(Sr VP-Jupiter)*
George Choquette *(Sr VP-Engrg)*
Mike Cook *(Sr VP)*
John Corrigan *(Sr VP)*
Estil Hoversten *(Sr VP)*
Tom Hsu *(Sr VP)*
Robert Kepley *(Sr VP-Engrg)*
Sandi Kerentoff *(Sr VP-Admin & HR)*
Ashok Mehta *(Sr VP)*
Vinod Shukla *(Sr VP)*
David Zatloukal *(Sr VP-North American Ops)*
Matthew Mohebbi *(VP & Gen Mgr-Mobile Satellite Grp)*
Robert O. Feierbach *(VP-Sls & Mktg-Intl Div)*
Dan Fraley *(VP-Engrg)*
Advertising Agencies:
GlobalWorks
220 5th Ave
New York, NY 10001
Tel.: (212) 252-8800
Fax: (212) 252-0002

White & Partners
13665 Dulles Technology Dr Ste 150
Herndon, VA 20171-4607
Tel.: (703) 793-3000
Fax: (703) 793-1495
Toll Free: (800) 211-0874

HYDROFLEX, INC.
301 E El Segundo Blvd
El Segundo, CA 90245
Tel.: (310) 301-8187
Fax: (310) 821-9886
E-mail: h2opros@hydroflex.com
Web Site: www.hydroflex.com
Approx. Number Employees: 5
Business Description:
Camera Equipment Mfr & Motion Picture Production Services
S.I.C.: 3861; 7359
N.A.I.C.S.: 333315; 532490
Media: 2-10
Personnel:
Peter Romano *(Pres)*

Key to Media (For complete agency information see *The Advertising Red Books-Agencies* edition):
1. Bus. Publs. 2. Cable T.V. 3. Catalogs & Directories. 4. Co-op Adv. 5. Consumer Mags. 6. D.M. to Bus. Estab.7. D.M. to Consumers 8. Daily Newsp. 9. Exhibits/Trade Shows 10. Foreign 11. Infomercial 12. Internet Adv.13. Multimedia 14. Network Radio 15. Network T.V. 16. Newsp. Distr. Mags. 17. Other 18. Outdoor (Posters, Transit) 19. Point of Purchase20. Premiums, Novelties 21. Product Samples 22. Special Events Mktg. 23. Spot Radio 24. Spot T.V. 25. Weekly Newsp. 26. Yellow Page Adv.

Brands & Products:
HYDROFLEX
HYDROFLO
HYDROPAR
HYDRORAMA
SEAPAR

ICAD, INC.
98 Spit Brook Rd Ste 100
Nashua, NH 03062
Tel.: (603) 882-5200
Fax: (603) 880-3843
Toll Free: (866) 280-2239
E-mail: info@icadmed.com
Web Site: www.icadmed.com
Approx. Rev.: $24,575,035
Approx. Number Employees: 143
Year Founded: 1984
Business Description:
Digital Image Scanners, Film Digitizers & Related Software for Applications in the Medical Imaging, Graphic Arts & Photographic Markets
S.I.C.: 3577; 5043; 7372
N.A.I.C.S.: 334119; 423410; 511210
Advertising Expenditures: $666,000
Media: 2-7-10
Personnel:
Lawrence Howard *(Chm)*
Kenneth M. Ferry *(CEO)*
Kevin C. Burns *(CFO, Treas & Exec VP-Fin)*
Jeffrey H. Barnes *(Exec VP-Global Comml Ops)*
Jonathan Go *(Sr VP-R&D)*
Stacey M. Stevens *(Sr VP-Mktg & Strategy)*
Donna Breault *(Dir-Mktg Comm)*
Brands & Products:
CADVUE
CLICKCAD
FULCRUM
ICAD
NEVER STOP LOOKING
SECOND LOOK
SPECTRALOOK
TOTALLOOK MAMMO ADVANTAGE
Advertising Agencies:
Lippert/Heilshorn & Associates, Inc.
800 Third Ave 17th Fl
New York, NY 10022
Tel.: (212) 838-3777
Fax: (212) 838-4568

PJA
12 Arrow St
Cambridge, MA 02138-5105
Tel.: (617) 492-5899
Fax: (617) 661-1530
Media Planning
— Allison Cherundolo *(Acct Exec)*

ICOP DIGITAL, INC.
16801 W 116th St
Lenexa, KS 66219
Tel.: (913) 338-5550
Toll Free: (866) 210-ICOP (Sls)
Toll Free: (866) 621-5500 (Support)
E-mail: info@icop.com
Web Site: icopdigital.com
Approx. Sls.: $8,423,365
Approx. Number Employees: 52
Business Description:
Security, Surveillance & Communications Solutions Provider
S.I.C.: 3291; 7382
N.A.I.C.S.: 327910; 561621
Advertising Expenditures: $208,000
Media: 2-7-10
Personnel:
David C. Owen *(Chm & CEO)*
Laura E. Owen *(Pres, COO & Dir)*
Mickie R. Koslofsky *(CFO)*
Brands & Products:
A VEIL OF PROTECTION
ADVANCING SURVEILLANCE TECHNOLOGY
ICOP
ICOP 20/20 VISION
ICOP DIGITAL
ICOP EXTREME WIRELESS MIC
ICOP GUARDIAN
ICOP IVAULT
ICOP LIVE
ICOP MODEL 20/20
ICOP MODEL 4000
ICOP PC VIEWER
ICOP SOLUTION

I.D. SYSTEMS, INC.
123 Tice Blvd
Woodcliff Lake, NJ 07677
Tel.: (201) 996-9000
Fax: (201) 996-9144
Toll Free: (866) 410-0152
E-mail: info@id-systems.com
Web Site: www.id-systems.com
E-Mail For Key Personnel:
Sales Director: sales@id-systems.com
Approx. Rev.: $25,861,000
Approx. Number Employees: 86
Year Founded: 1993
Business Description:
Wireless Asset Management Solutions
S.I.C.: 3663; 3679
N.A.I.C.S.: 334220; 334419
Advertising Expenditures: $271,000
Personnel:
Jeffrey M. Jagid *(Chm & CEO)*
Kenneth S. Ehrman *(Pres)*
Ned Mavrommatis *(CFO & Treas)*
Darryl Miller *(COO)*
Raju Kakarlapudi *(CIO)*
Todd Felker *(Exec VP-Mktg & Product Dev)*
Curt Lloyd *(Exec VP-Ops)*
Brands & Products:
AVRAMP
I.D. SYSTEMS INC.
OPTI-KAN
POWERFLEET
SAFENAV
TRUEUSE
VEHICLE ASSET COMMUNICATOR
VERIWISE
WIRELESS ASSET NET

IDT CORPORATION
520 Broad St
Newark, NJ 07102
Tel.: (973) 438-1000
Fax: (973) 438-1455
E-mail: cardinfo@corp.idt.net
Web Site: www.idt.net
Approx. Rev.: $1,401,449,000
Approx. Number Employees: 1,180
Year Founded: 1990
Business Description:
VoIP Telecommunications Services
S.I.C.: 4813; 7375
N.A.I.C.S.: 517310; 518111
Advertising Expenditures: $25,700,000
Media: 6-13-15-22-23-24
Personnel:
Howard S. Jonas *(Chm & CEO)*
James A. Courter *(Vice Chm)*
Ira A. Greenstein *(Pres)*
Bill Pereira *(CFO & Treas)*
Yona Katz *(COO-IDT Telecom)*
Samuel Jonas *(COO)*
Elliot Rothstein *(Chief Legal Officer)*
Mitch Silberman *(Chief Acctg Officer & Controller)*
Douglas W. Mauro *(Chief Tax Officer)*
Joyce J. Mason *(Gen Counsel, Sec & Exec VP)*
Liore Alroy *(Exec VP)*
Don Zamora *(Dir-Mktg)*
Brands & Products:
ABCGONLINE
BEEP2TALK
CLIC AQUI
CLICK2RESERVE
CLICK2TAKE
COLUMBIANA
CYBERSPACE KIDS
DEBIT TALK
DIPLOMATIC EXPO
DOMINICALL
EZ ROAD
FREEATLAST
GENIE
GIFTS FOR GAB
GLOBAL AMERICA
GLOBAL CALL
HEALINC
IDT
IMPERIAL TELECARD
INTERNET INDUSTRY & DESIGN
IP CENTRAL OFFICE
LA LINEA LATINA
LA UNIVERSAL
LOGINDATA
MEGA MEXICO
MEGATEL
MEXICALL
NET2DINE.COM
NET2TORAH
NETVENTURE
NO ONE DOES IT FOR LESS
NUBILL
NUBILL.COM
NUESTRA VOZ
NUPAGE
NUSSERVE
SKIPID
TRAVELER SOS
TV.TV
TV.TV BROADBAND NETWORK
VIRTURAL DIME
WEBONY
WEBONY.COM
THE WONDER OF BROADBAND
ZERODINERO

IEC ELECTRONICS CORP.
105 Norton St
Newark, NY 14513-1218
Tel.: (315) 331-7742
Fax: (315) 331-3547
E-mail: inq@iec-electronics.com
Web Site: www.iec-electronics.com
E-Mail For Key Personnel:
Public Relations: JSchlarbaum@iec-electronics.com
Approx. Sls.: $96,674,000
Approx. Number Employees: 567
Year Founded: 1966
Business Description:
Printed Circuit Board Assemblies, Electronic Products & Systems Mfr
S.I.C.: 3672; 3679
N.A.I.C.S.: 334412; 334419
Export
Media: 1-2-7-10-13
Personnel:
W. Barry Gilbert *(Chm & CEO)*
Jeffrey T. Schlarbaum *(Pres)*
Susan E. Topel-Samek *(CFO & VP)*
Donald S. Doody *(Exec VP-Ops)*
Brands & Products:
ABSOLUTELY, POSITIVELY, PERFECT AND ON-TIME
Advertising Agency:
Institutional Marketing Services
51 Locust Ave Ste 304
New Canaan, CT 06840
Tel.: (203) 972-9200
— John Nesbett *(Pres)*

IGO, INC.
Ste 200 17800 N Perimeter Dr
Scottsdale, AZ 85255-5433
Tel.: (480) 596-0061
Fax: (480) 596-0349
Web Site: www.igo.com/
Approx. Rev.: $43,357,000
Approx. Number Employees: 62
Year Founded: 1995
Business Description:
Portable & Handheld Computers Docking Stations & Power Products
S.I.C.: 3571; 3577
N.A.I.C.S.: 334111; 334119
Advertising Expenditures: $135,000
Personnel:
Michael J. Larson *(Chm)*
Michael D. Heil *(Pres & CEO)*
Darryl S. Baker *(CFO)*
Brian M. Roberts *(Gen Counsel, Sec & VP)*
Brian Dennison *(VP & Gen Mgr-Americas)*
Brands & Products:
CARDBUS
EASIDOCK
IGO
IGO AUTOPOWER
IGO AUTOPOWER 3000 SERIES
IGO DUALPOWER
IGO EVERYWHEREPOWER 3500 SERIES
IGO INTERNATIONAL PLUG ADAPTER KIT
IGO INTERNATIONAL TRAVEL ADAPTER
IGO MULTI-CARD READER
IGO NOTEBOOK CLEANING KIT
IGO TIP WALLET
IGO WALLPOWER
MAGMA
MOBILITY ELECTRONICS
PITCH DUO
QUICKPOINT
Advertising Agency:
Rogers Ruder Finn
1875 Century Park E Ste 200
Los Angeles, CA 90067-2504
Tel.: (310) 552-6922
Fax: (310) 552-9052

IKEGAMI ELECTRONICS (U.S.A.), INC.
(Holding of Ikegami Tsushinki Co., Ltd.)
37 Brook Ave
Maywood, NJ 07607
Tel.: (201) 368-9171

Key to Media (For complete agency information see *The Advertising Red Books-Agencies* edition):
1. Bus. Publs. 2. Cable T.V. 3. Catalogs & Directories. 4. Co-op Adv. 5. Consumer Mags. 6. D.M. to Bus. Estab.7. D.M. to Consumers
8. Daily Newsp. 9. Exhibits/Trade Shows 10. Foreign 11. Infomercial 12. Internet Adv.13. Multimedia 14. Network Radio
15. Network T.V. 16. Newsp. Distr. Mags. 17. Other 18. Outdoor (Posters, Transit) 19. Point of Purchase20. Premiums, Novelties
21. Product Samples 22. Special Events Mktg. 23. Spot Radio 24. Spot T.V. 25. Weekly Newsp. 26. Yellow Page Adv.

Ikegami Electronics (U.S.A.), Inc. — (Continued)

Fax: (201) 569-1626
E-mail: service@ikegami.com
Web Site: www.ikegami.com
Approx. Number Employees: 25
Year Founded: 1964
Business Description:
Sales of Broadcast Equipment & CCTV Cameras & Monitors
S.I.C.: 5065
N.A.I.C.S.: 423690
Import Export
Advertising Expenditures: $1,000,000
Media: 2-4-10
Distr.: Intl.; Natl.
Budget Set: Apr.
Personnel:
Sofia Ko *(CFO)*
Teri Zastrow *(Dir-Sls & Mktg)*
Brands & Products:
IKEGAMI
Advertising Agency:
MarComm Group, Inc.
10 Cuttermill Rd.
Great Neck, NY 11021
Tel.: (516) 829-0404
Fax: (516) 829-0472
(Professional Television Equipment)

INDUSTRIAL ELECTRONIC ENGINEERS, INC.

7723 Kester Ave
Van Nuys, CA 91405
Tel.: (818) 787-0311
Fax: (818) 787-3953
Toll Free: (800) 422-0867
E-mail: mail@ieeinc.com
Web Site: www.ieeinc.com
E-Mail For Key Personnel:
Marketing Director: ssmyers@ieeinc.com
Approx. Number Employees: 90
Year Founded: 1946
Business Description:
Mfr. of Multi-Platform Graphic Displays, Point-of-Sale Pole Displays & Rugged & Military Display Panels
S.I.C.: 3577; 3575
N.A.I.C.S.: 334119; 334113
Import Export
Advertising Expenditures: $250,000
Media: 7-10-13-20
Distr.: Intl.; Natl.
Budget Set: Sept.
Personnel:
Donald G. Gumpertz *(Chm)*
Thomas Whinfrey *(Pres & CEO)*
Michael Tubbs *(Dir-Ops)*
Jim Brahney *(Reg Mgr)*
Jodie Bennett *(Mgr-Sls)*
Gus Zamudio *(Mgr-Program)*
Elliot Shapiro *(Engr-Applications)*
Brands & Products:
ARGUS
ATLAS
ATLAS 2
CENTURY
DAYSTAR
DAYSTAR NOVA
FLIP
IEE
INDUSTRIAL ELECTRONIC ENGINEER
NOVA
PEP
SCANVUE
SHOPVUE
VIP

INFINEON TECHNOLOGIES NORTH AMERICA CORP.

(Sub. of Infineon Technologies AG)
640 N McCarthy Blvd
Milpitas, CA 95035
Tel.: (408) 503-2791
Fax: (408) 503-1791
E-mail: mitch.ahiers@infineon.com
Web Site: www.infineon.com
Approx. Number Employees: 2,800
Year Founded: 1982
Business Description:
Semiconductor Mfr
S.I.C.: 3674; 3679
N.A.I.C.S.: 334413; 334419
Media: 2-7-10-11-13
Personnel:
Jean-Baptiste Loire *(Pres)*
Andrew Prillwitz *(CFO)*
Shawn Slusser *(VP-Sls & Mktg)*

INFINERA CORPORATION

169 Java Dr
Sunnyvale, CA 94089
Tel.: (408) 572-5200
Fax: (408) 572-5343
E-mail: info@infinera.com
Web Site: www.infinera.com
Approx. Rev.: $454,352,000
Approx. Number Employees: 1,074
Year Founded: 2000
Business Description:
Digital Optical Networking Systems Mfr
S.I.C.: 3663; 3674; 3679
N.A.I.C.S.: 334220; 334413; 334419
Advertising Expenditures: $1,100,000
Media: 10-13-17-22
Personnel:
David F. Welch *(Co-Founder, CMO, Chief Strategy Officer & Exec VP)*
Drew Perkins *(Co-Founder & CTO)*
Kambiz Y. Hooshmand *(Chm)*
Thomas J. Fallon *(Pres & CEO)*
Michael O. McCarthy, III *(Chief Legal & Admin Officer)*
Scott A. Chandler *(VP-Strategic Sls)*
Dirk Corsus *(VP-Engrg)*
Ron Martin *(VP-Worldwide Sls)*
Deryck Robinson *(VP-Subsea Bus)*
Paul Whitney *(VP-HR)*
Vinay Rathore *(Sr Dir-Solutions Mktg)*

INFOCUS CORPORATION

(Sub. of Image Holdings Corporation)
13190 SW 68th Parkway Ste 200
Portland, OR 97223-8368
Tel.: (503) 207-4700
Fax: (503) 207-1937
Toll Free: (800) 294-6400
Web Site: www.infocus.com
Approx. Rev.: $255,685,000
Approx. Number Employees: 200
Year Founded: 1986
Business Description:
Digital Projectors Mfr
S.I.C.: 3651; 3577; 3861
N.A.I.C.S.: 334310; 333315; 334119
Import Export
Advertising Expenditures: $3,300,000
Media: 1-2-4-5-6-7-8-10-13-16-22
Distr.: Natl.
Personnel:
Robert G. O'Malley *(Pres & CEO)*
John Lap Shun Hui *(Pres, Treas & Sec)*
Lisa K. Prentice *(CFO, Sec & Sr VP-Fin)*
Thomson Chan *(VP-Asia Pacific Bus Unit)*
Jeremy Farren *(VP-Sls-Intl)*
Jim Reddy *(VP-Sls-America)*
Brands & Products:
ASK
ASKPROXIMA
THE BIG PICTURE
BRILLIANTCOLOR
DISPLAYLINK
INFOCUS
INFOCUS ENGINE
LEARN BIG
LITEPORT
LITEPRO
LITESHOW II
LP
PLAY BIG
PROJECTOR NET
PROXIMA
SCREENPLAY
SP
SPLIT SCREEN
WORK BIG
X2
Advertising Agency:
Edelman Public Relations Worldwide
888 SW 5th Ave Ste 1050
Portland, OR 97204
Tel.: (503) 227-5767

INFOSONICS CORPORATION

4350 Executive Dr Ste 100
San Diego, CA 92121-4204
Tel.: (858) 373-1600
Fax: (858) 373-1505
Toll Free: (800) 519-1599
E-mail: info@infosonics.com
Web Site: www.infosonics.com
Approx. Sls.: $72,530,000
Approx. Number Employees: 70
Year Founded: 1994
Business Description:
Wireless Handset & Accessory Distr
S.I.C.: 5065; 5731
N.A.I.C.S.: 423690; 443112
Advertising Expenditures: $1,156,000
Media: 2-5-10-13
Personnel:
Joseph Ram *(Founder, Pres & CEO)*
Vernon A. LoForti *(CFO)*
Brands & Products:
INFOSONICS

INSTANTEL INC.

(Sub. of Stanley Security Solutions, Inc.)
309 Legget Drive
Ottawa, ON K2K 3A3, Canada
Tel.: (613) 592-4642
Fax: (613) 592-4296
Toll Free: (800) 267-9111
E-mail: sales@instantel.com
Web Site: www.instantel.com
E-Mail For Key Personnel:
Sales Director: sales@instantel.com
Sales Range: $25-49.9 Million
Approx. Number Employees: 100
Year Founded: 1982
Business Description:
Vibration Monitoring Equipment Mfr
S.I.C.: 3679
N.A.I.C.S.: 334419
Media: 2-10
Personnel:
Bonnie Bewar *(Mgr-Sls)*
Brands & Products:
BLASTMATE
INSTANTEL
INSTANTEL AUTO CALL HOME
INSTANTEL BLASTWARE
INSTANTEL HISTOGRAM COMBO
MINIMATE
MINIMATE PLUS
MYCALL
XMARK

INSULET CORPORATION

9 Oak Park Dr
Bedford, MA 01730
Tel.: (781) 457-5000
Fax: (781) 457-5011
E-mail: careers@insulet.com
Web Site: www.myomnipod.com
Approx. Rev.: $96,966,000
Approx. Number Employees: 310
Year Founded: 2000
Business Description:
Insulin Infusion System Developer, Mfr & Marketer
S.I.C.: 3841
N.A.I.C.S.: 339112
Advertising Expenditures: $668,000
Personnel:
Duane M. DeSisto *(Pres & CEO)*
Brian Roberts *(CFO)*
Charles T. Liamos *(COO)*
R. Anthony Diehl *(Gen Counsel)*
Kevin Schmid *(VP-Ops & Engrg)*
Patrick Treanor *(VP-Sls)*

INTEGRA TELECOM, INC.

(Sub. of Integra Telecom Holdings, Inc.)
4690 Colorado St SE
Minneapolis, MN 55372
Tel.: (952) 226-7000
Fax: (612) 376-4411
Toll Free: (800) 435-4292
E-mail: mn-info@integratelecom.com
Web Site: www.integratelecom.com
Approx. Rev.: $274,526,000
Approx. Number Employees: 1,390
Business Description:
Telephone Equipment Services
S.I.C.: 4813; 4899
N.A.I.C.S.: 517110; 517310; 517910
Advertising Expenditures: $589,000
Media: 4-7-10
Personnel:
Kevin O'Hara *(Chm)*
Jim Heusgen *(Pres)*
Dudley R. Slater *(CEO)*
David Kunde *(Sr VP-ILEC Ops)*
Dan Wigger *(Sr VP-Minnesota & North Dakota)*
Brands & Products:
ESCHELON

INTEGRATED SILICON SOLUTION, INC.

1940 Zanker Rd
San Jose, CA 95112-4216
Tel.: (408) 969-6600
Fax: (408) 969-7800
E-mail: ir@issi.com
Web Site: www.issi.com
Approx. Sls.: $252,458,000
Approx. Number Employees: 452
Year Founded: 1988

Key to Media (For complete agency information see *The Advertising Red Books-Agencies* edition):
1. Bus. Publs. 2. Cable T.V. 3. Catalogs & Directories. 4. Co-op Adv. 5. Consumer Mags. 6. D.M. to Bus. Estab.7. D.M. to Consumers 8. Daily Newsp. 9. Exhibits/Trade Shows 10. Foreign 11. Infomercial 12. Internet Adv.13. Multimedia 14. Network Radio 15. Network T.V. 16. Newsp. Distr. Mags. 17. Other 18. Outdoor (Posters, Transit) 19. Point of Purchase20. Premiums, Novelties 21. Product Samples 22. Special Events Mktg. 23. Spot Radio 24. Spot T.V. 25. Weekly Newsp. 26. Yellow Page Adv.

Business Description:
Designer, Developer & Marketer of Memory Semiconductors
S.I.C.: 3674
N.A.I.C.S.: 334413
Advertising Expenditures: $35,000
Media: 17
Personnel:
Jimmy Shueh Mien Lee *(Chm)*
Kong Yeu Han *(Vice Chm)*
Scott D. Howarth *(Pres & CEO)*
John M. Cobb *(CFO, VP-Fin & Admin)*
Sanjiv Asthana *(Sr VP-Worldwide Sls)*
Ron Kalakuntla *(VP-Mktg)*
Sean Long *(Dir-Mktg)*
Brands & Products:
CAMTILE
ISSI
POWERSAVER
POWERSERVER
QUALITY, SERVICE, & SUPPORT
SIGMARAM

INTEL CORPORATION

2200 Mission College Blvd
Santa Clara, CA 95054-1537
Tel.: (408) 765-8080
Fax: (408) 765-9904
Toll Free: (800) 628-8686
E-mail: programs@intel.com
Web Site: www.intel.com
Approx. Rev.: $43,623,000,000
Approx. Number Employees: 82,500
Year Founded: 1968
Business Description:
Electronics & Semiconductors Mfr
S.I.C.: 3674; 3572; 7372
N.A.I.C.S.: 334413; 334112; 511210
Import Export
Advertising Expenditures: $1,800,000,000
Media: 2-3-5-6-7-8-9-10-13-15-16-19-20-22-24-25
Distr.: Intl.; Natl.
Budget Set: Annually
Personnel:
Jane E. Shaw *(Chm)*
Paul S. Otellini *(Pres & CEO)*
Stacy J. Smith *(CFO & Sr VP-Fin)*
Douglas F. Busch *(Sr VP & COO)*
James N. Johnson *(CIO & VP)*
Deborah Conrad *(CMO & VP)*
Andy D. Bryant *(Chief Admin Officer, Exec VP-Tech, Mfg & Enterprise Svcs)*
Justin R. Rattner *(CTO, VP & Dir-Labs)*
Arvind Sodhani *(Pres-Intel Capital & Exec VP)*
David Patterson *(Pres-Intel Federal LLC)*
A. Douglas Melamed *(Gen Counsel & Sr VP)*
Ravi Jacob *(Treas & VP-Fin)*
Cary I. Klafter *(Sec, VP-Legal Corp Affairs & Dir-Corp Legal)*
David Perlmutter *(Exec VP & Gen Mgr-Architecture Grp)*
Robert J. Baker *(Sr VP, Gen Mgr-Tech & Mfg Grp)*
Renee J. James *(Sr VP, Gen Mgr-Software & Svcs Grp)*
Thomas M. Kilroy *(Sr VP & Gen Mgr-Sls & Mktg Grp)*
Brian M. Krzanich *(Sr VP & Gen Mgr-Mfg & Supply Chain)*
Patricia Murray *(Sr VP & Dir-HR)*
Damian Artt *(Sr VP-Worldwide Wind River Sls & Svcs)*
James Campbell *(VP-Fin-Enterprise Svcs & Controller)*
Robert B. Crooke *(VP & Gen Mgr-Bus Client Grp)*
Shmuel Eden *(VP & Gen Mgr-PC Client Grp)*
Ron Friedman *(VP & Gen Mgr-Mobile Microprocessor Grp)*
Gordon Graylish *(VP & Gen Mgr-Enterprise Solutions Sls)*
Thomas R. MacDonald *(VP & Gen Mgr)*
Jeffrey P. McCrea *(VP-Mobility Grp & Gen Mgr-Consumer PC Grp)*
Christian Morales *(VP-Sls, Gen Mgr-EMEA & Mktg Grp)*
Sunil R. Shenoy *(VP-Digital Enterprise Grp & Gen Mgr-Enterprise Microprocessor Grp)*
Kirk Skaugen *(VP & Gen Mgr-Datacenter & Connected Sys Grp)*
Craig C. Brown *(VP-Tech, Dir-Materials & Mfg Grp)*
Laura G. Crone *(VP-Sls Mktg & Dir-Global Accts)*
Rama K. Shukla *(VP-Mobility Grp & Dir-Platform Program Office)*
Richard G.A. Taylor *(VP & Dir-HR)*
Suzan A. Miller *(VP& Deputy Gen Counsel)*
Timothy G. Hendry *(VP-Tech & manfrg grp)*
Arthur W. Roehm *(VP-Sls)*
Jacklyn A. Sturm *(VP-Fin)*
Lorie Wigle *(Gen Mgr-Eco Tech Program)*
William James Adams, Jr. *(Dir-Creative Innovation)*
Antony Barton *(Dir-Bus Insights & Market Res)*
Yan A. Borodovsky *(Sr Fellow-Intel & Dir-Advanced Lithography)*
Julie Coppernoll *(Dir-Mktg)*
Richard L. Coulson *(Dir-I/O Architecture)*
Joe Curley *(Dir-Mktg-Data Center Grp)*
David Ginsberg *(Dir-Insights & Market Res)*
Vikas Jain *(Dir-Product Mgmt)*
Neal R. Mielke *(Dir-Reliability Methods)*
R. Ravichandran *(Dir-Sls-South Asia)*
Tony Salvador *(Dir-Experience Insights Lab)*
Tonya DeGance *(Sr Mgr-Entertainment Alliances)*
Kathleen Malone *(Sr Mgr-Media-Global)*
Karen Regis *(Mgr-Consumer Mktg)*
Laurie Koehler *(Mgr-Consumer Campaigns Activation)*
Bill MacKenzie *(Mgr-Comm)*
Jeff Reese *(Mgr-Interactive Promos)*
Joshua M. Walden *(Mgr)*
Brands & Products:
ANYPOINT
BUNNYPEOPLE
CELERON
CELERON INSIDE
CENTRINO
CENTRINO INSIDE
CORE INSIDE
DIALOGIC
ENHANCED INTEL SPEEDSTEP
ETHEREXPRESS
FLASHFILE
I960
INSTANTIP
INTEL
INTEL ATOM
INTEL ATOM INSIDE
INTEL CORE
INTEL CREATE & SHARE
INTEL INSIDE
INTEL NETBURST
INTEL NETMERGE
INTEL NETSTRUCTURE
INTEL SINGLEDRIVER
INTEL STRATAFLASH
INTEL VIIV
INTEL VPRO
INTEL XSCALE
INTEL386
INTEL486
INTELDX2
INTELDX4
INTELSX2
INTRU
ITANIUM
ITANIUM INSIDE
THE JOURNEY INSIDE
MCS
MMX
MOBILE INTEL
NEHALEM-EX
OPLUS
PDCHARM
PENTIUM
PENTIUM INSIDE
REALPORT
REALPORT2
SKOOOL
SOUND MARK
STORAGEEXPRESS
STRONGARM
TOKENEXPRESS
VIIV INSIDE
VPRO INSIDE
VTUNE
XEON
XEON INSIDE
XIRCOM
Advertising Agencies:
CMD
1631 NW Thurman St
Portland, OR 97209-2558
Tel.: (503) 223-6794
Fax: (503) 223-2430
— Laurie Michelotti *(Acct Exec)*

FD Americas Public Affairs
1101 K St NW 9th Fl
Washington, DC 20005
Tel.: (202) 346-8800
Fax: (202) 346-8804

MRM Worldwide
622 3rd Ave
New York, NY 10017-6707
Tel.: (646) 865-6230
Fax: (646) 865-6264
(Intel.com)

OMD Worldwide
195 Broadway
New York, NY 10007
Tel.: (212) 590-7100
Media Buying & Planning

Tribal DDB San Francisco
555 Market St Ste 500
San Francisco, CA 94105
Tel.: (415) 732-2200
Fax: (415) 732-2295

Universal McCann
100 33rd St 8th Fl
New York, NY 10001
Tel.: (212) 883-4700

Venables, Bell & Partners
201 Post St Ste 200
San Francisco, CA 94108
Tel.: (415) 288-3300
Fax: (415) 421-3683
(Creative)
The Chase

INTERNATIONAL BUSINESS EXCHANGE CORPORATION

Ste 330 1 Chisholm Trl
Round Rock, TX 78681-5094
Mailing Address:
PO Box 1240
Round Rock, TX 78680-1240
Tel.: (512) 310-2966
Fax: (512) 310-8113
E-mail: ibectx@aol.com
Web Site: www.ibectx.com
Approx. Sls.: $7,500,000
Approx. Number Employees: 30
Year Founded: 1979
Business Description:
Business Services
S.I.C.: 7812
N.A.I.C.S.: 512110
Advertising Expenditures: $585,500
Media: 2-7-9-13-25
Distr.: Intl.; Natl.
Budget Set: Feb.
Personnel:
Jeff Hamilton *(CEO)*

INTERNATIONAL COMPONENTS CORPORATION

215 Mccormick Dr
Bohemia, NY 11716
Tel.: (631) 952-9595
Fax: (631) 952-9597
Toll Free: (800) 645-9154
E-mail: oemsales@icc107.com
Web Site: www.icc107.com
Sales Range: $50-74.9 Million
Approx. Number Employees: 65
Year Founded: 1970
Business Description:
Electronic Parts & Equipment Mfr
S.I.C.: 3675; 5065
N.A.I.C.S.: 334414; 423690
Import Export
Media: 2-4-6-7-10-11-13-17
Distr.: Intl
Budget Set: Oct.-Nov.
Personnel:
Irwin Friedman *(Pres)*
Fredric Grossman *(VP-Mktg & Sls)*
Brands & Products:
IC
INTERCAP
INTERVOX

INTERNATIONAL COMPONENTS CORPORATION

4 Westbrook Corporate Ctr Ste 900
Westchester, IL 60154
Tel.: (708) 836-3800
Fax: (708) 836-3801
Toll Free: (800) 210-1431
Toll Free: (800) 651-3087

Key to Media (For complete agency information see *The Advertising Red Books-Agencies* edition):
1. Bus. Publs. 2. Cable T.V. 3. Catalogs & Directories. 4. Co-op Adv. 5. Consumer Mags. 6. D.M. to Bus. Estab.7. D.M. to Consumers 8. Daily Newsp. 9. Exhibits/Trade Shows 10. Foreign 11. Infomercial 12. Internet Adv.13. Multimedia 14. Network Radio 15. Network T.V. 16. Newsp. Distr. Mags. 17. Other 18. Outdoor (Posters, Transit) 19. Point of Purchase20. Premiums, Novelties 21. Product Samples 22. Special Events Mktg. 23. Spot Radio 24. Spot T.V. 25. Weekly Newsp. 26. Yellow Page Adv.

International Components Corporation — (Continued)

E-mail: iccsales@iccus.com
Web Site: www.iccus.com
Approx. Number Employees: 750
Year Founded: 1967
Business Description:
Mfr. of Power Systems for Cellular Phones, Communications, Power Tools, Computer & Other Consumer Products Companies
S.I.C.: 3699
N.A.I.C.S.: 335999
Media: 4
Personnel:
Stephen M. McClure *(Pres & CEO)*
Brands & Products:
ELPAC POWER SYSTEMS
INTERNATIONAL COMPONENTS

INTERNATIONAL ELECTRONICS, INC.

(Sub. of Linear LLC)
1950 Camino Vida Roble Ste 150
Carlsbad, CA 92008
Tel.: (760) 438-7000
Fax: (800) 468-1340
Toll Free: (800) 421-1587
Web Site: www.ieib.com
Approx. Sls.: $14,120,979
Approx. Number Employees: 64
Year Founded: 1977
Business Description:
Electronic Access Control Equipment & Browser-Managed Security Platforms Distr & Mfr
S.I.C.: 3669; 3699; 3829
N.A.I.C.S.: 334290; 334519; 335999
Advertising Expenditures: $122,011
Media: 5-7-10
Personnel:
Jim Lynch *(Dir-Product Mgmt)*
Brands & Products:
BIOREAD
DOOR-GARD
DUOPROX
EZ-REX
GLASS-GARD
HUBMAX
IEI
ISOPROX
MAGCRD
MAGHICO
MINIMAX
POWERGARD
POWERKEY
PROXCARD
PROXKEY
PROX.PAD
PROXPOINT PLUS
PROXPRO
SECURED SERIES
SS-MINIPRO
SS-NT MAXIPRO
SS-PROXPOINTBK
SS-PROXPOINTGY
SS-PROXPRO-GY
SS-THINLINE
THINLINE
TRI-GARD
VOICEKEY
WIEGAND

INTERNATIONAL RECTIFIER CORPORATION

101 N Sepulveda Blvd
El Segundo, CA 90245
Tel.: (310) 726-8000
Fax: (310) 322-3332
E-mail: americas-tac@irf.com
Web Site: www.irf.com
Approx. Rev.: $1,176,577,000
Approx. Number Employees: 4,920
Year Founded: 1947
Business Description:
Power Management Semiconductors for Commercial, Industrial, Defense & Aerospace Use
S.I.C.: 3674
N.A.I.C.S.: 334413
Advertising Expenditures: $3,000,000
Media: 2-4-7-10-13-20
Distr.: Natl.
Personnel:
Richard J. Dahl *(Chm)*
Oleg Khaykin *(Pres & CEO)*
Ilan Daskal *(CFO & Exec VP)*
Michael Barrow *(COO & Exec VP)*
Timothy Bixler *(Gen Counsel, Sec & VP)*
Adam White *(Sr VP-Sls-Global)*
Chris Toth *(Exec Dir-IR)*
Brands & Products:
ACCELERATOR
BOSFET
CHIPSWITCH
COPPERSTRAP
DIRECTFET
DIRECTFETKY
FETKY
FLIPFET
FLIPKY
HEXFET
HEXFRED
HEXSENSE
IMOTION
INTERO
IPOWIR
MEGA-RAD
POWIRTAB
POWIRTRAIN
POWRIFSAFE
QUIETIR
SAFEIR
SMALLIR
SMARTRECTIFIER
SURECHIP
WARP SPEED
XPHASE

INTERPOINT CORPORATION

(Unit of Crane Electronics Group)
10301 Willows Rd Ne
Redmond, WA 98052
Mailing Address:
PO Box 97005
Redmond, WA 98073-9705
Tel.: (425) 882-3100
Fax: (425) 556-5061
Toll Free: (800) 822-8782
E-mail: power@crane-eg.com
Web Site: www.interpoint.com
Sales Range: $75-99.9 Million
Approx. Number Employees: 250
Year Founded: 1969
Business Description:
Power-Handling Products & Custom Microelectronics Mfr
S.I.C.: 3679; 3572
N.A.I.C.S.: 334419; 334112
Import Export
Media: 2-4-10-13-20
Distr.: Intl.; Natl.
Personnel:
Vince Piscopo *(Exec Dir-Sls-N America)*
Simon Abel *(Dir-Sls-Intl)*

INTERSIL CORPORATION

1001 Murphy Ranch Rd Ste 1
Milpitas, CA 95035-7912
Tel.: (408) 432-8888
Fax: (408) 434-5351
Toll Free: (888) INTERSIL
E-mail: investor@intersil.com
Web Site: www.intersil.com
Approx. Rev.: $822,400,000
Approx. Number Employees: 1,762
Year Founded: 1999
Business Description:
High Performance Analog Integrated Circuits Designer & Mfr
S.I.C.: 7389; 3674
N.A.I.C.S.: 541410; 334413
Advertising Expenditures: $4,700,000
Media: 2-7-8-10-13-17-23
Distr.: Natl.
Budget Set: Oct.
Personnel:
Gary E. Gist *(Chm)*
David B. Bell *(Pres & CEO)*
Jonathan Kennedy *(CFO & Sr VP)*
Thomas T. Tokos *(Gen Counsel, Sec & VP)*
Susan Hardman *(Sr VP-Analog Mixed Signal Grp)*
Vern Kelley *(Sr VP-HR)*
David Loftus *(Sr VP-Sls & Corp Mktg-Worldwide)*
Peter Oaklander *(Sr VP-Power Mgmt Grp)*
Sagar Pushpala *(Sr VP-Ops & Tech-Worldwide)*
Von Juni *(VP & Gen Mgr-Product)*
Michael Althar *(VP & Gen Mgr)*
Andrew Rhind *(VP & Gen Mgr)*
Paul Sferrazza *(VP & Gen Mgr)*
Terry Brophy *(VP-IT)*
Roberto Magnifico *(VP-Sls-Europe)*
Masato Nozaki *(VP-Sls-Japan)*
Adam Latham *(Dir-Corp Mktg)*
Chris Ludeman *(Sr Mgr-Mktg)*
Peter Blumenroether *(Sr Mktg Mgr)*
Kathryn Tucker *(Mktg Mgr-Video Products)*
Randy Pitts *(Mgr-Mktg)*
Debbie Timmerman *(Mgr-Mktg)*
Brands & Products:
BLOCK LOCK
COMMLINK
DYNAMIC-VID
ELANTEC
ENDURA
THE EVOLUTION OF ANALOG
FGA
INTELLITRIP
INTERSIL
ISIM
MIGHTYMUX
R3 TECHNOLOGY
SYNCHROFET
THERMAGUARD

INVISIBLE FENCE, INC.

(Sub. of Radio Systems Corporation)
10427 Electric Ave
Knoxville, TN 37932
Tel.: (610) 651-0999
Tel.: (865) 777-5404
Toll Free: (866) 804-1250
E-mail: webmaster@invisiblefence.com
Web Site: www.invisiblefence.com
Approx. Sls.: $12,400,000
Approx. Number Employees: 200
Year Founded: 1973
Business Description:
Electrical Equipment & Supplies
S.I.C.: 3699
N.A.I.C.S.: 335999
Brands & Products:
INVISIBLE FENCE
Advertising Agency:
St. John & Partners
5220 Belfort Rd Ste 400
Jacksonville, FL 32256-6017
Tel.: (904) 281-2500
Fax: (904) 281-0030

IPC SYSTEMS, INC.

(Sub. of IPC Systems Holdings Corp.)
Harborside Fin Ctr 1500 Plz 10 3 2nd St 15th Fl
Jersey City, NJ 07311
Tel.: (201) 253-2000
Fax: (201) 253-2361
Web Site: www.ipc.com
Approx. Rev.: $343,000,000
Approx. Number Employees: 900
Year Founded: 1998
Business Description:
Voice Over IP Technology & Integrated Network Management Services
S.I.C.: 7373; 4899; 7379
N.A.I.C.S.: 541512; 517910; 541519
Media: 10
Personnel:
Tim Whelan *(Pres, COO & Exec VP)*
Lance Boxer *(CEO)*
William McHale *(CFO & Sr VP)*
John McSherry *(Chief Admin Officer, Gen Counsel & Sr VP)*
David Brown *(Sr VP-Ops-Network Svcs)*
Marianne Leitch *(Sr VP-Global Svc Delivery)*
Pete Simms *(Sr VP-Global Trading Systems Ops)*
Tim Carmody *(VP-Global Engrg-Network Svcs)*
Brands & Products:
IPC
Advertising Agency:
Stein Rogan + Partners
432 Park Ave S
New York, NY 10016-8013
Tel.: (212) 213-1112
Fax: (212) 779-7305

IPCS, INC.

(Sub. of Sprint Nextel Corp.)
1901 N Roselle Rd Ste 500
Schaumburg, IL 60195
Tel.: (847) 885-2833
Fax: (847) 885-7125
E-mail: corporateinquires@ipcswirelessinc.com
Web Site: www.ipcswirelessinc.com
Approx. Rev.: $525,517,000
Approx. Number Employees: 535
Year Founded: 2000
Business Description:
Holding Company; Wireless Communications Products & Services
S.I.C.: 6719; 4812
N.A.I.C.S.: 551112; 517212

Key to Media (For complete agency information see *The Advertising Red Books-Agencies* edition):
1. Bus. Publs. 2. Cable T.V. 3. Catalogs & Directories. 4. Co-op Adv. 5. Consumer Mags. 6. D.M. to Bus. Estab.7. D.M. to Consumers 8. Daily Newsp. 9. Exhibits/Trade Shows 10. Foreign 11. Infomercial 12. Internet Adv.13. Multimedia 14. Network Radio 15. Network T.V. 16. Newsp. Distr. Mags. 17. Other 18. Outdoor (Posters, Transit) 19. Point of Purchase20. Premiums, Novelties 21. Product Samples 22. Special Events Mktg. 23. Spot Radio 24. Spot T.V. 25. Weekly Newsp. 26. Yellow Page Adv.

Advertising Expenditures: $16,200,000
Personnel:
John J. Peterman *(Sr VP-Sls)*

IPMOBILENET, INC.
16842 Von Karmen Ave Ste 200
Irvine, CA 92606
Tel.: (949) 417-4590
Fax: (949) 417-4591
Toll Free: (800) 348-1477
E-mail: ipmninfo@ipmn.com
Web Site: www.ipmn.com
Business Description:
Wireless Data Solutions
S.I.C.: 3669
N.A.I.C.S.: 334290
Media: 13
Personnel:
Frank Romanin *(Pres & CEO)*
Eric Tanner *(COO)*
Brian Purcell *(VP-Sls & Mktg)*
Brands & Products:
DATALINK
INTELLIGENT DIVERSITY RECEPTION
IP SERIES
IPMOBILENET
XPRESSNET

IRIDEX CORPORATION
1212 Terra Bella Ave
Mountain View, CA 94043-1824
Tel.: (650) 940-4700
Tel.: (650) 962-8100
Fax: (650) 940-4710
E-mail: info@iridex.com
Web Site: www.iridex.com
Approx. Rev.: $43,694,000
Approx. Number Employees: 145
Year Founded: 1989
Business Description:
Semiconductor-Based Laser Systems for Ophthalmology, Dermatology & Research
S.I.C.: 3845
N.A.I.C.S.: 334510
Advertising Expenditures: $307,000
Media: 2-7-10-16
Personnel:
Theodore A. Boutacoff *(Founder & CTO)*
William M. Moore *(Chm)*
Dominik Beck *(Pres & CEO)*
James H. Mackaness *(CFO)*
Eduardo Arias *(Sr VP-Intl Sls & Bus Dev)*
Brands & Products:
AURA-I
COOLSPOT
CW-PULSE
DIOLITE
DIOPEXY
EASYFIT
ENDOPROBE
FIBERCHECK
G-PROBE
GEMINI
IQ 577
IQ 810
IRIDEX
LYRA-I
MICRORUPTOR
OCULIGHT
OTOPROBE
SCANLITE
SMARTWARE
SYMPHONY
TRI-MODE
TRUECW
TRUFOCUS
VARILITE
VENUS-I

ITW PAKTRON
(Sub. of Illinois Tool Works Inc.)
1205 McConville Rd
Lynchburg, VA 24502-4535
Tel.: (434) 239-6941
Fax: (434) 239-4730
E-mail: itwpaktron@paktron.com
Web Site: www.paktron.com
Sales Range: $25-49.9 Million
Approx. Number Employees: 30
Year Founded: 1950
Business Description:
Film Capacitor Mfr
S.I.C.: 3679; 3675
N.A.I.C.S.: 334419; 334414
Export
Media: 7-10-11
Personnel:
Ian Clelland *(Gen Mgr)*
Tom Saunders *(Mgr-Tech Sls)*
Brands & Products:
ANGSTOR
CAPSTICK
QUENCHARC
SURFILM

JACO ELECTRONICS, INC.
145 Oser Ave
Hauppauge, NY 11788
Tel.: (631) 273-5500
Fax: (631) 273-5599
Toll Free: (800) 645-5112
E-mail: info@jacoelect.com
Web Site: www.jacoelectronics.com
Sales Range: $150-199.9 Million
Approx. Number Employees: 100
Year Founded: 1961
Business Description:
Electronic Components & Display Products Distr
S.I.C.: 5065
N.A.I.C.S.: 423690
Export
Media: 2-6
Budget Set: June
Personnel:
Joel H. Girsky *(Chm, Pres, CEO & Treas)*
Jeffrey D. Gash *(CFO, Exec VP-Fin & Sec)*
Robert Salvacchio *(Exec VP)*
Leslie Girsky *(Reg VP & VP-Sls)*
Jay Guthrie *(Dir-Mfg)*
Brands & Products:
JACO

JAN WIRELESS LLC
2945 E Bay Dr Ste C
Largo, FL 33771
Tel.: (727) 216-6975
E-mail: janwirelessfl@gmail.com
Web Site:
www.eastbayboostmobile.com
Business Description:
Mobile Broadband Services
N.A.I.C.S.: 517212
Media: 16-20-29
Personnel:
Jim Cunningham *(Owner)*
Sheila Eakes *(Mgr)*

JDR MICRODEVICES INC.
1850 S 10th St
San Jose, CA 95112
Tel.: (408) 494-1400
Fax: (408) 494-1420
Toll Free: (800) 538-5000
E-mail: sales@jdr.com
Web Site: www.jdr.com
E-Mail For Key Personnel:
Sales Director: sales@jdr.com
Approx. Number Employees: 35
Year Founded: 1979
Business Description:
Direct Marketer of Electronic Components
S.I.C.: 5961; 5065
N.A.I.C.S.: 454113; 423690
Media: 4-7-8-13
Brands & Products:
JDR
MCT

JOHANSON MANUFACTURING CORPORATION
301 Rockaway Vly Rd
Boonton, NJ 07005
Mailing Address:
PO Box 60
Memphis, TN 38101-0060
Tel.: (973) 334-2676
Fax: (973) 334-2954
E-mail: jmcsales@johansonmfg.com
Web Site: www.johansonmfg.com
Sales Range: $25-49.9 Million
Approx. Number Employees: 246
Year Founded: 1945
Business Description:
Trimmer Capacitors & Microwave Tuning Elements Mfr & Supplier
S.I.C.: 3675
N.A.I.C.S.: 334414
Import Export
Media: 2-4-7-10-11
Distr.: Natl.
Budget Set: Dec.
Personnel:
Nancy Johanson *(Owner)*
Brands & Products:
CERA-TRIM
DYNA-TRIM
EXACTUNE
EXACTUNE PM
GIGA-TRIM
POSI-TORQUE
RACK MOUNT VAC
RACK MOUNT VAC-PAK
SEAL-TRIM
THIN-TRIM

JUNO LIGHTING GROUP
(Sub. of Juno Lighting, Inc.)
12001 Exit 5 Pkwy
Fishers, IN 46038-7940
Tel.: (317) 849-1233
Fax: (317) 576-8006
E-mail: info@indylighting.net
Web Site: www.indylighting.net
Approx. Number Employees: 60
Year Founded: 1970
Business Description:
Mfr of Light Fixtures
S.I.C.: 3646
N.A.I.C.S.: 335122
Personnel:
Bill Morreal *(VP-Mktg)*
Advertising Agencies:
Advertising & Promotional Services, Inc. (Adpro, Inc.)
(d/b/a ADPRO, INC)
6 S 503 Wildwood Dr
Aurora, IL 60506
Tel.: (630) 801-9900
Fax: (630) 801-9663
Toll Free: (866) 895-2535

Carmichael Lynch
110 N 5th St
Minneapolis, MN 55403
Tel.: (612) 334-6000
Fax: (612) 334-6090
— Steve Solmonson *(Acct Exec-Juno Lighting)*

JVC U.S.A.
(Sub. of JVC America Corp.)
1700 Valley Rd
Wayne, NJ 07470
Tel.: (973) 317-5000
Fax: (973) 317-5110
Toll Free: (800) 247-3608
E-mail: webmaster@jvc.com
Web Site: www.jvc.com
Approx. Number Employees: 500
Year Founded: 1968
Business Description:
Household Audio & Video Equipment & Blank Media Distr
S.I.C.: 7699; 5045
N.A.I.C.S.: 811310; 423430
Import
Media: 6-10-18-19-22
Distr.: Natl.
Budget Set: Various
Personnel:
Hiro Ishizuka *(Pres & CEO)*
Craig Geiger *(Exec VP)*
Robert Mueller *(Exec VP)*
Karl Bearnarth *(Sr VP-Mktg)*
Dave Walton *(Asst VP-Mktg Comm)*
Tim Tokita *(Gen Mgr)*
Edgar Shane *(Gen Mgr-Engrg)*
Terry Shea *(Gen Mgr-Corp Comm)*
Gary Klasmeier *(Product Mgr-D-ILA Projectors)*
Lee Thompson *(Mgr-Mktg & Comm-Natl)*
Advertising Agency:
E2AMP
5354 Denny Ave Unit 126
North Hollywood, CA 91601
Tel.: (818) 252-0090
Fax: (818) 824-4904

KASTLE SYSTEMS LLC
1501 Wilson Blvd
Arlington, VA 22209
Tel.: (703) 528-8800
Fax: (703) 528-2103
Toll Free: (800) 448-3722
Web Site: www.kastle.com
E-Mail For Key Personnel:
Sales Director: mshortal@kastle.com
Approx. Number Employees: 450
Year Founded: 1972
Business Description:
Designer, Retailer, Installer & Servicer Electronic Security Systems
S.I.C.: 7382
N.A.I.C.S.: 561621
Export
Media: 2-7
Distr.: Natl.

Key to Media (For complete agency information see *The Advertising Red Books-Agencies* edition):
1. Bus. Publs. 2. Cable T.V. 3. Catalogs & Directories. 4. Co-op Adv. 5. Consumer Mags. 6. D.M. to Bus. Estab.7. D.M. to Consumers
8. Daily Newsp. 9. Exhibits/Trade Shows 10. Foreign 11. Infomercial 12. Internet Adv.13. Multimedia 14. Network Radio
15. Network T.V. 16. Newsp. Distr. Mags. 17. Other 18. Outdoor (Posters, Transit) 19. Point of Purchase20. Premiums, Novelties
21. Product Samples 22. Special Events Mktg. 23. Spot Radio 24. Spot T.V. 25. Weekly Newsp. 26. Yellow Page Adv.

Kastle Systems LLC — (Continued)

Personnel:
Piyush Sodha *(Co-Chm & CEO)*
R. Moleneri *(VP-New Prods)*
Peter DeVita *(Mgr-Trng)*
Andrea Steierman *(Mgr-Customer Svcs)*
Brands & Products:
KASTLE SYSTEMS
SECURITY.HANDHELD.

KEMET CORPORATION

2835 KEMET Way
Simpsonville, SC 29681
Mailing Address:
PO Box 5928
Greenville, SC 29606
Tel.: (864) 963-6300
Fax: (864) 963-6322
E-mail: investorrelations@kemet.com
Web Site: www.kemet.com
Approx. Sls.: $1,018,488,000
Approx. Number Employees: 11,000
Year Founded: 1990
Business Description:
Tantalum & Multilayer Ceramic Capacitors & Solid Aluminum Capacitors Mfr
S.I.C.: 3675; 5064
N.A.I.C.S.: 334414; 423620
Import Export
Advertising Expenditures: $250,000
Media: 2-13
Personnel:
Frank G. Brandenberg *(Chm)*
Per-Olof Loof *(CEO)*
William M. Lowe, Jr. *(CFO & Exec VP)*
Daniel E. LaMorte *(CIO & VP)*
Philip M. Lessner *(CTO & Sr VP)*
Richard M. Vosburgh *(Chief Talent Dev Officer & VP-Talent & Org Effectiveness)*
R. James Assaf *(Gen Counsel, Sec & VP)*
Conrado Hinojosa *(Exec VP-Tantalum Bus Grp)*
Charles C. Meeks, Jr. *(Exec VP-Ceramic, Film & Electrolytics Bus Grp)*
Robert Arguelles *(Sr VP-Operational Excellence & Quality)*
Marc Kotelon *(Sr VP-Global Sls)*
James A. Bruorton *(VP-Global Distr Sls)*
Richard Curley *(VP-Sls-EMEA)*
John J. Drabik *(VP-Sls-Americas)*
Donald Lung *(VP-Sls-Asia Pacific)*
Larry C. McAdams *(VP-HR)*
Daniel F. Persico *(VP-Strategic Mktg & Bus Dev)*
Dean W. Dimke *(Dir-Corp & Investor Comm)*
John Prymak *(Dir-Advanced Applications)*
Stanley Garrett *(Product Mgr-Technical)*
Bill Sloka *(Product Mgr)*
Jayson Young *(Product Mgr-Tantalum & Aluminum)*
Corey Antoniades *(Mgr-Technical Mktg)*
Brands & Products:
FE-CAP
FIT
HI-REL
KEMET
KEMET CHARGED
Advertising Agencies:
Athorn, Clark & Partners
38 E 32nd St 11th Fl
New York, NY 10016
Tel.: (212) 457-6140
Fax: (212) 457-6161

AutoCom Associates
74 W Long Lk Rd Ste 103
Bloomfield Hills, MI 48304-2770
Tel.: (248) 647-8621
Fax: (248) 642-2110

KENWOOD USA CORPORATION

(Sub. of Kenwood Corporation)
2201 E Dominguez St
Long Beach, CA 90801
Mailing Address:
PO Box 22745
Long Beach, CA 90801-5745
Tel.: (310) 639-9000
Fax: (310) 604-4488
Telex: 230-678758
Web Site: www.kenwoodusa.com
Approx. Number Employees: 300
Year Founded: 1960
Business Description:
Consumer Audio Electronics Mfr & Distr
S.I.C.: 7371
N.A.I.C.S.: 541511
Import Export
Advertising Expenditures: $8,000,000
Media: 1-3-5-6-10-11-13-19-23-25
Distr.: Intl.; Natl.
Budget Set: Mar.
Personnel:
Ryo Mizuhara *(Pres)*
Mark Jasin *(Sr VP & Gen Mgr)*
Keith Lehmann *(Sr VP-Consumer Electronics Sector)*
David Hoag *(Dir-Sls & Consumer Electronics Div)*
Tony Mercado *(Mgr-Mktg Dev)*

KESTER, INC.

(Sub. of Illinois Tool Works Inc.)
800 W Thorndale
Itasca, IL 60143
Tel.: (630) 616-4000
Fax: (630) 616-4044
Fax: (847) 699-5548 (Sls)
Toll Free: (800) 2KESTER
E-mail: customerservice@kester.com
Web Site: www.kester.com
E-Mail For Key Personnel:
President: rksavage@kester.com
Sales Range: $150-199.9 Million
Approx. Number Employees: 600
Year Founded: 1899
Business Description:
Solder & Solder Derivative Products Mfr
S.I.C.: 3339
N.A.I.C.S.: 331419
Media: 2-4-5-10-11-13
Distr.: Intl.; Natl.
Personnel:
Carmelle Giblin *(VP & Gen Mgr)*
Brands & Products:
BIO-KLEEN
KESTER LEAD-FREE SOLUTIONS
SE-CURE
SOLDERFORMS
ULTRA-SPHERES
ULTRAPURE

KEVLIN CORPORATION

(Sub. of Cobham Defence Systems Division)
596 Lowell St
Methuen, MA 01844
Tel.: (978) 557-2400
Fax: (978) 557-2800
Web Site: www.kevlin.com
Approx. Number Employees: 75
Year Founded: 1949
Business Description:
Microwave Devices for Uses in Military Commercial Radar Systems Design & Mfr
S.I.C.: 3679; 8111
N.A.I.C.S.: 334419; 541110
Export
Advertising Expenditures: $1,500,000
Media: 2-4-7-10-17
Distr.: Intl.; Natl.
Budget Set: Apr.
Personnel:
Andrew P. Pellerin *(Pres)*
Brands & Products:
IDA
KEVLIN MICROWAVE
MAST MICROWAVE
Advertising Agency:
M.R. Associates
162 Great Road
Acton, MA 01720
Tel.: (978) 263-0578
(Rotary Joints)

KIRKWOOD HOLDING, INC.

1239 Rockside Rd
Pampa, OH 44134
Tel.: (216) 267-6200
Fax: (216) 362-3812
E-mail: sales@kirkwood-ind.com
Web Site: www.kirkwood-ind.com
E-Mail For Key Personnel:
Sales Director: sales@kirkwood-ind.com
Approx. Number Employees: 200
Year Founded: 1944
Business Description:
Motor Commutators, Carbon Brushes, Springs & Related Products Mfr
S.I.C.: 3621; 3299
N.A.I.C.S.: 335312; 327999
Export
Advertising Expenditures: $200,000
Media: 2-4-7-10
Distr.: Natl.
Personnel:
L. Thomas Koechley *(Pres)*
Brands & Products:
BARLOK
CORTEM
KIRKWOOD
NIPPERT

KLIPSCH GROUP, INC.

(Sub. of Audiovox Corporation)
3502 Woodview Trace Ste 200
Indianapolis, IN 46268
Tel.: (317) 860-8100
Fax: (317) 860-9170
Toll Free: (800) 544-1482
E-mail: info@klipsch.com
Web Site: www.klipsch.com
Approx. Number Employees: 300
Year Founded: 1946
Business Description:
Audio Equipment Mfr & Marketer
S.I.C.: 3651
N.A.I.C.S.: 334310
Import Export
Media: 6-7-19-26
Distr.: Intl.; Natl.
Budget Set: May
Personnel:
Fred S. Klipsch *(Chm & CEO)*
Judy L. Klipsch *(Vice Chm)*
T.Paul Jacobs *(Pres & COO)*
Fred Farrar *(CFO & Treas)*
David P. Kelley *(Exec VP-Sls, North America & Asia Pacific)*
Michael F. Kilpsch *(Chief Legal Counsel & Exec VP-Global Supply)*
Michael Klipsch *(Chief Legal Counsel & Exec VP-Global Supply)*
Steve Klipsch *(Sr VP-Organizational Strategies)*
Nancy Mills *(Sr VP-Fin)*
Jeff Baer *(VP-Finance)*
Mark S. Casavant *(VP-Product Dev)*
Jim Garrett *(Dir-Mktg)*
Jill Escol *(Dir-Mktg)*
Jim Hunter *(Mgr-Engrg Ops)*
Brands & Products:
AURUM
BELLE KLIPSCH
FLUX TUBE
KI-272
KI-362
KLF-30
KLIPSCH
KLIPSCHORN
KM-2
KP-110
KP-250
KP-262
KPT-684
KPT-8001
KSM-12
KSM-15
KSM-8
KSW-12
KSW-15
KW-120-THX
LA SCALA
MICROTRACTRIX
MONSTER CABLE
P-10
PALLADIUM
PROMEDIA
REFERENCE
RS-10
SCR-1
SCR-2
SCR-3
SCW-2
SYNERGY SERIES
THX ULTRA

KNOLOGY INC.

1241 OG Skinner Dr
West Point, GA 31833-1789
Tel.: (706) 645-3000
Fax: (706) 642-0148
E-mail: mike-roddy@knology.com
Web Site: www.knology.com
Approx. Rev.: $459,546,000
Approx. Number Employees: 1,846
Business Description:
Cable, Phone & Internet Services
S.I.C.: 4812; 4813; 4841; 4899; 7375
N.A.I.C.S.: 517211; 515210; 517110; 517910; 518111
Advertising Expenditures: $7,655,000
Media: 7-8-13-15-18-22-23-24-25
Personnel:
Rodger L. Johnson *(Chm & CEO)*

Key to Media (For complete agency information see *The Advertising Red Books-Agencies* edition):
1. Bus. Publs. 2. Cable T.V. 3. Catalogs & Directories. 4. Co-op Adv. 5. Consumer Mags. 6. D.M. to Bus. Estab.7. D.M. to Consumers 8. Daily Newsp. 9. Exhibits/Trade Shows 10. Foreign 11. Infomercial 12. Internet Adv.13. Multimedia 14. Network Radio 15. Network T.V. 16. Newsp. Distr. Mags. 17. Other 18. Outdoor (Posters, Transit) 19. Point of Purchase20. Premiums, Novelties 21. Product Samples 22. Special Events Mktg. 23. Spot Radio 24. Spot T.V. 25. Weekly Newsp. 26. Yellow Page Adv.

M. Todd Holt *(Pres)*
Robert K. Mills *(CFO)*
Chad S. Wachter *(Gen Counsel, Sec & VP)*
Bret T. Mccants *(Exec VP-Ops)*
Weldon A. Feightner *(VP-Reg Ops)*
Anthony J. Palermo *(VP-Mktg)*
Richard D. Perkins *(VP-IT)*
Brad M. Vanacore *(VP-HR)*
Jason Clabo *(Gen Mgr-Augusta)*
Lee Endicott *(Gen Mgr-Charleston)*
Wade Lescord *(Mgr-Bus Sls-Charleston)*

KORRY ELECTRONICS CO.

(Sub. of Esterline Technologies Corporation)
11910 Beverly Park Rd
Everett, WA 98204
Tel.: (206) 281-1300
Fax: (425) 297-9876
Toll Free: (800) 257-8921
Web Site: www.korry.com
Sales Range: $150-199.9 Million
Approx. Number Employees: 580
Year Founded: 1989
Business Description:
Lighted Pushbutton Switches & Data Entry Panels Mfr
S.I.C.: 3613
N.A.I.C.S.: 335313
Media: 10
Personnel:
Dan McFeeley *(Pres)*
Robert Jacques *(VP-Sls)*
Brands & Products:
KORRY

KOSS CORPORATION

4129 N Port Washington Rd
Milwaukee, WI 53212
Tel.: (414) 964-5000
Fax: (414) 964-8615
Toll Free: (800) 872-5677
E-mail: customersupport@koss.com
Web Site: www.koss.com/
E-Mail For Key Personnel:
President: mjkoss@koss.com
Marketing Director: jmccurdy@koss.com
Approx. Sls.: $41,518,135
Approx. Number Employees: 65
Year Founded: 1953
Business Description:
Stereo Headphones & Accessories Designer, Mfr & Retailer
S.I.C.: 3651; 3661
N.A.I.C.S.: 334310; 334210
Import Export
Advertising Expenditures: $57,000
Media: 1-5-10-11-19-21
Distr.: Intl.; Natl.
Budget Set: Apr.
Personnel:
John C. Koss *(Chm)*
Michael J. Koss *(Vice Chm, Pres, CEO & COO)*
David D. Smith *(CFO, Sec & Exec VP)*
John C. Koss, Jr. *(VP-Sls)*
Cheryl Mike *(VP-HR)*
Brands & Products:
COBALT
FUN 'N FASHION
HOLD-A-PHONE
KOSS
NXSET
PLUG
POP GLOSS
PORTAPRO
QUIET ZONE 2000
SPORTAPRO
Advertising Agency:
Eichenbaum/Associates, Inc.
219 N Milwaukee St
Milwaukee, WI 53202-5818
Tel.: (414) 225-0011
Fax: (414) 225-0022

KRELL INDUSTRIES, INC.

45 Connair Rd
Orange, CT 06477-3650
Tel.: (203) 799-9954
Fax: (203) 799-9796
Fax: (203) 891-2028 (Sales)
E-mail: krell@krellonline.com
Web Site: www.krellonline.com
Approx. Number Employees: 38
Year Founded: 1980
Business Description:
Mfr. of Audio Equipment Including Amplifiers, Preamplifiers, Compact Disc Players, DVD Players, Surround Sound Processors, Digital-to-Analog Converters & Loudspeakers
S.I.C.: 3651; 5731
N.A.I.C.S.: 334310; 443112
Media: 2-4-5-6-10-13
Personnel:
Peter Mackay *(VP-Sls & Mktg-Intl)*
Bill McKiegan *(VP-Sls-US)*
Brands & Products:
CAST
CLASS A
KAV
KRELL
LAT
MASTER SERIES
SUSTAINED PLATEAU BIASING

KULICKE & SOFFA INDUSTRIES, INC.

1005 Virginia Dr
Fort Washington, PA 19034
Tel.: (215) 784-6000
Fax: (215) 784-6001
E-mail: investors@kns.com
Web Site: www.kns.com
Approx. Rev.: $762,784,000
Approx. Number Employees: 2,250
Year Founded: 1951
Business Description:
Semiconductor Wire Bonding Assembly Equipment Mfr
S.I.C.: 3559
N.A.I.C.S.: 333295
Export
Media: 4-7-11-13-17-25-26
Personnel:
MacDonell Roehm, Jr. *(Chm)*
Bruno Guilmart *(CEO)*
Jonathan H. Chou *(CFO)*
Clay Miller *(CIO & Sr VP-Shared Resources)*
Christian Rheault *(Sr VP-Bus Ops)*
Charles Salmons *(Sr VP)*
Brands & Products:
ACCUBUMP
ANALYZER
AREA ARRAY
ATLAS
AUTOCAD
BLADEPRO
CIC
CUPRA
DURAPLUS
ENDURO
HUB
KNET LT
KULICKE & SOFFA
MAXUMPLUS
NEXXUS
NOSWEEP
NOVA
NU-TEK
OZ TEK
PREMIER
QUATRIX
RADIX
SIGMA
SILICON
SPEEDTIP
WAFERPRO

KVH INDUSTRIES INC

50 Enterprise Ctr
Middletown, RI 02842
Tel.: (401) 847-3327
Fax: (401) 849-0045
E-mail: info@kvh.com
Web Site: www.kvh.com
Approx. Sls.: $112,242,794
Approx. Number Employees: 390
Year Founded: 1981
Business Description:
Mobile Satellite Communications Products Developer, Mfr & Marketer
S.I.C.: 3663; 3812
N.A.I.C.S.: 334220; 334511
Advertising Expenditures: $2,171,000
Media: 7-8-10
Personnel:
Martin A. Kits van Heyningen *(Chm, Pres & CEO)*
Arent H. Kits van Heyningen *(Chief Scientist)*
Patrick J. Spratt *(CFO)*
Robert Balog *(Sr VP-Engrg)*
Brent Bruun *(Sr VP-Sls & Bus Dev-Global)*
James S. Dodez *(VP-Mktg & Strategic Plng)*
Vivian Quenet *(VP-Sls-Asia Pacific)*
Christopher Watson *(Dir-Mktg)*
Brands & Products:
ACTIVEFIBER
AUTOCOMP
AZIMUTH
C100
DATASCOPE
E-CORE
ETRAC
GYROTRAC
INMARSAT
KVH
QUADRO
SAILCOMP
T-FOG
TACNAV
TACNAV II
TACNAV M100 GMENS
TACNAV TLS
TRACNET
TRACPHONE
TRACVISION
VELOCITY
VELOCITY ACCELERATION

L-1 SECURE CREDENTIALING, INC.

(Div. of L-1 Identity Solutions, Inc.)
296 Concord Rd Ste 302
Billerica, MA 01821-3487
Tel.: (978) 215-2400
Fax: (978) 952-2225
Web Site: www.l1id.com
Sales Range: $75-99.9 Million
Year Founded: 1996
Business Description:
Secure Credentialing Services
S.I.C.: 7373; 7389
N.A.I.C.S.: 541512; 561499
Advertising Expenditures: $400,000
Personnel:
Leo J. Sullivan *(Pres)*
Brands & Products:
BORDERGUARD
FACEEXPLORER
FACEFINDER
FACEPASS
FACETOOLS
IA-THENTICATE
PROOF
VIISAGE PROOF

L-3 AVIONICS SYSTEMS, INC.

(Sub. of L-3 Communications Corporation)
5353 52nd St SE
Grand Rapids, MI 49512
Tel.: (616) 949-6600
Fax: (616) 285-4224
E-mail: info.avionics@l-3com.com
Web Site: www.as.l-3com.com
Sales Range: $75-99.9 Million
Approx. Number Employees: 479
Year Founded: 1962
Business Description:
Cockpit Avionics Designer & Mfr
S.I.C.: 3812
N.A.I.C.S.: 334511
Import Export
Advertising Expenditures: $800,000
Media: 1-2-10-11-19-20-21
Distr.: Intl.; Natl.
Budget Set: Nov.
Personnel:
Jan LaFoy *(Pres)*
Larry Riddle *(VP-Sls & Mktg)*
Michelle Stevenson *(Mgr-Mktg)*
Brands & Products:
I-LINC
JET
LANDMARK
RGC350
SKYWATCH
STORMSCOPE

L-3 COMMUNICATIONS HOLDINGS INC.

600 3rd Ave
New York, NY 10016
Tel.: (212) 697-1111
Fax: (212) 805-5477
Web Site: www.l-3com.com
Approx. Sls.: $15,680,000,000
Approx. Number Employees: 67,000
Year Founded: 1997
Business Description:
Holding Company; Military Electronics & Communications Equipment Mfr
S.I.C.: 6719; 3663; 3669; 3769; 3812; 3823; 3825
N.A.I.C.S.: 551112; 334220; 334290; 334511; 334513; 334515; 336419
Media: 2-7-10-13
Personnel:
Michael T. Strianese *(Chm, Pres & CEO)*
Ralph G. D'Ambrosio *(CFO & Sr VP)*
Vincent T. Taylor *(CIO & VP)*

Key to Media (For complete agency information see *The Advertising Red Books-Agencies* edition):
1. Bus. Publs. 2. Cable T.V. 3. Catalogs & Directories. 4. Co-op Adv. 5. Consumer Mags. 6. D.M. to Bus. Estab.7. D.M. to Consumers
8. Daily Newsp. 9. Exhibits/Trade Shows 10. Foreign 11. Infomercial 12. Internet Adv.13. Multimedia 14. Network Radio
15. Network T.V. 16. Newsp. Distr. Mags. 17. Other 18. Outdoor (Posters, Transit) 19. Point of Purchase20. Premiums, Novelties
21. Product Samples 22. Special Events Mktg. 23. Spot Radio 24. Spot T.V. 25. Weekly Newsp. 26. Yellow Page Adv.

L-3 Communications Holdings Inc. — (Continued)

Dan Azmon *(Principal Acctg Officer, VP & Controller)*
John S. Mega *(Pres-NARDA Microwave-East & Corp VP)*
Robert W. Drewes *(Pres-Integrated Sys)*
James W. Dunn *(Pres-Link Simulation & Training)*
Todd W. Gautier *(Pres-Precision Engagement Sector)*
Steven Kantor *(Pres-Svcs Grp)*
Steven M. Post *(Gen Counsel, Sec & Sr VP)*
Curtis Brunson *(Exec VP-Corp Strategy & Dev)*
Richard A. Cody *(Corp Sr VP)*
Kathleen E. Karelis *(Sr VP & Sr Counsel)*
David G. Wessing *(VP & Gen Mgr)*
Allen E. Danzig *(VP, Asst Sec & Asst Gen Counsel)*
Ronald Mandler *(VP, Asst Gen Counsel & Asst Sec)*
David M. Reilly *(VP & Deputy Gen Counsel)*
Paul De Lia *(VP-Science & Tech)*
Ralph L. Denino *(VP-Procurement)*
John M. Hill *(VP-HR)*
Patrick M. Hughes *(VP-Intelligence & Counterterrorism)*
Vincent Jarvie *(VP-Corp Security)*
David Kinsinger *(VP & Chief Patent Counsel)*
Fred Piccirillo *(VP-Internal Audit & Corp Ethics Officer)*
David M. Rielly *(VP-HR)*
Kevin Byrne *(Dir-Product Mgmt)*
John S. Mitchell *(Engr-Technical Support)*
Brands & Products:
L3
Advertising Agency:
FD U.S. Communications, Inc. (d/b/a Financial Dynamics)
Wall St Plz 88 Pine St 32nd Fl
New York, NY 10005
Tel.: (212) 850-5600
Fax: (212) 850-5790

L-3 COMMUNICATIONS NARDA MICROWAVE-EAST

(Unit of L-3 Communications Corporation)
435 Moreland Rd
Hauppauge, NY 11788-3926
Tel.: (631) 231-1700
Fax: (631) 231-1711
E-mail: nardaeast@l-3com.com
Web Site: www.nardamicrowave.com
Sales Range: $100-124.9 Million
Approx. Number Employees: 331
Year Founded: 1954
Business Description:
Microwave & Ultra High Frequency Electronic Test Equipment, Components & Subsystems Mfr
S.I.C.: 3663; 3825
N.A.I.C.S.: 334220; 334515
Export
Media: 2-22
Distr.: Direct to Consumer; Intl.; Natl.
Budget Set: Apr.
Personnel:
John S. Mega *(Pres)*
Vinod Chitkara *(Sr VP-Sls & Mktg)*
Joe Merenda *(VP-Engrg)*
Walter Crofut *(Mgr-Mktg)*

L-3 INTERSTATE ELECTRONICS CORPORATION

(Sub. of L-3 Communications Corporation)
602 E Vermont Ave
Anaheim, CA 92805
Mailing Address:
PO Box 3117
Anaheim, CA 92803-3117
Tel.: (714) 758-0500
Fax: (714) 758-4111
Toll Free: (800) 854-6979
E-mail: iec.info@l-3com.com
Web Site: www.iechome.com
Sales Range: $50-74.9 Million
Approx. Number Employees: 600
Year Founded: 1956
Business Description:
Instrumentation & Missile Tracking Systems, Network Information Systems & Global Positioning System Technologies Mfr
S.I.C.: 3812; 3825
N.A.I.C.S.: 334511; 334515
Export
Advertising Expenditures: $100,000
Media: 2-10
Distr.: Intl.; Natl.
Budget Set: Dec.
Personnel:
Tom Walsh *(Pres)*
Robert Van Wechel *(Sr Chief Scientist)*
Greg Martz *(Mgr-Comm)*
Brands & Products:
TRUTRAK
XFACTOR
Advertising Agency:
The Rankin Group, Ltd.
17821 E 17th St Ste 270
Tustin, CA 92780-2137
Tel.: (714) 832-4100
Fax: (714) 282-8825

LABARGE, INC.

9900 Clayton Rd
Saint Louis, MO 63124
Mailing Address:
PO Box 14499
Saint Louis, MO 63178-4499
Tel.: (314) 997-0800
Fax: (314) 812-9438
E-mail: investorrelations@labarge.com
Web Site: www.labarge.com
E-Mail For Key Personnel:
Public Relations: colleen.clements@labarge.com
Approx. Sls.: $289,303,000
Approx. Number Employees: 1,560
Year Founded: 1953
Business Description:
Electronics & Interconnect Systems Designer & Mfr
S.I.C.: 3812; 3651; 3663; 3679
N.A.I.C.S.: 334511; 334220; 334310; 334418; 334419
Import Export
Media: 2-4-9-10-20-21-26
Distr.: Natl.; Reg.
Budget Set: Monthly
Personnel:
Craig E. Labarge *(Chm, Pres & CEO)*
Donald H. Nonnenkamp *(CFO, Sec & VP)*
Randy L. Buschling *(COO & VP)*
Colleen P. Clements *(Dir-Corp Comm)*
George Hayward *(Dir-Info Sys)*
Brian Stewart *(Dir-Operational Excellence)*
Mark Teubert *(Dir-Operational Excellence)*

LATTICE SEMICONDUCTOR CORPORATION

5555 NE Moore Ct
Hillsboro, OR 97124
Tel.: (503) 268-8000
Fax: (503) 268-8347
E-mail: sales@latticesemi.com
Web Site: www.latticesemi.com
Approx. Rev.: $297,768,000
Approx. Number Employees: 749
Year Founded: 1983
Business Description:
Programmable Logic Devices Mfr
S.I.C.: 3674
N.A.I.C.S.: 334413
Export
Media: 2-4-5-7-8-9-17-25
Distr.: Intl.
Personnel:
Patrick S. Jones *(Chm)*
Darin G. Billerbeck *(Pres & CEO)*
Joseph Bedewi *(CFO & VP-Fin)*
Byron Milstead *(Gen Counsel, Sec & VP)*
Sean P. Riley *(VP & Gen Mgr-High Density Solutions)*
Stacy Fender *(VP-Sls-Worldwide)*
Tim Schnettler *(Dir-Product Mktg)*
Brian Kiernan *(Mgr-Comm)*
Brands & Products:
E2CMOS
EXTREME PERFORMANCE
FLASHBAK
FLEXIFLASH
FLEXIMAC
FLEXIPCS
FREEDOMCHIP
GAL
GDX
GENERIC ARRAY LOGIC
HDL EXPLORER
IPEXPRESS
ISP
ISPATE
ISPCLOCK
ISPDOWNLOAD
ISPGAL
ISPGDS
ISPGDX
ISPGDX2
ISPGDXV
ISPJTAG
ISPLEVER
ISPLEVERCORE
ISPLSI
ISPMACH
ISPPAC
ISPTRACY
ISPVIRTUAL MACHINE
ISPVM
ISPXP
ISPXPLD
LATTICE
LATTICEEC
LATTICEECP
LATTICEECP & EC
LATTICEECP2
LATTICEECP2M
LATTICEMICO32
LATTICEMICO8
LATTICEXP
LATTICEXP2
LSC
MACHXO
ORCA
ORCASTRA
PAC-DESIGNER
PURESPEED
REVEAL
SILICON FOREST
SYSCONFIG
Advertising Agency:
Planned Marketing Solutions
5100 S.W. Macadam Ave., Ste. 420
Portland, OR 97201
Tel.: (503) 224-8892

LAW ENFORCEMENT ASSOCIATES CORPORATION

2609 Discovery Dr Ste 125
Raleigh, NC 27616
Tel.: (919) 872-6210
Tel.: (919) 554-4700
Fax: (919) 872-6431
Fax: (919) 556-6240
Toll Free: (800) 354-9669
E-mail: info@leacorp.com
Web Site: www.leacorp.com
Approx. Sls.: $5,575,872
Approx. Number Employees: 27
Year Founded: 1998
Business Description:
Undercover Surveillance Products Mfr & Marketer
S.I.C.: 7382; 3651
N.A.I.C.S.: 561621; 334310
Advertising Expenditures: $112,597
Media: 4-7-10
Personnel:
Anthony E. Rand *(Chm)*
Paul Briggs *(Pres, CEO & CFO)*
Jay Becker *(VP-Sls)*

LCC INTERNATIONAL, INC.

7900 W Park Dr Ste A315
McLean, VA 22102-4235
Tel.: (703) 873-2000
Fax: (703) 873-2100
E-mail: info@lcc.com
Web Site: www.lcc.com
Sales Range: $125-149.9 Million
Approx. Number Employees: 842
Year Founded: 1983
Business Description:
Wireless Voice & Data Turn-Key Services
S.I.C.: 4812; 4813; 8748
N.A.I.C.S.: 517212; 517211; 517310; 541690
Advertising Expenditures: $8,128,000
Media: 2-5-10-11
Personnel:
Louis Salamone, Jr. *(CFO & Exec VP)*
Carlo Baravalle *(Exec VP)*
Antonio Harnecker *(Sr VP-MEA Reg)*
Stan Schreuder *(Sr VP-Europe)*
Ananth Veluppillai *(Sr VP-Americas)*
John Buckholz *(VP-IT)*
Nancy O. Feeney *(VP-Ops)*
Brands & Products:
THE KNOWLEDGE THAT POWERS THE NETWORK
LCC
TOTALVIEW
WINDS
WIVIEW

Key to Media (For complete agency information see *The Advertising Red Books-Agencies* edition):
1. Bus. Publs. 2. Cable T.V. 3. Catalogs & Directories. 4. Co-op Adv. 5. Consumer Mags. 6. D.M. to Bus. Estab.7. D.M. to Consumers 8. Daily Newsp. 9. Exhibits/Trade Shows 10. Foreign 11. Infomercial 12. Internet Adv.13. Multimedia 14. Network Radio 15. Network T.V. 16. Newsp. Distr. Mags. 17. Other 18. Outdoor (Posters, Transit) 19. Point of Purchase20. Premiums, Novelties 21. Product Samples 22. Special Events Mktg. 23. Spot Radio 24. Spot T.V. 25. Weekly Newsp. 26. Yellow Page Adv.

LEXICON-HARMAN GOM, INC.
(Sub. of Harman Specialty Group)
1718 W Mishawaka Rd
Elkhart, IN 46517
Tel.: (516) 594-0300
E-mail: web@lexicon.com
Web Site: www.lexicon.com
Sales Range: $25-49.9 Million
Approx. Number Employees: 80
Year Founded: 1971
Business Description:
Digital Audio Equipment Mfr
S.I.C.: 3651
N.A.I.C.S.: 334310
Media: 6-13
Personnel:
John Batliner *(Pres)*
Brands & Products:
LOGIC7

LG ELECTRONICS CANADA, INC.
(Sub. of LG Electronics, Inc.)
550 Matheson Blvd E
Mississauga, ON L4Z 4G3, Canada
Tel.: (905) 568-6800
Fax: (905) 507-9649
E-mail: info@lg.com
Web Site: www.lg.com
Sales Range: $25-49.9 Million
Approx. Number Employees: 180
Business Description:
Electronic Appliances Whslr
S.I.C.: 7359
N.A.I.C.S.: 532210
Media: 15
Personnel:
Eric Agius *(Pres)*
Kevin Andrews *(Dir-Mktg)*
Frank Lee *(Mgr-Corp Mktg & Sponsorship)*
Brands & Products:
GOLDSTAR
Advertising Agency:
Y&R, Ltd.
60 Bloor Street West
Toronto, ON M4W 1J2, Canada
Tel.: (416) 961-5111
Fax: (416) 961-7890

LG ELECTRONICS U.S.A., INC.
(Sub. of LG Electronics, Inc.)
1000 Sylvan Ave
Englewood Cliffs, NJ 07632
Tel.: (201) 816-2000
Fax: (201) 816-0636
Toll Free: (800) 942-3786
Web Site: www.us.lge.com
Sales Range: $250-299.9 Million
Approx. Number Employees: 200
Year Founded: 1975
Business Description:
Home Appliances, Personal Computers & Consumer Electronics
S.I.C.: 5045; 5064
N.A.I.C.S.: 423430; 423620
Import
Media: 3-5-6-9-10-15-18-22
Distr.: Intl.; Natl.
Budget Set: Dec.
Personnel:
Sam Kim *(Pres)*
Jeff Hwang *(Pres-LG Electronics MobileComm U.S.A)*
James Fishler *(Sr VP-go-to-market Ops)*
Peter Reiner *(Sr VP-Mktg & Strategy-North America)*
Jay Vandenbree *(Sr VP-Home Entertainment Sls & Mktg)*
John B. Weinstock *(VP-Mktg-Home Entertainment & Home Appliances)*
Soon H. Kwon *(Head-Digital Appliance & Mktg-America, Asia, Middle East & Africa)*
Jacqueline Yu *(Sr Mgr-eCRM Digital Mktg)*
Jarett Quintana *(Coord-Sls)*
Advertising Agencies:
BrandBuzz
285 Madison Ave 22nd Fl
New York, NY 10017
Tel.: (212) 210-3879
Fax: (212) 210-3878

Fathom Communications
(Part of Omnicom Group of Companies)
437 Madison Ave
New York, NY 10022
Tel.: (212) 817-6600
Fax: (212) 415-3514

MPG Miami
5301 Blue Lagoon Dr Ste 850
Miami, FL 33126
Tel.: (305) 377-1907
Fax: (305) 337-1906

Ogilvy PR/New York
636 11th Ave
New York, NY 10036
Tel.: (212) 880-5200
Fax: (212) 884-1997

URi, Inc.
3542 Hayden Ave Ste A
Culver City, CA 90232
Tel.: (310) 360-1212
Fax: (310) 360-9003

Young & Rubicam Inc.
285 Madison Ave
New York, NY 10017-6401
Tel.: (212) 210-3000
Fax: (212) 490-9073
Something's Lurking

LG INFOCOMM U.S.A., INC.
(Sub. of LG Electronics, Inc.)
10225 Willow Creek Rd
San Diego, CA 92131
Tel.: (858) 635-5300
Fax: (858) 635-5399
Toll Free: (800) 793-8896
E-mail: lgcustomerservice@lge.com
Web Site: us.lge.com
Sales Range: $50-74.9 Million
Approx. Number Employees: 500
Year Founded: 1996
Business Description:
Wireless Communication Products & Services
S.I.C.: 5065; 3663
N.A.I.C.S.: 423690; 334220
Media: 10
Personnel:
Melissa Elkins *(Mgr-Pub Rels)*
Advertising Agencies:
Mindshare
498 7th Ave
New York, NY 10018
Tel.: (212) 297-7000
Fax: (212) 297-7001
LG Mobile

Smith & Jones
76 Main St
Sturbridge, MA 01566-1260
Tel.: (508) 347-7793
Fax: (508) 347-7796
LG Mobile

VML, Inc.
250 Richards Rd
Kansas City, MO 64116-4279
Tel.: (816) 283-0700
Fax: (816) 283-0954
Toll Free: (800) 990-2468
LG Mobile

THE LGL GROUP, INC.
2525 Shader Rd
Orlando, FL 32804
Tel.: (407) 298-2000
E-mail: jhealy@lglgroup.com
Web Site: www.lglgroup.com
E-Mail For Key Personnel:
President: John.Ferrara@lynch-mail.com
Approx. Rev.: $46,656,000
Approx. Number Employees: 233
Business Description:
Holding Company; Electronic Component Mfr
S.I.C.: 3679; 6719
N.A.I.C.S.: 334419; 551112
Import Export
Advertising Expenditures: $23,000
Media: 17
Personnel:
Marc J. Gabelli *(Chm)*
Greg P. Anderson *(Pres & CEO)*
R. LaDuane Clifton *(Chief Acctg Officer)*

LIBERTY MEDIA CORPORATION
12300 Liberty Blvd
Englewood, CO 80112
Tel.: (720) 875-5400
Toll Free: (877) 772-1518
Web Site: www.libertymedia.com
Approx. Rev.: $10,982,000,000
Approx. Number Employees: 24,000
Year Founded: 1990
Business Description:
Holding Company
S.I.C.: 6719
N.A.I.C.S.: 551112
Advertising Expenditures: $363,000,000
Personnel:
John C. Malone *(Chm)*
Gregory B. Maffei *(Pres & CEO)*
Tony G. Werner *(CTO & Sr VP)*
David J.A. Flowers *(Treas & Sr VP)*
Christopher W. Shean *(Sr VP & Controller)*
Mark D. Carleton *(Sr VP)*
William R. Fitzgerald *(Sr VP)*
Michael P. Zeisser *(Sr VP)*

LINEAR LLC
(Sub. of Nortek, Inc.)
1950 Camino Vida Roble Ste 150
Carlsbad, CA 92008-6517
Mailing Address:
PO Box 9003
Carlsbad, CA 92018-9003
Tel.: (760) 438-7000
Fax: (530) 283-3952
Toll Free: (800) 421-1587
E-mail: info@linearcorp.com
Web Site: www.linearcorp.com
Year Founded: 1961
Business Description:
Alarm Monitoring Components & Data Distribution Systems
S.I.C.: 3679; 3823
N.A.I.C.S.: 334419; 334513
Import Export
Advertising Expenditures: $200,000
Media: 2-9-10-11-17-19-20-25
Distr.: Natl.
Personnel:
Grant D. Rummell *(Chm & CEO)*
Dan Stottlemyre *(Pres)*
Gary Baker *(VP-Mktg)*
Charles Monts *(VP-Fin)*
John LaFond *(Dir-Sls)*
Brands & Products:
ACCESSBASE 2000
AE-1000
AE-500
AK-3
CHANNELPLUS
DELTA3
DUAL-824
DVS-1200
DVS-2400
DXR-701
DXR-702
DXSR-1504
DXSR-1508
FT-1
LSO50
MEGACODE
MULTICODE
OPENHOUSE
PERS-2400A
RE-1G
RE-1N
RE-1SS
SXR-64
Advertising Agency:
Newton Associates Marketing Communications, Inc.
527 Plymouth Rd Ste 411 Plymouth Woods
Plymouth Meeting, PA 19462
Tel.: (610) 964-9300
Fax: (610) 964-9306

LINEAR TECHNOLOGY CORP.
1630 McCarthy Blvd
Milpitas, CA 95035-7417
Tel.: (408) 432-1900
Fax: (408) 434-6441
Toll Free: (800) 4LINEAR
E-mail: contact@linear.com
Web Site: www.linear.com
Approx. Rev.: $1,483,962,000
Approx. Number Employees: 4,505
Year Founded: 1981
Business Description:
Semiconductors & Related Devices Mfr
S.I.C.: 3674
N.A.I.C.S.: 334413
Export
Advertising Expenditures: $3,700,000
Media: 1-2-4-5-7-9-10-11-13-18-20-21-22-25
Distr.: Intl.
Budget Set: June -July
Personnel:
Robert H. Swanson, Jr. *(Chm)*

Key to Media (For complete agency information see *The Advertising Red Books-Agencies* edition):
1. Bus. Publs. 2. Cable T.V. 3. Catalogs & Directories. 4. Co-op Adv. 5. Consumer Mags. 6. D.M. to Bus. Estab.7. D.M. to Consumers
8. Daily Newsp. 9. Exhibits/Trade Shows 10. Foreign 11. Infomercial 12. Internet Adv.13. Multimedia 14. Network Radio
15. Network T.V. 16. Newsp. Distr. Mags. 17. Other 18. Outdoor (Posters, Transit) 19. Point of Purchase20. Premiums, Novelties
21. Product Samples 22. Special Events Mktg. 23. Spot Radio 24. Spot T.V. 25. Weekly Newsp. 26. Yellow Page Adv.

Linear Technology Corp. — (Continued)

Lothar Maier *(CEO)*
Paul Coghlan *(CFO, Sec & VP-Fin)*
Alexander R. McCann *(COO & VP)*
Robert C. Dobkin *(CTO & VP-Engrg)*
Arthur F. Schneiderman *(Gen Counsel & Sec)*
Donald E. Paulus *(VP & Gen Mgr-D Power Products)*
Steve Pietkiewicz *(VP & Gen Mgr-S Power Products)*
Robert L. Reay *(VP & Gen Mgr-Mixed Signal Products)*
Erik Soule *(VP & Gen Mgr-Signal Conditioning Products)*
Richard Nickson *(VP-Sls-North America)*
David A. Quarles *(VP-Sls-Intl)*
Tony Armstrong *(Dir-Product Mktg-Power Products)*
John Hamburger *(Dir-Mktg Comm)*
Doug Dickinson *(Mgr-Media Rels)*
Dwight Somersett *(Mgr-Quality Assurance)*

Advertising Agency:
DRB Partners, Inc.
2635 N 1st St Ste 204
San Jose, CA 95134-2032
Tel.: (408) 943-0515
Fax: (408) 943-1904
Toll Free: (877) 234-2094

LONG'S ELECTRONICS, INC.

2630 5th Ave S
Irondale, AL 35210-1209
Tel.: (205) 956-6767
Fax: (205) 956-7325
Toll Free: (800) 633-3410
E-mail: info@longselectronics.com
Web Site: www.longselectronics.com
Sales Range: $25-49.9 Million
Approx. Number Employees: 40
Year Founded: 1977
Business Description:
Consumer Electronics & Audio-Visual Equipment Retailer
S.I.C.: 5731; 5999
N.A.I.C.S.: 443112; 453998
Media: 4-8-13-17-19-22
Distr.: Intl.; Natl.
Budget Set: Mar.
Personnel:
Roy Long *(Pres)*
Chris Long *(Mgr-Adv)*

LOUD TECHNOLOGIES INC.

16220 Wood-Red Rd NE
Woodinville, WA 98072
Tel.: (425) 892-6500
Fax: (425) 487-4337
Toll Free: (866) 858-5832
Toll Free: (800) 258-6883
Web Site: www.loudtechinc.com
Sales Range: $200-249.9 Million
Approx. Number Employees: 533
Year Founded: 1988
Business Description:
Professional Audio Equipment Mfr
S.I.C.: 3663; 3651
N.A.I.C.S.: 334220; 334310
Export
Advertising Expenditures: $4,100,000
Media: 1-2-10-13-17
Personnel:
Mark Graham *(Chm, Pres & CEO)*
Anthony Taylor *(VP & Mng Dir)*
Case Kuehn *(CFO & Sr VP)*
Yudhi Patel *(COO & Sr VP)*
Jeff Rocha *(VP & Gen Mgr)*
Brands & Products:
ALVAREZ
AMPEG
BLACKHEART
CRATE
EAW
LOUD TECHNOLOGIES INC.
MACKIE
TAPCO

LRAD CORPORATION

(Formerly American Technology Corporation)
15378 Ave of Science Ste 100
San Diego, CA 92128-3407
Tel.: (858) 676-1112
Fax: (858) 679-0545
E-mail: info@lradx.com
Web Site: www.lradx.com/site/
Approx. Rev.: $16,694,075
Approx. Number Employees: 36
Year Founded: 1980
Business Description:
Directed Sound Solutions & Services
S.I.C.: 3651; 5064
N.A.I.C.S.: 334310; 423620
Advertising Expenditures: $62,397
Media: 17
Personnel:
Thomas R. Brown *(Pres & CEO)*
Katherine H. McDermott *(CFO)*
Brands & Products:
CUTTING THROUGH
DIRECTEDACOUSTICS
DIRECTEDSOUND
DIRECTIVITY
GAS
HIDA
HSS
HYPER DIRECTIONAL
HYPERSONIC SOUND
LONG RANGE ACOUSTIC DEVICE
LRAD
MODAMP
MRAD
NEOPLANAR
PMT
PUREBASS
SFT
SHAPING THE FUTURE OF SOUND
SOUNDDIRECT
SOUNDSABER
SOUNDVECTOR
STRATIFIED FIELD

LSI SACO TECHNOLOGIES, INC.

(Sub. of LSI Industries Inc.)
7809 Trans Canada Hwy
Montreal, QC H4S 1L3, Canada
Tel.: (514) 745-0310
Fax: (514) 745-0315
Toll Free: (800) 991-7226
E-mail: tom@smartvision.com
Web Site: www.smartvision.com
E-Mail For Key Personnel:
President: fdj@smartvision.com
Sales Range: $10-24.9 Million
Approx. Number Employees: 35
Year Founded: 1987
Business Description:
Light Engines & Large-Format LED Video Screens Designer & Mfr
S.I.C.: 3651
N.A.I.C.S.: 334310
Media: 10
Personnel:
Fred Jalbout *(Pres & CEO)*
Jonathan Labbee *(VP-Mktg)*
Brands & Products:
SMARTVISION

LXE INC.

(Div. of EMS Technologies, Inc.)
125 Technology Pkwy
Norcross, GA 30092-2913
Tel.: (770) 447-4224
Fax: (770) 447-4397
E-mail: info@lxe.com
Web Site: www.lxe.com
Sales Range: $100-124.9 Million
Approx. Number Employees: 300
Business Description:
Mfr. of Radio-Data Linked Communications Systems & Bar Code Scanners
S.I.C.: 3663; 3575
N.A.I.C.S.: 334220; 334113
Personnel:
Stephen Newell *(Gen Mgr)*
Todd Baillie *(Mgr-Channel Sls-Americas)*
Advertising Agency:
EJW Associates, Inc.
Crabapple Village Office Park 1602 Abbey Ct
Alpharetta, GA 30004
Tel.: (770) 664-9322
Fax: (770) 664-9324

MAGNOLIA AUDIO VIDEO

(Sub. of Best Buy Co., Inc.)
6305 S 231st St
Kent, WA 98032-1872
Tel.: (253) 372-4434
Fax: (253) 372-4900
Toll Free: (800) 275-4434
Web Site: www.magnoliaav.com
Sales Range: $50-74.9 Million
Approx. Number Employees: 250
Year Founded: 1970
Business Description:
Retail Stereophonic Video Equipment; Car Stereos & Computers
S.I.C.: 5731
N.A.I.C.S.: 443112
Media: 4
Advertising Agency:
hawkeye
2828 Routh St Ste 300
Dallas, TX 75201
Tel.: (214) 659-5615
Fax: (214) 747-1897

MARANTZ AMERICA INC.

(Sub. of Marantz Japan Inc.)
1100 Maplewood Dr
Itasca, IL 60143
Tel.: (201) 762-6500
Fax: (201) 762-6670
Web Site: www.marantz.com
Approx. Number Employees: 15
Year Founded: 1953
Business Description:
Home Entertainment Equipment Retailer
S.I.C.: 5064
N.A.I.C.S.: 423620
Media: 4
Personnel:
Kevin Zarow *(VP-Sls & Mktg)*

MARCONI COMMUNICATIONS

(Div. of Telent Limited)
5900 Landerbrook Dr Ste 300
Cleveland, OH 44124-4019
Tel.: (440) 460-3600
Fax: (440) 460-3690
Toll Free: (800) 233-2334
Web Site: www.marconi.com
Approx. Number Employees: 250
Business Description:
Supplier of Integrated Access Solutions to Communications Providers
S.I.C.: 3661; 7629
N.A.I.C.S.: 334210; 811213
Import Export
Media: 1-2-4-5-7-9-10-13-19-20-21-22-25-26
Distr.: Intl.
Budget Set: Oct.
Brands & Products:
LORAIN

MARINE ELECTRIC SYSTEMS, INC.

550 Hyler
South Hackensack, NJ 07606
Tel.: (201) 531-8600
Fax: (201) 531-8606
E-mail: info@marineelectricsystems.com
Web Site:
www.marineelectricsystems.com
Approx. Number Employees: 15
Year Founded: 1945
Business Description:
Marine Monitoring & Control Systems Mfr
S.I.C.: 3823; 3825
N.A.I.C.S.: 334513; 334515
Export
Media: 10
Distr.: Intl.; Natl.
Budget Set: Dec.
Personnel:
Michael Epstein *(CEO)*
Caroline Coniglio *(CFO)*
Gary Mandell *(VP-Sls)*
Brands & Products:
CML MACARR
GALBRAITH-PILOT MARINE
MARINE ELECTRIC SYSTEMS
OCCIGERM

MARINE PARK COMPUTERS

3126 Avenue U
Brooklyn, NY 11229
Tel.: (718) 891-1878
Fax: (718) 891-4290
Toll Free: (800) 300-0615
Approx. Sls.: $50,000,000
Approx. Number Employees: 30
Year Founded: 1992
Business Description:
Computer, Camera & Video Equipment Retailer
S.I.C.: 5961; 5731
N.A.I.C.S.: 454113; 443112
Media: 6

MARTEK POWER ABBOTT, INC.

(Sub. of The Martek Power Group)
1111 Knox St
Torrance, CA 90502
Tel.: (310) 202-8820
Fax: (310) 836-4926
E-mail: sales.mpa@martekpower.com
Web Site:
www.martekpowerabbott.com

Key to Media (For complete agency information see *The Advertising Red Books-Agencies* edition):
1. Bus. Publs. 2. Cable T.V. 3. Catalogs & Directories. 4. Co-op Adv. 5. Consumer Mags. 6. D.M. to Bus. Estab.7. D.M. to Consumers
8. Daily Newsp. 9. Exhibits/Trade Shows 10. Foreign 11. Infomercial 12. Internet Adv.13. Multimedia 14. Network Radio
15. Network T.V. 16. Newsp. Distr. Mags. 17. Other 18. Outdoor (Posters, Transit) 19. Point of Purchase20. Premiums, Novelties
21. Product Samples 22. Special Events Mktg. 23. Spot Radio 24. Spot T.V. 25. Weekly Newsp. 26. Yellow Page Adv.

E-Mail For Key Personnel:
Sales Director: sales.mpa@martekpower.com
Sales Range: $10-24.9 Million
Approx. Number Employees: 200
Year Founded: 1961
Business Description:
Mfr. of Military & Aerospace Power & Electronic Systems
S.I.C.: 3679
N.A.I.C.S.: 334419
Export
Advertising Expenditures: $595,000
Media: 4-6-13
Distr.: Intl.; Natl.
Budget Set: Mar. -Apr.
Personnel:
Ahmad Innab *(Pres)*
Fred Lewin *(VP-Sls-Mktg)*
Brands & Products:
MIL/PAC

MAXELL CORPORATION OF AMERICA
(Sub. of Hitachi Maxell, Ltd.)
3 Garret Mountain Plz 3rd Fl Ste 300
Woodland Park, NJ 07424
Tel.: (201) 794-5900
Fax: (201) 796-8790
Toll Free: (800) 533-2836
E-mail: techsupp@maxell.com
Web Site: www.maxell-usa.com
Approx. Number Employees: 30
Business Description:
Audio & Video Appliances Sales
S.I.C.: 3652
N.A.I.C.S.: 334612
Media: 1-2-4-7-10-13-18-19-20-22
Personnel:
Masaru Kamemoto *(Pres)*
Pat Byrne *(Sr Mgr-Mktg)*
Charlotte Edwards *(Sls Mgr-Data Storage Grp-Natl)*
Rick Bright *(Mgr-Natl Sls-West)*
Advertising Agencies:
Kalmar Responsive Ad/Marketing Corp.
1 Blue Hill Plz PO Box 1501
Pearl River, NY 10965
Tel.: (845) 201-8035
Fax: (845) 201-8036

Manhattan Marketing Ensemble
443 Park Ave S 4th Fl
New York, NY 10016-7322
Tel.: (212) 779-2233
Fax: (212) 779-0825

MAXIM INTEGRATED PRODUCTS, INC.
120 San Gabriel Dr
Sunnyvale, CA 94086-5125
Tel.: (408) 737-7600
Fax: (408) 737-7194
E-mail: info2@maxim-ic.com
Web Site: www.maxim-ic.com
Approx. Rev.: $2,472,341,000
Approx. Number Employees: 9,370
Year Founded: 1983
Business Description:
Analog, Mixed-Signal, High-Frequency, & Digital Circuits Mfr, Designer, Developer & Marketer
S.I.C.: 3674
N.A.I.C.S.: 334413
Advertising Expenditures: $6,800,000
Media: 1-2-10-22
Personnel:
B. Kipling Hagopian *(Chm)*
Tunc Doluca *(Pres & CEO)*
Bruce E. Kiddoo *(CFO & Sr VP)*
Pirooz Parvarandeh *(CTO & Grp Pres-High Performance Analog Div)*
Vijay Ullal *(Grp Pres-Handheld Consumer Div)*
Ed Medlin *(Gen Counsel & VP)*
Vivek Jain *(Sr VP-Mfg Ops)*
Matthew J. Murphy *(Sr VP-Sls & Mktg-Worldwide)*
Christopher J. Neil *(Sr VP)*
Charles G. Rigg *(Sr VP-Admin)*
Jennifer E. Gilbert *(VP-Fin & Supply Chain Mgmt)*
Steve Yamasaki *(VP-HR)*
Andrew Baker *(Dir-Bus Mgmt)*
Patrick Long *(Dir)*
Brands & Products:
1 WIRE
ACTIVE RECTIFIER
AUTOSHUTDOWN
AUTOSHUTDOWN PLUS
BEYOND-THE-RAILS
BLUE DOT
CERAMAX
DALLASTAT
DIRECTDRIVE
DUAL MODE
DUALSPEED/BILEVEL
ECONOSCILLATOR
EE-MAIL
EZCASCADE
FLEAPOT
FOLDBACK MODE
FUELPACK
GLITCHCATHER
HYGROCHRON
I BUTTON
IDLE MODE
INNOVATION DELIVERED
LOAD PROBE
MAX-PHY
MAXIM
MAXQ
MEGABAUD
MICROLAN
MICROMONITOR
MSPB
NEXSAS
POWERMIND
QUERC
QUICK-PWM
QUICKIC
QUICKTOOLS
RAPID ADVANCE
RESOURCESMART
RF TO BITS
SECURE-LOCK
SIMPLE SWAPPER
SMART POWER SELECTOR
SMARTERSENSE
SMARTWIPER
SOT-POT
THERMOCHRON
TINI
TRUE SHUTDOWN
UCSP
UMAX
UNIQUEWARE
USIP
VARIABLESPEED/BILEVEL

MAXWELL TECHNOLOGIES, INC.
9244 Balboa Ave
San Diego, CA 92123-1505
Tel.: (858) 503-3300
Fax: (858) 503-3301
Toll Free: (877) 511-4324
E-mail: info@maxwell.com
Web Site: www.maxwell.com
E-Mail For Key Personnel:
Public Relations: msund@maxwell.com
Approx. Rev.: $121,882,000
Approx. Number Employees: 314
Year Founded: 1965
Business Description:
Power & Computing Components & Systems for Applications in Transportation, Telecommunications, Consumer & Industrial Electronics, Medical & Aerospace
S.I.C.: 3671; 3571; 3675
N.A.I.C.S.: 334411; 334111; 334414
Export
Advertising Expenditures: $256,000
Media: 2-4-7-10-13-16-20-22
Distr.: Intl.; Natl.
Budget Set: Aug.
Personnel:
Robert L. Guyett *(Chm)*
David J. Schramm *(Pres & CEO)*
Kevin S. Royal *(CFO, Treas, Sec & Sr VP)*
George Kreigler, III *(COO & Sr VP)*
Van M. Andrews *(Sr VP-Sls & Mktg)*
Larry Longden *(VP & Gen Mgr-Microelectronics Products)*
John M. Miller *(VP-Adv Transportation Applications)*
Michael W. Sund *(VP-Comm & IR)*
Brands & Products:
BOOSTCAP
CONDIS
LPT
MAXWELL TECHNOLOGIES
MORE POWER. MORE ENERGY. MORE IDEAS
POWERCACHE
POWERING THE FUTURE
RAD-COAT
RAD-PAK
RAD-STACK
THE ULTRACAPACITOR COMPANY
XRAY-PAK

MAYER ELECTRIC SUPPLY COMPANY INC.
3405 4th Ave S
Birmingham, AL 35222-2305
Tel.: (205) 583-3500
Fax: (205) 252-0315
Toll Free: (800) 866-3535
E-mail: mayer@mayerelectric.com
Web Site: www.mayerelectric.com
Approx. Sls.: $534,000,000
Approx. Number Employees: 850
Year Founded: 1930
Business Description:
Electrical Apparatus & Equipment Whslr & Distr
S.I.C.: 5063; 5065
N.A.I.C.S.: 423610; 423690
Import Export
Media: 2-5-22
Personnel:
Nancy Goedecke *(Chm & CEO)*
Charles Collat, Sr. *(Chm)*
Jim Summerlin *(Vice Chm)*
Wes Smith *(Pres)*
David L. Morgan *(CFO)*
Joe Llewellyn *(Dir-Corp Mktg)*
Glenn Goedecke *(Mgr)*

MCINTOSH LABORATORY INC.
(Sub. of D&M Holdings Inc.)
2 Chambers St
Binghamton, NY 13903-2699
Tel.: (607) 723-3512
Fax: (607) 724-0549
Toll Free: (800) 538-6576
E-mail: feedback@mcintoshlabs.com
Web Site: www.mcintoshlabs.com
Approx. Number Employees: 130
Business Description:
Home & Mobile Audio & Video Equipment Mfr
S.I.C.: 3651; 3829
N.A.I.C.S.: 334310; 334519
Media: 10-20
Personnel:
Sally Goff *(Mgr-Mktg & PR)*
Brands & Products:
C200
C2200
C45
C46
CR16
LD/HP
LS340
MC1201
MC2102
MC501
MCC404M
MCC602TM
MCD4000
MDA5000
MX406
PS112
RCT4
UR12
WS320
WS350
XRT28
XRT29
XRT30

MCT WORLDWIDE LLC
121 S 8th St Ste 960
Minneapolis, MN 55402
Tel.: (651) 414-6240
Tel.: (651) 414-6241
Fax: (612) 436-3242
Toll Free: (800) 628-1628
E-mail: info@mct.com
Web Site: www.mct.com
Sales Range: $10-24.9 Million
Approx. Number Employees: 50
Year Founded: 1972
Business Description:
Integrated Automation Solutions for the Global Semiconductor Test & Assembly Industry
S.I.C.: 3824; 3674; 3825
N.A.I.C.S.: 334514; 334413; 334515
Import Export
Media: 1-10
Personnel:
John Moon *(Pres & CEO)*
Bruce Ficks *(CFO)*
Brands & Products:
INFINITY SPC
MCT SMARTMARK
MCT TAPESTRY
SMARTMARK
SMARTSORT

Key to Media (For complete agency information see *The Advertising Red Books-Agencies* edition):
1. Bus. Publs. 2. Cable T.V. 3. Catalogs & Directories. 4. Co-op Adv. 5. Consumer Mags. 6. D.M. to Bus. Estab.7. D.M. to Consumers
8. Daily Newsp. 9. Exhibits/Trade Shows 10. Foreign 11. Infomercial 12. Internet Adv.13. Multimedia 14. Network Radio
15. Network T.V. 16. Newsp. Distr. Mags. 17. Other 18. Outdoor (Posters, Transit) 19. Point of Purchase20. Premiums, Novelties
21. Product Samples 22. Special Events Mktg. 23. Spot Radio 24. Spot T.V. 25. Weekly Newsp. 26. Yellow Page Adv.

MCT Worldwide LLC — (Continued)

SMARTTRAK
SMARTTRAK IBIS
SMARTTRAK SOFTWARE SUITE
TAPESTRY

MDU COMMUNICATIONS INTERNATIONAL, INC.

60-D Commerce Way
Totowa, NJ 07512
Tel.: (973) 237-9499
Fax: (573) 237-9287
Toll Free: (866) 286-9638
E-mail: info@mduc.com
Web Site: www.mduc.com
Approx. Rev.: $25,933,135
Approx. Number Employees: 135
Business Description:
Digital Satellite Television Programming & High-Speed Internet Services
S.I.C.: 4899
N.A.I.C.S.: 517910; 517410
Advertising Expenditures: $1,629,228
Personnel:
Sheldon B. Nelson *(Pres & CEO)*
Bradley D. Holmstrom *(Gen Counsel & Sec)*
Carmen Ragusa, Jr. *(VP-Fin & Admin)*

MEDIACOM COMMUNICATIONS CORPORATION

100 Crystal Run Rd
Middletown, NY 10941
Tel.: (845) 695-2600
Fax: (845) 695-2699
E-mail: resumes@mediacomcc.com
Web Site: www.mediacomcc.com
Approx. Rev.: $1,460,359,000
Approx. Number Employees: 4,410
Year Founded: 1995
Business Description:
Cable TV Multiple System Operator
S.I.C.: 4841
N.A.I.C.S.: 515210
Media: 3-13
Personnel:
Rocco B. Commisso *(Chm & CEO)*
Mark E. Stephan *(CFO & Exec VP)*
Joseph E. Young *(Gen Counsel, Sec, Sr VP & Mgr)*
John G. Pascarelli *(Exec VP-Ops)*
Brian M. Walsh *(Sr VP & Controller)*
Charles J. Bartolotta *(Sr VP-Enterprise)*
Calvin G. Craib *(Sr VP-Fin)*
Tapan Dandnaik *(Sr VP-Customer Svc & Fin Ops)*
Michael Rahimi *(Sr VP-Mktg & Consumer Svcs)*
Dan Templin *(Sr VP-Bus)*
J. R. Walden *(Sr VP-Tech)*
Italia Commisso Weinand *(Sr VP-Programming & HR)*
Thomas J. Larsen *(Grp VP-Legal & Pub Affairs)*
Steve Litwer *(Grp VP)*
Brands & Products:
MEDIACOM
MEDIACOM ECO BILLING
ONLINE
ONLINE INTRO
ONLINE MAX
Advertising Agency:
PK Network Communications
11 E 47th St 4th Fl
New York, NY 10017-7915
Tel.: (212) 888-4700
Fax: (212) 688-8832

MEGGITT SAFETY SYSTEMS, INC.

(Sub. of Meggitt PLC)
1915 Voyager Ave
Simi Valley, CA 93063-3386
Tel.: (805) 584-4100
Fax: (805) 578-3400
Web Site: www.meggittsafety.com
Approx. Sls.: $75,000,000
Approx. Number Employees: 200
Year Founded: 1947
Business Description:
Mfr. of Fire & Overheat Detection Systems For Aerospace & Commercial Applications
S.I.C.: 3728; 3669
N.A.I.C.S.: 336413; 334290
Advertising Expenditures: $4,000,000
Other: $4,000,000
Distr.: Intl.; Natl.
Budget Set: Oct.
Personnel:
Eric Chen *(CFO)*
Brands & Products:
WHITTAKER SAFETY EQUIPMENT

MERRIMAC INDUSTRIES INC.

(Sub. of Crane Co.)
41 Fairfield Pl
West Caldwell, NJ 07006
Tel.: (973) 575-1300
Fax: (973) 808-3906
E-mail: investor@merrimacind.com
Web Site: www.merrimacind.com
E-Mail For Key Personnel:
President: mnc@merrimacind.com
Approx. Sls.: $29,228,717
Approx. Number Employees: 207
Year Founded: 1954
Business Description:
Microwave & Radio Frequency Components & Subsystems Mfr.
S.I.C.: 3679; 3663
N.A.I.C.S.: 334419; 334220
Import Export
Advertising Expenditures: $54,000
Media: 2-4-10-21
Distr.: Intl.; Natl.
Budget Set: Jan.
Personnel:
Mason N. Carter *(Chm & CEO)*
Reynold K. Green *(COO & VP)*
Richard E. Dec *(VP-Corp Rels)*
Adriana Mazza *(VP-HR)*
Joe Mallon *(Mgr-Bus Dev)*
Brands & Products:
CUSTOMER DRIVEN RF MICROWAVE TECHNOLOGY
MERRIMAC
MICRO-MIX
MINI-MIX
MMFM
MULTI-MIX
MULTI-MIX PICO
MULTI MIX PICO RF
MULTI-MIX ZAPPER
PICO ZAPPER
SIP
TOTAL INTEGRATED PACKAGING SOLUTIONS
ZAPPER

METAL TEXTILES CORPORATION

(Sub. of United Capital Corp.)
970 New Durham Rd
Edison, NJ 08818
Tel.: (732) 287-0800
Fax: (732) 287-8546
Toll Free: (800) 222-0969
E-mail: sales@metexcorp.com
Web Site: www.metexcorp.com
E-Mail For Key Personnel:
Sales Director: sales@metexcorp.com
Sales Range: $75-99.9 Million
Approx. Number Employees: 200
Year Founded: 1964
Business Description:
Fabricated Wire Products Mfr
S.I.C.: 3496
N.A.I.C.S.: 332618
Import Export
Advertising Expenditures: $275,000
Media: 2-4-11
Distr.: Intl.; Natl.
Budget Set: Nov.
Personnel:
Greg Vongas *(Pres)*
Brands & Products:
DORNE & MARGOLIN
THERMASEAL

METHODE ELECTRONICS, INC.

7401 W Wilson Ave
Chicago, IL 60706-4548
Tel.: (708) 867-6777
Fax: (708) 867-6999
E-mail: info@methode.com
Web Site: www.methode.com
Approx. Sls.: $428,215,000
Approx. Number Employees: 2,743
Year Founded: 1946
Business Description:
Electronic Connectors, Controls & Power Distribution Systems Mfr
S.I.C.: 3678; 3674
N.A.I.C.S.: 334417; 334413
Export
Media: 10
Distr.: Intl.; Natl.
Budget Set: May
Personnel:
Warren L. Batts *(Chm)*
Donald W. Duda *(Pres & CEO)*
Douglas A. Koman *(CFO & VP-Fin)*
Thomas D. Reynolds *(Sr VP-Global Ops)*
Timothy R. Glandon *(VP & Gen Mgr-North America Ops)*
Theodore P. Kill *(VP-Global Sls)*
David Ciembronowicz *(Dir-Sls & Mktg)*
Brands & Products:
METHODE

METRO-GOLDWYN-MAYER STUDIOS, INC.

(Sub. of Metro-Goldwyn-Mayer Inc.)
(d/b/a MGM Studios, Inc.)
10250 Constellation Blvd
Los Angeles, CA 90067
Tel.: (310) 449-3000
Web Site: www.mgm.com/corporate/index.html
Year Founded: 1994
Business Description:
Motion Picture Production
S.I.C.: 7812
N.A.I.C.S.: 512110
Personnel:
Jim Packer *(Co-Pres-Worldwide Television)*
Harry E. Sloan *(CEO)*
Charles Cohen *(COO & Sr Exec VP)*
Erik Lomis *(Pres-Worldwide Theatrical Distr, Home Entertainment & Acq)*
Gary Marenzi *(Pres-Worldwide Television)*
Bruce Tuchman *(Pres-MGM Worldwide Networks)*
Scott Packman *(Gen Counsel, Sec & Exec VP)*
Steve Hendry *(Sr Exec VP-Fin)*
Gerald Ament *(Exec VP-Worldwide Television & Legal Affairs)*
Doug Finberg *(Exec VP-Mktg)*
Barry Gurstein *(Exec Dir-Global Mktg)*
Advertising Agency:
The Hogan Company
107 W 5th Ave
Knoxville, TN 37917
Tel.: (865) 951-1517
Fax: (865) 523-7300

MICREL, INC.

2180 Fortune Dr
San Jose, CA 95131
Tel.: (408) 944-0800
Fax: (408) 944-0970
E-mail: info@micrel.com
Web Site: www.micrel.com
E-Mail For Key Personnel:
Sales Director: sales@micrel.com
Approx. Rev.: $297,366,000
Approx. Number Employees: 837
Year Founded: 1978
Business Description:
Integrated Circuits Mfr
S.I.C.: 3674
N.A.I.C.S.: 334413
Advertising Expenditures: $472,000
Media: 2-7-10-13-21-26
Personnel:
Raymond D. Zinn *(Chm, Pres & CEO)*
Clyde R. Wallin *(CFO & VP-Fin)*
Thomas L. Credelle *(Sr VP-Engrg & Dev-Worldwide)*
Mansour Izadinia *(Sr VP-Analog Div)*
Brian Hedayati *(VP-Mktg-Analog Div)*
Bruce C. Larson *(VP-Analog Engrg)*
Carlos Mejia, Jr. *(VP-HR)*
David Schwartz *(VP-Worldwide Sls)*
Brands & Products:
ANYCLOCK
ANYGATE
ANYRATE
DAM
ECL PRO
EZANALOG
INNOVATION THROUGH TECHNOLOGY
ITTYBITTY
MICREL
MICREL MINI 8
MICRELNET
MICROWIRE
PRECISION EDGE
PWM
QWIKRADIO
RADIOWIRE
SUPER BETA PNP
SUPERLITE
TINYFET

Key to Media (For complete agency information see *The Advertising Red Books-Agencies* edition):
1. Bus. Publs. 2. Cable T.V. 3. Catalogs & Directories. 4. Co-op Adv. 5. Consumer Mags. 6. D.M. to Bus. Estab.7. D.M. to Consumers
8. Daily Newsp. 9. Exhibits/Trade Shows 10. Foreign 11. Infomercial 12. Internet Adv.13. Multimedia 14. Network Radio
15. Network T.V. 16. Newsp. Distr. Mags. 17. Other 18. Outdoor (Posters, Transit) 19. Point of Purchase20. Premiums, Novelties
21. Product Samples 22. Special Events Mktg. 23. Spot Radio 24. Spot T.V. 25. Weekly Newsp. 26. Yellow Page Adv.

MICRO NETWORKS CORP.
(Sub. of Spectrum Microwave, Inc.)
(d/b/a Spectrum Microwave)
324 Clark St
Worcester, MA 01606-1214
Tel.: (508) 852-5400
Fax: (508) 852-8456
E-mail: sales@mnc.com
Web Site: www.micronetworks.com
E-Mail For Key Personnel:
Sales Director: sales@mnc.com
Sales Range: $25-49.9 Million
Approx. Number Employees: 69
Year Founded: 1969
Business Description:
Hybrid Data Conversion Products
S.I.C.: 7373; 3825
N.A.I.C.S.: 541512; 334515
Export
Media: 2-4-7-10-11-21
Distr.: Intl.; Natl.
Budget Set: Jan.
Personnel:
Geoffrey Key *(Dir-Sls & Mktg)*

MICRON CORPORATION
89 Access Rd Ste 5
Norwood, MA 02062-5234
Tel.: (781) 769-5771
Fax: (781) 762-3531
Toll Free: (800) 456-0734
E-mail: info@microncorp.com
Web Site: www.microncorp.com
Sales Range: $10-24.9 Million
Approx. Number Employees: 27
Year Founded: 1982
Business Description:
Printed Circuit Board Assemblies Mfr
S.I.C.: 3672
N.A.I.C.S.: 334412
Export
Media: 6-26
Distr.: Intl.; Natl.
Budget Set: Nov.
Personnel:
William Theos *(Pres)*
James Theos *(VP-Mktg)*
Brands & Products:
ENERGAIRE
MICRON CORPORATION
RODAR

MICRONETICS, INC.
26 Hampshire Dr
Hudson, NH 03051-4922
Tel.: (603) 883-2900
Fax: (603) 882-8987
Web Site: www.mwireless.com
Approx. Sls.: $35,296,705
Approx. Number Employees: 188
Business Description:
Design & Manufacture of Intelligent Switches Noise Sources & Test Equipment
S.I.C.: 3679; 5065
N.A.I.C.S.: 334419; 423690
Advertising Expenditures: $46,818
Media: 2-10-22
Personnel:
Kevin P. Beals *(Pres & Sec)*
David Robbins *(CEO & Treas)*
Carl L. Lueders *(CFO)*
Brands & Products:
INNOVATION FOR THE FUTURE
MICRONETICS

MICROPAC INDUSTRIES INC.
905 E Walnut St
Garland, TX 75040
Tel.: (972) 272-3571
Fax: (972) 494-2281
E-mail: corporate@micropac.com
Web Site: www.micropac.com
Approx. Sls.: $23,070,000
Approx. Number Employees: 133
Year Founded: 1969
Business Description:
Integrated Microcircuits Distr
S.I.C.: 3674
N.A.I.C.S.: 334413
Advertising Expenditures: $784,000
Personnel:
Mark W. King *(CEO)*
Patrick Cefalu *(CFO, Principal Acctg Officer & Exec VP)*
Carol Cagle *(Mgr-Sls-Microcircuits Div)*
Dennis Granger *(Mgr-Sls-Reg-Microcircuits & Optoelectronics Div)*
Bill Holmes *(Mgr-Sls-Reg-Microcircuits & Optoelectronics Div)*
Dorothy Lindemann *(Mgr-Sls-Microcircuits Div)*
Cecil Miller *(Mgr-Quality-Microcircuits & Optoelectronics Div)*

MICROVISION, INC.
6222 185th Ave NE
Redmond, WA 98052-5034
Tel.: (425) 415-6847
Fax: (425) 415-6600
E-mail: info@microvision.com
Web Site: www.mvis.com
Approx. Rev.: $4,740,000
Approx. Number Employees: 108
Business Description:
Display & Imaging Products for Mobile Applications
S.I.C.: 3679; 3577; 8733
N.A.I.C.S.: 334419; 334119; 541710
Media: 10-22
Personnel:
Slade Gorton *(Chm)*
Alexander Y. Tokman *(Pres & CEO)*
Jeff T. Wilson *(CFO)*
Thomas M. Walker *(Gen Counsel, Sec & VP)*
Sridhar Madhavan *(VP-R&D & Product Dev)*
Brands & Products:
MICROVISION
NOMAD
PICOP
ROV
SHOWWX

MICROWAVE FILTER COMPANY, INC.
6743 Kinne St
East Syracuse, NY 13057-1215
Tel.: (315) 438-4700
Fax: (315) 463-1467
Toll Free: (800) 448-1666
E-mail: mfcsales@microwavefilter.com
Web Site: www.microwavefilter.com
Approx. Sls.: $4,691,522
Approx. Number Employees: 48
Business Description:
Electronic Filters for Processing Cable Televison, Radio & Other Signals
S.I.C.: 3679; 3663; 3677; 3826
N.A.I.C.S.: 334419; 334220; 334416; 334516
Media: 2-4-7-8-10-13-26
Personnel:
Robert R. Andrews *(Chm)*
Carl F. Fahrenkrug, Sr. *(Pres)*
Richard L. Jones *(CFO, Sec & VP)*
Paul W. Mears *(VP-Engrng)*

MILESTONE AV TECHNOLOGIES, INC.
8401 Eagle Creek Pkwy
Savage, MN 55378
Tel.: (952) 894-6280
Fax: (952) 894-6918
E-mail: info@milestone.com
Web Site: www.milestone.com
Sales Range: $200-249.9 Million
Approx. Number Employees: 330
Business Description:
Audio Visual, Mounting Equipment & Display Solutions Designer, Marketer & Distr
S.I.C.: 3651; 5064
N.A.I.C.S.: 334310; 423620
Advertising Expenditures: $1,334,000
Media: 2-4-5-6-7-8-9-10-16-25
Personnel:
Scott J. Gill *(CEO)*
Troy A. Peifer *(CFO)*
James G. Wohlford *(VP & Gen Mgr-Consumer Brands)*
Steven E. Durkee *(Gen Mgr-Comml Brands)*

MILLER & KREISEL SOUND CORPORATION
9207 Eton Ave
Chatsworth, CA 91311-5808
Tel.: (818) 701-7010
Fax: (818) 701-0369
E-mail: admin@mksound.com
Web Site: www.mksound.com
Approx. Number Employees: 85
Business Description:
Mfr of Sound Systems
S.I.C.: 3651
N.A.I.C.S.: 334310
Media: 6
Personnel:
Ken Kreisel *(Owner)*
Charles Back *(CFO, Sec & Exec VP)*
Brands & Products:
BACKFIRE
DIPOLE
DISCOVER DEEP BASS
K SERIES
MKPROFESSIONAL
TRIPOLE
XENON

MINI-SYSTEMS, INC.
20 David Rd
North Attleboro, MA 02760
Tel.: (508) 695-0203
Fax: (508) 695-6076
E-mail: rlamarre@mini-systemsinc.com
Web Site: www.mini-systemsinc.com
Approx. Sls.: $20,000,000
Approx. Number Employees: 200
Business Description:
Electronic Resistors Mfr
S.I.C.: 3676; 3674
N.A.I.C.S.: 334415; 334413
Media: 4-10
Personnel:
Glen Robertson *(Owner)*
Rick Charbonneau *(VP & Gen Mgr)*

Brands & Products:
MSIRP

MITEL NETWORKS CORPORATION
350 Legget Drive
PO Box 13089
Kanata, ON K2K 2W7, Canada
Tel.: (613) 592-2122
Fax: (613) 592-4784
E-mail: steve_spooner@mitel.com
Web Site: www.mitel.com
Approx. Rev.: $647,900,000
Approx. Number Employees: 2,362
Year Founded: 1971
Business Description:
Communications Solutions & Services
S.I.C.: 3663; 3661; 4899
N.A.I.C.S.: 334220; 334210; 517410
Export
Advertising Expenditures: $10,000,000
Media: 2-4-10
Distr.: Intl
Budget Set: Feb.
Personnel:
Terence H. Matthews *(Chm)*
Richard D. McBee *(Pres & CEO)*
Gwilym R. Funnell *(Mng Dir-Asia-Pacific Reg & VP)*
Roger K. Fung *(Mng Dir)*
Steven E. Spooner *(CFO)*
Ronald G. Wellard *(Exec VP-Product Dev & Ops)*
Kathy Enright *(VP-HR)*
Brands & Products:
HCI
INTER-TEL AXXESS
MITEL
MITEL ENTERPRISE
MITEL TOTALSOLUTION
MITEL UNIFIED COMMUNICATOR
NUPOINT UNIFIED MESSAGING
PANTHER
SMART-1
SPEAK@EASE
SPECTRALINK NETLINK
SPECTRUM
SUPERCONSOLE
SUPERSET 2
SUPERSET 3
SUPERSET 4
SUPERSET 7
SX-200
SX-200 DIGITAL
SX-200 EL
SX-200 LIGHT
SX-200 ML
SX-2000
SX-2000 LIGHT
SX-2000 MICRO LIGHT
SX-50
YOUR ASSISTANT

MITSUBISHI DIGITAL ELECTRONICS AMERICA, INC.
(Sub. of Mitsubishi Electric Corporation)
9351 Jeronimo Rd
Irvine, CA 92618-1904
Tel.: (949) 465-6000
Fax: (949) 465-6251
Toll Free: (800) 332-2119
Web Site: www.mitsubishi-tv.com
Approx. Number Employees: 360

Mitsubishi Digital Electronics America, Inc. — (Continued)

Business Description:
Upgradeable Projection Televisions, VCRs & Audio Products for Complete Home Theater Systems Mfr
S.I.C.: 3651; 3663
N.A.I.C.S.: 334310; 334220
Media: 6

Personnel:
Max Wasinger *(Exec VP)*
Shoichi Suwa *(Sr VP & Gen Mgr-Visual Sys Div)*
Frank DeMartin *(VP-Mktg)*
John Hwang *(Sr Product Mgr)*
Akihito Odakura *(Mgr-Bus Plng & Mktg)*

Advertising Agency:
GolinHarris
3200 Park Center Dr Ste 750
Costa Mesa, CA 92626
Tel.: (714) 662-5100
Fax: (714) 662-5198
LaserVue HDTV
LDD & DLP HDTVs

MMC ELECTRONICS AMERICA INC.

(Sub. of Mitsubishi Materials Corporation)
1314 N Plum Grove Rd
Schaumburg, IL 60173
Tel.: (847) 252-6360
Fax: (847) 519-1736
E-Mail For Key Personnel:
Marketing Director: glin@mmea.com
Sales Director: sales@mmea.com
Approx. Number Employees: 4
Year Founded: 1977

Business Description:
Electronic Components Distr
S.I.C.: 5065
N.A.I.C.S.: 423690
Import Export
Media: 13
Distr.: Natl.

Personnel:
Akihiko Ide *(Pres)*

MOLEX INCORPORATED

2222 Wellington Ct
Lisle, IL 60532-1682
Tel.: (630) 969-4550
Fax: (630) 968-8356
Toll Free: (800) 78MOLEX
E-mail: molex@molex.dk
Web Site: www.molex.com
Approx. Rev.: $3,587,334,000
Approx. Number Employees: 33,000
Year Founded: 1938

Business Description:
Mfr, Designer & Retailer of Electrical, Electronic & Fiber Optic Devices
S.I.C.: 3678; 3679
N.A.I.C.S.: 334417; 334419
Import Export
Advertising Expenditures: $5,453,000
Media: 1-2-4-5-7-10-11-13-20-21-22
Distr.: Intl.; Natl.
Budget Set: May

Personnel:
Frederick A. Krehbiel *(Co-Chm)*
John H. Krehbiel, Jr. *(Co-Chm)*
Martin P. Slark *(Vice Chm & CEO)*
Liam G. McCarthy *(Pres & COO)*
David D. Johnson *(CFO, Treas & Exec VP)*
Gary J. Matula *(CIO & Sr VP-Info Sys)*
K. Travis George *(Chief Acctg Officer & VP)*
Graham C. Brock *(Pres-Global Sls & Mktg Div & Exec VP)*
James E. Fleischhacker *(Pres-Global Comml Products Div & Exec VP)*
Katsumi Hirokawa *(Pres-Global Micro Products Div & Exec VP)*
J. Michael Nauman *(Pres-Global Integrated Products Div & Exec VP)*
Fred L. Krehbiel *(Sr VP-Tech Innovation)*
Ana G. Rodriguez *(Sr VP-Global HR)*
Adam Stanczak *(Mgr-Product)*
Tom Schoder *(Grp Product Mgr-Integrated Products)*
Ted Szarkowski *(Global Product Mgr-Integrated Products)*
Chip Walsh *(Global Product Mgr)*

Brands & Products:
6-PAK
ADVANTAGE
AERO-MOTIVE
AEROBAR
APPLICOM
AT-200
ATP-201
AVIKRIMP
AXID
BACKFLIP
BEAU
BEAUPLUG
BLC
BOSS
BRAD
BRAD HARRISON & DESIGN
BRADCOMMUNICATIONS
BRADCONNECTIVITY
BRADCONTROL
BRADPOWER
BRADPOWER & DESIGN
BSC
BSC II
C-GRID
C-GRID III
CHANGE
CLASPCON
CLIK-MATE
CLIPLOK
COAXID
COMPACTLAN
COMPAK-LOCK
COMPODRE
CONDOR
CONTURA
COOLFIN
CORE-LOCK
CRADLECON
CRC
DANIEL WOODHEAD
DATAGATE
DATAGATE PLUS
DECORA
DIRECT-LINK
DL-50
DMS-59
DS-50
DUALCON
DURACLIK
EAGLE
EASY-ON
EBBI
ECON-O-MITE
EDG
EDGELINE
EMILY
EMS-ENABLE
ENETMETER
EURO-C
EUROMATE
EUROMAX
EUROMOD
EUROSTYLE
EVERMATE
EXTREME CZPOWER
EXTREME HIGHCPOWER
EXTREME LPHPOWER
EXTREME MICROPOWER
EXTREME POWERBBC
EXTREME POWERDOCK
EXTREME POWEREDGE
EXTREME POWERMASS
EXTREME POWERPLUS
EXTREME TEN50POWER
EXTREME TEN60POWER
EXTREME ZPOWER
EZ BAR
EZ-CONN
FABRI-FIT
FACES
FASTJUNCTION
FAXENABLE
FINEADJUST
FLEXBEAM
FLEXJUMPER
FLEXPLANE
FLEXTRAN
FLIGHTFLEX
FLT4
FMP3
FOUR-DUCTOR
FRAMESTACK
GBX I-TRAC
H-DAC 64
HANDYLINK
HAWK
HAZTEX
HBMT
HD MEZZ
HDX
HISPEC
HISPEC GS
HMC
HS DOCK
HS MEZZ
HSAUTOLINK
HTC
HYPERJACK
ICOOL
IGRID
ILOCK
IMPACT
IMPACTNXT
INDUSTRIAL INTERFACES
INSULKRIMP
IPASS
IPASS+
JET-FLECS
KATT
KATT PDS
KRIMPTITE
LANELINK
LASERSTREAM
LFH
LI-24
LIGHTBAND
LIGHTDEALER
LITE-A-SITE
LOVOLT
LUMACORE
MACRO-LOCK
MAGKRIMP
MARKK
MAX-LOC
MCIA
METREC
MFB
MI II
MICRO-C
MICRO-C POLYPORT
MICRO-CHANGE
MICRO-FIT
MICRO-FIT 3.0
MICRO-FIT 3.0 BMI
MICRO-FIT BMI CPI
MICRO-FIT CPI
MICRO-LATCH
MICRO-LOCK
MICRO-PUSH
MICROBLADE
MICROCLASP
MICROCROSS
MIG
MILLI-GRID
MILLI-Z
MINI-AXID
MINI-C
MINI-C POLYPORT
MINI-CAM
MINI-CHANGE
MINI-FIT
MINI-FIT BMI
MINI-FIT BMI SLIDE-AND-LOCK
MINI-FIT CPI
MINI-FIT GW
MINI-FIT H20
MINI-FIT HCS
MINI-FIT HCS BMI
MINI-FIT HIGH CYCLE
MINI-FIT IDT
MINI-FIT JR.
MINI-FIT PLUS
MINI-FIT PLUS HCS
MINI-FIT RTC
MINI-FIT SMC
MINI-FIT SR.
MINI-FIT TPA
MINI-HMC
MINI-LATCH
MINI-LOCK
MINI-MAC
MINI MI II
MINI-PUSH
MINI-SPOX
MINI-X250
MINILAN
MITE-Y-PIN
MLX
MOBI-MATE
MOD-SNAP
MODLINK
MOLEX
MOLEX-ETC
MOLEX PREMISE NETWORKS
MOLIC
MP-200
MP-LOCK
MPIS
MPM
MTC
MULTI-TAP
MUSIC
MUXLINK
MV-396
MX
MX-250
MX-PLUS

Key to Media (For complete agency information see *The Advertising Red Books-Agencies* edition):
1. Bus. Publs. 2. Cable T.V. 3. Catalogs & Directories. 4. Co-op Adv. 5. Consumer Mags. 6. D.M. to Bus. Estab.7: D.M. to Consumers
8. Daily Newsp. 9. Exhibits/Trade Shows 10. Foreign 11. Infomercial 12. Internet Adv.13. Multimedia 14. Network Radio
15. Network T.V. 16. Newsp. Distr. Mags. 17. Other 18. Outdoor (Posters, Transit) 19. Point of Purchase20. Premiums, Novelties
21. Product Samples 22. Special Events Mktg. 23. Spot Radio 24. Spot T.V. 25. Weekly Newsp. 26. Yellow Page Adv.

MX120
MX150
MX150L
MX64
MXII
MXL-38999
MZP
NANO-CHANGE
NEOTEX
NET ALERT
NETALYTIX
NETMETER
NEXSTEP
NIAC
NYLAKRIMP
OFFICE BLOCK
OMNIGRID
ONE COMPANY A WORLD OF INNOVATION
OPTICAL SHUFFLE
ORIGIN
PANELMATE
PARALINK
PARALINK-P
PASSPORT
PENTA-CHANGE
PERMA-FIT
PERMA-SEAL
PHEONIX
PICO-CHANGE
PICO-CLASP
PICO-EZMATE
PICO-GOLD
PICO-GRID
PICO-SPOX
PICOBLADE
PICOFLEX
PICS SIMULATION
PINSETTER
PLATEAU HS DOCK
PLATEAU HS DOCK PG
PLATEAU HS MEZZ
PLATEAU TECHNOLOGY
POLYPORT
POW-R-BELT
POW-R-MATIC
POW-R-MITE
POW-R-TAG
POWER BLADZ
POWER DOCK
POWER EDGE
POWER MONITOR
POWER PLUS
POWER PLUS SR.
POWERCAT
POWERCAT 6
POWERRUN
PREMIUMGRADE
PREMO-FLEX
QF-50
QIK-FLECS
QUICK-CHANGE
RADIAL FIN
REALTIME
RESILIENTFLEX
RIPPN
RJ-LNXX
RKG
ROMEX
SABRE
SAFEWAY
SAFEWAY+
SDMO
SEE & SPLICE
SEMCONN
SERVICEGRADE
SHERLOCK
SIGNATURE
SILENT DRIVE
SL
SLICE IN A BOX
SLIDERZ
SLIMSTACK
SLT3S
SNAPMATE
SNAPPER
SOLDER CHARGE
SOLDER CHARGE TECHNOLOGY
SPECTRE
SPIRIT
SPOX
SPOX BMI
SST
STAC64
STREAMLINE
SUPER-SAFEWAY
SYNERGY
TDP
TELENABLE
TM-2000
TM-3000
TM-40
TM-42
TPA
TRACK-IT
TRANSCEND
TRIAD
TRIFURCON
TWIN-STACK
ULTI-MATE
ULTRA-LOCK
ULTRA+
UNIVERSAL PATCHING FRAME
USO
USP
VERSABLADE
VERSAKRIMP
VIBRAKRIMP
VPR
WAFERCON
WATERTITE
WIRE TRAP-LITE
X-LINK
XPRESS
XPRESS-LOCK
XRC
Z-ZONE
ZIFCON
ZIPCON
ZXP
ZYTON

Advertising Agencies:
Communication House, s.r.o.
Stefanikova 6
040 01
Kosice, Slovakia
Tel.: (421) 55 623 00 70
Fax: (421) 55 636 26 60

Gibbs & Soell - Chicago
2800 W Higgins Rd Ste 730
Hoffman Estates, IL 60169
Tel.: (847) 519-9150
Fax: (847) 519-1877

Moveo
1 Parkview Plz Ste 150
Oakbrook Terrace, IL 60181
Tel.: (630) 570-4800
Fax: (630) 571-3031

Sonnhalter
633 W Bagley Rd
Berea, OH 44017-1356
Tel.: (440) 234-1812
Fax: (440) 234-1890

MONITRONICS INTERNATIONAL, INC.
(Sub. of Ascent Media Group, LLC)
2350 Valley View Ln Ste 100
Dallas, TX 75234-5835
Mailing Address:
PO Box 814530
Dallas, TX 75381-4530
Tel.: (972) 243-7443
Fax: (972) 484-1393
Toll Free: (800) 447-9239
Web Site: www.monitronics.com
Sales Range: $250-299.9 Million
Approx. Number Employees: 700
Year Founded: 1994
Business Description:
Security Alarm Monitoring Systems
S.I.C.: 7382
N.A.I.C.S.: 561621
Export
Media: 2-5-7-10-13
Personnel:
Michael R. Haislip *(Pres & CEO)*
Michael R. Meyers *(CFO)*
Kelly Habbas *(CIO)*
Steve Baker *(VP-Sls)*
Mitch Clarke *(VP-Mktg & Mktg Devel)*
John M. Mejia *(VP-Customer Care)*
Bruce Mungiguerra *(VP-Sls & Dealer Dev)*
Reginald Blakely *(Product Mgr)*
Brands & Products:
MONITRONICS

MONOTYPE IMAGING HOLDINGS, INC.
500 Unicorn Park Dr
Woburn, MA 01801
Tel.: (781) 970-6000
Fax: (781) 970-6001
Web Site:
www.monotypeimaging.com
Approx. Rev.: $106,659,000
Approx. Number Employees: 251
Business Description:
Text Imaging Solutions
S.I.C.: 7371; 2759; 3669
N.A.I.C.S.: 541511; 323115; 334290
Advertising Expenditures: $2,800,000
Media: 1-6-7-8-10-13
Personnel:
Robert M. Givens *(Chm)*
Douglas J. Shaw *(Pres & CEO)*
Scott E. Landers *(CFO & Sr VP)*
Janet M. Dunlap *(Gen Counsel & VP)*
Jeffrey J. Burk *(Treas, VP & Asst Sec)*
John L. Seguin *(Exec VP)*
David L. Mccarthy *(VP & Gen Mgr)*
Steven R. Martin *(VP-Engrg)*
Patricia J. Money *(VP-HR)*
Advertising Agency:
Porter Novelli-Boston
2 Seaport Ln Ste 900
Boston, MA 02110
Tel.: (617) 897-8200
Fax: (617) 897-8203

MORSE WATCHMANS INC.
2 Morse Rd
Oxford, CT 06478-1040
Tel.: (203) 264-4949
Fax: (203) 264-8367
Toll Free: (800) 423-8256
E-mail: morse@morsewatchman.com
Web Site: www.morsewatchman.com
E-Mail For Key Personnel:
Marketing Director: fernando@morsewatchman.com
Approx. Sls.: $8,000,000
Approx. Number Employees: 45
Year Founded: 1882
Business Description:
Mfr. & Sale of Guard Tour Systems & Key Management Systems
S.I.C.: 3699; 3577
N.A.I.C.S.: 335999; 334119
Export
Media: 4
Distr.: Intl.; Natl.
Budget Set: Sept.
Personnel:
Fernando Pires *(VP-Sls-Mktg)*
Brands & Products:
THE BOSS
BOSS GUARD TOUR SYSTEM
KEY-PRO
KEY-RING
KEY-RINGS
KEYBANK
KEYWATCHER
POWERCHECK
TOUR-PRO

MOSAID TECHNOLOGIES INCORPORATED
11 Hines Rd Ste 203
Kanata, ON K2K 2X1, Canada
Tel.: (613) 599-9539
Fax: (613) 591-8148
E-mail: communications@mosaid.com
Web Site: www.mosaid.com
E-Mail For Key Personnel:
President: Lindgren@mosaid.com
Public Relations: ir@mosaid.com
Approx. Rev.: $69,593,935
Approx. Number Employees: 257
Year Founded: 1975
Business Description:
Mfr. of Semiconductors & Data Systems
S.I.C.: 3674
N.A.I.C.S.: 334413
Export
Media: 4-10-13
Personnel:
Carl P. Schlachte *(Chm)*
John C. Lindgren *(Pres & CEO)*
Joseph R. Brown *(CFO & VP)*
Phillip S. Shaer *(Gen Counsel, Sec & VP)*
Michael B. Vladescu *(VP-Licensing & Intellectual Property)*
Michael Salter *(Dir-IR & Corp Comm)*
Brands & Products:
MOSAID
MOSAID CLASS-IC

MOSYS INC.
3301 Olcott S
Santa Clara, CA 95054
Tel.: (408) 418-7500
Fax: (408) 418-7501
E-mail: ir@mosysinc.com
Web Site: www.mosysinc.com
Approx. Rev.: $15,563,000
Approx. Number Employees: 162
Year Founded: 1991
Business Description:
Memory Technologies for Semiconductor Industry & Electronic Product Manufacturers
S.I.C.: 3674

Key to Media (For complete agency information see *The Advertising Red Books-Agencies* edition):
1. Bus. Publs. 2. Cable T.V. 3. Catalogs & Directories. 4. Co-op Adv. 5. Consumer Mags. 6. D.M. to Bus. Estab.7. D.M. to Consumers
8. Daily Newsp. 9. Exhibits/Trade Shows 10. Foreign 11. Infomercial 12. Internet Adv.13. Multimedia 14. Network Radio
15. Network T.V. 16. Newsp. Distr. Mags. 17. Other 18. Outdoor (Posters, Transit) 19. Point of Purchase20. Premiums, Novelties
21. Product Samples 22. Special Events Mktg. 23. Spot Radio 24. Spot T.V. 25. Weekly Newsp. 26. Yellow Page Adv.

MoSys Inc. — (Continued)

N.A.I.C.S.: 334413
Advertising Expenditures: $1,000,000
Media: 2-10-13
Personnel:
Leonard Charles Perham *(Pres & CEO)*
James T. Sullivan *(CFO & VP-Fin)*
Sundari Mitra *(Exec VP-Engrg)*
Hem Hingarh *(VP-Engrg)*
Michael Miller *(VP-Tech Innovation & Sys Applications)*
Brands & Products:
1T-FLASH
1T-SRAM
MDRAM
MOSYS
Advertising Agency:
Shelton Group
12400 Coit Rd Ste 650
Dallas, TX 75251
Tel.: (972) 239-5119
Fax: (972) 239-2292

MOTOROLA CANADA LIMITED

(Sub. of Motorola Solutions, Inc.)
8133 Warden Avenue
Markham, ON L6G 1B3, Canada
Tel.: (090) 594-85200
Fax: (090) 594-85250
Telex: 6-969740
Web Site: www.motorola.ca
Sales Range: $100-124.9 Million
Year Founded: 1948
Business Description:
Cable TV Distribution Equipment, LAN Systems
S.I.C.: 3812
N.A.I.C.S.: 334511
Advertising Expenditures: $200,000
Media: 2-4-6-7-16
Distr.: Natl.
Budget Set: Jan.
Personnel:
Sean Miller *(Pres)*
Brands & Products:
CABLEOPTICS
STARLINE
Advertising Agencies:
Ogilvy & Mather
33 Yonge St
Toronto, ON M5E 1X6, Canada
Tel.: (416) 367-3573
Fax: (416) 363-2088

TWG Communications
101 Worthington St E Ste 433
North Bay, ON P1B 1G5, Canada
Tel.: (705) 472-1861
Fax: (705) 472-2343

MOTOROLA, INC.

(Name Changed to Motorola Solutions, Inc.)

MOTOROLA MOBILITY HOLDINGS, INC.

600 N US Highway 45
Libertyville, IL 60048
Tel.: (847) 523-5000
E-mail: info@motorola.com
Web Site: www.motorola.com/mobility
Approx. Rev.: $11,460,000,000
Approx. Number Employees: 19,000
Business Description:
Technologies, Products & Services for Mobile & Wireline Digital Communication, Information & Entertainment
S.I.C.: 3663
N.A.I.C.S.: 334220; 334290; 517212
Advertising Expenditures: $393,000,000
Personnel:
Sanjay K. Jha *(Chm & CEO)*
Daniel M. Moloney *(Pres)*
Marc Rothman *(Sr VP & CFO)*
Juergen Stark *(Sr VP & COO)*
Walt Oswald *(Corp VP & CIO)*
William Ogle *(Sr VP & CMO)*
Geoff Roman *(Sr VP & CTO)*
John Bucher *(Corp VP & Chief Strategy Officer)*
Scott A. Crum *(Sr VP & Chief People Officer)*
Mike Fleming *(Sr VP & Chief Supply Chain Officer)*
Frank Meng *(Pres-Greater China)*
Rob Hoxie *(Principal)*
Scott Offer *(Sr VP & Gen Counsel)*
John Burke *(Sr VP & Gen Mgr-Converged Experiences)*
John Cipolla *(Sr VP-Product Dev-Mobile Devices)*
Yossi Cohen *(Sr VP-Companion Products-Mobile Devices)*
Alain Mutricy *(Sr VP-Portfolio & Device Product Mgmt-Mobile Devices)*
Dave Rothschild *(Sr VP-Global Software Dev & Tech-Mobile Devices)*
Dale Stone *(Sr VP-Govt Rels)*
Jim Wicks *(VP & Dir-Consumer Experience Design-Mobile Devices)*
Rob Boverie *(Dir-Media-Americas)*

MOTOROLA SOLUTIONS, INC.

(Formerly Motorola, Inc.)
1303 E Algonquin Rd
Schaumburg, IL 60196-4041
Tel.: (847) 576-5000
Tel.: (847) 576-6899 (IR)
Fax: (847) 576-5372
Toll Free: (800) 331-6456
Web Site:
www.motorolasolutions.com
Approx. Sls.: $19,282,000,000
Approx. Number Employees: 51,000
Year Founded: 1928
Business Description:
Wireless & Broadband Telecommunications Equipment & Services
S.I.C.: 3663; 3577; 3661; 4812; 4899; 7379
N.A.I.C.S.: 334220; 334119; 334210; 517212; 517910; 541519
Advertising Expenditures: $502,000,000
Media: 2-3-4-5-6-7-8-9-10-11-13-14-15-18-19-20-22-23-24-25
Distr.: Intl.; Natl.
Personnel:
Gregory Q. Brown *(Pres & COO)*
Edward J. Fitzpatrick *(CFO)*
Leslie Jones *(CIO & Sr VP)*
Eduardo Conrado *(CMO & Sr VP)*
John K. Wozniak *(Chief Acctg Officer & Corp VP)*
Lewis Steverson *(Gen Counsel, Sec & Sr VP)*
Gene Delaney *(Exec VP-Product & Bus Ops)*
Bruce Brda *(Sr VP & Gen Mgr-Networks)*
Michele Aguilar Carlin *(Sr VP-HR)*
Mark F. Moon *(Sr VP-Sls & Field Ops)*
Karen P. Tandy *(Sr VP-Pub Affairs & Comm)*
Cathie Kozik *(Corp VP-IT)*
Kelly S. Mark *(Corp VP-Strategy & Staff Ops)*
Suzanne Cafferty *(Dir-Global Product Mktg)*
Vincent Kennedy *(Dir-Strategy-EMEA)*
Frank Lawler *(Dir-Creative)*
Kareen Kaur *(Sr Mgr-Interactive Mktg-Asia Pacific)*
Brands & Products:
ACCOMPLI
ASTRIA
ASTRO
BISTATIX
CANOPY
CHERRYPICKER
CLEARVISION
CLIQ
CN620
COMMANDER
CYBERSURFR
DIGITAL DNA
DIMETRA
DROID
DROID PRO
DTR410
DTR510
DTR550
DTR610
DTR650
ENTERPRISE SEAMLESS MOBILITY
ENVOY
FINDVIAMOTO
GETVIAMOTO
HOMESIGHT
IDEN
INTELLIGENCE EVERYWHERE
IRADIO
KDT800
KRZR
LCS 2000
M-CORE
M-VENTOR
MEDIACIPHER
ML910
MOTO
MOTORAZR
MOTORAZR MAXX VE
MOTORAZR2
MOTOROKR
MOTOROLA
MOTOSLVR
MOTOTRBO
MOTOWI4
MOTOZINE
NAVDISC
NETOPIA
OMNISTAR
ONCORE
PEBL
QUANTAR
RADIUS
RAZR
SATELLITE SERIES
SIMPLEFI
SIX SIGMA
STARCORE
STARLINE
SURFBOARD
TALKABOUT
TIMEPORT
VISUAL APB
V.SERIES
XPR
Advertising Agencies:
Anomaly Communications LLC
536 Broadway 11th Fl
New York, NY 10012
Tel.: (917) 595-2200
Fax: (917) 595-2299

BBDO Worldwide Inc.
(Sub. of Omnicom Group, Inc.)
1285 Ave of the Americas
New York, NY 10019-6028
Tel.: (212) 459-5000
Fax: (212) 459-6645
Rokr

BDS Marketing
10 Holland
Irvine, CA 92618
Tel.: (949) 472-6700
Fax: (949) 597-2220

Draftfcb
101 E Erie St
Chicago, IL 60611-2812
Tel.: (312) 425-5000
Fax: (312) 425-5010

GoConvergence
4545 36th St
Orlando, FL 32811
Tel.: (407) 235-3210
Fax: (407) 299-9907

Hill & Knowlton, Inc.
(Member of WPP)
825 3rd Ave 24th Fl
New York, NY 10022
Tel.: (212) 885-0300
Fax: (212) 885-0570
(Public Relations)

Ogilvy & Mather
(Sub. of WPP Group plc)
636 11th Ave
New York, NY 10036
Tel.: (212) 237-4000
Fax: (212) 237-5123

Ogilvy & Mather N America & Corporate
636 11th Ave
New York, NY 10036
Tel.: (212) 237-4000
Fax: (212) 237-5123

Weber Shandwick-Chicago
676 N St Clair Ste 1000
Chicago, IL 60611
Tel.: (312) 988-2400
Fax: (312) 988-2363
Motorola Mobility (Public Relations Agency of Record)

MTI INSTRUMENTS INC.

(Sub. of Mechanical Technology, Incorporated)
325 Washington Ave Ext
Albany, NY 12205-5505
Tel.: (518) 218-2500
Fax: (518) 218-2506
Toll Free: (800) 342-2203
E-mail: sales@mtiinstruments.com
Web Site: www.mtiinstruments.com
E-Mail For Key Personnel:
Sales Director: sales@mtiinstruments.com

Key to Media (For complete agency information see *The Advertising Red Books-Agencies* edition):
1. Bus. Publs. 2. Cable T.V. 3. Catalogs & Directories. 4. Co-op Adv. 5. Consumer Mags. 6. D.M. to Bus. Estab.7. D.M. to Consumers 8. Daily Newsp. 9. Exhibits/Trade Shows 10. Foreign 11. Infomercial 12. Internet Adv.13. Multimedia 14. Network Radio 15. Network T.V. 16. Newsp. Distr. Mags. 17. Other 18. Outdoor (Posters, Transit) 19. Point of Purchase20. Premiums, Novelties 21. Product Samples 22. Special Events Mktg. 23. Spot Radio 24. Spot T.V. 25. Weekly Newsp. 26. Yellow Page Adv.

Sales Range: $10-24.9 Million
Approx. Number Employees: 40
Business Description:
Electronic Instruments Mfr
S.I.C.: 3829; 8733
N.A.I.C.S.: 334519; 541710
Export
Media: 10
Personnel:
Rick Jones *(VP-Fin & Ops)*
Gordon Reid *(Sr Dir-Sls & Mktg-PE, MTI Instruments)*
Dave Kennison *(Dir-Sls-Aviation)*
Don Welch *(Dir-New Bus Dev)*
Brands & Products:
ACCUMEASURE 1500
ACCUMEASURE 5000
ACCUMEASURE 9000
FOTONIC
MICROTRAK 7000
MICROTRAK II
MTI-2000
PBS-4100
PBS-4100R
PROFORMA 300

MTI MICROFUEL CELLS INC.
(Sub. of Mechanical Technology, Incorporated)
431 New Karner Rd
Albany, NY 12205
Tel.: (518) 533-2222
Fax: (518) 533-2223
E-mail: sales.mtimicro@mechtech.com
Web Site: www.mtimicrofuelcells.com
E-Mail For Key Personnel:
Sales Director: sales.mtimicro@mechtech.com
Sales Range: $25-49.9 Million
Approx. Number Employees: 23
Year Founded: 2001
Business Description:
Developer & Marketer of Proprietary Direct Methanol Fuel Cells Systems as Future Power Sources for Wireless Electronic Devices
S.I.C.: 3692; 3691; 3699
N.A.I.C.S.: 335912; 335911; 335999
Media: 10
Personnel:
Peng K. Lim *(Chm & CEO)*
Jim Prueitt *(VP-Engrg & Ops)*
James Frawley *(Dir-Bus Dev)*

MTONE WIRELESS CORPORATION
3080 Olcott St Ste 100-A
Santa Clara, CA 95054
Tel.: (408) 986-8988
Fax: (408) 986-9309
Web Site: www.mtone.com
Sales Range: $10-24.9 Million
Approx. Number Employees: 322
Year Founded: 1994
Business Description:
Mobile Phone Service
S.I.C.: 4812; 7375
N.A.I.C.S.: 517212; 518111
Advertising Expenditures: $3,882,000
Media: 5-9-11-17-23-25
Personnel:
Victor Wang *(Pres & CEO)*
Peng Qiao *(COO)*

MULTI-FINELINE ELECTRONIX, INC.
(d/b/a MFlex)
3140 E Coronado St Ste A
Anaheim, CA 92806
Tel.: (714) 238-1488
Fax: (714) 996-3834
E-mail: info@mflex.com
Web Site: www.mflex.com
Approx. Sls.: $791,339,000
Approx. Number Employees: 11,800
Year Founded: 1984
Business Description:
Flexible Printed Circuits & Circuit Assemblies Mfr
S.I.C.: 3672
N.A.I.C.S.: 334412
Advertising Expenditures: $8,783,000
Personnel:
Philippe Lemaitre *(Chm)*
Reza A. Meshgin *(Pres & CEO)*
Thomas Liguori *(CFO & Exec VP)*
Matthew Wolk *(Chief Strategy Officer & VP-Corp Dev)*
Christine Besnard *(Gen Counsel, Sec & VP)*
Thomas Lee *(Exec VP-Ops & Program Mgmt)*
Don Pucci *(VP-Sls & Mktg)*

MUNICIPAL EMERGENCY SERVICES, INC.
(Sub. of Tyco Fire & Security)
15865 International Dr
Houston, TX 77032
Tel.: (281) 442-9190
Fax: (281) 442-9199
Toll Free: (800) 784-0404
E-mail: mkeltch@tycoint.com
Web Site: www.mesfire.com/
Approx. Number Employees: 170
Year Founded: 2001
Business Description:
Emergency Alarms
S.I.C.: 3669; 7382
N.A.I.C.S.: 334290; 561621
Media: 4-7-10
Personnel:
Steve Boubel *(Dir-Procurements)*
Advertising Agency:
Smiley Graphix
403 Lakemper Dr
Metamora, IL 61548
Tel.: (309) 383-2662

MURATA ELECTRONICS NORTH AMERICA, INC.
(Sub. of Murata Manufacturing Co., Ltd.)
2200 Lake Park Dr
Smyrna, GA 30080-7604
Tel.: (770) 436-1300
Fax: (770) 436-3030
E-mail: info@murata.com
Web Site: www.murata-northamerica.com
Approx. Number Employees: 150
Year Founded: 1973
Business Description:
Fixed & Variable Ceramic Capacitors & Related Products Distr
S.I.C.: 5065
N.A.I.C.S.: 423690
Import
Advertising Expenditures: $800,000
Media: 4-5-10
Distr.: Intl.; Natl.
Budget Set: Dec. -Jan.
Personnel:
David M. Kirk *(Pres & CEO)*
John Denslinger *(Exec VP)*
Hideo Sakamoto *(Exec VP)*
Tony Coalson *(Sr VP-Sls & Mktg)*
Scott Klettke *(Sr Mgr-RF & Microwave)*
Peter Tiller *(Sr Grp Product Mgr)*
Mitch Nozaki *(Sr Mgr-Product)*
Mark Waugh *(Product Mgr)*
Jerry Koby *(Mgr-Mktg)*
Tom Taylor *(Mgr-Accts-Global)*

NANOOPTO CORPORATION
(Sub. of API Technologies Corp.)
1600 Cottontail Ln
Somerset, NJ 08873-5112
Tel.: (732) 627-0808
Fax: (732) 627-9886
E-mail: info@nanoopto.com
Web Site: www.nanoopto.com
Approx. Sls.: $2,700,000
Approx. Number Employees: 31
Year Founded: 2000
Business Description:
Optical Chip & Nano-Structure Mfr.
S.I.C.: 3827
N.A.I.C.S.: 333314
Personnel:
Phillip DeZwirek *(Chm & CEO)*
Thomas Mills *(Pres & COO)*
Martin Moskovits *(Pres)*
Advertising Agency:
Interprose Inc.
2635 Steeplechase Dr
Reston, VA 20191
Tel.: (703) 860-0577
Fax: (703) 860-1623

NAPCO SECURITY SYSTEMS, INC.
333 Bayview Ave
Amityville, NY 11701
Tel.: (631) 842-9400
Fax: (631) 789-9292
Toll Free: (800) 645-9445
E-mail: salesinfo@naposecurity.com
Web Site: www.napcosecurity.com
E-Mail For Key Personnel:
Sales Director: salesinfo@napcosecurity.com
Approx. Sls.: $69,565
Approx. Number Employees: 774
Year Founded: 1969
Business Description:
Security Systems, Locking Devices & Access Control Security Products Mfr.
S.I.C.: 7382
N.A.I.C.S.: 561621
Import Export
Advertising Expenditures: $1,318,000
Media: 2-6-10-19
Distr.: Intl.; Natl.
Budget Set: June
Personnel:
Richard L. Soloway *(Chm, Pres & Sec)*
Kevin S. Buchel *(Treas, Sr VP-Ops & Fin)*
Michael Carrieri *(Sr VP-Engrg Dev)*
Jorge Hevia *(Sr VP-Sls & Mktg)*
Dave Sheffey *(VP-Sls-Eastern Reg)*
Dale Clement *(Reg Mgr-Sls)*
Joe Guernica *(Reg Mgr)*
Paul Hoey *(Reg Mgr-Sls)*
Scott Sager *(Reg Mgr-Sls)*
Richard Tare *(Reg Mgr-Sls)*
Kevin Kremposky *(Sls Mgr-Reg)*
Anne Gaudino *(Mgr-Intl Sls)*
Brands & Products:
CARDACCESS
CONTINENTAL INSTRUMENTS
CYPHER
DETECT COMPARE IMAGING DIAGNOSTICS
FIREWOLF
GEMINI
INFORMAX
IQ PROFILER
MAGNUM ALERT
MAGNUM FIRE ALERT
MICROTERM
MINITERM
NETLINK
POSITIVE ELECTRO-IMAGING TRACING
POWEREXIT
POWERMAG
QUICK LOADER
ROOM-ALERT
SIGNAL SELECTIVE PROCESSING
SIGNATURE PRODUCTS
SIRENLOCK
SMARTER SYSTEM
SMARTERM
SUPERTERM
TRILOGY
TURBO SUPERTERM
WIRELESS ADAPTIVE

NATIONAL SEMICONDUCTOR CORPORATION
2900 Semiconductor Dr
Santa Clara, CA 95051-0606
Mailing Address:
PO Box 58090
Santa Clara, CA 95052-8090
Tel.: (408) 721-5000
Fax: (408) 739-9803
Toll Free: (800) 272-9959
Telex: TWX 910-339-9240
E-mail: new.feedback@nsc.com
Web Site: www.national.com
Approx. Sls.: $1,520,400,000
Approx. Number Employees: 5,700
Year Founded: 1959
Business Description:
Integrated Circuits & Microprocessors Mfr
S.I.C.: 3674
N.A.I.C.S.: 334413
Export
Media: 1-4-7-10-11-13-20-22
Distr.: Intl.; Natl.
Budget Set: Apr.
Personnel:
Donald Macleod *(Chm & CEO)*
Lewis Chew *(CFO & Sr VP)*
Julie Wong *(CIO & VP)*
Ahmad Bahai *(CTO & Sr VP)*
Todd M. DuChene *(Gen Counsel, Sec & Sr VP)*
Detlev Kunz *(Sr VP & Gen Mgr-Product Grp)*
C. S. Liu *(Sr VP-Worldwide Mfg)*
Edward Sweeney *(Sr VP-Worldwide HR)*
Phil Gibson *(VP-Mktg & Web Ops)*
Sadanand Patil *(VP-Package Tech)*
Jeff Andersen *(Bus Dir)*
Ajay Padgaonkar *(Dir-Mktg)*

Key to Media (For complete agency information see *The Advertising Red Books-Agencies* edition):
1. Bus. Publs. 2. Cable T.V. 3. Catalogs & Directories. 4. Co-op Adv. 5. Consumer Mags. 6. D.M. to Bus. Estab.7. D.M. to Consumers
8. Daily Newsp. 9. Exhibits/Trade Shows 10. Foreign 11. Infomercial 12. Internet Adv.13. Multimedia 14. Network Radio
15. Network T.V. 16. Newsp. Distr. Mags. 17. Other 18. Outdoor (Posters, Transit) 19. Point of Purchase20. Premiums, Novelties
21. Product Samples 22. Special Events Mktg. 23. Spot Radio 24. Spot T.V. 25. Weekly Newsp. 26. Yellow Page Adv.

National Semiconductor Corporation — (Continued)

Brands & Products:
ANALOG EDGE
BI-FET
BLUETOOTH
DVMATICS
LME
MICROFIL
NATIONAL SEMICONDUCTOR
POWERWISE
SIMPLE SWITCHER
SOLARMAGIC
TRUTHERM
WEBENCH
WEBTHERM
WHISPERBUS
Advertising Agency:
Antenna Group, Inc.
135 Main St Ste 800
San Francisco, CA 94105-8110
Tel.: (415) 896-1800
Fax: (415) 896-1094

NAVCOM DEFENSE ELECTRONICS, INC.
(Div. of Deere & Company)
4323 Arden Dr
El Monte, CA 91731
Tel.: (626) 579-8689
Fax: (626) 444-7619
E-mail: nde@navcom.com
Web Site: www.navcom.com
Sales Range: $10-24.9 Million
Approx. Number Employees: 70
Year Founded: 1932
Business Description:
Designer & Mfr of Products Related to Altimetry, Radar, Tactical Air Navigation (TACAN), Beacons, Radios, Specialized Test Sets
S.I.C.: 3812
N.A.I.C.S.: 334511
Export
Media: 4-10-20
Distr.: Intl.; Natl.
Budget Set: Oct.
Personnel:
Clifford C. Christ *(CEO)*

NEC CORPORATION OF AMERICA
(Branch of NEC Corporation of America, Inc.)
10850 Gold Ctr Dr Ste 200
Rancho Cordova, CA 95670
Tel.: (916) 463-7000
Toll Free: (800) 733-1388
Web Site: www.necam.com
Approx. Number Employees: 50
Business Description:
Producer & Marketer of a Broad Range of Desktop & Mobile Computers & Servers
S.I.C.: 5045; 3572
N.A.I.C.S.: 423430; 334112
Media: 6-17-18-25
Distr.: Natl.

NEC CORPORATION OF AMERICA, INC.
(Sub. of NEC Corporation)
6555 N State Hwy 161
Irving, TX 75039-2402
Tel.: (214) 262-2000
Toll Free: (800) 338-9549
E-mail: lourdes.wojtecki@necam.com
Web Site: www.necamerica.com
Approx. Number Employees: 800
Year Founded: 1963
Business Description:
Mfr. & Sale of Communications Equipment
S.I.C.: 3661
N.A.I.C.S.: 334210
Import Export
Advertising Expenditures: $1,750,000
Media: 2-5-6-9-10-17-26
Distr.: Natl.
Budget Set: Apr.
Personnel:
Takayuki Okada *(Pres & CEO)*
Matt Pierce *(Sr VP-Sls & Mktg)*
Rocky Kler *(Gen Mgr-Optical Network Sys Division)*
John Wise *(Mgr-Mktg Comm)*
Brands & Products:
NEAX

NEONODE, INC.
(Sub. of Neonode, Inc.)
4000 Executive Pkwy Ste 200
San Ramon, CA 94583-4257
Tel.: (925) 355-2000
Fax: (925) 355-2020
Web Site: www.neonode.com
Sales Range: $25-49.9 Million
Approx. Number Employees: 40
Year Founded: 1961
Business Description:
Network Access & Communications Devices Mfr
S.I.C.: 3571; 3577; 3669; 3672
N.A.I.C.S.: 334111; 334119; 334290; 334412
Export
Advertising Expenditures: $661,000
Media: 2-4-5-13
Distr.: Intl.; Natl.
Personnel:
Greg Yamamoto *(Pres & CEO)*
David W. Brunton *(CFO)*
Leo Fang *(Exec VP)*
Nelson Abal *(VP-Sls)*
Brands & Products:
HIGHWIRE FAMILY
LINKWARE
SBE
VCOM
WANADAPT
WANPMC
WANPTMC

NEW AGE ELECTRONICS, INC.
(Div. of SYNNEX Corporation)
21950 Arnold Ctr Rd
Carson, CA 90810
Tel.: (511) 656-3333
Fax: (310) 549-6931
Toll Free: (800) 234-0300
E-mail: sales@newageinc.com
Web Site: www.newageinc.com
E-Mail For Key Personnel:
Sales Director: sales@newageinc.com
Approx. Rev.: $900,000,000
Approx. Number Employees: 175
Year Founded: 1988
Business Description:
Consumer Electronics, Office Equipment & Photography Equipment Distr
S.I.C.: 5044; 5045; 5731
N.A.I.C.S.: 423420; 423430; 443112
Media: 10-18
Personnel:
Fred Towns *(Pres)*
Michael Bertolani *(Mgr-Natl Sls)*
Roxanne Leone *(Mgr-Mktg)*
Advertising Agency:
Finn Partners
11400 W Olympic Blvd Ste 850
Los Angeles, CA 90064-1544
Tel.: (310) 479-9929
Fax: (310) 479-9989

NEXTEL PARTNERS, INC.
(Sub. of Sprint Nextel Corp.)
4500 Carillon Pt
Kirkland, WA 98033
Tel.: (425) 576-3600
Fax: (425) 576-3650
Toll Free: (888) 566-6111
E-mail: infoerate@nextelpartners.com
Web Site: www.nextelpartners.com
Sales Range: $1-4.9 Billion
Approx. Number Employees: 2,905
Business Description:
Wireless Communications Services
S.I.C.: 4812
N.A.I.C.S.: 517212
Advertising Expenditures: $75,200,000

NEXTWAVE WIRELESS INC.
12264 El Camino Real Ste 305
San Diego, CA 92130
Tel.: (619) 573-1570
E-mail: media@nextwave.com
Web Site: www.nextwave.com
Approx. Int. Income: $573,000
Approx. Number Employees: 11
Business Description:
Telecommunications Services; Wireless Network Operator
S.I.C.: 3663; 4812
N.A.I.C.S.: 334220; 517212
Media: 10
Personnel:
Allen B. Salmasi *(Chm)*
Francis J. Harding *(CFO & Exec VP)*
R. Andrew Salony *(Chief Admin Officer & Exec VP)*
Frank A. Cassou *(Chief Legal Counsel, Exec VP & Sec)*
Kevin M. Finn *(Dir)*
Brands & Products:
CORE
MEDIAFUSION
OPENCORE
TWONKYMEDIA

NHC COMMUNICATIONS, INC.
5450 Cote De Liesse
Mont Royal, QC H4P 1A5, Canada
Tel.: (514) 735-2741
Fax: (514) 735-8057
Toll Free: (800) 361-1965
E-mail: info@nhc.com
Web Site: www.nhc.com
Sales Range: $1-9.9 Million
Approx. Number Employees: 48
Year Founded: 1986
Business Description:
Physical-Layer High-Speed Switched Accessed Solutions for Voice & Data Networks Designer & Mfr
S.I.C.: 4812
N.A.I.C.S.: 517212
Advertising Expenditures: $350,000
Media: 2-7-10-13-20
Personnel:
Sylvain Abitbol *(CEO & Exec Officer-Mgmt)*
Andrew D. Lipman *(Sr Partner)*
Ralph Benatar *(CFO & Mgmt Exec)*
Sylvain Brossard *(VP-Fin Ops)*
Joe Teixeira *(VP-Res, Dev & Engrg)*
Marvin Garellek *(Dir-Mktg & Domestic Sls)*
Brands & Products:
CONTROLPOINT
XPOINT

NHT AUDIO, LLC
(d/b/a Now Hear This)
6400 Goodyear Rd
Benicia, CA 94510
Tel.: (707) 747-0122
Fax: (707) 747-1252
Fax: (707) 747-1273
Toll Free: (800) 648-9993
E-mail: sales@nhthifi.com
Web Site: www.nhthifi.com
Approx. Number Employees: 15
Year Founded: 1986
Business Description:
Design & Mfr of Audio/Video Loudspeaker Systems
S.I.C.: 3651
N.A.I.C.S.: 334310
Export
Advertising Expenditures: $500,000
Media: 5-6-19
Distr.: Intl.; Natl.
Budget Set: Nov.
Personnel:
Chris Byrne *(Partner)*
Brands & Products:
AR (ACOUSTIC RESEARCH)
NHT (NOW HEAR THIS)

NII HOLDINGS, INC.
1875 Explorer St Ste 1000
Reston, VA 20190
Tel.: (703) 390-5100
E-mail: ivan.montalvo@nii.com
Web Site: www.nii.com/
Approx. Rev.: $5,601,316,000
Approx. Number Employees: 13,500
Business Description:
Digital Wireless Communication Services
S.I.C.: 4812
N.A.I.C.S.: 517212
Advertising Expenditures: $155,100,000
Personnel:
Steven M. Shindler *(Chm)*
Steven P. Dussek *(CEO)*
Gokul Hemmady *(CFO & Exec VP)*
Alan Strauss *(CTO & Exec VP)*
Sergio Borges Chaia *(Pres/CEO-Nextel Brazil)*
Peter A. Foyo *(Pres-Nextel Mexico)*
Miguel E. Rivera *(Pres-Nextel Peru)*
Gary D. Begeman *(Gen Counsel & Exec VP)*

NORTECH SYSTEMS INCORPORATED
1120 Wayzata Blvd E Ste 201
Wayzata, MN 55391
Tel.: (952) 345-2244
Fax: (952) 473-2514
E-mail: investor@nortechsys.com
Web Site: www.nortechsys.com

Key to Media (For complete agency information see *The Advertising Red Books-Agencies* edition):
1. Bus. Publs. 2. Cable T.V. 3. Catalogs & Directories. 4. Co-op Adv. 5. Consumer Mags. 6. D.M. to Bus. Estab.7. D.M. to Consumers 8. Daily Newsp. 9. Exhibits/Trade Shows 10. Foreign 11. Infomercial 12. Internet Adv.13. Multimedia 14. Network Radio 15. Network T.V. 16. Newsp. Distr. Mags. 17. Other 18. Outdoor (Posters, Transit) 19. Point of Purchase20. Premiums, Novelties 21. Product Samples 22. Special Events Mktg. 23. Spot Radio 24. Spot T.V. 25. Weekly Newsp. 26. Yellow Page Adv.

Approx. Sls.: $99,820,069
Approx. Number Employees: 667
Year Founded: 1990
Business Description:
Wire Harnesses, Cables, Electromechanical Assemblies, Printed Circuit Boards & Higher-Level Assemblies for the Commercial & Defense Industries Mfr
S.I.C.: 3663; 3575; 3679; 8721
N.A.I.C.S.: 334220; 334113; 334418; 541219
Import Export
Advertising Expenditures: $167,000
Media: 17
Personnel:
Myron Kunin *(Chm)*
Michael J. Degen *(Pres & CEO)*
Richard G. Wasielewski *(CFO & Sr VP)*
Garry M. Anderly *(Treas & Sr VP-Corp Fin)*
Peter L. Kucera *(Sr VP-Corp Quality)*
Curtis J. Steichen *(Sr VP-Comml Ops)*

NOTIFIER CO.
(Sub. of Honeywell Security)
12 Clintonville Rd
Northford, CT 06472
Tel.: (203) 484-7161
Fax: (203) 484-7118
E-mail: webmaster@notifier.com
Web Site: www.notifier.com
Sales Range: $150-199.9 Million
Approx. Number Employees: 550
Year Founded: 1951
Business Description:
Mfr. of Fire Alarm & Emergency Lighting Products; Fire Alarm Control Panels & Compatible Indicating & Initiating Devices
S.I.C.: 3669
N.A.I.C.S.: 334290
Export
Media: 4-10-17-19-25
Distr.: Natl.
Personnel:
Mark Levy *(Pres)*
Peter Clark *(Mng Dir)*
W. Allen Fritts *(Exec VP)*
Brands & Products:
FIRE LITE
NOTI-FIRE-NET
NOTIFIER
ONYX SERIES
UNINET

NTELOS HOLDINGS CORP.
401 Spring Ln Ste 300
Waynesboro, VA 22980-4547
Mailing Address:
PO Box 1990
Waynesboro, VA 22980-7990
Tel.: (540) 946-3500
Fax: (540) 946-3595
Toll Free: (877) 468-83567
E-mail: customerfirst@ntelos.com
Web Site: www.ntelos.com
Approx. Rev.: $545,684,000
Approx. Number Employees: 1,445
Business Description:
Wireless Telecommunications Services
S.I.C.: 4813; 4812
N.A.I.C.S.: 517110; 517212
Advertising Expenditures: $14,500,000
Media: 1-2-10-22
Personnel:
Michael Huber *(Chm)*
James A. Hyde *(Pres & CEO)*
Conrad J. Hunter *(Pres & Exec VP-Wireless)*
Michael B. Moneymaker *(CFO, Treas, Sec & Exec VP)*
Mary McDermott *(Sr VP)*
Brands & Products:
HOMEFREE
NTELOS
Advertising Agency:
Barber Martin Agency
7400 Beaufont Springs Dr Ste 201
Richmond, VA 23225-5519
Tel.: (804) 320-3232
Fax: (804) 320-1729

NTN BUZZTIME, INC.
5966 La Place Court Ste 100
Carlsbad, CA 92008
Tel.: (760) 438-7400
Fax: (760) 438-3505
E-mail: advertising@buzztime.com
Web Site: www.ntn.com
Approx. Rev.: $25,309,000
Approx. Number Employees: 128
Year Founded: 1983
Business Description:
Interactive Entertainment Developer & Distr
S.I.C.: 4833; 2741; 7812; 7822; 7829; 7999
N.A.I.C.S.: 515120; 512110; 512120; 512199; 516110; 713990
Advertising Expenditures: $5,000
Media: 1-2-10-13
Personnel:
Jeffrey A. Berg *(Chm)*
Michael J. Bush *(CEO)*
Kendra Berger *(CFO)*
Christopher George *(CIO)*
Tony Duckett *(Exec VP-Sls)*
Brands & Products:
ASK IT ALREADY
BUZZTIME
BUZZTIME TRIVIA
COUNTDOWN
CROSS CHECKED
GLORY DAZE
IMMORTAL WORDS
LUNCHTIME TRIVIA
PLAYBACK
QB1
SHOWDOWN
SPORTS TRIVIA CHALLENGE
SPOTLIGHT
TOPIX
Advertising Agency:
Zenzi Communications
646 Valley Ave Ste C
Solana Beach, CA 92075
Tel.: (858) 523-9020
Fax: (858) 523-9670

NU HORIZONS ELECTRONICS CORP.
(Sub. of Arrow Electronics, Inc.)
70 Maxess Rd
Melville, NY 11747
Tel.: (631) 396-5000
Fax: (631) 396-5050
Toll Free: (888) 747-6846
E-mail: info@nuhorizons.com
Web Site: www.nuhorizons.com
E-Mail For Key Personnel:
President: andata@nuhorizons.com
Marketing Director: RMegling@nuhorizons.com
Approx. Sls.: $670,727,000
Approx. Number Employees: 779
Year Founded: 1982
Business Description:
High Technology Active Components, Memory Chips, Microprocessors, Digital & Linear Circuits, Diodes & Transistors Distr
S.I.C.: 5065
N.A.I.C.S.: 423690
Import Export
Advertising Expenditures: $269,000
Media: 5-7-13
Distr.: Natl.
Budget Set: Mar.
Personnel:
Arthur Nadata *(Chm & CEO)*
Martin Robert Kent *(Pres)*
Kurt Freudenberg *(Exec VP & CFO)*
Phil Gee *(Pres-Sls-Europe)*
Richard S. Schuster *(Pres-NIC Components Corp)*
Kent Smith *(Pres-Global Distr Div)*
Geoff Annesi *(Sr VP-Sls-Americas)*
Rita Megling *(Sr VP-Mktg)*
Steve A. Mussmacher *(Sr VP-Global Ops)*
Tom Dow *(VP-Sls-EMS Americas)*
Elaine Givner *(VP-HR)*
David Owens *(VP-Sls-Eastern Region)*
Burt Silverman *(VP-IT)*

NUMEREX CORP.
1600 Parkwood Cir Ste 500
Atlanta, GA 30339-2119
Tel.: (770) 693-5950
Fax: (770) 693-5951
E-mail: sales@numerex.com
Web Site: www.numerex.com
Approx. Sls.: $58,243,000
Approx. Number Employees: 125
Year Founded: 1992
Business Description:
Holding Company Comprised of Subsidiaries that Develop & Market Communication & Information Products & Services
S.I.C.: 3669; 3613; 3661
N.A.I.C.S.: 334290; 334210; 335313
Advertising Expenditures: $874,000
Personnel:
Stratton J. Nicolaides *(Chm & CEO)*
John G. Raos *(Vice Chm)*
Alan B. Catherall *(CFO & Exec VP)*
Michael A. Marett *(COO & Exec VP)*
Jeffrey O. Smith *(CTO & Exec VP)*
Louis Fienberg *(Exec VP-Corp Dev)*
Michael W. Lang *(Exec VP-Sls & Mktg)*
Brands & Products:
CELLEMETRY
FASTTRACK
FELIX
G-RFID
GPRSXPRESS
MACHINES TRUST US
NUMEREX
NUMEREX DNA
NUMEREX FAST
SMSXPRESS
UPLINK
Advertising Agency:
Zer0 to 5ive
28 S Waterloo Rd
Devon, PA 19333
Tel.: (617) 834-2190

NXP SEMICONDUCTORS
(Joint Venture of KKR & CO. L.P. , Bain Capital, LLC, Apax Partners LLP, AlpInvest Partners N.V. & Silver Lake Group, LLC)
1109 McKay Dr
San Jose, CA 95131
Tel.: (408) 434-3000
Fax: (408) 474-8103
Toll Free: (800) 447-1500
Web Site: www.nxp.com
Sales Range: $600-649.9 Million
Approx. Number Employees: 700
Year Founded: 1961
Business Description:
Semiconductor Mfr
S.I.C.: 3674
N.A.I.C.S.: 334413
Import Export
Media: 1-2-4-5-7-8-11-16-20-21
Distr.: Intl.; Natl.
Personnel:
Michael Noonen *(Exec VP-Global Sls)*
Frans Scheper *(Sr VP & Gen Mgr-Standard Products Applications)*
Simon McLean *(VP-Mktg & Standard Products)*
Gene Carter *(Product Mgr-Intl Microcontroller Bus)*
Kris Kendall *(Mgr-Mktg-Interface Products)*

OHMITE MANUFACTURING COMPANY
1600 Golf Rd Ste 850
Rolling Meadows, IL 60008
Tel.: (847) 258-0300
Fax: (847) 574-7522
Toll Free: (866) 9-OHMITE
E-mail: info@ohmite.com
Web Site: www.ohmite.com
Approx. Number Employees: 40
Year Founded: 1927
Business Description:
Resistors & Rheostats, Switches, Transformers, Ceramic Parts & Materials Mfr
S.I.C.: 3625; 3612
N.A.I.C.S.: 335314; 335311
Import Export
Advertising Expenditures: $250,000
Media: 2-4-5-7-10-21
Distr.: Intl.; Natl.
Budget Set: Nov. -Dec.
Personnel:
Steve Frediani *(Pres)*
Kirk Schwiebert *(Dir-Mktg)*
Brands & Products:
ACRASIL
AXIOHM
BROWN DEVIL
CAP RANGER
CORRIB
DEC-RANGER
DIVIDOHM
ECONO-MOX
LITTLE-DEMON
LITTLE-DEVIL
LITTLE REBEL
MAXI-MOX
METAL DEVIL
METAL-MITE
OHM-O-TONE
OHM-RANGER
OHMICONE

Key to Media (For complete agency information see *The Advertising Red Books-Agencies* edition):
1. Bus. Publs. 2. Cable T.V. 3. Catalogs & Directories. 4. Co-op Adv. 5. Consumer Mags. 6. D.M. to Bus. Estab.7. D.M. to Consumers
8. Daily Newsp. 9. Exhibits/Trade Shows 10. Foreign 11. Infomercial 12. Internet Adv.13. Multimedia 14. Network Radio
15. Network T.V. 16. Newsp. Distr. Mags. 17. Other 18. Outdoor (Posters, Transit) 19. Point of Purchase20. Premiums, Novelties
21. Product Samples 22. Special Events Mktg. 23. Spot Radio 24. Spot T.V. 25. Weekly Newsp. 26. Yellow Page Adv.

Ohmite Manufacturing Company — (Continued)

OHMITE
PECOS
POWER CHIP
POWER-MOX
POWR FILM
POWR-RIB
POWRFILM
PULSEATERS

OPLINK COMMUNICATIONS, INC.
46335 Landing Pkwy
Fremont, CA 94538
Tel.: (510) 933-7200
Fax: (510) 933-7300
E-mail: info@oplink.com
Web Site: www.oplink.com
Approx. Rev.: $198,803,000
Approx. Number Employees: 3,570
Year Founded: 1995
Business Description:
Fiber Optic Components & Integrated Optical Modules Mfr
S.I.C.: 3661; 3357; 3827
N.A.I.C.S.: 334210; 333314; 335921
Advertising Expenditures: $4,092,000
Media: 7-10-13
Personnel:
Joseph Y. Liu *(Chm & CEO)*
Shirley Yin *(CFO & Exec VP)*
Peter Lee *(COO)*
Stephen M. Welles *(Gen Counsel & VP)*
River Gong *(Sr VP-Worldwide Sls)*
Jim Li *(Sr VP-Engrg)*
Shawn Lin *(VP-Mktg)*
Roman Chuang *(Gen Mgr-Active BU)*
Brands & Products:
AWGM1
AWGM5
BTMS
CF0I050
CFOI100
CWDM 4/8 CH
CWDM OADMG 1x2
CWDM OADMG 2x2
DCPC
DWDMG 100GHZ 4/8CH
DWDMG 200GHZ 4/8 CH
DWFC 1X2
DWFC 1X3
DWFC 2X2
DWTC
EVOA T2
EVOA T3
GFFM
HWDMG1513/1315
ITMA
ITMS
IWMA
LLCWDM
LPTC
Mini SWDM59
MINI SWFC
MIOC3
MIOC4
MMFC 1X2
MMFC 2X2
MUX/DUX
MVOA-R
MVOA-T3
MWDMG1315
MWDMG1315/1513
MWDMG13CS
MWDMG1415/1514
MWDMG1514
MWDMG1598
MWDMG6470/7064
MWDMGCL
MWDMGCR/CB
MWDMGCSU
MWDMGFTTX
MWDMGLR/LB
MWDMGLSU
OADMG 100GHZ (1X2)
OADMG 100GHZ (2X2)
OADMG 200GHZ (1X2)
OADMG 200GHZ (2X2)
OFMS
OFMS 1X4
OFMS 1X8
OFMS CUSTOM
OFMS FULL 2X2
OFMS MINI (1:8)
OFMS MINI 1X4
OFMS MINI 1X8
OFMS MULTI-MODE
OFMS NET-READY 1+1
OFMS NET-READY (1:1)
OFMS SINGLE MODE
OFMS ULTRA-MINI
OIXSG
PBOC
PIPA
PIPD
PLCS
PLCS2
PMOC
PONM
QCPC
SWDM 53
SWDM 54
SWDM 59
SWDM53
SWDM54
SWDM59
SWFC 1X2
SWFC 1X3
SWFC1X4
SWTC
TCIHG
TRBG1EXNXXMX
TRBG1LXDXXSX
TRCE03KE2C000C3
TRPA03E2
TRPA03I1AXYS
TRPA03L1ExRS
TRPA03L2ExWS
TRPA03L2HXXXX
TRPA03L2IXXXX
TRPA03MM3XAS
TRPA12I1AXYM
TRPA12L1GxRM
TRPA12L2GxWM
TRPA12L2HXXXX
TRPA12L2IXXXX
TRPA12MM3XAS
TRPA12S1AXAM
TRPA48E2IXLMX
TRPA48E2IXXM
TRPA48E2ZXLMX
TRPA48I1 (ROHS)
TRPA48I1EXYM
TRPA48I2ExRM
TRPA48I2HXXXX
TRPA48I2IXXXX
TRPA48L1HxRM
TRPA48L2BXWM
TRPA48L2IXXXX
TRPA48S1 (ROHS)
TRPA48S1XXAM
TRPAFELXAXSS
TRPAFESMKXSS
TRPAG1EXJXNM
TRPAG1LXDxBM
TRPAG1SXLxES
TRPAG1VXIBMS
TRPAG1VXIXXXX
TRPAG1YXHXOM
TRPAG1YXHXXXX
TRPAG1YXZXAXMX
TRPAG1ZXIXGM
TRPAG1ZXIXXXX
TRPBFELXTXSX
TRPBG1LXDBXSX
TRPE03AI1C000E1
TRPE03AI1I000E1
TRPE03EL1C000E1
TRPE03EL1I000E1
TRPE03EL2C000E1
TRPE03EL2I000E1
TRPE12AI1C000E2
TRPE12AI1I000E2
TRPE12AS1C000E2
TRPE12AS1I000E2
TRPE12GL1C000E2
TRPE12GL1I000E2
TRPE12GL2C000E2
TRPE12GL2I000E2
TRPE48DS1C000E2
TRPE48DS1I000E2
TRPE48FI1C000E2
TRPE48FI1I000E2
TRPE48FI2C000E2
TRPE48FI2I000E2
TRPE48IL1C000E2
TRPE48IL1I000E2
TRPE48IL2C000E2
TRPE48IL2I000E2
TRPE48KE2C00010
TRPE48KE2C00020
TRPE48KE2C00030
TRPE48KE2C00040
TRPE48KE2C00050
TRPE48KE2C00060
TRPE48KE2C00070
TRPE48KE2C00080
TRPE48KE2C000E2
TRPE48KE2E00010
TRPE48KE2E00020
TRPE48KE2E00030
TRPE48KE2E00040
TRPE48KE2E00050
TRPE48KE2E00060
TRPE48KE2E00070
TRPE48KE2E00080
TRPE48KE2E000E2
TRPEG1CLXC000E2
TRPEG1CLXI000E2
TRPEG1EEXC000E2
TRPEG1EEXI000E2
TRPEG1HYXC000E2
TRPEG1HYXI000E2
TRPEG1JZXC000E2
TRPEG1JZXI000E2
TRPEG1KVXC000E1
TRPEG1KVXE000E1
TRPNFEMM3XSS
TRPW48E2OXXXX
TRPW48L2OXXXX
TRXA03I1 (ROHS)
TRXA03L1 (ROHS)
TRXA03L2 (ROHS)
TRXA12I1 (ROHS)
TRXA12L1 (ROHS)
TRXA12L2 (ROHS)
TRXA12MM (ROHS)
TRXA12S1 (ROHS)
TRXA48I2 (ROHS)
TRXA48L1 (ROHS)
TRXA48L2 (ROHS)
TRXAFEEX ZX (ROHS)
TRXAFELX (ROHS)
TRXAG1 SM (ROHS)
TRXAG1 SM (ROHS) EX
TRXAG1 SM (ROHS) LX
TRXAG1 SM (ROHS) YX
TRXAG1SX (ROHS)
TRXAG1VXIXMS (ROHS)
TRXAG1ZXM (ROHS)
TRXBG1EXM (ROHS)
TRXBG1LXM (ROHS)
TRXNFEMM (ROHS)
UFWC 1X2
UFWC 2X2
ULTRA-MINI
UTMS
UWDM 59
UWDM59
XGLRRXM
YOUR DESIGN & OMS PARTNER

OPTA SYSTEMS, LLC
(Sub. of Lotus Pacific Inc.)
(d/b/a GoVideo)
7835 E McClain Dr
Scottsdale, AZ 85260-1732
Tel.: (650) 579-3610
Fax: (480) 951-4404
Toll Free: (800) 736-7679
Web Site: www.govideo.com
Approx. Number Employees: 55
Year Founded: 1984
Business Description:
Developer & Marketer of Consumer Electronic Products & Home Theater
S.I.C.: 5064
N.A.I.C.S.: 423620
Import Export
Media: 2-4-6-7-8-9-10-17-19-20-22-24
Distr.: Natl.
Budget Set: Apr.
Personnel:
Sean Wang *(Chm)*
David Xiong *(CEO)*
Steve Davis *(CFO)*
Jerry Barbera *(Sr VP-Sls-Channel Mktg)*
Jim Smith *(VP-Mktg)*
Gil Miller *(Dir-Product Mktg)*
Brands & Products:
DUAL-DECK
GOVIDEO

OREGON SCIENTIFIC, INC.
(Sub. of Oregon Scientific Global Distribution Limited)
19861 SW 95th Ave
Tualatin, OR 97062
Tel.: (503) 783-5100
Fax: (503) 691-6208
Web Site: www.oregonscientific.com
Business Description:
Retailer of Electronic Consumer Products
S.I.C.: 5064
N.A.I.C.S.: 423620
Media: 6

ORTOFON, INC.
(Sub. of Ortofon A/S)
500 Executive Blvd Ste 102
Ossining, NY 10562-2563
Tel.: (914) 762-8646
Fax: (914) 762-8649
E-mail: info@ortofon.us
Web Site: www.ortofon.us

Key to Media (For complete agency information see *The Advertising Red Books-Agencies* edition):
1. Bus. Publs. 2. Cable T.V. 3. Catalogs & Directories. 4. Co-op Adv. 5. Consumer Mags. 6. D.M. to Bus. Estab.7. D.M. to Consumers
8. Daily Newsp. 9. Exhibits/Trade Shows 10. Foreign 11. Infomercial 12. Internet Adv.13. Multimedia 14. Network Radio
15. Network T.V. 16. Newsp. Distr. Mags. 17. Other 18. Outdoor (Posters, Transit) 19. Point of Purchase20. Premiums, Novelties
21. Product Samples 22. Special Events Mktg. 23. Spot Radio 24. Spot T.V. 25. Weekly Newsp. 26. Yellow Page Adv.

Approx. Number Employees: 15
Year Founded: 1946
Business Description:
Phonograph Cartridges, Components & Electronics
S.I.C.: 5064
N.A.I.C.S.: 423620
Export
Media: 8-13
Distr.: Natl.
Budget Set: July
Personnel:
Dee Hustinova *(Gen Mgr)*
Brands & Products:
ORTOFON

P&F USA
(Sub. of Funai Electric Co., Ltd.)
3015 Windward Plz Ste 100
Atlanta, GA 30005
Tel.: (678) 319-0439
Business Description:
Television Whslr
S.I.C.: 5731
N.A.I.C.S.: 443112
Personnel:
Ryo Fukuda *(Pres)*
Robert Hoglund *(CFO & Sr Controller)*
Todd Richardson *(Sr VP, Gen Mgr-Sls & Mktg)*
Keith Michael *(Dir-Mktg)*
Richard Dennis *(Mgr-Acctg)*
Advertising Agency:
Dentsu America, Inc.
32 Ave of the Americas 16th Fl
New York, NY 10013
Tel.: (212) 397-3333
Fax: (212) 397-3322

P2 SOLAR INC.
Unit 204 13569 76 Avenue
Surrey, BC V3W 2W3, Canada
Tel.: (605) 592-0047
Toll Free: (888) 945-4440
E-mail: info@p2solar.com
Web Site: www.p2solar.com
Approx. Int. Income: $62,630
Business Description:
Solar Power Systems Mfr
S.I.C.: 4931
N.A.I.C.S.: 221119
Advertising Expenditures: $40,010
Media: 17
Personnel:
Raj-Mohinder S. Gurm *(Pres & CEO)*
Jon T. Brainard *(VP-Corp Comm)*

PALOMAR TECHNOLOGIES INC.
(Sub. of Palomar Technologies Companies, LLC)
2728 Loker Ave W
Carlsbad, CA 92010
Tel.: (760) 931-3600
Fax: (760) 931-5191
Web Site:
www.palomartechnologies.com
E-Mail For Key Personnel:
Sales Director: sales@bonders.com
Approx. Sls.: $30,000,000
Approx. Number Employees: 50
Year Founded: 1998
Business Description:
Electronic Components Mfr
S.I.C.: 3679
N.A.I.C.S.: 334419
Import Export
Media: 10

Personnel:
Bruce W. Hueners *(Pres & CEO)*
Bradley Benton *(Reg Mgr-Acct)*
Brands & Products:
3500-II
6500

PANASONIC CORPORATION OF NORTH AMERICA
(Sub. of Panasonic Corporation)
1 Panasonic Way
Secaucus, NJ 07094-2917
Tel.: (201) 348-7755
Fax: (201) 392-6910
Toll Free: (800) 211-7262
E-mail: privacy@panasonic.com
Web Site: www.panasonic.com
Approx. Sls.: $8,000,000,000
Approx. Number Employees: 23,000
Year Founded: 1959
Business Description:
Mfr & Retailer of Radios, Televisions, Tape Recorders, Video Recorders & Players, Microwave Ovens, Business Equipment & Machines, VTR/CCTV Televisions & Equipment, Technics Audio & Professional Equipment, Industrial Products
S.I.C.: 5064; 5045
N.A.I.C.S.: 423620; 423430
Import Export
Media: 2-4-5-6-8-9-10-11-18-19-20-22-24
Distr.: Natl.
Personnel:
Joseph Taylor *(Chm & CEO)*
William Taylor *(Pres-Panasonic Digital Communications & Security)*
Carol DiStaulo *(Media Dir)*
James Reilly *(Dir-PR)*
Christopher Rice *(Sr Product Mgr-Imaging)*
Robert Ohme *(Asst Treas)*
Brands & Products:
LUMIX
PANASONIC
QUASAR
SEE THERE WHEN YOU CAN'T BE THERE
TECHNICS
Advertising Agencies:
Arnold Worldwide
101 Huntington Ave
Boston, MA 02199-7603
Tel.: (617) 587-8000
Fax: (617) 587-8004

Renegade, LLC
75 9th Ave 8th Fl
New York, NY 10011
Tel.: (646) 486-7700
Fax: (646) 486-7800

Sigma Group
690 Kinderkamack Rd Ste 203
Oradell, NJ 07649-1524
Tel.: (201) 261-1123
Fax: (201) 261-0399

PANASONIC ELECTRIC WORKS CORPORATION OF AMERICA
(Sub. of Panasonic Electric Works Co., Ltd.)
629 Central Ave
New Providence, NJ 07974
Tel.: (908) 464-3550
Fax: (908) 464-8513
Web Site: www.pewa.panasonic.com
Approx. Number Employees: 100
Year Founded: 1974
Business Description:
Electronic Components Mfr
S.I.C.: 5065; 3625
N.A.I.C.S.: 423690; 335314
Advertising Expenditures: $542,000
Media: 2-4-5
Distr.: Natl.
Budget Set: Nov.
Personnel:
Steve Cummins *(Dir-Mktg)*
Darin Pepple *(Sr Product Mgr-Imaging)*
Brands & Products:
PANASONIC

PANDUIT CORP.
17301 Ridgeland Ave
Tinley Park, IL 60477-3093
Tel.: (708) 532-1800
Fax: (708) 532-1811
Toll Free: (800) 777-3300
E-mail: info@panduit.com
Web Site: www.panduit.com
Sales Range: $400-449.9 Million
Approx. Number Employees: 3,500
Year Founded: 1953
Business Description:
Electrical Wiring Components, Network Wiring Systems & Electronic Connectors Mfr
S.I.C.: 3644; 3643
N.A.I.C.S.: 335932; 335931
Export
Media: 1-2-4-7-10
Distr.: Intl.; Natl.
Personnel:
Jack E. Caveney, Jr. *(Pres)*
Michael G. Kenny *(CFO)*
Alan Farrimond *(Sr VP-Europe)*
Ron Partridge *(Grp VP-Global Sls & Mktg)*
Paul M. Montgomery *(VP-Finance)*
Bernard T. Westapher *(VP-Sls & Mktg)*
Brands & Products:
BELT-TY
CABLEACCESS
CAD-CONNECT
CLINCHER
CONTOUR CRIMP
CONTOUR-TY
DAMP-SHRINK
DATA-PATCH
DISCO
DISCO-GRIP
DISCO-LOK
DISCOGRIP
DOME-TOP
DPOE
DRY-SHRINK
DURA-MARK
DURA-TY
EASY-MARK
EZAIR
FIBER-DUCT
FIBERRUNNER
FLAT PAN-POST
GIGA-PUNCH
GIGA-TX
HALAR
IN-CABINET
IN-LINE
INDUSTRIALNET
J-MOD
J-PRO
LABELCORE
MINI-COM
MINI-JACK
MINI-MOD
NETFRAME
NETKEY
NETMANAGER
NETRACK
NORYL
OPEN-ACCESS
OPTI-CORE
OPTI-CRIMP
OPTI-JACK
OPTICAM
OPTICOM
PAN-CLAMP
PAN-CODE
PAN-LUG
PAN-MARK
PAN-NET
PAN-PLUG
PAN-POLE
PAN-PUNCH
PAN-QUIK
PAN-STEEL
PAN-TERM
PAN-TY
PAN-WAY
PAN-WRAP
PAN-ZONE
PANACEA
PANDUCT
PANDUIT
PANTHER
PANVIEW
PANZONE
PATCHLINK
PATCHRUNNER
QUICKLOCK
QUICKNET
QUIKLOCK
REEL-SMART
SAFETY EASE
STA-STRAP
SUPER-GRIP
TAK-TAPE
TAK-TY
TEFZEL
ULTIMATE ID
ULTRA-CINCH
UNI-DIE
VIPER
WAVE-TY
Advertising Agency:
MarketSense
7020 High Grove Blvd
Burr Ridge, IL 60527-7599
Tel.: (630) 654-0170
Fax: (630) 654-0302
Toll Free: (800) 827-0170

PARK DISTRIBUTORS, INC.
347 Railroad Ave
Bridgeport, CT 06604-5424
Tel.: (203) 366-7200
Fax: (203) 335-3128
E-mail: sales@parkdistributors.com
Web Site: www.parkdistributors.com
E-Mail For Key Personnel:
Sales Director: sales@parkdistributors.com
Approx. Number Employees: 20
Year Founded: 1966
Business Description:
Electronics Distr
S.I.C.: 5065; 3625
N.A.I.C.S.: 423690; 335314
Media: 4-13

Key to Media (For complete agency information see *The Advertising Red Books-Agencies* edition):
1. Bus. Publs. 2. Cable T.V. 3. Catalogs & Directories. 4. Co-op Adv. 5. Consumer Mags. 6. D.M. to Bus. Estab.7. D.M. to Consumers
8. Daily Newsp. 9. Exhibits/Trade Shows 10. Foreign 11. Infomercial 12. Internet Adv.13. Multimedia 14. Network Radio
15. Network T.V. 16. Newsp. Distr. Mags. 17. Other 18. Outdoor (Posters, Transit) 19. Point of Purchase20. Premiums, Novelties
21. Product Samples 22. Special Events Mktg. 23. Spot Radio 24. Spot T.V. 25. Weekly Newsp. 26. Yellow Page Adv.

Park Distributors, Inc. — (Continued)

Personnel:
Alan Goodman *(Founder & Pres)*

PARKER CHOMERICS
(Div. of Parker Aerospace)
77 Dragon Ct
Woburn, MA 01801-1039
Tel.: (781) 935-4850
Fax: (781) 933-4318
E-mail: chomailbox@parker.com
Web Site: www.chomerics.com
Sales Range: $100-124.9 Million
Approx. Number Employees: 300
Year Founded: 1963
Business Description:
Electromagnetic Interference Shielding & Thermal Management Materials Mfr
S.I.C.: 2891; 3053
N.A.I.C.S.: 325520; 339991
Export
Media: 1-2-4-7-10-13-21
Distr.: Natl.
Personnel:
Dave Hill *(Gen Mgr-Chomerics Americas)*
Pete Marashio *(Mgr-Territory Sls)*
Brands & Products:
C-WING
CHO-BOND
CHO-CELL
CHO-FAB
CHO-FOIL
CHO-FORM
CHO-JAC
CHO-MASK
CHO-SEAL
CHO-SHIELD
CHO-SHRINK
CHO-SIL
CHO-SORB
CHO-THERM
COMBO STRIP
ECOPLATE
EMICLARE
MESH STRIP
METALEX
PARPHORM
POLA-H
PREMIER
SOFT-SHIELD
SPRING-LINE
SPRINGMESH
STREAMSHIELD
T-WING
THERM-A-FORM
THERM-A-GAP
THERMATTACH
THERMFLOW
WIN-SHIELD

PARLEX USA
(Sub. of Johnson Electric Holdings Limited)
One Parlex Pl
Methuen, MA 01844
Tel.: (978) 685-4341
Fax: (978) 685-8809
E-mail: flexcircuits@parlex.com
Web Site: www.parlex.com
Approx. Number Employees: 160
Year Founded: 1970
Business Description:
Mfr & Designer of Flexible Circuits, Laminated Cables, Value-Added Assemblies & Polymer Thick Film Products
S.I.C.: 3679; 3357; 3672
N.A.I.C.S.: 334418; 334412; 335921
Export
Advertising Expenditures: $1,000,000
Media: 2-4-11-17
Brands & Products:
FLEXILAYER
PALCOAT
PALCON
PALCORE
PALFLEX
PALSTRIP
PALYSOLDER
U-FLEX

PEAVEY ELECTRONICS CORPORATION
5022 Hartley Peavey Dr
Meridian, MS 39305-5422
Mailing Address:
PO Box 2898
Meridian, MS 39302-2898
Tel.: (601) 483-5365
Fax: (601) 486-1278
Toll Free: (877) 732-8391
E-mail: marketing@peavey.com
Web Site: www.peavey.com
Approx. Number Employees: 2,000
Year Founded: 1965
Business Description:
Mfr. of Portable Sound Equipment, Electric Musical Instruments, Guitars, Amplifiers, Microphones, Public Address Systems, Commercial Sound Equipment & Components; Guitars, Recording Equipment & Speakers
S.I.C.: 3651; 3931
N.A.I.C.S.: 334310; 339992
Import Export
Advertising Expenditures: $385,000
Media: 2-4-6-10-13-19-20
Distr.: Intl.; Natl.
Budget Set: Jan.
Personnel:
Hartley Peavey *(Owner)*
Mary Peavey *(Pres)*
Brands & Products:
AA
ACOUSTIC STAGE PACK
AMR
BAM
BANDIT
BASS STAGE PACK
BRIARWOOD
CLASSIC
COLOR CUE
COMBO
CREST AUDIO
CROPPER CLASSIC
DELTA BLUES
DELTABASS
DELTAFEX
DELTALINX
DIAMOND SERIES
DUAL DELTAFEX
ECOUSTIC
ESCORT
FEEDBACK FERRET
GENERATION
GENERATION EXP
GRIND
GUITAR STAGE PACK
HP SIGNATURE
HYPERVENT
IMPULSE
INTERNATIONAL SERIES
JACK DANIEL
JAZZ
JSX
KOSMOS
LIMITED
MEDIA MATRIX
MESSENGER
MILESTONE
MILLENNIUM
MINI-MONITOR
MONITOR
NASHVILLE
OMNIAC
PEAVEY
PEAVEY MAX
PENTA
PENTATONE
PREDATOR
PREDATOR PLUS
PRO 115
PRO 210
PRO 410
PRO 810
PVM
RAGE
RAPTOR
RAPTOR PLUS
ROTOR
SENIOR
SHEFFIELD
SIGNATURE SERIES
SOLO
STAGE PACK 3
STUDIO PRO
SUPREME
SWITCHCRAFT
TRANSFORMER
TRANSTUBE
TRIFLEX
TRIPLE XXX
V-TYPE
VALVEKING
WIGGY
WOLFGANG
XCON
XXL
Advertising Agency:
Peavey Electronic Advertising
5022 Hartley Peavey Dr
Meridian, MS 39305
Tel.: (601) 483-5365
Fax: (601) 486-1278

PERFORMANCE TECHNOLOGIES, INCORPORATED
205 Indigo Creek Dr
Rochester, NY 14626-5100
Tel.: (585) 256-0200
Fax: (585) 256-0791
E-mail: info@pt.com
Web Site: www.pt.com
Approx. Sls.: $27,946,000
Approx. Number Employees: 168
Year Founded: 1984
Business Description:
Supplier of Communications & Networking Solutions for a Wide Variety of Client Server, Telecommunications & Embedded Application Environments
S.I.C.: 3672; 3661
N.A.I.C.S.: 334412; 334210
Advertising Expenditures: $48,000
Media: 2-7-13
Personnel:
John M. Slusser *(Chm, Pres & CEO)*
Dorrance W. Lamb *(CFO & Sr VP)*
John J. Grana *(Sr VP-Products & Technologies)*
J. Patrick Rice *(Sr VP-Sls, Mktg & Svc)*
Deb Walker *(Sr Dir-Comml Mktg & Dir-Signaling Product Mgmt)*
Brands & Products:
ADVANCED MANAGED PLATFORMS
ADVANCEDMC
ADVANCEDTCA
CHANNEL7
CHANNELINK
COMLINK
COMPACTPCI
FLEXCONNECT
FLEXNAT
FLEXTUNNEL
INTEL NETSTRUCTURE
IPNEXUS
NEXUSWARE
PCI
PCI EXPRESS
PERFORMANCE TECHNOLOGIES
PICMG
POINT CODE EMULATION
SEGWAY
SIMPLY SMARTER SIGNALING
SIP SIGNALING BRIDGE
UNIPORTE

PHAZAR CORPORATION
101 SE 25th Ave
Mineral Wells, TX 76067
Mailing Address:
PO Box 520
Mineral Wells, TX 76068-0520
Tel.: (940) 325-3301
Fax: (940) 325-0716
Telex: 882-163
E-mail: HR@phazarcorp.com
Web Site: www.phazarcorp.com
Approx. Rev.: $8,399,586
Approx. Number Employees: 64
Year Founded: 1972
Business Description:
Holding Company
S.I.C.: 6719; 3663
N.A.I.C.S.: 551112; 334220
Import Export
Advertising Expenditures: $500,000
Media: 2-4-6-7-10-20-21
Distr.: Direct to Consumer; Natl.
Budget Set: Nov.
Personnel:
Garland P. Asher *(Pres & CEO)*
Deborah A. Inzer *(CFO, Treas & VP)*
Mark Allen *(Sr VP-Sls & Mktg)*
Phil Park *(Mgr-Mktg)*
Kathy Kindle *(Coord-IR)*
Brands & Products:
PHAZAR

PHILIPS ELECTRONICS NORTH AMERICA
(Group of Philips International B.V.)
3000 Minuteman Rd
Andover, MA 01810
Tel.: (800) 223-1828
Fax: (212) 536-0559
Toll Free: (800) 223-1828
E-mail: press.design@philips.com
Web Site: www.usa.philips.com

Key to Media (For complete agency information see *The Advertising Red Books-Agencies* edition):
1. Bus. Publs. 2. Cable T.V. 3. Catalogs & Directories. 4. Co-op Adv. 5. Consumer Mags. 6. D.M. to Bus. Estab.7. D.M. to Consumers
8. Daily Newsp. 9. Exhibits/Trade Shows 10. Foreign 11. Infomercial 12. Internet Adv.13. Multimedia 14. Network Radio
15. Network T.V. 16. Newsp. Distr. Mags. 17. Other 18. Outdoor (Posters, Transit) 19. Point of Purchase20. Premiums, Novelties
21. Product Samples 22. Special Events Mktg. 23. Spot Radio 24. Spot T.V. 25. Weekly Newsp. 26. Yellow Page Adv.

Sales Range: $5-14.9 Billion
Approx. Number Employees: 3,000
Year Founded: 1933
Business Description:
Mfr. of Consumer Electrical & Electronic Components
S.I.C.: 5064; 3651
N.A.I.C.S.: 423620; 334310
Import Export
Media: 3-6-9-15-16-17-18-24
Distr.: Intl.; Natl.
Personnel:
Reinier Jens *(Pres)*
Andrea Ragnetti *(CEO-Philips Consumer Style & Exec VP)*
Joseph Innamorati *(Sr VP & Chief Legal Counsel)*
Tracy Byers *(VP-Sls & Mktg)*
Brands & Products:
AMBX
BODYGROOM
CINEOS
DECT
HEARTSTART
NORELCO
PHOTOFRAME
PRESTIGO
SENSEO
SIMPLICITY
SONICARE
STREAMIUM
Advertising Agency:
Omnicom Group Inc.
437 Madison Ave 9th Fl
New York, NY 10022-7001
Tel.: (212) 415-3600
Fax: (212) 415-3530

PIONEER ELECTRONICS (USA) INC.
(Sub. of Pioneer Corporation)
1925 E Dominguez
Long Beach, CA 90810
Tel.: (310) 952-2000
Fax: (310) 952-2199
Toll Free: (800) 746-6337
Web Site: www.pioneerelectronics.com
E-Mail For Key Personnel:
Public Relations: pr-pioneer@pioneer-usa.com
Sales Range: $150-199.9 Million
Approx. Number Employees: 300
Year Founded: 1972
Business Description:
Consumer Electronics Sales
S.I.C.: 5064
N.A.I.C.S.: 423620
Import Export
Advertising Expenditures: $10,000,000
Media: 2-3-5-6-8-9-10-13-14-15-16-19-20-22-23-24-25
Distr.: Natl.
Personnel:
Masao Kawabata *(Chm & CEO)*
Russ Johnston *(Exec VP-Mktg & Product Plng)*
Matt Dever *(VP-Pro Sound & Visual Div)*
Roberta Tapp *(Dir-Mktg Comm)*
David Bales *(Mgr-Mktg-Audio Video Products)*
Advertising Agencies:
Atomic Public Relations
735 Market St 4th Fl
San Francisco, CA 94103
Tel.: (415) 402-0230
Fax: (415) 402-0237
Agency of Record
Brand Strategy
Event Support
Messaging
Positioning
Public Relations
Social Media

TBWA Chiat Day Los Angeles
5353 Grosvenor Blvd
Los Angeles, CA 90066
Tel.: (310) 305-5000
Fax: (310) 305-6000
Kuro Television

PLAINTREE SYSTEMS INC.
10 Didak Dr
Arnprior, ON K7S 0C3, Canada
Tel.: (613) 623-3434
Fax: (613) 623-4647
Toll Free: (888) 831-8300
E-mail: investor-relations@plaintree.com
Web Site: www.plaintree.com
E-Mail For Key Personnel:
Sales Director: sales@plaintree.com
Approx. Rev.: $11,248,338
Approx. Number Employees: 60
Year Founded: 1988
Business Description:
Infrared Transceivers Mfr for Wireless Networks
S.I.C.: 3661; 3577; 4812
N.A.I.C.S.: 334210; 334119; 517212
Advertising Expenditures: $1,105,000
Personnel:
William D. Watson *(Chm & VP-Mergers & Acq)*
William David Watson, II *(Pres & CEO)*
Lynn E. Saunders *(CFO)*
Brands & Products:
PLAINTREE SYSTEMS
WAVEBRIDGE
WAVESWITCH

PLANTRONICS, INC.
345 Encinal St
Santa Cruz, CA 95060-2132
Tel.: (831) 426-5858
Fax: (831) 426-6098
Fax: (888) 290-4519
Toll Free: (800) 544-4660
E-mail: plantronics@custhelp.com
Web Site: www.plantronics.com
Approx. Rev.: $683,602,000
Approx. Number Employees: 3,200
Year Founded: 1961
Business Description:
Lightweight Communications Headsets, Telephone Headset Systems, Accessories & Related Services Designer, Mfr & Marketer
S.I.C.: 3661
N.A.I.C.S.: 334210
Advertising Expenditures: $2,400,000
Media: 2-4-5-6-7-10-13-19-26
Distr.: Intl.; Natl.
Budget Set: Apr.
Personnel:
Marvin Tseu *(Chm)*
Kenneth S. Kannappan *(Pres & CEO)*
Barbara V. Scherer *(CFO, Sr VP-Fin & Admin)*
Ingrid van Den Hoogen *(CMO)*
Barry Margerum *(Chief Strategy Officer)*
Carsten Trads *(Pres-Clarity Div)*
Richard R. Pickard *(Gen Counsel, Sec & VP-Legal)*
Donald Houston *(Sr VP-Sls)*
Renee Niemi *(Sr VP)*
Larry Wuerz *(Sr VP-Worldwide Ops)*
Clay Hausmann *(VP-Corp Mktg)*
Mike Perkins *(VP-Product Dev & Tech)*
Brands & Products:
AMERIPHONE
BLUETOOTH
CLARITY
CLEARVOX
DUOPRO
DUOSET
ENCORE
FREEHAND
MIRAGE
PLANTRONICS
PRACTICA
SOUND INNOVATION
STARSET
SUPRA
SUPRAPLUS
TRISTAR
WALKER
Advertising Agency:
Wirestone
920 20th St
Sacramento, CA 95811
Tel.: (916) 446-6550
Fax: (916) 446-6551

PMC-SIERRA, INC.
1380 Bordeaux Dr
Santa Clara, CA 94089
Tel.: (408) 239-8000
Fax: (408) 492-9192
E-mail: publicrelations@pmc-sierra.com
Web Site: www.pmc-sierra.com
Approx. Rev.: $635,082,000
Approx. Number Employees: 1,449
Year Founded: 1983
Business Description:
Processors, Chips & Semiconductor Systems Solutions
S.I.C.: 3674
N.A.I.C.S.: 334413
Advertising Expenditures: $2,100,000
Media: 4-10-11
Personnel:
James V. Diller, Sr. *(Vice Chm)*
Gregory S. Lang *(Pres & CEO)*
Michael W. Zellner *(CFO)*
Colin C. Harris *(COO)*
Alinka Flaminia *(Gen Counsel, Corp Sec & VP)*
Raed O. Elmurib *(VP-Corp Dev & Gen Mgr-Microprocessor Products Div)*
Tom Sun *(VP & Gen Mgr-Broadband Wireless Div)*
Victor Vaisleib *(VP & Gen Mgr)*
Robert M. Liszt *(VP-Sls-Worldwide)*
Robert O'Dell *(VP-Mktg-Wireless Infrastructure & Networking (WIN) Div)*
Shai Shahar *(VP-Fin-FP&A)*
Art Miller *(Dir-Programs-WIN Div)*
Trey Oprendek *(Dir-Customer Mktg)*
Susan Shaw *(Mgr-Brand Comm)*
Brands & Products:
BRIC
COMET
MIPS
OCTALPHY
PALADIN
QUADPHY
UNI

POLK AUDIO, INC.
(Sub. of DEI Holdings, Inc.)
5601 Metro Dr
Baltimore, MD 21215
Tel.: (410) 358-3600
Fax: (410) 764-5266
Toll Free: (800) 377-7655
Telex: 87-993 POLK AUDIO BAL
E-mail: polkcs@polkaudio.com
Web Site: www.polkaudio.com
Sales Range: $25-49.9 Million
Approx. Number Employees: 75
Year Founded: 1972
Business Description:
Designer & Mfr of Home & Mobile Audio Equipment
S.I.C.: 3651
N.A.I.C.S.: 334310
Import Export
Media: 2-4-6-7-10-17
Distr.: Natl.
Personnel:
Jim Minarik *(Chm & CEO)*
Joe Tristani *(COO)*
Jeff Nemec *(Sr VP-Product Dev)*
Ben Newhall *(Sr VP-Sls & Mktg)*
Al Ballard *(VP-Mktg)*
Stu Lumsden *(VP-Engrg)*
Joe Phelps *(Dir-Sls-Personal Audio)*
Al Baron *(Mgr-Product Line)*
Dan Wakefield *(Mgr-Natl Sls-US)*

POLYCOM, INC.
4750 Willow Rd
Pleasanton, CA 94588-2708
Tel.: (925) 924-6000
Fax: (925) 924-6100
Toll Free: (800) 765-9266
E-mail: webmaster@polycom.com
Web Site: www.polycom.com
Approx. Rev.: $1,218,489,000
Approx. Number Employees: 3,230
Year Founded: 1990
Business Description:
Developer, Mfr & Marketer of Teleconferencing Equipment
S.I.C.: 3661
N.A.I.C.S.: 334210
Import Export
Advertising Expenditures: $21,000,000
Media: 2-13
Personnel:
David G. DeWalt *(Chm)*
Andrew M. Miller *(Pres & CEO)*
Michael R. Kourey *(CFO & Exec VP-Fin & Admin)*
Arijit Bose *(CIO & Sr VP-IT)*
Joseph B. Burton *(Sr VP, Chief Strategy Officer, CTO & Gen Mgr-Enterprise Provider)*
Sayed M. Darwish *(Chief Admin Officer, Gen Counsel, Sec & Exec VP)*
Sudhakar Ramakrishna *(Chief Dev Officer, Exec VP & Gen Mgr-Unified Comm Solutions)*
Tracey Newell *(Exec VP-Global Sls)*
Navin Mehta *(Sr VP-Global Svcs)*
Robert B. Steele *(Sr VP-Worldwide Ops)*
Bartus de Vries *(VP-Fin & Admin-Europe, Middle East & Africa)*
Danister Callistus De Almeida *(Dir-Partner Mktg-N America)*
Richard Grumet *(Dir-Svcs)*

Key to Media (For complete agency information see *The Advertising Red Books-Agencies* edition):
1. Bus. Publs. 2. Cable T.V. 3. Catalogs & Directories. 4. Co-op Adv. 5. Consumer Mags. 6. D.M. to Bus. Estab.7. D.M. to Consumers
8. Daily Newsp. 9. Exhibits/Trade Shows 10. Foreign 11. Infomercial 12. Internet Adv.13. Multimedia 14. Network Radio
15. Network T.V. 16. Newsp. Distr. Mags. 17. Other 18. Outdoor (Posters, Transit) 19. Point of Purchase20. Premiums, Novelties
21. Product Samples 22. Special Events Mktg. 23. Spot Radio 24. Spot T.V. 25. Weekly Newsp. 26. Yellow Page Adv.

Polycom, Inc. — (Continued)

Edgardo Colon *(Mgr-Sls & Mgr-Channel Caribe & Central America)*
Deane Jessep *(Mgr-New Zealand Reg)*

Brands & Products:
ACCORD
CAPSPACE
CLARITY BY POLYCOMM
CLASSSTATION
CLICK & VIEW
CMA
CONFERENCE COMPOSER
CONVENE
CONVERGED MANAGED APPLICATION
DISTRIBUTED MEDIA APPLICATION
EAGLEEYE
EYE CONNECT
GLOBAL MANAGEMENT SYSTEM
HDX 4000
HDX 8000
HDX 9000
IMAGESHARE
IMAGESHARE II
INNOVOX
INSTANT DESIGNER
INSTRUCTOR
IPOWER
IPRIORITY
KIRK
LOOK-AT-ME-BUTTON
LOST PACKET RECOVERY
LPR
MEDLINK
MEETINGSITE
MGC
MOBILE MEETING
MOBILE RESPONDER
NET ENGINE
NETWORK AWARE SCHEDULER
OBAM
PATHNAVIGATOR
PEOPLE ON CONTENT
PEOPLEPLUS CONTENT
POLYCOM
POLYCOM COMMUNICATOR
POLYCOM CONFERENCE SUITE
POLYCOM HD VOICE
POLYCOM ONE DIAL
POLYCOM PATH NAVIGATOR
POLYCOM SNAP
POLYCOM TELEPRESENCE EXPERIENCE
POLYCOM ULTIMATE HD
POLYCOM V500
POLYCOM VIDEO PLUS
POLYCOM VOICE PLUS
POWERCAM
POWERMIC
PRO-MOTION
PROXIAS
PVX
QSX
RAS
READICONVENE
READIMANAGER
READIRECORDER
READISERIES
READIVOICE
REALPRESENCE
RPX
RSS
SHOWSTATION
SIREN
SOUNDPOINT
SOUNDSTATION
SOUNDSTATION PREMIER
SOUNDSTATION PREMIER SATELLITE
SOUNDSTATION VTX 1000
SOUNDSTATION2
SOUNDSTATION2W
SOUNDSTRUCTURE
SPECTRA LINK
STEREOSURROUND
TPX
VBP
VCE
VIAVIDEO
VIDEO MEDIA CENTER
VIDEO NETWORK MANAGEMENT
VIEWSTATION
VISUAL CONCERT PC
VMS
VOICEPLUS
VOICESTATION
VORTEX
VSX
WEB COMMANDER

Advertising Agencies:
Loomis Group
345 Spear St Ste 110
San Francisco, CA 94105
Tel.: (415) 882-9494
Fax: (415) 882-7209

Motivo
205 E Third Ave Ste 303
San Mateo, CA 94401
Tel.: (650) 996-1108
Fax: (650) 532-0519

POLYVISION CORPORATION
(Sub. of Steelcase Inc.)
3970 Johns Creek Ct Ste 325
Suwanee, GA 30024
Tel.: (678) 542-3100
Fax: (678) 542-3200
Toll Free: (800) 631-4514
E-mail: info@polyvision.com
Web Site: www.polyvision.com
Sales Range: $150-199.9 Million
Approx. Number Employees: 1,150
Year Founded: 1954
Business Description:
Office Communication Products Mfr
S.I.C.: 2531; 2521; 2522
N.A.I.C.S.: 337127; 337211; 337214
Media: 2-7-10
Personnel:
Bob Crain *(Gen Mgr)*
Brands & Products:
COPYCAM
ROOMWIZARD
THUNDER EXPRESS
THUNDER PRO
WALK-AND-TALK

POSITIVEID CORPORATION
(d/b/a PositiveID)
1690 S Congress Ave Ste 200
Delray Beach, FL 33445
Tel.: (561) 805-8000
Fax: (561) 805-8001
Toll Free: (800) 970-2447
Web Site: www.positiveidcorp.com
Approx. Rev.: $3,093,000
Approx. Number Employees: 18
Business Description:
Human Implantable Radio Frequency Identification Microchip Mfr for Patient Identification
S.I.C.: 3669; 2836
N.A.I.C.S.: 334290; 325414
Advertising Expenditures: $200,000
Media: 2-10
Personnel:
Scott R. Silverman *(Chm)*
William J. Caragol *(CEO)*
Bryan Happ *(CFO & Sr VP)*
Brands & Products:
VERICHIP

POSITRON CORP.
7715 Loma Ct Ste A
Fishers, IN 46038
Tel.: (317) 576-0183
Fax: (317) 576-0358
Toll Free: (866) 613-7587
Web Site: www.positron.com
E-Mail For Key Personnel:
Sales Director: sales@positron.com
Approx. Sls.: $4,623,000
Approx. Number Employees: 27
Business Description:
Molecular Imaging Devices & Radiopharmaceutical Products Mfr
S.I.C.: 3845
N.A.I.C.S.: 334510
Advertising Expenditures: $133,338
Media: 17
Personnel:
Patrick G. Rooney *(Chm & CEO)*
Corey N. Conn *(CFO)*

POWER & TELEPHONE SUPPLY COMPANY
2673 Yale Ave
Memphis, TN 38112-3335
Tel.: (901) 324-6116
Fax: (901) 320-3082
Toll Free: (800) 238-7514
E-mail: info@ptsupply.com
Web Site: www.ptsupply.com
Sales Range: $100-124.9 Million
Approx. Number Employees: 1,500
Year Founded: 1963
Business Description:
Wholesale Telephones & Data Communications Equipment
S.I.C.: 5063; 5065
N.A.I.C.S.: 423610; 423690
Export
Media: 2-10-13
Personnel:
Jim Pentecost *(Pres)*
Mark Kaman *(CFO)*
Jim Drian *(Sr VP)*
Laburn R. Dye *(Sr VP)*
Daniel G. Melore *(Dir-Pur)*
Keith Cress *(Mgr-Mktg)*
Brands & Products:
POWER&TEL

POWER-ONE INC.
740 Calle Plano
Camarillo, CA 93012-8555
Tel.: (805) 987-8741
Fax: (805) 388-0476
Toll Free: (800) 678-9445
E-mail: investor.relations@power-one.com
Web Site: www.power-one.com
Approx. Sls.: $1,047,139,000
Approx. Number Employees: 3,470
Year Founded: 1973
Business Description:
AC/DC & DC/DC Power Supplies Mfr
S.I.C.: 3679; 3663; 3677
N.A.I.C.S.: 334418; 334220; 334416; 334419
Export
Advertising Expenditures: $830,000
Bus. Publs.: $450,000; Catalogs & Directories: $200,000; Exhibits/Trade Shows: $10,000; Foreign: $20,000; Internet Adv.: $10,000; Newsp. Distr. Mags.: $40,000; Other: $70,000; Product Samples: $10,000; Special Events Mktg.: $20,000
Distr.: Intl.; Natl.
Budget Set: Nov.
Personnel:
Jay Walters *(Chm)*
Richard J. Thompson *(Pres & CEO)*
Gary R. Larsen *(CFO & Sr VP-Fin)*
Steven Hogge *(Pres-Power Solutions Strategic Bus Unit)*
Alexander Levran *(Pres-Renewable Energy Solutions)*
Neil Dial *(Sr VP-Ops)*
Brands & Products:
AURORA
CHANGING THE SHAPE OF POWER
EXTERNAL ALARM UNIT
GALERO
HIQGRID
I.ILLUMINATION
INTEGRITY-ONE
NO-BUS
POWCOM
POWER-ONE
XSCEND
Z-ONE
Z-POL

POWERMAT USA, LLC
3000 N Pontiac Trl
Commerce Township, MI 48039
Tel.: (248) 668-6000
Fax: (248) 863-3100
Toll Free: (800) 753-3000
Web Site: www.powermat.com
Business Description:
Consumer Electronics; Develops, Designs & Sells Wireless Charging Devices
S.I.C.: 5065
N.A.I.C.S.: 423690
Personnel:
Ron Ferber *(Pres)*
Advertising Agencies:
Maxus Global
498 Seventh Ave
New York, NY 10018
Tel.: (212) 297-8300

Woods Witt Dealy & Sons, Inc.
110 W 40th St Ste 1902
New York, NY 10018
Tel.: (212) 768-1259
Fax: (212) 768-3520

POWERWAVE TECHNOLOGIES, INC.
1801 E Saint Andrew Pl
Santa Ana, CA 92705-5044
Tel.: (714) 466-1000
Fax: (714) 466-5800
Toll Free: (888) 797-9283
E-mail: info@pwav.com
Web Site: www.powerwave.com
Approx. Sls.: $591,461,000
Approx. Number Employees: 2,140
Business Description:
Designer & Mfr of Ultra-Linear Radio Frequency Power Amplifiers for Use in Wireless Communications
S.I.C.: 3663; 3679

Key to Media (For complete agency information see *The Advertising Red Books-Agencies* edition):
1. Bus. Publs. 2. Cable T.V. 3. Catalogs & Directories. 4. Co-op Adv. 5. Consumer Mags. 6. D.M. to Bus. Estab.7. D.M. to Consumers 8. Daily Newsp. 9. Exhibits/Trade Shows 10. Foreign 11. Infomercial 12. Internet Adv.13. Multimedia 14. Network Radio 15. Network T.V. 16. Newsp. Distr. Mags. 17. Other 18. Outdoor (Posters, Transit) 19. Point of Purchase20. Premiums, Novelties 21. Product Samples 22. Special Events Mktg. 23. Spot Radio 24. Spot T.V. 25. Weekly Newsp. 26. Yellow Page Adv.

N.A.I.C.S.: 334220; 334419
Advertising Expenditures: $2,600,000
Personnel:
Carl W. Neun *(Chm)*
Ronald J. Buschur *(Pres & CEO)*
Kevin T. Michaels *(CFO & Sec)*
J. Marvin Magee *(COO)*
Jake MacLeod *(Exec VP)*
Brands & Products:
AMR STREAMLINE
CLEAN SITE
NETWAY
NETWORK MANAGER
THE POWER IN WIRELESS
POWERWAVE
VERSAFLEX

PRECISION ELECTRONIC COIL MFG. CO.
(d/b/a Pacific Resistor Company)
18300 Oxnard St
Tarzana, CA 91356
Tel.: (818) 345-7811
Fax: (818) 345-1507
Toll Free: (800) 835-3355
E-mail: sales@pacificresistor.com
Web Site: www.pacificresistor.com
E-Mail For Key Personnel:
Sales Director: sales@pacificresistor.com
Approx. Number Employees: 45
Year Founded: 1953
Business Description:
Wire Wound Resistors, Networks & Customs Mfr
S.I.C.: 3676; 3677
N.A.I.C.S.: 334415; 334416
Export
Media: 2-4-26
Distr.: Direct to Consumer; Natl.
Budget Set: July
Brands & Products:
PRC

PRIMUS TELECOMMUNICATIONS GROUP, INCORPORATED
7901 Jones Branch Dr Ste 900
McLean, VA 22102-3338
Tel.: (703) 902-2800
Fax: (703) 902-2814
Toll Free: (888) 899-9900
E-mail: info@primustel.com
Web Site: www.primustel.com
Approx. Rev.: $764,947,000
Approx. Number Employees: 1,672
Year Founded: 1994
Business Description:
Integrated Telecommunications Services; International & Domestic Voice, Wireless, Internet, Voice-Over-Internet Protocol, Data & Hosting Services
S.I.C.: 4813
N.A.I.C.S.: 517110; 517310
Advertising Expenditures: $12,800,000
Media: 8-9-10-24-25
Personnel:
Peter D. Aquino *(Chm, Pres & CEO)*
Richard R. Ramlall *(Chief Comm Officer & Sr VP-Corp Dev)*
James C. Keeley *(Chief Acctg Officer, VP & Controller)*
Ravi Bhatia *(CEO-Australia)*
Christie A. Hill *(Gen Counsel, Sec & Sr VP)*
Advertising Agency:
Global Advertising Strategies
55 Broad St 19th Fl
New York, NY 10004
Tel.: (212) 964-0030
Fax: (212) 964-0040
Primus Wireless

PROFESSIONAL SECURITY TECHNOLOGIES LLC
43 River Rd
Nutley, NJ 07110-3411
Tel.: (973) 661-9000
Fax: (973) 661-3540
Toll Free: (888) 443-1100
Web Site: www.prosecurity.com
Sales Range: $50-74.9 Million
Approx. Number Employees: 20
Year Founded: 1967
Business Description:
Security Systems Installation & Services
S.I.C.: 7382
N.A.I.C.S.: 561621
Media: 2-4-7-8-9-13-20-25
Personnel:
Richard D. Rockwell *(Chm)*
Brands & Products:
PROFESSIONAL SECURITY TECHNOLOGIES
SECURITY EXPERTS FOR COMMERCIAL ENTERPRISES

PROFESSIONAL SOUND SERVICES, INC.
311 W 43rd St Ste 1100
New York, NY 10036
Tel.: (212) 586-1033
Fax: (212) 586-0970
Toll Free: (800) 883-1033
Web Site: www.pro-sound.com
Approx. Sls.: $2,300,000
Approx. Number Employees: 10
Business Description:
Audio Equipment Sales, Services & Rentals
S.I.C.: 7359
N.A.I.C.S.: 532299
Media: 2-6-10
Personnel:
Richard Topham, Jr. *(Pres)*

PROGRESSIVE DYNAMICS, INC.
507 Industrial Rd
Marshall, MI 49068-1750
Tel.: (269) 781-4241
Fax: (269) 781-7802
E-mail: sales@progressivedyn.com
Web Site: www.progressivedyn.com
E-Mail For Key Personnel:
Sales Director: sales@progressivedyn.com
Sales Range: $25-49.9 Million
Approx. Number Employees: 100
Year Founded: 1964
Business Description:
Mfr. of Twelve Volt Lighting & Power Convertors; Fibre Optic Light Sources; Patient Warming Devices
S.I.C.: 3679; 3647
N.A.I.C.S.: 334419; 336321
Import Export
Media: 2-4-7-10-11-17
Distr.: Intl.; Natl.
Personnel:
Thomas Phlipot *(Exec VP)*
Brands & Products:
CHARGE WIZARD
INTELI-POWER 9100
LIFE-AIR
QUIET SENSOR
SOFT-FLEX
TCMS
TCMS INTERFACE
TOTAL CHARGING MANAGEMENT SYSTEM
Advertising Agency:
Karlo Network
One Harper Run, Ste. 201
Battle Creek, MI 49014
Tel.: (269) 969-4300
Fax: (269) 969-4301
(Electrical Converters)

PROJECTS UNLIMITED, INC.
6300 Sand Lk Rd
Dayton, OH 45414-2649
Tel.: (937) 918-2200
Fax: (937) 918-2239
E-mail: info@pui.com
Web Site: www.pui.com
Sales Range: $200-249.9 Million
Approx. Number Employees: 100
Year Founded: 1940
Business Description:
Mfr of Solid State Audio Indicators, Audio Transducers, Power Transistor Pockets, & Electronic Assemblies & Sub-Assemblies
S.I.C.: 3672; 3679
N.A.I.C.S.: 334412; 334419
Import Export
Media: 2-4-6-7-8-10-11-21-26
Distr.: Intl.; Natl.
Budget Set: Nov.
Personnel:
David L. Wyse *(Pres)*
Brands & Products:
DIP-ALARM
DIP-FLASH
PROJECTS UNLIMITED

PROTECTION ONE, INC.
(Holding of GTCR Golder Rauner, LLC)
1035 N 3rd St Ste 101
Lawrence, KS 66044
Mailing Address:
PO Box 49292
Wichita, KS 67202
Tel.: (785) 856-5500
Fax: (785) 856-9700
Fax: (785) 856-9970
E-mail: dariusnevin@protectionone.com
Web Site: www.protectionone.com
E-Mail For Key Personnel:
Public Relations: robinlampe@protectionone.com
Approx. Rev.: $368,052,000
Approx. Number Employees: 2,600
Year Founded: 1988
Business Description:
Security Alarm Monitoring Services
S.I.C.: 1731; 7382
N.A.I.C.S.: 238210; 561621
Advertising Expenditures: $3,100,000
Media: 2-6-8-10-15-22-23-24-26
Personnel:
Timothy J. Whall *(CEO)*
Daniel M. Bresingham *(CFO)*
Sarah Strahm *(Chief Acctg Officer)*
Jamie Haenggi *(Chief Mktg & Customer Experience Officer)*
P. Gray Finney *(Gen Counsel, Sec & Sr VP)*
Bob Dale *(Sr VP-Residential & Comml Sls)*
Stephen Hopkins *(Sr VP-Ops & Corp Svcs)*
Joseph R. Sanchez *(Sr VP-Customer Ops)*
Lisa Ciappetta *(Sr Dir-Mktg)*

PROVISION HOLDING, INC.
9253 Eton Ave
Chatsworth, CA 91311
Tel.: (818) 775-1624
Fax: (818) 775-1628
E-mail: info@provision.tv
Web Site: www.provision3dmedia.com
Approx. Rev.: $209,354
Approx. Number Employees: 8
Year Founded: 2004
Business Description:
Holding Company; Interactive Display Technology Solutions
S.I.C.: 6719; 3679; 3993
N.A.I.C.S.: 551112; 334419; 339950
Advertising Expenditures: $59,814
Media: 17
Personnel:
Curt Thornton *(Pres & CEO)*

PTS ELECTRONICS CORPORATION
(Sub. of ModusLink Global Solutions, Inc.)
5233 S Hwy 37
Bloomington, IN 47401
Tel.: (812) 824-9331
Fax: (812) 824-2848
Toll Free: (800) 844-7871
E-mail: pts@ptscorp.com
Web Site: www.ptscorp.com
Sales Range: $25-49.9 Million
Approx. Number Employees: 550
Year Founded: 1967
Business Description:
Consumer Electronics Service Repair & Reverse Logistics Providers
S.I.C.: 7629
N.A.I.C.S.: 811219
Import Export
Media: 2-4-6-7-8-10-18-20
Distr.: Natl.
Budget Set: Feb.

PULSE ELECTRONICS CORPORATION
(Formerly Technitrol, Inc.)
1210 Northbrook Dr Ste 470
Trevose, PA 19053-8406
Tel.: (215) 355-2900
Fax: (215) 355-7397
Web Site: www.pulseelectronics.com
Approx. Sls.: $432,480,000
Approx. Number Employees: 16,100
Year Founded: 1947
Business Description:
Electronic Components Mfr
S.I.C.: 3679; 3674
N.A.I.C.S.: 334419; 334413
Import Export
Advertising Expenditures: $159,000
Media: 2-10
Distr.: Intl.; Natl.
Budget Set: Oct.
Personnel:
Ralph E. Faison *(Pres & CEO)*
Drew A. Moyer *(CFO & Sr VP)*

Key to Media (For complete agency information see *The Advertising Red Books-Agencies* edition):
1. Bus. Publs. 2. Cable T.V. 3. Catalogs & Directories. 4. Co-op Adv. 5. Consumer Mags. 6. D.M. to Bus. Estab.7. D.M. to Consumers 8. Daily Newsp. 9. Exhibits/Trade Shows 10. Foreign 11. Infomercial 12. Internet Adv.13. Multimedia 14. Network Radio 15. Network T.V. 16. Newsp. Distr. Mags. 17. Other 18. Outdoor (Posters, Transit) 19. Point of Purchase20. Premiums, Novelties 21. Product Samples 22. Special Events Mktg. 23. Spot Radio 24. Spot T.V. 25. Weekly Newsp. 26. Yellow Page Adv.

Pulse Electronics Corporation — (Continued)

Alan H. Benjamin *(COO)*
John R. D. Dickson *(CIO & Sr VP)*
Michael P. Ginnetti *(Chief Acctg Officer & Controller)*
John Houston *(Sr VP-Network & Wireless Products Grp)*
Roger Shahnazarian *(Sr VP-Production Ops)*
Jim Jacobson *(Dir-IR)*
Brands & Products:
AMI DODUCO
COMPONENTS FOR A MODERN WORLD
PULSE
TECHNITROL

Q-TECH CORPORATION

10150 W Jefferson Blvd
Culver City, CA 90232-3502
Tel.: (310) 836-7900
Fax: (310) 836-2157
E-mail: jerry.saklad@q-tech.com
Web Site: www.q-tech.com
Approx. Sls.: $17,000,000
Approx. Number Employees: 160
Year Founded: 1972
Business Description:
Oscillators Mfr
S.I.C.: 3679; 3825
N.A.I.C.S.: 334419; 334515
Media: 10
Personnel:
Richard Taylor *(Owner)*
Jerry Saklad *(Dir-Sls & Mktg)*

QSOUND LABS, INC.

2816 11 Street NE Suite 102
Calgary, AB T2E 7S7, Canada
Tel.: (403) 291-2492
Fax: (403) 250-1521
E-mail: info@qsound.com
Web Site: www.qsound.com
Sales Range: $1-9.9 Million
Approx. Number Employees: 21
Year Founded: 1988
Business Description:
Audio Enhancement Software Packages Developer
S.I.C.: 7372; 3651
N.A.I.C.S.: 511210; 334310; 334611
Advertising Expenditures: $963,255
Personnel:
David J. Gallagher *(Pres)*
Willis Liu *(Mgr-Tech Support)*
Brands & Products:
3D AUDIO THAT WORKS
AFFILIATEDIRECT
AUDIOPIX
CHOICEWORLD
IQ
IQFX
IQFX2
IQFX3
IQMS
IQMS2
LEADERS IN DIGITAL AUDIO INNOVATION
MICROQ
MQFX
MQSYNTH
Q1
Q123
Q2
Q2X
Q3
Q3D
Q3DINTERACTIVE
Q4
QBASS
QCOMMERCE
QCREATOR
QDVD
QEM
QHD
QLIMITER
QMAX
QMAXII
QMDX
QMIXER
QMP3D
QMSS
QRUMBLE
QSIZZLE
QSOFT3D
QSOUND
QSOUND 3D INTERACTIVE
QSURROUND
QSYS
QSYS/TDM
QSYSTEM
QTELNET
QTOOLS/AX
QTOOLS/SF
QVERB
QVOICE
QX
QX/TDM
QXPANDER
QXSDII
SCREAMING 3D AUDIO
ULTRAQ
VIRTUAL AUDIO

QUALITAU, INC.

950 Bemecia Ave
Sunnyvale, CA 94085
Tel.: (408) 522-9200
Fax: (408) 522-8110
E-mail: gadik@qualitau.com
Web Site: www.qualitau.com
Approx. Number Employees: 65
Year Founded: 1991
Business Description:
Reliability Test Equipment
S.I.C.: 3674
N.A.I.C.S.: 334413
Media: 10
Personnel:
Jacob Herschmann *(Pres)*
Gadi Krieger *(CEO)*
Nava Ben-Yehuda *(Controller & VP-Fin)*

QUAM-NICHOLS COMPANY

234 E Marquette Rd
Chicago, IL 60637-4091
Tel.: (773) 488-5800
Fax: (773) 488-6944
E-mail: qnc@qnc.com
Web Site: www.quamspeakers.com
Sales Range: $10-24.9 Million
Approx. Number Employees: 250
Year Founded: 1930
Business Description:
Commercial & Industrial Loudspeakers & Mounting Accessories
S.I.C.: 3651
N.A.I.C.S.: 334310
Import Export
Advertising Expenditures: $200,000
Media: 2-4-10-17-21
Distr.: Natl.
Budget Set: Mar.
Personnel:
William G. Little *(Pres & CEO)*
Larry Salzwedel *(VP-Sls & Mktg)*
Brands & Products:
QUAM
QUIKSPEC

QUAMTEL, INC.

(Formerly WQN)
14911 Quorum Dr Ste 140
Dallas, TX 75254
Tel.: (972) 361-1980
Fax: (469) 461-3917
Toll Free: (800) 731-7864
Web Site: www.quamtel.com
Approx. Rev.: $2,462,060
Approx. Number Employees: 17
Year Founded: 1996
Business Description:
Communications Services
S.I.C.: 4812; 7389
N.A.I.C.S.: 517212; 561421
Advertising Expenditures: $193,000
Media: 7-13
Personnel:
Robert S. Picow *(Chm)*
Stuart Ehrlich *(Pres & CEO)*

QUICKPLAY MEDIA INC.

190 Liberty St 2nd Fl
Toronto, ON M6K 3L5, Canada
Tel.: (416) 916-7529
Fax: (416) 535-2415
E-mail: investors@quickplay.com
Web Site: www.quickplay.com
E-Mail For Key Personnel:
Sales Director: sales@quickplay.com
Approx. Number Employees: 120
Business Description:
Mobile TV & Video Services
S.I.C.: 4812
N.A.I.C.S.: 517212
Personnel:
Wayne Purboo *(Co-Founder, Pres & CEO)*
John Coady *(COO)*
Samir Ahuja *(VP-Engrg & Product Solutions)*
Bruce Bishop *(VP-Fin)*
Mark Hyland *(VP-Mktg & Sls)*
Advertising Agency:
fama PR, Inc.
1 Broadway 16th Fl Kendall Sq
Cambridge, MA 02142
Tel.: (617) 758-4141
Fax: (617) 758-4101
Toll Free: (866) 326-2552

QUICKSET INTERNATIONAL, INC.

(Sub. of Moog Inc.)
3650 Woodhead Dr
Northbrook, IL 60062-1817
Tel.: (847) 498-0700
Fax: (847) 498-1258
Toll Free: (800) 247-6563
E-mail: info@quickset.com
Web Site: www.quickset.com
Sales Range: $10-24.9 Million
Approx. Number Employees: 58
Year Founded: 1933
Business Description:
Surveillance, Aerospace, Military, Emergency Vehicles, Videography, Electronic News Gathering & Communications Positioning Devices Mfr.
S.I.C.: 3861; 3625
N.A.I.C.S.: 333315; 335314
Export
Media: 2-4-5-6-7-10-13-19
Distr.: Intl.; Natl.
Personnel:
Andre Lareau *(Pres & CEO)*
Brian Hallstrom *(Mgr-Ops)*
Brands & Products:
APOLLO
GIBRALTAR
HERCULES
HUSKY
JUPITER
QUICKSET
QUICKTRAC
SAMSON

QWEST CORPORATION

(Sub. of Qwest Communications International Inc.)
1801 California St
Denver, CO 80202
Tel.: (303) 992-1400
Toll Free: (800) 899-7780
Web Site: www.qwest.com
Approx. Rev.: $9,271,000,000
Approx. Number Employees: 26,050
Year Founded: 1911
Business Description:
Wired Data, Internet, Video & Voice Telecommunications Services
S.I.C.: 4813
N.A.I.C.S.: 517110
Advertising Expenditures: $292,000,000
Personnel:
Edward A. Mueller *(Chm, Pres & CEO)*
Stefan Stein *(Chief Ethics & Compliance Officer)*
R. William Johnston *(Chief Acctg Officer, Sr VP & Controller)*
Stephanie G. Comfort *(Exec VP-Corp Strategy & Dev)*
Teresa A. Taylor *(Exec VP-Bus Markets Grp)*
Roland R. Thornton *(Exec VP)*
Robert D. Tregemba *(Exec VP-Network Ops)*
R. Steven Davis *(Sr VP-Pub Policy & Govt Rels)*

RADIO FREQUENCY SYSTEMS, INC.

200 Pond View Dr
Meriden, CT 06450-7195
Tel.: (203) 630-3311
Fax: (203) 634-2272
Toll Free: (800) 321-4700
E-mail: sales.americas@rfsworld.com
Web Site: www.rfsworld.com
E-Mail For Key Personnel:
Sales Director: sales.americas@rfsworld.com
Approx. Number Employees: 165
Year Founded: 1950
Business Description:
Wireless Telecommunications Infrastructure Products Mfr & Designer
S.I.C.: 3663; 3357
N.A.I.C.S.: 334220; 335921
Import
Media: 2-4-7-10-20-26
Distr.: Natl.
Budget Set: Oct.

Key to Media (For complete agency information see *The Advertising Red Books-Agencies* edition):
1. Bus. Publs. 2. Cable T.V. 3. Catalogs & Directories. 4. Co-op Adv. 5. Consumer Mags. 6. D.M. to Bus. Estab.7. D.M. to Consumers
8. Daily Newsp. 9. Exhibits/Trade Shows 10. Foreign 11. Infomercial 12. Internet Adv.13. Multimedia 14. Network Radio
15. Network T.V. 16. Newsp. Distr. Mags. 17. Other 18. Outdoor (Posters, Transit) 19. Point of Purchase20. Premiums, Novelties
21. Product Samples 22. Special Events Mktg. 23. Spot Radio 24. Spot T.V. 25. Weekly Newsp. 26. Yellow Page Adv.

Personnel:
William Bayne, Jr. *(Pres-Americas & WIS)*
Chris Jaeger *(Gen Mgr-Asia Pacific)*
Horst Spielkamp *(Gen Mgr)*
Zhu Du-qing *(Dir-Product Mgmt-Asia Pacific North)*
Chris Adams *(Product Mgr-Systems)*
Asad Zoberi *(Product Mgr)*
Paula Mennone-Preisner *(Specialist-Mktg & Comm)*
Brands & Products:
CELCALC
CELLFLEX
CELLITE
CELTOOLS
CELWAVE
THE CLEAR CHOICE
COMFLEX
COMPACTLINE
FLEXWELL
HELIFLEX
MAXIMIZER
MICRO-TENNA
OPTIMIZER
PENETRATOR
PERSUADER
RADIAFLEX
RAPID FIT
REMOTE TILT
SLIMLINE
STATIONMASTER

RADIO RESEARCH INSTRUMENT CO.

584 N Main St
Waterbury, CT 06704-3506
Tel.: (203) 753-5840
Fax: (203) 754-2567
E-mail: radiores@prodigy.net
Web Site: www.radiores.com/
Sales Range: $10-24.9 Million
Approx. Number Employees: 15
Year Founded: 1952
Business Description:
Radar Systems & Equipment Mfr
S.I.C.: 3812
N.A.I.C.S.: 334511
Import Export
Media: 2-4-7-10
Distr.: Natl.
Personnel:
P.J. Plishner *(Pres)*
Jane Barber *(Exec VP)*

RADIOSHACK CORPORATION

300 RadioShack Circle
Fort Worth, TX 76102-1964
Tel.: (817) 415-3011
Tel.: (817) 415-3700
Fax: (817) 415-6808
E-mail: investor.relations@radioshack.com
Web Site: www.radioshackcorporation.com
E-Mail For Key Personnel:
Public Relations: media.relations@radioshack.com
Approx. Rev.: $4,472,700,000
Approx. Number Employees: 35,100
Year Founded: 1919
Business Description:
Consumer Electronics & Accessories Retailer
S.I.C.: 5731; 5961; 5999
N.A.I.C.S.: 443112; 453998; 454111; 454113
Import Export
Advertising Expenditures: $206,100,000
Media: 3-4-6-9-13-14-15-16-23-24
Distr.: Intl.; Natl.
Personnel:
Julian C. Day *(Chm)*
James F. Gooch *(Pres & CEO)*
Dorvin D. Lively *(CFO, Chief Admin Officer & Exec VP)*
Sharon Stufflebeme *(CIO & Sr VP)*
Lee D. Appelbaum *(CMO & Exec VP)*
Mary Ann Doran *(Chief HR Officer & Sr VP-HR)*
Bryan E. Bevin *(Exec VP)*
Scott E. Young *(Chief Mdsg Officer & Exec VP)*
Darrell Brown *(Mgr-ODM Product Dev)*
Brands & Products:
RADIOSHACK
THE SHACK
Advertising Agencies:
Butler, Shine, Stern & Partners
20 Liberty Ship Way
Sausalito, CA 94965-3312
Tel.: (415) 331-6049
Fax: (415) 331-3524

imc2
12404 Park Central Ste 400
Dallas, TX 75251
Tel.: (214) 224-1000
Fax: (214) 224-1100

Mindshare
498 7th Ave
New York, NY 10018
Tel.: (212) 297-7000
Fax: (212) 297-7001
Media Buying & Planning Agency of Record

Overdrive
38 Everett St 2nd Fl
Boston, MA 02134
Tel.: (617) 254-5000
Fax: (617) 254-5003

PromoGroup
444 N Orleans St Ste 400
Chicago, IL 60610-4494
Tel.: (312) 467-1300
Fax: (312) 467-1311

Promotion Group Central-Dallas
9901 E Valley Ranch Pkwy
Irving, TX 75063
Tel.: (214) 614-3242

SBC Advertising
333 W Nationwide Blvd
Columbus, OH 43215
Tel.: (614) 891-7070
Fax: (614) 255-2600
Toll Free: (866) 891-7001

RANTEC MICROWAVE SYSTEMS, INC.

24003 Ventura Blvd
Calabasas, CA 91302
Tel.: (818) 223-5000
Fax: (818) 223-5089
Web Site: www.rantecmdm.com
Approx. Number Employees: 60
Year Founded: 1957
Business Description:
Microwave Antennas Mfr
S.I.C.: 3812; 3826
N.A.I.C.S.: 334511; 334516
Media: 8-10-21
Distr.: Intl.; Natl.
Budget Set: Oct.
Personnel:
Graham R. Wilson *(Pres)*
Carl Grindle *(CEO)*
Larry Miller *(Dir-Bus Dev)*
Mayo Overbeck *(Dir-Sls)*

RAULAND-BORG CORPORATION

1802 W Central Rd
Mount Prospect, IL 60052
Tel.: (847) 590-7100
Fax: (847) 632-8550
Toll Free: (800) 752-7725
E-mail: webmaster@rauland.com
Web Site: www.rauland.com
Approx. Number Employees: 300
Year Founded: 1948
Business Description:
Communication Systems for Health Care, Education & Corrections Fields Designer & Mfr; Professional Sound Reinforcement Systems
S.I.C.: 3661; 3663
N.A.I.C.S.: 334210; 334220
Import Export
Advertising Expenditures: $200,000
Media: 2-4-5-10-26
Distr.: Natl.
Budget Set: Oct.-Nov.
Personnel:
Norman Kidder *(Pres & CEO)*
Rick Stalkfleet *(CFO & VP)*
Carl Cox *(VP & Dir-Engrg)*
Maureen Pajerski *(VP-Sls & Mktg)*
Brands & Products:
ALL-AMERICAN
ASCOM
CHRONOCOM
DIRECTOR II
FIRE PLEX
RAULAND
RESPONDER
RESPONDER 4000
RESPONDER IV
RESPONDER NET
SECUREPLEX
SPECTRALINK
TELECENTER
TELENURSE

RAYMARINE INC.

(Sub. of Raymarine PLC)
21 Manchester St
Merrimack, NH 03054-4801
Tel.: (603) 881-5200
Fax: (603) 864-4756
Web Site: www.raymarine.com
Approx. Number Employees: 120
Business Description:
Marketing, Sales and Distribution of Marine Electronics
S.I.C.: 3812
N.A.I.C.S.: 334511
Personnel:
Dave Bimsthleger *(Pres)*
Kevin Murphy *(Sr VP-Fin)*
Larry Rencken *(VP-Sls)*
Sandra Soler *(VP-HR)*
Jameson Dery *(Dir-Product Support & Warranty)*
Jim Hands *(Dir-Mktg)*
Kevin Foley *(Mgr-IT)*
Advertising Agency:
Greenough Communications
9 Harcourt St
Boston, MA 02116
Tel.: (617) 275-6500
Fax: (617) 275-6501

RED PEACOCK INTERNATIONAL, INC.

19859 Nordhoff St
Northridge, CA 91324
Tel.: (818) 407-8822
Fax: (818) 407-8833
E-mail: info@redpeacock.com
Web Site: www.redpeacock.com
Sales Range: $25-49.9 Million
Approx. Number Employees: 9
Year Founded: 1997
Business Description:
Consumer Electronics Distr
S.I.C.: 5064
N.A.I.C.S.: 423620
Media: 4-10
Personnel:
Ruby G. Mansukhani *(Pres & COO)*
John Lalwani *(Exec VP)*
Lalchand S. Lalwani *(Exec VP)*

RELM WIRELESS CORPORATION

7100 Technology Dr
Melbourne, FL 32904-1525
Tel.: (321) 984-1414
Fax: (321) 984-0168
Toll Free: (800) 821-2900
E-mail: info@relm.com
Web Site: www.relm.com
E-Mail For Key Personnel:
Sales Director: sales@relm.com
Approx. Sls.: $25,954,000
Approx. Number Employees: 96
Year Founded: 1968
Business Description:
Mobile Radio Products Mfr
S.I.C.: 3663
N.A.I.C.S.: 334220
Import Export
Advertising Expenditures: $299,000
Personnel:
George N. Benjamin, III *(Chm)*
David P. Storey *(Pres & CEO)*
William P. Kelly *(CFO & Exec VP)*
Brands & Products:
BK RADIO
RELM
RELM/BK
RELM WIRELESS

RENESAS ELECTRONICS AMERICA INC.

(Sub. of Renesas Electronics Corp.)
2880 Scott Blvd
Santa Clara, CA 95050-2554
Tel.: (408) 588-6000
Fax: (408) 588-6130
Toll Free: (800) 366-9782
Web Site: www.am.renesas.com
Sales Range: $150-199.9 Million
Approx. Number Employees: 1,500
Year Founded: 1981
Business Description:
Semiconductor & Microcontroller Mfr
S.I.C.: 3674
N.A.I.C.S.: 334413
Import Export
Media: 1-2-4-7-8-10-20
Distr.: Natl.
Budget Set: Mar.

Key to Media (For complete agency information see *The Advertising Red Books-Agencies* edition):
1. Bus. Publs. 2. Cable T.V. 3. Catalogs & Directories. 4. Co-op Adv. 5. Consumer Mags. 6. D.M. to Bus. Estab.7. D.M. to Consumers 8. Daily Newsp. 9. Exhibits/Trade Shows 10. Foreign 11. Infomercial 12. Internet Adv.13. Multimedia 14. Network Radio 15. Network T.V. 16. Newsp. Distr. Mags. 17. Other 18. Outdoor (Posters, Transit) 19. Point of Purchase20. Premiums, Novelties 21. Product Samples 22. Special Events Mktg. 23. Spot Radio 24. Spot T.V. 25. Weekly Newsp. 26. Yellow Page Adv.

Renesas Electronics America Inc. — (Continued)

Personnel:
Daniel Mahoney *(Pres & CEO)*
David Weigand *(CFO & VP-Fin)*
Viren Patel *(CIO & VP)*
Harry Turner *(Gen Counsel, Sec & VP)*
Ali Sebt *(Exec VP)*
James Hettema *(VP-Computing & Comm Bus Unit)*
Sharon Maiden *(VP-HR & Admin)*
Shigehiko Satoh *(VP-Display Bus Unit)*
Jim Trent *(VP-Automotive)*
Makoto Sekine *(Gen Mgr-Advanced Process Dev)*
Denise Garibaldi *(Mgr-PR)*
Brands & Products:
ANALOG MASTER
FIP
K SERIES
NEC
OPENCAD DESIGN SYSTEM
V SERIES
V20
V20H
V25
V30
V30H
V40
V50
V800
V805
V810
V820
VR SERIES
VR4000
VR4000PC
VR4000SC
VR4200
VR4200LP
VR4200PC
VR4400
VR4400MC
VR4400PC
VR4400SC
Advertising Agency:
Dentsu America, Inc.
32 Ave of the Americas 16th Fl
New York, NY 10013
Tel.: (212) 397-3333
Fax: (212) 397-3322

RESEARCH IN MOTION LTD.
(d/b/a RIM)
295 Phillip Street
Waterloo, ON N2L 3W8, Canada
Tel.: (519) 888-7465
Fax: (519) 888-7884
E-mail: help@rim.com
Web Site: www.rim.com
Approx. Rev.: $19,907,000,000
Approx. Number Employees: 17,500
Year Founded: 1984
Business Description:
Designer, Mfr & Marketer of Wireless Solutions
S.I.C.: 3661; 3663; 4812
N.A.I.C.S.: 334210; 334220; 517212
Advertising Expenditures: $1,100,000,000
Media: 6-13-17
Personnel:
Michael Lazaridis *(Co-Chm, Pres & Co-CEO)*
James L. Balsillie *(Co-Chm & Co-CEO)*
Brian Bidulka *(CFO)*
Robin Bienfait *(CIO)*
Keith Pardy *(CMO)*
Larry Conlee *(COO-Product Dev & Mfg)*
Karima Bawa *(VP-Legal)*
Brian Wallace *(VP-Digital Mktg & Media)*
Larry Silver *(Dir-Federal Govt Solutions)*
Brands & Products:
ALWAYS ON, ALWAYS CONNECTED
BLACKBERRY BOLD
BLACKBERRY BUILT-IN
BLACKBERRY CONNECTION
BLACKBERRY CURVE
BLACKBERRY ENTERPRISE EDITION
BLACKBERRY EXCHANGE EDITION
BLACKBERRY INTERNET EDITION
BLACKBERRY NOTES EDITION
BLACKBERRY PEARL
BLACKBERRY STORM
BLACKBERRY SUREPRESS
BLACKBERRY TOUR
BLACKBERRY UNITE!
INTER@CTIVE
RIM
RIM 1802G
RIM 1902G
RIM 802D
RIM 850
RIM 850 WIRELESS HANDHELD
RIM 857
RIM 857 WIRELESS HANDHELD
RIM 902M
RIM 950
RIM 950 WIRELESS HANDHELD
RIM 957
RIM 957 WIRELESS HANDHELD
RIM WIRELESS HANDHELD
SURETYPE
Advertising Agencies:
72andSunny
6300 Arizona Cir
Los Angeles, CA 90045
Tel.: (310) 215-9009
Fax: (310) 215-9012
BlackBerry

Abbott Mead Vickers BBDO
151 Marylebone Rd
London, NW1 5QE, United Kingdom
Tel.: (44) 20 7616 3500
Fax: (44) 207 616 3600
BlackBerry

Brodeur Partners
855 Boylston St 2nd Fl
Boston, MA 02116-2622
Tel.: (617) 587-2800
Fax: (617) 587-2828

Hollywood Branded Inc.
110 Lomita St
El Segundo, CA 90245
Tel.: (310) 606-2030
Fax: (310) 606-2063

Quarry Integrated Communications
180 King St S
Waterloo, ON N2J 1P8, Canada
Tel.: (519) 570-2020
Fax: (519) 743-3053

RETZLAFF INCORPORATED
(d/b/a Celadon Incorporated)
50 Mitchell Blvd
San Rafael, CA 94903-2035
Tel.: (415) 472-1177
Fax: (415) 472-1179
E-mail: sales@celadon.com
Web Site: www.celadon.com
E-Mail For Key Personnel:
Sales Director: sales@celadon.com
Sales Range: $10-24.9 Million
Approx. Number Employees: 5
Year Founded: 1990
Business Description:
Custom Infrared Remote Control Devices
S.I.C.: 3625
N.A.I.C.S.: 335314
Media: 2-4-7-10-13
Distr.: Intl.; Natl.
Personnel:
Kathy Johnson *(Pres)*
Robert Z. Retzlaff *(CEO)*
Brands & Products:
CELADON
PIC-200
SC SERIES

REX AMERICAN RESOURCES CORPORATION
(Formerly Rex Stores Corporation)
2875 Needmore Rd
Dayton, OH 45414-4301
Tel.: (937) 276-3931
Fax: (937) 276-8643
E-mail: support@rexstores.com
Web Site: www.rexstores.com
Approx. Rev.: $301,674,000
Approx. Number Employees: 58
Year Founded: 1984
Business Description:
Investment Services
S.I.C.: 6289
N.A.I.C.S.: 523999
Advertising Expenditures: $8,533,000
Media: 4-9-25
Personnel:
Stuart A. Rose *(Chm & CEO)*
Zafar Rizvi *(Pres & COO)*
Douglas L. Bruggeman *(CFO, Treas & VP-Fin)*

REX STORES CORPORATION
(Name Changed to REX AMERICAN RESOURCES CORPORATION)

RF MICRO DEVICES, INC.
7628 Thorndike Rd
Greensboro, NC 27409-9421
Tel.: (336) 664-1233
Fax: (336) 931-7454
E-mail: info@rfmd.com
Web Site: www.rfmd.com
Approx. Rev.: $1,051,756,000
Approx. Number Employees: 3,726
Year Founded: 1991
Business Description:
Semiconductor Component Mfr
S.I.C.: 3674
N.A.I.C.S.: 334413
Advertising Expenditures: $300,000
Media: 2-4-10
Personnel:
Walter H. Wilkinson, Jr. *(Chm)*
Robert A. Bruggeworth *(Pres & CEO)*
William A. Priddy, Jr. *(CFO, Sec & VP-Admin)*
J. Forrest Moore *(CIO & VP-IT)*
Suzanne B. Rudy *(Compliance Officer, Treas, VP & Asst Sec)*
Steven E. Creviston *(Pres-Cellular Products Grp & VP)*
Norman A. Hilgendorf *(Pres-Multi-Market Products Grp & Corp VP)*
Jerry D. Neal *(Exec VP-Mktg & Strategic Dev)*
Ralph Knupp *(VP-HR)*
Gregory J. Thompson *(VP-Sls)*
Brands & Products:
BLUETOOTH
LEAD FRAME MODULE
POLARIS
POWERSTAR
RFMD
TOTAL RADIO
ULTIMATEBLUE
Advertising Agency:
The MWW Group
700 13th St NW
Washington, DC 20006
Tel.: (202) 585-2270
Fax: (202) 585-2273

RICHARDSON ELECTRONICS, LTD.
40W267 Keslinger Road
Lafox, IL 60147
Mailing Address:
PO Box 393
Lafox, IL 60147-0392
Tel.: (630) 208-2200
Tel.: (630) 208-3637 (Sales)
Fax: (630) 208-2550
Toll Free: (800) 348-5580
Telex: 283461
E-mail: info@rell.com
Web Site: www.rell.com
Approx. Sls.: $158,867,000
Approx. Number Employees: 295
Year Founded: 1947
Business Description:
Electronic Components, Equipment & Assemblies for Industrial Applications Distr
S.I.C.: 5065; 7373
N.A.I.C.S.: 423690; 541512
Import Export
Advertising Expenditures: $2,000,000
Media: 1-2-4-5-6-7-8-10-11-13-20-21-22
Distr.: Intl.; Natl.
Budget Set: May
Personnel:
Edward J. Richardson *(Chm, Pres, CEO & COO)*
Kathleen S. Dvorak *(CFO, Chief Strategy Officer & Exec VP)*
Michael Bauer *(Chief HR Officer & Sr VP)*
James M. Dudek, Jr. *(Chief Acctg Officer & Controller)*
Kyle C. Badger *(Gen Counsel, Sec & Exec VP)*
Robert J. Heise *(Exec VP & Gen Mgr-Display Sys Grp)*
Gregory J. Peloquin *(Exec VP & Gen Mgr-RF, Wireless & Power Div)*
Wendy Diddell *(Exec VP-Corp Dev)*
Bradley R. Knechtel *(Exec VP-Supply Chain Mgmt)*
Kevin M. Connor *(Sr VP-Mktg)*
Joseph C. Grill *(Sr VP-HR)*
Kathleen M. McNally *(Sr VP-Mktg Ops & Customer Support)*

Key to Media (For complete agency information see *The Advertising Red Books-Agencies* edition):
1. Bus. Publs. 2. Cable T.V. 3. Catalogs & Directories. 4. Co-op Adv. 5. Consumer Mags. 6. D.M. to Bus. Estab.7. D.M. to Consumers 8. Daily Newsp. 9. Exhibits/Trade Shows 10. Foreign 11. Infomercial 12. Internet Adv.13. Multimedia 14. Network Radio 15. Network T.V. 16. Newsp. Distr. Mags. 17. Other 18. Outdoor (Posters, Transit) 19. Point of Purchase20. Premiums, Novelties 21. Product Samples 22. Special Events Mktg. 23. Spot Radio 24. Spot T.V. 25. Weekly Newsp. 26. Yellow Page Adv.

Brands & Products:
AMPEREX
ANVIL
BROADCAST RICHARDSON
BURTEK
CETRON
ETERNAL GRAPHICS
IMAGE SYSTEMS
NATIONAL
PIXELINK
RF GAIN
RICHARDSON ELECTRONICS
WIMAX
Advertising Agency:
Richardson Electronics Ltd.
Advertising Group
(House Agency)
PO Box 393 40W267 Keslinger Rd.
Lafox, IL 60147-0393
Tel.: (630) 208-2200
Fax: (630) 208-2550
(Electron Tubes, Power Semiconductors, Display Products Security System)

ROCHE NIMBLEGEN, INC.
(Sub. of Roche Applied Science)
500 S Rosa Rd
Madison, WI 53719
Tel.: (608) 218-7600
Fax: (608) 218-7601 .
E-mail: info@nimblegen.com
Web Site: www.nimblegen.com
Sales Range: $10-24.9 Million
Approx. Number Employees: 135
Year Founded: 1999
Business Description:
Microarrays & Related Products Mfr & Marketer
S.I.C.: 2836; 8733
N.A.I.C.S.: 325414; 541710
Advertising Expenditures: $338,000
Media: 2-7-10-13-17
Personnel:
Frank Pitzer *(CEO)*
Andreas Gortz *(VP-Mktg)*

ROCKFORD CORPORATION
600 S Rockford Dr
Tempe, AZ 85281
Tel.: (480) 967-3565
Fax: (480) 967-8132
Web Site: www.rockfordcorp.com
Approx. Sls.: $52,975,000
Approx. Number Employees: 107
Year Founded: 1982
Business Description:
Household Audio & Video Equipment Mfr
S.I.C.: 3651; 3663
N.A.I.C.S.: 334310; 334220
Import Export
Advertising Expenditures: $1,000,000
Media: 4-7-8
Personnel:
Jerry E. Goldress *(Chm)*
William R. Jackson *(Pres)*
Richard G. Vasek *(CFO, Sec & VP-Fin)*
Dominick Aquilini *(Dir-Sls-Brax & Helix)*
Brands & Products:
INSTALLEDGE.COM
LIGHTNING AUDIO
ROCKFORD ACOUSTIC DESIGN
ROCKFORD CORPORATION
ROCKFORD FOSGATE

ROCKWELL AUTOMATION, INC.
1201 S 2nd St
Milwaukee, WI 53204-2410
Tel.: (414) 382-2000
Fax: (414) 382-4444
E-mail: njfranz@ra.rockwell.com
Web Site:
www.rockwellautomation.com
Approx. Sls.: $4,857,000,000
Approx. Number Employees: 19,000
Year Founded: 1903
Business Description:
Industrial Automation Power, Control & Information Products Mfr
S.I.C.: 3823; 3559; 3566; 3625; 3699
N.A.I.C.S.: 334513; 333298; 333612; 335314; 335999
Advertising Expenditures: $8,700,000
Media: 2-4-7-8-9-10-11-13-18
Distr.: Intl.; Natl.
Budget Set: June
Personnel:
Keith D. Nosbusch *(Chm & CEO)*
Theodore D. Crandall *(CFO & Sr VP)*
Sujeet Chand *(CTO & Sr VP-Advanced Tech)*
Douglas M. Hagerman *(Gen Counsel, Sec & Sr VP)*
Kent G. Coppins *(Gen Counsel-Tax & VP)*
John D. Cohn *(Sr VP-Bus Plng & Execution-Europe)*
Steven A. Eisenbrown *(Sr VP-Strategic Dev)*
Frank Kulaszewicz *(Sr VP-Architecture & Software)*
John P. McDermott *(Sr VP-Global Sls & Mktg)*
Blake Moret *(Sr VP-Control Products & Solutions)*
Robert A. Ruff *(Sr VP-Control Products & Solutions)*
Susan J. Schmitt *(Sr VP-HR)*
Martin Thomas *(Sr VP-Ops & Engrg Svcs)*
John M. Miller *(VP & Chief Intellectual Property Counsel)*
Ninveh Neuman *(Mktg Dir)*
John Bernaden *(Dir-Corp Comm)*
Keith Lester *(Mgr-PR)*
Keith Smith *(Engr-Applications)*
Brands & Products:
A-B IN OCTAGON
A.I. SERIES
ALLEN-BRADLEY
ALLEN-BRADLEY 1771 REMOTE I/O
ANORAD
ARENA
ARMOR
ARMORBLOCK
ARMORPOINT
AUTOMATION FAIR
AUTOMAX
BLOCK I/O
BRETER
CENTERLINE
CENTERONE
COMPACTBLOCK I/O
COMPLETE AUTOMATION
CONTROL TOWER
CONTROLLOGIX
DATA HIGHWAY II
DATA HIGHWAY PLUS
DATADISC
DEVICELOGIX
DH+
DHII
ELECTROGUARD
ENTEK
FACTORYTALK
FLEX
FLEX EX
GLOBAL MANUFACTURING SOLUTIONS
GML COMMANDER
GML ULTRA
GUARDMASTER
INTEGRATED ARCHITECTURE
INTELLICENTER
INVIEW
KINETIX
MICROLOGIX
MOBILEVIEW
ON-MACHINE
PANELVIEW
PANELVIEW LOGIX
PANELVIEW PLUS
PHOTOSWITCH
PICO
PICOGFX
PLC
PLC-2
PLC-3
PLC-5
POINT I/O
POINTBUS
POWERFLEX
PRO-SET
PROPACK DATA
QUICKCLAMP
ROCKWELL
ROCKWELL AUTOMATION
ROCKWELL SOFTWARE
RSAUTOMATION DESKTOP
RSBATCH
RSBIZWARE
RSBIZWARE BATCH
RSBIZWARE EPROCEDURE
RSBIZWARE PLANTMETRICS
RSEMULATE
RSENERGYMETRIX
RSFIELDBUS
RSLADDER
RSLINX
RSLOGIX
RSLOOP OPTIMIZER
RSMACC
RSNETWORX
RSPOWER
RSPRODUCTION
RSSQL
RSTESTSTAND
RSTRAINER
RSTUNE
RSVIEW
RSVIEW MACHINE EDITION
RSVIEW SUPERVISORY EDITION
RSVIEW32
SLC 500
SMC-FLEX
SOFTLOGIX
SPRECHER + SCHUH
TECHCONNECT
ULTRA
ULTRA MASTER
ULTRAWARE
VERSAVIEW
XM
Advertising Agencies:
Chletcos/Gallagher Inc.
63 Greene St Ste 602
New York, NY 10012
Tel.: (212) 334-2455
Fax: (212) 334-2463

Media II, Inc.
2778 SOM Center Rd Ste 200
Willoughby, OH 44094
Tel.: (440) 943-3600
Fax: (440) 943-3660

Padilla Speer Beardsley
1101 W River Pkwy Ste 400
Minneapolis, MN 55415-1241
Tel.: (612) 455-1700
Fax: (612) 455-1060

ROFIN-SINAR TECHNOLOGIES, INC.
40984 Concept Dr
Plymouth, MI 48170
Tel.: (734) 455-5400
Fax: (734) 455-2741
E-mail: info@rofin.com
Web Site: www.rofin-sinar.com
Approx. Sls.: $423,570,000
Approx. Number Employees: 1,822
Business Description:
Laser & Laser Systems Mfr
S.I.C.: 5084; 3699; 3827; 3845
N.A.I.C.S.: 423830; 333314; 334510; 335999
Media: 2-4-10-13
Personnel:
Peter Wirth *(Chm)*
Gunther Braun *(Pres & CEO)*
Ingrid Mittelstadt *(CFO)*
Brands & Products:
DC SLAB
EASYJEWEL
EASYMARK
EASYMARK II
MULTISCAN
PERFO
POWER LINE
SMG II
SMP II
STAR DISC
STAR SCRIBE
STARCUT
STARFIBER
STARMARK
STARPULSE
STARSHAPE
STARWELD
TRIAGON

ROGERS COMMUNICATIONS INC.
333 Bloor Street East 10th Floor
Toronto, ON M4W 1G9, Canada
Tel.: (416) 935-7777
Fax: (416) 935-3599
Toll Free: (888) ROGERS1
E-mail: info@rogers.com
Web Site: www.rogers.com
Approx. Rev.: $11,926,194,480
Approx. Number Employees: 28,985
Business Description:
Holding Company; Cable TV, Broadcasting, Mobile Communications & Telecommunication Services
S.I.C.: 4812; 4833; 4841; 6719
N.A.I.C.S.: 517212; 515120; 515210; 551112
Advertising Expenditures: $503,948,000
Personnel:
Alan D. Horn *(Chm)*
Edward S. Rogers *(Deputy Chm & Exec VP-Emerging Bus & Corp Dev)*

Key to Media (For complete agency information see *The Advertising Red Books-Agencies* edition):
1. Bus. Publs. 2. Cable T.V. 3. Catalogs & Directories. 4. Co-op Adv. 5. Consumer Mags. 6. D.M. to Bus. Estab.7. D.M. to Consumers
8. Daily Newsp. 9. Exhibits/Trade Shows 10. Foreign 11. Infomercial 12. Internet Adv.13. Multimedia 14. Network Radio
15. Network T.V. 16. Newsp. Distr. Mags. 17. Other 18. Outdoor (Posters, Transit) 19. Point of Purchase20. Premiums, Novelties
21. Product Samples 22. Special Events Mktg. 23. Spot Radio 24. Spot T.V. 25. Weekly Newsp. 26. Yellow Page Adv.

Rogers Communications Inc. — (Continued)

Philip B. Lind *(Vice Chm & Exec VP-Regulatory)*
Nadir H. Mohamed *(Pres & CEO)*
William W. Linton *(CFO & Exec VP-Fin)*
Jerry D. Brace *(CIO & Exec VP-IT)*
Robert F. Berner *(CTO & Exec VP)*
Kevin P. Pennington *(Chief HR Officer & Sr VP-HR)*
Robert W. Bruce *(Pres-Comm)*
David P. Miller *(Gen Counsel, Sec & Sr VP)*
Donald E. Moffatt *(Sr VP-Svc Strategy & Billing Systems)*
Melinda Mary Rogers *(Sr VP-Strategy & Dev)*
Thomas A. Turner Jr. *(VP-Sls)*
Bobby Sahni *(Sr Mgr & Head-Multicultural Mktg)*
Dan Coombes *(Dir-IR)*
John Fulton *(Dir-Content Dev)*
Deborah DeRoche *(Coord-IR)*

Brands & Products:
INNOVATING FOR LIFE
ROGERS

Advertising Agencies:
OMD Canada
67 Richmond St W 2nd Fl
Toronto, ON M5H 1Z5, Canada
Tel.: (416) 681-5600
Fax: (416) 681-5620
Media Planning & Buying

Publicis
111 Queen St E Ste 200
Toronto, ON M5C 1S2, Canada
Tel.: (416) 925-7733
Fax: (416) 925-7341
Branding

Rosetta
100 American Metro Blvd
Hamilton, NJ 08619
Tel.: (609) 689-6100
Fax: (609) 631-0184
Toll Free: (800) 374-6008

ROWE INTERNATIONAL CORP

(Holding of Harbour Group Ltd.)
4147 Eastern Ave SW Ste 200
Grand Rapids, MI 49507
Tel.: (616) 243-3633
Tel.: (616) 248-9409
Fax: (616) 247-6531
E-mail: service@roweinternational.com
Web Site: www.roweinternational.com
Approx. Number Employees: 125
Year Founded: 1909
Business Description:
Mfr of Vending Machines, Audio & Video Jukeboxes & Bill Changers
S.I.C.: 3651; 3579
N.A.I.C.S.: 334310; 333313
Export
Media: 2-4-7-10
Distr.: Natl.
Personnel:
Mike Maas *(Pres & CEO)*
John Margold *(Sr VP-Sls & Mktg)*
Brian Hoekstra *(Mgr-AMI)*
Brands & Products:
ENCORE
LASERSTAR NOSTALGIA
NETSTAR
STARLINK
STORM
SYMPHONY

RUDOLPH TECHNOLOGIES, INC.

(Sub. of Rudolph Technologies, Inc.)
4900 W 78th St
Bloomington, MN 55435-5410
Tel.: (952) 820-0080
Fax: (952) 820-0060
Web Site: www.augusttech.com
E-Mail For Key Personnel:
Marketing Director: marketing@augusttech.com
Sales Director: sales@augusttech.com
Sales Range: $50-74.9 Million
Approx. Number Employees: 254
Year Founded: 1992
Business Description:
Macro Defect Inspection & Analysis Products Mfr
S.I.C.: 3827; 3829
N.A.I.C.S.: 333314; 334519
Media: 2-10-13-22
Personnel:
Virginia Becker *(Mgr-Corp Comm)*
Reza Asgari *(Product Mgr-Wafer Scanner)*
Brands & Products:
AUGUST
DMS DECISION
DMSVISION
HARMONY ASR
TRUEADC
VERSASCOPE
Advertising Agency:
Next Communications
10249 Yellow Circle Dr
Minnetonka, MN 55343
Tel.: (952) 934-8220
Fax: (952) 934-2375
Creative

SABRE INDUSTRIES, INC.

(Holding of Corinthian Capital Group, LLC)
1120 Welsh Rd Ste 210
North Wales, PA 19454
Tel.: (267) 263-1300
Fax: (267) 263-1301
Toll Free: (888) 722-7350
E-mail: sales@sabrecom.com
Web Site:
www.sabreindustriesinc.com
Approx. Sls.: $302,063,000
Approx. Number Employees: 964
Business Description:
Wireless Communications Infrastructure Products & Ancillary Equipment
S.I.C.: 1623; 3663
N.A.I.C.S.: 237130; 334220
Advertising Expenditures: $326,000
Personnel:
James D. Mack *(Chm)*
Peter J. Sandore *(Pres & CEO)*
James M. Tholey *(CFO)*
Dan P. Baker *(VP & Gen Mgr-Integrated Svcs)*

SAE ENGINEERING, INC.

(Sub. of Hilby-Yates Inc.)
365 Reed St
Santa Clara, CA 95050
Tel.: (408) 987-9950
Fax: (408) 987-9960
Web Site: www.saeintl.com
Sales Range: $25-49.9 Million
Approx. Number Employees: 35
Year Founded: 1964
Business Description:
Mfr. of Electronic Interconnection Components for Integrated Products
S.I.C.: 3672
N.A.I.C.S.: 334412
Advertising Expenditures: $236,000
Media: 1-2-4-5-10-20
Distr.: Direct to Consumer; Intl.; Natl.
Budget Set: Oct.
Personnel:
Allan Pats *(Pres & CFO)*

SAM ASH MUSIC CORPORATION

278 Duffy Ave
Hicksville, NY 11801-3605
Mailing Address:
PO Box 9047
Hicksville, NY 11802-9047
Tel.: (516) 932-6400
Fax: (516) 938-1437
E-mail: sales@samash.com
Web Site: www.samashmusic.com
E-Mail For Key Personnel:
Sales Director: sales@samash.com
Approx. Number Employees: 1,600
Year Founded: 1924
Business Description:
Music Instrument & Sound Equipment Retail Stores
S.I.C.: 5736; 5731
N.A.I.C.S.: 451140; 443112
Import Export
Media: 4-8-23
Personnel:
Jerome W. Ash *(Chm)*
Paul J. Ash *(Pres)*
David Charles Ash *(CEO & Gen Counsel)*
Richard S. Ash *(CEO)*
Sam M. Ash *(Exec VP)*
Howard Mendelson *(Exec VP)*
Steven J. Prisco *(Dir-Mktg)*
Brands & Products:
BROWNSVILLE
CARLO ROBELLI
GROOVE PAK
GROOVE PERCUSSION
JEAN BAPTISTE
THE MUSICAL INSTRUMENT MEGASTORE
SAM ASH
SAMSON
STAGE WORKS
Advertising Agency:
Innovation Ads, Inc.
233 Broadway 21st Fl
New York, NY 10279
Tel.: (212) 509-5218
Fax: (866) 272-5129

SAMSUNG AMERICA, INC.

(Sub. of Samsung C&T Corporation)
105 Challenger Rd
Ridgefield Park, NJ 07660
Tel.: (201) 229-5000
Fax: (201) 229-5080
E-mail: info@samsungamerica.com
Web Site: www.samsungamerica.com
Business Description:
Commodities Trading & Marketing Services
S.I.C.: 6221; 6799
N.A.I.C.S.: 523130; 523910
Personnel:
K.I. Choo *(Pres & CEO)*
B. H. Huh *(CFO & Treas)*
Paul Holden *(CMO)*
Advertising Agencies:
Adwell Communications
3470 Wilshire Blvd Ste 540
Los Angeles, CA 90010
Tel.: (213) 380-8872
Fax: (213) 383-6438

The Barbarian Group
11 Beach St 10th Fl
New York, NY 10013
Tel.: (212) 343-4215
Fax: (212) 343-4216
Tweet Wrap

BDS Marketing
10 Holland
Irvine, CA 92618
Tel.: (949) 472-6700
Fax: (949) 597-2220

Jack Morton Worldwide
919 3rd Ave
New York, NY 10022
Tel.: (212) 401-7000
Fax: (212) 401-7010
TV

Leo Burnett Worldwide, Inc.
35 W Wacker Dr
Chicago, IL 60601-1723
Tel.: (312) 220-5959
Fax: (312) 220-3299

Starcom MediaVest Group
35 W Wacker Dr
Chicago, IL 60601-1723
Tel.: (312) 220-3535
Fax: (312) 220-6530
Media Buying

The VIA Group LLC
34 Danforth St Ste 309
Portland, ME 04101
Tel.: (207) 221-3000
Fax: (207) 761-9422

SAMSUNG ELECTRONICS AMERICA, INC.

(Sub. of Samsung Electronics Co., Ltd.)
105 Challenger Rd
Ridgefield Park, NJ 07660
Tel.: (201) 229-4000
Fax: (201) 229-4029
Web Site: www.samsung.com/us
Approx. Number Employees: 150
Year Founded: 1977
Business Description:
Electronic Products Distr
S.I.C.: 5064; 5045
N.A.I.C.S.: 423620; 423430
Import
Advertising Expenditures: $275,000,000
Media: 2-3-4-6-9-10-15-16-18-19-20-22
Distr.: Natl.
Personnel:
Chang-Soo Choi *(Vice Chm & CEO)*
Hoon Eom Young *(Co-Pres-Consumer Electronics Div)*
Jung Soo Shin *(Pres & CEO-South West Asia Ops)*

Key to Media (For complete agency information see *The Advertising Red Books-Agencies* edition):
1. Bus. Publs. 2. Cable T.V. 3. Catalogs & Directories. 4. Co-op Adv. 5. Consumer Mags. 6. D.M. to Bus. Estab.7. D.M. to Consumers
8. Daily Newsp. 9. Exhibits/Trade Shows 10. Foreign 11. Infomercial 12. Internet Adv.13. Multimedia 14. Network Radio
15. Network T.V. 16. Newsp. Distr. Mags. 17. Other 18. Outdoor (Posters, Transit) 19. Point of Purchase20. Premiums, Novelties
21. Product Samples 22. Special Events Mktg. 23. Spot Radio 24. Spot T.V. 25. Weekly Newsp. 26. Yellow Page Adv.

Ralph Santana *(CMO & Sr VP)*
Young Hwan Park *(Pres/CEO-Samsung Semiconductor)*
Tim Baxter *(Pres-Consumer Electronics Div)*
Bryan Hopkins *(Gen Counsel)*
John Garrison *(Exec VP)*
S.W. Hong *(Exec VP-Mktg-North America)*
David Steel *(Exec VP)*
Steven Cook *(Chief Strategic Mktg Officer & Sr VP)*
John Revie *(Sr VP)*
Joe Stinziano *(Sr VP-Sls-Consumer Electronics Div)*
Sam Akkapeddi *(VP-Sls)*
Doug Albregts *(VP-Sls & Mktg)*
Peggy Ang *(VP-Mktg Comm)*
Muzibul Khan *(VP)*
Stan Sands *(VP-Cable Sls)*
Randall R. Smith *(VP)*
Sun Hong Lim *(Dir-Strategic Mktg)*
Ethan Rasiel *(Dir-PR-Consumer Bus Div)*
Bret Berg *(Sr Mgr-Product Mktg)*
Jose Hernandez *(Sr Mgr Mktg)*
Kevin Schroll *(Product Mgr-Comml Display-Enterprise Bus Div)*

Brands & Products:
GALAXY TAB

Advertising Agencies:
Edelman
250 Hudson St
New York, NY 10013
Tel.: (212) 768-0550
Fax: (212) 704-0128
(Global Public Relations)

Merkle Inc.
7001 Columbia Gateway Dr
Columbia, MD 21046
Tel.: (443) 542-4000
Fax: (443) 542-4001

The MWW Group
1 Meadowlands Plz 6th Fl
East Rutherford, NJ 07073
Tel.: (201) 507-9500
Fax: (201) 507-0092
— Robyn Fink *(Acct Supvr)*

The VIA Group LLC
34 Danforth St Ste 309
Portland, ME 04101
Tel.: (207) 221-3000
Fax: (207) 761-9422

SAMSUNG SEMICONDUCTOR, INC.

(Sub. of Samsung Electronics America, Inc.)
3655 N 1st St
San Jose, CA 95134-1707
Tel.: (408) 544-4000
Fax: (408) 544-4980
Web Site: www.usa.samsungsemi.com
Approx. Number Employees: 1,000
Business Description:
Electronic Products Distr
S.I.C.: 5065; 5045
N.A.I.C.S.: 423690; 423430
Personnel:
Wan Hoon Hong *(Pres & CEO)*
Jim Elliott *(VP-Memory Mktg & Product Plng)*
Ana Molnar Hunter *(VP-Tech)*

Advertising Agency:
Cheil USA, Irvine
3351 Michelson Dr Ste 390
Irvine, CA 92612-7646
Tel.: (949) 975-7380
Fax: (949) 975-7399

SANMINA-SCI CORPORATION

2700 N 1st St
San Jose, CA 95134
Tel.: (408) 964-3500
Fax: (408) 964-3636
E-mail: info@sanmina-sci.com
Web Site: www.sanmina-sci.com
Approx. Sls.: $6,318,691,000
Approx. Number Employees: 36,503
Business Description:
Printed Circuit Board Assemblies Mfr & Testing & Assembly of Electronics Systems & Sub Systems
S.I.C.: 7359; 3672; 3679
N.A.I.C.S.: 532210; 334412; 334419
Media: 10
Personnel:
Jure Sola *(Chm & CEO)*
Steve Bruton *(Pres & GM-PCB Ops)*
Robert K. Eulau *(CFO & Exec VP)*
Manesh Patel *(CIO & Sr VP)*
Michael Tyler *(Gen Counsel, Sec & Exec VP)*
Dennis Young *(Exec VP-Sls & Mktg)*
Todd Schull *(Sr VP & Controller)*
Michael Kovacs *(Dir-Worldwide Corp Mktg & PR)*
Phillip Schoettlin *(Mgr-Bus Deve)*

Brands & Products:
BURIED CAPACITANCE
ECOBAY
ELECTRONICS MANUFACTURING SERVICES
FARADFLEX
INFINIBAND
OPTI-VIA
THE PREMIER EMS COMPANY
RAM-STACK
ZBC

Advertising Agency:
Hipmedia
Kneza Branimira 15
Zagreb, Croatia
Tel.: (385) 14880637
Fax: (385) 14814814

SANYO FISHER COMPANY

(Sub. of Sanyo North American Corporation)
21605 Plummer St
Chatsworth, CA 91311-4131
Mailing Address:
PO Box 2329
Chatsworth, CA 91313-2329
Tel.: (818) 998-7322
Fax: (818) 998-3533
Web Site: www.sanyo.com
Approx. Number Employees: 175
Year Founded: 1961
Business Description:
Sales & Marketing of Audio Systems, DVDs, Home Theatres, TVs, VCRs & other Electronic Equipment Including Integrated Component Systems
S.I.C.: 5065
N.A.I.C.S.: 423690
Import Export
Media: 2-4-5-6-10-18-19-23-26
Distr.: Natl.
Budget Set: Jan. -May

Personnel:
Sam Murata *(Pres)*
Paul D'Arcy *(Exec VP)*
Hiromoto Sekino *(Sr VP)*
Atsushi Kodera *(VP & Gen Mgr-Communications)*
Sam L. Malik *(VP & Gen Mgr)*
Steve Kawakami *(VP-Fin)*
John Lamb *(Sr Mgr-Mktg-Xacti)*
Eric Burr *(Mgr-Natl Mktg)*

SBA COMMUNICATIONS CORPORATION

5900 Broken Sound Pkwy NW
Boca Raton, FL 33487
Tel.: (561) 995-7670
Fax: (561) 998-3448
Toll Free: (800) 487-7483
E-mail: information@sbasite.com
Web Site: www.sbasite.com
Approx. Rev.: $626,619,000
Approx. Number Employees: 720
Year Founded: 1989
Business Description:
Wireless Communication Services
S.I.C.: 8711; 1623; 4812; 4899
N.A.I.C.S.: 541330; 237130; 517212; 517910
Media: 6-7-8
Personnel:
Jeffrey A. Stoops *(Pres & CEO)*
Brendan T. Cavanagh *(CFO & Sr VP)*
Jorge Grau *(CIO & VP)*
Brian D. Lazarus *(Chief Acctg Officer & VP)*
Kurt L. Bagwell *(Pres-Intl)*
Mark R. Ciarfella *(Sr VP-Ops)*
Jason V. Silberstein *(Sr VP-Property Mgmt)*
Jim D. Williamson *(Reg VP-Southeast)*
Jo Carol Rutherford *(VP-HR)*

SCANSOURCE, INC.

6 Logue Ct
Greenville, SC 29615
Tel.: (864) 288-2432
Fax: (864) 288-1165
Toll Free: (800) 944-2432
E-mail: info@scansource.com
Web Site: www.scansourceinc.com
E-Mail For Key Personnel:
Sales Director: sales@scansource.com
Approx. Sls.: $2,666,531,000
Approx. Number Employees: 1,370
Year Founded: 1992
Business Description:
Distr of Specialty Technology Products, Including Automatic Identification, Point of Sale & Telephony Equipment
S.I.C.: 5045; 5065
N.A.I.C.S.: 423430; 423690
Media: 4-5-7-10
Personnel:
Steven R. Fischer *(Chm)*
Xavier Cartiaux *(Pres-Europe)*
Michael L. Baur *(CEO)*
Richard P. Cleys *(CFO & VP-Fin)*
Buck Baker *(Pres-Comm)*
R. Scott Benbenek *(Pres-Worldwide Ops)*
John K. Black *(Pres-Catalyst Telecom)*
Elias Botbol *(Pres-Latin America)*
Jeff Yelton *(Pres-POS & Barcoding)*
John J. Ellsworth *(Gen Counsel, Sec & VP)*
Robert S. McLain, Jr. *(Exec VP-Corp Comm)*
Andrea D. Meade *(Exec VP-Ops & Corp Dev)*
Paul J. Constantine *(VP-Mdsg)*
Christopher Elrod *(VP-IT)*
Tony Sorrentino *(VP-Sls-ScanSource Security)*
Mary Gentry *(Dir-IR)*
Adrienne Annis *(Product Mgr-LXE)*
Blake Shurtz *(Product Mgr)*
Kim Hammond *(Mgr-Assets)*

Brands & Products:
CATALYST TELECOMM
EMPOWERING SOLUTION PROVIDERS
SCANSOURCE
SCANSOURCE COMMUNICATIONS
SCANSOURCE POS & BARCODING
SCANSOURCE SECURITY
WE HAVE GOT A SOLUTION FOR THAT

Advertising Agency:
Erwin-Penland
(Owned by Hill, Holliday, Connors, Cosmopulos, Inc., Member of the Interpublic Group)
125 E Broad St
Greenville, SC 29601
Tel.: (864) 271-0500
Fax: (864) 235-5941

SDI TECHNOLOGIES, INC.

1299 Main St
Rahway, NJ 07065-5024
Tel.: (732) 574-9000
Fax: (732) 574-2634
Toll Free: (800) 333-3092
Web Site: www.sdidirect.com
Sales Range: $50-74.9 Million
Approx. Number Employees: 400
Year Founded: 1956
Business Description:
Consumer Electronics Mfr
S.I.C.: 3651; 3661; 3679; 3873; 3944; 5064
N.A.I.C.S.: 334310; 334210; 334419; 334518; 339932; 423620
Import Export
Media: 4-5-6-8-10-13-15-19-21
Distr.: Natl.; Reg.
Budget Set: Nov.
Personnel:
Ely E. Ashkenazi *(Chm)*
Ezra S. Ashkenazi *(Pres)*
Harry Franco *(Sr VP)*
Chabetaye Chraime *(VP-Fin)*
Edward Nehmad *(VP-Pur)*
Evan Stein *(VP-Mktg)*

Brands & Products:
COLORTUNES
IHOME
RESON8
SDI
SOUNDESIGN

SEMTECH CORPORATION

200 Flynn Rd
Camarillo, CA 93012-8790
Tel.: (805) 498-2111
Fax: (805) 498-3804
E-mail: sales@semtech.com
Web Site: www.semtech.com
Approx. Sls.: $454,502,000
Approx. Number Employees: 982
Year Founded: 1960

Key to Media (For complete agency information see *The Advertising Red Books-Agencies* edition):
1. Bus. Publs. 2. Cable T.V. 3. Catalogs & Directories. 4. Co-op Adv. 5. Consumer Mags. 6. D.M. to Bus. Estab.7. D.M. to Consumers 8. Daily Newsp. 9. Exhibits/Trade Shows 10. Foreign 11. Infomercial 12. Internet Adv.13. Multimedia 14. Network Radio 15. Network T.V. 16. Newsp. Distr. Mags. 17. Other 18. Outdoor (Posters, Transit) 19. Point of Purchase20. Premiums, Novelties 21. Product Samples 22. Special Events Mktg. 23. Spot Radio 24. Spot T.V. 25. Weekly Newsp. 26. Yellow Page Adv.

Semtech Corporation — (Continued)

Business Description:
Mfr. of Analog & Mixed-Signal Semiconductor Products
S.I.C.: 3674
N.A.I.C.S.: 334413
Advertising Expenditures: $232,000
Media: 10-11
Distr.: Intl.; Natl.
Personnel:
Rockell N. Hankin *(Chm)*
James P. Burra *(Vice Chm)*
Mohan R. Maheswaran *(Pres & CEO)*
Emeka Chukwu *(CFO & VP)*
Michael J. Wilson *(CTO & Sr VP-Quality & Reliability)*
Alain Dantec *(Sr VP & Gen Mgr-Advanced Comm & Sensing Products)*
James J. Kim *(Sr VP-Sls & Mktg-Worldwide)*
Jeffrey T. Pohlman *(Sr VP-Protection Products)*
Simon Prutton *(VP & Gen Mgr-Power Mgmt Grp)*
Ken J. Barry *(VP-HR)*
Brands & Products:
ALPAC
C CLAMP
CHIPCLAMP
COMBI-SENSE
COMBI-SYNC
D CLAMP
E CLAMP
EMI CLAMP
ISOPAC
L CLAMP
METOXILITE
MICRO CLAMP
MICROBUDDY
NO-DRIFT
PIXIPOINT
POWER IT-PROTECT IT-CONNECT IT
R CLAMP
RAILCLAMP
SCREENCODER
SEMTECH
SLIMPAC
TODAY'S RESULTS...TOMORROW'S VISION
TOPSYNC
TRANS CLAMP
U BUDDY

SENSATA TECHNOLOGIES, INC.

(Sub. of SENSATA TECHNOLOGIES B.V.)
529 Pleasant St
Attleboro, MA 02703
Mailing Address:
PO Box 2964
Attleboro, MA 02703-0964
Tel.: (508) 236-3800
Fax: (508) 236-2266
Web Site: www.sensata.com
Approx. Number Employees: 200
Year Founded: 1916
Business Description:
Sensors & Control Instruments Designer, Mfr & Marketer
S.I.C.: 3829; 3613; 3679; 3699; 3822
N.A.I.C.S.: 334519; 334419; 334512; 335313; 335999
Media: 10
Personnel:
Martha Sullivan *(Pres, COO & Exec Dir)*
Robert Hureau *(Chief Acctg Officer, VP & Controller)*
Linda Megathlin *(Mgr-Comm-Worldwide)*
Advertising Agency:
Keiler & Company
304 Main St
Farmington, CT 06032-2985
Tel.: (860) 677-8821
Fax: (860) 676-8164

SENSOR SYSTEMS, LLC

2800 Anvil St N
Saint Petersburg, FL 33710-2943
Tel.: (727) 347-2181
Fax: (727) 347-7520
E-mail: info@vsensors.com
Web Site: www.vsensors.com
E-Mail For Key Personnel:
Sales Director: sales@vsensors.com
Sales Range: $10-24.9 Million
Approx. Number Employees: 120
Year Founded: 1998
Business Description:
Mfr. of Potentiometers, Pressure Transducers, Encoders & Value Added Assemblies
S.I.C.: 3643
N.A.I.C.S.: 335931
Import Export
Media: 2-4-6-10-21
Distr.: Intl.; Natl.
Budget Set: Sept.
Personnel:
Nancy Price *(Owner)*
Charles Nunziata *(Gen Mgr)*
Brands & Products:
SENSOR
TUFF-LINE

SENTRY TECHNOLOGY CORPORATION

1881 Lakeland Ave
Ronkonkoma, NY 11779
Tel.: (631) 739-2000
Fax: (631) 739-2124
Toll Free: (800) 645-4224
E-mail: sentry@sentrytechnology.com
Web Site: www.sentrytechnology.com
Sales Range: $10-24.9 Million
Approx. Number Employees: 35
Year Founded: 1997
Business Description:
Electronic Anti-Pilferage Security Devices & Closed Circuit Televisions
S.I.C.: 3669; 3663; 3812; 7382
N.A.I.C.S.: 334290; 334220; 334511; 561621
Import Export
Advertising Expenditures: $750,000
Media: 1-2-7-10-21-26
Distr.: Intl.; Natl.
Budget Set: Dec.
Personnel:
Peter L. Murdoch *(Chm, Pres & CEO)*
Joan E. Miller *(VP-Fin)*
Robert D. Furst Jr. *(Dir-SentryTech)*
Jonathan G. Granoff *(Dir-SentryTech)*
Brands & Products:
KNOGLO
KNOGO
KNOSCAPE
LCS PRO
MICRO-MAGNETIC
QUICKCHECK
SCAN-DE
SCANEZE
SECUREBOARD
SENTRY
SENTRY VISION
SILVER CLOUD
SPINE-TAG
STANDING WITH YOU.
TAIL-TAG
TYVEK

SEREFEX CORP.

4328 Corporate Square Blvd Ste D
Naples, FL 34104
Tel.: (239) 261-9975
E-mail: info@serefex.com
Web Site: www.serefex.com
Sales Range: $25-49.9 Million
Approx. Number Employees: 68
Year Founded: 1983
Business Description:
Roofing & Waterproofing Products & Services Including Building Inspection, Testing & Diagnostic Services
S.I.C.: 1761; 3444; 5211; 7389
N.A.I.C.S.: 238160; 332322; 444190; 541350
Advertising Expenditures: $172,163
Media: 8
Personnel:
Brian Dunn *(Pres, CEO & Sec)*
Shawn Williams *(COO)*

SEURA, INC.

1230 Ontario Rd
Green Bay, WI 54311
Tel.: (920) 337-1922
Fax: (920) 857-9490
Toll Free: (800) 957-3872
E-mail: contact@seura.com
Web Site: www.seura.com
Approx. Number Employees: 15
Business Description:
Television Mirrors Designer & Mfr
S.I.C.: 3663
N.A.I.C.S.: 334220
Media: 6-10-22
Personnel:
Gretchen Gilbertson *(Founder)*
Tim Gilbertson *(Founder)*
Advertising Agency:
Jennings & Company
436 Woodland Dr
Sarasota, FL 34234
Tel.: (941) 351-1005
Fax: (941) 351-0846
Pub Rels
— Linda Jennings *(Founder)*

SHAPE GLOBAL TECHNOLOGY, INC.

90 Community Dr
Sanford, ME 04073-5810
Tel.: (207) 324-5200
Fax: (207) 985-4617
Toll Free: (800) 627-5836
E-mail: info@shapeglobal.com
Web Site: www.shapenet.com
Approx. Number Employees: 400
Year Founded: 1973
Business Description:
Audio & Video Cassettes, Compact Disc Packaging & Data Storage Products, Computer Printer Cartridges & RDAT Cassettes Mfr
S.I.C.: 3089
N.A.I.C.S.: 326199
Export
Media: 2-4-7-10-22
Distr.: Intl.
Personnel:
Vincent Boragine *(Pres & CEO)*

SHARP ELECTRONICS CORPORATION

(Sub. of Sharp Corporation)
1 Sharp Plz
Mahwah, NJ 07430-2135
Tel.: (201) 529-8200
Fax: (201) 529-8425
Telex: 426903 SHARPAMMAWA
Web Site: www.sharpusa.com
Sales Range: $1-4.9 Billion
Approx. Number Employees: 1,000
Year Founded: 1962
Business Description:
Consumer Audio-Visual, Data & Communication Electronics & Home Appliances Mfr & Whslr
S.I.C.: 5044; 5065
N.A.I.C.S.: 423420; 423690
Import Export
Media: 2-3-5-6-7-9-10-13-14-15-16-18-19-20-22-23-24-26
Distr.: Natl.
Budget Set: Mar. -Oct.
Personnel:
Kozo Takahashi *(Chm & CEO)*
Robert Scaglione *(CMO)*
John Herrington *(Pres-Sharp Electronics Mktg Company of America)*
John Homlish *(VP-Home Entertainment Sls-Sharp Electronics Mktg Company)*
Mike Marusic *(VP-Mktg & Svc)*
Andrew Kritzer *(Assoc VP)*
Daisuke Koshima *(Gen Mgr-North & South America-Global Market Dev Grp)*
Bruce Fairchild *(Sr Dir-Channel Mktg)*
Neal Lattner *(Sr Dir-Mktg)*
Bruce Pollack *(Assoc Dir-Mktg)*
Paul Norton *(Dir-Western Reg Sls-Sharp Electronics Mktg Company of America)*
Bob Pleyer *(Sr Mgr-Product Mktg)*
Ellin Everson *(Sr Mgr-Mktg & Comm)*
George Grafanakis *(Sr Mgr-Product Mktg)*
Tony Favia *(Sr Product Mgr)*
Advertising Agencies:
Crenshaw Communications
7 West 18th St. 9th Fl
New York, NY 10011
Tel.: (212) 367-9700
Fax: (212) 367-9701

Deutsch New York
111 8th Ave 14th Fl
New York, NY 10011
Tel.: (212) 605-8000

SHENANDOAH TELECOMMUNICATIONS CO.

500 Shentel Way
Edinburg, VA 22824
Mailing Address:
PO Box 459
Edinburg, VA 22824-0459
Tel.: (540) 984-4141
Fax: (540) 984-8192
Toll Free: (800) 743-6835
E-mail: askus@shentel.net
Web Site: www.shentel.com

Key to Media (For complete agency information see *The Advertising Red Books-Agencies* edition):
1. Bus. Publs. 2. Cable T.V. 3. Catalogs & Directories. 4. Co-op Adv. 5. Consumer Mags. 6. D.M. to Bus. Estab.7. D.M. to Consumers 8. Daily Newsp. 9. Exhibits/Trade Shows 10. Foreign 11. Infomercial 12. Internet Adv.13. Multimedia 14. Network Radio 15. Network T.V. 16. Newsp. Distr. Mags. 17. Other 18. Outdoor (Posters, Transit) 19. Point of Purchase20. Premiums, Novelties 21. Product Samples 22. Special Events Mktg. 23. Spot Radio 24. Spot T.V. 25. Weekly Newsp. 26. Yellow Page Adv.

Approx. Rev.: $194,889,000
Approx. Number Employees: 589
Year Founded: 1981
Business Description:
Telephone Communication
S.I.C.: 4813; 5731
N.A.I.C.S.: 517110; 443112; 517310
Advertising Expenditures: $4,300,000
Personnel:
Christopher E. French *(Chm)*
Douglas C. Arthur *(Vice Chm)*
Adele M. Skolits *(CFO & VP-Fin)*
Earle A. Mackenzie *(COO & Exec VP)*
Ann E. Flowers *(Gen Counsel & VP-Legal)*
Rich Baughman *(VP-IT)*
Chris Kyle *(VP-Sls & Mktg-Cable)*
Ed McKay *(VP-Engrg & Plng)*
William L. Pirtle *(VP-Sls & Mktg-Wireless & Wireline)*
Brian Brooks *(Dir-Sls)*
Daniel R. Detamore-Hunsberger *(Dir-Compliance)*
Becky Nucilli *(Dir-HR)*
Dexter Torculas *(Dir-RS Engrg)*

SHOKAI FAR EAST LTD.
9 Elena Ct
Cortlandt Manor, NY 10567-7012
Tel.: (914) 736-3500
Fax: (914) 736-3656
E-mail: sales@shokaifareast.com
Web Site: www.shokaifareast.com
E-Mail For Key Personnel:
Sales Director: sales@shokaifareast.com
Sales Range: $10-24.9 Million
Approx. Number Employees: 60
Year Founded: 1960
Business Description:
OEM Components for Industry Mfr
S.I.C.: 5065
N.A.I.C.S.: 423690
Media: 6-20
Distr.: Intl.; Natl.
Personnel:
Michael B. Rubin *(Pres)*
Joe Weber *(VP-Mktg)*
Alan Weiss *(VP-Fin)*
Brands & Products:
SHOKAI
SHOKAI FAR EAST
WE MAKE YOUR IDEAS PROFITABLE

SHURE INCORPORATED
5800 Touhy Ave
Niles, IL 60714
Tel.: (847) 866-2200
Fax: (847) 600-1212
Toll Free: (800) 25SHURE
E-mail: info@shure.com
Web Site: www.shure.com
Approx. Number Employees: 300
Year Founded: 1925
Business Description:
Wired & Wireless Professional Microphones for Sound Reinforcement, Broadcasting, Recording, Land Mobile & Voice Input/Output Applications; Powered & Portable Mixers & Amplifiers for ENG, EFP & Sound Reinforcement; High-Fidelity Phonograph Cartridges; AMS Automatic Microphone Mixing Systems; Related Audio Circuitry Components & Accessories
S.I.C.: 3651; 3679
N.A.I.C.S.: 334310; 334419
Export
Media: 4-6-8-10-13-19-20
Distr.: Intl.; Natl.
Budget Set: June
Personnel:
Sandy LaMantia *(Pres & CEO)*
Ron Thompson *(COO & VP-Ops)*
Christine Schyvinck *(Exec VP-Global Mktg & Sls)*
Brands & Products:
ACRA-VECTOR
AMS
ARMO-DUR
AUDIO MASTER
AUXPANDER
BETA 57
BETA 58
BETA 98
BETA SERIES
BG SERIES
CONTROLLED MAGNETIC
DIVERSIPHASE
DYNETIC
EASYFLEX
HTS
INTELLIMIX
L SERIES
LX SERIES
MARCAD
MICROFLEX
MODULINK
PA SERIES
PERFORMANCE GEAR
POWER MASTER
POWER STATION
PRO MASTER
PROLOGUE
PSM
QUIET SPOT
SC SERIES
SHURE
SLENDYNE
STEREO SURROUND
SUPER TRACK
T SERIES
TRIPLE FLEX
UHF-R
ULX PROFESSIONAL
UNIDYNE
UNISPHERE
UT SERIES
VAGABOND
VERAFLEX
Advertising Agencies:
Formula PR
810 Parkview Dr N
El Segundo, CA 90245
Tel.: (310) 578-7050
Fax: (310) 578-7077
Agency of Record

Tom, Dick & Harry Advertising
350 W Erie 2nd Fl
Chicago, IL 60654
Tel.: (312) 327-9500
Fax: (312) 327-9501

SIEMENS FIRE SAFETY
(Div. of Siemens Building Technologies, Inc.)
8 Fernwood Rd
Florham Park, NJ 07932-1906
Tel.: (973) 593-2600
Fax: (973) 593-6670
E-mail: info@sbt.siemens.com
Web Site: www.buildingtechnologies.usa.siemens.com
Approx. Sls.: $67,200,000
Approx. Number Employees: 1,300
Year Founded: 1959
Business Description:
Fire Alarms, Early Warning Smoke & Fire Detection & Extinguishing Systems, Access Control Systems & Building Monitoring Systems Mfr
S.I.C.: 3822
N.A.I.C.S.: 334512
Media: 2-4-7-10-13
Distr.: Natl.
Brands & Products:
CYMPHANY
FIREPRINT
MXL
Advertising Agency:
BRUSHfire, Inc.
2 Wing Dr
Cedar Knolls, NJ 07927
Tel.: (973) 871-1700
Fax: (973) 871-1717

SIEMENS HEALTHCARE DIAGNOSTICS
(Div. of Siemens Healthcare Diagnostics)
1717 Deerfield Rd
Deerfield, IL 60015-0778
Tel.: (847) 267-5300
Fax: (847) 267-1699
Approx. Sls.: $1,739,200,000
Approx. Number Employees: 6,400
Year Founded: 1994
Business Description:
Clinical Diagnostics
S.I.C.: 2834; 8733
N.A.I.C.S.: 325412; 541710
Media: 6-9-17
Distr.: Natl.
Personnel:
Kathy Kennedy *(Sr VP-HR)*
Brands & Products:
AUTOSCAN
BEP
DIMENSION
QUADRIGA
STRATUS CS
STREAMLAB
SYSMEX
Advertising Agencies:
GrafikPharm, Inc.
1105 Market St Ste 100
Wilmington, DE 19801
Tel.: (302) 472-5909
Fax: (302) 652-8961

Reese, Tomases & Ellick, Inc. (RT&E)
1105 Market St Ste 100
Wilmington, DE 19801
Tel.: (302) 652-3211
Fax: (302) 428-3920
Toll Free: (888) 720-7561

SIEMENS INDUSTRY
(Formerly Siemens Energy & Automation Inc.)
(Sub. of Siemens Energy Automation GmbH)
3333 Old Milton Pkwy
Alpharetta, GA 30005-4437
Tel.: (770) 751-2000
Fax: (770) 740-2534
Toll Free: (800) 964-4114
E-mail: seainfo@sea.siemens.com
Web Site: www.sea.siemens.com
E-Mail For Key Personnel:
Public Relations: thomas.varney@siemens.com
Approx. Number Employees: 9,400
Year Founded: 1977
Business Description:
Electrical Motors, Switchgear & Power Switching Equipment, Regulator & Control Systems & Industrial & Building Systems Marketer & Mfr
S.I.C.: 3613; 3621
N.A.I.C.S.: 335313; 335312
Import Export
Media: 2-4-7-10-20-22
Distr.: Intl.; Natl.
Budget Set: July
Personnel:
Dennis Sadlowski *(Pres & CEO)*
Harry Volande *(CFO)*
Nico Nissink *(CIO)*
Tom Kopanski *(Sr VP-Sls)*
Michael A. Troy *(VP-HR)*
Dale Wilson *(VP-Sls)*
Brands & Products:
ACCESS
FURNAS
MURRAY
SENTRON

SIERRA WIRELESS INCORPORATED
13811 Wireless Way
Richmond, BC V6V 3A4, Canada
Tel.: (604) 231-1100
Fax: (604) 231-1109
E-mail: smyers@sierrawireless.com
Web Site: www.sierrawireless.com
Approx. Rev.: $650,341,000
Approx. Number Employees: 880
Year Founded: 1993
Business Description:
Wireless Data Communication Equipment Mfr
S.I.C.: 4812
N.A.I.C.S.: 517212
Media: 2-10
Personnel:
Jason W. Cohenour *(CEO)*
David G. McLennan *(CFO)*
Didier Dutronc *(Sr VP & Gen Mgr-M2M Embedded Solutions Bus)*
Daniel Schieler *(Sr VP & Gen Mgr-Mobile Computing Bus Unit)*
Emmanuel Walckenaer *(Sr VP & Gen Mgr-Solutions & Svcs)*
Andrew A. Berman *(Sr VP)*
Bill G. Dodson *(Sr VP-Ops)*
James B. Kirkpatrick *(Sr VP-Engrg, Mobile Computing Bus Unit)*
Pierre Teyssier *(Sr VP-Engrg & Reg Gen Mgr-Asia Pacific)*
Mike Ardelan *(VP-OEM Sls-World Wide)*
Steve Burrington *(VP-Worldwide Sys Engrg)*
Riley Hoyt *(VP-Engrg)*
Evan Jones *(VP-Engrg)*
Pat Watson *(VP-HR)*
Brands & Products:
ACEMANAGER
ACENET
ACEVIEW
ACEWARE
AIRCARD EXPRESSCARDS
AIRLINK
AIRLINK HELIX

Key to Media (For complete agency information see *The Advertising Red Books-Agencies* edition):
1. Bus. Publs. 2. Cable T.V. 3. Catalogs & Directories. 4. Co-op Adv. 5. Consumer Mags. 6. D.M. to Bus. Estab.7. D.M. to Consumers
8. Daily Newsp. 9. Exhibits/Trade Shows 10. Foreign 11. Infomercial 12. Internet Adv.13. Multimedia 14. Network Radio
15. Network T.V. 16. Newsp. Distr. Mags. 17. Other 18. Outdoor (Posters, Transit) 19. Point of Purchase20. Premiums, Novelties
21. Product Samples 22. Special Events Mktg. 23. Spot Radio 24. Spot T.V. 25. Weekly Newsp. 26. Yellow Page Adv.

Sierra Wireless Incorporated — (Continued)

AIRLINK PINPOINT X
AIRLINK PINPOINT XT
AIRLINK RAVEN X
APEX
COMPASS 597
COMPASS 885
COMPASS 888
CONNECT WITH MOBILE BROADBAND
EMPOWERED
HEART OF THE WIRELESS MACHINE
JUNXION BOX
SIERRA WIRELESS
SIERRA WIRELESS WATCHER
TRU-FLOW
TRU-INSTALL
TRU-LOCATE
TRU-POWERSAVE

SIGMATRON INTERNATIONAL, INC.
2201 Landmeier Rd
Elk Grove Village, IL 60007-2620
Tel.: (847) 956-8000
Fax: (847) 640-4528
Toll Free: (866) 225-3267
E-mail: info@sgmaintl.com
Web Site: www.sigmatronintl.com
Approx. Sls.: $151,728,084
Approx. Number Employees: 1,780
Business Description:
Electronic Components, Printed Circuit Board Assemblies & Box Build Electronic Products Mfr
S.I.C.: 5065; 3677
N.A.I.C.S.: 423690; 334416
Media: 2-10
Personnel:
John P. Chen *(Chm)*
Gary R. Fairhead *(Pres & CEO)*
Linda K. Frauendorfer *(CFO, Treas, Sec & VP-Fin)*
Gregory A. Fairhead *(Exec VP & Asst Sec)*
Raj B. Upadhyaya *(Exec VP-Ops-West Coast)*
John P. Sheehan *(VP, Dir-Supply Chain & Asst Sec)*
Curtis W. Campbell *(VP-Sls-West Coast Ops)*
Yousef M. Heidari *(VP-Engrg)*
Donald G. Madsen *(VP-Customer Svc-Hayward Ops)*
Dennis P. McNamara *(VP-Engrg)*
Stephen H. McNulty *(VP-Sls)*
Thomas F. Rovtar *(VP-IT)*
Frank Magallanes *(Mgr-Sls)*

SILICON LABORATORIES INC.
400 W Cesar Chavez
Austin, TX 78701
Tel.: (512) 416-8500
Fax: (512) 464-9444
Toll Free: (877) 444-3032
E-mail: pr@silabs.com
Web Site: www.silabs.com
Approx. Rev.: $493,341,000
Approx. Number Employees: 845
Year Founded: 1996
Business Description:
Mfr of High-Performance, Analog-Intensive Mixed-Signal IC's & Semiconductor Products
S.I.C.: 3669; 3674
N.A.I.C.S.: 334290; 334413
Advertising Expenditures: $1,400,000
Media: 2-5-10
Personnel:
Navdeep S. Sooch *(Chm)*
Necip Sayiner *(Pres & CEO)*
William G. Bock *(CFO, Sr VP-Fin & Admin)*
Paul V. Walsh, Jr. *(Chief Acctg Officer & VP-Fin)*
Jonathan D. Ivester *(Sr VP-Worldwide Ops)*
Mark Downing *(VP-Strategy & Bus Dev)*
Diane Marra Williams *(VP-HR)*
James Stansberry *(Gen Mgr-Audio Products)*
Brands & Products:
AERO
AEROFONE
C8051F01X
C8051F02X
C8051F04X
C8051F06X
C8051F0XX
C8051F12X/3X
C8051F2XX
C8051F30X
C8051F31X
C8051F336
C8051F33X
C8051F35X
C8051F36X
C8051F41X
C8051F70X/71X
C8051F9XX
C8051T606
C8051T60X
C8051T61X
C8051T63X
DSPLL
ISOMODEM
PROSLIC
SI2161/65
SI21XX
SI4702/03
SI4704/05
SI4707
SI4708/09
SI4710/11
SI4712/13
SI472X
SI4730/31
SI4734/35
SI4736/37
SI4738/39
SI474X
SILICON LABS
SIPHY
SIRX
USBXPRESS
ZIGBEE
Advertising Agency:
Cartis Group
1532 Ben Crenshaw Way
Austin, TX 78746
Tel.: (512) 476-2600
Fax: (512) 476-2626
Toll Free: (800) 479-2616

SILICONIX INCORPORATED
(Sub. of Vishay Intertechnology, Inc.)
2201 Laurelwood Rd
Santa Clara, CA 95054-1516
Tel.: (408) 988-8000
Fax: (408) 567-8950
Web Site: ir.vishay.com/phoenix.zhtml?c=113888&p=irol-newsArticle&t=Regular&id=154557&
Sales Range: $450-499.9 Million
Approx. Number Employees: 1,000
Business Description:
FETS, Integrated Circuits, MOS Power FETS, Analog Switches, Wideband Multiplexers & Smart Power ICs Mfr
S.I.C.: 3674
N.A.I.C.S.: 334413
Media: 2-4-5-7-8-11-20-21
Distr.: Intl.; Natl.
Budget Set: Oct.-Nov.

SIMPLEXGRINNELL LP
(Sub. of Tyco Fire & Security)
50 Technology Dr
Westminster, MA 01441-0001
Tel.: (978) 731-2500
Fax: (978) 731-7856
Toll Free: (800) 746-7539
Web Site: www.simplexgrinnell.com
Approx. Number Employees: 800
Year Founded: 1894
Business Description:
Fire Detection Systems, Fire Alarms, Fire Sprinklers, Fire Extinguishers & Fire Suppression Systems Mfr
S.I.C.: 9224; 7382
N.A.I.C.S.: 922160; 561621
Advertising Expenditures: $1,250,000
Media: 2-4-7-10-11-13-26
Distr.: Intl.
Budget Set: Sept.
Personnel:
Dave Baer *(VP-Sls & Mktg)*
Chris Woodcock *(Dir-Mktg Comm)*
Brands & Products:
ACTIVATION
AUTOCALL
CELESTRA
CROSSFIRE
PILOTEX
SAFELINC
SIMPLEX
TRUE ALARM
Advertising Agency:
Keiler & Company
304 Main St
Farmington, CT 06032-2985
Tel.: (860) 677-8821
Fax: (860) 676-8164

THE SINGING MACHINE COMPANY, INC.
6601 Lyons Rd Bldg A-7
Coconut Creek, FL 33073
Tel.: (954) 596-1000
Fax: (954) 596-2000
E-mail: info@singingmachine.com
Web Site: www.singingmachine.com
Approx. Sls.: $19,165,979
Approx. Number Employees: 23
Year Founded: 1982
Business Description:
Designs, Develops & Distributes a Full Line of Consumer-Oriented Karaoke Systems
S.I.C.: 3652; 5065
N.A.I.C.S.: 334612; 423690
Advertising Expenditures: $685,416
Media: 4-5-6-7-8-10-15-18-23
Personnel:
Carol Lau *(Chm)*
Gary Atkinson *(Interim CEO)*
Craig Edelman *(Mng Dir-Mktg & Corp Dev)*
Bernardo Melo *(VP-Global Sls & Mktg)*
John Steele *(VP-Sls-Intl)*
Fernando Reno *(Dir-Ops)*
Brands & Products:
G3504
G3521
G3523
G3531
G3601
G3603
G3631
G4448
G8856
G8858
G8862
ISM 370
THE LEADER IN HOME KARAOKE & BEYOND
POP CULTURE
THE SINGING MACHINE
SMM 106
SMM 107
SMM 111
SMM 112
SMM 117
SMM 205
SMVG 610
SOUND X
SOUND X KIDS

SION POWER CORPORATION
9040 S Rita Rd 20900 E Zira RD
Tucson, AZ 85756
Tel.: (520) 799-7500
Fax: (520) 799-7501
E-mail: info@sionpower.com
Web Site: www.sionpower.com
Approx. Sls.: $145,596,000
Approx. Number Employees: 60
Year Founded: 1988
Business Description:
Electrochemical Energy Storage Systems
S.I.C.: 8733
N.A.I.C.S.: 541710
Media: 10
Personnel:
Dennis Mangino *(CEO)*
Brands & Products:
SION POWER

SIXTH AVENUE ELECTRONICS, INC.
22 US Hwy 22 W
Springfield, NJ 07081
Tel.: (973) 467-3905
Fax: (973) 924-8457
Toll Free: (877) 684-2831
E-mail: helpdesk@6ave.com
Web Site: www.6ave.com
Approx. Number Employees: 340
Year Founded: 1984
Business Description:
Consumer Electronics Retailer
S.I.C.: 5731
N.A.I.C.S.: 443112
Advertising Expenditures: $6,000,000
Media: 1-3-5-7-8-9-14-18-19-22-23-25
Distr.: Natl.
Personnel:
Michael Temiv *(Pres)*
Brands & Products:
GREAT SERVICE AWAITS YOU
SIXTH AVENUE ELECTRONICS CITY

Key to Media (For complete agency information see *The Advertising Red Books-Agencies* edition):
1. Bus. Publs. 2. Cable T.V. 3. Catalogs & Directories. 4. Co-op Adv. 5. Consumer Mags. 6. D.M. to Bus. Estab.7. D.M. to Consumers
8. Daily Newsp. 9. Exhibits/Trade Shows 10. Foreign 11. Infomercial 12. Internet Adv.13. Multimedia 14. Network Radio
15. Network T.V. 16. Newsp. Distr. Mags. 17. Other 18. Outdoor (Posters, Transit) 19. Point of Purchase20. Premiums, Novelties
21. Product Samples 22. Special Events Mktg. 23. Spot Radio 24. Spot T.V. 25. Weekly Newsp. 26. Yellow Page Adv.

SKULLCANDY, INC.
1441 W Ute Blvd Ste 250
Park City, UT 84098
Tel.: (435) 940-1545
Toll Free: (888) 697-5855
E-mail: customerservice@skullcandy.com
Web Site: www.skullcandy.com
Approx. Rev.: $118,312,000
Approx. Number Employees: 132
Year Founded: 2003
Business Description:
Headphones & Other Audio Accessories Mfr & Distr
S.I.C.: 3651; 5065
N.A.I.C.S.: 334310; 423690
Personnel:
Rick Alden *(Founder)*
Jeremy Andrus *(CEO)*
Mitch Edwards *(CFO & Gen Counsel)*
Dan Levine *(Chief Mdsg Officer)*
Aaron Behle *(VP-Sls-Intl)*
Mike Carter *(VP-Mktg)*
Richard Sargente *(VP-Sls-North America)*
Brands & Products:
SKULLCANDY
Advertising Agency:
TrueAction
1075 1st Ave
King of Prussia, PA 19406
Tel.: (610) 491-7100
Fax: (610) 265-3528

SKYWORKS SOLUTIONS, INC.
20 Sylvan Rd
Woburn, MA 01801-1845
Tel.: (781) 376-3000
Fax: (781) 376-3100
Telex: 949436
E-mail: sales@skyworksinc.com
Web Site: www.skyworksinc.com
Approx. Rev.: $1,071,849,000
Approx. Number Employees: 3,700
Year Founded: 1962
Business Description:
Mfr of Electronic & Microwave Components
S.I.C.: 3674; 3679
N.A.I.C.S.: 334413; 334419
Import Export
Media: 4-13
Personnel:
David J. Aldrich *(Pres & CEO)*
Donald W. Palette *(CFO & VP)*
Mark V.B. Tremallo *(Gen Counsel, Sec & VP)*
Gregory L. Waters *(Exec VP & Gen Mgr-Front-End Solutions)*
Liama K. Griffin *(Sr VP-Sls & Mktg)*
Georgea M. Levan *(VP-HR)*
David B. Armstrong *(Sr Dir)*
Brands & Products:
AUTOSMART
BREAKTHROUGH SIMPLICITY
DCR
HELIOS
INNOVATION TO GO
INTERA
IPAC
LIPA
LYNX
PEGASUS
POLAR LOOP
SINGLE PACKET RADIO
SKYWORKS
SPR
SYSTEM SMART
TRANS-TECH

SL INDUSTRIES, INC.
520 Fellowship Rd Ste A114
Mount Laurel, NJ 08054-3400
Tel.: (856) 727-1500
Fax: (856) 727-1683
E-mail: slinfo@slindustries.com
Approx. Sls.: $189,768,000
Approx. Number Employees: 1,600
Year Founded: 1956
Business Description:
Advanced Power & Data Quality Products & Systems Mfr, Designer & Distr
S.I.C.: 3643; 1731; 3612; 3679; 3699; 5063
N.A.I.C.S.: 335931; 238210; 334419; 335311; 335999; 423610
Import Export
Advertising Expenditures: $192,000
Media: 17
Personnel:
Glen M. Kassan *(Chm)*
William T. Fejes, Jr. *(Pres & CEO)*
Louis J. Belardi *(CFO, Treas & Sec)*
Brands & Products:
CONDOR
TEALTRAN
TEALWATCH
TEALWAVE

SLI LIGHTING PRODUCTS INC.
(Sub. of Havell's Holdings International, LLC)
(d/b/a Havell's SLI)
122 E Laurel St
Mullins, SC 29574-3220
Tel.: (843) 464-0554
Fax: (843) 464-3820
Web Site: www.havell-soi.com
Approx. Number Employees: 100
Business Description:
Electric Lamps Sales
S.I.C.: 5063
N.A.I.C.S.: 423610
Advertising Agency:
Creative Marketing Alliance Inc.
191 Clarksville Rd
Princeton Junction, NJ 08550
Tel.: (609) 297-2222
Fax: (609) 799-7032

SLM ELECTRONICS
(Div. of St. Louis Music, Inc.)
1901 Congressional Dr
Saint Louis, MO 63146
Tel.: (314) 569-0141
Fax: (314) 569-0175
Toll Free: (800) 727-4512
Web Site: www.stlouismusic.com
Sales Range: $50-74.9 Million
Approx. Number Employees: 190
Business Description:
Amplifier Mfr
S.I.C.: 3651
N.A.I.C.S.: 334310
Advertising Expenditures: $2,000,000
Media: 2-6-8-13

SMARTERVILLE, INC.
(Holding of Sterling Partners)
1001 Fleet St
Baltimore, MD 21022
Tel.: (410) 843-6200
Toll Free: (888) 605-5055 (Customer Svc)
Web Site:
www.hookedonphonics.com
Approx. Number Employees: 500
Year Founded: 1987
Business Description:
Educational Products Publr
S.I.C.: 3944; 7372
N.A.I.C.S.: 339932; 511210
Media: 3-6-14-15-23-24
Personnel:
Andrew Morrison *(CEO)*
Paul Woodland *(CFO)*
Brands & Products:
HOOKED ON HANDWRITING
HOOKED ON MATH
HOOKED ON PHONICS
HOOKED ON SCHOOL SUCCESS
Advertising Agency:
Siquis, Ltd.
1340 Smith Ave Ste 300
Baltimore, MD 21209-3797
Tel.: (410) 323-4800
Fax: (410) 323-4113

SOLAR POWER, INC.
(Sub. of LDK Solar Co., Ltd.)
1115 Orlando Dr
Roseville, CA 95661
Tel.: (916) 745-0900
Fax: (916) 745-0999
Toll Free: (800) 548-8767
E-mail: info@solarpowerinc.net
Web Site: www.solarpowerinc.net
Approx. Sls.: $34,036,000
Approx. Number Employees: 217
Business Description:
Solar Power Systems Mfr & Installer
S.I.C.: 3612
N.A.I.C.S.: 335311
Advertising Expenditures: $131,000
Media: 7-8-13
Personnel:
Xiaofeng Peng *(Chm)*
Stephen C. Kircher *(Pres & CEO)*
Jeffrey G. Winzeler *(CFO)*
Robert Wood *(COO)*
Mike Anderson *(VP-Mktg)*
Alan M. Lefko *(VP-Fin)*

SOLITRON DEVICES, INC.
3301 Electronics Way
West Palm Beach, FL 33407-4636
Tel.: (561) 848-4311
Fax: (561) 863-5946
E-mail: info@solitrondevices.com
Web Site: www.solitrondevices.com
E-Mail For Key Personnel:
President: ssaraf@solitrondevices.com
Sales Director: sales@solitrondevices.com
Approx. Sls.: $8,933,000
Approx. Number Employees: 81
Year Founded: 1959
Business Description:
Power Transistors, Thick Film Hybrids, Field Effect Transistors, Integrated Circuits, Power Mosfet Modules, Power MOS Devices, Bipolar Power Thin Film Resistor Products Mfr
S.I.C.: 3674; 3676
N.A.I.C.S.: 334413; 334415
Import Export
Media: 2-4
Distr.: Intl.; Natl.
Personnel:
Shevach Saraf *(Chm, Pres, CEO & CFO)*
Brands & Products:
SOLITRON

SONANCE
212 Avenida Fabricante
San Clemente, CA 92672
Tel.: (949) 492-7777
Fax: (949) 361-2705
Toll Free: (800) 582-7777
Web Site: www.sonance.com
Business Description:
Mfr & Retailer of Audio Speaker Systems
S.I.C.: 3651
N.A.I.C.S.: 334310
Personnel:
Geoff Spencer *(Co-Founder)*
Scott Struthers *(Co-Founder)*
Patrick McGaughan *(COO)*
Brands & Products:
CINEMA SELECT
MERLOT
SONANCE
SYMPHONY
THINLINE
VIRTUOSO
Advertising Agency:
Nicoll Public Relations
1502 Providence Hwy Ste 2
Norwood, MA 02062
Tel.: (781) 762-9300
Fax: (781) 255-7777

SONICS, INC.
890 N McCarthy Blvd Ste 200
Milpitas, CA 95035
Tel.: (408) 457-2800
Tel.: (650) 605-6110 (Inv Rels)
Tel.: (650) 605-6151 (Pub Rels)
Fax: (408) 457-2899
E-mail: info@sonicsinc.com
Web Site: www.sonicsinc.com
Sales Range: $10-24.9 Million
Approx. Number Employees: 75
Business Description:
Semiconductor Devices & Related Products Mfr
S.I.C.: 3674
N.A.I.C.S.: 334413
Media: 5-10-17-22
Personnel:
Grant A. Pierce *(Pres & CEO)*
Martin M. Kovacich *(CFO)*
Raymond G. Brinks *(VP-Engrg)*

SONY CORPORATION OF AMERICA
(Sub. of Sony Corporation)
550 Madison Ave
New York, NY 10022
Tel.: (212) 833-6800
Fax: (212) 833-6956
E-mail: info@sony.com
Web Site: www.sony.com
Approx. Sls.: $19,887,886,762
Approx. Number Employees: 22,000
Business Description:
Holding Company
S.I.C.: 7812; 7832
N.A.I.C.S.: 512110; 512131
Personnel:
Howard Stringer *(Chm, CEO & Pres-Sony Corp)*
Robert S. Wiesenthal *(CFO & Exec VP)*
Philip Reitinger *(Chief Info Security Officer)*

Key to Media (For complete agency information see *The Advertising Red Books-Agencies* edition):
1. Bus. Publs. 2. Cable T.V. 3. Catalogs & Directories. 4. Co-op Adv. 5. Consumer Mags. 6. D.M. to Bus. Estab.7. D.M. to Consumers 8. Daily Newsp. 9. Exhibits/Trade Shows 10. Foreign 11. Infomercial 12. Internet Adv.13. Multimedia 14. Network Radio 15. Network T.V. 16. Newsp. Distr. Mags. 17. Other 18. Outdoor (Posters, Transit) 19. Point of Purchase20. Premiums, Novelties 21. Product Samples 22. Special Events Mktg. 23. Spot Radio 24. Spot T.V. 25. Weekly Newsp. 26. Yellow Page Adv.

Sony Corporation of America — (Continued)

Nicole Seligman *(Gen Counsel & Exec VP)*
Sean Carey *(Sr VP-Strategic Content Initiatives)*
Sam Levenson *(Sr VP-IR)*
Gary Podorowsky *(Sr VP)*
Stuart Redsun *(Sr VP-Corp Mktg)*
Tim Schaaff *(Sr VP-Software Dev)*
Caroline Sheu *(VP-Mktg)*
Steve Sommers *(VP-Mktg)*
Aaron Levine *(Product Mgr-HomeShare)*

Advertising Agencies:
BDS Marketing
10 Holland
Irvine, CA 92618
Tel.: (949) 472-6700
Fax: (949) 597-2220

Brierley & Partners
8401 N Central Expy Ste 1000 LB-37
Dallas, TX 75225-4403
Tel.: (214) 760-8700
Fax: (214) 743-5511

Deutsch LA
5454 Beethoven St
Los Angeles, CA 90066-7017
Tel.: (310) 862-3000
Fax: (310) 862-3100
Playstation 3

Draftfcb
101 E Erie St
Chicago, IL 60611
Tel.: (312) 425-5000
Fax: (312) 425-5010

Firstborn
630 9th Ave Ste 910
New York, NY 10036
Tel.: (212) 581-1100
Fax: (212) 765-7605
Digital Marketing
Make.believe
Mobile
OOH
Social

Universal McCann
100 33rd St 8th Fl
New York, NY 10001
Tel.: (212) 883-4700

SONY ELECTRONICS, INC.

(Sub. of Sony Corporation of America)
16450 W Bernardo Dr
San Diego, CA 92177
Tel.: (858) 942-2400
Business Description:
Holding Company; Household Audio & Video Equipment
S.I.C.: 3651; 7378
N.A.I.C.S.: 334310; 811212
Advertising Expenditures: $56,000,000
Personnel:
Stan Glasgow *(Chm)*
Phil Molyneux *(Pres & COO)*
Michael Fasulo *(CMO & Exec VP)*
Steve Haber *(Pres-Digital Reading Bus)*
Stuart Redsun *(Sr VP-Mktg)*
Marjorie Thomas *(Sr VP)*
Linda Turner *(Sr VP)*
Randy Waynick *(Sr VP-Mktg)*
Barbara Miller *(VP-Mktg)*
Steven Sommers *(VP-Mktg)*
Gary Mandle *(Sr Product Mgr)*
Kevin Sather *(Product Mgr-IT & Portable Audio Div)*
Kristine Willis *(Mgr-Media)*
Rob Manfredo *(Sr Specialist-PR)*

Advertising Agencies:
180 Los Angeles
1733 Ocean Ave 4th fl
Santa Monica, CA 90401
Tel.: (310) 382-1400
Fax: (310) 382-1401
— Matthew Elhardt *(Creative Dir-Boost Mobile & Sony)*

Atomic Public Relations
735 Market St 4th Fl
San Francisco, CA 94103
Tel.: (415) 402-0230
Fax: (415) 402-0237
Audio Products
Camcorders
Home Theater
PCs
Public Relations
Social Media
Tablets
US Agency of Record

Fallon London
Elsley Court
London, W1W 8BE, United Kingdom
Tel.: (44) 20 7494 9120
Fax: (44) 20 7494 9130
Bravia

HARTE-HANKS, INC.
9601 McAllister Freeway Ste 610
San Antonio, TX 78216
Tel.: (210) 829-9000
Fax: (210) 829-9403
Toll Free: (800) 456-9748
CRM Agency of Record

Ignited
2221 Park Pl
El Segundo, CA 90245
Tel.: (310) 773-3100
Fax: (310) 773-3101
VAIO TZ Notebook

Source Communications
433 Hackensack Ave 8th Fl
Hackensack, NJ 07601-6319
Tel.: (201) 343-5222
Fax: (201) 343-5710

ZAAZ
414 Olive Way Ste 500
Seattle, WA 98101
Tel.: (206) 341-9885
Fax: (206) 749-9868
Web Sites

SONY ELECTRONICS INC. MEDICAL SYSTEMS DIVISION

(Div. of Sony Electronics, Inc.)
1 Sony Dr
Park Ridge, NJ 07656
Tel.: (201) 930-1000
Fax: (201) 358-4977
Web Site: bssc.sel.sony.com
Approx. Number Employees: 170
Year Founded: 1946
Business Description:
Medical Electronics Mfr
S.I.C.: 3679; 5064
N.A.I.C.S.: 334419; 423620
Media: 10
Distr.: Natl.
Budget Set: July
Brands & Products:
ACCESS
THE ANSWER
AUTOMATED MUSIC SENSOR (AMS)
COLOR PURE FILTER
CYBER-SHOT
DESKTOP LIBRARY
DIRECT ACCESS
DISCMAN
DUAL ADJUST HEAD
DYNAMIC COLOR
DYNAMIC FOCUS
DYNAMIC PICTURE
DYNAMIC TRACKING
DYNAMICRON
ESPRIT
HIT
HOME MANAGEMENT HELPER
INDEXTRON
LEGATO LINEAR
MAGIC LINK
MATRIX SOUND
MAVICA
MAVICARD
MAVIGRAPH
MAVIPAK
MF TRINICON
MICROBLACK
MINI 8
MIRRORBLACK
MUSIC SHUTTLE
ONCE UPON A TIME ... (SVSC)
THE ONE AND ONLY
PANFOCUS
PC GLASSTRON
PCBACKER
PROFEEL
READY-FOCUS
REMOTE COMMANDER
RMO
SATICON
SDT
SMC-70
SMF TRINICON
SONY
SPEAKEASY
SPRESSA
SWING SEARCH
TAB MARKER INDEXING SYSTEM
TRINICON
TRINITONE
TRINITRON
TYPECODER
UNICOMMANDER
UNIMATCH
VELOCITY MODULATION
VIDEO 45
VIDEO 8
VIDEO EP
VIDEO LP
VIDEOSCOPE
WATCHCAM
WATCHMAN
WORLD BAND RADIO
X-TAL LOCK
ZONE PHONE

SOUND TECHNOLOGY, INC.

15732 Los Gatos Blvd #535
Los Gatos, CA 95032
Tel.: (408) 378-6540
Fax: (408) 378-6847
Telex: 357445
E-mail: info@soundtechnology.com
Web Site: www.soundtechnology.com
Approx. Number Employees: 12
Year Founded: 1969
Business Description:
Professional Audio Test & Measurement Equipment Mfr
S.I.C.: 3825; 3663
N.A.I.C.S.: 334515; 334220
Import Export
Advertising Expenditures: $250,000
Media: 10-17
Distr.: Intl.; Natl.
Budget Set: Sept.

SPECTRUM BRANDS, INC.

(Sub. of Spectrum Brands Holdings, Inc.)
601 Rayovac Dr
Madison, WI 53711-2497
Mailing Address:
PO Box 44960
Madison, WI 53744-4960
Tel.: (608) 275-3340
Web Site: www.spectrumbrands.com
Approx. Sls.: $2,567,011,000
Approx. Number Employees: 6,100
Year Founded: 1906
Business Description:
Holding Company; Batteries, Lighting Equipment & Personal Care Products Mfr & Whslr
S.I.C.: 6719; 3634; 3648; 3692; 5064
N.A.I.C.S.: 551112; 335129; 335211; 335912; 423620
Import Export
Advertising Expenditures: $37,520,000
Media: 2-3-6-7-9-12-13-15-18-19-20-25
Distr.: Intl.; Natl.
Budget Set: Oct.
Personnel:
David R. Lumley *(Pres)*
Anthony L. Genito *(CFO & Exec VP)*
John A. Heil *(Pres-Global Pet Supplies)*
Terry Lee Polistina *(Pres-Small Appliances)*
Eric Kenney *(Sr Dir-Mktg-Controls)*
Suzanne Fanning *(Dir-Mktg Comm-Remington Prods)*
Andy Van Wie *(Dir-Sls)*
Brands & Products:
BACKWOODS CUTTER
BACKYARD
BITE MD
BRILLIANT SOLUTIONS
CITROGUARD
CUTTER
CUTTER ADVANCED
GARDEN SAFE
HOT SHOT
HOT SHOT ANT KILLER PLUS4
MAXATTRAX
MAXATTRAX ULTRA
MORE POWER FOR YOUR MONEY
NO-PEST
PERMANONE
PRO LINE
RAYOVAC
REMINGTON
REPEL
REPEL LEMON EUCALYPTUS
REPEL SCENTED FAMILY FORMULA
REPEL SPORTSMEN FORMULA

Key to Media (For complete agency information see *The Advertising Red Books-Agencies* edition):
1. Bus. Publs. 2. Cable T.V. 3. Catalogs & Directories. 4. Co-op Adv. 5. Consumer Mags. 6. D.M. to Bus. Estab.7. D.M. to Consumers
8. Daily Newsp. 9. Exhibits/Trade Shows 10. Foreign 11. Infomercial 12. Internet Adv.13. Multimedia 14. Network Radio
15. Network T.V. 16. Newsp. Distr. Mags. 17. Other 18. Outdoor (Posters, Transit) 19. Point of Purchase20. Premiums, Novelties
21. Product Samples 22. Special Events Mktg. 23. Spot Radio 24. Spot T.V. 25. Weekly Newsp. 26. Yellow Page Adv.

REPEL SPORTSMEN MAX FORMULA
ROUGHNECK
SCHULTZ
SKINSATIONS
SPECTRUM BRANDS
SPORTSMAN
SUN & BUG STUFF
VALUE BRIGHT
WEATHER SHIELD
WORKHORSE

Advertising Agencies:
Manning Gottlieb OMD
Seymour Mews House
London, W1H 6BN, United Kingdom
Tel.: (44) 207 470 5300
Fax: (44) 207 412 0244
Media Buying & Planning
Remington
Russell Hobbs

Manning Selvage & Lee
1170 Peachtree St NE Ste 400
Atlanta, GA 30309-7677
Tel.: (404) 875-1444
Fax: (404) 892-1274

SPECTRUM CONTROL, INC.
8031 Avonia Rd
Fairview, PA 16415-2829
Tel.: (814) 474-2207
Fax: (814) 474-2208
E-mail: spectrum@spectrumcontrol.com
Web Site: www.spectrumcontrol.com
Approx. Sls.: $163,936,000
Approx. Number Employees: 1,631
Year Founded: 1968
Business Description:
Electromagnetic Interference & Radio Frequency Interference Suppression & Elimination Products Mfr
S.I.C.: 3679; 3663; 3675; 3677
N.A.I.C.S.: 334419; 334220; 334414; 334416
Import Export
Advertising Expenditures: $886,000
Media: 2-4-5-7-10
Distr.: Intl.; Natl.
Personnel:
Gerald Anthony Ryan *(Chm)*
Richard A. Southworth *(Pres & CEO)*
John P. Freeman *(CFO & Sr VP)*
James F. Toohey *(Gen Counsel & Sec)*
Lawrence G. Howanitz *(Sr VP & Bus Mgr-Spectrum Advanced Specialty Products)*
Brian F. Ward *(Sr VP & Bus Mgr-Spectrum Sensors & Controls)*
Robert J. McKenna *(Sr VP-New Bus & Resource Dev)*
Jeffrey S. Peters *(VP-IT)*
Tom Krahling *(Dir-Global Sales)*
Brands & Products:
QUIETSHIELD
SMARTSTART
SPECPOWER
SPECWAVE
Advertising Agency:
Altman-Hall Associates
235 W 7th St
Erie, PA 16501-1601
Tel.: (814) 454-0158
Fax: (814) 454-3266
(Filters & Connectors)

SR TELECOM & CO. S.E.C.
(Sub. of Groupe Lagasse Inc.)
8150 Trans Canada Hwy
Montreal, QC H4S 1M5, Canada
Tel.: (514) 335-1210
Fax: (514) 334-7783
E-mail: info@srtelecom.com
Web Site: www.srtelecom.com
Approx. Rev.: $82,440,680
Approx. Number Employees: 588
Year Founded: 1981
Business Description:
Wireless Access Technology Mfr
S.I.C.: 3663
N.A.I.C.S.: 334220
Media: 2-10
Personnel:
Michael J. Morris *(VP-Contracts & Legal)*
Brands & Products:
INSIGHT
METROFLEX
METROPOL
SHIFT
SR500
STRIDE2400
SWING
WL500

STANDARD MICROSYSTEMS CORPORATION
80 Arkay Dr
Hauppauge, NY 11788-8847
Mailing Address:
PO Box 18047
Hauppauge, NY 11788-8847
Tel.: (631) 435-6000
Fax: (631) 273-5550
Toll Free: (800) 443-7364
E-mail: custserv@smsc.com
Web Site: www.smsc.com
Approx. Rev.: $409,479,000
Approx. Number Employees: 1,026
Year Founded: 1971
Business Description:
Integrated Circuits Designer, Mfr & Distr
S.I.C.: 3674; 7371; 7379
N.A.I.C.S.: 334413; 541511; 541519
Import Export
Advertising Expenditures: $1,500,000
Media: 2-4-7-21
Distr.: Intl.; Natl.
Budget Set: Dec.
Personnel:
Christine King *(Pres & CEO)*
Kris Sennesael *(CFO & VP)*
Robert E. Hollingsworth *(Sr VP & Gen Mgr)*
Jeff VerHeul *(Sr VP-Engrg-Austin)*
Christian Thiel *(VP & Gen Mgr-Automotive Info Sys Grp)*
Andrew P. Solowey *(VP-HR)*
Carolynne Borders *(Sr Dir-Corp Comm & IR)*
Brands & Products:
ARCNET
CIRCLINK
LANCHECK
MOSTPEG
MULTISWITCH
MULTITRAK
NETDETACH
SMSC
STANDARD MICROSYSTEMS
SUCCESS BY DESIGN

STANTON MAGNETICS, INC.
(Sub. of The Stanton Group)
3000 SW 42nd St
Fort Lauderdale, FL 33312
Tel.: (954) 949-9600
Fax: (954) 316-1590
E-mail: info@stantonmagnetics.com
Web Site: www.stantondj.com
Approx. Number Employees: 30
Year Founded: 1961
Business Description:
Audio Equipment, Electronic Cartridges, Headphones, Preamplifiers, Stanton Record Care Products Mfr
S.I.C.: 3695
N.A.I.C.S.: 334613
Import Export
Advertising Expenditures: $200,000
Media: 4-6-9-11-17-19-20-22
Distr.: Natl.
Budget Set: Dec.
Personnel:
Marty Katz *(VP-Fin-Stanton Grp)*
Brands & Products:
FINALSCRATCH
STANTON MAGNETICS

STMICROELECTRONICS, INC.
(Sub. of STMicroelectronics N.V.)
750 Kanyon Dr
Coppell, TX 75019
Tel.: (972) 466-6000
Fax: (972) 466-6001
Fax: (972) 466-8130
Web Site: www.st.com
Approx. Number Employees: 1,400
Year Founded: 1957
Business Description:
Integrated Circuits & Computer Component Systems Mfr
S.I.C.: 3674
N.A.I.C.S.: 334413
Import Export
Media: 2-10
Distr.: Intl.; Natl.
Personnel:
Carmelo Papa *(Sr Exec VP & Gen Mgr-Indus & Multisegment Sector)*
Georges Auguste *(Exec VP-STMicroelectronics, Gen Mgr-Pkg & Test Mfg)*
Philippe Lambinet *(Exec VP, Gen Mgr-Home Entertainment & Displays)*
Otto Kosgalwies *(Exec VP-STMicroelectronics)*
Reza Kazerounian *(Sr VP-North America)*
Giordano Seragnoli *(Gen Mgr & Corp VP-Mfg)*
Patrice Chastagner *(Corp VP-HR)*
Archie Malone *(VP-Fin)*
Carlo Ottaviani *(Corp VP-Comm)*
Eric Aussedat *(Gen Mgr-Div)*
Maria Grazia Prestini *(Dir-Corp Media Relations)*
Michael Markowitz *(Dir-Technical Media Rels)*
Fabrizio Rossini *(Sr Mgr-IR)*

STRATOS INTERNATIONAL, INC.
(Sub. of Emerson Electric Co.)
7444 W Wilson Ave
Harwood Heights, IL 60706-4548
Tel.: (708) 867-9600
Fax: (507) 833-6224
E-mail: info@stratoslightwave.com
Web Site: www.stratosoptical.com
Sales Range: $150-199.9 Million
Approx. Number Employees: 524
Business Description:
Electronic Connectors & Controls; Power Distribution Systems Mfr
S.I.C.: 3674
N.A.I.C.S.: 334413
Advertising Expenditures: $400,000
Media: 4-10-13-17
Personnel:
Jim Peterson *(CIO & VP-IT)*
Richard C.E. Durrant *(Exec VP)*
Brands & Products:
STRATOS LIGHTWAVE
TSUNAMI

STRUTHERS ELECTRONICS CORPORATION
15 Harold Ct
Bay Shore, NY 11706-2202
Tel.: (631) 434-7586
Fax: (631) 434-7589
E-mail: struthers@vdot.net
Web Site: www.vdot.net
Sales Range: $10-24.9 Million
Approx. Number Employees: 50
Year Founded: 1962
Business Description:
Mfr of Waveguide/Coaxial High Power Switches & Directional Couplers
S.I.C.: 3679; 3825
N.A.I.C.S.: 334419; 334515
Export
Media: 2-4-10-11-20
Distr.: Intl.; Natl.
Budget Set: Dec.
Personnel:
Florence Isaacson *(Pres)*
Dan Gibbons *(Gen Mgr)*
Brands & Products:
STRUTHERS ELECTRONICS

SUNFIRE CORPORATION
(Sub. of The AVC Group, LLC)
1969 Kellogg Ave
Carlsbad, CA 92008
Tel.: (760) 710-0990
E-mail: info@sunfire.com
Web Site: www.sunfire.com
Sales Range: $1-9.9 Million
Approx. Number Employees: 40
Year Founded: 1994
Business Description:
Designer, Mfr & Marketer of Home Audio & Home Theater Electronics
S.I.C.: 5064; 3651; 3663
N.A.I.C.S.: 423620; 334220; 334310
Media: 6-10
Personnel:
Mark Weisenberg *(Gen Mgr)*
Brands & Products:
HRS
SOLITAIRE
SONIC HOLOGRAPHIC
SUNFIRE
TRACKING DOWNCONVERTER
XT SERIES

SUNRISE TELECOM, INC.
302 Enzo Dr
San Jose, CA 95138
Tel.: (408) 363-8000
Fax: (408) 363-8313
E-mail: info@sunrisetelecom.com
Web Site: www.sunrisetelecom.com

Key to Media (For complete agency information see *The Advertising Red Books-Agencies* edition):
1. Bus. Publs. 2. Cable T.V. 3. Catalogs & Directories. 4. Co-op Adv. 5. Consumer Mags. 6. D.M. to Bus. Estab.7. D.M. to Consumers 8. Daily Newsp. 9. Exhibits/Trade Shows 10. Foreign 11. Infomercial 12. Internet Adv.13. Multimedia 14. Network Radio 15. Network T.V. 16. Newsp. Distr. Mags. 17. Other 18. Outdoor (Posters, Transit) 19. Point of Purchase20. Premiums, Novelties 21. Product Samples 22. Special Events Mktg. 23. Spot Radio 24. Spot T.V. 25. Weekly Newsp. 26. Yellow Page Adv.

Sunrise Telecom, Inc. — (Continued)

Approx. Sls.: $50,582,000
Approx. Number Employees: 362
Year Founded: 1991
Business Description:
Service Verification Equipment Mfr to Diagnose Telecommunications & Internet Networks
S.I.C.: 3669; 4899
N.A.I.C.S.: 334290; 517910
Advertising Expenditures: $137,000
Media: 1-10-17
Personnel:
Henry P. Huff *(Chm)*
Bahaa Moukadam *(CEO)*
Lyron L. Bentovim *(CFO & COO)*
Kirk O. Williams *(Chief Legal Officer, Sec & Chief Compliance Officer)*
Jim Walker *(Chief Acctg Officer)*
Raymond Chong *(VP-Sls & Mktg-Asia Pacific Reg)*
Craig Easley *(VP-Mktg)*
Robert Heintz *(VP-Worldwide Sls)*
Peter Moulds *(VP-Sls)*
Brands & Products:
3010H
3010R
3GMASTER
AT2000HMQ
AT2500
CALAN
CM1000
GHEPARDO
GIGE
GTT
LANEXPLORER
LANTREND
NETRACKER
OCULIST
REALGATE
REALWORX
STT
SUNLITE
SUNLITE E1
SUNLITE GIGE
SUNRISE TELECOM
SUNSET
SUNSET 10G
SUNSET E20
SUNSET E20C
SUNSET ISDN
SUNSET MTT
SUNSET OCX
SUNSET SDH
SUNSET T10
TAMS
WE MAKE NETWORKS WORK
WINCOM II
WINQAM
WINREMOTE

SUNTRON CORPORATION
(Joint Venture of Thayer / Hidden Creek & Blum Capital Partners, L.P.)
2401 W Grandview Rd
Phoenix, AZ 85023-3112
Tel.: (602) 282-5059
Fax: (602) 282-1275
Toll Free: (888) 520-3382
E-mail: suntron@suntroncorp.com
Web Site: www.suntroncorp.com
Approx. Sls.: $320,786,000
Approx. Number Employees: 1,240
Business Description:
Electronic Manufacturing Services for Original Equipment Manufacturers; Joint Venture of Thayer Capital Partners L.P. & BLUM Capital Partners, L.P.
S.I.C.: 5065; 3577; 3672
N.A.I.C.S.: 423690; 334119; 334412
Media: 7
Personnel:
Ed Wheeler *(Pres & CEO)*
Jim Cogan *(Corp VP, Gen Mgr, VP-Global Supply Chain & Ops Plng)*
Micheal Moore *(VP-HR)*

SUPERIOR ESSEX, INC.
(Sub. of LS Cable Ltd.)
6120 Powers Ferry Rd Ste 150
Atlanta, GA 30339
Tel.: (770) 657-6000
Fax: (770) 657-6599
Web Site: www.superioressex.com
Approx. Sls.: $2,993,082,000
Approx. Number Employees: 4,500
Business Description:
Magnet Wire & Communications Cable Mfr
S.I.C.: 3357; 3496
N.A.I.C.S.: 335921; 331422; 332618; 335929
Advertising Expenditures: $1,200,000
Media: 7-10-13
Personnel:
Stephen M. Carter *(Pres & CEO)*
David S. Aldridge *(CFO, Treas & Exec VP)*
Justin F Deedy, Jr. *(Pres-Superior Essex Commun LP & Exec VP)*
J. David Reed *(Pres-Essex Grp & Exec VP)*
Marylove Sullenberger *(Gen Counsel, Sec & Exec VP)*
Tracye C Gilleland *(Sr VP-Fin & Controller)*
Debbie Baker-Oliver *(Sr VP-Corp Admin Svcs)*
Gayle Watson *(Mgr-Mktg Program)*

SUPERTEX, INC.
1235 Bordeaux Dr
Sunnyvale, CA 94089-1203
Tel.: (408) 222-8888
Fax: (408) 222-4800
Fax: (408) 222-4895
Toll Free: (800) 222-9884
E-mail: investors@supertex.com
Web Site: www.supertex.com
E-Mail For Key Personnel:
President: henryp@supertex.com
Public Relations: investors@supertex.com
Approx. Sls.: $83,172,000
Approx. Number Employees: 373
Year Founded: 1976
Business Description:
Mfr, Designer, Developer & Marketer of High Voltage Semiconductor Products for Sale to the Telecommunications, Medical, Instrumentation, Defense & Consumer Product Industries
S.I.C.: 3674
N.A.I.C.S.: 334413
Export
Media: 2-4-5-6-7-10-13-18
Distr.: Intl.; Natl.
Budget Set: Mar.
Personnel:
Henry C. Pao *(Pres & CEO)*
Phillip A. Kagel *(CFO & VP-Fin)*
Benedict C. K. Choy *(Sec & Sr VP-Tech Dev)*
Stephen Lin *(VP-Mktg & Bus Dev)*
William Petersen *(VP-Worldwide Sls)*
Kenneth Vickers *(Mgr-Marcom)*
Brands & Products:
FLEXSWITCH
SUPERTEX

SYMMETRICOM, INC.
2300 Orchard Pkwy
San Jose, CA 95131
Tel.: (408) 433-0910
Fax: (408) 428-7896
E-mail: world-info@symmetricom.com
Web Site: www.symmetricom.com
Approx. Rev.: $208,146,000
Approx. Number Employees: 570
Year Founded: 1956
Business Description:
Mfr., Designer & Marketer of Telecommunications Equipment & Linear & Mixed Signal Integrated Circuits
S.I.C.: 3661; 3825
N.A.I.C.S.: 334210; 334515
Export
Advertising Expenditures: $275,000
Media: 2-8-17
Distr.: Intl.; Natl.
Budget Set: June
Personnel:
Robert T. Clarkson *(Chm)*
David Cote *(Pres & CEO)*
Justin Spencer *(CFO)*
James Armstrong *(Exec VP & Gen Mgr-Comm Bus Unit)*
Daniel Scharre *(Exec VP & Gen Mgr-Govt Bus Unit)*
Phil Bourekas *(Exec VP-Mktg)*
Juan Dewar *(Exec VP-Worldwide Sls)*
Douglas Halbert *(Exec VP-Global Ops)*
William Minor, Jr. *(Exec VP-Global HR)*
Randy Brudzinski *(VP-Sls)*
Barry Dropping *(Sr Dir-Mktg)*
David Boone *(Dir-Product Line Mgmt)*
Paul Tuong *(Sr Product Mgr)*
Raillin Wirjo *(Sr Product Mgr)*
Ron Holm *(Mgr-Product Mktg)*
Doug Lowrie *(Mgr-Product Mktg)*
Paul Skoog *(Mgr-Product Mktg)*
Brands & Products:
AUDITSERVER
BESTIME
DOMAIN TIME
EFRATOM
EXACTIME
GOLONG
GOWIDE
MARK
RUBISOURCE
SMARTCLOCK
STAMPSERVER
STARLITE
STARLOC II
SYMMETRICOM
SYNCRAFT
SYNCSERVER
TELECOM SOLUTIONS
TELMAX
TIMECESIUM
TIMEEXPANDER
TIMEGPS
TIMEHUB
TIMEMONITOR
TIMEPICTRA
TIMEPROVIDER
TIMESCAN
TIMESCAN/CRAFT
TIMESOURCE
TIMEWATCH
TRUETIME
TRUSTED TIME
TSC
TYMMACHINE
TYMSERVE
VME-SG 2
WEBPROOF
X72
XL-GPS
XLI
XLI IEEE
XLI SAASM
XPRO
Advertising Agencies:
BroadPR Inc.
1770 Mass Ave
Cambridge, MA 02140
Tel.: (617) 868-5031
Fax: (617) 812-3088
Public Relations

Overdrive
38 Everett St 2nd Fl
Boston, MA 02134
Tel.: (617) 254-5000
Fax: (617) 254-5003

SYNERGISTICS, INC.
16 Tech Cir
Natick, MA 01760-1023
Tel.: (508) 655-1340
Fax: (508) 651-2902
Toll Free: (800) 433-7616
E-mail: sales@synergisticsinc.com
Web Site: www.synergisticsinc.com
E-Mail For Key Personnel:
Sales Director: sales@synergisticsinc.com
Sales Range: $10-24.9 Million
Approx. Number Employees: 20
Year Founded: 1960
Business Description:
Access Control Systems Mfr
S.I.C.: 7382
N.A.I.C.S.: 561621
Import Export
Media: 2-4-7-10-21
Distr.: Intl.; Natl.
Personnel:
Greg Goldman *(Pres & CEO)*
Pam Weber *(CFO)*
Brands & Products:
BUILDING WATCH
CITADEL
PRESIDIO
SECURE YOUR WORLD
SYNERGISTICS
WA-PAC
WAPAC PRO

SYNERGX SYSTEMS INC.
(Sub. of Firecom Inc.)
209 Lafayette Dr
Syosset, NY 11791-3939
Tel.: (516) 433-4700
Fax: (516) 433-1131
E-mail: info@synergxsystems.com
Web Site: www.synergxsystems.com
Approx. Rev.: $18,828,000
Approx. Number Employees: 41

Key to Media (For complete agency information see *The Advertising Red Books-Agencies* edition):
1. Bus. Publs. 2. Cable T.V. 3. Catalogs & Directories. 4. Co-op Adv. 5. Consumer Mags. 6. D.M. to Bus. Estab.7. D.M. to Consumers
8. Daily Newsp. 9. Exhibits/Trade Shows 10. Foreign 11. Infomercial 12. Internet Adv.13. Multimedia 14. Network Radio
15. Network T.V. 16. Newsp. Distr. Mags. 17. Other 18. Outdoor (Posters, Transit) 19. Point of Purchase20. Premiums, Novelties
21. Product Samples 22. Special Events Mktg. 23. Spot Radio 24. Spot T.V. 25. Weekly Newsp. 26. Yellow Page Adv.

Business Description:
Manufactures, Markets & Designs Data Communication Products & Systems with Applications in the Fire Alarm, Fire Safety, Security, Transit & Communications Industries
S.I.C.: 3669; 7382
N.A.I.C.S.: 334290; 561621
Media: 17
Personnel:
Paul Mendez *(Chm & CEO)*
John A. Poserina *(CFO, Treas, Sec & VP)*

SYSTEM SENSOR

(Sub. of Honeywell Life Safety)
3825 Ohio Ave
Saint Charles, IL 60174
Tel.: (630) 377-6580
Fax: (630) 377-6495
Toll Free: (800) 736-7672
E-mail: info@systemsensor.com
Web Site: www.systemsensor.com
Sales Range: $350-399.9 Million
Approx. Number Employees: 1,000
Year Founded: 1984
Business Description:
Sensor Equipment for Fire Alarm Systems Mfr
S.I.C.: 3669
N.A.I.C.S.: 334290
Export
Advertising Expenditures: $240,000
Media: 2-7-10
Distr.: Intl.; Natl.
Budget Set: Dec.
Personnel:
John Hakanson *(Pres)*
James B. Brown *(VP & GM-Intl)*
Cindy Edwards *(VP-Fin)*
Brands & Products:
ACCLIMATE
EXITPOINT
FILTREX
I3
INNOVAIR
MINI-ALERT
MULTI-ALERT
PINNACLE
SPECTRALERT
VIEW

T-MOBILE USA INC.

(Sub. of T-Mobile International AG & Co. KG)
12920 SE 38th St
Bellevue, WA 98006-1350
Tel.: (425) 378-4000
Fax: (425) 378-4040
Toll Free: (800) 866-2453
E-mail: mediarelations@t-mobile.com
Web Site: www.t-mobile.com
Sales Range: $15-24.9 Billion
Approx. Number Employees: 20,185
Year Founded: 1999
Business Description:
Digital Wireless Communications
S.I.C.: 4812
N.A.I.C.S.: 517212
Media: 2-3-6-8-10-13-15-18-19-23-24-31
Personnel:
Robert Dotson *(Vice Chm)*
Philipp Humm *(CEO)*
Brian Kirkpatrick *(CFO & Exec VP)*
Cole Brodman *(Chief Tech & Innovation Officer)*
Dave Miller *(Gen Counsel & Sr VP)*
Matt Millen *(VP-Small & Medium Bus Sls)*
Halle Hutchinson *(Dir-Integrated Mktg)*
T. Jason Young *(Dir-Consumer Mktg)*
Mark Stockdale *(Dir-Hispanic Mktg)*
Jim Pilcher *(Sr Mgr-Bus Dev)*
Advertising Agencies:
Ameredia, Inc.
101 Howard St Ste 380
San Francisco, CA 94105
Tel.: (415) 788-5100
Fax: (415) 449-3411
Mobile Phones (Multicultural Markets)

Big Fuel Communications LLC
298 5th Ave 5th Fl
New York, NY 10001
Tel.: (212) 616-6300
Fax: (212) 658-9226
Social Media Agency of Record

Conill Advertising, Inc.
3501 Sepulveda Blvd
Torrance, CA 90505-2538
Tel.: (310) 214-6400
Fax: (310) 214-6409

Hornall Anderson
Ste 1300 710 2nd Ave
Seattle, WA 98104-1712
Tel.: (206) 467-5800
Fax: (206) 467-6411
Sidekick

Optimedia International U.S.
375 Hudson St 7th Fl
New York, NY 10014
Tel.: (212) 820-3200
Fax: (212) 820-3300

Publicis West
424 2nd Ave W
Seattle, WA 98119-4013
Tel.: (206) 285-2222
Fax: (206) 273-4219
Whenever Minutes
T-Mobile@Home

TAITRON COMPONENTS INCORPORATED

28040 Harrison Pkwy
Valencia, CA 91355-4162
Tel.: (661) 257-6060
Fax: (661) 257-6415
Toll Free: (800) TAITRON
Toll Free: (800) TAITFAX (Facsimile)
E-mail: webadmin@taitroncomponents.com
Web Site:
www.taitroncomponents.com
Approx. Sls.: $7,189,000
Approx. Number Employees: 37
Year Founded: 1989
Business Description:
Contract Electronic Mfr & Distr of Transistors, Diodes & other Discrete Semiconductors, Optoelectronic Devices & Passive Components
S.I.C.: 5065
N.A.I.C.S.: 423690
Media: 10
Personnel:
Tzu Sheng Ku *(Chm)*
Stewart Wang *(Pres & CEO)*

TASER INTERNATIONAL, INC.

17800 N 85th St
Scottsdale, AZ 85255-6311
Tel.: (480) 905-2000
Fax: (480) 991-0791
Toll Free: (888) TASER-88
Toll Free: (800) 978-2737
Toll Free: (888) 827-3788
E-mail: ir@taser.com
Web Site: www.taser.com
E-Mail For Key Personnel:
Sales Director: sales@taser.com
Approx. Sls.: $86,930,019
Approx. Number Employees: 320
Business Description:
Mfr. of Electronic Control Devices
S.I.C.: 3829; 3489
N.A.I.C.S.: 334519; 332995
Advertising Expenditures: $700,000
Personnel:
Thomas P. Smith *(Co-Founder & Chm)*
Patrick W. Smith *(Co-Founder & CEO)*
Douglas E. Klint *(Pres & Gen Counsel)*
Daniel M. Behrendt *(CFO)*
Raymond G. Rivera *(CIO)*
Rick Guilbault *(VP-Trng & Education)*
Peter T. Holran *(VP-PR & Govt Affairs)*
Stephen D. Tuttle *(VP-Comm)*
Ted Murphy *(Dir-Mktg)*
Theron Neff *(Dir-Creative)*
Brands & Products:
ADVANCED TASER M18
ADVANCED TASER M26
AFID
AIR TASER
AUTO TASER
AXON
CHECKLOCK
EXOSKELETON
SHAPED PULSE
SHOCKWAVE
T-WAVE
TASER
TASER C2
TASER CAM
TASER MPH
TASER VDPM
TASER-WAVE
TASER X12
TASER X26
TASER X26C
TASER XREP
TRAD
X-RAIL
X26

TATUNG COMPANY OF AMERICA

(Sub. of Tatung Company)
2850 E El Presidio St
Long Beach, CA 90810-1119
Tel.: (310) 637-2105
Fax: (310) 637-8484
Toll Free: (800) 829-2850
E-mail: tushq@tatungusa.com
Web Site: www.tatungusa.com
Approx. Number Employees: 200
Year Founded: 1972
Business Description:
Mfr. & Marketer of Color TVs, Video Cassette Recorder & Portable Audio, Electric Fans, Compact Refrigerators, Cookers & Steamers, Color & Monochrome Monitor, Microwave Ovens, Desk-Top & Notebook Computers
S.I.C.: 3571; 3575
N.A.I.C.S.: 334111; 334113
Advertising Expenditures: $1,680,000
Media: 2-5-7-10-18-19-24
Distr.: Natl.
Budget Set: Nov. -Dec.
Personnel:
Larry Chen *(Mgr-Svc)*
Brands & Products:
AUDIOCOLOR

TDK-LAMBDA AMERICAS INC.

(Branch of TDK-Lambda Americas Inc.)
145 Marcus Blvd Ste 3
Hauppauge, NY 11788
Tel.: (631) 967-3000
Fax: (631) 967-3022
Toll Free: (800) 526-2325
Web Site: www.lambda-emi.com
Year Founded: 1945
Business Description:
Standard Switching & Linear Power Supplies, DC-DC Converters, Power Systems, Military Power Supplies & Systems
S.I.C.: 5065
N.A.I.C.S.: 423690
Import Export
Media: 2-4-7-10-17-20
Distr.: Intl.; Natl.
Budget Set: Mar.
Personnel:
David Norton *(VP-Mktg)*
John Breickner *(Product Mgr)*
Brands & Products:
LAMBDA
LAMBDA FASTRACK
LAMBDACARD
TELERACK
ULTRAFLEX SERIES
WATTBOX

TE CONNECTIVITY LTD.

(Formerly Tyco Electronics Corporation)
(Sub. of Tyco Electronics Ltd.)
1050 Westlakes Dr
Berwyn, PA 19312
Tel.: (610) 893-9800
Toll Free: (800) 522-6752
Web Site: www.te.com
Approx. Number Employees: 29,000
Year Founded: 1941
Business Description:
Solderless Terminals, Connectors, Relays, Wireless Components, Touch Screens, Circuit Protection Devices, Sealing Systems, Electronic Modules, Wire, Cable & Fiberoptic Components Mfr
S.I.C.: 3678; 3643
N.A.I.C.S.: 334417; 335931
Import Export
Media: 2-10-13
Distr.: Intl.
Budget Set: Sept.
Personnel:
Tom Lynch *(CEO)*
Terrence Curtin *(CFO & Exec VP)*
Alan Clarke *(Pres-Network Solutions)*
Chuck Dougherty *(Pres-Comm & Indus Solutions)*
Christopher Jurasek *(Pres-Wireless & Svcs)*
Bob Scott *(Gen Counsel & Exec VP)*
Cuong Do *(Sr VP-Corp Strategy & Bus Dev)*
Jane Leipold *(Sr VP-Global HR)*
Michael Robinson *(Sr VP-Ops)*

Key to Media (For complete agency information see *The Advertising Red Books-Agencies* edition):
1. Bus. Publs. 2. Cable T.V. 3. Catalogs & Directories. 4. Co-op Adv. 5. Consumer Mags. 6. D.M. to Bus. Estab.7. D.M. to Consumers
8. Daily Newsp. 9. Exhibits/Trade Shows 10. Foreign 11. Infomercial 12. Internet Adv.13. Multimedia 14. Network Radio
15. Network T.V. 16. Newsp. Distr. Mags. 17. Other 18. Outdoor (Posters, Transit) 19. Point of Purchase20. Premiums, Novelties
21. Product Samples 22. Special Events Mktg. 23. Spot Radio 24. Spot T.V. 25. Weekly Newsp. 26. Yellow Page Adv.

TE Connectivity Ltd. — (Continued)

Joan Wainwright *(Sr VP-Mktg & Comm)*
Michael Laub *(VP-Tech)*
John Roselli *(VP-Fin-Global Distr)*
Sabi Varma *(Gen Mgr)*
Eric Snyder *(Dir-Indus & Data Center)*

Brands & Products:
AMP
ASG
B&H
CHIPCOOLERS
CII
COEV
CORCOM
CRITCHLEY
ELASTOMERIC TECHNOLOGIES
ELO TOUCHSYSTEMS
HELLSTERN
HTS
IDENTO
LASER DIODE INC.
M/A-COM
OEG
PRECISION INTERCONNECT
PRODUCTS UNLIMITED
TDI

Advertising Agency:
DeCarolis Design & Marketing
476 S 1st St
San Jose, CA 95113
Tel.: (408) 947-1411
Fax: (408) 947-1570

TEAC AMERICA, INC.

(Sub. of TEAC Corporation)
7733 Telegraph Rd
Montebello, CA 90640-6537
Tel.: (323) 726-0303
Fax: (323) 727-7656
E-mail: webmaster@teac.com
Web Site: www.teac.com
Sales Range: $300-349.9 Million
Approx. Number Employees: 255
Year Founded: 1967

Business Description:
Electronic Audio & Video Equipment Systems, Recorders & Workstations Distr
S.I.C.: 5064; 5045
N.A.I.C.S.: 423620; 423430
Import Export
Media: 4-6-7-8-10-19-20-21
Distr.: Intl.; Natl.

Personnel:
Koichiro Nakamura *(Pres)*
Derek Davis *(COO & Exec VP)*
Les Luzar *(Sr VP-Sls & Mktg)*
Michael Townsen *(Dir-Sls-Consumer Electronics Div)*
Ken Hirata *(Mgr-Mktg & Commun)*
Tanja M. Pino *(Mgr-HR)*

Brands & Products:
ESOTERIC
TASCAM
TEAC

Advertising Agency:
The Rankin Group, Ltd.
17821 E 17th St Ste 270
Tustin, CA 92780-2137
Tel.: (714) 832-4100
Fax: (714) 282-8825
(Airborne Div., Data Storage Products and Information Products Divs.)

TECHNICAL SUPPORT SYSTEMS INC.

2232 Central Ave
Memphis, TN 38104
Tel.: (901) 398-5908
Fax: (901) 398-5914
E-mail: chip@techsupportsys.com
Web Site: www.techsupportsys.com
Approx. Sls.: $1,000,000
Approx. Number Employees: 6
Year Founded: 1984

Business Description:
Audio & Video Contractor
S.I.C.: 1731
N.A.I.C.S.: 238210
Media: 7-26

Personnel:
Chip Benson *(Pres)*
Mark Howard *(Office Mgr)*

TECHNITROL, INC.

(Name Changed to Pulse Electronics Corporation)

TECHNOLOGY RESEARCH CORPORATION

5250 140th Ave N
Clearwater, FL 33760-3728
Tel.: (727) 535-0572
Fax: (727) 535-4828
Toll Free: (800) 780-4324
E-mail: ctinfo@trci.net
Web Site: www.trci.net
Approx. Rev.: $34,833,000
Approx. Number Employees: 529
Year Founded: 1981

Business Description:
Portable Electrical Safety Products Designer, Mfr & Marketer; Power Monitoring & Control Equipment Supplier
S.I.C.: 5063; 3613; 3825; 8733
N.A.I.C.S.: 423610; 334515; 335313; 541710
Import Export
Advertising Expenditures: $166,000
Media: 17

Personnel:
Robert D. Woltil *(Interim CEO, CFO, Sec & VP-Fin)*
Richard C. O'Neal *(VP-Comml Sls & Mktg)*
Doug Tilghman *(VP-Engrg)*

Brands & Products:
BLACK JACKET
DRAG STRIP
ELECTRA CHECK
ELECTRIDUCT
FIRE SHIELD
FLAT PLUG
HD-PRO
SHOCK SHIELD
SURGE GUARD
TRC
YELLOW JACKET

TECHSONIC INDUSTRIES, INC.

(Sub. of Johnson Outdoors Inc.)
1220 Old Alpharetta Rd Ste 340
Alpharetta, GA 30005
Tel.: (770) 888-6292
Fax: (770) 888-9258
E-mail: cservices@johnsonoutdoors.com
Web Site: www.humminbird.com
Approx. Sls.: $60,000,000
Approx. Number Employees: 30
Year Founded: 1973

Business Description:
Mfr. of Marine Electronics
S.I.C.: 3812
N.A.I.C.S.: 334511
Export
Advertising Expenditures: $1,633,000
Bus. Publs.: $15,000; Catalogs & Directories: $200,000; Consumer Mags.: $1,000,000; D.M. to Bus. Estab.: $15,000; D.M. to Consumers: $40,000; Exhibits/Trade Shows: $15,000; Foreign: $25,000; Outdoor (Posters, Transit): $3,000; Premiums, Novelties: $15,000; Spot Radio: $5,000; Spot T.V.: $300,000
Budget Set: Sept.

Brands & Products:
FISH-EYE
LEGEND
PIRANHA
ZERCOM

TECHWELL INTERNATIONAL, INC.

(Sub. of Intersil Corporation)
408 E Plumeria Dr
San Jose, CA 95134
Tel.: (408) 435-3888
Fax: (408) 435-0588
E-mail: sales@techwellinc.com
Web Site: www.techwellinc.com
Approx. Rev.: $63,174,000
Approx. Number Employees: 206
Year Founded: 1997

Business Description:
Video Signal Integrated Circuit Designer, Marketer & Seller
S.I.C.: 3674; 3679
N.A.I.C.S.: 334413; 334419
Advertising Expenditures: $2,665,000

Personnel:
Fumihiro Kozato *(Founder, Pres & CEO)*
David Dong Wook Nam *(VP-Sls & Mktg)*

TELEDYNE MICROELECTRONIC TECHNOLOGIES

(Sub. of Teledyne Technologies Incorporated)
12964 Panama St
Los Angeles, CA 90066
Tel.: (310) 822-8229
Fax: (310) 822-3573
Toll Free: (800) 568-8711
Web Site: www.teledynemicro.com
Sales Range: $75-99.9 Million
Approx. Number Employees: 300
Year Founded: 1959

Business Description:
Traveling Wave Tubes, Microwave Subsystems, EW Systems, Solid State Amplifiers, High Power Amplifiers, Active Integrated Modules
S.I.C.: 3674
N.A.I.C.S.: 334413
Export
Advertising Expenditures: $300,000
Media: 2-4-7-10
Distr.: Intl.; Natl.
Budget Set: Nov. -Dec.

TELEGENIX INC.

(Sub. of Indel, Inc.)
1930 Olney Ave
Cherry Hill, NJ 08003-2016
Mailing Address:
PO Box 5550
Cherry Hill, NJ 08034-0511
Tel.: (856) 424-5220
Fax: (856) 424-0889
Toll Free: (800) 424-5220
E-mail: info@telegenix.com
Web Site: www.telegenix.com
E-Mail For Key Personnel:
Sales Director: sales@telegenix.com
Approx. Number Employees: 75
Year Founded: 1969

Business Description:
Mfr. of Data Communication, Traffic Control & Telemetry Systems
S.I.C.: 3669; 3577; 3679
N.A.I.C.S.: 334290; 334119; 334418
Export
Advertising Expenditures: $300,000
Media: 2-4-6-7-10-17
Distr.: Natl.

Personnel:
Joe Miller *(Pres)*

TELENAV, INC.

1130 Kifer Rd
Sunnyvale, CA 94086
Tel.: (408) 245-3800
Fax: (408) 245-0238
E-mail: media@telenav.com
Web Site: www.telenav.com
Approx. Rev.: $171,162,000
Approx. Number Employees: 942

Business Description:
Location Based Services Including Voice Guided Navigation On Mobile Phones
S.I.C.: 3669; 3679
N.A.I.C.S.: 334290; 334419
Advertising Expenditures: $182,000
Media: 17

Personnel:
H.P. Jin *(Co-Founder, Pres & CEO)*
Robert Rennard *(Co-Founder & CTO)*
Y.C. Chao *(Co-Founder & VP-R & D)*
Salman Dhanani *(Co-Founder & VP-Products)*
Douglas Miller *(CFO)*
Loren Hillberg *(Gen Counsel)*
Dariusz Paczuski *(VP-Mktg)*

Brands & Products:
TELENAV
TELENAV GPS NAVIGATOR
TELENAV SHOTGUN
TELENAV TRACK
TELENAV VEHICLE MANAGER
TELENAV VEHICLE TRACKER
WHEREBOUTZ

TELESCIENCES, INC.

2000 Midlantic Dr Ste 410
Mount Laurel, NJ 08054-1512
Tel.: (856) 866-1000
Fax: (856) 866-0185
E-mail: sales@telesciences.com
Web Site: www.telesciences.com
E-Mail For Key Personnel:
Sales Director: sales@telesciences.com
Approx. Number Employees: 180
Year Founded: 1967

Business Description:
Computer-Controlled Telephone Support Equipment
S.I.C.: 3669
N.A.I.C.S.: 334290
Media: 10
Distr.: Intl.; Natl.

Key to Media (For complete agency information see *The Advertising Red Books-Agencies* edition):
1. Bus. Publs. 2. Cable T.V. 3. Catalogs & Directories. 4. Co-op Adv. 5. Consumer Mags. 6. D.M. to Bus. Estab.7. D.M. to Consumers 8. Daily Newsp. 9. Exhibits/Trade Shows 10. Foreign 11. Infomercial 12. Internet Adv.13. Multimedia 14. Network Radio 15. Network T.V. 16. Newsp. Distr. Mags. 17. Other 18. Outdoor (Posters, Transit) 19. Point of Purchase20. Premiums, Novelties 21. Product Samples 22. Special Events Mktg. 23. Spot Radio 24. Spot T.V. 25. Weekly Newsp. 26. Yellow Page Adv.

Budget Set: Dec.
Personnel:
Mark Trudeau *(Pres & CEO)*
Rich Kraus *(VP-Sls-North America)*
Eric Liu *(VP-Sls)*
Larry Siegel *(VP-Mktg-Ventraq)*
Brands & Products:
TELESCIENCES

TELEX COMMUNICATIONS, INC.
(Name Changed to Bosch Communications Inc.)

TELKONET, INC.
10200 Innovation Dr Ste 300
Milwaukee, WI 53226
Tel.: (414) 233-0473
Fax: (414) 258-8307
Toll Free: (877) 838-2089
E-mail: ir@telkonet.com
Web Site: www.telkonet.com
Approx. Rev.: $11,258,776
Approx. Number Employees: 80
Year Founded: 1999
Business Description:
Powerline Communications Technology Systems Application Developer
S.I.C.: 4899; 3669; 7373
N.A.I.C.S.: 517910; 334290; 541512
Advertising Expenditures: $15,257
Media: 10
Personnel:
Anthony J. Paoni *(Chm)*
Jason L. Tienor *(Pres & CEO)*
Jeff Sobieski *(COO)*
Gerrit Reinders *(Exec VP-Global Sls & Mktg)*

TELLABS, INC.
1 Tellabs Ctr 1415 W Diehl Rd
Naperville, IL 60563
Tel.: (630) 798-8800
Fax: (630) 798-2000
E-mail: info@tellabs.com
Web Site: www.tellabs.com
Approx. Rev.: $1,642,300,000
Approx. Number Employees: 3,413
Year Founded: 1974
Business Description:
Holding Company; Telecommunications Equipment Designer & Marketer
S.I.C.: 3679; 3651; 3661; 3663; 3669; 6719
N.A.I.C.S.: 334418; 334210; 334220; 334290; 334310; 551112
Import Export
Media: 1-2-4-7-9-10-11-13-16-17-18-20-22-23-25
Distr.: Intl.; Natl.; Reg.
Budget Set: Sept.
Personnel:
Michael J. Birck *(Chm)*
Robert W. Pullen *(Pres & CEO)*
Jean K. Holley *(CIO & Exec VP)*
James M. Sheehan *(Chief Admin Officer, Gen Counsel & Exec VP)*
Vikram Saksena *(CTO & Exec VP)*
Thomas P. Minichiello *(Chief Acctg Officer & VP-Fin)*
Allan Thompson *(Principal-Mktg Analytics)*
John M. Brots *(Exec VP-Global Ops)*
Daniel P. Kelly *(Exec VP-Product Dev)*
Rizwan Khan *(Exec VP-Global Mktg)*
Brands & Products:
ACCESSMAX
ADVANCEDVOICE
ASSUREDETHERNET
CABLESPAN
FIBERDIRECT
THE FUTURE OF YOUR BUSINESS. STARTING NOW.
INTERGRATEDMOBILE
MEDIADIRECT
MULTISERVICE ACCESS PLATFORM
MULTISERVICEPLUS
PANORAMA
PROFESSIONAL & CONSULTING SERVICES
PROPARTNER
SIERRA
T SYMBOL
TELLABS
TELLIANT
TITAN
TRANSFORMING THE WAY THE WORLD COMMUNICATES
UNIVERSALDSL
Advertising Agencies:
Gerard Design
15 W. Jefferson Ave.
Naperville, IL 60540
Tel.: (630) 355-0775

Huntington Advertising, Inc.
4575 Weaver Pkwy Ste 500
Warrenville, IL 60555
Tel.: (630) 836-1850
Fax: (630) 836-1171

TELONIC BERKELEY, INC.
2825 Laguna Canyon Rd
Laguna Beach, CA 92651-1149
Mailing Address:
PO Box 277
Laguna Beach, CA 92652-0277
Tel.: (949) 494-9401
Fax: (949) 497-7331
Toll Free: (800) 854-2436
E-mail: info@telonicberkeley.com
Web Site: www.telonicberkeley.com
Approx. Sls.: $1,000,000
Approx. Number Employees: 13
Year Founded: 1958
Business Description:
Electronics Mfr
S.I.C.: 3679; 3669
N.A.I.C.S.: 334419; 334290
Export
Media: 2-4-7-10
Distr.: Intl
Personnel:
Kristi Tamaoki *(Gen Mgr)*

TERADYNE INC.
600 Riverpark Dr
North Reading, MA 01864
Tel.: (978) 370-2700
Fax: (617) 422-2910
Toll Free: (800) 227-1620
E-mail: investorrelations@teradyne.com
Web Site: www.teradyne.com
E-Mail For Key Personnel:
Public Relations: tom.newman@teradyne.com
Approx. Rev.: $1,608,650,000
Approx. Number Employees: 3,000
Year Founded: 1960
Business Description:
Automatic Test Equipment Designer & Mfr
S.I.C.: 3825; 3674; 8734
N.A.I.C.S.: 334515; 334413; 541380
Export
Advertising Expenditures: $800,000
Media: 2-4-7-10-11-17
Distr.: Intl.; Natl.
Personnel:
Albert Carnesale *(Chm)*
Michael A. Bradley *(Pres & CEO)*
Gregory R. Beecher *(CFO)*
Jeffrey R. Hotchkiss *(Pres-Sys Test Grp)*
Mark E. Jagiela *(Pres-Semiconductor Test Div)*
Charles Gray *(Gen Counsel, Sec & VP)*
Ben Sung *(Acct Mgr-Sls)*
Peter Predella *(Mgr-Corp Mktg Comm)*
Brands & Products:
4 TEL
BECAUSE TESTING MATTERS
BOARDWATCH
HD-OPTYX
HDM
HIGH DENSITY PLUS
INTEGRA
MAGNUM II
NEXLEV
SPECTRUM
STRATEGIST
TERADYNE
TESTNET
TESTSTATION
TRAX
X-FRAME
XSTAT
XSTATION
Advertising Agency:
InnoVision Media Group
3301 E Hill St Ste 401
Signal Hill, CA 90755
Tel.: (562) 961-3610
Fax: (562) 961-3616
Toll Free: (888) 843-9255

TERREMARK WORLDWIDE, INC.
(Sub. of Verizon Communications Inc.)
2 S Biscayne Blvd Ste 2800
Miami, FL 33131
Tel.: (305) 856-3200
Fax: (305) 856-8190
E-mail: info@terremark.com
Web Site: www.terremark.com
Approx. Rev.: $292,347,000
Approx. Number Employees: 859
Year Founded: 1980
Business Description:
Information Technology Infrastructure Services
S.I.C.: 7379; 7382
N.A.I.C.S.: 541519; 561621
Advertising Expenditures: $8,500,000
Media: 2-4-7-10-11-13-18-20-26
Personnel:
Manuel D. Medina *(Chm & CEO)*
Joseph R. Wright, Jr. *(Vice Chm)*
Jose A. Segrera *(CFO)*
Nelson Fonseca *(COO)*
Simon West *(CMO)*
Adam T. Smith *(Chief Legal Officer)*
Marvin Wheeler *(Chief Strategy Officer)*
Jamie Dos Santos *(Pres/CEO-Terremark Federal Grp)*
Herman Oggel *(Pres-Bus Unit-Europe)*
Barry Field *(Sr VP-U.S. Comml Sls)*
Brands & Products:
BEYOND AVAILABILITY
DIGITALOPS
FREEDOM OF CONNECTIVITY
HIGHLY MANAGED HOSTING
INFINISTRUCTURE
NAP OF THE AMERICAS
TERREMARK
TERREMARKS'S ENTERPRISE CLOUD
TERRENAP
Advertising Agency:
Edelman
80 SW 8th St Ste 2160
Miami, FL 33130
Tel.: (305) 358-9500
Fax: (305) 358-1270

TESSCO TECHNOLOGIES, INC.
11126 McCormick Rd
Hunt Valley, MD 21031-1494
Tel.: (410) 223-1000
Fax: (410) 527-0005
Toll Free: (800) 472-7373
E-mail: info@tessco.com
Web Site: www.tessco.com
Approx. Rev.: $605,219,200
Approx. Number Employees: 874
Year Founded: 1982
Business Description:
Wireless Communications Products Distr
S.I.C.: 5065; 7389
N.A.I.C.S.: 423690; 425120
Export
Advertising Expenditures: $1,932,200
Personnel:
Robert B. Barnhill, Jr. *(Chm, Pres & CEO)*
David M. Young *(CFO, Sec & Sr VP)*
Gerald T. Garland *(Sr VP-Solutions Dev & Product Mgmt)*
Douglas A. Rein *(Sr VP-Performance Sys Grp)*
Saeed Tofighi *(Sr VP-Market Dev & Sls)*
Brands & Products:
A SIMPLE WAY OF DOING BUSINESS BETTER
AIRSTREAM
DELIVERING EVERYTHING FOR WIRELESS
GIGAWAVE
GIGAWAVE TECHNOLOGIES
GOING BEYOND THE ORDINARY
LINKUPS
ORDERFLOW
SOLUTIONS THAT MAKE WIRELESS WORK
TERRAWAVE
TERRAWAVE SOLUTIONS
TESSCO
TESSCO TECHNOLOGIES
TESSCO.COM
VENTEV
VENTEV INNOVATIONS
THE VITAL LINK TO A WIRELESS WORLD
THE WIRELESS BULLETIN
THE WIRELESS GUIDE
THE WIRELESS JOURNAL
WIRELESS SOLUTIONS
THE WIRELESS UPDATE

Key to Media (For complete agency information see *The Advertising Red Books-Agencies* edition):
1. Bus. Publs. 2. Cable T.V. 3. Catalogs & Directories. 4. Co-op Adv. 5. Consumer Mags. 6. D.M. to Bus. Estab.7. D.M. to Consumers 8. Daily Newsp. 9. Exhibits/Trade Shows 10. Foreign 11. Infomercial 12. Internet Adv.13. Multimedia 14. Network Radio 15. Network T.V. 16. Newsp. Distr. Mags. 17. Other 18. Outdoor (Posters, Transit) 19. Point of Purchase20. Premiums, Novelties 21. Product Samples 22. Special Events Mktg. 23. Spot Radio 24. Spot T.V. 25. Weekly Newsp. 26. Yellow Page Adv.

Tessco Technologies, Inc. — (Continued)

YOUR TOTAL SOURCE
YOUR VIRTUAL INVENTORY
YOUR WIRELESS SUCCESS, NOTHING LESS

TEXAS INSTRUMENTS INCORPORATED
12500 TI Blvd
Dallas, TX 75243-4136
Mailing Address:
PO Box 660199
Dallas, TX 75266-0199
Tel.: (972) 995-2011
Tel.: (972) 995-3773
Fax: (972) 995-4360
Toll Free: (800) 336-5236
Toll Free: (800) 890-2600
E-mail: txn@ti.com
Web Site: www.ti.com
Approx. Rev.: $13,966,000,000
Approx. Number Employees: 28,412
Year Founded: 1930
Business Description:
Electronics, Semiconductors, Software Productivity Tools & Electrical Controls Mfr & Sales
S.I.C.: 3674; 3571; 3613
N.A.I.C.S.: 334413; 334111; 335313
Export
Advertising Expenditures: $42,000,000
Media: 2-5-6-7-10-11-13-18-20
Distr.: Intl.; Natl.
Personnel:
Richard K. Templeton *(Chm, Pres & CEO)*
Kevin P. March *(CFO & Sr VP)*
Melendy E. Lovett *(Pres-Education Tech & Sr VP)*
Joseph F. Hubach *(Gen Counsel, Sec & Sr VP)*
Brian T. Crutcher *(Sr VP & Gen Mgr-Embedded Processing & Custom Bus)*
R. Gregory Delagi *(Sr VP & Gen Mgr-Wireless Bus Unit)*
Kent Novak *(Sr VP & Gen Mgr-DLP Products)*
Steve Anderson *(Sr VP & Mgr-High Performance Analog-Worldwide)*
Michael J. Hames *(Sr VP & Mgr-Application Specific Products)*
David K. Heacock *(Sr VP & Mgr)*
Sami Kiriaki *(Sr VP, Mgr-Worldwide & Power Mgmt)*
John J. Szczsponik, Jr. *(Sr VP & Mgr-Sls & Mktg-Worldwide)*
Teresa L. West *(Sr VP & Mgr-Comm & IR)*
Gregg A. Lowe *(Sr VP-Analog)*
Kevin J. Ritchie *(Sr VP-Tech & Mfg Grp)*
Darla H. Whitaker *(Sr VP-HR-Worldwide)*
Dave Pahl *(Dir-IR)*
Mike Ryan-Todd *(Dir-Market Res)*
Olivier Monnier *(Mgr-Worldwide Mktg & Bus-Smart Grid Solutions)*
Chris Rongone *(Mgr-Fin Comm)*
Brands & Products:
ALANTRO
AUREUS
AUTO-BAND
AUTOCOMP
BENCHMARQ
BLUELINK
BQTINY
BRILLIANTCOLOR
BURR-BROWN
C2000
C20X
C24X
C28X
C5000
C54X
C55X
C5X
C6000
C62X
C64X
C67X
CODE COMPOSER STUDIO
CODEMAESTRO
D-CAP
DARKCHIP2
DAVINCI
DIGITAL LIGHT PROCESSING
DIGITAL THUNDER
DLP
DLP CINEMA
DLP COMPOSER
DSP/BIOS
DSP-SYNC
DYNAMICBLACK
EASYRF
EASYSCALE
EMBEDDED EDGE
EMU
EQUIBIT
EXCALIBUR
EXPRESSDSP
FILTERPRO
FLATLINK
FUSION DIGITAL POWER
GPLYNX
ICECRUSHER
IMPEDANCE TRACK
INCA
INNOVATOR
KLIXON
LINBICMOS
LINCMOS
LITTLE LOGIC
LYNXSOFT
MARCSTAR
MICROAMPLIFIER
MICROSTAR BGA
MICROSTAR JUNIOR
MUXIT
MY.TI
NANOFREE
NANOSTAR
NAVIGATOR
NAVILINK
OCHI-LYNX
OMAP
OMAP-VOX
OMAPI
OPAMPPRO
PANELBUS
PBCC
PCILYNX
POLA
POWER GAUGE
POWER TRENDS
POWERPAD
PREDICTIVE GATE DRIVE
PUMP SYSTEMALERT
PUREPATH DIGITAL
REAL WORLD SIGNAL PROCESSING
RTDX
SDQ
SINE ON
SMARTDM
SMARTREFLEX
SOUNDPLUS
SPACT
SPEEDPLUS
SPREETA
SSI
SWIFT
TAG-IT
TECHNOLOGY FOR INNOVATORS
TELINNOVATION
TELOGY NETWORKS, INC.
TEXAS INSTRUMENTS
TI-83 PLUS
TI NAVIGATOR
TI-NSPIRE
TI-OPC
TI-RFID
TI-SMARTVIEW
TI.COM
TIMEBUILDER
TIMECELL
TIMELINE
TIMEPILOT
TIRIS
TMS320
TPS40K
TRUEDRIVE
TURBODOX
ULTRAMEDIA
UNITRODE
VELOCITI
VLYNQ
VOICEVOYAGER
VOV
VOYAGE
WILINK
XDS
XDS510
XDS5100
XDS560
ZIGBEE
Advertising Agency:
M/C/C
8131 Lyndon B Johnson Fwy Ste 275
Dallas, TX 75251-1352
Tel.: (972) 480-8383
Fax: (972) 669-8447

THOMAS & BETTS CORPORATION
8155 T&B Blvd
Memphis, TN 38125-8888
Tel.: (901) 252-8000
Fax: (800) 816-7810
Fax: (901) 252-1354
Toll Free: (800) 816-7809
E-mail: elec_custserv@tnb.com
Web Site: www.tnb.com
Approx. Sls.: $2,004,366,000
Approx. Number Employees: 8,750
Year Founded: 1898
Business Description:
Electrical Connectors & Related Components Mfr
S.I.C.: 3678; 3643; 5063
N.A.I.C.S.: 334417; 335931; 423610
Import Export
Advertising Expenditures: $16,900,000
Media: 1-2-4-5-7-10-16-19-20-21-26
Distr.: Intl.; Natl.
Budget Set: Aug.
Personnel:
Dominic J. Pileggi *(Chm & CEO)*
Charles L. Treadway *(Pres & COO)*
William E. Weaver, Jr. *(CFO & Sr VP)*
W. David Smith, Jr. *(Chief Compliance Officer, Asst Sec & Asst Gen Counsel)*
Ned Camuti *(Pres-Electrical Div-US)*
Nathalie Pilon *(Pres-Canada)*
Fabrice Van Bell *(Pres-Europe, Middle East, Africa & Asia)*
James R. Wiederholt *(Pres-Steel Structures)*
J. N. Raines *(Gen Counsel, Sec & VP)*
Peggy Gann *(Sr VP-HR & Admin)*
Imad Hajj *(Sr VP-Intl & Operational Dev)*
Joseph Dicianni *(VP-IT)*
Jim Feeney *(VP-Sls)*
Anna Negrini *(Mgr-Customer Svc)*
Brands & Products:
BATTPAC
BLACKBURN
BOWERS
CANSTRUT
CARLON
CARLON FLEX-PLUS
CARLON MULTI-GARD
CARLON PLENUM-GARD
CARLON RESI-GARD
CARLON RISER-GARD
CATAMOUNT
CENTER LOK
COL-TY
COLOR-KEYED
CURRENT TECHNOLOGY
CYBEREX
DELTEC
DIAMOND
DRAGON TOOTH
E-KLIPS
E-Z CODE
E-Z-GROUND
E.K. CAMPBELL
ELASTIMOLD
EMERGI-LITE
EVER-LOK
EXPRESS TRAY
FLEXSHELL
FURSE
FURSEWELD
HAZLUX
HOMAC
IBERVILLE
JOSLYN
KINDORF
KING COBRA
KOLD-N-KLOSE
LRC
LUMACELL
MARRETTE
MEYER
MICROLECTRIC
MIPCO
NUTEK
OCAL
OMNI-PLUS
OMNILINK
PARTEX
POS-E-KON
RED DOT
REZNOR
RUSSELLSTOLL
SACHS
SHAMROCK
SHIELD-KON
SHRINK-KON
SHUREFLEX
SHURESEAL
SNAP-N-SEAL

Key to Media (For complete agency information see *The Advertising Red Books-Agencies* edition):
1. Bus. Publs. 2. Cable T.V. 3. Catalogs & Directories. 4. Co-op Adv. 5. Consumer Mags. 6. D.M. to Bus. Estab.7. D.M. to Consumers
8. Daily Newsp. 9. Exhibits/Trade Shows 10. Foreign 11. Infomercial 12. Internet Adv.13. Multimedia 14. Network Radio
15. Network T.V. 16. Newsp. Distr. Mags. 17. Other 18. Outdoor (Posters, Transit) 19. Point of Purchase20. Premiums, Novelties
21. Product Samples 22. Special Events Mktg. 23. Spot Radio 24. Spot T.V. 25. Weekly Newsp. 26. Yellow Page Adv.

SPEC-KON
STA-KON
STAR TECK
STEEL CITY
SUPERSTRUT
T&B
T&B EXPRESS TRAY
TAYLOR
THOMAS & BETTS
TY-DUCT
TY-FAST
TY-GRIP
TY-MET
TY-RAP
UNION
Advertising Agency:
Walker & Associates, Inc.
5100 Poplar Ave Ste 2812
Memphis, TN 38137
Tel.: (901) 522-1100
Fax: (901) 522-1101

THOMSON BROADCAST & MULTIMEDIA INC.

(Sub. of Grass Valley France S.A.)
104 Feeding Hills Rd
Southwick, MA 01077-9349
Tel.: (413) 998-1100
Tel.: (413) 569-5939
Fax: (413) 569-0679
Toll Free: (800) 688-3669
Web Site:
www.thomsongrassvalley.net
Approx. Number Employees: 65
Year Founded: 1972
Business Description:
Mfr of Television Broadcasting & Transmission Equipment
S.I.C.: 3663; 3651; 3669
N.A.I.C.S.: 334220; 334290; 334310
Export
Media: 2-4-7-10-11-17-20
Distr.: Natl.
Personnel:
Richard E. Fiore *(Sr VP-Sls)*
Joe Turbolski *(VP-Mktg)*

THOMSON INC.

(Sub. of Technicolor S.A.)
101 W 103 St
Indianapolis, IN 46290-1024
Mailing Address:
PO Box 1976
Indianapolis, IN 46206-1976
Tel.: (317) 587-3000
Fax: (317) 587-6765
E-mail: info@thomson.net
Web Site: www.thomson.net
Approx. Number Employees: 9,000
Business Description:
Research, Distribution, Sales, Leasing & Service of Television Receivers, Home Video Cassette Recorders, Color Picture Tubes, Audio & Communications Equipment
S.I.C.: 3651; 3861
N.A.I.C.S.: 334310; 333315
Media: 3-6-9-14-15-17-18-23-24-25
Distr.: Intl.; Natl.
Personnel:
Frank E. Dangeard *(Chm & CEO)*
Brands & Products:
ACCUBRITE
ACCUCIRCUIT
ACCUCOLOR
ACCUMATIC
ACCUTINT
ACCUTOUCH
AIRCON
BATHMATE
CABLEGUARD
COLORAMA
COLORTRAK
COMMAND PERFORMANCE
DIMENSIA
DOG
HELP
HI LITE
HIS MASTER'S VOICE
HOME MINDER
KID-CORDER
KITCHEN COMPANION
LIVING COLOR
MAGIC BRAIN & DESIGN
MASTER TENNA
MINIKIN
NEO-VISION
NUMITRON
PERMACHROME
PHOTOPHONE
PRO WONDER
PROSCAN
RCA DIGITAL SATELLITE SYSTEM (DSS)
SELECTAVISION
SILVERAMA
SK
SLIM DESIGN
SMALL WONDER
TRANS VISTA
TURBO 1000
VICTOR
VICTROLA
XL-100
XTENDED-LIFE

THX LTD.

1600 Los Gamos Dr Ste 231
San Rafael, CA 94903
Tel.: (415) 492-3900
Fax: (415) 492-3988
Web Site: www.thx.com
Business Description:
Home Entertainment Technology
S.I.C.: 3651
N.A.I.C.S.: 334310
Media: 10-17-20
Personnel:
Tim Rosa *(VP-Mktg)*

TII NETWORK TECHNOLOGIES, INC.

141 Rodeo Dr
Edgewood, NY 11717-8378
Tel.: (631) 789-5000
Fax: (631) 789-5063
Toll Free: (888) 844-4720
E-mail: customerservice@tiinettech.com
Web Site: www.tiinettech.com
Approx. Sls.: $54,498,000
Approx. Number Employees: 75
Year Founded: 1964
Business Description:
Mfr of Telephone Network Interface & Protection Products, Surge Protection, Fiber Optics & Specialized Electronic Devices
S.I.C.: 3613; 3612; 3677
N.A.I.C.S.: 335313; 334416; 335311
Import Export
Advertising Expenditures: $85,000
Media: 2-4-10
Distr.: Natl.
Budget Set: May
Personnel:
Charles H. House *(Chm)*
Kenneth A. Paladino *(Pres & CEO)*
Stacey L. Moran *(CFO, Treas, Sec & VP-Fin)*
Michael Dawe *(VP-Sls-UK, Europe, Asia & Oceania)*
Walter Fay *(VP-Sls & Mktg)*
Monica Gonzalez-Greer *(VP-Sls-Latin America & Caribbean)*
Thomas J. Smith *(VP-Engrg & Matls)*
Brands & Products:
ADVANCEMAN
ANGLE DRIVER
AUTO-JACK
BIG MAC
FAILSAFE
IN-LINE
TFS
THOR
TII
TII LIGHTING SHIELD
TOTEL FAILSAFE

TIMES FIBER COMMUNICATIONS, INC.

(Sub. of Amphenol Corporation)
358 Hall Ave
Wallingford, CT 06492
Mailing Address:
PO Box 384
Wallingford, CT 06492-7006
Tel.: (203) 265-8500
Fax: (203) 265-8422
Toll Free: (800) 677-CATV
E-mail: info@timesfiber.com
Web Site: www.timesfiber.com
Sales Range: $200-249.9 Million
Approx. Number Employees: 400
Year Founded: 1948
Business Description:
Coaxial Cable Mfr
S.I.C.: 3357
N.A.I.C.S.: 335929
Export
Advertising Expenditures: $300,000
Media: 2-4-5-10-11-26
Distr.: Natl.
Personnel:
Martin H. Loeffler *(Chm)*
Adam Norwitt *(Pres & CEO)*
Diana Reardon *(CFO)*
Edward Wetmore *(Gen Counsel)*
Brands & Products:
FLEXIBLE FEEDER
SEMIFLEX
T10 DROP CABLE
T10 SEMIFLEX
T10 TELEDROP
TELEDROP
TFC HEADEND DROP CABLE
TX10 SEMIFLEX

TOKO AMERICA, INC.

(Sub. of Toko, Inc.)
1250 Feehanville Dr
Mount Prospect, IL 60056-6009
Tel.: (847) 297-0070
Fax: (847) 699-7864
Toll Free: (800) PIK-TOKO
E-mail: info@tokoam.com
Web Site: www.tokoam.com
E-Mail For Key Personnel:
President: jonodera@tokoam.com
Sales Range: $10-24.9 Million
Approx. Number Employees: 90
Year Founded: 1965
Business Description:
Electronic Components
S.I.C.: 5065
N.A.I.C.S.: 423690
Import Export
Media: 1-2-4-7-10-13-20-21-22
Personnel:
Janet Byrne *(Mgr-Marcom)*

TOPFLIGHT CORPORATION

277 Commerce Dr
Glen Rock, PA 17327-8625
Tel.: (717) 227-5400
Fax: (717) 227-1415
Toll Free: (800) 233-9386
Web Site: www.topflight.com
Approx. Number Employees: 130
Year Founded: 1943
Business Description:
Printed Pressure-Sensitive Adhesive Materials for Electronic Switches; Labels & Nameplates
S.I.C.: 2672
N.A.I.C.S.: 322222
Media: 1-2-4-7-10-13-17-21
Distr.: Natl.; Reg.
Personnel:
E. W. Huber *(Chm)*
Rodney Stone *(CEO & Pres)*
Brands & Products:
INNOVATIVE PRINTING AND CONVERTING SOLUTIONS
LABEL SECURE
OPERATION ELIMINATE
RFID EASY
SMART PARTS
TOPFLIGHT

TOSHIBA AMERICA CONSUMER PRODUCTS, LLC

(Sub. of Toshiba America, Inc.)
82 Totowa Rd
Wayne, NJ 07470-3114
Tel.: (973) 628-8000
Fax: (973) 628-1875
Toll Free: (800) 361-3811
E-mail: customer_support@tacp.com
Web Site: www.tacp.toshiba.com
Sales Range: $10-24.9 Million
Approx. Number Employees: 100
Year Founded: 1989
Business Description:
Televisions, DVD Players, Air Conditioners, Industrial Video Systems, Satellite Receivers, Lamps & Other Consumer Electronics
S.I.C.: 3651; 5064; 7629
N.A.I.C.S.: 334310; 423620; 811211
Media: 2-6-7-8-10-13-19-20-21-22-23-24
Personnel:
Atsushi Murasawa *(Pres & CEO)*
Karen Gentoso *(VP & Controller)*

TOSHIBA AMERICA ELECTRONIC COMPONENTS, INC.

(Sub. of Toshiba America, Inc.)
19900 Macarthur Blvd Ste 400
Irvine, CA 92612-8434
Tel.: (949) 623-2900
Fax: (949) 474-1805
Web Site: www.toshiba.com/taec
Approx. Number Employees: 712
Year Founded: 1989
Business Description:
Mfr. of Microelectronics
S.I.C.: 3679; 3674

Key to Media (For complete agency information see *The Advertising Red Books-Agencies* edition):
1. Bus. Publs. 2. Cable T.V. 3. Catalogs & Directories. 4. Co-op Adv. 5. Consumer Mags. 6. D.M. to Bus. Estab.7. D.M. to Consumers 8. Daily Newsp. 9. Exhibits/Trade Shows 10. Foreign 11. Infomercial 12. Internet Adv.13. Multimedia 14. Network Radio 15. Network T.V. 16. Newsp. Distr. Mags. 17. Other 18. Outdoor (Posters, Transit) 19. Point of Purchase20. Premiums, Novelties 21. Product Samples 22. Special Events Mktg. 23. Spot Radio 24. Spot T.V. 25. Weekly Newsp. 26. Yellow Page Adv.

Toshiba America Electronic Components, Inc. — (Continued)

N.A.I.C.S.: 334419; 334413
Personnel:
Hideya Sakaida *(Pres & CEO)*
Stephen Marlow *(Exec VP)*
Hideya Yamaguchi *(Exec VP)*
Tokuhiro Matsuda *(VP-Bus Devel-Discrete Bus Unit)*
Doug Ryan *(VP-Mktg)*
Advertising Agency:
Tsantes Consulting Group
1825 Constitution Ct
San Jose, CA 95124
Tel.: (408) 309-9926
Semiconductors

TOSHIBA AMERICA, INC.

(Sub. of Toshiba Corporation)
1251 Ave of the Americas Ste 4110
New York, NY 10020-1104
Tel.: (212) 596-0600
Fax: (212) 593-3875
Web Site: www.toshiba.com
Approx. Number Employees: 9,500
Year Founded: 1989
Business Description:
Holding Company; TVs, Radios, Tape Recorders, CD Players, Stereos, Microwave Ovens, VCRs, Video Cameras & Coffee Makers Mfr
S.I.C.: 3651; 3631
N.A.I.C.S.: 334310; 335221
Export
Advertising Expenditures: $10,000,000
Media: 2-4-5-6-7-9-10-13-16-19-20-23-24-25-26
Distr.: Natl.
Budget Set: Apr.
Personnel:
Hitoshi Otsuka *(Pres & CEO)*
Stephen Marlow *(Exec VP)*
Clayton Bond *(Sr VP-Display Devices & Components)*
Shardul Kazi *(Sr VP-Sys LSI Grp Tech)*
Advertising Agencies:
Goodness Mfg.
6922 Hollywood Blvd 12th Fl
Los Angeles, CA 90028
Tel.: (310) 845-3035
Fax: (310) 845-3470
Consumer Electronics Computers (Agency of Record)

KSL Media, Inc.
15910 Ventura Blvd 9th Fl
Los Angeles, CA 91436
Tel.: (818) 461-5900
Fax: (818) 461-1373

Ted Barkus Company, Inc.
8017 Anderson St
Philadelphia, PA 19118
Tel.: (215) 545-0616

TRACFONE WIRELESS, INC.

(Affil. of AMERICA MOVIL, S.A.B. DE C.V.)
9700 NW 112 Ave
Miami, FL 33178-1504
Tel.: (305) 640-2000
Fax: (305) 640-2070
Web Site: www.tracfone.com
Approx. Sls.: $270,000,000
Approx. Number Employees: 500
Year Founded: 1996
Business Description:
Prepaid Wireless Communication Services
S.I.C.: 4813; 4812
N.A.I.C.S.: 517310; 517212
Media: 6-13
Personnel:
F. J. Pollak *(Pres & CEO)*
Gustavo Blanco *(CFO)*
Steve Ritter *(Chief Service Officer)*
Derek Hewitt *(Sr VP-Mktg)*
Peter Distler *(Sr Dir-Mobile Mktg)*
David May *(Dir-New Bus)*
Kim O'Connell *(Dir-Interactive Mktg & ECommerce)*
Juan Pacheco *(Dir-Handsets, Accessories & Packaging)*
Brands & Products:
NET10
TRACFONE
Advertising Agency:
droga5
400 Lafayette 5th Fl
New York, NY 10003
Tel.: (917) 237-8888
Fax: (917) 237-8889
Net10

TRANS-LUX CORPORATION

26 Pearl St
Norwalk, CT 06850
Tel.: (203) 853-4321
Fax: (203) 852-0836
Fax: (203) 866-9496
Toll Free: (800) 243-5544
E-mail: investor@trans-lux.com
Web Site: www.trans-lux.com
E-Mail For Key Personnel:
Sales Director: sales@trans.com
Approx. Rev.: $24,307,000
Approx. Number Employees: 150
Year Founded: 1919
Business Description:
Programmable Electronic Display Systems & Telecommunications Products Mfr, Designer, Renter, Seller & Servicer
S.I.C.: 3679; 3993; 3999; 7832
N.A.I.C.S.: 334419; 339950; 339999; 512131
Export
Advertising Expenditures: $54,000
Media: 1-2-7-10-11-18-19-20
Distr.: Intl.; Natl.
Budget Set: Dec.
Personnel:
Glenn J. Angiolillo *(Chm)*
J. M. Allian *(Pres & CEO)*
Angela D. Toppi *(CFO & Exec VP)*
Al L. Miller *(Exec VP)*
Karl P. Hirschauer *(Sr VP-Engrg)*
Thomas F. Mahoney *(Sr VP-Sls)*
Brands & Products:
CAPTIVUE
COLORWALL
DATAWALL
DYNAWALL
FAIR-PLAY
GRAPHIXMAX
GRAPHIXWALL
INFOWALL
ISEWRITE
LED JET
LED NEWSJET
MENUWALL
PICTUREWALL
PROLINE
PROMOWALL
RAINBOWWALL
SPECTRALENS
SPORTS INFORMATION DISPLAY
SPORTSTICKER
TRANS-LUX
VISIONWRITER
WINDOWRITER
Advertising Agency:
Mason & Kichar Recruitment Advertising
260 Amity Rd
Woodbridge, CT 06525
Tel.: (203) 392-0252
Fax: (203) 392-0255

TRANSCAT, INC.

35 Vantage Point Dr
Rochester, NY 14624-1151
Tel.: (585) 352-7777
Tel.: (585) 352-9720
Fax: (585) 352-7788
Fax: (585) 352-5422
E-mail: sales@transcat.com
Web Site: www.transcat.com
E-Mail For Key Personnel:
Sales Director: sales@transcat.com
Approx. Rev.: $91,186,000
Approx. Number Employees: 313
Year Founded: 1964
Business Description:
Professional Grade Test, Measurement & Calibration Instrumentation Distribution; Calibration & Repair Services
S.I.C.: 3824; 5049; 7629
N.A.I.C.S.: 334514; 423490; 811219
Media: 4-5-7-8-10-13-26
Personnel:
Carl E. Sassano *(Chm)*
Charles P. Hadeed *(Pres, CEO & COO)*
John J. Zimmer *(CFO & Sr VP-Fin)*
Michael P. Craig *(VP-HR)*
Lori L. Drescher *(VP-Sls Ops)*
John P. Hennessy *(VP-Sls & Mktg)*
James Daugherty *(Dir-Wind Energy Sls)*
Brands & Products:
BETTER BY EVERY MEASURE
CALTRAK
TRANSCAT

TRANSICO INCORPORATED

(d/b/a EECO Switch)
880 Columbia St
Brea, CA 92821
Tel.: (714) 835-6000
Fax: (714) 482-9429
Toll Free: (800) 854-3808
E-mail: sales@eecoswitch.com
Web Site: www.eecoswitch.com
E-Mail For Key Personnel:
Sales Director: sales@eecoswitch.com
Approx. Sls.: $5,000,000
Approx. Number Employees: 20
Year Founded: 1947
Business Description:
Electronics Mfr
S.I.C.: 3625
N.A.I.C.S.: 335314
Import Export
Media: 2-4-7-10
Distr.: Intl.; Natl.
Personnel:
Wen-Hu Tu *(Chm)*
Dane Hoiberg *(Pres & CEO)*
Steve Potter *(VP-Fin)*
Richard Soden *(VP-Mktg & Sls)*
Brands & Products:
EECO
EECO KEYPAD
EECO SWITCH
ELASTOMER KEYPADS
MICRO-DIP
MINI-DIP
PRINTED CIRCUIT BOARDS
SOFKEY
STRIPSWITCH
THUMBPOT
THUMBWHEEL

TRANSWITCH CORPORATION

3 Enterprise Dr
Shelton, CT 06484
Tel.: (203) 929-8810
Fax: (203) 926-9453
E-mail: txc-comments@transwitch.com
Web Site: www.transwitch.com
Approx. Rev.: $49,822,000
Approx. Number Employees: 233
Business Description:
Digital & Mixed Signal Semiconductors for High-Speed Telecommunications & Computer Networking Equipment
S.I.C.: 3674; 4899
N.A.I.C.S.: 334413; 517910
Media: 10
Personnel:
Gerald F. Montry *(Chm)*
M. Ali Khatibzadeh *(Pres & CEO)*
Robert A. Bosi *(CFO & VP)*
Kris Shankar *(Sr VP-Worldwide Sls & Mktg)*
Michael Macari *(VP-Engrg & Ops)*
Brands & Products:
CELLBUS
CONNECTIVITY ENGINES
CUBIT
CUBIT-PRO
ENGINES FOR GLOBAL CONNECTIVITY
ENVOY-XE
HD-PXL
SALI-25C
SARA
SARA-2
SARA-LITE
SARA-NIC
TRANSWITCH
TXC
XBERT

TRIAD SPEAKERS, INC.

15835 NE Cameron Blvd
Portland, OR 97230
Tel.: (503) 256-2600
Fax: (503) 256-5966
Toll Free: (800) 666-6316
Web Site: www.triadspeakers.com
Approx. Sls.: $7,000,000
Approx. Number Employees: 45
Year Founded: 1982
Business Description:
Mfr. of Home Theater & Stereo Loudspeakers
S.I.C.: 3651
N.A.I.C.S.: 334310
Media: 6
Personnel:
Larry Pexton *(Owner)*
Mike Budd *(Dir-Sls-Natl)*
Paul Scarpelli *(Dir-Sls & Mktg)*
Paul Teixeira *(Mgr-Mktg)*

Key to Media (For complete agency information see *The Advertising Red Books-Agencies* edition):
1. Bus. Publs. 2. Cable T.V. 3. Catalogs & Directories. 4. Co-op Adv. 5. Consumer Mags. 6. D.M. to Bus. Estab.7. D.M. to Consumers 8. Daily Newsp. 9. Exhibits/Trade Shows 10. Foreign 11. Infomercial 12. Internet Adv.13. Multimedia 14. Network Radio 15. Network T.V. 16. Newsp. Distr. Mags. 17. Other 18. Outdoor (Posters, Transit) 19. Point of Purchase20. Premiums, Novelties 21. Product Samples 22. Special Events Mktg. 23. Spot Radio 24. Spot T.V. 25. Weekly Newsp. 26. Yellow Page Adv.

Brands & Products:
INCEILING
INCORNER
INROOM
INWALL
ONWALL
TRIAD
UNIQUE SOLUTIONS... CUSTOM MADE DAILY
UNIQUESOLUTIONSTRIAD
Advertising Agency:
Muto Communications, LLC
PO Box 537
Port Jefferson, NY 11777
Tel.: (516) 662-5374
Tel.: (631) 849-4301
Fax: (631) 849-4301
Public Relations

TRION, INC.
(Joint Venture of Onex Corporation & Canada Pension Plan Investment Board)
101 McNeill Rd
Sanford, NC 27330-9451
Tel.: (919) 775-2201
Fax: (919) 777-6399
Toll Free: (800) 884-0002
Telex: 823143 Trion UF
E-mail: customerservice@trioninc.com
Web Site: www.trioniaq.com
E-Mail For Key Personnel:
Sales Director: sales@trioninc.com
Sales Range: $10-24.9 Million
Approx. Number Employees: 150
Year Founded: 1947
Business Description:
Electronic Air Cleaners Mfr
S.I.C.: 3564; 3585
N.A.I.C.S.: 333411; 333415
Import Export
Advertising Expenditures: $350,000
Media: 2-4-5-7-10-13-19-20
Distr.: Intl.; Natl.
Budget Set: Oct.
Personnel:
Mike Howell *(VP-Sls-Mktg)*
Colin O'Connell *(VP-Sls & Mktg)*
Brands & Products:
AIR BOSS
MAX 5
MODULAR FILTERPAC
SMOKE ELIMINATOR
TRIDEX
TRION
TRION RX
VENT FOG/IMP
WELDY 2000

TYCO ELECTRONICS - CORCOM
(Branch of TE Connectivity Ltd.)
620 S Butterfield Rd
Mundelein, IL 60060-9457
Tel.: (847) 680-7400
Fax: (847) 680-8169
Toll Free: (800) 468-2023
E-mail: corcomtechhelp@tycoelectronics.com
Web Site: www.corcom.com
Approx. Number Employees: 500
Year Founded: 1955
Business Description:
Radio Frequency Interference Filters Mfr
S.I.C.: 3677; 3678
N.A.I.C.S.: 334416; 334417
Import Export
Media: 2-4-7-10-17
Distr.: Natl.
Brands & Products:
CORCOM

TYCO ELECTRONICS CORPORATION
(Name Changed to TE Connectivity Ltd.)

ULTICOM, INC.
(Holding of Platinum Equity, LLC)
1020 Briggs Rd
Mount Laurel, NJ 08054
Tel.: (856) 787-2700
Tel.: (856) 787-2760 (Sales)
Fax: (856) 866-2033
Toll Free: (888) 395-6664
E-mail: ir@ulticom.com
Web Site: www.ulticom.com
E-Mail For Key Personnel:
Sales Director: sales@ulticom.com
Approx. Rev.: $45,838,000
Approx. Number Employees: 202
Business Description:
Signaling Software Solutions
S.I.C.: 7373; 7371
N.A.I.C.S.: 541512; 541511
Media: 2-5-7-10-13
Personnel:
Bruce D. Swail *(CEO)*
James McArdle *(VP-Sls)*
Brands & Products:
SIGNALWARE
ULTICOM

UNIDEN AMERICA CORPORATION
(Sub. of Uniden Corporation)
4700 Amon Carter Blvd
Fort Worth, TX 76155-2207
Tel.: (817) 858-3300
Fax: (817) 858-3228
Telex: 27-2296 UCA IND
E-mail: webmaster@uniden.com
Web Site: www.uniden.com
Approx. Number Employees: 250
Year Founded: 1979
Business Description:
Mfr. of Consumer & Commercial Electronics Specializing in Radio Communication Equipment
S.I.C.: 5065
N.A.I.C.S.: 423690
Import Export
Media: 2-3-4-5-6-9-10-11-12-19-23
Distr.: Intl.; Natl.
Budget Set: Sept.
Personnel:
Bill Dorr *(Sr VP-Mktg)*
Tomoko Kato *(Administrator-Mktg)*
Brands & Products:
BEARCAT
EXTEND A PHONE
IMPULSE
POWERMAX 5.8 GHZ

UNILUX, INC.
59 N 5th St
Saddle Brook, NJ 07663-6113
Tel.: (201) 712-1266
Fax: (201) 712-1366
Toll Free: (800) 522-0801
E-mail: unilux@unilux.com
Web Site: www.unilux.com
Sales Range: $10-24.9 Million
Approx. Number Employees: 35
Year Founded: 1962
Business Description:
Strobe Lights for Industrial Surface Inspection, Film & Video Production & Special Applications Designer & Mfr
S.I.C.: 3648; 3651
N.A.I.C.S.: 335129; 334310
Import Export
Media: 2-4-7-10
Distr.: Direct to Business
Budget Set: Dec.
Personnel:
Steven A. Hirsh *(Chm)*
Mike Simonis *(Pres)*
Brands & Products:
BEACON
CADET
CENTURION
CENTURION 701
GUARDIAN
HI-LIGHTER
LITHO-LITE
MITI-LITE
Q-EYE
SCOUT
SENTRY
UNILUX

UNITED CHEMI-CON, INC.
(Sub. of Nippon Chemi-Con Corporation)
9801 W Higgins Rd Ste 430
Rosemont, IL 60018
Tel.: (847) 696-2000
Fax: (847) 696-9278
E-mail: info@chemi-con.com
Web Site: www.chemi-con.com
Approx. Number Employees: 40
Year Founded: 1970
Business Description:
Electronic Component Mfr
S.I.C.: 3679
N.A.I.C.S.: 334419
Media: 4
Personnel:
N. Kakizaki *(Pres)*

UNIVERSAL DISPLAY CORPORATION
Princeton Crossroads Corp Ctr 375 Phillips Blvd
Ewing, NJ 08618
Tel.: (609) 671-0980
Fax: (609) 671-0995
E-mail: info@universaldisplay.com
Web Site: www.universaldisplay.com
Approx. Rev.: $30,544,380
Approx. Number Employees: 84
Business Description:
Organic Light Emitting Diode Technology Developer for Flat Panel Display Application
S.I.C.: 3674; 3648; 3679
N.A.I.C.S.: 334413; 334419; 335129
Media: 10
Personnel:
Sherwin I. Seligsohn *(Chm)*
Steven V. Abramson *(Pres & CEO)*
Sidney D. Rosenblatt *(CFO & Exec VP)*
Dean L. Ledger *(Exec VP)*
Mike Hack *(Gen Mgr-OLED Lighting, Custom Displays & Sr VP)*
Janice K. Mahon *(VP-Tech Commercialization & Gen Mgr-PHOLED Material Sls Bus)*
Brands & Products:
ACTIVE-MATRIX
FOLED
OVPD
P2OLED
PASSIVE-MATRIX
PHOLED
TOLED
UNIVERSAL DISPLAY CORPORATION
WOLED

UNIVERSAL ELECTRONICS, INC.
6101 Gateway Dr
Cypress, CA 90630-4841
Tel.: (714) 820-1000
Fax: (714) 820-1010
Web Site: www.uei.com
Approx. Sls.: $331,780,000
Approx. Number Employees: 1,843
Year Founded: 1986
Business Description:
Wireless Remote Control Technologies Developer & Mfr
S.I.C.: 3651; 3625
N.A.I.C.S.: 334310; 335314
Advertising Expenditures: $1,700,000
Media: 10
Personnel:
Paul D. Arling *(Chm & CEO)*
Bryan M. Hackworth *(CFO & Sr VP)*
Richard A. Firehammer Jr. *(Gen Counsel & Sr VP)*
Michael J. Koch *(Treas & VP-Fin)*
Paul J. M. Bennett *(Exec VP & Mng Dir-Europe)*
Mark S. Kopaskie *(Exec VP & Gen Mgr-US Ops)*
Louis S. Hughes *(Sr VP & Gen Mgr-Latin America)*
Ramzi S. Ammari *(Sr VP-Global Product Plng & Strategy)*
David C. H. Chong *(Sr VP-OEM-Bus Unit)*
Joseph E. Miketo *(Sr VP-Ops)*
Pamela L. Price *(Sr VP-Sls)*
Norman G. Sheridan *(Sr VP)*
Graham S. Williams *(Sr VP)*
Douglas J. Durrant *(VP-IT-Global)*
Stephen L. Gutman *(VP-Cable Sls-America)*
Patrick H. Hayes *(VP-Intellectual Property)*
Brands & Products:
ATLAS
ATLAS OCAP
BORA
CATALYST
CLICKER
CONTOUR
CONTROL 2
CONTROL-3
FOCUS
FORZA
GAMER
HELIX
IR BENDER
KAMELEON
MAX
MIDAS
MILLENIUM 4
MUNDIAL
NAVIGATOR
NEVO
NOVA
OMEGA

Key to Media (For complete agency information see *The Advertising Red Books-Agencies* edition):
1. Bus. Publs. 2. Cable T.V. 3. Catalogs & Directories. 4. Co-op Adv. 5. Consumer Mags. 6. D.M. to Bus. Estab.7. D.M. to Consumers 8. Daily Newsp. 9. Exhibits/Trade Shows 10. Foreign 11. Infomercial 12. Internet Adv.13. Multimedia 14. Network Radio 15. Network T.V. 16. Newsp. Distr. Mags. 17. Other 18. Outdoor (Posters, Transit) 19. Point of Purchase20. Premiums, Novelties 21. Product Samples 22. Special Events Mktg. 23. Spot Radio 24. Spot T.V. 25. Weekly Newsp. 26. Yellow Page Adv.

Universal Electronics, Inc. — (Continued)

OMMI
ONE FOR ALL
ORION
POLARIS
POTENZA
S4000
SCOUT
SPECTRUM
STEALTH
TAURUS
TITAN
TITAN MOXI
UNIVERSAL CRICKET
UNIVERSAL ELECTRONICS
VENTURE
XMP-2
ZAPPER
Advertising Agency:
Blanc & Otus Public Relations
60 Green St
San Francisco, CA 94111
Tel.: (415) 856-5100
Fax: (415) 856-5193

UNIVERSAL INSTRUMENTS CORPORATION

(Holding of Francisco Partners Management, LLC)
33 Broome Corporate Pk
Conklin, NY 13748
Mailing Address:
PO Box 825
Binghamton, NY 43902
Tel.: (607) 779-5000
Tel.: (607) 779-7522
Fax: (607) 779-2502
Toll Free: (800) 432-2607
E-mail: universal@uic.com
Web Site: www.uic.com
Approx. Number Employees: 2,000
Year Founded: 1919
Business Description:
Automated Electronic Assembly Equipment Mfr
S.I.C.: 3559
N.A.I.C.S.: 333298
Media: 2-4-7-10-11-13-20-22
Distr.: Intl.; Natl.
Budget Set: Nov.
Personnel:
Gene Heiser *(Corp VP-Sls)*
Sunny Chu *(Mgr-Mktg-Asia)*
Jeff Zopff *(Mgr-Mktg)*
Brands & Products:
ADVANTIS
APPLIED CONVEYOR ENGINEERING
CHIPJET
CIMLINK
DIMENSIONS
FLEXJET
GSM
GSM GENESIS PLATFORM
GSMX
GSMXS
LIGHTNING
MAGELLAN
MEGAVIEW
OMNIPLACE
ONSERTER
POLARIS
PRECISIONPRO
TECH ADVISOR
U-TEACH
UICS
UNISCAN
UNIVERSAL
UNIVERSALIGHT
UPTIME 100
VANTIS
VARI-CELL
VIRTUAL PROCESS ENGINEER

UNIVERSAL POWER GROUP, INC.

1720 Hayden Dr
Carrollton, TX 75006
Tel.: (469) 892-1122
Fax: (469) 892-1123
Toll Free: (866) 892-1122
E-mail: sales@upgi.com
Web Site: www.upgi.com
Approx. Sls.: $107,256,461
Approx. Number Employees: 91
Business Description:
Supply Chain Management Services; Supplier of Portable Power Supply Products
S.I.C.: 5065
N.A.I.C.S.: 423690
Advertising Expenditures: $480,000
Personnel:
William Kim Wah Tan *(Chm)*
Ian Colin Edmonds *(Pres, Interim CFO & CEO)*
Julie Sansom-Reese *(Sr VP-Fin)*
Mimi Tan *(Sr VP-Bus Dev & Mktg)*
Brands & Products:
ADVENTURE POWER
ALL-IN-ONE
CHARGE N' START
LET US POWER YOU
STARTER-UP
UNILOK
UNIVERSAL

UNIVERSAL RELAY

(Sub. of Park Distributors, Inc.)
347 Railroad Ave
Bridgeport, CT 06604-5424
Tel.: (203) 579-2140
Fax: (203) 579-2240
Toll Free: (800) 221-7616
E-mail: paul@park.com
Web Site: www.park.com
Approx. Sls.: $1,000,000
Approx. Number Employees: 18
Year Founded: 1947
Business Description:
Whslr of Electronic Relays
S.I.C.: 5065
N.A.I.C.S.: 423690
Export
Media: 4-8-17
Distr.: Intl.; Natl.
Budget Set: Jan.
Personnel:
Alan Goodman *(Owner)*

UNIVERSAL SECURITY INSTRUMENTS, INC.

11407 Cronhill Dr Ste A
Owings Mills, MD 21117
Tel.: (410) 363-3000
Fax: (410) 363-2218
E-mail: sales@universalsecurity.com
Web Site: www.universalsecurity.com
E-Mail For Key Personnel:
President: harvey@universalsecurity.com
Sales Director: sales@universalsecurity.com
Approx. Sls.: $13,249,604
Approx. Number Employees: 18
Year Founded: 1969
Business Description:
Residential Fire & Smoke Alarms Mfr & Distr
S.I.C.: 5065; 3679
N.A.I.C.S.: 423690; 334419
Import Export
Media: 4-5-6-10-11-19-21
Distr.: Intl.; Natl.
Budget Set: Monthly
Personnel:
Harvey B. Grossblatt *(Pres & CEO)*
James B. Huff *(CFO)*
Karen Yaggie *(Dir-Mktg)*
Brands & Products:
QUICK BLOCK
QUICK-DRAW
TALKABOUT
UNIVERSAL

UNIVISION COMMUNICATIONS INC.

(Holding of Broadcasting Media Partners, Inc.)
605 3rd Ave 12th Fl
New York, NY 10158
Tel.: (212) 455-5200
Web Site: www.univision.com
Approx. Rev.: $2,020,300,000
Approx. Number Employees: 3,922
Business Description:
Spanish-Language Media Holding Company
S.I.C.: 6719; 2741; 4832; 4833; 4841
N.A.I.C.S.: 551112; 515112; 515120; 515210; 516110
Personnel:
Haim Saban *(Chm)*
Randy Falco *(Pres & CEO)*
Andrew W. Hobson *(CFO, Chief Strategic Officer & Sr Exec VP)*
Roberto Llamas *(Chief HR Officer & Exec VP)*
Alexander P. Brown *(Pres-Sports)*
Cesar Conde *(Pres-Univision Networks)*
Kevin C. Conroy *(Pres-Interactive Media)*
Luis Fernandez *(Pres-Univision Studios)*
David Lawenda *(Pres-Adv Sls & Mktg)*
Peter Walker *(Pres-Univision Local Media)*
Mark Dante *(Exec VP-Station Grp Sls)*
Charlie Echeverry *(Exec VP-Interactive Media Sls)*
C. Douglas Kranwinkle *(Exec VP-Univision Television Grp)*
Peter J. Lazarus *(Exec VP-Sls & Mktg)*
Peter Lori *(Exec VP-Fin)*
Lisa McCarthy *(Exec VP)*
Tonia O'Connor *(Exec VP)*
Rick Alessandri *(Sr VP-Univision Enterprises)*
Cynthia Ashworth *(Sr VP)*
Jeff Browning *(Sr VP-Sls-Univision News)*
Carlos Deschapelles *(Sr VP-Sls-TeleFutura Network)*
Graciela Eleta *(Sr VP-Brand Solutions)*
Ivelisse Estrada *(Sr VP-Corp & Community Rels)*
Ruth Gaviria *(Sr VP-Corp Mktg)*
Emeli Gomez *(Sr VP-Mktg)*
Bob Gruters *(Sr VP-Client Dev Grp)*
David Neal *(Sr VP-Production-Sports-Miami)*
Trisha Pray *(Sr VP-Network Sls)*
Roberto Ruiz *(Sr VP-Brand Solutions-Client Dev Grp)*
Peter Scanlon *(Sr VP-Sls Plng & Analysis)*
Christian Martinez *(Reg VP)*
Mary McEvilly *(VP & Gen Mgr)*
Sara Hasson *(VP-Client Dev Group-Automotive)*
Brands & Products:
UNIVISION
Advertising Agencies:
MVC
9205 Alabama Ave Ste E
Chatsworth, CA 91311
Tel.: (818) 718-2005
Fax: (818) 718-2582

Y&R Puerto Rico, Inc.
PO Box 366288
San Juan, PR 00936-6288
Tel.: (787) 622-6500
Fax: (787) 793-3013

UNIVISION RADIO

(Div. of Univision Communications Inc.)
3102 Oak Lawn Ave Ste 215
Dallas, TX 75219-4259
Tel.: (214) 525-7700
Fax: (214) 525-7750
Web Site: www.univision.net/corp/en/urg.jsp
Sales Range: $350-399.9 Million
Approx. Number Employees: 55
Year Founded: 1974
Business Description:
Spanish Language Radio Broadcasting Services
S.I.C.: 4832
N.A.I.C.S.: 515112
Import Export
Personnel:
Jose Valle *(Pres)*
Timothy Ward *(CFO & Sr VP)*
Mitch Kline *(Exec VP)*
Brands & Products:
KLUE
KRCD
KSOL
KTNQ
WQBA
Advertising Agency:
El Creative, Inc.
3816 San Jacinto
Dallas, TX 75204
Tel.: (214) 742-0700

UQM TECHNOLOGIES, INC.

4120 Speciality Pl
Longmont, CO 80504
Mailing Address:
PO Box 439
Frederick, CO 80530
Tel.: (303) 278-2002
Fax: (303) 278-7007
E-mail: sales@uqm.com
Web Site: www.uqm.com
Approx. Rev.: $9,021,302
Approx. Number Employees: 79
Year Founded: 1967
Business Description:
Permanent Magnet Electric Motors & Controls for Electric & Hybrid Vehicles

Key to Media (For complete agency information see *The Advertising Red Books-Agencies* edition):
1. Bus. Publs. 2. Cable T.V. 3. Catalogs & Directories. 4. Co-op Adv. 5. Consumer Mags. 6. D.M. to Bus. Estab.7. D.M. to Consumers 8. Daily Newsp. 9. Exhibits/Trade Shows 10. Foreign 11. Infomercial 12. Internet Adv.13. Multimedia 14. Network Radio 15. Network T.V. 16. Newsp. Distr. Mags. 17. Other 18. Outdoor (Posters, Transit) 19. Point of Purchase20. Premiums, Novelties 21. Product Samples 22. Special Events Mktg. 23. Spot Radio 24. Spot T.V. 25. Weekly Newsp. 26. Yellow Page Adv.

S.I.C.: 3679; 3612; 3621; 3714
N.A.I.C.S.: 334419; 335311; 335312; 336322
Media: 2-10-13
Personnel:
William G. Rankin *(Chm)*
Eric R. Ridenour *(Pres & CEO)*
Donald A. French *(CFO, Treas & Sec)*
Ronald M. Burton *(Sr VP-Ops)*
Jon F. Lutz *(VP-Engrg)*
Douglas K. Smeltzer *(Mgr-Sls)*
Brands & Products:
POWERPHASE
UQM

US CELLULAR CO.
(Sub. of United States Cellular Corporation)
881 S Perryville Rd
Rockford, IL 61108-4339
Tel.: (815) 399-1111
Fax: (815) 399-1231
E-mail: info@uscellular.com
Web Site: www.uscellular.com
Sales Range: $25-49.9 Million
Approx. Number Employees: 100
Business Description:
Telephone Communications
S.I.C.: 4899
N.A.I.C.S.: 517910
Personnel:
Dan Schedler *(Sr Dir-Brand Mgmt)*
Advertising Agencies:
Lapiz
35 W Wacker Dr 12th Fl
Chicago, IL 60601
Tel.: (312) 220-5000
Fax: (312) 220-6212
Hispanic Agency of Record

TargetCom, LLC
444 N Michigan Ave 33rd Fl
Chicago, IL 60611-3905
Tel.: (312) 822-1100
Fax: (312) 822-9628
Toll Free: (877) 423-7837

VALENCE TECHNOLOGY, INC.
12303 Technology Blvd Ste 950
Austin, TX 78727-6128
Tel.: (512) 527-2900
Fax: (512) 527-2910
Toll Free: (888) VALENCE
E-mail: webmaster@valence.com
Web Site: www.valence.com
Approx. Rev.: $45,882,000
Approx. Number Employees: 433
Year Founded: 1989
Business Description:
High Performance, Cost Effective Battery Mfr
S.I.C.: 3692
N.A.I.C.S.: 335912
Advertising Expenditures: $21,000
Media: 17
Personnel:
Carl E. Berg *(Chm)*
Robert L. Kanode *(Pres & CEO)*
Donald E. Gottschalk *(Acting CFO & Controller)*
Roger A. Williams *(Gen Counsel)*
Randall J. Adleman *(VP-Sls & Mktg)*
Brands & Products:
SAPHION
U-CHARGE
VALENCE

Advertising Agency:
Lois Paul & Partners
150 Presidential Way
Woburn, MA 01801
Tel.: (781) 782-5000
Fax: (781) 782-5999

VALPEY-FISHER CORPORATION
75 South St
Hopkinton, MA 01748-2204
Tel.: (508) 435-6831
Fax: (508) 497-6377
Toll Free: (800) 982-5737
E-mail: sales@valpeyfisher.com
Web Site: www.valpeyfisher.com
Approx. Sls.: $14,716,169
Approx. Number Employees: 60
Year Founded: 1931
Business Description:
Crystal Oscillators & Transducers Mfr
S.I.C.: 3699; 3823; 3829
N.A.I.C.S.: 335999; 334513; 334519
Advertising Expenditures: $137,700
Media: 8
Personnel:
Ted Valpey, Jr. *(Chm)*
Michael J. Ferrantino, Jr. *(CEO)*
Michael J. Kroll *(CFO, Treas & VP)*
Walter Oliwa *(Sr VP-R&D)*
Dan Nehring *(VP-Engrg)*
John Fortune *(Dir-Sls & Mktg)*

VANSAN CORPORATION
16735 E Johnson Dr
City of Industry, CA 91745
Tel.: (626) 961-7211
Fax: (626) 369-9510
Toll Free: (800) 423-1829
E-mail: info@vansan.com
Web Site: www.vansan.com
Sales Range: $10-24.9 Million
Approx. Number Employees: 25
Year Founded: 1963
Business Description:
Lecterns, Audiovisual Equipment, Food & Beverage Carts & Retail Merchandising Carts Mfr & Distr
S.I.C.: 2531
N.A.I.C.S.: 337127
Export
Advertising Expenditures: $30,000
Media: 2-4-6-7-8-10-13-16-19-20-26
Distr.: Intl.; Natl.
Budget Set: July
Personnel:
Mark Vanlandingham *(Pres)*
Brands & Products:
VANSAN

VELODYNE ACOUSTICS, INC.
345 Digital Dr
Morgan Hill, CA 95037
Tel.: (408) 465-2800
Fax: (408) 779-9227
Toll Free: (800) VELODYNE
Web Site: www.velodyne.com
Approx. Number Employees: 70
Year Founded: 1983
Business Description:
Mfr. of Home Audio & Video Equipment
S.I.C.: 3651; 5731
N.A.I.C.S.: 334310; 443112
Media: 6-10
Personnel:
David Hall *(Founder & CEO & Chief Engr)*
Bruce Hall *(Pres)*

Houshang Vala *(Controller)*
David De Villevez *(Dir-Mfg)*
Doug Smith *(Dir-Sls-N America)*
Brands & Products:
DIGITAL DRIVE
MICROVEE
MINIVEE
SMS-1
SPL
VELODYNE
VX-10

VERMONT CIRCUITS INC.
76 Technology Dr
Brattleboro, VT 05301
Mailing Address:
PO Box 1890
Brattleboro, VT 05302-1890
Tel.: (802) 257-4571
Fax: (802) 257-0011
E-mail: pcbsales@vtcircuits.com
Web Site: www.vtcircuits.com
Approx. Number Employees: 90
Year Founded: 1989
Business Description:
Mfr. of Printed Circuit Boards
S.I.C.: 3672
N.A.I.C.S.: 334412
Advertising Expenditures: $500,000
Media: 7-10
Distr.: Reg.
Personnel:
James Lin *(Pres)*
Cheryl Bedard *(VP-Mktg & Sls)*

VERTEX STANDARD USA INC.
(Sub. of Vertex Standard Co., Ltd.)
10900 Walker St
Cypress, CA 90630
Tel.: (714) 827-7600
Fax: (714) 527-1494
Web Site: www.vxstd.com
Sales Range: $25-49.9 Million
Approx. Number Employees: 75
Year Founded: 1969
Business Description:
Two-Way Communications Equipment Handheld & Mobile Radios Mfr
S.I.C.: 5065
N.A.I.C.S.: 423690
Import Export
Media: 1-2-4-5-6-10-11-20-26
Distr.: Intl.; Natl
Budget Set: Oct.
Personnel:
Hermie Fama *(VP-Fin)*
Leann Griebner *(Sr Mgr-Mktg-Global)*
Brands & Products:
HORIZON

VICON INDUSTRIES, INC.
89 Arkay Dr
Hauppauge, NY 11788
Tel.: (631) 952-2288
Fax: (631) 951-2288
Toll Free: (800) 645-9116
E-mail: sales@vicon-cctv.com
Web Site: www.vicon-cctv.com
Approx. Sls.: $48,681,122
Approx. Number Employees: 180
Year Founded: 1967
Business Description:
Designer & Mfr Video Systems & System Components
S.I.C.: 3669; 3663; 3812
N.A.I.C.S.: 334290; 334220; 334511
Import Export
Media: 2-4-5-7-10-26

Distr.: Direct to Consumer; Intl.; Natl.
Budget Set: Aug.
Personnel:
Kenneth M. Darby *(CEO)*
John M. Badke *(CFO & Sr VP-Fin)*
Bret M. McGowan *(VP-Sls & Mktg)*
Mark S. Provinsal *(VP-Mktg & Product Mgmt)*
Tom Cook *(Dir-East Sls)*
Marjorie Gurwin *(Dir-Mktg)*
Mark Leedy *(Dir-West Sls)*
Maria Bustamante *(Sls Mgr-Latin America & Caribbean-Territory)*
Edmond Quinones *(Sls Mgr-Asia Pacific Vicon Industries-Territory)*
J. C. Caine *(Mgr-Intl Sls)*
Kristen Dorr *(Mgr-HR)*
Brands & Products:
ARCHITECH
AURORA
AURORACORD
BASIC 2
COMPACLINE
DIGITEK
GENESYS
KOLLECTOR
KOLLECTOR ELITE
KOLLECTOR PRO
MATRIX 44
MATRIX 88
MEMSCAN
MODUPULSE
NETSWITCH
NOVA
OPTECH
P&T PAD
PHASE EIGHT
PROTECH
QUANTUM TSI
ROUGHNECK
SURVEYOR
VECTORCAM
THE VERIFIER
VICOAX
VICON
VICONNET
VIDEOLINK
VISTAR
VN-VIEWER
VPS

VIDEO DISPLAY CORPORATION
1868 Tucker Industrial Rd
Tucker, GA 30084
Tel.: (770) 938-2080
Fax: (770) 493-3563
Toll Free: (800) 241-5005
E-mail: vdc@videodisplay.com
Web Site: www.videodisplay.com
Approx. Sls.: $59,039,000
Approx. Number Employees: 310
Year Founded: 1975
Business Description:
Monochrome & Color Tubes & Flyback Transformers for Computer Data Display Terminals & Television Tubes Mfr & Importer; Computer Service & Large TV Sales to Service Companies; Consumer Electronic Replacement Parts & Accessories Distr
S.I.C.: 3671; 3679
N.A.I.C.S.: 334411; 334419
Import Export
Media: 2-4-7-11
Distr.: Intl.; Natl.

Video Display Corporation — (Continued)

Budget Set: Feb.
Personnel:
Ronald D. Ordway *(Chm, CEO & Treas)*
Gregory L. Osborn *(CFO)*
David A. Heiden *(Exec VP)*
Norma Mann *(Dir-IR)*
Brands & Products:
VIDEO DISPLAY

VIRGIN MOBILE CANADA

(Sub. of BCE INC.)
720 King St W
Suite 905
M5V2T3
Toronto, ON Canada
Tel.: (888) 999-2321
Fax: (888) 999-9470
Web Site: www.virginmobile.ca
Business Description:
Mobile Telecommunications
S.I.C.: 4812
N.A.I.C.S.: 517212
Personnel:
Robert Blumenthal *(Pres)*
Advertising Agency:
Teehan+Lax
460 Richmond St W Ste 301
Toronto, ON M5V 1Y1, Canada
Tel.: (416) 340-8666
Fax: (416) 340-0777

VIRGIN MOBILE USA, INC.

(Sub. of Sprint Nextel Corp.)
10 Independence Blvd
Warren, NJ 07059
Tel.: (908) 607-4000
E-mail: main@virginmobileusa.com
Web Site: www.virginmobileusa.com
Approx. Rev.: $1,323,493,000
Approx. Number Employees: 420
Year Founded: 2002
Business Description:
Mobile Telecommunications Services
S.I.C.: 4812
N.A.I.C.S.: 517212
Advertising Expenditures: $50,800,000
Media: 3-5-6-8-9-14-15-18-24-25
Personnel:
Ron Amram *(Dir-Media & Advocacy)*
Geraldine Morrison *(Dir-Mktg, Adv & Promos)*
Advertising Agencies:
Alliance Agency
200 5th Ave 4th Fl
New York, NY 10010
Tel.: (212) 546-1800
Fax: (212) 546-5549

CooperKatz & Company
205 Lexington Ave 5th Fl
New York, NY 10016
Tel.: (917) 595-3030
Fax: (917) 326-8997

Hanft Raboy & Partners
205 Hudson St 7th Fl
New York, NY 10013
Tel.: (212) 674-3100
Fax: (212) 228-7679

Mother New York
595 11th Ave
New York, NY 10036
Tel.: (212) 254-2800
Fax: (212) 254-6121
(Agency of Record)

SHIFT Communications LLC
20 Guest St Ste 200
Brighton, MA 02135
Tel.: (617) 779-1800
Fax: (617) 779-1899

VISHAY VITRAMON, INC.

(Sub. of Vishay Intertechnology, Inc.)
10 Main St
Monroe, CT 06468
Mailing Address:
PO Box 544
Bridgeport, CT 06601-0544
Tel.: (203) 268-6261
Fax: (203) 452-5670
Fax: (203) 261-4446
Sales Range: $50-74.9 Million
Approx. Number Employees: 195
Year Founded: 1948
Business Description:
Mfr. of Electronic Capacitors
S.I.C.: 3675
N.A.I.C.S.: 334414
Import Export
Media: 2-10-17
Distr.: Natl.
Personnel:
Gerald Paul *(Pres)*
Pat Gormally *(Dir-Prod Mktg)*
Brands & Products:
VITRAMON

VISTA POINT TECHNOLOGIES, INC.

(Sub. of Flextronics International Ltd.)
1613 Santa Clara Dr Ste 100
Roseville, CA 95661-3542
Tel.: (408) 576-7000
Web Site: www.vptech.com
Sales Range: $75-99.9 Million
Approx. Number Employees: 3,200
Business Description:
Computer Monitor, Camera Module, Power Supply & Electronic Component Developer & Mfr
S.I.C.: 3679
N.A.I.C.S.: 334419
Advertising Expenditures: $70,000
Media: 10

VITESSE SEMICONDUCTOR CORPORATION

741 Calle Plano
Camarillo, CA 93012-8543
Tel.: (805) 388-3700
Fax: (805) 987-5896
Toll Free: (800) VITESSE
E-mail: pressrelations@vitesse.com
Web Site: www.vitesse.com
Approx. Rev.: $165,990,000
Approx. Number Employees: 467
Year Founded: 1984
Business Description:
Integrated Circuits Mfr
S.I.C.: 3674
N.A.I.C.S.: 334413
Advertising Expenditures: $100,000
Media: 17
Personnel:
Edward Rogas, Jr. *(Chm)*
Christopher R. Gardner *(CEO)*
Martin S. McDermut *(CFO)*
Paul Browne *(VP-Engrg)*
Roy Carew *(VP-Quality, Product & Test Engrg)*
Martin Nuss *(VP-Tech & Strategy)*
Steve M. Perna *(VP-Product Mktg)*
Brian Jaroszewski *(Sr Product Mgr)*
Brands & Products:
ACTIPHY
ASIC-FRIENDLY
BARRINGTON
CAMPBELL
CAMPBELL-I
ECOETHERNET
ELSTREE
EQ TECHNOLOGY
FAIROAKS
FIBRETIMER
FOCUS16
FOCUSCONNECT
G-ROCX
GATWICK
GIGASTREAM
HAWX
HEATHROW
HOVCAT
HOVCAT192
HOVCAT192E
HOVCAT48
HOVCAT48E
HOVCATE
IQ2200
LANSING
LOVCAT
MAKING NEXT-GENERATION NETWORKS A REALITY.
MEIGS
MEIGS-II
MEIGS-IIE
NEXSAS
OCTALMAC
PACEMAKER
PERFECTREACH
SCHAUMBURG
SFP PRO
SIMLIPHY
SMART-LINK
SNOOP LOOP
SPARX
STANSTED
STAPLEFORD
STAX
SUPER FEC
TIMESTREAM
VERIPHY
VERSACAT
VITESSE
VSCOPE
VSTAX
XFP PRO

VIZIO, INC.

39 Tesla
Irvine, CA 92618
Tel.: (949) 428-2525
Toll Free: (888) 849-4623
E-mail: sales@vizio.com
Web Site: www.vizio.com
E-Mail For Key Personnel:
Sales Director: sales@vizio.com
Approx. Sls.: $2,000,000,000
Year Founded: 2002
Business Description:
Flat-Panel Television Mfr
S.I.C.: 5064
N.A.I.C.S.: 423620
Personnel:
William Wang *(Owner & CEO)*
Kyle Wescoat *(CFO & VP)*
John Morriss *(VP & Gen Mgr)*
Laynie Newsome *(VP-Sls)*
Jason Maciel *(Dir-Mktg & Adv)*
Advertising Agencies:
L7 Creative Communications
5927 Balfour Ct Ste 104
Carlsbad, CA 92008
Tel.: (760) 931-0777
Toll Free: (877) 572-7888

ONE/x
6300 Wilshire Blvd Ste 1505
Los Angeles, CA 90048
Tel.: (310) 289-4422
Fax: (310) 289-4423
HDTV

Venables, Bell & Partners
201 Post St Ste 200
San Francisco, CA 94108
Tel.: (415) 288-3300
Fax: (415) 421-3683

VOICE MOBILITY INTERNATIONAL, INC.

645 Fort Street Suite 107
Victoria, BC V8W 1G2, Canada
Tel.: (250) 978-5050
Fax: (250) 978-5052
Toll Free: (866) 799-5577
E-mail: infoline@voicemobility.com
Web Site: www.voicemobility.com
Approx. Sls.: $97,107
Business Description:
Messaging Communications Applications
S.I.C.: 7373; 3669; 7372
N.A.I.C.S.: 541512; 334290; 511210
Advertising Expenditures: $715,564
Personnel:
James J. Hutton *(CEO)*
Mike Seeley *(VP-Global Sls)*

VONAGE HOLDINGS CORPORATION

23 Main St
Holmdel, NJ 07733
Tel.: (732) 528-2600
Fax: (732) 834-0189
E-mail: info@vonage.com
Web Site: www.vonage.com
Approx. Rev.: $885,042,000
Approx. Number Employees: 1,140
Year Founded: 2000
Business Description:
Local & Long Distance Telephone Connection Services; Broadband Internet Access Services
S.I.C.: 4813
N.A.I.C.S.: 517110; 517310
Advertising Expenditures: $142,753,000
Media: 13-15-24
Personnel:
Jeffrey Adam Citron *(Chm)*
Marc P. Lefar *(CEO)*
Barry L. Rowan *(CFO, Chief Admin Officer & Exec VP)*
Scott Ballantyne *(CMO)*
Brands & Products:
BANDWIDTH SAVER
NETWORK AVAILABILITY NUMBER
REFER-A-FRIEND
SIMUL-RING
TOLL FREE PLUS
V-PORTAL
VOICEMAIL PLUS
VONAGE
VONAGE SOFTPHONE
VONAGE V-PHONE
VONAGE VISUAL VOICEMAIL

Advertising Agencies:
Merkle Inc.
7001 Columbia Gateway Dr
Columbia, MD 21046
Tel.: (443) 542-4000
Fax: (443) 542-4001
Direct Campaigns

PHD
(An Omnicom Company)
220 E 42nd 7th Fl
New York, NY 10017
Tel.: (212) 894-6600
Fax: (212) 894-4100

TBWA Chiat Day New York
488 Madison Ave
New York, NY 10022
Tel.: (212) 804-1000
Fax: (212) 804-1200

VRINGO, INC.
18 E 16th St 7th Fl
New York, NY 10003
Tel.: (646) 448-8210
Web Site: www.vringo.com
Approx. Rev.: $211,000
Approx. Number Employees: 26
Year Founded: 2006
Business Description:
Video Ringtones Applications for Mobile Phones
S.I.C.: 4899; 7829
N.A.I.C.S.: 517910; 512199
Media: 8-10-13-17
Personnel:
Seth M. Siegel *(Co-Founder)*
Andrew Perlman *(Pres & Dir)*
Jonathan Medved *(CEO)*
Stuart Frohlich *(COO)*
Ellen Cohl *(VP-Fin & Governance)*

VULCAN, INC.
400 E Berry Ave
Foley, AL 36535-2833
Mailing Address:
PO Box 1850
Foley, AL 36536-1850
Tel.: (251) 943-7000
Tel.: (251) 943-2645
Fax: (251) 943-9270
Toll Free: (888) 846-2728
E-mail: vulcan1@vulcaninc.com
Web Site: www.vulcaninc.com
E-Mail For Key Personnel:
President: RLee@vulcaninc.com
Approx. Number Employees: 200
Year Founded: 1935
Business Description:
Traffic Control Signs Mfr
S.I.C.: 3469; 3993
N.A.I.C.S.: 332116; 339950
Advertising Expenditures: $200,000
Media: 2-4-10-19
Distr.: Natl.
Personnel:
Cater Lee *(Founder & Chm)*
Robert W. Lee *(CEO)*
Brands & Products:
LIGHTS MANAGER
MARKINGS MANAGER
REPORT MANAGER
ROADSIDE MANAGER
SERVICE MANAGER
SHOP MANAGER
SIGN MANAGER
SIGNAL MANAGER
SYSTEM MANAGER
VIMMS
VULCAN

VUZIX CORPORATION
75 Town Centre Dr
Rochester, NY 14623
Tel.: (585) 359-5900
Fax: (585) 359-4172
E-mail: sales@vuzix.com
Web Site: www.vuzix.com
Approx. Sls.: $12,255,414
Approx. Number Employees: 65
Business Description:
Video Eyewear Devices Designer, Mfr, Marketer & Sales
S.I.C.: 3651; 3679; 3827
N.A.I.C.S.: 334310; 333314; 334419
Advertising Expenditures: $771,132
Media: 2-4-5-6-7-8-10-13-17-19-22
Personnel:
Paul J. Travers *(Pres & CEO)*
Grant Russell *(CFO, Treas & Exec VP-Bus Dev)*
Stephen J. Glaser *(VP-Sls & Mktg-Defense)*
Gary VanCamp *(VP-Low-Vision Assist Products)*
Mike Hallett *(Dir-Sls-Consumer)*
Peter Artz *(Dir-Mfg)*
Vincent J. Ferrer *(Dir-Engrg)*
Advertising Agency:
Max Borges Agency
3050 Biscayne Blvd Ste 701
Miami, FL 33137
Tel.: (305) 576-1171
Fax: (305) 402-6373
— Greg Mondshein *(Acct Exec)*

WABASH TECHNOLOGIES, INC.
(Holding of Sun Capital Partners, Inc.)
1375 Swan St
Huntington, IN 46750
Tel.: (260) 355-4100
Fax: (260) 355-4265
E-mail: sales@wabashtech.com
Web Site: www.wabashtech.com
E-Mail For Key Personnel:
Sales Director: sales@wabashtech.com
Sales Range: $100-124.9 Million
Approx. Number Employees: 85
Year Founded: 1946
Business Description:
Sensor Technology Products Mfr
S.I.C.: 3677; 3625
N.A.I.C.S.: 334416; 335314
Import Export
Media: 2-4-10
Distr.: Natl.
Budget Set: Sept.
Personnel:
Stephen Dow *(Pres & CEO)*
Brands & Products:
WABASH

WARD LEONARD ELECTRIC COMPANY, INC.
401 Watertown Rd
Thomaston, CT 06787
Tel.: (860) 283-5801
Fax: (860) 283-5777
Web Site: www.wardleonard.com
Sales Range: $1-9.9 Million
Approx. Number Employees: 50
Year Founded: 1812
Business Description:
Electrical & Electronic Control Products
S.I.C.: 3625
N.A.I.C.S.: 335314
Media: 2-7-9-19-25-26
Distr.: Intl.; Natl.
Personnel:
Jon Carter *(CEO)*
Brands & Products:
POWER SOLUTIONS WHEN THE STAKES ARE HIGH
WARD LEONARD

WAUKESHA ELECTRIC SYSTEMS
(Unit of SPX Corporation)
400 S Prairie Ave
Waukesha, WI 53186-5969
Tel.: (262) 547-0121
Fax: (262) 521-0145
Toll Free: (800) 835-2732
Web Site: www.waukeshaelectric.com
Sales Range: $125-149.9 Million
Approx. Number Employees: 400
Business Description:
Power Transformers
S.I.C.: 3612; 7629
N.A.I.C.S.: 335311; 811219
Media: 10
Personnel:
Tom Brockley *(Pres)*

WEGENER CORPORATION
Tech Park/Johns Creek 11350
Technology Cir
Duluth, GA 30097
Tel.: (770) 814-4000
Fax: (770) 623-0698
E-mail: info@wegener.com
Web Site: www.wegener.com
Approx. Rev.: $8,921,419
Approx. Number Employees: 49
Year Founded: 1977
Business Description:
Holding Company; Satellite Communications Electronics Mfr
S.I.C.: 3663; 3679; 4832; 4899
N.A.I.C.S.: 334220; 334419; 515111; 517410
Import Export
Advertising Expenditures: $128,000
Media: 17
Personnel:
Robert A. Placek *(Chm)*
C. Troy Woodbury, Jr. *(Pres & CEO)*
James T. Traicoff *(CFO)*
Elaine Miller *(VP-HR)*
Brands & Products:
COMPEL
IPUMP
MEDIAPLAN
NAVE
SPOTTRAC
UNITY
WEGENER

WESCO INTERNATIONAL INC.
225 W Station Sq Dr Ste 700
Pittsburgh, PA 15219-1136
Tel.: (412) 454-2200
Fax: (412) 454-2505
E-mail: international@wescodist.com
Web Site: www.wescodist.com
Approx. Sls.: $5,063,862,000
Approx. Number Employees: 6,800
Business Description:
Distr of Electrical & Industrial Supplies
S.I.C.: 5045; 5063; 5084
N.A.I.C.S.: 425110; 423610; 423830
Personnel:
Roy W. Haley *(Chm)*
John J. Engel *(Pres & CEO)*
Richard P. Heyse *(CFO & VP)*
Stephen A. Van Oss *(COO & Sr VP)*
Daniel A. Brailer *(Treas & VP-IR & Legal)*
Diane E. Lazzaris *(VP-Legal Affairs)*
Kimberly G. Windrow *(VP-HR)*
Allan A. Duganier *(Dir-Internal Audit)*
Brands & Products:
WESCO BUYERS GUIDE
WESCO DISTRIBUTION
Advertising Agency:
Impressions-A.B.A. Industries, Inc.
393 Jericho Tpk
Mineola, NY 11501
Tel.: (516) 739-3210
Fax: (516) 739-9246

WESTINGHOUSE LIGHTING CORPORATION
12401 McNulty Rd
Philadelphia, PA 19154-1004
Tel.: (215) 671-2000
Fax: (215) 464-4115
Toll Free: (800) 999-2226
Web Site: www.westinghouselighting.com
Approx. Sls.: $91,800,000
Approx. Number Employees: 450
Year Founded: 1946
Business Description:
Decorative Electrical & Lighting Products, Door Chimes & Wall Plates Mfr, Distributor & Marketer
S.I.C.: 3645; 5063
N.A.I.C.S.: 335121; 423610
Import Export
Media: 2-4-10-17-19
Distr.: Natl.
Personnel:
Raymond Angelo *(Pres-Westinghouse Lighting & Owner)*
Stanley Angelo *(Chm)*
Kathleen Katz *(Sr Dir-Mktg)*
Brands & Products:
ABINGTON
ALLOY
ANGELIQUE
ANGELO
ANGELO FAN BRACE
ANGELO SUITE
APOLLO
APOLLO ELITE
ART DECO
ART METRO
AUSTORIA
AVIATOR
BALLERINA
BAROQUE
BASEBALL
BETHANY
BLAKELY
CAPISTRANO
CARERRA
CASA MONTEREY
CASANOVA
CHANCELLOR
CHATEAU
CHELSEA HARBOR
COMET
CONCERTO
CONTEMPRA
CONTEMPRA TRIO

Key to Media (For complete agency information see *The Advertising Red Books-Agencies* edition):
1. Bus. Publs. 2. Cable T.V. 3. Catalogs & Directories. 4. Co-op Adv. 5. Consumer Mags. 6. D.M. to Bus. Estab.7. D.M. to Consumers 8. Daily Newsp. 9. Exhibits/Trade Shows 10. Foreign 11. Infomercial 12. Internet Adv.13. Multimedia 14. Network Radio 15. Network T.V. 16. Newsp. Distr. Mags. 17. Other 18. Outdoor (Posters, Transit) 19. Point of Purchase20. Premiums, Novelties 21. Product Samples 22. Special Events Mktg. 23. Spot Radio 24. Spot T.V. 25. Weekly Newsp. 26. Yellow Page Adv.

Westinghouse Lighting Corporation — (Continued)

CONTRACTOR'S CHOICE
COPENHAGEN
CORINTHIAN SUPREME
CORSICA
CRUSADER
DECORLITE
EASTGATE
ECOMAX
EDWARDIAN
ELITE
ELLIPSE
ENCHANTE
ENERGY STAR
EURO-STYLE
EURO SWIRL
EYE SAVER
FAN MASTER
FLORA ROYALE
FORLI
FRENCH QUARTER
GEORGIAN
GRECO
HALOGEN HALOMAX
HALOMAX
HELIX
HELIX FUSION
HERCULES
HIGHLAND
HYANNIS PORT
IMPERIAL
INSTALOC
JEWEL
JULIUS ES
JUPITER
LAFAYETTE
LAUREL WOODS
LILY FIELDS
MAPLE GROVE
MICHELANGELO COLLECTION
MIDDLETOWN
MILANO
MIMOSA
NAPA VALLEY
NEWTOWN
NOVA
NURTURELITE
OAK HARBOR
ODYSSEY
OPULENCE
OPUS
PACIFIC PARADISE
PARS
PETITE
PORTICO
PRINCESS
PRINCESS AMBIANCE
PRINCESS RADIANCE
PROPELLER
PROTEGE
PROVINCIAL
RAPHAEL
REALITE
REVIVAL
SAF-T-BAR
SAF-T-BOX
SAF-T-BRACE
SAF-T-GRID
SAF-T-PAN
SAINT CHARLES
SAINT TROPEZ
SAN JUAN
SAN MORITZ
SAN SEBASTIAN
SANTE FE
SAVONA
SAVONA ES
SEDONA
SIENNA
SILVERDALE ES
SOCCER
ST. CHARLES
ST. TROPEZ
SWIRL
TACOMA
TARREGA
TAYLOR HILL
TORINO
TRADITIONAL
TRANSITIONS
TREVOR
TURBO SWIRL
VECTOR
VECTOR ELITE
VERANDAH BREEZE
VERONA
VIENNA ES
VINTAGE
WAVE FORM
WAVE FORM DELUXE
WESTINGHOUSE LIGHT BULBS
WICKER
WILLOW BREEZE
WINCHESTER
WYNDHAM
YORKSHIRE

WESTINGHOUSE SOLAR

(Formerly AKEENA SOLAR, INC.)
1475 S Bascom Ave Ste 101
Campbell, CA 95008
Tel.: (408) 402-9400
Toll Free: (888) 253-3628
Web Site:
www.westinghousesolar.com/
Approx. Sls.: $8,653,390
Approx. Number Employees: 34
Year Founded: 2001
Business Description:
Solar Power Systems Designer & Installer
S.I.C.: 1623; 1731
N.A.I.C.S.: 237130; 238210
Advertising Expenditures: $1,000,000
Media: 13-17
Personnel:
Barry Cinnamon *(Owner)*
Jeff Kiel *(Exec VP-Sls & Mktg)*
Gary Mull *(VP-Mktg)*
Jeff Brown *(Dir-Dev)*
Advertising Agency:
Carmichael Lynch Spong
110 N 5th St
Minneapolis, MN 55403
Tel.: (612) 375-8555
Fax: (612) 375-8501

WHITE ELECTRICAL CONSTRUCTION CO.

1730 Chattahoochee Ave NW
Atlanta, GA 30318-2112
Mailing Address:
PO Box 19629
Atlanta, GA 30325-0629
Tel.: (404) 351-5740
Fax: (404) 355-5823
Toll Free: (888) 519-4483
Web Site: www.white-electrical.com
E-Mail For Key Personnel:
Sales Director: roconnor@white-electrical.com
Sales Range: $50-74.9 Million
Approx. Number Employees: 530
Year Founded: 1910
Business Description:
Electrical Construction & Maintenance Services
S.I.C.: 1731
N.A.I.C.S.: 238210
Advertising Expenditures: $200,000
Media: 2-4-7-13-22-26
Distr.: Natl.
Budget Set: Sept.
Personnel:
Gary N. Clodfelter *(Pres)*
Marshall Combs *(CFO)*
Greg Hough *(Branch Mgr)*
Brands & Products:
WHITE ELECTRICAL

WHITE'S ELECTRONICS

1011 Pleasant Vly Rd
Sweet Home, OR 97386-1034
Tel.: (541) 367-6121
Fax: (541) 367-2968
Toll Free: (800) 547-6911
E-mail: info@whiteselectronics.com
Web Site: www.whiteselectronics.com
Approx. Number Employees: 100
Year Founded: 1950
Business Description:
Mfr. of Electronic Metal Detection Equipment
S.I.C.: 3812
N.A.I.C.S.: 334511
Import Export
Advertising Expenditures: $1,000,000
Media: 2-4-5-6-7-8-10-13-15-16-19-23-24
Distr.: Intl.; Natl.
Budget Set: July
Personnel:
Alan Holcombe *(Mgr-Mktg)*
Peam Godell *(Mgr-Production)*
Melissa Wise *(Mgr-Adv)*
Brands & Products:
BEACHHUNTER
BEACHHUNTER ID
BULLSEYE PINPOINTER
DFX
GMT
IDX PRO
MXT
PRISM
PRIZM II
PRIZM III
PRIZM IV
PRIZM V
QXT PRO
SURF PI PRO
WHITE'S
WHITE'S AUTOSCAN
XL PRO
XLT
Advertising Agency:
White's Advertising Agency
1011 Pleasant Vly Rd
Sweet Home, OR 97386
Tel.: (541) 367-6121
Fax: (541) 367-6629
Toll Free: (800) 547-6911

WIELAND ELECTRIC INC.

(Sub. of Wieland Electric GmbH)
49 Intl Rd
Burgaw, NC 28425-4434
Tel.: (910) 259-5050
Fax: (910) 259-3691
E-mail: salesUSA@wielandinc.com
Web Site: www.wielandinc.com
E-Mail For Key Personnel:
Sales Director: salesusa@wielandinc.com
Approx. Number Employees: 18
Year Founded: 1968
Business Description:
Sale of Conductive Wiring Components
S.I.C.: 5065; 5063
N.A.I.C.S.: 423690; 423610
Import Export
Brands & Products:
STOCKO
WIELAND
Advertising Agency:
Technell, Inc.
81 Nutmeg Ln
Stamford, CT 06905
Tel.: (203) 609-9065
Fax: (203) 609-9065

WINCHESTER ELECTRONICS CORP.

(Holding of Audax Management Company, LLC)
62 Barnes Industrial Rd N
Wallingford, CT 06492
Tel.: (203) 741-5400
Fax: (203) 741-5500
Web Site:
www.winchesterelectronics.com
Approx. Number Employees: 160
Year Founded: 1941
Business Description:
Electronic Connector Products
S.I.C.: 5065
N.A.I.C.S.: 423690
Import Export
Advertising Expenditures: $400,000
Media: 4-10
Distr.: Natl.
Budget Set: July
Personnel:
Michael P. Driscoll *(Chm)*
Kevin S. Perhamus *(CEO)*
Brands & Products:
COMPACTPCI
HIGH DENSITY PLUS
METCON-2
QC-SMA

WIND ENERGY AMERICA, INC.

12100 Singletree Ln Ste 100
Eden Prairie, MN 55344
Tel.: (952) 746-1234
Fax: (952) 746-1201
E-mail: info@windenergyamerica.com
Web Site:
www.windenergyamerica.com
Approx. Rev.: $42,142
Approx. Number Employees: 3
Year Founded: 1980
Business Description:
Power Generating Windmills Owner & Operator
S.I.C.: 4931
N.A.I.C.S.: 221119
Media: 7-10-13
Distr.: Intl.
Budget Set: June
Personnel:
Donald Blakstad *(Chm)*
Melvin E. Wentz *(CEO)*

WINEGARD COMPANY

3000 Kirkwood St
Burlington, IA 52601-2000
Tel.: (319) 754-0600

Key to Media (For complete agency information see *The Advertising Red Books-Agencies* edition):
1. Bus. Publs. 2. Cable T.V. 3. Catalogs & Directories. 4. Co-op Adv. 5. Consumer Mags. 6. D.M. to Bus. Estab.7. D.M. to Consumers 8. Daily Newsp. 9. Exhibits/Trade Shows 10. Foreign 11. Infomercial 12. Internet Adv.13. Multimedia 14. Network Radio 15. Network T.V. 16. Newsp. Distr. Mags. 17. Other 18. Outdoor (Posters, Transit) 19. Point of Purchase20. Premiums, Novelties 21. Product Samples 22. Special Events Mktg. 23. Spot Radio 24. Spot T.V. 25. Weekly Newsp. 26. Yellow Page Adv.

Fax: (319) 754-0787
E-mail: csvc@winegard.com
Web Site: www.winegard.com
Sales Range: $50-74.9 Million
Approx. Number Employees: 300
Year Founded: 1954
Business Description:
Mfr. of Television Reception Products
S.I.C.: 3663; 3651
N.A.I.C.S.: 334220; 334310
Export
Advertising Expenditures: $250,000
Media: 2-4-10-13-17-24
Distr.: Intl.; Natl.
Budget Set: Dec.
Personnel:
Randy Winegard *(Pres & CEO)*
Jim Riffel *(Dir-Satellite Bus Grp)*
Dave Chiswell *(Reg Mgr)*
John Schweizer *(Reg Mgr-Midwest)*
Karen Anderson *(Mgr-Natl Sls-Residential Satellite)*
Jude Bliss *(Mgr-Mktg Svcs)*
Keith Larson *(Mgr-Natl Sls)*
Grant Whipple *(Mgr-Natl Sls)*
Brands & Products:
CHROMSTAR II
CLEARLY THE WORLD'S BEST
DIGITAL MAGIC
GHOSTKILLER
HIDEAWAY
KILLER
METROSTAR
MOVIN' VIEW
PROSTAR
PROSTAR 1000
ROADSTAR
SENSAR
SQUARE SHOOTER
SQUARESHOOT
TV MAN
WINEGARD

WINLAND ELECTRONICS, INC.
1950 Excel Dr
Mankato, MN 56001-5903
Tel.: (507) 625-7231
Fax: (507) 387-2488
Toll Free: (800) 635-4269
E-mail: info@winland.com
Web Site: www.winland.com
Approx. Sls.: $3,317,000
Approx. Number Employees: 7
Year Founded: 1972
Business Description:
Designs & Manufactures Custom Electronic Controls & Assemblies for Original Equipment Manufacturer (OEM) Customers
S.I.C.: 3823; 3669; 3679
N.A.I.C.S.: 334513; 334290; 334418; 334419
Advertising Expenditures: $21,000
Media: 17
Personnel:
Thomas J. Goodmanson *(Chm)*
Brian D. Lawrence *(CFO & Sr VP)*
David A. Kuklinski *(VP-Sls & Mktg)*
Brands & Products:
ENVIROALERT
POWER-OUT ALERT
TEMP & HUMIDITY ALERTS
VEHICLE ALERT
WATERBUG ALERT
WINLAND ELECTRONICS
YOUR ENVIRONMENTAL SECURITY

WIRELESS RONIN TECHNOLOGIES INC.
Baker Tech N Plz 5929 Baker Rd Ste 475
Minnetonka, MN 55345
Tel.: (952) 564-3500
Fax: (952) 974-7887
Toll Free: (866) 418-3439
Toll Free: (888) 369-7678 (Sales)
E-mail: info@wirelessronin.com
Web Site: www.wirelessronin.com
Approx. Sls.: $8,567,000
Approx. Number Employees: 66
Year Founded: 2000
Business Description:
Wireless Communications Development
S.I.C.: 7373; 3669; 4812
N.A.I.C.S.: 541512; 334290; 517212
Advertising Expenditures: $45,000
Media: 10
Personnel:
Stephen F. Birke *(Chm)*
Scott W. Koller *(Pres & CEO)*
Darin P. McAreavey *(CFO & Sr VP)*
Scott N. Ross *(Gen Counsel, Sec & VP)*
Alan D. Buterbaugh *(Sr VP, Content Engrg & Gen Mgr-Canadian Ops)*
Brands & Products:
DYNAMIC DIGITAL SIGNAGE
RONINCAST

WIRELESS TELECOM GROUP, INC.
25 Eastmans Rd
Parsippany, NJ 07054-3702
Tel.: (973) 386-9696
Fax: (973) 386-9191
E-mail: info@noisecom.com
Web Site: www.noisecom.com
Approx. Sls.: $24,564,226
Approx. Number Employees: 101
Year Founded: 1985
Business Description:
Solid State Noise Sources, Noise Based Test Equipment & Wireless Telecommunication Test Equipment Mfr
S.I.C.: 3824; 3829
N.A.I.C.S.: 334514; 334519
Advertising Expenditures: $358,248
Media: 2-4-7-10
Personnel:
Adrian R. Nemcek *(Chm)*
Paul Genova *(CEO & CFO)*
Robert Censullo *(CFO)*
Joseph Debold *(Sr VP-Global Sls & Mktg)*
Brands & Products:
NOISECOM

WIRELESS XCESSORIES GROUP, INC.
1840 County Line Rd Ste 301
Huntingdon Valley, PA 19006
Tel.: (215) 322-4600
Fax: (888) 233-0220
Fax: (215) 322-4606
Toll Free: (800) 233-0013
Web Site: www.wirexgroup.com
Sales Range: $10-24.9 Million
Approx. Number Employees: 85
Year Founded: 1985
Business Description:
Wireless Aftermarket Accessories Whslr
S.I.C.: 5064; 4812
N.A.I.C.S.: 423620; 517212
Media: 13-18-19
Personnel:
Stephen Rade *(Pres & CEO)*
Ronald E. Badke *(CFO)*
Susan Rade *(VP & Acct Mgr-Sls)*
Dan Kenderdine *(VP-Pur & Bus Dev)*
Anna Pollack *(Acct Mgr-Sls & Mktg)*
Amy Sutter *(Acct Mgr-Sls & Mktg)*
Kathleen Garland *(Mgr-HR)*
Dawn Kenderdine *(Mgr-Warehouse)*
Christine Mayo *(Mgr-Credit & Customer Svc)*

WIREMOLD/LEGRAND
(Sub. of Legrand S.A.)
60 Woodlawn St
West Hartford, CT 06110-2326
Tel.: (860) 233-6251
Fax: (860) 232-2062
Toll Free: (800) 621-0049
E-mail: webmaster@wiremold.com
Web Site: www.wiremold.com
E-Mail For Key Personnel:
Sales Director: sales@wiremold.com
Approx. Number Employees: 900
Year Founded: 1900
Business Description:
Supplier of Wire Management Solutions for Lighting, Electrical, Electronic & Communication Markets
S.I.C.: 3644; 3643
N.A.I.C.S.: 335932; 335931
Export
Media: 1-2-3-4-6-7-8-10-13-19-20-21-22
Distr.: Natl.
Budget Set: Nov.
Personnel:
Michael Gambino *(CEO)*
John Hoffman *(Exec VP-sls & Market Dev)*
Don Torrant *(Dir-Mktg & Comm)*
Matt Martinez *(Project Mgr)*
Greg Crane *(Mgr-Distibutor Mktg)*
Linda Taylor *(Product Bus Mgr)*
Brands & Products:
1200 SERIES
1500 SERIES
2300 SERIES
2300D SERIES
2600 SERIES
400 SERIES
4FFATC FLUSH
525 SERIES
5400 SERIES
800 SERIES
862 SERIES
863 SERIES
880MP MODULINK
881 RACHET PRO
882C SERIES
884C SERIES
AC SERIES
ACCESS 5000
AF SERIES
AMD8 POKE-THRU
AV3 POKE-THRU
C9 POKE-THRU
CABINETMATE
CABLEMATE
CABLESMART
CABLOFIL
CHAN-L-WIRE
CORDMATE
CORDMATE II
CORDUCT
CORNERMATE
CRFB SERIES
CZE SERIES
DATA-FENCE
DEQUORUM
ECLIPSE PN03
ECLIPSE PN03L
ECLIPSE PN05
ECLIPSE PN10
EVOLUTION
FIT POKE-THRU
FLAMESTOPPER
FLEXIBLE PANCAKE
FLOORPORT
FLUSHDUCT
METER READER
MULTIFLEX SERIES
N-R-G-FLOR
NM2000 PLUGMOLD
NM2000 RACEWAY
OMNIBOX
PERMA POWER
PLUG-IN OUTLET CENTER
POWER COMMANDER
POWER COMMANDER IQ
POWER COMMANDER PDU
POWER COMMANDER PLUS
PSRC9 SERIES
RACK MOUNT
RC3 POKE-THRU
RC4 POKE-THRU
RC7 POKE-THRU
RC91GHBTC POKE-THRU
RC92GHBTC POKE-THRU
RC9AFFTC POKE-THRU
RC9AM2TC POKE-THRU
RC9AMD POKE-THRU
RESOURCE
RFB11 A/V
RFB6
RFB6 SERIES
RFB9 A/V
RFE SERIES
SAF SERIES
SENTREX
SNAPICOIL
SOURCE I
SOURCE II
SPECMATE LADDER
SPECMATE SOLID BOTTOM
SPECMATE TRAY
SPECMATE TYPE I
SPECMATE WALL
TABLESOURCE
UNIDUCT 2700
UNIDUCT 2800
UNIDUCT 2900
WALKERCELL
WALKERDECK
WALKERDUCT
WALKERDUCT PRO
WALKERFLEX
WALLDUCT MEDICAL
WFMB SERIES
WIRE BASKET TRAY
WIREWAY
ZONEMASTER
Advertising Agency:
Mintz & Hoke Communications Group
40 Tower Ln
Avon, CT 06001-4222
Tel.: (860) 678-0473
Fax: (860) 679-9850
(Product Mktg., Image Advertising, All Pub. Rels. & Wire Management Systems)
— William Field *(V.P.)*

Key to Media (For complete agency information see *The Advertising Red Books-Agencies* edition):
1. Bus. Publs. 2. Cable T.V. 3. Catalogs & Directories. 4. Co-op Adv. 5. Consumer Mags. 6. D.M. to Bus. Estab.7. D.M. to Consumers
8. Daily Newsp. 9. Exhibits/Trade Shows 10. Foreign 11. Infomercial 12. Internet Adv.13. Multimedia 14. Network Radio
15. Network T.V. 16. Newsp. Distr. Mags. 17. Other 18. Outdoor (Posters, Transit) 19. Point of Purchase20. Premiums, Novelties
21. Product Samples 22. Special Events Mktg. 23. Spot Radio 24. Spot T.V. 25. Weekly Newsp. 26. Yellow Page Adv.

WJ COMMUNICATIONS INCORPORATED
(Sub. of TriQuint Semiconductor, Inc.)
401 River Oaks Pkwy
San Jose, CA 95134-1916
Tel.: (408) 577-6200
Fax: (408) 577-6621
Toll Free: (800) 951-4401
Toll Free: (800) 876-6093
E-mail: info@wj.com
Web Site: www.wj.com
Approx. Sls.: $43,944,000
Approx. Number Employees: 132
Year Founded: 1957
Business Description:
Radio Frequency Semiconductors Designer & Supplier
S.I.C.: 3674; 3663
N.A.I.C.S.: 334413; 334220
Export
Media: 2-4-10-13
Distr.: Intl.; Natl.
Budget Set: Jan.
Personnel:
Morteza Saidi *(VP-Engrg)*
Claudia Lin *(Mgr-Editorial & PR)*
Advertising Agency:
Shelton Group
12400 Coit Rd Ste 650
Dallas, TX 75251
Tel.: (972) 239-5119
Fax: (972) 239-2292

WQN
(Name Changed to QUAMTEL, INC.)

XO HOLDINGS, INC.
13865 Sunrise Valley Dr
Herndon, VA 20171
Tel.: (703) 547-2000
Fax: (703) 547-2881
E-mail: chad.couser@xo.com
Web Site: www.xo.com
Approx. Rev.: $1,529,241,000
Approx. Number Employees: 3,654
Year Founded: 1994
Business Description:
Holding Company;
Telecommunications Services
S.I.C.: 4813; 6719
N.A.I.C.S.: 517110; 551112
Advertising Expenditures: $400,000
Media: 2
Personnel:
Carl Celian Icahn *(Chm)*
Laura W. Thomas *(CFO)*
Rob Geller *(CIO)*
Ernie Ortega *(Pres-Carrier Svcs)*
Daniel J. Wagner *(Pres-Bus Svcs)*
Heather Burnet Gold *(Sr VP-External Affairs)*
Terri Burke *(VP-HR)*
Gail Kowalski *(Product Mgr)*
Brands & Products:
XO

YAMAHA ELECTRONICS CORPORATION USA
(Affil. of Yamaha Corporation)
6660 Orangethorpe Ave
Buena Park, CA 90620
Tel.: (714) 522-9105
Fax: (714) 670-0108
E-mail: yecsupport@yamaha.com
Web Site: www.yamaha.com
Approx. Number Employees: 50
Year Founded: 1973
Business Description:
Mfr. of Stereo Components & Systems
S.I.C.: 5064
N.A.I.C.S.: 423620
Export
Advertising Expenditures: $2,000,000
Media: 2-3-4-7-8-10-11-13-19-24
Distr.: Natl.
Brands & Products:
DPX-1000
THE FUTURE OF MUSIC AND SOUND
HX SERIES
RX-Z1
RX-Z9
YST-SW1500
YST-SW215
Advertising Agency:
Giles Communications, LLC
2975 Westchester Ave Ste 402
Purchase, NY 10577
Tel.: (914) 644-3500
Fax: (914) 696-4120

YARDNEY TECHNICAL PRODUCTS, INC.
(Sub. of Ener-Tek International, Inc.)
82 Mechanic St
Pawcatuck, CT 06379-2154
Tel.: (860) 599-1100
Fax: (860) 599-3903
Toll Free: (800) 717-2586
E-mail: webmaster@yardney.com
Web Site: www.yardney.com
E-Mail For Key Personnel:
Marketing Director: Aretakis@yardney.com
Sales Range: $10-24.9 Million
Approx. Number Employees: 175
Year Founded: 1944
Business Description:
High Energy & Power Density Specialty Batteries Mfr
S.I.C.: 3691; 3692
N.A.I.C.S.: 335911; 335912
Export
Media: 2-4-11
Distr.: Intl.; Natl.
Budget Set: Nov.
Personnel:
Vincent A. Yevoli *(Pres & COO)*
Alexander P. Karpinski *(VP-Engrg)*
Anthony M. Aretakis *(Dir-Mktg & Sls)*
Brands & Products:
ALUPOWER
LITHION
SEACEL
SILVERCEL

ZACK ELECTRONICS, INC.
1070 Hamilton Rd
Duarte, CA 91010-2741
Tel.: (626) 303-0655
Fax: (626) 303-8694
Toll Free: (800) 466-0449
E-mail: info@zackelectronics.com
Web Site: www.zackelectronics.com
Approx. Number Employees: 10
Year Founded: 1931
Business Description:
Audio & Video Installation Equipment Distr
S.I.C.: 5065
N.A.I.C.S.: 423690
Media: 2-4-10-26
Personnel:
Dennis Awad *(Pres)*
Brands & Products:
ZACK

ZAGG INCORPORATED
3855 S 500 W Ste J
Salt Lake City, UT 84115
Tel.: (801) 263-0699
Toll Free: (800) 700-9244
E-mail: president@zagg.com
Web Site: www.zagg.com
Approx. Sls.: $76,135,025
Approx. Number Employees: 156
Business Description:
Protective Coverings, Audio Accessories & Power Solutions for Consumer Electronic & Hand-Held Devices Designer, Mfr & Distr
S.I.C.: 3651; 2671; 3669; 3679; 5065
N.A.I.C.S.: 334310; 322221; 334290; 334419; 423690
Advertising Expenditures: $5,067,377
Media: 3-13-14-15-19-23-24
Personnel:
Robert G. Pedersen, II *(Co-Founder, Chm, Pres & CEO)*
Brian S. Packer *(Mng Dir)*
Brandon T. O'Brien *(CFO)*
Derek Smith *(VP-Sls & Mktg)*
Brands & Products:
INVISIBLESHIELD

ZARLINK SEMICONDUCTOR INC.
400 March Rd
Ottawa, ON K2K 3H4, Canada
Tel.: (613) 592-0200
Fax: (613) 592-1010
E-mail: corporate@zarlink.com
Web Site: www.zarlink.com
Approx. Rev.: $220,141,000
Approx. Number Employees: 584
Year Founded: 1973
Business Description:
Mfr of Semiconductors for Communications & Healthcare Industries
S.I.C.: 3674
N.A.I.C.S.: 334413
Media: 7-10
Personnel:
Kirk K. Mandy *(Pres & CEO)*
Andre Levasseur *(CFO & Sr VP-Fin)*
Gary Tanner *(COO)*
Stan Swirhun *(CTO & CMO)*
Renato Pontello *(Gen Counsel, Sec & VP-Legal)*
Stephen J. Swift *(Sr VP & Gen Mgr-Medical Products Grp)*
Eileen Speirs *(VP-HR)*
Edward Goffin *(Mgr-Corp Comm)*
Advertising Agency:
Pinnacle Marketing Communications Ltd.
Prosperity House Dawlish Drive
Pinner, HA5 5LN, United Kingdom
Tel.: (44) 20 8869 9339
Fax: (44) 20 8868 4373

ZCOLO
(Formerly FiberNet Telecom Group, Inc.)
(Sub. of Zayo Group, LLC)
220 W 42nd St
New York, NY 10036
Tel.: (212) 405-6200
Fax: (212) 405-6262
Toll Free: (800) 342-3768
E-mail: zcolosales@zayo.com
Web Site: www.zcolo.com
Sales Range: $50-74.9 Million
Approx. Number Employees: 73
Business Description:
Fiber-Optic Networks Owner & Operator
S.I.C.: 3357; 4813
N.A.I.C.S.: 335921; 517110
Media: 7-18-22
Personnel:
Steve M. Finnerty *(VP-Sls)*

ZEBRA TECHNOLOGIES CORPORATION
475 Half Day Rd Ste 500
Lincolnshire, IL 60069
Tel.: (847) 634-6700
Fax: (847) 913-8766
Toll Free: (866) 230-9494
E-mail: dfox@zebra.com
Web Site: www.zebra.com
Approx. Sls.: $956,848,000
Approx. Number Employees: 2,750
Year Founded: 1969
Business Description:
On-Demand Bar Code Label Printers & Related Supplies
S.I.C.: 3577; 2672; 3553
N.A.I.C.S.: 334119; 322222; 333210
Export
Advertising Expenditures: $7,115,000
Personnel:
Michael A. Smith *(Chm)*
Anders Gustafsson *(CEO)*
Michael C. Smiley *(CFO & Treas)*
Jim L. Kaput *(Gen Counsel, Sec & Sr VP)*
Gerhard Cless *(Exec VP)*
Hugh K. Gagnier *(Sr VP-Ops)*
Philip Gerskovich *(Sr VP-Corp Dev)*
Michael H. Terzich *(Sr VP-Global Sls & Mktg)*
Ashley Ford *(VP & Gen Mgr-North America)*
Jim McWilson *(VP-Strategic Accts & Govt Sls-North America)*
Deborah Murphy *(VP-Global Mktg)*
Brands & Products:
STRIPE
VALUE-LINE
ZEBRA
ZPLZ
Advertising Agencies:
Ogilvy Public Relations Worldwide
636 11th Ave
New York, NY 10036
Tel.: (212) 880-5200
Fax: (212) 370-4636

Strategic Communications Group
1400 Spring St Ste 330
Silver Spring, MD 20910
Tel.: (301) 408-4500
Fax: (301) 408-4506
Card Printer Solutions

ZENITH ELECTRONICS CORP.
(Sub. of LG Electronics, Inc.)
2000 Millbrook Dr
Lincolnshire, IL 60069-3630
Tel.: (847) 941-8000
Fax: (847) 941-8200
Web Site: www.zenith.com
E-Mail For Key Personnel:
Public Relations: jtaylor@zenith.com

Key to Media (For complete agency information see *The Advertising Red Books-Agencies* edition):
1. Bus. Publs. 2. Cable T.V. 3. Catalogs & Directories. 4. Co-op Adv. 5. Consumer Mags. 6. D.M. to Bus. Estab.7. D.M. to Consumers 8. Daily Newsp. 9. Exhibits/Trade Shows 10. Foreign 11. Infomercial 12. Internet Adv.13. Multimedia 14. Network Radio 15. Network T.V. 16. Newsp. Distr. Mags. 17. Other 18. Outdoor (Posters, Transit) 19. Point of Purchase20. Premiums, Novelties 21. Product Samples 22. Special Events Mktg. 23. Spot Radio 24. Spot T.V. 25. Weekly Newsp. 26. Yellow Page Adv.

Approx. Number Employees: 160
Year Founded: 1918
Business Description:
TV, Video Cassette Recorders, Power Supplies, Video Display, CATV & STV Equipment & Accessories Mfr & Whlsr
S.I.C.: 3651; 3671
N.A.I.C.S.: 334310; 334411
Import Export
Advertising Expenditures: $6,000,000
Media: 5-6-7-9-15-18-19-20-23-24-25
Distr.: Natl.
Personnel:
John I. Taylor *(VP-Pub Rels)*
Brands & Products:
ZENITH
Advertising Agency:
Ogilvy & Mather
(Sub. of WPP Group plc)
636 11th Ave
New York, NY 10036
Tel.: (212) 237-4000
Fax: (212) 237-5123

ZIPIT WIRELESS

200 N Main St
Greenville, SC 29601
Tel.: (864) 451-5500
Fax: (864) 451-5505
Toll Free: (866) 92ZIPIT
Web Site: www.zipitwireless.com
Approx. Number Employees: 10
Business Description:
Wireless Instant Messaging Device Mfr & Distr
S.I.C.: 4812
N.A.I.C.S.: 517212
Personnel:
Frank Greer *(Pres & CEO)*
Advertising Agency:
The Brandon Agency
3023 Church St
Myrtle Beach, SC 29577
Tel.: (843) 916-2000
Fax: (843) 916-2050
— Reid Harper *(Acct Exec)*

ZYNEX, INC.

9990 Park Meadows Dr
Lone Tree, CO 80124
Tel.: (303) 703-4906
Fax: (800) 495-6695
Toll Free: (800) 495-6670
E-mail: info@zynexmed.com
Web Site: www.zynexmed.com
Approx. Rev.: $24,085,000
Approx. Number Employees: 164
Year Founded: 1996
Business Description:
Electromedical Equipment Mfr
S.I.C.: 3845
N.A.I.C.S.: 334510
Advertising Expenditures: $26,000
Media: 17
Personnel:
Thomas Sandgaard *(CEO)*
Anthony A. Scalese *(CFO)*
James Miller *(Pres-Zynex NeuroDiagnostic Inc.)*
David Empey *(Dir-Regulatory Compliance)*
Brands & Products:
E-WAVE
ELPHA
NEUROMOVE
TRUWAVE
VALUTENS
ZYNEX MEDICAL

Key to Media (For complete agency information see *The Advertising Red Books-Agencies* edition):
1. Bus. Publs. 2. Cable T.V. 3. Catalogs & Directories. 4. Co-op Adv. 5. Consumer Mags. 6. D.M. to Bus. Estab.7. D.M. to Consumers 8. Daily Newsp. 9. Exhibits/Trade Shows 10. Foreign 11. Infomercial 12. Internet Adv.13. Multimedia 14. Network Radio 15. Network T.V. 16. Newsp. Distr. Mags. 17. Other 18. Outdoor (Posters, Transit) 19. Point of Purchase20. Premiums, Novelties 21. Product Samples 22. Special Events Mktg. 23. Spot Radio 24. Spot T.V. 25. Weekly Newsp. 26. Yellow Page Adv.

Fabrics, Yarns & Sewing Notions

Knit Goods — Needlework — Sewing Notions

A.C. MOORE ARTS & CRAFTS, INC.
130 AC Moore Dr
Berlin, NJ 08009-9500
Tel.: (856) 768-4930
Fax: (856) 753-4725
Web Site: www.acmoore.com
Approx. Sls.: $448,058,000
Approx. Number Employees: 1,449
Year Founded: 1985
Business Description:
Traditional & Contemporary Arts & Crafts Merchandise Retailer
S.I.C.: 5945
N.A.I.C.S.: 451120
Import
Advertising Expenditures: $26,900,000
Media: 5-14-22-25
Personnel:
Joseph A. Jeffries *(CEO)*
David Stern *(CFO, Chief Admin Officer & Exec VP)*
David Abelman *(Chief Mktg & Mdsg Officer & Exec VP)*
Rodney B. Schriver *(Chief Acctg Officer, VP & Controller)*
Amy Rhoades *(Gen Counsel & Sr VP)*
Richard Arthur *(VP-Mktg & Adv)*
Joette Metzler *(VP-Supply Chain Support)*

ALBANY INTERNATIONAL CORP.
216 Airport Dr
Rochester, NH 03867
Mailing Address:
PO Box 1907
Albany, NY 12201-1907
Tel.: (518) 445-2200
Fax: (518) 445-2250
Toll Free: (800) 833-3836
E-mail: Investor_Relations@albint.com
Web Site: www.albint.com
Approx. Sls.: $914,356,000
Approx. Number Employees: 5,000
Year Founded: 1895
Business Description:
Paper-Machine Clothing & Industrial Products Mfr
S.I.C.: 2211
N.A.I.C.S.: 313210
Import Export
Media: 2-7-10-21
Distr.: Intl.; Natl.
Budget Set: Oct. -Nov.
Personnel:
Erland E. Kailbourne *(Chm)*
Joseph G. Morone *(Pres & CEO)*
John B. Cozzolino *(CFO & Treas)*
Dawne H. Wimbrow *(CIO & VP-Global Info Svcs)*
Robert A. Hansen *(CTO & Sr VP)*
Ralph M. Polumbo *(Chief Admin Officer & Sr VP-HR)*
David M. Pawlick *(Chief Acctg Officer, VP & Controller)*
Daniel A. Halftermeyer *(Pres-PMC)*
Michael J. Joyce *(Pres-Applied Technologies)*
Charles J. Silva, Jr. *(Gen Counsel, Sec & VP)*
Joseph M. Gaug *(Assoc Gen Counsel & Asst Sec)*
Brands & Products:
DURA-DRIVE
DURA-DRY
DURABELT
DURAGRIP
DURAGRIP-S
DURAGUARD
DURAGUARD-S
DURAMAX
GLOSSBELT
PRESSBELT
PRIMALOFT
PYROPEL
RAPID-ROLL
TRANSBELT
VENTABELT
Advertising Agency:
Verde PR & Consulting
PO Box 9028
Durango, CO 81302
Tel.: (970) 259-3555
PrimaLoft

ALLIED FELT GROUP
(Group of Central Shippee, Inc.)
46 Star Lake Rd
Bloomingdale, NJ 07403-1244
Tel.: (973) 838-1616
Fax: (973) 838-8273
Toll Free: (800) 631-8968
Web Site: www.thefeltpeople.com
Approx. Number Employees: 12
Year Founded: 1928
Business Description:
Felt for Crafts & Hobbies
S.I.C.: 5199; 2511
N.A.I.C.S.: 424990; 337122
Media: 2-6-7-21-26
Distr.: Natl.
Budget Set: Nov. -Dec.
Personnel:
Donald A. Hubner *(CEO)*
Brands & Products:
CUSHIONAIR
DURASTIFF
TEMPORA
WILLI-CLOTH

ALPHA ASSOCIATES, INC.
145 Lehigh Ave
Lakewood, NJ 08701
Tel.: (732) 634-5700
Fax: (732) 634-1430
Toll Free: (800) 631-5399
E-mail: guest@alphainc.com
Web Site: www.alphainc.com
Approx. Number Employees: 115
Year Founded: 1968
Business Description:
Resin Coated & Laminated Fabrics
S.I.C.: 2295
N.A.I.C.S.: 313320
Import Export
Advertising Expenditures: $200,000
Media: 4-5-13-16-20-21-26
Distr.: Intl.; Natl.
Personnel:
A. Louis Avallone *(Chm & CEO)*
Christopher J. Avallone *(Pres & COO)*
John T. Baxter *(VP-Sls & Mktg)*
Brands & Products:
ALPHA-ALAFLEX
ALPHA-HU-AL
ALPHA-MARITEX
ALPHA-MOTIVE
ALPHA-SIL
ALPHA-SONIC
ALPHA-WELD
ALPHAGLAS
CLEANGARD
GOLDENGARD
HYPALON
NEOPRENE
THERMAGARD
VAN
VERMICULITE
WELDFLEX
WELDGARD

AMERICAN & EFIRD, INC.
(Sub. of Ruddick Corporation)
22 American St
Mount Holly, NC 28120-2150
Mailing Address:
PO Box 507
Mount Holly, NC 28120
Tel.: (704) 827-4311
Fax: (704) 827-0974
Toll Free: (800) 453-5128
E-mail: northamerica.homepage@amefird.com
Web Site: www.amefird.com
E-Mail For Key Personnel:
Sales Director: aesales@amefird.com
Sales Range: $1-9.9 Million
Approx. Number Employees: 5,000
Year Founded: 1891
Business Description:
Industrial Sewing Thread Mfr
S.I.C.: 2284; 2281
N.A.I.C.S.: 313113; 313111
Import Export
Advertising Expenditures: $300,000
Media: 1-2-3-4-7-10-13-18-20-21-26
Distr.: Intl.; Natl.
Personnel:
Fred A. Jackson *(Pres)*
Craig G. Stover *(Sr VP-Fin)*
A. Knox Winget, III *(Sr VP-Global Supply Chain Ops)*
Mark Hatton *(Dir-Mktg)*
Brands & Products:
A&E
ANESYST
QUALITY, SERVICE, VALUE...THERE IS A DIFFERENCE
SIGNATURE
THREADUCATION
Advertising Agency:
Corder Philips, Inc.
508 W 5th St Ste 100
Charlotte, NC 28202
Tel.: (704) 333-3924
Fax: (704) 358-0134
(Thread)

AMERICAN TRADITIONAL DESIGNS
442 1st NH Tpke
Northwood, NH 03261

Key to Media (For complete agency information see *The Advertising Red Books-Agencies* edition):
1. Bus. Publs. 2. Cable T.V. 3. Catalogs & Directories. 4. Co-op Adv. 5. Consumer Mags. 6. D.M. to Bus. Estab.7. D.M. to Consumers 8. Daily Newsp. 9. Exhibits/Trade Shows 10. Foreign 11. Infomercial 12. Internet Adv.13. Multimedia 14. Network Radio 15. Network T.V. 16. Newsp. Distr. Mags. 17. Other 18. Outdoor (Posters, Transit) 19. Point of Purchase20. Premiums, Novelties 21. Product Samples 22. Special Events Mktg. 23. Spot Radio 24. Spot T.V. 25. Weekly Newsp. 26. Yellow Page Adv.

Tel.: (603) 942-8100
Fax: (603) 942-8919
Fax: (800) 448-6654
Toll Free: (800) 448-6656
E-mail: info@momenta.com
Web Site: www.momenta.com
Approx. Sls.: $2,300,000
Approx. Number Employees: 14
Year Founded: 1979
Business Description:
Arts & Crafts Supplies
S.I.C.: 3952; 2679
N.A.I.C.S.: 339942; 322299
Media: 4-10-13
Personnel:
Michael Barker *(CEO)*
Brands & Products:
3D STICKER FX
AMERICAN TRADITIONAL DESIGNS
CATS & DOGS COLLECTION
CROP YOUR PASSION
LIL' JEWELS
LIL' TEMPLATES

ASSOCIATED FABRICS CORPORATION

15-01 Pollitt Dr Unit 7
Fair Lawn, NJ 07410
Tel.: (800) 232-4077
Fax: (866) 710-3850
Fax: (212) 260-3531
E-mail: info@afcfabrics.com
Web Site: www.afc-fabrics.com
Sales Range: $10-24.9 Million
Approx. Number Employees: 10
Year Founded: 1928
Business Description:
Theatrical Fabrics
S.I.C.: 2261; 2299; 5949
N.A.I.C.S.: 313311; 313312; 451130
Media: 4-13
Personnel:
Isaac H. Stevens *(Pres)*
Bruce Nocera *(Dir-Sls)*
Sam Samson *(Dir-Ops)*

BARNHART INDUSTRIES, INC.

3690 Hwy M
Imperial, MO 63052-2932
Tel.: (636) 942-3133
Fax: (636) 948-3152
Toll Free: (800) 325-9973
Web Site: www.orthoband.com
Approx. Number Employees: 25
Year Founded: 1939
Business Description:
Mfr. of Soft Goods
S.I.C.: 3965; 3843
N.A.I.C.S.: 339993; 339114
Import Export
Media: 2-4-5-7-8-10-19-20-21
Distr.: Intl.
Budget Set: Dec.
Personnel:
Kenneth J. DeWoskin *(Owner)*
Anna Boehm *(Pres)*
Brands & Products:
BARNHART INDUSTRIES
FEMININE BOUTIQUE
HANGEROOS
KOOK-A-ROO
ORTHOBAND
ORTHOSTRAP

BELTON INDUSTRIES, INC.

1205 Hamby Rd
Belton, SC 29627
Tel.: (864) 338-5711
Fax: (800) 851-2688
Toll Free: (800) 845-8753
E-mail: customerservice@beltonindustries.com
Web Site: www.beltonindustries.com
Approx. Number Employees: 200
Year Founded: 1916
Business Description:
Specialty Fabrics Mfr
S.I.C.: 2299; 2211
N.A.I.C.S.: 314999; 313210
Import Export
Advertising Expenditures: $750,000
Media: 4-7-10-17-21
Distr.: Natl.
Personnel:
Carroll B. Hart, Sr. *(Pres)*
Brands & Products:
ANTI-WASH
CORRAL CARPET
DEKOWE
GEOCOIR
GEOJUTE
UDDERGUARD

BEST MANUFACTURING GROUP LLC

(Holding of GHCL Limited)
10 Exchange Pl Unit 22
Jersey City, NJ 07302-3917
Tel.: (201) 356-3800
Fax: (201) 356-3815
Toll Free: (800) 843-3233
Web Site: www.bestmfg.com
Approx. Number Employees: 1,020
Year Founded: 1914
Business Description:
Mfr. of Men's & Women's Washable Apparel; Wholesale Textiles
S.I.C.: 2389; 2299
N.A.I.C.S.: 315299; 313312
Import Export
Advertising Expenditures: $300,000
Media: 2-4-7-10
Distr.: Natl.
Personnel:
Scott Korman *(Chm)*

BLOCKSOM & COMPANY

450 St John Rd Ste 710 PO Box 2007
Michigan City, IN 46360-7351
Tel.: (219) 874-3231
Fax: (219) 874-9785
Toll Free: (800) 745-1408
E-mail: gpickford@blocksom.com
Web Site: www.roofsaver.com
Approx. Number Employees: 100
Year Founded: 1919
Business Description:
Mfr. of Filtered Products & Bridge Vents
S.I.C.: 2299
N.A.I.C.S.: 314999
Import Export
Media: 2-4-10-17-19
Distr.: Natl.
Budget Set: Dec.
Personnel:
Andrew Swan *(Pres)*
Ken Smith *(VP-Fin)*
Georgia Pickford *(Mgr-Customer Svc)*
Brands & Products:
COIRTEX
PAR FILTERS
PARATEX
ROOF SAVER

BUTTERICK, MCCALL & VOGUE PATTERN COMPANY

120 Broadway
New York, NY 10271-2006
Tel.: (212) 465-6800
Fax: (212) 465-6891
Web Site: www.mccallpattern.com
Approx. Number Employees: 36
Business Description:
Publisher of Magazines, Catalogs & Books
S.I.C.: 2741; 2721
N.A.I.C.S.: 511199; 511120
Media: 4
Personnel:
Robin Davies *(Pres)*
John Kobiskie *(CFO)*
Brands & Products:
BUTTERICK, MCCALL AND VOGUE PATTERN COMPANY
BUTTERICK PATTERNS
MCCALL PATTERNS
VOGUE PATTERNS
WALLIES MURALS

CALICO CORNERS

(Div. of Everfast Inc.)
203 Gale Ln
Kennett Square, PA 19348-1735
Tel.: (610) 444-9700
Fax: (610) 444-1221
Toll Free: (800) 213-6366
Web Site: www.calicocorners.com
Approx. Sls.: $1,500,000
Approx. Number Employees: 100
Business Description:
Retailer of Decorative Fabrics
S.I.C.: 5949; 5131
N.A.I.C.S.: 451130; 424310
Media: 4-6-8-20-21
Distr.: Natl.
Budget Set: Mar. -Sept.
Personnel:
Bert Kerstetter *(Chm)*
Roy Simpson *(Pres)*
Jan Jessup *(Dir-Comm)*
Linda Emmons *(Mgr-Mktg)*
Advertising Agency:
Ambit Advertising and Public Relations
2601 E OakLand Park Blvd Ste 301
Fort Lauderdale, FL 33306
Tel.: (954) 568-2100
Fax: (954) 568-2888

CARON INTERNATIONAL

(Sub. of National Spinning Company, Inc.)
1481 W 2nd St
Washington, NC 27889-4157
Mailing Address:
PO Box 222
Washington, NC 27889
Tel.: (252) 975-7111
Web Site: www.caron.com
Approx. Number Employees: 400
Year Founded: 1916
Business Description:
Mfr. of Consumer Yarns & Craft Kits
S.I.C.: 2281; 5949
N.A.I.C.S.: 313111; 451130
Import Export
Media: 5-6-19-21
Distr.: Natl.
Personnel:
Matt Rauschenbach *(Pres)*
Jan Kahn *(VP-Sls)*
Brands & Products:
CARON
GRANDMA'S BEST
NATURA
WONDERART

CENTRAL SHIPPEE, INC.

46 Star Lk Rd
Bloomingdale, NJ 07403
Tel.: (973) 838-1100
Fax: (973) 838-8273
Toll Free: (800) 631-8968
E-mail: felt@webspan.net
Web Site: www.centralshippee.com
Approx. Number Employees: 25
Year Founded: 1926
Business Description:
Mfr of Felt, Fabrics & Accessories
S.I.C.: 5199; 2511
N.A.I.C.S.: 424990; 337122
Import Export
Media: 2-4-6-7-8-10-20-22-26
Distr.: Intl.; Natl.
Budget Set: Nov. -Dec.
Personnel:
Donald A. Hubner *(Chm & CEO)*
C. E. Hubner, Jr. *(Pres & COO)*
E. Brower *(CFO)*
Brands & Products:
CENTRAL SHIPPEE
CUSHIONAIR
DURAFELT
SHOW AND SELL
SHOW FELT
STAR CRAFT
TEMPORA

COATS & CLARK INC.

(Sub. of Coats Group Limited)
3430 Toringdon Way Ste 301
Charlotte, NC 28277
Tel.: (704) 329-5800
Fax: (704) 329-5899
Toll Free: (800) 631-0965
Web Site: www.coatsandclark.com
Approx. Number Employees: 125
Business Description:
Sewing Thread, Dual Duty Plus Threads, Crochet Cotton, Embroidery Threads, Zippers, Narrow Fabrics, Red Heart Yarns, Needlework Kits & Instruction Books
S.I.C.: 2284
N.A.I.C.S.: 313113
Import Export
Advertising Expenditures: $700,000
Media: 2-6-10-19-20
Distr.: Natl.
Budget Set: June
Personnel:
Donald Armstrong *(VP-Fin)*
Dale Sutherland *(VP-Sls & Mktg)*
Dale Swanner *(VP-Sls)*
Brands & Products:
ANCHOR
AUNT LYDIA
BATES
DUAL DUTY PLUS
J&P COATS
RED HEART
SOUTH MAID

CONCORD FABRICS INC

462 7th Ave
New York, NY 10018
Tel.: (212) 760-0300
Fax: (212) 563-3746
Toll Free: (800) 223-5678

Key to Media (For complete agency information see *The Advertising Red Books-Agencies* edition):
1. Bus. Publs. 2. Cable T.V. 3. Catalogs & Directories. 4. Co-op Adv. 5. Consumer Mags. 6. D.M. to Bus. Estab.7. D.M. to Consumers 8. Daily Newsp. 9. Exhibits/Trade Shows 10. Foreign 11. Infomercial 12. Internet Adv.13. Multimedia 14. Network Radio 15. Network T.V. 16. Newsp. Distr. Mags. 17. Other 18. Outdoor (Posters, Transit) 19. Point of Purchase20. Premiums, Novelties 21. Product Samples 22. Special Events Mktg. 23. Spot Radio 24. Spot T.V. 25. Weekly Newsp. 26. Yellow Page Adv.

Concord Fabrics Inc — (Continued)

Approx. Number Employees: 250
Business Description:
Woven & Knitted Fabrics Mfr
S.I.C.: 2211; 2241
N.A.I.C.S.: 313210; 313221
Media: 2-7-10
Distr.: Natl.
Budget Set: Dec.
Brands & Products:
ANDOVER
MAKOWER

CONRAD INDUSTRIES, INC.
PO Box 695
Weaverville, NC 28787-0695
Tel.: (828) 645-3015
Fax: (800) 355-3581
Toll Free: (800) 438-4285
Web Site: www.abemblem.com
E-Mail For Key Personnel:
Sales Director: sales@abemblem.com
Approx. Number Employees: 120
Year Founded: 1962
Business Description:
Swiss Embroidered Emblems Mfr
S.I.C.: 2261
N.A.I.C.S.: 313311
Import Export
Advertising Expenditures: $600,000
Media: 2-4-6-10-13
Distr.: Intl.; Natl.
Budget Set: Jan.
Personnel:
Bernhard Conrad *(Owner)*
Andrew Nagle *(Exec VP)*

COOLEY GROUP, INC.
50 Esten Ave
Pawtucket, RI 02860-4840
Tel.: (401) 724-9000
Fax: (401) 725-4190
E-mail: info@cooleygroup.com
Web Site: www.cooleygroup.com
Approx. Number Employees: 150
Year Founded: 1926
Business Description:
Mfr. of Coated Fabrics for Building Materials
S.I.C.: 8748
N.A.I.C.S.: 541618
Media: 7-13-21
Personnel:
P. Robert Siener, Jr. *(Chm)*
Jeff Flath *(Pres)*
Steve Siener *(VP & Bus Mgr)*
Diane Rose *(Mgr-Adv)*
Brands & Products:
ARMOR SHELL
C3
COOLANCHOR
COOLEY-BRITE
COOLEY-BRITE II
COOLEY-BRITE LITE
COOLEY GROUP
COOLEY LITE
COOLEY MAGIC
COOLFLEX
COOLGRIP
COOLGUARD
COOLMASK
COOLMESH
COOLMESH 5600
COOLMESH PREMIUM
COOLMESH RENAISSANCE
COOLPRO
COOLSHIELD
COOLTHANE
COOLTHANE TANK
COOLTRANS
DREAMSCAPE
ENVIROFLEX
EVOLUTION
GRETAG
ILLUSIONS
NUR
OIL BOOM
SCITEX
SEAMLESS WIDE SIGN
VUTEK
WEATHERTYTE
WHERE CHEMISTRY MAKES THE DIFFERENCE

COPLAND FABRICS, INC.
1714 Carolina Mill Rd
Burlington, NC 27217-7837
Tel.: (336) 226-0272
Fax: (336) 226-6452
E-mail: sales@coplandfabrics.com
Web Site: www.coplandfabrics.com
E-Mail For Key Personnel:
Sales Director: sales@coplandfabrics.com
Approx. Number Employees: 400
Year Founded: 1941
Business Description:
Mfr. of Broad Woven Synthetic Fabrics
S.I.C.: 2211
N.A.I.C.S.: 313210
Media: 4-10
Distr.: Natl.
Personnel:
Glenn R. Gehlbach *(VP & Sls Mgr)*
Larry Hulighan *(VP-Sls & Mgr-Hospitality)*
Brands & Products:
COPLAND FABRICS
COPLAND INDUSTRIES
CUDDLE CLOTH
INTENSE

COTTON INCORPORATED CONSUMER MARKETING HEADQUARTERS
(Div. of Cotton Incorporated)
488 Madison Ave
New York, NY 10022
Tel.: (212) 413-8300
Fax: (212) 413-8377
E-mail: info@cottoninc.com
Web Site: www.cottoninc.com
Approx. Number Employees: 24
Year Founded: 1971
Business Description:
Cotton Promotional Services
S.I.C.: 8742
N.A.I.C.S.: 541613
Advertising Expenditures: $27,873,000
Media: 2-3-6-10-11-13-14-15-19-22
Personnel:
Berrye Worsham *(Pres & CEO)*
Richmond S. HendeeRichmond *(VP-Mktg Svcs)*
Robert Nichols *(Sr Dir)*
Richmond Hendee *(Dir-Mktg)*
Robin Merlo *(Dir-Mktg Comm)*
Bill Rearick *(Dir-Finishing Res)*
Glenn Sciachitano *(Dir-Adv)*
Shawn Steiner *(Dir-Pub Rels)*
Jerry Lin *(Acct Mgr-Global)*
Sherry Wu *(Acct Mgr-Global)*
Gloria Borriello *(Mgr-Adv)*
Advertising Agency:
DDB New York
437 Madison Ave
New York, NY 10022-7001
Tel.: (212) 415-2000
Fax: (212) 415-3506

CRAFTEX MILLS INC. OF PENNSYLVANIA
450 Sentry Pkwy E
Blue Bell, PA 19422-2319
Mailing Address:
PO Box 3017
Blue Bell, PA 19422-0795
Tel.: (610) 941-1212
Fax: (610) 941-7171
Web Site: www.craftex.com
Approx. Number Employees: 255
Year Founded: 1903
Business Description:
Mfr. of Upholstery Materials & Fabrics
S.I.C.: 2211
N.A.I.C.S.: 313210
Import Export
Advertising Expenditures: $500,000
Media: 2-4-10-17
Distr.: Intl.; Natl.
Personnel:
Robert M. Blum *(Pres)*
Robert Proske *(CFO & Sr VP)*
Brands & Products:
AVORA
BOUTIQUE
CONSUTURA
CRAFTEX MILLS
CRYPTON
TREVIRA

CROWN PRINCE, INC.
5695 W Franklin Dr
Franklin, WI 53132
Tel.: (414) 421-5400
Fax: (414) 421-3970
Approx. Sls.: $8,000,000
Approx. Number Employees: 200
Business Description:
Embroidery & Screen Printing Services
S.I.C.: 2759
N.A.I.C.S.: 323113
Import
Media: 10
Distr.: Natl.
Personnel:
Dave Scrima *(CFO)*

DESIGNTEX GROUP INC.
(Sub. of Steelcase Inc.)
200 Varick St 8th Fl
New York, NY 10014-7433
Tel.: (212) 886-8100
Fax: (212) 886-8219
Web Site: www.designtex.com
Sales Range: $10-24.9 Million
Approx. Number Employees: 70
Business Description:
Textile Design & Sales
S.I.C.: 5131
N.A.I.C.S.: 424310
Media: 10
Personnel:
Thomas Hamilton *(Pres)*
George Whalen *(CFO)*
Jamie Berg *(Mgr-Product Dev-Wallcovering)*
Brands & Products:
1+1
JM LYNNE
YVES GONNET

THE DIXIE GROUP, INC.
104 Nowlin Ln Ste 101
Chattanooga, TN 37421
Tel.: (423) 510-7000
Telex: 810-573-5284
E-mail: jon.faulkner@dixiegroup.com
Web Site: www.thedixiegroup.com
Approx. Sls.: $231,322,000
Approx. Number Employees: 1,150
Year Founded: 1920
Business Description:
Floorcovering Products, Carpet Yarns, High-End Residential & Contract Commercial Carpet & Designer Rugs Mfr & Sale
S.I.C.: 2273; 2281
N.A.I.C.S.: 314110; 313111
Export
Media: 2-6-7-10-19-22
Distr.: Natl.
Budget Set: Sept. -Oct.
Personnel:
Daniel K. Frierson *(Chm)*
Jon A. Faulkner *(CFO & VP)*
D. Kennedy Frierson, Jr. *(COO & VP)*
Paul B. Comiskey *(Pres-Residential & VP)*
Kenneth L. Dempsey *(Pres-Comml & VP)*
W. Derek Davis *(VP-HR)*
Kim Hamrick *(Mgr-Mktg)*
Brands & Products:
FABRICA
MASLAND

THE DMC CORPORATION
(Sub. of Dollfus Mieg & Cie, S.A.)
Port Kearny Bldg 10F 77 S Hackensack Ave
Kearny, NJ 07032
Tel.: (973) 589-0606
Fax: (973) 589-3744
E-mail: dmcusa@dmc.fr
Web Site: www.dmc-usa.com
Approx. Number Employees: 25
Year Founded: 1934
Business Description:
Art Needlework, Threads, Accessories & Craft Products
S.I.C.: 5949
N.A.I.C.S.: 451130
Import
Advertising Expenditures: $750,000
Media: 2-4-6-7-8-19-21
Distr.: Natl.
Budget Set: Aug.
Personnel:
Joseph McCade *(CEO)*
Sharlene Dinolso *(VP-Sls)*
Steve Mancuso *(VP-Mktg)*
Brands & Products:
DMC
LINEA
TRADITIONS

DRAPER KNITTING CO., INC.
28 Draper Ln
Canton, MA 02021-1555
Tel.: (781) 828-0029
Fax: (781) 828-3034
E-mail: kdraper@draperknitting.com
Web Site: www.draperknitting.com
Approx. Number Employees: 50
Year Founded: 1984
Business Description:
Mfr. of Knitted Fabrics, Safety Fabrics & Non-Woven Fabrics
S.I.C.: 2257; 2297

Key to Media (For complete agency information see *The Advertising Red Books-Agencies* edition):
1. Bus. Publs. 2. Cable T.V. 3. Catalogs & Directories. 4. Co-op Adv. 5. Consumer Mags. 6. D.M. to Bus. Estab.7. D.M. to Consumers
8. Daily Newsp. 9. Exhibits/Trade Shows 10. Foreign 11. Infomercial 12. Internet Adv.13. Multimedia 14. Network Radio
15. Network T.V. 16. Newsp. Distr. Mags. 17. Other 18. Outdoor (Posters, Transit) 19. Point of Purchase20. Premiums, Novelties
21. Product Samples 22. Special Events Mktg. 23. Spot Radio 24. Spot T.V. 25. Weekly Newsp. 26. Yellow Page Adv.

N.A.I.C.S.: 313241; 313230
Import Export
Media: 2-6-20-21
Distr.: Natl.
Personnel:
Kristin Draper *(Pres & Mgr-Mktg & Dev)*
Alice Argentine *(Office Mgr)*
Susan Cordo *(Mgr-Network)*
David Wedge *(Mgr-Technical Fabric Dev & Product)*
Brands & Products:
BASOFIL
ECO PILE
EQUI PILE
HIGHLAND BLENDS
HOLOMEDIC
KEVLAR
LENZING-FR
NOMEX
PANOX
PBI
Advertising Agency:
The Laidlaw Group, LLC
337 Summer St
Boston, MA 02210
Tel.: (617) 423-2801
Fax: (617) 423-2802

E-Z BOWZ, LLC
903 Parkway Ste 129
Gatlinburg, TN 37738
Tel.: (865) 277-7461
Fax: (865) 279-7462
Toll Free: (800) 311-6529
E-mail: info@ezbowz.com
Web Site: www.ezbowz.com
Approx. Number Employees: 9
Year Founded: 1993
Business Description:
Craft Supply Whslr
S.I.C.: 3944; 5092
N.A.I.C.S.: 339932; 423920
Media: 2-4-5-6-7-8-10-11-19-21
Distr.: Intl.
Personnel:
Art Cavender *(Vice Chm & CEO)*
Lea Cavender *(Pres)*
Brands & Products:
ANGEL BOWZ
E-Z BOWMAKER
E-Z BOWZ
E-Z CRAFT
E-Z ROSE & FLOWER MAKER
FAIRY BOWZ
MIRACLE BOW
MOSAIC MANIA
SANTA BOWZ
TREASURE KEEPER

EYE CATCHERS
1547 N State St
Lehi, UT 84043
Mailing Address:
PO Box 823
Lehi, UT 84043-0823
Tel.: (801) 766-2388
E-mail: cpturton@eyecatchers-solaray.com
Web Site: www.eyecatchers-solaray.com
Approx. Sls.: $1,000,000
Approx. Number Employees: 4
Year Founded: 1968
Business Description:
Sequins, Holographic Films & Computer Vinyl Mfr
S.I.C.: 3993
N.A.I.C.S.: 339950
Export
Media: 1-2-4-7-8-10-19-21-26
Distr.: Intl.; Natl.
Budget Set: Nov.
Personnel:
Jennifer Turton *(Owner)*
Brands & Products:
EYE CATCHERS
HOLOGRAPH
SOLARAY

EZ QUILTING
(Div. of Wm. Wright Company)
85 S St
West Warren, MA 01092
Tel.: (413) 436-7732
Fax: (413) 436-9785
Toll Free: (800) 660-0415
Web Site: www.wrights.com
Approx. Number Employees: 50
Year Founded: 1952
Business Description:
Sewing Notions, Quilting & Crafts Mfr
S.I.C.: 5949
N.A.I.C.S.: 451130
Import Export
Advertising Expenditures: $250,000
Media: 10-13-16-24
Distr.: Natl.
Budget Set: Oct. -Nov.
Personnel:
Monica Dobson *(Mgr-Mktg)*
Brands & Products:
DESIGNED FOR QUILTERS BY QUILTERS
EASY TRI-MATE
FLEXDESIGN RULE
QUILTS TO COME HOME TO
SEAMS RIGHT
TRI-RECS

FAB INDUSTRIES CORP.
98 Cutter Mill Rd Ste 412
Great Neck, NY 11021
Tel.: (516) 498-3200
Fax: (516) 829-0783
E-mail: fabindus@mindspring.com
Web Site: www.fab-industries.com
Sales Range: $25-49.9 Million
Approx. Number Employees: 475
Year Founded: 1966
Business Description:
Warp Knit & Laminated Fabrics Mfr
S.I.C.: 2258; 2211; 2253; 2254
N.A.I.C.S.: 313249; 313210; 315191; 315192
Export
Media: 4-10
Distr.: Natl.
Personnel:
Steven S. Myers *(Pres & COO)*
David A. Miller *(CFO, Treas & VP-Fin)*
Sam Hiatt *(Exec VP)*

FEDERAL FOAM TECHNOLOGIES INC.
(Sub. of Federal International Inc.)
600 Wisconsin Dr
New Richmond, WI 54017-2608
Tel.: (715) 246-9500
Fax: (715) 246-9599
Toll Free: (800) 898-9559
E-mail: sales@federalfoam.com
Web Site: www.federalfoam.com
E-Mail For Key Personnel:
Sales Director: sales@federalfoam.com
Sales Range: $25-49.9 Million
Approx. Number Employees: 95
Year Founded: 1946
Business Description:
Flexible Cellular & Plastic Materials Mfr
S.I.C.: 3086; 2299
N.A.I.C.S.: 326150; 314999
Media: 2-4-6-7-8-10-13-19-21-22-23-26
Distr.: Natl.
Personnel:
Wyman Smith *(Pres)*
William Jwanouskos *(CFO)*
Mike Pemble *(Dir-DP)*
Dale Kautz *(Mgr-Ops)*
Todd Kidder *(Mgr-Natl Sls)*
Jon Seeger *(Mgr-Environmental)*
Greg Windsperge *(Mgr-Sls)*
Brands & Products:
CHIROPRACTIC IMPRESSIONS
CRESCENT PRODUCTS
MARTIAL ARTS MAT
STERLING COLLECTION
THE SWAIN SPORTSMAT

THE FELTERS GROUP
5965 Hwy 221
Roebuck, SC 29376-0228
Mailing Address:
PO Box 228
Roebuck, SC 29376
Tel.: (864) 576-7900
Fax: (864) 574-5235
Toll Free: (800) 845-7596
E-mail: billa@felters.com
Web Site: www.felters.com
Approx. Number Employees: 200
Year Founded: 1898
Business Description:
Needle Mechanical Roll Felts & Fabricated Nonmetallic Materials Mfr
S.I.C.: 2297; 3469
N.A.I.C.S.: 313230; 332116
Import Export
Advertising Expenditures: $300,000
Media: 2-4-21
Distr.: Direct to Consumer; Natl.
Budget Set: Oct.
Personnel:
Gern Lowe *(Pres)*
Brands & Products:
THE FELTERS GROUP
FIRMAFLEX
FOAM SAFE
QUILT SAFE
SLEEP SAFE

FREUDENBERG NONWOVENS LIMITED PARTNERSHIP
(Sub. of Freudenberg & Co. Kommanditgesellschaft)
3500 Industrial Dr Eno Industrial Park
Durham, NC 27704
Tel.: (919) 620-3900
Fax: (919) 620-3945
Toll Free: (800) 40-VILENE
E-mail: vilene.usa@fvna.com
Web Site: www.freudenberg.de
Sales Range: $125-149.9 Million
Approx. Number Employees: 25
Year Founded: 1952
Business Description:
Nonwoven Textiles for Apparel, Industry & Air Filtration, Home Decorating Crafts, Full Range of Interlinings, Non-Woven, Woven & Knit
S.I.C.: 2297; 5023
N.A.I.C.S.: 313230; 423220
Import Export
Advertising Expenditures: $300,000
Media: 1-2-4-6-7-10-11-12-19-20-21
Distr.: Intl.; Natl.
Budget Set: Jan.
Personnel:
John McNabb *(Gen Mgr)*

G&K SERVICES INC.
5995 Opus Pkwy Ste 500
Minnetonka, MN 55343
Tel.: (952) 912-5500
Fax: (952) 912-5999
E-mail: srcarlson@gkservices.com
Web Site: www.gkservices.com
Approx. Rev.: $828,861,000
Approx. Number Employees: 7,500
Year Founded: 1902
Business Description:
Uniform Supplier & Facilities Services
S.I.C.: 7213; 7218; 7389
N.A.I.C.S.: 812331; 561499; 812332
Advertising Expenditures: $1,200,000
Media: 2-4-7-10-13-20-22-26
Distr.: Natl.
Budget Set: Mar.
Personnel:
M. Lenny Pippin *(Chm)*
Douglas A. Milroy *(CEO)*
Jeffrey L. Wright *(CFO & Exec VP)*
Karen S. Kirwan *(CIO & VP)*
Jeffrey L. Cotter *(Gen Counsel, Sec & VP)*
Dave Euson *(Sr VP-Mktg)*
Jacqueline T. Punch *(Sr VP-HR)*
Richard J. Stutz *(Sr VP-Ops & Sourcing)*
Michael F. Woodard *(VP-IT)*
Brands & Products:
ENHANCING IMAGE & SAFETY THROUGH INNOVATION
EXCEED
G AND K SERVICES
IMAGE GUARD
PROSURA
PROTECT
Advertising Agency:
The Zimmerman Group
21940 Minnetonka Blvd
Excelsior, MN 55331
Tel.: (952) 470-8830
Fax: (952) 470-8807

GILMORE & QUINN INDUSTRIES INC.
150 Wesley St
South Hackensack, NJ 07606-1510
Tel.: (201) 487-4492
Fax: (201) 343-4175
Approx. Number Employees: 20
Year Founded: 1990
Business Description:
Belt Backings, Beltings & Plastic Extrusions
S.I.C.: 3111; 2299
N.A.I.C.S.: 316110; 314999
Import Export
Media: 2-7-10-21
Distr.: Natl.
Budget Set: Nov.
Personnel:
Robert Siegel *(Pres)*
Joshua Gat *(VP & Gen Mgr)*

Key to Media (For complete agency information see *The Advertising Red Books-Agencies* edition):
1. Bus. Publs. 2. Cable T.V. 3. Catalogs & Directories. 4. Co-op Adv. 5. Consumer Mags. 6. D.M. to Bus. Estab.7. D.M. to Consumers
8. Daily Newsp. 9. Exhibits/Trade Shows 10. Foreign 11. Infomercial 12. Internet Adv.13. Multimedia 14. Network Radio
15. Network T.V. 16. Newsp. Distr. Mags. 17. Other 18. Outdoor (Posters, Transit) 19. Point of Purchase20. Premiums, Novelties
21. Product Samples 22. Special Events Mktg. 23. Spot Radio 24. Spot T.V. 25. Weekly Newsp. 26. Yellow Page Adv.

Gilmore & Quinn Industries Inc. — (Continued)

Brands & Products:
DURA BAC
PERMAFUZE

GLEN RAVEN, INC.
1831 N Park Ave
Glen Raven, NC 27217
Tel.: (336) 227-6211
Fax: (336) 226-8133
E-mail: garments@glenraven.com
Web Site: www.glenraven.com
Approx. Number Employees: 115
Year Founded: 1880
Business Description:
Textile Mill Products Mfr; Specialty Yarns, Upholstery Fabrics Mfr & Marketer; Dyeing & Finishing Operations
S.I.C.: 2281; 2211
N.A.I.C.S.: 313111; 313210
Import Export
Advertising Expenditures: $825,000
Media: 6-9-10-17-19-25
Distr.: Natl.
Budget Set: June
Personnel:
Allen E. Gant, Jr. *(Pres & CEO)*
Gary Smith *(CFO, Treas & Sr VP)*
Charlie Edgerton *(Pres-Glen Raven Logistics)*
Carl E. Wallace, Jr. *(Gen Counsel, Sec & Sr VP)*
William S. Chandler, Jr. *(VP-HR)*
Rob Lord *(Dir-Logistics-Glen Raven Logistics)*
Sue Rich *(Mgr-Mktg)*
Brands & Products:
BANGUARD
DICKSON
ERADI-LITE
GLEN RAVEN
NITE-LITE
OPERA
SUNBRELLA
SUNBRITE
SUR LAST
Advertising Agency:
Wray Ward Marketing Communications
900 Baxter St
Charlotte, NC 28204
Tel.: (704) 332-9071
Fax: (704) 375-5971
Fabrics

GREENWOOD MILLS, INC.
300 Morgan Ave
Greenwood, SC 29646-2641
Tel.: (864) 229-2571
Toll Free: (800) 847-5929
Web Site: www.greenwoodmills.com
Approx. Number Employees: 500
Year Founded: 1889
Business Description:
Mfr. of Fabrics for Men's, Women's & Children's Wear; Uniform & Career Apparel; Home Furnishings
S.I.C.: 2211
N.A.I.C.S.: 313210
Import Export
Advertising Expenditures: $1,500,000
Media: 1-2-4-7-10-16-20
Distr.: Natl.
Budget Set: Oct.
Personnel:
James C. Self *(Pres & COO)*
Tommy Davis *(CFO & Exec VP)*
Wade Harter *(VP-Engrng)*

GUDEBROD, INC.
274 Shoemaker Rd
Pottstown, PA 19464-6434
Tel.: (610) 327-4050
Fax: (610) 327-4588
E-mail: sales@gudebrod.com
Web Site: www.gudebrod.com
E-Mail For Key Personnel:
Sales Director: sales@gudebrod.com
Approx. Number Employees: 170
Year Founded: 1870
Business Description:
Mfr. of Thread, Umbilical Tape, Dental Floss, Fishlines, Electronic Lacing Tapes & Cords
S.I.C.: 2824; 2298
N.A.I.C.S.: 325222; 314991
Import Export
Media: 4-5-6-10-21
Distr.: Intl.; Natl.
Personnel:
Nat LeGrande *(Pres)*
Steve Gorsky *(CFO)*
William LeGrande *(Mgr-Sls & Mktg)*
Brands & Products:
CHAMPION
EZ-DUB
FOLD AWAY
GUDEBROD
HT
MONARCH
NCP
SUPER G
TRIMAR

GUILFORD PERFORMANCE TEXTILES
(Holding of Cerberus Capital Management, L.P.)
1001 Military Cutoff Rd Ste 300
Wilmington, NC 28405
Mailing Address:
PO Box 26969
Greensboro, NC 27419-6969
Tel.: (910) 794-5800
E-mail: custserv@gfd.com
Web Site: www.guilfordproducts.com
Sales Range: $150-199.9 Million
Approx. Number Employees: 2,650
Year Founded: 1946
Business Description:
Textile Production for Automobiles & Apparel
S.I.C.: 2392; 2258; 2299
N.A.I.C.S.: 314129; 313249; 314999
Import Export
Media: 2-7-10-17
Personnel:
David Thursfield *(Chm)*
Shannon White *(CEO)*
Marc Bourhis *(CFO)*
Bruce Smith *(COO & VP)*
Robert W. Nolan *(Exec VP)*
Tony Millington *(VP & Dir-Ops-Europe)*
Joe Cottone *(VP-Strategy & Integration)*
Alan R. Mackinnon *(VP-Automotive Sls)*
Leslie Rundell *(Mgr-Mktg)*
Brands & Products:
CANCEL STAT
COTTON FIESTA
DRI-Q
GUILFAST
SPUNFLEX
STAT STAR
VANGARD

HANCOCK FABRICS, INC.
1 Fashion Way
Baldwyn, MS 38824-8547
Tel.: (662) 365-6000
Tel.: (662) 842-2834
Fax: (662) 842-2834
E-mail: consumerdiv@hancockfabrics.com
Web Site: www.hancockfabrics.com
Approx. Sls.: $275,465,000
Approx. Number Employees: 4,300
Year Founded: 1957
Business Description:
Fashion Textile & Home Decor Materials & Sewing Equipment Whslr & Retailer
S.I.C.: 5949; 5961
N.A.I.C.S.: 451130; 454111
Advertising Expenditures: $10,100,000
Media: 3-5-6-8-9-10-13-15-16-19-22-23-24-26
Distr.: Natl.
Budget Set: Jan.
Personnel:
Steven D. Scheiwe *(Chm)*
Steven R. Morgan *(Pres & CEO)*
Robert W. Driskell *(CFO & Exec VP)*
Blake A. Fohl *(CMO)*
Hugh Hargett *(Sr VP-Wholesale Trade)*
Linda Gail Moore *(Sr VP-Mdsg & Mktg)*
William A. Sheffield *(Sr VP-Distr)*
William D. Smothers *(Sr VP-Real Estate)*
Susan van Benten *(Sr VP-Mdsg)*
Susan Zewicke *(Sr VP-Store Ops)*
Larry D. Fair *(VP-Fin)*
Stacey Gross *(VP-Ecommerce)*
Brands & Products:
DISCOVER THE DESIGNER IN YOU
HANCOCK FABRICS
LAUREN HANCOCK COLLECTION

HARODITE INDUSTRIES, INC.
66 S St
Taunton, MA 02780
Tel.: (508) 824-6961
Fax: (508) 880-0696
Web Site: www.harodite.com
Approx. Number Employees: 100
Year Founded: 1910
Business Description:
Mfr. of Finished Textiles
S.I.C.: 2211; 2261
N.A.I.C.S.: 313210; 313311
Import Export
Media: 2-4-7-10-11-17
Distr.: Intl.; Natl.
Personnel:
Michael P. Albert *(Chm)*
Aaron M. Albert *(Pres & CEO)*
J. Luis Suarez *(CFO)*
Antonio Gomez *(Gen Mgr)*
Donna Adams *(Dir-Quality)*
Frank Grace *(Dir-Product Dev)*
Dale Fulgham *(Reg Mgr-Sls)*
Joe Buckley *(Mgr)*
Jean Jardim *(Mgr-HR)*
Mitchell Knee *(Mgr-Reg Sls-NE)*
Ozzie Medeiros *(Mgr-Ops)*
Brands & Products:
EDGELOK
ETACOL
EZ-CREASE
HAROCOL
HAROFILM
HAROFIT
HAROFORM
HARONET
HAROPRESS
HAROSHAPE
HAROSTRETCH
STAFLEX

HERCULITE PRODUCTS, INC.
(Sub. of Aberdeen Road Company)
PO Box 435 105 E Sinking Spring Ln
Emigsville, PA 17318-0435
Tel.: (717) 764-1192
Fax: (717) 764-5211
Toll Free: (800) 772-0036
E-mail: customercare@herculite.com
Web Site: www.herculite.com
Approx. Number Employees: 50
Business Description:
Industrial & Safety Fabrics
S.I.C.: 2295
N.A.I.C.S.: 313320
Export
Media: 2-7-10
Distr.: Intl.
Budget Set: June -Dec.
Personnel:
Peter Mckernan *(Pres & CEO)*
Paul Moeller *(CFO & VP)*
Deena J. Davis *(Coord-Mktg)*
Brands & Products:
AQUATEX
AQUATEX II
ARCHITENT
ARCHITENT WIDESIDE
AUSTENITIC
BANNER-UP
BANTEX
BANTEX UNIVERSAL
CENTURION
COASTLINE PLUS
COLORGUARD
COMFORT
FUSION
HERCULEX
HERCULITE
HERCULITE AUSTENITIC PROTECTION FABRICS
LECTROLITE
LECTROLITE COMFORT
RAIN-KLEEN
REGATTA
SENTINEL
SERENE
SURE-CHEK
SURE-CHEK COMFORT
SURE-CHEK FUSION
SURE-THANE
VANGUARD
WIDESIDE

HERITAGE LACE INC.
309 S St
Pella, IA 50219
Tel.: (641) 628-4949
Fax: (641) 628-1689
Toll Free: (800) 354-0668
E-mail: inquire@heritagelace.net
Web Site: www.heritagelace.com
Approx. Number Employees: 70

Key to Media (For complete agency information see *The Advertising Red Books-Agencies* edition):
1. Bus. Publs. 2. Cable T.V. 3. Catalogs & Directories. 4. Co-op Adv. 5. Consumer Mags. 6. D.M. to Bus. Estab.7. D.M. to Consumers
8. Daily Newsp. 9. Exhibits/Trade Shows 10. Foreign 11. Infomercial 12. Internet Adv.13. Multimedia 14. Network Radio
15. Network T.V. 16. Newsp. Distr. Mags. 17. Other 18. Outdoor (Posters, Transit) 19. Point of Purchase20. Premiums, Novelties
21. Product Samples 22. Special Events Mktg. 23. Spot Radio 24. Spot T.V. 25. Weekly Newsp. 26. Yellow Page Adv.

Year Founded: 1983
Business Description:
Mfr. & Marketing & Import of Lace
S.I.C.: 5023; 2392
N.A.I.C.S.: 423220; 314129
Import Export
Media: 2-4-6-7-10-19-21
Distr.: Natl.
Personnel:
Dan Decook *(Co-CEO)*
Tim Heerema *(Co-CEO)*
Brands & Products:
A MOTHER'S LOVE
ABUNDANCE
ALLIUM
ANGEL
ANGELS
APPLE BASKET
BASKET WEAVE
BEACH
BETHLEHEM
BIRDHOUSE
BLACK
BLESSING OF CHRISTMAS
BLOSSOM
BLUE CHECK
BOG
BRICK QUADRANT
BUTTERFLIES
CABIN IN THE WOODS
CAMEL
CAMEO ROSE
CANDLE
CANDY CONE
CARNEO ROSE
CATS HAVE STAFF
CATS MEOW
CHAPEL
CHERRIES
CHERRY-O
CHRISTMAS SLEIGH RIDE
CHRISTMAS TREE
CHURCH
CLASSIC
COTTAGE GARDEN
COUNTRY GARDEN
CRIMSON
CRIMSON CHECK
CROSS
CUTEST LITTLE BABY
DAISY
DAISY TRO
DOGWOOD
DOVE
DRAPE SHADES
DYNASTY
EDEN
ENCORE
ENGLISH COUNTRY ROSE
ENGLISH IVY
FAITH
FELINE FRIENDS
FERN
FLEURETTE
FLORAL
FLORAL BOUQUET
FLORAL TRELLIS
FLORAL URN
FLORIADE
FLOWER GARDEN
FLOWER POTS
FLOWER POWER
FOLK ANGELS
FRUIT BASKET
GABRIELLE PLAID
GARDEN GLORY
GERANIUMS
GIVE THANKS
GOD BLESS AMERICA
GOD'S PROMISES
GRADMA
GRADMAS ROCK
GRANDMA
GRAPEVINE
GREATEST GIFT
GREEN REVERSIBLE
GREENBRIER
GROW WITH LOVE
HEADACHE
HEART TO HEART
HEAVEN
HEAVEN SENT
HEIRLOOM
HERITAGE LACE
HOLIDAY EMBROIDERED
HOLLY
HOLLY JOLLY CHRISTMAS
HOLLY RIBBON
HOME SWEET HOME
HOMESPUN
HONEYCOMB
HOUSE
HOUSE CAT
IT'S A BOY
IT'S A GIRL
IVORY
IVY BELLPULL
JINGLE BELLS
JOYFUL ANGEL
LACY
LEAVES
LES FLEURS
LET HEAVEN
LET IT SNOW
LIGHTHOUSE
LILY OF THE DAY
LINDSEY PLAID
LINEN HOLLY
LIVE WELL
LOVE
LOVE EWE
MACRAME
MADELINE PLAID
MARQUISE
MERRY CHRISTMAS
MITTEN
MITTEN 4 SALE
MOCHA
MONOGRAMS
MOSS TWEED
MOTHER ROSE
MS. UNDERSTOOD
MYSTIQUE
NATIVITY
NATURE SING
NAVY
NO PALCE LIKE HOME
O HOLY NIGHT
OATMEAL TWEED
ORNAMENTS
PEARLS
PERSIMMON
PINEAPPLE
PINECONE
PINECONE HOLLY
PLATES BELLPULL
PRETTY IN PURPLE
PRIMROSE
PRINCESS
QUILT PATCH
QUILT SCRAPS
RED REVERSIBLE
REMBRANDT
ROBIN EGG QUADRANT
ROBINWOOD PLAID
ROOSTER
ROSE
ROSEBUD
SAGE
SAGE BORDER STRIPE
SANDSTONE PLAID
SANTA CLAUS
SARAH PLAID
SCANDIA
SCATTER JOY
SEASCAPE
SET SAIL
SHEER DIVINE
SILVER POINSETTIA
SIMPLE BLESSINGS
SIMPLICTY
SIMPLY DIVINE
SKY BLUE
SNOW KISSES
SNOW PHOTO
SNOW TIME
SNOWFLAKE
SNOWMEN
SNOWNMAN
SOFT YELLOW
SPICE PLAID
STAR
STAR OF WONDER
STUART PLAID
SUMMERSET
SUNFLOWER
SWEETEST FLOWER
TAN
TAN HOUND'S TOOTH
TANE
TEA ROSE
TEDDY STOCKING
TEE TIME
TRACERY
TULIP
VICTORIA
VICTORIAN ROSE
VINEYARD
VINTAGE ROSE
WARM FUZZIES
WELCOME
WELCOME FRIENDS
WHAT WE KNOW
WHATEVER YOU ARE
WHITE FLOWER
WHITE PINE
WHITE ROSE
WILD FLOWERS
WILDWOOD
WINDMILL
WINDSOR
WINTER GREENS
WONDERFUL COUNSELOR

HERRSCHNERS, INC.
2800 Hoover Rd
Stevens Point, WI 54481-7103
Tel.: (715) 341-4554
Tel.: (715) 342-0741 (Acctg)
Fax: (715) 341-2250
Toll Free: (800) 441-0838
E-mail: help@herrschners.com
Web Site: www.herrschners.com
Approx. Number Employees: 200
Year Founded: 1899
Business Description:
Sales of Needlework Hobbycrafts
S.I.C.: 5961; 5949
N.A.I.C.S.: 454113; 451130
Media: 4-6-8-13
Distr.: Direct to Consumer; Natl.
Budget Set: Various
Personnel:
Ted Hesemann *(CEO)*
John Gritzmacher *(VP-Mdsg)*
David Verhage *(VP-Fin)*
Brands & Products:
HERRSCHNERS

HIRSCH INTERNATIONAL CORP.
50 Engineers Rd
Hauppauge, NY 11788
Mailing Address:
PO Box 18004
Hauppauge, NY 11788
Tel.: (631) 436-7100
Fax: (631) 436-7054
E-mail: info@hirschintl.com
Web Site:
www.hirschinternational.com
Approx. Sls.: $42,527,000
Approx. Number Employees: 138
Year Founded: 1970
Business Description:
Distr of Computerized Embroidery Equipment & Supplies; Developer of Computer Software Programs & Lessor of Computerized Embroidery Equipment
S.I.C.: 5084
N.A.I.C.S.: 423830
Advertising Expenditures: $305,000
Media: 2-5-10-13
Distr.: Natl.
Budget Set: Nov.
Personnel:
Paul Gallagher *(Pres, CEO & COO)*
Kristof Janowski *(Exec VP-Sls & Mktg)*
Brands & Products:
THE FABRIC OF YOUR SUCCESS
HIRSCH
MICROSMART

HONEYWELL NYLON LLC
(Sub. of Honeywell International Inc.)
101 Columbia Rd
Morristown, NJ 07960-4640
Tel.: (877) 841-2840
Fax: (480) 353-3020
Toll Free: (800) 247-0557
Web Site: www51.honeywell.com/sm/polymers/
Sales Range: $25-49.9 Million
Approx. Number Employees: 14
Year Founded: 1929
Business Description:
Nylon, Nylon Yarn, Fiber Tinitermediate, Caprolactam & Polycaprolactam Mfr
S.I.C.: 2282
N.A.I.C.S.: 313112
Import Export
Advertising Expenditures: $7,500,000
Media: 2-5-6-7-9-10-15-19-21-23-24
Distr.: Natl.
Brands & Products:
BASOFIL
CREATE
POWERSILK
SAVANT
SHIMMEREEN
SILKY TOUCH
ULTRA TOUCH
ZEFSPORT
ZEFTRON
ZEFTRON 200
ZEFTRON 2000
ZEFTRON 2000 ZX

Key to Media (For complete agency information see *The Advertising Red Books-Agencies* edition):
1. Bus. Publs. 2. Cable T.V. 3. Catalogs & Directories. 4. Co-op Adv. 5. Consumer Mags. 6. D.M. to Bus. Estab.7. D.M. to Consumers 8. Daily Newsp. 9. Exhibits/Trade Shows 10. Foreign 11. Infomercial 12. Internet Adv.13. Multimedia 14. Network Radio 15. Network T.V. 16. Newsp. Distr. Mags. 17. Other 18. Outdoor (Posters, Transit) 19. Point of Purchase20. Premiums, Novelties 21. Product Samples 22. Special Events Mktg. 23. Spot Radio 24. Spot T.V. 25. Weekly Newsp. 26. Yellow Page Adv.

HORIZON DESIGNS, INC.
5308 Parklane Dr Ste 1
Kearney, NE 68847
Tel.: (308) 237-2213
Fax: (308) 237-3048
Toll Free: (800) 445-1804
E-mail: hdi@horizondesigns.com
Web Site: www.horizondesigns.com
Approx. Number Employees: 25
Year Founded: 1982
Business Description:
Mfr., Importer & Marketer of Sewn Products with Embroidery & Screenprints
S.I.C.: 2393; 2759
N.A.I.C.S.: 314911; 323113
Advertising Expenditures: $200,000
Media: 2-4-7-10-13
Distr.: Natl.
Personnel:
Susan C. Bigg *(Owner & Pres)*
Stephanie Dickey *(VP-Sls & Creative Dev)*
Jason Kounovsky *(Dir-Art)*
Brands & Products:
HORIZON DESIGNS
LET HORIZON DESIGN FOR YOU

INTERFACE, INC.
2859 Paces Ferry Rd SE Ste 2000
Atlanta, GA 30339-6216
Tel.: (770) 437-6800
Fax: (706) 882-0500
Web Site: www.interfaceinc.com
Approx. Sls.: $961,827,000
Approx. Number Employees: 3,421
Year Founded: 1973
Business Description:
Commercial Carpets Mfr
S.I.C.: 2273
N.A.I.C.S.: 314110
Import Export
Advertising Expenditures: $600,000
Media: 1-2-3-4-6-7-8-10-11-13
Distr.: Natl.
Budget Set: Nov.
Personnel:
Ray C. Anderson *(Chm)*
Daniel T. Hendrix *(Pres & CEO)*
Patrick C. Lynch *(CFO & Sr VP)*
Robert A. Coombs *(Sr VP-Asia Pacific)*
Lindsey K. Parnell *(Sr VP-Europe Floorcoverings)*
John R. Wells *(Sr VP-Americas Floorcoverings)*
Rhonda Mitchell *(Dir-Mktg)*
Brands & Products:
ACADEMIC
ADAPTATIONS
AGNONA
AMAZING
AMPLIFIED
ANCIENT SPIRAL
ARCHITECTURE
BALANCE
BAMBOO GROVE
BENTLEY PRINCE STREET
BIOBAC
BIOMORPH
BOARDWALK
BOUCLE GRID
BOX GARDEN
BRABOURNE
CABANA
CAMPANA
CANOPY
CARIBBEAN
CASTLE BAY
CESTINO
CHARLES RIVER
CHENILLE WARP
CLARITY
COIR
COMMON THREADS
CUBIC
CUBISM
DECO
EARTH
EMAKI
ENTENDRE
ENTROBEAN
ENTROPY
ENTRY LEVEL
EQUAL SPACE
EQUATION
EQUATOR
EQUILIBRIUM
FALLING WATER
FAMILY TREE
FINER THINGS
FLOR
FOGLIA
FREQUENCY
FURROWS
FUTURE TILE
GARDEN PATCH
GEOMETRY
GINKGO LEAF
GINZA
GIST
GLASBAC
GRADIENT
GRILLWORK
HAPPENING
HEARTFELT
HEIRLOOM
HEUGA
HIGH PLAINS
HOME
HOME MOVIES
HUEGA
HYPERION
ICONIC
INTERCELL
INTERFACE FLOORING SYSTEMS
INTERFACEFABRIC
INTERFACEFLOR
INTERFOLD
INTERPLAY
INTERPOINT
INTERSECT
INTERSEPT
INTERSTAT
INTERTWIST
INTERVIEW
JAKARTA
JAPANESE FERN
KABUKI
KAMALA
KILIM MOTIF
KINESIS
KINGS ROAD
KOI
LASSO
LATE NIGHT TV
LEADER
LIBRA
LINE UP
LOOP DE LOOP
LOWELL
LUSH LEAF
LUSSO
MALPENSA
MANTRA
MARRAKESH
MATSURI
MEADOW
MEDITATIONS
MENAGERIE
METAMORPHIC
MILANO
MILL CITY
MISSION ZERO
MODERNISM
MONTENAPO
MOORFIELD
MORE MONSTERS UNDER THE BED
MORNING COFFEE
NATURE TRAILS
NEEDLEWORK
NERVI
NEW STRATFORD
NEXT IN LINE
NIKKO
OLIO
ORBIT
PAINT BOX
PANORAMA
PASSAGEWAY
PAST
PATCHWORK
PAWTUCKET FALLS
PEAK DISTRICT
PIACENZA
PIANTA
PIZZO
PLAIN WEAVE
PLUSH CROC
POLESTAR
POP
PRECAST
PRESENT
PRINCE STREET HOUSE & HOME
PRODUCER
PROFILE
PSYCHEDELIC
RAIN FOREST
RENOVISIONS
RESKU
RE:SOURCE
ROBIE HOUSE
ROUTE 66
RUGGED TERRAIN
SAMURAI
SATORI
SCAN
SCRIBBLE
SERENDIPITY
SEWN UP
SHE LOVES ME
SHIZEN
SILK ROUTE
SISAL TWIST
SOFT CHORD
SOFTSISAL
SOLID FOUNDATION
SOLID GROUND
SOMERSET
SOUTHERN PLAINS
SPACED OUT
SPAGO
SUPER FLOR
SYMBIOSIS
SYNCHRONICITY
TALIESIN
TATAMI
TEKNIT
TEKSOLUTIONS
TERRA
TERRATEX
TESSUTO
THICK AND THIN
THICKET
TIBETAN FOREST
TONAL
TOY POODLE
TRANSFORMATION
TURBULENCE
UNDERCURRENT
UPWARDLY MOBILE
URBAN GRID
VENEER
VESTITO
VIENNA SWIRL
VISCONTI
WALKING ON AIR
WALKING ON CLOUDS
WIDE WALE
WILLOW
WIND
WOODLAND WAY
WORKING CLASS
Advertising Agency:
Godfrey Advertising
40 N Christian St
Lancaster, PA 17602
Tel.: (717) 393-3831
Fax: (717) 393-1403

INTERNATIONAL TEXTILE GROUP, INC.
(Holding of W.L. Ross & Co., LLC)
804 Green Valley Rd Ste 300
Greensboro, NC 27408
Mailing Address:
PO Box 26540
Greensboro, NC 27415-6540
Tel.: (336) 379-6220
Fax: (336) 379-6043
E-mail: info@itg-global.com
Web Site: www.itg-global.com
E-Mail For Key Personnel:
Public Relations: sides.delores@burlington.com
Approx. Sls.: $616,130,000
Approx. Number Employees: 8,700
Year Founded: 2004
Business Description:
Automotive, Apparel & Interior Furnishings Fabric & Textile Mfr & Distr
S.I.C.: 2211; 2261; 2299; 2392
N.A.I.C.S.: 313210; 313311; 314129; 314999
Advertising Expenditures: $200,000
Media: 2-4-5-6-7-8-9-10-19-25
Distr.: Natl.
Personnel:
Wilbur L. Ross, Jr. *(Chm)*
Joseph L. Gorga *(Pres & CEO)*
Gail A. Kuczkowski *(Chief Acctg Officer & VP)*
Kenneth T. Kunberger *(Pres-ITG Apparel & Specialty Fabrics)*
Neil W. Koonce *(Gen Counsel & VP)*
Jeffrey H. Peck *(Exec VP-ITG Apparel & Specialty Fabrics)*
Robert E. Garren *(VP-HR & Corp Comm)*
Barbara Sorkin *(VP-Corp Comm)*
Delores Sides *(Dir-Corp Comm & HR)*
Brands & Products:
AUTHENTECH COLLECTION
BURLINGTON
CONE DENIM
MCS
RAEFORD

Key to Media (For complete agency information see *The Advertising Red Books-Agencies* edition):
1. Bus. Publs. 2. Cable T.V. 3. Catalogs & Directories. 4. Co-op Adv. 5. Consumer Mags. 6. D.M. to Bus. Estab.7. D.M. to Consumers 8. Daily Newsp. 9. Exhibits/Trade Shows 10. Foreign 11. Infomercial 12. Internet Adv.13. Multimedia 14. Network Radio 15. Network T.V. 16. Newsp. Distr. Mags. 17. Other 18. Outdoor (Posters, Transit) 19. Point of Purchase20. Premiums, Novelties 21. Product Samples 22. Special Events Mktg. 23. Spot Radio 24. Spot T.V. 25. Weekly Newsp. 26. Yellow Page Adv.

WEATHERMAX

JANLYNN CORPORATION

2070 W Dover Rd
Chicopee, MA 01022
Tel.: (413) 543-7500
Fax: (018) 005-265966
E-mail: customerserv@janlynn.com
Web Site: www.janlynn.com
Approx. Number Employees: 130
Year Founded: 1979
Business Description:
Mfr & Retailer of Crafts & Stitchery Kits
S.I.C.: 2261; 2389
N.A.I.C.S.: 313311; 315299
Advertising Expenditures: $100,000
Media: 4-5-8-10-11-19
Distr.: Natl.
Budget Set: Jan.
Personnel:
John F. Kozub *(Pres & CEO)*
Brands & Products:
COMPUTERCRAFTS
JANLYNN
MAKE IT COOL
PAINT POTTERY
STAMPS HAPPEN
STRING ALONG

JEFFREY KLEIN RIBBON DESIGNS

176 E 7th St
Paterson, NJ 07524
Tel.: (973) 684-4671
Fax: (973) 684-1136
E-mail: myownribbon@aol.com
Approx. Number Employees: 35
Business Description:
Floral & Satin Ribbons Designer & Retailer
S.I.C.: 2241; 2299
N.A.I.C.S.: 313221; 314999
Media: 2-4-7-10-13-17
Distr.: Natl.
Personnel:
Jeffrey Klein *(Pres)*

JELLIFF CORPORATION

354 Pequot Ave
Southport, CT 06890
Tel.: (203) 259-1615
Fax: (203) 255-7908
Toll Free: (800) 364-9502
E-mail: sales@jelliff.net
Web Site: www.jelliff.com
E-Mail For Key Personnel:
Sales Director: sales@jelliff.net
Approx. Number Employees: 100
Year Founded: 1880
Business Description:
Mfr. of Wire, Wire Cloth, Fabricated-Mesh Products & Electrical Resistance Wire
S.I.C.: 3496
N.A.I.C.S.: 332618
Import Export
Media: 2-4-7-8-13-21-26
Distr.: Direct to Consumer; Natl.
Budget Set: Jan.
Personnel:
W. F. Wheeler *(Chm)*
Gelff Wheele *(Pres)*
Brands & Products:
JELLIFF

JHB INTERNATIONAL, INC.

1955 S Quince St
Denver, CO 80231
Tel.: (303) 751-8100
Fax: (303) 752-0608
E-mail: sales@buttons.com
Web Site: www.buttons.com
E-Mail For Key Personnel:
Sales Director: sales@buttons.com
Approx. Sls.: $24,000,000
Approx. Number Employees: 65
Year Founded: 1969
Business Description:
Buttons Distr
S.I.C.: 5131
N.A.I.C.S.: 424310
Media: 4-6-10
Personnel:
James Barr, IV *(Owner)*
Allen Willis *(CFO)*
Lisa Lambright *(Dir-Sls-Mktg)*
Brands & Products:
BUTTON LADY
IT'S ALL IN THE DETAILS
JHB INTERNATIONAL

JO-ANN STORES INC.

5555 Darrow Rd
Hudson, OH 44236
Tel.: (330) 656-2600
Fax: (330) 463-6675
Toll Free: (888) 739-4120
Web Site: www.joann.com
Approx. Sls.: $2,079,000,000
Approx. Number Employees: 21,453
Year Founded: 1943
Business Description:
Fabric, Crafts & Related Products
S.I.C.: 5949
N.A.I.C.S.: 451130
Import
Advertising Expenditures: $72,900,000
Media: 4-8-10-13-16-26
Distr.: Direct to Consumer; Reg.
Budget Set: July
Personnel:
Darrell D. Webb *(Chm)*
Travis Smith *(CEO)*
James Kerr *(CFO & Exec VP)*
David B. Goldston *(Gen Counsel, Sec & Sr VP)*
Kenneth Haverkost *(Exec VP-Store Ops)*
Lisa Greb *(Dir-Corp Comm)*
Margaret Skinner *(Dir-Corp Comm)*
Brands & Products:
JO-ANN
JO-ANN FABRIC & CRAFTS STORES
JOANN.COM
THE OFFICIAL JOANN

JOHN R. LYMAN COMPANY

60 Depot St
Chicopee, MA 01014
Mailing Address:
PO Box 157
Chicopee, MA 01014-0157
Tel.: (413) 598-8344
Fax: (413) 592-4112
Toll Free: (800) 628-8606
E-mail: jrlcsales@johnrlyman.com
Web Site: www.johnrlyman.com
E-Mail For Key Personnel:
President: wwright@johnrlyman.com
Sales Range: $10-24.9 Million
Approx. Number Employees: 120
Year Founded: 1906
Business Description:
Specialty Wipes Mfr
S.I.C.: 2392
N.A.I.C.S.: 314129
Import Export
Advertising Expenditures: $50,000
Media: 2-10-13
Personnel:
William S. Wright *(Pres)*
Bill Lynch *(VP-Sls & Mktg)*
Brands & Products:
ADVANTAGE
LYMAN
LYMTECH

LION BRAND YARN COMPANY

135 Kero Rd
Carlstadt, NJ 07072
Tel.: (212) 243-8995
Fax: (201) 824-3918
Toll Free: (800) 258-YARN
E-mail: lionyarn@aol.com
Web Site: www.lionbrand.com
Approx. Number Employees: 20
Year Founded: 1878
Business Description:
Hand Knitting Yarn Mfr & Whslr
S.I.C.: 5199
N.A.I.C.S.: 424990
Import Export
Media: 4-5-7-10-20
Distr.: Natl.
Budget Set: Jan.
Personnel:
Dean Blumenthal *(COO & Exec VP)*
Ilana Rabinowitz *(VP-Mktg)*
Brands & Products:
CHUNKY USA
COTTON-EASE
FISHERMEN'S WOOL
FUN FUR
GLITTERSPUN
HOMESPUN
JAMIE
JAMIE-CLASSIC
JAMIE POMPADOUR
JIFFY
MAGIC STRIPES
MONET
POLARSPUN
POUND OF LOVE
WOOL-EASE

LION BROTHERS COMPANY, INC.

10246 Reisterstown Rd
Owings Mills, MD 21117
Tel.: (410) 363-1000
Fax: (410) 363-0181
Toll Free: (800) 365-6543
E-mail: webmaster@lionbrothers.com
Web Site: www.lionbrothers.com
Sales Range: $10-24.9 Million
Approx. Number Employees: 100
Year Founded: 1899
Business Description:
Decoration, Identification & Commemoration Products Mfr
S.I.C.: 2261
N.A.I.C.S.: 313311
Import Export
Advertising Expenditures: $400,000
Media: 2-4-7-10
Distr.: Intl.; Natl.
Budget Set: Sept.
Personnel:
Susan J. Ganz *(CEO)*
Cesar Aguilar *(Exec VP-Sls & Mktg)*

MART FILTER CORPORATION

(Sub. of American Performance Industries)
109 McNeill Rd
Sanford, NC 27330
Mailing Address:
PO Box 969
Sanford, NC 27331-0969
Tel.: (919) 775-7321
Fax: (919) 776-0121
Toll Free: (800) 438-3348
E-mail: info@ap-industries.com
Web Site: www.ap-industries.com
Approx. Number Employees: 55
Year Founded: 1970
Business Description:
Filters Mfr
S.I.C.: 3564
N.A.I.C.S.: 333411
Media: 2-10

MARY MAXIM, INC.

2001 Holland Ave
Port Huron, MI 48060
Mailing Address:
PO Box 5019
Port Huron, MI 48061-5019
Tel.: (810) 987-2000
Fax: (810) 987-5056
Toll Free: (800) 962-9504
E-mail: info@marymaxim.com
Web Site: www.marymaxim.com
Approx. Number Employees: 150
Year Founded: 1952
Business Description:
Mail Order Retailer of Needlework & Craft Kits
S.I.C.: 5961; 5949
N.A.I.C.S.: 454113; 451130
Import Export
Media: 4-6-9-10-13-20
Distr.: Natl.
Budget Set: Apr.
Brands & Products:
MARY MAXIM

MILLIKEN & COMPANY

920 Milliken Rd
Spartanburg, SC 29304
Mailing Address:
PO Box 1922
Spartanburg, SC 29304-1926
Tel.: (864) 503-2020
Fax: (864) 503-2100
E-mail: info@milliken.com
Web Site: www.milliken.com
Sales Range: $1-4.9 Billion
Approx. Number Employees: 11,000
Year Founded: 1865
Business Description:
Textiles & Chemicals Mfr
S.I.C.: 2211; 2899
N.A.I.C.S.: 313210; 325998
Import Export
Media: 4-6-7-10-21-22
Distr.: Natl.
Personnel:
Joseph M. Salley *(Pres & CEO)*
Scott Hunter *(Mgr-Mktg (Global))*
Brands & Products:
ALPHASAN
CLEAN-TEX
DIVISIONS
MILLIKEN
MILLIKEN-KEX
PALADIN
TEGRIS
YES ESSENTIALS

Key to Media (For complete agency information see *The Advertising Red Books-Agencies* edition):
1. Bus. Publs. 2. Cable T.V. 3. Catalogs & Directories. 4. Co-op Adv. 5. Consumer Mags. 6. D.M. to Bus. Estab.7. D.M. to Consumers 8. Daily Newsp. 9. Exhibits/Trade Shows 10. Foreign 11. Infomercial 12. Internet Adv.13. Multimedia 14. Network Radio 15. Network T.V. 16. Newsp. Distr. Mags. 17. Other 18. Outdoor (Posters, Transit) 19. Point of Purchase20. Premiums, Novelties 21. Product Samples 22. Special Events Mktg. 23. Spot Radio 24. Spot T.V. 25. Weekly Newsp. 26. Yellow Page Adv.

Milliken & Company — (Continued)

Advertising Agency:
Erwin-Penland
(Owned by Hill, Holliday, Connors, Cosmopulos, Inc., Member of the Interpublic Group)
125 E Broad St
Greenville, SC 29601
Tel.: (864) 271-0500
Fax: (864) 235-5941
YES Essentials

MOMENTUM TEXTILES INC.

17811 Fitch
Irvine, CA 92614-6001
Tel.: (949) 833-8886
Fax: (949) 833-9233
E-mail: customerservice@memo.com
Web Site: www.memosamples.com
Approx. Number Employees: 100
Year Founded: 1993
Business Description:
Piece Goods & Notions
S.I.C.: 5131; 2211
N.A.I.C.S.: 424310; 313210
Import Export
Media: 10
Personnel:
Roger Arciniega *(CEO)*
Joanne Corrao *(CFO)*
Brands & Products:
AMENITY
APERTURE
ATTACHE
BANDWIDTH
BETULA
BLACK & WHITE
BOTANIQUE
DECIMAL
FORAY
HABITAT
ICON
INTAGLIO
MOMENTUM TEXTILES
PARAGON
PERENNIAL
PRIVE
SOMA
STRADA
Advertising Agency:
Slaughter Group
2031 11th Ave S
Birmingham, AL 35205
Tel.: (205) 871-9020
Fax: (205) 252-2691

MOORE COMPANY

36 Beach St
Westerly, RI 02891
Tel.: (401) 596-2817
Fax: (401) 596-6801
E-mail: info@themooreco.com
Web Site: www.themooreco.com
Approx. Number Employees: 1,500
Year Founded: 1909
Business Description:
Fabric Finishing; Warp Knit, Manmade Fiber, Narrow Woven Fabrics, Pressure Sensitive Tape, Rubber, Thread, Mechanical Rubber Goods, Battery Separators & Wood
S.I.C.: 2299; 2241
N.A.I.C.S.: 313312; 313221
Media: 2-4-6-9-10-21
Distr.: Intl.; Natl.
Personnel:
Thomas F. Moore *(Chm)*
Dana Barlo *(Pres & CEO)*
Brands & Products:
AMERSIL FILPAP
DARLINGTON
FULFLEX
GEORGE C MOORE
MOELLER
RESOURCE TO THE WORLD'S MOST SUCCESSFUL BRANDS

MOUNT VERNON MILLS, INC.

(Sub. of R.B. Pamplin Corporation)
503 S Main St
Mauldin, SC 29662
Mailing Address:
PO Box 100
Mauldin, SC 29662
Tel.: (864) 688-7100
Fax: (864) 688-7101
E-mail: helpdesk@mvmills.com
Web Site: www.mvmills.com
Approx. Number Employees: 3,500
Year Founded: 1847
Business Description:
Textiles & Home Furnishings Mfr
S.I.C.: 2211; 2281
N.A.I.C.S.: 313210; 313111
Import Export
Advertising Expenditures: $799,000
Media: 1-2-4-5-6-7-8-10-21
Distr.: Natl.
Personnel:
Roger W. Chastain *(CEO)*
Don Henderson *(VP & Gen Mgr)*

NAME MAKER INC.

PO Box 43821
Atlanta, GA 30336-0821
Tel.: (404) 691-2237
Fax: (404) 691-7711
Toll Free: (800) 241-2890
E-mail: label@mindspring.com
Web Site: www.namemaker.com
Approx. Sls.: $3,000,000
Approx. Number Employees: 20
Year Founded: 1938
Business Description:
Mfr. of York Name Tapes, Laundry Marking Pens, Luggage Tags, Personalized Woven Labels & Name Labels
S.I.C.: 2299
N.A.I.C.S.: 313312
Import Export
Media: 2-4-6-7-8-10-19
Distr.: Intl.; Natl.
Budget Set: Jan.
Personnel:
Bernard M. Bryan *(Pres)*

NARROW FABRIC INDUSTRIES CORP.

(Holding of Cheynet S.A.S)
701 W Reading Ave
Reading, PA 19611
Mailing Address:
701 Reading Ave
Reading, PA 19611-1013
Tel.: (610) 376-2891
Fax: (610) 376-2869
Toll Free: (800))523-8118
E-mail: cmiller@narrowfabric.com
Web Site: www.narrowfabric.com
E-Mail For Key Personnel:
President: cmiller@narrowfabric.com
Marketing Director: mcoldren@narrowfabric.com
Approx. Number Employees: 100
Year Founded: 1900
Business Description:
Mfr. of Narrow Elastics for Use in Lingerie & Foundation Trades
S.I.C.: 2241; 2257
N.A.I.C.S.: 313221; 313241
Media: 7-20-21
Distr.: Intl.
Personnel:
Gregoire Giraud *(Chm)*
Charles Miller *(Pres & COO)*
John Althouse *(Dir-Engrg)*
Nancy Leinbach *(Dir-Tech)*
Ed LaSota *(Mgr-Safety)*

NATIONAL BANNER COMPANY, INC.

(d/b/a NABCO)
11938 Harry Hines Blvd
Dallas, TX 75234-5919
Tel.: (972) 241-2131
Fax: (972) 241-6282
Fax: (800) 468-0700
Toll Free: (800) 527-0860
E-mail: info@nationalbanner.com
Web Site: www.nationalbanner.com
Approx. Number Employees: 185
Year Founded: 1952
Business Description:
Mfr. of Banners, Pennants, Flags & Decals
S.I.C.: 3993
N.A.I.C.S.: 339950
Export
Media: 2-4-10-11-20-26
Distr.: Intl.; Natl.
Personnel:
Abraham Goldfarb *(Chm & Pres)*
Brands & Products:
NABCO

NATIONAL SPINNING COMPANY, INC.

1140 Avenue of the Americas Ste 1700
New York, NY 10036
Tel.: (212) 382-6400
Fax: (212) 382-6450
Toll Free: (800) 868-7104
Web Site: www.natspin.com
Approx. Number Employees: 1,500
Year Founded: 1921
Business Description:
Mfr & Importer of Spun Yarns for Knitting, Weaving & Home Crafts
S.I.C.: 2281; 2299
N.A.I.C.S.: 313111; 313312
Advertising Expenditures: $200,000
Bus. Publs.: $75,000; Consumer Mags.: $100,000; Spot T.V.: $25,000
Distr.: Intl.; Natl.
Budget Set: Nov.
Personnel:
Joseph Leff *(Chm)*
Morgan Miller *(Vice Chm)*
Jim Chesnutt *(Pres & CEO)*
Bob Miller *(Sr VP)*
Robert Gordon *(Mgr-NY Sls)*
Brands & Products:
ADVANTAGE
CARON
DICKSON
MICROSUEDE
SAYELLE
SUN SHARP
SUNBRELLA
ULTRASPUN
VYBRAN
WINTUK

PARKDALE MILLS INC.

531 Cottonblossom Cir
Gastonia, NC 28054
Tel.: (704) 874-5000
Fax: (704) 874-5176
Toll Free: (800) 331-1843
E-mail: sales@parkdalemills.com
Web Site: www.parkdalemills.com
E-Mail For Key Personnel:
Sales Director: sales@parkdalemills.com
Approx. Number Employees: 3,650
Year Founded: 1916
Business Description:
Cotton & Cotton Blend Yarns Mfr
S.I.C.: 2281
N.A.I.C.S.: 313111
Import Export
Advertising Expenditures: $3,000,000
Media: 4-6-8-26
Distr.: Natl.
Budget Set: Nov. -Dec.
Personnel:
W. Duke Kimbrell *(Chm)*
Anderson D. Warlick *(Pres & CEO)*
Charles Heilig *(Exec VP)*
Freddie Harris *(VP-Hosiery Sls)*
Brands & Products:
COOLMAX
PARKDALE

PENDLETON WOOLEN MILLS, INC.

220 NW Broadway
Portland, OR 97209-3509
Mailing Address:
PO Box 3030
Portland, OR 97209
Tel.: (503) 226-4801
Fax: (503) 535-5827
Fax: (503) 273-2599
Toll Free: (800) 649-1512
E-mail: webmail@pendleton-usa.com
Web Site: www.pendleton-usa.com
Approx. Number Employees: 1,500
Year Founded: 1863
Business Description:
Mfr & Whslr of Men's & Women's Sportswear
S.I.C.: 2337; 2311
N.A.I.C.S.: 315234; 315222
Import Export
Advertising Expenditures: $2,500,000
Media: 4-6-7-8-10-13-18-19-20-23
Distr.: Natl.
Budget Set: Aug.
Personnel:
John Bishop *(Chm & VP)*
Broughton Bishop *(Vice Chm)*
C. M. Bishop *(Pres)*
Robert Mathis *(CFO)*
Bob Christnacht *(Mgr-Mktg-Sls)*
Brands & Products:
CLASSIC
GOOD FOR LIFE
HIGH GRADE WESTERN WEAR
MEN'S SPORTSWEAR
ORIGINAL
PENDLETON

PLAINS COTTON COOPERATIVE ASSOCIATION

3301 E 50th St
Lubbock, TX 79404

Key to Media (For complete agency information see *The Advertising Red Books-Agencies* edition):
1. Bus. Publs. 2. Cable T.V. 3. Catalogs & Directories. 4. Co-op Adv. 5. Consumer Mags. 6. D.M. to Bus. Estab.7. D.M. to Consumers 8. Daily Newsp. 9. Exhibits/Trade Shows 10. Foreign 11. Infomercial 12. Internet Adv.13. Multimedia 14. Network Radio 15. Network T.V. 16. Newsp. Distr. Mags. 17. Other 18. Outdoor (Posters, Transit) 19. Point of Purchase20. Premiums, Novelties 21. Product Samples 22. Special Events Mktg. 23. Spot Radio 24. Spot T.V. 25. Weekly Newsp. 26. Yellow Page Adv.

Mailing Address:
PO Box 2827
Lubbock, TX 79408-2827
Tel.: (806) 763-8011
Fax: (806) 762-7400
Toll Free: (800) 333-8011
E-mail: webmaster@pcca.com
Web Site: www.pcca.com
Approx. Rev.: $922,000,000
Approx. Number Employees: 1,350
Year Founded: 1953
Business Description:
Marketing & Merchandising Raw Cotton to Domestic & Foreign Mills; Mfr of Denims
S.I.C.: 5159; 2211
N.A.I.C.S.: 424590; 313210
Import Export
Media: 2-7-9-22
Personnel:
Wally Darneille *(Pres & CEO)*
Sam Hill *(Treas & VP-Fin)*
John Johnson *(Dir-Pub Rels, Legislative Affairs & Corp Sec)*
Jack Mathews *(VP-Fabric Sls & Product Dev)*
Jim Taylor *(VP-Admin & HR)*
Joe Tubb *(VP-Info Sys)*
Lonnie Winters *(VP-Mktg)*
Grady Martin *(Dir-Sls)*
Lee Phenix *(Dir-Personnel)*
Chris Ford *(Sls Mgr)*
Carlos Garcia *(Mgr-Export Sls)*
Brands & Products:
TELCOT

POLARTEC LLC
(Holding of Versa Capital Management, Inc.)
46 Stafford St
Lawrence, MA 01841
Tel.: (978) 685-6341
Fax: (978) 975-2595
Web Site: www.polartec.com
Approx. Number Employees: 1,000
Year Founded: 1906
Business Description:
Outdoor Apparel Fabrics
S.I.C.: 2211; 2297
N.A.I.C.S.: 313210; 313230
Advertising Expenditures: $4,650,000
Media: 2-4-5-6-9-10-19-21-22
Distr.: Intl.
Budget Set: Aug.
Personnel:
Andrew Vecchione *(Pres & COO)*
Jonathan Adelman *(Exec VP-Sls & Mktg)*
Kathy Skala *(Dir-HR)*
Natalie Newton *(Laboratory Mgr)*
Brands & Products:
POLARFLEECE
POLARTEC
POLARTEC CLASSIC
POLARTEC POWER DRY
POLARTEC POWER SHIELD
POLARTEC POWER STRETCH
POLARTEC THERMAL PRO
POLARTEC WINDBLOC
Advertising Agencies:
Backbone Media LLC
65 N 4th St Ste 1
Carbondale, CO 81623
Tel.: (970) 963-4873
Fax: (303) 265-9854
Toll Free: (866) 963-4873
Doner
25900 Northwestern Hwy
Southfield, MI 48075
Tel.: (248) 354-9700
Fax: (248) 827-8440
High Performance Fabrics
Neoshell

POLYMER GROUP, INC.
(Holding of The Blackstone Group L.P.)
9335 Harris Corners Pkwy Ste 300
Charlotte, NC 28269
Tel.: (704) 697-5186
Tel.: (704) 697-5100
Fax: (704) 697-5121
Toll Free: (800) 631-5594
E-mail: normand@pginw.com
Web Site: www.polymergroupinc.com
Approx. Sls.: $882,652,000
Approx. Number Employees: 3,100
Year Founded: 1992
Business Description:
Nonwovens & Oriented Polymer Materials Mfr
S.I.C.: 2211; 2297; 2392
N.A.I.C.S.: 313210; 313230; 314129
Import Export
Media: 11
Personnel:
William B. Hewitt *(Chm)*
Veronica M. Hagen *(CEO)*
Dennis Norman *(CFO)*
Mike Hale *(COO)*
Daniel Rikard *(Gen Counsel, Sec & VP)*
Dale Tyson *(VP-Fin, Controller & Treas)*
William Spencer *(VP & Gen Mgr-Canada)*
Richard Ferencz *(VP-Engrg & Design)*
Brands & Products:
APEX
CHICOPEE
CHIX
DURAWIPE XTRA
MEDISOFT
SPINLACE
SUPERSOFT
ULTRA
Advertising Agency:
JMC Marketing Communications & PR
10 Pearl St
Kingston, NY 12401
Tel.: (845) 331-1200
Fax: (845) 331-1431
Toll Free: (800) 459-3003

PRECISION FABRICS GROUP INC.
301 N Elm St Ste 600
Greensboro, NC 27401
Tel.: (336) 510-8000
Fax: (336) 510-8004
Toll Free: (888) 733-5759
Web Site: www.precisionfabrics.com
Sales Range: $150-199.9 Million
Approx. Number Employees: 48
Business Description:
Mfr. of Synthetic Broadwoven Fabrics
S.I.C.: 2211; 2241
N.A.I.C.S.: 313210; 313221
Personnel:
Patrick J. Burns *(Co-CEO)*
Walter G. Jones *(Co-CEO)*
Terry Montgomery *(VP)*
Rich Bliton *(Dir-Bus)*
John Smith *(Mgr-Market)*
Brands & Products:
AEGIS
AEGIS MICROBE SHIELD
DERMATHERAPY
DIAMONDDRY
DURAWRITE 5500
THE FABRIC OF INNOVATION
INTEGRITY
JUMPMASTER
KEVLAR
MAGNAWRITE 7300
NEXUS
PEEL PLY
PRECISION FABRICS
PRISTINE
SOFTGUARD
ULTRAWRITE 6000
Advertising Agency:
Bouvier Kelly Inc.
212 S Elm St Ste 200
Greensboro, NC 27401-2631
Tel.: (336) 275-7000
Fax: (336) 275-9988

PRYM CONSUMER USA
(Sub. of Prym Consumer GmbH & Co. KG)
950 Brisack Rd
Spartanburg, SC 29303
Tel.: (864) 576-5050
Fax: (864) 587-3353
Toll Free: (800) 845-4948
Web Site: www.dritz.com
Approx. Number Employees: 120
Year Founded: 1924
Business Description:
Sewing Notions, Straight Pins, Safety Pins, Snap Fasteners, Needles, Thimbles, Buttons, Special Wire Forms, Scissors & Shears, Elastics, Clothing Care Items Mfr & Distr
S.I.C.: 5131
N.A.I.C.S.: 424310
Import
Media: 2-3-4-6-7-10-19-21-22
Distr.: Natl.
Budget Set: Oct.
Personnel:
Hans H. Koehl *(Chm)*
Johan Starrenburg *(CEO)*
Paul Inskip *(VP-Sls & Mktg)*
Grant A. Webb, III *(VP-Fin)*
Brands & Products:
COLLINS
DRITZ
INTERIOR EXPRESSIONS
OMNIGRID
PRYM

RELIABLE OF MILWAUKEE
(Formerly Reliable Knitting Works, Inc.)
1126 S 70th St #112-3
Milwaukee, WI 53214-5705
Tel.: (414) 272-5084
Fax: (414) 272-6443
Toll Free: (800) 336-6876
Web Site:
www.reliableofmilwaukee.com
Approx. Number Employees: 35
Year Founded: 1911
Business Description:
Mfr. of Infants', Children's, Teens', Misses' & Men's Knit Headwear; Slippers; Polar Boots; Golf Club Covers
S.I.C.: 2253; 2252
N.A.I.C.S.: 315191; 315119
Import Export
Advertising Expenditures: $100,000
Media: 4-5-9-10-13-19-20-21
Distr.: Natl.
Budget Set: Various
Personnel:
Mark Blutstein *(Pres)*
Morton Blutstein *(Exec VP & Gen Mgr)*
John Johnson *(Sr VP)*
Brands & Products:
CLUB SOX
ESCENTIALS
FOOT-LITES
HALPER
MUKLUKS
PENTHOUSE SKI WEAR
POLAR BOOTS
QUIET WEAR
RELIABLE
SCUFFIE FOOTLIGHTS
SCUFFIES
SHELETS
SLUMBER SOX
SOFTONES

RETAIL & SPECIALTY FABRICS
(Div. of Springs Global, Inc.)
454 S Anderson Ave Ste 400
Rock Hill, SC 29730
Tel.: (803) 547-1500
Fax: (803) 324-6529
Toll Free: (800) 572-5771
E-mail: info@specialtylinens.com
Approx. Number Employees: 400
Business Description:
Fabric For Home Sewing & Specialty Trades
S.I.C.: 2211
N.A.I.C.S.: 313210
Advertising Expenditures: $800,000
Media: 2-4-6-7-10-19-24
Distr.: Natl.
Brands & Products:
DAISYKINGDOM
QUILTERS ONLY
SPRINGMAID
WAMSUTTA

RHODE ISLAND TEXTILE COMPANY, INC.
211 Columbus Ave
Pawtucket, RI 02861-3404
Mailing Address:
PO Box 999
Pawtucket, RI 02862-0999
Tel.: (401) 722-3700
Fax: (401) 726-2840
Toll Free: (800) 556-6488
E-mail: ritextile@ritextile.com
Web Site: www.ritextile.com
Sales Range: $50-74.9 Million
Approx. Number Employees: 900
Year Founded: 1913
Business Description:
Mfr. of Elastic & Non-Elastic Narrow Fabrics, Knits, Braids & Webbing
S.I.C.: 2241; 2298
N.A.I.C.S.: 313221; 314991
Advertising Expenditures: $200,000
Media: 4

Key to Media (For complete agency information see *The Advertising Red Books-Agencies* edition):
1. Bus. Publs. 2. Cable T.V. 3. Catalogs & Directories. 4. Co-op Adv. 5. Consumer Mags. 6. D.M. to Bus. Estab. 7. D.M. to Consumers 8. Daily Newsp. 9. Exhibits/Trade Shows 10. Foreign 11. Infomercial 12. Internet Adv. 13. Multimedia 14. Network Radio 15. Network T.V. 16. Newsp. Distr. Mags. 17. Other 18. Outdoor (Posters, Transit) 19. Point of Purchase 20. Premiums, Novelties 21. Product Samples 22. Special Events Mktg. 23. Spot Radio 24. Spot T.V. 25. Weekly Newsp. 26. Yellow Page Adv.

Rhode Island Textile Company, Inc. — (Continued)

Personnel:
Paul M. Mahoney *(Pres-Indus Sls)*

THE ROBERT ALLEN GROUP, INC.
(Sub. of Decor Holdings, Inc.)
225 Foxboro Blvd
Foxboro, MA 02035
Tel.: (508) 339-9151
Fax: (508) 261-9297
Toll Free: (800) 333-3777
E-mail: admin@robertallendesign.com
Web Site: www.robertallendesign.com
Approx. Number Employees: 530
Business Description:
Fabrics & Textiles Distr
S.I.C.: 5023
N.A.I.C.S.: 423220
Media: 6
Personnel:
Ron Cordover *(Chm & CEO)*
Jeffrey A. Cordover *(Pres)*
Greg Tarver *(Exec VP)*
Judy Fishman *(Sr VP-HR)*
Peter Routsis *(VP-Mktg)*
Jennie Wilde *(VP-Design & Mdsg)*

RUDDICK CORPORATION
301 S Tryon St Ste 1800
Charlotte, NC 28282-1995
Tel.: (704) 372-5404
Fax: (704) 372-6409
Web Site: www.ruddickcorp.com
Approx. Sls.: $4,400,450,000
Approx. Number Employees: 25,200
Year Founded: 1968
Business Description:
Holding Company; Retail Supermarket Operator; Industrial Sewing & Embroidery Thread & Technical Textiles Mfr & Distr
S.I.C.: 5411; 2284
N.A.I.C.S.: 445110; 313113
Export
Advertising Expenditures: $22,068,000
Media: 5
Personnel:
Thomas W. Dickson *(Chm, Pres & CEO)*
John B. Woodlief *(CFO & VP-Fin)*
Frederick J. Morganthall, II *(Pres-Harris Teeter)*
Brands & Products:
AMERICAN & EFIRD
HARRIS TEETER
HUNTER
Advertising Agencies:
Corder Philips, Inc.
508 W 5th St Ste 100
Charlotte, NC 28202
Tel.: (704) 333-3924
Fax: (704) 358-0134

Mass Connections, Inc.
13131 E 166th St
Cerritos, CA 90703
Tel.: (562) 365-0200
Fax: (562) 365-0201
Toll Free: (800) 275-6650

THE RUG BARN INC.
(Sub. of The InterTech Group, Inc.)
Hwy 28 Bypass Industrial Park Rd
Abbeville, SC 29620-1187
Tel.: (864) 446-2123
Fax: (864) 643-1788
E-mail: webmaster@therugbarn.com
Web Site: www.therugbarn.com
Approx. Number Employees: 100
Business Description:
Mfr. of Throws, Pillows & Tapestries
S.I.C.: 2211; 2392
N.A.I.C.S.: 313210; 314129
Advertising Expenditures: $50,000
Catalogs & Directories: 50%; D.M. to Consumers: 50%
Distr.: Natl.
Brands & Products:
RUG BARN CUSTOMS

RUSSELL CORPORATION
(Sub. of Fruit of the Loom, Inc.)
3330 Cumberland Blvd Ste 800
Atlanta, GA 30339
Tel.: (678) 742-8000
Fax: (678) 742-8300
E-mail: webmaster@russellcorp.com
Web Site: www.russellcorp.com
Sales Range: $1-4.9 Billion
Approx. Number Employees: 15,500
Year Founded: 1902
Business Description:
Active Wear & Other Apparel Mfr, Designer & Marketer; Uniform Supplier
S.I.C.: 2299; 2211; 2253
N.A.I.C.S.: 313312; 313210; 315191
Import Export
Advertising Expenditures: $48,000,000
Media: 4-5-6-13-18-23-24
Personnel:
Edsel W. Flowers *(Sr VP-HR)*
Brands & Products:
AAI
BIKE
HUFFY SPORTS
JERZEES
MOSSY OAK
MOVING COMFORT
RUSSELL
RUSSELL ARTWEAR
RUSSELL ATHLETIC
SPALDING

SEFAR AMERICA, INC.
(Sub. of Sefar Holding AG)
120 Mt Holly By-Pass
Lumberton, NJ 08048
Tel.: (609) 613-5000
Fax: (609) 267-1750
Web Site: www.sefar.us
Approx. Number Employees: 190
Year Founded: 1927
Business Description:
Synthetic Fabrics, Wire Meshes & Supplies Mfr
S.I.C.: 3496; 2297
N.A.I.C.S.: 332618; 313230
Import Export
Media: 2-4-7-10-21
Distr.: Natl.
Budget Set: Oct.
Personnel:
Dave Koebcke *(Pres)*

SHILLCRAFT, INC.
PO Box 325
Bonsall, CA 92003
Tel.: (951) 674-4307
Fax: (951) 674-4325
E-mail: support@shillcraft.com
Web Site: www.shillcraft.com
Approx. Sls.: $7,600,000
Approx. Number Employees: 25
Year Founded: 1949
Business Description:
Supplier of Mail Order Crafts; Latch Hook Rug Kits & Accessories
S.I.C.: 5961; 5131
N.A.I.C.S.: 454113; 424310
Import Export
Advertising Expenditures: $750,000
Media: 2-3-4-5-6-7-8-10-12-13-16-19-24-25-26
Distr.: Intl.; Natl.
Budget Set: July
Personnel:
Mike Gordon *(CFO & VP-Fin)*
Keith Wehberg *(VP-Mktg)*
Lloyd Zucker *(VP-Sls)*

SINGER SEWING COMPANY
(Sub. of SVP Worldwide, LLC)
1224 Heil Quaker Blvd
La Vergne, TN 37086-3515
Tel.: (615) 213-0880
Fax: (615) 213-0994
Web Site: www.singerco.com
Sales Range: $75-99.9 Million
Approx. Number Employees: 75
Year Founded: 1851
Business Description:
Sewing Machine Designer, Mfr & Distr
S.I.C.: 3559; 5064; 5084
N.A.I.C.S.: 333298; 423620; 423830
Media: 2-3-6-8-9
Personnel:
William F. Andrews *(Chm)*
Gary Jones *(Pres-Mass Market)*
Caroline Weaver *(VP-Global Mktg)*
Brands & Products:
SINGER
Advertising Agency:
White/Thompson, LLC
1808 Patterson St
Nashville, TN 37203
Tel.: (615) 321-1033
Fax: (615) 321-1038
Toll Free: (888) 795-4260
— Sherri Jones *(Acct. Exec.)*

SPRINGS GLOBAL, INC.
205 N White St
Fort Mill, SC 29716-0070
Mailing Address:
PO Box 70
Fort Mill, SC 29716
Tel.: (803) 547-1500
Fax: (803) 547-1636
E-mail: wamsutta@springs.com
Web Site: www.springs.com
E-Mail For Key Personnel:
President: crandall.bowles@springs.com
Approx. Number Employees: 19,500
Year Founded: 1887
Business Description:
Finished Fabrics, Home Furnishings & Window Treatments
S.I.C.: 2211; 2273
N.A.I.C.S.: 313210; 314110
Import Export
Media: 4-5-6-8-9-10-19-20-21-23
Distr.: Intl.; Natl.
Personnel:
Josue Christiano Gomes da Silva *(Chm & CEO)*
Tom O'Connor *(Pres)*
Harvey Simon *(Pres-Private Label BU)*
Brands & Products:
AMERICAN LIFESTYLE
BALI
BAYPORT
BEAULIEU
BLUE JEAN TEDDY
BURLINGTON HOUSE
CRYSTAL PLEAT
CUSTOM DESIGNS
DAISY KINGDOM
DUNDEE
FASHION PLEAT
GRABER
HUMPHREYS CORNER
THE LEARNING LINE
LITTLE TIKES
NANIK
REGAL
SPRINGMAID
TEXMADE
WABASSO
WAMSUTTA
WAMSUTTA BABY
WOODLINES

STRETCH & SEW INC.
PO Box 25306
Tempe, AZ 85285-5306
Tel.: (480) 966-1462
Fax: (480) 966-1914
Toll Free: (800) 547-7717
E-mail: stretchsew@worldnet.att.net
Web Site: www.stretch-and-sew.com
Approx. Number Employees: 3
Year Founded: 1967
Business Description:
Sewing Products Retailer
S.I.C.: 5131
N.A.I.C.S.: 424310
Media: 4-6-8-9-11-19-21-25-26
Distr.: Intl.; Natl.
Budget Set: Sept. -Oct.
Brands & Products:
STRETCH & SEW

SWIFT GALEY
(Sub. of Swift Galey)
980 Ave of the Americas
New York, NY 10018
Tel.: (212) 465-3000
Tel.: (212) 465-3088 (Spanish)
Fax: (212) 465-3025
Fax: (212) 465-3024
Web Site: www.swiftgaley.com
Approx. Number Employees: 6
Year Founded: 1987
Business Description:
Textiles & Denim Mfr
S.I.C.: 5131; 2211
N.A.I.C.S.: 424310; 313210
Media: 2-9
Brands & Products:
SWIFT DENIM
Advertising Agency:
Jouard Wozniak Advertising & Design
30 Fairview Pl.
Montclair, NJ 07043
Tel.: (973) 655-1313

TRIMTEX CO. INC.
400 Park Ave
Williamsport, PA 17701-4930

Key to Media (For complete agency information see *The Advertising Red Books-Agencies* edition):
1. Bus. Publs. 2. Cable T.V. 3. Catalogs & Directories. 4. Co-op Adv. 5. Consumer Mags. 6. D.M. to Bus. Estab.7. D.M. to Consumers 8. Daily Newsp. 9. Exhibits/Trade Shows 10. Foreign 11. Infomercial 12. Internet Adv.13. Multimedia 14. Network Radio 15. Network T.V. 16. Newsp. Distr. Mags. 17. Other 18. Outdoor (Posters, Transit) 19. Point of Purchase20. Premiums, Novelties 21. Product Samples 22. Special Events Mktg. 23. Spot Radio 24. Spot T.V. 25. Weekly Newsp. 26. Yellow Page Adv.

Tel.: (570) 326-9135
Fax: (570) 326-4250
E-mail: info@trimtex.com
Web Site: www.trimtex.com
Sales Range: $50-74.9 Million
Approx. Number Employees: 20
Year Founded: 1919
Business Description:
Braided, Knitted & Woven Trimmings & Tapes; Functional Braids, Specification Tapes & Braids; Coatings & Finishing of Trims
S.I.C.: 2241; 2257
N.A.I.C.S.: 313221; 313241
Import Export
Media: 10-21
Distr.: Natl.
Budget Set: Dec.
Personnel:
Larry Epstein *(Pres & CEO)*
Doris Stevens *(Controller)*
James Fink *(Dir-Pur)*
Brands & Products:
TRIMTEX

UNIROYAL ENGINEERED PRODUCTS LLC

1800 2nd St Ste 970
Sarasota, FL 34236
Tel.: (608) 873-6631
Fax: (941) 906-8582
Toll Free: (877) 628-4248
E-mail: info@naugahyde.com
Web Site: www.naugahyde.com
Sales Range: $25-49.9 Million
Approx. Number Employees: 8
Year Founded: 1992
Business Description:
Coated Fabrics Mfr & Sales
S.I.C.: 2295
N.A.I.C.S.: 313320
Media: 7-10
Personnel:
H.F. Curd *(Chm & CEO)*
Larry Bressler *(VP-Sls)*
Brands & Products:
ALL-AMERICAN
ALLURE
BEAUTYGARD
BELLINGHAM
BOURBON STREET
BURKSHIRE
CHAMEA
CHELSEA
CITY LIGHTS
DOLPHIN
DURAN BLACK
ENGLISH PUB
EXPRESSIONS
MARBLESTONE
NAUGAHYDE
NAUGALEATHER
NAUGASATIN
NAUGASOFT
NAUGASYLK
NEOCHROME
OAKWOOD
OXEN
PHOENIX
REALTREE
ROGUE
SOUTHAMPTON
SPIRIT MILLENNIUM
STA-SOFT
STRATFORD
SURFSIDE
TUSK
TWILIGHT
UNIVERSAL
ZODIAC

VELCRO USA INC.

(Sub. of Velcro Industries N.V.)
406 Brown Ave
Manchester, NH 03103-7202
Tel.: (603) 669-4880
Fax: (603) 669-9271
Toll Free: (800) 225-0180
E-mail: marketing@velcro.com
Web Site: www.velcro.com
Approx. Number Employees: 650
Business Description:
Fasteners & Related Products for Consumer & Industrial Use
S.I.C.: 3965; 2241
N.A.I.C.S.: 339993; 313221
Export
Advertising Expenditures: $600,000
Media: 1-2-4-5-6-7-10-13-19-20-21-26
Distr.: Natl.
Budget Set: Nov.
Personnel:
Katherine Pries *(Mgr-Indus Div)*
Advertising Agencies:
Brewer Associates Marketing Communications
39555 Orchard Hill Pl Ste 600
Novi, MI 48375
Tel.: (734) 458-7180
Transportation Technologies Division

ThomasBoston Advertising, A Thomas Marketing Services Corporation Business
105 Ash St
Hopkinton, MA 01748-1928
Tel.: (508) 497-8900
Fax: (508) 497-8900
Toll Free: (800) 452-6231
— Thomas G. Lanen *(Acct. Exec.)*

VICTOR FORSTMANN, INC.

(Sub. of Victor Innovatex Inc.)
(d/b/a The Forstmann Company)
161 Nathaniel Dr
Dublin, GA 31027
Mailing Address:
PO Box 1049
Dublin, GA 31040
Tel.: (478) 275-5400
Fax: (478) 275-5647
Toll Free: (800) 233-2544
Web Site: www.forstmann.com
E-Mail For Key Personnel:
Marketing Director: TWinkler@forstmann.com
Approx. Number Employees: 154
Year Founded: 1904
Business Description:
Mfr. & Marketer of Apparel & Specialty Fabrics
S.I.C.: 2211; 8742
N.A.I.C.S.: 313210; 541613
Import Export
Media: 2-4-7-9-10-11-13-20-21
Distr.: Natl.
Personnel:
Richard Duval *(Pres & CEO)*
Brands & Products:
ANDOVER
ARCADE BILLIARD CLOTH
CABARET
CASUWOOL
FORSTMANN
HOCKANUM FABRIC
SPEEDBALL
WORUMBO FABRIC

VICTOR INNOVATEX INC.

2805 90th St
Saint-Georges, QC G6A 1K1, Canada
Tel.: (418) 227-9897
Fax: (418) 228-8985
E-mail: info@victorgroup.com
Web Site: www.victor-innovatex.com
E-Mail For Key Personnel:
President: rduval@lainages-victor.com
Approx. Number Employees: 150
Year Founded: 1947
Business Description:
Fabric & Apparel Mfr
S.I.C.: 2211; 2299
N.A.I.C.S.: 313210; 314999
Import Export
Media: 1-2-7-11-21
Distr.: Natl.
Personnel:
Alain Duval *(Pres & CEO)*
Melanie Thabet *(VP-Sls-Mktg)*

VICTOR INNOVATIVE TEXTILES

(Sub. of Victor Innovatex Inc.)
941 Grinnell St 81 Commerce Dr
Fall River, MA 02720-5215
Mailing Address:
PO Box 2139
Fall River, MA 02722-2139
Tel.: (508) 678-1951
Web Site: www.victorgroup.com
Approx. Sls.: $151,664,000
Approx. Number Employees: 1,008
Year Founded: 1941
Business Description:
Upholstery & Fabric Mfr
S.I.C.: 2211; 2299
N.A.I.C.S.: 313210; 314999
Export
Advertising Expenditures: $284,000
Media: 2-7-10-13-25
Distr.: Intl.
Budget Set: Nov. -Dec.
Personnel:
Alain Duval *(Pres & CEO)*
Cynthia L. Gordan *(Gen Counsel, Sec & VP)*
M. Beatrice Spires *(VP-Design & Mdsg)*
Brands & Products:
DAVOL
QUAKER FABRIC
QUAKER PLUSH
QUAKER SUEDE
WHITAKER R COLLECTION

WESTCHESTER LACE & TEXTILES INC.

3901 Liberty Ave
North Bergen, NJ 07047-2538
Tel.: (201) 864-2150
Fax: (201) 864-2116
Toll Free: (800) 699-5223
E-mail: sales002@westchesterlace.com
Web Site: www.westchesterlace.com
E-Mail For Key Personnel:
Sales Director: sales002@westchesterlace.com
Approx. Number Employees: 18
Year Founded: 1959
Business Description:
Knitted Lace, Elastics & Prints Mfr
S.I.C.: 2258
N.A.I.C.S.: 313249
Export
Media: 2-6-13
Distr.: Natl.
Personnel:
Lenny Edelson *(Pres)*
Jeffrey Edelson *(Exec VP)*

WM. WRIGHT COMPANY

(Sub. of Conso International Corporation)
85 S St
West Warren, MA 01092
Mailing Address:
PO Box 398
West Warren, MA 01092-0398
Tel.: (413) 436-7732
Fax: (413) 436-9785
Toll Free: (877) 597-4448
E-mail: help@wrights.com
Web Site: www.wrights.com
Approx. Number Employees: 400
Year Founded: 1897
Business Description:
Mfr. of Sewing Notions, Quilting & Crafts
S.I.C.: 2299; 5949
N.A.I.C.S.: 314999; 451130
Import Export
Advertising Expenditures: $100,000
Media: 2-4-5-7-9-10-13-19-21-25
Distr.: Natl.
Personnel:
Jerry Cohn *(Pres & CEO)*
Richard Gaffney *(CIO)*
Kimberly James *(Sr VP-Natl Sls)*
Scott Smith *(Sr VP-Sls)*
Patricia Desantis *(VP-Mktg)*
Brands & Products:
BONDEX
BOYE NEEDLE
BOYE PERFECTION POINTS
CROCHETMASTER
EZ QUILTING
NEEDLEMASTER
WRIGHTS
WRIGHTS. SHARE THE EXCITEMENT!

WOOLRICH, INC.

Two Mill St
Woolrich, PA 17779
Tel.: (570) 769-6464
Fax: (570) 769-6234
E-mail: service@woolrich.com
Web Site: www.woolrich.com
Approx. Number Employees: 650
Year Founded: 1830
Business Description:
Wool & Blends Cloth, Work & Sport Garments, Down Filled Garments, Ski Wear, Blankets, Upholstery Wall Paneling Fabric & Licensing
S.I.C.: 2311; 2329
N.A.I.C.S.: 315222; 315228
Import Export
Media: 2-4-5-8-10-13-14-18-20-21-22
Personnel:
James Griggs *(Pres)*
Brian Mangione *(Exec VP)*
Brent Hollowell *(VP-Mktg)*
Richard Insley *(VP-Mdsg)*
Jerry Rinder *(VP-Sls)*
Bob Spagnoletti *(VP-Fin)*
David May *(Dir-Ecommerce)*

Woolrich, Inc. — (Continued)

Brands & Products:
175TH ANNIVERSARY STOCKMAN KNIFE
BIG WOOLLY
MEN'S BERTUCCI
THE ORIGINAL OUTDOOR CLOTHING COMPANY
TEN-MILE
TRASK
WOOLRICH

YKK CORPORATION OF AMERICA

(Sub. of YKK Corporation)
1 Parkway Ctr 1850 Pkwy Pl SE Ste 300
Marietta, GA 30067-8258
Tel.: (770) 261-6120
Fax: (770) 261-6148
Toll Free: (888) YKKINFO
E-mail: feedback@ykk-usa.com
Web Site: www.ykkamerica.com
Approx. Number Employees: 28
Year Founded: 1960
Business Description:
Zippers, Buttons, Hook & Loop Fasteners Mfr
S.I.C.: 3965
N.A.I.C.S.: 339993
Export
Advertising Expenditures: $500,000
Media: 1-2-4-7-10-13-18-19-20-21
Distr.: Natl.
Personnel:
Alex Gregory *(Pres & CEO)*
Brands & Products:
COSMOLON
DECATHLON
ECHELON
FASTEN MATES
POWERHOOK
SMARTTOUCH
VISLON
YKK
YKK AP
ZIPLON
Advertising Agency:
Freebairn & Co.
3475 Lenox Rd Ste 900
Atlanta, GA 30326
Tel.: (404) 237-9945
Fax: (404) 231-2214
(All)

YKK SNAP FASTENERS AMERICA INC.

(Sub. of YKK Corporation of America)
302 Factory Ave
Lawrenceburg, KY 40342-0240
Mailing Address:
PO Box 240
Lawrenceburg, KY 40342
Tel.: (502) 839-6971
Fax: (502) 839-6525
Toll Free: (800) 786-2561
E-mail: sales@universal-fasteners.com
Web Site: www.ykksnap-america.com
E-Mail For Key Personnel:
Sales Director: sales@universal-fasteners.com
Approx. Number Employees: 230
Year Founded: 1895
Business Description:
Metal Buttons, Snap Fasteners, Rivets, Hooks & Eyes, Loops, Slides, Attaching Machines Mfr
S.I.C.: 3965; 3452
N.A.I.C.S.: 339993; 332722
Import Export
Media: 2
Distr.: Natl.
Budget Set: Sept.
Personnel:
Steve Furuki *(Pres)*
Brands & Products:
ELITE
SNAPET

Key to Media (For complete agency information see *The Advertising Red Books-Agencies* edition):
1. Bus. Publs. 2. Cable T.V. 3. Catalogs & Directories. 4. Co-op Adv. 5. Consumer Mags. 6. D.M. to Bus. Estab.7. D.M. to Consumers 8. Daily Newsp. 9. Exhibits/Trade Shows 10. Foreign 11. Infomercial 12. Internet Adv.13. Multimedia 14. Network Radio 15. Network T.V. 16. Newsp. Distr. Mags. 17. Other 18. Outdoor (Posters, Transit) 19. Point of Purchase20. Premiums, Novelties 21. Product Samples 22. Special Events Mktg. 23. Spot Radio 24. Spot T.V. 25. Weekly Newsp. 26. Yellow Page Adv.

Farm Equipment & Supplies

Cream Separators — Dairy Supplies — Farm Machinery — Farm Tools — Farm Tractors — Feed Grinders — Fences — Gates — Harnesses — Hay Bailers — Irrigation Systems — Plows — Seeding Machines — Sprayers — Wagons — Well Machinery

AG-MEIER INDUSTRIES LLC
1000 E 6th Ave
Belton, TX 76513-2804
Tel.: (254) 939-3731
Fax: (254) 939-0721
Toll Free: (800) 634-3597
E-mail: info@chicagometal.com
Web Site: www.ag-meier.net
Sales Range: $1-9.9 Million
Approx. Number Employees: 50
Year Founded: 1947
Business Description:
Mfr. of Farm Implements
S.I.C.: 5083; 1541
N.A.I.C.S.: 423820; 236210
Export
Advertising Expenditures: $200,000
Media: 4-7-8-10-20-21
Distr.: Intl.; Natl.
Budget Set: July
Personnel:
Lyle Meier *(Owner & Pres)*
Brands & Products:
ARMADILLO
BR75
BRONCO
COLT
DISC
ED
FRP
MOHAWK
MQH
MUSTANG
PT
QHD
REAR BLADES
SPS
STALLION
THOROUGHBRED
TPMA
UFT
XL

AGCO CORPORATION
4205 River Green Pkwy
Duluth, GA 30096
Tel.: (770) 813-9200
Fax: (770) 813-6040
E-mail: corporate.relations@agcocorp.com
Web Site: www.agcocorp.com
Approx. Sls.: $6,896,600,000
Approx. Number Employees: 14,300
Year Founded: 1990
Business Description:
Agricultural Equipment Mfr, Marketer & Distr
S.I.C.: 3523; 3423; 3535; 5083
N.A.I.C.S.: 333111; 332212; 333922; 423820
Import Export
Advertising Expenditures: $53,400,000
Media: 2-4-5-7-8-10-13-19-23
Distr.: Intl.; Natl.
Personnel:
Martin H. Richenhagen *(Chm, Pres & CEO)*
Andrew H. Beck *(CFO & Sr VP)*
Robert S. Greenberg *(CIO & VP)*
Debra E. Kuper *(Gen Counsel, Corp Sec & VP)*
Andre Mueller Carioba *(Sr VP & Gen Mgr-South America)*
Gary L. Collar *(Sr VP & Gen Mgr-EMEA, Australia & New Zealand)*
Robert B. Crain *(Sr VP & Gen Mgr-North America)*
Garry L. Ball *(Sr VP-Engrg)*
David L. Caplan *(Sr VP-Matls Mgmt-Worldwide)*
Randy G. Hoffman *(Sr VP-Global Sls & Mktg & Product Mgmt)*
Lucinda B. Smith *(Sr VP-HR)*
Hans-Bernd Veltmaat *(Sr VP-Mfg & Quality)*
Hubertus Muehlhaeuser *(VP-Strategy & Integration & Gen Mgr-Eastern Europe & Asia)*
Greg Peterson *(Dir-IR)*
Brands & Products:
AG-CHEM
AGCO
AUTO-GUIDE
E3
FALCON II
FARMHAND
GLENCOE
NEW IDEA
ROGATOR
SGIS
SOILTEQ
SPRA-COUPE
SUNFLOWER
TERRAGATOR
TYE
WHITE
WILLMAR
YOUR AGRICULTURE COMPANY
Advertising Agency:
Broadhead + Co.
123 N 3rd St Ste 507
Minneapolis, MN 55401
Tel.: (612) 623-8000
Fax: (612) 623-4810

ALAMO GROUP OF ILLINOIS
(Sub. of ALAMO GROUP INC.)
1020 S Sangamon Ave
Gibson City, IL 60936
Tel.: (217) 784-4261
Fax: (217) 784-4326
Toll Free: (800) 221-2855
Web Site: www.mw-gear.com
Sales Range: $50-74.9 Million
Approx. Number Employees: 150
Year Founded: 1949
Business Description:
Farm Equipment Retailer
S.I.C.: 3523
N.A.I.C.S.: 333111
Media: 1-2-5-6-8-10-19-23
Distr.: Natl.
Budget Set: Nov.
Brands & Products:
DYNA DRIVE
EARTHMASTER

ALAMO GROUP TX, INC
(Sub. of ALAMO GROUP INC.)
1502 E Walnut St
Seguin, TX 78155-5202
Mailing Address:
PO Box 712
Seguin, TX 78156-0712
Tel.: (830) 379-1480
Fax: (830) 372-9687
Toll Free: (877) 408-3297
Toll Free: (800) 882-5762
E-mail: parts@servis-rhino.com
Web Site: www.servis-rhino.com
Sales Range: $150-199.9 Million
Approx. Number Employees: 410
Year Founded: 1930
Business Description:
Rotary Cutters, Rear Mounted Blades, Tillage & Field Cultivators Mfr
S.I.C.: 5083
N.A.I.C.S.: 423820
Advertising Expenditures: $300,000
Media: 2-4-5-10-11-19
Distr.: Intl.; Natl.
Budget Set: Oct.
Brands & Products:
FL15
RHINO
SERVIS
TURF FLEX
TWISTER

ALFA LAVAL INC.
(Sub. of Alfa Laval AB)
5400 International Trade Dr
Richmond, VA 23231
Tel.: (804) 222-5300
Fax: (804) 236-3276
E-mail: customerservice.usa@alfalaval.com
Web Site: www.alfalaval.com
Approx. Number Employees: 100
Year Founded: 1883
Business Description:
Milk Plant Separators, Clarifiers, Standardizers, Coolers, Industrial & Marine Centrifugals, Heat Exchangers & Food Processing Equipment, Flow Equipment; Pumps, Valves & Fittings; Computer Based Supervisory & Control Systems
S.I.C.: 3556; 3823
N.A.I.C.S.: 333294; 334513
Import Export
Media: 1-2-4-7-10-20
Distr.: Natl.
Budget Set: Sept.
Personnel:
Anders Narvinger *(Chm)*
Alessandro Terenghi *(Pres & CEO)*
Parvez H. Kader *(Mng Dir)*
Thomas Thuresson *(CFO)*
Svante Karlsson *(Pres-Process Tech Div)*
Ulf Granstrand *(Exec VP-Technology)*
Peter Leifland *(Exec VP)*
Peter Torstensson *(Sr VP-Corp Comm)*
Charles Bresette *(VP-Comm)*
Subodh Raina *(Gen Mgr)*
Maurizio Mazza *(Product Mgr)*

AMEREQUIP CORPORATION
1015 Calumet Ave
Kiel, WI 53042
Tel.: (920) 894-7063
Fax: (920) 894-3799
E-mail: info@amerequip.com
Web Site: www.amerequip.com
Approx. Number Employees: 195
Year Founded: 1920

Key to Media (For complete agency information see *The Advertising Red Books-Agencies* edition):
1. Bus. Publs. 2. Cable T.V. 3. Catalogs & Directories. 4. Co-op Adv. 5. Consumer Mags. 6. D.M. to Bus. Estab.7. D.M. to Consumers
8. Daily Newsp. 9. Exhibits/Trade Shows 10. Foreign 11. Infomercial 12. Internet Adv.13. Multimedia 14. Network Radio
15. Network T.V. 16. Newsp. Distr. Mags. 17. Other 18. Outdoor (Posters, Transit) 19. Point of Purchase20. Premiums, Novelties
21. Product Samples 22. Special Events Mktg. 23. Spot Radio 24. Spot T.V. 25. Weekly Newsp. 26. Yellow Page Adv.

Amerequip Corporation — (Continued)

Business Description:
Industrial & Farming Equipment: Compact Loaders, Post Hole Diggers, Back Hoes Mfr
S.I.C.: 3523; 3537
N.A.I.C.S.: 333111; 333924
Export
Media: 2-10
Distr.: Intl.; Natl.
Budget Set: Sept. -Oct.
Personnel:
Mike Vander Zanden *(Pres & CEO)*
Brands & Products:
AMEREQUIP

ANIMAL REPRODUCTION SYSTEMS

(Div. of Dupree, Inc.)
14395 Ramona Ave
Chino, CA 91710-5740
Tel.: (909) 597-4889
Fax: (909) 597-3043
Toll Free: (800) 300-5143
E-mail: arssales@dupreeinc.com
Web Site: www.arssales.com
Year Founded: 1980
Business Description:
Animal Breeding Supplies Mfr
S.I.C.: 0279
N.A.I.C.S.: 112990
Media: 2-4-10
Brands & Products:
ARS
BIO-FLITE
E-Z FREEZIN
E-Z MIXIN
K-Y

AQUACENTER INC.

166 Seven Oaks Rd
Leland, MS 38756
Tel.: (662) 378-2861
Fax: (662) 378-2862
Toll Free: (800) 748-8921
Web Site: www.aquacenterinc.com
Sales Range: $1-9.9 Million
Approx. Number Employees: 7
Year Founded: 1987
Business Description:
Aquaculture Equipment, Products & Services Distr
S.I.C.: 5191
N.A.I.C.S.: 424910
Media: 4
Personnel:
Robert Jones *(Pres)*

ARETT SALES CORPORATION

1152 Marlkress Rd
Cherry Hill, NJ 08003-2314
Tel.: (856) 751-1224
Fax: (856) 751-0604
Fax: (856) 751-7167
Toll Free: (800) 257-8220
E-mail: mail@arett.com
Web Site: www.arett.com
E-Mail For Key Personnel:
President: lchesbrough@arett.com
Marketing Director: mlibrett@arett.com
Approx. Number Employees: 230
Year Founded: 1951
Business Description:
Farm, Lawn & Garden Supplies Distr
S.I.C.: 5191
N.A.I.C.S.: 424910
Import Export
Media: 5-10
Personnel:
Lindsey Chesbrough *(Pres)*
Cathy Schappert *(CFO)*
Mauri Librett *(VP-Mktg)*

ARIENS COMPANY INC.

655 W Ryan St
Brillion, WI 54110-1072
Tel.: (920) 756-2141
Fax: (920) 756-2407
E-mail: info@ariens.com
Web Site: www.ariens.com
E-Mail For Key Personnel:
President: dariens@ariens.com
Sales Director: mthuecks@ariens.com
Sales Range: $75-99.9 Million
Approx. Number Employees: 700
Year Founded: 1933
Business Description:
Mowers, Tillers, Tractors & Snow Blowers Mfr
S.I.C.: 3524
N.A.I.C.S.: 333112
Import Export
Advertising Expenditures: $2,000,000
Media: 2-3-4-5-6-10-11-13-15-18-19-20-26
Distr.: Intl.; Natl.
Budget Set: July
Personnel:
Mike Ariens *(Chm)*
Daniel Ariens *(Pres & CEO)*
Stewart Witkov *(CFO & Exec VP)*
Brands & Products:
ARIENS
COMPACT SNO-THROS
DELUXE SNO-THROS
HYDRO
PROFESSIONAL SNO-THROS
SINGLE-STAGE SNO-THROS
SMARTER BY THE YARD
SNO-THRO
SPORT-ZOOMS
ZOOMS

ART'S-WAY MANUFACTURING CO., INC.

5556 Hwy 9
Armstrong, IA 50514
Mailing Address:
PO Box 288
Armstrong, IA 50514-0288
Tel.: (712) 864-3131
Fax: (712) 864-3154
E-mail: info@artsway-mfg.com
Web Site: www.artsway-mfg.com
Approx. Sls.: $28,951,378
Approx. Number Employees: 163
Year Founded: 1956
Business Description:
Agricultural Equipment Mfr
S.I.C.: 3523
N.A.I.C.S.: 333111
Export
Advertising Expenditures: $282,000
Media: 1-2-5-6-7-8-10-13-14-20-25
Distr.: Natl.
Budget Set: Nov.
Personnel:
J. Ward McConnell, Jr. *(Chm)*
Carrie L. Majeski *(Pres, CEO & CFO)*
Jason Feucht *(Dir-Fin)*
Kent Kollasch *(Mgr-Info Svc)*
Kevin Zahrt *(Mgr-Sls & Mktg)*
Brands & Products:
ART'S WAY
ART'S WAY A TRADITION OF QUALITY SINCE 1956
CATTLEMAXX
GRIXXER
SUPRAMIX

A.T. FERRELL COMPANY, INC.

1440 S Adams St
Bluffton, IN 46714-9793
Tel.: (260) 824-3400
Fax: (260) 824-5463
Toll Free: (800) 248-8318
E-mail: info@atferrell.com
Web Site: www.atferrell.com
Approx. Number Employees: 50
Year Founded: 1869
Business Description:
Process Equipment Mfr of Products for Agricultural & Industrial Use
S.I.C.: 3523; 3537
N.A.I.C.S.: 333111; 333924
Import Export
Media: 2-4-10
Distr.: Intl.; Natl.
Budget Set: Jan.
Personnel:
Steve Stuller *(Pres, HR Exec)*
Brands & Products:
A.T. FERRELL
CLIPPER
FARMATIC
FERRELL-ROSS
MIX-MILL
MONARCH
NUTRI-BLENDER
SENTRY

AUTOMATIC EQUIPMENT MANUFACTURING CO.

(d/b/a Blue Ox)
Indus Pk 1 Mill Rd
Pender, NE 68047
Tel.: (402) 385-3051
Fax: (402) 385-3360
Toll Free: (888) 425-5382
E-mail: info@blueox.us
Web Site: www.aemfg.com
Sales Range: $25-49.9 Million
Approx. Number Employees: 125
Year Founded: 1925
Business Description:
Mfr. of Earthmovers, Guidance Systems, Rollermills & Mixers; Towing Products
S.I.C.: 3799; 3532
N.A.I.C.S.: 336999; 333131
Import Export
Advertising Expenditures: $600,000
Media: 1-2-4-5-6-7-8-10-11-13-16-19-20-21-22-24-26
Distr.: Intl.; Natl.
Budget Set: Oct.
Personnel:
Ellen Kietzmann *(VP-Sls & HR)*
Brands & Products:
ACCLAIM
ADVENTURER
AMBASSADOR
APOLLO
AUTOSTOP
AVENTA II
BLUE OX
BRAKESAFE PULL
BRAKESAFE PUSH
DUNCAN
KARGARD
NAVIGATOR
ROLLMIX
TOADSTOP
TOADSTOP II

BEHLEN MFG. CO.

4025 E 23rd St
Columbus, NE 68601-8501
Tel.: (402) 564-3111
Fax: (402) 563-7405
E-mail: behlen@behlenmfg.com
Web Site: www.behlenmfg.com
Approx. Number Employees: 800
Year Founded: 1936
Business Description:
Grain Handling & Manufacture of Storage Systems, Grain Bins, Berico Crop Dryers, Metal Building Systems, Roof Systems, Fencing, Strip Joining Presses, Big Bin Grain Storage Bins, Livestock Waters, Gates, Cattle Handling Equipment & Poly Livestock Drinkers
S.I.C.: 5084; 3448; 3523
N.A.I.C.S.: 423830; 332311; 333111
Export
Advertising Expenditures: $850,000
Bus. Publs.: $340,000; D.M. to Consumers: $510,000
Distr.: Intl.; Natl.
Budget Set: Nov.
Personnel:
Phil Raimondo *(Co-CEO)*
Tony Raimondo *(Co-CEO)*
Lyle Burbach *(Pres-Ag, Diversified Products-Intl & Sr VP)*
Richard F. Casey *(Sr VP-Fin)*
Steve Becker *(Gen Mgr-Behlen Building Sys)*
Brands & Products:
AG STAR
BEHLEN
BEHLEN COUNTRY
BERICO DRYERS
BIG BIN
BIG VALLEY
CLASSIC
CURVET
DUBL-PANL
EDGE
EXCEL
FARMASTER
HORSEMAN'S CHOICE
M1 MANUAL SILENCER
NEK-STENDER
POLY TUFF
PREMIER
QUARTERMASTER
RANCHMASTER
S-SPAN
UNIVERSAL
Advertising Agency:
BMC Advertising
4025 E 23rd St
Columbus, NE 68601-8501
Tel.: (402) 564-3111
Fax: (402) 563-7405
(Building Systems, Farmaster/Big Valley/Universal/Agstar Livestock Equipment, Berico Dryers and Grain Storage Bins)

BERG EQUIPMENT CO.

2700 W Veterans Pkwy
Marshfield, WI 54449
Mailing Address:
PO Box 507
Marshfield, WI 54449-0507

Key to Media (For complete agency information see *The Advertising Red Books-Agencies* edition):
1. Bus. Publs. 2. Cable T.V. 3. Catalogs & Directories. 4. Co-op Adv. 5. Consumer Mags. 6. D.M. to Bus. Estab.7. D.M. to Consumers 8. Daily Newsp. 9. Exhibits/Trade Shows 10. Foreign 11. Infomercial 12. Internet Adv.13. Multimedia 14. Network Radio 15. Network T.V. 16. Newsp. Distr. Mags. 17. Other 18. Outdoor (Posters, Transit) 19. Point of Purchase20. Premiums, Novelties 21. Product Samples 22. Special Events Mktg. 23. Spot Radio 24. Spot T.V. 25. Weekly Newsp. 26. Yellow Page Adv.

Tel.: (715) 384-2151
Fax: (715) 387-6777
Toll Free: (800) 494-1738
E-mail: bergeq@tznet.com
Web Site: www.bergequipment.com
Sales Range: $10-24.9 Million
Approx. Number Employees: 25
Year Founded: 1919
Business Description:
Barn Cleaners & Barn Equipment, Manure Pumps, Automatic Feeding Equipment & Barn Ventilation
S.I.C.: 3523; 3564
N.A.I.C.S.: 333111; 333412
Advertising Expenditures: $100,000
Media: 2-4-10-19
Distr.: Direct to Consumer; Natl.
Budget Set: Oct.
Personnel:
Vernon R. Berg, Jr. *(Pres)*
Robert Augustine *(Coord-Adv)*

Brands & Products:
ASSY
BERG
BUILDS EVERYTHING BETTER
FREE STALL PAD
HYDRO-MAN IV
SAND MARK
SIMPLEX
SIMPLEX DAIRY PAD

BLAIN SUPPLY, INC.
(d/b/a Blain's Farm & Fleet)
3507 E Racine St PO Box 391
Janesville, WI 53546
Tel.: (608) 754-2821
Fax: (608) 741-1455
E-mail: info@farmandfleet.com
Web Site: www.farmandfleet.com
Sales Range: $10-24.9 Million
Approx. Number Employees: 4,000
Year Founded: 1955
Business Description:
Retail Store
S.I.C.: 5083; 5072
N.A.I.C.S.: 423820; 423710
Media: 13-19
Personnel:
Robert S. Blain *(Owner)*
Harland Schraufnagel *(Pres)*
Jane Blain Gilbertson *(Exec VP)*

Brands & Products:
BLAIN'S FARM & FLEET

BLOOM MANUFACTURING, INC.
1443 220th St
Independence, IA 50644-9124
Tel.: (319) 827-1139
Fax: (319) 827-1140
Toll Free: (800) 394-1139
E-mail: sales@bloommfg.com
Web Site: www.bloommfg.com
E-Mail For Key Personnel:
Sales Director: sales@bloommfg.com
Approx. Sls.: $2,000,000
Approx. Number Employees: 20
Year Founded: 1910
Business Description:
Industrial & Farm Grain Equipment
S.I.C.: 3536; 3599
N.A.I.C.S.: 333923; 332710
Media: 2-4-6-7-8-9-11-21-23-25-26
Distr.: Direct to Consumer; Natl.
Personnel:
Mark Collett *(Pres)*
Michael Hunzeker *(Mgr-Mktg)*

Brands & Products:
BLOOM MANUFACTURING
LIFT SAFE
POWER-FLITE

BOUMATIC LLC
(Holding of Madison One Holdings)
1919 S Stoughton Rd
Madison, WI 53716
Mailing Address:
PO Box 8050
Madison, WI 53708
Tel.: (608) 222-3484
Fax: (608) 222-9314
E-mail: sales@boumatic.com
Web Site: www.boumatic.com
E-Mail For Key Personnel:
Sales Director: sales@boumatic.com
Year Founded: 1953
Business Description:
Dairy Equipment Mfr
S.I.C.: 3523
N.A.I.C.S.: 333111
Import Export
Advertising Expenditures: $500,000
Media: 1-5-6-8-10-11-20-21-25
Distr.: Intl.; Natl.
Budget Set: Oct.
Personnel:
John Kopps *(Owner)*

Brands & Products:
AGRI-COMP
AIR-STAR
ALOE SOFT TEAT DIP
BOU-MATIC PULSATOR
BOU-MATIC ROBOTICS
BOU-MATIC SHELL
BOVI-KOTE
COWTRAKKER
COWTRAKKER PID
DARI-KOOL FALLING
DARI-KOOL GLACIER
DARI-KOOL INSTA-KOOL
DARI-KOOL PLATE COOLER
EXCEL PLUS CIP CLEANER
FLO-SOAR
FLO-STAR LINEAR
FLO-STAR SUPREME CLAW
JET-VENT
KLEEN AND DRI
MAXIKLEEN
POWERLINE
THERMA-STOR
UDDERDINE
XPRESSWAY

BRILLION IRON WORKS, INC.
(Sub. of ACCURIDE CORPORATION)
200 Park Ave
Brillion, WI 54110-1145
Mailing Address:
PO Box 127
Brillion, WI 54110-0127
Tel.: (920) 756-3720
Fax: (920) 756-3409
Toll Free: (800) 409-9749
E-mail: biwfesales@brillionironworks.com
Web Site: www.brillionfarmeq.com
Sales Range: $1-9.9 Million
Approx. Number Employees: 1,000
Year Founded: 1893
Business Description:
Mfr. of Farm Equipment
S.I.C.: 0762; 3523
N.A.I.C.S.: 115116; 333111
Export
Media: 1-2-5-6-8-10-11-13-19-20-23-25
Distr.: Natl.
Personnel:
Michael Irish *(Gen Mgr-Sls)*

Brands & Products:
BRILLION
COMPACTION COMMANDER
LAND COMMANDER
SOIL COMMANDER
TURFMAKER

Advertising Agency:
Charleston/Orwig, Inc.
515 W North Shore Dr
Hartland, WI 53029-8312
Tel.: (262) 563-5100
Fax: (262) 563-5101
(Farm Equipment)

BURDEN SALES COMPANY
1015 W O St
Lincoln, NE 68528
Tel.: (402) 474-4055
Fax: (402) 474-5198
Toll Free: (800) 488-3407
E-mail: info@surpluscenter.com
Web Site: www.surpluscenter.com
Sales Range: $10-24.9 Million
Approx. Number Employees: 45
Year Founded: 1967
Business Description:
Mail Order Sales of Farm Machinery
S.I.C.: 5999
N.A.I.C.S.: 453998
Advertising Expenditures: $400,000
Media: 4-5-6-7-8-13-25-26
Distr.: Direct to Consumer; Natl.
Budget Set: Annually
Personnel:
David P. Burden *(Pres)*
Chris Cole *(VP-Sls)*

BUSH HOG, INC.
(Sub. of ALAMO GROUP INC.)
2501 Griffin Ave
Selma, AL 36703-1918
Mailing Address:
PO Box 1039
Selma, AL 36702-1039
Tel.: (334) 874-2700
Fax: (334) 874-2701
E-mail: info@bushhog.com
Web Site: www.bushhog.com
Sales Range: $100-124.9 Million
Approx. Number Employees: 400
Year Founded: 1951
Business Description:
Landscape & Farm Equipment Mfr
S.I.C.: 3523
N.A.I.C.S.: 333111
Export
Advertising Expenditures: $350,000
Media: 2-6-10-11-19-20
Distr.: Intl.; Natl.
Budget Set: Jan.
Personnel:
Bob Moore *(VP-Sls & Mktg)*
Tom Taylor *(VP-Sls & Mktg)*
Jimmy Anderson *(Gen Mgr-Sls)*

Brands & Products:
BUSH HOG

Advertising Agency:
Forward Consulting
2158 Airport Blvd
Mobile, AL 36606
Tel.: (251) 472-9400

BUSHWHACKER ASSOCIATES, INC.
(Sub. of Bethurum Research & Development, Inc.)
PO Box 345
Rancho Mirage, CA 92270-0345
Tel.: (760) 346-3019
Fax: (760) 346-7037
Toll Free: (800) 422-2687
E-Mail For Key Personnel:
Public Relations: shirleyb@bethurum.com
Year Founded: 1989
Business Description:
Agricultural & Home Insect Control Products
S.I.C.: 2879
N.A.I.C.S.: 325320
Import
Advertising Expenditures: $200,000
Media: 1-2-4-6-7-9-10-13-18-19-21-23-24-25
Distr.: Intl.
Budget Set: Monthly
Personnel:
Shirley Bethurum *(Pres)*

CARVER, INC.
1 Lummus Dr
Savannah, GA 31407
Mailing Address:
PO Box 4259
Savannah, GA 31407
Tel.: (912) 447-9000
Fax: (912) 447-9250
Toll Free: (800) 458-6687
E-mail: mailbox@carver-inc.com
Web Site: www.carver-inc.com
Approx. Number Employees: 100
Year Founded: 1842
Business Description:
Mfr. of Oil Seed Processing Machinery, Screening & Separating Equipment
S.I.C.: 3556
N.A.I.C.S.: 333294
Export
Media: 2-13
Distr.: Intl.; Natl.
Budget Set: Dec.
Personnel:
Stephen Marbut *(Pres & CEO)*

Brands & Products:
2000 SERIES
DENSE PAK
GEMINI
GUMP
HI-CEL
TRU-LINE

CHS INC.
5500 Cenex Dr
Inver Grove Heights, MN 55077-1733
Mailing Address:
PO Box 64089
Saint Paul, MN 55164-0089
Tel.: (651) 355-6000
Fax: (651) 355-6432
Toll Free: (800) 232-3639
Telex: 297-060
Web Site: www.chsinc.com
E-Mail For Key Personnel:
Public Relations: lani.jordan@chsinc.com
Approx. Rev.: $25,267,931,000
Approx. Number Employees: 7,641
Year Founded: 1998
Business Description:
Farm Supply Co-Operative; Petroleum

Key to Media (For complete agency information see *The Advertising Red Books-Agencies* edition):
1. Bus. Publs. 2. Cable T.V. 3. Catalogs & Directories. 4. Co-op Adv. 5. Consumer Mags. 6. D.M. to Bus. Estab.7. D.M. to Consumers
8. Daily Newsp. 9. Exhibits/Trade Shows 10. Foreign 11. Infomercial 12. Internet Adv.13. Multimedia 14. Network Radio
15. Network T.V. 16. Newsp. Distr. Mags. 17. Other 18. Outdoor (Posters, Transit) 19. Point of Purchase20. Premiums, Novelties
21. Product Samples 22. Special Events Mktg. 23. Spot Radio 24. Spot T.V. 25. Weekly Newsp. 26. Yellow Page Adv.

CHS INC. — (Continued)

Products; Fertilizer; Agricultural Chemicals; Tires; Batteries & Accessories; Agricultural Equipment; Farm Management Services; Grain Marketing; Flour Milling; Food Processing
S.I.C.: 5191; 2075; 5153; 5159
N.A.I.C.S.: 424910; 311222; 424510; 424590
Import Export
Advertising Expenditures: $8,366,000
Media: 2-7-10
Personnel:
Michael Toelle *(Chm)*
Robert Bass *(First Vice Chm)*
Carl M. Casale *(Pres & CEO)*
David A. Kastelic *(CFO & Exec VP)*
Jay D. Debertin *(COO & Exec VP-Energy & Foods)*
Beth E. Nordin *(CIO & VP)*
Theresa Egan *(Chief Acctg Officer, VP-Acctg & Controller)*
Mark L. Palmquist *(COO-Ag Bus & Exec VP)*
Lisa A. Zell *(Gen Counsel & Sr VP)*
Randy Knecht *(Treas & Asst Sec)*
Patrick M. Kluempke *(Exec VP-Corp Svcs)*
Rick Browne *(Sr VP)*
Paul Culver *(Sr VP-Propane)*
Lynden E. Johnson *(Sr VP-Bus Solutions)*
Kevin L. Williams *(Sr VP-Energy Sls)*
Jim Bareksten *(Dir-Govt Affairs)*
Annette Degnan *(Dir-Mktg Comm)*
Doug Dorfman *(Dir-Mktg & Retail Dev)*
Lani Jordan *(Dir-Corp Comm)*
Kristine Thompson *(Dir-Mktg Comm)*
Brian Kuhl *(Mgr-Bus Solutions)*
Brands & Products:
CENEX
CHS
HONEYSOY
OUR ENERGY COMES THROUGH RESOURCES FOR ENRICHING LIVES
SAVORYSOY
Advertising Agency:
Colle+McVoy
400 1st Ave N Ste 700
Minneapolis, MN 55401-1954
Tel.: (612) 305-6000
Fax: (612) 305-6500

CNH AMERICA LLC

(Holding of CNH Global N.V.)
6900 Veterans Blvd
Burr Ridge, IL 60527
Tel.: (630) 887-2233
E-mail: investorrelations@cnh.com
Web Site: www.cnh.com
Year Founded: 1842
Business Description:
Agricultural, Construction & Mechanical Equipment Mfr
S.I.C.: 3531; 3523
N.A.I.C.S.: 333120; 333111
Import Export
Media: 2-3-4-5-6-7-8-10-11-13-18-19-20-23-24-26
Distr.: Intl.; Natl.
Budget Set: Aug.
Personnel:
Michael Going *(Gen Counsel, Sr VP & Sec)*
Brands & Products:
AUSTOFT
BRAUD
CASE
CASE IH
CNH CAPITAL
CONCORD
DMI
FIATALLIS
FLEXI-COIL
KOBELCO
STEYR
TYLER
Advertising Agencies:
Colle+McVoy
400 1st Ave N Ste 700
Minneapolis, MN 55401-1954
Tel.: (612) 305-6000
Fax: (612) 305-6500
— Jamie Moran *(Acct Supvr)*
— Josette Hutchinson *(Acct Exec)*

Slack Barshinger & Partners, Inc.
233 N Michigan Ave Ste 3050
Chicago, IL 60601
Tel.: (312) 970-5800
Fax: (312) 970-5850
Toll Free: (800) 888-6197

CONRAD FAFARD, INC.

(Sub. of Syngenta Professional Products)
770 Silver St
Agawam, MA 01001-0790
Mailing Address:
PO Box 790
Agawam, MA 01001-0790
Tel.: (413) 786-4343
Fax: (413) 789-3425
Toll Free: (800) 732-8667
Web Site: www.fafard.com
Approx. Sls.: $76,000,000
Approx. Number Employees: 240
Year Founded: 1954
Business Description:
Agricultural Products Supplier
S.I.C.: 5191
N.A.I.C.S.: 424910
Media: 10-17
Personnel:
Keelan Pulliam *(Pres)*
Jack Cunningham *(VP-Fin)*
Jacqui Arnold *(Sr Mgr)*
Bruce Adams *(Mgr-Pro Market)*
Steve Young *(Mgr-Northern District Sls)*

CONVERTED ORGANICS, INC.

137A Lewis Wharf
Boston, MA 02110
Tel.: (617) 624-0111
Fax: (617) 624-0333
Toll Free: (877) 665-0444
Web Site:
www.convertedorganics.com
Approx. Rev.: $3,525,325
Approx. Number Employees: 26
Year Founded: 2003
Business Description:
Organic Soil Amendment & Fertilizer Product Mfr
S.I.C.: 0711; 2875
N.A.I.C.S.: 115112; 325314
Personnel:
Edward J. Gildea *(Pres & CEO)*
David R. Allen *(CFO & Exec VP)*
David A. Flannery *(VP-Sls, Mktg & Ops)*
Advertising Agency:
Crossbow Group, LLC
136 Main St
Westport, CT 06880
Tel.: (203) 222-2244
Fax: (203) 226-7838

CORN STATES HYBRID SERVICE, LLC

(Sub. of Monsanto Company)
2505 McKinley Ave
Des Moines, IA 50321-2309
Tel.: (515) 285-3091
Fax: (515) 285-6802
Toll Free: (800) 247-5202
Web Site: www.monsanto.com/who_we_are/locations/unitedstates/iowa.asp
Approx. Sls.: $25,000,000
Approx. Number Employees: 80
Business Description:
Seed Brokerage Services
S.I.C.: 5191
N.A.I.C.S.: 424910
Media: 2-4
Distr.: Intl.; Natl.
Budget Set: Jan.
Personnel:
Tim O'Leary *(Brand Mgr)*

CRANE PUMPS & SYSTEMS INC.

(Sub. of Crane Fluid Handling)
420 3rd St
Piqua, OH 45356-3918
Mailing Address:
PO Box 603
Piqua, OH 45356-0603
Tel.: (937) 773-2442
Fax: (937) 773-2238
E-mail: cranepumps@cranepumps.com
Web Site: www.cranepumps.com
Sales Range: $100-124.9 Million
Approx. Number Employees: 300
Business Description:
Pumps & Cleaning Systems Mfr
S.I.C.: 3561
N.A.I.C.S.: 333911
Import Export
Media: 2-4-10-20-26
Distr.: Intl.; Natl.
Budget Set: Sept.
Brands & Products:
BARNES
CROWN
DEMING
PROSSER
SELLERS

CRESCENT RESOURCES, LLC

(Joint Venture of Duke Energy Corporation)
400 S Tryon St Ste 1300
Charlotte, NC 28285
Tel.: (980) 321-6000
Toll Free: (866) 800-1429
E-mail: crescentnews@crescent-resources.com
Web Site:
www.crescentresources.com
Approx. Sls.: $11,354,250
Approx. Number Employees: 100
Year Founded: 1969
Business Description:
Real Estate Development & Land Management; Joint Venture Between Duke Energy Corporation & Morgan Stanley Real Estate Fund
S.I.C.: 6531; 6552; 9532
N.A.I.C.S.: 531390; 237210; 925120
Personnel:
Lawrence A. Corson *(Pres & CEO)*
Nina Shor *(Gen Counsel)*
Mike Burnett *(Sr VP)*
Margaret Jennesse *(Sr VP-Residential Div)*
Robert Zeiller *(Reg VP)*
Alice Zwahlen *(VP-HR)*
Jason Holwerda *(Dir-Leasing)*
Advertising Agency:
Abernathy MacGregor Group, Inc.
501 Madison Ave 13th Fl
New York, NY 10022-5617
Tel.: (212) 371-5999
Fax: (212) 371-7097

CRUSTBUSTER-SPEED KING, INC.

2300 E Trl St
Dodge City, KS 67801-9023
Tel.: (620) 227-7106
Fax: (620) 227-7130
E-mail: crustbuster@crustbuster.com
Web Site: www.crustbuster.com
Sales Range: $100-124.9 Million
Approx. Number Employees: 95
Year Founded: 1960
Business Description:
Retailer & Whslr of Farm Tillage, Seeding & Other Farming Equipment
S.I.C.: 5083
N.A.I.C.S.: 423820
Media: 2-7-10-19-23
Distr.: Natl.
Budget Set: July
Personnel:
Donald F. Hornung *(Pres & CEO)*
Brands & Products:
BELT VEYOR
BOLL BUGGY
CRUSTBUSTER
Advertising Agency:
Arrow Printing Co. Inc.
115 W Woodland
Salina, KS 67402
Tel.: (785) 825-8124
Fax: (785) 825-0784
(Farm Machinery)

DANUSER MACHINE COMPANY, INC.

500 E 3rd St
Fulton, MO 65251-1679
Mailing Address:
PO Box 368
Fulton, MO 65251-1679
Tel.: (573) 642-2246
Fax: (573) 642-2240
E-mail: sales@danuser.com
Web Site: www.danuser.com
E-Mail For Key Personnel:
Sales Director: sales@danuser.com
Approx. Number Employees: 65
Year Founded: 1910
Business Description:
Mfr. of Digger Tractor Attachments, Earth Drills, Specialized OEM Metal Components & Construction Diggers
S.I.C.: 3523; 3531
N.A.I.C.S.: 333111; 333120
Export
Media: 6-10

Key to Media (For complete agency information see *The Advertising Red Books-Agencies* edition):
1. Bus. Publs. 2. Cable T.V. 3. Catalogs & Directories. 4. Co-op Adv. 5. Consumer Mags. 6. D.M. to Bus. Estab.7. D.M. to Consumers 8. Daily Newsp. 9. Exhibits/Trade Shows 10. Foreign 11. Infomercial 12. Internet Adv.13. Multimedia 14. Network Radio 15. Network T.V. 16. Newsp. Distr. Mags. 17. Other 18. Outdoor (Posters, Transit) 19. Point of Purchase20. Premiums, Novelties 21. Product Samples 22. Special Events Mktg. 23. Spot Radio 24. Spot T.V. 25. Weekly Newsp. 26. Yellow Page Adv.

Distr.: Intl.
Budget Set: Nov. -Dec.
Personnel:
Jerry Danuser *(Pres)*
Betty Smola *(Mgr-Acctg)*
Brands & Products:
DANUSER
Advertising Agency:
Woodruff Sweitzer, Inc.
501 Fay St Ste 110
Columbia, MO 65201
Tel.: (573) 875-7917
Fax: (573) 874-7979
Toll Free: (888) 300-7485

DEERE & COMPANY
(d/b/a John Deere)
1 John Deere Pl
Moline, IL 61265-8010
Tel.: (309) 765-8000
Fax: (309) 765-5671
Web Site: www.deere.com
E-Mail For Key Personnel:
Public Relations: goldenken@johndeere.com
Approx. Rev.: $26,004,600,000
Approx. Number Employees: 55,700
Year Founded: 1837
Business Description:
Commercial & Farm Tractor, Mower, Truck & Utility Vehicle Developer & Mfr; Financial Services
S.I.C.: 5083; 3523; 3531; 6141
N.A.I.C.S.: 423820; 333111; 333120; 522220
Import Export
Advertising Expenditures: $154,000,000
Media: 1-2-4-5-6-8-10-15-19-23-24-25-26
Distr.: Intl.; Natl.
Budget Set: June
Personnel:
Samuel R. Allen *(Chm & CEO)*
James M. Field *(CFO & Sr VP)*
Barry W. Schaffter *(Sr VP-Intelligent Solutions Grp & CIO-Agriculture & Turf Div)*
David C. Everitt *(Pres-Ant Div Tractor Flash-Turs & Intl)*
James A. Israel *(Pres-John Deere Credit)*
Michael J. Mack, Jr. *(Pres-Worldwide Construction & Forestry Div)*
John C. Roberts *(Pres-John Deere Water)*
Markwart Von Pentz *(Pres-Agricultural Div-Europe, Africa, South America)*
David P. Werning *(Pres-John Deere Landscapes)*
James R. Jenkins *(Gen Counsel & Sr VP)*
Douglas C. Devries *(Sr VP-Global Mktg Svcs)*
Jean Gilles *(Sr VP-Power Sys, Mobile Equipment Technologies & Advanced Tech)*
Max A. Guinn *(Sr VP-Global Platform-Crop Harvesting)*
Robert C. Hove *(Sr VP-Customer Mktg & Sls)*
Daniel C. McCabe *(Sr VP-Sls & Mktg-US & Canada)*
Stephen Pullin *(Sr VP-Intl Lending Worldwide Fin Svcs Div)*
Randal A. Sergesketter *(Sr VP-Engrg & Mfg)*
Lawrence W. Sidwell *(Sr VP-Credit & Ops-US & Canada)*
John J. Dalhoff *(VP & Comptroller)*
Frances B. Emerson *(VP-Corp Comm & Global Brand Mgmt)*
Klaus G. Hoehn *(VP-Advanced Tech & Engrg)*
Mertroe B. Hornbuckle *(VP-HR)*
James R. Jabanoski *(VP-IT)*
Mary K. W. Jones *(VP-Global HR)*
Gary L. Medd *(VP-Internal Audit)*
Stefan von Stegmann *(VP-Sls & Mktg-Agricultural Div)*
Bill Becker *(Dir-Brand Mngmt)*
Gregg Breningmeyer *(Dir-Sls-Mktg)*
Ken Golden *(Dir-Global Pub Rels)*
Doug Laufenberg *(Product Mktg Mgr-Construction)*
David Niederkorn *(Mgr-Mktg Comm & Consumer Dev)*
Dean Anderson *(Mgr-Product Dev)*
Brett Errthum *(Mgr)*
Bill Klutho *(Mgr-Strategic PR)*
Tracy Lanier *(Mgr-Golf Product)*
Tim Meister *(Mgr-Mktg)*
Molly Reddish *(Mgr)*
Bob Tyler *(Mgr-Mktg)*
Gregory Weekes *(Mgr-Product Mktg)*
Don Worner *(Mgr-Mktg)*
Brands & Products:
AUTOTRAC
BUCK
COMPRESSERATORS
EZTRAK
GATOR
GREENSTAR
HARVESTLAB
ITEC
JDLINK
JDOFFICE
M-GATOR
MACHINEFINDER
MAXEMERGE
NOTHING RUNS LIKE A DEERE
POWERTECH PLUS
PROGATOR
SELECT SERIES
STARFIRE
SURFACR WATER PRO
SWATH CONTROL PRO
TRAIL BUCK
WORKSHITE PRO
Z-TRAK
Advertising Agencies:
The Buntin Group
1001 Hawkins St
Nashville, TN 37203-4758
Tel.: (615) 244-5720
Fax: (615) 244-6511
Clothing

Clean Design, Inc.
10 Laboratory Dr Bldg 2 Ste 200
Research Triangle Park, NC 27709
Tel.: (919) 544-2193
Fax: (919) 473-2200

eCreative Group, Inc.
PO Box 66
Independence, IA 50644
Tel.: (319) 334-5115
Fax: (319) 334-3752

KRT Marketing
3685 Mt Diablo Blvd Ste 255
Lafayette, CA 94549-3776
Tel.: (925) 284-0444
Fax: (925) 284-0448
Recruitment

Targetbase
7850 N Belt Line Rd
Irving, TX 75063-6098
Tel.: (972) 506-3400
Fax: (972) 506-3505
Toll Free: (866) 506-7850

Yeck Brothers Company
2222 Arbor Blvd
Dayton, OH 45439-1522
Tel.: (937) 294-4000
Fax: (937) 294-6985
Toll Free: (800) 417-2767

DEGELMAN INDUSTRIES LTD.
272 Industrial Dr
PO Box 830
Regina, SK S4P 3B1, Canada
Tel.: (306) 543-4447
Fax: (306) 543-2140
Toll Free: (800) 667-3545
E-mail: sales@degelman.com
Web Site: www.degelman.com
E-Mail For Key Personnel:
Sales Director: sales@degelman.com
Approx. Number Employees: 125
Year Founded: 1962
Business Description:
Farm Equipment
S.I.C.: 3523
N.A.I.C.S.: 333111
Import Export
Media: 2-7-10
Distr.: Intl.; Natl.
Budget Set: Oct.
Personnel:
Wilfred Degelman *(Pres)*
Roland Degelman *(Gen Mgr)*
Jack Degelman *(Mgr-Mktg)*
Brands & Products:
DEGELMAN
DIECI
ICE BREAKER
SHUTTLEKART
SIDEARM
SIGNATURE
SNOW BUCKET
SPEEDBLADE
STRAWMASTER
STRONGBOX

ECOLAB - ALCIDE
(Sub. of Ecolab Inc.)
8561 154th Ave NE
Redmond, WA 98052
Tel.: (425) 882-2555
Fax: (425) 861-0173
Sales Range: $75-99.9 Million
Business Description:
Research, Development & Commercialization of Unique Chemical Compounds; Food & Beverage Division
S.I.C.: 8734
N.A.I.C.S.: 541380
Advertising Expenditures: $207,965
Media: 5-10
Brands & Products:
4XLA
ALCIDE
DIPPINGOLD
EXSPOR
HOOFTECT
LD
PRE-GOLD
SANOVA
SILVERQUICK
UDDERGOLD
UDDERGOLD 5 STAR
UDDERGOLD PLUS
UDDERMINT
WOOLOVER

EVH MANUFACTURING COMPANY, LLC
4895 Red Bluff Rd
Loris, SC 29569
Tel.: (843) 756-4051
Fax: (843) 756-4436
Toll Free: (888) 990-2555
E-mail: evhmfg@evhmfg.com
Web Site: www.evhmfg.com
E-Mail For Key Personnel:
Sales Director: sales@evhmfg.com
Approx. Sls.: $5,000,000
Approx. Number Employees: 39
Year Founded: 1956
Business Description:
Mfr. of Farm Equipment; Agricultural Sprayers, Landscape Equipment & Nursery Equipment
S.I.C.: 3523
N.A.I.C.S.: 333111
Import Export
Advertising Expenditures: $300,000
Media: 2-10
Distr.: Reg.
Budget Set: July
Personnel:
Mike Todd *(Gen Mgr)*
Brands & Products:
HARDEE

FARMERS NATIONAL COMPANY
11516 Nicholas St Ste 100
Omaha, NE 68154-8016
Tel.: (402) 496-3276
Fax: (402) 496-7956
Toll Free: (800) 346-2650
E-mail: info@farmers-national.com
Web Site: www.farmersnational.com
Sales Range: $25-49.9 Million
Approx. Number Employees: 65
Year Founded: 1929
Business Description:
Farm & Ranch Management Services & Real Estate Sales
S.I.C.: 0762; 6531
N.A.I.C.S.: 115116; 531210
Advertising Expenditures: $650,000
Media: 8-13-26
Personnel:
Jim Farrell *(Pres & CEO)*
David Knutson *(CFO, Treas & Sr Exec VP)*
Jerry Warner *(Chief Mgmt Officer & Exec VP)*
Larry Hinrichs *(Exec Officer-Insurance Sls)*
Monty Meusch *(Area Mgr-Sls)*
Susan Christensen *(Mgr-Mktg)*
Pam Grap *(Coord-Real Estate Closing & Licensing)*
Brands & Products:
FARMERS NATIONAL COMPANY

FARMTRAC
111 Fairview St
Tarboro, NC 27886
Mailing Address:
PO Box 1139

Key to Media (For complete agency information see *The Advertising Red Books-Agencies* edition):
1. Bus. Publs. 2. Cable T.V. 3. Catalogs & Directories. 4. Co-op Adv. 5. Consumer Mags. 6. D.M. to Bus. Estab.7. D.M. to Consumers
8. Daily Newsp. 9. Exhibits/Trade Shows 10. Foreign 11. Infomercial 12. Internet Adv.13. Multimedia 14. Network Radio
15. Network T.V. 16. Newsp. Distr. Mags. 17. Other 18. Outdoor (Posters, Transit) 19. Point of Purchase20. Premiums, Novelties
21. Product Samples 22. Special Events Mktg. 23. Spot Radio 24. Spot T.V. 25. Weekly Newsp. 26. Yellow Page Adv.

Farmtrac — (Continued)

Tarboro, NC 27866-1139
Tel.: (252) 823-4151
Fax: (252) 823-4576
Web Site: www.farmtrac.com
Approx. Number Employees: 175
Year Founded: 1941
Business Description:
Farm Machinery & Equipment Mfr
S.I.C.: 3523; 3448
N.A.I.C.S.: 333111; 332311
Import Export
Advertising Expenditures: $300,000
Media: 2-4-5-6-7-8-9-10-14-16-20-23-25-26
Distr.: Reg.
Budget Set: Aug.
Personnel:
Pranab Ghosal *(Pres)*
Alton H. Cobb, Jr. *(VP-Fin)*
Brands & Products:
FARMTRAC
HYDROSTATIC
LANDTRAC
LONGTRAC

FLINT NEW HOLLAND INC.

3266 E Bristol Rd
Burton, MI 48529
Tel.: (810) 744-2030
Fax: (810) 744-0444
E-mail: flintnewholland@sbcglobal.net
Web Site: www.newholland.com
Approx. Number Employees: 15
Business Description:
Supplier of Tractors
S.I.C.: 5083; 5082
N.A.I.C.S.: 423820; 423810
Media: 10

GANDY COMPANY

528 Gandrud Rd
Owatonna, MN 55060-2185
Tel.: (507) 451-5430
Fax: (507) 451-2857
Toll Free: (800) 443-2476
E-mail: custsrv@gandy.net
Web Site: www.gandy.net
Approx. Number Employees: 25
Year Founded: 1936
Business Description:
Granular Chemical Applicators, Fertilizer Spreaders & Air Seeders Mfr
S.I.C.: 3523; 3524
N.A.I.C.S.: 333111; 333112
Import Export
Media: 1-4-6-10-11-13
Distr.: Intl.; Natl.
Budget Set: Nov.
Personnel:
Dale E. Gandrud *(Pres)*
Cindy Barta *(Mgr-Ops)*
Doug Snorek *(Mgr-Sls & Mktg)*
Brands & Products:
GANDY
THE GRANULAR APPLICATOR PEOPLE
ORBIT-AIR
ORBIT-FLOW
PEDAL PARTNER
SWEEP MASTER
TURF TENDER

GREAT PLAINS MANUFACTURING, INCORPORATED

1525 E North St
Salina, KS 67402-5060
Tel.: (785) 823-3276
Fax: (785) 822-5600
Toll Free: (800) 255-0132
E-mail: hrcontact@greatplainsmfg.com
Web Site: www.greatplainsmfg.com
E-Mail For Key Personnel:
Sales Director: sales@greatplainsmfg.com
Approx. Number Employees: 1,000
Year Founded: 1976
Business Description:
Mfr. of Agricultural Planting, Spraying & Cultivating Equipment & Landscaping Products; Provider of Trucking Services; Provider of Financing Services
S.I.C.: 3523
N.A.I.C.S.: 333111
Import Export
Advertising Expenditures: $500,000
Media: 2-5-6-13-23
Distr.: Natl.
Personnel:
Roy Applequist *(Founder & Pres)*
Daniel Rauchholz *(Pres-Great Plains Intl)*
Sherwin Fast *(Pres-Great Plains Trucking)*
Rick Hanson *(Pres-Great Plains Div)*
Brands & Products:
DISCOVATOR
ELIMINATOR
GREAT PLAINS
LAND PRIDE
PLAINS PLOW
SEED-LOK
SETTING THE PACE THROUGH INNOVATION
SUB-SOILER
TURBO-TILL
VANTAGE
VERTI-TILL

GREEN EARTH TECHNOLOGIES, INC.

10 Bank St Ste 680
White Plains, NY 10532
Fax: (877) 438-3293
Toll Free: (877) 438-4761
Web Site: www.getgreenearth.com
Approx. Sls.: $2,430,000
Approx. Number Employees: 8
Business Description:
Environmentally Safe Cleaning & Lawn Care Products Mfr & Marketer
S.I.C.: 2842; 0711
N.A.I.C.S.: 325612; 115112
Advertising Expenditures: $1,855,000
Personnel:
Jeffrey Loch *(Founder, Pres & CMO)*
William Jefferson Marshall *(Chm)*
Greg D. Adams *(CFO & COO)*
Brands & Products:
G-CLEAN
G-DISPOSOIL
G-GLASS
G-OIL
G-SCENT
G-TILE
G-TIRE
G-WASH
G-WHEEL
GETGREEN !
GREEN EARTH TECHNOLOGIES
SAVE THE EARTH SACRIFICE NOTHING
Advertising Agency:
Gregory FCA
27 W Athens Ave Ste 200
Ardmore, PA 19003
Tel.: (610) 642-8253
Fax: (610) 642-1258
Fax: (610) 649-9029
Toll Free: (800) 499-4734
Environmentally-Safe Consumer Products

THE GREGORY MFG. CO.

506 Oak Dr
Lewiston Woodville, NC 27849-9224
Mailing Address:
PO Box 269
Lewiston Woodville, NC 27849-0269
Tel.: (252) 348-2531
Fax: (252) 348-2400
Toll Free: (800) 233-4734
E-mail: gregorymfg@coastalnet.com
Web Site: www.gregorymfg.com
Approx. Number Employees: 100
Year Founded: 1984
Business Description:
Mfr. of Tobacco Harvesters, Peanut Combines & Agricultural Machinery, Highway Brush Cutting Equipment, Tree Shears & Industrial Fork Lifts
S.I.C.: 3523; 3537
N.A.I.C.S.: 333111; 333924
Export
Media: 1-2-4-6-8-9-10-11-13-17-20-25-26
Distr.: Intl.; Natl.
Budget Set: Jan. -Feb.
Personnel:
Charles E. Gregory *(Pres)*
Brands & Products:
AUTOMATIC 2-ROW
CH-55
CRUSTER
GERGORY
GREGORY G-195 BUSH AXE
HUSTLER PEANUT
PULL TYPE STRIPPER
ROANOKE
ROANOKE-HUSTLER FORKLIFTS
SB-110 CUTTER

GRIFFIN GREENHOUSE & NURSERY SUPPLIES, INC.

1619 Main St
Tewksbury, MA 01876
Tel.: (978) 851-4346
Fax: (978) 851-0012
E-mail: tnoop@griffinmail.com
Web Site: www.griffins.com
Sales Range: $75-99.9 Million
Approx. Number Employees: 85
Year Founded: 1947
Business Description:
Greenhouse & Nursery Supplies
S.I.C.: 5193; 5261
N.A.I.C.S.: 424930; 444220
Media: 10
Personnel:
Rick Hyslip *(Pres & CFO)*
Kenneth M. Hyslip, Sr. *(CEO)*
Craig Hyslip *(COO)*
Ken Hyslip, Jr. *(Exec VP)*
Dave Morin *(VP-Mktg & Pur)*

GROWMARK, INC.

1701 N Towanda Ave
Bloomington, IL 61701-2090
Tel.: (309) 557-6000
Fax: (309) 829-8532
E-mail: contactus@growmark.com
Web Site: www.growmark.com
Approx. Rev.: $4,422,306,000
Approx. Number Employees: 745
Year Founded: 1927
Business Description:
Agricultural Cooperative
S.I.C.: 9641; 6163
N.A.I.C.S.: 926140; 522310
Personnel:
Dan Kelley *(Chm & Pres)*
Rick Nelson *(Vice Chm)*
John Reifsteck *(Vice Chm)*
Jeff Solberg *(CEO)*
Tim Piper *(CIO & Dir-Info Tech)*
Brent Bostrom *(Gen Counsel & VP)*
Dennis Farmer *(Sr VP-Member Svcs)*
Kreg Ruhl *(Sr Mgr-Market-Nitrogen)*
Mark Dehner *(Mgr-Mktg Refined & Renewable Fuels)*
Brian Hundman *(Mgr-Ops-Plant Food)*
Kel Kelly *(Mgr-Economic & Market Res)*
Steve Kubsch *(Mgr-Transport Ops & Compliance)*
Jeff Mosley *(Mgr-Sys & Programming)*
Advertising Agency:
Kaiser Marketing, Inc.
11400 W Olympic Blvd Ste 600
Los Angeles, CA 90064
Tel.: (310) 479-8999
Fax: (310) 479-0414

HARPER INDUSTRIES, INC.

(d/b/a DewEze Manufacturing)
151 E Hwy 160
Harper, KS 67058-8201
Tel.: (620) 896-7381
Fax: (620) 896-7129
Toll Free: (800) 835-1042
E-mail: info@deweze.com
Web Site: www.deweze.com
E-Mail For Key Personnel:
President: penner@deweze.com
Approx. Number Employees: 85
Year Founded: 1998
Business Description:
Mfr. of Agricultural Machinery, Round Bale Handling & Feeding Equipment & Grounds Maintenance Equipment
S.I.C.: 3523; 3594
N.A.I.C.S.: 333111; 333996
Import Export
Media: 2-5-7-10-13-20-25
Distr.: Intl.; Natl.
Budget Set: Nov. -Oct.
Personnel:
A. Timothy Penner *(CEO)*
Luke Thornton *(Mgr-Sls)*
Heber Ramer *(Mgr-Engrg)*
Brands & Products:
ATM MOWERS
DEWEZE
GOOSSEN
HARPER

HAWKEYE STEEL PRODUCTS, INC.

609 Hwy 16 W
Houghton, IA 52631
Tel.: (319) 469-4141
Fax: (319) 469-4402
Toll Free: (800) 553-1791

Key to Media (For complete agency information see *The Advertising Red Books-Agencies* edition):
1. Bus. Publs. 2. Cable T.V. 3. Catalogs & Directories. 4. Co-op Adv. 5. Consumer Mags. 6. D.M. to Bus. Estab.7. D.M. to Consumers 8. Daily Newsp. 9. Exhibits/Trade Shows 10. Foreign 11. Infomercial 12. Internet Adv.13. Multimedia 14. Network Radio 15. Network T.V. 16. Newsp. Distr. Mags. 17. Other 18. Outdoor (Posters, Transit) 19. Point of Purchase20. Premiums, Novelties 21. Product Samples 22. Special Events Mktg. 23. Spot Radio 24. Spot T.V. 25. Weekly Newsp. 26. Yellow Page Adv.

E-mail: sales@hawkeyesteel.com
Web Site: www.hawkeyesteel.com
E-Mail For Key Personnel:
Sales Director: sales@hawkeyesteel.com
Approx. Number Employees: 60
Year Founded: 1920
Business Description:
Livestock Feeders & Waterers, Poultry Equipment, Grain Bins
S.I.C.: 3523; 3556
N.A.I.C.S.: 333111; 333294
Import Export
Media: 2-5-9-10-11-14-18-19-21-23-25
Distr.: Intl.; Natl.
Budget Set: Jan. -July
Personnel:
Marvin Bricker *(Co-Pres)*
Thomas W. Wenstrand *(Co-Pres)*
Brands & Products:
BROWER
CONRAD-AMERICAN
HAWKEYE
POLAR-MAX
PRIDE OF THE FARM
SPAN-TECH

HENKE MACHINE - BUFFALO EQUIPMENT
(Sub. of Sinca Industries, Inc.)
2281 16th Ave
Columbus, NE 68601-3513
Mailing Address:
PO Box 848
Columbus, NE 68602-0848
Tel.: (402) 562-0014
Fax: (402) 562-5530
E-mail: hbsales@megavision.com
Approx. Number Employees: 63
Year Founded: 1945
Business Description:
Agricultural Equipment
S.I.C.: 3523
N.A.I.C.S.: 333111
Import Export
Media: 1-4-5-6-8-9-10-11-13-14-16-18-19-20-22-23-26
Distr.: Intl.; Natl.
Budget Set: June
Personnel:
Doug Stevens *(Pres)*
Brands & Products:
BUFFALO
BUFFALO CULTIVATOR
BUFFALO DESIGN
BUFFALO FLAIL SHREDDER
BUFFALO RESIDUE CLIPPERS
BUFFALO RIDGE RUNNERS
BUFFALO SCOUT II
BUFFALO SLOT PLANTER
BUFFALO TILL PLANTER
HENKE
KWIKCUTTER
QUARTER-TURN
SCOUT II
THMR

HERD SEEDER COMPANY, INC.
2383 S US Hwy 35
Logansport, IN 46947-6625
Tel.: (574) 753-6311
Fax: (574) 722-4106
E-mail: info@herdseeder.com
Web Site: www.herdseeder.com
Approx. Sls.: $1,210,519
Approx. Number Employees: 19
Year Founded: 1948
Business Description:
Power Broadcast Seeder-Spreaders Mfr
S.I.C.: 3523
N.A.I.C.S.: 333111
Import Export
Media: 2-4-7-9-10-18-25
Distr.: Natl.
Brands & Products:
HERD
HERD SURE FEED
THOMPSON SEEDER CO.
WE HAVE IT ALL FROM BIG TO SMALL

HIGHWAY EQUIPMENT COMPANY
1330 76th Ave SW
Cedar Rapids, IA 52404
Tel.: (319) 363-8281
Fax: (319) 632-3080
Fax: (800) 363-8267
Toll Free: (800) 363-1771
E-mail: information@highwayequipment.com
Web Site: www.highwayequipment.com
Approx. Number Employees: 106
Year Founded: 1939
Business Description:
Mfr. of Hi-Way Deicing Spreaders, Road Maintenance Equipment, Fertilizer & Lime Spreaders
S.I.C.: 3531; 3523
N.A.I.C.S.: 333120; 333111
Export
Media: 1-2-4-5-7-8-10-13-18-19-20
Distr.: Intl.; Natl.
Budget Set: June
Personnel:
Matthew W. Rissi *(Owner)*
Rochelle Shepard *(Pres)*
Michael Dean *(Product Mgr)*
Brands & Products:
AERO SPREAD
DISPLACER SERIES SNOWPLOWS
G-4
HI-WAY
HI-WAY AUTUMNMATE
NEW LEADER
PREMIERE SERIES DUMP BODIES
SUPER P
XT3 MULTI-PURPOSE DUMP BODIES

HINIKER COMPANY
58766 240st St
Mankato, MN 56001
Tel.: (507) 625-6621
Fax: (507) 625-5883
Toll Free: (800) 433-5620
E-mail: hiniker@hiniker.com
Web Site: www.hiniker.com
Approx. Number Employees: 170
Year Founded: 1967
Business Description:
Mfr. of Farm Machinery & Equipment, Snow Plows, Water Purification Equipment & Electronic Controllers
S.I.C.: 3523; 3824
N.A.I.C.S.: 333111; 334514
Import Export
Media: 1-2-4-5-6-7-8-10-11-13-18-23-26
Distr.: Intl.; Natl.
Budget Set: Nov.
Personnel:
Vincent J. Tomlonovic *(Gen Mgr)*
Mark Miller *(Mgr-Adv & Mktg)*
Brands & Products:
CENTURY
COSTER
COSTER ENGINEERING
DUAL TRACK
FOX BRADY
HINIKER
QUICK-HITCH
Advertising Agency:
Lime Valley Marketing
101 N. Second St.
Mankato, MN 56001
Tel.: (507) 345-8500
(Snowplows & Agricultural Equipment)

HUTCHINSON/MAYRATH INDUSTRIES INC.
(Div. of Global Industries Inc.)
514 W Crawford St
Clay Center, KS 67432-2345
Mailing Address:
PO Box 629
Clay Center, KS 67432-0629
Tel.: (785) 632-2161
Fax: (785) 632-5964
Toll Free: (800) 523-6993
Web Site: www.mayrath.com
Approx. Sls.: $8,000,000
Approx. Number Employees: 150
Business Description:
Farm Equipment Mfr
S.I.C.: 3532; 3556
N.A.I.C.S.: 333131; 333294
Import Export
Media: 2-5-6-10
Distr.: Natl.
Personnel:
Cliff Williams *(Pres)*
Dwight Benninga *(VP-Engrg)*
Gary Gregg *(VP-Sls & Mktg)*
Gary Matteson *(VP-Fin)*
Alejandro Merino *(Reg Sls Mgr)*
Tom Sigg *(Reg Sls Mgr-Asia)*

HYPRO
(Sub. of Pentair Pump Group, Inc.)
375 5th Ave NW
New Brighton, MN 55112-3239
Tel.: (651) 766-6300
Fax: (651) 766-6600
Toll Free: (800) 424-9776
Telex: 4310109
E-mail: sales@hypropumps.com
Web Site: www.hypropumps.com
E-Mail For Key Personnel:
Sales Director: sales@hypropumps.com
Sales Range: $50-74.9 Million
Approx. Number Employees: 289
Year Founded: 1947
Business Description:
Pumps & Accessories Mfr
S.I.C.: 3561
N.A.I.C.S.: 333911
Import Export
Advertising Expenditures: $500,000
Media: 1-2-4-7-10-11-19-20
Distr.: Direct to Consumer; Intl.; Natl.; Reg.
Budget Set: Oct.
Personnel:
Greg Tufte *(Dir-Mktg)*
Brands & Products:
AQUA TIGER
BIG TWIN
FOAMPRO
HYPRO
POWERLINE
SHERTECH
SMALL TWIN

INGERSOLL PRODUCTS COMPANY
(Sub. of Amerop Products)
11323 Steeplechase Pkwy
Orland Park, IL 60467-5898
Tel.: (773) 264-7800
E-mail: sales@ingersoll-products.com
Web Site: www.ingersoll-products.com
E-Mail For Key Personnel:
President: bwright@ingersoll-products.com
Sales Director: sales@ingersoll-products.com
Approx. Number Employees: 150
Year Founded: 1884
Business Description:
Mfr of Plow Discs & Blades for Farming Machinery
S.I.C.: 3523
N.A.I.C.S.: 333111
Import Export
Media: 2-4-5-10
Distr.: Intl.; Natl.
Budget Set: Oct.
Brands & Products:
DURA-FACED
F BLADE
INGERSOLL
N BLADE
V BLADE

INTERMOUNTAIN FARMERS ASSOCIATION
1147 W 2100 South
Salt Lake City, UT 84119-1533
Tel.: (801) 972-2122
Fax: (801) 972-2186
Web Site: www.ifa-coop.com
Sales Range: $100-124.9 Million
Approx. Number Employees: 400
Year Founded: 1923
Business Description:
Feed & Farm Supplies Whslr; Farming Community Retail Stores Owner & Operator
S.I.C.: 5191; 5999
N.A.I.C.S.: 424910; 453998
Advertising Expenditures: $465,000
Media: 5-8-9-19-23-25-26
Distr.: Natl.
Personnel:
Layne B. Anderson *(Pres)*
Spence P. Lloyd *(CFO & Sr VP)*
W. Brad Camp *(VP-Mktg-IFA Country Stores)*
Bryan Coulter *(VP-Ops)*
Brands & Products:
BIRDSNACK
CARDINALS' CHOICE
CHICKADEES' CHOICE
FARM & RANCH
FAVORITE
FINCH DELIGHT
FLYERS' CHOICE
HELPING TO GROW THE THINGS YOU LOVE.
IFA

Key to Media (For complete agency information see *The Advertising Red Books-Agencies* edition):
1. Bus. Publs. 2. Cable T.V. 3. Catalogs & Directories. 4. Co-op Adv. 5. Consumer Mags. 6. D.M. to Bus. Estab.7. D.M. to Consumers
8. Daily Newsp. 9. Exhibits/Trade Shows 10. Foreign 11. Infomercial 12. Internet Adv.13. Multimedia 14. Network Radio
15. Network T.V. 16. Newsp. Distr. Mags. 17. Other 18. Outdoor (Posters, Transit) 19. Point of Purchase20. Premiums, Novelties
21. Product Samples 22. Special Events Mktg. 23. Spot Radio 24. Spot T.V. 25. Weekly Newsp. 26. Yellow Page Adv.

Intermountain Farmers Association — (Continued)

SCIENCE DIET
SCIENCE DIET ADVANCED PROTECTION
SHELL-LESS SELECT
SUN PRO
SUN PRO FELINE
SUN PRO LITE
SUN PRO PREMIUM ADULT
SUN PRO SELECT
SUN PRO SELECT PUPPY
SUNPRO ADULT
WESTERN SUN
WOODPECKERS' PICK

JOHN DEERE CONSUMER & COMMERCIAL EQUIPMENT, INC.

(Div. of Deere & Company)
2000 John Deere Run
Cary, NC 27513
Tel.: (919) 804-2000
Fax: (919) 804-2343
Web Site: www.johndeere.com
Sales Range: $100-124.9 Million
Approx. Number Employees: 350
Business Description:
Sales, Customer Service & Marketing For John Deere Products
S.I.C.: 3524
N.A.I.C.S.: 333112
Personnel:
Robert C. Hove *(Sr VP-Customer Mktg)*
Jennifer Cox *(Mgr-PR & Media)*
Brands & Products:
JOHN DEERE
Advertising Agencies:
IMRE
909 Ridgebrook Rd Ste 300
Baltimore, MD 21152
Tel.: (410) 821-8220
Fax: (410) 821-5619

Targetbase
202 CentrePort Dr Ste 400
Greensboro, NC 27409
Tel.: (972) 506-3400
Fax: (336) 665-3855

JOHN DEERE LTD.

(Sub. of Deere & Company)
295 Hunter Road
PO Box 1000
Grimsby, ON L3M 4H5, Canada
Tel.: (905) 945-9281
Fax: (905) 945-0341
Web Site: www.johndeere.com
Sales Range: $1-4.9 Billion
Approx. Number Employees: 300
Business Description:
Mfr & Distr of Industrial & Farm Equipment
S.I.C.: 3523; 3423; 3446; 3535
N.A.I.C.S.: 333111; 332212; 332323; 333922
Media: 2-4-6-10-14-15-19-23-24
Distr.: Natl.
Budget Set: Sept.
Personnel:
Dave Chipak *(Mgr-Sls Branch)*
Mary Dawson *(Coord-Adv)*
Brands & Products:
SABRE
Advertising Agency:
Mindshare
160 Bloor St E Ste 600
Toronto, ON M4W 0A2, Canada
Tel.: (416) 987-5100
Fax: (416) 987-5245

KELLY RYAN EQUIPMENT COMPANY

900 Kelly Ryan Dr
Blair, NE 68008
Tel.: (402) 426-2151
Fax: (402) 426-2186
Toll Free: (800) 640-6967
Web Site: www.kryan.com
E-Mail For Key Personnel:
Sales Director: sales@kryan.com
Sales Range: $1-9.9 Million
Approx. Number Employees: 50
Year Founded: 1945
Business Description:
Mfr. of Farming Machinery & Equipment
S.I.C.: 3523; 3535
N.A.I.C.S.: 333111; 333922
Advertising Expenditures: $50,000
Media: 2-7-8-10-13
Distr.: Natl.
Budget Set: Apr.
Personnel:
Steven L. Cook *(Pres)*
James P. Ryan *(CEO)*
Brands & Products:
KELLY RYAN
Advertising Agency:
Smith, Kaplan, Allen & Reynolds, Inc.
111 S 108th Ave
Omaha, NE 68154-2699
Tel.: (402) 330-0110
Fax: (402) 330-8791
Toll Free: (866) 330-0112
(Farm Equipment)

KRAUSE CORPORATION

305 S Monroe St PO Box 2707
Hutchinson, KS 67501-1728
Tel.: (620) 663-6161
Fax: (620) 663-6943
Toll Free: (800) 957-2873
E-mail: sales@krauseco.com
Web Site: www.krauseco.com
E-Mail For Key Personnel:
Sales Director: sales@krauseco.com
Sales Range: $50-74.9 Million
Approx. Number Employees: 230
Year Founded: 1916
Business Description:
Farm Equipment, Disc Harrows, Chisel Plows, Field Cultivators, Grain Drills & Trash Compaction Equipment Mfr
S.I.C.: 3523; 3589
N.A.I.C.S.: 333111; 333319
Export
Advertising Expenditures: $500,000
Media: 2-8-9-10-11-13-19-20-23-25
Distr.: Natl.
Budget Set: Oct.
Brands & Products:
DOMINATOR
KRAUSE
PATHFIND'R
ROCK-FLEX
SUPERSEAL
Advertising Agency:
Swanson Russell Associates
14301 FNB Pkwy Ste 312
Omaha, NE 68154-5299
Tel.: (402) 393-4940
Fax: (402) 393-6926

KUBOTA TRACTOR CORPORATION

(Sub. of Kubota Corporation)
3401 Del Amo Blvd
Torrance, CA 90503
Tel.: (310) 370-3370
Fax: (310) 370-2370
E-mail: info@kubota.com
Web Site: www.kubota.com
Approx. Number Employees: 131
Year Founded: 1972
Business Description:
Distr Tractors, Excavators, Lawn & Garden Equipment & Outdoor Power Products
S.I.C.: 5083
N.A.I.C.S.: 423820
Import
Media: 1-2-3-4-5-6-7-8-9-10-18-19-20-23-24-25-26
Distr.: Natl.
Budget Set: Sept.
Personnel:
Yuichi Kitao *(Pres)*
Keith Rohrbacker *(Product Mgr)*
Peggy Horkan *(Mgr-Adv & PR)*
Advertising Agencies:
Paulsen Marketing Communications, Inc.
(d/b/a Paulsen AgriBranding)
3510 S 1st Ave Cir
Sioux Falls, SD 57105-5807
Tel.: (605) 336-1745
Fax: (605) 336-2305
(All)

Woodruff Sweitzer, Inc.
501 Fay St Ste 110
Columbia, MO 65201
Tel.: (573) 875-7917
Fax: (573) 874-7979
Toll Free: (888) 300-7485

LIMONEIRA COMPANY

1141 Cummings Rd
Santa Paula, CA 93060
Tel.: (805) 525-5541
E-mail: info@limoneira.com
Web Site: www.limoneira.com
Approx. Rev.: $54,284,000
Approx. Number Employees: 206
Year Founded: 1893
Business Description:
Agribusiness, Real Estate, Energy & Resource Management Services
S.I.C.: 0139; 4931; 4941; 6531; 9511
N.A.I.C.S.: 111998; 221119; 221310; 531390; 924110
Advertising Expenditures: $88,000
Media: 17
Personnel:
Alan M. Teague *(Chm)*
John W. Blanchard *(Vice Chm)*
Robert M. Sawyer *(Vice Chm)*
Harold S. Edwards *(Pres & CEO)*
Joseph Rumley *(CFO)*
Alex M. Teague *(Sr VP)*
John Carter *(Dir-Global Sls)*

LOCKWOOD MANUFACTURING, INC.

(Div. of Crary Industries)
237 12th St NW
West Fargo, ND 58078
Mailing Address:
PO Box 849
West Fargo, ND 58078-0849
Tel.: (701) 282-5520
Fax: (701) 282-9522
Toll Free: (800) 247-7335
E-mail: lockwood@crary.com
Web Site: www.lockwoodmfg.com
Approx. Number Employees: 200
Year Founded: 1935
Business Description:
Specialized Farm Equipment
S.I.C.: 3999
N.A.I.C.S.: 339999
Import Export
Advertising Expenditures: $300,000
Media: 2-4-6-7-8-10-13-18-26
Distr.: Intl.; Natl.
Budget Set: Jan.

LUNDELL ENTERPRISES, INC.

5134 Hwy 3
Cherokee, IA 51012
Tel.: (712) 225-5181
Fax: (712) 225-5185
Toll Free: (800) 831-4841
E-mail: brooksm@lundellent.com
Web Site: www.lundellent.com
Approx. Sls.: $3,000,000
Approx. Number Employees: 50
Year Founded: 1945
Business Description:
Farm Replacement Parts Distr & Recycling Equipment Mfr
S.I.C.: 3559; 3523
N.A.I.C.S.: 333298; 333111
Export
Media: 2-7-8-10-19
Distr.: Natl.
Personnel:
Steven J. Lundell *(Chm, Pres & CEO)*

MILLER CHEMICAL & FERTILIZER CORPORATION

(Sub. of Alco Industries, Inc.)
120 Radio Rd
Hanover, PA 17331-1139
Mailing Address:
PO Box 333
Hanover, PA 17331-0333
Tel.: (717) 632-8921
Fax: (717) 632-4581
Web Site: www.millerchemical.com
Approx. Number Employees: 60
Year Founded: 1939
Business Description:
Non-Hazardous Crop Protection Adjuvants & Nutritional Agrochemicals Mfr & Marketer
S.I.C.: 2879; 2873
N.A.I.C.S.: 325320; 325311
Import Export
Media: 10-18
Personnel:
Charles H. Svec *(Pres)*
Jackie Walker *(Dir-Pur)*
Brands & Products:
MILLER
NUFILMS
NUTRILEAF
VAPORGARD

MILLER MANUFACTURING COMPANY

(Div. of Veeck Enterprises, Inc.)
2910 Waters Rd Ste 150
Eagan, MN 55121
Tel.: (651) 982-5100

Key to Media (For complete agency information see *The Advertising Red Books-Agencies* edition):
1. Bus. Publs. 2. Cable T.V. 3. Catalogs & Directories. 4. Co-op Adv. 5. Consumer Mags. 6. D.M. to Bus. Estab.7. D.M. to Consumers 8. Daily Newsp. 9. Exhibits/Trade Shows 10. Foreign 11. Infomercial 12. Internet Adv.13. Multimedia 14. Network Radio 15. Network T.V. 16. Newsp. Distr. Mags. 17. Other 18. Outdoor (Posters, Transit) 19. Point of Purchase20. Premiums, Novelties 21. Product Samples 22. Special Events Mktg. 23. Spot Radio 24. Spot T.V. 25. Weekly Newsp. 26. Yellow Page Adv.

Fax: (651) 982-5101
E-mail: miller@thevision.net
Web Site: www.miller-mfg.com
Approx. Number Employees: 25
Year Founded: 1934
Business Description:
Agriculture Machinery & Recycling Systems Mfr
S.I.C.: 3523
N.A.I.C.S.: 333111
Export
Media: 2-7-10
Distr.: Reg.
Personnel:
Dan Ferrise *(CEO)*
Brands & Products:
MILLER

MILLER-ST. NAZIANZ, INC.

511 E Main St
Saint Nazianz, WI 54232-0127
Tel.: (920) 773-2121
Fax: (920) 773-1200
Toll Free: (800) 247-5557
E-mail: info@millerstn.com
Web Site: www.millerstn.com
Approx. Rev.: $130,000,000
Approx. Number Employees: 150
Year Founded: 1899
Business Description:
Farm Equipment Mfr & Wholesaler
S.I.C.: 3523; 5083
N.A.I.C.S.: 333111; 423820
Import Export
Media: 8-10
Personnel:
John C. Miller *(Pres & CEO)*
Brands & Products:
AG-BAG
AIR MASTER II
ATLAS
CONDOR
HAY BUDDY
HYDRAFLEX
MERTZ
MILLER
MILLER PRO
NITRO
POCLAIN
SILVER WHEELS
TEEJET
TORQ-TRAC
VICTOR

MY-D HAN-D MFG. INC.

10881 McArtor Rd
Dodge City, KS 67801-6763
Tel.: (620) 225-0263
Fax: (620) 225-1807
E-mail: info@mydhandsales.com
Web Site: www.mydhandsales.com
Sales Range: $10-24.9 Million
Approx. Number Employees: 18
Year Founded: 1961
Business Description:
Cattle, Feed & Grain Handling Equipment Mfr; Cattle Handling Equipment, Bale Handling Equipment, Tillage Equipment, Seed Drills, Seed Cleaners, Grain Augers, Corn & Hay Elevators, 12V Past Hole Diggers & Oil Field Equipment Distr
S.I.C.: 3523; 3586
N.A.I.C.S.: 333111; 333913
Export
Media: 2-5-10-20-23-24
Distr.: Direct to Consumer; Intl.; Natl.
Personnel:
Kevin Tieben *(Pres)*
Patricia Tieben *(Treas & Sec)*
Brands & Products:
MY-D HAN-D

NOVUS INTERNATIONAL, INC.

20 Research Park Dr
Saint Louis, MO 63304
Tel.: (314) 576-8886
Fax: (314) 576-2148
E-mail: contact@novusint.com
Web Site: www.novusint.com
Sales Range: $400-449.9 Million
Approx. Number Employees: 200
Year Founded: 1991
Business Description:
Products & Services to the Animal & Agricultural Industry
S.I.C.: 2048; 8732
N.A.I.C.S.: 311119; 541910
Export
Media: 2-10-11-20-21
Distr.: Intl.
Personnel:
Thad Simons *(Pres & CEO)*
Joyce Cacho *(Chief Sustainability Officer)*
Giovanni Gasperoni *(Exec VP-Sls & Mktg)*
Hiro Saito *(Gen Mgr)*
Brands & Products:
ACIDOMIX
ACTIVATE
AGRADO
ALIMET
CIBENZA
CLARADIGM
IDEA
MINTREX
NATUGUARD
NOVAPOR
NOVUS
NUTRICHLOR
OASIS
OMNI
OMNIPRO
PERFORMANCE THROUGH INNOVATION
QUINGUARD
SANTOQUIN
SEQUENT
ZORIEN

OMAHA STANDARD, INC.

(Sub. of Palfinger USA Inc)
3501 S 11th St
Council Bluffs, IA 51501-3633
Tel.: (712) 328-7444
Fax: (712) 328-8383
Toll Free: (800) 279-2201
E-mail: os@omahastd.com
Web Site: www.omahastd.com
Approx. Sls.: $35,000,000
Approx. Number Employees: 250
Year Founded: 1926
Business Description:
Truck Bodies Mfr
S.I.C.: 3711; 3536
N.A.I.C.S.: 336211; 333923
Advertising Expenditures: $300,000
Media: 2-7-10
Distr.: Natl.
Personnel:
Jim Moser *(Co-Pres)*
Mark Whaley *(Exec VP)*
Elizabeth Moser *(Mgr-Mktg)*
Leslie Schueman *(Mgr-Customer Svc)*

ORSCHELN FARM & HOME L.L.C.

(Sub. of Orscheln Management Co.)
1800 Overcenter Dr
Moberly, MO 65270-1521
Tel.: (660) 263-4335
Fax: (660) 269-3500
Web Site: www.orscheln.com
Approx. Number Employees: 115
Year Founded: 1960
Business Description:
Operators of Farm & Home Stores
S.I.C.: 5191; 5251
N.A.I.C.S.: 424910; 444130
Import Export
Personnel:
William L. Onscheln *(Pres)*
Barb Westhues *(Sr VP & Controller)*
Advertising Agency:
True Media
29 S 9th St Ste 201
Columbia, MO 65201
Tel.: (573) 443-8783
Fax: (573) 443-8784

OWENSBORO GRAIN COMPANY, INC.

822 E 2nd St
Owensboro, KY 42303-3301
Tel.: (270) 926-2032
Fax: (270) 686-6509
Approx. Number Employees: 150
Year Founded: 1906
Business Description:
Agricultural Services
S.I.C.: 2075; 5153
N.A.I.C.S.: 311222; 424510
Export
Media: 4-5-13
Personnel:
Robert Hicks *(Pres)*
Jeffrey L. Erb *(CFO)*
Brands & Products:
QUALISOY
SOYMAX

PAUL MUELLER COMPANY

1600 W Phelps St
Springfield, MO 65802
Mailing Address:
PO Box 828
Springfield, MO 65801-0928
Tel.: (417) 831-3000
Fax: (417) 575-9669
Toll Free: (800) 683-5537
Web Site: www.muel.com
E-Mail For Key Personnel:
Sales Director: sales@muel.com
Approx. Sls.: $129,632,938
Approx. Number Employees: 729
Year Founded: 1940
Business Description:
Stainless Steel Processing Equipment Mfr
S.I.C.: 3443; 3556
N.A.I.C.S.: 332313; 332420; 333294
Import Export
Media: 2-4-5-7-10-13-20-26
Distr.: Intl.; Natl.
Budget Set: Oct.-Nov.
Personnel:
William R. Patterson *(Chm)*
David T. Moore *(Pres & CEO)*
Marcelino Rodriguez *(CFO)*
Donald E. Golik *(Exec VP)*
Brands & Products:
ACCU-THERM
AVALANCHE
E-STAR
FRE-HEATER
HIPERFORM
HYBRID
MAXIMICE
MUELLER
MUELLER MATIC
MULTITUBE/SPIRAL-FLOW
PAUL MUELLER
PYROPURE
SENTRY
TEMP-PLATE
VAPURE

PENNINGTON SEED INC.

(Sub. of Central Garden & Pet Company)
1280 Atlanta Hwy
Madison, GA 30650-0290
Tel.: (706) 342-1234
Fax: (706) 342-9644
Web Site: www.penningtonseed.com
Sales Range: $10-24.9 Million
Approx. Number Employees: 150
Business Description:
Mfr. of Consumer Lawn & Garden Products
S.I.C.: 0181; 2873
N.A.I.C.S.: 111422; 325311
Brands & Products:
APPLAUD
ARGENTINE
BACKSPIN
BANDANA
BARE SPOT REPAIR
BERMUDA TRIANGLE
BIRD-KOTE
BLUE BONNET
BLUE STAR
BUFFALO PALS
CENTIPEDE
CHATEAU
DENSE SHADE
DICHONDRA
DURANA
DUSTER
ELIMINATOR
ENVIRO BLEND
ENVIRO-BLUE
ENVIRO SHADE
EUREKA
EXEDA
FAIRWAY CLASSIC
FALL LAWN
FINELAWN
FLYER II
FUZZY
GLADE
GOURMET MIX
GRO TEC
INDEPENDENCE
INTEGRA
JET
KENTUCKY 31
KWIK GRASS
L-93
MAXIDE
MAXQ
MERIT
MID-ATLANTIC
MIDNIGHT

Key to Media (For complete agency information see *The Advertising Red Books-Agencies* edition):
1. Bus. Publs. 2. Cable T.V. 3. Catalogs & Directories. 4. Co-op Adv. 5. Consumer Mags. 6. D.M. to Bus. Estab.7. D.M. to Consumers 8. Daily Newsp. 9. Exhibits/Trade Shows 10. Foreign 11. Infomercial 12. Internet Adv.13. Multimedia 14. Network Radio 15. Network T.V. 16. Newsp. Distr. Mags. 17. Other 18. Outdoor (Posters, Transit) 19. Point of Purchase20. Premiums, Novelties 21. Product Samples 22. Special Events Mktg. 23. Spot Radio 24. Spot T.V. 25. Weekly Newsp. 26. Yellow Page Adv.

Pennington Seed Inc. — (Continued)

MIDWEST BLEND
MISTY
MOHAWK
MORNING STAR
NATURAL SPRINGS NECTAR
NEW ENGLAND
NEW YORK STATE
NORTHERN BLEND
PANAMA
PENKOTED
PENN G-6
PENN-SPEED PLUS
PENN TUF TURF
PENNCROSS
PENNEAGLE
PENNINGTON GREEN
PENNLINKS
PENNSYLVANIA STATE
PENNWAY
PENSACOLA
PLANTATION
PRINCESS 77
PRO LANSCAPERS MIX
PRO SELECT
PROFESSIONAL
RACKMASTER
REBEL
ROYAL BLEND
RUGGED WEAR
SAHARA
SAINT AUGUSTINE
SALTY
SENTRY
SHADY LAWN
SHINING STAR
SIGNATURE SERIES
SIGNIA
SONATA
STRIKE
SULTAN
SUN & SHADE
SUNNY LAWN
SUPER STAR
SUPREME
SYDNEY
TRIAD
VIRTUE
WIND DANCE
WIND STAR
YUMA
ZENITH ZOYSIA

Advertising Agency:
Rhea + Kaiser
Naperville Financial Ctr 400 E Diehl Rd Ste 500
Naperville, IL 60563-1342
Tel.: (630) 505-1100
Fax: (630) 505-1109

THE PERRY COMPANY

500 S Vly Mills Dr
Waco, TX 76711
Tel.: (254) 756-2139
Fax: (254) 756-2166
Toll Free: (800) 792-3246
E-mail: info@perry-co.com
Web Site: www.perry-co.com
E-Mail For Key Personnel:
Sales Director: sales@perry-co.com
Approx. Number Employees: 25
Year Founded: 1946
Business Description:
Mfr. & Distributor of Pickup Truck Accessories & Farm Implements
S.I.C.: 3523; 3714
N.A.I.C.S.: 333111; 336399
Export
Media: 2-3-4-5-6-9-10-11-19-23-24-25-26
Distr.: Natl.
Budget Set: Oct.
Personnel:
Jeff Weaver *(Pres)*
Brands & Products:
PERRY
RENEGADE

PRO-FAC COOPERATIVE, INC.

590 Willow Brook Office Park
Fairport, NY 14450
Mailing Address:
PO Box 30682
Rochester, NY 14603-0682
Tel.: (585) 218-4210
Fax: (585) 218-4241
E-mail: info@agrilinkfoods.com
Web Site: www.profaccoop.com
Approx. Sls.: $2,869,000
Approx. Number Employees: 4
Year Founded: 1960
Business Description:
Agricultural Marketing Cooperative Services
S.I.C.: 5141; 5148
N.A.I.C.S.: 424410; 424480
Advertising Expenditures: $23,900,000
Personnel:
Peter R. Call *(Pres)*
Steve Wright *(CEO, Sec & Gen Mgr)*
Allan W. Overhiser *(Treas & First VP)*
Steven D. Koinzan *(Second VP)*
Shari Burgo *(Asst Sec & Asst Treas)*
David Mehalick *(Asst Sec & Asst Treas)*
Chris Jagel *(Asst Sec)*
Thomas Willett *(Asst Treas)*

PURDEL, COOPERATIVE AGRO-ALIMENTAIRE

155 Saint Jean Baptiste
Bic, QC G0L 1B0, Canada
Tel.: (418) 736-4363
Fax: (418) 736-8267
Toll Free: (800) 463-4445
E-mail: purdel@globetter.qc.ca
Web Site: www.purdel.qc.ca
Sales Range: $25-49.9 Million
Approx. Number Employees: 125
Year Founded: 1928
Business Description:
Seafood, Agricultural Machinery, Biological Fertilizers, Feeds & Seeds
S.I.C.: 3523
N.A.I.C.S.: 333111
Export
Media: 2-6-10-18-26
Distr.: Intl.
Budget Set: Nov.
Personnel:
Jean Paul Theriault *(Dir-Gen)*

PYCO INDUSTRIES, INC.

2901 Ave A
Lubbock, TX 79404-2231
Tel.: (806) 747-3434
Fax: (806) 744-3221
Web Site: www.pycoindustries.com
Approx. Number Employees: 330
Year Founded: 1936
Business Description:
Cooperative Cotton Seed Processor
S.I.C.: 2079; 5159
N.A.I.C.S.: 311223; 424590
Media: 7
Personnel:
Gail Kring *(Pres)*
Robert Lacy *(Sr VP-Mktg)*
Tony Morton *(VP-Fin)*
Jeff Tucker *(Dir-IT)*
Kelly Jack *(Mgr-Transportation Mktg)*
Brands & Products:
PLAINMANS

RAIN BIRD CORPORATION

1000 Sierra Madre
Azusa, CA 91702
Tel.: (626) 963-9311
Fax: (626) 812-3411
Web Site: www.rainbird.com
Approx. Number Employees: 175
Year Founded: 1933
Business Description:
Sprinklers & Valves & Controllers & All Encompassing Automatic Systems Mfr
S.I.C.: 3494; 3432
N.A.I.C.S.: 332919; 332913
Export
Media: 4-10-19-20-21
Distr.: Intl.; Natl.
Budget Set: Nov.
Personnel:
Nick Kaleyias *(CFO)*
Dave Johnson *(Dir-Corp Mktg)*
Shane Russell *(Mgr-Ops)*
Brands & Products:
DANCING WATERS
FALCON
FLO-MANAGER
MAXI
MAXICOM2
MEMORY ARC
MICRO-BIRD
MINI-PAW
POP-A-WAY
RAIN BIRD
RAIN CURTAIN
RAIN GUN
STEELHEAD
SURE POP
TOUGH BIRD
UNI-FIT
XERI-BIRD
XERI-MAN
XERIGATION
Advertising Agencies:
Heinzeroth Marketing Group
415 Y Blvd
Rockford, IL 61107-3059
Tel.: (815) 967-0929
Fax: (815) 967-0983

The Pollack PR Marketing Group
1901 Ave of the Stars Ste 1040
Los Angeles, CA 90067
Tel.: (310) 556-4443
Fax: (310) 286-2350

Swanson Russell Associates
1222 P St
Lincoln, NE 68508-1425
Tel.: (402) 437-6400
Fax: (402) 437-6401

R.B. PAMPLIN CORPORATION

805 SW Broadway Ste 2400
Portland, OR 97205-3341
Tel.: (503) 248-1133
Fax: (503) 248-1175
E-mail: mstewart@pamplincorporation.com
Web Site: www.pamplin.org
Sales Range: $550-599.9 Million
Approx. Number Employees: 4,000
Year Founded: 1957
Business Description:
Holding Company
S.I.C.: 6719
N.A.I.C.S.: 551112
Media: 2-6-9-22-25-26
Distr.: Natl.
Budget Set: Nov. -Dec.
Personnel:
Robert B. Pamplin, Jr. *(Chm, Pres & CEO)*
David Hastings *(VP-Fin)*

REINKE MANUFACTURING COMPANY, INC.

5325 Reinke Rd
Deshler, NE 68340
Tel.: (402) 365-7251
Fax: (402) 365-4370
E-mail: international@reinke.com
Web Site: www.reinke.com
Sales Range: $10-24.9 Million
Approx. Number Employees: 300
Year Founded: 1954
Business Description:
Agricultural Irrigation Equipment Mfr; Steel Tubing & Oil Casing; Truck Trailers
S.I.C.: 3523
N.A.I.C.S.: 333111
Export
Advertising Expenditures: $500,000
Media: 2-4-6-7-10-11-18-23-24
Distr.: Intl.; Natl.
Personnel:
Victor Johnson *(CFO & VP-Fin)*
Tim Goldhammer *(VP-Mktg)*
Carla Deepe *(Mgr-Adv)*
Brands & Products:
ALUMIGATOR
ELECROGATOR
MAXIGATOR
MORE RIGHT THAN RAIN
NAVIGATOR
ON-TRAC
REINKE

RENTZEL PUMP MANUFACTURING, LP

1301 N Globe Ave
Lubbock, TX 79408
Tel.: (405) 360-7865
Fax: (405) 360-7832
E-mail: pumpsys@flash.net
Web Site: www.rentzelpump.com
E-Mail For Key Personnel:
Sales Director: sales@rentzelpump.com
Approx. Sls.: $40,000,000
Approx. Number Employees: 15
Year Founded: 1878
Business Description:
Pumps & Fertilizer Spreaders & Sprayers Mfr
S.I.C.: 5084
N.A.I.C.S.: 423830
Import Export
Media: 5-10-20
Distr.: Natl.
Budget Set: May
Personnel:
Randall M. Rentzel *(Pres)*
Lupe Montalvo *(Office Mgr)*

Key to Media (For complete agency information see *The Advertising Red Books-Agencies* edition):
1. Bus. Publs. 2. Cable T.V. 3. Catalogs & Directories. 4. Co-op Adv. 5. Consumer Mags. 6. D.M. to Bus. Estab.7. D.M. to Consumers 8. Daily Newsp. 9. Exhibits/Trade Shows 10. Foreign 11. Infomercial 12. Internet Adv.13. Multimedia 14. Network Radio 15. Network T.V. 16. Newsp. Distr. Mags. 17. Other 18. Outdoor (Posters, Transit) 19. Point of Purchase20. Premiums, Novelties 21. Product Samples 22. Special Events Mktg. 23. Spot Radio 24. Spot T.V. 25. Weekly Newsp. 26. Yellow Page Adv.

RITCHIE INDUSTRIES, INC.
120 S Main St
Conrad, IA 50621
Mailing Address:
PO Box 730
Conrad, IA 50621-0730
Tel.: (641) 366-2525
Fax: (641) 366-2551
Toll Free: (800) 747-0222
E-mail: info@ritchiefount.com
Web Site: www.ritchiefount.com
Approx. Number Employees: 100
Year Founded: 1921
Business Description:
Mfr. & Distr. of Livestock Watering Equipment
S.I.C.: 3523
N.A.I.C.S.: 333111
Export
Advertising Expenditures: $150,000
Media: 2-5-6-7-10-13-20
Distr.: Intl.; Natl.
Budget Set: Nov. -Dec.
Personnel:
Leon Yantis *(Pres)*
Brands & Products:
CATTLEMASTER
COMMANDER
OMNIFOUNT
PORK KING
RITCHIE
STALL FOUNT
THRIFTY KING
WATERMASTER
WATERMATIC
WATERMATIC 150S
WATERS 'EM RIGHT
Advertising Agency:
Graphic Arts Inc.
506 SW 10th Ave
Topeka, KS 66612
Tel.: (785) 354-8596

R.M. WADE & CO.
10025 SW Allen Blvd
Beaverton, OR 97005-4124
Mailing Address:
PO Box 8769
Portland, OR 97208-8769
Tel.: (503) 641-1865
Fax: (503) 626-8298
Web Site: www.generalimp.com
Approx. Number Employees: 150
Year Founded: 1865
Business Description:
Distr of Farm & Outdoor Power Equipment
S.I.C.: 5083
N.A.I.C.S.: 423820
Media: 4-7-9-13-26
Distr.: Intl.; Natl.
Personnel:
Buz Nelson *(Pres)*

SALT RIVER PROJECT
1521 N Project Dr
Tempe, AZ 85281
Tel.: (602) 236-8833
Fax: (602) 236-5444
E-mail: bizcenter@srpnet.com
Web Site: www.srpnet.com
Approx. Rev.: $2,521,970,000
Approx. Number Employees: 4,328
Year Founded: 1910
Business Description:
Power & Irrigation Services
S.I.C.: 4931
N.A.I.C.S.: 221119
Personnel:
David Rousseau *(Pres)*
David G. Areghini *(Gen Mgr-Power-Engrg)*
Richard M. Hayslip *(Gen Mgr)*
Richard H. Silverman *(Gen Mgr)*
John F. Sullivan *(Gen Mgr-Water Grp)*
Sergio Carlos *(Mgr-Adv & Brand)*
David Strohmeyer *(Sr Strategist-Adv)*
Brands & Products:
DELIVERING MORE THAN POWER
SRP
SRP PAYCENTERS
SRP POWERWISE
Advertising Agency:
FD Americas Public Affairs
1101 K St NW 9th Fl
Washington, DC 20005
Tel.: (202) 346-8800
Fax: (202) 346-8804

SCHAEFF INCORPORATED
(Sub. of Quantum Value Partners, LP)
7402 W 100th Pl
Bridgeview, IL 60455-2406
Tel.: (708) 430-5301
Fax: (708) 430-6803
E-mail: info@schaeffinc.com
Web Site: www.schaeffinc.com
Approx. Number Employees: 250
Year Founded: 1947
Business Description:
Electric, Stand-Up & Counter-Balance Forklift Mfr
S.I.C.: 3537
N.A.I.C.S.: 333924
Export
Media: 2-4-10
Distr.: Natl.
Budget Set: Nov.
Personnel:
Bob Litchev *(Pres)*
Brands & Products:
ELECTRIC STANDUP COUNTER BALANCED
SCHAEFF

SEEDBURO EQUIPMENT CO.
2293 S Mt Prospect Rd
Chicago, IL 60018-2914
Tel.: (312) 738-3700
Fax: (312) 738-5329
Toll Free: (800) 284-5779
E-mail: sales@seedburo.com
Web Site: www.seedburo.com
E-Mail For Key Personnel:
Marketing Director: tsnader@seedburo.com
Sales Director: sales@seedburo.com
Approx. Sls.: $5,000,000
Approx. Number Employees: 20
Year Founded: 1912
Business Description:
Moisture Testers, Conveyors, Seed Counters, Grain Feed Seed Testing Equipment Mfr & Distr
S.I.C.: 5083; 3523
N.A.I.C.S.: 423820; 333111
Export
Media: 2-4-7-10
Distr.: Intl.; Natl.
Budget Set: Apr.
Personnel:
Tom Runyon *(Pres)*
Katherine A. Reading *(VP-Sls)*
Timothy G. Snader *(Mgr-Sls)*
Brands & Products:
BURROWS
COUNT-A-PAK
SEEDBURO
VAC-A-SAMPLE

SHIVVERS INC.
614 W English St
Corydon, IA 50060-0467
Mailing Address:
PO Box 467
Corydon, IA 50060-0467
Tel.: (641) 872-1005
Fax: (641) 872-1593
Toll Free: (800) 245-9093
E-mail: shivvers@shivvers.com
Web Site: www.shivvers.com
Approx. Number Employees: 100
Year Founded: 1968
Business Description:
Mfr. of Grain Drying Equipment And Power Equipment
S.I.C.: 5083
N.A.I.C.S.: 423820
Media: 2-4-7-10-17
Distr.: Natl.
Personnel:
Carl Shivvers *(Founder)*
Ron Raasch *(CFO)*
Brands & Products:
BLUE FLAME DRYER
CIRCU-LATOR
CIRCU-LATOR II
COMPUDRY
DRI-FLO
SHIVVERS

SIMPLICITY MANUFACTURING, INC.
(Sub. of Briggs & Stratton Power Products Group LLC)
500 N Spring St
Port Washington, WI 53074-1752
Mailing Address:
PO Box 997
Port Washington, WI 53074-0997
Tel.: (262) 377-5450
E-mail: info@simplicitymfg.com
Web Site: www.simplicitymfg.com
Sales Range: $150-199.9 Million
Approx. Number Employees: 550
Year Founded: 1922
Business Description:
Mfr. of Outdoor Power Equipment
S.I.C.: 3524; 5261
N.A.I.C.S.: 333112; 444220
Export
Media: 1-3-5-6-7-8-10-11-14-18-19-20-23-24-26
Distr.: Intl.; Natl.
Brands & Products:
AGCO
CLEANSWEEP
COMMAND
COMMAND V-TWIN
DAIHATSU DIESEL
FERRIS
MASSEY FERGUSON
SIMPLICITY
V-TWIN
VANGUARD V-TWIN
Advertising Agency:
BVK
250 W Coventry Ct #300
Milwaukee, WI 53217-3972
Tel.: (414) 228-1990
Fax: (414) 228-7561
Toll Free: (888) 347-3212

SIOUX STEEL COMPANY
196 1/2 E 6th St
Sioux Falls, SD 57104-5929
Mailing Address:
PO Box 1265
Sioux Falls, SD 57101-1265
Tel.: (605) 336-1750
Fax: (605) 357-8597
Fax: (605) 336-2528
Toll Free: (800) 557-4689
E-mail: info@siouxsteel.com
Web Site: www.siouxsteel.com
Approx. Number Employees: 200
Year Founded: 1918
Business Description:
Livestock Equipment, Grain Handling Equipment & Front End Loaders for Tractors Mfr
S.I.C.: 3523
N.A.I.C.S.: 333111
Advertising Expenditures: $200,000
Media: 2-5-6-7-8-9-10-18-19-20-25
Distr.: Natl.
Budget Set: Sept.
Personnel:
Phillip Rysdon *(Pres)*
Scott Rysdon *(CEO & VP)*
Deon Carriere *(Mgr-Sls)*
Brands & Products:
PRO TEC
SIOUX
SOUND INVESTMENT. SOLID RETURN.
TOMBSTONE BULLTUFF

SPOT SYSTEMS
(Div. of Wisdom Industries, Inc.)
17582 Gothard St
Huntington Beach, CA 92647-6214
Tel.: (714) 842-7114
Fax: (714) 842-7853
Toll Free: (800) 854-7649
Sales Range: $1-9.9 Million
Business Description:
Mfr. & Retailer of Orchard Heating & Drip Irrigation Systems & Equipment
S.I.C.: 3567
N.A.I.C.S.: 333994
Advertising Expenditures: $250,000
Media: 4-5-6-10-18-26
Distr.: Intl.; Natl.
Budget Set: Sept.
Personnel:
Jesus Ochoa *(Mgr-Sls)*
Brands & Products:
MICRO SPRINKLER
ORCHARD
SPOT DRIP
VORTEX

TRACTOR SUPPLY CO. INC.
200 Powell Pl
Brentwood, TN 37027
Tel.: (615) 440-4000
Fax: (615) 277-4608
Web Site: www.tractorsupply.com
Approx. Sls.: $3,638,336,000
Approx. Number Employees: 7,900
Year Founded: 1938
Business Description:
Tractor Parts & Farm Supply Sales
S.I.C.: 5013; 5261; 5999
N.A.I.C.S.: 423120; 444220; 453910; 453998
Import

Key to Media (For complete agency information see *The Advertising Red Books-Agencies* edition):
1. Bus. Publs. 2. Cable T.V. 3. Catalogs & Directories. 4. Co-op Adv. 5. Consumer Mags. 6. D.M. to Bus. Estab.7. D.M. to Consumers
8. Daily Newsp. 9. Exhibits/Trade Shows 10. Foreign 11. Infomercial 12. Internet Adv.13. Multimedia 14. Network Radio
15. Network T.V. 16. Newsp. Distr. Mags. 17. Other 18. Outdoor (Posters, Transit) 19. Point of Purchase20. Premiums, Novelties
21. Product Samples 22. Special Events Mktg. 23. Spot Radio 24. Spot T.V. 25. Weekly Newsp. 26. Yellow Page Adv.

Tractor Supply Co. Inc. — (Continued)

Advertising Expenditures: $48,600,000
Media: 3-8-15-16-19-22-23-24
Personnel:
James F. Wright *(Chm & CEO)*
Gregory A. Sandfort *(Pres & Chief Mdsg Officer)*
Anthony F. Crudele *(CFO, Treas & Exec VP)*
Stanley L. Ruta *(COO & Exec VP)*
Joel A. Cherry *(Gen Counsel)*
Kimberly D. Vella *(Sr VP-HR)*
John D. Wendler *(Sr VP-Mktg)*
Steven K. Braun *(VP-E-Commerce)*
Randy Guiler *(Dir-IR)*
Brands & Products:
AMERICAN FARMLAND
BARNYARD
BENEFUL
BIT & BRIDLE
BLAZER INTERNATIONAL
BREYER
CAREFRESH
CARHARTT
CARRY-ON TRAILER
CATCHMASTER
C.E. SCHMIDT
CHAMPION POWER EQUIPMENT
COUNTRYLINE
DIAMOND
DUMOR
DUMOR NUTRISOURCE
EVERGREEN
FIRST ALERT ESCAPE
FIRST ALERT PLUG
FIX-A-THRED
FREIGHTLINER CENTURY AMERICAN JOURNEY TRUCK
GREEN SEASONS
GROUNDWORKS
HARVEST GARDEN HOSE
HARVEST SUPREME
HILL'S
HOG RING
HUSKEE
INTERNATIONAL
IVOMEC IVERMECTIN
JOB SMART
KENWORTH
LAMS
LEATHERMAN
MACK VISION
MASTERHAND
MILEPOST
MINOT
NATURAL CHOICE
NUTRISOURCE
PAWS 'N CLAWS
PB BLASTER PENETRANT
PETERBILT
PRO PLAN
PRO SERIES
PRODUCERS PRIDE
PRONTO BIG N' TUF
PURINA
RANCH HAND
RED SHED
REELED HORSE
REESE FARM & RANCH
RETRIEVER
ROYAL WING
SCHUMACHER
SCIENCE DUET
SHELTER LOGIC
SLIME
THE STUFF YOU NEED OUT HERE
TRAILER TONGUE
TRAVELLER
TRIMBRITE
TSC
WEATHERMASTER
WORK FORCE
Advertising Agencies:
Communications Associates Marketing, LLC
7051 Hwy 70 S Ste 340
Nashville, TN 37221
Tel.: (615) 662-2999
Fax: (615) 662-2444

Dye, Van Mol & Lawrence
209 7th Ave N
Nashville, TN 37219-1802
Tel.: (615) 244-1818
Fax: (615) 780-3301

FD U.S. Communications, Inc.
(d/b/a Financial Dynamics)
Wall St Plz 88 Pine St 32nd Fl
New York, NY 10005
Tel.: (212) 850-5600
Fax: (212) 850-5790

Marketing Support, Inc.
200 E Randolph Dr Ste 5000
Chicago, IL 60601
Tel.: (312) 565-0044
Fax: (312) 946-6100

TRADEWINDS FEEDS LLC

2339 Tacoma Ave S
Tacoma, WA 98402-1409
Tel.: (253) 272-4887
Fax: (253) 272-1911
Web Site: www.tradewindsbirdsandfeed.com
Approx. Number Employees: 1
Year Founded: 1996
Business Description:
Animal Feed Whslr
S.I.C.: 5153; 5083
N.A.I.C.S.: 424510; 423820
Media: 9-10-26
Distr.: Natl.
Budget Set: Feb. -Nov.
Personnel:
Patty Galloway *(Owner)*
Steve Galloway *(Owner)*
Brands & Products:
TRADEWINDS

VALENT U.S.A. CORP.

(Sub. of Sumitomo Chemical Company, Ltd.)
1333 N California Blvd Ste 600
Walnut Creek, CA 94596-8025
Tel.: (925) 256-2700
Fax: (925) 256-2776
Toll Free: (800) 682-5368
Web Site: www.valent.com
Year Founded: 1988
Business Description:
Development & Sales of Agrochemicals
S.I.C.: 5169; 2899
N.A.I.C.S.: 424690; 325998
Media: 10
Personnel:
Trevor Thorley *(Pres & COO)*
Jamie Nielson *(Brand Mgr-Valor)*
Rick Kraus *(Product Mgr)*
Carlos Granadino *(Mgr-Product Dev)*
Alan Kennedy *(Mgr-Western Reg)*
John Pawlak *(Mgr-Product Dev-Valor)*
Kelli Woodwick *(Mgr-Mktg)*

VERMEER MANUFACTURING COMPANY

1210 Vermeer Rd E
Pella, IA 50219-7660
Tel.: (641) 628-3141
Fax: (641) 621-7722
E-mail: info@vermeer.com
Web Site: www.vermeer.com
Sales Range: $500-549.9 Million
Approx. Number Employees: 3,000
Year Founded: 1948
Business Description:
Mfr. of Industrial Ditchers, Stump Cutters, Rock Cutters, Cable Plows, Tree Spades, Brush Chippers, Large Round Hay Balers & Rakes
S.I.C.: 3531; 3523
N.A.I.C.S.: 333120; 333111
Export
Media: 1-2-4-5-7-10-11-13-19-22-26
Distr.: Intl.; Natl.
Budget Set: Aug.
Personnel:
Robert Vermeer *(Chm)*
Mary Vermeer Andringa *(Pres & COO)*
Steve Van Dusseldorp *(CFO)*
Doug Hundt *(VP-Mktg & Sls)*
Randy Jones *(Gen Mgr-Environmental)*
Lincoln Austad *(Project Mgr)*
Jimmy Price *(Project Mgr)*
Mark Cooper *(Product Mgr)*
Chris Nichols *(Product Mgr-Environ)*
Brands & Products:
ATLAS BORE PLANNER
AUTOFEED II
AUTOSWEEP
COMMANDER
DURABULL
EVACUATOR
FIELDCALC
FIRESTICK
FLEXTRAK
INTERRAGATOR
NAVIGATOR
NAVTEC
RENEGADE
ROCKFIRE
SITESTAR
TEC 2000
TEC 2000.2
TERRAFIRE
TOP GUN
VERMEER

WEATHERTEC CORPORATION

5645 E Clinton Ave
Fresno, CA 93727-1308
Tel.: (559) 291-5555
Fax: (559) 294-8802
Toll Free: (800) 835-7836
E-mail: info@weathertec.com
Web Site: www.weathertec.com
Approx. Number Employees: 50
Year Founded: 1970
Business Description:
Mfr. of Irrigation Equipment
S.I.C.: 3494; 3523
N.A.I.C.S.: 332919; 333111
Export
Media: 1-2-5-6-7-10-26
Distr.: Intl.; Natl.
Budget Set: Nov. -Dec.
Personnel:
Jason Snyder *(Dir-Sls & Mktg)*
Brands & Products:
ALPHA SERIES VALVE-IN-HEAD
ENVIRONMENTAL CONTROL THROUGH IRRIGATION
G-50
TURF ROTORS
WEATHER TEC

WESTFALIA-SURGE INC.

(Sub. of WestfaliaSurge GmbH)
1880 Country Farm Dr
Naperville, IL 60563-1089
Tel.: (630) 369-8100
Fax: (630) 369-9875
Toll Free: (800) 323-1667
Telex: 254-561
Web Site: www.westfaliasurge.com
Approx. Number Employees: 100
Year Founded: 1906
Business Description:
Dairy Farm Equipment & Sanitation Products, Dairy Supplies & Animal Health Products
S.I.C.: 5083; 3523
N.A.I.C.S.: 423820; 333111
Export
Advertising Expenditures: $750,000
Media: 2-4-5-7-8-10-11-19-20
Distr.: Intl.; Natl.
Budget Set: Sept.
Personnel:
Vern Foster *(Pres)*
Brands & Products:
DAIRYPLAN C21
LOBE BLAST
MAGNUM AUTOROTOR 90
METATRON 21
ORACID PLUS
SURGE
TEAM
VICTORY

WHITE RIVER COOPERATIVE INC.

610 Church St
Loogootee, IN 47553
Tel.: (812) 295-4835
Tel.: (812) 254-4250
Fax: (812) 295-4755
Fax: (812) 875-2146
Web Site: www.whiterivercoop.com/
Sales Range: $25-49.9 Million
Approx. Number Employees: 10
Year Founded: 1924
Business Description:
Animal Seeds Distr
S.I.C.: 5191; 5171
N.A.I.C.S.: 424910; 424710
Media: 4-9-13-23

WINPOWER INC.

(Div. of Winco Generators)
225 S Cordva Ave
Le Center, MN 56057
Mailing Address:
PO Box 495
Saint Peter, MN 56082
Tel.: (507) 357-6700
Fax: (507) 357-6580
Toll Free: (800) 327-1301 (Sls.)
E-mail: afredrickson@winpowerinc.com
Web Site: www.winpowerinc.com
E-Mail For Key Personnel:
Sales Director: sales@winpowerinc.com
Approx. Number Employees: 27
Year Founded: 1925

Key to Media (For complete agency information see *The Advertising Red Books-Agencies* edition):
1. Bus. Publs. 2. Cable T.V. 3. Catalogs & Directories. 4. Co-op Adv. 5. Consumer Mags. 6. D.M. to Bus. Estab.7. D.M. to Consumers 8. Daily Newsp. 9. Exhibits/Trade Shows 10. Foreign 11. Infomercial 12. Internet Adv.13. Multimedia 14. Network Radio 15. Network T.V. 16. Newsp. Distr. Mags. 17. Other 18. Outdoor (Posters, Transit) 19. Point of Purchase20. Premiums, Novelties 21. Product Samples 22. Special Events Mktg. 23. Spot Radio 24. Spot T.V. 25. Weekly Newsp. 26. Yellow Page Adv.

Business Description:
Diesel/Tractor Mfr Driven Generators & Gasoline Electric Plants
S.I.C.: 5063
N.A.I.C.S.: 423610
Import Export
Media: 2-7-8
Distr.: Intl.; Natl.
Budget Set: Oct.
Personnel:
Ralph Call *(CEO)*
Brands & Products:
POWRPAK
WINPOWER

WYFFEL'S HYBRIDS, INC.
13344 US Hwy 6
Geneseo, IL 61254
Tel.: (309) 944-8334
Fax: (309) 944-8338
Toll Free: (800) 369-7833
E-mail: wsales@wyffels.com
Web Site: www.wyffels.com
Approx. Number Employees: 90
Business Description:
Hybrid Seed Corn Developer & Marketer
S.I.C.: 0115
N.A.I.C.S.: 111150
Advertising Expenditures: $200,000
Media: 2-8-10-13-14-18-23
Distr.: Reg.
Budget Set: Jan.
Personnel:
William Wyffel, Jr. *(Pres & Co-Owner)*
Robert Wyffel *(Co-Owner)*
Brian Humphries *(VP-Sls)*
Brands & Products:
AGRISURE
CLEARFIELD
FASTFILL
HERCULEX
LIBERTYLINK
LIGHTNING
MARKET CHOICES
PIONEER
PONCHO
ROUNDUP READY
WYFFELS
YIELDGARD

YETTER MANUFACTURING CO., INC.
109 S McDonough St
Colchester, IL 62326
Tel.: (309) 776-4111
Fax: (309) 776-3222
Toll Free: (800) 447-5777
E-mail: info@yetterco.com
Web Site: www.yetterco.com
Approx. Number Employees: 140
Year Founded: 1930
Business Description:
Farm Equipment Mfr
S.I.C.: 3523; 2519
N.A.I.C.S.: 333111; 337125
Export
Advertising Expenditures: $300,000
Media: 2-4-5-6-7-10-13
Distr.: Intl.; Natl.
Budget Set: Apr.
Personnel:
Bernard Whalen *(Pres)*
Patrick Whalen *(VP-Mktg)*
Susan Wherley *(Mgr-Adv)*
Brands & Products:
AVENGER
CUT 'N FEED
MAGNUM
MAVERICK
MAXIMIZER
SHARK TOOTH
SYSTEMS ONE
TITAN
T.O.W.
TUFFWEAR
VIPER
YETTER

Key to Media (For complete agency information see *The Advertising Red Books-Agencies* edition):
1. Bus. Publs. 2. Cable T.V. 3. Catalogs & Directories. 4. Co-op Adv. 5. Consumer Mags. 6. D.M. to Bus. Estab.7. D.M. to Consumers 8. Daily Newsp. 9. Exhibits/Trade Shows 10. Foreign 11. Infomercial 12. Internet Adv.13. Multimedia 14. Network Radio 15. Network T.V. 16. Newsp. Distr. Mags. 17. Other 18. Outdoor (Posters, Transit) 19. Point of Purchase20. Premiums, Novelties 21. Product Samples 22. Special Events Mktg. 23. Spot Radio 24. Spot T.V. 25. Weekly Newsp. 26. Yellow Page Adv.

Financial Services

Banks — Boards of Trade — Credit Cards — Investment Companies — Investment Advisory Services — Savings & Loan Associations — Security & Commodity Brokers — Stock Exchanges

1ST CONSTITUTION BANCORP
2650 Route 130 & Dey Rd
Cranbury, NJ 08512
Mailing Address:
PO Box 634
Cranbury, NJ 08512
Tel.: (609) 655-4500
Fax: (609) 655-5653
E-mail: main@1stconstitution.com
Web Site: www.1stconstitution.com
Approx. Rev.: $33,538,450
Approx. Number Employees: 126
Year Founded: 1999
Business Description:
Bank Holding Company
S.I.C.: 6029; 6712
N.A.I.C.S.: 522110; 551111
Advertising Expenditures: $140,975
Media: 17
Personnel:
Charles S. Crow, III *(Chm)*
Robert F. Mangano *(Pres & CEO)*
Joseph M. Reardon *(Treas & Sr VP)*
Anthony J. Denucci *(VP & Dir-Info Svcs)*

1ST FRANKLIN FINANCIAL CORPORATION
135 E Tugalo St
Toccoa, GA 30577
Mailing Address:
PO Box 880
Toccoa, GA 30577-0880
Tel.: (706) 886-7571
Fax: (706) 282-0355
E-mail: info@1ff.com
Web Site: www.first-franklin.com
E-Mail For Key Personnel:
Marketing Director: klovern@1ffc.com
Approx. Int. Income: $103,150,144
Approx. Number Employees: 1,042
Year Founded: 1941
Business Description:
Consumer Financial Services
S.I.C.: 6141; 6163
N.A.I.C.S.: 522291; 522310
Advertising Expenditures: $7,500,000
Personnel:
Ben F. Cheek III *(Chm & Pres)*
Ben F. Cheek, IV *(Vice Chm)*
Virginia C. Herring *(Pres)*
A. Roger Guimond *(CFO & Exec VP)*
J. Michael Culpepper *(COO)*
C. Michael Haynie *(Exec VP-HR)*
Karen S. Lovern *(Exec VP)*

1ST SOURCE BANK
(Holding of 1st Source Corporation)
100 N Michigan St
South Bend, IN 46601-1630
Tel.: (574) 235-2000
Fax: (574) 235-2297
Web Site: www.1stsource.com
Sales Range: $125-149.9 Million
Approx. Number Employees: 1,000
Year Founded: 1863
Business Description:
Commercial Banking Services
S.I.C.: 6029
N.A.I.C.S.: 522110
Media: 2-3-6-7-8-18-23-24-26
Personnel:
Christopher J. Murphy III *(Chm, Pres & CEO)*
Allen R. Qualey *(Pres & COO-Specialty Fin Grp)*
Wellington D. Jones, III *(Pres)*
John B. Griffith *(Exec VP-Admin)*
James R. Seitz *(Exec VP-Community Banking)*
Steven J. Wessell *(Exec VP-Private Banking, Wealth Mgmt, Asset Advisors, Investment)*
Robert T Ax *(Sr VP & Reg VP)*
Larry E. Mayers *(Sr VP & Reg VP)*
Donald E. Miller *(Sr VP-Ops & Grp Head)*
Steven E. Bonine *(Sr VP-Personal Asset Mgmt Div)*
James S. Jackson *(Sr VP-Funds Mgmt)*
Joseph T. Kuzmitz *(Sr VP-Bus Banking Grp)*
Tina H. Perkins *(Sr VP-HR)*
Todd Bemenderfer *(Asst VP)*
Al Borchelt *(Asst VP)*
Brad K. Bucher *(Asst VP)*
Andrea Colson *(Asst VP)*
Julianna Herring *(Asst VP)*
Larry M. Ort *(Asst VP)*
Melissa A. Collins *(Dir-Mktg)*

1ST UNITED BANCORP, INC.
1 N Federal Hwy
Boca Raton, FL 33432
Tel.: (561) 362-3400
Tel.: (561) 362-3435
Fax: (561) 362-3436
Toll Free: (877) 362-3411
Web Site: www.1stunitedbankfl.com
Approx. Rev.: $61,215,000
Approx. Number Employees: 292
Business Description:
Bank Holding Company
S.I.C.: 6712; 6029
N.A.I.C.S.: 551111; 522110
Advertising Expenditures: $165,000
Media: 8-9-22-25
Personnel:
Warren S. Orlando *(Chm)*
John Marino *(Pres & CFO)*
Rudy E. Schupp *(CEO)*
H. William Spute, Jr. *(Exec VP)*
Wade E. Jacobson *(Chief Lending Officer)*
Lawrence Ostermayer *(Sr VP-Credit Admin)*

401KEXCHANGE.COM INC.
2230 Jog Rd
Greenacres City, FL 33415
Tel.: (561) 439-5252
Fax: (561) 439-1388
Toll Free: (877) 777-4015
E-mail: support@401kexchange.com
Web Site: www.401kexchange.com
E-Mail For Key Personnel:
President: fbastein@401kexchange.com
Approx. Number Employees: 65
Year Founded: 1998
Business Description:
401K & Pension Administration Information & Services
S.I.C.: 6371
N.A.I.C.S.: 525110
Media: 8-10-13
Personnel:
Randy Mysel *(Pres & COO)*

ABINGTON BANCORP, INC.
180 Old York Rd
Jenkintown, PA 19046
Tel.: (215) 886-8280
Fax: (215) 887-4100
E-mail: abington@abingtonbank.com
Web Site:
www.abingtonbankonline.com
Approx. Rev.: $53,957,936
Approx. Number Employees: 137
Business Description:
Bank Holding Company
S.I.C.: 6712; 6029
N.A.I.C.S.: 551111; 522110
Advertising Expenditures: $545,816
Media: 8-9-22-23-24-25
Personnel:
Robert W. White *(Chm, Pres & CEO)*
Jack J. Sandoski *(CFO)*

ABSOLUTE LIFE SOLUTIONS, INC.
(Formerly Shimmer Gold, Inc.)
45 Broadway 6th Fl
New York, NY 10006
Tel.: (212) 201-4070
Year Founded: 2006
Business Description:
Life Settlement Services
S.I.C.: 6289
N.A.I.C.S.: 523999
Advertising Expenditures: $30,700
Media: 17
Personnel:
Avrohom Oratz *(Pres & CEO)*
Joshua Yifat *(CFO & Treas)*

ACCEL PARTNERS
428 University Ave
Palo Alto, CA 94301
Tel.: (650) 614-4800
Fax: (650) 614-4880
E-mail: siliconvalley@accel.com
Web Site: www.accel.com
Approx. Number Employees: 40
Year Founded: 1984
Business Description:
Venture Capital Firm
S.I.C.: 6289
N.A.I.C.S.: 523999
Personnel:
Arthur C. Patterson *(Co-Founder)*
Sukhinder Singh Cassidy *(CEO)*
Theresia Gouw Ranzetta *(Gen Partner)*
James W. Breyer *(Partner)*
John C. Colligan *(Partner)*
Robert Glaser *(Partner)*
James R. Swartz *(Partner)*
Richard Wong *(Partner)*
Brands & Products:
ACCEL
Advertising Agency:
bite communications ltd.
(Part of the Next Fifteen Group)
The Character Building 41B Beavor Lane

London, W6 9BL, United Kingdom
Tel.: (44) 20 8741 1123
Fax: (44) 20 8741 2790

ACCELERATED ACQUISITIONS V, INC.

12720 Hillcrest Rd Ste 1045
Dallas, TX 75230
Tel.: (972) 388-1950
Fax: (972) 388-1973
Toll Free: (888) 616-6639
Approx. Number Employees: 4
Year Founded: 2008
Business Description:
Investment Services
S.I.C.: 6289
N.A.I.C.S.: 523999
Advertising Expenditures: $850,000
Personnel:
Donald Kelly *(Pres, COO & Sec)*
Richard Aland *(CEO, CFO & Treas)*

ACCESS NATIONAL CORPORATION

1800 Robert Fulton Dr Ste 310
Reston, VA 20191
Tel.: (703) 871-2100
Fax: (703) 766-3386
Toll Free: (800) 931-0370
E-mail: smlinton@accessnationalbank.com
Web Site:
www.accessnationalbank.com
Approx. Rev.: $69,803,000
Approx. Number Employees: 277
Year Founded: 1999
Business Description:
Bank Holding Company
S.I.C.: 6712
N.A.I.C.S.: 551111
Advertising Expenditures: $2,762,000
Personnel:
Michael W. Clarke *(Pres & CEO)*
Charles Wimer *(CFO & Exec VP)*
Robert C. Shoemaker *(Exec VP)*

ACE CASH EXPRESS, INC.

(Holding of JLL Partners Inc.)
1231 Greenway Dr Ste 600
Irving, TX 75038-9904
Tel.: (972) 550-5000
Fax: (972) 550-5150
E-mail: acepresident@acecashexpress.com
Web Site: www.acecashexpress.com
Approx. Rev.: $309,909,000
Approx. Number Employees: 3,061
Year Founded: 1968
Business Description:
Check Cashing, Bill Payment & Short-Term Consumer Loan Services
S.I.C.: 6061; 6099; 6141
N.A.I.C.S.: 522130; 522291; 522390
Advertising Expenditures: $5,449,000
Media: 19
Personnel:
Jay B. Shipowitz *(Pres & CEO)*
Douglas A. Lindsay *(CFO)*
Joe B. Edwards *(CIO & Sr VP-IT)*
Allen J. Klose *(CMO)*
Ted M. Eades *(Gen Counsel & Sr VP)*
James R. Gibbs *(Sr VP-HR)*
Eric C. Norrington *(Sr VP-Pub Affairs)*
Victor Faszczuk *(VP-Sls)*
Brands & Products:
ACE
ACE CASH EXPRESS

ACNB CORPORATION

16 Lincoln Sq
Gettysburg, PA 17325
Mailing Address:
PO Box 3129
Gettysburg, PA 17325
Tel.: (717) 334-3161
Fax: (717) 334-9319
Toll Free: (888) 338-2262
E-mail: info@acnb.com
Web Site: www.acnb.com
Approx. Rev.: $56,812,000
Approx. Number Employees: 281
Year Founded: 1983
Business Description:
Bank Holding Company
S.I.C.: 6712; 6029
N.A.I.C.S.: 551111; 522110
Advertising Expenditures: $1,158,000
Personnel:
Ronald L. Hankey *(Chm)*
Frank Elsner, III *(Vice Chm)*
Thomas A. Ritter *(Pres & CEO)*
David W. Cathell *(CFO)*
Lynda L. Glass *(COO & Corp Compliance Officer)*

ADAMS COUNTY NATIONAL BANK INC.

(Sub. of ACNB Corporation)
16 Lincoln Sq
Gettysburg, PA 17325
Mailing Address:
PO Box 3129
Gettysburg, PA 17325
Tel.: (717) 334-3161
Fax: (717) 334-9319
Toll Free: (888) 338-2262
E-mail: info@acnb.com
Web Site: www.acnb.com
Approx. Sls.: $37,897,000
Approx. Number Employees: 225
Year Founded: 1857
Business Description:
Banking Services
S.I.C.: 6029
N.A.I.C.S.: 522110
Advertising Expenditures: $369,000
Media: 8-13-18
Personnel:
Ronald L. Hankey *(Chm)*
Thomas A. Ritter *(Pres & CEO)*
David W. Cathell *(CFO)*
Laurie A. Laub *(Sr VP & Chief Credit Officer)*
John M. Kiehl *(Chief Risk Officer & Sr VP)*
Lynda L. Glass *(Exec VP-Banking Svcs)*
Sandra A. Deaner *(Sr VP-HR)*
Paul H. Ketterman, Jr. *(Sr VP & Sr Trust Officer)*
Dorothy K. Puhl *(Sr VP-Info Sys)*
Carl L. Ricker *(Sr VP & Chief Lending Officer)*
L. John Hicks *(First VP)*
Dennis R. Hollinger *(First VP)*
R. Mark Purdy *(First VP)*
Advertising Agency:
Holton Sentivan and Gury
7 E Skippack Pike
Ambler, PA 19002
Tel.: (215) 619-7600
Fax: (215) 619-7621

THE ADAMS NATIONAL BANK

(Sub. of Premier Financial Bancorp, Inc.)
1130 Connecticut Ave
Washington, DC 20036
Tel.: (202) 772-3600
Fax: (202) 835-3871
E-mail: customerservice@adamsbank.com
Web Site: www.adamsbank.com
Sales Range: $10-24.9 Million
Approx. Number Employees: 60
Year Founded: 1978
Business Description:
Commercial Banking
S.I.C.: 6029
N.A.I.C.S.: 522110
Media: 7-8-13
Personnel:
Boris Orcev *(Pres)*
Karen E. Troutman *(CFO)*

ADP TAXWARE

(Div. of Automatic Data Processing, Inc.)
401 Edgewater Pl Ste 260
Wakefield, MA 01880
Tel.: (781) 557-2600
Fax: (781) 557-2606
Toll Free: (877) 835-7268
Toll Free: (877) TAXWARE
Toll Free: (877) 829-9273
E-mail: info@taxware.com
Web Site: www.taxware.com
Sales Range: $50-74.9 Million
Approx. Number Employees: 180
Business Description:
Tax & Accounting Software
S.I.C.: 7371; 7373
N.A.I.C.S.: 541511; 541512
Media: 4-6-13
Personnel:
Ken Zemba *(Sr VP-Tech)*
Jim Panagas *(VP-Mktg)*
Matthew S. Walsh *(Dir-Tax Res)*
Brands & Products:
TAXWARE
Advertising Agency:
Aloft Group, Inc.
26 Parker St
Newburyport, MA 01950
Tel.: (978) 462-0002
Fax: (978) 462-4337

ADVANCE AMERICA, CASH ADVANCE CENTERS, INC.

135 N Church St
Spartanburg, SC 29306
Tel.: (864) 342-5600
Fax: (864) 342-5612
Toll Free: (866) 640-4227
E-mail: info@advanceamerica.net
Web Site: www.advanceamerica.net
Approx. Rev.: $600,233,000
Approx. Number Employees: 5,839
Year Founded: 1997
Business Description:
Cash Advance Services
S.I.C.: 6141
N.A.I.C.S.: 522291
Advertising Expenditures: $24,137,000
Media: 7-8-15-19-20-22-24-26
Personnel:
William M. Webster, IV *(Chm & CEO)*
John Patrick O'Shaughnessy *(Pres, CEO & CFO)*
James A. Ovenden *(CFO & Exec VP)*
Advertising Agency:
Erwin-Penland
(Owned by Hill, Holliday, Connors, Cosmopulos, Inc., Member of the Interpublic Group)
125 E Broad St
Greenville, SC 29601
Tel.: (864) 271-0500
Fax: (864) 235-5941

ADVANCED SETTLEMENTS, INC.

(Sub. of National Financial Partners Corp.)
2101 Park Ctr Dr Ste 220
Orlando, FL 32835
Tel.: (407) 296-7373
Fax: (407) 296-7377
Toll Free: (800) 561-4148
E-mail: sales@advancedsettlements.com
Web Site:
www.advancedsettlements.com
E-Mail For Key Personnel:
Sales Director: sales@advancedsettlements.com
Sales Range: $125-149.9 Million
Approx. Number Employees: 50
Business Description:
Life Settlement Services
S.I.C.: 7389; 7319
N.A.I.C.S.: 561499; 541870; 561439; 561990
Media: 2-10
Personnel:
Matthew Ganovsky *(Co-Pres-Product Underwriting & Broker-Relships)*
Scott Kirby *(Co-Pres-Bus Dev & Compliance)*
Sean McNealy *(Co-Pres)*
Jeff Hallman *(Sr VP-Bus Dev)*
Dan Beatty *(VP-Sls & Ops)*
Karen Teller *(VP-Fin)*
Tom Offutt *(Dir-Compliance)*

ADVANTA CORP.

(Filed Ch 11 Bankruptcy #913931 on 11/09/09 in U.S. Bankruptcy Ct, Dist of DE, Wilmington)
Welsh & McKean Rds PO Box 844
Spring House, PA 19477
Tel.: (215) 657-4000
Fax: (215) 444-5906
E-mail: abswebmaster@advanta.com
Web Site: www.advanta.com
Sales Range: $450-499.9 Million
Approx. Number Employees: 841
Year Founded: 1951
Business Description:
Financial Services, Mortgages, Business Credit Cards, Equipment Leases, Insurance & Deposit Products
S.I.C.: 6141; 6029
N.A.I.C.S.: 522291; 522110; 522210
Advertising Expenditures: $20,560,000
Media: 2-7-9-25
Distr.: Natl.
Personnel:
Dennis Alter *(Chm & CEO)*
William A. Rosoff *(Vice Chm & Pres)*
Philip M. Browne *(CFO)*
Elizabeth H. Mai *(Chief Admin Officer, Gen Counsel, Sec & Sr VP)*
Catherine Reid *(VP-Commun)*
Advertising Agencies:
Red Tettemer & Partners
1 S Broad St 24th Fl
Philadelphia, PA 19107
Tel.: (267) 402-1410

Key to Media (For complete agency information see *The Advertising Red Books-Agencies* edition):
1. Bus. Publs. 2. Cable T.V. 3. Catalogs & Directories. 4. Co-op Adv. 5. Consumer Mags. 6. D.M. to Bus. Estab.7. D.M. to Consumers 8. Daily Newsp. 9. Exhibits/Trade Shows 10. Foreign 11. Infomercial 12. Internet Adv.13. Multimedia 14. Network Radio 15. Network T.V. 16. Newsp. Distr. Mags. 17. Other 18. Outdoor (Posters, Transit) 19. Point of Purchase20. Premiums, Novelties 21. Product Samples 22. Special Events Mktg. 23. Spot Radio 24. Spot T.V. 25. Weekly Newsp. 26. Yellow Page Adv.

Advanta Corp. — (Continued)

Fax: (267) 402-1458

Star Group Communications, Inc.
(d/b/a The Star Group)
220 Laurel Rd
Voorhees, NJ 08043
Tel.: (856) 782-7000
Fax: (856) 782-5699

AGFIRST FARM CREDIT BANK

(Affil. of Federal Farm Credit Banks Funding Corporation)
1401 Hampton St
Columbia, SC 29201
Tel.: (803) 799-5000
Fax: (803) 254-1776
Web Site: www.agfirst.com
Approx. Number Employees: 325
Business Description:
Agricultural Lending Institution
S.I.C.: 6159; 6163
N.A.I.C.S.: 522298; 522310
Personnel:
Felton A. Lowrey *(Pres & CEO)*
Charl L. Butler *(CFO)*
Advertising Agency:
Freebairn & Co.
3475 Lenox Rd Ste 900
Atlanta, GA 30326
Tel.: (404) 237-9945
Fax: (404) 231-2214

AGSOUTH FARM CREDIT

40 S Main St
Statesboro, GA 30458-0718
Tel.: (912) 764-9091
Fax: (912) 764-9546
Toll Free: (800) 633-9091
E-mail: info@agsouthfc.com
Web Site: www.agsouthfc.com
Approx. Number Employees: 16
Year Founded: 1916
Business Description:
Agricultural Credit Association
S.I.C.: 6141
N.A.I.C.S.: 522291
Media: 5-7-13
Personnel:
A. Harvey Lemmon *(Chm)*
Bill J. Spigener, Jr. *(CEO)*
Alisa D. Gunter *(CFO)*

ALASKA PACIFIC BANCSHARES, INC.

2094 Jordan Ave
Juneau, AK 99801
Tel.: (907) 790-5195
Fax: (907) 789-5902
Web Site:
www.alaskapacificbank.com
Approx. Rev.: $11,375,000
Approx. Number Employees: 60
Year Founded: 1935
Business Description:
Bank Holding Company
S.I.C.: 6035; 6712
N.A.I.C.S.: 522120; 551111
Advertising Expenditures: $183,000
Media: 7-9-10-13-18-19-20-23-25-26
Personnel:
William A. Corbus *(Chm)*
Maxwell S. Rule *(Vice Chm)*
Craig E. Dahl *(Pres & CEO)*
Leslie Dahl *(Pres & CEO)*
Julie M. Pierce *(CFO & Sr VP)*
Christopher P. Bourque *(COO & Sr VP)*
John Robertson *(Chief Credit Officer & Sr VP)*

ALASKA PACIFIC BANK

(Sub. of Alaska Pacific Bancshares, Inc.)
2094 Jordan Ave
Juneau, AK 99801
Tel.: (907) 586-1010
Fax: (907) 789-5902
E-mail: info@alaskapacificbank.com
Web Site:
www.alaskapacificbank.com
E-Mail For Key Personnel:
Marketing Director: grivas@alaskapacificbank.com
Sales Range: $10-24.9 Million
Approx. Number Employees: 44
Year Founded: 1935
Business Description:
Banking Services
S.I.C.: 6035
N.A.I.C.S.: 522120
Media: 7-8-9-13-20-23-24-25
Personnel:
Roger Grummett *(Chm)*
Craig E. Dahl *(Pres & CEO)*
Julie Pierce *(CFO & Sr VP)*
John Robertson *(Chief Credit Officer & Sr VP)*
Scott Shaub *(Officer-Mktg)*

ALLIANCE BANCORP, INC. OF PENNSYLVANIA

541 Lawrence Rd
Broomall, PA 19008-3599
Tel.: (610) 353-2900
Fax: (610) 359-6908
Toll Free: (800) 550-4387
Web Site: www.allianceanytime.com
Approx. Rev.: $20,881,068
Approx. Number Employees: 74
Business Description:
Bank Holding Company
S.I.C.: 6712; 6029; 6035
N.A.I.C.S.: 551111; 522110; 522120
Advertising Expenditures: $306,000
Personnel:
William E. Hecht *(Chm)*
Dennis D. Cirucci *(Pres & CEO)*
Peter J. Meier *(CFO & Exec VP-Alliance Bank)*
Janet R. Bryan *(VP & Dir-Deposit Svcs)*
Norma K. Browne *(Asst VP-Ops)*
Diann Snyder *(Asst VP)*

ALLIANCE BANKSHARES CORPORATION

14200 Park Meadow Dr Ste 200 S
Chantilly, VA 20151
Tel.: (703) 814-7200
Fax: (703) 378-7210
Web Site: www.alliancebankva.com
Approx. Rev.: $28,997,000
Approx. Number Employees: 62
Business Description:
Bank Holding Company
S.I.C.: 6141; 6712
N.A.I.C.S.: 522210; 551111
Advertising Expenditures: $77,000
Media: 17
Personnel:
Donald W. Fisher *(Chm)*
William M. Drohan *(Vice Chm)*
William E. Doyle, Jr. *(Pres & CEO)*
Jean S. Houpert *(Interim CFO & Sr VP)*
John B. McKenny, III *(Sr VP & Chief Credit Officer)*
Craig W. Sacknoff *(Exec VP-Alliance Bank)*
Brands & Products:
WHERE BANKING IS TODAY AND TOMORROW

ALLY FINANCIAL INC.

(Holding of FIM Holdings LLC)
Mailcode 482 B10 A68
Detroit, MI 48265
Tel.: (313) 656-6970
Web Site: www.ally.com
Approx. Rev.: $16,768,000,000
Approx. Number Employees: 14,400
Year Founded: 1997
Business Description:
Holding Company; Consumer & Commercial Lending, Automotive Financing, Insurance & Mortgage Services
S.I.C.: 6719; 6022; 6099; 6141; 6159; 7515
N.A.I.C.S.: 551112; 522190; 522220; 522291; 522292; 522298; 522390; 532112
Advertising Expenditures: $202,000,000
Personnel:
Franklin W. Hobbs *(Chm)*
William F. Muir *(Pres)*
Michael A. Carpenter *(CEO)*
Clifford A. Skelton *(COO & CTO)*
Sanjay Gupta *(CMO)*
David J. DeBrunner *(Chief Acctg Officer, VP & Controller)*
Thomas Marano *(Chief Capital Markets Officer & CEO-Mortgage Ops)*
William B. Solomon, Jr. *(Gen Counsel & VP)*
James G. Mackey *(Grp VP & Interim CFO)*
Don Ferguson *(Dir-Minority Dealer Dev)*
Susanne Gehrling *(Mgr-Comm)*
Brands & Products:
GMAC
GMAC FINANCIAL SERVICES
Advertising Agencies:
Campbell-Ewald
30400 Van Dyke Ave
Warren, MI 48093-2368
Tel.: (586) 574-3400
Fax: (586) 575-9925
(Auto Financing & Leasing)

G2 Worldwide
200 5th Ave
New York, NY 10010
Tel.: (212) 537-3700
Fax: (212) 546-2425

Grey New York
777 3rd Ave
New York, NY 10017-1401
Tel.: (212) 546-2000
Fax: (212) 546-1495

AMB FINANCIAL CORP.

8230 Hohman Ave
Munster, IN 46321-1578
Tel.: (219) 836-5870
Fax: (219) 836-5883
E-mail: amb@ambfinancial.com
Web Site: www.ambfinancial.com
Approx. Rev.: $9,465,855
Approx. Number Employees: 37
Year Founded: 1993
Business Description:
Bank Holding Company
S.I.C.: 6035; 6712
N.A.I.C.S.: 522120; 551111
Advertising Expenditures: $201,828
Personnel:
Clement B. Knapp Jr. *(Chm)*
Michael Mellon *(Pres & CEO)*
Steven A. Bohn *(CFO & VP)*

AMBOY BANCORPORATION

3590 US Hwy 9 S
Old Bridge, NJ 08857
Tel.: (732) 591-8700
Fax: (732) 591-0705
Toll Free: (800) 942-6269
E-mail: mailbox@amboybank.com
Web Site: www.amboybank.com
Sales Range: $100-124.9 Million
Approx. Number Employees: 28
Business Description:
Bank Holding Company
S.I.C.: 6712
N.A.I.C.S.: 551111
Media: 7-8-9-10-13-18-19-23-25
Personnel:
George G. Scharpf *(Pres & CEO)*
Dennis Kane *(Dir-Mktg)*

AMCORE FINANCIAL, INC.

501 7th St
Rockford, IL 61104-1242
Tel.: (815) 968-2241
Fax: (815) 961-2727
Toll Free: (888) 426-2673
Web Site: www.amcore.com
Approx. Rev.: $275,146,000
Approx. Number Employees: 962
Year Founded: 1982
Business Description:
Bank Holding Company
S.I.C.: 6712
N.A.I.C.S.: 551111
Advertising Expenditures: $2,838,000
Personnel:
Judith Carre Sutfin *(CFO & Exec VP)*
Thomas R. Szmanda *(Chief Retail Officer & Exec VP)*
Brands & Products:
AMCORE
MAKING IT EASY FOR YOU

AMERICAN BANK INCORPORATED

4029 W Tilghman St
Allentown, PA 18104-1619
Tel.: (610) 366-1800
Fax: (610) 366-1900
E-mail: service@pcbanker.com
Web Site: www.pcbanker.com
Sales Range: $25-49.9 Million
Approx. Number Employees: 46
Business Description:
Bank Holding Company
S.I.C.: 6712; 6029; 6163
N.A.I.C.S.: 551111; 522110; 522310
Advertising Expenditures: $70,000
Media: 7-8-9-20
Personnel:
Mark W. Jaindl *(Pres)*
Harry C. Birkhimer *(CFO & Sr VP)*
Robert W. Turner *(Sr VP)*
Mary Hodrick *(Dir-Mktg)*

Key to Media (For complete agency information see *The Advertising Red Books-Agencies* edition):
1. Bus. Publs. 2. Cable T.V. 3. Catalogs & Directories. 4. Co-op Adv. 5. Consumer Mags. 6. D.M. to Bus. Estab.7. D.M. to Consumers 8. Daily Newsp. 9. Exhibits/Trade Shows 10. Foreign 11. Infomercial 12. Internet Adv.13. Multimedia 14. Network Radio 15. Network T.V. 16. Newsp. Distr. Mags. 17. Other 18. Outdoor (Posters, Transit) 19. Point of Purchase20. Premiums, Novelties 21. Product Samples 22. Special Events Mktg. 23. Spot Radio 24. Spot T.V. 25. Weekly Newsp. 26. Yellow Page Adv.

AMERICAN CENTURY COMPANIES, INC.
4500 Main St
Kansas City, MO 64111-1816
Tel.: (816) 531-5575
Fax: (816) 340-7270
Toll Free: (800) 345-2021
Web Site: www.americancentury.com
Approx. Number Employees: 2,900
Year Founded: 1958

Business Description:
Investment Brokerage Advisory Service; Mutual Funds
S.I.C.: 6282; 7374
N.A.I.C.S.: 523930; 518210

Personnel:
Chris Doyle *(VP-Corp PR)*

Advertising Agency:
KRT Marketing
3685 Mt Diablo Blvd Ste 255
Lafayette, CA 94549-3776
Tel.: (925) 284-0444
Fax: (925) 284-0448

AMERICAN CENTURY INVESTMENTS
(Sub. of American Century Companies, Inc.)
4500 Main St
Kansas City, MO 64111-1816
Tel.: (816) 531-5575
Fax: (816) 340-7962
Web Site: www.americancentury.com
Approx. Number Employees: 2,000

Business Description:
Investment Management Services
S.I.C.: 6289
N.A.I.C.S.: 523999

Media: 2-9-22
Distr.: Natl.

Personnel:
James E. Stowers, III *(Founder)*
Jonathan Thomas *(Pres & CEO)*
Jon Zindel *(CFO)*
Barry Fink *(COO & Exec VP)*
Phillip N. Davidson *(Chief Investment Officer-U.S. Value Equity & Sr VP)*
Enrique Chang *(Chief Investment Officer & Exec VP)*
G. David MacEwen *(Chief Investment Officer-Fixed Income, Sr VP & Mgr-Portfolio)*
Joseph Craven *(Sr VP & Head-North American Institutional Bus)*
Rich Weiss *(Sr VP & Sr Mgr-Portfolio-Asset Allocation Portfolios)*
Troy Beaver *(VP-Mktg)*
Bing Chen *(Mgr-Value Added Sls)*
Anthony Han *(Mgr-Portfolio)*

Advertising Agencies:
KRT Marketing
3685 Mt Diablo Blvd Ste 255
Lafayette, CA 94549-3776
Tel.: (925) 284-0444
Fax: (925) 284-0448
Recruitment

Sullivan Higdon & Sink Incorporated
2000 Central
Kansas City, MO 64108-2022
Tel.: (816) 474-1333
Fax: (816) 474-3427
Toll Free: (800) 809-0884

AMERICAN EQUITY INVESTMENT LIFE HOLDING COMPANY
6000 Westown Pkwy
West Des Moines, IA 50266
Mailing Address:
PO Box 71216
West Des Moines, IA 50325
Tel.: (515) 221-0002
Fax: (515) 221-9947
Toll Free: (888) 221-1234
Web Site: www.american-equity.com
Approx. Rev.: $1,285,592,000
Approx. Number Employees: 360
Year Founded: 1995

Business Description:
Holding Company; Annuity & Life Insurance Products
S.I.C.: 6719; 6311
N.A.I.C.S.: 551112; 524113
Advertising Expenditures: $800,000

Media: 2-7-8-10

Personnel:
John M. Matovina *(Vice Chm, CFO & Treas)*
Terry A. Reimer *(COO & Exec VP)*
Debra J. Richardson *(Chief Admin Officer, Exec VP & Sec)*
James M. Gerlach *(Exec VP)*
Wendy C. Waugaman *(Exec VP)*
Julie L. LaFollette *(Dir-IR)*

Advertising Agency:
Doner
25900 Northwestern Hwy
Southfield, MI 48075
Tel.: (248) 354-9700
Fax: (248) 827-8440

AMERICAN EQUITY MORTGAGE INC.
11933 Westline Industrial Dr
Saint Louis, MO 63146
Tel.: (314) 878-9999
Fax: (314) 878-6338
Web Site: www.americanequity.com
Approx. Sls.: $52,393,277
Approx. Number Employees: 500
Year Founded: 1992

Business Description:
Mortgage Bankers & Loan Correspondents
S.I.C.: 6163
N.A.I.C.S.: 522310

Personnel:
Deanna Daughhetee *(Pres & CEO)*
Kari Cool *(Dir-Mktg)*

Brands & Products:
AMERICAN EQUITY MORTGAGE
THE FUTURE BELONGS TO YOU

Advertising Agencies:
Ackermann PR
1111 Northshore Dr Ste N-400
Knoxville, TN 37919
Tel.: (865) 584-0550
Fax: (865) 588-3009
Toll Free: (866) 896-4069
Toll Free: (888) 414-7787

Doner
25900 Northwestern Hwy
Southfield, MI 48075
Tel.: (248) 354-9700
Fax: (248) 827-8440

AMERICAN EXPRESS COMPANY
3 World Financial Ctr 200 Vesey St
New York, NY 10285-4805
Tel.: (212) 640-2000
Fax: (212) 619-9230
Web Site: www.americanexpress.com
Approx. Rev.: $22,950,000,000
Approx. Number Employees: 61,000
Year Founded: 1850

Business Description:
Diversified Financial & Travel; International Banking, Life Insurance, Publishing, Information Services, Asset Management Services & Consumer Lending
S.I.C.: 6141; 4724; 6099
N.A.I.C.S.: 522291; 522320; 522390; 561510
Advertising Expenditures: $595,000,000
Media: 2-3-6-9-15-16-18-23-24
Distr.: Direct to Consumer; Intl.; Natl.
Budget Set: Dec. -Jan.

Personnel:
Kenneth I. Chenault *(Chm & CEO)*
Edward P. Gilligan *(Vice Chm)*
Daniel T. Henry *(CFO & Exec VP)*
Stephen Squeri *(CIO & Grp Pres-Svcs-Global)*
John D. Hayes *(CMO & Head-Global Adv, Brand Mgmt)*
Ashwini Gupta *(Pres-Risk, Info Mgmt, Exec VP, Banking & Chief Risk Officer)*
Douglas E. Buckminster *(Pres-Intl Consumer & Small Bus Svcs)*
William H. Glenn *(Pres-Global Merchant Svcs)*
Daniel H. Schulman *(Grp Pres-Enterprise Growth)*
Susan Sobbott *(Pres-OPEN)*
Louise M. Parent *(Gen Counsel & Exec VP)*
Joan Lordi C. Amble *(Exec VP & Comptroller)*
Denise Pickett *(Exec VP & Gen Mgr-OPEN Product Mgmt & Acq)*
L. Kevin Cox *(Exec VP-HR)*
Kim C. Goodman *(Exec VP)*
David Messenger *(Exec VP)*
Thomas Schick *(Exec VP-Corp Affairs & Comm)*
Arne Christenson *(Sr VP-Govt Affairs)*
Marie Devlin *(Sr VP-Adv, Media & Sponsorships-Global)*
Ed Jay *(Sr VP-Business Insights)*
Peter Lurie *(Sr VP-Strategic Partnerships & Bus Dev-Enterprise Growth Grp)*
Mary Shinder *(VP & Gen Mgr-Bus Charge Cards, Brand & Product Mgmt)*
Joe Bihlmier *(VP-Media-Global)*
Debra Regan *(VP-Mktg-Digital Bus Svcs)*
Felicia Chiles *(Dir-Internet Acq-External Programs)*
Stephanie Gay *(Dir-Online Mktg & Bus Analysis)*
Carrie Granit *(Dir-Online Acq)*
Stacy Gratz *(Dir-Digital Brand & Social Media)*
Jeffrey Harouche *(Dir-Strategy & Plng)*
Tamar Shapiro *(Dir-Digital Analytics & Bus Insights)*
Rita Solodar *(Dir-Web Analytics)*
Leanna Beck *(Sr Mgr-Mktg)*
Laura Busker *(Sr Mgr-Innovation & Bus Dev)*
Judith Geis *(Sr Mgr-Mktg)*
Aniket Gune *(Sr Mgr-Social Media Acq Strategy)*
Mythily Kamath *(Sr Mgr-Mktg-Acq)*
Carolina Lasso *(Sr Mgr-Online Partnerships-Acq)*
Brooke Pederson *(Sr Mgr-Mktg)*
Nicole Schlesinger *(Sr Mgr-Interactive Dev)*
Marie Thomas *(Sr Mgr-Digital Mktg Experience)*
Ashley Lee McGrail *(Mgr-Mktg-Merchant Svcs)*
Jeannie Chu *(Mgr-Media & Sponsorships)*
Caitlin Lowie *(Mgr-Corp Affairs & Comm)*
Liz O'Pray *(Mgr-Adv)*
Sam Yoo *(Mgr-Prospect Online Acq Display Media)*

Brands & Products:
AMERICAN EXPRESS
AMEXMAIL SERVICES
BILLINGWATCH
BLUE CASH
BLUE FOR BUSINESS
BLUE FOR STUDENTS
BLUE FROM AMERICAN EXPRESS
BLUELOOT
CARDMEMBER
CENTURION
CHEQUES FOR TWO
DEPARTURES
DON'T LEAVE HOME WITHOUT IT
DON'T LEAVE HOME WITHOUT THEM
DON'T LEAVE HOMEPAGES WITHOUT IT
EXPRESS
EXPRESS APPROVAL
FOOD & WINE
GLOBAL ASSIST
HILTON HHONORS
MEMBERSHIP REWARDS
OFFER ZONE
ONLINE EXTRAS
OPEN: THE SMALL BUSINESS NETWORK
OPTIMA
PLATINUM CARD
PRIVATE PAYMENTS
SHOPAMEX
SIGN & TRAVEL
SKY MILES
SKYGUIDE
TRAVEL & LEISURE
TRAVELFUNDS
TRAVELFUNDS DIRECT
TRUE EARNINGS
TRUE GRACE

Advertising Agencies:
Bernard Hodes Group
790 E Broward Blvd Fl 4 Ste 400
Fort Lauderdale, FL 33301
Tel.: (954) 966-3500
Fax: (954) 989-3085

The Cooper Group
381 Park Ave S Eighth Fl
New York, NY 10016-8806
Tel.: (212) 696-2512
Fax: (212) 696-2516

CP+B
3390 Mary St Ste 300

Key to Media (For complete agency information see *The Advertising Red Books-Agencies* edition):
1. Bus. Publs. 2. Cable T.V. 3. Catalogs & Directories. 4. Co-op Adv. 5. Consumer Mags. 6. D.M. to Bus. Estab.7. D.M. to Consumers 8. Daily Newsp. 9. Exhibits/Trade Shows 10. Foreign 11. Infomercial 12. Internet Adv.13. Multimedia 14. Network Radio 15. Network T.V. 16. Newsp. Distr. Mags. 17. Other 18. Outdoor (Posters, Transit) 19. Point of Purchase20. Premiums, Novelties 21. Product Samples 22. Special Events Mktg. 23. Spot Radio 24. Spot T.V. 25. Weekly Newsp. 26. Yellow Page Adv.

American Express Company — (Continued)

Coconut Grove, FL 33133
Tel.: (305) 859-2070
Fax: (305) 854-3419
OPEN

CP+B Boulder
6450 Gunpark Dr
Boulder, CO 80301
Tel.: (303) 628-5100
Fax: (303) 516-0227

Digitas Inc.
33 Arch St
Boston, MA 02110
Tel.: (617) 867-1000
Fax: (617) 867-1111
(US Direct Marketing)

Digitas, Inc.
355 Park Ave S
New York, NY 10010-1706
Tel.: (212) 610-5000
Fax: (212) 350-7850
Small Business Saturday

Earthbound Media Group
14988 Sand Canyon Ave Studio 5
Irvine, CA 92618
Tel.: (949) 857-4000
Fax: (949) 857-4004
Toll Free: (866) 623-2784

ID Media
(Part of the Interpublic Group of Companies)
100 W 33rd St
New York, NY 10001
Tel.: (212) 907-7011
Fax: (212) 907-7290

Jaffe & Partners
148 Madison Ave 12th Fl
New York, NY 10016-5109
Tel.: (212) 696-5555
Fax: (212) 696-4998

Maslansky, Luntz & Partners
1101 King St Ste 110
Alexandria, VA 22314
Tel.: (703) 358-0080
Fax: (703) 358-0089

Mindshare
498 7th Ave
New York, NY 10018
Tel.: (212) 297-7000
Fax: (212) 297-7001
(Media Planning & Placement)
OPEN

Momentum Worldwide
250 Hudson St
New York, NY 10013
Tel.: (646) 638-5400
Fax: (646) 638-5401

o2kl
10 W 18th St 6th Fl
New York, NY 10011
Tel.: (646) 829-6239
Fax: (646) 839-6254

Ogilvy & Mather
(Sub. of WPP Group plc)
636 11th Ave
New York, NY 10036
Tel.: (212) 237-4000
Fax: (212) 237-5123
(TV, Print & Radio Advertising)
— David Carson *(Exec Dir-Creative)*

OgilvyAction
636 W 11th Ave
New York, NY 10036
Tel.: (212) 297-8000
Fax: (212) 297-8006

OgilvyAction
22 W 19th St 10th Fl
New York, NY 10011-4204
Tel.: (212) 627-4101
Fax: (212) 627-4106
Toll Free: (800) 343-4101

Serino Coyne LLC
(Sub. of Omnicom Group Inc.)
1515 Broadway 36th Fl
New York, NY 10036-8901
Tel.: (212) 626-2700
Fax: (212) 626-2799
Gold Card Events
— Roger Micone *(Grp Dir)*

Team One
(Sub. of Saatchi & Saatchi Advertising Worldwide)
1960 E Grand Ave
El Segundo, CA 90245-5059
Tel.: (310) 615-2000
Fax: (310) 322-7565
Private Jet Travel

AMERICAN FEDERAL BANK

215 5th St N
Fargo, ND 58102
Tel.: (701) 461-5900
Fax: (701) 461-5970
Web Site:
www.americanfederalbank.com
Approx. Number Employees: 27
Business Description:
Federal Savings Institutions
S.I.C.: 6035; 6163
N.A.I.C.S.: 522120; 522310
Media: 2
Advertising Agency:
Soter Associates Inc.
209 N 400 W
Provo, UT 84601-2746
Tel.: (801) 375-6200
Fax: (801) 375-6280

AMERICAN FINANCIAL GROUP, INC.

1 E 4th St
Cincinnati, OH 45202-3715
Tel.: (513) 579-2121
Fax: (513) 579-2113
E-mail: AFGInvestorRelations@gaic.com
Web Site: www.afginc.com
Approx. Rev.: $4,497,000,000
Approx. Number Employees: 5,100
Year Founded: 1940
Business Description:
Holding Company; Property & Casualty Insurance, Tax-Deferred Annuities, Life & Health Insurance
S.I.C.: 6331; 6311; 6719
N.A.I.C.S.: 524126; 524113; 551112
Media: 2-4-9-10
Distr.: Intl.; Natl.
Personnel:
Carl Henry Lindner *(Chm)*
S. Craig Lindner *(Co-CEO, Pres & Dir)*
Carl H. Lindner, III *(Co-Pres & Co-CEO)*
Piyush K. Singh *(CIO & VP)*
James E. Evans *(Gen Counsel & Sr VP)*
Karl J. Grafe *(Sec, VP & Asst Gen Counsel)*
Keith A. Jensen *(Sr VP)*
Thomas E. Mischell *(Sr VP-Tax)*
Annette D Gardner *(VP & Asst Treas)*
James C. Kennedy *(Deputy Gen Counsel & VP)*
Michelle A. Gillis *(VP-HR, Enterprise Svcs, Event & Conference Dept)*
John R. Rogers *(Asst VP-Enterprise Svcs, Event & Conference Svcs)*
Diane Weidner *(Asst VP-IR)*

AMERICAN HOME PARTNERS, INC.

1154 Highland Ave
Cheshire, CT 06410
Tel.: (203) 699-3400
Fax: (866) 963-5680
Toll Free: (800) 328-3380
E-mail: hsanti@amhp.net
Web Site:
www.americanhomepartners.com
Sales Range: $1-9.9 Million
Approx. Number Employees: 35
Year Founded: 1946
Business Description:
Home Mortgage Services
S.I.C.: 6163
N.A.I.C.S.: 522310
Media: 2-6

AMERICAN INCORPORATORS LTD.

1220 N Market St Ste 808
Wilmington, DE 19801
Tel.: (302) 421-5752
Fax: (302) 421-5753
Toll Free: (800) 421-2661
E-mail: info@ailcorp.com
Web Site: www.ailcorp.com
Sales Range: $1-9.9 Million
Approx. Number Employees: 25
Business Description:
Company Incorporating Services
S.I.C.: 7389
N.A.I.C.S.: 561499
Media: 6
Personnel:
Murray H. Sawyer, Jr. *(Chm)*
Ann Shilton *(Exec VP)*

AMERICAN LAND LEASE, INC.

(Sub. of Green Courte Partners, LLC)
380 Park Pl Blvd Ste 200
Clearwater, FL 33759
Tel.: (727) 726-8868
Fax: (727) 726-6700
Toll Free: (800) 826-6069
Web Site:
www.americanlandlease.com
Approx. Rev.: $38,651,000
Approx. Number Employees: 195
Business Description:
Real Estate Investment Trust
S.I.C.: 6513; 6798
N.A.I.C.S.: 531110; 525930
Advertising Expenditures: $1,916,000
Media: 8-16-18-22
Personnel:
Randall K. Rowe *(Chm)*
Shannon E. Smith *(CFO & COO)*
Ben Allen *(Gen Counsel, Sec & VP)*

AMERICAN NATIONAL BANKSHARES INC.

628 Main St
Danville, VA 24541
Tel.: (434) 792-5111
Fax: (434) 792-1582
Toll Free: (800) 240-8190
E-mail: petrovichn@amnb.com
Web Site: www.amnb.com
Approx. Rev.: $44,464,000
Approx. Number Employees: 242
Business Description:
National Commercial Banks
S.I.C.: 6029; 6141
N.A.I.C.S.: 522110; 522210
Advertising Expenditures: $229,000
Media: 7-8-9
Personnel:
Charles H. Majors *(Pres & CEO)*
William W. Traynham *(CFO & Sr VP)*
S. Cabell Dudley, Jr. *(Chief Lending Officer & Exec VP)*
Jeffrey V. Haley *(Exec VP)*
R. Helm Dobbins *(Sr VP)*
Dabney T.P. Gilliam Jr. *(Sr VP)*
Karen P. Kinnier *(Sr VP & Reg Exec)*

AMERICAN RIVER BANKSHARES

3100 Zinfandel Dr Ste 450
Rancho Cordova, CA 95670
Tel.: (916) 851-0123
E-mail: investor.relations@amrb.com
Web Site: www.amrb.com
Approx. Rev.: $27,510,000
Approx. Number Employees: 111
Business Description:
Bank Holding Company
S.I.C.: 6029; 6712
N.A.I.C.S.: 522110; 551111
Advertising Expenditures: $232,000
Personnel:
Charles D. Fite *(Chm)*
Roger J. Taylor *(Vice Chm)*
David T. Taber *(Pres & CEO-American River Bankshares)*
Mitchell A. Derenzo *(CFO & Exec VP)*
Douglas E. Tow *(Chief Credit Officer & Exec VP)*
Kevin B. Bender *(COO-American River Bankshares & Exec VP)*

AMERICAN SECURITIES LLC

299 Park Ave 34th Fl
New York, NY 10171-4011
Tel.: (212) 476-8000
Fax: (212) 697-5524
E-mail: info@american-securities.com
Web Site: www.american-securities.com
Sales Range: $1-4.9 Billion
Approx. Number Employees: 25
Year Founded: 1947
Business Description:
Private Equity Firm
S.I.C.: 6289
N.A.I.C.S.: 523999
Media: 13
Personnel:
Michael G. Fisch *(Pres & CEO)*
Anthony Grillo *(Mng Dir)*
Charles D. Klein *(Mng Dir)*
Matthew F. LeBaron *(Mng Dir)*

Key to Media (For complete agency information see *The Advertising Red Books-Agencies* edition):
1. Bus. Publs. 2. Cable T.V. 3. Catalogs & Directories. 4. Co-op Adv. 5. Consumer Mags. 6. D.M. to Bus. Estab.7. D.M. to Consumers 8. Daily Newsp. 9. Exhibits/Trade Shows 10. Foreign 11. Infomercial 12. Internet Adv.13. Multimedia 14. Network Radio 15. Network T.V. 16. Newsp. Distr. Mags. 17. Other 18. Outdoor (Posters, Transit) 19. Point of Purchase20. Premiums, Novelties 21. Product Samples 22. Special Events Mktg. 23. Spot Radio 24. Spot T.V. 25. Weekly Newsp. 26. Yellow Page Adv.

Kevin S. Penn *(Mng Dir)*
Paul Rosetti *(Mng Dir)*
Marc L. Saiontz *(Mng Dir)*
Larry First *(Mng Dir)*
Bill Fry *(Mng Dir)*
David L. Horing *(Mng Dir)*
Gregory J. Nolff *(CFO)*
David Maue *(Chief Admin Officer)*
Judie Feng *(Principal)*
Matthew S. Levine *(Principal)*
Scott M. Wolff *(Principal)*
Lee Dranikoff *(Sr Dir-Resources Grp)*
Anne T. Board *(Dir-External Rels)*
David L. Cohen *(Dir-Human Capital)*
Larry D. Greene *(Dir-Ops Excellence)*
David H. Kahn *(Dir-Investment Dev)*
J. Kelly McGowan *(Dir-Info Sys & Tech)*
Ee-Ping Ong *(Dir-Asia-Pacific Strategy)*
Amy Sodha *(Dir-IR)*
Jun Tao *(Dir-Asia-Pacific Ops)*
Eric M. Schwartzfarb *(Assoc Dir-Investment Dev)*

AMERICAN STUDENT ASSISTANCE
100 Cambridge St Ste 1600
Boston, MA 02114
Tel.: (617) 426-9434
Fax: (617) 728-4256
Web Site: www.amsa.com
Approx. Sls.: $36,725,000
Business Description:
Student Loan Marketing Association
S.I.C.: 6159; 6141
N.A.I.C.S.: 522298; 522291
Personnel:
Paul C. Combe *(Pres)*
Michael Finn *(CFO)*
Sue Burton *(Mng Dir-Consumer Product & Mktg)*
Martha Corrales *(Reg Mgr-Acct)*
Steve Smith *(Reg Mgr-Acct)*
Jonathan Phelan *(Product Mgr)*
Alessandra Lanza *(Mgr-PR)*
Caroline Menendez *(Mgr-Bus Dev-Northeast & Intl)*
Brands & Products:
AMERICAN STUDENT ASSISTANCE
THINK ABOUT TOMORROW
Advertising Agency:
Brodeur Partners
855 Boylston St 2nd Fl
Boston, MA 02116-2622
Tel.: (617) 587-2800
Fax: (617) 587-2828
Financial Wellness Programs

AMERICANWEST BANCORPORATION
(Filed Ch 11 Bankruptcy #1006097 on 10/28/10 in U.S. Bankruptcy Ct, Eastern Dist of Spokane, Washington)
41 W Riverside Ave Ste 400
Spokane, WA 99201
Tel.: (509) 467-6993
Fax: (509) 465-9681
E-mail: info@awbank.net
Web Site: www.awbank.net
Approx. Rev.: $108,638,000
Approx. Number Employees: 531
Year Founded: 1983
Business Description:
Bank Holding Company
S.I.C.: 6712
N.A.I.C.S.: 551111
Advertising Expenditures: $553,000
Media: 7-8-9
Personnel:
Craig D. Eerkes *(Chm)*
Wade A. Griffith *(CIO)*
Jay B. Simmons *(Gen Counsel)*
B. Nicole Sherman *(Chief Banking Officer & Exec VP)*

AMERICASBANK CORP.
(Sub. of Capital Funding Group Inc.)
500 York Rd
Towson, MD 21204
Tel.: (410) 823-0500
Fax: (410) 823-6685
E-mail: info@americasbank.com
Web Site: www.americasbank.com
E-Mail For Key Personnel:
President: AGRever@mail.bcpl.lib.md.us
Approx. Int. Income: $3,263,000
Approx. Number Employees: 50
Year Founded: 1927
Business Description:
Bank Holding Company; Commercial Banking
S.I.C.: 6035; 6029; 6712
N.A.I.C.S.: 522120; 522110; 551111
Advertising Expenditures: $61,306
Media: 7-8-13
Personnel:
A. Patrick Linton *(Pres & CEO)*
A. Gary Rever *(CFO)*
Ellen R. Fish *(Dir-Community Banking)*
Brands & Products:
A FAMILY OF COMMUNITY BANKS
AMERICANBANK

AMERIPRISE FINANCIAL, INC.
1099 Ameriprise Financial Ctr
Minneapolis, MN 55474
Tel.: (612) 671-3131
Fax: (612) 671-5112
Toll Free: (800) 386-2042
E-mail: laura.c.gagnon@ampf.com
Web Site: www.ameriprise.com
Approx. Rev.: $9,976,000,000
Approx. Number Employees: 10,472
Year Founded: 1894
Business Description:
Financial Planning, Products & Services for Individual, Business & Institutional Clients
S.I.C.: 6282; 6289
N.A.I.C.S.: 523930; 523920; 523999
Media: 1-3-5-6-8-9-15-24-26
Distr.: Direct to Consumer; Natl.
Budget Set: July
Personnel:
James M. Cracchiolo *(Chm & CEO)*
Walter S. Berman *(CFO & Exec VP)*
Kim Michele Sharan *(CMO & Pres-Fin Plng, Retirement & Wealth Strategies)*
John Robert Woerner *(Pres-Insurance & Chief Strategy Officer)*
David K. Stewart *(Chief Acctg Officer, Sr VP & Controller)*
Joseph Edward Sweeney *(Pres-Advice & Wealth Mgmt Products & Svcs)*
John C. Junek *(Gen Counsel & Exec VP)*
Kelli A. Hunter *(Exec VP-HR)*
Glen Salow *(Exec VP-Svcs Del & Tech)*
Deirdre N. Davey *(Sr VP)*
Stuart Burkhoff *(VP-Media & Sponsorship)*
Stacy Housman *(Dir-Pub Comm)*
Ryan Lund *(Dir-Comm)*
Chris Reese *(Dir-PR)*
Keith Dieruf *(Sr Mgr-Interactive Mktg)*
Jill Fochs *(Sr Mgr-Mktg)*
Charlie Keller *(Sr Mgr-Media Rels)*
Advertising Agencies:
Initiative
1 Dag Hammarskjold Plz
New York, NY 10017
Tel.: (212) 605-7000
Fax: (917) 305-4003

Velocity Sports & Entertainment
230 East Ave 3rd Fl
Norwalk, CT 06855
Tel.: (203) 831-2000
Fax: (203) 831-2300

Yamamoto Moss and Mackenzie Marketing
252 First Ave N
Minneapolis, MN 55401
Tel.: (612) 375-0180
Fax: (612) 342-2424
Toll Free: (888) 375-9910

AMERIQUEST MORTGAGE COMPANY INC.
(Sub. of Ameriquest Capital Corporation)
1100 W Town and Country Rd
Orange, CA 92868-4600
Tel.: (714) 541-9960
Fax: (714) 972-9313
Web Site:
www.ameriquestmortgage.com
Approx. Number Employees: 400
Year Founded: 1994
Business Description:
Mortgage Lending Services
S.I.C.: 6163
N.A.I.C.S.: 522310
Import Export
Media: 3-14-15-22-23-24

AMERIS BANCORP
310 1st St SE
Moultrie, GA 31768
Mailing Address:
PO Box 3668
Moultrie, GA 31776-3668
Tel.: (229) 890-1111
Fax: (229) 890-2235
Web Site: www.amerisbank.com
Approx. Rev.: $154,319,000
Approx. Number Employees: 709
Year Founded: 1980
Business Description:
Bank Holding Company
S.I.C.: 6029; 6712
N.A.I.C.S.: 522110; 551111
Advertising Expenditures: $566,000
Media: 7-8-9-13-17-18-23-24-25-26
Personnel:
Daniel B. Jeter *(Chm)*
Edwin W. Hortman, Jr. *(Co-Pres & CEO)*
Andrew B. Cheney *(Co-Pres & COO)*
Dennis J. Zember Jr. *(CFO & Exec VP)*
Gregory H. Walls *(CIO)*
Cindi H. Lewis *(Chief Admin Officer, Sec & Exec VP)*
Jon S. Edwards *(Exec VP & Dir-Credit Admin)*

AMERITRADE CANADA, INC.
(Sub. of TD Waterhouse Canada Inc.)
120 Adelaide St W Ste 916
Toronto, ON M5H 171, Canada
Tel.: (416) 363-9045
Fax: (416) 306-4101
Toll Free: (866) 328-3522
E-mail: service@ameritradecanada.com
Web Site:
www.ameritradecanada.com
Approx. Number Employees: 18
Year Founded: 2000
Business Description:
Brokerage & Related Financial Services
S.I.C.: 6211
N.A.I.C.S.: 523110
Media: 8-13-20-22-25

AMERIX CORPORATION
(Holding of Ascend One Corporation)
8930 Stanford Blvd
Columbia, MD 21045-5805
Tel.: (410) 910-1834
Fax: (410) 910-2832
Toll Free: (877) 260-1490
E-mail: info@amerix.com
Web Site: www.amerix.com
E-Mail For Key Personnel:
Marketing Director: jkotula@amerix.com
Public Relations: clucas@amerix.com
Sales Range: $75-99.9 Million
Approx. Number Employees: 590
Year Founded: 1996
Business Description:
Consumer Debt Management Programs
S.I.C.: 7389
N.A.I.C.S.: 541199
Media: 6-8-13
Personnel:
Bernie Dancel *(Chm & CEO)*
Michael Croxson *(Pres)*
Robert Miller *(CFO)*
Clarky Lucas *(Sr Dir-Pub Rels)*
Joe Kotula *(Dir-Adv & Internet Mktg)*
Brands & Products:
AMERIX
FREEDOM POINT

AMEX BANK OF CANADA
(Sub. of American Express Travel Related Services Company, Inc.)
101 McNabb St
Markham, ON L3R 4H8, Canada
Mailing Address:
1211 Denison Street Unit 18
Markham, ON L3R 4B3, Canada
Tel.: (905) 474-8000
Fax: (905) 474-1035
Web Site:
www.americanexpress.com/canada
Sales Range: $125-149.9 Million
Year Founded: 1853
Business Description:
Charge & Credit Cards
S.I.C.: 6141
N.A.I.C.S.: 522210
Advertising Expenditures: $10,000,000
Media: 6-13-15
Distr.: Natl.
Personnel:
Howard Grosfield *(Chm, Pres & CEO)*
Rob McClain *(VP-Mktg)*

Key to Media (For complete agency information see *The Advertising Red Books-Agencies* edition):
1. Bus. Publs. 2. Cable T.V. 3. Catalogs & Directories. 4. Co-op Adv. 5. Consumer Mags. 6. D.M. to Bus. Estab.7. D.M. to Consumers
8. Daily Newsp. 9. Exhibits/Trade Shows 10. Foreign 11. Infomercial 12. Internet Adv.13. Multimedia 14. Network Radio
15. Network T.V. 16. Newsp. Distr. Mags. 17. Other 18. Outdoor (Posters, Transit) 19. Point of Purchase20. Premiums, Novelties
21. Product Samples 22. Special Events Mktg. 23. Spot Radio 24. Spot T.V. 25. Weekly Newsp. 26. Yellow Page Adv.

AMSCOT CORPORATION
(Sub. of Amscot Holdings Inc.)
(d/b/a Amscot Financial Corporation)
8430 N Armenia Ave
Tampa, FL 33604
Tel.: (813) 932-4339
Toll Free: (800) 801-4444
Web Site: www.amscotfinancial.com
Approx. Number Employees: 250
Year Founded: 1989
Business Description:
Tax Return Preparation & Other Financial Services
S.I.C.: 7291; 6099; 6371
N.A.I.C.S.: 541213; 522390; 525990
Personnel:
Ian A. MacKechnie *(Chm & CEO)*
Advertising Agency:
Ad Partners Inc.
9800 4th St N Ste 200
Saint Petersburg, FL 33702
Tel.: (727) 289-8900
Fax: (727) 289-8999

AMSCOT HOLDINGS INC.
8430 N Armenia Ave PO Box 25137
Tampa, FL 33622
Tel.: (813) 637-6100
Fax: (813) 637-6260
Web Site: www.amscotfinancial.com
Approx. Sls.: $10,000,000
Approx. Number Employees: 12
Business Description:
Tax Return Preparation & Other Financial Services
S.I.C.: 7291; 6371
N.A.I.C.S.: 541213; 525990
Media: 18-22-24
Personnel:
Ian Mackechnie *(Chm & CEO)*
Brands & Products:
AMSCOT
Advertising Agency:
Ad Partners Inc.
9800 4th St N Ste 200
Saint Petersburg, FL 33702
Tel.: (727) 289-8900
Fax: (727) 289-8999

AMTRUST FINANCIAL SERVICES, INC.
59 Maiden Ln 6th Fl
New York, NY 10038
Tel.: (212) 220-7120
Fax: (212) 220-7130
Web Site: www.amtrustgroup.com
Approx. Rev.: $1,002,457,000
Approx. Number Employees: 1,400
Business Description:
Property & Casualty Insurance Services
S.I.C.: 6411; 6331
N.A.I.C.S.: 524210; 524126
Personnel:
Michael Karfunkel *(Chm)*
Barry D. Zyskind *(Pres & CEO)*
Ronald E. Pipoly, Jr. *(CFO)*
Michael J. Saxon *(COO)*
Christopher M. Longo *(CIO)*
Max G. Caviet *(Pres-AmTrust Intl Insurance Ltd/AmTrust Intl Underwriters Ltd)*
Stephen B. Ungar *(Gen Counsel & Sec)*
Harry Schlachter *(Treas & Sr VP-Fin)*
Advertising Agency:
Richards Communications
3201 Enterprise Pkwy Ste 400
Beachwood, OH 44122
Tel.: (216) 514-7800
Fax: (216) 514-7801

ANCHOR FUNDING SERVICES, INC.
10801 Johnston Rd Ste 210
Charlotte, NC 28226
Tel.: (704) 542-2533
Fax: (704) 542-4724
Toll Free: (866) 789-3863
E-mail: bgreen@anchorfundingservices.com
Web Site:
www.anchorfundingservices.com
Approx. Rev.: $2,514,394
Approx. Number Employees: 8
Business Description:
Financial Funding Services
S.I.C.: 6799; 6371
N.A.I.C.S.: 523910; 525990
Advertising Expenditures: $255,000
Personnel:
Brad Bernstein *(Pres)*

ANDROSCOGGIN SAVINGS BANK
30 Lisbon St
Lewiston, ME 04240
Tel.: (207) 784-9164
Fax: (207) 786-4782
Toll Free: (800) 927-3344
Web Site:
www.androscogginbank.com
Approx. Int. Income: $26,808,000
Approx. Number Employees: 155
Year Founded: 1870
Business Description:
Community Bank
S.I.C.: 6035
N.A.I.C.S.: 522120
Personnel:
Paul H. Andersen *(Pres & COO)*
Steven A. Closson *(CEO)*
Chris Logan *(Sr VP)*
Victoria Elwell *(VP & Mgr-Market)*
Bob Stone *(VP & Mgr-Bus & Govt Svcs)*
Leo Soucy *(VP-Sr Investment Advisor)*
Lindy Fogg *(Asst VP & Mgr-Market)*
Lena Hann *(Asst VP & Mgr-Market)*
Brands & Products:
ABFREE
ANDROSCOGGIN BANK
PARTNERS
PARTNERS PLUS
Advertising Agency:
McClain Marketing Group
75 Washington Ave
Portland, ME 04101
Tel.: (207) 761-8372
Fax: (207) 780-0155

ANGEL ACQUISITION CORP.
1802 N Carson St Ste 212-3018
Carson City, NV 89701
Tel.: (775) 887-0670
Fax: (775) 887-0738
E-mail: contact@angelacquisitions.com
Web Site: www.angelacquisitions.com
Approx. Rev.: $1,416,727
Approx. Number Employees: 1
Year Founded: 1999
Business Description:
Investment & Financial Services; Mortgage Broker
S.I.C.: 6289; 6163; 6371
N.A.I.C.S.: 523999; 522310; 525990
Advertising Expenditures: $23,370
Media: 17
Personnel:
Vincent R. Molinari *(Chm)*
H. Steven Bonenberger *(CEO, Pres, Board Member)*

ANNAPOLIS BANCORP, INC.
1000 Bestgate Rd Ste 400
Annapolis, MD 21401-3023
Tel.: (410) 224-4455
Fax: (410) 224-3132
Toll Free: (800) 582-2651
E-mail: rlerner@bankannapolis.com
Web Site: www.bankannapolis.com
Approx. Rev.: $21,668,000
Approx. Number Employees: 91
Year Founded: 1988
Business Description:
Bank Holding Company
S.I.C.: 6029; 6712
N.A.I.C.S.: 522110; 551111
Advertising Expenditures: $251,000
Personnel:
Richard M. Lerner *(Chm)*
Stanley J. Klos, Jr. *(Vice Chm)*
Edward J. Schneider *(CFO & Treas)*
Brands & Products:
ANNAPOLIS BANCORP
BANK ANNAPOLIS
BANK EASY BANK LOCAL

APPLE BANK FOR SAVINGS
122 E 42nd St 9th Fl
New York, NY 10168
Tel.: (212) 224-6400
Fax: (212) 224-6589
Toll Free: (800) 722-6888
E-mail: custline@apple-bank.com
Web Site: www.applebank.com
E-Mail For Key Personnel:
Marketing Director: nrichman@apple-bank.com
Approx. Rev.: $139,882,000
Approx. Number Employees: 785
Year Founded: 1863
Business Description:
Provider of Full Service Banking Services
S.I.C.: 6035
N.A.I.C.S.: 522120
Media: 2-8-9-16-18-20-25-26
Distr.: Reg.
Budget Set: Jan.
Personnel:
Alan Shamoon *(Chm, Pres & CEO)*
Bruce A. Herman *(Sec & Sr VP)*
Susan B. Goro *(Sr VP & Dir-HR)*
James G. Matera *(Sr VP & Dir-Consumer Banking)*
Vincent D. Baldino *(Sr VP)*
George Bossis *(Sr VP)*
Antonio Pietrantuono *(Sr VP-MIS)*
Roberta F. Thomson *(Sr VP-Comml Mortgages)*
Brands & Products:
BASIC VALUE CHECKING
GOLD VALUE NOW CHECKING ACCOUNT
GRAND YIELD SAVINGS
SURE ACCESS
SURE CREDIT
SURE LINE
SURE LOAN
Advertising Agency:
Apple Bank Ad Group
(House Agency)
277 Park Ave., 40th Fl.
New York, NY 10172
Tel.: (212) 224-6400
Fax: (212) 224-6589
(All Bank Products)

APPLIED CARD SYSTEMS INC.
5401 Brokensound Blvd NW
Boca Raton, FL 33487
Tel.: (561) 995-8820
Fax: (561) 994-5881
Toll Free: (866) 227-5627
E-mail: acshr@appliedcard.com
Web Site: www.appliedcard.com
Approx. Number Employees: 250
Year Founded: 1987
Business Description:
Credit Card Processing
S.I.C.: 6099
N.A.I.C.S.: 522320
Media: 10
Personnel:
Charlie Albano *(Pres & COO)*
Rocco Abessinio *(CEO)*

ARES CAPITAL-WASHINGTON, DC OFFICE
(Sub. of ARES CAPITAL CORPORATION)
1919 Pennsylvania Ave NW
Washington, DC 20006-3404
Tel.: (202) 721-6100
Fax: (202) 721-6101
Approx. Rev.: $318,686,000
Approx. Number Employees: 107
Year Founded: 1958
Business Description:
Private Equity & Business Development Services
S.I.C.: 6289
N.A.I.C.S.: 523999
Advertising Expenditures: $500,000
Media: 7
Personnel:
Penni F. Roll *(CFO)*
Suzanne V. Sparrow *(Mgr-Transition)*

ARLINGTON ASSET INVESTMENT CORP.
1001 19th St N
Arlington, VA 22209-1722
Tel.: (703) 312-9500
Fax: (703) 312-9501
Toll Free: (800) 846-5050
E-mail: ir@arlingtonasset.com
Web Site: www.arlingtonasset.com
Approx. Rev.: $42,881,000
Approx. Number Employees: 10
Year Founded: 1989
Business Description:
Investment Banking & Securities Brokerage Services
S.I.C.: 6211; 6798
N.A.I.C.S.: 523120; 523110; 525930
Media: 2-6-9-10-13-15-22-24-25
Personnel:
Eric F. Billings *(Chm & CEO)*
J. Rock Tonkel, Jr. *(Pres & COO)*
Kurt R. Harrington *(CFO & Exec VP)*
Robert S. Smith *(COO & Exec VP)*
Brian J. Bowers *(Chief Investment Officer & Portfolio Mgr)*
Frank B. Glassner *(CEO-Compensation Design Grp)*

Key to Media (For complete agency information see *The Advertising Red Books-Agencies* edition):
1. Bus. Publs. 2. Cable T.V. 3. Catalogs & Directories. 4. Co-op Adv. 5. Consumer Mags. 6. D.M. to Bus. Estab.7. D.M. to Consumers
8. Daily Newsp. 9. Exhibits/Trade Shows 10. Foreign 11. Infomercial 12. Internet Adv.13. Multimedia 14. Network Radio
15. Network T.V. 16. Newsp. Distr. Mags. 17. Other 18. Outdoor (Posters, Transit) 19. Point of Purchase20. Premiums, Novelties
21. Product Samples 22. Special Events Mktg. 23. Spot Radio 24. Spot T.V. 25. Weekly Newsp. 26. Yellow Page Adv.

Patrick Keeley *(Exec VP & Co-Head-Investment Banking)*
James C. Neuhauser *(Exec VP & Co-Head-Investment Banking)*
James T. Hill *(Mng Dir-Fin Institutions)*
Claire F. Newman *(Dir-Sls)*

ARROW FINANCIAL CORPORATION
250 Glen St
Glens Falls, NY 12801-3505
Tel.: (518) 745-1000
Fax: (518) 745-1976
E-mail: information@arrowbank.com
Web Site: www.arrowfinancial.com
Approx. Rev.: $104,061,000
Approx. Number Employees: 481
Year Founded: 1983
Business Description:
Bank Holding Company
S.I.C.: 6029
N.A.I.C.S.: 522110
Advertising Expenditures: $1,024,000
Personnel:
Thomas L. Hoy *(Chm, Pres & CEO)*
Terry Goodemote *(Sr VP & Chief Credit Officer)*
Karen E. Guiseppe *(Dir-Internal Audit)*

ASHEVILLE SAVINGS BANK SSB
11 Church St
Asheville, NC 28801
Tel.: (828) 254-7411
Fax: (828) 252-1512
E-mail: info@ashevillesavingsbank.com
Web Site: www.ashevillesavings.com
Approx. Number Employees: 178
Year Founded: 1936
Business Description:
Federal Savings Institutions
S.I.C.: 6035; 6163
N.A.I.C.S.: 522120; 522310
Import Export
Personnel:
Suzanne DeFerie *(Pres & CEO)*
Fred A. Martin *(CIO & Exec VP)*
Troy Favaron *(Comml Loan Officer)*
Brenda Gillespie *(Comml Loan Officer)*
David Kozak *(Chief Lending Officer & Exec VP)*
Vikki Bailey *(Sr VP-Exec Mktg)*
Jonna Bradham *(VP-HR)*
Susan Pike *(Area Mgr-Retail)*
Advertising Agency:
Publicis in Mid America
200 S Meridian St Ste 500
Indianapolis, IN 46225-1076
Tel.: (317) 639-5135
Fax: (317) 639-5134

ASHFORD HOSPITALITY TRUST, INC.
14185 Dallas Pkwy Ste 1100
Dallas, TX 75254
Tel.: (972) 490-9600
Fax: (972) 980-2705
E-mail: tripp.sullivan@ahtreit.com
Web Site: www.ahtreit.com
Approx. Rev.: $841,365,000
Approx. Number Employees: 67
Business Description:
Real Estate Investment Trust
S.I.C.: 6798
N.A.I.C.S.: 525930
Advertising Expenditures: $3,400,000
Media: 5
Personnel:
Archie Bennett, Jr. *(Chm)*
Douglas A. Kessler *(Pres)*
Montgomery J. Bennett *(CEO)*
Mark L. Nunneley *(Chief Acctg Officer)*
David A. Brooks *(COO, Gen Counsel & Sec)*
Tripp Sullivan *(Principal & Sr VP)*
Donald J. Denzin *(Sr VP-HR)*
Larry Doyle *(Sr VP-Asset Mgmt)*

ASSET ACCEPTANCE CAPITAL CORP.
28405 Van Dyke Ave
Warren, MI 48093
Mailing Address:
PO Box 2037
Warren, MI 48090-2037
Tel.: (586) 939-9600
Fax: (586) 446-7825
Toll Free: (800) 545-9931
E-mail: customerservice@assetacceptance.com
Web Site: www.assetacceptance.com
Approx. Rev.: $198,399,820
Approx. Number Employees: 1,206
Year Founded: 1962
Business Description:
Debt & Accounts Receivables Collection Services
S.I.C.: 6141; 7322; 8742
N.A.I.C.S.: 522210; 522291; 541611; 561440
Advertising Expenditures: $2,863,000
Personnel:
Nathaniel F. Bradley, IV *(Chm)*
Rion B. Needs *(Pres & CEO)*
Reid E. Simpson *(Sr VP, CFO, Asst Sec & Treas)*
Todd Langusch *(CIO & VP)*
Edwin L. Herbert *(Gen Counsel, Sec & VP)*
Deborah L. Everly *(Chief Acq Officer & Sr VP)*
Deanna S. Hatmaker *(VP-HR & Corp Comm)*
Brands & Products:
AACC
RETURNING VALUE TO OUR CREDIT DRIVEN ECONOMY
TAKING YOU FROM THE RED TO THE BLACK

ASSOCIATED BANC-CORP
1200 Hansen Rd
Green Bay, WI 54304-5448
Tel.: (920) 491-7000
Fax: (920) 491-7090
Toll Free: (800) 682-4989
E-mail: shareholders@associatedbank.com
Web Site: www.associatedbank.com
Approx. Rev.: $1,151,649,000
Approx. Number Employees: 4,894
Year Founded: 1970
Business Description:
Bank Holding Company
S.I.C.: 6712; 6029
N.A.I.C.S.: 551111; 522110
Advertising Expenditures: $18,385,000
Media: 2-8-9-20
Personnel:
Mark J. Mcmullen *(Vice Chm-Assocd Bank N.A.)*
Philip B. Flynn *(Pres & CEO)*
Joseph B. Selner *(CFO & Exec VP)*
Christopher Del Moral-Niles *(Deputy CFO)*
Mark D. Quinlan *(CIO, Exec VP & Dir-Ops & Tech)*
Brian R. Bodager *(Chief Admin Officer, Gen Counsel, Sec & Exec VP)*
Oliver Buechse *(Chief Strategy Officer & Exec VP)*
Scott S. Hickey *(Chief Credit Officer & Exec VP)*
Arthur G. Heise *(Chief Risk Officer & Exec VP)*
Robert Timothy Watson *(Treas & Exec VP)*
Judith M. Docter *(Exec VP & Dir-HR)*
Breck Hanson *(Exec VP & Dir-Comml Real Estate)*
Nicholas Papachristou *(Exec VP & Dir-Mktg)*
David L. Stein *(Exec VP & Dir-Retail Banking)*
Gordon J. Weber *(Exec VP & Dir-Corp Banking)*
Mark Sander *(Exec VP-Comml Banking)*
Laura Kahl *(Sr VP & Dir-ECommerce Mktg)*

ASTORIA FEDERAL SAVINGS & LOAN
(Sub. of Astoria Financial Corporation)
1 Astoria Federal Plz
Lake Success, NY 11042
Tel.: (516) 488-2400
E-mail: banking@astoriafederal.com
Web Site: www.astoriafederal.com
Sales Range: $125-149.9 Million
Year Founded: 1888
Business Description:
Federal Savings Institutions
S.I.C.: 6035
N.A.I.C.S.: 522120
Advertising Expenditures: $6,600,000
Personnel:
George L. Engelke, Jr. *(Chm & CEO)*
Gerard C. Keegan *(Vice Chm & Chief Admin Officer)*
Monte N. Redman *(Pres, CEO & Dir-Astoria Fin Corp)*
Frank E. Fusco *(CFO, Treas & Exec VP)*
Robert J. DeStefano *(CIO & Sr VP)*
Alan P. Eggleston *(Gen Counsel, Exec VP & Sec-Astoria Fin Corp)*
Anthony S. DiContanzo *(Sr VP & Dir-Taxes)*
Brian T. Edwards *(Sr VP & Dir-Mktg)*
William J. Mannix *(Sr VP & Dir-Audit)*
Robert T. Volk *(Sr VP & Dir-Retail Banking)*
Thomas E. Lavery *(Deputy Gen Counsel & Sr VP)*
Josie Callari *(Sr VP)*
Ira M. Yourman *(Sr VP-Loan Administration)*
Advertising Agency:
LoBo & Petrocine, Inc.
95 Broadhollow Rd Ste D
Melville, NY 11747
Tel.: (631) 421-3142
Fax: (631) 421-3783

ASTORIA FINANCIAL CORPORATION
1 Astoria Federal Plz
Lake Success, NY 11042-1085
Tel.: (516) 327-3000
Fax: (516) 327-7461
E-mail: ir@astoriafederal.com
Web Site: www.astoriafederal.com
Approx. Rev.: $936,487,000
Approx. Number Employees: 1,467
Year Founded: 1993
Business Description:
Bank Holding Company
S.I.C.: 6712; 6029; 6035
N.A.I.C.S.: 551111; 522110; 522120
Advertising Expenditures: $6,466,000
Media: 2
Personnel:
George L. Engelke, Jr. *(Chm & CEO)*
Gerard C. Keegan *(Vice Chm & Chief Admin Officer)*
John J. Conefry Jr. *(Vice Chm)*
Monte N. Redman *(Pres & COO)*
Frank E. Fusco *(CFO, Treas & Exec VP)*
Alan P. Eggleston *(Gen Counsel, Sec & Exec VP)*
Arnold K. Greenberg *(Exec VP)*
Gary T. McCann *(Exec VP)*
Peter J. Cunningham *(First VP-IR)*
Advertising Agency:
Curran & Connors, Inc.
3455 Peachtree Rd NE 5th Fl
Atlanta, GA 30326-3236
Tel.: (404) 239-3979
Toll Free: (800) 435-.0406

ATHENS BANCSHARES CORPORATION
106 Washington Ave
Athens, TN 37303
Tel.: (423) 745-1111
Approx. Rev.: $18,934,806
Approx. Number Employees: 88
Year Founded: 2009
Business Description:
Bank Holding Company
S.I.C.: 6029; 6712
N.A.I.C.S.: 522110; 551111
Advertising Expenditures: $184,695
Media: 17
Personnel:
Larry D. Wallace *(Chm)*
Jeffrey L. Cunningham *(Pres & CEO)*
Michael R. Hutsell *(CFO, COO, Treas & VP)*

ATLANTIC COAST FEDERAL CORPORATION
505 Haines Ave
Waycross, GA 31501
Tel.: (912) 283-4711
Fax: (912) 284-2284
Toll Free: (800) 342-2824
E-mail: info@atlanticcoastbank.net
Web Site: www.atlanticcoastbank.net
Approx. Rev.: $52,883,000
Approx. Number Employees: 153
Year Founded: 2003
Business Description:
Holding Company
S.I.C.: 6712
N.A.I.C.S.: 551111
Advertising Expenditures: $584,000
Personnel:
Jay S. Sidhu *(Chm)*
Forrest W. Sweat Jr. *(Vice Chm)*
Robert J. Larison, Jr. *(Pres & CEO)*
G. Thomas Frankland *(Pres & CEO-Interim)*
Thomas B. Wagers, Sr. *(COO)*
Herman T. Klinger Jr. *(CIO & Sr VP)*
Phillip S. Buddenbohm *(Chief Risk Officer & Sr VP)*

Key to Media (For complete agency information see *The Advertising Red Books-Agencies* edition):
1. Bus. Publs. 2. Cable T.V. 3. Catalogs & Directories. 4. Co-op Adv. 5. Consumer Mags. 6. D.M. to Bus. Estab.7. D.M. to Consumers 8. Daily Newsp. 9. Exhibits/Trade Shows 10. Foreign 11. Infomercial 12. Internet Adv.13. Multimedia 14. Network Radio 15. Network T.V. 16. Newsp. Distr. Mags. 17. Other 18. Outdoor (Posters, Transit) 19. Point of Purchase20. Premiums, Novelties 21. Product Samples 22. Special Events Mktg. 23. Spot Radio 24. Spot T.V. 25. Weekly Newsp. 26. Yellow Page Adv.

Atlantic Coast Federal Corporation — (Continued)

Denise A. Horton *(Market Pres-Florida)*
Diane S. Wade *(Sr VP-Corp Banking)*
Advertising Agency:
Caraway.Grammel.Group
4899 Belfort Rd Ste 202
Jacksonville, FL 32256
Tel.: (904) 208-5244
Fax: (904) 208-5245
Toll Free: (877) 442-0386

ATLANTIC SOUTHERN FINANCIAL GROUP, INC.

1701 Bass Rd
Macon, GA 31210
Tel.: (478) 476-2170
Fax: (478) 405-9157
E-mail: cellis@newsouthernbank.com
Web Site: www.atlanticsouthernbank.com
Approx. Rev.: $50,851,655
Approx. Number Employees: 162
Business Description:
Bank Holding Company
S.I.C.: 6712; 6029; 6035
N.A.I.C.S.: 551111; 522110; 522120
Advertising Expenditures: $344,680
Media: 17
Personnel:
William A. Fickling, III *(Chm)*
Edward P. Loomis, Jr. *(Pres)*
Carol W. Soto *(CFO & Exec VP)*
Brands & Products:
ATLANTICSOUTHERN FINANCIAL GROUP
Advertising Agency:
HHB Advertising
1873 Hardeman Ave Ste A
Macon, GA 31201
Tel.: (478) 464-0272
Fax: (478) 464-0236

AXEL JOHNSON INC.

(Sub. of Axel Johnson Gruppen AB)
155 Spring St 6th Fl
New York, NY 10012
Tel.: (646) 291-2445
Fax: (212) 966-9516
Web Site: www.axeljohnson.com
Approx. Managed Assets: $4,800,000,000
Year Founded: 1920
Business Description:
Investment Services
S.I.C.: 6289
N.A.I.C.S.: 523999
Export
Advertising Expenditures: $1,000,000
Media: 4-6
Distr.: Natl.
Budget Set: Nov.
Personnel:
Michael D. Milligan *(Pres & CEO)*
Ben J. Hennelly *(CFO & Exec VP)*
John C. Pascale *(Exec VP-Tax)*
Erika M. Cafarella *(Mgr-Corp Dev)*

AZOY TAX

4901 NW 17th Way Ste 301
Fort Lauderdale, FL 33309
Tel.: (954) 229-1652
Fax: (954) 229-1653
E-mail: eazoy@azoytax.com
Web Site: www.azoytax.com
Business Description:
Tax Controversies Specialist; IRS Representation, Business Consultation, Tax Preparation & Accounting & Payroll
S.I.C.: 7291; 6371
N.A.I.C.S.: 541213; 525990
Media: 9-25
Personnel:
Eduardo A. Azoy *(Pres)*

BAKER BOYER BANCORP

7 W Main St
Walla Walla, WA 99362
Tel.: (509) 525-2000
Fax: (509) 526-1444
Toll Free: (800) 234-7923
E-mail: info@bakerboyer.com
Web Site: www.bakerboyer.com
Approx. Rev.: $30,333,000
Approx. Number Employees: 170
Year Founded: 1986
Business Description:
Bank Holding Company
S.I.C.: 6029; 6712
N.A.I.C.S.: 522110; 551111
Advertising Expenditures: $204,000
Personnel:
Megan F. Clubb *(Chm, Pres & CEO)*
Mark A. Hess *(COO & Exec VP)*
Jon S. Bren *(Exec VP & Mgr-Wealth Mgmt Svcs Div)*
Lyle W. Hansen *(Exec VP & Mgr-Banking)*
Brands & Products:
BAKER BOYER
GUIDING YOU TO A BRIGHTER FINANCIAL FUTURE

BALTIMORE COUNTY SAVINGS BANK

(Sub. of BCSB Bancorp, Inc.)
4111 E Joppa Rd Ste 300
Baltimore, MD 21236-2289
Tel.: (410) 256-5000
Fax: (410) 529-0147
E-mail: info@bcsb.net
Web Site: www.baltcosavings.com
Sales Range: $100-124.9 Million
Approx. Number Employees: 50
Business Description:
Banking Services
S.I.C.: 6035
N.A.I.C.S.: 522120
Media: 7-8-13
Personnel:
Joseph J. Bouffard *(Pres & CEO)*
Anthony Cole *(CFO & Exec VP)*
Dave Meadows *(Gen Counsel, Sec & Exec VP)*
Advertising Agency:
A. Bright Idea
210 Archer St
Bel Air, MD 21014
Tel.: (410) 836-7180
Fax: (410) 836-0186

BANCFIRST CORPORATION

101 N Broadway Ave Ste 101
Oklahoma City, OK 73102
Tel.: (405) 270-1086
Fax: (405) 270-1089
E-mail: rforaker@bancfirst.com
Web Site: www.bancfirst.com
Approx. Rev.: $240,836,000
Approx. Number Employees: 1,532
Year Founded: 1984
Business Description:
Bank Holding Company
S.I.C.: 6712; 6029
N.A.I.C.S.: 551111; 522110
Advertising Expenditures: $4,720,000
Personnel:
William O. Johnstone *(Vice Chm & CEO-Council Oak Partners LLC)*
K. Gordon Greer *(Vice Chm)*
Dennis L. Brand *(Pres & CEO-BancFirst)*
David E. Rainbolt *(CEO-BancFirst Corp)*
Randy P. Foraker *(Treas, Exec VP & Chief Risk Officer)*
James R. Daniel *(Principal Exec Officer)*
H. E. Rainbolt *(Principal Exec Officer)*
Scott Copeland *(Exec VP)*
Joe T. Shockley, Jr. *(Exec VP)*
Robert M. Neville *(Sr VP-Investments)*
J. Michael Rogers *(Sr VP-HR)*

BANCLEASING INC.

(Sub. of Varilease Technology Finance Group Inc.)
3409 N Central Expy Ste 200
Plano, TX 75023
Tel.: (972) 562-7480
Fax: (972) 562-2082
Toll Free: (877) 274-5327
E-mail: info@bancleasing.com
Web Site: www.bancleasing.com
Approx. Number Employees: 30
Year Founded: 1998
Business Description:
Financial Information Technology
S.I.C.: 7359
N.A.I.C.S.: 532490
Advertising Expenditures: $300,000
Media: 10
Brands & Products:
CASH FLOW LEASE

BANCO POPULAR NORTH AMERICA - CALIFORNIA REGIONAL OFFICE

(Branch of Banco Popular North America)
888 S Disneyland Dr Ste 500
Anaheim, CA 92802-1846
Tel.: (714) 864-5056
Fax: (714) 864-5101
Web Site: www.bancopopular.com
Sales Range: $75-99.9 Million
Approx. Number Employees: 248
Year Founded: 1993
Business Description:
Commercial Banking Services
S.I.C.: 6029
N.A.I.C.S.: 522110
Media: 2-4-7-8-9-10-14-18-22-23-24-25
Personnel:
Adrianna Staker *(Mgr-Mktg & Creative Svcs)*

BANCORP OF NEW JERSEY, INC.

1365 Palisade Ave
Fort Lee, NJ 07024
Tel.: (201) 944-8600
Fax: (201) 944-8618
Web Site: www.bonj.net
Approx. Rev.: $17,344,000
Approx. Number Employees: 41
Year Founded: 2006
Business Description:
Bank Holding Company
S.I.C.: 6712
N.A.I.C.S.: 551111
Advertising Expenditures: $51,000
Media: 7-8
Personnel:
Albert F. Buzzetti *(Chm & CEO)*
Michael Lesler *(Pres & COO)*
Diane M. Spinner *(Exec VP & Chief Admin Officer)*

BANCORPSOUTH, INC.

1 Mississippi Plz 201 S Spring St
Tupelo, MS 38804
Mailing Address:
PO Box 789
Tupelo, MS 38802-0789
Tel.: (662) 680-2000
Fax: (662) 678-7263
Toll Free: (888) 797-7711
E-mail: ebanking@bxs.com
Web Site: www.bancorpsouth.com
Approx. Rev.: $582,762,000
Approx. Number Employees: 4,311
Year Founded: 1982
Business Description:
Bank Holding Company
S.I.C.: 6712; 6029; 6035; 6211
N.A.I.C.S.: 551111; 522110; 522120; 523110
Advertising Expenditures: $6,377,000
Media: 2-7-8-9-13-18-20-23-24-26
Distr.: Direct to Consumer; Reg.
Budget Set: Oct. -Nov.
Personnel:
Aubrey B. Patterson, Jr. *(Chm & CEO)*
James Virgil Kelley *(Pres & COO)*
William L. Prater *(CFO)*
Gary C. Bonds *(Principal Acctg Officer & Sr VP)*
David N. Wright *(Reg Pres)*
Don J. Giardina *(Pres-Birmingham Branch)*
Ty Warren *(Pres-Little Rock-AR)*
Cathy S. Freeman *(Sec & Exec VP)*
Larry D Bateman *(Exec VP)*
Gary R. Harder *(Exec VP)*
James Ronald Hodges *(Exec VP)*
W. James Threadgill, Jr. *(Exec VP)*
W. O. Jones *(Sr VP)*
Will Fisackerly *(VP & Dir-IR)*
Brands & Products:
BANCORP SOUTH
RIGHT WHERE YOU ARE
Advertising Agencies:
Stone Ward
225 E Markham St Ste 450
Little Rock, AR 72201-1629
Tel.: (501) 375-3003
Fax: (501) 375-8314

Tom Robinson Associates
One Mississippi Plaza, Ste. 609
Tupelo, MS 38801
Tel.: (662) 844-2654
(Banking Services)

BANCTRUST

(Formerly The Peoples BancTrust Company, Inc.)
(Sub. of BancTrust Financial Group, Inc.)
310 Broad St
Selma, AL 36701
Tel.: (334) 875-1000
Fax: (334) 875-1010

Key to Media (For complete agency information see *The Advertising Red Books-Agencies* edition):
1. Bus. Publs. 2. Cable T.V. 3. Catalogs & Directories. 4. Co-op Adv. 5. Consumer Mags. 6. D.M. to Bus. Estab.7. D.M. to Consumers 8. Daily Newsp. 9. Exhibits/Trade Shows 10. Foreign 11. Infomercial 12. Internet Adv.13. Multimedia 14. Network Radio 15. Network T.V. 16. Newsp. Distr. Mags. 17. Other 18. Outdoor (Posters, Transit) 19. Point of Purchase20. Premiums, Novelties 21. Product Samples 22. Special Events Mktg. 23. Spot Radio 24. Spot T.V. 25. Weekly Newsp. 26. Yellow Page Adv.

Approx. Int. Income: $62,860,054
Approx. Number Employees: 275
Year Founded: 1984
Business Description:
Bank Holding Company
S.I.C.: 6029; 6712
N.A.I.C.S.: 522110; 551111
Advertising Expenditures: $70,000
Media: 8-9-18-23
Personnel:
John G. Chisolm *(Exec VP-Comml Div)*
Roberta Leach *(Dir-Mktg)*

BANCTRUST FINANCIAL GROUP, INC.

100 Saint Joseph St
Mobile, AL 36652
Tel.: (251) 431-7800
Fax: (251) 431-7851
E-mail: customerservicesbtfg@banktrustonline.com
Web Site: www.banctrustfinancialgroupinc.com
Approx. Rev.: $104,480,000
Approx. Number Employees: 549
Year Founded: 1986
Business Description:
Bank Holding Company
S.I.C.: 6712; 6029
N.A.I.C.S.: 551111; 522110
Advertising Expenditures: $186,000
Media: 17
Personnel:
W. Bibb Lamar, Jr. *(Pres & CEO)*
F. Michael Johnson *(CFO, Sec & Exec VP)*
Bruce C. Finley, Jr. *(Exec VP & Sr Loan Officer)*
Edward T. Livingston *(Pres-Central Div-BankTrust & Exec VP)*
Michael D. Fitzhugh *(Exec VP)*
Brands & Products:
BANC TRUST
OUR INTEREST IS YOU

BANGOR SAVINGS BANK INC.

3 State St
Bangor, ME 04401
Tel.: (207) 942-5211
Fax: (207) 941-2713
Toll Free: (877) BANGOR1
E-mail: CustomerService@bangor.com
Web Site: www.bangor.com
E-Mail For Key Personnel:
Marketing Director: moorej@bangorsavings.com
Approx. Int. Income: $92,900,000
Approx. Number Employees: 600
Year Founded: 1852
Business Description:
Financial Services
S.I.C.: 6035
N.A.I.C.S.: 522120
Import Export
Personnel:
James Conlon *(Pres & CEO)*
Bruce Nickerson *(CFO, Treas & Exec VP)*
John A. Moore *(Sr VP)*
Gary A. Quintiliani *(Sr VP)*
Advertising Agency:
FORGE worldwide
142 Berkeley St
Boston, MA 02116
Tel.: (617) 262-4800

BANK LEUMI USA

(Sub. of Bank Leumi Le-Israel B.M.)
579 5th Ave
New York, NY 10017-1917
Tel.: (917) 542-2343
Fax: (917) 542-2254
Toll Free: (800) 892-5430
Web Site: www.bankleumiusa.com
Approx. Int. Income: $180,846,000
Approx. Number Employees: 447
Year Founded: 1954
Business Description:
International Banking
S.I.C.: 6029
N.A.I.C.S.: 522110
Media: 2-4-8-9-17-20-22-25
Distr.: Direct to Consumer; Reg.
Budget Set: Oct.
Personnel:
Uzi Rosen *(CEO)*
Sidney Gottesman *(COO)*
Ira Romoff *(Exec VP & Risk Mgr & Chief Credit Officer)*
John P. McGann *(Chief Compliance Officer-Branch Banking, Exec VP & Dir-HR)*
Raymond P. Cooney *(Chief Risk Officer & Sr VP)*
Maryellen Chomsky *(VP & Compliance Officer)*
Robert R. Giordano *(Treas & Exec VP)*
Michael W. Santimauro *(Treas & Sr VP-Admin)*
Yair Talmor *(Sr Exec VP & Dir-Ops)*
Chaim Fromowitz *(Exec VP & Dir-Banking-Intl Svcs)*
Herzl Rahimi *(Sr VP & Chief Internal Auditor)*
Gloria Bucher *(Sr VP-Corp Fin)*
Ron Ciborowski *(Sr VP-Loan Opers & Check Processing)*
Michaela Klein *(Sr VP-Intl Lending)*
Joseph A. Sciarillo *(Sr VP)*
Richard Silverstein *(Sr VP)*
Haim V. Sion *(Sr VP)*
Hillel Waxman *(Sr VP-Preferred Customer Unit)*
Leslie B. Kahle *(VP & Dir-Mktg)*
Brands & Products:
BANK LEUMI

BANK OF AMERICA

(Unit of Bank of America, N.A.)
1100 N King St
Wilmington, DE 19884-0131
Tel.: (302) 453-9930
Fax: (302) 458-3100
Web Site: www.bankofamerica.com
Sales Range: $1-4.9 Billion
Approx. Number Employees: 26,300
Year Founded: 1982
Business Description:
Bank Holding Company
S.I.C.: 6029; 6099; 6712
N.A.I.C.S.: 522110; 522320; 551111
Advertising Expenditures: $421,965,000
Media: 7-8-11-13-31
Personnel:
Randolph D. Lerner *(Chm)*
Steffen W. Parratt *(Mng Dir)*
Kenneth Vecchione *(CFO)*
Michael Bailey *(Officer-Mortgage Loan)*
Anne M. Finucane *(Officer-Mktg & Strategy-Global)*
Kathryn Condon *(Sr VP)*
Stephen R. Crowley *(Sr VP-Payments Delivery Exec)*
Jim Denny *(Sr VP-eCommerce Program Mgmt)*
Emily McCormack *(VP & Mgr-Social Media)*
Aimee Wroten *(Asst VP & Specialist-Ecommerce Mktg)*
Cathy Walton *(Mgr-Bus Change Capability)*
Brands & Products:
MBNA
WORLDPOINTS
Advertising Agency:
Starcom USA
35 W Wacker Dr
Chicago, IL 60601
Tel.: (312) 220-3535
Fax: (312) 220-6530
Media Agency of Record

BANK OF AMERICA CORPORATION

Bank of America Corporate Ctr 100 N Tryon St
Charlotte, NC 28255-0001
Tel.: (704) 386-5681
Fax: (704) 386-6699
Web Site: www.bankofamerica.com
Approx. Rev.: $134,194,000,000
Approx. Number Employees: 288,000
Year Founded: 1960
Business Description:
Bank Holding Company; Commercial, Investment & Wealth Management Banking Services
S.I.C.: 6029; 6141; 6211; 6282; 6289; 6712; 6733
N.A.I.C.S.: 522110; 522210; 523110; 523920; 523930; 523991; 523999; 551111
Import Export
Media: 3-13-15-17-31
Personnel:
Charles O. Holliday, Jr. *(Chm)*
Charles H. Noski *(Vice Chm)*
Brian T. Moynihan *(CEO)*
Joseph T. Buckley *(Mng Dir & Restaurant Analyst)*
Bruce Thompson *(CFO)*
David C. Darnell *(Co-COO)*
Thomas K. Montag *(Co-COO)*
Anne M. Finucane *(CMO & Chief Strategy Officer)*
J. Steele Alphin *(Chief Admin Officer & Exec-Global Personnel)*
Neil A. Cotty *(Chief Acctg Officer)*
Bob Arth *(Pres-Northeast US-Bus Capital Div)*
Keith T. Banks *(Pres-Global Wealth & Investment Mgmt)*
Catherine P. Bessant *(Pres-Global Corp Banking)*
Charles F. Bowman *(Pres-Market)*
Rick Bregman *(Pres-Market)*
Bruce Denby *(Pres-Chicago Market)*
Barbara J. Desoer *(Pres-Home Loans & Insurance)*
Diane Dickerson *(Pres-Kansas State)*
John Mostofi *(Pres-Western Div)*
Martin Richards *(Pres-Market)*
Thomas C. Woodward *(Pres-Pennsylvania Market)*
Edward P. O'Keefe *(Gen Counsel)*
Harold E. Blatt *(Exec VP-Southeast & Atlantic US)*
Joyce White *(Exec VP)*
Stephen R. Hinrichs *(Sr VP & Mgr-Mktg)*
Philip D. Armstrong *(Sr VP-Mktg, Exec-Online & Mobile Banking)*
James D. Cockey *(Sr VP-Central US & Canada)*
Shawn Lancelot *(Sr VP)*
Jay Livingston *(Sr VP-Global Mktg)*
Joseph P. Powers *(Sr VP)*
Craig Rosato *(SVP & Consumer Risk Exec)*
George Sherman *(Sr VP)*
Xavier Soosai *(Sr VP-Platform Solutions & Tech Refresh)*
Hari Gopalkrishnan *(Mng Dir-IT)*
David J. Flannery *(Global Head-Leveraged Fin)*
Claire Huang *(Head-Mktg)*
Jim Smith *(Asst VP & Consultant-System)*
Kevin Stitt *(Dir-IR)*
Advertising Agencies:
BBDO New York
1285 Ave of the Americas 7th Fl
New York, NY 10019-6028
Tel.: (212) 459-5000
US Olympic Team Banking

BBDO North America
1285 Ave of the Americas
New York, NY 10019-6028
Tel.: (212) 459-5000
Fax: (212) 459-6814

BBDO Worldwide Inc.
(Sub. of Omnicom Group, Inc.)
1285 Ave of the Americas
New York, NY 10019-6028
Tel.: (212) 459-5000
Fax: (212) 459-6645

BLM Quantum
247 Tottenham Court Road
London, W1T 7QX, United Kingdom
Tel.: (44) 207 182 6400
Fax: (44) 20 7287 8769

Bodden Partners
102 Madison Ave
New York, NY 10016-7417
Tel.: (212) 328-1111
Fax: (212) 328-1100

The Brand Union London
11-33 Saint John Street
London, EC1M 4PJ, United Kingdom
Tel.: (44) 20 7559 7000
Fax: (44) 20 7559 7001

D.L. Blair Inc.
1548 Front St
Blair, NE 68008-1641
Tel.: (402) 426-4701
Fax: (402) 426-4706

Don Jagoda Associates, Inc.
100 Marcus Dr
Melville, NY 11747-4229
Tel.: (631) 454-1800
Fax: (631) 454-1834

Fishburn Hedges
77 Kingsway
London, WC2B 6SR, United Kingdom
Tel.: (44) 20 7839 4321
Fax: (44) 20 7242 4202

Key to Media (For complete agency information see *The Advertising Red Books-Agencies* edition):
1. Bus. Publs. 2. Cable T.V. 3. Catalogs & Directories. 4. Co-op Adv. 5. Consumer Mags. 6. D.M. to Bus. Estab.7. D.M. to Consumers
8. Daily Newsp. 9. Exhibits/Trade Shows 10. Foreign 11. Infomercial 12. Internet Adv.13. Multimedia 14. Network Radio
15. Network T.V. 16. Newsp. Distr. Mags. 17. Other 18. Outdoor (Posters, Transit) 19. Point of Purchase20. Premiums, Novelties
21. Product Samples 22. Special Events Mktg. 23. Spot Radio 24. Spot T.V. 25. Weekly Newsp. 26. Yellow Page Adv.

Bank of America Corporation — (Continued)

FutureBrand
300 Park Ave S 7th FL
New York, NY 10010
Tel.: (212) 931-6300
Fax: (212) 931-6310

Hauser Advertising Inc.
309 Bellino Dr
Pacific Palisades, CA 90272
Tel.: (310) 459-5911
Fax: (310) 459-5919

hawkeye
325 Arlington Ave Ste 700
Charlotte, NC 28203
Tel.: (704) 344-7900
Fax: (704) 344-7920

hawkeye
2828 Routh St Ste 300
Dallas, TX 75201
Tel.: (214) 659-5615
Fax: (214) 747-1897

Innis Maggiore
4715 Whipple Ave NW
Canton, OH 44718-2651
Tel.: (330) 492-5500
Fax: (330) 492-5568
Toll Free: (800) 460-4111

Lopez Negrete Communications, Inc.
3336 Richmond Ave Ste 200
Houston, TX 77098
Tel.: (713) 877-8777
Fax: (713) 877-8796
Hispanic Advertising

Lopez Negrete Communications West, Inc.
2222 W Olive Ave
Burbank, CA 91506
Tel.: (713) 877-8777
Fax: (818) 524-2016
Toll Free: (888) 398-0657

Mangos
10 Great Valley Pkwy
Malvern, PA 19355-1316
Tel.: (610) 296-2555
Fax: (610) 640-9291

Octagon
800 Connecticut Ave 2nd Fl
Norwalk, CT 06854
Tel.: (203) 354-7400
Fax: (203) 354-7401

Organic, Inc.
555 Market St 4th Fl
San Francisco, CA 94105
Tel.: (415) 581-5300
Fax: (415) 581-5400

Orion Trading
1 Dag Hammarskjod Plz 2nd Fl
New York, NY 10017
Tel.: (212) 605-7000
Fax: (212) 605-7448

PointRoll Inc.
951 E Hector St
Conshohocken, PA 19428
Tel.: (267) 558-1300
Fax: (267) 285-1141
Toll Free: (800) 203-6956

Response Media, Inc.
3155 Medlock Bridge Rd
Norcross, GA 30071-1423
Tel.: (770) 451-5478
Fax: (770) 451-4929

RF Binder
950 3rd Ave 7th Fl
New York, NY 10022
Tel.: (212) 994-7600
Fax: (212) 994-7597

RF Binder Partners
160 Gould St Ste 115
Needham, MA 02494-2300
Tel.: (781) 455-8250
Fax: (781) 455-8233

Riester-Robb
132 W Pierpont Ave Ste 300
Salt Lake City, UT 84101-1102
Tel.: (801) 532-7333
Fax: (801) 532-6029

SangAm & Associates
3435 Wilshire Blvd Ste 2880
Los Angeles, CA 90010
Tel.: (213) 252-6320
Fax: (213) 252-9055

Sportsmark Management Group, Ltd. (d/b/a Sportsmark)
781 Lincoln Ave Ste 380
San Rafael, CA 94901
Tel.: (415) 461-5801
Fax: (415) 461-5804

Starcom USA
35 W Wacker Dr
Chicago, IL 60601
Tel.: (312) 220-3535
Fax: (312) 220-6530

Story Worldwide
87 Wall St
Seattle, WA 98121
Tel.: (206) 336-3001
Fax: (206) 336-3030

TPN Inc.
9400 N Central Expwy Ste 1500
Dallas, TX 75231-5044
Tel.: (214) 692-1522
Fax: (214) 692-8316

Waylon Ad, Inc.
100 S 4th St Ste 600
Saint Louis, MO 63102-1822
Tel.: (314) 231-6123
Fax: (314) 231-6012

The Weinstein Organization, Inc.
1 S Wacker Dr Ste 1670
Chicago, IL 60606-4670
Tel.: (312) 214-2900
Fax: (312) 214-1120

Wong, Doody, Crandall, Wiener
1011 Western Ave Ste 900
Seattle, WA 98104
Tel.: (206) 624-5325
Fax: (206) 624-2369

Wong, Doody, Crandall, Wiener
8500 Steller Dr Ste 5
Culver City, CA 90232-2427
Tel.: (310) 280-7800
Fax: (310) 280-7780

Wunderman
(Worldwide Headquarters)
285 Madison Ave
New York, NY 10017
Tel.: (212) 941-3000
Fax: (212) 210-5454

BANK OF AMERICA GLOBAL WEALTH & INVESTMENT MANAGEMENT

(Div. of Bank of America, N.A.)
100 Federal St
Boston, MA 02110-1802
Tel.: (866) 826-8989
Fax: (617) 434-6943
Toll Free: (800) 841-4000
Web Site: www.bankofamerica.com
Approx. Rev.: $7,923,000,000
Approx. Number Employees: 47,500
Business Description:
Investment & Wealth Management Services
S.I.C.: 6282; 6211; 6733
N.A.I.C.S.: 523920; 523110; 523930; 523991
Media: 2-3-6-7-8-9-10-13-18-19-22-23-24-25
Distr.: Natl.
Budget Set: Sept.
Personnel:
Colin Mulligan *(Sr VP-Sls Mgmt)*
Claire Huang *(Head-Mktg)*

BANK OF AMERICAN FORK

33 E Main St
American Fork, UT 84003
Tel.: (801) 756-7681
Fax: (801) 763-6666
E-mail: customercare@bankaf.com
Web Site: www.bankaf.com
Sales Range: $25-49.9 Million
Approx. Number Employees: 250
Year Founded: 1913
Business Description:
Banking Services
S.I.C.: 6029
N.A.I.C.S.: 522110
Media: 7-8-13-20
Personnel:
Richard T. Beard *(Pres & CEO)*
Brian Thompson *(CFO)*
Tracey Larson *(Asst VP-Org Dev & Dir-Policy)*
Chaille Mackie *(Asst VP & Mgr-Ops)*
Mark Purcell *(Asst VP)*
Lynette Hilgenberg *(Dir-Mktg)*
Cooper Thomas *(Asst Mgr-Ops)*
Angie Allen *(Mgr-Ops-Saratoga Springs)*
Michael Miner *(Mgr-Ops-Pleasant Grove)*
Kerry Robinson *(Mgr-Ops-Orem)*
Shereen Street *(Mgr-Ops-Murray)*
Advertising Agency:
Riester-Robb
132 W Pierpont Ave Ste 300
Salt Lake City, UT 84101-1102
Tel.: (801) 532-7333
Fax: (801) 532-6029

BANK OF COMMERCE HOLDINGS

1901 Churn Creek Rd
Redding, CA 96002
Tel.: (530) 772-3952
Tel.: (530) 722-3939
Toll Free: (800) 421-2575
E-mail: main@reddingbankofcommerce.com
Web Site:
www.reddingbankofcommerce.com
Approx. Rev.: $62,209,000
Approx. Number Employees: 313
Year Founded: 1982
Business Description:
Bank Holding Company
S.I.C.: 6712; 6029
N.A.I.C.S.: 551111; 522110
Advertising Expenditures: $322,000
Personnel:
Kenneth R. Gifford, Jr. *(Chm)*
Patrick J. Moty *(Pres & CEO)*
Samuel D. Jimenez *(CFO & Exec VP)*
Caryn A. Blais *(CIO & Sr VP)*
Debbie A. Sylvester *(Chief Admin Officer & Sr VP)*
Randall S. Eslick *(Reg Pres-Roseville Div)*
Linda J. Miles *(Exec VP & Asst Sec)*
Theodore Cumming *(Sr VP & Lending Grp Mgr)*
Robert A. Matranga *(Sr VP & Lending Grp Mgr)*
Robert J. O'Neil *(Sr VP & Reg Credit Mgr-Roseville Bank of Commerce)*
Brands & Products:
REDDING BANK OF COMMERCE
ROSEVILLE BANK OF COMMERCE

BANK OF FLORIDA CORPORATION

1185 Immokalee Rd
Naples, FL 34110
Tel.: (239) 254-2100
Toll Free: (866) 226-5352
Web Site:
www.bankoffloridaonline.com
Approx. Rev.: $80,332,000
Approx. Number Employees: 218
Year Founded: 1998
Business Description:
Bank Holding Company
S.I.C.: 6712; 6029
N.A.I.C.S.: 551111; 522110
Advertising Expenditures: $500,000
Personnel:
Michael T. Putziger *(Chm)*
Joe B. Cox *(CEO & CFO)*
Craig D. Sherman *(Exec VP)*

BANK OF GRANITE CORPORATION

23 N Main St
Granite Falls, NC 28630
Mailing Address:
PO Box 128
Granite Falls, NC 28630-0128
Tel.: (828) 496-2000
Fax: (828) 496-2077
E-mail: bfry@bankofgranite.com
Web Site: www.bankofgranite.com
Approx. Rev.: $53,582,000
Approx. Number Employees: 195
Year Founded: 1906
Business Description:
Bank Holding Company
S.I.C.: 6712; 6029; 6141
N.A.I.C.S.: 551111; 522110; 522291
Media: 3-7-8-18-20-23-24-26
Personnel:
John N. Bray *(Chm)*
Paul M. Fleetwood, III *(Vice Chm)*
R. Scott Anderson *(Pres, CEO & Sec)*

Key to Media (For complete agency information see *The Advertising Red Books-Agencies* edition):
1. Bus. Publs. 2. Cable T.V. 3. Catalogs & Directories. 4. Co-op Adv. 5. Consumer Mags. 6. D.M. to Bus. Estab.7. D.M. to Consumers 8. Daily Newsp. 9. Exhibits/Trade Shows 10. Foreign 11. Infomercial 12. Internet Adv.13. Multimedia 14. Network Radio 15. Network T.V. 16. Newsp. Distr. Mags. 17. Other 18. Outdoor (Posters, Transit) 19. Point of Purchase20. Premiums, Novelties 21. Product Samples 22. Special Events Mktg. 23. Spot Radio 24. Spot T.V. 25. Weekly Newsp. 26. Yellow Page Adv.

Jerry A. Felts *(CFO & COO)*
D. Mark Stephens *(CIO & Sr VP)*
Gayle H. Harris *(Chief Credit Officer & Sr VP)*
Karen Beal Warlick *(Chief Admin Officer & Sr VP)*
Cindy E. Hamrick *(VP & Officer-SEC Reporting)*
Jeff W. Prince *(Officer-Banking)*
Sheila R. Taylor *(VP & Dir-Training)*
Donna M. Harris *(Asst VP)*
Angela R. Lovelace *(Asst VP)*
Andrea J. McGowan *(Asst VP)*
Cheryl M. Mrozek *(Asst VP)*

Advertising Agency:
E.B. Wall + Associates
1520 Harper Ave NW
Lenoir, NC 28645
Tel.: (828) 757-0047
Fax: (828) 758-7394

BANK OF HAWAII CORPORATION

130 Merchant St
Honolulu, HI 96813
Mailing Address:
PO Box 2900
Honolulu, HI 96846-0001
Tel.: (808) 537-8580
Fax: (808) 537-8440
Toll Free: (888) 643-3888
E-mail: corpcommunication@boh.com
Web Site: www.boh.com
E-Mail For Key Personnel:
Public Relations:
corpcommunication@boh.com

Approx. Rev.: $720,509,000
Approx. Number Employees: 2,400
Year Founded: 1897

Business Description:
Bank Holding Company; Commercial Banking & Financial Services
S.I.C.: 6712; 6029; 6211
N.A.I.C.S.: 551111; 522110; 523110
Advertising Expenditures: $5,000,000

Media: 1-2-3-4-5-6-7-8-9-10-11-13-18-19-20-22-23-24-25-26
Distr.: Direct to Consumer; Intl.; Natl.
Budget Set: Aug.

Personnel:
Peter S. Ho *(Chm, Pres & CEO)*
Kent T. Lucien *(Vice Chm & CFO)*
LeAnn R. Piper *(VP & Sr Trust Officer-Personal Trust Dept)*
Kenneth M. Sheffield *(VP-Trust & Private Client Svcs)*
Lewis Slusher, Jr. *(VP & Compliance Officer-Corp Compliance Dept)*
Lea M. Nakamura *(Sr VP-Treasury Dept)*
James C. Polk *(Exec VP)*
Charlene Fernandez *(Sr VP & Mgr-Ops/Underwriting)*
Shanae A. Souza *(Sr VP-Mortgage Banking Div)*
Darlene-Inez Kekoolani *(Sr VP-HR & Mgr-Compensation & Benefits)*
Coleen Shoji *(Sr VP & Mgr)*
Diane Y. Higa *(Sr VP)*
Ai Wah Ng *(Sr VP-Wholesale Credit)*
Dorinda N. Collier *(VP-Customer Relationship Center)*
Debra Kenui *(VP & Mgr-Cash Mgmt Svc)*
Robyn Tanaka *(VP & Mgr-Retail Credit Analytics & Reporting)*
Marlene J. L. Pestana-Gualdarama *(Asst VP & Mgr-Contact Center)*

Brands & Products:
BANK OF HAWAII
PACIFIC CENTURY BANK
PACIFIC CENTURY LEASING

THE BANK OF KENTUCKY FINANCIAL CORPORATION

111 Lookout Farm Dr
Crestview Hills, KY 41017
Mailing Address:
PO Box 577
Florence, KY 41022
Tel.: (859) 372-9740
Fax: (857) 824-8729
E-mail: info@bankofkyhb.com
Web Site: www.bankofkyhb.com
Approx. Rev.: $87,396,000
Approx. Number Employees: 298
Year Founded: 1993
Business Description:
Bank Holding Company
S.I.C.: 6712; 6029
N.A.I.C.S.: 551111; 522110
Advertising Expenditures: $1,168,000
Media: 7-8-13
Personnel:
Rodney S. Cain *(Chm)*
Robert W. Zapp *(Pres & CEO)*
Martin J. Gerrety *(CFO & Exec VP)*

BANK OF MARIN BANCORP

504 Redwood Blvd Pell Plaza
Novato, CA 94947
Mailing Address:
PO Box 2039
Novato, CA 94948
Tel.: (415) 763-4520
E-mail: nancyboatwright@bankofmarin.com
Web Site: www.bankofmarin.com
Approx. Rev.: $66,878,000
Approx. Number Employees: 203
Business Description:
Bank Holding Company
S.I.C.: 6712; 6029
N.A.I.C.S.: 551111; 522110
Advertising Expenditures: $459,000
Personnel:
Joel Sklar *(Chief Medical Officer-Marin General Hospital & Chm)*
Russell A. Colombo *(Pres & CEO)*
Christina J. Cook *(CFO & Exec VP)*
Kevin K. Coonan *(Chief Credit Officer & Exec VP)*
Peter Pelham *(Exec VP)*
Nancy Rinaldi Boatright *(Sr VP & Asst Corp Sec)*
Nancy Jones *(Mgr-Client Svcs)*

BANK OF MCKENNEY

20718 First St
McKenney, VA 23872
Tel.: (804) 478-4434
Fax: (804) 478-4704
Web Site: www.bankofmckenney.com
Approx. Rev.: $11,887,731
Approx. Number Employees: 63
Year Founded: 1906
Business Description:
Banking Services
S.I.C.: 6029
N.A.I.C.S.: 522110
Advertising Expenditures: $65,093
Media: 17
Personnel:
William D. Allen, III *(Chm)*
Richard M. Liles *(Pres & CEO)*
James B. Neville Jr. *(CFO & Exec VP)*
Lynda P. Cunningham *(COO & Sr VP)*
Michelle Stone Fitch *(First VP-Ops & Support)*
Mark H. Stevens *(First VP-Credit Admin)*

BANK OF NASHVILLE

(Sub. of Synovus Financial Corp.)
401 Church St
Nashville, TN 37219-8986
Tel.: (615) 271-2000
Fax: (615) 271-2119
E-mail: info@bankofnashville.com
Web Site: www.bankofnashville.com
Sales Range: $25-49.9 Million
Approx. Number Employees: 98
Business Description:
Commercial Banking Services
S.I.C.: 6029
N.A.I.C.S.: 522110
Advertising Expenditures: $1,000,000
Media: 4-13-18
Personnel:
J. Hunter Atkins *(Chm)*
Richard Brad *(Sr VP)*
Roger Cathey *(Sr VP)*
Michael Davenport *(Sr VP)*
Dwayne Snider *(Sr VP)*
Betty Benoit *(Mgr-Bus Dev)*
Advertising Agency:
Bill Hudson & Associates, Inc., Advertising & Public Relations
1701 W End Ave
Nashville, TN 37203
Tel.: (615) 259-9002
Fax: (615) 256-0105

THE BANK OF NEW YORK MELLON CORPORATION

1 Wall St
New York, NY 10286-0001
Tel.: (212) 495-1784
Fax: (212) 809-9528
Web Site: www.bnymellon.com
Approx. Rev.: $10,697,000,000
Approx. Number Employees: 48,000
Year Founded: 2007
Business Description:
Bank Holding Company
S.I.C.: 6141; 6029; 6712
N.A.I.C.S.: 522210; 522110; 551111
Media: 2-6-7-8-9-11-13-18-19-20-23-25
Distr.: Direct to Consumer; Natl.
Budget Set: Dec.
Personnel:
Gerald L. Hassell *(Chm, Pres & CEO)*
Andrew J. Bell *(Mng Dir)*
John M. Roy *(Mng Dir)*
Richard P. Stanley *(Mng Dir & Sr Counsel)*
Thomas P. Gibbons *(CFO)*
Kurt D. Woetzel *(Chief Admin Officer, Head-Global Ops & Tech)*
David Cruikshank *(Exec VP & CEO-Treasury Svcs)*
Timothy F. Keaney *(CEO-BNY Mellon Asset Servicing)*
Karen B. Peetz *(CEO-Fin Markets & Treas Svcs)*
Scott Freidenrich *(Treas & Exec VP)*
Thomas A. Price *(Treas & EVP)*
John A. Fiore *(Exec VP & Head-Investor Svcs Tech)*
Paul Bodart *(Exec VP)*
Thomas V. Ford *(Exec VP-Securities Lending Division)*
Andrew Gordon *(Exec VP)*
Richard F. Mahoney *(Exec VP)*
Fred J. Ricciardi *(Exec VP)*
Patrick Tadie *(Exec VP)*
James Vallone *(Exec VP)*
Ciro J. Vitiello *(Exec VP)*
Len Blaifeder *(VP & Dir-Adv & Direct Mktg)*
Advertising Agencies:
Avicom Marketing Communications
2120 Pewaukee Rd Ste 200
Waukesha, WI 53188
Tel.: (262) 547-8000
Fax: (262) 547-1900

Concept Farm
43 W 24th St 5th Fl
New York, NY 10010
Tel.: (212) 463-9939
Fax: (212) 463-7032

DDB New York
437 Madison Ave
New York, NY 10022-7001
Tel.: (212) 415-2000
Fax: (212) 415-3506

Silver Communications, Inc.
35 E 21st St 7th Fl
New York, NY 10010
Tel.: (212) 387-8500
Fax: (212) 387-7875

THE BANK OF NOVA SCOTIA

(d/b/a Scotiabank)
Scotia Plaza
Toronto, ON M5H 1H1, Canada
Tel.: (416) 866-6161
Fax: (416) 866-3750
Telex: WUI 6719400
E-mail: email@scotiabank.com
Web Site: www.scotiabank.com
Approx. Int. Income: $16,530,883,880
Approx. Number Employees: 70,772
Year Founded: 1832
Business Description:
International Banking Services
S.I.C.: 6029; 6035; 6163; 6211; 6282
N.A.I.C.S.: 522110; 522120; 522310; 523110; 523120; 523930
Advertising Expenditures: $244,670,000
Media: 5-9-11-13-15-19-20-22-25
Budget Set: June -July
Personnel:
Arthur Richard Andrew Scace *(Chm)*
Sarabjit S. Marwah *(Vice Chm & COO)*
Mike Durland *(Grp Head-Global Capital Markets, Co-CEO-Scotia Capital)*
Luc A. Vanneste *(CFO & Exec VP)*
Stephen Hart *(Chief Credit Officer & Exec VP)*
Timothy P. Hayward *(Exec VP & Chief Admin Officer-Intl Banking)*
Alberta G. Cefis *(Exec VP & Head-Global Transaction Banking)*
Wendy Hannam *(Exec VP-Sls & Svc, Products, Mktg & Intl Banking)*
Jeffrey C. Heath *(Exec VP & Grp Treas)*
Robin S. Hibberd *(Exec VP-Retail Products & Svcs-Canadian Banking)*

Key to Media (For complete agency information see *The Advertising Red Books-Agencies* edition):
1. Bus. Publs. 2. Cable T.V. 3. Catalogs & Directories. 4. Co-op Adv. 5. Consumer Mags. 6. D.M. to Bus. Estab.7. D.M. to Consumers 8. Daily Newsp. 9. Exhibits/Trade Shows 10. Foreign 11. Infomercial 12. Internet Adv.13. Multimedia 14. Network Radio 15. Network T.V. 16. Newsp. Distr. Mags. 17. Other 18. Outdoor (Posters, Transit) 19. Point of Purchase20. Premiums, Novelties 21. Product Samples 22. Special Events Mktg. 23. Spot Radio 24. Spot T.V. 25. Weekly Newsp. 26. Yellow Page Adv.

The Bank of Nova Scotia — (Continued)

Dieter W. Jentsch *(Exec VP-Latin America)*
Barbara Mason *(Exec VP-Wealth Mgmt)*
Kim B. Mckenzie *(Exec VP-IT & Solutions)*
Jane Rowe *(Exec VP)*
Brian Maloney *(Sr VP-Scotia Capital Project Fin)*
Patrick N. Rooney *(Sr VP-Corp Credit)*
Robert Atkinson *(VP-Real Estate & Hospitality Fin)*
Richard White *(VP-Brand & Mktg)*
Sylvia D. Chrominska *(Grp Head-Global HR & Comm)*
Stephen D. McDonald *(Head-Global Corp & Investment Banking)*
Christine Clouston *(Mgr-Client Relationships & Market Lead)*

Brands & Products:
AUTOPILOT
CASHSTOP
EXCELSIOR
EXECUTIVE MONEY MASTER
GETTING THERE SAVINGS PROGRAM
GICS WITH GUTS
GOLDCHOICE
MATCH-A-PAYMENT
MISS-A-PAYMENT
MONEY MASTER
PAY YOURSELF TOO PLAN
POWERCHEQUING
REALITY CHECK
SCOTIA
SCOTIA 2020
SCOTIA BANKING ADVANTAGE
SCOTIA BUSINESS LINK
SCOTIA CANAM
SCOTIA DIRECT
SCOTIA GAIN PLAN
SCOTIA LEASING
SCOTIA ONLINE
SCOTIA PLAN
SCOTIA PLUS
SCOTIA POWERCHEQUING
SCOTIA PROFESSIONAL
SCOTIA REWARDS
SCOTIA TOTAL EQUITY
SCOTIA ULTIMATE
SCOTIA VALUE
SCOTIABANK
SCOTIABANK VALUE
SCOTIABANK.CA
SCOTIABANK.COM
SCOTIABUSINESS
SCOTIABUSINESS ELECTRONIC BANKING
SCOTIACARD
SCOTIACLUB
SCOTIACONNECT
SCOTIAFARM
SCOTIAGOLD
SCOTIAGOLD PASSPORT
SCOTIALINE
SCOTIAPAY
TELESCOTIA
THINKING AHEAD
THE ULTIMATE
THE ULTIMATE LADDERED

BANK OF SOUTH CAROLINA CORPORATION

256 Meeting St
Charleston, SC 29401
Tel.: (843) 724-1500
Fax: (843) 724-1513
E-mail: information@banksc.com
Web Site: www.banksc.com
Approx. Rev.: $14,216,533
Approx. Number Employees: 71
Year Founded: 1986
Business Description:
Bank Holding Company
S.I.C.: 6712; 6029
N.A.I.C.S.: 551111; 522110
Media: 8
Personnel:
Hugh C. Lane, Jr. *(Pres & CEO)*
Sheryl G. Sharry *(CFO & Exec VP)*
Fleetwood S. Hassell *(Exec VP)*
Janice B. Stanley *(Asst Sec)*

BANK OF THE CAROLINAS CORPORATION

135 Boxwood Village Dr
Mocksville, NC 27028
Tel.: (336) 751-5755
Fax: (336) 751-4222
Web Site:
www.bankofthecarolinas.com
Approx. Rev.: $26,131,000
Approx. Number Employees: 108
Year Founded: 2006
Business Description:
Bank Holding Company
S.I.C.: 6712
N.A.I.C.S.: 551111
Advertising Expenditures: $228,000
Personnel:
Stephen R. Talbert *(Pres & CEO)*
Eric E. Rhodes *(CFO & Exec VP-Ops Center)*
Ed Jordan *(COO-Lexington & Exec VP)*
Harry E. Hill *(Exec VP)*

BANK OF THE CASCADES

(Sub. of CASCADE BANCORP)
1100 NW Wall St
Bend, OR 97701-1935
Tel.: (541) 617-3500
Tel.: (541) 385-6200
Fax: (541) 382-8780
Toll Free: (877) 617-3400
E-mail: cascades@botc.com
Web Site: www.botc.com
Sales Range: $75-99.9 Million
Approx. Number Employees: 220
Year Founded: 1976
Business Description:
Commercial & Consumer Banking
S.I.C.: 6029
N.A.I.C.S.: 522110
Media: 7-8-9-13-18-23-24
Personnel:
Michael J Delvin *(Pres & COO)*
Patricia L. Moss *(CEO)*
Gregory D. Newton *(CFO & Exec VP)*
Michael Allison *(Chief Credit Officer & Exec VP)*
Frank R. Weis *(Chief Credit Officer & Exec VP)*
Peggy L. Biss *(Chief HR Officer & Exec VP)*

BANK OF THE OZARKS, INC.

17901 Chenal Pkwy PO Box 8811
Little Rock, AR 72231-8811
Tel.: (501) 978-2265
Fax: (501) 978-2350
Toll Free: (800) 274-4482
E-mail: info@bankozarks.com
Web Site: www.bankozarks.com
Approx. Int. Income: $157,972,000
Approx. Number Employees: 881
Year Founded: 1981
Business Description:
Bank Holding Company
S.I.C.: 6712; 6029
N.A.I.C.S.: 551111; 522110
Advertising Expenditures: $2,076,000
Personnel:
George Gleason *(Chm & CEO)*
Mark Ross *(Vice Chm, Pres & COO)*
Greg McKinney *(CFO & Chief Acctg Officer)*
Danny Criner *(Pres-Northern Div)*
C. E. Dougan *(Pres-Western Div)*
Scott Hastings *(Pres-Leasing Div)*
Gene Holman *(Pres-Mortgage Div)*
Rex Kyle *(Pres-Trust & Wealth Mgmt Div)*
Darrel Russell *(Pres-Central Div)*
Michael J. Ptak *(Gen Counsel)*
Tim Hicks *(Sr VP-Corp Fin)*
John Jenkins *(Sr VP)*
George J. Schaefer *(VP & Mgr-Mtg Sls)*
Drew Barnes *(Asst VP-Treasury Mgmt)*
Meg Binz *(Asst VP)*
Marlene Bown *(Asst VP)*
Brannan Hester *(Asst VP)*
Jennifer Ruhlman *(Asst VP)*
Christie Davenport *(Mgr-Benton)*
Brands & Products:
BANK OF THE OZARKS

BANK OF THE SIERRA, INC.

86 N Main St
Porterville, CA 93257
Tel.: (559) 782-4900
Fax: (559) 782-4994
Toll Free: (888) 454-2265
E-mail: info@bankofthesierra.com
Web Site: www.bankofthesierra.com
Approx. Number Employees: 500
Year Founded: 1977
Business Description:
State Commercial Bank
S.I.C.: 6029
N.A.I.C.S.: 522110
Import Export
Media: 9
Personnel:
Morris A. Tharp *(Chm)*
James C. Holly *(Pres & CEO)*
Kenneth Taylor *(CFO & Exec VP)*
James F. Gardunio *(Chief Credit Officer & Exec VP)*
Kevin McPhaill *(Chief Banking Officer & Exec VP)*
Robert H. Tienken *(Sec)*
Richard H. Davis *(Sr VP & Dir-IT)*
Brands & Products:
BANK OF THE SIERRA
SIERRA HSA

BANK OF THE WEST

(Sub. of BancWest Corporation)
180 Montgomery St
San Francisco, CA 94104
Tel.: (925) 942-8300
Fax: (925) 943-1224
Toll Free: (800) 488-BANK
Web Site: www.bankofthewest.com
Approx. Number Employees: 10,700
Year Founded: 1874
Business Description:
Banking Services
S.I.C.: 6029
N.A.I.C.S.: 522110
Media: 4-7-8-9-13-18-20-23-24-26
Personnel:
J. Michael Shepherd *(Chm & CEO)*
Steve Glenn *(Vice Chm & Chief Admin Officer)*
Maura Markus *(Pres & COO)*
Andrew Rosen *(CMO)*
William Even *(Sr Exec VP & Chief Credit Officer)*
Donald R. Ward *(Chief Admin Officer & Sr Exec VP)*
Vanessa Washington *(Gen Counsel, Sec & Exec VP)*
Scott Germer *(Sr Exec VP & Mgr-Risk)*
Paul T. Wible *(Sr Exec VP-Natl Fin Grp)*
Norma J. Waters *(Exec VP & Specialty Products Head-Retail & Bus Banking)*
Susan H. Fowler *(Exec VP & Dir-HR)*
Ross Biatek *(Exec VP & Gen Auditor)*
Robert Dalrymple *(Exec VP-Great Plains Div)*
Mark Glasky *(Exec VP)*
James R. Kennedy *(Exec VP)*
Martin Resch *(Exec VP)*
Roger Sturdevant *(Exec VP)*
John Thomason *(Exec VP)*
Gina Wolley *(Exec VP)*
Ralph Anthony *(Sr VP-Fin Integration & Tax)*
Mark Beecher *(Sr VP-Sls & Mktg)*
Art Crawford *(Sr VP-Consumer Fin Admin)*
Lori Rivers *(Sr VP-Sys & Project Office)*
Advertising Agencies:
Heat
Pier 33 S 3rd Fl
San Francisco, CA 94111
Tel.: (415) 477-1999
Fax: (415) 477-1990
Agency of Record
— Nei Caetano *(Dir-Creative)*

The Laster Group
5407 N Mesa St 2nd Fl
El Paso, TX 79912
Tel.: (915) 581-7900
Fax: (915) 581-0087

BANK OF TUSCALOOSA

(Sub. of Synovus Financial Corp.)
22100 Jack Warner Pkwy
Tuscaloosa, AL 35401
Tel.: (205) 345-6200
Fax: (205) 345-5853
Web Site: www.bankoftuscaloosa.com
Sales Range: $25-49.9 Million
Approx. Number Employees: 100
Business Description:
Banking
S.I.C.: 6029
N.A.I.C.S.: 522110
Personnel:
Mark Sullivan *(Pres & CEO)*
Advertising Agency:
TotalCom Marketing, Inc.
922 20th Ave
Tuscaloosa, AL 35401-2307
Tel.: (205) 345-7363
Fax: (205) 345-7373

BANK OF UTAH

(Sub. of BOU Bancorp, Inc.)
2605 Washington Blvd
Ogden, UT 84401-3626

Key to Media (For complete agency information see *The Advertising Red Books-Agencies* edition):
1. Bus. Publs. 2. Cable T.V. 3. Catalogs & Directories. 4. Co-op Adv. 5. Consumer Mags. 6. D.M. to Bus. Estab.7. D.M. to Consumers
8. Daily Newsp. 9. Exhibits/Trade Shows 10. Foreign 11. Infomercial 12. Internet Adv.13. Multimedia 14. Network Radio
15. Network T.V. 16. Newsp. Distr. Mags. 17. Other 18. Outdoor (Posters, Transit) 19. Point of Purchase20. Premiums, Novelties
21. Product Samples 22. Special Events Mktg. 23. Spot Radio 24. Spot T.V. 25. Weekly Newsp. 26. Yellow Page Adv.

Tel.: (801) 409-5000
Fax: (801) 409-5187
E-mail: info@bankofutah.com
Web Site: www.bankofutah.com
Approx. Number Employees: 300
Year Founded: 1970
Business Description:
Banking
S.I.C.: 6029
N.A.I.C.S.: 522110
Media: 2-4-7-8-9-18-20-22-23-25
Personnel:
Frank W. Browning *(Chm)*
Douglas L. DeFries *(Pres)*
Roger G. Shumway *(Chief Credit Officer & Exec VP)*
K. Darrel May *(Sr VP & Mgr-HR)*
Branden P. Hansen *(Sr VP-Residential Lending)*
Scott H. Parkinson *(Sr VP)*
Jason Tonioli *(VP-Mktg Mgr)*
Kelly Crane *(VP & Mgr-Relationship)*
Wendy B. Parker *(VP-Banking Opers)*
Terry Miller *(Mgr- Central Office)*
Lennis L. Hall *(Auditor)*

BANK RHODE ISLAND
(Sub. of Bancorp Rhode Island, Inc.)
1 Turks Head Pl
Providence, RI 02903
Mailing Address:
PO Box 9488
Providence, RI 02940-9488
Tel.: (401) 456-5000
Fax: (401) 456-5029
Web Site: www.bankri.com
Sales Range: $100-124.9 Million
Approx. Number Employees: 210
Year Founded: 1996
Business Description:
Banking Services
S.I.C.: 6029; 6163
N.A.I.C.S.: 522110; 522310
Advertising Expenditures: $800,000
Media: 7-13-18-22
Personnel:
Merrill W. Sherman *(Pres & CEO)*
Linda H. Simmons *(CFO & Treas)*
Robert H. Wischnowsky *(CIO)*
Peter D. Costa *(Sr VP & Dir)*
Kenneth Burnett *(Sr VP & Team Leader)*
Peter Walsh *(Sr VP)*
Paul Gennari *(VP-Admin Svcs & Dir)*
Joe Beck *(Dir-IT)*
Peter Flaningan *(Chief Auditor)*

BANKATLANTIC
(Sub. of BankAtlantic Bancorp, Inc.)
1750 E Sunrise Blvd
Fort Lauderdale, FL 33310
Tel.: (954) 764-3111
Fax: (954) 585-3198
Fax: (954) 760-5489
Toll Free: (800) 741-1700
E-mail: ecustomerare@bankatlantic.com
Web Site: www.bankatlantic.com
E-Mail For Key Personnel:
Public Relations: hharvey@bankatlantic.com
Sales Range: $150-199.9 Million
Year Founded: 1952
Business Description:
Federal Savings Bank
S.I.C.: 6035; 6531
N.A.I.C.S.: 522120; 531210
Media: 8-25
Personnel:
Jarett S. Levan *(CEO)*
Lloyd DeVaux *(COO)*
Ken Binger *(Pres-Bus Banking)*
Charles Mohr *(Pres-Retail Banking)*
Douglas A. Tuttle *(Pres-Market)*
Bill Horton *(Sr VP)*
Jeffrey Chiger *(Sr VP)*
Michelle Kulzer *(Sr VP & Dir-Fin Intelligence)*
Perry Alexander *(Sr VP-CRE Lending)*
Russell L. Burdsall *(Sr VP-Mortgage Svcs)*
Andrew Meran *(Sr VP-Special Assets)*
Nancy L. Merolla *(VP & Mgr-Relationship)*
Monica Silva Ribeiro *(VP & Mgr-Market)*
Matthew Shull *(Asst VP & Mgr-Customer Risk)*
Jennifer Valade *(Asst VP & Mgr-Fin Intelligence Unit)*
Michael Shallenburg *(Reg Mgr-Market)*
Charles Morton *(Branch Mgr)*

BANKATLANTIC BANCORP, INC.
(Sub. of BFC FINANCIAL CORPORATION)
2100 W Cypress Creek Rd
Fort Lauderdale, FL 33309
Mailing Address:
PO Box 8608
Fort Lauderdale, FL 33310-8608
Tel.: (954) 940-5000
Fax: (954) 940-5489
Toll Free: (800) 226-0051
Web Site:
www.bankatlanticbancorp.com
Approx. Rev.: $283,321,000
Approx. Number Employees: 1,210
Year Founded: 1994
Business Description:
Bank Holding Company
S.I.C.: 6035; 6712
N.A.I.C.S.: 522120; 551111
Advertising Expenditures: $8,598,000
Media: 2-7-8-9-10-17-23-24-25
Distr.: Direct to Consumer; Reg.
Budget Set: Oct.
Personnel:
Alan B. Levan *(Chm & CEO)*
John E. Abdo *(Vice Chm)*
Jarett S. Levan *(Pres)*
Valerie C. Toalson *(CFO & Exec VP)*
Lloyd B. Devaux *(COO & Exec VP)*
Lewis F. Sarrica *(Chief Investment Officer & Exec VP)*
Jay C. McClung *(Chief Risk Officer & Exec VP)*
Susan D. McGregor *(Chief Talent Officer & Exec VP)*
Patrick Southworth *(Pres-Comml Real Estate)*
Douglas K. Freeman *(Chief Corp Banking Exec & Exec VP)*
Patricia Lefebvre *(Chief Retail Banking Officer & Exec VP)*
Leo Hinkley *(Sr VP)*
Brian Smith *(Chief Info Security Officer & Sr VP)*
Sharon Lyn *(VP & Mgr-IR & Corp Comm)*
Donna Rouzeau *(Asst VP-IR & Corp Commun)*
Advertising Agency:
Boardroom Communications Inc.
1776 N Pine Island Rd Ste 320
Plantation, FL 33322
Tel.: (954) 370-8999
Fax: (954) 370-8892
Pub Rels

BANKFINANCIAL CORPORATION
15W060 N Frontage Rd
Burr Ridge, IL 60527
Tel.: (708) 747-2000
Toll Free: (800) 894-6900
Web Site: www.bankfinancial.com
Approx. Rev.: $72,064,000
Approx. Number Employees: 310
Business Description:
Bank Holding Company
S.I.C.: 6712; 6035
N.A.I.C.S.: 551111; 522120
Advertising Expenditures: $1,277,000
Personnel:
F. Morgan Gasior *(CEO)*
James J. Brennan *(Gen Counsel, Sec & Exec VP)*
Gregg T. Adams *(Exec VP-Mktg & Sls)*
Paul A. Cloutier *(Exec VP)*
Elizabeth A. Doolan *(Sr VP & Controller)*
Brands & Products:
BANKFINANCIAL
HELPING YOU DO MORE

BANKPLUS BELZONI MISSISSIPPI
(Sub. of Bancplus Corporation)
202 E Jackson St
Belzoni, MS 39038
Tel.: (662) 247-1811
Fax: (662) 247-3313
Web Site: www.bankplus.net
Approx. Rev.: $99,749,000
Approx. Number Employees: 18
Business Description:
State Trust Companies Accepting Deposits, Commercial
S.I.C.: 6029
N.A.I.C.S.: 522110
Personnel:
William A. Ray *(Pres & CEO)*
Advertising Agency:
The Ramey Agency LLC
3100 N State St Ste 300
Jackson, MS 39216
Tel.: (601) 898-8900
Fax: (601) 898-8999
Toll Free: (800) 594-0754

BANNER CORPORATION
10 S First Ave
Walla Walla, WA 99362
Mailing Address:
PO Box 907
Walla Walla, WA 99362-0265
Tel.: (509) 527-3636
Fax: (509) 526-8898
Toll Free: (800) 272-9933
E-mail: bannerbank@bannerbank.com
Web Site: www.banrbank.com
Approx. Rev.: $247,230,000
Approx. Number Employees: 1,015
Year Founded: 1995
Business Description:
Bank Holding Company
S.I.C.: 6712; 6029; 6035; 6141
N.A.I.C.S.: 551111; 522110; 522120; 522291
Advertising Expenditures: $7,639,000
Personnel:
Gary L. Sirmon *(Chm)*
Jesse G. Foster *(Vice Chm)*
Mark J. Grescovich *(Pres & CEO)*
Lloyd W. Baker *(CFO & Exec VP)*
Steven W. Rust *(CIO & Exec VP)*
Richard B. Barton *(Chief Lending Officer & Exec VP)*
Douglas M. Bennett *(Exec VP-Real Estate Lending Ops)*
Tyrone J. Bliss *(Exec VP)*
Paul E. Folz *(Exec VP-Community Banking)*
Cynthia D. Purcell *(Exec VP)*
Gary W. Wagers *(Exec VP-Retail Products & Svcs)*
John T. Wagner *(Exec VP-Corp Admin)*

BAR HARBOR BANK & TRUST
(Sub. of Bar Harbor Bankshares)
82 Main St
Bar Harbor, ME 04609
Mailing Address:
PO Box 400
Bar Harbor, ME 04609-0400
Tel.: (207) 288-3314
Fax: (207) 288-4560
Toll Free: (888) 853-7100
E-mail: info@bhbt.com
Web Site: www.bhbt.com
Sales Range: $25-49.9 Million
Approx. Number Employees: 56
Year Founded: 1887
Business Description:
Personal & Commercial Banking & Trust Services
S.I.C.: 6029; 6035; 6733
N.A.I.C.S.: 522110; 522120; 523991
Advertising Expenditures: $500,000
Media: 7-13-18-20
Personnel:
Joseph M. Murphy *(Chm, Pres & CEO)*
Gerald Shencavitz *(CFO, COO, Treas & Exec VP)*
Michael W. Bonsey *(Sr VP-Credit Admin & Risk Mngmt)*
Gregory W. Dalton *(Sr VP)*
Ray Frohnapfel *(Sr VP-Ops)*
Stephen M. Leackfeldt *(Sr VP-Retail Banking)*
Marsha C. Sawyer *(Sr VP)*
Adam Robertson *(VP-Bus Banking & Fin Svcs)*

BARTLETT & CO.
(Sub. of Legg Mason, Inc.)
600 Vine St Ste 2100
Cincinnati, OH 45202-3896
Tel.: (513) 621-4612
Fax: (513) 621-6462
Toll Free: (800) 800-4612
Web Site: www.bartlett1898.com
Sales Range: $125-149.9 Million
Approx. Number Employees: 47
Year Founded: 1898
Business Description:
Investment Management & Financial Planning Services
S.I.C.: 6282; 6211
N.A.I.C.S.: 523920; 523110; 523930
Media: 6-14-22
Personnel:
James A. Miller *(Chm)*
Kelley J. Downing *(Pres & CEO)*
Michael S. Cambron *(Mng Dir)*
Laura Humphrey *(Dir-Mktg)*
Jason M. Kiss *(Dir-Res & Sr Portfolio Mgr)*

Bartlett & Co. — (Continued)
Smith Hickenlooper, III *(Sr Mgr-Portfolio)*
Marilyn Osborn *(Sr Mgr-Portfolio)*
Shawn L. Fishbaugh *(Sr Mgr-Portfolio)*
James B. Hagerty *(Sr Mgr-Portfolio)*
Kenneth L. Schlachter *(Sr Mgr-Portfolio)*
Terrence T. Kelly *(Sr Portfolio Mgr)*
James B. Reynolds *(Sr Portfolio Mgr)*
Troy R. Snider *(Mgr-Portfolio)*
Brands & Products:
OUR GOAL IS REACHING YOURS

BAY BANKS OF VIRGINIA, INC.
100 S Main St
Kilmarnock, VA 22482-1869
Tel.: (804) 435-1171
Fax: (804) 435-0543
Toll Free: (800) 435-1140
E-mail: aroberts@banklanc.com
Web Site: www.bankoflancaster.com
Approx. Rev.: $18,523,330
Approx. Number Employees: 80
Year Founded: 1930
Business Description:
Bank Holding Company
S.I.C.: 6029
N.A.I.C.S.: 522110
Advertising Expenditures: $127,000
Media: 9
Personnel:
Robert F. Hurliman *(Chm)*
Austin L. Roberts, III *(Pres & CEO)*
Deborah M. Evans *(CFO)*

BAY NATIONAL CORPORATION
2328 W Joppa Rd
Lutherville, MD 21093
Tel.: (410) 494-2580
Fax: (410) 494-2589
Web Site: www.baynational.com
Approx. Rev.: $12,912,147
Approx. Number Employees: 37
Business Description:
Bank Holding Company
S.I.C.: 6141; 6712
N.A.I.C.S.: 522210; 551111
Advertising Expenditures: $158,697
Media: 17
Personnel:
Charles L. Maskell, Jr. *(Chm)*
Hugh W. Mohler *(Pres)*
David E. Borowy *(CFO)*
Curt H.G. Heinfelden *(Sr VP-Cash Mgmt)*
Gilbert F. Kennedy, III *(Sr VP-Corp Banking-Bay Natl Bank)*
Charles J. Fleury, IV *(Sr VP)*
Robert W. Freeman *(Sr VP)*
Gregory J. Olinde *(Sr VP)*

BAY STATE SAVINGS BANK
28 Franklin St
Worcester, MA 01608
Tel.: (508) 890-9000
Fax: (508) 792-5217
Toll Free: (800) 244-8161
Web Site:
www.baystatesavingsbank.com
Sales Range: $125-149.9 Million
Approx. Number Employees: 100
Business Description:
State Trust Companies Accepting Deposits
S.I.C.: 6029
N.A.I.C.S.: 522110
Personnel:
Peter B. Alden *(Pres & CEO)*
Robert Duquette *(CFO)*
Paul Gildody *(COO & Exec VP)*
Diane M. Giampa *(VP-HR & Mktg)*
Christine M. Lucier *(Asst VP & Branch Mgr)*
Brands & Products:
BAY STATE
BAY STATE ONLINE
MINUTEMAN
WE TAKE BANKING PERSONALLY.
Advertising Agency:
Davis Advertising, Inc.
306 Main St
Worcester, MA 01608-1550
Tel.: (508) 752-4615
Fax: (508) 421-8001

BAYLAKE CORP.
217 N 4th Ave
Sturgeon Bay, WI 54235
Mailing Address:
PO Box 9
Sturgeon Bay, WI 54235-0009
Tel.: (920) 743-5551
Fax: (920) 746-3984
Toll Free: (800) 267-3610
Web Site: www.baylake.com
Approx. Rev.: $54,005,000
Approx. Number Employees: 272
Year Founded: 1976
Business Description:
Bank Holding Company
S.I.C.: 6029
N.A.I.C.S.: 522110
Import Export
Advertising Expenditures: $259,000
Personnel:
Robert W. Agnew *(Co-Chm)*
Richard A. Braun *(Co-Chm)*
Robert J. Cera *(Pres & CEO)*
Kevin L. Laluzerne *(CFO)*
Brands & Products:
BAYLAKE CORP.

BB&T CORPORATION
200 W 2nd St
Winston Salem, NC 27101-4019
Mailing Address:
PO Box 1250
Winston Salem, NC 27102-1250
Tel.: (336) 733-2000
Fax: (336) 733-2470
Toll Free: (800) 226-5228
Web Site: www.bbandt.com
Approx. Rev.: $11,072,000,000
Approx. Number Employees: 31,400
Year Founded: 1872
Business Description:
Bank Holding Company
S.I.C.: 6712; 6029; 6035; 6099; 6141; 6159; 6163; 6211; 6221; 6282; 6289; 6733
N.A.I.C.S.: 551111; 522110; 522120; 522210; 522220; 522291; 522292; 522310; 522390; 523110; 523140; 523920; 523991; 523999
Advertising Expenditures: $50,000,000
Media: 2-3-4-6-7-8-9-13-14-15-17-18-19-22-23-24-26
Personnel:
Kelly S. King *(Chm & CEO)*
Daryl N. Bible *(CFO & Sr Exec VP)*
Steven B. Wiggs *(CMO & Sr Exec VP)*
Ricky K. Brown *(Sr Exec VP & Mgr-Banking Network)*
Barbara F. Duck *(Sr Exec VP & Mgr-Enterprise Risk)*
Donna C. Goodrich *(Sr Exec VP & Mgr-Deposit Svcs)*
Robert E. Greene *(Sr Exec VP & Mgr-Admin Svcs)*
C. Leon Wilson, III *(Sr Exec VP & Mgr-Ops Div)*
Clarence Keel *(Sr VP-Shareholder Svcs)*
Mark E. McRae *(Sr VP-Central & Dir-Portfolio-North Florida Reg)*
Mike L. Nichols *(Sr VP-External Reporting)*
Jon Bass *(Dir-Mktg & Adv Strategy)*
Robert A. Denham *(Dir-Corp & Exec Comm)*
Tamera Gjesdal *(Mgr-IR)*
Advertising Agencies:
Luquire George Andrews, Inc.
(dba LGA)
4201 Congress St Ste 400
Charlotte, NC 28209
Tel.: (704) 552-6565
Fax: (704) 552-1972
Agency of Record
Advertising
Media
Promotions
Public Relations
— Lauren Sammerson *(VP-Pub Rel)*

Machado/Garcia-Serra Publicidad, Inc.
(d/b/a MGSCOMM)
1790 Coral Way
Miami, FL 33145
Tel.: (305) 444-4647
Fax: (305) 856-2687

BBVA COMPASS BANK
(Sub. of Banco Bilbao Vizcaya Argentaria, S.A.)
15 S 20th St
Birmingham, AL 35233-2000
Mailing Address:
PO Box 10566
Birmingham, AL 35296-0002
Tel.: (205) 297-3000
Fax: (205) 297-7836
Toll Free: (800) 239-2265
E-mail: feedback@compassweb.com
Web Site: www.bbvacompass.com/
Year Founded: 1964
Business Description:
Savings, Loans, Commercial & Investment Banking Services
S.I.C.: 6029; 6035; 6163; 6211
N.A.I.C.S.: 522110; 522120; 522310; 523110
Advertising Expenditures: $5,000,000
Media: 2-4-6-7-8-9-10-13-17-18-19-20-25-26
Distr.: Direct to Consumer; Reg.
Budget Set: Nov.
Personnel:
John Dietrich *(Product Mgr-Small Bus)*
Tom Sumrall *(Mgr)*
Advertising Agencies:
GSD&M
828 W 6th St
Austin, TX 78703-5420
Tel.: (512) 242-4736
Fax: (512) 242-4700
Creative

MPG
(Div. of HAVAS)
195 Broadway 12th Fl
New York, NY 10007
Tel.: (646) 587-5000
Fax: (646) 587-5005
Media Buying

BCB BANCORP, INC.
104 110 Avenue C
Bayonne, NJ 07002
Tel.: (201) 823-0700
Fax: (201) 339-0403
Web Site: www.bcbbancorp.com
Approx. Rev.: $53,962,000
Approx. Number Employees: 123
Business Description:
Bank Holding Company
S.I.C.: 6035; 6029; 6712
N.A.I.C.S.: 522120; 522110; 551111
Advertising Expenditures: $336,000
Media: 7-8-9-25
Personnel:
Mark D. Hogan *(Chm)*
Donald Mindiak *(Pres & CEO)*
Kenneth D. Walter *(CFO)*
Thomas M. Coughlin *(COO, Chief Acctg Officer & VP)*

BCSB BANCORP, INC.
4111 E Joppa Rd Ste 300
Baltimore, MD 21236-2289
Tel.: (410) 256-5000
Fax: (410) 256-0261
E-mail: info@bcsb.net
Web Site: www.baltcosavings.com
Approx. Rev.: $31,268,000
Approx. Number Employees: 139
Year Founded: 1955
Business Description:
Bank Holding Company
S.I.C.: 6035
N.A.I.C.S.: 522120
Advertising Expenditures: $388,000
Media: 9-14-22
Personnel:
Henry V. Kahl *(Chm)*
H. Adrian Cox *(Vice Chm)*
Joseph J. Bouffard *(Pres & CEO)*
Brands & Products:
BCSB

BDO SEIDMAN, LLP
(Sub. of Brussels Worldwide Service BVBA)
100 Pk Ave
New York, NY 10017
Tel.: (212) 885-8000
Fax: (212) 697-1299
Web Site: www.bdo.com
Approx. Number Employees: 1,200
Year Founded: 1910
Business Description:
Accounting, Tax & Management Consulting
S.I.C.: 8721
N.A.I.C.S.: 541211
Personnel:
James Blinka *(Partner-Taxes)*
Michael Burke *(Partner)*
Bridget Goris-Klein *(Partner-Taxes)*
Advertising Agency:
Seiter & Miller Advertising, Inc.
460 Park Ave S
New York, NY 10016
Tel.: (212) 843-9900
Fax: (212) 843-9901
(Creative, Media)

Key to Media (For complete agency information see *The Advertising Red Books-Agencies* edition):
1. Bus. Publs. 2. Cable T.V. 3. Catalogs & Directories. 4. Co-op Adv. 5. Consumer Mags. 6. D.M. to Bus. Estab.7. D.M. to Consumers
8. Daily Newsp. 9. Exhibits/Trade Shows 10. Foreign 11. Infomercial 12. Internet Adv.13. Multimedia 14. Network Radio
15. Network T.V. 16. Newsp. Distr. Mags. 17. Other 18. Outdoor (Posters, Transit) 19. Point of Purchase20. Premiums, Novelties
21. Product Samples 22. Special Events Mktg. 23. Spot Radio 24. Spot T.V. 25. Weekly Newsp. 26. Yellow Page Adv.

BEACON FEDERAL BANCORP, INC.

6611 Manlius Center Rd
East Syracuse, NY 13057
Tel.: (315) 433-0111
Fax: (315) 362-6633
Toll Free: (888) 256-3800
Web Site: www.beaconfederal.com
Approx. Rev.: $58,649,000
Approx. Number Employees: 136
Business Description:
Bank Holding Company
S.I.C.: 6712; 6029; 6035
N.A.I.C.S.: 551111; 522110; 522120
Advertising Expenditures: $478,000
Personnel:
Timothy P. Ahern *(Chm)*
Ross J. Prossner *(Pres & CEO)*
Darren T. Crossett *(COO & Sr VP)*
J. David Hammond *(Chief Lending Officer & Sr VP)*
Randy J. Wiley *(Treas & Sr VP)*
Kathleen Russell *(VP-HR)*

BEDERSON & COMPANY LLP

405 Northfield Ave Ste 102
West Orange, NJ 07052
Tel.: (973) 736-3333
Fax: (973) 736-3367
Fax: (973) 736-8786
Toll Free: (888) 222-8268
E-mail: info@bederson.com
Web Site: www.bederson.com
Approx. Number Employees: 70
Business Description:
Accounting Services
S.I.C.: 8721
N.A.I.C.S.: 541219
Media: 2
Personnel:
Edward P. Bond *(Partner)*
Steven P. Bortnick *(Partner)*
Seymour Bressler *(Partner)*
Jeffrey E. Callahan *(Partner)*
Robert L. Fischbein *(Partner)*
Timothy J. King *(Partner)*
Elwood I. Lerman *(Partner)*
Charles S. Lunden *(Partner)*
Mark A. Mazza *(Partner)*
Norman J. Parness *(Partner)*
James H. Ruitenberg *(Partner)*
Jules Schneider *(Partner)*
Matthew Schwartz *(Partner)*
Kenneth Winslow *(Partner)*
P. Dermot O'Neill *(Sr Mgr)*

BENEFICIAL BANK

(Sub. of Beneficial Mutual Bancorp, Inc.)
510 Walnut St
Philadelphia, PA 19106
Tel.: (215) 864-6000
Fax: (215) 864-6177
Web Site: www.thebeneficial.com
Sales Range: $125-149.9 Million
Business Description:
Banking Services
S.I.C.: 6029
N.A.I.C.S.: 522110
Personnel:
Gerard P. Cuddy *(Pres & CEO)*
Thomas D. Cestare *(CFO)*
Robert J. Bush *(Exec VP)*
Denise Kassekert *(Chief Relationship Banking Officer & Exec VP)*
Andrew J. Miller *(Asst VP)*
Advertising Agency:
LevLane Advertising/PR/Interactive
100 Penn Sq E
Philadelphia, PA 19107
Tel.: (215) 825-9600
Fax: (215) 809-1900

BENEFICIAL MUTUAL BANCORP, INC.

510 Walnut St 19th Fl
Philadelphia, PA 19106
Tel.: (215) 864-6000
Fax: (215) 864-6177
Toll Free: (800) 742-5272
Web Site: www.thebeneficial.com
Approx. Rev.: $224,734,000
Approx. Number Employees: 754
Year Founded: 2004
Business Description:
Bank Holding Company
S.I.C.: 6712
N.A.I.C.S.: 551111
Advertising Expenditures: $5,898,000
Personnel:
Gerard P. Cuddy *(Chm, Pres & CEO)*
Andrew J. Miller *(Chief Lending Officer)*
Robert J. Bush *(Exec VP)*
Denise Kassekert *(Chief Relationship Banking Officer & Exec VP)*

THE BERKSHIRE BANK

(Sub. of Berkshire Bancorp Inc.)
160 Broadway
New York, NY 10038
Tel.: (212) 791-5362
Fax: (212) 791-5367
Web Site: www.berkbank.com
Sales Range: $1-9.9 Million
Approx. Number Employees: 2
Year Founded: 1989
Business Description:
Personal & Commercial Banking Services
S.I.C.: 6029
N.A.I.C.S.: 522110
Export
Media: 7-8-9-10-11-13-20-22
Personnel:
Moses Krausz *(Pres & CEO)*
David Lukens, Jr. *(CFO & Exec VP)*
Allison M. Powell *(COO & Sr VP)*
Stanley Wong *(Chief Risk Officer & Sr VP)*
Michael Carroll *(Sr VP & Comml Reg Exec)*

BERKSHIRE BANK

(Formerly Rome Bancorp, Inc.)
(Sub. of Berkshire Hills Bancorp, Inc.)
100 W Dominick St
Rome, NY 13440-5810
Tel.: (315) 336-7300
Fax: (315) 336-5440
Approx. Rev.: $20,037,000
Approx. Number Employees: 93
Year Founded: 1999
Business Description:
Bank Holding Company
S.I.C.: 6035; 6712
N.A.I.C.S.: 522120; 551111
Advertising Expenditures: $125,000
Media: 8-10-13-18-20-22-23-26
Personnel:
Charles M. Sprock *(Chm)*
David C. Nolan *(CFO & Exec VP)*
Barbara M. Chilluffo *(Asst VP & Officer-Bus Dev)*
Albert Casab *(Officer-Loan)*
Patricia B. Hamer *(Officer-Loan)*
Karin M. Reiss *(Officer-Loan)*
Deniece M. Zeller *(Officer-Loan)*
D.Bruce Fraser *(VP-Security, HR & Compliance)*
Mary K. Chmielewski *(Asst VP-Branch Administrator)*
James M. Hamer *(Asst VP)*
Leonard P. Hite *(Asst VP & Info Security Officer)*
Sally M. Roseboom *(Asst VP)*
Christine G. Ruben *(Asst VP & Offficer-HR)*
Michele M. Smith *(Asst VP)*
Robert F. Vonbargen *(Asst VP)*
Pamela S. Barber *(Mgr-Deposit)*
Deborah L. Curtis *(Mgr-Branch-New Hartford)*
Susan Hert *(Mgr-Lee Branch)*
Karen Wells *(Mgr-Branch-West Rome)*
Sharon A. Hansen *(Asst Treas)*
Carol F. Izzo *(Asst Sec)*

BFC FINANCIAL CORPORATION

2100 West Cypress Creek Rd
Fort Lauderdale, FL 33309
Mailing Address:
PO Box 5403
Fort Lauderdale, FL 33310
Tel.: (954) 940-4900
Tel.: (954) 940-4995
Fax: (954) 940-4910
E-mail: investorrelations@bfcfinancial.com
Web Site: www.bfcfinancial.com
Approx. Rev.: $682,676,000
Approx. Number Employees: 5,084
Business Description:
Diversified Investment Holding Company
S.I.C.: 6289; 6719
N.A.I.C.S.: 523999; 551112
Advertising Expenditures: $8,598,000
Personnel:
Alan B. Levan *(Chm & CEO)*
John E. Abdo *(Vice Chm)*
John K. Grelle *(CFO & Exec VP)*
Leo Hinkley *(Officer-IR)*
Sharon Lyn *(VP-IR & Mgr-Corp Comm)*
Brands & Products:
BFC
BUILDING FOREMOST COMPANIES

BIOMS MEDICAL CORP.

(Name Changed to Medwell Capital Corp.)

BIZFILINGS

(Unit of Wolters Kluwer Financial & Compliance Services)
8040 Excelsior Dr Ste 200
Madison, WI 53717
Tel.: (608) 827-5300
Fax: (608) 827-5501
Toll Free: (800) 981-7183
E-mail: info@bizfilings.com
Web Site: www.bizfilings.com
Approx. Number Employees: 50
Business Description:
Incorporation Services
S.I.C.: 7389
N.A.I.C.S.: 561499; 541199
Media: 13
Personnel:
Jodi Kukla *(Dir-Mktg)*
Karen Nathan *(Dir-Product Mgmt)*

BLACKHAWK BANCORP INC.

400 Broad St
Beloit, WI 53511
Mailing Address:
PO Box 719
Beloit, WI 53511-0719
Tel.: (608) 364-8911
Fax: (608) 364-1500
E-mail: nethelp@blackhawkbank.com
Web Site: www.blackhawkbank.com
Approx. Rev.: $35,278,000
Approx. Number Employees: 149
Business Description:
Bank Holding Company
S.I.C.: 6035; 6712
N.A.I.C.S.: 522120; 551111
Advertising Expenditures: $430,000
Personnel:
R. Richard Bastian, III *(Pres & CEO)*
Todd J. James *(CFO & Exec VP)*
Todd Larson *(Sr VP-Bus Banking)*

BLACKROCK, INC.

55 E 52nd St
New York, NY 10055
Tel.: (212) 754-5300
Fax: (212) 935-1370
E-mail: invrel@blackrock.com
Web Site: www.blackrock.com
Approx. Rev.: $8,612,000,000
Approx. Number Employees: 9,127
Year Founded: 1998
Business Description:
Equity, Fixed Income, Asset Management & Alternative Investment Products & Services
S.I.C.: 6722; 6211; 6282; 6289
N.A.I.C.S.: 525910; 523110; 523120; 523920; 523930; 523999
Advertising Expenditures: $169,200,000
Media: 2-11-13
Personnel:
Laurence Douglas Fink *(Chm & CEO)*
Blake R. Grossman *(Vice Chm)*
Susan L. Wagner *(Vice Chm)*
Kendrick R. Wilson *(Vice Chm)*
Robert Steven Kapito *(Pres)*
Ann Marie Petach *(Sr Mng Dir & CFO)*
Charles S. Hallac *(COO & Sr Mng Dir)*
J. Richard Kushel *(Sr Mng Dir & Head-Portfolio Mgmt)*
Scott Thiel *(Mng Dir & CIO-Fixed Income)*
Joseph Feliciani, Jr. *(Mng Dir & Chief Acctg Officer)*
Edwin N. Conway *(Mng Dir & Head-Institutional Bus-Global Client Grp-US & Canada)*
Michael Fredericks *(Mng Dir & Head-Retail-BlackRock Multi Asset Client Solutions-US)*
Michael Huebsch *(Mng Dir & Head-BlackRock Multi Asset Client Solutions)*
Frank Porcelli *(Mng Dir & Head-Retail Bus-US)*
John Howard Blevins *(Mng Dir & Deputy Chief Compliance Officer)*
Peter Fisher *(Mng Dir)*
Richard J. Schiffman *(Mng Dir)*
Mark Blair *(CMO)*
Chris Leavy *(Chief Investment Officer-Fundamental Equity-US)*
Rick Rieder *(Chief Investment Officer-Fixed Income)*
Gordy Abel *(Dir-Media-Global)*

Key to Media (For complete agency information see *The Advertising Red Books-Agencies* edition):
1. Bus. Publs. 2. Cable T.V. 3. Catalogs & Directories. 4. Co-op Adv. 5. Consumer Mags. 6. D.M. to Bus. Estab.7. D.M. to Consumers 8. Daily Newsp. 9. Exhibits/Trade Shows 10. Foreign 11. Infomercial 12. Internet Adv.13. Multimedia 14. Network Radio 15. Network T.V. 16. Newsp. Distr. Mags. 17. Other 18. Outdoor (Posters, Transit) 19. Point of Purchase20. Premiums, Novelties 21. Product Samples 22. Special Events Mktg. 23. Spot Radio 24. Spot T.V. 25. Weekly Newsp. 26. Yellow Page Adv.

BlackRock, Inc. — (Continued)

Advertising Agency:
Ogilvy & Mather
(Sub. of WPP Group plc)
636 11th Ave
New York, NY 10036
Tel.: (212) 237-4000
Fax: (212) 237-5123

BLOCK FINANCIAL INC.

20343 N Hayden Rd Ste 105 141
Scottsdale, AZ 85255
Fax: (877) 230-0744
Toll Free: (866) 278-0903
E-mail: kblock@mail.bkst.com
Web Site: www.blockfinancial.com
E-Mail For Key Personnel:
President: mark@blockfinancial.com
Year Founded: 1993
Business Description:
Financial Services
S.I.C.: 6282; 6163
N.A.I.C.S.: 523930; 522310
Media: 13-26

BLOOMBERG L.P.

731 Lexington Ave
New York, NY 10022
Tel.: (212) 318-2000
Fax: (917) 369-5000
E-mail: info@bloomberg.com
Web Site: www.bloomberg.com
Sales Range: $5-14.9 Billion
Approx. Number Employees: 10,000
Year Founded: 1981
Business Description:
Multimedia Financial Information Systems Including: TV, Cable, Radio, Magazines, Newspapers & Terminals
S.I.C.: 7383
N.A.I.C.S.: 519110
Media: 2-3-11-13-14
Personnel:
Tom Secunda *(Founder & Partner)*
Michael R. Bloomberg *(Founder)*
Peter T. Grauer *(Chm)*
Daniel L. Doctoroff *(Pres & CEO)*
Maureen A. McGuire *(CMO)*
Norman Pearlstine *(Chief Content Officer)*
Kevin Sheekey *(Chm-Bloomberg Govt & Global Head-Comm & Govt Rels)*
Paul Bascobert *(Pres-BusinessWeek)*
Matt Winkler *(Editor-in-Chief)*
Katherine Rizzo *(Editor)*
Meridith Webster *(Dir-Comm & Pub Affairs)*
Brands & Products:
B-TRADE
BLOOMBERG ACTIONPLUS
BLOOMBERG AFFILIATE.COM
BLOOMBERG BONDTRADER
BLOOMBERG BUSINESS NEWS
BLOOMBERG CLIENTBOOK
BLOOMBERG CONNEX
BLOOMBERG EXCHANGETRADER
BLOOMBERG FINANCIAL MARKETS
BLOOMBERG FINANCIAL NEWS
THE BLOOMBERG FORUM
BLOOMBERG GOLD LIST
BLOOMBERG GRADE
BLOOMBERG INFORMATION RADIO
BLOOMBERG INFORMATION TV
BLOOMBERG INVESTIMENTI
BLOOMBERG LEGAL
BLOOMBERG MARKETS
BLOOMBERG MONEY
BLOOMBERG NEWS
BLOOMBERG PERSONAL
BLOOMBERG PERSONAL BOOKSHELF
BLOOMBERG PERSONAL FINANCE
BLOOMBERG POWERMATCH
BLOOMBERG PRESS
BLOOMBERG PROFESSIONAL
BLOOMBERG PROFESSIONAL LIBRARY
BLOOMBERG RADIO
BLOOMBERG SMALL BUSINESS
BLOOMBERG TELEVISION
BLOOMBERG TRADEBOOK
THE BLOOMBERG TRAVELER
BLOOMBERG UNIVERSITY
BLOOMBERG VOICE
BLOOMBERG WEALTH MANAGER
BLOOMBERG.COM
BTRD
BTV
CLIENTBOOK
COMPANY CONNECTION
G-TRADE
GLOBAL TRADEBOOK
GRADE
MONEY, MARKETS & MORE
MONEYCAST
NEGOCIOS BLOOMBERG
NEWS THAT MOVES MARKETS
ON INVESTING
OPEN BLOOMBERG
THE POWER OF INFORMATION
SPEX, THE BLOOMBERG
TRADEBOOK
Advertising Agency:
J. Walter Thompson Company (d/b/a JWT)
466 Lexington Ave
New York, NY 10017-3140
Tel.: (212) 210-7000
Fax: (212) 210-7299
Agency of Record

BLUE VALLEY BAN CORP

11935 Riley St
Overland Park, KS 66213
Tel.: (913) 338-1000
Fax: (913) 338-2801
E-mail: ir@bankbv.com
Web Site: www.bankbv.com
Approx. Rev.: $38,922,000
Approx. Number Employees: 167
Year Founded: 1989
Business Description:
Bank Holding Company
S.I.C.: 6029; 6712
N.A.I.C.S.: 522110; 551111
Advertising Expenditures: $190,000
Media: 17
Personnel:
Robert D. Regnier *(Chm, Pres & CEO)*
Mark A. Fortino *(CFO & Exec VP)*

BMW FINANCIAL SERVICES NA, LLC

(Sub. of BMW of North America, LLC)
300 Chestnut Rdg Rd
Woodcliff Lake, NJ 07677-7739
Mailing Address:
PO Box 1227
Westwood, NJ 07675-1227
Tel.: (201) 307-4000
Fax: (201) 307-4095
Web Site: www.bmwusa.com
Approx. Rev.: $83,000,000
Approx. Number Employees: 400
Year Founded: 1993
Business Description:
Automobile Finance Leasing
S.I.C.: 6141
N.A.I.C.S.: 522220
Personnel:
Jim Gonnell *(Pres)*
Advertising Agency:
G2 Worldwide
200 5th Ave
New York, NY 10010
Tel.: (212) 537-3700
Fax: (212) 546-2425

BNC BANCORP

1226 Eastchester Dr
High Point, NC 27265
Tel.: (336) 869-9200
Fax: (336) 889-8451
Web Site: www.bankofnc.com
Approx. Rev.: $123,823,000
Approx. Number Employees: 358
Year Founded: 2002
Business Description:
Bank Holding Company
S.I.C.: 6712; 6029
N.A.I.C.S.: 551111; 522110
Advertising Expenditures: $1,994,000
Media: 7-8
Personnel:
Thomas R. Sloan *(Chm)*
W. Swope Montgomery, Jr. *(Pres & CEO)*
David B. Spencer *(CFO & Exec VP)*
Richard D. Callicutt, II *(COO & Exec VP)*
Thomas M. Nelson *(Chief Credit Officer)*
Reid Marks *(Mgr-Comml Banking)*

BOFI HOLDING, INC.

12777 High Bluff Dr Ste 100
San Diego, CA 92130-2224
Tel.: (858) 350-6200
Fax: (858) 350-0443
E-mail: investors@bankofinternet.com
Web Site: www.bofiholding.com
Approx. Int. Income: $93,888,000
Approx. Number Employees: 90
Business Description:
Bank Holding Company
S.I.C.: 6712; 2741; 6035
N.A.I.C.S.: 551111; 516110; 522120
Advertising Expenditures: $444,000
Media: 13
Personnel:
Theodore C. Allrich *(Chm)*
Nicholas A. Mosich *(Vice Chm)*
Gregory Garrabrants *(Pres & CEO)*
Andrew J. Micheletti *(CFO & Exec VP)*
Brands & Products:
BANK OF INTERNET USA
BOFI HOLDING

BOK FINANCIAL CORPORATION

Bank of Oklahoma Tower PO Box 2300
Tulsa, OK 74192-0001
Tel.: (918) 588-6000
Fax: (918) 588-6853
Web Site: www.bokf.com
Approx. Rev.: $851,082,000
Approx. Number Employees: 4,432
Year Founded: 1910
Business Description:
Financial Holding Company
S.I.C.: 6029; 6712
N.A.I.C.S.: 522110; 551111
Media: 2-6-8-9-18-23-24-25-26
Personnel:
George B. Kaiser *(Chm)*
Stanley A. Lybarger *(Pres & CEO)*
Steven E. Nell *(CFO & Exec VP)*
Donald T. Parker *(CIO & Exec VP)*
Jim Huntzinger *(Chief Investment Officer)*
Charles E. Cotter *(Chief Credit Officer & Exec VP)*
John C. Morrow *(Chief Acctg Officer & Sr VP)*
Ben Cowen *(Pres-Mortgage Grp)*
Daniel H. Ellinor *(Sr Exec VP)*
Charles Garcia *(Exec VP & Head-Treasury Svcs & Intl)*
Scott Grauer *(Exec VP-Wealth Mgmt Div)*
Stacy C. Kymes *(Sr VP & Controller)*
Randy Blattner *(Sr VP & Dir-Enterprise Architecture)*
Alan Nykiel *(Sr VP & Dir-Corp Mktg)*
Gregory Wagner *(Sr VP & Reg Branch Mgr-Sls & Svc-Consumer Div)*
Leslie Swafford *(Sr VP & Sr Mgr-Mktg)*
Clint Dishman *(Sr VP & Mgr-Strategic Investment Advisory Grp)*
Priscilla Dougherty *(Sr VP & Mgr-CCS/CAS)*
Nelson Justice *(Sr VP & Mgr-Reg Branch-Sls & Svc-Consumer Div)*
David Lamb *(Sr VP & Mgr-Relationship)*
Martha McGuire *(Sr VP-Lending Mgr-Comml Div)*
Daniel Norton *(Sr VP & Mgr-Reconciliation & Control-Fin/Admin Div)*
David Stephens *(Sr VP & Mgr-Acctg & Reporting)*
David Vinall *(Sr VP & Mgr-Reg Branch-Sls & Svc-Consumer Div)*
Stephen Wyett *(Sr VP & Mgr-Market-Trust Div)*
Paula Barrington *(Sr VP)*
Cynthia Batt *(Sr VP-Wealth Mgmt Div)*
Michael Brown *(Sr VP)*
Peter Carey *(Sr VP-Comml Div)*
Scott Deatherage *(Sr VP-Contact Center Ops)*
Steve Fulbright *(Sr VP-Infrastructure Svcs)*
Bryan Geiger *(Sr VP)*
Frank McKeon *(Sr VP)*
Jeffrey Reid *(Sr VP-Talent Acq)*
Jane Romine *(Sr VP)*
David Roten *(Sr VP & Sr Div Controller)*
Sherri Rowton *(Sr VP-PFS Credit Support-Trust Div)*
Dale Updegrove *(Sr VP-Credit Admin)*
Christopher Graber *(Mng Dir-Merchant Banking-Comml Banking Div & VP)*
Aaron Clark *(VP & Sr Mgr-Portfolio-Trust Div)*
Megan Elsis *(VP & Branch Mgr IV-Consumer Div)*
Roger W. Randol *(VP & Branch Mgr IV)*
Tiffany Stewart *(VP & Branch Mgr IV-Consumer Div)*
Dawn Walker *(VP & Branch Mgr IV-Consumer Div)*

Key to Media (For complete agency information see *The Advertising Red Books-Agencies* edition):
1. Bus. Publs. 2. Cable T.V. 3. Catalogs & Directories. 4. Co-op Adv. 5. Consumer Mags. 6. D.M. to Bus. Estab.7. D.M. to Consumers
8. Daily Newsp. 9. Exhibits/Trade Shows 10. Foreign 11. Infomercial 12. Internet Adv.13. Multimedia 14. Network Radio
15. Network T.V. 16. Newsp. Distr. Mags. 17. Other 18. Outdoor (Posters, Transit) 19. Point of Purchase20. Premiums, Novelties
21. Product Samples 22. Special Events Mktg. 23. Spot Radio 24. Spot T.V. 25. Weekly Newsp. 26. Yellow Page Adv.

Matt C. Crew *(VP & Mgr-Acct-Comml Banking Div)*
Claudia M. Cepeda *(VP & Product Mgr-Retirement & Institutional Svcs Product)*
Melissa Adams *(VP & Mgr-Investment Performance-Consumer Banking and Wealth Mgmt)*
Melissa Bowman *(VP & Mgr-Ops-V Loan Documentation)*
Leona Brasiola *(VP & Mgr-Ops-Ops & Tech Div)*
Timothy Carver *(VP & Mgr-Bus Application Delivery)*
Kati M. Christ *(VP & Mgr-Acct-Comml Banking Div)*
Shelly Connolly *(VP & Mgr-HR)*
Ryan Davis *(VP & Mgr-Production Svcs)*
William Denison *(VP & Mgr-Land-Trust Oil & Gas)*
Brian Dugan *(VP & Mgr-Institutional Wealth Mgmt Relationship)*
Stephen T. Grider *(VP & Mgr-Institutional Wealth Mgmt Relationship)*
Rich Hubbard *(VP & Mgr-Bus Perfomance Measurement)*
Lisa Kirk *(VP & Mgr-Bus Application Delivery)*
David Lowell *(VP & Mgr-Sls-BOSC Div)*
Christine McQueen *(VP & Mgr-Credit Svc Loan Boarding & Servicing Grp)*
Dena Milburn *(VP & Mgr-Leasing)*
Brian Schmidtberger *(VP & Market Mgr-Portfolio Mgmt-Trust Div)*
James Striegel *(VP & Mgr-Institutional Wealth Mgmt Relationship)*
Kelly Thornton, Sr. *(VP & Mgr-HR Support)*
Jan Tyler *(VP & Mgr-Product)*
Lisa J. Chesbro *(VP-Treasury Svcs-Bank of Oklahoma)*
Thomas Dye *(VP-Pur & Office Svc-Ops & Tech Div)*
Gareld Gill *(VP-TransFund Participant Svcs-Comml Banking Div)*
Suzanne Hagen *(VP-IT)*
Ginger S. Holley *(VP & Sls Officer-Treasury)*
Ryan Morris *(VP & PFS Banker-Consumer Banking & Wealth Mgmt Div)*
Jay L. Smith *(VP-PFS Banker III-Consumer Banking & Wealth Mgmt Div)*
Brian Warden *(VP-Corp Banking)*
Jesse Boudiette *(Dir-Corp Comm)*
Michael D. Nalley *(Dir-Corp Real Estate)*
Mark Pryce *(Dir-Sr Institutional Municipal Underwriter)*
Kevin Rubin *(Dir-Process Engrg)*
Rick Rademeyer *(Product Mgr)*
Dorothy Lowman *(Mgr-Ops & Tech Div)*
Andrea Myers *(Mgr-Media Rels)*
Jeffrey Garcia *(Engr-Process)*

Advertising Agency:
Littlefield Brand Development
1350 S Boulder Ave Ste 500
Tulsa, OK 74119-3214
Tel.: (918) 295-1000
Fax: (918) 295-1001

BOLLAM, SHEEDY, TORANI & CO.
(Name Changed to BST)

BOREL PRIVATE BANK & TRUST COMPANY
(Holding of BOSTON PRIVATE FINANCIAL HOLDINGS, INC.)
160 Bovet Rd Ste 100
San Mateo, CA 94402
Tel.: (650) 378-3700
Fax: (650) 378-3774
E-mail: info@borel.com
Web Site: www.borel.com
Sales Range: $25-49.9 Million
Approx. Number Employees: 90
Year Founded: 1980
Business Description:
Banking Services
S.I.C.: 6029; 8721
N.A.I.C.S.: 522110; 541219
Advertising Expenditures: $1,700,000
Media: 2-4-7-8-13
Personnel:
Sherie S. Dodsworth *(Chm)*
Harold A. Fick *(Vice Chm)*
James C. Garvey *(Pres & CEO)*
Stephen A. Rossi *(CFO)*
Mark K. McDonald *(Chief Creative Officer)*
Nancy E. Johnson *(Sr Trust & Investment Officer)*
Carol J. Olson *(Sr Ops Officer)*
Bruce K. Farrell *(Chief Lending Officer & Exec VP)*
Arlie D. Ferguson *(Exec VP)*
Emanuela M. Allgood *(Sr VP & Mgr-Special Projects)*
William M. Bordin *(Sr VP & Mgr-Deposit Sls)*
Diana Landi *(Sr VP & Mgr-Mktg)*
Jon R. Sandstrom *(Sr VP & Mgr-Tech)*
Martha A. Johnson Mastracci *(Specialist-Mortgage, Sr VP)*
Jeanne Barrett *(Sr VP & Trust Officer)*
D. Mark Brosche *(Sr VP)*
Krista M. Conover *(Sr VP & Trust Officer)*
Vahan Derounian *(Sr VP-Mortgage Lending)*
Christopher Glud *(Loan Group Leader & Sr VP)*
Christopher C. Greene *(Sr VP & Comml Loan Officer)*
Lynne C. Johnston *(Sr VP & Trust Officer)*
Constance I. Katsaros *(Sr VP-HR & Strategic Dev)*
Veronica C. Morsello *(Sr VP & Residential Mortgage Officer)*
Kathy A. Nevarez *(Operations Officer, Sr VP)*
Stanley Rubin *(Sr VP & Sr Loan Officer)*
Katie S. Seedman *(Sr VP & Private Banking Officer)*
Clancy Swanson Stein *(Sr VP & Comml Loan Officer)*
Susan M. Colliver *(VP & Mgr-Deposit Relationship)*
Janis M. Fong *(VP & Mgr-Deposit Relationship)*
Linda S. Manzon *(VP & Mgr-New Accounts Admin)*
Teresa J. Nazarian *(Mgr-Teller Dept, VP)*
Wyman C. Wong *(VP & Mgr-Deposit Relationship)*
Leland N. Wong *(VP & Supvr-Trust Ops)*
Barbara L. Evers *(Dir-Mktg)*
Wanda Alfaro *(Mgr-San Francisco Office)*
Stephen B. Fick *(Mgr-Los Altos Office)*
Deborah Pappas *(Mgr-Palo Alto Office)*

THE BOSTON COMPANY ASSET MANAGEMENT, LLC
(Sub. of The Bank of New York Mellon Corporation)
1 Boston Pl
Boston, MA 02108-4407
Tel.: (617) 722-7029
Fax: (617) 722-7516
E-mail: info@thebostoncompany.com
Web Site:
www.thebostoncompany.com
Sales Range: $550-599.9 Million
Approx. Number Employees: 2,500
Year Founded: 1875
Business Description:
Financial Services Firm
S.I.C.: 6029; 6282
N.A.I.C.S.: 522110; 523930
Media: 2-7
Distr.: Intl.; Natl.
Budget Set: Dec.
Personnel:
Bart Grenier *(Chm & CEO)*
John Truschel *(Chief Investment Officer & Exec VP)*
Richard K. Watson, Jr. *(Exec VP & Head-Distr)*
Nicole C. Zimmerman *(Dir-HR)*

BOSTON PRIVATE BANK & TRUST COMPANY
(Holding of BOSTON PRIVATE FINANCIAL HOLDINGS, INC.)
10 Post Office Sq
Boston, MA 02109
Tel.: (617) 912-1900
Fax: (617) 912-4550
E-mail: info@bostonprivatebank.com
Web Site:
www.bostonprivatebank.com
Sales Range: $100-124.9 Million
Approx. Number Employees: 227
Year Founded: 1986
Business Description:
Federal Savings & Loan & Investment Products
S.I.C.: 6029
N.A.I.C.S.: 522110
Media: 2-8-13-18
Personnel:
Mark D. Thompson *(Pres & CEO)*
Anne L. Randall *(CFO, Chief Admin Officer & Exec VP)*
George G. Schwartz *(COO, Treas & Exec VP-Deposit & Cash Mgmt)*
Gary L. Garber *(CIO)*
Thomas K. Anderson *(Chief Investment Officer-Investment Mgmt & Trust Grp & Sr VP)*
James C. Brown *(Chief Lending Officer & Exec VP)*
Amy E. Hunter *(Exec VP & Dir-Mktg)*
James D. Henderson *(Exec VP-Investment Mgmt & Trust)*
John J. Sullivan *(Exec VP-Residential Lending)*
Ralph Letner *(Sr VP)*
Robert H. Rudnick *(Sr VP-Comml Banking Grp)*
Mary Ann Manning *(VP & Mgr-Mktg Comm)*
Pilar Pueyo *(Dir-HR)*
Advertising Agency:
Trinity Communications, Inc.
180 Canal St
Boston, MA 02114
Tel.: (617) 292-7300
Fax: (617) 292-7400

BOTETOURT BANKSHARES, INC.
19747 Main St
Buchanan, VA 24066
Tel.: (540) 473-1173
Fax: (540) 473-3936
E-mail: info@bankofbotetourt.com
Web Site: www.bankofbotetourt.com
Approx. Rev.: $18,129,851
Approx. Number Employees: 89
Year Founded: 1997
Business Description:
Bank Holding Company
S.I.C.: 6141; 6029; 6712
N.A.I.C.S.: 522210; 522110; 551111
Advertising Expenditures: $148,000
Media: 17
Personnel:
H. Watts Steger, III *(Chm, Pres & CEO)*
Michelle A. Alexander *(CFO & Sr VP)*

BOTTOMLINE TECHNOLOGIES (DE), INC.
325 Corporate Dr
Portsmouth, NH 03801
Tel.: (603) 436-0700
Fax: (603) 742-6556
Toll Free: (800) 243-2528
E-mail: info@bottomline.com
Web Site: www.bottomline.com
Approx. Rev.: $189,381,000
Approx. Number Employees: 880
Year Founded: 1989
Business Description:
Developer of Laser Check Printing, Electronic Payment, Check Fraud Avoidance & Electronic Remittance Software Systems
S.I.C.: 7372; 7371
N.A.I.C.S.: 511210; 334611; 541511
Import Export
Advertising Expenditures: $1,200,000
Media: 10
Personnel:
Joseph L. Mullen *(Chm)*
Robert A. Eberle *(Pres & CEO)*
Kevin M. Donovan *(CFO)*
John Mason *(CIO)*
Richard A. Bell *(Sr VP & Gen Mgr-Fin Process Solution-North America)*
Thomas D. Gaillard *(Sr VP & Gen Mgr-Transactional Svcs-North America)*
Michael Lane *(Sr VP & Gen Mgr-Global Banking & Fin Svcs)*
Andrew Mintzer *(Sr VP-Product Strategy & Delivery)*
John Kelly *(Gen Mgr-Legal Solutions)*
Paul J. Fannon *(Grp Dir-Sls-Europe)*
Karen Fettig *(Sr Dir-Svcs & Product Mgmt)*
Marcus Hughes *(Dir-Global Mktg)*
Brands & Products:
BOTTOMLINE BUSINESS EXCHANGE
BOTTOMLINE PRINT MANAGER
BOTTOMLINE TECHNOLOGIES

Key to Media (For complete agency information see *The Advertising Red Books-Agencies* edition):
1. Bus. Publs. 2. Cable T.V. 3. Catalogs & Directories. 4. Co-op Adv. 5. Consumer Mags. 6. D.M. to Bus. Estab.7. D.M. to Consumers
8. Daily Newsp. 9. Exhibits/Trade Shows 10. Foreign 11. Infomercial 12. Internet Adv.13. Multimedia 14. Network Radio
15. Network T.V. 16. Newsp. Distr. Mags. 17. Other 18. Outdoor (Posters, Transit) 19. Point of Purchase20. Premiums, Novelties
21. Product Samples 22. Special Events Mktg. 23. Spot Radio 24. Spot T.V. 25. Weekly Newsp. 26. Yellow Page Adv.

Bottomline Technologies (de), Inc. — (Continued)

CHECKDEFENSE
CREATEARCHIEVE
CREATE!FORM
ESEND
FORMSCAPE
INVIEW AP
LEGAL EXCHANGE
MEDEX
MEDFORMS
NETTRANSACT
PAYBASE
QUICKRECORD
TRANSFORM
TROY
WEBSERIES

BPW ACQUISITION CORP.

(Sub. of The Talbots, Inc.)
750 Washington Blvd
Stamford, CT 06901
Tel.: (203) 653-5800
Approx. Number Employees: 4
Year Founded: 2007
Business Description:
Investment Services
S.I.C.: 6289
N.A.I.C.S.: 523999
Personnel:
Gary S. Barancik *(CEO)*
Advertising Agency:
Sard Verbinnen & Co.
630 3rd Ave 9th Fl
New York, NY 10017
Tel.: (212) 687-8080
Fax: (212) 687-8344

BREMER FINANCIAL CORPORATION

445 Minnesota St Ste 2000
Saint Paul, MN 55101-2135
Mailing Address:
PO Box 1000
Lake Elmo, MN 55042
Tel.: (651) 227-7621
Fax: (651) 312-3550
Toll Free: (800) 392-0301
E-mail: info@bremer.com
Web Site: www.bremer.com
E-Mail For Key Personnel:
Public Relations: rbbuck@bremer.com
Approx. Int. Income: $222,399,000
Approx. Number Employees: 1,800
Year Founded: 1943
Business Description:
Bank Holding Company
S.I.C.: 6029
N.A.I.C.S.: 522110
Personnel:
Terry M. Cummings *(Chm)*
Robert B. Buck *(CFO & Exec VP)*
Susan Klasen Albrecht *(Sr VP & Dir-Wealth Plng Svcs)*
Teresa Morrow *(Sr VP-Comm/Comm Dev)*
Brands & Products:
BREMER
Advertising Agency:
Bolin Marketing & Advertising
2523 Wayzata Blvd Ste 300
Minneapolis, MN 55405
Tel.: (612) 374-1200
Fax: (612) 377-4226

BRIDGE BANCORP, INC.

2200 Montauk Hwy
Bridgehampton, NY 11932
Tel.: (631) 537-1000
Fax: (631) 537-1835
Web Site: www.bridgenb.com
Approx. Rev.: $52,332,000
Approx. Number Employees: 206
Year Founded: 1910
Business Description:
Banking Services
S.I.C.: 6712; 6029
N.A.I.C.S.: 551111; 522110
Advertising Expenditures: $546,000
Media: 22
Personnel:
Marcia Z. Hefter *(Chm)*
Dennis A. Suskind *(Vice Chm)*
Kevin M. O'Connor *(Pres & CEO)*
Howard H. Nolan *(CFO, Chief Administrative Officer, Treas, Sec & Sr Exec VP)*
Sandra K. Novick *(CMO, Sec & Sr VP)*
Sarah A. Quinn *(Chief Acctg Officer, VP & Controller)*
James J. Manseau *(Exec VP)*
Kevin L. Santacroce *(Exec VP)*
Deborah McGrory *(Sr VP & Dir-HR)*
Seamus Doyle *(Sr VP)*
Maureen P. Mougios *(VP & Dir-Risk Mgmt)*
Deborah Cosgrove *(Asst VP & Branch Mgr-Admin)*
Robert Curtin *(Asst VP & Branch Mgr-Southold)*
Marion Stark *(Asst VP & Branch Mgr)*
Caroline Kalish *(Asst VP & Mgr-Data Processing Ops)*
Brands & Products:
THE BANK YOU CAN TALK TO
BNB MASTER MONEY
BRIDGE E-PAY
BRIDGEHAMPTON NATIONAL BANK

BRIDGEHAMPTON NATIONAL BANK

(Sub. of Bridge Bancorp, Inc.)
2200 Montauk Hwy
Bridgehampton, NY 11932
Tel.: (631) 537-1000
Fax: (631) 537-1835
Web Site: www.bridgenb.com
Sales Range: $50-74.9 Million
Approx. Number Employees: 150
Business Description:
Banking Services
S.I.C.: 6029
N.A.I.C.S.: 522110
Media: 22
Personnel:
Kevin M. O'Connor *(Pres & CEO)*
Howard H. Nolan *(CFO, Chief Admin Officer & Sr Exec VP)*
Thomas H. Simson *(CIO)*
Seamus Doyle *(Sr VP & Sr Lending Officer)*
Sharon Abbondondelo *(Asst VP)*
Deborah McGrory *(Dir-HR)*
Deborah Cosgrove *(Mgr-Facilities)*

BRIEFING.COM

555 Airport Blvd Ste 150
Burlingame, CA 94010
Tel.: (650) 347-2220
Fax: (650) 347-2223
Toll Free: (800) 752-3013
Web Site: www.briefing.com
E-Mail For Key Personnel:
Sales Director: crhymes@briefing.com
Approx. Sls.: $6,500,000
Approx. Number Employees: 40
Business Description:
Online Stock Market Analysis
S.I.C.: 6099
N.A.I.C.S.: 522320
Media: 7-8-13-18-19-20-21-24
Personnel:
Dick Green *(Chm)*
Cass Rhymes *(Sr VP)*
Kimberly DuBord *(Dir-Res)*
Robert V. Green *(Sr Strategist-Investment)*
Damon Southward *(Chief Market Strategist)*
Patrick O'Hare *(Chief Market Analyst)*
Jim Schroeder *(Technical Analyst)*
Brands & Products:
BRIEFING ADVISOR
BRIEFING IN PLAY
BRIEFING INSTITUTIONAL
BRIEFING PROFESSIONAL
BRIEFING TRADER
BRIEFING.COM

BRITTON & KOONTZ CAPITAL CORPORATION

500 Main St
Natchez, MS 39120-3364
Mailing Address:
PO Box 1407
Natchez, MS 39121-1407
Tel.: (601) 445-5576
Fax: (601) 445-2488
Toll Free: (866) .4BK-BANK
E-mail: info@bkbank.com
Web Site: www.bkbank.com
Approx. Rev.: $23,067,087
Approx. Number Employees: 3
Year Founded: 1982
Business Description:
Bank Holding Company
S.I.C.: 6141; 6029; 6035; 6712
N.A.I.C.S.: 522210; 522110; 522120; 551111
Advertising Expenditures: $179,450
Media: 17
Personnel:
Robert R. Punches *(Chm)*
W. Page Ogden *(Pres & CEO)*
William M. Salters *(CFO, Treas & Controller)*
Jarrett E. Nicholson *(COO & Chief Credit Policy Officer)*
Donita Martin *(Pres-Vicksburg Market & Chief Deposit Officer)*
Steve Barbera *(Chief Deposit Officer)*

BRITTON & KOONTZ FIRST NATIONAL BANK

(Sub. of Britton & Koontz Capital Corporation)
500 Main St
Natchez, MS 39120-3364
Tel.: (601) 445-5576
Fax: (601) 445-2488
E-mail: answers@bkbank.com
Web Site: www.bkbank.com
Sales Range: $10-24.9 Million
Approx. Number Employees: 50
Year Founded: 1836
Business Description:
Full Banking Services
S.I.C.: 6029
N.A.I.C.S.: 522110
Media: 7-8-18
Personnel:
W. Page Ogden *(Pres & CEO)*
William M. Salters *(CFO & Treas)*
Christopher Maxwell *(CTO & Sr VP)*
Frances B. Cothren *(Sr VP)*

BROADRIDGE FINANCIAL SOLUTIONS INC.

1981 Marcus Ave
Lake Success, NY 11042
Tel.: (516) 472-5400
Web Site: www.broadridge.com
Approx. Rev.: $2,209,200,000
Approx. Number Employees: 5,400
Year Founded: 1965
Business Description:
Financial Services Industry Outsourcing Services
S.I.C.: 7374; 7389
N.A.I.C.S.: 518210; 561499
Advertising Expenditures: $1,900,000
Personnel:
Arthur F. Weinbach *(Chm)*
John Hogan *(Pres & COO)*
Richard J. Daly *(CEO)*
Dan Sheldon *(CFO & VP)*
Stefanie Shelley *(CMO)*
Susan Certoma *(Pres-Brokerage Processing Svcs)*
Adam D. Amsterdam *(Gen Counsel, Sec & VP)*
Timothy C. Gokey *(Chief Corp Dev Officer & Sr VP)*
J. Peter Benzie *(VP-Sls)*
Paul Clark *(Sr Mgr-Strategy & Product-Securities Processing Solutions-Intl)*
Cindy Volker *(Product Mgr-Mktg Comm)*

BROADWAY FEDERAL BANK, F.S.B.

(Sub. of Broadway Financial Corporation)
4800 Wilshire Blvd
Los Angeles, CA 90010
Tel.: (323) 634-1700
Fax: (323) 634-1717
Web Site:
www.broadwayfederalbank.com
Sales Range: $25-49.9 Million
Approx. Number Employees: 68
Year Founded: 1946
Business Description:
Federal Savings & Loan
S.I.C.: 6035; 6163
N.A.I.C.S.: 522120; 522310
Advertising Expenditures: $1,500,000
Media: 1-7-8-13
Personnel:
Paul C. Hudson *(Chm & CEO)*
Wayne-Kent A. Bradshaw *(Pres & COO)*
Samuel Sarpong *(CFO)*
Wilbur A. McKesson, Jr. *(Chief Loan Officer & Sr VP)*
Karen Hudson *(Dir-PR)*

BROOKLINE BANCORP, INC.

160 Washington St
Brookline, MA 02445
Mailing Address:
PO Box 470469
Brookline, MA 02447-0469
Tel.: (617) 730-3500
Fax: (617) 730-3552
Web Site: www.brooklinebank.com

Key to Media (For complete agency information see *The Advertising Red Books-Agencies* edition):
1. Bus. Publs. 2. Cable T.V. 3. Catalogs & Directories. 4. Co-op Adv. 5. Consumer Mags. 6. D.M. to Bus. Estab.7. D.M. to Consumers 8. Daily Newsp. 9. Exhibits/Trade Shows 10. Foreign 11. Infomercial 12. Internet Adv.13. Multimedia 14. Network Radio 15. Network T.V. 16. Newsp. Distr. Mags. 17. Other 18. Outdoor (Posters, Transit) 19. Point of Purchase20. Premiums, Novelties 21. Product Samples 22. Special Events Mktg. 23. Spot Radio 24. Spot T.V. 25. Weekly Newsp. 26. Yellow Page Adv.

Approx. Int. Income: $130,109,000
Approx. Number Employees: 245
Year Founded: 1998
Business Description:
Bank Holding Company
S.I.C.: 6712
N.A.I.C.S.: 551111
Advertising Expenditures: $997,000
Media: 7-8
Personnel:
Joseph J. Slotnik *(Acting Chm)*
Paul A. Perrault *(Pres & CEO)*
Paul R. Bechet *(CFO & Treas)*
Advertising Agency:
Hurley Chandler & Chaffer
2757 Pawtucket Ave Ste 200
East Providence, RI 02914
Tel.: (401) 273-5530
Fax: (401) 331-2061

BROOKLYN FEDERAL BANCORP, INC.

81 Court St
Brooklyn, NY 11201
Tel.: (718) 855-8500
Fax: (718) 858-5174
E-mail: info@brooklynbank.com
Web Site: www.brooklynbank.com
Approx. Int. Income: $34,111,000
Approx. Number Employees: 74
Business Description:
Bank Holding Company
S.I.C.: 6712; 6029; 6035
N.A.I.C.S.: 551111; 522110; 522120
Advertising Expenditures: $100,000
Media: 17
Personnel:
Daniel O. Reich *(Chm)*
Angelo J. Di Lorenzo *(Vice Chm)*
Richard A. Kielty *(Pres & CEO)*
Michael A. Trinidad *(CFO, VP & Ethics Officer)*
Wendy R. Bermudez *(Asst VP-Retail Banking/Ops)*
Edward Bolmarcich *(Officer-Residential Mortgage Originations & Mgr)*
Marilyn Alberici *(Sr VP)*
Salvatore Gargaro *(Sr VP, Sr Retail Banking Officer-Ops)*
Erica Minott *(Asst VP & Asst Controller)*
Joseph Raucci *(Asst VP, Asst Sec & Asst Fin Officer)*

BRUNSWICK BANCORP

439 Livingston Ave
New Brunswick, NJ 08901
Tel.: (732) 247-5800
Fax: (732) 247-5996
E-mail: bbt@brunswickbank.com
Web Site: www.brunswickbank.com
Sales Range: $1-9.9 Million
Approx. Number Employees: 48
Year Founded: 1984
Business Description:
Bank Holding Company
S.I.C.: 6712; 6029; 6035
N.A.I.C.S.: 551111; 522110; 522120
Advertising Expenditures: $50,637
Media: 8
Personnel:
Roman T. Gumina *(Chm)*
Frederick H. Perrine *(Vice Chm)*
Thomas A. Fornale *(CFO, Sec & Sr VP)*
Michael A. Studney *(CIO & Sr VP)*
Frank J. Gumina, III *(VP, Counsel, Compliance Officer & BSA Officer)*
Russell Jaeschke *(Chief Lending Officer & Sr VP)*
Patricia Gerhartz *(VP & Asst Sec)*

BRYN MAWR BANK CORPORATION

801 Lancaster Ave
Bryn Mawr, PA 19010
Tel.: (610) 525-1700
Tel.: (610) 687-4268
E-mail: gmateer@bmtc.com
Web Site: www.bmtc.com
Approx. Rev.: $94,171,000
Approx. Number Employees: 325
Business Description:
Bank Holding Company
S.I.C.: 6141; 6029; 6712
N.A.I.C.S.: 522210; 522110; 551111
Import Export
Advertising Expenditures: $1,142,000
Personnel:
Frederick C. Peters, II *(Chm, Pres & CEO)*
Joseph Duncan Smith *(CFO & Exec VP)*
Joseph G. Keefer *(Chief Lending Officer & Exec VP)*
Geoffrey L. Halberstadt *(Chief Credit Policy Officer, Sec & Exec VP)*
Alison E. Gers *(Exec VP-Retail Banking, Ops, IT & Mktg)*
Francis J. Leto *(Exec VP-Wealth Mgmt Div)*

BST

(Formerly Bollam, Sheedy, Torani & Co.)
26 Computer Dr W
Albany, NY 12205
Tel.: (518) 459-6700
Fax: (518) 459-8492
Toll Free: (800) 724-6700
E-mail: info@bstco.com
Web Site: www.bstco.com
Approx. Number Employees: 55
Year Founded: 1976
Business Description:
Financial & Management Consulting Services
S.I.C.: 8721
N.A.I.C.S.: 541211
Media: 10-26
Personnel:
Joseph A. Torani *(Chm & Mng Partner)*
Robert J. Sheedy *(Pres)*
John R. Johnson *(Mng Partner)*
Richard O. Bollam *(Partner)*
William G. Reynolds *(Partner)*

C&F FINANCIAL CORPORATION

802 Main St
West Point, VA 23181
Mailing Address:
PO Box 391
West Point, VA 23181-0391
Tel.: (804) 843-2360
Fax: (804) 843-3017
E-mail: customerservice@cffc.com
Web Site: www.cffc.com
Approx. Rev.: $99,548,000
Approx. Number Employees: 544
Year Founded: 1994
Business Description:
Bank Holding Company
S.I.C.: 6712; 6029
N.A.I.C.S.: 551111; 522110
Advertising Expenditures: $614,000
Personnel:
Larry G. Dillon *(Chm, Pres & CEO)*
Thomas F. Cherry *(CFO & Exec VP)*

CADENCE FINANCIAL CORPORATION

301 E Main St
Starkville, MS 39760
Mailing Address:
PO Box 1187
Starkville, MS 39759
Tel.: (662) 323-1341
Fax: (662) 338-5049
Toll Free: (800) 636-7622
Web Site: www.cadencebanking.com
E-Mail For Key Personnel:
President: mabernathy@nbc-bank.com
Approx. Rev.: $101,182,000
Approx. Number Employees: 428
Year Founded: 1984
Business Description:
National Commercial Bank
S.I.C.: 6141; 6029
N.A.I.C.S.: 522210; 522110
Export
Advertising Expenditures: $724,000
Media: 13
Personnel:
Lewis F. Mallory, Jr. *(Chm & CEO)*
Mark A. Abernathy *(Pres & COO)*
Richard Thomas Haston *(CFO & Exec VP)*
J. Aubrey Adair *(Chief Acctg Officer & VP)*

CAISSE DE DEPOT ET PLACEMENT DU QUEBEC

1000 Pl Jean-Paul-Riopelle
Montreal, QC H2Z 2B3, Canada
Tel.: (514) 842-3261
Fax: (514) 842-4833
Telex: 55-61874
E-mail: info@lacaisse.com
Web Site: www.lacaisse.com
Sales Range: $1-4.9 Billion
Approx. Number Employees: 700
Year Founded: 1965
Business Description:
Public Investment Portfolio Management
S.I.C.: 6282; 6289
N.A.I.C.S.: 523920; 523999
Media: 2-6
Personnel:
Robert Tessier *(Chm)*
Michael Sabia *(Pres & CEO)*
Normand Provost *(COO & Exec VP-Private Equity)*
Roland Lescure *(Chief Investment Officer & Exec VP)*
Claude Bergeron *(Chief Risk Officer & Exec VP)*
Daniel Fournier *(Pres-Real Estate Grp & Exec VP-Real Estate)*
Denis Couture *(Exec VP-Pub Affairs)*
Oliver Fratzscher *(Chief Economist & Exec VP)*
Jean-Luc Gravel *(Exec VP-Equity Markets Investment Mgmt)*
Philippe Ithurbide *(Exec VP-Overlay Strategies)*

CALAMOS ASSET MANAGEMENT INC

2020 Calamos Ct
Naperville, IL 60563-2787
Tel.: (630) 245-7200
Fax: (630) 245-6335
Toll Free: (800) 582-6959
E-mail: mthielen@calamos.com
Web Site: www.calamos.com
Approx. Rev.: $326,039,000
Approx. Number Employees: 318
Business Description:
Investment Management Services
S.I.C.: 6289; 6211; 6282
N.A.I.C.S.: 523999; 523110; 523930
Advertising Expenditures: $14,266,000
Personnel:
John P. Calamos, Sr. *(Chm, CEO & Co-Chief Investment Officer)*
James F. Baka *(Pres & Exec VP-Wealth Mgmt)*
Nick P. Calamos *(Pres-Investments & Co-Chief Investment Officer)*
James J. Boyne *(Pres-Distr & Ops)*
Randall T. Zipfel *(COO-Investments, Sr VP & IT)*
Geoffrey Davis *(Sr VP & Head-Intermediary Distr-London)*
Nimish S. Bhatt *(Sr VP & Dir-Ops)*
Vincenzo Falbo *(Sr VP & Dir-Intl Bus)*
Gary J. Felsten *(Sr VP & Dir-HR)*
Brands & Products:
CALAMOS
STRATEGIES FOR SERIOUS MONEY
Advertising Agency:
csFinancialWorks
656 W Randolph St
Chicago, IL 60661
Tel.: (312) 382-9000

CALIFORNIA BANK & TRUST

(Sub. of Zions Bancorporation)
11622 El Camino Real 2nd Fl
San Diego, CA 92130-2049
Tel.: (858) 793-7400
Fax: (858) 793-7438
Toll Free: (800) 254-2265
E-mail: info@calbanktrust.com
Web Site: www.calbanktrust.com
E-Mail For Key Personnel:
Marketing Director: borgs@calbt.com
Approx. Int. Income: $414,300,000
Approx. Number Employees: 1,474
Year Founded: 1998
Business Description:
Banking Services
S.I.C.: 6029
N.A.I.C.S.: 522110
Media: 2-4-6-7-8-9-10-11-13-16-17-18-19-20-22-23-24-25-26
Distr.: Reg.
Budget Set: May-Nov.
Personnel:
David E. Blackford *(Pres & CEO)*
Dennis Uyemura *(Mng Dir & CFO)*
George Bryce *(Mng Dir & Chief Credit Officer-Comml)*
Michael Permenter *(Mng Dir & Chief Credit Officer-Real Estate)*
Allen W. Severson *(Mng Dir-Acq)*
Scott Monson *(Mng Dir & Reg Exec Dir-Comml Banking)*
Frank Lee *(CIO & Exec VP)*
Jeffrey Hill *(Gen Counsel & Exec VP)*

Key to Media (For complete agency information see *The Advertising Red Books-Agencies* edition):
1. Bus. Publs. 2. Cable T.V. 3. Catalogs & Directories. 4. Co-op Adv. 5. Consumer Mags. 6. D.M. to Bus. Estab.7. D.M. to Consumers
8. Daily Newsp. 9. Exhibits/Trade Shows 10. Foreign 11. Infomercial 12. Internet Adv.13. Multimedia 14. Network Radio
15. Network T.V. 16. Newsp. Distr. Mags. 17. Other 18. Outdoor (Posters, Transit) 19. Point of Purchase20. Premiums, Novelties
21. Product Samples 22. Special Events Mktg. 23. Spot Radio 24. Spot T.V. 25. Weekly Newsp. 26. Yellow Page Adv.

California Bank & Trust — (Continued)

Betty Rengifo Uribe *(Exec VP & Head-Bus & Personal Banking)*
Gary Green *(Exec VP & Mgr-Comml Banking-Orange County)*
William Gunnell *(Exec VP & Mgr-Comml Banking-Los Angeles)*
Paul Herman *(Exec VP & Mgr-Small Bus Lending)*
Robert Chaulk *(Exec VP)*
Frank Henry *(Exec VP)*
Torran Nixon *(Exec VP)*
Lori Poole *(Exec VP)*
Mark Young *(Exec VP)*
Steven Borg *(Sr VP & Dir-Corp Mktg)*
Susan Brown *(Sr VP & Grp Mgr-Mktg)*
Jill Faucher *(VP & Mgr-Mktg Comm)*
Nelson Strickler *(VP-Corp Mktg)*

Brands & Products:
BUSINESS CASHLINE
COST SAVER CHECKING

Advertising Agency:
ES Advertising
6222 Wilshire Blvd Ste 302
Los Angeles, CA 90048
Tel.: (323) 964-9001
Fax: (323) 964-9801

CALIFORNIA FIRST NATIONAL BANCORP

18201 Von Karman Ave Ste 800
Irvine, CA 92612
Tel.: (949) 255-0500
Fax: (949) 255-0501
Toll Free: (800) 496-4640
E-mail: custservice@calfirstbancorp.com
Web Site: www.calfirstbancorp.com
Approx. Rev.: $34,874,000
Approx. Number Employees: 179
Business Description:
Bank Holding Company; Financial Services & Leasing
S.I.C.: 6289; 6029; 6712
N.A.I.C.S.: 523999; 522110; 551111
Media: 7-13
Personnel:
Patrick E. Paddon *(Chm, Pres & CEO)*
S. Leslie Jewett *(CFO)*
Glen T. Tsuma *(COO & Sec)*

CALVIN B. TAYLOR BANKSHARES, INC.

24 N Main St
Berlin, MD 21811
Tel.: (410) 641-1700
Fax: (410) 641-0543
E-mail: taylorbk@dmv.com
Web Site: www.taylorbank.com
Approx. Rev.: $19,397,259
Approx. Number Employees: 89
Year Founded: 1995
Business Description:
Bank Holding Company
S.I.C.: 6029
N.A.I.C.S.: 522110
Advertising Expenditures: $180,336
Media: 17
Personnel:
Reese F. Cropper, Jr. *(Chm)*
Raymond M. Thompson *(Pres & CEO)*

CAMBRIDGE CREDIT COUNSELING CORP.

67 Hunt St
Agawam, MA 01001
Tel.: (413) 821-8900
Fax: (413) 789-7183
Toll Free: (800) 527-7595
Toll Free: (800) 897-2200
E-mail: feedback@cambridgecredit.org
Web Site: www.cambridgecredit.org
Approx. Number Employees: 260
Year Founded: 1996
Business Description:
Debt Counseling; Financial Education, Credit & Debt Management Services
S.I.C.: 7299; 6099; 8299
N.A.I.C.S.: 812990; 522390; 611710
Media: 2-6-8-13
Personnel:
Alfred H. Colonna, Jr. *(Chm)*
Christopher A. Viale *(Pres, CEO & Dir)*
Thomas W. Hebert *(CFO & Treas)*

CAMBRIDGE SAVINGS BANK

(Sub. of Cambridge Financial Group, Inc.)
1374 Massachusetts Ave
Cambridge, MA 02138-3822
Mailing Address:
PO Box 380206
Cambridge, MA 02238-9906
Tel.: (617) 864-8700
Fax: (617) 441-4226
Toll Free: (800) 864-BANK
E-mail: info@cambridgesavings.com
Web Site:
www.cambridgesavings.com
Approx. Number Employees: 300
Year Founded: 1834
Business Description:
Banking Services
S.I.C.: 6035
N.A.I.C.S.: 522120
Advertising Expenditures: $500,000
Media: 2-7-8-9-17-18-19-20-22-23-24-25-26
Distr.: Direct to Consumer; Reg.
Personnel:
Robert M. Wilson *(Pres & CEO)*
Wayne F. Patenaude *(CFO)*
Marie S. Lodi *(Chief HR Officer, Chief Mktg Officer & Sr VP)*
Mark T. Tracy *(CTO & Sr VP)*
Stephen J. Coukos *(Gen Counsel & Exec VP)*
Douglas J. Faithfull *(Exec VP)*
Susan Lapierre *(Sr VP & CRA Officer)*
Brian A. Farrell *(Sr VP & Bank Auditor)*
Terri M. Gavin *(Sr VP-Acct & Fin)*
Mary M. Kearney *(Sr VP)*
Ian MacDonald *(Sr VP-Mktg)*

CAMCO FINANCIAL CORPORATION

814 Wheeling Ave
Cambridge, OH 43725-8685
Tel.: (740) 435-2020
Fax: (740) 435-2021
E-mail: ir@advantagebank.com
Web Site: www.advantagebank.com
Approx. Rev.: $48,185,000
Approx. Number Employees: 228
Year Founded: 1970
Business Description:
Bank Holding Company
S.I.C.: 6712; 6029; 6035
N.A.I.C.S.: 551111; 522110; 522120
Import Export
Advertising Expenditures: $358,000
Media: 9-13-18-20-24-25-26
Personnel:
James E. Huston *(Pres & CEO)*
John E. Kirksey *(CFO, Treas & Sr VP)*
Laurence S. Christ *(Chief Credit Officer & Sr VP)*
Troy D. Greenwalt *(Chief Lending Officer & Sr. VP)*
David Caldwell *(Sr VP-Retail Banking)*
James W. Chugg *(Sr VP-HR)*
Mark A. Olson *(Sr VP-Residential & Consumer Lending)*
Edward A. Wright *(Sr VP-Ops)*
Brands & Products:
WHAT YOU NEED. WHEN YOU NEED IT
Advertising Agency:
Conrad, Phillips & Vutech, Inc.
1398 Goodale Blvd
Columbus, OH 43212
Tel.: (614) 224-3887
Fax: (614) 222-0737

CAMDEN NATIONAL BANK, INC.

(Sub. of Camden National Corporation)
2 Elm St
Camden, ME 04843-1903
Mailing Address:
PO Box 310
Camden, ME 04843
Tel.: (207) 236-9131
Fax: (207) 236-6256
Toll Free: (800) 887-7874
E-mail: info@camdennational.com
Web Site: www.camdennational.com
Sales Range: $50-74.9 Million
Approx. Number Employees: 325
Year Founded: 1875
Business Description:
National Commercial Banks
S.I.C.: 6029
N.A.I.C.S.: 522110
Advertising Expenditures: $4,400,000
Media: 4-7-8-13-18
Personnel:
Karen W. Stanley *(Chm)*
Gregory A. Dufour *(Pres & CEO)*
Debra Jordan *(CFO, Principal Fin & Acctg Officer & Sr VP)*
Timothy Nightingale *(Exec VP & Sr Lending Officer)*
Susan M. Westfall *(Sr VP & Controller)*
Vera Rand *(Sr VP & Reg Comml Mgr)*
Joanne T. Campbell *(Sr VP-Risk Mgmt)*
June B. Parent *(Sr VP-Retail Banking)*
Jack Williams *(Sr VP)*
Jane Dagley *(Mgr-Market & VP)*
Ward I. Graffam *(VP & Mgr-Comml-Southern & Central Reg)*
Chris Nolan *(VP-Info Sys)*
Scott Fernald *(Asst VP-Midcoast Reg)*
Brands & Products:
WHATEVER IT TAKES

CANADA MORTGAGE & HOUSING CORPORATION

700 Montreal Rd
Ottawa, ON K1A 0P7, Canada
Tel.: (613) 748-2000
Fax: (613) 748-2098
E-mail: chic@cmhc-schl.gc.ca
Web Site: www.cmhc-schl.gc.ca
Approx. Number Employees: 1,900
Year Founded: 1946
Business Description:
Mortgage Financing Services
S.I.C.: 6163
N.A.I.C.S.: 522310
Export
Media: 3-14-15-20-23-24
Personnel:
Dino Chiesa *(Chm)*
Karen A. Kinsley *(Pres & CEO)*
D.V. Tyler *(Gen Counsel)*
Coleen Volk *(VP-Fin)*

CANADIAN COMMERCIAL CORPORATION

50 O'Connor St 11th Fl
Ottawa, ON K1A 0S6, Canada
Tel.: (613) 996-0034
Fax: (613) 995-2121
Toll Free: (800) 748-8191 (Canada)
E-mail: reception@ccc.ca
Web Site: www.ccc.ca
Sales Range: $1-4.9 Billion
Approx. Number Employees: 125
Year Founded: 1946
Business Description:
Export Contracting Services
S.I.C.: 7389; 9611
N.A.I.C.S.: 561499; 926110
Media: 10-22
Personnel:
Robert C. Kay *(Chm)*
Marc Whittingham *(Pres & CEO)*
Tamara Parschin-Rybkin *(Gen Counsel, Corp Sec & VP-Legal Svcs)*
Emilie Girard-Ruel *(Mgr-Comm)*

CANADIAN IMPERIAL BANK OF COMMERCE

(d/b/a CIBC)
Commerce Court North 10th Floor
Toronto, ON M5L 1A2, Canada
Tel.: (416) 980-2211
Fax: (416) 363-5347
Toll Free: (800) 465-2422
E-mail: pas@cibc.com
Web Site: www.cibc.com
Approx. Rev.: $14,656,711,680
Approx. Number Employees: 42,354
Year Founded: 1867
Business Description:
Commercial Bank
S.I.C.: 6029
N.A.I.C.S.: 522110
Advertising Expenditures: $200,776,800
Media: 2-5-6-7-8-9-22-23-24-26
Budget Set: Nov. -Dec.
Personnel:
Charles Sirois *(Chm)*
Richard E. Venn *(Deputy Chm, Mng Dir & Sr Exec VP)*
David Hay *(Vice Chm-Investment Banking)*
Gerald T. Mccaughey *(Pres & CEO)*
Andre LaJeunesse *(Mng Dir & Head-Fixed Income, Currencies & Distribution-Asia)*
Duncan Rule *(Mng Dir & Head-FX Trading)*
Michael G. Capatides *(Chief Admin Officer & Gen Counsel)*
Ken Kilgour *(Sr Exec VP & Chief Risk Officer)*
Ron A. Lalonde *(Sr Exec VP-Tech & Ops)*
David Williamson *(Sr Exec VP-CIBC & Grp Head-Retail & Bus Banking)*

Key to Media (For complete agency information see *The Advertising Red Books-Agencies* edition):
1. Bus. Publs. 2. Cable T.V. 3. Catalogs & Directories. 4. Co-op Adv. 5. Consumer Mags. 6. D.M. to Bus. Estab.7. D.M. to Consumers 8. Daily Newsp. 9. Exhibits/Trade Shows 10. Foreign 11. Infomercial 12. Internet Adv.13. Multimedia 14. Network Radio 15. Network T.V. 16. Newsp. Distr. Mags. 17. Other 18. Outdoor (Posters, Transit) 19. Point of Purchase20. Premiums, Novelties 21. Product Samples 22. Special Events Mktg. 23. Spot Radio 24. Spot T.V. 25. Weekly Newsp. 26. Yellow Page Adv.

Colette Delaney *(Sr VP-GIC's, Deposits & Payments-CIBC Retail Markets)*
Cheryl Longo *(Sr VP-Card Products-CIBC Retail Markets)*
Mary Lou Frazer *(Sr Dir-Investor & Fin Comm)*
Doug Maybee *(Dir-External Comm & Media Rels)*

Brands & Products:
CIBC
CIBC 60 PLUS ADVANTAGE
CIBC ADVANTAGE
CIBC AEROGOLD
CIBC AEROMORTGAGE
CIBC AVENTURA
CIBC BIZLINE
CIBC BUSINESS OPERATING ACCOUNT
CIBC CREDITSMART
CIBC ESCALATING RATE GICS
CIBC EVERYDAY
CIBC EXPRESS SWITCH
CIBC INVESTOR'S EDGE
CIBC PREMIERSERVICE
CIBC PREMIUM GROWTH ACCOUNT
CIBC PRIVATE WEALTH MANAGEMENT
CIBC UNLIMITED
CONVENIENCE CARD
DIVIDEND CARD
DIVIDEND PLATINUM
FOR WHAT MATTERS.

Advertising Agencies:
BAM Strategy
420 McGill Ste 400
Montreal, QC H2Y 2G1, Canada
Tel.: (514) 875-1500
Fax: (514) 875-2108
Toll Free: (888) BAM4550

Organic, Inc.
555 Market St 4th Fl
San Francisco, CA 94105
Tel.: (415) 581-5300
Fax: (415) 581-5400

Publicis Montreal
3530 Blvd St- Laurent St 400
Montreal, QC H2X 2V1, Canada
Tel.: (514) 285-1414
Fax: (514) 842-5907

Publicis Toronto
(Sub. of Publicis SA)
111 Queen St E Ste 200
Toronto, ON M5C 1S2, Canada
Tel.: (416) 925-7733
Fax: (416) 925-7341

CANADIAN WESTERN BANK

10303 Jasper Ave Ste 2300
Edmonton, AB T5J 3X6, Canada
Tel.: (780) 423-8888
Fax: (780) 423-8897
E-mail: InvestorRelations@cwbank.com
Web Site: www.cwbankgroup.com
Approx. Int. Income: $568,080,787
Approx. Number Employees: 1,800
Year Founded: 1984
Business Description:
Banking
S.I.C.: 6211
N.A.I.C.S.: 523110
Media: 2-8-10-18-20-22-26

Personnel:
Allan W. Jackson *(Chm)*
Larry M. Pollock *(Pres & CEO)*
Tracey C. Ball *(CFO & Exec VP)*
Darrell R. Jones *(CIO & Sr VP)*
Gail L. Harding *(Gen Counsel, Sec & Sr VP)*
Ricki L. Golick *(Treas & Sr VP)*
William J. Addington *(Exec VP)*
Chris H. Fowler *(Exec VP)*
Randy W. Garvey *(Exec VP)*
Brian J. Young *(Exec VP)*
Michael N. Halliwell *(Sr VP & Reg Gen Mgr)*
Gregory J. Sprung *(Sr VP & Reg Gen Mgr)*
Jack C. Wright *(Sr VP & Reg Gen Mgr)*
Richard R. Giplin *(Sr VP-Credit Risk Mgmt)*
Carolyn J. Graham *(Sr VP & Chief Accountant)*
Uve Knaak *(Sr VP-HR)*
James O. Burke *(VP-Equipment Financing Grp)*
Peter K. Morrison *(VP-Mktg & Product Dev)*
Carl Knowler *(Dir-Mktg)*
Stan B. Plaisier *(Dir-Porfolio Mgmt)*

Brands & Products:
CANADIAN WESTERN BANK
CANADIAN WESTERN TRUST
THINK WESTERN

CAPE BANCORP, INC.

225 N Main St
Cape May Court House, NJ 08210
Tel.: (609) 465-5600
Fax: (609) 465-9040
Web Site: www.capebanknj.com
Approx. Rev.: $53,120,000
Approx. Number Employees: 190
Business Description:
Bank Holding Company; Savings Bank
S.I.C.: 6029; 6035; 6712
N.A.I.C.S.: 522110; 522120; 551111
Advertising Expenditures: $397,000
Media: 8-9-23-24-25
Personnel:
Agostino R. Fabietti *(Chm)*
Michael D. Devlin *(Pres & CEO)*
Guy Hackney *(CFO & Exec VP)*
Robert J. Boyer *(COO & Exec VP)*
James F. McGowan, Jr. *(Chief Credit Officer & Exec VP)*
Michele Pollack *(Chief Lending Officer & Exec VP)*
Kathryn M. Steiger *(Sr VP-Residential Loans)*

CAPITAL BANK CORPORATION

333 Fayetteville St Ste 700
Raleigh, NC 27601
Tel.: (919) 645-6400
Tel.: (919) 645-0868
Fax: (919) 645-6353
E-mail: customerservice@capitalbank-nc.com
Web Site: www.capitalbank-nc.com
Approx. Rev.: $93,271,000
Approx. Number Employees: 389
Year Founded: 1997
Business Description:
Bank Holding Company
S.I.C.: 6712; 6029
N.A.I.C.S.: 551111; 522110
Advertising Expenditures: $1,887,000

Personnel:
Oscar A. Keller, III *(Chm)*
B. Grant Yarber *(Pres & CEO)*
Michael R. Moore *(CFO)*
Jennifer Benefield *(Chief Admin Officer)*
David B. Therit *(Chief Acctg Officer)*
David Morgan *(Chief Banking Officer)*
Teresa White *(Chief HR & Trng Officer)*
Paul Angell *(Sr VP)*
Brad Day *(Dir-Compliance & Head-Compliance & Reporting)*
Ziad Fatayer *(Asst Gen Mgr-Retail Dept)*
Prudy Frederick *(Dir-Mktg)*
Roger F. Plott *(Dir-Comml Svcs)*
Joyce Dunn *(Mgr-Comml Svcs)*

CAPITAL CITY BANK GROUP, INC.

217 N Monroe St
Tallahassee, FL 32301
Tel.: (850) 671-0300
E-mail: bobs@ccbg.com
Web Site: www.ccbg.com
Approx. Rev.: $3,133,000
Approx. Number Employees: 975
Business Description:
Banking Services
S.I.C.: 6141
N.A.I.C.S.: 522210
Advertising Expenditures: $600,000
Media: 6-7-8-18-19-25-26
Personnel:
William G. Smith, Jr. *(Chm, Pres & CEO)*
J. Kimbrough Davis *(CFO & Exec VP)*
Beth H. Corum *(Chief People Officer & Pres-Capital City Svcs Company)*
Brooke Hallock *(Chief Brand Officer)*
Edward G. Canup *(Exec VP-Comml Real Estate Lending)*
William D. Colledge *(Exec VP-MetroCommunity Banking)*
Noel A. Ellis *(Exec VP-Credit Admin)*
Mitchell R. Englert *(Exec VP-Community Banking)*
Karen H. Love *(Exec VP-Residential Lending)*
Dale A. Thompson *(Exec VP-Credit Admin)*
Edwin N. West, Jr. *(Exec VP-Sls Leadership)*
Karen Hager *(Sr VP)*
Brands & Products:
CAPITAL CITY BANK

CAPITAL CROSSING PREFERRED CORPORATION

(Name Changed to EOS PREFERRED CORPORATION)

CAPITAL FINANCIAL HOLDINGS, INC.

1 Main St N
Minot, ND 58703-3189
Tel.: (701) 837-9600
Fax: (701) 857-1892
Toll Free: (877) 814-6379
Web Site:
www.capitalfinancialholdings.com
Approx. Rev.: $19,391,807
Approx. Number Employees: 22
Year Founded: 1987
Business Description:
Financial Holding Company; Investment Advisory, Asset Management, Insurance Brokerage, Securities Brokerage & Dealing Services
S.I.C.: 6719; 6211; 6282; 6371
N.A.I.C.S.: 551112; 523110; 523120; 523920; 523930; 525110
Advertising Expenditures: $27,903
Media: 17
Personnel:
Jeffrey Alan Cummer *(Chm)*
Jacqueline L. Case *(Interim Pres)*
John Carlson *(Interim CEO)*
Valarie Hoskin *(Interim CFO & Treas)*

CAPITAL ONE BANK (USA), N.A.

(Sub. of Capital One Financial Corporation)
275 Broadhollow Rd
Melville, NY 11747-4823
Mailing Address:
PO Box 8914
Melville, NY 11747
Tel.: (631) 844-1376
Toll Free: (877) 694-9111
Web Site: www.capitalonebank.com
E-Mail For Key Personnel:
Marketing Director: marketing@nfb.com
Sales Range: $1-4.9 Billion
Approx. Number Employees: 7,546
Year Founded: 1980
Business Description:
Commercial Banking Services
S.I.C.: 6029
N.A.I.C.S.: 522110
Media: 2-3-9-14-18-20-22-25-26
Personnel:
Lynn Pike *(Pres)*
James Jackson *(Pres-Mid Atlantic Reg & Exec VP-Branch Distr)*
David Dineen *(Pres-Montgomery County Market & Sr VP-Private Banking-Mid Atlanti)*
Eric Lawrence *(Pres-Arlington, Alexandria & Southern Fairfax Market & Sr VP)*
Kimberly Conte *(Pres-Loudon & Fairfax Counties Market & VP)*
Doug Kennedy *(Pres-New Jersey State)*
Ricky Otey *(Pres-Capital One Bank of Texas)*
Tony Pica *(Pres-Market-Suffolk County)*
Michael C. Slocum *(Pres-New York State)*
Robert M. Stuart, Jr. *(Pres-Louisiana State)*
Katherine Busser *(Exec VP)*
Carolyn A. Drexel *(Exec VP)*
Nancy Martel *(Sr VP-Loan Ops)*
Adam Ostrach *(Sr VP)*
Jeff E. Pfeffer *(Sr VP)*
Denis O'Leary *(Dir-Portfolio Mgmt)*
Advertising Agency:
Horizon Media, Inc.
75 Varick St
New York, NY 10013
Tel.: (212) 220-5000
Toll Free: (800) 633-4201
Media Buying

CAPITAL ONE FINANCIAL CORPORATION

1680 Capital One Dr
McLean, VA 22102

Key to Media (For complete agency information see *The Advertising Red Books-Agencies* edition):
1. Bus. Publs. 2. Cable T.V. 3. Catalogs & Directories. 4. Co-op Adv. 5. Consumer Mags. 6. D.M. to Bus. Estab.7. D.M. to Consumers
8. Daily Newsp. 9. Exhibits/Trade Shows 10. Foreign 11. Infomercial 12. Internet Adv.13. Multimedia 14. Network Radio
15. Network T.V. 16. Newsp. Distr. Mags. 17. Other 18. Outdoor (Posters, Transit) 19. Point of Purchase20. Premiums, Novelties
21. Product Samples 22. Special Events Mktg. 23. Spot Radio 24. Spot T.V. 25. Weekly Newsp. 26. Yellow Page Adv.

Capital One Financial Corporation — (Continued)

Tel.: (703) 720-1000
E-mail: investor.relations@capitalone.com
Web Site: www.capitalone.com
Approx. Int. Income: $15,353,000,000
Approx. Number Employees: 27,826
Year Founded: 1994
Business Description:
Financial Holding Company; Banking & Credit Card Financial Services
S.I.C.: 6141; 6029; 6719
N.A.I.C.S.: 522210; 522110; 522291; 551112
Advertising Expenditures: $1,400,000,000
Media: 3-6-8-9-13-14-15-22-24
Personnel:
Richard D. Fairbank *(Chm, Pres & CEO)*
Gary L. Perlin *(CFO)*
Robert M. Alexander *(CIO)*
William Cilluffo *(Pres-Intl Card)*
Rob Livingston *(Pres-Capital One Canada)*
Lynn A. Pike *(Pres-Banking Bus)*
Ryan M. Schneider *(Pres-Card)*
John G. Finneran, Jr. *(Gen Counsel & Corp Sec)*
Suzanne Hammett *(Exec VP & Chief Comml Credit Risk Officer)*
Richard Lyon *(Exec VP)*
Michael C. Slocum *(Exec VP-Capital Ones Comml Banking Bus)*
Jeff Elgin *(VP)*
Scot H. Goodman *(Mng VP-Audit, Info Sys & Enterprise Projects)*
Marc Mentry *(Mng VP-Adv, Media/ Creative Strategy)*
Marty Wilson *(VP-IT)*
Michael W. Azevedo *(Head-Banking Ops)*
Christine Landi *(Sr Dir-Brand Mktg)*
Ted Moon *(Dir-Online Media & Brand Adv)*
Jeff Norris *(Dir-IR)*
Rajesh Lalwaney *(Sr Mgr)*
Kevin Orsi *(Sr Brand Mgr)*
Michael Tsang *(Brand Mgr-Channel Acq Mktg)*
Brands & Products:
BLANK CHECK
CAPITAL ONE
CAPITAL ONE BUSINESS
NO HASSLE
WHAT'S IN YOUR WALLET?
Advertising Agencies:
360i
28 W 23rd St 6th Fl
New York, NY 10010
Tel.: (212) 703-7201
Toll Free: (888) 360-9360

BBDO Atlanta
3500 Lenox Rd NE Ste 1900
Atlanta, GA 30326-4232
Tel.: (404) 231-1700
Fax: (404) 841-1893

Bergman Group
4880 Sadler Rd Ste 220
Glen Allen, VA 23060
Tel.: (804) 225-0600
Fax: (804) 225-0900

company c marketing
160 Varick St
New York, NY 10013
Tel.: (212) 561-6000
Fax: (212) 463-8643

Halogen Response Media
1675 Broadway
New York, NY 10019
Tel.: (212) 468-3627
Fax: (212) 468-3940

hawkeye
2828 Routh St Ste 300
Dallas, TX 75201
Tel.: (214) 659-5615
Fax: (214) 747-1897

Horizon Media, Inc.
75 Varick St
New York, NY 10013
Tel.: (212) 220-5000
Toll Free: (800) 633-4201
Media

JWT Inside
3867 Ruckman Ave
Las Vegas, NV 89129-5565
Tel.: (702) 395-2570
Fax: (702) 395-2766

PromoGroup
444 N Orleans St Ste 400
Chicago, IL 60610-4494
Tel.: (312) 467-1300
Fax: (312) 467-1311

Re:Think Group
700 Canal St 5th Fl
Stamford, CT 06902
Tel.: (203) 357-9004
Fax: (203) 357-9006

CAPITAL Z

(Holding of Paine & Partners, LLC)
230 Park Ave S
New York, NY 10003-1528
Tel.: (212) 965-0800
Fax: (212) 965-2301
Web Site: www.capitalz.com
Approx. Number Employees: 30
Business Description:
Investment Services
S.I.C.: 6289
N.A.I.C.S.: 523999
Media: 2-8
Personnel:
Laurence Cheng *(Chm & Chief Investment Officer)*
Roland V. Bernardon *(CFO)*
Craig Fisher *(Gen Counsel)*
Jeffrey Bergman *(VP-Fin)*
Robin Prager *(Mgr-Acctg)*
Allen Tam *(Asst Controller)*

CAPITALSOURCE INC.

5404 Wisconsin Ave 2nd Fl
Chevy Chase, MD 20815
Tel.: (301) 841-2700
Fax: (301) 841-2340
Toll Free: (866) 695-3457
E-mail: mailinfo@capitalsource.com
Web Site: www.capitalsource.com
Approx. Int. Income: $639,641,000
Approx. Number Employees: 625
Business Description:
Commercial Finance Services
S.I.C.: 6141; 6163; 6211
N.A.I.C.S.: 522210; 522291; 522310; 523120
Media: 2
Personnel:
John K. Delaney *(Chm)*
Steven A. Museles *(Co-CEO)*
James J. Pieczynski *(Co-CEO)*
Donald F. Cole *(CFO)*
Joseph A. Kenary *(Chief Investment Officer)*
Bryan D. Smith *(Chief Acctg Officer)*
Laird M. Boulden *(Pres-Corp Fin Grp)*
Bryan M. Corsini *(Exec VP)*
Dennis Oakes *(Sr VP-IR)*
Ryan Golding *(Mng Dir-Leveraged Fin Grp)*
Michael Weiss *(Dir-Comm)*
Brands & Products:
CAPITAL SOURCE & DESIGN
CAPITALSOURCE
Advertising Agencies:
Crosby Marketing Communications
705 Melvin Ave Ste 200
Annapolis, MD 21401-1540
Tel.: (410) 626-0805
Fax: (410) 269-6547

HLB Communications, Inc.
875 N Michigan Ave
Chicago, IL 60611-1896
Tel.: (312) 649-0371
Fax: (312) 649-1119

CAPITOL BANCORP LTD.

200 Washington Sq N 4th Fl
Lansing, MI 48933
Tel.: (517) 487-6555
Fax: (517) 374-2576
E-mail: communications@capitolbancorp.com
Web Site: www.capitolbancorp.com
Approx. Rev.: $188,138,000
Approx. Number Employees: 1,002
Year Founded: 1990
Business Description:
Holding Company
S.I.C.: 6712; 6029
N.A.I.C.S.: 551111; 522110
Advertising Expenditures: $1,168,000
Personnel:
Joseph D. Reid *(Chm & CEO)*
Lawrence Connell *(Co-Vice Chm)*
Michael L. Kasten *(Co-Vice Chm)*
Lyle W. Miller *(Co-Vice Chm)*
Cristin K. Reid *(Pres)*
Nicholas G. Hahn *(Interim CFO)*
Gregory R. Bixby *(CIO)*
Bruce D. Jones *(Pres-Southeast Region)*
John S. Lewis *(Pres-Mid-Michigan Investment Co.)*
Bruce A. Thomas *(Pres-Bank Ops)*
Brian K. English *(Gen Counsel)*
Clifford G. Sheldon *(Exec VP & Cashier)*
John J. Wilkins *(Exec VP)*
Brian W. Astle *(Sr VP-Credit Admin)*
Carrie L. Dickinson *(Sr VP-Credit Admin)*
James R. Rose, Jr. *(Sr VP-Credit Admin)*
John Nixon III *(First VP-Capitol Wealth Advisors)*
Kathleen Slocum *(VP-Wealth Advisors)*
Art R. Aguirre *(Dir-Credit Risk)*
Richard Houseworth *(Dir-Govt Rels)*
Angela M. Kimber *(Dir-Comm)*
Charles J. McDonald *(Dir-Product Dev & Mgmt)*
Kelly D. Miller *(Dir-Specialty Fin)*
Kenneth I. Myers *(Dir-Risk Mgmt)*
Linda D. Pavona *(Dir-Corp Rels)*
Rebecca M. Hills *(Asst Dir-Acctg)*
Deanna L. Brock *(Sr Mgr-Ops)*
Christopher R. Cobb *(Mgr-Dev & Automation)*
David S. Groenewoud *(Mgr-Corp Fin)*
Charles D. Turpie *(Mgr-Loan)*
Michael M. Moran *(Chief-Capital Markets)*
Brands & Products:
THE ART OF BANKING
SMALLER BANKS BIGGER SERVICE

CAPITOL CITY BANCSHARES, INC.

562 Lee St
Atlanta, GA 30310
Tel.: (404) 752-6067
Fax: (404) 752-5862
Web Site: www.capitolcitybank-atl.com
Approx. Rev.: $18,156,162
Approx. Number Employees: 70
Year Founded: 1998
Business Description:
Bank Holding Company
S.I.C.: 6029; 6712
N.A.I.C.S.: 522110; 551111
Advertising Expenditures: $52,415
Media: 17
Personnel:
William Thomas *(Chm)*
George G. Andrews *(Pres & CEO)*

CAPITOL FEDERAL FINANCIAL, INC.

700 S Kansas Ave
Topeka, KS 66603-3894
Mailing Address:
PO Box 3505
Topeka, KS 66601-3505
Tel.: (785) 235-1341
Fax: (785) 231-6264
E-mail: jwempe@capfed.com
Web Site: www.capfed.com
Approx. Rev.: $408,462,000
Approx. Number Employees: 600
Year Founded: 1999
Business Description:
Bank Holding Company
S.I.C.: 6712; 6029
N.A.I.C.S.: 551111; 522110
Advertising Expenditures: $6,027,000
Media: 7-8-13
Budget Set: Oct.
Personnel:
John B. Dicus *(Chm, Pres & CEO)*
Kent G. Townsend *(CFO, Treas & Exec VP)*
Rick C. Jackson *(Exec VP)*
Larry K. Brubaker *(Exec VP)*
Brands & Products:
CAPITOL FEDERAL

CAPLEASE, INC.

1065 Ave of the Americas
New York, NY 10018
Tel.: (212) 217-6300
Fax: (212) 217-6301
E-mail: info@caplease.com
Web Site: www.caplease.com

Key to Media (For complete agency information see *The Advertising Red Books-Agencies* edition):
1. Bus. Publs. 2. Cable T.V. 3. Catalogs & Directories. 4. Co-op Adv. 5. Consumer Mags. 6. D.M. to Bus. Estab.7. D.M. to Consumers 8. Daily Newsp. 9. Exhibits/Trade Shows 10. Foreign 11. Infomercial 12. Internet Adv.13. Multimedia 14. Network Radio 15. Network T.V. 16. Newsp. Distr. Mags. 17. Other 18. Outdoor (Posters, Transit) 19. Point of Purchase20. Premiums, Novelties 21. Product Samples 22. Special Events Mktg. 23. Spot Radio 24. Spot T.V. 25. Weekly Newsp. 26. Yellow Page Adv.

Approx. Rev.: $166,415,000
Approx. Number Employees: 19
Year Founded: 1994
Business Description:
Real Estate Investment Trust
S.I.C.: 6798
N.A.I.C.S.: 525930
Advertising Expenditures: $145,000
Media: 17
Personnel:
Paul H. Mcdowell *(Chm & CEO)*
William R. Pollert *(Pres)*
Shawn P. Seale *(CFO & Sr VP)*
Robert Blanz *(Chief Investment Officer & Sr VP)*
John E. Warch *(Chief Acctg Officer & Sr VP)*
Paul Hughes *(Gen Counsel, Sec & VP)*

CAPSTAR PARTNERS, LLC
600 Congress Ave Ste 1400
Austin, TX 78701
Tel.: (512) 340-7800
Fax: (512) 340-7840
Web Site: www.capstarpartners.com
Sales Range: $25-49.9 Million
Approx. Number Employees: 30
Business Description:
Private Equity Firm
S.I.C.: 6289
N.A.I.C.S.: 523999
Personnel:
R. Steven Hicks *(Pres & Partner)*
Advertising Agency:
The Dozier Company
2547 Farrington St
Dallas, TX 75207-6607
Tel.: (214) 744-2800
Fax: (214) 744-1240

CARDINAL BANK N.A.
(Sub. of Cardinal Financial Corp.)
8270 Greensboro Dr Ste 500
McLean, VA 22102
Tel.: (703) 584-3400
Fax: (703) 584-3410
Toll Free: (800) 473-3247
Web Site: www.cardinalbank.com
Sales Range: $10-24.9 Million
Approx. Number Employees: 110
Year Founded: 1998
Business Description:
Full Banking Services
S.I.C.: 6029; 6159
N.A.I.C.S.: 522110; 522292
Media: 4-7-8-9-10-13-18-20-22-23-25-26
Personnel:
Bernard H. Clineburg *(Chm & CEO)*
William T. Mundy *(Mng Dir, Exec VP-Trust & Investments)*
Mark A. Wendel *(CFO & Exec VP)*
Alice P. Frazier *(COO & Exec VP)*
Christopher W. Bergstrom *(Chief Risk Officer & Exec VP)*
Robert E Bradecamp *(Treas & Exec VP)*
Cynthia A. Cole *(Exec VP & Dir-Mktg)*
Paulette Cross *(Exec VP & Dir-Mktg)*
Dennis M. Griffith *(Chief Lending Officer & Exec VP)*
Eleanor D. Schmidt *(Exec VP & Compliance Officer)*
Cheryl L. Steinbacher *(Sr VP & Dir-HR)*
Seth Carter *(Sr VP)*
Jeffrey R. DiMeglio *(Sr VP)*
William O'Connor *(Sr VP & Sr Credit Officer)*
Richard F. Schoen *(Sr VP)*
Hilary J. Blackburn *(VP-Product Dev & Ecommerce)*
Tahiya Kettles *(Asst VP & Mgr-Arlington)*
Cynthia Stirling *(Asst VP & Mgr-Banking Center)*
Laurie Hunt *(Asst VP)*
Martha Wilson *(Asst VP-Comml Lending)*
Brands & Products:
CARDINAL ESCROW MANAGER
CARDINAL ONLINE BANKING
CARDINAL ONLINE COMMERCIAL BANKING

CARDINAL FINANCIAL CORP.
8270 Greensboro Dr Ste 500
McLean, VA 22102
Tel.: (703) 584-3400
Fax: (703) 691-8075
Toll Free: (800) 473-3247
E-mail: mark.wendel@cardinalbank.com
Web Site: www.cardinalbank.com
Approx. Rev.: $124,022,000
Approx. Number Employees: 417
Year Founded: 1997
Business Description:
Bank Holding Company
S.I.C.: 6141; 6029; 6712
N.A.I.C.S.: 522210; 522110; 551111
Advertising Expenditures: $2,084,000
Personnel:
Bernard H. Clineburg *(Chm & CEO)*
Kendal E. Carson *(Pres)*
Mark A. Wendel *(CFO & Exec VP)*
Alice P. Frazier *(COO & Exec VP)*
Eleanor D. Schmidt *(Chief Compliance Officer & Exec VP)*
Christopher W. Bergstrom *(Chief Risk Officer & Exec VP)*
Robert E. Bradecamp *(Treas & Exec VP)*
Jennifer L. Deacon *(Sec, Sr VP & Controller)*
Dennis M. Griffith *(Chief Lending Officer & Exec VP)*
David W. Frasier *(Exec VP & Dir-Audit)*
Karen S. Denas *(Sr VP-Retail Admin)*
Janice A. Cross *(VP & Asst Sec)*
Brands & Products:
CARDINAL

CARDTRONICS, INC.
3250 Briarpark Dr Ste 400
Houston, TX 77042
Tel.: (832) 308-4000
Fax: (832) 308-4001
Toll Free: (800) 786-9666
E-mail: service@cardtronics.com
Web Site: www.cardtronics.com
Approx. Rev.: $532,078,000
Approx. Number Employees: 535
Year Founded: 1989
Business Description:
Automatic Teller Machines Owner & Operator
S.I.C.: 6099
N.A.I.C.S.: 522320
Advertising Expenditures: $1,000,000
Personnel:
Dennis F. Lynch *(Chm)*
Steven A. Rathgaber *(CEO)*
J. Chris Brewster *(CFO)*
Jerry Garcia *(CIO)*
Tom Pierce *(CMO)*
Erich Bradley Conrad *(Chief Acctg Officer)*
Michael H. Clinard *(Pres-Global Svcs)*
Rick Updyke *(Pres-Bus Grp-US)*
Michael E. Keller *(Gen Counsel & Sec)*
James Bettinger *(Exec VP-Global Ops)*
Carleton K. Thompson, III *(Exec VP-Domestic ATM Svcs)*
Thomas E. Upton *(Exec VP-Acq)*
Lloyd L. Nobles *(Sr VP)*
Joel Antonini *(VP-Mktg)*

CAROLINA BANK HOLDINGS, INC.
101 N Spring St
Greensboro, NC 27410
Mailing Address:
PO Box 10209
Greensboro, NC 27404
Tel.: (336) 288-1898
Fax: (336) 286-5553
E-mail: info@carolinabank.com
Web Site: www.carolinabank.com
Approx. Rev.: $46,289,000
Approx. Number Employees: 155
Year Founded: 2000
Business Description:
Bank Holding Company
S.I.C.: 6029; 6712
N.A.I.C.S.: 522110; 551111
Advertising Expenditures: $699,000
Personnel:
Gary N. Brown *(Chm)*
Robert T. Braswell *(Pres & CEO)*
Thomas Allen Liles *(CFO & Exec VP)*
Daniel D. Hornfeck *(Chief Credit Officer & Exec VP)*
Phillip C. Carmac *(Pres-Div & Sr VP)*
Gunnar N. R. Fromen *(Loan Officer-Comml & Exec VP)*
F. Virginia Grimes *(Sr VP, Branch Coord & Mgr)*
Gerald W Church *(Sr VP & Officer-Market Exec)*
H Dean Sexton *(Sr VP & Comml Loan Officer)*
Nicole Sammons *(VP & Mgr-Loan Ops)*
Sharon A. Williams *(VP & Mgr-Ops)*
Orentho T Stewart *(Asst VP & Mgr-Branch)*
Frank Harris *(Asst VP & Mortgage Loan Officer)*

CARROLLTON BANK
(Sub. of Carrollton Bancorp)
344 N Charles St Ste 300
Baltimore, MD 21201
Tel.: (410) 536-7386
Fax: (410) 536-7365
Toll Free: (800) 222-6566
E-mail: responsecenter@carroltonbank.com
Web Site: www.carrolltonbank.com
Sales Range: $50-74.9 Million
Approx. Number Employees: 149
Year Founded: 1903
Business Description:
State Commercial Bank
S.I.C.: 6029
N.A.I.C.S.: 522110
Advertising Expenditures: $250,000
Media: 7-8-20-22-23-25
Personnel:
Robert A. Altieri *(Pres & CEO)*
Michael J. Camiel *(Sr VP & Chief Credit Officer)*
Rich Hunt *(Sr VP & Dir-Comml Banking)*
Gary M. Jewell *(Sr VP-Electronic Banking)*
Deanna Lintz *(Sr VP-Branch Admin)*
Lola B. Stokes *(Sr VP-Compliance)*
Donna Smith *(VP & Dir-Security)*
Joyce F. Murphy *(VP-Electronic Banking)*
Cathy Regan *(VP-HR)*
Sally Rogers *(VP-Trng)*
Eunice W. Taylor *(VP-Electronic Banking)*
Victor Zubar *(VP-MIS)*
Gary Allgeier *(Asst VP-Fin)*
William Brown *(Asst VP-DP)*
Patricia Harris *(Asst VP-Branch Admin)*
Robert J. Tolson *(Asst VP-Loan Servicing)*
Tari Mitchell *(Assoc VP)*
Jeanette Neal *(Dir-Mktg)*

CARUSO AFFILIATED
101 The Grove Dr
Los Angeles, CA 90036
Tel.: (323) 900-8100
Fax: (323) 900-8101
E-mail: mail@carusoaffiliated.com
Web Site: www.carusoaffiliated.com
Approx. Sls.: $23,800,000
Approx. Number Employees: 90
Business Description:
Investment Holding Company
S.I.C.: 6719; 6512
N.A.I.C.S.: 551112; 531120
Personnel:
Rick J. Caruso *(Pres & CEO)*
Dave Reston *(CFO)*
Paul J. Kurzawa *(COO)*
David B. Silva *(Gen Counsel & Exec VP)*
Jennifer Gordon *(Sr VP-Events & PR)*
Rick Lemmo *(Sr VP-Community Rels)*
Bret M. Nielsen *(Sr VP-Leasing & Asset Mgmt)*
Daniel J. Burgner *(Exec VP-Strategic Alliances & Entertainment)*
Michael McManus *(Exec VP-Dev)*
Thomas A. Veje *(Exec VP-Construction)*
David W. Williams *(Exec VP-Architecture)*
Robert G. Johnson *(Sr VP & Controller)*
Jackie Levy *(Sr VP-Ops)*
Matt Middlebrook *(Sr VP-Dev)*
Galit Shokrian *(Sr VP-Mktg)*
Peter Hayden *(VP-Engrg)*
Advertising Agency:
One Eighteen Advertising
12400 Wilshire Blvd Ste 540
Los Angeles, CA 90025
Tel.: (310) 442-0118
Fax: (310) 442-0141

CARVER FEDERAL SAVINGS BANK
(Sub. of Carver Bancorp Inc)
75 W 125th St
New York, NY 10027-4512
Tel.: (212) 876-4747
Tel.: (718) 230-2900
E-mail: customer.service@carverbank.com

Key to Media (For complete agency information see *The Advertising Red Books-Agencies* edition):
1. Bus. Publs. 2. Cable T.V. 3. Catalogs & Directories. 4. Co-op Adv. 5. Consumer Mags. 6. D.M. to Bus. Estab.7. D.M. to Consumers 8. Daily Newsp. 9. Exhibits/Trade Shows 10. Foreign 11. Infomercial 12. Internet Adv.13. Multimedia 14. Network Radio 15. Network T.V. 16. Newsp. Distr. Mags. 17. Other 18. Outdoor (Posters, Transit) 19. Point of Purchase20. Premiums, Novelties 21. Product Samples 22. Special Events Mktg. 23. Spot Radio 24. Spot T.V. 25. Weekly Newsp. 26. Yellow Page Adv.

Carver Federal Savings Bank — (Continued)

Web Site: www.carverbank.com
Sales Range: $25-49.9 Million
Approx. Number Employees: 110
Year Founded: 1948
Business Description:
Full Banking Services
S.I.C.: 6035
N.A.I.C.S.: 522120
Advertising Expenditures: $250,000
Media: 6-8-9-23-25
Personnel:
Deborah C. Wright *(Chm)*
Chris A. McFadden *(CFO & Exec VP)*
Margaret Floyd *(Sr VP & Officer-HR)*
David Toner *(Sr VP & Controller)*
James H. Bason *(Chief Lending Officer & Sr VP)*
Advertising Agency:
Platform Media
155 E 55th St Ste 4D
New York, NY 10022
Tel.: (212) 330-7515

CASCADE BANCORP

1100 NW Wall St
Bend, OR 97701
Mailing Address:
PO Box 369
Bend, OR 97701
Tel.: (541) 617-3500
Tel.: (541) 385-6205
Fax: (541) 382-8780
Toll Free: (877) 617-3400
E-mail: debbieb@botc.com
Web Site: www.botc.com
Approx. Rev.: $98,353,000
Approx. Number Employees: 432
Business Description:
Bank Holding Company
S.I.C.: 6029; 6141; 6712
N.A.I.C.S.: 522110; 522291; 551111
Advertising Expenditures: $930,000
Personnel:
Gary L. Hoffman *(Chm)*
Patricia L. Moss *(Pres & CEO)*
Michael J Delvin *(Pres & COO)*
Gregory D. Newton *(CFO & Exec VP)*
Michael Allison *(Chief Credit Officer & Exec VP)*
Peggy L. Biss *(Chief HR Officer & Exec VP)*
Debbie C. Amerongen *(Chief Deposit Officer & Exec VP)*
Michael M. Mooney *(Pres-Idaho Reg)*
William A. Haden *(Exec VP-Southern Oregon & Reg Mgr)*
Walter O. Krumbholz *(Exec VP-Northwest Oregon & Reg Mgr)*
Julie A. Miller *(Exec VP & Reg Mgr-Central Oregon)*
Brands & Products:
CASCADE BANCORP

CASCADE FINANCIAL CORPORATION

2828 Colby Ave
Everett, WA 98201
Tel.: (425) 339-5500
Fax: (425) 259-8512
E-mail: scenter@cascadebank.com
Web Site: www.cascadebank.com
Approx. Rev.: $90,139,000
Approx. Number Employees: 200
Year Founded: 1916
Business Description:
Bank Holding Company
S.I.C.: 6022; 6029; 6712
N.A.I.C.S.: 522190; 522110; 551111
Advertising Expenditures: $810,000
Media: 2-4-7-8-9-18-20-23-25-26
Personnel:
Dennis R. Murphy *(Chm)*
Carol Kobuke Nelson *(Pres & CEO)*
Debra Johnson *(Chief Acctg Officer, Sr VP, CFO & Controller)*
Robert G. Disotell *(Exec VP & Chief Credit Officer)*
LeAnne M. Harrington *(Chief Admin Officer & Exec VP)*
Steven R. Erickson *(Exec VP-Bus Banking)*
Debbie E. Mcleod *(Exec VP-Retail Banking)*
Brands & Products:
CASCADE BANK
REAL PEPOPLE. REAL SOLUTIONS

CASH AMERICA INTERNATIONAL, INC.

Cash America Intl Bldg 1600 W 7th St
Fort Worth, TX 76102-2599
Tel.: (817) 335-1100
Fax: (817) 570-1225
E-mail: customer_service@cashamericaonline.com
Web Site: www.cashamerica.com
Approx. Rev.: $1,293,339,000
Approx. Number Employees: 6,017
Year Founded: 1984
Business Description:
Secured Non-Recourse Lending Services
S.I.C.: 6159; 5999; 6733
N.A.I.C.S.: 522298; 453998; 523991
Advertising Expenditures: $32,000,000
Personnel:
Jack R. Daugherty *(Chm)*
Daniel R. Feehan *(Pres & CEO)*
Dennis J. Weese *(Pres & COO-Retail Svcs Div)*
Thomas A. Bessant Jr. *(CFO & Exec VP)*
J. Curtis Linscott *(Gen Counsel, Sec & Exec VP)*
Austin D. Nettle *(Treas & VP-Fin)*
David J. Clay *(Sr VP-Fin)*
David J. Hurrell *(Sr VP-New Sys Dev)*
Mary L. Jackson *(Sr VP-Corp Affairs)*
Clint D. James *(Sr VP-HR)*
John M. Kenny *(Sr VP-IT)*
Roberto Martinez *(Sr VP-Mktg & Strategy)*
Aditya K. Garg *(VP-Infrastructure & Architecture)*
Brands & Products:
BECAUSE SOME THINGS CAN'T UNTIL PAYDAY
CASH AMERICA
CASH WHEN IT COUNTS
EASY SECURE,THE SEARCH ENDS
EZ CASH SUPERPAWN WHERE EVERYBODY SHOPS
GET THE CASH KEEP THE CAR
MAKE ANYDAY PAYDAY
MAXCASH
MAXCASH PAYDAY LOANS
MR PAYROLL
NATIONAL JEWELRY LIQUIDATION CENTRE
PAYDAY ADVANCE CASH AMERICA
REAL FAST REAL EASY
SUPERPAWN

CASH FLOW GENERATOR

(Sub. of TIGRENT INC.)
1612 E Cape Coral Pkwy
Cape Coral, FL 33904
Tel.: (239) 542-0643
Fax: (239) 540-6562
Toll Free: (800) 496-1874
E-mail: info@cashflowgenerator.com
Web Site: www.cashflowgenerator.com
Sales Range: $125-149.9 Million
Approx. Number Employees: 100
Year Founded: 1995
Business Description:
Financial Information Services
S.I.C.: 6289
N.A.I.C.S.: 523999
Export
Advertising Expenditures: $5,000,000
Media: 1-2-3-4-5-6-7-8-9-10-11-12-13-14-15-17-20-23-24-25
Distr.: Intl.
Personnel:
Lisa Marino *(Publications Dir)*
Brands & Products:
CASH FLOW BOOT CAMP
CASH FLOW GENERATOR
FLASH CASH COURSE
LEGRAND GROUP
MILLIONAIRE SUCCESS SYSTEM
MILLIONAIRE TRAINING WORKSHOP
QUICK-TURN
RESULTS PUBLISHING, INC.
SDI DIRECT
SDI INTERNET SERVICES
Advertising Agency:
SDI Marketing
(House Agency)
9799 Old Saint Augustine Rd.
Jacksonville, FL 32250
Tel.: (904) 886-2985 (x104)

THE CASH STORE FINANCIAL SERVICES INC.

17631 103rd Ave
Edmonton, AB T5S 1N8, Canada
Tel.: (780) 408-5110
Fax: (780) 408-5122
E-mail: information@csfinancial.ca
Web Site: www.csfinancial.ca
Approx. Rev.: $217,048,714
Year Founded: 2001
Business Description:
Payday Advance Lending Services
S.I.C.: 6141
N.A.I.C.S.: 522291
Advertising Expenditures: $5,978,756
Media: 5
Personnel:
Gordon J. Reykdal *(Chm & CEO)*
Barret J. Reykdal *(Pres & COO)*
Nancy Bland *(CFO)*
Michael J.L. Thompson *(Sec & Sr VP)*
Dave Park *(VP-HR)*
Werner Pietrzyk *(VP-Internal Audit)*
Stacey Shenfield *(VP-IT)*
Michael Zvonkovic *(VP-Fin)*
Tracy Nadiger *(Gen Mgr-Mktg & Comm)*

CATERPILLAR FINANCIAL SERVICES CORPORATION

(Sub. of Caterpillar, Inc.)
2120 West End Ave
Nashville, TN 37203-1031
Tel.: (615) 341-1000
Fax: (615) 341-8596
Web Site: www.finance.cat.com
Approx. Rev.: $2,552,000,000
Approx. Number Employees: 1,572
Year Founded: 1981
Business Description:
Finance & Leasing of Industrial Equipment & Machinery
S.I.C.: 7353; 6141; 6159
N.A.I.C.S.: 522210; 522220; 522291; 522298; 532412
Personnel:
Kent M. Adams *(Pres)*
James A. Duensing *(CFO & Exec VP)*
Michael G. Sposato *(Gen Counsel)*
Brands & Products:
CAT ACCESSACCOUNT
Advertising Agency:
Beyer & Associates LLC
Associated Bank Plaza 411 Hamilton Blvd Ste 1908
Peoria, IL 61602
Tel.: (309) 497-0100
Fax: (309) 497-0105
Cat AccessAccount

CATHAY GENERAL BANCORP, INC.

777 N Broadway
Los Angeles, CA 90012
Tel.: (213) 625-4700
Fax: (213) 625-1368
Toll Free: (800) 9CATHAY
E-mail: information@cathaybank.com
Web Site: www.cathaybank.com
E-Mail For Key Personnel:
President: dunson_cheng@cathaybank.com
Approx. Rev.: $489,594,000
Approx. Number Employees: 1,010
Year Founded: 1962
Business Description:
State Commercial Banks
S.I.C.: 6022; 6029
N.A.I.C.S.: 522190; 522110
Import Export
Advertising Expenditures: $2,488,000
Media: 7-8-13
Personnel:
Dunson K. Cheng *(Chm, Pres & CEO)*
Heng W. Chen *(CFO, Treas & Exec VP)*
Peter Wu *(Exec Vice Chm & COO)*
Kim R. Bingham *(Chief Credit Officer & Exec VP)*
Perry P. Oei *(Gen Counsel, Sec & Sr VP)*
Anthony M. Tang *(Exec VP)*
Irwin Wong *(Exec VP-Branch Admin)*
Monica Chen *(Asst Sec)*

CBIZ, INC.

6050 Oaktree Blvd Ste 500
Cleveland, OH 44131-6951
Tel.: (216) 447-9000
Fax: (216) 447-9007
Toll Free: (800) ASKCBIZ
Web Site: www.cbiz.com

Key to Media (For complete agency information see *The Advertising Red Books-Agencies* edition):
1. Bus. Publs. 2. Cable T.V. 3. Catalogs & Directories. 4. Co-op Adv. 5. Consumer Mags. 6. D.M. to Bus. Estab.7. D.M. to Consumers
8. Daily Newsp. 9. Exhibits/Trade Shows 10. Foreign 11. Infomercial 12. Internet Adv.13. Multimedia 14. Network Radio
15. Network T.V. 16. Newsp. Distr. Mags. 17. Other 18. Outdoor (Posters, Transit) 19. Point of Purchase20. Premiums, Novelties
21. Product Samples 22. Special Events Mktg. 23. Spot Radio 24. Spot T.V. 25. Weekly Newsp. 26. Yellow Page Adv.

Approx. Rev.: $732,505,000
Approx. Number Employees: 5,250
Year Founded: 1996
Business Description:
Accounting, Tax & Employee Benefit Consulting Services
S.I.C.: 8721; 7291; 7389; 8742
N.A.I.C.S.: 541219; 541213; 541611; 561499
Media: 2-6-7-10-14-23
Personnel:
Steven L. Gerard *(Chm & CEO)*
Jerome P. Grisko Jr. *(Pres & COO)*
Ware H. Grove *(CFO & Sr VP)*
Mark M. Waxman *(CMO)*
George A. Dufour *(CTO & Sr VP)*
G. Darrell Hulsey *(Pres-Medical Mgmt Prof)*
David J. Sibits *(Pres-Fin Svcs)*
Michael W. Gleespen *(Gen Counsel & Sec)*
Joseph George *(Exec VP & Dir-Property & Casualty)*
Teresa Bur *(Sr VP-HR)*
Michael P. Kouzelos *(Sr VP-Strategic Initiatives)*
Robert A. O'Byrne *(Sr VP-Benefits & Insurance Svcs)*
Frank Campagna *(Dir-Midwest)*
Daniel Hughes *(Dir-Tax & Bus Svcs Div)*
Emily Reilly *(Dir-Underwriting)*
Thomas Krysanick *(Sr Mgr-Tax)*
Nan Coverdale *(Mgr-Acct-Property & Casualty)*
Paul Soos *(Mgr-Anti-Fraud Svcs Practice)*
Victor Szerpicki *(Mgr-Acctg)*
Advertising Agency:
Dix & Eaton Incorporated
200 Public Sq Ste 1400
Cleveland, OH 44114
Tel.: (216) 241-0405
Fax: (216) 241-3070

CBOE HOLDINGS, INC.
400 S LaSalle St
Chicago, IL 60605
Tel.: (312) 786-5600
Fax: (312) 786-7409
Web Site: www.cboe.com
Approx. Rev.: $437,104,000
Approx. Number Employees: 581
Business Description:
Holding Company; Options Board Operations
S.I.C.: 6719; 6231
N.A.I.C.S.: 551112; 523210
Advertising Expenditures: $5,500,000
Personnel:
William J. Brodsky *(Chm & CEO)*
Edward T. Tilly *(Vice Chm)*
Edward J. Joyce *(Pres & COO)*
Alan J. Dean *(CFO, Treas & Exec VP)*
David S. Reynolds *(Chief Acctg Officer)*
Joanne Moffic-Silver *(Gen Counsel, Sec & Exec VP)*
Richard G. DuFour *(Exec VP)*
Gerald T. O'Connell *(Exec VP)*
Edward L. Provost *(Exec VP)*
Phillip M. Slocum *(Exec VP)*
Patrick J. Fay *(Sr VP)*

CCFNB BANCORP, INC.
232 East St
Bloomsburg, PA 17815
Tel.: (570) 784-4400
Fax: (570) 784-3912
Web Site: www.firstcolumbiabank.com
Approx. Rev.: $32,899,000
Approx. Number Employees: 185
Year Founded: 1983
Business Description:
Bank Holding Company
S.I.C.: 6712; 6029
N.A.I.C.S.: 551111; 522110
Advertising Expenditures: $224,000
Media: 8
Personnel:
Glenn E. Halterman *(Chm)*
Lance O. Diehl *(Pres & CEO)*
Jeffrey T. Arnold *(CFO & Treas)*

CENTER BANCORP, INC.
2455 Morris Ave
Union, NJ 07083-0007
Tel.: (908) 688-9500
Fax: (908) 688-3043
Web Site: www.centerbancorp.com
Approx. Rev.: $51,186,000
Approx. Number Employees: 159
Year Founded: 1982
Business Description:
Bank Holding Company
S.I.C.: 6141; 6029; 6712
N.A.I.C.S.: 522210; 522110; 551111
Advertising Expenditures: $268,000
Media: 6-7-8-9-10-18-20-22-23-24-25-26
Personnel:
Alexander A. Bol *(Chm)*
Anthony C. Weagley *(Pres & CEO)*
Vincent N. Tozzi *(CFO, Treas & VP)*
Julie D'Aloia *(Sr VP & Branch Mgr-Corp Headquarters)*
Lori A. Wunder *(Sr VP-Ops)*

CENTER FINANCIAL CORPORATION
3435 Wilshire Blvd Ste 700
Los Angeles, CA 90010
Tel.: (213) 251-2222
Web Site: investor.centerbank.com
Approx. Rev.: $121,919,000
Approx. Number Employees: 638
Year Founded: 2000
Business Description:
Bank Holding Company
S.I.C.: 6712; 6029; 6035
N.A.I.C.S.: 551111; 522110; 522120
Advertising Expenditures: $1,426,000
Personnel:
Jin Chul Jhung *(Chm)*
Richard S. Cupp *(Pres & CEO)*
Sook Goo *(COO & Exec VP)*
Jason K. Kim *(Chief Credit Officer & Exec VP)*
Lisa Kim Pai *(Chief Risk Officer, Exec VP, Gen Counsel & Corp Sec)*
Douglas J. Goddard *(CFO-Interim)*
Angie Yang *(Sr VP-IR)*

CENTRA FINANCIAL HOLDINGS, INC.
990 Elmer Prince Dr Ste 100
Morgantown, WV 26505
Tel.: (304) 598-2000
Fax: (304) 598-2435
Web Site: www.centrabank.com
Approx. Rev.: $70,051,000
Approx. Number Employees: 245
Year Founded: 1999
Business Description:
Bank Holding Company
S.I.C.: 6712; 6029
N.A.I.C.S.: 551111; 522110
Advertising Expenditures: $1,591,000
Personnel:
John T. Fahey *(Founder & Sr VP)*
Douglas J. Leech *(Chm, Pres & CEO)*
Kevin D. Lemley *(CFO, Treas & VP)*
E. Richard Hilleary *(Sr VP)*

CENTRAL BANCORP, INC.
399 Highland Ave
Somerville, MA 02144-2516
Tel.: (617) 628-4000
Fax: (617) 629-4219
E-mail: ebanker@centralbk.com
Web Site: www.centralbk.com
Approx. Rev.: $27,363,000
Approx. Number Employees: 92
Year Founded: 1915
Business Description:
Bank Holding Company
S.I.C.: 6712; 6029; 6035
N.A.I.C.S.: 551111; 522110; 522120
Advertising Expenditures: $163,000
Media: 8-25
Personnel:
John D. Doherty *(Chm & CEO)*
William P. Morrissey *(Pres)*
Paul S. Feeley *(CFO, Treas & Sr VP)*
Bryan E. Greenbaum *(Sr VP-Retail Banking)*
Rhoda K. Astone *(VP & Clerk)*

CENTRAL FEDERAL CORPORATION
2923 Smith Rd
Fairlawn, OH 44333
Tel.: (330) 666-7979
Fax: (330) 666-7959
Web Site: www.cfbankonline.com
Approx. Rev.: $14,411,000
Approx. Number Employees: 62
Year Founded: 1892
Business Description:
Bank Holding Company
S.I.C.: 6712; 6029
N.A.I.C.S.: 551111; 522110
Advertising Expenditures: $52,000
Media: 17
Personnel:
Jerry F. Whitmer *(Chm)*
Therese Ann Liutkus *(Pres, CFO & Treas)*
Eloise L. Mackus *(CEO)*
Laura L. Martin *(Asst Sec)*

CENTRAL PACIFIC FINANCIAL CORPORATION
220 S King St
Honolulu, HI 96813
Mailing Address:
PO Box 3590
Honolulu, HI 96811-3590
Tel.: (808) 544-0500
Fax: (808) 531-2875
Telex: 634261 CENPAC
Web Site:
www.centralpacificbank.com/
Approx. Int. Income: $160,754,000
Approx. Number Employees: 838
Year Founded: 1954
Business Description:
Bank Holding Company
S.I.C.: 6029; 6712
N.A.I.C.S.: 522110; 551111
Advertising Expenditures: $2,531,000
Media: 7-8-20
Personnel:
Crystal K. Rose *(Chm)*
John C. Dean, Jr. *(Pres & CEO)*
Denis K. Isono *(CFO & Exec VP)*
Agnes Catherine Ngo *(Chief Admin Officer & Exec VP)*
Raymond William Wilson *(Chief Credit Officer & Exec VP)*
David Hudson *(Exec VP & Mgr-Community Banking)*
Karen K. Street *(Sr VP-HR-Central Pacific Bank)*

CENTRAL VALLEY COMMUNITY BANCORP
7100 N Financial Dr
Fresno, CA 93720
Tel.: (559) 298-1775
Fax: (559) 323-3460
E-mail: customerservice@cvcb.com
Web Site: www.cvcb.com
Approx. Rev.: $39,734,000
Approx. Number Employees: 200
Year Founded: 2000
Business Description:
Bank Holding Company
S.I.C.: 6029; 6712
N.A.I.C.S.: 522110; 551111
Advertising Expenditures: $699,000
Personnel:
Daniel N. Cunningham *(Chm)*
Daniel J. Doyle *(Pres & CEO)*
David A. Kinross *(CFO & Sr VP)*
Gary Quisenberry *(Sr VP-Comml & Bus Banking)*
Lydia E. Shaw *(Sr VP-Consumer & Retail Banking)*
Thomas Sommer *(Sr VP & Administrator-Credit)*
Cathy Chatoian *(VP & Mgr-Cash Mgmt)*
Terry Crawford *(VP & Mgr-Agricultural Lending Grp)*
Daniel Demmers *(VP & Mgr-Info Svcs)*
Diane Hamp *(VP & Mgr-Loan Servicing)*
Tim Harris *(VP & Mgr-Private Banking)*
Jeff Pace *(VP & Mgr-Real Estate Dept)*
Debbie Cohen *(Dir-Mktg)*
Brands & Products:
CENTRAL VALLEY COMMUNITY BANK
QUICK BUSINESS CREDIT
STRONG. SOLID. UNCHANGING VALUES
Advertising Agency:
Cohen Communications
1201 W Shaw Ave
Fresno, CA 93711
Tel.: (559) 222-1322
Fax: (559) 221-4376

CENTRAL VIRGINIA BANKSHARES, INC.
2036 New Dorset Rd
Powhatan, VA 23139-0039
Mailing Address:
PO Box 39
Powhatan, VA 23139-0039
Tel.: (804) 403-2000
Toll Free: (888) 282-4030
Web Site: www.centralvabank.com
Approx. Rev.: $25,722,000
Approx. Number Employees: 79
Year Founded: 1986
Business Description:
Bank Holding Company
S.I.C.: 6712
N.A.I.C.S.: 551111

Key to Media (For complete agency information see *The Advertising Red Books-Agencies* edition):
1. Bus. Publs. 2. Cable T.V. 3. Catalogs & Directories. 4. Co-op Adv. 5. Consumer Mags. 6. D.M. to Bus. Estab.7. D.M. to Consumers
8. Daily Newsp. 9. Exhibits/Trade Shows 10. Foreign 11. Infomercial 12. Internet Adv.13. Multimedia 14. Network Radio
15. Network T.V. 16. Newsp. Distr. Mags. 17. Other 18. Outdoor (Posters, Transit) 19. Point of Purchase20. Premiums, Novelties
21. Product Samples 22. Special Events Mktg. 23. Spot Radio 24. Spot T.V. 25. Weekly Newsp. 26. Yellow Page Adv.

Central Virginia Bankshares, Inc. — (Continued)

Advertising Expenditures: $197,000
Media: 17
Personnel:
James T. Napier *(Chm)*
Herbert E. Marth, Jr. *(Pres & CEO)*
Robert B. Eastep *(CFO & Sr VP)*
Leslie S. Cundiff *(Sr VP)*

CENTRUE FINANCIAL CORPORATION
7700 Bonhomme Ave
Saint Louis, MO 63105
Tel.: (314) 505-5500
E-mail: kurt.stevenson@centrue.com
Web Site: www.centrue.com
Approx. Rev.: $59,662,000
Approx. Number Employees: 292
Year Founded: 1982
Business Description:
Bank Holding Company
S.I.C.: 6712; 6029; 6035
N.A.I.C.S.: 551111; 522110; 522120
Advertising Expenditures: $391,000
Personnel:
Dennis J. McDonnell *(Chm)*
Thomas A. Daiber *(Pres & CEO)*
Kurt R. Stevenson *(CFO)*
Robert L. Davidson *(Chief Investment Officer, ALCO Mgr & Exec VP)*
Kenneth A. Jones *(Exec VP & Chief Credit Officer)*
Diane F. Leto *(Exec VP, Head-Ops & Chief Risk Officer)*
Steven E. Flahaven *(Exec VP & Head-Comml Banking)*
Heather M. Hammitt *(Exec VP, Head-HR & Corp Comm)*
May Jane Raymond *(Exec VP & Head-Retail Banking)*
Roger D. Dotson *(Exec VP-Ops & IT & Loans)*
James J. Kerley, Jr. *(Exec VP & Sr Lender)*
Everett J. Solon *(Head-Mortgage Banking)*
Brands & Products:
CENTRUE

CENTURY BANK & TRUST
100 W Chicago St
Coldwater, MI 49036
Tel.: (517) 278-1500
Fax: (517) 278-1642
E-mail: IBanking@Centurybt.com
Web Site: www.centurybt.com
Approx. Int. Income: $17,000,000
Approx. Number Employees: 125
Business Description:
Regional Bank
S.I.C.: 6029; 6163
N.A.I.C.S.: 522110; 522310
Advertising Expenditures: $200,000
Media: 7-8-9-13-18-20-23
Distr.: Direct to Consumer; Reg.
Budget Set: Oct.
Personnel:
James Sobeske *(Pres & CEO)*
Rebecca Duke *(Dir-Adv)*

CHAMPION MORTGAGE CO., INC.
(Div. of Nationstar Mortgage LLC)
2 Gatehall Dr Ste 2
Parsippany, NJ 07054
Toll Free: (800) 242-6746
E-mail: jsupport@jakebrake.com
Web Site: www.championmortgage.com
Approx. Sls.: $120,000,000
Approx. Number Employees: 1,000
Year Founded: 1981
Business Description:
Mortgage Banking
S.I.C.: 6159; 6163
N.A.I.C.S.: 522292; 522310
Media: 8-13-24
Personnel:
Joseph P. Goryeb *(Chm & CEO)*
Brands & Products:
CHAMPION

CHARLES SCHWAB & COMPANY, INC.
(Sub. of The Charles Schwab Corporation)
211 Main Street
San Francisco, CA 94104-4122
Tel.: (415) 636-7000
Fax: (415) 667-3484
Toll Free: (800) 435-4000
Web Site: www.schwab.com
E-Mail For Key Personnel:
Public Relations: public.relations@schwab.com
Approx. Number Employees: 23,000
Year Founded: 1974
Business Description:
Financial Services, Discount Stock Broker, Electronic Brokerage, Mutual Funds
S.I.C.: 6211
N.A.I.C.S.: 523120
Advertising Expenditures: $129,550,000
Media: 2-3-4-5-6-8-9-11-13-14-15-16-19-22-23-24-25-26
Distr.: Intl.
Budget Set: Nov.
Personnel:
Ben Stuart *(Sr VP-Brand & Digital Mktg)*
Melanie Lowe *(Mng Dir-Interactive)*
Mike Naughton *(VP-Media)*
Randa Ghnaim *(Dir-Employee Comm)*
Kate O'Connor *(Dir-eBus)*
Brands & Products:
CYBERTRADER
ONESOURCE
SCHWABFUNDS
SCHWABPLAN
TELEBROKER
USTRUST
Advertising Agencies:
AKQA, Inc.
118 King St 6th Fl
San Francisco, CA 94107
Tel.: (415) 645-9400
Fax: (415) 645-9420

CRT/tanaka
101 W Commerce Rd
Richmond, VA 23224
Tel.: (804) 675-8100
Fax: (804) 675-8183

Daniel J. Edelman, Inc.
(d/b/a Edelman)
200 E Randolph St Fl 63
Chicago, IL 60601-6705
Tel.: (312) 240-3000
Fax: (312) 240-2900

Euro RSCG Worldwide HQ
350 Hudson St
New York, NY 10014-4504
Tel.: (212) 886-2000
Fax: (212) 886-2016

PHD
(An Omnicom Company)
220 E 42nd 7th Fl
New York, NY 10017
Tel.: (212) 894-6600
Fax: (212) 894-4100

Whitespeed
29672 Zuma Bay Way
Malibu, CA 90265
Tel.: (310) 869-9979
Fax: (310) 899-3199

CHARTER FINANCIAL CORPORATION
(Sub. of First Charter MHC)
1233 O.G. Skinner Dr
West Point, GA 31833
Tel.: (706) 645-1391
Fax: (706) 645-1370
E-mail: bbonner@charterbank.net
Web Site: www.charterbk.com
Approx. Rev.: $67,468,515
Approx. Number Employees: 250
Business Description:
Bank Holding Company
S.I.C.: 6712; 6029
N.A.I.C.S.: 551111; 522110
Advertising Expenditures: $789,593
Personnel:
Robert L. Johnson *(Chm, Pres & CEO)*
Curtis R. Kollar *(CFO & Sr VP)*
William C. Gladden *(Sec & Sr VP)*
Advertising Agency:
FD Americas Public Affairs
1101 K St NW 9th Fl
Washington, DC 20005
Tel.: (202) 346-8800
Fax: (202) 346-8804

CHASE CARD SERVICES, INC.
(Sub. of JPMorgan Chase & Co.)
360 Bay St
San Francisco, CA 94133
Tel.: (415) 477-9028
Web Site: www.chase.com
Year Founded: 1889
Business Description:
Credit Card Services
S.I.C.: 6141
N.A.I.C.S.: 522210
Media: 8-13
Personnel:
Anthony F. Vuoto *(Pres-Wamu Card Svcs)*
Rob Rosenblatt *(Gen Mgr-Loyalty Chase Card Svcs)*
Bridget Mccalla *(Mktg-Mgr)*
Brands & Products:
PROVIDIAN
Advertising Agency:
McGarry Bowen, LLC
601 W 26th St Ste 1150
New York, NY 10001
Tel.: (212) 598-2900
Fax: (212) 598-2996
Cinema
Local Broadcast TV
National Broadcast TV
Online
Print
Sweepstakes
Ultimate Rewards Loyalty Program

CHASE EDUCATION FINANCE
(Sub. of JPMorgan Chase & Co.)
10304 Spotsylvania Ave Ste 100
Fredericksburg, VA 22408-8602
Tel.: (540) 374-1600
Fax: (540) 374-1981
Toll Free: (800) 762-6441
E-mail: customerservice@cfsloans.com
Web Site: www.cfsloans.com
Sales Range: $150-199.9 Million
Approx. Number Employees: 806
Year Founded: 1998
Business Description:
Student Loans
S.I.C.: 6141
N.A.I.C.S.: 522291
Advertising Expenditures: $25,000,000
Media: 8-13
Personnel:
J. Barry Morrow *(Pres & CEO)*
John A. Reeves *(Exec VP-Govt Rels)*
Craig Anderson *(Sr VP)*
Ann Collier *(Sr VP-Corp Commun)*
Brands & Products:
COLLEGIATE FUNDING SERVICES

CHECK-N-GO FINANCIAL CORP.
(d/b/a Check-N-Go)
7755 Montgomery Rd Ste 400
Cincinnati, OH 45236
Tel.: (513) 336-7735
Fax: (513) 229-6743
Toll Free: (800) 561-2274
E-mail: hrrecruiting@checkngo.com
Web Site: www.checkngo.com
E-Mail For Key Personnel:
President: ddavis@cngfinancial.com
Approx. Number Employees: 2,200
Year Founded: 1994
Business Description:
Check-Cashing Services & Payday Loans
S.I.C.: 6099
N.A.I.C.S.: 522320
Import Export
Advertising Expenditures: $1,000,000
Media: 8-15-18-23-24-25-26
Personnel:
A. David Davis *(Pres & CEO)*
Miriam Giachetto *(VP-Strategic Mktg)*
Brands & Products:
CHECK-N-GO
SIMPLE.MONEY.SOLUTIONS.

CHECKFREE CORPORATION
(Name Changed to Fiserv, Inc.)

CHECKMASTERS.COM, INC.
12 E Broadway St
Shelbyville, IN 46176
Tel.: (317) 392-0772
Fax: (317) 392-0773
Toll Free: (800) 492-0772
E-mail: info@checkmasters.com
Web Site: www.checkmasters.com
Approx. Number Employees: 9
Year Founded: 1993
Business Description:
Check Cashing Store & Tobacco Seller
S.I.C.: 6099; 5993
N.A.I.C.S.: 522390; 453991
Media: 13

Key to Media (For complete agency information see *The Advertising Red Books-Agencies* edition):
1. Bus. Publs. 2. Cable T.V. 3. Catalogs & Directories. 4. Co-op Adv. 5. Consumer Mags. 6. D.M. to Bus. Estab.7. D.M. to Consumers 8. Daily Newsp. 9. Exhibits/Trade Shows 10. Foreign 11. Infomercial 12. Internet Adv.13. Multimedia 14. Network Radio 15. Network T.V. 16. Newsp. Distr. Mags. 17. Other 18. Outdoor (Posters, Transit) 19. Point of Purchase20. Premiums, Novelties 21. Product Samples 22. Special Events Mktg. 23. Spot Radio 24. Spot T.V. 25. Weekly Newsp. 26. Yellow Page Adv.

Personnel:
Talmage Thompson *(Owner)*

CHEMICAL FINANCIAL CORPORATION

235 E Main St
Midland, MI 48640-0569
Mailing Address:
PO Box 569
Midland, MI 48640-0569
Tel.: (989) 839-5350
Fax: (989) 839-5255
Toll Free: (800) 867-9757
Web Site: www.chemicalbankmi.com
Approx. Rev.: $252,902,000
Approx. Number Employees: 1,608
Year Founded: 1973
Business Description:
Bank Holding Company
S.I.C.: 6712; 6029
N.A.I.C.S.: 551111; 522110
Advertising Expenditures: $2,400,000
Personnel:
David B. Ramaker *(Chm, Pres & CEO)*
Lori A. Gwizdala *(CFO)*
Thomas W. Kohn *(Exec VP-Community Banking)*
John D. Hatfield *(VP & Dir-Mktg)*
Brands & Products:
CHEMICAL BANK
PREFERRED REWARDS
WE THINK YOU'LL LIKE THE CHEMISTRY

CHEMUNG FINANCIAL CORPORATION

1 Chemung Canal Plz
Elmira, NY 14901
Tel.: (607) 737-3711
Fax: (607) 735-2035
Toll Free: (800) 836-3711
E-mail: info@chemungcanal.com
Web Site: www.chemungcanal.com
Approx. Rev.: $62,390,606
Approx. Number Employees: 317
Year Founded: 1985
Business Description:
State Commercial Banks
S.I.C.: 6141
N.A.I.C.S.: 522210
Import Export
Advertising Expenditures: $712,842
Personnel:
David J. Dalrymple *(Chm)*
Ronald M. Bentley *(Pres & CEO)*
John R. Battersby Jr. *(CFO, Treas & Exec VP)*
Leslie J. Distin *(VP & Trust Officer-Binghamton)*
Jane H. Adamy *(Sec & Sr VP)*
Melinda A. Sartori *(Exec VP-Trust & Investment Svcs)*
Norman R. Ward *(Sr VP & Chief Auditor)*
Richard G. Carr *(Sr VP-Bus Client Svcs)*
Michael J. Crimmins *(Sr VP-Support Svcs)*
Elizabeth T. Dalrymple *(Sr VP-Trust & Estate Admin)*
Louis C. DiFabio *(Sr VP-Retail Client svcs)*
Douglas R. Johnson *(Sr VP & Reg Trust Exec)*
Linda M. Struble *(Sr VP-HR)*
Michael J. Wayne *(Sr VP-Mktg Svcs)*
Thomas J. Whitaker *(Sr VP-Fin-Chemung Canal Trust Company)*
Robert A. Roemmelt, Jr. *(VP & Branch Mgr-Arnot Road Office)*
Joseph W. Ahern *(VP & Reg Trust Mgr)*
Lucimar Foo-Siam Escudero *(VP & Mgr-Credit-Chemung Canal Trust Company)*
Larry W. Rudawsky *(VP & Mgr-Retirement Svcs)*
John J. Sentigar *(VP & Mgr-IT)*
Judy L. Barton *(VP-Bank Ops)*
Celeste D. Knickerbocker *(VP-Fin)*
Edward Morton, IV *(VP & Private Banker)*
Kenneth J. Wilson *(VP-Chemung Canal Bank)*
Kerry L. Oetting *(Asst VP & Sr Mgr-Retirement Plan)*
Michael J. Battersby *(Asst VP & Branch Mgr-Horseheads)*
Richard W. Carroll *(Asst VP & Branch Mgr-Watkins Glen)*
Sandra L. Grooms *(Asst VP & Branch Mgr-Ithaca)*
Megan B. Horton *(Asst VP & Branch Mgr-Owego)*
Eileen M. McCarthy *(Asst VP-Trust & Mgr-Investment Admin Svcs)*
Gary K. Earley *(Asst VP & Trust Officer)*
Craig B. Heffner *(Asst VP-Comml Lending)*
Scott T. Heffner *(Asst VP-Mktg)*
Mary L. Keefe *(Asst VP-e-Bus Svcs)*
Sandra J. Martinichio *(Asst VP-Trust Tax Svcs)*
Tina M. McGurgan *(Asst VP-IT)*
Mary Anne Narosky *(Asst VP-Bus Client Svcs)*
Joan M. Smith *(Asst VP-Fin)*
Debra L. Stanton *(Asst VP-ISO & CFSA-Chemung Canal Trust Co)*
Theresa A. Wagner *(Asst VP-Deposit Ops)*
David A. Wakeman *(Asst VP-Resource Recovery)*
Deborah A. Cram *(Asst Treas & Mgr-Chemung Canal Trust)*
Pamela D. Burns *(Mgr-Employment)*
Matthew T. Keefe *(Administrator-Chemung Canal Trust)*

CHESAPEAKE FINANCIAL SHARES, INC.

PO Box 1419
Kilmarnock, VA 22482
Tel.: (804) 435-1181
Fax: (804) 435-3490
E-mail: corporate@chesbank.com
Web Site: www.chesbank.com
Approx. Rev.: $44,609,159
Approx. Number Employees: 200
Business Description:
Bank Holding Company
S.I.C.: 6029; 6712
N.A.I.C.S.: 522110; 551111
Advertising Expenditures: $707,388
Personnel:
Jeffrey M. Szyperski *(Chm, Pres & CEO)*
Douglas D. Monroe, Jr. *(Vice Chm)*
John H. Hunt, II *(CFO, Sec & Exec VP)*

CHEVIOT FINANCIAL CORP.

(Sub. of Cheviot Mutual Holding Company)
3723 Glenmore Ave
Cheviot, OH 45211-4744
Tel.: (513) 661-0457
Fax: (513) 389-3312
Web Site: www.cheviotsavings.com
Approx. Rev.: $16,761,000
Approx. Number Employees: 52
Business Description:
Bank Holding Company
S.I.C.: 6712; 6029; 6035; 6141
N.A.I.C.S.: 551111; 522110; 522120; 522291
Advertising Expenditures: $197,000
Media: 17
Personnel:
Thomas J. Linneman *(Pres & CEO)*
Scott T. Smith *(CFO)*

CHEVY CHASE BANK, F.S.B.

(Sub. of Capital One Financial Corporation)
7501 Wisconsin Ave
Bethesda, MD 20814-6525
Tel.: (240) 497-4101
Fax: (240) 497-4110
Toll Free: (800) 987-2265
E-mail: info@chevychasebank.com
Web Site: www.chevychasebank.com
Sales Range: $550-599.9 Million
Approx. Number Employees: 3,400
Year Founded: 1969
Business Description:
Banking Service
S.I.C.: 6035; 6411
N.A.I.C.S.: 522120; 524210
Advertising Expenditures: $1,800,000
Media: 2-8-13-18-19-20-22
Personnel:
Robert D. Broeksmit *(Pres-B.F. Saul Mortgage Company)*
Thomas H. McCormick *(Gen Counsel & Exec VP)*
Brands & Products:
CHANGE EXPRESS
CHEVY CHASE

CHICOPEE BANCORP, INC.

70 Center St
Chicopee, MA 01013
Mailing Address:
PO Box 300
Chicopee, MA 01014-0300
Tel.: (413) 594-6692
Toll Free: (800) 662-0974
E-mail: HR@chicopeesavings.com
Web Site: www.chicopeesavings.com
Approx. Rev.: $27,483,000
Approx. Number Employees: 119
Year Founded: 2006
Business Description:
Bank Holding Company
S.I.C.: 6035; 6029; 6712
N.A.I.C.S.: 522120; 522110; 551111
Advertising Expenditures: $501,000
Media: 23-24
Personnel:
William J. Wagner *(Pres & CEO)*
Guida R. Sajdak *(CFO & Sr VP)*
Russell J. Omer *(Exec VP-Lending)*
Maria J.C. Aigner *(Sr VP-HR)*
Kathi Donahue *(Sr VP)*
Luke Kettles *(Sr VP)*
Darlene M. Libiszewski *(Sr VP-IT)*
Maria C. Desmarais *(Coord-Investments)*
Advertising Agency:
Jasin Advertising Inc.
28 Bedford Rd
Springfield, MA 01107-1212
Tel.: (413) 736-9072
Fax: (413) 736-4013

CHITTENDEN BANK

(Sub. of People's United Financial, Inc.)
2 Burlington Sq
Burlington, VT 05401-4412
Tel.: (802) 658-4000
Fax: (802) 660-1222
Toll Free: (800) 545-2236
Web Site: www.chittenden.com
Sales Range: $200-249.9 Million
Approx. Number Employees: 670
Year Founded: 1906
Business Description:
Full Service Financial Institution
S.I.C.: 6029
N.A.I.C.S.: 522110
Media: 2-4-6-7-8-9-10-13-23-24-25
Personnel:
Michael L. Seaver *(Pres-Vermont)*
Matthew Durkee *(Sr VP-Regional Fin Svcs)*
Brian Loveless *(Sr VP & Bank Fin Officer)*
Kathy Schirling *(Dir-Mktg & Community Svcs)*

CHOICEONE FINANCIAL SERVICES, INC.

109 E Division St
Sparta, MI 49345
Tel.: (616) 887-7366
Fax: (616) 887-7990
E-mail: ch1info@choiceone.com
Web Site: www.choiceone.com
Approx. Rev.: $27,530,000
Approx. Number Employees: 109
Business Description:
Bank Holding Company
S.I.C.: 6029; 6712
N.A.I.C.S.: 522110; 551111
Advertising Expenditures: $168,000
Media: 17
Personnel:
Donald VanSingel *(Vice Chm)*
James A. Bosserd *(Pres & CEO)*
Thomas L. Lampen *(CFO & VP)*

CHRYSLER FINANCIAL COMPANY, LLC

(Holding of Cerberus Capital Management, L.P.)
27777 Inkster Rd
Farmington Hills, MI 48334-5326
Mailing Address:
PO Box 9223
Farmington Hills, MI 48333-9223
Tel.: (248) 427-6800
Fax: (248) 427-6600
Toll Free: (800) 556-8172
Telex: 23 0663
Web Site: www.chryslerfinancial.com
Business Description:
Automotive Financing Services
S.I.C.: 6141
N.A.I.C.S.: 522220; 522291
Advertising Expenditures: $10,000,000
Media: 2-3-6-9-10-14-15-19
Distr.: Intl.; Natl.
Personnel:
Thomas F. Gilman *(CEO)*
Leland Wilson *(CFO)*
Darryl R. Jackson *(COO)*
Tracy L. Hackman *(Gen Counsel, Sec & VP)*
Mark Manzo *(VP-Sls & Mktg-US)*

Key to Media (For complete agency information see *The Advertising Red Books-Agencies* edition):
1. Bus. Publs. 2. Cable T.V. 3. Catalogs & Directories. 4. Co-op Adv. 5. Consumer Mags. 6. D.M. to Bus. Estab.7. D.M. to Consumers 8. Daily Newsp. 9. Exhibits/Trade Shows 10. Foreign 11. Infomercial 12. Internet Adv.13. Multimedia 14. Network Radio 15. Network T.V. 16. Newsp. Distr. Mags. 17. Other 18. Outdoor (Posters, Transit) 19. Point of Purchase20. Premiums, Novelties 21. Product Samples 22. Special Events Mktg. 23. Spot Radio 24. Spot T.V. 25. Weekly Newsp. 26. Yellow Page Adv.

Chrysler Financial Company, LLC — (Continued)

Machelle McAdory *(VP-HR & Admin Svcs)*

CIB MARINE BANCSHARES, INC.

1930 W Bluemound Rd Ste D
Waukesha, WI 53186
Tel.: (262) 695-6010
Fax: (262) 695-6014
E-mail: shareholderrelations@cibmarine.com
Web Site: www.cibmarine.com
Approx. Rev.: $31,359,000
Approx. Number Employees: 137
Year Founded: 1985
Business Description:
Bank Holding Company
S.I.C.: 6712; 6029
N.A.I.C.S.: 551111; 522110
Advertising Expenditures: $317,000
Personnel:
John P. Hickey, Jr. *(Chm)*
Charles J. Ponicki *(Pres & CEO)*
Patrick J. Straka *(CFO)*
Daniel J. Rasmussen *(Gen Counsel)*

CIT GROUP INC.

11 W 42nd St
New York, NY 10036
Mailing Address:
One Cit Dr
Livingston, NJ 07039
Tel.: (212) 461-5200
E-mail: info@cit.com
Web Site: www.cit.com
E-Mail For Key Personnel:
Public Relations: kelly.gipson@cit.com
Approx. Rev.: $6,362,500,000
Approx. Number Employees: 3,778
Year Founded: 1908
Business Description:
Bank Holding Company; Commercial Financing, Lending & Asset Management Services
S.I.C.: 6712; 6141; 6159; 6211; 6371
N.A.I.C.S.: 551111; 522220; 522294; 523110; 525990
Advertising Expenditures: $10,850,000
Bus. Publs.: $1,000,000; Cable T.V.: $500,000; Consumer Mags.: $1,000,000; D.M. to Bus. Estab.: $250,000; Daily Newsp.: $2,600,000; Exhibits/Trade Shows: $500,000; Internet Adv.: $100,000; Network T.V.: $4,900,000
Distr.: Natl.
Budget Set: Dec.
Personnel:
John A. Thain *(Chm & CEO)*
Nelson J. Chai *(Pres)*
William J. Koslo, Jr. *(Grp Head-Capital Markets & Mng Dir)*
W. Taylor Kamp *(Mng Dir, Head-Corp M & A)*
Jerry Jeram *(Mng Dir & Chief Petroleum Engr)*
E. Scott Medla *(Mng Dir)*
Scott T. Parker *(CFO)*
Umar Farooq *(Chief Sls Officer & Exec VP-Corp Strategy)*
Al Spada *(Chief Sls Officer-Comml & Indus & Exec VP)*
Robert C. Rowe *(Chief Credit Officer & Exec VP)*
James P. Shanahan, Jr. *(Chief Compliance Officer & Sr VP)*
Lisa K. Polsky *(Exec VP & Chief Risk Officer)*
Paul G. Petrylak *(Pres-Insurance Svcs, Exec VP & Head-Corp Svcs & Procurement)*
Jim Hudak *(Pres-CIT Comm, Media & Entertainment, Co-Head-Corp Fin)*
Ron Arrington *(Pres-Vendor Fin)*
George Cashman *(Pres-CIT Rail Resources)*
Randy Chesler *(Pres-Consumer Fin)*
John F. Daly *(Pres-Trade Fin)*
Peter Gaw *(Pres-Energy)*
Jeff Knittel *(Pres-Transportation Fin)*
Dan Mahoney *(Pres-Vendor Healthcare)*
Chris Reilly *(Pres-Small Bus Lending)*
Steven N. Warden *(Pres-Healthcare)*
Scott Kellman *(CEO-Care Investment Trust)*
Robert J. Ingato *(Gen Counsel, Sec & Exec VP)*
Glenn Votek *(Exec VP & Treas)*
Margaret D. Tutwiler *(Exec VP, Head-Comm & Mktg & Govt Rels)*
Kenneth A. Brause *(Exec VP & Dir-IR)*
Michael Baresich *(Global CIO & Exec VP)*
Pete Connolly *(Exec VP & Bus Leader)*
Cathleen Crowley-Piscitell *(Exec VP-Comml Real Estate)*
Tony Diaz *(Exec VP-Aerospace-Comml Airlines)*
Raymond J. Quinlan *(Exec VP-Banking)*
Michael E. Roemer *(Exec VP & Chief Auditor)*
Lisa D. Zonino *(Exec VP & Global Head-HR)*
Carol Hayles *(Sr VP & Controller)*
Jonathan Macey *(Sr VP-External Reporting / Accting Policy)*
David A. Davis *(Sr VP)*
Peter Mulroy *(Sr VP & Intl Mgr-Comml Svcs)*
Si Ming Li *(Mng Dir-Vendor Fin-Asia)*
Tom Westdyk *(Mng Dir-Comm/Media/Entertainment-Comm)*
Mark Ebanks *(VP & Reg Dir)*
C. Curtis Ritter *(VP & Dir-Comm & Media Rels)*
Paul Carmedelle *(VP & Dir-Mktg & Customer Integration)*
Volker Fabian *(VP & Dir-Mktg)*
Debbie Haeringer *(VP & Dir-Mktg-Vendor Fin)*
Daniel Infanti *(VP & Dir-Mktg & Adv)*
Lydia Mihalek *(VP-Mktg Comm, PR & Media)*
Steve Reedy *(Sr Dir)*
Abby Cohn *(Mgr-Mktg & Adv)*
Marc Heller *(Mgr-Northeast Regional & CIT Comml Svcs)*

Advertising Agencies:
IQ Interactive
280 Interstate N Cir SE Ste 300
Atlanta, GA 30339
Tel.: (404) 255-3550
Fax: (770) 956-8014

kirshenbaum bond senecal + partners
160 Varick St 4th Fl
New York, NY 10013
Tel.: (212) 633-0080
Fax: (212) 463-8643

CITIFINANCIAL CREDIT COMPANY

(Sub. of Citi Consumer Banking)
300 Saint Paul Pl
Baltimore, MD 21202-2120
Tel.: (410) 332-3000
Fax: (410) 332-3489
Toll Free: (800) 995-2274
Web Site: www.citifinancial.com
Sales Range: $300-349.9 Million
Approx. Number Employees: 900
Year Founded: 1999
Business Description:
Consumer Financial Services
S.I.C.: 6141; 6159
N.A.I.C.S.: 522291; 522210; 522292
Personnel:
Mary McDowell *(Pres)*
Advertising Agency:
GlobalHue
Ste 1600 4000 Town Ctr
Southfield, MI 48076
Tel.: (248) 223-8900
Fax: (248) 304-8877

CITIGROUP INC.

399 Park Ave
New York, NY 10043
Tel.: (212) 559-1000
Fax: (212) 793-3946
Toll Free: (800) 285-3000
E-mail: investorrelations@citi.com
Web Site: www.citigroup.com
Approx. Rev.: $111,465,000,000
Approx. Number Employees: 260,000
Year Founded: 1998
Business Description:
Banking & Financial Services Holding Company
S.I.C.: 6712; 6029; 6141
N.A.I.C.S.: 551111; 522110; 522210; 522291
Advertising Expenditures: $1,415,000,000
Media: 2-3-6-7-8-11-13-15-20-22-24
Personnel:
Richard D. Parsons *(Chm)*
Hamid Biglari *(Head-Emerging Markets & Vice Chm-Citicorp)*
Lewis B. Kaden *(Vice Chm-Citigroup)*
Peter Orszag *(Vice Chm-Global Banking Bus)*
Stephen R. Volk *(Vice Chm-Citigroup)*
John P. Havens *(Pres, COO & CEO-Institutional Clients Grp)*
Vikram S. Pandit *(CEO)*
Atul Dubey *(Mng Dir, COO-Securities & Fund SerVs)*
James Bardrick *(Mng Dir & Co-Head-Banking-EMEA)*
Dickson Chu *(Mng Dir)*
Sheree Stomberg *(Mng Dir)*
Catherine Weir *(Mng Dir)*
Simon Yates *(Mng Dir)*
John C. Gerspach *(CFO)*
Zion Shohet *(COO-Institutional Clients Grp)*
Mark Rufeh *(Chief Admin Officer & Head-Productivity-Institutional Clients Grp)*
Don Callahan *(Chief Admin Officer & Chief Ops/Tech Officer)*
Jeffrey R. Walsh *(Chief Acctg Officer & Controller)*
Dermot Boden *(Chief Brand Officer)*
Manuel Medina-Mora *(Chm/CEO-Latin America, Mexico & CEO-Consumer Banking-Americas)*
Pamela P. Flaherty *(Pres/CEO-Citi Foundation & Dir-Corp Citizenship Citi)*
Mary McDowell *(Pres/CEO-Consumer Banking-North America)*
George Award *(CEO-Consumer Fin-Citi Holdings)*
Michael L. Corbat *(CEO-Citi Holdings)*
Paul Galant *(CEO-Citi Global Enterprise Payments)*
Judson C. Linville *(CEO-Citi Cards)*
Fernando Quiroz Robles *(CEO-Markets/Banking-Latin America-Institutional Clients Grp)*
Enrique Zorrilla Fullaondo *(CEO-Banamex)*
Michael S. Helfer *(Gen Counsel & Corp Sec-Citigroup)*
Edward Skyler *(Exec VP-Global Pub Affairs)*
Anthony Carbone *(Sr VP & Bus Mgr-Compliance Architecture)*
Renee Cashion Anderson *(Sr VP-Digital Acq Mktg)*
Aarathi Reddy *(Sr VP)*
Ethan Green *(VP-Corp Sponsorships & Mktg)*
Rick Bartlett *(Head-Equity for the Americas)*
Elyssa Gray *(Head-Creative & Media)*
Carl E. Levinson *(Head-Productivity Improvement & Re-Engrg-Citi)*
Paul McKinnon *(Head-HR & Citigroup)*
Alysia Poe *(Editor-CitiVelocity.com)*
Paul Horn *(Global Product Dir-Citi Comml Cards)*
Alak Das *(Dir-Investment Tech)*
Mark Ingall *(Dir-Global Mktg)*
Bill Johnson *(Dir)*
Augusto Juanes *(Dir-Payment Instruments & Mktg-Banamex-Global Consumer Grp)*
Douglas Tienken *(Dir-Agency & Trust Sls-Global Transaction Svcs Bus)*
Glenn Curtis *(Mgr-Market Intelligence-Depositary Receipts Svcs)*
Carlos Gutierrez *(Mgr)*
Molly Millerwise Meiners *(Mgr-Corp Media Rels)*
Bonnie Howard *(Auditor)*
Brands & Products:
AADVANTAGE
AT&T UNIVERSAL SAVINGS & REWARDS CARD
AT&T UNIVERSAL SAVINGS PLATINUM CARD
BANAMEX
BLOOMINGDALE'S CREDIT CARD
CITGO PLUS CREDIT CARD
CITI
CITI / AADVANTAGE AMERICAN EXPRESS CARD
CITI ALTERNATIVE INVESTMENTS
CITI BRONZE / AADVANTAGE MASTERCARD
CITI BRONZE / AADVANTAGE WORLD MASTERCARD
CITI CARDS
CITI CASHRETURNS MASTERCARD
CITI CHAIRMAN AMERICAN EXPRESS CARD
CITI DIAMOND PREFERRED CARD
CITI DIVIDEND PLATINUM SELECT MASTERCARD
CITI FORWARD

Key to Media (For complete agency information see *The Advertising Red Books-Agencies* edition):
1. Bus. Publs. 2. Cable T.V. 3. Catalogs & Directories. 4. Co-op Adv. 5. Consumer Mags. 6. D.M. to Bus. Estab.7. D.M. to Consumers 8. Daily Newsp. 9. Exhibits/Trade Shows 10. Foreign 11. Infomercial 12. Internet Adv.13. Multimedia 14. Network Radio 15. Network T.V. 16. Newsp. Distr. Mags. 17. Other 18. Outdoor (Posters, Transit) 19. Point of Purchase20. Premiums, Novelties 21. Product Samples 22. Special Events Mktg. 23. Spot Radio 24. Spot T.V. 25. Weekly Newsp. 26. Yellow Page Adv.

CITI FORWARD BY MYSPACE
CITI GOLD / AADVANTAGE WORLD MASTERCARD
CITI HILTON HHONORS VISA SIGNATURE CARD
CITI INSTITUTIONAL CLIENTS GROUP
CITI INVESTMENT RESEARCH
CITI MICROFINANCE
CITI MTVUTM PLATINUM SELECT VISA
CITI PLATINUM AMERICAN EXPRESS
CITI PLATINUM SELECT / AADVANTAGE WORLD MASTERCARD
CITI PLATINUM SELECT MASTERCARD
CITI PREMIERPASS AMERICAN EXPRESS
CITI PREMIERPASS CARD
CITI PREMIERPASS CARD - ELITE LEVEL
CITI PREMIERPASS / EXPEDIA.COM CARD
CITI PREMIERPASS / EXPEDIA.COM CARD - ELITE LEVEL
CITI PRIVATE BANK
CITI PROFESSIONAL
CITI PROFESSIONAL CARD WITH THANKYOU NETWORK
CITI SECURED MASTERCARD
CITI SELECT / AADVANTAGE AMERICAN EXPRESS CARD
CITIBANK
CITIBUSINESS
CITIBUSINESS / AADVANTAGE VISA
CITIBUSINESS CARD WITH THANKYOU
CITIFINANCIAL
CITIGROUP
CITIINSURANCE
CITIMORTGAGE
EXXONMOBIL PERSONAL CARD
THE HOME DEPOT
MACY'S CREDIT CARD
MASTERCARD
PHILLIPS 66-CONOCO-76 PERSONAL CARD
PRIMERICA
SEARS CARD
SHELL CARD
SUNOCO CARD
WOMEN & CO.

Advertising Agencies:
Draftfcb
101 E Erie St
Chicago, IL 60611
Tel.: (312) 425-5000
Fax: (312) 425-5010

GlobalHue
Ste 1600 4000 Town Ctr
Southfield, MI 48076
Tel.: (248) 223-8900
Fax: (248) 304-8877
CitiFinancial Branding

Hydra Group, Inc.
8800 Wilshire Blvd 2nd Fl
Beverly Hills, CA 90211
Tel.: (310) 659-5755
Fax: (310) 659-5855

La Comunidad
6400 Biscayne Blvd
Miami, FL 33138
Tel.: (305) 993-5700
Tel.: (305) 865-9600
Fax: (305) 865-9609

MEC, Global HQ, New York
825 7th Ave
New York, NY 10019-6014
Tel.: (212) 474-0000
Fax: (212) 474-0020
Fax: (212) 474-0003

Merkley + Partners
(Sub. of Omnicom Group, Inc.)
200 Varick St
New York, NY 10014-4810
Tel.: (212) 366-3500
Fax: (212) 805-7445

Publicis USA
(Sub. of Publicis, S.A., Paris, France)
4 Herald Sq 950 6th Ave
New York, NY 10001
Tel.: (212) 279-5550
Fax: (212) 279-5560

CITIGROUP INVESTOR SERVICES, INC.

(Sub. of Citigroup Inc.)
105 Eisenhower Pkwy
Roseland, NJ 07068-1640
Tel.: (973) 461-2500
Fax: (973) 461-5663
Web Site: www.citi.com
Approx. Rev.: $842,852,000
Approx. Number Employees: 5,000
Year Founded: 1989
Business Description:
Fund Management & Alternative Investment Services
S.I.C.: 6722; 6211
N.A.I.C.S.: 525910; 523110
Media: 8-10

CITIZENS BANCORP

208 Providence Mine Rd Ste 122
Nevada City, CA 95959
Tel.: (530) 478-6000
Web Site: www.citizensbanknc.com
Approx. Rev.: $24,401,902
Approx. Number Employees: 81
Business Description:
Bank Holding Company
S.I.C.: 6712
N.A.I.C.S.: 551111
Advertising Expenditures: $223,045
Personnel:
Kenneth E. Baker *(Chm)*
Gary D. Gall *(Pres & CEO)*
Susann C. Trevena *(CFO & Exec VP)*

CITIZENS BANCSHARES CO.

515 Washington St
Chillicothe, MO 64601
Tel.: (660) 646-5500
Fax: (660) 646-1041
Web Site: www.ebankcbt.com
Sales Range: $10-24.9 Million
Approx. Number Employees: 350
Year Founded: 1994
Business Description:
Bank Holding Company
S.I.C.: 6712; 6029; 6035
N.A.I.C.S.: 551111; 522110; 522120
Import Export
Media: 3-4-9-13-25
Personnel:
William Young *(Pres)*

Brands & Products:
CITIZENS BANK AND TRUST
JEEP

CITIZENS BANK & SAVINGS COMPANY

200 S Jackson Ave
Russellville, AL 35653
Tel.: (256) 332-1710
Fax: (256) 718-4727
E-mail: citizensbank@cbsbank.com
Web Site: www.cbsbank.com
Sales Range: $500-549.9 Million
Approx. Number Employees: 200
Year Founded: 1906
Business Description:
Banking Services
S.I.C.: 6029
N.A.I.C.S.: 522110
Personnel:
Cecil Batchelor *(Chm)*
Greg Batchelor *(Vice Chm)*
Dennis Upchurch *(Pres & CEO)*
Roy Walton *(CFO & Exec VP)*
Renee Pezzi *(Sr VP & Dir-Res)*
Advertising Agency:
TotalCom Marketing, Inc.
922 20th Ave
Tuscaloosa, AL 35401-2307
Tel.: (205) 345-7363
Fax: (205) 345-7373

CITIZENS COMMUNITY BANCORP, INC.

2174 EastRidge Ctr
Eau Claire, WI 54701
Mailing Address:
PO Box 218
Altoona, WI 54720
Tel.: (715) 836-9994
Fax: (715) 830-4086
E-mail: info@citizenscommunityfederal.net
Web Site: www.citizenscommunityfederal.net
Approx. Rev.: $32,759,000
Approx. Number Employees: 193
Business Description:
Bank Holding Company
S.I.C.: 6712
N.A.I.C.S.: 551111
Advertising Expenditures: $173,000
Media: 17
Personnel:
Richard McHugh *(Chm)*
Thomas C. Kempen *(Vice Chm)*
Edward H. Schaefer *(Pres & CEO)*
Timothy J. Cruciani *(COO)*
Rebecca M. Johnson *(Sr VP-MIC, Controller & Acctg)*

CITIZENS FIRST CORPORATION

1065 Ashley Street
Bowling Green, KY 42103
Tel.: (270) 393-0700
Web Site: www.citizensfirstbank.com
Approx. Rev.: $20,458,000
Approx. Number Employees: 89
Year Founded: 1975
Business Description:
Holding Company; Commercial Banking Services
S.I.C.: 6712; 6029; 6035; 6141; 6289
N.A.I.C.S.: 551111; 522110; 522120; 522210; 522291; 523999
Advertising Expenditures: $281,000
Personnel:
M. Todd Kanipe *(Pres & CEO)*
Steve Marcum *(CFO & Exec VP)*
Carolyn Harp *(Exec VP & Officer-Corp Trng)*
Jana Stanley *(Loan Svcs Officer)*
Jeff Warren *(Officer-IT & Facilities)*
Lewis Bauer *(Pres-Community)*
Scott Brown *(Pres-Simpson County Community)*
Jim Lee *(Pres-Barren County Community)*
Carrie Taylor *(Pres-Warren County Community)*
Carla Wuertzer *(Pres-Hart County Community)*
Kim Thomas *(Exec VP-Community Banking & Private Client Grp)*
Kim Harmon *(Sr VP & Acctg Officer)*
Kent Mcbrayer *(Sr VP-Comml Lending)*

CITIZENS HOLDING COMPANY

521 Main St
Philadelphia, MS 39350
Tel.: (601) 656-4692
Fax: (601) 656-4264
E-mail: rsmith@tcbphila.com
Web Site: www.citizensholdingcompany.com
Approx. Rev.: $45,546,821
Approx. Number Employees: 244
Year Founded: 1982
Business Description:
Bank Holding Company
S.I.C.: 6712; 6029
N.A.I.C.S.: 551111; 522110
Advertising Expenditures: $669,472
Personnel:
Greg L. McKee *(Pres & CEO)*
Robert T. Smith *(CFO & Treas)*
Herbert A. King *(Pres-King Engrg Associates)*

CITIZENS REPUBLIC BANCORP, INC.

1 Citizens Banking Ctr 328 S Saginaw St
Flint, MI 48502-2401
Tel.: (810) 766-7500
Fax: (810) 342-7090
E-mail: custserv@citizensbanking.com
Web Site: www.citizensbanking.com
Approx. Rev.: $579,103,000
Approx. Number Employees: 2,026
Year Founded: 1980
Business Description:
Bank Holding Company
S.I.C.: 6712; 6029; 6035; 6163; 6211
N.A.I.C.S.: 551111; 522110; 522120; 522310; 523110
Advertising Expenditures: $7,146,000
Media: 2-3-8-9-10-14-18-19-23-24-25-26
Distr.: Reg.
Budget Set: Sept.
Personnel:
James L. Wolohan *(Chm)*
Cathleen H. Nash *(Pres & CEO)*
Lisa T. McNeely *(CFO & Exec VP)*
Mark W. Widawski *(Chief Credit Officer & Exec VP)*
Brad Faubel *(Mgr-Sr Credit Officer Team)*
Thomas W. Gallagher *(Gen Counsel, Sec & Exec VP)*

Key to Media (For complete agency information see *The Advertising Red Books-Agencies* edition):
1. Bus. Publs. 2. Cable T.V. 3. Catalogs & Directories. 4. Co-op Adv. 5. Consumer Mags. 6. D.M. to Bus. Estab.7. D.M. to Consumers 8. Daily Newsp. 9. Exhibits/Trade Shows 10. Foreign 11. Infomercial 12. Internet Adv.13. Multimedia 14. Network Radio 15. Network T.V. 16. Newsp. Distr. Mags. 17. Other 18. Outdoor (Posters, Transit) 19. Point of Purchase20. Premiums, Novelties 21. Product Samples 22. Special Events Mktg. 23. Spot Radio 24. Spot T.V. 25. Weekly Newsp. 26. Yellow Page Adv.

Citizens Republic Bancorp, Inc. — (Continued)

Louise N. O'Connell *(Exec VP & Gen Auditor)*
Susan P. Brockett *(Exec VP-HR)*
Stephen V. Figliuolo *(Exec VP & Corp Risk Officer)*
Judith L. Klawinski *(Exec VP-Core Banking)*
Peter W. Ronan *(Exec VP-Wealth Mgmt)*
Clinton A. Sampson *(Exec VP-Comml Banking)*
Joseph C. Czopek *(Sr VP & Controller)*
Advertising Agencies:
Harrison Media
24416 Crocker Blvd
Clinton Township, MI 48036
Tel.: (586) 465-3855
Fax: (586) 465-2726

Ogilvy & Mather
(Sub. of WPP Group plc)
636 11th Ave
New York, NY 10036
Tel.: (212) 237-4000
Fax: (212) 237-5123

CITIZENS SOUTH BANKING CORPORATION

519 S New Hope Rd
Gastonia, NC 28054-4040
Mailing Address:
PO Box 2249
Gastonia, NC 28053-2249
Tel.: (704) 868-5200
Fax: (704) 868-5212
Toll Free: (888) 309-4636
Toll Free: (800) 218-8619
Web Site: www.citizenssouth.com
Approx. Rev.: $71,051,000
Approx. Number Employees: 202
Business Description:
Bank Holding Company
S.I.C.: 6712; 6029
N.A.I.C.S.: 551111; 522110
Advertising Expenditures: $333,000
Personnel:
David W. Hoyle *(Chm)*
Ben R. Rudisill, II *(Vice Chm)*
Kim S. Price *(Pres & CEO)*
Gary F. Hoskins *(CFO, Treas & Exec VP)*
Paul L. Teem *(Chief Admin Officer, Sec & Exec VP)*
Kenneth A. Icenhour *(Exec VP & Chief Risk Officer)*

CITY HOLDING COMPANY

25 Gatewater Rd
Charleston, WV 25313
Mailing Address:
PO Box 7520
Charleston, WV 25356-0520
Tel.: (304) 769-1100
Fax: (304) 769-1111
E-mail: vikki.evans@cityholding.com
Web Site: www.cityholding.com
Approx. Rev.: $170,855,000
Approx. Number Employees: 805
Year Founded: 1983
Business Description:
Bank Holding Company
S.I.C.: 9121; 6029; 6712
N.A.I.C.S.: 921120; 522110; 551111
Advertising Expenditures: $3,692,000
Media: 19-20
Personnel:
Philip L. Mclaughlin *(Chm)*
Charles R. Hageboeck *(Pres & CEO)*
David L. Bumgarner *(CFO)*
Jeffrey D. Legge *(CIO)*
John A. Derito *(Exec VP-Comml Banking)*
Craig G. Stilwell *(Exec VP-Retail)*

CITY NATIONAL BANK

(Sub. of City Holding Company)
344 17th St
Ashland, KY 41101
Tel.: (606) 325-4789
Fax: (606) 326-2801
Web Site: www.cityholding.com
Sales Range: $10-24.9 Million
Approx. Number Employees: 20
Year Founded: 1995
Business Description:
Banking Services
S.I.C.: 6035; 6163
N.A.I.C.S.: 522120; 522310
Advertising Expenditures: $444,000
Media: 7-8-13
Personnel:
Donny McKenzie *(VP-Community Rels Officer)*
Warren Watts *(Exec VP)*
Debbie Hackworth *(Sr VP)*
Scott Sennett *(Sr VP)*
Kelly Shepherd *(Sr VP)*
Clay Spradlin *(Sr VP)*
Ron Mccloud *(Branch Mgr)*

CITY NATIONAL CORPORATION

555 S Flower St
Los Angeles, CA 90071
Tel.: (310) 888-6000
Fax: (310) 888-6045
Toll Free: (800) 773-7100
Web Site: www.cnb.com
Approx. Int. Income: $830,196,000
Approx. Number Employees: 3,178
Year Founded: 1968
Business Description:
Bank Holding Company
S.I.C.: 6029; 6035; 6712
N.A.I.C.S.: 522110; 522120; 551111
Advertising Expenditures: $20,100,000
Media: 2-7-10-19-23-25
Distr.: Direct to Consumer; Reg.
Budget Set: Aug.
Personnel:
Russell D. Goldsmith *(Chm & CEO)*
Bram Goldsmith *(Chm)*
George H. Benter, Jr. *(Vice Chm)*
Christopher J. Carey *(CFO & Exec VP)*
John J. Beale *(CIO & Exec VP)*
Brian Fitzmaurice *(Chief Credit Officer & Exec VP)*
Michael B. Cahill *(Gen Counsel, Sec & Exec VP)*
Rodney F. Banks *(Exec VP-Comml Banking)*
Robert Brant *(Exec VP-Northern CA)*
Kevin P. Dunigan *(Exec VP-Core Banking)*
Mark J. Forbes *(Exec VP-Real Estate)*
Richard Gershen *(Exec VP-Wealth Mgmt)*
Martha Henderson *(Exec VP-Entertainment)*
Robert M. Iritani *(Exec VP-Specialty Banking Div)*
Marianne Lamutt *(Exec VP-HR)*
Gwen T. Miller *(Exec VP-Private Banking, Los Angeles)*
Thomas R. Miller *(Exec VP-Mktg)*
Michael Pagano *(Exec VP-Private Client Svcs)*
John Pedersen *(Exec VP & Sr Risk Mngmt Officer)*
T. Richard Shier *(Exec VP-Banking & Investment Svcs)*
Christopher J. Warmuth *(Exec VP)*
Paul C. Stowell *(Sr VP-Media Rels)*
Cary Walker *(Sr VP)*
Brands & Products:
CALIFORNIA'S PREMIER PRIVATE AND BUSINESS BANK
CITY NATIONAL CORPORATION
Advertising Agency:
Grey Los Angeles
3500 W Olive Ave Ste 700
Burbank, CA 91505
Tel.: (818) 531-0800
Fax: (818) 531-0701

CLAYTON HOLDINGS, INC.

(Holding of Greenfield Partners LLC)
2 Corporate Dr
Shelton, CT 06484
Tel.: (203) 926-5600
Fax: (203) 926-5750
Toll Free: (888) 449-4055
Web Site: www.clayton.com
Approx. Rev.: $152,596,588
Approx. Number Employees: 413
Business Description:
Mortgage-Related Loan & Securities Transaction Management, Credit Risk Monitoring & Management Services
S.I.C.: 7389; 6099; 8748
N.A.I.C.S.: 561499; 522320; 541618
Advertising Expenditures: $1,117,325
Personnel:
Paul T. Bossidy *(Pres & CEO)*
Thomas Gere *(Sr Mng Dir)*
Peter Kushel *(CFO)*
Steven L. Cohen *(Gen Counsel, Sec & Sr VP)*
Conrad Vasquez *(Exec VP-Ops)*

CLIFTON SAVINGS BANCORP, INC.

1433 Van Houton Ave
Clifton, NJ 07015
Tel.: (973) 473-2200
Toll Free: (888) 562-6727
E-mail: info@cliftonsavings.com
Web Site: www.cliftonsavings.com
Approx. Rev.: $46,849,000
Approx. Number Employees: 89
Year Founded: 1928
Business Description:
Bank Holding Company; Commercial Banking Services
S.I.C.: 6712; 6035
N.A.I.C.S.: 551111; 522120
Advertising Expenditures: $279,000
Media: 8
Personnel:
John A. Celentano, Jr. *(Chm)*
Walter Celuch *(Pres, CEO & Sec)*
Christine R. Piano *(CFO & Exec VP)*
Bart D'Ambra *(COO & Exec VP)*
Stephen A. Hoogerhyde *(Chief Lending Officer & Exec VP)*
Linda Fisher *(Loan Officer & VP)*
Susan L. Horant *(Security Officer & VP)*
Ted Munley *(Sr VP)*
Claire L. Giancola *(VP & Mgr-Trng)*
Carol Campbell *(Asst VP)*
Christine Chudzik *(Asst VP)*
Kathryn Hochstaedt *(Asst VP)*
Maceda M. Kehoe *(Asst VP)*
Mary Ann Mac Kinnon *(Asst VP)*
Edyta Koc *(Asst VP)*
Maria Kosmider *(Asst VP)*
Bridget McFadden *(Asst VP)*
Carmen Miller *(Asst VP)*
Maryann Moran *(Asst VP)*
Kathryn Statzer-Dumas *(Asst VP)*
Beata Stec *(Asst VP)*
Evelyn M. Wiatrak *(Asst VP)*
Marysue Alegre *(Asst Treas)*
Wanda Czopek *(Asst Treas)*
Mary K. Farkas *(Asst Sec)*
Diane Gagliostro *(Asst Sec)*
Jeffrey Kohl *(Asst Treas)*
Teresa Masiuk *(Asst Sec)*
Joann M. McGuire *(Asst Treas)*
Joann M. McGuire *(Asst Treas)*
Klara Papp *(Asst Treas)*
Klara Papp *(Asst Treas)*
Krystyna Plaza *(Asst Treas)*
Geraldine Rambaldi *(Asst Treas)*
Carolann Shucai *(Asst Treas)*
Ashley Singh *(Asst Treas)*
Alicja Stolarz *(Asst Treas)*
Doris Swetiltschnyj *(Asst Treas)*
Anita Veljanovska *(Asst Treas)*

CLIFTON SAVINGS BANK, S.L.A.

(Sub. of Clifton Savings Bancorp, Inc.)
1433 Van Houten Ave PO Box 2149
Clifton, NJ 07015-2149
Tel.: (973) 473-2200
Fax: (973) 473-0451
E-mail: info@cliftonsavings.com
Web Site: www.cliftonsavings.com/locations_clifton_1433.html
Sales Range: $1-9.9 Million
Approx. Number Employees: 30
Business Description:
Banking Services
S.I.C.: 6029
N.A.I.C.S.: 522110
Personnel:
Walter Celuch *(Pres)*
Advertising Agency:
George P. Clarke Advertising, Inc.
27 E 21st St 2nd Fl
New York, NY 10010
Tel.: (212) 545-7400
Fax: (212) 545-7433

CME GROUP, INC.

20 S Wacker Dr
Chicago, IL 60606-7413
Tel.: (312) 930-1000
Fax: (312) 466-4410
Toll Free: (866) 716-7274
E-mail: info@cmegroup.com
Web Site: www.cmegroup.com
Approx. Rev.: $3,003,700,000
Approx. Number Employees: 2,570
Business Description:
Holding Company; Commodities Exchange
S.I.C.: 6719; 6231
N.A.I.C.S.: 551112; 523210
Advertising Expenditures: $16,740,000
Media: 2-4-7-9-10-11-13-25
Distr.: Intl.; Natl.
Budget Set: Nov. -Dec.

Key to Media (For complete agency information see *The Advertising Red Books-Agencies* edition):
1. Bus. Publs. 2. Cable T.V. 3. Catalogs & Directories. 4. Co-op Adv. 5. Consumer Mags. 6. D.M. to Bus. Estab.7. D.M. to Consumers 8. Daily Newsp. 9. Exhibits/Trade Shows 10. Foreign 11. Infomercial 12. Internet Adv.13. Multimedia 14. Network Radio 15. Network T.V. 16. Newsp. Distr. Mags. 17. Other 18. Outdoor (Posters, Transit) 19. Point of Purchase20. Premiums, Novelties 21. Product Samples 22. Special Events Mktg. 23. Spot Radio 24. Spot T.V. 25. Weekly Newsp. 26. Yellow Page Adv.

Personnel:
Terrence A. Duffy *(Chm)*
Charles P. Carey *(Vice Chm)*
Phupinder S. Gill *(Pres)*
Craig Steven Donohue *(CEO)*
Kevin Kometer *(Mng Dir & CIO)*
Hilda Harris Piell *(Mng Dir & Chief HR Officer)*
James V. Pieper *(Mng Dir & Chief Acctg Officer)*
Dean P. Payton *(Mng Dir & Chief Regulatory Officer)*
James E. Parisi *(Mng Dir & CFO-Fin & Corp Dev)*
Kathleen M. Cronin *(Mng Dir, Gen Counsel & Sec)*
Michael O'Connell *(Mng Dir-Clearing Solutions)*
Sean Keating *(Mng Dir & Head-CME Grp-New York)*
Timothy W. Smith *(Mng Dir & Assoc Gen Counsel)*
Christopher K. Bowen *(Mng Dir & Chief Regulatory Counsel)*
Tina Lemieux *(Mng Dir)*
Anita S. Liskey *(Mng Dir)*
Philip J. Papesh *(Mng Dir)*
Richard H. Redding *(Mng Dir)*
Robin S. Ross *(Mng Dir)*
Derek Sammann *(Mng Dir)*
Bryan T. Durkin *(COO, Mng Dir-Products & Svcs)*
Kimberly S. Taylor *(Pres-CME Clearing House Div)*
Howard Hopkins *(Mng Dir-Client Dev & Sls-Comml Corp)*
Christopher E. Mead *(Mng Dir-Mktg)*
John W. Pietrowicz *(Mng Dir-Bus Dev & Corp Fin)*
Rick Romeo *(Mng Dir-Fin Plng & Analysis)*
Sesh Sundaram *(Mng Dir-Software Engrg)*
Julie M. Winkler *(Mng Dir-Res & Product Dev)*
Michael Barston *(Dir)*
Thomas Boggs *(Dir-Equity Products)*
Felix J. Carabello *(Dir-Alternative Investment Products)*
Sunil Cutinho *(Dir)*
Kate Darcy *(Dir-Market Education)*
Charles Farra *(Dir)*
Helen Flanagan *(Dir)*
Dmitriy Glinberg *(Dir-Risk Sys Dev)*
John Harangody *(Dir-Commodity Products)*
Phillip Hatzopoulos *(Dir-Client Dev & Sls)*
Brian J. McElligott *(Dir-Info Products)*
Allan L. Schoenberg *(Dir-Corp Comm)*
Brett Vietmeier *(Dir)*

Brands & Products:
CME GROUP

Advertising Agencies:
Geto & deMilly Inc.
276 5th Ave Ste 806
New York, NY 10001
Tel.: (212) 686-4551
Fax: (212) 213-6850

VSA Partners, Inc.
600 W Chicago Ave
Chicago, IL 60654
Tel.: (312) 427-6413
Toll Free: (877) 422-1311

CME GROUP, INC.
(Branch of CME Group, Inc.)
141 W Jackson Blvd
Chicago, IL 60606-2994
Tel.: (312) 435-3500
Fax: (312) 341-3312
Fax: (312) 341-3392 (Executive Offices)
E-mail: news@cmegroup.com
Web Site: www.cmegroup.com
Approx. Rev.: $621,091,008
Approx. Number Employees: 662
Year Founded: 1848
Business Description:
Futures & Options Exchange
S.I.C.: 6231; 6221
N.A.I.C.S.: 523210; 523140
Media: 2-7-8-9-13-25
Distr.: Intl.; Natl.
Budget Set: Oct.
Personnel:
Charles P. Carey *(Vice Chm)*
Bryan T. Durkin *(COO, Mng Dir-Products & Svcs)*
William McKnight Farrow, III *(CIO & Exec VP)*
Kimberly S Taylor *(Pres-CME Clearing House Div)*
Carol Burke *(Gen Counsel & Exec VP)*
Christopher Malo *(Exec VP-Mktg & Bus Dev)*
James G. Bennett *(Sr VP-Tech Solutions)*
Celesta S. Jurkovich *(Sr VP-Govt Rels)*
Joseph F. Benning *(Sr Economist-Bus Dev Dept)*

Brands & Products:
CBOT

Advertising Agency:
Media Two Interactive
319 W Martin St Ste 200
Raleigh, NC 27601
Tel.: (919) 553-1246
Fax: (919) 882-9162
Toll Free: (877) 553-1246

CMS BANCORP, INC.
123 Main St Ste 750
White Plains, NY 10601
Tel.: (914) 422-2700
Web Site: www.cmsbk.com
Approx. Rev.: $12,455,000
Approx. Number Employees: 42
Business Description:
Bank Holding Company
S.I.C.: 6712; 6029
N.A.I.C.S.: 551111; 522110
Advertising Expenditures: $201,000
Media: 17
Personnel:
Thomas G. Ferrara *(Chm)*
John E. Ritacco *(Pres & CEO)*
Stephen E. Dowd *(CFO & Sr VP)*
Christopher Strauss *(Sr VP & Sr Lending Officer)*

CNB CORPORATION
1400 3rd Ave
Conway, SC 29526
Mailing Address:
PO Box 320
Conway, SC 29528
Tel.: (843) 248-5721
Tel.: (843) 248-7118
Fax: (843) 381-0152
E-mail: banker@conwaynationalbank.com
Web Site:
www.conwaynationalbank.com
Approx. Rev.: $47,506,000
Approx. Number Employees: 250
Year Founded: 1985
Business Description:
Bank Holding Company
S.I.C.: 6141; 6029; 6712
N.A.I.C.S.: 522210; 522110; 551111
Import Export
Advertising Expenditures: $396,000
Personnel:
Harold G. Cushman, Jr. *(Chm)*
W. Jennings Duncan *(Pres & CEO)*
L. Ford Sanders II *(CFO, Treas & Exec VP)*
William R. Benson *(Sr VP)*

CNB FINANCIAL CORPORATION
1 S 2nd St
Clearfield, PA 16830
Mailing Address:
PO Box 42
Clearfield, PA 16830
Tel.: (814) 765-9621
Fax: (814) 765-4511
E-mail: wfalger@bankcnb.com
Web Site: www.bankcnb.com
Approx. Rev.: $71,378,000
Approx. Number Employees: 261
Year Founded: 1983
Business Description:
Bank Holding Company
S.I.C.: 6029; 6712
N.A.I.C.S.: 522110; 551111
Advertising Expenditures: $620,000
Personnel:
Dennis L. Merrey *(Chm)*
Joseph B. Bower, Jr. *(Pres & CEO)*
Charles R. Guarino *(CFO & VP)*

Brands & Products:
CNB

COASTAL BANKING COMPANY, INC.
36 Sea Island Pkwy
Beaufort, SC 29907
Tel.: (843) 522-1228
Fax: (843) 524-4510
E-mail: info@coastalbanking.com
Web Site: www.coastalbanking.com
Approx. Rev.: $30,184,779
Approx. Number Employees: 124
Year Founded: 2000
Business Description:
Bank Holding Company
S.I.C.: 6141; 6712
N.A.I.C.S.: 522210; 551111
Advertising Expenditures: $139,654
Media: 17
Personnel:
Gary Horn *(Pres)*
Michael G. Sanchez *(CEO)*
Paul R. Garrigues *(CFO & Exec VP)*

COASTAL FEDERAL BANK
(Sub. of Coastal Financial Corp.)
2619 Oak St
Myrtle Beach, SC 29577-3129
Tel.: (843) 205-2000
Fax: (843) 205-2488
Web Site: www.coastalfederal.com
Approx. Number Employees: 500
Year Founded: 1954
Business Description:
Banking Services
S.I.C.: 6035
N.A.I.C.S.: 522120
Advertising Expenditures: $750,000
Media: 3-6-7-8-9-13-18-19-20-22-24-25-26
Personnel:
Jerry Rexroad *(CFO & Exec VP)*
Jimmy Graham *(CIO & Exec VP)*
Robert Douglas *(Exec VP-HR)*
Brands & Products:
COASTAL
COASTALFEDERALINVESTORS

CODORUS VALLEY BANCORP, INC.
105 Leader Heights Rd PO Box 2887
York, PA 17405
Tel.: (717) 747-1519
Fax: (717) 747-0633
Toll Free: (888) 846-1970
E-mail: support@peoplesbanknet.com
Web Site: www.peoplesbanknet.com
Approx. Rev.: $51,601,000
Approx. Number Employees: 185
Business Description:
Banking Services
S.I.C.: 6712
N.A.I.C.S.: 551111
Advertising Expenditures: $626,000
Personnel:
Rodney L. Krebs *(Chm)*
Larry J. Miller *(Vice Chm, Pres & CEO)*
Jann Allen Weaver *(CFO, Chief Acctg Officer, Treas & Asst Sec)*

COLONIAL FINANCIAL SERVICES, INC.
2745 S Delsea Dr
Vineland, NJ 08360
Tel.: (856) 205-0058
Fax: (856) 451-5110
Web Site: www.colonialbankfsb.com
Approx. Rev.: $27,866,000
Approx. Number Employees: 93
Business Description:
Bank Holding Company
S.I.C.: 6141; 6712
N.A.I.C.S.: 522210; 551111
Advertising Expenditures: $208,000
Personnel:
Albert A. Fralinger, Jr. *(Chm)*
Gregory J. Facemyer *(Vice Chm)*
Edward J. Geletka *(Pres & CEO)*
L. Joseph Stella III *(CFO & Exec VP)*
William F. Whelan *(COO & Exec VP)*
Richard W. Dapp *(Chief Credit Officer & Sr VP)*
J. Steven Sammartino *(Sr VP & Sr Comml Lender)*
Marie E. Davis *(Officer-Ops)*
Joseph Sidebotham, Sr. *(Sr VP, Controller & Corp Sec)*
Jody K. Hirata *(Sr VP-Bus Dev)*
Thomas Davies *(VP & Asst Sec)*
Vicki T. Cannizzaro *(VP-Tech & Product Dev)*
Christine Marciano *(Asst VP)*
Annette Massari *(Asst VP)*
Pauline Smith *(Asst Treas)*

COLONY BANKCORP, INC.
115 S Grant St
Fitzgerald, GA 31750
Mailing Address:
PO Box 989
Fitzgerald, GA 31750
Tel.: (229) 426-6000
Fax: (229) 426-6039

Key to Media (For complete agency information see *The Advertising Red Books-Agencies* edition):
1. Bus. Publs. 2. Cable T.V. 3. Catalogs & Directories. 4. Co-op Adv. 5. Consumer Mags. 6. D.M. to Bus. Estab.7. D.M. to Consumers
8. Daily Newsp. 9. Exhibits/Trade Shows 10. Foreign 11. Infomercial 12. Internet Adv.13. Multimedia 14. Network Radio
15. Network T.V. 16. Newsp. Distr. Mags. 17. Other 18. Outdoor (Posters, Transit) 19. Point of Purchase20. Premiums, Novelties
21. Product Samples 22. Special Events Mktg. 23. Spot Radio 24. Spot T.V. 25. Weekly Newsp. 26. Yellow Page Adv.

Colony Bankcorp, Inc. — (Continued)
Web Site: www.colonybank.com
Approx. Rev.: $68,744,568
Approx. Number Employees: 285
Business Description:
Bank Holding Company
S.I.C.: 6712; 6029
N.A.I.C.S.: 551111; 522110
Advertising Expenditures: $653,000
Personnel:
L. Morris Downing *(Chm)*
Edward J. Harrell *(Vice Chm)*
Al D. Ross *(Pres & CEO)*
Terry L. Hester *(CFO)*

COLORADO FEDERAL SAVINGS BANK

8400 E Prentice Ave Ste 545
Greenwood Village, CO 80111
Tel.: (303) 793-3555
Fax: (303) 793-3560
E-mail: colorado@noemail.com
Web Site:
www.coloradofederalbank.com
Approx. Sls.: $170,000,000
Approx. Number Employees: 10
Business Description:
Federal Savings Banks
S.I.C.: 6035
N.A.I.C.S.: 522120
Media: 2-10-13
Personnel:
Brad Dietz *(CFO)*
Pat Fogerty *(Exec VP)*

THE COLUMBIA BANK

(Holding of Fulton Financial Corporation)
7168 Columbia Gateway Dr
Columbia, MD 21046
Tel.: (410) 423-8000
Fax: (410) 884-5809
E-mail: info@thecolumbiabank.com
Web Site: www.thecolumbiabank.com
Sales Range: $50-74.9 Million
Approx. Number Employees: 360
Business Description:
Commercial Banking Services
S.I.C.: 6029
N.A.I.C.S.: 522110
Advertising Expenditures: $929,000
Media: 7-8-9-13-18-23-24-26
Personnel:
John M. Bond, Jr. *(Chm)*
John A. Scaldara, Jr. *(Pres & CEO)*
Michael T. Galeone *(Exec VP-Retail Banking)*
Albert D. Karfonta *(Exec VP)*
Robert W. Locke *(Exec VP)*

COLUMBIA BANKING SYSTEM, INC.

1301 A Street
Tacoma, WA 98401
Tel.: (253) 305-1900
Fax: (253) 305-0317
E-mail: columbiabank@columbiabank.com
Web Site: www.columbiabank.com
Approx. Int. Income: $185,879,000
Approx. Number Employees: 1,092
Year Founded: 1993
Business Description:
Bank Holding Company
S.I.C.: 6141; 6029
N.A.I.C.S.: 522210; 522110
Advertising Expenditures: $1,943,000
Personnel:
William Toycen Weyerhaeuser *(Chm)*
Melanie J. Dressel *(Pres & CEO)*
Gary R. Schminkey *(CFO & Exec VP)*
Andrew L. Mcdonald *(Chief Credit Officer & Exec VP)*
Clint E. Stein *(Chief Acctg Officer)*
Kent L. Roberts *(Exec VP & Dir-HR)*
Nina Maurer *(Sr VP)*
JoAnne Coy *(VP-Corp Comm)*

COLUMBUS BANK AND TRUST COMPANY

(Sub. of Synovus Financial Corp.)
1148 Broadway
Columbus, GA 31902-0120
Mailing Address:
PO Box 120
Columbus, GA 31902
Tel.: (706) 649-4900
Fax: (706) 649-2214
E-mail: info@cscolumbusbankandtrust.com
Web Site:
www.columbusbankandtrust.com
Sales Range: $50-74.9 Million
Approx. Number Employees: 365
Business Description:
Banking Services
S.I.C.: 6029
N.A.I.C.S.: 522110
Media: 4-8-13-18
Personnel:
William R. Blanchard *(Pres & CEO)*
Tommy Prescott *(CFO)*
Nina Elmore *(Sr VP & Dir-Mktg)*

COMDATA CORPORATION

(Joint Venture of Thomas H. Lee Partners, L.P. & Fidelity National Financial, Inc.)
5301 Maryland Way
Brentwood, TN 37027-5055
Tel.: (615) 370-7000
Fax: (615) 370-7771
Toll Free: (800) 266-3282
E-mail: info@comdata.com
Web Site: www.comdata.com
Approx. Sls.: $243,000,000
Approx. Number Employees: 1,800
Year Founded: 1969
Business Description:
Payment Processing Services
S.I.C.: 6099; 7374
N.A.I.C.S.: 522320; 518210
Media: 2-6-7-10-16
Distr.: Natl.
Personnel:
Steve Stevenson *(Pres)*
Michael Henricks *(CFO & Sr VP-Fin)*
Lisa Peerman *(Gen Counsel, Sec & Sr VP)*
Scott Phillips *(Exec VP & Gen Mgr-Corp Payment Solutions)*
Randy Morgan *(Exec VP-Sls)*
Walt Hannabass *(Sr VP-Credit & Collections)*
Todd Joseph *(Sr VP-IT)*
Greg Koren *(Sr VP-Sls)*
Tracey Power *(Sr VP-HR)*
Kedran Whitten *(Sr VP-Mktg & Product Mgmt)*
Keela Wofford *(Sr VP)*
Trisha Torrado *(VP-Mktg & Comm)*

COMERICA INCORPORATED

Comerica Bank Tower 1717 Main St
Dallas, TX 75201
Tel.: (214) 589-1400
Toll Free: (800) 521-1190
E-mail: info@comerica.com
Web Site: www.comerica.com
Approx. Rev.: $2,642,000,000
Approx. Number Employees: 8,636
Year Founded: 1973
Business Description:
Bank Holding Company
S.I.C.: 6712; 6029; 6035; 6163; 6211
N.A.I.C.S.: 551111; 522110; 522120; 522310; 523110
Advertising Expenditures: $4,000,000
Media: 1-2-3-6-7-8-9-10-13-14-15-16-18-19-20-23-24-25-26
Distr.: Natl.
Budget Set: Nov.
Personnel:
Ralph W. Babb, Jr. *(Chm & CEO-Comerica Incorporated & Comerica Bank)*
Curtis C. Farmer *(Vice Chm-The Retail Bank & Wealth & Institutional Mgmt)*
Elizabeth S. Acton *(CFO & Exec VP)*
Paul R. Obermeyer *(CIO & Exec VP)*
Jim Weber *(CMO)*
Brian Foley *(Chief Credit Officer & Sr VP)*
J. Michael Fulton *(Pres-Comerica Bank-Western Market)*
Thomas D. Ogden *(Pres-Comerica Bank-Michigan Market)*
David K. Skolnik *(Pres-Asset Mgmt Grp)*
Michael H. Michalak *(Interim Treas)*
Jon W. Bilstrom *(Exec VP-Governance, Regulatory Rels & Legal Affairs)*
David E. Duprey *(Exec VP & Gen Auditor)*
Dale E. Greene *(Exec VP-The Bus Bank)*
E. Mark Gregory *(Exec VP-Middle Market Banking)*
Ronald P. Marcinelli *(Exec VP-Natl Bus Fin)*
Robert D. McDermott *(Exec VP-Fin)*
Marvin J. Elenbaas *(Sr VP & Controller)*
Elizabeth J. Correa *(Sr VP)*
Linda D. Forte *(Sr VP-Bus Affairs)*
Eddie Gates *(Sr VP & Regl Mgr)*
Edward T. Gwilt *(Sr VP)*
Jerry Iwata *(Sr VP)*
Dana Johnson *(Sr VP)*
Todd McDonald *(Sr VP)*
Cassandra McKinney *(Sr VP-Retail Product & Sales Mgmt)*
Patricia McCann *(VP & Mgr-Natl Civic Affairs)*
Darlene P. Persons *(Dir-IR)*
Roslyn Samalik *(Grp Mgr-Loan)*
Brands & Products:
COMERICA CENTRAL
COMERICA TM CONNECT
COMERICA TM CONNECT DESKTOP
COMERICA TM CONNECT FILE TRANSFER
COMERICA TM CONNECT WEB
COMERICA WEB BANKING FOR SMALL BUSINESS
COMERICA WEB BILL PAY
COMERICA WEBBANKING
COMERICA'S HOME EQUITY FLEXLINE
COMTRAC
PLATINUM CIRCLE
RICH REWARDS
SPECTRUM OF CHOICE
WE LISTEN. WE UNDERSTAND. WE MAKE IT WORK
Advertising Agency:
Enlighten
3027 Miller Rd
Ann Arbor, MI 48103
Tel.: (734) 668-6678
Fax: (734) 668-1883

COMINAR REAL ESTATE INVESTMENT TRUST

455 Rue Marais
Quebec, QC G1M 3A2, Canada
Tel.: (418) 681-8151
Fax: (418) 681-2946
Toll Free: (866) COMINAR
E-mail: info@cominar.com
Web Site: www.cominar.com
Approx. Rev.: $289,249,111
Year Founded: 1998
Business Description:
Real Estate Investment Trust
S.I.C.: 6798
N.A.I.C.S.: 525930
Media: 4-7-11
Personnel:
Robert Despres *(Chm)*
Michel Dallaire *(Pres & CEO)*
Michel Berthelot *(CFO & Exec VP)*
Alain Dallaire *(Exec VP-Ops)*
Scott McCrea *(Exec VP-Atlantic Provinces)*
Michel Ouellette *(Exec VP-Acq & Dev)*
Todd Bechard *(VP-Fin-Atlantic Provinces)*
Richard Nolin *(VP-Retail)*
Jocelyn Tremblay *(Dir-Leasing)*

COMMERCE BANCSHARES, INC.

1000 Walnut
Kansas City, MO 64106
Mailing Address:
PO Box 419248
Kansas City, MO 64141-6248
Tel.: (816) 234-2000
Fax: (816) 234-2019
Toll Free: (800) 892-7100
Telex: 4-2374
E-mail: mymoney@commercebank.com
Web Site: www.commercebank.com
Approx. Int. Income: $729,478,000
Approx. Number Employees: 4,389
Year Founded: 1966
Business Description:
Bank Holding Company
S.I.C.: 6029; 6712
N.A.I.C.S.: 522110; 551111
Advertising Expenditures: $17,294,000
Media: 2-6-8-9-10-18-19-20-23-24-25-26
Distr.: Natl.
Budget Set: Oct.
Personnel:
David W. Kemper *(Chm, Pres & CEO)*
Jonathan M. Kemper *(Vice Chm)*
Seth M. Leadbeater *(Co-Vice Chm)*
Charles G. Kim *(CFO)*
Eric Steinhouse *(CMO & Exec VP)*
Robert C. Matthews Jr. *(Chief Credit Officer, Exec VP & Mgr-Risk)*
J. Daniel Stinnett *(Gen Counsel, Sec & VP)*

Key to Media (For complete agency information see *The Advertising Red Books-Agencies* edition):
1. Bus. Publs. 2. Cable T.V. 3. Catalogs & Directories. 4. Co-op Adv. 5. Consumer Mags. 6. D.M. to Bus. Estab.7. D.M. to Consumers 8. Daily Newsp. 9. Exhibits/Trade Shows 10. Foreign 11. Infomercial 12. Internet Adv.13. Multimedia 14. Network Radio 15. Network T.V. 16. Newsp. Distr. Mags. 17. Other 18. Outdoor (Posters, Transit) 19. Point of Purchase20. Premiums, Novelties 21. Product Samples 22. Special Events Mktg. 23. Spot Radio 24. Spot T.V. 25. Weekly Newsp. 26. Yellow Page Adv.

Kevin G. Barth *(Exec VP)*
V. Raymond Stranghoener *(Exec VP)*
Sara E. Foster *(Sr VP)*
Michael J. Petrie *(Sr VP)*
Robert J. Rauscher *(Sr VP)*
Jeanne D. Howard *(Dir-Reg Mktg & PR)*
Advertising Agencies:
Bernstein-Rein Advertising, Inc.
4600 Madison Ave Ste 1500
Kansas City, MO 64112-3016
Tel.: (816) 756-0640
Fax: (816) 399-6000
Toll Free: (800) 571-6246

BKV Inc.
10561 Barkley St Ste 200
Overland Park, KS 66212
Tel.: (913) 648-8333
Fax: (913) 648-5024

Rubenstein Associates, Inc.
1345 Ave of the Americas Fl 30
New York, NY 10105-0109
Tel.: (212) 843-8000
Fax: (212) 843-9200

COMMERCEBANK HOLDING CORPORATION
(Sub. of Mercantil Servicios Financieros, C.A.)
220 Alhambra Cir
Coral Gables, FL 33134
Tel.: (305) 460-8701
Fax: (305) 460-4010
E-mail: questions@commercebankfl.com
Web Site: www.commercebankfl.com
Approx. Int. Income: $128,186,000
Approx. Number Employees: 615
Year Founded: 1979
Business Description:
Commercial Banking Services
S.I.C.: 6029
N.A.I.C.S.: 522110
Media: 6
Personnel:
Gustavo Marturet *(Chm)*
Tere Benach *(Sr VP-Mktg)*

COMMERCIAL BANCSHARES, INC.
118 S Sandusky Ave
Upper Sandusky, OH 43351
Tel.: (419) 294-5781
Fax: (419) 294-2350
Web Site: www.csbanking.com
Approx. Rev.: $17,921,000
Approx. Number Employees: 81
Year Founded: 1995
Business Description:
Bank Holding Company
S.I.C.: 6029; 6712
N.A.I.C.S.: 522110; 551111
Advertising Expenditures: $213,000
Media: 17
Personnel:
Michael A. Shope *(Chm)*
Stanley K. Kinnett *(Vice Chm)*
Robert E. Beach *(Pres & CEO)*
Scott A. Oboy *(CFO)*

COMMERCIAL BANK & TRUST OF PENNSYLVANIA
(Sub. of Commercial National Financial Corporation)
900 Ligonier St
Latrobe, PA 15650
Mailing Address:
PO Box 429
Latrobe, PA 15650-0429
Tel.: (724) 539-3501
Fax: (724) 537-9966
Toll Free: (800) 803BANK
Web Site: www.cbthebank.com
Sales Range: $50-74.9 Million
Approx. Number Employees: 120
Year Founded: 1934
Business Description:
State Commercial Bank
S.I.C.: 6029; 6163
N.A.I.C.S.: 522110; 522310
Media: 7-8-9-13-25
Personnel:
Gregg E. Hunter *(Vice Chm, Pres & CEO)*
Wendy S. Schmucker *(Treas, Sec & Sr VP)*
Susan R. Skoloda *(VP, Asst Sec & Asst Treas)*

COMMERCIAL NATIONAL FINANCIAL CORPORATION
900 Ligonier St
Latrobe, PA 15650
Tel.: (724) 539-3501
Fax: (724) 537-9966
E-mail: wschmucker@cbthebank.com
Web Site: www.cnbthebank.com
Approx. Rev.: $21,125,000
Approx. Number Employees: 92
Year Founded: 1986
Business Description:
Bank Holding Company
S.I.C.: 6712; 6029
N.A.I.C.S.: 551111; 522110
Advertising Expenditures: $170,000
Media: 17
Personnel:
George V. Welty *(Chm)*
Gregg E. Hunter *(Vice Chm, Pres & CEO)*
Thomas D. Watters *(CFO & Exec VP)*
Wendy S. Schmucker *(Treas, Sec & Sr VP)*
Susan R. Skoloda *(VP, Asst Sec & Asst Treas)*

COMMONWEALTH BANKSHARES, INC.
403 Boush St
Norfolk, VA 23510
Tel.: (757) 446-6900
Fax: (757) 446-6986
E-mail: ewoodward@bocmail.net
Web Site: www.bankofthecommonwealth.com
Approx. Rev.: $64,736,976
Approx. Number Employees: 191
Year Founded: 1988
Business Description:
Bank Holding Company
S.I.C.: 6141; 6029; 6712
N.A.I.C.S.: 522210; 522110; 551111
Advertising Expenditures: $142,755
Media: 17
Personnel:
Richard J. Tavss *(Chm)*
Chris Beisel *(Chief Credit Officer)*
Cynthia A. Sabol *(CFO & Exec VP)*

COMMUNITY BANCORP
4811 US Rte 5
Derby, VT 05829
Mailing Address:
PO Box 259
Derby, VT 05829-0259
Tel.: (802) 334-7915
Fax: (802) 334-8266
E-mail: derby@communitynationalbank.com
Web Site: www.communitynationalbank.com
Approx. Rev.: $29,328,285
Approx. Number Employees: 137
Year Founded: 1851
Business Description:
Bank Holding Company
S.I.C.: 6712; 6141; 6289
N.A.I.C.S.: 551111; 522210; 523999
Advertising Expenditures: $414,902
Personnel:
Stephen P. Marsh *(Chm & CEO)*
Candace A. Patenaude *(Chief Acctg Officer)*
Kathryn M. Austin *(Exec VP)*
Brands & Products:
TOTALLY KIDS CLUB

COMMUNITY BANK, N.A.
(Sub. of Community Bank System, Inc.)
5790 Widewaters Pkwy
De Witt, NY 13214-1883
Tel.: (315) 445-2282
Fax: (315) 445-2997
E-mail: customerservice@communitybankna.com
Web Site: www.communitybankna.com
Sales Range: $450-499.9 Million
Approx. Number Employees: 1,500
Year Founded: 1992
Business Description:
Savings, Loan & Investment Banking Services
S.I.C.: 6029; 6035; 6163; 6211; 6289
N.A.I.C.S.: 522110; 522120; 522310; 523110; 523999
Advertising Expenditures: $484,000
D.M. to Consumers: $4,000; Daily Newsp.: $155,000; Other: $186,000; Premiums, Novelties: $25,000; Special Events Mktg.: $50,000; Spot Radio: $50,000; Spot T.V.: $14,000
Distr.: Reg.
Budget Set: Aug.
Personnel:
Mark E. Tryniski *(Pres & CEO)*
Scott A. Kingsley *(CFO)*
Bernadette R. Barber *(Chief HR Officer & Sr VP)*
Brian D. Donahue *(Exec VP & Chief Banking Officer)*
Timothy J. Baker *(Sr VP & Dir-Special Projects)*
Harold M. Wentworth *(Sr VP, Dir-Sls & Mktg)*
Brands & Products:
BANKEASE

COMMUNITY BANK SHARES OF INDIANA, INC.
101 W Spring St
New Albany, IN 47150
Mailing Address:
PO Box 939
New Albany, IN 47151-0939
Tel.: (812) 944-2224
Fax: (812) 949-6812
E-mail: custsrv@yourcommunitybank.com
Web Site: www.cbinonline.com
Approx. Rev.: $43,308,000
Approx. Number Employees: 191
Year Founded: 1991
Business Description:
Bank Holding Company
S.I.C.: 6029; 6712
N.A.I.C.S.: 522110; 551111
Advertising Expenditures: $495,000
Personnel:
Gary L. Libs *(Chm)*
Steven R. Stemler *(Vice Chm)*
James D. Rickard *(Pres & CEO)*
Paul A. Chrisco *(CFO & Exec VP)*
Michael Bauer *(Chief Credit Officer & Exec VP)*
Bill Wright *(Treas, Exec VP & Dir-Plng)*
Kevin J. Cecil *(Exec VP)*
J. Robert McIlvoy *(Sr VP)*
M. Diane Murphy *(Sr VP & Community Rels Officer)*

COMMUNITY BANK SYSTEM, INC.
5790 Widewaters Pkwy
De Witt, NY 13214-1883
Tel.: (315) 445-2282
Fax: (315) 445-2997
Toll Free: (800) 724-2262
Web Site: www.communitybankna.com
Approx. Rev.: $337,073,000
Approx. Number Employees: 1,627
Year Founded: 1983
Business Description:
Bank Holding Company
S.I.C.: 6029; 6712
N.A.I.C.S.: 522110; 551111
Advertising Expenditures: $2,000,000
Personnel:
Paul M. Cantwell, Jr. *(Chm)*
Mark E. Tryniski *(Pres & CEO)*
Scott A. Kingsley *(CFO & Exec VP)*
J. David Clark *(Sr VP & Chief Credit Officer)*
Joseph J. Lemchak *(Chief Investment Officer & Sr VP)*
J. Michael Wilson *(CTO & Sr VP)*
Bernadette R. Barber *(Chief HR Officer & Sr VP)*
Robert P. Matley *(Pres-Pennsylvania Banking)*
Timothy J. Baker *(Sr VP & Dir-Special Projects)*
Harold M. Wentworth *(Sr VP & Dir-Sls & Mktg)*
Claire F. Lagarry *(Sr VP & Mgr-Retail Banking)*
Richard M. Heidrick *(Sr VP-Retail Banking Admin)*

COMMUNITY BANKERS TRUST CORPORATION
4235 Innslake Dr Ste 200
Glen Allen, VA 23060
Tel.: (804) 934-9999
Web Site: www.cbtrustcorp.com
Approx. Rev.: $60,570,000
Approx. Number Employees: 287
Year Founded: 2005
Business Description:
Bank Holding Company
S.I.C.: 6712
N.A.I.C.S.: 551111
Advertising Expenditures: $345,000
Personnel:
Alexander F. Dillard, Jr. *(Chm)*

Key to Media (For complete agency information see *The Advertising Red Books-Agencies* edition):
1. Bus. Publs. 2. Cable T.V. 3. Catalogs & Directories. 4. Co-op Adv. 5. Consumer Mags. 6. D.M. to Bus. Estab.7. D.M. to Consumers 8. Daily Newsp. 9. Exhibits/Trade Shows 10. Foreign 11. Infomercial 12. Internet Adv.13. Multimedia 14. Network Radio 15. Network T.V. 16. Newsp. Distr. Mags. 17. Other 18. Outdoor (Posters, Transit) 19. Point of Purchase20. Premiums, Novelties 21. Product Samples 22. Special Events Mktg. 23. Spot Radio 24. Spot T.V. 25. Weekly Newsp. 26. Yellow Page Adv.

Community Bankers Trust Corporation — (Continued)

Troy A. Peery, Jr. *(Vice Chm)*
Rex L. Smith, III *(Pres & CEO)*
Bruce E. Thomas *(CFO & Sr VP)*
Patrick J. Tewell *(Chief Acctg Officer & Sr VP)*

COMMUNITY CAPITAL CORPORATION

1402-C Hwy 72 W
Greenwood, SC 29649
Mailing Address:
PO Box 218
Greenwood, SC 29648-0218
Tel.: (864) 941-8200
Tel.: (864) 941-8242
Fax: (864) 941-8283
E-mail: llee@capitalbanksc.com
Web Site: www.comcapcorp.com
Approx. Rev.: $41,711,000
Approx. Number Employees: 171
Year Founded: 1988
Business Description:
Bank Holding Company
S.I.C.: 6029; 6712
N.A.I.C.S.: 522110; 551111
Advertising Expenditures: $22,468
Media: 7-8-13
Personnel:
Patricia C. Hartung *(Chm)*
William G. Stevens *(Pres & CEO)*

COMMUNITY CENTRAL BANK CORPORATION

100 N Main St
Mount Clemens, MI 48043-5605
Mailing Address:
PO Box 7
Mount Clemens, MI 48046-0007
Tel.: (586) 783-4500
Fax: (586) 783-9471
E-mail: raycolonius@communitycentralbank.com
Web Site:
www.communitycentralbank.com
Approx. Rev.: $38,367,000
Approx. Number Employees: 89
Year Founded: 1996
Business Description:
Bank Holding Company
S.I.C.: 6029; 6712
N.A.I.C.S.: 522110; 551111
Advertising Expenditures: $426,000
Personnel:
Salvatore Cottone *(Chm)*
Ray T. Colonius *(CFO)*
Sam A. Locricchio *(Exec VP)*

COMMUNITY FINANCIAL CORPORATION

38 N Central Ave
Staunton, VA 24402-1209
Tel.: (540) 886-0796
Fax: (540) 885-0643
E-mail: rsavidge@cbnk.com
Web Site: www.cbnk.com
Approx. Rev.: $31,674,190
Approx. Number Employees: 162
Year Founded: 1986
Business Description:
Bank Holding Company
S.I.C.: 6712
N.A.I.C.S.: 551111
Advertising Expenditures: $522,072
Media: 8
Personnel:
James R. Cooke, Jr. *(Chm)*
P. Douglas Richard *(Vice Chm)*
Norman C. Smiley, III *(Pres & CEO)*
R. Jerry Giles *(CFO & Sr VP)*
Benny N. Werner *(COO & Sr VP)*
John J. Howerton *(Sr VP-Retail Banking)*
Clarence W. Keel *(Sr VP-Hampton Roads Reg)*
Lyle A. Moffett *(Sr VP-Lending)*
Brands & Products:
OUR NAME REALLY DOES SAY IT ALL

COMMUNITY FINANCIAL SHARES, INC.

357 Roosevelt Rd
Glen Ellyn, IL 60137
Tel.: (630) 545-0900
Fax: (630) 545-0399
Web Site: www.cbwge.com
Approx. Rev.: $15,614,000
Approx. Number Employees: 77
Year Founded: 2000
Business Description:
Bank Holding Company
S.I.C.: 6035; 6029; 6712
N.A.I.C.S.: 522120; 522110; 551111
Advertising Expenditures: $296,000
Personnel:
Donald H. Fischer *(Chm)*
Scott W. Hamer *(Pres & CEO)*
Christopher P. Barton *(Exec VP-Community Bank-Wheaton/Glen Ellyn)*

COMMUNITY NATIONAL BANK OF THE LAKEWAY AREA

225 W First North St
Morristown, TN 37814
Tel.: (423) 587-2345
Fax: (423) 587-3326
E-mail: investor@cnbla.com
Web Site: www.cnbla.com
Approx. Rev.: $6,748,555
Approx. Number Employees: 34
Business Description:
Banking Services
S.I.C.: 6029
N.A.I.C.S.: 522110
Advertising Expenditures: $318,000
Personnel:
Samuel F. Grigsby, Jr. *(Chm & CEO)*
Charles A. Hughes *(Pres)*
Darwin K. Kilday *(CFO, Sec & Exec VP)*
Brandon S. Stubblefield *(CIO & VP-Ops)*
Patricia A. Bowman *(Auditor)*
Thomas D. Rush, Jr. *(Exec VP-Lending)*
Jay C. Setser *(Asst VP)*

COMMUNITY PARTNERS BANCORP

1250 Hwy 35 S
Middletown, NJ 07748
Tel.: (732) 706-9009
E-mail: info@tworiverbank.com
Web Site: www.tworiverbank.com
Approx. Rev.: $33,190,000
Approx. Number Employees: 139
Business Description:
Bank Holding Company
S.I.C.: 6029; 6712
N.A.I.C.S.: 522110; 551111
Advertising Expenditures: $232,000
Personnel:
Charles T. Parton *(Chm)*
Joseph F. X. O'Sullivan *(Vice Chm)*
Frank J. Patock, Jr. *(Vice Chm)*
William D. Moss *(Pres & CEO)*
A. Richard Abrahamian *(CFO & Exec VP-Two River Community Bank)*

COMMUNITY SHORES BANK CORPORATION

1030 W Norton Ave
Muskegon, MI 49441
Tel.: (231) 780-1800
Fax: (231) 780-1860
E-mail: service@communityshores.com
Web Site:
www.communityshores.com
Approx. Rev.: $13,552,834
Approx. Number Employees: 58
Year Founded: 1998
Business Description:
Bank Holding Company
S.I.C.: 6712
N.A.I.C.S.: 551111
Advertising Expenditures: $76,000
Media: 1-8-9-18-25
Personnel:
Gary F. Bogner *(Chm)*
Robert L. Chandonnet *(Vice Chm)*
Heather D. Brolick *(Pres & CEO)*
Tracey A. Welsh *(CFO & Sr VP)*

COMMUNITY STATE BANK

(Sub. of Union Bancorporation)
1500 Main St
Union Grove, WI 53182
Tel.: (262) 878-3763
Fax: (262) 878-3009
E-mail: info@communitystatebank.net
Web Site:
www.communitystatebank.net
Approx. Number Employees: 110
Business Description:
Banking Services
S.I.C.: 6029
N.A.I.C.S.: 522110
Media: 8-9-10-25
Personnel:
Peter Huck *(Chm)*
Steven M. Bell *(Pres & CEO)*
Dennis Berg *(Credit Review Officer & Sr VP)*
Jeff Nielsen *(Asst VP, Webmaster & Officer-Mktg)*
Charles Daul *(Electronic Banking Officer)*
Dave Albrecht *(Exec VP)*
Kris Bernstein *(Sr VP-Personnel & Asst Security Officer)*
Sue Young *(Asst VP & Security Officer)*
Heidi Conde *(Asst VP & Mortgage Loan Officer)*
Kelly Hill *(Asst VP & Mortgage Loan Officer)*
Bonnie Leffelman *(Asst VP & Loan Officer)*

COMMUNITY WEST BANCSHARES

445 Pine Ave
Goleta, CA 93117-3709
Tel.: (805) 692-5821
Fax: (805) 692-2897
E-mail: contact@communitywest.com
Web Site: www.communitywest.com
Approx. Rev.: $43,249,000
Approx. Number Employees: 120
Year Founded: 1983
Business Description:
Financial Services Holding Company
S.I.C.: 6029
N.A.I.C.S.: 522110
Advertising Expenditures: $344,000
Personnel:
William R. Peeples *(Chm)*
Lynda J. Nahra *(Pres & CEO)*
Charles G. Baltuskonis *(CFO & Exec VP)*
Richard M Favor *(Exec VP & Chief Credit Officer)*
Susan C. Thompson *(Sr VP & Controller)*
Don W. Macaulay *(Sr VP & Reg Mgr-Bus Banking)*
James K. Battglias *(Sr VP & SlsMgr-SBA Western Reg)*
David A. Dickinson *(Sr VP-Comml Real Estate Lending)*
James D Gray *(Sr VP-Mortgage Div)*
Cynthia M. Hooper *(Sr VP-SBA Lending)*
Chris Lem *(Sr VP-Compliance & Risk Mgmt)*
Bernard R. Merry, Sr. *(Sr VP-Mortgage Div)*
Deborah L. Scott *(Sr VP-IT)*
Carlyn Smith *(Sr VP-Ops)*
Brands & Products:
MY COMMUNITY MY BANK

COMPASS BANK

(Sub. of Banco Bilbao Vizcaya Argentaria, S.A.)
4500 Mercantile Plz Ste 300
Fort Worth, TX 76137
Tel.: (817) 547-1150
Fax: (817) 270-1111
Web Site: www.bbvacompass.com/special/200910/wire/locations/texas.cfm
Sales Range: $75-99.9 Million
Approx. Number Employees: 601
Year Founded: 1996
Business Description:
Bank Holding Company
S.I.C.: 6712; 6289
N.A.I.C.S.: 551111; 523999
Advertising Expenditures: $1,332,000
Personnel:
Tom C. Nichols *(Chm & CEO)*
Don Cosby *(CFO & Exec VP)*
Ray Owen *(Exec VP)*
Laurie Jurhs *(Sr VP & Mgr-Ops)*
Barry Allison *(Sr VP)*
Hector Almeida *(Sr VP)*
F. James Volk *(Sr VP)*
Rex Castle *(VP-HR)*
Brands & Products:
STATE NATIONAL

COMPASS DIVERSIFIED HOLDINGS

61 Wilton Rd 2nd Fl
Westport, CT 06880
Tel.: (203) 221-1703
Web Site:
www.compassdiversifiedholdings.com
Approx. Rev.: $1,657,609,000
Approx. Number Employees: 399
Year Founded: 2005
Business Description:
Investment Trust
S.I.C.: 6733
N.A.I.C.S.: 525920
Advertising Expenditures: $6,100,000

Key to Media (For complete agency information see *The Advertising Red Books-Agencies* edition):
1. Bus. Publs. 2. Cable T.V. 3. Catalogs & Directories. 4. Co-op Adv. 5. Consumer Mags. 6. D.M. to Bus. Estab.7. D.M. to Consumers 8. Daily Newsp. 9. Exhibits/Trade Shows 10. Foreign 11. Infomercial 12. Internet Adv.13. Multimedia 14. Network Radio 15. Network T.V. 16. Newsp. Distr. Mags. 17. Other 18. Outdoor (Posters, Transit) 19. Point of Purchase20. Premiums, Novelties 21. Product Samples 22. Special Events Mktg. 23. Spot Radio 24. Spot T.V. 25. Weekly Newsp. 26. Yellow Page Adv.

Personnel:
James J. Bottiglieri *(CFO)*
I. Joseph Massoud *(CEO-Compass Grp Diversified Holdings)*

COMPASS GROUP DIVERSIFIED HOLDINGS LLC

(Group of Compass Diversified Holdings)
61 Wilton Rd 2nd Fl
Westport, CT 06880
Tel.: (203) 221-1703
Web Site:
www.compassdiversifiedholdings.com
Year Founded: 2005
Business Description:
Investment Holding Company
S.I.C.: 6719; 6289
N.A.I.C.S.: 551112; 523999
Advertising Expenditures: $3,300,000
Personnel:
C. Sean Daay *(Chm)*
Alan B. Offenberg *(CEO)*
James J. Bottiglieri *(CFO & Exec VP)*
Advertising Agency:
KCSA Strategic Communications (Kanan, Corbin, Schupak & Aronow, Inc.)
880 3rd Ave 6th Fl
New York, NY 10022
Tel.: (212) 682-6300
Fax: (212) 697-0910

COMPUCREDIT CORPORATION

(Sub. of CompuCredit Holdings Corporation)
Five Concourse Pkwy Ste 400
Atlanta, GA 30328
Tel.: (770) 828-2000
Toll Free: (888) 522CCRT
E-mail: corpinfo@compucredit.com
Web Site: www.compucredit.com
Sales Range: $1-4.9 Billion
Approx. Number Employees: 3,924
Year Founded: 1996
Business Description:
Credit & Related Financial Services
S.I.C.: 6141
N.A.I.C.S.: 522210; 522291
Media: 6-7-8-14-15-22-23-24
Personnel:
David G. Hanna *(Chm & CEO)*
Richard W. Gilbert *(Vice Chm & COO)*
Richard R. House, Jr. *(Pres)*
J. Paul Whitehead, III *(CFO)*
Rohit H. Kirpalani *(Gen Counsel)*
Richard C. Bricker, Jr. *(Dir-Internal Audit)*
Brands & Products:
ASPIRE CLASSIC
ASPIRE DIAMOND
ASPIRE PLATINUM
ASPIRE VISA
COMPUCREDIT
PURPOSE MONEY

CONSOLIDATED CREDIT COUNSELING SERVICES, INC.

5701 W Sunrise Blvd
Fort Lauderdale, FL 33313
Tel.: (954) 484-3328
Fax: (954) 233-3305
Toll Free: (800) 320-9929
E-mail: supervisor@consolidatedcredit.org
Web Site: www.consolidatedcredit.org
Approx. Number Employees: 4
Business Description:
Debt Management & Credit Counseling Services
S.I.C.: 7299
N.A.I.C.S.: 812990
Media: 6-8
Personnel:
Howard S. Dvorkin *(Founder)*
Gary Herman *(Pres)*
Alex Bort *(Dir-Online Mktg)*
April M.J. Lewis *(Dir-Corp Comm)*

CONSUMER CREDIT COUNSELING SERVICES

(d/b/a CredAbility)
100 Edgewood Ave NE Ste 1500
Atlanta, GA 30303
Tel.: (404) 527-7630
Fax: (404) 527-7632
Toll Free: (800) 251-2227
Web Site: www.credability.org
Approx. Sls.: $17,700,000
Approx. Number Employees: 60
Business Description:
Credit Counseling Services
S.I.C.: 7323; 6099
N.A.I.C.S.: 561450; 522390
Media: 17
Personnel:
Suzanne E. Boas *(Pres)*
Mark Cole *(COO & Exec VP)*
Dan Brown *(Sr VP & CIO)*

CONSUMER PORTFOLIO SERVICES, INC.

19500 Jamboree Rd
Irvine, CA 92618
Tel.: (949) 753-6800
Fax: (949) 753-4846
E-mail: webmaster@consumerportfolio.com
Web Site:
www.consumerportfolio.com
Approx. Rev.: $155,185,000
Approx. Number Employees: 435
Year Founded: 1991
Business Description:
Automotive Financial Services Company
S.I.C.: 3711; 6141; 6159
N.A.I.C.S.: 336111; 522291; 522298
Advertising Expenditures: $12,000,000
Personnel:
Charles E. Bradley, Jr. *(Pres & CEO)*
Jeffery P. Fritz *(CFO & Sr VP)*
Robert E. Riedl *(Chief Investment Officer & Sr VP)*
Mark A. Creatura *(Gen Counsel & Sr VP)*
Teri L. Clements *(Sr VP-Org)*
Curtis K. Powell *(Sr VP-Mktg)*
Chris Terry *(Sr VP-Svcs)*

CONTINUITY CONTROL

5 Science Park 3rd Fl
New Haven, CT 06511
Toll Free: (866) 631-5556
Web Site: www.continuity.net
Year Founded: 2008
Business Description:
Financial Technology
S.I.C.: 7372
N.A.I.C.S.: 511210
Personnel:
Andy Greenawalt *(Founder & CEO)*
Jim Kisch *(Chief Strategy Officer)*
Joel Nimety *(Sr VP-Tech)*
Advertising Agency:
William Mills Agency
300 W Wieuca Rd Bldg 1 Ste 300
Atlanta, GA 30342
Tel.: (678) 781-7200
Fax: (678) 781-7239
Toll Free: (800) 504-3077

THE CORPORATE EXECUTIVE BOARD COMPANY

1919 N Lynn St
Arlington, VA 22209
Tel.: (571) 303-3000
Fax: (571) 303-3100
Toll Free: (866) 913-2632
E-mail: info@executiveboard.com
Web Site: www.executiveboard.com
Approx. Rev.: $438,907,000
Approx. Number Employees: 1,879
Year Founded: 1983
Business Description:
Business Research & Analysis Services
S.I.C.: 8742; 8732
N.A.I.C.S.: 541611; 541910
Advertising Expenditures: $1,900,000
Personnel:
Thomas L. Monahan, III *(Chm & CEO)*
Richard S. Lindahl *(CFO)*
Melody L. Jones *(Chief HR Officer)*
Anthony Williams *(Exec Dir-Govt Practice)*
Brands & Products:
WHAT THE BEST COMPANIES DO

CORTLAND SAVINGS & BANKING CO.

(Sub. of Cortland Bancorp, Inc.)
194 W Main St
Cortland, OH 44410-1445
Tel.: (330) 637-8040
Fax: (330) 638-3018
E-mail: cbinfo@cortland-banks.com
Web Site: www.cortland-banks.com
Sales Range: $50-74.9 Million
Approx. Number Employees: 169
Year Founded: 1984
Business Description:
State Commercial Banking Services
S.I.C.: 6029
N.A.I.C.S.: 522110
Import Export
Media: 9
Personnel:
James M. Gasior *(Pres & CEO)*
Stanley P. Feret *(Chief Lending Officer)*
Timothy Carney *(Exec VP)*
Craig M. Phythyon *(VP & Asst Controller)*
Stephen A. Telego, Sr. *(VP-HR)*
Sarah Smith *(Dir-Mktg)*

COSTAR GROUP, INC.

1331 L St NW
Washington, DC 20005
Tel.: (202) 346-6500
Fax: (202) 346-6370
Fax: (800) 613-1301
Fax: (202) 346-6600
Toll Free: (800) 204-5960
Toll Free: (877) 739-0486
E-mail: info@costor.com
Web Site: www.costar.com
E-Mail For Key Personnel:
President: aflorance@costar.com
Approx. Rev.: $226,260,000
Approx. Number Employees: 1,389
Year Founded: 1987
Business Description:
Information Services to the Commercial Real Estate Industry
S.I.C.: 7389; 6531
N.A.I.C.S.: 561499; 531390
Advertising Expenditures: $3,000,000
Media: 2-8-10-13
Personnel:
Andrew C. Florance *(Founder, Pres & CEO)*
Michael R. Klein *(Chm)*
Brian J. Radecki *(CFO)*
Frank Simuro *(CIO)*
Jonathan Coleman *(Gen Counsel & Sec)*
Frank A. Carchedi *(Sr VP-Corp Dev)*
Jennifer L. Kitchen *(Sr VP-Res)*
John L. Stanfill *(Sr VP-Sls & Customer Svc)*
Tim Trainor *(Dir-Comm & Mng Editor-CoStar News)*
Michael Glick *(Dir-Dev)*
Walter Page *(Dir-Res-Property & Portfolio Res-Boston)*
Bill Tracy *(Dir-Sls-Adv)*
Brands & Products:
COSTAR ADVERTISING
COSTAR COMMERCIAL MLS
COSTAR COMPS EXPRESS
COSTAR COMPS PROFESSIONAL
COSTAR CONNECT
COSTAR EXCHANGE
COSTAR GROUP
COSTAR LISTINGS EXPRESS
COSTAR MARKET REPORT
COSTAR PROFESSIONAL DIRECTORY
COSTAR PROPERTY EXPRESS
COSTAR PROPERTY PROFESSIONAL
COSTAR SHOWCASE
COSTAR TENANT
METROPOLIS

COUNSEL CORPORATION

40 King St W Ste 3200
Toronto, ON M5H 3Y2, Canada
Tel.: (416) 866-3000
Fax: (416) 866-3061
E-mail: info@counselcorp.com
Web Site: www.counselcorp.com
Approx. Rev.: $37,528,235
Approx. Number Employees: 30
Year Founded: 1979
Business Description:
Investments; Management; Telecommunications
S.I.C.: 6282
N.A.I.C.S.: 523930
Advertising Expenditures: $127,000
Media: 17
Personnel:
Allan C. Silber *(Chm & CEO)*
Morris Perlis *(Vice Chm)*
Stephen Weintraub *(CFO, Sec & Exec VP)*
Kenneth J. Finkelstein *(Pres/CEO-Private Equity)*
R. Adam Levy *(Corp Counsel & Sr VP-Corp Dev)*
Howard Wortzman *(Sr VP-Real Estate Investments)*
Steven Walters *(Dir-Real Estate Acq)*

COUNTRYWIDE FINANCIAL CORPORATION

(Sub. of Bank of America Corporation)
4500 Park Granada

Key to Media (For complete agency information see *The Advertising Red Books-Agencies* edition):
1. Bus. Publs. 2. Cable T.V. 3. Catalogs & Directories. 4. Co-op Adv. 5. Consumer Mags. 6. D.M. to Bus. Estab.7. D.M. to Consumers
8. Daily Newsp. 9. Exhibits/Trade Shows 10. Foreign 11. Infomercial 12. Internet Adv.13. Multimedia 14. Network Radio
15. Network T.V. 16. Newsp. Distr. Mags. 17. Other 18. Outdoor (Posters, Transit) 19. Point of Purchase20. Premiums, Novelties
21. Product Samples 22. Special Events Mktg. 23. Spot Radio 24. Spot T.V. 25. Weekly Newsp. 26. Yellow Page Adv.

Countrywide Financial Corporation — (Continued)

Calabasas, CA 91302
Tel.: (818) 225-3000
Fax: (818) 888-6636
Web Site: www.countrywide.com
Sales Range: $1-4.9 Billion
Approx. Number Employees: 3,613
Year Founded: 1969
Business Description:
Commercial Banking
S.I.C.: 6159; 6029; 6141
N.A.I.C.S.: 522292; 522110; 522291; 522298
Media: 2-3-4-6-7-8-10-13-14-15-19-20-22
Distr.: Natl.
Budget Set: Dec.
Personnel:
Andrew Gissinger *(Pres & COO)*
Carlos Garcia *(Exec Mng Dir-Banking-Insurance Opers)*
David Sambol *(Exec Mng Dir)*
Andrew S. Bielanski *(Sr Mng Dir-Mktg)*
Thomas H. Boone *(Sr Mng Dir-Loan Admin)*
Richard Deleo *(Sr Mng Dir-Loan Administration)*
Todd Dal Porto *(Mng Dir)*
David Doyle *(Exec VP-Consumer Direct Production)*
Buddy E. Billingsley *(Dir-Assoc)*
Brands & Products:
ADVANTIDGE
EDGE
EXECUTIVE BROKER
LOCK N' SHOP
MORTGAGE EXPERT
MORTGAGE MONEY MOVER
PERKS

COWEN GROUP, INC.
599 Lexington Ave
New York, NY 10022
Tel.: (212) 845-7900
E-mail: cowen.us-communications@cowen.com
Web Site: www.cowen.com
Approx. Rev.: $233,810,000
Approx. Number Employees: 533
Year Founded: 1918
Business Description:
Investment Banking Services
S.I.C.: 6289; 6211
N.A.I.C.S.: 523999; 523120
Advertising Expenditures: $12,400,000
Media: 2-4-7-9-10-13-16-18-22
Personnel:
Peter Anthony Cohen *(Chm & CEO)*
Michael R. Costa *(Vice Chm-Investment Banking & Head-Mergers & Acq)*
Marran H. Ogilvie *(Partner & Mng Dir)*
Amrit Agrawal *(Mng Dir & Head-TMT Capital Markets)*
Ray Cameron *(Mng Dir & Head-Corp Access)*
David Ketsdever *(Mng Dir & Head-Tech Investment Banking)*
Leonard Sheer *(Mng Dir & Head-Debt Capital Markets)*
Tim Slaughter *(Mng Dir & Head-Fixed Income Distr)*
Jeff Porphy *(Mng Dir)*
Stephen A. Lasota *(CFO)*
Jeffrey Marc Solomon *(Chief Strategy Officer)*
Barry J. Tarasoff *(Dir-Res)*

CREDIT ACCEPTANCE CORPORATION
25505 W 12 Mile Rd Ste 3000
Southfield, MI 48034-8339
Tel.: (248) 353-2700
Fax: (248) 353-9776
E-mail: ir@creditacceptance.com
Web Site: www.credaccept.com
Approx. Rev.: $442,135,000
Approx. Number Employees: 862
Year Founded: 1972
Business Description:
Financial Services
S.I.C.: 6141; 6159
N.A.I.C.S.: 522210; 522291; 522298
Advertising Expenditures: $400,000
Media: 7-8-10-18
Personnel:
Donald A. Foss *(Founder & Chm)*
Brett A. Roberts *(CEO)*
Kenneth S. Booth *(CFO & Chief Acctg Officer)*
John P. Neary *(CIO)*
Charles A. Pearce *(Chief Legal Officer)*
Michael W. Knoblauch *(Sr VP-Loan Servicing)*
Brands & Products:
CREDIT ACCEPTANCE
WE CHANGE LIVES!

CREDIT ONE BANK
585 Pilot Rd
Las Vegas, NV 89119
Tel.: (702) 269-1000
Fax: (702) 269-1260
E-mail: info@creditonebank.com
Web Site: www.creditonebank.com
Sales Range: $50-74.9 Million
Approx. Number Employees: 750
Business Description:
National Commercial Banks
S.I.C.: 6029
N.A.I.C.S.: 522110
Personnel:
Robert Dejong *(Pres & CEO)*
Mamta Kapoor *(Sr VP-Mktg)*
Carrie Bradley *(Asst Controller)*
Advertising Agency:
SCPF
1688 Meridian Ave Ste 200
Miami Beach, FL 33139
Tel.: (305) 674-3222
Fax: (305) 695-2777

CREDIT SUISSE SECURITIES (USA) LLC
(Sub. of Credit Suisse (USA), Inc.)
11 Madison Ave
New York, NY 10010
Tel.: (212) 325-2000
Fax: (212) 538-3395
E-mail: info@credit-suisse.com
Web Site: www.credit-suisse.com
Approx. Number Employees: 9,050
Year Founded: 1934
Business Description:
Investment & Merchant Banking Services
S.I.C.: 6211; 6282
N.A.I.C.S.: 523110; 523930
Media: 2-6-9-11-16-25
Distr.: Intl.; Natl.; Reg.
Personnel:
Brady Dougan *(CEO)*
Amy Grossman *(Mng Dir)*
Neil Moskowitz *(Mng Dir)*
Nancy Smith *(Dir-Mktg)*
Advertising Agency:
McCann Erickson Worldwide
622 3rd Ave
New York, NY 10017-6707
Tel.: (646) 865-2000
Fax: (646) 487-9610

CRESCENT FINANCIAL CORPORATION
1005 High House Rd
Cary, NC 27513
Tel.: (919) 460-7770
Fax: (919) 460-2512
E-mail: virtualbanker@crescentstatebank.com
Web Site: www.crescentstatebank.com
Approx. Rev.: $55,690,572
Approx. Number Employees: 156
Business Description:
Bank Holding Company
S.I.C.: 6712; 6029; 6035
N.A.I.C.S.: 551111; 522110; 522120
Advertising Expenditures: $613,456
Personnel:
Bruce I. Howell *(Chm)*
James A. Lucas, Jr. *(Vice Chm)*
Michael G. Carlton *(Pres & CEO)*
Bruce W. Elder *(CFO)*

CRESTLINE FUNDING CORP.
18851 Bardeen Ave
Irvine, CA 92612-1520
Tel.: (949) 863-8600
Fax: (949) 863-8601
E-mail: info@crestlinefunding.com
Web Site: www.crestlinefunding.com
Sales Range: $10-24.9 Million
Approx. Number Employees: 50
Year Founded: 1994
Business Description:
Full-Service Mortgage Company
S.I.C.: 6163
N.A.I.C.S.: 522310
Advertising Expenditures: $750,000
Media: 6-8-9-13-23
Personnel:
Scott Brown *(Pres & CEO)*
Brad Helman *(CFO)*
Eric Paluncich *(Controller)*
Brands & Products:
YOUR FRIEND IN THE MORTGAGE BUSINESS

CROGHAN BANCSHARES, INC.
323 Croghan St
Fremont, OH 43420
Tel.: (419) 332-7301
Fax: (419) 355-2266
E-mail: ibank@croghan.com
Web Site: www.croghancolonialbank.com
Approx. Rev.: $26,519,000
Approx. Number Employees: 140
Year Founded: 1984
Business Description:
Banking Services
S.I.C.: 6141; 6029
N.A.I.C.S.: 522210; 522110
Advertising Expenditures: $192,000
Media: 17
Personnel:
Rick M. Robertson *(Pres & CEO)*
Kendall W. Rieman *(CFO & COO)*
Barry F. Luse *(Sec, VP & Sr Mgr)*
Thomas J. Elder, Jr. *(VP & Sr Mgr)*

CROWELL, WEEDON & CO.
1 Wilshire Blvd 26th Fl
Los Angeles, CA 90017-3876
Tel.: (213) 620-1850
Fax: (213) 244-9388
Toll Free: (800) 277-0319
E-mail: crowell@crowellweedon.com
Web Site: www.crowellweedon.com
Approx. Number Employees: 312
Year Founded: 1932
Business Description:
Provider of Investment Services
S.I.C.: 6211; 6282
N.A.I.C.S.: 523120; 523930
Personnel:
Andrew E. Crowell *(CEO, Mng Partner & COO)*
Alan Griffin *(Partner)*
James L. Cronk *(COO)*
Advertising Agency:
The Phelps Group
901 Wilshire Blvd
Santa Monica, CA 90401-1854
Tel.: (310) 752-4400
Fax: (310) 752-4444

CULLEN/FROST BANKERS, INC.
100 W Houston St
San Antonio, TX 78205-1414
Mailing Address:
PO Box 1600
San Antonio, TX 78296-1600
Tel.: (210) 220-4011
Fax: (210) 220-4325
Toll Free: (877) 714-4932
E-mail: frostbank@frostbank.com
Web Site: www.frostbank.com
Approx. Rev.: $899,372,000
Approx. Number Employees: 3,777
Year Founded: 1977
Business Description:
Bank Holding Company
S.I.C.: 6712; 6029; 6035; 6163; 6211
N.A.I.C.S.: 551111; 522110; 522120; 522310; 523110
Advertising Expenditures: $15,087,000
Media: 3-6-8-10-13-15-18-22-23-24-26
Budget Set: Dec. -Jan.
Personnel:
Richard W. Evans, Jr. *(Chm & CEO)*
Dave Beck *(Pres & Chief Bus Banking Officer)*
Phillip D. Green *(CFO & Grp Exec VP)*
William L. Perotti *(Grp Exec VP, Chief Credit Officer & Chief Risk Officer)*
Paul J. Olivier *(Grp Exec VP & Chief Consumer Banking Officer)*
Paul H. Bracher *(Pres-State Reg)*
Stan McCormick *(Gen Counsel, Sec & Exec VP)*
Richard Kardys *(Grp Exec VP-Fin Mgmt Grp)*
Emily A. Skillman *(Grp Exec VP-HR)*
Advertising Agency:
McGarrah Jessee
205 Brazos
Austin, TX 78701
Tel.: (512) 225-2000

Key to Media (For complete agency information see *The Advertising Red Books-Agencies* edition):
1. Bus. Publs. 2. Cable T.V. 3. Catalogs & Directories. 4. Co-op Adv. 5. Consumer Mags. 6. D.M. to Bus. Estab.7. D.M. to Consumers 8. Daily Newsp. 9. Exhibits/Trade Shows 10. Foreign 11. Infomercial 12. Internet Adv.13. Multimedia 14. Network Radio 15. Network T.V. 16. Newsp. Distr. Mags. 17. Other 18. Outdoor (Posters, Transit) 19. Point of Purchase20. Premiums, Novelties 21. Product Samples 22. Special Events Mktg. 23. Spot Radio 24. Spot T.V. 25. Weekly Newsp. 26. Yellow Page Adv.

Fax: (512) 225-2020

CULLMAN BANCORP, INC.

316 2nd Ave SW
Cullman, AL 35055
Tel.: (256) 734-1740
Fax: (256) 734-5344
Web Site:
www.cullmansavingsbank.com
Approx. Rev.: $13,120,000
Approx. Number Employees: 37
Business Description:
Bank Holding Company
S.I.C.: 6712; 6035
N.A.I.C.S.: 551111; 522120
Advertising Expenditures: $75,000
Media: 17
Personnel:
John A. Riley, III *(Pres & CEO)*
Michael C. Duke *(CFO & Sr VP)*
Robin O'Berry *(Sec & Sr VP)*
Alan R. Wood *(Exec VP)*
Robin Parson *(Sr VP & Dir-Savings)*

CUNA MUTUAL INSURANCE SOCIETY

(d/b/a CUNA Mutual Group)
5910 Mineral Point Rd
Madison, WI 53705
Mailing Address:
PO Box 391
Madison, WI 53701-0391
Tel.: (608) 238-5851
Fax: (608) 238-0830
Toll Free: (800) 356-2644
E-mail: marketing@cunamutual.com
Web Site: www.cunamutual.com
E-Mail For Key Personnel:
Public Relations: sydney.lindner@cunamutual.com
Approx. Rev.: $2,764,000,000
Approx. Number Employees: 4,500
Year Founded: 1935
Business Description:
Holding Company; Insurance, Asset Management & Financial Services
S.I.C.: 6719; 6282; 6289; 6411; 6733; 6799
N.A.I.C.S.: 551112; 523910; 523920; 523930; 523991; 523999; 524298
Media: 2-3-4-7-10-18-20-21-24
Distr.: Intl.; Natl.
Budget Set: Jan.
Personnel:
Joseph J. Gasper *(Vice Chm)*
Jeff Post *(Pres & CEO)*
Gerald Pavelich *(CFO & Exec VP)*
David Marks *(Chief Investment Officer & Exec VP)*
David Lundgren *(Chief Admin Officer & Exec VP)*
Robert Trunzo *(Chief Sls Officer & Exec VP-Sls)*
Jim Buchheim *(VP-PR & Comm)*
Rick Uhlmann *(Sr Mgr-Media Rels)*
Maripat Blankenheim *(Mgr-Media Rels)*
Phil Tschudy *(Mgr-Media Rels)*
Advertising Agencies:
Alternative Marketing Solutions, Inc.
342 Nutt Rd
Phoenixville, PA 19460-3910
Tel.: (610) 783-1320
Fax: (610) 783-1324

hawkeye
2828 Routh St Ste 300
Dallas, TX 75201
Tel.: (214) 659-5615
Fax: (214) 747-1897

hawkeye
325 Arlington Ave Ste 700
Charlotte, NC 28203
Tel.: (704) 344-7900
Fax: (704) 344-7920

Johnson Direct
250 N Sunnyslope Rd Ste 203
Brookfield, WI 53005
Tel.: (262) 782-2750
Fax: (262) 782-2751
Toll Free: (800) 710-2750

Laughlin/Constable, Inc.
360 N Michigan Ave 12th Fl
Chicago, IL 60601
Tel.: (414) 272-2400
Fax: (312) 422-5901

Yamamoto Moss and Mackenzie Marketing
252 First Ave N
Minneapolis, MN 55401
Tel.: (612) 375-0180
Fax: (612) 342-2424
Toll Free: (888) 375-9910

DALRADA FINANCIAL CORPORATION

10601-G Tierrasanta Blvd Ste 3440
San Diego, CA 92124
Tel.: (877) 325-7232
Fax: (858) 277-3448
Toll Free: (877) GETCOLOR
E-mail: inquiries@dalrada.com
Web Site: www.dalrada.com
Sales Range: $50-74.9 Million
Approx. Number Employees: 75
Year Founded: 1982
Business Description:
Holding Company; Human Resources & Other Administrative & Business Support Services
S.I.C.: 8741; 7363; 7389
N.A.I.C.S.: 561110; 561320; 561499
Import Export
Advertising Expenditures: $84,000
Media: 4-7-10-13-19
Distr.: Natl.
Personnel:
Angela L. Costello *(COO & VP-Sales-All Staffing)*
Jay Partin *(Chief Admin Officer & Exec VP)*
Eric W. Gaer *(CEO- Solvis Grp)*
William Brann *(Exec VP-Staffing Svcs)*

DANFORTH ASSOCIATES, INC.

1 Hollis St Ste 206
Wellesley, MA 02482
Tel.: (781) 235-9100
Fax: (781) 235-8028
Toll Free: (800) 443-4427
Web Site:
www.danforthassociates.com
Sales Range: Less than $1 Million
Approx. Number Employees: 4
Year Founded: 1936
Business Description:
Investment Management Services
S.I.C.: 6289
N.A.I.C.S.: 523999
Media: 2-6-8-9-25
Distr.: Reg.
Personnel:
Peter Alhart *(Pres & CIO)*

DANVERS BANCORP, INC.

1 Conant St
Danvers, MA 01923
Tel.: (978) 777-2200
Toll Free: (800) 771-8200
Toll Free: (888) 849-6046
Web Site: www.danversbank.com
Approx. Rev.: $132,378,000
Approx. Number Employees: 331
Year Founded: 1998
Business Description:
Bank Holding Company
S.I.C.: 6035; 6712
N.A.I.C.S.: 522120; 551111
Advertising Expenditures: $1,272,000
Personnel:
Kevin T. Bottomley *(Chm, Pres & CEO)*
L. Mark Panella *(CFO & Exec VP)*
James J. Mccarthy *(COO & Exec VP)*
Michael W. McCurdy *(Exec VP)*
John J. O'Neil *(Exec VP & Sr Lending Officer)*
Brands & Products:
DANVERSBANK
MY CALL CHECKING
MY SCHOOL
MY SONGS
MY WORLD

DCB FINANCIAL CORP.

110 Riverbend Ave
Lewis Center, OH 43035
Tel.: (740) 657-7010
Tel.: (740) 657-7930
Fax: (740) 657-7901
E-mail: jwolf@dcb-t.com
Web Site: www.dcbfinancialcorp.com
Approx. Rev.: $34,233,000
Approx. Number Employees: 152
Year Founded: 1997
Business Description:
Banking Services
S.I.C.: 6029
N.A.I.C.S.: 522110
Advertising Expenditures: $412,000
Media: 8
Personnel:
David J. Folkwein *(Chief Lending Officer & Exec VP-Corp Banking)*
John A. Ustaszewski *(CFO & Sr VP)*
Thomas R. Whitney *(Gen Counsel & Exec VP)*
Brian E. Stanfill *(Sr VP-HR & Ops)*
Barbara S. Walters *(Sr VP-Retail Banking)*
Jay D. Wolf *(VP-Mktg & Customer Rels)*

DEALERTRACK HOLDINGS, INC.

1111 Marcus Ave Ste M04
Lake Success, NY 11042
Tel.: (516) 734-3600
Toll Free: (877) 357-8725
Web Site: www.dealertrack.com
Approx. Rev.: $243,826,000
Approx. Number Employees: 1,200
Business Description:
Software & Data Solutions for Automotive Retail Industry for Auto Loans
S.I.C.: 7373; 6371; 7372
N.A.I.C.S.: 541512; 511210; 525990
Advertising Expenditures: $1,000,000
Media: 2-5-7-9-10-13-22-25
Personnel:
Mark F. O'Neil *(Chm & CEO)*
Eric D. Jacobs *(CFO, Chief Admin Officer & Sr VP)*
Richard McLeer *(CIO & Sr VP)*
Ann M. Herrera *(Sr VP-HR)*
Raj Sundaram *(Sr VP-Solutions & Svcs Grp-DealerTrack)*
Rick G. Von Pusch *(Sr VP-Sls & Mktg-Intl)*
Mark Brown *(VP-Mktg)*
Advertising Agency:
RF Binder Partners
950 3rd Ave 7th Fl
New York, NY 10022
Tel.: (212) 994-7600
Fax: (212) 994-7597

DEARBORN BANCORP, INC.

1360 Porter St
Dearborn, MI 48124
Tel.: (313) 565-5700
Fax: (313) 561-2291
E-mail: jeff.karafa@cbdear.com
Web Site: www.cbdear.com
Approx. Int. Income: $46,973,000
Approx. Number Employees: 191
Year Founded: 1992
Business Description:
Bank Holding Company
S.I.C.: 6141; 6029
N.A.I.C.S.: 522210; 522110
Advertising Expenditures: $237,000
Personnel:
John E. Demmer *(Chm)*
Michael J. Ross *(Pres & CEO)*
Jeffrey L. Karafa *(CFO & Sr VP)*
Robert Grant *(Pres-Oakland Reg)*
John A. Lindsey *(Pres-Oakland Reg)*

DEBT RESOLVE, INC.

150 White Plains Rd Ste 108
Tarrytown, NY 10591
Tel.: (914) 949-5500
Fax: (914) 428-3044
E-mail: info@debtresolve.com
Web Site: www.debtresolve.com
Approx. Rev.: $127,332
Approx. Number Employees: 4
Year Founded: 1997
Business Description:
Financial Services Computer Software Developer
S.I.C.: 7372
N.A.I.C.S.: 511210
Personnel:
James D. Burchetta *(Founder & Co-Chm)*
James G. Brakke *(Co-Chm & CEO)*
David M. Rainey *(Pres & CFO)*
Jonathan C. Rich *(Exec VP & Head-Investment Banking)*
Tony Sakovsky *(VP-IT)*
Rene A. Samson *(VP-IT)*
Brands & Products:
DEBTRESOLVE
DR SYSTEM
RESOLVED. WITH DIGNITY
Advertising Agency:
Rubenstein Public Relations
1345 Ave of the Americas
New York, NY 10105
Tel.: (212) 843-8000
Fax: (212) 843-9200

DEBTSCAPE, INC.

1304 Concourse Dr Ste 100
Linthicum, MD 21090

Key to Media (For complete agency information see *The Advertising Red Books-Agencies* edition):
1. Bus. Publs. 2. Cable T.V. 3. Catalogs & Directories. 4. Co-op Adv. 5. Consumer Mags. 6. D.M. to Bus. Estab.7. D.M. to Consumers 8. Daily Newsp. 9. Exhibits/Trade Shows 10. Foreign 11. Infomercial 12. Internet Adv.13. Multimedia 14. Network Radio 15. Network T.V. 16. Newsp. Distr. Mags. 17. Other 18. Outdoor (Posters, Transit) 19. Point of Purchase20. Premiums, Novelties 21. Product Samples 22. Special Events Mktg. 23. Spot Radio 24. Spot T.V. 25. Weekly Newsp. 26. Yellow Page Adv.

Debtscape, Inc. — (Continued)

Fax: (410) 859-3600
Toll Free: (888) 929-3328
E-mail: cs@debtscape.org
Web Site: www.debtscape.org
Approx. Number Employees: 100
Business Description:
Non-profit Credit & Debt Counseling Services
S.I.C.: 8748
N.A.I.C.S.: 541618
Media: 17
Personnel:
Dave Hensel *(Owner)*

DELOITTE & TOUCHE USA LLP

10 Westport Rd
Wilton, CT 06897-4522
Mailing Address:
PO Box 820
Wilton, CT 06897-0820
Tel.: (203) 761-3000
Fax: (203) 761-3000
Fax: (203) 834-2200
Toll Free: (800) 676-7736
Web Site: www.deloitte.com
Approx. Rev.: $8,769,000,000
Approx. Number Employees: 30,000
Year Founded: 1895
Business Description:
Accounting, Auditing, Tax & Management Consulting Services
S.I.C.: 8742; 7373; 8721
N.A.I.C.S.: 541611; 541219; 541512
Media: 2-3-4-7-9-13-25-26
Distr.: Intl.; Natl.
Personnel:
Sharon L. Allen *(Chm)*
Mark Edmunds *(Vice Chm & Reg Mng Partner-Northern Pacific)*
Anne Taylor *(Vice Chm & Reg Mng Partner-Mid America)*
Barry Salzberg *(CEO)*
Robin S. Lineberger *(CEO-Federal Govt Svcs)*
Karen R. Bowman *(Principal)*
Mary Cassidy *(Principal)*
Elizabeth Krentzman *(Principal)*
Suzanne Gylfe *(VP-Mktg)*
Vessa Playfair *(Head-Corp Affairs & Comm)*
Jon Warshowsky *(Editor-in-Chief-Deloitte Review)*
Gopal Ramasamy *(Dir)*
Paul Vogel *(Dir)*
John Keller *(Sr Mgr-Brand & Reputation)*
Brian Rutter *(Sr Mgr-Strategy & Ops)*
Angie Hazard *(Mgr-Talent Acq-Natl)*
John C. Pappas *(Mgr-PR-Natl)*
Shelley Pfaendler *(Mgr-PR-Natl)*
James C. Smith *(Mgr-Market Intelligence)*
Brands & Products:
DELOITTE REVIEW
Advertising Agency:
Keiler & Company
304 Main St
Farmington, CT 06032-2985
Tel.: (860) 677-8821
Fax: (860) 676-8164
(Accounting Firm Services)

DESERT COMMUNITY BANK

(Sub. of East West Bank)
12530 Hesperia Rd
Victorville, CA 92392
Mailing Address:
PO Box 1349
Victorville, CA 92393-1349
Tel.: (760) 243-2140
Fax: (760) 243-5048
E-mail: info@dcbk.org
Web Site: www.dcbk.org
Approx. Int. Income: $36,497,000
Approx. Number Employees: 172
Business Description:
Commercial Banking Services
S.I.C.: 6029; 6163
N.A.I.C.S.: 522110; 522310
Media: 8-13
Personnel:
Ralph Knipstein *(VP & Mgr-Special Access)*

DIGITAL INSIGHT CORPORATION

(Sub. of Intuit Inc.)
(d/b/a Intuit Financial Institutions Division)
26025 Mureau Rd
Calabasas, CA 91302-3103
Tel.: (818) 871-0000
Fax: (818) 878-7555
Toll Free: (888) 344-4674
Web Site: www.digitalinsight.com
Sales Range: $200-249.9 Million
Approx. Number Employees: 800
Year Founded: 1995
Business Description:
Online Banking Services for Mid-Market Banks & Credit Unions
S.I.C.: 7372; 7379
N.A.I.C.S.: 511210; 541519
Media: 7-10
Personnel:
Sasan Goodarzi *(Pres & Sr VP-Fin Institutions Div-Intuit)*
Bob J. Meagher *(Exec VP)*
CeCe Morken *(Exec VP)*
Katherine M. Jansen *(Sr VP)*
Advertising Agencies:
Glyphix Advertising
6964 Shoup Ave
West Hills, CA 91307
Tel.: (818) 704-3994
Fax: (818) 704-8850

The Ledlie Group
2970 Peachtree Rd Ste 805
Atlanta, GA 30305
Tel.: (404) 266-8833
Fax: (404) 266-9620

DIME COMMUNITY BANCSHARES, INC.

209 Havemeyer St
Brooklyn, NY 11211
Tel.: (718) 782-6200
Fax: (718) 486-7535
Fax: (718) 963-1075
Toll Free: (800) 321-3463
E-mail: einfo@dimewill.com
Web Site: www.dsbwdirect.com
Approx. Rev.: $222,849,000
Approx. Number Employees: 365
Year Founded: 1864
Business Description:
Bank Holding Company
S.I.C.: 6035
N.A.I.C.S.: 522120
Advertising Expenditures: $1,441,000
Personnel:
Vincent F. Palagiano *(Chm & CEO)*
Michael P. Devine *(Pres & COO)*
Kenneth J. Mahon *(CFO & Exec VP)*
Timothy B. King *(Chief Risk Officer & Exec VP)*
Michael Pucella *(Chief Acctg Officer & Exec VP)*
Terence J. Mitchell *(Chief Retail Officer & Exec VP)*
Kenneth A. Ceonzo *(Sr VP-Investor Rels)*

DIRECT MEDIA MILLARD, INC.

(Sub. of Infogroup Inc.)
10 Vose Farm Rd
Peterborough, NH 03458
Mailing Address:
PO Box 890
Peterborough, NH 03458-0890
Tel.: (402) 836-5100
Web Site: www.dmminfo.com
Sales Range: $75-99.9 Million
Approx. Number Employees: 240
Year Founded: 1977
Business Description:
List Management & Brokerage Services
S.I.C.: 7331; 8742
N.A.I.C.S.: 541860; 541611
Media: 2-7-13
Personnel:
Jeff Kelley *(Pres)*
Ben Perez *(Sr VP-Strategic & Bus Dev)*
Lilliane LeBel *(VP-Bus Intelligence)*
Heidi Thibodeau *(VP-Sls & Brokerage)*
Paddy Upton *(Acct Dir)*
Audrey Wallis *(Acct Dir)*
Lisa Williams *(Dir)*
Nicole Bartholomew *(Sr Mgr-Product)*
Brands & Products:
RFMPLUS

DISCOVER FINANCIAL SERVICES

2500 Lake Cook Rd
Riverwoods, IL 60015
Tel.: (224) 405-0900
Fax: (224) 405-4993
Toll Free: (800) 347-2683
E-mail: mediarelations@discoverfinancial.com
Web Site: www.discoverfinancial.com
Approx. Rev.: $8,241,217,000
Approx. Number Employees: 10,300
Year Founded: 1986
Business Description:
Credit Card Issuing Services
S.I.C.: 6141; 6099; 6371
N.A.I.C.S.: 522210; 522320; 525990
Media: 2-3-5-6-7-8-9-10-13-14-15-18-19-20-21-22-23-24-26-31
Personnel:
David W. Nelms *(Chm & CEO)*
Roger C. Hochschild *(Pres & COO)*
Carlos Minetti *(Pres & Exec VP-Consumer Banking-Ops)*
Diane E. Offereins *(Pres & Exec VP-Payment Svcs)*
Harit Talwar *(Pres & Exec VP-US Cards)*
R. Mark Graf *(Chief Acctg Officer, CFO & Exec VP)*
Glenn Schneider *(CIO & Sr VP)*
Kathryn Mcnamara Corley *(Gen Counsel, Sec & Exec VP)*
Christine Y. Homer *(Gen Counsel, VP & Sec-Student Lending Bus)*
James V. Panzarino *(Chief Credit Risk Off & Exec VP)*
Julie Loeger *(Sr VP-Brand & New Accts)*
Richard Brown *(Sr Mgr-Internet Acq & Mgr-Mktg Strategy)*
Brands & Products:
DINERS CLUB
DISCOVER
DISCOVER CARD
DISCOVER CLASSIC CARD
DISCOVER GOLD CARD
DISCOVER PLATINUM CARD
THE MILES CARD FROM DISCOVER CARD
Advertising Agencies:
MediaCom
498 7th Ave
New York, NY 10018
Tel.: (212) 912-4200
Fax: (212) 508-4386
(Discover Card, Media Buying/ Planning)

TargetCom, LLC
444 N Michigan Ave 33rd Fl
Chicago, IL 60611-3905
Tel.: (312) 822-1100
Fax: (312) 822-9628
Toll Free: (877) 423-7837

Tom, Dick & Harry Advertising
350 W Erie 2nd Fl
Chicago, IL 60654
Tel.: (312) 327-9500
Fax: (312) 327-9501

DISCOVER STUDENT LOANS

(Formerly The Student Loan Corporation)
(Sub. of Discover Financial Services)
750 Washington Blvd
Stamford, CT 06901
Tel.: (203) 975-6320
Fax: (203) 975-6299
Web Site: www.discoverstudentloans.com
Approx. Rev.: $981,772,000
Approx. Number Employees: 248
Year Founded: 1992
Business Description:
Educational Credit Services
S.I.C.: 6141
N.A.I.C.S.: 522291
Advertising Expenditures: $1,366,000
Media: 2-31
Personnel:
Michael J. Reardon *(CEO)*
Joseph P. Guage *(CFO)*

DITECH.COM

(Sub. of Residential Capital, LLC)
3200 Park Ctr Dr Ste 150
Costa Mesa, CA 92626
Tel.: (714) 800-5800
Fax: (714) 800-5801
Toll Free: (800) 803-7656
Web Site: www.ditech.com
Sales Range: $10-24.9 Million
Approx. Number Employees: 1,400
Year Founded: 1995
Business Description:
Mortgage Banker
S.I.C.: 6163
N.A.I.C.S.: 522310
Media: 3-8-9-10-13-14-15-18-20-23-24

Key to Media (For complete agency information see *The Advertising Red Books-Agencies* edition):
1. Bus. Publs. 2. Cable T.V. 3. Catalogs & Directories. 4. Co-op Adv. 5. Consumer Mags. 6. D.M. to Bus. Estab.7. D.M. to Consumers 8. Daily Newsp. 9. Exhibits/Trade Shows 10. Foreign 11. Infomercial 12. Internet Adv.13. Multimedia 14. Network Radio 15. Network T.V. 16. Newsp. Distr. Mags. 17. Other 18. Outdoor (Posters, Transit) 19. Point of Purchase20. Premiums, Novelties 21. Product Samples 22. Special Events Mktg. 23. Spot Radio 24. Spot T.V. 25. Weekly Newsp. 26. Yellow Page Adv.

Advertising Agency:
Anthem Worldwide
77 Maiden Ln 4th Fl
San Francisco, CA 94108
Tel.: (415) 896-9399
Fax: (415) 896-9387

DOLLAR FINANCIAL CORP.
1436 Lancaster Ave
Berwyn, PA 19312-1288
Tel.: (610) 296-3400
Fax: (610) 296-7844
E-mail: info@dfg.com
Web Site: www.dfg.com
Approx. Rev.: $610,927,000
Approx. Number Employees: 4,966
Year Founded: 1990
Business Description:
Holding Company; Loans, Check Cashing & Pawn Services
S.I.C.: 6719; 6099; 6141; 6159
N.A.I.C.S.: 551112; 522291; 522298; 522390
Advertising Expenditures: $8,800,000
Personnel:
Jeffrey A. Weiss *(Chm & CEO)*
Randy Underwood *(CFO)*
Norman Miller *(COO & Exec VP)*
Mike Coury *(CIO)*
William M. Athas *(Chief Acctg Officer)*
Sydney Franchuk *(Chm-Natl Money Mart & Exec VP)*
Roy W. Hibberd *(Gen Counsel & Sr VP)*
Carole Cross *(Sr VP-E-Commerce)*
Pete Sokolowski *(Corp Treas & Sr VP-Fin)*

DOLLAR FINANCIAL GROUP INC.
(Sub. of Dollar Financial Corp.)
1436 Lancaster Ave Ste 300
Berwyn, PA 19312
Tel.: (610) 296-3400
Fax: (610) 296-7844
Web Site: www.dfg.com
Sales Range: $100-124.9 Million
Approx. Number Employees: 70
Year Founded: 1990
Business Description:
Financial Services
S.I.C.: 6289
N.A.I.C.S.: 523999
Import Export
Advertising Expenditures: $7,406,000
Media: 8-10-19
Personnel:
Jeffrey A. Weiss *(Chm & CEO)*
Randall Underwood *(CFO & Exec VP)*
Sydney Franchuk *(Chm-Natl Money Mart & Exec VP)*
William M. Athas *(Controller & Sr VP-Fin)*
Peter Sokolowski *(Corp Treas & Sr VP-Fin)*
Melissa Soper *(Sr VP-Corp Admin)*

DOMINICK & DOMINICK, LLC
150 E 52nd St 3rd Fl
New York, NY 10022
Tel.: (212) 558-8800
Fax: (212) 750-6255
E-mail: info@dominickanddominick.com
Web Site: www.dominickanddominick.com
Approx. Number Employees: 100
Year Founded: 1870
Business Description:
Security & Commodity Services
S.I.C.: 6211; 6221
N.A.I.C.S.: 523120; 523130
Media: 13-17
Personnel:
Michael Campbell *(Pres, CEO & Exec Mgmt)*
Robert Reilly *(COO & Exec Mgmt)*
Borce Milreski *(CIO)*
Kevin McKay *(Gen Counsel & Exec Mgmt)*
Henry Hsu *(Sr VP)*

DORAL FINANCIAL CORPORATION
1451 Franklin D Roosevelt Ave
San Juan, PR 00920-2717
Tel.: (787) 474-6700
Fax: (787) 767-9098
E-mail: lgigante@doralbankny.com
Web Site: www.doralfinancial.com
Approx. Int. Income: $401,521,000
Approx. Number Employees: 1,352
Year Founded: 1972
Business Description:
Financial & Banking Services
S.I.C.: 6712; 6029; 6099; 6159; 6289
N.A.I.C.S.: 551111; 522110; 522292; 522390; 523999
Advertising Expenditures: $8,917,000
Personnel:
Glen R. Wakeman *(Pres & CEO)*
Javier J. Abreu *(CIO & VP-IT)*
Enrique R. Ubarri-Baragano *(Chief Compliance Officer, Exec VP & Gen Legal Counsel)*
Maurice Spagnoletti *(Exec VP, Head-Mortgage & Retail Banking)*
Christopher Poulton *(Chief US Ops Officer & Exec VP)*
Frederick C. Teed *(Exec VP-Banking Ops)*
Robert E. Wahlman *(Chief Fin, Investment Officer & Exec VP)*
Denise Segarra Sacarello *(Sr VP & Dir-Mortgage Grp)*
Lucienne Gigante *(VP-IR & Corp Comm)*

THE DREYFUS CORPORATION
(Sub. of The Bank of New York Mellon Corporation)
200 Park Ave
New York, NY 10166
Tel.: (212) 922-6000
Fax: (212) 922-7533
Toll Free: (888) 271-4994
E-mail: info@dreyfus.com
Web Site: www.dreyfus.com
Sales Range: $900-999.9 Million
Approx. Number Employees: 2,000
Year Founded: 1951
Business Description:
Mutual Funds, Investment & Management
S.I.C.: 6799; 6211; 6282; 6289
N.A.I.C.S.: 523910; 523110; 523120; 523920; 523930; 523999
Media: 2-3-6-9-25-26
Distr.: Natl.
Personnel:
Jon Baum *(Chm & CEO)*
J. David Officer *(Vice Chm & COO)*
Phil Maisano *(Vice Chm & Chief Investment Officer)*
J. Charles Cardona *(Pres)*
Penny Hill *(Exec VP)*
Patrice Kozlowski *(Sr VP-Corp Commun)*
Robert Tobin *(Sr VP-Branding & Digital Dev)*
Jennifer Scherz *(Asst VP-Digital Mktg)*
Steven Raab *(Product Mgr)*
Brands & Products:
DREYFUS

DUFF & PHELPS CORPORATION
55 E 52nd St 31 Fl
New York, NY 10055
Tel.: (212) 871-2000
Toll Free: (866) 282-8258
E-mail: noah.gottdiener@duffandphelps.com
Web Site: www.duffandphelps.com
Approx. Rev.: $375,031,000
Approx. Number Employees: 1,039
Year Founded: 1932
Business Description:
Financial Advisory & Investment Banking Services
S.I.C.: 6371; 6211; 6289
N.A.I.C.S.: 525990; 523110; 523999
Media: 2
Personnel:
Noah Gottdiener *(Chm, Pres & CEO)*
Michael Braverman *(Mng Dir)*
Andrew Capitman *(Mng Dir)*
Marty Dauer *(Mng Dir)*
Michael H. Dolan *(Mng Dir)*
Frank La Greca *(Mng Dir)*
Jacob Silverman *(Mng Dir)*
Randal Stephenson *(Mng Dir)*
Charles J. Wahle *(Mng Dir)*
Patrick M. Puzzuoli *(CFO & Exec VP)*
Brett Marschke *(COO & Exec VP)*
Edward S. Forman *(Gen Counsel, Sec & Exec VP)*
Advertising Agency:
Doremus
(Sub. of Omnicom Group, Inc.)
200 Varick St 11Fl
New York, NY 10014-4810
Tel.: (212) 366-3000
Fax: (212) 366-3060

DWS INVESTMENTS DISTRIBUTORS, INC.
(Sub. of Deutsche Bank Aktiengesellschaft)
222 S Riverside Plz
Chicago, IL 60606-5808
Tel.: (212) 454-6778
Web Site: www.dws-investments.com
Approx. Number Employees: 500
Year Founded: 1948
Business Description:
Investment Management Services
S.I.C.: 6211; 6282
N.A.I.C.S.: 523120; 523930
Advertising Expenditures: $15,000,000
Media: 2-3-5-6-7-9-14-15-18-20-22-23-24-25-26
Personnel:
Tom Eggars *(Pres & CEO)*
Greg Kiesel *(Mng Dir & Head-Equity Sls)*
Jared Dolce *(Dir-High Grade Credit Sls)*
Robert Garofolo *(Dir-Institutional Client Grp)*
Chris O'Hea *(Dir-Institutional Client Grp)*
Brands & Products:
KEMPER FUNDS

E-LOAN, INC.
(Sub. of Banco Popular North America - California Regional Office)
6230 Stoneridge Mall Rd
Pleasanton, CA 94588
Tel.: (925) 847-6200
Fax: (925) 847-0831
Toll Free: (800) 356-2622
Toll Free: (888) 533-5333
E-mail: client@eloan.com
Web Site: www.eloan.com
Sales Range: $125-149.9 Million
Approx. Number Employees: 930
Year Founded: 1997
Business Description:
Mortgages, Auto Loans, Credit Cards & Small Business Loans
S.I.C.: 6163
N.A.I.C.S.: 522310
Advertising Expenditures: $36,600,000
Media: 2-3-8-10-13-15-24
Personnel:
Christian A. Larsen *(Chm)*
Alberto J. Paracchini *(CFO)*
Harold Bonnikson *(Sr VP-First Mortgage Div)*
Scott McKinlay *(Sr VP-Corp Dev)*
Brands & Products:
A BETTER WAY TO GET A LOAN
E-LOAN
RADICALLY SIMPLE
Advertising Agency:
Merkley + Partners
(Sub. of Omnicom Group, Inc.)
200 Varick St
New York, NY 10014-4810
Tel.: (212) 366-3500
Fax: (212) 805-7445

EAGLE BANCORP, INC.
7815 Woodmont Ave
Bethesda, MD 20814
Tel.: (301) 986-1800
Fax: (301) 986-8529
E-mail: info@eaglebankmd.com
Web Site: www.eaglebankmd.com
Approx. Rev.: $105,900,000
Approx. Number Employees: 292
Year Founded: 1997
Business Description:
Bank Holding Company
S.I.C.: 6712; 6029; 6035
N.A.I.C.S.: 551111; 522110; 522120
Advertising Expenditures: $1,100,000
Media: 7-8-9-23-24-25
Personnel:
Ronald D. Paul *(Chm, Pres & CEO)*
Robert P. Pincus *(Vice Chm)*
James H. Langmead *(CFO & Exec VP)*
Susan G. Riel *(COO & Exec VP)*
Thomas D. Murphy *(Pres-Community Banking)*
Robert Hoffman *(Exec VP & Interim Chief Lending Officer)*
Laurence E. Bensignor *(Sr VP)*

EAGLE BANCORP MONTANA, INC.
1400 Prospect Ave
Helena, MT 59601
Mailing Address:
PO Box 4999
Helena, MT 59604

Key to Media (For complete agency information see *The Advertising Red Books-Agencies* edition):
1. Bus. Publs. 2. Cable T.V. 3. Catalogs & Directories. 4. Co-op Adv. 5. Consumer Mags. 6. D.M. to Bus. Estab.7. D.M. to Consumers 8. Daily Newsp. 9. Exhibits/Trade Shows 10. Foreign 11. Infomercial 12. Internet Adv.13. Multimedia 14. Network Radio 15. Network T.V. 16. Newsp. Distr. Mags. 17. Other 18. Outdoor (Posters, Transit) 19. Point of Purchase20. Premiums, Novelties 21. Product Samples 22. Special Events Mktg. 23. Spot Radio 24. Spot T.V. 25. Weekly Newsp. 26. Yellow Page Adv.

EAGLE BANCORP MONTANA, INC. — (Continued)

Tel.: (406) 442-3080
Fax: (406) 457-4035
Web Site: www.americanfederalsavingsbank.com
Approx. Sls.: $18,500,000
Approx. Number Employees: 81
Year Founded: 2009
Business Description:
Bank Holding Company
S.I.C.: 6712
N.A.I.C.S.: 551111
Advertising Expenditures: $438,000
Personnel:
Larry A. Dreyer *(Chm)*
Peter J. Johnson *(Pres & CEO)*
Clinton J. Morrison *(CFO & Sr VP)*

EAGLE FINANCIAL SERVICES, INC.

2 E Main St PO Box 391
Berryville, VA 22611
Tel.: (540) 955-2510
Fax: (540) 955-5233
E-mail: customerservice@bankofclarke.com
Web Site: www.bankofclarke.com
Approx. Rev.: $33,288,000
Approx. Number Employees: 155
Year Founded: 1991
Business Description:
Bank Holding Company
S.I.C.: 6712
N.A.I.C.S.: 551111
Advertising Expenditures: $409,000
Media: 9-18-23-24-25
Personnel:
Thomas T. Gilpin *(Chm)*
Robert W. Smalley, Jr. *(Vice Chm)*
John R. Milleson *(Pres & CEO)*
Kathleen J. Chappell *(CFO & VP)*
James W. McCarty, Jr. *(Chief Admin Officer)*
Teresa Hoffman *(Branch Mgr, Loan Officer)*
Steve Hyson *(Branch Mgr, Loan Officer)*
Libba Pendleton *(Sr VP)*
Kristie Peterson *(VP-Lending & Branch Mgr-Winchester)*
Judy Bowman *(Asst VP-Lending & Branch Mgr-Boyce)*
Angie Edwards *(Asst VP-Lending & Branch Mgr-Millbrook)*
Linda Garman *(Asst VP-Lending & Branch Mgr-Sunnyside)*
Cindy Larrick *(Asst VP-Lending & Branch Mgr-Kernstown)*
Betty Weller *(Asst VP-Lending & Branch Mgr-Stephens City)*
Regina Baldwin *(Branch Mgr-Winchester)*

EAGLEBANK

(Sub. of Eagle Bancorp, Inc.)
7815 Woodmont Ave
Bethesda, MD 20814
Tel.: (301) 986-1800
Fax: (301) 986-8529
Web Site: www.eaglebankmd.com
Sales Range: $25-49.9 Million
Approx. Number Employees: 130
Year Founded: 1998
Business Description:
Banking Services
S.I.C.: 6029
N.A.I.C.S.: 522110
Media: 2-7-8-9-13-18-22-23-24-25
Personnel:
Ronald D. Paul *(Chm & CEO)*
Robert P. Pincus *(Vice Chm)*
Robert R. Hoffman *(Chief Admin Lending Officer & Exec VP)*
Navas Heine *(Chief Lending Officer-Comml & Indus & Exec VP)*
Thomas Murphy *(Pres-Retail Banking)*
Martha Foulon-Tonat *(Exec VP)*
Antonio F. Marquez *(Exec VP)*
Mercedes Alvarez *(Sr VP & Dir-Mktg)*
Russell McNish *(Sr VP & Dir-HR)*
Terrence C. Weber *(Sr VP & Mgr-Fin Reporting & Control)*
Laurence E. Bensignor *(Sr VP)*
Robert R. Giraldi *(Sr VP)*
Douglas L. Vigen *(Sr VP)*
P. Lucas Flynn *(VP)*
Yulissa Guerra *(Asst VP & Branch Mgr)*
Linda Licata *(Asst VP & Branch Mgr)*
Ngozi Agugua *(Asst VP)*
Courtney Michelle *(Asst VP-HR)*
Deborah C. Shumaker *(Dir-Bus Dev)*
Linda Lacy *(Mgr-IT)*
Joan Pawloski *(Mgr-Loan Admin)*
Brands & Products:
WE'RE LISTENING

EARLYBIRDCAPITAL INC.

275 Madison Ave
New York, NY 10016
Tel.: (212) 661-0200
Fax: (212) 661-4936
Toll Free: (877) EARLYBIRD
E-mail: info@earlybirdcapital.com
Web Site: www.earlybirdcapital.com
Sales Range: $1-9.9 Million
Approx. Number Employees: 30
Year Founded: 2000
Business Description:
Private, Equity-Focused Investment Banking Services
S.I.C.: 6159; 6082; 6141
N.A.I.C.S.: 522298; 522220; 522292; 522293; 522294
Advertising Expenditures: $350,000
Media: 13
Personnel:
David Nussbaum *(Chm)*
Steven Levine *(Pres & CEO)*
Eileen Moore *(CFO & Exec VP)*

THE EAST CAROLINA BANK

(Sub. of ECB Bancorp, Inc.)
35050 US Hwy 264
Engelhard, NC 27824
Tel.: (252) 925-9411
Fax: (252) 925-3839
Web Site: www.ecbbancorp.com
Sales Range: $10-24.9 Million
Approx. Number Employees: 225
Year Founded: 1919
Business Description:
State-Chartered, Independent, Community Bank
S.I.C.: 6029
N.A.I.C.S.: 522110
Advertising Expenditures: $250,000
Media: 3-9-10-13-22-23-24-25-26
Personnel:
R. S. Spencer, Jr. *(Chm)*
George Thomas Davis, Jr. *(Vice Chm)*
A. Dwight Utz *(Pres & CEO)*
Thomas M. Crowder *(CFO & Exec VP)*
T. Olin Davis *(Chief Credit Officer & Exec VP)*
J. Dorson White, Jr. *(Chief Specialized Bus Officer & Exec VP)*
James J. Burson *(Chief Revenue Officer & Exec VP)*
Mimi Van Nortwick *(Sr VP-Bus, Treasury Svcs Div & Mgr-Product Dev)*
Gary M. Adams *(Dir-Fin Reporting)*
Brands & Products:
OUTER BANKER

EASTERN BANK CORPORATION

265 Franklin St
Boston, MA 02110
Tel.: (617) 897-1008
Fax: (781) 598-7679
Toll Free: (800) 327-8376
E-mail: info@easternbk.com
Web Site: www.easternbank.com
Approx. Rev.: $402,395,000
Approx. Number Employees: 1,900
Business Description:
Bank Holding Company
S.I.C.: 6712
N.A.I.C.S.: 551111
Advertising Expenditures: $2,000,000
Personnel:
Richard E. Holbrook *(Chm & CEO)*
Robert F. Rivers *(Vice Chm)*
Jan A. Miller *(Pres & Exec VP-Comml Banking)*
Charles M. Johnston *(CFO & Exec VP)*
Daniel J. Sullivan *(Sr VP & Chief Credit Officer)*
Lloyd L. Hamm, Jr. *(Chief Admin Officer)*
Terence A. McGinnis *(Gen Counsel & Sr VP)*
John F. McKinlay *(Treas & Sr VP-Support Svcs)*
Joseph J. Bartolotta *(Exec VP-Mktg & Product Mgmt-Support Svcs)*
Barbara J. Heinemann *(Exec VP-Ops & Tech)*
Cynthia C. Merkle *(Exec VP)*
Joseph F. Riley *(Exec VP)*
David A. Ahlquist *(Sr VP & Controller)*
Joseph B. Bator *(Sr VP-Bus Banking)*
John P. Brodrick *(Sr VP-Mortgage Banking)*
Michael T. Bulman *(Sr VP-Comml & Indus Lending)*
Mark P. Coryea *(Sr VP-Fin)*
Wendy L. de Villiers *(Sr VP-Support Svcs)*
Stephen J. DiPrete *(Sr VP-Bus Banking)*
Philip S. Dunn *(Sr VP-Support Svcs)*
Kenneth C. Dyment *(Sr VP-Consumer Fin)*
John P. Farmer *(Sr VP-Support Svcs)*
Pamela M. Feingold *(Sr VP-Community Dev)*
Daniel C. Field *(Sr VP-Comml & Indus Lending)*
Joseph H. Holland *(Sr VP-Comml & Indus Lending)*
Mary Ann Jordan *(Sr VP-Institutional Svcs)*
Karl C. Renney *(Sr VP-Support Svcs)*
Kevin M. Shea *(Sr VP-Support Svcs)*
Nancy Huntington Stager *(Sr VP-HR)*
Paula Murphy-Roux *(VP & Dir-Trng & Dev)*
Paul J. Pierre *(VP, Dir-Employment & Employee Rels)*
Anthony C. Rizzo *(VP & Mgr-Reg Sls)*
Advertising Agency:
Conover Tuttle Pace
77 N Washington St
Boston, MA 02114
Tel.: (617) 412-4000
Fax: (617) 412-4411

EASTERN BANK CORPORATION-SOUTH REGION HEADQUARTERS

(Sub. of Eastern Bank Corporation)
151 Campanelli Dr
Middleboro, MA 02346
Tel.: (508) 946-3000
Fax: (508) 946-3030
Fax: (508) 946-3034
Toll Free: (800) 649-3330
Web Site: www.easternbank.com
Year Founded: 1847
Business Description:
Bank
S.I.C.: 6035; 6141
N.A.I.C.S.: 522120; 522291
Media: 20
Distr.: Reg.
Personnel:
Richard Holbrook *(Chm & CEO)*
John Wainwright *(Mgr-Branch)*

EASTERN INSURANCE HOLDINGS, INC.

25 Race Ave
Lancaster, PA 17603
Tel.: (717) 396-7095
Toll Free: (888) 654-7100
E-mail: responsecenter@elhins.com
Web Site: www.easterninsuranceholdings.com
Approx. Rev.: $117,616,000
Approx. Number Employees: 171
Business Description:
Holding Company
S.I.C.: 6331; 6719
N.A.I.C.S.: 524126; 551112
Advertising Expenditures: $946,000
Personnel:
Bruce Matthew Eckert *(Vice Chm)*
Michael Leonard Boguski *(Pres & CEO)*
Kevin M. Shook *(CFO)*
Robert A. Gilpin *(Sr VP-Field Ops & Mktg)*

EASTERN VIRGINIA BANKSHARES, INC.

330 Hospital Rd
Tappahannock, VA 22560
Mailing Address:
PO Box 1005
Tappahannock, VA 22560
Tel.: (804) 443-8400
Tel.: (804) 443-8429
Fax: (804) 445-1047
Toll Free: (866) 443-3826
E-mail: info@rtco.com
Web Site: www.evb.org
Approx. Rev.: $63,502,000
Approx. Number Employees: 314
Year Founded: 1997
Business Description:
Bank Holding Company
S.I.C.: 6141; 6029; 6712
N.A.I.C.S.: 522210; 522110; 551111
Advertising Expenditures: $944,000

Key to Media (For complete agency information see *The Advertising Red Books-Agencies* edition):
1. Bus. Publs. 2. Cable T.V. 3. Catalogs & Directories. 4. Co-op Adv. 5. Consumer Mags. 6. D.M. to Bus. Estab.7. D.M. to Consumers 8. Daily Newsp. 9. Exhibits/Trade Shows 10. Foreign 11. Infomercial 12. Internet Adv.13. Multimedia 14. Network Radio 15. Network T.V. 16. Newsp. Distr. Mags. 17. Other 18. Outdoor (Posters, Transit) 19. Point of Purchase20. Premiums, Novelties 21. Product Samples 22. Special Events Mktg. 23. Spot Radio 24. Spot T.V. 25. Weekly Newsp. 26. Yellow Page Adv.

Personnel:
W. Rand Cook *(Chm)*
F. L. Garrett, III *(Vice Chm)*
Joe A. Shearin *(Pres & CEO)*
Joseph H. James, Jr. *(COO & Exec VP)*
Kecia B. Ware *(CIO & Sr VP)*
James S. Thomas *(Chief Credit Officer & Exec VP)*
J. Lloyd Railey *(Exec VP & Chief Risk Officer)*
Thomas J. McKittrick *(Sr VP & Comml Lending Officer)*
Gerald B. Riendeau, Jr. *(Sr VP & Chief Deposit Officer)*
Patricia H. Gallagher *(Sec & Dir-Strategic Plng)*
M. Robin Jett *(Sr VP & Dir-HR)*
Betty R. Miller *(Sr VP & Reg Mgr-Retail)*
Edwin P. Jones *(Sr VP & Reg Mgr-Retail)*
John L. Muller *(Sr VP & Comml Lending Officer)*
Linda L. Grow *(VP & Branch Mgr)*
Renee B. Perkins *(VP & Branch Mgr)*
James E. Johnson *(Gen Mgr)*

EATON VANCE CORP.

2 International Pl
Boston, MA 02110
Tel.: (617) 482-8260
Fax: (617) 482-2396
Toll Free: (800) 225-6265
E-mail: mpier@eatonvance.com
Web Site: www.eatonvance.com
Approx. Rev.: $1,121,661,000
Approx. Number Employees: 1,094
Year Founded: 1924
Business Description:
Investment Adviser; Investment Company Shares Distr
S.I.C.: 6282
N.A.I.C.S.: 523930
Advertising Expenditures: $1,500,000
Media: 2-6-9
Distr.: Natl.
Budget Set: Various
Personnel:
Thomas E. Faust, Jr. *(Chm, Pres, CEO & Chief Investment Officer)*
Robert J. Whelan *(CFO, Treas & VP)*
Frederick S. Marius *(Chief Legal Officer, Sec & VP)*
Jeffrey P. Beale *(Chief Admin Officer & VP)*
Laurie G. Hylton *(Chief Acctg Officer & VP)*
Duncan W. Richardson *(Exec VP & Chief Equity Investment Officer)*
Stephen W. Clarke *(Pres-Navigate Fund Solutions LLC)*
Brands & Products:
EATON VANCE

ECB BANCORP, INC.

35050 US Hwy 264
Engelhard, NC 27824
Mailing Address:
PO Box 337
Engelhard, NC 27824-0337
Tel.: (252) 925-9411
Fax: (252) 925-8491
E-mail: ecbonline@ecbbancorp.com
Web Site: www.ecbbancorp.com/
Approx. Rev.: $51,802,000
Approx. Number Employees: 233
Year Founded: 1998
Business Description:
Bank Holding Company
S.I.C.: 6029; 6712
N.A.I.C.S.: 522110; 551111
Media: 9-13
Personnel:
R. S. Spencer, Jr. *(Chm)*
George Thomas Davis, Jr. *(Vice Chm)*
A. Dwight Utz *(Pres & CEO)*
Thomas M. Crowder *(CFO & Exec VP)*
T. Olin Davis *(Chief Credit Officer & Exec VP)*
J. Dorson White, Jr. *(Chief Specialized Bus Officer & Exec VP)*
Gary M. Adams *(Sr VP & Dir-Fin Reporting)*
Mimi W. van Nortwick *(Sr VP-Treasury Svcs)*

EDGAR ONLINE, INC.

11200 Rockville Pike
Rockville, MD 20852
Tel.: (203) 852-5666
Fax: (203) 852-5667
Toll Free: (800) 416-6651
E-mail: investor@edgar-online.com
Web Site: www.edgar-online.com
Approx. Rev.: $19,468,000
Approx. Number Employees: 143
Year Founded: 1995
Business Description:
Internet Based Business & Financial Information Services
S.I.C.: 7389; 2741
N.A.I.C.S.: 561421; 516110; 519190
Advertising Expenditures: $243,000
Media: 7-8-10-13-16
Personnel:
John M. Connolly *(Chm)*
Robert J. Farrell *(Pres & CEO)*
David J. Price *(CFO & COO)*
David A. Frankel *(CMO)*
Paul Sappington *(Chief Software Officer & VP)*
Steven Friedman *(Gen Counsel)*
Ed McDonnell *(Exec VP-Worldwide Field Sls & Delivery)*
Brands & Products:
EDGAR
EDGAR ONLINE

EDUCATIONAL COIN COMPANY

291 Uppr N Rd
Highland, NY 12528-0892
Tel.: (845) 691-6100
Fax: (845) 691-4974
E-mail: robin@educationalcoin.com
Web Site: www.educationalcoin.com
Approx. Number Employees: 14
Year Founded: 1960
Business Description:
Genuine World Coins & Bank Notes Distr
S.I.C.: 8743; 5094
N.A.I.C.S.: 541820; 423940
Media: 2-4-7-10-21
Distr.: Intl.; Natl.
Personnel:
David Laties *(Owner)*
Robin Danziger *(Dir-Mktg)*

EDWARD D. JONES & CO., LP

(Holding of THE JONES FINANCIAL COMPANIES, L.L.L.P.)
(d/b/a Edward Jones)
12555 Manchester Rd
Saint Louis, MO 63131
Mailing Address:
PO Box 66906
Saint Louis, MO 63166-6906
Tel.: (314) 515-2000
Fax: (314) 515-3269
E-mail: john.boul@edwardjones.com
Web Site: www.edwardjones.com
Sales Range: $1-4.9 Billion
Approx. Number Employees: 30,000
Year Founded: 1871
Business Description:
Securities Brokerage & Investment Services
S.I.C.: 6211
N.A.I.C.S.: 523110; 523120
Media: 2-6-8-10-22-23-24-26
Distr.: Reg.
Personnel:
James D. Weddle *(CEO & Mng Partner)*
Steve Novik *(CFO & Gen Partner)*
Brad Iverson *(Principal & CMO)*
Gina House *(Dir-Online Mktg)*
Mark Eckert *(Mgr-Adv Programs)*
Colleen Raley *(Mgr-Adv)*
Carol Schwent *(Team Leader-Mktg Insight)*
Brands & Products:
EDWARD JONES
MAKING SENSE OF INVESTING
Advertising Agencies:
Cramer-Krasselt
225 N Michigan Ave
Chicago, IL 60601-7601
Tel.: (312) 616-9600
Fax: (312) 616-3839
(Creative, Media, Online, Direct Marketing, Social Media, Search)

Cramer-Krasselt Public Relations
225 N Michigan Ave
Chicago, IL 60601-7601
Tel.: (312) 616-9600

ELECTRONIC TRANSFER, INC.

3107 E Mission Ave
Spokane, WA 99202
Tel.: (509) 924-6730
Fax: (509) 924-6621
Toll Free: (800) 757-5453
E-mail: mike@electronictransfer.com
Web Site: www.electronictransfer.com
Sales Range: $50-74.9 Million
Approx. Number Employees: 10
Year Founded: 1989
Business Description:
Commercial Financial Services
S.I.C.: 6099
N.A.I.C.S.: 522320
Media: 4-6-7-10-13-26
Personnel:
Michael Knudtson *(Pres)*
Bob Donegan *(Dir-Mktg)*

THE ELMIRA SAVINGS BANK, FSB

333 E Water St
Elmira, NY 14902-9967
Tel.: (607) 734-3374
Fax: (607) 732-4007
E-mail: info@elmirasavingsbank.com
Web Site:
www.elmirasavingsbank.com
Approx. Int. Income: $25,141,000
Approx. Number Employees: 96
Business Description:
Commercial Banking Services
S.I.C.: 6029
N.A.I.C.S.: 522110
Media: 3-7-8-10-13-18-20-23-24-26
Personnel:
John Brand, III *(Vice Chm)*
Michael P. Hosey *(Pres & CEO)*
Thomas M. Carr *(COO & Exec VP)*
Kevin J Berkley *(Sr VP-Lending)*
Gary O. Short *(Sr VP)*
Donna Tangorre *(VP)*
Joseph L. Walker *(VP)*
Deborah L. Adams *(Asst VP)*
Philip J. Collins *(Asst VP)*
Susan M Cook *(Asst VP)*
Kimberly A Elliott *(Asst VP-Retail Svcs)*
Mark A. Terpolilli *(Asst VP)*

EMCLAIRE FINANCIAL CORP.

612 Main St
Emlenton, PA 16373
Tel.: (724) 867-2311
Fax: (724) 867-9326
E-mail: info@farmersnb.com
Web Site: www.emclairefinancial.com
Approx. Rev.: $26,058,000
Approx. Number Employees: 115
Business Description:
Bank Holding Company
S.I.C.: 6029; 6712
N.A.I.C.S.: 522110; 551111
Advertising Expenditures: $130,000
Media: 17
Personnel:
William C. Marsh *(Chm, Pres & CEO)*
David L. Cox *(Vice Chm)*
Matthew J. Lucco *(CFO & Treas)*
Danyell L. Bundy *(Asst VP & Dir-Branch Banking)*
Raymond M. Lawton *(Asst Sec)*

EMDEON, INC.

(Joint Venture of Hellman & Friedman LLC & General Atlantic LLC)
(d/b/a Emdeon Business Services)
3055 Lebanon Pike Ste 1000
Nashville, TN 37214
Tel.: (615) 932-3000
Fax: (615) 564-4667
Web Site: www.emdeon.com
Approx. Rev.: $1,002,152,000
Approx. Number Employees: 3,000
Business Description:
Revenue Cycle Management & Clinical Communication Services; Owned by General Atlantic LLC & Hellman & Friedman LLC
S.I.C.: 6099; 7389
N.A.I.C.S.: 522320; 561499
Media: 7-10-13-22
Personnel:
Tracy L. Bahl *(Chm)*
George I. Lazenby, IV *(CEO)*
Bob A. Newport, Jr. *(CFO)*
Damien Creavin *(CIO)*
Gregory T. Stevens *(Gen Counsel, Sec & Exec VP)*
J. Philip Hardin *(Exec VP-Provider Svcs)*
Gary D. Stuart *(Exec VP-Payer Svcs)*
Adam A. Hameed *(Sr VP-Data & Analytics Solutions)*
Tommy Lewis *(Sr VP-Corp Comm)*
Mark Lyle *(Sr VP-Pharmacy Svcs)*
Frank Manzella *(Sr VP-Corp Dev)*
Miriam Paramore *(Sr VP-Clinical Svcs & Govt Affairs)*
Tom Turi *(Sr VP-Fin Svcs)*
Susan Byrd *(VP-HR)*

Key to Media (For complete agency information see *The Advertising Red Books-Agencies* edition):
1. Bus. Publs. 2. Cable T.V. 3. Catalogs & Directories. 4. Co-op Adv. 5. Consumer Mags. 6. D.M. to Bus. Estab.7. D.M. to Consumers
8. Daily Newsp. 9. Exhibits/Trade Shows 10. Foreign 11. Infomercial 12. Internet Adv.13. Multimedia 14. Network Radio
15. Network T.V. 16. Newsp. Distr. Mags. 17. Other 18. Outdoor (Posters, Transit) 19. Point of Purchase20. Premiums, Novelties
21. Product Samples 22. Special Events Mktg. 23. Spot Radio 24. Spot T.V. 25. Weekly Newsp. 26. Yellow Page Adv.

EMIGRANT SAVINGS BANK
5 E 42nd St
New York, NY 10017-6904
Tel.: (212) 850-4000
Fax: (212) 850-4963
E-mail: info@emigrant.com
Web Site: www.emigrant.com
Sales Range: $550-599.9 Million
Approx. Number Employees: 1,373
Year Founded: 1850
Business Description:
Savings Banking, Real Estate Mortgage & Personal Loans
S.I.C.: 6035; 6311
N.A.I.C.S.: 522120; 524113
Media: 8-9-10-13-14-19-20-22-23-25-26
Distr.: Direct to Consumer; Reg.
Budget Set: May
Personnel:
Howard Milstein *(Chm, Pres & CEO)*
James C. Woolsey *(Vice Chm)*
Douglas Diamond *(CMO)*
Ted Morehouse *(Sr VP-Mktg)*
Eileen Lyon *(VP-Mktg)*
Peter Perroni *(Asst VP-Telecom)*
Advertising Agency:
The Milford Agency
335 Madison Ave 14th Fl
New York, NY 10017
Tel.: (212) 350-2373
Fax: (212) 350-2394

EMPRISE BANK
(Sub. of Emprise Financial Corporation)
257 N Broadway
Wichita, KS 67202
Mailing Address:
PO Box 2970
Wichita, KS 67201-2601
Tel.: (316) 383-4400
Fax: (316) 383-4399
Web Site: www.emprisebank.com
Approx. Number Employees: 350
Year Founded: 1989
Business Description:
Regional Bank
S.I.C.: 6029
N.A.I.C.S.: 522110
Media: 2-6-9-17-25-26
Distr.: Direct to Consumer; Reg.
Budget Set: Dec.
Personnel:
Mike D. Michaelis *(Chm)*
Thomas A. Page *(Pres)*
Tom Veatch *(CFO)*
Galen K. Nelson *(Exec VP)*

EMPRISE FINANCIAL CORPORATION
257 N Broadway St
Wichita, KS 67202
Tel.: (316) 383-4400
Fax: (316) 383-4397
Web Site: www.emprisebank.com
Approx. Number Employees: 380
Business Description:
State Commercial Banks
S.I.C.: 6029
N.A.I.C.S.: 522110
Personnel:
W. A. Michaelis, Jr. *(Chm)*
Thomas A. Page *(Pres)*
Roger E. Hastings *(Chief Investment Officer & Sr VP)*
Brands & Products:
EMPRISE BANK

Advertising Agency:
Associated Advertising Agency, Inc.
330 N Mead Ste 200
Wichita, KS 67202
Tel.: (316) 683-4691
Fax: (316) 683-1990

ENB FINANCIAL CORP.
31 E Main St
Ephrata, PA 17522
Tel.: (717) 733-4181
Fax: (717) 733-7034
Web Site: www.epnb.com
Approx. Rev.: $39,714,000
Approx. Number Employees: 171
Year Founded: 2008
Business Description:
Bank Holding Company
S.I.C.: 6712
N.A.I.C.S.: 551111
Advertising Expenditures: $445,000
Personnel:
Aaron L. Groff, Jr. *(Chm, Pres & CEO)*

ENCORE BANCSHARES, INC.
9 Greenway Plz Ste 1000
Houston, TX 77046-0900
Tel.: (713) 787-3100
Fax: (713) 267-7770
Web Site: www.encorebank.com
Approx. Rev.: $100,546,000
Approx. Number Employees: 315
Year Founded: 2000
Business Description:
Bank Holding Company
S.I.C.: 6712; 6035
N.A.I.C.S.: 551111; 522120
Advertising Expenditures: $617,000
Personnel:
James Samuel D'Agostino, Jr. *(Chm)*
Preston M. Moore *(Pres & CEO)*
L. Anderson Creel *(CFO & Exec VP)*
Rhonda L. Carroll *(Chief Compliance Officer, Corp Sec & Sr VP)*
Stephanie Pollock *(Chief Acctg Officer, Sr VP & Controller)*
Thomas N. Ray *(Pres-Florida)*
Robert D. Mrlik *(Exec VP)*
Patrick Oakes *(Exec VP)*
Brands & Products:
ENCORE
ENCOREBANK

ENCORE CAPITAL GROUP, INC.
8875 Aero Dr Ste 200
San Diego, CA 92123
Tel.: (858) 560-2600
Toll Free: (877) 445-4581
E-mail: paul.grinberg@encorecapitalgroup.com
Web Site:
www.encorecapitalgroup.com
Approx. Rev.: $381,308,000
Approx. Number Employees: 1,900
Business Description:
Investment & Credit Collection Services
S.I.C.: 7322; 6099
N.A.I.C.S.: 522320; 522390; 561440
Personnel:
George Lund *(Chm)*
J. Brandon Black *(Pres & CEO)*
Paul Grinberg *(CFO & Exec VP)*
Olivier Baudoux *(CIO & Sr VP-Info Tech)*
James Syran *(CMO & Sr VP-Ops)*
Gregory L. Call *(Gen Counsel, Sec & Sr VP)*
Steve Gonabe *(Sr VP-HR)*
Brian Enneking *(VP-Consumer Mktg)*
Advertising Agency:
MSLGROUP
1675 Broadway 9th Floor
New York, NY 10019-5865
Tel.: (212) 468-4200
Fax: (212) 468-3007
Government Affairs
Investor Relations
Media Relations
Reputation Management

ENERGY SERVICES OF AMERICA CORPORATION
100 Industrial Ln
Huntington, WV 25702
Tel.: (304) 399-6300
Fax: (304) 399-1096
Web Site:
www.energyservicesofamerica.com
Approx. Rev.: $218,287,753
Approx. Number Employees: 1,190
Year Founded: 2006
Business Description:
Investment Services
S.I.C.: 6289
N.A.I.C.S.: 523999
Advertising Expenditures: $24,056
Media: 17
Personnel:
Marshall T. Reynolds *(Chm & CEO)*
Edsel R. Burns *(Pres)*
Larry A. Blount *(CFO)*

ENTERPRISE BANCORP INC.
222 Merrimack St
Lowell, MA 01852
Tel.: (978) 459-9000
Fax: (978) 441-9083
E-mail: shareholders@ebtc.com
Web Site: www.ebtc.com
Approx. Rev.: $76,592,000
Approx. Number Employees: 333
Business Description:
Bank Holding Company
S.I.C.: 6712; 6029
N.A.I.C.S.: 551111; 522110
Advertising Expenditures: $2,204,000
Personnel:
George L. Duncan *(Chm)*
Arnold S. Lerner *(Vice Chm)*
Richard W. Main *(Pres)*
John P. Clancy, Jr. *(CEO)*
James A. Marcotte *(CFO, Treas & Exec VP)*
Stephen J. Irish *(COO & Exec VP)*
Robert R. Gilman *(Exec VP-Admin & Comml Lender)*
Michael K. Sullivan *(Sr VP & Controller)*
JoAnne McQuilkin *(Sr VP & Dir-Credit)*
John Bukala *(Mgr-Regal Comml Banking & Sr VP)*
John P. Harrington *(Asst Sec)*

ENVESTNET, INC.
35 E Wacker Dr Ste 2400
Chicago, IL 60601
Tel.: (312) 827-2800
Fax: (312) 827-2801
Toll Free: (866) 924-8912
E-mail: marketing@envestnet.com
Web Site: www.envestnet.com
Approx. Rev.: $98,052,000
Approx. Number Employees: 457
Year Founded: 2004
Business Description:
Web-Based Investment Solutions
S.I.C.: 6211; 2741
N.A.I.C.S.: 523120; 516110; 523110
Advertising Expenditures: $1,160,000
Media: 2-10-22
Personnel:
Brandon Thomas *(Co-Founder & CIO-Portfolio Mgmt Consultants)*
James Lumberg *(Co-Founder, Exec VP-Bus Dev & Envestnet)*
Judson Taft Bergman *(Chm & CEO)*
William Crager *(Pres)*
Marion Asnes *(Mng Dir & CMO)*
Mark Osmond *(Mng Dir)*
Peter D'Arrigo *(CFO)*
Charles Tennant *(COO)*
William Rubino, Jr. *(Chief Admin Officer)*
Timothy S. Stearns *(Chief Compliance Officer & Sr VP)*
Seth Wager *(Sr VP & Investment Officer)*
Shelly O'Brien *(Gen Counsel)*
Christopher Curtis *(Treas & Sr VP)*
Michael Apker *(Exec VP-Strategic Dev-Envestnet)*
Lori Hardwick *(Exec VP-Advisory Svcs)*
Karen McCue *(Exec VP)*
Viggy Mokkarala *(Exec VP-Product Grp-Envestnet)*
Babu Sivadasan *(Exec VP-Engrg)*
Mark Gerard *(Sr VP & Dir-Portfolio Strategies)*
Dale Seier *(Sr VP-Fin)*
Eric Fowler *(Mng Dir-Product Dev)*
Mark Diehl *(VP & Reg Dir)*
Maria McCaffrey *(VP & Reg Dir-NW)*
Mark Olson *(VP & Dir-Advisory Svcs)*
Brett Bennett *(Dir-Res)*

EOS PREFERRED CORPORATION
(Formerly Capital Crossing Preferred Corporation)
(Sub. of Lehman Brothers Holdings Inc.)
1271 Ave of the Americas 46th Fl
New York, NY 10020
Tel.: (212) 377-1503
Approx. Rev.: $8,692,000
Approx. Number Employees: 4
Year Founded: 1998
Business Description:
Real Estate Investment Trust
S.I.C.: 6798; 6163
N.A.I.C.S.: 525930; 522310
Import Export
Advertising Expenditures: $2,000,000
Media: 4-8-13
Personnel:
Thomas O'Sullivan *(Chm & Pres)*
Robert J. Leist, Jr. *(CFO)*

EQUIFAX INC.
1550 Peachtree St NW
Atlanta, GA 30309
Mailing Address:
PO Box 740241
Atlanta, GA 30374
Tel.: (404) 885-8000
Fax: (404) 885-8872
Toll Free: (888) 202-4025
E-mail: investor@equifax.com

Key to Media (For complete agency information see *The Advertising Red Books-Agencies* edition):
1. Bus. Publs. 2. Cable T.V. 3. Catalogs & Directories. 4. Co-op Adv. 5. Consumer Mags. 6. D.M. to Bus. Estab.7. D.M. to Consumers 8. Daily Newsp. 9. Exhibits/Trade Shows 10. Foreign 11. Infomercial 12. Internet Adv.13. Multimedia 14. Network Radio 15. Network T.V. 16. Newsp. Distr. Mags. 17. Other 18. Outdoor (Posters, Transit) 19. Point of Purchase20. Premiums, Novelties 21. Product Samples 22. Special Events Mktg. 23. Spot Radio 24. Spot T.V. 25. Weekly Newsp. 26. Yellow Page Adv.

Web Site: www.equifax.com
Approx. Rev.: $1,859,500,000
Approx. Number Employees: 6,500
Year Founded: 1899
Business Description:
Credit, Financial, Public Record & Information-Based Administrative Services
S.I.C.: 7323; 6022; 7322; 7389
N.A.I.C.S.: 561450; 519190; 522190; 561440
Export
Advertising Expenditures: $32,600,000
Media: 4-7-13-17-26
Distr.: Intl.; Natl.
Budget Set: Aug.
Personnel:
Richard F. Smith *(Chm & CEO)*
Lee Adrean *(CFO & Corp VP)*
David C. Webb *(CIO)*
Paul J. Springman *(CMO)*
Kent E. Mast *(Chief Legal Officer & Corp VP)*
Andy S. Bodea *(Chief Global Ops Officer)*
J. Dann Adams *(Pres-TALX Corp)*
Rodolfo O. Ploder *(Pres-US Consumer Info Solutions)*
Rajib Roy *(Pres-Tech & Analytical Svcs)*
Nuala M. King *(Sr VP & Controller)*
Jeffrey L. Dodge *(Sr VP-IR)*
John T. Hartman *(Sr VP-Corp Dev)*
Ray Killebrew *(Asst VP-Experience Design)*
Jeff Flory *(Dir-Enterprise Bus)*
Jeff Schwartzel *(Dir-Enterprise Bus)*
Christian Taylor *(Dir-Mktg)*
Steve Smith *(Engr-Voice Comm)*
Brands & Products:
CREDIT RANKINGS
CREDIT REPORT
CREDIT WATCH
EQUIFAX
FICO
HOME VALUATOR
ID PATROL
MORTGAGE MATCH
RATE FINDER
SCORE POWER
SCORE WATCH
Advertising Agency:
Digitas Inc
1447 Peachtree St Ste 900
Atlanta, GA 30309
Tel.: (404) 460-1010
Fax: (404) 460-1009
Brand Marketing
CRM
Digital
Equifax Personal Information Solutions (Creative & Media Agency of Record)
Mobile
Social
Television

EQUIFIRST CORPORATION
(Sub. of Barclays Bank Plc)
500 Forest Point Cir
Charlotte, NC 28273-5601
Tel.: (704) 679-4400
Fax: (704) 625-4500
Web Site: www.equifirst.com
Approx. Rev.: $14,400,000
Approx. Number Employees: 450
Year Founded: 1990
Business Description:
Mortgage Bankers
S.I.C.: 6163
N.A.I.C.S.: 522310
Media: 2-10
Brands & Products:
EQUIFIRST
NON-CONFORMING RESULTS

EQUIINSURANCE, LLC
6839 Main St
Miami Lakes, FL 33014
Tel.: (305) 557-5578
Fax: (305) 557-5197
Web Site: www.equiinsurance.com
Approx. Number Employees: 16
Business Description:
Insurance Agency
S.I.C.: 6411
N.A.I.C.S.: 524210
Media: 8
Personnel:
Frank Fernandez *(Owner)*

EQUITY GROUP INVESTMENTS, LLC
2 N Riverside Plz Ste 1500 6 F
Chicago, IL 60606
Tel.: (312) 466-4001
Fax: (312) 466-3311
Approx. Number Employees: 90
Year Founded: 1968
Business Description:
Holding Company
S.I.C.: 6719
N.A.I.C.S.: 551112
Media: 2-4-7-8
Distr.: Intl.; Natl.
Budget Set: Jan.
Personnel:
Samuel Zell *(Chm)*
Philip Tinkler *(CFO)*
David J. Contis *(Pres-Real Estate)*

EQUITY METHODS, LLC
(Sub. of Merrill Lynch & Co., Inc.)
14614 N Kierland Blvd Ste S 190
Scottsdale, AZ 85254
Tel.: (480) 998-3515
Fax: (480) 998-0862
Toll Free: (866) 998-3515
E-mail: info@equitymethods.com
Web Site: www.equitymethods.com
Sales Range: Less than $1 Million
Approx. Number Employees: 50
Year Founded: 1998
Business Description:
Employee Stock Option Consulting Services
S.I.C.: 8748; 6211; 6282; 6289; 6799; 8742
N.A.I.C.S.: 541618; 523110; 523910; 523920; 523930; 523999; 541611; 541613
Media: 10
Personnel:
Melissa Kirk *(VP-Tech & Infrastructure)*
Takis Makridis *(Exec Dir)*
Scott Cummins *(Engineer-Storage & Sys)*

EQUITY SERVICES, INC.
(Sub. of National Life Insurance Company)
1 National Life Dr
Montpelier, VT 05604-1000
Tel.: (802) 229-3900
Fax: (802) 229-3596
Toll Free: (800) 344-7437
E-mail: info@equity-services.com
Web Site: www.equity-services.com
Sales Range: $800-899.9 Million
Approx. Number Employees: 30
Year Founded: 1968
Business Description:
Broker & Dealer in Mutual Fund Shares & Other Securities
S.I.C.: 6211
N.A.I.C.S.: 523120
Advertising Expenditures: $500,000
Media: 2-7-8-9-10-13-14-20-22
Distr.: Natl.
Budget Set: Oct. -Dec.
Personnel:
Dan Randall *(Sr VP-Products-Advisory Svcs)*
Brands & Products:
CAPITAL ARCHITECT
SENTINEL GROUP FUNDS, INC.
SENTINEL PA TAX FREE TRUST

ERNST & YOUNG GLOBAL LIMITED
5 Times Sq
New York, NY 10036-6530
Tel.: (212) 773-3000
Fax: (212) 773-1655
Fax: (212) 773-6350
Telex: 760 7796
E-mail: webmaster@ey.com
Web Site: www.ey.com
Sales Range: $15-24.9 Billion
Approx. Number Employees: 130,000
Year Founded: 1989
Business Description:
Audit, Tax & Financial Advisory Services
S.I.C.: 8721; 7291
N.A.I.C.S.: 541219; 541211; 541213
Media: 2-3-7-9-10-11-13-15-18-22-23-26
Distr.: Intl.; Natl.
Budget Set: Oct.
Personnel:
James Turley *(Chm & CEO)*
Beth A. Brooke *(Vice Chm-Pub Policy)*
Mark A. Weinberger *(Vice Chm-Tax)*
Victoria Cochrane *(Mng Partner-Q & RM-Global)*
Jeffery H. Dworken *(Global Mng Partner-Ops & Fin)*
Sam Fouad *(Mng Partner-People-Global)*
Patrick Gounelle *(Mng Partner)*
Jim Hassert *(Co-Area Mng Partner-FE)*
Steve Howe *(Mng Partner-Americas)*
Herman Hulst *(Global Mng Partner-Client Svc & Accts)*
John Murphy *(Mng Partner-Global Markets)*
Mark Otty *(Mng Partner-EMEIA Area-Europe, Middle East, India & Africa)*
David Sun *(Co-Area Mng Partner-FE)*
John C. Distefano *(Partner & Head-Healthcare Sector-Natl)*
Timothy T. Griffy *(Partner)*
Christoph Gross *(Area COO-EMEIA)*
Andrew W. Patterson *(Principal)*
Chris Pockney *(Principal)*
George K. Tsantes *(Principal-Info Security Advisory Svcs)*
Brian L. Ferrell *(Exec Dir)*
Robert Brand *(Dir-Natl Mktg)*
Daniel Lawrence *(Dir-Corp Comm)*
Charles Perkins *(Dir-Media Rels)*
Michelle Wolf *(Sr Assoc-Media)*
Rhonda Jacobs *(Sr Mgr)*
Deborah Nixon *(Sr Mgr)*
Karen M. Brady *(Mgr-Tax, Human Capital & Mobility-Global)*
Marc Meyer *(Strategist-Social Media & Digital)*
Advertising Agencies:
GlobalWorks
220 5th Ave
New York, NY 10001
Tel.: (212) 252-8800
Fax: (212) 252-0002

MediaVest USA
1675 Broadway
New York, NY 10019
Tel.: (212) 468-4000
Fax: (212) 468-4110

ESB FINANCIAL CORPORATION
600 Lawrence Ave
Ellwood City, PA 16117
Tel.: (724) 758-5584
Fax: (724) 758-0576
Web Site: www.esbbank.com
Approx. Rev.: $89,331,000
Approx. Number Employees: 230
Year Founded: 1915
Business Description:
Bank Holding Company
S.I.C.: 6712; 6029; 6035
N.A.I.C.S.: 551111; 522110; 522120
Advertising Expenditures: $608,000
Personnel:
William B. Salsgiver *(Chm)*
Herbert S. Skuba *(Vice Chm)*
Charlotte A. Zuschlag *(Pres & CEO)*
Charles P. Evanoski *(CFO, Grp Sr VP & Principal Acctg Officer)*
Richard E. Canonge *(Treas & Sr VP)*
Robert A. Ackerman *(Sr VP-Audit & Loan Review)*
Robert J. Colalella *(Sr VP-Mktg)*
John W. Donaldson II *(Sr VP-Lending)*
Teresa Krukenberg *(Sr VP-Bus Dev)*
Ronald J. Mannarino *(Sr VP)*
Todd F. Palkovich *(Sr VP)*
Mark A. Platz *(Sr VP-IT)*
Ronald E. Pompeani *(Sr VP)*
Marilyn Scripko *(Sr VP)*
John T. Stunda *(Sr VP-HR)*

ESSA BANCORP, INC.
200 Palmer St
Stroudsburg, PA 18360
Tel.: (570) 421-0531
Web Site: www.essabank.com
Approx. Rev.: $55,965,000
Approx. Number Employees: 187
Business Description:
Bank Holding Company
S.I.C.: 6712; 6029
N.A.I.C.S.: 551111; 522110
Advertising Expenditures: $626,000
Personnel:
John E. Burrus *(Chm)*
Gary S. Olson *(CEO)*
Allan A. Muto *(CFO & Exec VP)*
Robert S. Howes, Jr. *(Sr VP)*
Advertising Agency:
Riger Advertising Agency, Inc.
53 Chenango St
Binghamton, NY 13902
Tel.: (607) 723-7441
Fax: (607) 723-7623

Key to Media (For complete agency information see *The Advertising Red Books-Agencies* edition):
1. Bus. Publs. 2. Cable T.V. 3. Catalogs & Directories. 4. Co-op Adv. 5. Consumer Mags. 6. D.M. to Bus. Estab.7. D.M. to Consumers 8. Daily Newsp. 9. Exhibits/Trade Shows 10. Foreign 11. Infomercial 12. Internet Adv.13. Multimedia 14. Network Radio 15. Network T.V. 16. Newsp. Distr. Mags. 17. Other 18. Outdoor (Posters, Transit) 19. Point of Purchase20. Premiums, Novelties 21. Product Samples 22. Special Events Mktg. 23. Spot Radio 24. Spot T.V. 25. Weekly Newsp. 26. Yellow Page Adv.

ESSEX BANK
(Sub. of Community Bankers Trust Corporation)
323 Prince St
Tappahannock, VA 22560-0965
Mailing Address:
PO Box 965
Tappahannock, VA 22560-0965
Tel.: (804) 443-4343
Fax: (804) 443-9472
Toll Free: (800) 443-5524
E-mail: info@essexbank.com
Web Site: www.essexbank.com
Sales Range: $10-24.9 Million
Approx. Number Employees: 40
Year Founded: 1926
Business Description:
Community Bank Services
S.I.C.: 6029
N.A.I.C.S.: 522110
Advertising Expenditures: $62,903
Media: 7-8-13-20-22
Personnel:
Rex L. Smith, III *(Pres & CEO)*
Bruce E. Thomas *(CFO & Exec VP)*

E*TRADE FINANCIAL CORPORATION
1271 Ave of the Americas 14th Fl
New York, NY 10022
Tel.: (646) 521-4300
Fax: (888) 276-9771
E-mail: ir@etrade.com
Web Site: www.etrade.com
Approx. Rev.: $2,077,875,000
Approx. Number Employees: 2,962
Year Founded: 1982
Business Description:
Holding Company; Online Securities Brokerage & Financial Services
S.I.C.: 6719; 6035; 6099; 6211
N.A.I.C.S.: 551112; 519130; 522120; 522320; 523110; 523120
Advertising Expenditures: $114,400,000
Media: 2-3-6-8-9-11-13-14-15-16-22-23-24-25
Personnel:
Robert Allan Druskin *(Chm)*
Steven J. Freiberg *(CEO)*
Matthew J. Audette *(CFO & Exec VP)*
Gregory Framke *(COO, CIO & Exec VP)*
Nicholas A. Utton *(CMO & Exec VP)*
Paul Brandow *(Chief Risk Officer & Exec VP)*
Andrew Goodman *(Chief HR Officer & Exec VP)*
Karen Wall *(Chief HR Officer & Exec VP)*
Robert V. Burton *(Pres-E*Trade Bank)*
Peter Knitzer *(Pres-E*TRADE Bank)*
Karl A. Roessner *(Gen Counsel, Sec & Exec VP)*
Susan Hickey *(Sr VP-Corp Comm)*
Michael Thomas *(Dir-eMktg)*
Anna Klayman *(Sr Mgr-Mktg)*
Craig Shiffrin *(Sr Mgr-Mktg)*
Michael Selvaggio *(Mgr-Mktg)*
Brands & Products:
COMPLETE IRA
ETRADE
Advertising Agencies:
Direct Partners
4755 Alla Rd
Marina Del Rey, CA 90292-6311
Tel.: (310) 482-4200
Fax: (310) 482-4201
(E*Trade Bank)

Grey New York
777 3rd Ave
New York, NY 10017-1401
Tel.: (212) 546-2000
Fax: (212) 546-1495

IMC Strategy Lab
401 W 45th St Ste 4C
New York, NY 10036
Tel.: (917) 257-3523
Toll Free: (800) 845-3779

StrawberryFrog
60 Madison Ave Ph
New York, NY 10010
Tel.: (212) 366-0500

EVANS BANCORP, INC.
14-16 N Main St
Angola, NY 14006
Tel.: (716) 926-2000
Fax: (716) 926-2005
E-mail: shareholderinfo@evansnational.com
Web Site: www.evansbancorp.com
Approx. Rev.: $44,050,000
Approx. Number Employees: 224
Year Founded: 1988
Business Description:
Bank Holding Company
S.I.C.: 6712; 6029
N.A.I.C.S.: 551111; 522110
Advertising Expenditures: $627,000
Media: 17
Personnel:
Phillip Brothman *(Chm)*
John R. O'Brien *(Vice Chm)*
David J. Nasca *(Pres & CEO)*
Howard M. Martin, Jr. *(CIO & Sr VP)*
Susan J. Harold *(VP & Dir-HR)*

EVERBANK FINANCIAL CORP.
(Holding of Sageview Capital LP)
501 Riverside Rd
Jacksonville, FL 32202
Tel.: (904) 281-6000
Fax: (904) 281-6165
Web Site: www.everbank.com
Approx. Rev.: $672,700,000
Approx. Number Employees: 2,200
Business Description:
Bank Holding Company
S.I.C.: 6712
N.A.I.C.S.: 551111
Advertising Expenditures: $8,978,000
Personnel:
Robert M. Clements *(Chm & CEO)*
Gary A. Meeks *(Vice Chm)*
W. Blake Wilson *(Pres & CFO)*
Michael C. Koster *(Exec VP)*
John S. Surface *(Exec VP)*
Frank O. Trotter *(Exec VP)*
Deborah Moore *(VP & Sr Mgr-Mktg)*
Jason Coots *(VP-Mktg)*

EXCHANGE BANK
545 4th St
Santa Rosa, CA 95401-6323
Mailing Address:
PO Box 403
Santa Rosa, CA 95402-0403
Tel.: (707) 524-3000
Tel.: (707) 524-3213
Fax: (707) 579-4745
Web Site: www.exchangebank.com
Approx. Rev.: $96,498,000
Approx. Number Employees: 490
Year Founded: 1890
Business Description:
Banking Services
S.I.C.: 6035
N.A.I.C.S.: 522120
Advertising Expenditures: $614,000
Personnel:
C. William Reinking *(Chm & CEO)*
Charles R. Bartley *(Vice Chm)*
William R. Schrader *(Pres)*
Bruce DeCrona *(COO & Exec VP)*
Gary W. Searby *(CIO & Sr VP)*
V. Anthony Ghisla *(Chief Credit Officer & Sr VP)*
Brad Hunter *(Chief Risk Officer & Sr VP)*
Samuel Brown *(Exec VP-Wealth Mgmt)*
Howard Daulton *(Sr VP & Mgr-Corp Bus Dev)*
Nina G. Drake *(Sr VP & Dir HR & Training)*
Ed Gomez *(Sr VP-Credit Admin)*
Gary Hartwick *(Sr VP & Chief Credit Risk Officer)*
Steve Herron *(Sr VP)*
Greg Jahn *(Chief Investment Mgr & Sr VP)*
Louise M. Mason *(Sr VP)*
Rolf Nelson *(Sr VP-Retail Banking & Sls)*

EXTRACO BANKS
(Sub. of Extraco Corporation)
1700 N Valley Mills Dr
Waco, TX 76710
Tel.: (254) 776-0160
Fax: (254) 761-2149
Web Site: www.extracobanks.com
Approx. Rev.: $7,744,000
Approx. Number Employees: 50
Business Description:
National Commercial Banks
S.I.C.: 6029; 6163
N.A.I.C.S.: 522110; 522310
Personnel:
Boyce Brown *(CEO)*
Advertising Agency:
Proof Advertising
114 W 7th St Ste 500
Austin, TX 78701
Tel.: (512) 345-6658
Fax: (512) 345-6227

EZCORP, INC.
1901 Capital Pkwy
Austin, TX 78746-7613
Tel.: (512) 314-3400
Fax: (512) 314-3404
Toll Free: (800) 873-7296
E-mail: invrel@ezcorp.com
Web Site: www.ezcorp.com
Approx. Rev.: $733,045,000
Approx. Number Employees: 4,900
Year Founded: 1989
Business Description:
Pawnshops & Payday Loan Stores Operator
S.I.C.: 3581; 5999; 6159
N.A.I.C.S.: 333311; 453998; 522298
Advertising Expenditures: $2,200,000
Media: 8-10-19-23-24-26
Distr.: Reg.
Personnel:
Sterling B. Brinkley *(Chm)*
Paul E. Rothamel *(Pres & CEO)*
Stephen A. Stamp *(CFO & Sr VP)*
Robert Jackson *(CIO & VP)*
Daniel M. Chism *(Chief Acctg Officer & VP)*
Joe Borbely *(Pres-EZMONEY Americas)*
Eric Fosse *(Pres-Pawn Americas)*
Thomas H. Welch, Jr. *(Gen Counsel, Sec & Sr VP)*
Connie L. Kondik *(Deputy Gen Counsel)*
Mark E. Kuchenrither *(Sr VP-Strategic Dev)*
Anthony Sanders *(Sr VP-HR)*
John R. Kissick *(VP-Strategic Dev)*
Brands & Products:
EZCORP
EZMONEY
EZPAWN

F&M BANK CORP.
205 S Main St PO Box 1111
Timberville, VA 22853
Tel.: (540) 896-8941
Fax: (540) 896-2840
E-mail: neilhayslett@farmersandmerchants.biz
Web Site: www.farmersandmerchants.biz
Approx. Rev.: $31,558,821
Approx. Number Employees: 141
Year Founded: 1983
Business Description:
Bank Holding Company
S.I.C.: 6712; 6029
N.A.I.C.S.: 551111; 522110
Advertising Expenditures: $191,449
Media: 17
Personnel:
Thomas L. Cline *(Chm)*
Dean W. Withers *(Pres & CEO)*
Neil W. Hayslett *(CFO & Exec VP)*

FACTSET MERGERSTAT, LLC
(Sub. of FactSet Research Systems Inc.)
2950 31st St Bldg T Ste 130
Santa Monica, CA 90405
Tel.: (800) 455-8871
Fax: (310) 829-4855
Toll Free: (800) 455-8871
E-mail: info@mergerstat.com
Web Site: www.mergerstat.com
Sales Range: $10-24.9 Million
Approx. Number Employees: 25
Year Founded: 1963
Business Description:
Online Integrated Database Services for Financial Institutions
S.I.C.: 2741; 6371
N.A.I.C.S.: 516110; 525990
Media: 7-10-13

FARM BUREAU BANK FSB
(Sub. of FB Bancorp)
17300 Henderson Pass
San Antonio, TX 78232-1568
Mailing Address:
PO Box 33427
San Antonio, TX 78265-3427
Tel.: (210) 637-4800
Fax: (210) 637-4824
Toll Free: (800) 492-3276
E-mail: services@farmbureaubank.com
Web Site: www.farmbureaubank.com
Approx. Number Employees: 87
Year Founded: 1999

Key to Media (For complete agency information see *The Advertising Red Books-Agencies* edition):
1. Bus. Publs. 2. Cable T.V. 3. Catalogs & Directories. 4. Co-op Adv. 5. Consumer Mags. 6. D.M. to Bus. Estab.7. D.M. to Consumers 8. Daily Newsp. 9. Exhibits/Trade Shows 10. Foreign 11. Infomercial 12. Internet Adv.13. Multimedia 14. Network Radio 15. Network T.V. 16. Newsp. Distr. Mags. 17. Other 18. Outdoor (Posters, Transit) 19. Point of Purchase20. Premiums, Novelties 21. Product Samples 22. Special Events Mktg. 23. Spot Radio 24. Spot T.V. 25. Weekly Newsp. 26. Yellow Page Adv.

Business Description:
Banking Services
S.I.C.: 6035
N.A.I.C.S.: 522120
Advertising Expenditures: $500,000
Media: 2-7-8-13
Personnel:
Larry J. Lanie *(Pres & CEO)*
Thomas Jaeger *(CFO)*
Mark Cromer *(Sr VP)*
Sheri Fletcher *(Mgr-Mktg-Sls)*

FARMERS & MERCHANTS BANCORP

111 W Pine St
Lodi, CA 95240-2184
Mailing Address:
PO Box 3000
Lodi, CA 95241-1902
Tel.: (209) 367-2300
Fax: (209) 367-2467
Toll Free: (800) 888-1498
E-mail: internetbank@fmbonline.com
Web Site: www.fmbonline.com
Approx. Rev.: $101,646,000
Approx. Number Employees: 306
Year Founded: 1999
Business Description:
Bank Holding Company
S.I.C.: 6712; 6029
N.A.I.C.S.: 551111; 522110
Media: 2-8-9-20-23-25-26
Distr.: Reg.
Budget Set: Nov.
Personnel:
Kent A. Steinwert *(Chm, Pres & CEO)*
Stephen W. Haley *(CFO & Exec VP)*
Richard S. Erichson *(Exec VP & Sr Credit Officer)*

FARMERS CAPITAL BANK CORPORATION

PO Box 309
Frankfort, KY 40602-0309
Tel.: (502) 227-1668
Fax: (502) 227-1692
E-mail: info@farmerscapital.com
Web Site: www.farmerscapital.com
Approx. Rev.: $123,861,000
Approx. Number Employees: 512
Year Founded: 1982
Business Description:
Financial Holding Company
S.I.C.: 6029
N.A.I.C.S.: 522110
Media: 6-8-23
Personnel:
Frank W. Sower, Jr. *(Chm)*
Lloyd C. Hillard, Jr. *(Pres & CEO)*
C. Douglas Carpenter *(CFO, Sec & Sr VP)*
Jean T. Harrod *(Gen Counsel, VP & Sec)*
Kaye Hall *(Sr VP-Fin)*
Linda L. Faulconer *(VP-HR)*
Mark A. Hampton *(VP-Fin)*
Janelda R. Mitchell *(VP-Mktg)*
Teresa Tipton *(Asst VP-HR)*

FARMERS NATIONAL BANC CORP.

20 S Broad St
Canfield, OH 44406
Tel.: (330) 533-3341
Fax: (330) 533-6365
E-mail: exec@fnbcanfield.com
Web Site: www.fnbcanfield.com
Approx. Rev.: $61,575,000
Approx. Number Employees: 268
Business Description:
National Commercial Banks
S.I.C.: 6022; 6029
N.A.I.C.S.: 522190; 522110
Advertising Expenditures: $637,000
Personnel:
Frank L. Paden *(Chm & Sec)*
John S. Gulas *(Pres & CEO)*
Carl D. Culp *(Treas & Exec VP)*
Kevin J. Helmick *(Sr VP-Wealth Mgmt/ Retail Banking)*
Mark Nicastro *(VP & Dir-HR)*
Bradley S. Henderson *(VP-Facilities Mgmt & Security)*
Raymond Calcagni *(Asst VP & Mgr-Comml Lending)*
Mary Jane Naples *(Asst VP & Mgr-Overdraft Privilege)*
Susan E. Better *(Asst VP-Corp Svcs Admin)*
Thomas Supko *(Asst VP & Compliance Officer)*

FASIG-TIPTON CO. INC.

2400 Newtown Pike
Lexington, KY 40511-8469
Mailing Address:
PO Box 13610
Lexington, KY 40583-3610
Tel.: (859) 255-1555
Fax: (859) 254-0794
E-mail: info@fasigtipton.com
Web Site: www.fasigtipton.com
Sales Range: $200-249.9 Million
Approx. Number Employees: 100
Year Founded: 1898
Business Description:
Thoroughbred Horses Auction Sales
S.I.C.: 5961
N.A.I.C.S.: 454112
Advertising Expenditures: $300,000
Media: 2-4-8-13-24
Distr.: Intl.; Natl.
Personnel:
Boyd T. Browning *(Pres & CEO)*
Tim Boyce *(Dir-Sls)*
Terence Collier *(Dir-Mktg)*
Max Hodge *(Dir-Client Svcs)*
Peter Penny *(Dir-Sls)*
William Meissner *(Plant Mgr)*
Advertising Agency:
Trapp Communications
1701-B Alexandria Dr
Lexington, KY 40504-2149
Tel.: (859) 277-6868
Fax: (859) 277-8588

THE FAUQUIER BANK

(Sub. of Fauquier Bankshares Inc)
10 Courthouse Sq
Warrenton, VA 20186
Tel.: (540) 347-2700
Fax: (540) 349-9533
Toll Free: (800) 638-3798
E-mail: webmaster@fauquierbank.com
Web Site: www.fauquierbank.com
Sales Range: $50-74.9 Million
Approx. Number Employees: 154
Year Founded: 1902
Business Description:
Bank
S.I.C.: 6029
N.A.I.C.S.: 522110
Media: 3-7-8-9-23-25-26
Personnel:
Randy Kent Ferrell *(Pres & CEO)*
Eric Peter Graap *(CFO & Exec VP)*

FAUQUIER BANKSHARES INC

10 Courthouse Sq
Warrenton, VA 20186
Tel.: (540) 347-2700
Fax: (540) 349-0268
Toll Free: (800) 638-3798
E-mail: infor@fauquierbank.com
Web Site: www.fauquierbank.com
Approx. Rev.: $33,035,782
Approx. Number Employees: 144
Year Founded: 1984
Business Description:
Bank Holding Company
S.I.C.: 6712; 6029
N.A.I.C.S.: 551111; 522110
Advertising Expenditures: $331,162
Media: 9-20-23-24
Personnel:
John B. Adams, Jr. *(Chm)*
Randolph T. Minter *(Vice Chm)*
Randy Kent Ferrell *(Pres & CEO)*
Eric Peter Graap *(CFO & Exec VP)*

FCSTONE GROUP, INC.

(Sub. of INTL FCStone Inc.)
1251 NW Briarcliff Pkwy Ste 800
Kansas City, MO 64116
Tel.: (816) 410-7120
Fax: (816) 741-8895
Toll Free: (800) 255-6381
Toll Free: (800) 422-3087
Toll Free: (866) 730-2424
E-mail: lauras@fcstone.com
Web Site: www.fcstone.com
Approx. Rev.: $337,526,000
Approx. Number Employees: 448
Year Founded: 1924
Business Description:
Commodity Risk Management
Consulting & Trading Services
S.I.C.: 6221; 8742
N.A.I.C.S.: 523130; 523140; 541611
Media: 10-13
Personnel:
Clarence C. Delbridge *(Exec VP-Compliance)*
Greg Greves *(Sr VP)*
Robert Mortenson *(Reg VP)*
Kyle Smith *(Reg Dir)*
Chris Aberle *(Dir-Natl Sls & Bus Dev)*
Kathy Holmes *(Dir-HR)*
Joe Bedore *(Mgr-Floor Ops)*
Jack Gilhooly *(Mgr-Futures Direct)*
Zesiewicz Theresa *(Mgr-Office)*
Rebecca Becker *(Admin Coord)*

FEDERAL AGRICULTURAL MORTGAGE CORPORATION

(d/b/a Farmer Mac)
1133 21st St NW Ste 600
Washington, DC 20036
Tel.: (202) 872-7700
Fax: (202) 872-7713
Toll Free: (800) 879-3276
Web Site: www.farmermac.com
Approx. Rev.: $243,685,000
Approx. Number Employees: 58
Year Founded: 1988
Business Description:
Mortgages & Agricultural Real Estate
Loans to American Farmers & Rural Homeowners
S.I.C.: 6163; 6159
N.A.I.C.S.: 522310; 522292; 522298
Media: 5
Personnel:
Lowell L. Junkins *(Chm)*
Michael A. Gerber *(Pres & CEO)*
Timothy L. Buzby *(Sr VP, CFO & Treas)*
Tom D. Stenson *(COO & Exec VP-Agricultural Fin)*
Jerome G. Oslick *(Gen Counsel, Sr VP & Corp Sec)*
Brands & Products:
AGPOWER
AGVANTAGE
FARMER MAC
FINANCING RURAL AMERICA
PART-TIME FARM
READY, SET, GROW

FEDERAL DEPOSIT INSURANCE CORPORATION

(d/b/a FDIC)
550 17th St Northwest
Washington, DC 20429
Tel.: (202) 736-0000
Fax: (202) 898-3543
E-mail: communications@fdic.gov
Web Site: www.fdic.gov
Sales Range: $1-4.9 Billion
Approx. Number Employees: 2,500
Year Founded: 1933
Business Description:
Federal Deposit Insurance Corporation (FDIC)
S.I.C.: 6399; 9311
N.A.I.C.S.: 524128; 921130
Media: 2-7-10
Personnel:
Sheila C. Bair *(Chm)*
John Bovenzi *(Deputy Chm & COO)*
Steven O. App *(CFO & Deputy to Chm)*
Michael Krimminger *(Gen Counsel)*
Thomas J. Dujenski *(Reg Dir-Supervision & Consumer Protection-Atlanta)*
Kristie K. Elmquist *(Reg Dir-Dallas)*
Daniel E. Frye *(Reg Dir)*
Mark C. Schmidt *(Reg Dir-DSC)*
Andrew Gray *(Dir-Pub Affairs Office)*
Mark Pearce *(Dir-Depositor & Consumer Protection Div)*
Sandra L. Thompson *(Dir-Risk Mgmt Supervision Div)*
Jim Wigand *(Dir-Complex Fin Institutions)*
Luke Brown *(Assoc Dir)*
Advertising Agencies:
Clayton-Davis & Associates, Incorporated
230 S Bemiston Ave Ste 1400
Clayton, MO 63105-3643
Tel.: (314) 862-7800
Fax: (314) 721-5171

G&G Advertising, Inc.
811 Silver SW
Albuquerque, NM 87102
Tel.: (505) 843-8113
Fax: (505) 843-7774

FEDERAL FARM CREDIT BANKS FUNDING CORPORATION

10 Exchange Pl Ste 1401
Jersey City, NJ 07302
Tel.: (201) 200-8000
Fax: (201) 200-8080
E-mail: webmaster@farmcredit-ffcb.com

Key to Media (For complete agency information see *The Advertising Red Books-Agencies* edition):
1. Bus. Publs. 2. Cable T.V. 3. Catalogs & Directories. 4. Co-op Adv. 5. Consumer Mags. 6. D.M. to Bus. Estab.7. D.M. to Consumers 8. Daily Newsp. 9. Exhibits/Trade Shows 10. Foreign 11. Infomercial 12. Internet Adv.13. Multimedia 14. Network Radio 15. Network T.V. 16. Newsp. Distr. Mags. 17. Other 18. Outdoor (Posters, Transit) 19. Point of Purchase20. Premiums, Novelties 21. Product Samples 22. Special Events Mktg. 23. Spot Radio 24. Spot T.V. 25. Weekly Newsp. 26. Yellow Page Adv.

Federal Farm Credit Banks Funding Corporation — (Continued)

Web Site: www.farmcredit-ffcb.com
Sales Range: $1-9.9 Million
Approx. Number Employees: 50
Year Founded: 1983
Business Description:
Agricultural Financial Services
S.I.C.: 6371
N.A.I.C.S.: 525990
Advertising Expenditures: $400,000
Media: 2-4-9-19-21-22
Distr.: Natl.
Budget Set: Oct.
Personnel:
J. Less Guthrie *(Chm)*
John J. Breena *(Mng Dir-Admin)*
Kathleen Mullarkey *(Gen Counsel & Sec)*
Glenn Doran *(Sr VP)*
Brands & Products:
FEDERAL FARM CREDIT BANKS FUNDING

FEDERAL HOME LOAN MORTGAGE CORPORATION

(d/b/a Freddie Mac)
8200 Jones Branch Dr
McLean, VA 22102-3110
Tel.: (703) 903-2000
Toll Free: (800) 424-5401
E-mail: corprel@freddiemac.com
Web Site: www.freddiemac.com
Approx. Int. Income: $109,956,000,000
Approx. Number Employees: 5,231
Year Founded: 1970
Business Description:
Federally Sponsored Home Mortgage Credit Services
S.I.C.: 6163; 6159
N.A.I.C.S.: 522310; 522298
Media: 6-8-10-13
Personnel:
Charles E. Haldeman, Jr. *(CEO)*
Ross J. Kari *(CFO)*
Raymond G. Romano *(Chief Credit Officer & Exec VP)*
Robert D. Mailloux *(Sr VP, Controller & Acctg Officer)*
Ralph F. Boyd, Jr. *(Exec VP-Community Relations)*
Robert E. Bostrom *(Gen Counsel & Exec VP)*
Paul G. George *(Exec VP-HR)*
Michael C. May *(Exec VP-Multifamily)*
Subha V. Barry *(Sr VP & Chief Diversity Officer)*
Donald J. Bisenius *(Sr VP-Single Family Credit Guarantee Bus)*
Hollis McLoughlin *(Sr VP-External Rels)*
Paul E. Mullings *(Sr VP-Single Family Sourcing)*
David R. Palombi *(Sr VP-Corp & Mktg Comm)*
Sharon McCail *(VP-Pub Relations)*
Mike McRoberts *(VP-Production & Sls-Multifamily)*
Brands & Products:
AFFORDABLE GOLD
AFFORDABLE MERIT RATE
AFFORDABLE SECONDS
BPODIRECT
COMMUNITY GOLD
CREDIT WORKS
DON'T BORROW TROUBLE
FREDDIE MAC
FREDDIE SUBS
GOLD CASH
GOLD CASH XTRA
GOLD CONNECTION
GOLD MEASURE
GOLD PERSPECTIVE
GOLD RUSH
GOLDWORKS
HOME POSSIBLE
HOMESTEPS
MAKING HOME AFFORDABLE
MI ACCESS
MULTISUITE
PMMS
PROGRAM PLUS
REFERENCE BILLS
REFERENCE BONDS
REFERENCE NOTES
REFERENCE POINT
REFERENCE REMIC
RELIEF REFINANCE MORTAGES
REMIC
REO MANAGER
WE MAKE HOME POSSIBLE
Advertising Agency:
NAS Recruitment Communications
1623 Forrest Dr Ste 100
Annapolis, MD 21403
Tel.: (410) 280-3505
Fax: (410) 280-3506

FEDERAL NATIONAL MORTGAGE ASSOCIATION

(d/b/a Fannie Mae)
3900 Wisconsin Ave NW
Washington, DC 20016-2806
Tel.: (202) 752-7000
Fax: (202) 752-3868
E-mail: headquarters@fanniemae.com
Web Site: www.fanniemae.com
Approx. Rev.: $154,270,000,000
Approx. Number Employees: 7,300
Year Founded: 1968
Business Description:
Home Mortgage Financial Services
S.I.C.: 6163
N.A.I.C.S.: 522310
Media: 2
Distr.: Natl.
Budget Set: Jan.
Personnel:
Philip A. Laskawy *(Chm)*
Michael J. Williams *(Pres & CEO)*
David C. Hisey *(Exec VP & Deputy CFO)*
Susan R. McFarland *(CFO & Exec VP)*
Timothy J. Mayopoulos *(Chief Admin Officer, Gen Counsel & Exec VP)*
Michael A. Shaw *(Chief Credit Officer & Exec VP)*
Douglas G. Duncan *(Chief Economist & VP)*
Kenneth J. Bacon *(Exec VP-Housing & Community Dev)*
David Benson *(Exec VP-Capital Markets)*
David M. Johnson *(Exec VP)*
Linda K. Knight *(Exec VP & Program Exec)*
Kenneth J. Phelan *(Exec VP-Enterprise Risk Mgmt)*
Edward G. Watson *(Exec VP-Ops & Tech)*
Edna Figueora *(Sr Product Mgr-Fannie Mae)*

FEDERAL REALTY INVESTMENT TRUST

1626 E Jefferson St
Rockville, MD 20852-4041
Tel.: (301) 998-8100
Fax: (301) 998-3700
Toll Free: (800) 658-8980
E-mail: IR@federalrealty.com
Web Site: www.federalrealty.com
Approx. Rev.: $544,674,000
Approx. Number Employees: 238
Year Founded: 1962
Business Description:
Equity Real Estate Investment Services
S.I.C.: 6798
N.A.I.C.S.: 525930
Personnel:
Donald C. Wood *(Pres & CEO)*
Andrew P. Blocher *(CFO, Principal Acctg Officer, Treas & Sr VP)*
Dawn M. Becker *(COO & Exec VP)*
Melissa Solis *(Chief Acctg Officer & VP)*
Jeffrey S. Berkes *(Pres-West Coast)*
Don Briggs *(Sr VP-Dev)*
Debbie Colson *(Sr VP-Legal Ops)*
Chris Weilminster *(Sr VP-Leasing)*
Wayne Christmann *(VP & Dir-Asset Mgmt-East Coast)*
Lisa Denson *(VP-IT & Special Projects)*
Vikki Kayne *(VP-Mktg & Corp Comm)*
Vicki Quinn *(VP-Mktg & Commun)*
Jeffrey R. Chamber *(Sr Dir-Dev & Acq-West Coast)*
Patrick Inaba *(Sr Dir-Tenant Svcs)*
Steve LaBold *(Sr Dir-Acq-Northeast Reg)*
Michael Khouri *(Dir-Leasing)*
Advertising Agency:
Ed Kiley Public Relations
133 Jersey St
San Francisco, CA 94114-3820
Tel.: (415) 826-0785

FEDERAL TRUST BANK

(Sub. of Federal Trust Corporation)
312 W 1st St
Sanford, FL 32771
Tel.: (407) 323-1833
Fax: (407) 302-4595
E-mail: info@federaltrust.com
Web Site: www.federaltrust.com
Sales Range: $10-24.9 Million
Approx. Number Employees: 75
Year Founded: 1988
Business Description:
Commercial Savings Bank
S.I.C.: 6035
N.A.I.C.S.: 522120
Advertising Expenditures: $400,000
Media: 4-7-8-9-10-13-20-22-25
Personnel:
Robert W. Paiano *(Pres)*
Winifred Chatman *(VP & Mgr-Sls)*

FEDERAL TRUST CORPORATION

(Sub. of The Hartford Financial Services Group, Inc.)
312 W 1st St Ste 110
Sanford, FL 32771
Mailing Address:
PO Box 1867
Sanford, FL 32772-1867
Tel.: (407) 323-1833
Fax: (407) 323-1833
E-mail: info@federaltrust.com
Web Site: www.federaltrust.com
Approx. Int. Income: $30,597,000
Approx. Number Employees: 89
Year Founded: 1989
Business Description:
Bank Holding Company
S.I.C.: 6035; 6712
N.A.I.C.S.: 522120; 551111
Advertising Expenditures: $314,000
Personnel:
Robert W. Paiano *(Pres)*

FEDERATED INVESTORS, INC.

Federated Investors Tower 1001 Liberty Ave
Pittsburgh, PA 15222-3779
Tel.: (412) 288-1900
Fax: (412) 288-1171
Toll Free: (800) 341-7400
E-mail: Investors@federatedinv.com
Web Site: www.federatedinvestors.com
Approx. Rev.: $951,943,000
Approx. Number Employees: 1,334
Year Founded: 1955
Business Description:
Investment Management Services
S.I.C.: 6282; 6211; 6722
N.A.I.C.S.: 523920; 523120; 525910
Advertising Expenditures: $10,110,000
Media: 2-6-9
Personnel:
John F. Donahue *(Co-Founder & Chm)*
Richard B. Fisher *(Co-Founder & Vice Chm)*
Gordon Joseph Ceresino *(Vice Chm)*
John B. Fisher *(Pres & CEO-Federated Advisory Companies)*
J. Christopher Donahue *(CFO & Treas)*
Stephen F. Auth *(CIO & Exec VP)*
Thomas E. Territ *(Pres-Federated Securities Corp)*
Eugene F. Maloney *(Exec VP)*
Thomas S. Schinabeck *(VP, Mgr-Sls & Western Reg)*
David W. Cook *(VP & Mgr-Portfolio)*
Bryan M. Burke *(Dir-Retirement Plan Sls)*
Albert Morabito *(Dir-Global Trading Ops)*
Colin B. Starks *(Dir-Sls-Natl)*
Douglas C. Noland *(Sr Mgr-Portfolio-Federated Market Opportunity Fund)*
Jonathan E. Gold *(Portfolio Mgr-Federated Kaufmann Team)*
John Leibee *(Portfolio Mgr-Federated Kaufmann Team)*
David Tice *(Chief Portfolio Strategist)*
Brands & Products:
EDGENET
FEDERATED
VALUE OUR EXPERIENCE
Advertising Agencies:
Krome Communications
The Bank Tower 307 4th Ave
Pittsburgh, PA 15222
Tel.: (412) 471-0840
Fax: (412) 471-0246

MCM Communications, Inc.
6101 Penn Ave Ste 601

Key to Media (For complete agency information see *The Advertising Red Books-Agencies* edition):
1. Bus. Publs. 2. Cable T.V. 3. Catalogs & Directories. 4. Co-op Adv. 5. Consumer Mags. 6. D.M. to Bus. Estab.7. D.M. to Consumers 8. Daily Newsp. 9. Exhibits/Trade Shows 10. Foreign 11. Infomercial 12. Internet Adv.13. Multimedia 14. Network Radio 15. Network T.V. 16. Newsp. Distr. Mags. 17. Other 18. Outdoor (Posters, Transit) 19. Point of Purchase20. Premiums, Novelties 21. Product Samples 22. Special Events Mktg. 23. Spot Radio 24. Spot T.V. 25. Weekly Newsp. 26. Yellow Page Adv.

Pittsburgh, PA 15206
Tel.: (412) 362-1211
Fax: (412) 362-1011

FEDFIRST FINANCIAL CORPORATION
Donner at 6th St
Monessen, PA 15062
Tel.: (724) 684-6800
Fax: (724) 684-4851
E-mail: Info@firstfederal-savings.com
Web Site: www.firstfederal-savings.com
Approx. Rev.: $19,247,000
Approx. Number Employees: 90
Business Description:
Bank Holding Company
S.I.C.: 6035; 6712
N.A.I.C.S.: 522120; 551111
Advertising Expenditures: $131,000
Media: 17
Personnel:
Patrick G. O'Brien *(Pres & CEO)*
Jamie L. Prah *(CFO & Sr VP)*
Henry B. Brown, III *(Sr VP-Production & Credit)*
Geraldine A. Ferrara *(VP & Mgr-Branch Sls & Admin)*
DaCosta Smith, III *(VP & Mgr-HR)*

FENTURA FINANCIAL, INC.
175 N Leroy St
Fenton, MI 48430
Tel.: (810) 629-2263
Fax: (810) 750-8762
E-mail: suzannew@fentura.com
Web Site: www.fentura.com
Approx. Rev.: $19,850,000
Approx. Number Employees: 130
Year Founded: 1898
Business Description:
Bank Holding Company
S.I.C.: 6141; 6029; 6163; 6712
N.A.I.C.S.: 522210; 522110; 522310; 551111
Advertising Expenditures: $101,000
Media: 17
Personnel:
Forrest A. Shook *(Chm)*
Thomas P. McKenney *(Vice Chm)*
Donald L. Grill *(Pres & CEO)*
Douglas J. Kelley *(CFO & Sr VP)*
Ronald L. Justice *(Sr VP)*
Dennis E. Leyder *(Sr VP)*
Holly J. Pingatore *(Sr VP-Info Sys)*
Kristina M. Premo *(Sr VP-HR)*

FIDELITY BANCORP INC.
1009 Perry Hwy
Pittsburgh, PA 15237
Tel.: (412) 367-3300
Fax: (412) 364-3360
E-mail: admin@fidelitybank-pa.com
Web Site: www.fidelitybancorp-pa.com
Approx. Rev.: $31,453,000
Approx. Number Employees: 128
Year Founded: 1993
Business Description:
Bank Holding Company
S.I.C.: 6029
N.A.I.C.S.: 522110
Advertising Expenditures: $332,000
Personnel:
Christopher S. Green *(Chm)*
Richard G. Spencer *(Pres & CEO)*
Lisa L. Griffith *(CFO, Treas & Sr VP)*
Michael A. Mooney *(Exec VP)*
Richard L. Barron *(Asst Sec)*

FIDELITY BANK
(Sub. of Fidelity Southern Corporation)
3490 Piedmont Rd
Atlanta, GA 30305
Mailing Address:
PO Box 105075
Atlanta, GA 30348
Tel.: (404) 639-6500
Fax: (404) 814-8118
E-mail: investorinfo@stmi.com
Web Site: www.lionbank.com
Sales Range: $25-49.9 Million
Approx. Number Employees: 400
Year Founded: 1974
Business Description:
Operator of Commercial Banks
S.I.C.: 6029
N.A.I.C.S.: 522110
Media: 6-9-13-17-18-19-23
Personnel:
James B. Miller, Jr. *(Chm & CEO)*
H. Palmer Proctor, Jr. *(Pres)*
Stephen H. Brolly *(CFO)*
David Buchanan *(Exec VP)*
Sue Cole *(VP-Mktg)*
Brands & Products:
FIDELITY BANK

FIDELITY D & D BANCORP INC.
Blakely & Drinker STS
Dunmore, PA 18512
Tel.: (570) 342-8281
Fax: (570) 346-5724
Toll Free: (800) 388-4380
E-mail: fidelity@fddbank.com
Web Site: www.the-fidelity.com
Approx. Int. Income: $27,579,974
Approx. Number Employees: 159
Year Founded: 1903
Business Description:
Bank Holding Company
S.I.C.: 6029; 6712
N.A.I.C.S.: 522110; 551111
Advertising Expenditures: $524,868
Personnel:
Patrick J. Dempsey *(Chm)*
Michael J. McDonald *(Vice Chm)*
Daniel J. Santaniello *(Pres & CEO)*
Salvatore R. Defrancesco Jr. *(CFO & Exec VP)*
Barbara A. Shimkus *(Asst VP & IR Officer)*

FIDELITY INVESTMENT CO. INC.
(Sub. of Fidelity Financial Corporation)
100 E English St
Wichita, KS 67202
Tel.: (316) 265-2261
Fax: (316) 268-7494
Web Site: www.fidelitybank.com
Approx. Rev.: $370,592
Approx. Number Employees: 400
Business Description:
Investment Holding Companies, Except Banks
S.I.C.: 6719; 6552
N.A.I.C.S.: 551112; 237210
Personnel:
Clark Bashton *(Chm)*
Stuart Grief *(Chief HR Officer & Exec VP)*
Julie Selig *(Dir-Media)*
Kendra Kontz *(Brand Mgr-Mktg)*

Advertising Agency:
EMI Strategic Marketing, Inc.
15 Broad St
Boston, MA 02109
Tel.: (617) 224-1101
Fax: (617) 224-1190

FIDELITY SOUTHERN CORPORATION
3490 Piedmont Rd Ne Ste 1550
Atlanta, GA 30305
Mailing Address:
PO Box 105075
Atlanta, GA 30348-5075
Tel.: (404) 639-6500
Fax: (404) 814-8060
Toll Free: (888) 248-5466
E-mail: ibsmgr@fnb-lion.com
Web Site: www.lionbank.com
Approx. Rev.: $138,193,000
Approx. Number Employees: 559
Business Description:
Bank Holding Company
S.I.C.: 6029; 6035; 6163; 6712
N.A.I.C.S.: 522110; 522120; 522310; 551111
Advertising Expenditures: $995,000
Personnel:
James B. Miller, Jr. *(Chm & CEO)*
H. Palmer Proctor, Jr. *(Pres)*
Stephen H. Brolly *(CFO)*

FIDUCIAL, INC.
(Sub. of Fiducial)
10100 Old Columbia Rd
Columbia, MD 21046
Tel.: (410) 910-5885
Fax: (410) 910-5901
Toll Free: (800) 434-3824
E-mail: info@fiducial.com
Web Site: www.fiducial.com
Approx. Number Employees: 80
Business Description:
Accounting Services
S.I.C.: 8741
N.A.I.C.S.: 561110
Media: 2
Personnel:
Bill Morice *(Dir-Field Ops)*

FIFTH THIRD BANCORP
Fifth Third Ctr 38 Fountain Sq Plz
Cincinnati, OH 45263
Fax: (513) 534-0629
Toll Free: (800) 972-3030
E-mail: 53investigation@security.53.com
Web Site: www.53.com
Approx. Rev.: $7,218,000,000
Approx. Number Employees: 20,838
Year Founded: 1975
Business Description:
Bank Holding Company
S.I.C.: 6011; 6029
N.A.I.C.S.: 521110; 522110
Export
Media: 2-6-8-9-10-13-18-20-23-24
Distr.: Reg.
Budget Set: Oct.
Personnel:
William M. Isaac *(Chm)*
Kevin T. Kabat *(Pres & CEO)*
Daniel T. Poston *(CFO & Exec VP)*
Greg D. Carmichael *(COO & Exec VP)*
Joseph R. Robinson *(CIO & Exec VP)*
Sidney C. Deloatch, III *(CIO-Comml Bank & Sr VP)*
Larry Magnesen *(CMO & Sr VP)*
Paul L. Reynolds *(Chief Admin Officer, Sec & Exec VP)*
Nancy R. Phillips *(Chief HR Officer & Exec VP)*
Mary E. Tuuk *(Chief Risk Officer & Exec VP)*
Yvonne Nabors *(Project Mgr-Principal)*
Mahesh Sankaran *(Treas & Sr VP)*
Bruce K. Lee *(Exec VP)*
Robert A. Sullivan *(Exec VP)*
Brian T. Mauntel *(Sr VP & Head-Bus Banking)*
Rob Rankin *(Sr VP & Head-Bus Dev/Natl Rels-Fin Institution Svcs Grp)*
Mark D. Hazel *(Sr VP & Controller)*
Robert Shaffer *(Sr VP & Dir-Fin Audit)*
Mark Erhardt *(Sr VP & Dir-Customer Segmentation)*
Jeff Ficke *(Sr VP & Dir-Treasury Mgmt)*
David Gottmann *(Sr VP & Dir-Check Svcs)*
Joe Pappano *(Sr VP & Dir-Merchant Sls-Processing Solutions)*
Jeff Richardson *(Sr VP & Dir-IR/Corp Analysis)*
Mike Butera *(Sr VP-Distr Strategy & Customer Analytics)*
Jean S. Hilliard *(Sr VP)*
Ed Owens, III *(Sr VP)*
Eric Puleo *(First VP & Mgr-IT Svc Delivery)*
Debra Decourcy *(VP & Dir-Corp Comm)*
Lesley DeCator *(VP & Mgr-Debit Mktg Program)*
Joe Chapline *(VP-Mktg)*
Nick Hamilton *(Asst VP)*
Pete Ludeman *(Asst VP-External Reporting)*
Michael Pento *(Asst VP)*
Charles N. Reeves *(Dir-Special Assets)*
Rodney Baker *(Sr Mgr-Applications Dev)*
Katherine Ebacher *(Mgr-Cash Vault Product)*
Brian Young *(Mgr-Retail Ops & Integrations)*
Brands & Products:
BANK MART
FIFTH THIRD
Advertising Agencies:
Haworth Marketing & Media Company
TCF Tower 10th Fl 121 S 8th St
Minneapolis, MN 55402
Tel.: (612) 677-8900
Fax: (612) 677-8901

Leo Burnett Worldwide, Inc.
35 W Wacker Dr
Chicago, IL 60601-1723
Tel.: (312) 220-5959
Fax: (312) 220-3299
Advertising
Agency of Record
Digital
Marketing Communications

FIFTH THIRD BANK, INDIANA (SOUTHERN)
(Affil. of Fifth Third Bancorp)
20 NW 3rd St
Evansville, IN 47708-0001
Mailing Address:
PO Box 778
Evansville, IN 47705-0778

Key to Media (For complete agency information see *The Advertising Red Books-Agencies* edition):
1. Bus. Publs. 2. Cable T.V. 3. Catalogs & Directories. 4. Co-op Adv. 5. Consumer Mags. 6. D.M. to Bus. Estab.7. D.M. to Consumers
8. Daily Newsp. 9. Exhibits/Trade Shows 10. Foreign 11. Infomercial 12. Internet Adv.13. Multimedia 14. Network Radio
15. Network T.V. 16. Newsp. Distr. Mags. 17. Other 18. Outdoor (Posters, Transit) 19. Point of Purchase20. Premiums, Novelties
21. Product Samples 22. Special Events Mktg. 23. Spot Radio 24. Spot T.V. 25. Weekly Newsp. 26. Yellow Page Adv.

Fifth Third Bank, Indiana (Southern) — (Continued)

Tel.: (812) 456-3400
Fax: (812) 456-3496
Toll Free: (800) 777-3949
Web Site: www.53.com
E-Mail For Key Personnel:
Marketing Director: lloyd.winnecke@53.com
Sales Range: $1-4.9 Billion
Approx. Number Employees: 23,000
Year Founded: 1983
Business Description:
Bank Holding Company
S.I.C.: 6029
N.A.I.C.S.: 522110
Media: 2-3-4-6-7-8-9-15-17-18-19-20-22-23-24
Distr.: Direct to Consumer; Reg.
Personnel:
Lloyd Winnecke *(Sr VP & Dir- Mktg)*
Nancy Byrd *(VP-HR)*
Michelle Moore *(Asst VP)*

FIFTH THIRD BANK, NORTHWESTERN OHIO, N.A.

(Affil. of Fifth Third Bancorp)
606 Madison Ave
Toledo, OH 43604-1111
Tel.: (419) 259-7890
Fax: (419) 259-7169
Web Site: www.53.com
Approx. Int. Income: $126,178,000
Approx. Number Employees: 880
Business Description:
Banking
S.I.C.: 6029
N.A.I.C.S.: 522110
Personnel:
Robert W. LaClair *(Pres & CEO)*
Karen Fraker *(Sr VP)*
Jeffrey S. Langenderfer *(VP & Reg Mgr-Sls)*
Advertising Agency:
Hart Associates, Inc.
1915 Indian Wood Cir
Maumee, OH 43537-4002
Tel.: (419) 893-9600
Fax: (419) 893-9070

FINANCIAL ENGINES, INC.

1804 Embarcadero Rd
Palo Alto, CA 94303-3341
Tel.: (650) 565-4900
Fax: (650) 565-4905
Toll Free: (888) 443-8577
E-mail: ir@financialengines.com
Web Site: www.financialengines.com
Approx. Rev.: $71,271,000
Approx. Number Employees: 303
Year Founded: 1996
Business Description:
Portfolio Management, Investment Advice, Retirement Assistance & Online Investing Services
S.I.C.: 6282; 2741; 6371
N.A.I.C.S.: 523920; 516110; 523930; 525990
Advertising Expenditures: $2,000,000
Media: 13
Personnel:
Paul G. Koontz *(Chm)*
Jeffrey N. Maggioncalda *(Pres & CEO)*
Raymond J. Sims *(CFO & Exec VP)*
Christopher L. Jones *(Chief Investment Officer & Exec VP-Investment Mgmt)*
Anne S. Tuttle *(Gen Counsel & Exec VP)*
Kenneth M. Fine *(Exec VP-Mktg)*
Garry W. Hallee *(Exec VP-Tech & Svc Delivery)*
Lawrence M. Raffone *(Exec VP-Sls & Client Svcs)*
Deborah J. Behrman *(VP-HR)*
Marci Pelletier *(Sr Mgr-Mktg)*
Brands & Products:
ADVICE LIGHT
ADVICESERVER
FINANCIAL ENGINES
FINENG
FORECASTER
RETIREMENT HELP FOR LIFE
WE MAKE IT PERSONAL
Advertising Agency:
PARTNERS+simons
25 Drydock Ave 8th Fl
Boston, MA 02210
Tel.: (617) 330-9393
Fax: (617) 330-9394

FINANCIAL INSTITUTIONS, INC.

220 Liberty St
Warsaw, NY 14569-1465
Tel.: (585) 786-1100
Fax: (585) 786-5254
E-mail: info@fiiwarsaw.com
Web Site: www.fiiwarsaw.com
Approx. Rev.: $115,963,000
Approx. Number Employees: 616
Year Founded: 1931
Business Description:
Bank Holding Company
S.I.C.: 6712; 6029
N.A.I.C.S.: 551111; 522110
Import Export
Advertising Expenditures: $949,000
Personnel:
John E. Benjamin *(Chm)*
Peter G. Humphrey *(Pres & CEO)*
Karl Krebs *(CFO & Exec VP)*
Ronald Mitchell McLaughlin *(CIO & Exec VP)*
George Daniel Hagi *(Exec VP & Chief Risk Officer)*
Martin K. Birmingham *(Reg Pres-Comml Markets & Sr VP)*
John J. Witkowski *(Reg Pres-Retail Banking & Sr VP)*
Kevin B. Klotzbach *(Treas & Sr VP)*
Sonia M. Dumbleton *(Sr VP & Controller)*
Bruce H. Nagle *(Sr VP & Dir-HR)*
Steven R. Ambrose *(Sr VP & Mgr-Workout Asset Grp)*
David R. Caster *(Sr VP)*
Martin T. Griffith *(Sr VP)*
Richard J. Harrison *(Sr VP & Sr Retail Lending Administrator)*
Kenneth V. Winn *(Sr VP & Sr Credit Administrator)*
Matthew T. Murtha *(VP-Mktg)*

FINANCIAL PACIFIC LEASING, LLC

(Holding of Flexpoint Ford, LLC)
3455 S 344th Way Ste 300
Federal Way, WA 98001
Mailing Address:
PO Box 4568
Federal Way, WA 98063
Tel.: (253) 568-6000
Fax: (253) 568-2222
Toll Free: (800) 447-7107
E-mail: finpac@finpac.com
Web Site: www.finpac.com
Sales Range: $25-49.9 Million
Approx. Number Employees: 120
Business Description:
Specialized Commercial Finance Company that Leases Business-Essential Equipment to Small Businesses
S.I.C.: 7389; 7319
N.A.I.C.S.: 561499; 541870; 561439; 561990
Media: 7
Personnel:
Paul Manzel *(Pres & CEO)*
Peter A. Davis *(CFO, Sec & Sr VP)*
Terey N. Jennings *(Sr VP-Bus Dev)*
Bruce Spencer *(Sr VP-Credit & Ops)*

FINOTEC GROUP, INC.

228 E 45th St Ste 1801
New York, NY 10017
Tel.: (718) 513-3620
Toll Free: (866) 243-0771
E-mail: contact@finotec.com
Web Site: www.finotec.com
Approx. Rev.: $2,799,764
Approx. Number Employees: 45
Business Description:
Financial Services
S.I.C.: 6371; 6082; 6211; 6221
N.A.I.C.S.: 525990; 522293; 523120; 523140
Advertising Expenditures: $670,387
Media: 9-10-13-25
Personnel:
Didier Essemini *(Chm, Pres, CEO & CFO)*

FIRST BANCORP OF INDIANA, INC.

5001 Davis Lant Dr
Evansville, IN 47715
Mailing Address:
PO Box 1111
Evansville, IN 47706-1111
Tel.: (812) 492-8100
Tel.: (812) 492-8104
Fax: (812) 421-4107
E-mail: president@fbei.net
Web Site: www.firstfedevansville.com
Approx. Rev.: $19,560,261
Approx. Number Employees: 83
Business Description:
Bank Holding Company
S.I.C.: 6712; 6029; 6035
N.A.I.C.S.: 551111; 522110; 522120
Advertising Expenditures: $246,882
Personnel:
Harold Duncan *(Chm)*
Michael H. Head *(Pres & CEO)*
George Jeffrey Smith *(CFO & Treas)*

THE FIRST BANCSHARES, INC.

6480 Hwy 98 W
Hattiesburg, MS 39404
Mailing Address:
PO Box 15549
Hattiesburg, MS 39404
Tel.: (601) 450-8888
Fax: (601) 579-9213
E-mail: info@firstbankslo.com
Web Site: www.thefirstbank.com
Approx. Rev.: $27,348,775
Approx. Number Employees: 148
Year Founded: 1996
Business Description:
Bank Holding Company
S.I.C.: 6712
N.A.I.C.S.: 551111
Advertising Expenditures: $261,727
Personnel:
E. Ricky Gibson *(Chm)*
J. Douglas Seidenburg *(Vice Chm)*
Milton Ray Cole, Jr. *(Pres & CEO)*
DeeDee Lowery *(CFO)*

THE FIRST BANCSHARES, INC.

(d/b/a First Home Savings Bank)
142 E 1st St
Mountain Grove, MO 65711
Mailing Address:
PO Box 777
Mountain Grove, MO 65711
Tel.: (417) 926-5151
Fax: (417) 926-4362
Web Site: www.fhsb.com
Approx. Int. Income: $8,253,003
Approx. Number Employees: 75
Year Founded: 1993
Business Description:
Bank Holding Company
S.I.C.: 6141; 6029; 6035; 6712
N.A.I.C.S.: 522210; 522110; 522120; 551111
Advertising Expenditures: $221,616
Personnel:
R. Bradley Weaver *(Chm & CEO)*
Lannie E. Crawford *(Pres)*
Ronald J. Walters *(CFO, Treas & Sr VP)*

FIRST BANK OF DELAWARE

(Sub. of REPUBLIC FIRST BANCORP, INC.)
1000 Rocky Run Pkwy
Wilmington, DE 19803-1455
Tel.: (302) 529-5984
Fax: (302) 529-5987
Web Site: www.fbdel.com
Sales Range: $10-24.9 Million
Approx. Number Employees: 7
Business Description:
Banking Services
S.I.C.: 6029
N.A.I.C.S.: 522110
Advertising Expenditures: $79,000
Media: 9-25
Personnel:
Harry D. Madonna *(Chm)*
Alonzo J. Primus *(CEO)*
Benjamin Watts *(CFO & Sr VP)*

FIRST BANKS, INC.

135 N Meramec Ave
Clayton, MO 63105-3751
Tel.: (314) 854-4600
Fax: (314) 854-5454
Toll Free: (800) 760-2265
Web Site: www.firstbanks.com
Approx. Rev.: $391,365,000
Approx. Number Employees: 1,380
Year Founded: 1978
Business Description:
Bank Holding Company
S.I.C.: 6712; 6029
N.A.I.C.S.: 551111; 522110
Advertising Expenditures: $1,483,000
Personnel:
James F. Dierberg *(Chm)*
Terrance M. McCarthy *(Pres & CEO)*
Lisa K. Vansickle *(CFO & Sr VP)*
Gary S. Pratte *(Chief Credit Officer & Exec VP)*
John G. Kitson *(Chief HR Officer & Sr VP)*

Key to Media (For complete agency information see *The Advertising Red Books-Agencies* edition):
1. Bus. Publs. 2. Cable T.V. 3. Catalogs & Directories. 4. Co-op Adv. 5. Consumer Mags. 6. D.M. to Bus. Estab.7. D.M. to Consumers 8. Daily Newsp. 9. Exhibits/Trade Shows 10. Foreign 11. Infomercial 12. Internet Adv.13. Multimedia 14. Network Radio 15. Network T.V. 16. Newsp. Distr. Mags. 17. Other 18. Outdoor (Posters, Transit) 19. Point of Purchase20. Premiums, Novelties 21. Product Samples 22. Special Events Mktg. 23. Spot Radio 24. Spot T.V. 25. Weekly Newsp. 26. Yellow Page Adv.

Peter D. Wimmer *(Gen Counsel, Sec & Sr VP)*
F. Christopher McLaughlin *(Exec VP & Dir-Retail)*
Mary P. Sherrill *(Exec VP & Dir-Ops & Tech)*
Laura Schumacher *(Sr VP & Dir-Risk Mgmt/Audit)*
Edwin E. Laws *(Sr VP-Fin)*

FIRST BUSEY CORPORATION

100 W University Ave
Champaign, IL 61820
Tel.: (217) 365-4516
Fax: (217) 365-4879
Toll Free: (800) 67BUSEY
Web Site: www.busey.com
Approx. Rev.: $218,936,000
Approx. Number Employees: 866
Year Founded: 1980
Business Description:
Financial Holding Company
S.I.C.: 6712; 6029; 6211; 6371
N.A.I.C.S.: 551111; 522110; 523110; 525990
Media: 2
Personnel:
Gregory B. Lykins *(Chm)*
Van A. Dukeman *(Pres & CEO)*
David B. White *(CFO & Exec VP)*
Leanne C. Heacock *(CIO)*
Robert F. Plecki, Jr. *(Chief Credit Officer)*
Barbara J. Harrington *(Exec VP & Chief Risk Officer)*
Susan E. Abbott *(Chief Retail Officer & Exec VP)*
Brands & Products:
BUSEY
OVERDRAFT ADVANTAGE

FIRST CALIFORNIA FINANCIAL GROUP, INC.

3027 Townsgate Rd Ste 300
Westlake Village, CA 91361
Tel.: (805) 322-9655
E-mail: investorrelations@fcalgroup.com
Web Site: www.fcbank.com
Approx. Rev.: $68,146,000
Approx. Number Employees: 248
Business Description:
Bank Holding Company
S.I.C.: 6712
N.A.I.C.S.: 551111
Advertising Expenditures: $48,000
Media: 17
Personnel:
Robert E. Gipson *(Chm)*
John W. Birchfield *(Vice Chm)*
Chong Guk Kum *(Pres & CEO)*
Romolo C. Santarosa *(CFO)*
Diane Dickerson *(CMO & Sr VP)*
William Schack *(Chief Credit Officer & Exec VP)*
Advertising Agency:
PondelWilkinson Inc.
1880 Century Park E Ste 350
Los Angeles, CA 90067
Tel.: (310) 279-5980
Fax: (310) 279-5988

FIRST CAPITAL BANCORP, INC.

4222 Cox Rd Ste 200
Glen Allen, VA 23060
Tel.: (804) 273-1160
Fax: (804) 527-0195
E-mail: wranson@1capitalbank.com
Web Site: www.1capitalbank.com
Approx. Rev.: $27,479,736
Approx. Number Employees: 82
Year Founded: 1998
Business Description:
Bank Holding Company
S.I.C.: 6712; 6029
N.A.I.C.S.: 551111; 522110
Advertising Expenditures: $176,711
Media: 7-8
Personnel:
Grant S. Grayson *(Chm)*
Richard W. Wright, Jr. *(Vice Chm)*
Robert G. Watts, Jr. *(Pres & CEO)*
John M. Presley *(CEO & Mng Dir)*
William W. Ranson *(CFO)*
Katherine K. Wagner *(COO & Sr VP)*
K.Bradley Hildebrandt *(Exec VP & Sr Lender)*
Patricia A. Cuccia *(Sr VP & Mgr-Ops)*
Barry P. Almond *(Sr VP-Retail Banking & Sr Leader)*
William D. Bien, Jr. *(Sr VP & Sr Comml Lender)*

FIRST CAPITAL, INC.

220 Federal Dr NW
Corydon, IN 47112
Mailing Address:
PO Box 130
Corydon, IN 47112
Tel.: (812) 738-2198
Fax: (812) 738-2202
E-mail: dnessmith@firstharrison.com
Web Site: www.firstharrison.com
Approx. Rev.: $25,740,000
Approx. Number Employees: 118
Year Founded: 1998
Business Description:
Bank Holding Company
S.I.C.: 6712; 6035
N.A.I.C.S.: 551111; 522120
Advertising Expenditures: $208,000
Personnel:
James Gordon Pendleton *(Chm)*
William W. Harrod *(Pres & CEO)*
Michael Chris Frederick *(CFO, Treas & Sr VP)*
Samuel E. Uhl *(COO)*

FIRST CASH FINANCIAL SERVICES, INC.

690 E Lamar Blvd Ste 400
Arlington, TX 76011-3864
Tel.: (817) 460-3947
Fax: (817) 461-7019
Web Site: www.firstcash.com
Approx. Rev.: $431,147,000
Approx. Number Employees: 4,700
Year Founded: 1988
Business Description:
Specialty Consumer Financial Services & Related Retail Products
S.I.C.: 6289; 6099; 6141; 6159
N.A.I.C.S.: 523999; 522291; 522298; 522390
Advertising Expenditures: $1,519,000
Media: 13-19
Personnel:
Rick L. Wessel *(Chm & CEO)*
Phillip Eric Powell *(Chm)*
R. Douglas Orr *(CFO & Exec VP)*
Stephen Coffman *(COO)*
John C. Powell *(Sr VP & Dir- Info Tech)*

FIRST CENTURY BANKSHARES INC.

500 Federal St
Bluefield, WV 24701
Tel.: (304) 325-8181
Fax: (304) 325-9735
E-mail: online@firstcentury.com
Web Site: www.firstcentury.com
Approx. Rev.: $22,614,000
Approx. Number Employees: 146
Business Description:
National Commercial Banks
S.I.C.: 6029
N.A.I.C.S.: 522110
Advertising Expenditures: $210,000
Personnel:
R. W. Wilkinson *(Chm)*
Robert M. Jones, Jr. *(Vice Chm)*
Frank W. Wilkinson *(Pres & CEO-First Century Bank)*
J. Ronald Hypes *(CFO & Sr VP)*
Jeffrey L. Forlines *(Chief Credit Officer & Sr VP)*
William E. Albert *(Sr VP & Cashier)*

FIRST CITIZENS BANC CORP

100 E Water St
Sandusky, OH 44870
Tel.: (419) 625-4121
Fax: (419) 627-3359
E-mail: jomiller@citizensbankco.com
Web Site: www.fcza.com
Approx. Rev.: $61,406,000
Approx. Number Employees: 290
Business Description:
Bank Holding Company
S.I.C.: 6712
N.A.I.C.S.: 551111
Advertising Expenditures: $391,000
Personnel:
David A. Voight *(Chm)*
James O. Miller *(Chm/Pres/CEO-The Citizens Banking Company, Pres & CEO)*
Paul J. Stark *(Chief Credit Officer & Sr VP)*
Pat Cromeell *(Privacy Officer)*
James E. McGookey *(Gen Counsel, Sec & Sr VP)*
Todd A. Michel *(Sr VP & Controller)*
Richard J. Dutton *(Sr VP)*
Charles C. Riesterer *(Sr VP-Lending)*

FIRST CITIZENS BANCSHARES, INC.

4300 Six Forks Rd
Raleigh, NC 27609
Tel.: (919) 716-7000
Fax: (919) 716-7074
Web Site: www.firstcitizens.com
Approx. Rev.: $1,375,582,000
Approx. Number Employees: 4,421
Year Founded: 1986
Business Description:
Bank Holding Company
S.I.C.: 6712
N.A.I.C.S.: 551111
Advertising Expenditures: $8,111,000
Media: 2-6-7-8-9-18-20-23-24-25-26
Distr.: Natl.
Budget Set: Dec.
Personnel:
Frank B. Holding, Jr. *(Chm & CEO)*
Hope Holding Connell *(Co-Vice Chm)*
Frank Brown Holding, Sr. *(Co-Vice Chm)*
Edward L. Willingham, IV *(Pres)*

FIRST CITIZENS BANCSHARES, INC.

1st Citizens Pl
Dyersburg, TN 38024
Tel.: (731) 285-4410
Fax: (731) 287-4440
Web Site: www.firstcitizens-bank.com
Approx. Rev.: $59,206,000
Approx. Number Employees: 259
Year Founded: 1982
Business Description:
National Commercial Banks
S.I.C.: 6029
N.A.I.C.S.: 522110
Import Export
Advertising Expenditures: $703,000
Personnel:
Jeffrey D. Agee *(Pres & CEO)*

FIRST COMMONWEALTH FINANCIAL CORPORATION

22 N 6th St
Indiana, PA 15701
Mailing Address:
PO Box 400
Indiana, PA 15701-0400
Tel.: (724) 349-7220
E-mail: dlawry@fcbanking.com
Web Site: www.fcbanking.com
Approx. Rev.: $317,594,000
Approx. Number Employees: 1,443
Year Founded: 1928
Business Description:
Bank Holding Company
S.I.C.: 6712; 6029
N.A.I.C.S.: 551111; 522110
Advertising Expenditures: $2,200,000
Media: 8-9-10-25
Personnel:
John J. Dolan *(Pres & CEO)*
Robert E. Rout *(CFO & Exec VP)*
Sue A. McMurdy *(CIO & Exec VP)*
I. Robert Emmerich *(Chief Credit Officer-First Commonwealth Bank & Exec VP)*
Matthew C. Tomb *(Chief Risk Officer, Sr VP & Assoc Gen Counsel)*
Thaddeus J. Clements *(Exec VP-Strategic Resources)*
J. Eric Renner *(Exec VP-Consumer Svcs)*
Teresa Ciambotti *(Sr VP & Controller)*
Orlando V. Fulgenzio, III *(Sr VP-Mktg Mgr)*
Wendy S. Bell *(Sr VP)*
Leonard V. Lombardi *(Sr VP & Chief Audit Exec)*
R. John Previte *(Sr VP-Investments)*
Susie Barbour *(Supvr-Media Rels)*
Advertising Agency:
Mullen
40 Broad St
Boston, MA 02109
Tel.: (617) 226-9000
Fax: (617) 226-9100

FIRST COMMUNITY BANCSHARES, INC.

One Community Pl
Bluefield, VA 24605
Mailing Address:
PO Box 989
Bluefield, VA 24605-0989
Tel.: (276) 326-9000
Fax: (276) 326-9010
E-mail: marketing@fcbinc.com
Web Site: www.fcbinc.com

Key to Media (For complete agency information see *The Advertising Red Books-Agencies* edition):
1. Bus. Publs. 2. Cable T.V. 3. Catalogs & Directories. 4. Co-op Adv. 5. Consumer Mags. 6. D.M. to Bus. Estab.7. D.M. to Consumers 8. Daily Newsp. 9. Exhibits/Trade Shows 10. Foreign 11. Infomercial 12. Internet Adv.13. Multimedia 14. Network Radio 15. Network T.V. 16. Newsp. Distr. Mags. 17. Other 18. Outdoor (Posters, Transit) 19. Point of Purchase20. Premiums, Novelties 21. Product Samples 22. Special Events Mktg. 23. Spot Radio 24. Spot T.V. 25. Weekly Newsp. 26. Yellow Page Adv.

First Community Bancshares, Inc. — (Continued)

Approx. Rev.: $144,090,000
Approx. Number Employees: 683
Year Founded: 1990
Business Description:
Bank Holding Company
S.I.C.: 6712; 6029
N.A.I.C.S.: 551111; 522110
Advertising Expenditures: $1,584,000
Media: 8-9-25
Personnel:
William P. Stafford, II *(Chm)*
John M. Mendez *(Pres & CEO)*
David D. Brown *(CFO)*
Robert L. Schumacher *(Gen Counsel & Sr VP)*
Robin D. Brown *(Dir-HR & Mktg)*
Pat Crapps *(Mgr-Retail)*
Timothy R. Langfitt *(Coord-Comml Banking)*

Advertising Agency:
Woodbine
210 S Cherry St
Winston Salem, NC 27101-5231
Tel.: (336) 724-0450
Fax: (336) 724-6725
Agency of Record

FIRST COMMUNITY BANK CORPORATION OF AMERICA

9001 Belcher Rd
Pinellas Park, FL 33782
Tel.: (727) 520-0987
Web Site: www.efirstcommbank.com
Approx. Rev.: $24,463,000
Approx. Number Employees: 90
Year Founded: 1985
Business Description:
Bank Holding Company
S.I.C.: 6029; 6712
N.A.I.C.S.: 522110; 551111
Advertising Expenditures: $23,000
Media: 17
Personnel:
Kenneth P. Cherven *(CEO)*
Donna M. Donovan *(COO & Exec VP)*
Thomas P. Croom *(Exec VP & Sr Credit Officer)*
Clifton E. Tufts *(Exec VP)*
Anna Thrombley *(Sr VP-HR)*
David K. Meehan *(Dir)*
Robert M. Menke *(Dir)*

FIRST COMMUNITY CORPORATION

5455 Sunset Blvd
Lexington, SC 29072
Tel.: (803) 951-2265
Tel.: (803) 951-0555
Fax: (803) 951-1722
Web Site: www.firstcommunitysc.com
Approx. Rev.: $31,355,000
Approx. Number Employees: 147
Business Description:
Bank Holding Company
S.I.C.: 6141; 6029; 6712
N.A.I.C.S.: 522210; 522110; 551111
Media: 17
Personnel:
Mitchell M. Willoughby *(Chm)*
J. Thomas Johnson *(Vice Chm)*
Michael C. Crapps *(Pres & CEO)*
Joseph G. Sawyer *(CFO)*
Kevin T. Adams *(Officer-Market Exec)*
Jeff A. Branum *(Mortgage Officer)*
Harry A. Deith *(Comml Lending Officer)*
Brenda S. Hartsell *(Mortgage Officer)*
J. Ted Nissen *(Grp Banking Officer)*
David K. Proctor *(Sr Credit Officer)*

FIRST COMMUNITY FINANCIAL CORPORATION

2 N Main St
Mifflintown, PA 17059
Tel.: (717) 436-2144
Fax: (717) 436-2345
E-mail: jskauffman@fnbmifflintown.com
Web Site: www.fnbmifflintown.com
Approx. Rev.: $20,940,000
Approx. Number Employees: 69
Year Founded: 1984
Business Description:
Bank Holding Company
S.I.C.: 6712; 6029
N.A.I.C.S.: 551111; 522110
Advertising Expenditures: $99,000
Media: 8
Personnel:
John P. Henry, III *(Chm)*
Roger Shallenberger *(Vice Chm)*
Jody D. Graybill *(Pres & CEO)*
Richard R. Leitzel *(CFO, Chief Acctg Officer & VP)*

FIRST DATA CORPORATION

(Holding of KKR & CO. L.P.)
5565 Glenridge Connector NE Ste 2000
Atlanta, GA 30342
Tel.: (404) 890-2000
Toll Free: (800) 735-3362
E-mail: chip.swearngan@firstdata.com
Web Site: www.firstdatacorp.com
Approx. Rev.: $10,380,400,000
Approx. Number Employees: 23,765
Year Founded: 1989
Business Description:
Credit, Debit, Smart Card & Store-Value Card Issuing & Merchant Transaction Processing Services; Internet Commerce Solutions; Money Transfers & Money Orders; Check Processing & Verification Services
S.I.C.: 6099; 6141
N.A.I.C.S.: 522320; 522210; 522390
Advertising Expenditures: $39,500,000
Distr.: Intl.; Natl.
Personnel:
Joe W. Forehand *(Chm)*
Jonathan J. Judge *(CEO)*
Raymond E. Winborne *(CFO & Exec VP)*
Kevin Kern *(Exec VP & CTO)*
John Elkins *(Pres-First Data- Intl Regs)*
Edward A. Labry, III *(Pres-North America)*
David R. Money *(Gen Counsel & Exec VP)*
Peter W. Boucher *(Exec VP-HR)*
Mark Herrington *(Exec VP-Global Product Mgmt & Innovation)*
Silvio Tavares *(Sr VP & Head-IR)*
Shawn Anderson *(Chief Procurement Officer & Sr VP)*
Chip Swearngan *(Sr VP-Global Comm & IR)*
Kevin Barry *(Gen Mgr-STAR Debit Network)*
Steve Boehm *(Dir-Global Product Mgmt & Innovation)*
Nancy Etheredge *(Dir-Corp Comm)*
Peter Korpady *(Mgr-Sls)*
Andy Payment *(Mgr-Comm)*
Claudio Rillo *(Mgr-IT)*

Brands & Products:
CONNECTPAY
FD100
FD300
FD50
FIRST DATA
REMITCO

Advertising Agencies:
Heinrich Marketing
1350 Independence St
Denver, CO 80215
Tel.: (303) 233-8660
Fax: (303) 239-5373
Toll Free: (800) 356-5036

Peak Creative Media
1801 Boulder St Ste 200
Denver, CO 80202-2658
Tel.: (303) 295-3373
Fax: (303) 455-3363

SapientNitro Atlanta
500 North Park Town Center 1100 AbernathyRd NE
Atlanta, GA 30328
Tel.: (770) 407-3400
Fax: (770) 407-3401
Agency of Record
Brand Identity

FIRST FEDERAL BANCSHARES OF ARKANSAS, INC.

1401 Hwy 62/65 N
Harrison, AR 72601
Mailing Address:
PO Box 550
Harrison, AR 72602-0550
Tel.: (870) 741-7641
Fax: (870) 365-8369
Toll Free: (800) 345-2539
E-mail: aic@ffbh.com
Web Site: www.ffbh.com
Approx. Rev.: $39,279,000
Approx. Number Employees: 218
Year Founded: 1996
Business Description:
Bank Holding Company
S.I.C.: 6712; 6029
N.A.I.C.S.: 551111; 522110
Advertising Expenditures: $263,000
Media: 8-9-14-15-25
Personnel:
Larry J. Brandt *(Chm & CEO)*
John Paul Hammerschmidt *(Chm)*
Sherri R. Billings *(CFO)*
Tommy W. Richardson *(Exec VP & COO)*

FIRST FINANCIAL BANKSHARES, INC.

400 Pine St
Abilene, TX 79601-5128
Mailing Address:
PO Box 701
Abilene, TX 79604-0701
Tel.: (325) 627-7155
Fax: (325) 627-7393
Toll Free: (800) 588-7000
E-mail: investorrelations@ffin.com
Web Site: www.ffin.com
Approx. Rev.: $199,177,000
Approx. Number Employees: 1,000
Year Founded: 1956
Business Description:
Bank Holding Company
S.I.C.: 2759; 6029; 6035; 6163; 6211; 6712
N.A.I.C.S.: 323119; 522110; 522120; 522310; 523110; 551111
Advertising Expenditures: $1,239,000
Media: 8-17
Personnel:
F. Scott Dueser *(Chm, Pres & CEO)*
J.Bruce Hildebrand *(CFO, Treas, Sec & Exec VP)*
Bob Goodner *(Compliance Officer)*
Daniel A. Ortiz *(Officer-Comm Loans)*
Gary S. Gragg *(Exec VP-Lending)*
Gary L. Webb *(Exec VP-Ops)*
Tommy J. Barrow *(Sr VP-Lending)*
Courtney Jordan *(Sr VP-Trng & Education)*
Michele P. Stevens *(Sr VP-Mktg)*
David Hogan *(Dir-IR & Corp Comm)*
Gaila N. Kilpatrick *(Asst Sec)*

FIRST FINANCIAL HOLDINGS, INC.

2440 Mall Dr
Charleston, SC 29406
Tel.: (843) 529-5933
Fax: (843) 529-5929
E-mail: investorrelations@firstfinancialholdings.com
Web Site: www.firstfinancialholdings.com
Approx. Rev.: $252,185,000
Approx. Number Employees: 1,129
Year Founded: 1987
Business Description:
Banking Services
S.I.C.: 6712; 6035; 6411
N.A.I.C.S.: 551111; 522120; 524210
Advertising Expenditures: $1,801,000
Media: 2-3-6-7-8-9-10-13-18-19-20-22-23-24-25-26
Personnel:
Paula Harper Bethea *(Chm)*
Thomas J. Johnson *(Vice Chm)*
R. Wayne Hall *(Pres & CEO)*
Blaise B. Bettendorf *(CFO & Exec VP)*
Joseph W. Amy *(Chief Credit Officer & Exec VP)*
J. Dale Hall *(Chief Banking Officer & Exec VP)*
Dorothy B. Wright *(Sec & Sr VP-IR)*
Charles F. Baarcke, Jr. *(Exec VP-Market Dev & Sr Bus Dev Officer)*
John L. Ott, Jr. *(Exec VP)*
R. Bruce Copeland, Jr. *(Sr VP-Mktg & PR)*

Advertising Agency:
On Ideas, Inc.
6 E Bay St Ste 100
Jacksonville, FL 32202-5422
Tel.: (904) 354-2600
Fax: (904) 354-7226

FIRST FINANCIAL GROUP OF AMERICA

(Sub. of American Fidelity Assurance Company)
515 N Sam Houston Pkwy E
Houston, TX 77060-4034
Tel.: (281) 847-8422
Fax: (281) 847-8423
Toll Free: (800) 523-8422

Key to Media (For complete agency information see *The Advertising Red Books-Agencies* edition):
1. Bus. Publs. 2. Cable T.V. 3. Catalogs & Directories. 4. Co-op Adv. 5. Consumer Mags. 6. D.M. to Bus. Estab.7. D.M. to Consumers 8. Daily Newsp. 9. Exhibits/Trade Shows 10. Foreign 11. Infomercial 12. Internet Adv.13. Multimedia 14. Network Radio 15. Network T.V. 16. Newsp. Distr. Mags. 17. Other 18. Outdoor (Posters, Transit) 19. Point of Purchase20. Premiums, Novelties 21. Product Samples 22. Special Events Mktg. 23. Spot Radio 24. Spot T.V. 25. Weekly Newsp. 26. Yellow Page Adv.

E-mail: info@ffga.com
Web Site: www.ffga.com
Approx. Number Employees: 150
Business Description:
Securities Broker & Dealer
S.I.C.: 6411
N.A.I.C.S.: 524210
Media: 13-17
Personnel:
Larry Forrester *(CFO)*

FIRST FINANCIAL SERVICE CORPORATION
2323 Ring Rd
Elizabethtown, KY 42701
Mailing Address:
PO Box 5006
Elizabethtown, KY 42702-5006
Tel.: (270) 765-2131
Fax: (270) 765-2135
Toll Free: (800) 314-2265
E-mail: internetservices@ffsbky.com
Web Site: www.ffsbky.com
Approx. Rev.: $67,666,000
Approx. Number Employees: 315
Year Founded: 1990
Business Description:
Bank Holding Company
S.I.C.: 6035; 6029; 6712
N.A.I.C.S.: 522120; 522110; 551111
Advertising Expenditures: $844,000
Media: 7-8-13
Budget Set: Dec.
Personnel:
Walter D. Huddleston *(Chm)*
Gregory S. Schreacke *(Pres)*
B. Keith Johnson *(CEO)*
Anne Moran *(Chief Retail Officer & Exec Officer)*
Rebecca Wells *(Sr VP)*
Susan Bradbury *(VP & Mgr-Banking Center)*
Larry Hawkins *(Mgr-Special Asset)*

FIRST FRANKLIN CORPORATION
(Sub. of Cheviot Financial Corp.)
4750 Ashwood Dr
Cincinnati, OH 45241
Tel.: (513) 469-8000
Fax: (513) 469-5360
E-mail: info@franklinsavings.com
Web Site: www.franklinsavings.com/
Approx. Rev.: $19,672,681
Approx. Number Employees: 73
Year Founded: 1883
Business Description:
Bank Holding Company
S.I.C.: 6035; 6163
N.A.I.C.S.: 522120; 522310
Advertising Expenditures: $144,777
Media: 17
Personnel:
John J. Kuntz *(Chm, Pres & CEO)*
Daniel T. Voelpel *(CFO & Sr VP)*
Kim McBride *(Coord-Mktg)*

FIRST GUARANTY BANCSHARES, INC.
400 E Thomas St
Hammond, LA 70401
Tel.: (985) 345-7685
Approx. Rev.: $60,955,000
Approx. Number Employees: 246
Business Description:
Bank Holding Company
S.I.C.: 6712
N.A.I.C.S.: 551111
Advertising Expenditures: $400,000
Personnel:
Marshall T. Reynolds *(Chm)*
Michael R. Sharp *(Pres)*
Eric Dosch *(CFO)*

FIRST HORIZON NATIONAL CORPORATION
165 Madison Ave
Memphis, TN 38103-2723
Mailing Address:
PO Box 84
Memphis, TN 38101-0084
Tel.: (901) 523-4444
Fax: (901) 523-4945
Toll Free: (800) 489-4040
Telex: 5-3800
E-mail: InvestorRelations@FirstHorizon.com
Web Site: www.fhnc.com
Approx. Rev.: $18,359,780,000
Approx. Number Employees: 5,435
Year Founded: 1864
Business Description:
Bank Holding Company
S.I.C.: 6712; 6029; 6159
N.A.I.C.S.: 551111; 522110; 522292
Advertising Expenditures: $22,074,000
Media: 2-3-6-7-8-9-10-13-16-18-19-20-22-23-24-25-26
Distr.: Intl.; Natl.
Budget Set: Dec.
Personnel:
Michael D. Rose *(Chm)*
Bryan Jordan *(Pres & CEO)*
Greg Jardine *(Chief Credit Officer)*
James F. Keen *(Exec VP, Principal Acctg Officer & Chief Acctg Officer)*
John M. Daniel *(Chief HR Officer & Exec VP)*
Charles G. Burkett *(Pres-Banking)*
Charles T. Tuggle, Jr. *(Exec VP & Gen Counsel)*
Thomas C. Adams, Jr. *(Exec VP & Treasurer)*
Clyde A. Billings, Jr. *(Corp Sec, Sr VP & Asst Gen Counsel)*
Kim Cherry *(Exec VP-Corp Comm)*
Christine Munson *(Exec VP-Corp Banking)*
Brands & Products:
ALL THINGS FINANCIAL
FIRST HORIZON NATIONAL CORPORATION

FIRST INTERSTATE BANCSYSTEM, INC.
401 N 31st St
Billings, MT 59116-0001
Mailing Address:
PO Box 30918
Billings, MT 59116-0918
Tel.: (406) 255-5390
Tel.: (406) 255-5000
Fax: (406) 255-5350
E-mail: info@firstinterstatebank.com
Web Site: www.firstinterstatebank.com
Approx. Int. Income: $314,546,000
Approx. Number Employees: 1,723
Year Founded: 1968
Business Description:
Bank Holding Company
S.I.C.: 6712; 6029; 6035
N.A.I.C.S.: 551111; 522110; 522120
Advertising Expenditures: $3,200,000
Personnel:
Thomas W. Scott *(Chm)*
James R. Scott *(Vice Chm)*
Lyle R. Knight *(Pres & CEO)*
Terrill R. Moore *(CFO & Exec VP)*
Edward Garding *(COO & Exec VP)*
Robert M. Cerkovnik *(Chief Credit Officer & Sr VP)*
Brands & Products:
FIRST INTERSTATE BANK

FIRST INVESTORS FINANCIAL SERVICES GROUP, INC.
675 Bering Dr Ste 710
Houston, TX 77057-2129
Tel.: (713) 977-2600
Fax: (800) 528-2384
Toll Free: (800) 603-4484
E-mail: customer.service@fifsg.com
Web Site: www.fifsg.com
Approx. Rev.: $48,632,000
Approx. Number Employees: 241
Year Founded: 1988
Business Description:
Indirect Automobile Financing Services
S.I.C.: 6141; 6371
N.A.I.C.S.: 522291; 525990
Import Export
Advertising Expenditures: $2,878,000
Media: 8
Personnel:
Tommy A. Moore, Jr. *(Pres & CEO)*
Bennie H. Duck *(CFO, Treas, Sec & Exec VP)*
Blaise Rodon *(COO & Sr VP)*

FIRST KEYSTONE COMMUNITY BANK
111 W Front St
Berwick, PA 18603
Tel.: (570) 752-3671
Fax: (570) 752-4022
Toll Free: (888) 759-2266
E-mail: info@fkcbank.com
Web Site: www.fkcbank.com
Approx. Rev.: $43,912,000
Approx. Number Employees: 163
Year Founded: 1983
Business Description:
State Commercial Banks
S.I.C.: 6029
N.A.I.C.S.: 522110
Advertising Expenditures: $273,000
Personnel:
John E. Arndt *(Owner-Arndt Insurance Agency)*
Robert E. Bull *(Chm)*
Matthew P. Prosseda *(CEO)*
Diane C.A. Rosler *(CFO)*
John G. Gerlach *(Pres-Pocono Community Bank)*
Barbara Robbins *(Sr VP-Deposit & Mgr-Ops)*

FIRST M&F CORPORATION
134 W Washington St
Kosciusko, MS 39090
Tel.: (662) 289-5121
Fax: (662) 289-8084
Toll Free: (800) 379-5465
E-mail: raven@mfbank.com
Web Site: www.mfbank.com
Approx. Rev.: $92,213,000
Approx. Number Employees: 499
Business Description:
Bank Holding Company
S.I.C.: 6712; 6029
N.A.I.C.S.: 551111; 522110
Advertising Expenditures: $1,136,000
Personnel:
Hugh S. Potts, Jr. *(Chm & CEO)*
Jeffrey B. Lacey *(Pres & Chief Banking Officer-Merchants & Farmers)*
John G. Copeland *(CFO & Exec VP)*
George Broadstreet *(Pres-Clinton)*
Jeff Cousar *(Pres-Oxford)*
Mark Jordan *(Pres-Brandon)*
Clay McWilliams *(Pres-Cleveland)*
Frank Street *(Pres-Canton)*
Michael Crandall *(Exec VP & Mgr-Middle Mississippi Reg)*
Robert K. Autry, Jr. *(Exec VP-Admin)*
Kin Kinney *(Exec VP)*

FIRST MARINER BANCORP
1501 S Clinton St
Baltimore, MD 21224
Tel.: (410) 342-2600
Fax: (410) 563-1594
E-mail: custserv@1stmarinerbank.com
Web Site: www.1stmarinerbank.com
Approx. Rev.: $83,413,000
Approx. Number Employees: 647
Year Founded: 1995
Business Description:
Bank Holding Company
S.I.C.: 6712; 6029
N.A.I.C.S.: 551111; 522110
Advertising Expenditures: $633,000
Personnel:
Edwin F. Hale, Sr. *(Chm & CEO)*
Mark A. Keidel *(Pres & COO)*
Paul B. Susie *(CFO)*
George H. Mantakos *(Exec VP)*
Robert P. Warr *(Sr VP-Commercial Loan Svcs)*

FIRST MARINER BANK
(Sub. of FIRST MARINER BANCORP)
3301 Boston St
Baltimore, MD 21224
Tel.: (410) 342-2600
Fax: (410) 558-4264
Toll Free: (888) 561BANK
E-mail: custserv@1stmarinerbank.com
Web Site: www.1stmarinerbank.com
Sales Range: $100-124.9 Million
Approx. Number Employees: 438
Year Founded: 1995
Business Description:
Commercial Bank
S.I.C.: 6029; 6163
N.A.I.C.S.: 522110; 522310
Advertising Expenditures: $600,000
Media: 7-8-18-20-23-24
Personnel:
Edwin F. Hale, Sr. *(Chm & CEO)*
Daniel E. McKew *(Pres)*
Paul B. Susie *(CFO)*
Mark A. Keidel *(COO & Exec VP)*
Robert P. Warr *(Exec VP & Chief Risk Officer)*

FIRST MERCHANTS CORPORATION
200 E Jackson St
Muncie, IN 47305
Mailing Address:
PO Box 792
Muncie, IN 47305-0792
Tel.: (765) 747-1500
Fax: (765) 747-1473
E-mail: jobs@firstmerchants.com
Web Site: www.firstmerchants.com

Key to Media (For complete agency information see *The Advertising Red Books-Agencies* edition):
1. Bus. Publs. 2. Cable T.V. 3. Catalogs & Directories. 4. Co-op Adv. 5. Consumer Mags. 6. D.M. to Bus. Estab.7. D.M. to Consumers
8. Daily Newsp. 9. Exhibits/Trade Shows 10. Foreign 11. Infomercial 12. Internet Adv.13. Multimedia 14. Network Radio
15. Network T.V. 16. Newsp. Distr. Mags. 17. Other 18. Outdoor (Posters, Transit) 19. Point of Purchase20. Premiums, Novelties
21. Product Samples 22. Special Events Mktg. 23. Spot Radio 24. Spot T.V. 25. Weekly Newsp. 26. Yellow Page Adv.

First Merchants Corporation — (Continued)

Approx. Rev.: $248,122,000
Approx. Number Employees: 1,178
Year Founded: 1982
Business Description:
Bank Holding Company
S.I.C.: 6712
N.A.I.C.S.: 551111
Advertising Expenditures: $1,797,000
Personnel:
Charles E. Schalliol *(Chm)*
Michael C. Rechin *(Pres & CEO)*
Mark K. Hardwick *(CFO & Exec VP)*
David W. Spade *(Chief Credit Officer & Sr VP)*
Jami L. Bradshaw *(Chief Acctg Officer & Sr VP)*
Michael J. Stewart *(Chief Banking Officer & Exec VP)*
Kimberly J. Ellington *(Sr VP & Dir-HR)*
Robert R. Connors *(Sr VP-Ops & Tech)*
Cynthia G. Holaday *(VP-Shareholder Rels)*

FIRST MIDWEST BANCORP INC.

1 Pierce Pl Ste 1500
Itasca, IL 60143
Tel.: (630) 875-7450
Fax: (630) 875-7369
Toll Free: (800) 322-3623
E-mail: investor.relations@firstmidwest.com
Web Site: www.firstmidwest.com
Approx. Int. Income: $328,867,000
Approx. Number Employees: 1,820
Year Founded: 1982
Business Description:
Bank Holding Company
S.I.C.: 6712; 6029; 6035; 6163; 6211; 6321
N.A.I.C.S.: 551111; 522110; 522120; 522310; 523110; 524130
Advertising Expenditures: $7,313,000
Media: 9-20-25-26
Personnel:
Robert P. O'Meara *(Chm)*
Michael L. Scudder *(Pres & CEO)*
Paul F. Clemens *(CFO)*
Cynthia A. Lance *(Corp Sec & Exec VP)*

FIRST MUTUAL BANK

(Div. of Washington Federal Savings Bank, Inc.)
400 108th Ave NE
Bellevue, WA 98004-5562
Tel.: (425) 455-7300
Fax: (425) 455-7330
Toll Free: (800) 735-7303
E-mail: webmaster@firstmutual.com
Web Site: www.firstmutual.com
Sales Range: $25-49.9 Million
Approx. Number Employees: 164
Year Founded: 1953
Business Description:
Stock Savings Bank
S.I.C.: 6029
N.A.I.C.S.: 522110
Advertising Expenditures: $1,000,000
Media: 7-8-10-13-18-20-22-23-26
Personnel:
Victor Mizumori *(VP & Mgr-Community Bus Banking)*
Advertising Agency:
Vander Houwen Public Relations, Inc.
8575 SE 76th Pl
Mercer Island, WA 98040
Tel.: (206) 236-6300
Fax: (206) 236-1715

FIRST NATIONAL COMMUNITY BANCORP, INC.

102 E Drinker St
Dunmore, PA 18512
Tel.: (570) 346-7667
Fax: (570) 348-6426
E-mail: fncb@fncb.com
Web Site: www.fncb.com
Approx. Rev.: $66,737,000
Approx. Number Employees: 271
Year Founded: 1997
Business Description:
Bank Holding Company
S.I.C.: 6029; 6712
N.A.I.C.S.: 522110; 551111
Import Export
Advertising Expenditures: $713,000
Personnel:
Dominick L. DeNaples *(Vice Chm)*
Gerard A. Champi *(Interim Pres & CEO)*
Edward J. Lipkus III *(CFO & Exec VP)*
James M. Bone, Jr. *(CIO & Exec VP)*
Robert J. Mancuso *(Chief Admin Officer & First Sr VP)*
Sandra E. Laughlin *(Chief Risk Officer & Exec VP)*
William E. Keating *(Asst VP & Officer-Comml)*
Thomas P. Tulaney *(Sr Exec VP & Mgr-Corp Sls Div)*
Patrick J. Barrett *(Sr VP & Mgr-Comml Lending)*
Cathy J. Conrad *(Sr VP & Mgr-Credit Admin)*
Jonathan T. Grande *(Sr VP & Mgr-Asset Recovery)*
Richard F. Post, Jr. *(Sr VP & Mgr-Loan Review Div)*
Joe Earys *(Sr VP-Credit & Branch Admin)*
Lisa L. Kinney *(Sr VP & Retail Lending Officer)*
Donna M. Czerw *(VP & Mgr-Retail Ops)*
Paul S. Dunda *(VP & Mgr-Info Svcs)*
Thomas C. Lunney *(VP & Mgr-Property)*
Eileen R. Farber-Bonk *(Asst VP & Reg Mgr)*
Madolyn A. MacArthur *(Asst VP & Reg Mgr)*
Marilyn K. Dolphin *(Asst VP & Mgr-Community Office)*
Christine A. Gresh *(Asst VP & Mgr-Community Office)*
Bernice A. Shipp *(Asst VP & Mgr-Community Office)*
Jason A. Bohenek *(Asst VP & Supvr-Acctg)*
Michael J. Germano, III *(Asst VP & Special Assets Officer)*
Richard D. Padula *(Asst VP-Mortgage Loan Originator)*
Lucy E. Singer *(Asst VP & Grp Mgr)*
Germaine T. Helcoski *(Asst Auditor)*
Joseph P. Stupak *(Auditor-Internal)*
Advertising Agency:
DeLuca Frigoletto Advertising, Inc.
108 N Washington Ave
Scranton, PA 18503
Tel.: (570) 344-8339
Fax: (570) 344-8345

FIRST NATIONAL CORPORATION

112 W King St
Strasburg, VA 22657
Tel.: (540) 465-9121
Fax: (540) 465-5946
E-mail: info@firstbank-va.com
Web Site: www.therspowerinone.com
Approx. Rev.: $33,278,000
Approx. Number Employees: 155
Business Description:
Bank Holding Company
S.I.C.: 6029
N.A.I.C.S.: 522110
Advertising Expenditures: $398,000
Personnel:
Douglas C. Arthur *(Chm)*
Byron A. Brill *(Vice Chm)*
Scott C. Harvard *(Pres & CEO)*
M. Shane Bell *(CFO & Exec VP)*
Dennis A. Dysart *(COO & Exec VP)*
Marshall J. Beverley Jr. *(Exec VP & Sr Trust Officer)*

FIRST NATIONWIDE LENDING, INC.

1990 Main St Ste 750
Sarasota, FL 34236
Tel.: (941) 256-3729
Fax: (941) 847-0658
Toll Free: (866) 446-0053
E-mail: info@mynationwidelending.com
Web Site: www.mynationwidelending.com
Business Description:
Correspondent Lending Services
S.I.C.: 6099
N.A.I.C.S.: 522320
Advertising Expenditures: $200,000
Media: 13
Personnel:
John King *(Pres & CEO)*

FIRST NIAGARA BANK

(Holding of FIRST NIAGARA FINANCIAL GROUP, INC.)
6950 S Transit Rd
Lockport, NY 14094
Mailing Address:
PO Box 514
Lockport, NY 14095-0514
Tel.: (716) 625-7500
Fax: (716) 625-8681
Toll Free: (800) 421-0004
Web Site: www.fnfg.com
Sales Range: $10-24.9 Million
Year Founded: 1870
Business Description:
Savings, Investment, Loan & Commercial Banking & Insurance Services
S.I.C.: 6035; 6029; 6163; 6211; 6289; 6331; 6371; 6411
N.A.I.C.S.: 522120; 522110; 522310; 523110; 523999; 524210; 524292; 524298; 525190
Advertising Expenditures: $1,500,000
Media: 2-7-8-10-13-21-22
Personnel:
John R. Koelmel *(Pres & CEO)*
Michael W. Harrington *(CFO)*
Elizabeth A. Bauman *(Chief Admin Officer)*
John Mineo *(Chief Risk Officer, Gen Counsel, Sec & Sr VP)*
G. Gary Berner *(Exec VP)*
Daniel E. Cantara, III *(Reg Pres-WNY & Exec VP-Comml Bus)*
Frank J. Polino *(Exec VP-Ops)*
Daniel A. Dintino, Jr. *(Sr VP)*
Annette M. Kajtoch *(Sr VP-Consumer Banking)*
Kevin M. O'Bryan *(Sr VP-Credit Admin)*
Michael Wydysh *(VP-Bus Banking Relationship)*
Brands & Products:
OUR FIRST PRIORITY IS YOU
Advertising Agency:
Eric Mower and Associates
211 West Jefferson St.
Syracuse, NY 13202
Tel.: (315) 466-1000
Fax: (315) 466-2000

FIRST NIAGARA BANK

(Formerly NewAlliance Bancshares, Inc.)
(Holding of FIRST NIAGARA FINANCIAL GROUP, INC.)
195 Church St
New Haven, CT 06510-2009
Tel.: (203) 784-5000
Fax: (203) 789-2812
Approx. Rev.: $411,973,000
Approx. Number Employees: 951
Year Founded: 2003
Business Description:
Bank Holding Company
S.I.C.: 6712; 6029; 6035
N.A.I.C.S.: 551111; 522110; 522120
Advertising Expenditures: $4,584,000
Media: 2-3-6-7-8-9-18-20-23-24-25-26
Distr.: Reg.
Budget Set: Feb.
Personnel:
Peyton R. Patterson *(Chm, Pres & CEO)*
Cecil Eugene Kirby, Jr. *(Pres & Exec VP)*
Glenn I. MacInnes *(CFO & Exec VP)*
Gail E. D. Brathwaite *(COO & Exec VP)*
Donald T. Chaffee *(Exec VP & Chief Credit Officer)*
Koon-Ping Chan *(Chief Risk Officer & Exec VP)*
Mark F. Doyle *(Chief Acctg Officer)*
Paul A. Mccraven *(Sr VP)*
David Deonarine *(Mgr-Bus Dev & Asst-VP)*
Don Schmitt *(Asst VP & Mgr-Relationship)*
Susan Swain *(Asst VP)*
Mike Kaczorowski *(Mgr-Relationship)*

FIRST NIAGARA FINANCIAL GROUP, INC.

726 Exchange St Ste 618
Buffalo, NY 14210
Tel.: (716) 819-5500
Fax: (716) 625-8681
Toll Free: (800) 421-0004
Toll Free: (800) 201-6621
E-mail: leslie.garrity@fnfg.com
Web Site: www.fnfg.com
Approx. Rev.: $932,203,000
Approx. Number Employees: 3,791
Year Founded: 1998

Key to Media (For complete agency information see *The Advertising Red Books-Agencies* edition):
1. Bus. Publs. 2. Cable T.V. 3. Catalogs & Directories. 4. Co-op Adv. 5. Consumer Mags. 6. D.M. to Bus. Estab.7. D.M. to Consumers
8. Daily Newsp. 9. Exhibits/Trade Shows 10. Foreign 11. Infomercial 12. Internet Adv.13. Multimedia 14. Network Radio
15. Network T.V. 16. Newsp. Distr. Mags. 17. Other 18. Outdoor (Posters, Transit) 19. Point of Purchase20. Premiums, Novelties
21. Product Samples 22. Special Events Mktg. 23. Spot Radio 24. Spot T.V. 25. Weekly Newsp. 26. Yellow Page Adv.

Business Description:
Bank Holding Company
S.I.C.: 6712; 6029; 6035; 6163; 6211; 6289; 6371; 6411
N.A.I.C.S.: 551111; 522110; 522120; 522310; 523110; 523999; 524210; 524292; 524298
Advertising Expenditures: $10,281,000
Personnel:
G. Thomas Bowers *(Chm)*
David M. Zebro *(Vice Chm)*
John R. Koelmel *(Pres & CEO)*
Gregory W. Norwood *(CFO)*
Gray M. Crosby *(COO & Exec VP)*
John Petrey *(CIO)*
Michael W. Harrington *(Chief Investment Officer & Treas)*
Elizabeth A. Bauman *(Chief Admin Officer)*
Daniel E. Cantara, III *(Exec VP-Comml Bus & Reg Pres-WNY)*
Robert Kane *(Pres-Market-Eastern Pennsylvania Bus)*
John Mineo *(Gen Counsel, Sec & Sr VP-Corp Risk Mgmt)*
Frank J. Polino *(Exec VP-Ops)*
Oliver Sommer *(Exec VP-Corp Dev)*
David Lanzillo *(Sr VP & Sr Dir-Corp Comm)*
Ram Shankar *(Sr VP & Sr Dir-IR)*
Thomas Fontana *(Sr VP & Reg Mgr-Sls-Retail Banking-Western Pennsylvania)*
Scott Fisher *(Sr VP & Mgr-Retail Admin)*
Mark Rendulic *(Sr VP-Retail Banking)*
Leslie G. Garrity *(First VP-Corp Affairs)*
Kirstin L. Benwitz *(Asst VP & Mgr-Branch)*
Bobby Huddleston *(Reg Mgr-Sls & Investments)*
Brands & Products:
BUSINESSWISE
FIRSTNIAGARA
GET BACK TO BASICS
MONEYPRO
ULTRA FLEX HOME EQUITY
Advertising Agencies:
Jay Advertising, Inc.
(A Subsidiary of The Interpublic Group of Companies)
170 Linden Oaks
Rochester, NY 14625-2836
Tel.: (585) 264-3600
Fax: (585) 264-3650
Toll Free: (800) 836-6800

Travers Collins & Company
726 Exchange St Ste 500
Buffalo, NY 14210-1495
Tel.: (716) 842-2222
Fax: (716) 842-6424

FIRST PACTRUST BANCORP, INC.
610 Bay Blvd
Chula Vista, CA 91910
Mailing Address:
PO Box 227
Chula Vista, CA 91912
Tel.: (619) 691-1519
Fax: (619) 691-1350
Toll Free: (877) 411-2265
E-mail: FPTB@pacifictrustbank.com
Web Site: www.firstpactrustbancorp.com
Approx. Rev.: $40,944,000
Approx. Number Employees: 95
Year Founded: 2002
Business Description:
Bank Holding Company
S.I.C.: 6712; 6029
N.A.I.C.S.: 551111; 522110
Advertising Expenditures: $232,000
Media: 17
Personnel:
Alvin L. Majors *(Chm)*
Gregory A. Mitchell *(Pres & CEO)*
Marangal Domingo *(CFO & Exec VP)*
Melanie M. Stewart *(Exec VP-Lending)*
Regan J. Lauer *(Sr VP & Controller)*
Lisa R. Goodwin *(Sr VP-Info Sys)*
Violeta Trajano *(VP & Mgr-Acctg)*
Sandra Guerra *(VP-Training & Coord)*
Lisa Moss *(VP-HR & Bank Security Officer)*
Brands & Products:
FIRST PACTRUST

FIRST PLACE FINANCIAL CORP.
185 E Market St
Warren, OH 44481
Mailing Address:
PO Box 551
Warren, MI 44482-0551
Tel.: (330) 373-1221
Fax: (330) 393-5578
E-mail: investor.relations@fpfc.net
Web Site: www.firstplacebank.com
Approx. Rev.: $206,591,000
Approx. Number Employees: 839
Year Founded: 1998
Business Description:
Bank Holding Company
S.I.C.: 6712; 6029; 6035
N.A.I.C.S.: 551111; 522110; 522120
Advertising Expenditures: $2,005,000
Media: 9-20-23-25
Personnel:
Samuel A. Roth *(Chm)*
Steven R. Lewis *(Pres & CEO)*
David W. Gifford *(CFO & Corp Exec VP)*
Albert P. Blank *(Pres/COO-First Place Bank)*
Brian E. Hoopes *(CIO & Corp Exec VP)*
Dominique K. Stoeber *(Chief Retail Officer)*
J. Craig Carr *(Gen Counsel, Sec & Corp Exec VP)*
Robert J. Kowalski *(Exec VP-HR)*
R. Bruce Wenmoth *(Exec VP-Lending)*
Brands & Products:
ALL UNDER ONE ROOF
FIRST PLACE

FIRST PREMIER BANK
(Sub. of United National Corporation)
601 S Minnesota Ave
Sioux Falls, SD 57104
Tel.: (605) 357-3000
Fax: (605) 357-3180
Web Site: www.firstpremier.com
Approx. Int. Income: $50,923,000
Approx. Number Employees: 192
Business Description:
Commercial Banking Services
S.I.C.: 6029
N.A.I.C.S.: 522110
Media: 2-6
Personnel:
Dana J. Dykhouse *(Pres & CEO)*
Darrell Schmith *(CFO)*
Bill O'Connor *(VP)*
Katie Kennett *(Mgr-Treasury Svcs)*

FIRST REAL ESTATE INVESTMENT TRUST NEW JERSEY CO.
505 Main St
Hackensack, NJ 07601
Tel.: (201) 487-1500
Fax: (201) 487-7881
Approx. Rev.: $44,053,000
Approx. Number Employees: 22
Business Description:
Real Estate Investment Trust; Shopping Center, Property Operation
S.I.C.: 6798; 6512; 6513
N.A.I.C.S.: 525930; 531110; 531120
Advertising Expenditures: $163,000
Media: 17
Personnel:
Robert S. Hekemian, Jr. *(Chm & CEO)*
Donald W. Barney *(Pres, CFO & Treas)*
Alan Tubin *(CFO)*

FIRST ROBINSON FINANCIAL CORPORATION
501 E Main St
Robinson, IL 62454
Tel.: (618) 544-8621
Fax: (618) 544-7506
Web Site: www.frsb.net
Approx. Rev.: $10,878,000
Approx. Number Employees: 54
Business Description:
Bank Holding Company
S.I.C.: 6712
N.A.I.C.S.: 551111
Advertising Expenditures: $258,000
Personnel:
Rick L. Catt *(Pres & CEO)*
Jamie E. McReynolds *(CFo, Sec & VP)*

FIRST SAVINGS FINANCIAL GROUP INC.
501 E Lewis & Clark Pkwy
Clarksville, IN 47129
Tel.: (812) 283-0724
Web Site: www.fsbbank.net/ASP/home.asp
Approx. Rev.: $29,178,000
Approx. Number Employees: 130
Business Description:
Bank Holding Company
S.I.C.: 6712
N.A.I.C.S.: 551111
Advertising Expenditures: $360,000
Media: 17
Personnel:
Michael F. Ludden *(Chm)*
Larry W. Myers *(Pres & CEO)*
John P. Lawson, Jr. *(COO)*

FIRST SECURITY BANCORP INC.
314 N Spring St
Searcy, AR 72143
Tel.: (501) 279-3400
Fax: (501) 279-3455
Web Site: www.fsbank.com
Approx. Number Employees: 41
Year Founded: 1980
Business Description:
Bank Holding Company
S.I.C.: 6712
N.A.I.C.S.: 551111
Import Export
Advertising Expenditures: $208,000
Media: 7-8
Personnel:
Reynie Rutledge *(Pres & CEO)*

FIRST SECURITY GROUP, INC.
531 Broad St
Chattanooga, TN 37402-2613
Tel.: (423) 308-2000
Tel.: (423) 266-2000
Fax: (423) 308-2015
Fax: (423) 308-2081
E-mail: clusk@fsgbank.com
Web Site: www.fsgbank.com
Approx. Rev.: $64,419,000
Approx. Number Employees: 302
Year Founded: 1999
Business Description:
Bank Holding Company
S.I.C.: 6712; 6029
N.A.I.C.S.: 551111; 522110
Advertising Expenditures: $155,000
Media: 17
Personnel:
Ralph E. Coffman, Jr. *(Interim Chm, Pres, Interim CEO & COO)*
Debbie Frank *(Trust Ops Officer)*
Sandy Chambers *(Sr VP-Wealth Mgmt)*
Deborah Blue *(Dir-HR)*
Frank Lewis *(Mgr-Portfolio)*

FIRST SOUTH BANCORP, INC.
1311 Carolina Ave
Washington, NC 27883
Mailing Address:
PO Box 2047
Washington, NC 27889
Tel.: (252) 946-4178
Fax: (252) 946-3873
E-mail: info@firstsouthnc.com
Web Site: www.firstsouthnc.com
Approx. Rev.: $53,714,907
Approx. Number Employees: 268
Year Founded: 1902
Business Description:
Bank Holding Company
S.I.C.: 6035; 6029
N.A.I.C.S.: 522120; 522110
Advertising Expenditures: $148,380
Media: 17
Personnel:
Frederick N. Holscher *(Chm)*
Marshall T. Singleton *(Vice Chm)*
Thomas A. Vann *(Pres & CEO)*
William L. Wall *(CFO, Sec & Exec VP)*
J. Randy Woodson *(COO & Exec VP-First South Bank)*
Larry W. Mallard *(COO)*
Lori Rozier *(Asst Sec, Asst VP & Officer-Mortgage)*
Mary Boyd *(Exec VP-Mortgage Loan Servicing)*
Sherry L. Correll *(Exec VP-Bank Ops)*
James W. Hoose Jr. *(Exec VP)*
Paul S. Jaber *(Exec VP-Mortage Lending)*
Joseph M. Johnson *(Sr VP)*
Dennis A. Nichols *(Sr VP & Area Exec-Neuse Reg)*
Robert C. Pfeiffer *(Sr VP)*

Key to Media (For complete agency information see *The Advertising Red Books-Agencies* edition):
1. Bus. Publs. 2. Cable T.V. 3. Catalogs & Directories. 4. Co-op Adv. 5. Consumer Mags. 6. D.M. to Bus. Estab.7. D.M. to Consumers
8. Daily Newsp. 9. Exhibits/Trade Shows 10. Foreign 11. Infomercial 12. Internet Adv.13. Multimedia 14. Network Radio
15. Network T.V. 16. Newsp. Distr. Mags. 17. Other 18. Outdoor (Posters, Transit) 19. Point of Purchase20. Premiums, Novelties
21. Product Samples 22. Special Events Mktg. 23. Spot Radio 24. Spot T.V. 25. Weekly Newsp. 26. Yellow Page Adv.

FIRST STATE BANCORPORATION
7900 Jefferson St NE
Albuquerque, NM 87109
Tel.: (505) 241-7500
Fax: (505) 241-7606
E-mail: banker@fcbnm.com
Web Site: www.fsbnm.com
Approx. Rev.: $195,924,000
Approx. Number Employees: 542
Year Founded: 1988
Business Description:
Bank Holding Company
S.I.C.: 6029; 6712
N.A.I.C.S.: 522110; 551111
Advertising Expenditures: $3,000,000
Media: 7-8
Personnel:
H. Patrick Dee *(Pres & CEO)*
Christopher C. Spencer *(CFO & Sr VP)*
Jed Fanning *(Exec VP & Chief Credit Officer)*
Marshall G. Martin *(Sec, Counsel & Exec VP)*
Thomas E. Bajusz *(Sr VP)*
Theresa A. Gabel *(Sr VP-HR & Inter Comm)*
Bobby Nafus *(Sr VP-Const Loans & Retail & Mortgage Lending)*
James E. Warden *(Sr VP-Branch Admin & Retail Svcs)*
Marie Alvarez *(VP & Mgr-Relationship)*
Bernadette Trujillo *(VP & Mgr)*
Wendy Harris *(VP-HR)*
Christie White *(VP-Audit & Compliance)*
Jacob Armijo *(Gen Mgr & Dir-Program)*

FIRST TENNESSEE BANK, N.A.
(Holding of FIRST HORIZON NATIONAL CORPORATION)
165 Madison Ave Fl 13
Memphis, TN 38103-2723
Mailing Address:
PO Box 84
Memphis, TN 38101-0084
Tel.: (901) 523-4444
Web Site: www.ftb.com
Sales Range: $800-899.9 Million
Year Founded: 1864
Business Description:
Savings, Loans & Commercial Banking Services
S.I.C.: 6029; 6035; 6159; 6163
N.A.I.C.S.: 522110; 522120; 522292; 522310
Personnel:
Michael D. Rose *(Chm)*
Charles Burkett *(Pres & CEO)*
Marlin L. Mosby, III *(CFO & Exec VP)*
John P. O'Connor, Jr. *(Exec VP & Chief Credit Officer)*
James F. Keen *(Exce VP, Principal Acctg Officer & Chief Accounting Officer)*
Peter F. Makowiecki *(Pres-Mortgage Banking)*
Harry A. Johnson, III *(Gen Counsel & Exec VP)*
John M. Daniel *(Exec VP-HR-First Horizon)*
Herbert H. Hilliard *(Exec VP-Govt Rels, CRA & Risk Mgmt)*
Thomas C. Owens *(Sr VP & Mgr-Comml Real Estate Market-East Tennessee)*
Dan Billingsley *(VP & Mgr-Portfolio)*
John Cantrell *(VP & Mgr-Relationship-Comml Real Estate Div)*
Jennifer B. Hyers *(VP & Relationship Mgr)*
Heather McKinney *(VP & Mgr-Relationship-Private Client Svcs Div)*
Drew Rodgers *(VP)*
Matt Synowiez *(Mgr-Comml Relationship-Comml Banking Div)*
Derrick Williams *(Mgr)*
Advertising Agency:
Thompson & Company Marketing Communications
50 Peabody Pl
Memphis, TN 38103-3667
Tel.: (901) 527-8000
Fax: (901) 527-3697

FIRST WEST VIRGINIA BANCORP, INC.
1701 Warwood Ave
Wheeling, WV 26003
Mailing Address:
PO Box 4075
Wheeling, WV 26003-0417
Tel.: (304) 277-1100
Fax: (304) 277-4705
E-mail: infosupport@progbank.com
Web Site: www.progbank.com
Approx. Rev.: $13,834,477
Approx. Number Employees: 96
Business Description:
Bank Holding Company
S.I.C.: 6029
N.A.I.C.S.: 522110
Advertising Expenditures: $88,932
Media: 8-9-24-25
Personnel:
Sylvan J. Dlesk *(Chm, Pres & CEO)*
Francie P. Reppy *(CFO, Chief Admin Officer, Treas & Exec VP)*
Brad D. Winwood *(COO, Chief Investment Officer & VP)*

FIRST WESTERN BANK & TRUST
900 S Broadway
Minot, ND 58701
Tel.: (701) 852-3711
Fax: (701) 857-7212
E-mail: info@fwbt.com
Web Site: www.bankfirstwestern.com
Sales Range: $50-74.9 Million
Approx. Number Employees: 75
Business Description:
Bank & Lending Institution
S.I.C.: 6029
N.A.I.C.S.: 522110
Personnel:
J. H. Hoeven *(Chm)*
Laurie Johnson *(Trust Ops Officer)*
Dee Johnson-Balentine *(Mktg Officer & HR Officer)*
Rich Campbell *(Chief Lending Officer & Exec VP)*
JoAnn Holtz *(Sr VP)*
Gordy Knudsvig *(Sr VP-Leasing)*
Dave Kuschel *(Sr VP-Comml Lending)*
Chris Lamoureux *(Sr VP & Trust Officer)*
Pam Aschenbrenner *(Asst VP)*
Chad Howard *(Mgr-Sys & Network)*
Advertising Agency:
Odney
1400 W Century Ave
Bismarck, ND 58503
Tel.: (701) 222-8721
Fax: (701) 222-8172
Toll Free: (888) 500-8721

FIRSTBANK CORPORATION
311 Woodworth Ave
Alma, MI 48801
Tel.: (989) 463-3131
Fax: (989) 466-2042
Web Site: www.firstbank-corp.com
Approx. Rev.: $84,211,000
Approx. Number Employees: 435
Year Founded: 1985
Business Description:
Bank Holding Company
S.I.C.: 6712; 6029
N.A.I.C.S.: 551111; 522110
Advertising Expenditures: $1,684,000
Personnel:
William E. Goggin *(Chm)*
Samuel G. Stone *(CFO & Exec VP)*
Christopher T. Holmes *(Sr VP)*

FIRSTBANK HOLDING COMPANY OF COLORADO, INC.
12345 W Colfax Ave
Lakewood, CO 80215
Tel.: (303) 232-3000
Fax: (303) 235-1047
E-mail: info@efirstbank.com
Web Site: www.efirstbank.com
Approx. Number Employees: 1,300
Year Founded: 1963
Business Description:
Holding Company
S.I.C.: 6035
N.A.I.C.S.: 522120
Import Export
Personnel:
Brian Jensen *(Sr VP-Mktg)*
Advertising Agency:
TDA Advertising & Design
1500 Pearl St Ste 300
Boulder, CO 80302
Tel.: (303) 247-1180
Fax: (303) 247-1214

FIRSTMERIT CORPORATION
3 Cascade Plz 7th Fl
Akron, OH 44308-1103
Tel.: (330) 996-6300
Fax: (330) 384-7133
Web Site: www.firstmerit.com
Approx. Rev.: $754,926,000
Approx. Number Employees: 3,058
Year Founded: 1981
Business Description:
Bank Holding Company
S.I.C.: 6712; 6035
N.A.I.C.S.: 551111; 522120
Advertising Expenditures: $9,581,000
Media: 7-8
Personnel:
Paul G. Greig *(Chm, Pres & CEO)*
Terrence E. Bichsel *(CFO & Exec VP)*
William P. Richgels *(Chief Credit Officer & Exec VP)*
Larry A. Shoff *(CTO & Exec VP)*
Mark N. DuHamel *(Treas & Exec VP)*
N. James Brocklehurst *(Exec VP-Retail Banking)*
Terri L. Cable *(Exec VP)*
Timothy A. Cahill *(Exec VP)*
Kenneth A. Dorsett *(Exec VP-Wealth Mgmt Svcs)*
David G. Goodall *(Exec VP-Comml Banking)*
Jack R. Gravo *(Exec VP)*
Christopher J. Maurer *(Exec VP-HR)*
Terry E. Patton *(Exec VP-Risk Mgmt)*
Judith A. Steiner *(Exec VP-Risk Mgmt)*
Mark Cicchinelli *(Sr VP & Mng DirCustomer Contact Center)*
Douglas Douglas K. Winget *(Sr VP & Group Head-FirstMerit Bank Bus Credit-FirstMerit Bank)*
Robert S. Jacob *(Sr VP-Admin)*
Mark Mosley *(Sr VP)*
Lucia Pileggi *(Sr VP-FirstMerit Bank)*
Eric Thompson *(Sr VP)*
Dina Anzevino *(Mgr-Wealth-FirstMerit Bank)*
Brands & Products:
FIRSTMERIT
Advertising Agency:
WhiteSpace Creative
24 N High St Ste 200
Akron, OH 44308
Tel.: (330) 762-9320
Fax: (330) 763-9323

FIRSTRADE SECURITIES, INC.
13325 37th Ave
Flushing, NY 11354
Tel.: (718) 961-6600
Fax: (718) 961-3919
E-mail: service@firstrade.com
Web Site: www.firstrade.com
Approx. Rev.: $2,100,000
Approx. Number Employees: 25
Year Founded: 1985
Business Description:
Security Brokers & Dealers
S.I.C.: 6211
N.A.I.C.S.: 523120
Personnel:
John Liu *(Chm & CEO)*
Advertising Agency:
SendTraffic.com, Inc.
450 7th Ave
New York, NY 10123
Tel.: (212) 273-1141
Fax: (845) 215-0101
Toll Free: (866) 487-2334

FIRSTRUST SAVINGS BANK
15 E Rdg Pike Ste 400
Conshohocken, PA 19428
Tel.: (610) 238-5000
Fax: (610) 238-5061
Toll Free: (800) 222-2265
E-mail: info@firstrust.com
Web Site: www.firstrust.com
Sales Range: $100-124.9 Million
Approx. Number Employees: 350
Year Founded: 1934
Business Description:
Financial Institution; Banking Services
S.I.C.: 6035; 6029
N.A.I.C.S.: 522120; 522110
Media: 8-18
Personnel:
Daniel B. Green *(Chm)*
Richard J. Green *(Vice Chm & CEO)*
Timothy J. Abell *(Pres & COO)*
Peter Nolan *(CFO & Sr VP)*
Joseph F. Mikotaitis *(Gen Counsel & Exec VP)*
Gayle Dietrich *(Sr Retail Product Mgr)*
Brands & Products:
FIRSTPAY
FIRSTRUST
FIRSTSAVER
FIRSTSITE
READYDEPOSIT

Key to Media (For complete agency information see *The Advertising Red Books-Agencies* edition):
1. Bus. Publs. 2. Cable T.V. 3. Catalogs & Directories. 4. Co-op Adv. 5. Consumer Mags. 6. D.M. to Bus. Estab.7. D.M. to Consumers 8. Daily Newsp. 9. Exhibits/Trade Shows 10. Foreign 11. Infomercial 12. Internet Adv.13. Multimedia 14. Network Radio 15. Network T.V. 16. Newsp. Distr. Mags. 17. Other 18. Outdoor (Posters, Transit) 19. Point of Purchase20. Premiums, Novelties 21. Product Samples 22. Special Events Mktg. 23. Spot Radio 24. Spot T.V. 25. Weekly Newsp. 26. Yellow Page Adv.

Advertising Agency:
Mangos
10 Great Valley Pkwy
Malvern, PA 19355-1316
Tel.: (610) 296-2555
Fax: (610) 640-9291
Agency of Record

FISERV, INC.
(Formerly CheckFree Corporation)
(Sub. of Fiserv, Inc.)
4411 E Jones Bridge Rd
Norcross, GA 30092-1615
Tel.: (678) 375-3000
Web Site: www.fiserv.com
E-Mail For Key Personnel:
Public Relations: jdwicks@checkfree.com
Sales Range: $900-999.9 Million
Approx. Number Employees: 4,300
Year Founded: 1981
Business Description:
Electronic Commerce Processing Services & Software Products
S.I.C.: 7374
N.A.I.C.S.: 518210
Export
Advertising Expenditures: $5,800,000
Media: 2-6-10-13-14-15-21
Personnel:
Andy Freundlich *(Sr VP-Strategic Bus Dev)*
Jay Pila *(Sr VP-Sls & Investment Svcs)*
Judy DeRango Wicks *(VP-Corp Comm)*
Wade Coleman *(Dir-Global Comm)*
Ann S. Cave *(Sr Mgr-PR-Digital Channels & Electronic Payments)*
Julie Keaton *(Mgr-Pub Rel)*
Advertising Agencies:
Atomic Fusion
1350 Spring St NW Ste 475
Atlanta, GA 30309
Tel.: (404) 897-1920
Fax: (404) 897-1923

Schwartz Communications, Inc.
230 3rd Ave
Waltham, MA 02451
Tel.: (781) 684-0770
Fax: (781) 684-6500
Pub Rels

FISERV LENDING SOLUTIONS
(Sub. of Fiserv, Inc.)
707 Grant St Ste 300
Pittsburgh, PA 15219
Tel.: (412) 261-4791
Web Site: www.orders.fiservls.com
Sales Range: $300-349.9 Million
Approx. Number Employees: 250
Business Description:
Mortgage Industry Technology Solutions
S.I.C.: 6541; 6531
N.A.I.C.S.: 541191; 531320
Media: 7-8

FLAGSTAR BANCORP, INC.
(Holding of MatlinPatterson Global Advisers LLC)
5151 Corporate Dr
Troy, MI 48098-2639
Tel.: (248) 312-2000
Fax: (248) 312-6833
Toll Free: (800) 642-0039
E-mail: investors@flagstar.com
Web Site: www.flagstar.com
Approx. Rev.: $951,417,000
Approx. Number Employees: 3,279
Business Description:
Bank Holding Company
S.I.C.: 6712; 6035
N.A.I.C.S.: 551111; 522120
Advertising Expenditures: $10,300,000
Personnel:
Joseph P. Campanelli *(Chm, Pres & CEO)*
Paul D. Borja *(CFO)*
Matthew I. Roslin *(Chief Legal Officer & Exec VP)*
Todd McGowan *(Chief Risk Officer & Exec VP)*
Alessandro P. Dinello *(Pres-Retail Banking)*
Marshall Soura *(Exec VP & Dir-Corp Svcs)*
Gregory Lutin *(Exec VP & Natl Sls Mgr)*
Matthew A. Kerin *(Exec VP-Mortgage Banking & Warehouse)*
Salvatore J. Rinaldi *(Exec VP)*
Brands & Products:
FLAGSTAR
THE NEW WAVE IN BANKING
Advertising Agency:
Simons Michelson Zieve, Inc.
900 Wilshire Dr Ste 102
Troy, MI 48084-1634
Tel.: (248) 362-4242
Fax: (248) 362-2014

FLAGSTAR BANK, FSB
(Sub. of Flagstar Bancorp, Inc.)
5151 Corporate Dr
Troy, MI 48098-2639
Tel.: (248) 312-2000
Fax: (248) 238-4729
Toll Free: (800) 945-7700
Web Site: www.flagstar.com
Approx. Number Employees: 2,500
Business Description:
Federal Savings & Loan
S.I.C.: 6035
N.A.I.C.S.: 522120
Personnel:
Paul D. Borja *(CFO)*
Daniel Landers *(Chief Credit Officer & Exec VP)*
Michael Maher *(Chief Acctg Officer & Exec VP)*
Steven J. Issa *(Pres-New England Market, Exec VP & Mng Dir-Comml Banking)*
Michael J. Tierney *(Pres-Midwest Market, Exec VP & Mng Dir-Retail Banking)*
Barbara J. Fischer *(Exec VP & Dir-Bank Ops)*
Alessandro DeNillo *(Exec VP)*
Matthew A. Kerin *(Exec VP-Mortgage Banking & Warehouse)*
Salvatore J. Rinaldi *(Exec VP)*
Advertising Agency:
Simons Michelson Zieve, Inc.
900 Wilshire Dr Ste 102
Troy, MI 48084-1634
Tel.: (248) 362-4242
Fax: (248) 362-2014

FLEETCOR TECHNOLOGIES, INC.
655 Engineering Dr Ste 300
Norcross, GA 30092-2830
Tel.: (770) 449-0479
Fax: (770) 449-3471
Toll Free: (800) 877-9019
E-mail: jobs@fleetcor.com
Web Site: www.fleetcor.com
Approx. Rev.: $433,841,000
Approx. Number Employees: 1,197
Year Founded: 2000
Business Description:
Management Services for Business Fleets; Fuel Card Processing
S.I.C.: 6099; 7389
N.A.I.C.S.: 522320; 488490
Advertising Expenditures: $9,800,000
Personnel:
Ronald F. Clarke *(Chm, Pres & CEO)*
Eric R. Dey *(CFO)*
Van E. Huff *(CIO)*
Benton C. Routh *(CMO & Pres-Petroleum Marketer Private Label Programs Div)*
Timothy J. Downs *(Pres-Corp Lodging Consultants)*
Eric Lind *(Pres-Petroleum Marketer CFN Programs)*
William J. Schmit *(Pres-Major Oil Card Programs)*
Andrew Blazye *(CEO-FleetCor-Europe)*
Sean Bowen *(Gen Counsel & Sr VP)*
Robert P. Brandes *(Exec VP-Global Universal Products)*
Ken Greenway *(Exec VP-Corp Inititaitves)*
Scott C. Ruoff *(Exec VP-Corp Dev)*
H. Steve Smith *(Exec VP-Strategic Partnerships)*
Susan Fischer *(VP-Online & Direct Mktg)*
Brands & Products:
FLEETCOR
THE GLOBAL FLEET CARD COMPANY
Advertising Agency:
Blue Sky Agency
950 Lowery Blvd Ste 30
Atlanta, GA 30318
Tel.: (404) 876-0202
Fax: (404) 876-0212

FLORIDA BANK GROUP, INC.
201 N Franklin St Ste 2800
Tampa, FL 33602
Tel.: (813) 367-5270
Fax: (813) 367-5289
E-mail: customerservice@flbank.com
Web Site: www.flbank.com/
Approx. Rev.: $42,671,000
Approx. Number Employees: 146
Business Description:
Bank Holding Company
S.I.C.: 6712; 6029
N.A.I.C.S.: 551111; 522110
Media: 7-8-9-13-25
Personnel:
Susan Martinez *(Chm, Pres & CEO)*
John R. Garthwaite *(CFO, Chief Investment Officer, Treas & Exec VP)*

FLORIDA COMMUNITY BANKS, INC.
1400 N 15th St
Immokalee, FL 34142
Tel.: (239) 657-3171
Fax: (239) 657-8482
Web Site: www.floridacommunitybank.net
Sales Range: $25-49.9 Million
Approx. Number Employees: 180
Year Founded: 1923
Business Description:
Banking Services
S.I.C.: 6029
N.A.I.C.S.: 522110
Advertising Expenditures: $412,000
Personnel:
Stephen L. Price *(Chm, Pres & CEO)*
Guy W. Harris *(CFO)*
William Strohm *(COO & Sr VP)*
Douglas Buchanan *(Sr VP & Chief Credit Officer)*
Jeffrey S. Bush *(Sr VP-HR)*
Bio V. Soukkay *(VP & Dir-IT)*
Tawanna Concepcion *(VP & Reg Mgr)*
Gary Wrage *(VP-Internal Audit)*
Karen Guthrie *(Asst VP-Bookkeeping)*
Audrey Kinchen *(Asst VP-HR)*
Deborah Rasnake *(Asst VP-Bookkeeping)*
Rhonda Rigsby *(Asst VP-Credit)*
Angela Sealey *(Asst VP-Loans)*
Andy Connell *(Mgr-IT)*

FLORIDA HOUSING FINANCE CORPORATION
227 N Bronough St Ste 5000
Tallahassee, FL 32301-1329
Tel.: (850) 488-4197
Fax: (850) 488-9809
E-mail: info@floridahousing.com
Web Site: www.floridahousing.org
Approx. Rev.: $250,000,000
Approx. Number Employees: 150
Year Founded: 1980
Business Description:
Mortgage Assistance Services
S.I.C.: 6159; 6163
N.A.I.C.S.: 522292; 522310
Media: 22-24
Personnel:
Barb Goltz *(CFO)*
Susan Parks *(CIO)*
Wellington Meffert *(Gen Counsel)*
Stephen P. Auger *(Exec Dir)*

FLUSHING FINANCIAL CORPORATION
1979 Marcus Ave Ste E 140
Lake Success, NY 11042
Mailing Address:
PO Box 540050
Flushing, NY 11354-0050
Tel.: (718) 961-5400
Web Site: www.flushingsavings.com
Approx. Rev.: $237,928,000
Approx. Number Employees: 345
Year Founded: 1994
Business Description:
Bank Holding Company
S.I.C.: 6035; 6163; 6712
N.A.I.C.S.: 522120; 522310; 551111
Advertising Expenditures: $2,300,000
Personnel:
John E. Roe, Sr. *(Chm)*
John R. Buran *(Pres & CEO)*
David W. Fry *(CFO & Exec VP)*
Maria A. Grasso *(COO & Exec VP)*
Francis W. Korzekwinski *(Chief Real Estate Lending Officer & Exec VP)*
Barbara A. Beckmann *(Sr VP & Dir-Ops)*
Brands & Products:
FFIC

Key to Media (For complete agency information see *The Advertising Red Books-Agencies* edition):
1. Bus. Publs. 2. Cable T.V. 3. Catalogs & Directories. 4. Co-op Adv. 5. Consumer Mags. 6. D.M. to Bus. Estab.7. D.M. to Consumers
8. Daily Newsp. 9. Exhibits/Trade Shows 10. Foreign 11. Infomercial 12. Internet Adv.13. Multimedia 14. Network Radio
15. Network T.V. 16. Newsp. Distr. Mags. 17. Other 18. Outdoor (Posters, Transit) 19. Point of Purchase20. Premiums, Novelties
21. Product Samples 22. Special Events Mktg. 23. Spot Radio 24. Spot T.V. 25. Weekly Newsp. 26. Yellow Page Adv.

FLUSHING SAVINGS BANK INC.
(Sub. of Flushing Financial Corporation)
1979 Marcus Ave Ste E 140
Lake Success, NY 11042
Tel.: (718) 961-5400
Fax: (718) 539-1025
E-mail: flushing@aol.com
Web Site: www.flushingsavings.com
Sales Range: $75-99.9 Million
Approx. Number Employees: 243
Year Founded: 1929
Business Description:
Federal Savings Institutions
S.I.C.: 6035; 6163
N.A.I.C.S.: 522120; 522310
Import Export
Media: 2-3-4-6-7-8-9-10-13-14-16-18-20-23-24-25-26
Personnel:
John R. Buran *(Pres & CEO)*
David W. Fry *(CFO & Exec VP)*
Maria A. Grasso *(COO & Exec VP)*
Francis W. Korzekwinski *(Exec VP & Chief Real Estate Lending Officer)*
Henry A. Braun *(Sr VP)*
Chris Y. Hwang *(Sr VP)*
Advertising Agency:
Elser & Aucone, Inc.
521 5th Ave Ste 630
New York, NY 10175
Tel.: (212) 867-3300
Fax: (212) 867-3761
(All Types)

FMR LLC
(d/b/a Fidelity Investments)
82 Devonshire St
Boston, MA 02109-3605
Tel.: (617) 563-7000
Fax: (617) 476-6150
Toll Free: (800) 343-3548
E-mail: fidelitycorporateaffairs@fmr.com
Web Site: www.fidelity.com
Sales Range: $5-14.9 Billion
Approx. Number Employees: 44,000
Year Founded: 1946
Business Description:
Mutual Funds, Life Insurance, Banking, Retirement & Financial Services
S.I.C.: 6289; 6211; 6282; 6371
N.A.I.C.S.: 523999; 523110; 523120; 523920; 523930; 525110
Advertising Expenditures: $87,414,000
Media: 2-3-6-7-8-9-10-14-15-17-23-24-25
Distr.: Natl.
Personnel:
Edward C. Johnson, III *(Chm & CEO)*
Rodger A. Lawson *(Pres)*
Abigail P. Johnson *(Pres-Personal, Workplace & Institutional Svcs)*
Gerard McGraw *(Pres-Fidelity Institutional)*
Ed Orazem *(Pres-Family Office Svcs unit)*
Scott W. Dell'Orfano *(Exec VP & Mgr-Natl Sls-Fidelity Registered Investm)*
Michael E. Wilens *(Dir-Client Mgmt-Retirement Unit)*
Brands & Products:
FIDELITY ADVISOR FUNDS
FIDELITY ANYWHERE
FIDELITY E-LEARNING
FIDELITY NETBENEFITS
Advertising Agency:
Arnold Worldwide
101 Huntington Ave
Boston, MA 02199-7603
Tel.: (617) 587-8000
Fax: (617) 587-8004

F.N.B. CORPORATION
1 FNB Blvd
Hermitage, PA 16148
Tel.: (724) 981-6000
Fax: (724) 983-3309
Toll Free: (888) 555-5455
Web Site: www.fnbcorporation.com
Approx. Rev.: $489,693,000
Approx. Number Employees: 2,241
Year Founded: 1974
Business Description:
Bank Holding Company
S.I.C.: 6712
N.A.I.C.S.: 551111
Advertising Expenditures: $5,300,000
Personnel:
William B. Campbell *(Chm)*
Brian F. Lilly *(Vice Chm & COO)*
Vincent J. Delie, Jr. *(Pres)*
Stephen J. Gurgovits, Sr. *(CEO)*
Vincent J. Calabrese *(CFO)*
James Orie *(Chief Legal Officer)*
Scott D. Free *(Treas & Sr VP)*
Louise Lowrey *(Exec VP)*
Timothy G. Rubritz *(Sr VP & Controller)*

FNB UNITED CORP.
150 S Fayetteville St
Asheboro, NC 27203
Mailing Address:
PO Box 1328
Asheboro, NC 27203
Tel.: (336) 626-8300
Fax: (336) 626-8374
E-mail: mark.severson@myyesbank.com
Web Site: www.myyesbank.com/
Approx. Rev.: $113,824,000
Approx. Number Employees: 426
Year Founded: 1985
Business Description:
Bank Holding Company
S.I.C.: 6029; 6712
N.A.I.C.S.: 522110; 551111
Advertising Expenditures: $2,056,000
Personnel:
Eugene B. Mclaurin, II *(Vice Chm)*
R. Larry Campbell *(Pres & CEO-Interim)*
Mark A. Severson *(Exec VP & Treas)*
Chandalar McMillian *(Asst Sec)*
Brands & Products:
YES YOU CAN. YES WE CAN.

FNBH BANCORP, INC.
101 E Grand River Ave
Howell, MI 48843
Tel.: (517) 546-3150
Fax: (517) 546-6275
E-mail: info@fnbsite.com
Web Site: www.fnbsite.com
Approx. Rev.: $17,781,224
Approx. Number Employees: 85
Year Founded: 1988
Business Description:
Bank Holding Company
S.I.C.: 6029; 6035; 6163; 6211; 6712
N.A.I.C.S.: 522110; 522120; 522310; 523110; 551111
Advertising Expenditures: $27,000
Media: 17
Personnel:
Philip C. Utter *(Chm)*
Stanley B. Dickson, Jr. *(Vice Chm)*
Ronald L. Long *(Pres & CEO)*
Mark J. Huber *(CFO & Sr VP)*
Michael N. Wieclaw *(VP & Credit Officer)*
Dennis P. Gehringer *(Sr VP-Comml Lender)*
Nancy Morgan *(Sr VP-HR)*
Patricia Griffith *(VP & Dir-Ops)*

FONDS DE SOLIDARITE DES TRAVAILLEURS DU QUEBEC
545 E Cremazie St Ste 200
Montreal, QC H2M 2W4, Canada
Tel.: (514) 383-8383
Fax: (514) 383-2502
Web Site: www.fondsftq.com
Approx. Rev.: $255,316,612
Approx. Number Employees: 460
Business Description:
Economic Development Services
S.I.C.: 9611; 6289
N.A.I.C.S.: 926110; 523999
Advertising Expenditures: $4,764,564
Personnel:
Yves Derosby *(Owner)*
Henri Masse *(Chm)*
Yvon Bolduc *(Pres & CEO)*
Janie C. Beique *(VP-Legal Affairs & Corp Sec)*
Gaetan Moirn *(Exec VP Investments)*
Gaetan Morin *(Exec VP-Investments)*
Jacques Bernier *(Sr VP-IT, Telecom & Indus Innovations)*
Denis Leclerc *(Sr VP-Shareholder)*
Michel Pontbriand *(Sr VP-Ends)*
Lucie Lebeuf *(VP-Portfolio Investment Strategies & Procurement-Quebec)*

FORSTMANN LITTLE & CO.
767 5th Ave 45th Fl
New York, NY 10153
Tel.: (212) 355-5656
Fax: (212) 759-9059
Approx. Number Employees: 17,034
Year Founded: 1978
Business Description:
Private Equity Firm
S.I.C.: 6289
N.A.I.C.S.: 523999
Media: 2-7-9-17
Distr.: Intl.; Natl.
Personnel:
Theodore J. Forstmann *(Founder & General Partner)*
Chris A. Davis *(Gen Partner)*
Advertising Agency:
Sard Verbinnen & Co.
630 3rd Ave 9th Fl
New York, NY 10017
Tel.: (212) 687-8080
Fax: (212) 687-8344

FPB BANCORP, INC.
1301 SE Port St Lucie Blvd
Port Saint Lucie, FL 34952
Tel.: (772) 398-1388
Fax: (772) 398-1399
Toll Free: (888) 398-5777
Web Site: www.1stpeoplesbank.com
Approx. Rev.: $13,924,000
Approx. Number Employees: 68
Year Founded: 1999
Business Description:
Bank Holding Company
S.I.C.: 6029; 6712
N.A.I.C.S.: 522110; 551111
Advertising Expenditures: $126,000
Media: 17
Personnel:
Gary A. Berger *(Chm)*
David W. Skiles *(Pres & CEO)*
Paul A. Zinter *(Mng Partner)*
Nancy E. Aumack *(CFO)*
Marge Riley *(COO & Exec VP)*
Melissa M. Favorite *(Sr VP)*
Stephen J. Krumfolz *(Sr VP)*
Randy J. Riley *(Sr VP- Comml Lending)*
William V. West *(Sr VP- Comml Lending)*
Sarah Baker *(Asst VP)*
Pete Ferlalte *(Asst VP-Network Admin)*
Jillian A. Lopez *(Asst VP & HR Officer)*
Brenda K. Parmelee *(Asst VP)*
Christina M. Saltos *(Asst VP)*

FRANCIS DAVID CORPORATION
(d/b/a Electronic Merchant Systems)
5005 Rockside Rd Ste PH100
Independence, OH 44131
Tel.: (216) 524-0900
Fax: (216) 524-9540
Toll Free: (800) 726-2117
E-mail: info@emscorporate.com
Approx. Number Employees: 250
Year Founded: 1987
Business Description:
Credit Card Processing Services
S.I.C.: 5044; 7359
N.A.I.C.S.: 423420; 532490
Advertising Expenditures: $250,000
Media: 4-9-17-25
Distr.: Natl.
Personnel:
Dan Neistadt *(Pres)*
Brands & Products:
ELECTRONIC MERCHANTS SYSTEM

FRANKLIN FINANCIAL SERVICES CORPORATION
20 S Main St
Chambersburg, PA 17201
Mailing Address:
PO Box 6010
Chambersburg, PA 17201
Tel.: (717) 264-6116
Fax: (717) 261-3545
Toll Free: (888) 264-6116
E-mail: info@fmtrust.com
Web Site: www.fmtrustonline.com
Approx. Rev.: $52,650,000
Approx. Number Employees: 263
Year Founded: 1983
Business Description:
Bank Holding Company
S.I.C.: 6712
N.A.I.C.S.: 551111
Advertising Expenditures: $1,300,000
Personnel:
Charles M. Sioberg *(Chm)*
William E. Snell, Jr. *(Pres & CEO)*
Mark R. Hollar *(CFO & Treas)*

FRANKLIN RESOURCES, INC.
(d/b/a Franklin Templeton Investments)
1 Franklin Pkwy Bldg 970 1st Fl
San Mateo, CA 94403

Key to Media (For complete agency information see *The Advertising Red Books-Agencies* edition):
1. Bus. Publs. 2. Cable T.V. 3. Catalogs & Directories. 4. Co-op Adv. 5. Consumer Mags. 6. D.M. to Bus. Estab.7. D.M. to Consumers 8. Daily Newsp. 9. Exhibits/Trade Shows 10. Foreign 11. Infomercial 12. Internet Adv.13. Multimedia 14. Network Radio 15. Network T.V. 16. Newsp. Distr. Mags. 17. Other 18. Outdoor (Posters, Transit) 19. Point of Purchase20. Premiums, Novelties 21. Product Samples 22. Special Events Mktg. 23. Spot Radio 24. Spot T.V. 25. Weekly Newsp. 26. Yellow Page Adv.

Tel.: (650) 312-2000
Fax: (650) 312-5606
Toll Free: (800) 632-2350
E-mail: investmentservices@frk.com
Web Site: www.franklintempleton.com
Approx. Rev.: $5,852,999,000
Approx. Number Employees: 7,900
Year Founded: 1948
Business Description:
Holding Company; Investment Management Services
S.I.C.: 6099; 6211; 6282; 6719
N.A.I.C.S.: 522320; 523120; 523920; 551112
Advertising Expenditures: $158,458,000
Media: 1-2-4-5-6-8-9-11-16-18-22-25-26
Distr.: Direct to Consumer; Natl.
Personnel:
Charles B. Johnson *(Chm)*
Rupert Harris Johnson, Jr. *(Vice Chm)*
Gregory Eugene Johnson *(Pres & CEO)*
Kenneth A. Lewis *(CFO & Exec VP)*
Rick Frisbie, Jr. *(Chief Admin Officer & Sr VP)*
Craig S. Tyle *(Gen Counsel & Exec VP)*
Vijay C. Advani *(Exec VP-Global Distr)*
Jennifer M. Johnson *(Exec VP-Ops & Tech)*
John M. Lusk *(Exec VP-Portfolio Ops)*
Dan O'Lear *(Exec VP-Advisory Svcs-US)*
William Y. Yun *(Exec VP-Alternative Strategies)*
Leslie M. Kratter *(Sr VP & Asst Sec)*
Penelope S. Alexander *(VP-HR)*
Lincoln Baca *(VP-Registered Investment Advisor Division)*
Holly E. Gibson *(VP-Corp Comm)*
Wenning Jung *(VP-Franklin Templeton Real Estate Advisors)*
Pierre Caramazza *(Head-Registered Investment Advisor Sls Unit)*
Sonal Desai *(Dir-Res-Intl Bonds-Franklin Templeton Fixed Income)*
Brands & Products:
1-800/DIAL BEN
1-888-FRANKLIN
A SMARTER WAY TO INVEST FOR COLLEGE
ADVISOR BUSINESS BUILDERS
BISSETT
FIDUCIARY TRUST
FRANKLIN
FRANKLIN TEMPLETON INVESTMENTS
GAIN FROM OUR PERSPECTIVE
MUTUAL SERIES
TEMPLETON
Advertising Agencies:
Collaborate Communications, Inc.
445 Bush St 3rd Fl
San Francisco, CA 94108
Tel.: (415) 651-1200
Fax: (415) 651-1299

M&C Saatchi
204 Solitaire Plz
Gurgaon, 122 002, India
Tel.: (91) 124 4659000-29
Fax: (91) 91 124 4659003
(Franklin Templeton Investments)

FRONTIER BANK
(Sub. of Union Bank, N.A.)
332 SW Everett Mall Way
Everett, WA 98204
Tel.: (425) 514-0731
Fax: (425) 514-0718
Web Site: www.frontierbank.com
Sales Range: $125-149.9 Million
Approx. Number Employees: 500
Business Description:
Commercial Bank
S.I.C.: 6029
N.A.I.C.S.: 522110
Advertising Expenditures: $1,750,000
Media: 7-8-9-18-20-22-23-24-25-26
Personnel:
Patrick M. Fahey *(CEO)*
Carol E. Wheeler *(CFO)*
Robert W. Robinson *(Exec VP & Chief Credit Officer)*

FROST COMPANY
6830 Lee Hwy
Chattanooga, TN 37421-2444
Tel.: (423) 855-4047
Fax: (423) 855-1438
E-mail: info@frostcompany.net
Web Site: www.frostcollc.com
Sales Estimate: $5-9.9 Million
Approx. Number Employees: 15
Business Description:
Bookkeeping & Tax Services
S.I.C.: 8721
N.A.I.C.S.: 541219
Media: 3-5-9-19-23-24
Distr.: Reg.
Budget Set: Dec. -June
Personnel:
Robert P. Frost *(Owner)*
James B. Frost *(Chm)*

FTI CONSULTING, INC.
777 Flagler Dr Ste 1500
West Palm Beach, FL 33401
Tel.: (561) 515-1900
Toll Free: (800) 334-5701
E-mail: info@fticonsulting.com
Web Site: www.fticonsulting.com
Approx. Rev.: $1,401,461,000
Approx. Number Employees: 3,527
Year Founded: 1982
Business Description:
Financial Restructuring, Litigation Support, Performance & Compliance Consulting Services
S.I.C.: 8742; 7389; 8748
N.A.I.C.S.: 541611; 541618; 561499
Advertising Expenditures: $20,700,000
Media: 22
Personnel:
Dennis J. Shaughnessy *(Chm)*
Dominic DiNapoli *(Vice Chm, COO & Exec VP)*
Jack B. Dunn, IV *(Pres & CEO)*
William M. Isaac *(Sr Mng Dir & Head-Fin Institutions Grp)*
David R. Alfaro *(Sr Mng Dir)*
Mark Bezant *(Sr Mng Dir)*
Albert S. Conly *(Sr Mng Dir)*
Mark Dewar *(Sr Mng Dir)*
Neal Hochberg *(Sr Mng Dir & Practice Leader)*
Ryan Johnson *(Sr Mng Dir)*
Sanjeev Khemlani *(Sr Mng Dir)*
John Klick *(Sr Mng Dir)*
Christopher J. Osborne *(Sr Mng Dir)*
Vicky Pryce *(Sr Mng Dir)*
James Schweikert *(Sr Mng Dir)*
Wendy Shapss *(Sr Mng Dir)*
Simon Strong *(Sr Mng Dir)*
Daryl Teshima *(Sr Mng Dir)*
Conor P. Tully *(Sr Mng Dir)*
Greg Watson *(Sr Mng Dir)*
Harvey Weinreb *(Sr Mng Dir)*
Daniel J. Castleman *(Mng Dir)*
David G. Bannister *(CFO, Chief Development & Exec VP)*
Greg Wills *(CIO)*
Roger D. Carlile *(Chief Admin Officer & Exec VP)*
John A. MacColl *(Chief Risk Officer & Exec VP)*
Catherine M. Freeman *(Chief Acctg Officer, Sr VP & Controller)*
Eric B. Miller *(Gen Counsel & Exec VP)*
Brands & Products:
FTI
TRIALMAX
Advertising Agencies:
FD U.S. Communications, Inc.
(d/b/a Financial Dynamics)
Wall St Plz 88 Pine St 32nd Fl
New York, NY 10005
Tel.: (212) 850-5600
Fax: (212) 850-5790

LEC
12 E Ohio St
Chicago, IL 60611-5311
Tel.: (312) 670-0077
Fax: (312) 670-4477
Toll Free: (800) 731-6171

FULTON BANK MORTGAGE
(Holding of Fulton Financial Corporation)
4429 Bonney Rd Ste 100
Virginia Beach, VA 23462
Tel.: (757) 463-2265
Fax: (757) 463-8786
Toll Free: (877) 791-2516
E-mail: info@resourcebankonline.com
Web Site: www.resourcebankonline.com
Sales Range: $50-74.9 Million
Approx. Number Employees: 120
Year Founded: 1988
Business Description:
Community Bank Services
S.I.C.: 6029; 6163
N.A.I.C.S.: 522110; 522310
Media: 2-9-10-25

FULTON FINANCIAL CORPORATION
1 Penn Sq
Lancaster, PA 17602-2853
Mailing Address:
PO Box 4887
Lancaster, PA 17604-4887
Tel.: (717) 291-2411
Fax: (717) 295-4792
Web Site: www.fult.com
E-Mail For Key Personnel:
Public Relations: lwakeley@fultonbank.com
Approx. Rev.: $930,275,000
Approx. Number Employees: 3,530
Year Founded: 1982
Business Description:
Financial Services Holding Company
S.I.C.: 6371; 6712
N.A.I.C.S.: 525990; 551111
Advertising Expenditures: $8,823,000
Personnel:
R. Scott Smith, Jr. *(Chm & CEO)*
E. Philip Wenger *(Pres & COO)*
Charles J. Nugent *(CFO & Sr Exec VP)*
Craig H. Hill *(Sr Exec VP-HR)*
Beth Ann L. Chivinski *(Exec VP & Controller)*
Kay E. Burky *(Sr VP-Corp & Mgr-Trng)*
Louis J. Yoka, III *(Sr VP & Mgr-Compensation & Benefits)*
Mark A. Crowe *(Sr VP & Deputy Gen Counsel)*
Michael J. DePorter *(Sr VP & Asst Corp Controller)*
Amy L. Sahm *(VP & Mgr-InterNatl Grp)*
Steven R. Horst *(VP-Legal Dept)*
Melinda K. Herr *(Mgr-Employment)*
Natalie A. Rose *(Mgr-Intl Retail Svcs)*
Anthony R. Shelly *(Mgr-Lock Box & Remittance)*
Michelle McGovern *(Coord-ECommerce Admin)*

GAIN CAPITAL HOLDINGS, INC.
Bedminster One 135 Route 202/206
Bedminster, NJ 07921
Tel.: (908) 731-0700
Fax: (908) 731-0777
E-mail: pr@gaincapital.com
Web Site: www.gaincapital.com
Approx. Rev.: $190,773,000
Approx. Number Employees: 329
Year Founded: 1999
Business Description:
Investment Banking & Securities Dealing & Internet Publishing & Trading Services
S.I.C.: 6211; 2741; 6371
N.A.I.C.S.: 523110; 516110; 525990
Advertising Expenditures: $38,400,000
Media: 2-7-8-10-11-13-17-23-24
Personnel:
Peter Quick *(Chm)*
Glenn H. Stevens *(CEO)*
Henry C. Lyons *(CFO)*
Andrew Haines *(CIO)*
Samantha Roady *(CMO)*
Daryl J. Carlough *(Chief Acctg Officer)*
Alexander Bobinski *(Exec VP-Ops)*
Kenneth O'Brien *(Sr VP-Intl Ops)*

GALE REAL ESTATE SERVICES COMPANY
(Sub. of Mack-Cali Realty Corporation)
4 Becker Farm Rd
Roseland, NJ 07068
Tel.: (973) 577-2500
Fax: (973) 422-9520
Web Site: www.thegalecompany.com
Sales Range: $1-4.9 Billion
Approx. Number Employees: 500
Year Founded: 1984
Business Description:
Real Estate & Investment Services
S.I.C.: 6531; 6289; 6519
N.A.I.C.S.: 531390; 523999; 531190
Media: 2-4-6-7-8-9-10-18-25-26
Distr.: Reg.
Personnel:
Stanley C. Gale *(Founder)*
Mark Yeager *(Pres)*

Key to Media (For complete agency information see *The Advertising Red Books-Agencies* edition):
1. Bus. Publs. 2. Cable T.V. 3. Catalogs & Directories. 4. Co-op Adv. 5. Consumer Mags. 6. D.M. to Bus. Estab.7. D.M. to Consumers 8. Daily Newsp. 9. Exhibits/Trade Shows 10. Foreign 11. Infomercial 12. Internet Adv.13. Multimedia 14. Network Radio 15. Network T.V. 16. Newsp. Distr. Mags. 17. Other 18. Outdoor (Posters, Transit) 19. Point of Purchase20. Premiums, Novelties 21. Product Samples 22. Special Events Mktg. 23. Spot Radio 24. Spot T.V. 25. Weekly Newsp. 26. Yellow Page Adv.

Gale Real Estate Services Company — (Continued)

Stephen P. Trapp *(Pres-Gale Construction)*
Lorraine B. Kucinski *(Sr VP)*
Gabe Sasso *(Sr VP)*

GAMCO INVESTORS, INC.

1 Corp Ctr
Rye, NY 10580-1422
Tel.: (914) 921-5100
Fax: (914) 921-5392
Web Site: www.gabelli.com
Approx. Rev.: $280,380,000
Approx. Number Employees: 222
Year Founded: 1977
Business Description:
Asset Manager & Financial Services
S.I.C.: 6289; 6211; 6282; 6719
N.A.I.C.S.: 523999; 523120; 523920; 551112
Media: 2-6-7-8-25
Distr.: Natl.
Personnel:
Mario Joseph Gabelli *(Chm & CEO-GAMCO Investors, Inc)*
Robert S. Zuccaro *(CFO)*
Henry G. Van Der Eb *(Sr VP)*
Barbara G. Marcin *(Mgr-Portfolio-Gabelli Dividend & Income Trust Inc)*

GATE CITY BANK

500 2nd Ave N
Fargo, ND 58102
Tel.: (701) 293-2400
Fax: (701) 293-2566
Web Site: www.gatecitybank.com
Sales Range: $10-24.9 Million
Approx. Number Employees: 310
Year Founded: 1923
Business Description:
Federal Savings Banks
S.I.C.: 6035
N.A.I.C.S.: 522120
Personnel:
Steven J. Swiontek *(Chm, Pres & CEO)*
Alan E. Erickson *(CFO)*
Blaise P. Johnson *(Dir-Lending)*
Lance R. Wolf *(Dir-Retail Banking)*
Kimberly R. Shuckhart *(Mgr-HR)*
Brands & Products:
AMERICAN EXPRESS
FOR A BETTER WAY OF LIFE.
GATE CITY BANK
MAKE IT HAPPEN
Advertising Agency:
Odney
1400 W Century Ave
Bismarck, ND 58503
Tel.: (701) 222-8721
Fax: (701) 222-8172
Toll Free: (888) 500-8721

GE CAPITAL

(Div. of General Electric Capital Corporation)
901 Main Ave Ste 800
Norwalk, CT 06851
Tel.: (203) 750-2900
Fax: (203) 840-6494
Toll Free: (888) 964-8897
Web Site: www.gecapital.com
Business Description:
Consumer Lending Services
S.I.C.: 6141; 6163
N.A.I.C.S.: 522291; 522210; 522310
Personnel:
Mark W. Begor *(Pres & CEO)*
Margaret Keane *(Pres & CEO)*
Glenn Marino *(Pres/CEO-Sls Fin)*
Steve Liguori *(Exec Dir-Global Mktg)*
Advertising Agency:
Hill & Knowlton (UK) Ltd.
20 Soho Square
London, W1A 1PR, United Kingdom
Tel.: (44) 20 7413 3000
Fax: (44) 20 7413 3111

GE COMMERCIAL DISTRIBUTION FINANCE

(Sub. of GE Vendor Financial Services)
5595 Trillium Blvd
Hoffman Estates, IL 60192
Tel.: (847) 747-6800
Fax: (847) 747-7455
Toll Free: (800) 292-2872
Web Site: www.gecdf.com
Sales Range: $1-4.9 Billion
Approx. Number Employees: 1,100
Year Founded: 1975
Business Description:
Financial Services
S.I.C.: 6289
N.A.I.C.S.: 523999
Media: 2-7-10-20
Personnel:
Scott Danahey *(Mng Partner)*

GENERAL FINANCE CORPORATION

39 E Union St
Pasadena, CA 91103
Tel.: (626) 584-9722
Fax: (626) 795-8090
E-mail: info@generalfinance.com
Web Site: www.generalfinance.com
Approx. Rev.: $156,309,000
Approx. Number Employees: 226
Year Founded: 2005
Business Description:
Investment Services
S.I.C.: 6289
N.A.I.C.S.: 523999
Advertising Expenditures: $2,478,000
Personnel:
Lawrence P. Glascott, III *(Chm)*
Ronald F. Valenta *(Pres, CEO & Dir)*
Theodore Mourouzis *(Pres & COO)*
Charles E. Barrantes *(CFO & Exec VP)*
John O. Johnson *(COO)*
Robert Allan *(CEO-Royal Wolf)*
Jeffrey A. Kluckman *(Exec VP-Bus Dev)*

GENESIS SECURITIES, LLC.

50 Broad St Ste 288
New York, NY 10004
Tel.: (212) 668-0888
Fax: (212) 668-0880
E-mail: info@gndt.com
Web Site: www.gndt.com
Approx. Rev.: $1,800,000
Approx. Number Employees: 20
Year Founded: 1999
Business Description:
Security Broker/Dealer Security/ Commodity Exchange
S.I.C.: 6211
N.A.I.C.S.: 523120
Brands & Products:
GENESIS SECURITY
SOGOTRADE
Advertising Agency:
SendTraffic.com, Inc.
450 7th Ave
New York, NY 10123
Tel.: (212) 273-1141
Fax: (845) 215-0101
Toll Free: (866) 487-2334

GENEVA FINANCIAL CORPORATION

100 N Centre Ave Ste 300
Rockville Centre, NY 11570
Tel.: (516) 255-1700
Fax: (516) 255-9660
Sales Range: $1-9.9 Million
Approx. Number Employees: 60
Business Description:
Financial Services
S.I.C.: 6163
N.A.I.C.S.: 522310
Media: 7-8-10-17-22
Personnel:
Stanley C. Kreitman *(Chm)*
Keith Haffner *(Pres & CEO)*

GENWORTH FINANCIAL, INC.

6620 W Broad St
Richmond, VA 23230
Tel.: (804) 281-6000
Tel.: (804) 484-3821 (Intl)
Fax: (804) 662-2414
Toll Free: (888) 436-9678
Toll Free: (888) GENWORTH
E-mail: contactus@genworth.com
Web Site: www.genworth.com
Approx. Rev.: $10,089,000,000
Approx. Number Employees: 6,500
Year Founded: 1871
Business Description:
Life Insurance, Long Term Care Insurance, Annuity, Investment Services, Mortgage Insurance & Employee Benefit Services
S.I.C.: 6321; 6163; 6282; 6289; 6311; 6331
N.A.I.C.S.: 524130; 522310; 523930; 523999; 524113; 524126
Advertising Expenditures: $32,000,000
Media: 2-3-5-6-7-9-13-15-22
Personnel:
Michael D. Fraizer *(Chm, Pres & CEO)*
Ronald D. Cordes *(Co-Chm)*
Kevin D. Schneider *(Sr VP-Genworth, Pres & CEO-US Mortgage Insurance)*
Scott J. McKay *(CIO & Sr VP-Ops & Quality)*
Myra Rothfeld *(CMO-Genworth Fin Wealth Mgmt, Inc.)*
Ronald P. Joelson *(Chief Investment Officer & Sr VP)*
Tim Knepp *(Chief Investment Officer-Asset Mgmt)*
Rohit Gupta *(Chief Comml Officer & Sr VP)*
Patrick B. Kelleher *(Pres/CEO-Retirement & Protection)*
Robert J. Brannock *(Pres-Europe)*
Chris Grady *(Pres-Insurance Distr & Mktg)*
Thomas M. Stinson *(Pres-Insurance Products)*
Gurinder S. Ahluwalia *(CEO-Genworth Fin Wealth Mgmt, Inc.)*
Amy R. Corbin *(CFO-Retirement & Protection & Sr VP)*
Leon E. Roday *(Gen Counsel, Sec & Sr VP)*
Jim Bennison *(Sr VP-Strategy & Capital Markets-Genworth Mortgage Insurance)*
Sean Curley *(Sr VP-Asset Mgmt)*
Barbara Faurot *(Sr VP-Comm)*
Timothy Herr *(Sr VP & Leader-BGA Channel)*
Michael Kim *(Sr VP)*
Martin P. Klein *(Sr VP)*
Michael S. Laming *(Sr VP-HR)*
Roger Levy *(Sr VP-Govt Rels)*
Al Orendorff *(Sr VP-PR)*
Joseph J. Pehota *(Sr VP-Corp Dev)*
Laurence M. Richmond *(Sr VP-PR & Brand)*
Terry Souers *(VP-PR-US Mortgage Insurance)*
Yokima Cureton *(Sr Mgr-PR)*
Gary Hensley *(Coord-Sls)*
Tom Topinka *(Coord-Community Rel)*
Brands & Products:
CLEARCOURSE
GENWORTH FINANCIAL
TOTAL LIVING COVERAGE
Advertising Agencies:
Allegro Communications, Inc.
401 W Saint Charles Rd
Lombard, IL 60148
Tel.: (630) 495-1600
Fax: (630) 495-1601

Ketchum
(Part of Omnicom)
1285 Ave of the Americas
New York, NY 10019
Tel.: (646) 935-3900
Fax: (646) 935-4482

Landor Associates
110 Shillito Pl
Cincinnati, OH 45202-2361
Tel.: (513) 419-2300
Fax: (513) 221-3532

McMurry
1010 E Missouri Ave
Phoenix, AZ 85014
Tel.: (602) 395-5850
Fax: (602) 248-2925
Toll Free: (888) MCMURRY
Toll Free: (888) 626-8779

Targetbase
7850 N Belt Line Rd
Irving, TX 75063-6098
Tel.: (972) 506-3400
Fax: (972) 506-3505
Toll Free: (866) 506-7850

Ulled Communicacion
Maria de Molina 37 3rd Floor Right
28006
Madrid, Spain
Tel.: (34) 91 564 04 96
Fax: (34) 91 411 75 24

GEORGIA-CAROLINA BANCSHARES, INC.

3527 Wheeler Rd
Augusta, GA 30909
Tel.: (706) 731-6600
Fax: (706) 731-6601
E-mail: internetbanking@firstbankofga.com
Web Site: www.firstbankofga.com

Key to Media (For complete agency information see *The Advertising Red Books-Agencies* edition):
1. Bus. Publs. 2. Cable T.V. 3. Catalogs & Directories. 4. Co-op Adv. 5. Consumer Mags. 6. D.M. to Bus. Estab.7. D.M. to Consumers 8. Daily Newsp. 9. Exhibits/Trade Shows 10. Foreign 11. Infomercial 12. Internet Adv.13. Multimedia 14. Network Radio 15. Network T.V. 16. Newsp. Distr. Mags. 17. Other 18. Outdoor (Posters, Transit) 19. Point of Purchase20. Premiums, Novelties 21. Product Samples 22. Special Events Mktg. 23. Spot Radio 24. Spot T.V. 25. Weekly Newsp. 26. Yellow Page Adv.

Approx. Rev.: $37,655,000
Approx. Number Employees: 160
Year Founded: 1997
Business Description:
Bank Holding Company
S.I.C.: 6029; 6712
N.A.I.C.S.: 522110; 551111
Advertising Expenditures: $237,000
Media: 2-9-13-25
Personnel:
Samuel A. Fowler Jr. *(Chm)*
George H. Inman *(Vice Chm)*
Remer Y. Brinson, III *(Pres & CEO)*
Thomas J. Flournoy *(CFO & Sr VP)*
Thomas M. Bird *(Exec VP)*
Lynn Holley *(Sr VP)*
William W. McCartney *(Sr VP)*
W. Cameron Nixon *(Sr VP & Sr Lending Officer)*

GERMAN AMERICAN BANCORP, INC.

711 Main St
Jasper, IN 47546
Tel.: (812) 482-1314
Fax: (812) 482-0721
Web Site:
www.germanamericanbancorp.com
Approx. Rev.: $81,136,000
Approx. Number Employees: 396
Year Founded: 1983
Business Description:
Bank Holding Company
S.I.C.: 6022; 6029; 6712
N.A.I.C.S.: 522190; 522110; 551111
Advertising Expenditures: $1,255,000
Media: 8-9-13-16-18-23-25
Personnel:
Mark A. Schroeder *(Chm, Pres & CEO)*
Bradley M. Rust *(CFO & Exec VP)*
Clay W. Ewing *(Pres-Retail Fin Svcs)*
Dave Mitchell *(Sr VP)*
Brands & Products:
GERMAN AMERICAN
GERMAN AMERICAN BANCORP
STRONG TIES. STRONG SOLUTONS.

GFI GROUP INC.

55 Water St
New York, NY 10041
Tel.: (212) 968-4100
Fax: (212) 968-2386
E-mail: info@gfigroup.com
Web Site: www.gfigroup.com
Approx. Rev.: $862,113,000
Approx. Number Employees: 1,990
Year Founded: 1987
Business Description:
Derivatives Trading & Brokerage Services
S.I.C.: 6211; 6231
N.A.I.C.S.: 523120; 523210
Import Export
Media: 2-10
Personnel:
Michael A. Gooch *(Chm & CEO)*
Colin Heffron *(Pres)*
Nick Brown *(Mng Dir & Head-Fin Product Brokerage-North America)*
Richard Giles *(Mng Dir, Head-Commodities & Energy Brokerage-North America)*
Jim Higgins *(Mng Dir & Head-Credit Brokerage-North American)*
Julian Swain *(Mng Dir & Head-London)*
Scott Tatham *(Mng Dir & Head-Asia)*
Michael Cosgrove *(Mng Dir)*
James A. Peers *(CFO)*
Ron Levi *(COO)*
J.Christopher Giancarlo *(Exec VP & Corp Dev)*
Scott Fitzpatrick *(Head-Sls)*
Sheena Griffiths *(Dir-HR-Global)*
Chris Ann Casaburri *(Mgr-IR)*
Advertising Agency:
Walek & Associates
317 Madison Ave Ste 2300
New York, NY 10017
Tel.: (212) 889-4113
Fax: (212) 889-7174
Public Relations

GILMAN CIOCIA, INC.

11 Raymond Ave
Poughkeepsie, NY 12603-2342
Tel.: (845) 485-3300
Fax: (845) 483-9332
E-mail: gilmanandciocia@gilcio.com
Web Site: www.gilcio.com
Approx. Rev.: $41,483,000
Approx. Number Employees: 195
Year Founded: 1982
Business Description:
Income Tax Preparation & Financial Planning Services
S.I.C.: 6282; 7291; 8721; 8741; 8742
N.A.I.C.S.: 523930; 541213; 541219; 541611; 561110
Advertising Expenditures: $1,300,000
Media: 8-9-10-18-22-23-24-25
Personnel:
James C. Ciocia *(Chm)*
Michael P. Ryan *(Pres & CEO)*
Karen Fisher *(Chief Acctg Officer & Treas)*
Ted Finkelstein *(Gen Counsel, Sec & VP)*
Carole Enisman *(Exec VP-Ops)*
John F. Levy *(Dir-Lead)*

GLACIER BANCORP, INC.

49 Commons Loop
Kalispell, MT 59901-2679
Tel.: (406) 756-4200
Fax: (406) 756-3518
Toll Free: (800) 735-4371
E-mail: investor@glacierbancorp.com
Web Site: www.glacierbancorp.com
Approx. Rev.: $288,402,000
Approx. Number Employees: 1,517
Year Founded: 1990
Business Description:
Bank Holding Company
S.I.C.: 6712
N.A.I.C.S.: 551111
Advertising Expenditures: $6,477,000
Personnel:
Everit A. Sliter *(Chm)*
Michael J. Blodnick *(Pres & CEO)*
Ronald J. Copher *(CFO & Treas)*
Mark D. MacMillan *(CIO)*
Don Chery *(Chief Admin Officer & Exec VP)*
April D. Kelso *(Corp Compliance Officer)*
Ryan T. Screnar *(Sr VP & Dir)*
Marcia L. Johnson *(Sr VP)*
Barry L. Johnston *(Sr VP-Credit Admin)*
Robin S. Roush *(Sr VP-HR)*
James J. Joslin *(VP-Internal Audit)*
Glenn G. Nelson *(Dir-Info Tech)*
T. J. Frickle *(Mgr-Enterprise & Wide Risk)*

GLACIER BANK

(Holding of Glacier Bancorp, Inc.)
202 Main St
Kalispell, MT 59901-4454
Tel.: (406) 756-4200
Fax: (406) 756-4298
Toll Free: (800) 735-4371
E-mail: glacier@glacierbank.com
Web Site: www.glacierbank.com
Approx. Rev.: $39,196,000
Approx. Number Employees: 198
Year Founded: 1955
Business Description:
Savings, Loans & Commercial Banking Services
S.I.C.: 6029; 6035; 6163
N.A.I.C.S.: 522110; 522120; 522310
Media: 7-8-13
Personnel:
Everit A. Sliter *(Chm)*
Michael J. Blodnick *(Pres & CEO)*
Dennis S. Beams *(Chief Credit Officer-Small Bus Admin Loan & Exec VP)*
Pam Butler *(Sr VP & Office Mgr)*
Don Lloyd *(Sr VP-Small Bus Admin Loan)*
James Ness *(Chief Deposit Officer & Sr VP)*
Gary Sparr *(VP & Office Mgr)*
Cheryl Zobenica *(VP & Office Mgr)*
Sandy Garrett *(Asst VP)*
Carol Hoerner *(Asst VP)*
Deb Broadbent *(Mgr-HR)*
Advertising Agency:
Schuman Advertising
307 1st Ave E # 19 Kalispell
Kalispell, MT 59901
Tel.: (406) 752-8172
Fax: (406) 752-8174
— Ray Schuman *(Owner & Acct. Exec.)*

GLEN BURNIE BANCORP

101 Crain Hwy SE
Glen Burnie, MD 21227
Tel.: (410) 766-3300
Fax: (410) 787-8570
E-mail: thebankofglenburnie@bogb.net
Web Site:
www.thebankofglenburnie.com
Approx. Rev.: $20,077,574
Approx. Number Employees: 118
Year Founded: 1949
Business Description:
Bank Holding Company
S.I.C.: 6712; 6029
N.A.I.C.S.: 551111; 522110
Advertising Expenditures: $240,177
Personnel:
John E. Demyan *(Chm)*
Michael G. Livingston *(Pres & CEO)*
Frederick W. Kuethe, III *(Pres)*
John E. Porter *(CFO & Sr VP)*
Barbara J. Elswick *(Chief Lending Officer & Sr VP)*
Brands & Products:
GLEN BURNIE

THE GLENMEDE TRUST COMPANY

1650 Market St Ste 1200
Philadelphia, PA 19103
Tel.: (215) 419-6000
Fax: (215) 419-6199
Web Site: www.glenmede.com
Sales Range: $75-99.9 Million
Approx. Number Employees: 180
Year Founded: 1956
Business Description:
Investment Trust Services
S.I.C.: 6282; 6732
N.A.I.C.S.: 523920; 813211
Media: 2
Personnel:
Gordon B. Fowler *(Pres, CEO & Chief Investment Officer)*
A. E. Piscopo *(Pres & CEO)*
James R. Belanger *(Mng Dir, Corp Counsel & Dir-Bus Assurance)*
Staney Broadbent *(Mng Dir & Dir-Bus Dev Mgr)*
Dave Prickril *(Dir-Portfolio Mgmt & Mng Dir)*
Peter J. Zuleba *(Mng Dir & Dir-Equity Mgmt)*
Laura A. Williamson *(COO)*
Kristine Plourde *(Officer-Mktg)*
Laura LaRosa *(First VP & Dir-Fixed Income)*
Vladimir de Vassal *(Dir-Quantitative Res-Glenmede Investment Mgmt LP)*
Jason Pride *(Dir-Investment Strategy)*
Stephen Mahoney *(Mgr-Fixed Income-Portfolio)*
Paul T. Sullivan *(Mgr-Glenmede Investment Mgmt LP)*

GLOBAL CASH ACCESS HOLDINGS, INC.

3525 E Post Rd Ste 120
Las Vegas, NV 89120
Tel.: (702) 855-3000
Fax: (702) 855-3040
Fax: (866) 972-4371
Toll Free: (800) 833-7110
E-mail: corpinfo@gcamail.com
Web Site:
www.globalcashaccess.com
Approx. Rev.: $605,590,000
Approx. Number Employees: 419
Business Description:
Holding Company; Gaming Industry Cash Access & Financial Data Intelligence Services
S.I.C.: 6719; 5044; 6371; 7374
N.A.I.C.S.: 551112; 423420; 518210; 525990
Advertising Expenditures: $100,000
Media: 10-13
Budget Set: Dec.
Personnel:
E. Miles Kilburn *(Chm)*
Scott H. Betts *(Pres, CEO & Sec)*
Mary E. Higgins *(CFO & Exec VP)*
David D. Johnson *(Gen Counsel & Exec VP)*
Michael Scott Dowty *(Exec VP-Bus Dev)*
Mari Ellis *(Exec VP-Dev & Tech)*
David J. Lucchese *(Exec VP-Sls)*
Kurt Sullivan *(Sr VP-Central Credit & Check Svcs)*
Brands & Products:
ACM
CASINO CASH PLUS
CASINO MARKETING SERVICES
CENTRALCREDIT
EDITH
GCA
POWERCASH
QUICKJACK
QUIKCASH

Key to Media (For complete agency information see *The Advertising Red Books-Agencies* edition):
1. Bus. Publs. 2. Cable T.V. 3. Catalogs & Directories. 4. Co-op Adv. 5. Consumer Mags. 6. D.M. to Bus. Estab.7. D.M. to Consumers
8. Daily Newsp. 9. Exhibits/Trade Shows 10. Foreign 11. Infomercial 12. Internet Adv.13. Multimedia 14. Network Radio
15. Network T.V. 16. Newsp. Distr. Mags. 17. Other 18. Outdoor (Posters, Transit) 19. Point of Purchase20. Premiums, Novelties
21. Product Samples 22. Special Events Mktg. 23. Spot Radio 24. Spot T.V. 25. Weekly Newsp. 26. Yellow Page Adv.

GLOBAL CASH ACCESS HOLDINGS, INC. — (Continued)

QUIKCASH PLUS
QUIKMARKETING
QUIKMESSAGING
QUIKREPORTS
QUIKTICKET
QUIKWAGER
STRETCH YOUR LIMITS
TRANSACTION THAT COUNT

GLOBAL PAYMENTS INC.

10 Glenlake Pkwy N Tower
Atlanta, GA 30328
Tel.: (770) 829-8000
Fax: (770) 829-8224
Toll Free: (800) 560-2960
E-mail: info@globalpay.com
Web Site: www.globalpaymentsinc.com
Approx. Rev.: $1,859,802,000
Approx. Number Employees: 3,753
Business Description:
Electronic Payment Processing Solutions & Money Transfers
S.I.C.: 6099
N.A.I.C.S.: 522320
Advertising Expenditures: $1,700,000
Media: 2-6-8-10
Personnel:
Paul R. Garcia *(Chm & CEO)*
James G. Kelly *(Pres & COO)*
David E. Mangum *(CFO & Exec VP)*
Guido F. Sacchi *(CIO)*
Morgan M. Schuessler *(Chief Admin Officer & Exec VP)*
Joseph C. Hyde *(Pres-Intl)*
Suellyn P. Tornay *(Gen Counsel & Exec VP)*

GMAC HOME SERVICES LLC

(Div. of Brookfield Residential Property Services)
2021 Spring Rd Ste 300
Oak Brook, IL 60523
Tel.: (630) 214-1600
Fax: (630) 214-1215
E-mail: info@gmacrealestate.com
Web Site: www.gmacrealestate.com
Year Founded: 1998
Business Description:
Real Estate Services
S.I.C.: 6531
N.A.I.C.S.: 531390
Media: 2-6-8
Personnel:
Jeff Gutowsky *(VP-Mktg & Comm)*

GMAC MORTGAGE, LLC

(Sub. of GMAC Residential Holding Corp.)
1100 Virginia Dr
Fort Washington, PA 19034
Tel.: (215) 734-8899
Web Site: www.gmacmortgage.com
Approx. Number Employees: 2,400
Business Description:
Mortgage Services
S.I.C.: 6163
N.A.I.C.S.: 522310
Media: 2-6-7-8-9-14
Distr.: Direct to Consumer; Natl.; Reg.
Budget Set: Nov. -Dec.
Personnel:
Thomas Marano *(CEO)*
Advertising Agency:
FD U.S. Communications, Inc.
(d/b/a Financial Dynamics)
Wall St Plz 88 Pine St 32nd Fl
New York, NY 10005
Tel.: (212) 850-5600
Fax: (212) 850-5790

GOINDUSTRY USA, INC.

(Sub. of GoIndustry-DoveBid plc)
11425 Cronhill Dr
Owings Mills, MD 21117
Tel.: (410) 654-7500
Fax: (410) 654-5876
Toll Free: (800) 722-3334
Web Site: www.go-dove.com/auctions/paymentinfo.asp
Approx. Number Employees: 56
Year Founded: 1998
Business Description:
Industrial Machinery Appraisal & Auction Services
S.I.C.: 5961; 5963
N.A.I.C.S.: 454112; 454390
Media: 6-7-8-16
Personnel:
Tim Lynch *(CEO)*

GOLDLEAF FINANCIAL SOLUTIONS, INC.

(Sub. of Jack Henry & Associates, Inc.)
(d/b/a ProfitStars)
350 Technology Blvd Ste 200
Norcross, GA 30071
Tel.: (678) 966-0844
E-mail: pbiz@pbizinc.com
Web Site: www.goldleaf.com
Approx. Rev.: $81,573,000
Approx. Number Employees: 493
Year Founded: 1991
Business Description:
Financial & Retail Institution Deposit Automation & Payment Processing Software & Services
S.I.C.: 7372; 7373; 7374
N.A.I.C.S.: 511210; 518210; 541512
Import Export
Advertising Expenditures: $281,000
Personnel:
Henry M. Baroco *(Pres-Retail Mdsg Svc Automation)*
Brian R. Geisel *(Exec VP, Enterprise Payments)*
W. Todd Shiver *(Exec VP-Sls & Mktg)*
Brands & Products:
BUSINESSMANAGER
COLLECTIONS MANAGER
GOLDLEAF FINANCIAL SOLUTIONS
IDENTIFICATION MANAGER
LENDING NETWORK
LINE MANAGER
MARKETING MANAGER
MEDCASH MANAGER

THE GOLDMAN SACHS GROUP, INC.

200 West St 29th Fl
New York, NY 10282
Tel.: (212) 902-1000
Fax: (212) 902-3000
Web Site: www.goldmansachs.com
Approx. Rev.: $39,161,000,000
Approx. Number Employees: 35,700
Year Founded: 1869
Business Description:
Bank Holding Company; Investment Banking, Trading & Principal Investments, Asset Management & Securities Services
S.I.C.: 6712; 6211; 6282; 6289; 6733
N.A.I.C.S.: 551111; 523110; 523120; 523920; 523930; 523991; 523999
Media: 1-2-7-9-11-13-22-25
Distr.: Intl.; Natl.
Budget Set: Dec.
Personnel:
Lloyd C. Blankfein *(Chm & CEO)*
J. Michael Evans *(Co-Vice Chm & Head-Global Growth Markets)*
James A. Johnson *(Vice Chm)*
Michael S. Sherwood *(Co-Vice Chm)*
John S. Weinberg *(Co-Vice Chm)*
Gary D. Cohn *(Pres & COO)*
Christopher A. Cole *(Mng Dir)*
Edith W. Cooper *(Mng Dir)*
Gordon E. Dyal *(Mng Dir)*
Isabelle Ealet *(Mng Dir)*
Edward K. Eisler *(Mng Dir)*
Edward C. Forst *(Mng Dir)*
Richard A. Friedman *(Mng Dir)*
Richard J. Gnodde *(Mng Dir)*
David B. Heller *(Mng Dir)*
Dane Holmes *(Mng Dir)*
Kevin W. Kennedy *(Mng Dir)*
Gwen R. Libstag *(Mng Dir)*
Masanori Mochida *(Mng Dir)*
Donald R. Mullen *(Mng Dir)*
Timothy J. O'Neill *(Mng Dir)*
Pablo J. Salame *(Mng Dir)*
Harvey M. Schwartz *(Mng Dir)*
David M. Solomon *(Mng Dir)*
Steven H. Strongin *(Mng Dir)*
Yoel Zaoui *(Mng Dir)*
David A. Viniar *(CFO & Exec VP)*
Sarah E. Smith *(Chief Acctg Officer)*
Gregory K. Palm *(Co-Gen Counsel, Co-Sec & Exec VP)*
Esta E. Stecher *(Co-Gen Counsel, Co-Sec & Exec VP)*
Alan M. Cohen *(Exec VP & Head-Global Compliance)*
David May *(VP Global Mktg)*
Advertising Agencies:
Andreoli/MS&L
Av Ibirapuera, 2332 Torre 1 - 14 andar
04028-002
Sao Paulo, SP Brazil
Tel.: (55) 11 3169 9300
Fax: (55) 11 3169 9317

R/GA
350 W 39th St
New York, NY 10018-1402
Tel.: (212) 946-4000
Fax: (212) 946-4010

Young & Rubicam Inc.
285 Madison Ave
New York, NY 10017-6401
Tel.: (212) 210-3000
Fax: (212) 490-9073

GOLDSMITH, AGIO, HELMS & LYNNER

(Name Changed to Lazard Middle Market LLC)

GOUVERNEUR BANCORP, INC.

(Sub. of Cambray Mutual Holding Company)
42 Church St
Gouverneur, NY 13642
Tel.: (315) 287-2600
Fax: (315) 287-3340
Toll Free: (888) 817-0020
Web Site: www.gouverneurbank.com
Sales Range: $1-9.9 Million
Approx. Number Employees: 32
Business Description:
Bank Holding Company
S.I.C.: 6712; 6035
N.A.I.C.S.: 551111; 522120
Media: 7-8-9-25
Personnel:
Gregory Langevin *(Chm)*
Charles C. Vanvleet *(Pres & CEO)*

GOUVERNEUR SAVINGS & LOAN ASSOCIATION

(Sub. of Gouverneur Bancorp, Inc.)
42 Church St
Gouverneur, NY 13642-1416
Tel.: (315) 287-2600
Fax: (315) 287-3340
Toll Free: (888) 817-0020
E-mail: gsla@bankmail.com
Web Site: www.gouverneurbank.com
Approx. Number Employees: 33
Year Founded: 1892
Business Description:
Savings & Loan Institution
S.I.C.: 6035
N.A.I.C.S.: 522120
Media: 7-8-9-13-25
Personnel:
Charles Van Vleet *(Pres & CEO)*
Kim Adams *(CFO & VP)*
Kathleen Mcintosh *(Treas)*

GRANT THORNTON INTERNATIONAL LTD.

175 W Jackson Blvd 20th Fl
Chicago, IL 60604
Tel.: (312) 856-0001
Fax: (312) 565-4719
E-mail: info@gti.org
Web Site: www.gti.org
Sales Range: $1-4.9 Billion
Approx. Number Employees: 22,000
Year Founded: 1924
Business Description:
Accounting, Auditing, Tax & Management Consulting Services
S.I.C.: 8742; 8721
N.A.I.C.S.: 541611; 541219
Import Export
Media: 2-9-10
Distr.: Natl.
Personnel:
David C. McDonnell *(CEO)*
Tricia Conahan *(CMO)*
Stephan Chipman *(CEO-US)*
Kate Speirs *(Head-Comm)*
April Mackenzie *(Exec Dir-Pub Policy)*
Barry Barber *(Dir-Audit & Quality Control-Worldwide)*
Robert M. Leavy *(Divisional Dir-Americas)*
John Vita *(Dir-Natl Comm)*
Amy Mauch *(US Brand Mgr)*
Mary Nessling *(Mgr-Pur)*
Brands & Products:
GRANT THORNTON

GRAYSON BANKSHARES, INC.

113 W Main St
Independence, VA 24348
Mailing Address:
PO Box 186
Independence, VA 24348-0186
Tel.: (276) 773-2811
Fax: (276) 773-3890
Web Site: www.graysonnationalbank.com

Key to Media (For complete agency information see *The Advertising Red Books-Agencies* edition):
1. Bus. Publs. 2. Cable T.V. 3. Catalogs & Directories. 4. Co-op Adv. 5. Consumer Mags. 6. D.M. to Bus. Estab. 7. D.M. to Consumers 8. Daily Newsp. 9. Exhibits/Trade Shows 10. Foreign 11. Infomercial 12. Internet Adv. 13. Multimedia 14. Network Radio 15. Network T.V. 16. Newsp. Distr. Mags. 17. Other 18. Outdoor (Posters, Transit) 19. Point of Purchase 20. Premiums, Novelties 21. Product Samples 22. Special Events Mktg. 23. Spot Radio 24. Spot T.V. 25. Weekly Newsp. 26. Yellow Page Adv.

Approx. Rev.: $21,320,514
Approx. Number Employees: 118
Year Founded: 1992
Business Description:
Bank Holding Company
S.I.C.: 6712; 6029; 6035; 6141
N.A.I.C.S.: 551111; 522110; 522120; 522291
Advertising Expenditures: $179,800
Media: 9-20-25
Personnel:
Julian L. Givens *(Chm)*
Jacky K. Anderson *(Pres & CEO)*
Blake M. Edwards, Jr. *(CFO)*

GREAT AMERICAN BANCORP, INC.

1311 S Neil St
Champaign, IL 61820
Mailing Address:
PO Box 1010
Champaign, IL 61824-1010
Tel.: (217) 356-2265
Fax: (217) 356-2502
E-mail: jadams@356bank.com
Web Site:
www.greatamericanbancorp.com
Approx. Rev.: $10,464,000
Approx. Number Employees: 66
Business Description:
Bank Holding Company
S.I.C.: 6712
N.A.I.C.S.: 551111
Media: 8-9-18-20-23-24-25
Personnel:
Ronald E. Guenther *(Chm)*
George R. Rouse *(Pres & CEO)*
Jane F. Adams *(CFO, Treas & Sec)*

GREAT SOUTHERN BANCORP, INC.

1451 E Battlefield Rd
Springfield, MO 65804
Mailing Address:
PO Box 9009
Springfield, MO 65808-9009
Tel.: (417) 887-4400
Fax: (417) 895-4517
Toll Free: (800) 749-7113
E-mail: intbanking@greatsouthernbank.com
Web Site:
www.greatsouthernbank.com
Approx. Rev.: $205,143,000
Approx. Number Employees: 814
Year Founded: 1989
Business Description:
Bank Holding Company
S.I.C.: 6712; 6029; 6035
N.A.I.C.S.: 551111; 522110; 522120
Advertising Expenditures: $1,488,000
Personnel:
William V. Turner *(Chm)*
Joseph W. Turner *(Pres & CEO)*
Brands & Products:
CASHBUILDER
GREAT SOUTHERN

GREATER HUDSON BANK, N.A.

643 Rte 211 E
Middletown, NY 10941
Tel.: (845) 695-7400
Web Site:
www.greaterhudsonbank.com
Approx. Rev.: $7,272,000
Business Description:
Banking Services

S.I.C.: 6029
N.A.I.C.S.: 522110
Advertising Expenditures: $194,000
Media: 8
Personnel:
Kenneth J. Torsoe *(Chm)*
Edward T. Lutz *(Vice Chm)*
Daniel E. Rifkin *(Co-Vice Chm)*
Eric J. Wiggins *(Pres & CEO)*
F. Thomas Cornelius *(CFO & Sr VP)*
Lynne C. Allan *(COO)*
Gregory B. Monteith *(Chief Lending Officer & Sr VP)*

GREEN BANKSHARES, INC.

100 N Main St
Greeneville, TN 37743-4992
Tel.: (423) 639-5111
Web Site: www.greenbankusa.com
Approx. Rev.: $153,408,000
Approx. Number Employees: 730
Year Founded: 1985
Business Description:
Bank Holding Company
S.I.C.: 6712; 6029; 6035; 6141
N.A.I.C.S.: 551111; 522110; 522120; 522210
Import Export
Advertising Expenditures: $2,388,000
Personnel:
Stephen M. Rownd *(Chm & CEO)*
Kenneth R. Vaught *(Pres & COO)*
Michael J. Fowler *(CFO & Sr VP)*
William C. Adams, Jr. *(CIO & Sr VP)*
Brands & Products:
GREENE COUNTY BANCSHARES

GREEN DOT CORPORATION

605 E Huntington Dr Ste 205
Monrovia, CA 91016
Tel.: (626) 739-3942
Web Site: www.greendot.com
Approx. Rev.: $363,888,000
Approx. Number Employees: 352
Year Founded: 1999
Business Description:
Prepaid Credit Card Issuer
S.I.C.: 6141
N.A.I.C.S.: 522210
Advertising Expenditures: $7,000,000
Media: 5-13-16-19
Personnel:
Steven W. Streit *(Chm, Pres & CEO)*
John L. Keatley *(CFO)*
William D. Sowell *(COO)*
Mark T. Troughton *(Pres-Cards & Network)*
John C. Ricci *(Gen Counsel)*
Matt Kohler *(VP-Mktg)*
Brands & Products:
GREEN DOT
Advertising Agency:
Horizon Media, Inc.
75 Varick St
New York, NY 10013
Tel.: (212) 220-5000
Toll Free: (800) 633-4201

GREENE COUNTY BANCORP, INC.

302 Main St
Catskill, NY 12414
Tel.: (518) 943-2600
Fax: (518) 622-2663
Web Site:
www.thebankofgreenecounty.com
Approx. Int. Income: $27,699,000
Approx. Number Employees: 107

Business Description:
Bank Holding Company
S.I.C.: 6712
N.A.I.C.S.: 551111
Advertising Expenditures: $308,000
Personnel:
Martin C. Smith *(Chm)*
Donald E. Gibson *(Pres & CEO)*
Michelle M. Plummer *(CFO, COO & Exec VP)*
Cynthia DuPilka *(VP-Branch Admin & BSA Officer)*
Stephen E. Nelson *(Chief Lending Officer & Exec VP)*
Martha Keeler *(VP & Dir-Mktg)*
Carmela Hendricks *(Asst VP-Ops)*
Rick Fernandez *(Mgr-IT Sys)*
Barbara Spring *(Mgr-Loan Servicing)*

GREENLIGHT FINANCIAL SERVICES

18200 Von Karman Ave Ste 300
Irvine, CA 92612
Tel.: (949) 798-2400
Fax: (949) 428-6460
Fax: (949) 756-7140
Toll Free: (866) 66FASTER
E-mail: sales@greenlightloans.com
Web Site: www.greenlightloans.com
E-Mail For Key Personnel:
Sales Director: sales@greenlightloans.com
Sales Range: $10-24.9 Million
Approx. Number Employees: 40
Year Founded: 2001
Business Description:
Mortgage Services
S.I.C.: 6159
N.A.I.C.S.: 522292
Media: 3-22-23-24
Personnel:
Stacey Sommer *(COO)*
Brands & Products:
GREENLIGHT
Advertising Agencies:
Kovel/Fuller
9925 Jefferson Blvd
Culver City, CA 90232-3505
Tel.: (310) 841-4444
Fax: (310) 841-4599

The Rose Group
9925 Jefferson Blvd 2nd Fl
Culver City, CA 90232
Tel.: (310) 280-3710
Fax: (310) 280-3715

GS FINANCIAL CORPORATION

3798 Veterans Blvd
Metairie, LA 70002
Tel.: (504) 457-6220
Fax: (504) 457-6227
Web Site: www.gsfinancialcorp.com
Approx. Rev.: $15,730,000
Approx. Number Employees: 54
Year Founded: 1996
Business Description:
Bank Holding Company
S.I.C.: 6035; 6712
N.A.I.C.S.: 522120; 551111
Advertising Expenditures: $76,000
Media: 17
Personnel:
Albert J. Zahn, Jr. *(Chm)*
Stephen E. Wessel *(Pres & CEO)*
Stephen F. Theriot *(CFO)*
Bruce A. Scott *(Exec VP)*

GUARANTY BANCSHARES, INC.

100 W Arkansas St
Mount Pleasant, TX 75455
Mailing Address:
PO Box 1158
Mount Pleasant, TX 75456-1158
Tel.: (903) 572-9881
Fax: (903) 572-9658
Toll Free: (888) 572-9881
E-mail: guaranty@gnty.com
Web Site: www.gnty.com
Approx. Rev.: $51,337,000
Approx. Number Employees: 250
Year Founded: 1980
Business Description:
Bank Holding Company
S.I.C.: 6029; 6712
N.A.I.C.S.: 522110; 551111
Advertising Expenditures: $357,000
Media: 7-8
Personnel:
Arthur B. Scharlach, Jr. *(Chm & CEO)*
Tyson T. Abston *(Pres)*
Cappy Payne *(CFO & Sr Exec VP)*
Craig Roberts *(Pres-Guaranty Bond Bank)*
Martin Bell *(Sr VP)*
Kirk L. Lee *(Sr VP)*
Brands & Products:
GUARANTY BANK

GUARANTY FEDERAL BANCSHARES, INC.

1341 W Battlefield Rd
Springfield, MO 65807
Tel.: (417) 520-4333
Fax: (417) 520-3607
E-mail: webmaster@gbankmo.com
Web Site: www.gfed.com
Approx. Rev.: $36,681,507
Approx. Number Employees: 146
Year Founded: 1997
Business Description:
Bank Holding Company
S.I.C.: 6029; 6035; 6712
N.A.I.C.S.: 522110; 522120; 551111
Advertising Expenditures: $300,000
Media: 6-7-9-25
Personnel:
Don M. Gibson *(Chm)*
Jack L. Barham *(Vice Chm)*
Shaun A. Burke *(CEO)*
Carter Peters *(CFO, COO & Exec VP)*
Mark McFatridge *(COO)*
H. Michael Mattson *(Exec VP & Chief Lending Officer)*
Carlye Wannenmacher *(VP-Dir-Mktg)*
Brands & Products:
KEEP YOUR SAVINGS CLOSE TO HOME
STRENGTH GROWTH VISION

GUARDIAN GROUP OF FUNDS LTD.

(Affil. of Bank of Montreal)
Commerce Ct W Ste 4100
Toronto, ON M5L 1G6, Canada
Mailing Address:
PO Box 577
Toronto, ON M5L 1G6, Canada
Tel.: (416) 947-4011
Fax: (416) 364-9169
E-mail: info@ggof.com
Web Site: www.ggof.com
Approx. Number Employees: 110

Key to Media (For complete agency information see *The Advertising Red Books-Agencies* edition):
1. Bus. Publs. 2. Cable T.V. 3. Catalogs & Directories. 4. Co-op Adv. 5. Consumer Mags. 6. D.M. to Bus. Estab.7. D.M. to Consumers 8. Daily Newsp. 9. Exhibits/Trade Shows 10. Foreign 11. Infomercial 12. Internet Adv.13. Multimedia 14. Network Radio 15. Network T.V. 16. Newsp. Distr. Mags. 17. Other 18. Outdoor (Posters, Transit) 19. Point of Purchase20. Premiums, Novelties 21. Product Samples 22. Special Events Mktg. 23. Spot Radio 24. Spot T.V. 25. Weekly Newsp. 26. Yellow Page Adv.

Guardian Group of Funds Ltd. — (Continued)

Year Founded: 2001
Business Description:
Mutual Funds
S.I.C.: 6722
N.A.I.C.S.: 525910
Media: 2
Personnel:
Ross Kappele *(Pres)*
Debbie Stansens *(VP-Mktg Svcs)*

H&R BLOCK, INC.

1 H&R Block Way
Kansas City, MO 64105
Tel.: (816) 854-3000
E-mail: partnerships@hrblock.com
Web Site: www.handrblock.com
Approx. Rev.: $3,774,296,000
Approx. Number Employees: 7,900
Year Founded: 1955
Business Description:
Holding Company; Income Tax Preparation, Temporary Help, Computer Information & Communications Services
S.I.C.: 6719; 6794; 7291; 7299; 7363; 8721
N.A.I.C.S.: 551112; 533110; 541211; 541213; 561320; 812199
Advertising Expenditures: $264,200,000
Media: 3-8-9-11-13-14-15-18-19-23-24-25-26
Distr.: Natl.
Budget Set: Sept.
Personnel:
Robert A. Gerard *(Chm)*
William C. Cobb *(Pres & CEO)*
Jeffrey T. Brown *(CFO & Sr VP)*
Richard Agar *(CIO & Sr VP)*
Robert Turtledove *(CMO & Sr VP)*
Phil Mazzini *(Pres-Retail Tax)*
Jim Ash *(Gen Counsel)*
Kathryn Fulton *(Sr VP-Govt Rels & Pub Policy)*
Jason Houseworth *(Sr VP-Digital Tax Solutions)*
Tammy S. Serati *(Sr VP-HR)*
Scott Gulbransen *(Dir-Social Media)*
Patrick Mumman *(Sr Mgr-Acq & Dev)*
Brands & Products:
BLOCK PREMIUM
H&R BLOCK
Advertising Agencies:
Due North Communications Inc.
35 The Esplanade 2nd Fl
Toronto, ON M5E 1Z4, Canada
Tel.: (416) 862-8181
Fax: (416) 862-9553

Fallon Worldwide
901 Marquette Ave Ste 2400
Minneapolis, MN 55402
Tel.: (612) 758-2345
Fax: (612) 758-2346
Agency of Record
Never Settle for Less
— Pete Leacock *(Acct Dir)*
— Chris Lawrence *(Acct Exec)*

HL2 Inc.
542 First Ave S Ste 400
Seattle, WA 98104
Tel.: (206) 223-0055
Fax: (206) 223-9665

Lapiz
35 W Wacker Dr 12th Fl
Chicago, IL 60601
Tel.: (312) 220-5000
Fax: (312) 220-6212
Hispanic Market

OMD Chicago
225 N Michigan Ave 19th Fl
Chicago, IL 60601-7757
Tel.: (312) 324-7000
Fax: (312) 324-8201
(Media Agency of Record)

PointRoll Inc.
951 E Hector St
Conshohocken, PA 19428
Tel.: (267) 558-1300
Fax: (267) 285-1141
Toll Free: (800) 203-6956

HABIF, AROGETI & WYNNE, LLP

5 Concourse Pkwy Ste 1000
Atlanta, GA 30328
Tel.: (404) 892-9651
Fax: (404) 602-4684
Toll Free: (800) 792-9651
E-mail: info@hawcpa.com
Web Site: www.hawcpa.com
Approx. Sls.: $24,000,000
Approx. Number Employees: 200
Year Founded: 1952
Business Description:
Accounting, Tax & Consulting Services
S.I.C.: 7291; 8721; 8748
N.A.I.C.S.: 541211; 541213; 541219; 541618
Personnel:
James Arogeti *(Co-Founder & Partner)*
Merrill D. Wynne *(Co-Founder & Partner)*
J. Dan Simms *(CEO & Partner)*
Robert J. Arogeti *(Partner-Advisory & Bus Svcs Grp)*
Jana Bledsoe *(Partner-Audit Grp)*
Rob Casey *(Partner-Audit Grp)*
Edward D. Deck *(Partner-Audit Grp)*
Yelena Epova *(Partner-Tax Grp)*
Baron J. Frankel *(Partner-Litigation Consulting Svcs Grp)*
Darrin Friedrich *(Partner-Tax Grp)*
Jeff Grosoff *(Partner-Audit Grp)*
Frank H. Gudger *(Partner-Audit Grp)*
Lisa C. Haynor *(Partner-Advisory & Bus Svcs Grp)*
Kurt Huntzinger *(Partner-Audit Grp)*
Marc L. Kanne *(Partner-Advisory & Bus Svcs Grp)*
Alex Knight *(Partner-Advisory & Bus Svcs Grp)*
Mitchell S. Kopelman *(Partner-Tax Grp)*
Richard Kopelman *(Partner-Audit Grp)*
Kim McConkey *(Partner-Audit Grp)*
Jonathan L. Miller *(Partner-Advisory & Bus Svcs Grp)*
Richard A. Rubin *(Partner-Advisory & Bus Svcs Grp)*
Advertising Agency:
TG Madison
3340 Peachtree Rd NE Ste 2850
Atlanta, GA 30326-1027
Tel.: (404) 262-2623
Tel.: (404) 267-4421 (President's Number)
Fax: (404) 237-2811

HAMPTON ROADS BANKSHARES, INC.

999 Waterside Dr Ste 200
Norfolk, VA 23510
Tel.: (757) 217-1000
Web Site: www.bankofhamptonroads.com
Approx. Rev.: $140,837,000
Approx. Number Employees: 750
Year Founded: 2001
Business Description:
Bank Holding Company
S.I.C.: 6712; 6029
N.A.I.C.S.: 551111; 522110
Advertising Expenditures: $888,000
Personnel:
John A. B. Davies, Jr. *(Pres & CEO)*
Stephen P. Theobald *(CFO & Exec VP)*
Lorelle L. Fritsch *(Chief Acctg Officer)*
Glenn R. Astolfi *(Pres/COO-Gateway Bank Mortgage, Inc.)*
Chris Corchiani *(CEO-Gateway Bank Mortgage, Inc.)*
Douglas J. Glenn *(Gen Counsel & Exec VP)*
Michael J. Sykes *(Sr VP & Project Mgr-Special Assets)*

HANCOCK BANK

(Holding of Hancock Holding Company)
(d/b/a Hancock Bank of Mississippi)
1 Hancock Plz
Gulfport, MS 39502
Tel.: (228) 868-4000
Tel.: (228) 868-4377
Fax: (228) 868-4675
Toll Free: (800) 448-8812
E-mail: service@hancockbank.com
Web Site: www.hancockbank.com
Sales Range: $300-349.9 Million
Approx. Number Employees: 1,500
Year Founded: 1899
Business Description:
Commercial Bank
S.I.C.: 6029
N.A.I.C.S.: 522110
Advertising Expenditures: $2,000,000
Media: 4-7-8-13
Personnel:
Carl J. Chaney *(Pres & CEO)*
Robert A. Seals *(Sr VP & Dir-Mktg)*
Renee Lester *(Mgr)*
Diana Nixon *(Mgr-Small Bus Products)*
Roland E. Pittman *(Mgr)*
Brands & Products:
HANDYCALL
Advertising Agency:
GodwinGroup
284 Debuys Rd
Biloxi, MS 39531-2611
Tel.: (601) 354-5711
Fax: (228) 388-8782

HANCOCK HOLDING COMPANY

1 Hancock Plz 2510 14th St
Gulfport, MS 39501-1947
Tel.: (228) 868-4000
Fax: (228) 868-4303
Toll Free: (800) 522-6542
E-mail: paul_guichet@hancockbank.com
Web Site: www.hancockbank.com
Approx. Int. Income: $352,558,000
Approx. Number Employees: 2,271
Year Founded: 1984
Business Description:
Bank Holding Company
S.I.C.: 6712; 6029
N.A.I.C.S.: 551111; 522110
Advertising Expenditures: $5,597,000
Media: 9-10-25
Personnel:
Carl J. Chaney *(Pres & CEO)*
John M. Hairston *(CEO & COO)*
Michael M. Achary *(CFO & Exec VP)*
Sam B. Kendricks *(Chief Credit Officer & Sr VP)*
Clifton J. Saik *(Chief Wealth Mgmt Officer & Exec VP)*
Edward G. Francis *(Chief Comml Banking Officer & Exec VP)*
Richard T. Hill *(Chief Retail Banking Officer & Exec VP)*
Joy Lambert Phillips *(Gen Counsel & Exec VP)*
Gerald S. Dugal *(Treas & Sr VP)*
D. Shane Loper *(Chief Risk & Admin Officer & Exec VP)*
Robert A. Seals *(Sr VP & Dir-Mktg)*
Sandra A. Wilbourn *(Sr VP & Dir-Corp Compliance)*
Alfreda A. Horne *(Sr VP)*
Brands & Products:
HANCOCK
HANCOCK BANK
Advertising Agency:
GodwinGroup
284 Debuys Rd
Biloxi, MS 39531-2611
Tel.: (601) 354-5711
Fax: (228) 388-8782

HANMI FINANCIAL CORPORATION

3660 Wilshire Blvd Penthouse Ste A
Los Angeles, CA 90010
Tel.: (213) 382-2200
Fax: (213) 384-8608
Web Site: www.hanmifinancial.com
Approx. Rev.: $169,918,000
Approx. Number Employees: 431
Year Founded: 2000
Business Description:
Bank Holding Company
S.I.C.: 6712; 6029; 6035; 6163; 6211
N.A.I.C.S.: 551111; 522110; 522120; 522310; 523110
Advertising Expenditures: $2,394,000
Media: 7-8-9-13-18-22-23-24-25
Personnel:
Joseph K. Rho *(Chm)*
Jay S. Yoo *(Pres & CEO)*
Brian E. Cho *(CFO & Exec VP)*

THE HARRIS BANK N.A.

(Sub. of Harris Bancorp, Inc.)
111 W Monroe St
Chicago, IL 60603-4096
Mailing Address:
PO Box 755
Chicago, IL 60690-0755
Tel.: (312) 461-2121
Fax: (312) 293-4780
Toll Free: (888) 340BANK
E-mail: webinfo@harrisbank.com
Web Site: www.harrisbank.com
Sales Range: $650-699.9 Million
Approx. Number Employees: 6,850
Year Founded: 1882
Business Description:
Commercial Banking Services
S.I.C.: 6029; 6035
N.A.I.C.S.: 522110; 522120

Key to Media (For complete agency information see *The Advertising Red Books-Agencies* edition):
1. Bus. Publs. 2. Cable T.V. 3. Catalogs & Directories. 4. Co-op Adv. 5. Consumer Mags. 6. D.M. to Bus. Estab.7. D.M. to Consumers 8. Daily Newsp. 9. Exhibits/Trade Shows 10. Foreign 11. Infomercial 12. Internet Adv.13. Multimedia 14. Network Radio 15. Network T.V. 16. Newsp. Distr. Mags. 17. Other 18. Outdoor (Posters, Transit) 19. Point of Purchase20. Premiums, Novelties 21. Product Samples 22. Special Events Mktg. 23. Spot Radio 24. Spot T.V. 25. Weekly Newsp. 26. Yellow Page Adv.

Advertising Expenditures: $6,000,000
Media: 1-2-3-4-7-8-9-10-13-18-19-20-22-23-24-25-26
Distr.: Direct to Consumer; Reg.
Budget Set: Nov.
Personnel:
Ellen Costello *(Pres & CEO)*
Pam C. Piarowski *(CFO & Sr VP)*
Justine Fedak *(Sr VP & Head-Mktg & Customer Strategies)*
Ivy Bennett *(Sr VP-Mktg & Customer Strategies)*
Deirdre Drake *(Sr VP-HR)*
Kathleen Campbell *(VP-Sls, Mgr-Svc Reporting & Analytics)*
Christina Jarzabek *(Mgr-Product & Channel)*
Brands & Products:
HARRIS
HARRIS ADVANTEDGE
HARRISDIRECT
Advertising Agency:
Element 79
(Part of the Omincom Group)
200 E Randolph St 33rd Fl
Chicago, IL 60601
Tel.: (312) 233-8100
Fax: (312) 233-8298

HAWTHORN BANCSHARES, INC.

300 SW Longview Blvd
Lees Summit, MO 64081
Tel.: (816) 347-8100
Toll Free: (800) 761-8362
Web Site:
www.hawthornbancshares.com
Approx. Rev.: $69,219,398
Approx. Number Employees: 309
Year Founded: 1992
Business Description:
Bank Holding Company
S.I.C.: 6712; 6029
N.A.I.C.S.: 551111; 522110
Advertising Expenditures: $1,272,046
Personnel:
David T. Turner *(Chm, Pres & CEO)*
Dean McCracken *(Sr Credit Officer)*
Kathleen L. Bruegenhemke *(Sec & Sr VP)*

H.D. VEST, INC.

(Sub. of Wells Fargo & Company)
6333 N State Hwy 161 4th Fl
Irving, TX 75038-2216
Tel.: (972) 870-6000
Fax: (972) 870-6128
E-mail: webmaster@hdvest.com
Web Site: www.hdvest.com
Sales Range: $1-4.9 Billion
Approx. Number Employees: 350
Year Founded: 1986
Business Description:
Financial Planning Services
S.I.C.: 6211; 6371
N.A.I.C.S.: 523120; 525990
Import Export
Media: 2-7-10
Personnel:
Roger Ochs *(Pres)*
Melissa Draughton *(Exec Mgr-Trng & Events)*
Tim O'Brien *(Mgr-HR)*

HEARTLAND BANCSHARES INC.

420 N Morton St
Franklin, IN 46131
Tel.: (317) 738-3915
Fax: (317) 736-5022
E-mail: jeff.joyce@hcb-in.com
Web Site: www.hcb-in.com
Approx. Rev.: $13,929,000
Approx. Number Employees: 84
Year Founded: 1997
Business Description:
Bank Holding Company
S.I.C.: 6712; 6029
N.A.I.C.S.: 551111; 522110
Advertising Expenditures: $273,000
Personnel:
John R. Norton, III *(Chm)*
Steven L. Bechman *(Pres & CEO)*
Jackie McNeelan *(Sr VP)*
Jeffrey L. Goben *(Exec VP)*
Jeffery D. Joyce *(Sr VP & Controller)*
R. Trent McWilliams *(Sr VP-Bus Dev)*

HEARTLAND FINANCIAL USA, INC.

1398 Central Ave
Dubuque, IA 52004
Tel.: (563) 589-2000
E-mail: webmaster@dubuquebank.com
Web Site: www.htlf.com
Approx. Rev.: $251,261,000
Approx. Number Employees: 1,066
Year Founded: 1981
Business Description:
Bank Holding Company
S.I.C.: 6712; 6029
N.A.I.C.S.: 551111; 522110
Import Export
Advertising Expenditures: $3,830,000
Media: 7-8-9-17-18-23-25
Personnel:
Mark C. Falb *(Vice Chm)*
Thomas L. Flynn *(Vice Chm)*
Lynn B. Fuller *(Pres & CEO)*
John K. Schmidt *(CFO, COO & Exec VP)*
Kenneth J. Erickson *(Chief Credit Officer & Exec VP)*
Janet M. Quick *(Chief Acctg Officer & Sr VP-Fin)*
David J. Kapler *(Gen Counsel)*
Lois K. Pearce *(Sr VP-Corp Sec)*
Tom Peckosh *(Head-Equity Portfolio Mgmt-Wealth Mgmt Grp)*
John J. Berg *(Exec VP-Mktg & Sls)*
Brian J. Fox *(Exec VP-Ops)*
Bruce J. Rehmke *(Exec VP-Wealth Mgmt Grp)*
Frank E. Walter *(Exec VP-Comml Sls)*
David Wick *(Sr VP-Program Dir)*
LuAnn Bowman *(Sr VP & Dir-Retail Trng)*
Polly Hauser *(Sr VP & Dir-Sls-Wealth Mgmt Grp)*
Doris Hannan *(Sr VP & Mgr-Deposit Ops)*
Sharon Yonda *(Sr VP & Mgr-Loan Ops)*
Edward Borchert *(Sr VP-Credit Admin)*
Michael Dillman *(Sr VP-Credit Admin)*
Robert Eby *(Sr VP-Credit Admin)*
Douglas J. Horstmann *(Sr VP-Lending)*
Nelson Klavitter *(Sr VP-Ops)*
Julie L. Shanahan *(Sr VP-Teller Ops)*
Marti A. Vandemore *(Sr VP-Info Svcs)*
Nancy Wilson *(Sr VP-HR)*
Teresa Rowe *(Asst VP-Compliance)*
Connie Thienes *(Product Mgr)*

HEARTLAND PAYMENT SYSTEMS, INC.

90 Nassau St 2nd Fl
Princeton, NJ 08542-4520
Tel.: (609) 683-3831
Fax: (609) 683-3815
Toll Free: (888) 798-3131
E-mail: nancy.gross@e-hps.com
Web Site:
www.heartlandpaymentsystems.com
Approx. Rev.: $1,864,337,000
Approx. Number Employees: 2,612
Year Founded: 1997
Business Description:
Credit Card Processing Services
S.I.C.: 8721; 6099; 6141; 7374
N.A.I.C.S.: 541214; 518210; 522210; 522320
Personnel:
Robert O. Carr *(Chm & CEO)*
Robert H.B. Baldwin, Jr. *(Pres)*
Maria Rueda *(CFO)*
Martin A. Moretti *(Chief Svc Officer)*
David J. Hogan *(Exec Dir-Major Accts)*
Alan Sims *(Exec Dir-Gateway Tech)*
Sanford C. Brown *(Reg Dir)*
Maria Jones *(Product Mgr)*
Brands & Products:
GIVE SOMETHING BACK NETWORK
HEARTLAND CARD PROCESSING
HEARTLAND CHECK MANAGEMENT
HEARTLAND CONNECT
HEARTLAND EXPRESS FUNDS
HEARTLAND GIFT CARDS
HEARTLAND LAUNDRY SOLUTIONS
HEARTLAND LENDING SERVICES
HEARTLAND MICROPAYMENTS
HEARTLAND ONLINE MERCHANT CENTER
HEARTLAND ONLINE PAYMENT
HEARTLAND PAYMENT SYSTEM
HEARTLAND PAYMENT SYSTEMS
HEARTLAND PAYROLL SERVICES
HEARTLAND TABLE SIDE
HEARTLAND WEB CONNECT
Advertising Agency:
Gregory FCA
27 W Athens Ave Ste 200
Ardmore, PA 19003
Tel.: (610) 642-8253
Fax: (610) 642-1258
Fax: (610) 649-9029
Toll Free: (800) 499-4734

HERITAGE COMMERCE CORP.

150 Almaden Blvd
San Jose, CA 95113-2000
Tel.: (408) 947-6900
Fax: (408) 947-6910
E-mail: heritage@herbank.com
Web Site:
www.heritagecommercecorp.com
Approx. Rev.: $63,820,000
Approx. Number Employees: 181
Year Founded: 1998
Business Description:
Bank Holding Company
S.I.C.: 6712; 6029; 6163
N.A.I.C.S.: 551111; 522110; 522310
Advertising Expenditures: $395,000
Media: 7-8-10-13
Personnel:
Jack W. Conner *(Chm)*
Walter T. Kaczmarek *(Pres)*
Lawrence D. Mcgovern *(CFO & Exec VP)*
Dan T. Kawamoto *(Chief Admin Officer & Exec VP)*
Raymond A. Parker *(Exec VP-Banking Div)*
Diana Oliveira *(VP & Dir-Mktg)*

HERITAGE FINANCIAL CORPORATION

201 5th Ave SW
Olympia, WA 98501
Mailing Address:
PO Box 1578
Olympia, WA 98507-1578
Tel.: (360) 943-1500
Fax: (360) 352-0864
E-mail: hfwa@heritagebankwa.com
Web Site:
www.heritagebankwaonline2.com
Approx. Rev.: $81,020,000
Approx. Number Employees: 321
Year Founded: 1997
Business Description:
Bank Holding Company
S.I.C.: 6712; 6029
N.A.I.C.S.: 551111; 522110
Advertising Expenditures: $494,000
Media: 7-8-10
Personnel:
Donald V. Rhodes *(Chm)*
Brian L. Vance *(Pres & CEO)*
Donald J. Hinson *(CFO & Sr VP)*
Jeffrey J. Deuel *(COO)*
Lisa L. Welander *(CIO & VP)*
Kaylene M. Lahn *(Sr VP & Corp Sec)*
Edward D. Cameron *(Exec VP)*
Cindy Huntley *(Dir-Mktg & Sr VP-Retail Banking)*
Sabrina C. Robison *(VP & Dir-HR)*

HF FINANCIAL CORP.

225 S Main Ave
Sioux Falls, SD 57104
Mailing Address:
PO Box 5000
Sioux Falls, SD 57117-5000
Tel.: (605) 333-7556
Fax: (605) 333-7621
Toll Free: (800) 244-2149
E-mail: info@homefederal.com
Web Site: www.homefederal.com
Approx. Rev.: $63,285,000
Approx. Number Employees: 310
Year Founded: 1991
Business Description:
Bank Holding Company
S.I.C.: 6712; 6029; 6035
N.A.I.C.S.: 551111; 522110; 522120
Advertising Expenditures: $856,000
Personnel:
Curtis L. Hage *(Chm, Pres & CEO)*
Charles T. Day *(Vice Chm)*
Brent R. Olthoff *(CFO, Treas & Sr VP)*
Michael Westberg *(Chief Credit Officer & Sr VP)*
Stephen M. Bianchi *(Sr VP & Pres-Twin Cities Market)*
Darrel L. Posegate *(Exec VP)*
David A. Brown *(Sr VP-Community Banking)*
Jon M Gadberry *(Sr VP-Wealth Mgmt)*
Mary F. Hitzemann *(Sr VP-HR)*
Natalie A. Sundvold *(Sr VP-Svcs & Support)*

Key to Media (For complete agency information see *The Advertising Red Books-Agencies* edition):
1. Bus. Publs. 2. Cable T.V. 3. Catalogs & Directories. 4. Co-op Adv. 5. Consumer Mags. 6. D.M. to Bus. Estab.7. D.M. to Consumers 8. Daily Newsp. 9. Exhibits/Trade Shows 10. Foreign 11. Infomercial 12. Internet Adv.13. Multimedia 14. Network Radio 15. Network T.V. 16. Newsp. Distr. Mags. 17. Other 18. Outdoor (Posters, Transit) 19. Point of Purchase20. Premiums, Novelties 21. Product Samples 22. Special Events Mktg. 23. Spot Radio 24. Spot T.V. 25. Weekly Newsp. 26. Yellow Page Adv.

HFF, INC.
1 Oxford Ctr 301 Grant St Ste 600
Pittsburgh, PA 15219
Tel.: (412) 281-8714
Fax: (412) 281-2792
E-mail: InvestorRelations@hfflp.com
Web Site: www.hfflp.com
Approx. Rev.: $139,972,000
Approx. Number Employees: 427
Business Description:
Commercial Real Estate & Capital Markets Services
S.I.C.: 6531; 6289
N.A.I.C.S.: 531390; 523999
Advertising Expenditures: $400,000
Media: 17
Personnel:
Steve Heldenfels *(Owner)*
John H. Pelusi, Jr. *(Exec Mng Dir)*
Todd Armstrong *(Sr Mng Dir)*
John Brownlee *(Sr Mng Dir)*
John Duffy *(Sr Mng Dir)*
Jaime Fink *(Sr Mng Dir)*
Susan L. Hill *(Sr Mng Dir)*
Mike Kavanau *(Sr Mng Dir)*
Andrew Levy *(Sr Mng Dir)*
Roberto Casas *(Mng Dir)*
Tom Goodson *(Mng Dir)*
Bill Miller *(Mng Dir)*
John S. Sebree *(Mng Dir)*
Ryan Shore *(Mng Dir)*
Kevin Smith *(Mng Dir)*
Andrew Weir *(Mng Dir)*
Gregory R. Conley *(CFO)*
Nancy O. Goodson *(COO)*
Matt Mitchell *(Dir-Multi-Housing Grp-Tampa)*
Doug Childers *(Assoc Dir)*

HIBERNIA HOMESTEAD BANCORP, INC.
325 Carondelet St
New Orleans, LA 70130
Tel.: (504) 522-3203
Fax: (504) 301-9707
Web Site:
www.hiberniahomesteadbank.com
Approx. Rev.: $6,032,000
Business Description:
Bank Holding Company
S.I.C.: 6712
N.A.I.C.S.: 551111
Advertising Expenditures: $103,000
Media: 17
Personnel:
Patrick W. Browne, Jr. *(Chm)*
A. Peyton Bush, III *(Pres & CEO)*
Donna T. Guerra *(CFO & Exec VP)*

HILCO INDUSTRIAL, LLC
(Sub. of Hilco Trading Co., Inc.)
31555 W Fourteen Mile Rd Ste 207
Farmington Hills, MI 48334
Tel.: (616) 732-1800
Fax: (248) 254-9995
Web Site: www.hilcoind.com
Business Description:
Equity Investment Services
S.I.C.: 6289
N.A.I.C.S.: 523999
Personnel:
Robert Levy *(Mng Partner)*
Stephan Wolf *(Mng Partner)*
Marsha Fales-Wright *(VP-Mktg)*
Advertising Agency:
LRC Marketing
31555 W 14 Mile Rd Ste 207
Farmington Hills, MI 48334
Tel.: (248) 254-9999
Fax: (248) 254-9995

HILL BARTH & KING LLC
7680 Market St
Youngstown, OH 44512
Tel.: (330) 758-8613
Fax: (330) 758-0357
Web Site: www.hbkcpa.com
Approx. Sls.: $24,500,000
Approx. Number Employees: 200
Business Description:
Certified Public Accountant
S.I.C.: 8721
N.A.I.C.S.: 541211
Media: 6
Personnel:
M. Allegretti *(CEO & Mng Partner)*
Richard A. Keyse *(Principal)*

HILLCREST BANK, N.A.
(Sub. of NBH Holdings Corp.)
11111 W 95th St
Overland Park, KS 66214-1846
Tel.: (913) 324-6400
Toll Free: (800) 681-1776
Web Site: www.hillcrestbank.com
Approx. Number Employees: 80
Year Founded: 1987
Business Description:
Commercial Banking Services
S.I.C.: 6029
N.A.I.C.S.: 522110
Personnel:
G. Timothy Laney *(Pres & CEO)*
Kathy Gordon *(First VP & Branch Coord)*
Advertising Agency:
Meers Advertising
1811 Walnut St
Kansas City, MO 64108
Tel.: (816) 474-2920
Fax: (816) 474-2925
Toll Free: (800) 259-7346

HILLS BANCORPORATION
131 Main St
Hills, IA 52235
Tel.: (319) 679-2291
Fax: (319) 679-2180
E-mail: hillsbank@hillsbank.com
Web Site: www.hillsbank.com
Approx. Rev.: $115,086,000
Approx. Number Employees: 350
Year Founded: 1982
Business Description:
Bank Holding Company
S.I.C.: 6712; 6029
N.A.I.C.S.: 551111; 522110
Advertising Expenditures: $2,058,000
Personnel:
Ronald E. Stutsman *(Chm & VP)*
Dwight O. Seegmiller *(Pres & CEO)*
James G. Pratt *(CFO, Chief Acctg Officer, Treas, Sec & Sr VP)*

HINGHAM INSTITUTION FOR SAVINGS
55 Main St
Hingham, MA 02043
Tel.: (781) 749-2200
Fax: (781) 740-4889
E-mail: pcbank24@hinghamsavings.com
Web Site: www.hinghamsavings.com
Approx. Int. Income: $46,825,000
Approx. Number Employees: 79
Year Founded: 1834
Business Description:
State-Chartered Savings Bank
S.I.C.: 6035; 6029
N.A.I.C.S.: 522120; 522110
Advertising Expenditures: $1,450,000
Media: 3-7-8-18-20-23
Personnel:
Robert H. Gaughen, Jr. *(Pres & CEO)*
Joan Reydel *(Asst VP-Retail Lending)*

HMN FINANCIAL, INC.
1016 Civic Center Dr NW
Rochester, MN 55903
Mailing Address:
PO Box 6057
Rochester, MN 55901
Tel.: (507) 535-1200
Fax: (507) 535-1300
Toll Free: (888) 644-4142 (Investor Relations)
Web Site: www.hmnf.com
Approx. Rev.: $55,541,000
Approx. Number Employees: 225
Year Founded: 1994
Business Description:
Bank Holding Company
S.I.C.: 6712; 6035
N.A.I.C.S.: 551111; 522120
Advertising Expenditures: $384,184
Personnel:
Timothy R. Geisler *(Chm)*
Bradley C. Krehbiel *(Pres)*
Jon J. Eberle *(CFO, Treas & Sr VP)*
Dwain C. Jorgensen *(Sr VP)*
Susan K. Kolling *(Sr VP)*

HOLMGREN & ASSOCIATES
1900 Mountain Blvd
Oakland, CA 94611
Tel.: (510) 339-2121
Fax: (510) 339-1004
Web Site:
www.mortgageholmgren.com
Sales Range: Less than $1 Million
Approx. Number Employees: 14
Year Founded: 1989
Business Description:
Mortgage Brokers
S.I.C.: 6159
N.A.I.C.S.: 522292
Media: 9-13-18-22-25-26
Personnel:
John K. Holmgren *(Owner & Pres)*
Cheryl Reyner *(Mgr-Mktg)*

HOME BANCORP, INC.
503 Kaliste Saloom Rd
Lafayette, LA 70508
Tel.: (337) 237-1960
Fax: (337) 264-9280
Web Site: www.home24bank.com
Approx. Rev.: $38,140,318
Approx. Number Employees: 143
Year Founded: 2008
Business Description:
Bank Holding Company
S.I.C.: 6712; 6035
N.A.I.C.S.: 551111; 522120
Advertising Expenditures: $634,000
Media: 3-8-9-23-24-25
Personnel:
Michael P. Maraist, III *(Chm)*
John W. Bordelon *(Pres & CEO)*
Darren E. Guidry *(CFO)*
Joseph B. Zanco *(CFO)*
Scott T. Sutton *(COO)*

HOME BANCSHARES, INC.
719 Harkrider St Ste 100
Conway, AR 72032
Mailing Address:
PO Box 966
Conway, AR 72033
Tel.: (501) 328-4715
Tel.: (501) 328-4657
E-mail: info@homebancshares.com
Web Site: www.homebancshares.com
Approx. Rev.: $216,171,000
Approx. Number Employees: 698
Year Founded: 1998
Business Description:
Bank Holding Company
S.I.C.: 6712; 6029
N.A.I.C.S.: 551111; 522110
Advertising Expenditures: $2,033,000
Personnel:
John W. Allison *(Chm)*
Robert H. Adcock, Jr. *(Vice Chm)*
C. Randall Sims *(CEO)*
Randy E. Mayor *(CFO & Treas)*
Brian S. Davis *(Chief Acctg Officer & IR Officer)*
Kevin D. Hester *(Chief Lending Officer)*

HOME FEDERAL BANCORP, INC.
500 12th Ave S
Nampa, ID 83651
Tel.: (208) 466-4634
Fax: (208) 468-5001
Web Site: www.myhomefed.com
Approx. Rev.: $54,213,000
Approx. Number Employees: 430
Year Founded: 1920
Business Description:
Bank Holding Company
S.I.C.: 6712; 6035
N.A.I.C.S.: 551111; 522120
Advertising Expenditures: $1,200,000
Personnel:
Daniel L. Stevens *(Chm)*
Len E. Williams *(Pres & CEO)*
Eric Nadeau *(CFO, Treas, Sec & Exec VP)*
Steven D. Emerson *(Exec VP-Comml Banking)*
R. Shane Correa *(Chief Banking Officer & Exec VP)*
Lynn Sander *(VP-Community Rels)*
Brands & Products:
HOME FEDERAL
HOME FEDERAL BANCORP

HOMEBANC
(Sub. of HomeBanc N.A.)
659 W Lumsden Rd
Brandon, FL 33511
Tel.: (813) 655-8877
Toll Free: (888) 291-2822
Web Site: www.homebanc.com/
Sales Range: $1-9.9 Million
Approx. Number Employees: 24
Business Description:
Mortgage Loan Broker
S.I.C.: 6163
N.A.I.C.S.: 522310
Media: 6
Personnel:
Michael T. Alea *(Sr VP & Reg Mortgage Mgr)*

HOPFED BANCORP, INC.
4155 Lafayette Rd
Hopkinsville, KY 42240
Tel.: (270) 885-1171

Key to Media (For complete agency information see *The Advertising Red Books-Agencies* edition):
1. Bus. Publs. 2. Cable T.V. 3. Catalogs & Directories. 4. Co-op Adv. 5. Consumer Mags. 6. D.M. to Bus. Estab.7. D.M. to Consumers 8. Daily Newsp. 9. Exhibits/Trade Shows 10. Foreign 11. Infomercial 12. Internet Adv.13. Multimedia 14. Network Radio 15. Network T.V. 16. Newsp. Distr. Mags. 17. Other 18. Outdoor (Posters, Transit) 19. Point of Purchase20. Premiums, Novelties 21. Product Samples 22. Special Events Mktg. 23. Spot Radio 24. Spot T.V. 25. Weekly Newsp. 26. Yellow Page Adv.

Fax: (270) 889-0313
E-mail: info@bankwithheritage.com
Web Site: www.bankwithheritage.com
Approx. Rev.: $63,523,000
Approx. Number Employees: 252
Year Founded: 1997
Business Description:
Bank Holding Company
S.I.C.: 6712; 6029; 6035
N.A.I.C.S.: 551111; 522110; 522120
Advertising Expenditures: $1,304,000
Personnel:
Gilbert E. Lee *(Chm)*
Thomas I. Miller *(Vice Chm)*
John E. Peck *(Pres & CEO)*
Billy C. Duvall *(CFO, Treas & Sr VP)*
Michael L. Woolfolk *(COO & Exec VP)*
Michael F. Stalls *(Chief Credit Officer & Sr VP)*

HORIZON BANCORP
515 Franklin Square
Michigan City, IN 46360
Tel.: (219) 879-0211
Fax: (219) 873-2626
Fax: (219) 873-2628
Toll Free: (888) 904-2265
Web Site: www.accesshorizon.com
Approx. Int. Income: $68,491,000
Approx. Number Employees: 312
Year Founded: 1873
Business Description:
Bank Holding Company
S.I.C.: 6712; 6029; 6035
N.A.I.C.S.: 551111; 522110; 522120
Advertising Expenditures: $787,000
Personnel:
Robert C. Dabagia *(Chm)*
Craig M. Dwight *(Pres & CEO)*
Mark E. Secor *(CFO)*
Thomas H. Edwards *(Exec VP)*
James D. Neff *(Exec VP)*

HSBC BANK CANADA
(Sub. of HSBC North America Holdings Inc)
Ste 300 885 W Georgia St
Vancouver, BC V6C 3E9, Canada
Tel.: (604) 685-1000
Fax: (604) 641-2506
Telex: 4507750 HONGGROUP VCR
E-mail: info@hsbc.com
Web Site: www.hsbc.ca
Approx. Rev.: $2,539,918,260
Approx. Number Employees: 6,000
Year Founded: 1981
Business Description:
Retail & Commercial Banking Services
S.I.C.: 6029
N.A.I.C.S.: 522110
Advertising Expenditures: $1,500,000
Media: 2-3-4-5-6-8-9-10-15-19-20-22-23-24-25-26
Distr.: Natl.
Budget Set: Aug.
Personnel:
Samuel Minzberg *(Chm)*
J. Lindsay Gordon *(Pres & CEO)*
Graham McIsaac *(CFO)*
Sandra Stuart *(CTO & Chief Svcs Officer)*
Mark Watkinson *(Exec VP-Comml Banking & Pres-Central & Eastern Canada Reg)*
Brad Meredith *(Exec VP-Investment Banking & Markets)*
Sarah Morgan-Silvester *(Exec VP)*
Margaret Willis *(Exec VP-Personal Fin Svcs & Wealth Mgmt)*
Neil D. Johansen *(Mng Dir-Merchant Banking)*
John K. Philp *(Mng Dir-Merchant Banking-Toronto)*
Paul S. Eldridge *(Dir-Merchant Banking-Toronto)*
Daniel G. Jacques *(Dir-Merchant Banking-Calgary)*
Paul W. Rowe *(Dir-Merchant Banking-Edmonton)*
Brands & Products:
CORE BANKING
LOCAL AREA MARKETING
SUBSIDIARY BANKING

HSBC BANK USA, INC.
(Sub. of HSBC North America Holdings Inc)
452 5th Ave
New York, NY 10018-2706
Tel.: (212) 525-5000
Fax: (212) 525-0355
Toll Free: (800) 975-4722
Toll Free: (800) 975HSBC
Web Site: www.us.hsbc.com
Approx. Number Employees: 10,800
Year Founded: 1980
Business Description:
Commercial & International Banking, Mortgage & Deposit Banking, Precious Metals Trading, Futures Trading & Commodities Brokerage Services & Financial & Facility Services
S.I.C.: 6082; 6799
N.A.I.C.S.: 522293; 523910
Advertising Expenditures: $426,000
Media: 2-3-4-6-7-8-9-11-18-19-20-23-24-25-26
Distr.: Direct to Consumer; Intl.; Natl.
Personnel:
Stephen Keith Green *(Chm)*
Ashley Parker *(Reg Pres)*
David J. Noble *(Mng Dir)*
Gerard Mattia *(CFO)*
Brendan McDonagh *(COO)*
Aimee Daniels *(Reg Pres-Mid-Atlantic & Exec VP)*
Andy Ireland *(Reg Pres-Upstate Retail Banking & Exec VP)*
Janet Burak *(Gen Counsel & Sr Exec VP)*
Kevin Martin *(Sr Exec VP-Personal Fin Svcs & Mktg)*
Jeanne Ebersole *(Exec VP & Head-HR)*
James Bryski *(Sr VP-Comml Banking Unit)*
Paul Cronin *(Sr VP)*
Robert Wexler *(VP & Mgr-Premier Relationship)*
Advertising Agencies:
Added Value USA
11 Madison Ave 12th Fl
New York, NY 10010
Tel.: (212) 532-5500
Fax: (212) 548-4724

J. Walter Thompson Company
(d/b/a JWT)
466 Lexington Ave
New York, NY 10017-3140
Tel.: (212) 210-7000
Fax: (212) 210-7299
— Josh Kilmer-Purcell *(Dir-Creative)*

HSBC FINANCE CORPORATION
(Sub. of HSBC North America Holdings Inc)
26525 N Riverwoods Blvd
Mettawa, IL 60045
Tel.: (224) 544-2000
Fax: (847) 205-7401
Toll Free: (800) 975-4722
E-mail: investor.relations.usa@us.hsbc.com
Web Site: www.hsbcusa.com/hsbc_finance
Approx. Rev.: $9,775,000,000
Approx. Number Employees: 6,650
Year Founded: 1878
Business Description:
Consumer Lending Services
S.I.C.: 6141; 6099; 6163
N.A.I.C.S.: 522291; 522210; 522310; 522320
Advertising Expenditures: $32,360,000
Media: 2-4-6-7-8-9-10-11-13-14-15-18-19-20-21-23-24-26
Distr.: Intl.; Natl.
Personnel:
Brendan P. McDonagh *(Chm)*
Patrick J. Burke *(CEO)*
Jon R. Bottorff *(Exec VP & CFO)*
Eli Sinyak *(Chief Tech & Svcs Officer & Sr Exec VP)*
Thomas M. Detelich *(Pres-Consumer & Mortgage Lending)*
Susan B. Jewell *(Gen Counsel & Exec VP)*
Patrick D. Schwartz *(Sec, Exec VP & Deputy Gen Counsel)*
Jon N. Couture *(Sr Exec VP-HR)*
Susan E. Artmann *(Exec VP-Taxpayer Fin Svcs)*
William H. Kesler *(Exec VP)*
Loren C. Klug *(Exec VP-Strategy & Analysis)*
Mark A. Melas *(Exec VP-Corp Real Estate)*
Lisa M. Sodeika *(Exec VP-Corp Affairs)*
Jeff Branflick *(Sr VP-Mktg)*
Iain J. Mackay *(Grp Dir-Fin)*

HSBC INSURANCE SERVICES
(Sub. of HSBC Finance Corporation)
200 Somerset Corporate Blvd
Bridgewater, NJ 08807
Tel.: (908) 203-2100
Fax: (908) 203-4201
Sales Range: $10-24.9 Million
Approx. Number Employees: 200
Year Founded: 1887
Business Description:
Insurance Services
S.I.C.: 6411; 6099; 6331; 8742
N.A.I.C.S.: 524210; 522320; 524126; 541611
Media: 7-8-9-11-15-19-23-24-25-26
Distr.: Reg.
Brands & Products:
BENEFICIAL CREDIT SERVICE
BENEFICIAL INSURANCE GROUP
TAX MASTERS

HUNTINGTON BANCSHARES INCORPORATED
41 S High St Huntington Ctr
Columbus, OH 43287
Tel.: (614) 480-8300
Fax: (614) 480-5284
Toll Free: (800) 480-2265
E-mail: investor.relations@huntington.com
Web Site: www.huntington.com
Approx. Rev.: $3,187,250,000
Approx. Number Employees: 11,341
Year Founded: 1966
Business Description:
Bank Holding Company
S.I.C.: 6712; 6029; 6035; 6163; 6211; 6289
N.A.I.C.S.: 551111; 522110; 522120; 522310; 523110; 523999
Personnel:
Stephen D. Steinour *(Chm, Pres & CEO)*
Jeffrey Chapman *(Exec Mng Dir-Capital Markets Bus)*
Donald R. Kimble *(CFO & Sr Exec VP)*
James V. Cannella *(Pres-Asset Based Lending)*
Peter Dunlap *(Pres-Insurance)*
Richard J. Remiker *(Pres-Equipment Fin Grp)*
Richard A. Cheap *(Vice President and Director,Gen Counsel & Sec)*
Mary W. Navarro *(Sr Exec VP & Dir-Retail & Bus Banking)*
Mark Thompson *(Sr Exec VP & Dir-Strategy & Bus Segment Performance)*
David S. Anderson *(Exec VP & Controller)*
Melinda Ackerman *(Exec VP)*
Eric N. Sutphin *(Exec VP & Chief Auditor)*
Norman P. Bertke *(Sr VP, Dir-Corp Real Estate & Facilities)*
Todd Beekman *(Sr VP, Asst Dir-IR)*
Neal R. Shipley *(Sr VP-Pittsburgh Reg & Mgr-Comml Banking)*
Jay Gould *(Sr VP)*
Thomas P. Reed *(Sr VP, Principal Fin & Acctg Officer)*
Shahed Zaman *(VP & Mgr-Retail Banking-Greater Cleveland Region)*
Scott Brewer *(Dir-Corp Dev)*
Jeri Grier-Ball *(Dir-Commun)*
Randall Stickler *(Dir-Comml Real Estate)*
Brands & Products:
A BANK INVESTED IN PEOPLE
GLOBAL TRADE ACCESS
HUNTINGTON
HUNTINGTON AT WORK
HUNTINGTON FUNDS
HUNTINGTON PARK
HUNTINGTON PAYMENT FREEDOM
HUNTINGTON SMARTTAX
HUNTINGTON VISUAL ARCHIVE
PLATINUM PLUS
WORLDPOINTS
Advertising Agencies:
Engauge Communications
375 N Front St Ste 400
Columbus, OH 43215
Tel.: (614) 573-1010
Fax: (614) 573-1011

MPG
(Div. of HAVAS)
195 Broadway 12th Fl
New York, NY 10007
Tel.: (646) 587-5000
Fax: (646) 587-5005

Key to Media (For complete agency information see *The Advertising Red Books-Agencies* edition):
1. Bus. Publs. 2. Cable T.V. 3. Catalogs & Directories. 4. Co-op Adv. 5. Consumer Mags. 6. D.M. to Bus. Estab.7. D.M. to Consumers 8. Daily Newsp. 9. Exhibits/Trade Shows 10. Foreign 11. Infomercial 12. Internet Adv.13. Multimedia 14. Network Radio 15. Network T.V. 16. Newsp. Distr. Mags. 17. Other 18. Outdoor (Posters, Transit) 19. Point of Purchase20. Premiums, Novelties 21. Product Samples 22. Special Events Mktg. 23. Spot Radio 24. Spot T.V. 25. Weekly Newsp. 26. Yellow Page Adv.

THE HUNTINGTON NATIONAL BANK

(Sub. of Huntington Bancshares Incorporated)
Huntington Ctr 41 S High St
Columbus, OH 43287
Mailing Address:
PO Box 1558
Columbus, OH 43216-1558
Tel.: (614) 480-8300
E-mail: direct@huntington.com
Web Site: www.huntington.com
Sales Range: $1-4.9 Billion
Approx. Number Employees: 7,935
Year Founded: 1866
Business Description:
Retail & Commercial Banking Services
S.I.C.: 6035; 6029; 6141; 6211
N.A.I.C.S.: 522120; 522110; 522291; 523110
Import Export
Media: 2-6-7-8-9-11-13-18-20-23-24-25-26
Distr.: Reg.
Personnel:
Stephen D. Steinour *(Chm, Pres & CEO)*
Donald R. Kimble *(CFO, Treas & Sr Exec VP)*
David Clifton *(CMO)*
James E. Kunk *(Pres-Central Ohio Reg)*
Diane L. Dougherty *(Sr VP & Dir-Collections)*
Deborah L. Stein *(Sr VP)*
Maureen Brown *(VP & Mgr-PR)*
Gary Smith *(Asst VP)*
Jeff Evans *(Sr Acct Exec-Asset Based Lending)*
Brands & Products:
A BANK INVESTED IN PEOPLE
HUNTINGTON
Advertising Agency:
Arnold Worldwide
101 Huntington Ave
Boston, MA 02199-7603
Tel.: (617) 587-8000
Fax: (617) 587-8004
Employee Communications
In-Branch Ads
Promotions
Social Media Marketing
Traditional Advertising
Web

HURON CONSULTING GROUP INC.

550 W Van Buren St
Chicago, IL 60607
Tel.: (312) 583-8700
Fax: (312) 583-8701
Web Site:
www.huronconsultinggroup.com
Approx. Rev.: $604,600,000
Approx. Number Employees: 1,757
Year Founded: 2002
Business Description:
Business Consulting Services
S.I.C.: 8748
N.A.I.C.S.: 541618
Advertising Expenditures: $5,200,000
Media: 22
Personnel:
George E. Massaro *(Vice Chm)*
James H. Roth *(Pres & CEO)*
Ryan Bengtson *(Mng Dir)*
J. Kevin Blodgett *(Mng Dir)*
Richard D. Caruso *(Mng Dir)*
Khaled Dajani *(Mng Dir)*
Delphine Mendez de Leon *(Mng Dir)*
Timothy J. Fournier *(Mng Dir)*
Paul Johnson *(Mng Dir)*
Michael J. Roberts *(Mng Dir)*
Robin Snasdell *(Mng Dir)*
Philip Strzalka *(Mng Dir)*
Larry E. Stuckey, II *(Mng Dir)*
Emmanuel Tzavlakis *(Mng Dir)*
Amy Wall *(Mng Dir)*
C. Mark Hussey *(CFO & Treas)*
James K. Rojas *(COO)*
Vincent A. Marin *(CIO)*
Diane E. Ratekin *(Gen Counsel & VP)*
Gordon J. Mountford *(Exec VP-Huron Healthcare)*
Jennifer Frost Hennagir *(Dir)*
Brands & Products:
EXPERIENCE. REDEFINED.
HURON

HYPERCOM CORPORATION

8888 E Raintree Dr Ste 300
Scottsdale, AZ 85260
Tel.: (602) 504-5000
Tel.: (602) 504-5383 (Media Rels)
Fax: (602) 866-5380
Toll Free: (877) HYPERCOM
E-mail: info-us@hypercom.com
Web Site: www.hypercom.com
Approx. Rev.: $468,449,000
Approx. Number Employees: 1,431
Year Founded: 1978
Business Description:
End-to-End Electronic Payment Solutions, Including Card Payment Systems, Peripherals, Network Products, Ascendent Software & E-Commerce Payment Solutions
S.I.C.: 6099; 3577
N.A.I.C.S.: 522320; 334119
Advertising Expenditures: $400,000
Media: 2-7-9-10-11-19-25
Personnel:
Norman Stout *(Chm)*
Philippe Tartavull *(Pres & CEO)*
Thomas B. Sabol *(CFO)*
Douglas J. Reich *(Chief Compliance Officer, Gen Counsel, Corp Sec & Sr VP)*
David S. Cronin *(Pres/Mng Dir-North America)*
Clint Jones *(Mng Dir-Latin America)*
Heidi R. Goff *(Sr VP-Global Strategic Accts)*
Nassrin Tavakoli *(Sr VP-Global Engrg)*
Scott M. Tsujita *(Sr VP-Fin, IR & Treasury)*
Michel Sohrabi *(VP & Gen Mgr-Scandinavia, Benelux, VP-Mktg NEMEA)*
T. K. Cheung *(VP-Quality & Security)*
Connie Festa *(VP-Sls-HBNet)*
William Rossiter *(VP-Mktg)*
Pete Schuddekopf *(VP-Media & Industry Rels)*
Stuart Taylor *(VP-Global Solutions & Mktg)*
Monica Mitjans *(Sr Dir-Mktg)*
Brands & Products:
ARTEMA
ARTEMA MODULAR
ATMCONNECT
AVT.COMPACT
CERTAINT 100
EFT-MASTER
EFTSEC
ENCRYPTING PIN PAD V5
EPIC
EPICRECEIPTS
EPOS-INFOCOMMERCE
FASTPOS
FPE32
H2210
H2220
HKLM
HTMS
HYBRID CARD CONTROLLER
HYPERCOM
HYPERCOMVIEW
HYPERSAFE
HYPERWARE
ICE
ICE-PAC
IEN 2500
IN-TACT
ITERM-MASTER
K1200
LOGARITHM
MCS.SOFT
MEDCOMPACT
MEDHYBRID
MEDMODULAR
MEGANAC
ODT
OPTIMUM
P1300
PAY-BY-CUSTOMER
PV1310
REAL PAY
S10
S9
SMARTPAYMENTS
SURELOAD
T7PLUS
TERM-MASTER
TERM-MASTER SUITE
TRUSTED TRANSACTIONS
VHDT
WYMIX
WYNID

IBERIABANK CORPORATION

200 W Congress St
Lafayette, LA 70501
Tel.: (337) 521-4003
Tel.: (337) 521-4012 (Investor Relations)
E-mail: investor@iberiabank.com
Web Site: www.iberiabank.com
Approx. Rev.: $530,261,000
Approx. Number Employees: 2,099
Year Founded: 1994
Business Description:
Bank Holding Company
S.I.C.: 6712; 6029
N.A.I.C.S.: 551111; 522110
Media: 7-8-13
Personnel:
William H. Fenstermaker *(Chm)*
Michael J. Brown *(Vice Chm & COO)*
Jefferson G. Parker *(Vice Chm & Mgr-Brokerage, Trust & Wealth Mgmt)*
E. Stewart Shea III *(Vice Chm)*
Daryl G. Byrd *(Pres & CEO)*
Anthony J. Restel *(CFO & Sr VP)*
H. Gregg Strader *(Chief Credit Officer & Exec VP)*
James B. Gburek *(Chief Risk Officer & Exec VP)*
Kevin Rafferty *(Pres-Market)*
Robert B. Worley, Jr. *(Gen Counsel & Exec VP)*
George J. Becker III *(Sec, Exec VP & Dir-Org Dev)*
John R. Davis *(Sr Exec VP-Fin & IR)*
Elizabeth A. Ardoin *(Exec VP & Dir-Comm)*
Robert M. Kottler *(Exec VP & Dir-Retail & Small Bus)*
Elise Latimer *(Exec VP & Dir-Enterprise Risk Mgmt)*
Lewis P. Rogers *(Exec VP & Mgr-Internal Audit)*
M. Cleland Powell, III *(Exec VP)*
Brands & Products:
LIFE DOESN'T WAIT.

IBW FINANCIAL CORP.

4812 Georgia Ave NW
Washington, DC 20011
Tel.: (202) 722-2000
E-mail: info@industrial-bank.com
Web Site: www.industrial-bank.com
Sales Range: $10-24.9 Million
Approx. Number Employees: 160
Year Founded: 1994
Business Description:
Bank Holding Company
S.I.C.: 6712; 6029
N.A.I.C.S.: 551111; 522110
Advertising Expenditures: $204,000
Media: 6-8-25
Personnel:
B. Doyle Mitchell, Jr. *(Pres & CEO)*
Thomas L. Wilson *(CFO & Sr VP)*
Rodney Epps *(COO & Sr VP)*
Patricia Mitchell *(Exec VP-Retail & Sls Ops)*
Hermond Palmer *(VP & Dir-Mktg)*
Rafael Soriano *(Mktg Assoc)*

IDEAL LENDING SOLUTIONS

5589 Okeechobee Blvd Ste 101
West Palm Beach, FL 33417
Tel.: (561) 202-8406
Fax: (561) 282-6215
E-mail: info@ideallending.net
Web Site: www.ideallending.net
Business Description:
Residential & Commercial Mortgage Lending
S.I.C.: 6163
N.A.I.C.S.: 522310
Media: 13
Personnel:
Wilson Enriquez *(Pres)*

IESI-BFC LTD.

400 Applewood Crescent 2nd Floor
Vaughan, ON L4K 0C3, Canada
Tel.: (905) 532-7510
Fax: (905) 532-7580
E-mail: corporate.communications@bficanada.com
Web Site: www.bficanada.com
Approx. Rev.: $1,429,765,000
Approx. Number Employees: 6,575
Business Description:
Holding Company; Waste Services
S.I.C.: 6719; 4953; 4959
N.A.I.C.S.: 551112; 562219; 562998
Advertising Expenditures: $2,303,000
Personnel:
James J. Forese *(Chm)*
Charles F. Flood *(Vice Chm)*
Joseph D. Quarin *(Pres & COO)*
Keith A. Carrigan *(CEO)*
Thomas J. Cowee *(CFO & VP)*
Gordon D. Peckham *(Chief Dev Officer & Sr VP)*

Key to Media (For complete agency information see *The Advertising Red Books-Agencies* edition):
1. Bus. Publs. 2. Cable T.V. 3. Catalogs & Directories. 4. Co-op Adv. 5. Consumer Mags. 6. D.M. to Bus. Estab.7. D.M. to Consumers
8. Daily Newsp. 9. Exhibits/Trade Shows 10. Foreign 11. Infomercial 12. Internet Adv.13. Multimedia 14. Network Radio
15. Network T.V. 16. Newsp. Distr. Mags. 17. Other 18. Outdoor (Posters, Transit) 19. Point of Purchase20. Premiums, Novelties
21. Product Samples 22. Special Events Mktg. 23. Spot Radio 24. Spot T.V. 25. Weekly Newsp. 26. Yellow Page Adv.

Ivan R. Cairns *(Gen Counsel & Exec VP)*
Joseph Rajotte *(VP-Western Canada)*
William P.M. Herman *(VP-Fin & Controller)*
Edward L. Apuzzi *(VP & Reg Mgr-Northeast Reg)*
Chaya Cooperberg *(VP-IR & Corp Comm)*
Ronald Neese *(VP-Info Sys)*
Scott Richards *(VP-Internal Audit)*

IHOMEOWNERS, INC.
24003 Ventura Blvd Bldg A
Calabasas, CA 91302
Tel.: (818) 999-4070
Fax: (818) 332-4230
Toll Free: (800) 410-1955
Sales Range: $1-9.9 Million
Approx. Number Employees: 60
Year Founded: 1996
Business Description:
Home Listings, Mortgage Generation, Insurance, Moving, Home Improvement & Repair, Decorating & Other Related Services
S.I.C.: 6163
N.A.I.C.S.: 522310
Media: 2-8-13
Personnel:
John Hasenhauer *(Pres)*
William McCoy *(CEO)*
Mike Hasenauer *(Mgr-New Bus Dev)*
Brands & Products:
4HOMES
4INSURANCE.COM
IHOMEOWNER.COM
LOANWEB.COM

IHS HEROLD, INC.
(Sub. of IHS Inc.)
14 Westport Ave
Norwalk, CT 06851
Tel.: (203) 847-3344
Fax: (203) 847-5566
Toll Free: (800) 475-6561
E-mail: accounts@herold.com
Web Site: www.herold.com
E-Mail For Key Personnel:
Sales Director: sales@herold.com
Sales Range: $10-24.9 Million
Approx. Number Employees: 70
Year Founded: 1948
Business Description:
Energy Industry Research & Consulting Services
S.I.C.: 6282; 8742
N.A.I.C.S.: 523930; 541613
Media: 10
Distr.: Direct to Consumer; Natl.
Personnel:
John Cannon *(Dir-Sls)*

IMPERIAL HOLDINGS, INC.
(Formerly Imperial Holdings, LLC)
701 Park of Commerce Blvd Ste 301
Boca Raton, FL 33487
Tel.: (561) 995-4200
Fax: (866) 664-9405
Toll Free: (888) 364-6775
E-mail: info@imprl.com
Web Site: www.imprl.com
Approx. Rev.: $76,896,089
Approx. Number Employees: 131
Year Founded: 2006
Business Description:
Holding Company; Insurance Financing Services
S.I.C.: 6411; 6371; 6719
N.A.I.C.S.: 524298; 525990; 551112
Advertising Expenditures: $5,100,000
Personnel:
Antony Mitchell *(Chm & CEO)*
Jonathan Neuman *(Pres & COO)*
Richard S. O'Connell, Jr. *(CFO & Chief Credit Officer)*
Anne Dufour Zuckerman *(Gen Counsel)*

IMPERIAL HOLDINGS, LLC
(Name Changed to Imperial Holdings, Inc.)

INCHARGE INSTITUTE OF AMERICA, INC.
5750 Major Blvd Ste 300
Orlando, FL 32819
Tel.: (407) 291-7770
Fax: (407) 532-5650
Toll Free: (800) 565-8953
E-mail: mediarelations@incharge.org
Web Site: www.incharge.org
Approx. Number Employees: 250
Business Description:
Personal Finance Education & Credit Counseling
S.I.C.: 7323
N.A.I.C.S.: 561450
Media: 8-13-24
Personnel:
Etta Money *(Pres)*
Brands & Products:
BRIGHTSCORE
INCHARGE
MILITARY MONEY

INDEPENDENCE FEDERAL SAVINGS BANK
1229 Connecticut Ave NW
Washington, DC 20036
Tel.: (202) 628-5500
Fax: (202) 626-7106
E-mail: information@ifsb.com
Web Site: www.ifsb.com
Approx. Rev.: $10,557,000
Approx. Number Employees: 30
Year Founded: 1968
Business Description:
Retail & Commercial Banking Services
S.I.C.: 6035; 6029; 6163
N.A.I.C.S.: 522120; 522110; 522310
Advertising Expenditures: $900,000
Media: 7-8-13
Personnel:
Elliott S. Hall *(Chm)*
Robert B. Isard *(Vice Chm)*
Kevin Merrick *(Asst VP-Lending)*
Darrell T. Holloman, Sr. *(Mgr-Acctg)*

INDEPENDENT BANK CORPORATION
230 W Main St
Ionia, MI 48846-1665
Mailing Address:
PO Box 491
Ionia, MI 48846-0491
Tel.: (616) 527-9450
Fax: (616) 527-4004
E-mail: info@ibcp.com
Web Site: www.ibcp.com
Approx. Rev.: $220,664,000
Approx. Number Employees: 982
Year Founded: 1973
Business Description:
Bank Holding Company
S.I.C.: 6712; 6029
N.A.I.C.S.: 551111; 522110
Advertising Expenditures: $2,712,000
Media: 8-19-20
Personnel:
Jeffrey A. Bratsburg *(Chm)*
William Brad Kessel *(Pres)*
Michael M. Magee, Jr. *(CEO)*
Robert N. Shuster *(CFO)*
Stefanie M. Kimball *(Exec VP & Chief Lending Officer)*
David C. Reglin *(Exec VP-Retail Banking)*
Laurinda M. Neve *(Sr VP-HR)*

INDEPENDENT BANK CORP.
288 Union St
Rockland, MA 02370
Tel.: (781) 878-6100
Fax: (616) 527-4004
E-mail: information@rocklandtrust.com
Web Site: www.rocklandtrust.com
Approx. Rev.: $249,630,000
Approx. Number Employees: 919
Year Founded: 1992
Business Description:
Bank Holding Company
S.I.C.: 6712; 6029; 6035
N.A.I.C.S.: 551111; 522110; 522120
Advertising Expenditures: $2,171,000
Media: 7-8-13
Personnel:
Thomas J. Teuten *(Chm)*
Christopher Oddleifson *(Pres & CEO)*
Denis K. Sheahan *(CFO)*
Edward F. Jankowski *(COO & CTO)*
David B. Smith *(Chief Investment Officer & Sr VP)*
Barry H. Jensen *(Chief Acctg Officer, Sr VP & Controller)*
Edward H. Seksay *(Gen Counsel)*
Robert D. Cozzone *(Treas & Sr VP)*
Jane L. Lundquist *(Exec VP, Dir-Retail Banking & Corp Mktg)*
Gerard F. Nadeau *(Exec VP-Comml Leasing)*
Raymond G. Fuerschbach *(Sr VP-HR)*

INDIANA COMMUNITY BANCORP
501 Washington St
Columbus, IN 47201
Tel.: (812) 522-1592
Fax: (812) 378-4663
Web Site: www.myindianabank.com
Approx. Rev.: $57,495,000
Approx. Number Employees: 203
Year Founded: 1990
Business Description:
Bank Holding Company
S.I.C.: 6712; 6029
N.A.I.C.S.: 551111; 522110
Advertising Expenditures: $1,025,000
Personnel:
John K. Keach, Jr. *(Chm, Pres & CEO)*
Mark T. Gorski *(CFO, Treas, Sec & Exec VP)*
Melissa Arnold McGill *(Chief Acctg Officer, Sr VP & Controller)*
Judy Webster *(Asst VP-Mktg Officer)*
Roger D. Eisenbarth *(Sr VP)*
Heather Shonkwiler *(Asst VP-Bus Dev)*

ING DIRECT
(Sub. of ING Groep N.V.)
111 Gordon Baker Rd Ste 110
Toronto, ON M2H 3R1, Canada
Tel.: (416) 497-5157
Fax: (416) 758-5356
E-mail: clientservices@ingdirect.ca
Web Site: www.ingdirect.ca
Approx. Number Employees: 840
Business Description:
Investing, Savings Bank & Individual Loan Services
S.I.C.: 6035
N.A.I.C.S.: 522120
Personnel:
Peter Aceto *(Pres & CEO)*
Andrew Zimakas *(VP-Mktg)*
Advertising Agencies:
Horizon Print Services Group
75 Varick St
New York, NY 10017
Tel.: (212) 916-8600
Fax: (212) 916-8653

John St.
172 John Street
Toronto, ON M5T 1X5, Canada
Tel.: (416) 348-0048
Fax: (416) 348-0050
Brand Strategy
Creative
Strategic Counsel

Trafficbuyer Digital
215 Park Ave S Ste 1303
New York, NY 10003
Tel.: (212) 642-8460

INTEGRA BANK CORPORATION
21 SE 3rd St
Evansville, IN 47708-0868
Mailing Address:
PO Box 868
Evansville, IN 47705-0868
Tel.: (812) 464-9800
Fax: (812) 464-9825
E-mail: info@integrabank.com
Web Site: www.integrabank.com
Approx. Rev.: $153,413,000
Approx. Number Employees: 517
Year Founded: 1985
Business Description:
Bank Holding Company
S.I.C.: 6712; 6029; 6035
N.A.I.C.S.: 551111; 522110; 522120
Advertising Expenditures: $1,774,000
Media: 7-8-11-13-14-15
Personnel:
Michael J. Alley *(Chm)*
Michael B. Carroll *(CFO & Exec VP)*
John W. Key *(Chief Credit & Risk Officer & Exec VP)*
Roger M. Duncan *(Pres-Evansville Reg, Exec VP & Retail Mgr-Community Markets)*
Wendell Burkhart *(Exec VP-Operational Risk Mgmt)*
Dan J. Carwile *(Exec VP)*
Roger D. Watson *(Exec VP)*
Robert Alexander *(Sr VP)*
Lisa Rheinhardt *(Asst VP-Bank Security Act)*
Brands & Products:
BANKANYTIME
INTEGRA BANK

INTERACTIVE BROKERS GROUP, INC.
One Pickwick Plz
Greenwich, CT 06830

Key to Media (For complete agency information see *The Advertising Red Books-Agencies* edition):
1. Bus. Publs. 2. Cable T.V. 3. Catalogs & Directories. 4. Co-op Adv. 5. Consumer Mags. 6. D.M. to Bus. Estab.7. D.M. to Consumers
8. Daily Newsp. 9. Exhibits/Trade Shows 10. Foreign 11. Infomercial 12. Internet Adv.13. Multimedia 14. Network Radio
15. Network T.V. 16. Newsp. Distr. Mags. 17. Other 18. Outdoor (Posters, Transit) 19. Point of Purchase20. Premiums, Novelties
21. Product Samples 22. Special Events Mktg. 23. Spot Radio 24. Spot T.V. 25. Weekly Newsp. 26. Yellow Page Adv.

Interactive Brokers Group, Inc. — (Continued)

Tel.: (203) 618-5700
Fax: (203) 618-5770
E-mail: media@interactivebrokers.com
Web Site: www.interactivebrokers.com
Approx. Rev.: $988,317,000
Approx. Number Employees: 857
Year Founded: 1977
Business Description:
Securities Trading
S.I.C.: 6799; 6211
N.A.I.C.S.: 523910; 523110
Personnel:
Thomas Peterffy *(Chm, Pres & CEO)*
Earl H. Nemser *(Vice Chm)*
Mike Domka *(Mng Dir)*
Gerald Perez *(Mng Dir)*
Paul J. Brody *(CFO, Treas & Sec)*
Thomas A. Frank *(CIO & Exec VP)*
Milan Galik *(Sr VP-Software Dev)*
Dawn Sun *(Reg Dir-Sls)*
Greg Novak *(Dir-Reg Sls)*
Brands & Products:
INTERACTIVE BROKERS GROUP
Advertising Agency:
Gearon Hoffman Inc.
88 Broad St
Boston, MA 02110
Tel.: (617) 247-1522
Fax: (617) 247-6821

INTERACTIVE DATA CORPORATION
(Joint Venture of Warburg Pincus LLC & Silver Lake Group, LLC)
32 Crosby Dr
Bedford, MA 01730-1448
Tel.: (781) 687-8500
Fax: (781) 687-8005
E-mail: info@interactivedata.com
Web Site: www.interactivedata.com
Sales Range: $500-549.9 Million
Approx. Number Employees: 2,500
Business Description:
Real-Time Market Data to Individual Investors; Owned by Silver Lake Group, LLC & Warburg Pincus LLC
S.I.C.: 0762; 6029; 6221; 6289; 8748
N.A.I.C.S.: 115116; 522110; 523140; 523999; 541690
Advertising Expenditures: $6,255,000
Media: 2-7-8-10-13
Personnel:
Mason P. Slaine *(Chm, Pres & CEO)*
Elizabeth Duggan *(Mng Dir)*
Vincent A. Chippari *(CFO & Sr VP)*
Jay Nadler *(COO)*
Alex Goor *(CIO)*
Mary Ivaliotis *(CMO)*
Mark Hepsworth *(Pres-Institutional Bus)*
Andrea H. Loew *(Gen Counsel, Sec & Exec VP)*
Carol Sweeney *(Gen Counsel & Sr VP)*
Jeff Banker *(Exec VP-Real-Time Market Data & Trading Solutions)*
Matt Goldstein *(Mgr-Bus Dev)*

INTERACTIVE DATA PRICING & REFERENCE DATA, INC.
(Joint Venture of Warburg Pincus LLC & Silver Lake Group, LLC)
32 Crosby Dr
Bedford, MA 01730-1448
Tel.: (781) 687-8500
Fax: (781) 687-8289
Fax: (781) 687-8005
E-mail: info@interactivedata.com
Web Site: www.interactivedata.com
Sales Range: $400-449.9 Million
Business Description:
Securities Information Services
S.I.C.: 7389; 6231
N.A.I.C.S.: 519190; 523210
Media: 2
Personnel:
Raymond L. D'Arcy *(Pres-Sls & Mktg-Institutional Bus Dev)*
Mark Hepsworth *(Pres-Institutional Bus)*
Brands & Products:
MUNIVIEW

INTERCONTINENTALEXCHANGE, INC.
2100 RiverEdge Pkwy Ste 500
Atlanta, GA 30328
Tel.: (770) 857-4700
Fax: (770) 951-1307
Web Site: www.theice.com
Approx. Rev.: $1,149,944,000
Approx. Number Employees: 933
Business Description:
Energy, Agricultural, Credit & Currency Commodity Contracts Trading & Clearing Services
S.I.C.: 6099; 6211; 6221; 6231
N.A.I.C.S.: 522320; 523110; 523130; 523210
Advertising Expenditures: $3,300,000
Personnel:
Jeffrey C. Sprecher *(Chm & CEO)*
Charles A. Vice *(Pres & COO)*
Scott A. Hill *(CFO & Sr VP)*
David S. Goone *(Chief Strategic Officer & Sr VP)*
Edwin D. Marcial *(CTO & Sr VP)*
Thomas W. Farley *(Pres/COO-ICE Futures US)*
David J. Peniket *(Pres/COO-ICE Futures Europe)*
Christopher S. Edmonds *(Pres-ICE Trust)*
Johnathan H. Short *(Gen Counsel, Sec & Sr VP)*
Brands & Products:
COCOA
COFFEE C
COTTON NO. 2
FCOJ-A
ICE DATA
INTERCONTINENTALEXCHANGE
SUGAR-NO.11
SUGAR-NO.16

INTERNATIONAL BANCSHARES CORPORATION
1200 San Bernardo Ave
Laredo, TX 78042-1359
Tel.: (956) 722-7611
Fax: (956) 726-6637
E-mail: wedomore@iboc.com
Web Site: www.ibc.com
Approx. Int. Income: $458,769,000
Approx. Number Employees: 2,964
Year Founded: 1979
Business Description:
Bank Holding Company
S.I.C.: 6712; 6029
N.A.I.C.S.: 551111; 522110
Advertising Expenditures: $9,149,000
Personnel:
Dennis E. Nixon *(Chm, Pres & CEO)*
R. David Guerra *(Pres & CEO)*
Imelda Navarro *(CFO, COO & Sr Exec VP)*
Pat Stewart *(Pres-Svc Center)*
Advertising Agency:
KGBTexas
1919 Oakwell Farms Pky, Ste 100
San Antonio, TX 78218
Tel.: (210) 826-8899
Fax: (210) 826-8872

INTERNATIONAL MONETARY SYSTEMS, LTD.
16901 W Glendale Dr
New Berlin, WI 53151
Tel.: (262) 780-3640
Fax: (262) 780-3655
Toll Free: (800) 559-8515
Web Site: www.internationalmonetary.com
Approx. Rev.: $13,704,307
Year Founded: 1985
Business Description:
Holding Company; Trade Exchanges & Barter Networks Owner, Manager & Operator
S.I.C.: 6719; 7389
N.A.I.C.S.: 551112; 425120; 561499
Advertising Expenditures: $140,014
Media: 17
Personnel:
Donald F. Mardak *(Pres & CEO)*
David Powell *(CFO)*
John E. Strabley, Jr. *(Exec VP)*
Dale L. Mardak *(Sr VP)*

INTERSECTIONS INC.
3901 Stonecroft Blvd
Chantilly, VA 20151
Mailing Address:
PO Box 222455
Chantilly, VA 20153-2455
Tel.: (703) 488-6100
Toll Free: (800) 695-7536
E-mail: media@intersections.com
Web Site: www.intersections.com
Approx. Rev.: $364,136,000
Approx. Number Employees: 787
Business Description:
Identity Management Solutions
S.I.C.: 7374; 6099; 7372; 7382; 7389
N.A.I.C.S.: 518210; 511210; 522390; 561499; 561621
Advertising Expenditures: $2,800,000
Personnel:
Michael R. Stanfield *(Chm & CEO)*
John G. Scanlon *(CFO & Exec VP)*
Neal B. Dittersdorf *(Exec VP, Chief Legal Officer)*
Steven A. Schwartz *(Exec VP-Consumer Svcs)*
Madalyn C. Behneman *(Principal Finl Officer & Sr VP-Fin & Acctg)*
Joe Mason *(Sr VP-Consumer Solutions)*
Brands & Products:
IDENTITY GUARD
INTERSECTIONS

INTERVEST BANCSHARES CORPORATION
1 Rockefeller Plz Ste 400
New York, NY 10020-1903
Tel.: (212) 218-2800
Fax: (212) 218-2808
Web Site: www.intervestnatbank.com
Approx. Rev.: $109,182,000
Approx. Number Employees: 73
Year Founded: 1993
Business Description:
Bank Holding Company
S.I.C.: 6712; 6029
N.A.I.C.S.: 551111; 522110
Advertising Expenditures: $71,000
Media: 17
Personnel:
Lowell S. Dansker *(Chm)*
Keith A. Olsen *(Pres)*
John J. Arvonio *(CFO)*
Diane S. Rathburn *(VP-Ops & Mgr-HR)*
Elizabeth Macias *(VP-IT, Sys & Security- Intervest National Bank)*

INTUIT GREENPOINT
(Div. of Intuit Canada Limited)
400 138th Ave SE
Calgary, AB T2G 4Z6, Canada
Tel.: (780) 466-9996
Fax: (800) 792-4044
Toll Free: (866) 313-5032
E-mail: customerservice_canada@intuit.com
Web Site: www.accountant.intuit.ca
Sales Range: $75-99.9 Million
Business Description:
Accounting & Tax Preparation Software
S.I.C.: 7372; 7291
N.A.I.C.S.: 511210; 541213
Media: 7-10
Brands & Products:
INTRA
PROFILE
Advertising Agency:
Maverick Public Relations
37 Madison Ave
Toronto, ON M5R 2S2, Canada
Tel.: (416) 640-5525
Fax: (416) 640-5524

INTUIT INC.
2700 Coast Ave
Mountain View, CA 94043
Mailing Address:
PO Box 7850
Mountain View, CA 94039-7850
Tel.: (650) 944-6000
Fax: (650) 944-3699
Toll Free: (800) 446-8848
E-mail: investor_relations@intuit.com
Web Site: www.intuit.com
Approx. Rev.: $3,851,000,000
Approx. Number Employees: 8,000
Year Founded: 1983
Business Description:
Accounting & Tax Preparation Software Publisher & Online Banking Services
S.I.C.: 7372; 7291; 7379; 8721
N.A.I.C.S.: 511210; 541213; 541219; 541519
Advertising Expenditures: $141,500,000
Media: 3-7-8-13-23
Personnel:
Scott D. Cook *(Founder)*
William V. Campbell *(Chm)*
Brad D. Smith *(Pres & CEO)*
R. Neil Williams *(CFO & Sr VP)*
Sasan K. Goodarzi *(CIO & Sr VP)*
Tayloe Stansbury *(CTO & Sr VP)*
Sherry Whiteley *(Chief HR Officer & Sr VP)*

Key to Media (For complete agency information see *The Advertising Red Books-Agencies* edition):
1. Bus. Publs. 2. Cable T.V. 3. Catalogs & Directories. 4. Co-op Adv. 5. Consumer Mags. 6. D.M. to Bus. Estab.7. D.M. to Consumers 8. Daily Newsp. 9. Exhibits/Trade Shows 10. Foreign 11. Infomercial 12. Internet Adv.13. Multimedia 14. Network Radio 15. Network T.V. 16. Newsp. Distr. Mags. 17. Other 18. Outdoor (Posters, Transit) 19. Point of Purchase20. Premiums, Novelties 21. Product Samples 22. Special Events Mktg. 23. Spot Radio 24. Spot T.V. 25. Weekly Newsp. 26. Yellow Page Adv.

Per-Kristian Halvorsen *(Chief Innovation Officer & Sr VP)*
Alexander M. Lintner *(Pres-Global Bus Div)*
Laura A. Fennell *(Gen Counsel, Sec & Sr VP)*
Kiran M. Patel *(Exec VP & Gen Mgr-Small Bus Grp)*
Ginny Lee *(Sr VP & Gen Mgr-Employee Mgmt Solutions)*
Steve Malik *(Sr VP & Gen Mgr-Intuit Health Grp)*
Daniel R. Maurer *(Sr VP & Gen Mgr-Consumer Grp)*
Jill A. Ward *(Sr VP & Gen Mgr-Acctg Professionals Div & Health Grp)*
Nora Denzel *(Sr VP-Big Data, Social Design & Mktg)*
Caroline F. Donahue *(Sr VP-Sls & Channel Mktg)*
Eric Dunn *(Sr VP-Payments Initiatives)*
CeCe Morken *(VP & Gen Mgr-Fin Svcs)*
Seth Greenberg *(VP-Media & Digital Mktg-Global)*
Diane Ueberle *(Head-Mktg & Brand)*
Cheryl Hassoldt *(Sr Mgr-Mktg)*
Christopher Battles *(Product Mgr-Payments)*
Megan Bhattacharyya *(Product Mgr)*
John Flora *(Product Mgr-Fin Svcs Grp)*
Mary Lunnebord *(Sr Product Mgr)*
Dan Bishop *(Mgr-Digital Mktg)*
Allison Ganz *(Mgr-Social Mobile Media)*
Michelle Makowski *(Mgr-Consumer Web Strategy)*
Craig Reddie *(Grp Mgr-Mobile Alliances)*

Brands & Products:
ASSISTED PAYROLL
BASIC PAYROLL
DIGITAL INSIGHT
EASYACCT
ECLIPSE
ENHANCED PAYROLL
INTUIT
INTUIT PAYROLL
INTUIT REAL ESTATE SOLUTIONS
ITSDEDUCTIBLE
LACERTE
MASTER BUILDER
PROSERIES
QUICKBASE
QUICKBOOKS
QUICKBOOKS ENTERPRISE SOLUTIONS
QUICKBOOKS ONLINE BASIC
QUICKBOOKS ONLINE PLUS
QUICKBOOKS PREMIER
QUICKBOOKS PREMIER ACCOUNTANT
QUICKBOOKS PRO
QUICKBOOKS SIMPLE START
QUICKEN
QUICKEN.COM
QUICKTAX
TURBOTAX

Advertising Agency:
Dailey & Associates
(Sub. of The Interpublic Group of Cos., Inc.)
8687 Melrose Ave Ste G300
West Hollywood, CA 90069-5701
Tel.: (310) 360-3100
Fax: (310) 360-0810

INVESCO LTD.

1555 Peachtree St NE Ste 1800
Atlanta, GA 30309
Tel.: (404) 892-0896
Fax: (404) 962-8176
Toll Free: (800) 241-5477
E-mail: contactus@invesco.com
Web Site: www.invesco.com
Approx. Rev.: $3,487,700,000
Approx. Number Employees: 5,617
Year Founded: 1935
Business Description:
Holding Company; Investment Management Services
S.I.C.: 6719; 6282; 6289
N.A.I.C.S.: 551112; 523920; 523999
Advertising Expenditures: $21,000,000
Media: 2-10-15-17
Personnel:
Rex D. Adams *(Chm)*
Martin L. Flanagan *(Pres & CEO)*
Colin D. Meadows *(Sr Mng Dir & Chief Admin Officer)*
John S. Markwalter Jr. *(Sr Mng Dir & CEO-Private Wealth Mgmt)*
Mark G. Armour *(Sr Mng Dir & Head-Worldwide Institutions)*
James I. Robertson *(Sr Mng Dir, Head-Invesco Perpetual & Continental Europe-UK)*
Philip A. Taylor *(Sr Mng Dir & Head-North American Retail)*
K. Stuart Peskin *(Mng Dir)*
Loren M. Starr *(CFO)*
Andrew Schlossberg *(Chief Mktg Officer)*
Roderick G. H. Ellis *(Chief Acctg Officer & Controller)*
David Bass *(Dir-Asset Mgmt)*
Bill Hensel *(Dir-Media Rels)*

Brands & Products:
AIM
ATLANTIC TRUST
INVESCO
INVESCO PERPETUAL

Advertising Agency:
Leo Burnett Worldwide, Inc.
35 W Wacker Dr
Chicago, IL 60601-1723
Tel.: (312) 220-5959
Fax: (312) 220-3299
Financial Services

INVESTOOLS INC.

(Sub. of TD AMERITRADE Holding Corporation)
4211 S 102nd St
Omaha, NE 68127
Tel.: (402) 597-8464
E-mail: investor.relations@investools.com
Web Site: www.investools.com
Sales Range: $25-49.9 Million
Approx. Number Employees: 15
Business Description:
Investor Education Advisory Newsletters
S.I.C.: 6163
N.A.I.C.S.: 522310
Personnel:
Jeff Goesner *(Dir-Fin & IR)*
Kim Hillyer *(Sr Mgr-Comm & Pub Affairs)*

Advertising Agency:
DiMassimo Goldstein
(d/b/a DIGO Brands)
220 E 23rd St
New York, NY 10010
Tel.: (212) 253-7500
Fax: (646) 507-5850
(Financial Education)

INVESTORPLACE MEDIA, LLC

9201 Corporate Blvd
Rockville, MD 20850
Tel.: (301) 250-2200
Fax: (301) 926-4351
E-mail: investorplace@investorplace.com
Web Site: www.investorplace.com
Business Description:
Investing Newsletters & Websites for the Individual Investor
S.I.C.: 6282
N.A.I.C.S.: 523930
Advertising Expenditures: $15,000,000
Media: 2-8-13
Personnel:
John Coyle *(CEO)*
Christopher Marrett *(Sr VP & Sr Grp Publr)*
Reagan Brown *(Gen Mgr)*

INVESTORS BANCORP, INC.

101 JFK Pkwy
Short Hills, NJ 07078
Tel.: (973) 924-5100
E-mail: dcama@isbnj.com
Web Site: www.isbnj.com
Approx. Rev.: $455,228,000
Approx. Number Employees: 844
Business Description:
Bank Holding Company
S.I.C.: 6712; 6035
N.A.I.C.S.: 551111; 522120
Advertising Expenditures: $1,860,000
Personnel:
Robert M. Cashill *(Chm)*
Kevin Cummings *(Pres & CEO)*
Thomas F. Splaine, Jr. *(CFO & Sr VP)*
Domenick A. Cama *(COO & Sr Exec VP)*
Kelly Pecoraro *(Chief Acctg Officer)*
Richard S. Spengler *(Chief Lending Officer & Exec VP)*

INVESTORS CAPITAL HOLDINGS, LTD.

230 Broadway East
Lynnfield, MA 01940
Tel.: (781) 593-8565
Fax: (781) 593-9464
Toll Free: (800) 949-1422
E-mail: info@investorscapital.com
Web Site: www.investorscapital.com
E-Mail For Key Personnel:
President: tmurphy@investorscapital.com
Approx. Rev.: $85,253,965
Approx. Number Employees: 83
Business Description:
Security Broker & Dealer; Investment Advisory & Asset Management Services
S.I.C.: 6221; 6211; 6282
N.A.I.C.S.: 523130; 523120; 523920; 523930
Advertising Expenditures: $200,000
Media: 7-10-13
Personnel:
Theodore E. Charles *(Chm)*
Timothy B. Murphy *(Pres & CEO)*
Kathleen L. Donnelly *(CFO & Chief Acctg Officer)*

IOWA FIRST BANCSHARES CORP.

300 E 2nd St
Muscatine, IA 52761
Mailing Address:
PO Box 539
Muscatine, IA 52761
Tel.: (563) 263-4221
Fax: (563) 262-4213
E-mail: info@fnbmusc.com
Web Site: www.fnbmusc.com
Approx. Rev.: $25,890,000
Approx. Number Employees: 130
Year Founded: 1984
Business Description:
Bank Holding Company
S.I.C.: 6712; 6029
N.A.I.C.S.: 551111; 522110
Advertising Expenditures: $185,000
Media: 17
Personnel:
D. Scott Ingstad *(Chm, Pres & CEO)*
Kim K. Bartling *(COO, Treas & Exec VP)*
Charla Schafer *(VP-Mktg)*

IPAYMENT, INC.

(Holding of iPayment Investors, LP)
40 Burton Hills Blvd Ste 415
Nashville, TN 37215
Tel.: (615) 665-1858
Web Site: www.ipaymentinc.com
Approx. Rev.: $699,174,000
Approx. Number Employees: 334
Year Founded: 1992
Business Description:
Credit & Debit Card-Based Payment Processing Services for Small Merchants
S.I.C.: 7389; 6099
N.A.I.C.S.: 561499; 522390
Advertising Expenditures: $142,000
Media: 10-13
Personnel:
Carl A. Grimstad *(Pres)*
Gregory S. Daily *(CEO)*
Mark C. Monaco *(CFO)*
Afshin M. Yazdian *(Gen Counsel, Sec & Exec VP)*
Robert S. Torino *(Exec VP & Asst Sec)*

IRONSTONE BANK

(Sub. of First Citizens BancShares, Inc.)
10865 Haynes Bridge Rd
Alpharetta, GA 30022
Tel.: (770) 777-8960
Fax: (770) 777-6792
Web Site: www.ironstonebank.com
Sales Range: $10-24.9 Million
Approx. Number Employees: 45
Year Founded: 1997
Business Description:
Banking Services
S.I.C.: 6029
N.A.I.C.S.: 522110
Media: 6
Personnel:
Geary Kinnett *(Exec VP & Reg Exec)*

ISABELLA BANK CORPORATION

401 N Main St
Mount Pleasant, MI 48858

Key to Media (For complete agency information see *The Advertising Red Books-Agencies* edition):
1. Bus. Publs. 2. Cable T.V. 3. Catalogs & Directories. 4. Co-op Adv. 5. Consumer Mags. 6. D.M. to Bus. Estab.7. D.M. to Consumers
8. Daily Newsp. 9. Exhibits/Trade Shows 10. Foreign 11. Infomercial 12. Internet Adv.13. Multimedia 14. Network Radio
15. Network T.V. 16. Newsp. Distr. Mags. 17. Other 18. Outdoor (Posters, Transit) 19. Point of Purchase20. Premiums, Novelties
21. Product Samples 22. Special Events Mktg. 23. Spot Radio 24. Spot T.V. 25. Weekly Newsp. 26. Yellow Page Adv.

Isabella Bank Corporation — (Continued)

Tel.: (989) 772-9471
Fax: (989) 775-5501
Toll Free: (800) 651-9111
E-mail: shareholderrelations@isabellabank.com
Web Site: www.isabellabank.com

Approx. Rev.: $66,517,000
Approx. Number Employees: 338
Year Founded: 1988

Business Description:
Financial Services Holding Company; Banking, Employee Leasing & Financial Information Services
S.I.C.: 6712; 6029; 7363; 7389
N.A.I.C.S.: 551111; 519190; 522110; 561330
Advertising Expenditures: $833,000

Personnel:
David J. Maness *(Chm)*
Dennis P. Angner *(Pres & CFO)*
Richard J. Barz *(CEO)*
Steven Pung *(COO)*
Peggy L. Wheeler *(Sr VP & Controller)*
Liz Gregus *(Asst VP)*

ISTA NORTH AMERICA INC.
(Sub. of ista International GmbH)
3655 Northpoint Pkwy Ste 150
Alpharetta, GA 30005-2025
Tel.: (678) 336-2200
E-mail: info@ista-na.com
Web Site: www.ista-na.com

Business Description:
Consumption-Dependent Energy, Water & Ancillary Costs Billing & Meter Installation Services
S.I.C.: 7389; 7322; 7338
N.A.I.C.S.: 561499; 561410; 561440; 561990

Personnel:
Ruediger Neubauer *(CEO)*
John Lis *(Sr VP)*
Phil Neeves *(VP-Sls & Mktg-Central Reg)*
Ron Brinkley *(Gen Mgr)*

Advertising Agency:
Bailey Gardiner Inc.
444 W. Beech St Ste 400
San Diego, CA 92101
Tel.: (619) 295-8232
Fax: (619) 295-8234
(Utility Expense Management)

ITEX CORPORATION
3326 160th Ave SE Ste 100
Bellevue, WA 98008
Tel.: (425) 463-4000
Fax: (425) 463-4041
E-mail: investor@itex.com
Web Site: www.itex.com

Approx. Rev.: $16,925,000
Approx. Number Employees: 35
Year Founded: 1982

Business Description:
Retail Trade & Barter Exchange
S.I.C.: 5999; 1799
N.A.I.C.S.: 453998; 238990
Import Export
Advertising Expenditures: $102,000
Media: 4-7

Personnel:
Steven White *(Chm, CEO & Interim CFO)*

JACKSON HEWITT TAX SERVICE INC.
3 Sylvan Way
Parsippany, NJ 07054
Tel.: (973) 630-1040
Fax: (973) 496-2785
Toll Free: (800) 234-1040
E-mail: corporatecommunications@jtax.com
Web Site: www.jacksonhewitt.com
Approx. Rev.: $213,762,000
Approx. Number Employees: 305
Business Description:
Tax Preparation Services
S.I.C.: 7291
N.A.I.C.S.: 541213
Advertising Expenditures: $36,400,000
Media: 5-8-18-23-24
Personnel:
Margaret Milner Richardson *(Chm)*
Philip H. Sanford *(Pres & CEO)*
Daniel P. O'Brien *(CFO, Treas & Exec VP)*
Debra Dowd *(CMO)*
Mark Steber *(Chief Tax Officer)*
Richard P. Enchura *(Pres-Tax Svcs of America Inc & Sr VP)*
Steven L. Barnett *(Gen Counsel, Sec & Exec VP)*
Duane R. Mora *(Sr VP-Franchise Ops & Sls)*
Michael J. LaCosta *(Dir-PR)*
Brands & Products:
DEDUCTIONS@WORK
FLEX PAY
GET MORE IN RETURN
HOLIDAY EXPRESS LOAN PROGRAM
IPOWER
JACKSON HEWITT
JACKSON HEWITT CASHCARD
REFER A FRIEND
TAX SERVICE
WE KNOW SO MUCH ABOUT TAXES WE CAN HELP ANYBODY
Advertising Agency:
22squared
1170 Peachtree St NE 15th Fl
Atlanta, GA 30309-7649
Tel.: (404) 347-8700
Fax: (404) 347-8800
Creative
Media
Online Ads

JACKSONVILLE BANCORP, INC.
100 N Laura St 10th Fl
Jacksonville, FL 32202-3613
Tel.: (904) 421-3040
Fax: (904) 421-3078
Toll Free: (888) 699-5292
E-mail: customerservice@jaxbank.com
Web Site: www.jaxbank.com
Approx. Rev.: $25,136,000
Approx. Number Employees: 102
Year Founded: 1997
Business Description:
Bank Holding Company
S.I.C.: 6712; 6029; 6035
N.A.I.C.S.: 551111; 522110; 522120
Advertising Expenditures: $471,000
Personnel:
Donald E. Roller *(Chm)*
Gilbert J. Pomar, III *(Pres & CEO)*
Price W. Schwenck *(CEO)*
Valerie A. Kendall *(CFO & Exec VP)*
Scott M. Hall *(Chief Credit Officer & Exec VP)*
Barry Chandler *(Pres-Beaches City)*

JANNEY MONTGOMERY SCOTT LLC
(Sub. of The Penn Mutual Life Insurance Company)
1801 Market St
Philadelphia, PA 19103-1675
Tel.: (215) 665-6000
Fax: (215) 564-9597
Toll Free: (800) 526-6397
Web Site: www.jmsonline.com
Approx. Number Employees: 1,800
Year Founded: 1832
Business Description:
Investments
S.I.C.: 6211
N.A.I.C.S.: 523120
Advertising Expenditures: $35,230,000
Media: 2-6-13-17-20
Personnel:
Rudolph C. Sander *(Chm)*
Timothy Scheve *(Pres & CEO)*
Thomas Ferraro *(Mng Dir & Head-Equities)*
Brent Giese *(Mng Dir & Head-Whole Loan Bus)*
Charles Mather *(Mng Dir)*
Michael Solomon *(Mng Dir)*
Christopher White *(Mng Dir)*
Robert J. Thielmann *(CIO)*
Jordie Maine *(Exec VP & Head-Capital Markets)*
David S. Penn *(Exec VP & Dir-Wealth Mgmt Svcs)*
Karen Shakowske *(Sr VP & Dir-Mktg Comm)*
Francis J. McAleer, Jr. *(Sr VP)*
David Mullan *(First VP-Ops)*
Edward Walters *(Dir-Products & Res)*
Advertising Agencies:
Omnico Promotions, Ltd.
PO Box 713
Mount Kisco, NY 10549
Tel.: (914) 241-1648
Fax: (914) 241-1649

Reese, Tomases & Ellick, Inc. (RT&E)
1105 Market St Ste 100
Wilmington, DE 19801
Tel.: (302) 652-3211
Fax: (302) 428-3920
Toll Free: (888) 720-7561

JANUS CAPITAL GROUP, INC.
151 Detroit St
Denver, CO 80206
Tel.: (303) 333-3863
Fax: (303) 336-7497
Toll Free: (800) 628-1577
E-mail: janus_info@janus.com
Web Site: www.janus.com
Approx. Rev.: $1,015,700,000
Approx. Number Employees: 1,119
Year Founded: 1969
Business Description:
Investment Management Services
S.I.C.: 6289; 6282; 6722
N.A.I.C.S.: 523999; 523920; 525910
Advertising Expenditures: $27,800,000
Media: 2-6-9-25
Personnel:
Steven L. Scheid *(Chm)*
Richard Mac Coy Weil *(CEO)*
Chris Furman *(Mng Dir)*
Gregory Alan Frost *(CFO & Exec VP)*
Robin C. Beery *(CMO & Exec VP)*
David Kowalski *(Chief Compliance Officer & Sr VP)*
Jonathan Coleman *(Co-Chief Investment Officer-Janus Capital Mgmt & Portfolio Mgr)*
Gibson Smith *(Co-Chief Investment Officer-Janus Capital Mgmt & Portfolio Mgr)*
Brennan A. Hughes *(Chief Acctg Officer & VP)*
Stephen H. Belgrad *(Treas & VP-Fin)*
George S. Batejan *(Sr VP & Global Head-Tech & Ops)*
Edward DeMarino *(VP & Dir)*
James F. Woods, Jr. *(Exec Dir-Consultant Rels)*
Mike Malinsky *(Reg Dir-Retirement-Fin Institutions-East)*
Stephen Dedyo *(Dir-Bus Dev-Global)*
Ginger Fanning *(Dir-Bus Dev-Global)*
James P. Goff *(Dir-Res)*
Gregory Kolb *(Asst Mgr-Portfolio)*
Brands & Products:
INTECH
JANUS
Advertising Agencies:
s2 Marketing + Communications, Inc.
656 W Randolph Ste 3E
Chicago, IL 60661
Tel.: (312) 382-9000

Teamspirit
78 Cowcross St
London, EC1M 6HE, United Kingdom
Tel.: (44) 20 7438 9400
Fax: (44) 20 7438 9420

JDSU
(Formerly American Bank Note Holographics, Inc.)
(Sub. of JDS Uniphase Corporation)
2 Applegate Dr
Trenton, NJ 08691-2342
Tel.: (609) 632-0800
Fax: (609) 632-0850
Web Site: www.jdsu.com
Sales Range: $25-49.9 Million
Approx. Number Employees: 111
Business Description:
Holograms for Credit & Transaction Cards
S.I.C.: 2754; 2759; 2791
N.A.I.C.S.: 323111; 323119; 323122
Media: 10
Personnel:
Michael T. Banahan *(VP-Sls)*
Adam L.A. Scheer *(Sr Dir-Bus Dev & Strategic Mktg)*
Brands & Products:
HOLOCAP
HOLOCARD
HOLOGARD
HOLOMAG
HOLOSEAL
HOLOSLEEVE

JEFFERIES GROUP, INC.
520 Madison Ave 12th Fl
New York, NY 10022
Tel.: (212) 284-2550
Fax: (203) 708-5922

Key to Media (For complete agency information see *The Advertising Red Books-Agencies* edition):
1. Bus. Publs. 2. Cable T.V. 3. Catalogs & Directories. 4. Co-op Adv. 5. Consumer Mags. 6. D.M. to Bus. Estab.7. D.M. to Consumers 8. Daily Newsp. 9. Exhibits/Trade Shows 10. Foreign 11. Infomercial 12. Internet Adv.13. Multimedia 14. Network Radio 15. Network T.V. 16. Newsp. Distr. Mags. 17. Other 18. Outdoor (Posters, Transit) 19. Point of Purchase20. Premiums, Novelties 21. Product Samples 22. Special Events Mktg. 23. Spot Radio 24. Spot T.V. 25. Weekly Newsp. 26. Yellow Page Adv.

E-mail: info@jefco.com
Web Site: www.jefferies.com
Approx. Rev.: $2,797,346,000
Approx. Number Employees: 3,084
Business Description:
Holding Company; Securities & Investment Banking Firm
S.I.C.: 6719; 6099; 6211; 6282; 6289; 6733
N.A.I.C.S.: 551112; 522320; 523110; 523120; 523920; 523991; 523999
Advertising Expenditures: $500,000
Media: 2-4-7-11-17-22
Distr.: Natl.
Personnel:
Richard B. Handler *(Chm, Pres & CEO)*
Charles J. Hendrickson *(Chief Credit Officer, Mng Dir & Treas)*
David Bohn *(Mng Dir & Head-Private Placements-Equity Capital Markets Bus)*
Ashley Delp *(Mng Dir & Head-US Equity Syndicate)*
Hitoshi Masumizu *(Mng Dir & Head-MBS/ABS Grp-Asia)*
David W. Bradley *(Mng Dir & Global Head-Indus Investment Banking)*
Todd Carnevale *(Mng Dir & Head-Municipal Yield Trading)*
Steven Hulett *(Mng Dir, Co-Head-MBS & ABS Grp-Europe)*
Thomas J. O'Leary *(Mng Dir & Head-Intl Equity Sls)*
Rob Stewart *(Mng Dir, Head-Aerospace & Defence Investment Banking-US)*
Robert A. Arrieta *(Mng Dir)*
Robert A. Bayer, Jr. *(Mng Dir)*
James McGinley *(Mng Dir)*
Kenneth M. Usdin *(Mng Dir)*
Peregrine C. Broadbent *(CFO & Exec VP)*
Patrice Blanc *(Pres-Futures Div)*
Marc Allison *(Sr VP)*
Daniel A. Brierley *(Sr VP)*
Marion Guilbert *(Sr VP-Sls-MBS)*
Dennis Hollands *(Sr VP-Sls-MBS/ABS)*
Roland T. Kelly *(Sr VP)*
Nathaniel Morse *(Sr VP-Distressed Trading)*
Jason O'Brien *(Sr VP)*
Edward Tunstall *(Sr VP-Sls-MBS/ABS)*
Amin Arjomand *(Mng Dir-Distressed Sls)*
Dung Nguyen *(Mng Dir-Healthcare Investment Banking)*
Alexander Yavorsky *(Mng Dir-Fin Institutions Investment Banking Grp)*
Brands & Products:
JEFFERIES
Advertising Agency:
Leo Burnett Business
160 Varick St 5th Fl
New York, NY 10013
Tel.: (646) 840-8350
Fax: (646) 840-8360

JEFFERSON BANCSHARES, INC.
120 Evans Ave
Morristown, TN 37814
Mailing Address:
PO Box 1198
Morristown, TN 37816-1198
Tel.: (423) 586-8421
Fax: (423) 581-5134
Fax: (423) 587-2605
E-mail: custserve@jeffersonfederal.com
Web Site: www.jeffersonfederal.com
Approx. Rev.: $34,077,000
Approx. Number Employees: 136
Year Founded: 1963
Business Description:
Bank Holding Company
S.I.C.: 6712; 6029; 6035
N.A.I.C.S.: 551111; 522110; 522120
Advertising Expenditures: $226,000
Media: 17
Personnel:
H. Scott Reams *(Chm)*
Anderson L. Smith *(Pres & CEO)*
Jane P. Hutton *(CFO, Treas & Sec)*
Anthony J. Carasso *(Pres-Knoxville Region)*
Janet J. Ketner *(Exec VP)*

JEFFERSON WELLS INTERNATIONAL, INC.
(Sub. of MANPOWER INC.)
100 Manpower Pl 4th Fl
Milwaukee, WI 53212
Tel.: (262) 957-3400
Fax: (262) 957-3401
Toll Free: (800) 826-5099
Web Site: www.jeffersonwells.com
Sales Range: $25-49.9 Million
Approx. Number Employees: 90
Business Description:
Tax, Technology Risk Management, Internal Audit & Control & Finance & Accounting Professional Services
S.I.C.: 7389
N.A.I.C.S.: 561499
Media: 6-7-9-10
Personnel:
Mike Touhey *(Pres & COO)*
Kris Best *(VP-Fin & IT)*
John LeBlanc *(VP-Product Mgmt & HR)*
Jill Blazek *(Dir-Mktg)*
Ronald A. Joma *(Mgr-Engagement & Risk Advisory Svcs)*
Advertising Agency:
Bader Rutter & Associates, Inc.
13845 Bishops Dr
Brookfield, WI 53005
Tel.: (262) 784-7200
Fax: (262) 938-5595
Toll Free: (888) 742-2337

JEFFERSONVILLE BANCORP
4866 State Rte 52
Jeffersonville, NY 12748
Mailing Address:
PO Box 398
Jeffersonville, NY 12748
Tel.: (845) 482-4000
Fax: (845) 482-3544
E-mail: information@jeffbank.com
Web Site: www.jeffbank.com/invest.asp
E-Mail For Key Personnel:
President: rwalter@jeffbank.com
Approx. Rev.: $24,795,000
Approx. Number Employees: 131
Year Founded: 1982
Business Description:
Bank Holding Company
S.I.C.: 6712; 6029
N.A.I.C.S.: 551111; 522110
Advertising Expenditures: $268,000
Personnel:
Kenneth C. Klein *(Chm)*
Raymond L. Walter *(Vice Chm)*
Wayne V. Zanetti *(Pres & CEO)*
John A. Russell *(CFO & Sr VP)*
Virginia Sanborn *(Controller, Asst Cashier & Officer-SOX)*
Tatiana Hahn *(Chief Lending Officer & Sr VP)*
George Kinne, Jr. *(Sr VP & Sr Loan Officer)*

J.H. COHN LLP
4 Becker Farm Rd
Roseland, NJ 07068
Tel.: (973) 228-3500
Fax: (973) 228-0330
Fax: (972) 228-0330
Toll Free: (888) 542-6461
Web Site: www.jhcohn.com
Approx. Sls.: $45,000,000
Approx. Number Employees: 350
Business Description:
Certified Public Accountant
S.I.C.: 8721
N.A.I.C.S.: 541211
Personnel:
Thomas J. Marino *(Partner & CEO)*
Brands & Products:
J.H COHN
Advertising Agency:
Peppercom
470 Park Ave S 5th Fl
New York, NY 10016
Tel.: (212) 931-6100
Fax: (212) 931-6159

J.K. HARRIS & CO. LLC
208 St James Ave Ste A
Goose Creek, SC 29445
Tel.: (843) 576-2255
Fax: (888) 576-2052
Toll Free: (888) 283-9922
E-mail: johnharris@jkharris.com
Web Site: www.jkharris.com
Sales Range: $300-349.9 Million
Approx. Number Employees: 470
Year Founded: 1997
Business Description:
Tax & Audit Representation & Tax Return Preparation Services
S.I.C.: 7291; 8742
N.A.I.C.S.: 541213; 541611
Media: 3-9-13-15-24-25
Personnel:
John K. Harris *(Owner)*
Oscar Luykenaar *(CFO, Exec VP-Fin & Admin)*
Gail Peck *(Pres-Mortgage Svcs)*
Josh Baker *(Exec VP-Client Advocacy)*
Bob Harris *(Exec VP-Ops)*
Richard Bassak *(VP-IT)*
Vicki Gorin *(VP-HR)*
Monica Linder *(VP-Legal Affairs)*
Gina Anton *(Dir-Comm)*
Brands & Products:
J.K. HARRIS
WE SOLVE IRS PROBLEMS
Advertising Agency:
Media Placement Group
5901 Broken Sound Pkwy NW Ste 225
Boca Raton, FL 33487-2773
Tel.: (561) 988-2181
Fax: (561) 988-2182

J.P. MORGAN ASSET MANAGEMENT HOLDINGS INC.
(Sub. of JPMorgan Chase & Co.)
270 Park Ave
New York, NY 10017
Tel.: (212) 483-2323
Fax: (212) 508-3778
Toll Free: (800) 218-4782
Web Site: www.jpmorgan.com
Sales Range: $550-599.9 Million
Approx. Number Employees: 1,000
Business Description:
International Brokers, Money Management, Investment Bankers
S.I.C.: 6722
N.A.I.C.S.: 525910
Media: 2-4-6-9-19-26
Distr.: Natl.
Personnel:
James Dimon *(Chm & CEO)*
George Gatch *(CEO)*
Michael Falcon *(Mng Dir & Head-Retirement-US & Canada)*

JPMORGAN CHASE & CO.
270 Park Ave
New York, NY 10017
Tel.: (212) 270-6000
Tel.: (212) 270-9300 (Exec Offices)
Web Site: www.jpmorganchase.com
Approx. Rev.: $102,694,000,000
Approx. Number Employees: 240,000
Year Founded: 1799
Business Description:
Bank Holding Company; Commercial & Investment Banking & Other Financial Services
S.I.C.: 6712; 6029; 6141; 6211; 6289
N.A.I.C.S.: 551111; 522110; 522291; 523110; 523999
Advertising Expenditures: $2,070,000,000
Media: 2-3-6-7-8-9-10-11-14-15-18-19-22-23-24-25-26
Distr.: Direct to Consumer; Natl.
Personnel:
James Dimon *(Chm, Pres & CEO)*
T. Andrew Smith *(Mng Dir)*
Robert M. Tas *(Mng Dir)*
Douglas L. Braunstein *(CFO)*
Guy Chiarello *(CIO)*
Frank J. Bisignano *(Chief Admin Officer)*
Ina R. Drew *(Chief Investment Officer)*
Achilles O. Macris *(Chief Investment Officer)*
Richard Sabo *(Chief Investment Officer)*
Heidi G. Miller *(Pres-Intl)*
Michael J. Cavanagh *(CEO-Treasury & Securities Svcs)*
Charles W. Scharf *(CEO-Retail Fin Svcs)*
James E. Staley *(CEO-Investment Bank Div)*
Yardise Jones *(VP & Sr Mgr-Online Innovation & New Capabilities)*
Philip F. Bleser *(Head-Comml Banking)*
Liesl Leach *(Head-Mktg & Adv)*
Jay Mandelbaum *(Head-Strategy & Bus Dev)*
Rob Kidder *(Asst VP & Mgr-Mktg)*
Marianne Samenko *(Sr Dir)*

Key to Media (For complete agency information see *The Advertising Red Books-Agencies* edition):
1. Bus. Publs. 2. Cable T.V. 3. Catalogs & Directories. 4. Co-op Adv. 5. Consumer Mags. 6. D.M. to Bus. Estab.7. D.M. to Consumers 8. Daily Newsp. 9. Exhibits/Trade Shows 10. Foreign 11. Infomercial 12. Internet Adv.13. Multimedia 14. Network Radio 15. Network T.V. 16. Newsp. Distr. Mags. 17. Other 18. Outdoor (Posters, Transit) 19. Point of Purchase20. Premiums, Novelties 21. Product Samples 22. Special Events Mktg. 23. Spot Radio 24. Spot T.V. 25. Weekly Newsp. 26. Yellow Page Adv.

JPMorgan Chase & Co. — (Continued)

Peter L. Scher *(Dir-Global Govt Rels & Public Policy)*
Jack Stephenson *(Dir-Mobile & E-Commerce & Payments)*

Advertising Agencies:
Gotham Direct
353 Lexington Ave 14th Fl
New York, NY 10016
Tel.: (212) 279-1474
Fax: (212) 279-1475

McGarry Bowen, LLC
601 W 26th St Ste 1150
New York, NY 10001
Tel.: (212) 598-2900
Fax: (212) 598-2996

PointRoll Inc.
951 E Hector St
Conshohocken, PA 19428
Tel.: (267) 558-1300
Fax: (267) 285-1141
Toll Free: (800) 203-6956

Zenith Media Services
(Regional Headquarters for ZenithOptimedia, the Americas)
299 W Houston St 10th Fl
New York, NY 10014-4806
Tel.: (212) 859-5100
Fax: (212) 727-9495
Meida Buying

JPMORGAN CHASE - MIDWEST REGIONAL OFFICE

(Unit of JPMorgan Chase Bank, N.A.)
10 S Dearborn
Chicago, IL 60603
Tel.: (312) 732-1164
Tel.: (312) 732-7007 (media relations)
Fax: (312) 732-3366
Web Site: www.jpmorganchase.com
Sales Range: $1-4.9 Billion
Approx. Number Employees: 12,000
Business Description:
Retail Financial & Commercial Banking Services
S.I.C.: 6799; 6211; 6282; 6289
N.A.I.C.S.: 523910; 523110; 523120; 523920; 523930; 523999
Personnel:
William M. Daley *(Chm)*

Advertising Agency:
Lapiz
35 W Wacker Dr 12th Fl
Chicago, IL 60601
Tel.: (312) 220-5000
Fax: (312) 220-6212
Multicultural

JUNIATA VALLEY FINANCIAL CORP.

Bridge & Main Streets PO Box 66
Mifflintown, PA 17059-0066
Tel.: (717) 436-8275
Fax: (717) 436-7551
E-mail: joann.mcminn@jvbonline.com
Web Site: www.jvbonline.com
Approx. Rev.: $25,508,000
Approx. Number Employees: 119
Year Founded: 1983
Business Description:
Bank Holding Company
S.I.C.: 6712; 6029; 6141
N.A.I.C.S.: 551111; 522110; 522210
Advertising Expenditures: $127,000
Media: 8-17
Personnel:
Philip E. Gingerich, Jr. *(Chm)*
Timothy I. Havice *(Vice Chm)*
Marcie A. Barber *(Pres & CEO)*
JoAnn N. McMinn *(CFO & Sr VP)*
Pamela S. Eberman *(Sr VP-HR)*
Steven T. Kramm *(Sr VP-Ops & Tech)*
Donald E. Shawley *(Sr VP-Trust & Investment Mgmt Div)*

KEARNY FINANCIAL CORP.

120 Passaic Ave
Fairfield, NJ 07004-3510
Tel.: (973) 244-4500
Toll Free: (800) 273-3406
Web Site: www.kearnyfederalsavings.com/ir_corporate_profile.asp
Approx. Int. Income: $93,108,000
Approx. Number Employees: 274
Year Founded: 1884
Business Description:
Bank Holding Company
S.I.C.: 6712; 6035
N.A.I.C.S.: 551111; 522120
Advertising Expenditures: $907,000
Media: 1-4-8
Personnel:
John J. Mazur, Jr. *(Chm)*
Craig L. Montanaro *(CEO)*
Eric B. Heyer *(CFO & Sr VP)*
William C. Ledgerwood *(COO)*
Albert E. Gossweiler *(Chief Investment Officer, Treas & Sr VP)*
Patrick M. Joyce *(Chief Lending Officer & Sr VP)*
Sharon Jones *(Corp Sec & Sr VP)*
Erika Sacher Parisi *(Sr VP & Branch Administrator)*

KEEPONPROSPECTING.COM

(Div. of Response Mail Express Inc.)
4910 Savarese Cir
Tampa, FL 33634
Tel.: (813) 885-8200
Fax: (813) 885-8201
Toll Free: (877) 233-7787
Web Site: www.keeponprospecting.com
Approx. Number Employees: 160
Year Founded: 2003
Business Description:
Sales Lead Services
S.I.C.: 7319; 7389
N.A.I.C.S.: 561499; 541870; 561439; 561990
Media: 2
Personnel:
Jorge Villar *(Founder & COO)*

KENTUCKY BANCSHARES, INC.

339 Main St
Paris, KY 40362-0157
Mailing Address:
PO Box 157
Paris, KY 40362-0157
Tel.: (859) 987-1795
Fax: (859) 987-5829
Toll Free: (800) 467-1939
E-mail: customerservice@kybank.com
Web Site: www.kybank.com
Approx. Rev.: $40,841,976
Approx. Number Employees: 184
Business Description:
Bank Holding Company
S.I.C.: 6029; 6035; 6712
N.A.I.C.S.: 522110; 522120; 551111
Advertising Expenditures: $443,604
Personnel:
Louis Prichard *(Pres & CEO)*
Gregory J. Dawson *(CFO)*
B. Proctor Caudill, Jr. *(Mgr-Special Projects)*

KEYBANK

(Sub. of KeyCorp)
100 Dutch Hill Rd
Orangeburg, NY 10962
Tel.: (845) 398-2280
Fax: (845) 365-2130
Web Site: www.key.com
Sales Range: $75-99.9 Million
Approx. Number Employees: 5
Year Founded: 1969
Business Description:
Bank
S.I.C.: 6029; 6163
N.A.I.C.S.: 522110; 522310
Media: 4-7-8-9-13-18-20-23-24-25-26
Personnel:
Kip Clarke *(Dir-KNB Corp Center)*
Frank Civitalla *(Mgr)*

KEYCORP

127 Public Sq
Cleveland, OH 44114-1221
Tel.: (216) 689-6300
Toll Free: (800) 539-2968
E-mail: keyexpress@keybank.com
Web Site: www.key.com
Approx. Rev.: $5,362,000,000
Approx. Number Employees: 15,301
Year Founded: 1825
Business Description:
Bank Holding Company
S.I.C.: 6211; 6029; 6712; 6733
N.A.I.C.S.: 523110; 522110; 523991; 551111
Advertising Expenditures: $30,000,000
Media: 2-3-4-6-7-8-9-13-14-17-18-19-20-22-23-24-25-26
Distr.: Direct to Consumer; Reg.
Budget Set: Sept.-Oct.
Personnel:
Thomas C. Stevens *(Vice Chm & Chief Admin Officer)*
Beth Mooney *(Pres & CEO)*
Richard Vonk *(Pres)*
Robert Montgomery *(Mng Dir)*
Jeffrey B. Weeden *(CFO & Sr Exec VP)*
Alvin B. Coppolo *(CIO & Exec VP)*
Stephen E. Yates *(CIO & Exec VP)*
Karen R. Haefling *(CMO & Chief Comm Officer)*
Charles S. Hyle *(Chief Risk Officer & Exec VP)*
Robert L. Morris *(Chief Acctg Officer)*
Jan Allen Ackley *(VP-Mktg Officer)*
Hugh Donlon *(Pres-Northeast Reg)*
Christopher M. Gorman *(Pres-Key Corp Bank)*
Timothy J. King *(Pres-Retail Banking Ops)*
William Koehler *(Pres-Key Community Bank)*
Wes Lawrence *(Pres-Northwest Region-KeyBank)*
Gary Quenneville *(Pres-Western New York District)*
Robert Wagner *(CEO-Victory Capital Mgmt)*
Paul N. Harris *(Gen Counsel, Sec & Exec VP)*
Joseph M. Vayda *(Treas & Exec VP)*
Amy K. Carlson *(Exec VP & Grp Head-Debt Capital Markets, Origination & Structurin)*
Cindy P. Crotty *(Exec VP & Head-Comml Bank Segment-Key Community Banking)*
Robert A. Deangelis *(Exec VP & Head-Consumer Bank Segment-Key Community Banking)*
Michael H. Dulan *(Exec VP & Head-Bus Banking Segment-Key Community Bank)*
Timothy J. Lathe *(Exec VP & Head-Wealth Mgmt Segment)*
Jeffery J. Weaver *(Exec VP)*
Margot J. Copeland *(Exec VP & Dir-Corp Diversity & Philanthropy)*
Michael P. Barnum *(Exec VP)*
Alan Buffington *(Exec VP-Keybank)*
E.J. Burke *(Exec VP)*
Pam Carson *(Exec VP, Grp Exec-Global Treasury Mgmt & Global Trade Svcs)*
George E. Emmons, Jr. *(Exec VP)*
Thomas E. Helfrich *(Exec VP)*
Carol Klimas *(Exec VP & Head of the Wealth Management Segment)*
Bruce D. Murphy *(Exec VP)*
Vernon L. Patterson *(Exec VP-IR)*
Andy R. Tyson *(Exec VP)*
Mark J. R. Williams *(Exec VP)*
Mary Ellen Good *(Sr VP)*
Richard Owens *(Sr VP)*
Peter D. Wheeler *(Sr VP-Global Treasury Mgmt Grp)*
Dean Ilijasic *(Dir-Consumer Innovation)*
Stan Ghys *(Product Mgr)*

Brands & Products:
KEY.COM

Advertising Agencies:
Dix & Eaton Incorporated
200 Public Sq Ste 1400
Cleveland, OH 44114
Tel.: (216) 241-0405
Fax: (216) 241-3070

Roop & Co.
925 Euclid Ave Ste 650
Cleveland, OH 44115-1408
Tel.: (216) 902-3800
Fax: (216) 902-3807

KIRTLAND CAPITAL PARTNERS

3201 Enterprise Pkwy Ste 200
Beachwood, OH 44122
Tel.: (216) 593-0100
Fax: (216) 593-0240
E-mail: firstinitialnestor@kirtlandcapital.com
Web Site: www.kirtlandcapital.com
Approx. Number Employees: 11
Year Founded: 1977
Business Description:
Private Equity Firm
S.I.C.: 6289
N.A.I.C.S.: 523999
Personnel:
John G. Nestor *(Chm, CEO & Sr Mng Partner)*
John F. Turben *(Chm)*
Michael T. DeGrandis *(CFO & Mng Partner)*

Key to Media (For complete agency information see *The Advertising Red Books-Agencies* edition):
1. Bus. Publs. 2. Cable T.V. 3. Catalogs & Directories. 4. Co-op Adv. 5. Consumer Mags. 6. D.M. to Bus. Estab.7. D.M. to Consumers
8. Daily Newsp. 9. Exhibits/Trade Shows 10. Foreign 11. Infomercial 12. Internet Adv.13. Multimedia 14. Network Radio
15. Network T.V. 16. Newsp. Distr. Mags. 17. Other 18. Outdoor (Posters, Transit) 19. Point of Purchase20. Premiums, Novelties
21. Product Samples 22. Special Events Mktg. 23. Spot Radio 24. Spot T.V. 25. Weekly Newsp. 26. Yellow Page Adv.

Robert Fines *(Mng Partner)*
Thomas N. Littman *(Mng Partner)*
James A. Foley *(Partner)*
David R. Menning *(VP & Dir-Bus Dev)*
Advertising Agency:
Roop & Co.
925 Euclid Ave Ste 650
Cleveland, OH 44115-1408
Tel.: (216) 902-3800
Fax: (216) 902-3807

KKR & CO. L.P.
9 W 57th St Ste 4200
New York, NY 10019
Tel.: (212) 750-8300
Fax: (212) 750-0003
Web Site: www.kkr.com
Approx. Int. Income: $226,824,000
Approx. Number Employees: 698
Year Founded: 1976
Business Description:
Private Equity Firm
S.I.C.: 6289; 6282
N.A.I.C.S.: 523999; 523930
Media: 2
Distr.: Intl.; Natl.
Personnel:
Henry R. Kravis *(Co-Founder, Co-Chm & Co-CEO)*
George R. Roberts *(Co-Founder, Co-Chm & Co-CEO)*
Scott C. Nuttall *(Gen Partner & Head-Fin Svcs)*
Deryck C. Maughan *(Partner & Head-Fin Institutions Grp)*
Perry Golkin *(Partner)*
Kenneth B. Mehlman *(Partner)*
Paul E. Raether *(Partner)*
George Bilicic *(Mng Dir & Head-Infrastructure)*
Kaveh Samie *(Mng Dir & Head-Middle East & North Africa)*
Kenneth W. Freeman *(Mng Dir)*
Suzanne Donohoe *(Mng Dir & Head-Client/Partnership Grp)*
William J. Janetschek *(CFO)*
Edward Brandman *(CIO)*
Todd A. Fisher *(Chief Admin Officer)*
William J. Eckert, IV *(Chief Acctg Officer)*
Peter M. Fasolo *(Chief Talent Officer)*
Ned Moran *(Principal-IT)*
David J. Sorkin *(Gen Counsel)*
Alexander Navab, Jr. *(Head-Media & Comm)*
Peter McKillop *(Dir-Global Comm)*
Lee D. Stern *(Dir-Investments)*

KKR FINANCIAL HOLDINGS LLC
555 California St 50th Fl
San Francisco, CA 94104-1701
Tel.: (415) 315-3620
Fax: (415) 391-3077
E-mail: kfninfo@kkr.com
Web Site: www.kkr.com
Approx. Rev.: $505,359,000
Business Description:
Holding Company; Corporate Debt Security & Bond Investment Services
S.I.C.: 6719; 6211; 6289; 6722
N.A.I.C.S.: 551112; 523110; 523999; 525910
Personnel:
Paul M. Hazen *(Chm)*
Jamie M. Weinstein *(Mng Dir)*
Christopher A. Sheldon *(Mng Dir)*
William B. Fisher *(Exec Officer-Asset Mgmt)*
Michael McFerran *(Exec Officer-Asset Mgmt)*
Laurie Poggi *(Exec Officer-Asset Mgmt)*
William C. Sonneborn *(Exec Officer-Asset Mgmt)*
Jeffrey B. Van Horn *(Exec Officer-Asset Mgmt)*
Advertising Agency:
Kekst & Co.
437 Madison Ave
New York, NY 10022
Tel.: (212) 593-2655
Fax: (212) 521-4900

KNIGHT CAPITAL GROUP, INC.
545 Washington Blvd
Jersey City, NJ 07310
Tel.: (201) 222-9400
Fax: (201) 557-6853
Toll Free: (800) 544-7508
E-mail: mwyrwas@knight.com
Web Site: www.knighttradinggroup.com
Approx. Rev.: $1,149,056,000
Approx. Number Employees: 1,326
Year Founded: 1995
Business Description:
Securities Trading Services
S.I.C.: 6211
N.A.I.C.S.: 523120; 523110
Personnel:
Thomas M. Joyce *(Chm & CEO)*
Steven Bisgay *(CFO & Sr Mng Dir)*
Leonard J. Amoruso *(Sr Mng Dir & Gen Counsel)*
Robert N. Stein *(Sr Mng Dir & Head-Global Asset Mgmt)*
Steven J. Sadoff *(Exec VP, Global Head-Ops, Svcs & Tech)*
James P. Smyth *(Exec VP & Sr Relationship Officer)*
Gregory C. Voetsch *(Exec VP-Head Global Equities)*
Margaret E. Wyrwas *(Sr Mng Dir-Comm, Mktg & IR)*
Bronwen Bastone *(Mng Dir-HR)*
Didier Bankole *(VP-Sls)*
Brands & Products:
KNIGHT
Advertising Agency:
Doremus
(Sub. of Omnicom Group, Inc.)
200 Varick St 11Fl
New York, NY 10014-4810
Tel.: (212) 366-3000
Fax: (212) 366-3060

KODIAK VENTURE PARTNERS, L.P.
Bay Colony Corp Ctr 1000 Winter St Ste 3800
Waltham, MA 02451
Tel.: (781) 672-2500
Fax: (781) 672-2501
E-mail: contact@kodiakvp.com
Web Site: www.kodiakvp.com
Approx. Sls.: $676,000,000
Approx. Number Employees: 100
Year Founded: 1999
Business Description:
Equity Investment Firm
S.I.C.: 6289
N.A.I.C.S.: 523999
Personnel:
Dave Furneaux *(Founder & Mng Partner)*
Chip Meakem *(Mng Partner)*
Lou Volpe *(Mng Partner)*
Andrey Zarur *(Mng Partner)*
W. David Lee *(Operating Partner)*
Penny Breen *(VP-Fin)*
Advertising Agency:
PAN Communications
300 Brickstone Sq 7th Fl
Andover, MA 01810
Tel.: (978) 474-1900
Fax: (978) 474-1903

KPMG LLP
(Affil. of KPMG International)
3 Chestnut Ridge Rd
Montvale, NJ 07645-0435
Tel.: (201) 307-7000
Fax: (201) 930-8617
Web Site: www.us.kpmg.com
Sales Range: $1-4.9 Billion
Approx. Number Employees: 23,897
Year Founded: 1897
Business Description:
Audit, Tax & Advisory Services
S.I.C.: 8721; 7291
N.A.I.C.S.: 541211; 541213; 541219
Media: 2-9-22-25
Distr.: Natl.
Personnel:
John B. Veihmeyer *(Chm & CEO)*
Thomas Bibby *(Partner)*
Jack Taylor *(Mng Dir)*
Chris Goodman *(CMO)*
Thomas G. Wilde *(Principal)*
Vicki Gault *(Sr Dir-Advisory Comm)*
Dan Ginsburg *(Sr Dir-Corp Comm)*
Deborah Primano *(Sr Dir-Tax Comm)*
Ray Zardetto *(Sr Dir-Comm)*
George Ledwith *(Dir-Global External Comm)*
John D. Stone *(Dir-Advisory Svcs)*
Curtis Topper *(Dir)*

LABRANCHE & CO., LLC
(Sub. of LaBranche & Co Inc.)
33 Whitehall St
New York, NY 10004
Tel.: (212) 425-1144
Web Site: www.labranche.com
Sales Range: $650-699.9 Million
Business Description:
Stock Brokerage Services
S.I.C.: 6211
N.A.I.C.S.: 523120
Personnel:
Alfred O. Hayward, Jr. *(Exec VP & Dir)*
Advertising Agency:
KCSA Strategic Communications
(Kanan, Corbin, Schupak & Aronow, Inc.)
880 3rd Ave 6th Fl
New York, NY 10022
Tel.: (212) 682-6300
Fax: (212) 697-0910

LAKE SHORE BANCORP, INC.
125 E 4th St
Dunkirk, NY 14048-2226
Tel.: (716) 366-4070
E-mail: kathy.kaus@lakeshoresavings.com
Web Site: www.lakeshoresavings.com
Approx. Rev.: $23,380,000
Approx. Number Employees: 100
Business Description:
Bank Holding Company; Federally-Chartered Savings & Loan Services
S.I.C.: 6712; 6029; 6035
N.A.I.C.S.: 551111; 522110; 522120
Advertising Expenditures: $419,000
Media: 8
Personnel:
Michael E. Brunecz *(Chm)*
Gary W. Winger *(Vice Chm)*
Daniel P. Reininga *(Pres & CEO)*
Rachel A. Foley *(CFO)*
Janinne F. Dugan *(Officer-HR)*
Nicole May *(Compliance Officer)*
Katherine A. Kaus *(Chief Lending Officer & Sr VP)*

LAKELAND FINANCIAL CORPORATION
202 E Center St PO Box 1387
Warsaw, IN 46581-1387
Tel.: (574) 267-6144
Fax: (574) 267-6063
Toll Free: (888) 522-2265
E-mail: david.findlay@lakecitybank.com
Web Site: www.lakecitybank.com
Approx. Rev.: $145,034,000
Approx. Number Employees: 467
Year Founded: 1983
Business Description:
Holding Company
S.I.C.: 6029
N.A.I.C.S.: 522110
Advertising Expenditures: $446,000
Personnel:
Michael L. Kubacki *(Chm & CEO)*
David M. Findlay *(Pres)*
Kevin L. Deardorff *(Exec VP)*
Charles D. Smith *(Exec VP)*
James D. Westerfield *(Sr VP-Wealth Advisory)*

LANDMARK BANCORP, INC.
701 Poyntz Ave
Manhattan, KS 66502-6052
Tel.: (785) 565-2000
Fax: (785) 537-0619
Toll Free: (800) 318-8997
E-mail: lnbmail@banklandmark.com
Web Site: www.banklandmark.com
Approx. Rev.: $33,491,000
Approx. Number Employees: 207
Business Description:
Holding Company
S.I.C.: 6029; 6712
N.A.I.C.S.: 522110; 551111
Advertising Expenditures: $617,000
Personnel:
Larry L. Schugart *(Chm)*
Patrick L. Alexander *(Pres & CEO)*
Mark A. Herpich *(CFO)*

LANDRUM CO.
801 E Broadway
Columbia, MO 65201
Tel.: (573) 449-3911
Fax: (573) 875-1468
Web Site: www.thelandrumcompany.com
Sales Range: $25-49.9 Million
Approx. Number Employees: 700
Business Description:
National Trust Companies With Deposits, Commercial
S.I.C.: 6029
N.A.I.C.S.: 522110
Personnel:
Marcus Landrum *(Chm)*

Key to Media (For complete agency information see *The Advertising Red Books-Agencies* edition):
1. Bus. Publs. 2. Cable T.V. 3. Catalogs & Directories. 4. Co-op Adv. 5. Consumer Mags. 6. D.M. to Bus. Estab.7. D.M. to Consumers
8. Daily Newsp. 9. Exhibits/Trade Shows 10. Foreign 11. Infomercial 12. Internet Adv.13. Multimedia 14. Network Radio
15. Network T.V. 16. Newsp. Distr. Mags. 17. Other 18. Outdoor (Posters, Transit) 19. Point of Purchase20. Premiums, Novelties
21. Product Samples 22. Special Events Mktg. 23. Spot Radio 24. Spot T.V. 25. Weekly Newsp. 26. Yellow Page Adv.

Landrum Co. — (Continued)

Advertising Agency:
True Media
29 S 9th St Ste 201
Columbia, MO 65201
Tel.: (573) 443-8783
Fax: (573) 443-8784

LAPORTE BANCORP, INC.
710 Indiana Ave
La Porte, IN 46350
Tel.: (219) 362-7511
E-mail: webmaster@thelpsb.com
Web Site:
www.laportesavingsbank.com
Approx. Rev.: $24,685,000
Approx. Number Employees: 103
Business Description:
Bank Holding Company
S.I.C.: 6035; 6712
N.A.I.C.S.: 522120; 551111
Advertising Expenditures: $240,000
Media: 6-8-9-25
Personnel:
Paul G. Fenker *(Chm)*
Jerry L. Mayes *(Vice Chm)*
Lee A. Brady *(Pres & CEO)*
Michele M. Thompson *(CFO & Exec VP)*
Bruce R. Fisher *(Sr VP-Mortgage Lending)*

LAUREL COLLEGIATE LOAN
(Sub. of Union Federal Savings Bank)
31 St James Ave
Boston, MA 02116
Toll Free: (866) 576-0685
Web Site:
www.laurelcollegiateloans.com
Sales Range: $125-149.9 Million
Business Description:
Student Loan Processing
S.I.C.: 6163
N.A.I.C.S.: 522310
Media: 13
Personnel:
Jack Kopinsky *(CEO)*

LAZARD FRERES & CO., LLC
(Sub. of Lazard Group LLC)
30 Rockefeller Plz
New York, NY 10020-0002
Tel.: (212) 632-6000
Fax: (212) 632-6060
Web Site: www.lazard.com
Approx. Number Employees: 1,300
Year Founded: 1858
Business Description:
Financial Advisory Services
S.I.C.: 6211
N.A.I.C.S.: 523120
Advertising Expenditures: $550,000
Media: 2-9
Distr.: Reg.
Budget Set: Oct.
Personnel:
Vernon E. Jordan, Jr. *(Partner)*
Douglas C. Taylor *(Mng Dir)*

LAZARD MIDDLE MARKET LLC
(Formerly Goldsmith, Agio, Helms & Lynner, LLC)
(Div. of Lazard Freres & Co., LLC)
225 S 6th St 46th Fl
Minneapolis, MN 55402
Tel.: (612) 339-0500
Fax: (612) 339-0507
Web Site: www.lazardmm.com
Sales Range: $25-49.9 Million
Approx. Number Employees: 80
Year Founded: 1977
Business Description:
Investment Banking Services
S.I.C.: 6211; 6282; 6289
N.A.I.C.S.: 523110; 523930; 523999
Personnel:
Michael F. Mcfadden *(Co-CEO)*
David J. Solomon *(Co-CEO)*
Gerald M. Caruso, Jr. *(Mng Dir)*
Andrew Torgove *(Mng Dir)*
Robert I. Burns, Jr. *(Mng Dir)*
James R. Clancy *(Mng Dir)*
Joseph M. Conte *(Mng Dir)*
Robin J. Engelson *(Mng Dir)*
James Frommelt *(Mng Dir)*
David L. Hallett *(Mng Dir)*
David G. Iverson *(Mng Dir)*
Kevin G. Jach *(Mng Dir)*
Terry A. Lynner *(Mng Dir)*
Stephen Miles *(Mng Dir)*
Ben S. Axelrod *(Dir)*
Kevin A. Janicki *(Dir)*
John A. Waldock, Jr. *(Dir)*
Advertising Agency:
Mindframe, Inc.
212 3rd Ave N Ste 586
Minneapolis, MN 55401-1440
Tel.: (612) 204-0320

LEGACY BANCORP, INC.
Legacy Financial Center 99 North St
Pittsfield, MA 01201
Tel.: (413) 443-4421
Fax: (413) 442-8153
Toll Free: (800) 292-6634
E-mail: paul.bruce@legacybanks.com
Web Site: www.legacy-banks.com
Approx. Rev.: $44,157,000
Approx. Number Employees: 173
Year Founded: 2005
Business Description:
Bank Holding Company
S.I.C.: 6035; 6029; 6712
N.A.I.C.S.: 522120; 522110; 551111
Advertising Expenditures: $1,047,000
Personnel:
J. Williar Dunlaevy *(Chm)*
Paul H. Bruce *(CFO & Sr VP-IR)*
Kimberly A. Matthews *(Gen Counsel & Sr VP)*
Richard M. Sullivan *(Sr VP-Comml Real Estate)*

LEGG MASON, INC.
100 International Dr
Baltimore, MD 21202
Tel.: (410) 539-0000
Fax: (410) 528-3999
Toll Free: (877) 534-4627
Web Site: www.leggmason.com
E-Mail For Key Personnel:
Public Relations: publicrelations@leggmason.com
Approx. Rev.: $2,784,317,000
Approx. Number Employees: 3,395
Year Founded: 1899
Business Description:
Asset Management Services
S.I.C.: 6211; 6282
N.A.I.C.S.: 523110; 523920
Media: 8-13
Personnel:
Mark Raymond Fetting *(Chm & CEO)*
Peter H. Nachtwey *(CFO)*
Thomas P. Lemke *(Gen Counsel & Exec VP)*
Timothy F. Munoz *(Sr VP & Head-Corp Mktg & Comm)*
F. Barry Bilson *(Sr VP)*
Elisabeth N. Spector *(Sr VP)*
Alan F. Magleby *(Mng Dir-IR & Comm)*
Peter Andersson *(Dir-Bus Dev)*
Mary Athridge *(Dir-Corp Comm)*
James Cahill *(Dir-Bus Dev)*
Advertising Agency:
Brotman Winter Fried Communications
111 Park Pl
Falls Church, VA 22046
Tel.: (703) 534-4600
Fax: (703) 536-2255

LEUCADIA NATIONAL CORPORATION
315 Park Ave S
New York, NY 10010
Tel.: (212) 460-1900
Fax: (212) 598-4869
Web Site: www.leucadia.com
Approx. Rev.: $1,320,004,000
Approx. Number Employees: 2,414
Year Founded: 1968
Business Description:
Holding Company
S.I.C.: 6719; 6289
N.A.I.C.S.: 551112; 523999
Export
Advertising Expenditures: $16,000,000
Media: 2-4-6-7-8-9-10-11-14-18-23-24-25
Distr.: Intl.; Natl.
Personnel:
Ian M. Cumming *(Chm)*
Joseph S. Steinberg *(Pres)*
Joseph A. Orlando *(CFO & VP)*
Justin R. Wheeler *(Pres-Asset Mgmt Grp)*
Laura E. Ulbrandt *(Sec & Asst VP)*
Thomas E. Mara *(Exec VP)*

LIBERTY BANCORP, INC.
16 W Franklin St
Liberty, MO 64068
Tel.: (816) 781-4822
Fax: (816) 781-6851
Web Site: www.banklibertykc.com
Approx. Rev.: $22,209,602
Approx. Number Employees: 84
Year Founded: 1955
Business Description:
Bank Holding Company
S.I.C.: 6712; 6029
N.A.I.C.S.: 551111; 522110
Advertising Expenditures: $313,000
Media: 3-6-9-20-23-24-25
Personnel:
Daniel G. O'Dell *(Chm)*
Brent M. Giles *(CEO)*
Marc J. Weishaar *(CFO & Sr VP)*
Ken Honeck *(Chief Deposit Officer)*
Mark E. Hecker *(Chief Lending Officer & Sr VP)*
Shawna Croucher *(Asst VP & Branch Mgr-Independence)*
Debbie Kincaid *(Asst VP & Branch Mgr-Boardwalk)*
Tara Wehri *(Asst VP & Branch Mgr)*

LIBERTY BANK INC.
315 Main St
Middletown, CT 06457
Tel.: (860) 344-7200
Toll Free: (888) 570-0773
Web Site: www.liberty-bank.com
Approx. Int. Income: $77,289,000
Approx. Number Employees: 500
Year Founded: 1825
Business Description:
Financial Services
S.I.C.: 6035; 6163
N.A.I.C.S.: 522120; 522310
Media: 2-4-7-8-9-13-15-16-19-20-21-22-23-24-26
Distr.: Direct to Consumer
Budget Set: Oct.
Personnel:
Thomas J. Pastorello *(CFO)*
Melanie Joy *(Sr VP)*
Brands & Products:
LIBERTY BANK

LIFELOCK INC.
60 E Rio Salado Pkwy Ste 400
Tempe, AZ 85281
Tel.: (480) 682-5100
Web Site: www.lifelock.com
Sales Range: $125-149.9 Million
Approx. Number Employees: 100
Year Founded: 2005
Business Description:
Identity Theft Prevention Services
S.I.C.: 7389
N.A.I.C.S.: 519190
Media: 3
Personnel:
Todd Davis *(Co-Founder, Chm & CEO)*
Andy Corbin *(Pres & COO)*
Patrick Pendleton *(CIO)*
Marvin Davis *(CMO)*
Mike Prusinski *(Sr VP- Corp Comm)*
Tami Nealy *(Dir-Pub Affairs)*
Amanda Lomont *(Sr Mgr-Product Mktg)*
Advertising Agencies:
IMAGES USA
1320 Ellsworth Industrial Blvd
Atlanta, GA 30318
Tel.: (404) 892-2931
Fax: (404) 892-8651

The Lavidge Company
2777 E Camelback Rd Ste 300
Phoenix, AZ 85016
Tel.: (480) 998-2600
Fax: (480) 998-5525

McCann Erickson/Los Angeles
5700 Wilshire Blvd Ste 225
Los Angeles, CA 90036
Tel.: (323) 900-7100
Fax: (323) 900-7111
Creative Agency of Record

McCann Erickson/Salt Lake City
32 Exchange Pl Ste 200
Salt Lake City, UT 84111-5151
Tel.: (801) 257-7700
Fax: (801) 257-7799
Creative Agency of Record

McCann Worldgroup
600 Battery St
San Francisco, CA 94111
Tel.: (415) 262-5600
Fax: (415) 262-5400
Creative Agency of Record

Key to Media (For complete agency information see *The Advertising Red Books-Agencies* edition):
1. Bus. Publs. 2. Cable T.V. 3. Catalogs & Directories. 4. Co-op Adv. 5. Consumer Mags. 6. D.M. to Bus. Estab.7. D.M. to Consumers 8. Daily Newsp. 9. Exhibits/Trade Shows 10. Foreign 11. Infomercial 12. Internet Adv.13. Multimedia 14. Network Radio 15. Network T.V. 16. Newsp. Distr. Mags. 17. Other 18. Outdoor (Posters, Transit) 19. Point of Purchase20. Premiums, Novelties 21. Product Samples 22. Special Events Mktg. 23. Spot Radio 24. Spot T.V. 25. Weekly Newsp. 26. Yellow Page Adv.

LINCOLN NATIONAL CORPORATION
(d/b/a Lincoln Financial Group)
150 Radner Chester Rd
Philadelphia, PA 19102-2112
Tel.: (484) 583-1400
E-mail: MediaRelations@LFG.com
Web Site: www.lfg.com
Approx. Rev.: $10,407,000,000
Approx. Number Employees: 8,270
Year Founded: 1905
Business Description:
Diversified Financial, Investment, Retirement Planning & Insurance Services
S.I.C.: 6321; 6282; 6289; 6311
N.A.I.C.S.: 524130; 523930; 523999; 524113; 524114
Advertising Expenditures: $30,700,000
Media: 2-7
Distr.: Natl.
Personnel:
William H. Cunningham *(Chm)*
Dennis R. Glass *(Pres & CEO)*
Randal J. Freitag *(CFO & Exec VP)*
Jamie DePeau *(Corp CMO)*
Casey J. Trumble *(Sr VP and Chief Accounting Officer)*
Lisa M. Bettinger-Buckingham *(Chief HR Officer & Exec VP)*
Robert William Dineen *(Pres-Lincoln Fin Network & CEO-Lincoln Fin Advisors)*
Charles C. Cornelio *(Pres-Defined-Contribution Bus)*
Mark E. Konen *(Pres-Insurance & Retirement Solutions)*
Frederick J. Crawford *(Exec VP, Head-Corp Dev & Investments)*
Jen Warne *(Sr VP & Head-Talent)*
Duane L. Bernt *(Head-Fin & Strategy-Defined Contribution Bus)*
David Wozniak *(Head-Adv)*
Brands & Products:
A. LINCOLN
ABE
AMERICAN LEGACY
CHOICEPLUS
CLEAR SOLUTIONS IN A COMPLEX WORLD
DIRECTOR
GROUP RESOURCE
HELLO FUTURE
LINCOLN
LINCOLN FINANCIAL GROUP
LINCOLN LIFE
LINCOLN LIFE DIRECTOR
LINCOLN NATIONAL
LINCOLN SILHOUETTE DESIGN
LNC
LNRM
LUS
MONEYGUARD
MULTI-FUND
SECURELINE
SPECIAL ALTERNATIVES
Advertising Agency:
Tierney Communications
(A Div. of the Interpublic Group of Companies)
The Bellevue 200 S Broad St
Philadelphia, PA 19102-3803
Tel.: (215) 790-4100
Fax: (215) 790-4363

LIQUIDATION WORLD INCORPORATED
3880 29th Street Northeast
Calgary, AB T1Y 6B6, Canada
Tel.: (403) 250-1222
Fax: (403) 291-1306
Toll Free: (877) SAVEBUX
E-mail: webmaster@liquidationworld.com
Web Site: www.lwstores.com
Approx. Rev.: $156,285,969
Approx. Number Employees: 1,700
Year Founded: 1986
Business Description:
Marketer of Merchandise from Bankruptcies, Receiverships, Close-Outs & Insurance Claims
S.I.C.: 5399
N.A.I.C.S.: 452990
Media: 3-9-25
Personnel:
Craig Graham *(Interim Pres)*
Lynda Murray *(Exec VP-Mktg)*
Jim Charbeneau *(VP-Mdsg)*
Corrie Prince *(VP-HR)*
Chris Rath *(Interim VP-Fin)*
Gary Kelly *(Dir-Distr & Logistics)*
Chad Richardson *(Dir-Info Sys)*

LIQUIDNET HOLDINGS, INC.
498 7th Ave 12th Fl
New York, NY 10018
Tel.: (646) 674-2000
Fax: (646) 674-2003
E-mail: info@liquidnet.com
Web Site: www.liquidnet.com
Sales Range: $300-349.9 Million
Approx. Number Employees: 379
Year Founded: 1999
Business Description:
Holding Company; Securities Brokerage Services
S.I.C.: 6211; 6719
N.A.I.C.S.: 523120; 551112
Media: 17-22
Personnel:
Seth Merrin *(Founder & CEO)*
William Maw *(CFO)*
Howard Meyerson *(Chief Compliance Officer & Gen Counsel)*
Ase Edstron *(Head-Mktg)*

LONG POINT CAPITAL LLC
600 5th Ave 23rd Fl
New York, NY 10020
Tel.: (212) 593-1800
Fax: (212) 593-1888
Web Site: www.longpointcapital.com
Approx. Sls.: $56,800,000
Approx. Number Employees: 10
Business Description:
Investment Bankers
S.I.C.: 6211
N.A.I.C.S.: 523110
Personnel:
Gerry Boylan *(Mng Dir)*
John Morgan *(Mng Dir)*
Ira Starr *(Mng Dir)*
William Ughetta *(Mng Dir)*
Eric Von Stroh *(Mng Dir)*
Advertising Agency:
Artichoke Creative
590 Hygeia Ave
Encinitas, CA 92024
Tel.: (760) 753-8663
Fax: (760) 454-2795

LOOMIS, SAYLES & COMPANY, L.P.
(Joint Venture of Caisse Nationale des Caisses d'Epargne et de Prevoyance & Banque Federale des Banques Populaires)
1 Financial Ctr
Boston, MA 02111-2621
Tel.: (617) 482-2450
Fax: (617) 482-1985
Toll Free: (800) 343-2029
Web Site: www.loomissayles.com
E-Mail For Key Personnel:
Marketing Director: mclough@loomissayles.com
Approx. Managed Assets: $140,900,000,000
Approx. Number Employees: 200
Year Founded: 1926
Business Description:
Securities Investment & Fund Management Services
S.I.C.: 6211; 6282
N.A.I.C.S.: 523110; 523920
Advertising Expenditures: $300,000
Media: 2-5-7-9-11-25
Distr.: Direct to Consumer; Natl.
Budget Set: Sept.
Personnel:
Dan Fuss *(Vice Chm)*
Robert J. Blanding *(CEO)*
Kevin Charleston *(CFO)*
Mark Baribeau *(CIO & VP)*
Lauriann Kloppenburg *(CIO-Equities)*
Jae Park *(Chief Investment Officer-Fixed Income)*
Jean Loewenberg *(Gen Counsel)*
Kathleen Gaffney *(VP & Mgr-Fixed Income Portfolio)*
Christopher Lazzaro *(VP & Mgr-Client Portfolio)*
Will Averill *(VP)*
Chuck Koeniger *(VP-Institutional Sls-Public Fund Plan Sponsors)*
Chris Perkin *(VP-Defined Contribution Investment)*
John Gallagher *(Dir-Institutional Svcs)*

LOUISIANA BANCORP, INC.
1600 Veterans Memorial Blvd
Metairie, LA 70005
Tel.: (504) 834-1190
Fax: (504) 835-2373
Web Site: www.bankofneworleans.net
Approx. Rev.: $17,130,000
Approx. Number Employees: 63
Business Description:
Bank Holding Company
S.I.C.: 6035; 6029; 6712
N.A.I.C.S.: 522120; 522110; 551111
Advertising Expenditures: $132,000
Media: 17
Personnel:
Lawrence J. LeBon, III *(Chm, Pres & CEO)*
John P. Leblanc *(CFO & Sr VP)*

LPL FINANCIAL CORPORATION
(Joint Venture of Hellman & Friedman LLC & TPG Capital, L.P.)
1 Beacon St 22nd Fl
Boston, MA 02108-3107
Tel.: (617) 423-3644
Web Site: www.lpl.com
Approx. Number Employees: 250
Business Description:
Securities Brokerage
S.I.C.: 6211
N.A.I.C.S.: 523120
Personnel:
Mark S. Casady *(Chm & CEO)*
Esther M. Stearns *(Pres & COO)*
Christopher Feeney *(CIO & Mng Dir)*
John J. McDermott, Jr. *(Mng Dir & Chief Enterprise Risk Mgmt Officer)*
Steven M. Black *(Mng Dir & Chief Risk Officer)*
William E. Dwyer *(Pres-Natl Sls/Mktg & Mng Dir)*
Stephanie L. Brown *(Mng Dir, Gen Counsel & Sec)*
Derek Bruton *(Mng Dir & Sls Mgr-Natl)*
Robert J. Moore *(CFO)*
Burt White *(Chief Investment Officer)*
Thomas Lux *(Chief Acctg Officer & Exec VP)*
Mark Barnett *(Exec VP-IR)*
Andy Kalbaugh *(Exec VP-Bus Consulting)*
William P. Morrissey *(Exec VP-Bus Dev)*
Cynthia K. Swank *(Exec VP-Svc Value Commitment)*
Jeffrey R. Buchheister *(Sr VP-Regulatory Controls & Commissions-Broker/Dealer Support Svc)*
Brad Cornell *(Sr VP-Sponsor Rels)*
Craig Kamis *(Sr VP-Bus Dev & Recruiting)*
Michael Watson *(Sr VP-Bus Consulting-San Diego)*
Advertising Agency:
Carton Donofrio Partners, Inc.
100 N Charles St 15th Fl
Baltimore, MD 21201
Tel.: (410) 576-9000
Fax: (410) 528-8809

LSB FINANCIAL CORP.
101 Main St
Lafayette, IN 47902
Mailing Address:
PO 1628
Lafayette, IN 47902-1628
Tel.: (765) 742-1064
Fax: (765) 742-1507
Toll Free: (800) 704-3084
E-mail: lsbmail@lsbank.com
Web Site: www.lsbank.com
Approx. Rev.: $21,975,000
Approx. Number Employees: 89
Year Founded: 1994
Business Description:
Financial Holding Company
S.I.C.: 6035; 6712
N.A.I.C.S.: 522120; 551111
Advertising Expenditures: $282,000
Media: 7-8-9-13-20-25
Personnel:
Mariellen M. Neudeck *(Chm)*
Randolph F. Williams *(Pres & CEO)*
Mary Jo David *(CFO, Sec & VP)*

LYDIAN BANK & TRUST
(Div. of Lydian Bank & Trust)
701 N Franklin St
Tampa, FL 33602
Tel.: (813) 227-9300
Fax: (813) 464-2894
Web Site: www.lydianbank.com
Approx. Number Employees: 6
Business Description:
Banking Services
S.I.C.: 6029

Key to Media (For complete agency information see *The Advertising Red Books-Agencies* edition):
1. Bus. Publs. 2. Cable T.V. 3. Catalogs & Directories. 4. Co-op Adv. 5. Consumer Mags. 6. D.M. to Bus. Estab.7. D.M. to Consumers 8. Daily Newsp. 9. Exhibits/Trade Shows 10. Foreign 11. Infomercial 12. Internet Adv.13. Multimedia 14. Network Radio 15. Network T.V. 16. Newsp. Distr. Mags. 17. Other 18. Outdoor (Posters, Transit) 19. Point of Purchase20. Premiums, Novelties 21. Product Samples 22. Special Events Mktg. 23. Spot Radio 24. Spot T.V. 25. Weekly Newsp. 26. Yellow Page Adv.

Lydian Bank & Trust — (Continued)

N.A.I.C.S.: 522110
Media: 6

THE LYONS NATIONAL BANK

(Sub. of Lyons Bancorp, Inc.)
35 Williams St
Lyons, NY 14489
Tel.: (315) 946-4871
Fax: (315) 946-6215
E-mail: lnbweb@redsuspenders.com
Web Site: bankwithlnb.com/
Approx. Number Employees: 30
Business Description:
Provider of Banking Services
S.I.C.: 6029
N.A.I.C.S.: 522110
Personnel:
Robert A. Schick *(CFO)*
Advertising Agency:
Archer Communications, Inc.
252 Alexander St
Rochester, NY 14607-2515
Tel.: (585) 461-1570
Fax: (585) 461-5313

M&T BANK CORPORATION

1 M&T Plaza
Buffalo, NY 14203
Tel.: (716) 842-5445
Fax: (716) 842-4306
E-mail: ir@mtb.com
Web Site: www.mtb.com
Approx. Rev.: $3,837,895,000
Approx. Number Employees: 12,031
Year Founded: 1969
Business Description:
Bank Holding Company
S.I.C.: 6029; 6035; 6163; 6211; 6712
N.A.I.C.S.: 522110; 522120; 522310; 523110; 551111
Advertising Expenditures: $41,869,000
Media: 2-3-4-6-7-8-9-10-12-18-19-20-22-23-24-25-26
Distr.: Reg.
Budget Set: Oct.
Personnel:
Robert G. Wilmers *(Chm & CEO)*
Jorge G. Pereira *(Vice Chm)*
Michael P. Pinto *(Vice Chm)*
Robert E. Sadler, Jr. *(Vice Chm)*
Mark J. Czarnecki *(Pres)*
Rene F. Jones *(CFO & Exec VP)*
Michele D. Trolli *(CIO & Exec VP)*
Peter Eliopoulos *(CMO)*
Robert J. Bojdak *(Chief Credit Officer & Exec VP)*
Christopher D. Randall *(Pres/CEO-M&T Securities)*
Peter G. Newman *(Pres-Southern New York Reg)*
D. Scott N. Warman *(Treas & Exec VP)*
James J. Beardi *(Exec VP)*
Stephen J. Braunscheidel *(Exec VP)*
Atwood Collins, III *(Exec VP)*
Brian E. Hickey *(Exec VP)*
Kevin J. Pearson *(Exec VP)*
Michael R. Spychala *(Sr VP & Controller)*
John L. D'Angelo *(Sr VP & Gen Auditor)*
Abbas Merchant *(Sr VP-Mktg)*
Michael S. Piemonte *(Sr VP)*
Thomas Esposito *(Grp VP-Consumer Capital Markets Dept)*
Ayan Das Gupta *(Grp VP)*
Clifford P. Johnson *(Grp VP)*
Jeffrey A. Livermore *(Grp VP)*
Christopher E. Tolomeo *(Grp VP)*
John T. Roberts, II *(VP & Mgr-Bus Banking Relationship-Howard County)*
Michael J. Shank *(VP & Mgr-Bus Banking)*
Jeffrey M. Balcom *(VP & Asst Sec)*
Randall A. Krolewicz *(VP & Asst Sec)*
Donald J. MacLeod *(VP & Asst Sec)*
Brian R. Yoshida *(Asst Sec & VP-Admin)*
David P. Rutecki *(VP-Admin)*
Kathleen M. Dewyea *(Asst VP)*
Rakesh Iyer *(Asst VP-Strategy & Analytics-Online & Direct Mktg)*
Alexander J. Craig *(Mgr-Portfolio)*
Eric Morales *(Mgr-Relationship-Central Virginia Middle Market Banking)*
Steve Schumer *(Mgr-Relationship)*
Deborah R. Pokerwinski *(Asst Sec)*
Brands & Products:
M&T BANK
UNDERSTANDING WHAT'S IMPORTANT
Advertising Agency:
Crowley Webb & Associates
268 Main St Ste 400
Buffalo, NY 14202-4108
Tel.: (716) 856-2932
Fax: (716) 856-2940

MACANDREWS & FORBES HOLDINGS INC.

35 E 62nd St
New York, NY 10021
Tel.: (212) 572-8600
Fax: (212) 572-8400
E-mail: info@macandrewsandforbes.com
Web Site: www.macandrewsandforbes.com
Approx. Number Employees: 19,800
Year Founded: 1983
Business Description:
Holding Company
S.I.C.: 6719; 2087; 2099; 2844; 2869; 3631; 3635; 3949; 7819
N.A.I.C.S.: 551112; 311930; 311942; 325199; 325620; 335212; 335221; 339920; 512191
Media: 6-15-18
Distr.: Natl.
Personnel:
Ronald O. Perelman *(Chm & CEO)*
Paul G. Savas *(CFO & Exec VP)*
Barry F. Schwartz *(Chief Admin Officer & Exec Vice Chm)*
Jim Gillece *(Chief People Officer & Sr VP-Human Capital Mgmt)*
Eric A. Rose *(Exec VP-Life Sciences)*
Christine Taylor *(Sr VP-Corp Comm)*

MACATAWA BANK CORPORATION

10753 Macatawa Dr
Holland, MI 49424
Mailing Address:
PO Box 3119
Holland, MI 49422-3119
Tel.: (616) 820-1444
Fax: (616) 494-7644
Toll Free: (877) 820-2265
E-mail: connect@macatawabank.com
Web Site: www.macatawabank.com
Approx. Int. Income: $76,003,000
Approx. Number Employees: 327
Year Founded: 2002
Business Description:
Bank Holding Company
S.I.C.: 6712; 6029
N.A.I.C.S.: 551111; 522110
Advertising Expenditures: $946,000
Personnel:
Richard L. Postma *(Chm)*
Ronald L. Haan *(Pres & CEO)*
Jon W. Swets *(CFO & Sr VP)*
Renae L. S. Eckland *(CIO & Sr VP)*
Craig A. Hankinson *(Chief Credit Officer & Sr VP)*
Vicki K. Denboer *(Sr VP-Retail Lending)*
Jill A. Walcott *(Sr VP)*
Brad Kolean *(VP & Mgr)*
Christine M. Bart *(VP-Mktg)*
Amy L. Ziel *(VP-HR)*
Jason Balgavy *(Mgr-Portfolio)*
Brands & Products:
MACATAWA
MACATAWA CONNECT
MOOOLAH KIDS CLUB
THE WAY BANKING SHOULD BE

MACKINAC FINANCIAL CORPORATION

130 S Cedar St
Manistique, MI 49854
Tel.: (906) 341-8401
Fax: (906) 341-8578
Web Site: www.bankmbank.com
Approx. Int. Income: $25,635,000
Approx. Number Employees: 110
Year Founded: 1974
Business Description:
Bank Holding Company
S.I.C.: 6712; 6029
N.A.I.C.S.: 551111; 522110
Advertising Expenditures: $297,000
Personnel:
Paul D. Tobias *(Chm)*
Kelly W. George *(Pres & CEO)*
Ernie R. Krueger *(CFO & Exec VP)*

MADISON NATIONAL BANCORP, INC.

888 Veterans Memorial Hwy Ste 400
Hauppauge, NY 11788
Tel.: (631) 348-6999
Fax: (631) 348-0099
E-mail: bseider@madisonnational.com
Web Site: www.madisonnational.com
Approx. Int. Income: $17,594,327
Business Description:
Bank Holding Company
S.I.C.: 6712; 6029
N.A.I.C.S.: 551111; 522110
Advertising Expenditures: $315,988
Personnel:
Gerald Kaiser *(Co-Founder)*
Donald Musso *(Co-Founder)*
Daniel L. Murphy *(Chm & CEO)*
Michael P. Puorro *(Pres)*
William P. Mackey *(CFO & Exec VP)*
Bonnie Seider *(Corp Sec & Sr VP)*
Thomas N. Gilmartin *(Chief Lending Officer & Exec VP)*
Stella M. Mendes *(Chief Retail Officer & Exec VP)*

MAGYAR BANCORP, INC.

(Holding of Magyar Bancorp, MHC)
400 Somerset St
New Brunswick, NJ 08903
Tel.: (732) 342-7600
Fax: (732) 249-2391
E-mail: customerservice@magbank.com
Web Site: www.magbank.com
Approx. Rev.: $27,415,000
Approx. Number Employees: 87
Business Description:
Bank Holding Company
S.I.C.: 6712; 6029; 6035; 6163
N.A.I.C.S.: 551111; 522110; 522120; 522310
Advertising Expenditures: $157,000
Personnel:
Joseph J. Lukacs, Jr. *(Chm)*
Thomas Lankey *(Vice Chm)*
John S. Fitzgerald *(Pres & CEO)*
Jon R. Ansari *(CFO & Sr VP)*
Advertising Agency:
Zullo Associates
1 Academy St
Princeton, NJ 08540
Tel.: (609) 683-1800
Fax: (609) 683-4773

MAINSTREET BANKSHARES, INC.

1075 Spruce Street
Martinsville, VA 24112
Tel.: (276) 632-8054
Fax: (276) 632-8043
E-mail: information@msbsinc.com
Web Site: www.msbsinc.com
Approx. Rev.: $12,117,933
Approx. Number Employees: 51
Year Founded: 1999
Business Description:
Bank Holding Company
S.I.C.: 6712
N.A.I.C.S.: 551111
Advertising Expenditures: $75,639
Media: 17
Personnel:
Joel R. Shepherd *(Chm)*
Larry A. Heaton *(Pres & CEO)*
Brenda H. Smith *(CFO, Sec & Exec VP)*
Christopher A. Ames *(VP & IT Officer)*
Sonya B. Smith *(VP-Ops & Compliance Officer)*
M. Catherine Frazier *(Loan Ops Officer)*
Judy H. McNeely *(Asst Sec)*

MALVERN FEDERAL BANCORP, INC.

42 E Lancaster Ave
Paoli, PA 19301
Tel.: (610) 644-9400
Web Site: www.malvernfederal.com
Approx. Rev.: $35,089,353
Approx. Number Employees: 90
Business Description:
Bank Holding Company
S.I.C.: 6712; 6035
N.A.I.C.S.: 551111; 522120
Advertising Expenditures: $735,484
Media: 3-8-9-18-23-24-25
Personnel:
F. Claire Hughes, Jr. *(Chm)*
John B. Yerkes, Jr. *(Vice Chm)*
Ronald Anderson *(Pres & CEO)*
Dennis Boyle *(CFO, Treas & Sr VP)*
William E. Hughes, Jr. *(Sr VP & Chief Lending Officer)*

Key to Media (For complete agency information see *The Advertising Red Books-Agencies* edition):
1. Bus. Publs. 2. Cable T.V. 3. Catalogs & Directories. 4. Co-op Adv. 5. Consumer Mags. 6. D.M. to Bus. Estab.7. D.M. to Consumers 8. Daily Newsp. 9. Exhibits/Trade Shows 10. Foreign 11. Infomercial 12. Internet Adv.13. Multimedia 14. Network Radio 15. Network T.V. 16. Newsp. Distr. Mags. 17. Other 18. Outdoor (Posters, Transit) 19. Point of Purchase20. Premiums, Novelties 21. Product Samples 22. Special Events Mktg. 23. Spot Radio 24. Spot T.V. 25. Weekly Newsp. 26. Yellow Page Adv.

MANULIFE FINANCIAL CORPORATION
200 Bloor Street East
Toronto, ON M4W 1E5, Canada
Tel.: (416) 926-0100
Fax: (416) 926-5454
Toll Free: (888) 626-8543
Telex: 6217896
E-mail: corporate_communications@manulife.com
Web Site: www.manulife.com
Approx. Rev.: $36,830,664,440
Approx. Number Employees: 24,000
Year Founded: 1887
Business Description:
Insurance & Investment Management Services
S.I.C.: 6289; 6311; 6321; 6331; 6411
N.A.I.C.S.: 523999; 524113; 524114; 524126; 524130; 524210; 524298; 525190
Media: 2-5-10
Personnel:
Gail C.A. Cook-Bennett *(Chm)*
Donald A. Guloien *(Pres & CEO)*
Indren Naidoo *(Pres & CEO)*
Paul L. Rooney *(Pres & CEO-Canada)*
Michael W. Bell *(CFO & Sr Exec VP)*
Joseph Cooper *(CIO & Exec VP-Global Svcs)*
Dawn Marchand *(CMO)*
Warren A. Thomson *(Chief Investment Officer & Sr Exec VP)*
Simon R. Curtis *(Chief Actuary & Exec VP)*
Beverly S. Margolian *(Chief Risk Officer & Exec VP)*
James R. Boyle *(Pres-Fin Svcs)*
Jean-Paul Bisnaire *(Gen Counsel & Sr Exec VP-Bus Dev)*
Robert A. Cook *(Sr Exec VP & Gen Mgr-Asia)*
Bruce Gordon *(Sr Exec VP & Gen Mgr)*
Geoffrey G. Crickmay *(Exec VP & Gen Mgr)*
Marianne Harrison *(Exec VP & Gen Mgr)*
Diane M. Bean *(Exec VP)*
J. Roy Firth *(Exec VP-Individual Wealth Mgmt)*
Scott Hartz *(Exec VP-Gen Acct Investments)*
Hugh C. McHaffie *(Exec VP-US Wealth Mgmt)*
Carey Hoch *(Sr VP & Head-Mktg)*
Andrew Arnott *(Sr VP)*
Peter Bethlenfalvy *(Sr VP-Fin Regulations)*
Donna Lindell *(VP-Corp Comm)*
Brands & Products:
MANULIFE
MANULIFE FINANCIAL
Advertising Agencies:
Anderson DDB Sante.Vie.Esprit.
3500 Blvd De Maisonneuve St W Ste 610
Montreal, QC H3Z 3C1, Canada
Tel.: (514) 844-9505
Fax: (514) 842-9871

The Henderson Robb Group
401 Bay St Ste 1600
Toronto, ON M5H 2Y4, Canada
Tel.: (416) 362-8262

RMG:Connect - Toronto
160 Bloor St E
Toronto, ON M4W 3P7, Canada
Tel.: (416) 926-7300
Fax: (416) 926-7497

MARKETAXESS HOLDINGS INC.
299 Park Ave
New York, NY 10171
Tel.: (212) 813-6000
Fax: (212) 813-6390
Toll Free: (877) 638-0037
E-mail: uscs@marketaxess.com
Web Site: www.marketaxess.com
Approx. Rev.: $146,228,000
Approx. Number Employees: 229
Year Founded: 2000
Business Description:
Holding Company; Financial Transaction Processing & Securities Trading Services
S.I.C.: 6719; 6099; 6211; 7372; 7379
N.A.I.C.S.: 551112; 511210; 522320; 523110; 541519
Advertising Expenditures: $2,882,000
Media: 7-10-22
Personnel:
Richard M. McVey *(Chm & CEO)*
T. Kelley Millet *(Pres)*
Antonio L. DeLise *(CFO)*
James N.B. Rucker *(Chief Ops, Credit & Risk Officer)*
Nicholas Themelis *(CIO)*
Charles R. Hood *(Gen Counsel)*
Cordelia Boise *(Head-HR)*
Brands & Products:
BONDTICKER
DEALERAXESS
EXCEL ADD IN
FIX MESSAGING
LIQUIDITYBRIDGE
MARKETAXESS
SOAP WEB
STP MESSENGER

MARSHALL & ILSLEY CORPORATION
770 N Water St
Milwaukee, WI 53202-3509
Tel.: (414) 765-7700
Fax: (414) 298-2921
Web Site: www.micorp.com
Approx. Rev.: $2,168,178,000
Approx. Number Employees: 9,137
Year Founded: 1959
Business Description:
Bank Holding & Diversified Financial Services
S.I.C.: 6712; 6029; 6289
N.A.I.C.S.: 551111; 522110; 523999
Media: 2-4-6-7-8-9-10-13-14-15-18-19-20-21-22-25-26
Personnel:
Mark F. Furlong *(Chm, Pres & CEO)*
Gregory A. Smith *(CFO & Sr VP)*
Randall J. Erickson *(Chief Admin Officer, Gen Counsel & Sr VP)*
Mark R. Hogan *(Sr VP & Chief Credit Officer)*
Beth D. Knickerbocker *(Sr VP & Chief Risk Officer)*
Michael C. Smith *(Treas & Sr VP)*
Thomas R. Ellis *(Exec VP)*
Patty Cadorin *(Sr VP-Corp Comm, VP-M & I Foundation)*
Ryan R. Deneen *(Sr VP & Dir-Corp Tax)*
Paul J. Renard *(Sr VP & Dir-HR)*
Thomas A. Root *(Sr VP & Dir-Audit)*
Kenneth C. Krei *(Sr VP)*
Thomas J. O'Neill *(Sr VP)*
John L. Roberts *(Sr VP)*
Jodi B. Payne *(VP & Mgr-State Tax)*
Advertising Agency:
Harland Clarke Corp.
10931 Laureate Dr
San Antonio, TX 78249
Tel.: (210) 697-8888
Toll Free: (800) 382-0818

MASTERCARD INC.
2000 Purchase St
Purchase, NY 10577-2405
Tel.: (914) 249-2000
Fax: (914) 249-4206
E-mail: investor_relations@mastercard.com
Web Site: www.mastercard.com
Approx. Rev.: $5,539,000,000
Approx. Number Employees: 5,600
Year Founded: 1966
Business Description:
Holding Company; Credit Card Issuing
S.I.C.: 6141; 6099; 6719
N.A.I.C.S.: 522210; 522320; 522390; 551112
Advertising Expenditures: $162,000,000
Media: 3-5-6-7-8-11-13-14-15-17-18-22-23-24-31
Personnel:
Richard N. Haythornthwaite *(Chm)*
Ajaypal S. Banga *(Pres & CEO)*
Martina Hund-Mejean *(CFO)*
Alfredo Gangotenato *(CMO)*
Andrea Forster *(Chief Acctg Officer & Controller)*
Noah J. Hanft *(Gen Counsel, Sec & Officer-Franchise Integrity)*
Tara Maguire *(Grp Exec-Corp Plng & Fin Analysis)*
Wendy J. Murdock *(Chief Product Officer)*
Gary J. Flood *(Pres-Global Products & Solutions)*
Walter M. Macnee *(Pres-Intl Markets)*
Chris A. McWilton *(Pres-US Markets)*
Robert Reeg *(Pres-Global Tech & Ops)*
Kevin J. Stanton *(Pres-MasterCard Canada)*
Laura Kelly *(Exec VP)*
June Schult *(Sr Leader-Bus, Head-Mktg-South East & South Asia)*
Gaetano Carboni *(Grp Exec & Gen Mgr-Western Continental Europe)*
Jay Mandel *(Mgr-Global Digital Mktg)*
Cathleen Conforti *(Mgr-Product-PayPass)*
Michael F. McEneney *(Deputy Gen Counsel)*
John Sulca *(Asst Controller)*
Brands & Products:
THE BEST WAY TO PAY FOR EVERYTHING THAT MATTERS
CIRRUS
GOLD MASTERCARD
LODGEMASTER
MAESTRO
MAESTRO E-COMMERCE
MASTER ROADASSIST
MASTERCARD
MASTERCARD CORPORATE CARD
MASTERCARD CORPORATE EXECUTIVE CARD
MASTERCARD CORPORATE FLEET CARD
MASTERCARD CORPORATE MULTI CARD
MASTERCARD CORPORATE PURCHASING CARD
MASTERCARD EXECUTIVE BUSINESSCARD
MASTERCARD GOVERNMENT FLEET CARD
MASTERCARD GOVERNMENT INTEGRATED CARD
MASTERCARD GOVERNMENT PURCHASING CARD
MASTERCARD GOVERNMENT TRAVEL CARD
MASTERCARD INCENTIVE CARD
MASTERCARD INSTALLMENT CARD
MASTERCARD MARKET ADVISOR
MASTERCARD MARKETACCESS
MASTERCARD MASTERTAGGER
MASTERCARD MATCH
MASTERCARD MEETING CARD
MASTERCARD OPEN DATA STORAGE
MASTERCARD PAYPASS
MASTERCARD PAYROLL CARD
MASTERCARD PROFESSIONAL CARD
MASTERCARD PROJECT CARD
MASTERCARD PUBLIC SECTOR FLEET CARD
MASTERCARD PUBLIC SECTOR MULTI CARD
MASTERCARD PUBLIC SECTOR PAYMENT SOLUTIONS
MASTERCARD PUBLIC SECTOR PURCHASING CARD
MASTERCARD PUBLIC SECTOR TRAVEL CARD
MASTERCARD RELOCATION CARD
MASTERCARD REWARDS
MASTERCARD TRAVEL PER DIEM CARD
MASTERCARD TRAVELERS CHEQUE
MASTERMONEY BUSINESSCARD
MASTERPURCHASE
MASTERTRIP
ONESMART MASTERCARD
PLATINUM MASTERCARD
REPOWER
TITANIUM MASTERCARD
VIRTUAL MASTERCARD
WORLD ELITE MASTERCARD
WORLD MASTERCARD
Advertising Agencies:
BLUE
1 Maritime Sq
Singapore, 099253, Singapore
Tel.: (65) 6333 3336
Fax: (65) 6336 6334

CoreBrand
122 W 27th St 9th Fl
New York, NY 10001
Tel.: (212) 329-3030
Fax: (212) 329-3031

Dentino Marketing
515 Executive Dr
Princeton, NJ 08540
Tel.: (609) 454-3202
Fax: (609) 454-3239

Everett Studios

Key to Media (For complete agency information see *The Advertising Red Books-Agencies* edition):
1. Bus. Publs. 2. Cable T.V. 3. Catalogs & Directories. 4. Co-op Adv. 5. Consumer Mags. 6. D.M. to Bus. Estab.7. D.M. to Consumers
8. Daily Newsp. 9. Exhibits/Trade Shows 10. Foreign 11. Infomercial 12. Internet Adv.13. Multimedia 14. Network Radio
15. Network T.V. 16. Newsp. Distr. Mags. 17. Other 18. Outdoor (Posters, Transit) 19. Point of Purchase20. Premiums, Novelties
21. Product Samples 22. Special Events Mktg. 23. Spot Radio 24. Spot T.V. 25. Weekly Newsp. 26. Yellow Page Adv.

MasterCard Inc. — (Continued)

5 N Greenwich Rd
Armonk, NY 10504
Tel.: (914) 997-2200
Fax: (914) 997-2479

Impressions-A.B.A. Industries, Inc.
393 Jericho Tpk
Mineola, NY 11501
Tel.: (516) 739-3210
Fax: (516) 739-9246

MacLaren McCann Canada Inc.
10 Bay St
Toronto, ON M5J 2S3, Canada
Tel.: (416) 594-6000
Fax: (416) 643-7030
Fax: (416) 643-7027
(Mastercard Canada)

McCann Erickson/New York
622 3rd Ave
New York, NY 10017
Tel.: (646) 865-2000
Fax: (646) 487-9610
Creative
World Mastercard

MRM Worldwide
622 3rd Ave
New York, NY 10017-6707
Tel.: (646) 865-6230
Fax: (646) 865-6264

OSL Communications
1100 Ave des Canadiens Gare
Windsor Bureau C-18
Montreal, QC H3B 2S2, Canada
Tel.: (514) 849-9627
Fax: (514) 849-7935

R/GA
350 W 39th St
New York, NY 10018-1402
Tel.: (212) 946-4000
Fax: (212) 946-4010
Global Digital Agency of Record

Rasky Baerlein Strategic Communications
70 Franklin St 3rd Fl
Boston, MA 02110
Tel.: (617) 443-9933
Fax: (617) 443-9944

Roberts Communications Inc.
64 Commercial St
Rochester, NY 14614-1010
Tel.: (585) 325-6000
Fax: (585) 325-6001

Sigma Group
690 Kinderkamack Rd Ste 203
Oradell, NJ 07649-1524
Tel.: (201) 261-1123
Fax: (201) 261-0399

Tanen Directed Advertising
12 S Main St Ste 401
Norwalk, CT 06854-2980
Tel.: (203) 855-5855
Fax: (203) 855-5865

Taylor
350 Fifth Ave Ste 3800
New York, NY 10118
Tel.: (212) 714-1280
Fax: (212) 695-5685

TracyLocke
1999 Bryan St Ste 2800
Dallas, TX 75201
Tel.: (214) 259-3500
Fax: (214) 259-3550

Universal McCann
100 33rd St 8th Fl
New York, NY 10001
Tel.: (212) 883-4700
U.S. Media

The Vidal Partnership
228 E 45th St 11th Fl
New York, NY 10017-3303
Tel.: (646) 356-6600
Fax: (212) 661-7650

Waggener Edstrom
225 108th Ave NE Ste 700
Bellevue, WA 98004-5737
Tel.: (425) 638-7000
Fax: (425) 638-7001

MASTERCARD INTERNATIONAL, INC.

(Sub. of MasterCard Inc.)
2000 Purchase St
Purchase, NY 10577
Tel.: (914) 249-2000
Fax: (914) 249-4260
Web Site: www.mastercardintl.com
Sales Range: $650-699.9 Million
Approx. Number Employees: 2,700
Year Founded: 1966
Business Description:
Credit Card & Financial Services
S.I.C.: 6099
N.A.I.C.S.: 522320; 522390
Advertising Expenditures: $30,000,000
Media: 2-3-6-15-16-17-18-24
Distr.: Intl.; Natl.
Budget Set: Aug.
Personnel:
Robert W. Selander *(CEO)*
Martina Hund-Mejean *(CFO)*
Lawrence Flanagan *(CMO & Exec VP)*
Alfredo Gangotena *(CMO)*
Noah J. Hanft *(Chief Compliance Officer, Gen Counsel & Sec)*
Gary J. Flood *(Pres-Global Products & Solutions)*
Walter M. Macnee *(Pres-Intl Markets)*
Chris A. McWilton *(Pres-US Markets-MasterCard Worldwide)*
Robert Reeg *(Pres-MasterCard Technologies-Worldwide)*
Melissa Ballenger *(Principal & Controller)*
Chris Jogis *(Sr VP-Consumer Mktg)*
Ai June Schult *(Sr Leader-Bus, Head-Mktg-South East & South Asia)*
Advertising Agencies:
Arnold Worldwide
101 Huntington Ave
Boston, MA 02199-7603
Tel.: (617) 587-8000
Fax: (617) 587-8004

Dentino Marketing
515 Executive Dr
Princeton, NJ 08540
Tel.: (609) 454-3202
Fax: (609) 454-3239

Impressions-A.B.A. Industries, Inc.
393 Jericho Tpk
Mineola, NY 11501
Tel.: (516) 739-3210
Fax: (516) 739-9246

McCann Erickson/New York
622 3rd Ave
New York, NY 10017
Tel.: (646) 865-2000
Fax: (646) 487-9610
Creative

R/GA
350 W 39th St
New York, NY 10018-1402
Tel.: (212) 946-4000
Fax: (212) 946-4010
Global Digital Agency of Record

Roberts Communications Inc.
64 Commercial St
Rochester, NY 14614-1010
Tel.: (585) 325-6000
Fax: (585) 325-6001

Universal McCann
100 33rd St 8th Fl
New York, NY 10001
Tel.: (212) 883-4700
U.S. Media

The Vidal Partnership
228 E 45th St 11th Fl
New York, NY 10017-3303
Tel.: (646) 356-6600
Fax: (212) 661-7650

MASTERCARD WORLDWIDE INC.

(Div. of MasterCard International, Inc.)
2200 Mastercard Blvd
O Fallon, MO 63366-7263
Tel.: (636) 722-6100
Fax: (314) 523-2805
Web Site: www.mastercard.com
Sales Range: $400-449.9 Million
Approx. Number Employees: 1,000
Business Description:
Short-Term Business Credit Institutions
S.I.C.: 6141
N.A.I.C.S.: 522210
Personnel:
Alfredo Gangotena *(CMO-Global)*
Eileen Simon *(Chief Franchise Dev Officer)*
Vicky S. Bindra *(Pres-Asia Pacific, Middle East & Africa)*
Michael Miebach *(Pres-Middle East & Africa Div)*
Timothy H. Murphy *(Pres-United States)*
Ajay Bhalla *(Exec VP)*
Eddie Grobler *(Exec VP)*
Denzil Lawson *(Sr VP & Gen Mgr-Middle East & Levant)*
Cathleen Conforti *(Sr VP & Mgr-Global PayPass Product)*
Cheryl Guerin *(Sr VP-Global Digital Mktg)*
Ed McLaughlin *(Sr VP-RPPS)*
Benjamin Jankowski *(Grp Head-Global Media)*
Matthew Lanford *(Head-Prepaid Product Mgmt -Europe)*
Deborah Hsu Serianni *(Head-Global Consumer Mktg Grp)*
Jon Briggs *(Dir-Channel Plng & Strategic Partnerships-US)*
Sharon Hamilton *(Dir-Media & New Channels-Global)*
Advertising Agencies:
Taylor
350 Fifth Ave Ste 3800
New York, NY 10118
Tel.: (212) 714-1280
Fax: (212) 695-5685

Weber Shandwick-Minneapolis
8000 Norman Ctr Dr Ste 400
Minneapolis, MN 55437
Tel.: (952) 832-5000
Fax: (952) 831-8241
— Jessi Newman *(Acct Exec)*

MAXIMUS, INC.

11419 Sunset Hills Rd
Reston, VA 20190-5207
Tel.: (703) 251-8500
Fax: (703) 251-8240
Toll Free: (800) MAXIMUS
E-mail: info@maximus.com
Web Site: www.maximus.com
Approx. Rev.: $831,749,000
Approx. Number Employees: 6,834
Year Founded: 1975
Business Description:
Government Consulting & Government Operations
S.I.C.: 9199; 7371; 7373; 7379; 7389; 8742; 8748
N.A.I.C.S.: 921190; 541511; 541512; 541519; 541611; 541618; 561499
Media: 2-5
Personnel:
Peter B. Pond *(Chm)*
Raymond B. Ruddy *(Vice Chm)*
Richard A. Montoni *(Pres & CEO)*
David N. Walker *(CFO)*
John F. Boyer *(Pres/Gen Mgr-MAXIMUS Federal Svcs)*
Bruce L. Caswell *(Pres/Gen Mgr-Health Svcs Segment)*
Akbar Piloti *(Pres/Gen Mgr-Human Svcs)*
David R. Francis *(Gen Counsel & Sec)*
Brands & Products:
ASSET FOCUS
ASSETMAXX
CHDR
CJIS
COURTVIEW
CRIS
EVENTSECURE
FACILITYFOCUS
FLEETFOCUS
FLYSECURE
FUELFOCUS
HELPING GOVERNMENT SERVE THE PEOPLE
JAILVIEW
JURYMAX
JURYVIEW
JUSTICEMAX
MAXE2 SYSTEM
MAXIMUS
MAXREG
MAXSTAR
MAXTRACK
RAILFOCUS
RECORDVIEW

Key to Media (For complete agency information see *The Advertising Red Books-Agencies* edition):
1. Bus. Publs. 2. Cable T.V. 3. Catalogs & Directories. 4. Co-op Adv. 5. Consumer Mags. 6. D.M. to Bus. Estab.7. D.M. to Consumers 8. Daily Newsp. 9. Exhibits/Trade Shows 10. Foreign 11. Infomercial 12. Internet Adv.13. Multimedia 14. Network Radio 15. Network T.V. 16. Newsp. Distr. Mags. 17. Other 18. Outdoor (Posters, Transit) 19. Point of Purchase20. Premiums, Novelties 21. Product Samples 22. Special Events Mktg. 23. Spot Radio 24. Spot T.V. 25. Weekly Newsp. 26. Yellow Page Adv.

SCHOOLMAX
SECURITY ENFORCER
SMARTCARDS
TIENET
WORKQWEST

Advertising Agency:
Enten & Associates, Inc.
8120 Woodmont Ave Ste 550
Bethesda, MD 20814-2761
Tel.: (301) 913-0010
Fax: (301) 913-5484

MB FINANCIAL, INC.

800 W Madison St
Chicago, IL 60607-2630
Tel.: (847) 653-4800
Fax: (847) 653-2293
Toll Free: (888) 422-6562
E-mail: contactus@mbfinancial.com
Web Site: www.mbfinancial.com
Approx. Rev.: $615,396,000
Approx. Number Employees: 1,703
Year Founded: 2001
Business Description:
Bank Holding Company
S.I.C.: 6712
N.A.I.C.S.: 551111
Advertising Expenditures: $6,465,000
Personnel:
Thomas H. Harvey *(Chm)*
James N. Hallene *(Vice Chm)*
Mitchell S. Feiger *(Pres & CEO)*
Jill E. York *(CFO & VP)*

MCCOMBS ENTERPRISES

755 E Mulberry Ave Ste 600
San Antonio, TX 78212
Tel.: (210) 821-6523
Fax: (210) 821-5860
Web Site: www.redmac.com
Approx. Number Employees: 33
Year Founded: 1944
Business Description:
Holding Company
S.I.C.: 6289
N.A.I.C.S.: 523999
Media: 8-18-22-23-24-25
Personnel:
B. J. McCombs *(Chm & COO)*
Gary V. Woods *(Pres)*
Steve Cummings *(CFO)*
Terell McCombs *(VP-Contracts & Procurement)*

MCG CAPITAL CORPORATION

1100 Wilson Blvd Ste 3000
Arlington, VA 22209
Tel.: (703) 247-7500
Fax: (703) 247-7505
E-mail: mcg@mcgcapital.com
Web Site: www.mcgcapital.com
Approx. Rev.: $89,569,000
Approx. Number Employees: 63
Year Founded: 1998
Business Description:
Capital Investments, Business Development & Portfolio Management Services
S.I.C.: 6289; 6282; 6719; 8742; 8748
N.A.I.C.S.: 523999; 523920; 541611; 541618; 551112
Media: 10-13-17
Personnel:
Richard W. Neu *(Chm)*
Steven F. Tunney *(Pres & CEO)*
William B. Ford *(Sr VP & Mng Dir)*
Douglas H. Gilbert *(Mng Dir)*
Andrew J. Jacobson *(Mng Dir)*
E. Peter Malekian *(Mng Dir)*
Robert L. Marcotte *(Mng Dir)*
Thomas P. Mcloughlin *(Mng Dir)*
John S. Patton, Jr. *(Mng Dir)*
Stephen J. Bacica *(CFO & Exec VP)*
Kevin Madden *(CIO & Exec VP)*
Linda A. Nimmons *(Chief Acctg Officer)*
Samuel G. Rubenstein *(Gen Counsel & Exec VP)*
B. Hagen Saville *(Exec VP)*
Derek R. Thomas *(Exec VP-Risk Mgmt & Investment Underwriting)*
Kathryn Killeen *(Sr VP-Sponsorship & Underwriting)*

MCGLADREY & PULLEN, LLP

3600 American Blvd W 3rd Fl
Bloomington, MN 55431-4502
Tel.: (952) 835-9930
Fax: (952) 921-7702
Toll Free: (866) 835-8474
E-mail: information@rsmi.com
Web Site: www.mcgladrey.com
Sales Range: $250-299.9 Million
Approx. Number Employees: 3,000
Year Founded: 1926
Business Description:
Auditing & Accounting Services
S.I.C.: 8721; 8742
N.A.I.C.S.: 541211; 541219; 541611
Media: 2-6-7-10
Personnel:
Jerry Bourassa *(Chm)*
Joe Adams *(CEO & Mng Partner)*
Joseph Dennis *(Exec Partner-Assurance Svcs)*
Jeff Johannesen *(Partner)*
Kristi Kennedy *(Partner)*
Kaye Lauritsen *(Partner)*
Joseph Mazza *(Partner)*
Mitch Gorochow *(Exec Mng Dir)*
Rene Ordogne *(CFO)*
Rick Day *(Dir-Natl Acctg)*

MEDALLION FINANCIAL CORP.

437 Madison Ave 38th Fl
New York, NY 10022
Tel.: (212) 328-2100
Fax: (212) 328-2121
Toll Free: (877) MEDALLION
E-mail: alvinmurstein@medallionfinancial.com
Web Site: www.medallion.com
Approx. Rev.: $40,786,000
Approx. Number Employees: 122
Year Founded: 1996
Business Description:
Specialty Finance Services
S.I.C.: 6371; 6141; 6289; 7319; 9311
N.A.I.C.S.: 525990; 522220; 523999; 541890; 921130
Advertising Expenditures: $51,565
Media: 2-4-7-13-26
Personnel:
Alvin Murstein *(Chm & CEO)*
Andrew M. Murstein *(Pres)*
Larry D. Hall *(CFO & Sr VP)*
Brian S. O'Leary *(COO & Chief Credit Officer)*
Jeffrey Yin *(Gen Counsel & Chief Compliance Officer)*
Marie Russo *(Sec & Sr VP)*
Michael J. Kowalsky *(Exec VP)*
Advertising Agencies:
Innovative Internet Marketing Solutions
900 Northrop Rd Ste F
Wallingford, CT 06492
Tel.: (203) 265-2424
Fax: (203) 265-4914

Zahor Design Office
20 N Van Brunt St
Englewood, NJ 07631
Tel.: (201) 567-2608
Fax: (201) 567-1208

MEDWELL CAPITAL CORP.

(Formerly BioMS Medical Corp.)
6030 88 Street
Edmonton, AB T6E 6G4, Canada
Tel.: (780) 413-7152
Fax: (780) 408-3040
Toll Free: (866) 701-6033
E-mail: info@medwellcapital.com
Web Site: www.medwellcapital.com
Approx. Rev.: $1,157,778
Approx. Number Employees: 15
Business Description:
Biotechnology Services
S.I.C.: 2836; 2834
N.A.I.C.S.: 325414; 325412
Personnel:
Clifford D. Giese *(Chm)*
Kevin A. Giese *(Pres & CEO)*
Nitin Kaushal *(Mng Dir & Exec VP)*
Brent Johnston *(CFO)*
Tony Hesby *(Exec VP-Corp Affairs)*
Richard Brown *(VP-Comml Dev)*
Ryan Giese *(VP-Corp Comm)*
Advertising Agency:
Renmark Financial Communications, Inc.
1550 Metcalfe Ste 502
Montreal, QC H3A 1X6, Canada
Tel.: (514) 939-3989
Fax: (514) 939-3717

MELITTA USA INC.

(Sub. of Melitta Unternehmensgruppe Bentz KG)
13925 58th St N
Clearwater, FL 33760-3721
Tel.: (727) 535-2111
Fax: (727) 535-7376
Web Site: www.melitta.com
Approx. Number Employees: 191
Business Description:
Mfr. of Coffee
S.I.C.: 2095; 3634
N.A.I.C.S.: 311920; 335211
Import Export
Personnel:
Marty Miller *(Pres & CEO)*
Chris Hillman *(VP-Mktg)*
Brands & Products:
MELITTA COFFEE
MELITTA FILTERPAPER
Advertising Agency:
FKQ Advertising + Marketing
15351 Roosevelt Blvd
Clearwater, FL 33760-3534
Tel.: (727) 539-8800
Fax: (866) 707-6648

MERCANTILE BANK CORPORATION

310 Leonard St NW
Grand Rapids, MI 49504-4224
Tel.: (616) 406-3000
Fax: (616) 406-3737
Web Site: www.mercbank.com
Approx. Rev.: $97,387,000
Approx. Number Employees: 219
Business Description:
Bank Holding Company
S.I.C.: 6712; 6029
N.A.I.C.S.: 551111; 522110
Advertising Expenditures: $906,000
Media: 10-22
Personnel:
Michael H. Price *(CEO)*
Charles E. Christmas *(CFO, Treas & Sr VP)*
Robert B. Kaminski, Jr. *(COO, Exec VP & Sec)*
Advertising Agency:
FUSE/ideas
255 Elm St Ste 201
Somerville, MA 02144
Tel.: (617) 776-5800
Fax: (617) 776-5821
Agency of Record
Broadcast
Online & Social Media
Print

MERCHANTS BANCSHARES, INC.

275 Kennedy Dr
South Burlington, VT 05403
Mailing Address:
PO Box 1009
Burlington, VT 05402
Tel.: (802) 658-3400
Fax: (802) 865-1874
Web Site: www.mbvt.com
Approx. Rev.: $71,893,000
Approx. Number Employees: 303
Year Founded: 1865
Business Description:
Bank Holding Company
S.I.C.: 6022; 6029; 6712
N.A.I.C.S.: 522190; 522110; 551111
Advertising Expenditures: $1,372,000
Media: 7-8
Personnel:
Raymond C. Pecor, Jr. *(Chm)*
Michael R. Tuttle *(Pres & CEO)*
Janet P. Spitler *(CFO, Treas & Sr VP)*
Brands & Products:
AUTOLYNX
COMMERCELYNX
FREEDOMLYNX
VERMONT MATTERS

MERIDIAN INTERSTATE BANCORP, INC.

(Sub. of East Boston Savings Bank)
10 Meridian St
East Boston, MA 02128
Tel.: (617) 567-1500
Web Site: www.ebsb.com
Approx. Rev.: $93,780,000
Approx. Number Employees: 272
Year Founded: 2006
Business Description:
Bank Holding Company
S.I.C.: 6035; 6712
N.A.I.C.S.: 522120; 551111
Advertising Expenditures: $1,241,000
Personnel:
Richard J. Gavegnano *(Chm & CEO)*
Deborah J. Jackson *(Pres & COO)*
Mark L. Abbate *(CFO)*

MERRILL LYNCH & CO., INC.

(Sub. of Bank of America Corporation)
Bank of America Corp Ctr 100 N Tryon St
Charlotte, NC 28255
Tel.: (704) 386-5681
Toll Free: (800) 637-7455
E-mail: investor_relations@ml.com

Key to Media (For complete agency information see *The Advertising Red Books-Agencies* edition):
1. Bus. Publs. 2. Cable T.V. 3. Catalogs & Directories. 4. Co-op Adv. 5. Consumer Mags. 6. D.M. to Bus. Estab.7. D.M. to Consumers 8. Daily Newsp. 9. Exhibits/Trade Shows 10. Foreign 11. Infomercial 12. Internet Adv.13. Multimedia 14. Network Radio 15. Network T.V. 16. Newsp. Distr. Mags. 17. Other 18. Outdoor (Posters, Transit) 19. Point of Purchase20. Premiums, Novelties 21. Product Samples 22. Special Events Mktg. 23. Spot Radio 24. Spot T.V. 25. Weekly Newsp. 26. Yellow Page Adv.

Merrill Lynch & Co., Inc. — (Continued)
Web Site: www.ml.com
Approx. Rev.: $28,189,000,000
Approx. Number Employees: 64,200
Year Founded: 1885
Business Description:
Holding Company; Wealth Management, Capital Markets & Advisory Services
S.I.C.: 6211; 6221; 6282; 6289; 6331; 6371; 6719; 6722; 6733
N.A.I.C.S.: 523110; 523120; 523130; 523140; 523920; 523930; 523991; 523999; 525110; 525120; 525190; 525910; 525920; 525990; 551112
Advertising Expenditures: $692,000,000
Media: 2-4-6-7-8-9-10-11-13-14-15-18-19-21-22-23-24-25-26
Distr.: Intl.; Natl.
Personnel:
Brian Moynihan *(Chm)*
Robert Qutub *(CFO)*
Peter D. Taube *(Chief Acctg Officer & Controller)*
Thomas K. Montag *(Pres-Global Banking & Markets)*
Frank Petrilli *(Sr VP)*
Advertising Agencies:
J. Walter Thompson Company
(d/b/a JWT)
466 Lexington Ave
New York, NY 10017-3140
Tel.: (212) 210-7000
Fax: (212) 210-7299

Pantin/Beber Silverstein Public Relations
(Part of the Beber Silverstein Group)
3361 SW 3rd Ave
Miami, FL 33145-3911
Tel.: (305) 856-9800
Fax: (305) 857-0027

MERRILL MERCHANTS BANK
(Sub. of People's United Financial, Inc.)
(d/b/a Merrill Bank)
201 Main St
Bangor, ME 04401-0925
Tel.: (207) 942-4800
Fax: (207) 945-4712
E-mail: info@merrillmerchants.com
Web Site: www.merrillmerchants.com
Sales Range: $50-74.9 Million
Approx. Number Employees: 144
Year Founded: 1992
Business Description:
Commercial Banking Services
S.I.C.: 6029
N.A.I.C.S.: 522110
Media: 4-7-8-13
Personnel:
William P. Lucy *(Pres & CEO)*

MERRIMAN CURHAN FORD GROUP, INC.
600 California St 9th Fl
San Francisco, CA 94108
Tel.: (415) 248-5600
E-mail: investor_relations@mcfco.com
Web Site: www.mcfco.com
Approx. Rev.: $49,263,042
Approx. Number Employees: 94
Business Description:
Investment Banking & Securities Dealing
S.I.C.: 6211
N.A.I.C.S.: 523120; 523110
Advertising Expenditures: $139,000
Media: 17
Personnel:
D. Jonathan Merriman *(Co-Founder)*
Ronald L. Chez *(Co-Chm)*
Joe Minton *(Mng Dir & Head-Derivatives)*
Peter V. Coleman *(CFO, COO & Sec)*
Michael C. Doran *(Gen Counsel)*
Eric Wold *(Dir-Equity Res)*

METRO BANCORP, INC.
3801 Paxton St
Harrisburg, PA 17111
Tel.: (717) 412-6301
Toll Free: (800) 653-6104
Web Site: www.mymetrobank.com
Approx. Rev.: $126,627,000
Approx. Number Employees: 724
Year Founded: 1999
Business Description:
Bank Holding Company
S.I.C.: 6712; 6029
N.A.I.C.S.: 551111; 522110
Advertising Expenditures: $2,751,000
Personnel:
Gary L. Nalbandian *(Pres & CEO)*
Mark A. Zody *(CFO)*
Peter J. Ressler *(Gen Counsel & Sec)*
Victoria G. Chieppa *(Sr VP-Ops)*

METROCORP BANCSHARES, INC.
9600 Bellaire Blvd Ste 252
Houston, TX 77036
Tel.: (713) 776-3876
Fax: (713) 414-3507
E-mail: metrobank@metrobank-na.com
Web Site: www.metrobank-na.com
Approx. Rev.: $85,014,000
Approx. Number Employees: 291
Year Founded: 1987
Business Description:
Bank Holding Company
S.I.C.: 6712; 6029
N.A.I.C.S.: 551111; 522110
Import Export
Media: 10-17-18-20-22
Personnel:
Don J. Wang *(Chm)*
George M. Lee *(Vice Chm, Pres & CEO)*
David C. Choi *(CFO)*
David Tai *(Sec & Exec VP)*

MFS INVESTMENT MANAGEMENT
(Sub. of Sun Life Assurance Company of Canada (U.S.))
500 Boylston St
Boston, MA 02116
Tel.: (617) 954-5000
Fax: (617) 954-6620
Toll Free: (800) 637-2929
Web Site: www.mfs.com
Approx. Number Employees: 2,521
Year Founded: 1924
Business Description:
Manages & Distributes Mutual Funds, Annuities & Services
S.I.C.: 6722
N.A.I.C.S.: 525910
Media: 8-13
Distr.: Natl.; Reg.
Personnel:
J. Robert Manning *(Chm & CEO)*
Michael Roberge *(Pres & Chief Investment Officer)*
Ravi Venkataraman *(Sr Mng Dir)*
Christine Girvan *(Mng Dir)*
Amrit Kanwal *(CFO & Exec VP)*
Elizabeth Palmer *(VP & Dir-Product Mngmt)*
Sean Spaulding *(VP & Dir-Mktg-Intl)*
Liz Larson *(VP-Comm)*
John Reilly *(Dir-Media Rels)*

MG FINANCIAL LLC
(Sub. of Rosenthal Collins Group, LLC)
40 Exchange Pl 12th Fl
New York, NY 10005
Tel.: (212) 835-0100
Fax: (212) 835-0101
Toll Free: (888) MGFOREX
E-mail: pr@mgforex.com
Web Site: www.mgforex.com
Approx. Number Employees: 35
Year Founded: 1992
Business Description:
Foreign Exchange Trading Services
S.I.C.: 6221
N.A.I.C.S.: 523130
Media: 6-13
Personnel:
Ian McFarlane *(Chm)*
Oleg Tcoupronn *(Compliance Officer)*
Brands & Products:
ALERT!FX
DEALSTATION
MGFOREX

MICROBILT CORPORATION
(Sub. of Bristol Investments, Ltd.)
1640 Airport Rd Ste 115
Kennesaw, GA 30144
Tel.: (770) 218-4400
Fax: (770) 218-4992
Toll Free: (800) 884-4747
E-mail: microbilt@microbilt.com
Web Site: www.microbilt.com
Approx. Number Employees: 47
Year Founded: 1978
Business Description:
Risk Management & Business Consulting Services
S.I.C.: 8742; 7389
N.A.I.C.S.: 541611; 561499
Media: 2-7-10-13-20
Personnel:
Walt Wojciechowski *(CEO)*
Robert Raleigh *(Pres-Board-Dirs)*
Mike Garretson *(Sr VP & Gen Mgr)*
Chris Atkins *(VP-Fin)*
Todd Milner *(Head-Sls)*
Steve White *(Product Mgr)*
Brands & Products:
MICROBILT
SMARTTARGET

MICROFINANCIAL INCORPORATED
16 New England Executive Pk Ste 200
Burlington, MA 01803
Tel.: (781) 994-4800
Fax: (781) 994-4710
E-mail: info@microfinancial.com
Web Site: www.microfinancial.com
Approx. Rev.: $50,929,000
Approx. Number Employees: 118
Year Founded: 1987
Business Description:
Financing Services
S.I.C.: 6159; 6141; 7359
N.A.I.C.S.: 522298; 522220; 532420
Media: 10-13
Personnel:
Richard F. Latour *(Pres & CEO)*
James R. Jackson, Jr. *(CFO & VP)*
Stephen J. Constantino *(VP-HR)*
Steven J. LaCreta *(VP-Legal & Lessee Rels)*
Brands & Products:
GIVING BUSINESS THE CREDIT IT DESERVES
MICROFINANCIAL
THE ONLY FINANCING SOURCE YOU WILL EVER NEED

MID PENN BANCORP, INC.
349 Union St
Millersburg, PA 17061
Tel.: (717) 692-2133
Fax: (717) 692-4861
Toll Free: (800) 468-9716
E-mail: mpbank@epix.net
Web Site: www.midpennbank.com
Approx. Rev.: $33,562,000
Approx. Number Employees: 158
Year Founded: 1991
Business Description:
Bank Holding Company
S.I.C.: 6029; 6712
N.A.I.C.S.: 522110; 551111
Advertising Expenditures: $679,000
Media: 10-19-20-22
Personnel:
Edwin D. Schlegel *(Chm)*
Robert C. Grubic *(Vice Chm)*
Rory G. Ritrievi *(Pres & CEO)*
Kevin W. Laudenslager *(CFO & Exec VP)*

MID PENN BANK
(Sub. of Mid Penn Bancorp, Inc.)
349 Union St
Millersburg, PA 17061-1611
Tel.: (717) 692-2133
Fax: (717) 692-4861
E-mail: mpbank@epix.net
Web Site: www.midpennbank.com
Sales Range: $50-74.9 Million
Approx. Number Employees: 150
Year Founded: 1868
Business Description:
Bank Services
S.I.C.: 6029; 8721
N.A.I.C.S.: 522110; 541219
Advertising Expenditures: $150,000
Media: 7-8-10-13-18-23-26
Personnel:
Edwin D. Schlegel *(Chm)*
Rory G. Ritrievi *(Pres & CEO)*
Kevin W. Laudenslager *(CFO & Exec VP)*
Sheri Brown *(VP & Sr Credit Officer)*
Amy Mountain *(VP & Dir-Mktg)*
Edward P. Williams *(Asst VP & Dir-Fin Reporting)*

THE MIDDLEBURG BANK
(Sub. of Middleburg Financial Corporation)
111 W Washington St
Middleburg, VA 20117
Tel.: (703) 777-6327

Key to Media (For complete agency information see *The Advertising Red Books-Agencies* edition):
1. Bus. Publs. 2. Cable T.V. 3. Catalogs & Directories. 4. Co-op Adv. 5. Consumer Mags. 6. D.M. to Bus. Estab.7. D.M. to Consumers 8. Daily Newsp. 9. Exhibits/Trade Shows 10. Foreign 11. Infomercial 12. Internet Adv.13. Multimedia 14. Network Radio 15. Network T.V. 16. Newsp. Distr. Mags. 17. Other 18. Outdoor (Posters, Transit) 19. Point of Purchase20. Premiums, Novelties 21. Product Samples 22. Special Events Mktg. 23. Spot Radio 24. Spot T.V. 25. Weekly Newsp. 26. Yellow Page Adv.

Fax: (703) 737-3426
Web Site: www.middleburgbank.com
Sales Range: $75-99.9 Million
Approx. Number Employees: 185
Business Description:
Financial Institution
S.I.C.: 6029
N.A.I.C.S.: 522110
Personnel:
Joseph Landon Boling *(Chm)*
Gary R. Shook *(Pres & CEO)*
Jeffrey H. Culver *(COO & Exec VP)*
Robert Steve Miller, Jr. *(CMO & Sr VP)*
Arch A. Moore, III *(Chief Lending Officer & Exec VP)*
Suzanne K. Withers *(Sr VP-HR & Organizational Dev)*
Advertising Agency:
Davis & Company
1705 Baltic Ave
Virginia Beach, VA 23451
Tel.: (757) 627-7373
Fax: (757) 627-4257

MIDDLEBURG FINANCIAL CORPORATION
111 W Washington St
Middleburg, VA 20117
Mailing Address:
PO Box 5
Middleburg, VA 20118
Tel.: (703) 777-6327
Fax: (703) 737-3426
E-mail: client-service-center@middleburgbank.com
Web Site: www.middleburgbank.com
Approx. Rev.: $74,034,000
Approx. Number Employees: 350
Business Description:
Bank Holding Company
S.I.C.: 6712; 6141
N.A.I.C.S.: 551111; 522210
Advertising Expenditures: $1,071,000
Personnel:
Joseph Landon Boling *(Chm)*
Gary Ross Shook *(Pres & CEO)*
Raj Mehra *(CFO & Exec VP)*
Jeffrey H. Culver *(COO & Exec VP)*
Suzanne K. Withers *(Sr VP-HR & Organizational Dev)*

MIDDLEFIELD BANC CORP.
15985 E High St PO Box 35
Middlefield, OH 44062
Tel.: (440) 632-1666
Fax: (440) 632-1700
E-mail: info@amstock.com
Web Site: www.middlefieldbank.com
Approx. Rev.: $31,717,000
Approx. Number Employees: 108
Business Description:
Bank Holding Company
S.I.C.: 6029; 6712
N.A.I.C.S.: 522110; 551111
Advertising Expenditures: $401,000
Personnel:
Richard T. Coyne *(Chm)*
Thomas G. Caldwell *(Pres & CEO)*
Donald L. Stacy *(CFO & Treas)*
James R. Heslop, II *(COO & Exec VP)*
Kathleen M. Johnson *(Chief Acctg Officer, VP & Sec)*
Gail Neikirk *(Asst VP & Sec)*
Jay P. Giles *(Sr VP & Sr Loan Officer)*
Teresa M. Hetrick *(Sr VP-Ops & Admin)*
Dennis E. Linville *(Sr VP)*
Mary Gerbasi *(VP & Office Mgr)*
Karen Branham *(Asst VP)*
Dale Moore *(Asst VP-Network Admin)*
Marlin J. Moschell *(Asst VP-Orwell Lending)*
Thomas R. Neikirk *(Asst VP)*

MIDSOUTH BANCORP, INC.
102 Versailles Blvd
Lafayette, LA 70501
Mailing Address:
PO Box 3745
Lafayette, LA 70502-3745
Tel.: (337) 237-8343
Fax: (337) 267-4434
Toll Free: (800) 213-2265
E-mail: support@midsouthbank.com
Web Site: www.midsouthbank.com
Approx. Rev.: $62,981,000
Approx. Number Employees: 389
Business Description:
Bank Holding Company
S.I.C.: 6029; 6712
N.A.I.C.S.: 522110; 551111
Advertising Expenditures: $2,013,123
Media: 1-10-22
Personnel:
J. B. Hargroder *(Vice Chm)*
C. R. Cloutier *(Pres & CEO)*
James R. McLemore, Jr. *(CFO & Sr Exec VP)*
Gerald G. Reaux, Jr. *(COO)*
Alexander Calicchia *(CMO)*
Troy Cloutier *(Chief Banking Officer & Sr Exec VP)*
Carolyn Lay *(Chief Retail Officer)*
Lorraine Miller *(Sr VP & Dir-Mergers & Acq)*
Christopher J. Levanti *(Sr VP-Credit Admin)*
Jennifer S. Fontenot *(Mgr-Banking Center)*

MIDSOUTH BANK N.A.
(Sub. of MidSouth Bancorp, Inc.)
102 Versailles Blvd
Lafayette, LA 70501
Mailing Address:
PO Box 3745
Lafayette, LA 70502
Tel.: (337) 237-8343
Fax: (337) 593-3271
Toll Free: (800) 213BANK
E-mail: support@midsouthbank.com
Web Site: www.midsouthbank.com
Sales Range: $75-99.9 Million
Approx. Number Employees: 187
Year Founded: 1985
Business Description:
Commercial Bank
S.I.C.: 6029
N.A.I.C.S.: 522110
Media: 2-7-8-9-10-13-20-22-23-25-26
Personnel:
C. R. Cloutier *(Pres & CEO)*
James R. McLemore, Jr. *(CFO & Sr Exec VP)*
Gerald G. Reaux, Jr. *(COO)*
Alexander Calicchia *(CMO & Exec VP)*
John Nichols *(Chief Credit Officer & Exec VP)*
Troy Cloutier *(Chief Banking Officer & Sr Exec VP)*
Paul Judice *(City Pres & Sr VP)*
Michael Lea *(Dir-Mktg)*
Jennifer S. Fontenot *(Mgr-Banking Center)*

MIDWEST BANC HOLDINGS, INC.
Midwest Ctr 501 W North Ave
Melrose Park, IL 60160
Tel.: (708) 865-1053
Fax: (708) 865-7013
E-mail: investorsrelations@midwestbank.com
Web Site: www.midwestbanc.com
Approx. Rev.: $167,638,000
Approx. Number Employees: 416
Year Founded: 1983
Business Description:
Bank Holding Company
S.I.C.: 6141; 6029; 6035; 6211; 6712
N.A.I.C.S.: 522210; 522110; 522120; 523110; 551111
Media: 1-10-20
Personnel:
Roberto R. Herencia *(Pres & CEO)*
Thomas J. Bell, III *(Chief Investment Officer, Treas & Exec VP-Midwest Bank & Trust)*
Jonathan P. Gilfillan *(Exec VP & Head-Comml Real Estate Lending Div)*
Advertising Agency:
s2 Marketing + Communications, Inc.
656 W Randolph Ste 3E
Chicago, IL 60661
Tel.: (312) 382-9000

MILLENNIUM BANKSHARES CORPORATION
1601 Washington Plz N
Reston, VA 20190
Tel.: (703) 464-0100
Fax: (703) 464-0064
E-mail: info@millenniumbankshares.com
Web Site: www.millenniumbankshares.com
Approx. Int. Income: $9,960,000
Approx. Number Employees: 58
Business Description:
Bank Holding Company
S.I.C.: 6029; 6712
N.A.I.C.S.: 522110; 551111
Advertising Expenditures: $221,000
Media: 1-10-22
Personnel:
John F. Novak *(Pres & CEO)*
Mark Jeffries *(CFO & Exec VP)*
Marcus Perry *(Chief Lending Officer & Exec VP)*
Edward W. Lull *(Sr VP-Lending)*

MINDEN BANCORP, INC.
100 MBL Bank Dr
Minden, LA 71055
Tel.: (318) 371-4156
E-mail: info@mblminden.com
Web Site: www.mblminden.com
Approx. Rev.: $9,737,000
Approx. Number Employees: 30
Business Description:
Bank Holding Company
S.I.C.: 6712
N.A.I.C.S.: 551111
Advertising Expenditures: $45,000
Media: 17
Personnel:
A. David Evans *(Chm)*
Jack E. Byrd, Jr. *(Pres & CEO)*
Becky T. Harrell *(CFO, Chief Acctg Officer & Treas)*

M.L. STERN & CO., LLC
(Name Changed to Southwest Securities, Inc.)

MODIFYUTAH.ORG
734 E Utah Valley Dr Ste 200
American Fork, UT 84003
Tel.: (801) 772-3535
Fax: (801) 206-0479
Toll Free: (800) 400-1850
E-mail: info@modifyutah.org
Web Site: www.modifyutah.org
Approx. Number Employees: 30
Business Description:
Loan Modification Services
S.I.C.: 6163
N.A.I.C.S.: 522310
Media: 13-18-22-23-24
Personnel:
Alain Templeman *(Pres)*

MONARCH FINANCIAL HOLDINGS, INC.
1435 Crossways Blvd
Chesapeake, VA 23320
Tel.: (757) 389-5111
Web Site: www.monarchbank.com
Approx. Rev.: $92,776,221
Approx. Number Employees: 513
Business Description:
Bank Holding Company
S.I.C.: 6712
N.A.I.C.S.: 551111
Advertising Expenditures: $350,163
Personnel:
Jeffrey F. Benson *(Chm)*
Lawton H. Baker *(Vice Chm)*
William F. Rountree, Jr. *(Pres)*
Brad E. Schwartz *(CEO)*
Lynette Harris *(CFO, Sec, Treas & Exec VP)*
Andrew N. Lock *(Chief Credit Officer & Exec VP)*
Barbara N. Lane *(Exec VP-Property Mgmt)*
Nancy B. Porter *(Exec VP-Sls & Mktg)*

THE MONEY TREE INC.
114 S Broad St
Bainbridge, GA 39817
Tel.: (229) 246-6536
Fax: (229) 243-7977
Toll Free: (877) 468-7878
Web Site: www.themoneytreeinc.com
Approx. Int. Income: $11,807,508
Approx. Number Employees: 296
Business Description:
Debenture Investment Services
S.I.C.: 6289; 6282; 6371
N.A.I.C.S.: 523999; 523930; 525990
Advertising Expenditures: $325,676
Personnel:
Bradley D. Bellville *(Pres)*
Steven P. Morrison *(CFO)*
Clayton Penhallegon *(Second VP-Investments)*
Dellhia Franklin *(VP-Customer Svc)*

MONEY4GOLD HOLDINGS, INC.
(Name Changed to Upstream Worldwide, Inc.)

MONEYGRAM INTERNATIONAL, INC.
(Holding of Thomas H. Lee Partners, L.P.)
2828 N Harwood St 15th Fl

Key to Media (For complete agency information see *The Advertising Red Books-Agencies* edition):
1. Bus. Publs. 2. Cable T.V. 3. Catalogs & Directories. 4. Co-op Adv. 5. Consumer Mags. 6. D.M. to Bus. Estab.7. D.M. to Consumers 8. Daily Newsp. 9. Exhibits/Trade Shows 10. Foreign 11. Infomercial 12. Internet Adv.13. Multimedia 14. Network Radio 15. Network T.V. 16. Newsp. Distr. Mags. 17. Other 18. Outdoor (Posters, Transit) 19. Point of Purchase20. Premiums, Novelties 21. Product Samples 22. Special Events Mktg. 23. Spot Radio 24. Spot T.V. 25. Weekly Newsp. 26. Yellow Page Adv.

MoneyGram International, Inc. — (Continued)

Dallas, TX 75201
Tel.: (214) 999-7552
Toll Free: (800) 328-5678
Web Site: www.moneygram.com
Approx. Rev.: $1,166,653,000
Approx. Number Employees: 1,570
Year Founded: 1940
Business Description:
Payment & Money Order Processing Services
S.I.C.: 6099
N.A.I.C.S.: 522320
Advertising Expenditures: $40,200,000
Media: 2-7-10-14-15-19-20-22
Distr.: Natl.
Budget Set: Oct.
Personnel:
Pamela H. Patsley *(Chm & CEO)*
James E. Shields *(CFO & Exec VP)*
Juan Agualimpia *(CMO & Exec VP)*
Phyllis Skene-Stimac *(Chief Compliance Officer & Sr VP)*
Aaron Henry *(Chief Privacy Officer, Sr VP & Assoc Gen Counsel-Global Regulator)*
Timothy C. Everett *(Gen Counsel & Exec VP)*
Daniel J. O'Malley *(Exec VP-Americas)*
Steven Piano *(Exec VP-HR)*
J. Lucas Wimer *(Exec VP-Ops & Tech)*
Patricia Sullivan *(Sr VP-Comm)*
Corinna Ulrich *(VP, Assoc Gen Counsel & Asst Sec)*
Brands & Products:
EXPRESSPAYMENT
FLASHPAY
MONEYGRAM
TRAVELERSEXPRESS
Advertising Agencies:
Draftfcb Cape Town
183 Main Road
7700
Cape Town, South Africa
Tel.: (27) 21 680 7600
Fax: (27) 21 680 7602

Global Advertising Strategies
55 Broad St 19th Fl
New York, NY 10004
Tel.: (212) 964-0030
Fax: (212) 964-0040

MONTGOMERY BANK
(Sub. of Montgomery Bancorporation Inc.)
(d/b/a First National Bank, The)
1 Montgomery Bank Plz
Sikeston, MO 63801
Tel.: (573) 471-2275
Fax: (573) 472-5405
Web Site: www.montgomerybank.com
Approx. Number Employees: 105
Business Description:
National Commercial Banks
S.I.C.: 6029
N.A.I.C.S.: 522110
Personnel:
Jeff Sutton *(Reg Pres)*
Ken Wrtbrodt *(CEO)*
Gary Pewitt *(CFO)*
Ryan Harper *(COO)*
Michelle Worth *(Br Mgr)*

Advertising Agency:
Hughes
1141 S 7th St
Saint Louis, MO 63104
Tel.: (314) 571-6300

MORGAN KEEGAN, INC.
(Sub. of Regions Financial Corporation)
Morgan Keegan Tower 50 Frnt St
Memphis, TN 38103
Tel.: (901) 524-4100
Fax: (901) 579-4406
Toll Free: (800) 366-7426
Telex: 6974324
E-mail: info@morgankeegan.com
Web Site: www.morgankeegan.com
Sales Range: $1-4.9 Billion
Approx. Number Employees: 1,000
Year Founded: 1969
Business Description:
Investment Firm
S.I.C.: 6211; 6798
N.A.I.C.S.: 523120; 525930
Media: 8-9-13-25
Distr.: Direct to Consumer; Natl.
Budget Set: June
Personnel:
Allen B. Morgan, Jr. *(Chm)*
Robert J. Glenn *(Exec Mng Dir-Equity Capital Markets)*
Robert A. Baird *(Exec Mng Dir)*
Jonathan Ruykhaver *(Mng Dir)*
E. Carl Krausnick, Jr. *(Pres-Equity Capital Markets)*
Chip Grayson *(Dir-Investment Banking)*
William T. Hughes *(Dir-Fin Svcs)*
Jerome Dattel *(Reg Mgr)*

MORGAN STANLEY
1585 Broadway
New York, NY 10036
Tel.: (212) 761-4000
Toll Free: (888) 368-5351
E-mail: mediainquiries@morganstanley.com
Web Site: www.morganstanley.com
Approx. Rev.: $31,622,000,000
Approx. Number Employees: 62,542
Year Founded: 1935
Business Description:
Bank Holding Company; Institutional Securities, Wealth & Asset Management Services
S.I.C.: 6712; 6029; 6211; 6282; 6289; 6371
N.A.I.C.S.: 551111; 522110; 523110; 523120; 523920; 523999; 524292
Advertising Expenditures: $1,247,000,000
Personnel:
John J. Mack *(Chm)*
Benjamin P. Jenkins, III *(Vice Chm-Retail Banking Grp)*
William Wicker *(Vice Chm-Investment Banking-Natural Resources Grp)*
James P. Gorman *(Pres & CEO)*
Jay Mantz *(Pres & CIO-Real Estate Investing)*
Colm Kelleher *(Co-Pres-Institutional Securities)*
Paul J. Taubman *(Co-Pres-Institutional Securities)*
Jay Dweck *(Mng Dir & Head-Strategies & Tech, Institutional Securities)*
Kevin Dunleavy *(Mng Dir-Sls & Trading)*
Stephen C. Daffron *(Mng Dir)*
Schuyler Grow *(Mng Dir)*
Robert Mansley *(Mng Dir)*
Jean-Philippe Barade *(Mng Dir)*
Eric Bischof *(Mng Dir)*
Simon Greenshields *(Mng Dir)*
Robert Rooney *(Mng Dir)*
Ruth Porat *(CFO & Exec VP)*
Thomas R. Nides *(COO, Chief Admin Officer, Sec & Exec VP)*
Jim Rosenthal *(COO)*
Ramona G. Boston *(CMO)*
Francis P. Barron *(Chief Legal Officer)*
Kenneth M deRegt *(Chief Risk Officer)*
Jonathan Kindred *(Pres-Morgan Stanley Japan Securities Co, Ltd)*
Cece S. Sutton *(Pres-Retail Banking Grp)*
Eric F. Grossman *(Gen Counsel-Americas & Global Head-Litigation)*
Smith Barney *(Gen Counsel)*
Thomas Kelleher *(Exec VP)*
Christine Bacon *(VP & Dir-Adv)*
Neville Godley *(VP-Institutional Equities Div)*
Colin Bryce *(Head-Europe Institutional Sls/Trading & Co-Head-Global Commodity)*
Michael Eck *(Head-Retail Banking)*
Karen Jamesley *(Global Head-HR)*
Jonathan Pruzan *(Co-Head-Global Fin Institutions Grp)*
Luis Arriola *(Exec Dir)*
Candido Viyella *(Exec Dir)*
Juan-Luis Perez *(Global Dir-Res)*
Paul C. Wirth *(Dir-Fin)*
Philip Lader *(Sr Advisor)*
Advertising Agencies:
Leo Burnett USA
35 W Wacker Dr
Chicago, IL 60601-1723
Tel.: (312) 220-5959
Fax: (312) 220-3299

The Martin Agency
One Shockoe Plz
Richmond, VA 23219-4132
Tel.: (804) 698-8000
Fax: (804) 698-8001
Agency of Record
Brand Creative Development
Strategic Planning

StrawberryFrog
60 Madison Ave Ph
New York, NY 10010
Tel.: (212) 366-0500

MORGAN STANLEY SMITH BARNEY LLC
(Joint Venture of Morgan Stanley & Citigroup Inc.)
388 Greenwich St
New York, NY 10013-2375
Tel.: (212) 761-4000
Fax: (212) 793-9086
E-mail: info@smithbarney.com
Web Site: www.morganstanleysmithbarney.com
Approx. Number Employees: 12,400
Year Founded: 2009
Business Description:
Wealth Management Services; Owned by Morgan Stanley 51% & Citigroup Inc. 49%
S.I.C.: 6282; 6289
N.A.I.C.S.: 523920; 523999
Advertising Expenditures: $20,000,000
Media: 2-4-6-22-25
Personnel:
Charles D. Johnston *(Pres)*
James P. Gorman *(CEO)*
Jim A. Rosenthal *(COO)*
Craig Pfeiffer *(CMO)*
Bernard J. Fasciano *(Sr VP & Dir-Portfolio Mgmt)*
Stephanie L. Nallia *(Sr VP & Fin Advisor)*
James A. Richardson *(First VP & Fin Advisor)*
Kate E. Salsman *(Second VP & Fin Advisor)*
Katen Fletcher *(Dir-Pro Alliance Group)*
James J. Tracy *(Dir-Consulting Group)*

MORLEY FINANCIAL SERVICES
(Sub. of Principal Financial Group, Inc.)
1300 SW 5th Ave Ste 3300
Portland, OR 97201-3193
Tel.: (503) 620-7899
Tel.: (503) 484-9300
Fax: (866) 330-6841
E-mail: clientservice@morley.com
Web Site: www.morley.com
Sales Range: $100-124.9 Million
Approx. Number Employees: 28
Year Founded: 1982
Business Description:
Investment Advisory Services
S.I.C.: 6282; 6722
N.A.I.C.S.: 523930; 525910
Media: 26
Personnel:
Tim Stumpff *(Pres)*
William Finley *(Chief Investment Officer)*
Ronald Heath *(Mng Dir-Sls & Mktg)*

MORNINGSTAR, INC.
22 W Washington St
Chicago, IL 60602
Tel.: (312) 696-6000
Fax: (312) 696-6024
Fax: (312) 696-6001
Toll Free: (800) 735-0700
E-mail: newsroom@morningstar.com
Web Site: www.morningstar.com
Approx. Rev.: $555,351,000
Approx. Number Employees: 3,225
Year Founded: 1984
Business Description:
Investment Research & Software for Individual & Professional Investors
S.I.C.: 2721; 2741; 6211; 6282; 6289; 7389
N.A.I.C.S.: 523930; 511120; 516110; 519190; 523120; 523920; 523999
Advertising Expenditures: $7,361,000
Media: 2-6-7-8-9-10-13-16-17-18-20-22-25
Personnel:
Joe Mansueto *(Chm & CEO)*
Scott Cooley *(CFO)*
Chris Boruff *(Pres-Software Div)*
Peng Chen *(Pres-Global Investment Mgmt Div)*
Bevin Desmond *(Pres-Intl Ops & Global HR)*
Kishore Gangwani *(Pres-Real Time Data Bus)*

Key to Media (For complete agency information see *The Advertising Red Books-Agencies* edition):
1. Bus. Publs. 2. Cable T.V. 3. Catalogs & Directories. 4. Co-op Adv. 5. Consumer Mags. 6. D.M. to Bus. Estab.7. D.M. to Consumers
8. Daily Newsp. 9. Exhibits/Trade Shows 10. Foreign 11. Infomercial 12. Internet Adv.13. Multimedia 14. Network Radio
15. Network T.V. 16. Newsp. Distr. Mags. 17. Other 18. Outdoor (Posters, Transit) 19. Point of Purchase20. Premiums, Novelties
21. Product Samples 22. Special Events Mktg. 23. Spot Radio 24. Spot T.V. 25. Weekly Newsp. 26. Yellow Page Adv.

Kunal Kapoor *(Pres-Equity Data & Individual Investor Software)*
Elizabeth Kirscher *(Pres-Data Div)*
Catherine Gillis Odelbo *(Pres-Equity Res)*
Richard E. Robbins *(Gen Counsel & Sec)*
Mary Uribe *(Sr VP-Adv)*
John Rekenthaler *(VP-Res)*
Melissa Chlopecki *(Product Mgr)*
Frank O'Connor *(Product Mgr-Variable Annuity Database)*
Brands & Products:
CLEARFUTURE
INSTANT X-RAY
MORNINGSTAR
MORNINGSTAR ADVISOR
MORNINGSTAR ADVISOR WORKSTATION
MORNINGSTAR DIRECT
MORNINGSTAR FUNDINVESTOR
MORNINGSTAR FUNDS 500
MORNINGSTAR INDEXES
MORNINGSTAR INVESTMENT GUIDES
MORNINGSTAR INVESTMENT PROFILES
MORNINGSTAR MANAGED PORTFOLIOS
MORNINGSTAR MUTUAL FUNDS
MORNINGSTAR PRINCIPIA
MORNINGSTAR STOCKINVESTOR
MORNINGSTAR STOCKS 500
MORNINGSTARADVISOR.COM
MORNINGSTAR.COM
Advertising Agency:
Schwartz Public Relations Associates, Inc.
444 Park Ave S 12th Fl
New York, NY 10016-7321
Tel.: (212) 677-8700
Fax: (212) 254-2507

THE MOTLEY FOOL, INC.
2000 Duke St 4th FL
Alexandria, VA 22314
Tel.: (703) 838-3665
Fax: (703) 254-1999
Toll Free: (888) 665-3665
E-mail: cs@fool.com
Web Site: www.fool.com
Approx. Number Employees: 200
Year Founded: 1993
Business Description:
Investment Information Publisher
S.I.C.: 2741; 6282
N.A.I.C.S.: 511199; 523930
Media: 12-13-23
Personnel:
Scott Shedler *(Pres)*
Tom Gardner *(CEO)*
Ollen Douglass *(CFO)*
Brands & Products:
FOOL PRO
FOOLISH FOUR
FOOLMART
FOOL'S SCHOOL
THE MOTLEY FOOL
RULE BREAKER
RULE MAKER
TO EDUCATE, AMUSE & ENRICH

MOUNTAIN NATIONAL BANCSHARES, INC.
300 E Main St
Sevierville, TN 37862
Tel.: (865) 428-7990
Web Site: www.bankmnb.com
Approx. Rev.: $29,206,365
Approx. Number Employees: 150
Year Founded: 2002
Business Description:
Bank Holding Company
S.I.C.: 6712; 6029
N.A.I.C.S.: 551111; 522110
Advertising Expenditures: $122,670
Media: 17
Personnel:
Dwight B. Grizzell *(Pres & CEO)*
Richard A. Hubbs *(CFO & Sr VP)*
Michael L. Brown *(COO & Exec VP)*
Grace D. McKinzie *(Chief Lending Officer & Exec VP)*

MSB FINANCIAL CORP.
1902 Long Hill Rd
Millington, NJ 07946-0417
Tel.: (908) 647-4000
Fax: (908) 647-6196
Toll Free: (800) 264-5578
E-mail: investorinfo@millingtonsb.com
Web Site:
www.millingtonsbonline.com
Approx. Rev.: $17,495,000
Approx. Number Employees: 51
Year Founded: 1911
Business Description:
Holding Company
S.I.C.: 6712
N.A.I.C.S.: 551111
Advertising Expenditures: $223,000
Personnel:
Albert N. Olsen *(Chm)*
Gary T. Jolliffe *(Pres, CEO & Treas)*
Jeffrey E. Smith *(CFO & VP)*
Nancy E. Schmitz *(Chief Lending Officer, Sec & VP)*
Michael A. Shriner *(Exec VP)*
Betty Zangari *(VP & Asst Sec)*
Amra Bashir *(Asst Treas)*
Sandra Bentivegna *(Asst Treas)*
Kathleen Kardan *(Asst Treas)*
Linda Zito *(Asst Sec)*

MSCI INC.
1 Chase Manhattan Plz 44th Fl
New York, NY 10005
Tel.: (212) 804-3900
Fax: (212) 804-2919
E-mail: info@msci.net
Web Site: www.mscibarra.com
Approx. Rev.: $662,901,000
Approx. Number Employees: 878
Business Description:
Equity, Fixed Income & Hedge Fund Developer & Management Services
S.I.C.: 6289; 2721
N.A.I.C.S.: 523999; 511120
Media: 7-8-10-13-17-19
Personnel:
Henry A. Fernandez *(Chm & CEO)*
Peter Zangari *(Mng Dir & Head-Equity Portfolio Mgmt Analytics Bus)*
Remy Briand *(Mng Dir)*
Anand S. Iyer *(Mng Dir)*
David C. Brierwood *(COO)*
David M. Obstler *(COO)*
Gary Retelny *(Pres-Institutional Shareholder Svcs Inc. & Sec)*

MUTUALFIRST FINANCIAL, INC.
(d/b/a Mutual Bank)
110 E Charles St
Muncie, IN 47305-2400
Mailing Address:
PO Box 551
Muncie, IN 47308-0551
Tel.: (765) 747-2800
Fax: (765) 289-1201
Toll Free: (800) 382-8031
E-mail: market@mfsbank.com
Web Site: www.mfsbank.com
Approx. Rev.: $80,476,854
Approx. Number Employees: 363
Year Founded: 1999
Business Description:
Bank Holding Company
S.I.C.: 6029; 6035; 6163; 6712
N.A.I.C.S.: 522110; 522120; 522310; 551111
Advertising Expenditures: $1,224,000
Personnel:
David W. Heeter *(Pres & CEO)*
Christopher D. Cook *(CFO, Treas & Sr VP)*
Gary Kern *(CIO & VP)*
Patrick C. Botts *(Exec VP)*
John H. Bowles *(Sr VP/Mgr-Consumer Banking)*
Max Courtney *(Sr VP)*
Sharon Ferguson *(Sr VP)*
James L. Widner *(Sr VP)*
Lesley Neal *(Controller & Asst VP)*
Connie Bower *(Asst VP)*
Crystal L. Bradford *(Asst VP)*
Bill Curl *(Asst VP)*
Mitch Goon *(Asst VP)*
Lila Piper *(Asst VP)*
Karyn Kruger *(Mgr-Ops)*

NARA BANCORP, INC.
3731 Wilshire Blvd Ste 1000
Los Angeles, CA 90010
Tel.: (213) 639-1700
Fax: (213) 639-1717
Web Site: www.narabank.com
Approx. Rev.: $174,917,000
Approx. Number Employees: 376
Year Founded: 1988
Business Description:
Bank Holding Company
S.I.C.: 6029; 6712
N.A.I.C.S.: 522110; 551111
Advertising Expenditures: $1,671,000
Media: 7-8-13-22-23
Personnel:
Ki Suh Park *(Chm)*
Alvin D. Kang *(Pres & CEO)*
Philip E. Guldeman *(CFO & Exec VP)*
Bonnie Lee *(COO & Exec VP)*
Ellen Lee *(Chief Compliance Officer & Interim Chief Risk Officer)*
Mark Lee *(Exec VP & Chief Credit Officer)*
Kathi Duncan *(Chief Corp Svcs Officer)*
Shumun Mona Chui *(Sr VP & Mgr-IT)*
Kyu Kim *(Sr VP & Mgr-Eastern Reg)*
Anna Chung *(Sr VP & District Mgr)*

NASB FINANCIAL, INC.
12498 S Hwy 71
Grandview, MO 64030
Tel.: (816) 765-2200
Fax: (816) 316-4504
E-mail: info@nasb.com
Web Site: www.nasb.com
Approx. Rev.: $126,796,000
Approx. Number Employees: 414
Year Founded: 1998
Business Description:
Bank Holding Company
S.I.C.: 6035; 6712
N.A.I.C.S.: 522120; 551111
Import Export
Advertising Expenditures: $5,612,000
Media: 2-10-18-22
Personnel:
David H. Hancock *(Chm & CEO)*
Keith B. Cox *(Pres)*
Rhonda Nyhus *(CFO)*
Paul L. Thomas *(Exec VP & Chief Credit Officer)*
Wade Hall *(Sr VP)*
Bruce Thielen *(Sr VP-Loans)*

THE NASDAQ OMX GROUP, INC.
1 Liberty Plz
New York, NY 10006
Tel.: (212) 401-8700
Fax: (212) 401-1024
Toll Free: (877) 536-2737
Web Site: www.nasdaqomx.com
Approx. Rev.: $3,197,000,000
Approx. Number Employees: 2,395
Business Description:
Securities Exchange
S.I.C.: 6211; 6231
N.A.I.C.S.: 523120; 523210
Advertising Expenditures: $15,000,000
Media: 9-14-15-23-24
Personnel:
H. Furlong Baldwin *(Chm)*
Robert Greifeld *(Pres & CEO)*
Lee Shavel *(CFO & Exec VP-Corp Strategy)*
Anna M. Ewing *(CIO & Exec VP)*
John L. Jacobs *(CMO-Global Index Products & Mktg Grp & Exec VP)*
Edward S. Knight *(Chief Regulatory Officer, Gen Counsel & Exec VP)*
Bruce E. Aust *(Exec VP-Global Corp Client Grp)*
Hans-Ole Jochumsen *(Exec VP-Transaction Svcs Nordics & Global Data Products)*
Eric Noll *(Exec VP-Transaction Svcs)*
Nelson Griggs *(Sr VP & Head-Global Corp Client Grp-Asia Pacific)*
Frank De Maria *(Sr VP-Global Corp Comm)*
Carl-Magnus Hallberg *(Sr VP-Global IT Svcs Ops)*
Brian Hyndman *(Sr VP-Global Data Products)*
Jill Dodge *(Mng Dir-Mktg-Global)*
Joe Christinat *(Head-Media Rels & VP-Corp Comm)*
Jameel Aalim-Johnson *(Assoc VP)*
Dave Howland *(Dir-Creative)*
Meg Sharp *(Dir-Mktg Comm)*
Lindsey Peters *(Assoc Dir-Mktg-Global)*
Daniel Farrow *(Sr Web Developer)*
Brands & Products:
NASDAQ OMX
Advertising Agencies:
Gong Communications
1 Blandford St
London, W1U 3DA, United Kingdom
Tel.: (44) 20 7935 4800

McCann Erickson Worldwide
622 3rd Ave
New York, NY 10017-6707

The NASDAQ OMX Group, Inc. — (Continued)

Tel.: (646) 865-2000
Fax: (646) 487-9610

McKinney
(d/b/a McKinney Silver)
318 Blackwell St
Durham, NC 27701
Tel.: (919) 313-0802
Fax: (919) 313-0805

NATIONAL BANCSHARES CORPORATION

112 W Market St
Orrville, OH 44667
Tel.: (330) 682-1010
Fax: (330) 682-4740
E-mail: onlinebanking@fnborrville.com
Web Site: www.discoverfirstnational.com
Approx. Rev.: $18,691,000
Approx. Number Employees: 113
Business Description:
Bank Holding Company
S.I.C.: 6141; 6029; 6712
N.A.I.C.S.: 522210; 522110; 551111
Advertising Expenditures: $301,154
Personnel:
David C. Vernon *(Pres & CEO)*
James R. VanSickle *(Chief Acctg Officer & Sr VP)*
Thomas M. Fast *(Sr VP & Sr Loan Officer)*
Harold D. Berkey *(VP-Comml Banking)*
Angela L. Smith *(Asst Controller)*
Dean M. Karhan *(Asst VP & Mgr)*
Cindy A. Wagner *(Asst VP & Mgr Mayflower Office)*
Kathy J. Barnes *(Asst VP)*
Laura R. Yoder *(Asst VP)*
Janice M. Zacharias *(Mgr-Office)*

NATIONAL BANK OF CANADA

600 de la Gauchetiere West National Bank Tower
Montreal, QC H3B 4L2, Canada
Tel.: (514) 394-5000
Fax: (514) 394-8434
Telex: 525181
E-mail: investorrelations@nbc.ca
Web Site: www.nbc.ca
Approx. Rev.: $2,947,446,260
Approx. Number Employees: 17,747
Business Description:
Banking Services
S.I.C.: 6029
N.A.I.C.S.: 522110
Advertising Expenditures: $34,314,000
Personnel:
Jean E. Douville *(Chm)*
Louis Vachon *(Pres & CEO)*
Charles Guay *(Pres & CEO-Natl Bank Securities)*
William Bonnell *(Mng Dir)*
Patricia Curadeau-Grou *(CFO & Exec VP)*
Rejean Levesque *(Exec VP-Personal & Comml Banking)*
Luc Paiement *(Exec VP-Wealth Mgmt)*
Ricardo Pascoe *(Exec VP-Fin Markets)*
Eric Bujold *(Sr VP & Mng Dir-Wealth Mgmt)*
Richard Barriault *(Sr VP-Taxation)*
Alain Brunet *(Sr VP-Insurance)*
John B. Cieslak *(Sr VP)*
Jean Dagenais *(Sr VP-Fin, Taxation & IR)*
Pierre Dubreuil *(Sr VP)*
Michael Hanley *(Sr VP-Ops & Strategic Initiatives Office)*
Lynn Jeanniot *(Sr VP-HR & Corp Affairs)*
Martin Ouellet *(Sr VP-Corp Treasury)*
Kathleen Zicat *(Sr VP-Sls & Svc-Personal Banking)*
Suzanne Cote *(VP-Legal Affairs)*
Nathalie Lauzier *(VP-SME Market)*
France Roy Maffei *(VP-Customer Rels)*
Daniel Poissant *(VP-Personal Banking)*
Pierre Therrien *(VP-Private Banking)*
Helene Baril *(Dir-IR)*
Denis Dube *(Dir-Pub Rel)*

NATIONAL BANK OF INDIANAPOLIS CORPORATION

107 N Pennsylvania Ste 700
Indianapolis, IN 46204
Tel.: (317) 261-9000
Fax: (317) 261-9696
Toll Free: (877) 233-9500
Web Site: www.nbofi.com
Approx. Rev.: $61,378,000
Approx. Number Employees: 267
Year Founded: 1993
Business Description:
Bank Holding Company
S.I.C.: 6029; 6712
N.A.I.C.S.: 522110; 551111
Media: 8-20
Personnel:
Michael S. Maurer *(Chm)*
Morris L. Maurer *(CEO)*
Debra L. Ross *(CFO & Sr VP)*
Philip B. Roby *(COO)*
Brands & Products:
DIAMOND CAPITAL MANAGEMENT
THE NATIONAL BANK OF INDIANAPOLIS
PRIVATE PORTRAIT

NATIONAL BANK OF SOUTH CAROLINA

(Sub. of Synovus Financial Corp.)
1221 Main St
Columbia, SC 29201-3212
Tel.: (803) 929-2145
Fax: (803) 929-2064
Web Site: www.banknbsc.com
Sales Range: $200-249.9 Million
Approx. Number Employees: 600
Year Founded: 1905
Business Description:
Bank Holding Company
S.I.C.: 6029; 6712
N.A.I.C.S.: 522110; 551111
Media: 1-2-3-4-7-8-9-18-19-20-23-24-25-26
Distr.: Reg.
Budget Set: Aug.
Personnel:
William L. Pherigo *(Chm)*
C. W Garnett *(Pres & CEO)*
Sharon Duke *(Sr VP-Mktg)*
Frank W. Brumley *(Advisory Dir)*

NATIONAL BANKSHARES, INC.

101 Hubbard St
Blacksburg, VA 24060
Mailing Address:
PO Box 90002
Blacksburg, VA 24062-9002
Tel.: (540) 951-6300
Fax: (540) 951-6324
Toll Free: (800) 552-4123
E-mail: jrakes@nbbank.com
Web Site: www.nationalbankshares.com
Approx. Rev.: $57,486,000
Approx. Number Employees: 220
Year Founded: 1986
Business Description:
Bank Holding Company
S.I.C.: 6141; 6029; 6712
N.A.I.C.S.: 522210; 522110; 551111
Advertising Expenditures: $163,000
Media: 7-8-9-13-20-25
Personnel:
James G. Rakes *(Chm, Pres & CEO)*
James M. Shuler *(Vice Chm)*
David K. Skeens *(CFO & Treas)*
F. Brad Denardo *(Exec VP)*

NATIONAL FOUNDATION FOR CREDIT COUNSELING

801 Roder Rd Ste 900
Silver Spring, MD 20910-3372
Tel.: (202) 677-4300
Fax: (301) 495-5623
E-mail: questions@nfcc.org
Web Site: www.nfcc.org
Approx. Number Employees: 15
Year Founded: 1951
Business Description:
Nonprofit Credit Counseling Services
S.I.C.: 8611
N.A.I.C.S.: 813910
Media: 6-13-15
Personnel:
Susan C. Keating *(Pres & CEO)*
Paul Weiss *(CFO & Chief of Staff)*
William Binzel *(Sr VP)*

NATIONAL PENN BANCSHARES, INC.

Philadelphia & Reading Aves
Boyertown, PA 19512-0547
Mailing Address:
PO Box 547
Boyertown, PA 19512-0547
Tel.: (610) 705-9101
Fax: (610) 369-6118
Toll Free: (800) 822-3321
E-mail: international@natpennbank.com
Web Site: www.nationalpennbancshares.com
Approx. Int. Income: $387,249,000
Approx. Number Employees: 1,728
Year Founded: 1982
Business Description:
Bank Holding Company
S.I.C.: 6712; 6029
N.A.I.C.S.: 551111; 522110
Advertising Expenditures: $7,400,000
Personnel:
Thomas A. Beaver *(Chm)*
Wayne R. Weidner *(Vice Chm)*
Scott V. Fainor *(Pres & CEO)*
Michael J. Hughes *(CFO & Exec VP)*
Keene S. Turner *(Chief Acctg Officer)*
Gary L. Rhoads *(Treas & Exec VP)*
Michelle H. Debkowski *(Exec VP-Fin & IR)*
Carl F. Kovacs *(Exec VP-Ops & Tech)*
Carey Babczak *(Sr VP)*
Kelli Domizio *(Asst VP)*
Lisa Lightcap *(Asst VP)*
F. Mitchell *(Asst VP)*
John McCausland *(Dir-Corp Plng)*

NATIONAL PENN BANK

(Holding of National Penn Bancshares, Inc.)
Philadelphia & Reading Ave
Boyertown, PA 19512-0547
Tel.: (610) 369-6340
Fax: (610) 369-6627
Toll Free: (800) 822-3321
E-mail: information@nationalpennbank.com
Web Site: www.nationalpennbank.com
Sales Range: $250-299.9 Million
Approx. Number Employees: 723
Year Founded: 1874
Business Description:
Providers of Banking Services
S.I.C.: 6029
N.A.I.C.S.: 522110
Personnel:
Scott V. Fainor *(Pres & CEO)*
Gary L. Rhoads *(CFO)*
Timothy A. Day *(Mgr-Natl)*
Advertising Agency:
Stiegler, Wells, Brunswick & Roth, Inc.
(d/b/a SWB&R)
3865 Adler Pl
Bethlehem, PA 18017-9000
Tel.: (610) 866-0611
Fax: (610) 866-8650

NATIONWIDE HEALTH PROPERTIES, INC.

610 Newport Center Dr Ste 1150
Newport Beach, CA 92660
Tel.: (949) 718-4400
Fax: (949) 759-6876
E-mail: investorrelations@nhp-reit.com
Web Site: www.nhp-reit.com
Approx. Rev.: $439,251,000
Approx. Number Employees: 41
Year Founded: 1985
Business Description:
Real Estate Investment Trust
S.I.C.: 6798
N.A.I.C.S.: 525930
Advertising Expenditures: $700,000
Media: 2-25
Distr.: Natl.
Budget Set: Dec.
Personnel:
Douglas M. Pasquale *(Chm, Pres & CEO)*
Abdo H. Khoury *(CFO, Chief Portfolio Officer & Exec VP)*
Donald D. Bradley *(Chief Investment Officer & Exec VP)*
David M. Boitano *(Sr VP & Sr Investment Officer-West)*
Stephen F. Graham *(VP & Sr Investment Officer-South Central & Southeast)*
William Henry *(VP & Sr Investment Officer-Midwest)*
Robert G. Noonan *(VP & Sr Investment Officer-Northeast)*
Derrick D. Pete *(Sr VP-Corp Dev)*

NAUGATUCK VALLEY FINANCIAL CORPORATION

333 Church St
Naugatuck, CT 06770

Key to Media (For complete agency information see *The Advertising Red Books-Agencies* edition):
1. Bus. Publs. 2. Cable T.V. 3. Catalogs & Directories. 4. Co-op Adv. 5. Consumer Mags. 6. D.M. to Bus. Estab.7. D.M. to Consumers 8. Daily Newsp. 9. Exhibits/Trade Shows 10. Foreign 11. Infomercial 12. Internet Adv.13. Multimedia 14. Network Radio 15. Network T.V. 16. Newsp. Distr. Mags. 17. Other 18. Outdoor (Posters, Transit) 19. Point of Purchase20. Premiums, Novelties 21. Product Samples 22. Special Events Mktg. 23. Spot Radio 24. Spot T.V. 25. Weekly Newsp. 26. Yellow Page Adv.

Tel.: (203) 720-5000
Web Site: www.nvsl.com
Approx. Rev.: $31,826,000
Approx. Number Employees: 128
Business Description:
Bank Holding Company
S.I.C.: 6712; 6035
N.A.I.C.S.: 551111; 522120
Advertising Expenditures: $344,000
Personnel:
Carlos S. Batista *(Chm)*
John C. Roman *(Pres & CEO)*
Lee R. Schlesinger *(CFO & Sr VP)*
Dominic J. Alegi, Jr. *(Exec VP)*
Mark S. Graveline *(Sr VP)*
William C. Nimons *(Sr VP)*

NAVIGANT CONSULTING, INC.
30 S Wacker Dr Ste 3100
Chicago, IL 60606
Tel.: (312) 583-5700
Fax: (312) 583-5701
Toll Free: (800) 621-8390
E-mail: inquiries@navigantconsulting.com
Web Site: www.navigantconsulting.com
Approx. Rev.: $703,660,000
Approx. Number Employees: 2,359
Year Founded: 1983
Business Description:
Litigation, Financial, Healthcare, Energy & Operational Consulting Services
S.I.C.: 8742; 8748
N.A.I.C.S.: 541611; 541618
Media: 13
Personnel:
William M. Goodyear *(Chm & CEO)*
Julie M. Howard *(Pres & COO)*
William E. Dickenson *(Exec Mng Dir, Leader-Practice Area & Energy practice)*
Edward R. Casas *(Mng Dir & Co-Head-Capital Advisor)*
Jerry J. Capell *(Mng Dir)*
Thomas A. Nardi *(CFO & Exec VP)*
Andrew Bosman *(Chief Mktg & Comm Officer)*
Monica Weed *(Gen Counsel, Sec & VP)*
Jennifer Moreno *(Exec Dir-IR)*
Alma Angotti *(Dir-Disputes & Investigations Practice-Washington)*
Carrie Grapenthin *(Dir-Corp Comm & Mktg)*
Kristin Kruska *(Deputy Gen Counsel)*
Harry L. Hutcherson Jr. *(Independent Contract Consultant)*
Advertising Agency:
Design Reactor, Inc.
675 Campbell Technology Pkwy Ste 250
Campbell, CA 95008
Tel.: (408) 341-1190
Fax: (408) 341-8777

NBS TECHNOLOGIES INC.
(Sub. of Brookfield Asset Management Inc.)
703 Evans Ave Ste 400
Toronto, ON M9C 5E9, Canada
Tel.: (416) 621-1911
Fax: (416) 621-8875
E-mail: info@nbstech.com
Web Site: www.nbstech.com
Sales Range: $50-74.9 Million
Approx. Number Employees: 222
Year Founded: 1975
Business Description:
Credit Card & Plastic Card Related Services
S.I.C.: 6141
N.A.I.C.S.: 522210
Export
Advertising Expenditures: $287,246
Media: 2-7-10-26
Distr.: Intl.; Natl.
Budget Set: Oct.
Personnel:
Kirk Hamilton *(Pres & CEO)*
Bryan Hills *(Pres & CEO)*
Brands & Products:
NBS ADVANTAGE
NBS HORIZON
NBS HORIZON EVOLUTION
NBS IMAGEMASTER IMX2
NBS JAVELIN
NBS WAFER PACKING SOLUTIONS
UBIQ SOFTWARE

NCO GROUP, INC.
(Holding of One Equity Partners LLC)
507 Prudential Rd
Horsham, PA 19044
Tel.: (215) 441-3000
Fax: (215) 411-3908
Toll Free: (800) 220-2274
Web Site: www.ncogroup.com
Approx. Rev.: $1,602,163,000
Approx. Number Employees: 25,200
Year Founded: 1926
Business Description:
Accounts Receivable Management & Collection Services
S.I.C.: 7322
N.A.I.C.S.: 561440
Media: 2-8-10
Personnel:
Michael J. Barrist *(Chm & CEO)*
Stephen W. Elliott *(Pres & CEO)*
Ronald A. Rittenmeyer *(Pres & CEO)*
John R. Schwab *(CFO, Exec VP-Fin & Treas)*
Steven Leckerman *(COO & Exec VP)*
Joshua Gindin *(Gen Counsel & Exec VP)*
Albert Zezulinski *(Exec VP)*
Brands & Products:
ATTORNEY NETWORK SERVICES
NCOEPAYMENTS
Advertising Agency:
VisualMax
630 9th Ave Ste 414
New York, NY 10036
Tel.: (212) 925-2938
Fax: (212) 202-3905

NCO RECEIVABLES MANAGEMENT SOLUTIONS
(Sub. of NCO Group, Inc.)
(d/b/a NCO Financial Systems, Inc.)
4000 E 5th Ave
Columbus, OH 43219
Tel.: (614) 827-7549
Fax: (614) 827-7802
E-mail: webmaster@nationalrevenue.com
Web Site: www.nationalrevenue.com
Sales Range: $600-649.9 Million
Approx. Number Employees: 4,000
Business Description:
Collection Agency Services
S.I.C.: 7322
N.A.I.C.S.: 561440
Media: 2-7-10-13

NELNET, INC.
121 S 13th St Ste 201
Lincoln, NE 68508
Tel.: (402) 458-3038
Fax: (402) 458-2399
E-mail: investorrelations@nelnet.net
Web Site: www.nelnet.com
Approx. Rev.: $1,061,500,000
Approx. Number Employees: 2,200
Year Founded: 1977
Business Description:
Student Loan Products & Services
S.I.C.: 6141; 9311
N.A.I.C.S.: 522291; 921130
Import Export
Advertising Expenditures: $8,046,000
Media: 2-6-7-13-20-22
Personnel:
Michael S. Dunlap *(Chm & CEO)*
Stephen F. Butterfield *(Vice Chm)*
Jeffrey R. Noordhoek *(Pres)*
Terry J. Heimes *(CFO)*
William J. Munn *(Chief Legal Officer, Gen Counsel, Sec & Corp Governance Officer)*
Timothy A. Tewes *(Pres/CEO-Nelnet Bus Solutions)*
Todd M. Eicher *(Exec Dir-Nelnet Enrollment Solutions)*
Brands & Products:
KWIKPAY
NCONCERT
NELNET
NGENIUS
NSERVICE
NTERACT
NTERCHANGE
NTRUST

NETSPEND HOLDINGS, INC.
701 Brazos St Ste 1300
Austin, TX 78701-2582
Tel.: (512) 532-8200
Web Site: www.netspend.com
Approx. Rev.: $275,387,000
Approx. Number Employees: 507
Business Description:
Holding Company
S.I.C.: 6719
N.A.I.C.S.: 551112
Advertising Expenditures: $100,000
Media: 17
Personnel:
Charles J. Harris *(Pres)*
Daniel R. Henry *(CEO)*
George W. Gresham *(CFO)*
Christopher T. Brown *(Gen Counsel & Sec)*
Thomas A. Cregan *(Exec VP-Sls & Distr)*
James DeVoglaer *(Exec VP-IT)*
Anh Hatzopoulos *(Exec VP-Online Bus Dev)*
James Jerome *(Exec VP-Card Ops)*

NEW ALLIANCE BANCSHARES, INC.
(Name Changed to First Niagara Bank)

NEW BEACON FINANCIAL CORPORATION
221 E Palmetto Park Rd
Boca Raton, FL 33432
Tel.: (561) 910-2981
Fax: (561) 431-3214
Toll Free: (800) 320-4001
E-mail: info@newbeaconfinancial.com
Web Site: www.newbeaconfinancial.com
Business Description:
Forward & Reverse Mortgage Broker
S.I.C.: 6163
N.A.I.C.S.: 522310
Media: 23
Personnel:
Thomas Simpson *(Pres)*

NEW CENTURY BANCORP, INC.
700 W Cumberland St
Dunn, NC 28335
Tel.: (910) 892-7080
Fax: (910) 892-9225
E-mail: investor@newcenturybanknc.com
Web Site: www.newcenturybanknc.com
Approx. Rev.: $36,288,000
Approx. Number Employees: 135
Year Founded: 2003
Business Description:
Bank Holding Company
S.I.C.: 6712; 6029; 6035
N.A.I.C.S.: 551111; 522110; 522120
Advertising Expenditures: $387,000
Personnel:
J. Gary Ciccone *(Chm)*
Clarence L. Tart Jr. *(Vice Chm)*
William L. Hedgepeth, II *(Pres & CEO)*
Lisa F. Campbell *(CFO, COO & Exec VP)*
Joseph Daniel Fisher *(Chief Credit Officer & Exec VP)*
Joan I. Patterson *(Chief Deposit Ops Officer & Exec VP)*

NEW ENGLAND BANCSHARES, INC.
855 Enfield St
Enfield, CT 06082
Tel.: (860) 253-5200
Fax: (860) 253-5205
Web Site: www.nebankct.com
Approx. Rev.: $35,585,000
Approx. Number Employees: 121
Business Description:
Bank Holding Company
S.I.C.: 6712; 6029
N.A.I.C.S.: 551111; 522110
Advertising Expenditures: $282,000
Media: 17
Personnel:
Peter T. Dow *(Chm)*
David J. O'Connor *(Pres & CEO)*
Scott D. Nogles *(CFO & Exec VP)*
Charles J. Desimone, Jr. *(Chief Credit Officer, Chief Risk Officer & Exec VP)*
John F. Parda *(Chief Loan Officer & Exec VP)*
Anthony M. Mattioli *(Pres-Market)*
Michael J. Marcucci *(Exec VP)*
Peter W. McClintock *(Exec VP-Retail Div)*

NEW ENGLAND REALTY ASSOCIATES LIMITED PARTNERSHIP
39 Brighton Ave
Allston, MA 02134-2301
Tel.: (617) 783-0039

Key to Media (For complete agency information see *The Advertising Red Books-Agencies* edition):
1. Bus. Publs. 2. Cable T.V. 3. Catalogs & Directories. 4. Co-op Adv. 5. Consumer Mags. 6. D.M. to Bus. Estab.7. D.M. to Consumers
8. Daily Newsp. 9. Exhibits/Trade Shows 10. Foreign 11. Infomercial 12. Internet Adv.13. Multimedia 14. Network Radio
15. Network T.V. 16. Newsp. Distr. Mags. 17. Other 18. Outdoor (Posters, Transit) 19. Point of Purchase20. Premiums, Novelties
21. Product Samples 22. Special Events Mktg. 23. Spot Radio 24. Spot T.V. 25. Weekly Newsp. 26. Yellow Page Adv.

New England Realty Associates Limited Partnership — (Continued)
Fax: (617) 783-0568
E-mail: nera@thehamiltoncompany.com
Web Site: www.thehamiltoncompany.com/nera/nerainvestor.htm
Approx. Rev.: $33,166,110
Year Founded: 1977
Business Description:
Residential & Commercial Real Estate Acquirer, Developer, Investor, Operator & Sales
S.I.C.: 6513; 6512; 6798
N.A.I.C.S.: 531110; 525930; 531120
Advertising Expenditures: $70,074
Media: 17
Personnel:
Ronald Brown *(Pres)*
Sally Starr *(Dir-IR)*

NEW HAMPSHIRE THRIFT BANCSHARES, INC.
9 Main St The Carriage House
Newport, NH 03773
Tel.: (603) 863-0886
Fax: (603) 863-7980
Toll Free: (800) 281-5772
E-mail: info@lakesunbank.com
Web Site: www.lakesunbank.com
Approx. Rev.: $48,930,775
Approx. Number Employees: 215
Business Description:
Bank Holding Company
S.I.C.: 6035; 6029; 6163; 6712
N.A.I.C.S.: 522120; 522110; 522310; 551111
Advertising Expenditures: $432,063
Media: 8-10-22
Personnel:
Stephen W. Ensign *(Chm & CEO)*
Stephen R. Theroux *(Vice Chm, Pres, CFO & COO)*
Laura Jacobi *(Chief Acctg Officer)*
Scott Laughinghouse *(Sr VP-Comml Lending)*

NEW VALLEY CORPORATION
(Sub. of New Valley Holdings Inc.)
100 SE 2nd St 32nd Fl
Miami, FL 33131-2158
Tel.: (305) 579-8000
Fax: (305) 579-8001
E-mail: info@amstock.com
Web Site: www.newvalley.com
Sales Range: $1-9.9 Million
Approx. Number Employees: 12
Year Founded: 1851
Business Description:
Real Estate Holding Company
S.I.C.: 6552
N.A.I.C.S.: 237210
Export
Media: 1-2-3-4-5-7-9-10-15-19-20-23-24-26
Distr.: Natl.
Budget Set: Nov.
Personnel:
Richard J. Lampen *(Gen Counsel & Exec VP)*

NEW YORK COMMERCIAL BANK
(Sub. of New York Community Bancorp, Inc.)
1 Suffolk Sq 1601 Veterans Memorial Hwy
Islandia, NY 11749
Tel.: (631) 348-0888
Fax: (631) 348-0542
Toll Free: (888) LICB-888
Web Site: www.newyorkcommercialbank.com
Sales Range: $25-49.9 Million
Approx. Number Employees: 101
Year Founded: 1989
Business Description:
Commercial Banking Services
S.I.C.: 6029
N.A.I.C.S.: 522110
Media: 4-7-10-13-22
Personnel:
Joseph R. Ficalora *(Pres & CEO)*
Douglas C. Manditch *(COO & Sr Exec VP)*
Spiros J. Voutsinas *(Pres/CEO-Atlantic Bank Div)*
Kenneth M. Scheriff *(Exec VP)*
Advertising Agency:
George P. Clarke Advertising, Inc.
27 E 21st St 2nd Fl
New York, NY 10010
Tel.: (212) 545-7400
Fax: (212) 545-7433

NEWBRIDGE BANCORP
1501 Highwoods Blvd Ste 400
Greensboro, NC 27410
Tel.: (336) 369-0900
E-mail: info@lsbnc.com
Web Site: www.lsbnc.com
Approx. Rev.: $109,420,000
Approx. Number Employees: 481
Year Founded: 1982
Business Description:
Bank Holding Company
S.I.C.: 6029; 6712
N.A.I.C.S.: 522110; 551111
Advertising Expenditures: $1,594,000
Media: 7-8-9-17-18-19-20-22-23-25
Personnel:
Michael S. Albert *(Chm)*
Barry Z. Dodson *(Vice Chm)*
Pressley A. Ridgill *(Pres & CEO)*
Wes Budd *(Chief Credit Officer & Exec VP)*
Richard M. Cobb *(Chief Acctg Officer, Sr VP & Controller)*
Ramsey K. Hamadi *(CFO-NewBridge Bancorp, NewBridge Bank & Exec VP)*
Robin Hager *(Chief Resource Officer-NewBridge Bank & Exec VP)*
Terry N. Freeman *(Sr VP)*
Brands & Products:
NEWBRIDGE BANCORP

NFCO INC.
2121 Brooks St
Neenah, WI 54956
Mailing Address:
PO Box 729
Neenah, WI 54956
Tel.: (920) 725-7000
Fax: (920) 729-3661
Web Site: www.nfco.com
Sales Range: $300-349.9 Million
Approx. Number Employees: 1,000
Business Description:
Investment Holding Companies, Except Banks
S.I.C.: 6719; 3321
N.A.I.C.S.: 551112; 331511
Media: 4

NICHOLAS FINANCIAL, INC.
2454 N McMullen-Booth Rd Bldg C
Clearwater, FL 33759
Tel.: (727) 726-0763
Fax: (727) 726-2140
E-mail: info@nicfn.com
Web Site: www.nicholasfinancial.com
Approx. Rev.: $62,773,526
Approx. Number Employees: 291
Year Founded: 1981
Business Description:
Direct Consumer Loans & Purchaser of Installment Sales Contracts from Automobile Dealers for Used Cars & Light Trucks
S.I.C.: 6141
N.A.I.C.S.: 522291
Advertising Expenditures: $1,242,337
Personnel:
Peter L. Vosotas *(Chm, Pres & CEO)*
Ralph T. Finkenbrink *(CFO, Sec & Sr VP)*
Michael J. Marika *(CIO)*
Douglas W. Marohn *(Sr VP-Branch Ops)*
Matthew J. Foget *(VP-Mktg)*
Stephanie M. Crist *(Dir-HR)*
Sotirios A. Kakalis *(Dir-Loss Recovery)*

NOMURA SECURITIES INTERNATIONAL, INC.
(Sub. of Nomura Holding America Inc.)
2 World Financial Ctr Bldg B
New York, NY 10281-1008
Tel.: (212) 667-9300
Fax: (212) 667-1058
Toll Free: (888) NOMURA6
Web Site: www.nomura.com
E-Mail For Key Personnel:
Public Relations: rpiscitelli@us.nomura.com
Approx. Number Employees: 1,000
Year Founded: 1927
Business Description:
Securities & Investment Banking Services
S.I.C.: 6211; 6282
N.A.I.C.S.: 523110; 523120; 523920
Import Export
Advertising Expenditures: $1,000,000
Media: 1-2-9-10-11
Distr.: Natl.
Budget Set: July
Personnel:
Shigesuke Kashiwagi *(Pres & CEO)*
Ciaran O'Kelly *(Sr Mng Dir & Head-Equities-Americas)*
Paul Sheard *(Mng Dir, Chief Economist & Head-Economic Res)*
Michael Hill *(Mng Dir & Global Co-Head-Natural Resources & Power)*
Thomas Rosen *(Mng Dir & Head-Americas Power, Utilities, & Renewables)*
James DeNaut *(Mng Dir)*
Brian Foran *(Mng Dir)*
Lori Lancaster *(Mng Dir)*
Surat Maheshwari *(Mng Dir)*
James Merli *(Mng Dir)*
Craig Phares *(Mng Dir)*
Takahide Mizuno *(CIO & Exec VP)*
Thomas Barber *(Mng Dir-Natural Resources Banking)*
Mark Govoni *(Head-Program Sls Trading & Index Analytics-US)*
Ralph Piscitelli *(Exec Dir-Corp Comm)*
Gerald Casey *(Dir)*

NORTH CENTRAL BANCSHARES, INC.
825 Central Ave
Fort Dodge, IA 50501
Tel.: (515) 576-7531
Fax: (515) 576-2051
Web Site: www.firstfederaliowa.com
Approx. Rev.: $29,951,592
Approx. Number Employees: 137
Business Description:
Bank Holding Company
S.I.C.: 6712; 6035
N.A.I.C.S.: 551111; 522120
Advertising Expenditures: $366,681
Personnel:
David M. Bradley *(Chm & CEO)*
C. Thomas Chalstrom *(Pres & COO)*
Jane M. Funk *(CFO & Treas)*
Kirk A. Yung *(Sr VP)*
Brooke Ruddy *(Mktg Comm Dir)*

NORTH PENN BANCORP, INC.
216 Adams Ave
Scranton, PA 18503-1692
Tel.: (570) 344-6113
Fax: (570) 344-5626
Web Site: www.northpennbank.com
Approx. Rev.: $8,280,000
Approx. Number Employees: 34
Business Description:
Bank Holding Company
S.I.C.: 6035; 6712
N.A.I.C.S.: 522120; 551111
Advertising Expenditures: $32,000
Media: 17
Personnel:
Frederick L. Hickman *(Pres & CEO)*
Joseph F. McDonald *(CFO)*
Thomas J. Dziak *(Exec VP & Sr Lending Officer)*
Thomas A. Byrne *(Sr VP & Comml Lending Officer)*

NORTHEAST BANCORP
500 Canal St
Lewiston, ME 04240
Mailing Address:
PO Box 2017
Lewiston, ME 04241-2017
Tel.: (207) 786-3245
Toll Free: (800) 284-5989
E-mail: neinformation@northeastbank.com
Web Site: www.northeastbank.com
Approx. Rev.: $43,407,662
Approx. Number Employees: 229
Business Description:
Bank Holding Company
S.I.C.: 6712; 6029
N.A.I.C.S.: 551111; 522110
Advertising Expenditures: $566,000
Personnel:
Judith E. Wallingford *(Chm)*
John Rosmarin *(Vice Chm)*
Chris Delamater *(Pres & CEO)*
James D. Delamater *(Pres & CEO)*
Robert S. Johnson *(CFO & Sr VP)*
Marcel Blais *(COO)*
Craig Linscott *(Sr VP-Northeast Bank Insurance Grp)*
Leslie L. Couper *(Mgr)*
Brands & Products:
NO ORDINARY ADVICE
NO ORDINARY BANK
NORTHEAST BANK

Key to Media (For complete agency information see *The Advertising Red Books-Agencies* edition):
1. Bus. Publs. 2. Cable T.V. 3. Catalogs & Directories. 4. Co-op Adv. 5. Consumer Mags. 6. D.M. to Bus. Estab.7. D.M. to Consumers 8. Daily Newsp. 9. Exhibits/Trade Shows 10. Foreign 11. Infomercial 12. Internet Adv.13. Multimedia 14. Network Radio 15. Network T.V. 16. Newsp. Distr. Mags. 17. Other 18. Outdoor (Posters, Transit) 19. Point of Purchase20. Premiums, Novelties 21. Product Samples 22. Special Events Mktg. 23. Spot Radio 24. Spot T.V. 25. Weekly Newsp. 26. Yellow Page Adv.

TOGETHER, WE'LL GET YOU THERE

THE NORTHERN TRUST COMPANY

50 S LaSalle St
Chicago, IL 60603
Tel.: (312) 630-6000
Web Site: www.northerntrust.com
Approx. Number Employees: 7,000
Year Founded: 1889
Business Description:
Banking Services
S.I.C.: 6029; 6035
N.A.I.C.S.: 522110; 522120
Advertising Expenditures: $2,500,000
Media: 2-6-7-8-9-10-19-25
Distr.: Reg.
Budget Set: Sept.
Personnel:
Frederick H. Waddell *(Pres & CEO)*
Shundrawn A. Thomas *(Mng Dir & Head-Global Bus-Exchange Traded Funds Grp)*
Peter Jordan *(Mng Dir)*
Orie L. Dudley *(Chief Investment Officer)*
Steven L. Fradkin *(Pres-Corp & Institutional Svcs)*
William Morrison *(Pres-Personal Fin Svcs)*
Kelly R. Welsh *(Gen Counsel & Exec VP)*
Rose A. Ellis *(Asst Gen Counsel & Corp Sec)*
Timothy P. Moen *(Exec VP, Head-HR & Admin)*
John P. Grube *(Exec VP)*
Marie Dzanis *(Sr VP & Head-Exchange Traded Funds Sls & Servicing)*
Lawrence Au *(Sr VP)*
Brands & Products:
NORTHERN TRUST
WHAT REALLY MATTERS

NORTHERN TRUST CORPORATION

50 S La Salle St
Chicago, IL 60675-0001
Tel.: (312) 630-6000
Fax: (312) 630-1512
Web Site: www.northerntrust.com
Approx. Rev.: $2,729,000,000
Approx. Number Employees: 12,800
Year Founded: 1889
Business Description:
Bank Holding Company
S.I.C.: 6141; 6029; 6035; 6733
N.A.I.C.S.: 522210; 522110; 522120; 523991
Media: 2-6
Personnel:
Frederick H. Waddell *(Chm & CEO)*
Sherry S. Barrat *(Vice Chm)*
David C. Blowers *(Pres & CEO-Midwest Reg)*
Miles S. Milton *(Mng Dir & Sr VP)*
William L. Morrison *(CFO & Exec VP)*
Peter Cherecwich *(COO & Head-Global Fund Svcs)*
Patricia K Bartler *(Chief Ethics Officer, Sr VP & Chief Compliance Officer)*
Lloyd A. Wennlund *(Exec VP & Pres-Northern Institutional Fund Families)*
Steven L. Fradkin *(Pres-Corp & Institutional Svcs)*
Stephen N. Potter *(Pres-Global Investments)*
Douglas P. Regan *(Pres-Wealth Mgmt)*
Jana Raye Schreuder *(Pres-Personal Fin Svcs)*
Joyce M. St. Clair *(Pres-Ops & Tech)*
Stephen Biff Bowman *(CEO-EMEA)*
Kelly R. Welsh *(Gen Counsel & Exec VP)*
William R. Dodds *(Treas & Exec VP)*
Rose A. Ellis *(Sec & Asst Gen Counsel)*
Jeffrey D. Cohodes *(Exec VP & Head-Corp Risk Mgmt)*
Aileen B. Blake *(Exec VP & Controller)*
Marianne G. Doan *(Exec VP)*
Wilson Leech *(Exec VP)*
Connie L. Lindsey *(Exec VP)*
Lyle Logan *(Exec VP)*
R. Hugh Magill *(Exec VP)*
Timothy P. Moen *(Exec VP-HR & Admin)*
Brian P. Ovaert *(Exec VP)*
Lee S. Selander *(Exec VP)*
Jean E. Sheridan *(Exec VP)*
John Skjervem *(Exec VP)*
Ian Baillie *(Sr VP & Mng DirLuxembourg Office)*
Kelly King Dibble *(Sr VP & Dir-Pub Affairs & Govt Rels)*
Beverly J. Fleming *(Sr VP & Dir-IR)*
Sharon Cohen *(Sr VP)*
Jeffrey W. Conover *(Sr VP)*
Kevin Hardy *(Sr VP)*
Peter Jacobs *(Sr VP-Mutual Fund Product Mgmt)*
Grant Johnsey *(Sr VP)*
Kelly Mannard *(Sr VP-Global Mktg & Comm)*
Rohan Singh *(Sr VP)*
Louisa Taylor *(Sr VP)*
Jason J. Tyler *(Head-Corp Strategy)*
Jon Dunham *(Dir-Asset Servicing Sls-North America)*
David McPhillips *(Dir-Consultant Rels & Transition Mgmt Strategist)*
Lee Woolley *(Dir-Advisory Svcs)*
Kathy Dugan *(Product Mgr)*
Paul Finlayson *(Product Mgr-Alternative Assets)*
Jim Haran *(Product Mgr-Investment Risk & Analytical Svcs)*
Brands & Products:
NORTHERN TRUST
Advertising Agencies:
Digney & Company Public Relations
1680 N Vine St Ste 1105
Hollywood, CA 90028
Tel.: (323) 993-3000

Downtown Partners Chicago
200 E Randolph St 34th Fl
Chicago, IL 60601
Tel.: (312) 552-5800
Tel.: (312) 552-5804
Fax: (312) 552-2330

MC2 Marketing Inc.
13131 E 166th St
Cerritos, CA 90703-2202
Tel.: (562) 365-0200
Fax: (562) 365-0201

Octagon EMEA
100 Boulevard du Souverain
1170
Brussels, Belgium
Tel.: (32) 2 661 2874

s2 Marketing + Communications, Inc.
656 W Randolph Ste 3E
Chicago, IL 60661
Tel.: (312) 382-9000

Team One
(Sub. of Saatchi & Saatchi Advertising Worldwide)
1960 E Grand Ave
El Segundo, CA 90245-5059
Tel.: (310) 615-2000
Fax: (310) 322-7565

NORTHFIELD SAVINGS BANK INC.

33 S Main St
Northfield, VT 05663-6703
Tel.: (802) 476-2400
Fax: (802) 476-5532
E-mail: nsb@nsbvt.com
Web Site: www.nsbvt.com
Approx. Number Employees: 150
Year Founded: 1867
Business Description:
State Commercial Banks
S.I.C.: 6029
N.A.I.C.S.: 522110
Import Export
Personnel:
Brian C. Harwood *(Chm)*
Thomas N. Pelletier *(Pres & CEO)*
Christine Martin *(Security Officer)*
Cory B. Richardson *(Sr VP-Comml)*
Gail Theodoseau *(Branch Mgr)*
Donna Bohonnon *(Mgr-Bethel)*
Eileen Bradley *(Mgr-Northfield & Administrator-Central Vermont Branch)*
Tracy Davis *(Mgr-Williston Road)*
Suzanne Grenier *(Mgr-Williston Road)*
Wendy Kellett *(Mgr-Waterbury)*
Kathy LaCross *(Mgr-Williston & Administrator-Chittenden County Branch)*
Delora J. Livingston *(Mgr-Randolph)*
Polly P. Thomas *(Mgr-Opers)*
Tim Sargent *(Engr-Network)*
Advertising Agency:
Spike Advertising Inc.
27 Kilburn St
Burlington, VT 05401
Tel.: (802) 951-1700
Fax: (802) 951-1705

NORTHRIM BANCORP, INC.

3111 C St
Anchorage, AK 99503
Mailing Address:
PO Box 241489
Anchorage, AK 99524-1489
Tel.: (907) 562-0062
Fax: (907) 562-1758
Toll Free: (800) 478-2265
E-mail: investors@nrim.com
Web Site: www.northrim.com
Approx. Rev.: $62,075,000
Approx. Number Employees: 268
Year Founded: 1990
Business Description:
Bank Holding Company
S.I.C.: 6035; 6029; 6712
N.A.I.C.S.: 522120; 522110; 551111
Import Export
Advertising Expenditures: $1,300,000
Personnel:
R. Marc Langland *(Chm & CEO)*
Joseph M. Beedle *(Pres)*
Joseph M. Schierhorn *(CFO & Exec VP)*
Christopher N. Knudson *(COO & Exec VP)*
Sig Casiano *(Officer-Construction Loan & VP)*
Ray Dinger *(Officer-Comml Real Estate Loan & VP)*
Mark Edwards *(VP & Comml Loan Officer)*
Sandi Garnand *(VP & Comml Loan Officer)*
Kathy Martin *(Officer-Construction Loan & VP)*
Jim Miller *(VP & Comml Loan Officer)*
Sharon Wright *(Officer-Loan Documentation & VP)*
Erika Bills *(Officer-Bus Dev & Asst VP)*
Julee Drennan *(Officer-HR & Asst VP)*
Glenna Hartman *(Asst VP & Credit Admin Officer)*
Jesse Janssen *(Asst VP & Comml Loan Officer)*
Heidi Moes *(Officer-Loan Servicing & Asst VP)*
Rick Pinkerton *(Asst VP & Loan Review Officer)*
Paula Sanders-Grau *(Officer-Comml Cash Mgmt & Asst VP)*
Russ Sharpton *(Asst VP & Comml Loan Officer)*
Melissa Stewart *(Asst VP & Comml Loan Officer)*
Mildred Sy *(Officer-Loan Quality Assurance & Asst VP)*
Nancy Wilson *(Asst VP & Deposit Compliance Officer)*
Cathy Wright *(Officer-Loan Admin Support & Asst VP)*
Bill Simpson *(Officer-Special Credits)*
Sandra Walters *(Officer-Loan)*
Steve Hartung *(Exec VP & Quality Assurance Officer)*
Audrey Amundson *(Sr VP, Controller & Mgr-Acctg)*
Blythe Campbell *(Sr VP-Mktg & Mgr-Comm)*
Catherine Claxton *(Sr VP & Mgr-Comml Real Estate Lending)*
Ken Ferguson *(Sr VP-Comml Real Estate Lending Mgr)*
Leonard Horst *(Sr VP & Mgr-Comml Loan)*
Daniel Lowell *(Sr VP & Mgr-Northrim Funding Svcs)*
Tara Tetzlaff *(Sr VP & Mgr-Residential Construction Lending)*
Suzanne Whittle *(Sr VP & Mgr-Info Svcs)*
Lynn Wolfe *(Sr VP & Mgr-Loan Support Svcs)*
Dennis Bingham *(Sr VP-Loan Admin)*
Carolyn Jennings *(Sr VP & Administrator-Branch)*
Victor P. Mollozzi *(Sr VP- Bus & Community Dev)*
Jeanine Lillo *(VP-Acctg & Asst Controller)*
Benjamin Craig *(VP & Mgr-Info Sys)*
Sheri Gower *(VP & Mgr-HR)*
Janet Holland *(VP & Mgr-Facilities)*
Mary Perez *(VP-Branch Admin & Mgr-Sls & Svc)*
Amber Zins *(VP & Mgr-Internal Audit)*
Lynn Akers *(Asst VP & Branch Mgr)*

Key to Media (For complete agency information see *The Advertising Red Books-Agencies* edition):
1. Bus. Publs. 2. Cable T.V. 3. Catalogs & Directories. 4. Co-op Adv. 5. Consumer Mags. 6. D.M. to Bus. Estab.7. D.M. to Consumers
8. Daily Newsp. 9. Exhibits/Trade Shows 10. Foreign 11. Infomercial 12. Internet Adv.13. Multimedia 14. Network Radio
15. Network T.V. 16. Newsp. Distr. Mags. 17. Other 18. Outdoor (Posters, Transit) 19. Point of Purchase20. Premiums, Novelties
21. Product Samples 22. Special Events Mktg. 23. Spot Radio 24. Spot T.V. 25. Weekly Newsp. 26. Yellow Page Adv.

Northrim BanCorp, Inc. — (Continued)

Cindy Cevasco *(Asst VP & Branch Mgr)*
Regina Jackson *(Asst VP & Branch Mgr)*
Fiona Johnson *(Asst VP & Branch Mgr)*
Tammy Kosa *(Asst VP & Branch Mgr)*
Amy Penrose *(Asst VP & Branch Mgr)*
Fran Ponge *(Asst VP & Branch Mgr)*
Rodlynn Smallwood *(Asst VP & Branch Mgr)*
Rina Suesue *(Asst VP & Branch Mgr)*
Angela Freeman *(Asst VP & Trng Mgr)*
Josie Thayer *(Asst VP & Mgr-Electronic Bus Svcs)*
Robin Bettisworth *(Asst VP & Supvr-Audit)*
Kelly Lykins-Longlet *(Mgr-Risk)*
Latosha Dickinson *(Asst Controller)*

NORTHWAY FINANCIAL, INC.

9 Main St
Berlin, NH 03570
Tel.: (603) 752-1171
Fax: (603) 752-6291
E-mail: cse@northwaybank.com
Web Site: www.northwaybank.com
Sales Range: $25-49.9 Million
Approx. Number Employees: 245
Business Description:
Bank Holding Company
S.I.C.: 6029; 6712
N.A.I.C.S.: 522110; 551111
Advertising Expenditures: $386,000
Personnel:
William J. Woodward *(CEO)*
Richard P. Orsillo *(CFO & Sr VP)*

NORTHWEST BANCORPORATION INC.

421 W Riverside Ave Ste 113
Spokane, WA 99201
Tel.: (509) 456-8888
Fax: (509) 742-6669
Web Site: www.inb.com
Approx. Rev.: $24,834,546
Approx. Number Employees: 109
Business Description:
State Commercial Banks
S.I.C.: 6141
N.A.I.C.S.: 522210
Advertising Expenditures: $51,685
Media: 17
Personnel:
Anthony D. Bonanzino *(Chm)*
Freeman Duncan *(Vice Chm)*
Randall L. Fewel *(Pres & CEO)*
Holly A. Austin *(CFO & Sr VP)*
Holly A. Poquette *(CFO)*
Scott Southwick *(Exec VP)*
Doug Beaudoin *(Sr VP)*
Mark Dresback *(Sr VP)*
Elizabeth Herndon *(Sr VP & Branch Administrator)*
Stanly Anderson *(VP & Mgr-IT)*

NORTHWEST BANCSHARES, INC.

100 Liberty St
Warren, PA 16365-2353
Tel.: (814) 726-2140
Tel.: (814) 728-7263 (Shareholder Relations)
Fax: (814) 728-7716
Toll Free: (800) 859-1000 (Shareholder Relations)
E-mail: nwsbinfo@nwbcorp.com
Web Site: www.northwestsavingsbank.com
Approx. Rev.: $370,568,000
Approx. Number Employees: 1,722
Year Founded: 2001
Business Description:
Bank Holding Company
S.I.C.: 6712; 6029; 6035
N.A.I.C.S.: 551111; 522110; 522120
Advertising Expenditures: $3,742,000
Media: 2-3-9-10-18-23-25-26
Personnel:
William J. Wagner *(Pres & CEO)*
William W. Harvey, Jr. *(CFO & Exec VP)*
Andrew C. Young *(CIO-Northwest Bank)*
Steven G. Fisher *(Exec VP-Banking Svcs)*
Timothy A. Huber *(Chief Lending Officer & Exec VP)*
Gregory C. LaRocca *(Exec VP-Investment & Trust Svcs)*
Gerald J. Ritzert *(Sr VP & Controller)*
Robert Bablak, Jr. *(Sr VP-Community Banking)*
John M. Beard *(Sr VP-Northwest Savings Bank)*
Julia W. McTavish *(Sr VP-HR)*
Richard F. Seibel *(Sr VP-Risk Mgmt-Northwest Savings Bank)*

NORTHWEST SAVINGS BANK

(Sub. of Northwest Bancshares, Inc.)
100 Liberty St PO Box 128
Warren, PA 16365-2353
Tel.: (814) 726-2140
Fax: (814) 728-7720
Web Site:
www.northwestsavingsbank.com
Sales Range: $1-9.9 Million
Approx. Number Employees: 12
Year Founded: 1896
Business Description:
Personal & Commercial Banking Services
S.I.C.: 6029; 6035
N.A.I.C.S.: 522110; 522120
Personnel:
William J. Wagner *(Pres & CEO)*
William W. Harvey, Jr. *(CFO & Exec VP)*
Michael G. Smelko *(Chief Credit Officer & Exec VP)*
Gregory C. LaRocca *(Exec VP & Sec)*
Steven G. Fisher *(Exec VP-Banking Svcs)*
Timothy A. Huber *(Chief Lending Officer & Exec VP)*
Robert Bablak, Jr. *(Sr VP-Community Banking)*
Richard F. Seibel *(Sr VP-Risk Mgmt)*
David E. Westerburg *(Mgr-Ops)*
Advertising Agency:
Partnership Advertising
11 Pinchot Ct Ste 100
Amherst, NY 14228
Tel.: (716) 689-2222
Fax: (716) 689-2468

NORWOOD FINANCIAL CORP.

717 Main St
Honesdale, PA 18431
Tel.: (570) 253-1455
Fax: (570) 253-3725
E-mail: info@waynebank.com
Web Site: www.norwoodfc.com
Approx. Rev.: $29,751,000
Approx. Number Employees: 113
Business Description:
Bank Holding Company
S.I.C.: 6141; 6029
N.A.I.C.S.: 522210; 522110
Advertising Expenditures: $187,000
Media: 17
Personnel:
John E. Marshall *(Chm)*
Lewis J. Critelli, Jr. *(Pres & CEO)*
William S. Lance *(CFO)*
Edward C. Kasper *(Sr VP)*
Joseph A. Kneller *(Sr VP)*
John H. Sanders *(Sr VP)*
Sandra Halas *(Asst VP)*

NUVEEN INVESTMENTS, INC.

(Holding of Madison Dearborn Partners, LLC)
333 W Wacker Dr
Chicago, IL 60606
Tel.: (312) 917-7700
Fax: (312) 917-8049
Web Site: www.nuveen.com
Approx. Rev.: $662,759,000
Approx. Number Employees: 902
Year Founded: 1898
Business Description:
Investment Services
S.I.C.: 6289
N.A.I.C.S.: 523999
Advertising Expenditures: $11,253,000
Media: 2-3-5-6-7-8-9-10-13-15-23-24-25
Distr.: Natl.
Budget Set: Oct.
Personnel:
John P. Amboian *(Chm & CEO)*
Mary Keefe *(Mng Dir & Dir-Compliance)*
Glenn R. Richter *(COO & Chief Admin Officer)*
John L. MacCarthy *(Gen Counsel, Sec & Exec VP)*
William Adams, IV *(Exec VP-US Structured Products)*
Chris Fitzgerald *(Sr VP)*
Kathleen H. Cardoza *(VP-Corp Comm)*
Advertising Agency:
Planit
500 E Pratt St 10th Fl
Baltimore, MD 21202
Tel.: (410) 962-8500
Fax: (410) 962-8508

NYSE AMEX LLC

(Div. of NYSE Group, Inc.)
11 Wall St
New York, NY 10005-1905
Tel.: (212) 656-2065
Fax: (212) 656-5549
E-mail: nyseeuronextoffice@nyx.com
Web Site: www.nyse.com
Sales Range: $75-99.9 Million
Approx. Number Employees: 200
Year Founded: 1921
Business Description:
Securities & Commodities Exchange
S.I.C.: 6231
N.A.I.C.S.: 523210
Advertising Expenditures: $12,000,000
Media: 1-2-3-4-6-7-8-9-10-11-14-15-16-17-18-20-22-23-24-25
Distr.: Intl.; Natl.; Reg.
Budget Set: Oct. -Apr.
Personnel:
Claudia Crowley *(CEO & Chief Regulatory Officer)*
Andrew Brandman *(Chief Admin Officer & Exec VP)*
Stephane Biehler *(Chief Acctg Officer & Controller)*
Steve Crutchfield *(CEO-NYSE Amex Options)*
Lawrence Liebowitz *(Exec VP)*
Joseph Mecane *(Exec VP)*
Janet Kissane *(Sr VP)*
Janice O'Neill *(Sr VP-Corp Compliance)*
Advertising Agency:
DDB Worldwide Communications Group Inc.
(Sub. of Omnicom Group, Inc.)
(Corporate Headquarters)
437 Madison Ave 5nd Fl
New York, NY 10022-7001
Tel.: (212) 415-2000
Fax: (212) 415-3414

NYSE GROUP, INC.

(Div. of NYSE Euronext)
11 Wall St
New York, NY 10005-1905
Tel.: (212) 656-3000
Fax: (212) 656-2126
Web Site: www.nyse.com
Sales Range: $250-299.9 Million
Business Description:
Holding Company; Securities & Commodities Exchanges
S.I.C.: 6719; 6231
N.A.I.C.S.: 551112; 523210
Advertising Expenditures: $22,200,000
Media: 1-2-6-7-9-10-25
Distr.: Natl.
Budget Set: Mar.
Personnel:
Marshall N. Carter *(Deputy Chm)*
Duncan L. Niederauer *(CEO)*
Michael S. Geltzeiler *(CFO & Grp Exec VP)*
Lawrence Leibowitz *(COO)*
Andrew T. Brandman *(Chief Admin Officer & Exec VP)*
John K. Halvey *(Gen Counsel & Grp Exec VP)*
Miguel Athayde Marques *(Exec VP & Head-Indices)*
Mary L. Brienza *(Exec VP & Gen Auditor)*
John F. Malitzis *(Exec VP-Market Surveillance)*
Richard C. Adamonis *(Sr VP-Corp Comm)*
Salvatore Pallante *(Sr VP-Member Firm Regulation)*
Mark H. Wille *(Sr VP-Ops-NYSE Euronext)*
Anand K. Ramtahal *(VP-Member Firm Regulation)*
Tarak Achiche *(Head-Info Sys)*
Gunjali Trikha *(Product Mgr)*
David Mann *(Mgr-Corp Comm)*
Brands & Products:
ARCA
NEW YORK STOCK EXCHANGE
NYSE
THE WORLD PUTS ITS STOCK IN US

Key to Media (For complete agency information see *The Advertising Red Books-Agencies* edition):
1. Bus. Publs. 2. Cable T.V. 3. Catalogs & Directories. 4. Co-op Adv. 5. Consumer Mags. 6. D.M. to Bus. Estab.7. D.M. to Consumers 8. Daily Newsp. 9. Exhibits/Trade Shows 10. Foreign 11. Infomercial 12. Internet Adv.13. Multimedia 14. Network Radio 15. Network T.V. 16. Newsp. Distr. Mags. 17. Other 18. Outdoor (Posters, Transit) 19. Point of Purchase20. Premiums, Novelties 21. Product Samples 22. Special Events Mktg. 23. Spot Radio 24. Spot T.V. 25. Weekly Newsp. 26. Yellow Page Adv.

Advertising Agencies:
Euro RSCG Worldwide
350 Hudson St
New York, NY 10014-4504
Tel.: (212) 886-2000
Fax: (212) 886-2016
Toll Free: (800) 937-0233

Euro RSCG Worldwide HQ
350 Hudson St
New York, NY 10014-4504
Tel.: (212) 886-2000
Fax: (212) 886-2016

MPG
(Div. of HAVAS)
195 Broadway 12th Fl
New York, NY 10007
Tel.: (646) 587-5000
Fax: (646) 587-5005

OAK RIDGE FINANCIAL SERVICES, INC.

2211 Oak Ridge Rd
Oak Ridge, NC 27310
Tel.: (336) 644-9944
E-mail: twayne@bankofoakridge.com
Web Site: www.bankofoakridge.com
Approx. Rev.: $22,276,000
Approx. Number Employees: 88
Business Description:
Bank Holding Company
S.I.C.: 6029; 6712
N.A.I.C.S.: 522110; 551111
Advertising Expenditures: $1,368,000
Personnel:
Douglas G. Boike *(Chm)*
Ronald O. Black *(Pres & CEO)*
Thomas W. Wayne *(CFO & Exec VP)*
L. William Vasaly III *(Chief Credit Officer & Exec VP)*

OAK STREET FINANCIAL SERVICES, INC.

11595 N Meridian St Ste 400
Carmel, IN 46032
Tel.: (317) 805-3200
Fax: (317) 805-3151
Web Site:
www.oakstreetmortgage.com
Sales Range: $10-24.9 Million
Approx. Number Employees: 660
Year Founded: 1999
Business Description:
Real Estate Investment Trust
S.I.C.: 6163
N.A.I.C.S.: 522310
Media: 7-8-10
Brands & Products:
OAK STREET
YOU'RE CLOSER THAN YOU THINK

OCEAN SHORE HOLDING CO.

1001 Asbury Ave
Ocean City, NJ 08226
Tel.: (609) 399-0012
Fax: (609) 399-3614
Toll Free: (800) 771-7990
E-mail: service@ochome.com
Web Site: www.ochome.com
Approx. Rev.: $41,119,376
Approx. Number Employees: 137
Business Description:
Bank Holding Company
S.I.C.: 6712; 6029; 6035
N.A.I.C.S.: 551111; 522110; 522120
Advertising Expenditures: $432,746
Personnel:
Steven E. Brady *(Pres & CEO)*
Donald F. Morgenweck *(CFO & Sr VP)*
Anthony J. Rizzotte *(Exec VP & Chief Lending Officer)*
Kim M. Davidson *(Exec VP)*

OCEANFIRST BANK

(Sub. of OceanFirst Financial Corp.)
975 Hooper Ave
Toms River, NJ 08753
Tel.: (732) 240-4500
Toll Free: (888) OCEAN-33
Web Site: www.oceanfirstonline.com
Year Founded: 1902
Business Description:
Retail, Commercial & Investment Banking Services
S.I.C.: 6035; 6029; 6163; 6211; 6733
N.A.I.C.S.: 522120; 522110; 522310; 523110; 523991
Media: 3-4-7-8-9-13-18-20-23-25
Personnel:
John R. Garbarino *(Chm & CEO)*
Vito R. Nardelli *(Pres & COO)*
Michael J. Fitzpatrick *(CFO & Exec VP)*
Joseph J. Lebel, III *(Chief Lending Officer & First Sr VP)*
Advertising Agency:
Winning Edge Communications
205 Rockingham Row
Princeton, NJ 08540
Tel.: (609) 275-4747
Fax: (609) 452-7212

OCEANFIRST FINANCIAL CORP.

975 Hooper Ave
Toms River, NJ 08753
Tel.: (732) 240-4500
Fax: (732) 349-5070
Web Site: www.oceanfirstonline.com
Approx. Rev.: $116,679,000
Approx. Number Employees: 358
Year Founded: 1996
Business Description:
Bank Holding Company
S.I.C.: 6712; 6029; 6035
N.A.I.C.S.: 551111; 522110; 522120
Media: 3-4-7-8-9-13-18-20-23-25
Personnel:
John R. Garbarino *(Chm & CEO)*
Vito R. Nardelli *(Pres & COO)*
Michael J. Fitzpatrick *(CFO)*
Joseph J. Lebel, III *(Chief Lending Officer & First Sr VP)*
Steven J. Tsimbinos *(Gen Counsel & First Sr VP)*
Brands & Products:
OCEANFIRST BANK

OHIO LEGACY CORP

600 S Main St
North Canton, OH 44720
Tel.: (330) 499-1900
E-mail: jane.marsh@ohiolegacybank.com
Web Site: www.ohiolegacycorp.com
Approx. Rev.: $7,719,056
Approx. Number Employees: 50
Year Founded: 1999
Business Description:
Bank Holding Company
S.I.C.: 6712; 6029
N.A.I.C.S.: 551111; 522110
Advertising Expenditures: $100,208
Media: 7-8
Personnel:
Wilbur R. Roat *(Chm)*
Rick L. Hull *(Pres & CEO)*
Jane E. Marsh *(CFO, Sec & Sr VP)*
Denise M. Penz *(COO & Mgr-Wealth & Exec VP)*

OLD LINE BANCSHARES, INC.

1525 Pointer Ridge Place
Bowie, MD 20716
Tel.: (301) 645-0333
E-mail: customerservice@oldlinebank.com
Web Site: www.oldlinebank.com
Approx. Rev.: $19,860,833
Approx. Number Employees: 69
Business Description:
Bank Holding Company
S.I.C.: 6712; 6029
N.A.I.C.S.: 551111; 522110
Advertising Expenditures: $61,816
Media: 17
Personnel:
Frank Lucente, Jr. *(Vice Chm)*
James W. Cornelsen *(CEO)*
Christine M. Rush *(CFO, Sec & Exec VP)*
Joseph E. Burnett *(Chief Lending Officer & Sr VP)*
Craig E. Clark *(Mgr-Validation)*

OLD MUTUAL ASSET MANAGEMENT

(Sub. of Old Mutual plc)
200 Clarendon St Fl 53
Boston, MA 02116
Tel.: (617) 369-7300
Fax: (617) 369-7400
E-mail: info@oldmutualus.com
Web Site: www.oldmutualus.com
Approx. Number Employees: 70
Year Founded: 1980
Business Description:
Holding Company for US Subsidiaries
S.I.C.: 8721
N.A.I.C.S.: 541219
Distr.: Natl.
Personnel:
Peter L. Bain *(Pres & CEO)*
Linda Tilton Gibson *(COO & Exec VP)*
Matthew J. Appelstein *(Exec VP & Head-Distr-Global)*
Kevin M. Hunt *(Chief Sls & Mktg Officer & Exec VP)*
Michael Raso *(Sr VP & Dir-Institutional Retirement)*
Advertising Agency:
Kilgannon
1360 Peachtree St Ste 700
Atlanta, GA 30309
Tel.: (404) 876-2800
Fax: (404) 876-2830

OLD NATIONAL BANCORP

1 Main St
Evansville, IN 47708
Mailing Address:
PO Box 718
Evansville, IN 47705-0718
Tel.: (812) 464-1294
Fax: (812) 464-1567
Toll Free: (800) 731-BANK
E-mail: shareholderservices@oldnational.com
Web Site: www.oldnational.com
Approx. Rev.: $466,998,000
Approx. Number Employees: 2,491
Year Founded: 1982
Business Description:
Bank Holding Company
S.I.C.: 6029; 6035; 6163; 6211; 6289; 6311; 6321; 6331; 6361; 6399; 6411; 6712
N.A.I.C.S.: 522110; 522120; 522310; 523110; 523999; 524113; 524114; 524126; 524127; 524128; 524210; 551111
Media: 7-8-9-10
Personnel:
Robert G. Jones *(Pres & CEO)*
Christopher A. Wolking *(CFO & Sr Exec VP)*
Kathy A. Schoettlin *(CMO & Exec VP)*
Daryl D Moore *(Exec VP & Chief Credit Officer)*
Allen R. Mounts *(Chief Admin Officer & Exec VP)*
Candice J. Rickard *(Exec VP & Chief Risk Officer)*
Kendra L. Vanzo *(Chief HR Officer & Exec VP)*
Barbara A. Murphy *(Sr Exec VP & Chief Banking Officer)*
Richard W. Dube *(Exec VP, Chief Audit Executive & Chief Ethics Officer)*
Annette W. Hudgions *(Exec VP & Chief Client Svcs Officer)*
Dan L. Doan *(Reg CEO)*
Dennis P. Heishman *(Reg CEO)*
Randall D. Reichmann *(Reg CEO)*
James A. Sandgren *(Reg CEO)*
Donald A. Schroeder *(CEO-Bus Partner Sls)*
James C. Ryan, III *(Exec VP & Dir-Corp Strategy)*
Jeffrey L. Knight *(Exec VP & Chief Legal Counsel)*
Lynell J. Walton *(Sr VP & Dir-IR)*
Christopher A. Wilson *(VP & Mgr-Comml Relationship)*
Jim Schmidt *(Asst Treas)*
Brands & Products:
BANKCONNECT
COMMUNITY HERO CHECKING
OLD NATIONAL
OLD NATIONAL BANK
OLD NATIONAL ONLINE
OLD NATIONAL REACH

OLD POINT FINANCIAL CORPORATION

1 W Mellen St
Hampton, VA 23663
Tel.: (757) 728-1200
Tel.: (757) 728-1231
E-mail: info@oldpoint.com
Web Site: www.oldpoint.com
Approx. Rev.: $53,529,000
Approx. Number Employees: 309
Year Founded: 1984
Business Description:
Bank Holding Company
S.I.C.: 6712; 6029
N.A.I.C.S.: 551111; 522110
Import Export
Advertising Expenditures: $654,000
Personnel:
Robert F. Shuford, Sr. *(Chm, Pres & CEO)*
Laurie D. Grabow *(CFO-Old Point Natl Bank & Exec VP)*

Key to Media (For complete agency information see *The Advertising Red Books-Agencies* edition):
1. Bus. Publs. 2. Cable T.V. 3. Catalogs & Directories. 4. Co-op Adv. 5. Consumer Mags. 6. D.M. to Bus. Estab.7. D.M. to Consumers 8. Daily Newsp. 9. Exhibits/Trade Shows 10. Foreign 11. Infomercial 12. Internet Adv.13. Multimedia 14. Network Radio 15. Network T.V. 16. Newsp. Distr. Mags. 17. Other 18. Outdoor (Posters, Transit) 19. Point of Purchase20. Premiums, Novelties 21. Product Samples 22. Special Events Mktg. 23. Spot Radio 24. Spot T.V. 25. Weekly Newsp. 26. Yellow Page Adv.

Old Point Financial Corporation — (Continued)

Ervin Black *(Exec VP-CRA & Compliance Officer-Old Point Nationa)*
Melissa L. Burroughs *(Exec VP)*

OLD SECOND BANCORP, INC.

37 S River St
Aurora, IL 60506-4173
Tel.: (630) 892-0202
Fax: (630) 892-9630
E-mail: SupportCenter@oldsecond.com
Web Site: www.o2bancorp.com
Approx. Rev.: $151,591,000
Approx. Number Employees: 522
Business Description:
Holding Company
S.I.C.: 6029
N.A.I.C.S.: 522110
Advertising Expenditures: $1,461,000
Personnel:
William B. Skoglund *(Chm, Pres & CEO)*
J. Douglas Cheatham *(CFO & Exec VP)*
James L. Eccher *(COO & Exec VP)*
Walter Alexander *(Sr Dir)*

OLIVER WYMAN, INC.

(Sub. of Marsh & McLennan Companies Inc.)
(d/b/a Oliver Wyman Group)
1166 Ave of the Americas
New York, NY 10036-2708
Tel.: (212) 345-8000
Fax: (212) 345-8075
Web Site: www.oliverwyman.com
Sales Range: $50-74.9 Million
Approx. Number Employees: 250
Business Description:
Management Consulting Services
S.I.C.: 8742
N.A.I.C.S.: 541611
Personnel:
John P. Drzik *(Pres & CEO)*
Matthew Cunningham *(CFO)*
Partha Bose *(CMO)*
Dana Bolton *(Gen Counsel)*
Scott McDonald *(Head-Fin Svcs)*
Advertising Agency:
Weber Shandwick
(Sub. of The Interpublic Group of Companies)
919 3rd Ave
New York, NY 10022
Tel.: (212) 445-8000
Fax: (212) 445-8001

OMNIAMERICAN BANCORP, INC.

1320 S University Dr Ste 900
Fort Worth, TX 76107
Tel.: (817) 367-4640
Web Site: www.omniamerican.com
Approx. Rev.: $66,546,000
Approx. Number Employees: 292
Year Founded: 2009
Business Description:
Bank Holding Company
S.I.C.: 6029; 6712
N.A.I.C.S.: 522110; 551111
Advertising Expenditures: $719,000
Personnel:
Elaine Anderson *(Chm)*
John F. Sammons, Jr. *(Vice Chm)*
Tim Carter *(Pres & CEO)*
Deborah B. Wilkinson *(CFO & Sr Exec VP)*
Terry M. Almon *(COO & Sr Exec VP)*
T. L. Arnold *(Exec VP & Chief Credit Officer)*
Wendy Gary *(Exec VP-Consumer Lending)*
Maria Jones *(Exec VP)*
David Johnson *(Sr VP-Comml Lending)*

ONEIDA FINANCIAL CORP.

182 Main St
Oneida, NY 13421-1676
Tel.: (315) 363-2000
Fax: (315) 366-3709
Web Site: www.oneidabank.com
Approx. Rev.: $46,668,281
Approx. Number Employees: 319
Year Founded: 1998
Business Description:
Bank Holding Company
S.I.C.: 6035; 6712
N.A.I.C.S.: 522120; 551111
Advertising Expenditures: $529,901
Media: 7-17
Personnel:
Richard B. Myers *(Chm)*
Michael R. Kallet *(Pres & CEO)*
Eric E. Stickels *(CFO & Exec VP)*
Thomas H. Dixon *(Chief Credit Officer & Exec VP)*
Lori Torrey *(Office Mgr)*

ONEIDA SAVINGS BANK

(Sub. of Oneida Financial Corp.)
182 Main St
Oneida, NY 13421
Tel.: (315) 363-2000
Fax: (315) 366-3709
E-mail: service@oneidabank.com
Web Site: www.oneidabank.com
Sales Range: $50-74.9 Million
Approx. Number Employees: 120
Year Founded: 1866
Business Description:
Banking
S.I.C.: 6035; 6029
N.A.I.C.S.: 522120; 522110
Advertising Expenditures: $150,000
Media: 3-7-8-18-20-22-23-24-26
Personnel:
Michael R. Kallet *(Pres & CEO)*
Eric E. Stickels *(CFO & Exec VP)*
Thomas H. Dixon *(Chief Credit Officer & Exec VP)*
Deresa Durkee *(Treas & Sr VP)*
Russell Brewer *(Sr VP-Bus Banking)*
Mark Cavanagh *(Sr VP-Mortgage Banking Sls)*
Kathleen J. Donegan *(Sr VP-Retail Banking)*
Randall R. Kennedy *(Sr VP-Managed Assets)*
Chuck Stevens *(Sr VP-Trust & Investment Svcs)*
Deborah S. Stickels *(Sr VP-Mortgage Ops)*
Gina Rossi *(VP-Mktg & Brand Dev)*
Terry Maphia *(Asst VP & Dir-HR)*
Kathryn S. Woodbury *(Dir-Internal Audit)*
Amanda Relyea *(Mgr-Consumer Banking)*
Brands & Products:
YOUR LINK TO A BRIGHTER FUTURE

ONEUNITED BANK

(Sub. of One United Bank)
3683 Crenshaw Blvd
Los Angeles, CA 90016-4849
Tel.: (323) 295-3381
Fax: (323) 293-7746
Toll Free: (877) ONE-UNITED
Web Site: www.oneunited.com
Approx. Number Employees: 72
Year Founded: 1991
Business Description:
Banking & Financial Services
S.I.C.: 6029
N.A.I.C.S.: 522110
Media: 9-22-25
Personnel:
Kevin Cohee *(Chm & CEO)*
Teri Williams *(Pres)*

ONLINE RESOURCES CORPORATION

4795 Meadow Wood Ln Ste 300
Chantilly, VA 20151
Tel.: (703) 653-3100
Fax: (703) 653-3105
Toll Free: (866) 606-3000
E-mail: info@orcc.com
Web Site: www.orcc.com
Approx. Rev.: $149,513,000
Approx. Number Employees: 603
Year Founded: 1989
Business Description:
Web-Based Financial Services
S.I.C.: 6099; 8721
N.A.I.C.S.: 522320; 541219
Media: 10-13
Personnel:
John C. Dorman *(Co-Chm)*
Joseph L. Cowan *(Pres & CEO)*
Catherine A. Graham *(CFO & Exec VP)*
Janie M. West *(CMO)*
Ronald J. Bergamesca *(Exec VP-Banking Svcs)*
Robert R. Craig *(Exec VP-eCommerce Svcs)*
Sheila Narayan *(Exec VP-Corp Ops)*
William T. Kinnelly *(Sr VP-Card & Credit Svcs)*
William J. Michael *(Sr VP-Corp Sys Ops)*
Holly Palmeri *(Sr VP-Client Svcs)*
Daniel F. Ritten *(Sr VP-Sls & Distr)*
David M. Stafford *(Sr VP-Professional Svcs)*
Beth Halloran *(Sr Dir-Corp Comm)*
Brands & Products:
CLIENT CONSOLE
CONNECT
ENROLLMENT
ICM
LOCKBOX
MONEY HQ
ONE-TIME PAY
ONLINE RESOURCES
PAYANYONE
QUOTIEN
REAL-TIME DIGITAL SCANLINE
SERVICE FEE
VIRTUAL COLLECTION AGENT

OPEN SOLUTIONS, INC.

(Holding of The Carlyle Group, LLC)
455 Winding Brook Dr
Glastonbury, CT 06033-4335
Tel.: (860) 652-3155
Fax: (860) 652-3156
Toll Free: (800) 226-5674
E-mail: info@opensolutions.com
Web Site: www.opensolutions.com
Sales Range: $150-199.9 Million
Approx. Number Employees: 2,100
Year Founded: 1992
Business Description:
Software Development & Management Services
S.I.C.: 7373; 7371; 7379
N.A.I.C.S.: 541512; 541511; 541519
Media: 2-7-9-10-13-22
Personnel:
Louis Hernandez, Jr. *(Chm & CEO)*
Stephen J. Cameron *(Pres)*
John W. Frederick *(CFO & Exec VP)*
David Mitchell *(CMO & Sr VP)*
Rashid Desai *(CTO & Exec VP)*
Thomas N. Tartaro *(Chief Admin Officer & Corp Exec VP)*
Sam Boggs *(Exec VP-Ops)*
Santo Cannone *(Exec VP-Grp Sls)*
Rob Johnson *(Sr VP-Acct Mgmt)*
George McGourty *(Sr VP-Strategic Channels)*
Greg O'Brien *(Sr VP-HR)*
Marvin Goldwasser *(Dir-Mktg)*
Brands & Products:
THE COMPLETE BANKING SOLUTION
THE COMPLETE CREDIT UNION SOLUTION
CVIEW
CYBERSUITE
E-COMMERCE BANKER
E-COMMERCE MART
THE OPEN SOLUTIONS ENABLING PLATFORM
PROFIT VISION
THE SOUND COMMERCIAL LOAN DOCUMENTER
THE SOUND CONSUMER LOAN MANAGEMENT SYSTEM
THE SOUND MORTGAGE MANAGEMENT SYSTEM
Advertising Agency:
First Experience Communications
701 Hebron Ave
Glastonbury, CT 06033
Tel.: (860) 657-3815
Fax: (860) 657-4379
Toll Free: (800) 426-5170

OPPENHEIMERFUNDS, INC.

(Sub. of Massachusetts Mutual Life Insurance Company)
2 World Financial Ctr 225 Liberty St 11th Fl
New York, NY 10281-1008
Mailing Address:
PO Box 5270
Denver, CO 80217-5270
Tel.: (212) 323-0200
Web Site:
www.oppenheimerfunds.com
Approx. Rev.: $256,005,234
Approx. Number Employees: 1,380
Year Founded: 1978
Business Description:
Holding Company; Asset Management Services
S.I.C.: 6719; 6211; 6282; 6289; 6733
N.A.I.C.S.: 551112; 523110; 523920; 523991; 523999
Personnel:
William F. Glavin, Jr. *(CEO)*
Martha Willis *(CMO)*
James F. Bailey *(CTO & Sr VP)*

Darren Walsh *(Pres-OppenheimerFunds Svcs)*
Geoffrey Craddock *(Exec VP & Dir-Risk Mgmt & Asset Allocation)*
Philip Parrotta *(Sr VP, Head-Integrated Mktg & Dir-Creative)*
John Damian *(Dir-Value Equities, Sr VP & Portfolio Mgr)*
Kathleen Beichert *(Sr VP & Dir-Retirement Plans)*
Kimberly Mustin *(Sr VP & Global Head-Strategic Accounts)*
Jennifer Kane Heathwood *(VP & Dir-Brand Mktg)*
Advertising Agency:
Euro RSCG Worldwide
350 Hudson St
New York, NY 10014-4504
Tel.: (212) 886-2000
Fax: (212) 886-2016
Toll Free: (800) 937-0233
Agency of Record
Digital
Television

OPTIONSXPRESS HOLDINGS, INC.

311 W Monroe St Ste 1000
Chicago, IL 60606-4663
Mailing Address:
PO Box 2197
Chicago, IL 60690-2197
Tel.: (312) 630-3300
Fax: (312) 629-5256
Toll Free: (888) 280-8020
E-mail: nedb@optionsxpress.com
Web Site: www.optionsxpress.com
Approx. Rev.: $231,444,000
Approx. Number Employees: 408
Business Description:
Online Brokerage Services
S.I.C.: 6289; 6211; 6799
N.A.I.C.S.: 523120; 523110; 523910; 523999
Advertising Expenditures: $14,816,000
Media: 2-13
Personnel:
James A. Gray *(Chm)*
Ned W. Bennett *(Vice Chm)*
David A. Fisher *(CEO)*
Adam DeWitt *(CFO)*
Paul Eppen *(CMO)*
Thomas E. Stern *(Chief Admin Officer)*
Brands & Products:
AUTO-TRADING WITH XECUTE
ONE-CANCELS-OTHER
ONE-TRIGGERS-OTHER
ONE TRIGGERS TWO
OPTIONSXPRESS
TRAILING STOPS
XTEND

ORIENTAL FINANCIAL GROUP INC

Oriental Ctr 10th Fl Professional Offices Park
San Juan, PR 00926
Mailing Address:
PO Box 191429
San Juan, PR 00919-1429
Tel.: (787) 771-6800
Fax: (787) 771-6770
Toll Free: (888) 502-4053
Toll Free: (800) 981-5554
E-mail: portega@orientalfg.com
Web Site: www.orientalfg.com
Approx. Rev.: $308,931,000
Approx. Number Employees: 717
Year Founded: 1964
Business Description:
Diversified Financial Services
S.I.C.: 6029; 6035
N.A.I.C.S.: 522110; 522120
Advertising Expenditures: $4,978,000
Personnel:
Jose J. Gil De Lamadrid *(Chm)*
Jose Rafael Fernandez *(Vice Chm, Pres & CEO)*
Norberto Gonzalez *(CFO & Exec VP)*
Carlos J. Nieves *(COO & Sr Exec VP)*
Ganesh Kumar *(COO & Exec VP)*
Jose Fernandez Richards *(Exec VP & Chief Mktg Officer)*
Julio R. Micheo *(Chief Investment Officer, Treas & Sr Exec VP)*
Jose Ramon Gonzalez *(Sr Exec VP-Banking & Corp Dev)*
Cesar A. Ortiz *(Sr VP & Controller)*
Rafael Cruz *(Sr VP-Compliance)*
Carlos Andres Vina *(Sr VP & Audit Gen)*

ORITANI FINANCIAL CORP.

370 Pascack Rd
Washington, NJ 07676
Mailing Address:
PO Box 1329
Washington, NJ 07676-1329
Tel.: (201) 664-5400
Fax: (201) 497-1223
E-mail: customerservice@oritiani.com
Web Site: investor.oritani.com
Approx. Int. Income: $105,339,000
Approx. Number Employees: 150
Business Description:
Bank Holding Company
S.I.C.: 6712
N.A.I.C.S.: 551111
Advertising Expenditures: $665,000
Personnel:
Kevin J. Lynch *(Pres & CEO)*
John M. Fields, Jr. *(CFO & Exec VP)*
Thomas Guinan *(Chief Legal Officer & Exec VP)*
Rosanne P. Buscemi *(Chief Compliance Officer & Sr VP)*
Anne Mooradian *(Chief HR Officer & Sr VP)*
Philip Wyks *(Sec & Sr VP)*
Leonard S. Carlucci *(Sr VP)*

ORRSTOWN FINANCIAL SERVICES, INC.

77 E Kings St
Shippensburg, PA 17257
Mailing Address:
PO Box 250
Shippensburg, PA 17257
Tel.: (717) 532-6114
Fax: (717) 532-9342
E-mail: info@orrstown.com
Web Site: www.orrstown.com
Approx. Rev.: $82,216,000
Approx. Number Employees: 275
Business Description:
State Commercial Banks
S.I.C.: 6029
N.A.I.C.S.: 522110
Advertising Expenditures: $456,000
Personnel:
Joel R. Zullinger *(Chm)*
Jeffrey W. Coy *(Vice Chm)*
Thomas R. Quinn, Jr. *(Pres & CEO)*
Kenneth R. Shoemaker *(Pres)*
Bradley S. Everly *(CFO & Treas)*
Jeffrey W. Embly *(Chief Compliance Officer & Exec VP)*
Douglas P. Barton *(Chief Acctg Officer & Sr VP)*
Philip E. Fague *(Chief Mortgage, Consumer, Investment Officer, Exec VP & Asst Sec)*
Barbara E. Brobst *(Sr VP)*
Lauren Shutt *(Sr VP)*
Benjamin S. Stoops *(Sr VP & Chief Of Tech)*
Stephen C. Caldwell *(VP & Dir-HR)*

ORTHOSYNETICS, INC.

545 S Nolen Dr Ste 300
Southlake, TX 76092
Tel.: (817) 416-7408
Toll Free: (888) 622-7645
Web Site: www.orthosynetics.com
Approx. Number Employees: 2,741
Year Founded: 1985
Business Description:
Operational, Financial, Marketing & Administrative Services to Orthodontic Centers
S.I.C.: 8021; 7389
N.A.I.C.S.: 621210; 561499
Advertising Expenditures: $16,000,000
Media: 2-7-18-23-24
Personnel:
William Jones *(Pres)*
Chris W. Roussos *(CEO)*
Cathy M. Green *(CFO)*

OTC MARKETS GROUP INC.

(Formerly Pink OTC Markets Inc.)
304 Hudson St 2nd Fl
New York, NY 10013
Tel.: (212) 896-4400
Fax: (212) 868-3848
E-mail: ir@otcmarkets.com
Web Site: www.otcmarkets.com
Approx. Rev.: $24,031,661
Approx. Number Employees: 53
Year Founded: 1913
Business Description:
Pricing & Financial Information for the OTC Securities Market; Company Information Publisher
S.I.C.: 6289
N.A.I.C.S.: 523999
Advertising Expenditures: $2,082,939
Media: 2-7-13
Personnel:
R. Cromwell Coulson *(Pres & CEO)*
Wendy Fraulo *(CFO)*
Emilia Sherifova *(CIO)*
Carl Giangrasso *(Pres-OTC Link)*
Timothy Ryan *(Mng Dir-Sls & Bus Dev)*
Daniel Brasier *(Dir-Bus Dev-OTCQX)*
Brands & Products:
PINK OTC MARKETS
PINK SHEETS
YELLOW SHEETS

PACIFIC & WESTERN CREDIT CORP.

140 Fullarton St Ste 2002
London, ON N6A 5P2, Canada
Tel.: (519) 645-1919
Fax: (519) 645-2060
E-mail: telm@pwbank.com
Web Site: www.pwbank.com
Approx. Int. Income: $63,211,668
Approx. Number Employees: 57
Year Founded: 2002
Business Description:
Bank & Financial Services Holding Company
S.I.C.: 6712; 6029; 6099
N.A.I.C.S.: 551111; 522110; 522320
Media: 4
Personnel:
C. Scott Ritchie *(Chm)*
David R. Taylor *(Pres & CEO)*
Barry D. Walter *(CFO & Sr VP)*
Shawn Clarke *(CIO, VP-Corp Dev & Enterprise Risk)*
Richard M. D. Vanlerberghe *(Gen Counsel & Sec)*
John W. Asma *(Sr VP-Structured Fin & Treas)*
Avery Pennarun *(Exec VP-Software Dev)*
Neil Beaton *(Sr VP-Strategic Initiatives)*
Ross P. Duggan *(Sr VP-Lending)*
Nick Kristo *(Sr VP-Credit & Admin)*
Jonathan F. P. Taylor *(Sr VP-HR & Ops)*
Moe A. Danis *(VP-Lease Fin)*
Rick Coates *(Asst VP)*
Steve Creery *(Asst VP)*
Wade MacBain *(Dir-IR)*

PACIFIC CONTINENTAL CORPORATION

111 W 7th Ave
Eugene, OR 97401-2622
Tel.: (541) 686-8685
Fax: (541) 344-2807
Toll Free: (877) 231-BANK
Toll Free: (877) 231-2265
E-mail: banking@therightbank.com
Web Site: www.therightbank.com
Approx. Rev.: $68,082,000
Approx. Number Employees: 263
Year Founded: 1972
Business Description:
Bank Holding Company
S.I.C.: 6029; 6712
N.A.I.C.S.: 522110; 551111
Advertising Expenditures: $569,000
Personnel:
Robert A. Ballin *(Chm)*
Donald G. Montgomery *(Vice Chm)*
Roger S. Busse *(Pres & COO)*
Charlotte Boxer *(Pres & Dir-Comml Real Estate Markets)*
Mitchell J. Hagstrom *(Pres & Dir-Eugene Market)*
Daniel J. Hempy *(Pres & Dir-Portland Market)*
Hal M. Brown *(CEO)*
Michael A. Reynolds *(CFO & Exec VP)*
Patricia Haxby *(CIO & Exec VP)*
Casey Hogan *(Chief Credit Officer & Exec VP)*
Rachel L. Ulrich *(Exec VP & Dir-HR)*
Maecey Castle *(VP & Dir-Corp Comm)*
Angie Stone *(VP & Reg Mgr-Svc)*
Brands & Products:
BUSINESS MASTERCARD
PACIFIC CONTINENTAL
THE RIGHT BANK

PACIFIC FINANCIAL CORPORATION

1011 S Boone St
Aberdeen, WA 98520

Key to Media (For complete agency information see *The Advertising Red Books-Agencies* edition):
1. Bus. Publs. 2. Cable T.V. 3. Catalogs & Directories. 4. Co-op Adv. 5. Consumer Mags. 6. D.M. to Bus. Estab.7. D.M. to Consumers 8. Daily Newsp. 9. Exhibits/Trade Shows 10. Foreign 11. Infomercial 12. Internet Adv.13. Multimedia 14. Network Radio 15. Network T.V. 16. Newsp. Distr. Mags. 17. Other 18. Outdoor (Posters, Transit) 19. Point of Purchase20. Premiums, Novelties 21. Product Samples 22. Special Events Mktg. 23. Spot Radio 24. Spot T.V. 25. Weekly Newsp. 26. Yellow Page Adv.

PACIFIC FINANCIAL CORPORATION — (Continued)

Tel.: (360) 533-8870
Fax: (360) 533-0489
Toll Free: (888) 366-3267
Web Site: www.thebankofpacific.com
Approx. Rev.: $39,311,000
Approx. Number Employees: 222
Business Description:
Bank Holding Company
S.I.C.: 6029; 6712
N.A.I.C.S.: 522110; 551111
Advertising Expenditures: $395,000
Personnel:
Gary C. Forcum *(Chm)*
Dennis A. Long *(CEO)*
John Van Dijk *(Pres, COO & Exec VP)*
Denise Portmann *(CFO, Chief Acctg Officer & Treas)*
Lynn Paylor *(VP-Personnel)*

PACIFIC PREMIER BANK
(Sub. of Pacific Premier Bancorp Inc.)
1600 Sunflower Ave 2nd Fl
Costa Mesa, CA 92626
Tel.: (714) 431-4000
Fax: (714) 433-3000
Toll Free: (866) 353-1476
E-mail: info@ppbi.net
Web Site: www.ppbi.net
Sales Range: $25-49.9 Million
Approx. Number Employees: 100
Year Founded: 1983
Business Description:
Commercial Bank
S.I.C.: 6029
N.A.I.C.S.: 522110
Advertising Expenditures: $150,000
Media: 7-8-13
Personnel:
Steven R. Gardner *(Pres & CEO)*
Kent Smith *(CFO, Treas & Sr VP)*
Edward E. Wilcox *(Chief Banking Officer & Exec VP)*
William R. Owen *(VP, Dir-Warehouse Facility & Banker-Bus)*

PALMETTO BANCSHARES, INC.
306 E North St
Greenville, SC 29601
Tel.: (864) 255-7960
Tel.: (864) 250-6061 (Pub Rel)
Fax: (864) 255-7990
Toll Free: (800) 725-2265
E-mail: cjamison@palmettobank.com
Web Site: www.palmettobank.com
Approx. Rev.: $56,627,000
Approx. Number Employees: 394
Year Founded: 1982
Business Description:
Bank Holding Company
S.I.C.: 6029; 6712
N.A.I.C.S.: 522110; 551111
Import Export
Media: 8-17
Personnel:
L. Leon Patterson *(Chm)*
Samuel L. Erwin *(Pres & CEO)*
Roy D. Jones *(CFO)*
Lee S. Dixon *(COO & Chief Risk Officer)*
Anna Miles *(Dir-Mktg)*
Advertising Agencies:
Gibbons/Peck
7 S Laurens St Ste 200
Greenville, SC 29601
Tel.: (864) 232-0927
Fax: (864) 232-2213

Jackson Marketing Group
2 Task Ct
Greenville, SC 29607
Tel.: (864) 272-3000
Fax: (864) 272-3040

PARK BANCORP, INC.
5400 S Pulaski Rd
Chicago, IL 60632
Tel.: (773) 582-8616
Fax: (773) 582-2801
Web Site: www.parkfed.com
Approx. Rev.: $9,905,000
Approx. Number Employees: 57
Business Description:
Bank Holding Company
S.I.C.: 6035; 6712
N.A.I.C.S.: 522120; 551111
Advertising Expenditures: $184,000
Media: 7
Personnel:
David A. Remijas *(Chm & CEO)*
Richard J. Remijas, Jr. *(Pres & COO)*
Victor E. Caputo *(CFO, Treas & Sec)*
Paul J. Lopez *(Chief Lending Officer-Park Federal Savings Bank & Sr VP)*

PARK NATIONAL CORPORATION
50 N 3rd St
Newark, OH 43058
Mailing Address:
PO Box 3500
Newark, OH 43058-3500
Tel.: (740) 349-8451
Fax: (740) 349-3787
E-mail: main@parknationalbank.com
Web Site: www.parknationalcorp.com
Approx. Rev.: $423,013,000
Approx. Number Employees: 1,969
Year Founded: 1905
Business Description:
Multi-Bank Holding Company
S.I.C.: 6029; 6712
N.A.I.C.S.: 522110; 551111
Advertising Expenditures: $4,197,000
Personnel:
C. Daniel DeLawder *(Chm & CEO)*
Harry O. Egger *(Vice Chm)*
David L. Trautman *(Pres & Sec)*
John W. Kozak *(CFO)*
Brady T. Burt *(Chief Acctg Officer)*
Cindy Kosik *(Mgr-Admin)*
Advertising Agency:
Baker Creative
386 Main St
Groveport, OH 43125
Tel.: (614) 836-3845
Toll Free: (877) BAKER03

PARKVALE FINANCIAL CORPORATION
4220 William Penn Hwy
Monroeville, PA 15146-2774
Tel.: (412) 373-7200
Fax: (412) 856-3943
Web Site: www.parkvale.com
Approx. Rev.: $74,378,000
Approx. Number Employees: 362
Year Founded: 1987
Business Description:
Bank Holding Company
S.I.C.: 6712; 6029
N.A.I.C.S.: 551111; 522110
Media: 2-7-8-13-23-24
Personnel:
Robert D. Pfischner *(Chm)*
Robert J. McCarthy, Jr. *(Vice Chm)*
Gilbert A. Riazzi *(CFO, CIO & Sr VP)*
Robert A. Stephens *(Chief Lending Officer & Sr VP)*
Gail B. Anwyll *(Sr VP-HR, Mktg, Sls & Trng)*
Thomas R. Ondek *(Sr VP-Deposit Ops)*
Matthew J. Husak *(VP & Dir-Audit & Compliance Risk)*
Christopjer M. Trombetta *(VP & Mgr-Comml Svcs)*
Thomas A. Webb *(VP & Mgr-Consumer, Mortgage Lending & Asset Mgmt)*

PARKVALE SAVINGS BANK
(Sub. of Parkvale Financial Corporation)
4220 William Penn Hwy
Monroeville, PA 15146
Tel.: (412) 373-7200
Fax: (412) 856-3943
E-mail: hr@parkvale.com
Web Site: www.parkvale.com
Sales Range: $50-74.9 Million
Approx. Number Employees: 150
Year Founded: 1968
Business Description:
Banking Services
S.I.C.: 6035
N.A.I.C.S.: 522120
Import Export
Media: 7-8-9-13-23-25
Personnel:
Robert J. McCarthy Jr. *(Vice Chm)*
Gilbert A. Riazzi *(CFO, CIO & Sr VP)*
Patricia A. Lowe *(VP-Branch Ops)*
Gail B. Anwyll *(Sr VP-HR, Mktg, Sls & Trng)*
Thomas R. Ondek *(Sr VP-Deposit Ops)*
Christopher M. Trombetta *(VP & Mgr-Comml Svcs)*
Thomas A. Webb *(VP-Mgr-Consumer & Mortgage Lending & Asset Mgmt)*
James M. Urban *(Asst VP)*

PATAPSCO BANCORP
1301 Merritt Blvd
Baltimore, MD 21222
Tel.: (410) 285-1010
Fax: (410) 285-7751
E-mail: webmail@patapscobank.com
Web Site: www.patapscobank.com
Approx. Rev.: $14,611,000
Approx. Number Employees: 61
Year Founded: 1995
Business Description:
Bank Holding Company
S.I.C.: 6035; 6712
N.A.I.C.S.: 522120; 551111
Advertising Expenditures: $42,000
Media: 17
Personnel:
Thomas P. O'Neill *(Chm)*
Michael J. Dee *(Pres)*
William C. Wiedel, Jr. *(CFO & Sr VP)*
Laurence S. Mitchell *(Chief Lending Officer)*
Linda Linz *(Sr VP-Branch Admin & Ops)*
Linda Lynz *(Sr VP-Branch Admin & Ops)*
Phil P. Phillips *(Sr VP-Loan Admin)*
Keith Zickar *(VP-Comml Lending)*
Francis C. Broccolino *(VP & Mgr-Real Estate)*

PATHFINDER BANCORP, INC.
214 W 1st St
Oswego, NY 13126
Tel.: (315) 343-0057
Fax: (315) 342-9403
E-mail: contactus@pathfinderbank.com
Web Site: www.pathfinderbancorpinc.com
Approx. Rev.: $21,159,000
Approx. Number Employees: 95
Business Description:
Bank Holding Company
S.I.C.: 6035; 6712
N.A.I.C.S.: 522120; 551111
Advertising Expenditures: $268,000
Personnel:
Janette Resnick *(Chm)*
Thomas W. Schneider *(Pres & CEO)*
James A. Dowd *(CFO & Sr VP)*
Melissa A. Miller *(COO & Sr VP)*
Edward A. Mervine *(Gen Counsel & Sr VP)*

PATRIOT NATIONAL BANCORP, INC.
900 Bedford St
Stamford, CT 06901
Tel.: (203) 324-7500
Fax: (203) 324-8877
Toll Free: (800) 762-7620
Web Site: www.pnbdirect.com
Approx. Rev.: $37,963,131
Approx. Number Employees: 148
Year Founded: 1994
Business Description:
Bank Holding Company
S.I.C.: 6029
N.A.I.C.S.: 522110
Advertising Expenditures: $312,621
Personnel:
Michael A. Carrazza *(Chm)*
Christopher D. Maher *(Pres & CEO)*
Robert F. O'Connell *(CFO & Sr Exec VP)*
Philip W. Wolford *(COO)*
Michael A. Capodanno *(Sr VP & Controller)*
Brands & Products:
PATRIOT

PAULSON CAPITAL CORP.
811 SW Naito Pkwy Ste 200
Portland, OR 97204
Tel.: (503) 243-6000
Fax: (503) 243-6018
Web Site: www.paulsoninvestment.com
Approx. Rev.: $18,094,472
Approx. Number Employees: 63
Business Description:
Holding Company; Investment Services
S.I.C.: 6719; 6289
N.A.I.C.S.: 551112; 523999
Advertising Expenditures: $119,443
Media: 17
Personnel:
Chester L.F. Paulson *(Chm, Pres & CEO)*
Jacqueline M. Paulson *(Chm)*
Murray G. Smith *(CFO)*

Key to Media (For complete agency information see *The Advertising Red Books-Agencies* edition):
1. Bus. Publs. 2. Cable T.V. 3. Catalogs & Directories. 4. Co-op Adv. 5. Consumer Mags. 6. D.M. to Bus. Estab.7. D.M. to Consumers 8. Daily Newsp. 9. Exhibits/Trade Shows 10. Foreign 11. Infomercial 12. Internet Adv.13. Multimedia 14. Network Radio 15. Network T.V. 16. Newsp. Distr. Mags. 17. Other 18. Outdoor (Posters, Transit) 19. Point of Purchase20. Premiums, Novelties 21. Product Samples 22. Special Events Mktg. 23. Spot Radio 24. Spot T.V. 25. Weekly Newsp. 26. Yellow Page Adv.

PAYCHEX, INC.
911 Panorama Trail S
Rochester, NY 14625-0397
Tel.: (585) 385-6666
Fax: (585) 383-3428
Toll Free: (800) 322-7292
Web Site: www.paychex.com
Approx. Rev.: $2,084,300,000
Approx. Number Employees: 12,400
Year Founded: 1971
Business Description:
Payroll Processing, Human Resources & Benefits Outsourcing Solutions for Small to Medium-Sized Businesses
S.I.C.: 8721; 7363
N.A.I.C.S.: 541214; 541219; 561330
Media: 2-4-7-8-10-13-26
Personnel:
B. Thomas Golisano *(Chm)*
Martin Mucci *(Pres & CEO)*
Efrain Rivera *(CFO, Treas & Sr VP)*
Stephanie L. Schaeffer *(Chief Legal Officer, Sec & VP)*
Mark A. Bottini *(Sr VP-Sls)*
Michael E. Gioja *(Sr VP-IT, Product Mgmt & Dev)*
Daniel A. Canzano *(VP-IT)*
Andrew B. Childs *(VP-Mktg)*
John M. Morphy *(VP-Fin)*
Janice A. Nearen-Bell *(VP-Sls)*
Martin Stowe *(VP-HR Svcs Ops)*
Christian A. Timol *(VP-Major Market Svcs Sls)*
Laurie L. Zaucha *(VP-HR & Organizational Dev)*
Laura Saxby Lynch *(Dir-Corp Comm)*
John Welch *(Dir-Real Estate, Pur & Facilities)*
Becky Cania *(Program Mgr-Pub Rel)*
Lisa Fleming *(Mgr-Pub Rel Programs)*
Joni McManus *(Mgr-Adv)*
Gregory S. Peel *(Mgr-Reg Sls)*
Brands & Products:
FLEXIBLE SPENDING ACCOUNT
MMS
PAYCHEX
PAYCHEX ONLINE PAYROLL
PAYCHEX PREMIER
PAYLINK
PREMIUM ONLY PLAN
PREVIEW
READYCHEX
REPORTLINK
SOLUTIONS FROM HIRE TO RETIRE
SUI
TAXPAY
TIME IN A BOX
Advertising Agencies:
Adam Communications
2601 Lac De Ville Blvd
Rochester, NY 14618
Tel.: (585) 271-4010
Fax: (585) 271-4102

Roberts Communications Inc.
64 Commercial St
Rochester, NY 14614-1010
Tel.: (585) 325-6000
Fax: (585) 325-6001

PAYMENT PROCESSING INC.
8200 Central Ave
Newark, CA 94560
Tel.: (510) 795-2290
Fax: (510) 795-2299
Fax: (800) 900-7487
Toll Free: (800) 774-6462
E-mail: information@paypros.com
Web Site: www.paypros.com
Approx. Number Employees: 200
Business Description:
Billing & Bookkeeping Service
S.I.C.: 8721
N.A.I.C.S.: 541219
Personnel:
Eddie Myers *(Pres & COO)*
Chuck Smith *(CEO)*
Chuck Riegel *(Partner & Exec VP-Software Products)*
John Malnar *(CFO)*
Mark Goddard *(Sr VP-Merchant Ops)*
Martin Hawke *(Sr VP)*
Allen Genereux *(VP-Fin)*
Anthony Gin *(Dir-Bus Dev)*
Brands & Products:
PAYMENT PROCESSING
PCCHARGE
PCCHARGE PAYMENT SERVER
PCCHARGE PRO
PPI PAYMOVER
Advertising Agency:
Crossroads Public Relations
136 E Morgan St Ste 100
Raleigh, NC 27601
Tel.: (919) 821-2822
Fax: (919) 834-0448

PEAPACK-GLADSTONE BANK
(Sub. of Peapack-Gladstone Financial Corporation)
190 Main St
Gladstone, NJ 07934
Tel.: (908) 234-0700
Fax: (908) 234-0711
E-mail: info@pgbank.com
Web Site: www.pgbank.com
Sales Range: $150-199.9 Million
Approx. Number Employees: 300
Year Founded: 1921
Business Description:
Banking Services
S.I.C.: 6029
N.A.I.C.S.: 522110
Media: 4-7-8-13-20-22-26
Personnel:
Frank A. Kissel *(Chm & CEO)*
Robert M. Rogers *(Pres & COO)*
Jeff Carfora *(CFO & Exec VP)*
Hubert P. Clarke *(CIO & Sr VP-Info Sys)*
Vincent A. Spero *(Chief Lending Officer & Exec VP)*
Finn M. W. Caspersen *(Gen Counsel & Exec VP)*
Bridget J. Walsh *(Sr VP & Dir-HR)*
Michael J. Giacobello *(Sr VP-Retail Sls)*
Katherine M. Kremin *(Sr VP & Sr Ops Officer)*
Denise M. Pace *(VP & Dir-Mktg)*
Sarah Krieger *(VP, Mgr-Portfolio-PGB Trust & Investments)*
Rohinton Madon *(VP-HR)*
Jennifer Corcoran Johnson *(Asst VP & Branch Mgr-Whitehouse)*
Richard B. Barfuss *(Asst VP-Fin Modeling & Analysis)*
Lynda A. Cross *(Asst VP)*

PEAPACK-GLADSTONE FINANCIAL CORPORATION
500 Hills Dr Ste 300
Bedminster, NJ 07921
Tel.: (908) 234-0700
Fax: (908) 234-0795
E-mail: birmingham@pgbank.com
Web Site: www.pgbank.com
Approx. Rev.: $75,037,000
Approx. Number Employees: 284
Business Description:
Bank Holding Company
S.I.C.: 6712; 6029
N.A.I.C.S.: 551111; 522110
Advertising Expenditures: $691,000
Media: 13-17
Personnel:
Frank A. Kissel *(Chm & CEO)*
Robert M. Rogers *(Pres & COO)*
Jeffrey J. Carfora *(CFO & Exec VP)*
Hubert P. Clarke *(CIO & Sr VP)*
Marjorie A. Dzwonczyk *(Compliance Officer)*
Vincent A. Spero *(Chief Lending Officer)*
Finn M. W. Caspersen, Jr. *(Gen Counsel)*
Mary M. Russell *(Sr VP & Comptroller)*
Bridget J. Walsh *(Sr VP, Dir-HR-Loan & Admin)*
Karen M. Chiarello *(Sr VP & Auditor)*
Robert A. Buckley *(Sr VP & Branch Admin-Loan & Admin)*
Michael J. Giacobello *(Sr VP-Retail Sls)*
Richard J. Ragoza *(Sr VP & Sr Credit Officer)*
John M. Bonk *(First VP, Dir-Bus Dev-PGB Trust & Investments)*
John E. Creamer *(First VP-PGB Trust & Investment)*
John C. Kautz *(First VP & Sr Investment Officer-PGB Trust & Investment)*
Michael Pylypyshyn *(First VP-PGB Trust & Investment)*
Denise M. Pace *(VP, Dir-Mktg-Loan & Admin)*
James R. Housman *(VP, Dir-Tax-PGB Trust & Investments)*
Rene B. Merghart *(VP & Dir-Facilities)*
Paula L. Palermo *(VP, Dir-Sls-Loan & Admin)*

PENN TREATY AMERICAN CORPORATION
3440 Lehigh St
Allentown, PA 18103
Tel.: (469) 287-7044
E-mail: info@penntreatyamerican.com
Web Site: www.penntreatyamerican.com
Sales Range: $75-99.9 Million
Approx. Number Employees: 322
Year Founded: 1972
Business Description:
Holding Company; Accident, Health, Life & Disability Insurance; Long-Term Care & Home Health Care Products Distr
S.I.C.: 6321; 6311; 6411; 6719
N.A.I.C.S.: 524114; 524113; 524210; 551112
Media: 2-10
Personnel:
Eugene J. Woznicki *(Chm & CEO)*
Sean T. Mullen *(CFO)*
Jim Von Bruchhaeuser *(CMO)*
Jane Menin Bagley *(Sr VP, Corp Counsel & Corp Sec)*
Michael F. Grill *(Treas & Comptroller)*
Stephen R. LaPierre *(Exec VP-Insurance Ops)*
James M. Heyer *(Sr VP-Risk Mgmt)*
Brands & Products:
THE ASSISTED LIVING PLUS
THE INDEPENDENT LIVING
LTC SOLUTION
LTC WORKS!
PENN TREATY AMERICAN
THE PERSONAL FREEDOM
THE SECURED RISK
SMART SENSIBLE LONG TERM CARE INSURANCE

PENSECO FINANCIAL SERVICES CORPORATION
150 N Washington Ave
Scranton, PA 18503-1843
Tel.: (570) 346-7741
Fax: (570) 969-2743
Toll Free: (800) 327-0394
Web Site: www.pennsecurity.com
Approx. Rev.: $53,897,000
Approx. Number Employees: 224
Year Founded: 1902
Business Description:
Bank Holding Company
S.I.C.: 6141; 6029; 6282; 6712
N.A.I.C.S.: 522210; 522110; 523930; 551111
Advertising Expenditures: $605,000
Media: 8-9
Personnel:
D. William Hume *(Chm)*
Craig W. Best *(Pres & CEO)*
Michael G. Ostermayer *(Chief Investment Officer & VP-Trust Svcs)*
Denise A. Belton *(Customer Svc Officer)*
Robert E. Diehl *(Collections Officer)*
Barbara Garofoli *(Customer Svc Officer)*
Kimberly A. Kelly *(Customer Svc Officer)*
Jennifer Lee *(Customer Svc Officer)*
Robert W. McDonald *(Tax Officer)*
Kristen R. Noll *(Asst Trust Officer)*
Charles Penn *(Computer Ops Officer)*
Sharon L. Thauer *(Customer Svc Officer)*
Carol Trezzi *(Trust Ops Officer)*
David R. Weiland *(Cost Acctg Officer)*
Melissa M. Wicksnes *(Customer Svc Officer)*
Otto P. Robinson, Jr. *(Gen Counsel)*
Richard E. Grimm *(Treas, Exec VP & Head-Credit Div)*
Susan M. Bray *(Asst Controller & Asst Treas)*
Paula M. DePeters *(Asst VP & Asst Treas)*
Andrew A. Kettel Jr. *(Exec VP & Head-Private Banking Div)*
Greg D. Misterman *(Exec VP & Head-Corp Lending Div)*
Patrick Scanlon *(Sr VP, Controller & Head-Fin Div)*
Stanley H. Cohen *(Sr VP & Head-Retail Banking Div)*
Richard P. Rossi *(Sr VP & Head-HR Div)*
Lynn Peters Thiel *(Sr VP, Head-Plng & Dev Div)*
Karen L. Thomas *(Sr VP & Mktg Mgr)*
William J. Calpin Jr. *(Sr VP & Mgr-Trust Svcs)*
James Tobin *(Sr VP)*

Key to Media (For complete agency information see *The Advertising Red Books-Agencies* edition):
1. Bus. Publs. 2. Cable T.V. 3. Catalogs & Directories. 4. Co-op Adv. 5. Consumer Mags. 6. D.M. to Bus. Estab.7. D.M. to Consumers 8. Daily Newsp. 9. Exhibits/Trade Shows 10. Foreign 11. Infomercial 12. Internet Adv.13. Multimedia 14. Network Radio 15. Network T.V. 16. Newsp. Distr. Mags. 17. Other 18. Outdoor (Posters, Transit) 19. Point of Purchase20. Premiums, Novelties 21. Product Samples 22. Special Events Mktg. 23. Spot Radio 24. Spot T.V. 25. Weekly Newsp. 26. Yellow Page Adv.

Penseco Financial Services Corporation — (Continued)

Paula A. Ralston Nenish *(VP & Dir-Internal Audit)*
Beth S. Wolff *(Asst VP & Mgr-New Acct Product)*
Mark M. Bennett *(Asst VP & Asst Sec)*
Carol Curtis McMullen *(Asst VP & Asst Sec)*
Aleta Sebastianelli *(Asst VP & Asst Sec)*

PENSON WORLDWIDE, INC.

1700 Pacific Ave Ste 1400
Dallas, TX 75201
Tel.: (214) 765-1100
Web Site: www.penson.com
Approx. Rev.: $310,617,000
Approx. Number Employees: 985
Year Founded: 1995
Business Description:
Holding Company; Securities & Futures Trade Execution, Custody, Clearing & Settlement Services
S.I.C.: 6099; 6211; 6221; 6289; 6719
N.A.I.C.S.: 523120; 522320; 523110; 523130; 523140; 523999; 551112
Media: 1-2-7-11-13
Personnel:
Daniel P. Son *(Co-Founder & Vice Chm)*
Roger J. Engemoen, Jr. *(Chm)*
Bryce Engel *(Pres & COO)*
Philip A. Pendergraft *(CEO)*
Kevin W. McAleer *(CFO & Principal Acctg Officer)*
William McLemore *(CIO-Global & Sr VP)*
Andrew B. Koslow *(Gen Counsel & Exec VP-Strategic Investments)*
Richard Anspacher *(Sr VP)*
David Mudie *(Head-Sls)*
Amanda McCutcheon *(Mgr-Corp Comm)*

PEOPLES BANCORP INC.

138 Putnam St
Marietta, OH 45750-2923
Mailing Address:
PO Box 738
Marietta, OH 45750-0738
Tel.: (740) 373-3155
Fax: (740) 374-2020
Toll Free: (800) 374-6123
E-mail: bank@peoplesbancorp.com
Web Site: www.peoplesbancorp.com
Approx. Rev.: $120,930,000
Approx. Number Employees: 534
Year Founded: 1980
Business Description:
Bank Holding Company
S.I.C.: 6712; 6029; 6035; 6163; 6211; 6411
N.A.I.C.S.: 551111; 522110; 522120; 522310; 523110; 524298
Advertising Expenditures: $59,532
Media: 7
Personnel:
Richard E. Ferguson *(Chm)*
Paul T. Theisen *(Vice Chm)*
Charles W. Sulerzyski *(Pres & CEO)*
Edward G. Sloane, Jr. *(CFO, Treas & Exec VP)*
Timothy H. Kirtley *(Chief Credit Officer & Exec VP)*
Rose Nardi *(Chief Investment Officer-Peoples Fin Advisors & Sr VP)*
Daniel K. McGill *(Chief Comml Lending Officer & Exec VP)*
Rhonda L. Mears *(Gen Counsel)*
Carol A. Schneeberger *(Exec VP-Ops)*
Jim Barengo *(Sr VP)*
Laura J. Cox *(VP-Mktg)*
Laura Covault *(Mgr-Agency)*

PEOPLES BANCORP OF NORTH CAROLINA, INC.

518 W C St
Newton, NC 28658
Tel.: (828) 464-5620
Tel.: (828) 464-5663
Fax: (828) 464-5671
Toll Free: (800) 948-7195
Web Site: www.peoplesbanknc.com
Approx. Rev.: $61,564,000
Approx. Number Employees: 244
Business Description:
Bank Holding Company
S.I.C.: 6029
N.A.I.C.S.: 522110
Advertising Expenditures: $714,000
Media: 1-7-13
Personnel:
Robert C. Abernethy *(Chm)*
Tony W. Wolfe *(Pres & CEO)*
A. Joseph Lampron *(CFO, Corp Treas & Exec VP)*
William D. Cable, Sr. *(COO, Exec VP & Asst Treas)*
Joseph F. Beaman Jr. *(Chief Admin Officer, Sec & Exec VP)*

PEOPLES BANCORPORATION, INC.

1818 E Main St
Easley, SC 29640
Tel.: (864) 859-2265
Fax: (864) 859-0285
E-mail: patti.jensen@peoplesbc.com
Web Site: www.peoplesbc.com
Approx. Rev.: $31,128,000
Approx. Number Employees: 107
Year Founded: 1992
Business Description:
Bank Holding Company
S.I.C.: 6712; 6029
N.A.I.C.S.: 551111; 522110
Advertising Expenditures: $177,000
Media: 7-8-17
Personnel:
George B. Nalley, Jr. *(Chm)*
E. Smyth McKissick III *(Vice Chm)*
L. Andrew Westbrook, III *(Pres & CEO)*
Robert E. Dye, Jr. *(CFO & Sr VP)*
William B. West *(Exec VP)*
Patricia A. Jensen *(Sr VP & Controller)*

THE PEOPLES BANCTRUST COMPANY, INC.

(Name Changed to BancTrust)

PEOPLES FEDERAL BANCSHARES, INC.

435 Market St
Brighton, MA 02135
Tel.: (617) 254-0707
E-mail: lcote@pfsb.com
Web Site: www.pfsb.com
Approx. Rev.: $23,026,000
Approx. Number Employees: 60
Business Description:
Bank Holding Company
S.I.C.: 6712
N.A.I.C.S.: 551111
Advertising Expenditures: $140,000
Media: 17
Personnel:
Maurice H. Sullivan, Jr. *(Chm & CEO)*
Thomas J. Leetch, Jr. *(Pres & COO)*
Christopher Lake *(CFO & Sr VP)*
James J. Gavin *(Exec VP)*

PEOPLES FINANCIAL CORPORATION

152 Lameuse Ave
Biloxi, MS 39530
Tel.: (228) 435-5511
Fax: (228) 435-8410
Toll Free: (800) 873-6468
E-mail: investorrelations@thepeoples.com
Web Site: www.thepeoples.com
Approx. Rev.: $39,788,925
Approx. Number Employees: 185
Year Founded: 1984
Business Description:
Bank Holding Company
S.I.C.: 6712; 6029
N.A.I.C.S.: 551111; 522110
Advertising Expenditures: $580,000
Media: 8
Personnel:
Chevis C. Swetman *(Chm)*
Dan Magruder *(Vice Chm)*
Lauri A. Wood *(CFO & Sr VP)*
Thomas J. Sliman *(CIO & Sr VP)*
Robert M. Tucei *(Chief Credit Officer & Sr VP)*

PEOPLES FINANCIAL SERVICES CORP.

82 Franklin Ave PO Box A
Hallstead, PA 18822
Tel.: (570) 879-2175
Fax: (570) 879-4372
Toll Free: (888) 868-3858
E-mail: pnbank@peoplesnatbank.com
Web Site: www.peoplesnatbank.com
Approx. Rev.: $29,867,000
Approx. Number Employees: 124
Business Description:
Bank Holding Company
S.I.C.: 6141; 6712
N.A.I.C.S.: 522210; 551111
Advertising Expenditures: $403,000
Personnel:
William E. Aubrey, II *(Chm)*
Alan W. Dakey *(Pres & CEO)*
Scott A. Seasock *(CFO & Sr VP)*

PEOPLES STATE BANK

(Sub. of PSB Financial Corporation)
880 San Antonio Ave
Many, LA 71449
Tel.: (318) 256-2071
Fax: (318) 256-4343
E-mail: info@peoplesstate.com
Web Site: www.peoplesstate.com
Approx. Number Employees: 168
Business Description:
Commercial Banking Services
S.I.C.: 6029
N.A.I.C.S.: 522110
Personnel:
John J. Blake, III *(Pres, CEO & Dir)*
Clay Abington *(Chief Risk Officer & Sr VP)*
Advertising Agency:
pushtwentytwo
22 W Huron
Pontiac, MI 48342
Tel.: (248) 335-9500
Fax: (248) 335-7848

PEOPLES TRUST COMPANY

888 Dunsmuir St 14th Fl
Vancouver, BC V6C 3K4, Canada
Tel.: (604) 683-2881
Fax: (604) 331-3469
Toll Free: (800) 663-0324
E-mail: people@peoplestrust.com
Web Site: www.peoplestrust.com
E-Mail For Key Personnel:
President: frank@peoplestrust.com
Sales Range: $10-24.9 Million
Approx. Number Employees: 80
Year Founded: 1985
Business Description:
Residential Mortgages; Commercial & Industrial Real Estate Financing; Mortgage Banking; Mortgage Financing; Deposit Services; Mortgage Backed Securities; Retirement Savings Plan
S.I.C.: 6159
N.A.I.C.S.: 522294
Media: 2-4-8-13
Distr.: Direct to Consumer; Natl.
Budget Set: Nov.
Personnel:
Eskandar Ghermezian *(Chm)*
Frank A. Renou *(Pres & CEO)*
Derek Peddlesden *(COO & Exec VP)*
Barrie M. Battley *(Sr VP)*
Dennis Aitken *(VP & Reg Mgr-Prairiesany)*
Brian D. Kennedy *(VP & Reg Mgr)*
Jeanette Curtis *(Sr Mgr-Deposit Svcs)*

PEOPLE'S UNITED BANK

(Sub. of People's United Financial, Inc.)
850 Main St
Bridgeport, CT 06604-4917
Tel.: (203) 338-7171
Fax: (800) 772-1090
E-mail: custserv@peoples.com
Web Site: www.peoples.com
Sales Range: $350-399.9 Million
Approx. Number Employees: 3,000
Year Founded: 1842
Business Description:
Diversified Financial Services
S.I.C.: 6029; 6289
N.A.I.C.S.: 522110; 523999
Import Export
Advertising Expenditures: $99,000,000
Personnel:
John P. Barnes *(Pres & CEO)*
Armando F. Goncalves *(Pres-People's United Bank-South)*
Paul D. Burner *(CFO & Sr Exec VP)*
Michael J. Casparino *(Pres-People's United Bank-North)*
Robert R. D'Amore *(Sr Exec VP-Retail & Bus Banking)*
Brian F. Dreyer *(Sr Exec VP-Comml Banking)*
David Norton *(Sr Exec VP-HR)*
Hank Mandel *(Exec VP-Org Effectiveness)*
Linda M. Cheever *(Sr VP-Corp Fin)*
David S. Marsh *(Sr VP & Chief Applications Officer-IT Div)*
Valerie C. Carlson *(First VP-Corp Comm)*
Brent Di Giorgio *(Dir-External Comm)*

Key to Media (For complete agency information see *The Advertising Red Books-Agencies* edition):
1. Bus. Publs. 2. Cable T.V. 3. Catalogs & Directories. 4. Co-op Adv. 5. Consumer Mags. 6. D.M. to Bus. Estab.7. D.M. to Consumers 8. Daily Newsp. 9. Exhibits/Trade Shows 10. Foreign 11. Infomercial 12. Internet Adv.13. Multimedia 14. Network Radio 15. Network T.V. 16. Newsp. Distr. Mags. 17. Other 18. Outdoor (Posters, Transit) 19. Point of Purchase20. Premiums, Novelties 21. Product Samples 22. Special Events Mktg. 23. Spot Radio 24. Spot T.V. 25. Weekly Newsp. 26. Yellow Page Adv.

Advertising Agency:
The VIA Group LLC
34 Danforth St Ste 309
Portland, ME 04101
Tel.: (207) 221-3000
Fax: (207) 761-9422
Agency of Record
Brand Positioning

PEOPLE'S UNITED FINANCIAL, INC.

850 Main St 11th Fl
Bridgeport, CT 06604
Tel.: (203) 338-7171
Tel.: (203) 338-4114
Fax: (203) 338-3665
Toll Free: (800) 894-0300
E-mail: custserv@peoples.com
Web Site: www.peoples.com
Approx. Rev.: $828,800,000
Approx. Number Employees: 4,528
Year Founded: 1850
Business Description:
Bank Holding Company
S.I.C.: 6035; 6712
N.A.I.C.S.: 522120; 551111
Import Export
Advertising Expenditures:
$14,100,000
Personnel:
John P. Barnes *(Pres & CEO)*
Kirk W. Walters *(CFO & Sr Exec VP)*
David A. Bodor *(Exec VP & Chief Credit Officer)*
Lee C. Powlus *(Chief Admin Officer & Exec VP)*
Chantal D. Simon *(Sr Exec VP & Chief Risk Officer)*
Armando F. Goncalves *(Pres-Southern Connecticut/New York)*
Michael J. Casparino *(Pres-Northern Connecticut)*
Robert E. Trautmann *(Gen Counsel & Sr Exec VP)*
R. David Rosato *(Sr VP & Treas)*
Susan D. Stanley *(Sec, Sr VP & Sr Corp Counsel)*
Robert R. D'Amore *(Sr Exec VP-Retail & Bus Banking)*
Vincent R. Cianciolo *(Exec VP)*
Jeffrey Hoyt *(Sr VP & Controller)*
David P. Berey *(Sr VP-Comml Lending)*
Christina M. Bliven *(Sr VP-Fin Plng & Analysis)*
Peter M. Brestovan *(Sr VP-Real Estate Svcs)*
Timothy P. Crimmins, Jr. *(Sr VP)*
Harold F. Geissler *(Sr VP-Comml Lending)*
Florence F. Izzo *(Sr VP-Loan & Wealth Mgmt Ops)*
Walter W. Kaercher *(Sr VP)*
Samuel A. Ladd, III *(Sr VP)*
Sara M. Longobardi *(Sr VP-Customer Relationship Dev)*
Patricia A. Manion *(Sr VP-Direct Banking & Deposit Ops)*
Susan A. Matlos *(Sr VP-Fin Svcs)*
Thomas J. Pantello *(Sr VP-Comml Real Estate)*
Frances Ricci *(Sr VP & Sr Corp Counsel)*
Peter J. Scotch, Jr. *(Sr VP-Consumer Deposit Products)*
Linda A. Stempek *(Sr VP-Bus Svcs)*
Maria A. Stolfi *(Sr VP-HR)*
Marie A. Thresher *(Sr VP)*
Wayne C. Walker *(Sr VP-Residential & Consumer Lending)*
Valerie C. Carlson *(First VP-Corp Comm)*
Hank Mandel *(Exec Dir)*
Brent Di Giorgio *(Dir-External Comm)*

PHH CORPORATION

3000 Leadenhall Rd
Mount Laurel, NJ 08054
Mailing Address:
PO Box 5452
Mount Laurel, NJ 08054-5452
Tel.: (856) 917-1744
Fax: (856) 917-4326
Toll Free: (800) 449-8767
E-mail: customer.service@mortgagefamily.com
Web Site: www.phh.com
E-Mail For Key Personnel:
Marketing Director: marketing@phh.com
Public Relations: karen.mccallson@phh.com
Approx. Rev.: $2,438,000,000
Approx. Number Employees: 5,610
Year Founded: 1946
Business Description:
Direct Consumer Mortgages & Fleet Management Services
S.I.C.: 6163; 6141; 6289
N.A.I.C.S.: 522310; 522220; 523999
Advertising Expenditures: $3,000,000
Personnel:
Jerome J. Selitto *(Pres & CEO)*
David J. Coles *(Interim CFO, Interim Chief Acctg Officer & Interim Exec VP)*
Glen A. Messina *(COO)*
Jeff S. Bell *(CIO & Sr VP)*
Adele T. Barbato *(Chief HR Officer & Sr VP)*
William F. Brown *(Gen Counsel, Sec & Sr VP)*
Mark E. Johnson *(Treas & Sr VP)*
George J. Kilroy *(Exec VP-Fleet)*
Milton Prime *(Sr VP)*
Karen McCallson *(VP-PR)*
Brands & Products:
PHH
PHH ARVAL
PHH MORTGAGE

PIE TECHNOLOGIES

1588 Oak Bridge Ter
Powhatan, VA 23139
Tel.: (804) 744-5900
Fax: (804) 744-9351
E-mail: btatum@pietech.com
Web Site: www.pietech.com
Sales Range: $10-24.9 Million
Approx. Number Employees: 33
Year Founded: 1997
Business Description:
Financial Planning Software Developer
S.I.C.: 7371
N.A.I.C.S.: 541511
Import Export
Media: 10
Personnel:
Bob Curtis *(Pres)*
Brands & Products:
MONEYGUIDEPRO

PIEDMONT FEDERAL SAVINGS BANK

16 W 3rd St
Winston Salem, NC 27101
Mailing Address:
PO Box 215
Winston Salem, NC 27102
Tel.: (336) 770-1000
E-mail: rwagner@piedmontfederal.com
Web Site: www.piedmontfederal.com
Sales Range: $800-899.9 Million
Approx. Number Employees: 50
Year Founded: 1903
Business Description:
Commercial Banking Services
S.I.C.: 6035; 6029; 6163
N.A.I.C.S.: 522120; 522110; 522310
Advertising Expenditures: $300,000
Media: 6-13-18-23-24
Personnel:
Richard F. Wagner, Jr. *(Pres & CEO)*
Michael L. Hauser *(COO & Exec VP)*
Lisa Snowden *(Sec & Sr VP-HR)*
M. Dean Browder *(Sr VP-Savings Admin)*
Bruce B. Humphries *(Sr VP-Branch Admin)*
Wanda Merschel *(Sr VP-Bus Dev)*
Darrell N. Newton *(Sr VP-Credit & Underwriting)*
J. Robert Sanders, Jr. *(Sr VP-Loan Origination)*
Brands & Products:
PIEDMONT FEDERAL

PINK OTC MARKETS INC.

(Name Changed to OTC Markets Group Inc.)

PINNACLE FINANCIAL PARTNERS, INC.

150 3rd Ave S Ste 900
Nashville, TN 37201
Tel.: (615) 744-3700
Fax: (615) 744-3810
Toll Free: (866) 404-6143
Web Site: www.pnfp.com
Approx. Rev.: $239,663,410
Approx. Number Employees: 765
Year Founded: 2000
Business Description:
Bank Holding Company
S.I.C.: 6029; 6035; 6163; 6211; 6712
N.A.I.C.S.: 522110; 522120; 522310; 523110; 551111
Advertising Expenditures: $259,000
Personnel:
Robert A. McCabe, Jr. *(Chm)*
M. Terry Turner *(Pres & CEO)*
Harold R. Carpenter *(CFO)*
Hugh M. Queener *(Chief Admin Officer & Exec VP)*
Martha B. Olsen *(Chief People Officer)*
Charles McMahan *(Exec VP & Sr Credit Officer)*
J. Edward White *(Exec VP & Sr Lending Officer)*
Nathan Hunter *(Pres-Pinnacle Knoxville)*
Joanne B. Jackson *(Exec VP & Mgr-Client Svcs)*
Barry Moody *(Exec VP & Mgr-Pinnacle Asset Mgmt)*
Distefano Mike *(Exec VP-Pinnacle Knoxville)*
R. Dale Floyd *(Sr VP & Mgr-Client Advisory Grp)*
Kim Jenny *(Sr VP & Sr Program Mgr)*
M. Glenn Layne *(Sr VP & Credit Officer)*
Scott Ractliffe *(Sr VP)*
Brands & Products:
PINNACLE

PIONEER INVESTMENTS

(Sub. of UniCredito Italiano S.p.A.)
60 State St
Boston, MA 02109-1800
Tel.: (617) 742-7825
Fax: (617) 422-4223
E-mail: us.work@pioneerinvestments.com
Web Site:
www.pioneerinvestments.com
Approx. Number Employees: 700
Year Founded: 1956
Business Description:
Investment Management, Mutual Funds & Private Accounts, Mutual Fund Share Distribution & Shareholder Services for Mutual Funds
S.I.C.: 6722
N.A.I.C.S.: 525910
Export
Personnel:
Bill Taylor *(Mng Dir, Head-Bus Dev & Investment Only)*
Joseph Kringdon *(Pres-Pioneer Funds Distributor, Exec VP & Head-US Retail Distr)*
Steven Graziano *(Exec VP)*
Paul Mahan *(Sr VP & Dir-Investment Only)*
Thomas Jones *(Sr VP & Dir-Wealth Mgmt Channel)*
Advertising Agency:
Corporate Communications, Inc.
65 Seavey St
North Conway, NH 03860
Tel.: (603) 356-7011

PIPER JAFFRAY COMPANIES

800 Nicollet Mall Ste 800
Minneapolis, MN 55402
Tel.: (612) 303-6000
Fax: (612) 303-8199
Toll Free: (800) 333-6000
E-mail: susan.l.beatty@pjc.com
Web Site: www.piperjaffray.com
Approx. Rev.: $530,074,000
Approx. Number Employees: 1,053
Year Founded: 1895
Business Description:
Holding Company; Investment Banking & Institutional Securities Firm Services
S.I.C.: 6719; 6211
N.A.I.C.S.: 551112; 523110
Personnel:
Andrew S. Duff *(Chm & CEO)*
Thomas P. Schnettler *(Pres & COO)*
Lois E. Quam *(Mng Dir-Alternate Investments)*
David Castagna *(Mng Dir & Co-Head-Tech Investment Banking)*
Stuart Duty *(Mng Dir & Global Co-Head-Health Care Investment Banking)*
Larry Zimmerman *(Mng Dir & Head-Indus)*
Debbra L. Schoneman *(CFO)*
R. Todd Firebaugh *(Chief Admin Officer)*
Timothy L. Carter *(Chief Acctg Officer)*
James L. Chosy *(Gen Counsel & Sec)*
John Gibas *(Mng DirInstitutional Mktg & Sls)*
P. Jonathan Heroux *(Mng Dir-Pub Fin Investment Banking)*

Key to Media (For complete agency information see *The Advertising Red Books-Agencies* edition):
1. Bus. Publs. 2. Cable T.V. 3. Catalogs & Directories. 4. Co-op Adv. 5. Consumer Mags. 6. D.M. to Bus. Estab.7. D.M. to Consumers
8. Daily Newsp. 9. Exhibits/Trade Shows 10. Foreign 11. Infomercial 12. Internet Adv.13. Multimedia 14. Network Radio
15. Network T.V. 16. Newsp. Distr. Mags. 17. Other 18. Outdoor (Posters, Transit) 19. Point of Purchase20. Premiums, Novelties
21. Product Samples 22. Special Events Mktg. 23. Spot Radio 24. Spot T.V. 25. Weekly Newsp. 26. Yellow Page Adv.

Piper Jaffray Companies — (Continued)

Susan Beatty *(VP-PR & Comm)*
Frank E. Fairman *(Head-Pub Fin Svcs)*
Benjamin T. May *(Head-Yield & Structured Products)*
Jon W. Salveson *(Head-Investment Banking)*
Jennifer A. Olson-Goude *(Dir-IR)*

Advertising Agency:
Preston Kelly
222 First Ave NE
Minneapolis, MN 55413
Tel.: (612) 843-4000
Fax: (612) 843-3900

PLAINS CAPITAL CORPORATION

2323 Victory Ave Ste 1400
Dallas, TX 75219
Tel.: (214) 252-4100
Web Site: www.plainscapital.com
Approx. Rev.: $650,608,000
Approx. Number Employees: 3,000
Year Founded: 1987
Business Description:
Bank Holding Company
S.I.C.: 6712; 6029
N.A.I.C.S.: 551111; 522110
Advertising Expenditures: $2,800,000
Personnel:
Alan B. White *(Chm & CEO)*
Jerry Schaffner *(Pres & CEO-PlainsCapital Bank)*
James R. Huffines *(Pres & COO-PlainsCapital Corporation)*
John A. Martin *(CFO)*
W. Allen Custard, III *(Exec VP-Corp Dev & Strategic Plng)*
Jeff Isom *(Exec VP-Fin & Acctg)*
Roseanna McGill *(Exec VP-Strategic Initiatives)*

PLATTE VALLEY FINANCIAL SERVICE COMPANIES INC.

1212 Cir Dr
Scottsbluff, NE 69363-0137
Tel.: (308) 632-7004
Fax: (308) 632-7039
Toll Free: (888) 632-7004
E-mail: info@pvbankne.com
Web Site: www.pvbankne.com
Sales Range: $550-599.9 Million
Approx. Number Employees: 200
Year Founded: 1934
Business Description:
Bank Holding Company
S.I.C.: 6712; 6029; 6411
N.A.I.C.S.: 551111; 522110; 524298
Media: 6-9-23-25
Personnel:
H. Hod Kosman *(Chm, Pres & CEO)*
James E. Kozal *(CFO, COO & Exec VP)*
Donald F. Roth *(COO, Sec & Exec VP)*
Jody Miles *(Sr VP & Comptroller)*
Sandy Massey *(Sr VP & Dir-HR)*
Mark Payne *(Sr VP & Mgr-IT)*
Janet Ewald *(Sr VP, Compliance Officer & Auditor)*
Mindy Burbach *(Asst VP & Dir-Mktg)*

PLUMAS BANCORP

35 S Lindan Ave
Quincy, CA 95971
Tel.: (530) 283-7305
Fax: (530) 283-3557
E-mail: elizabeth.kuipers@plumasbank.com
Web Site: www.plumasbank.com
Approx. Rev.: $29,241,000
Approx. Number Employees: 146
Business Description:
Bank Holding Company
S.I.C.: 6712; 6029
N.A.I.C.S.: 551111; 522110
Advertising Expenditures: $252,000
Personnel:
Daniel E. West *(Chm)*
Terrance J. Reeson *(Vice Chm & Sec)*
Andrew J. Ryback *(Interim Pres & CEO)*
Monetta Rose Dembosz *(Exec VP, Mgr-Bank Ops & Network Admin)*
Richard L. Belstock *(Interim CFO & Sr VP)*
Elizabeth Kuipers *(VP & Mgr-Mktg & IR)*
Brands & Products:
LOCAL PEOPLE SERVING LOCAL NEEDS
PLUMAS BANK

PNC BANK

(Branch of PNC Bank, Philadelphia & Southern New Jersey)
2465 Whitehorse Mercerville Rd
Hamilton, NJ 08619
Tel.: (609) 586-8737
Sales Range: $75-99.9 Million
Approx. Number Employees: 200
Year Founded: 1924
Business Description:
Full-Service Bank
S.I.C.: 6029
N.A.I.C.S.: 522110
Advertising Expenditures: $1,500,000
Media: 4-6-7-8-13-23
Personnel:
Lucy Elomia *(Reg Pres)*

THE PNC FINANCIAL SERVICES GROUP, INC.

1 PNC Plaza 249 5th Ave
Pittsburgh, PA 15222-2707
Tel.: (412) 762-2000
Fax: (412) 762-7829
Toll Free: (888) 762-2265
E-mail: investor.relations@pnc.com
Web Site: www.pnc.com
Approx. Int. Income: $11,150,000,000
Approx. Number Employees: 44,817
Year Founded: 1983
Business Description:
Bank Holding Company
S.I.C.: 6712; 6029; 6035; 6099; 6163; 6211; 6289
N.A.I.C.S.: 551111; 522110; 522120; 522310; 522320; 523110; 523999
Advertising Expenditures: $20,000,000
Media: 2-3-4-6-7-8-9-17-19-22-23-24-25-26
Distr.: Natl.
Budget Set: Aug.
Personnel:
James E. Rohr *(Chm & CEO)*
William S. Demchak *(Sr Vice Chm)*
Thomas K. Whitford *(Vice Chm)*
Joseph C. Guyaux *(Pres)*
Mark Stevens *(Mng Dir)*
Richard J. Johnson *(CFO)*
Karen Larrimer *(Exec VP & CMO)*
Randall C. King *(Pres-PFGI Capital Corp & Sr VP)*
David Boyle *(Pres-Michigan & NW Ohio)*
Richard DeVore *(Pres-Detroit & Southeast Michigan Reg)*
Helen P. Pudlin *(Gen Counsel)*
Diana Reid *(Exec VP)*
Gregory H. Kozich *(Sr VP & Controller)*
William H. Callihan *(Sr VP & Dir-IR)*
Stacey L. Gannon *(VP & Sr Mgr-Relationship-Wealth Mgmt)*
Lisa Leake *(VP & Sr Brand Mgr)*
Aimee LeWinter *(VP & Mgr-Comml Banking Relationship)*
Kristin Mohn *(Mgr-Comm)*
Brands & Products:
ACTIVEPAY
AUTOALERTS
CAPITAL DIRECTIONS
CHOICE PLAN
CUSTOMIZED BANKING
LEADING THE WAY
PINACLE
PNC
PNC MERCHANT SERVICES
PREMIUM PLAN
REFLEX
RETIREMENT DIRECTIONS
VESTED INTEREST
Advertising Agencies:
AdAsia Communications, Inc.
85 Fifth Ave 7th Fl
New York, NY 10003
Tel.: (212) 871-6886
Fax: (212) 871-6883

Doner
25900 Northwestern Hwy
Southfield, MI 48075
Tel.: (248) 354-9700
Fax: (248) 827-8440

PORTER BANCORP, INC.

2500 Eastpoint Pkwy
Louisville, KY 40223
Tel.: (502) 499-4800
Fax: (502) 499-4811
E-mail: support@pbibank.com
Web Site: www.pbibank.com
Approx. Rev.: $97,989,000
Approx. Number Employees: 286
Year Founded: 1988
Business Description:
Bank Holding Company
S.I.C.: 6712
N.A.I.C.S.: 551111
Advertising Expenditures: $408,000
Personnel:
J. Chester Porter *(Chm)*
Maria L. Bouvette *(Pres & CEO)*
Phil W. Barnhouse *(CFO)*
E. Todd Young *(COO)*
Avery K. Matney, Jr. *(Pres-Southern Reg)*
C. Bradford Harris *(Gen Counsel & Exec VP)*
Fred Catlett *(Exec VP)*

POTOMAC BANCSHARES INC.

111 E Washington St
Charles Town, WV 25414
Tel.: (304) 725-8431
Fax: (304) 725-0059
Web Site: www.bankatbct.com
Approx. Rev.: $17,980,000
Approx. Number Employees: 89
Business Description:
State Commercial Banks
S.I.C.: 6029
N.A.I.C.S.: 522110
Advertising Expenditures: $176,000
Media: 17
Personnel:
John C. Skinner, Jr. *(Chm)*
Robert F. Baronner, Jr. *(Pres & CEO)*
Gayle Marshall Johnson *(CFO & Sec)*
David W. Irvin *(Exec VP)*

PRE-PAID LEGAL SERVICES, INC.

1 Pre-Paid Way
Ada, OK 74820-5605
Mailing Address:
PO Box 145
Ada, OK 74821-0145
Tel.: (580) 436-1234
Fax: (580) 421-6305
Toll Free: (800) 654-7757
E-mail: investor@pplsi.com
Web Site: www.prepaidlegal.com
E-Mail For Key Personnel:
Public Relations: investor@pplsi.com
Approx. Rev.: $453,936,000
Approx. Number Employees: 680
Year Founded: 1972
Business Description:
Legal Service Membership Plans
S.I.C.: 7389; 8111
N.A.I.C.S.: 541199; 541110
Media: 17
Personnel:
Harland C. Stonecipher *(Chm)*
Mark Brown *(Co-CEO, CMO & Sr VP)*
Steve Williamson *(CFO)*
Randy Harp *(COO)*
Keri Prince *(Gen Counsel)*
Vicky Mapp *(VP-IT)*
Wilburn Smith *(Dir-Natl Mktg)*
Jamie Anderson *(Mgr-Membership Admin)*
Sheila Burris *(Mgr-Mktg Svcs)*
Keith Davis *(Mgr-Grp Mktg)*
Brands & Products:
LIFE EVENTS LEGAL PLAN
PRE-PAID LEGAL SERVICES

PREMIERWEST BANCORP

503 Airport Rd
Medford, OR 97504
Mailing Address:
PO Box 40
Medford, OR 97504
Tel.: (541) 618-6020
Fax: (541) 774-4166
Toll Free: (800) 708-4378
E-mail: investorrelations@premierwestbank.com
Web Site: www.premierwestbank.com
Approx. Rev.: $80,313,000
Approx. Number Employees: 477
Business Description:
Bank Holding Company
S.I.C.: 6712
N.A.I.C.S.: 551111
Advertising Expenditures: $801,000
Personnel:
John A. Duke *(Chm)*
Patrick G. Huycke *(Vice Chm)*
James M. Ford *(Pres & CEO)*
Douglas N. Biddle *(CFO & Exec VP)*
Richard R. Hieb *(COO, Sec & Sr Exec VP)*
Owen Atkinson *(CIO & Sr VP)*

Key to Media (For complete agency information see *The Advertising Red Books-Agencies* edition):
1. Bus. Publs. 2. Cable T.V. 3. Catalogs & Directories. 4. Co-op Adv. 5. Consumer Mags. 6. D.M. to Bus. Estab.7. D.M. to Consumers 8. Daily Newsp. 9. Exhibits/Trade Shows 10. Foreign 11. Infomercial 12. Internet Adv.13. Multimedia 14. Network Radio 15. Network T.V. 16. Newsp. Distr. Mags. 17. Other 18. Outdoor (Posters, Transit) 19. Point of Purchase20. Premiums, Novelties 21. Product Samples 22. Special Events Mktg. 23. Spot Radio 24. Spot T.V. 25. Weekly Newsp. 26. Yellow Page Adv.

Jill Marie Borovansky *(Sr VP & Dir-Internal Audit)*
Carrie Brownell *(Sr VP & Dir-HR)*
Don Dahrens *(Sr VP & Dir-Credit Examination)*
James V. Earley *(Sr VP & Mgr-Asset Recovery Grp)*
Mario Callegari *(Sr VP & Administrator-Branch Credit)*
Bob Dumilieu *(Sr VP & Reg Administrator)*
Richard Russell *(Sr VP-Reg Administrator)*
Susan Stuart *(Sr VP & Compliance Officer)*
Kathy Trautman *(Sr VP-Reg Administrator)*
Shawna Sloan *(Mgr-Internal Audit)*

PREVISOR INC.
(Branch of PreVisor Inc.)
650 3rd Ave S Ste 1300
Minneapolis, MN 55402
Tel.: (612) 843-1059
Fax: (770) 642-6115
Toll Free: (800) 447-2266
E-mail: sales@previsor.com
Web Site: www.previsor.com
E-Mail For Key Personnel:
Sales Director: sales@previsor.com
Approx. Number Employees: 40
Business Description:
Staffing Services
S.I.C.: 8299
N.A.I.C.S.: 611710
Media: 10-13-18
Personnel:
Tony Anello *(Sr VP-Sls)*

PRICEWATERHOUSECOOPERS LLP - USA
(d/b/a PwC USA)
300 Madison Ave
New York, NY 10017-6204
Tel.: (646) 471-4000 (Corp)
Tel.: (646) 471-3000
Fax: (646) 471-4444
Fax: (813) 268-6000
Web Site: www.pwc.com/us
E-Mail For Key Personnel:
Public Relations: david.nestor@us.pwc.com
Year Founded: 1982
Business Description:
Accounting, Tax Preparation, Risk Management, Business Assurance, Human Resource, Regulatory, Operational Management & Advisory Services
S.I.C.: 8721; 7291; 7361; 7389; 8742; 8748
N.A.I.C.S.: 541211; 541213; 541219; 541611; 541612; 541618; 561499
Media: 2-3-4-9-10-13-15-17-20-22-25
Distr.: Natl.
Personnel:
Robert E. Moritz *(Chm & Sr Partner)*
Donald V. Almeida *(Vice Chm-Client Svc-US Assurance Practice)*
Michael F. Swanick *(Partner)*
Mike Burwell *(CFO)*
John Carter *(Chief Admin Officer)*
Edwin Boswell *(Principal-US Advisory People)*
Thomas P. Degarmo *(Principal)*
Brian Snarzyk *(Principal)*
Javier H. Rubinstein *(Gen Counsel-Global)*
David L. Nestor *(Head-Pub Rel)*
Mike Davies *(Dir-Comm & Pub Rel-Global)*
Phil Hulley *(Dir)*

PRIMERICA FINANCIAL SERVICES, INC.
(Sub. of Primerica, Inc.)
3120 Breckinridge Blvd
Duluth, GA 30099
Tel.: (770) 381-1000
Fax: (770) 564-6110
Web Site: www.primerica.com
Approx. Sls.: $1,980,000,000
Approx. Number Employees: 1,800
Year Founded: 1977
Business Description:
Insurance & Asset Management Services
S.I.C.: 6411; 6211; 6282
N.A.I.C.S.: 524210; 523120; 523930
Media: 2-8-9-25
Distr.: Natl.
Personnel:
D. Richard Williams *(Co-CEO)*
Alison Rand *(CFO)*
David Wade *(CIO)*
Mark Supic *(Exec VP-Corp Rels)*
Jeffrey Shirley *(Reg VP)*

PRINCETON FINANCIAL SYSTEMS, INC.
(Sub. of State Street Corporation)
600 College Rd E
Princeton, NJ 08540
Tel.: (609) 987-2400
Fax: (609) 987-9320
Web Site: www.pfs.com
Sales Range: $650-699.9 Million
Business Description:
Portfolio Management & Accounting Systems Services
S.I.C.: 6282
N.A.I.C.S.: 523930
Media: 10
Personnel:
John Kuhn *(Product Mgr)*
Cyndi Flanagan *(Mgr-Global Mktg)*
Brands & Products:
PRINCETON FINANCIAL SYSTEMS

PRINCETON NATIONAL BANCORP, INC.
606 S Main St
Princeton, IL 61356
Tel.: (815) 875-4444
Fax: (815) 872-0247
E-mail: pnbc@citizens1st.com
Web Site: www.pnbc-inc.com
Approx. Rev.: $61,058,000
Approx. Number Employees: 275
Year Founded: 1981
Business Description:
Bank Holding Company
S.I.C.: 6712; 6029
N.A.I.C.S.: 551111; 522110
Advertising Expenditures: $751,000
Media: 8-13-20-23-26
Personnel:
Thomas D. Ogaard *(Pres & CEO)*
Rodney Stickle *(CFO)*
Todd D. Fanning *(COO & Exec VP)*
Craig O. Wesner *(Gen Mgr)*

PRINCIPAL FINANCIAL GROUP, INC.
711 High St
Des Moines, IA 50392-0001
Mailing Address:
801 Grand Ave
Des Moines, IA 50392-0490
Tel.: (515) 247-5111
Fax: (515) 246-5475
Toll Free: (800) 986-3343
Toll Free: (800) 533-1390
E-mail: connect@principal.com
Web Site: www.principal.com
Approx. Rev.: $9,158,600,000
Approx. Number Employees: 13,627
Year Founded: 1879
Business Description:
Financial Products & Services Including Retirement & Investment Services, Life & Health Insurance, Mortgage Banking to Businesses, Individuals & Institutional Clients
S.I.C.: 6311; 6289; 6321; 6411; 6719
N.A.I.C.S.: 524113; 523999; 524114; 524210; 524298; 551112
Media: 1-2-3-5-6-7-8-9-10-13-15-18-23-25-26
Distr.: Natl.
Budget Set: Oct.
Personnel:
Larry Donald Zimpleman *(Chm, Pres & CEO)*
Terry Lillis *(CFO & Sr VP)*
Gary P. Scholten *(CIO & Sr VP)*
Mary A. O'Keefe *(CMO & Sr VP)*
Julia M. Lawler *(Chief Investment Officer & Sr VP)*
Ellen Z. Lamale *(Chief Risk Officer & Sr VP)*
Luis Valdes *(Pres-Latin America & Sr VP)*
John E. Aschenbrenner *(Pres-Insurance & Fin Svcs)*
James P. McCaughan *(Pres-Global Asset Mgmt)*
Norman R. Sorensen *(Pres-Intl Asset Mgmt & Accumulation)*
Ned A. Burmeister *(COO-Principal Intl & Sr VP &)*
Karen E. Shaff *(Gen Counsel & Exec VP)*
Joyce N. Hoffman *(Sec & Sr VP)*
Greg Elming *(Sr VP & Controller)*
Rex Auyeung *(Sr VP)*
Gregory J. Burrows *(Sr VP-Retirement & Investor Svcs)*
Nora M. Everett *(Sr VP-Retirement & IR)*
Thomas J. Graf *(Sr VP-IR)*
Carey G. Jury *(Sr VP-Health)*
Timothy J. Minard *(Sr VP-Retirement Distr)*
Deanna Strable-Soethout *(Sr VP-Individual Life & Specialty Benefits)*
Bill Fox *(Reg VP-Disability Income)*
Gretchen Barress *(VP-Sls, Retirement Svcs)*
Susan Houser *(Head-PR)*
Theresa McConeghey *(Asst VP-SBD Products)*
Tuba Malinowski *(Dir-Mktg)*
Brands & Products:
DOING BUSINESS WITH THE PRINCIPAL
FROM HERE TO SECURITY
PERLS
PRINCIPAL
THE PRINCIPAL
PRINCIPAL ANNUITY LEGACY
PRINCIPAL BANK
PRINCIPAL BANK VISA
PRINCIPAL E-DISTRIBUTION SERVICES
THE PRINCIPAL FINANCIAL GROUP
THE PRINCIPAL FINANCIAL WELL-BEING INDEX
PRINCIPAL HEALTH NEWS
PRINCIPAL IRA EXCHANGE
PRINCIPAL PROVIDER SERVICE CENTER
PRINCIPAL REIMBURSEMENT ARRANGEMENT
PRINCIPAL RETURN-TO-WORK RESOURCES
PRINCIPAL ROLLOVER CHOICE
PRINCIPAL TOTAL RETIREMENT SUITE
PRINCIPAL WORK SECURE
PROCEED TO HEALTH ASSESSMENTS
RETIREMENT SERVICE CENTER
ROTH IRA
SAFE HARBOR
TRADITIONAL IRA
WE'LL GIVE YOU AN EDGE
Advertising Agency:
TBWA Chiat Day Los Angeles
5353 Grosvenor Blvd
Los Angeles, CA 90066
Tel.: (310) 305-5000
Fax: (310) 305-6000

PRIVATEBANCORP INC.
120 S LaSalle St
Chicago, IL 60603
Tel.: (312) 564-2000
Fax: (312) 683-7111
E-mail: pbadmin@theprivatebank.com
Web Site: www.privatebancorp.com
Approx. Rev.: $601,171,000
Approx. Number Employees: 1,060
Business Description:
Bank Holding Company
S.I.C.: 6712; 6029
N.A.I.C.S.: 551111; 522110
Media: 6-8
Personnel:
Ralph B. Mandell *(Co-Founder & Chm)*
Larry D. Richman *(Pres & CEO-PrivateBancorp)*
Karen B. Case *(Exec Mng Dir & Pres-Comml Real Estate)*
Bruce R. Hague *(Pres-Natl Comml Banking & Exec Mng Dir)*
Bruce S. Lubin *(Pres-Comml, Specialty Banking-Illinois & Exec Mng Dir)*
Kevin M. Killips *(CFO & Mng Dir)*
C. Brant Ahrens *(Mng Dir & COO)*
Elizabeth Cummings *(Mng Dir & CIO)*
Kevin J. Van Solkema *(Chief Credit Officer & Mng Dir)*
Joan Schellhorn *(Chief HR Officer & Mng Dir)*
Leonard Wiatr *(Mng Dir & Chief Risk Officer)*
Jennifer R. Evans *(Mng Dir, Gen Counsel & Corp Sec)*
Hammad Pirzada *(Treas & Mng Dir)*
Brands & Products:
CDARS
FOCUS. EXECUTION. CONTINUITY. CONFIDENTIALITY.
PRIVATEBANCORP
THE PRIVATEBANK

Key to Media (For complete agency information see *The Advertising Red Books-Agencies* edition):
1. Bus. Publs. 2. Cable T.V. 3. Catalogs & Directories. 4. Co-op Adv. 5. Consumer Mags. 6. D.M. to Bus. Estab.7. D.M. to Consumers
8. Daily Newsp. 9. Exhibits/Trade Shows 10. Foreign 11. Infomercial 12. Internet Adv.13. Multimedia 14. Network Radio
15. Network T.V. 16. Newsp. Distr. Mags. 17. Other 18. Outdoor (Posters, Transit) 19. Point of Purchase20. Premiums, Novelties
21. Product Samples 22. Special Events Mktg. 23. Spot Radio 24. Spot T.V. 25. Weekly Newsp. 26. Yellow Page Adv.

PrivateBancorp Inc. — (Continued)

Advertising Agency:
Tom, Dick & Harry Advertising
350 W Erie 2nd Fl
Chicago, IL 60654
Tel.: (312) 327-9500
Fax: (312) 327-9501

PROSERO INCORPORATED

1200 Ashwood Pkwy Ste 450
Atlanta, GA 30338-4749
Tel.: (678) 731-8500
Fax: (678) 731-8700
E-mail: info@procero.net
Web Site: www.prosero.net
Sales Range: $1-9.9 Million
Approx. Number Employees: 100
Year Founded: 1999
Business Description:
Procurement Outsourcing Services
S.I.C.: 6289
N.A.I.C.S.: 523999
Advertising Expenditures: $200,000
Media: 2-7-13
Brands & Products:
PROSERO

PROSPERITY BANCSHARES, INC.

Prosperity Bank Plaza 4295 San Felipe
Houston, TX 77027-2942
Tel.: (713) 693-9300
Fax: (713) 693-9309
E-mail: investor.relations@prosperitybanktx.com
Web Site: www.prosperitybanktx.com
Approx. Rev.: $438,370,000
Approx. Number Employees: 1,708
Year Founded: 1983
Business Description:
Bank Holding Company
S.I.C.: 6712; 6029
N.A.I.C.S.: 551111; 522110
Personnel:
Peter E. Fisher *(Vice Chm & Gen Counsel)*
H. E. Timanus, Jr. *(Vice Chm)*
David Zalman *(Sr Chm & CEO)*
David Hollaway *(CFO)*
Randy D. Hester *(Chief Lending Officer)*
Brands & Products:
PROSPERITY BANCSHARES
PROSPERITY BANK
Advertising Agency:
MMG
PO Box 2148
Cypress, TX 77410-2148
Tel.: (281) 894-7070

PROVIDENT COMMUNITY BANCSHARES, INC.

2700 Celanese Rd
Rock Hill, SC 29732
Tel.: (803) 325-9400
Fax: (864) 429-1884
Toll Free: (888) 427-9002
Web Site: www.providentonline.com
Approx. Rev.: $20,141,000
Approx. Number Employees: 69
Year Founded: 1994
Business Description:
Bank Holding Company
S.I.C.: 6035; 6029; 6712
N.A.I.C.S.: 522120; 522110; 551111
Advertising Expenditures: $41,000
Media: 17
Personnel:
Carl L. Mason *(Chm)*
Dwight V. Neese *(Pres & CEO)*
Mark F. Pack *(Pres & Chief Credit Officer)*
Richard H. Flake *(CFO & Exec VP)*
Lud W. Vaughn *(COO & Exec VP)*
Wanda J. Wells *(Chief Admin Officer, Sr VP & Crop Sec)*
Carolyn H. Belue *(Sr VP & Ops Admin Officer)*
John T. Poole, Jr. *(Sr VP & Reg Exec)*
Brenda Billardello *(VP, Dir-Trng & Banking Sles Mgr)*
Henry G. Alexander *(VP & Mgr-Comml Relationships)*
Holly Coffer *(Asst VP)*

PROVIDENT FINANCIAL HOLDINGS, INC.

3756 Central Ave
Riverside, CA 92506
Tel.: (951) 686-6060
Fax: (951) 782-6132
E-mail: service@myprovident.com
Web Site: www.myprovident.com
Approx. Int. Income: $58,689,000
Approx. Number Employees: 436
Year Founded: 1956
Business Description:
Banking Holding Company
S.I.C.: 6712; 6029
N.A.I.C.S.: 551111; 522110
Media: 7-8-9-20-22-23-25-26
Personnel:
Craig G. Blunden *(Chm & CEO)*
Donavon P. Ternes *(Pres, CFO, COO & Sec)*
Lilian Salter *(CIO & Sr VP)*
Richard L. Gale *(Sr VP-Provident Bank Mortgage)*
Kathryn R. Gonzales *(Sr VP-Retail Banking)*
David S. Weiant *(Chief Lending Officer & Sr VP)*
Deborah Hill *(VP-HR)*
Brands & Products:
PROVIDENT
PROVIDENT BANK

PROVIDENT FINANCIAL SERVICES, INC.

239 Washington St
Jersey City, NJ 07302
Tel.: (732) 590-9200
Toll Free: (800) 448-7768
E-mail: ken.wagner@providentnj.com
Web Site: www.providentnj.com
Approx. Rev.: $286,534,000
Approx. Number Employees: 863
Year Founded: 2002
Business Description:
Bank Holding Company
S.I.C.: 6712; 6035
N.A.I.C.S.: 551111; 522120
Advertising Expenditures: $4,049,000
Media: 6-8-11
Personnel:
Christopher P. Martin *(Chm, Pres & CEO)*
Thomas M. Lyons *(CFO & Exec VP)*
Frank S. Muzio *(Chief Acctg Officer & Sr VP)*
John F. Kuntz *(Gen Counsel & Sec)*
Kenneth J. Wagner *(Sr VP-IR)*
Brands & Products:
HASSEL FREE BANKING FOR BUSY PEOPLE
THE PROVIDENT BANK
Advertising Agency:
RM International
300 Lighting Way
Secaucus, NJ 07094
Tel.: (201) 902-1418

PROVIDENT NEW YORK BANCORP

400 Rella Blvd
Montebello, NY 10901
Tel.: (845) 369-8040
Fax: (845) 369-8066
Web Site: www.providentbanking.com
Approx. Rev.: $146,975,000
Approx. Number Employees: 497
Business Description:
Bank Holding Company
S.I.C.: 6712
N.A.I.C.S.: 551111
Advertising Expenditures: $3,252,000
Personnel:
William F. Helmer *(Chm)*
Dennis L. Coyle *(Vice Chm)*
Jack L. Kopnisky *(Pres & CEO)*
Paul A. Maisch *(CFO & Exec VP)*
Daniel G. Rothstein *(Chief Risk Officer, Gen Counsel & Exec VP)*
Stephen G. Dormer *(Exec VP-Comml Lending & Strategic Plng)*
Richard O. Jones *(Exec VP-Bus Svcs)*
Carl Capuano *(Sr VP)*
John J. Fitzpatrick *(Sr VP)*
Alfred Friedman *(Chief Auditor & Sr VP)*
William Lamadore *(Sr VP)*

PRUDENTIAL FINANCIAL, INC.

751 Broad St
Newark, NJ 07102-3777
Tel.: (973) 802-6000
Fax: (973) 802-4479
Toll Free: (800) THEROCK
Web Site: www.prudential.com
Approx. Rev.: $38,414,000,000
Approx. Number Employees: 41,044
Year Founded: 1875
Business Description:
Insurance, Real Estate & Financial Investment Services
S.I.C.: 6311; 6099; 6289; 6371; 6531
N.A.I.C.S.: 524113; 522320; 523999; 525990; 531390
Advertising Expenditures: $105,000,000
Media: 2-3-6-8-9-11-13-14-15-16-17-18-20-23-24-26
Distr.: Natl.
Budget Set: Sept.
Personnel:
John Robert Strangfeld, Jr. *(Chm, Pres & CEO)*
Mark B. Grier *(Vice Chm)*
Arvind Rajan *(Mng Dir, Head-Quantitative Res & Risk Mgmt)*
Ric Abel *(Mng Dir)*
Clifford Axelson *(Mng Dir)*
David Brooker *(Mng Dir)*
Robert Derrick *(Mng Dir)*
Jeffrey L. Dickson *(Mng Dir)*
Scott Fischer *(Mng Dir)*
Charles King *(Mng Dir)*
Randall Kob *(Mng Dir)*
Richard J. Carbone *(CFO & Exec VP)*
Charles E. Lowrey *(COO & Exec VP)*
Kara Segreto *(CMO-Retirement)*
Helen M. Galt *(Chief Risk Officer, Sr VP, Company Actuary)*
John W. Greene, Jr. *(Pres-Agency Distr)*
Peter Green *(Principal)*
Susan L. Blount *(Gen Counsel & Sr VP)*
Robert C. Golden *(Exec VP-Ops & Sys)*
Billy Greer *(Sr VP)*
Andrew Mako *(Sr VP-Products Mktg & Strategic Initiatives)*
Mitchell Reed *(Sr VP)*
Sharon C. Taylor *(Sr VP-HR)*
Ching-Meei Chang *(VP-Product Performance & Actuary)*
John Ehrle *(VP-Sls)*
Peter Bandarenko *(Dir-Natl Sls & Advanced Markets)*
Frank Boesch *(Dir-Customer Mktg & Acq)*
Craig Cooperman *(Dir-Search & eMktg Campaigns)*
Uttara Patla *(Dir-Internal Comm)*
Todd Stauffacher *(Dir-Bus Intelligence)*
Cynthia Crossland *(Mgr-Transition)*
Ted Yoon *(Mgr-Digital Strategy)*
Brands & Products:
GROWING AND PROTECTING YOUR WEALTH
PRUDENTIAL

PSB HOLDINGS, INC.

1905 W Stewart Ave
Wausau, WI 54402-1686
Tel.: (715) 842-2191
Fax: (715) 842-3418
E-mail: scattanach@psbwi.com
Web Site: www.psbwi.com
Approx. Rev.: $35,028,000
Approx. Number Employees: 126
Business Description:
Bank Holding Company
S.I.C.: 6141; 6029; 6712
N.A.I.C.S.: 522210; 522110; 551111
Advertising Expenditures: $355,000
Personnel:
Gordon P. Gullickson *(Chm)*
Peter W. Knitt *(Pres & CEO)*
Scott M. Cattanach *(CFO, Treas, Sec & Sr VP)*

PULASKI FINANCIAL CORP.

12300 Olive Blvd
Creve Coeur, MO 63141-6434
Tel.: (314) 878-2210
Fax: (314) 878-7130
E-mail: jobs@pulaskibankstl.com
Web Site: www.pulaskibankstl.com
Approx. Rev.: $79,944,668
Approx. Number Employees: 457
Business Description:
Bank Holding Company
S.I.C.: 6712; 6035
N.A.I.C.S.: 551111; 522120
Advertising Expenditures: $566,000
Media: 9-20-23-24-25
Personnel:
Stanley J. Bradshaw *(Chm)*
Lee S. Wielansky *(Vice Chm)*
Gary W. Douglass *(Pres & CEO)*
Paul J. Milano *(CFO, Treas, Sec, Sr VP & Controller)*
Brian Boyles *(Pres-Mortgage Div)*

Key to Media (For complete agency information see *The Advertising Red Books-Agencies* edition):
1. Bus. Publs. 2. Cable T.V. 3. Catalogs & Directories. 4. Co-op Adv. 5. Consumer Mags. 6. D.M. to Bus. Estab.7. D.M. to Consumers 8. Daily Newsp. 9. Exhibits/Trade Shows 10. Foreign 11. Infomercial 12. Internet Adv.13. Multimedia 14. Network Radio 15. Network T.V. 16. Newsp. Distr. Mags. 17. Other 18. Outdoor (Posters, Transit) 19. Point of Purchase20. Premiums, Novelties 21. Product Samples 22. Special Events Mktg. 23. Spot Radio 24. Spot T.V. 25. Weekly Newsp. 26. Yellow Page Adv.

PUTNAM COUNTY SAVINGS BANK INC.
2477 Rte 6
Brewster, NY 10509-0417
Mailing Address:
PO Box 417
Brewster, NY 10509-0417
Tel.: (845) 279-7101
Fax: (845) 279-9175
Web Site: www.pcsb.com
Approx. Number Employees: 88
Year Founded: 1871
Business Description:
Financial Services
S.I.C.: 6035
N.A.I.C.S.: 522120
Personnel:
Daniel S. Ryan *(Chm, Pres & CEO)*
Advertising Agency:
Problem Solvers, Inc.
(Sub. of Elser & Aucone, Inc.)
521 5th Ave Ste 630
New York, NY 10175
Tel.: (212) 687-5590
Fax: (212) 867-3761

PUTNAM INVESTMENTS, LLC
(Sub. of Great-West Lifeco, Inc.)
1 Post Office Sq
Boston, MA 02109
Tel.: (617) 292-1000
Fax: (800) 250-8211
Web Site: www.putnam.com
Approx. Number Employees: 3,500
Business Description:
Investment Management Services
S.I.C.: 6722; 6282; 8742
N.A.I.C.S.: 525910; 523930; 541611
Personnel:
Robert L. Reynolds *(Pres & CEO)*
Jeffrey R. Carney *(Sr Mng Dir & Head-Global Mktg & Products)*
William T. Connolly *(Sr Mng Dir & Head-Global Distribution)*
Mark McKenna *(Mng Dir & Head-Mktg & Comm)*
Nick C. Thakore *(Mng Dir & Portfolio Mgr-Putnam Voyager Fund)*
Robert D. Ewing *(Mng Dir & Grp Leader-Domestic Equity)*
Scott Sipple *(Mng Dir)*
Walter C. Donovan *(Chief Investment Officer)*
Anne Lundberg *(Sr VP & Mgr-Consultant Rels-Midwest Reg)*
David Depew *(Mgr-Risk)*
Advertising Agencies:
Hill Holliday
53 State St
Boston, MA 02109
Tel.: (617) 366-4000

Trinity Communications, Inc.
180 Canal St
Boston, MA 02114
Tel.: (617) 292-7300
Fax: (617) 292-7400

PVF CAPITAL CORP.
30000 Aurora Rd
Solon, OH 44139
Tel.: (440) 248-7171
Fax: (440) 542-6063
E-mail: info@parkviewfederal.com
Web Site: www.parkviewfederal.com
Approx. Rev.: $32,981,776
Approx. Number Employees: 159
Year Founded: 1994
Business Description:
Bank Holding Company
S.I.C.: 6712
N.A.I.C.S.: 551111
Advertising Expenditures: $204,089
Media: 2-6-9-18-23-24-25
Personnel:
Mark D. Grossi *(Chm)*
Robert J. King, Jr. *(Pres & CEO)*
James H. Nicholson *(CFO & Exec VP)*
William J. Harr, Jr. *(Sr VP-Lending)*
Mei-Lan Chang *(VP-Info Sys)*
Adeline Novak *(VP-HR)*
J. Thomas Peyton *(VP-Info Sys)*

Q LOTUS HOLDINGS, INC.
1221 Brickell Ave Ste 934
Miami, FL 33131
Tel.: (786) 245-7615
E-mail: info@qlotuspe.com
Web Site: www.qlotuspe.com
Business Description:
Investment Services
S.I.C.: 6289
N.A.I.C.S.: 523999
Advertising Expenditures: $369,000
Personnel:
Marckensie S. Theresias *(Chm & Pres)*
Gary A. Rosenberg *(CEO)*
Robert H. Daskal *(CFO)*
Daniel Kurzweil *(COO)*

QC HOLDINGS, INC.
9401 Indian Creek Pwy Ste 1500
Overland Park, KS 66210
Tel.: (913) 234-5000
Fax: (913) 234-5500
Toll Free: (866) 660-2243
E-mail: receptionist@qcholdings.com
Web Site: www.qcholdings.com
Approx. Rev.: $188,088,000
Approx. Number Employees: 1,681
Year Founded: 1992
Business Description:
Payday Loan Stores Operator
S.I.C.: 6141
N.A.I.C.S.: 522291
Advertising Expenditures: $2,400,000
Personnel:
Don Early *(Chm & CEO)*
Mary Lou Andersen *(Vice Chm & Sec)*
Darrin J. Andersen *(Pres & COO)*
Douglas E. Nickerson *(CFO)*
Robert L. Albin *(Sr VP)*

QCR HOLDINGS, INC.
3551 7th St Ste 204
Moline, IL 61265
Tel.: (309) 736-3584
Fax: (309) 736-3149
Web Site: www.qcbt.com
Approx. Rev.: $95,503,254
Approx. Number Employees: 343
Year Founded: 1993
Business Description:
Bank Holding Company
S.I.C.: 6712; 6029
N.A.I.C.S.: 551111; 522110
Advertising Expenditures: $991,243
Media: 22
Personnel:
James J. Brownson *(Chm)*
Douglas M. Hultquist *(Pres & CEO)*
Todd A. Gipple *(CFO, COO & Exec VP)*
William M. Tank *(Chief Credit Officer & Exec VP)*
M. Randolf Westlund *(Chief Investment Officer & Exec VP)*
Victor J. Quinn *(Exec VP & Dir-Funds Mgmt)*
John A. Rodriguez *(Exec VP-Deposit Ops & Informational Svcs)*
Cathie S. Whiteside *(Exec VP-Corp Strategy & Branding)*
Jill A. DeKeyser *(Sr VP & Dir-HR)*
Shawna M. Graham *(Sr VP & Dir-Risk Mgmt)*
R. Timothy Harding *(Sr VP & Dir-Internal Audit)*
Shellee R. Showalter *(Sr VP & Dir-Fin & Budgeting)*
Kathleen M. Francque *(Sr VP-Correspondent Banking & Info Svcs)*
John R. Oakes *(VP, Controller & Dir-Fin Reporting)*
Pamela J. Goodwin *(VP & Mgr-Loan Ops)*
Beth L. Easteria *(Asst VP-Deposit Ops & Mgr-Electronic Banking)*

QUEENS COUNTY SAVINGS BANK
(Div. of New York Community Bank)
13665 Roosevelt Ave
Flushing, NY 11354
Tel.: (516) 683-4408
Fax: (718) 460-4844
Web Site: www.nycb.com
Approx. Int. Income: $134,800,992
Approx. Number Employees: 120
Year Founded: 1993
Business Description:
Non-Federal Savings Institutions
S.I.C.: 6035
N.A.I.C.S.: 522120
Import Export
Media: 10
Personnel:
John Lee *(Mgr)*

QUEST CAPITAL CORP.
(Name Changed to Sprott Resource Lending Corp.)

QUICKEN LOANS, INC.
(Sub. of RockBridge Growth Equity LLC)
1050 Woodward Ave
Detroit, MI 48226
Tel.: (734) 805-5000
Fax: (734) 805-7075
Toll Free: (800) 863-4332
E-mail: help@quickenloans.com
Web Site: www.quickenloans.com
Approx. Number Employees: 3,600
Business Description:
Online Retail Mortgage Lender
S.I.C.: 6531
N.A.I.C.S.: 522310
Personnel:
Dan Gilbert *(Founder & Chm)*
Patrick McInnis *(Pres & COO)*
William Emerson *(CEO)*
Robert Walters *(Chief Economist & VP)*
Advertising Agency:
Anthem Worldwide
77 Maiden Ln 4th Fl
San Francisco, CA 94108
Tel.: (415) 896-9399
Fax: (415) 896-9387

QUOTEMEDIA, INC.
17100 Shea Blvd Ste 230
Fountain Hills, AZ 85268
Tel.: (480) 905-7311
E-mail: billing@quotemedia.com
Web Site: www.quotemedia.com
Approx. Rev.: $7,804,805
Approx. Number Employees: 50
Business Description:
Financial Stock Market Data, Market News Feeds, Market Research Information & Financial Software Solutions
S.I.C.: 4311; 2741
N.A.I.C.S.: 491110; 516110
Advertising Expenditures: $360,000
Personnel:
R. Keith Guelpa *(Co-Founder, Pres & CEO)*
Robert J. Thompson *(Chm)*
Keith J. Randall *(CFO, Sec & VP)*
Advertising Agency:
Christensen
14 Wall St Ste 2001
New York, NY 10005
Tel.: (212) 618-1978

RABIN WORLDWIDE, INC.
650 Townsend Ctr Ste 480
San Francisco, CA 94103-6225
Tel.: (415) 522-5700
Fax: (415) 522-5701
Toll Free: (800) 421-2144
E-mail: info@rabin.com
Web Site: www.rabin.com
Approx. Sls.: $50,000,000
Approx. Number Employees: 20
Business Description:
Financial Services for Businesses in Transition
S.I.C.: 5961
N.A.I.C.S.: 454112
Media: 2
Personnel:
Richard Reese *(Pres)*
Michael Bank *(Sr VP)*

RABO CAPITAL SERVICES, INC.
(Sub. of Cooperatieve Centrale Raiffeisen-Boerenleenbank B.A.)
(d/b/a Rabobank International - U.S.A.)
245 Park Ave
New York, NY 10167
Tel.: (212) 916-7800
Web Site:
www.rabobankamerica.com/wholesale/index.jsp
Approx. Number Employees: 200
Year Founded: 1980
Business Description:
Corporate Banking, Financial Market & Merger Advisory Services
S.I.C.: 6211; 6082; 6099; 6282
N.A.I.C.S.: 523110; 522293; 522390; 523930
Media: 2-7-8-13-24-26
Advertising Agency:
Doremus
(Sub. of Omnicom Group, Inc.)
200 Varick St 11Fl
New York, NY 10014-4810
Tel.: (212) 366-3000
Fax: (212) 366-3060

RAMPART CAPITAL CORPORATION
16401 Country Club Dr
Crosby, TX 77532
Tel.: (713) 223-4610
Fax: (713) 223-4814
Web Site: www.rampart-capital.com

Key to Media (For complete agency information see *The Advertising Red Books-Agencies* edition):
1. Bus. Publs. 2. Cable T.V. 3. Catalogs & Directories. 4. Co-op Adv. 5. Consumer Mags. 6. D.M. to Bus. Estab.7. D.M. to Consumers
8. Daily Newsp. 9. Exhibits/Trade Shows 10. Foreign 11. Infomercial 12. Internet Adv.13. Multimedia 14. Network Radio
15. Network T.V. 16. Newsp. Distr. Mags. 17. Other 18. Outdoor (Posters, Transit) 19. Point of Purchase20. Premiums, Novelties
21. Product Samples 22. Special Events Mktg. 23. Spot Radio 24. Spot T.V. 25. Weekly Newsp. 26. Yellow Page Adv.

Rampart Capital Corporation — (Continued)

Sales Range: $1-9.9 Million
Approx. Number Employees: 6
Year Founded: 1994
Business Description:
Financial & Business Services
S.I.C.: 6552; 1531
N.A.I.C.S.: 237210; 236117
Media: 9
Personnel:
C.W. Janke *(Chm & CEO)*
J.H. Carpenter *(Pres & COO)*

RAYMOND JAMES FINANCIAL, INC.
The Raymond James Fin Ctr 880 Carillon Pkwy
Saint Petersburg, FL 33716-2749
Tel.: (727) 567-1000
Toll Free: (800) 248-8863
Web Site: www.raymondjames.com
Approx. Rev.: $2,979,516,000
Approx. Number Employees: 7,200
Year Founded: 1962
Business Description:
Investment & Financial Planning
S.I.C.: 6719; 6211; 6282
N.A.I.C.S.: 551112; 523110; 523120; 523930
Media: 2-3-6-9-14-15-17-22-23-24-26
Distr.: Natl.
Personnel:
Thomas A. James *(Chm)*
Francis S. Godbold *(Vice Chm)*
Paul C. Reilly *(CEO)*
Jeffrey P. Julien *(CFO & Exec VP-Fin)*
Chet B. Helck *(COO)*
J. Timothy Eitel *(CIO & Sr VP)*
Angela M. Biever *(Chief Admin Officer)*
Dennis W. Zank *(Pres-Raymond James & Assoc)*
Richard K. Riess *(CEO-Eagle Asset Mgmt & Exec VP-Asset Mgmt)*
Paul L. Matecki *(Gen Counsel & Sr VP)*
Thomas R. Tremaine *(Exec VP-Ops, Admin-Raymond James & Associates)*
Jeffrey E. Trocin *(Exec VP-Equity Capital Markets)*
Trudy Bixby *(Sr VP-Customer Ops)*
Denise Ganster Samson *(Sr VP-Ops)*
Van C. Sayler *(Sr VP-Fixed Income-Raymond James & Associates)*
Pam Ward *(Sr VP-HR)*
Jonathan Oorlog *(VP-Fin Reporting)*
Anthea Penrose *(Mgr-PR)*
Brands & Products:
RAYMOND JAMES
Advertising Agencies:
Dukas Public Relations, Inc.
100 W 26th St 2nd Fl
New York, NY 10001
Tel.: (212) 704-7385
Fax: (212) 242-3646

Fitzgerald+CO
3060 Peachtree Rd NW
Atlanta, GA 30305
Tel.: (404) 504-6900
Fax: (404) 239-0548

Martin/Williams Advertising Inc.
(A Member of Omnicom Group)
60 S 6th St Ste 2800
Minneapolis, MN 55402-4428
Tel.: (612) 340-0800
Fax: (612) 342-9700

RJ Communications
880 Carillon Pkwy
Saint Petersburg, FL 33716
Tel.: (727) 567-8711
Fax: (727) 567-8927
Toll Free: (800) 248-8863
(Financial Services)

RBC BANCORPORATION (USA)
(Sub. of Royal Bank of Canada)
3201 Beechleaf Ct
Raleigh, NC 27604
Tel.: (919) 788-5938
Fax: (919) 788-7502
Toll Free: (888) 680-5064
Web Site: www.rbcbankusa.com
E-Mail For Key Personnel:
Marketing Director: tearley@centura.com
Sales Range: $650-699.9 Million
Approx. Number Employees: 5,500
Year Founded: 1990
Business Description:
Bank Holding Company
S.I.C.: 6712; 6029; 6035
N.A.I.C.S.: 551111; 522110; 522120
Media: 7-8-13-23-24-26
Personnel:
Jim Westlake *(Chm & CEO)*
John Holcomb *(Vice Chm)*
Reggie Davis *(Pres)*
Glenn McCoy *(CFO)*
Dan Wall *(Exec VP & Chief Credit/Risk Officer)*
Tracy Stevenson *(Exec VP-Sls Strategy)*
Joe Cooper *(Sr VP-Tech & Ops)*
Blake Coules *(Sr VP-Real Estate & Asset Resolution)*
Susan Uchida *(VP-HR)*
Advertising Agencies:
The Buntin Group
1001 Hawkins St
Nashville, TN 37203-4758
Tel.: (615) 244-5720
Fax: (615) 244-6511

Buntin Out-of-Home Media
1001 Hawkins St
Nashville, TN 37203-4758
Tel.: (615) 244-5720
Fax: (615) 244-6511

Capstrat
1201 Edwards Mill Rd 1st Fl
Raleigh, NC 27607-3625
Tel.: (919) 828-0806
Fax: (919) 834-7959

Vargas & Amigos Inc.
3055 Waterfront Cir
Marietta, GA 30062-5659
Tel.: (770) 992-9771
Fax: (770) 992-9778

RBC CAPITAL MARKETS
(Unit of RBC Capital Markets Corporation)
2 Embarcadero Ctr Ste 1200
San Francisco, CA 94111
Tel.: (415) 633-8500
Fax: (415) 633-8635
Toll Free: (800) 652-1030
E-mail: info@rbccm.com
Web Site: www.rbccm.com
Year Founded: 1858
Business Description:
Equity Research Investment
S.I.C.: 6211
N.A.I.C.S.: 523120
Media: 2-4-5-6-9-16-25-26
Distr.: Reg.
Budget Set: Mar.
Personnel:
Dan Asma *(Pres)*
Anthony George Gero *(Sr VP)*
Jake Herman *(Mgr-Natl Sls)*
Jaimie Barry *(Coord-Mktg-Reg)*

RBC WEALTH MANAGEMENT
(Unit of RBC Wealth Management)
345 California St
San Francisco, CA 94104
Tel.: (415) 445-8500
Fax: (415) 398-7434
Fax: (415) 391-9586
Toll Free: (800) 557-8876
Web Site: www.rbcwm-usa.com
Sales Range: $1-4.9 Billion
Approx. Number Employees: 1,000
Year Founded: 1858
Business Description:
Investment & Trading Services
S.I.C.: 6211
N.A.I.C.S.: 523120
Media: 2-4-5-6-9-16-25-26
Distr.: Reg.
Budget Set: Mar.
Personnel:
H. H. Hardee *(Chief Investment Officer & Sr VP)*

REALTY INCOME CORPORATION
600 La Terraza Blvd
Escondido, CA 92025-3873
Tel.: (760) 741-2111
Fax: (760) 741-2235
E-mail: contact@realtyincome.com
Web Site: www.realtyincome.com
Approx. Rev.: $345,009,000
Approx. Number Employees: 79
Business Description:
Real Estate Investment Trust
S.I.C.: 6798
N.A.I.C.S.: 525930
Media: 10
Personnel:
Thomas A. Lewis, Jr. *(Vice Chm & CEO)*
Gary M. Malino *(Pres & COO)*
Paul M. Meurer *(CFO, Treas & Exec VP)*
John P. Case *(Chief Investment Officer & Exec VP)*
Michael R. Pfeiffer *(Gen Counsel, Sec & Exec VP)*
Richard G. Collins *(Exec VP-Portfolio Mgmt)*
Laura S. King *(Sr VP & Asst Gen Counsel)*
Robert J. Israel *(Sr VP-Res)*
Sumit Roy *(Sr VP-Real Estate Acq)*
Tere H. Miller *(VP-Corp Comm & IR)*
Scott Kohnen *(Dir-Res)*

REFCO INC.
1 World Financial Center 200 Liberty St Tower A
New York, NY 10281
Tel.: (212) 693-7000
Fax: (212) 693-7831
E-mail: webmaster@refco.com
Web Site: www.refco.com
Sales Range: $1-4.9 Billion
Approx. Number Employees: 2,434
Year Founded: 1969
Business Description:
Holding Company
S.I.C.: 6719
N.A.I.C.S.: 551112
Media: 2-13

REGIONS FINANCIAL CORPORATION
1900 5th Ave N
Birmingham, AL 35203
Tel.: (205) 944-1300
Fax: (205) 580-3915
Toll Free: (800) 734-4667
Telex: 59-6259
E-mail: list.underwood@regions.com
Web Site: www.regions.com
Approx. Int. Income: $4,689,000,000
Approx. Number Employees: 27,829
Year Founded: 1971
Business Description:
Bank Holding Company
S.I.C.: 6712; 6029; 6141
N.A.I.C.S.: 551111; 522110; 522291
Media: 6-8-9-13-14-15-18-20-23-24-25
Personnel:
O. B. Grayson Hall, Jr. *(Pres & CEO)*
Terry Katon *(Mng Dir & Head-Comml Loan Syndications)*
David J. Turner, Jr. *(CFO & Sr Exec VP-Exec Council & Operating Committee)*
Scott Peters *(CMO & Sr Exec VP-Operating Committee)*
Christopher Michaud *(CTO-Regions Insurance Grp)*
David B. Edmonds *(Chief Admin Officer)*
Brad Kimbrough *(Chief Acctg Officer, Exec VP & Controller)*
Bill Ritter *(Pres-Central Reg & Sr VP)*
Fournier J. Gale, III *(Gen Counsel & Sr Exec VP)*
Lynetta Tipton Steed *(Exec VP & Head-Community Banking Div)*
J. Kenneth Alderman *(Exec VP)*
John Barton *(Exec VP-Healthcare Grp)*
Joel Daves *(Exec VP)*
Guillermo R. Araoz *(Sr VP & Dir-Equity Res)*
Allen Oakley *(Sr VP & Mgr-Fin & Institutional Grp)*
Linda Germany Childs *(Sr VP-Corp Comm)*
David Sozio *(Mng Dir-Tech & Defense Banking Grp)*
Brands & Products:
REGIONS
Advertising Agency:
Luckie & Company
600 Luckie Dr Ste 150
Birmingham, AL 35223-2429
Tel.: (205) 879-2121
Fax: (205) 877-9855

RENASANT BANK
(Formerly Crescent Bank)
(Div. of Renasant Bank)
7 Caring way
Jasper, GA 30143
Mailing Address:
PO Box 668

Key to Media (For complete agency information see *The Advertising Red Books-Agencies* edition):
1. Bus. Publs. 2. Cable T.V. 3. Catalogs & Directories. 4. Co-op Adv. 5. Consumer Mags. 6. D.M. to Bus. Estab.7. D.M. to Consumers
8. Daily Newsp. 9. Exhibits/Trade Shows 10. Foreign 11. Infomercial 12. Internet Adv.13. Multimedia 14. Network Radio
15. Network T.V. 16. Newsp. Distr. Mags. 17. Other 18. Outdoor (Posters, Transit) 19. Point of Purchase20. Premiums, Novelties
21. Product Samples 22. Special Events Mktg. 23. Spot Radio 24. Spot T.V. 25. Weekly Newsp. 26. Yellow Page Adv.

Jasper, GA 30143
Tel.: (678) 454-2266
Fax: (678) 454-2299
Toll Free: (800) 872-7941
E-mail: btrivedi@crescentbank.com
Web Site: www.crescentbank.com
Approx. Rev.: $48,667,801
Approx. Number Employees: 164
Year Founded: 1989
Business Description:
Bank Holding Company
S.I.C.: 8732; 6029; 6712
N.A.I.C.S.: 541910; 522110; 551111
Media: 7-8-13
Personnel:
John S. Dean, Sr. *(Chm)*
J. Donald Boggus, Jr. *(Pres & CEO)*
Bonnie B. Boling *(Exec VP-Retail Admin-Crescent Bank)*
A. Bradley Rutledge *(Exec VP-Chief Loan Admin)*

RENASANT CORPORATION
209 Troy St
Tupelo, MS 38804-4827
Tel.: (662) 680-1001
Fax: (662) 680-1234
E-mail: info@renasant.com
Web Site: www.renasantbank.com
Approx. Rev.: $165,339,000
Approx. Number Employees: 996
Year Founded: 1982
Business Description:
Bank Holding Company
S.I.C.: 6712; 6029; 6035; 6141; 6411
N.A.I.C.S.: 551111; 522110; 522120; 522291; 524298
Import Export
Advertising Expenditures: $3,747,000
Personnel:
Michael D. Ross *(Pres)*
Edward Robinson McGraw *(CEO)*
Stuart R. Johnson *(CFO & Sr Exec VP)*
J. Scott Cochran *(Pres-Renasant Mississippi & Exec VP)*
Stephen M. Corban *(Gen Counsel & Sr Exec VP)*
Larry R. Mathews *(Sr Exec VP, Dir-Sls & Mktg)*
R. Rick Hart *(Exec VP)*
Phyllis C. Drope *(Sr VP)*

REPUBLIC BANCORP, INC.
601 W Market St
Louisville, KY 40202-2745
Tel.: (502) 584-3600
Fax: (502) 584-3753
Toll Free: (888) 584-3600
E-mail: info@republicbank.com
Web Site: www.republicbank.com
Approx. Rev.: $281,131,000
Approx. Number Employees: 744
Year Founded: 1998
Business Description:
Bank Holding Company
S.I.C.: 6029; 6712
N.A.I.C.S.: 522110; 551111
Media: 2-3-4-7-8-10-13-18-20-23-24-26
Personnel:
Steven E. Trager *(Chm & CEO)*
A. Scott Trager *(Pres)*
Kevin Sipes *(CFO)*
Michael Sadofsky *(Sr VP-Mktg)*
Lisa Butcher *(Mgr-Private Banking & VP)*

REPUBLIC BANK & TRUST COMPANY
(Sub. of Republic Bancorp, Inc.)
601 W Market St
Louisville, KY 40202
Tel.: (502) 584-3600
Fax: (502) 584-3753
Toll Free: (888) 782-3333
E-mail: info@republicbank.com
Web Site: www.republicbank.com
Sales Range: $250-299.9 Million
Approx. Number Employees: 650
Year Founded: 1982
Business Description:
Full Banking Services
S.I.C.: 6029; 6163
N.A.I.C.S.: 522110; 522310
Media: 4-7-8-18-20
Personnel:
Scott Trager *(Pres)*
Steven E. Trager *(CEO)*
Kevin Sipes *(CFO)*
Michael Sadofsky *(Sr VP-Mktg)*
Karen McGee *(VP & Mgr-Treasury Mgmt Ops)*

REPUBLIC FIRST BANCORP, INC.
50 S 16th St Ste 2400
Philadelphia, PA 19102
Tel.: (215) 735-4422
Fax: (215) 735-0508
Web Site: www.rfbkonline.com
Approx. Rev.: $43,148,000
Approx. Number Employees: 210
Year Founded: 1988
Business Description:
Bank Holding Company
S.I.C.: 6282; 6029
N.A.I.C.S.: 523920; 522110
Import Export
Advertising Expenditures: $379,000
Media: 17
Personnel:
Harry D. Madonna *(Chm & CEO)*
Frank A. Cavallaro *(CFO)*
Carol Hunter *(Sr VP & Chief Credit Officer)*
Patrick J. Morris *(Exec VP & Head-Comml Real Estate Grp)*

THE RESERVE GROUP
3560 W Market St Ste 300
Akron, OH 44333
Tel.: (330) 665-2900
Fax: (330) 665-2906
E-mail: info@reservegroup.com
Web Site: www.reservegroup.com
Approx. Number Employees: 3,000
Year Founded: 1995
Business Description:
Private Equity Firm
S.I.C.: 6289
N.A.I.C.S.: 523999
Media: 13-18
Personnel:
Richard M. Hamlin, Sr. *(Chm)*
Mark Hamlin, Jr. *(Pres & CEO)*
James D. Vantiem *(Exec VP)*

REVERA INC.
55 Standish Court 8th Fl
Mississauga, ON L5R 4B2, Canada
Tel.: (289) 360-1200
Fax: (289) 360-1201
Web Site: www.reveraliving.com
Sales Range: $800-899.9 Million
Approx. Number Employees: 6,000
Business Description:
Retirement Residences Operations
S.I.C.: 8059
N.A.I.C.S.: 623311
Media: 2-8-10-18-22-23-24-26
Personnel:
Derek J. Watchorn *(Pres & CEO)*
Alan Torrie *(COO)*
Frank Cerrone *(Gen Counsel, Sec & Sr VP)*
Mario Bedard *(Exec VP-Real Estate)*
Sheri Annable *(Sr VP-Fin)*
David Hamilton *(Sr VP-Devel & Construction)*
Mike Hubbert *(Sr VP)*
Stuart Lindeman *(Sr VP)*
Chris Mason *(Sr VP)*
Michael Miceli *(Sr VP)*
Tim Benson *(VP-IR & Corp Fin)*

RIOCAN REAL ESTATE INVESTMENT TRUST
2300 Yonge St Ste 500
PO Box 2386
Toronto, ON M4P 1E4, Canada
Tel.: (416) 866-3033
Fax: (416) 866-3020
Toll Free: (800) 465-2733
E-mail: inquiries@riocan.com
Web Site: www.riocan.com
E-Mail For Key Personnel:
Marketing Director: marketing@riocan.com
Approx. Rev.: $903,693,340
Approx. Number Employees: 598
Year Founded: 1993
Business Description:
Real Estate Investment Trust
S.I.C.: 6798
N.A.I.C.S.: 525930
Media: 2-10
Personnel:
Paul V. Godfrey *(Chm)*
Edward Sonshine *(Pres & CEO)*
Raghunath Davloor *(CFO, Sec & Sr VP)*
Frederic A. Waks *(COO & Exec VP)*
John Ballantyne *(Sr VP-Asset Mgmt)*
Michael Connolly *(Sr VP-Construction)*
Jonathan Gitlin *(Sr VP-Investments)*
Danny Kissoon *(Sr VP-Ops)*
Donald MacKinnon *(Sr VP-Real Estate Fin)*
Jordan Robins *(Sr VP-Plng & Dev)*
Jeff Ross *(Sr VP-Leasing)*
Suzanne Marineau *(VP-HR)*
Maria Rico *(VP-Fin Reporting)*
Christian W. Green *(Dir-IR & Compliance)*
Suanne Maureau *(Mgr-HR)*
Brands & Products:
RIO CAN

RISKMETRICS GROUP, INC.
(Sub. of MSCI Inc.)
1 Chase Manhattan Plz 44th Fl
New York, NY 10005
Tel.: (212) 981-7475
E-mail: sarah.cohn@riskmetrics.com
Web Site: www.riskmetrics.com
Approx. Rev.: $303,361,000
Approx. Number Employees: 1,103
Year Founded: 1994
Business Description:
Financial Planning, Risk & Wealth Management Services
S.I.C.: 6289; 6211; 6282; 6371
N.A.I.C.S.: 523999; 523110; 523930; 525990
Media: 7-10-17
Personnel:
Marc Ethan Berman *(CEO)*

RIVER BANK
(Sub. of LSB Corporation)
30 Massachusetts Ave
North Andover, MA 01845
Tel.: (978) 725-7670
Fax: (978) 725-7680
Web Site: www.riverbk.com
Sales Range: $1-4.9 Billion
Year Founded: 1868
Business Description:
Federal Reserve Bank
S.I.C.: 6035; 6029; 6163
N.A.I.C.S.: 522120; 522110; 522310
Advertising Agency:
White Rhino Productions, Inc.
41 Second Ave
Burlington, MA 01803
Tel.: (781) 270-4545
Fax: (781) 270-5151

RIVER VALLEY BANCORP
430 Clifty Dr
Madison, IN 47250
Mailing Address:
PO Box 1590
Madison, IN 47250-0590
Tel.: (812) 273-4949
Fax: (812) 273-4944
Toll Free: (800) 994-4849
E-mail: contactus@rvfbank.com
Web Site: www.rvfbank.com
Approx. Rev.: $22,536,000
Approx. Number Employees: 77
Year Founded: 1997
Business Description:
Saving & Loan Holding Company
S.I.C.: 6035; 6712
N.A.I.C.S.: 522120; 551111
Advertising Expenditures: $413,000
Media: 6-9-25
Personnel:
Fred W. Koehler *(Chm)*
Matthew P. Forrester *(Pres & CEO)*
Vickie Grimes *(CFO & VP)*
Crystal Barnes *(Compliance Officer)*
Sheri Furnish *(Officer-Loan)*
Katherine Rundall *(Officer-Loan)*
Andrew W. Ward *(Officer-Loan)*
Anthony D. Brandon *(Exec VP)*
Loy Skirvin *(VP-HR)*
Rick Nelson *(Asst VP-Madison Office)*
Alicia Berry *(Mgr-Electronic Svc Sls)*
Laura Denning *(Mgr-Loan Processing)*
Roger Smith *(Mgr-Acctg)*
Teresa Smith *(Mgr-Data Processing)*
Mary Ellen Wehner *(Mgr-Comml Loan Ops)*
Debbie Finnegan *(Auditor-Internal)*
Brands & Products:
RIVER VALLEY BANCORP

RIVERVIEW BANCORP, INC.
900 Washington St Ste 900
Vancouver, WA 98660
Tel.: (360) 693-6650
Fax: (360) 693-6275
Toll Free: (888) 834-6561
Web Site: www.riverviewbank.com
Approx. Rev.: $43,214,000
Approx. Number Employees: 238
Business Description:
Savings Bank Holding Company

RIVERVIEW BANCORP, INC. — (Continued)

S.I.C.: 6035
N.A.I.C.S.: 522120
Advertising Expenditures: $627,000
Personnel:
Patrick Sheaffer *(Chm & CEO)*
Ronald A. Wysaske *(Pres & COO)*
Kevin J. Lycklama *(CFO & Exec VP)*
David A. Dahlstrom *(Chief Credit Officer & Exec VP)*
James D. Baldovin *(Exec VP -Retail Banking)*
Kim J. Capeloto *(Exec VP-Mktg & Ops)*
John A. Karas *(Exec VP)*
Krista Holland *(Sr VP-HR-Riverview Community Bank)*

RIVERVIEW COMMUNITY BANK
(Sub. of RIVERVIEW BANCORP, INC.)
315 SW 5th Ave
Portland, OR 97204
Tel.: (503) 221-5801
Fax: (503) 221-6242
Web Site: www.apbank.com
Sales Range: $1-9.9 Million
Approx. Number Employees: 32
Year Founded: 1979
Business Description:
Personal & Commercial Banking
S.I.C.: 6029
N.A.I.C.S.: 522110
Media: 7-8-13-22
Personnel:
Patrick Sheaffer *(Chm & CEO)*
Ronald A. Wysaske *(Pres & COO)*
Kim J. Capeloto *(Exec VP)*
Steven Plambeck *(Sr VP & Dir-Medical Banking)*

RIVERVIEW FINANCIAL CORPORATION
(d/b/a Halifax National)
3rd & Market Streets
Halifax, PA 17032
Tel.: (717) 896-3433
Fax: (717) 896-8599
Web Site: www.halifaxnational.com
Approx. Rev.: $13,890,000
Approx. Number Employees: 55
Business Description:
Bank Holding Company
S.I.C.: 6712; 6029
N.A.I.C.S.: 551111; 522110
Advertising Expenditures: $64,000
Media: 17
Personnel:
David W. Hoover *(Chm)*
Kirk D. Fox *(Pres)*
Robert M. Garst *(CEO)*
Theresa M. Wasko *(CFO)*
Paul B. Zwally *(Chief Lending Officer & Exec VP)*

ROCKVILLE FINANCIAL INC.
(Sub. of Rockville Financial MHC, Inc.)
25 Park St
Rockville, CT 06066
Tel.: (860) 291-3600
Web Site: www.rockvillebank.com
Approx. Rev.: $85,103,000
Approx. Number Employees: 236
Business Description:
Bank Holding Company
S.I.C.: 6029; 6712
N.A.I.C.S.: 522110; 551111
Advertising Expenditures: $1,134,000
Personnel:
Raymond H. Lefurge, Jr. *(Founder & Chm)*
Michael A. Bars *(Vice Chm & Partner)*
William H. W. Crawford, IV *(Pres, CEO & Sr Exec VP)*
John T. Lund *(CFO, Treas & Sr VP)*
Ratna Ray *(CIO)*
Richard Trachimowicz *(Exec VP)*
Darlene S. White *(Sr VP & Officer-Ops)*
Christopher E. Buchholz *(Exec VP)*
Richard DiChiara *(Sr VP & Retail Banking Officer)*
Mark A. Kucia *(Sr VP & Comml Banking Officer)*
Laurie A. Rosner *(Sr VP-Mktg & Admin Svcs Officer)*

RODMAN & RENSHAW CAPITAL GROUP, INC.
1251 Ave of the Americas 20th Fl
New York, NY 10020
Tel.: (212) 356-0500
Fax: (212) 581-5690
E-mail: info@rodm.com
Web Site: www.rodmanandrenshaw.com
Approx. Rev.: $83,615,000
Approx. Number Employees: 131
Business Description:
Investment Banking Services
S.I.C.: 6211; 6282; 7389
N.A.I.C.S.: 523110; 523930; 561499
Advertising Expenditures: $1,582,000
Personnel:
Wesley K. Clark *(Chm)*
Michael Vasinkevich *(Vice Chm, Sr Mng Dir & Partner)*
Edward Rubin *(CEO)*
John J. Borer, III *(Sr Mng Dir & Head-Investment Banking)*
F. Alger Boyer *(Mng Dir)*
David Strupp *(Mng Dir)*
David Jay Horin *(CFO)*
Xen A. Galinas *(Mng Dir-Investment Banking Grp-Rodman & Renshaw, LLC)*
Gordon K. Johnson *(Mng Dir-Healthcare Investment Banking-Rodman & Renshaw, LLC)*

ROMA FINANCIAL CORPORATION
Washington Town Center Office 2300 Rt 33
Robbinsville, NJ 08691
Tel.: (609) 223-8300
Toll Free: (877) 227-5787
Web Site: www.romabank.com
Approx. Rev.: $73,782,000
Approx. Number Employees: 317
Business Description:
Bank Holding Company: Federally-Chartered Mutual Holding Company
S.I.C.: 6035; 6029; 6289; 6712
N.A.I.C.S.: 522120; 522110; 523999; 551111
Advertising Expenditures: $827,000
Media: 7-23-24
Personnel:
Maurice T. Perilli *(Chm)*
Peter A. Inverso *(Pres & CEO)*
Sharon L. Lamont *(CFO)*
Madhusudhan Kotta *(Treas & Sr VP)*
C. Keith Pericoloso *(Exec VP)*
Robert W. Sumner *(Sr VP-IT)*
Peter Villa *(Sr VP-Lending)*
Barry J. Zadworny *(Sr VP-Compliance)*

ROMA FINANCIAL CORP.
(Sub. of Roma Financial Corporation)
2300 Rte 33
Robbinsville, NJ 08691-1411
Tel.: (609) 223-8300
Fax: (609) 223-8209
Toll Free: (888) 440-ROMA
Web Site: www.romabank.com
Approx. Number Employees: 120
Year Founded: 1920
Business Description:
Federal Savings Institutions
S.I.C.: 6035
N.A.I.C.S.: 522120
Import Export
Media: 2
Personnel:
Barry Zadworny *(Sr VP-Compliance)*
C. Keith Pericoloso *(VP-Ops & Gen Mgr)*
Richard Rosall *(VP & Asst Controller)*

ROME BANCORP, INC.
(Name Changed to Berkshire Bank)

ROSLYN SAVINGS BANK
(Div. of New York Community Bank)
1 Jericho Plz
Jericho, NY 11753
Tel.: (516) 942-6000
Fax: (516) 942-6065
Web Site: www.roslyn.com
Sales Range: $550-599.9 Million
Approx. Number Employees: 780
Year Founded: 1876
Business Description:
Banking
S.I.C.: 6035; 6163
N.A.I.C.S.: 522120; 522310
Advertising Expenditures: $2,000,000
Media: 4-7-8-13-22

ROTHSCHILD INC.
(Sub. of Rothschilds Continuation Holdings AG)
1251 Ave of the Americas 51st Fl
New York, NY 10020-1104
Tel.: (212) 403-3500
Fax: (212) 403-3501
E-mail: info@rothschild.com
Web Site: www.rothschild.com
Approx. Number Employees: 300
Year Founded: 1967
Business Description:
Investment Banking; Trading & Venture Capital
S.I.C.: 6211; 6282
N.A.I.C.S.: 523110; 523930
Media: 2-8-9-11-17
Distr.: Natl.
Personnel:
Roger H. Kimmel *(Vice Chm)*
John D. Mcgurk *(Partner)*
Laurence S. Grafstein *(Mng Dir)*
Todd R. Snyder *(Mng Dir)*
Mark K. Tavel *(Mng Dir)*
Steven H. Tishman *(Mng Dir)*

ROTHSCHILD NORTH AMERICA INC.
(Sub. of Rothschilds Continuation Holdings AG)
1251 Ave Of The Americas
New York, NY 10020-1104
Tel.: (212) 403-3500
Fax: (212) 403-3501
Web Site: www.rothschild.com
Approx. Number Employees: 250
Year Founded: 1987
Business Description:
Investment Services
S.I.C.: 6211; 6159
N.A.I.C.S.: 523110; 522298
Advertising Expenditures: $600,000
Media: 2-8-9-11
Distr.: Natl.
Personnel:
David de Rothschild *(Chm)*
Christopher Lawrence *(Deputy Chm-Global Investment Banking)*
Jim Lawrence *(CEO)*
David Resnick *(Mng Dir & Co-Head-Investment Banking)*

ROTHSTEIN KASS & CO. PC
4 Becker Farm Rd Ste 2
Roseland, NJ 07068
Tel.: (973) 994-6666
Fax: (973) 994-0337
Web Site: www.rkco.com
Approx. Sls.: $42,000,000
Approx. Number Employees: 750
Business Description:
Certified Public Accountant
S.I.C.: 8721
N.A.I.C.S.: 541211
Media: 2
Personnel:
Steven Kass *(Co-CEO & Co-Mng Principal)*
Carl J. Scheuten *(Partner)*
Austine Olson *(Dir-Mktg)*

ROYAL BANCSHARES OF PENNSYLVANIA, INC.
732 Montgomery Ave
Narberth, PA 19072
Tel.: (610) 668-4700
Fax: (610) 668-1185
Toll Free: (800) 417-5198
E-mail: info@royalbankamerica.com
Web Site: www.royalbankpa.com
Approx. Int. Income: $57,262,000
Approx. Number Employees: 155
Year Founded: 1982
Business Description:
Savings Bank Holding Company
S.I.C.: 6141
N.A.I.C.S.: 522210
Advertising Expenditures: $109,000
Media: 4-7-8-13-18
Personnel:
Robert R. Tabas *(Chm & CEO)*
Murray Stempel, III *(Vice Chm)*
James J. McSwiggan *(Pres & COO)*
Robert A. Kuehl *(CFO)*
Douglas J.R. Smith *(Exec VP & Chief Credit Officer)*
Marc Sanders *(Dir-Mktg)*

ROYAL BANK OF CANADA
(d/b/a RBC Financial Group)
Royal Bank Plaza 200 Bay Street
PO Box 1
Toronto, ON M5J 2J5, Canada
Tel.: (416) 974-5151
Fax: (416) 955-7800
Web Site: www.royalbank.com
Approx. Rev.: $35,257,925,680
Approx. Number Employees: 72,126
Year Founded: 1869

Key to Media (For complete agency information see *The Advertising Red Books-Agencies* edition):
1. Bus. Publs. 2. Cable T.V. 3. Catalogs & Directories. 4. Co-op Adv. 5. Consumer Mags. 6. D.M. to Bus. Estab.7. D.M. to Consumers 8. Daily Newsp. 9. Exhibits/Trade Shows 10. Foreign 11. Infomercial 12. Internet Adv.13. Multimedia 14. Network Radio 15. Network T.V. 16. Newsp. Distr. Mags. 17. Other 18. Outdoor (Posters, Transit) 19. Point of Purchase20. Premiums, Novelties 21. Product Samples 22. Special Events Mktg. 23. Spot Radio 24. Spot T.V. 25. Weekly Newsp. 26. Yellow Page Adv.

Business Description:
Bank Holding Company
S.I.C.: 6712; 6029; 6035; 6141; 6211; 6282; 6411; 6531; 6733
N.A.I.C.S.: 551111; 522110; 522120; 522291; 523110; 523920; 523991; 524298; 531390
Media: 2-6-9-13-15-17-25
Distr.: Intl.; Natl.
Budget Set: June
Personnel:
Douglas McGregor *(Chm & Co-CEO-Capital Markets)*
Gordon M. Nixon *(Pres & CEO)*
Janice R. Fukakusa *(CFO & Chief Admin Officer)*
David McKay *(Grp Head-Banking-Canada)*
Barbara G. Stymiest *(Group Head-Strategy, Treasury & Corp Svcs)*
Raymond Chouinard *(Dir-Media & PR)*
Rina Cortese *(Dir-Media Rels)*
Greg Skinner *(Dir-Comm)*
Judi Levita *(Mgr-Media Rels)*
Jamie Mitchell *(Mgr-Media Rels)*
Dano Spooner *(Mgr-Comm)*
Michael Volpatti *(Mgr-Donations)*
Advertising Agencies:
BBDO Toronto
2 Bloor St W
Toronto, ON M4W 3R6, Canada
Tel.: (416) 972-1505
Fax: (416) 972-5656

The Buntin Group
1001 Hawkins St
Nashville, TN 37203-4758
Tel.: (615) 244-5720
Fax: (615) 244-6511

CloudRaker
1435 rue Saint-Alexandre
Montreal, QC H3A 2G4, Canada
Tel.: (514) 499-0005
Fax: (514) 499-0525

MacLaren McCann Direct (M2D)
10 Bay St
Toronto, ON M5J 2S3, Canada
Tel.: (416) 594-6000
Fax: (416) 64-3 7030

Organic, Inc.
555 Market St 4th Fl
San Francisco, CA 94105
Tel.: (415) 581-5300
Fax: (415) 581-5400

RP FUNDING
2700 Westhall Ln Ste 120
Maitland, FL 32250
Tel.: (321) 397-4420
Web Site: www.myrpfunding.com
Business Description:
Full Service Mortgage Lender
S.I.C.: 6163
N.A.I.C.S.: 522310
Media: 8
Personnel:
Robert Palmer *(Pres)*

RSI
(Div. of Gallagher Benefit Services, Inc.)
501 Fellowship Rd Ste 201
Mount Laurel, NJ 08054-3404
Tel.: (856) 234-6111
Fax: (856) 234-8328
Toll Free: (800) 394-6111
Web Site: www.rsionline.com
E-Mail For Key Personnel:
President: dfriedman@rsionline.com
Sales Director: wkaiser@rsionline.com
Sales Range: $50-74.9 Million
Approx. Number Employees: 100
Business Description:
Employee Benefits Management Consulting Services
S.I.C.: 8742; 6411; 8748
N.A.I.C.S.: 541611; 524298; 541618
Media: 2-13
Personnel:
David J. Friedman *(Pres)*
William H. Kaiser *(VP-Sls & Consulting)*
Sharyn Spitznagel *(Dir-HR)*
Ralph A. Catillo *(Mgr-Benefits Consulting)*
Bonnie D'Amico *(Mgr-Benefit Svcs)*
Bob Flanders *(Mgr-Consulting Support)*

RURBAN FINANCIAL CORP.
401 Clinton St
Defiance, OH 43512-2662
Tel.: (419) 783-8950
Fax: (419) 784-4085
E-mail: rfcinv@rurban.net
Web Site: www.rurbanfinancial.net
Approx. Rev.: $50,382,439
Approx. Number Employees: 239
Year Founded: 1983
Business Description:
Bank Holding Company
S.I.C.: 6712; 6029
N.A.I.C.S.: 551111; 522110
Advertising Expenditures: $445,656
Media: 9-18-23-25
Personnel:
Richard L. Hardgrove *(Chm)*
Mark A. Klein *(Pres & CEO)*
Anthony V. Cosentino *(CFO & Exec VP)*
Henry R. Thiemann *(Pres-RDSI)*
Michelle Baker *(Dir-HR)*
Nichole Wichman *(Mgr-Mktg)*

RUSSELL INVESTMENT GROUP
(Sub. of Northwestern Mutual Life Insurance Company)
909 A St
Tacoma, WA 98402-5111
Tel.: (253) 572-9500
Fax: (253) 591-3495
E-mail: info@russell.com
Web Site: www.russell.com
Approx. Number Employees: 1,400
Year Founded: 1936
Business Description:
International Finance Consulting, Investment Management, Communication & Record Keeping Services for Defined Contribution Plans, Securities Brokerage
S.I.C.: 6282
N.A.I.C.S.: 523930; 523920
Personnel:
Andrew S. Doman *(CEO)*
Greg Nott *(Chief Investment Officer-Canada)*
Advertising Agency:
Doremus
(Sub. of Omnicom Group, Inc.)
200 Varick St 11Fl
New York, NY 10014-4810
Tel.: (212) 366-3000
Fax: (212) 366-3060

RYDEX DISTRIBUTORS, LLC
(Sub. of Security Benefit Corporation)
(d/b/a Rydex SGI)
9601 Blackwell Rd Ste 500
Rockville, MD 20850
Tel.: (301) 296-5406
Tel.: (301) 296-5100
Fax: (301) 296-5101
Toll Free: (800) 820-0888
E-mail: rydexshareholderservices@sg-investors.com
Web Site: www.rydex-sgi.com
Approx. Managed Assets: $22,000,000,000
Approx. Number Employees: 300
Year Founded: 1993
Business Description:
Asset Management Services
S.I.C.: 6282; 6289
N.A.I.C.S.: 523930; 523999
Personnel:
Richard M. Goldman *(CEO)*
Michael P. Byrum *(Chief Investment Officer)*
Nick Bonos *(Sr VP-Fund Svcs)*
Mike Dellapa *(Dir-Investment Res)*
Dawn Kahler *(Dir-Corp Comm)*
Advertising Agency:
TargetCast tcm
909 3rd Ave 31st Fl
New York, NY 10022
Tel.: (212) 500-6900
Fax: (212) 500-6880

SALARY.COM, INC.
(Sub. of Kenexa Corporation)
160 Gould St Ste 300
Needham, MA 02451
Tel.: (781) 851-8000
Toll Free: (866) SALARY1
E-mail: ir@salary.com
Web Site: www.salary.com
Approx. Rev.: $45,750,000
Approx. Number Employees: 528
Year Founded: 1999
Business Description:
On-Demand Compensation & Performance Management Solutions
S.I.C.: 2741; 7373; 8748
N.A.I.C.S.: 516110; 541512; 541618
Advertising Expenditures: $515,000
Media: 10-13
Personnel:
Yong Zhang *(COO & Pres-Global Ops)*
Brent Kleiman *(Sr VP-Mktg & Strategy)*
Brands & Products:
COMPANALYST
COMPANALYST EXECUTIVE
COMPPLANNER
CONNECTING PEOPLE,PAY & PERFORMANCE
DAD SALARY WIZARD
MOM SALARY WIZARD
ON-DEMAND HR DATA & SOFTWARE
PERSONAL SALARY WIZARD
SALARY WIZARD
SALARY.COM
TALENT MANAGER
WHAT ARE YOU WORTH
Advertising Agency:
Schwartz Communications, Inc.
230 3rd Ave
Waltham, MA 02451
Tel.: (781) 684-0770
Fax: (781) 684-6500
— Bill Keeler *(Acct Exec)*

SALEM FIVE CENTS SAVINGS BANK
(d/b/a Salem Five)
210 Essex St
Salem, MA 01970-3705
Tel.: (978) 745-5555
Fax: (978) 745-0861
Toll Free: (800) 322-2265
E-mail: mail@salemfive.com
Web Site: www.salemfive.com
Sales Range: $25-49.9 Million
Approx. Number Employees: 400
Year Founded: 1855
Business Description:
Consumer & Commercial Banking Services
S.I.C.: 6029; 6035; 6163
N.A.I.C.S.: 522110; 522120; 522310
Media: 7-8-9-13-18-22-23-24-25
Personnel:
William H. Mitchelson *(Chm)*
Joseph M. Gibbons *(Pres & CEO)*
Ping Yin Chai *(CFO & Exec VP)*
Kim A. Meader *(Exec VP)*
John S. Hall *(Sr VP & Mgr-Comml Banking-Salem Five Bank)*
Dawn M. Dillon *(Sr VP)*
Janis C. Dodge *(Sr VP-Consumer Banking)*
Keith D. Graham *(Sr VP-Aviation Lending)*
Bruce Potter *(Sr VP)*
Jay S. Spahr *(Sr VP)*
Brands & Products:
AROUND THE CORNER - AROUND THE WORLD
BANKING WITH YOU IN MIND
DIRECTBANKING.COM
GOLD STAR CHECKING
GOLD STAR SAVER
PLATINUM PLUS
SALEM FIVE
SALEM FIVE ACCESSLINE
SALEM FIVE WORLDACCESS
STAR CHECKING
ULTIMATE ACCOUNT

SALISBURY BANCORP, INC.
5 Bissell St
Lakeville, CT 06039-1868
Mailing Address:
PO Box 1868
Lakeville, CT 06039
Tel.: (860) 435-9801
Fax: (860) 435-0631
Toll Free: (800) 222-9801
E-mail: sbt@salisburybank.com
Web Site: www.salisburybank.com
Approx. Rev.: $29,963,000
Approx. Number Employees: 126
Year Founded: 1848
Business Description:
Bank Holding Company; Bank & Trust Services
S.I.C.: 6035; 6029; 6712
N.A.I.C.S.: 522120; 522110; 551111
Media: 7-8-13
Personnel:
Michael A. Varet *(Chm)*
Richard J. Cantele, Jr. *(Pres & CEO)*
Ian McMahon *(CFO)*
Todd M. Clinton *(CTO, Sr VP & Chief Compliance Officer)*

Key to Media (For complete agency information see *The Advertising Red Books-Agencies* edition):
1. Bus. Publs. 2. Cable T.V. 3. Catalogs & Directories. 4. Co-op Adv. 5. Consumer Mags. 6. D.M. to Bus. Estab.7. D.M. to Consumers
8. Daily Newsp. 9. Exhibits/Trade Shows 10. Foreign 11. Infomercial 12. Internet Adv.13. Multimedia 14. Network Radio
15. Network T.V. 16. Newsp. Distr. Mags. 17. Other 18. Outdoor (Posters, Transit) 19. Point of Purchase20. Premiums, Novelties
21. Product Samples 22. Special Events Mktg. 23. Spot Radio 24. Spot T.V. 25. Weekly Newsp. 26. Yellow Page Adv.

Salisbury Bancorp, Inc. — (Continued)

Diane E.R. Johnstone *(Sr VP & Trust Officer)*
Geoffrey Talcott *(Sr VP & Chief Lending Officer)*
William J. Lambert *(VP & Trust Officer)*
Sharon A. Pilz *(VP-Salisbury Bank & Trust Company)*
Alton E. Golden *(Exec Officer & Branch Asst-Retail Banking)*
Linda F. Decker *(Branch Mgr-Sharon Office & Asst Treas)*
Jerry Baldwin *(Exec VP)*
Melanie Neely *(VP-Fin-Salisbury Bank & Trust Company)*
Robin Foley *(Asst VP-Loan Origination)*
Robert Lotz *(Asst VP-Fin)*
Doug Cahill *(Dir-HR)*
Betsy Devino *(Branch Mgr-Canaan Office)*
Georgann Farnum *(Branch Mgr-Egremont Office)*
Melissa Galm *(Branch Mgr-Lakeville Office)*
Alice Kent *(Branch Mgr-Salisbury Office)*
Nancy Missaggia *(Branch Mgr)*
Diane Palmer *(Mgr-Deposit Ops)*
Sharon Renzetti *(Mgr-Deposit Opers)*

SALISBURY BANK & TRUST COMPANY

(Sub. of Salisbury Bancorp, Inc.)
5 Bissell St
Lakeville, CT 06039-1868
Tel.: (860) 435-9801
Fax: (860) 435-0631
E-mail: sbt@salisburybank.com
Web Site: www.salisburybank.com
E-Mail For Key Personnel:
President: jp@salisbury-bank.com
Sales Range: $25-49.9 Million
Approx. Number Employees: 120
Year Founded: 1925
Business Description:
Bank &Trust Services
S.I.C.: 6029
N.A.I.C.S.: 522110
Advertising Expenditures: $2,500,000
Media: 7-8-10-13
Personnel:
Michael A. Varet *(Chm)*
Richard J. Cantele, Jr. *(Pres & CEO)*
John Francis Foley *(CFO & Treas)*
Diane E.R. Johnstone *(Sr VP & Trust Officer)*
Peter J. Riley *(Asst VP & Comml Credit Mgr)*

SANDERS MORRIS HARRIS GROUP, INC.

JP Morgan Chase Twr 600 Travis St Ste 5800
Houston, TX 77002
Tel.: (713) 224-3100
Fax: (713) 224-1101
Toll Free: (800) 900-4611
Web Site: www.smhgroup.com
E-Mail For Key Personnel:
President: r.e.garrison@smhg.net
Approx. Rev.: $168,843,000
Approx. Number Employees: 529
Business Description:
Holding Company; Wealth Management & Institutional Banking Services
S.I.C.: 6712; 6211; 6282
N.A.I.C.S.: 551111; 523110; 523120; 523920; 523930
Advertising Expenditures: $3,900,000
Personnel:
George Lester Ball *(Chm & CEO)*
Don A. Sanders *(Vice Chm)*
Fredric M. Edelman *(Pres)*
Frederic L. Saalwachter *(Mng Dir & Head-Energy Investment Banking)*
Humbert B. Powell *(Mng Dir)*
Rick Berry *(CFO)*
Pamela Caloway *(Asst Sec)*

SANDY SPRING BANCORP, INC.

17801 Georgia Ave
Olney, MD 20832
Tel.: (301) 774-6400
Fax: (301) 260-0044
Toll Free: (800) 399-5919
E-mail: info@sandyspringbank.com
Web Site: www.sandyspringbank.com
Approx. Rev.: $194,342,000
Approx. Number Employees: 711
Business Description:
Bank Holding Company; Savings, Loans, Commercial & Investment Banking Services
S.I.C.: 6712; 6029; 6035; 6163; 6289
N.A.I.C.S.: 551111; 522110; 522120; 522310; 523999
Media: 8-9-10-23-25
Personnel:
Robert L. Orndorff, Jr. *(Chm)*
Daniel J. Schrider *(Pres & CEO)*
Philip J. Mantua *(CFO & Exec VP)*
Frank H. Small *(COO-Sandy Spring Bank & Exec VP)*
R. Stephen Geoffray *(Pres-Insurance)*
Ronald E. Kuykendall *(Gen Counsel, Sec & Exec VP)*
R. Louis Caceres *(Exec VP-Sandy Spring Bank)*
Joseph J. O'Brien, Jr. *(Exec VP-Sandy Spring Bank)*
Michael A. Bateman *(Sr VP & Dir-Corp Dev)*
Brands & Products:
BANK EXPRESS
SANDY SPRING BANK
Advertising Agency:
Cornerstone
10715 Little Patuxent Pkwy Ste 120
Columbia, MD 21044
Tel.: (410) 727-2131
Fax: (443) 367-5911

SANDY SPRING BANK

(Holding of Sandy Spring Bancorp, Inc.)
17801 Georgia Ave
Olney, MD 20832
Tel.: (301) 774-6400
Fax: (301) 260-0600
Toll Free: (800) 399-5919
E-mail: communityrelations@sandyspringbank.com
Web Site: www.sandyspringbank.com
Sales Range: $800-899.9 Million
Year Founded: 1868
Business Description:
Savings, Loans, Commercial & Investment Banking Services
S.I.C.: 6035; 6029; 6163; 6211
N.A.I.C.S.: 522120; 522110; 522310; 523110
Advertising Expenditures: $750,000
Media: 7-8-13
Personnel:
Daniel J. Schrider *(Pres & CEO)*
Philip J. Mantua *(CFO & Exec VP)*
Frank H. Small *(COO & Exec VP)*
Jeffrey A. Welch *(Chief Credit Officer & Exec VP)*
R. Louis Caceres *(Exec VP-Wealth Mgmt)*
Jay O'Brien *(Exec VP-Comml Banking Grp)*
Patrick Shurney *(Sr VP)*
Frederic G. Burke, Jr. *(Sr VP & Mgr-Investment Mgmt & Fiduciary Svcs Div)*

SANTA BARBARA BANK & TRUST

(Formerly First Bancshares Inc.)
(Sub. of Pacific Capital Bancorp)
995 Higuera St
San Luis Obispo, CA 93401
Tel.: (805) 541-6100
Fax: (805) 783-5199
Toll Free: (866) 733-2756
Web Site: www.ssbt.com
Sales Range: $1-9.9 Million
Year Founded: 1980
Business Description:
State Commercial Banks
S.I.C.: 6029; 6163
N.A.I.C.S.: 522110; 522310
Media: 22-23
Personnel:
George Leis *(Pres & COO)*
Harry Polland *(Sr VP-Lending)*
Donna Milne *(VP-Retail Banking)*
Julie Alonso *(Asst VP-Fin & Acctg)*
Brands & Products:
ABOVE AND BEYOND BANKING

SANTA FE FINANCIAL CORPORATION

(Sub. of InterGroup Corporation)
10940 Wilshire Blvd Ste 2150
Los Angeles, CA 90024
Tel.: (310) 889-2500
Fax: (310) 889-2510
Web Site: intgla.com/santafe.html
Approx. Rev.: $33,234,000
Approx. Number Employees: 3
Business Description:
Commercial & Residential Real Estate Investment
S.I.C.: 6289; 6531
N.A.I.C.S.: 523999; 531390
Advertising Expenditures: $278,000
Personnel:
John V. Winfield *(Chm, Pres & CEO)*
Michael G. Zybala *(Gen Counsel, Sec & VP)*

SANTANDER HOLDINGS USA, INC.

(Holding of BANCO SANTANDER, S.A.)
75 State St
Boston, MA 02109
Tel.: (617) 346-7200
Toll Free: (877) 768-2265
Web Site: www.santanderconsumerusa.com
Approx. Rev.: $5,813,958,000
Approx. Number Employees: 10,515
Year Founded: 1987
Business Description:
Bank Holding Company
S.I.C.: 6712; 6035; 6211
N.A.I.C.S.: 551111; 522120; 523120
Advertising Expenditures: $52,362
Media: 2-8-10
Personnel:
Juan Guillermo Sabater *(CFO)*
Juan Davila *(Chief Risk Mgmt Officer)*
Nuno G. Matos *(Jr Acct Officer)*
Richard A. Toomey *(Gen Counsel)*
Andrew P. Gully *(Sr VP & Mng Dir-Corp Affairs)*
William Hartz *(Sr VP)*
Stacey V. Weikel *(Sr VP-IR & Strategic Plng)*
Jose Castello Orta *(Mng Dir-Global Banking & Markets)*
Roy J. Lever *(Mng Dir-Retail Banking)*
Francisco J. Simon *(Mng Dir-HR)*
Ellen Molle *(Dir-Corp Affairs)*
Advertising Agency:
PARTNERS+simons
25 Drydock Ave 8th Fl
Boston, MA 02210
Tel.: (617) 330-9393
Fax: (617) 330-9394

THE SAVANNAH BANCORP, INC.

25 Bull St
Savannah, GA 31401-2642
Mailing Address:
PO Box 188
Savannah, GA 31401-3140
Tel.: (912) 629-6486
Fax: (912) 629-6487
E-mail: webmaster@savb.com
Web Site: www.savb.com
Approx. Rev.: $55,240,000
Approx. Number Employees: 188
Year Founded: 1989
Business Description:
Bank Holding Company
S.I.C.: 6712; 6141
N.A.I.C.S.: 551111; 522210
Advertising Expenditures: $377,000
Personnel:
J. Wiley Ellis *(Chm)*
Robert H. Demere, Jr. *(Vice Chm)*
John C. Helmken, II *(Pres & CEO)*
Michael W. Harden, Jr. *(CFO)*
R. Stephen Stramm *(Exec VP-Lending)*

SAXON MORTGAGE, INC.

(Sub. of Morgan Stanley)
4708 Mercantile Dr N
Fort Worth, TX 76137
Tel.: (804) 967-7400
Fax: (804) 967-7408
Web Site: www.saxononline.com
Sales Range: $450-499.9 Million
Approx. Number Employees: 550
Business Description:
Residential Mortgages & Services
S.I.C.: 6163; 6099
N.A.I.C.S.: 522310; 522390
Media: 8-13-17
Personnel:
Richard A. Kraemer *(Chm)*
Mark E. Trentmann *(CIO)*
Laurie A. Gaines *(Sr VP-Strategy & Svcs)*
James Smith *(Sr Mgr-Foreclosure Controls)*

SCBT FINANCIAL CORPORATION

520 Gervais St
Columbia, SC 29201-3046

Key to Media (For complete agency information see *The Advertising Red Books-Agencies* edition):
1. Bus. Publs. 2. Cable T.V. 3. Catalogs & Directories. 4. Co-op Adv. 5. Consumer Mags. 6. D.M. to Bus. Estab.7. D.M. to Consumers
8. Daily Newsp. 9. Exhibits/Trade Shows 10. Foreign 11. Infomercial 12. Internet Adv.13. Multimedia 14. Network Radio
15. Network T.V. 16. Newsp. Distr. Mags. 17. Other 18. Outdoor (Posters, Transit) 19. Point of Purchase20. Premiums, Novelties
21. Product Samples 22. Special Events Mktg. 23. Spot Radio 24. Spot T.V. 25. Weekly Newsp. 26. Yellow Page Adv.

Tel.: (803) 771-2265
Fax: (803) 531-0524
Toll Free: (800) 277-2175
E-mail: info@jssb.com
Web Site: www.scbandt.com
Approx. Rev.: $293,089,000
Approx. Number Employees: 1,015
Year Founded: 1985
Business Description:
Bank Holding Company
S.I.C.: 6712; 6029
N.A.I.C.S.: 551111; 522110
Advertising Expenditures: $2,497,000
Personnel:
Robert R. Horger *(Chm)*
Dwight W. Frierson *(Vice Chm)*
Robert R. Hill, Jr. *(Pres & CEO)*
Donald E. Pickett *(CFO & Exec VP)*
John C. Pollok *(COO & Sr Exec VP)*
Bruce Harrison *(CIO & Exec VP)*
Nathaniel A. Barber *(Sr VP)*
Arthur P. Swanson *(Reg Pres-Charleston & Exec VP)*
Michael E. Coggin *(Reg Pres-Upstate & Sr VP)*
F. Gene McConnell, Jr. *(Reg Pres-Orangeburg & Sr VP)*
John S. Goettee *(Pres-Midlands)*
A. Todd Harward *(Pres-Wealth Mgmt Grp)*
John F. Windley *(Pres-SCBT N.A)*
Richard C. Mathis *(Treas & Exec VP)*
Renee R. Brooks *(Sec & Sr VP)*
Dane H. Murray *(Sr Exec VP-Retail Banking)*
J. Alex Shuford, III *(Exec VP & Mgr-Correspondent Banking)*
Lesley Dunn *(Exec VP-Support Div)*
Michael A. Komar *(Sr VP & Gen Auditor)*
James B. Brant *(Sr VP-Correspondent Banking)*
Lesley Lampert *(Sr VP & Compliance Officer)*
Greg A. Lapointe *(Sr VP)*
Bill Medich *(Sr VP & Exec-Charleston Area)*

SCHLUMBERGER LIMITED
5599 San Felipe 17th Fl
Houston, TX 77056
Tel.: (713) 513-2000
E-mail: irsupport@slb.com
Web Site: www.slb.com
Approx. Rev.: $27,447,000,000
Approx. Number Employees: 108,000
Year Founded: 1927
Business Description:
Holding Company; Oilfield Services, Electronic Equipment & Components
S.I.C.: 6719; 1389; 1623
N.A.I.C.S.: 551112; 213112; 237120
Advertising Expenditures: $8,000,000
Media: 17-25
Personnel:
Andrew F.J. Gould *(Chm & CEO)*
Ashok Belani *(Pres)*
Simon Ayat *(CFO)*
Paal Kibsgaard *(COO)*
Bryan L. Dudman *(Pres-Drilling Tools & Remedial)*
Catherine MacGregor *(Pres-Wireline)*
Sophie Zurquiyah-Rousset *(Pres-Data & Consulting Svcs)*
Dalton Boutte *(Exec VP)*
Rodney Nelson *(VP-Comm)*
Doug Pferdehirt *(VP-Corp Dev & Comm)*
Paul Clent *(Product Mgr)*
Robert Bergeron *(Mgr-IR)*
Brands & Products:
ATHOS
AVOCET
BHA
BORTEX
BORVIEW
CHARISMA
COUGAR
CPS-3
DECIDE!
ECLIPSE
ECLIPSE SIMOPT
ELANPLUS
EXPEDITOR
FLOGRID
GEOFRAME
GEOPLAT
GEOVIZ
IESX
IN-SITU
LITHO
MERAK
MERAK FLOMATIC
METRIS
OSPREY
PETREL
PIPESIM
PREPLUS
PVTI
PROSOURCE
Q-TECHNOLOGY
RESLINK
RESSUM
SCAL
SCHLUMBERGER
SEISCLASS
STRUCTVIEW
SUBSEA
VOLTS
VX TECHNOLOGY
Advertising Agency:
Schlumberger Ltd.
210 Schlumberger Dr
Sugar Land, TX 77478
Tel.: (281) 285-8500
Fax: (281) 285-8970

SCOTTRADE, INC.
12800 Corp Hill Dr
Saint Louis, MO 63131-1834
Tel.: (314) 965-1555
Fax: (314) 543-6280
Toll Free: (800) 619SAVE
E-mail: mediarelations@scottrade.com
Web Site: www.scottrade.com
Approx. Number Employees: 1,000
Year Founded: 1980
Business Description:
Online Trading
S.I.C.: 6211; 6282
N.A.I.C.S.: 523120; 523930
Export
Media: 3-9-11-13-24-25-26
Personnel:
Rodger O. Riney *(Founder & CEO)*
Patricia Milon *(Exec VP & Chief Counsel)*
Kelly Doria *(Dir-PR)*
Justin Gioia *(Dir-Branding & Mktg Comm)*
Craig Ransom *(Dir-Corp Comm)*
Wende Rhodes *(Dir-Branch Admin)*
Kimberly Wells *(Dir-Brand Mgmt & Digital Mktg)*
Tom Trinity *(Asst Dir-Dev)*
Kristin Grupas *(Mgr-Customer Education)*
Erica Hubbard *(Mgr-Enterprise Security)*
Camisha Reed *(Mgr-IT Asset)*
Carrie Trent *(Mgr-PR)*
Leslie Vitt *(Mgr-Internal Audit)*
Brands & Products:
MORE BROKER FOR YOUR MONEY
SCOTTRADE
SCOTTRADE ELITE
SCOTTRADE.COM
SCOTTRADER
SCOTTSAVE.COM
Advertising Agency:
Gearon Hoffman Inc.
88 Broad St
Boston, MA 02110
Tel.: (617) 247-1522
Fax: (617) 247-6821

SEAWAY VALLEY CAPITAL CORPORATION
10 18 Park Str 2nd Fl
Gouverneur, NY 13642
Tel.: (315) 287-1122
Web Site:
www.seawayvalleycapitalcorp.com
Approx. Rev.: $21,894,746
Approx. Number Employees: 20
Year Founded: 2007
Business Description:
Venture Capital & Private Equity Investment Services
S.I.C.: 6289
N.A.I.C.S.: 523999
Advertising Expenditures: $472,368
Personnel:
Thomas W. Scozzafava *(Pres & CEO)*

SECURITY FEDERAL CORPORATION
238 Richland Ave W
Aiken, SC 29801
Tel.: (803) 641-3000
Fax: (803) 502-2407
E-mail: bank@securityfederalbank.com
Web Site:
www.securityfederalbank.com
Approx. Rev.: $50,537,301
Approx. Number Employees: 202
Business Description:
Bank Holding Company
S.I.C.: 6035; 6712
N.A.I.C.S.: 522120; 551111
Advertising Expenditures: $393,287
Personnel:
T. Clifton Weeks *(Chm)*
Timothy W. Simmons *(Pres & CEO)*
Roy G. Lindburg *(CFO & Exec VP)*
Marian A. Shapiro *(Exec VP)*
Anthony Ateca *(Sr VP)*
William O Boyte, III *(Sr VP-Construction Lending-SC Midlands)*
Thomas R. Crawford, Jr. *(Sr VP-Georgia Market Area)*
Richard T. Harmon *(Sr VP-Mortgage Lending)*
Carol P. McCleskey *(Sr VP-Branch Admin)*
Paul T. Rideout *(Sr VP)*
Lynn B. Shepard *(Sr VP-Ops)*
Gabriele C. Dukes *(VP-Fin Counseling)*
Donald J. Krafnick *(VP-HR)*
Thomas H. Wessell *(VP-IT)*

SECURITY NATIONAL FINANCIAL CORPORATION
5300 S 360 W Ste 250
Salt Lake City, UT 84123-4600
Mailing Address:
PO Box 57250
Salt Lake City, UT 84157
Tel.: (801) 264-1060
Fax: (801) 265-9882
Toll Free: (800) 574-7117
E-mail: contact@securitynational.com
Web Site: www.securitynational.com
Approx. Rev.: $168,529,557
Approx. Number Employees: 607
Year Founded: 1979
Business Description:
Life, Health Insurance Services; Annuities; Cemetery & Mortuary Operations; Mortgage Loan Broker
S.I.C.: 6311; 6163; 6282; 6321; 6553
N.A.I.C.S.: 524113; 522310; 523930; 524114; 812220
Advertising Expenditures: $2,122,000
Personnel:
George R. Quist *(Chm & CEO)*
Scott M. Quist *(Pres & COO)*
Stephen M. Sill *(CFO, Treas & VP)*
Christie Q. Overbaugh *(Sr VP-Internal Ops)*

SEI INVESTMENTS COMPANY
1 Freedom Valley Dr
Oaks, PA 19456-1100
Tel.: (610) 676-1000
Fax: (610) 676-2995
Toll Free: (800) 342-5734
E-mail: shortterminvestments@seic.com
Web Site: www.seic.com
Approx. Rev.: $900,835,000
Approx. Number Employees: 2,240
Year Founded: 1968
Business Description:
Outsourced Investment & Fund Processing for Banks, Trust Companies & Investment Managers
S.I.C.: 6099; 7376
N.A.I.C.S.: 522320; 541513
Advertising Expenditures: $600,000
Media: 2-4
Distr.: Intl.; Natl.
Personnel:
Alfred P. West, Jr. *(Chm & CEO)*
Patrick Disney *(Mng Dir)*
Kathy C. Heilig *(Chief Acctg Officer & Controller)*
N. Jeffrey Klauder *(Gen Counsel & Exec VP)*
Edward D. Loughlin *(Exec VP-Institutional Grp)*
Stephen G. Meyer *(Exec VP)*
Joseph P. Ujobai *(Exec VP-Private Banks)*
Wayne M. Withrow *(Exec VP-SEI Advisor Network)*
Cedric Bucher *(Dir-Client Investment Strategy)*
Donna Delpo *(Product Mgr)*
Brands & Products:
NEW WAYS. NEW ANSWERS.
SEI
TREASURYPOINT.COM

Key to Media (For complete agency information see *The Advertising Red Books-Agencies* edition):
1. Bus. Publs. 2. Cable T.V. 3. Catalogs & Directories. 4. Co-op Adv. 5. Consumer Mags. 6. D.M. to Bus. Estab.7. D.M. to Consumers
8. Daily Newsp. 9. Exhibits/Trade Shows 10. Foreign 11. Infomercial 12. Internet Adv.13. Multimedia 14. Network Radio
15. Network T.V. 16. Newsp. Distr. Mags. 17. Other 18. Outdoor (Posters, Transit) 19. Point of Purchase20. Premiums, Novelties
21. Product Samples 22. Special Events Mktg. 23. Spot Radio 24. Spot T.V. 25. Weekly Newsp. 26. Yellow Page Adv.

SEI Investments Company — (Continued)

Advertising Agency:
Braithwaite Communications
100 Penn Sq E Ste 480
Philadelphia, PA 19107
Tel.: (215) 564-3200
Fax: (215) 564-3455

SEVERN BANCORP, INC.

200 Westgate Cir Ste 200
Annapolis, MD 21401
Tel.: (410) 260-2000
Fax: (410) 841-6296
Toll Free: (800) 752-5854
E-mail: info@severnbank.com
Web Site: www.severnbank.com
Approx. Rev.: $52,278,000
Approx. Number Employees: 116
Business Description:
Bank Holding Company
S.I.C.: 6141; 6029; 6035; 6163
N.A.I.C.S.: 522210; 522110; 522120; 522310
Advertising Expenditures: $422,000
Personnel:
Alan J. Hyatt *(Chm & Pres)*
Melvin E. Meekins, Jr. *(Vice Chm)*
Thomas G. Bevivino *(CFO & Exec VP)*
Phillip V. Jones, Jr. *(COO & Exec VP)*
James Orazi *(Sr VP-Mortgage Ops)*

SHAREBUILDER CORPORATION

(Sub. of ING Bank, fsb)
83 S Kings St Ste 700
Seattle, WA 98104
Tel.: (206) 805-0800
Fax: (206) 805-0803
E-mail: webpartners@sharebuilder.com
Web Site: www.sharebuilder.com
Sales Range: $10-24.9 Million
Approx. Number Employees: 250
Year Founded: 1996
Business Description:
Financial & Investment Services
S.I.C.: 6211; 6371
N.A.I.C.S.: 523110; 525990
Media: 13
Personnel:
Dan Greenshields *(Pres)*
Paul Swegle *(Gen Counsel)*
Advertising Agencies:
DDB Seattle
1000 2nd Ave Ste 1000
Seattle, WA 98104
Tel.: (206) 442-9900
Fax: (206) 223-6309

YellowHammer Media Group, LLC
111 W 28th St Ste 2B
New York, NY 10001
Tel.: (646) 490-9841

SHIMMER GOLD, INC.

(Name Changed to Absolute Life Solutions, Inc.)

SHISEIDO AMERICAS CORPORATION

(Sub. of Shiseido Company Ltd. - International Division)
178 Bauer Dr
Oakland, NJ 07436-3105
Tel.: (201) 337-3750
Fax: (201) 337-3862
Web Site: www.shiseido.com
Approx. Rev.: $134,400,000
Approx. Number Employees: 200
Year Founded: 1988
Business Description:
Holding Company; Back Office Operations & Financial Services
S.I.C.: 6719
N.A.I.C.S.: 551112
Personnel:
Shuichi Tanaka *(Chm & CEO)*
Advertising Agency:
Dentsu America, Inc.
32 Ave of the Americas 16th Fl
New York, NY 10013
Tel.: (212) 397-3333
Fax: (212) 397-3322

SHORE BANCSHARES, INC.

18 E Dover St
Easton, MD 21601
Tel.: (410) 822-1400
Fax: (410) 820-7180
E-mail: info@rtco.com
Web Site: www.shbi.net
Approx. Rev.: $73,502,000
Approx. Number Employees: 304
Year Founded: 1996
Business Description:
Bank Holding Company
S.I.C.: 6029; 6712
N.A.I.C.S.: 522110; 551111
Advertising Expenditures: $347,000
Personnel:
Christopher F. Spurry *(Chm)*
Lloyd L. Beatty, Jr. *(Pres & COO)*
W. Moorhead Vermilye *(CEO)*
Brands & Products:
BANKING. INSURANCE. INVESTMENTS.
SHORE BANCSHARES, INC.

SI FINANCIAL GROUP, INC.

803 Main St
Willimantic, CT 06226
Tel.: (860) 423-4581
Fax: (860) 423-9001
E-mail: webmaster@savingsinstitute.com
Web Site: www.savingsinstitute.com
Approx. Rev.: $50,560,000
Approx. Number Employees: 237
Year Founded: 2004
Business Description:
Holding Company
S.I.C.: 6712; 6035
N.A.I.C.S.: 551111; 522120
Advertising Expenditures: $791,000
Personnel:
Henry P. Hinckley *(Chm)*
Rheo Arthur Brouillard *(Pres & CEO)*
Brian J. Hull *(CFO & Exec VP)*
Laurie L. Gervais *(Sr VP & Corp Sec)*
William E. Anderson Jr. *(Sr VP)*
Michael J. Moran *(Sr VP & Sr Credit Officer)*

SIEBERT FINANCIAL CORP.

885 3rd Ave Fl 17
New York, NY 10022-4834
Tel.: (212) 644-2400
Fax: (212) 486-2784
Toll Free: (877) 327-8379
E-mail: info@siebertnet.com
Web Site: www.siebertnet.com
Approx. Rev.: $20,770,000
Approx. Number Employees: 70
Year Founded: 1996
Business Description:
Financial Services
S.I.C.: 6799; 6211
N.A.I.C.S.: 523910; 523110; 523120
Advertising Expenditures: $400,000
Media: 2-3-6-7-9-10-15-22-23-24-25-26
Personnel:
Muriel F. Siebert *(CEO)*
Joseph M. Ramos, Jr. *(CFO & Exec VP)*
Jeanne M. Rosendale *(Gen Counsel & Exec VP)*
Ameen Esmail *(Exec VP)*
Laura Gross *(Sr VP-Mktg & e-Bus)*
John Lally *(Sr VP)*
David Haywood *(Dir-Res)*

SIEMENS CORPORATION

(Sub. of Siemens Aktiengesellschaft)
527 Madison Ave 8th Flr
New York, NY 10022
Tel.: (212) 258-4000
Fax: (212) 258-4035
Toll Free: (800) SIEMENS
E-mail: usa.800siemens@siemens.com
Web Site: www.usa.siemens.com
Approx. Sls.: $18,800,001,024
Approx. Number Employees: 25
Year Founded: 1847
Business Description:
Holding & Finance Company for Power Generation & Transmission Systems, Industrial Building Systems, Drives, Automation Systems, Communication Systems & Networks, Defense Electronics, Transportation & Automotive Systems, Medical Engineering
S.I.C.: 3612; 3844
N.A.I.C.S.: 335311; 334517
Import Export
Advertising Expenditures: $25,000,000
Media: 1-2-3-4-5-6-7-8-9-10-13-15-16-18-19-20-22-23-24-26
Distr.: Natl.
Personnel:
Uriel J. Sharef *(Chm)*
Eric Spiegel *(Pres & CEO)*
Harry A. Feuerstein *(CFO)*
Thomas Haas *(CMO)*
E. Robert Lupone *(Gen Counsel, Sec & Sr VP)*
Richard Brait *(Gen Counsel)*
James Whaley *(Sr VP-Comm & Mktg)*
Kathleen A. Ambrose *(Sr VP-Govt Affairs Office)*
Michael Panigel *(Sr VP-HR)*
Brands & Products:
CALL STAT
CEREC
DULUX
ECAT
EDX-P
MAMMOMAT
MEVATRON
MICOR
MINIMED
PHONEMAIL
SIMATIC
Advertising Agency:
Publicis USA
(Sub. of Publicis, S.A., Paris, France)
4 Herald Sq 950 6th Ave
New York, NY 10001
Tel.: (212) 279-5550
Fax: (212) 279-5560
(Creative)

SIERRA BANCORP

86 N Main St
Porterville, CA 93257-1930
Tel.: (559) 782-4900
E-mail: ktaylor@bankofthesierra.com
Web Site: www.sierrabancorp.com
Approx. Rev.: $81,692,000
Approx. Number Employees: 318
Business Description:
Bank Holding Company
S.I.C.: 6029; 6712
N.A.I.C.S.: 522110; 551111
Advertising Expenditures: $1,979,000
Personnel:
Morris A. Tharp *(Chm)*
James C. Holly *(Pres & CEO)*
Kenneth R. Taylor *(CFO & Exec VP)*
James F. Gardunio *(Chief Credit Officer & Exec VP)*
Kevin J. Mcphaill *(Chief Banking Officer & Exec VP)*
Thomas Y. Yamaguchi *(Treas & Sr VP)*
Cindy L. Dabney *(Sr VP & Controller)*
Hope Attenhofer *(Sr VP & Dir-Mktg)*
Mona M. Carr *(Sr VP & Dir-Ops)*
Rick Davis *(Sr VP & Dir-Info Tech)*
Donald L. Sowers *(Sr VP & Dir-HR)*
Jeri L. Eubanks *(Sr VP & General Credit Administrator)*
Larry J. Mueller *(Sr VP & General Credit Adminstrator)*
Ronda Day *(VP & Dir-Compliance)*
Linda S. Hudspeth *(VP & Dir-Loan Ops)*
Sherri Jackson *(VP & Dir-Real Estate Ops)*
Kathy Lostetter *(VP & Dir-Trng)*
James Stewart *(VP & Mgr-Leasing)*
Frank W. Wittich Jr. *(VP & Mgr-Special Assets Center)*

SKAGIT STATE BANCORP, INC.

301 E Fairhaven Ave
Burlington, WA 98233
Tel.: (360) 755-0411
Fax: (360) 755-9675
Web Site: www.skagitbank.com
Approx. Rev.: $32,152,000
Approx. Number Employees: 164
Business Description:
Bank Holding Company
S.I.C.: 6712
N.A.I.C.S.: 551111
Advertising Expenditures: $708,000
Personnel:
B. Marvin Omdal *(Chm)*
Michael F. Janicki *(Vice Chm)*
Cheryl R. Bishop *(Pres & CEO)*
Carla F. Tucker *(CFO & Sr VP)*

SLM CORPORATION

(d/b/a Sallie Mae)
12061 Bluemont Way
Reston, VA 20190
Mailing Address:
PO Box 9532
Wilkes Barre, PA 18773-9532
Tel.: (703) 810-3000

Key to Media (For complete agency information see *The Advertising Red Books-Agencies* edition):
1. Bus. Publs. 2. Cable T.V. 3. Catalogs & Directories. 4. Co-op Adv. 5. Consumer Mags. 6. D.M. to Bus. Estab.7. D.M. to Consumers 8. Daily Newsp. 9. Exhibits/Trade Shows 10. Foreign 11. Infomercial 12. Internet Adv.13. Multimedia 14. Network Radio 15. Network T.V. 16. Newsp. Distr. Mags. 17. Other 18. Outdoor (Posters, Transit) 19. Point of Purchase20. Premiums, Novelties 21. Product Samples 22. Special Events Mktg. 23. Spot Radio 24. Spot T.V. 25. Weekly Newsp. 26. Yellow Page Adv.

Fax: (703) 810-7053
Fax: (703) 984-5042
Toll Free: (888) 272-5543
E-mail: newslinkeditor@salliemae.com
Web Site: www.salliemae.com
Approx. Rev.: $6,776,323,000
Approx. Number Employees: 7,600
Year Founded: 1973
Business Description:
Funding & Servicing Support for Higher Education Loans
S.I.C.: 6163; 6141; 6159
N.A.I.C.S.: 522310; 522210; 522291; 522298
Media: 2-4-5-6-7-8-10-13-20
Distr.: Direct to Consumer; Natl.; Reg.
Budget Set: Sept.
Personnel:
Anthony P. Terracciano *(Chm)*
Albert L. Lord *(Vice Chm & CEO)*
John F. Remondi *(Pres & COO)*
Jonathan C. Clark *(CFO & Exec VP)*
Karen Kotowski *(CIO & Sr VP)*
Joe DePaulo *(CMO & Exec VP)*
David West *(Sr VP & Chief Credit Officer)*
Paul Thome *(Pres-Sallie Mae Bank)*
Laurent C. Lutz *(Exec VP & Gen Counsel)*
Ted Morris *(Sr VP & Controller)*
Dana Albertini *(Sr VP)*
Tom Anderson *(Sr VP-Consumer Channel)*
Somsak Chivavibul *(Sr VP)*
Charles Colligan *(Sr VP)*
Keith D'Ambra *(Sr VP-Loan Consolidation)*
Mark Daly *(Sr VP-Corp Fin)*
Kenneth Fischbach *(Sr VP-Corp Fin)*
Tim Hynes *(Sr VP-Credit)*
John Kane *(Sr VP-Collections)*
Jonathan E. Kroehler *(Sr VP-Consumer Contact Centers)*
Jerry Maher *(Sr VP-Fin Institution Sls & Guarantor Bus Dev)*
Michael Maier *(Sr VP-Lending)*
Renee R. Mang *(Sr VP-Originations, Implementation & Servicing)*
Paul Mayer *(Sr Vp-Corp Dev)*
Steven J. McGarry *(Sr VP-IR)*
Steve O'Connell *(Sr VP)*
Timothy Staley *(Sr VP-Tech)*
April Stercula *(Sr VP-Loan Ops)*
Andy Wachtel *(Sr VP)*
Dennis Wentworth *(Sr VP-Higher Education Sls)*
Marcos Bronfman *(VP-Fin Plng & Analysis)*
Denise Chaisson *(VP-Sls-Higher Education)*
Mark Lloyd *(VP-Sls Mgmt)*
Charles Parker *(VP-Credit Sls Solutions & Trng)*
Mark Rein *(VP-Corp Fin)*
Brands & Products:
ACADEMIC MANAGEMENT SERVICES CORP
CLASS
COLLEGE ANSWERS
COLLEGESERV
EDNOTES
EDUCATION LEADS US
EXPORTSS
FULL CIRCUIT
GENERAL REVENUE CORP.
GRADEXCEL
GREAT REWARDS
K-12 FAMILY EDUCATION LOAN
NELLIE MAE
NOBODY LENDS YOU MORE SUPPORT
PIONEER CREDIT RECOVERY
PORTSS
POWERED BY SALLIE MAE
SALLIE MAE
SALLIE MAE EDUCATION LOAN
THE SALLIE MAE FUND
SALLIE MAE MBA LOANS
SELECT STEP
SIGNATURE EDUCATION LOAN
SIGNATURE SELECT
SLM CORPORATION
SMART LOAN
STUDENT LOAN FUNDING
SWIFTPAY
TRUECAREERS
TUITION ANSWER
WHIZKID
WIREDSCHOLAR
Advertising Agency:
OLSON
1625 Hennepin Ave
Minneapolis, MN 55403
Tel.: (612) 215-9800
Fax: (612) 215-9801
— Kevin DiLorenzo *(Acct Supvr)*

SOMERSET HILLS BANCORP
155 Morristown Rd
Bernardsville, NJ 07924
Mailing Address:
PO Box 237
Bernardsville, NJ 07924
Tel.: (908) 221-0100
Fax: (908) 221-1514
E-mail: customerservice@somersethillsbank.com
Web Site:
www.bankofsomersethills.com
Approx. Rev.: $15,687,000
Approx. Number Employees: 60
Year Founded: 1997
Business Description:
Bank Holding Company
S.I.C.: 6712; 6163
N.A.I.C.S.: 551111; 522310
Advertising Expenditures: $189,000
Media: 17
Personnel:
Edward B. Deutsch *(Chm)*
Stewart E. McClure, Jr. *(CEO & Pres)*
William S. Burns *(CFO)*
Donald P. Theobald, Jr. *(Sr VP & Controller)*
Brands & Products:
SOMERSET HILLS
SOMERSET HILLS BANCORP

SOMERSET VALLEY BANK
(Holding of Fulton Financial Corporation)
103 W End Ave
Somerville, NJ 08876
Tel.: (908) 541-9500
Fax: (908) 541-6464
Sales Range: $25-49.9 Million
Approx. Number Employees: 108
Year Founded: 1991
Business Description:
Community Banking Services
S.I.C.: 6029
N.A.I.C.S.: 522110
Media: 3-7-8-13-18-23-24-26

SONOMA NATIONAL BANK
(Sub. of STERLING FINANCIAL CORPORATION)
801 4th St
Santa Rosa, CA 95404
Tel.: (707) 579-2265
Fax: (707) 569-7636
Web Site: www.snbank.com
Sales Range: $50-74.9 Million
Approx. Number Employees: 172
Year Founded: 1985
Business Description:
Holding Company; Commercial Banking Services
S.I.C.: 6029
N.A.I.C.S.: 522110
Import Export
Advertising Expenditures: $515,000
Personnel:
Jane M. Baker *(CFO & Sr VP)*

SOUTHCOAST FINANCIAL CORPORATION
530 Johnnie Dodds Blvd
Mount Pleasant, SC 29464
Tel.: (843) 884-0504
Fax: (843) 884-2886
Toll Free: (877) 884-0504
E-mail: info@southcoastbank.com
Web Site: www.southcoastbank.com
Approx. Rev.: $25,780,704
Business Description:
Bank Holding Company
S.I.C.: 6712; 6029
N.A.I.C.S.: 551111; 522110
Advertising Expenditures: $139,462
Media: 17
Personnel:
L. Wayne Pearson *(Chm & CEO)*
William A. Coates *(Vice Chm)*
William C. Heslop *(CFO & Sr VP)*
William B. Seabrook *(Exec VP-Retail Banking)*

SOUTHEASTERN BANK FINANCIAL CORPORATION
3530 Wheeler Rd
Augusta, GA 30909
Tel.: (706) 738-6990
Fax: (702) 738-2350
E-mail: customerservice@georgiabankandtrust.com
Web Site:
www.georgiabankandtrust.com
Approx. Rev.: $69,874,000
Approx. Number Employees: 349
Year Founded: 1988
Business Description:
Bank Holding Company
S.I.C.: 6011; 6029; 6712
N.A.I.C.S.: 521110; 522110; 551111
Media: 7-8
Personnel:
Robert W. Pollard, Jr. *(Chm)*
R. Daniel Blanton *(Pres & CEO)*
Ronald L. Thigpen *(COO & Exec VP)*
Sonya M. Hanson *(VP & Dir-Mktg)*
Brands & Products:
CARING CONNECTING DOING THE RIGHT THING
GEORGIA BANK & TRUST

SOUTHEASTERN BANKING CORP.
1010 Northway St
Darien, GA 31305
Mailing Address:
PO Box 455
Darien, GA 31305-0455
Tel.: (912) 264-3307
Fax: (912) 437-2294
E-mail: seb@southeasternbank.com
Web Site:
www.georgiabankandtrust.com
Approx. Rev.: $21,350,781
Approx. Number Employees: 143
Year Founded: 1980
Business Description:
Bank Holding Company
S.I.C.: 6029
N.A.I.C.S.: 522110
Import Export
Advertising Expenditures: $282,337
Media: 9-18-25
Personnel:
Cornelius P. Holland III *(Pres & CEO)*

THE SOUTHERN BANC COMPANY, INC.
221 S 6th St
Gadsden, AL 35901
Mailing Address:
PO Box 1130
Gadsden, AL 35902
Tel.: (256) 543-3860
Fax: (256) 543-3864
E-mail: services@sobanco.com
Web Site: www.sobanco.com
Approx. Rev.: $4,815,817
Approx. Number Employees: 31
Business Description:
Bank Holding Company
S.I.C.: 6712; 6035
N.A.I.C.S.: 551111; 522120
Advertising Expenditures: $57,212
Media: 2-24
Personnel:
Gates Little *(Pres)*
James B. Little, Jr. *(Chief Investment Officer)*
Brands & Products:
SOBANCO
SOUTHERN BANK

SOUTHERN COMMUNITY FINANCIAL CORP.
4605 Country Club Rd
Winston Salem, NC 27104
Tel.: (336) 768-8500
Fax: (336) 768-2437
Toll Free: (888) 768-2666
E-mail: info@villagebankva.com
Web Site:
www.smallenoughtocare.com
Approx. Rev.: $96,244,000
Approx. Number Employees: 301
Business Description:
Bank Holding Company
S.I.C.: 6029; 6712
N.A.I.C.S.: 522110; 551111
Advertising Expenditures: $925,000
Media: 9-18-23
Personnel:
F. Scott Bauer *(Chm & CEO)*
James G. Chrysson *(Vice Chm)*
Jeffrey T. Clark *(Pres)*
James Hastings *(CFO & Exec VP)*
James C. Monroe *(Treas & Sr VP)*
Merle B. Andrews *(Exec VP & Sr Operating Officer)*
Robert L. Davis, Jr. *(Exec VP & Comml Banking Exec)*
Suzie Dixon *(VP-Mktg)*

Key to Media (For complete agency information see *The Advertising Red Books-Agencies* edition):
1. Bus. Publs. 2. Cable T.V. 3. Catalogs & Directories. 4. Co-op Adv. 5. Consumer Mags. 6. D.M. to Bus. Estab.7. D.M. to Consumers 8. Daily Newsp. 9. Exhibits/Trade Shows 10. Foreign 11. Infomercial 12. Internet Adv.13. Multimedia 14. Network Radio 15. Network T.V. 16. Newsp. Distr. Mags. 17. Other 18. Outdoor (Posters, Transit) 19. Point of Purchase20. Premiums, Novelties 21. Product Samples 22. Special Events Mktg. 23. Spot Radio 24. Spot T.V. 25. Weekly Newsp. 26. Yellow Page Adv.

SOUTHERN CONNECTICUT BANCORP INC.
215 Church St
New Haven, CT 06510
Tel.: (203) 782-1100
E-mail: info@scbancorp.com
Web Site: www.scbancorp.com
Approx. Rev.: $8,160,657
Approx. Number Employees: 33
Year Founded: 2000
Business Description:
Bank Holding Company
S.I.C.: 6712; 6029
N.A.I.C.S.: 551111; 522110
Advertising Expenditures: $14,321
Media: 7-8
Personnel:
Elmer F. Laydon *(Chm)*
Alphonse F. Spadaro, Jr. *(Vice Chm)*
Sunil Pallan *(Interim Pres)*
Stephen V. Ciancarelli *(CFO & Sr VP)*
Anthony M. Avellani *(Chief Acctg Officer & VP)*
Rosemarie A. Romano *(Corp Sec, First VP & Dir-HR)*

SOUTHERN MISSOURI BANCORP, INC.
531 Vine St
Poplar Bluff, MO 63901
Mailing Address:
PO Box 520
Poplar Bluff, MO 63902-0520
Tel.: (573) 778-1800
Fax: (573) 686-2920
E-mail: ebanking@smbtonline.com
Web Site: www.smbtonline.com
Approx. Rev.: $45,549,949
Approx. Number Employees: 146
Year Founded: 1966
Business Description:
Bank Holding Company
S.I.C.: 6029; 6035; 6712
N.A.I.C.S.: 522110; 522120; 551111
Advertising Expenditures: $252,404
Personnel:
Samuel H. Smith *(Chm)*
L. Douglas Bagby *(Vice Chm)*
Greg A. Steffens *(Pres & CEO)*
Christy Frazier-Moore *(Mng Dir)*
Matt Funke *(CFO)*
Kimberly Capps *(COO & Treas)*
William D. Hribovsek *(Sr VP)*
William Hirtz *(Mgr-Customer Svcs)*

SOUTHSIDE BANCSHARES INC.
1201 S Beckham Ave
Tyler, TX 75701
Mailing Address:
PO Box 1079
Tyler, TX 75701
Tel.: (903) 531-7111
Fax: (903) 592-3692
E-mail: info.lending@southside.com
Web Site: www.southside.com
Approx. Rev.: $182,770,000
Approx. Number Employees: 578
Year Founded: 1983
Business Description:
Bank Holding Company
S.I.C.: 6141; 6029
N.A.I.C.S.: 522210; 522110
Import Export
Advertising Expenditures: $2,319,000
Personnel:
B. G. Hartley *(Chm & CEO)*
Robbie N. Edmonson *(Vice Chm)*
Sam Dawson *(Pres & Sec)*
Lee R. Gibson *(CFO)*
Julie N. Shamburger *(Chief Acctg Officer)*

SOUTHWEST GEORGIA FINANCIAL CORPORATION
201 1st St SE
Moultrie, GA 31768
Tel.: (229) 985-1120
Fax: (229) 985-0251
E-mail: investorinfo@sgfc.com
Web Site: www.sgfc.com
E-Mail For Key Personnel:
Public Relations: peggy.weeks@sgfc.com
Approx. Rev.: $18,105,786
Approx. Number Employees: 123
Year Founded: 1928
Business Description:
Bank Holding Company
S.I.C.: 6029
N.A.I.C.S.: 522110
Advertising Expenditures: $177,402
Media: 17
Personnel:
Michael J. McLean *(Chm)*
Richard L. Moss *(Vice Chm)*
Dewitt Drew *(Pres & CEO)*
Charles R. Lemons *(Pres & CEO-Empire Fin Svcs)*
George R. Kirkland *(Treas & Sr VP)*
Sansbury C. Wallace *(Exec VP)*
Morris I. Bryant *(Sr VP)*
Robert M. Carlton *(Sr VP)*
Geraldine A. Ferrone Luff *(Sr VP)*
Geraldine A. Ferrone *(Sr VP)*
Vayden L. Murphy, Jr. *(Sr VP)*
Bell D. Paul *(Sr VP)*
Randall L. Webb, Jr. *(Sr VP)*
Blanton J. Larry *(VP & Dir-Insurance)*

SOUTHWEST SECURITIES, INC.
(Formerly M.L. Stern & Co., LLC)
(Sub. of SWS Group, Inc.)
8350 Wilshire Blvd
Beverly Hills, CA 90211
Tel.: (323) 658-4400
Fax: (323) 658-2232
Toll Free: (800) 765-2200
Web Site: www.swst.com
Sales Range: $200-249.9 Million
Approx. Number Employees: 150
Year Founded: 1980
Business Description:
Asset Management & Investment Banking Services
S.I.C.: 6211; 6282
N.A.I.C.S.: 523120; 523110; 523930
Media: 8-9-23
Personnel:
Milford L. Stern *(Pres)*
Miles Benickes *(Exec VP-Municipal Bond Trading)*
Peter Cappos *(Sr VP & Reg Dir-Sls)*
Stacy Stern *(Sr VP & Reg Dir-Sls)*
Neil Hattem *(Sr VP & Branch Mgr)*
Jeff Margolis *(Sr VP)*
Mike Cavanaugh *(Sr VP)*
Greg Flack *(Sr VP-Municipal Bond Trading)*
John Gresham *(Sr VP-Res)*
Don Lewis *(Sr VP-Corp/Govt Bonds & UIT Trading)*
Todd Smith *(Sr VP)*
Randy Stern *(Sr VP-Closed-End Funds)*
Michael Urman *(Sr VP-Mktg & Ops)*
Ray Baker *(First VP-Equity Trading)*
Edward Barnett *(VP & Wealth Mgr)*
Steven Lee *(Mgr-Regional Sls)*

SPROTT RESOURCE LENDING CORP.
(Formerly QUEST CAPITAL CORP.)
Suite 1028 550 Burrard Street
Vancouver, BC V6C 2B5, Canada
Tel.: (604) 687-8378
Fax: (604) 682-3941
Toll Free: (800) 318-3094
E-mail: info@questcapcorp.com
Web Site: www.sprottlending.com/
Approx. Int. Income: $9,395,328
Approx. Number Employees: 15
Year Founded: 1984
Business Description:
Merchant Banking Services
S.I.C.: 6211; 6289
N.A.I.C.S.: 523110; 523999
Media: 10
Personnel:
A. Murray Sinclair *(Chm)*
Peter Grosskopf *(Pres & CEO)*
Jim Grosdanis *(CFO)*
Derek Wasson *(Sr VP)*

STANDARD & POOR'S FINANCIAL SERVICES LLC
(Sub. of The McGraw-Hill Companies Inc.)
55 Water St
New York, NY 10041
Tel.: (888) 843-4772
Fax: (212) 438-7290
E-mail: questions@sandp.com
Web Site:
www.standardandpoors.com
Sales Range: $1-4.9 Billion
Approx. Number Employees: 7,500
Business Description:
Statistical Reports, Credit Ratings & Risk Solutions
S.I.C.: 8748; 6282
N.A.I.C.S.: 541690; 523930
Media: 2-7-10-11
Distr.: Natl.
Personnel:
Douglas Peterson *(Pres)*
Jitendra Sharma *(Exec Mng Dir)*
Gerald Creagh *(Exec Mng Dir)*
Adam H. Schuman *(Exec Mng Dir & Assoc Gen Counsel)*
Paul Coughlin *(Exec Mng Dir-Corp & Govt Ratings)*
David Jacob *(Exec Mng Dir-Structured Fin Ratings)*
Alexander J. Matturri, Jr. *(Exec Mng Dir-Portfolio Svcs)*
Joanne W. Rose *(Exec Mng Dir-Structured Fin)*
Tom Schiller *(Exec Mng Dir & Region Head-Asia-Pacific)*
Vladimir Y. Stadnyk *(Exec Mng Dir)*
Randall Winn *(Exec Mng Dir-Fin Data & Analytics Fin)*
David M. Blitzer *(Mng Dir)*
Mark Adelson *(Chief Credit Officer)*
Sam Stovall *(Chief Investment Strategist)*
Patrick Milano *(Exec VP-Ops Svcs)*
Rita Bulger *(Sr VP-Global Regulatory Affairs)*
Joe Held *(Sr VP-IT)*
Catherine Mathis *(Sr VP-Mktg & Comm)*
Elizabeth Ventura *(Sr VP-Mktg & Comm)*
John Weisenseel *(Sr VP-Fin)*
Shari Stein *(VP-Corp Mktg & Brand Mgmt)*
James C. Daly *(VP-HR)*
Martin Goldberg *(Head-Model Quality Review & Sr Dir-Quantitative Analytics Res Grp)*
Chris Atkins *(Dir-Fin & Acctg)*
Lynn Cohn *(Dir-Market Dev)*
Jaimee Gordesky *(Sr Mgr-Mktg)*
Rachel Shain *(Mgr-Comm)*
Brands & Products:
ADVISOR INSIGHT
ADVISOR INSIGHT STREET
AIM
ANALYSTS HANDBOOK
ANNA SERVICE BUREAU
ASIA MARKETSCOPE
BANK LOAN AND RECOVERY RATINGS
BOND GUIDE
CDO EVALUATOR
CDS ACCELERATOR
CDS XPRESS
CLASSICDIRECT
COMPUSTAT DATA
COMPUSTAT GLOBAL
COMPUSTAT NORTH AMERICA
COMPUSTAT XPRESSFEED
COMPUSTAT XPRESSFEED LOADER
CONSULTANT DIRECTORY
CORPORATE CREDIT RATINGS
CORPORATE GOVERNANCE EVALUATIONS & SCORES
CORPORATE PROFILES QUANTITATIVE STOCK REPORTS
CORPORATE TRACKER
CORPORATION RECORDS
CREDITMODEL
CREDITPRO
CREDITWEEK
CREDITWIRE
CREDITWIRE JAPAN
CUSIP ISID PLUS ACCESS
CUSIP MASTER SERVICE
CUSIP_DB
DACSS
DEFAULT FILTER
DISCLOSURE DIRECTORY
DIVIDEND RECORD
EUROPEAN MARKETSCOPE
EUROTHESYS LIFE & NON LIFE
EXECUCOMP
GICS DIRECT
GICS HISTORY
GLOBAL RATINGS HANDBOOK
INDEX ALERT
INDEX ALERT-AUSTRALIA
INDUSTRY SURVEYS (GLOBAL)
ISID-PLUS
KENNYBASE
KENNYWEB
LEVELS
LIQUID
LOSSSTATS
LOSSSTATS MODEL
MARKETSCOPE
MASTERFEED
MMD ACCESS
MMD MAILING LISTS
NETADVANTAGE

Key to Media (For complete agency information see *The Advertising Red Books-Agencies* edition):
1. Bus. Publs. 2. Cable T.V. 3. Catalogs & Directories. 4. Co-op Adv. 5. Consumer Mags. 6. D.M. to Bus. Estab.7. D.M. to Consumers
8. Daily Newsp. 9. Exhibits/Trade Shows 10. Foreign 11. Infomercial 12. Internet Adv.13. Multimedia 14. Network Radio
15. Network T.V. 16. Newsp. Distr. Mags. 17. Other 18. Outdoor (Posters, Transit) 19. Point of Purchase20. Premiums, Novelties
21. Product Samples 22. Special Events Mktg. 23. Spot Radio 24. Spot T.V. 25. Weekly Newsp. 26. Yellow Page Adv.

PROFESSIONAL INVESTOR INSIGHT
RATINGS IQUERY
RATINGSDIRECT
RATINGSDIRECT ASIA
RATINGSDIRECT CANADA
RATINGSDIRECT CORPORATIONS & UTILITIES
RATINGSDIRECT FINANCIAL INSTITUTIONS
RATINGSDIRECT GLOBAL ISSUERS
RATINGSDIRECT INSURANCE
RATINGSDIRECT LATIN AMERICA
RATINGSDIRECT PACIFIC
RATINGSDIRECT PUBLIC FINANCE
RATINGSDIRECT SOVEREIGNS
RATINGSDIRECT STRUCTURED FINANCE
RATINGSXPRESS-CREDIT RATINGS
RATINGSXPRESS-CREDIT RESEARCH
RESEARCH INSIGHT
RESEARCH INSIGHT ON THE WEB
S&P INDICES
VALORDATA BROWSER
VALORDATA FEED

STANDARD FINANCIAL CORP.

2640 Monroeville Blvd
Monroeville, PA 15146
Tel.: (412) 856-0363
Web Site: www.standardbankpa.com
Approx. Rev.: $20,466,000
Approx. Number Employees: 88
Year Founded: 2010
Business Description:
Bank Holding Company
S.I.C.: 6712
N.A.I.C.S.: 551111
Advertising Expenditures: $81,000
Media: 17
Personnel:
Terence L. Graft *(Chm)*
Dale A. Walker *(Vice Chm)*
Timothy K. Zimmerman *(Pres & CEO)*
Colleen M. Brown *(CFO)*
Paul A. Knapp *(Chief Comml Loan Officer & Sr VP)*

STATE BANCORP, INC.

Two Jericho Plz
Jericho, NY 11753
Tel.: (516) 465-2200
Fax: (516) 465-6700
Toll Free: (866) 782-8325
E-mail: info@statebankofli.com
Web Site: www.statebankofli.com
Approx. Rev.: $84,767,000
Approx. Number Employees: 289
Year Founded: 1985
Business Description:
Bank Holding Company
S.I.C.: 6029; 6712
N.A.I.C.S.: 522110; 551111
Import Export
Advertising Expenditures: $775,000
Personnel:
Thomas E. Christman *(Chm)*
Thomas M. O'Brien *(Pres & CEO)*
Brian K. Finneran *(CFO & Exec VP)*
Anthony J. Morris *(CMO & Corp Planning Officer)*
Patricia M. Schaubeck *(Gen Counsel)*
Deborah A. Kendric *(Dir-Corp Comm)*

STATE BANK OF LONG ISLAND

(Sub. of STATE BANCORP, INC.)
699 Hillside Ave
New Hyde Park, NY 11040-2512
Tel.: (516) 465-2200
Fax: (516) 437-1032
E-mail: pamsupport@statebankofli.com
Web Site: www.statebankofli.com
Sales Range: $10-24.9 Million
Approx. Number Employees: 50
Year Founded: 1966
Business Description:
State Commercial Bank
S.I.C.: 6029; 6163
N.A.I.C.S.: 522110; 522310
Import Export
Personnel:
Thomas M. O'Brien *(Pres & CEO)*
Brian K. Finneran *(CFO & Exec VP)*
Thomas Iadanza *(Chief Lending Officer)*
Philip J. Nardella *(VP-Fin)*
Thomas A. Arnone *(Dir-Compliance)*
Advertising Agency:
Kalmar Responsive Ad/Marketing Corp.
1 Blue Hill Plz PO Box 1501
Pearl River, NY 10965
Tel.: (845) 201-8035
Fax: (845) 201-8036

STATE STREET CORPORATION

1 Lincoln St
Boston, MA 02111
Tel.: (617) 786-3000
Fax: (617) 664-4299
E-mail: ir@statestreet.com
Web Site: www.statestreet.com
Approx. Rev.: $8,953,000,000
Approx. Number Employees: 28,670
Year Founded: 1792
Business Description:
Investment Services
S.I.C.: 6712; 6029; 6282; 8742; 8748
N.A.I.C.S.: 551111; 522110; 523930; 541611; 541618
Advertising Expenditures: $42,000,000
Media: 2-4-9-11-13-20-22-25-26
Distr.: Intl.
Budget Set: Aug.
Personnel:
Joseph L. Hooley *(Chm, Pres & CEO)*
Joseph C. Antonellis *(Vice Chm)*
William H. Cunningham *(Sr Mng Dir)*
Doug Stern *(Sr Mng Dir & Global Head-Bus Dev & Client Svc)*
Yvonne Wong *(Mng Dir & Head-Bus Dev-Asia Pacific)*
Tom Forrester *(Mng Dir & Head-Ops-Kansas City)*
Edward J. Resch *(CFO & Exec VP)*
Christopher P. Perretta *(CIO & Exec VP)*
Hannah Grove *(Exec VP & Chief Mktg Officer)*
Marc P. Brown *(Chief Admin Officer & Exec VP)*
Jeffrey N. Carp *(Chief Legal Officer & Exec VP)*
Andrew Kuritzkes *(Chief Risk Officer & Exec VP)*
David C. Phelan *(Gen Counsel & Exec VP)*
David J. Gutschenritter *(Treas & Exec VP)*
Stefan M. Gavell *(Exec VP & Head-Regulatory, Indus & Govt Affairs)*
Edward J. O'Brien *(Exec VP & Head-Securities Fin)*
Peter O'Neill *(Exec VP, Head-Global Markets & Global Svcs-Asia-Pacific)*
James S. Phalen *(Exec VP & Head-Global Ops, Tech & Product Dev)*
David Puth *(Exec VP & Head-State Street Global Markets)*
Alison A. Quirk *(Exec VP & Head-Global HR)*
Nicholas J. Bonn *(Exec VP)*
Drew J. Breakspear *(Exec VP & Gen Auditor)*
James C. Caccivio *(Exec VP-Corp Advisory Svcs)*
Timothy J. Caverly *(Exec VP)*
Joseph W. Chow *(Exec VP)*
Donald E. Conover *(Exec VP)*
Jeff Conway *(Exec VP)*
Maureen P. Corcoran *(Exec VP)*
Albert J. Cristoforo *(Exec VP)*
Jayne K. Donahue *(Exec VP & Gen Auditor)*
Sharon E. Donovan Hart *(Exec VP)*
Gary E. Enos *(Exec VP)*
Pamela D. Gormley *(Exec VP)*
Alan D. Greene *(Exec VP)*
Gunjan Kedia *(Exec VP)*
John L. Klinck *(Exec VP-Global Head of Corp Dev & Global Relationship Mgmt)*
Nancy Loucks *(Exec VP)*
Madge M. Meyer *(Exec VP)*
Douglas J. Miller *(Exec VP)*
George A. Russell, Jr. *(Exec VP)*
Mark J. Snyder *(Exec VP)*
Anne P. Tangen *(Exec VP)*
Brian Walsh *(Exec VP)*
Michael L. Williams *(Exec VP)*
Michael J. Wilson *(Exec VP)*
Caroline M. Carmichael *(Sr VP)*
William C. Pryor *(Sr VP & Mgr Investment Analytics)*
Madeleine Egger *(Head-Vienna Office & Country Mgr-Austria)*
Thomas E. Eichenberger *(Sr Dir-Bus Dev)*
Brands & Products:
SSGA
STATE STREET
Advertising Agency:
Kelliher Samets Volk
212 Battery St
Burlington, VT 05401-5281
Tel.: (802) 862-8261
Fax: (802) 863-4724
Media Planning & Placement — Bob Smith *(Acct Exec)*

STELLARONE CORPORATION

590 Peter Jefferson Pkwy Ste 250
Charlottesville, VA 22911
Tel.: (434) 964-2217
Web Site: www.vfgi.net
Approx. Rev.: $161,191,000
Approx. Number Employees: 838
Business Description:
Bank Holding Company
S.I.C.: 6712
N.A.I.C.S.: 551111
Import Export
Advertising Expenditures: $1,100,000
Media: 17
Personnel:
Raymond D. Smoot, Jr. *(Chm)*
H. Wayne Parrish *(Vice Chm)*
O. R. Barham, Jr. *(Pres & CEO)*
Jeffrey W. Farrar *(CFO & Exec VP)*
Litz H. Van Dyke *(COO & Exec VP)*
Christine L. Lewis *(Officer & Corp Sec)*

STERLING BANCORP

650 5th Ave
New York, NY 10019
Tel.: (212) 757-3300
Fax: (212) 490-8852
E-mail: customerservice@sterlingbancorp.com
Web Site: www.sterlingbancorp.com
Approx. Int. Income: $97,190,000
Approx. Number Employees: 558
Year Founded: 1929
Business Description:
Bank Holding Company
S.I.C.: 6712; 6029
N.A.I.C.S.: 551111; 522110
Advertising Expenditures: $3,167,000
Media: 2-4-6-7-8-9-10-19-20-22-23-26
Distr.: Natl.
Budget Set: Jan.
Personnel:
John C. Millman *(Pres)*
Louis J. Cappelli *(CEO)*
John W. Tietjen *(CFO & Exec VP)*
Allen Gershlak *(Pres-Sterling Resource Funding Corp)*
Kenneth E. Cohen *(Sr VP-Comml Real Estate)*
Jeffrey S. Fliegel *(Sr VP)*
John B. McCormack *(Sr VP)*
Michael J. Scheller *(Sr VP)*
Thomas Braunstein *(First VP-Middle Market Banking)*
Salvator Costa *(First VP-Professional Banking Grp)*
Anthony Grosso *(First VP-Sterling National Bank)*
Sadia Affrin *(VP & Branch Mgr-Sterling Natl Bank)*
Elizabeth Forgione *(VP & Branch Mgr-Sterling Natl Bank)*
Rosemarie Henry *(VP & Branch Mgr-Sterling Natl Bank)*
Michael Madeo *(VP & Branch Mgr-Sterling Natl Bank)*
Brands & Products:
EZCERT
TIMEFRAME

STERLING BANCSHARES, INC.

2950 N Loop W Ste 1200
Houston, TX 77092
Tel.: (713) 466-8300
Fax: (713) 466-3117
E-mail: info@banksterling.com
Web Site: www.banksterling.com
Approx. Rev.: $238,872,000
Approx. Number Employees: 946
Year Founded: 1974
Business Description:
Bank Holding Company
S.I.C.: 6712; 6029
N.A.I.C.S.: 551111; 522110
Advertising Expenditures: $1,500,000
Media: 8-9-14-15-20-22-23-24
Personnel:
J. Downey Bridgwater *(Chm, Pres & CEO)*
Zach L. Wasson *(CFO & Exec VP)*
Deborah A. Dinsmore *(Chief Ops Officer, CIO & Exec VP)*
Robert S. Smith *(Chief Credit Officer & Exec VP)*

Key to Media (For complete agency information see *The Advertising Red Books-Agencies* edition):
1. Bus. Publs. 2. Cable T.V. 3. Catalogs & Directories. 4. Co-op Adv. 5. Consumer Mags. 6. D.M. to Bus. Estab.7. D.M. to Consumers 8. Daily Newsp. 9. Exhibits/Trade Shows 10. Foreign 11. Infomercial 12. Internet Adv.13. Multimedia 14. Network Radio 15. Network T.V. 16. Newsp. Distr. Mags. 17. Other 18. Outdoor (Posters, Transit) 19. Point of Purchase20. Premiums, Novelties 21. Product Samples 22. Special Events Mktg. 23. Spot Radio 24. Spot T.V. 25. Weekly Newsp. 26. Yellow Page Adv.

Sterling Bancshares, Inc. — (Continued)
Wanda S. Dalton *(Chief HR Officer & Exec VP)*
James W. Goolsby, Jr. *(Gen Counsel & Exec VP)*
Allen D. Brown *(Exec VP)*
Graham B. Painter *(Exec VP)*
Christopher D. Reid *(VP & Dir-IR)*
Susannah M. Griffin *(VP-Corp Comm)*

Advertising Agency:
Marion Montgomery Inc.
2412 South Blvd
Houston, TX 77098
Tel.: (713) 523-7900

STERLING FINANCIAL CORPORATION
111 N Wall St
Spokane, WA 99201-0609
Tel.: (509) 227-5389
Fax: (509) 358-6161
E-mail: customer.service@sterlingsavings.com
Web Site: www.sterlingfinancialcorporation.com
Approx. Rev.: $582,098,000
Approx. Number Employees: 2,498
Year Founded: 1983
Business Description:
Bank Holding Company
S.I.C.: 6712; 6035; 6163
N.A.I.C.S.: 551111; 522120; 522310
Advertising Expenditures: $11,536,000
Personnel:
Leslie S. Biller *(Chm)*
J. Gregory Seibly *(Pres & CEO)*
Patrick J. Rusnak *(CFO)*
Ezra A. Eckhardt *(COO)*
Robert G. Butterfield *(Principal Acctg Officer, Sr VP & Controller)*
Andrew J. Schultheis *(Gen Counsel & Exec VP)*
Jennifer Lutz *(Coord-PR)*

STEWARDSHIP FINANCIAL CORPORATION
630 Godwin Ave
Midland Park, NJ 07432
Tel.: (201) 444-7100
Fax: (201) 251-1184
Toll Free: (877) 844-2265
E-mail: customerservice@asbnow.com
Web Site: www.snl.com/irweblinkx/corporateprofile.aspx?iid=1032760
Approx. Rev.: $37,371,000
Approx. Number Employees: 112
Year Founded: 1984
Business Description:
Bank Holding Company
S.I.C.: 6029; 6712
N.A.I.C.S.: 522110; 551111
Advertising Expenditures: $523,000
Personnel:
William C. Hanse *(Chm)*
Michael A. Westra *(Vice Chm)*
Paul Van Ostenbridge *(Pres & CEO)*
Julie E. Holland *(Chief Risk Officer & Sr VP)*
John W. Hain *(Sr VP)*
Robert C. Vliet *(Sr VP)*
Mary Beth Steiginga *(Asst Sec)*

STONEHAM BANK
80 Montvale Ave
Stoneham, MA 02180
Tel.: (781) 438-0430
Toll Free: (888) 402-2265
Web Site: www.stonehambank.com
Approx. Number Employees: 70
Year Founded: 1887
Business Description:
Federal Savings Institutions
S.I.C.: 6035; 6163
N.A.I.C.S.: 522120; 522310
Media: 6-17
Personnel:
Robert H. Skelley *(Chm)*
Donald R. Clarke *(Vice Chm)*
Janice Houghton *(Pres & CEO)*
John P. Speakman *(COO & Exec VP)*
Janet Spencer *(Sr VP-Comml & Construction Loans)*

Advertising Agency:
Stackpole & Partners Advertising
222 Merrimac St
Newburyport, MA 01950
Tel.: (978) 463-6600
Fax: (978) 463-6610

STRATEGIC TAX SOLUTIONS
4553 9th Ave SW Ste B
Fargo, ND 58103
Tel.: (701) 356-8600
Fax: (701) 356-8601
E-mail: rick@protaxsolutions.net
Web Site: www.protaxsolutions.net
Business Description:
Tax Preparation & Planning, Accounting & Bookkeeping, Payroll, Business Consulting & New Corporation Setup
S.I.C.: 7291; 8721; 8748
N.A.I.C.S.: 541213; 541214; 541219; 541618
Media: 8
Personnel:
Rick Morris *(Owner)*

SUMMIT FINANCIAL GROUP, INC.
300 N Main St PO Box 179
Moorefield, WV 26836
Tel.: (304) 530-1000
E-mail: tsherman@summitfgi.com
Web Site: www.summitfgi.com
Approx. Int. Income: $79,672,000
Approx. Number Employees: 234
Year Founded: 1996
Business Description:
Financial Services
S.I.C.: 6029; 6099
N.A.I.C.S.: 522110; 522320
Advertising Expenditures: $198,000
Media: 17
Personnel:
Oscar M. Bean *(Chm)*
George R. Ours, Jr. *(Vice Chm)*
H. Charles Maddy III *(Pres & CEO)*
Robert S. Tissue *(CFO & Sr VP)*
Scott C. Jennings *(COO & Sr VP)*
Patrick N. Frye *(Chief Credit Officer & Sr VP)*
Julie R. Cook *(Chief Acctg Officer & VP)*
Douglas T. Mitchell *(Chief Banking Officer & Sr VP)*
Jerry Endsley *(Sr Acct Exec)*

SUMMIT STATE BANK
500 Bicentennial Way
Santa Rosa, CA 95403
Mailing Address:
PO Box 6188
Santa Rosa, CA 95406-0188
Tel.: (707) 568-6000
Toll Free: (800) 428-5008
E-mail: summitonline@summitstatebank.com
Web Site: www.summitstatebank.com
Approx. Int. Income: $21,554,000
Approx. Number Employees: 49
Business Description:
Federal Savings Bank
S.I.C.: 6035
N.A.I.C.S.: 522120
Advertising Expenditures: $206,000
Personnel:
John C. Lewis *(Chm)*
Thomas M. Duryea *(Pres & CEO)*
Dennis E. Kelley *(CFO & Sr VP)*
Linda Bertauche *(COO & Sr VP)*
Jacqueline A. Peterson *(Reg VP)*
Patty Hoagland *(VP-IT)*
Gail Baker *(Asst VP & Branch Mgr)*
Judy Reynolds *(Asst VP & Branch Mgr)*

SUN BANCORP, INC.
226 W Landis Ave
Vineland, NJ 08360
Tel.: (856) 691-7700
Fax: (856) 691-9187
Fax: (856) 507-1181
Toll Free: (800) 691-7701
Web Site: www.sunnb.com
Approx. Rev.: $161,115,000
Approx. Number Employees: 625
Year Founded: 1985
Business Description:
Bank Holding Company
S.I.C.: 6029
N.A.I.C.S.: 522110
Advertising Expenditures: $2,453,000
Media: 2-22
Personnel:
Sidney R. Brown *(Vice Chm, Treas & Sec)*
Thomas X. Geisel *(Pres & CEO)*
Robert B. Crowl *(CFO & Exec VP)*
A. Bruce Dansbury *(Exec VP)*
Edward A. Malandro *(Exec VP-Consumer Banking)*
Thomas J. Townsend *(Exec VP & Chief Bank Officer)*
Heather Newcomb *(VP, Dir-PR & Comm)*

SUN LIFE ASSURANCE COMPANY OF CANADA
(Sub. of Sun Life Financial Inc.)
100 Simcoe St Ste 115
Toronto, ON M5H 1J9, Canada
Tel.: (647) 788-2415
Fax: (416) 408-4824
Toll Free: (800) 471-3941
Web Site: www.sunlife.ca/
Approx. Number Employees: 13
Year Founded: 1987
Business Description:
Distibutor of Mutual Funds
S.I.C.: 6211
N.A.I.C.S.: 523120
Media: 13-17
Personnel:
Donald A. Stewart *(CEO)*
Dan Buttenhan *(Mng Dir)*

SUN LIFE FINANCIAL INC.
150 King Street West
Toronto, ON M5H 1J9, Canada
Tel.: (416) 979-9966
Fax: (416) 979-4853
Toll Free: (800) SUNLIFE
E-mail: webmaster@sunlife.com
Web Site: www.sunlife.com
Approx. Rev.: $13,210,222,640
Approx. Number Employees: 14,755
Year Founded: 1871
Business Description:
Life Insurance & Financial Services
S.I.C.: 6722; 6311
N.A.I.C.S.: 525910; 524113
Media: 2-3-6-7-8-10-13-15-17-25
Distr.: Intl.
Budget Set: Jan.
Personnel:
Ronald W. Osborne *(Chm)*
Jon A. Boscia *(Pres)*
Donald A. Stewart *(CEO)*
Colm J. Freyne *(CFO & Exec VP)*
Paul O. Petrelli *(CFO & Sr VP)*
Dean A. Connor *(COO)*
Mark S. Saunders *(CIO & Exec VP)*
Mary De Paoli *(CMO & Sr VP)*
Stephen C. Peacher *(Chief Investment Officer & Exec VP)*
Michael P. Stramaglia *(Chief Risk Officer & Exec VP)*
Robert W. Wilson *(Chief Actuary & Sr VP)*
K. Louise McLaren *(Chief HR Officer & Sr VP)*
Keith Gubbay *(Chief Actuary-Sun Life Fin US & VP)*
Robert J. Sharkey *(Chief Actuary)*
Christine I. Mackiw *(VP-Records Mgmt)*
Kevin P. Dougherty *(Pres-Sun Life Global Investments & Pres-Sun Life Financial Canada)*
Dikran Ohannessian *(Pres-Sunlife Asia)*
Westley V. Thompson *(Pres-Sun Life Fin-US)*
Thomas A. Bogart *(Gen Counsel & Exec VP-Bus Dev)*
Stephen C. Kicinski *(Treas & Sr VP)*
Joan M. Wilson *(Sec & Sr VP)*
Stephen L. Deschenes *(Sr VP & Gen Mgr-Annuities Div)*
Michael Shunney *(Sr VP-Employee Benefits Grp & Gen Mgr)*
Greta R. Cusworth *(Sr VP-Intl Initiatives)*
Wayne A. Daniel *(Sr VP-Reinsurance)*
Michael J. O'Connor *(Sr VP-Tax)*
Kevin Strain *(Sr VP-Individual Insurance & Investments)*
Lesley Thomson *(VP-Actuary)*
Lori Bak *(VP-Mktg & Bus Dev)*
B. Dustin Ball *(VP-Strategic Initiatives-Asia)*
Frank Switzer *(VP-Corp Comm)*

Advertising Agencies:
Adams & Knight Advertising/Public Relations
80 Avon Meadow Ln
Avon, CT 06001
Tel.: (860) 676-2300
Fax: (860) 676-1940

Grey Canada
1881 Yonge St Ste 800
Toronto, ON M4S 3C4, Canada
Tel.: (416) 486-0700
Fax: (416) 486-8907

NATIONAL Public Relations
2001 McGill College Ave Ste 800
Montreal, QC H3A 1G1, Canada

Key to Media (For complete agency information see *The Advertising Red Books-Agencies* edition):
1. Bus. Publs. 2. Cable T.V. 3. Catalogs & Directories. 4. Co-op Adv. 5. Consumer Mags. 6. D.M. to Bus. Estab.7. D.M. to Consumers 8. Daily Newsp. 9. Exhibits/Trade Shows 10. Foreign 11. Infomercial 12. Internet Adv.13. Multimedia 14. Network Radio 15. Network T.V. 16. Newsp. Distr. Mags. 17. Other 18. Outdoor (Posters, Transit) 19. Point of Purchase20. Premiums, Novelties 21. Product Samples 22. Special Events Mktg. 23. Spot Radio 24. Spot T.V. 25. Weekly Newsp. 26. Yellow Page Adv.

Tel.: (514) 843-7171
Fax: (514) 843-6976

Weber Shandwick
10/F Oxford House Taikoo Place
Quarry Bay, China (Hong Kong)
Tel.: (852) 2845 1008
Fax: (852) 2868 0224

SUN TRUST BANK, ATLANTA

PO Box 4625
Atlanta, GA 30302
Toll Free: (800) 568-3476
Advertising Agency:
Cookerly Public Relations
3500 Lenox Rd 1 Alliance Ctr Ste 510
Atlanta, GA 30326
Tel.: (404) 816-2037
Fax: (404) 816-3037

SUNBELT BUSINESS ADVISORS NETWORK, LLC

(Sub. of Merrymeeting, Inc.)
7100 E Pleasant Valley Rd Ste 300
Independence, OH 44131
Tel.: (216) 674-0645
Fax: (216) 674-0650
Toll Free: (877) 392-6278
E-mail: etp@sunbeltnetwork.com
Web Site: www.sunbeltnetwork.com
Approx. Rev.: $16,000,000
Approx. Number Employees: 3
Year Founded: 1979
Business Description:
Franchised Business Brokerage Services
S.I.C.: 7389
N.A.I.C.S.: 541990
Advertising Expenditures: $250,000
Media: 2-6-9-10-13-23-24
Personnel:
Matt Ottaway *(Pres)*
John Davies *(CEO)*
Brands & Products:
SUNBELT BUSINESS ADVISORS
SUNBELT BUSINESS BROKERS

SUNTRUST BANK, NASHVILLE REGION

(Sub. of SunTrust Banks, Inc.)
201 4th Ave N
Nashville, TN 37219
Mailing Address:
PO Box 305110
Nashville, TN 37230-5110
Tel.: (615) 748-4000
Fax: (615) 748-4279
Sales Range: $450-499.9 Million
Approx. Number Employees: 1,800
Business Description:
Full Banking Services
S.I.C.: 6029
N.A.I.C.S.: 522110
Advertising Expenditures: $2,160,000
Media: 2-4-6-7-8-9-13-18-23-24-25-26
Distr.: Direct to Consumer; Reg.
Budget Set: Sept.
Personnel:
Robert McNeilly *(Pres & CEO)*

SUNTRUST BANKS, INC.

303 Peachtree St NE
Atlanta, GA 30308-3201
Tel.: (404) 588-7711
Fax: (404) 332-3875
E-mail: michael.mccoy@suntrust.com
Web Site: www.suntrust.com
Approx. Int. Income: $6,343,000,000
Approx. Number Employees: 29,056
Year Founded: 1984
Business Description:
Bank Holding Company
S.I.C.: 6712; 6029; 6035
N.A.I.C.S.: 551111; 522110; 522120
Advertising Expenditures: $156,700,000
Media: 2-8-10-13-20-22-23
Personnel:
William H. Rogers, Jr. *(Pres & CEO)*
Laura Kaplan *(Mng Dir & Head-Private Wealth)*
Aleem Gillani *(CFO)*
Timothy E. Sullivan *(CIO)*
Rilla Delorier *(CMO & Exec VP)*
David F. Dierker *(Chief Admin Officer & Exec VP)*
Ernest N. Dawal *(Chief Investment Officer-Private Wealth Mgmt)*
Thomas E. Panther *(Chief Acctg Officer, Sr VP & Controller)*
Kenneth J. Carrig *(Chief HR Officer & Corp Exec VP)*
Thomas E. Freeman *(Chief Risk Officer)*
John Geraghty *(Exec VP)*
Steve Shriner *(Chief Consumer Credit Officer)*
Johnny B. Moore, Jr. *(Pres/CEO-Memphis Reg Ops)*
John G. Stallings *(Pres/CEO-Mid-Atlantic Div)*
David Stevens *(Pres/CEO-Central Carolina Reg)*
Raymond D. Fortin *(Gen Counsel)*
Willem-Jan O. Hattink *(Exec VP & Head-Private Wealth Mgmt)*
William Newell *(Exec VP & Head-Bus-Comml Line)*
Gay O. Abbott *(Exec VP-Comml Bus)*
Brad Dinsmore *(Exec VP-Consumer Banking & Private Wealth Mgmt)*
Craig Smith *(Exec VP)*
Jarrette A. White, III *(Exec VP)*
Robert Blair *(Sr VP & Head-Comml Card Svcs)*
Cathy Linton *(Sr VP & Dir-Adv & Comm)*
Kristopher Dickson *(Sr VP)*
Ryan Shim *(Sr VP-Wealth & Investments)*
Terry Vacheron *(Sr VP & Corp Dir-Tax)*
Gaetana Rampley *(VP & Assoc-Adv)*
Bill Holt *(Head-Bus Banking)*
J. MacGregor Tisdale *(Mgr-Comml Team)*
Brands & Products:
BE READY FOR LIFE
LIVE SOLID. BANK SOLID
SUNTRUST
Advertising Agency:
Cookerly Public Relations
3500 Lenox Rd 1 Alliance Ctr Ste 510
Atlanta, GA 30326
Tel.: (404) 816-2037
Fax: (404) 816-3037

SUNWEST BANK

17542 17th St
Tustin, CA 92780-1960
Tel.: (714) 730-4400
Tel.: (714) 730-4444
Fax: (714) 730-9465
Toll Free: (800) 330-9890
E-mail: info@sunwestbank.com
Web Site: www.sunwestbank.com
Approx. Int. Income: $43,285,000
Approx. Number Employees: 126
Year Founded: 1981
Business Description:
Commercial Bank
S.I.C.: 6029
N.A.I.C.S.: 522110
Advertising Expenditures: $228,000
Media: 7-8-9
Personnel:
Eric D. Hovde *(Chm)*
Chris Walsh *(Pres)*
Glenn E. Gray *(CEO)*
Jason Raefski *(CFO & Exec VP)*
Brad Hoover *(Chief Credit Officer & Exec VP)*
Marshell Montgomery *(Chief Compliance Officer & Exec VP)*
Milton Flores *(Chief Acctg Officer & Sr VP)*
Andrew Stines *(Chief Risk Officer & Sr VP)*
Andy Phillips *(Pres-Northern Arizona Market)*
Brian Constable *(Chief Comml Banking Officer & Exec VP)*
John Houten *(Exec VP-Corp Dev)*
Kenneth Smith *(Sr VP & Reg Mgr)*
Andrew Lamb *(Sr VP & Mgr-Relationship-Newport Beach)*
Ann Lobosky *(Sr VP & Mgr-HR)*
Kendra Coffey *(Sr VP-Bank Ops)*
Matt Rogers *(Sr VP)*
Robert L. Cafaro *(VP & Branch Mgr-Sls)*
Tony Rodriguez *(VP & Mgr-Sls-San Clemente Branch)*
Lisa Sacquety *(VP & Mgr-Relationship)*
Brands & Products:
SUNWEST BANK
SUNWEST BANK ONLINE
SUNWEST BANK RAPID REMID
Advertising Agency:
The Artime Group
65 N Raymond Ave Ste 205
Pasadena, CA 91103-3947
Tel.: (626) 583-1855
Fax: (626) 583-1861

SUPERIOR BANCORP

17 N 20th St
Birmingham, AL 35203
Tel.: (205) 327-1400
Tel.: (205) 327-3547
Fax: (205) 324-8060
Web Site: www.superiorbank.com
Approx. Rev.: $175,661,000
Approx. Number Employees: 828
Year Founded: 1997
Business Description:
Holding Company; Commercial Bank & Trust
S.I.C.: 6712; 6029
N.A.I.C.S.: 551111; 522110
Advertising Expenditures: $2,530,000
Media: 7-8-9-18-23-25-26
Personnel:
C. Marvin Scott *(Chm & CEO)*
Rick D. Gardner *(Pres)*
David R. Hiden *(CIO)*
A. Fox Defuniak, III *(Pres-Birmingham Market)*
George J. Hall *(Pres-Florida & Corp Banking Exec)*
William H. Caughan *(Gen Counsel & Sec)*
Chris Gossett *(Exec VP)*
Donna Earnest *(Dir-Mktg)*

SUSQUEHANNA BANCSHARES, INC.

26 N Cedar St
Lititz, PA 17543-7000
Mailing Address:
PO Box 1000
Lititz, PA 17543
Tel.: (717) 626-4721
Fax: (717) 626-1874
Web Site: www.susquehanna.net
Approx. Int. Income: $613,695,000
Approx. Number Employees: 2,836
Year Founded: 1982
Business Description:
Bank Holding Company
S.I.C.: 6712; 6029
N.A.I.C.S.: 551111; 522110
Advertising Expenditures: $9,058,000
Personnel:
William John Reuter *(Chm & CEO)*
Eddie L. Dunklebarger *(Vice Chm)*
Drew K. Hostetter *(CFO & Exec VP)*
Gregory A. Duncan *(COO & Exec VP)*
Edward Balderston Jr. *(Chief Admin Officer, Code of Ethics Officer & Exec VP)*
Michael M. Quick *(Chief Corp Credit Officer & Exec VP)*
Rodney A. Lefever *(CTO & Sr VP)*
Edward J. Wydock *(Chief Risk Officer & Sr VP)*
Lisa M. Cavage *(Sec & Counsel & Sr VP)*
Bernard Allen Francis, Jr. *(Sr VP & Grp Exec)*
Michael E. Hough *(Sr VP)*
Joseph R. Lizza *(Sr VP)*
John H. Montgomery *(Sr VP)*
Advertising Agencies:
Donovan Advertising & Marketing Services
180 W Airport Rd
Lititz, PA 17543
Tel.: (717) 560-1333
Fax: (717) 560-2034

IntelliMedia-DBC
1200 River Rd Ste 300 E
Conshohocken, PA 19428
Tel.: (215) 957-0300
Fax: (484) 342-3602

SUSSEX BANCORP

200 Munsonhurst Rd Rt 517
Franklin, NJ 07416-0353
Tel.: (973) 827-2914
Fax: (973) 827-2926
E-mail: comments@sussexbank.com
Web Site: www.sussexbank.com
Approx. Rev.: $26,639,000
Approx. Number Employees: 106
Year Founded: 1976
Business Description:
Bank Holding Company
S.I.C.: 6141; 6712
N.A.I.C.S.: 522210; 551111
Advertising Expenditures: $178,000
Media: 17
Personnel:
Donald L. Kovach *(Chm)*
Edward J. Leppert *(Vice Chm)*

Key to Media (For complete agency information see *The Advertising Red Books-Agencies* edition):
1. Bus. Publs. 2. Cable T.V. 3. Catalogs & Directories. 4. Co-op Adv. 5. Consumer Mags. 6. D.M. to Bus. Estab.7. D.M. to Consumers 8. Daily Newsp. 9. Exhibits/Trade Shows 10. Foreign 11. Infomercial 12. Internet Adv.13. Multimedia 14. Network Radio 15. Network T.V. 16. Newsp. Distr. Mags. 17. Other 18. Outdoor (Posters, Transit) 19. Point of Purchase20. Premiums, Novelties 21. Product Samples 22. Special Events Mktg. 23. Spot Radio 24. Spot T.V. 25. Weekly Newsp. 26. Yellow Page Adv.

Sussex Bancorp — (Continued)

Anthony Labozzetta *(Pres & CEO)*
Steven M. Fusco *(CFO & Exec VP)*

SVB FINANCIAL GROUP

3003 Tasman Dr
Santa Clara, CA 95054-1191
Tel.: (408) 654-7400
Fax: (408) 496-2405
E-mail: cswest@svb.com
Web Site: www.svb.com
Approx. Rev.: $461,731,000
Approx. Number Employees: 1,357
Year Founded: 1983
Business Description:
Financial Services Company
S.I.C.: 6712; 6029; 6371
N.A.I.C.S.: 551111; 522110; 525990
Media: 2-4-6-7-8-9-10-22-25
Personnel:
Alex W. Hart *(Chm)*
Harry W. Kellogg, Jr. *(Vice Chm-Silicon Valley Bank & Head-Strategic Relationships)*
Gregory W. Becker *(Pres)*
Kenneth Parmalee Wilcox *(CEO)*
Gerald Brady *(Mng Dir)*
Michael Descheneaux *(CFO)*
Brian K. Dennehy *(CMO)*
Marc J. Verissimo *(Chief Strategy Officer & Chief Risk Officer)*
Kamran Husain *(Chief Acctg Officer)*
Mary Dent *(Gen Counsel)*
Chris Edmonds-Waters *(Head-HR)*
Jason Carone *(Sr Mgr-ePayments & Cash Mgmt Ops)*
Advertising Agency:
VSA Partners, Inc.
600 W Chicago Ave
Chicago, IL 60654
Tel.: (312) 427-6413
Toll Free: (877) 422-1311

SWISS AMERICA TRADING CORPORATION

15018 N Tatum Blvd
Phoenix, AZ 85032
Tel.: (602) 788-4653
Fax: (602) 788-4655
E-mail: info@swissamerica.com
Web Site: www.swissamerica.com
Approx. Number Employees: 10
Year Founded: 1982
Business Description:
Business & Investment Services Relating to US Rare Coins & Precious Metals
S.I.C.: 7389; 6282
N.A.I.C.S.: 561499; 523930
Media: 3
Personnel:
Craig R. Smith *(Chm)*
Steve Carnow *(Gen Mgr)*
Pat Mershon *(Mgr-Ops)*
Dean Heskin *(Sr Acct Exec)*
Advertising Agency:
FAME - Financially Acclaimed Marketing Enterprises, Inc.
15018 N Tatum Blvd
Phoenix, AZ 85032
Tel.: (602) 788-4653

T BANCSHARES, INC.

16000 Dallas Pkwy Ste 125
Dallas, TX 75248
Tel.: (972) 720-9000
Fax: (972) 720-9025
E-mail: ib_help@tbank.com
Web Site: www.tbank.com
Approx. Rev.: $15,647,000
Approx. Number Employees: 25
Business Description:
Bank Holding Company
S.I.C.: 6712; 6029
N.A.I.C.S.: 551111; 522110
Advertising Expenditures: $139,000
Media: 7-8-9-23-25
Personnel:
Dan Basso *(Chm)*
Patrick Howard *(Pres & CEO)*
Craig Barnes *(Chief Credit Officer & Exec VP)*
Charles Holmes *(Exec VP)*
Matthew Smith *(VP-IT-T Bank)*

T. ROWE PRICE ASSOCIATES, INC.

(Sub. of T. Rowe Price Group Inc.)
100 E Pratt St
Baltimore, MD 21202-1009
Tel.: (410) 345-2000
Fax: (410) 345-2349
Toll Free: (800) 225-5132
E-mail: info@troweprice.com
Web Site: www.troweprice.com
Sales Range: $1-4.9 Billion
Approx. Number Employees: 4,000
Year Founded: 1937
Business Description:
Investment Management Firm
S.I.C.: 6722; 6289
N.A.I.C.S.: 525910; 523999
Media: 2-3-6-7-8-9-15-25
Distr.: Direct to Consumer; Natl.
Budget Set: Sept.
Personnel:
Brian C. Rogers *(Chm)*
James A.C. Kennedy *(Pres & CEO)*
James S. Riepe *(Mng Dir)*
Kenneth V. Moreland *(CFO)*
Michael Olsheski *(VP-Media)*
Wayne Melia *(Head-Ops & Tech)*
Advertising Agency:
J. Walter Thompson Company (d/b/a JWT)
466 Lexington Ave
New York, NY 10017-3140
Tel.: (212) 210-7000
Fax: (212) 210-7299

T. ROWE PRICE GROUP INC.

100 E Pratt St
Baltimore, MD 21202-1009
Tel.: (410) 345-2000
Fax: (410) 345-2394
Toll Free: (800) 638-7890
E-mail: info@troweprice.com
Web Site: www.troweprice.com
Approx. Rev.: $2,370,700,000
Approx. Number Employees: 5,052
Year Founded: 2000
Business Description:
Investment & Financial Services
S.I.C.: 6221; 6282
N.A.I.C.S.: 523140; 523930
Advertising Expenditures: $86,900,000
Personnel:
Brian C. Rogers *(Chm)*
Edward C. Bernard *(Vice Chm)*
James A.C. Kennedy *(Pres & CEO)*
Kenneth V. Moreland *(CFO)*
Henry H. Hopkins *(Chief Legal Officer)*
Natalie Calarie Widdowson *(VP-Mktg)*
Lea Wray *(Asst VP)*
Mike Gitlin *(Dir-Fixed Income Div)*
Thomas Kazmierczak, Jr. *(Product Mgr)*
Brands & Products:
INVEST WITH CONFIDENCE
T. ROWE PRICE
Advertising Agency:
Carton Donofrio Partners, Inc.
100 N Charles St 15th Fl
Baltimore, MD 21201
Tel.: (410) 576-9000
Fax: (410) 528-8809

TAYLOR CAPITAL GROUP INC

9550 W Higgins Rd
Rosemont, IL 60018
Tel.: (847) 653-7978
E-mail: investor.relations@coletaylor.com
Web Site: www.taylorcapitalgroup.com
Approx. Rev.: $281,199,000
Approx. Number Employees: 591
Year Founded: 1969
Business Description:
Bank Holding Company
S.I.C.: 6029; 6163; 6712
N.A.I.C.S.: 522110; 522310; 551111
Advertising Expenditures: $1,500,000
Personnel:
Bruce W. Taylor *(Chm)*
Jeffrey W. Taylor *(Vice Chm)*
Mark A. Hoppe *(Pres & CEO)*
Randall T. Conte *(CFO)*
Steven H. Shapiro *(Gen Counsel & Sr VP)*
Linda Hamilton *(Dir-HR)*
Caroline Carramusa *(Office Mgr)*
Ilene Stevens *(Coord-IR)*

TCF FINANCIAL CORPORATION

200 Lake St E
Wayzata, MN 55391-1693
Mailing Address:
Mail Code EX0 03 A
Wayzata, MN 55391
Tel.: (612) 661-6500
Fax: (952) 745-2773
Web Site: www.tcfbank.com
Approx. Rev.: $1,507,862,000
Approx. Number Employees: 4,978
Year Founded: 1923
Business Description:
Bank Holding Company
S.I.C.: 6712; 6029
N.A.I.C.S.: 551111; 522110
Advertising Expenditures: $17,134,000
Media: 17
Personnel:
William A. Cooper *(Chm & CEO)*
Barry N. Winslow *(Vice Chm & Chief Risk Officer)*
Gregory J. Pulles *(Vice Chm)*
Neil W. Brown *(Pres & COO)*
Thomas F. Jasper *(CFO)*
Earl Stratton *(CIO & Exec VP-TCF Bank)*
Craig R. Dahl *(Chm-TCF Equipment Finance, Inc. & Exec VP-Wholesale Banking)*
William Henak *(Pres/COO-TCF Equipment Fin, Inc.)*
David M. Stautz *(Exec VP & Controller)*
Brands & Products:
OPEN SEVEN DAYS
TCF
TCF EXPRESS TELLERS
TOTALLY FREE

TCW GROUP INC.

(Sub. of SG Asset Management SA)
865 S Figueroa St Ste 1800
Los Angeles, CA 90017
Tel.: (213) 244-0000
Web Site: www.tcw.com
Approx. Number Employees: 500
Year Founded: 1971
Business Description:
Financial Advisors
S.I.C.: 6289; 6282
N.A.I.C.S.: 523999; 523930
Personnel:
Robert A. Day *(Chm)*
Marc I. Stern *(Vice Chm & CEO)*
Thomas E. Larkin, Jr. *(Vice Chm)*
Charles W. Baldiswieler *(Pres, CEO & Grp Mng Dir)*
Hilary G.D. Lord *(Mng Dir & Chief Compliance Officer)*
Tad Rivelle *(Chief Investment Officer & Grp Mng Dir)*
Eric Arentsen *(Mng Dir-US Fixed Income)*
Jeffrey B. Anderson *(Mng Dir)*
David S. DeVito *(Chief Admin Officer & Exec VP)*
Joseph M. Burschinger *(Chief Risk Officer, Exec VP & Head-Investment Ops)*
Michael E. Cahill *(Gen Counsel & Exec VP)*
Mark W. Gibello *(Exec VP)*
Dennis J. McCarthy *(Sr VP-Defined Contribution Mktg)*
Advertising Agency:
Molecular
The Arsenal of the Charles 343 Arsenal St
Watertown, MA 02472
Tel.: (617) 218-6500
Fax: (617) 218-6700

TD AMERITRADE HOLDING CORPORATION

4211 S 102nd St
Omaha, NE 68127-1031
Mailing Address:
PO Box 3288
Omaha, NE 68103-0288
Tel.: (402) 331-7856
Fax: (402) 597-7789
Toll Free: (800) 237-8692
E-mail: amtdinfo@ameritrade.com
Web Site: www.amtd.com
Approx. Rev.: $2,560,691,000
Approx. Number Employees: 5,240
Year Founded: 1971
Business Description:
Retail Discount Brokerage & Related Financial Services Including Electronic Trading, Market Data & Research
S.I.C.: 6211
N.A.I.C.S.: 523120; 523110
Advertising Expenditures: $250,000,000
Media: 3-6-8-9-10-13-15-19-22

Key to Media (For complete agency information see *The Advertising Red Books-Agencies* edition):
1. Bus. Publs. 2. Cable T.V. 3. Catalogs & Directories. 4. Co-op Adv. 5. Consumer Mags. 6. D.M. to Bus. Estab.7. D.M. to Consumers
8. Daily Newsp. 9. Exhibits/Trade Shows 10. Foreign 11. Infomercial 12. Internet Adv.13. Multimedia 14. Network Radio
15. Network T.V. 16. Newsp. Distr. Mags. 17. Other 18. Outdoor (Posters, Transit) 19. Point of Purchase20. Premiums, Novelties
21. Product Samples 22. Special Events Mktg. 23. Spot Radio 24. Spot T.V. 25. Weekly Newsp. 26. Yellow Page Adv.

Personnel:
W. Edmund Clark *(Vice Chm-TD Ameritrade & Pres/CEO-TD Bank Grp)*
Fredric J. Tomczyk *(Pres & CEO)*
John Bunch *(Pres & Retail Distribution)*
Joseph H. Moglia *(CEO)*
William J. Gerber *(CFO & Exec VP)*
Marvin W. Adams *(COO & CIO)*
Phillip A. Bowman *(CMO)*
Bryce Engel *(Chief Brokerage Officer & Sr VP)*
Tom Bradley *(Pres-TD Ameritrade Institutional)*
Ellen L. S. Koplow *(Gen Counsel, Sec & Exec VP)*
Peter Sidebottom *(Exec VP-Product, Mktg & Client Experience)*
Laurine M. Garrity *(Sr VP)*
Tom Sosnoff *(Sr VP-Strategic Initiatives)*
Brands & Products:
AMERITRADE
AMERITRADE ADVANCED ANALYZER
AMERITRADE ADVISOR SERVICES
AMERITRADE APEX
AMERITRADE CLEARING SERVICES
AMERITRADE CORPORATE SERVICES
AMERITRADE IZONE
AMERITRADE PLUS
AMERITRADE PRO
AMERITRADE STREAMER
AMERIVEST
QUOTESCOPE
SNAPTICKET
SUPER STREAMMACHINE
TRADE TRIGGERS
Advertising Agencies:
Goodby, Silverstein & Partners, Inc.
(Part of Omnicom Group, Inc.)
720 California St
San Francisco, CA 94108-2404
Tel.: (415) 392-0669
Fax: (415) 788-4303
Creative

Karsh & Hagan Communications, Inc.
2399 Blake St Ste 160
Denver, CO 80205-2108
Tel.: (303) 296-8400
Fax: (303) 296-2015

MediaVest USA
1675 Broadway
New York, NY 10019
Tel.: (212) 468-4000
Fax: (212) 468-4110
Active Trader/Long-Term Investor Retail Business

OgilvyOne Worldwide
636 11th Ave
New York, NY 10036
Tel.: (212) 237-4000
Fax: (212) 237-5123

TD BANK US HOLDING COMPANY
(Sub. of The Toronto-Dominion Bank)
2 Portland Sq
Portland, ME 04112
Mailing Address:
PO Box 9540
Portland, ME 04112-9540
Tel.: (207) 761-8500
Fax: (207) 761-8534
Toll Free: (800) 462-3666
Web Site: www.tdbank.com
Approx. Number Employees: 20,953
Year Founded: 1986
Business Description:
Bank Holding Company
S.I.C.: 6712
N.A.I.C.S.: 551111
Advertising Expenditures: $30,381,000
Personnel:
William J. Ryan *(Chm)*
Bharat B. Masrani *(Pres & CEO)*
Stephen J. Boyle *(CFO & Exec VP-Fin)*
Edward P. Schreiber *(Chief Risk Officer & Exec VP)*
Jacquelynn E. Henke *(Officer-Real Estate Green Strategy)*
Fred Graziano *(Pres-Reg Retail Banking)*
Joseph F. Nemia *(Exec VP & Head-Asset Based Lending)*
Mark Santasieri *(Sr VP)*
Shaun McIntyre *(VP-Municipal Lending-Govt Banking Div)*
Bryan Feuerberg *(Asst VP & Mgr-Field Mktg)*
Jordan Butterworth *(Mgr-Comml Loan Specialist)*
Michael F. Downes *(Mgr-Loan Servicing & Reputational Risk)*
Advertising Agency:
The Vidal Partnership
228 E 45th St 11th Fl
New York, NY 10017-3303
Tel.: (646) 356-6600
Fax: (212) 661-7650

TD WATERHOUSE SECURITIES, INC.
(Sub. of TD Waterhouse Group, Inc.)
31 W 52nd St
New York, NY 10019-6118
Tel.: (212) 668-1674
Fax: (212) 809-1651
Toll Free: (800) 934-4448
Web Site: www.tdameritrade.com
Approx. Number Employees: 1,600
Year Founded: 1979
Business Description:
Securities; Brokerage Firm
S.I.C.: 6211; 6282
N.A.I.C.S.: 523120; 523930
Advertising Expenditures: $1,000,000
Media: 2-3-4-8-9-10-13-14-15-18-25
Distr.: Natl.
Brands & Products:
ADVISORDIRECT
IRACESS
TRADEDIRECT
TRANSFERDIRECT

TEAMSTAFF, INC.
1 Executive Dr Ste 130
Somerset, NJ 08873-4002
Tel.: (732) 748-1700
Fax: (732) 748-3206
Toll Free: (877) 523-9897
Toll Free: (866) 352-5304
Web Site: www.teamstaff.com
Approx. Rev.: $40,874,000
Approx. Number Employees: 37
Year Founded: 1969
Business Description:
Payroll Service Bureau, Contract Employment, Employee Leasing & Temporary Medical Staffing
S.I.C.: 7361; 7363; 8721
N.A.I.C.S.: 561310; 541214; 561320; 561330
Advertising Expenditures: $26,000
Media: 17
Personnel:
Frederick G. Wasserman *(Chm)*
Zachary C. Parker *(Pres & CEO)*
John E. Kahn *(CFO)*
John F. Armstrong *(Exec VP-Corp Dev)*
Brands & Products:
TEAMSTAFF

TECHE HOLDING COMPANY
1120 Jefferson Ter
New Iberia, LA 70560
Tel.: (337) 560-7151
Fax: (337) 365-7130
Toll Free: (800) 256-1500
E-mail: info@teche.com
Web Site: www.teche.com
Approx. Rev.: $57,296,000
Approx. Number Employees: 237
Business Description:
Bank Holding Company
S.I.C.: 6035; 6712
N.A.I.C.S.: 522120; 551111
Media: 10
Personnel:
Patrick O. Little *(Chm)*
J. L. Chauvin *(CFO, Treas & Sr VP)*
Darryl R. Broussard *(Sr VP & Chief Lending Officer)*
W. Ross Little, Jr. *(Sec & Sr VP-Sls & Mktg)*
Martin M. Vasquez *(Mgr-Loan Ops-Teche Federal Bank)*
Brands & Products:
WE WANT TO BE YOUR BANKER

TELECHECK SERVICES, INC.
(Sub. of First Data Corporation)
5251 Westheimer Rd
Houston, TX 77056-5412
Tel.: (713) 331-7600
Fax: (713) 331-7713
Toll Free: (800) 927-0599
Web Site: www.telecheck.com
Sales Range: $125-149.9 Million
Approx. Number Employees: 1,300
Year Founded: 1964
Business Description:
Check Guarantee & Verification Services
S.I.C.: 6099
N.A.I.C.S.: 522320
Advertising Expenditures: $500,000
Media: 2-7-10-16
Distr.: Intl.; Natl.
Budget Set: Sept.
Personnel:
Jody Soper *(Dir-Mktg & Commun)*
Brands & Products:
TELECHECK

TENNESSEE COMMERCE BANCORP, INC.
381 Mallory Station Rd Ste 207
Franklin, TN 37067-8264
Tel.: (615) 599-2274
Fax: (615) 599-2275
E-mail: info@tncommercebank.com
Web Site: www.tncommercebank.com
Approx. Rev.: $83,761,000
Approx. Number Employees: 99
Year Founded: 2000
Business Description:
Bank Holding Company
S.I.C.: 6712
N.A.I.C.S.: 551111
Advertising Expenditures: $96,000
Media: 17
Personnel:
Michael R. Sapp *(Pres)*
Frank Perez *(CFO)*
H. Lamar Cox *(COO & Sec)*
John Burton *(Sr VP-Direct Lending & Mortgage)*
Doug Rogers *(Sr VP & Natl Lending Exec)*

TERRA NOVA FINANCIAL GROUP, INC.
(Name Changed to TNFG Corporation)

TEXAS CAPITAL BANCSHARES, INC.
2000 McKinney Ave Ste 700
Dallas, TX 75201
Tel.: (214) 932-6600
Fax: (214) 932-6604
E-mail: customerservice@texascapitalbank.com
Web Site: www.texascapitalbank.com
Approx. Rev.: $312,073,000
Approx. Number Employees: 699
Year Founded: 1998
Business Description:
Bank Holding Company
S.I.C.: 6712; 6029
N.A.I.C.S.: 551111; 522110
Advertising Expenditures: $819,000
Media: 7-8-22
Personnel:
James R. Holland, Jr. *(Chm)*
George F. Jones, Jr. *(Pres & CEO)*
David Cargill *(Pres, COO & Chief Lending Officer)*
Peter B. Bartholow *(CFO)*
James C. White *(COO & Exec VP)*
Julie Anderson *(Exec VP & Controller)*
Russell Hartsfield *(Exec VP)*
Myrna Vance *(Dir-IR)*
Brands & Products:
BANKDIRECT
BANKNOW
THE BEST BUSINESS BANK IN TEXAS
THE CAPITAL BANK

TF FINANCIAL CORPORATION
3 Penns Trl
Newtown, PA 18940-3433
Tel.: (215) 579-4000
Fax: (215) 579-2380
E-mail: dstewart@thirdfedbank.com
Web Site: www.thirdfedbank.com
Approx. Rev.: $36,851,000
Approx. Number Employees: 162
Year Founded: 1921
Business Description:
Bank Holding Company
S.I.C.: 6035
N.A.I.C.S.: 522120
Advertising Expenditures: $469,000
Media: 9-22-25
Personnel:
Robert N. Dusek *(Chm)*
Kent C. Lufkin *(Pres & CEO)*
Dennis R. Stewart *(CFO & Exec VP)*

TF Financial Corporation — (Continued)
Floyd P. Haggar *(Chief Lending Officer & Sr VP)*
Elizabeth Kaspern *(Sr VP-Retail Banking)*

THIRD FEDERAL SAVINGS & LOAN ASSOCIATION
(Sub. of TFS Financial Corporation)
7007 Broadway Ave
Cleveland, OH 44105
Tel.: (216) 441-6000
Fax: (216) 441-7030
Web Site: www.thirdfederal.com
E-Mail For Key Personnel:
Public Relations: monica.martines@thirdfederal.com
Sales Range: $550-599.9 Million
Approx. Number Employees: 2,000
Year Founded: 1938
Business Description:
Federal Savings Institutions
S.I.C.: 6035
N.A.I.C.S.: 522120
Media: 4-7-8-13-18-20-23-24-26
Personnel:
Marc A. Stefanski *(Pres & CEO)*
David S. Huffman *(CFO)*
Ralph M. Betters *(CIO)*
Marianne Piterans *(Dir-HR)*
Steve Roth *(Product Mgr)*
Brands & Products:
THIRD FEDERAL

THOMAS WEISEL PARTNERS LLC
(Sub. of Stifel Financial Corp.)
1 Montgomery St
San Francisco, CA 94104
Tel.: (415) 364-2500
Fax: (415) 364-2695
Toll Free: (888) 267-3700
E-mail: twpinfo@tweisel.com
Web Site: www.tweisel.com
E-Mail For Key Personnel:
Sales Director: pslivon@tweisel.com
Approx. Rev.: $196,712,000
Approx. Number Employees: 453
Year Founded: 1998
Business Description:
Investment Banking, Brokerage, Research & Asset Management Services
S.I.C.: 6211; 6289
N.A.I.C.S.: 523110; 523120; 523999
Media: 2-9-10
Personnel:
Anthony V. Stais *(Sr Mng Dir & Head-Trading)*
Paul Silvon *(Sr Mng Dir)*
Seth Ferguson *(Mng Dir & Co-Head-Mergers & Acq-Global)*
Steven Levy *(Mng Dir)*
Christopher Poggi *(Mng Dir)*
Paul C. Slivon *(Mng Dir)*
John Soden *(Mng Dir)*
Shaugn Stanley *(Chief Admin Officer)*
Mark P. Fisher *(Gen Counsel)*
R. Keith Gay *(Dir-Res)*

THOMSON REUTERS MARKETS
(Div. of Thomson Reuters - Corporate Headquarters)
3 Times Sq
New York, NY 10006
Tel.: (646) 223-4000
E-mail: tfonlinerequests@thomson.com
Web Site: www.thomsonreuters.com/business_units/financial
Approx. Rev.: $2,186,000,000
Approx. Number Employees: 9,300
Business Description:
Information & Technology Solutions to the Worldwide Financial Community
S.I.C.: 2731
N.A.I.C.S.: 511130
Media: 2-4-7-8-13-16-18-19-20-22-25
Personnel:
David Turner *(CFO & Exec VP)*
Lee Ann Daly *(CMO & Exec VP)*
Pete Dorogoff *(CMO)*
Chris Ahearn *(Pres-Reuters Media)*
Eric Frank *(Pres-Investment & Advisory)*
Christopher Perry *(Pres-Markets Division, Americas)*
Jon Robson *(Pres-Enterprise)*
Matthew Burkley *(CFO-Sls & Trading)*
Nancy Gardner *(Gen Counsel & Exec VP)*
Priscilla Hughes *(Gen Counsel-Americas)*
John Reid-Dodick *(Global Head-HR)*
David Schlesinger *(Editor-in-Chief-Reuters News)*
Brands & Products:
BASELINE
DISCLOSURE
EARNINGS.COM
I/B/E/S
IFR
ILX SYSTEMS
INVESTEXT
THOMSON ADVISOR
VESTEK

TIB FINANCIAL CORP.
599 9th St N Ste 101
Naples, FL 34102
Tel.: (239) 263-3344
Toll Free: (800) 233-6330
E-mail: eservice@tibbank.com
Web Site: www.tibbank.com
Sales Range: $75-99.9 Million
Approx. Number Employees: 391
Year Founded: 1974
Business Description:
Bank Holding Company
S.I.C.: 6712; 6029; 6035
N.A.I.C.S.: 551111; 522110; 522120
Media: 6-7-8-13-18-19-20-22-25-26
Personnel:
Roger Eugene Taylor *(Chm & CEO)*
Christopher G. Marshall *(CFO)*

TIDELANDS BANCSHARES, INC.
875 Lowcountry Blvd
Mount Pleasant, SC 29464
Tel.: (843) 388-8433
Fax: (843) 388-8081
Toll Free: (888) 877-8433
E-mail: info@tidelandsbank.com
Web Site: www.tidelandsbank.com
Approx. Rev.: $30,726,878
Approx. Number Employees: 82
Year Founded: 2002
Business Description:
Bank Holding Company
S.I.C.: 6712; 6211
N.A.I.C.S.: 551111; 523110
Advertising Expenditures: $250,000
Personnel:
Alan W. Jackson *(Acting Pres & CFO)*
Thomas H. Lyles *(Acting CEO, Chief Admin Officer & Board Member)*

TIMBERLAND BANCORP, INC.
624 Simpson Ave
Hoquiam, WA 98550
Tel.: (360) 533-4747
Fax: (360) 533-4743
Toll Free: (800) 562-8761
E-mail: customerservice@timberlandbank.com
Web Site: www.timberlandbank.com
Approx. Rev.: $42,292,000
Approx. Number Employees: 250
Year Founded: 1997
Business Description:
Bank Holding Company
S.I.C.: 6712; 6035
N.A.I.C.S.: 551111; 522120
Advertising Expenditures: $829,000
Media: 10-22
Personnel:
Michael R. Sand *(Pres & CEO)*
Dean J. Brydon *(CFO, Sec & Exec VP)*
Kathie M. Bailey *(COO & Sr VP)*
Marci A. Basich *(Treas & Sr VP)*

TITANIUM ASSET MANAGEMENT CORP.
(Holding of Clal Finance Ltd.)
777 E Wisconsin Ave
Milwaukee, WI 53202-5310
Tel.: (414) 765-1980
Fax: (414) 765-1998
Web Site: www.ti-am.com
Approx. Rev.: $23,570,000
Approx. Number Employees: 78
Year Founded: 2007
Business Description:
Holding Company; Investment Advisory & Asset Management Services
S.I.C.: 6719; 6282
N.A.I.C.S.: 551112; 523920; 523930
Advertising Expenditures: $256,000
Personnel:
Robert Emmett Kelly, Jr. *(Co-Chm)*
Tal Raz *(Co-Chm)*
Emmanuel Gill *(Vice Chm)*
Robert Patrick Brooks *(CEO & Mng Dir)*
Brian L. Gevry *(COO, Mng Dir & Co-Head-Fixed Income)*
Robert J. Siefert *(Mng Dir & Co-Head-Fixed Income)*
Jonathan Hoenecke *(CFO & Sec)*

TMX FINANCE LLC
(d/b/a TitleMax)
15 Bull St Ste 200
Savannah, GA 31401
Tel.: (912) 525-2675
E-mail: investors@titlemax.biz
Web Site: www.titlemax.biz
Business Description:
Automobile Title Lending Services for Consumers with Limited Access to Credit
N.A.I.C.S.: 522291
Media: 13-15-18-26
Personnel:
John W. Robinson, III *(Pres)*
Tracy Young *(CEO)*
Donald E. Thomas *(CFO)*
Robert Alan Parks *(Chief Acctg Officer)*

TMX GROUP, INC.
3rd Fl 130 King St W
Toronto, ON M5X 1J2, Canada
Tel.: (416) 947-4670
Fax: (416) 947-4254
E-mail: info@tsx.com
Web Site: www.tsx.com
Approx. Rev.: $544,455,343
Approx. Number Employees: 849
Business Description:
Holding Company; Stock Exchanges
S.I.C.: 6719; 6231
N.A.I.C.S.: 551112; 523210
Media: 2-7-13
Personnel:
Thomas Kloet *(CEO)*
Michael S. Ptasznik *(CFO)*
Brenda Hoffman *(CIO & Sr VP)*
Alain Miquelon *(Pres/CEO-Montreal Exchange)*
Eric Sinclair *(Pres-TMX Datalinx & Grp Head-Data Svcs)*
Sharon Pel *(Sr VP-Legal & Bus Affairs)*
Mary Lou Hukezalie *(VP-HR)*
Carolyn Quick *(Dir-Corp Comm)*

TNFG CORPORATION
(Formerly Terra Nova Financial Group, Inc.)
2305 Cedar Springs Rd Ste 100
Dallas, TX 75201
Tel.: (214) 954-0324
Web Site: www.tnfgcorp.com
Sales Range: $10-24.9 Million
Approx. Number Employees: 65
Year Founded: 1990
Business Description:
Holding Company
S.I.C.: 6719
N.A.I.C.S.: 551112
Advertising Expenditures: $604,828
Personnel:
Bernay Box *(CEO)*
Murrey Wanstrath *(CFO, COO & Treas)*
Brands & Products:
TERRA NOVA FINANCIAL

THE TORONTO-DOMINION BANK
(d/b/a TD Bank Financial Group)
Toronto Dominion Center
Toronto, ON M5K 1A2, Canada
Mailing Address:
PO Box 1
Toronto, ON M5K 1A2, Canada
Tel.: (416) 982-8222
Fax: (416) 982-5671
Telex: 6524267
E-mail: customer.services@td.com
Web Site: www.td.com
Approx. Rev.: $24,867,280,120
Year Founded: 1855
Business Description:
International Banking Services
S.I.C.: 6029
N.A.I.C.S.: 522110
Advertising Expenditures: $424,163,600
Media: 7-8-14-15
Personnel:
Brian Michael Levitt *(Chm)*
Frank J. McKenna *(Deputy Chm)*
Andrea S. Rosen *(Vice Chm)*
W. Edmund Clark *(Pres & CEO)*
Timothy D. Hockey *(Pres, CEO-TD Canada Trust & Grp Head-Canadian Banking)*

Key to Media (For complete agency information see *The Advertising Red Books-Agencies* edition):
1. Bus. Publs. 2. Cable T.V. 3. Catalogs & Directories. 4. Co-op Adv. 5. Consumer Mags. 6. D.M. to Bus. Estab.7. D.M. to Consumers 8. Daily Newsp. 9. Exhibits/Trade Shows 10. Foreign 11. Infomercial 12. Internet Adv.13. Multimedia 14. Network Radio 15. Network T.V. 16. Newsp. Distr. Mags. 17. Other 18. Outdoor (Posters, Transit) 19. Point of Purchase20. Premiums, Novelties 21. Product Samples 22. Special Events Mktg. 23. Spot Radio 24. Spot T.V. 25. Weekly Newsp. 26. Yellow Page Adv.

Robert E. Dorrance *(CEO, Pres-TD Securities & Grp Head-Wholesale Banking)*
Colleen M. Johnston *(CFO & Grp Head-Fin)*
Kevin Kessinger *(CIO & Exec VP)*
Dominic J. Mercuri *(CMO & Exec VP)*
Mark R. Chauvin *(Exec VP & Chief Risk Officer)*
Karen Clarke-Whistler *(Chief Environ Officer-Fin Grp)*
Bharat B. Masrani *(Pres/CEO-TD Bank)*
Christopher A. Montague *(Gen Counsel, Exec VP-Legal & Compliance)*
Riaz Ahmed *(Exec VP-Corp Dev & Grp Strategy)*
Theresa L. Currie *(Exec VP-HR, Corp & Pub Affairs)*
Beata Caranci *(Assoc VP & Deputy Chief Economist)*
Lyne Beauregard Fisher *(Sr Mgr-IR)*

THE TORONTO STOCK EXCHANGE INC.

(Sub. of TMX Group, Inc.)
130 King St W
Toronto, ON M5X 1J2, Canada
Tel.: (416) 947-4700
Tel.: (416) 947-4670
Fax: (416) 947-4662
Fax: (416) 365-2224 (TSX Venture)
Toll Free: (888) 873-8392
Toll Free: (877) 421-2369 (TSX Venture)
E-mail: info@tsx.com
Web Site: www.tsx.com
Sales Range: $200-249.9 Million
Approx. Number Employees: 510
Business Description:
Equities Market
S.I.C.: 6231
N.A.I.C.S.: 523210
Media: 2-7-10-13-20-22
Personnel:
Wayne C. Fox *(Chm)*
Tom Kloet *(CEO)*
Michael S. Ptasznik *(CFO)*
Kevan Cowan *(Pres-TSX Markets, Grp Head-Equities)*
Robert Fotheringham *(Sr VP-Equities Trading)*
Christine A. Ellison *(VP-HR)*

TOTALBANK CORP.

(Sub. of Banco Popular Espanol, S.A.)
2720 Coral Way
Miami, FL 33145
Tel.: (305) 448-6500
Fax: (305) 448-8201
E-mail: contactus@totalbank.com
Web Site: www.totalbank.com
Sales Range: $25-49.9 Million
Approx. Number Employees: 250
Year Founded: 1974
Business Description:
Commercial Banking Services
S.I.C.: 6029; 6035; 6163
N.A.I.C.S.: 522110; 522120; 522310
Import Export
Media: 6
Personnel:
Jorge Rossell *(Chm & CEO)*
Luis de la Aguilera *(Pres & CMO)*
Diego Villamizar *(Mng Dir & Sr VP)*
Jose Marina *(CFO & Exec VP)*
Lyan Fernandez *(COO & Exec VP)*
David Hitt *(Sr VP & Sr Intl Personal Banker)*
Benigno Pazos *(Exec VP-Debt Restru)*
Thomas Baschoff *(Exec VP-Insurance Premium Fin)*
Lourdes Rey-Wilson *(Exec VP-HR)*
Elsa Soler *(Sr VP & Controller)*
Andres Collazo *(Sr VP & Mgr-Bank Ops)*
Daniel Diaz *(Sr VP)*
Fabricio Gomez *(Sr VP-Debt Restructure Div)*
Maritza Jaime *(Sr VP-Credit Admin)*
Mark Leider *(Sr VP)*
Alex Pascual *(Sr VP-Lending Div)*
Eduardo Quiros *(Sr VP)*
William Turner *(Sr VP-Credits)*
Noel Rosquette *(VP & Mgr-Mktg)*
Emy Ruiz *(VP & Mgr-Global Trade)*
Brands & Products:
BANK WITH TOTAL CONFIDENCE
Advertising Agency:
Everett Clay Associates
6161 Blue Lagoon Dr Ste 270
Miami, FL 33126
Tel.: (305) 261-6222
Fax: (305) 262-9977

TOUCHMARK BANCSHARES, INC.

3651 Old Milton Pkwy
Alpharetta, GA 30005
Tel.: (770) 407-6700
Web Site: www.touchmarknb.com
Approx. Rev.: $8,919,316
Approx. Number Employees: 26
Year Founded: 2007
Business Description:
Bank Holding Company
S.I.C.: 6712
N.A.I.C.S.: 551111
Advertising Expenditures: $210,466
Personnel:
Jayendrakuma J. Shah *(Chm)*
Pin Pin Chau *(Pres & CEO)*
Jorge L. Forment *(CFO)*

TOWER BANCORP, INC.

112 Market St
Harrisburg, PA 17101
Tel.: (717) 231-2700
Web Site: www.towerbancorp.com
Approx. Rev.: $88,515,000
Approx. Number Employees: 846
Year Founded: 1983
Business Description:
Bank Holding Company; Commercial Banking Services
S.I.C.: 6712; 6029
N.A.I.C.S.: 551111; 522110
Advertising Expenditures: $1,087,000
Personnel:
Andrew Samuel *(Chm)*
Jeffrey Renninger *(Pres & COO)*
Mark S. Merrill *(CFO)*
Kristofer A. Paul *(Chief Acctg Officer & VP)*
Janak Amin *(Pres/CEO-Graystone)*
Jeffrey B. Shank *(Exec VP)*

TOWER BANK & TRUST COMPANY

(Sub. of Tower Financial Corporation)
116 E Berry St
Fort Wayne, IN 46802
Tel.: (260) 427-7000
Fax: (260) 427-7180
Web Site: www.towerbank.net
Sales Range: $25-49.9 Million
Approx. Number Employees: 94
Business Description:
Banking Services
S.I.C.: 6029
N.A.I.C.S.: 522110
Personnel:
Michael D. Cahill *(Pres & CEO)*
Wendell Bontrager *(Chief Lending-ficer & Exec VP)*
Advertising Agency:
Ferguson Advertising Inc.
803 S Calhoun St 6th Fl
Fort Wayne, IN 46802-2319
Tel.: (260) 426-4401
Fax: (260) 422-6417

TOWNEBANK

5716 High St
Portsmouth, VA 23703
Tel.: (757) 638-7500
Fax: (757) 484-7544
Web Site: www.townebankonline.com
Approx. Int. Income: $161,081,000
Approx. Number Employees: 600
Year Founded: 1998
Business Description:
Banking Services
S.I.C.: 6029
N.A.I.C.S.: 522110
Media: 2-6-9-16-24-25
Personnel:
G. Robert Aston, Jr. *(Chm & CEO)*
Thomas C. Broyles *(Vice Chm)*
William A. Copeland, Jr. *(Vice Chm)*
John W. Failes *(Vice Chm)*
Ernest F. Hardee *(Vice Chm)*
Clyde E. McFarland, Jr. *(CFO & Sr Exec VP)*
William Littreal *(COO & Sr Exec VP)*
Keith D. Horton *(Chief Admin Officer & Sr Exec VP)*
J. Morgan Davis *(Pres/CEO-Towne Fin Svcs Grp)*
Jacqueline B. Amato *(Pres-Mortgage)*
Anne C.H. Conner *(Pres-Williamsburg)*
William I. Foster, III *(Pres-Norfolk)*
Herbert R. Hamlet *(Pres-Chesapeake)*
Gerald L. Passaro *(Pres-Real Estate Finance Grp)*
Paul Ward Robinett, Jr. *(Pres-Portsmouth)*
William D. Sessoms, Jr. *(Pres-Virginia Beach)*
Brian K. Skinner *(Pres-Peninsula)*
William T. Hodsden *(Exec VP & Reg Mgr-Retail Banking)*
Dawn S. Glynn *(Exec VP-Private Banking)*
Thomas L. Hasty, III *(Exec VP-Risk Mgmt)*
U. Starr Oliver *(Exec VP-Mktg & Retail Banking)*
Advertising Agency:
Seventh Point
4752 Euclid Rd
Virginia Beach, VA 23462-3823
Tel.: (757) 473-8152
Fax: (757) 473-9825
Toll Free: (800) 951-6226

TRACINDA CORPORATION

150 S Rodeo Dr Ste 250
Beverly Hills, CA 90212
Tel.: (310) 271-0638
Fax: (310) 271-3416
Sales Range: $1-4.9 Billion
Approx. Number Employees: 10
Year Founded: 1969
Business Description:
Holding Company
S.I.C.: 6719
N.A.I.C.S.: 551112
Advertising Expenditures: $109,497,100
Personnel:
Kirkor Kerkorian *(CEO & Pres)*

TRADESTATION GROUP, INC.

8050 SW 10th St Ste 4000
Plantation, FL 33324
Tel.: (954) 652-7000
Fax: (954) 652-7300
Toll Free: (800) 556-2022
E-mail: sales@tradestation.com
Web Site: www.tradestation.com
Approx. Rev.: $128,972,000
Approx. Number Employees: 392
Year Founded: 1982
Business Description:
Direct-Access Brokerage Services; Computer Trading Platforms
S.I.C.: 7372; 6211
N.A.I.C.S.: 523110; 511210; 523120
Export
Advertising Expenditures: $6,200,000
Media: 2-7-8-10-13-15
Personnel:
Salomon Sredni *(Chm & CEO)*
David H. Fleischman *(CFO, Treas & VP-Fin)*
John Roberts *(COO)*
Edward Codispoti *(Chief Acctg Officer)*
Marc J. Stone *(Gen Counsel, Sec & VP-Corp Dev)*
Brands & Products:
EASYLANGUAGE
OPTIONSTATION
RADARSCREEN
SUPERCHARTS
SYSTEM WRITER
TRADESTATION

TRANSUNION LLC

(Sub. of TransUnion Corp.)
555 W Adams St 6th Fl
Chicago, IL 60661-3614
Tel.: (312) 258-1717
Tel.: (312) 985-2540 (Pub Rels)
Fax: (312) 466-6865
E-mail: contactdesk@transunion.com
Web Site: www.transunion.com
E-Mail For Key Personnel:
Public Relations: coneal@transunion.com
Sales Range: $150-199.9 Million
Approx. Number Employees: 4,100
Year Founded: 1968
Business Description:
Credit Bureau Services
S.I.C.: 7323
N.A.I.C.S.: 561450
Personnel:
Siddharth N. Mehta *(Pres & CEO)*
David Emery *(COO)*
Heather Battison *(Sr Dir-Mktg)*
Advertising Agencies:
Cramer-Krasselt
225 N Michigan Ave
Chicago, IL 60601-7601
Tel.: (312) 616-9600
Fax: (312) 616-3839
Creative & Media
Consumer Credit Management

Key to Media (For complete agency information see *The Advertising Red Books-Agencies* edition):
1. Bus. Publs. 2. Cable T.V. 3. Catalogs & Directories. 4. Co-op Adv. 5. Consumer Mags. 6. D.M. to Bus. Estab.7. D.M. to Consumers 8. Daily Newsp. 9. Exhibits/Trade Shows 10. Foreign 11. Infomercial 12. Internet Adv.13. Multimedia 14. Network Radio 15. Network T.V. 16. Newsp. Distr. Mags. 17. Other 18. Outdoor (Posters, Transit) 19. Point of Purchase20. Premiums, Novelties 21. Product Samples 22. Special Events Mktg. 23. Spot Radio 24. Spot T.V. 25. Weekly Newsp. 26. Yellow Page Adv.

TransUnion LLC — (Continued)

TrueCredit.com

Cramer-Krasselt Public Relations
225 N Michigan Ave
Chicago, IL 60601-7601
Tel.: (312) 616-9600
TrueCredit.com
Public Relations
Consumer Credit Management

TREE.COM, INC.
11115 Rushmore Dr
Charlotte, NC 28277
Tel.: (704) 541-5351
Fax: (704) 541-1824
E-mail: tree.com-investor.relations@tree.com
Web Site: www.tree.com
Approx. Rev.: $198,181,000
Approx. Number Employees: 900
Year Founded: 1998
Business Description:
Online Lending & Financial Services
S.I.C.: 6163
N.A.I.C.S.: 522310
Advertising Expenditures: $69,790,000
Personnel:
Douglas R. Lebda *(Chm & CEO)*
Gabriel Dalporto *(CMO)*
Christopher Hayek *(Chief Acctg Officer & Sr VP)*
Tamara Kotronis *(Sr VP-Fin Plng, Analysis & IR)*
Robert Iadanza, Jr. *(Sr Acct Mgr-Sls)*
Brands & Products:
EDUCATIONDEGREESOURCE.COM

TRI-COUNTY FINANCIAL CORPORATION
3035 Leonardtown Rd
Waldorf, MD 20601
Tel.: (301) 645-5601
Fax: (301) 885-1437
E-mail: info@cbtc.com
Web Site: www.cbtc.com
Approx. Rev.: $39,536,987
Approx. Number Employees: 131
Year Founded: 1989
Business Description:
Bank Holding Company
S.I.C.: 6029; 6712
N.A.I.C.S.: 522110; 551111
Advertising Expenditures: $399,802
Media: 8-18-25
Personnel:
Michael L. Middleton *(Chm, Pres & CEO)*
William J. Pasenelli *(CFO)*

TRIAD FINANCIAL SM LLC
(Joint Venture of The Goldman Sachs Group, Inc., GTCR Golder Rauner, LLC & Hunter's Glenn/Ford, Ltd.)
5201 Rufe Snow Dr
North Richland Hills, TX 76180
Tel.: (714) 373-8300 (Huntington Beach)
Fax: (714) 890-8499
Toll Free: (877) 631-6200 (Texas HQ)
E-mail: triadcommunications@triadfinancial.com
Web Site: www.triadfinancial.com
Approx. Int. Income: $461,092,000
Approx. Number Employees: 700
Year Founded: 1989
Business Description:
Automotive Credit & Loan Services
S.I.C.: 6141; 6099
N.A.I.C.S.: 522220; 522390
Advertising Expenditures: $3,997,000
Personnel:
Gerald J. Ford *(Co-Chm)*
Carl B. Webb *(Co-Chm)*
Timothy M. O'Connor *(Sr VP)*
David L. Satterfield *(Sr VP-Ops)*

TRICITY BANKSHARES CORPORATION
6400 S 27th St
Oak Creek, WI 53154
Tel.: (414) 761-1610
Fax: (414) 423-2291
Web Site: www.tcnb.com
Approx. Rev.: $80,987,210
Approx. Number Employees: 399
Year Founded: 1970
Business Description:
Bank Holding Company
S.I.C.: 6029
N.A.I.C.S.: 522110
Advertising Expenditures: $1,018,000
Personnel:
Ronald Puetz *(Chm, Pres & CEO)*
Scott A. Wilson *(Treas, Sec & Exec VP)*

TRICO BANCSHARES
63 Constitution Dr
Chico, CA 95973
Tel.: (530) 898-0300
Fax: (530) 898-0310
Toll Free: (800) 922-8742
Web Site: www.tricountiesbank.com
Approx. Rev.: $137,267,000
Approx. Number Employees: 680
Year Founded: 1974
Business Description:
Bank Holding Company
S.I.C.: 6712; 6029
N.A.I.C.S.: 551111; 522110
Advertising Expenditures: $2,340,000
Personnel:
William J. Casey *(Chm)*
Richard P. Smith *(Pres & CEO)*
Thomas J. Reddish *(CFO & Exec VP)*
Craig Carney *(Chief Credit Officer-Tri Counties Bank & Exec VP)*
Daniel K. Bailey *(Exec VP-Retail Banking-Tri Counties Bank)*
Richard O'Sullivan *(Exec VP-Wholesale Banking-Tri Counties Bank)*
Richard Miller *(Sr VP & Dir-HR-Tri Counties Bank)*
Raymond Rios *(Sr VP & Mgr-Info Sys)*
Nicole Johansson *(Mgr-Mktg)*
Chad Stevenson *(Mgr-Sls & Merchant Card)*
Kay Armstrong *(Coord-Direct Banking)*
John McCaw *(Coord-BillPay Svcs)*
Rachelle Savagno *(Coord-BillPay Svcs)*
Karen Shapland *(Coord-Real Property Valuation)*
Toni Wilson *(Coord-Client Svcs)*
Suzanne Youngs *(Coord-Acctg & Shareholder Rels)*

TRUSTCO BANK CORP NY
5 Sarnowski Dr
Glenville, NY 12302
Mailing Address:
PO Box 1082
Schenectady, NY 12301-1082
Tel.: (518) 377-3311
Fax: (518) 381-3668
Toll Free: (800) 670-3110
Web Site: www.trustcobank.com
Approx. Int. Income: $128,148,000
Approx. Number Employees: 738
Year Founded: 1981
Business Description:
Bank Holding Company
S.I.C.: 6029; 6712
N.A.I.C.S.: 522110; 551111
Advertising Expenditures: $3,000,000
Personnel:
Robert James McCormick *(Pres & CEO)*
William Joseph Purdy *(Chm)*
Robert T. Cushing *(CFO & Exec VP)*
Scot R. Salvador *(Chief Banking Officer & Exec VP)*
Sharon J. Parvis *(VP & Asst Sec)*
Brands & Products:
TRUSTCO
TRUSTCO BANK
YOUR HOME TOWN BANK

TRUSTMARK CORPORATION
248 E Capitol St
Jackson, MS 39201-2503
Mailing Address:
PO Box 291
Jackson, MS 39205-0291
Tel.: (601) 208-5111
Fax: (601) 208-6684
Toll Free: (800) 844-2000
Web Site: www.trustmark.com
Approx. Rev.: $574,145,000
Approx. Number Employees: 2,490
Year Founded: 1968
Business Description:
Bank Holding Company
S.I.C.: 6712; 6035; 6163; 6211; 6289
N.A.I.C.S.: 551111; 522120; 522310; 523110; 523999
Advertising Expenditures: $1,400,000
Personnel:
Daniel A. Grafton *(Chm)*
Gerard R. Host *(Pres & CEO)*
Melissa King *(Mgr-Sls)*
Melanie A. Morgan *(Asst Sec)*
Brands & Products:
TRUSTMARK

TRUSTMARK NATIONAL BANK
(Holding of Trustmark Corporation)
248 E Capitol St
Jackson, MS 39201-2503
Mailing Address:
PO Box 291
Jackson, MS 39205-0291
Tel.: (601) 208-5111
Fax: (601) 949-6684
Toll Free: (800) 844-2000
Web Site: www.trustmark.com
Sales Range: $800-899.9 Million
Year Founded: 1889
Business Description:
Savings, Loans, Commercial & Investment Banking Services
S.I.C.: 6035; 6029; 6163; 6211
N.A.I.C.S.: 522120; 522110; 522310; 523110
Media: 9-15-18
Personnel:
Daniel A. Grafton *(Chm)*
Gerard R. Host *(Pres & CEO)*
James S. Lenoir *(CFO)*
Glynn Ingram *(CIO & Exec VP)*
Leland R. Mitchell, III *(Pres-Corp Residential)*
Douglas H. Ralston *(Pres-Wealth Mgmt)*
Harry M. Walker *(Pres-Jackson Metro)*
Mike Zito, Jr. *(Pres-Brokerage Svcs)*
George C. Gunn *(Exec VP)*
Breck W. Tyler *(Exec VP)*
Ferol W. Hettick *(Sr VP & Dir-Compliance)*
Joseph C. Gibbs, Jr. *(Sr VP-e-Bus Svcs)*
Letitia C. Hughes *(Sr VP)*
David W. Martin *(Sr VP)*
Kenneth W. Sickels *(Sr VP)*
Theresa Jones *(Asst VP-Central Document Preparation Dept)*
C. Scott Woods *(Mgr-Comm,Insurance Svcs)*
Melanie A. Morgan *(Asst Sec)*
Advertising Agency:
Godwin Advertising Agency, Inc. (d/b/a GodwinGroup)
1 Jackson Pl 188 E Capitol St Ste 800
Jackson, MS 39201
Tel.: (601) 354-5711
Fax: (601) 960-5869

UBS FINANCIAL SERVICES INC.
(Sub. of UBS AG)
1285 Ave of the Americas
New York, NY 10019
Tel.: (212) 713-2000
Fax: (212) 713-9818
Web Site: www.ubs.com
Sales Range: $1-4.9 Billion
Approx. Number Employees: 16,000
Year Founded: 1879
Business Description:
Holding Company; Investment Advisory Services, Securities Brokerage Services, Investment Banking & Related Services
S.I.C.: 6211; 6221
N.A.I.C.S.: 523120; 523140
Media: 2-3-6-18
Personnel:
Robert Wolf *(Chm)*
Gary Timmerman *(Mng Dir & Head-US Mortgage Fin)*
Cheryl Jones *(Dir-Digital & Online Mktg)*
Pat Pilkonis *(Dir-Adv)*
Advertising Agencies:
The Edelman Group
110 W 40th St Ste 2302
New York, NY 10018
Tel.: (212) 825-9200
Fax: (212) 825-1900

Publicis New York
4 Herald Sq 950 6th Ave
New York, NY 10001
Tel.: (212) 279-5550
Fax: (212) 279-5560

UCBH HOLDINGS, INC.
555 Montgomery St
San Francisco, CA 94111
Tel.: (415) 315-2800
Fax: (415) 441-5227
Toll Free: (800) 821-3899
Telex: 6737076 USB UW
E-mail: ucbhir@unitedcb.com
Web Site: www.ibankunited.com
E-Mail For Key Personnel:

Key to Media (For complete agency information see *The Advertising Red Books-Agencies* edition):
1. Bus. Publs. 2. Cable T.V. 3. Catalogs & Directories. 4. Co-op Adv. 5. Consumer Mags. 6. D.M. to Bus. Estab.7. D.M. to Consumers 8. Daily Newsp. 9. Exhibits/Trade Shows 10. Foreign 11. Infomercial 12. Internet Adv.13. Multimedia 14. Network Radio 15. Network T.V. 16. Newsp. Distr. Mags. 17. Other 18. Outdoor (Posters, Transit) 19. Point of Purchase20. Premiums, Novelties 21. Product Samples 22. Special Events Mktg. 23. Spot Radio 24. Spot T.V. 25. Weekly Newsp. 26. Yellow Page Adv.

President: twu@unitedcb.com
Sales Range: $650-699.9 Million
Approx. Number Employees: 1,542
Year Founded: 1998
Business Description:
Bank Holding Company
S.I.C.: 6712; 6029; 6035
N.A.I.C.S.: 551111; 522110; 522120
Media: 7-8-13
Personnel:
Joseph J. Jou *(Chm)*
Doreen Woo Ho *(Pres & CEO)*
Craig S. On *(CFO & Exec VP)*
Daniel M. Gautsch *(Exec VP, Chief Risk Officer & Chief Compliance Officer)*
Jonas B. Miller *(Treas & Sr VP)*
John M. Cinderey *(Exec VP & Dir-Coml Banking)*
William J. Laraia *(Exec VP)*
Sylvia Loh *(Exec VP)*
Douglas J. Mitchell *(Sr VP-Corp Dev)*
David Yu *(Exec VP)*
Burton D. Thompson *(Sr VP & Controller)*
Martha F. Perry *(Sr VP & Dir-Fin Plng & Analysis)*
Dennis A. Lee *(Sr VP, Asst Sec & Corp Counsel)*
Robert C. Nagel *(Sr VP & Chief Audit Exec)*
Brands & Products:
UNITED COMMERCIAL BANK

UDR, INC.

1745 Shea Center Dr Ste 200
Highlands Ranch, CO 80129
Tel.: (720) 283-6120
Fax: (720) 283-2451
E-mail: ir@udrt.com
Web Site: www.udrt.com
Approx. Rev.: $646,596,000
Approx. Number Employees: 1,547
Year Founded: 1972
Business Description:
Real Estate Investment Trust Services
S.I.C.: 6798
N.A.I.C.S.: 525930
Advertising Expenditures: $6,400,000
Media: 2-4-6-9-10-16-17-25-26
Distr.: Natl.; Reg.
Personnel:
James D. Klingbeil *(Chm)*
Lynne B. Sagalyn *(Vice Chm)*
Thomas W. Toomey *(Pres & CEO)*
David L. Messenger *(CFO & Sr VP)*
R. Scott Wesson *(CIO)*
James M. Wallace *(Chief Tax Officer & VP)*
Ella Neyland *(Treas-IR & Exec VP)*
Thomas P. Simon *(Treas & Sr VP)*
Richard A. Giannotti *(Exec VP-Redev)*
Matthew T. Akin *(Sr VP-Acq & Dispositions)*
Harry Alcock *(Sr VP-Asset Mgmt)*
Mark M. Culwell, Jr. *(Sr VP-Dev)*
Jerry A. Davis *(Sr VP-Property Ops)*
William S. Deniger, Jr. *(Sr VP-Transactions)*
Katie Miles-Ley *(Sr VP-HR)*
Rodney A. Neuheardt *(Sr VP)*
Thomas A. Spangler *(Sr VP-Bus Dev)*
S. Douglas Walker *(Sr VP-Transactions)*
Teresa L. Barker *(VP & Dir-Area)*
Kathryn O. Clem *(VP & Dir-Area)*
Terry D. Fulbright *(VP & Dir-Ancillary Svcs)*
Louis N. Kovalsky *(VP & Dir-Area)*
Dennis E. Sandidge *(VP & Dir-Area)*
Steven H. Taraborelli *(VP & Dir-Sls & Mktg)*
Jerrie A. Berning *(VP-Trng & Dev)*
R. Bruce Blanton *(VP-Info Sys)*
Nellcine Ford *(VP-HR)*
William E. Schart *(VP-Trng & Dev)*

UMB FINANCIAL CORPORATION

1010 Grand Blvd
Kansas City, MO 64106-2008
Mailing Address:
PO Box 419226
Kansas City, MO 64141-6226
Tel.: (816) 860-7930
Fax: (816) 860-7610
Toll Free: (800) 821-2171
Telex: 816-860-5675
Web Site: www.umb.com
Approx. Rev.: $706,877,000
Approx. Number Employees: 3,355
Year Founded: 1967
Business Description:
Bank Holding Company
S.I.C.: 6712; 6029; 6035; 6141; 6211; 6282; 6411; 6722; 6733
N.A.I.C.S.: 551111; 522110; 522120; 522291; 523110; 523920; 523930; 523991; 524210; 525910
Advertising Expenditures: $13,309,000
Media: 2-3-4-6-7-8-9-10-18-20-23-24-25-26
Distr.: Direct to Consumer; Reg.
Budget Set: Oct.
Personnel:
Michael D. Hagedorn *(Vice Chm, CFO & Chief Admin Officer)*
Clyde Francis Wendel *(Vice Chm & Exec VP-UMB Bank & Asset Mgmt)*
Peter J. deSilva *(Pres & COO)*
John Mariner Kemper *(CEO)*
Michael F. Jackson *(CTO & SVP)*
Larry Smith *(Exec VP-Organizational Effectiveness)*
Craig L. Anderson *(Chm/CEO-Kansas & West Central Reg)*
Thomas W. Chulick *(Chm/CEO-UMB Bank-St Louis)*
James A. Sangster *(Pres-UMB Bank, NA & Exec VP)*
Jon M. Robinson *(Pres-UMB Bank Colorado)*
Gil L. Trout *(CEO-UMB Bank-Reg)*
John P. Zader *(CEO-UMB Fund Svcs)*
Dennis R. Rilinger *(Gen Counsel & Exec VP)*
Terry W. D'Amore *(Exec VP & Dir-UMB Bank)*
Daryl S. Hunt *(Exec VP-Ops & Tech Grp)*
David D. Kling *(Exec VP)*
Heather Kemper Miller *(Exec VP-Sls, Mktg & Comm)*
Douglas F. Page *(Chief Lending Officer & Exec VP)*
Brian J. Walker *(Sr VP & Controller)*
Brands & Products:
COMMERCIALCARD
SHAREHOLDER VIEW
STATEMENTLOOK
UMB TRUSTDIRECT
UNITEPLUS
Advertising Agency:
Barkley
1740 Main St
Kansas City, MO 64108
Tel.: (816) 842-1500
(Full Line of Products; Industrial & Consumer)

UMPQUA HOLDINGS CORPORATION

1 SW Colombia St Ste 1200
Portland, OR 97258
Mailing Address:
PO Box 1820
Roseburg, OR 97470
Tel.: (503) 727-4100
Fax: (971) 544-3750
Toll Free: (866) 486-7782
E-mail: customerservice@umpquabank.com
Web Site: www.umpquabank.com
E-Mail For Key Personnel:
President: raydavis@umpquabank.com
Approx. Rev.: $564,500,000
Approx. Number Employees: 2,185
Year Founded: 1953
Business Description:
Bank Holding Company
S.I.C.: 6712; 6029
N.A.I.C.S.: 551111; 522110
Media: 7-8-13
Personnel:
Allyn C. Ford *(Chm)*
Raymond P. Davis *(Pres & CEO)*
Ronald L. Farnsworth *(CFO & Exec VP)*
Brad F. Copeland *(COO & Sr Exec VP)*
Colin Eccles *(CIO & Exec VP)*
Mark Wardlow *(Chief Credit Officer & Exec VP)*
Steven L. Philpott *(Gen Counsel & Exec VP)*
Neal T. McLaughlin *(Treas & Exec VP)*
Barbara J. Baker *(Exec VP-Cultural Enhancement)*
Lani C. Hayward *(Exec VP-Creative Strategies)*
Daniel A. Sullivan *(Exec VP-Strategic Initiatives)*
Eve Callahan *(Sr VP-Corp Comm)*
Brands & Products:
UMPQUA BANK
Advertising Agency:
Creature
1508 10th Ave
Seattle, WA 98122
Tel.: (206) 625-6994
Fax: (206) 625-6904

UNION BANK, N.A.

(Holding of UnionBanCal Corporation)
400 California St
San Francisco, CA 94104
Mailing Address:
PO Box 7104
San Francisco, CA 94120-7104
Tel.: (415) 765-0400
Fax: (415) 765-2220
Telex: 188612 UNIONBK UT
Web Site: www.uboc.com
Approx. Number Employees: 10,227
Year Founded: 1864
Business Description:
Commercial Banking Services
S.I.C.: 6029; 6082
N.A.I.C.S.: 522110; 522293
Advertising Expenditures: $36,803,000
Media: 6-8-9-13-18-23-24
Distr.: Direct to Consumer; Reg.
Budget Set: Sept.
Personnel:
John F. Woods *(Vice Chm & CFO)*
John C. Erickson *(Vice Chm & Chief Corp Banking Officer)*
Timothy H. Wennes *(Vice Chm & Chief Retail Banking Officer)*
Arthur G. Smith *(CMO)*
JoAnn M. Bourne *(Sr Exec VP-Corp Deposits & Global Treasury Mgmt)*
Paul E. Fearer *(Sr Exec VP & Dir-HR)*
Todd H. Baker *(Exec VP & Dir-Corp Strategy)*
Linda F. Betzer *(Exec VP-Ops)*
Robert A. McNeely *(Exec VP)*
Bradley Shairson *(Exec VP)*
Michael Campbell *(Sr VP-Credit Admin)*
Chris Merrywell *(Sr VP-Wealth Mgmt Grp)*
Scott Camp *(Reg VP-Northern California & Central Valley-Bus Banking Grp)*
Robbin Narike Preciado *(Exec Dir-Retail Programs & Community Banking Programs)*
John Calhoun *(Reg Dir-Personal Trust)*
Joanne Curran *(Mgr-External Comm)*
Advertising Agencies:
Hawk Media, Inc.
PO Box 623
Diablo, CA 94528
Tel.: (415) 860-2500
Fax: (925) 855-1843

MeadsDurket
6863 Friars Rd
San Diego, CA 92108-1121
Tel.: (619) 574-0808
Fax: (619) 574-1644

Round2 Communications, LLC
10866 Wilshire Blvd Ste 900
Los Angeles, CA 90024
Tel.: (310) 481-8040
Fax: (310) 571-1827

Stephenson Group
37 Hollow Brook Rd
Califon, NJ 07830
Tel.: (908) 439-3660
Fax: (908) 439-3268

UNION BANKSHARES, INC.

20 Lower Main St
Morrisville, VT 05661
Mailing Address:
PO Box 667
Morrisville, VT 05661
Tel.: (802) 888-6600
Fax: (802) 888-4921
E-mail: info@unionbankvt.com
Web Site: www.unionbankvt.com
Approx. Rev.: $28,841,485
Approx. Number Employees: 160
Year Founded: 1982
Business Description:
Bank Holding Company
S.I.C.: 6712; 6029
N.A.I.C.S.: 551111; 522110
Advertising Expenditures: $283,000
Media: 9-23-25-26

Key to Media (For complete agency information see *The Advertising Red Books-Agencies* edition):
1. Bus. Publs. 2. Cable T.V. 3. Catalogs & Directories. 4. Co-op Adv. 5. Consumer Mags. 6. D.M. to Bus. Estab.7. D.M. to Consumers
8. Daily Newsp. 9. Exhibits/Trade Shows 10. Foreign 11. Infomercial 12. Internet Adv.13. Multimedia 14. Network Radio
15. Network T.V. 16. Newsp. Distr. Mags. 17. Other 18. Outdoor (Posters, Transit) 19. Point of Purchase20. Premiums, Novelties
21. Product Samples 22. Special Events Mktg. 23. Spot Radio 24. Spot T.V. 25. Weekly Newsp. 26. Yellow Page Adv.

Union Bankshares, Inc. — (Continued)

Personnel:
Richard C. Sargent *(Chm)*
Kenneth D. Gibbons *(Pres & CEO)*
Marsha A. Mongeon *(CFO, Treas & VP)*
JoAnn A. Tallman *(Asst Sec)*

UNION FIRST MARKET BANKSHARES CORPORATION

111 Virginia St Ste 200
Richmond, VA 23219
Tel.: (804) 633-5031
Fax: (804) 633-1800
E-mail: invrelations@ubsh.com
Web Site: www.ubsh.com
Approx. Rev.: $237,119,000
Approx. Number Employees: 1,005
Year Founded: 1993
Business Description:
Bank Holding Company
S.I.C.: 6712; 6029
N.A.I.C.S.: 551111; 522110
Advertising Expenditures: $1,200,000
Personnel:
Ronald L. Hicks *(Chm)*
W. Tayloe Murphy, Jr. *(Vice Chm)*
David J. Fairchild *(Pres)*
G. William Beale *(CEO)*
D. Anthony Peay *(CFO & Exec VP)*
Olen Thomas *(CMO & Sr VP)*
Douglas F. Woolley, III *(Exec VP & Chief Credit Officer)*
John C. Neal *(Chief Banking Officer & Exec VP)*
Janis Orfe *(Gen Counsel, Sec & Exec VP)*
Elizabeth M. Bentley *(Exec VP & Dir-Retail Banking)*
Rex A. Hockemeyer *(Exec VP, Dir-IT & Ops)*
David S. Wilson *(Exec VP-Ops & Tech)*
Rawley H. Watson, III *(Dir-Internal Audit)*

UNION NATIONAL FINANCIAL CORPORATION

570 Lausch Ln Ste 300
Lancaster, PA 17601
Tel.: (717) 492-2222
Fax: (717) 492-2212
E-mail: mgainer@uncb.com
Web Site: www.uncb.com
Approx. Rev.: $25,582,000
Approx. Number Employees: 119
Year Founded: 1987
Business Description:
Bank Holding Company
S.I.C.: 6712; 6029
N.A.I.C.S.: 551111; 522110
Advertising Expenditures: $211,000
Personnel:
Mark D. Gainer *(Chm, Pres & CEO)*
James R. Godfrey *(Vice Chm)*
Michael D. Peduzzi *(CFO, Principal Acctg Officer, Treas & Exec VP)*
Stephen D. Staman *(Exec VP)*

UNIONBANCAL CORPORATION

(Sub. of The Bank of Tokyo-Mitsubishi UFJ, Ltd.)
400 California St
San Francisco, CA 94104
Tel.: (415) 765-2969
Tel.: (415) 765-0400
Fax: (415) 765-2220
Web Site: www.uboc.com
Approx. Rev.: $3,749,000,000
Approx. Number Employees: 10,715
Year Founded: 1996
Business Description:
Bank Holding Company
S.I.C.: 6712; 6029; 6035; 6211
N.A.I.C.S.: 551111; 522110; 522120; 523110
Advertising Expenditures: $50,000,000
Media: 17
Personnel:
Kyota Omori *(Chm)*
John F. Woods *(Vice Chm & CFO)*
Mark W. Midkiff *(Vice Chm & Chief Risk Officer)*
Timothy H. Wennes *(Vice Chm & Chief Retail Banking Officer)*
Masashi Oka *(Pres & CEO)*
Brian Hawley *(Pres-Retail Banking)*
Masamichi Yasuda *(Deputy CFO, Chief Liaison Officer & Sr Exec VP)*
James Yee *(CIO & Sr Exec VP)*
Arthur G. Smith *(CMO)*
Lynn A. Sullivan *(Chief Compliance Officer & Exec VP)*
Morris W. Hirsch *(Gen Counsel, Sec & Sr Exec VP)*
Pierre P. Habis *(Sr Exec VP & Head-Branch Banking)*
Paul E. Fearer *(Sr Exec VP & Dir-HR)*
Joann M. Bourne *(Sr Exec VP-Corp Deposits & Global Treasury Mgmt)*
Steven L. Glaser *(Exec VP-Retail Banking)*
Ronald H. Kendrick *(Exec VP)*
David Jochim *(Sr VP)*
Justin Miller *(Dir-Legal Specialty Grp)*
Michael Feldman *(Mgr-Natl Sls)*

UNITED BANCORP, INC.

201 S 4th St
Martins Ferry, OH 43935
Tel.: (740) 633-0445
Fax: (740) 633-1448
Web Site: www.unitedbancorp.com
Approx. Rev.: $24,984,000
Approx. Number Employees: 146
Year Founded: 1983
Business Description:
Bank Holding Company
S.I.C.: 6712; 6029
N.A.I.C.S.: 551111; 522110
Advertising Expenditures: $357,000
Personnel:
James W. Everson *(Chm, Pres & CEO)*
Randall M. Greenwood *(CFO, Treas & Sr VP)*
Scott A. Everson *(COO & Sr VP)*
Michael A. Lloyd *(CIO & VP)*
Elmer K. Leeper *(Chief Retail Banking Officer & VP)*
James A. Lodes *(Chief Lending Officer & VP)*

UNITED BANCORP, INC.

2723 S State St
Ann Arbor, MI 48104
Tel.: (517) 423-8373
Fax: (517) 423-4176
E-mail: info@ubat.com
Web Site: www.ubat.com
Approx. Int. Income: $39,770,000
Approx. Number Employees: 224
Year Founded: 1985
Business Description:
Bank Holding Company
S.I.C.: 6712; 6029; 6141; 6733
N.A.I.C.S.: 551111; 522110; 522291; 523991
Import Export
Advertising Expenditures: $610,000
Personnel:
James C. Lawson *(Chm)*
James D. Buhr *(Vice Chm)*
Robert K. Chapman *(Pres & CEO)*
Randal J. Rabe *(CFO & Exec VP)*
Judith Brooks *(Fin Acctg Officer)*
Diane Higgins *(Collections Officer)*
Linda Lips *(Fin Acctg Officer)*
Steven W. Schwartz *(Treas & Sr VP)*
Gary D. Haapala *(Exec VP-Wealth Mgmt)*
Dale L. Chadderdon *(Sr VP-Fin)*
Thomas C. Gannon *(Sr VP-HR)*
Kathy McCrate *(Sr VP-Risk Mgmt)*
Lisa Mason *(VP & Internal Auditor)*
Amanda M. Hart *(VP-Deposit Ops)*

UNITED BANCORPORATION OF ALABAMA, INC.

200 E Nashville Ave
Atmore, AL 36502
Mailing Address:
PO Drawer 8
Atmore, AL 36504
Tel.: (251) 446-6000
Fax: (251) 446-6087
Web Site: www.unitedbank.com
Approx. Rev.: $24,538,221
Approx. Number Employees: 180
Year Founded: 1982
Business Description:
Bank Holding Company
S.I.C.: 6712; 6029
N.A.I.C.S.: 551111; 522110
Advertising Expenditures: $276,039
Personnel:
William J. Justice *(Chm)*
David D. Swift, Sr. *(Vice Chm)*
Robert R. Jones, III *(Pres & CEO)*
Allen O. Jones, Jr. *(CFO & Treas)*
Brands & Products:
YOUR HOMETOWN ADVANTAGE

UNITED BANCSHARES, INC.

100 S High St
Columbus Grove, OH 45830
Tel.: (419) 659-2141
Fax: (419) 659-2069
E-mail: info@theubank.com
Web Site: www.theubank.com
Approx. Rev.: $33,981,914
Approx. Number Employees: 150
Year Founded: 1985
Business Description:
Bank Holding Company
S.I.C.: 6712; 6029
N.A.I.C.S.: 551111; 522110
Advertising Expenditures: $546,025
Media: 8-10-13-18-23-24-26
Personnel:
James N. Reynolds *(Chm)*
Daniel W. Schutt *(Pres & CEO)*
Brian D. Young *(CFO, Treas & Exec VP)*
Richard M. Adams, Jr. *(Exec VP)*

UNITED BANK

(Sub. of United Bancorporation of Alabama, Inc.)
200 E Nashville Ave
Atmore, AL 36502
Mailing Address:
PO Box 8
Atmore, AL 36504
Tel.: (251) 446-6000
Fax: (251) 446-6089
Web Site: www.ubankal.com
Sales Range: $125-149.9 Million
Year Founded: 1918
Business Description:
Commercial Banking Services
S.I.C.: 6029
N.A.I.C.S.: 522110
Personnel:
Robert R. Jones, III *(Pres & CEO)*
Allen O. Jones, Jr. *(CFO & Sr VP)*
Advertising Agency:
TotalCom Marketing, Inc.
922 20th Ave
Tuscaloosa, AL 35401-2307
Tel.: (205) 345-7363
Fax: (205) 345-7373

UNITED BANKSHARES, INC.

300 United Center 500 Virginia St E
Charleston, WV 25301
Tel.: (304) 424-8800
Fax: (304) 424-8805
Toll Free: (800) 345-4862
Web Site: www.ubsi-wv.com
Approx. Rev.: $385,585,000
Approx. Number Employees: 1,451
Year Founded: 1982
Business Description:
Bank Holding Company
S.I.C.: 6712; 6029; 6035; 6163; 6211
N.A.I.C.S.: 551111; 522110; 522120; 522310; 523110
Advertising Expenditures: $3,338,000
Media: 7-8-13
Personnel:
Richard M. Adams, Jr. *(Chm & CEO)*
Steven E. Wilson *(CFO, Treas & Exec VP)*
James B. Hayhurst *(Exec VP)*
John Neuner, III *(Exec VP)*
Craige Smith *(Exec VP)*
Joe L. Wilson *(Exec VP)*
Advertising Agency:
Fahlgren Mortine
4030 Easton Station Ste 300
Columbus, OH 43219
Tel.: (614) 383-1500
Fax: (614) 383-1501

UNITED COMMUNITY BANCORP

(Holding of United Community MHC)
92 Walnut St
Lawrenceburg, IN 47025
Tel.: (812) 537-4822
Fax: (812) 537-5769
Web Site: www.bankucb.com
Approx. Rev.: $22,493,000
Approx. Number Employees: 95
Business Description:
Bank Holding Company
S.I.C.: 6712; 6029
N.A.I.C.S.: 551111; 522110
Advertising Expenditures: $378,000
Personnel:
Ralph B. Sprecher *(Chm)*
William F. Ritzmann *(Pres & CEO)*
Vicki A. March *(CFO & Sr VP-Fin)*
Elmer G. McLaughlin *(COO, Sec & Exec VP)*
James W. Kittle *(Sr VP-Lending)*
W. Michael McLaughlin *(Sr VP-Ops)*
Eugene B. Seitz, II *(Asst Sec)*

Key to Media (For complete agency information see *The Advertising Red Books-Agencies* edition):
1. Bus. Publs. 2. Cable T.V. 3. Catalogs & Directories. 4. Co-op Adv. 5. Consumer Mags. 6. D.M. to Bus. Estab.7. D.M. to Consumers 8. Daily Newsp. 9. Exhibits/Trade Shows 10. Foreign 11. Infomercial 12. Internet Adv.13. Multimedia 14. Network Radio 15. Network T.V. 16. Newsp. Distr. Mags. 17. Other 18. Outdoor (Posters, Transit) 19. Point of Purchase20. Premiums, Novelties 21. Product Samples 22. Special Events Mktg. 23. Spot Radio 24. Spot T.V. 25. Weekly Newsp. 26. Yellow Page Adv.

UNITED COMMUNITY BANKS, INC.
125 Hwy 515 E
Blairsville, GA 30512
Tel.: (706) 781-2265
Toll Free: (866) 270-7200
E-mail: investor_relations@ucbi.com
Web Site: www.ucbi.com
Approx. Rev.: $341,122,000
Approx. Number Employees: 1,763
Year Founded: 1988
Business Description:
Bank Holding Company
S.I.C.: 6712; 6029; 6035; 6141; 6211
N.A.I.C.S.: 551111; 522110; 522120; 522291; 523110
Advertising Expenditures: $4,625,000
Personnel:
Robert L. Head, Jr. *(Chm)*
W. C. Nelson, Jr. *(Vice Chm)*
Jimmy C. Tallent *(Pres & CEO)*
Rex S. Schuette *(CFO & Exec VP)*
Guy W. Freeman *(COO & Exec VP)*
David P. Shearrow *(Exec VP & Chief Risk Officer)*
Craig Metz *(Exec VP-Mktg)*
William M. Gilbert *(Sr VP-Retail Banking)*
Brands & Products:
THE BANK THAT SERVICE BUILT
UNITED COMMUNITY BANK

UNITED COMMUNITY FINANCIAL CORP.
275 Federal Plz W
Youngstown, OH 44503
Mailing Address:
PO Box 1111
Youngstown, OH 44501
Tel.: (330) 742-0500
Fax: (330) 742-0532
Toll Free: (888) 822-4751
E-mail: info@homesavings.com
Web Site: www.ucfconline.com
E-Mail For Key Personnel:
President: dmckay@hslonline.com
Approx. Sls.: $132,641,000
Approx. Number Employees: 557
Year Founded: 1998
Business Description:
Bank Holding Company
S.I.C.: 6712; 6035
N.A.I.C.S.: 551111; 522120
Advertising Expenditures: $860,000
Personnel:
Richard J. Schiraldi *(Chm)*
Patrick W. Bevack *(Pres & CEO)*
Jude J. Nohra *(Gen Counsel & Sec)*
Karen DeAmicis *(VP-Retail Sls & Svc Support-The Home Savings & Loan Company)*
Richard Michaels *(Asst VP, Branch Sls Mgr)*
Claudia Newhard *(Asst VP, Branch Sls Mgr)*
Troy Adair *(Asst VP)*

UNITED DOMINION REALTY L.P.
(Sub. of UDR, Inc.)
1745 Shea Center Dr
Highlands Ranch, CO 80129
Tel.: (720) 283-6120
Web Site: www.udr.com/corporate-overview/contact-us
Approx. Rev.: $352,089,000
Business Description:
Investment & Management Services
S.I.C.: 6289
N.A.I.C.S.: 523999
Advertising Expenditures: $2,300,000
Personnel:
Thomas W. Toomey *(CEO)*

UNITED SECURITY BANCSHARES
2126 Inyo St
Fresno, CA 93721
Tel.: (559) 248-4930
Fax: (559) 248-5088
Toll Free: (888) 683-6030
E-mail: info@unitedsecuritybank.com
Web Site:
www.unitedsecuritybank.com
Approx. Rev.: $38,429,000
Approx. Number Employees: 132
Year Founded: 1987
Business Description:
Bank Holding Company
S.I.C.: 6712; 6029
N.A.I.C.S.: 551111; 522110
Advertising Expenditures: $73,000
Media: 17
Personnel:
Dennis R. Woods *(Chm, Pres & CEO)*
Kenneth L. Donahue *(CFO & Sr VP)*
David L. Eytcheson *(COO & Sr VP)*
Rhodlee A. Braa *(Chief Credit Officer & Sr VP)*
William F. Scarborough *(Chief Banking Officer & Sr VP)*

UNITED SECURITY BANCSHARES, INC.
131 W Front St
Thomasville, AL 36784
Mailing Address:
PO Box 249
Thomasville, AL 36784-0249
Tel.: (334) 636-5424
Fax: (334) 636-9606
Fax: (334) 636-0479
Web Site: www.firstusbank.com
Approx. Rev.: $54,993,805
Approx. Number Employees: 297
Year Founded: 1983
Business Description:
Bank Holding Company
S.I.C.: 6712; 6029
N.A.I.C.S.: 551111; 522110
Import Export
Advertising Expenditures: $397,000
Personnel:
Robert Steen *(Principal Fin Officer, Principal Acctg Officer, Treas & Exec VP)*
J. Daniel Matheson, III *(Investment Officer)*
William D. Morgan *(Asst VP & Asst Sec)*

UNITED STATES 12 MONTH NATURAL GAS FUND, LP
(Sub. of United States Commodity Funds, LLC)
1320 Harbor Bay Pkwy Ste 145
Alameda, CA 94502
Tel.: (510) 522-3336
Approx. Rev.: $23,527
Year Founded: 2007
Business Description:
Investment Fund
S.I.C.: 6722
N.A.I.C.S.: 525910
Advertising Expenditures: $78,224
Media: 17
Personnel:
Nicholas D. Gerber *(CEO)*
Howard Mah *(CFO & Sec)*

UNITED STATES HEATING OIL FUND, LP
(Sub. of United States Commodity Funds, LLC)
1320 Harbor Bay Pkwy Ste 145
Alameda, CA 94502
Tel.: (510) 522-3336
Web Site:
www.unitedstatesheatingoilfund.com
Approx. Rev.: $528,840
Approx. Number Employees: 20
Year Founded: 2007
Business Description:
Heating & Oil Investment Fund Services
S.I.C.: 6722
N.A.I.C.S.: 525910
Advertising Expenditures: $78,224
Media: 17
Personnel:
Howard Mah *(Mng Dir, CFO & Sec)*
Andrew F. Ngim *(Mng Dir & Treas)*
Robert L. Nguyen *(Mng Dir)*
Nicholas D. Gerber *(Mgr-USCF Portfolio)*

UNITED STATES MINT
801 9th St NW
Washington, DC 20220
Tel.: (202) 354-7500
Tel.: (202) 354-7227 (Pub Rels)
Fax: (202) 756-6200
Toll Free: (800) USAMINT
Web Site: www.usmint.gov
Sales Range: $1-4.9 Billion
Approx. Number Employees: 2,500
Year Founded: 1792
Business Description:
Coins & Coin Related Products
S.I.C.: 9311
N.A.I.C.S.: 921130
Advertising Expenditures: $12,134,000
Media: 6-7-9-13-15-23-24-25
Distr.: Natl.
Brands & Products:
50 STATE QUARTERS
THE UNITED STATES MINT
UNITED STATES MINT SILVER PROOF SET
Advertising Agencies:
Campbell-Ewald
30400 Van Dyke Ave
Warren, MI 48093-2368
Tel.: (586) 574-3400
Fax: (586) 575-9925

Chess Communications Group
901 E Fayette St
Baltimore, MD 21202-4731
Tel.: (410) 732-7400
Fax: (410) 563-0045
Toll Free: (800) 551-0158

UNITED STATES SHORT OIL FUND, LP
(Sub. of United States Commodity Funds, LLC)
c/o United States Commodity Funds LLC 1320 Harbor Bay Pkwy Ste 145
Alameda, CA 94502
Tel.: (510) 522-9600
Fax: (510) 522-3338
Web Site:
www.unitedstatescommodityfunds.com
Approx. Rev.: $1,147,191
Approx. Number Employees: 5
Year Founded: 2008
Business Description:
Investment Fund Services
S.I.C.: 6722
N.A.I.C.S.: 525910
Advertising Expenditures: $78,224
Media: 17
Personnel:
Howard Mah *(CFO & Sec)*
Nicholas D. Gerber *(Mgr-Portfolio)*

UNITED TENNESSEE BANKSHARES, INC.
170 W Broadway
Newport, TN 37821-2857
Tel.: (423) 623-6088
Fax: (423) 625-0301
E-mail: customerservice@newportfederalbank.com
Web Site:
www.newportfederalbank.com
Sales Range: $1-9.9 Million
Approx. Number Employees: 30
Year Founded: 1997
Business Description:
Bank Holding Company
S.I.C.: 6712; 6029; 6035
N.A.I.C.S.: 551111; 522110; 522120
Media: 7-8-9-23-25
Personnel:
J. William Myers *(Chm)*
Chris Triplett *(Pres & CEO)*

UNITED WESTERN BANCORP, INC.
700 17th St Ste 2100
Denver, CO 80202
Tel.: (303) 595-9898
Fax: (303) 390-0952
E-mail: info@uwbank.com
Web Site:
www.unitedwesternbancorp.com
Approx. Int. Income: $101,507,000
Approx. Number Employees: 224
Year Founded: 1993
Business Description:
Bank Holding Company
S.I.C.: 6712; 6029; 6035
N.A.I.C.S.: 551111; 522110; 522120
Media: 7-8-13-26
Personnel:
Guy A. Gibson *(Chm)*
William D. Snider *(Vice Chm)*
Benjamin C. Hirsh *(CFO & Chief Acctg Officer)*
Michael J. McCloskey *(COO)*
Jeffrey R. Leventhal *(Gen Counsel, Sec & Sr VP)*
Jeffrey D. Thompson *(Exec VP)*
Brands & Products:
UNITED WESTERN BANCORP
Advertising Agency:
Silverman Heller Associates
1100 Glendon Ave PH-1
Los Angeles, CA 90024
Tel.: (310) 208-2550
Fax: (310) 208-0931
Investor Relations Consultation

UNITY BANCORP, INC.
(d/b/a Unity Bank)
64 Old Highway 22
Clinton, NJ 08809-1380
Tel.: (908) 730-7630

Key to Media (For complete agency information see *The Advertising Red Books-Agencies* edition):
1. Bus. Publs. 2. Cable T.V. 3. Catalogs & Directories. 4. Co-op Adv. 5. Consumer Mags. 6. D.M. to Bus. Estab.7. D.M. to Consumers 8. Daily Newsp. 9. Exhibits/Trade Shows 10. Foreign 11. Infomercial 12. Internet Adv.13. Multimedia 14. Network Radio 15. Network T.V. 16. Newsp. Distr. Mags. 17. Other 18. Outdoor (Posters, Transit) 19. Point of Purchase20. Premiums, Novelties 21. Product Samples 22. Special Events Mktg. 23. Spot Radio 24. Spot T.V. 25. Weekly Newsp. 26. Yellow Page Adv.

Unity Bancorp, Inc. — (Continued)

Fax: (908) 730-9430
Toll Free: (800) 618-2265
E-mail: unitydirect@unitybank.com
Web Site: www.unitybank.com
Approx. Rev.: $49,104,000
Approx. Number Employees: 167
Year Founded: 1991
Business Description:
Bank Holding Company
S.I.C.: 6022; 6029; 6712
N.A.I.C.S.: 522190; 522110; 551111
Advertising Expenditures: $624,000
Media: 7-8-13-20
Personnel:
David D. Dallas *(Chm)*
Allen Tucker *(Vice Chm)*
James A. Hughes *(Pres)*
Alan J. Bedner, Jr. *(CFO & Exec VP)*
Mark Dirado *(CIO)*
Ray Kenwell *(Chief Lending Officer & Exec VP)*
John J. Kauchak *(Chief Deposit Officer & Exec VP)*
David L. Hensley *(Sr VP)*

UNITY BANK

(Sub. of Unity Bancorp, Inc.)
64 Old Hwy 22
Clinton, NJ 08809
Tel.: (908) 730-7300
Fax: (908) 713-4388
Toll Free: (800) 540-4790
E-mail: info@unitybank.com
Web Site: www.unitybank.com
Sales Range: $50-74.9 Million
Approx. Number Employees: 140
Year Founded: 1991
Business Description:
Banking
S.I.C.: 6029
N.A.I.C.S.: 522110
Advertising Expenditures: $2,000,000
Media: 4-7-8-13
Personnel:
James A. Hughes *(Pres & CEO)*
Alan J. Bedner, Jr. *(CFO)*
John J. Kauchak *(COO & Exec VP)*
Rosemary Fellner *(Asst VP-Mktg)*

UNIVERSITY BANCORP, INC.

2015 Washtenaw Ave
Ann Arbor, MI 48104-3656
Tel.: (734) 741-5858
Fax: (734) 741-5859
E-mail: information@university-bank.com
Web Site: www.university-bank.com
Approx. Rev.: $21,814,739
Approx. Number Employees: 81
Year Founded: 1988
Business Description:
Bank Holding Company; 45.81% Owned by Orpheus Capital, Limited Partnership
S.I.C.: 6712; 6029
N.A.I.C.S.: 551111; 522110
Advertising Expenditures: $255,193
Media: 7-8-23-25
Personnel:
Stephen Lange Ranzini *(Chm & Pres)*
Charles McDowell *(Chm)*
Melanie Myjak *(VP & Internal Auditor)*

UNIVEST CORPORATION OF PENNSYLVANIA

Univest Plz 14 N Main St
Souderton, PA 18964
Mailing Address:
PO Box 64197
Souderton, PA 18964
Tel.: (215) 721-2400
Fax: (215) 721-2427
Toll Free: (800) 660-4276
E-mail: customersupport@univest.net
Web Site: www.univest.net
Approx. Rev.: $125,421,000
Approx. Number Employees: 551
Business Description:
Financial Holding Company; Banking, Investing & Insurance Services
S.I.C.: 6712; 6029; 6163; 6211; 6411; 6719
N.A.I.C.S.: 551111; 522110; 522310; 523110; 524210; 551112
Advertising Expenditures: $1,840,000
Personnel:
William S Aichele *(Chm, Pres & CEO)*
K. Leon Moyer *(Vice Chm)*
Duane J. Brobst *(Chief Risk Officer & Exec VP)*
Barry L Stoltzfus *(Exec VP & Mgr-Wealth Mgmt & Trust Grp)*
Gary Brown *(Sr VP & Sr Fin Advisor)*
Timothy Swartley *(Sr VP & Sr Trust Officer)*
Karen Elizabeth Tejkl *(Sr VP)*
Kim Detwiler *(VP & Dir-Corp Comm)*
Brands & Products:
UNIVEST
UNIVEST CORPORATION OF PENNSYLVANIA

UPROMISE, INC.

(Sub. of SLM Corporation)
95 Wells Ave Ste 160
Newton, MA 02459
Tel.: (617) 454-6400
E-mail: info@upromise.com
Web Site: www.upromise.com
Approx. Sls.: $67,100,000
Approx. Number Employees: 300
Year Founded: 2001
Business Description:
Financial Services for Educational Savings
S.I.C.: 6289; 6371; 8299
N.A.I.C.S.: 523999; 525990; 611710
Advertising Expenditures: $200,000
Media: 13
Personnel:
David Coppins *(Pres)*
Jeff Howkins *(Pres-Upromise Investments)*
Michael Libenson *(Sr VP, Gen Mgr-Grocery Svcs)*
Edwin Twomey *(Product Mgr)*
Brands & Products:
UPROMISE
Advertising Agencies:
Centra360
1400 Old Country Rd Ste 420
Westbury, NY 11590-5119
Tel.: (516) 997-3147
Fax: (516) 334-7798

JL Media, Inc.
1600 Rte 22 E
Union, NJ 07083-3415
Tel.: (908) 687-8700
Fax: (908) 687-9280

UPSTREAM WORLDWIDE, INC.

(Formerly Money4Gold Holdings, Inc.)
200 E Broward Blvd Ste 1200
Fort Lauderdale, FL 33301
Tel.: (954) 915-1550
E-mail: info@upstreamworldwide.com
Web Site:
www.upstreamworldwide.com
Approx. Rev.: $32,547,898
Approx. Number Employees: 25
Year Founded: 2003
Business Description:
Electronics & Precious Metals Recycling & Sales
S.I.C.: 7389; 5093; 6371
N.A.I.C.S.: 561499; 423930; 525990
Advertising Expenditures: $15,223,698
Media: 3-8-15
Personnel:
Scott Frohman *(Chm)*
Charles Wallace *(Pres & COO)*
Douglas Feirstein *(CEO)*
Daniel Brauser *(CFO)*
Michael Brachfeld *(Chief Acctg Officer & VP-Fin)*

U.S. BANCORP

800 Nicollet Mall Ste 1500
Minneapolis, MN 55402
Tel.: (651) 466-3000
Toll Free: (800) 872-2657
Web Site: www.usbancorp.com
Approx. Int. Income: $12,158,000,000
Approx. Number Employees: 56,000
Business Description:
Bank Holding Company
S.I.C.: 6712; 6029; 6035; 6211; 6733
N.A.I.C.S.: 551111; 522110; 522120; 523110; 523991
Media: 2-6-7-8-9-10-13-17-18-19-20-22-23-24-26
Distr.: Natl.; Reg.
Budget Set: Jan.
Personnel:
Richard K. Davis *(Chm, Pres & CEO)*
Andrew Cecere *(Vice Chm & CFO)*
Richard C. Hartnack *(Vice Chm)*
Joseph C. Hoesley *(Vice Chm-Comml Real Estate)*
Pamela A. Joseph *(Vice Chm)*
Richard B. Payne, Jr. *(Vice Chm)*
Timothy J. Leach *(Chief Investment Officer)*
P. W. Parker *(Chief Credit Officer & Exec VP)*
Richard J. Hidy *(Chief Risk Officer & Exec VP)*
Lee R. Mitau *(Gen Counsel & Exec VP)*
Jennie P. Carlson *(Exec VP-HR)*
Judith T. Murphy *(Exec VP-PR & IR)*
Ralph Bernstein *(Sr VP-Healthcare Payment Solutions)*
Steven W. Dale *(Sr VP-Media Rels)*
Rich Martino *(Sr VP-Market Analytics & Performance Solutions)*
Anthony Vuoto *(Gen Mgr-Retail Payment Solutions-US Bank)*
Brands & Products:
FIRSTAR
U.S. BANCORP
Advertising Agency:
Empower MediaMarketing (MEDIA THAT WORKS)
1111 Saint Gregory St
Cincinnati, OH 45202
Tel.: (513) 871-9454
Fax: (513) 871-1804

U.S. GLOBAL INVESTORS, INC.

7900 Callaghan Rd
San Antonio, TX 78229-2327
Tel.: (210) 308-1234
Fax: (210) 308-1217
Toll Free: (800) 873-8637
E-mail: shsvc@usfunds.com
Web Site: www.us-global.com
Approx. Rev.: $35,030,153
Approx. Number Employees: 79
Year Founded: 1983
Business Description:
Investment Manager & Advisor
S.I.C.: 6282; 8742
N.A.I.C.S.: 523920; 523930; 541611
Advertising Expenditures: $406,955
Media: 7-8-13-26
Personnel:
Jerold H. Rubinstein *(Chm)*
Roy David Terracina *(Vice Chm)*
Susan B. Mcgee *(Pres & Gen Counsel)*
Frank E. Holmes *(CEO & Chief Investment Officer)*
Catherine A. Rademacher *(CFO)*
John Derrick *(Dir-Res)*
Susan K. Filyk *(Dir-Mktg)*
Ralph P. Aldis *(Mgr-Portfolio)*
Mickael Ding *(Mgr-Portfolio)*
Brian K. Hicks *(Mgr-Portfolio)*
Evan W. Smith *(Mgr-Portfolio)*
Tim Steinle *(Mgr-Portfolio)*
Brands & Products:
ABC INVESTMENT PLAN
U.S.GLOBAL INVESTORS INC

USA FINANCIAL MARKETING CORPORATION

6020 E Fulton St
Ada, MI 49301
Tel.: (616) 676-2288
Fax: (800) 280-5262
Toll Free: (800) 530-9872
E-mail: usaf@usa-financial.com
Web Site: www.usa-financial.com
Sales Range: $50-74.9 Million
Approx. Number Employees: 35
Year Founded: 1988
Business Description:
Financial Services
S.I.C.: 8748; 6099; 7319; 7389; 8299
N.A.I.C.S.: 561499; 522320; 541618; 541870; 561439; 561990; 611710
Media: 2-13
Personnel:
Michael D. Walters *(Chm & CEO)*
Brent D. Enders *(Pres)*
Mark R. Mersman *(CMO)*
David D. Radde *(Exec VP-Mktg)*
Angela M. Versluis *(Exec VP-Logistics)*
Matthew R. Hoogterp *(VP-Mktg-Annuities & Income)*
Jade A. Rossback *(Mktg Mgr-Case Design)*
Brands & Products:
PLUG-N-RUN
USA FINANCIAL

USA TECHNOLOGIES, INC.

100 Deerfield Ln Ste 140
Malvern, PA 19355
Tel.: (610) 989-0340
Fax: (610) 989-0344
Toll Free: (800) 633-0340
E-mail: shareholders@usatech.com
Web Site: www.usatech.com
Approx. Rev.: $12,020,123
Approx. Number Employees: 40
Year Founded: 1992

Key to Media (For complete agency information see *The Advertising Red Books-Agencies* edition):
1. Bus. Publs. 2. Cable T.V. 3. Catalogs & Directories. 4. Co-op Adv. 5. Consumer Mags. 6. D.M. to Bus. Estab.7. D.M. to Consumers
8. Daily Newsp. 9. Exhibits/Trade Shows 10. Foreign 11. Infomercial 12. Internet Adv.13. Multimedia 14. Network Radio
15. Network T.V. 16. Newsp. Distr. Mags. 17. Other 18. Outdoor (Posters, Transit) 19. Point of Purchase20. Premiums, Novelties
21. Product Samples 22. Special Events Mktg. 23. Spot Radio 24. Spot T.V. 25. Weekly Newsp. 26. Yellow Page Adv.

Business Description:
Wireless, Cashless, Micro-Transactions & Networking Services
S.I.C.: 6099; 4812; 7379; 7389
N.A.I.C.S.: 522320; 517212; 541519; 561499
Advertising Expenditures: $72,000
Media: 2-5-7-13
Personnel:
George R. Jensen, Jr. *(Chm & CEO)*
Stephen P. Herbert *(Pres & COO)*
David M. Demedio *(CFO)*
Brands & Products:
BEXPRINT
BUSINESS EXPRESS
CM2IQ
COOLERMISER
CREATING VALUE THROUGH INNOVATION
E-PORT
E-SUDS
ENERGYMISER
EPORT CONNECT
EZ-APN
INTELLIGENT VENDING
PC EXPRESS
PLUGMISER
SNACKMISER
TRANSACT
USA TECHNOLOIES
VENDINGMISER
VM2IQ

VALLEY FINANCIAL CORPORATION
36 Church Ave SW
Roanoke, VA 24011
Tel.: (540) 342-2265
Fax: (540) 342-4514
E-mail: bjmitchell@myvalleybank.com
Web Site: www.myvalleybank.com
Approx. Rev.: $35,838,000
Approx. Number Employees: 124
Year Founded: 1995
Business Description:
Bank Holding Company
S.I.C.: 6712; 6029; 6035
N.A.I.C.S.: 551111; 522110; 522120
Advertising Expenditures: $296,000
Personnel:
George W. Logan *(Chm)*
Abney S. Boxley, III *(Vice Chm)*
Kimberly B. Snyder *(CFO & Exec VP)*
JoAnn M. Lloyd *(CIO & Sr VP)*
Edward C. Martin *(Chief Credit Officer & Sr VP)*
Mary P. Hundley *(Chief Risk Officer & Sr VP)*
Andrew B. Agee *(Chief Lending Officer & Sr VP)*
Connie W. Stanley *(Chief Retail Banking Officer & Sr VP)*
R. Grayson Goldsmith *(Sr VP & Mgr-Bus Banking Grp)*

VALLEY NATIONAL BANCORP
1455 Valley Rd
Wayne, NJ 07470
Tel.: (973) 305-8800
Fax: (973) 696-2044
Toll Free: (800) 522-4100
E-mail: investorrelations@valleynationalbank.com
Web Site: www.valleynationalbank.com
Approx. Rev.: $768,139,000
Approx. Number Employees: 2,720
Year Founded: 1983
Business Description:
Bank Holding Company
S.I.C.: 6712; 6029; 6035; 6163; 6211
N.A.I.C.S.: 551111; 522110; 522120; 522310; 523110
Advertising Expenditures: $3,372,000
Media: 2-7-8-13-17
Personnel:
Gerald Howard Lipkin *(Chm, Pres & CEO)*
Alan D. Eskow *(CFO, Sec & Exec VP)*
Peter Crocitto *(COO & Sr Exec VP)*
Robert E. Farrell *(Chief Credit Officer & Exec VP)*
Robert J. Mulligan *(Chief Admin Officer & Exec VP)*
Albert L. Engel *(Chief Retail Lending Officer & Exec VP)*
Robert M. Meyer *(Chief Comml Lending Officer & Exec VP)*
Anthony M. Bruno, Jr. *(Pres-Wealth Mgmt & Insurance Svcs)*
Bernadette M. Mueller *(Exec VP & Dir-Sls & Client Dev)*
James G. Lawrence *(Exec VP)*
Mitchell L. Crandell *(Sr VP & Controller)*
Stephen P. Davey *(Sr VP)*
Robert A. Ewing *(Sr VP)*
Thomas Sparkes *(Sr VP)*
Advertising Agency:
Rebolucion, LLC
22 W 23rd St 3rd Fl
New York, NY 10010
Tel.: (212) 229-0700
Fax: (212) 229-0770
(Hispanic Marketing)

VALUE FINANCIAL SERVICES, INC.
(Sub. of EZCORP, Inc.)
1063 Maitland Ctr Commons Blvd Ste 200
Maitland, FL 32751-7436
Tel.: (407) 339-0064
Fax: (407) 339-6608
E-mail: info@vfservices.com
Web Site: www.vfservices.com
Approx. Rev.: $87,814,000
Approx. Number Employees: 530
Year Founded: 1994
Business Description:
Small, Secured, Non-Recourse Consumer Loans (Pawn Loans) & Related Services
S.I.C.: 6159; 5932; 6163
N.A.I.C.S.: 522298; 453310; 522310
Advertising Expenditures: $203,000
Media: 9-20-23-25
Personnel:
Wilton Whitcomb *(CFO)*

THE VANGUARD GROUP, INC.
100 Vanguard Blvd
Malvern, PA 19355
Tel.: (610) 669-1000
Fax: (610) 669-6605
Toll Free: (800) 662-6773
Web Site: www.vanguard.com
Approx. Number Employees: 12,000
Year Founded: 1975
Business Description:
Mutual Fund Company
S.I.C.: 6722
N.A.I.C.S.: 525910
Advertising Expenditures: $20,000,000
Media: 6-8-9-13-14-15-22-25
Personnel:
William McNabb, III *(Chm & CEO)*
Paul Heller *(Mng Dir & CIO)*
R. Gregory Barton *(Mng Dir-Institutional Investor Grp)*
Glenn Reed *(Mng Dir)*
Heidi Stam *(Gen Counsel)*
Kathleen Gubanich *(Mng Dir-HR)*
Shannon Nutter-Wiersbitzky *(Dir-Mktg Res)*
Wayne Park *(Sr Mgr-Adv)*
Rebecca Cohen *(Mgr-Pub Rel)*
Louise DiFilippo *(Mgr-Dev & Production)*
Lauren Shapiro *(Mgr-Adv)*
Karen Eriksen *(Coord-Media)*
Brands & Products:
ADMIRAL
EXPLORER
FINANCIAL PLANNER
FLAGSHIP
FUNDACCESS
PLAIN TALK
PLAINTALK
UNMATCHABLE VALUE FOR INVESTORS
VANGUARD
VANGUARD BROKERAGE SERVICES
VANGUARD ETF
VANGUARD FINANCIAL ADVISOR SERVICES
VANGUARD IRA
VANGUARD LIFESTRATEGY
VANGUARD LIFETIME INCOME PROGRAM
VANGUARD PLAN SPONSOR BRIDGE
VANGUARD TOTAL BOND MARKET INDEX FUND SIGNAL
VANGUARD UNMATCHABLE EXCELLENCE
VANGUARDADVANTAGE
VANGUARD.COM
VIPER
VISION
VOYAGER
VOYAGER SELECT SERVICES
VOYAGER SERVICES
Advertising Agencies:
MediaCom
498 7th Ave
New York, NY 10018
Tel.: (212) 912-4200
Fax: (212) 508-4386
Media

TBC Inc.
900 S Wolfe St
Baltimore, MD 21231
Tel.: (410) 347-7500
Fax: (410) 986-1299

VML-New York
285 Madison Ave
New York, NY 10017
Tel.: (212) 210-3653
Fax: (212) 880-7543
Interactive Digital

Young & Rubicam Inc.
285 Madison Ave
New York, NY 10017-6401
Tel.: (212) 210-3000
Fax: (212) 490-9073

VENGROFF WILLIAMS & ASSOCIATES, INC.
2211 Fruitville Rd
Sarasota, FL 34237
Tel.: (941) 363-5200
Fax: (941) 363-5300
E-mail: moreinfo@vwainc.com
Web Site: www.vwainc.com
Approx. Number Employees: 200
Year Founded: 1963
Business Description:
Financial & Accounting Services
S.I.C.: 7322; 6371; 8721
N.A.I.C.S.: 561440; 525990; 541219
Media: 10
Personnel:
Harvey Vengroff *(Founder)*
Robert Williams *(Chm & CEO)*
Joel Vengroff *(Pres)*
Robert Sherman *(Pres-California & Dir-Mktg)*

VIAD CORP.
1850 N Central Ave Ste 800
Phoenix, AZ 85004-4545
Tel.: (602) 207-4000
Fax: (602) 207-5900
E-mail: ir@viad.com
Web Site: www.viad.com
Approx. Rev.: $844,761,000
Approx. Number Employees: 3,350
Year Founded: 1914
Business Description:
Diversified Holding Company: Marketing, Events, Travel & Recreation Services
S.I.C.: 8742; 4789; 6719; 7389
N.A.I.C.S.: 541611; 488999; 551112; 561920
Media: 2-7
Personnel:
Paul B. Dykstra *(Chm, Pres & CEO)*
Ellen M. Ingersoll *(CFO)*
G. Michael Latta *(Chief Acctg Officer & Controller)*
Michael M. Hannan *(Pres-Travel & Recreation Grp)*
Scott E. Sayre *(Gen Counsel & Sec)*
Suzanne Pearl *(VP-HR & Admin)*
Brands & Products:
TRAVELERS EXPRESS

VIEWPOINT FINANCIAL GROUP, INC.
1309 W 15th St
Plano, TX 75075
Tel.: (972) 578-5000
Fax: (469) 467-1020
E-mail: mary.rische@viewpointbank.com
Web Site: www.viewpointbank.com
Approx. Rev.: $148,849,000
Approx. Number Employees: 581
Business Description:
Holding Company
S.I.C.: 6035; 6061; 6712
N.A.I.C.S.: 522120; 522130; 551111
Advertising Expenditures: $1,285,000
Personnel:
Garold R. Base *(Pres & CEO)*
James C. Parks *(COO & Exec VP)*
Liz German *(Chief HR Officer & Sr VP)*
Rick M. Robertson *(Chief Banking Officer & Exec VP)*

Key to Media (For complete agency information see *The Advertising Red Books-Agencies* edition):
1. Bus. Publs. 2. Cable T.V. 3. Catalogs & Directories. 4. Co-op Adv. 5. Consumer Mags. 6. D.M. to Bus. Estab.7. D.M. to Consumers
8. Daily Newsp. 9. Exhibits/Trade Shows 10. Foreign 11. Infomercial 12. Internet Adv.13. Multimedia 14. Network Radio
15. Network T.V. 16. Newsp. Distr. Mags. 17. Other 18. Outdoor (Posters, Transit) 19. Point of Purchase20. Premiums, Novelties
21. Product Samples 22. Special Events Mktg. 23. Spot Radio 24. Spot T.V. 25. Weekly Newsp. 26. Yellow Page Adv.

VIEWPOINT FINANCIAL GROUP, INC. — (Continued)

Mark E. Hord *(Gen Counsel, Sec & Exec VP)*
Patrick J. Ramsier *(Chief Comml Real Estate Officer & Sr VP)*
Yvonne Stewart *(VP & Mgr-Relationship)*
Camille Ussery *(VP)*
Todd Carter *(Asst VP & Mgr-Private Client)*

VILLAGE BANK & TRUST FINANCIAL CORP.

15521 Midlothian Tpke Ste 200
Midlothian, VA 23113
Tel.: (804) 897-3900
Fax: (804) 897-9043
E-mail: customerservice@villagebank.com
Web Site: www.villagebank.com
Approx. Rev.: $41,172,505
Approx. Number Employees: 198
Business Description:
Bank Holding Company
S.I.C.: 6712
N.A.I.C.S.: 551111
Advertising Expenditures: $308,598
Personnel:
Craig D. Bell *(Chm)*
Donald J. Balzer, Jr. *(Vice Chm)*
Jerry W. Mabry *(Pres & CEO)*
Thomas W. Winfree *(Pres & CEO)*
C. Harril Whitehurst *(CFO & Sr VP)*
Raymond E. Sanders *(COO & Sr VP)*
Dennis Falk *(Treas, Sr VP & Controller)*
Rebecca Kline *(Sr VP-Retail Banking)*
Robert R. Staples *(VP & Dir-HR)*
David G. Fahy *(VP & Mgr-Residential Construction Lending)*
Mary A. Szulczewski *(VP & Mgr-Loan Admin)*
Bob Thomas *(VP-IT)*
Dawn T. Grosik *(Asst VP & Branch Mgr-Courthouse Branch)*
Charissa Lynn Johnson *(Asst VP & Branch Mgr-Clover Hill Branch)*
Vivian Kelly *(Asst VP & Branch Mgr-Chester Branch)*
Susan Wilhelm *(Asst VP & Branch Mgr-Brandermill Branch)*
George Pulliam *(Asst VP & Mgr-Powhatan Branch)*
Deborah M. Golding *(Asst VP & Exec Asst)*
Dorothy J. McCool *(Asst VP & Bus Devel Officer-Midlothian Branch)*
Kathy J. Naworal *(Asst VP & Credit Policy Officer)*
Jane S. Preston *(Asst VP-HR)*

VIRGINIA COMMERCE BANCORP, INC.

5350 Lee Hwy
Arlington, VA 22207
Tel.: (703) 534-0700
Fax: (703) 534-1782
E-mail: bankinfo@vcbonline.com
Web Site: www.vcbonline.com
Approx. Rev.: $152,523,000
Approx. Number Employees: 210
Year Founded: 1999
Business Description:
Bank Holding Company
S.I.C.: 6029; 6712
N.A.I.C.S.: 522110; 551111
Advertising Expenditures: $941,000
Media: 17
Personnel:
W. Douglas Fisher *(Chm)*
David M. Guernsey *(Vice Chm)*
Peter A. Converse *(CEO)*
Wilmer L. Tinley, Jr. *(Interim CFO)*
Patricia M. Ostrander *(Chief Admin Officer)*
Richard B. Anderson, Jr. *(Chief Lending Officer)*
Steven A. Reeder *(Chief Deposit Officer)*
William K. Beauchesne *(Exec VP)*

VISA, INC.

PO Box 8999
San Francisco, CA 94128-8999
Tel.: (415) 932-2100
E-mail: globemedia@visa.com
Web Site: www.corporate.visa.com
Approx. Rev.: $8,065,000,000
Approx. Number Employees: 6,800
Business Description:
Credit Card & Electronic Payment Services
S.I.C.: 6141; 6099
N.A.I.C.S.: 522210; 522320
Advertising Expenditures: $918,000,000
Media: 2-3-5-6-7-8-11-13-15-17-22-24
Personnel:
Joseph W. Saunders *(Chm & CEO)*
John M. Partridge *(Pres)*
Byron H. Pollitt *(CFO)*
Michael L. Dreyer *(CIO)*
Antonio Lucio *(CMO, Chief Strategy & Corp Dev Officer-Global)*
Ellen Richey *(Chief Enterprise Risk Officer)*
Eduardo Erana *(Reg Pres-Latin America & Caribbean)*
William M. Sheedy *(Pres-North America)*
Elizabeth Buse *(CEO-Intl)*
Joshua R. Floum *(Gen Counsel)*
Jennifer Bazante *(Head-Global Brand & Sponsorship Mktg)*
Oliver Jenkyn *(Global Head-Strategy & Corp Dev)*
Rick Leweke *(Global Head-HR)*
Jason Alderman *(Sr Dir-Corp Rels)*
Victoria Hyde-Dunn *(Dir-IR)*
George Perry *(Sr Product Mgr-Mobile Banking Svcs)*
Una Somerville *(Global Head-Customer Svc & Implementation)*
Advertising Agencies:
AKQA, Inc.
118 King St 6th Fl
San Francisco, CA 94107
Tel.: (415) 645-9400
Fax: (415) 645-9420

Eleven Inc.
445 Bush St 8th Fl
San Francisco, CA 94108
Tel.: (415) 707-1111
Fax: (415) 707-1100

Greer, Margolis, Mitchell, Burns & Associates (GMMB)
1010 Wisconsin Ave NW Ste 800
Washington, DC 20007-3674
Tel.: (202) 338-8700
Fax: (202) 338-2334
Corporate Identity

OMD Worldwide
195 Broadway
New York, NY 10007
Tel.: (212) 590-7100
(Media Planning & Buying)

TBWA/Worldwide
(Sub. of Omnicom Group, Inc.)
488 Madison Ave 5th Fl
New York, NY 10022-5702
Tel.: (212) 804-1300
Fax: (212) 804-1333

VISA INTERNATIONAL

(Sub. of Visa, Inc.)
900 Metro Ctr Blvd
Foster City, CA 94404
Tel.: (650) 432-3200
Fax: (650) 432-3087
Web Site: www.visa.com
Sales Range: $250-299.9 Million
Business Description:
Transactions, Credit & Collections & Electronic Payment Systems
S.I.C.: 6099
N.A.I.C.S.: 522320
Personnel:
Elizabeth Buse *(CEO-Intl)*
Joshua R. Floum *(Gen Counsel & Sec)*
Don Davis *(Sr VP & Global Head-Real Estate)*
Michael Lynch *(Sr VP)*
Stacey Pinkerd *(Sr VP-Product)*
Advertising Agency:
Wieden + Kennedy UK Limited
16 Hanbury Street
London, E1 6QR, United Kingdom
Tel.: (44) 207 194 7000
Fax: (44) 207 194 7100
World Cup Sponsorship

VISA U.S.A., INC.

(Sub. of Visa, Inc.)
900 Metro Center Blvd
Foster City, CA 94404-2172
Mailing Address:
PO Box 194607
San Francisco, CA 94119-4607
Tel.: (650) 432-3200
Tel.: (415) 932-2100
Web Site: www.usa.visa.com
Sales Range: $1-4.9 Billion
Approx. Number Employees: 2,500
Year Founded: 1970
Business Description:
Electronic Payment & Credit Card Administration Services
S.I.C.: 6141; 6099
N.A.I.C.S.: 522210; 522320
Advertising Expenditures: $360,000
Media: 1-2-3-4-5-6-7-8-9-10-13-14-15-18-20-22-23-24-31
Distr.: Intl.; Natl.
Budget Set: June
Personnel:
John M. Partridge *(Pres)*
Joshua R. Floum *(Gen Counsel)*
Michael Lynch *(Sr VP)*
Kevin Burke *(Head-Global Mktg & Strategy)*
Gerry Sweeney *(Head-eCommerce & Authentication)*
Alex Robinson Hinkle *(Dir-Loyalty Mktg)*
Brands & Products:
VISA
VISA BUSINESS CARD
VISA BUXX
VISA CLASSIC CARD
VISA DEBIT CARD
VISA GOLD CARD
VISA INFINITE
VISA PLATINUM
VISA SIGNATURE
VISA SMART
VISA TRAVEL VOUCHERS
VISA TRAVELERS CHEQUES
Advertising Agencies:
AKQA, Inc.
118 King St 6th Fl
San Francisco, CA 94107
Tel.: (415) 645-9400
Fax: (415) 645-9420
Visa Signature

Fleishman-Hillard Inc.
4745 Alla Rd
Marina Del Rey, CA 90292-6311
Tel.: (310) 482-4270
Fax: (310) 482-4271

National Response Group
PO Box 245
Kentfield, CA 94914-0245
Tel.: (415) 457-2200
Fax: (415) 456-3227

TBWA Chiat Day Los Angeles
5353 Grosvenor Blvd
Los Angeles, CA 90066
Tel.: (310) 305-5000
Fax: (310) 305-6000
Check Card

VISION BANCSHARES, INC.

(Sub. of Park National Corporation)
2201 W 1st St
Gulf Shores, AL 36542
Mailing Address:
PO Box 4649
Gulf Shores, AL 36547
Tel.: (251) 967-4212
Fax: (251) 967-4213
Web Site: www.visionbankfsb.com/home/home
Sales Range: $75-99.9 Million
Approx. Number Employees: 180
Year Founded: 1999
Business Description:
Bank Holding Company
S.I.C.: 6035; 6712
N.A.I.C.S.: 522120; 551111
Advertising Expenditures: $297,000
Media: 7-8-13-20-22
Personnel:
Tracy Stewart *(Gen Mgr)*

VIST BANK

(Sub. of VIST Financial Corp.)
1240 Broadcasting Rd
Wyomissing, PA 19610
Mailing Address:
PO Box 6219
Wyomissing, PA 19610
Tel.: (610) 478-9922
Fax: (610) 288-1892
Web Site: www.vistfc.com
Sales Range: $125-149.9 Million
Year Founded: 1894
Business Description:
Commerical Bank
S.I.C.: 6029
N.A.I.C.S.: 522110
Media: 7-8-9-13-25

Key to Media (For complete agency information see *The Advertising Red Books-Agencies* edition):
1. Bus. Publs. 2. Cable T.V. 3. Catalogs & Directories. 4. Co-op Adv. 5. Consumer Mags. 6. D.M. to Bus. Estab.7. D.M. to Consumers 8. Daily Newsp. 9. Exhibits/Trade Shows 10. Foreign 11. Infomercial 12. Internet Adv.13. Multimedia 14. Network Radio 15. Network T.V. 16. Newsp. Distr. Mags. 17. Other 18. Outdoor (Posters, Transit) 19. Point of Purchase20. Premiums, Novelties 21. Product Samples 22. Special Events Mktg. 23. Spot Radio 24. Spot T.V. 25. Weekly Newsp. 26. Yellow Page Adv.

Personnel:
Robert D. Davis *(Pres & CEO)*
Paula Baron *(VP-Mktg)*

VIST FINANCIAL CORP.

1240 Broadcasting Rd
Wyomissing, PA 19610
Tel.: (610) 208-0966
Fax: (610) 926-9824
Fax: (610) 372-5705
Toll Free: (888) 238-3330
Web Site: www.vistfc.com/
Approx. Rev.: $84,704,000
Approx. Number Employees: 295
Year Founded: 1986
Business Description:
Holding Company; Banking Services
S.I.C.: 6022; 6029; 6712
N.A.I.C.S.: 522190; 522110; 551111
Advertising Expenditures: $1,011,000
Personnel:
Alfred J. Weber *(Chm)*
Frank C. Milewski *(Vice Chm)*
Robert D. Davis *(Pres & CEO)*
Edward C. Barrett *(CFO & Exec VP)*
John F. Acanfora *(CIO)*
Paula N. Barron *(CMO & Sr VP)*
Terry F. Favilla *(Treas & Sr VP)*
Jenette L. Eck *(Sr VP & Corp Sec)*
Christina S. Mcdonald *(Chief Retail Banking Officer & Exec VP)*

Brands & Products:
PROVIDING KNOWLEDGE DELIVERING SOLUTIONS
VIST FINANCIAL

WACCAMAW BANKSHARES, INC.

110 N JK Powell Blvd
Whiteville, NC 28472
Tel.: (910) 641-0044
Fax: (910) 641-0978
E-mail: waccamaw@waccamawbank.com
Web Site: www.waccamawbank.com
Approx. Rev.: $29,797,921
Approx. Number Employees: 129
Business Description:
Bank Holding Company
S.I.C.: 6029; 6712
N.A.I.C.S.: 522110; 551111
Advertising Expenditures: $311,000
Personnel:
Alan W. Thompson *(Chm & Interim CEO)*
Geoffrey Hopkins *(Pres)*
David A. Godwin *(CFO & Sr VP)*
Freda H. Gore *(COO & Sr VP)*
Richard C. Norris *(Chief Credit Officer & Exec VP)*
Anthony M. Henry *(Chief Credit Officer-Credit Admin & Asst VP)*
Gracie B. McClary *(VP & Officer-Compliance)*
Jennifer Noble *(Officer-Area Ops & Asst VP)*
Kim T. Hutchens *(Sr VP & Chief Dir-HR)*
Kim Neisler *(VP & Mgr-Waccamaw Mortgage Svcs)*
Sheri Gibson *(VP-Retail Sls & Mktg)*
Tamra Cannon *(Asst VP & Area Mgr-South Carolina)*
Kim Felts *(Asst VP & Branch Mgr)*
George Benton *(Asst VP & Credit Dept Mgr-Credit Admin)*
Michelle Brown *(Asst VP & Consumer Lender)*
Michael A. Lewis *(Asst VP & Ops/ Security Officer)*
Janet Smith *(Asst VP & Credit Review Mgr-Credit Admin)*

WADDELL & REED FINANCIAL, INC.

6300 Lamar Ave
Shawnee Mission, KS 66202
Tel.: (913) 236-2000
Tel.: (913) 236-1880 (Investor Rels)
Fax: (913) 236-2017
Toll Free: (800) 532-2757
E-mail: jobs@waddell.com
Web Site: www.waddell.com
Approx. Rev.: $1,044,885,000
Approx. Number Employees: 1,485
Year Founded: 1937
Business Description:
Mutual Funds & Life Insurance
S.I.C.: 6799; 6211; 6282; 6722
N.A.I.C.S.: 523910; 523110; 523120; 523930; 525910
Advertising Expenditures: $4,700,000
Media: 1-3-5-7-8-9-13-18-20-23-24-25-26
Distr.: Natl.
Budget Set: Jan.
Personnel:
Henry John Herrmann *(Chm & CEO)*
Michael L. Avery *(Chief Investment Officer, Pres & Portfolio Mgr)*
Daniel P. Connealy *(CFO & Sr VP)*
Michael D. Strohm *(COO & Sr VP)*
Thomas W. Butch *(CMO & Exec VP)*
Daniel C. Schulte *(Chief Legal Officer & Sr VP)*
John E Sundeen *(Chief Admin Officer & Sr VP)*
Brent K. Bloss *(Chief Acctg Officer, Treas & Sr VP-Fin)*

Brands & Products:
FINANCIAL ADVISORS
WADDELL & REED FINANCIAL SERVICES

WAINWRIGHT BANK & TRUST COMPANY

(Sub. of Eastern Bank Corporation)
63 Franklin St
Boston, MA 02110
Tel.: (617) 478-4000
Fax: (617) 478-4080
Toll Free: (800) 444BANK
Web Site: www.wainwrightbank.com
Approx. Rev.: $50,115,000
Approx. Number Employees: 145
Year Founded: 1987
Business Description:
Commercial Banking Services
S.I.C.: 6029
N.A.I.C.S.: 522110
Media: 7-8-13-18
Personnel:
Robert Alan Glassman *(Co-Chm)*
John Michael Plukas *(Co-Chm)*
Jan A. Miller *(Pres & CEO)*
James J. Barrett *(CFO & Sr VP)*
Martha A. Dean *(CIO, Sr VP & Ops Officer)*
Carolyn E. Crowley *(Sr VP-Private Banking)*
Pamela C. Feingold *(Sr VP-Community Dev Lending)*
Darryl J. Fess *(Sr VP-Comml Real Estate Lending)*
Michael Lindberg *(Sr VP)*
Aime O'Donovan *(Sr VP-HR)*
Liliana P. Sanchez *(Sr VP)*
Henri A. Soucy *(Sr VP)*
Steven F. Young *(Sr VP-Comm & Mktg)*
David Dolbashian *(VP)*
Mei See Law-Sandson *(VP-Credit)*
Nancy Mahoney *(VP-Deposit Svcs)*
Stephen G. Markos *(VP-Retail Banking)*
Joseph P. Orefice *(VP-IT)*
Edward M. Sugrue *(VP-Retail Banking)*
Timothy W. Tracey *(VP)*
Roseline Alexandre *(Asst VP-Retail Banking)*
Irene K. Berry *(Asst VP-Deposit Svcs)*
Stig N. Bjornebye *(Asst VP)*
Nicholas P. Calos *(Asst VP-Retail Banking)*
Richard B. Golden *(Asst VP-Credit)*
Robert A. Johnson *(Asst VP-Residential & Consumer Lending)*
Douglas K. Lennan *(Asst VP-Retail Banking)*
Maria L. Lucas *(Asst VP-Retail Banking)*
Ramon Marrero *(Asst VP-Retail Banking)*
Tatyana A. Melnik *(Asst VP)*
Ethelbert N. Onyeokoro *(Asst VP-Retail Banking)*
David C. Pennybaker, Jr. *(Asst VP-Comml Lending)*
Mark C. Stevens *(Asst VP)*
Julie A. Walker *(Asst VP-Deposit Svcs)*
Thomas P. Walsh *(Asst VP-Retail Banking)*
Peter J. Benotti *(Mgr-Computer Ops)*
Christopher W. Scoville *(Mgr-Community Dev Relationship)*

Brands & Products:
COMMUNITYROOM.NET
SOCIALLY PROGRESSIVE BANKING

WASHINGTON FEDERAL INC.

425 Pike St
Seattle, WA 98101
Tel.: (206) 624-7930
Tel.: (206) 777-8246 (Investor Rels)
Fax: (206) 624-2334
E-mail: info@washingtonfederal.com
Web Site: www.washingtonfederal.com
Approx. Rev.: $783,990,000
Approx. Number Employees: 1,165
Year Founded: 1994
Business Description:
Bank Holding Company; Savings & Loan Institution
S.I.C.: 6712; 6029; 6035
N.A.I.C.S.: 551111; 522110; 522120
Media: 8-9-25-26
Personnel:
Roy M. Whitehead *(Chm, Pres & CEO)*
Brent J. Beardall *(CFO & Exec VP)*
Mark A. Schoonover *(Chief Credit Officer & Exec VP)*
Leo Clark *(Gen Counsel)*
Keith D. Taylor *(Sr VP & Treas-Corp Real Estate)*
Linda S. Brower *(EVP-HR & Deposit Ops)*
Edwin C. Hedlund *(EVP-Mortgage & Consumer Lending)*
Jack B. Jacobson *(Exec VP-Comml Real Estate & Chief Lending Officer)*
James E. Cady *(Sr VP-Credit Admin)*
Rick J. Collette *(Sr VP-Bus Dev & Bus Banking Div)*
Cathy E. Cooper *(Sr VP-Mktg & Comm)*
Thomas F. Kenney *(Sr VP)*
Barbara A. Murphy *(Sr VP-Internal Audit)*
Terry O. Permenter *(Sr VP-DP)*
Dale R. Sullivan *(Sr VP-Credit Admin)*
Colleen E. Wells *(Sr VP-Wholesale Underwriting)*
Patrick J. Carson *(VP-BDM Permanent Lending)*
Andy Pohlman *(Mgr-Community Bus Banking Sls)*
Dennis Zender *(Asst Mgr-Investor Rels & Mktg)*

Brands & Products:
WASHINGTON FEDERAL
WASHINGTON FEDERAL SAVINGS

WASHINGTON TRUST BANCORP, INC.

23 Broad St
Westerly, RI 02891-1879
Mailing Address:
PO Box 512
Westerly, RI 02891-0512
Tel.: (401) 348-1200
Fax: (401) 348-1347
Toll Free: (800) 475-2265
E-mail: ebeckel@washtrust.com
Web Site: www.washtrust.com
Approx. Rev.: $171,727,000
Approx. Number Employees: 481
Year Founded: 1984
Business Description:
Bank Holding Company
S.I.C.: 6029; 6712
N.A.I.C.S.: 522110; 551111
Advertising Expenditures: $1,633,000
Personnel:
Joseph J. MarcAurele *(Chm, Pres & CEO)*
Gerald J. Fogarty, Jr. *(Mng Dir-Washington Trust Investors)*
Marie J. Langlois *(Mng Dir-Washington Trust Investors)*
David V Devault *(CFO, Sec & Sr Exec VP)*
James M. Vesey *(Chief Credit Officer & Exec VP)*
Dennis L. Algiere *(Chief Compliance Officer, Sr VP & Dir-Community Affairs)*
Mary M. Mcgoldrick *(Chief Investment Officer & Sr VP)*
Stephen M. Bessette *(Exec VP-Retail Lending)*
Galan George Daukas *(Exec VP-Wealth Mgmt)*
B. Michael Rauh *(Exec VP-Sls, Svc & Delivery)*
Harvey C. Perry, II *(Sr VP & Dir-Non-Profit Resources)*
James J. Walther *(Sr VP & Dir-Intl Audit)*
Carl M. Amaral *(Sr VP-Retail Branch Admin)*
Philip L. Friend *(Sr VP-Retail Lending)*
Russell W. Hahn *(Sr VP-Comml Lending)*
Rogean B. Makowski *(Sr VP-Wealth Mgmt Client Svcs)*
Brenda H. Senak *(Sr VP-Risk Mgmt)*
Julia Anne M. Slom *(Sr VP-Comml Real Estate Grp)*

Key to Media (For complete agency information see *The Advertising Red Books-Agencies* edition):
1. Bus. Publs. 2. Cable T.V. 3. Catalogs & Directories. 4. Co-op Adv. 5. Consumer Mags. 6. D.M. to Bus. Estab.7. D.M. to Consumers
8. Daily Newsp. 9. Exhibits/Trade Shows 10. Foreign 11. Infomercial 12. Internet Adv.13. Multimedia 14. Network Radio
15. Network T.V. 16. Newsp. Distr. Mags. 17. Other 18. Outdoor (Posters, Transit) 19. Point of Purchase20. Premiums, Novelties
21. Product Samples 22. Special Events Mktg. 23. Spot Radio 24. Spot T.V. 25. Weekly Newsp. 26. Yellow Page Adv.

WATERSTONE FINANCIAL, INC.
11200 W Plank Ct
Wauwatosa, WI 53226
Tel.: (414) 761-1000
Web Site: www.wsbonline.com
Approx. Rev.: $128,926,000
Approx. Number Employees: 595
Business Description:
Bank Holding Company
S.I.C.: 6035; 6712
N.A.I.C.S.: 522120; 551111
Advertising Expenditures: $1,259,000
Personnel:
Douglas S. Gordon *(Pres & CEO)*
Richard C. Larson *(CFO & Sr VP)*
Dave C. Hoerig *(VP & Sr Delinquent Loans Officer)*
Jodi L. Johnson *(Asst VP & Asst Compliance Officer)*
William F. Bruss *(Gen Counsel, Sr VP, Compliance Officer & Head-HR & Legal Dept)*
Kurt Andre *(Sr VP & Sr Comml Loan Officer-Wauwatosa Savings Bank)*
Judy L. Gebhard *(Head-Retail Delivery & Asst VP)*
Collette Kendzierski *(Head-Deposits Ops & Asst VP)*
Therese M. Pekar *(Head-Customer Svcs & Asst VP)*
Mark Gerke *(Controller & Asst VP)*
Megan A. Liebmann *(Asst VP & Dir-Mktg-Wauwatosa Savings Bank)*
Judith M. Wagner *(Asst VP & Asst Controller)*
Sally R. McFadden *(Asst VP-Employee Benefits Administrator)*
Bryan J. Olen *(Asst VP & Dept Head-Asset Mgmt, Securit, Facilities)*

WATERTOWN SAVINGS BANK INC.
60 Main St
Watertown, MA 02472-4413
Tel.: (617) 928-9000
Fax: (617) 972-9390
E-mail: support@watertownsavings.com
Web Site:
www.watertownsavings.com
Approx. Number Employees: 150
Year Founded: 1870
Business Description:
Savings Institution
S.I.C.: 6035; 6163
N.A.I.C.S.: 522120; 522310
Media: 6-17
Personnel:
Ronald D. Dean *(Chm & CEO)*
Brett W. Dean *(Pres)*
Richard Tatarczuk *(CFO & Sr VP)*
James H. Barwell *(Sr VP)*
Randall A. Buck *(Sr VP)*
Frederick Proia *(Sr VP)*
Carole Katz *(VP-Mktg)*
Craig McKenna *(VP-Security & Compliance-AMLP)*
Leslie M. Peters *(VP-HR)*
Julie A. Griffin *(Mgr)*
Advertising Agency:
Stackpole & Partners Advertising
222 Merrimac St
Newburyport, MA 01950
Tel.: (978) 463-6600
Fax: (978) 463-6610

WAUSAU FINANCIAL SYSTEMS INC.
(Holding of Frontenac Company)
875 Indianhead Dr
Mosinee, WI 54455-9512
Tel.: (715) 359-0427
Fax: (715) 241-2288
E-mail: info@wausaufs.com
Web Site: www.wausaufs.com
Sales Range: $100-124.9 Million
Approx. Number Employees: 400
Year Founded: 1974
Business Description:
Computers, Peripherals & Software
S.I.C.: 7373; 5045
N.A.I.C.S.: 541512; 423430
Import Export
Personnel:
Bill Fenimore *(Chm)*
Gary Cawthorne *(Pres)*
Stuart Coppens *(CFO)*
Tim Patneaude *(COO, CIO & Exec VP)*
Keith Williams *(Sr VP-HR)*
Christian Zegal *(VP-Mktg)*
Advertising Agency:
Zizzo Group Marketing + PR + New Media
648 N Plankinton Ave Ste 270
Milwaukee, WI 53203
Tel.: (414) 319-5700
Fax: (414) 319-5717

WAYNE BANK
(Sub. of Norwood Financial Corp.)
717 Main St
Honesdale, PA 18431
Mailing Address:
PO Box 269
Honesdale, PA 18431
Tel.: (570) 253-1455
Fax: (570) 253-3725
E-mail: info@waynebank.com
Web Site: www.waynebank.com
Sales Range: $25-49.9 Million
Approx. Number Employees: 125
Year Founded: 1871
Business Description:
Community Bank
S.I.C.: 6029
N.A.I.C.S.: 522110
Advertising Expenditures: $240,000
Media: 2-4-7-8-9-10-13-18-20-23-25-26
Personnel:
Lewis J. Critelli *(Pres & CEO)*
Edward C. Kasper *(Exec VP-Comml Loans)*
Sandra Halas *(Sr VP)*
John H. Sanders *(Sr VP-Retail Bank)*

WAYNE SAVINGS BANCSHARES, INC.
151 N Market St
Wooster, OH 44691
Tel.: (330) 264-5767
Fax: (330) 264-5908
Toll Free: (800) 414-1103
E-mail: waynesavings@sssnet.com
Web Site: www.waynesavings.com
Approx. Rev.: $19,816,000
Approx. Number Employees: 96
Year Founded: 1899
Business Description:
Bank Holding Company
S.I.C.: 6712; 6035
N.A.I.C.S.: 551111; 522120
Advertising Expenditures: $37,000
Media: 17
Personnel:
James C. Morgan *(Chm)*
Rodney C. Steiger *(Pres & CEO)*
Myron Swartzentruber *(CFO & Sr VP)*

WEBBANK
(Sub. of Steel Partners Holdings Ltd.)
6440 S Wasatch Blvd Ste 300
Salt Lake City, UT 84121
Tel.: (801) 993-5025
Fax: (801) 993-5015
Toll Free: (888) 881-3789
Web Site: www.webbank.com
Sales Range: $50-74.9 Million
Approx. Number Employees: 20
Business Description:
Financial Advisory Services & Products
S.I.C.: 6141; 6371; 6733
N.A.I.C.S.: 522220; 523991; 525990
Media: 13
Personnel:
Kelly Barnett *(CFO & Sr VP)*
Todd Tlumley *(VP-Loan Review & Mgr-Collection)*
Robin Riggs *(Dir)*

WEBSTER CITY FEDERAL BANCORP
820 Des Moines St
Webster City, IA 50595-2120
Tel.: (515) 832-3071
Fax: (515) 832-3085
Toll Free: (866) 263-0293
E-mail: wcfinfo@webcityfed.com
Web Site: www.webcityfed.com
Approx. Rev.: $5,256,682
Approx. Number Employees: 24
Business Description:
Bank Holding Company
S.I.C.: 6029; 6712
N.A.I.C.S.: 522110; 551111
Advertising Expenditures: $40,000
Media: 9-20-23-25-26
Personnel:
Stephen Mourlam *(Pres & CEO)*
Sheila M. Scott *(Sec & Asst VP)*
Kyle Swon *(Exec VP)*

THE WEISS GROUP INC.
15430 Endeavour Dr
Jupiter, FL 33478
Tel.: (561) 627-3300
Fax: (561) 625-6685
Toll Free: (800) 289-9222
Web Site: www.weissgroupinc.com
Approx. Number Employees: 100
Year Founded: 1971
Business Description:
Financial Newsletter & Health Newsletter Publisher; Investment Advisors
S.I.C.: 6282; 2711
N.A.I.C.S.: 523930; 511110
Advertising Expenditures: $300,000
Media: 2-4-7-8-9-10-13-25
Distr.: Intl.; Natl.
Budget Set: Dec. -Jan.
Personnel:
Martin D. Weiss *(Founder, Chm & Editor-Money & Markets)*
Thomas J. Clarke, Jr. *(CEO)*
Tracey Butz *(COO)*
Brands & Products:
WEISS GROUP
WEISS MONEY MANAGEMENT
WEISS RATINGS
WEISS RESEARCH

WELLS FARGO ADVISORS, LLC
(Holding of Wells Fargo & Company)
1 N Jefferson Ave
Saint Louis, MO 63103-2205
Tel.: (314) 955-3000
Fax: (314) 955-2890
Toll Free: (877) 835-7877
Web Site:
www.wellsfargoadvisors.com
Approx. Rev.: $8,700,000,000
Approx. Number Employees: 30,200
Year Founded: 1934
Business Description:
Securities Brokerage, Investment Banking, Financial Advisory, Trust & Asset Management Services; Owned 77% by Wachovia Corporation & 23% by Prudential Financial, Inc.
S.I.C.: 6282; 6211; 6733
N.A.I.C.S.: 523110; 523120; 523920; 523930; 523991
Media: 1-2-3-4-5-6-7-8-9-10-13-14-15-17-18-19-20-22-23-24-25-26
Distr.: Natl.
Budget Set: Feb.
Personnel:
Daniel J. Ludeman *(Pres & CEO)*
Erik O'Neill *(Mng Dir)*
Peter Deakos *(Pres-Venality)*
Advertising Agency:
Eric Mower and Associates
211 West Jefferson St.
Syracuse, NY 13202
Tel.: (315) 466-1000
Fax: (315) 466-2000

WELLS FARGO & COMPANY
420 Montgomery St
San Francisco, CA 94104-1205
Tel.: (515) 221-5600
Tel.: (415) 396-4000
Toll Free: (800) 956-4442
Toll Free: (800) 869-3557
Toll Free: (866) 878-5865
Web Site: www.wellsfargo.com
Approx. Int. Income: $52,796,000,000
Approx. Number Employees: 158,900
Year Founded: 1852
Business Description:
Bank & Financial Holding Company; Commercial Banking, Consumer Lending, Insurance & Other Financial Services
S.I.C.: 6712; 6029; 6141; 6163; 6331; 6361; 6411
N.A.I.C.S.: 551111; 522110; 522291; 522310; 524126; 524127; 524298
Advertising Expenditures: $572,000,000
Media: 2-7-8-9-13-14-15-18-23-24-26
Distr.: Natl.
Personnel:
John G. Stumpf *(Chm, Pres & CEO)*
Anthony P. Gallo *(Mng Dir)*
Brian Statfeld *(Mng Dir)*
Timothy J. Sloan *(CFO & Sr Exec VP)*
Sylvia Reynolds *(CMO)*
Jeff Rademann *(Reg Pres)*
Kim M Young *(Pres-Community Banking-Southern California)*
James M. Strother *(Gen Counsel & Exec VP)*
Laurel A. Holschuh *(Sec, Sr VP & Asst Gen Counsel)*

Key to Media (For complete agency information see *The Advertising Red Books-Agencies* edition):
1. Bus. Publs. 2. Cable T.V. 3. Catalogs & Directories. 4. Co-op Adv. 5. Consumer Mags. 6. D.M. to Bus. Estab.7. D.M. to Consumers 8. Daily Newsp. 9. Exhibits/Trade Shows 10. Foreign 11. Infomercial 12. Internet Adv.13. Multimedia 14. Network Radio 15. Network T.V. 16. Newsp. Distr. Mags. 17. Other 18. Outdoor (Posters, Transit) 19. Point of Purchase20. Premiums, Novelties 21. Product Samples 22. Special Events Mktg. 23. Spot Radio 24. Spot T.V. 25. Weekly Newsp. 26. Yellow Page Adv.

Lawrence P. Haeg, Sr. *(Sr Exec VP-Corp Comm)*
Diana L Starcher *(Head-Phone BankSM & Exec VP-Bank)*
Oscar Suris *(Exec VP & Head-Corp Comm)*
Richard D. Levy *(Exec VP & Controller)*
Caryl J. Athanasiu *(Exec VP)*
Ellen Haude *(Exec VP)*
Kevin McCabe *(Chief Auditor & Exec VP)*
Avid Modjtabai *(Exec VP-Tech & Ops)*
Kevin A. Rhein *(Exec VP-Card Svcs & Consumer Lending)*
Eric D Shand *(Exec VP)*
Lisa J Stevens *(Exec VP)*
Sara Wardell-Smith *(Exec VP-Foreign Exchange & Intl Treasury Mgmt)*
Alan Elias *(Sr VP & Head-Wholesale Bank Comm)*
Alec Hughes *(Sr VP & Reg Dir-Mktg)*
Carey Parker *(Sr VP-Online Sls & Dir-Mktg)*
Katy Frohling *(Sr VP-Brand Mgmt)*
Maggie Mui *(Sr VP)*
Derick McGee *(VP & Dir-Product Mgmt)*
Steve Godfrey *(Head-Foreign Exchange E-Commerce Div)*
Mary S. Wenzel *(Dir-Environmental Affairs)*
Peter Ho *(Product Mgr-Card Svcs & Consumer Lending)*
Christine Smith *(Product Mgr)*

Advertising Agencies:
Acento Advertising, Inc.
2254 S Sepulveda Blvd
Los Angeles, CA 90064
Tel.: (310) 943-8300
Fax: (310) 943-8310
Hispanic
— Robert Orci *(Contact)*

DAE Advertising, Inc.
71 Stevenson St Ste 750
San Francisco, CA 94105
Tel.: (415) 341-1280
Fax: (415) 296-8378
Asian
— Fanny Chew *(Contact)*
— Krittaya Boonma *(Contact)*

DDB Los Angeles
340 Main St
Venice, CA 90291
Tel.: (310) 907-1500
Fax: (310) 907-1571

Euro RSCG Worldwide - San Francisco
1355 Sansome St
San Francisco, CA 94111
Tel.: (415) 345-7700
Fax: (415) 345-7705
Activation & Usage Programs
Credit Cards
Direct Marketing
Rewards
— Ernie Lageson *(Contact)*

The Marketing Arm
1999 Bryan St Ste 1800
Dallas, TX 75201-3125
Tel.: (214) 259-3200
Fax: (214) 259-3201
Sports Marketing & Sponsorships
— Andrew Robinson *(Contact)*

Muse Communications
9543 Culver Blvd 2nd Fl
Culver City, CA 90232
Tel.: (310) 945-4100
Fax: (310) 945-4110
African American
— J. Melvin Muse *(Contact)*
— Shelley Yamane *(Contact)*

OMD Los Angeles
5353 Grosvenor Blvd
Los Angeles, CA 90066
Tel.: (310) 301-3600
Fax: (646) 278-8000

Performics
180 N LaSalle Ste 1100
Chicago, IL 60601
Tel.: (312) 739-0222
Fax: (312) 739-0223
Paid Search Campaigns for Home Equity
— Linda Khoshaba *(Contact)*
— Sara Rohman *(Contact)*

WELLS FARGO FINANCIAL, INC.
(Div. of Wells Fargo & Company)
800 Walnut St
Des Moines, IA 50309
Tel.: (515) 243-2131
Fax: (515) 557-7666
Web Site: www.financial.wellsfargo.com
Approx. Number Employees: 16,500
Year Founded: 1897
Business Description:
Financial Services
S.I.C.: 6141; 6159
N.A.I.C.S.: 522210; 522220; 522291; 522292; 522298
Advertising Expenditures: $400,000
Catalogs & Directories: $200,000;
D.M. to Consumers: $200,000
Distr.: Natl.
Budget Set: Dec.-Jan.
Personnel:
Alan Blenner *(Exec VP & Chief Credit Officer)*
David R. Kvamme *(Pres-US Consumer)*
Patricia J. McFarland *(Sec & Exec VP)*
Michael R. McCoy *(Div Pres & Bus Mgr)*
Brands & Products:
NORWEST
SUPREME
SWIFT

WELLS FINANCIAL CORP.
53 First St SW
Wells, MN 56097
Tel.: (507) 553-3151
Fax: (507) 553-6295
E-mail: jmoll@wellsfederal.com
Web Site: www.wellsfinancialcorp.com
Approx. Rev.: $18,758,000
Approx. Number Employees: 95
Year Founded: 1994
Business Description:
Bank Holding Company
S.I.C.: 6035; 6712
N.A.I.C.S.: 522120; 551111
Advertising Expenditures: $238,000
Personnel:
Lonnie R. Trasamar *(Pres)*
James Sauer *(COO)*
James D. Moll *(Officer-Fin & Acctg)*

WES-STATE MORTGAGE INC.
1450 W 7th Ave
Eugene, OR 97402-4424
Tel.: (541) 485-4741
Fax: (541) 683-6385
Toll Free: (800) 569-4816
E-mail: info@wes-state.com
Web Site: www.wes-state.com
Approx. Number Employees: 5
Year Founded: 1976
Business Description:
Mortgage & Financing Services
S.I.C.: 6163
N.A.I.C.S.: 522310
Media: 2
Personnel:
George Ropchan *(Founder & Pres)*

WESBANCO, INC.
1 Bank Plz
Wheeling, WV 26003
Tel.: (304) 234-9000
Fax: (304) 234-4736
Toll Free: (800) 328-3369
E-mail: wesbanco@wesbanco.com
Web Site: www.wesbanco.com
Approx. Rev.: $236,528,000
Approx. Number Employees: 1,377
Year Founded: 1870
Business Description:
Bank Holding Company
S.I.C.: 6029
N.A.I.C.S.: 522110
Advertising Expenditures: $2,300,000
Media: 7-8-13
Personnel:
James C. Gardill *(Chm)*
Paul M. Limbert *(Pres)*
Dennis G. Powell *(COO & Exec VP)*
Peter W. Jaworski *(Chief Credit Officer & Exec VP)*
Brent E. Richmond *(Treas & Exec VP)*
John W. Moore *(Exec VP-HR)*
Jerome B. Schmitt *(Exec VP)*
Michael L. Perkins *(Sr VP-Risk Mgmt)*
Stephen J. Lawrence *(VP & Auditor)*
Douglas Molmar *(Mktg Mgr)*
Brands & Products:
BY ALL ACCOUNTS, BETTER.
WESBANCO

WESCO FINANCIAL CORPORATION
(Sub. of Blue Chip Stamps)
301 E Colorado Blvd Ste 300
Pasadena, CA 91101-1901
Tel.: (626) 585-6700
Fax: (626) 449-1455
Web Site: www.wescofinancial.com
Approx. Rev.: $765,703,000
Approx. Number Employees: 6
Year Founded: 1959
Business Description:
Holding Company; Insurance Services, Furniture Rental & Steel Service Center Operator
S.I.C.: 6719; 5051; 6289; 6321; 6331; 6411; 7359
N.A.I.C.S.: 551112; 423510; 523999; 524126; 524130; 524298; 532299; 532310
Advertising Expenditures: $10,622,000
Personnel:
Charles T. Munger *(Chm, Pres & CEO)*
Jeffery L. Jacobson *(CFO & VP)*

WEST SUBURBAN BANCORP, INC.
711 S Meyers Rd
Lombard, IL 60148
Tel.: (630) 629-4200
Fax: (630) 629-0278
E-mail: wsbmarketing@aol.com
Web Site: www.westsuburbanbank.com
Approx. Rev.: $92,506,000
Approx. Number Employees: 481
Year Founded: 1987
Business Description:
Bank Holding Company
S.I.C.: 6029; 6411; 6712
N.A.I.C.S.: 522110; 524210; 551111
Import Export
Advertising Expenditures: $997,000
Personnel:
Kevin J. Acker *(Chm & CEO)*
Duane G. Debs *(Pres & CFO)*
Keith W. Acker *(COO)*
Michael P. Brosnahan *(VP, Sr VP & Community Reinvestment Acct Officer)*

WESTAMERICA BANCORPORATION
1108 Fifth Ave
San Rafael, CA 94901
Tel.: (415) 257-8000
Toll Free: (800) 848-1088
E-mail: investments@westamerica.com
Web Site: www.westamerica.com
Approx. Rev.: $282,609,000
Approx. Number Employees: 1,015
Year Founded: 1884
Business Description:
Bank Holding Company
S.I.C.: 6712; 6029
N.A.I.C.S.: 551111; 522110
Advertising Expenditures: $880,000
Media: 7-9-13-20-22-23-25-26
Personnel:
David L. Payne *(Chm, Pres & CEO)*
Robert A. Thorson *(CFO & Sr VP)*
Jennifer J. Finger *(Treas & Sr VP)*
Dennis R. Hansen *(Sr VP-Ops & Sys)*
Russell W. Rizzardi *(Sr VP-Credit Admin)*
David L. Robinson *(Sr VP-Banking Div)*
James J. Schneck *(VP & Auditor)*
Nick Lane *(Asst VP-Adv)*
Brands & Products:
REMEDY
REMEDY CHECK PROTECTION
WESTAMERICA BANK
YOUR COMMUNITY BANKER

WESTERN ALLIANCE BANCORPORATION
One E Washington St Ste 1400
Phoenix, AZ 85004
Tel.: (602) 389-3500
E-mail: dgibbons@westernalliancebancorp.com
Web Site: www.westernalliancebancorp.com
Approx. Rev.: $328,649,000
Approx. Number Employees: 908
Business Description:
Bank Holding Company
S.I.C.: 6029; 6712

Key to Media (For complete agency information see *The Advertising Red Books-Agencies* edition):
1. Bus. Publs. 2. Cable T.V. 3. Catalogs & Directories. 4. Co-op Adv. 5. Consumer Mags. 6. D.M. to Bus. Estab.7. D.M. to Consumers 8. Daily Newsp. 9. Exhibits/Trade Shows 10. Foreign 11. Infomercial 12. Internet Adv.13. Multimedia 14. Network Radio 15. Network T.V. 16. Newsp. Distr. Mags. 17. Other 18. Outdoor (Posters, Transit) 19. Point of Purchase20. Premiums, Novelties 21. Product Samples 22. Special Events Mktg. 23. Spot Radio 24. Spot T.V. 25. Weekly Newsp. 26. Yellow Page Adv.

Western Alliance Bancorporation — (Continued)

N.A.I.C.S.: 522110; 551111
Advertising Expenditures: $6,463,000
Media: 17
Personnel:
Robert G. Sarver *(Chm & CEO)*
Kenneth A. Vecchione *(Pres & COO)*
Dale Gibbons *(CFO & Exec VP)*
Merrill S. Wall *(Chief Admin Officer & Exec VP)*
Robert R. McAuslan *(Chief Credit Officer & Exec VP)*
Susan C. Thompson *(Principal Acctg Officer, Sr VP & Corp Controller)*
James C. DeVolld *(Exec VP-Admin-Norther Nevada)*
Gerald Cady *(Exec VP-Admin-California)*
Duane Froeschle *(Exec VP-Credit Admin)*
Bruce E. Hendricks *(Exec VP-Admin-Southern Nevada)*
James H. Lundy *(Exec VP-Admin-Arizona)*
Dennis Rygwalski *(Exec VP-Tech & Ops)*
Kelly Ardrey *(Sr VP)*
Lary Dunn *(Sr VP-Credit Admin)*

WESTERN CAPITAL RESOURCES, INC.
(Holding of Blackstreet Capital Management, LLC)
11550 I St Ste 150
Omaha, NE 68137
Tel.: (402) 551-8888
Fax: (402) 715-4202
E-mail: deb@pqhwireless.com
Approx. Rev.: $17,978,447
Approx. Number Employees: 205
Business Description:
Consumer Loan Broker
S.I.C.: 6163
N.A.I.C.S.: 522310
Advertising Expenditures: $360,000
Personnel:
John Quandahl *(CFO & COO)*

WESTERN FINANCIAL GROUP, INC.
1010 24th St SE
High River, AB T1V 2A7, Canada
Tel.: (403) 652-2663
Fax: (403) 652-2661
Toll Free: (866) THEWEST
E-mail: info@westernfinancialgroup.net
Web Site: www.westernfinancialgroup.net
Approx. Rev.: $233,771,305
Approx. Number Employees: 1,400
Year Founded: 1995
Business Description:
Acquirer & Operator of Insurance & Financial Brokerage Businesses
S.I.C.: 6221
N.A.I.C.S.: 523140
Personnel:
Jim Dinning *(Chm)*
Bill Yuill *(Vice Chm)*
Scott A. Tannas *(Pres & CEO)*
Catherine A. Rogers *(CFO, Sec & Exec VP-Fin & Admin)*
Tom C. Dutton *(Exec VP)*
Devin Tretiak *(Mgr-Learning)*
Brands & Products:
WESTERN FINANCIAL GROUP
Advertising Agency:
True Media
29 S 9th St Ste 201
Columbia, MO 65201
Tel.: (573) 443-8783
Fax: (573) 443-8784

WESTERN LIBERTY BANCORP
8363 W Sunset Rd Ste 350
Las Vegas, NV 89113
Tel.: (702) 966-7400
Approx. Rev.: $1,638,000
Approx. Number Employees: 40
Year Founded: 2007
Business Description:
Bank Holding Company
S.I.C.: 6712
N.A.I.C.S.: 551111
Advertising Expenditures: $79,000
Media: 17
Personnel:
Michael B. Frankel *(Chm)*
Terrence L. Wright *(Vice Chm)*
William E. Martin *(CEO)*
George A. Rosenbaum, Jr. *(CFO)*

THE WESTERN UNION COMPANY
12500 E Belford Ave
Englewood, CO 80112
Mailing Address:
PO Box 6992
Greenwood Village, CO 80155-6992
Tel.: (720) 332-1000
Fax: (720) 332-4753
Toll Free: (866) 405-5012
E-mail: westernunion.ir@westernunion.com
Web Site: www.westernunion.com
Approx. Rev.: $5,192,700,000
Approx. Number Employees: 7,000
Business Description:
Money Transfer Services for Consumers & Businesses; Electronic Bill-Payment Services & Consumer Message Services
S.I.C.: 6099
N.A.I.C.S.: 522320
Export
Advertising Expenditures: $201,400,000
Personnel:
Hikmet Ersek *(Pres & CEO)*
Scott T. Scheirman *(CFO & Exec VP)*
Diane Scott *(CMO & Exec VP)*
Stewart Stockdale *(Pres-The Americas & Exec VP-Global Cards/Global Key Accounts)*
David G. Yates *(Pres-Bus Dev & Innovation & Exec VP)*
David Schlapbach *(Gen Counsel & Exec VP)*
Guy Battista *(Exec VP)*
Robin Heller *(Exec VP-Ops & IT)*
Grover Wray *(Exec VP-HR)*
Carter Hunt *(Sr VP-Strategic Accounts & Bus Dev-America)*
Michael A. Salop *(Sr VP-IR)*
Drina C. Yue *(Sr VP-Asia Pacific)*
Patricia Zamora-Riingen *(Sr VP)*
Julie Cannava *(Dir-Digital Mktg & Content-Global)*
Daniel Lee *(Dir-Risk Mgmt)*
Brands & Products:
QUICK CASH
QUICK COLLECT
WESTERN UNION
WESTERN UNION MONEY TRANSFER
YES!
Advertising Agencies:
Bromley Communications
401 E Houston St
San Antonio, TX 78205-2615
Tel.: (210) 244-2000
Fax: (210) 244-2442
(Hispanic Marketing)

Leo Burnett, Ltd.
Warwick Building Kensington Village
London, W14 8HQ, United Kingdom
Tel.: (44) 207 751 1800
Fax: (44) 207 348 3855

Profero
Centro 3 19 Mandela St
London, NW1 0DU, United Kingdom
Tel.: (44) 20 7387 2000
Fax: (44) 20 7529 8700

Publicis Hong Kong
23/F 1063 Kings Road
Hong Kong, China (Hong Kong)
Tel.: (852) 2590 5888
Fax: (852) 2856 9905

WHITNEY HOLDING CORPORATION
228 Saint Charles Ave
New Orleans, LA 70130
Mailing Address:
PO Box 61260
New Orleans, LA 70161-1260
Tel.: (504) 586-7272
Fax: (504) 552-4851
Toll Free: (800) 347-7272
E-mail: investor.relations@whitneybank.com
Web Site: www.whitneybank.com
Approx. Rev.: $593,515,000
Approx. Number Employees: 2,672
Year Founded: 1961
Business Description:
Bank Holding Company
S.I.C.: 6029; 6035; 6163; 6211; 6289; 6712
N.A.I.C.S.: 522110; 522120; 522310; 523110; 523999; 551111
Advertising Expenditures: $4,167,000
Media: 2-3-4-9-13-14-15-16-18-23-25-26
Distr.: Reg.
Personnel:
John C. Hope, III *(Chm)*
Carl J. Chaney *(Pres & CEO)*
Thomas L. Callicutt Jr. *(CFO & Sr Exec VP)*
James C. McElroy *(Chief Investment Officer)*
David J. Palozzola *(Pres-Whitney Securities, LLC)*
Joseph S. Schwertz *(Gen Counsel, Sec & Exec VP)*
Francisco DeArmas *(Exec VP-Ops & Tech)*
Mark Duthu *(Exec VP-Trust & Wealth Mgmt)*
David P. Frady *(Exec VP-Comml Banking Div)*
Suzanne C. Thomas *(Exec VP-Credit Admin)*
Luis C. Garza *(Sr VP & Dir-Internat Banking)*
Duane J. Abadie *(Sr VP-New Orleans Sls)*
James S. Corbett *(Sr VP)*
Walter M. Kelly *(Sr VP-Residential Mortgage Lending)*
Stephen C. Lacy *(Sr VP)*
Sharon Lee *(Sr VP-Retail Banking-Western Reg)*
Gary L. Lorio *(Sr VP-Corp Banking-New Orleans)*
Kenneth L. Martinez *(Sr VP-Corp Banking-New Orleans)*
L. Biff Motley *(Sr VP-Retail Banking & Mktg)*
Harry C. Stahel *(Sr VP-Corp Banking-New Orleans)*
Allen L. Harvell *(VP & Mgr-Comml Banking-Pinellas)*
Brands & Products:
WHITNEY
Advertising Agency:
Peter A. Mayer Advertising, Inc.
324 Camp St
New Orleans, LA 70130-2804
Tel.: (504) 581-7191
Fax: (504) 581-3009
(Financial Services)

THE WILBER CORPORATION
(Sub. of Community Bank System, Inc.)
(d/b/a Wilber National Bank)
245 Main St
Oneonta, NY 13820
Tel.: (607) 432-1700
Fax: (607) 433-4161
Fax: (607) 433-4161, ext. 6074334184
Web Site: www.wilberbank.com
Approx. Rev.: $52,523,000
Approx. Number Employees: 261
Business Description:
Bank Holding Company
S.I.C.: 6022; 6029; 6141; 6712
N.A.I.C.S.: 522190; 522110; 522210; 551111
Advertising Expenditures: $528,000
Personnel:
Brian R. Wright *(Chm)*
Alfred S. Whittet *(Vice Chm)*
Joseph E. Sutaris *(CFO, Treas, Sec & Exec VP)*
Brands & Products:
WILBER
WILBER CORPORATION

WILHELMINA INTERNATIONAL, INC.
200 Crescent Ct Ste 1400
Dallas, TX 75201
Tel.: (214) 661-7488
Fax: (210) 302-0414
Web Site: www.wilhelmina.com
Approx. Rev.: $48,965,000
Approx. Number Employees: 78
Business Description:
Holding Company
S.I.C.: 6719
N.A.I.C.S.: 551112
Advertising Expenditures: $206,000
Media: 17
Personnel:
Mark E. Schwarz *(Chm & CEO)*
Sean Patterson *(Pres)*

WILLAMETTE MANAGEMENT ASSOCIATES
8600 W Bryn Mawr Ave
Chicago, IL 60631

Key to Media (For complete agency information see *The Advertising Red Books-Agencies* edition):
1. Bus. Publs. 2. Cable T.V. 3. Catalogs & Directories. 4. Co-op Adv. 5. Consumer Mags. 6. D.M. to Bus. Estab.7. D.M. to Consumers
8. Daily Newsp. 9. Exhibits/Trade Shows 10. Foreign 11. Infomercial 12. Internet Adv.13. Multimedia 14. Network Radio
15. Network T.V. 16. Newsp. Distr. Mags. 17. Other 18. Outdoor (Posters, Transit) 19. Point of Purchase20. Premiums, Novelties
21. Product Samples 22. Special Events Mktg. 23. Spot Radio 24. Spot T.V. 25. Weekly Newsp. 26. Yellow Page Adv.

Tel.: (773) 399-4300
Fax: (773) 399-4310
E-mail: info@willamette.com
Web Site: www.willamette.com
Sales Range: $25-49.9 Million
Approx. Number Employees: 50
Business Description:
Appraisers, Except Real Estate
S.I.C.: 8748
N.A.I.C.S.: 541618
Personnel:
Curtis R. Kimball *(Mng Dir)*
James G. Rabe *(Mng Dir)*
Robert F. Reilly *(Mng Dir)*
Robert P. Schweihs *(Mng Dir)*
Charles A. Wilhoite *(Mng Dir)*
Timothy J. Meinhart *(Principal)*
Hale Chan *(Dir-Mktg Comm)*
Pamela Garland *(Sr Mgr)*
Advertising Agency:
Gibbs & Soell, Inc.
60 E 42nd St
New York, NY 10165
Tel.: (212) 697-2600
Fax: (212) 697-2646
(Advisory Services)

WILLIAM BLAIR & COMPANY LLC
222 W Adams St
Chicago, IL 60606-5312
Tel.: (312) 236-1600
Fax: (312) 236-9660
E-mail: info@wmblair.com
Web Site: www.wmblair.com
Sales Range: $350-399.9 Million
Approx. Number Employees: 800
Year Founded: 1935
Business Description:
Investment Services
S.I.C.: 6211
N.A.I.C.S.: 523120
Media: 1-2-6-10-13-18-19-20-23-24
Personnel:
Edgar D. Jannotta *(Chm)*
E. David Coolidge *(Vice Chm)*
Daniel Daul *(Mng Dir, Co-Head-Fin Tech & IT Security)*
Brian Doyle *(Mng Dir & Head-Intl)*
Brandon Lower *(Mng Dir & Head-Fin Sponsors)*
Brent Smith *(Mng Dir)*
James Wildman *(Mng Dir)*
Timothy L. Burke *(CFO)*
James Connors *(CTO)*
Isidora Lagos *(Principal, Head-Brand Mktg & Comm)*
Stephen Campbell *(Principal & Mgr-Ops)*
Colin Williams *(Principal & Co-Mgr)*
Harvey H. Bundy III *(Principal)*
Arthur J. Simon *(Gen Counsel)*
William J. Roddy *(Head-Institutional Sls & Trading Opers)*
Dmitry Krasnik *(Dir)*
Robert D. Newman *(Dir-Res)*
Tony Zimmer *(Dir)*
Karl Brewer *(Portfolio Mgr-Growth Fund)*
Darryl Hill *(Mgr-Mktg)*
Mike Balkin *(Co-Mgr-Small-Cap Growth)*
Brands & Products:
A TRADIITON OF GROWTH
R DOCS
WILLIAM BLAIR & COMPANY

WILMINGTON SAVINGS FUND SOCIETY, FEDERAL SAVINGS BANK
(Sub. of WSFS Financial Corporation)
(d/b/a WSFS Bank)
500 Delaware Ave
Wilmington, DE 19801
Mailing Address:
PO Box 1889
Wilmington, DE 19899-1889
Tel.: (302) 792-6000
Fax: (302) 571-7215
Toll Free: (888) 973-7226
E-mail: info@wsfsbank.com
Web Site: www.wsfsbank.com
Sales Range: $150-199.9 Million
Approx. Number Employees: 300
Year Founded: 1832
Business Description:
Federal Savings Bank
S.I.C.: 6035
N.A.I.C.S.: 522120
Advertising Expenditures: $1,100,000
Media: 2-7-8-18-20
Distr.: Direct to Consumer
Budget Set: Oct.
Personnel:
Mark A. Turner *(Pres & CEO)*
Rodger Levenson *(Exec VP & Dir-Comml Banking)*
Richard M. Wright *(Exec VP & Dir-Retail Banking)*
Janis L. Julian *(Sr VP-Director of Community Strategy)*
Deborah Robert *(Sr VP-Dir of Retail Lending)*

WILMINGTON TRUST CORPORATION
1100 N Market St
Wilmington, DE 19890-0001
Tel.: (302) 651-1000
Fax: (302) 651-8937
Toll Free: (800) 441-7120
E-mail: IR@wilmingtontrust.com
Web Site: www.wilmingtontrust.com
Approx. Rev.: $763,300,000
Approx. Number Employees: 2,793
Year Founded: 1903
Business Description:
Holding Company; Wealth Advisory, Corporate Client & Regional Banking Services
S.I.C.: 6712
N.A.I.C.S.: 551111
Advertising Expenditures: $7,600,000
Media: 6-8-9
Distr.: Natl.
Budget Set: Nov.
Personnel:
Donald E. Foley *(Chm & CEO)*
Robert V.A. Harra, Jr. *(Pres & COO)*
Stephen P. Winterstein *(Mng Dir & Head-Strategy-Municipal Fixed Income)*
Jim McGinley *(Mng Dir)*
David Reed Gibson *(CFO)*
Chick Pinto *(CMO & Sr VP)*
Jack E. Steil *(Pres-Mid Atlantic Reg)*
Michael A. Digregorio *(Exec VP, Gen Counsel & Sec)*
William J. Farrell II *(Exec VP)*
Mark A. Graham *(Exec VP)*
Kevyn N. Rakowski *(Sr VP & Controller)*
J. William Benintende *(VP-PR & Mktg Comm)*
Brian Waldron *(Dir-Online Mktg & ECommerce)*
Ronald K. Pendleton *(Mgr-Trust Conversion Risk & Quality)*
Advertising Agencies:
Pirozzolo Company Public Relations
PO Box 812-909
Wellesley, MA 02482
Tel.: (781) 235-9911
Fax: (781) 235-9898

Planet Central
16740 Birkdale Commons Pkwy Ste 206
Huntersville, NC 28078
Tel.: (704) 875-9028
Fax: (704) 875-9763

Quattro Direct LLC
1175 Lancaster Ave
Berwyn, PA 19312
Tel.: (610) 993-0070
Fax: (610) 993-0057

Quorum Integrated, Inc.
816 Evanson Rd PO Box 1057
Hockessin, DE 19707
Tel.: (302) 239-4822
Fax: (302) 239-1224

WH2P, Inc.
3704 Kennett Pike Ste 400
Wilmington, DE 19807
Tel.: (302) 479-8330
Fax: (866) 480-9518
Toll Free: (866) 480-9518

WILSHIRE BANCORP INC.
3200 Wilshire Blvd
Los Angeles, CA 90010
Tel.: (213) 387-3200
Fax: (213) 427-6562
Web Site: www.wilshirebank.com
E-Mail For Key Personnel:
President: soobongmin@wilshirebank.com
Approx. Rev.: $192,332,000
Approx. Number Employees: 388
Year Founded: 1980
Business Description:
Banking Services
S.I.C.: 6029; 6163
N.A.I.C.S.: 522110; 522310
Advertising Expenditures: $1,400,000
Personnel:
Steven S. Koh *(Chm)*
Jae Whan Yoo *(Pres & CEO)*
Alex Koh *(CFO & Exec VP)*

WILSHIRE ENTERPRISES, INC.
100 Eagle Rock Ave
East Hanover, NJ 07936
Tel.: (201) 420-2796
Fax: (201) 420-6012
Toll Free: (888) 697-3962
Web Site:
www.wilshireenterprisesinc.com
Approx. Rev.: $8,649,000
Approx. Number Employees: 5
Business Description:
Property Investment & Management Services
S.I.C.: 6289; 6531
N.A.I.C.S.: 523999; 531312
Advertising Expenditures: $113,000
Media: 17
Personnel:
Sherry Wilzig Izak *(Chm & CEO)*
David Morrow *(COO & Principal Acctg Officer)*

WILSON BANK HOLDING COMPANY
623 W Main St
Lebanon, TN 37087
Tel.: (615) 444-2265
Fax: (615) 443-7117
E-mail: info@wilsonbank.com
Web Site: www.wilsonbank.com
Approx. Int. Income: $76,180,000
Approx. Number Employees: 349
Year Founded: 1992
Business Description:
Bank Holding Company
S.I.C.: 6029; 6712
N.A.I.C.S.: 522110; 551111
Import Export
Advertising Expenditures: $813,000
Personnel:
Mackey Bentley *(Chm)*
James Randall Clemons *(Pres & CEO)*
Lisa Pominski *(CFO & Sr VP)*
Herbert Elmer Richerson *(Exec VP)*

WIND POINT PARTNERS
676 N Michigan Ave Ste 3700
Chicago, IL 60611
Tel.: (312) 255-4800
Fax: (312) 255-4820
E-mail: info@wppartners.com
Web Site: www.wppartners.com
Sales Range: $100-124.9 Million
Approx. Number Employees: 27
Year Founded: 1983
Business Description:
Private Equity Firm
S.I.C.: 6289
N.A.I.C.S.: 523999
Media: 13
Personnel:
Nathan Brown *(Mng Dir)*
Mark Burgett *(Mng Dir)*
Robert Cummings *(Mng Dir)*
Rich Kracum *(Mng Dir)*
Michael Solot *(Mng Dir)*
James TenBroek *(Mng Dir)*
Alex Washington *(Mng Dir)*
LeAnn Kilarski *(CFO)*
Michael Nelson *(Principal)*
Rebecca Vanderlake Converse *(Dir-IR, Mktg & Comm)*

WIPRO GALLAGHER SOLUTIONS
(Sub. of Wipro Limited)
18001 Old Cutler Rd 651
Miami, FL 33157
Tel.: (305) 251-6654
Fax: (866) 483-2061
Toll Free: (800) 989-9998
E-mail: info@gogallagher.com
Web Site: www.gogallagher.com
E-Mail For Key Personnel:
Marketing Director: sales@gogallagher.com
Approx. Number Employees: 100
Year Founded: 1985
Business Description:
Mortgage Banking Origination & Solutions Software
S.I.C.: 7371
N.A.I.C.S.: 541511
Media: 1-2-7-10-11-13-20
Distr.: Intl.; Natl.
Budget Set: Oct.

Wipro Gallagher Solutions — (Continued)

Personnel:
Joey McDuffee *(Head-Sls & Mktg)*
Chris Anderson *(Gen Mgr)*

Brands & Products:
DIALOG HELPER
GALLAGHER MILLENNIUM
GFS EXECUTIVE INFORMATION SYSTEM
GFS NAVIGATOR
LAPSYNC
NETOXYGEN
RULE & PROFILE ADMINISTRATION

WISDOMTREE INVESTMENTS, INC.

380 Madison Ave 21st Fl
New York, NY 10017
Tel.: (866) 909-9473
Toll Free: (866) 909-9473
Web Site: www.wisdomtree.com
Sales Range: $50-74.9 Million
Approx. Number Employees: 50

Business Description:
Investment Services
S.I.C.: 6289; 6722
N.A.I.C.S.: 523999; 525910

Personnel:
Michael H. Steinhardt *(Chm)*
Bruce Lavine *(Pres & COO)*
Jonathan Steinberg *(CEO)*
Amit Muni *(CFO & Exec VP-Fin)*
Peter Ziemba *(Gen Counsel, Exec VP-Bus & Legal Affairs)*

Advertising Agency:
KCSA Strategic Communications (Kanan, Corbin, Schupak & Aronow, Inc.)
880 3rd Ave 6th Fl
New York, NY 10022
Tel.: (212) 682-6300
Fax: (212) 697-0910

WISS & COMPANY LLP

354 Eisenhower Pkwy
Livingston, NJ 07039
Tel.: (973) 994-9400
Fax: (973) 992-6760
E-mail: jcampo@wiss.com
Web Site: www.wiss.com
Approx. Number Employees: 90
Year Founded: 1969

Business Description:
Accounting & Consulting Services
S.I.C.: 8721
N.A.I.C.S.: 541211
Media: 2-7-10-13-22

Personnel:
Jeffrey Campo *(Mng Partner)*
Russell L. Faye *(Partner-Real Estate Svcs)*
Lisa Calick *(Dir-HR)*
Rhonda Nelson *(Dir-Mktg)*
Randy B. Cohen *(Sr Mgr-Audit)*
Diana Miller *(Mgr)*

WORDEN BROTHERS, INC.

Five Oaks Ofc Pk 4905 Pine Cone Dr
Durham, NC 27707
Tel.: (919) 408-0542
Fax: (919) 408-0545
Toll Free: (800) 776-4940
E-mail: support@worden.com
Web Site: www.worden.com
Approx. Number Employees: 80

Business Description:
Free Stock Market Software, Databases, Investing Advice & Seminars
S.I.C.: 7373; 2731
N.A.I.C.S.: 541512; 511130
Media: 5-13

Personnel:
Chris Worden *(Owner)*
Michael Thompson *(Dir-Bus & Client Rels)*

Brands & Products:
ACCUTICK
BALANCE OF POWER
BLOCKS
EASYSCAN
MONEYSTREAM
STOCKFINDER
TC2000
TCNET
TELECHART
TELECHART 2000
TIME SEGMENTED VOLUME
WORDEN

WORLD ACCEPTANCE CORPORATION

108 Frederick St
Greenville, SC 29607-2532
Mailing Address:
PO Box 6429
Greenville, SC 29606-6429
Tel.: (864) 298-9800
Fax: (864) 298-9810
Web Site: www.worldacceptance.com
E-Mail For Key Personnel:
Public Relations: aamwac@aol.com
Approx. Rev.: $491,445,103
Approx. Number Employees: 3,292
Year Founded: 1962

Business Description:
Finance & Loan Services
S.I.C.: 6141
N.A.I.C.S.: 522210; 522291
Advertising Expenditures: $13,100,000

Personnel:
A. Alexander McLean, III *(Chm & CEO)*
Mark C. Roland *(Pres & COO)*
Kelly Malson *(CFO, Treas & Sr VP)*
Judson K. Chapin, III *(Gen Counsel, Sec & Sr VP)*
Daniel Clinton Dyer *(Sr VP-Central Div)*
Marilyn M. Messer *(Sr VP-HR)*
Francisco Javier Sauza Del Pozo *(Sr VP-Mexico)*
Jeff L. Tinney *(Sr VP-Western Div)*
James Daniel Walters *(Sr VP-Southern Div)*
Yvette Drake *(VP & Dir-Mktg)*
Brent R. Cooler *(Asst Sec & VP-Acctg)*
Keith T. Littrell *(Asst Sec & VP-Tax)*

W.P. CAREY & CO., LLC

50 Rockefeller Plz 2nd Fl
New York, NY 10020-1605
Tel.: (212) 492-1100
Fax: (212) 492-8922
Toll Free: (800) 972-2739
E-mail: webmarketing@wpcarey.com
Web Site: www.wpcarey.com
Approx. Rev.: $235,876,000
Approx. Number Employees: 156
Year Founded: 1973

Business Description:
Corporate Financing & Real Estate Investment Banking Services
S.I.C.: 6512; 6282; 6531
N.A.I.C.S.: 531390; 523930; 531120; 531210

Personnel:
William Polk Carey *(Chm)*
Trevor P. Bond *(Pres & CEO)*
Mark J. DeCesaris *(CFO & Mng Dir)*
Thomas E. Zacharias *(Mng Dir & COO)*
Susan C. Hyde *(Mng Dir)*
Jan F. Karst *(Mng Dir)*
Anne Coolidge Taylor *(Mng Dir)*
Yvonne Cheng *(Mng Dir)*
Jason E. Fox *(Mng Dir)*
Gino Sabatini *(Mng Dir)*
John D. Miller *(Chief Investment Officer)*
Thomas J. Ridings, Jr. *(Chief Acctg Officer & Exec Dir)*
Douglas E. Barzelay *(Gen Counsel)*
Donna M. Neiley *(Sr VP-Asset Mgmt)*
David G. Termine *(First VP)*
Hsin-Cha Hsu *(Second VP-CPA Funds)*
Jeffrey S. Lefleur *(Exec Dir)*
Kathleen Barthmaier *(Dir)*
Chad Edmonson *(Dir)*
Darren R. Postel *(Dir)*
Katie Rebmann *(Mgr-Ops)*

Brands & Products:
CPA
INVESTING FOR THE LONG RUN
W.P CARLEY

Advertising Agency:
Bell Pottinger Public Affairs
5th Fl Holborn Gate
London, WC1V 7QC, United Kingdom
Tel.: (44) 20 7861 2400
Fax: (44) 20 7861 2401
(European Operations)

WSB HOLDINGS, INC.

4201 Mitchellville Rd Ste 300
Bowie, MD 20716
Tel.: (301) 352-3120
Tel.: (301) 352-3100
Fax: (301) 352-3110
Toll Free: (888) 843-7250
Toll Free: (866) 546-7485
E-mail: info@twsb.com
Web Site: www.twsb.com
Approx. Rev.: $21,410,708
Approx. Number Employees: 119
Year Founded: 1982

Business Description:
Banking Services
S.I.C.: 6035; 6029
N.A.I.C.S.: 522120; 522110
Advertising Expenditures: $321,449
Media: 7-8-13

Personnel:
William J. Harnett *(Chm)*
Kevin P. Huffman *(Pres & COO)*
Phillip C. Bowman *(CEO)*
Jeff Donohue *(VP & Product Mgr)*

WSFS FINANCIAL CORPORATION

500 Delaware Ave
Wilmington, DE 19801
Tel.: (302) 792-6000
Fax: (302) 571-7172
E-mail: customerservice@wsfsbank.com
Web Site: www.wsfsbank.com
E-Mail For Key Personnel:
President: sschoenhals@wsfsbank.com
Marketing Director: RLevenson@wsfsbank.com
Sales Director: SArnold@wsfsbank.com
Public Relations: SArnold@wsfsbank.com
Approx. Rev.: $212,518,000
Approx. Number Employees: 695

Business Description:
Bank Holding Company
S.I.C.: 6029; 6035; 6289; 6712
N.A.I.C.S.: 522110; 522120; 523999; 551111
Media: 2-3-4-7-8-9-13-18-19-20-22-23-25-26
Distr.: Direct to Consumer; Reg.
Budget Set: Jan. -Dec.

Personnel:
Marvin N. Schoenhals *(Chm)*
Charles G. Cheleden *(Vice Chm)*
Mark A. Turner *(Pres & CEO)*
Stephen A. Fowle *(CFO & Exec VP)*
Alice M. Fredericks *(Chief Investment Officer)*
John L. Olsen *(Gen Counsel & Sr VP)*
Peggy H. Eddens *(Exec VP & Dir-Human Capital Mgmt)*
Rodger Levenson *(Exec VP & Dir-Comml Banking)*
Richard M. Wright *(Exec VP-Retail Banking & Mktg)*
David H. Hargarten *(Sr VP & Dir-Mktg)*
Deborah A. Markwood *(Sr VP & Dir-Trust Svcs)*
William M. Byrne *(Sr VP-Comml Banking)*

Brands & Products:
CASH CONNECT
WE STAND FOR SERVICE
WSFS
WSFS BANK

Advertising Agency:
StarShipley
135 S West St
Wilmington, DE 19801
Tel.: (302) 434-8700
Fax: (302) 434-8701

YADKIN VALLEY FINANCIAL CORPORATION

209 N Bridge St
Elkin, NC 28621-3404
Mailing Address:
PO Box 888
Elkin, NC 28621-0888
Tel.: (336) 526-6300
Web Site: www.yadkinvalleybank.com
Approx. Rev.: $121,140,000
Approx. Number Employees: 548
Year Founded: 2006

Business Description:
Bank Holding Company
S.I.C.: 6712; 6029
N.A.I.C.S.: 551111; 522110
Advertising Expenditures: $995,000

Personnel:
Ralph L. Bentley *(Chm)*
Joseph H. Towell *(Pres & CEO)*
Jan H. Hollar *(CFO & Exec VP)*
Harry M. Davis *(Professor-Fin)*

YORK SECURITIES, INC.

E Bldg 160 Broadway 7th Fl
New York, NY 10038

Key to Media (For complete agency information see *The Advertising Red Books-Agencies* edition):
1. Bus. Publs. 2. Cable T.V. 3. Catalogs & Directories. 4. Co-op Adv. 5. Consumer Mags. 6. D.M. to Bus. Estab.7. D.M. to Consumers 8. Daily Newsp. 9. Exhibits/Trade Shows 10. Foreign 11. Infomercial 12. Internet Adv.13. Multimedia 14. Network Radio 15. Network T.V. 16. Newsp. Distr. Mags. 17. Other 18. Outdoor (Posters, Transit) 19. Point of Purchase20. Premiums, Novelties 21. Product Samples 22. Special Events Mktg. 23. Spot Radio 24. Spot T.V. 25. Weekly Newsp. 26. Yellow Page Adv.

Tel.: (212) 349-9700
Fax: (212) 619-1593
Toll Free: (800) 221-3154
E-mail: info@yorksec.com
Web Site: www.yorktrade.com
Approx. Number Employees: 25
Year Founded: 1979
Business Description:
Discount Broker
S.I.C.: 6211; 6282
N.A.I.C.S.: 523110; 523930
Media: 13
Personnel:
David Corcoran *(Pres)*
Marie Califano *(CFO)*

ZECCO TRADING
PO Box 60670
Pasadena, CA 91116
Fax: (626) 529-7077
Toll Free: (877) 700-7862
E-mail: customerservice@zeccotrading.com
Web Site: www.zecco.com
Approx. Number Employees: 40
Business Description:
Online Brokerage Services
S.I.C.: 6411
N.A.I.C.S.: 524210
Media: 13
Personnel:
Jeroen Veth *(Founder & VP)*
Michael Seser *(Pres)*
Michael Raneri *(CEO)*
Allard Luchsinger *(COO)*
Francesco Matteini *(Gen Counsel & Chief Compliance Officer)*
Frank O'Conner *(Dir-Brokerage Products)*
Advertising Agency:
Dukas Public Relations, Inc.
100 W 26th St 2nd Fl
New York, NY 10001
Tel.: (212) 704-7385
Fax: (212) 242-3646

THE ZIEGLER COMPANIES, INC.
200 S Wacker Dr Ste 2000
Chicago, IL 60606
Tel.: (920) 739-2364
Fax: (312) 263-5217
Toll Free: (800) 797-4272
E-mail: info@ziegler.com
Web Site: www.ziegler.com
Approx. Rev.: $88,748,000
Approx. Number Employees: 311
Year Founded: 1902
Business Description:
Holding Company; Financial Services
S.I.C.: 6211; 6282
N.A.I.C.S.: 523110; 523930
Advertising Expenditures: $1,380,000
Media: 2-4-6-8-9-10-16-19-25-26
Personnel:
Geoffrey B. Shields *(Chm)*
Thomas R. Paprocki *(CEO)*
Jeffrey C. Vredenbregt *(CFO & Sr Mng Dir)*
Thomas S. Ross *(Sr Mng Dir & Chief Credit Officer)*
Gary P. Engle *(Sr Mng Dir)*
Angelique David *(Gen Counsel & Sec)*
Brands & Products:
EXTRAS
STAMPS
ZIEGLER
Advertising Agencies:
Marcel Media
445 W Erie Ste 211
Chicago, IL 60654
Tel.: (312) 255-8044
Fax: (866) 643-7506
SEO Agency of Record

Phoenix Marketing Group, Inc.
6750 Maple Terr
Milwaukee, WI 53213
Tel.: (414) 771-1044
Fax: (414) 771-1084

ZIONS BANCORPORATION
1 S Main St 15th Fl
Salt Lake City, UT 84133
Tel.: (801) 524-4787
Fax: (801) 524-4805
E-mail: info@zionsbank.com
Web Site: www.zionsbancorporation.com
Approx. Rev.: $2,760,307,000
Approx. Number Employees: 10,524
Year Founded: 1961
Business Description:
Bank Holding Company
S.I.C.: 6712
N.A.I.C.S.: 551111
Advertising Expenditures: $26,465,000
Media: 2-3-4-5-6-7-8-9-10-13-18-19-20-22-23-24-25-26
Personnel:
Harris H. Simmons *(Chm, Pres & CEO)*
Doyle L. Arnold *(Vice Chm & CFO)*
John T. Itokazu *(CIO & Exec VP)*
Kenneth E. Peterson *(Chief Credit Officer & Exec VP)*
Bruce K. Alexander *(CEO-Vectra Bank Colorado & Exec VP)*
Aldon Scott Anderson *(CEO-Zions First National Bank & Exec VP)*
David E. Blackford *(CEO-California Bank & Trust & Exec VP)*
Dallas E. Haun *(CEO-Nevada State Bank & Exec VP)*
Keith D. Maio *(CEO-National Bank of Arizona & Exec VP)*
Scott J. McLean *(CEO-Amegy Bank of Texas & Exec VP)*
Stanley D. Savage *(CEO-Commerce Bank of Washington & Exec VP)*
Thomas E. Laursen *(Gen Counsel & Exec VP)*
George Mark Feiger *(Exec VP-Wealth Mgmt)*
W. David Hemingway *(Exec VP-Capital Markets & Investments)*
Connie Linardakis *(Exec VP-HR)*
Dean L. Marotta *(Exec VP-Risk Mgmt)*
Ronald L. Johnson *(Sr VP-Credit Examination)*
Alvin Lee *(Sr VP-Corp Dev)*
Norman W. Merritt *(Sr VP-Compliance)*
Jennifer A. Smith *(Sr VP-Internal Audit)*
H. Walter Young *(Sr VP-Corp Fin)*
Advertising Agencies:
Crowell Advertising, Marketing and PR
12 S 400 W 2nd Fl
Salt Lake City, UT 84101
Tel.: (801) 531-0533
Fax: (801) 531-0547

Love Communications
546 S 200 W
Salt Lake City, UT 84101
Tel.: (801) 519-8880
Fax: (801) 519-8884

The Orton Group, Inc.
204 E 900 S
Salt Lake City, UT 84111-4215
Tel.: (801) 596-2100
Fax: (801) 596-2151

Richter7
280 S 400 W Ste 200
Salt Lake City, UT 84101
Tel.: (801) 521-2903
Fax: (801) 359-2420

ZIONS FIRST NATIONAL BANK, N.A.
(Sub. of Zions Bancorporation)
1 S Main St
Salt Lake City, UT 84111
Tel.: (801) 974-8800
Fax: (801) 524-4772
Toll Free: (800) 789-8800
E-mail: info@zionsbank.com
Web Site: www.zionsbank.com
Sales Range: $650-699.9 Million
Approx. Number Employees: 2,700
Year Founded: 1873
Business Description:
Banking Services
S.I.C.: 6029
N.A.I.C.S.: 522110
Media: 2-8-9-18-19-20-23-24
Distr.: Intl.; Natl.
Budget Set: Dec.
Personnel:
Harris H. Simmons *(Chm)*
Aldon Scott Anderson *(Pres & CEO)*
Kay B. Hall *(CFO & Exec VP)*
Steve Houston *(Exec VP & Chief Credit Officer)*
Michael Morris *(Exec VP & Exec Dir-Real Estate)*
Rob Brough *(Exec VP-Mktg & Comm)*
Lori Chillingworth *(Exec VP-Small Bus Div)*
John D'Arcy *(Exec VP & Sr Lending Officer-Specialty Bus Banking)*
George B. Hofmann, III *(Exec VP-Bus Banking)*
Diana E. Kirk *(Exec VP-Private Client Svcs Div)*
LeeAnne B. Linderman *(Exec VP-Retail Branch Banking Div)*
Peter J. Morgan *(Exec VP-Real Estate Dept-Natl)*
Susan Speer *(Exec VP)*
Mark Garfield *(VP & Reg Mgr)*
Brands & Products:
ZIONS BANK
Advertising Agency:
Richter7
280 S 400 W Ste 200
Salt Lake City, UT 84101
Tel.: (801) 521-2903
Fax: (801) 359-2420

ZURICH NORTH AMERICA SURETY & FINANCIAL ENTERPRISES
(Sub. of Zurich Holding Company of America, Inc.)
3910 Keswick Rd
Baltimore, MD 21211
Tel.: (410) 366-1000
Fax: (410) 338-1403
Toll Free: (800) 821-4635
Telex: 87 805
E-mail: info@zurichna.com
Web Site: www.zurichna.com
Approx. Number Employees: 1,400
Year Founded: 1980
Business Description:
Fidelity & Surety Bonding & Property & Casualty Insurance
S.I.C.: 6331
N.A.I.C.S.: 524126
Advertising Expenditures: $150,000
Media: 2-7-10-23-24
Distr.: Natl.; Reg.
Budget Set: Oct. -Dec.
Personnel:
Terry D. Gray *(Pres-Construction)*
Eleanor S. Barnard *(CMO & Head-Distr)*
Dave Bowers *(Exec VP-Law)*
James D. Engel *(Exec VP-Custom Svc)*

Key to Media (For complete agency information see *The Advertising Red Books-Agencies* edition):
1. Bus. Publs. 2. Cable T.V. 3. Catalogs & Directories. 4. Co-op Adv. 5. Consumer Mags. 6. D.M. to Bus. Estab.7. D.M. to Consumers 8. Daily Newsp. 9. Exhibits/Trade Shows 10. Foreign 11. Infomercial 12. Internet Adv.13. Multimedia 14. Network Radio 15. Network T.V. 16. Newsp. Distr. Mags. 17. Other 18. Outdoor (Posters, Transit) 19. Point of Purchase20. Premiums, Novelties 21. Product Samples 22. Special Events Mktg. 23. Spot Radio 24. Spot T.V. 25. Weekly Newsp. 26. Yellow Page Adv.

Flour & Cereals

Breakfast Foods — Flour — Mixes

ADM MILLING CO.
(Div. of Archer-Daniels-Midland Company)
8000 W 110th St
Overland Park, KS 66210-2312
Tel.: (913) 491-9400
Fax: (913) 491-0035
Web Site: www.e-adm.com/srch/srch_lsearch.asp
E-Mail For Key Personnel:
Sales Director: m-marsh@corp.admworld.com
Sales Range: $50-74.9 Million
Approx. Number Employees: 100
Business Description:
Flour; Dry Milling of Grains Mfr
S.I.C.: 2041
N.A.I.C.S.: 311211
Media: 2-4
Personnel:
Mark Kolkhorst *(Pres-Milling & Cocoa & VP)*
Loren Urquhart *(VP-Sls)*
Advertising Agency:
Jones & Thomas, Inc.
788 N Sunnyside Rd
Decatur, IL 62522-1156
Tel.: (217) 423-1889
Fax: (217) 425-0680
— Bill Lehmann *(V.P.-Strategic Plng.)*

AMERICAN POP CORN COMPANY
1 Fun Pl
Sioux City, IA 51108
Tel.: (712) 239-1232
Fax: (712) 239-1268
E-mail: email@jollytime.com
Web Site: www.jollytime.com
E-Mail For Key Personnel:
Marketing Director: tome@jollytime.com
Approx. Number Employees: 150
Year Founded: 1914
Business Description:
Popcorn Mfr
S.I.C.: 2099
N.A.I.C.S.: 311999
Export
Media: 2-6-9-15-19-24
Personnel:
Carlton Smith *(Owner)*
Garrett K. Smith *(Pres)*
Don Townley *(Treas & Sr VP)*
Tom Elsen *(VP-Mktg)*
Steve Juisenga *(VP-Sls)*
Tracy Boever *(Dir-PR & Mktg Comm)*
Brands & Products:
AMERICAN'S BEST
THE BIG CHEEZ
BLAST O BUTTER
BLAST O BUTTER LIGHT
BUTTER-LICIOUS
BUTTER LICIOUS LIGHT
CRISPY 'N WHITE
CRISPY 'N WHITE LIGHT
HAPPY TIME
HEALTHY POP
JOLLY TIME
KETTLE MANIA
POLY BAG
WHITE & BUTTERY
Advertising Agency:
Barkley
1740 Main St
Kansas City, MO 64108
Tel.: (816) 842-1500
Jolly Time Pop Corn

ARCHER-DANIELS-MIDLAND COMPANY
4666 Faries Pkwy
Decatur, IL 62526-5666
Mailing Address:
PO Box 1470
Decatur, IL 62525-1820
Tel.: (217) 424-5200
Fax: (217) 424-5447
Toll Free: (800) 637-5843
E-mail: info@admworld.com
Web Site: www.admworld.com
Approx. Sls.: $80,676,000,000
Approx. Number Employees: 30,700
Year Founded: 1902
Business Description:
Agricultural Commodities Processor
S.I.C.: 2046; 2041; 2075; 2079; 2083; 5261
N.A.I.C.S.: 311221; 311211; 311213; 311222; 311223; 311225; 444220
Import Export
Media: 2
Distr.: Intl.; Natl.
Personnel:
Patricia A. Woertz *(Chm, Pres & CEO)*
John Daniel Rice *(Vice Chm)*
Ray G. Young *(CFO & Sr VP)*
Juan R. Luciano *(COO & Exec VP)*
Craig E. Huss *(Chief Risk Officer & Sr VP)*
Vanessa L. Vargas-Land *(Ethics Officer & VP)*
Mark A. Bemis *(Pres-Corn Bus Unit & Sr VP)*
Matthew J. Jansen *(Pres-Oilseeds Bus Unit & Sr VP)*
Joseph Daniel Taets *(Pres-Agricultural Svcs Bus & Sr VP)*
Mark L. Kolkhorst *(Pres-Milling & Cocoa & VP)*
Ismael Roig *(Pres-Asia-Pacific & VP)*
Janice K. Binger *(Pres-Natural Health & Nutrition)*
Scott Fredericksen *(Pres-Rail Container & Supply Chain Transportation Segment)*
David J. Smith *(Gen Counsel, Sec & Exec VP)*
Vikram Luthar *(Treas & VP-Fin)*
Michael D'Ambrose *(Sr VP-HR)*
Steven J. Cassady *(VP-Procurement)*
Mark J. Cheviron *(VP-Corp Security & Svcs)*
Kurt M. Johnson *(Dir-Bus Dev)*
David Weintraub *(Dir-External Comm)*
Karl Locascio *(Mgr-Mktg)*
Stuart E. Funderburg *(Asst Sec & Asst Gen Counsel)*
Scott A. Roberts *(Asst Sec & Asst Gen Counsel)*
Ronald S. Bandler *(Asst Treas)*
Brands & Products:
ADM CLINTOSE
ALINCO
AMBROSIA
ARC T U872 D CAR FOR F250
ARC T871 LT CARML F125
ARCHER RC
ARCHER SOYBEAN OIL
ARCON
ARCON F
ARCON S
ARCON SM
ARCON T
ARCON T F125
ARCON T F125 CARAMEL
ARCON T F250
ARCON T F250 CARAMEL
ARCON T MINCED
ARCON T MINCED 180
ARCON T MINCED 180 CARAMEL
ARCON T MINCED 300
ARCON T MINCED 300 CARAMEL
ARCON T STRIP
ARCON T STRIP 5 CARAMEL
ARCON VF
ARDEX
ARDEX AF
ARDEX- F
AREX F-DISP
ARLAC P
ARLAC S
AYTEX P
BEAKIN
BIOSAP
CALIBER
CALIBER DC
CANOLA
CAPSULEC
CARDIOAID
CARDIOAID-CZ
CARDIOAID-M
CARDIOAID-S
CITROSOL 502
CITROSOL 503
CLINTOSE
CLINTOSE CR 18
CLINTOSE CR 24
CLINTOSE CR10
CLINTOSE CR15
CORNSWEET
CORNSWEET 42
CORNSWEET 42 80% SOLIDS
CORNSWEET 55
CORNSWEET 90
CORNSWEET HFCS 90
CULTURETECH
DE-MOL DRY
DE-MOL FLAKE
DE ZAAN
DECANOX
DECANOX MTS-30
DECANOX MTS-50
DECANOX MTS-70
DECANOX MTS-90
DRI-MOL 60
DRI-MOL 604
DRI-MOL DRY
DRI-MOL FLAKE
DRI-MOL R
ECOTONE
EDIGEL
EDKO 76
ENERTIA
ENVIROSTRIP
ESTRIP

Key to Media (For complete agency information see *The Advertising Red Books-Agencies* edition):
1. Bus. Publs. 2. Cable T.V. 3. Catalogs & Directories. 4. Co-op Adv. 5. Consumer Mags. 6. D.M. to Bus. Estab.7. D.M. to Consumers
8. Daily Newsp. 9. Exhibits/Trade Shows 10. Foreign 11. Infomercial 12. Internet Adv.13. Multimedia 14. Network Radio
15. Network T.V. 16. Newsp. Distr. Mags. 17. Other 18. Outdoor (Posters, Transit) 19. Point of Purchase20. Premiums, Novelties
21. Product Samples 22. Special Events Mktg. 23. Spot Radio 24. Spot T.V. 25. Weekly Newsp. 26. Yellow Page Adv.

FEED GRADE
FIBERSOL-2
GOLDEN GLUTEN
HONI-BAKE
HONI-BAKE 705
HONI-BAKE DRY
HONI-BAKE HS DRY
HONI-BAKE MB DRY
HONI-FLAKE
HONI-FLAKE 705
HONI-FLAKE DRY
HYDRO-FRACTIONATED
HYDROGENATED
IGR MINERALS
IVORY
JELTEC
KANSAS DIAMOND
LIQUIDGOLD
LYSORB 218
LYSORB 220
MARQUIS
MEATBIND
MERCKENS
MIDLAND HARVEST
MIREL
MONARCH
THE NATURE OF WHAT'S TO COME
NC-3000
NOVALIPID
NOVASOY
NOVASOY 40% DIRECT COMPRESS
NOVATOL
NOVAXAN
NOVAXAN XANTHAN GUM 200 MESH
NOVAXAN XANTHAN GUM 40 MESH
NOVAXAN XANTHAN GUM 80 MESH DUST FREE
NOVAXAN XANTHAN GUM DISPERSIBLE
NOVAXAN XANTHAN GUM PET FOOD
NUSUN
NUTREON
NUTRIPASS
NUTRISOY
NUTRISOY NEXT
OKO
OPTIXAN
OPTIXAN T
OPTIXAN XANTHAN GUM 40 MESH
OPTIXAN XANTHAN GUM DISPERSIBLE
OPTIXAN XANTHAN GUM TRANSPARENT
PANAID
PANALITE
PANIPLEX
PANISTAY
PARTIALLY HYDRO
PAYGEL
PERFORMIX
PFL
PFL ISOLATED
PILLSBURY
PRO-FAM
PRO-FAM 646
PRO-FAM 648
PRO-FAM 780
PRO-FAM 781
PRO-FAM 825
PRO-FAM 875
PRO-FAM 891
PRO-FAM 892
PRO-FAM 922
PRO-FAM 931
PRO-FAM 932
PRO-FAM 955
PRO-FAM 974
PRO-FAM H200
PROLITE
PROLITE 100
PROLITE 200
PROLITE LOW FLAVOR
PROSTART
PROVIM ESP
PROVIM ESP VITAL
R&R 551
READIGEL
RESOURCEFUL BY NATURE
RUMA-PASS
SMARTBIND
SOFT TOUCH
SOY7
SOYCOMIL
SOYLEC
SOYLEC A-10
SOYLEC C-15
STABLEC
SUPERB
SUPERB SELECT
SUPERB SELECT NU-SUN
SUPERB SELECT POWER-SUN
SUPERGLUTEN
SWEEET N NEAT 65 GMF
SWEET N NEAT
SWEET N NEAT 2000
SWEET N NEAT 3000
SWEET N NEAT 4000
SWEET N NEAT 50
SWEET N NEAT 5000
SWEET N NEAT TACK BLEND
SWEET N NEAT TACK BLEND S
SWEET N NEAT TACK BLEND T
SWEET N NEAT TS DRY
SWEET N NEAT TS OIL
THERMOLEC
TVC
TVP
ULTRALEC
VEGEFULL
WHETPRO
WHETPRO 75
WHETPRO 80
WHETPRO 82
WHETSTAR
YELKIN
YELKIN 1018
YELKIN DS
YELKIN GOLD
YELKIN SS
YELKIN T
YELKIN TS
YELKINOL AC
YUCATAN

AUTHENTIC SPECIALTY FOODS, INC.

(Div. of Grupo Kuo, S.A.B. de C.V.)
4340 Eucalyptus Ave
Chino, CA 91710-9705
Tel.: (909) 631-2000
Fax: (909) 631-2100
Toll Free: (888) 236-2272
Web Site: www.asf-inc.com
Sales Range: $100-124.9 Million
Approx. Number Employees: 300
Year Founded: 1917
Business Description:
Mfr. of Mexican Salsa, Sauces & Spices
S.I.C.: 2035; 2099
N.A.I.C.S.: 311941; 311942
Media: 19-23-24
Distr.: Reg.
Budget Set: Mar.
Personnel:
Samuel E Hillin *(CFO & Principal Acctg Officer)*
Brands & Products:
EMBASA
LA VICTORIA

THE BIRKETT MILLS

163 Main St
Penn Yan, NY 14527
Tel.: (315) 536-3311
Fax: (315) 536-6740
Web Site: www.thebirkettmills.com
Approx. Sls.: $6,500,000
Approx. Number Employees: 40
Year Founded: 1797
Business Description:
Flour & Grain Products Mfr
S.I.C.: 2041; 5999
N.A.I.C.S.: 311211; 453998
Export
Media: 5-6-8-10-17-19-21-23-25
Distr.: Natl.
Budget Set: Sept.-Nov.
Personnel:
Jeffrey S. Gifford *(Pres)*
Brands & Products:
BESSIE
BIRKETT'S
FIRST PRIZE
FLEX A FLO
LARROWE'S
MUL-TEX
POCONO
PURITAN
WOLFF'S

CONAGRA FOODS, INC.

1 ConAgra Dr
Omaha, NE 68102-5001
Tel.: (402) 595-4000
Tel.: (402) 595-5210 (Corp Comm)
Tel.: (402) 595-4154 (IR)
Fax: (402) 595-4707
Web Site: www.conagrafoods.com
Approx. Sls.: $12,079,400,000
Approx. Number Employees: 24,400
Year Founded: 1919
Business Description:
Flour Milling, Grain Merchandising & Poultry Products
S.I.C.: 2034; 0182; 2015; 2075; 2079; 2098
N.A.I.C.S.: 311423; 111411; 311222; 311223; 311225; 311615; 311823
Advertising Expenditures: $371,900,000
Media: 3-6-9-15-16-18-23-24
Distr.: Natl.
Personnel:
Steven F. Goldstone *(Chm)*
Gary M. Rodkin *(CEO)*
John F. Gehring *(CFO & Exec VP)*
Joan K. Chow *(CMO & Exec VP)*
Brian L. Keck *(Chief Admin Officer & Exec VP)*
Dean Hollis *(Pres/COO-Consumer Products)*
Doug Knudsen *(Pres-Food Sls)*
Paul Maass *(Pres-Comml Foods)*
David Palfenier *(Pres-Grocery Div)*
Colleen Batcheler *(Gen Counsel, Corp Sec & Exec VP)*
Albert D. Bolles *(Exec VP-Res, Quality & Innovation)*
Greg L. Smith *(Exec VP-Supply Chain)*
Ryan Clark *(VP & Gen Mgr-Hunt's & Ro*Tel Brands)*
Mark A. Duffy *(VP & Gen Mgr-Spicetec Flavors & Seasonings)*
Teresa Paulsen *(VP-Corp Comm)*
Fernando Arriola *(Sr Dir-Media)*
John Lindell *(Brand Dir-Healthy Choice)*
Daniel Marple *(Brand Dir)*
Audy Baack *(Dir-Mktg)*
Stephanie K. Childs *(Dir-Comm)*
Annabelle Nogueira *(Sr Mktg Mgr)*
Brands & Products:
ACT II
ANDY CAPP'S
ANGELA MIA
AWARD
BANQUET
BIG MAMA SAUSAGE
BLUE BONNET
BROADCAST
BROWN 'N SERVE
CAFE STEAMERS
CHEF BOYARDEE
CONAGRA MILLS
COOK'S
CRUNCH 'N MUNCH
CULTURELLE
DAVID
DENNISON'S
ECKRICH READY CRISP
EGG BEATERS
FERNANDO'S
FIDDLE FADDLE
FIRECRACKER
FLEISCHMANN'S
FRESH MIXERS
GEBHARDT
GILARDI FOODS
GILROY
GOLDEN CUISINE
GULDEN'S
HEALTHY CHOICE
HEBREW NATIONAL
HUNT'S
J.HUNGERFORD SMITH
JIFFY POP
KID CUISINE
LA CHOY
LAMB WESTON
LAMB WESTON INLAND VALLEY
LIBBY'S
LIGHTLIFE
LONGMONT
LUCK'S
LUNCHMAKERS
MANWICH
MARIE CALLENDER'S
THE MAX
MOVE OVER BUTTER
ORVILLE REDENBACHER'S
PAM
PAM PROFESSIONAL
PARKAY
PATIO
PEMMICAN
PENROSE
PETER PAN
POPPYCOCK
RANCH STYLE
REDDI-WIP
RO TEL
ROSARITA
SLIM JIM
SNACK PACK
SPICETEC
SQUEEZ 'N GO

Key to Media (For complete agency information see *The Advertising Red Books-Agencies* edition):
1. Bus. Publs. 2. Cable T.V. 3. Catalogs & Directories. 4. Co-op Adv. 5. Consumer Mags. 6. D.M. to Bus. Estab.7. D.M. to Consumers 8. Daily Newsp. 9. Exhibits/Trade Shows 10. Foreign 11. Infomercial 12. Internet Adv.13. Multimedia 14. Network Radio 15. Network T.V. 16. Newsp. Distr. Mags. 17. Other 18. Outdoor (Posters, Transit) 19. Point of Purchase20. Premiums, Novelties 21. Product Samples 22. Special Events Mktg. 23. Spot Radio 24. Spot T.V. 25. Weekly Newsp. 26. Yellow Page Adv.

ConAgra Foods, Inc. — (Continued)

SWISS MISS
VANCAMP
WESSON
WOLF

Advertising Agencies:
DDB San Francisco
555 Market St 5th Fl
San Francisco, CA 94105
Tel.: (415) 732-3600
Fax: (415) 732-3636

The Geppetto Group
95 Morton St 8th Fl
New York, NY 10014-3336
Tel.: (212) 462-8140
Fax: (212) 462-8197

Leo Burnett Worldwide, Inc.
35 W Wacker Dr
Chicago, IL 60601-1723
Tel.: (312) 220-5959
Fax: (312) 220-3299

The Marketing Store
701 E 22nd St
Lombard, IL 60148
Tel.: (630) 693-1400
Fax: (630) 932-5200

SapientNitro USA, Inc.
215 Park Ave S 2nd Fl
New York, NY 10003-1603
Tel.: (212) 206-1005
Fax: (212) 206-8510
Hebrew National

Schafer Condon Carter
168 N Clinton
Chicago, IL 60661
Tel.: (312) 464-1666
Fax: (312) 464-0628
ConAgra Foodservice

Spark Communications
222 Merchandise Mart Plz Ste 550
Chicago, IL 60654-1032
Tel.: (312) 970-8400
Fax: (312) 970-8464
Fax: (312) 970-8409
Digital Media Agency of Record
Digital Media Planning & Buying

Strahan Advertising
1940 Old Tustin Ave
Santa Ana, CA 92705
Tel.: (714) 547-6383
Fax: (714) 547-5463

Venables, Bell & Partners
201 Post St Ste 200
San Francisco, CA 94108
Tel.: (415) 288-3300
Fax: (415) 421-3683
Orville Redenbacher
Slim Jim

WonderGroup
312 Plum St Ste 1000
Cincinnati, OH 45202-2618
Tel.: (513) 357-2950
Fax: (513) 651-1162

CONTINENTAL MILLS, INC.

18125 Andover Park W
Tukwila, WA 98188-4704
Tel.: (253) 872-8400
Fax: (206) 299-3935
Web Site: www.continentalmills.com
Approx. Number Employees: 661
Year Founded: 1928
Business Description:
Mfr. of Prepared Flour
S.I.C.: 2045; 2038
N.A.I.C.S.: 311822; 311412
Media: 7-25
Personnel:
John M. Heily *(Chm, Pres & CEO)*
Bob Wallach *(Sr VP-Sls & Mktg)*
Brands & Products:
ALPINE
CLASSIC HEARTH
EAGLE MILLS
GHIRARDELLI
GRAIN GOURMET
KRUSTEAZ
KRUSTEAZ CARBSIMPLE
MY BRANDS
SNOQUALMIE FALLS
Advertising Agency:
Publicis USA
(Sub. of Publicis, S.A., Paris, France)
4 Herald Sq 950 6th Ave
New York, NY 10001
Tel.: (212) 279-5550
Fax: (212) 279-5560

GENERAL MILLS CANADA CORP.

(Sub. of General Mills, Inc.)
5825 Explorer Dr
Mississauga, ON L4W 5P6, Canada
Tel.: (905) 212-4000
Fax: (905) 212-4122
Web Site: www.generalmills.com
Sales Range: $100-124.9 Million
Approx. Number Employees: 300
Year Founded: 1954
Business Description:
Packaged Foods
S.I.C.: 5142
N.A.I.C.S.: 424420
Import
Media: 1-5-6-8-10-13-15-16-19-21-22-24-26
Distr.: Natl.
Budget Set: Jan.
Personnel:
Doug McGillivray *(VP-Mktg)*
Advertising Agency:
Cossette Communication-Marketing
502 King St W
Toronto, ON M5V 1L7, Canada
Tel.: (416) 922-2727
Fax: (416) 922-9450
Fibre 1 Cereal
Oatmeal Crisp

GENERAL MILLS, INC.

1 General Mills Blvd
Minneapolis, MN 55426-1347
Tel.: (763) 764-7600
Fax: (763) 764-7384
Toll Free: (800) 328-1144
E-mail: media.line@genmills.com
Web Site: www.generalmills.com
Approx. Sls.: $14,796,500,000
Approx. Number Employees: 33,000
Year Founded: 1928
Business Description:
Food & Flour Mfr
S.I.C.: 2043; 2024; 2034; 2045; 2096; 2099
N.A.I.C.S.: 311230; 311423; 311520; 311822; 311919; 311999
Export
Advertising Expenditures: $843,700,000
Media: 3-6-8-9-13-15-16-18-19-21-23-24
Distr.: Intl.; Natl.
Personnel:
Kendall J. Powell *(Chm & CEO)*
Donal Leo Mulligan *(CFO & Exec VP)*
Kenneth L. Thome *(Sr VP & Deputy CFO)*
Mark W. Addicks *(CMO & Sr VP)*
Gary Chu *(Pres-Greater China & Sr VP)*
Juliana L. Chugg *(Pres-Meals & Sr VP)*
David P. Homer *(Pres-Gen Mills Canada & Sr VP)*
John T. Machuzick *(Pres-Bakeries, Food Svcs & Sr VP)*
Christina L. Shea *(Pres-General Mills Foundation & Sr VP-External Rels)*
Ann W.H. Simonds *(Pres-Pillsbury USA & Sr VP)*
Jeffrey L. Harmening *(Pres-Big G Cereals & VP)*
Michele S. Meyer *(Pres-Small Planet Foods & VP)*
Maria S. Morgan *(Pres-Food Svcs & VP)*
Becky O'Grady *(Pres-Yoplait & VP)*
Peter J. Capell *(Pres-Intl)*
Christi L. Strauss *(CEO-Cereal Partners Worldwide & Sr VP)*
Ian R. Friendly *(COO-US Retail & Exec VP)*
Christopher D. O'Leary *(COO-Intl & Exec VP)*
Roderick A. Palmore *(Chief Compliance, Risk Mgmt Officer, Gen Counsel, Sec & Exec VP)*
Y. Marc Belton *(Exec VP-Global Strategy, Growth & Mktg Innovation)*
John Church *(Sr VP-Supply Chain)*
Michael Lee Davis *(Sr VP-Global HR)*
Rory A. Delaney *(Sr VP)*
Peter C. Erickson *(Sr VP-Innovation, Tech & Quality)*
James H. Murphy *(Sr VP-Global Strategy & Growth)*
Lucio Rizzi *(Sr VP)*
Ray Joncas *(Dir-Mktg)*
Cheryl Welch *(Dir-Mktg)*
Jim Cuene *(Dir-Interactive Mktg)*
Rodolfo Rodriguez *(Dir-Multicultural Mktg)*
Karl Schmidt *(Dir-Promotion Mktg)*
Martin Abrams *(Sr Manager-Mktg)*
Matt Beliveau *(Sr Mgr-HR, Supply Chain Logistics & Sls)*
Julie Fleigle *(Brand Mgr-Haagen-Dazs Shops)*
Julie Michelutti *(Brand Mgr-Haagen-Dazs Shops)*
Rohan Thakur *(Brand Mgr)*
Dan Stangler *(Mgr-Mktg)*
Hyun Oh *(Mktg Mgr)*
Arya Badiyan *(Mgr-Global Mktg)*
Scott Dorman *(Mgr-Mktg)*
Hyun Mee Graves *(Mgr-Mktg)*
Derek Herbst *(Mgr-Mktg)*
Jamie Kinnear *(Mgr-Mktg)*
Amy Sweeney *(Mgr-Mktg)*
Muffie Taggett *(Mgr-Adv & Branding)*
Brands & Products:
APPLE CINNAMON CHEERIOS
BACOS BITS
BASIC 4
BERRY BERRY KIX
BERRY BURST CHEERIOS
BETTY CROCKER
BIG G CEREALS
BISQUICK
BOO BERRY
BOWL APPETIT
BUGLES
CASCADIAN FARM
CASCADIAN FARM PURELY O'S
CHEERIOS
CHEX
CHEX MIX
CHEX RICE
CHEX WHEAT
CHICKEN HELPER
CINNAMON GRAHAMS
CINNAMON TOAST CRUNCH
CLUSTERS
COCOA PUFFS
COLOMBO
COOKIE CRISP
COUNT CHOCULA
COUNTRY CORN FLAKES
DIABLITOS UNDERWOOD
FIBER ONE
FIBREONE
FORNO DE MINAS
FRANKEN BERRY
FRESCARINI
FROSTED WHEATIES
FRUIT BY THE FOOT
FRUIT GUSHERS
FRUIT ROLL-UPS
FRUIT SHAPES
FRUIT SNACKS
GARDETTO'S
GO-GURT
GOLD MEDAL
GOLDEN GRAHAMS
GOLDEN LAYERS
GRANDS!
GREEN GIANT
HAAGEN-DAZS
HAMBURGER HELPER
HELPER
HONEY NUT CHEERIOS
HONEY NUT CLUSTERS
JENO'S
JUS-ROL
KIX
KNACK AND BACK
LA SALTENA
LARABAR
LATINA
LUCKY CHARMS
MILK 'N CEREAL BARS
MUIR GLEN
MULTI GRAIN CHEERIOS
NATURE VALLEY
NOURISHING LIVES
OATMEAL CRISP
OLD EL PASO
PET-RITZ
PILLSBURY
PILLSBURY PIZZA MINIS
PILLSBURY PIZZA POPS
PIZZA ROLLS
POTATO BUDS
PROGRESSO
PURE GOODNESS
RAISIN NUT BRAN
REESES PEANUT BUTTER PUFFS

Key to Media (For complete agency information see *The Advertising Red Books-Agencies* edition):
1. Bus. Publs. 2. Cable T.V. 3. Catalogs & Directories. 4. Co-op Adv. 5. Consumer Mags. 6. D.M. to Bus. Estab.7. D.M. to Consumers 8. Daily Newsp. 9. Exhibits/Trade Shows 10. Foreign 11. Infomercial 12. Internet Adv.13. Multimedia 14. Network Radio 15. Network T.V. 16. Newsp. Distr. Mags. 17. Other 18. Outdoor (Posters, Transit) 19. Point of Purchase20. Premiums, Novelties 21. Product Samples 22. Special Events Mktg. 23. Spot Radio 24. Spot T.V. 25. Weekly Newsp. 26. Yellow Page Adv.

SIMPLY STEAM
SNACKIN' CAKE
SUDDENLY SALAD
SUPERMOIST
TASTE YOU CAN BELIEVE IN
TEAM CHEERIOS
TOASTER SCRAMBLES
TOASTER STRUDEL
TOTAL
TOTAL RAISIN BRAN
TOTINO'S
TRIX
TRIX YOGURT
TUNA HELPER
V. PEARL
WANCHAI FERRY
WARM DELIGHT MINIS
WHEATIES
WONDRA
YOPLAIT
YOPLAIT/COLOMBO
YOPLAIT DELIGHTS
YOPLAIT KIDS
YOPLAIT YO-PLUS
YOPLUS LIGHT

Advertising Agencies:
Bromley Communications
401 E Houston St
San Antonio, TX 78205-2615
Tel.: (210) 244-2000
Fax: (210) 244-2442

Burrell
233 N Michigan Ave Ste 2900
Chicago, IL 60601
Tel.: (312) 297-9600
Fax: (312) 297-9601
(African-American Marketing)

Campbell Mithun, Inc.
Campbell Mithun Tower 222 S 9th St
Minneapolis, MN 55402-3389
Tel.: (612) 347-1000
Fax: (612) 347-1515
Nature Valley Granola Bars
Caribou Coffee Bars

Carol H. Williams Advertising
875 N Michigan Ave Ste 2750
Chicago, IL 60611
Tel.: (312) 836-7900
Fax: (312) 836-7919

Casanova Pendrill, LLC
275-A McCormick Ave Ste 100
Costa Mesa, CA 92626-3369
Tel.: (714) 918-8200
Fax: (714) 918-8295
(Hispanic Market)

Cone
(A Member of Omnicom Group)
855 Boylston St
Boston, MA 02116
Tel.: (617) 227-2111
Fax: (617) 523-3955

Fallon Minneapolis
901 Marquette Ave Ste 2400
Minneapolis, MN 55402
Tel.: (612) 758-2345
Fax: (612) 758-2346
Toll Free: (866) 758-2345
(Totino's)

GolinHarris
(Part of the Interpublic Group of Companies)
111 E Wacker Dr 11th Fl
Chicago, IL 60601-4306
Tel.: (312) 729-4000
Fax: (312) 729-4010
Fiber One
— Vanessa Mason *(Acct Exec)*
— Kristen Roskowski *(Acct Exec)*

OLSON
1625 Hennepin Ave
Minneapolis, MN 55403
Tel.: (612) 215-9800
Fax: (612) 215-9801
Interactive
— Michael Kraabel *(Creative Dir)*

Publicis Modem
One Selleck St 2nd Fl
Norwalk, CT 06855
Tel.: (203) 295-0615
Fax: (203) 299-7060
Totino's Pizza Rolls

Publicis Modem & Dialog, East
75 Ninth Ave 4th Fl
New York, NY 10011
Tel.: (212) 336-3300
Fax: (212) 326-3356
Totino's Pizza Rolls

Saatchi & Saatchi New York
375 Hudson St
New York, NY 10014-3660
Tel.: (212) 463-2000
Fax: (212) 463-9855
(Pillsbury, Progresso Light Soups, Cheerios, Honey Nut Cheerios, Country Corn Flakes, Corn Total, Total, Kix, Berry Berry Kix, Lucky Charms, Monster Cereals, Trix, Cocoa Puffs, Fiber One, Clusters, Circus Fun Cereal, Squeezit, Fruit Wrinkles)
— Peter Moore Smith *(Exec VP & Exec Dir-Creative)*

Zenith Media Services
(Regional Headquarters for ZenithOptimedia, the Americas)
299 W Houston St 10th Fl
New York, NY 10014-4806
Tel.: (212) 859-5100
Fax: (212) 727-9495
(Media Planning & Buying)

HODGSON MILL, INC.

(Sub. of Siemer Milling Company)
1100 Stevens Ave
Effingham, IL 62401
Tel.: (217) 347-0105
Fax: (217) 347-0198
Toll Free: (800) 347-0105
E-mail: customerservice@hodgson.com
Web Site: www.hodgsonmill.com
Approx. Number Employees: 45
Year Founded: 1882

Business Description:
Whole Grain Mill & Mix Plant
S.I.C.: 2041; 2045
N.A.I.C.S.: 311211; 311822

Media: 2-4-6-10-13

Personnel:
Paul Kirby *(Exec VP)*
Ray Martin *(VP-Sls & Mktg)*

Advertising Agency:
Dayton Communications, Inc.
1120 NW 14th St
Portland, OR 97209
Tel.: (503) 233-9352
Fax: (503) 241-7386

HOUSE-AUTRY MILLS INC.

PO Box 460
Four Oaks, NC 27524
Tel.: (919) 963-6200
Fax: (919) 963-6458
E-mail: info@house-autrymillsinc.com
Web Site: www.house-autry.com
Approx. Rev.: $7,000,000
Approx. Number Employees: 80
Year Founded: 1812
Business Description:
Corn Meal Mfr
S.I.C.: 2041
N.A.I.C.S.: 311211
Advertising Agency:
French/West/Vaughan, Inc.
112 E Hargett St
Raleigh, NC 27601
Tel.: (919) 832-6300
Fax: (919) 832-6360

KASHI COMPANY

(Sub. of Kellogg Company)
Ste 500 4275 Executive Sq
La Jolla, CA 92037-1477
Mailing Address:
PO Box 8557
La Jolla, CA 92038
Tel.: (858) 274-8870
Fax: (858) 274-8894
E-mail: info@kashi.com
Web Site: www.kashi.com
E-Mail For Key Personnel:
Marketing Director: marketing@kashi.com
Public Relations: pr@kashi.com
Sales Range: $25-49.9 Million
Approx. Number Employees: 75
Year Founded: 1984
Business Description:
Health Food Breakfast & Snacks Mfr
S.I.C.: 2041
N.A.I.C.S.: 311211
Media: 6
Personnel:
David DeSouza *(VP & Gen Mgr)*
Sarah Lowrey Ceccarelli *(Sr Mgr-Mktg & Innovation)*
John Henry Siedlecki *(Sr Mgr-Brand Mktg & Innovation)*
Kristin Honey *(Office Mgr)*
Lara Gish *(Brand Mgr)*
Erin D. Becker *(Mgr-Customer Mktg)*
Nancy Knight *(Mgr-Quality)*
Brands & Products:
CHEWY GRANOLA BARS
COCOA BEACH
GOLEAN
GOLEAN BARS
GOLEAN CEREAL
GOLEAN CRUNCH
GOLEAN HOT CEREAL
GOLEAN SHAKES
GOLEAN WAFFLES
GOOD FRIENDS
GOOD FRIENDS CINNA-RAISIN CRUNCH
HEART TO HEART
HEART TO HEART OATMEAL
HEART TO HEART WAFFLES
HERITAGE FOODS
KASHI
KASHI 7 WHOLE GRAIN PILAF
KASHI FLAKES
KASHI HONEY ALMOND FLAX
KASHI HONEY PUFFS
KASHI MEDLEY
KASHI MOUNTAIN MEDLEY
KASHI NUGGETS
KASHI ORCHARD SPICE
KASHI PEANUT PEANUT BUTTER
KASHI PILAF
KASHI PUFFS
KASHI TRAIL MIX
KASHI VIVE
ORGANIC PROMISE
ORGANIC PROMISE AUTUMN WHEAT
ORGANIC PROMISE CRANBERRY SUNSHINE
ORGANIC PROMISE STRAWBERRY FIELDS
SUMMER BERRY
TLC COUNTRY CHEDDAR
TLC CRACKERS
TLC HONEY SESAME
TLC NATURAL RANCH
TLC ORIGINAL 7 GRAIN
VIVE

Advertising Agencies:
Amazon Advertising
30 Hotaling Pl Ste 100
San Francisco, CA 94111
Tel.: (415) 433-3004
Fax: (415) 433-3002

Starcom MediaVest Group
35 W Wacker Dr
Chicago, IL 60601-1723
Tel.: (312) 220-3535
Fax: (312) 220-6530

KELLOGG COMPANY

1 Kellogg Sq
Battle Creek, MI 49017-3534
Mailing Address:
PO Box 3599
Battle Creek, MI 49016-3599
Tel.: (269) 961-2000
Fax: (269) 961-2871
Toll Free: (800) 535-5644
E-mail: info@kelloggs.com
Web Site: www.kelloggcompany.com
Approx. Sls.: $12,397,000,000
Approx. Number Employees: 30,600
Year Founded: 1906
Business Description:
Ready-to-Eat Breakfast Cereals, Snacks & Beverage Products
S.I.C.: 2043; 2041; 2053
N.A.I.C.S.: 311230; 311211; 311813
Import Export
Advertising Expenditures: $1,091,000,000
Media: 1-3-6-8-10-11-13-15-18-19-21-22-24
Distr.: Natl.
Budget Set: Sept. -Oct.
Personnel:
Ronald L. Dissinger *(CFO)*
Brian S. Rice *(CIO & Sr VP)*
Mark R. Baynes *(CMO-Global & VP)*
Celeste A. Clark *(Chief Sustainability Officer & Sr VP-Global Pub Policy & External)*
Bradford J. Davidson *(Sr VP & Pres-North America)*

Key to Media (For complete agency information see *The Advertising Red Books-Agencies* edition):
1. Bus. Publs. 2. Cable T.V. 3. Catalogs & Directories. 4. Co-op Adv. 5. Consumer Mags. 6. D.M. to Bus. Estab.7. D.M. to Consumers
8. Daily Newsp. 9. Exhibits/Trade Shows 10. Foreign 11. Infomercial 12. Internet Adv.13. Multimedia 14. Network Radio
15. Network T.V. 16. Newsp. Distr. Mags. 17. Other 18. Outdoor (Posters, Transit) 19. Point of Purchase20. Premiums, Novelties
21. Product Samples 22. Special Events Mktg. 23. Spot Radio 24. Spot T.V. 25. Weekly Newsp. 26. Yellow Page Adv.

Kellogg Company — (Continued)

Paul T. Norman *(Sr VP & Pres-Kellogg Intl)*
Juan Pablo Villalobos *(Sr VP & Pres-US Morning Foods)*
Todd Penegor *(VP & Pres-US Snacks)*
Elisabeth Fleuriot *(Pres-France/ Benelux/Emerging markets)*
David J. Pfanzelter *(Pres-Specialty Channels & Kellogg Canada)*
Gary H. Pilnick *(Sec & Sr VP & Gen Counsel-Corp Dev)*
Russ Hockin *(Sr VP)*
Gregory D. Peterson *(Sr VP)*
Dennis W. Shuler *(Sr VP-Global HR)*
Kevin Smith *(Sr VP-Mktg Svcs-United States)*
Steven Sterling *(Sr VP-Global Supply Chain)*
Kathleen Wilson-Thompson *(Sr VP-Global HR)*
Margarget Bath *(VP-Res, Quality & Tech)*
Annunciata Cerioli *(VP-HR)*
Jenny Enochson *(Sr Dir-Mktg & Commun)*
Sandy Uridge *(Sr Dir)*
Rebeca Mitre *(Dir-Latinamerica Mktg)*
Gordon Sun *(Dir-Strategic Media)*
Andrea Borton *(Assoc Dir-Brand Mktg)*
Aaron Fetters *(Assoc Dir-Digital Strategy & Analytics-Global)*
Tamara Howe *(Assoc Dir-Brand Mktg-Global)*
Karl Miller *(Assoc Dir-Adult RTEC Innovation)*
John Ross *(Assoc Dir-Mktg Res)*
Don Cumming *(Brand Mgr-Morning Foods Adult)*
Angela Gusse *(Brand Mgr)*
LaKesha Hatch *(Brand Mgr-Special K)*

Brands & Products:
APPLE JACKS
APPLE RAISIN CRISP
AUSTIN
BITS CRASHERS
BRAN BUDS
CHEEZ-IT
CHIK PATTIES
CHIPS DELUXE
CINNABON
CINNAMON CRUNCH CRISPIX
CLUB
COCOA KRISPES
COMPLETE WHEAT BRAN FLAKES
CORN POPS
CRACKLIN' OAT BRAN
CRISPIX
EGGO
EGGO APPLE CINNAMON WAFFLES
EGGO BANANA BREAD WAFFLES
EGGO BUTTERMILK PANCAKES
EGGO NUTRI-GRAIN WHOLE GRAIN WAFFLES
EGGO NUTRI-GRAIN WHOLE WHEAT WAFFLES
EGGO SPECIAL K WAFFLES
EGGO TOASTER SWIRLZ
ERNIE KEEBLER
FAMOUS AMOS
FIBERPLUS
FROOT LOOPS
FROSTED FLAKES
FROSTED KRISPIES
FROSTED MINI-WHEATS
FRUIT HARVEST
FUDGE SHOPPE
GRILLERS PRIME
GRIPZ
HONEY CRUNCH CORN FLAKES
HONEY LOOPS
HONEY SMACKS
HYDROX
JACK'S
JACKSONS
JUMBO MULTI-GRAIN KRISPIES
KEEBLER
KEEBLER COOKIE CRUNCH
KEEBLER EL FUDGE
KELLOGG'S
KELLOGG'S CORN FLAKES
KELLOGG'S CORNFLAKE CRUMBS
KELLOGG'S CRUNCH
KELLOGG'S FROSTED FLAKES
KELLOGG'S KITCHEN
KELLOGG'S RACING
KELLOGG'S STUFFING MIX
KRISPY
LOMA LINDA
MARSHMALLOW FROOT LOOPS
MATCHBOX
MIGHTY TINY
MINI-SWIRLZ
MINI-WHEATS
MORNINGSTAR FARMS
MURRAY
MURRAY SUGAR FREE
NATURAL TOUCH
NATURAL TOUCH KAFFREE ROMA
NATURAL TOUCH NINE BEAN LOAF
NATURAL TOUCH VEGETARIAN TUNA
NICKELODEON
NUT & HONEY CRUNCH
NUTRI-GRAIN
NUTRI-GRAIN STRAWBERRY YOGURT
NUTRI-GRAIN VANILLA YOGURT
OPERATION
PLANTATION
POP-TARTS
POP-TARTS BROWN SUGAR CINNAMON
POP-TARTS CHOCOLATE FUDGE
POP-TARTS FROSTED HOT FUDGE SUNDAE
POP-TARTS LOW FAT STRAWBERRY
POP-TARTS RASPBERRY
POP-TARTS STRAWBERRY
POP-TARTS VANILLA CREME
POP-TARTS WILD BERRY
PRODUCT 19
RAISIN BRAN
READY CRUST
RICE KRISPIES
RICE KRISPIES TREATS
SANDIES
SAUSAGE PATTIES
SAUSAGE STYLE RECIPE CRUMBLES
SCOOBY DOO BERRY BONES
SMART START
SMART START ANTIOXIDANTS
SMORZ
SNAP! CRACKLE! POP!
SOFT BATCH
SPECIAL K
SPECIAL K BAR STRAWBERRY
SPECIAL K BLISS BAR
SPECIAL K PROTEIN SHAKE
SUNSHINE
TIGER POWER
TOASTEDS
TONY THE TIGER
TONY'S CINNAMON KRUNCHERS
TOUCAN SAM
TOWN HOUSE
VEGGIE CORN DOGS
VIENNA CREMES
VIENNA FINGERS
WHEATABLES
WONDERPETS!
WORTHINGTON
YOGOS
ZESTA

Advertising Agencies:
Biggs Gilmore Communications
261 E Kalamazoo Ave Ste 300
Kalamazoo, MI 49007-3841
Tel.: (269) 349-7711
Fax: (269) 349-3051
Pop Tarts
Rice Krispies

Brand Learning
Burgoine Quay 8 Lower Teddington Rd
Hampton Wick
Kingston upon Thames, KT1 4ER, United Kingdom
Tel.: (44) 2086148150

Epsilon Data Management, LLC
4301 Regent Blvd
Irving, TX 75063-2253
Tel.: (972) 582-9600
Fax: (972) 582-9700
Toll Free: (800) 309-0505
CRM
Database Marketing

Ketchum
6 PPG Pl
Pittsburgh, PA 15222-5425
Tel.: (412) 456-3500
Fax: (412) 456-3834

Leo Burnett Inc.
Western Bank World Plz 268 Munoz Rivera Ave Ste 1200
San Juan, PR 00918
Tel.: (787) 754-7760
Fax: (787) 754-4941
Special K-Sass

Leo Burnett Worldwide, Inc.
35 W Wacker Dr
Chicago, IL 60601-1723
Tel.: (312) 220-5959
Fax: (312) 220-3299
(Consolidated Creative Account, All-Bran, FiberPlus)
Crunchy Nut

Starcom USA
35 W Wacker Dr
Chicago, IL 60601
Tel.: (312) 220-3535
Fax: (312) 220-6530

THE KING ARTHUR FLOUR COMPANY, INC.

135 Rte 5 S
Norwich, VT 05055
Tel.: (802) 649-3881
Fax: (802) 649-3323
Toll Free: (800) 827-6836
E-mail: bakers@kingarthurflour.com
Web Site: www.kingarthurflour.com
Approx. Sls.: $61,000,000
Approx. Number Employees: 160
Year Founded: 1896
Business Description:
Retailer of Flour Products & Baking Utensils
S.I.C.: 2041; 2045; 5961
N.A.I.C.S.: 311211; 311822; 454113
Advertising Expenditures: $800,000
Media: 4-6-9-22-24
Distr.: Reg.
Budget Set: July
Personnel:
F. E. Sands, II *(Chm)*
Steve Voigt *(CEO)*
Karen Colberg *(VP & GM)*
Sarah McGinley-Smith *(Dir-Corp Comm)*
Tom Payne *(Dir-Mktg)*
Allison Rogers *(Mgr-Media Rels)*
Brands & Products:
DEDICATED TO THE PURE JOY OF BAKING
K.A.F KIDS
KING ARTHUR
QUEEN GUINEVERE
ROUND TABLE
Advertising Agencies:
Digital Flannel
PO Box 358
Woodstock, VT 05091
Tel.: (802) 457-3838

Kelliher Samets Volk
212 Battery St
Burlington, VT 05401-5281
Tel.: (802) 862-8261
Fax: (802) 863-4724

LITTLE CROW FOODS

201 S Detroit St
Warsaw, IN 46580
Tel.: (574) 267-7141
Fax: (574) 267-2370
Toll Free: (800) 288-2769
E-mail: customerservice@lcfmail.com
Web Site: www.littlecrowfoods.com
E-Mail For Key Personnel:
President: dennyfuller@littlecrowfoods.com
Sales Director: tomlawrence@littlecrowfoods.com
Approx. Number Employees: 57
Year Founded: 1903
Business Description:
Grain Food Products Mfr
S.I.C.: 2045; 2043
N.A.I.C.S.: 311822; 311230
Export
Advertising Expenditures: $800,000
Media: 5-6-8-9-14-18-19-20-21-23-24-25
Distr.: Reg.
Budget Set: Apr.
Personnel:
Denny Fuller *(Pres)*
Kim Fuller *(Exec VP)*
Greg Dearborn *(VP-Admin & Mgr-Pur)*
Tom Lawrence *(VP & Mgr-Sls)*
Ron Shipley *(VP & Mgr-Ops)*
Rich Utley *(VP & Mgr-Sls)*
Brands & Products:
BAKIN' MIRACLE
COCO WHEATS

Key to Media (For complete agency information see *The Advertising Red Books-Agencies* edition):
1. Bus. Publs. 2. Cable T.V. 3. Catalogs & Directories. 4. Co-op Adv. 5. Consumer Mags. 6. D.M. to Bus. Estab.7. D.M. to Consumers 8. Daily Newsp. 9. Exhibits/Trade Shows 10. Foreign 11. Infomercial 12. Internet Adv.13. Multimedia 14. Network Radio 15. Network T.V. 16. Newsp. Distr. Mags. 17. Other 18. Outdoor (Posters, Transit) 19. Point of Purchase20. Premiums, Novelties 21. Product Samples 22. Special Events Mktg. 23. Spot Radio 24. Spot T.V. 25. Weekly Newsp. 26. Yellow Page Adv.

FASTSHAKE
FRYIN' MAGIC
LITTLE CROW FOODS
MIRACLE MAIZE

MALT-O-MEAL COMPANY

80 S 8th St Ste 2700
Minneapolis, MN 55402-2100
Tel.: (612) 338-8551
Fax: (612) 359-5424
Toll Free: (800) 743-3029
E-mail: human_resources@malt-o-meal.com
Web Site: www.malt-o-meal.com
Sales Range: $500-549.9 Million
Approx. Number Employees: 1,000
Year Founded: 1919
Business Description:
Private & Branded Label Cereals Mfr
S.I.C.: 2043
N.A.I.C.S.: 311230
Media: 2-4-5-8-9-10-19-21-23-24
Distr.: Natl.
Budget Set: Oct.
Personnel:
Chris Neugent *(Pres & COO)*
Paul Norton *(VP-Sls & Mktg)*
Sally Literski *(Dir-Mktg-Hot Cereal)*
James Sophocleus *(Dir-Insights & Category Mgmt)*
Mike Allen *(Sls Mgr)*
Dan Lookretis *(Sls Mgr)*
Wes Witmer *(Sls Mgr)*
Brands & Products:
APPLE CINNAMON TOASTY O'S
APPLE ZINGS
BALANCE
BERRY COLOSSAL CRUNCH
CINNAMON TOASTER
COCO ROOS
COCOA DYNO-BITES
CORN BURSTS
CRISP 'N CRACKLING RICE
FROSTED FLAKES
FROSTED MINI SPOONERS
FRUITY DINO-BYTES
GOLDEN PUFFS
HONEY BUZZERS
HONEY GRAHAM TOASTERS
HONEY NUT TOASTY O'S
MALT-O-MEAL
MARSHMALLOW MATEYS
PUFFED RICE
PUFFED WHEAT
TOASTY O'S
TOOTIE FRUITIES

NATURE'S PATH FOODS INC.

9100 Van Horne Way
Richmond, BC V6X 1W3, Canada
Tel.: (604) 248-8777
Fax: (604) 248-8760
E-mail: cereal@naturespath.com
Web Site: www.naturespath.com
Approx. Number Employees: 200
Year Founded: 1985
Business Description:
Organic & Natural Breakfast Food Mfr
S.I.C.: 2043; 2051
N.A.I.C.S.: 311230; 311812
Media: 6-21
Personnel:
Arran B. Stephens *(Founder & Pres)*
Ratana Stephens *(Co-CEO & COO)*
Neil D. Mandleman *(CFO)*
Robert Patrizio *(VP-Fin)*
Rob Wardle *(Dir-Mktg)*
Maria Emmer Aanes *(Dir-Mktg & Comm)*
Maria Emmer-Aanes *(Dir-Mktg & Comm)*
Brands & Products:
AGAVE PLUS
AMAZON
EAT WELL. DO GOOD.
ECO PAC
ENVIROBOX
ENVIROKIDZ
FLAX PLUS
GINGER ZING
GORILLA MUNCH
HEMP PLUS
HERITAGE
HIKER+
HONEY
HONEY'D
KOALA CRISP
LIFESTREAM
MANNA
MAPLE CINN
MESA SUNRISE
NATURE'S PATH
OATY BITES
OPTIMUM
OPTIMUM POWER
OPTIMUM REBOUND
OPTIMUM SLIM
OPTIMUM ZEN
ORANGUTAN-O'S
PANDA PUFFS
POMEGRAN PLUS
POWER BREAKFAST
PUMPKIN FLAX PLUS
SHREDDED HERITAGE BITES
SMARTBRAN
SOY PLUS
SYNERGY
TENDER O'S
WHOLE O'S

NORTH DAKOTA MILL & ELEVATOR ASSOCIATION

1823 Mill Rd
Grand Forks, ND 58203-1535
Tel.: (701) 795-7000
Fax: (701) 795-7272
Toll Free: (800) 538-7721
Web Site: www.ndmill.com
Approx. Number Employees: 120
Year Founded: 1922
Business Description:
Flour Mfr; Terminal Elevator & Packaging Warehouse
S.I.C.: 2041; 2052
N.A.I.C.S.: 311211; 311821
Media: 2-9-10-14-18-20
Distr.: Natl.
Personnel:
Vance Taylor *(Pres & Gen Mgr)*
Ed Barchenger *(Controller & Mgr-Fin)*
Steve Sannes *(Mgr-Sls)*
Chris LeMoine *(Production Mgr)*
Mike Jones *(Mgr-Logistics)*
Bob Sombke *(Mgr-Quality Assurance)*
Brands & Products:
DAKOTA BRAVE
DAKOTA CHAMPION
DAKOTA DIAMOND
DAKOTA MAID
DAKOTA PRIDE
DURAKOTA
MILLER'S CHOICE

POST FOODS, LLC

(Sub. of Ralcorp Holdings, Inc.)
1 Upper Pond Rd Bldg E 2nd Fl
Parsippany, NJ 07054
Tel.: (973) 658-2300
Approx. Rev.: $1,100,000,000
Approx. Number Employees: 1,250
Business Description:
Breakfast Cereals Marketing
S.I.C.: 2043
N.A.I.C.S.: 311230
Personnel:
Bart Adlam *(Pres)*
Kelley Peters *(Sr Dir-Strategy)*
Neil Grossman *(Brand Mgr)*
Brands & Products:
ALPHA BITS
BRAN FLAKES
COCOA PEBBLES
FRUITY PEBBLES
GOLDEN CRISP
GRAPE-NUTS
HONEY BUNCHES OF OATS
HONEYCOMB
POST SELECTS BANANA NUT CRUNCH
POST SELECTS BLUEBERRY MORNING
POST SELECTS CRANBERRY ALMOND CRUNCH
POST SELECTS GREAT GRAINS
POST SELECTS MAPLE PECAN CRUNCH
RAISIN BRAN
SHREDDED WHEAT
WAFFLE CRISP
Advertising Agency:
LatinWorks Marketing, Inc.
206 E 9th St Capital Tower Fl 13
Austin, TX 78701
Tel.: (512) 479-6200
Fax: (512) 479-6024

THE QUAKER OATS COMPANY

(Sub. of PepsiCo Americas Foods)
555 W Monroe Ste 16-01
Chicago, IL 60604-9001
Mailing Address:
PO Box 049003
Chicago, IL 60604-9003
Tel.: (312) 821-1000
Fax: (312) 821-1594
Web Site: www.quakeroats.com
Sales Range: $1-4.9 Billion
Approx. Number Employees: 11,666
Year Founded: 1901
Business Description:
Grain-Based Foods & Beverages
S.I.C.: 2043
N.A.I.C.S.: 311230
Media: 6-9-11-15-16-21-24-25
Distr.: Intl.; Natl.
Budget Set: Apr.
Personnel:
Jaya Kumar *(Pres)*
Shelley Haus *(Dir-Mktg-Quaker Breakfast)*
Sari Winick *(Brand Mgr)*
Brands & Products:
3 MINUTOS MIXED CEREAL
CAP'N CRUNCH
COQUEIRO
CREUSLI
CRISP-UMS
FRESCAVENA
HARVEST CRUNCH
HOT OAT CRUNCH
KING VITAMIN
LIFE
LIVING PROOF
MAGICO
MOTHER'S
NEAR EAST
PASTA RONI
QUAKER
QUAKER 100% NATURAL CEREAL
QUAKER BAKERIES
QUAKER CHEWY
QUAKER DIPPS
QUAKER FRUIT & OATMEAL
QUAKER FRUIT & OATMEAL BITES
QUAKER FRUIT & OATMEAL TOASTABLES
QUAKER FRUT
QUAKER INSTANT OATMEAL
QUAKER MAGICA
QUAKER MAGICA CON SOJA
QUAKER MAIS SABOR
QUAKER MEU MINGAU
QUAKER OAT BRAN
QUAKER OATMEAL
QUAKER OATMEAL BREAKFAST SQUARES
QUAKER OATMEAL BROWN SUGAR BLISS
QUAKER OATMEAL HONEY NUT HEAVEN
QUAKER OATMEAL-TO-GO
QUAKER OATS
QUAKER OATSO SIMPLE
QUAKER OH'S!
QUAKER SOY CRISPS
QUAKER VITALY
QUAKES
QUICK 'N HEARTY
QUISP
RICE-A-RONI
SCOTT'S PORAGE OATS
SCOTT'S SO EASY OATS
SIMPLE HARVEST
SPUDZ
SUGAR PUFFS
TODDY
TODDYNHO
Advertising Agencies:
BBDO Toronto
2 Bloor St W
Toronto, ON M4W 3R6, Canada
Tel.: (416) 972-1505
Fax: (416) 972-5656

Goodby, Silverstein & Partners, Inc.
(Part of Omnicom Group, Inc.)
720 California St
San Francisco, CA 94108-2404
Tel.: (415) 392-0669
Fax: (415) 788-4303
(Creative)

Juniper Park
2 Bloor St W 6th Fl
Toronto, ON M4W 3R6, Canada
Tel.: (416) 413-7301
Fax: (416) 972-5486
Amazing Mornings Campaign

OMD-USA
195 Broadway
New York, NY 10007
Tel.: (212) 590-7100
Media

Tribal DDB Chicago
200 E Randolph St

The Quaker Oats Company — (Continued)

Chicago, IL 60601
Tel.: (312) 552-6000
Fax: (312) 552-2358
Digital Marketing
Quaker Oatmeal
Quaker Snack Bars
Quaker Rice Snacks
Quaker Simple Harvest
Quaker Life Cereal

RALCORP HOLDINGS, INC.
800 Market St
Saint Louis, MO 63101-2506
Mailing Address:
PO Box 618
Saint Louis, MO 63188-0618
Tel.: (314) 877-7000
Fax: (314) 877-7900
E-mail: investorrelations@ralcorp.com
Web Site: www.ralcorp.com
Approx. Sls.: $4,048,500,000
Approx. Number Employees: 10,800
Year Founded: 1994
Business Description:
Holding Company;Pasta, Cereal, Cookie & Cracker Mfr
S.I.C.: 2052; 2034; 2043; 6719
N.A.I.C.S.: 311821; 311230; 311423; 551112
Advertising Expenditures: $102,000,000
Media: 7-17
Personnel:
William P. Stiritz *(Chm)*
Kevin J. Hunt *(Co-Pres & Co-CEO)*
David P. Skarie *(Co-Pres & Co-CEO)*
Richard R. Koulouris *(Pres)*
Thomas G. Granneman *(Chief Acctg Officer & VP)*
Ronald D. Wilkinson *(Pres-Ralcorp Cereal Products & Corp VP)*
Gregory A. Billhartz *(Gen Counsel, Sec & Corp VP)*
Dave Waldman *(Mgr-Customer Mktg)*
Brands & Products:
BREMNER
CARRIAGE HOUSE
LINETTE QUALITY CHOCOLATES
MEDALLION FOODS, INC.
NUTCRACKER
RALCORP
RYKRISP
Advertising Agency:
Schupp Company, Inc.
401 Pine St
Saint Louis, MO 63102-2731
Tel.: (314) 421-5200
Fax: (314) 421-5554

ROMAN MEAL COMPANY
2101 S Tacoma Way
Tacoma, WA 98409
Tel.: (253) 475-0964
Fax: (253) 475-4708
E-mail: customerservice@romanmeal.com
Web Site: www.romanmeal.com
Approx. Number Employees: 25
Year Founded: 1927
Business Description:
Producers & Marketers of Whole Grain Bakery Goods, Cereals, Bakers Mixes & Other Bakery Goods
S.I.C.: 5149
N.A.I.C.S.: 424490
Advertising Expenditures: $4,500,000
D.M. to Consumers: $2,025,000; Daily Newsp.: $1,125,000; Exhibits/Trade Shows: $1,350,000
Distr.: Natl.
Budget Set: Aug.
Personnel:
Charles W. Matthaei *(Chm)*
Gary Jensen *(Pres)*
William L. Matthaei *(CEO)*
Brands & Products:
100% WHOLE GRAIN SNACK BARS
CREAM OF RYE
HARVEST RECIPE
NUTRI-BRAN
ROMAN LIGHT
ROMAN MEAL
ROMAN MEAL CARB AWARE
ROMAN MEAL COMPANY
ROMAN MEAL HIGH FIBER
ROMAN MEAL HONEY COCONUT ALMOND GRANOLA
ROMAN MEAL HONEY NUT & OAT BRAN
ROMAN MEAL HONEY WHEATBERRY
ROMAN MEAL HONEYBRAN
ROMAN MEAL MULTIGRAIN PLUS
ROMAN MEAL SEVEN GRAIN
ROMAN MEAL SUGAR FREE
ROMAN MEAL SUN GRAIN
ROMAN MEAL TWELVE GRAINS
Advertising Agency:
Grey Los Angeles
3500 W Olive Ave Ste 700
Burbank, CA 91505
Tel.: (818) 531-0800
Fax: (818) 531-0701

SOUTHERN BAKERIES, INC.
(Div. of Flowers Baking Company)
(d/b/a ButterKrust Bakery)
3355 W Memorial Blvd
Lakeland, FL 33815-1084
Tel.: (863) 682-1155
Fax: (863) 686-9252
Toll Free: (800) 283-8093
Web Site: www.bkbusa.com
Approx. Sls.: $70,000,000
Approx. Number Employees: 368
Year Founded: 1988
Business Description:
Bread, Rolls & Related Products Mfr
S.I.C.: 2051; 5149
N.A.I.C.S.: 311812; 424490
Import Export
Media: 8-19-21

THE UHLMANN CO.
1009 Central St
Kansas City, MO 64105
Tel.: (816) 221-8200
Fax: (816) 221-5504
Sales Range: $25-49.9 Million
Approx. Number Employees: 12
Year Founded: 1951
Business Description:
Producer & Distr of Grocery Flour; Investments & Real Estates
S.I.C.: 2041; 5153
N.A.I.C.S.: 311211; 424510
Media: 6-9
Distr.: Reg.
Personnel:
John W. Uhlmann *(Chm)*
Paul Uhlmann III *(Pres)*
Stanley P. Cyphers *(CFO)*
Judy Rasmussen *(Mgr-Sls-Food Svcs)*
Brands & Products:
CERESOTA
HECKERS
JUST ADD FRUIT

U.S. MILLS, LLC
(Holding of Susquehanna International Group, LLP)
200 Reservoir St
Needham, MA 02494-3191
Tel.: (781) 444-0440
Fax: (781) 444-3411
Web Site: www.usmillsinc.com
Sales Range: $10-24.9 Million
Approx. Number Employees: 12
Year Founded: 1908
Business Description:
Breakfast Food & Cereal Mfr
S.I.C.: 2043
N.A.I.C.S.: 311230
Import Export
Media: 5-9-19-20-23-24-25
Distr.: Natl.
Personnel:
William Bunn *(VP-Sls)*
Brands & Products:
EREWHON
FARINA
NEW MORNING
SKINNER'S
UNCLE SAM
Advertising Agency:
Gearon Hoffman Inc.
88 Broad St
Boston, MA 02110
Tel.: (617) 247-1522
Fax: (617) 247-6821
Farina
Skinner's
New Morning

VITERRA INC.
2625 Victoria Avenue
Regina, SK S4T 7T9, Canada
Tel.: (306) 569-4411
Tel.: (306) 569-4859 (IR)
Fax: (306) 569-5036
Fax: (306) 569-4400 (IR)
Toll Free: (866) 569-4411
E-mail: investor@viterra.ca
Web Site: www.viterra.ca
E-Mail For Key Personnel:
Public Relations: colleen.vancha@swp.com
Approx. Rev.: $8,411,663,190
Approx. Number Employees: 400
Year Founded: 1924
Business Description:
Holding Company; Grain & Agricultural Products Processor, Marketer & Distr
S.I.C.: 6719; 5153; 5159
N.A.I.C.S.: 551112; 424510; 424590
Media: 2-8-10-13-18-22-23-25-26
Personnel:
Thomas Birks *(Chm)*
Mayo M. Schmidt *(Pres & CEO)*
Rex McLennan *(CFO)*
Francis J. Malecha *(COO)*
Mike Brooks *(CIO & Sr VP)*
Rob Gordon *(Pres-South East Asia & Sr VP)*
James R. Bell *(Gen Counsel, Sec & Sr VP)*
Steven Berger *(Sr VP-HR & Transformation)*
Don Chapman *(Sr VP-Intl Grain)*
Raymond Dean *(Sr VP-Legal Svcs)*
Karl J. Gerrand *(Sr VP-Processing)*
Robert Miller *(Sr VP-Grain-North America)*
William D. Mooney *(Sr VP-Feed Products)*
Colleen Vancha *(Sr VP-IR & Corp Affairs)*
Doug Wonnacott *(Sr VP-Agri Products)*
Brands & Products:
AGPRO GRAIN
VITERRA

THE WEETABIX COMPANY, INC.
(Sub. of Weetabix Limited)
20 Cameron St
Clinton, MA 01510
Tel.: (978) 368-0991
Fax: (978) 365-7268
Web Site: www.weetabixusa.com
Approx. Number Employees: 240
Year Founded: 1932
Business Description:
Cereals & Industrial Ingredients Mfr & Distr
S.I.C.: 2043
N.A.I.C.S.: 311230
Advertising Expenditures: $700,000
Media: 6-15-17-19-21-24
Distr.: Intl.; Natl.
Personnel:
Chuck Green *(VP-Sls)*
Advertising Agency:
Crier Communications
9507 Santa Monica Blvd Ste 300
Beverly Hills, CA 90210
Tel.: (310) 274-1072
Fax: (310) 274-0611
— Shaina Zalma *(Sr Acct Exec)*

WILKINS-ROGERS INCORPORATED
27 Frederick Rd
Ellicott City, MD 21043-4759
Mailing Address:
PO Box 308
Ellicott City, MD 21041-0308
Tel.: (410) 465-5800
Fax: (443) 750-0163
Toll Free: (800) 735-3585
E-mail: info@washingtonqualityfoods.com
Web Site: www.wrmills.com
Sales Range: $25-49.9 Million
Approx. Number Employees: 155
Year Founded: 1913
Business Description:
Family Flours; Bakery Flours; Corn Meal; Prepared Baking Mixes; Bread & Cake Mixes
S.I.C.: 5461; 2041
N.A.I.C.S.: 445291; 311211
Export
Media: 2-5-7-9-11-14-19-21
Distr.: Reg.
Personnel:
George Grosse *(VP-Comml Mktg)*
Brands & Products:
BEATTIE'S
CROSS
INDIAN HEAD
MARTHA WASHINGTON
OLD TIME
RAGA MUFFINS
VELVETEX

Key to Media (For complete agency information see *The Advertising Red Books-Agencies* edition):
1. Bus. Publs. 2. Cable T.V. 3. Catalogs & Directories. 4. Co-op Adv. 5. Consumer Mags. 6. D.M. to Bus. Estab.7. D.M. to Consumers 8. Daily Newsp. 9. Exhibits/Trade Shows 10. Foreign 11. Infomercial 12. Internet Adv.13. Multimedia 14. Network Radio 15. Network T.V. 16. Newsp. Distr. Mags. 17. Other 18. Outdoor (Posters, Transit) 19. Point of Purchase20. Premiums, Novelties 21. Product Samples 22. Special Events Mktg. 23. Spot Radio 24. Spot T.V. 25. Weekly Newsp. 26. Yellow Page Adv.

WASHINGTON
WHITE LILLY

Key to Media (For complete agency information see *The Advertising Red Books-Agencies* edition):
1. Bus. Publs. 2. Cable T.V. 3. Catalogs & Directories. 4. Co-op Adv. 5. Consumer Mags. 6. D.M. to Bus. Estab.7. D.M. to Consumers 8. Daily Newsp. 9. Exhibits/Trade Shows 10. Foreign 11. Infomercial 12. Internet Adv.13. Multimedia 14. Network Radio 15. Network T.V. 16. Newsp. Distr. Mags. 17. Other 18. Outdoor (Posters, Transit) 19. Point of Purchase20. Premiums, Novelties 21. Product Samples 22. Special Events Mktg. 23. Spot Radio 24. Spot T.V. 25. Weekly Newsp. 26. Yellow Page Adv.

Food Processing & Manufacturing

Baking Powder — Butter — Canned Goods — Chocolate — Cocoa — Coffee — Condensed Milk — Condiments — Evaporated Milk — Extracts — Frozen — Fruits — Margarine — Meats — Preserves — Spices — Sugar — Tea — Vegetables

4C FOODS CORPORATION
580 Fountain Ave
Brooklyn, NY 11208-6002
Tel.: (718) 272-4242
Fax: (718) 272-2899
E-mail: inthekitchen@4c.com
Web Site: www.4c.com
Sales Range: $100-124.9 Million
Approx. Number Employees: 150
Year Founded: 1935
Business Description:
Mfr. of Bread Crumbs, Grated Cheese, Baking Crumbs, Coating Mixes, Rib Sauce, Ice Tea Mixes, Dehydrated Soup Mixes & Lemonade Drink Mixes
S.I.C.: 2099; 2086
N.A.I.C.S.: 311999; 312111
Media: 2-9-23-25
Distr.: Reg.
Budget Set: Nov.
Personnel:
John Celauro *(Pres)*
Nathan Celauro *(Pres-Sls)*
Brands & Products:
2GO
4C
HOMESTYLE
TEA2GO
TOTALLY LIGHT
Advertising Agency:
DKM Marketing Consultants Inc.
114 Dartmouth Rd.
Manhasset, NY 11030
Tel.: (516) 365-7260
(4C Iced Tea Mix, 4C Grated Cheese, 4C Bread Crumbs)

A. DUDA & SONS INC.
1200 Duda Trl
Oviedo, FL 32765-4504
Mailing Address:
PO Box 620257
Oviedo, FL 32762-0257
Tel.: (407) 365-2111
Fax: (407) 365-2010
E-mail: info@duda.com
Web Site: www.duda.com
Approx. Number Employees: 2,500
Year Founded: 1926
Business Description:
Agribusiness & Real Estate; Vegetable, Citrus & Sod Growers; Cattle; Crop Preparation
S.I.C.: 5261
N.A.I.C.S.: 444220
Import Export
Advertising Expenditures: $500,000
Media: 2-4-7-9-10-11-13-18-25
Distr.: Intl.
Personnel:
Ferdinand S. Duda *(Chm)*
David J. Duda *(CEO)*
Rick Alcocer *(Sr VP-Fresh Sls)*
Dan Duda *(Sr VP-Fresh Ops)*
Tommy Duda *(Sr VP-Land Matters and Mergers and Acq)*
Susan Howard *(Dir-Corp Commun)*
Brands & Products:
BERMUDA
CITRUS BELLE
DANDY
DUDA
EMPRESS ZOYSIA
FLORATAM
PALMETTO
REDICEL
SEVILLE
VIERA
Advertising Agency:
Chernoff Newman
2500 Maitland Center Pkwy Ste 104
Maitland, FL 32751-4165
Tel.: (407) 875-1919
Fax: (407) 875-0666
(Fresh Fruits & Vegetables; Real Estate)

A.C. KISSLING, INC.
161 E Allen St
Philadelphia, PA 19125-4144
Tel.: (215) 423-4700
Fax: (215) 425-0525
E-mail: ackissling@verizon.net
Sales Range: $10-24.9 Million
Approx. Number Employees: 10
Business Description:
Sauerkraut & Meats
S.I.C.: 5147
N.A.I.C.S.: 424470
Advertising Expenditures: $250,000
Media: 7
Distr.: Reg.
Budget Set: Dec.
Personnel:
Richard W. Kissling, Jr. *(Pres)*
Brands & Products:
A.C. KISSLING

ACH FOOD COMPANIES, INC.
(Sub. of Associated British Foods Plc)
7171 Goodlett Farms Pkwy
Cordova, TN 38016-4909
Tel.: (901) 381-3000
Fax: (901) 381-2968
Toll Free: (800) 691-1106
E-mail: info@achfood.com
Web Site: www.achfood.com
Approx. Number Employees: 250
Business Description:
Miscellaneous Food Products
S.I.C.: 2079; 2099
N.A.I.C.S.: 311225; 311999
Personnel:
Jeffrey A. Atkins *(COO)*
Charles F. Martin, III *(CMO & Exec VP)*
Carmen Sciackitano *(VP-Gen Counsel)*
Bill Puentes *(Dir-Mktg)*
Advertising Agencies:
Cramer-Krasselt
246 E Chicago St
Milwaukee, WI 53202
Tel.: (414) 227-3500
Fax: (414) 276-8710
Spice Islands

Lapiz
35 W Wacker Dr 12th Fl
Chicago, IL 60601
Tel.: (312) 220-5000
Fax: (312) 220-6212
(Mazola, Creative)

Tapestry Partners
35 W Wacker Dr
Chicago, IL 60601
Tel.: (312) 220-3535
Fax: (312) 220-6561
(Media Buying & Planning)

ADAMS EXTRACT & SPICE LLC
3217 Johnston Rd
Gonzales, TX 78629
Mailing Address:
PO Box 1726
Gonzales, TX 78629
Tel.: (830) 672-1850
Fax: (830) 672-8100
E-mail: spice@adamsextract.com
Web Site: www.adamsextract.com
Approx. Number Employees: 105
Year Founded: 1888
Business Description:
Mfr. of Vanilla, Butter Flavoring, Spices & Food Colors
S.I.C.: 5149; 2099
N.A.I.C.S.: 424490; 311999
Export
Media: 2-5-10-19-20
Distr.: Reg.
Personnel:
Clay Ruple *(Pres & CFO)*
Jennifer Hawkes *(Dir-HR)*
Beth Henderschott *(Mgr-Mktg)*
Brands & Products:
ADAMS
ADAMS BEST
ADAMS EXTRACT
ADAMS RESERVE

ADVANCED FOOD PRODUCTS LLC
(Sub. of BC-USA, Inc.)
402 S Custer Ave
New Holland, PA 17557
Tel.: (717) 355-8667
Fax: (717) 355-8848
E-mail: info@afpllc.com
Web Site: www.afpllc.com
Approx. Number Employees: 200
Business Description:
Aseptically Canned Puddings, Cheese Sauces & Nutritional Beverages Mfr
S.I.C.: 2099; 2022
N.A.I.C.S.: 311999; 311513
Export
Advertising Expenditures: $200,000
Bus. Publs.: $100,000; Other: $100,000
Personnel:
Miroslav Hosek *(Pres & CEO)*
Bill Dillon *(VP-Sls)*
Rich Kern *(VP-Sls)*
Audrey King *(Dir)*
Brands & Products:
ANDERSON'S
REAL FRESH
REGENT

AG PROCESSING INC.
12700 W Dodge Rd
Omaha, NE 68154-2154
Tel.: (402) 496-7809
Fax: (402) 498-2215
Toll Free: (800) 247-1345

E-mail: info@agp.com
Web Site: www.agp.com
Sales Range: $1-4.9 Billion
Approx. Number Employees: 250
Year Founded: 1983
Business Description:
Agricultural Services
S.I.C.: 5153; 2075
N.A.I.C.S.: 424510; 311222
Export
Media: 2-7-20
Personnel:
Martin P. Reagan *(CEO)*
J. Keith Spackler *(CFO, Asst Treas, Asst Sec & Grp VP-Fin)*
Larry Steier *(Gen Counsel & VP)*
John Campbell *(Sr VP)*
Charles A. Janiszewski *(Sr VP-Eng)*
Mike Maranell *(Sr VP)*
Gary L. Olsen *(Sr VP-Grain Ops)*
Michael Reed *(Sr VP-Info Sys)*
David E. Tegeder *(Sr VP-Refined Vegetable Oils)*
Duke Vair *(Sr VP-HR)*
Terry Voss *(Sr VP-Transportation)*
Brands & Products:
AEP
AGP
AMINOPLUS
MASTERFEEDS
SOYGOLD
Advertising Agency:
Swanson Russell Associates
14301 FNB Pkwy Ste 312
Omaha, NE 68154-5299
Tel.: (402) 393-4940
Fax: (402) 393-6926
— Susan Rehm *(V.P. & Acct. Supvr.)*

AGROFARMA BRANDS
669 County Rd 25
New Berlin, NY 13411
Tel.: (607) 847-6181
Fax: (607) 841-8847
E-mail: info@chobani.com
Web Site: www.chobani.com
Sales Range: $1-9.9 Million
Approx. Number Employees: 100
Year Founded: 2005
Business Description:
Dairy Products Mfr & Whslr
S.I.C.: 5143; 0241
N.A.I.C.S.: 424430; 112120
Media: 6-10-21-22
Personnel:
Hamdi Ulukaya *(Founder & Pres)*
Kyle O'Brien *(VP-Sls)*
Doron Stern *(VP-Mktg)*
Yvette Baumgarten-Borrack *(Reg Mgr-Southeast)*
Girish Patel *(Mgr-Quality Assurance)*
Brands & Products:
CHOBANI

AGROPUR COOPERATIVE
510 Rue Principale
Granby, QC J2G 7G2, Canada
Tel.: (450) 375-1991
Fax: (450) 375-2099
Telex: 5832510
E-mail: info@agropur.com
Web Site: www.agropur.com
Sales Range: $1-4.9 Billion
Approx. Number Employees: 5,000
Year Founded: 1938
Business Description:
Agricultural Cooperative; Dairy Production & Research
S.I.C.: 2026; 2022; 8733
N.A.I.C.S.: 311511; 311513; 541710
Import Export
Advertising Expenditures: $500,000
Media: 5-6-9-18-19-23-24
Distr.: Natl.
Budget Set: Aug.
Personnel:
Serge Riendeau *(Chm)*
Rene Grimard *(Vice Chm)*
Pierre Claprood *(CEO)*
Jocelyn Lauziere *(CFO)*
Robert Gour *(Pres-Fine Cheese Div)*
Louis Lefebvre *(Pres-Cheese & Functional Products Div)*
Serge Paquette *(Pres-Div Natrel)*
Benoit Gagnon *(Exec VP-Global Dev)*
Jean Brodeur *(VP-PR & Comm)*
Caroline Losson *(VP-Mktg)*
Scott McDonald *(VP-HR)*
Michel Pouliot *(VP-Research, Dev & Engrg)*
Michel St-Louis *(VP-Legal Affairs)*
Brands & Products:
AGROPUR SIGNATURE
ALLEGRO
BRIGHT
CANADIAN RESERVE
CHAMPFLEURY
CRINO
ISLAND FARMS
L'EXTRA
NATREL
OKA
OLYMPIC
QUEBON
SEALTEST
VAUDREUIL
YOPLAIT

ALFRED NICKLES BAKERY, INC.
26 N Main St
Navarre, OH 44662-1158
Tel.: (330) 879-5635
Fax: (330) 879-5896
E-mail: info@nicklesbakery.com
Web Site: www.nicklesbakery.com
Approx. Number Employees: 2,500
Year Founded: 1909
Business Description:
Baker of Bread, Buns, Sweet Goods (Including Sweet Rolls, Donuts, Cake) & Hard Rolls; Brown-n-Serve Rolls; English Muffins
S.I.C.: 2051
N.A.I.C.S.: 311812
Advertising Expenditures: $40,000
Media: 2-7-10-17-26
Distr.: Reg.
Budget Set: Dec. -Jan.
Personnel:
David A. Gardner *(Pres & CEO)*
Mark Sponseller *(Treas & VP-Fin)*
Christian Gardner *(Sr VP-Admin)*
Philip Gardner *(VP-Mktg)*
Brands & Products:
BANANA FLIPS
CREME STICKS
DESSERT CUPS
DONUT FAIRS
LIGHT 35
MIDWEST GRAIN
NICKLES

ALGOOD FOOD COMPANY
7401 Tradeport Dr
Louisville, KY 40258
Tel.: (502) 637-3631
Fax: (502) 637-1502
E-mail: jmelhuish@algoodfood.com
Web Site: www.algoodfood.com
Approx. Number Employees: 145
Year Founded: 1985
Business Description:
Peanut Butter, Jellies, Jams, Preserves & Salsa
S.I.C.: 2068; 2035
N.A.I.C.S.: 311911; 311941
Import Export
Media: 2
Distr.: Natl.
Budget Set: Dec.
Personnel:
Cecil C. Barnett *(Owner)*
Nick Melhuish *(Pres)*
James Melhuish *(VP)*
Brands & Products:
ALGOOD
ALGOOD OLD FASHIONED
ALGOOD RED LABEL
CAP'N KID

ALLEGRO COFFEE CO.
(Sub. of Whole Foods Market, Inc.)
12799 Claude Ct Bldg B Dock 4
Thornton, CO 80241
Tel.: (303) 444-4844
Fax: (303) 920-5468
Toll Free: (800) 666-4869
E-mail: info@allegrocoffee.com
Web Site: www.allegrocoffee.com
Sales Range: $25-49.9 Million
Approx. Number Employees: 50
Business Description:
Coffee Whslr
S.I.C.: 5411
N.A.I.C.S.: 445110
Media: 7-13
Personnel:
Jeff Teter *(Pres & Gen Mgr)*
Tara Cross *(Dir-Mktg)*
Brands & Products:
ALLEGRO COFFEE

ALLEN CANNING COMPANY
305 E Main St
Siloam Springs, AR 72761
Tel.: (479) 524-6431
Fax: (479) 524-3291
Web Site: www.allens.com
Approx. Number Employees: 125
Year Founded: 1926
Business Description:
Vegetable Packers of Sweet Potatoes, Whole Sliced & Diced White Potatoes, Fresh Lima Beans, Okra & Squash, Green Beans, Spinach, Fresh Southern Peas & Dried Beans
S.I.C.: 2033
N.A.I.C.S.: 311421
Export
Advertising Expenditures: $300,000
Media: 2-5-7-8-9-10-13-19-23
Distr.: Natl.
Budget Set: Jan.
Personnel:
Roderick L. Allen *(Chm & CEO)*
Michael D. Hubbard *(Sr VP-Sls)*
Brands & Products:
ALLENS
BUTTERFIELD
EAST TEXAS FAIR
FRESHLIKE
POPEYE
PRINCELLA
ROYAL PRINCE
SUGARY SAM
SUNSHINE
TRAPPEY'S
VEG-ALL
WAGON MASTER
Advertising Agency:
The Winnie Group
1942 East Lakewood St.
Springfield, MO 65804
Tel.: (417) 882-1512
Fax: (417) 882-7141
(Canning Products)

ALLIED OLD ENGLISH, INC.
100 Markley St
Port Reading, NJ 07064
Tel.: (732) 636-2060
Fax: (732) 636-2538
E-mail: info@alliedoldenglish.com
Web Site: www.alliedoldenglish.com
Approx. Number Employees: 70
Year Founded: 1951
Business Description:
Prepared Foods, Chinese Condiments, Molasses & Fruit Preserves
S.I.C.: 2099; 5812
N.A.I.C.S.: 311999; 722110
Import Export
Advertising Expenditures: $500,000
Media: 2-5-6-8-9-10-19-23-24-25
Distr.: Natl.
Budget Set: Jan.
Personnel:
Fred C. Ross *(CEO)*
Frank Gatti *(CFO)*
Brands & Products:
AH-SO
CHINA-PRIDE
DAI DAY
GRANDMOTHER'S
MEE TU
PLANTATION
POLYNESIAN
RIO GLANDE
SAUCY SUSAN
SORRELL RIDGE
SUN LUCK

ALPHA BAKING COMPANY
5001 W Polk St
Chicago, IL 60644
Tel.: (773) 261-6000
Fax: (773) 261-6065
E-mail: contact@alphabaking.com
Web Site: www.alphabaking.com
Approx. Number Employees: 400
Year Founded: 1977
Business Description:
Bakery Products Mfr
S.I.C.: 5149
N.A.I.C.S.: 424490
Media: 2-4-9-13-16-18-22-23-24-26
Personnel:
Michael Marcucci *(Chm & CEO)*
Lawrence L. Marcucci *(Pres)*
Robert G. Cruice *(Treas & Exec VP)*
Gary D. Narcisi *(VP-Frozen Food Svc & Retail)*
Brands & Products:
ALPHA
CABLE CAR
CASTLE
CUB FOODS
DOMINICK'S
GOLDEN HEARTH
JEWEL-OSCO

Key to Media (For complete agency information see *The Advertising Red Books-Agencies* edition):
1. Bus. Publs. 2. Cable T.V. 3. Catalogs & Directories. 4. Co-op Adv. 5. Consumer Mags. 6. D.M. to Bus. Estab.7. D.M. to Consumers 8. Daily Newsp. 9. Exhibits/Trade Shows 10. Foreign 11. Infomercial 12. Internet Adv.13. Multimedia 14. Network Radio 15. Network T.V. 16. Newsp. Distr. Mags. 17. Other 18. Outdoor (Posters, Transit) 19. Point of Purchase20. Premiums, Novelties 21. Product Samples 22. Special Events Mktg. 23. Spot Radio 24. Spot T.V. 25. Weekly Newsp. 26. Yellow Page Adv.

Alpha Baking Company — (Continued)

KREAMO
MARYANN
MEIJER
NATIONAL
S. ROSEN

ALTA-DENA CERTIFIED DAIRY, LLC
(Sub. of Dean Dairy Holdings, LLC)
17637 E Valley Blvd
City of Industry, CA 91744
Tel.: (626) 964-6401
Fax: (626) 854-4287
Toll Free: (800) MILK123
Toll Free: (800) 535-1369
Web Site: www.altadenadairy.com
Sales Range: $250-299.9 Million
Approx. Number Employees: 500
Year Founded: 1945
Business Description:
Mfr. of Dairy Products; Dairy Processor & Distr
S.I.C.: 2026; 2024
N.A.I.C.S.: 311511; 311520
Export
Advertising Expenditures: $500,000
Media: 2-3-4-5-8-10-18-19-21-22-23-24
Distr.: Natl.
Budget Set: Nov.
Brands & Products:
ALTA DENA

ALTO-SHAAM INC.
W 164 N 9221 Water St
Menomonee Falls, WI 53051-1401
Tel.: (262) 251-3800
Fax: (262) 251-2510
Fax: (800) 558-8744
E-mail: international@alto-shaam.com
Web Site: www.alto-shaam.com
Approx. Number Employees: 310
Year Founded: 1955
Business Description:
Mfr. of Food Service Machines
S.I.C.: 3589
N.A.I.C.S.: 333319
Import Export
Media: 17
Personnel:
Steve Maahs *(Pres)*
Karen Hansen *(CEO)*
Jack Scott *(Sr VP-Sls & Mktg)*
Joe Konop *(Mgr-Mktg)*
Brands & Products:
ALTO-SHAAM
COMBI-THERM
COMBIGUARD
ECOSMART
HALO HEAT
QUICKCHILLER
SMARTCLEAN

AMANA SOCIETY, INC.
506 39th Ave PO Box 189
Amana, IA 52203-8229
Tel.: (319) 622-7500
Fax: (319) 622-3119
Web Site: www.amanasociety.com
Approx. Number Employees: 325
Year Founded: 1932
Business Description:
Commercial Farming, General Stores, Feed Mills, Lumber Yards, Woolen Goods, Meat Products, Furniture & Bakery Products & Tourist Based Attractions
S.I.C.: 0139; 0279
N.A.I.C.S.: 111998; 112990
Import Export
Media: 3-5-6-7-8-9-13-18-19-21-23-24-25-26
Distr.: Natl.
Personnel:
John K. Peterson *(Pres & CEO)*
Brands & Products:
AMANA SOCIETY
COLONY
Advertising Agency:
Datahaus
PO Box 8
Amana, IA 52203
Tel.: (319) 622-6149

AMERICAN COFFEE COMPANY, INC.
640 Magazine St
New Orleans, LA 70130-3616
Tel.: (504) 581-7234
Fax: (504) 581-7518
Toll Free: (800) 554-7234
E-mail: info@frenchmarketcoffee.com
Web Site: www.frenchmarketcoffee.com
Approx. Number Employees: 100
Year Founded: 1890
Business Description:
Roasted Coffee, Chicory & Tea Mfr
S.I.C.: 2095
N.A.I.C.S.: 311920
Media: 5-6-20-23-25-26
Distr.: Natl.
Personnel:
Fraiser Bartlett *(Pres)*
Brands & Products:
FRENCH MARKET

AMERICAN CRYSTAL SUGAR COMPANY
101 3rd St N
Moorhead, MN 56560-1952
Tel.: (218) 236-4400
Fax: (218) 236-4422
E-mail: feedback@crystalsugar.com
Web Site: www.crystalsugar.com
E-Mail For Key Personnel:
Public Relations: jschweit@crystalsugar.com
Approx. Rev.: $1,203,897,000
Approx. Number Employees: 1,361
Year Founded: 1899
Business Description:
Sugar Producer
S.I.C.: 2063; 2061; 5261; 5499
N.A.I.C.S.: 311313; 311311; 444220; 445299
Advertising Expenditures: $1,067,000
Media: 2-6-7-8-9-18-20-23-24
Distr.: Reg.
Budget Set: Aug.
Personnel:
David A. Berg *(Pres & CEO)*
Thomas S. Astrup *(CFO)*
Joseph J. Talley *(COO)*
David L. Malmskog *(Dir-Economic Analysis, Asst Sec & Asst Treas)*
Mark L. Lembke *(Mgr-Fin Admin, Asst Sec & Asst Treas)*
Samuel S.M. Wai *(Treas & Asst Sec)*
Kevin S. Price *(Dir-Govt Affairs)*
Ronald K. Peterson *(Asst Treas, Asst Sec, Mgr-Acctg & Sys)*
Lisa M. Maloy *(Mgr-Treasury Ops & Asst Sec)*
Jeff Schweitzer *(Mgr-Pub Rels)*
Brands & Products:
CRYSTAL SUGAR
Advertising Agency:
Flint Communications, Inc. & Adfarm
101 N 10th St Ste 300
Fargo, ND 58107
Tel.: (701) 237-4850
Fax: (701) 234-9680

AMERICAN FOODS GROUP, LLC
(Sub. of Rosens Diversified, Inc.)
544 Acme St
Green Bay, WI 54302
Tel.: (920) 437-6330
Fax: (920) 436-6510
Web Site: www.americanfoodsgroup.com
Sales Range: $300-349.9 Million
Approx. Number Employees: 4,000
Year Founded: 1985
Business Description:
Holding Company; Beef & Pork Products Mfr & Whslr
S.I.C.: 6719; 0751; 2013; 5147
N.A.I.C.S.: 551112; 311611; 311612; 311613; 424470
Media: 2-4
Personnel:
Greg Benedict *(Pres & COO)*
Thomas J. Rosen *(CEO)*
Robert Elliott *(Pres-Brands Div)*
Don Mehesan *(Pres-Fresh Meat Div)*
Jeff Jones *(Exec VP-Boxed Beef & Trim Sls-Fresh Meat Div)*
Jerry Scott *(Exec VP-Fresh Meat Div)*
Steve Van Lannen *(Exec VP-Fresh Meat Div)*
Steve Giroux *(VP-Sls & Mktg)*
David Wilson *(VP-HR)*
Brands & Products:
AMERICAN FOODS GROUP
BLACK ANGUS RESERVE
GOLDEN PRAIRIE
GOLDEN SUPERB
GREAT AMERICAN HAMBURGERS
GREAT AMERICAN STEAKS
SERVER'S CHOICE
SHEBOYGAN
SMOKREST

AMERICAN INSTANTS, INC.
117 Bartley Flanders Rd
Flanders, NJ 07836
Tel.: (973) 584-8811
Fax: (973) 584-0444
E-mail: sales@americaninstants.com
Web Site: www.americaninstants.com
E-Mail For Key Personnel:
Sales Director: sales@americaninstants.com
Approx. Number Employees: 60
Year Founded: 1961
Business Description:
Instant Beverage Mfr
S.I.C.: 5149; 2095
N.A.I.C.S.: 424490; 311920
Media: 7-13-19-21
Personnel:
Thomas J. Roche *(Chm)*
Chris Roche *(CEO)*
Brands & Products:
AMERICAN INSTANTS
CAPPUCCINO SUPREME
DEEP RICH COFFEE SYSTEM
ESTEEMED SUPREME
HOT CHOCOLATE SUPREME
SHIVERY SHAKE

AMERICAN ITALIAN PASTA COMPANY
(Sub. of Ralcorp Holdings, Inc.)
1251 NW Briarcliff Pkwy Ste 500
Kansas City, MO 64116
Tel.: (816) 584-5000
Fax: (816) 584-5100
Toll Free: (877) EAT-PASTA
E-mail: smanson@aipc.com
Web Site: www.aipc.com
Approx. Rev.: $628,162,000
Approx. Number Employees: 675
Year Founded: 1988
Business Description:
Pasta Mfr & Marketer
S.I.C.: 2098; 2034; 2099
N.A.I.C.S.: 311823; 311423; 311999
Advertising Expenditures: $2,200,000
Media: 2-4-7-13-17-18-21-22-26
Personnel:
William R. Patterson *(Chm)*
Walter N. George *(Pres)*
Paul R. Geist *(CFO & Exec VP)*
Robert W. Schuller *(Chief Compliance Officer, Gen Counsel & Exec VP)*
Francesco Bonfanti *(Pres-Italy)*
Thomas J. Branich *(Sr VP-Retail Sls)*
Michael J. Kaczynski *(Sr VP-Retail Sls)*
Patrick D. Regan *(Sr VP-Consumer & Customer Brand Mktg)*
Chrystal L. Johnson *(VP-Info Sys)*
Pam Lane *(Mgr-Regulatory)*
Brands & Products:
AIPC
ANTHONY'S
GOLDEN GRAIN
HEARTLAND
LENSI
LUXURY
MARTHA GOOCH
MRS. GRASS
MUELLER'S
PENNSYLVANIA DUTCH
R&F
RONCO
Advertising Agency:
Linden Alschuler & Kaplan, Inc.
1251 Ave of the Americas Ste 940
New York, NY 10020
Tel.: (212) 575-4545
Fax: (212) 575-0519

AMERICAN RICE, INC.
(Sub. of SOS Corporacion Alimentaria, S.A.)
10700 N Fwy Ste 800
Houston, TX 77037-1158
Mailing Address:
PO Box 2587
Houston, TX 77252-2587
Tel.: (281) 272-8800
Fax: (281) 272-9707
Telex: 77-5839 ARI HOU
E-mail: info@amrice.com
Web Site: www.amrice.com
Approx. Number Employees: 360
Business Description:
Rice Producer
S.I.C.: 2044

Key to Media (For complete agency information see *The Advertising Red Books-Agencies* edition):
1. Bus. Publs. 2. Cable T.V. 3. Catalogs & Directories. 4. Co-op Adv. 5. Consumer Mags. 6. D.M. to Bus. Estab.7. D.M. to Consumers 8. Daily Newsp. 9. Exhibits/Trade Shows 10. Foreign 11. Infomercial 12. Internet Adv.13. Multimedia 14. Network Radio 15. Network T.V. 16. Newsp. Distr. Mags. 17. Other 18. Outdoor (Posters, Transit) 19. Point of Purchase20. Premiums, Novelties 21. Product Samples 22. Special Events Mktg. 23. Spot Radio 24. Spot T.V. 25. Weekly Newsp. 26. Yellow Page Adv.

N.A.I.C.S.: 311212
Advertising Expenditures: $500,000
Media: 2-6-7-8-10-18-19-21-22-23-25
Distr.: Natl.
Personnel:
Lee Adams *(Pres)*
Rick Arredondo *(CFO)*
Shelby Cater *(Mgr-Customer Svc-Intl)*
Brands & Products:
AA
ABU BINT
ABU BINT/GOLDEN CHOPSTICK
ADOLPHUS
BLUE RIBBON
BLUE RIBBON GOLDEN
CINTA AZUL
COLUSA ROSE
COMET
DRAGON
GREEN PEACOCK
PEAR BLOSSOM
WONDER
Advertising Agency:
K. Fernandez and Associates, LLC
8207 Callaghan Rd Ste 200
San Antonio, TX 78230-4736
Tel.: (210) 614-1052
Fax: (210) 614-1059

AMERICAN RICE, INC.
(Sub. of American Rice, Inc.)
10700 N Fwy Ste 800
Houston, TX 77037-1158
Tel.: (281) 272-8800
Fax: (281) 272-9682
E-mail: info@gruposos.com
Web Site: www.amrice.com
Approx. Number Employees: 47
Business Description:
Rice Marketer
S.I.C.: 7319; 7389
N.A.I.C.S.: 561499; 541870; 561439; 561990
Advertising Expenditures: $1,000,000
Media: 2-6-7-8-10-18-19-21-22-23-25
Distr.: Intl.
Budget Set: Apr.
Personnel:
Mike Macora *(VP-Sls)*
Karen Tigert *(Mgr-Sls Promos)*

AMERICAN SEAFOODS, LP
Marketplace Tower 2025 1st Ave Ste 900
Seattle, WA 98121
Tel.: (206) 374-1515
Fax: (206) 374-1516
E-mail: info@americanseafoods.com
Web Site:
www.americanseafoods.com
Sales Range: $500-549.9 Million
Approx. Number Employees: 1,100
Business Description:
Holding Company
S.I.C.: 6719; 2092
N.A.I.C.S.: 551112; 311712
Media: 2-7-10-11-13-19-20-21
Personnel:
Bernt O. Bodal *(Chm & CEO)*

AMERICAN SUGAR REFINING, INC.
(Sub. of Florida Crystal Corporation)
1 Federal St
Yonkers, NY 10705-1079
Tel.: (914) 963-2400
Fax: (914) 963-5213
Business Description:
Cane Sugar Refining Services
S.I.C.: 2062
N.A.I.C.S.: 311312
Media: 4-6-9-10-17-19-25
Distr.: Intl.; Natl.
Brands & Products:
COUNTRY CANE
FLOSWEET
JACK FROST

AMY'S KITCHEN, INC.
2330 Northpoint Pkwy
Santa Rosa, CA 95407
Mailing Address:
PO Box 4759
Petaluma, CA 95407
Tel.: (707) 578-7270
Fax: (707) 578-7995
Web Site: www.amys.com
Approx. Sls.: $200,000,000
Approx. Number Employees: 900
Year Founded: 1987
Business Description:
Health Food Mfr
S.I.C.: 2099
N.A.I.C.S.: 311999
Advertising Expenditures: $50,000
Media: 6-8-10
Personnel:
Andy Berliner *(Pres & CEO & Co-Owner)*
Rachel Berliner *(Co-Owner)*
Damien Threadgold *(Dir-Sls-UK)*
Michelle Erbs *(Mgr-Mktg)*
Tom Mello *(Mgr-Organic Agriculture)*
Errol Sober *(Mgr-Bus Dev & Natl Sls)*

ANDERSON ERICKSON DAIRY COMPANY
2420 E University Ave
Des Moines, IA 50317-6559
Tel.: (515) 265-2521
Fax: (515) 263-6301
E-mail: aedairy@aedairy.com
Web Site: www.aedairy.com
Sales Range: $25-49.9 Million
Approx. Number Employees: 520
Year Founded: 1930
Business Description:
Milk & Dairy Products Mfr
S.I.C.: 2026; 2086
N.A.I.C.S.: 311511; 312111
Advertising Expenditures: $100,000
Media: 4-5-17-21-22
Personnel:
James W. Erickson *(Chm)*
Miriam Erickson Brown *(Pres & CEO)*
Warren Erickson *(Pres/CEO-Anderson Erickson Dairy)*
Kim Peter *(Dir-Mktg)*
Brands & Products:
ANDERSON ERICKSON
ICY COLD TO GO!
YOLITE

ARDEN INTERNATIONAL LLC
(Sub. of Bellisio Foods, Inc.)
21150 Hamburg Ave
Lakeville, MN 55044-8060
Tel.: (952) 469-2000
Fax: (952) 985-5822
Toll Free: (800) ENTREES
Approx. Number Employees: 100
Year Founded: 1977
Business Description:
Food Processor; Prepared Frozen Food Entrees
S.I.C.: 2038
N.A.I.C.S.: 311412
Export
Media: 10-17
Distr.: Natl.; Reg.
Budget Set: Aug.
Personnel:
Kim Ewanika *(Sr Dir-Sls & Mktg Ops-Arden Culinary)*
Brands & Products:
ARDEN BRAND
ARDEN INTERNATIONAL KITCHENS
ARDENELLI'S
CHARRITO'S

ARMANINO FOODS OF DISTINCTION, INC.
30588 San Antonio St
Hayward, CA 94544
Tel.: (510) 441-9300
Fax: (510) 441-0101
Toll Free: (866) 553-5611
E-mail: warmaninofoods@armanino.biz
Web Site: www.armaninofoods.biz
Approx. Sls.: $22,879,412
Approx. Number Employees: 41
Year Founded: 1998
Business Description:
Italian-Style Frozen Food Mfr
S.I.C.: 2038
N.A.I.C.S.: 311412
Advertising Expenditures: $6,605
Media: 4-7-10-18-20-21-26
Personnel:
Douglas R. Nichols *(Chm)*
David B. Scatena *(Vice Chm)*
Edmond J. Pera *(Pres & CEO)*
Edgar Estonina *(CFO)*
Deborah Armanino LeBlanc *(Dir-Sls)*
Brands & Products:
ARMANINO
ARMANINO FOODS OF DISTINCTION INC.
BAY CITY
GARLIC ZING
ITALIAN HOLIDAY
Advertising Agency:
Lee & Associates, Inc.
145 S Fairfax Ave Ste 301
Los Angeles, CA 90036-2166
Tel.: (323) 938-3300
Fax: (323) 938-3305

ARMOUR-ECKRICH MEATS, LLC
4225 Naperville Rd Ste 600
Lisle, IL 60563
Tel.: (630) 281-5000
Fax: (630) 281-7670
Web Site: www.armour-eckrich.com
Approx. Number Employees: 250
Business Description:
Meats Processor & Distr
S.I.C.: 5147
N.A.I.C.S.: 424470
Media: 16-22
Personnel:
Michael Paribello *(Sr Dir-Mktg)*
Brands & Products:
ARMOUR
ARMOUR ECKRICH
ECKRICH
HEALTHY ONES
LUNCHMAKERS
MARGHERITA
MAYROSE
Advertising Agencies:
OMD-USA
195 Broadway
New York, NY 10007
Tel.: (212) 590-7100

Schafer Condon Carter
168 N Clinton
Chicago, IL 60661
Tel.: (312) 464-1666
Fax: (312) 464-0628

Spark Communications
222 Merchandise Mart Plz Ste 550
Chicago, IL 60654-1032
Tel.: (312) 970-8400
Fax: (312) 970-8464
Fax: (312) 970-8409

ASSOCIATED MILK PRODUCERS INC.
(d/b/a AMPI)
315 N Broadway
New Ulm, MN 56073
Tel.: (507) 354-8295
Fax: (507) 359-8651
Web Site: www.ampi.com
Sales Range: $10-24.9 Million
Approx. Number Employees: 60
Year Founded: 1969
Business Description:
Regional Dairy Products Cooperative
S.I.C.: 2023; 2021; 2022
N.A.I.C.S.: 311514; 311512; 311513
Media: 2
Distr.: Natl.
Personnel:
Paul Toft *(Chm)*
Ed Welch *(Pres & CEO)*
Sheryl Doering Meshke *(Sr VP-Pub Affairs & Corp Strategy)*
James Walsh *(Dir-Mktg)*
Brands & Products:
AMPI
COMPAKT REDDIES
STATE BRAND

ATALANTA CORPORATION
1 Atalanta Plz
Elizabeth, NJ 07206
Tel.: (908) 351-8000
Fax: (908) 351-1978
Web Site: www.atalanta1.com
Approx. Sls.: $235,000,000
Approx. Number Employees: 200
Year Founded: 1945
Business Description:
Canned Meats, Frozen Seafoods & Groceries, Cheeses & Specialty Items Importer & Distr
S.I.C.: 5149; 5143
N.A.I.C.S.: 424490; 424430
Import Export
Advertising Expenditures: $300,000
Media: 2-4-5-6-7-8-9-10-14-16-18-19-20-21-23
Distr.: Natl.
Budget Set: Nov.
Personnel:
Andrew Gellert *(Owner)*
Charles Stough *(CFO)*
Robert S. Gellert *(Exec VP)*
Jacque Folts *(Mgr-Mktg)*
Brands & Products:
ATALANTA
CALYPSO
CASA DIVA
CELEBRITY

Key to Media (For complete agency information see *The Advertising Red Books-Agencies* edition):
1. Bus. Publs. 2. Cable T.V. 3. Catalogs & Directories. 4. Co-op Adv. 5. Consumer Mags. 6. D.M. to Bus. Estab.7. D.M. to Consumers
8. Daily Newsp. 9. Exhibits/Trade Shows 10. Foreign 11. Infomercial 12. Internet Adv.13. Multimedia 14. Network Radio
15. Network T.V. 16. Newsp. Distr. Mags. 17. Other 18. Outdoor (Posters, Transit) 19. Point of Purchase20. Premiums, Novelties
21. Product Samples 22. Special Events Mktg. 23. Spot Radio 24. Spot T.V. 25. Weekly Newsp. 26. Yellow Page Adv.

Atalanta Corporation — (Continued)

DEL DESTINO
THE GOLDEN PIG
GREENLEAF
HAMNIK
INTERNATIONAL CHOICE
MARSHALL'S
MARTEL
MILL DANCE BRAND
NORDIC PRIDE
POLONAISE
ROYAL DANUBE
ROYAL KERRY
ROYAL MAHOUT
SHAHEEN
TIVOLI
TOP
WHITE CROWN
ZERTO

ATEECO, INC.

600 E Center St
Shenandoah, PA 17976
Tel.: (570) 462-2745
Fax: (570) 462-1392
Web Site: www.pierogies.com
Sales Range: $100-124.9 Million
Approx. Number Employees: 241
Business Description:
Ethnic Foods; Frozen
S.I.C.: 2038; 2099
N.A.I.C.S.: 311412; 311999
Personnel:
Thomas F. Twardzik *(Owner)*
Gary Lauerman *(Dir-Sls & Mktg-Mrs. T's Pierogies)*
Brands & Products:
MRS. T'S PIEROGIES
MRS.T'S
THE PERFECT PAIRING OF PASTA AND POTATOES
Advertising Agency:
Alcone Marketing Group
(Division of Omnicom Group, Inc.)
4 Studebaker
Irvine, CA 92618-2012
Tel.: (949) 770-4400
Fax: (949) 770-2957

A.V. OLSSON TRADING CO. INC.

2001 W Main St Ste 215
Stamford, CT 06902-4542
Tel.: (203) 969-2090
Fax: (203) 969-2098
Toll Free: (877) 929-3999
Web Site: www.avolsson.com
Approx. Sls.: $5,000,000
Approx. Number Employees: 40
Year Founded: 1920
Business Description:
Scandinavian Food Importer
S.I.C.: 5149
N.A.I.C.S.: 424490
Import
Media: 7-10-18-19-21
Distr.: Natl.
Personnel:
Kenneth Olsson *(Pres)*
Brands & Products:
ASCOT
BALLERINA
BEYOND GOURMET
CREAMY HAVARTI
GRADDOST
GULOST
HERRGARD
JULIA MARIE
LEKSAND
NORRGREVE SWISS
PRASTOST
SCANDIC FARMER
SCANDIC GRAND FONTINA
SCANDIC ORGANIC CHEDDAR
SKANSEN
SKANSEN HERRING
SWEDISH KITCHEN
VASTERBOTTEN

AZTECA FOODS, INCORPORATED

5005 S Nagle Ave
Chicago, IL 60638
Tel.: (708) 563-6600
Fax: (708) 563-0331
Toll Free: (800) 475-7997
E-mail: info@aztecafoods.com
Web Site: www.aztecafoods.com
E-Mail For Key Personnel:
President: arthur.velasquez@aztecafoods.com
Approx. Number Employees: 150
Year Founded: 1970
Business Description:
Tortillas, Salad Shells & Tortilla Chips Mfr
S.I.C.: 2099; 2096
N.A.I.C.S.: 311830; 311919
Export
Media: 2-3-5-7-9-10-19
Distr.: Natl.
Budget Set: Nov.-Dec.
Personnel:
Arthur R. Velasquez *(Chm)*
Renee Togher *(Pres)*
Joanne Velasquez *(Exec VP)*
Joseph Klomes *(VP-Fin)*
Dorothy Pigozzo *(VP-HR)*
Joe Rabaglia *(Mgr-Mktg)*
Brands & Products:
AZTECA
BUENA VIDA
IT'S ALWAYS A FIESTA WITH AZTECA
Advertising Agency:
Schafer Condon Carter
168 N Clinton
Chicago, IL 60661
Tel.: (312) 464-1666
Fax: (312) 464-0628
(Tortilla Chips)
— Jodi Schwartz *(Acct. Dir.)*

B&G FOODS, INC.

4 Gatehall Dr Ste 110
Parsippany, NJ 07054-4522
Tel.: (973) 401-6500
Fax: (973) 364-1037
E-mail: info@bgfoods.com
Web Site: www.bgfoods.com
E-Mail For Key Personnel:
President: dwenner@bgfoods.com
Approx. Sls.: $513,337,000
Approx. Number Employees: 749
Year Founded: 1889
Business Description:
Jams, Jellies, Spices, Pickles, Prepared Garlic, Bagel Chips, Snack Foods, Baked Beans & Wine Vinegar & Other Food Products Mfr
S.I.C.: 2033; 2035; 2099; 5142
N.A.I.C.S.: 311421; 311941; 311999; 424420
Import Export
Advertising Expenditures: $2,900,000
Media: 2-14-15-17-19
Distr.: Natl.
Personnel:
Stephen C. Sherrill *(Chm)*
David L. Wenner *(Pres & CEO)*
Robert C. Cantwell *(CFO & Exec VP-Fin)*
Scott E. Lerner *(Chief Compliance Officer, Gen Counsel, Sec & Exec VP)*
James H. Brown *(Exec VP)*
William F. Herbes *(Exec VP-Ops)*
Vanessa E. Maskal *(Exec VP-Sls & Mktg)*
William H. Wright *(Exec VP-Quality Assurance & R & D)*
Marvin Schwinder *(Dir-Mktg)*
Brands & Products:
AC'CENT
B&G
B&M
BLOCH & GUGGENHEIMER
BRER RABBIT
CREAM OF WHEAT
EMERIL'S
FOOD SERVICE
GRANDMA'S
GRANDMA'S MOLASSES
JOAN OF ARC
LAS PALMAS
MAPLE GROVE FARMS OF VERMONT
ORTEGA
POLANER
RED DEVIL
REGINA
SA-SON
TRAPPEY'S
UNDERWOOD
VERMONT MAID
WRIGHT'S
Advertising Agency:
Robert N. Pyle & Associates
1223 Potomac St NW
Washington, DC 20007
Tel.: (202) 333-8190
Fax: (202) 337-3809

BAKEMARK INGREDIENTS USA

(Sub. of CSM Bakery Supplies Division North America)
7351 Crider Ave
Pico Rivera, CA 90660-3705
Tel.: (562) 949-1054
Fax: (562) 949-1257
Web Site: www.bakemark.com
Approx. Number Employees: 450
Year Founded: 1928
Business Description:
Prepared Flour Mixes & Doughs; Bakery Products, Fruit Fillings & Icings
S.I.C.: 2045; 5149
N.A.I.C.S.: 311822; 424490
Import Export
Personnel:
Resugio Reynoso *(VP-Fin & Admin)*
Advertising Agency:
Travers Collins & Company
726 Exchange St Ste 500
Buffalo, NY 14210-1495
Tel.: (716) 842-2222
Fax: (716) 842-6424

BAKER COMMODITIES, INC.

4020 Bandini Blvd
Vernon, CA 90058-4605
Tel.: (323) 268-2801
Fax: (323) 268-5166
Web Site: www.bakercommodities.com
Approx. Number Employees: 610
Year Founded: 1937
Business Description:
Rendering Company; Animal Fats & Oils, Tallow, Feed Fat, Meat & Bone Meal Producer & Distr
S.I.C.: 2013; 2048
N.A.I.C.S.: 311613; 311119
Export
Advertising Expenditures: $50,000
Media: 2-7-8-10-20-21
Distr.: Natl.
Budget Set: Nov.
Personnel:
James M. Andreoli *(Pres & CEO)*
Dennis N. Luckey *(Exec VP)*
Larry Friend *(VP-Info Sys)*

BALCHEM CORPORATION

52 Sunrise Park Rd
New Hampton, NY 10958
Mailing Address:
PO Box 600
Slate Hill, NY 10973-0175
Tel.: (845) 326-5600
Tel.: (845) 355-5300
Fax: (845) 326-5742
Fax: (845) 326-5702
Toll Free: (800) 431-5641
E-mail: bcpexec@balchem.com
Web Site: www.balchem.com
Approx. Sls.: $255,071,000
Approx. Number Employees: 351
Year Founded: 1967
Business Description:
Developer, Mfr & Marketer of Specialty Performance Ingredients for the Food, Feed & Medical Sterilization Industries
S.I.C.: 6159; 2869; 5169
N.A.I.C.S.: 522294; 325199; 424690
Advertising Expenditures: $3,500,000
Personnel:
Dino A. Rossi *(Pres & CEO)*
Frank J. Fitzpatrick *(CFO, Treas & Asst Sec)*
Matthew Houston *(Gen Counsel & Sec)*
David F. Ludwig *(VP & Gen Mgr-ARC Specialty Prods)*
Robert T. Miniger *(VP-HR)*
Eric Smith *(VP-Mktg & Sls)*
Brands & Products:
BAKESHURE
BALCHEM CORPORATION
CONFECSHURE
FLAVORSHURE
MEATSHURE
NIASHURE
NITROSHURE
ON TARGET TO DELIVER
PHARMASHURE
REASHURE
VITASHURE

BALDUCCI'S LLC

(Holding of Irving Place Capital Management, L.P.)
10411 Motor City Dr Ste 500
Bethesda, MD 20817-1818
Tel.: (240) 403-2440
Fax: (240) 403-2520
Web Site: www.balduccis.com
Approx. Number Employees: 1,300
Year Founded: 1980

Key to Media (For complete agency information see *The Advertising Red Books-Agencies* edition):
1. Bus. Publs. 2. Cable T.V. 3. Catalogs & Directories. 4. Co-op Adv. 5. Consumer Mags. 6. D.M. to Bus. Estab.7. D.M. to Consumers
8. Daily Newsp. 9. Exhibits/Trade Shows 10. Foreign 11. Infomercial 12. Internet Adv.13. Multimedia 14. Network Radio
15. Network T.V. 16. Newsp. Distr. Mags. 17. Other 18. Outdoor (Posters, Transit) 19. Point of Purchase20. Premiums, Novelties
21. Product Samples 22. Special Events Mktg. 23. Spot Radio 24. Spot T.V. 25. Weekly Newsp. 26. Yellow Page Adv.

Business Description:
Specialty Food Stores, Restaurants & Catering Services
S.I.C.: 5411; 5812
N.A.I.C.S.: 445110; 722110; 722320
Advertising Expenditures: $100,000
Media: 7-8-9-13-22-23-25
Personnel:
Barbara Parasco *(CEO)*
Brands & Products:
BALDUCCI'S
CUSTOM CAKES
FOOD LOVER'S MARKET

BAR-S FOODS CO.
(Sub. of Sigma Foods Inc.)
3838 N Central Ave Ste 1900
Phoenix, AZ 85012-1957
Tel.: (602) 264-7272
Fax: (602) 285-5252
Web Site: www.bar-s.com
Sales Range: $500-549.9 Million
Approx. Number Employees: 1,560
Year Founded: 1981
Business Description:
Meat & Poultry Products Mfr
S.I.C.: 5147; 2022
N.A.I.C.S.: 311612; 311513
Advertising Expenditures: $1,000,000
Media: 2-5-6-7-8-9-10-13-18-19-20-21-22-23-24-25
Distr.: Reg.
Budget Set: Sept.
Personnel:
Timothy T. Day *(Chm & CEO)*
Warren Panico *(Pres & COO)*
James S. Kuykendall *(CFO & VP)*
Bryan Kuhn *(VP-Sls-Eastern Div)*
Brands & Products:
BAR-S
CHUCK WAGON
OLD WORLD PREMIUM
PRESIDENTS PRIDE
REX
VIRGINIA REEL

BARBER DAIRIES, INC.
(Sub. of Dean Dairy Holdings, LLC)
36 Barber Ct
Birmingham, AL 35209-6435
Tel.: (205) 942-2351
Fax: (205) 943-0297
E-mail: info@barbersdairy.com
Web Site: www.barbersdairy.com
Sales Range: $400-449.9 Million
Approx. Number Employees: 750
Year Founded: 1925
Business Description:
Processor & Packager of Milk & Milk Products
S.I.C.: 2026; 2024
N.A.I.C.S.: 311511; 311520
Media: 1-2-3-5-6-7-8-9-10-14-15-17-18-19-20-21-22-23-24-25-26
Distr.: Reg.
Budget Set: Sept.-Oct.
Personnel:
Valerir Meirs *(Mgr-Production)*
Brands & Products:
BARBER
DEAN
NUTRISH AB

BARBER FOODS, INC.
56 Milliken St
Portland, ME 04103
Tel.: (207) 482-5500
Fax: (207) 797-0286
Toll Free: (800) 577-2595
E-mail: customer_relations@barberfoods.com
Web Site: www.barberfoods.com
Approx. Number Employees: 700
Year Founded: 1955
Business Description:
Poultry Processing Services
S.I.C.: 2015; 2038
N.A.I.C.S.: 311615; 311412
Media: 6-8-10-20-23-25
Distr.: Natl.
Personnel:
David Barber *(CEO)*
Vicki Mann *(CFO)*
Mark Dvorozniak *(VP-Mktg)*
Brands & Products:
BARBER FOODS
MAKE DINNER. BETTER.
Advertising Agency:
Yellin/McCarron, Inc.
280 Summer St 4th Fl
Boston, MA 02210
Tel.: (617) 426-9211
Fax: (617) 426-7443

BARILLA AMERICA, INC.
(Sub. of Barilla Holding S.p.A.)
1200 Lakeside Dr
Bannockburn, IL 60015
Tel.: (847) 405-7500
Fax: (847) 405-7511
E-mail: consumerrelations@barilla-usa.com
Web Site: www.barillaus.com
Approx. Number Employees: 140
Year Founded: 1996
Business Description:
Pasta Mfr
S.I.C.: 2098
N.A.I.C.S.: 311823
Media: 6-15-24
Personnel:
Kirk Trofholz *(Pres)*
Guido Sciascia *(VP-Mktg)*
Craig Geiger *(Dir-Category Dev & Shopper Insights)*
Catherine Terry *(Mgr-Mktg-Wasa)*
Brands & Products:
BARILLA
BARILLA PLUS
Advertising Agency:
OMD Chicago
225 N Michigan Ave 19th Fl
Chicago, IL 60601-7757
Tel.: (312) 324-7000
Fax: (312) 324-8201
Media Buying & Planning

BASIC AMERICAN FOODS, INC.
2121 N Califor Blv Ste 400
Walnut Creek, CA 94596
Tel.: (925) 472-4000
Fax: (925) 472-4000
Web Site: www.baf.com
Approx. Number Employees: 2,500
Year Founded: 1933
Business Description:
Dehydrated Potatoes, Onions, Garlic & Refried Beans Mfr & Distr
S.I.C.: 2034; 2099
N.A.I.C.S.: 311423; 311999
Media: 2-7-10-20-21
Personnel:
George H. Hume *(Chm)*
Loren Kimura *(CEO)*
Jim Collins *(CFO)*
Mike Case *(Dir-IT)*
Brands & Products:
BASIC AMERICAN FOODS
CLASSIC CASSEROLE
GOLDEN GRILL
HOT SCOOPS
IDEAS YOU CAN BUILD ON
NATURE'S OWN
POTATO PEARLS
POTATO PEARLS EXCEL
QUICK-START
REDI SHRED
REGIONAL RECIPE
SANTIAGO

BAUMER FOODS INC.
2424 Edenborn Ave Ste 510
Metairie, LA 70001-1845
Tel.: (504) 482-5761
Fax: (504) 483-2425
E-mail: info@baumerfoods.com
Web Site: www.baumerfoods.com
Approx. Number Employees: 250
Year Founded: 1922
Business Description:
Barbecue Sauces Mfr
S.I.C.: 2033; 2035
N.A.I.C.S.: 311421; 311941
Import Export
Media: 4-8-13
Personnel:
Alvin A. Baumer, Jr. *(Pres & CEO)*
Brands & Products:
CRYSTAL
Advertising Agency:
Zehnder Communications, Inc.
650 Poydras St Ste 2450
New Orleans, LA 70130
Tel.: (504) 558-7778
Fax: (504) 558-7779
Toll Free: (877) 558-7778

BC-USA, INC.
(Sub. of Bongrain S.A.)
400 S Custer Ave
New Holland, PA 17557-9220
Tel.: (717) 355-8500
Fax: (717) 355-8561
Web Site: www.alouettecheese.com
Approx. Sls.: $120,000,000
Approx. Number Employees: 500
Business Description:
Cheese Products Mfr
S.I.C.: 2022
N.A.I.C.S.: 311513
Export
Media: 6-8-9-10-18-19-20-21-23
Distr.: Natl.
Personnel:
Frank Otis *(Pres)*
David Rozenberg *(Brand Mgr-Alouette Cheese)*
Brands & Products:
CREME DE BRIE
CREME FRAICHE
DELICE DE FRANCE
DELICO
FLEUR DE LAIT
FLEUR DE LAIT LIGHT
NEW HOLLAND
SALADENA

BEECH-NUT NUTRITION CORPORATION
(Sub. of Hero AG)
100 S 4th St Ste 1010
Saint Louis, MO 63102-1823
Tel.: (314) 436-7667
Fax: (314) 436-7679
Toll Free: (800) BEECH-NUT
Web Site: www.beechnut.com
Approx. Number Employees: 36
Year Founded: 1891
Business Description:
Baby Food Mfr
S.I.C.: 2032; 2099
N.A.I.C.S.: 311422; 311999
Personnel:
James Schneider *(Pres & CEO)*
Evan Eckman *(CMO)*
Brands & Products:
BABY'S FIRST
BEECH-NUT
BEECH-NUT STAGES
DHA PLUS YOGURT BLENDS WITH JUICE-MIXED BERRY
DHA PLUS YOGURT BLENDS WITH JUICE-TROPICAL FRUIT
GOOD EVENING
GOOD EVENING VEGGIE DELIGHT JUICE
GOOD MORNING
GOOD MORNING CHIQUITA BANANA JUICE WITH YOGURT
LET'S GROW
STAGES
TABLETIME
Advertising Agencies:
Design North, Inc.
8007 Douglas Ave
Racine, WI 53402
Tel.: (262) 639-2080
Tel.: (262) 898-1090
Fax: (262) 639-5230
Toll Free: (800) 247-8494

Palio
260 Broadway
Saratoga Springs, NY 12866
Tel.: (518) 584-8924
Fax: (518) 583-1560
(Let's Grow)

BEL BRANDS USA
(Sub. of Fromageries Bel S.A.)
25 NW Point Blvd Ste 1000
Elk Grove Village, IL 60007
Mailing Address:
PO Box 1974
Kaukauna, WI 54130-7074
Tel.: (847) 879-1900
Fax: (920) 788-9725
Toll Free: (800) 272-1224
E-mail: customerservicekk@belkauusa.com
Web Site: www.kaukauna.com
Approx. Number Employees: 400
Year Founded: 1949
Business Description:
Cheese Products Mfr & Producer
S.I.C.: 2022
N.A.I.C.S.: 311513
Advertising Expenditures: $4,000,000
Media: 1-3-5-6-9-10-16-19-20-21-23-24-25
Distr.: Natl.
Budget Set: Nov.

Key to Media (For complete agency information see *The Advertising Red Books-Agencies* edition):
1. Bus. Publs. 2. Cable T.V. 3. Catalogs & Directories. 4. Co-op Adv. 5. Consumer Mags. 6. D.M. to Bus. Estab.7. D.M. to Consumers
8. Daily Newsp. 9. Exhibits/Trade Shows 10. Foreign 11. Infomercial 12. Internet Adv.13. Multimedia 14. Network Radio
15. Network T.V. 16. Newsp. Distr. Mags. 17. Other 18. Outdoor (Posters, Transit) 19. Point of Purchase20. Premiums, Novelties
21. Product Samples 22. Special Events Mktg. 23. Spot Radio 24. Spot T.V. 25. Weekly Newsp. 26. Yellow Page Adv.

Bel Brands USA — (Continued)

Personnel:
Robert Gilbert *(Pres)*
Ann Legan *(VP-Mktg)*

Brands & Products:
BOURSIN
CONNOISSEUR
MINI BABYBEL
OWLS NEST

Advertising Agencies:
DDB Chicago
200 E Randolph St
Chicago, IL 60601
Tel.: (312) 552-6000
Fax: (312) 552-2370
Advertising Agency of Record
Boursin

OMD Worldwide
195 Broadway
New York, NY 10007
Tel.: (212) 590-7100
Media Buying

Porter Novelli
(Sub. of Omnicom Group, Inc.)
75 Varick St 6th Fl
New York, NY 10013
Tel.: (212) 601-8000
Fax: (212) 601-8101
Digital Agency of Record
Laughing Cow Wedges
Mini Babybel

Ryan Partnership
(dba D.L. Ryan Companies, Ltd.)
50 Danbury Rd
Wilton, CT 06897-4448
Tel.: (203) 210-3000
Fax: (203) 210-7926
Promotions

BELL-CARTER FOODS, INC.

3742 Mt Diablo Blvd
Lafayette, CA 94549-3682
Tel.: (925) 284-5933
Fax: (925) 284-2377
E-mail: lency.alex@bellcarter.com
Web Site: www.bellcarter.com
Approx. Number Employees: 300
Year Founded: 1930

Business Description:
Olive Processor
S.I.C.: 2033
N.A.I.C.S.: 311421
Advertising Expenditures: $300,000
Media: 2-4-6-7-10-13-19-20-21
Distr.: Natl.
Budget Set: Sept.

Personnel:
Paul McGinty *(VP-Sls)*

Brands & Products:
BELL-CARTER
BELL CARTER

BELLISIO FOODS, INC.

1201 Harmon Pl Ste 302
Minneapolis, MN 55403
Tel.: (612) 371-8222
E-mail: info@bellisiofoods.com
Web Site: www.bellisiofoods.com
Approx. Number Employees: 1,400
Year Founded: 1990

Business Description:
Frozen Food Specialties
S.I.C.: 2038
N.A.I.C.S.: 311412
Import Export
Media: 2-4-16-19-22

Personnel:
Jeno F. Paulucci *(Founder)*
Joel Conner *(Chm & CEO)*
Danette Bucsko *(CFO & Sr VP)*
Charles W. Pountney *(Sr Exec VP-Sls & Mktg)*

Brands & Products:
AUTHENTICO
HOMESTYLE BOWLS
HOT SUBS
LEAN GOURMET
MICHELINA'S
SIGNATURE
YU SING
ZAP'EMS

BEN E. KEITH COMPANY

1805 Record Crossing Rd
Dallas, TX 75235
Tel.: (214) 634-1500
Fax: (214) 638-4418
Web Site: www.benekeith.com
Approx. Number Employees: 3,500
Year Founded: 1906

Business Description:
Distr of Food Service Products & Anheuser-Busch Products
S.I.C.: 5141; 5181
N.A.I.C.S.: 424410; 424810
Advertising Expenditures: $375,000
Media: 2-10

Personnel:
Robert Hallam *(Chm & CEO)*
Howard Hallam *(Pres & COO)*
Mel Cockrell *(CFO & Treas)*
David Greenlee *(Gen Counsel & Sec)*
Barry Cook *(Dir-Mktg)*

BETTY CROCKER PRODUCTS

(Div. of General Mills, Inc.)
1 General Mills Blvd
Minneapolis, MN 55426

Mailing Address:
PO Box 9452
Minneapolis, MN 55440
Tel.: (763) 764-7600
Tel.: (763) 764-2311
Fax: (763) 764-8330
Toll Free: (800) 446-1898
Toll Free: (800) 328-8360
E-mail: bettycrocker@mail.genmills.com
Web Site: www.bettycrocker.com
Sales Range: $350-399.9 Million
Year Founded: 1969

Business Description:
Food Mfr
S.I.C.: 2043; 2041
N.A.I.C.S.: 311230; 311211
Media: 4-6-13-19-23-24
Distr.: Natl.

Brands & Products:
BETTY CROCKER KITCHENS

BICKEL'S SNACK FOODS, INC.

(Sub. of Hanover Foods Corporation)
1120 Zinns Quarry Rd
York, PA 17404-3533
Tel.: (717) 843-0738
Fax: (717) 181-1713
Toll Free: (800) 233-1933
Web Site: www.bickelssnacks.com
Sales Range: $100-124.9 Million
Approx. Number Employees: 180

Business Description:
Snack Food Mfr
S.I.C.: 2099; 2096
N.A.I.C.S.: 311999; 311919
Advertising Expenditures: $200,000
Media: 2-4-7-10-13
Distr.: Reg.

Brands & Products:
BONTON

BIMBO BAKERIES USA

(Plant of Bimbo Bakeries USA Inc.)
480 S Vail Ave
Montebello, CA 90640-4900
Tel.: (323) 720-6000
Fax: (323) 720-6015
Web Site: www.bimbobakeriesusa.com
Approx. Number Employees: 500
Year Founded: 1994

Business Description:
Mfr. of Bread & Related Products
S.I.C.: 2051
N.A.I.C.S.: 311812
Media: 7-8

Personnel:
Edgar Jarmaillo *(Dir-Ops)*
Liza Leszczuk *(Brand Mgr-Sandwich Thins)*

Brands & Products:
CLAIRE ROBINSON'S
FOUR-S
SUNSET HARVEST
WEBER'S BREAD

Advertising Agency:
Moroch Partners
3625 N Hall St Ste 1100
Dallas, TX 75219-5122
Tel.: (214) 520-9700
Fax: (214) 252-1724

BIMBO BAKERIES USA INC.

(Sub. of Grupo Bimbo, S.A.B. de C.V.)
255 Business Center Dr
Horsham, PA 19044
Tel.: (800) 984-0989
Fax: (610) 320-9286
E-mail: contactbbu@bimbobakeriesusa.com
Web Site: www.bimbobakeriesusa.com
Approx. Sls.: $1,200,000,000
Approx. Number Employees: 2,000
Year Founded: 1993

Business Description:
Baked Foods Mfr & Distr
S.I.C.: 5461; 5812
N.A.I.C.S.: 311811; 722310
Import Export
Advertising Expenditures: $15,000,000
Media: 17-22

Personnel:
Fernando Sanchez *(Brand Mgr-Bimbo)*

Advertising Agencies:
Legion Advertising
1425 Greenway Dr Ste 100
Arlington, TX 75038
Tel.: (817) 784-8544
Fax: (817) 385-0378

O'Leary and Partners
5000 Birch St Ste 1000
Newport Beach, CA 92660
Tel.: (949) 833-8006
Fax: (949) 833-9155
Entenmann's
Francisco
Orowheat

BIMBO BAKERIES USA INC.

(Plant of Bimbo Bakeries USA Inc.)
7301 S Fwy PO Box 937
Fort Worth, TX 76134-4004
Tel.: (817) 293-6230
Web Site: www.bimbobakeriesusa.com
Approx. Number Employees: 600
Year Founded: 1998

Business Description:
Bread Cake & Related Products
S.I.C.: 2099
N.A.I.C.S.: 311830
Import Export

Personnel:
Ronaldo Reyna *(Exec VP)*
Cristina Torres *(Brand Mgr-Bimbo)*

Brands & Products:
MRS BAIRD'S
OROWEAT

Advertising Agency:
Moroch Partners
3625 N Hall St Ste 1100
Dallas, TX 75219-5122
Tel.: (214) 520-9700
Fax: (214) 252-1724
(Mrs. Baird's brand)

BLUE DIAMOND GROWERS

1802 C St
Sacramento, CA 95811-1010

Mailing Address:
PO Box 1768
Sacramento, CA 95812-1768
Tel.: (916) 442-0771
Fax: (916) 446-8461
Telex: 377449
E-mail: mjansen@bdgrowers.com
Web Site: www.bluediamondgrowers.com
Approx. Rev.: $19,000,000
Approx. Number Employees: 1,000
Year Founded: 1910

Business Description:
Almonds, Macadamias, Hazelnuts, Pistachios & Almond Butter; Operator of Almond Research Center
S.I.C.: 0173; 8611
N.A.I.C.S.: 111335; 813910
Import Export
Advertising Expenditures: $3,000,000
Media: 2-6-7-9-23
Distr.: Intl.; Natl.
Budget Set: July

Personnel:
Clinton Shick *(Chm)*
Mark D Jansen *(Pres & CEO)*
Robert Donovan *(CFO)*
Kristen Arakaki *(Asst Mgr-Mktg)*

Brands & Products:
ALMOND ACCENTS
ALMOND FACTS
THE ALMOND PEOPLE
BLUE DIAMOND ALMONDS
BREEZE
CELEBRATION
CONFETTI
FROM THE VALLEYS OF CALIFORNIA
GOLDEN STATE
INVITATION
MINT'EES
NUT THINS
SMOKEHOUSE
SWEET'EES

Key to Media (For complete agency information see *The Advertising Red Books-Agencies* edition):
1. Bus. Publs. 2. Cable T.V. 3. Catalogs & Directories. 4. Co-op Adv. 5. Consumer Mags. 6. D.M. to Bus. Estab.7. D.M. to Consumers 8. Daily Newsp. 9. Exhibits/Trade Shows 10. Foreign 11. Infomercial 12. Internet Adv.13. Multimedia 14. Network Radio 15. Network T.V. 16. Newsp. Distr. Mags. 17. Other 18. Outdoor (Posters, Transit) 19. Point of Purchase20. Premiums, Novelties 21. Product Samples 22. Special Events Mktg. 23. Spot Radio 24. Spot T.V. 25. Weekly Newsp. 26. Yellow Page Adv.

BLUE RIDGE FARMS LLC
3301Atlantic Ave
Brooklyn, NY 11208
Tel.: (718) 827-9000
Fax: (718) 647-0052
Web Site: www.blueridgefarms.com
Sales Range: $10-24.9 Million
Approx. Number Employees: 400
Year Founded: 1933
Business Description:
Prepackaged Prepared Foods Mfr & Distr
S.I.C.: 2099
N.A.I.C.S.: 311991
Import Export
Media: 2-4-7-10-13
Distr.: Reg.
Budget Set: Feb.
Personnel:
Marvin Sussman *(Owner)*
Brands & Products:
BLUE RIDGE FARMS

BOB EVANS FARMS, INC.
3776 S High St
Columbus, OH 43207-4012
Mailing Address:
PO Box 7863
Columbus, OH 43207-0863
Tel.: (614) 491-2225
Fax: (614) 492-4949
Toll Free: (800) 272-7675
E-mail: customer_support@bobevans.com
Web Site: www.bobevans.com
Approx. Sls.: $1,676,906,000
Approx. Number Employees: 44,819
Year Founded: 1948
Business Description:
Restaurants Owner & Operator; Pork & Other Food Products Producer & Retailer
S.I.C.: 5812; 5045; 5142; 5147; 5421; 7389
N.A.I.C.S.: 722110; 311612; 424420; 425110; 425120; 445210
Advertising Expenditures: $49,311,000
Media: 3-4-5-8-9-10-16-17-18-19-20-22-23-24-25
Distr.: Reg.
Budget Set: Jan.
Personnel:
Steven A. Davis *(Chm & CEO)*
Harvey Brownlee *(Co-Pres & Chief Restaurant Ops Officer)*
Randall L. Hicks *(Co-Pres & Chief Concept Officer)*
Richard B. Green *(Interim CFO, Chief Compliance Officer & Chief Risk Officer)*
Donald J. Radkoski *(CFO, Treas & Sec)*
Paul F. DeSantis *(CFO, Treas & Asst Sec)*
J. Michael Townsley *(Pres-Bob Evans Foods)*
Mary L. Garceau *(Gen Counsel, Sec & VP)*
Joseph R. Eulberg *(Exec VP-HR)*
R. Earl Beery *(Sr VP-Food Products Ops)*
Richard D. Hall *(Sr VP-Supply Chain Mgmt)*
Kathleen E. North *(Sr VP-Restaurant Ops)*
Stephen A. Warehime *(Sr VP-Real Estate & Restaurant Dev)*
Chelsea Hamilton *(Mgr-Field Mktg Comm & PR)*
Brands & Products:

Brunner
11 Stanwix St 5th Fl
Pittsburgh, PA 15222-1312
Tel.: (412) 995-9500
Fax: (412) 995-9501
Agency of Record

BOB'S RED MILL NATURAL FOODS, INC.
13521 SE Pleasant Ct
Milwaukie, OR 97222
Tel.: (503) 654-3215
Fax: (503) 653-1339
E-mail: info@bobsredmill.com
Web Site: www.bobsredmill.com
Approx. Number Employees: 180
Business Description:
Mfr. of Natural Food Products
S.I.C.: 2041
N.A.I.C.S.: 311211
Media: 6-13
Personnel:
Robert Moore *(Founder)*
Dennis Gilliam *(Owner)*
John Wagner *(CFO)*
Matt Cox *(Mgr-Mktg)*
Brands & Products:
BOB'S RED MILL
GLUTEN FREE
TO YOUR GOOD HEALTH
Advertising Agency:
Koopman Ostbo
412 NW 8th Ave
Portland, OR 97209
Tel.: (503) 223-2168
Fax: (503) 223-1819

BOCA FOODS COMPANY
(Sub. of Kraft North America Commercial)
910 Mayer Ave PO Box 8995
Madison, WI 53708
Mailing Address:
PO Box 8995
Madison, WI 53708
Tel.: (608) 285-6950
Tel.: (608) 285-3311
Fax: (608) 285-3311
Web Site: www.bocaburger.com
Sales Range: $250-299.9 Million
Business Description:
Meat Alternative Food Products
S.I.C.: 2038
N.A.I.C.S.: 311412
Media: 6-13-19

BON SECOUR FISHERIES INC.
17449 Country Rd 49 S
Bon Secour, AL 36511
Tel.: (251) 949-7411
Fax: (251) 949-6478
E-mail: bonsec@bonsecourfisheries.com
Web Site:
www.bonsecourfisheries.com
Approx. Number Employees: 200
Year Founded: 1896
Business Description:
Fish & Seafoods Processor & Distr
S.I.C.: 2092; 2097
N.A.I.C.S.: 311712; 312113
Import Export
Media: 4-13-21-26
Personnel:
John Ray Nelson *(Chm)*
B. Frank Bailey *(CFO, Treas & Sec)*
Melanie Parker *(Dir-Info Sys)*
Pam Skinner *(Mgr-Credit)*
Brands & Products:
BON SECOUR
KING O SEAS
NELSON
NELSON'S

BRADY ENTERPRISES, INC.
167 Moore Rd
East Weymouth, MA 02189-2332
Mailing Address:
PO Box 890099
East Weymouth, MA 02189
Tel.: (781) 337-5000
Fax: (781) 337-9338
E-mail: info@brady-ent.com
Web Site: www.brady-ent.com
Approx. Number Employees: 80
Year Founded: 1964
Business Description:
Dry Food Products Mixing & Packaging Services; Stuffing & Seasonings Mfr
S.I.C.: 2099; 2034; 7389
N.A.I.C.S.: 311942; 311423; 311999; 561910
Media: 7
Distr.: Natl.
Budget Set: Nov.
Personnel:
William Gould *(Mgr-Sls & Mktg)*
Brands & Products:
BAR TENDER'S
BELL'S
BRADY ENTERPRISES

BRIDGFORD FOODS CORPORATION
1308 N Patt St
Anaheim, CA 92801-2551
Mailing Address:
PO Box 3773
Anaheim, CA 92803-3773
Tel.: (714) 526-5533
Fax: (714) 526-4360
Toll Free: (800) 527-2105
E-mail: info@bridgford.com
Web Site: www.bridgford.com
Approx. Sls.: $117,655,000
Approx. Number Employees: 530
Year Founded: 1931
Business Description:
Ready-to-Bake Frozen Bread, Rolls, Luncheon Meats, Biscuits & Dry Sausage
S.I.C.: 2038; 2045
N.A.I.C.S.: 311412; 311822
Import Export
Advertising Expenditures: $3,530,000
Media: 2-5-9-10-14-15-19-20-21-23-24-25-26
Distr.: Natl.
Budget Set: Oct.
Personnel:
Hugh William Bridgford *(Co-Founder & Chm)*
Allan L. Bridgford *(Sr Chm)*
William L. Bridgford *(Pres)*
Raymond F. Lancy *(CFO)*
Bruce H. Bridgford *(Pres-Bridgford Foods of California)*
John V. Simmons *(Pres-Frozen Foods Div)*
Daniel R. Yost *(Sr VP-Frozen Food Sls & Mktg)*
Brands & Products:
BRIDGFORD
DEMI-LOAF
THE FRESH BAKED IDEA COMPANY
MICRO-READY
READY-DOUGH

BROUGHTON FOODS COMPANY
(Sub. of Dean Foods Company)
1701 Greene St
Marietta, OH 45750-9816
Mailing Address:
PO Box 656
Marietta, OH 45750-0656
Tel.: (740) 373-4121
Fax: (740) 373-2861
Toll Free: (800) 283-2479
Web Site: www.broughtonfoods.com
Sales Range: $50-74.9 Million
Approx. Number Employees: 150
Year Founded: 1910
Business Description:
Dairy & Non-Dairy Foods Processor & Distr
S.I.C.: 2026
N.A.I.C.S.: 311511
Media: 2-3-5-9-10-18-19-21-22-23-24-25
Distr.: Reg.
Budget Set: Jan. -Dec.
Personnel:
David Broughton *(VP & Gen Mgr)*
Brands & Products:
BROUGHTON
DAIRYLANE
REAL CREAM
SOKREEM

BRUCE FOODS CORPORATION
Hwy 182 W
Cade, LA 70519
Tel.: (337) 365-8101
Fax: (337) 364-3742
Toll Free: (800) 299-9082
E-mail: info@brucefoodsla.com
Web Site: www.brucefoods.com
Approx. Number Employees: 900
Year Founded: 1928
Business Description:
Canned Vegetables, Seasonings, Mexican Food & Hot Sauce Mfr & Whslr
S.I.C.: 2099
N.A.I.C.S.: 311999
Import Export
Media: 2-3-5-6-8-9-10-13-18-19-21-23-24
Distr.: Intl.; Natl.
Budget Set: Aug.
Brands & Products:
BRUCE FOODS
BRUCE'S
BRUCE'S YAMS
CAJUN INJECTOR
CAJUN KING
CASA FIESTA
LOUISIANA GOLD
MEXENE CHILI
ORIGINAL LOUISIANA

Key to Media (For complete agency information see *The Advertising Red Books-Agencies* edition):
1. Bus. Publs. 2. Cable T.V. 3. Catalogs & Directories. 4. Co-op Adv. 5. Consumer Mags. 6. D.M. to Bus. Estab.7. D.M. to Consumers
8. Daily Newsp. 9. Exhibits/Trade Shows 10. Foreign 11. Infomercial 12. Internet Adv.13. Multimedia 14. Network Radio
15. Network T.V. 16. Newsp. Distr. Mags. 17. Other 18. Outdoor (Posters, Transit) 19. Point of Purchase20. Premiums, Novelties
21. Product Samples 22. Special Events Mktg. 23. Spot Radio 24. Spot T.V. 25. Weekly Newsp. 26. Yellow Page Adv.

Bruce Foods Corporation — (Continued)

Advertising Agency:
Ocean Bridge Group
1714 16th St
Santa Monica, CA 90404
Tel.: (310) 392-3200

BUMBLE BEE FOODS LLC

(Sub. of Lion Capital LLP)
9655 Gramett Rdg Dr
San Diego, CA 92123-2674
Mailing Address:
PO Box 85362
San Diego, CA 92186-5362
Tel.: (858) 715-4000
Fax: (858) 715-4321
Telex: 188908
Web Site: www.bumblebee.com
Sales Range: $900-999.9 Million
Approx. Number Employees: 1,700
Year Founded: 1985
Business Description:
Canned Tuna, Salmon, Oysters, Pet Food, Frozen Shrimp & Other Seafoods Mfr
S.I.C.: 2091; 2047
N.A.I.C.S.: 311711; 311111
Import Export
Media: 2-6-21-22
Personnel:
Christopher D. Lischewski *(Pres & CEO)*
Dave Melbourne *(Sr VP-Mktg)*
Michael McGowan *(VP-Procurement)*
Melvin Progar *(VP-Pur)*
Brands & Products:
BRUNSWICK
BUMBLE BEE
CLOVER LEAF
CORAL
KING OSCAR
LIFE IS FULL OF FLAVOR. BUMBLE BEE. YUM
ORLEANS
SWEET SUE
Advertising Agency:
McCann Erickson/Los Angeles
5700 Wilshire Blvd Ste 225
Los Angeles, CA 90036
Tel.: (323) 900-7100
Fax: (323) 900-7111

BUNGE LIMITED

50 Main St
White Plains, NY 10606-1901
Tel.: (914) 684-2800
Fax: (914) 684-3499
E-mail: bge.comm@bunge.com
Web Site: www.bunge.com
Approx. Sls.: $45,707,000,000
Approx. Number Employees: 33,021
Year Founded: 1818
Business Description:
Holding Company; Agribusiness
S.I.C.: 4221; 2046; 2061; 2075; 2079; 5153; 5191
N.A.I.C.S.: 493130; 311221; 311222; 311223; 311311; 424510; 424910
Media: 2-7-8-10-11-13-17
Personnel:
Alberto Weisser *(Chm & CEO)*
Jorge Born, Jr. *(Deputy Chm)*
Pedro Pullen Parente *(Pres & CEO-Bunge Brazil)*
Mario Alves Barbosa Neto *(Mng Dir-Fertilizer Div)*
Vicente C. Teixeira *(Chief Personnel Officer, Bunge Limited)*
Sergio Roberto Waldrich *(Pres-AgriBusiness Div-Bunge Brazil & CEO-Bunge Alimentos SA)*
Raul Padilla *(CEO-Bunge Product Lines & Mng Dir-Bunge Global Agribusiness)*
Jean-Louis Gourbin *(CEO-Bunge Europe)*
Soren Schroder *(CEO-Bunge North America)*
Christopher White *(CEO-Bunge Asia)*
Carla Heiss *(Asst Gen Counsel)*
Brands & Products:
BAKEALL
BAKERS IDEAL
BIPHOR
BUNGE
BUNICCI
CLEAR CHOICE
CREMOL
CUSTOM IMPERIAL OIL
E-Z COAT
ELITE
FARMETRICS
GOLDEN AWARD
GOLDEN GRIDDLE FRY
MARATHON
NUTRA-FRY
PEANUT SELECT
PENGUIN
PRO-FORMANCE
SHASTA
TEM-COTE
TEM-PLUS
TRI-CO
VICTOR
VITO
X-TRUDE

BURRIS LOGISTICS

501 SE 5th St
Milford, DE 19963-2022
Mailing Address:
PO Box 219
Milford, DE 19963
Tel.: (302) 422-4531
Fax: (302) 839-5175
Toll Free: (800) 805-8135
E-mail: info@burrislogistics.com
Web Site: www.burrislogistics.com
Sales Range: $350-399.9 Million
Approx. Number Employees: 1,000
Year Founded: 1939
Business Description:
Refrigerated Foods Distr
S.I.C.: 5142; 4222
N.A.I.C.S.: 424420; 493120
Media: 2-6-25
Personnel:
Jennifer Black *(Dir-Bus Analysis)*
Maggie Owens *(Dir-Mktg)*

BUSH BROTHERS & COMPANY

1016 E Weisgarber Rd
Knoxville, TN 37909
Tel.: (865) 588-7685
Fax: (865) 584-9337
Web Site: www.bushbeans.com
Approx. Number Employees: 700
Year Founded: 1908
Business Description:
Processed Dry Edible Beans & Other Canned Vegetables
S.I.C.: 2033; 2032
N.A.I.C.S.: 311421; 311422
Import
Advertising Expenditures: $1,000,000
Media: 2-3-5-6-9-10-12-13-15-19-20-21-23-24
Distr.: Reg.
Budget Set: Quarterly
Personnel:
Jim Ethier *(Chm)*
Phil Perkins *(Sr VP-Innovation & R&D)*
Randy Hansen *(Dir-Mktg)*
Brands & Products:
BUSH'S BEST
CHILI MAGIC
Advertising Agency:
Doner
25900 Northwestern Hwy
Southfield, MI 48075
Tel.: (248) 354-9700
Fax: (248) 827-8440

BUTTERBALL, LLC

(Joint Venture of Smithfield Foods, Inc. & Maxwell Foods, LLC)
1628 Garner Chapel Rd
Mount Olive, NC 28365
Mailing Address:
PO Box 589
Mount Olive, NC 28365
Tel.: (919) 658-6743
Fax: (919) 658-5865
Toll Free: (800) 523-4759
E-mail: BBTurkeyCo@aol.com
Web Site: www.butterball.com
Approx. Sls.: $1,095,000,000
Approx. Number Employees: 5,500
Year Founded: 1985
Business Description:
Turkey Processing
S.I.C.: 0253; 0254; 2015
N.A.I.C.S.: 112330; 112340; 311615
Personnel:
Rod Brenneman *(CEO)*
Ed Kascuta *(CFO)*
Gary R. Lenaghan *(VP-HR)*
Richie Jenkins *(Dir-Foodservice Mktg)*
Natalie Klooz Thompson *(Mgr-Mktg Innovation)*
Brands & Products:
BUTTERBALL
CAROLINA TURKEY
JUST PERFECT
LONGMONT
Advertising Agencies:
Howard, Merrell & Partners, Inc.
8521 Six Forks Rd 4th Fl
Raleigh, NC 27615-5278
Tel.: (919) 848-2400
Fax: (919) 848-2420

Marriner Marketing Communications, Inc.
10221 Wincopin Cir Ste 300
Columbia, MD 21044-3419
Tel.: (410) 715-1500
Fax: (410) 995-3609
Toll Free: (800) 268-6475
Foodservice Agency of Record

BUTTERBALL, LLC

(Joint Venture of Smithfield Foods, Inc. & Maxwell Foods, LLC)
1240 E Diehl Rd
Naperville, IL 60563
Tel.: (630) 955-3000
Toll Free: (800) BUTTERBALL
Web Site: www.butterball.com
Sales Range: $10-24.9 Million
Approx. Number Employees: 70
Year Founded: 1954
Business Description:
Turkey Processing
S.I.C.: 0253
N.A.I.C.S.: 112330
Advertising Expenditures: $3,000,000
Media: 6-9-16-17-20-21-23-24
Distr.: Natl.
Personnel:
Joe Nalley *(COO)*
Bill Klump *(Sr VP-Corp Mktg)*
Richard Sarvas *(VP & Gen Mgr-Whole Bird Products)*
Advertising Agency:
Daniel J. Edelman, Inc.
(d/b/a Edelman)
200 E Randolph St Fl 63
Chicago, IL 60601-6705
Tel.: (312) 240-3000
Fax: (312) 240-2900
Public Relations

BUTTERBALL, LLC

(Joint Venture of Smithfield Foods, Inc. & Maxwell Foods, LLC)
PO Box 1479
Longmont, CO 80502-1479
Tel.: (303) 776-6611
Fax: (303) 678-4120
Web Site: www.butterballcorp.com/content.aspx?pin=e8ccf04a-f4a9-4b84-8fea-b4c35bca3abb
Sales Range: $650-699.9 Million
Approx. Number Employees: 850
Year Founded: 1951
Business Description:
Turkey Processing
S.I.C.: 0253
N.A.I.C.S.: 112330
Media: 2-6-9-10-19
Distr.: Natl.
Personnel:
Frank Koekkoek *(Mgr-Plant)*
Brands & Products:
LONGMONT GOLDEN SUPREME
LONGMONT LITE SUPREME
LONGMONT SUPREME

C&H SUGAR COMPANY, INC.

(Sub. of American Sugar Refining, Inc.)
830 Loring Ave
Crockett, CA 94525
Tel.: (510) 787-2121
Fax: (510) 787-4420
Web Site: www.chsugar.com
Sales Range: $400-449.9 Million
Approx. Number Employees: 550
Year Founded: 1906
Business Description:
Sugars
S.I.C.: 2062
N.A.I.C.S.: 311312
Media: 17
Distr.: Reg.
Brands & Products:
C&H

CADBURY ADAMS CANADA INC.

(Sub. of Cadbury plc)
5000 Yonge Street Ste 2100
Toronto, ON M2N 7E9, Canada
Tel.: (416) 590-5000
Fax: (416) 590-5600
Web Site: www.canada.cadbury.com
Approx. Number Employees: 182

Key to Media (For complete agency information see *The Advertising Red Books-Agencies* edition):
1. Bus. Publs. 2. Cable T.V. 3. Catalogs & Directories. 4. Co-op Adv. 5. Consumer Mags. 6. D.M. to Bus. Estab.7. D.M. to Consumers
8. Daily Newsp. 9. Exhibits/Trade Shows 10. Foreign 11. Infomercial 12. Internet Adv.13. Multimedia 14. Network Radio
15. Network T.V. 16. Newsp. Distr. Mags. 17. Other 18. Outdoor (Posters, Transit) 19. Point of Purchase20. Premiums, Novelties
21. Product Samples 22. Special Events Mktg. 23. Spot Radio 24. Spot T.V. 25. Weekly Newsp. 26. Yellow Page Adv.

Business Description:
Candy & Other Confectionery Products Mfr
S.I.C.: 2064
N.A.I.C.S.: 311330
Personnel:
Stephanie Minna-Cass *(Mgr-Corp Comm)*
Advertising Agencies:
Cossette Inc.
801 Grande Allee Ouest Ste 200
Quebec, QC G1S 1C1, Canada
Tel.: (418) 647-2727
Fax: (418) 647-2564

Strategic Objectives
184 Front Street E 4th Floor
Toronto, ON M5A 4N3, Canada
Tel.: (416) 366-7735
Fax: (416) 366-2295

CAINS FOODS, L.P.

114 E Main St
Ayer, MA 01432-1832
Tel.: (978) 772-0300
Fax: (978) 772-9254
Toll Free: (800) 225-0601
E-mail: info@cainsfoods.com
Web Site: www.cainsfoods.com
E-Mail For Key Personnel:
President: dkeaveny@cainsfoods.com
Marketing Director: cjg@cainsfoods.com
Approx. Number Employees: 100
Year Founded: 1914
Business Description:
Salad Dressings & Sauces Mfr & Distr
S.I.C.: 2035
N.A.I.C.S.: 311941
Import Export
Media: 20-23-24-25
Distr.: Reg.
Personnel:
Denis J. Keaveny *(Pres)*
Ronald H. Adams *(CFO & VP-Fin & Admin)*
Christopher Katopis *(VP-Sls & Mktg)*
Douglas M. Orton *(VP-Food Svcs, Mktg & Sls)*
Joseph Samson *(Gen Mgr)*
Caroline Giuffrida *(Mgr-Mktg)*
Brands & Products:
BOTTOMS UP
CAINS
CAINS COUNTRY
CAROLINE'S DRESSING
DELINAISE
HEALTH SMART
OLDE CAPE COD
OXFORD
OXFORD CUSTOM BLEND
PLYMOUTH COLONY
RIVIERA
SALAD LITE
SANDWICH SENSATIONS

CAL-MAINE FOODS, INC.

3320 W Woodrow Wilson Ave
Jackson, MS 39209-3409
Mailing Address:
PO Box 2960
Jackson, MS 39207-2960
Tel.: (601) 948-6813
Fax: (601) 969-0905
E-mail: info@cmfoods.com
Web Site: www.calmainefoods.com
Approx. Sls.: $941,981,000
Approx. Number Employees: 2,100
Year Founded: 1969
Business Description:
Fresh Shell Egg Production, Grading, Packing & Sales
S.I.C.: 0252; 2099; 9641
N.A.I.C.S.: 112310; 311999; 926140
Advertising Expenditures: $2,098,000
Media: 7-8
Personnel:
Fred R. Adams, Jr. *(Chm)*
Richard K. Looper *(Vice Chm)*
Adolphus B. Baker *(Pres & CEO)*
Timothy A. Dawson *(CFO, Treas, Sec & VP)*
Sherman Miller *(COO & VP)*
James H. Neeld, III *(Gen Counsel)*
Matthew Arrowsmith *(VP-Sls-Egg)*
Jeff Hardin *(VP-Sls)*
Kyle Morris *(VP-Sls)*
Jack B. Self *(VP-Ops & Production)*
Brands & Products:
4-GRAIN
CAL-MAINE FOODS
CCF
EGG-LAND'S BEST
FARMHOUSE
RIO GRANDE
SUNUPS

CALAVO GROWERS, INC.

1141-A Cummings Rd
Santa Paula, CA 93060-9118
Mailing Address:
PO Box 712
Santa Paula, CA 93061-0712
Tel.: (805) 525-1245
Fax: (805) 921-3219
Toll Free: (800) 422-5286
E-mail: Info@calavo.com
Web Site: www.calavo.com
Approx. Sls.: $398,351,000
Approx. Number Employees: 1,157
Year Founded: 1924
Business Description:
Avocado Growers Marketing & Packaging Services
S.I.C.: 9641; 5142; 5148
N.A.I.C.S.: 926140; 424420; 424480
Import Export
Advertising Expenditures: $100,000
Media: 2-10-13-20
Distr.: Intl.; Natl.
Personnel:
Lecil E. Cole *(Chm)*
Arthur J. Bruno *(CFO, COO & Sec)*
Rob Wedin *(VP-Sls & Fresh Mktg)*
Brands & Products:
CALAVO
THE FIRST NAME IN AVOCADOS

CALIFORNIA MILK ADVISORY BOARD

3800 Cornucopia Way Ste D
Modesto, CA 95358-9494
Tel.: (209) 525-6875
Fax: (209) 525-6899
E-mail: askus@realcaliforniacheese.com
Web Site:
www.realcaliforniacheese.com
E-Mail For Key Personnel:
Public Relations: info@californiadairypressroom.com
Sales Range: $25-49.9 Million
Approx. Number Employees: 18
Year Founded: 1850
Business Description:
Milk, Cheese & Butter Advertising, Promotion & Market Development
S.I.C.: 2022
N.A.I.C.S.: 311513
Export
Advertising Expenditures: $18,000,000
Media: 3-6-10-15-18-19-20-22-24
Distr.: Reg.
Budget Set: Dec.
Personnel:
Stanley G. Andre *(CEO)*
Michael Freeman *(VP-Adv)*
Vars Injijian *(VP-Sls-Mktg)*
Phil Robnett *(VP-Mktg-Sls-Cheese)*
Brands & Products:
REAL CALIFORNIA
REAL CALIFORNIA CHEESE
Advertising Agencies:
Deutsch, Inc.
(A Lowe & Partners Company)
111 8th Ave 14th Fl
New York, NY 10011-5201
Tel.: (212) 981-7600
Fax: (212) 981-7525

Draftfcb
101 E Erie St
Chicago, IL 60611
Tel.: (312) 425-5000
Fax: (312) 425-5010

HipCricket
11241 Slater Ave NE Ste 201
Kirkland, WA 98033
Tel.: (425) 452-1111
Fax: (425) 827-1561

iDeutsch
111 8th Ave
New York, NY 10011-5201
Tel.: (212) 981-7600
Fax: (212) 981-7525

Ketchum
1050 Battery St
San Francisco, CA 94111-1209
Tel.: (415) 984-6100
Fax: (415) 984-6102

CAMERICAN INTERNATIONAL

(Sub. of Atalanta Corporation)
45 Eisenhower Dr
Paramus, NJ 07652-1452
Tel.: (201) 587-0101
Tel.: (201) 833-2000
Fax: (201) 587-2040
E-mail: cii@camerican-foods.com
E-Mail For Key Personnel:
President: labramso@camerican-foods.com
Approx. Number Employees: 39
Year Founded: 1916
Business Description:
Processing of Tuna, Pineapple & Specialty Foods
S.I.C.: 5149; 5963
N.A.I.C.S.: 424490; 722330
Import
Media: 6-7-9-25
Distr.: Reg.
Personnel:
Larry Abramson *(Pres)*
Jim Kopple *(Coord-Mktg)*
Brands & Products:
DEEP BLUE
GREAT OCEAN
ROYALTY

CAMPBELL COMPANY OF CANADA LTD

(Sub. of Campbell Soup Company)
60 Birmingham St
Toronto, ON M8V 2B8, Canada
Tel.: (416) 251-1131
Fax: (416) 253-8623
Toll Free: (800) 410-7687
Web Site: www.campbellsoup.ca
Sales Range: $400-449.9 Million
Approx. Number Employees: 800
Year Founded: 1930
Business Description:
Mfr., Distr & Retailer of Soup
S.I.C.: 2032
N.A.I.C.S.: 311422
Export
Advertising Expenditures: $10,000,000
Media: 2-4-5-6-7-8-11-13-15-18-19-20-22-23-24-25
Distr.: Intl.; Natl.
Budget Set: Mar.-May
Personnel:
Philip Donne *(Pres)*
Mark Childs *(VP-Mktg)*
G. Smith *(VP-HR)*
Brands & Products:
BISTO
CAMPBELL'S FOR LIFE
CHUNKY
GARDENNAY
GOLDEN AUTUMN
HABITANT
ONE METHOD. ENDLESS POSSIBILITIES
PACE
POWER 2 COOK
TEMPTING ISN'T IT?
V8
V8 SPLASH
Advertising Agencies:
BBDO Toronto
2 Bloor St W
Toronto, ON M4W 3R6, Canada
Tel.: (416) 972-1505
Fax: (416) 972-5656

Nolin BBDO
3575 Boulevard St-Laurent Suite 300
Montreal, QC H2X 2T7, Canada
Tel.: (514) 939-4100
Fax: (514) 939-4006

OMD Canada
67 Richmond St W 2nd Fl
Toronto, ON M5H 1Z5, Canada
Tel.: (416) 681-5600
Fax: (416) 681-5620

Y&R, Ltd.
60 Bloor Street West
Toronto, ON M4W 1J2, Canada
Tel.: (416) 961-5111
Fax: (416) 961-7890
(Chunky Soup)

CAMPBELL SOUP COMPANY

1 Campbell Pl
Camden, NJ 08103-1701
Tel.: (856) 342-4800
Fax: (856) 342-3878
Toll Free: (800) 257-8443

Key to Media (For complete agency information see *The Advertising Red Books-Agencies* edition):
1. Bus. Publs. 2. Cable T.V. 3. Catalogs & Directories. 4. Co-op Adv. 5. Consumer Mags. 6. D.M. to Bus. Estab.7. D.M. to Consumers
8. Daily Newsp. 9. Exhibits/Trade Shows 10. Foreign 11. Infomercial 12. Internet Adv.13. Multimedia 14. Network Radio
15. Network T.V. 16. Newsp. Distr. Mags. 17. Other 18. Outdoor (Posters, Transit) 19. Point of Purchase20. Premiums, Novelties
21. Product Samples 22. Special Events Mktg. 23. Spot Radio 24. Spot T.V. 25. Weekly Newsp. 26. Yellow Page Adv.

Campbell Soup Company — (Continued)

Telex: 845173
Web Site: www.campbellsoup.com
Approx. Sls.: $7,719,000,000
Approx. Number Employees: 17,500
Year Founded: 1869
Business Description:
Prepared Convenience Foods Mfr
S.I.C.: 2032; 2033; 2035; 2037; 2052; 2058; 2064; 2066; 2099
N.A.I.C.S.: 311422; 311320; 311330; 311411; 311421; 311813; 311821; 311941; 311999
Import Export
Advertising Expenditures: $133,000,000
Media: 3-5-6-8-9-11-13-16-17-19-21-22-23-24-25
Distr.: Intl.; Natl.
Budget Set: June
Personnel:
Denise M. Morrison *(Pres & CEO)*
B. Craig Owens *(CFO, Chief Admin Officer & Sr VP)*
Joseph Spagnoletti *(CIO & Sr VP)*
M. Carl Johnson, III *(Chief Strategy Officer & Sr VP)*
Rosalyn Taylor O'Neale *(Chief Diversity & Inclusion Officer & VP)*
Chris Delaney *(Pres-Asia Pacific)*
John Sechi *(Pres-Greater Europe)*
Mark R. Alexander *(Sr VP)*
Irene Chang Britt *(Sr VP)*
Jerry S. Buckley *(Sr VP-Pub Affairs)*
Sean M. Connolly *(Sr VP)*
Anthony P. DiSilvestro *(Sr VP-Fin)*
George Dowdie *(Sr VP-Global R&D)*
Ellen Oran Kaden *(Sr VP-Law & Govt Affairs)*
Larry S. McWilliams *(Sr VP)*
Nancy A. Reardon *(Sr VP)*
David R. White *(Sr VP)*
Andrew Brennan *(VP-Global Strategy, Advertising & Design)*
Kirk Elliott *(VP-Corp Strategy)*
David P. Stangis *(VP-Corp Social Responsibility & Sustainability)*
Kim Fremont Fortunato *(Dir-Childhood Obesity & Hunger Program)*
Thomas Griffiths *(Dir-Culinary)*
Beth Jolly *(Dir-Comm-Campbell North America)*
Colleen Milway *(Dir-Global Media)*
Kevin C. Parham *(Dir-Global Adv)*
Joe Ruiz *(Dir-Mdsg Strategies & Retail Ops North America)*
Juli Mandel Sloves *(Sr Mgr-Nutrition & Wellness Comm)*
Sophia Arsenlis *(Brand Mgr-V8 Fusion)*
Douglas Brand *(Sr Brand Mgr-Campbell's Chunky Soup)*
Jennifer Brownrigg *(Brand Mgr)*
Theresa McGlynn *(Brand Mgr)*
Ramesh Thiyagarajan *(Brand Mgr-Prego Italian Sauce)*
Mark Tumelty *(Brand Mgr)*
Jeff Jackson *(Mgr-Internet Mktg)*
Brands & Products:
ARNOTT'S
AWAY FROM HOME
BATCHELORS
BLA BRAND
CAMPBELL'S
CHUNKY
ERASCO
GOLDFISH
HEALTHY REQUEST
HEISSE TASSE
HOMEPRIDE
KITCHEN CLASSICS
LABELS FOR EDUCATION
LESIEUR
LIEBIG
MCDONELLS
NOURISHING PEOPLE'S LIVES EVERYWHERE,EVERY DAY
OXO
PACE
PEPPERIDGE FARM
PREGO
ROYCO
SEEDS
SELECT
SOUP AT HAND
SPAGHETTIOS
SUPPER BAKES
SWANSON
V-8
Advertising Agencies:
BBDO New York
1285 Ave of the Americas 7th Fl
New York, NY 10019-6028
Tel.: (212) 459-5000
(Select Soups, Select Harvest Soups, Red & White Soups, R&W, Swanson Broth, Home Cookin', Healthy R & W, Window, Healthy Request, Swanson Frozen Foods, LeMenu, Great Starts Breakfasts, New Products)
— Paul Reilly *(Sr. V.P.)*

Circle One
10 Norden Pl
Norwalk, CT 06854
Tel.: (203) 286-0550
Fax: (203) 286-0555

FCF Schmidt Public Relations, Inc.
630 W Germantown Pike Ste 400
Plymouth Meeting, PA 19462
Tel.: (610) 641-0395
Fax: (610) 941-0580
— Michelle Bauer *(Acct Exec)*

G2 USA
200 5th Ave
New York, NY 10010
Tel.: (212) 537-3700
Fax: (212) 537-3737
V8

MEC, Global HQ, New York
825 7th Ave
New York, NY 10019-6014
Tel.: (212) 474-0000
Fax: (212) 474-0020
Fax: (212) 474-0003
V8

Response Media, Inc.
3155 Medlock Bridge Rd
Norcross, GA 30071-1423
Tel.: (770) 451-5478
Fax: (770) 451-4929

Weber Shandwick-Chicago
676 N St Clair Ste 1000
Chicago, IL 60611
Tel.: (312) 988-2400
Fax: (312) 988-2363
V8 Fusion
— Kate Hartman *(Acct Exec-V8 Fusion)*

Y&R Puerto Rico, Inc.
PO Box 366288
San Juan, PR 00936-6288
Tel.: (787) 622-6500
Fax: (787) 793-3013

Young & Rubicam Inc.
285 Madison Ave
New York, NY 10017-6401
Tel.: (212) 210-3000
Fax: (212) 490-9073
V8

CANADIAN FISH EXPORTERS, INC.

(d/b/a CFE International)
600 Pleasant St
Watertown, MA 02471
Mailing Address:
PO Box 411
Watertown, MA 02471-0411
Tel.: (617) 924-8300
Fax: (617) 926-8214
Toll Free: (800) 225-4215
E-mail: cfe@cfeboston.com
Web Site: www.cfeboston.com
Approx. Sls.: $23,469,491
Approx. Number Employees: 25
Year Founded: 1972
Business Description:
Fish Whslr
S.I.C.: 5146
N.A.I.C.S.: 424460
Media: 10
Personnel:
Robert Metafora *(Chm & CEO)*
James Scannell *(Pres & COO)*
Janelle Calamari *(CFO & Treas)*
Raphael J. Santaella *(Asst VP-Sls & Mktg)*
Donna Metafora *(Mgr-Benefits)*
Angel Rio *(Mgr-Acct)*
Brands & Products:
BACALARICO
BUENA VENTRURA
COSSU
CRISTOBAL
FALCO
PINNA
ROSSELLA

CAPE COD POTATO CHIP COMPANY

(Sub. of Snyder's-Lance, Inc.)
100 Breeds Hill Rd
Hyannis, MA 02601-1860
Tel.: (508) 775-3358
Fax: (508) 775-2808
Toll Free: (888) 881-2447
E-mail: customer.service@capecodchips.com
Web Site: www.capecodchips.com
Sales Range: $50-74.9 Million
Approx. Number Employees: 150
Year Founded: 1980
Business Description:
Snack Food Mfr
S.I.C.: 2096
N.A.I.C.S.: 311919
Export
Media: 6-8-17-19-21-22
Distr.: Intl.; Natl.
Personnel:
Heidi Ford *(Dir-Mktg)*
Brands & Products:
CAPE COD
SHAPES OF THE CAPE

Advertising Agencies:
Ericho Public Relations
333 Mamaroneck Ave Ste 222
White Plains, NY 10605
Tel.: (914) 834-2199
Fax: (914) 834-2203

gkv Communications
The Cascade Bldg 1030 Hull St Ste 400
Baltimore, MD 21230
Tel.: (410) 539-5400
Fax: (410) 234-2441

CARGILL, INC.

15407 McGinty Rd W
Wayzata, MN 55391-2365
Mailing Address:
PO Box 9300
Minneapolis, MN 55440-9300
Tel.: (952) 742-7575
Fax: (952) 742-2185
Toll Free: (800) 227-4455
E-mail: financials@cargill.com
Web Site: www.cargill.com
Approx. Rev.: $116,579,000,000
Approx. Number Employees: 158,000
Year Founded: 1865
Business Description:
Crop & Livestock Products & Services; Food & Pharmaceutical Ingredient Development & Manufacturing; Industrial Processing & Risk Management Services
S.I.C.: 2099; 2048; 2834; 2869; 6289
N.A.I.C.S.: 311999; 311119; 325199; 325412; 523999
Import Export
Advertising Expenditures: $25,000,000
Media: 2-3-4-6-7-9-10-13-15-17-20-21-22-23-24-26
Distr.: Intl.; Natl.
Personnel:
Gregory R. Page *(Chm & CEO)*
David W. MacLennan *(CFO & Sr VP)*
Steven C. Euller *(Gen Counsel & Sec)*
David M. Larson *(Exec VP)*
William A. Buckner *(Sr VP)*
Paul D. Conway *(Sr VP)*
Richard D. Frasch *(Sr VP)*
Emery N. Koenig *(Sr VP)*
Sergio Rial *(Sr VP)*
Rita J. Heise *(Corp VP-IT)*
Peter Vrijsen *(Corp VP-HR)*
Tim Loesch *(Dir-Corp Affairs-Media Rels)*
Jane Naumkin *(Dir-HR)*
John Franklin *(Mktg Mgr)*
Asif Malik *(Mgr-Global Product Line (Vitamin E & Plant Sterols))*
Brands & Products:
ACCO FEEDS
ACTISTAR
ALBERGER
AQUAXCEL
ARTHRED
BARLIV
BIOH
CARGILL
CHAMPIONS CHOICE
CLEAR VALLEY
CLEARDEX
CLEARSWEET
COROWISE
DIAMOND CRYSTAL
DUST-OFF

Key to Media (For complete agency information see *The Advertising Red Books-Agencies* edition):
1. Bus. Publs. 2. Cable T.V. 3. Catalogs & Directories. 4. Co-op Adv. 5. Consumer Mags. 6. D.M. to Bus. Estab.7. D.M. to Consumers 8. Daily Newsp. 9. Exhibits/Trade Shows 10. Foreign 11. Infomercial 12. Internet Adv.13. Multimedia 14. Network Radio 15. Network T.V. 16. Newsp. Distr. Mags. 17. Other 18. Outdoor (Posters, Transit) 19. Point of Purchase20. Premiums, Novelties 21. Product Samples 22. Special Events Mktg. 23. Spot Radio 24. Spot T.V. 25. Weekly Newsp. 26. Yellow Page Adv.

EMCAP
EXCEL
EZ FILL
FIBER KRUNCH
FRESHZONE
GERKENS
GLACIER
GRAINWISE
HONEYSUCKLE
HONEYSUCKLE WHITE
ISOMALTIDEX
LECI-CHOLINE
LIBERTY
LOYALL
MALTIDEX
MANNIDEX
MASATHENTIC
MASTER CHEF
NOURISHING IDEAS, NOURISHING PEOPLE
NUTRENA
OLIGGO-FIBER
PROLIA
PROS PICK
PROSANTE
PROSANTE PLUS
RED CROSS
REGENASURE
REVEAL
SALTWISE
SATIN SWEET
SORBIDEX
STABITEX
STERLING SILVER
SUNNY FRESH
SWEET DESIGN
TAPIOCA
TENDER CHOICE
TEXTRATEIN
TRUVIA
WILBUR
XTEND
ZEROSE

Advertising Agencies:
Bailey Lauerman
1248 O St Ste 900
Lincoln, NE 68508-1460
Tel.: (402) 475-2800
Fax: (402) 475-5115
RAMP

Martin/Williams Advertising Inc.
(A Member of Omnicom Group)
60 S 6th St Ste 2800
Minneapolis, MN 55402-4428
Tel.: (612) 340-0800
Fax: (612) 342-9700
Grains Division

CARGILL KITCHEN SOLUTIONS
(Sub. of Cargill, Inc.)
206 W 4th St
Monticello, MN 55362-8524
Tel.: (763) 271-5600
Fax: (763) 271-5711
Toll Free: (800) USAEGGS
E-mail: usaeggs@cargill.com
Web Site: www.usaeggs.com
Approx. Number Employees: 400
Year Founded: 1966
Business Description:
Egg Products & Egg Based Entree Producers
S.I.C.: 2099
N.A.I.C.S.: 311999
Media: 7-8-10-19-20-21
Distr.: Natl.
Personnel:
Mary Thompson *(Pres)*
Helen Cummins *(Mgr-Mktg Comm)*
Brands & Products:
COUNTRY BLEND
COUNTRY BLEND ESL
COUNTRY GOLD
COUNTRY GOLD ESL
GOLDEN NATURE
GOLDEN NATURE ESL
PILLOW-PAK
SUN BREAK
SUNNY FRESH
SUNNY FRESH FREE
Advertising Agency:
Tartan Marketing
10467 93rd Ave N
Maple Grove, MN 55369
Tel.: (763) 391-7575
Fax: (763) 391-7576
Toll Free: (877) 321-7575

CARGILL MEAT SOLUTIONS
(Unit of Cargill Meat Solutions Corp.)
151 N Main St 1st Fl
Wichita, KS 67201
Tel.: (316) 291-2500
Fax: (316) 291-2550
Toll Free: (800) 532-5756
Web Site: www.cargillfoodservice.com
Approx. Number Employees: 1,000
Business Description:
Turkey Production
S.I.C.: 5144
N.A.I.C.S.: 424440
Export
Media: 3-6-7-9-18-19-20-24
Distr.: Reg.
Personnel:
John O'Carroll *(Pres)*
David Barocco *(VP-Sls)*
Nicole Johnson-Hoffman *(Gen Mgr)*
John Franklin *(Mgr-Mktg)*
Advertising Agencies:
Advertising & Promotional Services, Inc. (Adpro, Inc.)
(d/b/a ADPRO, INC)
6 S 503 Wildwood Dr
Aurora, IL 60506
Tel.: (630) 801-9900
Fax: (630) 801-9663
Toll Free: (866) 895-2535

Sullivan Higdon & Sink Incorporated
255 N Mead St
Wichita, KS 67202-2707
Tel.: (316) 263-0124
Fax: (316) 263-1084
Toll Free: (800) 577-5684

CARGILL SALT
(Unit of Cargill, Inc.)
12800 Whitewater Dr MS 21
Minnetonka, MN 55343
Mailing Address:
PO Box 5621
Minneapolis, MN 55440-5621
Tel.: (952) 984-8280
Fax: (952) 984-8715
Toll Free: (888) 385-7258
Web Site: www.cargillsalt.com
Approx. Number Employees: 85
Year Founded: 1865
Business Description:
Salt Product Mfr
S.I.C.: 2099; 5149
N.A.I.C.S.: 311942; 424490
Advertising Expenditures: $250,000
Media: 2-4-7-9-20-23-24
Distr.: Natl.
Budget Set: July
Personnel:
Dale Fehrenbach *(Pres -DI Zinc Technology)*
Ruth Kimmelshue *(Pres-Bus Unit Leader Cargill Salt)*
Brands & Products:
COLONIAL
DURA-CUBE
HALITE
RED CROSS
SALT SENSE
STERLING
SUN GEMS

CARGILL TURKEY PRODUCTS
(Div. of Cargill, Inc.)
1 Kratzer Ave
Harrisonburg, VA 22802-4567
Tel.: (540) 568-1400
Fax: (540) 568-1401
Toll Free: (800) 336-4003
Web Site: www.cargillturkey.com
Sales Range: $550-599.9 Million
Approx. Number Employees: 3,600
Year Founded: 1939
Business Description:
Poultry Processing; Feed Mill; Wholesale Building Supplies; Distribution Center
S.I.C.: 0253
N.A.I.C.S.: 112330
Export
Advertising Expenditures: $12,200,000
Media: 2-5-6-8-9-10-17-18-19-20-21-22-23-24
Distr.: Natl.
Budget Set: Dec.
Personnel:
John O'Carroll *(Pres)*
Advertising Agency:
Associated Advertising Agency, Inc.
330 N Mead Ste 200
Wichita, KS 67202
Tel.: (316) 683-4691
Fax: (316) 683-1990

CARGILL TURKEY PRODUCTS INC.
(Sub. of Cargill Turkey Products)
135 Huffman Dr
Dayton, VA 22821-0158
Tel.: (540) 879-2521
Fax: (540) 879-9656
E-mail: info@cargillturkey.com
Web Site: www.cargillturkey.com
Approx. Number Employees: 1,600
Year Founded: 1939
Business Description:
Turkey & Turkey Products Processing
S.I.C.: 2015
N.A.I.C.S.: 311615
Export
Advertising Expenditures: $4,000,000
Media: 5-6-9-10-19-21-23-24-25-26
Distr.: Intl.; Natl.
Budget Set: Nov.
Advertising Agency:
Square One, Inc.
1801 N Lamar Ste 375
Dallas, TX 75202
Tel.: (214) 749-1111
Fax: (214) 379-8499

CARL BUDDIG & COMPANY
950 W 175th St
Homewood, IL 60430-2027
Tel.: (708) 798-0900
Fax: (708) 798-3178
Toll Free: (800) 621-0868
Web Site: www.buddig.com
Approx. Number Employees: 400
Year Founded: 1943
Business Description:
Processor Smoked Meats & Other Meat Products
S.I.C.: 5147; 2022
N.A.I.C.S.: 311612; 311513
Import Export
Advertising Expenditures: $100,000
Media: 1-2-3-5-6-8-9-10-13-19-20-21-22-23-24-25
Distr.: Natl.
Budget Set: Sept.
Personnel:
Thomas R. Buddig *(Owner)*
Robert J. Buddig *(Co-CEO)*
Eugene J. Donaghey *(CFO)*
Michelle Fadeley *(Coord-Mktg)*
Brands & Products:
COUNTRY CUPBOARD
DELI CUTS
FAT FREDDIE
FIX QUIX
OLD WISCONSIN
Advertising Agency:
Jacobson Rost
233 N Water St 6th Fl
Milwaukee, WI 53202
Tel.: (414) 220-4888
Fax: (414) 220-4889

THE CARRIAGE HOUSE COMPANIES, INC.
(Sub. of Ralcorp Holdings, Inc.)
196 Newton St
Fredonia, NY 14063-1304
Tel.: (716) 673-1000
Fax: (716) 679-3480
E-mail: mjklanac@ralcorp.com
Web Site: www.carriagehousecos.com
Sales Range: $400-449.9 Million
Approx. Number Employees: 1,000
Year Founded: 1976
Business Description:
Mfr & Retailer of Private Label Food Products
S.I.C.: 2035; 2068; 2087; 2099
N.A.I.C.S.: 311941; 311911; 311930; 311999
Advertising Expenditures: $2,000,000
Media: 2-7-8-9-10-18-25
Distr.: Intl.; Natl.
Personnel:
Richard R. Koulouris *(Pres)*
Mike Klanac *(VP-Mktg)*
Brands & Products:
MAJOR PETER'S

CARVEL CORPORATION
(Sub. of FOCUS Brands, Inc.)
200 Glenridge Point Pkwy Ste 200
Atlanta, GA 30342
Tel.: (404) 255-3250
Fax: (404) 255-4978
E-mail: custsvcs@focusbrands.com
Web Site: www.carvel.com
Approx. Number Employees: 500
Year Founded: 1989

Key to Media (For complete agency information see *The Advertising Red Books-Agencies* edition):
1. Bus. Publs. 2. Cable T.V. 3. Catalogs & Directories. 4. Co-op Adv. 5. Consumer Mags. 6. D.M. to Bus. Estab.7. D.M. to Consumers 8. Daily Newsp. 9. Exhibits/Trade Shows 10. Foreign 11. Infomercial 12. Internet Adv.13. Multimedia 14. Network Radio 15. Network T.V. 16. Newsp. Distr. Mags. 17. Other 18. Outdoor (Posters, Transit) 19. Point of Purchase20. Premiums, Novelties 21. Product Samples 22. Special Events Mktg. 23. Spot Radio 24. Spot T.V. 25. Weekly Newsp. 26. Yellow Page Adv.

Carvel Corporation — (Continued)

Business Description:
Ice Cream Mfr & Distr
S.I.C.: 2024
N.A.I.C.S.: 311520
Import Export
Media: 25
Personnel:
Gary Bales *(Pres)*
Lori Peterson *(VP-Mktg)*
Lauren McGowen *(Mgr-Pub Rels)*
Heather Metzler *(Mgr-Franchise Mktg)*

CASS-CLAY CREAMERY
(Div. of Associated Milk Producers Inc.)
200 20th St North
Fargo, ND 58108
Mailing Address:
PO Box 2947
Fargo, ND 58108-2947
Tel.: (701) 293-6455
Fax: (701) 241-9154
Web Site: www.cassclay.com
E-Mail For Key Personnel:
Sales Director: greg@cassclay.com
Sales Range: $75-99.9 Million
Approx. Number Employees: 300
Year Founded: 1934
Business Description:
Dairy Product Mfr
S.I.C.: 2026; 2022
N.A.I.C.S.: 311511; 311513
Media: 2-7-9-10-18-21-23-24
Distr.: Reg.
Personnel:
Paul Morlock *(Dir-Sls)*
Brands & Products:
ABSOLUTELY NUTS
BISON CRUNCH
CALCI 1
CALCI SKIM
CASS-CLAY
DUSTY ROADS
FIGHTING SIOUX CHAMPIONSHIP CHIP
GOLDEN GOPHER
MUDDY SNEAKERS
NOG ROYALE
WE MAKE GOOD THINGS BETTER

CEDAR FARMS COMPANY, INC.
2100 Hornig Rd
Philadelphia, PA 19116
Tel.: (215) 934-7100
Fax: (215) 934-5851
Toll Free: (800) 220-2217
Web Site: www.cedarfarms.com
Approx. Number Employees: 200
Year Founded: 1925
Business Description:
Wholesale Dairy Products, Poultry, Frozen Foods, Meats, & Meat Products
S.I.C.: 5143; 5144
N.A.I.C.S.: 424430; 424440
Media: 13
Distr.: Reg.
Personnel:
Gus P. Pahidis *(Owner & Chm)*
Peter Pahides *(Pres & CEO)*
Michael Essaf *(Gen Mgr)*
Rose Cataldi *(Office Mgr)*
Brands & Products:
CEDAR FARMS

CELESTIAL SEASONINGS, INC.
(Sub. of The Hain Celestial Group, Inc.)
4600 Sleepytime Dr
Boulder, CO 80301-3292
Tel.: (303) 530-5300
Fax: (303) 581-1332
Toll Free: (800) 434-4246
E-mail: webmaster@celestialseasonings.com
Web Site: www.celestialseasonings.com
Sales Range: $125-149.9 Million
Approx. Number Employees: 275
Year Founded: 1969
Business Description:
Herbal & Specialty Teas Mfr
S.I.C.: 2095
N.A.I.C.S.: 311920
Import Export
Advertising Expenditures: $5,000,000
Media: 5-6-10-13-14-15-19-20-21-23-24
Distr.: Intl.; Natl.
Budget Set: Annually
Personnel:
Peter Burns *(Gen Mgr)*
Scott Graham *(Dir-Tea Product Dev)*
Jennifer Stolte *(Sr Brand Mgr)*
Brands & Products:
ALMOND SUNSET
ANTIOXIDANT EXTRA
AUTHENTIC GREEN TEA
BALI BLACK RASPBERRY
BENGAL SPICE
BLACK CHERRY BERRY
CANADIAN VANILLA MAPLE DECAF
CHAMOMILE GREEN TEA
CINNAMON APPLE SPICE
CLASSIC BLACK TEA
CLASSIC DECAF BLACK TEA
COMPLETE CARE
COOL BREW ICED TEAS
COUNTRY PEACH PASSION
CRANBERRY APPLE ZINGER
DECAF GREEN TEA
DECAF MANDARIN ORCHARD GREEN TEA
DECAF MINT GREEN TEA
DETOX AM TEA
DIET PARTNER
ECHINACEA COMPLETE CARE
ECHINACEA WELLNESS TEA
EMERALD GARDENS GREEN TEA
EMPERORS CHOICE
ENGLISH BREAKFAST
ENGLISH TOFFEE
GINGERBREAD SPICE
GINGEREASE TEA
GINGSENG ENERGY
GINKGOSHARP
GOLDEN HONEY DARJEELING
GOOD NITE CLEANSE
HARVEST CAMOMILE
HONEY LEMON GINSENG
HONEY VANILLA CHAMOMILE
ISLAND ORANGE SPICE
LEMON ZINGER
LEMON ZINGER GREEN TEA
MANDARIN ORANGE SPICE
METABO PARTNER
MINT MAGIC
MOOD MENDER
MORNING THUNDER
MOUNTAIN CHAI DECAF ORIGINAL
MOUNTAIN CHAI ORIGINAL
NUTCRACKER SWEET
ORGANIC PEPPERMINT TEA
PEACH APRICOT HONEYBUSH
PEPPERMINT HERB TEA
PERFECTLY PEAR
RAINBOW OF BERRIES
RASPBERRY GARDENS
RASPBERRY ZINGER
RED ZINGER
ROASTAROMA
SAPHARA
SLEEPYTIME
SLEEPYTIME EXTRA
STRAWBERRY KIWI
SUGAR PLUM SPICE
SUNBURST C
TANGERINE ORANGE ZINGER WITH VITAMIN C
TEA FOR AMERICA
TENSION TAMER
TENSION TAMER EXTRA
THROAT SOOTHERS
TOTAL ANTIOXIDANT
TROPICAL FRUIT ZINGER
TRUE BLUEBERRY
TUMMY MINT
TUSCANY ORANGE SPICE
VANILLA HAZELNUT
VERDE PEACH MIST
VICTORIAN EARL GREY
WILD BERRY ZINGER
Advertising Agencies:
Burson-Marsteller
222 Merchandise Mart Plz Ste 250
Chicago, IL 60654-1022
Tel.: (312) 596-3400
Fax: (312) 596-3600

TDA Advertising & Design
1500 Pearl St Ste 300
Boulder, CO 80302
Tel.: (303) 247-1180
Fax: (303) 247-1214

THE C.F. SAUER COMPANY
2000 W Broad St
Richmond, VA 23220-2006
Tel.: (804) 359-5786
Fax: (804) 359-2263
E-mail: consumer-information@cfsauer.com
Web Site: www.cfsauer.com
Approx. Number Employees: 200
Year Founded: 1887
Business Description:
Mfr. of Mayonnaise, Salad Products, Spices & Extracts
S.I.C.: 2099; 2035
N.A.I.C.S.: 311942; 311941
Import Export
Media: 2-5-19-23-24
Distr.: Reg.
Budget Set: Jan.
Personnel:
Conrad F. Sauer *(Pres & CEO)*
Bill Uhlik *(CFO)*
Mark A. Sauer *(Exec VP-Sls)*
Hollace Shaw *(Mgr)*
Brands & Products:
BAMA
DUKE'S
GOLD MEDAL
MRS. FILBERT'S
SAUER'S
SPICE HUNTER
Advertising Agency:
Planet Central
590 Springfield Ave
Berkeley Heights, NJ 07922
Tel.: (908) 665-9460
Fax: (908) 665-9463
(Duke's Mayonnaise)

CHAMPION NUTRITION, INC.
2615 Stanwell Dr
Concord, CA 94520
Tel.: (925) 689-1790
Fax: (925) 689-0821
E-mail: info@champion-nutrition.com
Web Site: www.champion-nutrition.com
Approx. Number Employees: 50
Year Founded: 1983
Business Description:
Nutritional Products
S.I.C.: 2834; 2833
N.A.I.C.S.: 325412; 325411
Media: 6
Brands & Products:
CHAMPION NUTRITION
CINNA-GRAHAM SLAM
ENDURANCE
PERFORMADE
REVENGE PRO
TRAIN LIKE A CHAMPION
ULTRAMET
WELLNESS NUTRITION
WIPEOUT

CHATTANOOGA BAKERY INC.
900 Manufacturers Rd
Chattanooga, TN 37405-3763
Tel.: (423) 267-3351
Fax: (423) 266-2169
Web Site: www.moonpie.com
Approx. Sls.: $13,900,000
Approx. Number Employees: 150
Year Founded: 1902
Business Description:
Commercial Bakeries
S.I.C.: 2051; 2052; 2099
N.A.I.C.S.: 311812; 311821; 311999
Advertising Expenditures: $1,000,000
Media: 2-5-13-16-17
Personnel:
Samuel H. Campbell, III *(Chm)*
Samuel H. Campbell, IV *(Pres & CEO)*
Keith Holt *(CFO & Controller)*
John Campbell *(VP-Sls)*
Tory Johnston *(VP-Mktg)*
Brands & Products:
CHATTANOOGA BAKERY
DOUBLE-DECKER
MOONPIE

CHERRY CENTRAL COOPERATIVE, INC.
1771 N US 31 S
Traverse City, MI 49684-0988
Tel.: (231) 946-1860
Fax: (231) 941-4167
E-mail: info@cherrycentral.com
Web Site: www.cherrycentral.com
Approx. Number Employees: 35
Year Founded: 1973
Business Description:
Processor & Marketer of Fresh Fruits & Vegetables
S.I.C.: 5142; 5149
N.A.I.C.S.: 424420; 424490
Import Export
Media: 1-2-5-10
Distr.: Natl.

Key to Media (For complete agency information see *The Advertising Red Books-Agencies* edition):
1. Bus. Publs. 2. Cable T.V. 3. Catalogs & Directories. 4. Co-op Adv. 5. Consumer Mags. 6. D.M. to Bus. Estab.7. D.M. to Consumers
8. Daily Newsp. 9. Exhibits/Trade Shows 10. Foreign 11. Infomercial 12. Internet Adv.13. Multimedia 14. Network Radio
15. Network T.V. 16. Newsp. Distr. Mags. 17. Other 18. Outdoor (Posters, Transit) 19. Point of Purchase20. Premiums, Novelties
21. Product Samples 22. Special Events Mktg. 23. Spot Radio 24. Spot T.V. 25. Weekly Newsp. 26. Yellow Page Adv.

Personnel:
Richard Bogard *(Pres)*
James Bryant *(Mktg Mgr-Sls)*
David Barger *(Mgr-Sls)*
Cheryl Saxton *(Mgr)*
Brent Tackett *(Mgr-Natl Sls)*
Frank Wolff *(Mgr-Natl Sls-Private Label)*

Brands & Products:
CHERRY CENTRAL

CHIQUITA BRANDS INTERNATIONAL, INC.

250 E 5th St
Cincinnati, OH 45202-4119
Tel.: (513) 784-8000
Fax: (513) 564-2920
Web Site: www.chiquita.com
Approx. Sls.: $3,227,432,000
Approx. Number Employees: 21,000
Year Founded: 1870
Business Description:
Food Producer, Processor & Distr
S.I.C.: 2037; 0139; 0161; 0174; 0179; 0711
N.A.I.C.S.: 311411; 111219; 111320; 111339; 111998; 115112
Advertising Expenditures: $62,000,000
Media: 2-6-10-11-19-20-24
Distr.: Intl.; Natl.
Personnel:
Fernando Aguirre *(Chm, Pres & CEO)*
Michael Sims *(CFO & Sr VP)*
Tanios Viviani *(CMO & Pres-Emerging Markets)*
Lori A. Ritchey *(Chief Acctg Officer & Controller)*
Joe Huston *(Pres-Chiquita Brands)*
Brian W. Kocher *(Pres-North America)*
Michel Loeb *(Pres-Europe)*
James E. Thompson *(Gen Counsel, Sec & Sr VP)*
Waheed Zaman *(Sr VP-Supply Chain & Procurement)*
Barbara Wagner *(VP, Asst Sec & Assoc Gen Counsel)*
George Jaksch *(Sr Dir-Corp Responsibility, Pub Affairs & Chiquita Fresh Europe)*
Michael Mitchell *(Dir-Corp Comm)*

Brands & Products:
A HEALTHY WAY TO START YOUR DAY
AMIGO
CALYPSO BREEZE
CHICO
CHIQUITA
CHIQUITA FRUIT BITES
CHIQUITA FRUIT SMOOTHIES
CHIQUITA JR.
CHIQUITA KIDS
CHIQUITA MINI'S
CHIQUITA PINEAPPLE BITES
CHIQUITA SOLUTIONS
CHIQUITA. YOUR PRODUCE SOLUTION
ENERGIZE, MAXIMIZE, CHIQUITA-TIZE
FRESH EXPRESS
FRUPAC
JUST FRESH FRUIT
KEEP CRISP
MISS CHIQUITA
PACIFIC GOLD
PRODUCE SOLUTIONS
QUITE POSSIBLY, THE WORLD'S PERFECT FOOD
SMOOTHIES
SPORTS BLAST
TROPICAL PARADISE
WHEN A LITTLE IS EXACTLY ENOUGH
WILD BERRY SPLASH

Advertising Agencies:
Dieste
1999 Bryan St Ste 2700
Dallas, TX 75201
Tel.: (214) 259-8000
Fax: (214) 259-8040

Doner
25900 Northwestern Hwy
Southfield, MI 48075
Tel.: (248) 354-9700
Fax: (248) 827-8440
(Bananas)

Full Steam Marketing & Design
60 W Market St Ste 150
Salinas, CA 93901
Tel.: (831) 757-4164
Fax: (831) 757-7574

Gotham Direct
353 Lexington Ave 14th Fl
New York, NY 10016
Tel.: (212) 279-1474
Fax: (212) 279-1475

CHIQUITA FRESH NORTH LLC

(Sub. of Chiquita Brands International, Inc.)
250 E 5th St
Cincinnati, OH 45202-4119
Tel.: (513) 784-8000
Fax: (513) 784-8030
Approx. Sls.: $2,400,000,000
Approx. Number Employees: 400
Business Description:
Bananas, Processed Food Products & Plantains Distr
S.I.C.: 0179; 0174
N.A.I.C.S.: 111339; 111320
Advertising Expenditures: $12,000,000
Consumer Mags.: $2,400,000; D.M. to Consumers: $4,800,000; Daily Newsp.: $2,400,000; Exhibits/Trade Shows: $2,400,000
Distr.: Natl.
Budget Set: Dec.
Personnel:
Robert F. Kistinger *(Pres)*

Advertising Agency:
Doner
25900 Northwestern Hwy
Southfield, MI 48075
Tel.: (248) 354-9700
Fax: (248) 827-8440
(Chiquita Bananas & Processed Foods)

CHR. HANSEN, INC.

(Sub. of Chr. Hansen Holding A/S)
9015 W Maple St
Milwaukee, WI 53214-4213
Tel.: (414) 607-5700
Fax: (414) 607-5959
Toll Free: (800) 558-0802
Web Site: www.chr-hansen.com
Approx. Number Employees: 300
Year Founded: 1878
Business Description:
Enzymes, Colorants & Cultures, Food Flavoring, Dairy & Agriculture Businesses, Media & Probiotics Mfr
S.I.C.: 2099; 2087
N.A.I.C.S.: 311999; 311930
Import Export
Media: 2-4-6-7-10-21
Distr.: Intl.; Natl.
Budget Set: Jan. -Dec.
Personnel:
Cecily Smith *(Mgr-Mktg-Europe, Food & Beverage Div)*

Brands & Products:
BETA STAR
BIOPLUS 2B
CHY-MAX
COLORMAX
DS6
DVS
EXACT
NUTRISH
PHAGE CONTROL
YO-FLEX

CHURNY COMPANY INC.

(Sub. of Kraft Foods Inc.)
1 Kraft Ct
Glenview, IL 60025
Tel.: (847) 646-5500
Fax: (847) 480-5591
Web Site: www.churny.com
Sales Range: $150-199.9 Million
Business Description:
Specialty Cheeses Mfr & Distr
S.I.C.: 5143
N.A.I.C.S.: 424430
Media: 6-9-25
Distr.: Natl.
Budget Set: Jan.

CITRUS WORLD, INC.

20205 US Hwy 27
Lake Wales, FL 33853-1111
Mailing Address:
PO Box 1111
Lake Wales, FL 33859-1111
Tel.: (863) 676-1411
Fax: (863) 678-9631
E-mail: info@floridasnatural.com
Web Site: www.floridasnatural.com
Sales Range: $600-649.9 Million
Approx. Number Employees: 975
Year Founded: 1934
Business Description:
Citrus Processors & Packagers; Agricultural Co-op
S.I.C.: 2033; 2037
N.A.I.C.S.: 311421; 311411
Import Export
Advertising Expenditures: $100,000
Media: 3-6-8-11-13-15-19-20
Distr.: Intl.; Natl.
Personnel:
Stephen M. Caruso *(CEO)*
Walt Lincer *(VP-Sls & Mktg)*
Dan McSpadden *(Dir-Mktg)*

Brands & Products:
BLUEBIRD
DONALD DUCK
GROWER'S STYLE
TEXSUN

C.J. VITNER CO.

4202 W 45th St
Chicago, IL 60632
Mailing Address:
4425 S Tripp
Chicago, IL 60632
Tel.: (773) 523-7900
Fax: (773) 523-9143
E-mail: info@vitners.com
Web Site: www.vitners.com
Approx. Number Employees: 450
Year Founded: 1928
Business Description:
Snack Foods
S.I.C.: 2096; 5145
N.A.I.C.S.: 311919; 424450
Advertising Expenditures: $228,000
Bus. Publs.: $10,000; Daily Newsp.: $8,000; Exhibits/Trade Shows: $15,000; Other: $30,000; Outdoor (Posters, Transit): $10,000; Product Samples: $10,000; Spot Radio: $160,000
Distr.: Reg.
Budget Set: Oct.
Personnel:
Edward Cepa *(Pres)*
William A. Vitner *(CEO)*
Steve Reusz *(CFO)*
Ed Szajuk *(Gen Mgr)*

Brands & Products:
THE CHICAGO STYLE SNACKS
RIDGETTS
VITNER'S

CLEAR SPRINGS FOODS, INC.

1500 E 4424 N Clear Lk Rd
Buhl, ID 83316
Tel.: (208) 543-4316
Fax: (208) 543-5608
Toll Free: (800) 635-8211
E-mail: csf@clearsprings.com
Web Site: www.clearsprings.com
Approx. Number Employees: 400
Year Founded: 1966
Business Description:
Distributor, Researcher & Farm Raiser of Rainbow Trout
S.I.C.: 0921; 2048
N.A.I.C.S.: 112511; 311119
Export
Advertising Expenditures: $300,000
Media: 2
Distr.: Intl.; Natl.
Budget Set: July
Personnel:
Ed White *(Pres & COO)*
Larry W. Cope *(CEO)*
Keith Quigley *(CFO, Treas & VP)*
Don Riffle *(VP-Mktg & Sls)*
Chris Howard *(Dir-Mktg)*

Brands & Products:
CLEAR CUTS
CLEAR SPRINGS FOODS
CLEAR SPRINGS KITCHEN
CREATIVE COMPONENTS
HERB & GARLIC SEASONED SPLASH!
PARMESAN CRUSTED SPLASH!
PECAN CRUSTED SPLASH!
PORTICO
PORTICO BOUNTY
PORTICO SIMPLY

Advertising Agency:
Scott, Inc. of Milwaukee
(dba Scott Advertising)
1031 N Astor St
Milwaukee, WI 53202-3324
Tel.: (414) 276-1080
Fax: (414) 276-3327

Key to Media (For complete agency information see *The Advertising Red Books-Agencies* edition):
1. Bus. Publs. 2. Cable T.V. 3. Catalogs & Directories. 4. Co-op Adv. 5. Consumer Mags. 6. D.M. to Bus. Estab.7. D.M. to Consumers 8. Daily Newsp. 9. Exhibits/Trade Shows 10. Foreign 11. Infomercial 12. Internet Adv.13. Multimedia 14. Network Radio 15. Network T.V. 16. Newsp. Distr. Mags. 17. Other 18. Outdoor (Posters, Transit) 19. Point of Purchase20. Premiums, Novelties 21. Product Samples 22. Special Events Mktg. 23. Spot Radio 24. Spot T.V. 25. Weekly Newsp. 26. Yellow Page Adv.

CLEMENTS FOODS COMPANY
6601 N Harvey
Oklahoma City, OK 73116-7911
Mailing Address:
PO Box 14538
Oklahoma City, OK 73113-0538
Tel.: (405) 842-3308
Fax: (405) 843-6894
Toll Free: (800) 654-8355
Web Site: www.clementsfoods.com
Approx. Number Employees: 250
Year Founded: 1954
Business Description:
Jellies, Preserves, Mayonnaise, Salad Dressing, Syrups, Mustard, Vinegar & Peanut Butter Mfr
S.I.C.: 2033; 2035
N.A.I.C.S.: 311421; 311941
Import Export
Advertising Expenditures: $700,000
Media: 2-5-9-19
Distr.: Reg.
Budget Set: Nov.
Personnel:
Richard H. Clements *(Chm & CFO)*
Edward B. Clements *(Pres)*
Robert H. Clements *(Exec VP)*
Brands & Products:
CLEMENTS
CLEMENTS FOODS COMPANY
DELICIOUS
GARDEN CLUB
LITTLE PIG
RIO DE ORO
SAVORY
WIN YOU

CLIF BAR INC.
1451 66th St
Emeryville, CA 94608
Tel.: (510) 558-7855
Fax: (510) 547-1199
Toll Free: (800) 354-3227
E-mail: custserv@clifbar.com
Web Site: www.clifbar.com
E-Mail For Key Personnel:
Public Relations: dmayer@clifbar.com
Approx. Number Employees: 215
Year Founded: 1997
Business Description:
Mfr. of Energy & Nutritional Foods
S.I.C.: 2052; 5149
N.A.I.C.S.: 311821; 424490
Advertising Expenditures: $7,000,000
Media: 3-6-23-24
Personnel:
Gary Erickson *(Owner & CEO)*
Jennifer Yun *(Brand Dir-Clif Kid)*
Dean Mayer *(Mgr-Comm)*
Brands & Products:
BUILDER'S
CLIF BAR
CLIF SHOT
CLIF SHOT BLOKS
LUNA BAR
MOJO BAR
NECTAR
ZBAR

CLOUGHERTY PACKING COMPANY
(Sub. of Hormel Foods Corporation)
(d/b/a Farmer John)
3049 E Vernon Ave
Los Angeles, CA 90058-1800
Mailing Address:
PO Box 58870
Los Angeles, CA 90058-0870
Tel.: (323) 583-4621
Fax: (323) 584-1699
E-mail: farmerjohn@farmerjohn.com
Web Site: www.farmerjohn.com
Sales Range: $500-549.9 Million
Approx. Number Employees: 1,400
Year Founded: 1931
Business Description:
Meat Packing Services
S.I.C.: 0751; 5147
N.A.I.C.S.: 311611; 311612
Export
Advertising Expenditures: $3,000,000
Media: 9
Distr.: Reg.
Budget Set: Sept.
Personnel:
Dennis Clougherty *(VP-Mktg)*
Brands & Products:
FARMER JOHN
Advertising Agencies:
Mendelsohn Zien Advertising LLC
11111 Santa Monica Blvd 21st Fl
Los Angeles, CA 90025-3356
Tel.: (310) 444-1990
Fax: (310) 444-9888
(Creative, Media Buying/Planning)

Riester Robb
1960 E Grand Ave Ste 260
El Segundo, CA 90245
Tel.: (310) 459-4499
Fax: (310) 392-2595

CLOVER STORNETTA FARMS INC.
5401 Old Redwood Hwy
Petaluma, CA 94954-1168
Mailing Address:
PO Box 750369
Petaluma, CA 94975-0369
Tel.: (707) 778-8448
Fax: (707) 778-9169
Toll Free: (800) 237-3317
E-mail: askclo@clover-stornetta.com
Web Site: www.clover-stornetta.com
Sales Range: $25-49.9 Million
Approx. Number Employees: 210
Year Founded: 1977
Business Description:
Dairy Products Mfr & Distr
S.I.C.: 2026; 0241; 2021; 2023; 5143
N.A.I.C.S.: 311511; 112120; 311512; 311514; 424430
Media: 18-22
Personnel:
Mike Keefer *(Owner)*
Dan Benedetti *(Chm)*
Marcus Benedetti *(Pres)*
Kevin Imm *(CEO)*
Mkulima Britt *(VP-Fin)*

COBURG DAIRY
(Sub. of National Dairy LLC)
5001 LaCross Rd
North Charleston, SC 29406
Mailing Address:
PO Box 63448
North Charleston, SC 29419-3448
Tel.: (843) 554-4870
Fax: (843) 745-5502
Web Site: www.coburgmilk.com
Approx. Number Employees: 300
Business Description:
Milk & Milk By-Products Processor
S.I.C.: 2026
N.A.I.C.S.: 311511
Advertising Expenditures: $200,000
Exhibits/Trade Shows: $100,000; Point of Purchase: $100,000
Distr.: Reg.
Budget Set: Various
Personnel:
Mike Watson *(Gen Mgr)*
Brands & Products:
COBURG

COCA-COLA NORTH AMERICA
(Div. of The Coca-Cola Company)
1 Coca Cola Plaza
Atlanta, GA 30313-2499
Tel.: (404) 676-2121
Fax: (404) 676-6792
Web Site: www.cocacola.com
Sales Range: $150-199.9 Million
Approx. Number Employees: 350
Business Description:
Orange Juice & Other Juices; Processing of Citrus Products; Dairy Products; Flavoring Extracts & Syrups Mfr
S.I.C.: 2037
N.A.I.C.S.: 311411
Advertising Expenditures: $50,000,000
Media: 1-2-3-5-6-8-9-15-18-19-20-21-22-23-24
Distr.: Natl.
Personnel:
J. Alexander M. Douglas, Jr. *(Pres & COO)*
Katie J. Bayne *(Pres & Gen Mgr-Sparkling Beverages)*
Dan Candeto *(CIO)*
Beatriz R. Perez *(Chief Sustainability Officer)*
Brian P. Kelley *(Pres-Bus Integration)*
Deryck van Rensburg *(Pres-Emerging Brands-US)*
Alison Lewis *(Sr VP-Mktg)*
Sonya Soutus *(Sr VP)*
Kathleen Ciaramello *(Reg VP)*
Dan A. Schafer *(VP-Comm & Pub Affairs)*
Reinaldo Padua *(Asst VP-Hispanic Mktg)*
Mike St. John *(Gen Mgr)*
Betty Kuphal *(Reg Dir-Media-Southeast Reg)*
William White *(Grp Brand Dir-Diet Coke)*
Sheri Bain *(Dir-Reg Media)*
Susan Stribling *(Dir-Comm)*
Jose Serafin *(Brand Mgr-Hispanic Mktg)*
Al Rondon *(Sr Brand Mgr-Hispanic Mktg)*
Jennifer McClure *(Mgr-Comm)*
Lyndell Morrissey *(Mgr-Comm)*
Debbie Vasquez *(Mgr-Shopper Mktg-Walmart-Central US)*
Advertising Agencies:
CP+B
3390 Mary St Ste 300
Coconut Grove, FL 33133
Tel.: (305) 859-2070
Fax: (305) 854-3419

CP+B Boulder
6450 Gunpark Dr
Boulder, CO 80301
Tel.: (303) 628-5100
Fax: (303) 516-0227

Leo Burnett Worldwide, Inc.
35 W Wacker Dr
Chicago, IL 60601-1723
Tel.: (312) 220-5959
Fax: (312) 220-3299

Starcom MediaVest Group
35 W Wacker Dr
Chicago, IL 60601-1723
Tel.: (312) 220-3535
Fax: (312) 220-6530

Wieden + Kennedy, Inc.
224 NW 13th Ave
Portland, OR 97209-2953
Tel.: (503) 937-7000
Fax: (503) 937-8000

THE COFFEE BEANERY LTD.
3429 Pierson Pl
Flushing, MI 48433-2413
Tel.: (810) 733-1020
Fax: (810) 733-1536
Toll Free: (800) 728-2326
E-mail: ops@coffeebeanery.com
Web Site: www.coffeebeanery.com
Approx. Number Employees: 200
Year Founded: 1976
Business Description:
Retail Gourmet Coffee Specialty Store
S.I.C.: 5499; 5149
N.A.I.C.S.: 445299; 424490
Media: 9-23-25-26
Distr.: Reg.
Budget Set: Nov.
Personnel:
JoAnne M Shaw *(Pres)*
Brands & Products:
BEANERY BLEND
CAFE CARMEL
COFFEE BEANERY
COFFEE BEANVAC
COFFEE PEOPLE WHO CARE
ESPRESSO PERFECTO
EZ GRIP
ICED FUDGE RIPPLE
ITALIAN ESPRESS
THE RIGHT ROAST

COFFEE HOLDING CO., INC.
3475 Victory Blvd
Staten Island, NY 10314
Tel.: (718) 832-0800
Fax: (718) 832-0892
Toll Free: (800) 458-2233
E-mail: info@coffeeholding.com
Web Site: www.coffeeholding.com
Approx. Sls.: $83,491,967
Approx. Number Employees: 67
Year Founded: 1972
Business Description:
Wholesale Coffee Roaster & Dealer
S.I.C.: 2095; 2033; 5149; 7999
N.A.I.C.S.: 311920; 311421; 424490; 713990
Advertising Expenditures: $41,724
Media: 17
Personnel:
Andrew Gordon *(Pres, CEO & CFO)*
David Gordon *(COO & Exec VP)*
Brands & Products:
5TH AVENUE
CAFE CARIBE
CAFE SUPREMO
COFFEE HOLDING CO., INC.
DON MANUEL
S AND W
VIA ROMA

Key to Media (For complete agency information see *The Advertising Red Books-Agencies* edition):
1. Bus. Publs. 2. Cable T.V. 3. Catalogs & Directories. 4. Co-op Adv. 5. Consumer Mags. 6. D.M. to Bus. Estab.7. D.M. to Consumers 8. Daily Newsp. 9. Exhibits/Trade Shows 10. Foreign 11. Infomercial 12. Internet Adv.13. Multimedia 14. Network Radio 15. Network T.V. 16. Newsp. Distr. Mags. 17. Other 18. Outdoor (Posters, Transit) 19. Point of Purchase20. Premiums, Novelties 21. Product Samples 22. Special Events Mktg. 23. Spot Radio 24. Spot T.V. 25. Weekly Newsp. 26. Yellow Page Adv.

COFFEEAM.COM
12230 Coming Hwy
Canton, GA 30155
Tel.: (678) 494-1915
Fax: (678) 494-3433
Toll Free: (800) 803-7774
E-mail: service@coffeeam.com
Web Site: www.coffeeam.com
Approx. Number Employees: 15
Year Founded: 1992
Business Description:
Online Coffee Roastery
S.I.C.: 5499; 5149; 5961
N.A.I.C.S.: 445299; 424490; 454111; 454113
Media: 4-13
Brands & Products:
COFFEEAM
PORTROYAL.COM

COLAVITA USA, INC.
2537 Brunswick Ave
Linden, NJ 07036-2433
Tel.: (908) 862-5454
Fax: (908) 862-4382
E-mail: usa@colavita.com
Web Site: www.colavita.com
Sales Range: $25-49.9 Million
Approx. Number Employees: 80
Year Founded: 1892
Business Description:
Importer & Distr Olive Oil, Pasta & Other Food Products
S.I.C.: 5149
N.A.I.C.S.: 424490
Import Export
Advertising Expenditures: $400,000
Media: 7-16
Distr.: Intl.; Natl.
Budget Set: Mar. -Apr.
Personnel:
John Profaci, Jr. *(Founder & Chm)*
Walter Willett *(Chm)*
Joseph R. Profaci *(Gen Counsel & VP)*
Robert J. Profaci *(Sec & VP-Pur)*
John A. Profaci *(VP-Mktg)*
Brands & Products:
COLAVITA
DAL RACCOLTO

COLOMBO BAKING COMPANY
(Sub. of Interstate Brands Corporation)
580 Julie Ann Way
Oakland, CA 94621
Tel.: (510) 635-4343
Fax: (510) 638-2004
Web Site: www.sourdoughbread.com
Approx. Number Employees: 150
Year Founded: 1886
Business Description:
Sourdough & French Bread Products Mfr
S.I.C.: 2051
N.A.I.C.S.: 311812
Export
Advertising Expenditures: $600,000
Media: 8-9-10-19-25
Distr.: Natl.
Budget Set: Oct.
Personnel:
John Vrattos *(Acct Mgr-Sls)*
Brands & Products:
COLOMBO
EMPEROR NORTON

COLONNA BROS., INC.
4102 Bergen Tpke
North Bergen, NJ 07047-2510
Tel.: (201) 864-1115
Fax: (201) 864-0144
E-mail: cbifoods@aol.com
Web Site: www.colonnabrothers.com
Sales Range: $10-24.9 Million
Approx. Number Employees: 50
Year Founded: 1918
Business Description:
Distributor of Cheese, Flavored Bread Crumbs, Plain Bread Crumbs, Private Label Packaging, Spices, Croutons & Stuffing Mix
S.I.C.: 2022; 2099
N.A.I.C.S.: 311513; 311999
Import Export
Advertising Expenditures: $450,000
Media: 2-9-17-18-19-21-23-24-26
Distr.: Reg.
Budget Set: Jan.
Personnel:
Peter Colonna *(Pres)*
Brands & Products:
COLONNA

COLONY BRANDS INC.
(Formerly The Swiss Colony, Inc.)
1112 7th Ave
Monroe, WI 53566-1364
Tel.: (608) 328-8400
Fax: (608) 328-8457
Web Site: www.swisscolony.com
Approx. Number Employees: 1,300
Year Founded: 1926
Business Description:
Mfr & Retailer of Cheese, Meats, Pastries, Candies, Fruits, Nuts & Gift Packs; Retail Operations; Dining Facilities
S.I.C.: 5961; 5143
N.A.I.C.S.: 454113; 424430
Import Export
Advertising Expenditures: $8,690,000
Cable T.V.: $25,000; Catalogs & Directories: $7,000,000; Consumer Mags.: $1,000,000; Daily Newsp.: $100,000; Network T.V.: $10,000; Newsp. Distr. Mags.: $500,000; Other: $25,000; Spot T.V.: $25,000; Yellow Page Adv.: $5,000
Distr.: Direct to Consumer; Natl.
Budget Set: Mar.-July
Personnel:
Pat Kubly *(Chm)*
John Baumann *(Pres & CEO)*
Ann Bush *(VP-Mdsg)*
Joseph Hunter *(VP-HR)*
Robert Vig *(VP-Data Center)*
Ryan Kubly *(Dir-Strategic Planning)*
Brands & Products:
SHARING HOLIDAY MOMENTS FOR GENERATIONS
SWISS COLONY

COMMUNITY COFFEE COMPANY LLC
3332 Partridge Ln
Baton Rouge, LA 70821
Tel.: (225) 368-3900
Fax: (225) 368-4510
Fax: (800) 643-8199
Toll Free: (800) 525-5583
E-mail: info@communitycoffee.com
Web Site: www.communitycoffee.com
Sales Range: $10-24.9 Million
Approx. Number Employees: 1,500
Year Founded: 1919
Business Description:
Mfr. of Roasted Coffee
S.I.C.: 2095
N.A.I.C.S.: 311920
Import
Media: 1-2-3-4-6-8-9-10-13-14-15-18-19-20-22-23-24-26
Personnel:
Matthew Saurage *(Pres)*
Brands & Products:
CAFE SPECIAL
COMMUNITY
HOLIDAY JAZZ
HOTEL BLEND
MOCHASIPPI
NEW ORLEAN BLEND
PRIVATE RESERVE
RED BAG
TEABAGS
Advertising Agency:
Encircle Marketing
1999 Bryan St 29th Fl
Dallas, TX 75201
Tel.: (214) 259-4000
Fax: (214) 259-4060

CONAGRA FOODS LAMB WESTON, INC.
(Sub. of ConAgra Foods, Inc.)
599 S Rivershore Ln
Eagle, ID 83616
Tel.: (208) 938-1047
Fax: (208) 388-4299
Toll Free: (800) 766-7783
E-mail: info@lambweston.com
Web Site: www.lambweston.com
Sales Range: $50-74.9 Million
Approx. Number Employees: 55
Year Founded: 1950
Business Description:
Frozen Potato & Other Frozen Food Products Mfr & Distr
S.I.C.: 2038; 5142
N.A.I.C.S.: 311412; 424420
Export
Media: 2-7-10-11-13-19-20
Distr.: Intl.
Budget Set: Feb.
Personnel:
Richard A. Porter *(Chm)*
Jeffery J. DeLapp *(Pres)*
Mark Hayden *(Sr VP-Sls & Customer Ops)*
Lisa Bescherer *(Sr Dir-Mktg)*
Helene Clark *(Dir-Mktg)*
Dan Downard *(Dir-HR)*
Ken Horn *(Dir-Natl Accts)*
Steve Hamm *(Mgr-Mktg)*
Advertising Agencies:
Bailey Lauerman
1248 O St Ste 900
Lincoln, NE 68508-1460
Tel.: (402) 475-2800
Fax: (402) 475-5115

Budco Creative Services
13700 Oakland Ave
Highland Park, MI 48203
Tel.: (313) 957-5100
Fax: (313) 957-5522
Toll Free: (888) BUDCO-40

Leo Burnett Company Ltd.
175 Bloor St E North Twr
Toronto, ON M4W 3R9, Canada
Tel.: (416) 925-5997
Fax: (416) 92-5 3443

The Marketing Store
701 E 22nd St
Lombard, IL 60148
Tel.: (630) 693-1400
Fax: (630) 932-5200

Strahan Advertising
1940 Old Tustin Ave
Santa Ana, CA 92705
Tel.: (714) 547-6383
Fax: (714) 547-5463
— Timothy D. Strahan *(Pres.)*

CONAGRA GROCERY PRODUCTS COMPANY, LLC
(Sub. of ConAgra Foods, Inc.)
215 W Diehl Rd
Naperville, IL 60563
Tel.: (630) 857-1000
Sales Range: $300-349.9 Million
Approx. Number Employees: 650
Year Founded: 1890
Business Description:
Grocery Products Mfr & Marketing
S.I.C.: 2033; 2079
N.A.I.C.S.: 311421; 311225
Media: 2-3-5-6-8-9-10-13-14-15-16-18-19-20-21-23-24
Distr.: Intl.; Natl.
Budget Set: Mar.
Brands & Products:
BEANEE WEENEE
BIG JOHNS
ROSARITA
SNACK PACK
SWISS MISS
WESSON
WOLF BRAND CHILI
Advertising Agency:
Leo Burnett Worldwide, Inc.
35 W Wacker Dr
Chicago, IL 60601-1723
Tel.: (312) 220-5959
Fax: (312) 220-3299
(Chef Boyardee & Healthy Choice)

CONOPCO
(Plant of Conopco)
(d/b/a Unilever Home & Personal Care USA)
75 Merritt Blvd
Trumbull, CT 06611
Tel.: (203) 377-8300
Tel.: (203) 381-3500
Fax: (203) 381-2199
Telex: 66140 LEVER UW
Web Site: www.unilever.com
Approx. Number Employees: 135
Year Founded: 1989
Business Description:
Cosmetics Mfr
S.I.C.: 2844
N.A.I.C.S.: 325620
Media: 2-4-5-6-7-8-9-10-15-16-19-20-21-23-24-25-26
Distr.: Natl.
Personnel:
Lisa Klauser *(VP-Mktg)*
Ian Amour *(Asst Brand Mgr)*
Mirja Kloss *(Brand Mgr)*
Harpreet S. Tibb *(Product Mgr)*

Key to Media (For complete agency information see *The Advertising Red Books-Agencies* edition):
1. Bus. Publs. 2. Cable T.V. 3. Catalogs & Directories. 4. Co-op Adv. 5. Consumer Mags. 6. D.M. to Bus. Estab.7. D.M. to Consumers
8. Daily Newsp. 9. Exhibits/Trade Shows 10. Foreign 11. Infomercial 12. Internet Adv.13. Multimedia 14. Network Radio
15. Network T.V. 16. Newsp. Distr. Mags. 17. Other 18. Outdoor (Posters, Transit) 19. Point of Purchase20. Premiums, Novelties
21. Product Samples 22. Special Events Mktg. 23. Spot Radio 24. Spot T.V. 25. Weekly Newsp. 26. Yellow Page Adv.

CONOPCO
(Plant of Unilever Foodsolutions)
(d/b/a Unilever Food Solutions)
1930 California Ave
Corona, CA 92881
Tel.: (951) 737-4000
Fax: (909) 737-1951
E-mail: hr@unilever.com
Web Site:
www.unileverfoodsolutions.us
Approx. Number Employees: 120
Year Founded: 1943
Business Description:
Custom Designer & Developer of Specialty Wet & Dry Food Products
S.I.C.: 2099
N.A.I.C.S.: 311999
Export
Media: 2-10-17
Distr.: Natl.
Budget Set: Jan.

CONSOLIDATED TEA CO., INC.
300 Merrick Rd Ste 202
Lynbrook, NY 11563-2503
Tel.: (516) 887-1144
Fax: (516) 887-1643
Approx. Number Employees: 10
Business Description:
Tea Products Mfr
S.I.C.: 5149
N.A.I.C.S.: 424490
Media: 6
Distr.: Natl.
Budget Set: Sept.
Personnel:
Elliot V. Labiner *(Pres)*
Brands & Products:
ANN JOY
COLUMBIA
SWEE-TOUCH-NEE
WHITE LILAC

CONWAY IMPORT CO. INC.
11051 Addison Ave
Franklin Park, IL 60131-1401
Tel.: (847) 455-5600
Fax: (847) 455-5630
E-mail: conwayinternet@mindspring.com
Web Site: www.conwaydressings.com
Approx. Number Employees: 90
Year Founded: 1910
Business Description:
Mfr. of Condiments; French Dressing, Mayonnaise & Processed Oil
S.I.C.: 2035; 2046
N.A.I.C.S.: 311941; 311221
Advertising Expenditures: $500,000
Media: 9-13
Personnel:
Scott P. Heineman *(Pres)*
Bob Burns *(VP-Mktg)*
Brands & Products:
CONWAY
LA-FLORA

CONWAY IMPORT CO. INC.
(Div. of Conway Import Co. Inc.)
4 Warehouse Ln
Elmsford, NY 10523-1542
Tel.: (914) 592-1311
Fax: (914) 592-1104
Web Site: www.conwaydressings.com
Approx. Number Employees: 4
Business Description:
Salad Dressings Mfr
S.I.C.: 2035
N.A.I.C.S.: 311941
Media: 2-23
Distr.: Natl.

COOKIES BY DESIGN, INC.
1865 Summit Ave Ste 605
Plano, TX 75074
Tel.: (972) 398-9536
Fax: (972) 398-9542
Toll Free: (800) 945-2665
Web Site: www.cookiesbydesign.com
Sales Range: $10-24.9 Million
Approx. Number Employees: 25
Business Description:
Cookie Products Mfr & Distr
S.I.C.: 6794
N.A.I.C.S.: 533110
Media: 4-6-13
Personnel:
Anthony Sirnans *(CFO)*
Brands & Products:
COOKIE BOUQUET
COOKIES BY DESIGN
GIFTS THAT TASTE AS GOOD AS THEY LOOK

COOPERATIVE REGIONS OF ORGANIC PRODUCER POOLS
(d/b/a Organic Valley)
1 Organic Way
La Farge, WI 54639
Tel.: (608) 625-3025
Toll Free: (888) 444-6455
E-mail: organic@orgnicvalley.coop
Web Site: www.organicvalley.coop
Sales Range: $200-249.9 Million
Approx. Number Employees: 350
Year Founded: 1988
Business Description:
Organic Food Producer & Marketer
S.I.C.: 2099; 0139
N.A.I.C.S.: 311999; 111998
Media: 6-10
Personnel:
Theresa Marquez *(CMO)*
Eric Newman *(VP-Sls)*
Angela Garrett *(Assoc Product Mgr-Organic Valley)*
Brands & Products:
CALIFORNIA PASTURES
FAMILY OF FARMS
GEN-O
NEW ENGLAND PASTURES
NORTHEAST PASTURES
NORTHWEST PASTURES
ORGANIC VALLEY
ROCKY MOUNTAIN PASTURES
STRINGLES
TEXAS PASTURES
Advertising Agency:
Haberman & Associates, Inc.
119 N 4th St Ste 301
Minneapolis, MN 55410
Tel.: (612) 338-3900
Fax: (612) 338-4844

CORN PRODUCTS INTERNATIONAL, INC.
5 Westbrook Corporate Ctr
Westchester, IL 60154
Tel.: (708) 551-2600
Fax: (708) 551-2570
Toll Free: (800) 443-2746
E-mail: corpcomm@cornproducts.com
Web Site: www.cornproducts.com
Approx. Sls.: $4,632,000,000
Approx. Number Employees: 10,700
Year Founded: 1906
Business Description:
Corn Refiner; Starches, Liquid Sweeteners & Other Corn-Derived Food Ingredients Supplier
S.I.C.: 2046; 0115; 2099
N.A.I.C.S.: 311221; 111150; 311999
Export
Media: 2-4-8-13-16-17-22
Distr.: Natl.
Personnel:
Ilene S. Gordon *(Chm, Pres & CEO)*
Cheryl K. Beebe *(CFO & Exec VP)*
Mary Ann Hynes *(Chief Compliance Officer, Gen Counsel, Sec & Sr VP)*
Julio dos Reis *(Pres-South America Ingredient Solutions & Sr VP)*
Jack C. Fortnum *(Pres-North America Div & VP)*
John F. Saucier *(Sr VP-Strategy & Global Bus Dev)*
Aaron H. Hoffman *(VP-IR & Corp Comm)*
Mark Lindley *(Dir-Corp Comm)*

COSTA FRUIT & PRODUCE INC.
18 Bunker Hill Indus Pk
Boston, MA 02129-1621
Tel.: (617) 241-8007
Fax: (617) 241-8718
E-mail: costasales@costafoods.com
Web Site: www.freshideas.com
Approx. Number Employees: 250
Year Founded: 1949
Business Description:
Fresh Fruits, Vegetables & Other Food Related Items Supplier & Whslr
S.I.C.: 5148; 5143
N.A.I.C.S.: 424480; 424430
Import Export
Advertising Expenditures: $500,000
Media: 7-8-10-13-17-19-20
Personnel:
Manuel R. Costa *(Pres & CEO)*
Kevin Linnehan *(CFO)*
Mike Scuderi *(Dir-Mktg)*
Romana Medeiros *(Dir-Mfg-Fresh Ideas)*
Barry Milanese *(Dir-Sls & Mktg)*
Linda Shea *(Dir)*
Joe Walsh *(Dir-MIS)*
Carmen Fuccillo *(Mgr-Natl Accounts)*
Karen Morrison *(Mgr)*
Chris Poirier *(Mgr-Ops)*

COUNTRY HOME BAKERS, INC.
(Sub. of J&J Snack Foods Corporation)
361 Benigno Blvd
Bellmawr, NJ 08031
Tel.: (856) 931-7052
Fax: (856) 931-7423
Toll Free: (800) 852-2253
E-mail: info@countryhomebakers.com
Web Site:
www.countryhomebakers.com
Sales Range: $10-24.9 Million
Approx. Number Employees: 500
Year Founded: 1959
Business Description:
Mfr. of Frozen Bread & Other Bakery Products
S.I.C.: 5149; 2053
N.A.I.C.S.: 424490; 311813
Export
Media: 2-4-7-10-17-19-20-21-22
Distr.: Natl.
Budget Set: Nov.
Personnel:
Jerry Shreiber *(CEO)*
Kelly Boyle *(Sr Product Mgr)*

CREST FOODS CO. INC.
905 Main St
Ashton, IL 61006
Tel.: (815) 453-7411
Fax: (815) 453-2646
Toll Free: (800) 435-6972
Web Site: www.crestfoods.com
Approx. Sls.: $32,507,117
Approx. Number Employees: 435
Year Founded: 1968
Business Description:
Dairy Stabilizers, Manufacturing & Contract Packaging
S.I.C.: 3556
N.A.I.C.S.: 333294
Media: 7-13-16
Personnel:
Jeffrey Meiners *(Pres)*
Steve Meiners *(VP-Corp Sls)*
Janet Sutton *(Mgr-Customer Svcs Dept)*

CROWLEY FOODS, INC.
(Sub. of HP Hood LLC)
93 Pennsylvania Ave
Binghamton, NY 13903
Mailing Address:
PO Box 549
Binghamton, NY 13902-0549
Tel.: (607) 779-3289
Fax: (607) 779-3439
Telex: 646095
Web Site: www.crowleyfoods.com
Approx. Number Employees: 1,000
Year Founded: 1904
Business Description:
Dairy, Frozen Desserts & Specialty Food Products Mfr
S.I.C.: 2026; 2024
N.A.I.C.S.: 311511; 311520
Advertising Expenditures: $225,000
Media: 2-4-7-10-17-20-21-22-23
Distr.: Natl.
Budget Set: Sept.
Personnel:
Scott Blake *(Sr VP-Ops)*
Brands & Products:
AXELROD
CROWLEY
GREENS
HAGAN
HELUVAGOOD
MAGGIO
PENN MAID
PENSUPREME
ROSENBERGERS
WEEKS

CROWN PRINCE, INC.
18581 Railroad St
City of Industry, CA 91748
Tel.: (626) 912-3700
Fax: (626) 854-0350
Toll Free: (800) 255-5063
E-mail: sales@crownprince.com
Web Site: www.crownprince.com
E-Mail For Key Personnel:
Marketing Director: dhines@crownprince.com
Sales Director: sales@crownprince.com

Key to Media (For complete agency information see *The Advertising Red Books-Agencies* edition):
1. Bus. Publs. 2. Cable T.V. 3. Catalogs & Directories. 4. Co-op Adv. 5. Consumer Mags. 6. D.M. to Bus. Estab.7. D.M. to Consumers 8. Daily Newsp. 9. Exhibits/Trade Shows 10. Foreign 11. Infomercial 12. Internet Adv.13. Multimedia 14. Network Radio 15. Network T.V. 16. Newsp. Distr. Mags. 17. Other 18. Outdoor (Posters, Transit) 19. Point of Purchase20. Premiums, Novelties 21. Product Samples 22. Special Events Mktg. 23. Spot Radio 24. Spot T.V. 25. Weekly Newsp. 26. Yellow Page Adv.

Sales Range: $10-24.9 Million
Approx. Number Employees: 50
Year Founded: 1948
Business Description:
Canned Seafood Importer
S.I.C.: 5149
N.A.I.C.S.: 424490
Import
Media: 2-3-6-8-9-10-14-17-19-20-23-25
Distr.: Natl.
Budget Set: Nov.
Personnel:
Robert Hoffman *(Owner)*
Dustan Hoffman *(Pres)*
Lawrence DeMarco *(Mgr-North Central Reg)*
Gary Gruettner *(Mgr-Sls-Natl)*
Denise Hines *(Mgr-Mktg)*
Ed Leavister *(Mgr-Sls-Eastern Reg)*
Brands & Products:
CROWN PRINCE
NATURAL
OCEAN PRINCE

CRYSTAL CREAM & BUTTER COMPANY

529 Kansas Ave
Modesto, CA 95321
Tel.: (209) 576-3400
Fax: (209) 576-3437
Toll Free: (866) 225-4821
E-mail: sales@crystal-milk.com
Web Site: www.crystal-milk.com
E-Mail For Key Personnel:
Sales Director: sales@crystal-milk.com
Public Relations: mike@crystal-milk.com
Sales Range: $150-199.9 Million
Approx. Number Employees: 630
Year Founded: 1901
Business Description:
Dairy Products Mfr
S.I.C.: 2026; 2021
N.A.I.C.S.: 311511; 311512
Export
Media: 18-19-23
Distr.: Reg.
Budget Set: Nov.
Personnel:
Jeff Foster *(Pres)*
Tom Van Autreve *(CFO)*
Brands & Products:
CRYSTAL
VITAFREZE
Advertising Agency:
Mering & Associates
1700 I St Ste 210
Sacramento, CA 95811
Tel.: (916) 441-0571
Fax: (916) 441-1370
(Cream & Butter; Milk & Milk By-Products; Ice Cream)
— Dave Mering *(Pres.)*

CTB INTERNATIONAL CORP.

(Holding of Berkshire Hathaway Inc.)
611 N Higbee St
Milford, IN 46542
Mailing Address:
PO Box 2000
Milford, IN 46542-2000
Tel.: (574) 658-4191
Fax: (574) 658-3471
E-mail: hr@ctbinc.com
Web Site: www.ctbinc.com
Sales Range: $100-124.9 Million
Approx. Number Employees: 1,300
Year Founded: 1995
Business Description:
Automated Feeding, Watering & Ventilation Systems Mfr
S.I.C.: 3523
N.A.I.C.S.: 333111
Export
Advertising Expenditures: $2,000,000
Media: 4-5-9-13-17-26
Personnel:
Victor Mancinelli *(Pres & CEO)*
Randy Eveler *(CFO & VP)*
Chuck Klippel *(VP & Gen Mgr-Production)*
Susan Hight *(Mgr-Corp Comm)*
Brands & Products:
AGILE MFG.
BROCK DOCK
BROCK SHUR-STEP
CHORE-MATIC
CHORE-TIME
DURA-CAGE
DURAMID
FANCOM
FLEX-AUGER
FLIP-TOP
GALV-A-WELD
HARMONIZER
LATCH-LOCK
MEAL-TIME
MEALMASTER FEEDKAR
MULTIFLO
POSIFLO
PYRAMID
RLX
ROXELL
SATELLITE
SHENANDOAH
SHUR-LOCK
SIBLEY
SOFT-TOUCH
SSS
STACO
SUPER 6
SWISH
TRIPLE CROWN
ULTRA-DRY
ULTRAFLO
ULTRAKAR
UNI-FRAME
WEIGH-MATIC
WELL-GARD

CUISINE SOLUTIONS, INC.

85 S Bragg St Ste 600
Alexandria, VA 22312-2793
Tel.: (703) 270-2900
Fax: (703) 750-1158
E-mail: webmaster@cuisinesolutions.com
Web Site: www.cuisinesolutions.com
Sales Range: $75-99.9 Million
Approx. Number Employees: 347
Year Founded: 1972
Business Description:
Prepared Frozen Entrees & Sauces Mfr
S.I.C.: 2038; 2037; 2099
N.A.I.C.S.: 311412; 311411; 311991
Export
Media: 2-4-7-10-21
Personnel:
Jean-Louis Vilgrain *(Chm)*
Stanislas Vilgrain *(Pres & CEO)*
Ronald Zilkowski *(CFO, Treas & Sec)*
L. Felipe Hasselmann *(COO)*
Gerard J. Bertholon *(Chief Strategy Officer & VP-Sls)*
Brian Vandiver *(Dir-Logistics)*
Brands & Products:
CUISINE SOLUTIONS
VOTRE PARTENAIRE CULINAIRE
YOUR CULINARY PARTNER

CUMBERLAND PACKING CORP.

2 Cumberland St
Brooklyn, NY 11205-1040
Tel.: (718) 858-4200
Fax: (718) 858-4785
E-mail: info@sweetnlow.com
Web Site: www.sweetnlow.com
Sales Range: $50-74.9 Million
Approx. Number Employees: 350
Business Description:
Sugar & Salt Substitutes Mfr
S.I.C.: 2869
N.A.I.C.S.: 325199
Media: 2-3-4-6-7-8-9-10-13-15-18-19-20-21-22-23-24-25-26
Distr.: Natl.
Budget Set: Oct.
Personnel:
Jeffrey Eisenstadt *(Pres)*
Mike Briskey *(Brand Mgr)*
Brands & Products:
BUTTER BUDS
NU-SALT
SWEET 'N LOW
Advertising Agency:
Mother New York
595 11th Ave
New York, NY 10036
Tel.: (212) 254-2800
Fax: (212) 254-6121
Agency of Record
Butter Buds
Creative Strategy
Interactive
NatraTaste
Nu-Salt
Outdoor
Package Design
Print
Stevia
Sugar in the Raw
Sween 'N Low
TV

CUSTOM CULINARY, INC.

(Sub. of Griffith Laboratories, Inc.)
2021 Swift Dr
Oak Brook, IL 60523
Tel.: (630) 928-4898
Fax: (630) 928-4899
Toll Free: (800) 621-8827
Web Site: www.customculinary.com
Approx. Number Employees: 56
Business Description:
Private-Label Soup Bases, Gravies & Sauces Mfr
S.I.C.: 2034; 2099
N.A.I.C.S.: 311423; 311999
Personnel:
Michael L. Minor *(Dir-Culinary Svcs)*
Brands & Products:
CUSTOM
CUSTOM GOLD LABEL
PANROAST
Advertising Agency:
Scott, Inc. of Milwaukee
(dba Scott Advertising)
1031 N Astor St
Milwaukee, WI 53202-3324
Tel.: (414) 276-1080
Fax: (414) 276-3327

DAIRY FARMERS OF AMERICA, INC.

PO Box 909700
Kansas City, MO 64190-9700
Tel.: (816) 801-6455
Fax: (816) 801-6456
Toll Free: (888) 332-6455
E-mail: media@dfamilk.com
Web Site: www.dfamilk.com
Sales Range: $5-14.9 Billion
Approx. Number Employees: 4,000
Year Founded: 1998
Business Description:
Dairy Marketing Services
S.I.C.: 9641; 2023; 2026
N.A.I.C.S.: 926140; 311511; 311514
Media: 10-13-14-18
Personnel:
Randy Mooney *(Chm)*
Rick Smith *(Pres & CEO)*
Mark Korsmeyer *(Pres-Global Dairy Products Grp & Exec VP)*
Joel Clark *(Sr VP-Acctg)*
David A. Geisler *(Sr VP-Legal & Admin)*
David Meyer *(Sr VP-Fin)*
John J. Wilson *(Sr VP & Chief Fluid Mktg Officer)*
Brands & Products:
BORDEN
CACHE VALLEY
CALPRO
DFA
ELSIE
HOTEL BAR
PLUGRA
SPORT SHAKE
SPORT SHAKE MAX
Advertising Agencies:
Bernstein-Rein Advertising, Inc.
4600 Madison Ave Ste 1500
Kansas City, MO 64112-3016
Tel.: (816) 756-0640
Fax: (816) 399-6000
Toll Free: (800) 571-6246

Sullivan Higdon & Sink Incorporated
255 N Mead St
Wichita, KS 67202-2707
Tel.: (316) 263-0124
Fax: (316) 263-1084
Toll Free: (800) 577-5684
Agency of Record-Cache Valley Dairy & Borden Cheese

DAIRYLEA COOPERATIVE INC.

5001 Brittonfield Pkwy
East Syracuse, NY 13057-9201
Tel.: (315) 433-0100
Fax: (315) 433-2345
Toll Free: (800) 654-8838
E-mail: webmaster@dairylea.com
Web Site: www.dairylea.com
Approx. Sls.: $1,100,000,000
Approx. Number Employees: 200
Year Founded: 1907
Business Description:
Marketing, Business & Economic Development, Financial, Investment, Insurance, Information Technology, Risk Management & Cooperative Trading Services to Dairy Farmers
S.I.C.: 0241
N.A.I.C.S.: 112120

Key to Media (For complete agency information see *The Advertising Red Books-Agencies* edition):
1. Bus. Publs. 2. Cable T.V. 3. Catalogs & Directories. 4. Co-op Adv. 5. Consumer Mags. 6. D.M. to Bus. Estab.7. D.M. to Consumers 8. Daily Newsp. 9. Exhibits/Trade Shows 10. Foreign 11. Infomercial 12. Internet Adv.13. Multimedia 14. Network Radio 15. Network T.V. 16. Newsp. Distr. Mags. 17. Other 18. Outdoor (Posters, Transit) 19. Point of Purchase20. Premiums, Novelties 21. Product Samples 22. Special Events Mktg. 23. Spot Radio 24. Spot T.V. 25. Weekly Newsp. 26. Yellow Page Adv.

Dairylea Cooperative Inc. — (Continued)

Media: 9-17-23
Distr.: Natl.
Budget Set: Mar.
Personnel:
Clyde E. Rutherford *(Pres)*
Gregory I. Wickham *(CEO)*
Ellen M O'Connor *(CFO)*
Brad Keating *(COO)*
Edward W. Bangel *(VP-Fin & Admin)*
Karen Cartier *(VP-Comm & Legislative Affairs)*

DAKOTA GROWERS PASTA COMPANY, INC.

(Sub. of Viterra Inc.)
1 Pasta Ave
Carrington, ND 58421-2500
Tel.: (701) 652-2855
Fax: (701) 652-3552
E-mail: webmaster@dakotagrowers.com
Web Site: www.dakotagrowers.com
Approx. Rev.: $297,438,000
Approx. Number Employees: 299
Year Founded: 1993
Business Description:
Pasta Mfr
S.I.C.: 2098; 2099
N.A.I.C.S.: 311823; 311999
Import Export
Advertising Expenditures: $2,808,000
Media: 6-8-13-15
Personnel:
Timothy J. Dodd *(Pres & CEO)*
Edward O. Irion *(CFO)*
Eldon Buschbom *(Reg VP-Ops)*
Susan M. Clemens *(VP-HR & Admin)*
Jack B. Hasper *(VP-Sls-Mktg)*
Radwan Ibrahim *(VP-Quality Assurance)*
Liz Reinhiller *(Dir-Mktg & PR)*
Brands & Products:
DAKOTA GROWERS PASTA
PASTA SANITA
YOUR SOURCE FOR PREMIUM PASTA
ZIA BRIOSA
Advertising Agency:
The Zimmerman Group
21940 Minnetonka Blvd
Excelsior, MN 55331
Tel.: (952) 470-8830
Fax: (952) 470-8807

DANISCO USA, INC.

(Sub. of Danisco A/S)
4 New Century Pkwy
New Century, KS 66031
Mailing Address:
PO Box 26
New Century, KS 66031-0026
Tel.: (913) 764-8100
Fax: (913) 764-5407
Toll Free: (800) 255-6837
Web Site: www.danisco.com
Approx. Number Employees: 250
Year Founded: 1975
Business Description:
Functional Food Ingredients Mfr & Retailer
S.I.C.: 2869; 2099
N.A.I.C.S.: 325199; 311999
Import Export
Advertising Expenditures: $200,000
Media: 2-10
Distr.: Natl.
Budget Set: Aug.
Personnel:
Steve St. Arnold *(VP-Fin-NAFTA Region)*
Brands & Products:
CREMODAN
DIMODAN
GRINDSTED
GRINDSTED CITREM
GRINDSTED LACTEM
GRINDSTED PGE
GRINDSTED PGME
GRINDSTED PS
GRINDSTED STS & SMS

THE DANNON COMPANY, INC.

(Sub. of Danone Foods Inc.)
Fl 3 100 Hillside Ave
White Plains, NY 10603-2862
Tel.: (914) 872-8400
E-mail: info@dannon.com
Web Site: www.dannon.com
Sales Range: $550-599.9 Million
Approx. Number Employees: 400
Year Founded: 1942
Business Description:
Mfr of Yogurt & Frozen Yogurt
S.I.C.: 2026
N.A.I.C.S.: 311511
Media: 6-7-8-9-10-16-19-20-23-24-25
Distr.: Natl.
Budget Set: Dec.
Personnel:
Juan Carlos Dalto *(Pres & CEO)*
Elio Pacheco *(Pres/Gen Mgr-Evian)*
Sergio Fuster *(Sr VP-Mktg)*
Luciano Lopez-May *(Sr VP-Sls)*
Eric O'Toole *(Sr VP-Foodservice & Restaurant Bus Unit)*
Alessandro Arosio *(VP-Mktg)*
Francois Blanckaert *(VP-Pur)*
Tony Cicio *(VP-HR)*
Michael Neuwirth *(Sr Dir-Pub Rels)*
Raman Sehgal *(Sr Mgr-Mktg)*
Mike Skousen *(Mgr-Bus Dev)*
Brands & Products:
ACTIMEL
COLOR CHANGING CRYSTALS
DANIMALS
DANNON
FRUSION
LIGHT 'N FIT
MYSTERY MIXINS
SPRINKL'INS
Advertising Agencies:
Edelman
250 Hudson St
New York, NY 10013
Tel.: (212) 768-0550
Fax: (212) 704-0128

Marketing Drive
800 Connecticut Ave 3rd Fl E
Norwalk, CT 06854
Tel.: (203) 857-6100
Fax: (203) 857-6171
Light 'n Fit

MPG
(Div. of HAVAS)
195 Broadway 12th Fl
New York, NY 10007
Tel.: (646) 587-5000
Fax: (646) 587-5005
— Adnan Brankovic *(VP & Grp Acct Dir-Dannon)*

VML-New York
285 Madison Ave
New York, NY 10017
Tel.: (212) 210-3653
Fax: (212) 880-7543

Young & Rubicam Inc.
285 Madison Ave
New York, NY 10017-6401
Tel.: (212) 210-3000
Fax: (212) 490-9073
Activia
Light & Fit 0% Plus
— Filipe Vasconcellos *(Acct Exec)*

DARIGOLD, INC.

PO Box 34377
Seattle, WA 98124-1377
Tel.: (206) 284-7220
Fax: (206) 281-3456
Toll Free: (800) 333-6455
Web Site: www.darigold.com
Approx. Number Employees: 1,160
Year Founded: 1918
Business Description:
Processor of Dairy Products
S.I.C.: 2023; 2026
N.A.I.C.S.: 311514; 311511
Export
Media: 1-2-3-4-5-10-17-18-19-20-21-22-23-24-26
Distr.: Direct to Insurance Agent or Broker; Reg.
Budget Set: Jan.
Personnel:
John Underwood *(Pres & CEO)*
John Wells *(CFO & Sr VP-Fin)*
Dermot Carey *(Sr VP-Ingredients Div)*
Brands & Products:
DAIRYGOLD
DARIGOLD
THE NATURAL SOURCE OF QUALITY
Advertising Agency:
Dave Syferd & Partners
2601 4th Ave Ste 600
Seattle, WA 98121
Tel.: (206) 262-0395
Fax: (206) 262-0915

DARLING INTERNATIONAL, INC.

251 O'Connor Ridge Blvd Ste 300
Irving, TX 75038
Tel.: (972) 717-0300
Fax: (972) 717-1588
E-mail: info@darlingii.com
Web Site: www.darlingii.com
E-Mail For Key Personnel:
Sales Director: sales@darlingii.com
Approx. Sls.: $724,909,000
Approx. Number Employees: 3,330
Year Founded: 1882
Business Description:
Animal By-Products & Used Cooking Oil Processor
S.I.C.: 2079; 2013
N.A.I.C.S.: 311225; 311613
Media: 2-7
Personnel:
Randall C. Stuewe *(Chm & CEO)*
John F. Sterling *(Gen Counsel, Sec & Exec VP)*
Neil Katchen *(Exec VP-Ops)*
John O. Muse *(Exec VP)*
Michael L. Rath *(Exec VP-Commodities & Risk Mgmt)*
Robert H. Seemann *(Exec VP-Sls & Svcs)*
Nick Borrelli *(Mgr-Accts)*

D'ARRIGO BROS. COMPANY

(d/b/a Andy Boy)
2177 Harris Rd
Salinas, CA 93908
Tel.: (831) 455-4500
Fax: (831) 455-4301
Web Site: www.andyboy.com
Approx. Number Employees: 900
Year Founded: 1927
Business Description:
Vegetables & Melons Producer
S.I.C.: 0161; 0139
N.A.I.C.S.: 111219; 111998
Import Export
Media: 7-10-11-13-22
Personnel:
Andrew A. D'Arrigo *(Chm)*
John D'Arrigo *(Pres)*
Margaret D'Arrigo-Martin *(Exec VP-Sls & Mktg)*
Dave Martinez *(Dir-Sls)*
Claudia Villalobos *(Mgr-Mktg)*
Brands & Products:
ANDY BOY
THE JOY OF HEALTHY LIFE

DAVID MICHAEL & CO. INC.

10801 Decatur Rd
Philadelphia, PA 19154-3209
Tel.: (215) 632-3100
Fax: (215) 637-3920
Toll Free: (800) DM-FLAVORS
E-mail: dmflavor@dmflavors.com
Web Site: www.dmflavors.com
Approx. Number Employees: 200
Year Founded: 1896
Business Description:
Mfr. of Flavorings for Processed Food Industry
S.I.C.: 2087; 2869
N.A.I.C.S.: 311930; 325199
Import Export
Personnel:
Skip Rosskam *(Pres & COO)*
Stuart Rosenbaum *(CIO & Partner)*
Jedd B. Stillman *(Treas & Sr VP)*
George Rosskam *(Exec VP)*
Steve A. Rosskam *(Exec VP)*
Steve Wilbur *(VP-Mktg)*
Marie Cummings *(Mgr-Food Applications & Product Dev)*
Luis Gayo *(Mgr-Ops)*
Russell Kauffman *(Mgr-Production)*
Erin Kate O'Donnell *(Mgr-Mktg)*
Brands & Products:
BEEF MATE
COFFEE TOPPER
DM CHOICE
HIT YOUR FLAVOR TARGET FASTER
MICHAEL THERMICS
MICHAELITE
MICHAELOK
MICHTEX
MIXEVAN
OLD TIME BODY & AGE
RAISINMATE
SUPER SUPREME
SUPERVAN
SUPREME
VANGUARD
Advertising Agency:
Star Group Communications, Inc.
(d/b/a The Star Group)

Key to Media (For complete agency information see *The Advertising Red Books-Agencies* edition):
1. Bus. Publs. 2. Cable T.V. 3. Catalogs & Directories: 4. Co-op Adv. 5. Consumer Mags. 6. D.M. to Bus. Estab.7. D.M. to Consumers 8. Daily Newsp. 9. Exhibits/Trade Shows 10. Foreign 11. Infomercial 12. Internet Adv.13. Multimedia 14. Network Radio 15. Network T.V. 16. Newsp. Distr. Mags. 17. Other 18. Outdoor (Posters, Transit) 19. Point of Purchase20. Premiums, Novelties 21. Product Samples 22. Special Events Mktg. 23. Spot Radio 24. Spot T.V. 25. Weekly Newsp. 26. Yellow Page Adv.

220 Laurel Rd
Voorhees, NJ 08043
Tel.: (856) 782-7000
Fax: (856) 782-5699

DEAN FOODS COMPANY

2711 N Haskell Ave Ste 3400
Dallas, TX 75204
Tel.: (214) 303-3400
Fax: (214) 303-3499
Toll Free: (800) 431-9214
Web Site: www.deanfoods.com
Approx. Sls.: $12,122,887,000
Approx. Number Employees: 25,780
Year Founded: 1925
Business Description:
Milk & Dairy Products, Soymilk & Organic Food Products Mfr & Distr
S.I.C.: 2024; 2026; 2099; 5143
N.A.I.C.S.: 311520; 311511; 311999; 424430
Export
Advertising Expenditures: $190,700,000
Media: 6-9-10-13-16-18-19-20-23-24-25
Distr.: Natl.
Budget Set: Sept.
Personnel:
Gregg L. Engles *(Chm & CEO)*
Shaun P. Mara *(CFO)*
Barbara D. Carlini *(CIO & Sr VP)*
Rick Zuroweste *(CMO & Sr VP)*
Scott Vopni *(Chief Acctg Officer & VP)*
Marguerite Copel *(Pres-Dean Foods Foundation & VP-Corp Comm)*
Steven J. Kemps *(Gen Counsel, Sec & Exec VP)*
Kelly Duffin-Maxwell *(Exec VP-R & D)*
Gregory A. McKelvey *(Chief Strategy & Transformation Officer & Exec VP)*
Gregg A. Tanner *(Chief Supply Chain Officer & Exec VP)*
Tommy Zanetich *(Exec VP-HR)*
Deborah B. Carosella *(Sr VP-Innovation)*
Rick Fehr *(Sr VP)*
William C. Tinklepaugh *(Sr VP-Govt & Indus Rels)*
Ronald H. Klein *(VP & Gen Mgr-Cultured Products)*
Nick Mysore *(Sr Dir-Market Res & Strategy)*
Brands & Products:
ALTA DENA
BARBER'S
BARBE'S
BERKELEY FARMS
BROUGHTON
BROWN'S DAIRY
COUNTRY DELITE
COUNTRY FRESH
CREAMLAND
CREATED BY NATURE. DELIVERED BY DEAN.
DAIRY FRESH
DEAN
DEAN'S
GANDY'S
GARELICK FARMS
HEALTHY FOODS, HEALTHY FAMILIES, HEALTHY BUSINESS.
HYGEIA
LEHIGH VALLEY
LOUIS TRAUTH
MAPLEHURST
MAYFIELD
MAYFIELD DAIRY
MCARTHUR
MCARTHUR DAIRY
MEADOW BROOK
MEADOW GOLD
MELODY FARMS
MODEL DAIRY
MOUNTAIN HIGH
OAK FARMS
OVER THE MOON
PET DAIRY
PRICE'S
PRICE'S CREAMERIES
PURITY
RACHEL'S
RACHEL'S ORGANIC
REITER
REITER DAIRY
ROBINSON
SCHENKEL'S ALL STAR
SCHEPPS
SKINNY COW MILK
SWISS DAIRY
T.G. LEE
T.G. LEE DAIRY
TUSCAN
Advertising Agency:
Leo Burnett Worldwide, Inc.
35 W Wacker Dr
Chicago, IL 60601-1723
Tel.: (312) 220-5959
Fax: (312) 220-3299
Alta Dena
Country Fresh
Dean's
Garelick Farms
Lead Creative Agency
Mayfield

DEL MONTE FOODS CO.

(Joint Venture of KKR & CO. L.P., Vestar Capital Partners, Inc. & Centerview Partners LLC)
1 Market @ The Landmark
San Francisco, CA 94105
Tel.: (415) 247-3000
Fax: (415) 247-3565
E-mail: media.relations@delmonte.com
Web Site: www.delmonte.com
Approx. Sls.: $3,739,800,000
Approx. Number Employees: 5,300
Year Founded: 1916
Business Description:
Canned Fruit, Vegetables, Seafood, Broth & Pet Food Producer; Owned by KKR & Co. L.P., Vestar Capital Partners, Inc. & Centerview Partners LLC
S.I.C.: 2033; 5149
N.A.I.C.S.: 311421; 424490
Import Export
Advertising Expenditures: $140,600,000
Media: 3-6-7-10-15-18-19-20-24
Distr.: Natl.
Budget Set: Apr.
Personnel:
Neil Harrison *(Interim CEO)*
Larry E. Bodner *(CFO & Exec VP-Fin)*
Nils Lommerin *(COO)*
William D. Pearce *(CMO & Sr VP)*
Richard W. Muto *(Chief HR Officer & Exec VP)*
Richard L. French *(Chief Acctg Officer, Sr VP & Controller)*
James G. Potter *(Gen Counsel, Sec & Sr VP)*
David W. Allen *(Exec VP-Ops)*
Timothy A. Cole *(Exec VP-Sls)*
Jennifer D. Garrison *(VP-IR, Corp Comm & Govt Rels)*
Carrie Schliemann *(Dir-Mktg-Pet Food)*
Doug Chavez *(Sr Mgr-Digital Mktg)*
Melinda Winter *(Sr Mgr-Brand)*
Carlos Cojulun *(Sr Brand Mgr)*
Scott Noble *(Mgr-Integrated Mktg)*
Brands & Products:
9LIVES
BALANCED BITES
CHEW LOTTA
COLLEGE INN
CONTADINA
DEL MONTE
DOGS JUST KNOW
EVERY INGREDIENT COUNTS
FAARM STAND SELECTS
THE FRESHEST IDEAS IN ITALIAN COOKING
FRUIT CHILLERS
FRUIT NATURALS
GRAVY TRAIN
KIBBLES 'N BITS
LETS PLAY
MAKE A MILK BONE MOMENT
MEATY BONE
MEET SONCRATES
MEOW MIX
MILK-BONE
MORE TASTE.MORE JOY
NATURE'S RECIPE
NOURISHING FAMILIES. ENRICHING LIVES. EVERY DAY.
PIT ROAD PETS
POUNCE
PUP-PERONI
PUP-PERONI RIBS
S&W
SKIPPY
SNAUSAGES
SNAUSAGES BREAKFASTBITES
SNAUSAGES IN A BLANKET
SNAUSAGES PARTY SNACK
SNAUSAGES PAW PRINTS
SNAUSAGES SNAW SOMEONES
STEAK CHEW
SUNFRESH
WHOLESOME GOODNESS
WHOLESOME MEDLEY
WOOF DAWN THE LAUGHS
Advertising Agencies:
Bates 141 Asia Pacific
(Bates Asia Headquarters)
33F Tower 1 Times Square
Causeway Bay, China (Hong Kong)
Tel.: (852) 21036333
Fax: (852) 25274086
(S&W)

Catalyst
475 Sansome St Ste 730
San Francisco, CA 94111
Tel.: (415) 655-4200

Coburn Communications
130 W 42nd St Ste 750
New York, NY 10036
Tel.: (212) 730-7277
Fax: (212) 730-4738
9Lives
— Kate Tuller *(Acct Exec)*

Draftfcb
101 E Erie St
Chicago, IL 60611
Tel.: (312) 425-5000
Fax: (312) 425-5010

Draftfcb West
1160 Battery St Ste 250
San Francisco, CA 94111
Tel.: (415) 820-8000
Fax: (415) 820-8087
Agency of Record

Full Steam Marketing & Design
60 W Market St Ste 150
Salinas, CA 93901
Tel.: (831) 757-4164
Fax: (831) 757-7574

The Geppetto Group
95 Morton St 8th Fl
New York, NY 10014-3336
Tel.: (212) 462-8140
Fax: (212) 462-8197

Smith Brothers Agency, LP
116 Federal St
Pittsburgh, PA 15212
Tel.: (412) 391-0555
Fax: (412) 391-3562

Vertical Marketing Network LLC
15147 Woodlawn Ave
Tustin, CA 92780
Tel.: (714) 258-2400, ext. 420
Fax: (714) 258-2409

DELTA PRIDE CATFISH, INC.

PO Box 271 South City Limits Rd
Isola, MS 38754
Tel.: (662) 962-3101
Fax: (662) 962-0114
Toll Free: (800) 421-1045
E-mail: info@deltapride.com
Web Site: www.countryselect.com
Approx. Number Employees: 550
Year Founded: 1981
Business Description:
Processor of Fresh & Frozen Farm-Raised Catfish; Farmer-Owned Cooperative
S.I.C.: 2092; 2091
N.A.I.C.S.: 311712; 311711
Export
Media: 5-10-17
Distr.: Natl.
Personnel:
David Allen *(Pres)*
Greg Griffith *(Mgr-Eastern Div)*
Paul Tischer *(Mgr-Logistics)*
Brands & Products:
DELTA PRIDE
DELTA PRIME

DERST BAKING COMPANY, LLC

(Sub. of Flowers Foods Bakeries Group, LLC)
1311 Mills B Ln Blvd
Savannah, GA 31405
Tel.: (912) 233-2235
Fax: (912) 234-3611
Web Site: www.derst.com
Sales Range: $250-299.9 Million
Approx. Number Employees: 500
Year Founded: 1867

Key to Media (For complete agency information see *The Advertising Red Books-Agencies* edition):
1. Bus. Publs. 2. Cable T.V. 3. Catalogs & Directories. 4. Co-op Adv. 5. Consumer Mags. 6. D.M. to Bus. Estab.7. D.M. to Consumers 8. Daily Newsp. 9. Exhibits/Trade Shows 10. Foreign 11. Infomercial 12. Internet Adv.13. Multimedia 14. Network Radio 15. Network T.V. 16. Newsp. Distr. Mags. 17. Other 18. Outdoor (Posters, Transit) 19. Point of Purchase20. Premiums, Novelties 21. Product Samples 22. Special Events Mktg. 23. Spot Radio 24. Spot T.V. 25. Weekly Newsp. 26. Yellow Page Adv.

Derst Baking Company, LLC — (Continued)

Business Description:
Bread, Cake & Related Products Mfr & Whslr
S.I.C.: 2051; 5461
N.A.I.C.S.: 311812; 311811
Media: 5-9-18-19-24
Personnel:
Paul Frankum *(Pres)*
Steve Morani *(Sr VP-Fin)*
Brands & Products:
CAPTAIN JOHN DERST

DI GIORGIO CORPORATION
(Sub. of Rose Partners LP)
380 Middlesex Ave
Carteret, NJ 07008-3446
Tel.: (732) 541-5555
Fax: (732) 541-3730
Web Site: www.whiterose.com
Sales Range: $1-4.9 Billion
Approx. Number Employees: 1,201
Year Founded: 1920
Business Description:
Wholesale Distr of Groceries
S.I.C.: 5141; 5143
N.A.I.C.S.: 424410; 424430
Media: 2-6-9-10-11-17-19-23
Distr.: Intl.; Natl.
Budget Set: Sept.
Brands & Products:
WHITE ROSE
Advertising Agency:
Crown Advertising and Marketing
245 Newtown Road Ste 103
Plainview, NY 11803
Tel.: (516) 470-2700
Fax: (516) 470-2712

DIEDRICH COFFEE, INC.
(Sub. of Green Mountain Coffee Roasters, Inc.)
28 Executive Park Ste 200
Irvine, CA 92614
Tel.: (949) 260-1600
Fax: (949) 260-6781
Toll Free: (800) 354-5282
E-mail: info@diedrich.com
Web Site: www.diedrich.com
Approx. Rev.: $62,310,000
Approx. Number Employees: 149
Year Founded: 1972
Business Description:
Coffee Roaster & Retailer
S.I.C.: 5499; 2095
N.A.I.C.S.: 445299; 311920
Advertising Expenditures: $125,000
Media: 2-4-7-13-17
Personnel:
Richard Scott McCreary *(Pres)*
Tina Bissonette *(VP-Fin)*
Brands & Products:
ANTIGUA MOCHA JAVA
BLACK TIGER
COFFEE PEOPLE
DIEDRICH
DIEDRICH COFFEE
FLOR DE APANAS
GLORIA JEANS
MORNING EDITION BLEND
NEPENTHE BLEND
WIENER MELANGE BLEND

DIEHL FOOD INGREDIENTS LLC
24 N Clinton St
Defiance, OH 43512-1807
Tel.: (419) 782-5010
Fax: (419) 783-4319
Toll Free: (800) 251-3033
E-mail: info@diehlinc.com
Web Site: www.diehlinc.com
Approx. Number Employees: 150
Year Founded: 1870
Business Description:
Milk Substitutes & Custom Products Mfr & Distr
S.I.C.: 2023; 2099
N.A.I.C.S.: 311514; 311999
Export
Advertising Expenditures: $50,000
Media: 4-9-17
Personnel:
Tim Small *(Gen Mgr)*
Brands & Products:
CENTENNIAL
CHOCO-CREAM
CHOCOMITE
COCOA RICHE
FIVE STAR
HOFBRAU
JERZEE
PARTY NOGG
VITAMITE

DIETRICH'S MILK PRODUCTS, LLC
(Joint Venture of Dairy Farmers of America, Inc. & Dairylea Cooperative Inc.)
100 McKinley Ave
Reading, PA 19605
Tel.: (610) 929-5736
Fax: (610) 921-9330
Toll Free: (800) 526-6455
E-mail: webmaster@dietrichsmilk.com
Web Site: www.dietrichsmilk.com
Approx. Number Employees: 110
Year Founded: 1998
Business Description:
Industrial Food Ingredients Mfr
S.I.C.: 2023; 2026
N.A.I.C.S.: 311514; 311511
Media: 2-7-8
Distr.: Natl.
Budget Set: Jan.

DIETZ & WATSON INC.
5701 Tacony St
Philadelphia, PA 19135-4311
Tel.: (215) 831-9000
Fax: (215) 831-1044
Toll Free: (800) 333-1974
Web Site: www.dietzandwatson.com
E-Mail For Key Personnel:
Marketing Director: Leni@dietzandwatson.com
Sales Director: sales@dietzandwatson.com
Sales Range: $200-249.9 Million
Year Founded: 1939
Business Description:
Deli Products Mfr., Processor & Distr
S.I.C.: 0751; 5147
N.A.I.C.S.: 311611; 311612
Media: 1-2-3-5-10-17-19-21-23-25
Personnel:
Ruth Eni *(Chm)*
Louis Eni *(Pres & CEO)*
Christopher Eni *(COO)*
Steve Riley *(Dir-Mktg)*
Brands & Products:
DIETZ & WATSON
GOURMET LITE

DOLE FOOD COMPANY, INC.
(Sub. of Dole Holding Company, LLC)
1 Dole Dr
Westlake Village, CA 91362-7300
Mailing Address:
PO Box 5132
Westlake Village, CA 91359-5132
Tel.: (818) 879-6600
Fax: (818) 874-4893
Telex: 340295
Web Site: www.dole.com
Approx. Rev.: $6,892,614,000
Approx. Number Employees: 37,600
Year Founded: 1851
Business Description:
Fruit, Vegetable, Flower & Juice Producer, Mfr & Distr
S.I.C.: 2099; 0161; 0174; 0175; 0179; 2033; 5148
N.A.I.C.S.: 311999; 111219; 111320; 111331; 111339; 311421; 424480
Import Export
Advertising Expenditures: $92,100,000
Media: 5-6-10-11-17-18-22-23-24
Distr.: Intl.; Natl.
Budget Set: Aug.
Personnel:
David H. Murdock *(Chm)*
David A. DeLorenzo *(Pres & CEO)*
Joseph S. Tesoriero *(CFO)*
Yoon J. Hugh *(Chief Acctg Officer, VP & Controller)*
C. Michael Carter *(Gen Counsel, Sec & Exec VP)*
Roberta Wieman *(Exec VP & Head-Staff)*
Scott A. Griswold *(Exec VP-Corp Dev)*
Sue Hagen *(Sr VP-HR & Indus Relations)*
Danko Stambuk *(Sr VP-Mfg)*
Chris Lock *(VP-Sls & Mktg, Foodservice)*
Marty Ordman *(VP-Mktg & Comm)*
Ronda Reed *(VP-Mktg)*
Dave Spare *(VP-Mktg & Bus Dev)*
David Bright *(Dir-Mktg)*
Charlotte Kavanagh *(Mgr-Sls Strategy-Fresh Vegetables-Supervalu)*
Silvana Kocovski *(Mgr-Sls Strategy-Fresh Vegetables-Canada)*
Brands & Products:
DOLE
Advertising Agencies:
B.A.R.C. Communications, Inc.
170 Columbus Ave 5th Fl
San Francisco, CA 94133-5128
Tel.: (415) 772-1989
Fax: (415) 772-8964

BFG Communications
6 Anolyn Ct
Bluffton, SC 29910
Tel.: (843) 837-9115
Fax: (843) 837-9225

Dailey & Associates
(Sub. of The Interpublic Group of Cos., Inc.)
8687 Melrose Ave Ste G300
West Hollywood, CA 90069-5701
Tel.: (310) 360-3100
Fax: (310) 360-0810

Daniels & Roberts, Inc.
209 N Seacrest Blvd Ste 209
Boynton Beach, FL 33435
Tel.: (561) 241-0066
Fax: (561) 241-1198
Toll Free: (800) 488-0066
(Fresh Fruits)

Flair Communications Agency, Inc.
214 W Erie St
Chicago, IL 60654
Tel.: (312) 943-5959
Toll Free: (800) 621-8317
(Promotions)

Gibraltar Associates
815 Connecticut Ave N W Ste 800
Washington, DC 20006
Tel.: (202) 879-5820
Fax: (202) 534-1701
Corporate Social Responsibility Communications Agency of Record

DOLE FRESH VEGETABLES
(Holding of DOLE FOOD COMPANY, INC.)
639 S Sanborn Rd
Salinas, CA 93901
Tel.: (831) 754-3519
Fax: (831) 753-7210
Toll Free: (800) 333-5454
Web Site: www.dole.com
Business Description:
Vegetable Production
S.I.C.: 0723; 2099
N.A.I.C.S.: 115114; 311999
Export
Advertising Expenditures: $4,000,000
Media: 2-4-5-6-7-8-11-13-18-25-26
Personnel:
Ray DeRiggi *(Pres & CEO)*
Roger D. Billingsley *(Sr VP-Tech & Product Dev)*
Michelle Gonsalves *(Dir-Mktg-Fresh Div)*
Chris Mayhew *(Dir-Mktg & Strategy)*
Robert Hall *(Brand Mgr-Value Added Salads)*
Brands & Products:
BACON LETTUCE TOSS
BANANA SHUFFLE
FALL HARVEST
GREENER SELECTIONS
JUST LETTUCE
MYGREENS
SPRING GARDEN
VERY VEGGIE

DON MIGUEL MEXICAN FOODS, INC.
1501 W Orangewood Ave
Orange, CA 92868
Tel.: (714) 634-8441
Fax: (714) 978-3743
Web Site: www.donmiguel.com
Approx. Number Employees: 20
Year Founded: 1908
Business Description:
Mfr. of Mexican Food Products
S.I.C.: 2032; 2038
N.A.I.C.S.: 311422; 311412
Media: 2-9-20-25
Distr.: Natl.
Brands & Products:
ALEX
AUTENTICO
THE BOMB
DON MIGUEL
EL CHARRITO
EXPRESS BOWL
GRILLWICH

Key to Media (For complete agency information see *The Advertising Red Books-Agencies* edition):
1. Bus. Publs. 2. Cable T.V. 3. Catalogs & Directories. 4. Co-op Adv. 5. Consumer Mags. 6. D.M. to Bus. Estab.7. D.M. to Consumers
8. Daily Newsp. 9. Exhibits/Trade Shows 10. Foreign 11. Infomercial 12. Internet Adv.13. Multimedia 14. Network Radio
15. Network T.V. 16. Newsp. Distr. Mags. 17. Other 18. Outdoor (Posters, Transit) 19. Point of Purchase20. Premiums, Novelties
21. Product Samples 22. Special Events Mktg. 23. Spot Radio 24. Spot T.V. 25. Weekly Newsp. 26. Yellow Page Adv.

LEAN OLE
LUCCA
PINATA
XLNT

DR PEPPER SNAPPLE GROUP, INC.
(Sub. of Dr Pepper Snapple Group, Inc.)
900 King St
Rye Brook, NY 10573
Mailing Address:
PO Box 3800
Stamford, CT 06905-0800
Tel.: (914) 612-4000
Fax: (914) 612-4100
E-mail: media.relations@motts.com
Web Site: www.motts.com
Sales Range: $500-549.9 Million
Approx. Number Employees: 1,300
Year Founded: 1842
Business Description:
Fruit & Vegetable Beverages & Sauces
S.I.C.: 2033; 5149
N.A.I.C.S.: 311421; 424490
Advertising Expenditures: $6,000,000
Media: 2-6-8-9-10-15-19-20-24-25
Distr.: Natl.
Budget Set: Jan.-July
Personnel:
Mark Cassidy *(Sr VP)*

DRISCOLL STRAWBERRY ASSOCIATES INC.
345 Westridge Dr
Watsonville, CA 95076-4169
Tel.: (831) 763-5100
Fax: (831) 761-1090
Toll Free: (800) 871-3333
E-mail: consumer@driscolls.com
Web Site: www.driscolls.com
Approx. Number Employees: 300
Year Founded: 1953
Business Description:
Fresh Fruit Supplier
S.I.C.: 5148; 5431
N.A.I.C.S.: 424480; 445230
Import Export
Media: 2-4-13-17
Personnel:
Miles Reiter *(Chm & CEO)*
Soren Bjorn *(Sr VP-Bus & Global Technologies-Intl)*
Michael Hollister *(VP-Sls & Mktg)*
Brands & Products:
DRISCOLL
THE FINEST BERRIES IN THE WORLD

DUNDEE CITRUS GROWERS ASSOCIATION
PO Box 1739
Dundee, FL 33838
Tel.: (863) 439-1574
Fax: (863) 439-1535
E-mail: info@dun-d.com
Web Site: www.dun-d.com
Approx. Number Employees: 400
Business Description:
Citrus Farming
S.I.C.: 0179
N.A.I.C.S.: 111339
Media: 20-21
Personnel:
Steve Callaham *(CEO & Exec VP)*
Brands & Products:
DUN-D

DURKEE-MOWER, INC.
2 Empire St
Lynn, MA 01902-1815
Tel.: (781) 593-8007
Fax: (781) 593-6410
Web Site: www.marshmallowfluff.com
Approx. Number Employees: 20
Year Founded: 1920
Business Description:
Mfr. of Sandwich Spreads & Marshmallow Toppings
S.I.C.: 2099
N.A.I.C.S.: 311340
Advertising Expenditures: $200,000
Media: 8-25
Distr.: Reg.
Budget Set: May
Personnel:
Donald D. Durkee *(Pres)*
Jonathan S. Durkee *(Treas & Exec VP)*
Dan Quirk *(Dir-Sls-Mktg)*
Brands & Products:
FLUFF STUFF
FLUFFERNUTTER
MARSHMALLOW FLUFF

DUTCH GOLD HONEY INC.
2220 Dutch Gold Dr
Lancaster, PA 17601-1941
Tel.: (717) 393-1716
Fax: (717) 393-8687
Toll Free: (800) 338-0587
E-mail: info@dutchgoldhoney.com
Web Site: www.dutchgoldhoney.com
E-Mail For Key Personnel:
President: ngamber@dutchgoldhoney.com
Sales Director: mlane@dutchgoldhoney.com
Sales Range: $50-74.9 Million
Approx. Number Employees: 85
Year Founded: 1946
Business Description:
Honey & Maple Syrup Mfr & Whslr
S.I.C.: 5149; 2099
N.A.I.C.S.: 424490; 311999
Import Export
Advertising Expenditures: $25,000
Media: 2-4-16-17-23-24
Personnel:
William R. Gamber, II *(Chm)*
Nancy J. Gamber *(CEO)*
Jill Clark *(VP-Mktg & Sls)*
Charles Schatzman *(VP-Fin & Admin)*
Brands & Products:
BLOSSOM HILL
DUTCH GOLD HONEY
HONEY IN THE ROUGH
MCLURE'S
MOORELAND
SWEETMEADOW FARMS

EASTERN FISH COMPANY
300 Frank W Burr Blvd
Teaneck, NJ 07666-6704
Tel.: (201) 801-0800
Fax: (201) 801-0802
Toll Free: (800) 526-9066
E-mail: everyone@easternfish.com
Web Site: www.easternfish.com
E-Mail For Key Personnel:
President: ebloom@easternfish.com
Approx. Sls.: $200,000,000
Approx. Number Employees: 30
Year Founded: 1974
Business Description:
Fish & Seafoods Importer & Producer
S.I.C.: 5146
N.A.I.C.S.: 424460
Import Export
Media: 6-10-21
Personnel:
Eric Bloom *(Chm)*
Brands & Products:
SAIL BRAND

E.D. SMITH FOODS, LTD.
(Sub. of TreeHouse Foods, Inc.)
944 Highway 8
Winona, ON L8E 5S3, Canada
Tel.: (905) 643-1211
Fax: (905) 643-3328
Toll Free: (800) 263-9246
Web Site: www.edsmith.com
Sales Range: $200-249.9 Million
Approx. Number Employees: 490
Year Founded: 1882
Business Description:
Salad Dressing, Jam & Sauce Mfr
S.I.C.: 2035; 2099
N.A.I.C.S.: 311941; 311999
Export
Media: 5-6-15-19-21-24
Distr.: Natl.
Brands & Products:
E.D. SMITH

EGGLAND'S BEST, INC.
1400 S. Trooper Rd., Ste 201
Jeffersonville, PA 19403
Toll Free: (800) 922-EGGS
Web Site: www.eggland.com
Approx. Number Employees: 13
Year Founded: 1988
Business Description:
Distributor & Marketer of Egg Products
S.I.C.: 6794; 8742
N.A.I.C.S.: 533110; 541613
Export
Media: 2-6-7-9-10-17-19-23-24
Distr.: Natl.
Budget Set: June
Personnel:
Charles Lanktree *(Pres & CEO)*
Kurt A. Misialek *(CFO & VP)*
David Rochon *(Sr VP)*
Steve Michella *(VP-Sls)*
John Cavaliere *(Dir-Mktg)*
Bart Slaugh *(Dir-Quality Assurance)*
Brands & Products:
BETTER TASTE. BETTER NUTRITION. BETTER EGGS
EB
EGGLAND'S BEST

EINSTEIN BROTHERS BAGELS
200 Fillmore St Ste 104
Denver, CO 80206
Tel.: (303) 355-8700
Web Site: www.einsteinbros.com
Approx. Rev.: $2,300,000
Approx. Number Employees: 77
Year Founded: 1996
Business Description:
Bagels
S.I.C.: 5461
N.A.I.C.S.: 445291
Personnel:
Bob Hartnett *(CEO)*
James O'Reilly *(Chief Concept Officer)*
Advertising Agency:
Young & Rubicam Chicago
233 N Michigan Ave 16th Fl
Chicago, IL 60601-5519
Tel.: (312) 596-3000
Fax: (312) 596-3130
Agency of Record

ELLENBEE-LEGGETT COMPANY INC.
3765 Port Union Rd
Fairfield, OH 45014-2207
Tel.: (513) 874-3200
Fax: (513) 874-3323
Toll Free: (800) 536-1613
E-mail: service@ellenbee.com
Web Site: www.ellenbee.com
Approx. Number Employees: 100
Year Founded: 1954
Business Description:
Foodservice Products Distr
S.I.C.: 5141; 5147
N.A.I.C.S.: 424410; 424470
Advertising Expenditures: $1,000,000
Media: 13-22
Personnel:
James E. Kite *(Pres)*
Tom Koeninger *(VP-Sls)*
Gaylene Smith *(Dir-Mktg)*
Brands & Products:
BRIAR STRE
BUTCHER BO
CUISINE IN
DOLE
ELLENBEE LEGGETT
FLAVOR PAC
GOLDEN TIG
HEINZ
LAMB
MINH
NUGGET
PACKER
PREMIER
RAPID RUSS
SARA LEE
SIMPLOT
SPRINGBROO
STOUFFER'S
TYSON

EMERALD DAIRY INC.
11990 Market St Ste 205
Reston, VA 20190
Tel.: (703) 867-9247
Fax: (678) 868-0633
E-mail: investors@emeralddairy.com
Web Site: www.emeralddairy.com
Approx. Sls.: $55,269,755
Approx. Number Employees: 1,449
Business Description:
Dairy
S.I.C.: 0241
N.A.I.C.S.: 112120
Advertising Expenditures: $1,697,274
Personnel:
Yang Yongshan *(Pres & CEO)*
Shu Kaneko *(CFO)*
Qin Si Bo *(COO)*
Yuan Yong Wei *(VP-Ops & Dir)*
Niu Wan Chen *(VP-Sls)*

EMPIRE KOSHER POULTRY, INC.
(Holding of Palisades Associates, Inc.)
Rte 5 PO Box 228
Mifflintown, PA 17059-9409
Tel.: (717) 436-5921
Fax: (717) 436-9269
Toll Free: (800) 233-7177
E-mail: empire@empirekosher.com
Web Site: www.empirekosher.com

Empire Kosher Poultry, Inc. — (Continued)

Sales Range: $75-99.9 Million
Approx. Number Employees: 1,100
Year Founded: 1938
Business Description:
Processor & Packer of Kosher Poultry
S.I.C.: 2015; 5812
N.A.I.C.S.: 311615; 722110
Export
Media: 2-5-6-7-8-9-10-13-19-20-21-25
Distr.: Intl.; Natl.
Budget Set: Dec.
Personnel:
Barry Rosenbaum *(VP-Sls & Mktg)*
Dennis Hutchings *(Dir-Art)*
Neenah Lauver *(Mgr-Mktg)*
Brands & Products:
DEAN
EMPIRE
EMPIRE KOSHER
GALIL
HADAS
HAROT

ENERGY BRANDS, INC.

(Unit of Coca-Cola North America)
(d/b/a Glaceau)
1720 Whitestone Expwy
Whitestone, NY 11357-3000
Tel.: (718) 746-0087
Fax: (718) 746-5775
E-mail: info@energybrands.com
Web Site: www.energybrands.com
Sales Range: $350-399.9 Million
Approx. Number Employees: 1,000
Year Founded: 1996
Business Description:
Bottled Water Mfr & Distr
S.I.C.: 2086
N.A.I.C.S.: 312111
Personnel:
J. Darius Bikoff *(Pres & CEO)*
Carol Dollard *(Sr VP)*
Rohan Oza *(Sr VP-Mktg-Glaceau)*
Matt Kahn *(Dir-Corp Mktg)*
Lisa Dewitt *(Assoc Mgr-Mktg-Glaceau)*
Brands & Products:
BALANCE
DEFENSE
ENDURANCE
ENERGY
ESSENTIAL
FOCUS
FORMULA
FRUITWATER
GLACEAU WATER+
MULTI-V
POWER-C
RESCUE
REVIVE
SMARTWATER
STRESS-B
VITAL-T
VITAMINWATER
Advertising Agencies:
Berlin Cameron United
100 Ave of the Americas 2nd Fl
New York, NY 10013
Tel.: (212) 824-2000
Fax: (212) 268-8454

MediaCom
498 7th Ave
New York, NY 10018
Tel.: (212) 912-4200
Fax: (212) 508-4386

EVERFRESH BEVERAGES INC.

(Sub. of National Beverage Corp.)
6600 E 9 Mile Rd
Warren, MI 48041
Tel.: (586) 755-9500
Fax: (586) 755-9587
Toll Free: (800) 755-9500
Web Site: www.everfreshjuice.com
Sales Range: $50-74.9 Million
Approx. Number Employees: 100
Business Description:
Juice & Juice-Enriched Products Mfr
S.I.C.: 4213
N.A.I.C.S.: 484121
Media: 5-7-9-10-17-18-19-23-25
Distr.: Natl.
Brands & Products:
ASANTE
NU ANCE
SHASTA
SPREE
VOODOO RAIN

F&A CHEESE CORPORATION

2040 Main St Ste 100
Irvine, CA 92623-9127
Tel.: (949) 221-8255
Fax: (949) 221-8256
E-mail: mgray@facheese.com
Web Site: www.facheese.com
Approx. Number Employees: 123
Year Founded: 1974
Business Description:
Cheese & Other Dairy Products Mfr
S.I.C.: 2022
N.A.I.C.S.: 311513
Import Export
Advertising Expenditures: $500,000
Media: 13-22
Personnel:
Frank Terranova, Jr. *(Pres)*
Dean Hatch *(Exec VP)*
Brands & Products:
REAL CALIFORNIA CHEESE

FARIBAULT FOODS, INC.

(Div. of Faribault Foods Inc.)
128 15th St NW
Faribault, MN 55021-3037
Tel.: (507) 331-1400
Fax: (507) 334-0243
Web Site: www.faribaultfoods.com
Approx. Number Employees: 300
Business Description:
Mfr. of Canned Vegetables
S.I.C.: 2033
N.A.I.C.S.: 311421
Export
Media: 2-8-10-13-16-18-20-21-25
Distr.: Reg.
Personnel:
Scott King *(Exec VP-Ops)*
Frank Lynch *(Exec VP-Sls & Mktg)*

FARMER BROTHERS COMPANY

20333 S Normandie Ave
Torrance, CA 90502
Tel.: (310) 787-5200
Fax: (310) 787-5412
E-mail: info@farmerbrotherscoffee.com
Web Site: www.farmerbroscousa.com
Approx. Sls.: $463,945,000
Approx. Number Employees: 1,820
Year Founded: 1912
Business Description:
Coffee, Spices, Restaurant Supplies
S.I.C.: 2095; 2099; 5149
N.A.I.C.S.: 311920; 311999; 424490
Export
Media: 7-13-21
Personnel:
Guenter W. Berger *(Chm)*
Jeffrey A. Wahba *(Interim Co-CEO, CFO & Treas)*
Patrick G. Criteser *(Interim Co-CEO)*
Larry B. Garrett *(Gen Counsel & Asst Sec)*
Drew H. Webb *(Exec VP)*
Mark A. Harding *(Sr VP-Ops)*
Brands & Products:
CAIN'S
CONSISTENTLY GOOD
FARMER BROTHERS
IRELAND
MCGARVEY
METROPOLITAN
PANACHE
PREBICA
SIERRA
SOMETHIN NEW IS BREWIN
SUPERIOR

FARMERS PRIDE, INC.

154 W Main St
Fredericksburg, PA 17026
Tel.: (717) 865-6626
Fax: (717) 865-7046
E-mail: info@bellandevans.com
Web Site: www.bellandevans.com
Approx. Number Employees: 1,000
Year Founded: 1939
Business Description:
Processor of Poultry
S.I.C.: 2015
N.A.I.C.S.: 311615
Media: 2-4-7-9-10
Distr.: Reg.
Personnel:
Scott I. Sechler *(Owner)*
J. Michael Good *(CEO)*
Thomas Stone *(Dir-Mktg)*
Brands & Products:
BELL & EVANS
FARMER'S PRIDE
FRESH. YOUNG. CHICKEN
Advertising Agency:
Allebach Advertising
117 N Main St
Souderton, PA 18964
Tel.: (215) 721-7693
Fax: (215) 721-7694

FARMERS RICE COOPERATIVE

2525 Natomas Pk Dr Ste 300
Sacramento, CA 95833-2933
Mailing Address:
PO Box 15223
Sacramento, CA 95851-1223
Tel.: (916) 923-5100
Fax: (916) 920-4295
Toll Free: (800) 326-2799
E-mail: webmaster@farmersrice.com
Web Site: www.farmersrice.com
Approx. Sls.: $129,525,000
Approx. Number Employees: 300
Year Founded: 1944
Business Description:
Rice Milling & Marketing
S.I.C.: 2044
N.A.I.C.S.: 311212
Export
Advertising Expenditures: $300,000
Media: 7-11
Personnel:
Charles R. Hoppin *(Vice Chm)*
Mike Sandrock *(Pres & CEO)*
Jim Dodson *(CFO, Sec & VP)*
H. Kirk Messick *(Sr VP)*
Kirk Messick *(Sr VP)*
Keith Hargrove *(VP-Mfg & Tech)*
Owen Hamilton *(Controller & Asst VP)*
Dave Jones *(Dir-Svcs)*

FARMLAND DAIRIES LLC

(Sub. of Grupo Industrial Lala S.A. de C.V.)
520 Main Ave
Wallington, NJ 07057-1830
Tel.: (973) 777-2500
Fax: (973) 249-3838
Web Site: www.farmlanddairies.com
Approx. Number Employees: 400
Year Founded: 1982
Business Description:
Dairy Products Mfr
S.I.C.: 2026; 2024
N.A.I.C.S.: 311511; 311520
Advertising Expenditures: $1,500,000
Media: 3-13-14-15-19-21-22-23-24-26
Personnel:
Martin Margherio *(Reg Mgr)*
Stephen Raiola *(Mgr-Mktg & Mdsg)*

FIRMENICH

(Sub. of Firmenich S.A.)
424 S Atchison St
Anaheim, CA 92805-4045
Mailing Address:
PO Box 3633
Anaheim, CA 92803-3633
Tel.: (714) 535-2871
Fax: (714) 535-2626
Web Site: www.firmenich.com
Approx. Number Employees: 130
Year Founded: 1895
Business Description:
Powdered Citrus Juices & Oils
S.I.C.: 2869; 2899
N.A.I.C.S.: 325199; 325998
Advertising Expenditures: $300,000
Media: 2-6-8-9
Distr.: Natl.
Budget Set: Oct.
Brands & Products:
ACM
BORDEN CAPS
CHIPPETTES
DURAROME
MCP
PECTIN
PERMA STABIL
SLIM SET

FIRST COLONY COFFEE & TEA COMPANY

204-222 W 22nd St
Norfolk, VA 23517-0005
Mailing Address:
PO Box 11005
Norfolk, VA 23517
Tel.: (757) 622-3658
Fax: (757) 623-1833
Toll Free: (800) 446-8555
E-mail: contact@firstcolonycoffee.com
Web Site: www.firstcolonycoffee.com
Approx. Number Employees: 85
Year Founded: 1902

Key to Media (For complete agency information see *The Advertising Red Books-Agencies* edition):
1. Bus. Publs. 2. Cable T.V. 3. Catalogs & Directories. 4. Co-op Adv. 5. Consumer Mags. 6. D.M. to Bus. Estab.7. D.M. to Consumers 8. Daily Newsp. 9. Exhibits/Trade Shows 10. Foreign 11. Infomercial 12. Internet Adv.13. Multimedia 14. Network Radio 15. Network T.V. 16. Newsp. Distr. Mags. 17. Other 18. Outdoor (Posters, Transit) 19. Point of Purchase20. Premiums, Novelties 21. Product Samples 22. Special Events Mktg. 23. Spot Radio 24. Spot T.V. 25. Weekly Newsp. 26. Yellow Page Adv.

Business Description:
Mfr. of Gourmet Tea & Coffee
S.I.C.: 2095
N.A.I.C.S.: 311920
Import Export
Media: 2-4-5-8-9-13-19-20-26
Distr.: Reg.
Budget Set: Sept. -Jan.
Personnel:
Charles Cortellini *(Pres & CEO)*
Brands & Products:
FIRST COLONY
FIRST COLONY COFFEE HOUSE BEVERAGE SYRUPS
FIRST COLONY DARK
FIRST COLONY ORGANIC
FIRST COLONY TRADITIONAL
LANGFORD BROTHERS
PRIVATE LABEL
RED BAG
SUSAN'S TEA
WATER ST.

FLEISCHMANN'S YEAST
(Sub. of Associated British Foods Plc)
240 Larkin Williams Industrial Ct
Fenton, MO 63026-2413
Tel.: (636) 349-8800
Fax: (636) 349-8825
E-mail: info@fleischmannsyeast.com
Web Site:
www.fleischmannsyeast.com
Approx. Number Employees: 200
Business Description:
Yeast & Other Baking Products Mfr
S.I.C.: 2099; 5149
N.A.I.C.S.: 311942; 424490
Import Export
Media: 2-4-6-7-10-15-16-22
Distr.: Natl.
Budget Set: July
Brands & Products:
BENCHMATE
FLEISCHMANN'S
RAPID RISE
Advertising Agency:
Delfino Marketing Communications, Inc.
400 Columbus Ave Ste 120S
Valhalla, NY 10595-1396
Tel.: (914) 747-1400
Fax: (914) 747-1430

FLORIDA CRYSTAL CORPORATION
(Sub. of FloSun Incorporated)
1 N Clematis St Ste 200
West Palm Beach, FL 33401-5551
Tel.: (561) 366-5100
Fax: (561) 366-5158
Toll Free: (877) 835-2828
E-mail: info@floridacrystals.com
Web Site: www.floridacrystals.com
Approx. Number Employees: 55
Year Founded: 1978
Business Description:
Cane Sugar Refining Services
S.I.C.: 2062
N.A.I.C.S.: 311312
Advertising Agency:
Barkley
1740 Main St
Kansas City, MO 64108
Tel.: (816) 842-1500

FLORIDA'S NATURAL GROWERS
(Div. of Citrus World, Inc.)
20205 US Hwy 27
Lake Wales, FL 33853
Mailing Address:
PO Box 1111
Lake Wales, FL 33859
Tel.: (863) 676-1411
Fax: (863) 676-5744
Web Site: www.floridasnatural.com
Approx. Number Employees: 800
Business Description:
Citrus Processors & Packagers; Agricultural Co-op
S.I.C.: 2033; 2037
N.A.I.C.S.: 311421; 311411
Media: 6-15-24
Personnel:
Steve Caruso *(CEO)*
Chip Hendry *(CFO)*
Robert Behr *(COO)*
Walt Zircer *(VP-Sls & Mktg)*
Dan McSpadden *(Dir-Mktg)*
Brands & Products:
FLORIDA'S NATURAL
FLORIDA'S NATURAL GROWERS' PRIDE
IT'S AS CLOSE TO THE GROVE AS YOU CAN GET
Advertising Agency:
22squared
1170 Peachtree St NE 15th Fl
Atlanta, GA 30309-7649
Tel.: (404) 347-8700
Fax: (404) 347-8800
Orange Juice

FLOWERS FOODS BAKERIES GROUP, LLC
(Sub. of Flowers Foods, Inc.)
112 E Jefferson St
Thomasville, GA 31792
Tel.: (229) 558-6445
Fax: (229) 225-3816
Web Site: www.flowersfoods.com
Sales Range: $1-4.9 Billion
Approx. Number Employees: 10,000
Year Founded: 1942
Business Description:
Baked Goods Mfr
S.I.C.: 2051
N.A.I.C.S.: 311812
Media: 9-24
Personnel:
Bradley K. Alexander *(Pres)*
Karyl H. Lauder *(Chief Acctg Officer & Sr VP)*

FLOWERS FOODS, INC.
1919 Flowers Cir
Thomasville, GA 31757-1137
Tel.: (229) 226-9110
Fax: (229) 225-3816
E-mail: info@flowersfoods.com
Web Site: www.flowersfoods.com
Approx. Sls.: $2,573,769,000
Approx. Number Employees: 8,800
Year Founded: 1919
Business Description:
Fresh & Frozen Bakery Foods Mfr
S.I.C.: 2051; 2052; 5142
N.A.I.C.S.: 311812; 311821; 424420
Import Export
Advertising Expenditures: $11,300,000
Media: 9-16-19-22-23-24-25
Distr.: Natl.; Reg.
Budget Set: Mar.
Personnel:
George E. Deese *(Chm & CEO)*
Allen L. Shiver *(Pres)*
R. Steve Kinsey *(CFO & Exec VP)*
Gene D. Lord *(COO & Exec VP)*
Karyl H. Lauder *(Chief Acctg Officer & Sr VP)*
Stephen R. Avera *(Gen Counsel, Sec & Exec VP)*
Michael A. Beaty *(Exec VP-Supply Chain)*
Marta Jones Turner *(Exec VP-Corp Rels)*
Donald A. Thriffiley, Jr. *(Sr VP-HR)*
D. Keith Hancock *(Mng Dir-Comm)*
Mary A. Krier *(VP-Comm & Corp Responsibility)*
Brent Bradshaw *(Brand Mgr)*
Brands & Products:
BLUEBIRD
BUNNY BREAD
BUTTERKRUST
CAPTAIN JOHN DERST'S
COBBLESTONE MILL
EUROPEAN BAKERS
FLOWERS FOODS
MI CASA
MRS. FRESHLEY'S
NATURE'S OWN
SUNBEAM
TESORITOS
WHITEWHEAT
Advertising Agency:
GolinHarris
1575 Northside Dr NW Bldg 200 Ste 200
Atlanta, GA 30318
Tel.: (404) 880-4600
Fax: (404) 523-3483

THE FOLGER COFFEE COMPANY
(Sub. of The J.M. Smucker Company)
1 Strawberry Ln
Orrville, OH 44667
Mailing Address:
PO Box 599
Cincinnati, OH 45202
Tel.: (330) 682-3000
Fax: (330) 684-6410
Web Site: www.folgers.com
Approx. Sls.: $1,600,000,000
Approx. Number Employees: 1,250
Year Founded: 1963
Business Description:
Coffee & Tea Products Mfr
S.I.C.: 2095
N.A.I.C.S.: 311920
Media: 9-14-15-23-24
Distr.: Natl.
Personnel:
Tim Smucker *(Chm & Co-CEO)*
Brands & Products:
FOLGERS
FOLGERS CLASSIC ROAST
FOLGERS GOURMET SELECTIONS
SIMPLY SMOOTH

FONA INTERNATIONAL INC.
1900 Averill Rd
Geneva, IL 60134-1601
Tel.: (630) 462-1414
Tel.: (630) 578-8600
Fax: (630) 462-8855
Fax: (630) 578-8601
E-mail: info@fona.com
Web Site: www.fona.com
Sales Range: $50-74.9 Million
Approx. Number Employees: 200
Year Founded: 1987
Business Description:
Extracts & Flavoring Products Developer
S.I.C.: 2099
N.A.I.C.S.: 311942
Media: 2-7-10
Personnel:
Joseph Slawek *(Founder, Pres & CEO)*
Terry Emmel *(VP & Gen Mgr)*
Tracy Cesario *(Dir-Corp Mktg & Comm)*

FOOD SERVICES OF AMERICA, INC.
(Sub. of Services Group of America, Inc.)
16100 N 71st St Ste 400
Scottsdale, AZ 85254
Mailing Address:
PO Box 84628
Seattle, WA 98124-5928
Tel.: (206) 933-5000
Fax: (206) 933-5282
E-mail: fsa_corporate@fsafood.com
Web Site: www.fsafood.com
Approx. Number Employees: 250
Year Founded: 1986
Business Description:
Fruit, Vegetable, Canned & Frozen Food Distr
S.I.C.: 5141; 5142
N.A.I.C.S.: 424410; 424420
Advertising Expenditures: $4,000,000
Media: 4-6-10
Distr.: Reg.
Budget Set: Nov.
Personnel:
Thomas J. Stewart *(Chm & CEO)*
Peter Smith *(CFO)*
Scott Bixby *(Chief Mdsg Officer & Sr VP)*
Randy Irvine *(Pres-Seattle Branch)*
Greg Bunker *(VP-Mdsg)*
Ernie Snyder *(VP-IT)*
Mike Callaghan *(Dir-Bus Dev)*
Jeff Chester *(Dir-Quality Assurance & Supplier Info)*
Paul Henderson *(Product Mgr)*
J. R. Fox *(Mgr-Beverage Ops)*
Brands & Products:
COLUMBIA VALLEY FARMS
DELLA VITA
ELITE
FLYING FLAG FISH HOUSE
MADRONA MARKET
PRIDE
RIO VIEJO
SIGNATURE
SNOBOY

FOREMOST FARMS USA COOPERATIVE
E 10889 A Penny Ln
Baraboo, WI 53913
Tel.: (608) 356-8316
Fax: (608) 355-6701
Toll Free: (800) 362-9196
Web Site: www.foremostfarms.com
Approx. Number Employees: 1,540
Year Founded: 1995
Business Description:
Dairy Cooperative Manufacturing
S.I.C.: 0241; 2026
N.A.I.C.S.: 112120; 311511

Key to Media (For complete agency information see *The Advertising Red Books-Agencies* edition):
1. Bus. Publs. 2. Cable T.V. 3. Catalogs & Directories. 4. Co-op Adv. 5. Consumer Mags. 6. D.M. to Bus. Estab.7. D.M. to Consumers
8. Daily Newsp. 9. Exhibits/Trade Shows 10. Foreign 11. Infomercial 12. Internet Adv.13. Multimedia 14. Network Radio
15. Network T.V. 16. Newsp. Distr. Mags. 17. Other 18. Outdoor (Posters, Transit) 19. Point of Purchase20. Premiums, Novelties
21. Product Samples 22. Special Events Mktg. 23. Spot Radio 24. Spot T.V. 25. Weekly Newsp. 26. Yellow Page Adv.

Foremost Farms USA Cooperative — (Continued)

Advertising Expenditures: $200,000
Media: 2-5-7-9-13
Personnel:
Ed Brooks *(Chm)*
David Fuhrmann *(Pres)*
Mike MacDonald *(VP-HR, Safety & Comm)*
Joan Behr *(Dir-Comm)*
Brands & Products:
BAKER'S SPECIAL
DAIRY BAKE
DARITEK
ECONOBAKE
GG GOLDEN GUERNSEY DAIRY
KIDS CAPS AND CASH
LACTOSE
MORNING GLORY
NUTRIMIX
NUTRITEK
REDDI-SPONGE
TEKLAC

FOSTER FARMS
1000 Davis St
Livingston, CA 95334-0457
Tel.: (209) 394-7901
Fax: (209) 394-6342
Toll Free: (800) 225-7227
E-mail: retailsales@fosterfarms.com
Web Site: www.fosterfarms.com
Sales Range: $1-4.9 Billion
Approx. Number Employees: 10,500
Year Founded: 1939
Business Description:
Poultry Processor & Distr
S.I.C.: 0254; 2015
N.A.I.C.S.: 112340; 311615
Advertising Expenditures: $10,000,000
Media: 1-6-7-8-10-13-15-18-19-20-21-22-23-24
Distr.: Reg.
Personnel:
Ron Foster *(CEO)*
John Landis *(CFO)*
Randy Boyce *(Gen Counsel & Sr VP)*
Bob Kellert *(Sr VP-Retail Sls)*
Tim Walsh *(Sr VP-HR)*
Greta Janz *(VP-Mktg)*
James Marnatti *(Dir-Environmental Affairs)*
Teresa Lenz *(Mgr-Consumer Affairs)*
Brands & Products:
FOSTER FARMS
PURE HONEST TO GOODNESS
SAVORY SERVINGS
Advertising Agencies:
Ad Group
785 Grant St.
Eugene, OR 97402
Tel.: (541) 345-2300
Fax: (541) 345-2550
(Foster Farms Poultry)

The Bravo Group
303 2nd St 9th Fl S Tower
San Francisco, CA 94107
Tel.: (415) 268-3380
Fax: (415) 268-3390

Fineman PR
330 Townsend St Ste 119
San Francisco, CA 94107
Tel.: (415) 392-1000
Fax: (415) 392-1099
Public Rels

Grupo Gallegos
401 E Ocean Blvd Ste 600
Long Beach, CA 90802
Tel.: (562) 256-3600
Fax: (562) 256-3620

FRED USINGER, INC.
1030 N Old World 3rd St
Milwaukee, WI 53203-1302
Tel.: (414) 276-9100
Fax: (414) 291-5277
Toll Free: (800) 558-9998
E-mail: info@usinger.com
Web Site: www.usinger.com
Approx. Number Employees: 200
Year Founded: 1880
Business Description:
Sausages Mfr
S.I.C.: 5147; 5812
N.A.I.C.S.: 311612; 722110
Import
Advertising Expenditures: $373,000
Multimedia: $1,000; Bus. Publs.: $30,000; Catalogs & Directories: $50,000; Consumer Mags.: $30,000; D.M. to Bus. Estab.: $5,000; D.M. to Consumers: $10,000; Exhibits/Trade Shows: $10,000; Internet Adv.: $5,000; Other: $85,000; Outdoor (Posters, Transit): $30,000; Point of Purchase: $10,000; Premiums, Novelties: $10,000; Product Samples: $20,000; Special Events Mktg.: $15,000; Spot Radio: $50,000; Spot T.V.: $10,000; Yellow Page Adv.: $2,000
Distr.: Natl.
Budget Set: Mar.
Personnel:
Fritz Usinger, IV *(Pres)*
Allen Weidler *(Sec & VP-Fin)*
Jon Gabe *(VP-Sls)*
Debra Usinger *(Dir-Corp Svcs-Retail Ops)*
Brands & Products:
USINGER'S
Advertising Agency:
CDC
1298 Martha Washington Dr.
Wauwatosa, WI 53213
Tel.: (414) 771-6003
(Sausage/Gift Boxes)

FREEZER QUEEN FOODS, INC.
(Sub. of Home Market Foods Incorporated)
975 Fuhrmann Blvd
Buffalo, NY 14203
Mailing Address:
PO Box 948
Buffalo, NY 14240-0948
Tel.: (716) 826-2500
Fax: (716) 824-4258
E-mail: info@freezerqueenfoods.com
Web Site: www.freezerqueenfoods.com
Approx. Number Employees: 500
Year Founded: 1959
Business Description:
Frozen Prepared Foods Mfr
S.I.C.: 5142; 5147
N.A.I.C.S.: 424420; 424470
Media: 5-13-16-21
Distr.: Natl.
Budget Set: Sept.

THE FREMONT COMPANY
802 N Front St
Fremont, OH 43420-1917
Tel.: (419) 334-8995
Fax: (419) 334-8120
E-mail: sales@sauerkraut.com
Web Site: www.fremontcompany.com
E-Mail For Key Personnel:
Sales Director: sales@sauerkraut.com
Approx. Number Employees: 200
Year Founded: 1905
Business Description:
Mfr. of Canned Foods: Sauerkraut, Barbecue Sauce & Ketchup
S.I.C.: 2033
N.A.I.C.S.: 311421
Export
Media: 9-25
Distr.: Natl.
Brands & Products:
F
FRANK'S
MISSISSIPPI BARBECUE SAUCE
SNOWFLOSS
Advertising Agency:
BIGfrontier Communications Group
600 W Van Buren Ste 507A
Chicago, IL 60607
Tel.: (312) 238-9308
Fax: (312) 602-2450

FRESH DEL MONTE PRODUCE INC.
241 Sevilla Ave
Coral Gables, FL 33134-3125
Mailing Address:
PO Box 149222
Coral Gables, FL 33114
Tel.: (305) 520-8400
Fax: (305) 567-0320
Toll Free: (800) 950-3683
E-mail: Contact-US-Executive-Office@freshdelmonte.com
Web Site: www.freshdelmonte.com
Approx. Sls.: $3,552,900,000
Approx. Number Employees: 42,000
Year Founded: 1892
Business Description:
Fresh-Cut Fruit, Vegetables & Other Fresh Produce Distr & Marketer
S.I.C.: 2033; 0161; 0171; 0174; 0175; 0179; 5148
N.A.I.C.S.: 311421; 111219; 111320; 111331; 111334; 111339; 424480
Advertising Expenditures: $17,500,000
Media: 2-8-11-13-19-20-21
Personnel:
Mohammad Abu-Ghazaleh *(Chm & CEO)*
Hani El-Naffy *(Pres & COO)*
Richard Contreras *(CFO & Sr VP)*
Bruce A. Jordan *(Gen Counsel, Sec & Sr VP)*
Jean-Pierre Bartoli *(Sr VP-Europe & Africa)*
Emanuel Lazopoulos *(Sr VP-Sls & Product Mgmt-North America)*
Paul Rice *(Sr VP-Ops-North America)*
Jimmy Tenazas *(Sr VP-Asia Pacific)*
Jose Antonio Yock *(Sr VP-Central America)*
Marissa R. Tenazas *(VP-HR)*
Brands & Products:
DEL MONTE
DEL MONTE GOLD
Advertising Agency:
Communication House
Akasaka Omotemachi Bldg#504
Tokyo, 107-0052, Japan
Tel.: (81) 3 5411 4841
Fax: (81) 3 5411 4844

FRESH MARK, INC.
1888 Southway St SW PO Box 571
Massillon, OH 44646
Tel.: (330) 832-7491
Fax: (330) 430-5658
Toll Free: (800) 860-6777
E-mail: jobs@freshmark.com
Web Site: www.freshmark.com
Approx. Number Employees: 1,400
Year Founded: 1920
Business Description:
Full Line Meat Processor
S.I.C.: 5147
N.A.I.C.S.: 311612; 424470
Import Export
Media: 2-4-10-16-18-19-23
Distr.: Reg.
Personnel:
Neil Genshaft *(Chm & CEO)*
Harry Valentino *(Pres & COO)*
Dave Cochenour *(CFO, Treas & VP)*
Kristin Clemmer *(Dir-Mktg)*
Alicia Pucky *(Mgr-Mktg)*
Brands & Products:
FRESH MARK
SUGARDALE
SUPERIOR'S

FRESHBREW COFFEE, LLC
11600 Big John St
Houston, TX 77038-3302
Tel.: (281) 847-2222
Fax: (281) 847-4444
E-mail: info@freshbrewgroup.com
Web Site: www.freshbrewgroup.com
Approx. Sls.: $5,000,000
Approx. Number Employees: 45
Year Founded: 1995
Business Description:
Mfr. of Coffee, Tea & Coffee Bags
S.I.C.: 2095
N.A.I.C.S.: 311920
Media: 2-6-9-10-18-19-20-21-23-24
Distr.: Intl.; Natl.
Budget Set: Mar.
Personnel:
Robert Sakowitz *(Chm)*
Dari Ansari *(Pres & CEO)*
Tom Duffy *(VP-Sls)*
Joseph Bolatto *(Dir-Customer Svc)*
Bill Duffy *(Dir-Sls Vending)*
Darrell Runyan *(Sls Exec Mgr)*
Brands & Products:
FRESH
MORNING TREAT
PERKUP

FRESHDIRECT, INC.
23-30 Borden Ave
Long Island City, NY 11101
Tel.: (718) 928-1000
Fax: (718) 928-1050
E-mail: service@freshdirect.com
Web Site: www.freshdirect.com
Approx. Number Employees: 1,300
Year Founded: 1999

Key to Media (For complete agency information see *The Advertising Red Books-Agencies* edition):
1. Bus. Publs. 2. Cable T.V. 3. Catalogs & Directories. 4. Co-op Adv. 5. Consumer Mags. 6. D.M. to Bus. Estab.7. D.M. to Consumers 8. Daily Newsp. 9. Exhibits/Trade Shows 10. Foreign 11. Infomercial 12. Internet Adv.13. Multimedia 14. Network Radio 15. Network T.V. 16. Newsp. Distr. Mags. 17. Other 18. Outdoor (Posters, Transit) 19. Point of Purchase20. Premiums, Novelties 21. Product Samples 22. Special Events Mktg. 23. Spot Radio 24. Spot T.V. 25. Weekly Newsp. 26. Yellow Page Adv.

Business Description:
Internet Grocery Shopping & Delivery Services
S.I.C.: 5411; 4215
N.A.I.C.S.: 445110; 492210
Media: 13
Personnel:
Jason Ackerman *(Founder, Vice Chm & CFO)*
Richard S. Braddock, Sr. *(Chm & CEO)*
Maria Coder *(Mgr-PR & Influencer Partnerships)*
Advertising Agencies:
Gotham Incorporated
150 E 42nd St 12th Fl
New York, NY 10017
Tel.: (212) 414-7000
Fax: (212) 414-7095

The MWW Group
1 Meadowlands Plz 6th Fl
East Rutherford, NJ 07073
Tel.: (201) 507-9500
Fax: (201) 507-0092

Peppercom
470 Park Ave S 5th Fl
New York, NY 10016
Tel.: (212) 931-6100
Fax: (212) 931-6159

FRIENDSHIP DAIRIES, INC.

1 Jericho Plz
Jericho, NY 11753-1680
Tel.: (585) 973-3031
Fax: (516) 719-3880
Toll Free: (800) 924-6328
E-mail: myfriends@friendshipdairies.com
Web Site: www.friendshipdairies.com
Approx. Number Employees: 30
Year Founded: 1913
Business Description:
Full Line of Cultured Dairy Products Mfr
S.I.C.: 2023; 2026
N.A.I.C.S.: 311514; 311511
Export
Advertising Expenditures: $2,005,000
Media: 2-6-8-9-10-13-19-20-21-22-23-24
Distr.: Reg.
Budget Set: Sept. -Oct.
Personnel:
Paige Pistone *(Dir-Mktg)*
Brands & Products:
FRIENDSHIP

FRY KRISP COMPANY

3360 Spring Arbor Rd
Jackson, MI 49203-3636
Tel.: (517) 784-8531
Fax: (517) 784-6585
E-mail: frykrisp@tds.net
Web Site: www.frykrisp.com
Sales Range: $10-24.9 Million
Approx. Number Employees: 10
Year Founded: 1950
Business Description:
Batter & Seasoning Mixes Mfr
S.I.C.: 2045
N.A.I.C.S.: 311822
Import Export
Media: 9-18-19-21-26
Distr.: Reg.
Personnel:
Richard G. Neuenfeldt *(Pres)*
Brands & Products:
FRY KRISP
OVEN KRISP

FUCHS NORTH AMERICA.

(Sub. of FUCHS-Gewurze GmbH)
9740 Reisterstown Rd
Owings Mills, MD 21117
Tel.: (410) 363-1700
Fax: (410) 363-6619
Toll Free: (800) 365-3229
E-mail: info@fuchsnorthamerica.com
Web Site: www.fuchsnorthamerica.com
Approx. Number Employees: 150
Year Founded: 1939
Business Description:
Dry Mustards, Spices, Seasonings & Capsicums Producer & Mfr
S.I.C.: 2099; 2087
N.A.I.C.S.: 311942; 311930
Import Export
Advertising Expenditures: $50,000
Media: 2-7-10-13-19-21-26
Distr.: Natl.
Personnel:
Nils Meyer-Pries *(Pres)*
Christopher Rodski *(CFO)*
Brands & Products:
A WORLD OF ADVANTAGES FOR OUR CUSTOMERS
BALANOX
BALTIMORE SPICE
CULINARY CHOICE
ENTICE WITH SPICE
MICROCONTROL

FULTON PROVISION COMPANY

(Sub. of Sysco Corporation)
16123 NE Airport Way
Portland, OR 97294
Mailing Address:
PO Box 301579
Portland, OR 97294-9579
Tel.: (503) 254-3000
Fax: (503) 408-5640
Web Site: www.sysco.com/aboutus/contactus.asp
Sales Range: $75-99.9 Million
Approx. Number Employees: 100
Business Description:
Food Products Wholesale Distr
S.I.C.: 5149
N.A.I.C.S.: 424490
Advertising Agency:
Maxwell PR
1600 SE Bybee Blvd Ste 202
Portland, OR 97202
Tel.: (503) 231-3086
Fax: (503) 231-3089
— Kim Van Syoc *(Acct Exec)*

FURMANO FOODS, INC.

770 Cannery Rd
Northumberland, PA 17857
Mailing Address:
PO Box 500
Northumberland, PA 17857
Tel.: (570) 473-3516
Fax: (570) 473-7367
Toll Free: (877) 877-6032
E-mail: sandy.bonshock@furmanos.com
Web Site: www.furmanos.com
Approx. Number Employees: 300
Year Founded: 1921
Business Description:
Processed Tomatoes & Vegetables
S.I.C.: 2033
N.A.I.C.S.: 311421
Import Export
Media: 1-2-4-5-6-7-9-10-11-13-16-17-18-19-20-21-22-23-25-26
Distr.: Intl.; Natl.
Personnel:
David N. Geise *(Pres & CEO)*
Ted Hancock *(CFO)*
Kermit Kohl *(VP-HR)*
Brands & Products:
BAK-N-BEANS
BELLA VISTA
CONTE
FURMANO'S
GREAT TASTE IS A FAMILY TRADITION
Advertising Agency:
Hunter
204 Julie Dr
Parkesburg, PA 19365
Tel.: (610) 857-2977
Fax: (610) 857-2984
Toll Free: (877) 363-0606

F.W. BRYCE, INC.

8 Pond Rd
Gloucester, MA 01930-1833
Tel.: (978) 283-7080
Fax: (978) 283-7647
E-mail: fwbryce@fwbryce.com
Web Site: www.fwbryce.com
Approx. Number Employees: 25
Year Founded: 1947
Business Description:
Importer & Distr of Frozen Seafood
S.I.C.: 5142
N.A.I.C.S.: 424420
Import Export
Media: 2-4-10-22
Personnel:
Keith Moores *(Pres)*
Ian W. Moores *(Gen Counsel)*
Patrick Burke *(Mgr-Sls-North Atlantic Reg)*
Glenn P. Hale *(Mgr-Chain Accts-Natl)*
Steven Lubelczyk *(Mgr-Bus Analytics)*
Justin Moores *(Mgr-Quality Assurance)*
Mary Murch *(Mgr-Inventory Control)*
Frank Souza *(Mgr-Ops)*
Mike Sullivan *(Mgr-Sls-Northeast Reg)*
Brands & Products:
ALLENS
ATLANTIC OCEAN
CASCABELL
F.W.BRYCE
MIQUELON
POLAR STAR
PRIME SELECTIONS
YOUR TRUSTED SOURCE FOR QUALITY SEAFOOD SINCE 1947

GALAXY NUTRITIONAL FOODS, INC.

(Joint Venture of Galaxy Partners LLC & Mill Road Capital, L.P)
6280 Hazeltine National Dr
Orlando, FL 32822
Tel.: (407) 855-5500
Fax: (407) 855-1099
Toll Free: (800) 808-2325
E-mail: galxquality@galaxyfoods.com
Web Site: www.galaxyfoods.com
Sales Range: $25-49.9 Million
Approx. Number Employees: 23
Year Founded: 1972
Business Description:
Vegetable Dairy Alternatives Mfr; Owned by Galaxy Partners LLC & Mill Road Capital, L.P
S.I.C.: 2022; 5499
N.A.I.C.S.: 311513; 445299
Import Export
Advertising Expenditures: $452,000
Media: 6-9-16-21-23-24-25
Personnel:
Richard Antonelli *(CEO)*
Brian O'Farrell *(CFO)*
Todd Porrier *(Exec VP-Ops & Product Dev)*
Jerry Schwartz *(Exec VP-Sls & Mktg)*
Sabrina Mak *(Dir-Sls)*
Corrina Merryman *(Mgr-Sls-Western Natural)*
Brands & Products:
A GALAXY OF SMART FOOD CHOICES
GALAXY NUTRITIONAL FOODS
GALAXY SUPER STIX
RICE
RICE VEGAN
VEGAN
VEGGIE
VEGGY
WHOLESOME VALLEY
WHOLESOME VALLEY ORGANIC
Advertising Agency:
Engauge Communications
1000 Legion Pl Ste 1250
Orlando, FL 32801
Tel.: (407) 649-8101
Fax: (407) 649-8686
Toll Free: (888) 448-4481

GARELICK FARMS, LLC

(Sub. of Dean Foods Company)
1199 W Central St
Franklin, MA 02038
Tel.: (508) 528-9000
Fax: (508) 520-3922
Web Site: www.garelickfarms.com
Sales Range: $300-349.9 Million
Approx. Number Employees: 650
Year Founded: 1931
Business Description:
Producer of Dairy Products & Juice
S.I.C.: 2026
N.A.I.C.S.: 311511
Media: 2-18-19-20-21-23-24-25-26
Personnel:
Stephen B. Lincoln *(Exec VP-Sls)*
Tom Davis *(VP & Gen Mgr)*
Brands & Products:
GARELICK FARMS
Advertising Agency:
Connelly Partners
46 Waltham St Fl 4
Boston, MA 02118
Tel.: (617) 956-5050
Fax: (617) 956-5054

GAY LEA FOODS CO-OPERATIVE LIMITED

5200 Orbitor Dr
Mississauga, ON L4W 5B4, Canada
Tel.: (905) 283-5222
Fax: (905) 283-5335
Toll Free: (888) 4GAYLEA
E-mail: contact@gayleafoodmembers.com

Key to Media (For complete agency information see *The Advertising Red Books-Agencies* edition):
1. Bus. Publs. 2. Cable T.V. 3. Catalogs & Directories. 4. Co-op Adv. 5. Consumer Mags. 6. D.M. to Bus. Estab.7. D.M. to Consumers 8. Daily Newsp. 9. Exhibits/Trade Shows 10. Foreign 11. Infomercial 12. Internet Adv.13. Multimedia 14. Network Radio 15. Network T.V. 16. Newsp. Distr. Mags. 17. Other 18. Outdoor (Posters, Transit) 19. Point of Purchase20. Premiums, Novelties 21. Product Samples 22. Special Events Mktg. 23. Spot Radio 24. Spot T.V. 25. Weekly Newsp. 26. Yellow Page Adv.

Gay Lea Foods Co-operative Limited — (Continued)

Web Site: www.gayleafoods.com
Sales Range: $125-149.9 Million
Approx. Number Employees: 400
Year Founded: 1958
Business Description:
Dairy Foods Producer
S.I.C.: 2023; 0241; 5143
N.A.I.C.S.: 311514; 112120; 424430
Media: 10-22
Personnel:
Mark Hamel *(Chm)*
Andrew MacGillivray *(Pres & CEO)*
John Rebry *(CFO & Treas)*
Larry HooK *(VP Sls & Mktg)*
David Jennison *(VP-Res & Product Dev)*
Bruce Ruth *(VP-HR)*
Jay Kirktown *(Dir-Indus Bus)*
Gerry Schafer *(Brand Mgr-Co-Pack)*
Brands & Products:
BLUEBERRY GINGER COTTAGE CHEESE
CHICKEN FLORENTINE NORDICA
CHINICHURRI COTTAGE CHEESE SALAD TOPPER
GAY LEA
GRILLED HAM WITH BRIE AND APPLE
LACTEEZE
NECTARINE WALDORF SALAD
NORDICA
NORDICA SUMMER DRESSING
ROAST BEEF AND HORSERADISH GRILLED CHESSE
SOUR CREAM
UPSIDE DOWN FRUIT AND WHITE CHOCLATE CAKE
ZESTY ITALIAN COTTAGE CHEESE SALAD TOPPER

GENERAL MILLS
(Div. of General Mills, Inc.)
1 General Mills Blvd
Minneapolis, MN 55426-1347
Mailing Address:
PO Box 9452
Minneapolis, MN 55440-1113
Tel.: (763) 764-7600
Fax: (800) 446-3334
Toll Free: (800) 967-5248
Web Site: www.yoplaitusa.com
Sales Range: $450-499.9 Million
Year Founded: 1977
Business Description:
Refrigerated Food Items; Yogurt
S.I.C.: 5143; 5141
N.A.I.C.S.: 424430; 424410
Media: 6-9-15-19-20-23-24-25
Distr.: Natl.
Personnel:
Rick Hosfield *(VP-Adv)*
Jim Cuene *(Dir-Interactive Mktg)*
Vanessa Reed *(Dir-Media Content Plng & Buying)*
Brent Shiely *(Sr Mgr-Brands & Digital Production-Intl)*
Stacy Aase *(Mgr-Promo)*
Vanessa Bush *(Mgr-Digital Editorial Content)*
Carrie Chang *(Mgr-Interactive Mktg)*
Robert Dircks *(Mgr-Mktg-Yoplait Frozen & Green Giant Innovation)*
Amy Halford *(Mgr-Relationship Mktg)*
Tim Rosen *(Mgr-Promo)*
Brands & Products:
COLUMBO
CUSTARD STYLE
GO-GURT
NOURICHE
TRIX
WHIPS
YOPLAIT
YUMSTERS
Advertising Agencies:
Brandimage Desgrippes & Laga
990 Skokie Blvd
Northbrook, IL 60062
Tel.: (847) 291-0500
Fax: (847) 291-0516

Saatchi & Saatchi New York
375 Hudson St
New York, NY 10014-3660
Tel.: (212) 463-2000
Fax: (212) 463-9855

GEORGE DE LALLO COMPANY INC.
6390 Route 30
Jeannette, PA 15644
Tel.: (724) 523-6577
Toll Free: (877) DELALLO
E-mail: info@delallo.com
Web Site: www.delallo.com
Approx. Number Employees: 109
Year Founded: 1950
Business Description:
Specialty Italian Food Products
S.I.C.: 5149; 5147
N.A.I.C.S.: 424490; 424470
Import Export
Personnel:
Francis X. DeLallo *(Pres & CEO)*
Brands & Products:
DELALLO
Advertising Agency:
Giant Ideas
100 1st Ave Ste 200
Pittsburgh, PA 15222
Tel.: (412) 566-5756
Fax: (412) 566-1510
Toll Free: (866) 45GIANT

GEORGE WESTON LIMITED
22 Saint Clair Ave E
Toronto, ON M4T 2S7, Canada
Tel.: (416) 922-2500
Fax: (416) 922-4395
E-mail: customer_service@weston.ca
Web Site: www.weston.ca
Approx. Sls.: $25,606,224,000
Approx. Number Employees: 145,000
Year Founded: 1882
Business Description:
Food Processing & Distr Services; Fresh & Frozen Bakeries, Dairy & Supermarket Operations
S.I.C.: 2051; 2092; 5411
N.A.I.C.S.: 311812; 311712; 445110
Export
Media: 1-7-8-13
Personnel:
W. Galen Weston *(Chm)*
Allan L. Leighton *(Deputy Chm)*
Peter B.M. Eby *(Vice Chm)*
Pavi Binning *(Pres)*
Rolando Sardellitti *(CFO & VP-Fin)*
Gordon A.M. Currie *(Chief Legal Officer & Exec VP)*
Robert A. Balcom *(Sr VP, Gen Counsel-Canada & Sec)*
Roy R. Conliffe *(Exec VP-Labour Rels)*
Robert G. Vaux *(Exec VP-Corp Dev)*
Franca Smith *(Sr VP & Controller)*
Scott Fullbright *(Sr VP & Gen Mgr-Dairy Div)*
Selena Sanderson *(Sr VP & Gen Mgr-Cookie & Crackers Div)*
Manny DiFilippo *(Sr VP-Risk Mgmt & Audit Svcs)*
J. Bradley Holland *(Sr VP-Tax)*
Lucy J. Paglione *(Sr VP-Pension & Benefits)*
Geoffrey H. Wilson *(Sr VP-Fin Svcs & IR)*
Michael N. Kimber *(VP-Legal Counsel)*
Darren Mahaffy *(VP-Mktg)*
Walter H. Kraus *(Sr Dir-Environ Affairs)*
Brands & Products:
ATLANTIC SUPERSTORE
BOBOLI
DUTCH COUNTRY
FORTINO'S
LOBLAW
MOULIN ROUGE
WESTON
ZEHR'S

GERBER PRODUCTS COMPANY
(Sub. of Nestle Healthcare Nutrition)
12 Vreeland Rd
Florham Park, NJ 07932
Tel.: (973) 593-7599
Fax: (973) 593-7600
Toll Free: (800) 443-7237
Web Site: www.gerber.com
Approx. Number Employees: 200
Business Description:
Baby Products Mfr
S.I.C.: 5149
N.A.I.C.S.: 424490
Personnel:
Kurt T. Schmidt *(CEO)*
Christina Mayadas Lawrence *(VP-Mktg-Infant Nutrition)*
Louis Hudyman *(Brand Mgr)*
Valerie Shukovsky *(Mgr-Mktg-Gerber Organic)*
Brands & Products:
GERBER ORGANIC
Advertising Agency:
ClearRiver Communications Group
2401 Eastlawn Dr
Midland, MI 48640
Tel.: (989) 631-9560
Fax: (989) 631-7977

GFI AMERICA, INC.
(d/b/a King's Deluxe Foods)
(Filed for Ch. 11 bankruptcy on 10/7/05)
Ste 600 1010 W Saint Germain St
Saint Cloud, MN 56301-3002
Tel.: (612) 872-6262
Fax: (612) 870-4955
Toll Free: (800) 669-8996
Web Site: www.kingsdeluxe.com
Approx. Number Employees: 500
Year Founded: 1974
Business Description:
Beef Processor
S.I.C.: 5147
N.A.I.C.S.: 311612
Media: 4-8-13-16-17
Brands & Products:
THE BEEF REVOLUTION
FORMAX
KING'S DELUXE
THE NATURAL
SMART BURGER
SMARTMEAT
SUPERNATURAL

GILSTER-MARY LEE CORPORATION
1037 State St
Chester, IL 62233
Tel.: (618) 826-2361
Fax: (618) 826-2973
Toll Free: (800) 851-5371
E-mail: webmaster@gilstermarylee.com
Web Site: www.gilstermarylee.com
Sales Range: $650-699.9 Million
Approx. Number Employees: 3,000
Year Founded: 1895
Business Description:
Private Label & Contract Mfr of Cake Mixes, Dry Drink Mixes, Dry Cereals, Macaroni, Potato Products, Popcorn & Pasta
S.I.C.: 2098; 2043
N.A.I.C.S.: 311823; 311230
Export
Media: 13
Distr.: Natl.
Personnel:
Donald E. Welge *(Pres & CEO)*
Michael W. Welge *(CFO)*
Delbert Dethrow *(VP & Mgr-Truck)*
Ron Tretter *(Asst VP-Engrng)*
Brands & Products:
CINCH
DUFF
GILSTER-MARY LEE
GML
HOSPITALITY
PY-O-MY

GLOBAL SMOOTHIE SUPPLY, INC.
4428 University Blvd
Dallas, TX 75205
Tel.: (214) 769-0836
E-mail: info@gssww.com
Web Site: www.gssww.com
Approx. Rev.: $16,923
Business Description:
Fresh-Fruit Smoothie Systems Supplier
S.I.C.: 3556
N.A.I.C.S.: 333294
Advertising Expenditures: $37,464
Media: 17
Personnel:
David C. Tiller *(Chm & CEO)*
Donald M. Roberts *(Vice Chm, CFO & Treas)*
Harry B. Ireland *(Vice Chm, Chief Legal Officer & Sec)*
Advertising Agency:
Revel
3001 Maple Ave Ste 501
Dallas, TX 75201
Tel.: (214) 397-0202
Fax: (214) 397-0203

GOLD PURE FOOD PRODUCTS CO., INC.
1 Brooklyn Rd
Hempstead, NY 11550-6619
Tel.: (516) 483-5600

Key to Media (For complete agency information see *The Advertising Red Books-Agencies* edition):
1. Bus. Publs. 2. Cable T.V. 3. Catalogs & Directories. 4. Co-op Adv. 5. Consumer Mags. 6. D.M. to Bus. Estab.7. D.M. to Consumers
8. Daily Newsp. 9. Exhibits/Trade Shows 10. Foreign 11. Infomercial 12. Internet Adv.13. Multimedia 14. Network Radio
15. Network T.V. 16. Newsp. Distr. Mags. 17. Other 18. Outdoor (Posters, Transit) 19. Point of Purchase20. Premiums, Novelties
21. Product Samples 22. Special Events Mktg. 23. Spot Radio 24. Spot T.V. 25. Weekly Newsp. 26. Yellow Page Adv.

Fax: (516) 483-5798
E-mail: generalcomments@goldshorseradish.com
Web Site: www.goldshorseradish.com
Approx. Number Employees: 70
Year Founded: 1932
Business Description:
Horseradish, Spare Rib Sauce, Kosher Foods, Sauces, Various Mustards & Vinegar Mfr
S.I.C.: 2035; 2099
N.A.I.C.S.: 311941; 311999
Import Export
Advertising Expenditures: $100,000
Media: 2-4-5-7-9-18-19-20-23
Distr.: Natl.
Budget Set: Jan.
Personnel:
Neil Gold *(Owner)*
Steve Gold *(Pres)*
Mark Gold *(Dir-Mktg & Adv)*
Brands & Products:
ARROW
BAKER'S MUSTARD
CHEF ALLEN'S
EXTRA CHUNKY
GOLD'S
NATHAN'S
NATHAN'S MUSTARD
OLD WORLD
SAUCY CHICKEN
SAUCY RIB
UNCLE DAVE'S
Advertising Agency:
Furman Roth Advertising
801 2nd Ave 14th Fl
New York, NY 10017-4706
Tel.: (212) 687-2300
Fax: (212) 687-0858
(Horse Radish, Mustard & Sauces)

GOLD'N PLUMP POULTRY, INC.

(Sub. of JFC Inc.)
4150 Second St S Ste 200
Saint Cloud, MN 56301-3994
Mailing Address:
PO Box 1106
Saint Cloud, MN 56302-1106
Tel.: (320) 251-3570
Fax: (320) 240-6250
Toll Free: (800) 892-8569
Toll Free: (800) 328-2838
E-mail: hr@goldnplump.com
Web Site: www.goldnplump.com
Sales Range: $200-249.9 Million
Approx. Number Employees: 65
Year Founded: 1926
Business Description:
Poultry Broilers, Hatchery & Processing
S.I.C.: 2015
N.A.I.C.S.: 311615
Export
Media: 3-4-5-6-8-9-10-17-18-19-20-21-22-23-24-25
Budget Set: June -Oct.
Personnel:
Don Helgeson *(Chm)*
Michael Helgeson *(CEO)*
Stephen Jurek *(Exec VP-Ops)*
Tim Wensman *(Exec VP)*
Tracy Miller *(Sr Mgr-Product Dev)*
Rory Bidinger *(Mgr-Brand Comm)*
Brands & Products:
GOLD'N PLUMP
GOLD'N PLUMP PREMIUM SELECTS
Advertising Agencies:
Gabriel deGrood Bendt
608 2nd Ave S Ste 129
Minneapolis, MN 55402
Tel.: (612) 547-5000
Fax: (612) 547-5090
Chicken
— Kris Fitzpatrick *(Acct Supvr)*

Maccabee Group, Inc.
211 N 1st St Ste 425
Minneapolis, MN 55401
Tel.: (612) 337-0087
Fax: (612) 337-0054
(Media Relations)

GONNELLA BAKING COMPANY

2006 W Erie St
Chicago, IL 60612-1318
Tel.: (312) 733-2020
Fax: (312) 733-7056
E-mail: webmaster@gonnella.com
Web Site: www.gonnella.com
Approx. Number Employees: 350
Year Founded: 1886
Business Description:
Bakers of French Bread & Rolls
S.I.C.: 2051; 5812
N.A.I.C.S.: 311812; 722110
Media: 10-13-18-26
Distr.: Reg.
Personnel:
Nick Marcucci *(Pres)*
Tom Marcucci *(VP)*
James Mazukelli *(Safety Dir)*
Brands & Products:
GONNELLA

THE GORTON GROUP

(Sub. of Nippon Suisan Kaisha, Ltd.)
128 Rogers St
Gloucester, MA 01930-5005
Tel.: (978) 283-3000
Fax: (978) 281-8295
E-mail: info@gortons.com
Web Site: www.gortons.com
Approx. Number Employees: 300
Year Founded: 1849
Business Description:
Seafood Processor
S.I.C.: 2091; 2092
N.A.I.C.S.: 311711; 311712
Import Export
Media: 2-6-7-9-13-15-19-21-23-24
Distr.: Natl.
Budget Set: Feb. -Apr.
Personnel:
Judson Reis *(Pres & CEO)*
Craig Roller *(Dir-Quality)*
Zach Soolman *(Dir-Consumer Mktg)*
Jan Velco Soolman *(Mgr-Brand Comm)*
Brands & Products:
GORTON'S
Advertising Agency:
TargetCast tcm
909 3rd Ave 31st Fl
New York, NY 10022
Tel.: (212) 500-6900
Fax: (212) 500-6880

GOYA FOODS, INC.

100 Seaview Dr
Secaucus, NJ 07094-1800
Tel.: (201) 348-4900
Fax: (201) 348-6609
E-mail: info@goya.com
Web Site: www.goya.com
Approx. Number Employees: 2,500
Year Founded: 1936
Business Description:
Mfr, Producer & Distr of Food Products; Purveyor of Rice, Beans, Condiments, Nectars & Authentic Latin American Specialties
S.I.C.: 5141
N.A.I.C.S.: 424410
Import
Advertising Expenditures: $10,000,000
Media: 2-4-6-7-8-9-10-11-13-18-21-24-25
Distr.: Natl.
Budget Set: June
Personnel:
Joseph Perez *(Sr VP)*
Nydia Ramos *(Dir-Mktg)*
Alvaro Serrano *(Product Mgr)*
Brands & Products:
CANILLA
FIESTA
GOLDEN CANILLA
GOYA
HOPPIN'S JOHN
IF IT'S GOYA IT HAS TO BE GOOD
MASAREPA BLANCA
MASARICA
PAELLA
SAZON GOYA
WHAT A WAY TO GOYA
Advertising Agency:
Republica
2153 Coral Way
Miami, FL 33145
Tel.: (305) 442-0977
Fax: (305) 443-1631

GRAIN PROCESSING CORPORATION

(Sub. of Muscatine Foods Corp.)
1600 Oregon St
Muscatine, IA 52761-1404
Tel.: (563) 264-4211
Tel.: (563) 264-4265 (Mktg)
Fax: (563) 264-4289
E-mail: sales@grainprocessing.com
Web Site: www.grainprocessing.com
E-Mail For Key Personnel:
Sales Director: sales@grainprocessing.com
Approx. Number Employees: 1,400
Year Founded: 1943
Business Description:
Corn-Based Products Mfr & Worldwide Marketer
S.I.C.: 2869; 2046; 2085
N.A.I.C.S.: 325199; 311221; 312140
Export
Media: 2-7-10-13
Personnel:
Gage A. Kent *(Chm & CEO)*
Diane Rieke *(Mgr-Mktg Commun)*
Brands & Products:
AQUATITE
AQUATITE RESIN ADDITION SYSTEM
CHARGEMASTER
COATMASTER
GEOMELT
GOLDEN GRIP
GPC
INSCOSITY
INSTANT PURE-COAT
KAPEL
MALTRIN
MALTRIN QD
MOUNTAIN MELT
PURE-BIND
PURE-COTE
PURE-DENT
PURE-GEL
PURE-SET
SEALMASTER
SECURE 'N SAFE
SOLULAC
SPRESS
SUPERBOND
WATER LOCK
ZEINA

GRANDMA BROWN'S BEANS, INC.

5837 Scenic Ave
Mexico, NY 13114-3481
Mailing Address:
PO Box 230
Mexico, NY 13114-0230
Tel.: (315) 963-7221
Fax: (315) 963-4072
E-mail: grandmabrownsbeans@verizon.net
Approx. Sls.: $2,500,000
Approx. Number Employees: 15
Year Founded: 1938
Business Description:
Baked Beans, Saucepan Beans, Bean Soup & Split Pea Soup Mfr
S.I.C.: 2032; 2033
N.A.I.C.S.: 311422; 311421
Import
Media: 2-5-6-8-9-19-21-22-23-25
Distr.: Direct to Consumer; Natl.
Budget Set: Jan.
Personnel:
Sandra L. Brown *(Chm & CEO)*
Brands & Products:
GRANDMA BROWN'S

GRAVYMASTER INC.

(Sub. of Richardson Brands Company)
16 Business Pk Dr
Branford, CT 06405-2924
Tel.: (203) 481-2276
Fax: (203) 488-8085
E-mail: info@gravy.com
Web Site: www.gravy.com
Approx. Number Employees: 45
Year Founded: 1935
Business Description:
Mfr of Seasoning & Browning Sauces
S.I.C.: 2035
N.A.I.C.S.: 311941
Export
Media: 2-6-9-19
Distr.: Natl.
Budget Set: Aug.
Personnel:
Don Boodie *(CEO)*
Brands & Products:
GRAVYMASTER

GRAY & COMPANY

2331 23rd Ave
Forest Grove, OR 97116
Mailing Address:
PO Box 218
Forest Grove, OR 97116-0218
Tel.: (503) 357-3141
Fax: (503) 357-8837
E-mail: customerservice@cherryman.com
Web Site: www.cherryman.com

Key to Media (For complete agency information see *The Advertising Red Books-Agencies* edition):
1. Bus. Publs. 2. Cable T.V. 3. Catalogs & Directories. 4. Co-op Adv. 5. Consumer Mags. 6. D.M. to Bus. Estab.7. D.M. to Consumers 8. Daily Newsp. 9. Exhibits/Trade Shows 10. Foreign 11. Infomercial 12. Internet Adv.13. Multimedia 14. Network Radio 15. Network T.V. 16. Newsp. Distr. Mags. 17. Other 18. Outdoor (Posters, Transit) 19. Point of Purchase20. Premiums, Novelties 21. Product Samples 22. Special Events Mktg. 23. Spot Radio 24. Spot T.V. 25. Weekly Newsp. 26. Yellow Page Adv.

Gray & Company — (Continued)

Sales Range: $50-74.9 Million
Approx. Number Employees: 500
Year Founded: 1908
Business Description:
Packaged Maraschino Cherry, Glazed Fruit & Coconut Mfr & Distr
S.I.C.: 5149; 2033
N.A.I.C.S.: 424490; 311421
Import Export
Advertising Expenditures: $300,000
Media: 2-7-9-17-26
Distr.: Natl.
Personnel:
James G. Reynolds *(Pres & CEO)*

THE GREAT LAKES CHEESE CO., INC.
17825 Great Lks Pkwy
Hiram, OH 44234-9677
Tel.: (440) 834-2500
Fax: (440) 834-1002
Web Site:
www.greatlakescheese.com
Approx. Number Employees: 1,700
Year Founded: 1958
Business Description:
Mfr., Packager & Distributor of Cheese
S.I.C.: 5143; 2022
N.A.I.C.S.: 424430; 311513
Import
Advertising Expenditures: $2,000,000
Media: 2-4-5-10-18-20-21-23
Distr.: Reg.
Personnel:
Hans Epprecht *(Owner)*
John W. Epprecht *(Owner)*
Gary Vanic *(Pres & CEO)*
Russell Mullins *(CFO)*
William H. Andrews *(VP-Sls)*
MaryJo Poumert *(VP-HR)*
Brands & Products:
A PASSION FOR EXCELLENCE
AMERICAN SLICE
GREAT LAKES
HOT PEPPER
OLD WORLD TRADITION

GREAT LAKES KRAUT CO., LLC
400 Clark St
Bear Creek, WI 54922
Tel.: (715) 752-4105
Fax: (715) 752-1308
E-mail: info@krispkraut.com
Web Site: www.krispkraut.com
Approx. Number Employees: 200
Year Founded: 1900
Business Description:
Mfr. of Sauerkraut
S.I.C.: 2033
N.A.I.C.S.: 311421
Media: 4-6-9-10-17-20-21-25
Personnel:
Ryan A. Downs *(Owner)*
Brands & Products:
KRRRRISPKRAUT
SILVER FLOSS

GREAT NORTHERN PRODUCTS, LTD.
804 Centerville Rd
Warwick, RI 02886-4397
Mailing Address:
PO Box 7622
Warwick, RI 02887-7622
Tel.: (401) 821-2400
Fax: (401) 821-2419
E-mail: domestic@northernproducts.com
Web Site: www.northernproducts.com
Sales Range: $50-74.9 Million
Approx. Number Employees: 24
Year Founded: 1989
Business Description:
Seafood, Meats, Cheese & Fruit Concentrates
S.I.C.: 5141
N.A.I.C.S.: 424410
Import Export
Media: 7-10-13
Personnel:
George Nolan *(Pres)*
Brands & Products:
CRUSTATEES
LANGLOIS
SEALICIOUS
THE WORLD OF GREAT NORTHERN

GRECIAN DELIGHT FOODS INC.
1201 Tonne Rd
Elk Grove Village, IL 60007-4925
Tel.: (847) 364-1010
Fax: (847) 364-1078
E-mail: webmaster@gonnella.com
Web Site: www.greciandelight.com
Sales Range: $50-74.9 Million
Approx. Number Employees: 200
Year Founded: 1974
Business Description:
Mediterranean Foods: Pita Breads, Gyros Meat & Greek Specialties Mfr
S.I.C.: 2099; 2051
N.A.I.C.S.: 311999; 311812
Import Export
Media: 19-23
Distr.: Natl.
Budget Set: Mar.
Personnel:
Peter Parthenis, Jr. *(Pres & CEO)*
Ted Sawicz *(COO)*
George Georganas *(VP-Procurement)*
Brands & Products:
ARTURO'S
FEISTY FETA
GRECIAN DELIGHT
OPAA!
PITA WRAP

GREEN MOUNTAIN COFFEE ROASTERS, INC.
33 Coffee Ln
Waterbury, VT 05676-8900
Tel.: (802) 244-5621
Fax: (802) 244-5436
Toll Free: (888) 879-4627
E-mail: investor.services@gmcr.com
Web Site:
www.greenmountaincoffee.com
Approx. Sls.: $1,356,775,000
Approx. Number Employees: 2,380
Year Founded: 1981
Business Description:
Coffee Mfr
S.I.C.: 2095; 5149
N.A.I.C.S.: 311920; 424490
Advertising Expenditures: $52,900,000
Media: 2-4-5-6-7-8-10-17-19-21-22-23
Distr.: Natl.
Budget Set: Sept.
Personnel:
Robert P. Stiller *(Chm)*
Lawrence J. Blanford *(Pres & CEO)*
Frances G. Rathke *(CFO & Treas)*
James K. Prevo *(CIO)*
Stephen L. Gibbs *(Chief Acctg Officer & VP)*
Richard Scott McCreary *(Pres-Specialty Coffee Bus Unit)*
Howard Malovany *(Gen Counsel, Sec & VP)*
Kathryn S. Brooks *(VP-Org Dev & HR & Internal Comm)*
Suzanne DuLong *(VP-IR & Corp Comm)*
James Travis, Jr. *(VP-Sls)*
T. J. Whalen *(VP-Mktg)*
Lindsey Bolger *(Sr Dir-Coffee Sourcing & Relationships)*
Derek Archambault *(Sr Brand Mgr)*
Ross Fenderson *(Brand Mgr)*
Don Holly *(Mgr-Corp Quality)*
Kathleen Shaffer *(Coord-IR)*
Brands & Products:
ALL CAFE ESCAPES
APPROPRIATE ROAST
AUTUMN HARVEST BLEND
BARISTA PRIMA COFFEEHOUSE
BETTER WORLD HOT COCOA
CAFE VERDE
CAFE VERMONT
DARK MAGIC
EARTH-FRIENDLY
GREAT COFFEE MADE EASY
GREAT COFFEE MAKES A WORLD OF DIFFERENCE
GREEN MOUNTAIN
GREEN MOUNTAIN COFFEE
GREEN MOUNTAIN COFFEE ROASTERS
GREEN MOUNTAIN COFFEE ROASTERS & DESIGN
GREEN MOUNTAIN NATURALS
GUATAMALAN FINCA DOS MARIAS
K-CUP
KEURIG
LAKE & LODGE
MOCHA ALMOND CHILLER
NANTUCKET BLEND
ORGANIC BLACK PARROT BLEND
ORGANIC HAZELNUT SELECT
ORGANIC HOUSE BLEND
ORGANIC MEXICAN SELECT
ORGANIC PERUVIAN SELECT
ORGANIC RAIN FOREST BLEND
ORGANIC SUMATRAN RESERVE
ORGANIC VIENNESE CINNAMON
PARTNERFARM
THE PERFECT PEACH
RAIN FOREST NUT
STEWARDSHIP
SUMMER SAFARI
TAPESTRY BLEND DARK
THE ULTIMATE OFFICE COFFEE
VERMONT COUNTRY BLEND
WILD MOUNTAIN BLUEBERRY
Advertising Agencies:
BrandBuzz
285 Madison Ave 22nd Fl
New York, NY 10017
Tel.: (212) 210-3879
Fax: (212) 210-3878

Sloane & Company LLC
(d/b/a Sloane & Company)
7 Times Sq Tower 17th Fl
New York, NY 10036
Tel.: (212) 486-9500
Fax: (212) 486-9094
Corporate Public Relations
Strategic Financial

GRIFFIN FOOD COMPANY
(Sub. of Griffin Holdings Inc.)
111 S Cherokee St
Muskogee, OK 74403
Tel.: (918) 687-6311
Fax: (918) 687-3579
E-mail: info@griffinfoods.com
Web Site: www.griffinfoods.com
Year Founded: 1908
Business Description:
Mfr. of Waffle Syrup, Coconut & Canned Foods, Preserves, Jellies, Salad Dressing & Mustards
S.I.C.: 2099
N.A.I.C.S.: 311999
Media: 5-6-9-10-19-21-23-24
Personnel:
John W. Griffin *(Founder & Pres)*
Brands & Products:
GRIFFIN JELLY
GRIFFIN SYRUP

GRIFFITH LABORATORIES, INC.
1 Griffith Ctr
Alsip, IL 60803-3408
Tel.: (708) 371-0900
Fax: (708) 597-3294
Toll Free: (800) 346-9494
E-mail: contactsales-us@griffithlabs.com
Web Site: www.griffithlabs.com
Approx. Number Employees: 2,500
Year Founded: 1919
Business Description:
Food Ingredients Mfr
S.I.C.: 2099
N.A.I.C.S.: 311942
Media: 1-2-4-7-10-21
Distr.: Intl.; Natl.
Budget Set: Sept.
Personnel:
Dean Griffith *(Chm)*
Herve de la Vauvre *(Pres & CEO-Worldwide)*
Joe Maslick *(CFO & Exec VP)*
Brian Griffith *(Pres-Asia-Pacific)*
James S. Legg *(Gen Counsel & VP)*
Drew M. Bandusky *(Sr VP-Global Bus Performance)*
Bill Frost *(Sr VP)*
Christine Carr *(VP-Mktg & Global Comm)*
Jeff Shinn *(VP-IT-Worldwide)*
Christopher Wood *(VP-Sls)*
Brands & Products:
CULINARY
GRIFFITH
INNOVA
PANROAST
PRAGUE POWDER
ROBUST
SAVOR NOTES
VEGAMINE

GRIFFITH LABORATORIES LTD.
(Holding of Griffith Laboratories, Inc.)
757 Pharmacy Ave
Scarborough, ON M1L 3J8, Canada
Tel.: (416) 288-3050
Fax: (416) 288-3481
Telex: 6 96 3562 GRIFLAB TOR
E-mail: contactsales-can@griffithlabs.com

Key to Media (For complete agency information see *The Advertising Red Books-Agencies* edition):
1. Bus. Publs. 2. Cable T.V. 3. Catalogs & Directories. 4. Co-op Adv. 5. Consumer Mags. 6. D.M. to Bus. Estab.7. D.M. to Consumers
8. Daily Newsp. 9. Exhibits/Trade Shows 10. Foreign 11. Infomercial 12. Internet Adv.13. Multimedia 14. Network Radio
15. Network T.V. 16. Newsp. Distr. Mags. 17. Other 18. Outdoor (Posters, Transit) 19. Point of Purchase20. Premiums, Novelties
21. Product Samples 22. Special Events Mktg. 23. Spot Radio 24. Spot T.V. 25. Weekly Newsp. 26. Yellow Page Adv.

Web Site: www.griffithlaboratories.com
Approx. Number Employees: 300
Year Founded: 1919
Business Description:
Mfr of Food Preparations; Rice Milling; Food Products Machinery
S.I.C.: 2034; 2099
N.A.I.C.S.: 311423; 311999
Export
Advertising Expenditures: $400,000
Media: 10
Distr.: Natl.
Personnel:
Dean Griffith *(Chm)*
Herve de la Vauvre *(Pres & CEO-Worldwide)*
Chris Savage *(Pres)*
Joe Maslick *(CFO & Exec VP)*
Wilf Costello *(Sr VP-Sls)*
Joyce Ballou *(Sr Dir-HR)*
Wendy Tai *(Mgr-HR)*

GROSVENOR MARKETING LTD.
(Sub. of R. Twining & Co. Ltd.)
777 Passaic Ave
Clifton, NJ 07012-1804
Tel.: (973) 591-0600
Fax: (973) 591-1700
Toll Free: (800) 631-0880
E-mail: info@twiningsnorthamera.com
Web Site: www.twiningsnorthamera.com
Approx. Sls.: $20,000,000
Approx. Number Employees: 25
Business Description:
Tea, Coffee, Cocoa & Spice Whslr.
S.I.C.: 5149
N.A.I.C.S.: 424490
Import
Media: 4-6-8-9-10-11-13-19-21-23-24-25
Distr.: Natl.

GRUMA CORPORATION
(Branch of Gruma Corporation)
(d/b/a Mission Foods)
1565 1st Ave NW
New Brighton, MN 55112-1948
Tel.: (651) 697-5500
Fax: (651) 697-0600
Web Site: www.missionfoods.com
Approx. Number Employees: 150
Business Description:
Tortilla Chips, Salsas & Other Snack Food Products Mfr & Distr
S.I.C.: 2099
N.A.I.C.S.: 311999
Personnel:
Norma Rojas *(Sr Dir-Mktg)*
Brands & Products:
MISSION
Advertising Agency:
Butler, Shine, Stern & Partners
20 Liberty Ship Way
Sausalito, CA 94965-3312
Tel.: (415) 331-6049
Fax: (415) 331-3524
Mission Foods

HAELAN PRODUCTS, INC.
18568 142nd Ave NE Bldg F
Woodinville, WA 98072-8520
Tel.: (425) 482-2645
Fax: (425) 482-2647
Toll Free: (866) 5-HAELAN
E-mail: info@haelan951.com
Web Site: www.haelan951.com
Approx. Number Employees: 10
Business Description:
Nutritional Supplements Distr
S.I.C.: 5122
N.A.I.C.S.: 424210
Media: 2-6-10
Brands & Products:
HAELAN 951
HAELAN PRODUCTS

THE HAIN CELESTIAL GROUP, INC.
58 S Service Rd
Melville, NY 11747-2342
Tel.: (631) 730-2200
Fax: (631) 730-2550
Toll Free: (800) 434-4246
E-mail: investorrelations@hain-celestial.com
Web Site: www.hain-celestial.com
Approx. Sls.: $1,130,257,000
Approx. Number Employees: 2,031
Year Founded: 1993
Business Description:
Natural & Organic Foods & Personal Care Products Mfr
S.I.C.: 2099; 2034; 2038; 2043; 2052; 2075; 2079; 2095; 2096; 2098; 2833; 2841; 2844
N.A.I.C.S.: 311999; 311222; 311223; 311230; 311412; 311423; 311821; 311823; 311919; 311920; 311991; 325411; 325611; 325620
Advertising Expenditures: $5,400,000
Media: 2-4-5-6-8-9-11-14-15-17-19-20-21-22-24
Personnel:
Irwin D. Simon *(Founder, Chm, Pres & CEO)*
Ira J. Lamel *(CFO & Exec VP)*
Maureen M. Putman *(CMO-Grocery & Snacks)*
Michael J. Speiller *(Chief Acctg Officer & Sr VP-Fin)*
Ellen B. Deutsch *(Chief Growth Officer & Sr VP)*
James R. Meiers *(Chief Supply Chain Officer-Grocery, Snacks & Personal Care)*
Beena G. Goldenberg *(Pres-Canada)*
John Carroll *(CEO-United States & Exec VP)*
Philippe Woitrin *(CEO-Europe)*
Denise M. Faltischek *(Gen Counsel & Sr VP)*
Mary Celeste Anthes *(Sr VP-Corp Rels)*
Benjamin Brecher *(Sr VP-Special Projects)*
Michael E. Calderon *(VP-IT)*
Dominic D. Myrand *(VP-HR)*
Brands & Products:

Story Worldwide
360 Lexington Ave 19th Fl
New York, NY 10017
Tel.: (212) 481-3452
Fax: (212) 213-1287
(Terra Chips)

HANOVER FOODS CORPORATION
1486 York St
Hanover, PA 17331-9570
Mailing Address:
PO Box 334
Hanover, PA 17331
Tel.: (717) 632-6000
Fax: (717) 637-2890
E-mail: jerry.neidigh@hanoverfoods.com
Web Site: www.hanoverfoods.com
Sales Range: $500-549.9 Million
Approx. Number Employees: 2,200
Year Founded: 1924
Business Description:
Canned & Frozen Foods
S.I.C.: 2033; 2032
N.A.I.C.S.: 311421; 311422
Import Export
Advertising Expenditures: $17,000,000
Media: 2-5-9-10-16-19-20
Distr.: Reg.
Budget Set: Apr.
Personnel:
John Warehime *(CEO)*
Peitro Giraffa *(Chief Acctg Officer, VP & Controller)*
Steven E. Robertson *(Treas)*
Gary Knisely *(Exec VP)*
Jerry Neidigh *(Mgr-Adv & Mktg)*
Brands & Products:
BICKEL'S
BON TON
CABANA
DRAPER KING COLE
GIBBS
HANOVER
MAKING MEALS EASY
MYERS
PHILLIPS
SPRING GLEN
SUN SPROUT
SUPERFINE
WEGE

HATFIELD QUALITY MEATS, INC.
(Sub. of Clemens Family Corporation)
2700 Clemens Rd
Hatfield, PA 19440-2834
Mailing Address:
PO Box 902
Hatfield, PA 19440-0902
Tel.: (215) 368-2500
Fax: (215) 362-1750
Toll Free: (800) 523-5291
Web Site: www.hatfieldqualitymeats.com
E-Mail For Key Personnel:
President: doug@hqm.com
Marketing Director: ryan@hqm.com
Sales Range: $400-449.9 Million
Approx. Number Employees: 1,400
Year Founded: 1895
Business Description:
Meat Packing
S.I.C.: 0751; 5147
N.A.I.C.S.: 311611; 311612
Export
Advertising Expenditures: $800,000
Media: 7-13
Personnel:
Douglas C. Clemens *(Pres)*
Philip A. Clemens *(CEO)*
Brands & Products:
BEAVER FALLS
BUTCHER WAGON
CHEF PLEASER
CHESAPEAK VALLEY FARMS
THE FRESHEST FOR YOUR FAMILY. GUARANTEED.
GOLD RIBBON
HATFIELD
JUMBO GRILLER
MEDFORD'S
PA DUTCH
PRIMA PORTA
TENDER PLUS
WILD BILL'S
YOUR FAMILY DESERVES THE FRESHEST
Advertising Agency:
Allebach Advertising
117 N Main St
Souderton, PA 18964
Tel.: (215) 721-7693
Fax: (215) 721-7694
— Kevin Schluth *(Acct Exec)*

HAWAII COFFEE COMPANY
(Sub. of Paradise Beverages, Inc.)
1555 Kalani St
Honolulu, HI 96817
Tel.: (808) 843-4202
Fax: (808) 847-7900
Toll Free: (800) 338-8353
Web Site: www.lioncoffee.com
Approx. Sls.: $25,000,000
Approx. Number Employees: 120
Year Founded: 1967
Business Description:
Coffee Processor & Marketer
S.I.C.: 5149; 2095
N.A.I.C.S.: 424490; 311920
Import Export
Media: 4-21-23-26
Distr.: Natl.
Personnel:
James M. Wayman *(Pres)*
Brands & Products:
HAWAIIAN ISLANDS TEA
LION
ROYAL KAUAI
ROYAL KONA
ROYAL MAUI

HAYDENERGY, INC.
200 W 58th St Ste 2C
New York, NY 10019-1432
Tel.: (212) 246-9343
Toll Free: (800) 255-1660
Web Site: www.naurahayden.com
Approx. Number Employees: 8
Business Description:
Health Food Products Mfr
S.I.C.: 5499; 5149
N.A.I.C.S.: 446191; 424490
Media: 2-6-7-9-19-23-25
Distr.: Natl.
Budget Set: Mar.
Personnel:
Naura Hayden *(Owner)*
Brands & Products:
DYNAMITE ENERGY SHAKE
DYNAMITE VITES

HEALTHY FAST FOOD, INC.
(Name Changed to U-Swirl, Inc.)

HEAVENS' BISTRO, INC.
2801 Ocean Park Blvd Ste 184
Santa Monica, CA 90405-2905
Tel.: (310) 281-1973
Toll Free: (888) HEAVNLY
Web Site: www.heavensbistro.com
Approx. Number Employees: 12
Business Description:
Frozen Pizza
S.I.C.: 2038

Key to Media (For complete agency information see *The Advertising Red Books-Agencies* edition):
1. Bus. Publs. 2. Cable T.V. 3. Catalogs & Directories. 4. Co-op Adv. 5. Consumer Mags. 6. D.M. to Bus. Estab.7. D.M. to Consumers 8. Daily Newsp. 9. Exhibits/Trade Shows 10. Foreign 11. Infomercial 12. Internet Adv.13. Multimedia 14. Network Radio 15. Network T.V. 16. Newsp. Distr. Mags. 17. Other 18. Outdoor (Posters, Transit) 19. Point of Purchase20. Premiums, Novelties 21. Product Samples 22. Special Events Mktg. 23. Spot Radio 24. Spot T.V. 25. Weekly Newsp. 26. Yellow Page Adv.

Heavens' Bistro, Inc. — (Continued)

N.A.I.C.S.: 311412
Media: 6
Personnel:
Eric Gault *(Pres)*
Brands & Products:
HEAVENS' BISTRO
THE PIZZA WITH ALL OF THE TASTE, NOT ON YOUR WAIST

HEINZ FROZEN FOOD COMPANY

(Sub. of H.J. Heinz Company)
357 6 Avn
Pittsburgh, PA 15222
Tel.: (412) 237-5700
Fax: (412) 237-3450
E-mail: info@heinz.com
Web Site: www.heinz.com
Sales Range: $500-549.9 Million
Approx. Number Employees: 1,000
Year Founded: 1983
Business Description:
Frozen Entrees & Side Dishes
S.I.C.: 2037; 2038
N.A.I.C.S.: 311411; 311412
Media: 8-10
Personnel:
William R. Johnson *(Chm, Pres & CEO)*
Scott O'hara *(Pres, CEO-Heinz North America & Exec VP)*

HEINZ NORTH AMERICA

(Sub. of H.J. Heinz Company)
357 6th Ave
Pittsburgh, PA 15222-2500
Mailing Address:
PO Box 57
Pittsburgh, PA 15230
Tel.: (412) 237-5757
Web Site: www.heinz.com
Sales Range: $550-599.9 Million
Approx. Number Employees: 2,500
Business Description:
Supplier of Canned Tuna & Pet Food Products
S.I.C.: 2047
N.A.I.C.S.: 311111
Export
Advertising Expenditures: $296,900,000
Media: 6-8-9-11-13-20-23-24
Personnel:
Jeffrey D. Kelly *(Dir-Corp Accounts)*
Patrick Macedo *(Brand Mgr-Ketchup)*
Frank Lubsey *(Assoc Mgr-Digital Mktg & Media)*
Brands & Products:
9-LIVES
9-LIVES MATURE
AMORE
CHARLIE'S LUNCH KIT
CYCLE
GRILL BITS
GRILL STIX
HOT DOGGIES
JERKY TREATS
KOZY KITTEN
MEATY BONES
REWARD
SNAUSAGES
Advertising Agency:
Smith Brothers Agency, LP
116 Federal St
Pittsburgh, PA 15212
Tel.: (412) 391-0555
Fax: (412) 391-3562

HELUVA GOOD, LLC

(Sub. of HP Hood LLC)
6551 Pratt Rd
Sodus, NY 14589
Mailing Address:
PO Box 410
Sodus, NY 14551
Tel.: (315) 483-6971
Fax: (315) 483-9927
Toll Free: (800) 323-2188
E-mail: consumeraffairs@heluvagood.com
Web Site: www.heluvagood.com
Approx. Number Employees: 150
Year Founded: 1939
Business Description:
Cheese, Dips, Salsa, Condiments & Dairy Products Mfr & Packager
S.I.C.: 5143; 2035
N.A.I.C.S.: 424430; 311941
Export
Media: 4-6-9-10-18-19-21-22-23-24
Budget Set: Sept.
Personnel:
John Snedeker *(VP-Sls & Gen Mgr)*
Brands & Products:
HELUVA GOOD
YOU'LL LOVE IT. WE SWEAR.

HERR FOODS INC.

273 Baltimore Pke
Nottingham, PA 19362-9788
Mailing Address:
PO Box 300
Nottingham, PA 19362
Tel.: (610) 932-9330
Fax: (610) 932-2137
E-mail: info@herrs.com
Web Site: www.herrsfood.com
Sales Range: $100-124.9 Million
Approx. Number Employees: 1,300
Year Founded: 1946
Business Description:
Snack Foods Mfr
S.I.C.: 2096; 2099
N.A.I.C.S.: 311919; 311999
Advertising Expenditures: $4,000,000
Media: 4-7-8-9-10-13-14-15-16-18-22
Personnel:
James M. Herr *(Chm & CEO)*
Ed Herr *(Pres)*
Phil Bernas *(Sr VP-Mfg)*
Daryl Thomas *(Sr VP-Sls & Mktg)*
Richard White *(Sr VP-HR)*
Fran Dolan *(VP-Mktg)*
Gerry Kluis *(VP-Fin)*
Joe Kuehner *(Gen Mgr-Sls)*
Brands & Products:
CHIPPER CLUB
HERR'S
HERR'S BACON & HORSERADISH
HERR'S CRUNCHY CHEESE STICKS
HERR'S JALAPENO
HERR'S KETTLE COOKED CHIPS
HERR'S OLD FASHIONED
HERR'S PHILLY CHEESE STEAK
HERR'S SOUR CREAM & ONION
HERR'S STIX
HERR'S WHITE CHEDDAR RANCH
MAKE HERR'S YOURS
MEXICAN CHEDDAR ON BLACK BEAN DIPPERS
NACHITAS
RUSSETT KETTLE COOKED POTATO CHIPS
WHOLE GRAIN
Advertising Agency:
Neiman Group
614 N Frnt St
Harrisburg, PA 17101-1057
Tel.: (717) 232-5554
Fax: (717) 232-7998

HICKORY FARMS, INC.

(Holding of Sun Capital Partners, Inc.)
1505 Holland Rd
Maumee, OH 43537-1620
Tel.: (419) 893-7611
Fax: (419) 893-0164
Toll Free: (800) 442-5671
E-mail: info@hickoryfarms.com
Web Site: www.hickoryfarms.com
Sales Range: $150-199.9 Million
Approx. Number Employees: 200
Year Founded: 1945
Business Description:
Specialty Food; Smoked Meats, Crackers & Snacks; Food Gift Packages
S.I.C.: 5499; 5961
N.A.I.C.S.: 445299; 454113
Advertising Expenditures: $1,000,000
Media: 4-6-7-8-9-15-19-21-23-24-25
Distr.: Natl.
Budget Set: Apr. -May
Personnel:
Mark Rodriguez *(Pres & CEO)*
James O'Neill *(VP-Retail & Wholesale Sls)*
Lisa Bryant *(Dir-PR)*
Christine Baron *(Mgr-Mktg)*
Brands & Products:
ACE SPECIALTY FOODS
ALMOND PLAZA
GOURMET REWARDS
HICKORY FARMS
MISSION ORCHARDS
PFAELZER BROTHERS
PINNACLE ORCHARDS
SQUIRES CHOICE

HIGH LINER FOODS INCORPORATED

100 Battery Point
Lunenburg, NS B0J 2C0, Canada
Tel.: (902) 634-8811
Fax: (902) 634-6228
E-mail: investor@highlinerfoods.com
Web Site: www.highlinerfoods.com
E-Mail For Key Personnel:
President: demonh@highlinerfoods.com
Public Relations: investor@highlinerfoods.com
Approx. Sls.: $613,814,394
Year Founded: 1899
Business Description:
Frozen Seafood Products Mfr
S.I.C.: 5146
N.A.I.C.S.: 445220
Import Export
Advertising Expenditures: $6,000,000
Media: 4-9-11-15-19-23-24-25
Distr.: Intl.; Natl.
Budget Set: Nov.
Personnel:
David J. Hennigar *(Chm)*
Henry E. Demone *(Pres & CEO)*
Keith A. Decker *(Pres & COO-High Liner Foods (USA) Inc)*
Mario P. Marino *(Pres & COO-Canadian Ops)*
Kelly L. Nelson *(CFO, Sec & Exec VP)*
Joanne E. Brown *(VP-HR)*
Paul W. Snow *(VP-Procurement)*
Bill DiMento *(Corp Dir-Sustainability)*
Brands & Products:
40 FATHOMS
CAPTAIN'S CATCH
FISHER BOY
FISHERINGS
FLORESTA
FPI
GINA ITALIAN VILLAGE
HEALTHY BAKE
HEALTHY CATCH
HIGH LINER
HIGH LINER FOODS
ITALIAN VILLAGE
LIGHT TONIGHT
MIRABEL
QUIK STIX
RAPIBARRITAS
RAPICOCINADOS
RINGOS
ROYAL SEA
SEA CUISINE
SEAFRESH
SENSIBLES
Advertising Agencies:
Full Contact Advertising
186 Lincoln St Ste 801E
Boston, MA 02111
Tel.: (866) 748-3700
Fax: (617) 249-0144
Toll Free: (866) 748-3700
Fisher Boy (Agency of Record)

NorBella Inc.
46 Plympton St
Boston, MA 02118
Tel.: (617) 542-1040
Media Buying & Planning

HIGH LINER FOODS (USA) INCORPORATED

(Sub. of High Liner Foods Incorporated)
18 Electronics Ave
Danvers, MA 01923
Tel.: (978) 777-2660
Fax: (978) 777-6849
E-mail: info@highlinerfoods.com
Web Site: www.highlinerfoodsusa.com
Approx. Number Employees: 250
Year Founded: 1899
Business Description:
Frozen Seafood Products Mfr
S.I.C.: 2092
N.A.I.C.S.: 311712
Import Export
Advertising Expenditures: $1,500,000
Media: 2-5-9-19-20-23
Distr.: Natl.
Budget Set: Sept.
Personnel:
Keith Decker *(Pres & COO)*
Advertising Agencies:
Full Contact Advertising
186 Lincoln St Ste 801E
Boston, MA 02111
Tel.: (866) 748-3700
Fax: (617) 249-0144
Toll Free: (866) 748-3700

Key to Media (For complete agency information see *The Advertising Red Books-Agencies* edition):
1. Bus. Publs. 2. Cable T.V. 3. Catalogs & Directories. 4. Co-op Adv. 5. Consumer Mags. 6. D.M. to Bus. Estab.7. D.M. to Consumers
8. Daily Newsp. 9. Exhibits/Trade Shows 10. Foreign 11. Infomercial 12. Internet Adv.13. Multimedia 14. Network Radio
15. Network T.V. 16. Newsp. Distr. Mags. 17. Other 18. Outdoor (Posters, Transit) 19. Point of Purchase20. Premiums, Novelties
21. Product Samples 22. Special Events Mktg. 23. Spot Radio 24. Spot T.V. 25. Weekly Newsp. 26. Yellow Page Adv.

NorBella Inc.
46 Plympton St
Boston, MA 02118
Tel.: (617) 542-1040

HILAND DAIRY FOODS COMPANY, LLC

(Joint Venture of Dairy Farmers of America, Inc. & Prairie Farms Dairy, Inc.)
1133 E Kearney St
Springfield, MO 65803
Mailing Address:
PO Box 2270
Springfield, MO 65801-2270
Tel.: (417) 862-9311
Fax: (417) 837-1106
E-mail: questionsandcomments@hilanddairy.com
Web Site: www.hilanddairy.com
Approx. Sls.: $50,000,000
Approx. Number Employees: 250
Year Founded: 1938
Business Description:
Dairy Processing & Distr
S.I.C.: 2026; 2024
N.A.I.C.S.: 311511; 311520
Media: 5-7-18-19-23-24
Distr.: Reg.
Budget Set: Apr.
Personnel:
Gary Aggus *(Pres & Gen Mgr)*
Brands & Products:
HILAND SOUR CREAM

H.J. HEINZ COMPANY

1 PPG Pl
Pittsburgh, PA 15222
Mailing Address:
P.O. Box 57
Pittsburgh, PA 15230
Tel.: (412) 456-5757
Fax: (412) 456-6128
Toll Free: (800) 255-5750
E-mail: contact@heinz.com
Web Site: www.heinz.com
Approx. Sls.: $10,706,588,000
Approx. Number Employees: 34,800
Year Founded: 1869
Business Description:
Ketchup, Condiments & Sauces, Frozen Foods, Baby Foods, Beans & Pasta Meals, Soups & Other Processed Foods Mfr
S.I.C.: 2035; 2034; 2038; 2096; 2098; 2099; 5142
N.A.I.C.S.: 311941; 311412; 311423; 311823; 311919; 311999; 424420
Export
Advertising Expenditures: $369,600,000
Media: 3-6-9-13-15-16-18-19-21-22-23-24
Distr.: Intl.
Budget Set: Dec.
Personnel:
William R. Johnson *(Chm, Pres & CEO)*
Arthur B. Winkleblack *(CFO & Exec VP)*
Isobel Thomson *(CIO)*
Daniel G. Milich *(Chief Strategy Officer & VP)*
Robert P. Ostryniec *(Chief Supply Chain Officer)*
Christopher Stockwell *(Chief Procurement Officer)*
David C. Moran *(Pres/CEO-Heinz Europe & Exec VP)*
C. Scott O'Hara *(Pres/CEO-Heinz North America & Exec VP)*
Brendan Foley *(Pres-Foodservice-US)*
Theodore N. Bobby *(Gen Counsel & Exec VP)*
Christopher Warmoth *(Exec VP-Asia Pacific)*
Edward J. McMenamin *(Sr VP-Fin)*
Michael D. Milone *(Sr VP-Infant & Enterprise Risk Mgmt)*
Margaret R. Nollen *(Sr VP-IR)*
Diane B. Owen *(Sr VP-Corp Audit)*
Mitchell A. Ring *(Sr VP-Bus Dev)*
Wendy Joyce *(VP-Mktg-Ore-Ida)*
Noel Geoffroy *(Mktg Dir)*
Jeffrey Godish *(Dir-Digital Mktg & Media)*
Rebecca Serafini *(Assoc Dir-Category Dev)*
Eric Dahmer *(Sr Brand Mgr-Heinz 57 Sauce)*
Jennifer McGurrin *(Brand Mgr-Smart Ones)*
Hein Kroft *(Mgr-External Affairs)*
Stephanie Ackerman *(Sr Coord)*

Brands & Products:

Abbott Mead Vickers BBDO
151 Marylebone Rd
London, NW1 5QE, United Kingdom
Tel.: (44) 20 7616 3500
Fax: (44) 207 616 3600
(Baby Food)

Brunner
11 Stanwix St 5th Fl
Pittsburgh, PA 15222-1312
Tel.: (412) 995-9500
Fax: (412) 995-9501
Ketchup Creativity Contest

Cramer-Krasselt
225 N Michigan Ave
Chicago, IL 60601-7601
Tel.: (312) 616-9600
Fax: (312) 616-3839
(Ore-Ida)

Cramer-Krasselt Public Relations
225 N Michigan Ave
Chicago, IL 60601-7601
Tel.: (312) 616-9600

EHS 4D
Phoenix Way
Cirencester, Glos GL7 1RY, United Kingdom
Tel.: (44) 1285 644744
Fax: (44) 1285 654952
(Baby Food)

Ferrara & Company
29 Airpark Rd
Princeton, NJ 08540
Tel.: (609) 924-4932
Fax: (609) 945-8700

Giant Ideas
100 1st Ave Ste 200
Pittsburgh, PA 15222
Tel.: (412) 566-5756
Fax: (412) 566-1510
Toll Free: (866) 45GIANT

Haygarth Group
28-31 High Street
London, SW19 5BY, United Kingdom
Tel.: (44) 20 8971 3300
Fax: (44) 20 8947 3700
(Baby Food)

Jack Horner Communications
671 Moore Rd Ste 100
King of Prussia, PA 19406
Tel.: (610) 768-3700
Fax: (610) 768-3701
Public Relations

M&C Saatchi plc
36 Golden Sq
London, W1F 9EE, United Kingdom
Tel.: (44) 20 7543 4500
Fax: (44) 20 7543 4501

Sigma International (Poland) Ltd.
Nowogrodzka 31
00-511
Warsaw, Poland
Tel.: (48) 22 628 04 88
Fax: (48) 22 629 96 14

TBWA/Vietnam
Unit 302 Satra Dong Khoi
Ho Chi Minh City, Vietnam
Tel.: (84) 8 3824 5315
Fax: (84) 8 3824 5318

Vibrant Media Ltd.
7th Floor
London, EC1A 4HY, United Kingdom
Tel.: (44) 207 239 0120
Fax: (44) 201 239 9396

Vitruvio Leo Burnett S.A.
Duque De Sevilla 3
28002
Madrid, Spain
Tel.: (34) 91 590 5000
Fax: (34) 91 590 5050

H.J. HEINZ CO. OF CANADA LTD.

(Sub. of H.J. Heinz Company)
90 Sheppard Avenue East Suite 400
North York, ON M2N 7K5, Canada
Tel.: (416) 226-5757
Fax: (416) 226-5064
Web Site: www.heinz.com
Approx. Sls.: $600,000,000
Approx. Number Employees: 125
Year Founded: 1909
Business Description:
Convenience Meals, Pet Foods & Treats, Infant Feeding Products & Specialty Condiments Mfr
S.I.C.: 2033
N.A.I.C.S.: 311421
Import Export
Advertising Expenditures: $5,000,000
Media: 6-9-15-19-23-25
Distr.: Natl.
Personnel:
Peter Luik *(Pres & CEO)*
Brian Arbique *(VP-Food Service & Retail Sls)*
Steven Oakes *(VP-Mktg)*
Holly Dickinson *(Mgr-Comm)*
Advertising Agency:
Genesis-Vizeum
22 St Claire Ave E Ste 500
Toronto, ON M4T 2S5, Canada
Tel.: (416) 967-7282
Fax: (416) 967-1395

HOBAN FOODS, INC.

1599 E Warren Ave
Detroit, MI 48207-1035
Tel.: (313) 833-1500
Fax: (313) 833-0629
Web Site: www.hobanfoods.com
Approx. Number Employees: 25
Year Founded: 1935
Business Description:
Wholesale Food Dist
S.I.C.: 5143; 5142
N.A.I.C.S.: 424430; 424420
Import Export
Media: 8-10-16
Distr.: Natl.
Budget Set: Dec.
Personnel:
Jeff Roth *(Chm)*
Donald C. Van Tiem *(Pres)*
Pat Sweet *(Office Mgr)*
Brands & Products:
HOBAN

HONEYBAKED HAM CO. OF OHIO

11935 Mason Montgomery Rd Ste 200
Cincinnati, OH 45249-3703
Tel.: (513) 583-9700
Fax: (513) 583-4190
Web Site: www.honeybakedforyou.com
Approx. Number Employees: 400
Year Founded: 1965
Business Description:
Ham Mfr
S.I.C.: 5421; 2099
N.A.I.C.S.: 445210; 311999
Advertising Expenditures: $1,000,000
Media: 2-4-6-7-8-9-14-18-21-23-25
Distr.: Natl.
Budget Set: Oct.
Brands & Products:
HONEYBAKED HAM

HORIZON ORGANIC DAIRY, LLC

(Sub. of WhiteWave Foods Company)
12002 Airport Way
Broomfield, CO 80021-2546
Tel.: (303) 635-4000
Fax: (303) 652-1371
Web Site: www.horizonorganic.com
Sales Range: $250-299.9 Million
Approx. Number Employees: 338
Year Founded: 1991
Business Description:
Mfr. of Organic Dairy Products
S.I.C.: 5499
N.A.I.C.S.: 445299
Advertising Expenditures: $1,500,000
Media: 6-7-10-13-17-19-20-21-23
Brands & Products:
GOOD FROM THE BEGINNING
HORIZON ORGANIC
ORGANIC COW OF VERMONT
PURE FROM THE BEGINNING
RACHEL'S ORGANIC
Advertising Agencies:
Hoffman/Lewis
1725 Montgomery St
San Francisco, CA 94111-1030
Tel.: (415) 434-8500
Fax: (415) 434-8484

Key to Media (For complete agency information see *The Advertising Red Books-Agencies* edition):
1. Bus. Publs. 2. Cable T.V. 3. Catalogs & Directories. 4. Co-op Adv. 5. Consumer Mags. 6. D.M. to Bus. Estab.7. D.M. to Consumers 8. Daily Newsp. 9. Exhibits/Trade Shows 10. Foreign 11. Infomercial 12. Internet Adv.13. Multimedia 14. Network Radio 15. Network T.V. 16. Newsp. Distr. Mags. 17. Other 18. Outdoor (Posters, Transit) 19. Point of Purchase20. Premiums, Novelties 21. Product Samples 22. Special Events Mktg. 23. Spot Radio 24. Spot T.V. 25. Weekly Newsp. 26. Yellow Page Adv.

Horizon Organic Dairy, LLC — (Continued)

Ketchum
E Randolph Ste 3600
Chicago, IL 60601-5925
Tel.: (312) 228-6800
Fax: (312) 228-6868
— Megan Severs *(Acct Exec)*

Sterling Rice Group
1801 13th St Ste 400
Boulder, CO 80302
Tel.: (303) 381-6400
Fax: (303) 444-6637

HORMEL FOODS CORPORATION

1 Hormel Pl
Austin, MN 55912-3680
Tel.: (507) 437-5611
Fax: (507) 437-5129
E-mail: publicrelations@hormel.com
Web Site: www.hormelfoods.com
Approx. Sls.: $7,220,719,000
Approx. Number Employees: 19,300
Year Founded: 1891
Business Description:
Meat & Food Products Mfr & Marketer
S.I.C.: 0751; 0259; 2013; 2015; 2099; 5147
N.A.I.C.S.: 311611; 112390; 311612; 311613; 311615; 311999
Export
Advertising Expenditures: $112,300,000
Media: 2-3-6-9-13-14-15-16-18-19-23-24
Distr.: Natl.
Budget Set: Aug.
Personnel:
Jeffrey M. Ettinger *(Chm, Pres & CEO)*
Jody H. Feragen *(CFO & Exec VP)*
Larry L. Vorpahl *(Pres-Consumer Products Sls & Grp VP)*
Lori J. Marco *(Gen Counsel & VP-External Affairs)*
James W. Cavanaugh *(Gen Counsel)*
Roland G. Gentzler *(Treas & VP-Fin)*
Ronald W. Fielding *(Exec VP-Corp Strategy)*
Daniel A. Hartzog *(Sr VP-Consumer Products Sls & VP)*
Kurt F. Mueller *(Sr VP-Consumer Products Sls & VP)*
Douglas R. Reetz *(Sr VP-Consumer Products Sls & VP)*
William F. Snyder *(Sr VP-Supply Chain)*
Richard A. Bross *(Grp VP)*
Robert A. Tegt *(Grp VP)*
Michael D. Tolbert *(Grp VP-Specialty Foods)*
Swen Neufeldt *(VP-Hormel Foods Intl & Dir-Bus Dev-Asia)*
D. Scott Aakre *(VP-Mktg-Grocery Products)*
Deanna T. Brady *(VP-Sls-Food Svc)*
Julie H. Craven *(VP-Corp Comm)*
David P. Juhlke *(VP-HR)*
Donald H. Kremin *(VP-Sls-Consumer Products)*
Russell C. Potter *(VP-Grocery Products Production)*
Jim Schroeder *(VP-Engrg)*
Fred D. Halvin *(Dir-Corp Dev)*
Kevin C. Jones *(Dir-IR)*
Thomas Raymond *(Dir-Environment Sustainability)*
Steven J. Venenga *(Dir-Mktg-Meat Products)*
Mark Mayer *(Grp Product Mgr-Ethnic Foods)*
Scott Weisenbeck *(Grp Product Mgr-Lunch & Snack Grp)*
Eric Steinbach *(Sr Product Mgr-Breakfast Meats)*
Jeffrey A. Grev *(Mgr-Merger & Acq)*
Ryan Vossler *(Mgr-Customer Bus-Club Team)*
Robert C. Wahlert *(Mgr-Merger & Acq)*
Brands & Products:
ALWAYS TENDER
BREAD READY
BUFALO
CAFE H
CALIFORNIA NATURAL
CARAPELLI
CHI-CHI'S
COMPLEATS
CREATE SOMETHING GOOD
CURE 81
DI LUSSO
DIAMOND CRYSTAL
DINTY MOORE
DONA MARIA
EL TORITO
FORMER JOHN
FRESH PANTRY
GRAND CHAMPION
GRANDE GOURMET
HERB-OX
HERDEZ
HIBACHI GRILL
HORMEL
HOUSE OF TSANG
JENNIE-O TURKEY STORE
KIDS KITCHEN
LITTLE SIZZLERS
LLOYD'S
MAGNIFOODS
MANNY'S
MARRAKESH EXPRESS
NATURAL CHOICE
NOT-SO-SLOPPY-JOE
OLD SMOKEHOUSE
PATAK'S
PELOPONNESE
PREP CHEF
SPAM
STAGG
TEZZATA
VALLEY FRESH
WRANGLERS
Advertising Agencies:
BBDO Minneapolis
150 S 5th St Ste 3500
Minneapolis, MN 55402-4200
Tel.: (612) 338-8401
Fax: (612) 656-0602
Old Smokehouse Steak Sauce Plus, Low-Salt Spam Luncheon Meat, Not So Sloppy Joe Sloppy Joe Sauce, Cure 81 Ham, Frank 'N Stuff, Little Sizzlers, Chicken by George, Hormel Chili, Hormel Chunk Meats, Bacon Bits, TopShelf, Mary Kitchen Beef Hash, Hormel Microwave Entrees, Spam Oven Roasted Turkey
Chi-Chi's

Burson-Marsteller
(Part of Young & Rubicam Brands, a Sub. of WPP Group plc)
230 Park Ave S
New York, NY 10003-1566
Tel.: (212) 614-4000
Fax: (212) 598-5407
Herdez
— Tracy Evans *(Acct Exec)*
— Murray Kalis *(Acct Exec)*

Marsteller Interactive
230 Park Ave S
New York, NY 10003-1502
Tel.: (212) 614-4824
Fax: (212) 59-8 5411
Internet Design Business

Riester
802 N 3rd Ave
Phoenix, AZ 85003
Tel.: (602) 462-2200
Fax: (602) 307-5811

HORMEL FOODS CORPORATION - FOODSERVICE DIVISION

(Div. of Hormel Foods Corporation)
1 Hormel Pl
Austin, MN 55912-3673
Tel.: (507) 437-5611
Fax: (507) 437-5838
Toll Free: (800) 723-8000
Web Site: www.hormelfoods.com
Sales Range: $150-199.9 Million
Approx. Number Employees: 400
Business Description:
Food for Restaurants & Other Foodservice Operations
S.I.C.: 5812; 5963
N.A.I.C.S.: 722310; 722330
Media: 2-4-7-10-20-21-22
Personnel:
Thomas R. Day *(Grp VP)*
Julie H. Craven *(VP-Corp Comm)*
Dennis B. Goettsch *(VP-Mktg)*
Jerry Whithaus *(Dir-Mktg Svcs)*
Advertising Agency:
J.T. Mega Marketing Communications
4020 Minnetonka Blvd
Minneapolis, MN 55416-4100
Tel.: (952) 929-1370
Fax: (952) 929-5417
Toll Free: (800) 923-6342

HOUSE OF RAEFORD FARMS, INC.

520 E Central Ave
Raeford, NC 28376-3020
Mailing Address:
PO Box 100
Raeford, NC 28376-3020
Tel.: (910) 875-5161
Fax: (910) 875-8300
Toll Free: (800) 8TURKEY
Web Site: www.houseofraeford.com
Approx. Number Employees: 2,000
Year Founded: 1962
Business Description:
Processor of Turkey & Chicken Products
S.I.C.: 2015; 0751
N.A.I.C.S.: 311615; 311611
Export
Media: 2-3-4-6-7-10-11-13-17-18-19-21
Distr.: Intl.; Natl.
Budget Set: Dec.
Personnel:
E. Marvin Johnson *(Chm)*
Don Taber *(Pres & COO)*
Robert Johnson *(CEO)*
Brenda Branch *(VP-Mktg & Sls)*
Harold Brock *(Mgr-Commodity & Export)*
Brands & Products:
HOUSE OF RAEFORD
LAKEWOOD PLANTATION
THE ONE WITH REAL TASTE

HP HOOD LLC

(Sub. of Catamount Dairy Holdings L.P.)
6 Kimball Ln
Lynnfield, MA 01940
Tel.: (617) 887-3000
Fax: (617) 887-8484
Toll Free: (800) 343-6592
Web Site: www.hphood.com
Sales Range: $1-4.9 Billion
Approx. Number Employees: 4,500
Year Founded: 1846
Business Description:
Producer & Marketer of Milk, Other Dairy Products & Citrus & Specialty Drinks
S.I.C.: 2026; 2024
N.A.I.C.S.: 311511; 311520
Import Export
Media: 13-18-24
Personnel:
John A. Kaneb *(Chm, Pres & CEO)*
Gary R. Kaneb *(CFO)*
Paul C. Nightingale *(Gen Counsel & Sr VP)*
Jeffrey J. Kaneb *(Exec VP)*
James F. Walsh *(Exec VP-Sls)*
H. Scott Blake *(Sr VP-Ops)*
Mike J. Suever *(Sr VP-R & D/Engrg/Procurement)*
Bruce W. Bacon *(VP-HR)*
Lynne M. Bohan *(VP-Pub Rel & Govt Affairs)*
Chris Ross *(VP-Mktg)*
Brands & Products:
HOOD

HULMAN & COMPANY

900 Wabash Ave
Terre Haute, IN 47807-3208
Mailing Address:
PO Box 150
Terre Haute, IN 47808-0150
Tel.: (812) 232-9446
Fax: (812) 478-7181
Web Site: www.clabbergirl.com
Approx. Number Employees: 750
Year Founded: 1850
Business Description:
Holding Company; Baking Powder, Corn Starch & Other Food Products Mfr & Distr; Motor Racetrack & Racing League Owner & Operator
S.I.C.: 6719; 2041; 2046; 2099; 7948; 7999
N.A.I.C.S.: 551112; 311211; 311221; 311999; 711212; 711219
Media: 2-6-9-20-21-23
Distr.: Natl.
Budget Set: Nov.
Personnel:
Mary Hulman George *(Chm)*
William Curtis Brighton *(Pres & CEO)*
Gary Morris *(COO-Clabber Girl)*
Jeffrey G. Belskus *(Pres/CEO-Indianapolis Motor Speedway Corp)*
Brands & Products:
RUMFORD NATURALS

Key to Media (For complete agency information see *The Advertising Red Books-Agencies* edition):
1. Bus. Publs. 2. Cable T.V. 3. Catalogs & Directories. 4. Co-op Adv. 5. Consumer Mags. 6. D.M. to Bus. Estab.7. D.M. to Consumers
8. Daily Newsp. 9. Exhibits/Trade Shows 10. Foreign 11. Infomercial 12. Internet Adv.13. Multimedia 14. Network Radio
15. Network T.V. 16. Newsp. Distr. Mags. 17. Other 18. Outdoor (Posters, Transit) 19. Point of Purchase20. Premiums, Novelties
21. Product Samples 22. Special Events Mktg. 23. Spot Radio 24. Spot T.V. 25. Weekly Newsp. 26. Yellow Page Adv.

Advertising Agency:
Dan Pipkin Advertising Agency, Inc.
429 N Walnut St
Danville, IL 61832
Tel.: (217) 446-1021
Fax: (217) 446-3062

HV FOOD PRODUCTS COMPANY

(Sub. of The Clorox Company)
1221 Broadway
Oakland, CA 94612-1837
Tel.: (510) 271-7000
Fax: (510) 832-1463
Web Site: www.clorox.com
Sales Range: $10-24.9 Million
Approx. Number Employees: 70
Business Description:
Salad Dressing Mixes Mfr
S.I.C.: 8741
N.A.I.C.S.: 561110
Media: 6-13-15-24
Brands & Products:
HIDDEN VALLEY
Advertising Agency:
DDB San Francisco
555 Market St 5th Fl
San Francisco, CA 94105
Tel.: (415) 732-3600
Fax: (415) 732-3636

ICELANDIC USA, INC.

(Sub. of Icelandic Group PLC)
190 Enterprise Dr
Newport News, VA 23603
Tel.: (757) 820-4000
Fax: (757) 888-6250
Web Site: www.icelandic.com
Approx. Number Employees: 600
Year Founded: 1947
Business Description:
Frozen Seafood Producer
S.I.C.: 2092; 5142
N.A.I.C.S.: 311712; 424420
Media: 7-10-16-19-20-21
Distr.: Natl.
Budget Set: Nov.
Personnel:
Evar Agnarsson *(Pres & CEO)*
Daniel Murphy *(Exec VP)*
Tom Sherman *(VP-Consumer Sls & Mktg)*
Michael Thome *(VP-Fin & Admin)*
Mary Arbegast *(Dir-Customer Svc)*
Brian Brizendine *(Dir-IT)*
Roger Riggs *(Dir-Commodity Sls)*
Debra Zartman *(Dir-HR)*
Vickie Dunn *(Mgr-Credit)*
Lisa Taylor *(Mgr-Corp Plng & Analysis)*
Brands & Products:
ICELANDIC
SEASTAR

ICICLE SEAFOODS, INC.

(Holding of Paine & Partners, LLC)
4019 21st Ave W
Seattle, WA 98199-1251
Mailing Address:
PO Box 79003
Seattle, WA 98119-7903
Tel.: (206) 282-0988
Fax: (206) 282-7222
E-mail: customerservice@icicleseafoods.com
Web Site: www.icicleseafoods.com
Sales Range: $300-349.9 Million
Approx. Number Employees: 2,000
Year Founded: 1965
Business Description:
Seafood Harvesting & Processing Services
S.I.C.: 2092; 2091
N.A.I.C.S.: 311712; 311711
Export
Media: 1-2-4-5-6-7-9-10-17-19-20-21-25
Distr.: Natl.
Personnel:
Dennis Guhlke *(CEO)*
John Boynton *(VP-Sls)*
Mark S. Sandvik *(VP-Sls)*
Rick Speed *(VP-Sls)*
Brands & Products:
ICICLE
SHIP AHOY

IDAHO FRESH-PAK INC.

529 N 3500 E
Lewisville, ID 83431-5035
Mailing Address:
PO Box 130
Lewisville, ID 83431-0130
Tel.: (208) 754-4686
Fax: (208) 754-0094
Toll Free: (800) 635-6100
E-mail: idahoan@idahoan.com
Web Site: www.idahoan.com
E-Mail For Key Personnel:
Marketing Director: ifp.drew@srv.net
Sales Director: ifp.todd@srv.net
Approx. Number Employees: 500
Year Founded: 1960
Business Description:
Mfr. of Dehydrated Fruits, Vegetables & Soups
S.I.C.: 2034; 2099
N.A.I.C.S.: 311423; 311999
Import Export
Media: 2-4-7-8-10-11-19-20-21-23-24-25
Distr.: Intl.; Natl.
Personnel:
Gordan Lewis *(Pres)*
Kerry Buck *(CFO)*
Drew Facer *(Exec VP-Retail)*
Dan Fitzgerald *(Dir-Mktg)*
Brands & Products:
IDAHOAN
Advertising Agencies:
Hunter Public Relations
41 Madison Ave Fl 5
New York, NY 10010-2202
Tel.: (212) 679-6600
Fax: (212) 679-6607

Riester
802 N 3rd Ave
Phoenix, AZ 85003
Tel.: (602) 462-2200
Fax: (602) 307-5811

IDAHO SUPREME POTATOES, INC.

614 E 800 N
Firth, ID 83236-0246
Mailing Address:
PO Box 246
Firth, ID 83236-0246
Tel.: (208) 346-6841
Fax: (208) 346-4104
E-mail: spud@idahosupreme.com
Web Site: www.idahosupreme.com
Approx. Number Employees: 350
Year Founded: 1966
Business Description:
Potato Processing Services
S.I.C.: 2034; 5148
N.A.I.C.S.: 311423; 424480
Export
Media: 7-10-17
Distr.: Natl.
Budget Set: July
Personnel:
Brad Chapman *(Mgr-Adv)*
Brands & Products:
GREAT POTATO PRODUCTS ANY WAY YOU SLICE IT!
IDAHO
IDAHO SUPREME
IDAHO SUPREME POTATO FLAKES
MASHED RED POTATOES
MOM'S CHOICE
PASTATO
STUFFED TATER

IMPERIAL SUGAR COMPANY

One Imperial Sq 8016 Highway 90A
Sugar Land, TX 77478-2961
Mailing Address:
PO Box 9
Sugar Land, TX 77487-0009
Tel.: (281) 491-9181
Fax: (281) 490-9879
Toll Free: (800) 727-8427
E-mail: isccustomerservice@imperialsugar.com
Web Site:
www.imperialsugarcompany.com
Approx. Sls.: $908,033,000
Approx. Number Employees: 694
Year Founded: 1843
Business Description:
Pure Cane Sugar Refiner, Packager & Distr
S.I.C.: 2062; 2061
N.A.I.C.S.: 311312; 311311
Export
Media: 5-6-7-8-9-11-13-17
Distr.: Reg.
Budget Set: Oct.
Personnel:
James J. Gaffney *(Chm)*
John C. Sheptor *(Pres & CEO)*
Hal P. Mechler *(CFO & Sr VP)*
Ronald L. Allen *(Corp Safety Officer)*
Louis T. Bolognini *(Gen Counsel, Sec & Sr VP)*
Patrick D. Henneberry *(Sr VP-Commodities & Sls)*
Ralph D. Clements *(VP-Mfg & Engrg)*
Brian T. Harrison *(VP-Tech)*
George Muller *(VP-Sls Plng, Supply Chain & IT)*
Brands & Products:
DIXIE CRYSTALS
GOLD 'N NATURAL
HOLLY
IMPERIAL
IMPERIAL SUGAR
REDI-MEASURE
SAVANNAH GOLD
SPRECKELS

INSTITUTION FOOD HOUSE, INC.

(Sub. of Alex Lee, Inc.)
543 12th St Dr NW
Hickory, NC 28603
Mailing Address:
PO Box 2947
Hickory, NC 28603
Tel.: (828) 725-4500
Fax: (828) 725-4553
E-mail: ifhinfo@ifh.com
Web Site: www.ifh.com
Sales Range: $250-299.9 Million
Approx. Number Employees: 511
Year Founded: 1966
Business Description:
Foodservice Distr
S.I.C.: 5141; 5142
N.A.I.C.S.: 424410; 424420
Media: 2-7
Personnel:
Brad Holma *(Dir-Purchasing & Mktg)*

INTERNATIONAL FIBER CORP.

(Holding of Swander Pace Capital, LLC)
50 Bridge St
North Tonawanda, NY 14120-6842
Tel.: (716) 693-4040
Fax: (716) 693-3528
Toll Free: (888) 698-1936
E-mail: info@ifcfiber.com
Web Site: www.ifcfiber.com
Approx. Number Employees: 250
Year Founded: 1926
Business Description:
Fiber Processor for Food, Cheese, Pharmaceutical, Pet Food & Industrial Applications
S.I.C.: 2823; 2299
N.A.I.C.S.: 325221; 314999
Import Export
Media: 2-4-7-10-11-13
Distr.: Intl.; Natl.
Personnel:
Dan Muth *(CEO)*
Jit Ang *(Exec VP-R&D)*
Mike Bailey *(Exec VP-Food Sls)*
Brian Finn *(Exec VP-Ops)*
Steve Godin *(Exec VP-Indus Sls)*
James Gramkee *(Accountant)*
Brands & Products:
ALPHA-CEL
FIBREX
FLOAM
JUSTFIBER
KEYCEL
NUTRAFIBER
QUALFLO
SOLKA-FLOC

J&J SNACK FOODS CORPORATION

6000 Central Hwy
Pennsauken, NJ 08109-4607
Tel.: (856) 665-9533
Fax: (856) 665-6718
Toll Free: (800) 486-9533, ext. 6130
E-mail: webmaster@jjsnack.com
Web Site: www.jjsnack.com
Approx. Sls.: $696,703,000
Approx. Number Employees: 2,700
Year Founded: 1971
Business Description:
Snack Foods, Frozen Desserts & Beverages Mfr, Marketer & Distr
S.I.C.: 2024; 2051; 2052; 2053
N.A.I.C.S.: 311520; 311812; 311813; 311821
Export
Advertising Expenditures: $2,751,000
Media: 2-3-4-6-9-10-15-18-19-20-23-24
Distr.: Natl.
Budget Set: Aug.

Key to Media (For complete agency information see *The Advertising Red Books-Agencies* edition):
1. Bus. Publs. 2. Cable T.V. 3. Catalogs & Directories. 4. Co-op Adv. 5. Consumer Mags. 6. D.M. to Bus. Estab.7. D.M. to Consumers
8. Daily Newsp. 9. Exhibits/Trade Shows 10. Foreign 11. Infomercial 12. Internet Adv.13. Multimedia 14. Network Radio
15. Network T.V. 16. Newsp. Distr. Mags. 17. Other 18. Outdoor (Posters, Transit) 19. Point of Purchase20. Premiums, Novelties
21. Product Samples 22. Special Events Mktg. 23. Spot Radio 24. Spot T.V. 25. Weekly Newsp. 26. Yellow Page Adv.

J&J Snack Foods Corporation — (Continued)

Personnel:
Gerald B. Shreiber *(Founder, Chm, Pres & CEO)*
Dennis G. Moore *(CFO, Treas, Sec & Sr VP)*
Robert M. Radano *(COO & Sr VP-Sls)*
Tom Hunter *(VP & Gen Mgr-Uptown Bakeries)*
Harry Fronjian *(VP-HR)*
John Griffith *(VP-IT)*
Robert J. Pape *(VP-Sls)*
Steven J. Taylor *(VP-Sls)*
Charles Tommolino *(VP-Sls-Food Svcs)*
T.J. Couzens *(Gen Mgr)*
Stacey Inglis-Baron *(Dir-Mktg)*
Brands & Products:
ARCTIC BLAST
BAKERS BEST
BAVARIAN
BENEFIT
CAMDEN CREEK
CHILL
COUNTRY HOME BAKERS
DADDY RAY'S
DOGSTERS
DUTCH TWIST
FRUIT-A-FREEZE
THE FUNNEL CAKE FACTORY
FUNNEL CAKE FRIES
GOURMET TWISTS
ICEE
ICEEBITS
LUIGI'S
LUIGI'S SWIRL
MARY B'S
MRS. GOODCOOKIE
POPPERS
PRETZEL FILLERS
PRETZELFILS
READI-BAKE
SHAPE UPS
SLUSH PUPPIE
SOFTSTIX
SUPERPRETZEL
TIO PEPE'S
UPTOWN
WHOLE FRUIT
Advertising Agency:
Brownstein Group
215 S Broad St 9th Fl
Philadelphia, PA 19107-5325
Tel.: (215) 735-3470
Fax: (215) 735-6298
SuperPretzel

JBS
(Formerly Swift & Company, E.A. Miller Inc.)
(Sub. of JBS USA Holding, Inc.)
410 N 200 W
Hyrum, UT 84319-1024
Tel.: (435) 245-6456
Fax: (435) 245-6634
Fax: (435) 245-5384
Web Site: www.jbsswift.com
Approx. Number Employees: 1,100
Year Founded: 1936
Business Description:
Meat Processing
S.I.C.: 5147
N.A.I.C.S.: 311612
Export
Media: 9-13-18-19
Distr.: Natl.
Budget Set: Aug.
Personnel:
Paul Barnard *(VP-Personnel)*

JBS USA HOLDING, INC.
(Sub. of JBS S.A.)
1770 Promontory Cir
Greeley, CO 80634
Tel.: (970) 506-8000
Web Site: www.jbsswift.com
Approx. Sls.: $2,478,734,000
Approx. Number Employees: 31,900
Business Description:
Holding Company; Beef Processing & Export
S.I.C.: 2013; 5147; 6719
N.A.I.C.S.: 311613; 424470; 551112
Advertising Expenditures: $5,600,000
Media: 5-8-16-19
Personnel:
Andre Nogueira de Souza *(CFO)*
William G. Trupkiewicz *(Chief Acctg Officer & Sec)*
Bill Rupp *(Pres-Beef Div)*
Robert Daubenspeck *(Head-HR)*

THE JEL SERT COMPANY
Route 59 and Conde St
West Chicago, IL 60185-0261
Tel.: (630) 231-7590
Fax: (630) 231-0093
Toll Free: (800) 323-2592
Web Site: www.jelsert.com
Approx. Number Employees: 420
Year Founded: 1926
Business Description:
Gelatin, Puddings & Ice Pops Mfr & Distr
S.I.C.: 2087; 2024
N.A.I.C.S.: 311930; 311520
Export
Advertising Expenditures: $2,000,000
Media: 2-5-6-11-13-14-15-19-20-21
Distr.: Intl.; Natl.
Budget Set: Oct.
Personnel:
Charles T. Wegner *(Chm & CEO)*
Kenneth Wegner *(Pres)*
Tony Damma *(CFO)*
Bob Clements *(VP-Sls & Mktg)*
Susie Frausto *(Sr Dir-Mktg)*
Mike Gomolski *(Mgr-Mktg)*
Steve Modaff *(Mgr-Mktg)*
Brands & Products:
COMIC COOLERS
FLA-VOR-ICE
FLAVOR-AID
FUDGE SHOPPE
MONDO FRUIT SQUEEZERS
MY-T-FINE
OTTER POPS
POOCH POPS
POP-ICE
ROYAL
WYLER'S

JENNIE-O TURKEY STORE, INC.
(Sub. of Hormel Foods Corporation)
2505 SW Willmar Ave
Willmar, MN 56201
Tel.: (320) 235-2622
Fax: (320) 231-7100
Toll Free: (800) 621-3505
Web Site: www.jennie-o.com
Sales Range: $900-999.9 Million
Approx. Number Employees: 7,000
Business Description:
Turkey Processor
S.I.C.: 2015; 0253
N.A.I.C.S.: 311615; 112330
Advertising Expenditures: $550,000
Media: 6-10-14-15-16-17-19-21-23-24
Distr.: Intl.; Natl.
Budget Set: Nov.
Personnel:
Robert A. Tegt *(Pres)*
John Court *(CFO & VP-)*
Glenn Leitch *(Sr VP-Commodity & Supply Chain)*
Steve Lykken *(Sr VP-Retail)*
Cris Eide *(Dir-Bus Dev)*
Sarah Anderson *(Mgr-Product Mktg)*
Brands & Products:
GRAND CHAMPION

THE J.M. SMUCKER COMPANY
1 Strawberry Lane
Orrville, OH 44667-0280
Mailing Address:
PO Box 197
Orrville, OH 44667
Tel.: (330) 682-3000
Tel.: (330) 684-1500
Fax: (330) 684-6410
Toll Free: (888) 550-9555
E-mail: investor.relations@jmsmucker.com
Web Site: www.smuckers.com
Approx. Sls.: $4,825,743,000
Approx. Number Employees: 4,500
Year Founded: 1897
Business Description:
Mfr & Marketer of Food Products
S.I.C.: 2033; 2099
N.A.I.C.S.: 311421; 311999
Import Export
Advertising Expenditures: $115,066,000
Media: 1-3-6-9-10-13-14-15-19-20-22-23-24
Distr.: Direct to Consumer; Intl.; Natl.
Personnel:
Timothy P. Smucker *(Chm & Co-CEO)*
Vincent C. Byrd *(Pres & COO)*
Richard K. Smucker *(Co-CEO)*
Mark R. Belgya *(CFO & Sr VP)*
Andrew G. Platt *(CIO & VP-Info Svcs)*
Steven Oakland *(Pres-US Retail-Smuckers Jif & Hungry Jack)*
Mark T. Smucker *(Pres-Retail Coffee-United States)*
Paul Smucker Wagstaff *(Pres-Oils & Baking-US Retail)*
Jeannette L. Knudsen *(Gen Counsel, Corp Sec & VP)*
Dennis J. Armstrong *(Sr VP-Logistics & Ops Support)*
Barry C. Dunaway *(Sr VP-Corp & Org Dev)*
Julia L. Sabin *(VP & Gen Mgr-Smucker Quality Beverages, Inc)*
John F. Mayer *(VP-Sls & Grocery Market)*
Brands & Products:

Alcone Marketing Group
(Division of Omnicom Group, Inc.)
4 Studebaker
Irvine, CA 92618-2012
Tel.: (949) 770-4400
Fax: (949) 770-2957

Carat
150 E 42nd St
New York, NY 10017
Tel.: (212) 689-6800
Fax: (212) 689-6005
Digital Media Planning & Buying
Traditional Media Planning & Buying

Flair Communications Agency, Inc.
214 W Erie St
Chicago, IL 60654
Tel.: (312) 943-5959
Toll Free: (800) 621-8317

Grey New York
777 3rd Ave
New York, NY 10017-1401
Tel.: (212) 546-2000
Fax: (212) 546-1495

Possible Worldwide
302 W Third St Ste 900
Cincinnati, OH 45202
Tel.: (513) 381-1380
Fax: (513) 381-0248

Saatchi & Saatchi
(Sub. of Publicis Groupe S.A.)
(Worldwide Headquarters)
375 Hudson St
New York, NY 10014-3660
Tel.: (212) 463-2000
Fax: (212) 463-9856

JOHANNA FOODS INC.
Johanna Farms Rd
Flemington, NJ 08822
Tel.: (908) 788-2200
Fax: (908) 788-2737
Toll Free: (800) 727-6700
E-mail: info@johannafoods.com
Web Site: www.johannafoods.com
Sales Range: $50-74.9 Million
Approx. Number Employees: 500
Business Description:
Food Mfr & Distr
S.I.C.: 2033; 2026
N.A.I.C.S.: 311421; 311511
Import Export
Media: 7-8-11-13-16-19-22-25
Distr.: Natl.
Budget Set: Dec.
Personnel:
Robert A. Facchina *(Pres & CEO)*
Don Griffin *(VP-HR)*
Brands & Products:
JOHANNA FOODS INC.
LA YOGURT
LIVE STRONGER. LIVE LONGER.
SABOR LATINO
SABOR LATINO NECTARS
SSIPS
TREE RIPE

THE JOHN C. MEIER GRAPE JUICE CO.
(Sub. of Meier's Wine Cellars, Inc.)
6955 Plainfield Rd
Cincinnati, OH 45236-3733
Tel.: (513) 891-2900
Fax: (513) 891-6370
Web Site: www.meierswinecellars.com
Approx. Number Employees: 30
Year Founded: 1934
Business Description:
Sparkling & Still Grape Juice Mfr
S.I.C.: 2033; 2084

Key to Media (For complete agency information see *The Advertising Red Books-Agencies* edition):
1. Bus. Publs. 2. Cable T.V. 3. Catalogs & Directories. 4. Co-op Adv. 5. Consumer Mags. 6. D.M. to Bus. Estab.7. D.M. to Consumers 8. Daily Newsp. 9. Exhibits/Trade Shows 10. Foreign 11. Infomercial 12. Internet Adv.13. Multimedia 14. Network Radio 15. Network T.V. 16. Newsp. Distr. Mags. 17. Other 18. Outdoor (Posters, Transit) 19. Point of Purchase20. Premiums, Novelties 21. Product Samples 22. Special Events Mktg. 23. Spot Radio 24. Spot T.V. 25. Weekly Newsp. 26. Yellow Page Adv.

N.A.I.C.S.: 311421; 312130
Advertising Expenditures: $600,000
Media: 9-10-23-25
Distr.: Natl.
Budget Set: Quarterly
Personnel:
Lynn Lubin *(Dir-Mktg)*
Brands & Products:
BRECKENRIDGE FARMS
MEIERS

JOHN COPE'S FOOD PRODUCTS, INC.
(Sub. of Farm Stand Foods)
156 W Harrisburg Ave
Rheems, PA 17570
Mailing Address:
759 Long Rd
Manheim, PA 17545-8613
Tel.: (717) 367-5142
Fax: (717) 367-7317
Toll Free: (800) 745-8211
E-mail: copes@copefoods.com
Web Site: www.copefoods.com
E-Mail For Key Personnel:
President: larry@copefoods.com
Sales Range: $10-24.9 Million
Approx. Number Employees: 130
Year Founded: 1900
Business Description:
Mfr Dried & Frozen Vegetables & Fruits
S.I.C.: 2037; 2034
N.A.I.C.S.: 311411; 311423
Import Export
Media: 1-2-8-9-10-13-18-19-21-22-23-26
Distr.: Reg.
Budget Set: Jan.
Personnel:
Akbar Boutorabi *(Mgr-Pkgng)*
Dar Soltani *(Mgr-Pur)*
Brands & Products:
DUTCH DELIGHT
JOHN COPE'S
JOHN COPE'S ORGANIC

JOHN MORRELL & CO.
(Sub. of Smithfield Foods, Inc.)
805 E Kemper Rd
Cincinnati, OH 45246
Tel.: (513) 346-3540
Fax: (513) 346-3557
E-mail: info@johnmorrell.com
Web Site: www.johnmorrell.com
Sales Range: $1-4.9 Billion
Approx. Number Employees: 6,700
Year Founded: 1827
Business Description:
Processed Meats & Fresh Pork Distributor & Marketer
S.I.C.: 0751
N.A.I.C.S.: 311611
Export
Advertising Expenditures: $914,000
Media: 1-4-5-6-9-10-19-21-23-24
Distr.: Natl.
Budget Set: May
Personnel:
Joseph B. Sebring *(Pres)*
Gary Junso *(VP-HR)*
Brands & Products:
DINNER BELL
E-Z CUT
GOOSE BRAND
HUNTER
JOHN MORRELL
JOHN MORRELL TENDER N JUICY
KRETSCHMAR
PEYTON'S
RATH BLACK HAWK
RODEO
TOBIN'S FIRST PRIZE
TOBIN'S MOTHER

JOHNSONVILLE SAUSAGE, LLC
PO Box 906
Sheboygan Falls, WI 53085
Tel.: (920) 453-6900
Fax: (920) 453-2203
Toll Free: (800) 556-BRAT
Toll Free: (800) 733-6900
Web Site: www.johnsonville.com
Approx. Number Employees: 1,000
Year Founded: 1945
Business Description:
Sausage Mfr
S.I.C.: 5147
N.A.I.C.S.: 311612
Media: 2-3-4-5-7-10-13-15-17-18-19-22-23-25-26
Distr.: Reg.
Budget Set: Jan.
Personnel:
Ralph C. Stayer *(Co-Owner, Chm & CEO)*
Launa Stayer Maloney *(Co-Owner)*
Bill Morgan *(Pres)*
Jim Mueller *(Dir-Mktg)*
Bruce Johnson *(Sr Brand Mgr)*
Cory Bouck *(Mgr-OD&L)*
Brands & Products:
BEDDAR WITH CHEDDAR
BEEF BRATS
BEEF SMOKIES
BEER BRATS
BEER 'N BRATWURST
BEER 'N CHEDDAR
DELI BITES
HOT N' SPICY
IRISH O'GARLIC
JOHNSONVILLE
LITTLE SMOKIES
NEW ORLEANS
OKTOBERFEST
ORIGINAL BRATWURST
STADIUM BRATS
VERMONT MAPLE SYRUP
Advertising Agencies:
Campbell Mithun, Inc.
Campbell Mithun Tower 222 S 9th St
Minneapolis, MN 55402-3389
Tel.: (612) 347-1000
Fax: (612) 347-1515

Cramer-Krasselt
225 N Michigan Ave
Chicago, IL 60601-7601
Tel.: (312) 616-9600
Fax: (312) 616-3839

Cramer-Krasselt
246 E Chicago St
Milwaukee, WI 53202
Tel.: (414) 227-3500
Fax: (414) 276-8710
(Creative)

JONES DAIRY FARM
800 Jones Ave
Fort Atkinson, WI 53538
Tel.: (920) 563-2431
Fax: (920) 563-6801
Toll Free: (800) 563-1004
Web Site: www.jonesdairyfarm.com
Approx. Number Employees: 365
Year Founded: 1889
Business Description:
Meat Processor
S.I.C.: 5147
N.A.I.C.S.: 424470
Export
Advertising Expenditures: $3,000,000
Media: 5-6-9-10-13-19-23-24
Distr.: Intl.; Natl.
Budget Set: Apr.
Personnel:
Phillip H. Jones *(Pres)*
Rick Lowry *(Sr VP-Sls & Mktg)*
Brands & Products:
COUNTRY-CARVED
GOLDEN BROWN
JONES

J.R. SIMPLOT COMPANY
999 Main St Ste 1300
Boise, ID 83702-9000
Mailing Address:
PO Box 27
Boise, ID 83707-0027
Tel.: (208) 336-2110
Fax: (208) 389-7515
Telex: 368432
E-mail: jrs_info@simplot.com
Web Site: www.simplot.com
Sales Range: $1-4.9 Billion
Approx. Number Employees: 10,100
Year Founded: 1955
Business Description:
Frozen Potato & Vegetable Products
S.I.C.: 2037
N.A.I.C.S.: 311411
Export
Personnel:
Scott R. Simplot *(Chm)*
Bill Whitacre *(Pres-Agribusiness Grp)*
Terry Uhling *(Gen Counsel, Sec & Sr VP)*
Brands & Products:
APEX
AVAIL
BRINGING EARTH'S RESOURCES TO LIFE
CONQUEST
EXTREME SUPREME
FREEZERFRIGE
GRAND VALLEY
IDAHOAN
INFINITY
MARINER
NATURALCRISP
NUTRISPHERE-N
OLD FASHIONED WAY
PANCAKE PODS
PAYETTE FARMS
PLATE-PERFECT
QUICKMASH
ROASTWORKS
SEASONEDCRISP
SELECT-RECIPE
SIMPLOT
SIMPLOT CLASSIC
SPUDSTERS
SUN CROP
TATER PALS
TOP CAT
TRUE RECIPE
UPSIDES
WE'RE ON YOUR SIDE
Advertising Agency:
Scott, Inc. of Milwaukee
(dba Scott Advertising)
1031 N Astor St
Milwaukee, WI 53202-3324
Tel.: (414) 276-1080
Fax: (414) 276-3327

J.R. SIMPLOT COMPANY FOOD GROUP
(Group of J.R. Simplot Company)
6360 S Federal Way
Boise, ID 83716
Mailing Address:
PO Box 9386
Boise, ID 83707
Tel.: (208) 384-8000
Fax: (208) 384-8022
Toll Free: (800) 572-7783
Web Site: www.simplotfoods.com
Approx. Number Employees: 200
Business Description:
Mfr. & Distr of Frozen Potatoes, Fruits & Vegetables
S.I.C.: 2037; 2869
N.A.I.C.S.: 311411; 325199
Advertising Expenditures: $200,000
Media: 2-4-10-11
Distr.: Intl.
Personnel:
Kevin Storms *(Sr VP-Intl Bus Dev)*
Brands & Products:
CORNADOS
CULINARY SELECT
INFINITY
ROASTWORKS
SIMPLOT CLASSICS
SIMPLOT FRENCH FRIES
SPUDSTERS
WE'RE ON YOUR SIDE

KAGOME, INC.
(Sub. of Kagome Co., Ltd.)
333 Johnston Rd
Los Banos, CA 93635-9768
Tel.: (209) 826-8850
Fax: (209) 826-8858
Web Site: www.kagomeusa.com
Sales Range: $450-499.9 Million
Approx. Number Employees: 1,942
Business Description:
Canned Tomatoe Products & Canned Soft Drinks Mfr
S.I.C.: 2033; 2035; 2086
N.A.I.C.S.: 311421; 311941; 312111
Personnel:
Roshie Mori *(Pres)*
Hiroshi Mori *(CFO)*
Advertising Agency:
Advertising & Promotional Services, Inc. (Adpro, Inc.)
(d/b/a ADPRO, INC)
6 S 503 Wildwood Dr
Aurora, IL 60506
Tel.: (630) 801-9900
Fax: (630) 801-9663
Toll Free: (866) 895-2535

KAUFFMAN POULTRY FARMS, INC.
8519 Leland Rd
Waterman, IL 60556
Tel.: (815) 264-3470
Fax: (815) 264-7820
E-mail: hoka@verizon.net
Web Site: www.hokaturkeys.com
Sales Range: Less than $1 Million
Sales Estimate: $5-9.9 Million
Approx. Number Employees: 10
Year Founded: 1933

Key to Media (For complete agency information see *The Advertising Red Books-Agencies* edition):
1. Bus. Publs. 2. Cable T.V. 3. Catalogs & Directories. 4. Co-op Adv. 5. Consumer Mags. 6. D.M. to Bus. Estab.7. D.M. to Consumers
8. Daily Newsp. 9. Exhibits/Trade Shows 10. Foreign 11. Infomercial 12. Internet Adv.13. Multimedia 14. Network Radio
15. Network T.V. 16. Newsp. Distr. Mags. 17. Other 18. Outdoor (Posters, Transit) 19. Point of Purchase20. Premiums, Novelties
21. Product Samples 22. Special Events Mktg. 23. Spot Radio 24. Spot T.V. 25. Weekly Newsp. 26. Yellow Page Adv.

Kauffman Poultry Farms, Inc. — (Continued)
Business Description:
Poultry Grower & Processor
S.I.C.: 0253
N.A.I.C.S.: 112330
Media: 17
Distr.: Reg.
Budget Set: Jan.
Personnel:
Robert Kauffman *(Pres)*
Tom Klopfenstein *(Gen Mgr)*
Brands & Products:
HO-KA
HOME OF SELECTED OVEN DRESSED

KAYEM FOODS, INC.
75 Arlington St
Chelsea, MA 02150
Tel.: (617) 889-1600
Fax: (617) 889-5931
Toll Free: (800) 426-6100
E-mail: stephan.monkiewicz@kayem.com
Web Site: www.kayem.com
Sales Range: $100-124.9 Million
Approx. Number Employees: 500
Year Founded: 1909
Business Description:
Meat Processor
S.I.C.: 0751; 5147
N.A.I.C.S.: 311611; 311612
Media: 2-4-7-23-24
Distr.: Reg.
Personnel:
Ralph Smith *(Pres & CEO)*
Stephan Monkiewicz *(Treas & Engr)*
Matt Monkiewicz *(VP-Mktg)*
Tricia Williams *(Assoc Dir-Mktg)*
Carl Colson *(Dir-Procurement)*
Bob Kufferman *(Sr Brand Mgr)*
Brands & Products:
BRATWURSHIP
DECOSTA
DEUTSCHMACHER
ESSEM
GENOA
GET FRESH WITH KAYEM
JORDAN'S
KAYEM
KIRSCHNER
MCKENZIE COUNTRY CLASSICS
MEISTERCHEF
SCHONLAND'S
SUNNY ISLE
TASTY BITE
TRIPLE M
WILLIAMS OF VERMONT
Advertising Agency:
Blitz Media-Direct
(Div. of The Linick Group, Inc.)
Linick Bldg 7 Putter Ln
Middle Island, NY 11953-0102
Tel.: (631) 924-8555
Fax: (631) 924-8555

KEMPS LLC
(Sub. of Crowley Foods, Inc.)
1270 Energy Ln
Saint Paul, MN 55108-5225
Tel.: (651) 379-6500
Fax: (612) 378-8398
Web Site: www.kemps.com
Approx. Number Employees: 75
S.I.C.: 2022
N.A.I.C.S.: 311513
Advertising Expenditures: $550,000
Media: 3-8-9-10-18-19-20-21-23-24-25
Personnel:
James B. Green *(Pres & CEO)*
Craig Kurr *(VP-Sls)*
Rachel A. Kyllo *(VP-Mktg)*
Christopher Thorpe *(VP-Fin)*

KEN'S FOODS, INC.
1 Dangelo Dr
Marlborough, MA 01752
Tel.: (508) 485-7540
Fax: (508) 485-6882
E-mail: service@kensfoods.com
Web Site: www.kensfoods.com
Approx. Number Employees: 500
Year Founded: 1958
Business Description:
Salad Dressing, Mayonnaise, Vinegar, Sauces & Syrups Mfr
S.I.C.: 2035
N.A.I.C.S.: 311941
Media: 2-4-17
Distr.: Reg.
Personnel:
Andy Crowley *(Pres)*
Brian Crowley *(Pres-Food Svc Sls)*
Brands & Products:
BORN IN A GREAT STEAK HOUSE
KEN'S
LITE ACCENTS
QUALITY DRESSINGS FOR GENERATIONS

KERRY INC.
(Sub. of Kerry Group plc)
3400 Millington Rd
Beloit, WI 53511
Tel.: (608) 363-1200
Fax: (608) 363-1429
Web Site: www.kerryingredients.com
Business Description:
Mfr & Distr of Food Products & Food Ingredients
S.I.C.: 2099; 2087
N.A.I.C.S.: 311999; 311930
Export
Media: 7-10-13
Personnel:
Gerry Behan *(COO)*

KERRY SAVORY, INC.
(Sub. of Kerry Inc.)
21612 88th Ave S
Kent, WA 98031-1918
Tel.: (253) 395-9400
Fax: (253) 395-3330
Approx. Number Employees: 90
Year Founded: 1883
Business Description:
Mfr of Spices & Custom Blended Seasonings & Whole Nuts
S.I.C.: 2099; 5145
N.A.I.C.S.: 311942; 424450
Import Export
Media: 2-5-6-8-9-10-11-18-19-20-21-23-24-26
Distr.: Pacific Basin; Reg.
Budget Set: Feb.
Personnel:
Greg Corder *(Gen Mgr)*
Brands & Products:
CHEF'S CLASSIC
COFFEE ACCENTS
CRESCENT
GOLD SHIELD

KETTLE FOODS, INC.
(Sub. of Diamond Foods, Inc.)
3125 Kettle Crt SE
Salem, OR 97301
Tel.: (503) 364-0399
Fax: (503) 371-1447
Web Site: www.kettlefoods.com
Sales Range: $150-199.9 Million
Approx. Number Employees: 200
Year Founded: 1978
Business Description:
Snack Food Mfr
S.I.C.: 2096
N.A.I.C.S.: 311919
Import Export
Personnel:
Julie Dunmire *(Brand Dir)*
Brands & Products:
BACKYARD BARBEQUE
KETTLE
KRINKLE CUT
ROASTER FRESH
TIAS
Advertising Agency:
MEI
55 Madison Ave 4th Fl
Morristown, NJ 07960
Tel.: (973) 285-3045
Fax: (973) 538-0503

KEY TECHNOLOGY, INC.
150 Avery St
Walla Walla, WA 99362
Tel.: (509) 529-2161
Fax: (509) 527-1331
E-mail: info@keytechnology.com
Web Site: www.key.net
Approx. Sls.: $115,804,000
Approx. Number Employees: 536
Year Founded: 1948
Business Description:
Process Automation Systems Designer, Mfr, Retailer & Servicer
S.I.C.: 3581; 3556; 3559
N.A.I.C.S.: 333311; 333220; 333294
Advertising Expenditures: $13,071,000
Media: 10
Personnel:
Charles H. Stonecipher *(Chm)*
David M. Camp *(Pres & CEO)*
John J. Ehren *(CFO & Sr VP)*
John C. Boutsikaris *(Sr VP-Global Sls & Aftermarket)*
Louis C. Vintro *(Sr VP-Bus Dev & Global Ops)*
James D. Ruff *(Gen Mgr-Integrated Solutions Grp)*
Bret Larreau *(Mgr-Product Mktg)*
Brands & Products:
ADR
AUTOMATED SOLUTIONS FOR PROCESSORS WORLDWIDE
C-BELT
FLUORAPTOR
FMALERT
FORTE
HI-FLO
HORIZON
IMPULSE
INTELLISORT
ISO-FLO
KEY
KEYWARE
KHROMASORT
MANTA
MARATHON
OPTYX
PRISM
PRISM 2
SMART SHAKER
TEGRA
TOBACCO SORTER 3
TOBACCO SORTER II
TURBO-FLO
VEG-MIX
VHS-OPTISORT

KEYSTONE COFFEE COMPANY
2230 Will Wool Dr Ste 100
San Jose, CA 95112
Tel.: (408) 998-2221
Fax: (408) 998-5021
E-mail: sales@keystonecoffee.com
Web Site: www.keystonecoffee.com
E-Mail For Key Personnel:
Sales Director: sales@keystonecoffee.com
Approx. Number Employees: 11
Year Founded: 1867
Business Description:
Coffee Roaster & Retailer
S.I.C.: 5499
N.A.I.C.S.: 445299
Advertising Expenditures: $1,500,000
Media: 7-10
Distr.: Reg.
Personnel:
Tim Wright *(Owner & Pres)*
Brands & Products:
KEYSTONE COFFEE

KIKKOMAN INTERNATIONAL INC.
(Sub. of Kikkoman Corporation)
50 California St Ste 3600
San Francisco, CA 94111
Tel.: (415) 956-7750
Fax: (415) 956-7760
Toll Free: (800) 944-0600
E-mail: info@kikkoman-usa.com
Web Site: www.kikkoman-usa.com
Approx. Number Employees: 45
Year Founded: 1957
Business Description:
Mfr. of Soy, Steak, Sweet & Sour, Stir Fry & Teriyaki Sauces & Seasoning Mixes
S.I.C.: 5149; 2035
N.A.I.C.S.: 424490; 311941
Import
Advertising Expenditures: $7,000,000
Media: 2-10
Distr.: Natl.
Budget Set: Oct.
Brands & Products:
PEARL
QUICK & EASY
Advertising Agencies:
Dentsu Communications, Inc.
32 Ave of Americas 16th Fl
New York, NY 10013
Tel.: (212) 660-6790
Fax: (212) 660-6797

Ketchum
1050 Battery St
San Francisco, CA 94111-1209
Tel.: (415) 984-6100
Fax: (415) 984-6102
(Food Service & Industrial)

mktg, inc.

Key to Media (For complete agency information see *The Advertising Red Books-Agencies* edition):
1. Bus. Publs. 2. Cable T.V. 3. Catalogs & Directories. 4. Co-op Adv. 5. Consumer Mags. 6. D.M. to Bus. Estab.7. D.M. to Consumers 8. Daily Newsp. 9. Exhibits/Trade Shows 10. Foreign 11. Infomercial 12. Internet Adv.13. Multimedia 14. Network Radio 15. Network T.V. 16. Newsp. Distr. Mags. 17. Other 18. Outdoor (Posters, Transit) 19. Point of Purchase20. Premiums, Novelties 21. Product Samples 22. Special Events Mktg. 23. Spot Radio 24. Spot T.V. 25. Weekly Newsp. 26. Yellow Page Adv.

75 9th Ave 3rd Fl
New York, NY 10011
Tel.: (212) 660-3800
Fax: (212) 660-3878

KING & PRINCE SEAFOOD CORPORATION

(Sub. of The Gorton Group)
1 King & Prince Blvd
Brunswick, GA 31520
Mailing Address:
PO Box 899
Brunswick, GA 31521-0899
Tel.: (912) 265-5155
Fax: (912) 264-2918
Toll Free: (800) 841-0205
E-mail: sales@kpseafood.com
Web Site: www.kpseafood.com
E-Mail For Key Personnel:
Marketing Director: marketing@kpseafood.com
Sales Director: sales@kpseafood.com
Approx. Number Employees: 350
Year Founded: 1949
Business Description:
Frozen & Processed Seafood Products Mfr
S.I.C.: 2092
N.A.I.C.S.: 311712
Import Export
Media: 2-5-7-10-11-13-19-21
Distr.: Intl.; Natl.
Budget Set: Oct.
Personnel:
John Flood *(Dir-Mktg)*
Brands & Products:
FLYING JIB
GOLDEN SHORE
GOLDEN SUPREME
GULFSTREAM
KING & PRINCE
OCEANWAY
Advertising Agency:
The Aristos Group
750 E Lake St
Wayzata, MN 55391
Tel.: (952) 449-4100
Fax: (952) 449-4119
— Jay Wissink *(Pres.)*

KING KOLD FROZEN FOODS, INC.

(Sub. of Vienna Sausage Mfg. Co.)
1920 Swarthmore Ave Ste 1
Lakewood, NJ 08701
Tel.: (732) 730-2157
Fax: (732) 730-9913
Web Site: www.kingkold.com
Approx. Number Employees: 75
Business Description:
Frozen Food Mfr
S.I.C.: 2499
N.A.I.C.S.: 321999
Media: 8-9-15-18-23-25
Distr.: Natl.
Budget Set: Apr.
Brands & Products:
KING KOLD
RATNER'S
RUTHIE & GUSSIE'S

KLOSTERMAN BAKING COMPANY, INC.

4760 Paddock Rd
Cincinnati, OH 45229-1004
Tel.: (513) 242-1004
Fax: (513) 242-8257
E-mail: comments@klostermanbakery.com
Web Site: www.klostermanbakery.com
Sales Range: $500-549.9 Million
Approx. Number Employees: 500
Year Founded: 1848
Business Description:
Baked Goods Mfr
S.I.C.: 2051
N.A.I.C.S.: 311812
Media: 5-8-26
Distr.: Reg.
Personnel:
Kenneth Klosterman, Sr. *(Chm)*
Kenneth Klosterman, Jr. *(Pres)*
Dennis Wiltshire *(Exec VP)*
Brands & Products:
BIG WHITE
CINCINNATI DELI RYES
DELI LINE
EUROPEAN HARVEST SIGNATURE
GIANT
HOLSUM
HOMESTYLE
VILLAGE PRIDE

KNOUSE FOODS COOPERATIVE INC.

800 Peach Glen Idaville Rd
Peach Glen, PA 17375
Tel.: (717) 677-8181
Fax: (717) 677-7069
E-mail: customerservice@knouse.com
Web Site: www.knouse.com
Approx. Number Employees: 1,800
Year Founded: 1949
Business Description:
Fruit Product Mfr
S.I.C.: 0175; 0762; 2033; 2034; 2037; 2086
N.A.I.C.S.: 111331; 115116; 311411; 311421; 311423; 312111
Export
Advertising Expenditures: $1,400,000
Media: 1-2-5-7-8-9-10-13-19-20-23-24-25
Distr.: Natl.
Budget Set: Feb.
Personnel:
Kenneth E. Guise, Jr. *(Pres & CEO)*
Thomas M. DeNisco *(CFO, VP & Gen Mgr)*
Richard Esser *(VP-Sls)*
Robert Fisher *(VP-Mktg)*
Ken Millage *(Mgr-Mktg)*
Brands & Products:
THE APPLE EXPERTS
APPLE TIME
KNOUSE FOODS
LINCOLN
LUCKY LEAF
MUSSELMAN'S
Advertising Agency:
Brunner
11 Stanwix St 5th Fl
Pittsburgh, PA 15222-1312
Tel.: (412) 995-9500
Fax: (412) 995-9501
(Musselman)

KOSTO FOOD PRODUCTS CO.

1325 N Old Rand Rd
Wauconda, IL 60084
Tel.: (847) 487-2600
Fax: (847) 487-2654
Web Site: www.kostofoods.com
Approx. Number Employees: 25
Year Founded: 1898
Business Description:
Desserts & Dessert Ingredients Mfr
S.I.C.: 2099
N.A.I.C.S.: 311999
Media: 2-16
Distr.: Reg.
Personnel:
Donald F. Colby *(Pres)*
Steven Colby *(Gen Mgr)*

KOWALSKI CO., INC.

2270 Holbrook Ave
Hamtramck, MI 48212
Tel.: (313) 873-8200
Fax: (313) 873-4220
E-mail: kowalski@cmconnect.net
Web Site: www.kowality.com
Approx. Number Employees: 225
Year Founded: 1920
Business Description:
Sausage, Ham, Bacon & Luncheon Meat Mfr
S.I.C.: 5147; 5421
N.A.I.C.S.: 311612; 445210
Media: 2-3-4-5-6-7-8-9-19-20-21-22-23-24-25-26
Distr.: Natl.
Budget Set: Nov. -Dec.

KOZY SHACK INC.

83 Ludy St
Hicksville, NY 11801
Tel.: (516) 870-3000
Fax: (516) 870-3001
Web Site: www.kozyshack.com
Sales Range: $100-124.9 Million
Approx. Number Employees: 330
Business Description:
Mfr. & Sales of Puddings
S.I.C.: 2099; 5149
N.A.I.C.S.: 311999; 424490
Personnel:
Vincent Gruppuso *(Chm)*
Sally Olivero *(CFO & VP)*
Janice McCarthy *(VP-Mktg)*
Brands & Products:
CREAMY
DULCE DE LECHE
EUROPEAN
KOZY SHACK
NATURAL
OLD FASHIONED
ORIGINAL
REAL
Advertising Agency:
BRUSHfire, Inc.
2 Wing Dr
Cedar Knolls, NJ 07927
Tel.: (973) 871-1700
Fax: (973) 871-1717

KRAFT CANADA INC.

(Sub. of Kraft International Commercial)
95 Moatfield Drive
Toronto, ON M3B 3L6, Canada
Tel.: (416) 441-5000
Fax: (416) 441-5059
Web Site: www.kraftcanada.com
Sales Range: $1-4.9 Billion
Approx. Number Employees: 4,500
Year Founded: 1920
Business Description:
Food Products Mfr & Distr
S.I.C.: 2099
N.A.I.C.S.: 311999
Media: 2-4-6-7-8-9-10-11-14-15-18-20-21-23-24-25
Distr.: Natl.
Personnel:
Irene B. Rosenfeld *(Chm & CEO)*
Mary Beth West *(CMO, Chief Category Officer & Exec VP)*
Sanjay Khosla *(Pres-Developing Markets & Exec VP)*
Richard G. Searer *(Pres-North America & Exec VP)*
Dino Bianco *(Pres-Kraft Canada)*
Marc Firestone *(Gen Counsel & Exec VP-Corp & Legal Affairs)*
David Brearton *(Exec VP-Ops)*
Karen May *(Exec VP-Global HR)*
Jean E. Spence *(Exec VP-Res, Dev & Quality)*
Franz-Josef Vogelsang *(Exec VP-Supply Chain)*
Tim Berman *(VP-Sls)*
Pamela Horvatis *(VP-Customer Sls-Convenience, Gas & Wholesale)*
Vanessa Grekov *(Sr Product Mgr-Peek Freans Lifestyle Selection Cookies)*
Kristi Murl *(Brand Mgr-Oreo)*
Natalie Redman *(Brand Mgr-Triscuit)*
Anne Farragher *(Brand Mgr-Peanut Butter Bears)*
Rena Nickerson *(Sr Brand Mgr-Maxwell House Coffee)*
Luke Cole *(Product Mgr-Tassimo)*
Karen Miyauchi *(Assoc Product Mgr-Tassimo)*
Shalini Kapur-Roncato *(Product Mgr-Tassimo)*
Jordon Fietje *(Mgr-Brand Mktg & Kids Cereals)*
Brands & Products:
SHREDDIES
Advertising Agencies:
Draftfcb Toronto
(Canadian Headquarters)
245 Eglinton Avenue East Suite 300
Toronto, ON M4P 3C2, Canada
Tel.: (416) 483-3600
Fax: (416) 489-8782
Oreo

Euro RSCG Toronto
473 Adelaide St W Ste 300
Toronto, ON M5V 1T1, Canada
Tel.: (416) 920-6864
Fax: (416) 920-5043

JWT Company Ltd.
160 Bloor St E
Toronto, ON M4W 3P7, Canada
Tel.: (416) 926-7300
Fax: (416) 926-7389

Leo Burnett Company Ltd.
175 Bloor St E North Twr
Toronto, ON M4W 3R9, Canada
Tel.: (416) 925-5997
Fax: (416) 92-5 3443

Ogilvy & Mather
33 Yonge St
Toronto, ON M5E 1X6, Canada
Tel.: (416) 367-3573
Fax: (416) 363-2088
— Kristi Karens *(Acct Dir)*

Kraft Canada Inc. — (Continued)

Starcom MediaVest Group
175 Bloor St E N Tower 10th Fl
Toronto, ON M4W 3R9, Canada
Tel.: (416) 928-3636
Fax: (416) 927-3202

Y&R, Ltd.
60 Bloor Street West
Toronto, ON M4W 1J2, Canada
Tel.: (416) 961-5111
Fax: (416) 961-7890

KRAFT FOOD INGREDIENTS

(Div. of Kraft Foods Inc.)
8000 Horizon Ctr Blvd
Memphis, TN 38133
Tel.: (901) 381-6500
Fax: (901) 381-6524
Toll Free: (800) 458-8324
Web Site:
www.kraftfoodingredients.com
Sales Range: $25-49.9 Million
Approx. Number Employees: 100
Year Founded: 1986
Business Description:
Food Products, Seasonings & Flavorings Mfr
S.I.C.: 5143; 5149
N.A.I.C.S.: 424430; 424490
Export
Media: 1-2-4-7-10-20-21-22
Distr.: Intl.; Natl.
Budget Set: Oct.
Personnel:
Mike Strauch *(VP & Gen Mgr)*
Andreas Schauffler *(Controller & Dir-Fin)*

KRAFT FOODS INC.

3 Lakes Dr
Northfield, IL 60093-2753
Tel.: (847) 646-2000
Fax: (847) 646-6005
Web Site: www.kraft.com
Approx. Rev.: $49,207,000,000
Approx. Number Employees: 127,000
Business Description:
Holding Company; Packaged Grocery Products
S.I.C.: 6719; 2022; 2043; 2096
N.A.I.C.S.: 551112; 311230; 311513; 311919
Advertising Expenditures: $2,269,000,000
Media: 2-3-4-5-6-7-8-9-10-11-13-14-15-18-19-20-21-22-23-24-25
Distr.: Natl.
Budget Set: Jan.
Personnel:
Irene B. Rosenfeld *(Chm & CEO)*
W. Anthony Vernon *(Pres & Exec VP)*
Krister Zackari *(Mng Dir)*
Mary Beth West *(CMO & Exec VP)*
Sanjay Khosla *(Pres-Intl & Exec VP)*
Christopher J. Baldwin *(Pres-Snacks)*
Dino Bianco *(Pres-Canada)*
Rhonda L. Jordan *(Pres-Health & Wellness)*
Bob Levi *(Pres-Global Walmart Sls)*
Nicholas Meriggioli *(Pres-Oscar Mayer)*
Michael Osanloo *(Pres-Grocery Bus-North America)*
Thomas H. Sampson *(Pres-Foodservice)*
Marc S. Firestone *(Gen Counsel & Exec VP-Corp & Legal Affairs)*
David Brearton *(Exec VP-Ops & Bus Svcs)*
Karen J. May *(Exec VP-Global HR)*
Sam B. Rovit *(Exec VP-Strategy)*
Jean E. Spence *(Exec VP-R & D & Quality)*
Jane Hilk *(Sr VP-Mktg)*
Kim Harris Jones *(Sr VP & Controller)*
Todd Abraham *(Sr VP-R & D)*
Dana Anderson *(Sr VP-Mktg, Strategy & Comm)*
Nancy Daigler *(Sr VP-Bus Unit Corp Affairs)*
Lance A. Friedmann *(Sr VP)*
Laura McCorvie *(Sr VP-Customer Growth & Shopper Mktg)*
Donald King *(VP-Mktg)*
Kim Bealle *(Sr Dir-Beverages & Consumer Mktg Grp)*
Stephen Chriss *(Sr Dir-Corp Scale & Mktg Partnerships)*
John Ghingo *(Sr Dir-Mktg & Oreo Global Growth Platform)*
Maurice Herrera *(Sr Dir-Mktg)*
Sean Marks *(Sr Dir-Mktg-Oscar Mayer)*
Amelia A. Strobel *(Sr Dir)*
Sara Braun *(Mktg Dir-Miracle Whip & Grey Poupon)*
David Ervin *(Dir-Breakthrough Innovation)*
Roxanne Bernstein *(Dir-Mktg)*
Sheldon Cummings *(Dir-Mktg-Walmart Shopper)*
Chitra Ebenezer *(Dir-Consumer Cohorts)*
Julie Fleischer *(Dir-CRM Content Strategy & Integration)*
Beth Goeddel *(Dir-Mktg)*
Gary Gruneberg *(Dir-Media Buying)*
Laurie M. Guzzinati *(Dir-Comm-Europe)*
Ed Kaczmarek *(Dir-Innovation-New Svcs)*
Clayton Wai-Poi *(Dir-Category Bus)*
Laure Morris *(Sr Mgr-Digtal Mktg & Media)*
Adam W. Butler *(Brand Mgr)*
Melissa Merchant *(Sr Brand Mgr-Beverages)*
Eileen Rosenfeld *(Sr Brand Mgr-Kraft Macaroni & Cheese)*
Steve Seigal *(Sr Brand Mgr-Nabisco 100 Calorie Packs)*
Daisie Siska *(Brand Mgr)*
Brigette Wolf *(Brand Mgr-Global Oreo Innovation)*
Adam Grablick *(Brand Mgr)*
Nicole Kulwicki *(Brand Mgr-Miracle Whip-Grey Poupon)*
Scott Marcus *(Sr Brand Mgr-Planters)*
Todd Midora *(Brand Mgr-Ritz Crackers)*
Arthur Sevilla *(Brand Mgr)*
Marisa Zimmerman *(Brand Mgr-KRAFT Singles)*
Carolina Yepes *(Mgr-Procurement-Mktg Resources)*
Brands & Products:
AIR CRISPS
ATHENOS
BAGEL-FULS
BAKER'S
BALANCE
BALANCE B KIDS
BARNUM'S ANIMALS
BETTER CHEDDARS
BOCA
BREAKSTONE'S
BULL'S-EYE
CAFE CREME
CALUMET
CAMEO
CAPRI-SUN
CERTO
CHEESE NIPS
CHEEZ WHIZ
CHIPS AHOY!
CHURNY
CLAUSSEN
CLIGHT
COMIDA KRAFT
COOL WHIP
CORN NUTS
COTE D'OR
COUNTRY TIME
CRACKER BARREL
CROWN PILOT
CRYSTAL LIGHT
D-ZERTA
DAD'S
DREAM WHIP
DUET
EASY MAC CUPS
FLAVOR CRISPS
GENERAL FOODS INTERNATIONAL COFFEES
GOOD SEASONS
GREY POUPON
HANDI-SNACKS
HARVEST MOON
HONEY MAID
JELL-O
JET-PUFFED
KNUDSEN
KOOL-AID
KRAFT
KRAFT MACARONI & CHEESE CRACKERS
KRAFT SINGLES
LIGHT N' LIVELY
LIVEACTIVE
LIVEACTIVE CHEWY GRANOLA BAR
LORNA DOONE
LOUIS RICH
LUNCHABLES
MALLOMARS
MARSHMALLOW TWIRLS
MAXIM
MAXWELL HOUSE
MIRACLE WHIP
NABISCO
NABISCO GARDEN HARVEST TOASTED CHIPS
NATURAL BRAN FLAKES
NEWTONS
NILLA
NUTTER BUTTER
OREO
OSCAR MAYER
OVEN FRY
PEAK FREANS
PECANZ
PHILADELPHIA
PLANTERS
POLLY-O
POSTUM
PREMIUM
RITZ
SANKA
SEVEN SEAS
SHAKE 'N BAKE
SNACKWELL'S
SOCIAL TEA
SOUTH BEACH LIVING
STELLA D'ORO
STONED WHEAT THINS
STOVE TOP
STOVE TOP QUICK CUPS
SURE-JELL
TANG
TASSIMO
TEDDY GRAHAMS
TEMP-TEE
TERRY'S
TOBLER
TOBLERONE
TRIDENT
TRISCUIT
TROLLI
VELVEETA
WHEAT THINS
WHEATSWORTH
YUBAN
Advertising Agencies:
360i
28 W 23rd St 6th Fl
New York, NY 10010
Tel.: (212) 703-7201
Toll Free: (888) 360-9360

Admerasia, Inc.
159 W 25th St 6th Fl
New York, NY 10001-7203
Tel.: (212) 686-3333
Fax: (212) 686-8998

AKQA, Inc.
118 King St 6th Fl
San Francisco, CA 94107
Tel.: (415) 645-9400
Fax: (415) 645-9420
Digiorno
Miracle Whip

Aspen Marketing Services
417 Canal St 6th Fl
New York, NY 10013-1902
Tel.: (212) 431-5300
Fax: (212) 431-5833
Crystal Light
— Tim Hanlon *(Acct Exec-Crystal Light)*

Carol H. Williams Advertising
1400 65th St Ste 200
Emeryville, CA 94608
Tel.: (510) 763-5200
Fax: (510) 763-9266

Copper-Brite, Inc.
1482 E Valley Rd Ste 29
Santa Barbara, CA 93108-1200
Tel.: (805) 565-1566
Fax: (805) 565-1394

Coyne Public Relations
14 Walsh Dr 2nd Fl
Parsippany, NJ 07054
Tel.: (973) 316-1665
Fax: (973) 316-6568
Capri Sun
Milk-Bone
Ritz
— Allison Greco *(Acct Exec)*
— Rachel Max *(Acct Exec-Capri Sun)*
— Molly Judge *(Acct Exec-Capri Sun)*

CP+B

Key to Media (For complete agency information see *The Advertising Red Books-Agencies* edition):
1. Bus. Publs. 2. Cable T.V. 3. Catalogs & Directories. 4. Co-op Adv. 5. Consumer Mags. 6. D.M. to Bus. Estab.7. D.M. to Consumers
8. Daily Newsp. 9. Exhibits/Trade Shows 10. Foreign 11. Infomercial 12. Internet Adv.13. Multimedia 14. Network Radio
15. Network T.V. 16. Newsp. Distr. Mags. 17. Other 18. Outdoor (Posters, Transit) 19. Point of Purchase20. Premiums, Novelties
21. Product Samples 22. Special Events Mktg. 23. Spot Radio 24. Spot T.V. 25. Weekly Newsp. 26. Yellow Page Adv.

3390 Mary St Ste 300
Coconut Grove, FL 33133
Tel.: (305) 859-2070
Fax: (305) 854-3419
Creative
Mac & Cheese
Milka Chocolate
Triscuit Crackers

CP+B Boulder
6450 Gunpark Dr
Boulder, CO 80301
Tel.: (303) 628-5100
Fax: (303) 516-0227
Mac & Cheese

Dan Klores Communications
(d/b/a dkc)
386 Park Ave S 10th Fl
New York, NY 10016
Tel.: (212) 685-4300
Fax: (212) 685-9024
Kool Aid
— Liz Anklow *(Acct Exec)*
— Debra Duffy *(Acct Exec)*

Daniel J. Edelman, Inc.
(d/b/a Edelman)
200 E Randolph St Fl 63
Chicago, IL 60601-6705
Tel.: (312) 240-3000
Fax: (312) 240-2900
Kraft Singles

Digitas, Inc.
111 E Wacker Dr Ste 1500
Chicago, IL 60601-4501
Tel.: (312) 729-0100
Fax: (312) 729-0111
(Salad Dressings, Online Marketing)

Digitas, Inc.
355 Park Ave S
New York, NY 10010-1706
Tel.: (212) 610-5000
Fax: (212) 350-7850
Planters

Digitas Inc.
33 Arch St
Boston, MA 02110
Tel.: (617) 867-1000
Fax: (617) 867-1111
Media Planning
— Robert Cross *(Sr VP-Media)*

Display Boys
17032 Murphy Ave
Irvine, CA 92614
Tel.: (949) 833-0100
Fax: (949) 838-0110
(Kraft Cheese)

DraftFCB
Miguel de Cervantes Saavedra #193
11520
Mexico, DF Mexico
Tel.: (52) 55 5350 7900
Fax: (52) 55 5282 4640
Clight

Draftfcb
101 E Erie St
Chicago, IL 60611-2812
Tel.: (312) 425-5000
Fax: (312) 425-5010
(Jell-O, Bull's-Eye Barbecue Sauce, General Foods International Coffee, Kraft Barbecue Sauce, Stove Top Stuffing, Kraft Macaroni & Cheese, Deluxe Macaroni & Cheese, Grated Parmesan, Louis Rich, Di Giorno Pasta & Sauce, Di Giorno Pizza, Tombstone Pizza, Velveeta, Kraft Pourable Salad Dressings)

Draftfcb
Minones 1856
C1414CTU
Buenos Aires, Argentina
Tel.: (54) 11 4789 7700
Fax: (54) 11 4789 7754
Oreo

Draftfcb New York
100 W 33rd St
New York, NY 10001
Tel.: (212) 885-3000
Fax: (212) 885-3300
Club Social Crackers
Kraft Cheese
Oreo

droga5
400 Lafayette 5th Fl
New York, NY 10003
Tel.: (917) 237-8888
Fax: (917) 237-8889
Athenos

EMAK Worldwide, Inc.
6330 San Vicente Blvd
Los Angeles, CA 90048-5425
Tel.: (323) 932-4300
Fax: (323) 932-4400

Euro RSCG 4D Impact
36 E Grand Ave
Chicago, IL 60611-3506
Tel.: (312) 799-7000
Fax: (312) 799-7100

Euro RSCG Worldwide
350 Hudson St
New York, NY 10014-4504
Tel.: (212) 886-2000
Fax: (212) 886-2016
Toll Free: (800) 937-0233

Euro RSCG Worldwide
36 E Grand Ave
Chicago, IL 60611-3506
Tel.: (312) 337-4400
Fax: (312) 337-5930
Fax: (312) 337-2316
(Salad Dressings, Interactive, Direct Marketing, Event Marketing)

Euro RSCG Worldwide HQ
350 Hudson St
New York, NY 10014-4504
Tel.: (212) 886-2000
Fax: (212) 886-2016
Ritz
Triscuits
Toasted Chips

FD Americas Public Affairs
1101 K St NW 9th Fl
Washington, DC 20005
Tel.: (202) 346-8800
Fax: (202) 346-8804

Horizon Media, Inc.
75 Varick St
New York, NY 10013
Tel.: (212) 220-5000
Toll Free: (800) 633-4201
Macaroni & Cheese

Hunter Public Relations
41 Madison Ave Fl 5
New York, NY 10010-2202
Tel.: (212) 679-6600
Fax: (212) 679-6607
Cheddar Explosion
Kraft Macaroni & Cheese

J. Walter Thompson Company
(d/b/a JWT)
466 Lexington Ave
New York, NY 10017-3140
Tel.: (212) 210-7000
Fax: (212) 210-7299
Cadbury - U.S. Creative
Stride

JWT
Alsina 465
C1087 AAE
Buenos Aires, Argentina
Tel.: (54) 1 1 4339 6100
Fax: (54) 1 1 4339 3675

JWT Canada
160 Bloor St E Ste 800
Toronto, ON M4W 3P7, Canada
Tel.: (416) 926-7300
Fax: (416) 967-2859

The Kaplan Thaler Group
825 8th Ave 34th Fl
New York, NY 10019
Tel.: (212) 474-5000
Fax: (212) 474-5702
Bagel-fuls

Lopez Negrete Communications, Inc.
3336 Richmond Ave Ste 200
Houston, TX 77098
Tel.: (713) 877-8777
Fax: (713) 877-8796
Kraft Singles

McGarry Bowen
515 N State St 29th Fl
Chicago, IL 60654
Tel.: (312) 239-6370
Fax: (312) 840-8396
Chips Ahoy
Fig Newtons
Kraft Barbecue Sauce
Kraft Mayonnaise
Kraft Salad Dressings
Lunchables
Miracle Whip
Nabisco 100 Calorie Packs
Oscar Mayer
Philadelphia Cream Cheese

McGarry Bowen, LLC
601 W 26th St Ste 1150
New York, NY 10001
Tel.: (212) 598-2900
Fax: (212) 598-2996

MediaVest USA
1675 Broadway
New York, NY 10019
Tel.: (212) 468-4000
Fax: (212) 468-4110
(Media Planning & Buying)
Nabisco

MMA
15 River Rd
Wilton, CT 06897
Tel.: (203) 834-3300
Fax: (203) 834-3333

Momentum
444 N Michigan Ave Ste 1700
Chicago, IL 60611
Tel.: (312) 245-3500
Fax: (312) 245-3550
(Salad Dressings, In-Store Marketing & Promotional)

MRM Worldwide
622 3rd Ave
New York, NY 10017-6707
Tel.: (646) 865-6230
Fax: (646) 865-6264
Philadelphia Brand

OgilvyAction
636 W 11th Ave
New York, NY 10036
Tel.: (212) 297-8000
Fax: (212) 297-8006
Maxwell House - Promotional

OgilvyAction
350 W Mart Center Dr Ste 1100
Chicago, IL 60654-1866
Tel.: (312) 527-3900
Fax: (312) 527-3327

OgilvyOne Worldwide
636 11th Ave
New York, NY 10036
Tel.: (212) 237-4000
Fax: (212) 237-5123
Maxwell House - Digital

OgilvyOne Worldwide
10 Imathias Street
15 344
Athens, Greece
Tel.: (30) 210 610 6900
Fax: (30) 210 610 6903

PointRoll Inc.
951 E Hector St
Conshohocken, PA 19428
Tel.: (267) 558-1300
Fax: (267) 285-1141
Toll Free: (800) 203-6956

Publicis Groupe S.A.
133 Ave des Champs-Elysee
75008
Paris, France
Tel.: (33) 1 44 43 70 00
Fax: (33) 1 44 43 75 25
Cadbury (Media Buying Agency)

Razorfish
821 2nd Ave Ste 1800
Seattle, WA 98104-2343
Tel.: (206) 816-8800
Fax: (206) 816-8808
Digital Agency
Lunchables

Response Media, Inc.
3155 Medlock Bridge Rd

Key to Media (For complete agency information see *The Advertising Red Books-Agencies* edition):
1. Bus. Publs. 2. Cable T.V. 3. Catalogs & Directories. 4. Co-op Adv. 5. Consumer Mags. 6. D.M. to Bus. Estab.7. D.M. to Consumers 8. Daily Newsp. 9. Exhibits/Trade Shows 10. Foreign 11. Infomercial 12. Internet Adv.13. Multimedia 14. Network Radio 15. Network T.V. 16. Newsp. Distr. Mags. 17. Other 18. Outdoor (Posters, Transit) 19. Point of Purchase20. Premiums, Novelties 21. Product Samples 22. Special Events Mktg. 23. Spot Radio 24. Spot T.V. 25. Weekly Newsp. 26. Yellow Page Adv.

Kraft Foods Inc. — (Continued)

Norcross, GA 30071-1423
Tel.: (770) 451-5478
Fax: (770) 451-4929

Saatchi & Saatchi
(Sub. of Publicis Groupe S.A.)
(Worldwide Headquarters)
375 Hudson St
New York, NY 10014-3660
Tel.: (212) 463-2000
Fax: (212) 463-9856
Trident

SS+K Agency
88 Pine St 30th Fl
New York, NY 10005
Tel.: (212) 274-9500
— Alvaro Rivera *(Dir-Art)*
— Nathan Phillips *(Copywriter)*

Starcom MediaVest Group
35 W Wacker Dr
Chicago, IL 60601-1723
Tel.: (312) 220-3535
Fax: (312) 220-6530
Lunchables

Sterling Rice Group
1801 13th St Ste 400
Boulder, CO 80302
Tel.: (303) 381-6400
Fax: (303) 444-6637

TBWA Chiat Day New York
488 Madison Ave
New York, NY 10022
Tel.: (212) 804-1000
Fax: (212) 804-1200
Planters

TBWA/Worldwide
(Sub. of Omnicom Group, Inc.)
488 Madison Ave 5th Fl
New York, NY 10022-5702
Tel.: (212) 804-1300
Fax: (212) 804-1333
Tassimo

Weber Shandwick
(Sub. of The Interpublic Group of Companies)
919 3rd Ave
New York, NY 10022
Tel.: (212) 445-8000
Fax: (212) 445-8001
Lunchables
Nabisco 100 Calorie Packs
Press Releases, Media Contact
Shake 'N Bake
— Theresa Renaldi *(Media Contact-Kraft Foods, Inc.)*
— Nicole Miller *(Acct Exec)*

Wieden + Kennedy, Inc.
224 NW 13th Ave
Portland, OR 97209-2953
Tel.: (503) 937-7000
Fax: (503) 937-8000
Velveeta Cheesy Skillets

KRAFT FOODS MANAGEMENT CENTER-TARRYTOWN

(Unit of Kraft Foods Inc.)
555 S Broadway
Tarrytown, NY 10591-5598
Tel.: (914) 425-2500
Fax: (914) 335-7508
E-mail: healthy@balance.com
Web Site: www.krafts.com
Sales Range: $100-124.9 Million
Approx. Number Employees: 130
Year Founded: 1992
Business Description:
Food Processing & Marketing Services
S.I.C.: 5141; 2086
N.A.I.C.S.: 424410; 312111
Import Export
Advertising Expenditures: $200,000
Media: 15-19-21-24
Personnel:
James Chambers *(Pres-Snacks & Confectionery-Kraft North America)*
Sivonne Davis *(Sr Brand Mgr-Kool-Aid)*
Joseph Lavin *(Mgr-Consumer Science)*
Advertising Agencies:
Admerasia, Inc.
159 W 25th St 6th Fl
New York, NY 10001-7203
Tel.: (212) 686-3333
Fax: (212) 686-8998

D.L. Blair Inc.
1051 Franklin Ave
Garden City, NY 11530
Tel.: (516) 746-3700
Fax: (516) 746-3889

Draftfcb New York
100 W 33rd St
New York, NY 10001
Tel.: (212) 885-3000
Fax: (212) 885-3300

EMAK Worldwide, Inc.
6330 San Vicente Blvd
Los Angeles, CA 90048-5425
Tel.: (323) 932-4300
Fax: (323) 932-4400

FD Americas Public Affairs
1101 K St NW 9th Fl
Washington, DC 20005
Tel.: (202) 346-8800
Fax: (202) 346-8804

Leo Burnett Worldwide, Inc.
35 W Wacker Dr
Chicago, IL 60601-1723
Tel.: (312) 220-5959
Fax: (312) 220-3299

Sterling Rice Group
1801 13th St Ste 400
Boulder, CO 80302
Tel.: (303) 381-6400
Fax: (303) 444-6637

KRAFT FOODS OSCAR MAYER

(Div. of Kraft Foods Global)
910 Mayer Ave
Madison, WI 53704-4256
Tel.: (608) 241-3311
Web Site: www.oscarmayer.com
Sales Range: $300-349.9 Million
Approx. Number Employees: 1,500
Year Founded: 1923
Business Description:
Wiener Mfr
S.I.C.: 0751
N.A.I.C.S.: 311611
Media: 2-3-6-14-15
Personnel:
Nick Meriggioli *(Pres-Oscar Mayer)*
Sean Marks *(Sr Dir-Mktg)*
Mindee Elam *(Brand Mgr-Lunchables)*
Peter M. Dunn *(Mgr-Mktg)*
Ed Roland *(Mgr-Mobile Mktg)*
Rachel Kerr *(Coord-Mobile Mktg)*
Advertising Agency:
Just Kid, Inc.
27 Ann St
Norwalk, CT 06854
Tel.: (203) 358-2120
Fax: (203) 523-7888

KRAFT NABISCO

(Div. of Kraft Foods Global)
100 DeForest Ave
East Hanover, NJ 07936
Mailing Address:
PO Box 1911
East Hanover, NJ 07936-1911
Tel.: (973) 503-2000
Fax: (973) 503-4884
Fax: (973) 682-6222
E-mail: info@kraft.com
Web Site: www.kraft.com
Sales Range: $450-499.9 Million
Approx. Number Employees: 1,000
Year Founded: 1896
Business Description:
Nuts, Snacks & Confections Mfr
S.I.C.: 2099
N.A.I.C.S.: 311999
Export
Media: 3-6-9-13-15-19-20-21-24
Distr.: Natl.

KRONOS PRODUCTS, INC.

1 Kronos Dr Glendale Hts
Glendale Heights, IL 60139
Tel.: (773) 847-2250
Fax: (773) 847-2492
Toll Free: (800) 621-0099
E-mail: info@kronosfoods.com
Web Site: www.kronosproducts.com
Approx. Number Employees: 145
Year Founded: 1975
Business Description:
Greek Meat Products, Baked Foods & Food Service Equipment Mfr & Marketer
S.I.C.: 5147; 2051
N.A.I.C.S.: 311612; 311812
Advertising Expenditures: $400,000
Media: 4-8-9-23-25
Distr.: Reg.
Personnel:
Pat Costello *(Pres & COO)*
Mike Austin *(CEO)*
Janet Carwell *(CFO)*
Brands & Products:
AUTHENTIC PITA
GYROKONES
JR. KRONOMATIC
KRONOMATIC
KRONOS
THE KRONOS PERFECT PORTION CONTROL SYSTEM
PERFECT PITA
SOUVLAKI

LA BREA BAKERY, INC.

(Sub. of IAWS Group Ltd.)
15963 Strathern St
Van Nuys, CA 91406
Tel.: (818) 742-4242
Fax: (818) 742-4276
Web Site: www.labreabakery.com
Business Description:
Bread Mfr & Retailer
S.I.C.: 2051
N.A.I.C.S.: 311812
Personnel:
John Yamin *(CEO)*
Rick Anderson *(CMO & Chief Comml Officer)*
Advertising Agency:
Tom, Dick & Harry Advertising
350 W Erie 2nd Fl
Chicago, IL 60654
Tel.: (312) 327-9500
Fax: (312) 327-9501

LA CIE MCCORMICK CANADA CO.

(Sub. of McCormick & Company, Incorporated)
600 Clarke Rd
PO Box 5788
London, ON N5V 3K5, Canada
Tel.: (519) 432-1166
Fax: (519) 673-0089
E-mail: info@mccormick.com
Web Site: www.mccormick.com
Sales Range: $250-299.9 Million
Approx. Number Employees: 550
Year Founded: 1989
Business Description:
Specialty Food Products, Seasonings, Flavorings & Food Decorations Mfr & Distr
S.I.C.: 2087; 2099
N.A.I.C.S.: 311942; 311930; 311999
Advertising Expenditures: $2,500,000
Media: 6-15-19-23
Distr.: Natl.
Budget Set: Dec.
Personnel:
Keith Gibbons *(Chm)*
Angela Francolini *(Pres & CEO)*
Brian Rainey *(VP-Sls & Mktg)*
Advertising Agency:
JWT Canada
160 Bloor St E Ste 800
Toronto, ON M4W 3P7, Canada
Tel.: (416) 926-7300
Fax: (416) 967-2859

LA PREFERIDA, INC.

3400 W 35th St
Chicago, IL 60632
Mailing Address:
PO Box 649
Marianna, AR 72360-0649
Tel.: (773) 254-7200
Fax: (773) 254-8546
E-mail: info@lapref.com
Web Site: www.lapreferida.com
Approx. Number Employees: 60
Year Founded: 1898
Business Description:
Ethnic Food Mfr & Distr
S.I.C.: 5149; 5148
N.A.I.C.S.: 424490; 424480
Export
Media: 5-6-8-17-19-23-24-25
Distr.: Natl.
Personnel:
David Steinbarth *(Owner)*
Richard Steinbarth *(Owner)*
Greg Gondek *(CFO)*
Brands & Products:
LA PREFERIDA

Key to Media (For complete agency information see *The Advertising Red Books-Agencies* edition):
1. Bus. Publs. 2. Cable T.V. 3. Catalogs & Directories. 4. Co-op Adv. 5. Consumer Mags. 6. D.M. to Bus. Estab.7. D.M. to Consumers 8. Daily Newsp. 9. Exhibits/Trade Shows 10. Foreign 11. Infomercial 12. Internet Adv.13. Multimedia 14. Network Radio 15. Network T.V. 16. Newsp. Distr. Mags. 17. Other 18. Outdoor (Posters, Transit) 19. Point of Purchase20. Premiums, Novelties 21. Product Samples 22. Special Events Mktg. 23. Spot Radio 24. Spot T.V. 25. Weekly Newsp. 26. Yellow Page Adv.

LACTALIS AMERICAN GROUP
(Sub. of Groupe Lactalis)
2376 S Park Ave
Buffalo, NY 14220
Tel.: (716) 823-6262
Fax: (716) 823-6454
Toll Free: (800) 828-7031
Web Site:
www.lactalisamericangroup.com
E-Mail For Key Personnel:
Marketing Director: donna.rippin@lactalis.us
Approx. Number Employees: 2,000
Year Founded: 1947
Business Description:
Mfr. Cheese
S.I.C.: 2022
N.A.I.C.S.: 311513
Import Export
Media: 1-2-3-4-5-6-8-10-13-17-19-20-21-22-23-24
Distr.: Natl.
Personnel:
Fredrick Bouisset *(Pres & CEO)*
John Zielinski *(CFO)*
Charles Hylkema *(VP-Fin)*
Donna Rippin *(Dir-Mktg)*
Angela Fisher *(Dir-Mktg)*
David Issenberg *(Mktg Mgr-Channel)*
James Binner *(Sls Mgr-Foodservice Div-East)*
Brands & Products:
GALBANI
MOZZARELLA FRESCA
PRECIOUS
PRESIDENT
SHAPESTERS
SORRENTO
STICKSTERS
STRINGSTERS
Advertising Agency:
Partners & Napier
192 Mill St Ste 600
Rochester, NY 14614
Tel.: (585) 454-1010
Fax: (585) 454-1575
Toll Free: (800) 274-4954

LANCASTER COLONY CORPORATION
37 W Broad St Ste 500
Columbus, OH 43215-4132
Tel.: (614) 224-7141
Fax: (614) 469-8219
Web Site: www.lancastercolony.com
Approx. Sls.: $1,089,946,000
Approx. Number Employees: 3,100
Year Founded: 1961
Business Description:
Holding Company; Specialty Foods, Candles & Glassware & Automotive Products
S.I.C.: 2035; 2038; 2099; 5144; 6719
N.A.I.C.S.: 311941; 311412; 311942; 424440; 551112
Export
Advertising Expenditures: $21,132,160
Media: 17
Distr.: Natl.
Personnel:
John B. Gerlach, Jr. *(Chm, Pres & CEO)*
Patricia Schnyder *(Exec Mng Dir)*
John L. Boylan *(CFO, Treas, VP & Asst Sec)*
Matthew R. Shurte *(Chief Ethics Officer, Sec & Gen Counsel)*
Richard W. Gentil *(Asst Treas)*
David M Segal *(Sr Corp Counsel & Asst Sec)*
Brands & Products:
AMISH KITCHEN
AUNT VI'S
BRODY
CANDLE-LITE
CARDINI'S
CHATHAM VILLAGE
COLONY
DEE ZEE
FOSTORIA
GIRARD'S
INDIANA GLASS
INN MAID
KONETA
LANCASTER COLONY
MAMMA BELLA
MARSHALL'S
MARY'S
MARZETTI
MOUNTAIN TOP
NEW YORK BRAND
NEW YORK FROZEN FOODS
OTRIA
PFEIFFER
PROTECTA
REAMES
ROMANOFF
SISTER SCHUBERT'S
TEXAS TOAST
T.MARZETTI

LANCASTER FINE FOODS, INC.
2320 Norman Rd
Lancaster, PA 17601
Tel.: (717) 397-9578
Fax: (717) 397-0941
Web Site:
www.lancasterfinefoods.com
Business Description:
Organic Food Mfr
N.A.I.C.S.: 311999
Media: 17
Personnel:
Doug Harris *(Pres)*
Brands & Products:
GREEN VALLEY RANCH FOODS

LAND O'LAKES, INC.
4001 Lexington Ave N
Arden Hills, MN 55126-2934
Mailing Address:
PO Box 64101
Saint Paul, MN 55164-0101
Tel.: (651) 481-2222
Fax: (651) 481-2000
Toll Free: (800) 328-9680
Telex: 910-563-3663
Web Site: www.landolakesinc.com
E-Mail For Key Personnel:
Public Relations: lboth@landolakes.com
Approx. Sls.: $12,039,259,000
Approx. Number Employees: 8,700
Year Founded: 1921
Business Description:
Dairy Products Producer
S.I.C.: 2021; 0241; 0252; 2022; 5143
N.A.I.C.S.: 311512; 112120; 112310; 311513; 424430
Export
Advertising Expenditures: $82,600,000
Media: 2-4-5-6-7-8-9-10-16-18-19-20-21-22-23-24-25
Distr.: Natl.; Reg.
Budget Set: Nov.
Personnel:
Pete Kappelman *(Chm)*
Rodney Schroeder *(Pres & COO)*
Christopher J. Policinski *(CEO)*
Daniel Knutson *(CFO)*
Alan Pierson *(COO-Dairy Foods Indus & Exec VP)*
Steve Dunphy *(COO-Retail Foods & Exec VP)*
Jerry Kaminski *(COO-Dairy Foods Indus & Exec VP)*
Mike Vande Logt *(COO-Seed & Exec VP)*
Fernando Palacios *(Exec VP-Ops & Supply Chain)*
Jim Fife *(Sr VP-Member & Pub Affairs)*
Karen Grabow *(Sr VP-Bus Dev Svcs & Govt Rels)*
Loren Heeringa *(Sr VP-HR)*
Peter Janzen *(Sr VP-Law & Intl Dev)*
Barry Wolfish *(Sr VP-Corp Mktg & Comm)*
Lydia Botham *(Dir)*
Brands & Products:
ALPINE LACE
CROPLAN GENETICS
LAND O' LAKES
PMI NUTRITION
WHERE SIMPLE GOODNESS BEGINS
YOUR PASSION. OUR PROMISE
Advertising Agencies:
Campbell Mithun, Inc.
Campbell Mithun Tower 222 S 9th St
Minneapolis, MN 55402-3389
Tel.: (612) 347-1000
Fax: (612) 347-1515
(Consumer & Foodservice Products)

Colle+McVoy
400 1st Ave N Ste 700
Minneapolis, MN 55401-1954
Tel.: (612) 305-6000
Fax: (612) 305-6500
Consumer Web Site
Creative
Development
Land O'Lakes Dairy Foods - Digital
Assignment
Production
Strategy

Eisenman Associates Inc.
401 Broadway 22nd Fl
New York, NY 10013
Tel.: (212) 941-0550
Fax: (212) 941-0710

J.T. Mega Marketing Communications
4020 Minnetonka Blvd
Minneapolis, MN 55416-4100
Tel.: (952) 929-1370
Fax: (952) 929-5417
Toll Free: (800) 923-6342

OLSON
1625 Hennepin Ave
Minneapolis, MN 55403
Tel.: (612) 215-9800
Fax: (612) 215-9801

LAVAZZA PREMIUM COFFEES CORP.
(Sub. of Luigi Lavazza S.p.A.)
3 Park Ave 28th Fl
New York, NY 10016
Tel.: (212) 725-8800
Fax: (212) 725-9475
Toll Free: (800) GOODCUP
E-mail: info@lavazzausa.com
Web Site: www.lavazza.com
Approx. Number Employees: 230
Year Founded: 1900
Business Description:
Coffee Mfr
S.I.C.: 5149
N.A.I.C.S.: 424490
Import
Advertising Expenditures: $1,000,000
Media: 2-4-6-10-13-21
Distr.: Natl.
Budget Set: Sept.
Personnel:
Ennio Ranaboldo *(CEO)*
Giuseppe Lavazza *(Dir-Strategic Marketing)*
Brands & Products:
LAVAZZA

LEA & PERRINS INC.
(Sub. of H.J. Heinz Company)
1501 Pollitt Dr
Fair Lawn, NJ 07410
Tel.: (201) 791-1600
Fax: (201) 791-8945
Web Site: www.leaperrins.com
Sales Range: $50-74.9 Million
Approx. Number Employees: 65
Business Description:
Worcestershire Sauce, Steak Sauce & Condiments Mfr
S.I.C.: 2035
N.A.I.C.S.: 311941
Import
Advertising Expenditures: $7,000,000
Media: 3
Distr.: Intl.; Natl.
Budget Set: Oct.
Advertising Agency:
Euro RSCG Barcelona
World Trade Center, Moll de Barcelona s/n
Barcelona, Spain
Tel.: (34) 93 341 0200
Fax: (34) 93 341 0201

THE LEAVITT CORPORATION
100 Santilli Hwy
Everett, MA 02149-1938
Mailing Address:
PO Box 490067
Everett, MA 02149-0998
Tel.: (617) 389-2600
Fax: (617) 387-9085
E-mail: markhintlian@teddie.com
Web Site: www.teddie.com
Sales Range: $50-74.9 Million
Approx. Number Employees: 62
Year Founded: 1924
Business Description:
Peanut Butter & Nut Products Mfr
S.I.C.: 2068
N.A.I.C.S.: 311911
Import Export
Media: 2-4-10-13-19
Distr.: Intl.; Natl.
Personnel:
James T. Hintlian *(Chm)*
Frank Ciampa *(VP-Pur)*

The Leavitt Corporation — (Continued)

Brands & Products:
RIVER QUEEN
TEDDIE
TEDDIE PEANUT BUTTER

LEON'S FINE FOODS, INC.
(d/b/a Leon's Texas Cuisine)
2100 N Redbud Blvd
McKinney, TX 75069
Mailing Address:
PO Box 1850
McKinney, TX 75070-1850
Tel.: (972) 529-5050
Fax: (972) 529-2244
Web Site: www.texascuisine.com
E-Mail For Key Personnel:
Sales Director: scott@texascuisine.com
Sales Range: $25-49.9 Million
Approx. Number Employees: 200
Year Founded: 1946
Business Description:
Snack Food Mfr & Distr
S.I.C.: 5147; 2099
N.A.I.C.S.: 311612; 311999
Export
Media: 6-26
Distr.: Natl.
Budget Set: Aug.
Personnel:
Bob L. Clements *(Pres)*
John Vroman *(Sr VP-Ops)*
Cindy Stephens *(VP-HR)*
Scott Elwonger *(Sls Dir)*
Brands & Products:
CORN DOGS
JALITOS
LEON'S TEXAS CUISINE

LEPAGE BAKERIES, INC.
Country Kitchen Plz
Auburn, ME 04211-1900
Mailing Address:
PO Box 1900
Auburn, ME 04211-1900
Tel.: (207) 783-9161
Fax: (207) 783-3300
E-mail: lbck@lepagebakeries.com
Web Site: www.lepagebakeries.com
Sales Range: $25-49.9 Million
Approx. Number Employees: 525
Year Founded: 1903
Business Description:
Mfr & Whslr of Bakery Products
S.I.C.: 2051; 5461
N.A.I.C.S.: 311812; 311811
Export
Media: 4-5-9-19-20-21-23-24
Distr.: Reg.
Budget Set: Aug.
Personnel:
Albert R. Lepage *(Chm)*
Andrew P. Barowsky *(Pres & CEO)*
Brands & Products:
BAROWSKY'S
COUNTRY KITCHEN
LEPAGE BAKERIES

LEPRINO FOODS COMPANY
1830 W 38th Ave
Denver, CO 80211
Tel.: (303) 480-2600
Fax: (303) 480-2605
Toll Free: (800) LEPRINO
E-mail: cheese@leprinofoods.com
Web Site: www.leprinofoods.com
Approx. Number Employees: 3,000
Year Founded: 1950
Business Description:
Cheese Mfr & Distr
S.I.C.: 2022
N.A.I.C.S.: 311513
Export
Media: 2-7-10-20-22
Distr.: Natl.
Personnel:
Larry Jensen *(Pres)*
James G. Leprino *(CEO)*
Ron Klump *(CFO)*
Richard Barz *(Sr VP-Quality Assurance & R & D)*
Kevin Burke *(Sr VP-Bus Dev-Global)*
Mike Reidy *(Sr VP-Procurement & Logistics & Bus Dev)*
Shane Cole *(Mgr-HR)*
Andrea Kroekel *(Mgr-Mktg Svcs)*
Brands & Products:
EGGREP PRO
GEL PRO
INNOVATIVE BULK RIBBON
LE-PRO
LEPRINO FOODS
NOBODY KNOWS MORE ABOUT MOZZARELLA
QLC
QUALITY-LOCKED
TEMP PRO
WALK THIS WHEY
WRAPPED RIBBON

LIDESTRI FOODS, INC.
815 W Whitney Rd
Fairport, NY 14450-1030
Tel.: (585) 377-7700
Fax: (585) 377-8150
Web Site: www.francescorinaldi.com
Approx. Sls.: $196,000,000
Approx. Number Employees: 500
Year Founded: 1937
Business Description:
Sauces & Condiments
S.I.C.: 2035
N.A.I.C.S.: 311941
Export
Advertising Expenditures: $7,000,000
Media: 2-9-10-14-15-20-21-23-24-25
Distr.: Reg.
Budget Set: July
Personnel:
John LiDestri *(Pres & CEO)*
Jan Vapere *(CFO)*
Edward P. Salzano *(COO & Exec VP-Mktg)*
Brands & Products:
FRANCESCO RINALDI
ULTRA DOLCE

LIFEWAY FOODS, INC.
6431 W Oakton St
Morton Grove, IL 60053
Tel.: (847) 967-1010
Fax: (847) 967-6558
E-mail: info@lifeway.net
Web Site: www.lifeway.net
Approx. Sls.: $58,499,893
Approx. Number Employees: 315
Year Founded: 1986
Business Description:
Specialty Dairy Products Mfr
S.I.C.: 0241; 2022; 2026; 2034
N.A.I.C.S.: 112120; 311423; 311511; 311513
Advertising Expenditures: $2,390,003
Media: 4-6-8-9-10-13-16-18-21-22-23-26
Personnel:
Mike Smolyansky *(Founder)*
Julie Smolyansky *(Pres & CEO)*
Ludmila Smolyansky *(CEO)*
Edward P. Smolyansky *(CFO)*
Marina Nikolenko *(Dir-Mktg)*
Brands & Products:
BASICS PLUS
GO WITH THE FLOW
IT'S PUDDING
KEFIR
LA FRUTA
LIFEWAY
PROBUGS
SLIM6
SOY TREAT
SWEET KISS

LIGHTLIFE FOODS
(Sub. of ConAgra Foods, Inc.)
153 Industrial Blvd
Turners Falls, MA 01376
Tel.: (413) 774-9000
Toll Free: (800) SOY-EASY
E-mail: info@lightlife.com
Web Site: www.lightlife.com
Sales Range: $75-99.9 Million
Approx. Number Employees: 150
Year Founded: 1979
Business Description:
Vegetarian & Soy Food Products Mfr
S.I.C.: 2099; 2034
N.A.I.C.S.: 311999; 311423
Media: 2-5-6-8-10-11-13-14-16-19-20-21-22-23-25
Personnel:
Darcy Zbinovec *(VP & Gen Mgr)*
Brands & Products:
SMART MENU

LITTLE LADY FOODS, INC.
2323 Pratt Blvd
Elk Grove Village, IL 60007-5918
Tel.: (847) 631-3500
Fax: (847) 806-0026
Toll Free: (800) 439-1440
E-mail: info@llf.com
Web Site: www.littleladyfoods.com
Approx. Number Employees: 180
Year Founded: 1961
Business Description:
Producer of Food & Customized Food Items
S.I.C.: 2038; 2099
N.A.I.C.S.: 311412; 311999
Import Export
Media: 1-2-3-4-5-6-7-9-10-18-19-20-21-22-25
Distr.: Intl.
Budget Set: Nov.
Personnel:
John T. Geocaris *(Owner)*
Dan Geocaris *(Vice Chm)*
Peter Cokinos *(Sr VP)*

LLOYDS BARBEQUE COMPANY
(Sub. of Hormel Foods Corporation)
1455 Mendota Hts Rd
Saint Paul, MN 55120-1002
Tel.: (800) 533-2000
Fax: (651) 681-1430
Toll Free: (800) 999-7427
E-mail: info@lloydsbbq.com
Web Site: www.lloydsbbq.com
Sales Range: $100-124.9 Million
Approx. Number Employees: 200
Year Founded: 1978
Business Description:
Cooked Meats From Purchased Meat
S.I.C.: 5147; 2099
N.A.I.C.S.: 311612; 311999
Advertising Agency:
Burson-Marsteller
222 Merchandise Mart Plz Ste 250
Chicago, IL 60654-1022
Tel.: (312) 596-3400
Fax: (312) 596-3600
— Erin Conn *(Acct Exec)*

LOUIS MAULL COMPANY
219 N Market
Saint Louis, MO 63102
Tel.: (314) 241-8410
Fax: (314) 241-9840
E-mail: info@maull.com
Web Site: www.maull.com
Sales Range: $10-24.9 Million
Approx. Number Employees: 20
Year Founded: 1897
Business Description:
Barbecue Sauce Mfr
S.I.C.: 2033
N.A.I.C.S.: 311421
Media: 2-5-9-14-18-24
Distr.: Reg.
Personnel:
David Ahner *(Corp Sec & VP-Sls)*
Brands & Products:
JALAPENO
MAULL'S
MAULL'S BARBECUE SAUCE
SMOKY

LSI INC.
39210 221st St
Alpena, SD 57312
Mailing Address:
PO Box 159
Alpena, SD 57312
Tel.: (605) 849-3367
Fax: (605) 849-8810
E-mail: info@lsiincsd.com
Approx. Number Employees: 470
Business Description:
Sausages & Other Prepared Meats
S.I.C.: 5147
N.A.I.C.S.: 311612
Personnel:
Terry Smith *(Pres)*
Jack Link *(CEO)*
Doug Walz *(Fin Controller)*
Jeff LeFever *(Dir-Mktg-Jack Link)*
Kathy Watson *(Dir-HR)*
Rick Tebay *(Plant Mgr)*
Cark Kappel *(Safety Mgr)*
Scott Mees *(Asst Plant Mgr)*
Brands & Products:
JACK LINKS
JACK LINKS BEEF JERKY
Advertising Agencies:
Atomic Playpen
701 Xenia Ave S Ste 200
Minneapolis, MN 55416
Tel.: (763) 231-3400
Fax: (763) 231-3401

Carmichael Lynch
110 N 5th St
Minneapolis, MN 55403
Tel.: (612) 334-6000
Fax: (612) 334-6090

Key to Media (For complete agency information see *The Advertising Red Books-Agencies* edition):
1. Bus. Publs. 2. Cable T.V. 3. Catalogs & Directories. 4. Co-op Adv. 5. Consumer Mags. 6. D.M. to Bus. Estab.7. D.M. to Consumers 8. Daily Newsp. 9. Exhibits/Trade Shows 10. Foreign 11. Infomercial 12. Internet Adv.13. Multimedia 14. Network Radio 15. Network T.V. 16. Newsp. Distr. Mags. 17. Other 18. Outdoor (Posters, Transit) 19. Point of Purchase20. Premiums, Novelties 21. Product Samples 22. Special Events Mktg. 23. Spot Radio 24. Spot T.V. 25. Weekly Newsp. 26. Yellow Page Adv.

Carmichael Lynch Spong
110 N 5th St
Minneapolis, MN 55403
Tel.: (612) 375-8555
Fax: (612) 375-8501

LUND FOOD HOLDINGS, INC.

4100 W 50th St
Edina, MN 55424-1200
Tel.: (952) 927-3663
Fax: (952) 927-3663
Web Site: www.lfhi.com
Sales Range: $25-49.9 Million
Approx. Number Employees: 5,500
Year Founded: 1939
Business Description:
Holding Company; Grocery, Bakery & Liquor Stores
S.I.C.: 5411
N.A.I.C.S.: 445110
Personnel:
Phil Lombardo *(VP-Sls & Mktg)*
Peter Kuhr *(Mgr-Product Dev)*
Brands & Products:
BYERLY'S
Advertising Agency:
Risdall Marketing Group
550 Main St
New Brighton, MN 55112-3271
Tel.: (651) 286-6700
Fax: (651) 631-2561
Toll Free: (888) RISDALL

LUND'S FISHERIES, INC.

997 Ocean Dr
Cape May, NJ 08204
Tel.: (609) 884-7600
Fax: (609) 884-0664
E-mail: info@lundsfish.com
Web Site: www.lundsfish.com
Approx. Number Employees: 130
Year Founded: 1954
Business Description:
Seafood Products Producer & Distr
S.I.C.: 5146
N.A.I.C.S.: 424460
Import Export
Media: 4-10-26
Personnel:
Jeff Reichle *(Pres)*
Brands & Products:
CONSIDER THE SOURCE!!!
LUND'S
SEA LEGEND BRAND
SUN COAST CALAMARI

M.A. GEDNEY COMPANY

2100 Stoughton Ave
Chaska, MN 55318
Tel.: (952) 448-2612
Fax: (952) 448-1790
Web Site: www.gedneypickle.com
Approx. Number Employees: 90
Business Description:
Pickles, Vinegar
S.I.C.: 2033
N.A.I.C.S.: 311421
Media: 13
Personnel:
Charles Weil *(Pres)*
Jess Traynor *(CFO)*
Brands & Products:
CAINS
DELMONTE
GEDNEY
STATE FAIR
Advertising Agency:
Gabriel deGrood Bendt
608 2nd Ave S Ste 129
Minneapolis, MN 55402
Tel.: (612) 547-5000
Fax: (612) 547-5090

MALLET & COMPANY, INC.

51 Arch St
Carnegie, PA 15106
Mailing Address:
PO Box 474
Carnegie, PA 15106-0474
Tel.: (412) 276-9000
Fax: (412) 276-9002
Toll Free: (800) 245-2757
E-mail: sales@malletoil.com
Web Site: www.malletoil.com
E-Mail For Key Personnel:
Sales Director: sales@malletoil.com
Approx. Number Employees: 90
Year Founded: 1939
Business Description:
Oils, Ingredients & Custom Food Processing Equipment
S.I.C.: 2099; 2079
N.A.I.C.S.: 311999; 311225
Media: 2-7-10
Distr.: Intl.; Natl.
Budget Set: Dec.
Personnel:
Robert I. Mallet *(Pres)*
Matt Karlovitz *(Mgr-Acct)*
Bob Wilhelm *(Mgr-Adv)*
Brands & Products:
EVERITE
EXA LUB
GOLDEN CANOLA
GOLDEN GLOW
HIFLEX
K LUBE
KAKE MATE
KOKO GOLD COCONUT OIL
LANCELOT
MELLO GOLD
MELLOW SUPREME
PIC 77
POLLY PEP
PRIME FRY
PROFORM CS
SATIN DONUT FRY
SATIN FRY
SATIN GLO
SATIN PLUS
SPARKLE
SUNNY GOLD
THRIFTEE
THRIFTEE GOLD
TOUCH O' GOLD PEANUT OIL
TRO LUBE
VEGALUBE

MANISCHEWITZ COMPANY

(Sub. of R.A.B. Holdings, Inc.)
1 Harmon Plz 10th Fl
Secaucus, NJ 07094
Tel.: (201) 333-3700
Tel.: (201) 553-1100
Fax: (201) 333-4007
E-mail: deborah.ross@manischewitz.com
Web Site: www.manischewitz.com
Approx. Number Employees: 240
Year Founded: 1888
Business Description:
Kosher Foods Mfr
S.I.C.: 2052; 2045
N.A.I.C.S.: 311821; 311822
Import Export
Media: 6-8-9-19-21-22-23-25
Distr.: Natl.
Budget Set: June
Personnel:
David Rossi *(Sr VP-Mktg)*
Brands & Products:
GOODMAN'S
GUILTLESS GOURMET
HOROWITZ MARGARETEN
MANISCHEWITZ
MISPACHA
MOTHER'S
MRS. ADLER'S
ROKEACH
SEASON

MAPLE LEAF CONSUMER FOODS

(Sub. of Maple Leaf Foods Inc.)
321 Courtland Avenue East
Kitchener, ON N2G 3X8, Canada
Mailing Address:
PO Box 130
Kitchener, ON N2G 3X8, Canada
Tel.: (519) 741-5000
Fax: (519) 749-7400
Toll Free: (800) 567-1890
Web Site: www.mapleleaf.ca
Sales Range: $750-799.9 Million
Approx. Number Employees: 1,100
Business Description:
Meat Products & Grocery Items for Retail & Food Service Markets Mfr
S.I.C.: 5147
N.A.I.C.S.: 311612
Media: 4-8-18-19-22-25-26
Distr.: Intl.; Natl.
Personnel:
Doug Gingrich *(VP-Sls & Mktg)*
Josh Van Bladel *(Mgr-Ops)*
Brands & Products:
HOTROD
HOTSTUFFS
LEAN LINKS
LEANSTUFFS
OKTOBERFEST
SCHNEIDERS
Advertising Agencies:
John St.
172 John Street
Toronto, ON M5T 1X5, Canada
Tel.: (416) 348-0048
Fax: (416) 348-0050

Noble
33 W Monroe St Ste 300
Chicago, IL 60603
Tel.: (312) 670-2900
Fax: (312) 670-7420
Toll Free: (800) 986-6253

MAPLE LEAF FOODS INC.

30 Saint Clair Ave W
Toronto, ON M4V 3A2, Canada
Tel.: (416) 926-2000
Fax: (416) 926-2018
E-mail: mapleleaffoods@consumerservicesemail.com
Web Site: www.mapleleaf.com
Approx. Rev.: $5,061,619,000
Approx. Number Employees: 21,000
Year Founded: 1927
Business Description:
Food Processor
S.I.C.: 2099
N.A.I.C.S.: 311999
Export
Advertising Expenditures: $28,000,000
Media: 4-6-8-11-13-14-15-18-19-20-21
Distr.: Intl.
Personnel:
G. Wallace F. McCain *(Chm)*
Michael H. McCain *(Pres & CEO)*
J. Scott McCain *(Pres & COO-Agribusiness Grp)*
E. Jeffrey Hutchinson *(CIO)*
Stephen Graham *(CMO)*
Douglas W. Dodds *(Chief Strategy Officer)*
Les Dakens *(Chief HR Officer & Sr VP)*
Randall Huffman *(Chief Food Safety Officer)*
Kevin P. Golding *(Pres-Rothsay)*
C. Barry Mclean *(Pres-Canada Bread Fresh Bakery)*
Real Menard *(Pres-Canada Bread Frozen Bakery)*
Simon Wookey *(Pres-Mapley Leaf Fresh Prepared Foods)*
Rocco Cappuccitti *(Sec, Sr VP-Transactions & Admin)*
Maryanne Chantler *(Sr VP & Gen Mgr-Canada Bread Fresh-Ontario)*
Bill Kaldis *(Sr VP-Logistics)*
Lynda J. Kuhn *(Sr VP-Comm)*
Deborah K. Simpson *(Sr VP-Fin)*
J. Nicholas Boland *(VP-Fin Projects)*
Patti Hamimpon *(Dir-Benefits)*
Brands & Products:
BEN'S
BURNS
CALIFORNIA GOLDMINER
CANINE PLUS
DEMPSTER'S
HEALTHY WAY
HYGRADE
LANDMARK FEEDS
MAPLE LEAF
MAPLE LEAF MEDALLION NATURALLY
MAPLE LEAF NATURES GOURMET
MAPLE LEAF PRIME NATURALLY
MAPLE LEAF SIMPLY FRESH
MEDALLION
NEW YORK BAGEL
NUTRIWHIP
OLIVIERI
PRIME
PRIME TURKEY
READY CRISP
SCHNEIDER FOODS
SHOPSY'S
SHUR-GAIN
SIMPLY SAVOUR
TENDERFLAKE
TOP DOGS
WE TAKE CARE

MAPLE LODGE FARMS LTD.

8301 Winston Churchill Blvd
Brampton, ON L6Y 0A2, Canada
Tel.: (905) 455-8340
Fax: (905) 455-8543
Toll Free: (888) 664-4444 (Canada)
Toll Free: (800) 463-3548 (US)
E-mail: customerservice@maplelodgefarms.com
Web Site: www.maplelodgefarms.com
Approx. Number Employees: 2,200
Year Founded: 1955

Key to Media (For complete agency information see *The Advertising Red Books-Agencies* edition):
1. Bus. Publs. 2. Cable T.V. 3. Catalogs & Directories. 4. Co-op Adv. 5. Consumer Mags. 6. D.M. to Bus. Estab.7. D.M. to Consumers 8. Daily Newsp. 9. Exhibits/Trade Shows 10. Foreign 11. Infomercial 12. Internet Adv.13. Multimedia 14. Network Radio 15. Network T.V. 16. Newsp. Distr. Mags. 17. Other 18. Outdoor (Posters, Transit) 19. Point of Purchase20. Premiums, Novelties 21. Product Samples 22. Special Events Mktg. 23. Spot Radio 24. Spot T.V. 25. Weekly Newsp. 26. Yellow Page Adv.

Maple Lodge Farms Ltd. — (Continued)
Business Description:
Poultry & Deli Products Processor & Mfr
S.I.C.: 2015; 2013
N.A.I.C.S.: 311615; 311613
Media: 2-5-10-19-20-21-22-23
Personnel:
Bob May *(Co-Chm)*
Jack May *(Co-Chm)*
Greg Scott *(CFO)*
Susan Grant *(VP-Mktg)*
Debi Kee *(VP-HR)*
Brands & Products:
MAPLE LODGE FARMS
SALSALITTA
TERIYAKI
ZABIHA HALAL

MAPLEHURST BAKERIES, INC.
(Sub. of Weston Bakeries Limited)
50 Maplehurst Dr
Brownsburg, IN 46112
Tel.: (317) 858-9000
Fax: (317) 858-9009
E-mail: webmaster@maplehurstbakeries.com
Web Site:
www.maplehurstbakeries.com
Approx. Number Employees: 500
Business Description:
Frozen Bakery Products for In-Store & Food Service Bakeries Mfr
S.I.C.: 2051; 5812
N.A.I.C.S.: 311812; 722110
Media: 2-9-10
Personnel:
Dave Winiger *(Pres)*

MAR-JAC HOLDINGS INC.
1020 Aviation Blvd
Gainesville, GA 30501-6839
Mailing Address:
PO Box 1017
Gainesville, GA 30503
Tel.: (770) 531-5000
Fax: (770) 531-5015
Toll Free: (800) 226-0561
E-mail: info@marjacpoultry.com
Web Site: www.marjacpoultry.com
Sales Range: $150-199.9 Million
Approx. Number Employees: 1,000
Year Founded: 1954
Business Description:
Holding Company; Poultry Slaughtering & Processing
S.I.C.: 2015; 6719
N.A.I.C.S.: 311615; 551112
Import Export
Advertising Expenditures: $500,000
Media: 7-13-25
Personnel:
Jamal Al-Baranzinji *(Pres)*
Mahmoud Mohamed *(VP-Fin)*

MARUCHAN INC.
(Sub. of Toyo Suisan Kaisha, Ltd.)
15800 Laguna Canyon Rd
Irvine, CA 92718
Tel.: (949) 789-2300
Fax: (949) 789-2350
Web Site: www.maruchan.com
Approx. Number Employees: 500
Year Founded: 1978
Business Description:
Mfr. of Dehydrated Instant Noodle Soups & Won Ton Soup & Related Products
S.I.C.: 2098; 2099
N.A.I.C.S.: 311823; 311999
Media: 5-6-9-14-19-21-25-26
Distr.: Intl.; Natl.
Budget Set: Apr.
Brands & Products:
JUMBOWL
MARUCHAN

MASSIMO ZANETTI BEVERAGE USA
(Sub. of Segafredo Zanetti S.p.A.)
200 Port Centre Pkwy
Portsmouth, VA 23704
Tel.: (757) 215-7300
Fax: (757) 215-7447
Web Site: www.mzb-usa.com
Approx. Number Employees: 1,275
Year Founded: 1932
Business Description:
Processing, Packaging & Marketing of Coffee & Tea Products
S.I.C.: 5149; 2099
N.A.I.C.S.: 424490; 311999
Media: 1-2-3-5-6-8-9-10-15-18-19-20-21-22-23-24-25
Distr.: Natl.
Budget Set: Apr.
Advertising Agency:
BCF
4500 Main St Ste 600
Virginia Beach, VA 23462
Tel.: (757) 497-4811
Fax: (757) 497-3684

THE MASTERSON COMPANY, INC.
4023 W Natl Ave
Milwaukee, WI 53215
Tel.: (414) 647-1132
Fax: (414) 647-1170
Toll Free: (800) 558-0990
E-mail: joemasterson@mastersoncompany.com
Web Site:
www.mastersoncompany.com
Approx. Number Employees: 150
Year Founded: 1848
Business Description:
Dessert Toppings Mfr
S.I.C.: 2099
N.A.I.C.S.: 311999
Media: 13-17-22
Distr.: Natl.
Personnel:
Joe A. Masterson *(CEO)*
Dave Erickson *(VP-Sls)*
Irene Groh *(Dir-Mktg & Sls)*

MAUI LAND & PINEAPPLE COMPANY, INC.
870 Haliimaile Rd
Makawao, HI 96768-9768
Tel.: (808) 877-3351
Fax: (808) 871-0953
E-mail: mlpcommunications@mlpmaui.com
Web Site: www.mauiland.com
Approx. Rev.: $41,954,000
Approx. Number Employees: 180
Year Founded: 1909
Business Description:
Land Holding & Operating Services for Agriculture & Resort Operations; Pineapple Production
S.I.C.: 2033; 0179; 9532
N.A.I.C.S.: 311421; 111336; 925120
Export
Advertising Expenditures: $651,000
Media: 7-10-22
Personnel:
Warren H. Haruki *(Chm & Interim CEO)*
Ryan L. Churchill *(Pres & COO)*
Tim T. Esaki *(CFO)*
Calvin H. Oda *(Sr VP)*
Karin Sagar *(VP & Corp Mktg)*

MAYFIELD DAIRY FARMS, LLC
(Sub. of Dean Dairy Holdings, LLC)
806 E Madison Ave
Athens, TN 37371-0310
Tel.: (423) 745-2151
Fax: (423) 745-9118
E-mail: info@mayfielddairy.com
Web Site: www.mayfielddairy.com
Sales Range: $300-349.9 Million
Approx. Number Employees: 600
Business Description:
Mfr. Of Fluid Milk & Ice Cream
S.I.C.: 2026; 2024
N.A.I.C.S.: 311511; 311520
Personnel:
Scottie Mayfield *(Pres)*
Robbie Roberts *(VP-Sls)*
Mary Williams *(Gen Mgr-Southeast)*
Mark Cox *(Sr Mgr-Project)*
Alan Owen *(Brand Mgr-Mktg-Dean Foods Southeast)*
Advertising Agency:
Waterhouse Public Relations
735 Broad St Ste 1004
Chattanooga, TN 37402
Tel.: (423) 643-4977
Fax: (423) 648-2929

MBM CORPORATION
2641 Meadowbrook Rd
Rocky Mount, NC 27801
Mailing Address:
PO Box 800
Rocky Mount, NC 27802
Tel.: (252) 985-7200
Fax: (252) 985-7241
Toll Free: (800) 233-2508
Sales Range: $1-4.9 Billion
Approx. Number Employees: 3,000
Year Founded: 1947
Business Description:
Food & Related Products Services to National Restaurant Chains
S.I.C.: 5812
N.A.I.C.S.: 722310
Media: 9-25
Personnel:
Jerry L. Wordsworth *(CEO)*
Jeffrey M. Kowalk *(CFO)*
Tim Ozment *(Dir-HR)*
Brands & Products:
DESTROYIT
TRIUMPH

MCARTHUR DAIRY, LLC
(Sub. of Dean Dairy Holdings, LLC)
240 NE 71st St
Miami, FL 33138
Tel.: (305) 514-8862
Fax: (305) 576-9203
Web Site: www.deanfoods.com
Sales Range: $150-199.9 Million
Year Founded: 1929
Business Description:
Dairy Product Mfr
S.I.C.: 0241
N.A.I.C.S.: 112120
Media: 2-10-17
Distr.: Reg.
Budget Set: Oct.
Personnel:
Scottie Mayfield *(Pres)*
Brad Abell *(VP & Gen Mgr)*

MCCAIN FOODS LIMITED
8800 Main St
Florenceville, NB E7L 1B2, Canada
Tel.: (506) 392-5541
Fax: (506) 392-8156
Web Site: www.mccain.com
Approx. Sls.: $6,361,420,000
Approx. Number Employees: 30,000
Year Founded: 1957
Business Description:
Frozen Food Mfr
S.I.C.: 2038
N.A.I.C.S.: 311412
Export
Personnel:
G. Wallace F. McCain *(Co-Founder & Vice Chm)*
Dirk Van de Put *(Pres & CEO)*
Kai Bockman *(Mng Dir)*
David Sanchez *(CFO)*
Roman Coba *(CIO)*
Christa Wessel *(Chief Legal Officer)*
Rick Ciccone *(Chief Supply Chain Officer)*
Fred Schaeffer *(CEO-Canada & Asia)*
Karen Basian *(VP-Strategy, Merger, Acquisitions & Innovation)*
Jeff Veysey *(VP-Sls & Food Svc)*
Brands & Products:
AH MCCAIN, YOU'VE DONE IT AGAIN!
BOSTON PRIDE
CATERPAC
CHIP WAGON
FRESH PAK
FRESHCHILL
GOOD FOOD. BETTER LIFE.
HARVEST PRIDE
INVISICOAT
IT'S ALL GOOD
MCCAIN
X-TREME FRIES
Advertising Agencies:
Beattie McGuinness Bungay
16 Short's Gardens
London, WC2H 9AU, United Kingdom
Tel.: (44) 207 632 0400
Fax: (44) 207 632 0401
Oven Chips

Principles Agency
Devonshire Ave St Ln
Leeds, LS8 1AW, United Kingdom
Tel.: (44) 113 226 2222
Fax: (44) 113 226 2223

MCCAIN FOODS USA INC.
(Sub. of McCain Foods Limited)
2275 Cabot Dr
Lisle, IL 60532-3653
Tel.: (630) 955-0400
Fax: (630) 857-4560
Web Site: www.mccainusa.com
Approx. Number Employees: 320
Year Founded: 1985
Business Description:
Pizza, Potato Product & Appetizer Mfr, Marketer & Distr
S.I.C.: 2037
N.A.I.C.S.: 311411
Personnel:
Frank van Schaayk *(CEO)*
Frank Finn *(Sr VP-Comml Ops)*

Key to Media (For complete agency information see *The Advertising Red Books-Agencies* edition):
1. Bus. Publs. 2. Cable T.V. 3. Catalogs & Directories. 4. Co-op Adv. 5. Consumer Mags. 6. D.M. to Bus. Estab.7. D.M. to Consumers 8. Daily Newsp. 9. Exhibits/Trade Shows 10. Foreign 11. Infomercial 12. Internet Adv.13. Multimedia 14. Network Radio 15. Network T.V. 16. Newsp. Distr. Mags. 17. Other 18. Outdoor (Posters, Transit) 19. Point of Purchase20. Premiums, Novelties 21. Product Samples 22. Special Events Mktg. 23. Spot Radio 24. Spot T.V. 25. Weekly Newsp. 26. Yellow Page Adv.

Joe Bybel *(VP-Mktg & Innovation)*
Dierdre Dickerson *(Dir-Corp Comm)*
Advertising Agency:
Schafer Condon Carter
168 N Clinton
Chicago, IL 60661
Tel.: (312) 464-1666
Fax: (312) 464-0628

MCILHENNY COMPANY

Hwy 329
Avery Island, LA 70513
Tel.: (337) 365-8173
Fax: (337) 369-6326
Toll Free: (800) 634-9599
E-mail: whatscooking@tabasco.com
Web Site: www.tabasco.com
Approx. Number Employees: 205
Year Founded: 1868
Business Description:
Mfr. of Pepper Sauces & Condiments
S.I.C.: 2035; 2099
N.A.I.C.S.: 311941; 311942
Import Export
Media: 2-4-6-8-10-11-13-14-15-18-20-21-22-23-24
Distr.: Intl.
Budget Set: Sept. -Oct.
Personnel:
Edward M. Simmons *(Chm)*
Paul C.P. McIlhenny *(Pres & CEO)*
Tony Simmons *(Exec VP)*
Lisa Bell *(VP-Info Sys)*
William Dunn *(VP-Retail-Foodservice Sls)*
Martin Manion *(VP-Corp Mktg)*
Stephen Romero *(VP-Sls-Intl)*
Michael Terrell *(VP-Fin)*
Jan Carroll *(Brand Mgr-Retail)*
Brands & Products:
COOK & LADDER
FAMILY OF FLAVORS
MCILHENNY FARMS
PEPPERFEST
TABASCO
Advertising Agencies:
The Food Group (Tampa)
14499 N Dalemabry Hwy Ste 130
Tampa, FL 33618
Tel.: (813) 933-0683
Fax: (813) 932-1232

Ogilvy & Mather
3530 Hayden Ave
Culver City, CA 90232
Tel.: (310) 280-2200
Fax: (310) 280-9473
Tabasco

MCKENZIES OF VERMONT, INC.

(Sub. of Kayem Foods, Inc.)
160 Flynn Ave
Burlington, VT 05401
Tel.: (802) 864-4585
Fax: (802) 651-7335
Approx. Number Employees: 10
Business Description:
Mfr Sausage Products
S.I.C.: 5147
N.A.I.C.S.: 424470
Media: 2-4-10
Distr.: Natl.
Budget Set: Nov.

MERISANT COMPANY

33 N Dearborn St Ste 200
Chicago, IL 60602
Tel.: (312) 840-6000
Fax: (312) 840-5101
Web Site: www.merisant.com
Sales Range: $200-249.9 Million
Approx. Number Employees: 430
Year Founded: 2000
Business Description:
Synthetic Sweetener Mfr & Marketer
S.I.C.: 5169; 2869
N.A.I.C.S.: 424690; 325199
Advertising Expenditures: $13,420,000
Media: 2-5-7-10-11-13-21
Personnel:
Paul R. Block *(Chm, Pres & CEO)*
Julie Wool *(CFO & VP)*
Richard Mewborn *(COO & VP)*
Jonathan Cole *(Gen Counsel, Sec & VP-Bus Dev)*
Brian Alsvig *(VP-Fin, Plng & Analysis)*
William Beuhner *(Dir-Sls-Food Service Channel)*
Brands & Products:
CANDEREL
CHUKER
DULCET
EQUAL
MISURA
MIVIDA
NUTRAVIA
NUTRIENTIA
PEPTIS PLUS
POTYI
RIDER SWEET
SABRO
SEMBLE
SUCARYL
SWEET SIMPLICITY
SWEETEX
SWEETMATE

METZ BAKING COMPANY

(Sub. of Sara Lee Corporation)
2883 S Hillock Ave
Chicago, IL 60608-5495
Tel.: (773) 376-7700
Fax: (773) 376-7917
Toll Free: (800) 659-4622
Web Site: www.saralee.com
Sales Range: $200-249.9 Million
Approx. Number Employees: 500
Business Description:
Bakery Products Mfr
S.I.C.: 2051
N.A.I.C.S.: 311812
Advertising Expenditures: $500,000
Media: 9-14-24-25
Distr.: Reg.
Budget Set: Nov.

MGP INGREDIENTS, INC.

100 Commercial St PO Box 130
Atchison, KS 66002-2666
Tel.: (913) 367-1480
Fax: (913) 367-0192
E-mail: steve.pickman@mgpingredients.com
Web Site: www.mgpingredients.com
Approx. Sls.: $247,915,000
Approx. Number Employees: 192
Year Founded: 1941
Business Description:
Flour, Vital Wheat Gluten, Wheat Starch & Food Grade Alcohol Mfr & Distr
S.I.C.: 2041; 2085; 2869
N.A.I.C.S.: 311211; 312140; 325199
Export
Advertising Expenditures: $224,000
Media: 2-4-7-10-13-18-26
Personnel:
John R. Speirs *(Chm)*
Timothy W. Newkirk *(Pres & CEO)*
Don Tracy *(CFO & VP-Fin)*
Randall M. Schrick *(Pres-ICP & VP-Engrg)*
William R. Thornton *(Corp Counsel)*
Donald Coffey *(Exec VP-R&D & Innovation)*
Robert G. Booe *(VP-Fin & Admin)*
David Dykstra *(VP-Alcohol Sls & Mktg)*
Jack Healy *(VP-Sls & Admin)*
Clodualdo Maningat *(VP-Application Tech & Technical Svcs)*
Steven J. Pickman *(VP-Corp Rels & Mktg Svcs)*
David E. Rindom *(VP-HR)*
Mike Lasater *(Dir-Sls-Natl)*
Mathew Collins *(Mgr-Corp Pur)*
Stephanie Symns *(Mgr-Comm Svcs)*
Arya Tulva *(Engr)*
Brands & Products:
ARISE
CREATING BETTER SOLUTIONS...NATURALLY
FIBERSYM
FP
HWG 2009
MGP
MGPI CHEWTEX
MGPI PET-TEX
MIDSOL
OMNI-SMOOTH
PASTA POWER
POLYTRITICUM
PREGEL
TERRATEK
WHEATEX
Advertising Agency:
Unicom Marketing Group
2875 S 25th Ave
Broadview, IL 60155
Tel.: (312) 738-1404
Fax: (708) 410-4501

MICHAEL FOODS, INC.

(Holding of GS Capital Partners L.P.)
301 Carlson Pkwy Ste 400
Minnetonka, MN 55305
Tel.: (952) 258-4000
Fax: (952) 258-4911
Toll Free: (800) 325-4270
Web Site: www.michaelfoods.com
E-Mail For Key Personnel:
Public Relations: mark.witmer@michaelfoods.com
Approx. Sls.: $1,542,779,000
Approx. Number Employees: 3,513
Year Founded: 1987
Business Description:
Refrigerated Grocery Products, Non-Frozen Potato Products & Fresh, Frozen & Dried Egg Products Producer & Distr; Owned 90% by Thomas H. Lee Partners
S.I.C.: 0252; 2034; 2099
N.A.I.C.S.: 112310; 311423; 311999
Import Export
Advertising Expenditures: $12,101,000
Media: 2-3-6-7-10-13-18-19-20-21-23-24-25
Distr.: Natl.
Personnel:
James E. Dwyer, Jr. *(Pres & CEO)*
Mark W. Westphal *(CFO & Sr VP)*
Susan Brau *(Assoc Mgr-Mktg)*
Brands & Products:
BETTER'N EGGS
CRYSTAL FARMS
DINERS' CHOICE
ESL MIX BNB
ESL MIX CARTON
ESL WHITE BNB
ESL WHITE CARTON
ESL WHOLE BNB
ESL WHOLE CARTON
ESL YOLK BNB
ESL YOLK CARTON
FARM FRESH FOODS
FRZ BLEND CARTON
FRZ EGGS D'LITE
FRZ MIX BNB
FRZ MIX CARTON
FRZ WHITE CARTON
FRZ WHOLE BNB
FRZ WHOLE CARTON
FRZ YOLK CARTON
KOHLER
LNC CARTON
M.G. WALDBAUM
NORTHERN STAR
PAPETTI'S
PCE EGG CURDS
PCE FILLED OMELETS
PCE LNC OMELETS
PCE PLAIN FRIED PATTIES
SIMPLY POTATOES
Advertising Agency:
J.T. Mega Marketing Communications
4020 Minnetonka Blvd
Minneapolis, MN 55416-4100
Tel.: (952) 929-1370
Fax: (952) 929-5417
Toll Free: (800) 923-6342
(MFI Foodservice)

MICROSOY CORP.

300 E MicroSoy Dr
Jefferson, IA 50129
Tel.: (515) 386-2100
Fax: (515) 386-3287
E-mail: info@microsoyflakes.com
Web Site: www.microsoyflakes.com
Approx. Number Employees: 9
Year Founded: 1991
Business Description:
Microsoyflakes Mfr
S.I.C.: 2075
N.A.I.C.S.: 311222
Media: 10
Personnel:
Terry Tanaka *(Pres)*
Brands & Products:
BETTER BITES
INNOVATE WITH ENDLESS POSSIBILITIES
MICROSOY

MILNE FOOD PRODUCTS, INC.

(Sub. of Wyckoff Farms, Inc.)
804 Bennett Ave
Prosser, WA 99350-1267
Tel.: (509) 786-2611
Fax: (509) 786-1724
E-mail: joes@milnefruit.com
Web Site: www.milnefruit.com
Approx. Number Employees: 70
Year Founded: 1956

Key to Media (For complete agency information see *The Advertising Red Books-Agencies* edition):
1. Bus. Publs. 2. Cable T.V. 3. Catalogs & Directories. 4. Co-op Adv. 5. Consumer Mags. 6. D.M. to Bus. Estab.7. D.M. to Consumers 8. Daily Newsp. 9. Exhibits/Trade Shows 10. Foreign 11. Infomercial 12. Internet Adv.13. Multimedia 14. Network Radio 15. Network T.V. 16. Newsp. Distr. Mags. 17. Other 18. Outdoor (Posters, Transit) 19. Point of Purchase20. Premiums, Novelties 21. Product Samples 22. Special Events Mktg. 23. Spot Radio 24. Spot T.V. 25. Weekly Newsp. 26. Yellow Page Adv.

Milne Food Products, Inc. — (Continued)

Business Description:
Fruit Juices, Fruit Purees, Blends, Premixes & Ingredients Mfr & Processor
S.I.C.: 2037
N.A.I.C.S.: 311411
Media: 2-10-21

Personnel:
Dave Wyckoff *(Chm & CEO)*
John J. Schroeder *(VP, Dir-Sls & Mktg)*
Randy Hageman *(Gen Mgr)*
Ed Thomas *(Dir-Quality Assurance)*
Rocky Brumley *(Mgr-Inside Sls)*
Shannon Elkins *(Mgr-Sls-Natl)*
Eric Johnson *(Mgr-Res & Dev & Product Dev)*

MINN-DAK FARMERS COOPERATIVE

7525 Red River Rd
Wahpeton, ND 58075-9705
Tel.: (701) 642-8411
Fax: (701) 642-6814
E-mail: smjohnson@mdf.coop
Web Site: www.mdf.coop
Approx. Rev.: $214,311,789
Approx. Number Employees: 313
Year Founded: 1972

Business Description:
Beet Sugar Mfr
S.I.C.: 2063
N.A.I.C.S.: 311313
Import Export
Advertising Expenditures: $19,875
Media: 17

Personnel:
Douglas Etten *(Chm)*
Brent Davison *(Vice Chm)*
David H. Roche *(Pres & CEO)*
Steven M. Caspers *(CFO & Exec VP)*
John Haugen *(VP-Engrg)*
Kevin R. Shannon *(Dir-Safety)*
Susan Johnson *(Mgr-Comm)*
John S. Nyquist *(Mgr-Pur)*
Greg J. Schmalz *(Mgr-HR)*
John Wieser *(Mgr-IT)*
Simone Sandberg *(Legal Counsel)*

Brands & Products:
BEACH SUGAR

MITSUI FOODS, INC.

(Sub. of Mitsui & Co., Ltd.)
35 Maple St
Norwood, NJ 07648
Tel.: (201) 750-2832
Fax: (201) 750-0145
Toll Free: (800) 777-2322
Telex: 6853452
Web Site: www.mitsui-foods.com
Approx. Number Employees: 50
Year Founded: 1953

Business Description:
Empress Brand Canned Foods Importers & Distr; Industrial Food Ingredients; Private Label Canned Products
S.I.C.: 5141
N.A.I.C.S.: 424410
Import Export
Media: 4-5-10-20-21-24

Personnel:
Mark Sims *(CFO & Sr VP)*
Philip Demarest *(VP-IT)*

Brands & Products:
EMPRESS
NOBILITY

MIZKAN AMERICAS, INC.

(Sub. of Mizkan Group Corporation)
1661 Feehanville Dr Ste 300
Mount Prospect, IL 60056
Tel.: (847) 590-0059
Fax: (847) 590-0638
Web Site: www.mizkan.com
Approx. Number Employees: 100

Business Description:
Liquid Condiments Mfr
S.I.C.: 2035; 2099
N.A.I.C.S.: 311941; 311999
Media: 2-4-7-10-17
Distr.: Natl.

Personnel:
Dennis Dedmond *(Sr VP-Mktg & Brand Mgmt)*
Dave Rotunno *(Exec Dir-Mktg)*

MODERN MUSHROOM FARMS, INC.

1330 Newark Rd
Toughkenamon, PA 19374

Mailing Address:
PO Box 340
Avondale, PA 19311
Tel.: (610) 268-3535
Fax: (610) 268-3099
E-mail: info@modernmush.com
Web Site: www.modernmush.com
Approx. Sls.: $25,000,000
Approx. Number Employees: 350
Year Founded: 1970

Business Description:
Mushrooms Producer
S.I.C.: 0182; 2099
N.A.I.C.S.: 111411; 311999
Import Export
Advertising Expenditures: $100,000
Media: 4-13-16-17-26

Personnel:
Charles J. Ciarrocchi, Jr. *(Pres)*

MONKS' BREAD

Abbey of the Genesee
Piffard, NY 14533
Tel.: (585) 243-0660
Fax: (585) 243-4816
E-mail: community@geneseeabbey.org
Web Site: www.geneseeabbey.org
Sales Range: $10-24.9 Million
Approx. Number Employees: 10
Year Founded: 1959

Business Description:
Monastery & Bread Bakers
S.I.C.: 8661; 2051
N.A.I.C.S.: 813110; 311812
Media: 10-18-19
Distr.: Reg.
Budget Set: Jan. -June

Personnel:
Jerome Machar *(Mgr-Prod)*

Brands & Products:
MONKS' BREAD
MONKS' FRUIT CAKES

MONTEREY GOURMET FOODS, INC.

(Sub. of Pulmuone Wildwood Inc.)
1528 Moffett St
Salinas, CA 93905-3342
Tel.: (831) 753-6262
Fax: (831) 753-6255
E-mail: info@montereypasta.com
Web Site: www.montereypasta.com
Approx. Rev.: $97,188,000
Approx. Number Employees: 311
Year Founded: 1989

Business Description:
Gourmet Pasta & Sauce Producer & Marketer
S.I.C.: 2098; 2033; 2099
N.A.I.C.S.: 311823; 311421; 311999
Advertising Expenditures: $125,000
Media: 2-4-14-15-16

Personnel:
Eric C. Eddings *(CEO)*
Joseph Stirlacci *(VP-Club Channel Sls)*

Brands & Products:
CARBSMART
CASUAL GOURMET
EMERALD VALLEY KITCHEN
MONTEREY GOURMET FOODS
MONTEREY PASTA
SONOMA

MONTEREY MUSHROOMS, INC.

260 Westgate Dr
Watsonville, CA 95076-2452
Tel.: (831) 763-5300
Fax: (831) 763-2300
Fax: (831) 763-0700
Toll Free: (800) 333-6874
E-mail: corp@montmush.com
Web Site: www.montmush.com
Approx. Number Employees: 2,100
Year Founded: 1971

Business Description:
Marketing, Growing & Processing of Mushrooms
S.I.C.: 0182; 2034
N.A.I.C.S.: 111411; 311423
Advertising Expenditures: $200,000
Media: 2-4-13-17-21

Personnel:
Shah Kazemi *(Pres & CEO)*
Ray Selle *(CFO)*
Brian Jenny *(Dir-Sls)*
Mike Stephan *(Dir-Sls)*

Brands & Products:
MONTEREY

MORGAN FOODS, INC.

90 W Morgan St
Austin, IN 47102-1741
Tel.: (812) 794-1170
Fax: (812) 794-1211
Toll Free: (800) 430-1780
Web Site: www.morganfoods.com
Approx. Number Employees: 400
Year Founded: 1899

Business Description:
Food Processing Services
S.I.C.: 2032; 2099
N.A.I.C.S.: 311422; 311942
Export
Advertising Expenditures: $300,000
Bus. Publs.: $30,000; Consumer Mags.: $30,000; Exhibits/Trade Shows: $240,000

Personnel:
John S. Morgan *(Chm & CEO)*
Daniel R. Slattery *(CFO & Sr VP)*
Larry M. Higdon *(VP-Pur)*
Dennis W. Murnane *(Mgr-Quality)*
Steve Zollman *(Mgr-Quality Assurance)*

Brands & Products:
AMERICAN BEAUTY
LITTLE CHEF

MRS. CUBBISON'S FOODS, INC.

(Sub. of Hostess Brands)
7240 E Gage Ave
City of Commerce, CA 90040
Tel.: (562) 231-1699
Tel.: (562) 231-1680
Fax: (562) 231-1691
E-mail: mrscubbisons@aol.com
Web Site: www.mrscubbisons.com
Sales Range: $1-9.9 Million
Approx. Number Employees: 100

Business Description:
Croutons, Poultry Dressing & Other Food Products Mfr
S.I.C.: 2051
N.A.I.C.S.: 311812
Export
Advertising Expenditures: $500,000
Media: 2-7-9-19-23-24-25
Distr.: Reg.
Budget Set: June

Brands & Products:
MRS. CUBBISON'S

Advertising Agency:
Lee & Associates, Inc.
145 S Fairfax Ave Ste 301
Los Angeles, CA 90036-2166
Tel.: (323) 938-3300
Fax: (323) 938-3305
— Leo Pearlstein *(Acct. Exec.)*

MURRY'S, INC.

8300 Pennsylvania Ave
Upper Marlboro, MD 20772
Tel.: (301) 420-6400
Fax: (301) 967-4816
Toll Free: (800) 638-0215
E-mail: corporate@murrys.com
Web Site: www.murrys.com
Approx. Number Employees: 250
Year Founded: 1948

Business Description:
Food Products, Specializing in Meat, Frozen & Packaged Goods
S.I.C.: 5963; 5142
N.A.I.C.S.: 454390; 424420
Advertising Expenditures: $3,000,000
Media: 3-5-8-9-10-19-23-24-25-26
Distr.: Natl.
Budget Set: Mar.

Personnel:
Ira Mendelson *(CEO)*
Brad Holland *(CFO)*
Matthew Young *(Exec VP)*
Gary Gold *(Sr VP)*
Stuart Mendelson *(Sr VP)*
Linda Ralph *(Dir-Mktg & Adv)*

Brands & Products:
FAMILY OF FINE FOODS
MURRY'S
W'NG-ITS

MY OWN MEALS, INC.

400 Lk Cook Rd
Deerfield, IL 60015
Tel.: (847) 948-1118
Fax: (847) 948-0468
E-mail: myownmeals@sbcglobal.net
Web Site: www.myownmeals.com
Approx. Number Employees: 130
Year Founded: 1986

Business Description:
Mfr. of Refrigeration-Free Ethnic Food Products, Kosher & Halal Meals & Military Rations
S.I.C.: 2099

Key to Media (For complete agency information see *The Advertising Red Books-Agencies* edition):
1. Bus. Publs. 2. Cable T.V. 3. Catalogs & Directories. 4. Co-op Adv. 5. Consumer Mags. 6. D.M. to Bus. Estab.7. D.M. to Consumers 8. Daily Newsp. 9. Exhibits/Trade Shows 10. Foreign 11. Infomercial 12. Internet Adv.13. Multimedia 14. Network Radio 15. Network T.V. 16. Newsp. Distr. Mags. 17. Other 18. Outdoor (Posters, Transit) 19. Point of Purchase20. Premiums, Novelties 21. Product Samples 22. Special Events Mktg. 23. Spot Radio 24. Spot T.V. 25. Weekly Newsp. 26. Yellow Page Adv.

N.A.I.C.S.: 311999
Export
Advertising Expenditures: $1,000,000
Media: 1-4-5-6-7-8-11-16-19-20-25
Distr.: Reg.
Brands & Products:
CHEESE TORTELLINI
FLORENTINE LASAGNA
J&M
MY KIND OF CHICKEN
MY KIND OF MEAL
MY OWN MEALS

NAKED JUICE COMPANY, INC.
(Sub. of Tropicana Products, Inc.)
935 W 8th St
Monrovia, CA 91016
Tel.: (626) 812-6022
Fax: (972) 334-3271
Web Site: www.nakedjuice.com
Sales Range: $150-199.9 Million
Approx. Number Employees: 80
Year Founded: 1985
Business Description:
Frozen Fruits, Fruit Juices, Canned & Preserved Fruit Mfr
S.I.C.: 2033
N.A.I.C.S.: 311421
Export
Advertising Expenditures: $1,000,000
Media: 4-6-7-9-10-16-23-24
Distr.: Natl.
Personnel:
Monty Sharma *(CEO)*
Brands & Products:
JUST PIKT
NAKED
Advertising Agency:
BLITZ
1453 3rd St Promenade Ste 420
Santa Monica, CA 90401
Tel.: (310) 551-0200
Fax: (310) 551-0022

NATIONAL BEEF PACKING COMPANY, LLC
(Sub. of U.S. Premium Beef, LLC)
12200 N Ambassador Dr Ste 500
Kansas City, MO 64163-1244
Mailing Address:
PO Box 20046
Kansas City, MO 64195-0046
Tel.: (816) 713-8800
Fax: (816) 713-8863
Toll Free: (800) 449BEEF
E-mail: nbpcontact@nationalbeef.com
Web Site: www.nationalbeef.com
Approx. Number Employees: 9,100
Year Founded: 1968
Business Description:
Meat Packing Plants
S.I.C.: 0751
N.A.I.C.S.: 311611
Import Export
Advertising Expenditures: $5,300,000
Media: 19-22
Personnel:
Steven D. Hunt *(Chm)*
Timothy M. Klein *(Pres & COO)*
Simon P. McGee *(CFO)*
Terry L. Wilkerson *(COO)*
Jay D. Nielsen *(Chief Acctg Officer & Treas)*
Bret G. Wilson *(Gen Counsel & VP)*
David L. Grosenheider *(Exec VP-Bus Plng & Analysis)*
Carey Hoskinson *(Exec VP-Beef Ops)*
Monte E. Lowe *(Exec VP-Sls & Mktg)*
Brands & Products:
BIOLOGIC
BLACK CANYON
CERTIFIED PREMIUM BEEF
IMPERIAL VALLEY
LEADING THE WAY IN QUALITY BEEF
NATIONAL BEEF
NATURESOURCE
NATUREWELL
VINTAGE NATURAL BEEF

NATIONAL BEEF PACKING COMPANY, LP
(Sub. of National Beef Packing Company, LLC)
2000 E Trl St
Dodge City, KS 67801-9018
Mailing Address:
PO Box 539
Dodge City, KS 67801-0539
Tel.: (620) 227-7135
Fax: (620) 338-4338
E-mail: info@nationalbeef.com
Web Site: www.nationalbeef.com
Approx. Number Employees: 2,000
Year Founded: 1962
Business Description:
Meat Packing
S.I.C.: 0751; 5147
N.A.I.C.S.: 311611; 311612
Advertising Expenditures: $3,300,000

NATIONAL ENZYME COMPANY
15366 US Hwy 160
Forsyth, MO 65653
Tel.: (417) 546-4796
Fax: (417) 546-6433
Toll Free: (800) 825-8545
E-mail: mail@nzimes.com
Web Site: www.nationalenzyme.com
Approx. Number Employees: 110
Year Founded: 1932
Business Description:
Mfr of Food Enzyme Products
S.I.C.: 2869; 5499
N.A.I.C.S.: 325199; 446191
Media: 6-7-8-13
Personnel:
Anthony Collier *(Owner & CEO)*
Elizabeth Cambar-Roney *(Sr Mgr-Accts)*
Scott Daniel *(Mgr-Mktg)*
Grace Yu Wen Lu *(Mgr-Sls-Intl & Mktg)*
Linda Sorenson *(Mgr-HR)*
Brands & Products:
BIOCORE
CERECALASE
ENZYME UNIVERSITY
INSOLASE
N ZIMES
SERRAZIMES

NATIONAL FRUIT PRODUCT COMPANY, INC.
551 Fairmont Ave
Winchester, VA 22601-3931
Tel.: (540) 662-3401
Fax: (540) 665-4671
Web Site: www.whitehousefoods.com
Approx. Number Employees: 400
Year Founded: 1908
Business Description:
Producer of Apple Related Products
S.I.C.: 2033; 2099
N.A.I.C.S.: 311421; 311942
Export
Advertising Expenditures: $3,500,000
Media: 2-3-5-6-8-9-10-19-20-21-22-23-24-25
Distr.: Natl.
Personnel:
Karen J. Colvin *(Asst Treas)*
Kathy Strawn *(VP-HR)*
Brands & Products:
ORCHARD BOY
REPUTATION
SHENANDOAH
SKYLAND
TWELVE OAKS
WHITE HOUSE

NATIONAL PORK BOARD
1776 NW 114th St
Clive, IA 50325-7073
Tel.: (515) 223-2600
Fax: (515) 223-2646
E-mail: info@pork.org
Web Site: www.pork.org
Sales Range: $50-74.9 Million
Approx. Number Employees: 70
Year Founded: 1969
Business Description:
Business Association for the Pork Industry
S.I.C.: 8611
N.A.I.C.S.: 813910
Advertising Expenditures: $9,500,000
Media: 3-5-6-10-11-13-15-18-19-22-23-24
Personnel:
Jim Meimann *(Exec VP-Governance & Opers)*
Ceci Snyder *(VP-Domestic Mktg)*
Barry Kenney *(Asst VP-Gen Svcs)*
Liz Wagstrom *(Asst VP-Science & Tech)*
Ernie Barnes *(Dir & Producer-Industry Svcs)*
Nicole Boettger *(Dir-Producer Svcs)*
Mark Boggess *(Dir-Animal Science)*
Kathy Codner *(Dir-Meeting Svcs)*
Chuck Cozad *(Dir-Tech Svcs & Strategy)*
Jill Criss *(Dir-HR)*
Pamela Johnson *(Dir-Consumer Commun)*
Kathryn Mennenga *(Dir-IT)*
Chris Oldt *(Dir-Art)*
Allan Stokes *(Dir-Environ Programs)*
Patrick Webb *(Dir-Swine Health Programs)*
Lynette Webster *(Dir-Acctg Opers)*
Stephen Gerike *(Mgr-Natl Foodservice Mktg)*
Howard Greenblatt *(Mgr-Natl Foodservice Mktg)*
Traci Rodemeyer *(Mgr-Pork Info)*
Teresa Roof *(Mgr-PR)*
Advertising Agencies:
Click Here, Inc.
8750 N Central Expy Ste 100
Dallas, TX 75231-6430
Tel.: (214) 891-5325
Fax: (214) 346-4870

Osborn & Barr Communications
Cupples Sta 914 Spruce St
Saint Louis, MO 63102
Tel.: (314) 726-5511
Fax: (314) 726-6350
Toll Free: (800) 666-1765
Toll Free: (888) BELIEF-2

Schafer Condon Carter
168 N Clinton
Chicago, IL 60661
Tel.: (312) 464-1666
Fax: (312) 464-0628
Agency of Record
Brand Development
Consumer Marketing Program

NATURAL SELECTION FOODS, LLC
(Holding of HM Capital Partners LLC)
(d/b/a Earthbound Farms)
1721 San Juan Hwy
San Juan Bautista, CA 95045
Tel.: (831) 623-7880
Fax: (831) 626-0467
Toll Free: (800) 690-3200
E-mail: info@ebfarm.com
Web Site: www.ebfarm.com
Approx. Number Employees: 1,200
Year Founded: 1984
Business Description:
Organic Vegetable Farming
S.I.C.: 0161; 0723
N.A.I.C.S.: 111219; 115114
Media: 6
Personnel:
Myra Goodman *(Co-Founder)*
Drew Goodman *(Pres & CEO)*
Todd Kodet *(Sr VP-Supply Mgmt)*
Tonya Antle *(VP-Sls & Mktg)*
Will Daniels *(VP-Sls)*
Samantha Cabaluna *(Dir-Comm)*

NATURE MADE NUTRITIONAL PRODUCTS INC.
(Sub. of Pharmavite LLC)
8510 Balboa Blvd PO Box 9606
Mission Hills, CA 91325
Tel.: (818) 221-6200
Fax: (818) 221-6644
Web Site: www.pharmavite.com
Business Description:
Vitamin Mfr
S.I.C.: 2834
N.A.I.C.S.: 325412
Personnel:
Jim Lundeen *(VP-Mktg)*
Advertising Agency:
Ogilvy & Mather
3530 Hayden Ave
Culver City, CA 90232
Tel.: (310) 280-2200
Fax: (310) 280-9473

NEOGEN CORPORATION
620 Lesher Pl
Lansing, MI 48912-1509
Tel.: (517) 372-9200
Fax: (517) 372-2006
Toll Free: (800) 234-5333
E-mail: inform@neogen.com
Web Site: www.neogen.com
Approx. Sls.: $172,683,000
Approx. Number Employees: 654
Year Founded: 1982
Business Description:
Food & Animal Safety Products Developer, Mfr & Marketer
S.I.C.: 2834; 2835; 2836; 3841
N.A.I.C.S.: 325412; 325413; 325414; 339112
Export
Advertising Expenditures: $600,000

Neogen Corporation — (Continued)

Personnel:
James L. Herbert *(Chm & CEO)*
Lon M. Bohannon *(Pres & COO)*
Steven J. Quinlan *(CFO & VP)*
Jennifer Rice *(VP & Sr Dir-Res)*

Brands & Products:
ACCUCLEAN
ACCUPOINT
ACCUSCAN
ACUMEDIA
AG-TEK
AGRI-SCREEN
AGRI-SCREEN TICKET
ALERT
ALUSHIELD
AMVET
BETASTAR
BIOPLATE
BIOSENTRY
BIOSENTRY ACID-A-FOAM
BIOSENTRY BIOCRES
BIOSENTRY BIOPHENE
BIOSENTRY BIOQUAT
BIOSENTRY CHLOR-A-FOAM
BOTTOMHOOF
BOTVAX
BREEDERSLEEVE
CALF EZE
CAT LOGO
CENTRUS
CHONDRO-ORAL
COLITAG
CORRECT
CYKILL
D3 NEEDLES
DC&R
DETECTABLE NEEDLES
DI-FENDER
DI-KILL
DR. FRANKS
E-Z BOND
E-Z CATCH
ELECTROJAC
ELISA TECHNOLOGIES
ENVIROCASTER
EQSTIM
EQUIMAX
EQUISLEEVE
FURAZONE
FUTURAPAD
GENE-TRAK
GENEQUENCE
GENESEEK
GNAT-AWAY
GNATURAL
GOLD NUGGET
GOLD WRAP
HACCO
HYGICULT
IDEAL
IMMUNOREGULIN
IMMUNOVET
INJECTO-STIK
INSIGHT
ISO-GRID
ISO-PRINE
JOLT
K-BLUE
K-BLUE SUBSTRATE
K-GOLD
LIVER 7
MAXISLEEVE
MEGASHOT
MICROBIOLOGY AT THE SPEED OF LIGHT
MINI-SHOT
MYCASEPTIC
NEEDLEGARD
NEO-GRID
NEOCOLUMN
NEOGEN
NEOGEN FLASK
NEOGENVET
NFZ
ONE BAD CAT
PADDOCK AND PASTURE
PANAKARE
PARVOSOL
PENZYM
PENZYME
POLYHAND
POLYSLEEVE
PORIDON
PRO-PISTOL
PRO-SHOT
PROFIX
PROFLEX
PROMAR
PROZAP
PYRIL-PAM
RAMIK
RENAKARE
REVEAL
REVIVE
RIVARD
RODEX
SAFETFLEX
SOLERIS
SPEC-TUSS
SPECTRASOL
SQUIRE
STAM-N-AID
STRESS-DEX
SURGICRYL
TCA PAINT
TETRASTAR
THRUSHCRUSHER
THYROKARE
TOPHOOF
TRI-HIST
TRI-SOXSUPRINE
TRIPLE BLOCK
TRIPLE CAST
TRIPLE CROWN
TRIPLE HEAT
TRYAD
URICON
URIKARE
VERATOX
VITA-15

NESTLE CANADA INC.
(Sub. of Nestle S.A.)
25 Sheppard Ave W
North York, ON M2N 6S8, Canada
Tel.: (416) 512-9000
Fax: (416) 218-2794
Web Site: www.nestle.ca
Approx. Number Employees: 3,400
Business Description:
Mfr of Chocolate Drinks, Coffee, Tea, Canned Foods, Pet Foods, & Other Food Products
S.I.C.: 2064
N.A.I.C.S.: 311330
Media: 5-6-10-15-18-19-21-23-25
Distr.: Natl.
Budget Set: Oct. -Dec.
Advertising Agencies:
JWT Company Ltd.
160 Bloor St E
Toronto, ON M4W 3P7, Canada
Tel.: (416) 926-7300
Fax: (416) 926-7389
Ice Cream

MacLaren McCann Canada Inc.
10 Bay St
Toronto, ON M5J 2S3, Canada
Tel.: (416) 594-6000
Fax: (416) 643-7030
Fax: (416) 643-7027

NESTLE USA - BEVERAGE DIVISION, INC.
(Div. of Nestle USA, Inc.)
800 N Brand Blvd Fl 21
Glendale, CA 91203-1229
Tel.: (818) 549-6000
Fax: (818) 549-6952
Web Site: www.nestleusa.com
Approx. Number Employees: 2,300
Business Description:
Coffee, Tea, Milk & Other Beverage Products Mfr
S.I.C.: 2095
N.A.I.C.S.: 311920
Personnel:
Bradley A. Alford *(CEO)*
Chad Patterson *(Mgr-Mktg-Nestle Jamba Energy)*
Advertising Agencies:
OIC
959 E Colorado Blvd Ste 230
Pasadena, CA 91106
Tel.: (626) 229-0931
Fax: (626) 229-9897

Threshold Interactive
13160 Mindanao Way
Marina Del Rey, CA 90292
Tel.: (310) 577-9800
Fax: (310) 577-9844

NESTLE USA, INC.
(Sub. of Nestle S.A.)
800 N Brand Blvd
Glendale, CA 91203-1245
Tel.: (818) 549-6000
Fax: (818) 549-6952
Toll Free: (800) 225-2270
Web Site: www.nestleusa.com
Sales Range: $5-14.9 Billion
Approx. Number Employees: 17,000
Year Founded: 1899
Business Description:
Beverages, Food Services, Foreign Trade, Nutrition, Pet Care & Sales
S.I.C.: 2023; 2033
N.A.I.C.S.: 311514; 311421
Import Export
Advertising Expenditures: $1,100,000,000
Media: 3-6-9-14-15-17-18-23-24-25
Distr.: Natl.
Personnel:
Bradley A. Alford *(Chm & CEO)*
Karen Crawford *(Dir-Media Adv & CRM)*
Meghaan Blauvelt *(Brand Mgr-Drumstick)*
Sanford Fink *(Sr Brand Mgr)*
Jessica Vasisht *(Brand Mgr)*
Kristen Mandel *(Mgr-Mktg)*
Jennifer Dahlgren *(Mgr-Mktg-Jack's Brand & Pizza Div Growth Channels)*
Cathy Dean *(Mgr-Mktg-Juice Innovation)*
Kristine Gardner *(Mgr-Consumer Mktg Technologies)*
Victoria Nuevo-Celeste *(Mgr-Innovation)*
Chad Patterson *(Mgr-Mktg-Beverage Div)*
Carleen Ramirez *(Mgr-Interactive Mktg)*
Brands & Products:
100 GRAND
ADDITIONS
ALBERS
ALPO CHEW-EEZ
ALPO DOG TREATS
ALPO MASTER'S CHOICE
BACI
BIT-O-HONEY
BUITONI
BUITONI REFRIGERATED PASTAS & SAUCES
BUTTERFINGER BB's
CARNATION ALSOY
CARNATION BABY CEREAL
CARNATION COCO SUPREME
CARNATION COFFEE-MATE
CARNATION EVAPORATED MILK
CARNATION FOLLOW-UP FORMULA
CARNATION GOOD START
CARNATION HOT COCOA
CARNATION INSTANT BREAKFAST
CHEF-MATE
CONDIMIX
CRUCIAL
DAVID & SONS SUNFLOWER SEEDS
DIGIORNO
DOLE
DREYER'S
DREYER'S GRAND ICE CREAM
DRUMSTICK
EUROPEAN STYLE
FRISKIES CANNED
FRISKIES CHEF'S BLEND
FRISKIES COME 'N GET IT
FRISKIES DRY
FRISKIES FANCY FEAST
FRISKIES GOURMET
FRISKIES KITTEN
FRISKIES MASTER'S CHOICE
FRISKIES MIGHTY DOG
FRISKIES MIGHTY DOG SENIOR
FRISKIES PRIME STEAKS
FRISKIES PRIME STRIPS
FRISKIES SENIOR
FRISKIES SPECIAL DIET
FUN DIP
GLYTROL
GOOBERS
GOOD START ESSENTIALS
GOOD START SUPREME
GRAND LIGHT
HAAGEN-DAZS
HOT POCKETS
IBD NUTRIVENT
ICECAP
JIM DANDY
LIBBY'S JUICE BLAST
LIBBY'S JUICY JUICE
LIBBY'S KERNS
LIBBY'S KERNS NECTARS
LIBBY'S PUMPKIN
LIK-M-AID
MAGGI
MILO
MINOR'S
MODULEN
NESCAFE CLASSICO
NESCAFE ICED COFFEE

Key to Media (For complete agency information see *The Advertising Red Books-Agencies* edition):
1. Bus. Publs. 2. Cable T.V. 3. Catalogs & Directories. 4. Co-op Adv. 5. Consumer Mags. 6. D.M. to Bus. Estab.7. D.M. to Consumers 8. Daily Newsp. 9. Exhibits/Trade Shows 10. Foreign 11. Infomercial 12. Internet Adv.13. Multimedia 14. Network Radio 15. Network T.V. 16. Newsp. Distr. Mags. 17. Other 18. Outdoor (Posters, Transit) 19. Point of Purchase20. Premiums, Novelties 21. Product Samples 22. Special Events Mktg. 23. Spot Radio 24. Spot T.V. 25. Weekly Newsp. 26. Yellow Page Adv.

NESCAFE MOUNTAIN BLEND
NESCAFE SUNRISE
NESPRESSO
NESQUIK POWDER
NESQUIK READY TO DRINK
NESQUIK SYRUP
NESTEA HERITAGE
NESTEA ICE TEASERS
NESTEA NUEVO TEA
NESTEA SUNTEA
NESTLE BUNCHA CRUNCH
NESTLE CRUNCH
NIPS
NUBASICS
NUTRIHEP
NUTRIRENAL
PEARSON'S NIPS
PEPTAMEN
PERUGINA
PERUGINA GIANDUIA
PERUGINA ORE LIETE
PETER'S BROC
PETER'S BROKEN ORINOCO
PETER'S BURGUNDY
PETER'S CHATHAM
PETER'S COMMANDER
PETER'S CREMA
PETER'S GIBRALTAR
PIXY STIX
POWERBAR
PROBALANCE
PUSH UPS
QUALITY STREET
RAISINETS
RENALCAL
REPLETE
SNO-CAPS
STOUFFER'S
STOUFFER'S ENTREES
STOUFFER'S FAMILY STYLE FAVORITES
STOUFFER'S FROZEN PIZZA
STOUFFER'S HEARTY PORTIONS
STOUFFER'S HOMESTYLE
STOUFFER'S LEAN CUISINE
STOUFFER'S LEAN CUISINE AMERICAN FAVORITES
STOUFFER'S LEAN CUISINE CAFE CLASSICS
STOUFFER'S LEAN CUISINE HEARTY PORTIONS
STOUFFER'S LEAN SKILLET SENSATIONS
STOUFFER'S OVEN SENSATIONS
STOUFFER'S SKILLET SENSATIONS
TOLL HOUSE MORSELS
TOLL HOUSE REFRIGERATED COOKIE DOUGH
TREASURES
TRIO
TRIO SUPREME
WILLY WONKA'S

Advertising Agencies:
Casanova Pendrill, LLC
275-A McCormick Ave Ste 100
Costa Mesa, CA 92626-3369
Tel.: (714) 918-8200
Fax: (714) 918-8295
(Beverage Division)

Dailey & Associates
(Sub. of The Interpublic Group of Cos., Inc.)
8687 Melrose Ave Ste G300
West Hollywood, CA 90069-5701
Tel.: (310) 360-3100
Fax: (310) 360-0810

Draftfcb
101 E Erie St
Chicago, IL 60611-2812
Tel.: (312) 425-5000
Fax: (312) 425-5010
DiGiorno (Agency of Record)

Euro RSCG Worldwide
350 Hudson St
New York, NY 10014-4504
Tel.: (212) 886-2000
Fax: (212) 886-2016
Toll Free: (800) 937-0233
(Nestle Prepared Foods Division)

Ketchum
(Part of Omnicom)
1285 Ave of the Americas
New York, NY 10019
Tel.: (646) 935-3900
Fax: (646) 935-4482
Dreyer's
Drumstick
Haagen-Dazs

McCann Erickson/Los Angeles
5700 Wilshire Blvd Ste 225
Los Angeles, CA 90036
Tel.: (323) 900-7100
Fax: (323) 900-7111
(Beverage Division, Prepared Foods Division, Nutrition Division & Pet Care Division)

OgilvyInteractive
636 11th Ave
New York, NY 10036
Tel.: (212) 237-4000
Fax: (212) 237-5123

OgilvyOne Worldwide
636 11th Ave
New York, NY 10036
Tel.: (212) 237-4000
Fax: (212) 237-5123
Digital/CRM Agency of Record - Wonka Brand
Nerds
Nestle Crunch
Raisenets
Spree
Sweet Tarts
Wonka Exceptionals Chocolate

Publicis Dallas
7300 Lonestar Dr
Plano, TX 75024
Tel.: (972) 628-7500
Fax: (972) 628-7864
(Beverage Division & Confections & Snacks Division)
Buitoni Pasta

Publicis USA
(Sub. of Publicis, S.A., Paris, France)
4 Herald Sq 950 6th Ave
New York, NY 10001
Tel.: (212) 279-5550
Fax: (212) 279-5560
Nescafe

NEW WORLD PASTA COMPANY

(Sub. of Ebro Puleva S.A.)
85 Shannon Rd
Harrisburg, PA 17112-2799
Mailing Address:
PO Box 126457
Harrisburg, PA 17112-6457
Tel.: (717) 526-2200
Fax: (717) 526-2468
Toll Free: (800) 730-5957
E-mail: nwpasta@casupport.com
Web Site: www.newworldpasta.com
Sales Range: $25-49.9 Million
Approx. Number Employees: 800
Year Founded: 1977
Business Description:
Mfr of Pasta Products
S.I.C.: 2098; 2099
N.A.I.C.S.: 311823; 311999
Advertising Expenditures: $1,000,000
Media: 6-16-19-23-26
Distr.: Natl.
Personnel:
Peter Smith *(CEO)*
Pankaj Talwar *(Sr VP & CMO)*

Brands & Products:
AMERICAN BEAUTY
CREAMETTE
GOODMAN
LANCIA
LIGHT 'N FLUFFY
MRS. WEISS
P&R
PRINCE
RONZONI
SAN GIORGIO
SKINNER
Advertising Agency:
Dailey & Associates
(Sub. of The Interpublic Group of Cos., Inc.)
8687 Melrose Ave Ste G300
West Hollywood, CA 90069-5701
Tel.: (310) 360-3100
Fax: (310) 360-0810

NEW ZEALAND LAMB COOPERATIVE, INC.

20 Westport Rd Ste 320
Wilton, CT 06897-4522
Tel.: (203) 529-9100
Fax: (203) 529-9101
Toll Free: (800) 438-5262
E-mail: shane@nzlamb.com
Web Site: www.nzlamb.com
E-Mail For Key Personnel:
President: shane@nzlamb.com
Marketing Director: peter@nzlamb.com
Sales Range: $50-74.9 Million
Approx. Number Employees: 75
Year Founded: 1962
Business Description:
Lamb Importer & Whslr
S.I.C.: 5147
N.A.I.C.S.: 424470
Advertising Expenditures: $250,000
Media: 2-6-7-9-19-23-24-25
Distr.: Natl.
Personnel:
Shane O'Hara *(Pres)*
Peter M. Gilligan *(VP-Sls & Mktg)*
Clay Nicholson *(Dir-Retail Sls)*
Christopher Thompson *(Dir-Culinary Devel)*
Marybeth Laleman *(Mgr-Eastern Region Sls)*
Kathleen Zavala *(Mgr-Western Region Sls)*

NEWLY WEDS FOODS, INC.

4140 W Fullerton Ave
Chicago, IL 60639-2106
Tel.: (773) 489-7000
Fax: (773) 489-2799
Toll Free: (800) 621-7521
E-mail: resumes@newlywedsfoods.com
Web Site: www.newlywedsfoods.com
Sales Range: $400-449.9 Million
Approx. Number Employees: 1,700
Year Founded: 1932
Business Description:
Mfr of Batter, Breadings, Multi-Grain Blends, Seasonings, Spices, Marinades & Capsicums
S.I.C.: 2045; 2052
N.A.I.C.S.: 311822; 311821
Import Export
Media: 2-4-7-10-13-21
Distr.: Intl.; Natl.
Budget Set: Sept.
Personnel:
Charles T. Angell *(Pres)*
Brian Johnson *(CFO)*
Bruce A. Leshinski *(Sr VP-Sls & Mktg)*
Jim Chin *(VP-Sls)*
Chris Swain *(VP-Engrng)*
Brands & Products:
BINDRIGHT
CUSTOMIZED TASTE TECHNOLOGY
FLAVORTRAK
NATUREGUARD
NEWLY WEDS ADHESION BATTERS
NEWLY WEDS FOODS
NEWLY WEDS SPECIALTY BATTERS

NEWMAN'S OWN, INC.

246 Post Rd E
Westport, CT 06880
Tel.: (203) 222-0136
Fax: (203) 227-5630
Toll Free: (800) 444-8705
E-mail: info@newmansown.com
Web Site: www.newmansown.com
Approx. Number Employees: 18
Year Founded: 1982
Business Description:
Spaghetti Sauce, Popcorn, Salad Dressing & Lemonade Mfr & Distr
S.I.C.: 2035; 2033
N.A.I.C.S.: 311941; 311421
Advertising Expenditures: $4,000,000
Media: 5-6-10-17-19-21
Distr.: Natl.
Budget Set: Apr.
Personnel:
Tom Indoe *(Pres & COO)*
Michael Harvard *(VP-Mktg)*
Brands & Products:
BANDITO SALSA
BUTTER BOOM
GORILLA GRAPE
GRAB-N-GO
INDUSTRIAL STRENGTH SPAGHETTI SAUCE
LIGHTEN UP!
NEWMAN'S OWN
NEWMAN'S OWN ORGANICS
ORANGE MANGO TANGO
RAZZ-MA-TAZZ RASPBERRY
WHITE CHEDDAR GENIUS FOOD
Advertising Agency:
Gotham Incorporated
150 E 42nd St 12th Fl

Key to Media (For complete agency information see *The Advertising Red Books-Agencies* edition):
1. Bus. Publs. 2. Cable T.V. 3. Catalogs & Directories. 4. Co-op Adv. 5. Consumer Mags. 6. D.M. to Bus. Estab.7. D.M. to Consumers 8. Daily Newsp. 9. Exhibits/Trade Shows 10. Foreign 11. Infomercial 12. Internet Adv.13. Multimedia 14. Network Radio 15. Network T.V. 16. Newsp. Distr. Mags. 17. Other 18. Outdoor (Posters, Transit) 19. Point of Purchase20. Premiums, Novelties 21. Product Samples 22. Special Events Mktg. 23. Spot Radio 24. Spot T.V. 25. Weekly Newsp. 26. Yellow Page Adv.

Newman's Own, Inc. — (Continued)

New York, NY 10017
Tel.: (212) 414-7000
Fax: (212) 414-7095

NISSIN FOODS (U.S.A.) INC.

(Sub. of Nissin Foods Holdings Co., Ltd.)
2001 W Rosecrans Ave
Gardena, CA 90249-2931
Tel.: (310) 327-8478
Fax: (310) 515-3751
E-mail: export@nissinfoods.com
Web Site: www.nissinfoods.com
Approx. Number Employees: 500
Year Founded: 1970
Business Description:
Instant Ramen Noodles Mfr
S.I.C.: 2098; 2038
N.A.I.C.S.: 311823; 311412
Export
Media: 6-9-13-20-22
Distr.: Natl.
Budget Set: Oct. -Nov.
Personnel:
Tak Naruto *(Pres)*
Ken Sasahara *(Pres)*
Brands & Products:
CUP NOODLES
NISSIN
TOP RAMEN
TWIN CUP NOODLES

N.K. HURST CO., INC.

230 W McCarty St
Indianapolis, IN 46225-1234
Mailing Address:
PO Box 985
Indianapolis, IN 46206-0985
Tel.: (317) 634-6425
Fax: (317) 638-1396
Toll Free: (800) HAM-BEEN
E-mail: info@nkhurst.com
Web Site: www.hurstbeans.com
Sales Range: $25-49.9 Million
Approx. Number Employees: 45
Year Founded: 1938
Business Description:
Packagers of Dried Bean Products
S.I.C.: 5153; 5149
N.A.I.C.S.: 424510; 424490
Media: 6-23-24
Distr.: Natl.
Budget Set: Nov.-Dec.
Personnel:
Rick Hurst *(Pres)*
Brands & Products:
15 BEAN SOUP
BEEF 15 BEAN SOUP
CAJUN 15 BEAN SOUP
CHICKEN 15 BEAN SOUP
CHILI 15 BEAN SOUP
HAMBEEN BLACK BEAN SALSA
HAMBEENS
N. K. HURST
PINTO HAMBEENS
QUICK BEANS
SPANISH AMERICAN BEAN SOUP
Advertising Agency:
MZD Advertising
8425 Woofield Crossing Blvd Ste 200 W
Indianapolis, IN 46240
Tel.: (317) 924-6271
Fax: (317) 925-3854
(Dried Beans)

NONNI'S FOOD COMPANY INC.

(Sub. of Vivartia Holding S.A.)
601 S Boulder Ave Ste 900
Tulsa, OK 74119
Tel.: (918) 560-4100
Fax: (918) 560-4108
Web Site: www.nonnisfoods.com
Approx. Number Employees: 60
Year Founded: 1988
Business Description:
Gourmet & Snack Food Mfr
S.I.C.: 2096; 2052
N.A.I.C.S.: 311919; 311821
Media: 8-19-20-24
Personnel:
Matt Duffy *(Dir-Mktg)*
Brands & Products:
BESTLIFE
NEW YORK STYLE
NONNI'S
OLD LONDON

NOON HOUR FOOD PRODUCTS, INC.

215 N Des Plaines St
Chicago, IL 60661-1140
Tel.: (312) 382-1177
Fax: (312) 382-9420
Sales Range: $25-49.9 Million
Approx. Number Employees: 75
Year Founded: 1876
Business Description:
Herring, Cheese & Specialty Pancakes Producer
S.I.C.: 5149; 2034
N.A.I.C.S.: 424490; 311423
Media: 2-4-7
Distr.: Natl.
Personnel:
Paul A. Buhl *(Pres)*
Brands & Products:
NOON HOUR

NORBEST, INC.

PO Box 890
Moroni, UT 84646
Mailing Address:
PO Box 1000
Midvale, UT 84047-1000
Tel.: (801) 566-5656
Fax: (888) 597-5416
Toll Free: (800) 453-5327
E-mail: norbest@norbest.com
Web Site: www.norbest.com
E-Mail For Key Personnel:
Marketing Director: preed@norbest.com
Approx. Number Employees: 1,200
Year Founded: 1930
Business Description:
Mfr of Fresh & Frozen Turkeys & Poultry Products
S.I.C.: 5144
N.A.I.C.S.: 424440
Export
Media: 2-5-7-9-10-18-19-20-21-23-24-25
Distr.: Natl.
Budget Set: Mar.
Personnel:
Steven R. Jensen *(Pres & CEO)*
Brands & Products:
BUDGET WISE
FAMILY PRIDE
FAMILY TRADITION
NORBEST
PLYMOUTH PRIDE
ROAST RITE
SWEETHEART
TASTI-LEAN
TURKEY. THE PERFECT PROTEIN

NORSE DAIRY SYSTEMS LLC

(Div. of Interbake Foods LLC)
1740 Joyce Ave
Columbus, OH 43219-1026
Mailing Address:
PO Box 1869
Columbus, OH 43216-1869
Tel.: (614) 294-4931
Fax: (614) 299-0538
Toll Free: (800) NDS-CONE
Web Site: www.norse.com
Approx. Number Employees: 250
Year Founded: 1995
Business Description:
Mfr. of Ice Cream Novelty Machines
S.I.C.: 3556; 2052
N.A.I.C.S.: 333294; 311821
Advertising Expenditures: $100,000
Media: 2-17
Personnel:
Nick Kosanovich *(VP-Sls & Mktg)*
Sue Paap *(Mgr-Mktg)*
Brands & Products:
NORSE DAIRY SYSTEMS

NORSELAND, INC.

1290 E Main St
Stamford, CT 06902-3555
Tel.: (203) 324-5620
Fax: (203) 325-3189
Web Site: www.norseland.com
Approx. Number Employees: 30
Year Founded: 1979
Business Description:
Dairy Products Distr
S.I.C.: 5143
N.A.I.C.S.: 424430
Import
Media: 5-6-19-20-23
Distr.: Natl.
Budget Set: Apr.-Sept.
Personnel:
John Solomon *(Pres)*
Brands & Products:
JARLSBERG
JARLSBERG LITE
Advertising Agency:
Zullo Associates
1 Academy St
Princeton, NJ 08540
Tel.: (609) 683-1800
Fax: (609) 683-4773

NU-VU FOODSERVICE SYSTEMS

(Sub. of The Middleby Corporation)
5600 13th St
Menominee, MI 49858
Tel.: (906) 863-4401
Fax: (906) 863-5889
Toll Free: (800) 338-9886
E-mail: sales@nu-vu.com
Web Site: www.nu-vu.com/index.html
Sales Range: $25-49.9 Million
Approx. Number Employees: 70
Year Founded: 1920
Business Description:
Steel & Aluminum Food Service & Meal Delivery Equipment
S.I.C.: 3556
N.A.I.C.S.: 333294
Export
Media: 4
Distr.: Natl.
Personnel:
Dede Kramer *(Reg Mgr-Sls-Western Reg)*

NULAID FOODS INC.

200 W 5th St
Ripon, CA 95366-2766
Mailing Address:
PO Box 397
Bridgeville, DE 19933-0397
Tel.: (209) 599-2121
Fax: (209) 599-5220
Toll Free: (800) 788-8871
E-mail: info@nulaid.com
Web Site: www.nulaid.com
Approx. Number Employees: 50
Year Founded: 1963
Business Description:
Packaged Egg Products Mfr & Distributor
S.I.C.: 5144
N.A.I.C.S.: 424440
Media: 6-13
Personnel:
Ernie Gemperle *(Chm)*
David Crockett *(Pres & CEO)*
Dean Peters *(VP-IT)*
Brands & Products:
ADDING VALUE THROUGH INNOVATION
NULAID
REDDIEGG
Advertising Agency:
Media Brokers International, Inc.
11720 Amberpark Drive Ste 600
Alpharetta, GA 30009
Tel.: (678) 514-6200
Fax: (678) 514-6299

NXT NUTRITIONALS HOLDINGS, INC.

933 E Columbus Ave Ste C
Holyoke, MA 01105
Tel.: (413) 533-9300
Toll Free: (800) 535-4315
E-mail: info@nxtnutritionals.com
Web Site: www.nxtnutritionals.com
Approx. Sls.: $187,516
Business Description:
All Natural Sweetener, Food & Beverage Products Mfr & Marketer
S.I.C.: 2099; 2037; 2833
N.A.I.C.S.: 311999; 311411; 325411
Advertising Expenditures: $617,787
Media: 13-16-17
Personnel:
Francis McCarthy *(Pres, CEO & Director)*
David Briones *(CFO)*
Richard M. Jordan *(Exec VP, Gen Mgr & Dir)*
Mark A. Giresi *(Dir)*
Brands & Products:
HEALTHY DAIRY
SUSTA
Advertising Agency:
JS2 Communications
661 N Harper Ave Ste 208
Los Angeles, CA 90048
Tel.: (323) 866-0880
Fax: (323) 866-0882
Public Relations Agency of Record
SUSTA Natural Sweetener

OAKHURST DAIRY

364 Forest Ave
Portland, ME 04101-2035

Key to Media (For complete agency information see *The Advertising Red Books-Agencies* edition):
1. Bus. Publs. 2. Cable T.V. 3. Catalogs & Directories. 4. Co-op Adv. 5. Consumer Mags. 6. D.M. to Bus. Estab.7. D.M. to Consumers
8. Daily Newsp. 9. Exhibits/Trade Shows 10. Foreign 11. Infomercial 12. Internet Adv.13. Multimedia 14. Network Radio
15. Network T.V. 16. Newsp. Distr. Mags. 17. Other 18. Outdoor (Posters, Transit) 19. Point of Purchase20. Premiums, Novelties
21. Product Samples 22. Special Events Mktg. 23. Spot Radio 24. Spot T.V. 25. Weekly Newsp. 26. Yellow Page Adv.

Tel.: (207) 772-7468
Fax: (207) 874-0714
Web Site: www.oakhurstdairy.com
Sales Range: $75-99.9 Million
Approx. Number Employees: 225
Year Founded: 1921
Business Description:
Milk Processing & Distr
S.I.C.: 2026; 5143
N.A.I.C.S.: 311511; 424430
Media: 13-14-15-23-24
Personnel:
William P. Bennett *(Pres & COO)*
Thomas A. Brigham *(CFO, Treas & Exec VP)*
Paul J. Connolly, Jr. *(CIO & VP-Tech Svcs)*
Joseph H. Hyatt *(VP-HR & Admin)*
James M. Lesser *(VP-Sls & Mktg)*
Althea Bennett McGirr *(Dir-Customer Svcs & Consumer Affairs)*
Denise Bean *(Mgr-Accts & Credit)*
David Green *(Mgr-Fleet)*
Linda S. Sheehy *(Mgr-Mktg Comm)*
Brands & Products:
THE NATURAL GOODNESS OF MAINE
NU-TRISH
OAKHURST

OBERWEIS DAIRY, INC.

951 Ice Cream Dr
North Aurora, IL 60542-8193
Tel.: (630) 897-6600
Fax: (630) 897-0562
Toll Free: (888) 645-5868
E-mail: info@oberweis.com
Web Site: www.oberweis.com
Sales Range: $25-49.9 Million
Approx. Number Employees: 427
Year Founded: 1927
Business Description:
Retail & Wholesale Milk, Ice Cream & Other Dairy Products
S.I.C.: 2026; 5963
N.A.I.C.S.: 311511; 454390
Import Export
Advertising Expenditures: $1,500,000
Media: 2-5-7-8-9-10-18-19-21-25-26
Distr.: Direct to Consumer; Natl.
Budget Set: Nov.
Personnel:
Jim Oberweis *(Chm)*
Joe Oberweis *(Pres & CEO)*
Elizabeth Craig *(VP-Retail Ops)*
Dan Rosier *(Dir-Brand Dev)*
Brands & Products:
OBERWEIS DAIRY

OCEAN MIST FARMS CORP.

10855 Ocean Mist Pkwy
Castroville, CA 95012-3229
Tel.: (831) 633-2144
Fax: (831) 633-0561
E-mail: sales@oceanmist.com
Web Site: www.oceanmist.com
E-Mail For Key Personnel:
Sales Director: sales@oceanmist.com
Approx. Number Employees: 100
Year Founded: 1924
Business Description:
Grower, Packer & Shipper of Artichokes, Broccoli, Sprouts, Anise, Romaine, Lettuce, Peas, Mixed Vegetables & Cauliflower
S.I.C.: 0723
N.A.I.C.S.: 115114
Export
Personnel:
Les Tottino *(Vice Chm)*
Edward Boutonnet *(CEO)*
Phil Taluban *(CFO)*
Katie Tossie *(Coord-Sls)*
Bob Polovneff *(Sls Mgr)*
Gary Silacci *(Sls Mgr)*
Afreen Malik *(Mgr-Food Safety)*
Jorge Suarez *(Mgr-HR)*
Kori Tuggle *(Mgr-Mktg)*
Herb Wong *(Mgr-Facilities)*
Brands & Products:
OCEAN MIST
Advertising Agency:
Full Steam Marketing & Design
60 W Market St Ste 150
Salinas, CA 93901
Tel.: (831) 757-4164
Fax: (831) 757-7574

OCEAN SPRAY CRANBERRIES, INC.

1 Ocean Spray Dr
Lakeville, MA 02347-1339
Tel.: (508) 946-1000
Fax: (508) 946-7704
Toll Free: (800) 662-3263
Telex: 710391598
Web Site: www.oceanspray.com
Sales Range: $1-4.9 Billion
Approx. Number Employees: 500
Year Founded: 1930
Business Description:
Co-op Mfr & Marketer of Cranberry & Grapefruit Products
S.I.C.: 2033; 0171
N.A.I.C.S.: 311421; 111334
Import Export
Advertising Expenditures: $20,000,000
Media: 3-5-6-8-9-10-13-15-19-20-21-22-23-24
Distr.: Natl.
Budget Set: Aug. -Sept.
Personnel:
Randy C. Papadellis *(Pres & CEO)*
Richard Lees *(CFO & Sr VP)*
Larry Martin *(VP-Mktg)*
Katie Morey *(VP-HR)*
Robert Carrell *(Dir-IT)*
Nina Gorman *(Dir-Adv)*
Kathie Cornelius *(Mgr-Corp Comm)*
Courtney Genovese *(Mgr-Bus Dev)*
Cindy Taccini *(Mgr-Pub Rels)*
Brands & Products:
CARIBBEAN COLADA
CITRUS AM
CRAISINS
CRAN APPLE
CRAN CHERRY
CRAN GRAPE
CRAN MANGO
CRAN ORANGE
CRAN RASPBERRY
CRAN STRAWBERRY
CRAN TANGERINE
CRANERGY
CRANFRUIT
CRANICOT
CRANTASTIC
CRAVE THE WAVE
DIET OCEAN SPRAY
JUICE JAM
LIGHT CRAN POMEGRANATE
LIGHT CRANGRAPE
LIGHT RUBY
MANDARIN MAGIC
OCEANSPRAY
REFRESHERS
RUBY
SPLENDA
WHITE CRANBERRY
Advertising Agencies:
Arnold Worldwide
101 Huntington Ave
Boston, MA 02199-7603
Tel.: (617) 587-8000
Fax: (617) 587-8004
(Cranberry & Grapefruit Beverages & Foods)

Connelly Partners
46 Waltham St Fl 4
Boston, MA 02118
Tel.: (617) 956-5050
Fax: (617) 956-5054

Media Concepts Corporation
25 N Main St
Assonet, MA 02702-1136
Tel.: (508) 644-3131
Fax: (508) 644-5201

Weber Shandwick
(Sub. of The Interpublic Group of Companies)
919 3rd Ave
New York, NY 10022
Tel.: (212) 445-8000
Fax: (212) 445-8001

ZenithOptimedia
299 W Houston St 11th Fl
New York, NY 10014
Tel.: (212) 859-5100
Fax: (212) 727-9495

ODOM'S TENNESSEE PRIDE SAUSAGE, INC.

1201 Neelys Bend Rd
Madison, TN 37115-5446
Tel.: (615) 868-1360
Fax: (615) 860-4703
Toll Free: (800) 327-6269
Web Site: www.tnpride.com
E-Mail For Key Personnel:
President: larry@tnpride.com
Marketing Director: hea@tnpride.com
Sales Director: sales@tnpride.com
Approx. Rev.: $60,000,000
Approx. Number Employees: 600
Year Founded: 1943
Business Description:
Producers of Sausage
S.I.C.: 5147
N.A.I.C.S.: 311612
Media: 5-9-10-19-20-21-22-23-24
Distr.: Intl.; Natl.
Budget Set: Apr. -Aug.
Personnel:
Larry D. Odom *(Pres)*
Harold Boone *(CFO)*
Jim Stonehocker *(COO & Exec VP)*
Jim Hea *(VP-Sls & Mktg)*
Mark Newell *(Dir-Mktg)*
Brands & Products:
TENNESSEE PRIDE

ODWALLA, INC.

(Unit of Coca-Cola North America)
120 Stone Pine Rd
Half Moon Bay, CA 94019-1783
Tel.: (650) 726-1888
Fax: (650) 560-9009
Toll Free: (800) 639-2552
E-mail: press@odwalla.com
Web Site: www.odwalla.com
Sales Range: $25-49.9 Million
Approx. Number Employees: 60
Year Founded: 1980
Business Description:
All-Natural, Freshly Squeezed & Nutritionally Fortified Juices & Smoothies Mfr & Distr
S.I.C.: 2033
N.A.I.C.S.: 311421
Advertising Expenditures: $5,000,000
Media: 2-4-13-14-15-16-18
Personnel:
James Steichen *(CFO & Sr VP-Fin)*
Susan M. Kirmayer *(VP-HR)*
Brands & Products:
C MONSTER
FEMME VITALE
MANGO TANGO
MO' BETA

OLD DUTCH FOODS, INC.

2375 Terminal Rd
Roseville, MN 55113-2530
Tel.: (651) 633-8810
Fax: (651) 633-8894
Toll Free: (800) 989-2447
E-mail: customerservice@olddutchfoods.com
Web Site: www.olddutchfoods.com
Approx. Number Employees: 500
Year Founded: 1958
Business Description:
Potato Chips, Corn Chips, Nuts, Popcorn, Pretzels & Other Snack Foods
S.I.C.: 2096; 2099
N.A.I.C.S.: 311919; 311999
Media: 5-6-8-10-18-19-23-24
Distr.: Reg.
Budget Set: Dec.
Personnel:
Steve Aanenson *(Pres & CEO)*
Trace Benson *(CFO)*
Matt Colford *(Dir-Product Mgmt & Mktg)*
Brands & Products:
DUTCH CRUNCH
OLD DUTCH

ON-COR FROZEN FOODS LLC

627 Landwehr Rd
Northbrook, IL 60062-2309
Tel.: (847) 205-1040
Fax: (847) 205-1070
Web Site: www.on-cor.com
Approx. Number Employees: 500
Year Founded: 1946
Business Description:
Frozen Foods Mfr
S.I.C.: 2038; 2099
N.A.I.C.S.: 311412; 311999
Media: 5-6-9-14-15-19-20-25
Distr.: Natl.
Personnel:
Howard Leafstone *(Sr VP)*
Brands & Products:
ON-COR
ON-COR CLASSICS
ON-COR TRADITIONALS
REDI-SERVE
Advertising Agency:
Blue Chip Marketing Worldwide
650 Dundee Rd Ste 250

Key to Media (For complete agency information see *The Advertising Red Books-Agencies* edition):
1. Bus. Publs. 2. Cable T.V. 3. Catalogs & Directories. 4. Co-op Adv. 5. Consumer Mags. 6. D.M. to Bus. Estab.7. D.M. to Consumers 8. Daily Newsp. 9. Exhibits/Trade Shows 10. Foreign 11. Infomercial 12. Internet Adv.13. Multimedia 14. Network Radio 15. Network T.V. 16. Newsp. Distr. Mags. 17. Other 18. Outdoor (Posters, Transit) 19. Point of Purchase20. Premiums, Novelties 21. Product Samples 22. Special Events Mktg. 23. Spot Radio 24. Spot T.V. 25. Weekly Newsp. 26. Yellow Page Adv.

On-Cor Frozen Foods LLC — (Continued)

Northbrook, IL 60062
Tel.: (847) 446-2114

ORANGE MAISON
(Div. of A. Lassonde, Inc.)
9424 Lengelier Blvd
Saint Leonard, QC H1P 3H8, Canada
Tel.: (514) 351-4010
Fax: (514) 351-1185
Web Site: www.orange-maison.ca
Approx. Number Employees: 16
Business Description:
Orange Juice & Spring Water Mfr
S.I.C.: 2037
N.A.I.C.S.: 311411
Media: 2-4-10-13-18-23-26
Brands & Products:
ORANGE MAISON

OREGON FREEZE DRY, INC.
525 25th Ave SW
Albany, OR 97322
Mailing Address:
PO Box 1048 97321
Albany, OR 97322
Tel.: (541) 926-6001
Fax: (541) 967-6527
Toll Free: (800) 547-4060
E-mail: international@ofd.com
Web Site: www.ofd.com
Approx. Sls.: $5,300,000
Approx. Number Employees: 330
Year Founded: 1963
Business Description:
Freeze Dried Foods & Non-Food Ingredients Mfr
S.I.C.: 5147; 2015
N.A.I.C.S.: 311612; 311615
Export
Media: 4-7-8-10-20-22
Distr.: Intl.; Natl.
Personnel:
Herbert Aschkenasy *(Chm, Pres & CEO)*
Philip Unverzagt *(CFO)*
Larry Von Deylen *(Sr VP)*
Walt Pebley *(Mgr-Technical)*
Brands & Products:
EASY MEAL
FRUIT CRISPS
MOUNTAIN HOUSE
NOUVELLE
OREGON FREEZE DRY
PERFECT HOST

OTT FOOD PRODUCTS
(Div. of Westin Foods, Inc.)
705 W Fairview Ave
Carthage, MO 64836-3724
Tel.: (417) 358-2585
Fax: (417) 358-4553
Toll Free: (800) 866-2585
E-mail: rickk@ottfoods.com
Web Site: www.ottfoods.com
Approx. Number Employees: 18
Year Founded: 1954
Business Description:
Salad Dressings & Barbecue Sauces Mfr
S.I.C.: 2035; 2033
N.A.I.C.S.: 311941; 311421
Media: 1-2-7-8
Distr.: Natl.
Brands & Products:
OTT

OWENS COUNTRY SAUSAGE, INC.
(Sub. of Owens Foods, Inc.)
1403 E Lookout Dr
Richardson, TX 75082-3074
Mailing Address:
PO Box 830249
Richardson, TX 75083-0249
Tel.: (972) 235-7181
Fax: (972) 498-9253
E-mail: information@owensinc.com
Sales Range: $125-149.9 Million
Approx. Number Employees: 250
Year Founded: 1928
Business Description:
Meat Products
S.I.C.: 5147
N.A.I.C.S.: 311612
Export
Advertising Expenditures: $600,000
Media: 9-18-19-23-24
Distr.: Reg.
Budget Set: May
Personnel:
Mike Townsley *(Pres & COO)*
Brands & Products:
BORDER BREAKFAST
OWEN'S COUNTRY SAUSAGE
OWEN'S SPRING CREEK

PACKRYT, INC.
87-500 Airport Blvd PO Box 728
Thermal, CA 92274
Tel.: (760) 399-5026
Fax: (760) 399-0093
E-mail: admin@redidate.com
Web Site: www.redidate.com
Approx. Number Employees: 100
Year Founded: 1974
Business Description:
Contract Packaging Services for Food Products
S.I.C.: 7389
N.A.I.C.S.: 561910
Advertising Expenditures: $500,000
Media: 6-7-13-19
Distr.: Intl.; Natl.
Budget Set: Sept.
Personnel:
George Jeffrey *(CEO)*
Jack Stutz *(COO)*
Lisa Zeise *(Dir-Technical)*
Mike Avon *(Mgr-Production)*
Rosa Mireles *(Mgr-Fin)*
Joe Hughes *(Supvr-Inventory)*
Corina Sanchez *(Supvr-Pur)*

PAMLICO PACKING COMPANY INCORPORATED
PO Box 336
Grantsboro, NC 28529
Tel.: (252) 745-3688
Fax: (252) 745-3272
E-mail: info@bestseafoods.com
Web Site: www.bestseafood.com
E-Mail For Key Personnel:
Sales Director: sales@bestseafood.com
Sales Range: $10-24.9 Million
Approx. Number Employees: 9
Year Founded: 1941
Business Description:
Mfr & Distr of Fresh & Frozen Packaged Fish
S.I.C.: 2092
N.A.I.C.S.: 311712

Advertising Agency:
Browning Advertising, Inc.
121 Chanlon Rd
New Providence, NJ 07974
Tel.: (908) 464-0000
Fax: (908) 790-5405

PARADISE, INC.
1200 Dr Martin Luther King Jr Blvd
Plant City, FL 33563-5155
Tel.: (813) 752-1155
Fax: (813) 754-3168
Toll Free: (800) 330-8952
Web Site: www.paradisefruitco.com
Approx. Sls.: $23,964,543
Approx. Number Employees: 275
Year Founded: 1961
Business Description:
Candied Fruit Mfr
S.I.C.: 2099
N.A.I.C.S.: 311999; 311340
Advertising Expenditures: $144,603
Media: 3-5-19-24
Distr.: Natl.
Personnel:
Melvin S. Gordon *(Chm & CEO)*
Randy S. Gordon *(Pres)*
Jack M. Laskowitz *(CFO & Treas)*
Mark H. Gordon *(Exec VP)*
Tracy W. Schulis *(Sr VP & VP-Sls)*
Ron Peterson *(VP-Sls)*
Brands & Products:
DIXIE
PARADISE
PENNANT
WHITE SWAN

PARMALAT CANADA INC.
(Sub. of Parmalat SpA)
405 The West Mall 10th Floor
Toronto, ON M9C 5J1, Canada
Tel.: (416) 626-1973
Fax: (416) 620-3123
Web Site: www.parmalat.ca
Approx. Rev.: $2,045,032,867
Approx. Number Employees: 2,974
Year Founded: 1997
Business Description:
Producer & Marketer of Dairy Products
S.I.C.: 2026; 2034; 2099
N.A.I.C.S.: 311511; 311423; 311999
Export
Media: 6-15-19-24
Distr.: Intl.
Personnel:
Alnashir Lakha *(Pres & CEO)*
Cheryl Smith *(Exec VP-Consumer & Trade Mktg)*
Brands & Products:
ASTRO
BALDERSON
BLACK DIAMOND
COLONIAL
OLIVINIA
SARGENTO

PASTORELLI FOOD PRODUCTS, INC.
162 N Sangamon St
Chicago, IL 60607-2210
Tel.: (312) 666-2041
Fax: (312) 666-2415
Toll Free: (800) 767-2829
E-mail: info@pastorelli.com
Web Site: www.pastorelli.com
Approx. Number Employees: 17
Year Founded: 1931
Business Description:
Italian Foods, Edible Oils & Vinegars
S.I.C.: 2032; 2033
N.A.I.C.S.: 311422; 311421
Import Export
Media: 4-5-6-7-9-10-17-19-21-23-24
Distr.: Natl.
Budget Set: Feb. -May
Personnel:
Richard Pastorelli *(Pres)*
Angela Pastorelli *(Treas)*
Brands & Products:
CAL-WEST
CAMEO
CONTINENTAL CHEF
ITALIAN CHEF
PASTORELLI
PASTORELLI FOUR CHEESE
PASTORELLI GARDEN MARINARA
PASTORELLI ORGANIC FOUR CHEESE
PASTORELLI ORGANIC GARDEN MARINARA
PASTORELLI ORGANIC SPICY ARRABBIATA
PASTORELLI ORGANIC ZESTY PUTTANESCA
PASTORELLI SPICY ARRABBIATA
PASTORELLI ZESTY PUTTANESCA
REGINA
VEGIOLA

PATRICK CUDAHY INC.
(Sub. of Smithfield Foods, Inc.)
1 Sweet Apple Wood Ln
Cudahy, WI 53110
Tel.: (414) 744-2000
Fax: (414) 744-4213
Toll Free: (800) 486-6900
Web Site: www.patrickcudahy.com
Sales Range: $400-449.9 Million
Approx. Number Employees: 2,000
Year Founded: 1888
Business Description:
Bacon, Ham & Sausage Products
S.I.C.: 5147
N.A.I.C.S.: 311612
Import Export
Advertising Expenditures: $500,000
Media: 5-9-19-23-24
Distr.: Intl.; Natl.
Budget Set: Feb.
Personnel:
William G. Otis *(Pres & COO)*
James E. Matthews *(Sr VP)*
Sue Harris *(VP-Quality Control & Mgr)*
Brands & Products:
AGAR AND CLASSIC
DANZIG
FLAVORTAINER
GOLDEN CRISP
HAMBASSADOR
HERITAGE
LA ABUELITA
LA FORTUNA
MONTE ROSA
PATRICK CUDAHY
PATRICK'S PRIDE
PAVONE
PORTION PERFECT
REALEAN
ROYALE
ROYALEAN
SWEET APPLE WOOD SMOKE
VENICIA

Key to Media (For complete agency information see *The Advertising Red Books-Agencies* edition):
1. Bus. Publs. 2. Cable T.V. 3. Catalogs & Directories. 4. Co-op Adv. 5. Consumer Mags. 6. D.M. to Bus. Estab.7. D.M. to Consumers 8. Daily Newsp. 9. Exhibits/Trade Shows 10. Foreign 11. Infomercial 12. Internet Adv.13. Multimedia 14. Network Radio 15. Network T.V. 16. Newsp. Distr. Mags. 17. Other 18. Outdoor (Posters, Transit) 19. Point of Purchase20. Premiums, Novelties 21. Product Samples 22. Special Events Mktg. 23. Spot Radio 24. Spot T.V. 25. Weekly Newsp. 26. Yellow Page Adv.

PB LEINER USA
(Sub. of Tessenderlo Chemie N.V.)
7001 N Brady St
Davenport, IA 52806
Tel.: (563) 386-8040
Fax: (516) 822-4044
Toll Free: (888) 919-9494
Web Site: www.gelatin.com
Approx. Number Employees: 6
Business Description:
Gelatin Mfr & Retailer
S.I.C.: 2899
N.A.I.C.S.: 325998
Import
Media: 2-7-10
Distr.: Intl.
Budget Set: Jan.

PECO FOODS INC.
1020 Lurleen Wallace Blvd N
Tuscaloosa, AL 35401
Tel.: (205) 345-4711
Fax: (205) 366-4535
E-mail: info@pecofoods.com
Web Site: www.pecofoods.com
Approx. Number Employees: 3,200
Year Founded: 1969
Business Description:
Poultry Hatchery Services
S.I.C.: 0254; 0251
N.A.I.C.S.: 112340; 112320
Import Export
Advertising Expenditures: $2,000,000
Media: 4-5-13-16
Personnel:
Mark Hickman *(Pres & CEO)*
Tommy Elliott *(CFO)*
Benny Bishop *(COO)*
Steve Conley *(Dir-HR)*
Bobby Wilburn *(Dir-Sls & Mktg)*

PEER FOODS INC.
1200 W 35th St Ste 5 E
Chicago, IL 60609-3214
Tel.: (773) 927-1440
Fax: (773) 927-9859
E-mail: support@peerfoods.com
Web Site: www.peerfoods.com
Approx. Sls.: $90,000,000
Approx. Number Employees: 12
Year Founded: 1943
Business Description:
Sausages & Other Prepared Meats
S.I.C.: 5147; 5812
N.A.I.C.S.: 311612; 722110
Import Export
Media: 4-13
Personnel:
Larry O'Connell *(Pres)*
Brands & Products:
MARIAH
PEER
Advertising Agency:
Gordon Hanrahan, Inc.
150 N Michigan Ave Ste 600
Chicago, IL 60601-7570
Tel.: (312) 372-0935
Fax: (312) 372-1409

PEPPERIDGE FARM, INC.
(Sub. of Campbell Soup Company)
595 Westport Ave
Norwalk, CT 06851-4413
Tel.: (203) 846-7000
Fax: (203) 846-7369
Toll Free: (888) 737-7374
Web Site: www.pepperidgefarm.com
E-Mail For Key Personnel:
President: pat_callaghan@pepperidgefarm.com
Sales Range: $150-199.9 Million
Approx. Number Employees: 325
Year Founded: 1937
Business Description:
Fresh & Frozen Bakery Products Mfr
S.I.C.: 2051; 2052
N.A.I.C.S.: 311812; 311821
Import Export
Media: 3-6-8-9-10-14-15-19-20-21-23-24
Distr.: Natl.
Personnel:
Patrick J. Callaghan *(Pres)*
Maureen Linder *(Sr VP-Fresh & Frozen Bakery)*
Suzanne Goodrich *(Dir-Bus)*
Nan Redmond *(Dir-Comm)*
Brands & Products:
BORDEAUX
BRUSSELS
CHANTILLY
CHEDDAR FINGERS
CHEF'S COLLECTION
CHESAPEAKE
CHESSMEN
CINNAMON FINGERS
COUNTRY CHUNK
FARMHOUSE
FLAVOR BLASTED
GENEVA
GOLDEN TWIST
GOLDFISH
GOLDFISH SANDWICH SNACKERS
LIDO
LISBON
MILANO
MINI BRUSSELS
MINI CHESSMEN
MINI MILANO
MINI MINT MILANO
NANTUCKET
NAPLES
ORLEANS
PEPPERIDGE FARM
PEPPERIDGE FARM CARB STYLE
PEPPERIDGE FARM CHOCOLATE HEAVEN
PEPPERIDGE FARM FARMHOUSE
PEPPERIDGE FARM GREAT BAKES
PIROUETTE
SAUSALITO
STOWE
SWIRL
TAHITI
TAHOE
VENISE
VERONA
WHIMS
WHOLE GRAIN WHITE LIGHT STYLE
WHOLE GRAIN WHITE SANDWICH
WHOLE GRAIN WHITE VERY THIN
Advertising Agencies:
DeVries Public Relations
30 E 60th St 14th Fl
New York, NY 10022
Tel.: (212) 891-0400
Fax: (212) 644-0291

The Geppetto Group
95 Morton St 8th Fl
New York, NY 10014-3336
Tel.: (212) 462-8140
Fax: (212) 462-8197
Goldfish

Young & Rubicam Inc.
285 Madison Ave
New York, NY 10017-6401
Tel.: (212) 210-3000
Fax: (212) 490-9073

PERDUE FARMS INCORPORATED
31149 Old Ocean City Rd
Salisbury, MD 21804-1806
Mailing Address:
PO Box 1537
Salisbury, MD 21802-1537
Tel.: (410) 543-3000
Fax: (410) 543-3532
Toll Free: (800) 473-7383
Web Site: www.perdue.com
Sales Range: $1-4.9 Billion
Approx. Number Employees: 21,215
Year Founded: 1920
Business Description:
Dressed Poultry, Chickens, Prime Chicken Parts, Oven Stuffer Roasters, Fresh Cornish Game Hens, Turkeys & Turkey Parts Processor & Producer
S.I.C.: 2015; 2075; 5144
N.A.I.C.S.: 311615; 311222; 424440
Import Export
Media: 1-6-7-8-9-15-16-19-21-22-23-24
Distr.: Reg.
Budget Set: Mar.
Personnel:
James A. Perdue *(Chm & CEO)*
Richard L. Willey *(Pres & Gen Mgr-AgriBusiness)*
Mark Garth *(Sr VP-Fin & Acctg)*
Andy Urban *(VP-Sls-Supermarket/CPG/Deli)*
Lisa Woodward *(Asst Mgr-Mktg)*
Brands & Products:
COOKIN' GOOD
FIT 'N EASY
FUN SHAPES
MEAL TIME STARTERS
MEALS & MORE
OVEN STUFFER
PERDUE
PERDUE DONE IT!
PERFECT PORTIONS
PRIME PARTS
SANDWICH BUILDERS
SHORT CUTS
TENDER & TASTY
Advertising Agency:
RJ Palmer LLC
156 W 56th St 5th Fl
New York, NY 10019-3800
Tel.: (212) 541-6770
Fax: (212) 541-6769
Agency of Record
Digital Planning & Buying

PERFECTION BAKERIES INC.
350 Pearl St
Fort Wayne, IN 46802-1508
Tel.: (260) 424-8245
Fax: (260) 424-0477
Toll Free: (800) 995-8245
Web Site: www.perfectionbakeries.com
Approx. Int. Income: $1,144,733,493
Year Founded: 1901
Business Description:
Wholesale Bread & Buns
S.I.C.: 2051
N.A.I.C.S.: 311812
Media: 5-9-14-18-19-20-23
Distr.: Reg.
Budget Set: Jan.
Personnel:
John F. Popp *(Pres)*
Joe Steele *(Chief Engrg Officer)*
Jay Miller *(Treas & Sr VP-Fin)*
John B. Popp *(VP-Mktg)*

PETER PAN SEAFOODS, INC.
(Sub. of Nichiro Corporation)
2200 6th Ave Ste 1000
Seattle, WA 98121
Tel.: (206) 728-6000
Fax: (206) 441-9090
E-mail: sales@ppsf.com
Web Site: www.ppsf.com
E-Mail For Key Personnel:
Sales Director: sales@ppsf.com
Approx. Sls.: $24,000,000
Approx. Number Employees: 376
Year Founded: 1914
Business Description:
Canned & Frozen Salmon, Crab, Halibut, Cod, Pollock & Herring Mfr
S.I.C.: 2092; 2091
N.A.I.C.S.: 311712; 311711
Import Export
Media: 2-4-5-6-9-10-11-19-21-23
Distr.: Intl.; Natl.
Budget Set: Apr.
Personnel:
Barry D. Collier *(Pres & CEO)*
Steven N. Chartier *(VP-Sls & Mktg)*
Kirk Koch *(VP-Fin & Acctg)*
Brands & Products:
DEMING'S
DOUBLE Q
GILLNETTERS BEST
HUMPTY DUMPTY
PETER PAN
SEABLENDS

PHILLIPS MUSHROOM FARMS
1011 Kaolin Rd
Kennett Square, PA 19348
Mailing Address:
PO Box 190
Kennett Square, PA 19348
Tel.: (610) 925-0520
Fax: (610) 925-0527
E-mail: info@phillipsgourmet.com
Web Site: www.phillipsmushroomfarms.com
Approx. Number Employees: 200
Year Founded: 1962
Business Description:
Specialty Mushroom Farming
S.I.C.: 0182; 5148
N.A.I.C.S.: 111411; 424480
Media: 2-8-13-21
Personnel:
Jim Angioletti *(Gen Mgr)*
Brands & Products:
BABY BELLA
BELLA BURGER
PHILLIPS MUSHROOM FARMS
SHROOMIES

THE PICTSWEET COMPANY
10 Pictsweet Dr
Bells, TN 38006
Tel.: (731) 663-7600
Fax: (800) 561-8810
Toll Free: (800) 367-7412
Web Site: www.pictsweet.com
Approx. Number Employees: 2,000
Year Founded: 1999

Key to Media (For complete agency information see *The Advertising Red Books-Agencies* edition):
1. Bus. Publs. 2. Cable T.V. 3. Catalogs & Directories. 4. Co-op Adv. 5. Consumer Mags. 6. D.M. to Bus. Estab.7. D.M. to Consumers 8. Daily Newsp. 9. Exhibits/Trade Shows 10. Foreign 11. Infomercial 12. Internet Adv.13. Multimedia 14. Network Radio 15. Network T.V. 16. Newsp. Distr. Mags. 17. Other 18. Outdoor (Posters, Transit) 19. Point of Purchase20. Premiums, Novelties 21. Product Samples 22. Special Events Mktg. 23. Spot Radio 24. Spot T.V. 25. Weekly Newsp. 26. Yellow Page Adv.

The Pictsweet Company — (Continued)

Business Description:
Holding Company
S.I.C.: 2037; 0161
N.A.I.C.S.: 311411; 111219
Media: 17
Personnel:
James I. Tankersley *(CEO)*
Carl W. Gruenewald, II *(CFO & Sr VP)*
Brands & Products:
PICTSWEET
TASTE THE QUALITY!

PICTSWEET FROZEN FOODS

(Div. of The Pictsweet Company)
10 Pictsweet Dr
Bells, TN 38006
Tel.: (731) 663-2346
Fax: (888) 662-7651
Approx. Number Employees: 200
Business Description:
Mfr. & Distributor of Frozen Vegetables
S.I.C.: 7389; 5045; 5142
N.A.I.C.S.: 425120; 424420; 425110
Media: 2-8-9-23-25
Distr.: Intl.
Personnel:
Julia Wells *(Dir-Mktg)*
Brands & Products:
PICTSWEET
UNITED FOOD
Advertising Agency:
United Media
(House Agency)
PO Box 119 Ten Pictsweet Dr.
Bells, TN 38006
Tel.: (901) 422-7600
(Frozen Vegetables)

PILGRIM'S PRIDE CORPORATION

(Sub. of JBS USA Holding, Inc.)
1770 Promontory Cir
Greeley, CO 80634-9038
Tel.: (970) 506-8000
Toll Free: (800) 824-1159
Toll Free: (800) 683-1968
E-mail: info@pilgrimspride.com
Web Site: www.pilgrimspride.com
Approx. Sls.: $6,881,629,000
Approx. Number Employees: 28,270
Year Founded: 1946
Business Description:
Poultry Processing Services
S.I.C.: 2015; 0251
N.A.I.C.S.: 311615; 112320
Import Export
Media: 2-6-19-21-23-24
Distr.: Intl.; Natl.
Personnel:
Wesley Mendonca Batista *(Chm)*
William W. Lovette *(Pres & CEO)*
Fabio Sandri *(CFO)*
William K. Snyder *(Chief Restructuring Officer)*
Jerry Wilson *(Exec VP-Sls & Mktg)*
David W. Hand *(Sr VP-Intl & Fresh Sls)*
Gary L. Rhodes *(VP-Corp Comm & IR)*
Dave Parr *(Dir-Prepared Foods)*
Bei Bei Hirshman *(Mgr-Sls-Far East)*
Darla Knight *(Mgr-Sls-EMEA)*
Brands & Products:
BREADED NUGGETS
BREADED TENDER
BUFFALO WINGS
CAJUN STYLE
CHIPOTLE
COUNTRY PRIDE
EASY ENTREES
EAT WELL
EAT WELL STAY HEALTHY
EGGSPLUS
FAJITA BREAST STRIPS
GOLD KIST
PETITE
PILGRIM'S PRIDE
PILGRIM'S SIGNATURE
POPCORN
PRIDE GAUCHO GRILLS
ROTISSERIE
ROUND HILL WHOLE
SMOKED YOUNG
WING-DINGS
WING ZINGS
WINGSATIONS
Advertising Agencies:
Boomm! Marketing & Communications
17 N Catherine Ave
La Grange, IL 60525
Tel.: (708) 352-9700
Fax: (708) 352-9701

Hollister Strategic Marketing Services
2701 Valwood Pkwy
Farmers Branch, TX 75324
Tel.: (972) 693-4141

The Richards Group, Inc.
8750 N Central Expy Ste 100
Dallas, TX 75231-6430
Tel.: (214) 891-5700
Fax: (214) 265-2933

The Wolf Agency
3900 Willow St Ste 250
Dallas, TX 75226
Tel.: (214) 965-0880
Fax: (214) 760-7518

PINES INTERNATIONAL, INC.

1992 E 1400 Rd
Lawrence, KS 66044
Tel.: (785) 841-6016
Fax: (785) 841-1252
Toll Free: (800) 697-4637
E-mail: pines@wheatgrass.com
Web Site: www.wheatgrass.com
Sales Range: Less than $1 Million
Approx. Number Employees: 20
Business Description:
Whole Foods Mfr.
S.I.C.: 8322
N.A.I.C.S.: 624210
Media: 4-6-13
Personnel:
Steve Malone *(Co-Founder & CEO)*
Ron Siebold *(Pres)*

PINNACLE FOODS FINANCE LLC

(Holding of The Blackstone Group L.P.)
1 Old Bloomfield Ave
Mountain Lakes, NJ 07046
Tel.: (973) 541-6620
Approx. Sls.: $2,436,703,000
Approx. Number Employees: 4,400
Business Description:
Holding Company; Food Mfr, Distr & Marketer
S.I.C.: 6719
N.A.I.C.S.: 551112
Advertising Expenditures: $40,725,000
Media: 3-6-7-8-9-13-15-16-17-22-24-25
Personnel:
Roger Deromedi *(Chm)*
Robert Gamgort *(CEO)*
Craig Steeneck *(CFO & Exec VP)*
Antonio F. Fernandez *(Chief Supply Chain Officer & Exec VP)*
Mark L. Schiller *(Pres-Duncan Hines Grocery Div & Exec VP)*
M. Kelley Maggs *(Gen Counsel, Sec & Sr VP)*
Lynne M. Misericordia *(Treas, Sr VP & Asst Sec)*
Sally Genster Robling *(Div Pres-Birds Eye Frozen Div & Exec VP)*
Raymond J. O'Brien *(Chief Customer Officer & Exec VP-Sls)*
Anthony C. Landretti *(Sr VP & Gen Mgr-Specialty Foods Div)*
John F. Kroeger *(VP & Deputy Gen Counsel)*
Andy Reicchgut *(VP-Mktg)*
Brandi Unchester *(Sr Brand Mgr)*
Advertising Agencies:
BBDO New York
1285 Ave of the Americas 7th Fl
New York, NY 10019-6028
Tel.: (212) 459-5000

Bender Hammerling Group Public Relations
546 Valley Rd
Montclair, NJ 07043
Tel.: (973) 744-0707
Fax: (973) 746-2199

MEI
55 Madison Ave 4th Fl
Morristown, NJ 07960
Tel.: (973) 285-3045
Fax: (973) 538-0503

TBWA Chiat Day New York
488 Madison Ave
New York, NY 10022
Tel.: (212) 804-1000
Fax: (212) 804-1200

PINNACLE FOODS GROUP LLC

(Sub. of Pinnacle Foods Finance LLC)
1 Old Bloomfield Ave
Mountain Lakes, NJ 07046
Tel.: (973) 541-6620
Web Site: www.pinnaclefoods.com
Sales Range: $800-899.9 Million
Approx. Number Employees: 3,100
Business Description:
Holding Company for Dry/Frozen Food Brands
S.I.C.: 6719; 2037; 2096; 2099
N.A.I.C.S.: 311991; 311411; 311919; 311999; 551112
Media: 13-15-24-29
Personnel:
Robert J. Gamgort *(CEO)*
Craig Steeneck *(CFO & Exec VP)*
Sally Genster-Robling *(CMO & Exec. VP)*
Michael J. Cramer *(Chief Admin Officer & Exec VP)*
Chris Kiser *(Chief Customer Officer)*
M. Kelley Maggs *(Gen Counsel, Sec & Sr VP)*
John F. Kroeger *(VP & Asst Gen Counsel)*
Lynne M. Misericordia *(Treas, Sr VP & Asst Sec)*
John L. Butler *(Exec VP-HR)*
Edward L. Sutter *(Exec VP-Supply Chain & Ops)*
Mark Parker *(Sr VP-Bus Dev)*
Jim Seiple *(Sr VP- Product Dev & Tech Svcs)*
Brandi Unchester *(Sr Brand Mgr-Frozen & Refrigerated Breakfasts)*
Brands & Products:
ARMOUR
AUNT JEMIMA
BERNSTEIN'S
BIRDS EYE FOODS
BROOKS
C&W
CELESTE
COMSTOCK
DUNCAN HINES
FRESHLIKE
HUNGRY-MAN
LENDER'S
LOG CABIN
MCKENZIE'S
MILWAUKEE'S
MRS. BUTTERWORTH'S
MRS. PAUL'S
NALLEY
SNYDER OF BERLIN
STEAMFRESH
SWANSON
TIM'S
VAN DE KAMP'S
VLASIC
WIEJSKE WYROBY
WILDERNESS

PLOCHMAN, INC.

1333 N Boudreau Rd
Manteno, IL 60950-9384
Tel.: (815) 468-3434
Fax: (815) 468-8755
Toll Free: (800) 84DIJON
Web Site: www.plochman.com
Approx. Number Employees: 90
Year Founded: 1852
Business Description:
Prepared Mustard Mfr
S.I.C.: 2035
N.A.I.C.S.: 311941
Import Export
Media: 2-19-20
Distr.: Natl.
Budget Set: Oct.-Nov.
Personnel:
Carl M. Plochman *(Chm)*
Carl M. Plochman III *(Pres & CEO)*
Diane Kintz *(CFO)*
Brands & Products:
CHILI DOG
HEARTY BAVARIAN
HONEY DIJON
KOSCIUSKO
MUSTARD LOVERS
NATURAL STONE GROUND
PLOCHMAN
PREMIUM DIJON
SPICY HONEY
SPICY HORSERADISH
SPICY PEPPA
SPOONABLE BARREL CONTAINER
SQUARE BARREL CONTAINER
ZESTY HORSERADISH

Key to Media (For complete agency information see *The Advertising Red Books-Agencies* edition):
1. Bus. Publs. 2. Cable T.V. 3. Catalogs & Directories. 4. Co-op Adv. 5. Consumer Mags. 6. D.M. to Bus. Estab.7. D.M. to Consumers 8. Daily Newsp. 9. Exhibits/Trade Shows 10. Foreign 11. Infomercial 12. Internet Adv.13. Multimedia 14. Network Radio 15. Network T.V. 16. Newsp. Distr. Mags. 17. Other 18. Outdoor (Posters, Transit) 19. Point of Purchase20. Premiums, Novelties 21. Product Samples 22. Special Events Mktg. 23. Spot Radio 24. Spot T.V. 25. Weekly Newsp. 26. Yellow Page Adv.

PLUM ORGANICS
1485 Park Ave
Emeryville, CA 94608
Toll Free: (877) 914-7586
Web Site: www.plumorganics.com
Approx. Number Employees: 30
Business Description:
Mfr & Distr of Organic Foods for Babies, Toddlers & Children
N.A.I.C.S.: 311999
Media: 29
Personnel:
Neil Grimmer *(CEO)*

POINSETTIA GROVES INC.
1481 US Hwy 1
Vero Beach, FL 32960-5733
Tel.: (772) 562-3356
Fax: (772) 562-3629
Toll Free: (800) 327-8624
E-mail: customer.service@poinsettiagroves.com
Web Site: www.poinsettiagroves.com
Sales Range: $10-24.9 Million
Approx. Number Employees: 50
Year Founded: 1947
Business Description:
Retailer of Citrus Fruits & Gift Packages
S.I.C.: 5961; 0179
N.A.I.C.S.: 454113; 111339
Media: 4-6-8-9-13-18-25-26
Distr.: Natl.
Personnel:
Jeb B. Hudson *(Pres)*
Brands & Products:
POINSETTIA GROVES

POLKA DOT DAIRY
110 17th St E
Hastings, MN 55033
Tel.: (651) 438-2793
Fax: (651) 438-2638
Web Site: www.polkadotdairy.com
Approx. Number Employees: 23
Year Founded: 1957
Business Description:
Dairy Producer
S.I.C.: 0241; 2022
N.A.I.C.S.: 112120; 311513
Advertising Expenditures: $1,000,000
Media: 2-8-9-23-24
Personnel:
Brenda Fahey *(Dir-Mktg)*

POM WONDERFUL, LLC
(Sub. of Roll International Corporation)
11444 W Olympic Blvd
Los Angeles, CA 90064
Tel.: (310) 966-5800
Fax: (310) 966-5801
E-mail: pr@pomwonderful.com
Web Site: www.pomwonderful.com
Sales Range: $150-199.9 Million
Approx. Number Employees: 60
Business Description:
Pomegranate Processor & Distr
S.I.C.: 2037
N.A.I.C.S.: 311411
Export
Media: 2-6-7-8-11-21
Personnel:
Lynda Resnick *(Owner)*
Matt Tupper *(Pres)*
Tina Wong *(Mgr-Mktg)*
Brands & Products:
THE ANTIOXIDANT SUPERPOWER
POM WONDERFUL
POMX ICED TEA

POMPEIAN, INC.
4201 Pulaski Hwy
Baltimore, MD 21224-1603
Tel.: (410) 276-6900
Fax: (410) 276-3764
Toll Free: (800) POMPEIAN
E-mail: sales@pompeian.com
Web Site: www.pompeian.com
E-Mail For Key Personnel:
Sales Director: sales@pompeian.com
Approx. Number Employees: 50
Business Description:
Olive Oil, Vinegar, Cooking Wines, Olives & Artichokes Importer
S.I.C.: 2079
N.A.I.C.S.: 311225
Import
Advertising Expenditures: $500,000
Media: 4-5-6-9-10-19-20-21-23
Distr.: Natl.
Budget Set: Dec.
Personnel:
Frank Patton *(Pres)*
Bill Monroe *(CEO)*
Bob Eckoff *(Mgr-Mktg & Sls)*
Brands & Products:
LIFE IS GOOD POMPEIAN MAKES IT BETTER.
MUSA
OLIVEXTRA PLUS
POMPEIAN
WHAT PUTS THE "VIRGIN" IN EXTRA VIRGIN OLIVE OIL?
Advertising Agency:
Block & DeCorso
3 Claridge Dr
Verona, NJ 07044-3000
Tel.: (973) 857-3900
Fax: (973) 857-4041

PRAIRIE FARMS DAIRY, INC.
1100 N Broadway St
Carlinville, IL 62626-1183
Tel.: (217) 854-2547
Fax: (217) 854-6426
E-mail: icebox@prairiefarms.com
Web Site: www.prairiefarms.com
Approx. Number Employees: 3,000
Year Founded: 1938
Business Description:
Dairy Food Products Mfr
S.I.C.: 2026
N.A.I.C.S.: 311511
Media: 2-9-17-18-19-20-22-23-24-25
Distr.: Reg.
Personnel:
Ed Mullins *(CEO)*
Mark Hopping *(VP & Mgr-Risk)*
Paul Benne *(VP-Fin)*
Larry King *(VP-Ice Cream Sls)*
Gary Lee *(VP-Mktg)*
William Montgomery *(Dir-Adv & Promo)*
Brands & Products:
PFKIDS
PRAIRIE FARMS
QUALITY, YOU CAN TASTE

PRECISION FOODS, INC.
(Sub. of Grain Processing Corporation)
11457 Olde Cabin Rd
Saint Louis, MO 63141-7139
Tel.: (314) 567-7400
Fax: (314) 567-7421
E-mail: info@precisionfoods.com
Web Site: www.precisionfoods.com
Approx. Number Employees: 28
Business Description:
Food Manufacturing Company
S.I.C.: 2034; 2035
N.A.I.C.S.: 311423; 311941
Personnel:
Gage A. Kent *(Chm)*
Jerry L. Fritz *(Pres)*
Brands & Products:
FROSTLINE
MILANI THICK-IT
Advertising Agency:
Design North, Inc.
8007 Douglas Ave
Racine, WI 53402
Tel.: (262) 639-2080
Tel.: (262) 898-1090
Fax: (262) 639-5230
Toll Free: (800) 247-8494

PRESIDENT GLOBAL CORPORATION
(Sub. of Uni-President Enterprises Corporation)
6965 Aragon Cir
Buena Park, CA 90620
Tel.: (714) 994-2990
Fax: (714) 523-3142
Web Site: www.tung-i.com
Approx. Number Employees: 70
Business Description:
Mfr. of Convenient Foods
S.I.C.: 5149; 2099
N.A.I.C.S.: 424490; 311999
Import Export
Media: 2-5-6-9-11-23-24-25
Personnel:
Ping C. Wu *(Owner, Pres & CEO)*
Brands & Products:
LUCKY
PRESIDENT
TUNG-I

PURITY DAIRIES, LLC
(Sub. of Dean Dairy Holdings, LLC)
360 Murfreesboro Rd
Nashville, TN 37210-2816
Mailing Address:
PO Box 100957
Nashville, TN 37224-0957
Tel.: (615) 244-1900
Tel.: (615) 760-2296
Fax: (615) 242-8547
Toll Free: (800) 804-6455
E-mail: whypurity@puritydairies.com
Web Site: www.puritydairies.com
Sales Range: $250-299.9 Million
Approx. Number Employees: 500
Year Founded: 1926
Business Description:
Mfr. of Dairy Products
S.I.C.: 2026; 2024
N.A.I.C.S.: 311511; 311520
Advertising Expenditures: $1,500,000
Media: 2-6-9-18-19-20-21-22-23-24-25-26
Personnel:
Mark Ezell *(Pres & Gen Mgr)*
Tim White *(VP & Mgr-Sls)*
Brands & Products:
GREAT TASTE SIMPLY AND PURE
PURITY MILK
SWEET ACIDOPHILUS

Q&B FOODS, INC.
(Sub. of Kewpie Corporation)
15547 First St
Irwindale, CA 91706-6201
Tel.: (626) 334-8090
Fax: (626) 969-1587
Toll Free: (800) 423-4505
Web Site: www.qbfoods.com
Approx. Number Employees: 85
Business Description:
Salad Dressing & Mayonnaise; Private Label & Co-Packing Mfr
S.I.C.: 2035
N.A.I.C.S.: 311941
Advertising Expenditures: $1,200,000
Media: 6-8-10-17-19
Distr.: Intl.; Natl.
Budget Set: Oct. -Nov.
Personnel:
Vern Robinius *(Pres)*
Kuniaki Ishikawa *(CEO)*
Jerry Shepherd *(Exec VP)*
Jeannie DeFlaviis *(VP-Fin)*
Koh Matsumoto *(Gen Mgr-Trading Div)*
Pamela Boswell *(Dir-Tech Svcs)*
Jim Collazo *(Mgr-Distr)*
Julie Hunter *(Mgr-Material Control)*
Alfredo Medina *(Mgr-Production)*
Tony Chavez *(Supvr-Distr)*
Brands & Products:
ORIENTAL CHEF

QUALITY BAKERS OF AMERICA COOPERATIVE, INC.
1055 Parsippany Blvd Ste 201
Parsippany, NJ 07054
Tel.: (973) 263-6970
Fax: (973) 263-0937
E-mail: info@qba.com
Web Site: www.qba.com
Approx. Number Employees: 4
Year Founded: 1922
Business Description:
Bakers Cooperative; Bread
S.I.C.: 8748
N.A.I.C.S.: 541618
Advertising Expenditures: $1,000,000
Media: 1-3-4-5-6-7-8-9-10-11-18-19-20-22-23-24-25
Distr.: Natl.
Budget Set: Oct.
Personnel:
Donald C. Cummings *(CFO)*
Brands & Products:
MISS SUNBEAM
POWER KIDS BREAD
QBA
SUNBEAM
SUNBEAM LITE
Advertising Agency:
Depersico Creative Group
1 Raymond Dr
Havertown, PA 19083
Tel.: (610) 789-4400
Fax: (610) 789-7133
Toll Free: (800) 645-1950

QUANTUM FOODS, INC.
750 S Schmidt Rd
Bolingbrook, IL 60440
Tel.: (630) 679-2300
Fax: (630) 679-1257
Toll Free: (800) 334-6328
E-mail: info@quantumfoods.com
Web Site: www.quantumfoods.com
Approx. Number Employees: 700
Year Founded: 1990

Key to Media (For complete agency information see *The Advertising Red Books-Agencies* edition):
1. Bus. Publs. 2. Cable T.V. 3. Catalogs & Directories. 4. Co-op Adv. 5. Consumer Mags. 6. D.M. to Bus. Estab.7. D.M. to Consumers 8. Daily Newsp. 9. Exhibits/Trade Shows 10. Foreign 11. Infomercial 12. Internet Adv.13. Multimedia 14. Network Radio 15. Network T.V. 16. Newsp. Distr. Mags. 17. Other 18. Outdoor (Posters, Transit) 19. Point of Purchase20. Premiums, Novelties 21. Product Samples 22. Special Events Mktg. 23. Spot Radio 24. Spot T.V. 25. Weekly Newsp. 26. Yellow Page Adv.

Quantum Foods, Inc. — (Continued)

Business Description:
Portion Controlled Meats for Food Services Mfr & Distr
S.I.C.: 5147
N.A.I.C.S.: 311612
Advertising Expenditures: $300,000
Media: 3-6-9-19-25
Distr.: Natl.
Budget Set: Sept.
Personnel:
Edward Bleka *(Founder & Owner)*
Brands & Products:
GREAT STEAKS!
PROVIDING PROTEIN AND MENU SOLUTIONS
QUANTUM FOODS
QUANTUM STEAKHOUSE
SIMPLY GOURMET

RALSTON FOODS

(Sub. of Ralcorp Holdings, Inc.)
800 Market St
Saint Louis, MO 63101-2506
Tel.: (314) 877-7000
Fax: (314) 877-7666
Web Site: www.ralstonfoods.com
Sales Range: $75-99.9 Million
Approx. Number Employees: 180
Year Founded: 1994
Business Description:
Private Label & Store Brand Breakfast Cereals Mfr
S.I.C.: 2043
N.A.I.C.S.: 311230
Media: 2-4-7-13-16-21
Personnel:
David P. Skarie *(Co-CEO)*
Brands & Products:
RALSTON FOODS

R.C. BIGELOW, INC.

201 Black Rock Tpke
Fairfield, CT 06825
Tel.: (203) 334-1212
Fax: (203) 576-0241
Toll Free: (888) BIGELOW
E-mail: info@bigelowtea.com
Web Site: www.rcbigelow.com
Approx. Number Employees: 425
Year Founded: 1945
Business Description:
Mfr. of Teas
S.I.C.: 2095
N.A.I.C.S.: 311920
Export
Media: 4-6-7
Distr.: Natl.
Budget Set: June
Personnel:
Eunice Bigelow *(Vice Chm)*
Cindy Bigelow *(Pres)*
Donald Janezic *(CFO)*
Marshall Adams *(Sr VP-Bus Devel & Strategic Plng)*
Robert Kelly *(VP-Mktg & Sls)*
Richard Whalen *(VP-HR)*
Elizabeth Fritz *(Mgr-Prod)*
Brands & Products:
APPLE CINNAMON
BIGELOW
CHINESE FORTUNE
CINNAMON STICK
CONSTANT COMMENT
CRANBERRY APPLE
THE ELEGANT SOFT DRINK
ENGLISH TEATIME
LEMON LIFT
MINT MEDLEY
PLANTATION MINT
RASPBERRY ROYALE
RED RASPBERRY
STERLING SILVER TEAS
SWEET DREAMS

READING PRETZEL MACHINERY CORPORATION

(d/b/a Reading Bakery Systems)
380 Old W Penn Ave
Robesonia, PA 19551-8903
Tel.: (610) 693-5816
Year Founded: 1978
Business Description:
Bakery Equipment Mfr
S.I.C.: 3556
N.A.I.C.S.: 333294
Media: 2-10
Advertising Agency:
Reese
955 Berkshire Blvd
Wyomissing, PA 19610-1229
Tel.: (610) 378-1835
Fax: (610) 378-1676

READY PAC PRODUCE, INC.

4401 Foxdale Ave
Irwindale, CA 91706
Tel.: (626) 856-8686
Fax: (626) 856-0088
Toll Free: (800) 800-7822
E-mail: info@readypacproduce.com
Web Site: www.readypacproduce.com
Approx. Number Employees: 2,200
Year Founded: 1969
Business Description:
Processor of Fresh-Cut Produce
S.I.C.: 2099; 5148
N.A.I.C.S.: 311991; 424480
Personnel:
Dennis Gertmenian *(Founder)*
Brands & Products:
AQUA PAC
BISTRO-TO-GO
LEAFY GREEN BLENDS
ORGANIC
READY FIXIN'S
READY PAC
Advertising Agency:
Dentsu America, Inc.
32 Ave of the Americas 16th Fl
New York, NY 10013
Tel.: (212) 397-3333
Fax: (212) 397-3322

REALLY COOL FOODS

(Sub. of Renaissance Food Group, LLC.)
1200 Enterprise Rd
Cambridge City, IN 47327
Tel.: (765) 478-6600
Web Site: www.reallycoolfoods.com
Business Description:
Natural Food Product Mfr.
S.I.C.: 2099
N.A.I.C.S.: 311991
Personnel:
Bob Clamp *(CEO)*
Dana Richardson *(VP-Mktg)*
Advertising Agencies:
Barker/DZP
455 Broadway
New York, NY 10013
Tel.: (212) 226-7336
Fax: (212) 226-7937

Bose Public Affairs Group
111 Monument Cir Ste 2700
Indianapolis, IN 46204
Tel.: (317) 684-5400

REDCO FOODS, INC.

(Sub. of Teekanne GmbH)
100 Northfield Dr
Windsor, CT 06095
Tel.: (860) 688-2121
Fax: (860) 688-7844
Toll Free: (877) 248-2477
Web Site: www.greentea.com
Approx. Number Employees: 100
Year Founded: 1985
Business Description:
Mfr. of Teas & Desserts
S.I.C.: 2095; 2024
N.A.I.C.S.: 311920; 311520
Advertising Expenditures: $2,000,000
Media: 4-5-6-9-10-13-18-19-21-23-24-25
Distr.: Natl.
Budget Set: Jan.
Personnel:
Doug Farrell *(Gen Mgr & Dir)*
Michele Peters *(Brand Mgr-Salada Tea & Red Rose Tea)*
Brands & Products:
HANSEN ISLAND
JUNKET
RED ROSE
SALADA
Advertising Agency:
Pinckney Hugo Group
760 W Genesee St
Syracuse, NY 13204-2306
Tel.: (315) 478-6700
Fax: (315) 426-1392
(Salada Green Tea)

REIDCO, INC.

(d/b/a Marion-Kay Spices)
1351 W US Hwy 50
Brownstown, IN 47220
Tel.: (812) 358-3000
Fax: (812) 358-3400
E-mail: info@marionkay.com
Web Site: www.marionkay.com
Approx. Number Employees: 20
Year Founded: 1927
Business Description:
Flavoring Extracts & Spices Retailer for Food Services Industry
S.I.C.: 2099; 5961
N.A.I.C.S.: 311942; 454113
Media: 2-4-6-7-8-10-13-20-22-26
Distr.: Natl.
Budget Set: Apr. -Nov.

REILY FOODS COMPANY

(Div. of William B. Reily & Co., Inc.)
640 Magazine St
New Orleans, LA 70130-3406
Mailing Address:
PO Box 60296
New Orleans, LA 70160-0296
Tel.: (504) 524-6131
Tel.: (504) 539-5200
Fax: (504) 539-5427
Toll Free: (800) 535-1961
E-mail: service@luzianne.com
Web Site: www.luzianne.com
Approx. Sls.: $200,000,000
Approx. Number Employees: 325
Year Founded: 1903
Business Description:
Mfr., Producer & Retailer of Coffee, Tea, Mayonnaise, Salad Dressings, Cake Flour, Peanut Butter & Cooking Oils
S.I.C.: 2035; 2099
N.A.I.C.S.: 311941; 311942
Export
Media: 1-4-6-8-9-10-19-20-21-23-24-25
Distr.: Natl.
Budget Set: Oct.
Personnel:
David Darraugh *(Pres)*
Don Simpson *(VP-Sls)*
Brands & Products:
A TRADITION OF GOOD EATING
Advertising Agency:
Optimedia International U.S.
375 Hudson St 7th Fl
New York, NY 10014
Tel.: (212) 820-3200
Fax: (212) 820-3300

RHODES INTERNATIONAL, INC.

PO Box 25487
Salt Lake City, UT 84123-0487
Tel.: (801) 972-0122
Fax: (801) 972-4310
Toll Free: (800) 695-0122
E-mail: customersatisfaction@rhodesbread.com
Web Site: www.rhodesbread.com
Approx. Number Employees: 450
Year Founded: 1964
Business Description:
Mfr. of Frozen Bread, Roll & Biscuit Dough
S.I.C.: 2051; 5812
N.A.I.C.S.: 311812; 722110
Advertising Expenditures: $1,000,000
Media: 5-6-9-19-23-24
Distr.: Natl.
Budget Set: Nov.
Personnel:
Ken Farnsworth, Jr. *(Owner)*
Brands & Products:
ANYTIME!
RHODES
SHOW YOUR LOVE BY WHAT YOU SERVE

RICELAND FOODS, INC.

2120 S Park Ave
Stuttgart, AR 72160-6822
Mailing Address:
PO Box 927
Stuttgart, AR 72160
Tel.: (870) 673-5500
Fax: (870) 673-5667
Telex: 536-464
E-mail: riceland@riceland.com
Web Site: www.riceland.com
E-Mail For Key Personnel:
Public Relations: BReed@riceland.com
Sales Range: $800-899.9 Million
Approx. Number Employees: 1,900
Year Founded: 1921
Business Description:
Rice & Soybean Milling Services; Farmer-Owned Cooperative
S.I.C.: 2044; 2079
N.A.I.C.S.: 311212; 311225
Export
Media: 6-8-9-23-24-25
Distr.: Natl.
Budget Set: Dec.-Jan.

Key to Media (For complete agency information see *The Advertising Red Books-Agencies* edition):
1. Bus. Publs. 2. Cable T.V. 3. Catalogs & Directories. 4. Co-op Adv. 5. Consumer Mags. 6. D.M. to Bus. Estab.7. D.M. to Consumers 8. Daily Newsp. 9. Exhibits/Trade Shows 10. Foreign 11. Infomercial 12. Internet Adv.13. Multimedia 14. Network Radio 15. Network T.V. 16. Newsp. Distr. Mags. 17. Other 18. Outdoor (Posters, Transit) 19. Point of Purchase20. Premiums, Novelties 21. Product Samples 22. Special Events Mktg. 23. Spot Radio 24. Spot T.V. 25. Weekly Newsp. 26. Yellow Page Adv.

Personnel:
Thomas C. Hoskyn *(Chm)*
Harry E. Loftis *(CFO & Sr VP)*
K. Danny Kennedy *(COO & Exec VP)*
Carl W. Brothers *(Sr VP)*
Jerry A. Delatte *(Sr VP-Domestic Food Svc)*
Terry Harris *(VP-Mktg)*
Richard M. Rorey *(VP-Rice Milling & Engrg)*
Dan Meins *(Dir-Mktg)*
Sherry Brantley *(Sls Mgr-Rice Feed Ingredients)*
Randy Johnson *(Sls Mgr-Private Label)*
Brands & Products:
CHEF-WAY
CHINA BUTTERFLY
DELTA STAR
LOTUS 103
ORIENTAL HARVEST
ORIENTAL STYLE
PAGODA
PERFECTION
RICE 'N EASY
RICELAND

RICH PRODUCTS CORPORATION

1 Robert Rich Way
Buffalo, NY 14213-1714
Mailing Address:
PO Box 245
Buffalo, NY 14240-0245
Tel.: (716) 878-8000
Fax: (716) 878-8765
Toll Free: (800) 45RICHS
Web Site: www.richs.com
Sales Range: $1-4.9 Billion
Approx. Number Employees: 7,500
Year Founded: 1945
Business Description:
Non-Dairy Products, Frozen Foods, Baked Goods & Seafood Mfr
S.I.C.: 2053; 2092
N.A.I.C.S.: 311813; 311712
Import Export
Media: 2-4-6-9-10-13-18-20-21-22-23-25-26
Distr.: Natl.
Budget Set: Dec.
Personnel:
Mindy Rich *(Vice Chm)*
William G. Gisel, Jr. *(Pres & CEO)*
James Deuschle *(CFO & Exec VP)*
Maureen O. Hurley *(Chief Admin Officer & Exec VP)*
Ray Burke *(Pres-Bakery Div)*
Richard Ferranti *(Pres-North America)*
Jack C. Kilgore *(Pres-Consumer Brands)*
Kevin Malchoff *(Pres-Intl)*
Wendy Barth *(Sr VP-Intl Mktg & R & D)*
Michael Bingham *(Sr VP)*
Dwight Gam *(VP-Comm)*
Brands & Products:
ALLEN
AVOSET
BETTERCREME
BYRON'S
CARING FOR CUSTOMERS LIKE ONLY A FAMILY CAN
CASA DIBERTACCHI
COFFEE RICH
DELLA SUPREMA
FARM RICH
GOLD LABEL
JON DONAIRE
MOTHER'S KITCHEN
ON TOP
PRESTO
RICH'S
RICH'S WELCOMES YOU LIKE ONLY A FAMILY CAN
SEAPAK
TIKI BAY
TRES RICHES
Advertising Agencies:
hyperQuake
205 W Fourth St Ste 1010
Cincinnati, OH 45202
Tel.: (513) 563-6555
Fax: (513) 563-6080
(Casa Di Bertacchi, Cookie Dough Nuggets, Farm Rich, French Meadow Bakery, Seapak Shrimp Co., World Catch)

Ignite Communications
11445 JohnsCreek Pkwy
Duluth, GA 30097
Tel.: (770) 232-1711
Fax: (770) 232-1722

Travers Collins & Company
726 Exchange St Ste 500
Buffalo, NY 14210-1495
Tel.: (716) 842-2222
Fax: (716) 842-6424
(Della Suprema)

RIVIANA FOODS INC.

(Sub. of Ebro Puleva S.A.)
2777 Allen Pkwy
Houston, TX 77019-2141
Mailing Address:
PO Box 2636
Houston, TX 77252-2636
Tel.: (713) 529-3251
Fax: (713) 529-1661
Web Site: www.riviana.com
Sales Range: $350-399.9 Million
Approx. Number Employees: 2,752
Year Founded: 1986
Business Description:
Branded & Private-Label Rice & Other Food Products Mfr, Marketer & Distr
S.I.C.: 2044; 2052
N.A.I.C.S.: 311212; 311821
Export
Advertising Expenditures: $5,000,000
Media: 5-8-9-11-18-19-20-21-22-23-24-25
Distr.: Intl.; Natl.
Personnel:
Antonio Hernandez Callejas *(Chm)*
Gregory S. Richardson *(VP & CFO)*
Elizabeth B. Woodard *(VP & Gen Counsel)*
Gerard J. Ferguson *(VP-HR)*
Paul A. Galvani *(VP-Mktg)*
Pankaj Talwar *(VP-Mktg-Consumer)*
Tim D. White *(VP-Fin)*
Enrique Zaragoza *(VP-Sls)*
Brands & Products:
CAROLINA
GOURMET HOUSE
MAHATMA
MINUTE RICE
RIVER
RIVIANA
S&W
SUCCESS
WATERMAID
Advertising Agency:
Barkley
1740 Main St
Kansas City, MO 64108
Tel.: (816) 842-1500
Minute Rice

ROSE PACKING COMPANY

65 S Barrington Rd
Barrington, IL 60010-9508
Tel.: (847) 381-5700
Fax: (847) 381-9424
E-mail: info@rosepacking.com
Web Site: www.rosepacking.com
Approx. Number Employees: 800
Year Founded: 1924
Business Description:
Mfr. & Whslr of Smoked Meat Products
S.I.C.: 5147
N.A.I.C.S.: 311612
Media: 2-4-7-8-9-10-19-26
Distr.: Natl.
Budget Set: Dec.-Jan.
Personnel:
Dwight Stiehl *(Pres & CEO)*
James O'Hara *(CFO)*
Peter Rose *(VP-Production)*
Jim Vandenbergh *(VP-Sls & Mktg)*
Keith Brixius *(Mgr-Sls-Western)*
Nick Ledanski *(Mgr-Sls-Military)*
Frank Vainisi *(Mgr-Sls-Eastern)*
Brands & Products:
BETTER MEATS. BETTER MEALS. BETTER MENU
ROSE PACKING

ROSENBERGERS DAIRIES, LLC

(Sub. of Crowley Foods, Inc.)
847 Forty Foot Rd
Hatfield, PA 19440
Mailing Address:
PO Box 901
Hatfield, PA 19440-0901
Tel.: (215) 855-9074
Tel.: (215) 412-4620 (Sales)
Fax: (215) 855-6486
Fax: (215) 412-5992 (Sales & Marketing)
Toll Free: (800) 355-9074
E-mail: info@rosenbergers.com
Web Site: www.rosenbergers.com
Approx. Number Employees: 280
Year Founded: 1925
Business Description:
Milk & Cream Producer & Retailer
S.I.C.: 2026; 0241; 5143
N.A.I.C.S.: 311511; 112120; 424430
Advertising Expenditures: $50,000
Daily Newsp.: $25,000; Other: $25,000
Brands & Products:
ROSENBERGERS

RUDOLPH FOODS COMPANY

6575 Bellefontaine Rd
Lima, OH 45804-4415
Mailing Address:
PO Box 509
Lima, OH 45802-0509
Tel.: (419) 648-3611
Fax: (419) 648-4087
Toll Free: (800) 241-7675
Toll Free: (800) 443-7675
E-mail: info@rudolphfoods.com
Web Site: www.rudolphfoods.com
Sales Range: $50-74.9 Million
Approx. Number Employees: 400
Year Founded: 1955
Business Description:
Pork Rinds & Cracklings Mfr
S.I.C.: 2096; 2099
N.A.I.C.S.: 311919; 311999
Export
Consumer Mags.: 50%; Exhibits/Trade Shows: 50%
Distr.: Reg.
Budget Set: Dec.
Personnel:
John E. Rudolph *(Chm)*
Richard M. Rudolph *(Pres)*
Brands & Products:
BACON SNAPS
GRANDPA JOHN'S
PEPE'S
RUDOLPH FOODS
SOUTHERN RECIPE

RUIZ FOOD PRODUCTS, INC.

501 S Alta Ave
Dinuba, CA 93618-2100
Mailing Address:
PO Box 37
Dinuba, CA 93618-0037
Tel.: (559) 591-5510
Fax: (559) 591-1593
Toll Free: (800) 477-6474
Telex: 559-591-6329
E-mail: contactus@ruizfoods.com
Web Site: www.ruizfoods.com
Sales Range: $150-199.9 Million
Approx. Number Employees: 2,600
Year Founded: 1966
Business Description:
Mfr. of Frozen Mexican Foods
S.I.C.: 2038; 2099
N.A.I.C.S.: 311412; 311999
Import Export
Media: 2-5-6-8-10-11-13-19-20-21-22-26
Distr.: Reg.
Personnel:
Fred Ruiz *(Co-Founder, Chm & CEO)*
Kimberly Ruiz Beck *(Co-Chm)*
Bryce B. Ruiz *(Pres & CEO)*
Glen Lee *(CFO)*
Mark Hannay *(Sr VP-Sls)*
Tony Caetano *(VP-HR)*
Kimberli Carroll *(VP-Sls & Mktg-Foodservice Div)*
George Turner *(VP-Pur)*
Pat Summers *(Dir-Media)*
Brands & Products:
A REAL MEXICAN FOOD COMPANY
APPETIZERS
CRUNCHEROS
EL MONTEREY
ENCHILADAS
GIGANTE
QUESADILLAS
RUIZ
TAMALES
TAQUITOS
TORNADOS
XX LARGE
Advertising Agency:
Summers Advertising
777 W Shaw Ave
Fresno, CA 93728
Tel.: (559) 222-7100

SAGE V FOODS, LLC

12100 Wilshire Blvd Ste 605
Los Angeles, CA 90025-7122

Key to Media (For complete agency information see *The Advertising Red Books-Agencies* edition):
1. Bus. Publs. 2. Cable T.V. 3. Catalogs & Directories. 4. Co-op Adv. 5. Consumer Mags. 6. D.M. to Bus. Estab.7. D.M. to Consumers
8. Daily Newsp. 9. Exhibits/Trade Shows 10. Foreign 11. Infomercial 12. Internet Adv.13. Multimedia 14. Network Radio
15. Network T.V. 16. Newsp. Distr. Mags. 17. Other 18. Outdoor (Posters, Transit) 19. Point of Purchase20. Premiums, Novelties
21. Product Samples 22. Special Events Mktg. 23. Spot Radio 24. Spot T.V. 25. Weekly Newsp. 26. Yellow Page Adv.

Sage V Foods, LLC — (Continued)

Tel.: (310) 820-4496
Fax: (310) 820-2559
E-mail: sales@sagevfoods.com
Web Site: www.sagevfoods.com
E-Mail For Key Personnel:
Sales Director: sales@sagevfoods.com
Sales Range: $10-24.9 Million
Approx. Number Employees: 10
Year Founded: 1992
Business Description:
Producer of Rice Based Ingredients for Use in Processed Foods
S.I.C.: 2044
N.A.I.C.S.: 311212
Media: 4-9-10-13-15-23-25-26
Distr.: Intl.; Natl.
Budget Set: Apr.
Personnel:
Pete Vegas *(Owner)*

SAN-J INTERNATIONAL, INC.

(Sub. of San-Jirushi)
2880 Sprouse Dr
Richmond, VA 23231-6039
Tel.: (804) 226-8333
Fax: (804) 226-8383
Toll Free: (800) 446-5500
E-mail: sales@san-j.com
Web Site: www.san-j.com
E-Mail For Key Personnel:
Sales Director: sales@san-j.com
Approx. Number Employees: 50
Year Founded: 1978
Business Description:
Fermented Soy-Based Sauces Mfr
S.I.C.: 2035
N.A.I.C.S.: 311941
Import Export
Media: 2-4-5-6-8-9-10-17-19-21-23-25
Distr.: Intl.; Natl.
Budget Set: Oct.
Personnel:
Takashi Sato *(Pres)*
Brands & Products:
SAN-J
Advertising Agency:
Gauger + Associates
360 Post St Ste 901
San Francisco, CA 94108
Tel.: (415) 434-0303
Fax: (415) 434-0524
— David Gauger *(Acct. Exec.)*

SANDERSON FARMS, INC.

127 Flynt Rd
Laurel, MS 39443
Mailing Address:
PO Box 988
Laurel, MS 39441-0988
Tel.: (601) 649-4030
Fax: (601) 426-1461
Toll Free: (800) 844-4030
Telex: SAN SON
E-mail: info@sandersonfarms.com
Web Site: www.sandersonfarms.com
Approx. Sls.: $1,925,445,000
Approx. Number Employees: 9,859
Year Founded: 1955
Business Description:
Production of Fresh Ice Pack Poultry, Whole Birds & Parts, Frozen Frying Chicken Parts, Corn Dogs & Prepared Entrees
S.I.C.: 2015; 0251
N.A.I.C.S.: 311615; 112320
Export
Advertising Expenditures: $637,000
Media: 2-6-7-8-9-13-23-24-25-26
Distr.: Natl.
Budget Set: Oct.
Personnel:
Joe F. Sanderson, Jr. *(Chm & CEO)*
Lampkin Butts *(Pres & COO)*
D. Michael Cockrell *(CFO & Treas)*
James A. Grimes *(Chief Acctg Officer & Sec)*
Bob Billingsley *(Dir-Dev)*
Doug Lee *(Dir-Processing)*
Neil Morgan *(Dir-Sls)*
Randy Pettus *(Dir-Production)*
Robin Robinson *(Dir-Org, Dev & Corp Comm)*
Brian Romano *(Dir-Admin)*
Hillary Burroughs *(Mgr-Mktg Svcs)*
Brands & Products:
100% CHICKEN. NATURALLY.
SANDERSON FARMS

SAPUTO BAKERY INC.

(Sub. of Saputo, Inc.)
8770 Langelier Boulevard Suite 230
Saint Leonard, QC H1T3C6, Canada
Tel.: (514) 326-3101
Fax: (514) 326-2772
Toll Free: (888) 529-2836
E-mail: grocerycanada@saputo.com
Web Site: www.cayer.ca
Approx. Number Employees: 75
Year Founded: 1954
Business Description:
Mfr. of Food Products, Pastry Products, Cookies & Crackers, Dehydrated Soups, Dry Bread Products
S.I.C.: 2051
N.A.I.C.S.: 311812
Export
Advertising Expenditures: $800,000
Media: 3-5-8-10-18-19-20-21-24-26
Distr.: Natl.
Budget Set: Aug.
Personnel:
Lionel Ettedgui *(Pres & COO)*
Brands & Products:
AH CARAMEL!
GRANNY'S
HOP & GO!
JOS.LOUIS
MAY WEST
PASSION FLAKIE
VACHON

SAPUTO CHEESE USA INC.

(Sub. of Saputo, Inc.)
25 Tri State International Ofc Ctr Ste 250
Lincolnshire, IL 60069-4453
Tel.: (847) 267-1100
Fax: (847) 267-1110
Web Site:
www.saputousafoodservice.com
Approx. Number Employees: 1,900
Year Founded: 1954
Business Description:
Matured & Processed Cheese
S.I.C.: 2022
N.A.I.C.S.: 311513
Media: 5-6-8-10-15-19-20-21-23-24
Distr.: Natl.
Budget Set: Oct.
Personnel:
Terry Brockman *(Pres & COO)*
Laurie Chapman *(Mgr-Mktg)*
Brands & Products:
FRIGO CHEESE HEADS

SAPUTO, INC.

6869 Metropolitan Blvd E
Montreal, QC H1P 1X8, Canada
Tel.: (514) 328-6662
Fax: (514) 328-3310
E-mail: saputo@saputo.com
Web Site: www.saputo.com
Approx. Rev.: $6,138,869,345
Approx. Number Employees: 10,200
Year Founded: 1954
Business Description:
Dairy & Bakery Products
S.I.C.: 2023
N.A.I.C.S.: 311514
Import Export
Media: 10-17-22
Personnel:
Emanuele Saputo *(Chm)*
Lino A. Saputo, Jr. *(Vice Chm, Pres & CEO)*
Claude Pinard *(Exec VP-Comm & Social Responsibility)*
Terry Brockman *(Pres/COO-Dairy Products Div-USA)*
Lionel Ettedgui *(Pres/COO-Bakery Div)*
Dino Dello Sbarba *(Pres/COO-Dairy Products Div-Canada)*
Louis Philippe Carriere *(Exec VP-Fin & Admin)*
Gaetane Wagner *(Exec VP-HR)*
Brands & Products:
1/2 LUNEMOON
AHCARAMEL!
ALEXIS DE PORTNEUF
ALTO
ARMSTRONG
AUTHENTIC
BARAKA
BARI
BAXTER
BIG DADDY
CARON
CAYER
DAIRYLAND
DANSCORELLA
DUVILLAGE 1860
FRIGO
FROMA-DAR
GARDENIA
GRANNY'S
HOP & GO
HOSTESS
JOS.LOUIS
LA PAULINA
LAITS GO
LUGANO
MAY WEST
MOLFINO
NEILSON
#1
NUTRILAIT
ORIGINAL
PACIFIC
PASSION FLAKIE
PRATO
RICREM
SAPUTO
TALUHET
TRADITION.PASSION.EVOLUTION.
VACHON

SARA LEE BAKERY GROUP

(Unit of Sara Lee Corporation)
3470 Rider Trl S
Earth City, MO 63045-1109
Tel.: (314) 259-7000
Fax: (314) 259-7131
Toll Free: (800) 449-4284
Web Site: www.saralee.com
Sales Range: $250-299.9 Million
Year Founded: 1927
Business Description:
Fresh Refrigerated & Frozen Bakery Services
S.I.C.: 2051
N.A.I.C.S.: 311812
Advertising Expenditures: $10,000,000
Media: 5-6-9-14-15-18-19-21-22-23-24-26
Distr.: Natl.
Personnel:
Tom Hayes *(Chief Supply Chain Officer)*

SARA LEE BAKERY GROUP

(Unit of Sara Lee Corporation)
2110 Chapman Hwy
Knoxville, TN 37920-1904
Tel.: (865) 573-1941
Fax: (865) 577-1592
Toll Free: (800) 654-SARA
Web Site: www.saralee.com
Sales Range: $800-899.9 Million
Approx. Number Employees: 1,300
Year Founded: 1864
Business Description:
Wholesale Bread, Rolls & Cake
S.I.C.: 5499
N.A.I.C.S.: 445299
Media: 3-13-18-23-24
Distr.: Reg.
Budget Set: Nov.

SARA LEE COFFEE & TEA

(Unit of Sara Lee Foodservice)
10 Empire Blvd
Moonachie, NJ 07074-1303
Tel.: (201) 807-9300
Fax: (201) 229-0006
Toll Free: (800) 800-2633
Sales Range: $50-74.9 Million
Approx. Number Employees: 100
Year Founded: 1903
Business Description:
Coffee, Tea & Hot Cocoa Mix Mfr & Distr
S.I.C.: 2095; 5812
N.A.I.C.S.: 311920; 722310
Import Export
Advertising Expenditures: $300,000
Media: 2-4-10
Distr.: Natl.

SARA LEE CORPORATION

3500 Lacey Rd
Downers Grove, IL 60515-5424
Tel.: (630) 598-6000
Toll Free: (800) 727-2533
Telex: 4330147
E-mail: Investor.Relations@saralee.com
Web Site: www.saralee.com
Approx. Sls.: $8,681,000,000
Approx. Number Employees: 21,000
Year Founded: 1939
Business Description:
Global Food & Consumer Products Mfr
S.I.C.: 5147; 2043; 2053; 5149
N.A.I.C.S.: 311612; 311230; 311813; 424490

Import Export
Advertising Expenditures: $282,000,000
Media: 1-2-3-4-6-7-8-9-10-11-13-15-16-18-19-20-21-22-23-24-25
Distr.: Intl.; Natl.

Personnel:
Jan Bennink *(Chm)*
Marcel H. M. Smits *(CEO)*
Mark A. Garvey *(CFO & Exec VP)*
Philippe Schaillee *(CMO)*
John P. Zyck *(Chief Acctg Officer & Controller)*
Michiel Herkemij *(CEO-Intl Beverage Bus & Exec VP)*
Paulette Dodson *(Gen Counsel & Sec)*
Shalabh Gupta *(Treas & Sr VP)*
Stephen J. Cerrone *(Exec VP-HR)*
B. Thomas Hansson *(Sr VP-Strategic Plng & Corp Dev)*
Randall White *(Sr VP-Corp Affairs)*
Chuck Hemmingway *(Brand Dir-Ball Park)*
Amy Grabow *(Dir-Mktg-Ball Park)*
Jon Harris *(Dir-Product Dev-Bulk & Sliced Meats)*
Greg Buck *(Sr Mgr-Consumer Activation)*
Christina Saikus *(Asst Brand Mgr-State Fair)*
Daniel Meyer *(Brand Mgr)*

Brands & Products:

Arc Worldwide
(Sub. of Publicis Groupe S.A.)
35 W Wacker Dr 15th Fl
Chicago, IL 60601
Tel.: (312) 220-3200
Fax: (312) 220-1995

Equinox Communications
22 Percy Street
London, W1T 2BS, United Kingdom
Tel.: (44) 20 7864 1950
Douwe Egberts

Grey New York
777 3rd Ave
New York, NY 10017-1401
Tel.: (212) 546-2000
Fax: (212) 546-1495

Ogilvy & Mather
Plaza Bapindo Bank Mandiri Tower
26 Fl
PO Box 2580
Jakarta, 12190, Indonesia
Tel.: (62) 21 526 626 1
Fax: (62) 21 526 626 3
(Brylcreem, She)

Publicis West
424 2nd Ave W
Seattle, WA 98119-4013
Tel.: (206) 285-2222
Fax: (206) 273-4219
Ball Park
Creative

Starcom MediaVest Group
35 W Wacker Dr
Chicago, IL 60601-1723
Tel.: (312) 220-3535
Fax: (312) 220-6530
(Consolidated Media Account)

TBWA Chiat Day Los Angeles
5353 Grosvenor Blvd
Los Angeles, CA 90066
Tel.: (310) 305-5000
Fax: (310) 305-6000
Jimmy Dean
Jimmy Dean D-Lights
Hillshire Farm

SARA LEE CORP.
(Div. of Sara Lee Corporation)
2411 Baumann Ave
San Lorenzo, CA 94580-1801
Tel.: (510) 276-1300
Fax: (510) 278-2177
Toll Free: (800) 328-2426
Web Site: www.saralee.com
Sales Range: $100-124.9 Million
Approx. Number Employees: 175
Business Description:
Bakery & Other Food Products
S.I.C.: 5147
N.A.I.C.S.: 311612
Media: 3-5-6-7-8-9-10-16-18-19-20-21-22-23-24-25
Distr.: Intl.; Natl.
Budget Set: July

SARA LEE FOODSERVICE
(Div. of Sara Lee Corporation)
3500 Lacey Rd
Downers Grove, IL 60515
Mailing Address:
PO Box 756
Neenah, WI 54957
Tel.: (630) 598-6000
Fax: (847) 595-6001
Toll Free: (800) 621-4100
Web Site: saraleefoodservice.com/
Sales Range: $150-199.9 Million
Approx. Number Employees: 300
Year Founded: 1908
Business Description:
Coffee, Tea, Dressings, Syrups, Hot Chocolate, Soup Bases, Spices & Other Food Products for Restaurants, Hotels & Institutions
S.I.C.: 2095; 5149
N.A.I.C.S.: 311920; 424490
Import Export
Media: 2-6-7-9-10-13-14-21-24-25-26
Distr.: Natl.
Budget Set: Nov.
Personnel:
Tom Hayes *(Chief Supply Chain Officer)*
Charlie McConnell *(Dir-Customer Mktg-Foodservice)*
Brands & Products:
DOUWE EGBERTS
JAVA COAST
JUSTIN LLOYD
KAYO
LAURENTIS
METROPOLITAN
PARADISE TROPICAL TEA
PREBICA
SUNTIPT
SUPERIOR

SARGENTO FOODS INC.
1 Persnickety Pl
Plymouth, WI 53073-3544
Tel.: (920) 893-8484
Fax: (920) 893-8399
Web Site: www.sargento.com
Sales Range: $500-549.9 Million
Approx. Number Employees: 1,300
Year Founded: 1953
Business Description:
Cheese Products Mfr
S.I.C.: 2022; 5812
N.A.I.C.S.: 311513; 722110
Media: 6-9-15-17-26
Distr.: Natl.
Personnel:
Michael Gordy *(Pres-Food Ingredient Div)*
Louie Gentine *(CEO)*
George Hoff *(CFO & Exec VP)*
Mike McEvoy *(Pres-Food Ingredients Div)*
David Vroom *(Sr VP & Gen Mgr-Sargento Culinary Solutions Div)*
Kristi Jankowski *(Sr VP-Innovation)*
Mark Gumm *(VP-Sls-Consumer Product Div)*
Sue Peterson *(VP-IT)*
Chip Schuman *(VP-Mktg-Consumer Products)*
Jane Gapinski *(Dir-Mktg Svcs)*
Katharine Richards *(Dir-Market Res)*
Kate Krier *(Sr Mgr-Market Res)*
Ken Tobey *(Sr Mgr-Analytics)*
Bryan Birling *(Mgr-New Bus Dev)*
Leathan Christensen *(Mgr-Natl Acct Sls)*
Rob Krause *(Mgr-Customer Res)*
Brands & Products:
ARTISAN BLENDS
BRISTO
MOOTOWN
SARGENTO
Advertising Agency:
GolinHarris
(Part of the Interpublic Group of Companies)
111 E Wacker Dr 11th Fl
Chicago, IL 60601-4306
Tel.: (312) 729-4000
Fax: (312) 729-4010

SARTORI FOOD CORPORATION
107 Pleasant View Rd
Plymouth, WI 53073-4948
Tel.: (920) 893-6061
Fax: (920) 892-2732
E-mail: info@sartorifoods.com
Web Site: www.sartorifoods.com
Approx. Number Employees: 95
Year Founded: 1939
Business Description:
Mfr. of Cheese; Natural & Processed
S.I.C.: 2022
N.A.I.C.S.: 311513
Import Export
Personnel:
James C. Sartori *(Owner)*
Bob McManus *(Dir-Sls-Natl)*
Brands & Products:
ASADERO
COTIJA
INTENSACHEDDAR
MEXICAN MEDLEY
PIAVE RETAGGIO
QUESADERO
SARTON FOOD
SARTORI FOOD
SARTORI FOODS
VIBRANTE SUPREME
VIBRANTE ULTRA
Advertising Agency:
COLANGELO
120 Tokeneke Rd
Darien, CT 06820
Tel.: (203) 662-6600
Fax: (203) 662-6601

SAU-SEA FOODS, INC.
670 Montauk Hwy
Water Mill, NY 11976
Tel.: (631) 726-0269
Fax: (631) 726-0272
Approx. Sls.: $16,000,000
Approx. Number Employees: 5
Year Founded: 1940
Business Description:
Shrimp Cocktails, Cocktail Sauce, Frozen Breaded Shrimp, Frozen Shrimp & Institutional Pack Cocktails Mfr & Retailer
S.I.C.: 5146; 5149
N.A.I.C.S.: 424460; 424490
Advertising Expenditures: $560,000
Media: 2-10
Distr.: Intl.; Natl.
Budget Set: Nov.
Personnel:
Antonio Estadella *(Pres)*
Ronnie Kaplan *(Office Mgr)*
Brands & Products:
SAU-SEA

SAVE-A-LOT, LTD.
(Sub. of SUPERVALU International)
100 Corporate Office Dr
Earth City, MO 63045-1528
Tel.: (314) 592-9100
Fax: (314) 592-9619
E-mail: communications@save-a-lot.com
Web Site: www.save-a-lot.com
Sales Range: $300-349.9 Million
Approx. Number Employees: 500
Year Founded: 1977
Business Description:
Foods Distr
S.I.C.: 5141; 5411
N.A.I.C.S.: 424410; 445110
Media: 3-13-15-17-18-19-23-25
Personnel:
Bill Shaner *(Pres & CEO)*
Nancy Santana *(Gen Counsel & VP)*
Mark Kotcher *(Dir-Brand Mktg & Design)*

SCHEPPS DAIRY
(Sub. of Dean Dairy Holdings, LLC)
3114 S Haskell Ave
Dallas, TX 75223-3100
Tel.: (214) 824-8163
Fax: (214) 818-3407
Web Site: www.scheppsdairy.com
Approx. Sls.: $915,000,000
Approx. Number Employees: 500
Year Founded: 1857
Business Description:
Dairy Products Mfr
S.I.C.: 2026
N.A.I.C.S.: 311511
Media: 6-16-18-22-23-24
Distr.: Natl.
Personnel:
Steve Schenkel *(Gen Mgr)*
Brands & Products:
THE DAIRY BEST

SCHMIDT BAKING CO., INC.
7801 Fitch Ln
Baltimore, MD 21236-3916
Tel.: (410) 668-8200
Fax: (410) 882-2051
E-mail: comments@schmidtbaking.com

Schmidt Baking Co., Inc. — (Continued)

Web Site: www.schmidtbaking.com
Approx. Number Employees: 638
Year Founded: 1886
Business Description:
Commercial Bakery
S.I.C.: 2051
N.A.I.C.S.: 311812
Media: 1-2-4-5-6-7-8-9-10-16-19-22-23-24-25-26
Personnel:
Steve Harris *(Dir-Mktg)*
Rick Koester *(Dir-Fin)*
Brands & Products:
BLUE RIBBON
OLD TYME
SCHMIDT BAKING
SUNBEAM

SCHREIBER FOODS, INC.

425 Pine St
Green Bay, WI 54301-5137
Mailing Address:
PO Box 19010
Green Bay, WI 54307-9010
Tel.: (920) 437-7601
Toll Free: (800) 344-0333
E-mail: schreiberweb@schreiberfoods.com
Web Site: www.schreiberfoods.com
Sales Range: $1-9.9 Million
Approx. Number Employees: 5,000
Year Founded: 1945
Business Description:
Dairy Products
S.I.C.: 5143; 2022; 2023; 2656; 3556
N.A.I.C.S.: 424430; 311513; 311514; 322215; 333294
Import Export
Media: 2-4-6-7-8-10-11-13-21-26
Distr.: Intl.
Personnel:
Larry P. Ferguson *(Chm)*
Mike Haddad *(CEO)*
Tom Andreoli *(CIO)*
Jerry Smyth *(Gen Counsel & VP)*
Robert Byrne *(Dir-Industry & Regulatory Affairs)*
Terry Moeller *(Dir-Mktg)*
Lana Dose *(Mgr-Mktg)*
Brands & Products:
AMERICAN HERITAGE
CLEARFIELD
COOPER
LAFERIA
LOV-IT
MENU
RASKAS
READY-CUT
SCHOOL CHOICE
SCHREIBER
Advertising Agency:
Barkley
1740 Main St
Kansas City, MO 64108
Tel.: (816) 842-1500
Cheeses

SCHULZE & BURCH BISCUIT COMPANY

1133 W 35th St
Chicago, IL 60609-1447
Tel.: (773) 927-6622
Fax: (773) 376-4528
Web Site: www.toastem.com
Approx. Number Employees: 500
Year Founded: 1923
Business Description:
Mfr. of Baked Goods
S.I.C.: 2051; 2052
N.A.I.C.S.: 311812; 311821
Media: 7-10
Distr.: Natl.; Reg.
Budget Set: Mar.
Personnel:
P. Salina *(COO & Gen Mgr)*
Steve Podracky *(Mktg Mgr)*
Brands & Products:
FLAVOR KIST
SNACKIN' FRUITS
TOAST'EM POP-UPS

THE SCHWAN FOOD COMPANY

115 W College Dr
Marshall, MN 56258
Tel.: (507) 532-3274
Fax: (507) 537-8226
Toll Free: (800) 533-5290
E-mail: questions@schwans.com
Web Site: www.theschwanfoodcompany.com
Sales Range: $1-4.9 Billion
Approx. Number Employees: 22,000
Year Founded: 1952
Business Description:
Frozen Food Mfr & Distr
S.I.C.: 2038; 2024
N.A.I.C.S.: 311412; 311520
Export
Advertising Expenditures: $10,000,000
Media: 6-9-11-13-24-25-26
Distr.: Natl.
Personnel:
Allan L. Schuman *(Chm)*
Greg Flack *(Pres, CEO & COO)*
Jim Clough *(Pres-Food Svc)*
Brian Sattler *(Gen Counsel & Exec VP-Admin)*
Kathy Bassininski *(Sr Dir-Mktg)*
Brands & Products:
ARCTIC EXPRESS
ASIAN SENSATIONS
CHICAGO TOWN
COYOTE GRILL
EDWARD'S
FRESCHETTA
HEIDI'S GOURMET DESSERTS
IMPROMPTU GOURMET
LARRY'S
MINH
MRS. SMITH'S
PROOF PERFECT
RED BARON
SCHWAN'S
TONY'S
WESTERN COUNTRY PIES
ZINGS
Advertising Agencies:
Brew
530 University Ave SE
Minneapolis, MN 55414
Tel.: (612) 331-7700
Fax: (612) 331-7704

Campbell Mithun, Inc.
Campbell Mithun Tower 222 S 9th St
Minneapolis, MN 55402-3389
Tel.: (612) 347-1000
Fax: (612) 347-1515
(Media & Promotional)

Cheetham Bell/JWT
Astley House Quay St
Manchester, M3 4AS, United Kingdom
Tel.: (44) 161 832 8884
Fax: (44) 161 835 1436
Chicago Town

SEA WATCH INTERNATIONAL, LTD.

8978 Glebe Pk Dr
Easton, MD 21601-7004
Tel.: (410) 822-7500
Fax: (410) 822-1226
Toll Free: (800) 732-2526
E-mail: sales@seaclam.com
Web Site: www.seaclam.com
E-Mail For Key Personnel:
Sales Director: sales@seaclam.com
Approx. Number Employees: 500
Year Founded: 1978
Business Description:
Canned & Frozen Clam Processing
S.I.C.: 2092; 2091
N.A.I.C.S.: 311712; 311711
Import Export
Advertising Expenditures: $100,000
Media: 2-10
Personnel:
Robert Brennan *(Pres & Partner)*
Brands & Products:
OLD SALT
SEA WATCH
SEAWATCH INTERNATIONAL

SENECA FOODS CORPORATION

3736 S Main St
Marion, NY 14505-9751
Tel.: (315) 926-8100
Fax: (315) 926-8300
Telex: 650-277-0604
E-mail: webmaster@senecafoods.com
Web Site: www.senecafoods.com
Approx. Sls.: $1,194,612,000
Approx. Number Employees: 3,000
Year Founded: 1949
Business Description:
Food Processor & Canner of Fruits & Vegetables
S.I.C.: 2033; 2037
N.A.I.C.S.: 311421; 311411
Import Export
Media: 6-8-9-10-15-19-20-21-24-25
Distr.: Natl.
Budget Set: July
Personnel:
Arthur S. Wolcott *(Chm)*
Kraig H. Kayser *(Pres & CEO)*
Roland E. Breunig *(CFO)*
Paul L. Palmby *(COO & Exec VP)*
Cynthia L. Fohrd *(Chief Admin Officer & Sr VP)*
John D. Exner *(Gen Counsel)*
Dean E. Erstad *(Sr VP-Sls)*
Frederick J. Baker *(VP & Gen Mgr-Ops-Fruit)*
James F. Mcclelland *(VP & Gen Mgr-Ops-Snack)*
Vincent J. Lammers *(VP-Procurement)*
Richard L. Waldorf *(VP-Ops-Customer Svc)*
Bruce Wolcott *(VP-Mktg)*
Jon A. Brekken *(Dir-Fin)*
Jane Sloan *(Dir-Credit & Collections)*
Sarah S. Mortensen *(Asst Sec)*
Brands & Products:
AUNT NELLIES
BLUE BOY
DIAMOND A
FESTAL
HARVEST MOON
LIBBY'S
PERFECTION
READ
SENECA
SENECA FARMS
STOKLEY
TIP TOP
Advertising Agency:
M&P Food Communications, Inc.
151 N Michigan Ave Ste 804
Chicago, IL 60601
Tel.: (312) 201-9101
Fax: (312) 201-9161

SENSIENT FLAVORS INC.

(Sub. of Sensient Technologies Corporation)
5600 W Raymond St
Indianapolis, IN 46241-4343
Tel.: (317) 243-3521
Fax: (317) 240-1524
Toll Free: (800) 445-0073
Web Site: www.sensient-tech.com
Sales Range: $650-699.9 Million
Approx. Number Employees: 350
Year Founded: 1903
Business Description:
Food & Beverage Flavorings Mfr
S.I.C.: 2087
N.A.I.C.S.: 311930
Import Export
Media: 2-7-10-11-13-21
Distr.: Intl.; Natl.
Budget Set: Sept.
Personnel:
James P. McCarthy *(Pres-Flavors & Fragrances Grp)*

SENSIENT TECHNOLOGIES CORPORATION

777 E Wisconsin Ave
Milwaukee, WI 53202-5304
Tel.: (414) 271-6755
Fax: (414) 347-3785
Fax: (414) 347-4794
Toll Free: (800) 558-9892
E-mail: corporate.communications@sensient-tech.com
Web Site: www.sensient-tech.com
Approx. Rev.: $1,201,412,000
Approx. Number Employees: 3,618
Year Founded: 1882
Business Description:
Colors, Flavors, Yeast, Dehydrated Vegetables & Seasonings Developer, Mfr & Marketer
S.I.C.: 1321; 2087; 2099
N.A.I.C.S.: 211112; 311930; 311999
Advertising Expenditures: $1,000,000
Media: 2-5-10-13-19-21
Distr.: Intl.
Budget Set: Dec.
Personnel:
Kenneth P. Manning *(Chm & CEO)*
Douglas S. Pepper *(Pres & COO)*
Richard F. Hobbs *(CFO & Sr VP)*
Peter G. Bradley *(Pres-Color Grp)*
Robert Wilkins *(Pres-Asia Pacific)*
John L. Hammond *(Gen Counsel, Sec & Sr VP)*
Christopher M. Daniels *(VP-HR)*
Gordon E. Hering *(VP-Mktg & Tech)*
Robert L. Menzl *(VP-IT)*
Richard J. Malin *(Asst Controller)*

Key to Media (For complete agency information see *The Advertising Red Books-Agencies* edition):
1. Bus. Publs. 2. Cable T.V. 3. Catalogs & Directories. 4. Co-op Adv. 5. Consumer Mags. 6. D.M. to Bus. Estab.7. D.M. to Consumers 8. Daily Newsp. 9. Exhibits/Trade Shows 10. Foreign 11. Infomercial 12. Internet Adv.13. Multimedia 14. Network Radio 15. Network T.V. 16. Newsp. Distr. Mags. 17. Other 18. Outdoor (Posters, Transit) 19. Point of Purchase20. Premiums, Novelties 21. Product Samples 22. Special Events Mktg. 23. Spot Radio 24. Spot T.V. 25. Weekly Newsp. 26. Yellow Page Adv.

Brands & Products:
SENSIENT
WE BRING LIFE TO PRODUCTS.

SHAMROCK FOODS COMPANY

2228 N Black Canyon Hwy
Phoenix, AZ 85009-2707
Tel.: (602) 272-6721
Fax: (602) 233-2791
E-mail: hiroxie@shamrockfoods.com
Web Site: www.shamrockfoods.com
Sales Range: $1-4.9 Billion
Approx. Number Employees: 2,700
Year Founded: 1922
Business Description:
Dairy Products Processing; Food Service Distr
S.I.C.: 0241; 5087; 5143; 5149; 5812
N.A.I.C.S.: 112120; 423850; 424430; 424490; 722310
Advertising Expenditures: $2,000,000
Cable T.V.: 5%; Other: 8%; Outdoor (Posters, Transit): 10%; Point of Purchase: 5%; Product Samples: 2%; Special Events Mktg.: 5%; Spot Radio: 15%; Spot T.V.: 50%
Personnel:
Norman P. McClelland *(Owner)*
Kent McClelland *(Pres)*
F. Phillips Giltner, III *(CFO)*
Rob Baxter *(CIO & VP)*
Larry F. Yancy *(Sr VP & Gen Mgr)*
Michael Krueger *(Sr VP)*
Kent Mullison *(Sr VP)*
Robert Beake *(VP-HR)*
Molly Watson *(Assoc Brand Mgr-Shamrock Farms)*
Michelle Daley *(Brand Mgr)*
Brands & Products:
ASPEN GOLD
BOUNTIFUL HARVEST
BRICKFIRE BAKERY
CHEF MARK
COBBLESTONE MARKET
CULINARY SECRETS
DELIVERING SATISFACTION. IT'S WHAT WE DO.
EVER
HIDDEN BAY
!INTROS!
KATY'S KITCHEN
PIERPORT
PRAIRIE CREEK
PROPAK
REJUV
RIDGELINE
SAN PABLO
SHAMROCK
SHAMROCK FARMS
SHAMROCK FOODS
SILVERBROOK
SMART SOURCE
SOUTHERN PEARL
TRESCERRO
VILLA FRIZZONI
WINDSCAPES
XTREME

SIGMA FOODS INC.

(Sub. of Sigma Alimentos, S.A. de C.V.)
110 Cypress Station Dr Ste 202
Houston, TX 77090
Tel.: (281) 999-6361
Fax: (281) 999-5957
E-mail: info@sigmafoodsusa.com
Web Site: www.sigmafoodsusa.com
Approx. Number Employees: 30
Business Description:
Refrigerated & Frozen Food Mfr & Distr
S.I.C.: 5142
N.A.I.C.S.: 424420
Advertising Agency:
Legion Advertising
1425 Greenway Dr Ste 100
Arlington, TX 75038
Tel.: (817) 784-8544
Fax: (817) 385-0378

SIMMONS FOODS INC.

601 N Hico
Siloam Springs, AR 72761
Mailing Address:
PO Box 430
Siloam Springs, AR 72761
Tel.: (479) 524-8151
Toll Free: (800) 346-7352
Web Site: www.simmonsfoods.com
Sales Range: $600-649.9 Million
Approx. Number Employees: 10,000
Year Founded: 1949
Business Description:
Fresh & Frozen Poultry Products Mfr & Distr
S.I.C.: 2015; 5144
N.A.I.C.S.: 311615; 424440
Export
Media: 8-10-11-13
Personnel:
Mark Simmons *(Chm)*
D. Michael Jones *(CFO)*
Todd Simmons *(COO)*
Gary Murphy *(Pres-Processing Ops)*
Jerry Laster *(Sr VP-Sls & Mktg)*
Steve Gardner *(VP-HR)*
Brands & Products:
SIMMONS

SIOUX HONEY ASSOCIATION

301 Lewis Blvd
Sioux City, IA 51101-2237
Mailing Address:
PO Box 388
Sioux City, IA 51102-0388
Tel.: (712) 258-0638
Fax: (712) 258-1332
E-mail: jrs_info@simplot.com
Web Site: www.suebee.com
Approx. Number Employees: 100
Year Founded: 1921
Business Description:
Honey Processor
S.I.C.: 5149
N.A.I.C.S.: 424490
Import Export
Advertising Expenditures: $2,000,000
Media: 2-4-6-7-9-13-14-15-19-20
Distr.: Natl.
Budget Set: June -July
Personnel:
Dave Allibon *(Pres & CEO)*
Vic Lund *(VP-Fin & Acctg)*
Brands & Products:
AMERICA'S HONEY
BRADSHAW'S
CLOVER MAID
SUE BEE
SUEBEE

SLIM-FAST FOODS COMPANY

(Sub. of Conopco, Inc.)
800 Sylvan Ave
Englewood Cliffs, NJ 07632
Tel.: (201) 567-8000
Toll Free: (800) SLIMFAST
E-mail: info@slimfast.com
Web Site: www.slim-fast.com
Approx. Number Employees: 150
Year Founded: 1990
Business Description:
Weight Loss Products Mfr & Retailer
S.I.C.: 2099; 5149
N.A.I.C.S.: 311999; 424490
Media: 8-15-21-22-25
Personnel:
Art Peters *(COO)*
Michael Kruyt *(VP-Global Mktg)*
Donna Barker *(Dir-Mktg)*
Virginia Blake West *(Dir-Brand Dev)*
Edward Kim *(Mgr-Direct Mktg)*
Brands & Products:
MEAL ON-THE-GO
OPTIMA
SLIM-FAST
Advertising Agency:
Daniels & Roberts, Inc.
209 N Seacrest Blvd Ste 209
Boynton Beach, FL 33435
Tel.: (561) 241-0066
Fax: (561) 241-1198
Toll Free: (800) 488-0066

SMALL PLANET FOODS INC.

(Sub. of General Mills, Inc.)
719 Metcalf St
Sedro Woolley, WA 98284-1420
Tel.: (360) 855-0100
Fax: (360) 855-0444
Web Site: www.smallplanetfoods.com
Sales Range: $75-99.9 Million
Approx. Number Employees: 70
Year Founded: 2000
Business Description:
Organic Foods Producer
S.I.C.: 2034; 2098; 5499
N.A.I.C.S.: 311423; 311823; 445299
Media: 6
Personnel:
Michele S. Meyers *(Pres)*
Tom Nientimp *(Dir-Mktg-Cascadian Farm)*
Brands & Products:
CASCADIAN FARM

SMITHFIELD FOODS, INC.

200 Commerce St
Smithfield, VA 23430
Tel.: (757) 365-3000
Fax: (757) 365-3017
Toll Free: (888) 366-6767
E-mail: information@smithfieldfoods.com
Web Site: www.smithfieldfoods.com/home.asp
Approx. Sls.: $12,202,700,000
Approx. Number Employees: 46,350
Year Founded: 1962
Business Description:
Meat Processing & Packing
S.I.C.: 5147; 0212; 0213; 0253; 0279; 0751; 2013; 2015
N.A.I.C.S.: 311612; 112111; 112210; 112330; 112990; 311611; 311613; 311615
Export
Advertising Expenditures: $102,500,000
Media: 2-4-6-7-8-9-10-14-15-18-20-21-23-24-25
Distr.: Natl.
Budget Set: Sept.
Personnel:
Charles Larry Pope *(Co-Pres & CEO)*
George H. Richter *(Co-Pres & COO)*
Robert W. Manly, IV *(CFO & Exec VP)*
Mansour T. Zadeh *(CIO)*
Michael H. Cole *(Chief Legal Officer, Sec & VP)*
Dennis H. Treacy *(Chief Sustainability Officer & Sr VP-Corp Affairs)*
Kenneth M. Sullivan *(Chief Acctg Officer & VP-Fin)*
Dhamu Thamodaran *(Chief Commodity Hedging Officer & Exec VP)*
Joseph W. Luter, IV *(Exec VP)*
Henry L. Morris *(Sr VP-Ops & Engrg)*
Keira L. Lombardo *(VP-IR & Corp Comm)*
James D. Schloss *(Corp VP-Sls & Mktg)*
Brands & Products:
ARMOUR
CARANDO
COOK'S
CURLY'S
ECKRICH
FARMLAND
FLAVORE
GOOD FOOD.RESPONSIBLY.
GWALTNEY
HEALTHY ONES
JOHN MORRELL
KRETSCHMAR
LYKES
MARGHERITA
PATRICK CUDAHY
THE PEANUT SHOP OF WILLIAMSBURG
QUICK-N-EASY
SMITHFIELD
SMITHFIELD PREMIUM
SUNNYLAND
Advertising Agency:
Championship Group, Inc.
1954 Airport Rd Ste 200
Atlanta, GA 30341
Tel.: (770) 457-5777
Fax: (770) 457-1248

THE SMITHFIELD PACKING CO., INC.

(Sub. of Smithfield Foods, Inc.)
501 N Church St PO Box 447
Smithfield, VA 23430
Tel.: (757) 357-4321
Fax: (757) 357-1686
Toll Free: (800) 444-9180
Web Site: www.smithfield.com
Approx. Number Employees: 9,330
Year Founded: 1936
Business Description:
Meat Processing
S.I.C.: 0751; 5147; 5421
N.A.I.C.S.: 311611; 311612; 445210
Advertising Expenditures: $109,400,000
Media: 2-4-6-7-8-9-10-19-21-23-24
Distr.: Natl.
Budget Set: Jan.
Personnel:
Tim Schellpeper *(Pres)*
Jere Null *(Sr VP-Sls-Fresh & Intl)*
Keller Watts *(Sr VP)*
James D. Schloss *(Corp VP-Sls & Mktg)*
Joe Weber *(VP-Sls)*

Key to Media (For complete agency information see *The Advertising Red Books-Agencies* edition):
1. Bus. Publs. 2. Cable T.V. 3. Catalogs & Directories. 4. Co-op Adv. 5. Consumer Mags. 6. D.M. to Bus. Estab.7. D.M. to Consumers 8. Daily Newsp. 9. Exhibits/Trade Shows 10. Foreign 11. Infomercial 12. Internet Adv.13. Multimedia 14. Network Radio 15. Network T.V. 16. Newsp. Distr. Mags. 17. Other 18. Outdoor (Posters, Transit) 19. Point of Purchase20. Premiums, Novelties 21. Product Samples 22. Special Events Mktg. 23. Spot Radio 24. Spot T.V. 25. Weekly Newsp. 26. Yellow Page Adv.

The Smithfield Packing Co., Inc.— (Continued)

Brands & Products:
HAMILTON EASY KARV
JAMESTOWN BRAND
LEAN GENERATION
LYKES
SMITHFIELD LEAN
SMITHFIELD PREMIUM
SUNNYLAND
Advertising Agency:
Lawler Ballard Van Durand
31 Inverness Center Pkwy Ste 110
Birmingham, AL 35242-4822
Tel.: (205) 995-1775
Fax: (205) 991-5141
(Fresh Pork)

SMOKEWOOD FOODS

1926 W Orangewood Ave Ste 101
Orange, CA 92868-2007
Tel.: (714) 634-4221
Fax: (714) 634-0481
E-mail: sales@smokewoodfoods.com
Web Site: www.smokewoodfoods.com
E-Mail For Key Personnel:
Sales Director: sales@smokewoodfoods.com
Approx. Number Employees: 5
Year Founded: 1948
Business Description:
Edible Bowl & Shell (Made From Wheat, Corn & Rice Flours) Mfr
S.I.C.: 2099
N.A.I.C.S.: 311830
Export
Advertising Expenditures: $400,000
Media: 8-9-19-20-23
Distr.: Direct to Consumer; Reg.
Personnel:
Van K. Reese *(VP-Sls)*
Brands & Products:
DEL ORO TACO TUBS
DEL ORO TOSTADA CROWNS
RIO RANCHO
SIX GUN
SIX GUN CHILI MIXIN'S

SMUCKER FOODS OF CANADA CO.

(Sub. of The J.M. Smucker Company)
80 Whitehall Dr
Markham, ON L3R 0P3, Canada
Tel.: (905) 940-9600
Fax: (905) 940-5969
Toll Free: (800) 268-3232
E-mail: info@jmsmucker.ca
Web Site: www.jmsmucker.com
Sales Range: $75-99.9 Million
Approx. Number Employees: 200
Year Founded: 1909
Business Description:
Food Products Mfr
S.I.C.: 2099
N.A.I.C.S.: 311999
Export
Advertising Expenditures: $2,000,000
Distr.: Natl.
Budget Set: Oct. -Dec.
Personnel:
Rob Morgan *(VP-Fin)*
Stephanie Gougeon *(Dir-HR)*
Danielle Rudra *(Dir-Mktg-Baking & Frozen)*
Brands & Products:
BICK'S
GOLDEN TEMPLE
OLD MILL
RED RIVER
ROBIN HOOD
Advertising Agency:
Ogilvy & Mather
33 Yonge St
Toronto, ON M5E 1X6, Canada
Tel.: (416) 367-3573
Fax: (416) 363-2088

SNYDER - BERLIN

(Formerly Birds Eye-Berlin)
(Plant of Pinnacle Foods Group LLC)
1313 Stadium St
Berlin, PA 15530-1446
Tel.: (814) 267-4641
Fax: (814) 267-5648
Toll Free: (800) 374-7949
Web Site: www.snyderofberlin.com
Sales Range: $300-349.9 Million
Business Description:
Potato Chips Mfr
S.I.C.: 2096; 2099
N.A.I.C.S.: 311919; 311999
Advertising Expenditures: $100,000
Media: 5-6-9-10-18-20-21-23
Distr.: Reg.
Personnel:
Ron Kereston *(Gen Mgr)*
Michele A. James *(Mgr-Mktg)*

SNYDER'S-LANCE, INC.

(Formerly Lance, Inc.)
13024 Ballantyne Corporate Pl Ste 900
Charlotte, NC 28277
Mailing Address:
PO Box 32395
Charlotte, NC 28232-2395
Tel.: (704) 554-1421
Fax: (704) 554-5562
Toll Free: (800) 438-1880
Toll Free: (800) 99-LANCE (Customer Svc)
E-mail: fresh@lance.com
Web Site: www.lance.com
Approx. Rev.: $979,835,000
Approx. Number Employees: 7,000
Year Founded: 1915
Business Description:
Snack Foods Mfr
S.I.C.: 2052; 2051; 2064; 2096
N.A.I.C.S.: 311821; 311330; 311812; 311919
Advertising Expenditures: $7,500,000
Media: 2-3-5-6-10-16-18-19-20-21-22-23-24-25-26
Distr.: Natl.
Personnel:
Michael A. Warehime *(Chm)*
David V. Singer *(CEO)*
Rick D. Puckett *(CFO, Treas & Exec VP)*
Glenn A. Patcha *(Sr VP-Sls & Mktg)*
Blake W. Thompson *(Sr VP-Supply Chain)*
Margaret E. Wicklund *(VP, Controller & Asst Sec)*
Alvaro Trinidad *(Sr Brand Mgr)*
Brands & Products:
CAPTAIN'S CHOICE
CAPTAIN'S WAFERS
CHEESE ON NIPCHEE
CHOC-O-LUNCH
GOLD N CHEES
LANCE
LANCE FRESH
LEM-O-LUNCH
MALT
NEKOT
NIPCHEE
ORIGINAL RUMBLE
OUTPOST BRAND
SHARP CHEDDAR
SOUR BLOOPS
STELLA D'ORO
STORMY
THUNDER
TOASTCHEE
TOASTY
TOM'S
VAN-O-LUNCH
Advertising Agency:
gkv Communications
The Cascade Bldg 1030 Hull St Ste 400
Baltimore, MD 21230
Tel.: (410) 539-5400
Fax: (410) 234-2441

SOLAE LLC

(Joint Venture of E.I. du Pont de Nemours & Company & Bunge Limited)
4300 Duncan Ave
Saint Louis, MO 63110
Mailing Address:
PO Box 88940
Saint Louis, MO 63188
Tel.: (314) 659-3380
Tel.: (314) 659-3000
Fax: (314) 659-5380
Toll Free: (800) 325-7108
Web Site: www.solae.com
Sales Range: $1-4.9 Billion
Approx. Number Employees: 3,500
Year Founded: 2003
Business Description:
Isolated Soy Protein Mfr; Owned 28% by E.I. du Pont de Nemours & Company & 72% by Bunge Limited
S.I.C.: 2824
N.A.I.C.S.: 325222
Media: 2-3-6-10
Personnel:
Craig F. Binetti *(Chm)*
Torkel Rhenman *(CEO)*
Michelle Fite *(VP-Global Strategy, Mktg & Specialty Bus)*
John Hoffmann *(Dir-Quality Assurance-Global)*
Jason E. Mann *(Grp Leader-Food Safety & HACCP-Global)*
Hector DeVitre *(Assoc Dir-Quality)*

SOUTHERN MINNESOTA BEET SUGAR COOPERATIVE

83550 County Rd 21 PO Box 500
Renville, MN 56284
Tel.: (320) 329-8305
Fax: (320) 329-4172
E-mail: info@smbsc.com
Web Site: www.smbsc.com
Approx. Number Employees: 320
Year Founded: 1972
Business Description:
Beet Sugar, Pulp & Molasses Mfr
S.I.C.: 2063; 2061
N.A.I.C.S.: 311313; 311311
Export
Media: 5
Brands & Products:
AGRICULTURAL LIMING MATERIAL
SMBSC

SOUTHERN SHELL FISH CO. INC.

501 Destrehan Ave
Harvey, LA 70058-2737
Mailing Address:
PO Box 97
Harvey, LA 70059-0097
Tel.: (504) 341-5631
Fax: (504) 341-5635
Sales Range: $1-9.9 Million
Approx. Number Employees: 8
Year Founded: 1988
Business Description:
Shrimp, Oysters & Crabmeat Preparer
S.I.C.: 2091; 2092
N.A.I.C.S.: 311711; 311712
Import Export
Media: 9
Distr.: Natl.
Brands & Products:
BLUE PLATE
DUNBAR
GULF KIST

SPECIALTY BAKERS, INC.

450 S State Rd
Marysville, PA 17053-1012
Mailing Address:
PO Box 130
Marysville, PA 17053-0130
Tel.: (717) 957-2131
Fax: (717) 957-0156
Web Site: www.sbiladyfingers.com
Approx. Number Employees: 300
Year Founded: 1901
Business Description:
Quick & Convenient Alternative to Cake Batters & Piecrusts for Bakers & Homemakers
S.I.C.: 2051
N.A.I.C.S.: 311812
Advertising Expenditures: $1,000,000
Media: 1-2-5-7-8-9-10-13-20-21
Distr.: Reg.
Personnel:
John L. Piotrowski *(Owner, Pres & CEO)*
Brands & Products:
COUNTRY BAKER
LADYFINGERS

SPECIALTY FOODS GROUP-FIELD PACKING DIV.

(Div. of Specialty Foods Group, Inc.)
6 Dublin Ln PO Box 20003 42304
Owensboro, KY 42301
Mailing Address:
PO Box 20003
Owensboro, KY 42304
Tel.: (270) 926-2324
Fax: (270) 926-5077
Toll Free: (800) 87FIELD
E-mail: vplane@sfgsaintfranceroad.com
Web Site: www.smgmeats.com
Sales Range: $150-199.9 Million
Approx. Number Employees: 500
Year Founded: 1914
Business Description:
Meat, Sausage & Smoked Meat Producer
S.I.C.: 0751; 2013; 5147
N.A.I.C.S.: 311611; 311612; 311613
Import Export
Media: 2-3-4-5-6-7-8-9-10-13-16-18-19-23-24-25
Distr.: Intl.; Natl.

Key to Media (For complete agency information see *The Advertising Red Books-Agencies* edition):
1. Bus. Publs. 2. Cable T.V. 3. Catalogs & Directories. 4. Co-op Adv. 5. Consumer Mags. 6. D.M. to Bus. Estab.7. D.M. to Consumers 8. Daily Newsp. 9. Exhibits/Trade Shows 10. Foreign 11. Infomercial 12. Internet Adv.13. Multimedia 14. Network Radio 15. Network T.V. 16. Newsp. Distr. Mags. 17. Other 18. Outdoor (Posters, Transit) 19. Point of Purchase20. Premiums, Novelties 21. Product Samples 22. Special Events Mktg. 23. Spot Radio 24. Spot T.V. 25. Weekly Newsp. 26. Yellow Page Adv.

Budget Set: Nov.
Personnel:
Keith Luedke *(VP-Sls)*
Brands & Products:
COMIDAS CASERAS
FIELD
FISCHER'S
KENTUCKIAN GOLD
KENTUCKY LEGEND

STAGG FOODS, INC.

(Sub. of Hormel Foods Corporation)
PO Box 800
Austin, MN 55912
Tel.: (507) 437-5611
Fax: (507) 437-5838
Toll Free: (800) 611-9778
Web Site: www.staggchili.com
Sales Range: $25-49.9 Million
Approx. Number Employees: 25
Year Founded: 1968
Business Description:
Canned Specialties Mfr
S.I.C.: 2032
N.A.I.C.S.: 311422
Media: 13
Advertising Agency:
Preston Kelly
222 First Ave NE
Minneapolis, MN 55413
Tel.: (612) 843-4000
Fax: (612) 843-3900

STAHMANN FARMS, INC.

22500 S Hwy 28
La Mesa, NM 88044
Tel.: (505) 526-2453
Fax: (505) 526-5760
Toll Free: (800) 654-6887
E-mail: customerservice@stahmanns.com
Web Site: www.stahmanns.com
Approx. Number Employees: 150
Year Founded: 1932
Business Description:
Producer & Sales of Pecans & Baked Goods
S.I.C.: 0173; 2068
N.A.I.C.S.: 111335; 311911
Media: 4-7-13-19-21
Distr.: Natl.
Personnel:
Sally A. Stahmann *(Pres & CEO)*
Judy Mitchell *(Controller)*
Brands & Products:
STAHMANNS

STAR FINE FOODS-BORGES USA

(Sub. of Aceites Borges Pont, S.A.)
4652 E Date Ave
Fresno, CA 93725
Tel.: (559) 498-2900
Fax: (559) 498-2920
E-mail: postmaster@starfinefoods.com
Web Site: www.starfinefoods.com
Approx. Number Employees: 24
Year Founded: 1898
Business Description:
Olive Oil, Wine Vinegar, Maraschino Cherries, Onions, Olives, Sundried Tomatoes, Pickle Specialties, Capers, Anchovies, Peppers, Jalapeno Peppers, Chili Peppers Importer
S.I.C.: 5149
N.A.I.C.S.: 424490
Import Export
Advertising Expenditures: $1,000,000
Media: 2-5-6-7-8-10-14-15-19-21-22-23-24-25
Distr.: Intl.; Natl.
Personnel:
Jeffrey Freeman *(Pres & CEO)*
Patti Andrade *(Sr VP-Mktg)*
Brands & Products:
STAR
Advertising Agency:
Hunter/Rossini/Boleslav
503 N Sweetzer Ave
West Hollywood, CA 90048-2605
Tel.: (323) 660-5941
Tel.: (323) 852-0851
(Oil, Vinegar, Capers, Olives, Cherries, Anchovies, Sun Dried Tomatoes)

STARBUCKS CORPORATION

2401 Utah Ave S
Seattle, WA 98134
Mailing Address:
PO Box 34067
Seattle, WA 98124-1067
Tel.: (206) 447-1575
Fax: (206) 447-0828
Toll Free: (800) 23-LATTE
E-mail: investorrelations@starbucks.com
Web Site: www.starbucks.com
Approx. Rev.: $8,963,500,000
Approx. Number Employees: 137,000
Year Founded: 1971
Business Description:
Specialty Coffee Roaster & Retailer
S.I.C.: 2095; 5499; 5812
N.A.I.C.S.: 311920; 445299; 722213
Advertising Expenditures: $5,600,000
Media: 6-8-9-23-25
Distr.: Intl.; Natl.
Personnel:
Howard D. Schultz *(Chm, Pres & CEO)*
Jeff Hansberry *(Pres, Global Consumer Products & Foodservice)*
Troy Alstead *(CFO, Chief Admin Officer & Exec VP)*
Annie Young-Scrivner *(CMO-Global)*
David Landau *(Chief Compliance Officer, Sr VP & Deputy Gen Counsel)*
Jinlong Wang *(Chm-Greater China & Sr VP)*
Julio Gutierrez *(Pres-Latin America & Sr VP)*
Vladan Armus *(Pres-Starbucks Coffee-Central & Eastern Europe)*
Cliff Burrows *(Pres-Starbucks Coffee US)*
John Culver *(Pres-Starbucks Coffee Intl)*
Michelle Gass *(Pres-Seattles Best Coffee)*
Arthur Rubinfeld *(Pres-Global Dev)*
Paula E. Boggs *(Gen Counsel, Sec & Exec VP)*
Kalen Holmes *(Exec VP-Partner Resources)*
Lucy Helm *(Deputy Gen Counsel & Sr VP-Global Bus)*
Chris Carr *(Sr VP-Northwest/Mountain Field Ops)*
Terry Davenport *(Sr VP-Mktg)*
Mary Egan *(Sr VP-Corp Strategy-Global)*
Willard Hay *(Sr VP-Coffee & Global Procurement)*
Cosimo Laporta *(Sr VP-Ops-Starbucks Coffee Intl)*
Michael Malanga *(Sr VP-Store Dev)*
Colin Moore *(Sr VP)*
Adam Brotman *(VP & Gen Mgr-Digital Ventures)*
Rachel Finke *(Dir-Packaged Coffee)*
Anthony Perez *(Sr Mgr-Concept Design-Global)*
Robert W. Taylor *(Bus Mgr-Sys Store Dev & Emerging Bus Sys)*
David Brewster *(Mgr-Content & Digital ventures)*
Ann-Marie Kurtz *(Mgr-Global Coffee & Tea Education)*
Michelle Malgesini *(Mgr-Mktg)*
Brands & Products:
AWAKE
BARISTA
BLACK APRON EXCLUSIVES
BRAZIL IPANEMA BOURBON
CAFE ESTIMA BLEND
CAFFE VERONA
CALM
CLOVER
COLOMBIA NARINO SUPREMO
DECAF CAFFE VERONA
DECAF ESPRESSO ROAST
DECAF KOMODO DRAGON BLEND
DECAF LIGHTNOTE BLEND
DECAF PIKE PLACE ROAST
DECAF SUMATRA
DOUBLESHOT
ESPRESSO ROAST
ETHIOPIA SIDAMO
ETHOS
FAIR TRADE BLEND
FRAPPUCCINO
GAZEBO BLEND
GOLD COAST BLEND
GUATEMALA ANTIGUA
GUATEMALA CASI CIELO
KOMODO DRAGON BLEND
LIGHTNOTE BLEND
OM
ORGANIC SERENA BLEND
PASSION
PIKE PLACE ROAST
REFRESH
SEATTLE'S BEST COFFEE
STARBUCKS
STARBUCKS COFFEE
STARBUCKS DISCOVERIES
STARBUCKS HEAR MUSIC
STARBUCKS VIA
TAZO
TORREFAZIONE ITALIA
VIA
YUKON BLEND
Advertising Agencies:
BBDO New York
1285 Ave of the Americas 7th Fl
New York, NY 10019-6028
Tel.: (212) 459-5000
(Creative)

Blast Radius
285 Madison Ave 12th Fl
New York, NY 10017
Tel.: (212) 925-4900
Fax: (212) 925-5247

Codilink S.r.l.
Reforma 444 Int.901, Col. Juarez
06600
Guadalajara, Mexico
Tel.: (52) 55 5207 8410
Fax: (52) 55 5207 8405

Creature
1508 10th Ave
Seattle, WA 98122
Tel.: (206) 625-6994
Fax: (206) 625-6904
Seattle's Best

Daniel J. Edelman, Inc.
(d/b/a Edelman)
200 E Randolph St Fl 63
Chicago, IL 60601-6705
Tel.: (312) 240-3000
Fax: (312) 240-2900

Draftfcb
101 E Erie St
Chicago, IL 60611
Tel.: (312) 425-5000
Fax: (312) 425-5010
(Direct Marketing, Loyalty Cards)

Grey Vancouver
1600 - 1500 W Georgia St
Vancouver, BC V6G 2Z6, Canada
Tel.: (604) 687-1001
Fax: (604) 682-1827
Toll Free: (877) 250-2275

GroundFloor Media, Inc.
1923 Market St
Denver, CO 80202
Tel.: (303) 865-8110
Fax: (303) 253-9763

MediaCom
498 7th Ave
New York, NY 10018
Tel.: (212) 912-4200
Fax: (212) 508-4386

STARKIST FOODS INC.

(Sub. of Dongwon F&B Co., Ltd.)
323 North Shore Dr Ste 600
Pittsburgh, PA 15212
Tel.: (412) 222-2200
Tel.: (412) 323-7400
Fax: (412) 222-4050
Toll Free: (800) 732-8812
Web Site: www.starkist.com
Sales Range: $550-599.9 Million
Approx. Number Employees: 5,000
Business Description:
Tuna, Sardines, Mackerel, Canned Cat Foods, Dry Cat Food, Soft Moist Cat Food, Dry Dog Food, Dog Snacks Mfr
S.I.C.: 2091; 2047
N.A.I.C.S.: 311711; 311111
Media: 2-4-6-9-14-15-18-19-20-21-23-24-25
Distr.: Intl.; Natl.
Personnel:
Donald J. Binotto *(Pres & CEO)*
H. K. Lee *(Treas, Sr VP & Controller)*
Patrick M. Moody *(Sr VP-Supply Chain)*
Melissa Murphy-Brown *(Sr VP-Corp Affairs & HR)*
Jan Tharp *(Sr VP-Supply Chain)*
Joe M. Tuza *(Sr VP-Mktg, Innovation & Technical Svcs)*
Brands & Products:
CHARLIE
CHARLIE'S LUNCH KIT
GOURMET CHOICE
PRIME CATCH
SELECT
STAR-KIST

Key to Media (For complete agency information see *The Advertising Red Books-Agencies* edition):
1. Bus. Publs. 2. Cable T.V. 3. Catalogs & Directories. 4. Co-op Adv. 5. Consumer Mags. 6. D.M. to Bus. Estab.7. D.M. to Consumers 8. Daily Newsp. 9. Exhibits/Trade Shows 10. Foreign 11. Infomercial 12. Internet Adv.13. Multimedia 14. Network Radio 15. Network T.V. 16. Newsp. Distr. Mags. 17. Other 18. Outdoor (Posters, Transit) 19. Point of Purchase20. Premiums, Novelties 21. Product Samples 22. Special Events Mktg. 23. Spot Radio 24. Spot T.V. 25. Weekly Newsp. 26. Yellow Page Adv.

StarKist Foods Inc. — (Continued)

STAR-KIST EATWELL
STARKIST FLAVOR FRESH POUCH
STARKIST TUNA CREATIONS

STEWARTS PRIVATE BLEND FOODS INC.
4110 W Wrightwood Ave
Chicago, IL 60639-2127
Tel.: (773) 489-2500
Fax: (773) 489-2148
Toll Free: (800) 654-2862
E-mail: info@stewarts.com
Web Site: www.stewarts.com
Approx. Number Employees: 55
Year Founded: 1913
Business Description:
Coffee, Tea & Allied Foods Mfr
S.I.C.: 2095
N.A.I.C.S.: 311920
Import Export
Media: 5-7-8-9-10-13-19-20-21-24-25-26
Distr.: Intl.; Natl.
Budget Set: Nov.
Personnel:
Bob Tomkins *(Dir-Mktg)*
Brands & Products:
STEWARTS

STOCK YARDS PACKING CO., INC.
(Joint Venture of KKR & CO. L.P. & Clayton, Dubilier & Rice, LLC)
340 N Oakley Blvd
Chicago, IL 60612
Mailing Address:
PO Box 12450
Chicago, IL 60612-0450
Tel.: (312) 733-6050
Fax: (312) 733-1746
Toll Free: (800) 621-3687
Toll Free: (877) STK-YARD
Toll Free: (800) 621-1119
E-mail: customerservice@stockyards.com
Web Site: www.stockyards.com
Sales Range: $125-149.9 Million
Approx. Number Employees: 100
Year Founded: 1893
Business Description:
Meat & Poultry Distr
S.I.C.: 5147
N.A.I.C.S.: 424470
Export
Distr.: Direct to Consumer; Natl.
Personnel:
Wes Ball *(Dir-Retail Bus)*
Brands & Products:
KING OF STEAKS
Advertising Agency:
GSP Marketing Services, Inc.
320 W Ohio St
Chicago, IL 60654
Tel.: (312) 944-3000
Fax: (312) 944-8587
(Steaks & Gourmet Food)

STONYFIELD FARM, INC.
(Sub. of Danone Foods Inc.)
10 Burton Dr
Londonderry, NH 03053
Tel.: (603) 437-4040
Fax: (603) 437-7594
Toll Free: (800) 776-2697
E-mail: info@stonyfield.com
Web Site: www.stonyfield.com
Approx. Number Employees: 230
Business Description:
Yogurt, Milk & Ice Cream Mfr
S.I.C.: 2024; 2026
N.A.I.C.S.: 311520; 311511
Media: 1-4-8-10-13-15-20-22-23
Personnel:
Gary Hirshberg *(Chm, Pres & CEO)*
Diane Carhart *(COO)*
Kasi Reddy *(Sr VP-Quality, Food Safety & R&D)*
Rolf Carlson *(VP-Pur)*
Alice Markowitz *(VP-Comm)*
Carol Billings *(Dir-Mktg Comm)*
Carrie Kocik *(Dir-Comm)*
Brands & Products:
O'SOY
STONYFIELD FARM
YO BABY
Advertising Agency:
Connelly Partners
46 Waltham St Fl 4
Boston, MA 02118
Tel.: (617) 956-5050
Fax: (617) 956-5054

STRETCH ISLAND FRUIT, INC.
4275 Executive Square Dr
La Jolla, CA 92037
Mailing Address:
PO Box 8557
La Jolla, CA 92038
Tel.: (360) 275-6050
Fax: (360) 275-6184
Toll Free: (800) 863-7836
E-mail: stretchisland@vasupport.com
Web Site: www.stretchislandfruit.com
Approx. Number Employees: 75
Business Description:
Natural Fruit Snacks Mfr
S.I.C.: 2034; 5149
N.A.I.C.S.: 311423; 424490
Media: 6

STROEHMANN BAKERIES
(Sub. of Stroehmann Bakeries, L.C.)
3996 Paxton St
Harrisburg, PA 17111-1423
Tel.: (717) 561-1790
Fax: (717) 564-9231
Web Site: www.stroehmann.com
Approx. Number Employees: 390
Year Founded: 1924
Business Description:
Bakery Services
S.I.C.: 2051
N.A.I.C.S.: 311812
Advertising Expenditures: $50,000
Media: 2-8-9-10-14-15-18-19-20-21-23-24
Distr.: Reg.
Budget Set: Feb.
Brands & Products:
D'ITALIANO
DUTCH COUNTRY
MAIER'S
STROEHMANN'S

STROEHMANN BAKERIES, L.C.
(Plant of Bimbo Bakeries USA Inc.)
255 Business Ctr Dr Ste 200
Horsham, PA 19044
Tel.: (215) 672-8010
Fax: (215) 672-6988
Web Site: www.stroehmann.com
Approx. Number Employees: 60
Year Founded: 1924
Business Description:
Bakery Services
S.I.C.: 2051; 5461
N.A.I.C.S.: 311812; 311811
Advertising Expenditures: $5,000,000
Media: 9-10-18-19-20-24
Distr.: Reg.
Personnel:
Tony Leta *(Gen Mgr)*
Brands & Products:
STROEHMANN
Advertising Agency:
Depersico Creative Group
1 Raymond Dr
Havertown, PA 19083
Tel.: (610) 789-4400
Fax: (610) 789-7133
Toll Free: (800) 645-1950

STROHMEYER & ARPE COMPANY
106 Allen Rd
Basking Ridge, NJ 07920
Tel.: (908) 580-9100
Fax: (908) 580-9300
E-mail: sales@strohmeyer.com
Web Site: www.strohmeyer.com
E-Mail For Key Personnel:
Sales Director: sales@strohmeyer.com
Approx. Number Employees: 8
Year Founded: 1882
Business Description:
Distr & Importer of Canned Fruits
S.I.C.: 5149
N.A.I.C.S.: 424490
Media: 2-4-10-13-21-23
Distr.: Natl.
Budget Set: Jan.
Personnel:
Charles Kocot *(Pres)*
Pierre Crawley *(VP-Mktg)*
Brands & Products:
KING PANTRY
PEPPADEW
S&A

STROM PRODUCTS LTD.
1500 Lakeside Dr Ste 110
Bannockburn, IL 60015-1234
Tel.: (847) 236-9676
Fax: (847) 267-1404
Toll Free: (800) 862-3311
E-mail: noyolks@stromproducts.com
Web Site: www.noyolks.com
Approx. Number Employees: 10
Year Founded: 1999
Business Description:
Food Products Whslr
S.I.C.: 5149
N.A.I.C.S.: 424490
Export
Advertising Expenditures: $1,900,000
Media: 3-15
Distr.: Natl.
Budget Set: Jan.
Personnel:
Robert B. Strom *(Pres & CTO)*
Gary Henke *(Pres)*
Brands & Products:
NO YOLKS
STROM PRODUCTS
WACKY MAC
WACKY MAC MACARONI & CHEESE DINNERS

SUBCO FOODS, INC.
1150 Commerce Dr
West Chicago, IL 60185
Tel.: (708) 338-4488
Fax: (630) 231-0678
E-mail: info@subcofoods.com
Web Site: www.subcofoods.com
Approx. Number Employees: 175
Year Founded: 1995
Business Description:
Food Preparations
S.I.C.: 2099
N.A.I.C.S.: 311999
Media: 4-7-13
Personnel:
Mas Khan *(Pres & CEO)*
Brands & Products:
FLAVOR TIME
LITE & FREE
ORCHARD PARK
SUBCO

SUBCO FOODS OF WISCONSIN
(Div. of Subco Foods, Inc.)
4350 S Taylor Dr
Sheboygan, WI 53081-8479
Tel.: (920) 457-7761
Fax: (920) 457-3899
E-mail: info@subcofoods.com
Web Site: www.subcofoods.com
Approx. Number Employees: 39
Year Founded: 1925
Business Description:
Mfr. of Private Label & Contract Sugar Free Sweetners, Dry Drink Mixes, Coffee Creamers, Gelatins, Puddings.
S.I.C.: 2023
N.A.I.C.S.: 311514
Export
Media: 6-7-13
Distr.: Natl.
Budget Set: Nov.
Personnel:
Mas Khan *(Pres & CEO)*

SUGAR CREEK PACKING CO.
2101 1 2 Kenskill Ave
Washington Court House, OH 43160-9311
Tel.: (740) 335-3586
Fax: (740) 335-7443
E-mail: Sales@sugarcreek.com
Web Site: www.sugarcreek.com
E-Mail For Key Personnel:
Sales Director: sales@sugarcreek.com
Approx. Number Employees: 550
Year Founded: 1966
Business Description:
Bacon Processor
S.I.C.: 5147; 0751
N.A.I.C.S.: 311612; 311611
Export
Media: 2-4-13-18
Personnel:
John G. Richardson *(Pres & CEO)*
Tom Bollinger *(CFO)*

SUN-MAID GROWERS OF CALIFORNIA
13525 S Bethel Ave
Kingsburg, CA 93631-9212
Tel.: (559) 896-8000
Fax: (559) 897-2362
E-mail: smaid@sunmaid.com
Web Site: www.sunmaid.com

Key to Media (For complete agency information see *The Advertising Red Books-Agencies* edition):
1. Bus. Publs. 2. Cable T.V. 3. Catalogs & Directories. 4. Co-op Adv. 5. Consumer Mags. 6. D.M. to Bus. Estab.7. D.M. to Consumers 8. Daily Newsp. 9. Exhibits/Trade Shows 10. Foreign 11. Infomercial 12. Internet Adv.13. Multimedia 14. Network Radio 15. Network T.V. 16. Newsp. Distr. Mags. 17. Other 18. Outdoor (Posters, Transit) 19. Point of Purchase20. Premiums, Novelties 21. Product Samples 22. Special Events Mktg. 23. Spot Radio 24. Spot T.V. 25. Weekly Newsp. 26. Yellow Page Adv.

Sales Range: $150-199.9 Million
Approx. Number Employees: 500
Year Founded: 1912
Business Description:
Producer & Distributor of Raisins, Dried Apricots, Peaches, Mixed Cut Fruit, Raisin Juice Concentrate, Dried Pears, Animal Feed & Gift Packs
S.I.C.: 5149
N.A.I.C.S.: 424490
Export
Advertising Expenditures: $7,000,000
Media: 2-6-8-9-10-14-15-18-21-23-24
Distr.: Intl.; Natl.
Personnel:
Jon Marthedal *(Chm)*
Pete J. Penner *(Vice Chm)*
Barry Kriebel *(Pres)*
Richard Emde *(CFO)*
Kayhan Hazrati *(Asst VP-Tech Svcs)*
Carsten Tietjen *(Dir-Intl Sls & Mktg)*
Brands & Products:
EARLY SEASON
FRUIT BITS
NATURE SNACKS
RAISIN D'LITE
REDS & YELLOWS
SUN-MAID
SUN-MAID BAKING RAISINS
VINE-MAID
Advertising Agencies:
McCann Erickson/Los Angeles
5700 Wilshire Blvd Ste 225
Los Angeles, CA 90036
Tel.: (323) 900-7100
Fax: (323) 900-7111
Sun-Maid Raisins

TargetCast tcm
909 3rd Ave 31st Fl
New York, NY 10022
Tel.: (212) 500-6900
Fax: (212) 500-6880

SUN-RYPE PRODUCTS LTD.
1165 Ethel St
Kelowna, BC V1Y 2W4, Canada
Tel.: (250) 470-6405
Tel.: (250) 470-6426
Fax: (250) 762-3611
Toll Free: (800) 533-8933
E-mail: investor@sunrype.com
Web Site: www.sunrype.com
Approx. Sls.: $144,547,121
Approx. Number Employees: 382
Year Founded: 1946
Business Description:
Food & Beverage Products Mfr & Marketer
S.I.C.: 2037; 2096; 2099
N.A.I.C.S.: 311411; 311919; 311999
Media: 8-15
Personnel:
Merv Geen *(Chm)*
Dave McAnerney *(Pres & CEO)*
Don VanderZwaag *(CFO & VP-Fin)*
Cameron Johnston *(VP-Sls & Mktg)*
Brands & Products:
APPLEWISE
FRUIT PLUS
FRUIT TO GO
FRUITSOURCE
FUNBITES
LIGHT & REFRESHING
REAL FRUIT GOODNESS
SUN-RYPE
VITA BURST
Advertising Agencies:
DDB Vancouver
1600-777 Hornby St
Vancouver, BC V6Z 2T3, Canada
Tel.: (604) 687-7911
Fax: (604) 640-4343

OMD Vancouver
777 Hornby Street Suite 1600
Vancouver, BC V6Z 2T3, Canada
Tel.: (604) 640-4336
Fax: (604) 640-4337
Media Buying

Tribal DDB Vancouver
1600-777 Hornby St
Vancouver, BC V6Z 2T3, Canada
Tel.: (604) 608-4451
Fax: (604) 640-4343

SUNKIST GROWERS, INC.
14130 Riverside Dr
Sherman Oaks, CA 91423-2313
Mailing Address:
PO Box 7888
Van Nuys, CA 91409-7888
Tel.: (818) 986-4800
Web Site: www.sunkist.com
Approx. Number Employees: 4,500
Year Founded: 1893
Business Description:
Non-Profit Co-operative Marketing Fresh Oranges, Lemons, Grapefruit & Tangerines
S.I.C.: 5148
N.A.I.C.S.: 424480
Import Export
Advertising Expenditures: $16,000,000
Media: 2-3-5-6-7-8-9-10-11-13-14-15-18-19-20-22-23-24-25
Distr.: Intl.; Natl.
Budget Set: Sept.
Personnel:
Nicholas L. Bozick *(Chm)*
Craig Armstrong *(Vice Chm)*
Gerald M. Denni *(Vice Chm)*
James P. Finch *(Vice Chm)*
Russell L. Hanlin, II *(Pres & CEO)*
Michael J. Wootton *(Sr VP-Corp Relations & Admin)*
Richard G. French *(VP-Fin)*
Julie DeWolf *(Dir-Mktg-Retail)*
Leland Wong *(Dir-Mktg)*
Brands & Products:
SUNKIST
Advertising Agency:
Gordon Hanrahan, Inc.
150 N Michigan Ave Ste 600
Chicago, IL 60601-7570
Tel.: (312) 372-0935
Fax: (312) 372-1409

SUNNY DELIGHT BEVERAGES CO.
(Holding of J.W. Childs Associates, L.P.)
6000 Creek Rd
Cincinnati, OH 45242
Tel.: (513) 483-3300
Fax: (513) 483-3396
Toll Free: (800) 395-5849
E-mail: service.fin@sunnyd.com
Web Site: www.sunnyd.com
Approx. Sls.: $550,000,000
Approx. Number Employees: 550
Business Description:
Fruit Drinks, Fruit Juices, Sweet Cider, Natural Juices & Nectars Mfr
S.I.C.: 2037
N.A.I.C.S.: 311411
Media: 15-22
Personnel:
William B. Cyr *(Pres & CEO)*
John R. Crossetti *(Sr VP-Sls-US)*
Rick Zimmerman *(Sr VP-Mktg & Innovation)*
Davette Shorter *(Dir-Natural Beverages)*
Ed Klene *(Brand Mgr)*
David Silver *(Brand Mgr-SunnyD)*
Brands & Products:
FRUIT2O
FRUITSIMPLE
SUNNY DELIGHT
SUNNYD
SUNNYD 100% JUICE
SUNNYD BAJA
SUNNYD INTENSE SPORT
VERYFINE
Advertising Agencies:
Exopolis, Inc.
3000 E Cesar Chavez
Austin, TX 78702
Tel.: (323) 662-8500
Fax: (512) 480-9860
Creative
Mobile
Social
SunnyD (Digital Agency of Record)
Web

The Gate Worldwide New York
11 E 26th St 14th Fl
New York, NY 10010
Tel.: (212) 508-3400
Fax: (212) 508-3543

The McRae Agency
2130 Walecitos Ste 348
La Jolla, CA 92037
Tel.: (480) 990-0282
Fax: (858) 459-1227
Swim to Success Program

SUNOPTA INGREDIENTS, INC.
(Sub. of SunOpta Inc.)
(d/b/a SunOpta Ingredients Group)
100 Apollo Dr
Chelmsford, MA 01824
Tel.: (781) 276-5100
Fax: (781) 276-5101
Toll Free: (800) 353-6782
E-mail: ingredients@sunopta.com
Web Site: www.sunopta-food.com/ingredients
Approx. Number Employees: 150
Year Founded: 1998
Business Description:
Texturizing Ingredients Added to Prepared Foods
S.I.C.: 2099
N.A.I.C.S.: 311999
Advertising Expenditures: $650,000
Media: 2-4-10-13-16
Personnel:
Douglas Shreves *(Pres)*
Jim Podolske *(Sr VP-Innovation & Sustainability)*
George Klesaris *(Grp VP-Fin)*
Collette Sizer *(Grp VP-Sls & Mktg)*
Laura Cooper *(Mgr-Mktg)*
Eloise Walker *(Mgr-Customer Svc)*

SUNRISE SOYA FOODS
729 Powell St
Vancouver, BC Canada
Tel.: (604) 253-2326
Fax: (604) 251-1083
Toll Free: (800) 661BEAN
E-mail: consumer-info@sunrise.com
Web Site: www.sunrise-soya.com
Approx. Number Employees: 200
Year Founded: 1957
Business Description:
Soybean Products Mfr
S.I.C.: 2075; 2079
N.A.I.C.S.: 311222; 311225
Media: 2-8-10-13-22
Personnel:
Peter Joe *(Owner, CEO & Gen Mgr)*
Paul Mitchell *(VP-Sls & Mktg)*
Sue Willems *(VP-Sls & Mktg)*
Brands & Products:
MANDARIN TOFU
PETE'S TOFU
SUNRISE SOYA FOODS
SUNRISE TOFU
Advertising Agency:
Hamazaki Wong Marketing Group
1155 Pender St W Ste 700
Vancouver, BC V6E 2P4, Canada
Tel.: (604) 669-8282
Fax: (604) 669-2288

SUNSWEET GROWERS, INC.
901 N Walton Ave
Yuba City, CA 95993-8634
Tel.: (530) 674-5010
Fax: (530) 751-5258
Toll Free: (800) 417-2253
E-mail: info@sunsweet.com
Web Site: www.sunsweet.com
Approx. Number Employees: 650
Year Founded: 1917
Business Description:
Dried Fruits Processor
S.I.C.: 2034; 2037
N.A.I.C.S.: 311423; 311411
Export
Advertising Expenditures: $1,000,000
Media: 1-2-4-6-8-10-11-13-14-15-16-19-20-21-22
Personnel:
Gary Thiara *(Chm)*
Tim D. Smith *(Vice Chm)*
Ana Spyres *(CFO & VP-Fin)*
Dane L. Lance *(COO)*
Steve Harris *(VP-Mktg)*
Brands & Products:
CALIFORNIA GOLD
CRANBERRY FRUITLINGS
LIGHTER BAKE
ORCHARD MIX
PLUMSMART
PLUMSMART LIGHT
SUNSWEET
SUNSWEET FRESH

SUNTORY INTERNATIONAL CORP.
(Sub. of Suntory Holdings Ltd.)
7 Times Sq 21st Fl
New York, NY 10036
Tel.: (212) 891-6600
Fax: (212) 891-6601
Web Site: www.suntory.com/group/food.html
Business Description:
Food Products Importer
S.I.C.: 7389

Key to Media (For complete agency information see *The Advertising Red Books-Agencies* edition):
1. Bus. Publs. 2. Cable T.V. 3. Catalogs & Directories. 4. Co-op Adv. 5. Consumer Mags. 6. D.M. to Bus. Estab.7. D.M. to Consumers 8. Daily Newsp. 9. Exhibits/Trade Shows 10. Foreign 11. Infomercial 12. Internet Adv.13. Multimedia 14. Network Radio 15. Network T.V. 16. Newsp. Distr. Mags. 17. Other 18. Outdoor (Posters, Transit) 19. Point of Purchase20. Premiums, Novelties 21. Product Samples 22. Special Events Mktg. 23. Spot Radio 24. Spot T.V. 25. Weekly Newsp. 26. Yellow Page Adv.

Suntory International Corp. — (Continued)

N.A.I.C.S.: 561499
Advertising Agency:
filter Advertising
160 Pearl St 2nd Fl
New York, NY 10005
Tel.: (212) 248-3028

SUPERIOR DAIRY, INC.
4719 Navarre Rd SW
Canton, OH 44706-2338
Tel.: (330) 477-4515
Fax: (330) 477-5908
Toll Free: (800) 683-2479
Web Site: www.superiordairy.com/
Approx. Number Employees: 260
Year Founded: 1922
Business Description:
Mfr. & Distr of Fluid Milk, Ice Cream, Novelties, Cottage Cheese, Sour Cream & Dip
S.I.C.: 2026; 2024
N.A.I.C.S.: 311511; 311520
Media: 2-7-10
Distr.: Reg.
Personnel:
Daniel P. Soehnlen *(Pres)*
Joseph A. Soehnlen *(CEO)*
Carolyn J. Schoeppner *(Coord-Customer Support)*
Barbara J. Green *(Dir-HR)*
Jill A. Frank *(Mgr-Benefits Admin)*
Al Soehnlen *(Mgr-Key Accts)*
J.P. Soehnlen *(Mgr-Pur)*
Brands & Products:
SUPERIOR

SUREQUEST SYSTEMS, INC.
3330 Keller Springs Ste 205
Carrollton, TX 75006
Tel.: (972) 238-7200
Fax: (972) 238-7733
E-mail: info@surequest.com
Web Site: www.surequest.com
Sales Range: $1-9.9 Million
Approx. Number Employees: 20
Year Founded: 1984
Business Description:
Dietary & Food Service Management Software, Menu Services & Dietary Consulting
S.I.C.: 7371; 7372; 8748
N.A.I.C.S.: 541511; 511210; 541618
Advertising Expenditures: $53,917
Media: 10
Personnel:
Tim J. Sudderth *(Pres & CEO)*
Stan Janczyk *(CFO)*
Alma Sudderth *(COO)*
Cris Sedbergh *(VP-Support Svcs-Trng)*
Brands & Products:
2SQUARED
SQUARE 1
SUREASSESS
SURELINK
SUREMENU
SUREQUEST
TECHNOLOGY THAT FEEDS AMERICA!
THREESQUARES

SWEET OVATIONS, LLC
1741 Tomlinson Rd
Philadelphia, PA 19116-3847
Tel.: (215) 676-3900
Fax: (215) 702-1015
E-mail: custserv@sweetovations.com
Web Site: www.sweetovations.com
Approx. Number Employees: 350
Year Founded: 1970
Business Description:
Processed Fruits for Food Services, Bakery & Dairy & Frozen Dessert Applications
S.I.C.: 2099
N.A.I.C.S.: 311999
Advertising Expenditures: $200,000
Media: 2-7-10-13-18-19-20-21-22
Distr.: Natl.
Budget Set: Feb.
Personnel:
Kevin Daugherty *(Pres)*

SWISHER HYGIENE INC.
(Formerly CoolBrands International, Inc.)
4725 Piedmont Row Dr Ste 400
Charlotte, NC 28210
Tel.: (704) 364-7707
Web Site: www.swisherhygiene.com
Approx. Rev.: $63,652,318
Approx. Number Employees: 1,077
Business Description:
Cleaning Products & Facility Cleaning Services
S.I.C.: 7349
N.A.I.C.S.: 561720
Export
Advertising Expenditures: $5,274,000
Media: 17
Personnel:
H. Wayne Huizenga *(Chm)*
Steven R. Berrard *(Pres & CEO)*
Hugh H. Cooper *(CFO & Treas)*
Thomas E. Aucamp *(Exec VP & Sec)*
Thomas C. Byrne *(Exec VP)*
Thomas LaMartina *(Sr VP-Ops)*

THE SWISS COLONY, INC.
(Name Changed to Colony Brands Inc.)

SWISS WATER DECAFFEINATED COFFEE INCOME FUND
(d/b/a Swiss Water Decaffeinated Coffee Company Inc.)
3131 Lake City Way
Burnaby, BC V5A 3A3, Canada
Tel.: (604) 420-4050
Fax: (604) 420-8711
Toll Free: (800) 667-6181
E-mail: info2@swisswater.com
Web Site: www.swisswater.com
Approx. Sls.: $30,495,669
Approx. Number Employees: 15
Business Description:
Decaffeinated Coffee Processing
S.I.C.: 2095; 6722
N.A.I.C.S.: 311920; 525910
Media: 6-10-11-13-15-18-21
Personnel:
David Rowntree *(Chm)*
Frank Dennis *(Pres & CEO)*
Sherry Tryssenaar *(CFO)*
Dave Wong *(Dir-Fin Plng & Treasury)*
Kathy Berardo *(Sr Mgr-Customer Relship)*
Dorota Impert *(Mgr-Customer Relationship)*
Andrea Piccolo *(Mgr-Customer Relationship)*
Brands & Products:
ORGANIC CASCADIA
QUADRA-SEAL
SWISS WATER

SYLVAN INC.
(Sub. of Snyder Associated Companies, Inc.)
90 Glade Dr
Kittanning, PA 16201
Tel.: (724) 543-3900
Fax: (724) 543-7583
E-mail: sylvan@sylvaninc.com
Web Site: www.sylvaninc.com
Approx. Number Employees: 900
Year Founded: 1937
Business Description:
Fungal Technology Services
S.I.C.: 0182
N.A.I.C.S.: 111411
Media: 2-4-11-13-17
Personnel:
Mark A. Snyder *(Chm)*
Gary D. Walker *(Pres)*
Donald E. Smith *(CFO)*
Monir K. Elzalaki *(Pres-Sylvan America)*
Mark P. Wach *(VP & Dir-Res)*
Brands & Products:
HAUSER
SOMYCEL
SYLVAN

T. MARZETTI COMPANY
(Sub. of Lancaster Colony Corporation)
1105 Schrock Rd Ste 300
Columbus, OH 43229-1174
Mailing Address:
PO Box 29163
Columbus, OH 43229-0163
Tel.: (614) 846-2232
Fax: (614) 848-8330
Web Site: www.marzetti.com
E-Mail For Key Personnel:
Marketing Director: danderson@marzetti.com
Sales Range: Less than $1 Million
Approx. Number Employees: 175
Year Founded: 1896
Business Description:
Salad Dressings, Frozen Pies, Frozen Bread & Refrigerated Chip Dips Mfr
S.I.C.: 2035; 2098
N.A.I.C.S.: 311941; 311823
Export
Advertising Expenditures: $4,500,000
Media: 2-6-9-10-17-19-21
Distr.: Natl.
Budget Set: June
Personnel:
Bruce Rosa *(Pres)*
Gary E. Thompson *(Exec VP-Specialty Foods Grp)*
Beverly Sandberg *(VP-Mktg)*
Schrade Radtke *(Sr Mgr-Mktg)*
Irena Castle *(Sr Brand Mgr)*
Brands & Products:
AMISH KITCHEN
CARDINI'S
CHATHAM VILLAGE
INN MAID
MAMMA BELLA
MARZETTI
MOUNTAIN TOP
NEW YORK
PFEIFFER
REAMES
ROMANOFF
SISTER SCHUBERT'S
T. MARZETTI'S
TEXAS BEST
Advertising Agencies:
Empower MediaMarketing (MEDIA THAT WORKS)
1111 Saint Gregory St
Cincinnati, OH 45202
Tel.: (513) 871-9454
Fax: (513) 871-1804

Fitzgerald+CO
3060 Peachtree Rd NW
Atlanta, GA 30305
Tel.: (404) 504-6900
Fax: (404) 239-0548

TABATCHNICK FINE FOODS, INC.
1230 Hamilton St
Somerset, NJ 08873-3343
Mailing Address:
PO Box 27
Boise, ID 83707-0027
Tel.: (732) 247-6668
Fax: (732) 247-6555
E-mail: ben@tabatchnick.com
Web Site: www.tabatchnick.com
E-Mail For Key Personnel:
President: ben@tabatchnick.com
Sales Range: $1-9.9 Million
Approx. Number Employees: 40
Year Founded: 1905
Business Description:
Mfr. & Distr of Frozen Soups
S.I.C.: 2038; 2092
N.A.I.C.S.: 311412; 311712
Advertising Expenditures: $300,000
Media: 8-9-25
Distr.: Natl.
Budget Set: Feb.
Personnel:
Benjamin Tabatchnick *(Pres & CEO)*
Robert Ingebretsen *(CFO)*
Barry Ansel *(Sr VP-Sls & Mktg)*
Bud Barry *(Engr)*
Brands & Products:
TABATCHNICK
Advertising Agency:
Frieze Advertising Inc.
223 State Rte 18
East Brunswick, NJ 08816-1913
Tel.: (732) 828-5800
Fax: (732) 545-8575

TASTY-TOPPINGS, INC.
2804 13th St
Columbus, NE 68602-0728
Tel.: (402) 564-1347
Fax: (402) 563-1469
Toll Free: (800) 228-4148
Web Site: www.dorothylynch.com
Sales Range: $1-9.9 Million
Approx. Number Employees: 25
Year Founded: 1964
Business Description:
Home Style Dressing
S.I.C.: 2035
N.A.I.C.S.: 311941
Advertising Expenditures: $1,500,000
Distr.: Reg.
Budget Set: Dec.
Personnel:
Mac Hull *(Pres)*
Brands & Products:
DOROTHY LYNCH

Key to Media (For complete agency information see *The Advertising Red Books-Agencies* edition):
1. Bus. Publs. 2. Cable T.V. 3. Catalogs & Directories. 4. Co-op Adv. 5. Consumer Mags. 6. D.M. to Bus. Estab.7. D.M. to Consumers
8. Daily Newsp. 9. Exhibits/Trade Shows 10. Foreign 11. Infomercial 12. Internet Adv.13. Multimedia 14. Network Radio
15. Network T.V. 16. Newsp. Distr. Mags. 17. Other 18. Outdoor (Posters, Transit) 19. Point of Purchase20. Premiums, Novelties
21. Product Samples 22. Special Events Mktg. 23. Spot Radio 24. Spot T.V. 25. Weekly Newsp. 26. Yellow Page Adv.

Advertising Agency:
Swanson Russell Associates
1222 P St
Lincoln, NE 68508-1425
Tel.: (402) 437-6400
Fax: (402) 437-6401

TATE & LYLE
(Sub. of Tate & Lyle PLC)
2200 E Eldorado St
Decatur, IL 62521-1578
Tel.: (217) 423-4411
Fax: (217) 421-2216
Web Site: www.tateandlyle.com
Approx. Number Employees: 5,000
Year Founded: 1898
Business Description:
Cereal Sweeteners Mfr
S.I.C.: 2043
N.A.I.C.S.: 311230
Personnel:
Matthew Wineinger *(Pres)*
Brands & Products:
GREGG
GREGG'S GOLD-N-SOFT
QUICK ELASTIC
Advertising Agency:
Bozell
1022 Leavenworth St
Omaha, NE 68102
Tel.: (402) 965-4434
Fax: (402) 965-4399

TAYLOR COMPANY
(Sub. of Carrier Commercial Refrigeration)
750 N Blackhawk Blvd
Rockton, IL 61072-2104
Tel.: (815) 624-8333
Fax: (815) 624-8000
Toll Free: (800) 255-0626
E-mail: info@taylor-company.com
Web Site: www.taylor-company.com
E-Mail For Key Personnel:
President: cwangaard@taylor-company.com
Sales Range: $150-199.9 Million
Approx. Number Employees: 500
Year Founded: 1920
Business Description:
Commercial Ice Cream, Milk Shake, Frozen Confection & Slush Machinery & Cooking Utensils
S.I.C.: 3556
N.A.I.C.S.: 333294
Personnel:
Greg McMaster *(Pres)*
Advertising Agency:
Foodmix Marketing Communications
103 W Arthur St
Elmhurst, IL 60126
Tel.: (630) 366-7500
Fax: (630) 366-7519

TEJON RANCH COMPANY
4436 Lebec Rd
Lebec, CA 93243
Mailing Address:
PO Box 1000
Lebec, CA 93243
Tel.: (661) 248-3000
Fax: (661) 248-2318
E-mail: bzoeller@tejonranch.com
Web Site: www.tejonranch.com
Approx. Rev.: $35,513,000
Approx. Number Employees: 129
Year Founded: 1843
Business Description:
Real Estate Developer
S.I.C.: 6512; 6552
N.A.I.C.S.: 531120; 237210
Advertising Expenditures: $227,000
Personnel:
Kent G. Snyder *(Chm)*
Robert A. Stine *(Pres & CEO)*
Allen E. Lyda *(CFO, Treas & VP)*
Joseph E. Drew *(Sr VP-Real Estate)*
Kathleen J. Perkinson *(Sr VP-Natural Resources)*
Barry Zoeller *(VP & Dir-Corp Comm)*
Dean Brown *(Dir-Construction)*

TETLEY USA INC.
(Sub. of Tata Global Beverages)
155 Chestnutridge Rd Fl 2
Montvale, NJ 07645
Tel.: (203) 929-9200
Fax: (203) 929-9263
E-mail: info@tetleyusa.com
Web Site: www.tetleyusa.com
Approx. Number Employees: 100
Year Founded: 1837
Business Description:
Producer & Retailer of Tea
S.I.C.: 2095
N.A.I.C.S.: 311920
Import Export
Advertising Expenditures: $1,500,000
Media: 6-8-9-11-13-15-18-19-20-23-25
Distr.: Natl.
Budget Set: Aug.
Personnel:
Barbara Roth *(Pres)*
Joe Zoby *(VP-Sls)*
Cathy Kolumbus *(Sr Mgr-Brand)*
Brands & Products:
TETLEY
TETLEY DRAWSTRING TEA BAGS
TETLEY ICED GOLD
TETLEY ICED TEA MIX
TETLEY MAKES IT BETTER
TETLEY ROUND TEA BAGS

T.G. LEE FOODS, LLC
(Sub. of Dean Dairy Holdings, LLC)
315 N Bumby Ave
Orlando, FL 32803
Tel.: (407) 894-4941
Fax: (407) 896-4757
Web Site: www.deanfoods.com
Sales Range: $150-199.9 Million
Approx. Number Employees: 350
Business Description:
Mfr. of Fresh Milk, Ice Cream, Cottage Cheese & Related Dairy Products; Powdered Non-Dairy Creamers; Prepared Foods; Pickles & Relishes; Cranberry Sauce & Relish, Salads & Salad Dressings; Liquid Ice Cream Mixes & Ice Cream Novelties
S.I.C.: 2026
N.A.I.C.S.: 311511
Media: 9-14-22-23
Distr.: Reg.
Personnel:
Bill Geovanadi *(Gen Mgr)*
Brands & Products:
T G LEE
Advertising Agency:
Chernoff Newman
1411 Gervais St 5th Fl
Columbia, SC 29201-3125
Tel.: (803) 254-8158
Fax: (803) 252-2016

TILLAMOOK COUNTY CREAMERY ASSOCIATION
4175 Hwy 101 N
Tillamook, OR 97141-7770
Tel.: (503) 842-4481
Fax: (503) 842-6039
E-mail: jobs@tillamookcheese.com
Web Site: www.tillamookcheese.com
Sales Range: $250-299.9 Million
Approx. Number Employees: 470
Year Founded: 1909
Business Description:
Mfr. of Cheddar Cheese, Ice Cream, Butter & Whey Powder Products
S.I.C.: 2022; 5191
N.A.I.C.S.: 311513; 424910
Export
Advertising Expenditures: $100,000
Media: 2-6-8-13-16-18-23
Distr.: Reg.
Budget Set: Sept.
Personnel:
Harold Strunk *(CEO)*
Kathleen Holstad *(Mgr-Product Mktg)*
Brands & Products:
BABY LOAF
SNACK BAR
TILLAMOOK
TILLAMOOK CHEESEBURGER
Advertising Agencies:
Four Stories
1801 NW Northrup St #200
Portland, OR 97209
Tel.: (503) 471-0683

Leopold Ketel & Partners
112 SW 1st Ave
Portland, OR 97204
Tel.: (503) 295-1918
Fax: (503) 295-3601
Tillamook Ice Cream-Television Spots

TONE BROTHERS, INC.
(Sub. of Associated British Foods Plc)
2301 SE Tones Dr
Ankeny, IA 50021-8790
Tel.: (515) 965-2711
Fax: (515) 965-2803
Toll Free: (800) 964-8663
E-mail: spice_advice@tones.com
Web Site: www.tones.com
Approx. Number Employees: 650
Year Founded: 1873
Business Description:
Mfr. of Spices, Flavoring Extracts, Food Colors, Cake Decorations & Dehydrated Vegetables
S.I.C.: 2099
N.A.I.C.S.: 311942
Import Export
Advertising Expenditures: $1,000,000
Media: 2-6-7-10-13-19
Distr.: Intl.; Natl.
Budget Set: May
Brands & Products:
DECACAKE
DURKEE
FRENCH'S
SPICE ADVICE
SPICE ISLANDS
TONE'S
TRADER'S CHOICE

TOPCO HOLDINGS INC.
7711 Gross Point Rd
Skokie, IL 60077
Tel.: (847) 676-3030
Fax: (847) 676-4949
E-mail: webmaster@topco.com
Web Site: www.topco.com
Approx. Number Employees: 400
Year Founded: 1944
Business Description:
Holding Company; Perishables Equipment & Supplies Mfr
S.I.C.: 5141
N.A.I.C.S.: 424410
Import Export
Media: 2-9-10-17-25
Personnel:
Steven K. Lauer *(Pres & CEO)*
Ian Grossman *(Sr VP)*
Kenneth Guy *(Sr VP-Acct Mgmt)*
Daniel Mazur *(Sr VP)*
Brands & Products:
FOOD CLUB
FULL CIRCLE
PET CLUB
TOP CARE
TOP CREST
TOPCO

TOWNSENDS, INC.
22855 Dupont Blvd
Georgetown, DE 19947
Tel.: (302) 855-7100 (Admin)
Fax: (302) 777-6660
Toll Free: (800) 422-4425
E-mail: info@townsends.com
Web Site: www.townsends.com
Approx. Number Employees: 3,000
Year Founded: 1937
Business Description:
Poultry Processing Plant
S.I.C.: 0752
N.A.I.C.S.: 115210
Export
Media: 5-7-10-11-13
Personnel:
Gene Mcdonald *(VP-Sls & Mktg)*
Brands & Products:
CHEF'S SELECT
PERFECT BREAST
PRISTINE CUISINE
RUBY DRAGON
SERVING YOUR POULTRY NEEDS!
SPEEDY BIRD
TOWNSEND

TRADER VIC'S GOURMET PRODUCTS, INC.
5650 Imhoff Dr Ste I
Concord, CA 94520
Tel.: (925) 675-6400
Fax: (925) 691-9956
Web Site: www.tradervics.com
Approx. Number Employees: 9
Year Founded: 1948
Business Description:
Supplier of Specialty Foods, Salad Dressings & Cocktail Mixes
S.I.C.: 2035; 2099
N.A.I.C.S.: 311941; 311999
Export
Media: 4-8-19-21-26
Distr.: Intl.; Natl.
Personnel:
Karim Aghai *(Mgr)*
Phahon Bunlert *(Mgr)*
Wong Chai *(Mgr)*
Gion Fetz *(Mgr)*
Takehiko Fujii *(Mgr)*
Masahiro Kimura *(Mgr)*
Pronchai Butipunka *(Exec Chef)*

Key to Media (For complete agency information see *The Advertising Red Books-Agencies* edition):
1. Bus. Publs. 2. Cable T.V. 3. Catalogs & Directories. 4. Co-op Adv. 5. Consumer Mags. 6. D.M. to Bus. Estab.7. D.M. to Consumers 8. Daily Newsp. 9. Exhibits/Trade Shows 10. Foreign 11. Infomercial 12. Internet Adv.13. Multimedia 14. Network Radio 15. Network T.V. 16. Newsp. Distr. Mags. 17. Other 18. Outdoor (Posters, Transit) 19. Point of Purchase20. Premiums, Novelties 21. Product Samples 22. Special Events Mktg. 23. Spot Radio 24. Spot T.V. 25. Weekly Newsp. 26. Yellow Page Adv.

Trader Vic's Gourmet Products, Inc. — (Continued)

Brands & Products:
KAFE-LA-TE
SENOR PICO
TRADER VIC'S

TREE TOP, INC.
220 E 2nd Ave
Selah, WA 98942-0248
Tel.: (509) 697-7251
Fax: (509) 698-1421
Fax: (509) 698-1463
Toll Free: (800) 542-4055
E-mail: faq@treetop.com
Web Site: www.treetop.com
E-Mail For Key Personnel:
President: tstokes@treetop.com
Sales Director: ereinhart@treetop.com
Sales Range: $100-124.9 Million
Approx. Number Employees: 1,156
Year Founded: 1960
Business Description:
Fruit Juice Mfr
S.I.C.: 2037; 2086
N.A.I.C.S.: 311411; 312111
Export
Advertising Expenditures: $2,125,000
Media: 5-6-7-9-10-11-13-19
Distr.: Natl.
Budget Set: Aug.
Personnel:
Tom Stokes *(Pres & CEO)*
Lindsay Buckner *(Sr VP-Field Svcs)*
Dan Hagerty *(Sr VP-Mktg & Sls)*
Tom Hurson *(Sr VP-Ingredient & Food Svc Sls)*
Nancy Buck *(VP-HR)*
Brenda Moore *(Product Mgr-Special Channels & Digital Media)*
Brands & Products:
REAL FRUIT FROM REAL PEOPLE
SENECA
TREE TOP
TRIM
Advertising Agency:
Cole & Weber United
221 Yale Ave N Ste 600
Seattle, WA 98109
Tel.: (206) 447-9595
Fax: (206) 233-0178

TREEHOUSE FOODS, INC.
2 Westbrook Corp Ctr Ste 1070
Westchester, IL 60154
Mailing Address:
PO Box 19057
Green Bay, WI 54307-9057
Tel.: (708) 483-1300
Fax: (708) 409-1062
E-mail: info@treehousefoods.com
Web Site: www.treehousefoods.com
Approx. Sls.: $1,817,024,000
Approx. Number Employees: 4,000
Year Founded: 1962
Business Description:
Pickles, Relishes, Sauces, Dressings & Cranberry Products Processor & Retailer
S.I.C.: 2033; 2035; 5147
N.A.I.C.S.: 311421; 311941; 424470
Export
Media: 2-8-19-21-26
Distr.: Reg.
Budget Set: Oct.
Personnel:
Sam K. Reed *(Chm & CEO)*
David B. Vermylen *(Pres & COO)*
Dennis F. Riordan *(CFO & Sr VP)*
Alan T. Gambrel *(Sr VP-HR & Chief Admin Officer)*
Harry J. Walsh *(Sr VP-TreeHouse & Pres-Bay Valley Foods, LLC)*
Danny J. Coning *(Sr VP)*
Erik T. Kahler *(Sr VP-Corp Dev)*
Brands & Products:
BENNETT'S
CREMORA
E.D. SMITH
FARMAN'S
HABITANT
HOFFMAN HOUSE
MOCHA MIX
NALLEY'S
PETER PIPER
RODDENBERRY'S NORTHWOODS
SAN ANTONIO FARMS
SCHWARTZ
SECOND NATURE
STEINFELD
TREEHOUSE

TRI-UNION SEAFOODS LLC
(Sub. of Thai Union Frozen Products Public Company Limited)
(d/b/a Chicken of the Sea)
9330 Scranton Rd Ste 500
San Diego, CA 92121
Tel.: (858) 558-9662
Fax: (858) 597-4282
Web Site: www.chickenofthesea.com
Approx. Number Employees: 95
Year Founded: 1988
Business Description:
Packager of Tuna Fish
S.I.C.: 2091; 5146
N.A.I.C.S.: 311711; 424460
Personnel:
Schue Wing Chan *(Pres & CEO)*
John Sawyyer *(Sr VP-Mktg)*
Brands & Products:
CHICKEN OF THE SEA
Advertising Agency:
Campbell-Ewald Los Angeles
8687 Melrose Ave Ste G510
West Hollywood, CA 90069
Tel.: (310) 358-4800
account strategy, creative, production, and media planning and buying.

TRIAD FOODS GROUP
191 Waukegan Rd Ste 300 N Field
Winnetka, IL 60093
Tel.: (847) 441-9696
Fax: (847) 441-5976
Approx. Sls.: $175,000,000
Approx. Number Employees: 12
Business Description:
Holding Company
S.I.C.: 5147; 6719
N.A.I.C.S.: 424470; 551112
Media: 17-19
Personnel:
John Stewart *(CEO)*
Brian Brucker *(COO)*

TROPICANA PRODUCTS, INC.
(Sub. of PepsiCo Beverages Americas)
1001 13th Ave E
Bradenton, FL 34208-2656
Tel.: (941) 747-4461
Fax: (941) 742-3205
Toll Free: (800) 435-0744
E-mail: info@tropicana.com
Web Site: www.tropicana.com
Sales Range: $750-799.9 Million
Approx. Number Employees: 1,800
Business Description:
Fruit Beverage Mfr
S.I.C.: 2033; 2086
N.A.I.C.S.: 311421; 312111
Media: 6
Brands & Products:
ALVALLE
COPELLA
FRUI'VITA
LOOZA
TROPICANA 100
TROPICANA COASTAL GROVES
TROPICANA PURE PREMIUM
TROPICANA PURE TROPICS
TROPICANA SEASON'S BEST
TROPICANA SMOOTHIES
TROPICANA TOUCHE DE LAIT
TROPICANA TWISTER
Advertising Agency:
BBDO Toronto
2 Bloor St W
Toronto, ON M4W 3R6, Canada
Tel.: (416) 972-1505
Fax: (416) 972-5656

TROYER POTATO PRODUCTS, INC.
810 Rte 97 S
Waterford, PA 16441
Tel.: (814) 796-2611
Fax: (814) 796-6757
Toll Free: (800) 458-0485
E-mail: info@troyerfarms.com
Web Site: www.troyerfarms.com
Approx. Number Employees: 200
Year Founded: 1967
Business Description:
Potato Chips, Pretzels & Corn Snack Products Mfr
S.I.C.: 2096
N.A.I.C.S.: 311919
Media: 7-9-10-13-19-20-23-24
Distr.: Reg.
Brands & Products:
DAN DEE
GOLDEN WAVE
TROYER FARM

TURBOCHEF TECHNOLOGIES, INC.
(Sub. of The Middleby Corporation)
4240 International Pkwy Ste 105
Carrollton, TX 75007-1969
Tel.: (214) 379-6000
Fax: (214) 340-8477
Toll Free: (800) 90TURBO
E-mail: parts@turbochef.com
Web Site: www.turbochef.com
Approx. Rev.: $108,106,000
Approx. Number Employees: 258
Year Founded: 1991
Business Description:
Proprietary Cooking Technologies Designer & Developer
S.I.C.: 3631; 3589
N.A.I.C.S.: 335221; 333319
Advertising Expenditures: $8,900,000
Media: 2-7-8-10-13
Personnel:
Paul P. Lehr *(Pres)*
Peter J. Ashcraft *(Sr VP-Global Sls & Bus Dev)*
James Pearl *(Sr VP)*
David Shave *(VP-Global Sls & Mktg)*
Brands & Products:
AIRSPEED TECHNOLOGY
C3
CHEFCOMM PRO
COOK NAVIGATOR
COOKWHEEL
HIGH H BATCH
HIGH H CONVEYOR 2020
HIGH H CONVEYOR 3240
I3
I5
TORNADO
TORNADO 2
TURBOCHEF
Advertising Agency:
mono
(Partially Owned by MDC Partners)
3036 Hennepin Ave
Minneapolis, MN 55408
Tel.: (612) 822-4135
Fax: (612) 454-4950
TurboChef Oven

TURKEY HILL DAIRY, INC.
(Sub. of Dillon Companies, Inc.)
2601 River Rd
Conestoga, PA 17516
Tel.: (717) 872-5461
Fax: (717) 871-9884
Toll Free: (800) 693-2479
E-mail: crela@turkeyhill.com
Web Site: www.turkeyhill.com
Sales Range: $100-124.9 Million
Approx. Number Employees: 500
Year Founded: 1931
Business Description:
Frozen Desserts, Milk & Drinks Processor & Mfr
S.I.C.: 2026; 2024
N.A.I.C.S.: 311511; 311520
Export
Media: 3-4-5-7-8-10-16-18-19-20-21-22-23-24
Distr.: Natl.; Reg.
Personnel:
Thomas A. Canuso *(VP-Sls)*
Lisa Hutchinson *(Mgr-Mktg)*
Melissa Mattilio *(Mktg Mgr-Consumer)*
Ian Cox *(Mgr-Warehouse & Supply Chain)*
Brands & Products:
CHOCOLATE MINT MOOSE TRACKS
MOOSE TRACKS
NUT 'N SWEETIE
NUTTY CHOCOLATE MOOSE TRACKS
TURKEY HILL
VENICE
Advertising Agencies:
Brandesign
981 Rt 33 W
Monroe Township, NJ 08831
Tel.: (609) 490-9700

Harmelin Media
525 Righters Ferry Rd
Bala Cynwyd, PA 19004-1315
Tel.: (610) 668-7900
Fax: (610) 668-9548

Pavone
1006 Market St
Harrisburg, PA 17101-2811
Tel.: (717) 234-8886
Fax: (717) 234-8940

Key to Media (For complete agency information see *The Advertising Red Books-Agencies* edition):
1. Bus. Publs. 2. Cable T.V. 3. Catalogs & Directories. 4. Co-op Adv. 5. Consumer Mags. 6. D.M. to Bus. Estab.7. D.M. to Consumers
8. Daily Newsp. 9. Exhibits/Trade Shows 10. Foreign 11. Infomercial 12. Internet Adv.13. Multimedia 14. Network Radio
15. Network T.V. 16. Newsp. Distr. Mags. 17. Other 18. Outdoor (Posters, Transit) 19. Point of Purchase20. Premiums, Novelties
21. Product Samples 22. Special Events Mktg. 23. Spot Radio 24. Spot T.V. 25. Weekly Newsp. 26. Yellow Page Adv.

TYSON FOODS, INC.
2200 Don Tyson Pkwy
Springdale, AR 72762-6999
Tel.: (479) 290-4000
Fax: (479) 290-4061
Toll Free: (800) 643-3410
Web Site: www.tyson.com
Approx. Sls.: $28,430,000,000
Approx. Number Employees: 115,000
Year Founded: 1935
Business Description:
Poultry, Pork & Beef Products, Tortilla Products & Animal Feed Ingredients Processor & Marketer
S.I.C.: 2015; 0254; 0259; 0751; 2013; 2048; 2099
N.A.I.C.S.: 311615; 112340; 112390; 311119; 311611; 311613; 311830
Export
Advertising Expenditures: $505,000,000
Media: 3-5-6-13-15-16-21-23-24
Distr.: Natl.
Budget Set: Aug.
Personnel:
John H. Tyson *(Chm)*
Donald D. Smith *(Pres & CEO)*
Dennis Leatherby *(CFO & Exec VP)*
James V. Lochner *(COO)*
Gary Cooper *(CIO & Sr VP)*
Craig J. Hart *(Chief Acctg Officer, Sr VP & Controller)*
David L. Van Bebber *(Gen Counsel & Exec VP)*
Archie Schaffer, III *(Exec VP-Corp Affairs)*
Craig Bacon *(Sr VP-R & D)*
Chris Daniel *(Sr VP-Beef Margin Mgmt)*
Kenneth J. Kimbro *(Sr VP-HR)*
Noel White *(Sr Grp VP-Tyson Fresh Meats)*
Donnie D. King *(Grp VP-Poultry & Prepared Foods)*
Bernard F. G. Leonard *(Grp VP-Food Svc)*
Jeff Webster *(Grp VP)*
Ruth Ann Wisener *(VP-IR & Asst Sec)*
Libby Lawson *(VP-PR)*
Sue Quillin *(VP-Sls Svcs)*
Bill Welsh *(VP-Mktg)*
Meredith Austin *(Mgr-Mktg)*
Brands & Products:
ANCHO GRILL
BATTER GOLD
BATTERSWEET
BIGTIME
BONICI
BONICI ITALIAN
BURGERITO
CARB CONSCIOUS
CHICKEN BITES
CHICKEN CURLS
CHICKEN FOR THE BURGER CROWD
CHICKEN GLAZERS
CHIK-BITS
CHOMPERS
CONVENIENCE WITHOUT COMPROMISE
COOPE DU JOUR
CRACKIN' UP FOR BREAKFAST
CRISPITOS
CROSSFIRES
CRUMBLES
CRUSTANO'S
DO WELL
DOING WHAT'S RIGHT!
DRUMS OF FIRE
EVENCOOK
FAST FINISH
FEEDING YOU LIKE A FAMILY
FLAVOR-REDI
FOODWISE
G2 DOUBLE GLAZED
GOLD' N HONEY
GOURMET SELECTION
GREAT ON THE GRILL
HAVE YOU HAD YOUR PROTEIN TODAY
HAYDEN HOUSE MICRO MAGIC
HIP DIPPERS
HONEY STUNG
HOT DELI-FRIED CHICKEN
HOT WINGS
IT'S WHAT YOUR FAMILY DESERVES
KID TESTED KID APPOVED
LADY ASTER
LOBSTER DELIGHTS
MALLARD'S
NATURE'S FARM
NEW COURSES
ORIGINAL WRAPS
ORVILLE & WILBUR'S
OSTEOCARE
OVEN EASY
PACIFIC MATE
PB&J ROLLUPS
PEPPER STINGERS
PEPPERONI OHZ!
PICKENS' FRIED CHICKEN
PLANT'ABLES
POUR OVERS
POWERED BY TYSON
PREMIUM CUT
PROJECT A+
PROSPECT FARMS
PROUDLY POWERING THE WORLD
RESTAURANT FAVORITES
RUSSER
SLUGGERS
SOUTHWEST BLACKENED WRAPS
SPECIALTIES DELIVERY
STINGERS
SUNSET STRIPS
TASTY BIRD
TASTY SELECTIONS
TASTYRIB
TENDERPRESSED SELECT
THICK 'N CRISPY
TIME TRIMMERS
TOPNOTES
TYSON
TYSON CLASSIC ANGUS
TYSON DELI ROTISSERIE
TYSON HOLLY FARMS
TYSON MARINATED RAW BREADED
TYSON TO GO
TYSON'S PRIDE
VICTORY WINGS
VWINGS
WEAVER
WILSON
WING BREAK
WINGAMAJIG
WINGS OF FIRE
WINGS ON THE FLY
WRIGHT
THE WRIGHT WING!
W.W. FLYERS
Advertising Agencies:
Arnold Worldwide
101 Huntington Ave
Boston, MA 02199-7603
Tel.: (617) 587-8000
Fax: (617) 587-8004
Natural, Anitbiotic-Free Chicken

CJRW Northwest
(Sub. of Cranford Johnson Robinson Woods)
4100 Corporate Center Dr Ste 300
Springdale, AR 72762
Tel.: (479) 442-9803
Fax: (479) 442-3092
Toll Free: (800) 599-9803

Cranford Johnson Robinson Woods
303 W Capitol Ave
Little Rock, AR 72201-3531
Tel.: (501) 975-6251
Fax: (501) 975-4241
Toll Free: (888) 383-2579
(School Fundraising Programs)

E. Morris Communications, Inc.
820 N Orleans St Ste 402
Chicago, IL 60610
Tel.: (312) 943-2900
Fax: (312) 943-5856
Toll Free: (877) 916-0007
Chicken, Beef & Pork Products
Natural, Antibiotic-Free Chicken

GolinHarris
(Part of the Interpublic Group of Companies)
111 E Wacker Dr 11th Fl
Chicago, IL 60601-4306
Tel.: (312) 729-4000
Fax: (312) 729-4010
(Public Relations)
Consumer Products

U-SWIRL, INC.
(Formerly Healthy Fast Food, Inc.)
1175 American Pacific Ste C
Henderson, NV 89074
Tel.: (702) 586-8700
Fax: (702) 568-0898
E-mail: corporate@u-swirl.com
Web Site: www.u-swirl.com
Approx. Rev.: $2,610,208
Approx. Number Employees: 9
Year Founded: 2005
Business Description:
Fast Food Restaurant Franchiser, Owner & Operator
S.I.C.: 5812
N.A.I.C.S.: 722211
Advertising Expenditures: $86,582
Media: 8-9-16-24-25
Personnel:
Henry E. Cartwright *(Chm, Pres & CEO)*
Dana Cartwright *(Mgr-Corp Trng & Dir-Store Ops-U-Swirl)*

UNILEVER CANADA INC.
(Sub. of Unilever PLC)
160 Bloor Street East Suite 1500
Toronto, ON M4W 3R2, Canada
Tel.: (416) 964-1857
Fax: (416) 964-5197
E-mail: corpaffairs.canada@unilever.com
Web Site: www.unilever.ca
Sales Range: $1-4.9 Billion
Approx. Number Employees: 450
Year Founded: 1890
Business Description:
Production of Food Products
S.I.C.: 2099
N.A.I.C.S.: 311999
Export
Advertising Expenditures: $750,000
Media: 2-5-6-7-8-9-10-15-18-19-21-23-24
Distr.: Natl.
Budget Set: Aug.
Personnel:
Christofer Luxon *(Pres & CEO)*
John Coyne *(VP & Gen Counsel)*
Bobby Kwon *(VP-Fin-North America Customer Dev)*
Jon Affleck *(Dir-Mktg)*
Sharon MacLeod *(Dir-Brand Building-Dove, Vaseline, Q-tips, Lever 2000)*
Michael White *(Dir-HR)*
Brands & Products:
BOVRIL
BREYERS
CITRUS STIX
CREAMSICLE
FLEISCHMANN'S
FUDGSICLE
HELLMANN'S MAYONNAISE
I CAN'T BELIEVE IT'S NOT BUTTER!
IMPERIAL
KIDWICH
OXO
PG TIPS
QUEBON
RED ROSE
REVELLO
SALADA
VIENNETTA
Advertising Agencies:
DDB Canada
33 Bloor Street East Suite 1700
Toronto, ON M4W 3T4, Canada
Tel.: (416) 925-9819
Fax: (416) 925-4180

Ogilvy & Mather
33 Yonge St
Toronto, ON M5E 1X6, Canada
Tel.: (416) 367-3573
Fax: (416) 363-2088
(Dove, Hellmann's)

UNILEVER UNITED STATES, INC.
(Sub. of Unilever PLC)
800 Sylvan Ave
Englewood Cliffs, NJ 07632-3113
Tel.: (201) 894-4000
Fax: (201) 894-2186
Web Site: www.unileverusa.com
Approx. Number Employees: 14,000
Year Founded: 1906
Business Description:
Food, Home & Personal Care Products Mfr; Owned 56% by Unilever N.V. & 44% by Unilever PLC
S.I.C.: 2035; 2034; 2052; 2087; 2096; 2098; 2099; 5999
N.A.I.C.S.: 311941; 311423; 311821; 311823; 311919; 311930; 311942; 311999; 446199
Import Export
Advertising Expenditures: $77,400,000
Media: 3-6-13-14-15-24
Distr.: Intl.; Natl.
Personnel:
Antoine de Saint Affrique *(Pres-Food)*

Key to Media (For complete agency information see *The Advertising Red Books-Agencies* edition):
1. Bus. Publs. 2. Cable T.V. 3. Catalogs & Directories. 4. Co-op Adv. 5. Consumer Mags. 6. D.M. to Bus. Estab.7. D.M. to Consumers
8. Daily Newsp. 9. Exhibits/Trade Shows 10. Foreign 11. Infomercial 12. Internet Adv.13. Multimedia 14. Network Radio
15. Network T.V. 16. Newsp. Distr. Mags. 17. Other 18. Outdoor (Posters, Transit) 19. Point of Purchase20. Premiums, Novelties
21. Product Samples 22. Special Events Mktg. 23. Spot Radio 24. Spot T.V. 25. Weekly Newsp. 26. Yellow Page Adv.

Unilever United States, Inc. — (Continued)

Kevin Havelock *(Pres-Refreshment Category)*
Dave Lewis *(Pres-Personal Care)*
Peter Ter Kulve *(CEO-Benelux)*
Eugenio Minvielle *(Exec VP-North American Bus)*
John C. Bird *(Sr VP)*
Neal Vorchheimer *(Sr VP-Fin)*
Lisa Klauser *(VP-Consumer & Customer Solutions)*
Luis Di Como *(VP-Media-America)*
Sharon Rossi *(VP-Customer Dev (Sls))*
Brad Simmons *(VP-Media-US)*
Brian Manning *(Sr Dir-Mktg-Bertolli)*
Dana Emery *(Dir-Mktg)*
Sarah Jensen *(Dir-Mktg)*
Srini Sripad *(Brand Dir)*
Ami Striker *(Dir-Mktg-Sunsilk)*
David Burrows *(Brand Dir-Building)*
Fernando Machado *(Brand Dir-Vaseline-Global)*
Javier Martin *(Mktg Dir-Unilever)*
Douglas Balentine *(Dir-Nutrition Science)*
Donna Barker *(Dir-Mktg)*
Marc Shaw *(Dir-Integrated Mktg)*
Srini Sripada *(Dir-Mktg)*
Barret Roberts *(Sr Mgr-Lead Comm)*
Naomi Cohen *(Assoc Brand Mgr-I Can't Believe It's Not Butter)*
Tatiana Hansell *(Sr Brand Mgr-Multicultural)*
Rob Master *(Brand Mgr-Dove)*
Rachel Porges *(Brand Mgr-Bertolli)*
Barry Sands *(Sr Brand Mgr)*
Sam Spencer *(Assoc Brand Mgr-Magnum Ice Cream)*
Shane Kent *(Mgr-Brand Mktg-Axe)*
Andre Mahoney *(Mgr-Mktg)*
Joseph Vizcarra *(Mgr-Integrated Mktg)*

Advertising Agencies:
AM/PM Advertising Inc.
345 Claremont Ave Ste 26
Montclair, NJ 07042
Tel.: (973) 824-8600
Fax: (646) 366-1168

Amalgamated Advertising LLC
145 W 30th St 7th Fl
New York, NY 10001
Tel.: (646) 878-1700
Fax: (646) 878-1787
Ben & Jerry's

BBH New York
32 Avenue of the Americas 19th Fl
New York, NY 10013
Tel.: (212) 812-6600
Fax: (212) 242-4110
Cleans Your Balls
— Armando Turco *(Acct Mgr)*

Braxton Strategic Group
54 Westbrook Rd
Westfield, NJ 07090
Tel.: (908) 209-3331

Burson-Marsteller
(Part of Young & Rubicam Brands, a Sub. of WPP Group plc)
230 Park Ave S
New York, NY 10003-1566
Tel.: (212) 614-4000
Fax: (212) 598-5407

Daniel J. Edelman, Inc.
(d/b/a Edelman)
200 E Randolph St Fl 63
Chicago, IL 60601-6705
Tel.: (312) 240-3000
Fax: (312) 240-2900

DDB Worldwide Communications Group Inc.
(Sub. of Omnicom Group, Inc.)
(Corporate Headquarters)
437 Madison Ave 5nd Fl
New York, NY 10022-7001
Tel.: (212) 415-2000
Fax: (212) 415-3414
(Savory Foods & Knorr in North America, Southern Europe, the United Kingdom, France & the Middle East)

Deutsch New York
111 8th Ave 14th Fl
New York, NY 10011
Tel.: (212) 605-8000

droga5
400 Lafayette 5th Fl
New York, NY 10003
Tel.: (917) 237-8888
Fax: (917) 237-8889
Suave

Edelman
250 Hudson St
New York, NY 10013
Tel.: (212) 768-0550
Fax: (212) 704-0128
Multicultural

The Edelman Group
110 W 40th St Ste 2302
New York, NY 10018
Tel.: (212) 825-9200
Fax: (212) 825-1900
Dove
— Randi Liodice *(Acct Exec)*
— Jessica Axelrod *(Acct Exec)*

Euro RSCG 4D Impact
2885 Pacific Dr Ste A
Norcross, GA 30071-1807
Tel.: (888) 788-5918
Fax: (770) 248-9014
Toll Free: (888) 788-5918

FKM
1800 W Loop S Ste 2100
Houston, TX 77027
Tel.: (713) 862-5100
Fax: (713) 869-6560
Bertolli Olive Oil

GolinHarris
(Part of the Interpublic Group of Companies)
111 E Wacker Dr 11th Fl
Chicago, IL 60601-4306
Tel.: (312) 729-4000
Fax: (312) 729-4010
Bertolli
Breyers
Klondike
— Lindsey Auslander *(Acct Exec)*

J. Walter Thompson Company
(d/b/a JWT)
466 Lexington Ave
New York, NY 10017-3140
Tel.: (212) 210-7000
Fax: (212) 210-7299
(Savory Foods & Knorr in Northern Europe, Latin America & Asia Pacific)
Sunsilk

M. Booth & Associates
300 Park Ave S 12th Fl
New York, NY 10010
Tel.: (212) 481-7000
Fax: (212) 481-9440
I Can't Believe It's Not Butter

Mekanism, Inc.
640 Second St 3rd Fl
San Francisco, CA 94107
Tel.: (415) 908-4000
Fax: (415) 908-3993
Lipton Brisk

Mindshare
498 7th Ave
New York, NY 10018
Tel.: (212) 297-7000
Fax: (212) 297-7001
(Media Agency for U.S.)
Axe
Degree
Dove
I Can't Believe It's Not Butter
Lynx
Suave
Sunsilk

Ogilvy & Mather
350 W Mart Ctr Dr Ste 1100
Chicago, IL 60654-1866
Tel.: (312) 856-8200
Fax: (312) 856-8207

Ogilvy & Mather
(Sub. of WPP Group plc)
636 11th Ave
New York, NY 10036
Tel.: (212) 237-4000
Fax: (212) 237-5123
Promise
— Cory Martin *(Acct Exec)*
— Alison Gragnano *(Exec Dir-Creative)*

OgilvyAction
350 W Mart Center Dr Ste 1100
Chicago, IL 60654-1866
Tel.: (312) 527-3900
Fax: (312) 527-3327

PointRoll Inc.
951 E Hector St
Conshohocken, PA 19428
Tel.: (267) 558-1300
Fax: (267) 285-1141
Toll Free: (800) 203-6956

Research Development & Promotions
(d/b/a RDP)
360 Menores Ave
Coral Gables, FL 33134
Tel.: (305) 445-4997
Fax: (305) 445-4221

Story Worldwide
20 Marshall St Ste 220
South Norwalk, CT 06854
Tel.: (203) 831-8700
Fax: (203) 299-0068
I Can't Believe It's Not Butter

Talent Resources
124 E 36th St Ste A
New York, NY 10016
Tel.: (212) 725-1005
Fax: (212) 725-0272

The VIA Group LLC
34 Danforth St Ste 309
Portland, ME 04101
Tel.: (207) 221-3000
Fax: (207) 761-9422

Weber Shandwick
(Sub. of The Interpublic Group of Companies)
919 3rd Ave
New York, NY 10022
Tel.: (212) 445-8000
Fax: (212) 445-8001
ALL
Degree
Hellmann's
Pond's
— Donna Walter *(Acct Exec)*
— Janna Porrevecchio *(Acct Exec)*
— Jennifer Scheftt *(Acct Exec)*
— Briana Haas *(Acct Exec-Pond's)*

Zullo Associates
1 Academy St
Princeton, NJ 08540
Tel.: (609) 683-1800
Fax: (609) 683-4773

UNISEA FOODS, INC.

(Sub. of Nippon Suisan Kaisha, Ltd.)
15400 NE 90th St Po 97019
Redmond, WA 98052-3524
Tel.: (425) 881-8181
Fax: (425) 861-5239
E-mail: info@unisea.com
Web Site: www.unisea.com
Approx. Sls.: $125,000,000
Approx. Number Employees: 50
Year Founded: 1974
Business Description:
Fish Products Processor
S.I.C.: 2092; 2091
N.A.I.C.S.: 311712; 311711
Import Export
Advertising Expenditures: $600,000
Media: 2-7-9-10-25
Distr.: Intl.; Natl.
Budget Set: Oct.
Personnel:
Terry Shaff *(Pres & CEO)*
Jim Donahue *(Dir-Mktg)*
Brands & Products:
CASCADE SELECT
DUTCH HARBOR
PRIDE OF ALASKA
UNISEA

UNITED DAIRY FARMERS, INC.

3955 Montgomery Rd
Cincinnati, OH 45212
Tel.: (513) 396-8700
Fax: (513) 396-8736
Toll Free: (800) 654-2809
E-mail: consumerrelations@udfinc.com
Web Site: www.udfinc.com
Approx. Number Employees: 75,300
Year Founded: 1940
Business Description:
Chain of Convenience Stores; Milk Processing, Ice Cream & Ices; Frozen Dairy Desserts

Key to Media (For complete agency information see *The Advertising Red Books-Agencies* edition):
1. Bus. Publs. 2. Cable T.V. 3. Catalogs & Directories. 4. Co-op Adv. 5. Consumer Mags. 6. D.M. to Bus. Estab.7. D.M. to Consumers 8. Daily Newsp. 9. Exhibits/Trade Shows 10. Foreign 11. Infomercial 12. Internet Adv.13. Multimedia 14. Network Radio 15. Network T.V. 16. Newsp. Distr. Mags. 17. Other 18. Outdoor (Posters, Transit) 19. Point of Purchase20. Premiums, Novelties 21. Product Samples 22. Special Events Mktg. 23. Spot Radio 24. Spot T.V. 25. Weekly Newsp. 26. Yellow Page Adv.

S.I.C.: 5411; 5143
N.A.I.C.S.: 445120; 424430
Advertising Expenditures: $1,000,000
Media: 4-7-8-9-10-18-19-20-23-24
Distr.: Direct to Consumer; Reg.
Personnel:
Brad Lindner *(Pres & CEO)*
Marilyn Mitchell *(CFO)*
John Luebbers *(VP-Sls & Mktg)*
David Lindner *(Dir-Mktg)*
Brands & Products:
BEECHWOOD FARMS
CHERRY CORDIAL
DEEP FREEZE
FARMERS MARKET
HAWAIIAN SUNDAE
HOMEMADE BRAND
KRAZY KREAMS
MAGIC MALT
MALTED MICRO SHAKE
MICRO MALT
MICROWAVEABLE MALT
MICROWAVEABLE SHAKE
MINUTE MALT
MINUTE SHAKE
NOTHING TASTES BETTER THAN HOMEMADE.
PREMIUM HOMEMADE ICE CREAM
QUEEN CITY ICE
UNITED DAIRY FARMERS
WOW COW
Advertising Agency:
Kling Marketing & Advertising
550 Anna Marie Ln
Cincinnati, OH 45247
Tel.: (513) 385-7370

UNITED EGG PRODUCERS

1720 Windward Concourse Ste 230
Alpharetta, GA 30005-2289
Tel.: (770) 360-9220
Fax: (770) 360-7058
E-mail: info@unitedegg.org
Web Site: www.unitedegg.org
Approx. Rev.: $19,000,000
Approx. Number Employees: 10
Year Founded: 1968
Business Description:
Food Marketing Cooperative
S.I.C.: 8611
N.A.I.C.S.: 813910
Media: 2-10-17
Personnel:
Gene Gregory *(Pres & CEO)*
Chad Gregory *(Sr VP)*
Sherry Shedd *(VP-Fin)*

UNITED NATURAL FOODS, INC.

313 Iron Horse Way
Providence, RI 02908
Tel.: (401) 528-0634
Toll Free: (800) 877-8898
Web Site: www.unfi.com
Approx. Sls.: $4,530,015,000
Approx. Number Employees: 6,900
Year Founded: 1985
Business Description:
Natural Foods Distr
S.I.C.: 5149; 5122; 5141
N.A.I.C.S.: 424490; 424210; 424410
Advertising Expenditures: $6,400,000
Media: 4-8-10-13-14-15-18-19-20-26
Personnel:
Michael S. Funk *(Chm)*
Gordon D. Barker *(Vice Chm)*
Steven L. Spinner *(Pres & CEO)*
Mark E. Shamber *(CFO, Treas & Sr VP)*
Eric A. Dorne *(CIO & Sr VP)*
Joseph J. Traficanti *(Chief Compliance Officer, Gen Counsel & Sr VP)*
Thomas A. Dziki *(Chief HR Officer, Chief Sustainability Officer & Sr VP)*
Thomas J. Grillea *(Pres-Woodstock Farms Mfg & Select Nutrition Distr)*
Kurt Luttecke *(Pres-Western Region)*
David A. Matthews *(Pres-UNFI Intl)*
Craig H. Smith *(Pres-Eastern Reg)*
Sean Griffin *(Sr VP-Natl Distr)*
John Stern *(Sr VP)*
Brands & Products:
AMERICA'S PREMIER CERTIFIED ORGANIC DISTRIBUTOR
BLUE MARBLE
DRIVEN BY NATURE
HEALTHY CLIPPINGS
UNFI
Advertising Agency:
The MWW Group
700 13th St NW
Washington, DC 20006
Tel.: (202) 585-2270
Fax: (202) 585-2273

UNITED STATES BAKERY

315 NE 10th Ave
Portland, OR 97232-2712
Tel.: (503) 731-5670
Fax: (503) 731-4888
E-mail: bakery_info@usbakery.com
Web Site: www.usbakery.com
Approx. Number Employees: 15
Year Founded: 1906
Business Description:
Commercial Bakery
S.I.C.: 2051
N.A.I.C.S.: 311812
Advertising Expenditures: $1,000,000
Media: 2-7-10-17
Distr.: Reg.
Budget Set: Nov.
Personnel:
Mark Albers *(Pres & COO)*
Bob Albers *(CEO)*
Jerry Boness *(CFO)*
Brands & Products:
AUNT HATTIE'S
BAY CITY
FRANZ
HOME RUN
NEW YORK BAGEL BOYS
OUTBACK
ROMAN MEAL
SEATTLE INTERNATIONAL
SMART NUTRITION
SNYDER'S
SVENHARD'S
WILLIAMS'

UNITED STATES SUGAR CORPORATION

111 Ponce de Leon Ave
Clewiston, FL 33440-3032
Tel.: (863) 983-8121
Fax: (863) 983-8181
Web Site: www.ussugar.com
Approx. Number Employees: 2,000
Year Founded: 1931
Business Description:
Sugar Cane, Raw & Refined Sugar & Molasses Producer
S.I.C.: 0133; 2061
N.A.I.C.S.: 111930; 311311
Media: 2-9-10-23-24-25
Distr.: Natl.; Reg.
Budget Set: Oct.
Personnel:
Robert H. Buker *(CEO)*
Gerard Bernard *(CFO & Exec VP)*
Carl Stringer *(CIO)*
Robert E. Coker *(Sr VP-Pub Affairs)*
Malcolm S. Wade *(Sr VP-Corp Strategy & Bus Dev)*
Charles F. Shide *(VP-HR)*
Judy C. Sanchez *(Dir-Corp Comm & Pub Affairs)*
Brands & Products:
SUGA-LIK
UNITED STATES SUGAR
Advertising Agency:
Wragg & Casas Public Relations, Inc.
1000 Brickell Ave Ste 400
Miami, FL 33131
Tel.: (305) 372-1234
Fax: (305) 372-8565

UPSTATE NIAGARA COOPERATIVE, INC.

25 Anderson Rd
Buffalo, NY 14225-4905
Tel.: (716) 892-3156
Fax: (716) 892-3157
E-mail: emailus@upstatefarms.com
Web Site: www.upstatefarms.com
Approx. Number Employees: 600
Year Founded: 1965
Business Description:
Food & Beverage Cooperative
S.I.C.: 2026; 2033
N.A.I.C.S.: 311511; 311421
Media: 2-5-7-9-10-13-18-19-20-21-22-23
Distr.: Reg.
Personnel:
Dan Wolf *(Pres)*
Bob Hall *(CEO)*
Timothy Harner *(Gen Counsel)*
Jim Murphy *(Dir-Quality Ops)*
Brands & Products:
BISON
INTENSE MILKS
TASTE UPSTATE FRESHNESS
UPSTATE FARMS
Advertising Agencies:
Butler/Till Media Services, Inc.
2349 Monroe Ave
Rochester, NY 14618
Tel.: (585) 473-3740
Fax: (585) 473-3862

Cenergy Communications, LLC (d/b/a Cenergy Sports)
728 Main St
East Aurora, NY 14052
Tel.: (716) 652-7400
Fax: (716) 652-7161
Crave

U.S. PREMIUM BEEF, LLC

12200 N Ambassador Dr
Kansas City, MO 64163-1244
Mailing Address:
PO Box 20103
Kansas City, MO 64195
Tel.: (816) 713-8800
Fax: (816) 713-8810
Toll Free: (866) 877-2525
E-mail: uspb@uspb.com
Web Site: www.uspremiumbeef.com
Approx. Sls.: $5,807,929,000
Approx. Number Employees: 9
Year Founded: 1996
Business Description:
Beef Marketing Services
S.I.C.: 9641; 0212; 0751
N.A.I.C.S.: 926140; 112111; 311611
Advertising Expenditures: $481,595
Personnel:
Mark Gardiner *(Chm)*
Steven D. Hunt *(CEO)*
Scott Miller *(CFO & Exec VP)*
Stan Linville *(COO & Exec VP)*
Danielle Imel *(Treas & Sr VP)*
Bill Miller *(VP-Comm)*
Tracy Thomas *(VP-Mktg)*
Lisa Phillips *(Dir-Ops)*

UTZ QUALITY FOODS, INC.

900 High St
Hanover, PA 17331-1639
Tel.: (717) 637-6644
Fax: (717) 633-5102
Toll Free: (800) 367-7629
E-mail: dlissette@utzsnacks.com
Web Site: www.utzsnacks.com
Sales Range: $150-199.9 Million
Approx. Number Employees: 2,200
Year Founded: 1921
Business Description:
Mfr. & Sales of Potato Chips, Pretzels, Popcorn & Gift Snacks
S.I.C.: 2096
N.A.I.C.S.: 311919
Media: 5-8-13-18-19-20-23-24-26
Distr.: Natl.
Personnel:
Tom Dempsey *(Pres)*
Todd Staub *(CFO & VP)*
Dylan Lissette *(Exec VP-Sls & Mktg)*
Les Erving *(Grp VP-Sls)*
George Neidere *(VP-HR)*
Tiffani Justh *(Brand Mgr)*
Brands & Products:
GRANDMA UTZ
HOME STYLE
KETTLE CLASSICS
MYSTIC
NATURAL
ORGANIC
REGULAR
SELECT
UTZ
Advertising Agency:
MGH, Inc.
100 Painters Mill Rd Ste 600
Owings Mills, MD 21117-7305
Tel.: (410) 902-5000
Fax: (410) 902-8712

VALLEY FIG GROWERS, INC.

2028 S 3rd St
Fresno, CA 93702
Tel.: (559) 237-3893
Fax: (559) 237-3898
E-mail: info@valleyfig.com
Web Site: www.valleyfig.com
Sales Range: $10-24.9 Million
Approx. Number Employees: 180
Year Founded: 1959
Business Description:
Figs Producer
S.I.C.: 0723; 2033
N.A.I.C.S.: 115114; 311421
Advertising Expenditures: $500,000
Media: 2-10-13
Personnel:
Paul Mesple *(Chm)*

Key to Media (For complete agency information see *The Advertising Red Books-Agencies* edition):
1. Bus. Publs. 2. Cable T.V. 3. Catalogs & Directories. 4. Co-op Adv. 5. Consumer Mags. 6. D.M. to Bus. Estab.7. D.M. to Consumers 8. Daily Newsp. 9. Exhibits/Trade Shows 10. Foreign 11. Infomercial 12. Internet Adv.13. Multimedia 14. Network Radio 15. Network T.V. 16. Newsp. Distr. Mags. 17. Other 18. Outdoor (Posters, Transit) 19. Point of Purchase20. Premiums, Novelties 21. Product Samples 22. Special Events Mktg. 23. Spot Radio 24. Spot T.V. 25. Weekly Newsp. 26. Yellow Page Adv.

Valley Fig Growers, Inc. — (Continued)

Michael Emigh *(Pres)*
Linda Cain *(VP-Mktg)*
James Gargiulo *(VP-Fin)*

Brands & Products:
BLUE RIBBON
FIGLETS
OLD ORCHARD
ORCHARD CHOICE
SUN-MAID
VALLEY FIG GROWERS

VALLEY ISLE PRODUCE, INC.

(d/b/a VIP Foodservice)
74 Hobron Ave PO Box 517
Kahului, HI 96732
Tel.: (808) 877-5055
Fax: (808) 877-4960
E-mail: contact@vipfoodservice.com
Web Site: www.vipfoodservice.com
Approx. Number Employees: 150
Year Founded: 1951
Business Description:
Packaged Frozen Goods; Fresh Fruits & Vegetables, Seafoods; General Line of Groceries; Fresh Meats, Paper Products & Sanitation Supplies Wholesale Distr
S.I.C.: 5142; 5141
N.A.I.C.S.: 424420; 424410
Media: 20-23
Personnel:
Nelson Okumura *(Pres)*
Alton Nakagawa *(VP-Fin)*
Stephen Smith *(VP-Pur)*
Lori Jio *(Mgr-HR)*

VAN HOUTTE, INC.

(Sub. of Green Mountain Coffee Roasters, Inc.)
8300 19th Ave
Montreal, QC H1Z 4J8, Canada
Tel.: (514) 593-7711
Fax: (514) 593-8755
Toll Free: (877) 593-7722
E-mail: webmaster@vanhoutte.com
Web Site: www.vanhoutte.com
Sales Range: $350-399.9 Million
Approx. Number Employees: 1,800
Year Founded: 1919
Business Description:
Coffee & Brewing Products Mfr
S.I.C.: 2095
N.A.I.C.S.: 311920
Media: 2-4-7-8-10-13-18-21-22
Personnel:
Gerard Geoffrion *(Pres & CEO)*
Michel Slight *(CFO & VP)*
Sylvain Toutant *(COO)*
Jean-Olivier Boucher *(Chief Legal Officer & VP)*
Robert Mann *(Sr VP-Coffee Svcs-Western Reg)*
Denis Sarrazin *(Sr VP-Coffee Svcs-Eastern Reg)*
Francois de l'Etoile *(VP & Gen Mgr-Cafe-Bistro Div)*
Denis Graus *(VP-Sls-Retail-Quebec)*
Michel Lajoie *(VP-Sls-Retail-Ontario/Western)*
Alberto Mouron *(VP-IT)*
Isabelle Pasquet-Geairon *(VP-Mktg)*
Marie-Claude Dessureault *(Dir-Coffee Expertise, Dev & Comm Tools)*
Brands & Products:
BRULERIE MONT ROYAL
BRULERIE ST. DENIS
LES CAFES ORIENT EXPRESS
VAN HOUTTE
Advertising Agencies:
Chapeau Publicity & Design
4030 Cote-Vertu Ste 104
Saint Laurent, QC H4R 1N4, Canada
Tel.: (514) 284-5489

Espresso communication et design
3863 boul St-Laurent bur 207
Montreal, QC H2W 1Y1, Canada
Tel.: (514) 286-9696
Fax: (514) 284-9152

VENTRE PACKING COMPANY, INC.

6050 Ct St Rd
Syracuse, NY 13206-1711
Tel.: (315) 463-2384
Fax: (315) 463-5897
Toll Free: (888) 472-8237
E-mail: enrico@enricos-ventre.com
Web Site: www.ventre.com
E-Mail For Key Personnel:
President: mventre@ventre.com
Approx. Number Employees: 50
Year Founded: 1938
Business Description:
Mfr. & Retailer of Spaghetti Sauces, Mexican Sauces, Seafood Cocktail Sauces, BBQ Sauces, Salsas, Ketchup & Dips
S.I.C.: 2033; 2099
N.A.I.C.S.: 311421; 311999
Import Export
Media: 1-4-5-6-8-10-17-18-20-25
Distr.: Natl.
Budget Set: Sept.
Personnel:
Martin Ventre *(Pres & CEO)*
Frank Ventre, Jr. *(Gen Counsel)*
Brands & Products:
DINO'S
ENRICO
ENRICO'S
MEDEI CUISINE

VENTURA COASTAL LLC

2325 Vista Del Mar Dr PO Box 69
Ventura, CA 93001-3751
Mailing Address:
PO Box 69
Ventura, CA 93001
Tel.: (805) 653-7000
Fax: (805) 653-7777
E-mail: rtorres@vcoastal.com
Sales Range: $10-24.9 Million
Approx. Number Employees: 100
Year Founded: 1952
Business Description:
Citrus Products
S.I.C.: 2037; 2087
N.A.I.C.S.: 311411; 311930
Import Export
Media: 2-7-10
Personnel:
William Borgers *(Pres & CEO)*
Joan Schomp *(VP-HR)*
Deanne Hoyt *(Mgr-Indus Sls)*

VENTURA FOODS, LLC

(Joint Venture of Mitsui & Co., Ltd. & CHS INC.)
40 Pointe Dr
Brea, CA 92821
Tel.: (714) 257-3700
Fax: (714) 257-3702
Toll Free: (877) 836-8872
Web Site: www.venturafoods.com
Sales Range: $650-699.9 Million
Approx. Number Employees: 1,840
Year Founded: 1995
Business Description:
Salad & Cooking Oil, Dairy Products, Flavorings & Spices Mfr
S.I.C.: 2079; 5149
N.A.I.C.S.: 311225; 424490
Import Export
Advertising Expenditures: $250,000
Media: 1-2-4-5-6-7-10-19-20-21
Distr.: Intl.; Natl.
Budget Set: Sept.
Personnel:
Christopher Furman *(Pres & CEO)*
Thomas G. McCarley *(Exec VP)*
B. Kelly Brintle *(Sr VP-Corp Strategy & Bus Devel)*
Steve Geske *(Sr VP)*
Terry Splane *(VP-Mktg)*
Brands & Products:
CHEF'S PRIDE
CHURN SPREAD
CINEMA GOLD
CITATION
CLASSIC GOURMET
COCOPOP BARS
DRESS ALL
DRI POP
EXTEND
GOLD-N-SOFT
GOLD-N-SWEET
GOLDEN TOP
GRANDIOSO
LOU ANA
MEL-FRY
MOR GOLD PLUS
PERFECTO PEANUT
PHASE
POP-ALL
POP TOP
POP'N LITE
POPPIN' TOPPIN'
PRIDE OF LIFE
SAFFOLA
SALAD BISTRO
SAVORY
SUNBURST
SUNGLOW
TRIUMPH
VENTURA
VENTURA CONCIERGE CUSTOMER
VO-POP
WHITE CAP
Advertising Agencies:
The Food Group (Los Angeles)
9714 Variel Ave
Chatsworth, CA 91311
Tel.: (818) 993-0304
Fax: (818) 993-0428
(Food Service Adv. - Gold N' Sweet, Classic Gourmet, Extend, White Cap, Savory)

Vertical Marketing Network LLC
15147 Woodlawn Ave
Tustin, CA 92780
Tel.: (714) 258-2400, ext. 420
Fax: (714) 258-2409

VERYFINE PRODUCTS, INC.

(Sub. of Sunny Delight Beverages Co.)
20 Harvard Rd
Littleton, MA 01460
Mailing Address:
PO Box 8005
Littleton, MA 01460
Tel.: (978) 742-3365
Fax: (978) 952-6245
Toll Free: (800) VERYFINE
E-mail: info@veryfine.com
Web Site: www.veryfine.com
E-Mail For Key Personnel:
Sales Director: retailsales@veryfine.com
Sales Range: $150-199.9 Million
Approx. Number Employees: 400
Year Founded: 1865
Business Description:
Pure Fruit Juices, Juice Cocktails & Juice Drinks Mfr & Sales
S.I.C.: 2086
N.A.I.C.S.: 312111
Media: 2-5-6-9-10-14-18-19-20-21-24
Distr.: Natl.
Budget Set: Oct.
Personnel:
Dan Gray *(Gen Mgr)*
Brands & Products:
FRUIT20
FRUIT2O PLUS
HEALTHY SOLUTIONS
NECTARS
VERYFINE
VERYFINE CHILLERS

VIENNA SAUSAGE MFG. CO.

2501 N Damen Ave
Chicago, IL 60647-2101
Tel.: (773) 278-7800
Fax: (773) 278-4759
Toll Free: (800) 366-3647
E-mail: info@viennabeef.com
Web Site: www.viennabeef.com
Approx. Number Employees: 300
Year Founded: 1893
Business Description:
Food Processor & Distr
S.I.C.: 5147; 5149
N.A.I.C.S.: 424470; 424490
Advertising Expenditures: $1,000,000
Media: 1-2-4-5-6-7-9-10-18-19-21
Distr.: Intl.; Natl.
Budget Set: Feb.
Personnel:
James W. Bodman *(CEO)*
Brands & Products:
BAGELDOG
BISTRO
CHIPICO
CORKY'S
FIREDOG
PIE PIPER
SPORT PEPPER
VIENNA

VIRGINIA DARE EXTRACT CO., INC.

882 3rd Ave
Brooklyn, NY 11232
Tel.: (718) 788-1776
Fax: (718) 768-3978
Toll Free: (800) 847-4500
E-mail: webinfo@virginiadare.com
Web Site: www.virginiadare.com
Approx. Number Employees: 175
Year Founded: 1923
Business Description:
Mfr. of Vanilla and other Flavoring Extracts for Food Products
S.I.C.: 2087
N.A.I.C.S.: 311930
Export
Advertising Expenditures: $200,000

Key to Media (For complete agency information see *The Advertising Red Books-Agencies* edition):
1. Bus. Publs. 2. Cable T.V. 3. Catalogs & Directories. 4. Co-op Adv. 5. Consumer Mags. 6. D.M. to Bus. Estab.7. D.M. to Consumers 8. Daily Newsp. 9. Exhibits/Trade Shows 10. Foreign 11. Infomercial 12. Internet Adv.13. Multimedia 14. Network Radio 15. Network T.V. 16. Newsp. Distr. Mags. 17. Other 18. Outdoor (Posters, Transit) 19. Point of Purchase20. Premiums, Novelties 21. Product Samples 22. Special Events Mktg. 23. Spot Radio 24. Spot T.V. 25. Weekly Newsp. 26. Yellow Page Adv.

Media: 2-4-10-20-21
Distr.: Intl.; Natl.
Budget Set: Sept.
Personnel:
Howard Smith, Jr. *(Pres)*
Stephen Balter *(VP-Fin)*
Paul Graffigna *(VP-Mktg)*
Christina Smith *(VP-Pur)*
Brands & Products:
PROSWEET
THINK OF US AS FALVOR
VIRGINIA DARE
Advertising Agency:
Poutray Pekar Associates
344 W Main St
Milford, CT 06460
Tel.: (203) 283-9511
Fax: (203) 283-9514
(Flavors)
— Carol Pekar *(Partner & Creative Dir.)*

VITA FOOD PRODUCTS, INC.
2222 W Lake St
Chicago, IL 60612-2210
Tel.: (312) 738-4500
Fax: (312) 738-3215
Web Site: www.vitafoodproducts.com
Approx. Sls.: $53,865,698
Approx. Number Employees: 178
Year Founded: 1928
Business Description:
Herring & Smoked-Fish Products
S.I.C.: 2091; 5146
N.A.I.C.S.: 311711; 424460
Export
Advertising Expenditures: $284,000
Media: 2-6-9-10-22-26
Distr.: Natl.
Budget Set: Aug.
Personnel:
Clifford K. Bolen *(Pres & CEO)*
Clark L. Feldman *(Sec & Exec VP)*
Brands & Products:
ELF
GRAND ISLE
OAK HILL FARMS
SCORNED WOMAN
VIRGINIA BRAND
VITA

WALDEN FARMS, INC.
1209 W St Georges Ave
Linden, NJ 07036-6117
Tel.: (908) 925-9494
Fax: (908) 925-9537
Toll Free: (800) 229-1706
E-mail: info@waldenfarms.com
Web Site: www.waldenfarms.com
Sales Range: $1-9.9 Million
Approx. Number Employees: 50
Year Founded: 1966
Business Description:
Mfr. of Salad Dressings, Dips & Fruit Spreads
S.I.C.: 2035
N.A.I.C.S.: 311941
Export
Advertising Expenditures: $260,000
Media: 2-4-6-7-8-9-13
Distr.: Natl.
Budget Set: Feb.
Personnel:
Mitchell Berko *(Pres)*
Brands & Products:
WALDEN FARMS

WATKINS INCORPORATED
150 Liberty St
Winona, MN 55987-3707
Tel.: (507) 457-3300
Fax: (507) 452-6723
Web Site: www.watkinsonline.com
Sales Range: $25-49.9 Million
Approx. Number Employees: 350
Year Founded: 1868
Business Description:
Mfr. & Retailer of Extracts, Spices, Health/Beauty Aids, Insecticides, Medicines & Food Specialties
S.I.C.: 2099; 2841
N.A.I.C.S.: 311942; 325611
Import Export
Advertising Expenditures: $850,000
Media: 1-4-8-10-15-20-21
Distr.: Direct to Consumer; Natl.
Budget Set: Sept.
Personnel:
Irwin Jacobs *(Owner)*
Mark E. Jacobs *(Pres)*
Stephen Nett *(CFO)*
J.R. Rigeley *(Exec VP-Sls & Mktg-J.R. Watkins Naturals)*
Brands & Products:
APOTHECARY
FIBERAID
FRESH WASH
J.R WATKINS
OLD RED BARN
PETRO-CARBO
SETTLZ
SOYNILLA
THERATEA
THERATRIM

WEILER & COMPANY, INC.
(Sub. of Henry Crown & Company)
1116 E Main St
Whitewater, WI 53190-2022
Tel.: (262) 473-5254
Fax: (262) 473-5867
E-mail: sales@weilerinc.com
Web Site: www.weilerinc.com
E-Mail For Key Personnel:
Sales Director: sales@weilerinc.com
Approx. Number Employees: 130
Year Founded: 1945
Business Description:
Heavy Duty Food Processing Equipment
S.I.C.: 3556
N.A.I.C.S.: 333294
Media: 7-10
Personnel:
Bill Wight *(VP-Product Dev & Engrg)*
Rick Hendrickson *(Mgr-Customer Svc)*
Mike Stapleton *(Mgr-Product Dev)*
Dave Stone *(Mgr-Mixing, Grinding, Europe & Middle East)*
Andy Wischmann *(Mgr-Sls-Intl)*
Brands & Products:
DOMINATOR
PIRANHA
WEILER

WELCH FOODS INC.
(Sub. of National Grape Co-Op Association, Inc.)
3 Concord Farms 575 Virginia Rd
Concord, MA 01742-9101
Tel.: (978) 371-1000
Fax: (978) 371-3860
Web Site: www.welchs.com
Approx. Number Employees: 1,258
Year Founded: 1869
Business Description:
Grape, Cranberry & Tomato Juices; Concentrates; Light Juice Cocktails; Grape Jelly & Jam; Squeezable Jelly, Jam & Preserves; Fruit Spreads Mfr
S.I.C.: 2033; 2037
N.A.I.C.S.: 311421; 311411
Export
Advertising Expenditures: $15,000,000
Media: 2-3-5-6-8-9-10-14-15-19-20-21-22-23-24
Distr.: Natl.
Budget Set: Apr.
Personnel:
Joseph Falcone *(Chm)*
Brad Irwin *(Pres & CEO)*
Vivian S.Y. Tseng *(Gen Counsel, Sec & VP)*
Brands & Products:
BAMA
WELCHADE
WELCH'S
WELCH'S CHILLED GRAPE JUICE
WELCH'S FRUIT JUICE BARS
WELCH'S GRAPE & CRANBERRY CONCENTRATES
WELCH'S GRAPE JELLY & JAM
WELCH'S JUICEMAKERS
WELCH'S LIGHT JUICE COCKTAILS
WELCH'S ORCHARD BLENDED JUICK COCKTAILS
WELCH'S PURPLE GRAPE JUICE
WELCH'S SPARKLING JUICE
WELCH'S SQUEEZABLES
WELCH'S TOMATO JUICE
WELCH'S TOTALLY FRUIT
WELCH'S WHITE GRAPE JUICE
Advertising Agency:
Porter Novelli
(Sub. of Omnicom Group, Inc.)
75 Varick St 6th Fl
New York, NY 10013
Tel.: (212) 601-8000
Fax: (212) 601-8101
Public Relations Agency of Record

WELCH'S INTERNATIONAL
(Div. of Welch Foods Inc.)
575 Virginia Rd
Concord, MA 01742
Tel.: (978) 371-1000
Fax: (978) 371-3649
Web Site: www.welchs.com
Approx. Number Employees: 200
Business Description:
Retailer & Marketer of Frozen Fruit Juices & Vegetables
S.I.C.: 2033; 2037
N.A.I.C.S.: 311421; 311411
Personnel:
Brad Irwin *(Pres & CEO)*
Michael J. Perda *(CFO)*
Matthew Wohl *(CMO)*
David Engelkemeyer *(VP-Ops & Tech)*
Advertising Agencies:
Maxus Global
498 Seventh Ave
New York, NY 10018
Tel.: (212) 297-8300
Media

The VIA Group LLC
34 Danforth St Ste 309
Portland, ME 04101
Tel.: (207) 221-3000
Fax: (207) 761-9422
Lead Creative Agency

WELLS' DAIRY, INC.
1 Blue Bunny Dr SW
Le Mars, IA 51031
Tel.: (712) 546-4000
Fax: (712) 548-3011
Toll Free: (800) 831-0830
E-mail: webmaster@bluebunny.com
Web Site: www.wellsdairy.com
Approx. Number Employees: 2,450
Year Founded: 1913
Business Description:
Ice Cream Novelty Products
S.I.C.: 2024; 2026
N.A.I.C.S.: 311520; 311511
Advertising Expenditures: $4,000,000
Media: 14-15-19
Distr.: Reg.
Personnel:
Michael Wells *(Pres & CEO)*
David Lyons *(Sr VP-Ops & Supply Chain)*
Jim Reynolds *(Sr VP-Sls, Mktg, R & D)*
Dave Smetter *(Dir-Mktg)*
Brands & Products:
AMAZON STORM
BIG BOPPER
BIG DOUBLE STRAWBERRY
BIG MISSISSIPPI MUD
BIG NEAPOLITAN
BIG SLICE
BIG VANILLA
BLUE BUNNY
BOMB POP
BON PETITES
BROWNIE EXTREME
BUNNY TRACKS
CARAMEL MUD SPLASH
CARAMEL PECAN PASSION
CHAMOY
CHAMP!
CHIPS GALORE!
CHOCOLATE CHAMPION
COFFEE BREAK
COOKIE CRAZE
COOL TUBES
DOUBLE FUDGE FRENZY
DOUBLE STRAWBERRY
DOUBLES
ELEPHANT STAMPEDE
FRIO GRANDE
FROZFRUIT
GEL BLASTS
HEALTH SMART
HEATH
JOLLY RANCHER
JUNGLE ADVENTURES
JUST PEACHY
LUCAS
ORANGE DREAM
PEANUT BUTTER PANIC
PELUCAS
PERSONALS
POINTS
SCOOPS
SLUSH POPS
STAR BAR
SUNDAE CRUNCH
SUPER CHUNKY COOKIE DOUGH
SUPER FUDGE BROWNIE
SUPREMES
SWEET FREEDOM
TWIRLIX
WEIGHTWATCHERS
WELLS

Key to Media (For complete agency information see *The Advertising Red Books-Agencies* edition):
1. Bus. Publs. 2. Cable T.V. 3. Catalogs & Directories. 4. Co-op Adv. 5. Consumer Mags. 6. D.M. to Bus. Estab.7. D.M. to Consumers 8. Daily Newsp. 9. Exhibits/Trade Shows 10. Foreign 11. Infomercial 12. Internet Adv.13. Multimedia 14. Network Radio 15. Network T.V. 16. Newsp. Distr. Mags. 17. Other 18. Outdoor (Posters, Transit) 19. Point of Purchase20. Premiums, Novelties 21. Product Samples 22. Special Events Mktg. 23. Spot Radio 24. Spot T.V. 25. Weekly Newsp. 26. Yellow Page Adv.

Wells' Dairy, Inc. — (Continued)

Advertising Agency:
Barkley
1740 Main St
Kansas City, MO 64108
Tel.: (816) 842-1500

WESTIN FOODS, INC.
11808 W Ctr Rd
Omaha, NE 68144-4397
Tel.: (402) 691-8800
Fax: (402) 691-7920
Toll Free: (800) 293-9783
E-mail: westin@westininc.com
Web Site: www.westinfoods.com
Approx. Number Employees: 250
Year Founded: 1971
Business Description:
Mfr & Distr of Food Products
S.I.C.: 5149; 2035; 2099
N.A.I.C.S.: 424490; 311941; 311999
Import
Advertising Expenditures: $250,000
Media: 6-7-9-13-16-19
Distr.: Natl.
Personnel:
Richard S. Westin *(Chm)*
Scott Carlson *(Pres & CEO)*
Brad Poppen *(COO)*
Steve Mercier *(Gen Mgr-Packaged Meats)*
Amy Hanna *(Dir-Creative)*
Brands & Products:
WESTIN
WESTIN FOODS

WESTON BAKERIES LIMITED
(Sub. of George Weston Limited)
2510 Shepherd Rd
Ottawa, ON K1B 45, Canada
Tel.: (416) 252-7323, ext. 6137495965
Fax: (416) 252-5159
Web Site:
www.westonfoodscanada.ca/
Approx. Number Employees: 22,500
Business Description:
Breads, Rolls, Cakes & Other Bakery Products Mfr
S.I.C.: 2051
N.A.I.C.S.: 311812
Media: 2-4-14-15-17-21-25
Distr.: Natl.
Budget Set: Oct. -Dec.
Personnel:
Ralph A. Robinson *(Pres-Weston Foods Canada)*
Colleen William *(Sr Product Mgr)*

WHITE ROSE FOODS
(Div. of Di Giorgio Corporation)
380 Middlesex Ave
Carteret, NJ 07008-3446
Tel.: (732) 541-5555
Fax: (732) 541-3730
Web Site: www.whiterose.com
Approx. Number Employees: 1,200
Business Description:
Wholesale Food Distribution
S.I.C.: 5141; 5143
N.A.I.C.S.: 424410; 424430
Media: 2-4-7-9-10-17
Distr.: Natl.
Budget Set: Sept.
Personnel:
Stephen R. Bokser *(Co-Chm & Co-CEO)*
Dennis Hickey *(Sr VP)*

WHITFIELD FOODS, INC.
1101 N Ct St
Montgomery, AL 36104
Mailing Address:
PO Box 791
Montgomery, AL 36101-0791
Tel.: (334) 263-2541
Fax: (334) 262-4203
Toll Free: (800) 633-8790
Web Site: www.alagasyrup.com/
Approx. Number Employees: 150
Year Founded: 1906
Business Description:
Fruit Drinks Packer & Distr, 100% Juices & Table Syrups
S.I.C.: 2099
N.A.I.C.S.: 311999
Media: 1-2-5-6-9-10-16-19-20-21-23-24-25-26
Distr.: Natl.
Personnel:
Les Massey *(Pres & CEO)*
Brands & Products:
ALAGA HOT SAUCE
ALAGA LIGHT CORN SYRUP
ALAGA ORIGINAL SYRUP
ALAGA SPICED APPLE CIDER
PLOW BOY SYRUP
TASTEE
YELLOW LABEL

WHOLESOME & HEARTY FOODS COMPANY
(Holding of Annex Capital Management LLC)
15615 Alton Pkwy Ste 350
Irvine, CA 92618
Tel.: (949) 255-2000
Fax: (949) 255-2010
Toll Free: (800) 459-7079
E-mail: cschwarz@gardenburger.com
Web Site: www.gardenburger.com
Approx. Number Employees: 156
Year Founded: 1985
Business Description:
Meatless Food Products Mfr & Distr
S.I.C.: 2038; 5149
N.A.I.C.S.: 311412; 424490
Advertising Expenditures: $602,000
Media: 2-6-9-13-16-19-20

WILD FLAVORS, INC.
(Sub. of Rudolf Wild GmbH & Co. KG)
1261 Pacific Ave
Erlanger, KY 41018
Tel.: (859) 342-3600
Fax: (859) 342-3610
Web Site: www.wildflavors.com
Sales Range: $50-74.9 Million
Approx. Number Employees: 425
Year Founded: 1994
Business Description:
Food & Beverage Flavorings, Colors & Other Ingredients Mfr
S.I.C.: 2087; 2099
N.A.I.C.S.: 311942; 311930; 311999
Media: 10
Personnel:
Michael Ponder *(Pres & CEO)*
Gary Massie *(CFO)*
Erik Donhowe *(COO)*
Louis Proietti *(Gen Counsel)*
Victoria de la Huerga *(Sr VP-Beverage & Strategy)*
Reed Lynn *(VP-Sls)*
Karen Eberts *(Sr Dir-Quality Mgmt & Food Safety)*
Linda Haering *(Sr Dir-HR)*
Donna Hansee *(Sr Dir-Mktg)*
Brands & Products:
CHEF'S SHORTCUTS
COLORS FROM NATURE
H.I.T.S.
LIGHTSHEILD
MAXIMMUNE
N.E.X.T.
ONLYSWEET
RESOLVER
SALTTRIM
SAVORCRAVE
WE CREATE GREAT TASTE
WILD

WILLIAMS FOODS, INC.
(Sub. of C.H. Guenther & Son, Inc.)
13301 W 99th St
Lenexa, KS 66215-1348
Tel.: (913) 888-4343
Fax: (913) 888-0727
Toll Free: (800) 255-6736
E-mail: info@williamsfoods.com
Web Site: www.williamsfoods.com
Approx. Number Employees: 200
Year Founded: 1937
Business Description:
Dry Seasoning & Canned Food Mfr
S.I.C.: 2099
N.A.I.C.S.: 311942; 311999
Advertising Expenditures: $400,000
Media: 9-10-19-20-21-23-24-25
Distr.: Natl.
Budget Set: Feb.
Personnel:
Adrian Bozarth *(Dir-Ops)*
Brands & Products:
GRANDMA'S
SUN-BIRD
TRADICIONES
WAGNER'S
WILLIAMS
WOLFERMANS

WILLIAMS SAUSAGE CO., INC.
5132 Old Troy Hickman Hwy
Union City, TN 38261
Tel.: (731) 885-5841
Fax: (731) 885-5884
Toll Free: (800) 844-4242
Web Site: www.williams-sausage.com
Sales Range: $25-49.9 Million
Approx. Number Employees: 200
Year Founded: 1958
Business Description:
Sausage Mfr & Distr
S.I.C.: 5147
N.A.I.C.S.: 311612
Advertising Expenditures: $3,000,000
Media: 10-18-20-23-24
Personnel:
Roger Williams *(Owner)*
Thomas Ray, Sr. *(Mgr-Plant)*
Brands & Products:
12 COUNTRY
OLE SOUTH
WILLIAMS COUNTRY SAUSAGE

WIN SCHULER FOODS
27777 Franklin Rd Ste 1520
Southfield, MI 48034-8261
Tel.: (248) 262-3450
Fax: (248) 262-3455
Approx. Number Employees: 11
Year Founded: 1993
Business Description:
Mfrs. of Snack Foods, Frozen Soups, Sauces, Salad Dressings & Cheese Spreads
S.I.C.: 2038; 2022
N.A.I.C.S.: 311412; 311513
Import Export
Advertising Expenditures: $300,000
Media: 4-8-9-19-21-22-23
Distr.: Reg.
Budget Set: Sept.
Personnel:
Robert P. Nunez *(Pres)*
Brands & Products:
BAR-SCHEEZE
BAR-SCHIPS
WIN SCHULER'S

WINDSOR QUALITY FOOD CO., LTD.
3355 W Alabama St Ste 730
Houston, TX 77098-1797
Tel.: (713) 843-5200
Fax: (713) 960-9709
Web Site: www.windsorfoods.com
Approx. Number Employees: 900
Year Founded: 1996
Business Description:
Mfr. of Frozen Foods
S.I.C.: 2038
N.A.I.C.S.: 311412
Media: 2-4-10-13-16-21-22
Personnel:
Greg Gieb *(Pres & CEO)*
Brad Kumin *(Dir-Mktg)*
Brands & Products:
BERNARDI
GOLDEN TIGER
ORIGINAL CHILI
ORIGINAL CHILI BOWL
WHITEY'S CHILI
WINDSOR FROZEN FOOD
WINDSOR FROZEN FOODS

THE WISCONSIN CHEESEMAN, INC.
301 Broadway Dr
Sun Prairie, WI 53590
Mailing Address:
PO Box 1
Madison, WI 53701-0001
Tel.: (608) 837-8535
Tel.: (608) 837-5166
Fax: (608) 825-6463
Fax: (608) 837-5493
Toll Free: (800) 698-1721
E-mail: customerservice@wisconsincheeseman.com
Web Site:
www.wisconsincheeseman.com
Approx. Number Employees: 220
Year Founded: 1946
Business Description:
Mail Order Food Gifts
S.I.C.: 5961; 2099; 5143
N.A.I.C.S.: 454113; 311999; 424430
Media: 2-4-8-10-21
Distr.: Natl.
Personnel:
Doug First *(VP-Direct Mktg)*
Roxanne Van Loon *(Dir-Product Dev)*
Lindsey Decker *(Mktg Comm Mgr)*
Brands & Products:
PECANBACKS
THE WISCONSIN CHEESEMAN

Key to Media (For complete agency information see *The Advertising Red Books-Agencies* edition):
1. Bus. Publs. 2. Cable T.V. 3. Catalogs & Directories. 4. Co-op Adv. 5. Consumer Mags. 6. D.M. to Bus. Estab.7. D.M. to Consumers 8. Daily Newsp. 9. Exhibits/Trade Shows 10. Foreign 11. Infomercial 12. Internet Adv.13. Multimedia 14. Network Radio 15. Network T.V. 16. Newsp. Distr. Mags. 17. Other 18. Outdoor (Posters, Transit) 19. Point of Purchase20. Premiums, Novelties 21. Product Samples 22. Special Events Mktg. 23. Spot Radio 24. Spot T.V. 25. Weekly Newsp. 26. Yellow Page Adv.

WORLD FINER FOODS, INC.
300 Broadacres Dr
Bloomfield, NJ 07003-3153
Tel.: (973) 338-0300
Fax: (973) 338-0382
E-mail: info@worldfiner.com
Web Site: www.worldfiner.com
E-Mail For Key Personnel:
President: fmuchel@worldfiner.com
Approx. Number Employees: 82
Year Founded: 1990
Business Description:
Specialty Foods Sales, Marketing & Distribution; Food Importer
S.I.C.: 5149
N.A.I.C.S.: 424490
Import
Advertising Expenditures: $2,000,000
Media: 2-4-6-9-10-16-19-25
Distr.: Natl.
Personnel:
Frank Muchel *(Pres)*
Barry O'Brien *(CFO)*
Todd Newstadt *(VP-Mktg)*
John H. Affel *(Dir-Mktg)*
Advertising Agency:
Benjamin & Ribaudo Advertising Inc.
212 W 35th St 10th Fl
New York, NY 10001
Tel.: (212) 465-2496
Fax: (212) 465-2497

WORLDWIDE FOOD PRODUCTS INC.
14707 94th Ave
Jamaica, NY 11435-4513
Tel.: (718) 658-4000
Fax: (718) 262-8006
Web Site: www.geishaseafood.com
Approx. Sls.: $45,000,000
Approx. Number Employees: 25
Year Founded: 1989
Business Description:
Mfr. of Seafood Products
S.I.C.: 5146
N.A.I.C.S.: 424460
Advertising Expenditures: $700,000
Media: 5-9-19-21
Distr.: Intl.; Natl.
Budget Set: Dec.
Brands & Products:
FARMER BOY
TRUNZ

YASHENG GROUP
805 Veterans Blvd Ste 228
Redwood City, CA 94063
Tel.: (650) 363-8345
Fax: (650) 363-0462
Fax: (650) 362-0478
E-mail: info@yashenggroup.com
Web Site: www.yashenggroup.com
Approx. Sls.: $849,454,265
Approx. Number Employees: 15,000
Year Founded: 2004
Business Description:
Holding Company; Agricultural Food & Agro-byproducts Cultivator, Processor, Marketer & Distr
S.I.C.: 6719
N.A.I.C.S.: 551112
Advertising Expenditures: $664,410
Personnel:
Chang Sheng Zhou *(Chm & CEO)*
Mei Ping Wu *(Pres & Sec)*
Hai Yun Zhuang *(CFO)*
Deng Fu Wand *(Gen Mgr)*

ZACKY FARMS, INC.
2020 S East Ave
Fresno, CA 93721
Tel.: (559) 486-2310
Tel.: (559) 443-2700 (Corp Office)
Tel.: (562) 641-2020 (Sales & Marketing)
Fax: (559) 443-2778
Fax: (562) 641-2040 (Sales & Marketing)
Toll Free: (800) 888-0235
Web Site: www.zacky.com
Sales Range: $300-349.9 Million
Approx. Number Employees: 2,800
Year Founded: 1946
Business Description:
Turkeys & Processed Meats
S.I.C.: 0253
N.A.I.C.S.: 112330
Advertising Expenditures: $1,000,000
Media: 2-7-10-17
Distr.: Reg.
Budget Set: Sept.
Personnel:
John Ross *(Pres & COO)*
Marcus Curry *(CFO)*
Ivy Quon *(Sr VP-Mktg & Admin)*
Lillian Zacky *(Dir-Consumer Affairs)*
Brands & Products:
ZACKY
ZACKY FARMS
Advertising Agency:
Klein Mickaelian Partners
5670 Wilshire Blvd Ste 1590
Los Angeles, CA 90036-5633
Tel.: (310) 556-0500
Fax: (310) 556-0949
(Chicken, Turkey, Process Meat)

ZATARAIN'S BRANDS, INC.
(Sub. of McCormick & Company, Incorporated)
82 1st St
Gretna, LA 70053
Mailing Address:
PO Box 347
Gretna, LA 70053
Tel.: (504) 367-2950
Fax: (504) 362-2004
E-mail: service@zatarain.com
Web Site: www.zatarain.com
Sales Range: $125-149.9 Million
Approx. Number Employees: 235
Year Founded: 1889
Business Description:
New Orleans-Style Foods Mfr
S.I.C.: 2099; 2035
N.A.I.C.S.: 311999; 311941
Import Export
Advertising Expenditures: $1,000,000
Media: 3-10-13-14-15-18-20-22-23-24
Distr.: Natl.
Personnel:
Regina Templet *(CFO)*
Brands & Products:
ZATARAIN'S

ZEPHYRHILLS SPRING WATER COMPANY
(Sub. of Nestle Waters North America Inc.)
6403 Harney Rd
Tampa, FL 33610
Tel.: (813) 621-2025
Fax: (813) 620-6862
Toll Free: (800) 950-9398
Toll Free: (800) 759-4926
Web Site: www.zephyrhillswater.com
Year Founded: 1960
Business Description:
Spring Water Producer
S.I.C.: 2086
N.A.I.C.S.: 312112
Media: 6-22-24
Personnel:
Kim E. Jeffery *(Pres & CEO)*

Key to Media (For complete agency information see *The Advertising Red Books-Agencies* edition):
1. Bus. Publs. 2. Cable T.V. 3. Catalogs & Directories. 4. Co-op Adv. 5. Consumer Mags. 6. D.M. to Bus. Estab.7. D.M. to Consumers 8. Daily Newsp. 9. Exhibits/Trade Shows 10. Foreign 11. Infomercial 12. Internet Adv.13. Multimedia 14. Network Radio 15. Network T.V. 16. Newsp. Distr. Mags. 17. Other 18. Outdoor (Posters, Transit) 19. Point of Purchase20. Premiums, Novelties 21. Product Samples 22. Special Events Mktg. 23. Spot Radio 24. Spot T.V. 25. Weekly Newsp. 26. Yellow Page Adv.

Food Retailers

Fruit & Vegetable Markets — Grocery Stores — Meat & Fish Markets — Retail Bakeries — Supermarkets

7-ELEVEN, INC.
(Sub. of Seven-Eleven Japan Co., Ltd.)
1722 Routh St Ste 1000
Dallas, TX 75201-2504
Mailing Address:
PO Box 711
Dallas, TX 75221-0711
Tel.: (972) 828-7011
Fax: (972) 828-7848
Web Site: www.7-eleven.com
Approx. Number Employees: 31,500
Year Founded: 1927
Business Description:
Convenience Store Operator
S.I.C.: 5411
N.A.I.C.S.: 445120
Advertising Expenditures: $38,900,000
Media: 2-3-6-15-17-18-23-24
Distr.: Natl.
Personnel:
Joseph M. DePinto *(Pres & CEO)*
Stanley W. Reynolds *(CFO & Exec VP)*
Darren M. Rebelez *(COO & Exec VP)*
Rita Bargerhuff *(CMO & VP)*
Dave Fenton *(Gen Counsel, Sec & Sr VP)*
Masaaki Asakura *(Exec VP)*
Carole Davidson *(Sr VP-Fin & Comm)*
Jesus Delgado-Jenkins *(Sr VP-Mdsg & Logistics)*
Krystin Mitchell *(Sr VP-HR)*
Jeffrey A. Schenck *(Sr VP-Franchise-Natl)*
Frank S. Gambina *(VP-Natl Franchise)*
Joe Strong *(VP-Chesapeake)*
Tom Gerrity *(Sr Dir-Store Brands)*
Dennis Phelps *(Sr Dir-Beverages)*
Laura Gordon *(Sr Brand Dir-Slurpee)*
Mark Hagen *(Sr Product Dir-Food Service)*
Margaret Chabris *(Dir-PR)*
Jay Wilkins *(Brand Mgr-Hot Beverages)*
Richard Forsshell *(Mgr-Mktg)*
Brands & Products:
7-ELEVEN
7-SELECT
BIG BITE
BIG BREW
BIG EATS BAKERY
BIG EATS DELI
BIG EATS DELUXE
BIG GULP
GO-GO TAQUITO
SLURP AND GULP
SLURPEE
SLURPEE SPLITZ-O
SPEAK OUT
SUPER BIG BURGER
SUPER BIG GULP
SUPER STRATA SLURPEE
X-TREME GULP
Advertising Agencies:
Brendy Barr Communications LLC
144 Knorrwood Ct
Oakland Township, MI 48306
Tel.: (248) 651-4858
Fax: (248) 651-4868

TracyLocke
1999 Bryan St Ste 2800
Dallas, TX 75201
Tel.: (214) 259-3500
Fax: (214) 259-3550

ACCORD INC.
(d/b/a Taco Time)
3300 Maple Valley Hwy
Renton, WA 98058
Tel.: (425) 226-6656
Fax: (425) 228-8226
Web Site: www.tacotimenw.com
Sales Range: $10-24.9 Million
Approx. Number Employees: 20
Business Description:
Franchiser of Restaurants
S.I.C.: 6794; 5812
N.A.I.C.S.: 533110; 722211
Media: 1-3-19-20-21-22-23-24
Personnel:
Mathew Tonkin *(Pres)*
Jim Tonkin *(CEO)*
Gretchen Everett *(Dir-Mktg & Adv)*

ACME MARKETS, INC.
(Div. of Albertson's, Inc.)
75 Valley Stream Pkwy
Malvern, PA 19355-1406
Tel.: (610) 889-4000
Fax: (610) 889-3039
Web Site: www.acmemarkets.com
Sales Range: $1-4.9 Billion
Approx. Number Employees: 18,000
Year Founded: 1891
Business Description:
Retail Food Stores
S.I.C.: 5411
N.A.I.C.S.: 445110
Media: 5-7-8-9-13-18-23-24-25
Distr.: Reg.
Budget Set: Jan.
Personnel:
Dan Sanders *(Pres)*
Advertising Agency:
Duncan & Associates Philadelphia
1150 1st Ave Ste 200
King of Prussia, PA 19406
Tel.: (610) 945-0201
Fax: (610) 945-0208

AFFILIATED FOOD STORES, INC.
(d/b/a Oklahoma Affiliated Food Stores)
4109 Vine St
Abilene, TX 79602
Mailing Address:
PO Box 2938
Abilene, TX 79602
Tel.: (325) 692-1440
Fax: (325) 692-0848
Sales Range: $150-199.9 Million
Approx. Number Employees: 150
Business Description:
Holding Company; Grocery Stores Owner & Operator
S.I.C.: 6719; 5411
N.A.I.C.S.: 551112; 445110
Media: 9-16-25
Personnel:
Darrell Earnest *(Pres & CEO)*

AFFILIATED FOODS, INC.
1401 W Farmers Ave
Amarillo, TX 79118-6134
Tel.: (806) 372-3851
Fax: (806) 374-3647
E-mail: afiama@afiama.com
Web Site: www.afiama.com
Sales Range: $900-999.9 Million
Approx. Number Employees: 1,000
Year Founded: 1946
Business Description:
Wholesale Food Cooperative
S.I.C.: 5141; 2026
N.A.I.C.S.: 424410; 311511
Media: 2-10-22
Distr.: Natl.
Budget Set: June
Personnel:
Roger Lowe *(Chm)*
Randy Arceneaux *(Pres, CEO & COO)*
Tammie Coffee *(CFO)*
Gene Blackburn *(Dir-HR)*
David Campsey *(Dir-Mktg)*
Dale Thomson *(Dir-New Accts)*
Bob Mitchusson *(Mgr-Adv)*
Brands & Products:
AFFILIATED

AFFILIATED FOODS MIDWEST INC.
1301 Omaha Ave
Norfolk, NE 68701
Tel.: (402) 371-0555
Fax: (402) 371-1884
E-mail: info@afmidwest.com
Web Site: www.afmidwest.com
Approx. Number Employees: 700
Year Founded: 1931
Business Description:
Distribution Center for Member-Owned Cooperative
S.I.C.: 5141; 5142
N.A.I.C.S.: 424410; 424420
Import
Media: 5-10-17-22
Personnel:
Marc King *(Chm)*
Marty W. Arter *(Pres)*
Duane Seversen *(CFO)*
Tim Goetsch *(Exec VP)*
Dave Engelhaupt *(Sr VP)*
Ron Kuhn *(Gen Mgr)*
Brands & Products:
AFFILIATED FOODS MIDWEST

AGRI-MARK, INC.
100 Milk St
Methuen, MA 01844-4600
Mailing Address:
PO Box 5800
Lawrence, MA 01842
Tel.: (978) 689-4442
Fax: (978) 794-8304
Web Site: www.agrimark.net
Approx. Number Employees: 700
Year Founded: 1980
Business Description:
Dairy Marketing Cooperative
S.I.C.: 2026; 2022
N.A.I.C.S.: 311511; 311513
Media: 2-5-21-22
Personnel:
Paul P. Johnston *(Pres & CEO)*

Key to Media (For complete agency information see *The Advertising Red Books-Agencies* edition):
1. Bus. Publs. 2. Cable T.V. 3. Catalogs & Directories. 4. Co-op Adv. 5. Consumer Mags. 6. D.M. to Bus. Estab.7. D.M. to Consumers 8. Daily Newsp. 9. Exhibits/Trade Shows 10. Foreign 11. Infomercial 12. Internet Adv.13. Multimedia 14. Network Radio 15. Network T.V. 16. Newsp. Distr. Mags. 17. Other 18. Outdoor (Posters, Transit) 19. Point of Purchase20. Premiums, Novelties 21. Product Samples 22. Special Events Mktg. 23. Spot Radio 24. Spot T.V. 25. Weekly Newsp. 26. Yellow Page Adv.

Robert Wellington *(Sr VP-Economics, Commun & Legislative Affairs)*
Douglas DiMento *(Dir-Comm)*

Brands & Products:
AGRI-MARK
CABOT
MCCADAM

AJINOMOTO U.S.A., INC.
(Sub. of Ajinomoto Company, Inc.)
One Parker Plz 400 Kelby St
Fort Lee, NJ 07024
Tel.: (201) 292-3200
Web Site: www.ajinomoto-usa.com
Approx. Number Employees: 50
Year Founded: 1956
Business Description:
Provider of Food Enhancement Products
S.I.C.: 5142; 5169
N.A.I.C.S.: 424420; 424690
Import Export
Media: 2-7-10
Distr.: Natl.
Budget Set: Jan.
Personnel:
Shinichi Suzuki *(Pres & CEO)*
Advertising Agencies:
Delfino Marketing Communications, Inc.
400 Columbus Ave Ste 120S
Valhalla, NY 10595-1396
Tel.: (914) 747-1400
Fax: (914) 747-1430
(Food Ingredients, Specialty Chemicals)

Dentsu America, Inc.
32 Ave of the Americas 16th Fl
New York, NY 10013
Tel.: (212) 397-3333
Fax: (212) 397-3322

Matrix Advertising Associates, Inc.
375 W Broadway 4th Fl
New York, NY 10012
Tel.: (212) 334-6600
Fax: (212) 334-6228

ALADDIN TEMP-RITE, LLC
(Sub. of Ali S.p.A.)
250 E Main St
Hendersonville, TN 37075
Mailing Address:
PO Box 2978
Hendersonville, TN 37077-2978
Tel.: (615) 537-3600
Fax: (888) 812-9956
Toll Free: (800) 888-8018
Web Site: www.aladdintemprite.com
E-Mail For Key Personnel:
Marketing Director: debbiewitt@aladdintemprite.com
Approx. Number Employees: 200
Year Founded: 1968
Business Description:
Mfr. of Insulated Food Service Systems for Hospitals, Correctional Facilities & Institutions
S.I.C.: 5047
N.A.I.C.S.: 423450
Advertising Expenditures: $1,000,000
Media: 1-2-7-10-11-13-17-20-21
Distr.: Direct; Intl.; Natl.
Budget Set: Jan.
Personnel:
Jeff Burns *(CFO)*
Debbie Witt *(Mgr-Adv & PR)*
Linda Kirkpatrick *(Coord-Mktg)*
Brands & Products:
CONVECT-RITE II
HEAT ON DEMAND
INSUL-PLUS
RITE TEMP
TEMP-RITE
TEMP-RITE II
TEMP RITE II EXCEL

ALBERTSON'S, INC.
(Sub. of SUPERVALU, Inc.)
250 Parkcenter Blvd
Boise, ID 83726-0020
Tel.: (208) 395-6200
Fax: (208) 395-6349
Toll Free: (877) 932-7948
E-mail: absfeedback@eds.com
Web Site: www1.albertsons.com
Sales Range: $15-24.9 Billion
Approx. Number Employees: 52,400
Year Founded: 1939
Business Description:
Retail Food & Drug Chain
S.I.C.: 5411; 5912
N.A.I.C.S.: 445110; 446110
Advertising Expenditures: $534,000,000
Media: 3-5-8-9-10-13-14-15-18-19-21-23-24-25-26
Distr.: Reg.
Budget Set: Dec.
Personnel:
Felicia D. Thornton *(CFO & Exec VP)*
Mike Clawson *(Pres-Intermountain West Div)*
Carl Jablonski *(Pres-Eastern Div)*
John R. Sims *(Gen Counsel & Exec VP)*
Ertharin Cousin *(Sr VP-Albertsons Foods)*
Dennis Bassler *(VP-Mktg & VP)*
John Colgrove *(VP-Mktg & VP)*
Keith DeMeyer *(VP-Commun)*
Ed Hanson *(VP-Mktg)*
Frank Yaksitch *(VP-Mktg & Mdsg)*
Brands & Products:
ALBERTSONS
JEWEL
OSCODRUG
SAVON
SUPERSAVER FOODS
Advertising Agencies:
DAE Advertising, Inc.
71 Stevenson St Ste 750
San Francisco, CA 94105
Tel.: (415) 341-1280
Fax: (415) 296-8378

Dailey & Associates
(Sub. of The Interpublic Group of Cos., Inc.)
8687 Melrose Ave Ste G300
West Hollywood, CA 90069-5701
Tel.: (310) 360-3100
Fax: (310) 360-0810

ALDI FOOD INC.
(Sub. of ALDI Group)
1200 N Kirk Rd
Batavia, IL 60510-1443
Tel.: (630) 879-8100
Fax: (630) 879-8410
Web Site: www.aldi.com
Approx. Number Employees: 80
Year Founded: 1945
Business Description:
Retailer of Groceries
S.I.C.: 5411
N.A.I.C.S.: 445110
Media: 9-23-24-25-26
Distr.: Reg.
Budget Set: Nov.
Personnel:
Chuck Youngstrom *(Pres)*
Terry Pfortmiller *(CFO)*
Brands & Products:
ALDI
Advertising Agency:
The MWW Group
111 E Wacker Dr 10th Fl
Chicago, IL 60601
Tel.: (312) 853-3131
Fax: (312) 853-0955

ALIMENTATION COUCHE-TARD INC.
Riverside Ofc Plz Ste 236 59th
Laval, QC H7G 4S7, Canada
Tel.: (450) 662-6632
Fax: (450) 662-6648
Toll Free: (800) 361-2612
E-mail: info@couche-tard.com
Web Site: www.couche-tard.com
Approx. Rev.: $16,439,600,000
Approx. Number Employees: 53,000
Year Founded: 1981
Business Description:
Convenience Store Operator
S.I.C.: 5411
N.A.I.C.S.: 445120; 445110
Advertising Expenditures: $31,100,000
Personnel:
Richard Fortin *(Chm)*
Alain Bouchard *(Pres & CEO)*
Raymond Pare *(CFO & VP)*
Brian Hannasch *(COO)*
Sylvain Aubry *(Sec & Sr Dir-Legal Affairs)*
Real Plourde *(Exec VP)*
Alain Brisebois *(Sr VP-Ops)*
Brands & Products:
7-JOURS
BECKER'S
CIRCLE K
COUCHE-TARD
DAIRY MART
DAISY MART
FROSTER
HANDY ANDY FOOD STORES
MAC'S
SLOCHE
SUNSHINE JOE
WINKS

THE ALMOND BOARD OF CALIFORNIA
1150 9th St Ste 1500
Modesto, CA 95354
Tel.: (209) 549-8262
Fax: (209) 549-8267
E-mail: staff@almondboard.com
Web Site: www.almondboard.com
Approx. Number Employees: 38
Business Description:
Almonds Marketer
S.I.C.: 9641
N.A.I.C.S.: 926140
Media: 6
Personnel:
Richard Waycott *(Pres & CEO)*
Melissa Mautz *(Mgr North American Consumer Mktg)*

ALON BRANDS, INC.
(Sub. of ALON USA ENERGY, INC.)
7616 LBJ Freeway 3rd Fl
Dallas, TX 75251
Tel.: (972) 367-3900
Web Site: www.alonusa.com
Approx. Rev.: $1,274,516,000
Approx. Number Employees: 2,014
Business Description:
Convenient Store Operations
S.I.C.: 5411
N.A.I.C.S.: 445120
Advertising Expenditures: $992,000
Personnel:
David Wiessman *(Chm)*
Kyle McKeen *(Pres & CEO)*
David Potter *(CFO)*
Judge A. Dobrient *(Sr VP-Wholesale Mktg)*
Joseph Lipman *(Sr VP-Retail)*
Michael Oster *(Sr VP-Mergers & Acq-USA)*

AMERICAN CONSUMERS, INC.
55 Hannah Way
Rossville, GA 30741
Mailing Address:
PO Box 2328
Fort Oglethorpe, GA 30742-2328
Tel.: (706) 861-3347
Fax: (706) 861-3364
Web Site: www.acop.com
Approx. Sls.: $32,937,845
Approx. Number Employees: 83
Year Founded: 1968
Business Description:
Supermarket Owner & Operator
S.I.C.: 5411
N.A.I.C.S.: 445110
Advertising Expenditures: $496,493
Personnel:
Paul R. Cook *(Chm, Pres, CEO, CFO & Treas)*
Todd Richardson *(COO & Exec VP)*

ARAMARK CANADA LTD.
(Sub. of ARAMARK Corporation)
811 Islington Ave
Toronto, ON M8Z 5W8, Canada
Mailing Address:
PO Box 950
Toronto, ON M8Z 5Y7, Canada
Tel.: (416) 255-1331
Fax: (416) 255-4706
E-mail: info@aramark.ca
Web Site: www.aramark.ca
Approx. Number Employees: 14,000
Year Founded: 1961
Business Description:
Service Management Company; Food Service, Vending, Office Coffee & Cleaning, Laundry & Housekeeping Services
S.I.C.: 8744; 5812; 7213; 7319; 7349; 7389
N.A.I.C.S.: 561210; 541870; 561439; 561499; 561720; 561790; 561990; 722110; 812331
Media: 2-7-9-10-13-19-22-26
Distr.: Intl.; Natl.
Budget Set: May
Personnel:
Karen Wetselaar *(CFO & VP-Fin)*
Lynn Ervin *(VP-HR)*

Key to Media (For complete agency information see *The Advertising Red Books-Agencies* edition):
1. Bus. Publs. 2. Cable T.V. 3. Catalogs & Directories. 4. Co-op Adv. 5. Consumer Mags. 6. D.M. to Bus. Estab.7. D.M. to Consumers 8. Daily Newsp. 9. Exhibits/Trade Shows 10. Foreign 11. Infomercial 12. Internet Adv.13. Multimedia 14. Network Radio 15. Network T.V. 16. Newsp. Distr. Mags. 17. Other 18. Outdoor (Posters, Transit) 19. Point of Purchase20. Premiums, Novelties 21. Product Samples 22. Special Events Mktg. 23. Spot Radio 24. Spot T.V. 25. Weekly Newsp. 26. Yellow Page Adv.

ARAMARK Canada Ltd. — (Continued)

Brands & Products:
ARAMARK

ARAMARK CORPORATION
1101 Market St
Philadelphia, PA 19107
Tel.: (215) 238-3000
Toll Free: (800) 272-6275
E-mail: webmaster@aramark.com
Web Site: www.aramark.com
Approx. Sls.: $12,571,676,000
Approx. Number Employees: 162,000
Year Founded: 1959
Business Description:
Holding Company; Food Services, Uniforms & Facilities Management Services
S.I.C.: 5812; 8744
N.A.I.C.S.: 722310; 561210
Media: 2-4-6-8-10-13-19-22
Distr.: Natl.
Personnel:
Joseph Neubauer *(Chm & CEO)*
L. Frederick Sutherland *(CFO & Exec VP)*
David Kausan *(CIO)*
Ira Cohn *(Pres-Bus & Indus Grp)*
Gary Crompton *(Pres-Bus Svcs)*
Frank Mendicino *(Pres-Strategic Assets)*
Bart Colli *(Gen Counsel, Sec & Exec VP)*
Christopher Holland *(Sr VP-Fin & Treas)*
Andrew C. Kerin *(Exec VP & Grp Pres-Food, Facility & Hospitality Svcs Segment)*
Lynn McKee *(Exec VP-HR)*
Joseph Munnelly *(Sr VP & Controller)*
Sandy Heilman *(VP-Sls & Mktg)*
Diane Coyne *(Sr Dir-Franchise Brands)*
Brands & Products:
ARAMARK
MANAGED SERVICES MANAGED BETTER
Advertising Agencies:
160over90
1 S Broad St 10th Fl
Philadelphia, PA 19107
Tel.: (215) 732-3200
Fax: (215) 732-1664

Allebach Advertising
117 N Main St
Souderton, PA 18964
Tel.: (215) 721-7693
Fax: (215) 721-7694

Cresta Group
1050 N State St
Chicago, IL 60610
Tel.: (312) 944-4700
Fax: (312) 944-1582

Karstan Communications
700 Doorbell Dr Ste 301
Oakville, ON L6K 3V3, Canada
Tel.: (905) 844-1900
Fax: (905) 844-5200

Noble
2215 W Chesterfield Blvd
Springfield, MO 65807-8650
Tel.: (417) 875-5000
Fax: (417) 875-5051

Toll Free: (800) 662-5390

ARBY'S RESTAURANT GROUP, INC.
(Sub. of WENDY'S/ARBY'S GROUP, INC.)
1155 Perimeter Ctr W 9th Fl
Atlanta, GA 30338
Tel.: (678) 514-4100
Fax: (678) 514-5330
Toll Free: (800) 487-2729
Web Site: www.arbys.com
Sales Range: $150-199.9 Million
Approx. Number Employees: 530
Year Founded: 1964
Business Description:
Restaurants
S.I.C.: 5812
N.A.I.C.S.: 722211
Media: 24
Personnel:
Hala G. Moddelmog *(Pres)*
Diana Petrovich-Tao *(COO)*
Steve Davis *(CMO)*
Kristina Jonathan *(VP-Digital & Social Media)*
Brian Kolodziej *(VP-Product Dev)*
Advertising Agencies:
BBDO Worldwide Inc.
(Sub. of Omnicom Group, Inc.)
1285 Ave of the Americas
New York, NY 10019-6028
Tel.: (212) 459-5000
Fax: (212) 459-6645
Creative

Doner
25900 Northwestern Hwy
Southfield, MI 48075
Tel.: (248) 354-9700
Fax: (248) 827-8440

ARDEN GROUP, INC.
2020 S Central Ave
Compton, CA 90220-5302
Mailing Address:
PO Box 512256
Los Angeles, CA 90051-0256
Tel.: (310) 638-2842
Fax: (310) 631-0950
E-mail: info@gelsonsvillage.com
Web Site: www.gelsons.com
Approx. Sls.: $417,065,000
Approx. Number Employees: 1,222
Year Founded: 1951
Business Description:
Supermarket Services
S.I.C.: 5541; 5399; 5411
N.A.I.C.S.: 447110; 445110; 445120; 452910
Import
Advertising Expenditures: $1,876,000
Media: 7-9-13-18-19-25
Personnel:
Bernard Briskin *(CEO)*
Laura J. Neumann *(CFO)*
Brenda McDaniel *(Sr VP)*
Brands & Products:
GELSONS
MAYFAIR

ASSOCIATED FOOD STORES, INC.
1850 W 2100 S
Salt Lake City, UT 84119
Tel.: (801) 973-4400
Fax: (801) 973-2158
Toll Free: (888) 574-7100
E-mail: afsweb@afstores.com
Web Site: www.afstores.com
Approx. Number Employees: 1,500
Year Founded: 1940
Business Description:
Distr of Groceries
S.I.C.: 5141; 5147
N.A.I.C.S.: 424410; 424470
Advertising Expenditures: $3,000,000
Media: 2-7-13-18-21-23-24-25
Personnel:
Rich Parkinson *(CEO)*
Robert Opray *(CFO)*
Steve Miner *(Pres-Market Dev Inc)*
Steve Reich *(VP-Mktg)*
Wayne Dalton *(Mgr-Creative Svcs)*
Brands & Products:
ASSOCIATED FOOD STORES
WESTERN FAMILY
Advertising Agency:
AFS Creative Services
1850 W 2100 S
Salt Lake City, UT 84119
Tel.: (801) 978-8516

ASSOCIATED WHOLESALE GROCERS, INC.
5000 Kansas Ave
Kansas City, KS 66106-1135
Mailing Address:
PO Box 2932
Kansas City, KS 66110-2932
Tel.: (913) 288-1000
Fax: (913) 288-1587
E-mail: contactawg@awginc.com
Web Site: www.awginc.com
Sales Range: $5-14.9 Billion
Approx. Number Employees: 2,000
Year Founded: 1926
Business Description:
Co-Operative Grocery Distr
S.I.C.: 5141
N.A.I.C.S.: 424410
Import
Advertising Expenditures: $300,000
Media: 2-8-9-15-16-23-24
Distr.: Reg.
Budget Set: Dec.-Jan.
Personnel:
Jerry Garland *(Pres & CEO)*
Robert C. Walker *(CFO & Exec VP)*
Scott Wilmosky *(Sr VP-Real Estate)*
Joe Busch *(VP-Sls)*
Steve Dillard *(VP-Corp Sls Dev)*
Brands & Products:
ALWAYS SAVE
ASSOCIATED WHOLESALE GROCERS
AWG

AWREY BAKERIES, INC.
(Holding of Monomoy Capital Partners, L.P.)
12301 Farmington Rd
Livonia, MI 48150-1747
Tel.: (734) 522-1100
Fax: (734) 522-1585
Toll Free: (800) 950-2253
Web Site: www.awrey.com
E-Mail For Key Personnel:
Marketing Director: leslye.davidson@awrey.com
Sales Range: $25-49.9 Million
Approx. Number Employees: 400
Year Founded: 1910
Business Description:
Bakery Goods Producer & Distr
S.I.C.: 2051
N.A.I.C.S.: 311812
Import Export
Media: 2-4-7-10-16-17-19-20-21
Distr.: Natl.
Budget Set: Oct.
Personnel:
Bob Wallace *(Pres & CEO-North America)*
Greg Gallagher *(CFO)*
Connie Holston *(VP-SE Sls)*
Leslie Davidson *(Dir-Mktg)*
Brands & Products:
AWREY
GRANDE
MAESTRO
MARQUISE
Advertising Agency:
The Northwest Group
28265 Beck Rd Ste C2
Wixom, MI 48393
Tel.: (248) 349-9480
Fax: (248) 349-9415
(Awrey, Marquise, Grande)

B&B CORPORATE HOLDINGS, INC.
927 S US Hwy 301
Tampa, FL 33619
Tel.: (813) 621-6411
Fax: (813) 622-8163
E-mail: info@bnbch.com
Approx. Number Employees: 450
Year Founded: 1923
Business Description:
Grocery Store Operator
S.I.C.: 6719; 5141; 5411
N.A.I.C.S.: 551112; 424410; 445110
Media: 5-8-9-10-13-18-19-20-22-23-24-26
Distr.: Direct to Consumer; Reg.
Personnel:
Jay Andrew Bever, Jr. *(Pres)*
Dave Easterman *(CFO)*
Kathy Hovatter *(Dir-Adv)*

BARI BEEF INTERNATIONAL
(Formerly Bari Importing Corp.)
3875 Bengert St
Orlando, FL 32808-4603
Tel.: (407) 298-0560
Fax: (407) 293-2032
E-mail: baripap@aol.com
Approx. Number Employees: 250
Year Founded: 1973
Business Description:
Importer of Italian Foods
S.I.C.: 5149; 5147
N.A.I.C.S.: 424490; 311612
Import Export
Advertising Expenditures: $400,000
Media: 4-7-8-10-11-13-22
Personnel:
Enzo Paparella *(Pres)*
Brands & Products:
BARI BRANDS

BARNIE'S COFFEE & TEA COMPANY
2126 Landstreet Rd Ste 300
Orlando, FL 32809
Tel.: (407) 854-6600
Fax: (407) 854-6601
Toll Free: (800) 284-1416
E-mail: customerservice@barniescoffee.com
Web Site: www.barniescoffee.com

Key to Media (For complete agency information see *The Advertising Red Books-Agencies* edition):
1. Bus. Publs. 2. Cable T.V. 3. Catalogs & Directories. 4. Co-op Adv. 5. Consumer Mags. 6. D.M. to Bus. Estab.7. D.M. to Consumers 8. Daily Newsp. 9. Exhibits/Trade Shows 10. Foreign 11. Infomercial 12. Internet Adv.13. Multimedia 14. Network Radio 15. Network T.V. 16. Newsp. Distr. Mags. 17. Other 18. Outdoor (Posters, Transit) 19. Point of Purchase20. Premiums, Novelties 21. Product Samples 22. Special Events Mktg. 23. Spot Radio 24. Spot T.V. 25. Weekly Newsp. 26. Yellow Page Adv.

E-Mail For Key Personnel:
Sales Director: sales@barniescoffee.com
Approx. Number Employees: 50
Year Founded: 1980
Business Description:
Coffee & Tea Shops
S.I.C.: 5499; 5719
N.A.I.C.S.: 445299; 442299
Import
Media: 5-7-9-17-18-19-23-25-26
Distr.: Reg.
Personnel:
Ronado Sirota *(CFO)*
Meredith McGrath *(Dir-Mktg)*
Brands & Products:
BARNIE'S
BARNIE'S COFFEE
DECAF BARNIE'S
DECAF COOL CAFE BLUES
DECAF SANTA'S WHITE CHRISTMAS
SANTA'S WHITE CHRISTMAS
WALKER'S

BASHAS' SUPERMARKETS
22402 S Basha Rd
Chandler, AZ 85248-4908
Mailing Address:
PO Box 488
Chandler, AZ 85244-0488
Tel.: (480) 895-9350
Fax: (480) 895-5371
Toll Free: (800) 755-7292
E-mail: bashas@synergypromo.com
Web Site: www.bashas.com
Approx. Rev.: $2,500,000,000
Approx. Number Employees: 14,300
Year Founded: 1932
Business Description:
Retail Grocery Stores
S.I.C.: 5411; 5149
N.A.I.C.S.: 445110; 424490
Advertising Expenditures: $8,350,000
Media: 2-6-8-9-16-18-20-22-23-24-25-26
Distr.: Reg.
Budget Set: Nov.
Personnel:
Edward N. Basha, Jr. *(Chm)*
Johnny Basha *(Vice Chm & Sr VP-Real Estate)*
James Buhr *(CFO & Sr VP-Fin)*
Edward N. Basha, III *(Sr VP-Legal & Fin Affairs)*
Ike Basha *(Sr VP-Support Svcs)*
Gregg Tucek *(VP-Legal Affairs-HR)*
Bryon Roberts *(Dir-Non Perishable & Gen Mgr)*
Kristy Nied *(Dir-Comm)*
Monica Sherbaum *(Dir-Adv)*
Ralph Woodward *(Dir-Ops)*
Christa Levine *(Brand Mgr-Bashas Family of Stores)*
Brands & Products:
BASHAS'
FOOD CLUB
FULL CIRCLE
PAWS
TOP CARE
TOP CREST
VALU TIME
Advertising Agency:
Arvizu Advertising & Promotions
3101 N Central Ave Ste 150
Phoenix, AZ 85012-2650
Tel.: (602) 279-4669
Fax: (602) 279-4977
(Food City, Bashas')
— Ray Arvizu *(Chief Exec. Officer)*

BASIC FOOD INTERNATIONAL, INC.
Ste 202 901 S Federal Hwy
Fort Lauderdale, FL 33316-1236
Tel.: (954) 467-1700
Fax: (954) 764-5110
Fax: (954) 462-0913
Telex: 514347-803198
E-mail: info@basicfood.com
Web Site: www.basicfood.com
Sales Range: $10-24.9 Million
Approx. Number Employees: 30
Year Founded: 1976
Business Description:
Whslr, Importer & Exporter of Fresh Fruits & Vegetables, Canned & Packaged Groceries, Frozen Meats, Poultry & Seafood
S.I.C.: 5146; 5142
N.A.I.C.S.: 424460; 424420
Import Export
Advertising Expenditures: $50,000
Media: 2-4-7-13-26
Personnel:
John P. Bauer *(Pres & CEO)*

B.C. TREE FRUITS LTD.
1473 Water St
Kelowna, BC V1Y 1J6, Canada
Tel.: (250) 470-4200
Fax: (250) 762-5571
Web Site: www.bctree.com
Sales Range: $1-9.9 Million
Approx. Number Employees: 43
Year Founded: 1936
Business Description:
Fruit & Vegetable Broker
S.I.C.: 5431
N.A.I.C.S.: 445230
Export
Media: 2-10
Distr.: Intl.
Budget Set: June
Personnel:
John Bernard *(CFO & Sec)*
Peter Austin *(Dir-Sls Canada)*
Rick Austin *(Dir-Sls)*
Adrian Abbott *(Mgr-Mktg Svcs)*

BEL AIR MARKETS
(Sub. of Raley's Inc.)
500 W Capitol Ave
West Sacramento, CA 95605-2624
Mailing Address:
PO Box 15618
Sacramento, CA 95852-1618
Tel.: (916) 373-3333
Fax: (916) 373-6351
E-mail: jobs@raleys.com
Web Site: www.raleys.com
Approx. Number Employees: 500
Year Founded: 1955
Business Description:
Retail Grocery
S.I.C.: 5411
N.A.I.C.S.: 445110
Media: 6-8-9-10-17-23-24-25-26
Distr.: Direct to Consumer; Reg.
Personnel:
Michael Teeo *(Pres & CEO)*

BELCANTO FOODS, LLC
(Sub. of Dairyland USA Corporation)
1300 Viele Ave
Bronx, NY 10474-7134
Tel.: (718) 497-3888
Fax: (718) 497-3799
E-mail: info@belcantofoods.com
Web Site: www.belcantofoods.com
Approx. Number Employees: 35
Year Founded: 1978
Business Description:
Importer & Distr of Specialty Food Products
S.I.C.: 5499; 5149
N.A.I.C.S.: 445299; 424490
Import
Media: 4-7-10-16-19-21-25-26
Distr.: Natl.
Personnel:
John Corbino *(Mgr-Import)*

BI-LO, LLC
(Holding of Lone Star Funds)
208 Industrial Blvd
Greenville, SC 29607
Mailing Address:
PO Box 99
Mauldin, SC 29662
Tel.: (864) 213-2500
Fax: (864) 234-6999
Toll Free: (800) 862-9293
Web Site: www.bi-lo.com
Approx. Rev.: $3,600,000,000
Approx. Number Employees: 23,500
Year Founded: 1961
Business Description:
Grocery Store Operator
S.I.C.: 5411
N.A.I.C.S.: 445110
Personnel:
Randall Onstead *(Chm)*
Michael Byars *(Pres & CEO)*
Anthea Jones *(Sr VP-Store Ops)*
Joan Miszak *(Sr VP-HR & Org Effectiveness)*
Bill Nasshan *(Sr VP-Mdsg & Mktg)*
Bruce Steadman *(Grp VP-Center Store)*
Kip Faulhaber *(VP-Sls, Mktg, Adv & Pricing)*
John Gianakas *(VP-Center Store Category Mgmt)*
Advertising Agency:
Erwin-Penland
(Owned by Hill, Holliday, Connors, Cosmopulos, Inc., Member of the Interpublic Group)
125 E Broad St
Greenville, SC 29601
Tel.: (864) 271-0500
Fax: (864) 235-5941

BIG Y FOODS, INC.
2145 Roosevelt Ave
Springfield, MA 01102
Tel.: (413) 784-0600
Fax: (413) 731-8135
Toll Free: (800) 828-2688
E-mail: regan@bigy.com
Web Site: www.bigy.com
Sales Range: $1-4.9 Billion
Approx. Number Employees: 9,500
Year Founded: 1936
Business Description:
Supermarkets
S.I.C.: 5411
N.A.I.C.S.: 445110
Import
Advertising Expenditures: $30,000,000
Media: 2-3-4-5-8-9-10-17-18-19-21-22-23-24-25-26
Distr.: Direct to Consumer; Reg.
Personnel:
Charles L. D'Amour *(Owner)*
Donald H. D'Amour *(Chm & CEO)*
Daniel Lescoe *(Sr VP-Mdsg)*
Michael S. Gold *(VP-Legal Affairs & Govt Relations)*
Jack Henry *(VP-HR)*
Kevin R. Regan *(VP-Fin)*
John Sarno *(VP-Info Sys)*
Phil Schneider *(VP-Sls)*
John Schnepp *(Dir-Adv)*
Casimir M. Tryba *(Dir-Food Safety)*
Brands & Products:
BIG Y
ONLY THE BEST FOR YOUR FAMILY FROM OURS
SAVINGS CLUB
WORLD CLASS MARKET
Advertising Agency:
Mars Advertising Group
(d/b/a UNIQUE CONCEPTS INTERNATIONAL)
25200 Telegraph Rd
Southfield, MI 48034
Tel.: (248) 936-2200
Fax: (248) 936-2760
Toll Free: (800) 521-9317
— Marilyn Barnett *(Acct. Exec.)*

BIGLARI HOLDINGS INC.
175 E Houston St Ste 1300
San Antonio, TX 78205
Tel.: (317) 633-4100
Web Site: www.biglariholdings.com
Approx. Rev.: $673,781,000
Approx. Number Employees: 20,000
Year Founded: 1934
Business Description:
Restaurant Chain Owner, Operator & Franchiser
S.I.C.: 5812
N.A.I.C.S.: 722110
Advertising Expenditures: $18,900,000
Media: 5-8-15-16-20
Personnel:
Sardar Biglari *(Chm & CEO)*
Philip L. Cooley *(Vice Chm)*
Duane E. Geiger *(Interim CFO)*
Dennis Roberts *(Sr VP-Ops Excellence)*
J. Michael Vance *(VP-IT & Plng)*
Brands & Products:
BANAWBERRY
BITS N PIECES
EXACTLY THE WAY YOU WANT IT
FAXASAK
IN SIGHT IT MIGHT BE RIGHT
SIPPABLE SUNDAE
STARWNILLA
STEAK N SHAKE FAMOUS FOR STEAKBURGERS
STEAK N SHAKE ITS A MEAL
STEAKBURGER
STOREFRONTDESIGN
TAKHOMACARD
TAKHOMACUP
VANOCHA
THE WING & CIRCLE
Advertising Agencies:
EchoPoint Media
407 N Fulton St
Indianapolis, IN 46202
Tel.: (317) 264-8400

Key to Media (For complete agency information see *The Advertising Red Books-Agencies* edition):
1. Bus. Publs. 2. Cable T.V. 3. Catalogs & Directories. 4. Co-op Adv. 5. Consumer Mags. 6. D.M. to Bus. Estab.7. D.M. to Consumers 8. Daily Newsp. 9. Exhibits/Trade Shows 10. Foreign 11. Infomercial 12. Internet Adv.13. Multimedia 14. Network Radio 15. Network T.V. 16. Newsp. Distr. Mags. 17. Other 18. Outdoor (Posters, Transit) 19. Point of Purchase20. Premiums, Novelties 21. Product Samples 22. Special Events Mktg. 23. Spot Radio 24. Spot T.V. 25. Weekly Newsp. 26. Yellow Page Adv.

Biglari Holdings Inc. — (Continued)

Fax: (317) 264-8401

kirshenbaum bond senecal + partners
160 Varick St 4th Fl
New York, NY 10013
Tel.: (212) 633-0080
Fax: (212) 463-8643

BISCUITVILLE, INC.
1414 Yanceyville St Ste 300
Greensboro, NC 27405-1753
Tel.: (336) 229-6671
Fax: (336) 553-3701
E-mail: info@biscuitville.com
Web Site: www.biscuitville.com
Approx. Number Employees: 750
Year Founded: 1966
Business Description:
Food Service Chain
S.I.C.: 5812
N.A.I.C.S.: 722211
Advertising Expenditures: $750,000
D.M. to Consumers: $375,000; Premiums, Novelties: $375,000
Distr.: Reg.
Personnel:
Maurice Jennings *(Founder & Chm)*
Burney Jennings *(Pres)*
Jeff May *(CFO & VP)*
Kellie Hicks *(Dir-Brand Dev & Mktg)*
Dan Hotchkiss *(Dir-Purchasing & Product Dev)*

BJ'S WHOLESALE CLUB, INC.
25 Research Dr
Westborough, MA 01581
Tel.: (508) 651-7400
Fax: (508) 651-6114
E-mail: investor@bjs.com
Web Site: www.bjs.com
Approx. Rev.: $10,877,239,000
Approx. Number Employees: 24,800
Year Founded: 1997
Business Description:
Warehouse Club Merchandising; Food & General Merchandise
S.I.C.: 5399; 5136; 5137
N.A.I.C.S.: 452910; 424320; 424330; 452990
Media: 4-5-8-13-18-23-24-26
Distr.: Natl.
Personnel:
Laura J. Sen *(Pres & CEO)*
Robert W. Eddy *(CFO & Exec VP)*
Peter Amalfi *(CIO & Exec VP)*
Susan Hoffman *(Chief People Officer & Sr VP-HR)*
Lon F. Povich *(Gen Counsel, Sec & Exec VP)*
Bruce L. Graham *(Sr VP & Gen Mdse Mgr)*
Cornel Catuna *(Exec VP-Club Ops)*
Christina M. Neppl *(Exec VP-Msdg & Logistics)*
Michael P. Atkinson *(Sr VP & Dir-Mktg & E-Commerce)*
John B. Mulleady *(Sr VP & Dir-Real Estate)*
Brands & Products:
BJ'S
BJ'S AUTO BUYING PROGRAM
BJ'S GAS
BJ'S HOME IMPROVEMENT
BJ'S OPTICAL DEPARTMENT
BJ'S PROPANE
BJ'S REWARDS
BJ'S REWARDS MEMBERSHIP
BJ'S TIRE CENTER
BJ'S.COM
INNER CIRCLE
WELLSLEY FARMS
Advertising Agency:
Connelly Partners
46 Waltham St Fl 4
Boston, MA 02118
Tel.: (617) 956-5050
Fax: (617) 956-5054

BLIMPIE INTERNATIONAL INC.
Ste 500 180 Interstate North Pkwy SE
Atlanta, GA 30339-2190
Tel.: (770) 984-2707
Fax: (770) 952-3558
Toll Free: (800) 447-6256
Web Site: www.blimpie.com
Sales Range: $25-49.9 Million
Approx. Number Employees: 110
Year Founded: 1964
Business Description:
Fast Food Restaurants Franchisor
S.I.C.: 5812
N.A.I.C.S.: 722211
Media: 3-8-9-23-24
Brands & Products:
AMERICA'S BEST DRESSED SANDWICH
BLIMPIE
BLIMPIE BEST
BLIMPIE BLAST
BLIMPIE BLUFFIN
BLIMPIE SUPER SUMMER
BLIMPIE XPRESS
CHILI OLE
COUNTING CARBS? COUNT ON BLIMPIE!
CRUNCH-A-BOWL
HAVE BLIMPIE WILL TRAVEL
I WANT MY BLIMPIE
IT'S A BEAUTIFUL THING
MAUI TACOS
PASTA CENTRAL
SMOOTHIE ISLAND
ZESTO PESTO

BOSTON PIZZA INTERNATIONAL, INC.
5500 Parkwood Way
Richmond, BC Canada
Tel.: (604) 270-1108
Fax: (604) 270-4168
E-mail: forresterj@bostonpizza.com
Web Site: www.bostonpizza.com
Approx. Number Employees: 100
Business Description:
Pizza Restaurant Franchisor
S.I.C.: 5499
N.A.I.C.S.: 445299
Media: 8-14-15-23-24
Personnel:
George C. Melville *(Co-Owner & Co-Chm)*
Walter James Treliving *(Co-Owner & Co-Chm)*
Mark G. Pacinda *(Pres & COO)*
Mike Cordoba *(CEO)*
Mark Powell *(CFO)*
Joanne Forrester *(VP-Mktg, Corp Svcs)*

BOZZUTO'S INC.
275 Schoolhouse Rd
Cheshire, CT 06410-1241
Tel.: (203) 272-3511
Fax: (203) 250-2954
Toll Free: (800) 243-9761
Web Site: www.bozzutos.com
Sales Range: $900-999.9 Million
Approx. Number Employees: 2,000
Year Founded: 1945
Business Description:
Wholesale Food Distr
S.I.C.: 5141; 5147
N.A.I.C.S.: 424410; 424470
Media: 4-8-9-10-13-18-19-20-22-23-24-25
Personnel:
Michael Bozzuto *(Chm, Pres & CEO)*
Kevin Daly *(Gen Counsel & VP)*
Steve Heggelke *(Sr VP-Mdsg)*
John Keeley *(Sr VP-Bus Tech Sys & Svcs)*
Dan Brock *(VP-Sls)*
Gail Handley *(VP-Customer Svc)*
Robert H. Wood *(VP-Fin)*
Bonnie Sirois *(Dir-Corp HR)*
Amy Yeager *(Dir-Adv & Comm)*
Bob Schooly *(Mgr-Reg Mdsg)*
Advertising Agency:
FKQ Advertising + Marketing
15351 Roosevelt Blvd
Clearwater, FL 33760-3534
Tel.: (727) 539-8800
Fax: (866) 707-6648

BROOKSHIRE GROCERY COMPANY
1600 W SW Loop 323
Tyler, TX 75701-8532
Mailing Address:
PO Box 1411
Tyler, TX 75710-1411
Tel.: (903) 534-3000
Fax: (903) 534-2206
Fax: (903) 534-2240
Web Site: www.brookshires.com
Sales Range: $1-4.9 Billion
Approx. Number Employees: 12,500
Year Founded: 1928
Business Description:
Retail Grocery Business, Supermarkets
S.I.C.: 5411
N.A.I.C.S.: 445110
Media: 8-9-13-19-25
Personnel:
Brad Brookshire *(Chm)*
Rick Rayford *(Pres & CEO)*
Carolyn Hutson *(CFO & Exec VP)*
Tim King *(CFO & Exec VP)*
John D'Anna *(CIO & Sr VP)*
Rick Ellis *(CMO & Sr VP)*
Mark Brookshire *(Exec Officer)*
Britt Brookshire *(Pres-Retail Ops Grp)*
Tim Brookshire *(Pres-HR & Fin)*
Russ Cooper *(Gen Counsel, Sec & Exec VP)*
Kevin Albritton *(Exec VP-Sls & Mktg)*
Kenny Holt *(Exec VP-HR)*
Mike Terry *(Exec VP-Retail Ops)*
Gregg Skelly *(Sr VP & Mgr-Super 1 Foods Div)*
Jim Cousineau *(Sr VP-Pharmacy Ops)*
David Krause *(Sr VP-Category Mgmt)*
Greg Nordyke *(Sr VP-Corp Dev)*
John Penn *(Sr VP-Retail Projects)*
Scott Reily *(Sr VP-Logistics)*
Trent Brookshire *(VP & Mgr-District 10)*
Rebecca Sanders *(VP-Mktg)*
Kevin Santone *(VP-Category Mgmt)*
Roger Story *(VP-Mdsg)*
Linda Wiggins *(VP-Sls Events)*
Philip Aldredge *(Dir-Mktg)*
Pete Leung *(Dir)*
Brands & Products:
BROOKSHIRE'S
BROOKSHIRE'S. THANK YOU FOR YOUR LOYALTY.
OLE FOODS
SUPER1FOODS

BRUNO'S SUPERMARKETS, LLC
(Holding of Lone Star Funds)
(Filed for Ch. 11 Bankruptcy on 2/5/2009)
1800 International Park Dr Ste 500
Birmingham, AL 35243
Tel.: (205) 916-5220
Fax: (205) 916-5261
Toll Free: (877) 927-8667
Web Site: www.brunos.com
Sales Range: $300-349.9 Million
Approx. Number Employees: 4,200
Year Founded: 1933
Business Description:
Supermarket Operator
S.I.C.: 5411
N.A.I.C.S.: 445110
Advertising Expenditures: $15,000,000
Media: 3-5-6-8-9-13-14-15-17-18-22-23-24-25-26
Personnel:
David West *(Chm)*
Jim Grady *(Chief Restructuring Officer)*
Brands & Products:
BRUNO'S
FOOD WORLD
Advertising Agency:
Godwin Advertising Agency, Inc. (d/b/a GodwinGroup)
1 Jackson Pl 188 E Capitol St Ste 800
Jackson, MS 39201
Tel.: (601) 354-5711
Fax: (601) 960-5869

BUTERA FINER FOODS INC.
1 Clock Twr Plz
Elgin, IL 60120-6918
Tel.: (847) 741-1010
Fax: (847) 741-9674
E-mail: buteramarket@yahoo.com
Web Site: www.buteramarket.com
Sales Range: $75-99.9 Million
Approx. Number Employees: 300
Year Founded: 1968
Business Description:
Food Stores
S.I.C.: 5411
N.A.I.C.S.: 445110
Advertising Expenditures: $1,700,000
Media: 7-9-16-19-25
Distr.: Reg.
Budget Set: Monthly
Personnel:
Joseph Butera *(Pres)*
Brands & Products:
BUTERA

BUTLER WHOLESALE PRODUCTS, INC.
37 Pleasant St
Adams, MA 01220-1739
Tel.: (413) 743-3885
Fax: (413) 743-3887

Key to Media (For complete agency information see *The Advertising Red Books-Agencies* edition):
1. Bus. Publs. 2. Cable T.V. 3. Catalogs & Directories. 4. Co-op Adv. 5. Consumer Mags. 6. D.M. to Bus. Estab.7. D.M. to Consumers 8. Daily Newsp. 9. Exhibits/Trade Shows 10. Foreign 11. Infomercial 12. Internet Adv.13. Multimedia 14. Network Radio 15. Network T.V. 16. Newsp. Distr. Mags. 17. Other 18. Outdoor (Posters, Transit) 19. Point of Purchase20. Premiums, Novelties 21. Product Samples 22. Special Events Mktg. 23. Spot Radio 24. Spot T.V. 25. Weekly Newsp. 26. Yellow Page Adv.

E-mail: info@butlerwholesale.com
Web Site: www.butlerwholesale.com
Approx. Number Employees: 65
Year Founded: 1915
Business Description:
Foodservice Distr
S.I.C.: 5141; 5142
N.A.I.C.S.: 424410; 424420
Media: 2-4

C&K MARKET, INC.

615 5th St
Brookings, OR 97415-9199
Tel.: (541) 469-3113
Fax: (541) 469-6717
E-mail: info@ckmarket.com
Web Site: www.ckmarket.com
Sales Range: $250-299.9 Million
Approx. Number Employees: 2,500
Year Founded: 1956
Business Description:
Operator of Supermarkets
S.I.C.: 5411
N.A.I.C.S.: 445110
Media: 9-13-18-26
Personnel:
Doug Nidiffer *(CEO)*
Brands & Products:
C&K MARKET
PRICE LESS FOODS
RAY'S
RAY'S FOOD PLACE
SHOP SMART

C&S WHOLESALE GROCERS, INC.

7 Corporate Dr
Keene, NH 03431
Tel.: (603) 354-7000
Fax: (603) 354-4690
E-mail: info@cswg.com
Web Site: www.cswg.com
Sales Range: $15-24.9 Billion
Approx. Number Employees: 12,000
Year Founded: 1918
Business Description:
Grocery Whslr
S.I.C.: 5141; 5142
N.A.I.C.S.: 424410; 424420
Media: 2-22
Personnel:
Rick Cohen *(Chm & CEO)*
Joe Caracappa *(CIO & Exec VP-Process Engrg)*
Michael Newbold *(Exec VP-Corp Dev & Gen Counsel)*
Scott Charlton *(Exec VP-Ops)*
Bruce Johnson *(Exec VP-HR)*
Bob Palmer *(Exec VP-Procurement, Mdsg, Mktg & Supply Chain)*
Richard Wyckoff *(Exec VP-Sls & Mktg & Chief Customer Officer)*
Tracy Moore *(Sr VP-Mdsg)*

CALFEE COMPANY OF DALTON, INC.

(d/b/a Favorite Markets)
1503 N Tibbs Rd
Dalton, GA 30720-2915
Tel.: (706) 226-4834
Fax: (706) 275-4417
E-mail: webmaster@favmkt.com
Web Site: www.favmkt.com
Approx. Number Employees: 800
Year Founded: 1989
Business Description:
Convenience Stores
S.I.C.: 5411; 5541
N.A.I.C.S.: 445120; 447190
Import Export
Advertising Expenditures: $650,000
Media: 2-4-13-16-17
Personnel:
Samuel D. Turner *(Chm & CEO)*
Joseph Turner *(CFO)*
Advertising Agency:
Falls Communications
50 Public Sq 25th Fl
Cleveland, OH 44113
Tel.: (216) 696-0229
Fax: (216) 696-0269

CALIFORNIA RAISIN MARKETING BOARD

2445 Capitol St Ste 200
Fresno, CA 93721
Tel.: (559) 248-0287
Fax: (559) 224-7016
E-mail: info@raisins.org
Web Site: www.loveyourraisins.com
Approx. Number Employees: 4
Business Description:
Promoter of California-Grown Raisins
S.I.C.: 8611
N.A.I.C.S.: 813910
Media: 2-6-8-10-13
Personnel:
Gary Schulz *(Pres)*
Larry Blagg *(Sr VP-Mktg)*
Rick O'Fallon *(Dir-Mktg)*
Advertising Agencies:
Fleishman-Hillard Inc.
300 Capitol Mall Ste 1100
Sacramento, CA 95814
Tel.: (916) 441-7606
Fax: (916) 441-7622

Thomas J. Payne Market Development
865 Woodside Way PO Box 281525
San Mateo, CA 94401-1611
Tel.: (650) 340-8311
Fax: (650) 340-8568

CANNATA'S CORPORATION

6307 W Park Ave
Houma, LA 70364-2235
Tel.: (504) 851-2253
Fax: (985) 873-9178
Toll Free: (800) 226-6282
E-mail: sales@houmanet.com
Web Site: www.cannatas.com
Sales Range: $25-49.9 Million
Approx. Number Employees: 350
Year Founded: 1959
Business Description:
Operate Grocery Stores
S.I.C.: 5812
N.A.I.C.S.: 722320
Import Export
Advertising Expenditures: $800,000
Media: 2-4-13-16
Brands & Products:
CANNATAS KING CAKE

CASEYS GENERAL STORES, INC.

1 Convenience Blvd
Ankeny, IA 50021
Tel.: (515) 965-6100
Fax: (515) 965-6160
Web Site: www.caseys.com
Approx. Rev.: $5,635,240,000
Approx. Number Employees: 9,013
Year Founded: 1967
Business Description:
Retailer of Gasoline, Prepared Foods & Fountain Items, Groceries & Other Merchandise
S.I.C.: 5411; 5013; 5149; 5541; 6794
N.A.I.C.S.: 445120; 424490; 441310; 447110; 533110
Advertising Expenditures: $1,000,000
Media: 4-13-16-18-22-25
Personnel:
Robert J. Myers *(Pres & CEO)*
William J. Walljasper *(CFO & Sr VP)*
Terry W. Handley *(COO)*
Julia L. Jackowski *(Gen Counsel & Corp Sr VP-HR)*
Eli J. Wirtz *(Gen Counsel & VP)*
Brian J. Johnson *(Sec & VP-Fin)*
Sam J. Billmeyer *(Sr VP-Logistics & Acq)*
Michael R. Richardson *(VP-Mktg)*
Advertising Agency:
Barkley
1740 Main St
Kansas City, MO 64108
Tel.: (816) 842-1500
Broadcast
Casey's (Agency of Record)
Creative
Marketing
Media Planning
Online
Print

CENTERPLATE, INC.

(Holding of Kohlberg & Company, LLC)
2187 Atlantic St
Stamford, CT 06902
Tel.: (203) 975-5900
Toll Free: (800) 698-6992
E-mail: info@centerplate.com
Web Site: www.centerplate.com
Sales Range: $1-4.9 Billion
Year Founded: 1995
Business Description:
Food Service, Catering & Merchandising Services Contractor
S.I.C.: 5812
N.A.I.C.S.: 722310; 722320
Media: 10
Personnel:
Joseph J. O'Donnell *(Chm)*
Desmond J. Hague *(Pres & CEO)*
Kevin Francis McNamara *(CFO, Chief Admin Officer & Exec VP)*
Chris Verros *(COO)*
Bob Pascal *(CMO)*
John Sergi *(Chief Design Officer)*
Keith Baxter Wilison King *(Gen Counsel, Sr VP & Sec)*
Hadi K. Monavar *(Exec VP-Strategic Plng)*
George Wooten *(Exec VP-Ops)*
Pat Bruhn *(Sr VP-Entertainment)*
Kyle Kandel *(Sr VP-Convention Centers-East)*
John Vingas *(Sr VP-Convention Centers-West)*
Gary Wattie *(Sr VP-New Bus Dev)*
Brands & Products:
CENTERPLATE
CRAVEABLE EXPERIENCES. RAVEABLE RESULTS.

CHECKERS DRIVE-IN RESTAURANTS, INC.

(Holding of Wellspring Capital Management LLC)
4300 W Cypress St Ste 600
Tampa, FL 33607-4159
Tel.: (813) 283-7000
Fax: (813) 283-7001
Web Site: www.checkers.com
Sales Range: $150-199.9 Million
Approx. Number Employees: 4,000
Year Founded: 1986
Business Description:
Drive-Through Hamburger Restaurants
S.I.C.: 5812
N.A.I.C.S.: 722211
Advertising Expenditures: $10,400,000
Media: 5-8-10-14-15-18-19-22-23-24-26
Personnel:
William P. Foley, II *(Chm)*
Enrique Silva *(Pres & CEO)*
Todd Lindsey *(CFO & Sr VP & Diver-Deep Sea)*
Terry Snyder *(CMO, Exec VP & Driver-Racecar)*
Brian Doster *(Gen Counsel, Sr VP & Boating Enthusiast)*
Adam Noyes *(Exec VP-Ops & Team Player)*
Lori Malcolm *(Sr VP-HR)*
David Masvidal *(Brand Mgr)*
Brands & Products:
BIG BUFORD
CHAMP BURGER
RALLY'S
YOU GOTTA EAT
Advertising Agency:
ML Rogers
102 Madison Ave 10th Fl
New York, NY 10016
Tel.: (212) 213-3833

CHEESECAKE FACTORY INCORPORATED

26901 Malibu Hills Rd
Calabasas Hills, CA 91301
Tel.: (818) 871-3000
Fax: (818) 871-3100
E-mail: jpeters@thecheesecakefactory.com
Web Site: www.thecheesecakefactory.com
Approx. Rev.: $1,659,404,000
Approx. Number Employees: 31,500
Year Founded: 1972
Business Description:
Restaurant Chain & Wholesale Bakery
S.I.C.: 5812; 2051; 5813
N.A.I.C.S.: 722211; 311812; 722110; 722410
Advertising Expenditures: $7,300,000
Media: 22
Personnel:
David Overton *(Chm & CEO)*
Michael E. Jannini *(Pres)*
W. Douglas Benn *(CFO & Exec VP)*
David M. Gordon *(COO & Sr VP)*
Jim Rasmussen *(CIO & Sr VP)*
Donald Evans *(CMO)*
Cheryl M. Slomann *(Chief Acctg Officer, VP & Controller)*
Max S. Byfuglin *(Pres-Cheesecake Factory Bakery Inc)*
Debby R. Zurzolo *(Gen Counsel, Sec & Exec VP)*
Dina R. Barmasse-Gray *(Sr VP-HR)*

Key to Media (For complete agency information see *The Advertising Red Books-Agencies* edition):
1. Bus. Publs. 2. Cable T.V. 3. Catalogs & Directories. 4. Co-op Adv. 5. Consumer Mags. 6. D.M. to Bus. Estab.7. D.M. to Consumers
8. Daily Newsp. 9. Exhibits/Trade Shows 10. Foreign 11. Infomercial 12. Internet Adv.13. Multimedia 14. Network Radio
15. Network T.V. 16. Newsp. Distr. Mags. 17. Other 18. Outdoor (Posters, Transit) 19. Point of Purchase20. Premiums, Novelties
21. Product Samples 22. Special Events Mktg. 23. Spot Radio 24. Spot T.V. 25. Weekly Newsp. 26. Yellow Page Adv.

Cheesecake Factory Incorporated — (Continued)

Keith Carango *(Sr VP-Bakery Ops)*
Russell Greene *(Sr VP-Ops Svcs)*
Donald Moore *(Sr VP-Kitchen Ops)*
Brands & Products:
BUFFALO BLASTS
THE CHEESECAKE FACTORY
THE CHEESECAKE FACTORY BAKERY
THE CHEESECAKE FACTORY BAKERY CAFE
THE CHEESECAKE FACTORY EXPRESS
GODIVA
GRAND LUX CAFE
KAHLUA
OREO
ROCKSUGAR PAN ASIAN KITCHEN
SPLENDA
WHITE CHOCOLATE RASPBERRY TRUFFLE
Advertising Agencies:
Ansira
15851 Dallas Pkwy Ste 725
Addison, TX 75001
Tel.: (972) 663-1100
Fax: (972) 663-1300

New Media Strategies
1100 Wilson Blvd Ste 1400
Arlington, VA 22209
Tel.: (703) 253-0050
Fax: (703) 253-0065

CITARELLA
2135 Broadway
New York, NY 10023
Tel.: (212) 874-0383
Fax: (212) 595-3738
E-mail: services@citarella.com
Web Site: www.citarella.com
Approx. Number Employees: 40
Year Founded: 1912
Business Description:
Gourmet & Specialty Grocer
S.I.C.: 5411
N.A.I.C.S.: 445110
Advertising Expenditures: $500,000
Media: 6-13-18-19
Personnel:
Joseph Gurrera *(Pres & CEO)*
Marc Oshima *(VP-Mktg)*
Brands & Products:
CITARELLA
Advertising Agency:
Redscope
619 W 54th St 7th Fl
New York, NY 10010
Tel.: (212) 505-3100
Fax: (212) 582-2152

COLORADO PRIME FOODS LLC
500 Bi County Blvd Ste 400
Farmingdale, NY 11735-3996
Tel.: (631) 694-1111
Fax: (631) 694-8493
Toll Free: (800) 365-2404
E-mail: info@reordermenu.com
Web Site: www.reordermenu.com
Sales Range: Less than $1 Million
Approx. Number Employees: 15
Year Founded: 1959
Business Description:
Home Food Service Company
S.I.C.: 5499
N.A.I.C.S.: 445299
Media: 4-13
Personnel:
Paul Roman *(CEO)*
Brands & Products:
COLORADO PRIME FOODS
WE'RE WHAT'S FOR DINNER!

CONVENIENT FOOD MART, INC.
(Sub. of CFM Holding Corporation)
467 N State St
Painesville, OH 44077-8009
Tel.: (440) 639-6515
Fax: (440) 639-6526
Toll Free: (800) 860-4844
E-mail: info@convenientfoodmart.com
Web Site:
www.convenientfoodmart.com
Sales Range: $300-349.9 Million
Approx. Number Employees: 225
Year Founded: 1958
Business Description:
Convenience Stores Franchiser & Operator
S.I.C.: 5411; 5541
N.A.I.C.S.: 445120; 447110
Advertising Expenditures: $7,000,000
Media: 5-8-9-18-19-20-23-24-25-26
Distr.: Natl.
Budget Set: Nov.
Personnel:
John C. Call *(Pres)*
Brands & Products:
CONVENIENT FOOD MART

THE COPPS CORPORATION
(Div. of Roundy's Supermarkets Inc.)
2828 Wayne St
Stevens Point, WI 54481-4169
Tel.: (715) 344-5900
Fax: (715) 344-7378
Web Site: www.copps.com
Sales Range: $600-649.9 Million
Approx. Number Employees: 2,500
Year Founded: 1982
Business Description:
Wholesale & Retail Groceries, Meat, Produce, Frozen Foods
S.I.C.: 5141; 5411
N.A.I.C.S.: 424410; 445110
Media: 8-13-16-20-21-25
Personnel:
Bob Mariano *(Pres)*
Brands & Products:
COPPS SQUAD FOR KIDS

COUSINS SUBMARINES, INC.
N83 W13400 Leon Rd
Menomonee Falls, WI 53051-3306
Tel.: (262) 253-7700
Fax: (262) 253-7710
Toll Free: (800) 238-9736
E-mail: info@cousinssubs.com
Web Site: www.cousinssubs.com
Approx. Sls.: $70,000,000
Approx. Number Employees: 850
Year Founded: 1972
Business Description:
Sub Sandwiches & Fast Food Franchiser
S.I.C.: 5812
N.A.I.C.S.: 722211
Media: 3-9-18-19-20-21-23-24-25-26
Distr.: Reg.
Budget Set: Oct. -Dec.
Personnel:
Kendall Richmond *(CFO)*
Larry Weissman *(VP-Mktg)*
Tom Laabs *(Sr Dir-Pur)*
Mark Cairns *(Dir-Franchising Sls)*
Joel Ferguson *(Dir-Dev)*
Justin McCoy *(Dir-Mktg)*
Brands & Products:
BETTER BREAD BETTER SUBS
COUSINS
COUSINS SUBS
Advertising Agency:
Zeppos & Associates, Inc.
400 E Mason St Ste 200
Milwaukee, WI 53202-3703
Tel.: (414) 276-6237
Fax: (414) 276-2322

CUB FOODS OF APPLETON INC.
(Sub. of SUPERVALU, Inc.)
1200 W Northland Ave
Appleton, WI 54914-1415
Tel.: (920) 739-6253
Fax: (920) 739-2648
Approx. Rev.: $11,800,000
Approx. Number Employees: 110
Business Description:
Grocery Stores
S.I.C.: 5411
N.A.I.C.S.: 445110
Media: 9-13-14-17-23
Personnel:
Keith R. Wyche *(Pres & CEO)*

CUB FOODS STORES
(Sub. of SUPERVALU, Inc.)
1801 Market dr
Stillwater, MN 55082-0009
Mailing Address:
PO Box 9
Stillwater, MN 55082
Tel.: (651) 430-2350
Fax: (651) 439-3190
Web Site: www.cub-foods.com
Sales Range: $150-199.9 Million
Approx. Number Employees: 300
Year Founded: 1968
Business Description:
Grocery Retailer
S.I.C.: 5411
N.A.I.C.S.: 445110
Media: 3-5-8-9-18-19-23-24-25
Distr.: Intl.; Natl.
Budget Set: Mar.
Personnel:
Chris Murphy *(Sr Mgr-Pub Rels & Consumer Affairs)*

CULINART, INC.
175 Sunnyside Blvd
Plainview, NY 11803-6769
Tel.: (516) 437-2700
Fax: (516) 437-6680
E-mail: pmurnane@culinartinc.com
Web Site: www.culinartinc.com
Approx. Number Employees: 800
Year Founded: 1994
Business Description:
Provider of Eating Place Services
S.I.C.: 5812; 8748
N.A.I.C.S.: 722310; 541618
Import Export
Media: 17
Personnel:
Joseph Pacifico *(Chm & CEO)*
Thomas Eich *(Pres)*
Vincent Stracquadanio *(CFO)*
Michael Pitkewicz *(VP-HR)*

CUMBERLAND FARMS, INC.
777 Dedham St PO Box 9178
Canton, MA 02021-1402
Tel.: (508) 270-1400
Fax: (781) 459-6624
Toll Free: (800) 225-9702
E-mail: customerservice@cumberlandfarms.com
Web Site: www.cumberlandfarms.com
Sales Range: $5-14.9 Billion
Approx. Number Employees: 7,000
Year Founded: 1939
Business Description:
Convenience Store & Gas Station Operator
S.I.C.: 5411; 5541
N.A.I.C.S.: 445120; 447110
Media: 8-9-13-19-20-21-23-25
Distr.: Reg.
Personnel:
Lily Haseotes Bentas *(Chm & CEO)*
Harry Brenner *(Pres & COO)*
Stephen Winslow *(CFO)*
Mark Howard *(Chief Legal Officer, Gen Counsel & Sec)*
Daniel D. Phaneuf *(Sr VP-Retail Ops)*
Edward Potkay *(Dir-Transportation & Fleet Svcs)*
Brands & Products:
CUMBERLAND FARMS
THE STOP THAT KEEPS YOU GOING.
Advertising Agency:
Warner Communications
41 Raymond St
Manchester, MA 01944
Tel.: (978) 526-1960
Fax: (978) 526-8206

CYTOSPORT, INC.
4795 Industrial Way
Benicia, CA 94510
Tel.: (707) 751-3942
Fax: (707) 748-5732
Web Site: www.cytosport.com
Approx. Rev.: $3,000,000
Approx. Number Employees: 40
Year Founded: 1997
Business Description:
Nutritional Products Mfr & Distr
S.I.C.: 5499
N.A.I.C.S.: 446191
Media: 18
Personnel:
Greg Pickett *(Founder, Pres & CEO)*
Nikki Brown *(VP-Mktg)*
Brands & Products:
CYTOCARB II
CYTOGAINER
CYTOMAX
CYTOMAX NATURAL
CYTOMAX PROTEIN
EVOPRO
FAST TWITCH
JOINT MATRIX
MONSTER AMINO
MONSTER MAIZE
MONSTER MASS
MONSTER MILK
MONSTER PUMP
MUSCLE MILK
MUSCLE MILK LIGHT
MUSCLE MILK 'N OATS
MUSCLE MILK NATURALS

Key to Media (For complete agency information see *The Advertising Red Books-Agencies* edition):
1. Bus. Publs. 2. Cable T.V. 3. Catalogs & Directories. 4. Co-op Adv. 5. Consumer Mags. 6. D.M. to Bus. Estab.7. D.M. to Consumers 8. Daily Newsp. 9. Exhibits/Trade Shows 10. Foreign 11. Infomercial 12. Internet Adv.13. Multimedia 14. Network Radio 15. Network T.V. 16. Newsp. Distr. Mags. 17. Other 18. Outdoor (Posters, Transit) 19. Point of Purchase20. Premiums, Novelties 21. Product Samples 22. Special Events Mktg. 23. Spot Radio 24. Spot T.V. 25. Weekly Newsp. 26. Yellow Page Adv.

MUSCLE MILK REFUEL
MUSCLE MILK TETRA

D'AGOSTINO SUPERMARKETS INC.

1385 Boston Post Rd
Larchmont, NY 10538-3904
Tel.: (914) 833-4000
Fax: (914) 833-4060
Web Site: www.dagnyc.com
Sales Range: $200-249.9 Million
Approx. Number Employees: 1,150
Year Founded: 1932
Business Description:
Operator of Supermarkets
S.I.C.: 5411
N.A.I.C.S.: 445110
Media: 9-18-22-23
Personnel:
Nicholas D'Agostino, Jr. *(Pres)*
Richard Lagreca *(VP-Fin)*

DAHL'S FOOD MART INC.

4343 Merle Hay Rd
Des Moines, IA 50310-1411
Tel.: (515) 276-4845
Fax: (515) 278-0012
E-mail: dahlsfeedback@dahlsfoods.com
Web Site: www.dahlsfoods.com
Approx. Number Employees: 1,600
Year Founded: 1951
Business Description:
Grocery Supermarkets
S.I.C.: 5194; 5411
N.A.I.C.S.: 424940; 445110
Media: 13
Personnel:
David Sinwell *(Pres)*
Ross Nixon *(COO & Exec VP)*
Mark Brase *(VP-Mktg)*
Brands & Products:
DAHL'S

DAWN FOOD PRODUCTS, INC.

3333 Sargeant Rd
Jackson, MI 49201-3473
Tel.: (517) 789-4400
Fax: (517) 789-4465
Web Site: www.dawnfoods.com
Sales Range: $1-4.9 Billion
Approx. Number Employees: 2,100
Year Founded: 1978
Business Description:
Mfr & Distr of Bakery Mixes, Ingredients & Supplies
S.I.C.: 2045; 5046
N.A.I.C.S.: 311822; 423440
Personnel:
Miles E. Jones *(Co-Chm)*
Ronald L. Jones *(Co-Chm)*
Carrie Jones-Barber *(CEO)*
David Knowlton *(CFO)*
Chip Potter *(Dir-Mktg)*
Brands & Products:
APPLE CRISP
BAKERS EASE
BAKERS SELECT
BASE A
BUT-R-CREME
DAWN
DIP QUIK
EXTEND-R
HERITAGE
LIBERTY
MAJESTIC
PAKS
RAISED
REGENCY
SELECT CHOCOLATE
SELECT DONUT
SNACKEES
TRADITIONAL RECIPE
VELVETOP
Advertising Agency:
Barkley
1740 Main St
Kansas City, MO 64108
Tel.: (816) 842-1500

DEAN & DELUCA, INC.

560 Broadway
New York, NY 10012-3938
Tel.: (212) 226-6800
Fax: (212) 334-2619
Toll Free: (800) 999-0306
E-mail: customerservice@deandeluca.com
Web Site: www.deandeluca.com
Approx. Number Employees: 800
Year Founded: 1977
Business Description:
Retailer of Gourmet Foods; Grocery & Deli Chain
S.I.C.: 5499; 5812
N.A.I.C.S.: 445299; 722211
Export
Media: 4-7-8-11-13-21
Personnel:
Justin Seamonds *(Pres)*
Tiena Manypenny *(VP-E-Commerce)*
Brands & Products:
DEAN & DELUCA
Advertising Agency:
Jajo, Inc.
200 N Broadway Ste 110
Wichita, KS 67202
Tel.: (316) 267-6700
Fax: (316) 267-3531

DEL FRISCO'S RESTAURANT GROUP, LLC

(Holding of Lone Star Funds)
125 N Market Ste 1300
Wichita, KS 67202
Tel.: (316) 264-8899
Fax: (316) 264-3282
Web Site: www.lonestarsteakhouse.com
Approx. Rev.: $152,543,000
Approx. Number Employees: 2,337
Business Description:
Restaurant Owner & Operator
S.I.C.: 5812
N.A.I.C.S.: 722110
Personnel:
Mark S. Mednansky *(CEO)*
Jon W. Howie *(CFO)*
April Scopa *(VP-HR & Trng)*
Tracy Hendrix *(Mgr-Mktg & Sls)*
Advertising Agency:
Neff + Associates, Inc.
The Novelty Bldg 15 S Third St 4th Fl
Philadelphia, PA 19106
Tel.: (215) 627-4747
Fax: (215) 923-6333

DEMOULAS SUPER MARKETS INC.

(d/b/a Market Basket)
875 E St
Tewksbury, MA 01876
Tel.: (978) 851-8000
Fax: (978) 640-8390
Sales Range: $1-4.9 Billion
Approx. Number Employees: 12,350
Year Founded: 1954
Business Description:
Supermarkets
S.I.C.: 5411
N.A.I.C.S.: 445110
Media: 5-16-19
Personnel:
William J. Shea *(Chm)*
Arthur Damoulas *(Pres)*
Donald Mulligan *(Treas & VP-Fin)*
Joseph Rockwell *(VP-Mdsg & Sls-Grocery)*

DIERBERGS MARKETS INC.

16690 Swingley Rdg Rd
Chesterfield, MO 63017-0758
Tel.: (636) 532-8884
Fax: (636) 812-1603
Web Site: www.dierbergs.com
Approx. Sls.: $575,000,000
Approx. Number Employees: 5,000
Year Founded: 1854
Business Description:
Supermarkets
S.I.C.: 5411
N.A.I.C.S.: 445110
Media: 13-19
Personnel:
Robert J. Dierberg *(Chm)*
F. Roger Dierberg *(Vice Chm)*
Gregory J. Dierberg *(Pres & CEO)*
Connie Hawley *(CFO & VP)*
Andrew J. Pauk *(COO & Sr VP)*
John Muckerman *(VP-Mktg & Adv)*
Linda Ryan *(VP-HR)*

DOMINICK'S FINER FOODS, LLC

(Sub. of Safeway Inc.)
711 Jorie Blvd
Oak Brook, IL 60523-4425
Tel.: (630) 891-5000
Fax: (630) 891-5210
Web Site: www.dominicks.com
Approx. Number Employees: 11,582
Year Founded: 1925
Business Description:
Owner & Operator of Grocery Stores
S.I.C.: 5411
N.A.I.C.S.: 445110
Media: 8-23-24-25
Distr.: Direct to Consumer; Reg.

DOT FOODS, INC.

1 Dot Way
Mount Sterling, IL 62353
Mailing Address:
PO Box 192
Mount Sterling, IL 62353
Tel.: (217) 773-4411
Fax: (217) 773-3321
Toll Free: (800) 366-3687
E-mail: webmaster@dotfoods.com
Web Site: www.dotfoods.com
Sales Range: $1-4.9 Billion
Approx. Number Employees: 3,000
Year Founded: 1960
Business Description:
Food Logistics Services
S.I.C.: 4225; 4222; 5149; 5812
N.A.I.C.S.: 493110; 424490; 493120; 722310
Personnel:
Patrick F. Tracy *(Chm)*
John M. Tracy *(CEO)*
William H. Metzinger *(CFO)*
Joe Tracy *(COO)*
James W. Tracy *(Gen Counsel)*
Dick Tracy *(Exec VP-Food Service)*
Jeff Bottorff *(VP-Quality-Trng)*
Michael J. Duggan *(VP-Sls)*
George Eversman *(VP-Retail)*
Scott C. Stamerjohn *(VP-Mktg)*
Dorcas Galloway *(Dir-Inside Sls)*
Brands & Products:
BUILD YOUR BUSINESS, NOT MORE BUILDINGS.
DOT
DOT EXPRESSWAY
DOT ON DEMAND
DOT SAMPLE EXPRESS
DOT VIRTUAL WAREHOUSE
Advertising Agency:
Hughes
1141 S 7th St
Saint Louis, MO 63104
Tel.: (314) 571-6300

EATERIES, INC.

1208 E Broadway Rd Ste 120
Tempe, AZ 85282
Tel.: (480) 347-3800
Fax: (480) 347-3810
Web Site: www.eateriesinc.com
E-Mail For Key Personnel:
Marketing Director: KristenM@eats-inc.com
Sales Range: $75-99.9 Million
Approx. Number Employees: 2,500
Year Founded: 1984
Business Description:
Owner, Operator & Franchiser of Casual Restaurants
S.I.C.: 5812; 5813
N.A.I.C.S.: 722110; 722410
Import
Media: 3-5-8-9-18-23-24-25
Distr.: Reg.
Personnel:
James M. Burke *(Co-Founder, Pres, COO & Asst Sec)*
Bradley L. Grow *(CFO, VP & Asst Sec)*
Marilyn Ruggles *(VP-Mktg)*
Lori Imel *(Mgr-Mktg)*
Brands & Products:
EATERIES
GARCIA'S
GARFIELD'S
PEPPERONI GRILL
Advertising Agency:
ROI Media
5801 E 41st St Ste 600
Tulsa, OK 74135-5628
Tel.: (918) 582-9777
Fax: (918) 592-6635
(Garfield's & Garcia's)
— Lester J. Boyle *(Acct. Exec.)*

EDEN FOODS INC.

701 Tecumseh Rd
Clinton, MI 49236-9589
Tel.: (517) 456-7424
Fax: (517) 456-6075
E-mail: info@edenfoods.com
Web Site: www.edenfoods.com
Sales Range: $25-49.9 Million
Approx. Number Employees: 80
Year Founded: 1968
Business Description:
Grocery & Related Services
S.I.C.: 5149; 2098
N.A.I.C.S.: 424490; 311823

Key to Media (For complete agency information see *The Advertising Red Books-Agencies* edition):
1. Bus. Publs. 2. Cable T.V. 3. Catalogs & Directories. 4. Co-op Adv. 5. Consumer Mags. 6. D.M. to Bus. Estab.7. D.M. to Consumers 8. Daily Newsp. 9. Exhibits/Trade Shows 10. Foreign 11. Infomercial 12. Internet Adv.13. Multimedia 14. Network Radio 15. Network T.V. 16. Newsp. Distr. Mags. 17. Other 18. Outdoor (Posters, Transit) 19. Point of Purchase20. Premiums, Novelties 21. Product Samples 22. Special Events Mktg. 23. Spot Radio 24. Spot T.V. 25. Weekly Newsp. 26. Yellow Page Adv.

Eden Foods Inc. — (Continued)

Import Export
Media: 6
Personnel:
Michael Potter *(Pres)*
James Hughes *(CFO)*
Jon Solomon *(Pur Dir)*
Sue Potter *(Mgr-Mktg)*
Brands & Products:
BIFA-15
EDEN
EDEN BIFA 15
EDEN ORGANIC
EDEN RANCH
EDEN SPRINGS
EDENBALANCE
EDENBLEND
EDENSOY
GOOD FOOD GOOD REASON HEALTH AND HAPPINESS
TETRA PAK
TWISTED PAIR
UNIVERSAL APPEAL
Advertising Agency:
Grey Singapore
No1 Magazine Road
Singapore, 059567, Singapore
Tel.: (65) 6511 7600
Fax: (65) 6223 8992
Eden Wasabi Chips

EINSTEIN NOAH RESTAURANT GROUP, INC.

555 Zang St Ste 300
Lakewood, CO 80228-1013
Tel.: (303) 568-8000
Fax: (303) 568-8039
E-mail: customerservice@enbc.com
Web Site: www.einsteinnoah.com
Approx. Rev.: $411,711,000
Approx. Number Employees: 6,796
Business Description:
Coffee Bars & Bagel Bakeries
S.I.C.: 2032; 5461; 5812
N.A.I.C.S.: 311422; 445291; 722213
Advertising Expenditures: $9,900,000
Media: 8-18-19-23-24
Personnel:
E. Nelson Heumann *(Chm)*
Jeffrey O'Neill *(Pres & CEO)*
Emanuel P.N. Hilario *(CFO)*
Daniel J. Dominguez *(COO)*
Rhonda J. Parish *(Chief Legal Officer & Sec)*
Robert E. Gowdy, Jr. *(Chief Acctg Officer & Controller)*
James P. O'Reilly *(Chief Concept Officer)*
Mike Ellis *(Exec VP-Franchise & Restaurant Dev)*
Brian Unger *(Exec VP-Ops)*
Jeff Keune *(VP-Mktg)*
Brands & Products:
CHESAPEAKE BAGEL BAKERY
EINSTEIN BROS
EINSTEIN NOAH RESTAURANT GROUP, INC.
NEW WORLD COFFEE
NOAH'S NEW YORK BAGELS
Advertising Agencies:
Fishman Public Relations
1161 Lk Cook Rd Ste E
Deerfield, IL 60015
Tel.: (847) 945-1300
Fax: (847) 945-3755

Young & Rubicam Chicago
233 N Michigan Ave 16th Fl
Chicago, IL 60601-5519
Tel.: (312) 596-3000
Fax: (312) 596-3130
Agency of Record
Creative, Digital & Media Campaigns

EMPIRE COMPANY LIMITED

115 King Street
Stellarton, NS B0K 1S0, Canada
Tel.: (902) 755-4440
Fax: (902) 755-6477
Telex: 19-36536
E-mail: paul.sobey@sobeys.ca
Web Site: www.empireco.ca
E-Mail For Key Personnel:
President: paul.sobey@sobeys.ca
Approx. Sls.: $16,029,200,000
Approx. Number Employees: 49,000
Year Founded: 1963
Business Description:
Holding Company; Supermarkets, Food Distr, Movie Theaters & Real Estate
S.I.C.: 5411; 6719
N.A.I.C.S.: 445110; 551112
Import
Media: 13-18-19
Personnel:
Robert P. Dexter *(Chm)*
Paul D. Sobey *(Pres & CEO)*
Paul V. Beesley *(CFO & Exec VP)*
John G. Morrow *(VP & Comptroller)*
Stewart H. Mahoney *(VP-Treasury & IR)*
Brands & Products:
OUR COMPLIMENTS
SMART CHOICE
SOBEYS

ENERLUME ENERGY MANAGEMENT CORP.

2 Broadway
Hamden, CT 06518-2614
Tel.: (203) 248-4100
Fax: (203) 230-8667
E-mail: info@enerlume.com
Web Site: www.enerlume.com
Sales Range: $1-9.9 Million
Approx. Number Employees: 59
Year Founded: 1986
Business Description:
Fluorescent Lighting Products Mfr
S.I.C.: 3646
N.A.I.C.S.: 335122
Media: 2-4-7-17-18
Personnel:
Patrick J. Healy *(Chm)*
John Ekregen *(Acting Pres)*
Ronald R. Sparks *(Pres-RS Svcs)*
Mark Cerreta *(Exec VP-Lindley)*

FARM FRESH INC.

(Sub. of SUPERVALU, Inc.)
853 Chimney Hill Shopping Ctr
Virginia Beach, VA 23452
Mailing Address:
PO Box 2250
Virginia Beach, VA 23450-2250
Tel.: (757) 306-7006
Fax: (757) 306-2218
Fax: (757) 306-2213
Fax: (757) 306-2215
Toll Free: (800) 280-6726
Web Site: www.farmfreshmarkets.com
Sales Range: $150-199.9 Million
Approx. Number Employees: 100
Year Founded: 1957
Business Description:
Supermarkets
S.I.C.: 5541; 5399; 5411
N.A.I.C.S.: 447110; 445110; 445120; 452910
Advertising Expenditures: $5,000,000
Media: 5-8-9-18-19-23-24
Distr.: Reg.
Budget Set: June
Personnel:
Gaelo de la Fuente *(Pres)*
Michael Griffith *(Sr VP-Engrg)*
Pat Campbell *(VP-Mdsg-Bakery)*
Chris VanParys *(VP-Mdsg-Perishable)*
Mike Johannsen *(Mgr-Mfg)*
Brands & Products:
FARM FRESH
RACK N' SACK
RICH FOOD
Advertising Agency:
Burford Company Advertising
125 E Main St
Richmond, VA 23219
Tel.: (804) 780-0354
Fax: (804) 780-0025

FARM STORES

18001 Old Cutler Rd Ste 370
Palmetto, FL 33157
Tel.: (305) 677-0616
Toll Free: (800) 726-3276
E-mail: customerservice@farmstores.com
Web Site: www.farmstores.com
Approx. Number Employees: 900
Year Founded: 1937
Business Description:
Convenience Food Stores; Gasoline Stations
S.I.C.: 5411
N.A.I.C.S.: 445120
Media: 9-13-14
Distr.: Direct to Consumer; Reg.
Personnel:
Carlos Bared *(CEO)*
Maurice Bared *(COO)*

FIESTA MART INC.

(Sub. of Grocers Supply Co., Inc.)
5235 Katy Fwy
Houston, TX 77007-2210
Mailing Address:
PO Box 7481
Houston, TX 77007
Tel.: (713) 869-5060
Fax: (713) 869-6197
E-mail: fmi@fiestamart.com
Web Site: www.fiestamart.com
Approx. Number Employees: 150
Year Founded: 1972
Business Description:
Supermarket Retailer
S.I.C.: 5411
N.A.I.C.S.: 445110
Media: 8-9-13-18-23-24
Distr.: Natl.; Reg.
Personnel:
Louis Katopodis *(Pres & CEO)*
Jim Cronan *(CIO)*
Keith Jacobsen *(Dir-Adv)*
Brands & Products:
FIESTA MART

THE FOOD EMPORIUM

(Sub. of The Great Atlantic & Pacific Tea Company, Inc.)
42 West 39th St
New York, NY 10018
Tel.: (212) 915-2202
Fax: (212) 915-2228
E-mail: thefooodemporium@aptea.com
Web Site: www.thefoodemporium.com
Approx. Sls.: $364,000,000
Approx. Number Employees: 40
Year Founded: 1979
Business Description:
Retail Supermarket Chain
S.I.C.: 5411
N.A.I.C.S.: 445110
Import Export
Advertising Expenditures: $6,000,000
Media: 5-6-7-8-9-11-13-14-16-19-22-23-25-26
Distr.: Direct to Consumer; Reg.
Personnel:
Bill Farlie *(Dir-Creative)*
Advertising Agency:
Benjamin & Ribaudo Advertising Inc.
212 W 35th St 10th Fl
New York, NY 10001
Tel.: (212) 465-2496
Fax: (212) 465-2497
(All Grocery Products-Print & Media)

FOOD LION, LLC

(Sub. of Delhaize America, Inc.)
2110 Executive Dr
Salisbury, NC 28147-9007
Mailing Address:
PO Box 1330
Salisbury, NC 28145-1330
Tel.: (704) 633-8250
Fax: (704) 630-5024
Toll Free: (800) 210-9569
Web Site: www.foodlion.com
Approx. Number Employees: 7,500
Year Founded: 1957
Business Description:
Supermarket Services
S.I.C.: 5411
N.A.I.C.S.: 445110
Advertising Expenditures: $3,000,000
Media: 5-8-9-13-16-18-24-25
Distr.: Direct to Consumer; Natl.
Budget Set: Aug.
Personnel:
Robert Canipe *(Sr VP-Corp Dev)*
Glenn Dixon *(VP & Deputy Gen Counsel)*
Greg Finchum *(VP-Retail Svcs)*
Ken Mills *(VP-Sls & Mktg)*
R. Kyle Mitchell *(VP-Construction & Engrg)*
Billy Zyliak *(Dir-Ops)*
Brands & Products:
ANGUS PRIDE
FOOD LION
KASH N' KARRY
SAVE 'N PACK
Advertising Agencies:
Ames Scullin O'Haire
245 Peachtree Center Ave 23rd Fl
Atlanta, GA 30303
Tel.: (404) 659-2769
Fax: (404) 659-7664

G&G Advertising
2804 3rd Ave N
Billings, MT 59101

Key to Media (For complete agency information see *The Advertising Red Books-Agencies* edition):
1. Bus. Publs. 2. Cable T.V. 3. Catalogs & Directories. 4. Co-op Adv. 5. Consumer Mags. 6. D.M. to Bus. Estab.7. D.M. to Consumers 8. Daily Newsp. 9. Exhibits/Trade Shows 10. Foreign 11. Infomercial 12. Internet Adv.13. Multimedia 14. Network Radio 15. Network T.V. 16. Newsp. Distr. Mags. 17. Other 18. Outdoor (Posters, Transit) 19. Point of Purchase20. Premiums, Novelties 21. Product Samples 22. Special Events Mktg. 23. Spot Radio 24. Spot T.V. 25. Weekly Newsp. 26. Yellow Page Adv.

Tel.: (406) 294-8113
Fax: (406) 294-8120
Toll Free: (800) 390-2892

THE FRED W. ALBRECHT GROCERY CO.
(d/b/a Acme Fresh Markets)
2700 Gilchrist Rd
Akron, OH 44305-4433
Tel.: (330) 733-2263
Fax: (330) 733-8782
Web Site: www.acmestores.com
Approx. Sls.: $259,000,000
Approx. Number Employees: 2,000
Year Founded: 1891
Business Description:
Grocery Store Operator
S.I.C.: 5411
N.A.I.C.S.: 445110
Media: 9-21-23-25
Personnel:
Steven Albrecht *(Pres & CEO)*
James Trout *(VP-Mdsg)*
Marilyn Guthier *(Dir-Consumer Mktg)*
David Nestor *(Dir-Adv)*
Brands & Products:
ACME

FRENCH MEADOW BAKERY, INC.
1000 Apollo Rd
Eagan, MN 55121
Tel.: (651) 286-7861
Fax: (651) 454-3327
Toll Free: (877) NO-YEAST
E-mail: info@frenchmeadow.com
Web Site: www.frenchmeadow.com
Approx. Sls.: $3,200,000
Approx. Number Employees: 72
Business Description:
Whslr & Retailer of Bakery Products
S.I.C.: 5149; 5461
N.A.I.C.S.: 424490; 311811
Media: 6
Brands & Products:
FRENCH MEADOW BAKERY
HEALTHSEED
HEALTHY HEMP
KAMUT
MEN'S BREAD
OUR DAILY BREAD
WOMAN'S BREAD

FRESH & EASY NEIGHBORHOOD MARKET INC
(Sub. of Tesco plc)
2120 Park Pl # 200
El Segundo, CA 90245-4741
Tel.: (310) 341-1200
Web Site: www.freshandeasy.com
Business Description:
Grocery Chain
S.I.C.: 5411
N.A.I.C.S.: 445110
Personnel:
James Dibbo, *(CFO)*
Advertising Agency:
Deutsch LA
5454 Beethoven St
Los Angeles, CA 90066-7017
Tel.: (310) 862-3000
Fax: (310) 862-3100

FRESH BRANDS, INC.
(Sub. of Certifresh Holdings Inc.)
2215 Union Ave
Sheboygan, WI 53081
Tel.: (920) 457-4433
Fax: (920) 457-6295
Web Site: www.fresh-brands.com
Sales Range: $650-699.9 Million
Approx. Number Employees: 2,400
Year Founded: 1912
Business Description:
Supermarket Retailer & Grocery Whslr
S.I.C.: 5411; 5141
N.A.I.C.S.: 445110; 424410
Advertising Expenditures: $2,443,000
Media: 4-5-6-13-16-18-19-22-23-24-25

THE FRESH MARKET, INC.
628 Green Valley Rd Ste 500
Greensboro, NC 27408-7099
Tel.: (336) 272-1338
Fax: (336) 272-5800
E-mail: rantandrave@freshmarket.net
Web Site: www.thefreshmarket.net
Approx. Sls.: $974,213,000
Approx. Number Employees: 7,300
Year Founded: 1982
Business Description:
Grocery Store Owner & Operator
S.I.C.: 5411
N.A.I.C.S.: 445110
Import
Advertising Expenditures: $1,737,000
Media: 8-10-13
Personnel:
Ray Berry *(Chm)*
Michael Barry *(Vice Chm)*
Brett Berry *(Vice Chm)*
Craig Carlock *(Pres & CEO)*
Lisa Klinger *(CFO)*
Sean Crane *(Sr VP-Store Ops)*
Marc Jones *(Sr VP-Mdsg & Mktg)*
Randy Kelley *(Sr VP-Real Estate & Dev)*
Jeff Short *(VP-Fin)*

FROSTY ACRES BRANDS, INC.
1225 Old Alpharetta Rd Ste 235
Alpharetta, GA 30005
Tel.: (678) 356-5400
Fax: (678) 356-0100
Toll Free: (800) 569-4821
E-mail: info@frostyacres.com
Web Site: www.frostyacres.com
Approx. Number Employees: 55
Year Founded: 1954
Business Description:
National Marketing & Food Buying Cooperative
S.I.C.: 5142; 5141
N.A.I.C.S.: 424420; 424410
Advertising Expenditures: $250,000
Media: 2-5-7-10-13-16
Distr.: Natl.
Budget Set: Jan.
Personnel:
George T. Watson *(Pres & CEO)*
Philli Eakinf *(CFO & VP)*
Cindy Naes *(Sr VP-Procurement & Mktg)*
Jake Marsh *(Reg VP-South)*
Georgia Barber *(Mgr-Mktg)*
Brands & Products:
BUTTERFUL
COCINA CASERA
F.A.B
FROSTY SEAS
FROSTY WHIP
GARDEN DELIGHT
OREFRESCO
SERVING AMERICA'S TABLES TODAY AND TOMORROW
TASTY TATERS

GELSON'S MARKETS
(Sub. of Arden Group, Inc.)
16400 Ventura Blvd Ste 240 PO Box 1802 91426
Encino, CA 91436-2123
Tel.: (818) 906-5700
Fax: (818) 990-7877
E-mail: info@gelsons.com
Sales Range: $75-99.9 Million
Approx. Number Employees: 200
Business Description:
Supermarkets
S.I.C.: 5411
N.A.I.C.S.: 445110
Media: 9-22-23
Personnel:
Bernard Briskin *(Chm & CEO)*
Robert E. Stiles *(Pres)*
Tom Frattali *(Sr VP-Grocery Pur & Mdsg & Distr)*
Donna Tyndall *(Sr VP-Store Ops)*

GENUARDI'S FAMILY MARKETS INC.
(Sub. of Safeway Inc.)
301 E Germantown Pike
Norristown, PA 19401
Tel.: (610) 277-6000
Fax: (610) 277-7783
E-mail: info@genuardis.com
Web Site: www.genuardis.com
Sales Range: $1-4.9 Billion
Approx. Number Employees: 6,500
Year Founded: 1920
Business Description:
Supermarket Operator
S.I.C.: 5411
N.A.I.C.S.: 445110
Media: 4-8-9-13-16-20-22-23-24
Personnel:
Glenn Davis *(CFO)*
Advertising Agency:
Dailey & Associates
(Sub. of The Interpublic Group of Cos., Inc.)
8687 Melrose Ave Ste G300
West Hollywood, CA 90069-5701
Tel.: (310) 360-3100
Fax: (310) 360-0810

GERLAND CORPORATION
3131 Pawnee St
Houston, TX 77054-3302
Tel.: (713) 746-3600
Fax: (713) 746-3621
Web Site: www.gerlands.com
Approx. Number Employees: 1,500
Year Founded: 1967
Business Description:
Grocery Stores
S.I.C.: 5411
N.A.I.C.S.: 445110
Media: 13-18-19-22
Personnel:
Kevin P. Doris *(Pres & CEO)*
Jeff Reeder *(CFO, Treas & VP)*
Rick Noeth *(Sr VP-Bakery-Ops)*

GIANT EAGLE AMERICAN SEAWAY FOODS
(Sub. of Giant Eagle, Inc.)
5300 Richmond Rd
Bedford, OH 44146
Tel.: (216) 292-7000
Fax: (216) 591-2804
Toll Free: (800) 362-8899
Approx. Number Employees: 5,800
Year Founded: 1987
Business Description:
Food Distr
S.I.C.: 5411; 5141
N.A.I.C.S.: 445110; 424410
Advertising Expenditures: $5,900,000
Media: 2-4-7-10
Distr.: Direct to Consumer; Reg.
Budget Set: Dec.
Personnel:
Anthony C. Rego *(Chm & CEO)*
Mary Winston *(CFO, Treas & Sr VP)*
Kevin Srigley *(Sr VP)*
Jean C. Colarik *(Dir-Retail HR)*
Brands & Products:
AMERICAN SEAWAY FOODS
EAGLE
RINI-REGO MARKETPLACE
RINI-REGO STOP-N-SHOP
SEAWAY

GIANT EAGLE, INC.
101 Kappa Dr
Pittsburgh, PA 15238-2809
Tel.: (412) 963-6200
Fax: (412) 968-1617
Toll Free: (800) 553-2324
E-mail: human.resources@gianteagle.com
Web Site: www.gianteagle.com
Sales Range: $5-14.9 Billion
Approx. Number Employees: 36,000
Year Founded: 1931
Business Description:
Grocery Products Whslr & Retailer
S.I.C.: 5411; 5141
N.A.I.C.S.: 445110; 424410
Advertising Expenditures: $22,000,000
Media: 5-8-9-10-17-23-24-25
Distr.: Direct to Consumer; Natl.
Budget Set: July
Personnel:
David S. Shapira *(Chm, Pres & CEO)*
Raymond J. Burgo *(Vice Chm)*
Russ Ross *(CIO)*
Laura Karet *(Chief Strategy Officer & Sr Exec VP)*
Mark Minnaugh *(Chief Acctg Officer & Exec VP)*
Ed Steinmetz *(Sr VP-Meat, Seafood & Prepared Foods)*
Kevin Srigley *(VP-Mktg)*
Rob Borella *(Sr Dir-Mktg)*
Chuck Porter *(Sr Dir)*
David Atkins *(Dir-Inedible)*
Brands & Products:
THE BAKE SHOP
EAGLE'S NEST
THE FAMOUS DELI
GETGO
GIANT EAGLE
THE GIFT GARDEN
IGGLE VIDEO
JAVA SONATA CAFE
LEAF & LADLE
MARKET DISTRICT
NATURE'S BASKET
PIZZA DI CASA
PROSERIES
RIVER CITY CHICKEN
Advertising Agencies:
NFM Group Inc.
320 Fort Duquesne Blvd 26 H

Key to Media (For complete agency information see *The Advertising Red Books-Agencies* edition):
1. Bus. Publs. 2. Cable T.V. 3. Catalogs & Directories. 4. Co-op Adv. 5. Consumer Mags. 6. D.M. to Bus. Estab.7. D.M. to Consumers
8. Daily Newsp. 9. Exhibits/Trade Shows 10. Foreign 11. Infomercial 12. Internet Adv.13. Multimedia 14. Network Radio
15. Network T.V. 16. Newsp. Distr. Mags. 17. Other 18. Outdoor (Posters, Transit) 19. Point of Purchase20. Premiums, Novelties
21. Product Samples 22. Special Events Mktg. 23. Spot Radio 24. Spot T.V. 25. Weekly Newsp. 26. Yellow Page Adv.

Giant Eagle, Inc. — (Continued)

Pittsburgh, PA 15222
Tel.: (412) 394-6400
Fax: (412) 394-6411
Event Marketing

RJW Media
5830 Ellsworth Ave Ste 200
Pittsburgh, PA 15232-1778
Tel.: (412) 361-6833
Fax: (412) 361-8005
(Media Buying)

Young & Rubicam Chicago
233 N Michigan Ave 16th Fl
Chicago, IL 60601-5519
Tel.: (312) 596-3000
Fax: (312) 596-3130

GIANT FOOD LLC

(Sub. of The Stop & Shop Supermarket Company)
(d/b/a Giant-Landover)
8301 Professional Pl Ste 115
Landover, MD 20785
Tel.: (781) 380-8000
Fax: (301) 618-4968
Web Site: www.giantfood.com
Year Founded: 1936
Business Description:
Supermarket Operator
S.I.C.: 5411; 5912
N.A.I.C.S.: 445110; 446110
Import Export
Media: 8-9-16-18-19-23-24-25
Distr.: Reg.
Personnel:
Carl Schlicker *(Pres & CEO)*
Paula A. Price *(CFO)*
Paula Labian *(Exec VP-HR)*
Brands & Products:
GIANT FOOD
SUPER G
YOU'VE GOT A GIANT ON YOUR SIDE

GIANT FOOD STORES, LLC

(Sub. of Ahold USA, Inc.)
1149 Harrisburg Pike
Carlisle, PA 17013-1665
Mailing Address:
PO Box 249
Carlisle, PA 17013-0249
Tel.: (717) 249-4000
Fax: (717) 960-1950
Web Site: www.giantpa.com
Approx. Number Employees: 22,000
Year Founded: 1923
Business Description:
Grocery Store Operator
S.I.C.: 5411
N.A.I.C.S.: 445110
Advertising Expenditures: $9,000,000
Media: 8-25-26
Personnel:
Rick Herring *(Pres)*
John Bussenger *(Exec VP-HR)*
Jamess Ferraro *(Exec VP-Real Estate & Construction)*
Peter Labbe *(Exec VP-Retail Ops)*
Jeff Martin *(Exec VP-Sls & Mdsg)*
Casper Meijer *(Exec VP)*
Jodie Daubert *(Sr VP-Perishables)*
Erik Keptner *(Sr VP-Mktg & Comm)*
Walt Lentz *(Sr VP-Supply Chain)*
Nancy Appleby *(VP-Adv & Mktg Plng)*
Mary Jane Jamrogowicz *(VP-IT)*
Sylvia Emberger *(Reg Dir)*
Charles Achuff *(Dir-IT)*
Ron Bagley *(Dir-Compact Formats)*
Lawrence Knorr *(Dir-Info Systems)*
Joe LaCagnia *(Dir-Real Estate)*
Tracy Pawelski *(Dir-Pub & Community Rels)*
Chuck Shank *(Dir-Ops)*
Greg Tobin, III *(Dir-Adv)*
Brands & Products:
EXTRA REWARDS
NATURE'S PROMISE
Advertising Agency:
Mullen
40 Broad St
Boston, MA 02109
Tel.: (617) 226-9000
Fax: (617) 226-9100

GLOBAL CONDIMENTS, INC.

415 E Calder Way
State College, PA 16801
Tel.: (814) 237-0134
Fax: (814) 237-1893
Web Site: www.herlocher.com
Approx. Rev.: $118,305
Business Description:
Internet Mustard, Salsa & Other Food Products Whslr
S.I.C.: 5961; 5149
N.A.I.C.S.: 454111; 424490
Advertising Expenditures: $22,614
Media: 17
Personnel:
Charles C. Herlocher, II *(Pres, CEO, CFO, Chief Acctg Officer & Sec)*

GO-MART INC.

(d/b/a U-Pak)
915 Riverside Dr
Gassaway, WV 26624
Tel.: (304) 364-8000
Fax: (304) 364-4690
E-mail: gomart@gomart.com
Sales Range: $300-349.9 Million
Approx. Number Employees: 50
Business Description:
Convenience Stores Independent
S.I.C.: 5411; 5541
N.A.I.C.S.: 445120; 447190
Media: 18
Personnel:
John D. Heater *(Pres)*
Paul Gaughan *(Gen Mgr)*
Glenn Long *(Dir-Mktg)*

GOLD STAR CHILI INC.

650 Lunken Pk Dr
Cincinnati, OH 45226
Tel.: (513) 231-4541
Fax: (513) 624-4415
Toll Free: (800) 643-0465
E-mail: info@goldstarchili.com
Web Site: www.goldstarchili.com
Sales Range: $75-99.9 Million
Approx. Number Employees: 150
Business Description:
Food Preparations & Vending
S.I.C.: 2099; 5812
N.A.I.C.S.: 311999; 722211
Media: 3-15-18-19-22-23
Personnel:
Mike Rohrkemper *(CEO)*
Basheer Daoud *(Dir-Real Estate & Dev)*
Charlie Howard *(Dir-Mktg)*
Mike Mason *(Dir-Ops)*
Advertising Agency:
Freedman, Gibson & White Inc.
100 E Business Way Ste 300
Cincinnati, OH 45241
Tel.: (513) 241-3900
Fax: (513) 241-2220

GOLUB CORPORATION

(d/b/a Price Chopper)
461 Nott St
Schenectady, NY 12308
Mailing Address:
PO Box 1074
Schenectady, NY 12301-1074
Tel.: (518) 355-5000
Fax: (518) 355-5728
Fax: (518) 355-0843
E-mail: webmaster@pricechopper.com
Web Site: www.pricechopper.com
Sales Range: $5-14.9 Billion
Approx. Number Employees: 24,500
Year Founded: 1932
Business Description:
Retail Grocery Chain
S.I.C.: 5541; 5399; 5411
N.A.I.C.S.: 447110; 445110; 445120; 452910
Import
Media: 8-13-16-19-22-26
Personnel:
Neil M. Golub *(Pres & CEO)*
Jerel Golub *(Pres & COO)*
John J. Endres *(CFO)*
William Kenneally *(Gen Counsel, Sec & Sr VP)*
Margaret Davenport *(VP-HR)*
Brands & Products:
PRICE CHOPPER
Advertising Agency:
Callahan Creek, Inc.
805 New Hampshire St
Lawrence, KS 66044-2739
Tel.: (785) 838-4774
Fax: (785) 838-4033

GORDON FOOD SERVICE INC.

333 50th St SW
Grand Rapids, MI 49548-5639
Mailing Address:
PO Box 1787
Grand Rapids, MI 49501
Tel.: (616) 530-7000
Fax: (616) 717-7600
Toll Free: (888) 437-3663
E-mail: info@gfs.com
Web Site: www.gfs.com
Sales Range: $100-124.9 Million
Approx. Number Employees: 7,000
Year Founded: 1897
Business Description:
Foodservice Distr
S.I.C.: 5812; 5142; 5149
N.A.I.C.S.: 722310; 424420; 424490
Media: 2-7-8-10-19
Personnel:
Jim Gordon *(Pres)*
Dan Gordon *(CEO)*
Jeff Maddox *(CFO)*
Tim Fatum *(Dir-HR)*
Rob Van Renterghem *(Dir-Mktg & Procurement)*
Alan Hooker *(Mgr-Cash)*
Brands & Products:
ARRAY
BRICKMAN'S
CROWN COLLECTION
GFS
GFS EXPERIENCE
GORDON FOOD SERVICE
GORDON SIGNATURE
GRAN SAZON
HARVEST VALLEY
HEARTHSTONE CLASSICS
KITCHEN ESSENTIALS
MARKON
MOSAIC
PEPPER MILL
PREMIUM ANGUS BEEF
PRIMO GUSTO
SERVSAFE
SIENNA BAKERY
TRADE EAST
TRIUMPH
Advertising Agency:
Queue Creative
410 S Cedar St Ste F
Lansing, MI 48912
Tel.: (517) 374-6600
Fax: (517) 374-4215

GRADE A MARKET INC.

360 Connecticut Ave
Norwalk, CT 06854
Tel.: (203) 838-0504
Fax: (203) 838-9215
Web Site: www.shoprite.com
Approx. Sls.: $172,462,084
Approx. Number Employees: 1,000
Business Description:
Independent Supermarket
S.I.C.: 5411
N.A.I.C.S.: 445110
Media: 9-16-25
Personnel:
Rocco Cingari *(Pres)*
Jim Tarantio *(CFO)*
Robert Procaccini *(Mgr-Adv)*

THE GREAT ATLANTIC & PACIFIC TEA COMPANY, INC.

(Sub. of Tengelmann Warenhandelsgesellschaft KG)
(d/b/a A&P)
(Filed Ch 11 Bankruptcy #10-24549 on 12/12/10 in U.S. Bankruptcy Court, Southern Dist of NY, White Plains)
2 Paragon Dr
Montvale, NJ 07645-1718
Tel.: (201) 573-9700
Fax: (201) 571-8719
E-mail: apcustomerrel@aptea.com
Web Site: www.aptea.com
Approx. Sls.: $8,078,455,000
Approx. Number Employees: 12,480
Year Founded: 1859
Business Description:
Supermarket Owner & Operator
S.I.C.: 5411; 5141
N.A.I.C.S.: 445110; 424410
Import Export
Advertising Expenditures: $92,100,000
Media: 1-2-5-6-7-8-9-10-18-19-20-23-24-25
Distr.: Natl.
Personnel:
Christian W.E. Haub *(Chm)*
Andreas Guldin *(Vice Chm & Chief Strategy Officer)*
Samuel M. Martin, III *(Pres & CEO)*
Frederic F. Brace *(CFO, Chief Admin Officer & Chief Restructuring Officer)*
Christopher W. McGarry *(Gen Counsel, Sec & Sr VP)*
Paul Hertz *(Exec VP-Ops)*

Key to Media (For complete agency information see *The Advertising Red Books-Agencies* edition):
1. Bus. Publs. 2. Cable T.V. 3. Catalogs & Directories. 4. Co-op Adv. 5. Consumer Mags. 6. D.M. to Bus. Estab.7. D.M. to Consumers
8. Daily Newsp. 9. Exhibits/Trade Shows 10. Foreign 11. Infomercial 12. Internet Adv.13. Multimedia 14. Network Radio
15. Network T.V. 16. Newsp. Distr. Mags. 17. Other 18. Outdoor (Posters, Transit) 19. Point of Purchase20. Premiums, Novelties
21. Product Samples 22. Special Events Mktg. 23. Spot Radio 24. Spot T.V. 25. Weekly Newsp. 26. Yellow Page Adv.

Tom O'Boyle *(Exec VP-Mdsg & Mktg)*
Carter Knox *(Sr VP-HR & Labor Rels)*
Rebecca Philbert *(Sr VP & Chief Mdsg & Mktg Officer)*
Marie Robinson *(Sr VP-Supply & Logistics)*

Brands & Products:
A&P
AMERICA'S CHOICE
BEST CELLARS
FOOD BASICS
FOOD EMPORIUM
HEALTH PRIDE
MASTER CHOICE
PATHMARK
SAV-A-CENTER
SAVINGS PLUS
SUPER FOODMART
SUPER FRESH
WALDBAUM'S

Advertising Agency:
Words and Pictures Creative Service, Inc.
141 Kinderkamack Rd
Park Ridge, NJ 07656
Tel.: (201) 573-0228
Fax: (201) 573-8966
Toll Free: (877) 573-0228

GRISTEDES FOODS, INC.

(Sub. of Red Apple Group, Inc.)
823 11th Ave
New York, NY 10019-3557
Tel.: (212) 956-5803
Tel.: (212) 956-5770
Fax: (212) 262-4979
Fax: (212) 247-4509
Web Site: www.gristedes.com
Sales Range: $300-349.9 Million
Approx. Number Employees: 4,000
Year Founded: 1888

Business Description:
Supermarket Chain & Holding Company
S.I.C.: 5411
N.A.I.C.S.: 445110
Advertising Expenditures: $1,394,169
Media: 4-8-13-21-23-24

Brands & Products:
GRISTEDES

GSC ENTERPRISES, INC.

130 Hillcrest Dr
Sulphur Springs, TX 75482
Tel.: (903) 885-7621
Fax: (903) 885-6928
Toll Free: (800) 231-1938
Web Site: www.grocerysupply.com
Sales Range: $25-49.9 Million
Approx. Number Employees: 1,100
Year Founded: 1947

Business Description:
Holding Company; Grocery Distr & Money Order Fulfillment Services
S.I.C.: 6719; 5141; 6099
N.A.I.C.S.: 551112; 424410; 522390
Export
Media: 10

Personnel:
Michael K. McKenzie *(Chm)*
Michael J. Bain *(Pres & CEO)*
Kerry Law *(CFO & VP-Fin)*
Ryan McKenzie *(COO & VP-Ops)*
Steve Rutherford *(Gen Counsel)*
Chad Bolton *(VP-IT)*
Steve Shing *(Corp VP-Sls & Mktg)*
Howard Stroud *(Dir-Mdsg & Pur)*
Theresa Toland *(Dir-HR)*
Tracey Ballard *(Mgr-Promos)*
Alex Bernal *(Mgr-Adv)*
Tony Chitwood *(Mgr-Dry Groceries)*
Pat Goggans *(Mgr-Snacks)*
Fred Miller *(Mgr-Svc)*
Teresa Reynolds *(Mgr-Water)*
Jeff Speicher *(Mgr-Frozen)*
Carole Wilks *(Mgr-Cigarettes)*

Brands & Products:
BIG ENOUGH FOR THE JOB, SMALL ENOUGH TO CARE
GSC
GSC ECARE

H&N FOODS INTERNATIONAL, INC.

5580 S Alameda St
Los Angeles, CA 90058-3426
Mailing Address:
PO Box 58626
Los Angeles, CA 90058-0626
Tel.: (415) 821-6637
Fax: (415) 821-7159
E-mail: info@hnfoods.com
Web Site: www.hnfoods.com
Sales Range: $150-199.9 Million
Approx. Number Employees: 150
Year Founded: 1981

Business Description:
Fish & Seafoods
S.I.C.: 5146; 5812
N.A.I.C.S.: 424460; 722110
Import Export
Media: 2-5-10

Personnel:
Hua T. Ngo *(Pres)*
Christine Ngo *(Exec VP)*

HAGGEN, INC.

2211 Rimland Dr
Bellingham, WA 98226
Mailing Address:
PO Box 9704
Bellingham, WA 98227-9704
Tel.: (360) 733-8720
Fax: (360) 650-8235
E-mail: web@haggen.com
Web Site: www.haggen.com
Sales Range: $700-749.9 Million
Approx. Number Employees: 4,000
Year Founded: 1933

Business Description:
Supermarket Chain Stores & Pharmacies Owner & Operator
S.I.C.: 5411; 5912
N.A.I.C.S.: 445110; 446110
Media: 8-9-13-18-19-23-24-25

Personnel:
Richard R. Haggen *(Co-Chm & Co-Owner)*
Donald E. Haggen *(Co-Chm)*
Clarence J. Gabriel *(Pres & CEO)*
Harrison Lewis *(CIO & VP)*
John Boyle *(Sr VP-Sls & Mktg)*
Tom Kenney *(VP-Fin)*
Scott Smith *(VP-Mktg)*
Becky Skaggs *(Dir-Consumer Affairs)*

Brands & Products:
FOOD CLUB
FULL CIRCLE
HAGGEN
HAGGEN C.A.R.D.
PAWS
TOPCARE
WHERE YOUR BEST MEALS BEGIN

Advertising Agency:
Davis-Elen Advertising, Inc.
865 S Figueroa St
Los Angeles, CA 90017-2543
Tel.: (213) 688-7000
Fax: (213) 688-7288

HANNAFORD BROTHERS CO.

(Sub. of Delhaize America, Inc.)
145 Pleasant Hill Rd
Scarborough, ME 04074-9309
Mailing Address:
PO Box 1000
Portland, ME 04104-5005
Tel.: (207) 883-2911
Fax: (207) 885-2859
E-mail: working@hannaford.com
Web Site: www.hannaford.com
Approx. Number Employees: 1,200
Year Founded: 1883

Business Description:
Retail Supermarkets
S.I.C.: 5411; 5912
N.A.I.C.S.: 445110; 446110
Import
Media: 2-6-8-9-14-15-18-23-24-25
Distr.: Direct to Consumer; Reg.
Budget Set: Aug.

Personnel:
Ron Hodge *(Pres)*
Chris Lewis *(CIO & Sr VP-IT)*
Tara L. Nau *(Center Mgr)*
Mike Norton *(Mgr-Comm)*

Brands & Products:
HANNAFORD FOOD AND DRUG
SHOP 'N SAVE

Advertising Agency:
Allen & Gerritsen
The Arsenal on the Charles 311 Arsenal St 4th Fl
Watertown, MA 02472
Tel.: (617) 926-4005
Fax: (617) 926-0133

HARKER'S DISTRIBUTION, INC.

801 6th St SW
Le Mars, IA 51031-1817
Mailing Address:
PO Box 1308
Le Mars, IA 51031-1308
Tel.: (712) 546-8171
Fax: (712) 546-3109
E-mail: service@harkers.com
Web Site: www.harkers.com
Sales Range: $200-249.9 Million
Approx. Number Employees: 550
Year Founded: 1906

Business Description:
Specialty Food Items
S.I.C.: 5142
N.A.I.C.S.: 424420
Advertising Expenditures: $100,000
Media: 1-2-7-10-19-21
Distr.: Midwest
Budget Set: Jan.

Personnel:
Dick Blackwell *(VP-Sls & Mktg)*

Brands & Products:
HARKER'S
HARKER'S FLAV-R-CUT
HARKER'S PREMIUM-CUT
HARKER'S TEND-R-CUT
SIGNATURE OF IOWA
SPECIALISTS IN CENTER-OF-THE PLATE
TEND-R-CUT

HARPS FOOD STORES, INC.

918 S Gutensohn Rd
Springdale, AR 72762-5165
Mailing Address:
PO Box 48
Springdale, AR 72765-0048
Tel.: (479) 751-7601
Fax: (479) 751-3625
Web Site: www.harpsfood.com
Approx. Number Employees: 3,000
Year Founded: 1930

Business Description:
Retail Groceries
S.I.C.: 5411
N.A.I.C.S.: 445110
Media: 9-18-21-22-23-24
Distr.: Direct to Consumer; Reg.

Personnel:
Roger Collins *(Chm & CEO)*
Kim Eskew *(Pres)*
Jim Antz *(CFO, VP-Fin & Admin)*
Frank Ray *(VP-HR)*
Huey Couch *(Mgr-Adv)*

Brands & Products:
HARP'S FOOD STORE
PRICECUTTER FOOD WAREHOUSE

Advertising Agency:
The Mullikin Agency
3418 W Sunset Ave.
Springdale, AR 72762
Tel.: (501) 756-0871
Fax: (501) 756-0871
(Retail Grocery Store)

HARRIS TEETER, INC.

(Sub. of Ruddick Corporation)
701 Crestdale Rd
Matthews, NC 28105
Mailing Address:
PO Box 10100
Matthews, NC 28106-1010
Tel.: (704) 844-3100
Fax: (704) 844-3138
Toll Free: (800) 432-6111
E-mail: info@harristeeter.com
Web Site: www.harristeeter.com
Sales Range: $1-4.9 Billion
Approx. Number Employees: 15,000
Year Founded: 1949

Business Description:
Supermarkets
S.I.C.: 5411
N.A.I.C.S.: 445110
Media: 8-9-13-19-23-24-25

Personnel:
Frederick J. Morganthall, II *(Pres)*
Jeff D. Sherman *(CFO & Sr VP-Fin)*
Daniel J. Bruni *(CIO & Sr VP)*
Jim Clendenen *(CIO)*
Jerry L. Clontz *(Sr VP-Ops)*
Bradley J. Graham *(Sr VP)*
C. Douglas Rhodes *(Sr VP-HR)*
Charles F. Corbeil *(Grp VP-Mktg)*
Rodney C. Antolock *(VP-Ops & Mdsg)*
Ted Harrington *(Dir-Diversity)*
Travis Hubbard *(Dir-Fresh Foods Mdsg)*

Brands & Products:
HARRIS TEETER
HARRIS TEETER NATURALS
HT TRADERS
HUNTER FARMS
PREMIER SELECTION
TOP CARE

Advertising Agencies:
Mass Connections, Inc.
13131 E 166th St

Key to Media (For complete agency information see *The Advertising Red Books-Agencies* edition):
1. Bus. Publs. 2. Cable T.V. 3. Catalogs & Directories. 4. Co-op Adv. 5. Consumer Mags. 6. D.M. to Bus. Estab.7. D.M. to Consumers 8. Daily Newsp. 9. Exhibits/Trade Shows 10. Foreign 11. Infomercial 12. Internet Adv.13. Multimedia 14. Network Radio 15. Network T.V. 16. Newsp. Distr. Mags. 17. Other 18. Outdoor (Posters, Transit) 19. Point of Purchase20. Premiums, Novelties 21. Product Samples 22. Special Events Mktg. 23. Spot Radio 24. Spot T.V. 25. Weekly Newsp. 26. Yellow Page Adv.

Harris Teeter, Inc. — (Continued)

Cerritos, CA 90703
Tel.: (562) 365-0200
Fax: (562) 365-0201
Toll Free: (800) 275-6650

Red Moon Marketing
4100 Coca-Cola Plz Ste 215
Charlotte, NC 28211
Tel.: (704) 366-1147
Fax: (704) 366-2283

HARRY & DAVID HOLDINGS, INC.

(Joint Venture of Wasserstein & Co., LP & Highfields Capital Management LP)
(d/b/a Harry and David)
(Filed Ch 11 Bankruptcy #11-108884 on 03/29/11 in U.S. Bankruptcy Ct, Dist of DE, Wilmington)
2500 S Pacific Hwy
Medford, OR 97501-2675
Tel.: (541) 864-2500
Fax: (800) 648-6640
Toll Free: (877) 322-1200
E-mail: service@harryanddavid.com
Web Site: www.hndcorp.com
Approx. Sls.: $426,774,000
Approx. Number Employees: 1,026
Business Description:
Gift Baskets, Mail-Order Flowers & Novelties Whslr & Direct Marketer; Owned 65% by Wasserstein & Co., LP & 34% by Highfields Capital Management LP
S.I.C.: 5947; 5193; 5961
N.A.I.C.S.: 453220; 424930; 454111; 454113
Advertising Expenditures: $65,097,000
Media: 4-8-13
Personnel:
Steven J. Heyer *(Chm)*
Kay Hong *(Interim CEO & Chief Restructuring Officer)*
Edward F. Dunlap *(CFO)*
Charles Hunsinger *(CIO & Sr VP)*
David Rogalski *(Chief Acctg Officer, VP & Controller)*
Bill Ihle *(Exec VP-Corp Rels)*
Peter D. Kratz *(Exec VP-Ops)*
Brands & Products:
CUSHMAN HONEYBELLS
FRUIT-OF-THE-MONTH CLUB
HARRY & DAVID
MOOSE MUNCH
ROYAL RIVIERA
TOWER OF TREATS
WOLFERMAN'S

HAWKEYE FOODSERVICE DISTRIBUTION

3550 2nd St
Coralville, IA 52241-3205
Tel.: (319) 645-2193
Fax: (319) 645-2742
Web Site:
www.hawkeyefoodservice.com
Approx. Number Employees: 387
Year Founded: 1921
Business Description:
Groceries Distr
S.I.C.: 5141; 5149
N.A.I.C.S.: 424410; 424490
Import Export
Media: 10-13

Personnel:
Jeff Braverman *(Pres)*
Steve Connor *(CFO)*

H.E. BUTT GROCERY COMPANY

646 S Main Ave
San Antonio, TX 78204-1210
Tel.: (210) 938-8000
Fax: (210) 938-8579
Web Site: www.heb.com
Sales Range: $5-14.9 Billion
Approx. Number Employees: 60,000
Year Founded: 1905
Business Description:
Grocery Store Operator
S.I.C.: 5411
N.A.I.C.S.: 445110
Advertising Expenditures: $1,000,000
Media: 2-4-7-8-10-19-20-23-24
Personnel:
Charles C. Butt *(Chm & CEO)*
Craig Boyan *(Pres & COO)*
Martin Otto *(CFO & Exec VP-Mdsg/ Procurement)*
Susan Wade *(Exec VP-Retailing)*
Jeff Thomas *(Sr VP & Gen Mgr-Central Texas)*
Cory Basso *(VP-Mktg & Adv & Branding)*
Brooke Brownlow *(VP-Benefits & HR)*
Dya Campos *(Dir-Pub Affairs)*
Leslie Lockett *(Dir-Pub Affairs)*
Shelley Parks *(Dir-Pub Affairs)*
Susan Ghertner *(Mgr-Environ)*
Brands & Products:
H.E.B
HERE EVERYTHING'S BETTER
MY H-E-B TEXAS LIFE
Advertising Agency:
The Richards Group, Inc.
8750 N Central Expy Ste 100
Dallas, TX 75231-6430
Tel.: (214) 891-5700
Fax: (214) 265-2933

HOMELAND STORES, INC.

(Sub. of Associated Wholesale Grocers, Inc.)
390 NE 36th St
Oklahoma City, OK 73105
Mailing Address:
PO Box 25008
Oklahoma City, OK 73125-0008
Tel.: (405) 290-3000
Fax: (405) 216-2266
Toll Free: (800) 522-5658
E-mail: info@homelandstores.com
Web Site: www.homelandstores.com
Sales Range: $500-549.9 Million
Approx. Number Employees: 50
Year Founded: 1987
Business Description:
Grocery Store Chain
S.I.C.: 5411
N.A.I.C.S.: 445110
Media: 1-4-5-8-9-13-14-15-16-18-19-20-21-22-23-24-25
Distr.: Natl.
Budget Set: Sept. -Dec.
Personnel:
Darryl Fitzgerald *(Pres & CEO)*
Sonny Sanchez *(Mgr-Category)*
Brands & Products:
HOMELAND
ONE CARD
WE'RE BETTER THAN EVER

HOUCHENS INDUSTRIES INC.

700 Church St
Bowling Green, KY 42101-5112
Mailing Address:
PO Box 90009
Bowling Green, KY 42102-9009
Tel.: (270) 843-3252
Fax: (270) 780-2877
Web Site:
www.houchensindustries.com
Sales Range: $1-4.9 Billion
Approx. Number Employees: 11,487
Year Founded: 1917
Business Description:
Diversified Holding Company
S.I.C.: 6719; 5411; 5999
N.A.I.C.S.: 551112; 445110; 453998
Media: 3-5-8-13-14-15-16-18-22-23-24-25
Personnel:
James Gipson *(Chm, Pres & CEO)*
Gordon Minter *(CFO)*
Sharon Grooms *(Dir-HR)*
Alan Larsen *(Dir-Mktg & Mdsg)*
Terry Cornell *(Mgr-Info Sys)*

THE H.T. HACKNEY COMPANY

502 S Gay St
Knoxville, TN 37902-1503
Mailing Address:
PO Box 238
Knoxville, TN 37901-0238
Tel.: (865) 546-1291
Fax: (865) 546-1501
E-mail: tommy.thomas@hthackney.com
Web Site: www.hthackney.com
Approx. Rev.: $3,550,000,000
Approx. Number Employees: 3,600
Year Founded: 1891
Business Description:
Food, Health & Beauty Items Distr
S.I.C.: 5141; 5172
N.A.I.C.S.: 424410; 424720
Import
Media: 2-10-19
Personnel:
William B. Sansom *(Chm, Pres & CEO)*
Mike Morton *(CFO & VP)*
Dean Ballinger *(COO & VP)*
Leonard Robinette *(CIO)*
Bruce Pearl *(VP-Mktg)*
Tommy Thomas *(Dir-Sls & Mktg)*
Heather Butler *(Mgr-Events)*

HUNGRY HOWIE'S PIZZA & SUBS INC.

30300 Stephenson Hwy
Madison Heights, MI 48071-1600
Tel.: (248) 414-3300
Fax: (248) 414-3301
Toll Free: (800) 624-8122
E-mail: hungryhinc@hungryhowies.com
Web Site: www.hungryhowies.com
Sales Range: $10-24.9 Million
Approx. Number Employees: 60
Year Founded: 1973
Business Description:
Fast-Food Restaurant Franchising Services
S.I.C.: 5812
N.A.I.C.S.: 722211
Import Export
Media: 8-15-16-24

Personnel:
Jeff Inke *(VP-Mktg)*
Nancy Cook *(Dir-HR)*
Steven E. Jackson *(Dir-Franchise Dev)*
Brands & Products:
CRISP 'N THIN CRUST
FLAVOURED CRUST
HOWIE WINGS
HUNGRY HOWIE'S PIZZA
THE ORIGINAL FLAVORED CRUST PIZZA
Advertising Agency:
Tattoo Projects
1920 Abbott St Ste 300
Charlotte, NC 28203
Tel.: (704) 900-7150
Flavored-Crust Pizza

HY-VEE, INC.

5820 Westown Pkwy
West Des Moines, IA 50266-8223
Tel.: (515) 267-2800
Fax: (515) 267-2817
Toll Free: (800) 289-8343
E-mail: hrmail@hy-vee.com
Web Site: www.hy-vee.com
Sales Range: $5-14.9 Billion
Approx. Number Employees: 50,000
Year Founded: 1930
Business Description:
Operator of Retail Foods, Bakeries & Drug Stores
S.I.C.: 5411; 5912
N.A.I.C.S.: 445110; 446110
Media: 8-10-18-19-22-23-24-25
Personnel:
Randy Edeker *(Pres)*
Richard N. Jurgens *(CEO)*
Ken Waller *(Chief Admin Officer & Exec VP)*
Ron Taylor *(Chief Admin Officer)*
Dennis Ausenhus *(Sr VP-Real Estate & Engrg)*
Sheela Laing *(VP-HR)*
Robert Wei *(Mgr-Chinese Express-Asbury Plaza Hy-Vee)*
Brands & Products:
AMANA
ANGUS MACBRIDE
BLUE RIBBON
COLLINS BLACK
COWBOY GRILLER
COWGIRL GRILLER
DI LUSSO
FULL CIRCLE
HEALTHMARKET
HOME HELPERS
HY-VEE FRESH HOME MEALS
HY-VEE SPLASH
HYVEE
JUICE SPLASH
KITCHEN HELPERS
LE TECHNIQ
LORD ISAACS
MAKING LIVES EASIER, HEALTHIER, HAPPIER
MIDWEST COUNTRY FARE
MOTHER'S CHOICE
PAWS PREMIUM
REDMOND
SNACK-IN-A-BOX
SOFT ESSENTIALS
SPARKLY
SPARKLY CLEAN
THIRSTY GIANT

Key to Media (For complete agency information see *The Advertising Red Books-Agencies* edition):
1. Bus. Publs. 2. Cable T.V. 3. Catalogs & Directories. 4. Co-op Adv. 5. Consumer Mags. 6. D.M. to Bus. Estab.7. D.M. to Consumers 8. Daily Newsp. 9. Exhibits/Trade Shows 10. Foreign 11. Infomercial 12. Internet Adv.13. Multimedia 14. Network Radio 15. Network T.V. 16. Newsp. Distr. Mags. 17. Other 18. Outdoor (Posters, Transit) 19. Point of Purchase20. Premiums, Novelties 21. Product Samples 22. Special Events Mktg. 23. Spot Radio 24. Spot T.V. 25. Weekly Newsp. 26. Yellow Page Adv.

Advertising Agency:
The Meyocks Group
6800 Lake Dr Ste 150
West Des Moines, IA 50266-2544
Tel.: (515) 225-1200
Fax: (515) 225-6400

IGA, INC.

8745 W Higgins Rd Ste 350
Chicago, IL 60631-2716
Tel.: (773) 693-4520
Fax: (773) 693-1271
Fax: (773) 693-4533
Web Site: www.igainc.com
Approx. Number Employees: 38
Year Founded: 1926
Business Description:
Supermarkets Licenser & Franchisor
S.I.C.: 5411
N.A.I.C.S.: 445110
Advertising Expenditures: $1,000,000
Media: 2-9-10-18-19-20-23-24-25
Distr.: Natl.
Budget Set: July -Dec.
Personnel:
Mark Batenic *(CEO)*
John Collins *(CFO)*
Douglas Fritsch *(Sr VP)*
Nick Liakopulos *(VP-IT)*
Barbara Wiest *(VP-Admin Events & Comm)*
Bill Overman *(Dir-Area Mktg)*
Brands & Products:
EXPLORE THE STORE
HOME TOWN GREEN
HOMETOWN PROUD
IGA
KIDS BEST
MUCHMORE
ROYAL GUEST
TABLERITE

INGLES MARKETS, INCORPORATED

2913 US Hwy 70 W
Black Mountain, NC 28711
Mailing Address:
PO Box 6676
Asheville, NC 28816-6676
Tel.: (828) 669-2941
Fax: (828) 669-3678
E-mail: rfreeman@ingles-markets.com
Web Site: www.ingles-markets.com
Approx. Sls.: $3,390,051,840
Approx. Number Employees: 7,896
Year Founded: 1963
Business Description:
Owner & Operator of Grocery Stores
S.I.C.: 5411
N.A.I.C.S.: 445110
Advertising Expenditures: $14,800,000
Media: 6-7-8-9-13-15-18-19-20-23-25-26
Distr.: Direct to Consumer; Reg.
Personnel:
James W. Lanning *(Pres & COO)*
Ronald B. Freeman *(CFO)*
Cynthia L. Brooks *(VP-HR)*
J. Thomas Outlaw, Jr. *(VP-Sls & Mktg)*
Michael Elliott *(Dir-Trng)*
Dan Spears *(Dir-Nonfoods)*
Brands & Products:
INGLES
INGLES BEST
LAURA LYNN
THE INGLES ADVANTAGE

INKO'S WHITE ICED TEA

435 E 70st
New York, NY 10021
Tel.: (917) 509-1903
Fax: (212) 472-0016
Toll Free: (866) 747-INKO
Web Site: www.healthywhitetea.com
Sales Range: $10-24.9 Million
Approx. Number Employees: 120
Business Description:
Iced Tea Retailer
S.I.C.: 5499
N.A.I.C.S.: 445299; 446191
Media: 1-7-10-20-21-22
Personnel:
Andy Schamisso *(Founder & Pres)*
Brands & Products:
INKO'S
WHAT WHITE TEA TASTES LIKE

INVENTURE FOODS, INC.

5050 N 40th St Ste 300
Phoenix, AZ 85018
Tel.: (623) 932-6200
Fax: (623) 522-2690
E-mail: info@inventuregroup.net
Web Site: www.inventuregroup.net
Approx. Rev.: $133,987,442
Approx. Number Employees: 389
Year Founded: 1986
Business Description:
Potato Chips & Snack Foods Distr
S.I.C.: 2034; 2038; 2096; 5145
N.A.I.C.S.: 311423; 311412; 311919; 424450
Advertising Expenditures: $669,256
Media: 3-8-10-13
Personnel:
Itzhak Reichman *(Chm)*
Terry McDaniel *(Pres & CEO)*
Steve Weinberger *(CFO, Sec & Treas)*
Rick Suchenski *(Sr VP-Sls & Mktg)*
Brands & Products:
BK FLAME BROILED FLAVORED POTATO
BOB'S TEXAS STYLE
BOB'S TEXAS STYLE BAR B QUE CHIPS
BOB'S TEXAS STYLE JALAPENO CHIPS
BOB'S TEXAS STYLE ORIGINAL POTATO CHIPS
BOB'S TEXAS STYLE SALT & CRACKED PEPPER
BOB'S TEXAS STYLE SALT & VINEGAR CHIPS
BOB'S TEXAS STYLE SWEET MAUI ONION POTATO CHIPS
BOB'S TEXAS STYLE THREE CHEESE JALAPENO
BOULDER CANYON
BOULDER CANYON CANYON CUT SALT & PEPPER
BOULDER CANYON CANYON CUT SOUR CREAM & CHIVE
BOULDER CANYON CANYON CUT TOTALLY NATURAL
BOULDER CANYON RICE & ADZUKI BEAN
BOULDER CANYON RICE & ADZUKI CHIPOTLE
BOULDER CANYON TOMATO & BASIL
BRAIDS PRETZELS
BUTTER PRETZEL BRAIDS
CANYON CUT
HONEY WHEAT PRETZEL BRAIDS
INTENSELY DIFFERENT
INVENTURE GROUP
MINI KNOTS
POORE BROTHERS
POORE BROTHERS BBQ RANCH CHIPS
POORE BROTHERS JALAPENO CHIPS
RADER FARMS
TATO SKINS
TATO SKINS CHEDDAR & BACON POTATO SKINS
TATO SKINS SOUR CREAM & ONION POTATO SKINS
TEXAS STYLE
TGI FRIDAY'S CHEESE PIZZA CHIPS

JAMBA, INC.

6475 Christie Ave Ste 150
Emeryville, CA 94608
Tel.: (510) 596-0100
Fax: (510) 653-0484
Toll Free: (800) 545-9972
E-mail: investors@jambajuice.com
Web Site: www..jambajuice.com
Approx. Rev.: $262,653,000
Approx. Number Employees: 5,900
Year Founded: 1990
Business Description:
Natural Fruit Drink Sales
S.I.C.: 5812
N.A.I.C.S.: 722211
Advertising Expenditures: $7,800,000
Media: 2-4-8-13-14-15-21-22
Personnel:
James D. White *(Chm, Pres & CEO)*
Karen L. Luey *(CFO & Sr VP)*
Susan Shields *(CMO & Sr VP)*
Bruce Schroder *(Pres-Store Ops)*
Michael Fox *(Gen Counsel & Sr VP)*
Steve Adkins *(Sr VP-Ops Svcs)*
Greg Schwartz *(Sr VP-Supply Chain)*
Julie Washington *(VP & Gen Mgr-Consumer Products)*
Renee Kempler *(Dir-Regal Brand Mktg)*
Julie Liu *(Dir-Product Mktg)*
Brands & Products:
3G CHARGER
ACAI SUPER-ANTIOXIDANT
ACAI TOPPER
ALL FRUIT SMOOTHIES
ALOHA PINEAPPLE
ANTI OXIDANT POWER
BANANA BERRY
BERRY FULFILLING
BERRY LIME SUBLIME
BERRY TOPPER
BLACKBERRY BLISS
BRIGHT EYED AND BLUEBERRY
CALCIUM
CARIBBEAN PASSION
CHOCOLATE MOO'D
CHUNKY STRAWBERRY TOPPER
CITRUS SQUEEZE
COLDBUSTER
CRANBERRY CRAZE
DAILY VITAMIN
ENERGY BOOST
ENLIGHTENED SMOOTHIES
FEMME BOOST
FIBER BOOST
FIT 'N FRUITFUL
GREEN CAFFEINE BOOST
HEART DEFENDER
IMMUNITY BOOST
JAMBA
JAMBA FUNCTIONALS
JAMBA JUICE
JAMBA MULTI-BOOST
JAMBA POWERBOOST
JUICIES
KIWI BERRY BURNER
MANGO-A-GO-GO
MANGO MANTRA
MANGO PEACH TOPPER
MATCHA GREEN TEA BLAST
MATCHA GREEN TEA SHOT
MEGA MANGO
ORANGE-A-PEEL
ORANGE BERRY BLITZ
ORANGE DREAM MACHINE
ORANGE MANGO PASSION
PEACH PERFECTION
PEACH PLEASURE
PEANUT BUTTER MOO'D
PERFORMANCE BOOST
POMEGRANATE HEART HAPPY
POMEGRANATE PARADISE
POMEGRANATE PICK-ME-UP
POWERBOOST
PROTEIN BERRY PIZZAZZ
PROTEIN BERRY WORKOUT
RAZZMATAZZ
SOY PROTEIN
STRAWBERRIES WILD
STRAWBERRRY ENERGIZER
STRAWBERRY NIRVANA
STRAWBERRY SURF RIDER
STRAWBERRY TSUNAMI
STRAWBERRY WHIRL
SUNRISE STRAWBERRY
VIBRANT-C
VIBRANT-C BOOST
WEIGHT BURNER
WHEY PROTEIN
Advertising Agency:
Grow Marketing
1606 Union St
San Francisco, CA 94123
Tel.: (415) 440-4769
Fax: (415) 440-4779
— Kara Burke *(Acct Exec)*

JEWEL-OSCO

(Div. of Albertson's, Inc.)
150 Pierce Rd
Itasca, IL 60143
Tel.: (630) 948-6000
Fax: (708) 531-6047
Toll Free: (800) JEWEL-61
Web Site: www.jewelosco.com
Approx. Number Employees: 35,000
Year Founded: 1899
Business Description:
Food & Drug Stores
S.I.C.: 5541; 5399; 5411
N.A.I.C.S.: 447110; 445110; 445120; 452910
Import
Media: 3-4-5-6-7-8-9-11-13-14-15-16-18-19-21-22-23-24-25-26
Distr.: Direct to Consumer; Natl.
Budget Set: Jan.
Personnel:
Brian Huff *(Pres)*
Nancy Chagares *(Sr VP-Mktg & Mdsg)*
Tim Corry *(VP-HR)*
Brands & Products:
JEWEL-OSCO
Advertising Agency:
R.J. Dale Advertising & Public Relations
205 N Michigan Ave
Chicago, IL 60601

Key to Media (For complete agency information see *The Advertising Red Books-Agencies* edition):
1. Bus. Publs. 2. Cable T.V. 3. Catalogs & Directories. 4. Co-op Adv. 5. Consumer Mags. 6. D.M. to Bus. Estab.7. D.M. to Consumers
8. Daily Newsp. 9. Exhibits/Trade Shows 10. Foreign 11. Infomercial 12. Internet Adv.13. Multimedia 14. Network Radio
15. Network T.V. 16. Newsp. Distr. Mags. 17. Other 18. Outdoor (Posters, Transit) 19. Point of Purchase20. Premiums, Novelties
21. Product Samples 22. Special Events Mktg. 23. Spot Radio 24. Spot T.V. 25. Weekly Newsp. 26. Yellow Page Adv.

Jewel-Osco — (Continued)

Tel.: (312) 644-2316
Fax: (312) 644-2688

JIMMY JOHNS FRANCHISE, LLC
2212 Fox Dr
Champaign, IL 61820
Tel.: (217) 356-9900
Fax: (217) 359-2956
Toll Free: (800) 546-6904
Web Site: www.jimmyjohns.com
Sales Range: $10-24.9 Million
Year Founded: 1983
Business Description:
Restaurant Franchise Operations
S.I.C.: 5812
N.A.I.C.S.: 722211
Personnel:
James John Liautaud *(Chm & CEO)*
Advertising Agency:
SpaceTime, Inc.
35 E Wacker Dr Ste 3100
Chicago, IL 60601-2307
Tel.: (312) 425-0800
Fax: (312) 425-0808

JOHN B. SANFILIPPO & SON, INC.
1703 N Randall Rd
Elgin, IL 60123-7820
Tel.: (847) 289-1800
Fax: (847) 289-1843
E-mail: ebulkfoods@jbssinc.com
Web Site: www.jbssinc.com
Approx. Sls.: $674,212,000
Approx. Number Employees: 1,400
Year Founded: 1922
Business Description:
Nuts, Snacks & Confections Mfr & Distr
S.I.C.: 2068; 0173; 2034; 2035; 2064; 2087; 2096; 2099
N.A.I.C.S.: 311911; 111335; 311330; 311340; 311423; 311919; 311930; 311941
Import Export
Advertising Expenditures: $6,493,000
Media: 2-4-5-8-9-10-19-21-23
Distr.: Intl.; Natl.
Budget Set: Sept.
Personnel:
Jeffrey T. Sanfilippo *(Chm & CEO)*
Michael J. Valentine *(Grp Pres, CFO & Sec)*
Jasper Brian Sanfilippo, Jr. *(Pres, COO & Asst Sec)*
James A. Valentine *(CIO)*
Michael G. Cannon *(Sr VP-Corp Ops)*
Robert J. Sarlls *(Sr VP-Consumer Sls, Strategy & Bus)*
Everardo Soria *(Sr VP-Pecan Ops & Procurement)*
Walter R. Tankersley, Jr. *(Sr VP-Procurement & Commodity Risk Mgmt)*
Frank S. Pellegrino *(VP-Fin & Controller)*
Howard Brandeisky *(VP-Mktg, Innovation & Customer Solutions)*
Jose Cabanin *(VP-Sls-Intl)*
Thomas J. Fordonski *(VP-HR)*
John H. Garoni *(VP-Comml Ingredient Sls)*
Everett Dudley *(Dir-Innovation)*
Herbert J. Marros *(Dir-Fin Reporting & Taxation)*
Julie Nargang *(Dir-Corp Mktg)*
Nathan Rucker *(Dir-Corp Continuous Improvement)*
Brands & Products:
ARMA
E-BULK FOODS
EVON'S
FISHER
FLAVOR TREE
JOHN B. SANFILIPPO & SON, INC.
ORCHARD VALLEY HARVEST
SUNSHINE COUNTRY
TEXAS PRIDE
Advertising Agency:
Blue Chip Marketing Worldwide
650 Dundee Rd Ste 250
Northbrook, IL 60062
Tel.: (847) 446-2114
Agency of Record
Creative
Interactive
Media

JORDANO'S, INC.
550 S Patterson Ave
Santa Barbara, CA 93111
Tel.: (805) 964-0611
Fax: (805) 964-3821
Toll Free: (800) 325-2278
E-mail: jordanos@jordanos.com
Web Site: www.jordanos.com
Approx. Number Employees: 500
Year Founded: 1915
Business Description:
Marketer & Whslr of Food, Beverages & Culinary Equipment
S.I.C.: 5181; 5182
N.A.I.C.S.: 424810; 424820
Import Export
Media: 2-4-7-13-22
Personnel:
Peter C. Jordano *(Pres & CEO)*
Jeffrey S. Jordano *(Pres)*
Michael Sieckowski *(CFO)*

K-VA-T FOOD STORES, INC.
(d/b/a Food City)
201 Trigg St PO Box 1158
Abingdon, VA 24210
Tel.: (276) 628-5503
Fax: (276) 623-5440
Toll Free: (800) 826-8451
E-mail: info@foodcity.com
Web Site: www.foodcity.com
Approx. Number Employees: 11,000
Year Founded: 1955
Business Description:
Supermarket Owner & Operator
S.I.C.: 5411; 5141
N.A.I.C.S.: 445110; 424410
Media: 2-3-5-6-7-8-9-13-16-18-19-20-21-22-23-24-25
Personnel:
Steven C. Smith *(Pres & CEO)*
Robert L. Neeley *(CFO, Treas, Sec & Sr VP)*
Jesse A. Lewis *(COO & Sr VP)*
Mike Tipton *(Dir-Produce Ops)*
Brands & Products:
FOOD CITY

KAHALA COLD STONE HOLDING COMPANY
9311 E Via De Ventura
Scottsdale, AZ 85258
Tel.: (480) 362-4800
Fax: (480) 362-4812
Toll Free: (866) 464-9467
Web Site: www.coldstonecreamery.com
Approx. Sls.: $408,000,000
Approx. Number Employees: 195
Year Founded: 1988
Business Description:
Fast Food Restaurant Franchise Holding Company
S.I.C.: 5812; 6794
N.A.I.C.S.: 722211; 533110
Media: 8-13-20-21-26
Personnel:
David Guarino *(Pres)*
Kevin Blackwell *(CEO)*
Chris Henry *(Exec VP-Dev & Licensing)*
Suzanne Schutz *(VP-Mktg)*
Cori Mozilo *(Mgr-Interactive Mktg)*
Brands & Products:
COLD STONE CREAMERY
Advertising Agency:
Santy Advertising
5080 N 40th St Ste 340
Phoenix, AZ 85018-2149
Tel.: (602) 952-1222
Fax: (602) 952-1433

KEY FOOD STORES CO-OPERATIVE, INC.
1200 S Ave
Staten Island, NY 10314
Tel.: (718) 370-4200
Fax: (718) 370-4225
Web Site: www.keyfoodstores.com
Sales Range: $50-74.9 Million
Approx. Number Employees: 100
Year Founded: 1937
Business Description:
Wholesale Food Co-Operative
S.I.C.: 5141; 5146; 5411; 5421; 5431
N.A.I.C.S.: 424410; 445110; 445210; 445220; 445230
Media: 7-9-18-22-25
Personnel:
Lawrence Mandell *(Pres)*
Dean Janeway *(CEO)*
Ken Nastro *(Dir-Adv & HR)*

KING KULLEN GROCERY COMPANY, INC.
185 Central Ave
Bethpage, NY 11714
Tel.: (516) 733-7100
Fax: (516) 827-6325
Web Site: www.kingkullen.com
Sales Range: $800-899.9 Million
Approx. Number Employees: 4,200
Year Founded: 1930
Business Description:
Grocery Store Operator
S.I.C.: 5411; 5912
N.A.I.C.S.: 445110; 446110
Media: 3-9-19-20-23-25
Distr.: Reg.
Personnel:
Bernard D. Kennedy *(Chm & Co-CEO)*
Brian C. Cullen *(Pres & COO)*
Ronald Colikin *(Co-CEO)*
Joseph Brown *(Pres-Wild by Nature Markets, VP-Sls & Mdsg)*
James F. Flynn *(Sr VP-Fin & Admin)*
James Ashley Johnston *(Dir-Real Estate)*
Advertising Agency:
Crown Advertising and Marketing
245 Newtown Road Ste 103
Plainview, NY 11803
Tel.: (516) 470-2700
Fax: (516) 470-2712
(Supermarkets)
— Tom Cullen *(Pres.)*

KINGS SUPER MARKETS, INC.
(Joint Venture of Angelo, Gordon & Co. L.P. & MTN Capital Partners)
700 Lanidex Plz
Parsippany, NJ 07054
Tel.: (973) 463-3200
Fax: (973) 463-6518
Toll Free: (800) 325-4647
E-mail: openline@kingssm.com
Web Site: www.kingswebsite.com
Sales Range: $400-449.9 Million
Approx. Number Employees: 2,250
Year Founded: 1936
Business Description:
Supermarkets
S.I.C.: 5411
N.A.I.C.S.: 445110
Media: 8-9-13-21-25
Personnel:
James A. Demme *(Chm)*
Judy Spires *(Pres & CEO)*
Fred Brohm *(Exec VP)*
Richard Durante *(Sr VP-Store Ops)*
Patricia Mikell *(Sr Dir-Mktg)*

KRASDALE FOODS INC.
65 W Red Oak Ln
White Plains, NY 10604
Tel.: (914) 694-6400
Fax: (914) 697-5225
E-mail: webmaster@krasdalefoods.com
Web Site: www.krasdalefoods.com
Sales Range: $200-249.9 Million
Approx. Number Employees: 650
Year Founded: 1908
Business Description:
Grocery Whslr
S.I.C.: 5141
N.A.I.C.S.: 424410
Media: 7-10-14-23
Personnel:
Charles A. Krasne *(Pres)*
Steve Silver *(CFO)*
David Poses *(Dir-Adv)*
Brands & Products:
AIM

THE KROGER CO.
1014 Vine St
Cincinnati, OH 45202-1141
Tel.: (513) 762-4000
Fax: (513) 762-1160
Telex: 212065
E-mail: kroger.investors@kroger.com
Web Site: www.kroger.com
Approx. Sls.: $82,189,000,000
Approx. Number Employees: 338,000
Year Founded: 1883
Business Description:
Grocery & Multi-Department Store Operator
S.I.C.: 5411; 5311; 5912
N.A.I.C.S.: 445110; 446110; 452111
Import
Advertising Expenditures: $533,000,000
Media: 3-9-17-18-19-23-24
Distr.: Natl.
Budget Set: Jan.
Personnel:
David B. Dillon *(Chm & CEO)*

Key to Media (For complete agency information see *The Advertising Red Books-Agencies* edition):
1. Bus. Publs. 2. Cable T.V. 3. Catalogs & Directories. 4. Co-op Adv. 5. Consumer Mags. 6. D.M. to Bus. Estab.7. D.M. to Consumers 8. Daily Newsp. 9. Exhibits/Trade Shows 10. Foreign 11. Infomercial 12. Internet Adv.13. Multimedia 14. Network Radio 15. Network T.V. 16. Newsp. Distr. Mags. 17. Other 18. Outdoor (Posters, Transit) 19. Point of Purchase20. Premiums, Novelties 21. Product Samples 22. Special Events Mktg. 23. Spot Radio 24. Spot T.V. 25. Weekly Newsp. 26. Yellow Page Adv.

W. Rodney McMullen *(Pres & COO)*
J. Michael Schlotman *(CFO & Sr VP)*
Calvin Kaufman *(Pres-Kroger Mfg & Grp VP)*
Kathy Kelly *(Pres-Kroger Personal Fin)*
Robert Moeder *(Pres-Central Div)*
Michael J. Stoll *(CEO-The Little Clinic)*
Paul W. Heldman *(Exec VP)*
Kathleen S. Barclay *(Sr VP-HR)*
Geoffrey Covert *(Sr VP-Retail Ops)*
Michael J. Donnelly *(Sr VP-Mdsg)*
M. Marnette Perry *(Sr VP)*
Michael J. Schlotman *(Sr VP)*
R. Pete Williams *(Sr VP)*
Jeffrey D. Burt *(Grp VP-Perishables Mdsg & Procurement)*
Kevin M. Dougherty *(Grp VP-Logistics)*
Carver L. Johnson *(Grp VP-Info Sys & Tech)*
Lynn Marmer *(Grp VP)*
Della Wall *(Grp VP-HR)*
Sukanya R. Madlinger *(VP-Mdsg)*
Nancy Moon-Eilers *(VP-Natural Foods Procurement & Mdsg)*
Linda Severin *(VP-Corp Brands)*
Keith Dailey *(Dir-External Corp Comm)*
Meghan Glynn *(Dir-Corp Comm)*
Jeff Hock *(Mgr-Mktg-Interactive & Mobile)*

Brands & Products:
BAKER'S
BARCLAY JEWELERS
BELL
CALA
CITY MARKET
DILLON
FOOD 4 LESS
FOODS CO.
FRED MEYER
FRED MEYER JEWELERS
FRY'S
GERBES
HILANDER
JAY C
KING SOOPERS
KROGER
KROGER FRESH FARE
KROGER'S ACTIVE LIFESTYLE
LITTMAN JEWELERS
NATURALLY PREFERRED
OWEN'S
PAY LESS
PRIVATE SELECTION
QFC
RALPHS
SMITH'S

Advertising Agency:
Fahlgren Mortine
4030 Easton Station Ste 300
Columbus, OH 43219
Tel.: (614) 383-1500
Fax: (614) 383-1501

KUNZLER & COMPANY, INC.

652 Manor St
Lancaster, PA 17603
Mailing Address:
PO Box 4747
Lancaster, PA 17604-4747
Tel.: (717) 299-6301
Fax: (717) 390-2170
Toll Free: (888) KUNZLER
E-mail: customerservice@kunzler.com
Web Site: www.kunzler.com
Approx. Number Employees: 500
Year Founded: 1901
Business Description:
Sausage, Bologna & Smoked Meat Whslr & Distr
S.I.C.: 5147; 0751
N.A.I.C.S.: 311612; 311611
Media: 4-7-9-13-16-17-21-22
Personnel:
Christian C. Kunzler, Jr. *(Chm)*
Christian C. Kunzler, III *(Pres & CEO)*
Steve C. Robinson *(Sr Dir-Sls & Mktg)*

KWIK TRIP INC.

1626 Oak St
La Crosse, WI 54602
Mailing Address:
PO Box 2107
La Crosse, WI 54602-2107
Tel.: (608) 781-8988
Fax: (608) 779-9252
E-mail: marketingdp@kwiktrip.com
Web Site: www.kwiktrip.com
E-Mail For Key Personnel:
Marketing Director: marketingdp@kwiktrip.com
Approx. Number Employees: 8,000
Year Founded: 1965
Business Description:
Convenience Store, Gas Station & Restaurant Owner & Operator
S.I.C.: 5541; 5411
N.A.I.C.S.: 447190; 445120
Media: 8-18-19-20-23-24-25
Distr.: Reg.
Budget Set: Dec.
Personnel:
Donald P. Zietlow *(Pres & CEO)*
Gary Gonczy *(Dir-Mktg & Adv)*

Brands & Products:
CAFE KARUBA
CINNAMON CINNSATIONS
DASH-IN GRILL
GLAZERS
HEARTY PLATTER
KWIK STAR
KWIK TRIP
KWIKERY BAKERY
NATURE'S TOUCH
TOBACCO OUTLET PLUS
URGE

LACKMANN CULINARY SERVICES

303 Crossways Pk Dr
Woodbury, NY 11797
Tel.: (516) 364-2300
Fax: (516) 364-9788
E-mail: info@lackmann.com
Web Site: www.lackmann.com
Approx. Number Employees: 30
Year Founded: 1964
Business Description:
Food Service Contractor
S.I.C.: 5812
N.A.I.C.S.: 722310
Advertising Expenditures: $2,000,000
Media: 2-4-7-10-13-22
Personnel:
Andrew Lackmann *(Co-Chm & Co-CEO)*
Matthew Lackmann *(Co-Chm & Co-CEO)*
Peter Alessio *(Pres & COO)*
Denise Drury *(Mgr-Employee Benefits)*

Brands & Products:
LACKMANN
LIGHTER BY CHOICE

LATE JULY SNACKS LLC

3166 Main St
Barnstable, MA 02630
Tel.: (508) 362-5859
Fax: (508) 362-5868
E-mail: info@latejuly.com
Web Site: www.latejuly.com
Sales Range: $10-24.9 Million
Approx. Number Employees: 20
Business Description:
Organic Snackfood Mfr
S.I.C.: 2052; 2096
N.A.I.C.S.: 311821; 311919
Media: 6-9
Personnel:
Nicole Dawes *(Co-Founder & CEO)*
Darby Ziruk *(Co-Pres)*

LEADING BRANDS, INC.

1500 W Georgia Street Suite 1800
Vancouver, BC V6G 2Z6, Canada
Tel.: (604) 685-5200
Fax: (604) 685-5249
Toll Free: (866) 685-5200
E-mail: info@lbix.com
Web Site: www.leadingbrandsinc.com
Approx. Sls.: $21,699,952
Approx. Number Employees: 87
Year Founded: 1986
Business Description:
Beverage Mfr, Distr, Retailer & Marketer
S.I.C.: 2086; 2096
N.A.I.C.S.: 312111; 311919; 312112
Advertising Expenditures: $450,000
Media: 13-19-22
Personnel:
Ralph D. McRae *(Chm & CEO)*
Marilyn Kerzner *(Dir-Corp Affairs)*

Brands & Products:
BRAND X
BRAND X ORIGINALS
CAESAR'S
COOL CANADIAN
COUNTRY HARVEST
DIE HARD
INFINITE HEALTH
INFINITY
LEADING BRANDS
LITEBLUE
NITRO
PUREBLUE
STOKED
TRUEBLUE
WE BUILD BRANDS

LOAF 'N JUG/MINI MART, INC.

(Div. of The Kroger Co.)
442 Keeler Pkwy
Pueblo, CO 81001
Tel.: (719) 948-3071
Fax: (719) 948-2602
E-mail: wecare@loafnjug.com
Web Site: www.loafnjug.com
Sales Range: $25-49.9 Million
Approx. Number Employees: 45
Year Founded: 1968
Business Description:
Convenience Store Owner & Operator
S.I.C.: 5411
N.A.I.C.S.: 445120
Media: 9-18-19-23
Distr.: Reg.
Budget Set: Sept. -Oct.
Personnel:
Arthur Stawski *(Head-Loaf N Jug & Pres-Mini Mart Inc)*
Russ Drury *(VP-Mktg-Kroger C-Store Grp)*

Advertising Agency:
Marketing Plus
3215 Lake Ave
Pueblo, CO 81004
Tel.: (719) 564-2180

LOBLAW COMPANIES LIMITED

(Sub. of George Weston Limited)
1 Presidents Choice Cir
Brampton, ON L6Y 5S5, Canada
Tel.: (416) 922-2500, ext. 9054592500
Tel.: (905) 459-2500
Fax: (905) 861-2602
Telex: 6-218848
E-mail: Customer_Service@loblaw.ca
Web Site: www.loblaw.ca
Approx. Sls.: $30,079,729,800
Approx. Number Employees: 139,000
Year Founded: 1956
Business Description:
Food Distr & Grocery Chain
S.I.C.: 5411
N.A.I.C.S.: 445110
Advertising Expenditures: $15,000,000
Media: 4-8-9-11-22-24
Budget Set: Oct. -Dec.
Personnel:
Galen G. Weston *(Chm)*
Vicente Trius *(Deputy Chm & Pres)*
Sarah R. Davis *(CFO)*
Gordon A.M. Currie *(Chief Legal Officer & Exec VP)*
Frank Rocchetti *(Exec VP & Chief Mdsg Officer)*
Mark Butler *(Exec VP-Ops-Central)*
Barry K. Columb *(Exec VP-Fin Svcs)*
Roy R. Conliffe *(Exec VP-Labour Rels)*
Grant B. Froese *(Exec VP-Mdsg)*
S. Jane Marshall *(Exec VP-Special Projects)*
Judy A. McCrie *(Exec VP-HR)*
Calvin McDonald *(Exec VP-Mktg & Customer Relationship Mgmt)*
Peter K. McMahon *(Exec VP-Supply Chain, Distr & IT)*
Amu Misra *(Exec VP-Ops)*
Robert A. Balcom *(Sr VP)*
Richard Dickson *(Sr VP-IT)*
Todd Friars *(Sr VP-Fin Sys & Processes)*
Craig R. Hutchinson *(Sr VP-Mktg)*
Jeremy Roberts *(Sr VP-Fin)*
Timothy J. Scott *(Sr VP-Internal Audit & Internal Control Compliance)*
Geoffrey H. Wilson *(Sr VP-IR)*
Michael N. Kimber *(VP & Legal Counsel)*
Elizabeth Margles *(VP-Pub Rel & Corp Comm)*
Karen Gumbs *(Sr Mgr-Corp Affairs)*
Martin Parrest *(Sr Mgr-ESB)*
Christina Calleja *(Mgr-Mktg Media)*

Advertising Agencies:
Manning Selvage & Lee
175 Bloor Street E Suite 801
Toronto, ON M4W 3R8, Canada
Tel.: (416) 967-3702
Fax: (416) 967-6414
President's Choice, Joe Fresh Style

Loblaw Companies Limited — (Continued)

Ove Design & Communications Ltd.
111 Queen Street East, Suite 555,
Toronto, ON M5C 1S2, Canada
Tel.: (416) 423-6228
Fax: (416) 423-2940

LOCAL & WESTERN OF TEXAS, INC.

5445 La Sierra
Dallas, TX 75231
Mailing Address:
PO Box 822463
Dallas, TX 75281
Tel.: (214) 750-6633
Fax: (214) 750-8359
Approx. Number Employees: 12
Year Founded: 1986
Business Description:
Meat Whslr & Distr
S.I.C.: 5142; 5147
N.A.I.C.S.: 424420; 424470
Media: 5-7-17
Personnel:
Gerald B. Darver *(Pres)*
Allen Darver *(VP-Sls & Mktg)*

LOPEZ FOODS INC.

9500 NW 4th St
Oklahoma City, OK 73127
Tel.: (405) 789-7500
Fax: (405) 499-0114
Web Site: www.lopezfoods.com
Approx. Sls.: $173,541,948
Approx. Number Employees: 500
Business Description:
Prepared Beef Products Mfr
S.I.C.: 5147
N.A.I.C.S.: 311612
Personnel:
Eduardo Sanchez *(CEO)*
Brands & Products:
PROCESS MEAT
Advertising Agency:
Estrada Communications Group, Inc
13729 Research Blvd Ste 610
Austin, TX 78750
Tel.: (512) 335-7776
Fax: (512) 335-2226

LOWE'S FOOD STORES, INC.

(Sub. of Alex Lee, Inc.)
1381 Old Mill Cir Ste 200
Winston Salem, NC 27103
Mailing Address:
PO Box 24908
Winston Salem, NC 27114-4908
Tel.: (336) 659-0180
Fax: (336) 768-4702
Toll Free: (800) 669-5693
Web Site: www.lowesfoods.com
Approx. Number Employees: 8,000
Year Founded: 1954
Business Description:
Supermarket Store Operator
S.I.C.: 5411
N.A.I.C.S.: 445110
Media: 8-9
Distr.: Direct to Consumer; Reg.
Personnel:
Barbara Saulpaugh *(VP-Mktg)*
Ronald W. Knedlik *(Controller & Dir-Fin)*
Lisa Selip *(Dir-Mktg)*
Advertising Agency:
PromoGroup
444 N Orleans St Ste 400
Chicago, IL 60610-4494
Tel.: (312) 467-1300
Fax: (312) 467-1311

MAC'S CONVENIENCE STORES, INC.

(Sub. of Alimentation Couche-Tard Inc.)
305 Milner Avenue 4th Floor
Toronto, ON M1B 3V4, Canada
Tel.: (416) 291-4441
Fax: (416) 291-4947
Toll Free: (800) 268-5574
E-mail: customer.service@macs.ca
Web Site: www.macs.ca
Approx. Number Employees: 150
Year Founded: 1963
Business Description:
Convenience & Specialty Retail Store Owner & Operator
S.I.C.: 5541
N.A.I.C.S.: 447110
Media: 9-18-23-24-25
Distr.: Intl.; Natl.
Budget Set: Oct. -Dec.
Personnel:
Richard Fortin *(CFO)*
Advertising Agency:
Bos Advertising
3970 Saint-Ambroise street
Montreal, QC H4C 2C7, Canada
Tel.: (514) 848-0010
Fax: (514) 373-2992

MAPCO EXPRESS, INC.

(Sub. of Delek US Holdings, Inc.)
7102 Commerce Way
Brentwood, TN 37027
Tel.: (615) 771-6701
Web Site: www.mapcoexpress.com
Sales Range: $800-899.9 Million
Approx. Number Employees: 175
Business Description:
Convenience Stores & Gasoline Pumping Stations
S.I.C.: 5541; 5411
N.A.I.C.S.: 447110; 445120
Media: 13-20-22
Personnel:
Igal Zamir *(Pres)*

MARSH SUPERMARKETS, INC.

(Holding of Sun Capital Partners, Inc.)
333 S Franklin Rd
Indianapolis, IN 46219-3350
Tel.: (317) 594-2100
Fax: (317) 594-2700
Fax: (317) 594-2704
Toll Free: (800) 382-8798
E-mail: info@marsh.net
Web Site: www.marsh.net
Sales Range: $1-4.9 Billion
Approx. Number Employees: 13,800
Year Founded: 1931
Business Description:
Supermarket & Convenience Store Operator; Catering Services
S.I.C.: 5411; 5812
N.A.I.C.S.: 445110; 722320
Advertising Expenditures: $23,700,000
Media: 2-3-5-6-7-8-9-19-23-24-25
Distr.: Direct to Consumer; Reg.
Budget Set: Feb. -Mar.
Personnel:
Joseph Kelley *(Chm, Pres & CEO)*
David C. Siegel *(Sr VP-Mdsg & Mktg Strategic Initiatives)*
Connie Gardner *(Sr Dir-Communtity Rels)*
Gary Cantrell *(Dir-Floral Mdsg)*
Advertising Agency:
Ron Foth Advertising
8100 N High St
Columbus, OH 43235-6400
Tel.: (614) 888-7771
Fax: (614) 888-5933

MARTIN'S FOODS

(Formerly Ukrop's Super Markets, Inc.)
(Sub. of Ahold USA, Inc.)
1149 Harrisburg Pke
Carlisle, PA 17013
Tel.: (888) 562-7846
Fax: (301) 618-4968
Web Site: www.martinsfoods.com
Approx. Number Employees: 5,500
Year Founded: 1937
Business Description:
Supermarkets
S.I.C.: 5411
N.A.I.C.S.: 445110
Advertising Expenditures: $15,000,000
Media: 5-10-16-17-19-20-22-25
Personnel:
James E. Ukrop *(Chm)*
David Naquin *(COO & Exec VP)*
John Zeheb *(VP-Fin)*
Jim Scanlon *(Dir-HR)*
Brands & Products:
FOOD CLUB
FULL CIRCLE
PAWS PREMIUM
TOP CARE
TOP CREST
UKROP
UKROP'S
WORLD CLASSICS TRADING COMPANY

MAVERIK COUNTRY STORES, INC.

880 W Ctr St
North Salt Lake, UT 84054-2913
Tel.: (801) 936-5557
Fax: (801) 936-1406
Toll Free: (800) 789-4455
Toll Free: (877) 936-5557
E-mail: customerservice@maverik.com
Web Site: www.maverik.com
E-Mail For Key Personnel:
Marketing Director: bcall@maverik.com
Approx. Sls.: $999,000,000
Approx. Number Employees: 3,500
Year Founded: 1930
Business Description:
Convenience Store & Gas Station Operator
S.I.C.: 5541; 5411
N.A.I.C.S.: 447190; 445120
Media: 16-18-19-23-24
Distr.: Direct to Consumer; Reg.
Personnel:
Michael Call *(Pres & CEO)*
Spencer Hewlett *(CFO)*
Lynn Call *(CIO)*
Glen Fullenger *(Dir-Mdsg)*
Brands & Products:
ADVENTURE CLUB CARD
ADVENTURE'S FIRST STOP
EXTREME COMBO
GLACIER RAIN
GREEN DAY
KICKSTART
MAVERIK
MAVERIK FLEET CARD
MAVERIK GIFT CARD
MAVERIK MASTERCARD

MCCORMICK & COMPANY, INCORPORATED

18 Loveton Circle
Sparks, MD 21152-6000
Tel.: (410) 771-7301
Fax: (410) 771-7462
Toll Free: (800) 632-5847
E-mail: Joyce_Brooks@Mccormick.com
Web Site: www.mccormick.com
Approx. Sls.: $3,336,800,000
Approx. Number Employees: 7,500
Year Founded: 1889
Business Description:
Mfr of Specialty Food Products, Seasonings & Flavorings & Baking Products
S.I.C.: 2099; 1796
N.A.I.C.S.: 311999; 238290; 311942
Import Export
Advertising Expenditures: $71,700,000
Media: 2-4-6-8-9-14-16-18-21-23-24
Distr.: Natl.
Budget Set: July
Personnel:
Alan D. Wilson *(Chm, Pres & CEO)*
John McCormick *(Partner)*
Gordon M. Stetz, Jr. *(CFO & Exec VP)*
Jeryl Wolfe *(CIO & VP-Supply Chain Strategy)*
Hamed Faridi *(Chief Science Officer)*
Lawrence E. Kurzius *(Pres-McCormick Intl Mgmt Committee)*
Charles T. Langmead *(Pres-US Indus Grp)*
Ken Stickevers *(Pres-Consumer Products)*
Malcolm Swift *(Pres-Europe, Middle East, Africa)*
Mark T. Timbie *(Pres-Consumer Foods-North America)*
W. Geoffrey Carpenter *(Gen Counsel, Sec & VP)*
Paul C. Beard *(Treas & Sr VP-Fin)*
Kenneth A. Kelly, Jr. *(Sr VP & Controller)*
Cecile K. Perich *(Sr VP-HR)*
Wendy P. Davidson *(VP & Gen Mgr-US & Latin America)*
Jill Pratt *(VP-Mktg-US Consumer Products Div)*
Lori Robinson *(VP-Corp Comm, Branding & Culinary Mktg)*
Laurie Harrsen *(Dir-PR & Consumer Comm)*
Andrew Foust *(Mgr-Mktg)*
Brands & Products:
AEROPLANE
BAG'N SEASON
BAKERS
BILLY BEE
CLUB HOUSE
DUCROS
EL GUAPO
FLAVORCELL
FRENCH VANILLA BLEND
GOLDEN DIPT

Key to Media (For complete agency information see *The Advertising Red Books-Agencies* edition):
1. Bus. Publs. 2. Cable T.V. 3. Catalogs & Directories. 4. Co-op Adv. 5. Consumer Mags. 6. D.M. to Bus. Estab.7. D.M. to Consumers 8. Daily Newsp. 9. Exhibits/Trade Shows 10. Foreign 11. Infomercial 12. Internet Adv.13. Multimedia 14. Network Radio 15. Network T.V. 16. Newsp. Distr. Mags. 17. Other 18. Outdoor (Posters, Transit) 19. Point of Purchase20. Premiums, Novelties 21. Product Samples 22. Special Events Mktg. 23. Spot Radio 24. Spot T.V. 25. Weekly Newsp. 26. Yellow Page Adv.

GOURMET COLLECTION
GRILL MATES
HANDY FILL
LAWRY'S
LEMON AND PEPPER
MCCORMICK
OLD BAY
PRODUCE PARTNERS
REAL FOOD MADE EASY!
SALAD SUPREME
SALAD TOPPINS
SCHILLING
SCHWARTZ
SETCO
SILVO
SIMPLY ASIA
STOCK-AID
THE TASTE YOU TRUST
THAI KITCHEN
VAHINE

Advertising Agencies:
Alcone Marketing Group
320 Post Rd
Darien, CT 06820-3605
Tel.: (203) 656-3555
Fax: (203) 656-4111

The Sawtooth Group
100 Woodbridge Ctr Dr Ste 102
Woodbridge, NJ 07095-1125
Tel.: (732) 636-6600
Fax: (732) 602-4214

Studiocom
191 Peachtree St NE Ste 4025
Atlanta, GA 30303
Tel.: (404) 541-9555
Online Advertising

Weber Shandwick-Chicago
676 N St Clair Ste 1000
Chicago, IL 60611
Tel.: (312) 988-2400
Fax: (312) 988-2363
US Consumer Products Div.

MEAT & SEAFOOD SOLUTIONS, LLC

(Formerly Southern Foods, Inc.)
(d/b/a Southern Foods)
3500 Old Battleground Rd
Greensboro, NC 27410
Mailing Address:
PO Box 26801
Greensboro, NC 27429
Tel.: (336) 545-3800
Fax: (336) 545-5296
Toll Free: (800) 441-FOOD
E-mail: sfoods@southernfoods.com
Web Site: www.southernfoods.com
Approx. Number Employees: 480
Year Founded: 1954
Business Description:
Retailer & Distr of Meat Products & Food Items
S.I.C.: 5147; 5143
N.A.I.C.S.: 424470; 424430
Media: 4-5-7-8-13-21-22-26
Personnel:
Bill Mutton *(Pres)*
Brands & Products:
CHEF DRIVEN, INGREDIENT DRIVEN
SOUTHERN FOODS

MINYARD FOOD STORES, INC.

8304 Esters Blvd Ste 860
Irving, TX 75063
Tel.: (972) 393-8700
Fax: (972) 393-8794
E-mail: jobs@minyards.com
Web Site: www.minyards.com
Approx. Sls.: $900,000,000
Approx. Number Employees: 230
Year Founded: 1932
Business Description:
Operator of Retail Groceries & Warehouse Distribution Center
S.I.C.: 5411; 5812
N.A.I.C.S.: 445110; 722310
Import
Advertising Expenditures: $1,000,000
Media: 4-8-9-13-21-22-23-24
Advertising Agency:
Promote Success PR
3745 Edgemont Dr.
Garland, TX 75042
Tel.: (214) 296-0984

MOE'S SOUTHWEST GRILL, LLC

(Sub. of FOCUS Brands, Inc.)
2915 Peachtree Rd
Atlanta, GA 30305
Tel.: (404) 442-8932
Fax: (404) 844-1363
E-mail: pr@moes.com
Web Site: www.moes.com
Sales Range: $250-299.9 Million
Year Founded: 2000
Business Description:
Fast-Food Franchiser
S.I.C.: 5812
N.A.I.C.S.: 722110; 722211
Personnel:
Mark Monroe *(Owner)*
Advertising Agency:
French/West/Vaughan, Inc.
112 E Hargett St
Raleigh, NC 27601
Tel.: (919) 832-6300
Fax: (919) 832-6360

MOODY DUNBAR INC.

2000 Waters Edge Dr
Johnson City, TN 37604
Tel.: (423) 952-0100
Fax: (423) 952-1001
Web Site: www.moodydunbar.com
Approx. Number Employees: 200
Year Founded: 1933
Business Description:
Canned Fruits & Specialties
S.I.C.: 2033
N.A.I.C.S.: 311421
Import Export
Advertising Expenditures: $500,000
Media: 4-17-22
Personnel:
Stanley K. Dunbar *(CEO)*
Edward Simmerly *(VP-Mktg)*
Brands & Products:
DUNBARS ROASTED RED PEPPERS
Advertising Agency:
Creative Energy Group Inc
3206 Hanover Rd
Johnson City, TN 37604
Tel.: (423) 926-9494
Fax: (423) 929-7222
Toll Free: (800) 926-9454

MORAN FOODS, INC.

(Sub. of SUPERVALU, Inc.)
(d/b/a Save-A-Lot Food Stores)
100 Corporate Ofc Dr
Earth City, MO 63045-1528
Tel.: (314) 592-9100
Fax: (314) 592-9619
E-mail: info@save-a-lot.com
Web Site: www.save-a-lot.com
Sales Range: $350-399.9 Million
Approx. Number Employees: 450
Business Description:
Food Distribution
S.I.C.: 5141; 5411
N.A.I.C.S.: 424410; 445110
Media: 13
Personnel:
Bill Shaner *(Pres & CEO)*

MORINAGA NUTRITIONAL FOODS, INC.

(Sub. of Morinaga Milk Industry Co., Ltd.)
2441 W 205th Ste C102
Torrance, CA 90501
Tel.: (310) 787-0200
Fax: (310) 787-2727
E-mail: info@morinu.com
Web Site: www.morinu.com
Approx. Sls.: $1,200,000
Approx. Number Employees: 12
Business Description:
Soybean Curd Importer & Seller
S.I.C.: 5153
N.A.I.C.S.: 424510
Import Export
Media: 6-9-20-21-25
Personnel:
Susan Bucher *(Dir-Mktg)*
Brands & Products:
MORINU

MORRISON MANAGEMENT SPECIALISTS, INC.

(Sub. of Compass Group USA, Inc.)
5801 Peachtree Dunwoody Rd
Atlanta, GA 30342-1503
Tel.: (404) 845-3330
Fax: (404) 845-3333
Toll Free: (800) 2CLIENT
E-mail: webmaster@iammorrison.com
Web Site: www.iammorrison.com
Approx. Number Employees: 10,000
Year Founded: 1996
Business Description:
Food, Nutrition & Dining Services to the Health Care & Senior Living Industries
S.I.C.: 8099
N.A.I.C.S.: 621999
Media: 7-8-13
Personnel:
Gene Dolloff *(Pres-Morrison Sr Dining)*
Michael Svagdis *(Pres-Morrison Healthcare Food Svcs)*
Gary Gaddy *(Exec VP-Sls)*
Jim Devos *(VP-Mktg)*
Andrea Woods *(Dir-Mktg Svcs)*
Brands & Products:
ON THE GO BISTRO
RITAZZA
SPICE OF LIFE

NASH-FINCH COMPANY

7600 France Ave S
Edina, MN 55435-5924
Mailing Address:
PO Box 355
Minneapolis, MN 55440-0355
Tel.: (952) 832-0534
Fax: (952) 844-1237
E-mail: investor@nashfinch.com
Web Site: www.nashfinch.com
Approx. Sls.: $4,991,979,000
Approx. Number Employees: 4,474
Year Founded: 1885
Business Description:
Wholesale Grocery Distr
S.I.C.: 5149; 5141; 5148
N.A.I.C.S.: 424490; 424410; 424480
Import Export
Advertising Expenditures: $59,900,000
Media: 2-3-4-5-8-9-18-19-20-22-23-24-25-26
Distr.: Reg.
Personnel:
Robert L. Bagby *(Chm)*
Alec C. Covington *(Pres & CEO)*
Robert B. Dimond *(CFO, Treas & Exec VP)*
Calvin S. Sihilling *(CIO & Exec VP)*
Christopher A. Brown *(Pres/COO-Nash Finch Wholesale & Exec VP)*
Edward L. Brunot *(Pres/COO-MDV)*
Kathleen M. Mahoney *(Gen Counsel, Sec & Exec VP)*
Jeffrey E. Poore *(Exec VP)*
Howard F. Befort *(Sr VP)*
Michael W. Rotelle, III *(Sr VP-HR)*
Brands & Products:
AVANZA
ECONO CARD
ECONOFOODS
FAMILY FRESH MARKET
FAMILY THRIFT CENTER
FOOD PRIDE
FRESH PLACE
NASH FINCH COMPANY
OUR FAMILY
OUR FAMILY PRIDE
PERFORMANCE DRIVEN
SUN MART
Advertising Agency:
FKQ Advertising + Marketing
15351 Roosevelt Blvd
Clearwater, FL 33760-3534
Tel.: (727) 539-8800
Fax: (866) 707-6648
— George Ferris *(Acct Exec)*

NATIONAL FOOD SALES, INC.

150 Calapooia St SW Ste B
Albany, OR 97321-2291
Tel.: (541) 924-2744
Fax: (541) 924-2745
Approx. Sls.: $4,000,000
Approx. Number Employees: 3
Year Founded: 1968
Business Description:
Frozen Fruits, Vegetables, French Fries & Juices Distr
S.I.C.: 5142
N.A.I.C.S.: 424420
Import Export
Media: 2-4-10-21
Distr.: Natl.
Budget Set: Mar.
Personnel:
James C. Decker *(Pres & CEO)*
Brands & Products:
NATIONAL FOOD SALES

NATIONAL FOOD STORES, INC.

(d/b/a Krauszer's)
76 National Rd

Key to Media (For complete agency information see *The Advertising Red Books-Agencies* edition):
1. Bus. Publs. 2. Cable T.V. 3. Catalogs & Directories. 4. Co-op Adv. 5. Consumer Mags. 6. D.M. to Bus. Estab.7. D.M. to Consumers
8. Daily Newsp. 9. Exhibits/Trade Shows 10. Foreign 11. Infomercial 12. Internet Adv.13. Multimedia 14. Network Radio
15. Network T.V. 16. Newsp. Distr. Mags. 17. Other 18. Outdoor (Posters, Transit) 19. Point of Purchase20. Premiums, Novelties
21. Product Samples 22. Special Events Mktg. 23. Spot Radio 24. Spot T.V. 25. Weekly Newsp. 26. Yellow Page Adv.

National Food Stores, Inc. — (Continued)

Edison, NJ 08817-2809
Tel.: (732) 287-2800
Fax: (732) 287-8064
Approx. Sls.: $110,000,000
Approx. Number Employees: 35
Year Founded: 1909
Business Description:
Convenience Stores Owner & Operator
S.I.C.: 5411
N.A.I.C.S.: 445120
Advertising Expenditures: $400,000
Media: 8-9-19-21-25
Distr.: Direct to Consumer; Reg.
Budget Set: Oct.
Personnel:
Harry Shah *(Pres)*
Brands & Products:
KRAUSZER'S

NEW LEAF BRANDS, INC.

9380 E Bahia Dr Ste A-201
Scottsdale, AZ 85260
Tel.: (201) 784-2400
Fax: (480) 483-2168
Toll Free: (800) 481-7169
E-mail: customerservice@bywd.com
Approx. Sls.: $3,457,168
Approx. Number Employees: 32
Business Description:
Dietary Supplement Developer, Distr & Marketer
S.I.C.: 5499; 2833; 2834; 2836
N.A.I.C.S.: 446191; 325411; 325412; 325414
Advertising Expenditures: $165,000
Media: 17
Personnel:
Eric Skae *(Founder, Chm & CEO)*
David Tsiang *(CFO)*
Angela Lamendola *(Mgr-Mktg)*

NEW YORK FRIES

400-1220 Yonge St
Toronto, ON Canada
Tel.: (416) 963-5005
Fax: (416) 963-4920
E-mail: mail@newyorkfries.com
Web Site: www.newyorkfries.com
Approx. Number Employees: 17
Year Founded: 1984
Business Description:
Fast Food Restaurant
S.I.C.: 5812; 2096
N.A.I.C.S.: 722211; 311919
Media: 13-18
Personnel:
Jay Gould *(Pres & CEO)*
Advertising Agency:
Media Experts
495 Wellington St W Ste 250
Toronto, ON M5V 1E9, Canada
Tel.: (416) 597-0707
Fax: (416) 597-9927
(Restaurant, Media Buying)

NIEMANN FOODS INC.

1501 N 12th St
Quincy, IL 62306
Tel.: (217) 221-5600
Fax: (217) 221-5920
Web Site: www.discountfoods.com
Approx. Number Employees: 75
Year Founded: 1917
Business Description:
Provider of Grocery Services
S.I.C.: 5411
N.A.I.C.S.: 445110
Import Export
Personnel:
Richard H. Niemann *(Pres & CEO)*
Chris Niemann *(CFO & Exec VP)*
Jim Cox *(Sr VP)*
Ron Cook *(VP & Dir-Mktg)*
Advertising Agency:
FKQ Advertising + Marketing
15351 Roosevelt Blvd
Clearwater, FL 33760-3534
Tel.: (727) 539-8800
Fax: (866) 707-6648

NOB HILL FOODS, INC.

(Sub. of Raley's Inc.)
8420 Church St
Gilroy, CA 95020-4229
Tel.: (800) 725-3977
Fax: (408) 842-1583
Web Site: www.raleys.com
Approx. Sls.: $400,000,000
Approx. Number Employees: 2,600
Year Founded: 1961
Business Description:
Supermarket Chain; Retail Grocer
S.I.C.: 5411
N.A.I.C.S.: 445110
Advertising Expenditures: $1,000,000
Media: 3-8-13-16-18-23-24
Distr.: Direct to Consumer; Reg.

OCEAN BEAUTY SEAFOODS, INC.

1100 W Ewing St
Seattle, WA 98127-1321
Tel.: (206) 285-6800
Fax: (206) 281-0820
E-mail: info@oceanbeauty.com
Web Site: www.oceanbeauty.com
Approx. Number Employees: 1,300
Year Founded: 1910
Business Description:
Distributor of Seafood
S.I.C.: 2091; 2092
N.A.I.C.S.: 311711; 311712
Advertising Expenditures: $100,000
Media: 2-10
Personnel:
Mark Palmer *(Pres & CEO)*
Tom Sunderland *(VP-Mktg & Comm)*
Jeo Frazier *(Mgr-Quality Control)*
Kevin Palmer *(Mgr-Natl Retail Sls-Seattle)*
Brands & Products:
BAY BEAUTY
CIRCLESEA
DEEP SEA
ECHO FALLS
ICY POINT
LASCCO
MCGOVERN
NATHAN'S
NEPTUNE
OCEAN BEAUTY
OCEAN BONITA
PILLAR ROCK
PINK BEAUTY
PIRATE
PORT CLYDE
RITE
RITE FOODS
ROYAL ALASKA
SEA CHOICE
SEARCHLIGHT
SOUND BEAUTY
SURF KING
THREE STAR
TRIBE OF TWO SHEIKS
XIP CAVIAR
Advertising Agency:
Nerland Agency Worldwide Partners
808 E St
Anchorage, AK 99501-3532
Tel.: (907) 274-9553
Tel.: (907) 274-9549 (Marketing)
Fax: (907) 274-9990

OHSMAN & SONS COMPANY INC.

311 3rd Ave Ste 106
Cedar Rapids, IA 52401-1934
Tel.: (319) 365-7546
Fax: (319) 365-7550
E-mail: mail@ohsman.com
Web Site: www.ohsman.com
Sales Range: $10-24.9 Million
Approx. Number Employees: 16
Year Founded: 1891
Business Description:
Cattle Hide Whslr
S.I.C.: 5159
N.A.I.C.S.: 424590
Import Export
Media: 10-21
Personnel:
Michael Ohsman *(Pres)*

OLD FASHION FOODS, INC.

5521 Collins Blvd
Austell, GA 30106-3653
Tel.: (770) 948-1177
Fax: (770) 739-3254
Toll Free: (800) 241-4722
E-mail: info@oldfashfd.com
Web Site: www.oldfashfd.com
Sales Range: $75-99.9 Million
Approx. Number Employees: 100
Year Founded: 1965
Business Description:
Variety Products Sales Through Vending Machines
S.I.C.: 5962; 7389
N.A.I.C.S.: 454210; 561990
Media: 3-5-7-9-13-16-18-19-20-23-24-25-26
Distr.: Reg.
Personnel:
Sheldon E. Smith *(Chm, Pres & CEO)*
Jerry W. Seneker *(Exec VP)*
Joseph C. Hulsey *(Sr VP-Fin)*
Terry C. Coker *(VP-Mktg)*
Advertising Agency:
Old Fashion Foods Advertising
5521 Collins Blvd SW
Austell, GA 30106
Tel.: (770) 948-1177
Fax: (770) 739-3254
(Vending Company)
— Terry Coker *(Dir.-Mktg.)*

ORANGE PEEL ENTERPRISES, INC.

(d/b/a Greens+)
2183 Ponce De Leon Cir
Vero Beach, FL 32960
Tel.: (772) 562-2766
Fax: (772) 562-9848
E-mail: info@greensplus.com
Web Site: www.greensplus.com
Approx. Sls.: $9,000,000
Approx. Number Employees: 26
Year Founded: 1990
Business Description:
Groceries & Health Food Whslr
S.I.C.: 5149
N.A.I.C.S.: 424490
Media: 6
Personnel:
Jude Deauville *(Founder & CEO)*
Christopher Daniels *(Mgr-Mktg)*
Brands & Products:
FIBER GREENS
FIBER GREENS+
GREENS
GREENS+
GREENS+ ENERGY BAR
HIPPO GLO
JUNGLE GREENS
JUNGLE GREENS+
LIZARD LUSTER
PRO-RELIEF
PRO-RELIEF+
PROTEIN GREENS
PROTEIN GREENS+
RHINO RUBDOWN
SALAMANDER SOOTHER
THERMO GREENS
THERMO GREENS+
ULTRAPURE

OREGON CHERRY GROWERS INC.

1520 Woodrow St NE
Salem, OR 97301
Tel.: (503) 364-8421
Fax: (503) 585-7710
Toll Free: (800) 367-2536
E-mail: mrm@orcherry.com
Web Site: www.orcherry.com
Approx. Sls.: $70,000,000
Approx. Number Employees: 250
Year Founded: 1932
Business Description:
Maraschino Cherries Process, Retailer & Whslr
S.I.C.: 0723; 2033
N.A.I.C.S.: 115114; 311421
Import Export
Advertising Expenditures: $800,000
Media: 4-10-13-16-18
Personnel:
Edward Johnson *(Pres & CEO)*
Danny Weeden *(CFO)*
Steve Travis *(VP-Sls)*
Brands & Products:
NATURAL BORDEAUX
NATURAL RED
OREGON CHERRY GROWERS
ROYAL WILLAMETTE

ORGANIC TO GO FOOD CORPORATION

3317 3rd Ave S
Seattle, WA 98134
Tel.: (206) 838-4670
Fax: (800) 861-7894
E-mail: customercare@organictogo.com
Web Site: www.organictogo.com
Sales Range: $10-24.9 Million
Approx. Number Employees: 251
Year Founded: 1994
Business Description:
Organic Food Stores & Cafes
S.I.C.: 5499; 5812
N.A.I.C.S.: 445299; 722110
Advertising Expenditures: $1,200,000
Personnel:
Richard Cervera *(Chm & CEO)*
Michael Gats *(CFO)*
Erica Gillespie *(VP-Retail Ops)*

Key to Media (For complete agency information see *The Advertising Red Books-Agencies* edition):
1. Bus. Publs. 2. Cable T.V. 3. Catalogs & Directories. 4. Co-op Adv. 5. Consumer Mags. 6. D.M. to Bus. Estab.7. D.M. to Consumers
8. Daily Newsp. 9. Exhibits/Trade Shows 10. Foreign 11. Infomercial 12. Internet Adv.13. Multimedia 14. Network Radio
15. Network T.V. 16. Newsp. Distr. Mags. 17. Other 18. Outdoor (Posters, Transit) 19. Point of Purchase20. Premiums, Novelties
21. Product Samples 22. Special Events Mktg. 23. Spot Radio 24. Spot T.V. 25. Weekly Newsp. 26. Yellow Page Adv.

PANERA BREAD COMPANY
8630 S Geyer Rd Ste 100
Saint Louis, MO 63127
Tel.: (314) 984-1000
Fax: (314) 633-7200
E-mail: contactus@panerabread.com
Web Site: www.panerabread.com
Approx. Rev.: $1,542,489,000
Approx. Number Employees: 15,900
Year Founded: 1981
Business Description:
Owner, Operator & Franchisor of Bakery Cafes
S.I.C.: 5812
N.A.I.C.S.: 722211
Advertising Expenditures: $27,400,000
Media: 1-10-18-19-20-21-22
Personnel:
Ronald M. Shaich *(Chm)*
William W. Moreton *(Pres & CEO)*
Jeffrey W. Kip *(CFO & Sr VP)*
John M. Maguire *(Co-COO & Exec VP)*
Cedric Vanzura *(Co-COO & Exec VP)*
Thomas C. Kish *(CIO & Sr VP)*
Michael Simon *(CMO & Sr VP)*
Scott Blair *(Chief Legal Officer, Gen Counsel & Sr VP)*
Michael J. Nolan *(Chief Dev Officer & Sr VP)*
Rebecca A. Fine *(Sr VP & Chief People Officer)*
Mark D. Wooldridge *(Chief Acctg Officer & Asst Controller)*
Mark A. Borland *(Sr VP & Chief Supply Chain Officer)*
Michael J. Kupstas *(Sr VP & Chief Franchise Officer)*
William H. Simpson *(Sr VP & Chief Company & Joint Venture Ops Officer)*
Scott G. Davis *(Chief Concept Officer & Exec VP)*
Craig Fetter *(Dir-Ops-Southwest Missouri & Arkansas Market)*
Kirsten Collins *(Mgr-Mktg)*
Brands & Products:
CRISPANI
FRESH BREAD MAKES FRIENDS
PANERA
PANERA BREAD
THE PANERA CARD
PINK RIBBON BAGGEL
VIA PANERA
YOU PICK TWO
Advertising Agencies:
Franco Public Relations Group
400 Renaissance Ctr Ste 1000
Detroit, MI 48243
Tel.: (313) 567-2300
Fax: (313) 567-4486

Looney Advertising and Design
7 N Mountain Ave
Montclair, NJ 07042
Tel.: (973) 783-0017
Tel.: (973) 220-0335
Fax: (973) 783-0613

The Phelps Group
901 Wilshire Blvd
Santa Monica, CA 90401-1854
Tel.: (310) 752-4400
Fax: (310) 752-4444

THE PANTRY, INC.
305 Gregson Dr PO Box 8019
Cary, NC 27511
Tel.: (919) 774-6700
Fax: (919) 775-5428
Toll Free: (800) 476-7574
E-mail: postmaster@thepantry.com
Web Site: www.thepantry.com
Approx. Rev.: $7,265,262,000
Approx. Number Employees: 6,378
Year Founded: 1967
Business Description:
Independent Convenience Store Operator
S.I.C.: 5411; 5541
N.A.I.C.S.: 445120; 447110
Advertising Expenditures: $4,600,000
Personnel:
Edwin J. Holman *(Chm & Interim CEO)*
Mark R. Bierley *(CFO & Sr VP)*
Paul M. Lemerise *(CIO)*
Keith S. Bell *(Sr VP-Fuels)*
John Joseph Fisher *(Sr VP-Food Svc)*
Brands & Products:
AUNT M'S
BEAN STREET COFFEE
BIG CHILL
CAMPUS STORE
CELESTE
THE CHILL ZONE
COWBOYS
ETNA
FAST LANE
FOOD CHIEF
GOLDEN GALLON
KANGAROO
KANGAROO EXPRESS
LIL' CHAMP
ON THE WAY
THE PANTRY
PETRO EXPRESS
QUICK STOP
SMOKERS EXPRESS
SPRINT
WORTH
Advertising Agency:
Largemouth Communications, Inc.
1007 Slater Rd, Ste 150
Durham, NC 27703
Tel.: (919) 459-6450
Fax: (919) 573-9139

PAPA MURPHY'S INTERNATIONAL, LLC
(Holding of Lee Equity Partners LLC)
8000 NE Pkwy Dr # 350
Vancouver, WA 98662
Tel.: (360) 260-7272
Fax: (360) 260-0500
Web Site: www.papamurphys.com
Approx. Number Employees: 65
Year Founded: 1981
Business Description:
Pizza Restaurant Operator & Franchisor
S.I.C.: 5812
N.A.I.C.S.: 722110
Media: 5-6-13-14-15-19-20
Personnel:
John D. Barr *(Chm & CEO)*
Ken Calwell *(Pres)*
Jenifer Anhorn *(CMO)*
Victoria Blackwell *(Gen Counsel)*
Advertising Agency:
Periscope
921 Washington Ave S
Minneapolis, MN 55415
Tel.: (612) 399-0500
Fax: (612) 399-0600
Toll Free: (800) 339-2103
(Agency of Record)

PARAMOUNT COFFEE COMPANY
130 N Larch St
Lansing, MI 48901
Tel.: (517) 372-5500
Fax: (517) 372-2870
Toll Free: (800) 968-1222
E-mail: pcc@paramountcoffee.com
Web Site: www.paramountcoffee.com
Business Description:
Coffee Distr
S.I.C.: 2095
N.A.I.C.S.: 311920
Media: 2-7-8-10
Personnel:
Steve Morris *(Pres & COO)*
Advertising Agency:
Queue Creative
410 S Cedar St Ste F
Lansing, MI 48912
Tel.: (517) 374-6600
Fax: (517) 374-4215

THE PASTENE COMPANIES, LTD.
330 Tpke St
Canton, MA 02021-2357
Tel.: (781) 830-8200
Fax: (781) 830-8225
Toll Free: (888) 727-8363
E-mail: sales@pastene.com
Web Site: www.pastene.com
E-Mail For Key Personnel:
Sales Director: sales@pastene.com
Approx. Number Employees: 50
Year Founded: 1874
Business Description:
Importer of Foods & Wines
S.I.C.: 5141; 5182
N.A.I.C.S.: 424410; 424820
Import
Media: 18-22-23
Distr.: Natl.
Personnel:
Christopher Tosi *(Chm)*
Mark Tosi *(Pres)*
John Franciosa *(CFO)*
Brands & Products:
PASTENE

PATHMARK STORES, INC.
(Sub. of The Great Atlantic & Pacific Tea Company, Inc.)
2 Paragon Dr
Montvale, NJ 07645
Tel.: (201) 573-9700
Fax: (201) 505-3054
E-mail: customers@pathmark.com
Web Site: www.pathmark.com
Approx. Sls.: $4,058,000,000
Approx. Number Employees: 7,400
Year Founded: 1968
Business Description:
Retail Chain Supermarkets
S.I.C.: 5411
N.A.I.C.S.: 445110
Advertising Expenditures: $41,600,000
Media: 5-8-9-13-19-23-24-25
Distr.: Reg.
Budget Set: Dec.
Personnel:
Dave Kelly *(Sr VP-Construction & Dev)*
Margaret Bigley *(Dir-Adv)*
Brands & Products:
ADVANTAGE CLUB
GET A LITTLE MORE
PATHMARK
Advertising Agencies:
Concrete Media
43 E Moonachie Rd
Hackensack, NJ 07601
Tel.: (201) 440-2626
Fax: (201) 440-3433

Grocery Shopping Network
900 Lumber Exchange Bldg 10 S 5th St
Minneapolis, MN 55402
Tel.: (612) 746-4232
Fax: (612) 746-4237
Toll Free: (888) 673-4663

MGSCOMM - New York City
817 Broadway 2nd Fl
New York, NY 10003
Tel.: (212) 204-8340
Fax: (212) 979-9357

PEAPOD, LLC
(Sub. of Ahold USA, Inc.)
9933 Woods Dr Ste 375
Skokie, IL 60077-1057
Tel.: (847) 583-9400
Fax: (847) 583-9494
Toll Free: (800) 573-2763
E-mail: info@peapod.com
Web Site: www.peapod.com
Approx. Number Employees: 1,800
Year Founded: 1989
Business Description:
Online Grocery Shopping Services
S.I.C.: 5411; 7379
N.A.I.C.S.: 445110; 541519
Import Export
Advertising Expenditures: $1,500,000
Media: 8-13
Personnel:
Andrew B. Parkinson *(Pres)*
John Burchard *(CIO & Sr VP)*
Thomas L. Parkinson *(CTO & Sr VP)*
Scott DeGraeve *(Sr VP & Gen Mgr)*
Michael Brennen *(Sr VP-Mktg & Customer Svc)*
Dave McHugh *(VP & Gen Mgr)*
Tony Stallone *(VP-Mdsg)*
Jonathan C. Wilson *(VP-IT)*
Peg Merzbacher *(Dir-Mktg)*
Brands & Products:
PEAPOD

PEET'S COFFEE & TEA, INC.
1400 Park Ave
Emeryville, CA 94608-3520
Mailing Address:
PO Box 12509
Berkeley, CA 94712-3509
Tel.: (510) 594-2100
Fax: (510) 594-2180
Toll Free: (800) 895-8387
Toll Free: (800) 999-2132
E-mail: info@peets.com
Web Site: www.peets.com
Approx. Rev.: $333,808,000
Approx. Number Employees: 765
Year Founded: 1966
Business Description:
Coffee Roaster & Online Merchant

Key to Media (For complete agency information see *The Advertising Red Books-Agencies* edition):
1. Bus. Publs. 2. Cable T.V. 3. Catalogs & Directories. 4. Co-op Adv. 5. Consumer Mags. 6. D.M. to Bus. Estab.7. D.M. to Consumers
8. Daily Newsp. 9. Exhibits/Trade Shows 10. Foreign 11. Infomercial 12. Internet Adv.13. Multimedia 14. Network Radio
15. Network T.V. 16. Newsp. Distr. Mags. 17. Other 18. Outdoor (Posters, Transit) 19. Point of Purchase20. Premiums, Novelties
21. Product Samples 22. Special Events Mktg. 23. Spot Radio 24. Spot T.V. 25. Weekly Newsp. 26. Yellow Page Adv.

Peet's Coffee & Tea, Inc. — (Continued)

S.I.C.: 2095; 5499
N.A.I.C.S.: 311920; 445299
Advertising Expenditures: $4,248,000
Media: 4-7-8-13-16-17-22-26
Personnel:
Jean-Michel Valette *(Chm)*
Patrick J. O'Dea *(Pres & CEO)*
Thomas P. Cawley *(CFO)*
Brands & Products:
AGED SUMATRA
ANNIVERSARY BLEND
ARABIAN MOCHA JAVA
ARABIAN MOCHA SANANI
BLEND 101
COLOMBIA
COSTA RICA
DECAF FRENCH ROAST
DECAF HOUSE BLEND
DECAF MAJOR DICKASON'S BLEND
DECAF MOCHA JAVA
DECAF SIERRA DORADA
DECAF SPECIAL BLEND
DECAF SUMATRA
DEEP ROASTING
DICKASON'S BLEND
ESPRESSO FORTE
ETHIOPIAN FANCY
FRENCH ROAST
GAIA ORGANIC BLEND
GARUDA BLEND
GUATEMALA
HOUSE BLEND
ITALIAN ROAST
JR RESERVE BLEND
KENYA
KONA
MADURO BLEND
MAJOR DICKASON'S BLEND
NEW GUINEA
PEABERRY
PEET'S COFFEE & TEA
PEET'S COFFEE GLOBAL JOURNEY
PEET'S.COM
PRIDE OF THE PORT
PUMPHREY'S BLEND
SIERRA DORADA
SNOW LEOPARD
SULAWESI-KALOSI
SUMATRA
SUMMER HOUSE
TOP BLEND
VIENNESE BLEND
Advertising Agency:
Eleven Inc.
445 Bush St 8th Fl
San Francisco, CA 94108
Tel.: (415) 707-1111
Fax: (415) 707-1100

PERFORMANCE FOOD GROUP COMPANY, LLC

(Holding of The Blackstone Group L.P.)
12500 W Creek Pkwy
Richmond, VA 23238-1110
Mailing Address:
PO Box 29269
Richmond, VA 23238
Tel.: (804) 484-7700
Fax: (804) 484-7701
E-mail: pfg@pfgc.com
Web Site: www.pfgc.com
Sales Range: $5-14.9 Billion
Approx. Number Employees: 7,200
Year Founded: 1987
Business Description:
Groceries & General Line Whslr & Distr
S.I.C.: 3556; 5046; 5141; 5142; 5148
N.A.I.C.S.: 333294; 423440; 424410; 424420; 424480
Import
Advertising Expenditures: $500,000
Media: 1-2-5-19-20
Distr.: Natl.
Budget Set: Sept.
Personnel:
George Holm *(Pres & CEO)*
Thomas Hoffman *(Pres, CEO-PFG Customized & Exec VP-Performance Food Grp)*
Mac Pearce *(Pres, CEO-Performance Foodservice & Exec VP-Performance Food Grp)*
Bob Evans *(CFO & Sr VP)*
Ernie Gilchrist *(Sr VP-Strategy & Innovation)*
Craig Hoskins *(Sr VP-Sls)*
Jane Manion *(Sr VP-HR)*
Brands & Products:
AFFLAB
BAY WINDS
BRILLIANCE
EMPIRES TREASURE
FIRST MARK
FRESH EXPRESS
GOURMET TABLE
GUEST HOUSE
HERITAGE OVENS
PFG CUSTOM CUT MEATS
POCAHONTAS
RAFFINATO
ROASTERS EXCHANGE
SONERO
VILLAGE GARDEN
WEST CREEK
Advertising Agency:
CRT/tanaka
101 W Commerce Rd
Richmond, VA 23224
Tel.: (804) 675-8100
Fax: (804) 675-8183

P.F. CHANG'S CHINA BISTRO, INC.

7676 E Pinnacle Peak Rd
Scottsdale, AZ 85255
Tel.: (480) 888-3000
Fax: (480) 888-3001
Toll Free: (866) PFCHANGS
Web Site: www.pfcb.com
Approx. Rev.: $1,242,799,000
Approx. Number Employees: 25,000
Year Founded: 1993
Business Description:
Owner & Operator of Full-Service Chinese Bistro Restaurants
S.I.C.: 5812; 5813
N.A.I.C.S.: 722110; 722410
Advertising Expenditures: $12,500,000
Media: 17-18-22-23-26
Distr.: Intl.
Personnel:
Richard L. Federico *(Chm & Co-CEO)*
F. Lane Cardwell, Jr. *(Pres)*
Robert T. Vivian *(Co-CEO)*
Mark D. Mumford *(CFO)*
Tracy M. Durchslag *(Chief Legal Officer & Corp Sec)*
R. Michael Welborn *(Pres-Global Brand Dev & Exec VP)*
Brands & Products:
PEI WEI
PEI WEI ASIAN DINER
P.F. CHANG'S
P.F. CHANG'S CHINA BISTRO
TANEKO JAPANESE TAVERN
Advertising Agency:
VITRO
(An MDC Partners Company)
625 Broadway Fl 4
San Diego, CA 92101-5403
Tel.: (619) 234-0408
Fax: (619) 234-4015

PHILLIPS FOODS INC.

1215 Fort Ave
Baltimore, MD 21220
Tel.: (443) 263-1200
Fax: (410) 837-8526
Toll Free: (888) 234-2722
E-mail: comments@phillipsfoods.com
Web Site: www.phillipsfoods.com
Sales Range: $200-249.9 Million
Approx. Number Employees: 500
Business Description:
Seafood Restaurant Operator & Seafood Product Sales
S.I.C.: 5812; 2092
N.A.I.C.S.: 722110; 311712
Personnel:
Steve Phillips *(Pres & CEO)*
Dean E. Flowers *(CFO & Exec VP)*
John Knorr *(Sr VP)*
James R. King *(VP-Fin)*
Honey Konicoff *(VP-Mktg)*
Brands & Products:
ASIAN RHYTHMS
MAKING SEAFOOD A BIGGER PART OF LIFE
PHILLIPS
STEAMER CREATIONS
Advertising Agencies:
Marriner Marketing Communications, Inc.
10221 Wincopin Cir Ste 300
Columbia, MD 21044-3419
Tel.: (410) 715-1500
Fax: (410) 995-3609
Toll Free: (800) 268-6475
NetPlus Marketing, Inc.
625 Ridge Pike Bldg E Ste 200
Conshohocken, PA 19428
Tel.: (610) 897-2380
Fax: (610) 897-2381
Interactive Marketing

PHILLIPS GOURMET, INC.

(Sub. of Phillips Mushroom Farms)
1011 Kaolin Rd PO Box 190
Kennett Square, PA 19348
Tel.: (610) 925-0520
Fax: (610) 925-0527
Web Site:
www.phillipsmushroomfarms.com
Business Description:
Prepared Gourmet Foods
S.I.C.: 2038
N.A.I.C.S.: 311412
Media: 2-4-8
Personnel:
Kevin Donovan *(Mgr-Sls)*

PRICE CHOPPER OPERATING CO., INC.

(Sub. of Golub Corporation)
501 Duanesburg Rd
Schenectady, NY 12306
Tel.: (518) 355-5000
Fax: (518) 355-3382
E-mail: webmaster@pricechopper.com
Web Site: www.pricechopper.com
Approx. Number Employees: 100
Business Description:
Retail Grocery Stores
S.I.C.: 5411
N.A.I.C.S.: 445110
Media: 5-8-9-10-17-18-22-23-24-25-26
Distr.: Reg.
Budget Set: Jan.
Personnel:
Neil M. Golub *(Pres & CEO)*
John Endres *(CFO, Treas & Sr VP-Fin)*
Jerel Golub *(COO & Exec VP)*
Greg Zeh *(CIO)*
Christina Maltbie *(VP & Asst Treas)*
Margaret Davenport *(Sr VP-HR)*
Al Provancher *(Reg VP-Ops)*
Mark Brown *(VP-Perishable Mdsg)*
Peter Cobuzzi *(VP-Mktg)*
Steven Duffy *(VP-Architectural Design & Pur Svcs)*
Lee E. French *(VP-Seafood Mdsg)*
Dave Hetfinger *(VP-Mdsg)*
Jim Mizeur *(VP-Strategic Initiatives)*
Bill Sweet *(VP-Engrg & Construction)*
Russell Zwanka *(VP-Sls, Mdsg & Mktg)*
Glen Bradley *(Dir-Loyalty Mktg & Bus Intelligence)*
Chester Pennacchia *(Dir-Construction)*
Jody Plonski *(Dir-Zone)*

PRIMO WATER CORPORATION

104 Cambridge Plaza Dr
Winston Salem, NC 27104
Tel.: (336) 331-4000
Fax: (336) 331-0319
Toll Free: (877) 266-5370
E-mail: kprimus@primowater.com
Web Site: www.primowater.com
Approx. Sls.: $44,607,000
Approx. Number Employees: 126
Year Founded: 2005
Business Description:
Purified Bottled Water & Water Dispensers Distr
S.I.C.: 5149; 2086
N.A.I.C.S.: 424490; 312112
Advertising Expenditures: $296,000
Media: 16-19
Personnel:
Billy D. Prim *(Chm, Pres & CEO)*
Mark Castaneda *(CFO)*
Michael Reeves *(Pres-Primo Direct)*
Michael S. Gunter *(Sr VP-Ops)*
Alan Leff *(VP-Quality & Production)*
Brands & Products:
AMERICAN GROWN BOTTLE
PIONEER
PRIMO
TASTE PERFECTION
ZERO WASTE BOTTLES

PROVIGO INC.

(Sub. of Loblaw Companies Limited)
400 Avenue Sainte Croix
Saint Laurent, QC H4N 3L4, Canada

Key to Media (For complete agency information see *The Advertising Red Books-Agencies* edition):
1. Bus. Publs. 2. Cable T.V. 3. Catalogs & Directories. 4. Co-op Adv. 5. Consumer Mags. 6. D.M. to Bus. Estab.7. D.M. to Consumers 8. Daily Newsp. 9. Exhibits/Trade Shows 10. Foreign 11. Infomercial 12. Internet Adv.13. Multimedia 14. Network Radio 15. Network T.V. 16. Newsp. Distr. Mags. 17. Other 18. Outdoor (Posters, Transit) 19. Point of Purchase20. Premiums, Novelties 21. Product Samples 22. Special Events Mktg. 23. Spot Radio 24. Spot T.V. 25. Weekly Newsp. 26. Yellow Page Adv.

Tel.: (514) 383-8800
Fax: (514) 383-3088
Web Site: www.provigo.ca
Approx. Number Employees: 500
Year Founded: 1969
Business Description:
Operator of Grocery Stores
S.I.C.: 5541
N.A.I.C.S.: 447110
Import Export
Advertising Expenditures: $1,000,000
Media: 4-7-8-9-11-15-18-19-20-23
Distr.: Intl.; Natl.
Budget Set: Oct.
Personnel:
Jocyanne Bourdeau *(Exec VP)*
Caroline Rousseau *(VP-HR)*
Jean-Paul Gauvin *(Mgr-HR & Labour Rels)*
Brands & Products:
PRESIDENT'S CHOICE
PROVIGO

PUBLIX SUPER MARKETS, INC.

3300 Publix Corporate Pkwy
Lakeland, FL 33811
Mailing Address:
PO Box 407
Lakeland, FL 33802-0407
Tel.: (863) 688-1188
Fax: (863) 284-5532
Toll Free: (800) 242-1227
E-mail: maria.brous@publix.com
Web Site: www.publix.com
E-Mail For Key Personnel:
Public Relations: clayton.hollis@publix.com
Approx. Rev.: $25,328,054,000
Approx. Number Employees: 70,000
Year Founded: 1930
Business Description:
Holding Company; Supermarket Chain Owner & Operator
S.I.C.: 6719; 5411
N.A.I.C.S.: 551112; 445110
Advertising Expenditures: $191,788,000
Media: 3-5-8-9-16-23-24-25-26
Distr.: Direct to Consumer; Reg.
Personnel:
Charles H. Jenkins, Jr. *(Chm)*
Hoyt R. Barnett *(Vice Chm)*
William E. Crenshaw *(CEO)*
David P. Phillips *(CFO & Treas)*
Laurie S. Zeitlin *(CIO & Sr VP)*
John A. Attaway, Jr. *(Gen Counsel, Sec & Sr VP)*
John T. Hrabusa *(Sr VP-HR)*
Randall T. Jones, Sr. *(Sr VP)*
Linda S. Kane *(VP & Asst Sec)*
Mark R. Irby *(VP-Mktg)*
Sharon A. Miller *(Exec Dir)*
Chuck Roskovich *(Reg Dir)*
Maria Brous *(Dir-Media & Community Rels)*
Marc Salm *(Dir-Counsel Risk Mgmt)*
Jason Holleman *(Brand Mgr-Fresh Foods)*
Liz Cruz *(Mgr-Mktg Sys)*
Shannon Patten *(Mgr-Media & Community Rels)*
Brenda Reid *(Mgr)*
Dwaine Stevens *(Mgr-Media & Community Rels)*
Brands & Products:
1-877-PBX-PTLS
APRON'S
CAFE PIX
COOL PIX
CRISPERS
DAILY PIX
DANISH BAKERY
EGGSTIRS
FAMILY STYLE
GET IT ALL TOGETHER
GREEN ROUTINE
HERITAGE
IT'S OUR PLEASURE
MORNING SONG
NUTRIGANICS
PLATO THE PUBLIXAURUS
PRESTO!
PUBLIX
PUBLIX ADVANTAGE BUY
PUBLIX BABY CLUB
PUBLIX FAMILYSTYLE
PUBLIX GRAPE
PUBLIX GREENWISE MARKET
PUBLIX HIGH QUALITY. LOW PRICES.
PUBLIX PARTNERS
PUBLIX PAWS
PUBLIX PIX
PUBLIX PLUS
PUBLIX PRESCHOOL PALS
PUBLIX.COM
PUBLIXDIRECT
PUBLIXDIRECT ONLINE SHOPPING. HOME DELIVERY
QUICK TAKES
START SOMETHING
STEAKHOUSE CUT
SYLLABUS
THE ULTIMATE TAILGATE PARTY
WEBB-IT 24
WHERE SHOPPING IS A PLEASURE
Advertising Agencies:
22squared
1170 Peachtree St NE 15th Fl
Atlanta, GA 30309-7649
Tel.: (404) 347-8700
Fax: (404) 347-8800

Matlock Advertising & Public Relations
107 Luckie St
Atlanta, GA 30303
Tel.: (404) 872-3200
Fax: (404) 876-4929

QDOBA MEXICAN GRILL INC.

(Sub. of Jack in the Box Inc.)
4865 Ward Rd Ste 500
Wheat Ridge, CO 80033
Tel.: (720) 898-2300
Fax: (720) 898-2396
E-mail: info@qdoba.com
Web Site: www.qdoba.com
Sales Range: $50-74.9 Million
Approx. Number Employees: 75
Year Founded: 1995
Business Description:
Mexican Restaurant Operator
S.I.C.: 5812
N.A.I.C.S.: 722211
Personnel:
Gary J. Beisler *(Pres & CEO)*
Richard Pugh *(COO)*
Eric Grundmeier *(VP-Pur & Distr)*
Bill McMillan *(VP-IT)*
Mike Speck *(VP-HR & Trng)*
David Craven *(Dir-Mktg)*
Advertising Agencies:
Amalgamated Advertising LLC
145 W 30th St 7th Fl
New York, NY 10001
Tel.: (646) 878-1700
Fax: (646) 878-1787

GroundFloor Media, Inc.
1923 Market St
Denver, CO 80202
Tel.: (303) 865-8110
Fax: (303) 253-9763

Horizon Media, Inc.
75 Varick St
New York, NY 10013
Tel.: (212) 220-5000
Toll Free: (800) 633-4201

QUAKER MAID MEATS INC.

521 Carroll St
Reading, PA 19611-2010
Tel.: (610) 376-1500
Fax: (610) 376-2678
E-mail: info@quakermaidmeats.com
Web Site: www.quakermaidmeats.com
Approx. Sls.: $29,410,954
Approx. Number Employees: 98
Year Founded: 1960
Business Description:
Prepared Meats
S.I.C.: 5147
N.A.I.C.S.: 311612
Import Export
Personnel:
Sergei Szortyka *(Pres)*
Brands & Products:
GINA LINA'S
MAMA LUCIA
QUAKER MAID
STEAK-UMM
Advertising Agency:
MEI
55 Madison Ave 4th Fl
Morristown, NJ 07960
Tel.: (973) 285-3045
Fax: (973) 538-0503

QUAKER VALLEY FOODS INC.

2701 Red Lion Rd
Philadelphia, PA 19114-1019
Tel.: (215) 992-0900
Fax: (215) 934-5028
Web Site: www.quakervalleyfoods.com
Approx. Sls.: $168,563,055
Approx. Number Employees: 300
Business Description:
Packaged Goods
S.I.C.: 5142
N.A.I.C.S.: 424420
Media: 4-7-13

QUALITY FOOD CENTERS, INC.

(Sub. of Fred Meyer, Inc.)
10116 NE 8th St
Bellevue, WA 98004-4148
Tel.: (425) 455-3761
Fax: (425) 462-2162
Toll Free: (800) 201-6261
Web Site: www.qfconline.com
Sales Range: $1-4.9 Billion
Approx. Number Employees: 6,500
Business Description:
Grocery Stores
S.I.C.: 5411
N.A.I.C.S.: 445110
Media: 8-9-19-23-24
Distr.: Natl.
Personnel:
Joe Fey *(Pres)*
Jeff Burt *(Grp VP-Perishables)*
Dean Olson *(Dir-Adv)*
Advertising Agency:
CB&S Advertising
3800 SE 22nd Ave
Portland, OR 97202
Tel.: (503) 797-3200

QUICK CHEK FOOD STORES INC.

3 Old Hwy 28
Whitehouse Station, NJ 08889
Tel.: (908) 534-2200
Fax: (908) 534-7216
E-mail: info@qchek.com
Web Site: www.qchek.com
Approx. Sls.: $200,000,000
Approx. Number Employees: 1,400
Year Founded: 1966
Business Description:
Convenience Stores
S.I.C.: 5411
N.A.I.C.S.: 445120
Import Export
Personnel:
Carlton C. Durling *(Founder)*
Dean C. Durling *(Pres)*
Mike Murphy *(Sr VP)*
Jeff Albanese *(Mgr-Real Estate)*
Advertising Agency:
Oxford Communications, Inc.
11 Music Mtn Blvd
Lambertville, NJ 08530
Tel.: (609) 397-4242
Fax: (609) 397-8863

QUIKTRIP CORPORATION

4705 S 129th East Ave
Tulsa, OK 74134-7008
Mailing Address:
PO Box 3475
Tulsa, OK 74101-3475
Tel.: (918) 615-7900
Fax: (918) 615-7377
Toll Free: (800) 947-4709
Web Site: www.quiktrip.com
E-Mail For Key Personnel:
Public Relations: pr@quiktrip.com
Approx. Sls.: $5,000,000,000
Approx. Number Employees: 6,663
Year Founded: 1958
Business Description:
Gasoline & Convenience Retail
S.I.C.: 5541; 5411
N.A.I.C.S.: 447190; 445120
Advertising Expenditures: $6,000,000
Media: 17-19
Distr.: Reg.
Personnel:
Chester Edward Cadieux, III *(Chm, Pres & CEO)*
James Denny *(VP-Mktg)*
Mike Thornbrugh *(Mgr-Pub & Govt Affairs)*
Brands & Products:
QUIK N' TASTEY
QUIKTRIP
SELECT BLEND
Advertising Agency:
The Richards Group, Inc.
8750 N Central Expy Ste 100
Dallas, TX 75231-6430

Key to Media (For complete agency information see *The Advertising Red Books-Agencies* edition):
1. Bus. Publs. 2. Cable T.V. 3. Catalogs & Directories. 4. Co-op Adv. 5. Consumer Mags. 6. D.M. to Bus. Estab.7. D.M. to Consumers
8. Daily Newsp. 9. Exhibits/Trade Shows 10. Foreign 11. Infomercial 12. Internet Adv.13. Multimedia 14. Network Radio
15. Network T.V. 16. Newsp. Distr. Mags. 17. Other 18. Outdoor (Posters, Transit) 19. Point of Purchase20. Premiums, Novelties
21. Product Samples 22. Special Events Mktg. 23. Spot Radio 24. Spot T.V. 25. Weekly Newsp. 26. Yellow Page Adv.

QuikTrip Corporation — (Continued)

Tel.: (214) 891-5700
Fax: (214) 265-2933

RALEY'S INC.
500 W Capitol Ave
West Sacramento, CA 95605-2624
Tel.: (916) 373-6370
Fax: (916) 373-6351
Fax: (916) 373-6126
E-mail: webmaster@raleys.com
Web Site: www.raleys.com
Sales Range: $1-4.9 Billion
Approx. Number Employees: 16,600
Year Founded: 1935
Business Description:
Supermarkets & Drug Stores
S.I.C.: 5411
N.A.I.C.S.: 445110
Import
Media: 8-9-13-16-18-19-20-21
Distr.: Direct to Consumer; Reg.
Budget Set: June
Personnel:
Joyce Raley Teel *(Owner & Co-Chm)*
James Teel *(Co-Chm)*
Donald Hall *(CFO)*
Michelle Cervantez *(CMO)*
Jennifer Crabb *(Gen Counsel)*
Jeffrey Szczesny *(Sr VP-HR)*
Joel Bartin *(VP-Mktg)*
Greg Korrigan *(VP-Sls)*
Brands & Products:
CELEBRATE FOOD CELEBRATE LIFE
FULL CIRCLE
RALEY'S
Advertising Agency:
Hoffman/Lewis
1725 Montgomery St
San Francisco, CA 94111-1030
Tel.: (415) 434-8500
Fax: (415) 434-8484

RALPHS GROCERY COMPANY
(Sub. of Fred Meyer, Inc.)
1100 W Artesia Blvd
Compton, CA 90220-5108
Mailing Address:
PO Box 54143
Los Angeles, CA 90054-0143
Tel.: (310) 884-9000
Fax: (310) 884-2601
E-mail: kroger.investors@kroger.com
Web Site: www.ralphs.com
Sales Range: $5-14.9 Billion
Approx. Number Employees: 34,600
Year Founded: 1873
Business Description:
Retail Grocery Stores
S.I.C.: 5411
N.A.I.C.S.: 445110
Advertising Expenditures: $1,300,000
Media: 1-8-9-14-15-16-19-22-23-24
Distr.: Reg.
Personnel:
Donna Giordano *(Pres)*
Paul Lammert *(CFO & Sr VP)*
John Schroder *(Grp VP-HR & Labor Rels)*
Terry O'Neil *(Mgr)*
Advertising Agency:
CB&S Advertising
3800 SE 22nd Ave
Portland, OR 97202
Tel.: (503) 797-3200

RESER'S FINE FOODS INC.
15570 SW Jenkins Rd
Beaverton, OR 97006
Tel.: (503) 643-6431
Fax: (503) 646-9233
Toll Free: (800) 333-6431
E-mail: marketing@resers.com
Web Site: www.resers.com
Sales Range: $300-349.9 Million
Approx. Number Employees: 1,700
Year Founded: 1951
Business Description:
Mfr. of Wholesale Specialty Food Items
S.I.C.: 2099; 5141
N.A.I.C.S.: 311999; 424410
Media: 2
Distr.: Natl.
Personnel:
Paul Leavy *(CFO)*
Peter Sirgy *(Sr VP-Sls & Mktg)*
Brands & Products:
AMERICAN CLASSICS
BAJA CAFE
DELSEY'S
DILLON'S
LYNN WILSON MEXICAN FOODS
LYNN WILSON'S
MAIN ST. BISTRO
MITIA
MRS. KINSER'S
MRS. WEAVERS
PACO RICO
PAPA LYNN
POTATO EXPRESS
RESER'S
SENSATIONAL SIDES
SIDARIS
STONEMILL KITCHENS
TORTILLAS SAN ANTONIO
WESTERN FAMILY

RICE EPICUREAN MARKET
5333 Gulfton St
Houston, TX 77081-2801
Mailing Address:
PO Box 159
Bellaire, TX 77402-0159
Tel.: (713) 662-7700
Fax: (713) 662-7757
E-mail: info@riceepicurean.com
Web Site: www.riceepicurean.com
Approx. Number Employees: 30
Year Founded: 1988
Business Description:
Grocery Stores; Rental Property Management
S.I.C.: 5411; 5812
N.A.I.C.S.: 445110; 722110
Advertising Expenditures: $250,000
Media: 8-9-13-16-25
Distr.: Reg.
Personnel:
Gary Friedlander *(Pres & COO)*
Bruce Levy *(CFO & Sr VP)*
Phil Cohen *(VP-Mktg)*
Kathy Gurwell *(Mgr-Adv)*

ROCKY MOUNTAIN CHOCOLATE FACTORY, INC.
265 Turner Dr
Durango, CO 81303
Tel.: (970) 259-0554
Fax: (970) 259-5895
Toll Free: (888) 525-2462 (Customer Service)
Toll Free: (800) 438-7623
Web Site: www.rmcf.com
Approx. Rev.: $31,127,971
Approx. Number Employees: 260
Year Founded: 1981
Business Description:
Chocolate Candy & Confections Mfr
S.I.C.: 2066; 2064
N.A.I.C.S.: 311320; 311330
Advertising Expenditures: $302,817
Personnel:
Franklin E. Crail *(Chm, Pres & CEO)*
Bryan J. Merryman *(CFO, COO & Treas)*
William K. Jobson *(CIO)*
Edward L. Dudley *(Sr VP-Sls & Mktg)*
Gregory L. Pope *(Sr VP-Dev)*
Donna L. Coupe *(VP-Franchise Support & Trng)*
Jay B. Haws *(VP-Creative)*
Jeremy M. Kinney *(VP-Fin)*
Brands & Products:
AMERICA'S CHOCOLATIER
BEAR CUBS
BEARS
THE PEAK OF PERFECTION IN HANDMADE CHOCOLATES
PEANUT BUTTER BUCKET
PEANUT BUTTER PAILS
ROCKY MOUNTAIN CHOCOLATE FACTORY
ROCKY MOUNTAIN MEDLEY
ROCKY MOUNTAIN MINTS
ROCKY MOUNTAIN SPLENDOR
ROCKY POP
SEAFOAM
SUGAR FREE DELIGHT
SWEET DREAMS
THE WORLD'S CHOCOLATIER

ROSAUERS SUPERMARKETS, INC.
(Sub. of URM Stores, Inc.)
1815 W Garland Ave
Spokane, WA 99205-2522
Mailing Address:
PO Box 9000
Spokane, WA 99209-9000
Tel.: (509) 326-8900
Fax: (509) 325-7645
Fax: (509) 328-2483
E-mail: info@rosauers.com
Web Site: www.rosauers.com
Approx. Number Employees: 60
Year Founded: 1939
Business Description:
Supermarket Chain
S.I.C.: 5411
N.A.I.C.S.: 445110
Media: 4-5-8-9-18-19-23-24-26
Distr.: Direct to Consumer; Reg.
Budget Set: July
Personnel:
Jeffrey Philipps *(Pres & CEO)*
Mike Shirts *(COO & Exec VP-Mktg)*
Paul Van Gordon *(VP-HR)*
Brands & Products:
ROSAUER'S

ROUNDY'S SUPERMARKETS INC.
(Holding of Willis Stein & Partners)
875 E Wisconsin Ave
Milwaukee, WI 53202
Mailing Address:
PO Box 473
Milwaukee, WI 53201-0473
Tel.: (414) 231-5000
Fax: (414) 231-7939
E-mail: vking@roundys.com
Web Site: www.roundys.com
Sales Range: $1-4.9 Billion
Approx. Number Employees: 21,000
Year Founded: 1952
Business Description:
Wholesale & Retail Food Distribution
S.I.C.: 5149
N.A.I.C.S.: 424490
Import
Advertising Expenditures: $3,000,000
Media: 7-8-9-18-19-20-21-23-24-26
Distr.: Reg.
Budget Set: Nov.
Personnel:
Robert A. Mariano *(CEO)*
Don Rosanova *(Exec VP-Ops)*
Ron Cooper *(Grp VP-Sls-Mktg)*
Lynn Guyer *(Dir-Organizational Comm)*
Edward G. Kitz *(Accountant)*
Brands & Products:
OLD TIME
PICK 'N SAVE
ROUNDY'S
Advertising Agency:
SMP Advertising
11500 W. Burleigh St.
Wauwatosa, WI 53222
Tel.: (414) 778-1373
(Food Wholesaler)

SAFEWAY INC.
5918 Stoneridge Mall Rd
Pleasanton, CA 94588-3229
Mailing Address:
PO Box 99
Pleasanton, CA 94566-0009
Tel.: (925) 467-3000
Fax: (925) 467-3321
Toll Free: (877) SAFEWAY
Web Site: www.safeway.com
Approx. Sls.: $41,050,000,000
Approx. Number Employees: 180,000
Year Founded: 1986
Business Description:
Food & Drug Retailer
S.I.C.: 5141; 5411
N.A.I.C.S.: 445120; 424410; 445110
Import Export
Advertising Expenditures: $523,700,000
Media: 3-5-8-9-15-16-17-18-19-23-24-25-26
Distr.: Reg.
Personnel:
Steven A. Burd *(Chm, Pres & CEO)*
Tom Schwilke *(Pres & Gen Mgr-Perishables)*
Robert L. Edwards *(CFO & Exec VP)*
Kenneth M. Shachmut *(CFO & Exec VP)*
David T. Ching *(CIO & Sr VP)*
Diane M. Dietz *(CMO & Exec VP)*
Larree M. Renda *(Exec VP & Chief Strategist & Admin Officer)*
Mir Aamir *(Pres-Customer Loyalty & Digital Tech)*
Kelly Griffith *(Pres-Mdsg)*
Scott Grimmett *(Pres-Denver Div)*
Michael R. Minasi *(Pres-Mktg)*
Steve Neibergall *(Pres-Eastern Div)*
Bruce L. Everette *(Exec VP-Retail Ops)*
David F. Bond *(Sr VP-Fin & Control)*
Joseph Ennen *(Sr VP-Consumer Brands)*
Carl Graziani *(Sr VP-Mktg Plng)*

Key to Media (For complete agency information see *The Advertising Red Books-Agencies* edition):
1. Bus. Publs. 2. Cable T.V. 3. Catalogs & Directories. 4. Co-op Adv. 5. Consumer Mags. 6. D.M. to Bus. Estab.7. D.M. to Consumers
8. Daily Newsp. 9. Exhibits/Trade Shows 10. Foreign 11. Infomercial 12. Internet Adv.13. Multimedia 14. Network Radio
15. Network T.V. 16. Newsp. Distr. Mags. 17. Other 18. Outdoor (Posters, Transit) 19. Point of Purchase20. Premiums, Novelties
21. Product Samples 22. Special Events Mktg. 23. Spot Radio 24. Spot T.V. 25. Weekly Newsp. 26. Yellow Page Adv.

Russell M. Jackson *(Sr VP-HR)*
Jonathan Mayes *(Sr VP-Govt Rel, Pub Affairs & Corp Social Responsibility)*
Melissa C. Plaisance *(Sr VP-Fin & IR)*
Darren Singer *(Sr VP-Pharmacy, Health & Wellness)*
David R. Stern *(Sr VP-Plng & Bus Dev)*
Jerry Tidwell *(Sr VP-Supply Ops)*
Donald P. Wright *(Sr VP-Real Estate & Engrg)*
Sheetal Khanna *(Dir-Brand Dev-Premium Brands)*
Brands & Products:
BASIC RED
BRIGHT GREEN
EATING RIGHT KIDS
INGREDIENTS FOR LIFE.
LUCERNE
MOM TO MOM
O ORGANICS
PRIMO TAGLIO
PRIORITY PET CARE
RANCHER'S RESERVE
SAFEWAY SELECT
SIGNATURE CAFE
WATERFRONT BISTRO
Advertising Agencies:
Alcone Marketing Group
(Division of Omnicom Group, Inc.)
4 Studebaker
Irvine, CA 92618-2012
Tel.: (949) 770-4400
Fax: (949) 770-2957

DDB Chicago
200 E Randolph St
Chicago, IL 60601
Tel.: (312) 552-6000
Fax: (312) 552-2370

PHD San Francisco
555 Market St 10th Fl
San Francisco, CA 94105
Tel.: (415) 356-1300
Fax: (415) 356-1301
Media Planning & Buying

Webb PR
6025 S Quebec St Ste 360
Centennial, CO 80111
Tel.: (303) 796-8888

SAKER SHOPRITES INC.

922 Hwy 33 Bldg 6 Ste 1
Freehold, NJ 07728-8452
Tel.: (732) 462-4700
Fax: (732) 294-2322
Web Site: www.shoprite.com
Approx. Number Employees: 6,850
Year Founded: 1958
Business Description:
Supermarket Owner & Retailer
S.I.C.: 5411; 5149
N.A.I.C.S.: 445110; 424490
Advertising Expenditures: $10,300,000
Media: 8-9-16-23-24-25
Personnel:
Maryanne Rego *(Dir-Adv)*

SAVE MART SUPERMARKETS

1800 Standiford Ave
Modesto, CA 95350-0180
Mailing Address:
PO Box 4278
Modesto, CA 95352-4278
Tel.: (209) 577-1600
Fax: (209) 577-3857
Toll Free: (800) 692-5710
Web Site: www.savemart.com
Approx. Number Employees: 10,500
Year Founded: 1952
Business Description:
Supermarket Chain
S.I.C.: 5411
N.A.I.C.S.: 445110
Media: 5-8-9-16-19-22-23-24-25
Personnel:
Robert M. Piccinini *(Chm & CEO)*

SCHNUCK MARKETS, INC.

11420 Lackland Rd
Saint Louis, MO 63146-3559
Tel.: (314) 994-9900
Fax: (314) 994-4465
Web Site: www.schnucks.com
Sales Range: $1-4.9 Billion
Approx. Number Employees: 15,642
Year Founded: 1939
Business Description:
Retail Grocery & Pharmaceutical Services; Restaurant & Baking Services
S.I.C.: 5411; 5912
N.A.I.C.S.: 445110; 446110
Advertising Expenditures: $200,000
Media: 8-13-19-20-22-25
Personnel:
Scott C. Schnuck *(Chm & CEO)*
Todd R. Schnuck *(Pres & COO)*
David Bell *(CFO)*
Robert J. Howard *(VP-Mktg)*
Gary Meyer *(VP-Fin)*
Ross E. Hutsle *(Dir-Facilities)*
Tom McMunn *(Dir-Private Brands Dev)*
Bob Mueller *(Dir-Pharmacy)*
Joane Taylor *(Dir-Consumer Affairs)*
Lori Willis *(Dir-Comm)*
Joe Duggan *(Mgr-Category)*
Brands & Products:
ACCU-PRICE
THE FRIENDLIEST STORES IN TOWN
SCHNUCKS
WE MAKE IT EASY

SEATTLE'S BEST COFFEE INTERNATIONAL

(Sub. of FOCUS Brands, Inc.)
200 Glenridge Point Pkwy Ste 200
Atlanta, GA 30342
Tel.: (404) 255-3250
Fax: (404) 255-4978
Toll Free: (800) 722-3190
Web Site: www.focusbrands.com
Approx. Number Employees: 500
Business Description:
Franchisor of Coffee Bars on Military Bases & International Markets
S.I.C.: 5812; 5499
N.A.I.C.S.: 722211; 445299
Personnel:
Michelle Gass *(Pres)*
Lenore Krentz *(Chief Admin Officer & CFO)*
Advertising Agency:
Creature
1508 10th Ave
Seattle, WA 98122
Tel.: (206) 625-6994
Fax: (206) 625-6904

SEDANO'S MANAGEMENT, INC.

3140 W 76th St
Hialeah, FL 33018
Tel.: (305) 824-1034
Fax: (305) 556-6981
E-mail: info@sedanos.com
Web Site: www.sedanos.com
Sales Range: $300-349.9 Million
Approx. Number Employees: 1,800
Year Founded: 1961
Business Description:
Grocery Store Chain
S.I.C.: 5411; 5912
N.A.I.C.S.: 445110; 446110
Media: 8-23-24
Personnel:
Manuel A. Herran *(Pres & CEO)*
Daniel Valdez *(VP-Fin & Mktg)*
Alfredo Guerra *(Mgr-IT)*
Advertising Agency:
Republica
2153 Coral Way
Miami, FL 33145
Tel.: (305) 442-0977
Fax: (305) 443-1631

SHAW'S SUPERMARKETS, INC.

(Div. of Albertson's, Inc.)
750 W Ctr St
West Bridgewater, MA 02379-1518
Tel.: (508) 313-3318
Fax: (508) 313-3112
Toll Free: (888) 477-4297
E-mail: resume@shaws.com
Web Site: www.shaws.com
Sales Range: $125-149.9 Million
Approx. Number Employees: 226
Year Founded: 1978
Business Description:
Supermarkets
S.I.C.: 5411; 8741
N.A.I.C.S.: 445110; 561110
Advertising Expenditures: $1,000,000
Media: 8-9-16-24-25
Distr.: Reg.

SHEARER'S FOODS INC.

(Holding of Mistral Equity Partners LLC)
692 Wabash Ave N
Brewster, OH 44613
Tel.: (330) 478-2179
Fax: (330) 767-3393
E-mail: info@shearers.com
Web Site: www.shearers.com
Approx. Sls.: $48,093,807
Approx. Number Employees: 290
Year Founded: 1974
Business Description:
Potato Chips & Similar Snacks
S.I.C.: 2096; 5145
N.A.I.C.S.: 311919; 424450
Personnel:
Scott W. Smith *(Pres)*
Robert Shearer *(CEO)*
Bill McCabe *(Sr VP-Sls & Mktg)*
Paul Smith *(Dir-Product Solutions)*
Brands & Products:
GRANDMA SHEARERS
SHEARERS
Advertising Agency:
Innis Maggiore
4715 Whipple Ave NW
Canton, OH 44718-2651
Tel.: (330) 492-5500
Fax: (330) 492-5568
Toll Free: (800) 460-4111

SHEETZ, INC.

5700 6th Ave
Altoona, PA 16602
Tel.: (814) 946-3611
Fax: (814) 946-4375
Toll Free: (800) 487-5444
Web Site: www.sheetz.com
Sales Range: $1-4.9 Billion
Approx. Number Employees: 10,650
Year Founded: 1952
Business Description:
Convenience Stores & Gasoline Stations
S.I.C.: 5541; 5411
N.A.I.C.S.: 447110; 445120; 447190
Media: 13-14-15-19-25
Personnel:
Stephen G. Sheetz *(Chm)*
Stanton R. Sheetz *(Pres & CEO)*
Mike Lorenz *(Exec VP-Petroleum Supply)*
Ray Ryan *(Exec VP-Distr & Sheet Bros Kitchen)*
Joseph M. Sheetz *(Exec VP-Fin)*
Louie Sheetz *(Exec VP-Mktg)*
Stephanie Doliveria *(VP-HR)*
George Medairy *(Dir-Corp IT)*
Brands & Products:
COFFEEZ
CUPO'CCINO
SHEETZ
SHWEETZ
Advertising Agencies:
Harmelin Media
525 Righters Ferry Rd
Bala Cynwyd, PA 19004-1315
Tel.: (610) 668-7900
Fax: (610) 668-9548
(Sheetz Brothers Coffeez, Media Buying)

Think, Inc.
2818 Smallman St
Pittsburgh, PA 15222
Tel.: (412) 281-9228
Fax: (412) 281-9243

SHERWOOD FOOD DISTRIBUTORS

12499 Evergreen Rd
Detroit, MI 48228
Tel.: (313) 659-7300
Fax: (313) 659-7509
E-mail: detroit@sherwoodfoods.com
Web Site: www.sherwoodfoods.com
Approx. Number Employees: 600
Year Founded: 1987
Business Description:
Wholesale Food Distributor
S.I.C.: 5147; 5144
N.A.I.C.S.: 424470; 424440
Advertising Expenditures: $500,000
Media: 8-13-17-22
Personnel:
Earl Ishbia *(CEO)*
Jason Ishbia *(CFO)*
Howard Ishbia *(Exec VP-Sls)*
Brands & Products:
SFD

SHOPRITE SUPERMARKETS, INC.

(Sub. of Wakefern Food Corporation)
176 N Main St

Key to Media (For complete agency information see *The Advertising Red Books-Agencies* edition):
1. Bus. Publs. 2. Cable T.V. 3. Catalogs & Directories. 4. Co-op Adv. 5. Consumer Mags. 6. D.M. to Bus. Estab.7. D.M. to Consumers
8. Daily Newsp. 9. Exhibits/Trade Shows 10. Foreign 11. Infomercial 12. Internet Adv.13. Multimedia 14. Network Radio
15. Network T.V. 16. Newsp. Distr. Mags. 17. Other 18. Outdoor (Posters, Transit) 19. Point of Purchase20. Premiums, Novelties
21. Product Samples 22. Special Events Mktg. 23. Spot Radio 24. Spot T.V. 25. Weekly Newsp. 26. Yellow Page Adv.

ShopRite Supermarkets, Inc. — (Continued)

Florida, NY 10921-1021
Tel.: (845) 651-4411
Fax: (845) 651-4469
Web Site: www.shoprite.com
Approx. Number Employees: 150
Year Founded: 1942
Business Description:
Supermarket Chain Operator
S.I.C.: 5411
N.A.I.C.S.: 445110
Export
Media: 4-5-8-9-13-14-15-19-21-22-23-24-25-26
Distr.: Direct to Consumer; Reg.
Budget Set: Sept. -Oct.
Personnel:
Denise Ryan *(Adv Dir)*

SKYLINE CHILI, INC.

4180 Thunderbird Ln
Fairfield, OH 45014
Tel.: (513) 874-1188
Fax: (513) 874-3591
Web Site: www.skylinechili.com
Approx. Rev.: $30,000,000
Approx. Number Employees: 700
Year Founded: 1949
Business Description:
Quick Service Restaurants Owner, Operator, Developer & Franchiser; Frozen Food Products Production & Sales
S.I.C.: 5812; 2038
N.A.I.C.S.: 722110; 311412
Advertising Expenditures: $2,000,000
Media: 3-9-13-18-19-20-22-23-24-25
Distr.: Direct to Consumer; Reg.
Budget Set: Oct.
Personnel:
Kevin R. McDonnell *(Chm, Pres & CEO)*
Debi Chitwood *(Sr VP-Ops)*
Phil Lewis *(Sr VP-Franchising)*
Brands & Products:
CONEY BITES
FRESH SELECT
IT'S SKYLINE TIME
LO-CARB CONEY BOWL
SKYFRIES
SKYLINE
SKYLINE CHILI
Advertising Agency:
Sunrise Advertising
700 Walnut St Ste 500
Cincinnati, OH 45202
Tel.: (513) 333-4100
Fax: (513) 333-4101
(Skyline Chili Restaurants)
— George Sabert *(V.P.)*

SMART & FINAL, INC.

(Holding of Apollo Management, L.P.)
600 Citadel Dr
City of Commerce, CA 90040
Tel.: (323) 869-7500
Fax: (323) 869-7860
E-mail: customerrelations@smartandfinal.com
Web Site: www.smartandfinal.com
Approx. Sls.: $2,104,473,000
Approx. Number Employees: 5,910
Year Founded: 1871
Business Description:
Wholesale Grocers & Restaurant & Grocery Items Supplier
S.I.C.: 5141
N.A.I.C.S.: 424410
Import
Advertising Expenditures: $26,700,000
Media: 2-5-7-9-10-15-19-21-23-25-26
Distr.: Reg.
Budget Set: Jan.
Personnel:
George G. Golleher *(Chm & CEO)*
John Golleher *(Pres & CEO)*
Dave Hirz *(Pres)*
Richard N. Phegley *(CFO & Sr VP)*
Richard A. Link *(Chief Acctg Officer, VP & Controller)*
Donald G. Alvarado *(Gen Counsel)*
C. Marie Robinson *(Sr VP-Supply Chain)*
Jeff D. Whynot *(Sr.VP-HR)*
Suzanne Mullins *(Grp VP-HR)*
Randall Oliver *(Dir-Corp Comm)*
Terry Johnson *(Mgr-Retail Maintenance)*
Brands & Products:
CHEF'S REVIEW
LA ROMANELA
MONTECITO
PROPRIDE
Advertising Agency:
Mass Connections, Inc.
13131 E 166th St
Cerritos, CA 90703
Tel.: (562) 365-0200
Fax: (562) 365-0201
Toll Free: (800) 275-6650

SMART BALANCE INC.

115 W Century Rd Ste 260
Paramus, NJ 07652-1432
Tel.: (201) 568-9300
Web Site: www.smartbalance.com
Approx. Sls.: $241,967,000
Approx. Number Employees: 69
Business Description:
Food & Beverage Processing Services
S.I.C.: 2099; 2033; 2782; 7389
N.A.I.C.S.: 311999; 311421; 323118; 561499
Advertising Expenditures: $25,868,000
Personnel:
Stephen B. Hughes *(Chm & CEO)*
Alan Gever *(CFO & Exec VP)*
Norman Matar *(Chief Counsel, Corp Sec & Exec VP)*
Peter Dray *(Exec VP-Ops & Product Dev)*
Austin Jacobus *(Exec VP-Foodservice, Indus & Intl)*
Terry Schulke *(Chief Customer Officer & Exec VP)*
Gerald Edel *(VP & Gen Mgr)*
Brett Meltzer *(VP & Gen Mgr-West)*
Jeff Scroggins *(VP & Gen Mgr-Mass-Club Channel)*
John Mintz *(VP-Fin & Strategy)*
David McCarty *(Dir-Mktg)*
Brands & Products:
BALANCING YOUR FATS
SMART BALANCE
Advertising Agencies:
Becker Guerry
107 Tindall Rd
Middletown, NJ 07748-2321
Tel.: (732) 671-6440
Fax: (732) 671-4350

MEI
55 Madison Ave 4th Fl
Morristown, NJ 07960
Tel.: (973) 285-3045
Fax: (973) 538-0503

TBC Inc.
900 S Wolfe St
Baltimore, MD 21231
Tel.: (410) 347-7500
Fax: (410) 986-1299

SMITH'S FOOD & DRUG CENTERS, INC.

(Sub. of Fred Meyer, Inc.)
1550 S Redwood Rd
Salt Lake City, UT 84104-5105
Mailing Address:
PO Box 30550
Salt Lake City, UT 84130
Tel.: (801) 974-1400
Fax: (801) 974-1676
Toll Free: (800) 444-8081
E-mail: investors@kroger.com
Web Site:
www.smithsfoodanddrug.com
Sales Range: $25-49.9 Million
Approx. Number Employees: 300
Year Founded: 1948
Business Description:
Grocery & Drug Stores Chain
S.I.C.: 5411; 5912
N.A.I.C.S.: 445110; 446110
Import
Media: 8-9-10-13-18-23-24-25-26
Distr.: Natl.
Budget Set: Aug.
Personnel:
Jai Hallsey *(CEO)*
Dirk Burningham *(Dir-Adv)*

SOBEYS INC.

(Sub. of Empire Company Limited)
123 Ford St
Stellarton, NS B0K 1S0, Canada
Tel.: (902) 752-8371
Fax: (902) 752-2960
E-mail: customer.service@sobeys.ca
Web Site: www.sobeys.ca
E-Mail For Key Personnel:
Marketing Director: duncan.reith@sobeys.ca
Public Relations: Andrew.Walker@sobeys.ca
Approx. Sls.: $12,609,215,488
Approx. Number Employees: 32,000
Year Founded: 1907
Business Description:
Food Distribution & Retail Services
S.I.C.: 5149
N.A.I.C.S.: 424490
Import
Advertising Expenditures: $29,444,227
Media: 8-9-11-18-20-23-24
Distr.: Intl.; Natl.
Personnel:
Bill McEwan *(Pres & CEO)*
Paul A. Jewer *(CFO)*
Dennis Folz *(Chief HR Officer & Exec VP)*
Ashim Khemani *(Chief Leadership Dev Officer)*
Karen McCaskill *(Gen Counsel, Sec & Sr VP)*
Sylvie Lachance *(Exec VP-Real Estate Dev)*
Francois Vimard *(Exec VP)*
L. Jane McDow *(Asst Sec)*
Brands & Products:
OUR COMPLIMENTS
SMART CHOICE

SPARTAN STORES, INC.

850 76th St SW
Grand Rapids, MI 49518
Mailing Address:
PO Box 8700
Grand Rapids, MI 49518-8700
Tel.: (616) 878-2000
Fax: (616) 878-2691
Toll Free: (800) 343-4422
E-mail: communications@spartanstores.com
Web Site: www.spartanstores.com
Approx. Sls.: $2,533,064,000
Approx. Number Employees: 4,100
Year Founded: 1917
Business Description:
Grocery Supplier & Retailer
S.I.C.: 5141; 5411
N.A.I.C.S.: 424410; 445110
Import
Advertising Expenditures: $14,200,000
Media: 2-4-8-13-22-26
Personnel:
Craig C. Sturken *(Chm)*
Dennis Eidson *(Pres & CEO)*
David M. Staples *(CFO & Exec VP)*
Alex J. DeYonker *(Gen Counsel, Sec & Exec VP)*
Theodore C. Adornato *(Exec VP-Retail Ops)*
Alan Hartline *(Exec VP-Mdsg & Mktg)*
Derek Jones *(Exec VP-Wholesale Ops)*
David deS Couch *(VP-IT)*
Thomas A. Van Hall *(VP-Fin)*
Brands & Products:
AROMA STREET
FRESH SELECTIONS
FULL CIRCLE
PAWS
SPARTAN
TOP CARE
VALUTIME

STACY'S PITA CHIP COMPANY, INC.

(Sub. of Frito-Lay, Inc.)
663 N St
Randolph, MA 02368
Tel.: (781) 961-2800
Fax: (781) 961-2830
Toll Free: (888) 33-CHIPS
Approx. Sls.: $60,000,000
Approx. Number Employees: 100
Year Founded: 1997
Business Description:
Snack Food Mfr & Retailer
S.I.C.: 2096
N.A.I.C.S.: 311919
Media: 6-18-21-22
Brands & Products:
STACY'S PITA CHIPS
STACY'S SOY THIN CRISPS
Advertising Agency:
The Castle Group
38 Third Ave Charlestown Navy Yard
Boston, MA 02129
Tel.: (617) 337-9500

Key to Media (For complete agency information see *The Advertising Red Books-Agencies* edition):
1. Bus. Publs. 2. Cable T.V. 3. Catalogs & Directories. 4. Co-op Adv. 5. Consumer Mags. 6. D.M. to Bus. Estab.7. D.M. to Consumers 8. Daily Newsp. 9. Exhibits/Trade Shows 10. Foreign 11. Infomercial 12. Internet Adv.13. Multimedia 14. Network Radio 15. Network T.V. 16. Newsp. Distr. Mags. 17. Other 18. Outdoor (Posters, Transit) 19. Point of Purchase20. Premiums, Novelties 21. Product Samples 22. Special Events Mktg. 23. Spot Radio 24. Spot T.V. 25. Weekly Newsp. 26. Yellow Page Adv.

Fax: (617) 337-9539

STATER BROS. MARKETS

(Sub. of Stater Brothers Holdings)
301 S Tippecanoe Ave
San Bernardino, CA 92408
Tel.: (909) 733-5000
Fax: (909) 379-0414
Toll Free: (877) 232-9300
Web Site: www.staterbros.com
Business Description:
Supermarket Services
S.I.C.: 5411
N.A.I.C.S.: 445110
Media: 4-8-16-18-21-22
Personnel:
Jack H. Brown *(Chm & CEO)*
Jim Lee *(Pres & COO)*
Phillip J. Smith *(CFO, Chief Acctg Officer & Exec VP-Fin)*
George Frahm *(Exec VP-Retail Ops & Admin)*
Dan Meyer *(Sr VP-Retail Ops)*
Dave Harris *(VP-Fin)*

STATER BROTHERS HOLDINGS

(Sub. of La Cadena Investments)
301 S Tippecanoe Ave
San Bernardino, CA 92408
Tel.: (909) 783-5000
Fax: (909) 783-3930
Web Site: www.staterbros.com
Approx. Sls.: $3,674,427,000
Approx. Number Employees: 18,000
Year Founded: 1936
Business Description:
Holding Company; Supermarkets
S.I.C.: 5411; 6719
N.A.I.C.S.: 445110; 551112
Advertising Expenditures: $28,100,000
Personnel:
Jack H. Brown *(Chm & CEO)*
Thomas W. Field, Jr. *(Vice Chm)*
James W. Lee *(Pres & COO)*
Phillip J. Smith *(CFO, Chief Acctg Officer & Exec VP)*
George A. Frahm *(Exec VP-Retail Ops & Admin)*
Dennis L. McIntyre *(Exec VP-Mktg)*
Dan Meyer *(Reg Sr VP-Retail Ops)*

STEUBEN FOODS INC.

15504 Liberty Ave
Jamaica, NY 11433-1038
Tel.: (718) 291-3333
Fax: (718) 291-0560
Sales Range: $250-299.9 Million
Approx. Number Employees: 240
Year Founded: 1981
Business Description:
Producer of Canned Specialties & Dairy Products
S.I.C.: 2099; 2026
N.A.I.C.S.: 311999; 311511
Import Export
Media: 5-17

THE STOP & SHOP SUPERMARKET COMPANY

(Sub. of Ahold USA, Inc.)
1385 Hancock St Quincy Ctr Plz
Quincy, MA 02169-5100
Mailing Address:
PO Box 1942
Boston, MA 02105-1942
Tel.: (617) 770-6040
Toll Free: (800) 767-7772
Web Site: www.stopandshop.com
Year Founded: 1914
Business Description:
Grocery Store Operator
S.I.C.: 5411
N.A.I.C.S.: 445110
Import Export
Media: 7-8-9-16-19-20-23-25
Distr.: Reg.
Personnel:
Carl Schlicker *(Pres & CEO)*
Paula A. Price *(CFO)*
Robin Michel *(Exec VP & Gen Mgr-Giant Landover)*
Jim Dwyer *(Exec VP-Strategy & Bus Dev)*
Paula Labian *(Exec VP-HR)*
Jeff Slater *(Exec VP-People)*
Stephen Vowles *(Sr VP-Mktg)*
Caryn Neidel *(Brand Mgr)*
Brands & Products:
STOP & SHOP
Advertising Agency:
Mullen
40 Broad St
Boston, MA 02109
Tel.: (617) 226-9000
Fax: (617) 226-9100

SUNSHINE RAISIN CORPORATION

PO Box 219 626 S 5th St
Fowler, CA 93625-0219
Tel.: (559) 834-5981
Fax: (559) 834-1756
E-mail: info@national-raisin.com
Web Site: www.national-raisin.com
Sales Range: $25-49.9 Million
Approx. Number Employees: 500
Year Founded: 1968
Business Description:
Supplier of Raisins
S.I.C.: 0723
N.A.I.C.S.: 115114
Advertising Expenditures: $200,000
Media: 2-13-17-22-26
Personnel:
Christina Lloyd *(Head-HR)*
Brands & Products:
BONNER
CHAMPION
NATIONAL RAISIN
THOMPSON

SUPER FRESH COMPANY

(Sub. of The Great Atlantic & Pacific Tea Company, Inc.)
2 Paragon Dr
Montvale, NJ 07645
Mailing Address:
PO Box 2945
Paterson, NJ 07509-2945
Tel.: (410) 594-7500
Fax: (410) 594-7619
Toll Free: (866) 443-7374
Web Site: www.superfreshfood.com
Approx. Number Employees: 3,500
Business Description:
Supermarket
S.I.C.: 5411
N.A.I.C.S.: 445110
Media: 8-9-18-23-24-25
Distr.: Reg.

SUPERVALU, INC.

7050 Flying Cloud Dr
Eden Prairie, MN 55344
Tel.: (952) 828-4000
Fax: (952) 828-8998
E-mail: sv.inquire@supervalu.com
Web Site: www.supervalu.com
E-Mail For Key Personnel:
President: Mike.Jackson@supervalu.com
Approx. Sls.: $37,534,000,000
Approx. Number Employees: 142,000
Year Founded: 1870
Business Description:
Wholesale Food Distr & Retailer
S.I.C.: 5141; 5147; 5411
N.A.I.C.S.: 424410; 424470; 445110
Import Export
Advertising Expenditures: $120,000,000
Media: 5-8-9-15-19-20-21-23-24-25
Distr.: Reg.
Budget Set: Oct.
Personnel:
Craig R. Herkert *(Pres & CEO)*
Sherry M. Smith *(CFO & Exec VP)*
Wayne Shurts *(CIO & Exec VP)*
Julie Dexter Berg *(CMO & Exec VP)*
Mark P. Anderson *(Pres/COO-Independent Bus)*
Peter J. Van Helden *(Pres-Retail Ops & Exec VP)*
David M. Oliver *(CFO-Supply Chain Svs, VP & Interim Controller)*
J. Andrew Herring *(Exec VP-Real Estate, Market Dev & Legal)*
Dave Pylipow *(Exec VP-HR & Comm)*
David McGlinchey *(Sr VP-Mdsg-Shaw's/Star Banners)*
Daniel J. Zvonek *(Grp VP-Fin, Mdsg, Mktg & Corp Plng)*
Leon Bergmann *(VP-Independent Sls Mktg & Mdsg)*
Jean A Giese *(Dir-IR)*
Adam Graham *(Brand Mgr)*
Kristin Parsons *(Brand Mgr)*
Brands & Products:
ALBERTSONS
COUNTY MARKET
CUB FOODS
CULINARY CIRCLE
FARM FRESH
IGA
JEWEL-OSCO
LUCKY
NEWMARKET
SAVE-A-LOT
SCOTT'S FOODS
SHOP 'N SAVE
SHOPPERS
SHOPPER'S FOOD WHAREHOUSE
SUPERVALU
TRADITION, EXCELLENCE AND FUTURE PROMISE.
WILD HARVEST
Advertising Agencies:
Compass Point Media
222 S 9th St
Minneapolis, MN 55402-3362
Tel.: (612) 347-6900
Fax: (612) 347-6969
Albertson's
Acme
Biggs
Cub Foods
Shop 'n Save
Bristol Farms
Farm Fresh & Pharmacy
Hornbacher's Jewel/Osco
Shaws/Star Market
Shoppers Food & Pharmacy

Dailey & Associates
(Sub. of The Interpublic Group of Cos., Inc.)
8687 Melrose Ave Ste G300
West Hollywood, CA 90069-5701
Tel.: (310) 360-3100
Fax: (310) 360-0810

FAME
60 S Sixth St Ste 2600
Minneapolis, MN 55402
Tel.: (612) 746-3263
Fax: (612) 746-3333
(Creative)

The Kaplan Thaler Group
825 8th Ave 34th Fl
New York, NY 10019
Tel.: (212) 474-5000
Fax: (212) 474-5702
Acme
Albertsons
Creative
Cub Foods
Digital Marketing
Direct Marketing
Jewel-Osco
Save-A-Lot
Shaw?s & Star Market

SUPERVALU, INC. - EASTERN REGION

(Div. of SUPERVALU, Inc.)
8258 Richfood Rd
Mechanicsville, VA 23116-2008
Tel.: (804) 746-6000
Fax: (804) 746-6144
Web Site: www.supervalu.com
Sales Range: $450-499.9 Million
Approx. Number Employees: 1,200
Business Description:
Groceries Whslr
S.I.C.: 5141
N.A.I.C.S.: 424410
Media: 6-9-25
Personnel:
Kevin Kamp *(Pres)*
Robert A. Mcgaw *(Dir-Consumer Mktg)*

SUPERVALU, INC., FOOD MARKETING DIVISION

(Div. of SUPERVALU, Inc.)
4815 Executive Blvd
Fort Wayne, IN 46808
Tel.: (260) 483-2146
Fax: (260) 482-6434
Web Site: www.supervalu.com/sv-webapp/contact/directory.jsp
Sales Range: $750-799.9 Million
Approx. Number Employees: 1,100
Business Description:
Wholesale Grocery Distribution
S.I.C.: 5411
N.A.I.C.S.: 445110
Media: 2-4-5-16-21-23-24-25
Distr.: Reg.
Budget Set: Sept.
Personnel:
Mike Schiffli *(Dir-Mktg-Ft Wayne DC)*

SUPERVALU, INC., HARRISBURG DIVISION

(Div. of SUPERVALU, Inc.)
3900 Industrial Rd
Harrisburg, PA 17110-2945
Mailing Address:

Key to Media (For complete agency information see *The Advertising Red Books-Agencies* edition):
1. Bus. Publs. 2. Cable T.V. 3. Catalogs & Directories. 4. Co-op Adv. 5. Consumer Mags. 6. D.M. to Bus. Estab.7. D.M. to Consumers 8. Daily Newsp. 9. Exhibits/Trade Shows 10. Foreign 11. Infomercial 12. Internet Adv.13. Multimedia 14. Network Radio 15. Network T.V. 16. Newsp. Distr. Mags. 17. Other 18. Outdoor (Posters, Transit) 19. Point of Purchase20. Premiums, Novelties 21. Product Samples 22. Special Events Mktg. 23. Spot Radio 24. Spot T.V. 25. Weekly Newsp. 26. Yellow Page Adv.

SUPERVALU, Inc., Harrisburg Division — (Continued)

PO Box 2261
Harrisburg, PA 17105-2261
Tel.: (717) 232-6821
Fax: (717) 257-4554
Toll Free: (800) 444-7424
Toll Free: (800) 256-2800
Web Site: www.supervalu.com
Sales Range: $1-4.9 Billion
Approx. Number Employees: 3,200
Year Founded: 1929
Business Description:
Food Distr
S.I.C.: 5141; 5411
N.A.I.C.S.: 424410; 445110
Advertising Expenditures: $5,000,000
Media: 2-3-4-6-7-8-9-10-18-19-21-23-24-25-26
Distr.: Reg.
Budget Set: Oct.
Brands & Products:
RICH FOOD

SWEETBAY LLC

(Sub. of Delhaize America, Inc.)
(d/b/a Sweetbay Supermarket)
3801 Sugar Palm Dr
Tampa, FL 33619-8301
Tel.: (813) 620-1139
Fax: (813) 627-9765
E-mail: communications@sweetbaysupermarket.com
Web Site: www.sweetbaysupermarket.com
Approx. Number Employees: 150
Year Founded: 1988
Business Description:
Supermarket Chain; Liquor & Drug Stores
S.I.C.: 5411; 5921
N.A.I.C.S.: 445110; 445310
Media: 18-24
Personnel:
Michael Vail *(Pres & COO)*
Lori Malcolm *(VP-HR)*

SYSCO CORPORATION

1390 Enclave Pkwy
Houston, TX 77077-2099
Tel.: (281) 584-1390
Fax: (281) 584-2721
Web Site: www.sysco.com
Approx. Sls.: $39,323,489,000
Approx. Number Employees: 46,000
Year Founded: 1969
Business Description:
Food, Food-Related & Food Service Industry Products Marketer & Wholesale Distr
S.I.C.: 5812; 5411; 5421
N.A.I.C.S.: 722110; 445110; 445210
Import
Media: 4-7-10-13
Personnel:
William J. DeLaney, III *(Pres & CEO)*
Robert C. Kreidler *(CFO & Exec VP)*
Twila M. Day *(CIO & Sr VP)*
G. Mitchell Elmer *(Chief Acctg Officer, Sr VP & Controller)*
Russell T. Libby *(Gen Counsel, Sec & VP)*
William B. Day *(Exec VP-Mdsg & Supply Chain)*
Michael W. Green *(Exec VP-Foodservice Ops-US)*
James D. Hope *(Exec VP-Bus Transformation)*
Larry G. Pulliam *(Exec VP-Foodservice Ops)*
Joseph R. Barton *(Sr VP-Sourcing)*
Kirk G. Drummond *(Sr VP-Sysco Bus Svcs)*
Alan Hasty *(Sr VP-Mdsg)*
Mike Headrick *(Sr VP-Foodservice Ops-South Reg)*
G. Kent Humphries *(Sr VP-Multi-Unit Sls)*
C. Frederick Lankford *(Sr VP-Distr Svcs)*
Paul T. Moskowitz *(Sr VP-HR)*
Scott A. Sonnemaker *(Sr VP-Foodservice Ops-Western Reg)*
Charles W. Staes *(Sr VP-Foodservice Ops-North Central Reg)*
Thomas P. Kurz *(Deputy Gen Counsel, Asst Sec & VP)*
Gregory W. Neely *(VP & Asst Controller)*
David L. Valentine *(VP & Asst Controller)*
John D. Holzem *(VP-IT)*
Julie O. Swan *(VP-Fin-Specialty Bus)*
Neil G. Theiss *(VP-Supply Chain Plng & Mdsg)*
Lucas Wagenaar *(VP-IT)*
Mark Wisnoski *(VP-HR)*
Toni R. Spigelmyer *(Dir-IR & Media Rels)*
Russell Raymond *(Mgr-Sls)*
Brands & Products:
BUTCHER'S BLOCK
GOOD THINGS COME FROM SYSCO
SYSCO
SYSCO CLASSIC
SYSCO IMPERIAL
SYSCO NATURAL
SYSCO RELIANCE
SYSCO SUPREME
Advertising Agency:
Adcetera Group
3000 Louisiana St
Houston, TX 77006
Tel.: (713) 522-8006
Fax: (713) 522-8018

SYSCO FOOD SERVICES OF ALBANY, LLC

(Sub. of Sysco Corporation)
1 Liebich Ln
Halfmoon, NY 12065-1421
Tel.: (518) 877-3200
Fax: (518) 877-3123
Toll Free: (800) 735-3341
Web Site: www.syscoalb.com
Sales Range: $400-449.9 Million
Approx. Number Employees: 600
Year Founded: 1936
Business Description:
Food Products Wholesale Distr
S.I.C.: 5149
N.A.I.C.S.: 424490
Advertising Expenditures: $300,000
Media: 9-10-25
Distr.: Natl.
Budget Set: Dec.
Personnel:
Ray Schiffer *(Pres)*
Mary Rogers *(CFO)*
Bill Fleming *(VP-Mdsg)*
Christine Lorusso *(Dir-Mktg)*

TAZO TEA COMPANY

(Sub. of Starbucks Corporation)
301 SE Second Ave
Portland, OR 97207
Mailing Address:
PO Box 66
Portland, OR 97207
Tel.: (503) 736-9005
Fax: (503) 231-8801
Toll Free: (800) 299-9445
Toll Free: (888) 436-2673
Web Site: www.tazo.com
Sales Range: $250-299.9 Million
Business Description:
Tea Retailers
S.I.C.: 2095
N.A.I.C.S.: 311920
Media: 8-10-13-21-22
Advertising Agencies:
Anvil Media, Inc.
310 NE Failing St.
Portland, OR 97212
Tel.: (503) 595-6050
Fax: (503) 223-1008

MediaVest USA
1675 Broadway
New York, NY 10019
Tel.: (212) 468-4000
Fax: (212) 468-4110

TC GLOBAL, INC.

3100 Airport Way S
Seattle, WA 98134
Tel.: (206) 233-2070
Fax: (206) 233-2077
Toll Free: (800) 968-8559
Web Site: www.tullyscoffeeshops.com/
Approx. Sls.: $39,570,000
Approx. Number Employees: 727
Year Founded: 1992
Business Description:
Coffee Stores
S.I.C.: 5499; 5812
N.A.I.C.S.: 445299; 722110
Advertising Expenditures: $563,000
Personnel:
Carl W. Pennington, Sr. *(Chm)*
Scott M. Pearson *(Pres & CEO)*
Catherine Campbell *(CFO & Controller)*
Cathy Campbel *(Gen Counsel & VP-Legal)*
Andrew Mun *(Gen Counsel & VP-Legal)*
Robert Martin *(VP-Mdsg & Production)*
Scott Earle *(VP-Mktg & Bus Dev)*
Brands & Products:
BELLACCINO
SPIN
TANGO
TULLY'S COFFEE
Advertising Agency:
Wong, Doody, Crandall, Wiener
1011 Western Ave Ste 900
Seattle, WA 98104
Tel.: (206) 624-5325
Fax: (206) 624-2369

TH FOODS INC.

2154 Harlem Rd
Loves Park, IL 61111
Tel.: (815) 636-9500
Fax: (815) 636-8400
Web Site: www.thfoods.com
Approx. Number Employees: 200
Business Description:
Snack Food Mfr
S.I.C.: 2052
N.A.I.C.S.: 311821
Personnel:
Terry Jessen *(Pres)*
James D. Garsow *(Dir-Mktg)*
Brands & Products:
MR CRISPERS
Advertising Agency:
Design North, Inc.
8007 Douglas Ave
Racine, WI 53402
Tel.: (262) 639-2080
Tel.: (262) 898-1090
Fax: (262) 639-5230
Toll Free: (800) 247-8494

TILLAMOOK CHEESE INC.

(Sub. of Tillamook County Creamery Association)
6855 SW Bayllor St
Tigard, OR 97223
Mailing Address:
PO Box 230667
Tigard, OR 97281-0667
Tel.: (503) 639-5512
Fax: (503) 639-7037
Web Site: www.tillamook.com
Approx. Number Employees: 15
Business Description:
Sales of Cheddar Cheese, Ice Cream, Butter & Whey Powder
S.I.C.: 5141
N.A.I.C.S.: 424410
Personnel:
Harold Strunk *(Pres & CEO)*
Mike Franklin *(Brand Mgr-Res)*
Brands & Products:
TILLAMOOK
Advertising Agency:
mono
(Partially Owned by MDC Partners)
3036 Hennepin Ave
Minneapolis, MN 55408
Tel.: (612) 822-4135
Fax: (612) 454-4950
Agency of Record

TOPS HOLDING CORPORATION

(Sub. of Morgan Stanley Private Equity)
6363 Main St
Williamsville, NY 14221
Tel.: (716) 635-5000
Web Site: www.topsmarkets.com
Approx. Sls.: $2,257,536,000
Approx. Number Employees: 12,700
Business Description:
Holding Company; Supermarket Owner & Operator
S.I.C.: 6719; 5411
N.A.I.C.S.: 551112; 445110
Advertising Expenditures: $23,175,000
Personnel:
Gary S. Matthews *(Chm)*
Frank Curci *(Pres & CEO)*
Kevin Darrington *(CFO & COO)*
Jack Barrett *(Sr VP-HR & Asst Sec)*
John Persons *(Sr VP-Ops)*

TOPS MARKETS, LLC

(Sub. of Tops Holding Corporation)
6363 Main St
Williamsville, NY 14221

Key to Media (For complete agency information see *The Advertising Red Books-Agencies* edition):
1. Bus. Publs. 2. Cable T.V. 3. Catalogs & Directories. 4. Co-op Adv. 5. Consumer Mags. 6. D.M. to Bus. Estab.7. D.M. to Consumers 8. Daily Newsp. 9. Exhibits/Trade Shows 10. Foreign 11. Infomercial 12. Internet Adv.13. Multimedia 14. Network Radio 15. Network T.V. 16. Newsp. Distr. Mags. 17. Other 18. Outdoor (Posters, Transit) 19. Point of Purchase20. Premiums, Novelties 21. Product Samples 22. Special Events Mktg. 23. Spot Radio 24. Spot T.V. 25. Weekly Newsp. 26. Yellow Page Adv.

Mailing Address:
PO Box 1027
Buffalo, NY 14240-1027
Tel.: (716) 635-5000
Toll Free: (800) 522-2522
E-mail: info@topsmarkets.com
Web Site: www.topsmarkets.com
Sales Range: $700-749.9 Million
Approx. Number Employees: 1,000
Year Founded: 1962
Business Description:
Grocery Store Operator
S.I.C.: 5411
N.A.I.C.S.: 445110
Import Export
Media: 3-5-6-8-9-13-18-19-20-21-22-23-24-25-26
Distr.: Natl.
Budget Set: Nov.
Personnel:
Frank Curci *(Pres)*
William R. Mills *(CFO & Sr VP)*
Kevin Darrington *(COO)*
Jack Barrett *(Sr VP-HR)*
John Persons *(Sr VP-Ops)*
Ron Ferri *(Reg VP-West)*
Mike Patti *(Reg VP-East)*
Diane Colgan *(VP-Sls & Mktg)*
Jeff Culhane *(VP-Perishable Mktg)*
Mike Metz *(VP-IT)*
Dave Bordonaro *(Dir-Non-Perishables)*
Gary Geitter *(Dir-Asset Protection)*
Jim Lane *(Dir-Meat & Seafood)*
Karl Oesterle *(Dir-Adv)*
Sam Qureshi *(Dir-Produce & Floral Mktg)*
Ken Schaeffer *(Dir-Fin & Budgets)*
Frank Wolff *(Dir-Pharmacy)*
Kristine Wydro *(Dir-HR)*
Katie McKenna *(Mgr-Comm & Pub Rels)*
Advertising Agency:
SKM Group
6350 Transit Rd
Depew, NY 14043
Tel.: (716) 989-3200
Fax: (716) 989-3220
— Amy Hurd *(Sr Acct Exec-TOPS Friendly Marke)*
— Kim Pasierb *(Sr Acct Exec-TOPS Friendly Marke)*

TOWN & COUNTRY GROCERY
210 E Murta St
Fredericktown, MO 63645
Tel.: (573) 783-5703
Fax: (573) 783-5962
Approx. Sls.: $173,300,000
Approx. Number Employees: 70
Business Description:
Independent Supermarket
S.I.C.: 5411
N.A.I.C.S.: 445110
Media: 9-13-23-25
Personnel:
Bob Hufford *(Pres)*

UNIFIED GROCERS, INC.
5200 Sheila St
City of Commerce, CA 90040
Mailing Address:
PO Box 513396
Los Angeles, CA 90051-1396
Tel.: (323) 264-5200
Toll Free: (800) 724-7762
E-mail: mediacontact@uwgrocers.com
Web Site: www.uwgrocers.com
Approx. Sls.: $3,921,059,000
Approx. Number Employees: 3,100
Year Founded: 1925
Business Description:
Wholesale Grocery Cooperative
S.I.C.: 5141; 5411
N.A.I.C.S.: 424410; 445110; 445120
Export
Advertising Expenditures: $700,000
Media: 2-5-7-10
Distr.: Reg.
Budget Set: July
Personnel:
Alfred A. Plamann *(Pres & CEO)*
Richard L. Wright *(Pres)*
Richard Martin *(CFO & Exec VP-Fin & Admin)*
Gary S. Herman *(CIO & VP-Info Svcs)*
Philip S. Smith *(Chief Mktg & Procurement Officer & Exec VP)*
Randall G. Scoville *(Chief Acctg Officer & VP-Acctg)*
Robert M. Ling, Jr. *(Gen Counsel, Exec VP & Sec)*
Christine Neal *(Treas & Sr VP-Fin)*
Joseph L. Falvey *(Sr VP-Sls)*
Daniel J. Murphy *(Sr VP-Retail Svcs & Perishables)*
Rodney L. Van Bebber *(Sr VP-Ops)*
Dirk T. Davis *(VP-Mktg)*
Donald E. Gilpin *(VP-HR)*
Robert E. Lutz *(VP-Procurement)*
Brands & Products:
COTTAGE HEARTH
GOLDEN CREME
MORE WAYS TO MAKE IT YOUR MARKET
SPECIAL VALUE
SPRINGFIELD
UNIFIED GROCERS
WESTERN FAMILY
Advertising Agency:
Unified Grocers Inc.
5200 Sheila St
Commerce, CA 90040
Tel.: (323) 264-5200
Fax: (323) 264-0320
Toll Free: (800) 724-7762

UNIFIED GROCERS, INC.
(Sub. of Unified Grocers, Inc.)
3301 S Norfolk St
Seattle, WA 98118-5648
Tel.: (206) 762-2100
Web Site: www.unifiedgrocers.com
Sales Range: $900-999.9 Million
Approx. Number Employees: 800
Year Founded: 1934
Business Description:
Wholesale Grocery Distr
S.I.C.: 5141; 5147
N.A.I.C.S.: 424410; 424470
Media: 2-4-7-10-17
Distr.: Reg.
Personnel:
Bob Ling *(General Counsel, Corp Sec & Exec VP)*
Carl D. Morley *(Exec Dir-Perishables)*
Advertising Agency:
Market Advertising
(House Agency)
3301 S. Norfolk St.
Seattle, WA 98118
Tel.: (206) 767-8750
Fax: (206) 463-7955
(Grocery Wholesale Distributor)

UNITED SUPERMARKETS, L.L.C.
7830 Orlando Ave
Lubbock, TX 79423-1942
Mailing Address:
PO Box 6840
Lubbock, TX 79493-6840
Tel.: (806) 791-0220
Fax: (806) 791-7491
E-mail: info@unitedtexas.com
Web Site: www.unitedtexas.com
Approx. Number Employees: 10,000
Year Founded: 1916
Business Description:
Grocery Store Chain
S.I.C.: 5411
N.A.I.C.S.: 445110
Advertising Expenditures: $10,500,000
Media: 3-5-6-8-9-10-13-18-19-20-21-22-23-24-25-26
Distr.: Reg.
Budget Set: Oct.
Personnel:
Robert Snell *(Chm)*
Gantt Bumstead *(Co-Pres)*
Matt Bumstead *(Co-Pres)*
Robert Taylor, Jr. *(Interim CEO)*
SuzAnn Kirby *(CFO)*
Sidney Hopper *(COO)*
Wes Jackson *(Sr VP-Sls & Mdsg)*
Joe Womble *(Reg VP-Lubbock)*
Matt Edwards *(Dir)*
Eddie Owens *(Dir-Corp Comm)*
Doug Pellock *(Dir-Facilities Support, Dev & Construction)*
Lou Moore *(Mgr-Benefits)*
Brands & Products:
UNITED SUPERMARKETS

UPTON TEA IMPORTS
34 Hayden Rowe St
Hopkinton, MA 01748-1842
Tel.: (508) 435-9988
Fax: (508) 435-9955
Toll Free: (800) 234-8327
Web Site: www.uptontea.com
Approx. Number Employees: 15
Year Founded: 1989
Business Description:
Tea Importer & Distributor
S.I.C.: 5961; 5149
N.A.I.C.S.: 454113; 424490
Media: 4-6-8
Personnel:
Thomas Eck *(Owner)*

URM STORES, INC.
7511 N Freya St PO Box 3365
Spokane, WA 99217-8004
Tel.: (509) 467-2620
Fax: (509) 466-9754
Web Site: www.urmstores.com
Approx. Number Employees: 1,920
Year Founded: 1921
Business Description:
Cooperative; Wholesale Grocery Distributor; Retail Grocery Services
S.I.C.: 5141; 5147
N.A.I.C.S.: 424410; 424470
Import
Media: 8-9-19-25
Distr.: Reg.
Personnel:
Dean Sonnenberg *(Pres & CEO)*
Lauri Bigej *(CFO)*
Brands & Products:
FAMILY FOODS
HARVEST FOODS
ROSAUERS
SUPER 1
SUPER1 FOOD
URM
YOKES

VILLAGE SUPER MARKET INC.
733 Mountain Ave
Springfield, NJ 07081
Tel.: (973) 467-2200
Fax: (973) 467-6582
Web Site: www.shoprite.com
Approx. Sls.: $1,261,825,000
Approx. Number Employees: 1,323
Year Founded: 1937
Business Description:
Supermarket Operator
S.I.C.: 5411; 5921
N.A.I.C.S.: 445110; 445310
Advertising Expenditures: $8,972,000
Media: 9
Distr.: Direct to Consumer; Reg.
Budget Set: Dec.
Personnel:
James Sumas *(Chm & CEO)*
Kevin R. Begley *(CFO & Treas)*
John J. Sumas *(VP, Gen Counsel & Head-Legal Dept)*
John P. Sumas *(Exec VP)*
Robert Sumas *(Exec VP)*
William Sumas *(Exec VP)*
Brands & Products:
VILLAGE
Advertising Agency:
Della Femina & Gianettino
98 Floral Ave Ste 201
New Providence, NJ 07974
Tel.: (908) 871-0100
Fax: (908) 871-0120
Toll Free: (800) 497-0622

VIP SALES COMPANY, INC.
6116 S Memorial Dr
Tulsa, OK 74133-1939
Tel.: (918) 252-5791
Fax: (918) 254-1667
Toll Free: (800) 800-7437
E-mail: webmaster@vipfoods.com
Web Site: www.vipfoods.com
E-Mail For Key Personnel:
Marketing Director: dbequette@vipfoods.com
Sales Director: sbeck@vipfoods.com
Approx. Number Employees: 30
Year Founded: 1967
Business Description:
Frozen Vegetables, Fruits, Rice Entrees & Smoothies Mfr, Marketer & Distr
S.I.C.: 5142
N.A.I.C.S.: 424420
Import Export
Media: 3-4-5-10-13-16-19-21-22-24-26
Distr.: Natl.
Budget Set: Sept.
Personnel:
Greg Costley *(Pres)*
Harry Bandelles *(CFO)*
Brands & Products:
FRESHER THAN FRESH
HOME FIXINS
QUALITY PLUS
QUICK FIX SIDES
QUICK OVERN CRISP

Key to Media (For complete agency information see *The Advertising Red Books-Agencies* edition):
1. Bus. Publs. 2. Cable T.V. 3. Catalogs & Directories. 4. Co-op Adv. 5. Consumer Mags. 6. D.M. to Bus. Estab.7. D.M. to Consumers
8. Daily Newsp. 9. Exhibits/Trade Shows 10. Foreign 11. Infomercial 12. Internet Adv.13. Multimedia 14. Network Radio
15. Network T.V. 16. Newsp. Distr. Mags. 17. Other 18. Outdoor (Posters, Transit) 19. Point of Purchase20. Premiums, Novelties
21. Product Samples 22. Special Events Mktg. 23. Spot Radio 24. Spot T.V. 25. Weekly Newsp. 26. Yellow Page Adv.

VIP Sales Company, Inc. — (Continued)

READY TO BLEND
STIR FRY
TAI PEI
USE LIKE FRESH
VEGGIE COMBOS
VIP
VIP HOME FIXINS
VIP QUALITY PLUS
VIP QUICK OVEN CRISPY
VIP QUICKFIX SIDES
VIP READY TO BLEND
VIP STIR-FRY
VIP USE LIKE FRESH
VIP VEGGIE COMBOS

VONS A SAFEWAY COMPANY

(Sub. of Safeway Inc.)
618 Michillinda Ave
Arcadia, CA 91007-6300
Mailing Address:
PO Box 513338
Los Angeles, CA 90051-1338
Tel.: (626) 821-7000
Fax: (626) 821-7933
Web Site: www.vons.com
Sales Range: $1-4.9 Billion
Approx. Number Employees: 22,000
Year Founded: 1906
Business Description:
Operator of Supermarkets
S.I.C.: 5411; 5912
N.A.I.C.S.: 445110; 446110
Media: 3-4-8-9-13-17-19-22-23-24-26
Distr.: Direct to Consumer; Reg.
Personnel:
Tom Keller *(Pres)*
Bruce L. Everette *(Exec VP)*
Larree M. Renda *(Exec VP-Ops)*
David F. Bond *(Sr VP-Fin)*
Melissa C. Plaisance *(Sr VP-Fin & IR)*
Jerry Tidwell *(Sr VP-Supply Ops)*
Larry Vanderdoes *(VP-Retail Ops)*
Advertising Agency:
Dailey & Associates
(Sub. of The Interpublic Group of Cos., Inc.)
8687 Melrose Ave Ste G300
West Hollywood, CA 90069-5701
Tel.: (310) 360-3100
Fax: (310) 360-0810

WAKEFERN FOOD CORPORATION

(d/b/a ShopRite)
600 York St
Elizabeth, NJ 07207
Mailing Address:
PO Box 7812
Edison, NJ 08818
Tel.: (908) 527-3300
Fax: (908) 527-3397
Toll Free: (800) 746-7748
E-mail: corpcomm@wakefern.com
Web Site: www.shoprite.com
Sales Range: $1-4.9 Billion
Approx. Number Employees: 50,000
Year Founded: 1945
Business Description:
Grocery Stores
S.I.C.: 5141; 5411
N.A.I.C.S.: 424410; 445110
Media: 3-8-9-16-18-19-22-23-24-25-26
Distr.: Natl.
Personnel:
Dean Janeway *(Pres & COO)*
Ken Jasinkiewicz *(CFO)*
James Watson *(Gen Counsel)*
Carol Lawton *(VP & Asst Sec)*
William Crombie *(VP-Corp Mdsg)*
Peter Rolandelli *(VP-Trng & Logistics)*
Thomas Drogaris *(Dir-Corp Svcs)*
Brands & Products:
ONE PLACE. YOUR PLACE.
SHOPRITE
Advertising Agencies:
Della Femina & Gianettino
98 Floral Ave Ste 201
New Providence, NJ 07974
Tel.: (908) 871-0100
Fax: (908) 871-0120
Toll Free: (800) 497-0622

Miller Advertising Agency Inc.
71 5th Ave 5th Fl
New York, NY 10003-3004
Tel.: (212) 929-2200
Fax: (212) 727-4734
Toll Free: (800) 229-6574

WALDBAUM'S SUPERMARKETS, INC.

(Sub. of The Great Atlantic & Pacific Tea Company, Inc.)
PO Box 3068
Paterson, NJ 07509
Tel.: (631) 582-9300
Fax: (718) 559-0901
Toll Free: (866) 44FRESH
E-mail: 18004waldbaums@aptea.com
Web Site: www.waldbaums.com
Approx. Number Employees: 6,500
Year Founded: 1904
Business Description:
Supermarket Chain
S.I.C.: 5541; 5399; 5411
N.A.I.C.S.: 447110; 445110; 445120; 452910
Media: 8-9-16-18-19-20-23-24-25
Distr.: Direct to Consumer; Reg.

WAWA, INC.

260 W Baltimore Pike
Media, PA 19063-5620
Tel.: (610) 358-8000
Fax: (610) 358-8878
Toll Free: (800) 444-9292
Web Site: www.wawa.com
Sales Range: $10-24.9 Million
Approx. Number Employees: 16,000
Year Founded: 1902
Business Description:
Convenience Store Operator
S.I.C.: 5411
N.A.I.C.S.: 445120
Media: 4-9-17-18-20-22-23-24-25
Distr.: Direct to Consumer; Reg.
Personnel:
Howard B. Stoeckel *(Pres & CEO)*
Carl Johnson *(CMO)*
Harry McHugh *(Sr VP-HR)*
Stephanie Capaccio *(Dir-Benefits & Risk Mgmt)*
Alfred J. Meaney *(Dir-Fuel Ops)*
Lori Bruce *(Mgr-Culture & Comm)*
David Edwards *(Mgr-Customer Svc)*
Don Kane *(Distr Mgr)*
Michael McCabe *(Mgr-Real Estate Tech)*
Brands & Products:
BUILT-TO-ORDER
CLASSIC
JUNIOR
SHORTI
SIZZLI
WAWA
Advertising Agencies:
The Archer Group
233 N King St
Wilmington, DE 19801
Tel.: (302) 429-9120
Fax: (302) 429-8720
Interactive Web Site
Online Media

The Richards Group, Inc.
8750 N Central Expy Ste 100
Dallas, TX 75231-6430
Tel.: (214) 891-5700
Fax: (214) 265-2933

WAYFIELD FOODS INC.

5145 Wellcome All Rd
Atlanta, GA 30349
Tel.: (404) 559-3200
Fax: (404) 559-3206
Web Site: www.wayfieldfoods.com
Approx. Sls.: $48,600,000
Approx. Number Employees: 500
Year Founded: 1982
Business Description:
Operator of Grocery Stores
S.I.C.: 5411
N.A.I.C.S.: 445110
Media: 9
Personnel:
Ron B. Edenfield *(Co-Founder & Pres)*
Cindy Edenfield *(CFO)*

WEGMANS FOOD MARKETS, INC.

1500 Brooks Ave
Rochester, NY 14603-0844
Mailing Address:
PO Box 30844
Rochester, NY 14603-0844
Tel.: (585) 328-2550
Fax: (585) 464-4669
Toll Free: (800) WEGMANS
E-mail: comments@wegmans.com
Web Site: www.wegmans.com
Sales Range: $1-4.9 Billion
Approx. Number Employees: 34,938
Year Founded: 1916
Business Description:
Retail Supermarkets
S.I.C.: 5411
N.A.I.C.S.: 445110
Advertising Expenditures: $850,000
Media: 6
Personnel:
Colleen Wegman *(Pres)*
James J. Leo *(CFO)*
Paul S. Speranza, Jr. *(Gen Counsel & Sec)*
Jack DePeters *(Exec VP-Ops)*
Mary Ellen Burris *(Sr VP-Consumer Affairs)*
Patty Kaminski *(Dir-Mktg)*
John Derby *(Dir-Adv)*
Marybeth Stewart *(Mgr-HR-New England Div)*
Brands & Products:
EAT WELL LIVE WELL
WEGMANS
WEGMANS PHARMACY
WEGMANS SMARTFILL
Advertising Agency:
Jay Advertising, Inc.
(A Subsidiary of The Interpublic Group of Companies)
170 Linden Oaks
Rochester, NY 14625-2836
Tel.: (585) 264-3600
Fax: (585) 264-3650
Toll Free: (800) 836-6800

WEIS MARKETS, INC.

1000 S 2nd St PO Box 471
Sunbury, PA 17801-0471
Tel.: (570) 286-4571
Fax: (570) 286-3286
Toll Free: (866) 999-9347
E-mail: feedback@weismarkets.com
Web Site: www.weismarkets.com
Approx. Sls.: $2,620,378,000
Approx. Number Employees: 17,700
Year Founded: 1912
Business Description:
Supermarket Operator
S.I.C.: 5411; 5999
N.A.I.C.S.: 445110; 453910
Advertising Expenditures: $25,100,000
Media: 3-5-8-9-18-19-23-24-25-26
Distr.: Reg.
Personnel:
Robert F. Weis *(Chm)*
Jonathan H. Weis *(Vice Chm & Sec)*
David J. Hepfinger *(Pres & CEO)*
Scott F. Frost *(CFO, Treas & VP)*
R. Graber *(Sr VP-Real Estate & Dev)*
James E. Marcil *(Sr VP-HR)*
Jay Ropietski *(Sr VP-Ops)*
Kurt Schertle *(Sr VP-Sls & Mdsg)*
Brad Kochenour *(Reg VP)*
Mike Mignola *(Reg VP)*
Bruno Garisto *(VP-Center Store Sls & Mdsg)*
Steve Davis *(Dir & Gen Mgr-HBC & Grocery Nonfoods)*
Jerry Hatch *(Reg Dir)*
Robert Cline *(Dir-Trng & Organizational Dev)*
Brian Holt *(Dir-Mktg)*
Regina Tator *(Dir-Private Brands)*
Geoffrey Wexler *(Dir-Deli & Prepared Foods)*
Janice Brown *(Mgr-District)*
Greg Oldright *(Mgr-Category)*
Brands & Products:
WHERE FRESHNESS MATTERS

WESTERN BEEF, INC.

47-05 Metropolitan Ave
Ridgewood, NY 11385-1046
Tel.: (718) 417-3770
Fax: (718) 628-2359
Web Site: www.westernbeef.com
Sales Range: $400-449.9 Million
Approx. Number Employees: 2,000
Year Founded: 1985
Business Description:
Full-Service Retail Supermarkets & Food Outlet Stores Owner & Operator
S.I.C.: 5411; 5421
N.A.I.C.S.: 445110; 445210
Media: 8-13-18-19-21
Personnel:
Tom Moronzoni *(CFO)*
Peter Castellana, Jr. *(Pres-Florida Div)*
Frank Castellana *(Exec VP-Plng)*

Key to Media (For complete agency information see *The Advertising Red Books-Agencies* edition):
1. Bus. Publs. 2. Cable T.V. 3. Catalogs & Directories. 4. Co-op Adv. 5. Consumer Mags. 6. D.M. to Bus. Estab.7. D.M. to Consumers 8. Daily Newsp. 9. Exhibits/Trade Shows 10. Foreign 11. Infomercial 12. Internet Adv.13. Multimedia 14. Network Radio 15. Network T.V. 16. Newsp. Distr. Mags. 17. Other 18. Outdoor (Posters, Transit) 19. Point of Purchase20. Premiums, Novelties 21. Product Samples 22. Special Events Mktg. 23. Spot Radio 24. Spot T.V. 25. Weekly Newsp. 26. Yellow Page Adv.

Michael Castellana *(Sr VP-Retail Opers)*
Santino Montalbano *(Dir-Real Estate)*
Brands & Products:
WE KNOW THE NEIGHBORHOOD!
WESTERN BEEF

WESTERN FAMILY HOLDING CO., INC.

6700 SW Sandburg St
Tigard, OR 97223-8008
Tel.: (503) 639-6300
Fax: (503) 684-3469
E-mail: info@westernfamily.com
Web Site: www.westernfamily.com
Approx. Rev.: $40,783
Year Founded: 1963
Business Description:
Private Label Groceries
S.I.C.: 5141; 5142
N.A.I.C.S.: 424410; 424420
Import Export
Advertising Expenditures: $1,000,000
Media: 4-13-19
Personnel:
Ronald S. King *(Pres)*
Pete Craven *(CFO & Sr VP)*
Bob Cutler *(Sr VP-Procurement)*
Charlie Rotta *(Grp VP-Intl)*
Steve Hauke *(VP-Sls)*
Steve Hockey *(VP-Sls & Mktg)*
Brands & Products:
SHUR FINE
WESTERN FAMILY

WHITE HEN PANTRY, INC.

(Sub. of 7-Eleven, Inc.)
Ste 300 700 E Butterfield Rd
Lombard, IL 60148-7701
Tel.: (630) 366-3100
Fax: (630) 366-3465
Web Site: www.whitehen.com
Sales Range: $500-549.9 Million
Approx. Number Employees: 100
Year Founded: 1965
Business Description:
Convenience Food Stores Operator
S.I.C.: 5411
N.A.I.C.S.: 445120
Brands & Products:
WHITE HEN PANTRY
Advertising Agency:
RPM Advertising
222 S Morgan St
Chicago, IL 60610
Tel.: (312) 455-8600
Fax: (312) 455-8617
Toll Free: (800) 475-2000

WHITEWAVE FOODS COMPANY

(Div. of Dean Foods Company)
12002 Airport Way
Broomfield, CO 80021
Tel.: (303) 635-4000
Fax: (303) 635-5000
E-mail: questions@whitewave.com
Web Site: www.whitewave.com
Sales Range: $1-4.9 Billion
Approx. Number Employees: 1,311
Year Founded: 1977
Business Description:
Organic Foods Distr
S.I.C.: 5149; 5499
N.A.I.C.S.: 424490; 445299
Advertising Expenditures: $2,000,000
Media: 4-6-8-9-10-11-13-16-17-21
Personnel:
Blaine McPeak *(Pres)*
Kelly Haecker *(CFO)*
Michael Ferry *(Pres-Horizon)*
Mike Keown *(Pres-Indulgent Brands)*
Roger Theodoredis *(Sr VP & Gen Counsel-Div)*
Doug Behrens *(Chief Customer Officer & Sr VP-Sls)*
Deborah B. Carosella *(Sr VP-Innovation)*
Thomas N. Zanetich *(Sr VP-HR)*
Jim Blumberg *(Dir-Consumer Promo)*
Carolina Fryer *(Brand Mgr)*
Jarod Ballentine *(Mgr-Digital Comm)*
Luana Hancock *(Mgr-Corp Comm)*
Brands & Products:
INTERNATIONAL DELIGHT
RACHEL'S
SOY A MELT
SUN SOY
WHITE WAVE
Advertising Agencies:
Arc Worldwide
(Sub. of Publicis Groupe S.A.)
35 W Wacker Dr 15th Fl
Chicago, IL 60601
Tel.: (312) 220-3200
Fax: (312) 220-1995
Silk Soymilk

Berlin Cameron United
100 Ave of the Americas 2nd Fl
New York, NY 10013
Tel.: (212) 824-2000
Fax: (212) 268-8454
Silk Soymilk

Engauge Communications
375 N Front St Ste 400
Columbus, OH 43215
Tel.: (614) 573-1010
Fax: (614) 573-1011

Leo Burnett Worldwide, Inc.
35 W Wacker Dr
Chicago, IL 60601-1723
Tel.: (312) 220-5959
Fax: (312) 220-3299
Silk Soy Milk

Sterling Rice Group
1801 13th St Ste 400
Boulder, CO 80302
Tel.: (303) 381-6400
Fax: (303) 444-6637
Horizon Organic

WHOLE FOODS MARKET - FLORIDA REGION

(Branch of Whole Foods Market, Inc.)
6451 N Federal Hwy Ste 101
Fort Lauderdale, FL 33308
Tel.: (954) 489-2100
Fax: (954) 489-2101
Web Site: www.wholefoods.com
Sales Range: $25-49.9 Million
Approx. Number Employees: 50
Business Description:
Natural & Organic Foods Supermarkets
S.I.C.: 5411
N.A.I.C.S.: 445110
Personnel:
Juan Nunez *(Pres)*
Advertising Agency:
wwdb integrated marketing
412 SE 13th St
Fort Lauderdale, FL 33316
Tel.: (954) 922-4332
Fax: (954) 923-0126

WHOLE FOODS MARKET, INC.

550 Bowie St
Austin, TX 78703
Tel.: (512) 477-4455
Fax: (512) 482-7000
E-mail: ir.questions@wholefoods.com
Web Site:
www.wholefoodsmarket.com
Approx. Sls.: $9,005,794,000
Approx. Number Employees: 54,000
Year Founded: 1978
Business Description:
Operator of Natural & Organic Food Supermarkets
S.I.C.: 5411; 5499
N.A.I.C.S.: 445110; 445299
Advertising Expenditures: $33,000,000
Media: 1-5-18-19-21-22
Personnel:
John B. Elstrott *(Chm)*
A.C. Gallo *(Pres & COO)*
John P. Mackey *(Co-CEO)*
Walter Robb *(Co-CEO)*
Glenda J. Flanagan *(CFO, Sec, Exec VP & Principal Acctg Officer)*
Mike Clifford *(CIO & VP)*
Jeff Turnas *(Pres-UK)*
Roberta Lang *(Gen Counsel & VP-Legal Affairs)*
James P. Sud *(Exec VP-Growth & Bus Dev)*
Lee Valkenaar *(Exec VP-Global Support)*
Michael Besancon *(Sr VP-Global Pur, Distr & Mktg)*
Bruce Silverman *(Grp VP)*
Edmund LaMacchia *(VP-Procurement & Perishables-Natl)*
Jim Speirs *(VP-Procurement-Non Perishables-Global)*
Bill McGowan *(Coord-Produce & Floral-North Atlantic Reg)*
Brands & Products:
365 EVERYDAY VALUE
TAKE BACK OUR PLATES
WHOLE FOODS
WHOLE FOODS MARKET
Advertising Agencies:
Cartis Group
1532 Ben Crenshaw Way
Austin, TX 78746
Tel.: (512) 476-2600
Fax: (512) 476-2626
Toll Free: (800) 479-2616

filter Advertising
160 Pearl St 2nd Fl
New York, NY 10005
Tel.: (212) 248-3028

WINCO FOODS, INC.

650 N Armstrong Pl
Boise, ID 83704-0825
Mailing Address:
PO Box 5756
Boise, ID 83705-0756
Tel.: (208) 377-0110
Fax: (208) 377-0474
Web Site: www.wincofoods.com
Approx. Rev.: $2,850,000,000
Approx. Number Employees: 13,000
Year Founded: 1967
Business Description:
Retail Grocery Chain
S.I.C.: 5411
N.A.I.C.S.: 445110
Import
Advertising Expenditures: $2,500,000
Media: 8-13-18-19-22-23-24
Personnel:
Steven Goddard *(Pres & CEO)*
Gary R. Piva *(CFO & Exec VP)*
Rich Charrier *(COO & Exec VP)*
Michael Read *(VP-Pub & Legal Affairs)*
David Van Etten *(VP-Engrg)*
Wayne Duncan *(Dir-Transportation)*
Steve Olds *(Dir-Indus Engrng)*
Brands & Products:
WINCO FOODS

WINN-DIXIE STORES, INC.

5050 Edgewood Ct
Jacksonville, FL 32254-3601
Mailing Address:
PO Box B
Jacksonville, FL 32203-0297
Tel.: (904) 783-5000
Fax: (904) 783-5294
Toll Free: (866) WINN-DIXIE
Web Site: www.winn-dixie.com
E-Mail For Key Personnel:
Public Relations: RobinMiller@winn-dixie.com
Approx. Sls.: $6,880,776,000
Approx. Number Employees: 47,000
Year Founded: 1925
Business Description:
Supermarkets Owner & Operator; Network of Distribution Centers; Processing & Manufacturing Plants; Truck Delivery Fleet; In-Store Banking Services; Pharmacies
S.I.C.: 5411; 5147; 5912
N.A.I.C.S.: 445110; 311612; 446110
Advertising Expenditures: $95,900,000
Media: 3-6-8-9-18-19-23-24-25
Distr.: Reg.
Personnel:
Peter L. Lynch *(Chm, Pres & CEO)*
Bennett L. Nussbaum *(CFO & Sr VP)*
Maura Hart *(CIO & Grp VP-Info Sys)*
D. Michael Byrum *(Chief Acctg Officer & VP)*
Timothy Williams *(Gen Counsel, Sec & Sr VP)*
Lynn Schweinfurth *(Treas & VP-Fin)*
Laurence B. Appel *(Sr VP-Retail Ops)*
Anita Dahlstrom-Gutel *(Sr VP-HR)*
Frank O. Eckstein *(Sr VP-Retail Ops)*
Matthew Gutermuth *(Grp VP-Pricing & Corp Brand)*
Mary Kellmanson *(Grp VP-Mktg)*
Phillip E. Pichulo *(Grp VP-Dev)*
Chrisopher L. Scott *(Grp VP-Logistics & Distr)*
Mark A. Sellers *(Grp VP-Ops)*
James Smits *(Grp VP-Perishables)*
Joey Medina *(Reg VP-Ops)*
Frank Thurlow *(Sr Dir-Meat)*
Anthony Agresta *(Dir-Brand Mgmt)*
Eric Harris *(Dir-IR)*
Robin Miller *(Dir-Comm)*
Mike Carter *(Sr Mgr-Produce & Floral)*
Brandon Benedicto *(Mgr-Database-Mktg)*
Dan Ryndak *(Mgr-Produce)*

Key to Media (For complete agency information see *The Advertising Red Books-Agencies* edition):
1. Bus. Publs. 2. Cable T.V. 3. Catalogs & Directories. 4. Co-op Adv. 5. Consumer Mags. 6. D.M. to Bus. Estab.7. D.M. to Consumers 8. Daily Newsp. 9. Exhibits/Trade Shows 10. Foreign 11. Infomercial 12. Internet Adv.13. Multimedia 14. Network Radio 15. Network T.V. 16. Newsp. Distr. Mags. 17. Other 18. Outdoor (Posters, Transit) 19. Point of Purchase20. Premiums, Novelties 21. Product Samples 22. Special Events Mktg. 23. Spot Radio 24. Spot T.V. 25. Weekly Newsp. 26. Yellow Page Adv.

Winn-Dixie Stores, Inc. — (Continued)

Brands & Products:
BARGAIN DEPOT
GETTING BETTER ALL THE TIME
SAVERITE
THRIFTWAY
WINN-DIXIE

Advertising Agencies:
On Ideas, Inc.
6 E Bay St Ste 100
Jacksonville, FL 32202-5422
Tel.: (904) 354-2600
Fax: (904) 354-7226

Zubi Advertising Services, Inc.
355 Alhambra Cir 10th Fl
Coral Gables, FL 33134-5006
Tel.: (305) 448-9824
Fax: (305) 460-6393

YOCREAM INTERNATIONAL INC.

5858 NE 87th Ave
Portland, OR 97220-1312
Tel.: (503) 256-3754
Fax: (503) 256-3976
Toll Free: (800) YOCREAM
E-mail: info@yocream.com
Web Site: www.yocream.com
Sales Range: $25-49.9 Million
Approx. Number Employees: 100
Year Founded: 1977
Business Description:
Produces, Markets & Sells Frozen Dessert, Snack & Beverage Items
S.I.C.: 2024
N.A.I.C.S.: 311520
Export
Advertising Expenditures: $405,000
Media: 2-11-13-14-15-16-18-19-25-26
Budget Set: Oct.
Personnel:
John N. Hanna *(Chm & CEO)*
W. Douglas Caudell *(CFO)*
Tyler Bargas *(Dir-Sls)*
Suzanne Gardner *(Dir-Mktg & Military Sls)*
Terry Lusetti *(Dir-IR)*
Terry Oftedal *(Dir-Supply Chain Ops)*
Hellen Horne *(Mgr-Inside Sls)*
Lori Lusetti *(Mgr-Dev)*
Gabby McClintock *(Mgr-Dev)*
Barbara Rhoades *(Mgr-Dev)*
Monica Zebryk *(Mgr-Dev)*

Brands & Products:
FRUITQUAKE
ICE BREAKERS
ITS A BELIEF
ITS A LIFESTYLE
JARRITOS
JOLLY RANCHER
JUST SAY YO
ORIGINAL TART
PURE ENVIRONMENT
PURE FOOD
PURE PLEASURE
SMOOTH & TASTY
TWIZZLERS
YO CAFFE
YOCAFFE LATTE
YOCREAM
YOCREAM FROZEN CUSTARD
YOGURT STAND

Key to Media (For complete agency information see *The Advertising Red Books-Agencies* edition):
1. Bus. Publs. 2. Cable T.V. 3. Catalogs & Directories. 4. Co-op Adv. 5. Consumer Mags. 6. D.M. to Bus. Estab.7. D.M. to Consumers
8. Daily Newsp. 9. Exhibits/Trade Shows 10. Foreign 11. Infomercial 12. Internet Adv.13. Multimedia 14. Network Radio
15. Network T.V. 16. Newsp. Distr. Mags. 17. Other 18. Outdoor (Posters, Transit) 19. Point of Purchase20. Premiums, Novelties
21. Product Samples 22. Special Events Mktg. 23. Spot Radio 24. Spot T.V. 25. Weekly Newsp. 26. Yellow Page Adv.

Furniture, Floor Coverings & Decorations

Antiques — Art Objects — Beds — Carpeting — Chairs — Draperies — Floor Coverings — Juvenile Furniture — Lamps — Mattresses — Outdoor Furniture — Paintings — Shades — Springs — Window Blinds — Window Shades

3 DAY BLINDS, INC.
25 Technology Dr Ste B100
Irvine, CA 92618
Tel.: (714) 634-4600
Fax: (949) 266-5819
Web Site: www.3dayblinds.com
Approx. Number Employees: 500
Year Founded: 1978
Business Description:
Mfr. of Window Coverings
S.I.C.: 2591; 5714
N.A.I.C.S.: 337920; 442291
Advertising Expenditures: $250,000
Media: 4-6-9
Personnel:
Kevin M. Rabbitt *(CEO)*
Opal Feerraro *(CFO)*
Kristen Harrigan *(Mgr-Adv Production)*
Brands & Products:
3 DAY BLINDS
IDESIGN

AARON BROTHERS, INC.
(Joint Venture of The Blackstone Group L.P. & Bain Capital, LLC)
1221 S Beltline Rd Ste 500
Coppell, TX 75019
Tel.: (214) 492-6200
Fax: (469) 759-5446
Toll Free: (888) 372-6464
Web Site: www.aaronbrothers.com
Sales Range: $75-99.9 Million
Year Founded: 1946
Business Description:
Custom Framing, Oil Paintings, Art Supplies, Easels & Art Studio Furniture, Framed Mirrors & Decorator Items
S.I.C.: 5945; 5999
N.A.I.C.S.: 451120; 453998
Import
Advertising Expenditures: $5,000,000
Media: 5-8-9-23-24-25-26
Distr.: Direct to Consumer; Reg.
Personnel:
Shawn Hearn *(VP-HR)*
Brands & Products:
AARON BROTHERS
KOLO
TIMEFRAME

AARON'S, INC.
309 E Paces Ferry Rd NE
Atlanta, GA 30305-2367
Tel.: (404) 231-0011
E-mail: aleksandra.nearing@aaronrents.com
Web Site: www.aaronrents.com
Approx. Rev.: $1,876,847,000
Approx. Number Employees: 10,400
Year Founded: 1955
Business Description:
Furniture, Consumer Electronics & Home Appliances Rental & Rent-to-Own Services
S.I.C.: 7359; 5712
N.A.I.C.S.: 532310; 442110; 532210
Advertising Expenditures: $31,000,000
Media: 2-4-6-8-9-18-19-20-22-23-24-26
Distr.: Natl.
Budget Set: Various
Personnel:
R. Charles Loudermilk, Sr. *(Chm)*
Robert C. Loudermilk, Jr. *(Pres & CEO)*
Gilbert L. Danielson *(CFO & Exec VP)*
William K. Butler, Jr. *(COO)*
John T. Trainor *(CIO & VP)*
James L. Cates *(Corp Sec & Sr Grp VP)*
Mitchell S. Paull *(Sr VP-Mdsg & Logistics)*
Tom Peterson *(VP-Mktg)*
Richard Lamprey *(Dir-Mktg-Sports)*
Mike Virok *(Dir-Adv)*
Aleksandra Nearing *(Mgr-Fin Reporting)*
Brands & Products:
AARON'S

ABC CARPET & HOME INC.
(d/b/a ABC Design Rugs)
888 Broadway Fl 4
New York, NY 10003
Tel.: (212) 473-3000
Fax: (212) 228-3273
E-mail: info@abchome.com
Web Site: www.abchome.com
Approx. Sls.: $39,437,724
Approx. Number Employees: 400
Business Description:
Home Furnishings
S.I.C.: 5712; 5719
N.A.I.C.S.: 442110; 442299
Media: 3-6-8-9-18-23-24-25-26
Personnel:
Paulette Cole *(Owner)*
Jerome Weinrib *(Chm)*
Dave Lauber *(CFO)*
Aliza Olin *(Coord-Mktg & PR)*

ACOUSTIC INNOVATIONS INC.
1377 Clint Moore Rd
Boca Raton, FL 33487
Tel.: (561) 995-0090
Fax: (561) 995-0290
Toll Free: (800) 983-6233
E-mail: enquire@acousticinnovations.com
Web Site: www.acousticinnovations.com
Approx. Number Employees: 35
Business Description:
Acoustic Panels & Custom Theater Seating Mfr
S.I.C.: 3296; 2531
N.A.I.C.S.: 327993; 337127
Media: 6
Personnel:
Jay Miller *(Owner)*

ADELPHI PAPER HANGINGS LLC
PO Box 135
Sharon Springs, NY 13459
Tel.: (518) 284-9066
Fax: (518) 284-3011
E-mail: info@adelphipaperhangings.com
Web Site: www.adelphipaperhangings.com
Sales Range: Less than $1 Million
Approx. Number Employees: 4
Business Description:
Historically-Accurate Wallpaper Reproduction
S.I.C.: 2531; 2499; 3589; 3999
N.A.I.C.S.: 337127; 321999; 333319; 339999
Media: 4-5-6
Personnel:
Steve Larson *(Co-Owner)*
Chris Ohrstrom *(Co-Owner)*

ADELPHIA LAMP & SHADE INC.
(d/b/a Remington Lamps)
2500 Gettysburg Rd
Camp Hill, PA 17011
Tel.: (717) 737-7120
Fax: (717) 737-7140
E-mail: info@remingtonlamp.com
Web Site: www.remingtonlamp.com
Approx. Number Employees: 50
Year Founded: 1935
Business Description:
Table Lamps & Shades Mfr
S.I.C.: 3645; 3641
N.A.I.C.S.: 335121; 335110
Media: 4-6-17
Distr.: Natl.
Personnel:
Alfred H. Denenberg *(Pres & Treas)*
Brands & Products:
REMINGTON

AFD CONTRACT FURNITURE, INC.
810 7th Ave
New York, NY 10019
Tel.: (212) 721-7100
Fax: (212) 721-7175
Web Site: www.afd-inc.com
Approx. Number Employees: 150
Year Founded: 1980
Business Description:
Office Furniture Sales
S.I.C.: 5712
N.A.I.C.S.: 442110
Advertising Expenditures: $1,250,000
Media: 2-7
Personnel:
Richard Aarons *(CEO)*

AGRISOLAR SOLUTIONS, INC.
1175 Osage St Ste 204
Denver, CO 80204
Tel.: (303) 623-5400
Web Site: www.agrisolarsolutions.com
Approx. Rev.: $4,607,957
Approx. Number Employees: 158
Year Founded: 1994
Business Description:
Residential & Commercial Window Fashion Franchisor; Window Fashion Software Developer & Licensor; Soft Window Treatment Products Mfr & Sales
S.I.C.: 5714; 6794; 7372
N.A.I.C.S.: 442291; 334611; 533110
Advertising Expenditures: $79,633
Media: 5
Personnel:
Arnold Tinter *(Founder, Pres & CFO)*
Chao Wei Liang *(Chm & CEO)*
Xue Mei Mo *(Sec & Dir)*
Brands & Products:
V2K

Key to Media (For complete agency information see *The Advertising Red Books-Agencies* edition):
1. Bus. Publs. 2. Cable T.V. 3. Catalogs & Directories. 4. Co-op Adv. 5. Consumer Mags. 6. D.M. to Bus. Estab.7. D.M. to Consumers 8. Daily Newsp. 9. Exhibits/Trade Shows 10. Foreign 11. Infomercial 12. Internet Adv.13. Multimedia 14. Network Radio 15. Network T.V. 16. Newsp. Distr. Mags. 17. Other 18. Outdoor (Posters, Transit) 19. Point of Purchase20. Premiums, Novelties 21. Product Samples 22. Special Events Mktg. 23. Spot Radio 24. Spot T.V. 25. Weekly Newsp. 26. Yellow Page Adv.

AgriSolar Solutions, Inc. — (Continued)

V2K INTERNATIONAL

AKIN INDUSTRIES INC.
113 Commerce Dr
Monticello, AR 71655
Tel.: (870) 367-6263
Fax: (870) 367-5230
E-mail: info@akinindustries.com
Web Site: www.akinindustries.com
Sales Range: $100-124.9 Million
Approx. Number Employees: 193
Business Description:
Wood Furniture Mfr
S.I.C.: 2511; 2512
N.A.I.C.S.: 337122; 337121
Advertising Expenditures: $50,000
Media: 2-4-7-8-10-16
Personnel:
John Akin *(Mgr-Sls)*

ALL STAR BLEACHERS, INC.
(Sub. of Penco Products, Inc.)
6550 New Tampa Hwy
Lakeland, FL 33815-3148
Tel.: (863) 687-3141
Fax: (813) 628-4254
Toll Free: (800) 875-3141
E-mail: info@allstarbleachers.com
Web Site: www.allstarbleachers.com
Sales Range: $25-49.9 Million
Approx. Number Employees: 75
Year Founded: 1946
Business Description:
Metal Bleacher & Stadium Seating Mfr
S.I.C.: 3499; 3441
N.A.I.C.S.: 332999; 332312
Media: 10
Personnel:
Neil Judy *(VP & Gen Mgr)*

AMERICAN DREW
(Div. of La-Z-Boy Greensboro, Inc.)
4620 Grandover Pkwy
Greensboro, NC 27407-8202
Mailing Address:
PO Box 26777
Greensboro, NC 27417-6777
Tel.: (336) 294-5233
Fax: (336) 315-4389
E-mail: americandrew@americandrew.com
Web Site: www.americandrew.com
Sales Range: $125-149.9 Million
Approx. Number Employees: 500
Year Founded: 1927
Business Description:
Bedroom & Dining Room Furniture Mfr
S.I.C.: 2542
N.A.I.C.S.: 337215
Advertising Expenditures: $400,000
Media: 2-4-7-10-19-20-24
Distr.: Natl.
Budget Set: Nov.
Personnel:
R. Jack Richardson, Jr. *(Pres)*
Terry James *(Dir-Mktg)*
Brands & Products:
AMERICAN DREW

AMERICAN FURNITURE COMPANY, INC.
(Sub. of La-Z-Boy Greensboro, Inc.)
(d/b/a American of Martinsville)
128 E Church St
Martinsville, VA 24112-2806
Tel.: (276) 638-2379
Tel.: (276) 632-2379
Fax: (276) 638-8810
Web Site:
www.americanofmartinsville.com
Sales Range: $300-349.9 Million
Approx. Number Employees: 800
Year Founded: 1906
Business Description:
Hospitality, Assisted-Living & Government Markets Furniture Supplier
S.I.C.: 5712; 2511
N.A.I.C.S.: 442110; 337122
Import Export
Advertising Expenditures: $325,000
Media: 2-4-10
Distr.: Natl.
Personnel:
Leo Vogel *(Sr VP-Sls & Mktg)*
Advertising Agency:
MarketSense
7020 High Grove Blvd
Burr Ridge, IL 60527-7599
Tel.: (630) 654-0170
Fax: (630) 654-0302
Toll Free: (800) 827-0170

AMERICAN LEATHER LP
4501 Mtn Creek Pkwy
Dallas, TX 75236
Tel.: (972) 296-9599
Fax: (972) 590-8859
E-mail: info@americanleather.com
Web Site: www.americanleather.com
Approx. Number Employees: 270
Business Description:
Custom-Made Leather Furniture Mfr
S.I.C.: 2512; 5712
N.A.I.C.S.: 337121; 442110
Media: 6
Personnel:
Bob Duncan *(CEO)*
Kelly Montgomery *(VP-Fin)*
Jill Shambo *(Mgr-Mktg)*
Brands & Products:
ABSTRACT
AMERICAN LEATHER
ANTIGO
BENNET
BLANCO
BRAXTON
BRECKENRIDGE
BUCK
BURROWS
CARLISLE
CARSON
CHOCOLATE GARDEN
CLAREMONT
CORONADO
COVINGTON
DAWSON
DILLON
DIZZY
ETHAN
FALL
FIRENZE GRAPE
FLOWER POWER
FRENCH KISS
GRAYSON
HAMPTON
HIP HOP
HOLDEN
HOUNDSTOOTH
INDIAN BLANKET
JACKS
JOE
KADEN
KEATON
KEIFER
KENDALL
LANSING
LINCOLN
LISBEN
LISBEN WEDGE
LLANO
LONDON
LOWY
MADRID
MASCHERONI
MATINEE
MENLO PARK
METROPOLOTAN
MISSONI
MODERN
MUSEUM
NOBHILL
NOLAN
ODYSSEY
OMNIROLL
ORLY
PALMS
PASTELS
PUEBLO
QUATTRO
RANDALL
RANGER
ROLLO
SALINA
SANDRA
SAVOY
SEVILLE
SILHOUETTE
SINCLAIR
SOHO
SONOMA
SUSSEX
TIFFANY
TOSCANA
TUCKER
TWEED
TYLER
UNO
VINCENT
WOODGRAIN
ZANE
ZURICH

AMERICAN WOODMARK CORPORATION
3102 Shawnee Dr
Winchester, VA 22601-4208
Mailing Address:
PO Box 1980
Winchester, VA 22604-8090
Tel.: (540) 665-9100
Fax: (540) 665-9322
E-mail: service@woodmark.com
Web Site:
www.americanwoodmark.com
Approx. Sls.: $452,589,000
Approx. Number Employees: 3,693
Year Founded: 1980
Business Description:
Kitchen Cabinets & Vanities Mfr & Distr
S.I.C.: 5031; 2434; 5039
N.A.I.C.S.: 423310; 337110; 423390
Advertising Expenditures: $30,000,000
Media: 4-5-10
Personnel:
Kent B. Guichard *(Chm, Pres & CEO)*
Jonathan H. Wolk *(CFO & Sr VP)*
Bradley S. Boyer *(Sr VP-Remodel Sls & Mktg)*
S. Cary Dunston *(Sr VP-Mfg & Logistics)*
Brands & Products:
AMERICAN WOODMARK CORPORATION
POTOMAC
SHENANDOAH
SHENANDOAH CABINETRY
TIMBERLAKE
WAYPOINT LIVING SPACES
Advertising Agency:
Gibbs & Soell - Raleigh
8521 Six Forks Rd Ste 300
Raleigh, NC 27615
Tel.: (919) 870-5718
Fax: (919) 870-8911
Toll Free: (800) 472-6616

AMISCO INDUSTRIES LTD.
(Sub. of Gestion Martin Poitras Inc)
33 5th St L Islet
Quebec, QC G0R 2C0, Canada
Tel.: (418) 247-5025
Fax: (800) 232-6614
Toll Free: (800) 361-6360
E-mail: info@amisco.com
Web Site: www.amisco.com
Approx. Sls.: $29,036,870
Approx. Number Employees: 150
Year Founded: 1954
Business Description:
Painted Tubular & Sheet Steel Residential Furniture Designer & Mfr
S.I.C.: 2514
N.A.I.C.S.: 337124
Media: 10
Personnel:
Rejean Poitras *(Chm, Pres & CEO)*
Claude Poitras *(VP-Admin & Fin)*
Brands & Products:
ADEN
AKERS
ALPHA
AMINA
AMISCO
ANDREW
ANDY
ANN
ANNABELLE
BARCELONA
BEN
BENNETT
BIANCA
BRADLEY
BRENT
BRITTANY
BRODIE
BRUCE
CAMELIA
CAMERON
CARDIN
CARLY
CAROLYN
CATE
CECILIA
CHARLES
CINDY
CRYSTAL
CYNTHIA
DALIA
DANA
DEE
DELANEY
DEREK
DIRK

Key to Media (For complete agency information see *The Advertising Red Books-Agencies* edition):
1. Bus. Publs. 2. Cable T.V. 3. Catalogs & Directories. 4. Co-op Adv. 5. Consumer Mags. 6. D.M. to Bus. Estab.7. D.M. to Consumers
8. Daily Newsp. 9. Exhibits/Trade Shows 10. Foreign 11. Infomercial 12. Internet Adv.13. Multimedia 14. Network Radio
15. Network T.V. 16. Newsp. Distr. Mags. 17. Other 18. Outdoor (Posters, Transit) 19. Point of Purchase20. Premiums, Novelties
21. Product Samples 22. Special Events Mktg. 23. Spot Radio 24. Spot T.V. 25. Weekly Newsp. 26. Yellow Page Adv.

EDWARD
EDWIN
ELEANOR
ELLA
ERIK
FAITH
FRANCESCA
GABRIEL
GINGER
GRAHAM
GRANT
HECTOR
IAN
IRINA
JANE
JASON
JULIA
JULIET
KAI
KARA
KARL
KARYNA
KEVIN
KRIS
KYLE
LEO
LILLY
LOLO
LUBA
LUCAS
LUIS
MADISON
MADRID
MAE
MAGGIE
MARCIA
MASON
MAT
MAXIM
MEG
MONACO
MUNICH
NAOMI
NATASHA
NEWTON
NICKY
NINA
ORION
OWEN
PABLO
PARIS
PATRICIA
PAUL
PAYTON
PENELOPE
PETUNIA
RAY
ROBERT
ROBERTSON
ROCKY
ROME
ROMY
RONNY
ROSE
SABRINA
SALLY
SAM
SAMSON
SERENA
SINGAPORE
SOFIA
SOPHY
SPENCER
TAMARA
TAMMY
TESSA
THEODORE
TIM
TINA
TOMMY
TORI
TRACY
TRISHA
VALENTINO
VANNA
VENUS
VICTOR
ZOE

AMTICO INTERNATIONAL, INC.
(Sub. of Amtico International Ltd.)
6480 Roswell Road
Atlanta, GA 30328
Tel.: (404) 267-1900
Fax: (404) 267-1901
Web Site:
www.amticointernational.com
Business Description:
Floor Tile Mfr
S.I.C.: 3253
N.A.I.C.S.: 327122
Media: 2-5-6-13-19-21
Advertising Agency:
Denmark Advertising & Public Relations
6000 Lake Forest Dr Ste 260
Atlanta, GA 30328
Tel.: (404) 256-3681
Fax: (404) 250-9626
Residential & Commercial Flooring

ANIMA DOMUS INC.
25 NE 39th St
Miami, FL 33137
Tel.: (305) 576-9088
Fax: (305) 567-9728
E-mail: design@animadomus.com
Web Site: www.animadomus.com
Approx. Number Employees: 10
Business Description:
Interior Design Services; Furniture Store Owner
S.I.C.: 7389; 5712
N.A.I.C.S.: 541410; 442110
Media: 4-6
Personnel:
Silvia Naziazeni *(Pres)*

ANTHRO CORPORATION
10450 SW Manhasset Dr
Tualatin, OR 97062
Tel.: (503) 691-2556
Fax: (503) 691-2409
Toll Free: (800) 325-3841
E-mail: anthroear@anthro.com
Web Site: www.anthro.com
Approx. Number Employees: 100
Business Description:
Mfr. & Sales of Office Furniture
S.I.C.: 2522; 2521
N.A.I.C.S.: 337214; 337211
Media: 6
Personnel:
Shoaib Tareen *(Pres)*
Brands & Products:
ANTHRO
ANTHROBENCH
ANTHROCART
CARL'S TABLE
CONVOI
ELEVATE
ENOOK
FAST AND FRIENDLY!
FIT SYSTEM
IDEA CART
SHOP ABOUT
TECHNOLOGY FURNITURE
ZIDO

ARIZONA WHOLESALE SUPPLY COMPANY
2020 E Univ Dr
Phoenix, AZ 85034-6731
Mailing Address:
PO Box 2979
Phoenix, AZ 85062-2979
Tel.: (602) 258-7901
Fax: (602) 258-8335
E-mail: builder@awsco.net
Web Site: www.builderappliances.com
Approx. Number Employees: 165
Year Founded: 1944
Business Description:
Electronic Products, Consumer Appliances & Flooring Distr
S.I.C.: 5064; 5065
N.A.I.C.S.: 423620; 423690
Import Export
Media: 2-4-7
Distr.: Reg.
Budget Set: Apr.
Personnel:
Terence W. Thomas *(Chm & Pres)*
William Parks *(VP-Sls-Building Prods)*

ARM'S REACH CONCEPTS, INC.
2081 N Oxnard Blvd PMB #187
Oxnard, CA 93030
Tel.: (805) 278-2559
Fax: (805) 604-7982
Toll Free: (800) 954-9353
E-mail: arc@armsreach.com
Web Site: www.armsreach.com
Business Description:
Children's Furniture Retailer
S.I.C.: 5021
N.A.I.C.S.: 423210
Media: 5-6-10
Personnel:
James J. McKenna *(Dir)*
Brands & Products:
ARM'S REACH
CATCH ALL
THE CLEAR-VUE
CO-SLEEPER
THE LITTLE PALACE
THE MINI CONVERTIBLE
SLEIGH BED

ARMSTRONG WORLD INDUSTRIES, INC.
2500 Columbia Ave
Lancaster, PA 17603
Mailing Address:
PO Box 3001
Lancaster, PA 17604-3001
Tel.: (717) 397-0611
Fax: (717) 396-6133
Web Site: www.armstrong.com
Approx. Sls.: $2,766,400,000
Approx. Number Employees: 9,800
Year Founded: 1860
Business Description:
Flooring, Ceiling & Cabinet Products Designer, Mfr & Distr
S.I.C.: 3996; 2431; 2434; 3299; 3448; 5211
N.A.I.C.S.: 326192; 321918; 327999; 332311; 337110; 444190
Import Export
Advertising Expenditures: $28,800,000
Media: 1-2-4-5-6-7-9-10-11-14-16-19-20-21-23-24
Distr.: Natl.
Budget Set: Sept.
Personnel:
James J. O'Connor *(Chm)*
Matthew J. Espe *(CEO)*
Thomas B. Mangas *(CFO & Sr VP)*
Victor D. Grizzle *(CEO-Armstrong Building Products & Exec VP)*
Frank J. Ready *(CEO-Armstrong Floor Products Worldwide & Exec VP)*
Laurie Israel-Cubell *(VP-Mktg & New Product Dev)*
Beth A. Riley *(VP-IR, Comm & Diversity)*
William C. Rodruan *(VP-Fin-Flooring Products-Americas)*
Brands & Products:
ALLWOOD
ARMSTRONG
ARTEFFECTS
AXIOM
BRUCE
CAPELLA
CAPZ
CERAMAGUARD
CIRRUS
CORLON
CORTEGA
CUSHIONSTEP
DESIGNER SOLARIAN
DLW
DUNE
EXCELON
FINE FISSURED
FUNDAMENTALS
HARTCO
HOMERWOOD
INFUSIONS
MEDINTECH
METALWORKS
NATURAL CREATIONS
NATURAL INSPIRATIONS
NATURE'S GALLERY
OPTIMA
PARK AVENUE
PROCONNECT
RHINOFLOOR
ROBBINS
SAHARA
SCALA
SECOND LOOK
SOUNDSCAPES
STRATAMAX
TECHZONE
TIMBERLAND
TOUGHGUARD
ULTIMA
WOODWORKS
Advertising Agency:
OMD-USA
195 Broadway
New York, NY 10007
Tel.: (212) 590-7100

ART VAN FURNITURE, INC.
6500 E 14 Mi Rd
Warren, MI 48092-1281
Tel.: (586) 939-0800
Fax: (586) 939-3055
Web Site: www.artvan.com
Sales Range: $500-549.9 Million
Approx. Number Employees: 3,000
Year Founded: 1959
Business Description:
Home Furnishings Retailer

Key to Media (For complete agency information see *The Advertising Red Books-Agencies* edition):
1. Bus. Publs. 2. Cable T.V. 3. Catalogs & Directories. 4. Co-op Adv. 5. Consumer Mags. 6. D.M. to Bus. Estab.7. D.M. to Consumers 8. Daily Newsp. 9. Exhibits/Trade Shows 10. Foreign 11. Infomercial 12. Internet Adv.13. Multimedia 14. Network Radio 15. Network T.V. 16. Newsp. Distr. Mags. 17. Other 18. Outdoor (Posters, Transit) 19. Point of Purchase20. Premiums, Novelties 21. Product Samples 22. Special Events Mktg. 23. Spot Radio 24. Spot T.V. 25. Weekly Newsp. 26. Yellow Page Adv.

Art Van Furniture, Inc. — (Continued)

S.I.C.: 5712
N.A.I.C.S.: 442110
Media: 5-8-9-13-18-19-20-22-23-24-26
Distr.: Reg.
Budget Set: Oct.
Personnel:
Art Van Elslander *(Founder & Chm)*
Gary Van Elslander *(Pres)*
Kim Yost *(CEO)*
Dan Baran *(VP-Info Sys, Ops & Logistics)*
Michael Bolton *(VP-Fin)*
Cathy DiSante *(VP-Adv)*
Diane Charles *(Dir-Corp Comm)*
Tom DeCorte *(Dir-Inventory Project)*
Bruce McDonald *(Dir-Creative)*
Diane Karageozian *(Mgr-Adv)*

ARTE DE MEXICO INCORPORATED

1000 Chestnut St
Burbank, CA 91506
Tel.: (818) 753-4559
Fax: (818) 563-1015
E-mail: sales@artedemexico.com
Web Site: www.artedemexico.com
E-Mail For Key Personnel:
Sales Director: sales@artedemexico.com
Approx. Number Employees: 200
Year Founded: 1972
Business Description:
Wood & Upholstered Household Furniture
S.I.C.: 2512; 2511
N.A.I.C.S.: 337121; 337122
Media: 4-6
Personnel:
Gerald Stoffers *(Pres)*

ARTHUR LAUER, INC.

47 Steve's Ln
Gardiner, NY 12525
Tel.: (845) 255-7871
Fax: (845) 255-7881
Toll Free: (800) 385-0030
Web Site: www.arthurlauer.com
Approx. Sls.: $11,000,000
Approx. Number Employees: 30
Year Founded: 1983
Business Description:
Mfr. of Teak Outdoor Furniture
S.I.C.: 2511; 2512
N.A.I.C.S.: 337122; 337121
Media: 4-8
Personnel:
Jeremy Smith *(Chief Strategy Officer)*
Sue Hamel *(VP-Mktg)*
Brands & Products:
ARTHUR LAUER
ASBURY
BALDWIN
BELLAMY
BERKELEY
BROCKDEN
CHANDLER
CHAPMAN
CHIPPENDALE
CLASSIC
CLASSIC ADIRONDACK
CONRAD
COOPER
DUNWOODY
EMMA
ENDECOTT
GALLAGHER
GRAYSON
HAWTHORNE
HUDSON VALLEY
INSPIRED OUTDOOR LIVING
LENNOX
LUTYENS
NANTUCKET
OLIVER
PETERSON
PIERPONT
PORTER
RIDLEY
SALTER
SAXE
SEDGWICK
ST. GEORGE
STEAMER
TALIAFERRO
TAYLOR
TUSCANY

ARTISTIC TILE INC.

520 Secaucus Rd
Secaucus, NJ 07094-2502
Tel.: (201) 864-7000
Fax: (201) 864-7008
Web Site: www.artistictile.com
E-Mail For Key Personnel:
Marketing Director: janmaclatchie@artistictile.com
Sales Range: $25-49.9 Million
Approx. Number Employees: 50
Business Description:
Bathroom Fixtures, Equipment & Supplies
S.I.C.: 5211; 1743
N.A.I.C.S.: 444190; 238340
Media: 1-4-8-10
Personnel:
Nancy Epstein *(Founder & CEO)*
Lauren Cherkas *(Pres-Retail)*
Laura Steele *(VP-Mktg)*
Brands & Products:
AIDA'S NILE
AKROS
AMBRA
ARCTIC
ARTISTIC TILE
BARBIERI
BRUSHETTA
CARBONO
CAVA CLADDING
CELESTIAL
CONTESSA
DUCHESSA BRECCIA
DUCHESSA SEMPLICE
EFFERVESCENCE
ENCORE
FIG-ARO
FRAMEWORKS
FUSIONI
GRIGIO E SABBIA
HAMPTONS BLEND
HAUTE COTURE
IRIDIUM
IRONWORKS
LA LEAF
LIVE
M. BUTTERFLY
MELANGE
MEZZANINE MINK
MUSEE
NOUVEAU
OCEANSIDE
ONICE MISTA
ONYX
OVATION
PACIFICA
PALAZZO
PAVAROTTI PEARL
PHANTOM
PRATT & LARSON
REGINA
RIVERSTONE
SALSA
SCALINI
SHIMMER
SIGNORA
SISAL
SOUTH SEA
STILO
TERRA D ITALIA
TROPIQUE
TUNISIAN
VINO E ORO
XILO

ASHLEY FURNITURE INDUSTRIES, INC.

1 Ashley Way
Arcadia, WI 54612-1218
Tel.: (608) 323-3377
Fax: (608) 323-6019
Web Site: www.ashleyfurniture.com
Approx. Number Employees: 13,400
Year Founded: 1945
Business Description:
Wood & Upholstered Furniture Mfr, Whslr & Retail Store Franchiser
S.I.C.: 2511; 2512; 6794
N.A.I.C.S.: 337122; 337121; 533110
Media: 3-15-24
Personnel:
Ronald G. Wanek *(Chm)*
Todd R. Wanek *(Pres & CEO)*
Stacy Roshto *(Dir-Web Strategy)*
Jim Evanson *(Mgr-Credit)*
Nicole Pierce *(Mgr-Adv)*
Brands & Products:
AFRICA
AIREDALE
ALADDIO
ALEXIS
ALLESANDRO
ALLURE
ALMA
ALMIRA
ALPINE
ALTURA
ANNABELLE
ANNETTE
ANNIKA
ANTHEA
ANTIGO
ANTIQUE
APOLLO
ARETJA
ARLINGTON
ASHEVILLE
ASHFAIR
ASHLEY
ASHTON
ATHALIE
AUBURN RIDGE
AUCKLAND
AXIOM
AXIS
BAHA-MOSAIC
BAILEY
BANERAS
BARA
BARLETTA ANTIQUE
BARRETTA
BARSTOW AVE
BASIL
BATYA
BAVARIA
BAXTER
BAYPORT
BEERNADINE
BELLA VISTA
BELLEVILLE
BERNADINE
BERRINGER
BESSIE
BIGHAM
BILTMORE
BITTERSWEET
BONGO
BOULEVARD
BOUNDARY
BOX OFFICE
BRADBURY
BRADINGTON
BRAVADA
BRENNAN
BRIDGEPORT
BRIETTA
BRILEY
BRINDA
BRITTANY
BRYANT
BURLINGTON
CALA
CALAIS
CALEY
CANA
CAPE MAY
CAPRESSO
CARESS
CARHA
CARLYLE
CARON
CARRIE
CASA MOLLINO
CASEY
CASSELLA
CASTLE HILL
CATALINA
CEDAR HEIGHTS
CEDAR SPRINGS
CELEBRITY
CELINA
CELINE
CHARADE
CHARISMA
CHARLETON
CHATEAU FRONTENAC
CHELSA
CHELSEA
CHESHIRE LANE
CIRCUS
CITYSCAPE
CLAREMONT
CLAREMORE
COLISTA
COLLINS AVENUE
COMPANERO
CONCHITA
CONCORD VINES
CONNOISSEUR
CONTEMPO
CONTEMPORARY
CONTINUUM
COTTAGE RETREAT
CREATIVE SPACES
CROSSTALK
CURIOSITY
CYNTHIA
DAGMAR
DAHLIA

Key to Media (For complete agency information see *The Advertising Red Books-Agencies* edition):
1. Bus. Publs. 2. Cable T.V. 3. Catalogs & Directories. 4. Co-op Adv. 5. Consumer Mags. 6. D.M. to Bus. Estab.7. D.M. to Consumers 8. Daily Newsp. 9. Exhibits/Trade Shows 10. Foreign 11. Infomercial 12. Internet Adv.13. Multimedia 14. Network Radio 15. Network T.V. 16. Newsp. Distr. Mags. 17. Other 18. Outdoor (Posters, Transit) 19. Point of Purchase20. Premiums, Novelties 21. Product Samples 22. Special Events Mktg. 23. Spot Radio 24. Spot T.V. 25. Weekly Newsp. 26. Yellow Page Adv.

DAISY
DALTON
DAMARA
DANBURY
DANETTE
DANIELLE
DANYL
DAW
DEBORAH
DECO
DEIDRA
DELAFIELD
DELICIA
DELORMY
DEMBE
DEMETRIUS
DEMI
DEMPSEY
DENALI
DEON
DEREK
DERICA
DESANA
DESDEMON
DEVEN
DEXTRA
DIALLO
DIAMANTA
DIANE
DIKMAN
DILLIAN
DODGER
DOLLY
DOLORES
DONATA
DONNA
DORIS
DORSET
DOVER
DRAKE
DREAMA
DRIFTER
DRINA
DUBOT
DUNBAR
DUNIXI
DUNJA
DUNNE
DURACORD
DURAHIDE
DURANGO
DURAPELLA
DURAPLUSH
DURRIYA
DYANI
DYLAN
EASTRIDGE
EBBA
ECLIPSE
EDNA
EDOLIE
EDWINA
EILIS
EIRENE
ELAINE
ELAN
ELBERTINE
ELCOTT
ELDRIDGE
ELECTA
ELFRIEDA
ELIORA
ELITA
ELIZA
ELIZABETH
ELLEMA
ELMA
ELOISE
ELTA
ELYSIA
EMA
EMELIA
ENCORE
ENDEAVOR
ENDURO
ENHANCE
ENID
ENNIS
ERICA
ERIN
ERIS
ESHE
ESPRIT
ESTHER
ETANA
ETHEL
EUDORA
EUGENIA
EULALIE
EUNICE
EUSTACIA
EVA
EVELINA
EXETER
EXPEDITION
EXPLORER
EXTON
FERRETTI
FLINT CREEK
FLORIAN
FRANCO
FRISCO
FRONTIER
FUSION
GEMINI
GLEN ABBEY
GLEN EAGLE
GRACE ELEGANCE
GREAT PLAINS
GUNSMOKE-CANYON
HALIFAX
HARGROVE
HAVERHILL
HEIRLOOM
HENTHORN
HERITAGE
HICKORY POINT
HIGHLAND PARK
HILL HOUSE
HUDSON
INGLEBROOK
INTRINSIC
ITASCA
JOLLIET HEIGHTS
JUST ROCKS
KELSEY
KENYA
KENYON
LAKELAND
LAMBERT
LANCASTER
LANDMARK
LATTICE
LEGION POINT
LINCOLN ROAD
LINDEN FALLS
LONGWORTH
LUSSANNE
MADRAS
MAIFAIR PLACE
MAISON
MANCHESTER
MANHATTAN
MARCOS-ESTATES
MARESSA
MARGILLES
MARQUEE
MARQUIS
MARRIETTA
MATRIX
MAYFIELD
MEDFORD
MENDAM
MERANO
MERINO
MIDNIGHT
MILFORD PARK
MILLENNIUM
MILLESTEAD
MIRANDA
MODENA
MONACO
MONARCH VALLEY
MONTICELLO
MONTOUR
MORTON
NAPLES
NEWHOUSE
NORTH BROOK
NORTHFORK CRAFTSMAN
OAK LORE
ODYSSEY
OMNI
OPTIMA
OPULENCE
ORLEANS FORGE
OXFORD
PAMPA
PAN CASARI
PANORAMA
PASCAL
PENROSE
PHEASANT
PHEASANT RUN
PINEDALE
PINELLA
PINTO
PLUM GROVE
PORT ROUGE
PORTICA
POSH
PRAIRIE VIEW
PRINTZ
PROTEGE
QUEEN ANNE
QUINTESSENTIALS
RAMONA
RANCHO
RANGOON
REGAL
RENAISSANCE
RENDEZVOUS
RICHLAND PINES
RIO MAR
RIVARD
ROBERTA
ROCK FALLS
ROMANOFF
ROSEWOOD
ROYALTY-GOLD
RUTHERFORD
RYLAND
SAFARI-BURLAP
SANDSTONE
SANGER
SANIBEL
SANTA BARBARA
SANTORI
SAVANAH
SCOTTSBLUFF
SEALY
SEDALLIA
SENECA
SERENGETI
SHELDON HARBOR
SHERWOOD
SIENNA
SILVER LAKE
SIMMONS
SIOUX
SOLANA
SONOMA
SORENTO
SOUTH BARSTOW
SOUTH SHORE
SOUTHPOINT
SPECTRA
SPIRIT RIDGE
SPOT
SPRING GREEN
STAGES
ST.LAURET
STRATUS
STRICKLY MISSION
SUMMIT
SUMMIT AVENUE
SURROUNDS
SUTCLIFFE
SWEETWATER OAKS
SYDNEY
TACOMA
TAFFETA TRELLIS
TEMPO
TENLEY
TEXTURED PEWTER
TIMBERLINE
TOILE
TOSCANA
TOVOLO
TRIBAL
TRIUMPH
TUSCANY
UPTON
URBANVILLE
VARIA
VENECIA
VENTURE
VERONA
VILLA MARIE
VITELLINO
WESTBROOK
WHILTON
WHISPERING
WIGEON
WILMIGTON HEIGHTS
WILSHIRE
WINDHAM
WINSLOW
YORK STREET

Advertising Agency:
Zimmerman Advertising
2200 W Commercial Blvd Ste 300
Fort Lauderdale, FL 33309-3064
Tel.: (954) 644-4000
Fax: (954) 731-2977
Toll Free: (800) 248-8522
(Creative & Media)

BABY TREND, INC.

(Filed Ch 11 Bankruptcy #934090 in U.S. Bankruptcy Ct, Central Dist of CA, Riverside)
1607 S Campus Ave
Ontario, CA 91761
Tel.: (909) 773-0018
Fax: (909) 773-0108
Toll Free: (800) 328-7363
E-mail: info@babytrend.com
Web Site: www.babytrend.com

Key to Media (For complete agency information see *The Advertising Red Books-Agencies* edition):
1. Bus. Publs. 2. Cable T.V. 3. Catalogs & Directories. 4. Co-op Adv. 5. Consumer Mags. 6. D.M. to Bus. Estab.7. D.M. to Consumers 8. Daily Newsp. 9. Exhibits/Trade Shows 10. Foreign 11. Infomercial 12. Internet Adv.13. Multimedia 14. Network Radio 15. Network T.V. 16. Newsp. Distr. Mags. 17. Other 18. Outdoor (Posters, Transit) 19. Point of Purchase20. Premiums, Novelties 21. Product Samples 22. Special Events Mktg. 23. Spot Radio 24. Spot T.V. 25. Weekly Newsp. 26. Yellow Page Adv.

Baby Trend, Inc. — (Continued)

Sales Range: $1-9.9 Million
Approx. Number Employees: 20
Year Founded: 1988
Business Description:
Baby Furniture, Strollers, Car Seats & Walkers Whslr
S.I.C.: 5021
N.A.I.C.S.: 423210
Media: 4-6-19
Personnel:
Denny Tsai *(Pres)*
Brands & Products:
BABY TREND
EXPEDITION
EZ FLEX-LOC
FLEX-LOC
SIT N STAND
SNAP-N-GO
TRENDSPORT
TRENDWALKER

BABYLICIOUS GEAR LTD.

5811 Blenheim St
Vancouver, BC Canada
Tel.: (604) 374-3300
Fax: (604) 736-1926
Toll Free: (866) 289-5210 (Customer Svc)
E-mail: tina@babylicious.ca
Web Site: www.babylicious.ca
Approx. Number Employees: 6
Business Description:
Baby Furniture & Bedding Mfr
S.I.C.: 2512; 2392
N.A.I.C.S.: 337121; 314129
Media: 5-6-13
Personnel:
Tina Barkley *(CEO & Chief Inspiration Off)*
Jennifer Henrey *(CFO)*
Brent Holliday *(COO)*

BACOVA GUILD, LTD.

(Sub. of Ronile, Inc.)
1000 Commerce Ctr Dr
Covington, VA 24426
Mailing Address:
PO Box 180
Low Moor, VA 24457
Tel.: (540) 863-2600
Fax: (540) 863-2645
E-mail: bacova@bacova.com
Web Site: www.bacova.com
Year Founded: 1957
Business Description:
Printed Accent Rugs, Printed Floor Mats & Bathroom Ensembles Mfr
S.I.C.: 2273; 2392; 2431; 2759
N.A.I.C.S.: 314110; 314129; 321918; 323113
Media: 4-7-10-11-19
Personnel:
Charlie Bowers *(Pres)*
Bob Delumyea *(CFO)*
David Woods *(Gen Mgr)*
Brad Houff *(Asst Gen Mgr)*
Kathy Fowlkes *(Bus Mgr & Dir-Trend)*
Donna Rodgers *(Dir-Design)*
Julie Dean *(Mgr-Customer Svc)*
Rick Lewis *(Mgr-Natl Sls)*
Judy Ryder *(Mgr-Quality Assurance)*
Jeff Strasser *(Engr)*
Brands & Products:
BACOVA

BAKER KNAPP & TUBBS INC.

(Sub. of Kohler Company)
222 Merchandise Mart Plz Ste 1414
Chicago, IL 60654
Tel.: (312) 329-9410
Fax: (312) 836-1370
Toll Free: (800) 59BAKER
E-mail: info@bakerfurniture.com
Web Site: www.bakerfurniture.com
Approx. Number Employees: 35
Year Founded: 1890
Business Description:
Mfr. of Reproduction Traditional & Contemporary Furniture
S.I.C.: 2511; 5021
N.A.I.C.S.: 337122; 423210
Advertising Expenditures: $1,000,000
Media: 1-2-5-6-10
Distr.: Natl.
Budget Set: Nov.
Personnel:
Rachel D. Kohler *(Group Pres-Interiors)*
James Nauyok *(VP-Mktg-Visual Display)*
Brands & Products:
BAKER
MASTERCRAFT
MILLING ROAD

BALL & BALL HARDWARE REPRODUCTIONS

463 W Lincoln Hwy
Exton, PA 19341
Tel.: (610) 363-7330
Fax: (610) 363-7639
Toll Free: (800) 257-3711
Web Site: www.ballandball.com
Approx. Number Employees: 25
Year Founded: 1932
Business Description:
Reproduction Hardware Mfr
S.I.C.: 3429; 5932
N.A.I.C.S.: 332510; 453310
Media: 4-6-10
Personnel:
Bill Ball *(Gen Mgr)*

BASSETT FURNITURE INDUSTRIES, INCORPORATED

3525 Fairystone Hwy
Bassett, VA 24055
Mailing Address:
PO Box 626
Bassett, VA 24055-0626
Tel.: (276) 629-6000
Fax: (276) 629-6333
Telex: 62035175
E-mail: bassett@bassettfurniture.com
Web Site: www.bassettfurniture.com
Approx. Sls.: $235,254,000
Approx. Number Employees: 1,254
Year Founded: 1902
Business Description:
Furniture Mfr & Retailer
S.I.C.: 2511; 2512; 5712
N.A.I.C.S.: 337122; 337121; 442110
Import Export
Advertising Expenditures: $8,462,000
Media: 2-8
Personnel:
Paul Fulton *(Chm)*
Robert H. Spilman, Jr. *(Pres & CEO)*
J. Michael Daniel *(Chief Acctg Officer & VP)*
Brands & Products:
5TH AVENUE
AMERICAN HEWN
ASPEN
BALI
BASSETT
BASSETT FURNITURE DIRECT
BEDDING & DREAM MAKER
BROADWAY
CAMBRIDGE
CLASSIC ELWAY
CLUB ROOM
COBBLESTONE
CONTINENTAL SKETCHBOOK
DEVON
EASTON
ENZIO
FAVERSHAM HALL
GRAYSON
GUILFORD
HAWTHORNE
HYDE PARK
LANCASTER
MONROE
MONTGOMERY
NEW AMERICAN LIVING
NEW TRADITIONS
OLYMPIA BAY
OXFORD
PANORAMA
RUE DE SEINE
SCARLETTE
SIMPLY YOURS
SLIPPER CHAIRS
TERRACE PLACE
TRINIDAD
VIEWPOINTS
VINTAGE ELWAY
WESTON

BAUHAUS USA, INC.

(Sub. of La-Z-Boy Incorporated)
1 Bauhaus Dr
Saltillo, MS 38866-6974
Tel.: (662) 869-2664
Fax: (662) 869-5910
E-mail: consumer@bauhaususa.com
Web Site: www.bauhaususa.com
Sales Range: $75-99.9 Million
Approx. Number Employees: 275
Business Description:
Furniture Mfr
S.I.C.: 2512
N.A.I.C.S.: 337121
Media: 11
Brands & Products:
BAUHAUS USA

BEAULIEU CANADA

(Sub. of Beaulieu Group, LLC)
335 Rue De Roxton
Acton Vale, QC J0H 1A0, Canada
Tel.: (450) 546-5000
Fax: (450) 546-5027
Toll Free: (800) 853-9048
Web Site: www.beaulieucanada.ca
Sales Range: $150-199.9 Million
Approx. Number Employees: 1,400
Year Founded: 1954
Business Description:
Mfr. of Tufted Carpet
S.I.C.: 2273
N.A.I.C.S.: 314110
Export
Advertising Expenditures: $3,000,000
Media: 2-5-6-7-8-10-19-22
Distr.: Intl.
Budget Set: Nov.-Dec.
Personnel:
Leslie Beaumont *(Dir-Mktg)*
Brands & Products:
BEAULIEU COMMERCIAL
BOLYU
CAMBRIDGE
CONCERT
CORONET
PEERLESS COMFORT
YOUR HOMESTYLE

BEAULIEU GROUP, LLC

(d/b/a Beaulieu of America)
1502 Coronet Dr
Dalton, GA 30720-2664
Tel.: (706) 278-6666
Fax: (706) 272-7305
E-mail: resinfo@beaulieu-usa.com
Web Site: www.beaulieu-usa.com
Approx. Number Employees: 6,800
Year Founded: 1978
Business Description:
Mfr. of Carpets & Rugs
S.I.C.: 2273; 2281
N.A.I.C.S.: 314110; 313111
Media: 10
Personnel:
Ralph Bow *(COO)*
Jeff Meadows *(Chief Mktg Officer)*
Patricia Flavin *(Sr VP-Mktg)*
Regina Duckett *(Mgr-Customer Svc)*
Mark Johnson *(Mgr-Tech Svcs)*
Ellen Moore *(Mgr-Residential Sls)*
Debby Parsons *(Mgr-HR)*
Laraine Thompson *(Mgr-Promo Goods)*
Christina Wright *(Mgr-After Sls)*
Brands & Products:
ACCOMODATION
ACCURACY
ADOBE VILLAGE
AFFECTIONATELY YOURS
AGELESS BEAUTY
ALLANTE
ALTERNATE
ANASTASIA
ASPECTS
ATTRIBUTE
AYLESBURY
BAKERS SQUARE
BALLYMORE
BAYPOINT
BAYTOWNE
BEAUJOLAIS
BEAULIEU
BEL AIR
BEL ROCK
BELIZE
BETTER YET
BLOCK PARTY
BOLTON
BOXWEAVE
BRAID
BRAZILIAN MAPLE
BROCADE
BROOKFIELD
BYRON BAY
CABO
CALADERA
CALIFORNIA DREAMER
CAREFREE LIVING
CARMEL COVE
CARRARA
CASANOVA
CASTAWAY
CASTLETOWN
CAYMAN

Key to Media (For complete agency information see *The Advertising Red Books-Agencies* edition):
1. Bus. Publs. 2. Cable T.V. 3. Catalogs & Directories. 4. Co-op Adv. 5. Consumer Mags. 6. D.M. to Bus. Estab.7. D.M. to Consumers 8. Daily Newsp. 9. Exhibits/Trade Shows 10. Foreign 11. Infomercial 12. Internet Adv.13. Multimedia 14. Network Radio 15. Network T.V. 16. Newsp. Distr. Mags. 17. Other 18. Outdoor (Posters, Transit) 19. Point of Purchase20. Premiums, Novelties 21. Product Samples 22. Special Events Mktg. 23. Spot Radio 24. Spot T.V. 25. Weekly Newsp. 26. Yellow Page Adv.

CEDAR STREET
CENTENNIAL
CENTER SQUARE
CENTER STAGE
CHARMING
CHESS CLUB
CHISWELL
CITATION
CITY BLOCK
CLAMOR
CLASSIC DREAMS
CLASSICAL PRODUCTIONS
CLEAR PERFORMANCE
COBBLE HILL
COLOR SPECTRUM
CONQUISTADOR
CONSORT
CONTENDER
CORDOBA
CORONADO BEACH
CORRIGANS COVE
COURTSHIP
CRITICS CHOICE
CURRENTS
DAMASCUS
DECOR
DEER VALLEY
DIAMOND BACK
DURANGO
EASTBORNE
EASY AS PIE
ELEVATIONS
EMBRACEABLE YOU
ENGLISH IVY
ESCAPADE
EVERYTHING NICE
EXETER
EXHUBERANCE
EXOTIC
EXTRAVAGANT
FIBERESSENCE
FIJI
FIREWORKS
FIRST CLASS
FIRST LOVE
FLOWER GARDEN
FLOWERING VINE
FOREVER AND EVER
FREE N EASY
FRENCH RIVIERA
FRISKY
GENTLE CARESS
GINGERWOOD
GLAMOURESQUE
GLENLO ABBEY
GOLDEN ANNIVERSARY
GOOD CHEER
GRAND CAYMAN
GRAND ILLUSIONS
GRANTHAM
GUARDIAN
HAPPY GO LUCKY
HEDGEROW
HERB GARDEN
HIDDEN TREASURE
HOLLYTEX
HOLLYWOOD HILLS
HUDDERSFIELD
HUGS N KISSES
HUNTINGTON
ICE PALACE
INTERMISSION
JAZZ
LA JOLLA
LA PALMA
LA PRADA
LAP OF LUXURY
LIVE IT UP
LONDON CLASSIC
LONG KEY
LOVE AFFAIR
THE LUXURY COLLECTION
LUXURYBAC
MADEIRA
MADISON AVE
MAGIC DECOR
MALLORY SQUARE
MAPLEWOOD
MATCHLESS
MIRADA
MONTANA MORN
NATURAL EXPRESSIONS
NATURAL FERN
NATURE WEAVE
NATURES GARDEN
NAVARRO
NEPAL
NETWORKS
NEVIS
NEW DIMENSIONS
NORTHWICH
NOTTINGHAM
OAHU
OCEAN BREEZE
ONE OF A KIND
OPERA HOUSE
OSBORNE
PALM BEACH
PALM SPRINGS
PARADOX
PARK AVENUE
PERENNIAL
PERMASHIELD
PERMASOFT
PETIT POINT
PLANTATION KEY
PLEATS N PLAIDS
POINT ROYALE
PRAIRIE MEADOWS
PREVIEW
PROGRESSION
PROMINENCE
RARE TREASURE
RAVINA
RAVING BEAUTY
RELIANCE
RENOVATION
RIGOROUS
RIVER DOWNS
ROMANCE
SAINT IVES
SALT N PEPPER
SCOTTISH HIGHLANDS
SEAGATE
SEDUCTIVE
SENSUOUS
SENTIMENTAL
SERENE
SHANGRILA
SHEER ELEGANCE
SHERWOOD PARK
SHIFTING SANDS
SHINING STAR
SIESTA KEY
SILVER ANNIVERSARY
SIMPLY BEAUTIFUL
SIMPLY IRRESISTIBLE
SISAL WEAVE
SNAZZY
SNUGGLES
SOFT N INVITING
SONORA
SOUTH BEACH
SOUTH HAMPTON
SOVEREIGN
SPIN CITY
SPLENDID BEAUTY
ST. KITTS
ST. LUCIA
ST. MARTIN
ST. VINCENT
STAINMASTER
STARLIGHT
STIMULATING
STONEHURST
STRATA
STRUCTURES
STYLED FOR LIVING
SUBLIMINAL
SUGAR N SPICE
SUPREME ELEGANCE
SUPREME LIVING
SUPREME LUXURY
SURE THING
SWEET SENSATIONS
SWEETHEART
TACTESSE
TAHITI
TALISMAN
TATTERSAIL
TEMPTING
THUNDER CREEK
TIMELESS TWIST
TREASURE
TRIBECCA
TRITON
TROPICAL PARADISE
TROPICAL SPLENDOR
TRUE LOVE
TRULY YOURS
TSUNAMI
TURNBRIDGE
TWIST N SHOUT
ULTIMA
ULTIMATE TEXTURE
ULTIMATE TWIST
VAIL
VENICE
VICTORY GARDEN
VILLAGE SQUARE
VISION
WARM EMBRACE
WAVERLY
WISTERIA
WOVEN ELEGANCE
WOVEN RATTAN
XTRALIFE

BELLACOR INC.

2425 Enterprise Dr Ste 900
Mendota Heights, MN 55120-1172
Tel.: (651) 294-2500
Fax: (651) 294-2595
Toll Free: (877) 723-5522
E-mail: marketing@bellacor.com
Web Site: www.bellacor.com
Sales Range: $1-9.9 Million
Approx. Number Employees: 50
Year Founded: 2000
Business Description:
Decorative Furniture Accessories Retailer
S.I.C.: 5719
N.A.I.C.S.: 442299
Media: 2-10-13
Personnel:
Michael M. Minsberg *(CEO)*
Jim Lawrence *(CFO)*
Chris Fowler *(Dir-Mktg)*

BELVEDERE USA CORPORATION

(Sub. of The Wella Corporation)
1 Belvedere Blvd
Belvidere, IL 61008
Tel.: (815) 544-3131
Fax: (815) 544-6747
Fax: (800) 626-9750
Toll Free: (800) 435-5491
Web Site: www.belvedere.com
E-Mail For Key Personnel:
Marketing Director: mshipley@belvedereco.com
Sales Range: $100-124.9 Million
Approx. Number Employees: 300
Year Founded: 1927
Business Description:
Beauty & Barber Furniture & Equipment Mfr
S.I.C.: 2531; 3589
N.A.I.C.S.: 337127; 333319
Export
Media: 2-4-5-7-8-10
Distr.: Natl.
Budget Set: Oct.
Personnel:
Horst Ackermann *(Owner)*
Barry Sanders *(Pres)*
Brands & Products:
ALPHA
BELLEVUE
FIRST LADY
FLO-TEMP
MONDO
WHIZ
Advertising Agency:
Heinzeroth Marketing Group
415 Y Blvd
Rockford, IL 61107-3059
Tel.: (815) 967-0929
Fax: (815) 967-0983

BEMCO ASSOCIATES, INC.

2720 S River Rd Ste 130
Des Plaines, IL 60018
Tel.: (847) 296-0080
E-mail: info@bemco.com
Web Site: www.bemco.com
Sales Range: $1-9.9 Million
Approx. Number Employees: 1
Year Founded: 1956
Business Description:
Mattress Licensing
S.I.C.: 2515
N.A.I.C.S.: 337910
Media: 4-6
Personnel:
Daryl Tarbutton *(Pres)*
Brands & Products:
BEMCO
ENJOY HEALTHY SLEEP
MEMORYREST
POSTURE COLLECTION
POSTURE ZONE SUSPENSION SYSTEM
SLEEP DIMENSIONS
USA GYMNAST COLLECTION

BERKLINE/BENCHCRAFT HOLDINGS LLC

(Holding of Sun Capital Partners, Inc.)
1 Berkline Dr
Morristown, TN 37813
Tel.: (423) 585-1500
Fax: (423) 585-4420
Toll Free: (800) 633-9313
E-mail: webadmin@benchcraft.com

Key to Media (For complete agency information see *The Advertising Red Books-Agencies* edition):
1. Bus. Publs. 2. Cable T.V. 3. Catalogs & Directories. 4. Co-op Adv. 5. Consumer Mags. 6. D.M. to Bus. Estab.7. D.M. to Consumers 8. Daily Newsp. 9. Exhibits/Trade Shows 10. Foreign 11. Infomercial 12. Internet Adv.13. Multimedia 14. Network Radio 15. Network T.V. 16. Newsp. Distr. Mags. 17. Other 18. Outdoor (Posters, Transit) 19. Point of Purchase20. Premiums, Novelties 21. Product Samples 22. Special Events Mktg. 23. Spot Radio 24. Spot T.V. 25. Weekly Newsp. 26. Yellow Page Adv.

Berkline/BenchCraft Holdings LLC — (Continued)

Web Site: www.berkline.com
Approx. Number Employees: 3,000
Year Founded: 1937
Business Description:
Recliners & Reclining Upholstered Living Room & Family Room Furniture Mfr
S.I.C.: 2512
N.A.I.C.S.: 337121
Import Export
Media: 2-4-5-7-8-9-10-21
Distr.: Natl.
Budget Set: Feb.
Personnel:
Robert Burch *(Pres & CEO)*
Brands & Products:
ADINA
ALEXANDRIA
ARLINGTON
AUTOMOTION
BARCELONA
BERGAMO
BERKLINE
BERKLINE BENCHCRAFT
BEVINGTON
BIG EASY
BORDEAUX
BRANSON
CHAISELOUNGER
CHAMPION
CIMMARON
COMFORTREST
CUDDLE
DREAMER
EASYLIFT
EASYOFF BACK
EPIC
ESPRIT
FARRINGTON
GEMINI
GRAVITY
HERMITAGE
HIDEAWAY
HORIZON
INTRIGUE
LIV-IN-ROOM
LONDON
LYNDON
MARSHALL
MASADA
MASSAGE
METRO
OASIS
POWERRECLINE
RADFORD
ROCK-A-LOUNGER
ROTHERHAM
SENTRY
SOLANO
SWANSEA
SYDNEY
TOUCHMOTION
TUSCANY
VIBRANT
WALLAWAY
WEXNER
Advertising Agency:
Horich Parks Lebow Advertising
101 Shilling Rd Ste 30
Hunt Valley, MD 21031
Tel.: (410) 329-1950
Fax: (410) 329-1210
Toll Free: (800) 878-8989

BERNHARDT DESIGN

(Formerly Bernhardt Furniture Company)
1839 Morganton Blvd SW
Lenoir, NC 28645-5338
Mailing Address:
PO Box 740
Lenoir, NC 28645-5338
Tel.: (828) 758-9811
Fax: (828) 759-6634
Toll Free: (800) 340-0240
Web Site: www.bernhardt.com
Approx. Number Employees: 2,000
Year Founded: 1889
Business Description:
Wood & Upholstered Dining Room, Living Room & Bedroom Furniture Importer, Mfr & Distr
S.I.C.: 2511; 2512
N.A.I.C.S.: 337122; 337121
Advertising Expenditures: $200,000
Media: 2-4-6-10
Personnel:
J. Rountree Collett *(Pres-Bernhardt Ventures)*
William B. Collett *(Exec VP & Gen Mgr-Bernhardt Residential Casegoods)*
Marissa Belvedere *(Mgr-Mktg)*
Heather Erdenmiller *(Mgr-Adv)*
Brands & Products:
ABRA
ADAGIO
ADELPHI
ALDER
ALEXANDER
ALGONQUIN
AMBASSADOR
AQUACADE
ARIA
ATHERTON
AVALON
AVENUE
AXIS
BANNOK
BELLAGIO
BERLIN
BLITZ
BOREAS
BOULEVARD
BRANDAU
BRELLIN
BRETTELLES
BRISA
BULL RUN
CAMERON
CAMINO
CANTATA
CAPRI
CARAVAN
CARAVELLE
CARLYLE
CARSON
CHANDLER
CHASE
CHINOOK
CIRQUE
CLARK
CONCERTO
COSTUME
COTILLION
CRAVAT
CROQUET
DELANEY
DENEVE
DIALECT
DILLON
DOLLAR
DUET
DUNHILL
EARTH QUAKE
ETAGE
FINESSE
FINISH LINE
FLORENCE
FULTON STREET
FUNDEMENTAL
GALA
GALLERY
GELLATIN
GEORGE
GO
GRAPHICA
HAT TRICK
HELENA
HYDROGEN
ILLUSION
IMAGE
INTERPOLATION
JUBILEE
JUNCTURE
KISMET
LARGO
LIFE LINE
LIFE STORY
LISBON
LIVINGSTON
LONDON
LUCKY STARS
MADELEINE
MADISON
MANHASSET
MARLOWE
MARTINI
MASQUERADE
MASTRAL
MEZZO
MILAN
MONTRIO
MOREAU
NEWBERRY
NIGHT SKY
OBERLIN
ONE
OPERA
ORBIT
OXFORD
PARIS
PASSAGE
PAUSE
PERIMETER
PESARO
PING PONG
PORTRAIT
PRAGUE
PRELUDE
PROVIDENCE
PYRAMID
RALEIGH COURT
RAPINA
REGENCY
RELAY
RICHMOND
RIDGWOOD
RING TOSS
ROSE GARDEN
SEATTLE
SEDONA
SENTRY
SERENADE
SHERIDAN
SHIFT
SHIMMER
SINCLAIR
SKY DANCER
SKY LARK
SPELLBOUND
SPOTLIGHT
ST. ELIENNE
ST. GERMAIN
ST. MICHAEL
STACKING
STADIUM
STRADE
STRATA
STUDIO
TEMPO
THEA ARIZONA
TITANIUM
TRELLIS
TRIBECA
TRILOGY
ULTIMA LEATHER
ULTRALEATHER
UNTRATECH 7000
VALENCIA
VENDOME
VIENNA
VISIONS
VISTA
VOLTAIRE
VORTAX
WAKE FOREST
WANDER
WATER FALL
WATER LINE
WAVE
WAVERLY
WILLOW
WILSHIRE
WINTHROPE
ZENITH
ZINC
ZOE

BIELECKY BROTHERS, INC.

50-22 72nd St
Woodside, NY 11377
Tel.: (718) 424-4764
Tel.: (212) 753-2355 (NY Showroom)
Fax: (718) 898-4737
Fax: (212) 751-9369 (NY Showroom)
E-mail: bielecky@bieleckybrothers.com
Web Site: www.bieleckybrothers.com
Approx. Sls.: $1,000,000
Approx. Number Employees: 50
Business Description:
Handcrafted Rattan, Cane & Wicker Furniture Mfr
S.I.C.: 2519
N.A.I.C.S.: 337125
Media: 2
Distr.: Natl.
Personnel:
Eddy Bielecky *(Pres)*
Advertising Agency:
Michael Chaves Advertising, Inc.
10 E 21st St
New York, NY 10010
Tel.: (212) 677-5480
Fax: (212) 529-7633

BLINDS TO GO (CANADA) INC.

(Sub. of Blinds To Go Inc.)
3510 Blvd Saint Joseph E
Montreal, QC H1X 1W6, Canada
Tel.: (514) 255-4000
Fax: (514) 259-9992
Web Site: www.blindstogo.com/support_storelocator.php
Approx. Number Employees: 3,510
Year Founded: 1954

Key to Media (For complete agency information see *The Advertising Red Books-Agencies* edition):
1. Bus. Publs. 2. Cable T.V. 3. Catalogs & Directories. 4. Co-op Adv. 5. Consumer Mags. 6. D.M. to Bus. Estab.7. D.M. to Consumers 8. Daily Newsp. 9. Exhibits/Trade Shows 10. Foreign 11. Infomercial 12. Internet Adv.13. Multimedia 14. Network Radio 15. Network T.V. 16. Newsp. Distr. Mags. 17. Other 18. Outdoor (Posters, Transit) 19. Point of Purchase20. Premiums, Novelties 21. Product Samples 22. Special Events Mktg. 23. Spot Radio 24. Spot T.V. 25. Weekly Newsp. 26. Yellow Page Adv.

Business Description:
Mfr. & Retailer of Window Blinds
S.I.C.: 2591
N.A.I.C.S.: 337920
Media: 13
Personnel:
David Shiller *(Chm)*

BLINDS TO GO INC.

70 Wood Ave S 1st Fl
Iselin, NJ 08830
Tel.: (514) 255-4000
Fax: (732) 906-0888
Toll Free: (800) BLINDS7
E-mail: jjoassainte@blindstogo.com
Web Site: www.blindstogo.com
Sales Range: $50-74.9 Million
Approx. Number Employees: 600
Year Founded: 1999
Business Description:
Window Covering Parts & Accessories
S.I.C.: 5023; 5719
N.A.I.C.S.: 423220; 442299
Media: 24
Personnel:
Nkere Udofia *(Vice Chm)*
Brands & Products:
BLINDS TO GO
LE MARCHE DU
Advertising Agency:
French/West/Vaughan, Inc.
112 E Hargett St
Raleigh, NC 27601
Tel.: (919) 832-6300
Fax: (919) 832-6360
(Public Relations)

BLU DOT DESIGN & MANUFACTURING, INC.

3236 California St NE
Minneapolis, MN 55418
Tel.: (612) 782-1844
Approx. Rev.: $8,000,000
Approx. Number Employees: 19
Year Founded: 1996
Business Description:
Whol Furniture
S.I.C.: 5021
N.A.I.C.S.: 423210
Personnel:
John Christakos *(CEO)*
Advertising Agency:
mono
(Partially Owned by MDC Partners)
3036 Hennepin Ave
Minneapolis, MN 55408
Tel.: (612) 822-4135
Fax: (612) 454-4950

BOGDANCO CONSULTING

541 F Cowper St
Palo Alto, CA 94301
Mailing Address:
555 Bryant St Ste 458
Palo Alto, CA 94301
Tel.: (650) 823-9313
Fax: (650) 618-2542
E-mail: info@bogdanco.com
Web Site: www.bogdanco.com
E-Mail For Key Personnel:
President: bogdan@bogdanco.com
Approx. Number Employees: 5
Year Founded: 1999
Business Description:
Product Design Firm offering Mechanical Engineering & Industrial Design Services
S.I.C.: 7389
N.A.I.C.S.: 541420
Advertising Expenditures: $250,000
Media: 4-7-10-13
Personnel:
Mario Bogdan *(CEO & Product Design Engr)*
Brands & Products:
BALL FRAME 25
BOGDANCO
STAR COASTERS
TOOTHY FROG

BR-111 IMPORT & EXPORT, INC.

12800 NW 107th Ct
Medley, FL 33178
Tel.: (305) 882-8842
Fax: (800) 577-2711
Toll Free: (800) 525-BR111
E-mail: wood@br111.com
Web Site: www.br111.com
Approx. Number Employees: 45
Business Description:
Hardwood Flooring Sales
S.I.C.: 5023
N.A.I.C.S.: 423220
Media: 6-10
Personnel:
Ricardo Moraes *(Pres)*
Jason Strong *(Exec VP)*
Keith Barrette *(Mgr-Ops & Mktg)*

BRAYTON

(Div. of Coalesse)
250 Swathmore Ave
High Point, NC 27263-1931
Mailing Address:
PO Box 7288
High Point, NC 27264-7288
Tel.: (336) 434-4151
Fax: (336) 434-8247
Fax: (888) 413-5161
Toll Free: (800) 627-6770
Web Site: www.brayton.com
Sales Range: $100-124.9 Million
Approx. Number Employees: 326
Year Founded: 1973
Business Description:
Office Furniture Mfr
S.I.C.: 2521; 2522
N.A.I.C.S.: 337211; 337214
Media: 2-4-10
Personnel:
Gina Chapman-Cox *(VP-Sls)*
Lisa Clark *(VP-Customer Experience-Coalesse)*
Kathy Turner *(VP-HR)*

BROWN JORDAN INTERNATIONAL COMPANY

(Sub. of Brown Jordan International)
1801 N Andrews Ave
Pompano Beach, FL 33069
Tel.: (954) 960-1117
Fax: (954) 960-1849
E-mail: contact@brownjordan.com
Web Site: www.brownjordan.com
Sales Range: $350-399.9 Million
Approx. Number Employees: 1,814
Year Founded: 1945
Business Description:
Mfr. of Stainless Steel, Aluminum, Teak & Woven Luxury Leisure Furniture
S.I.C.: 2512; 2514
N.A.I.C.S.: 337121; 337124
Import Export
Media: 2-4-6-7-10
Distr.: Intl.; Natl.
Personnel:
Jim Kemp *(Dir-Product Dev)*
Rashna Carmicle *(Dir-Mktg & Comm)*
Brands & Products:
BROWN JORDAN
CASUAL LIVING
CHARTER
LOEWENSTEIN
POMPEII
STUART CLARK
TEXACRAFT
TROPIC CRAFT
VINEYARD
WABASH VALLEY
WINSTON
WOODSMITHS

BROYHILL FURNITURE INDUSTRIES, INC.

(Sub. of Furniture Brands International, Inc.)
1 Broyhill Pk
Lenoir, NC 28633-0003
Tel.: (828) 758-3111
Fax: (828) 758-3538
Toll Free: (800) 327-6944
E-mail: hr@broyhillfurniture.com
Web Site: www.broyhillfurn.com
Sales Range: $250-299.9 Million
Approx. Number Employees: 850
Year Founded: 1905
Business Description:
Bedroom, Dining Room & Occasional, Casual Furniture & Upholstery Mfr
S.I.C.: 2511; 2512
N.A.I.C.S.: 337122; 337121
Import Export
Media: 3-4-6-10-16-24
Distr.: Intl.; Natl.
Budget Set: Sept. -Oct.
Personnel:
Mark E. Stephens *(Pres)*
Brands & Products:
BROYHILL
Advertising Agency:
Symetri
6520 Airport Center Dr Ste 208
Greensboro, NC 27409
Tel.: (336) 285-0940

BRUNSCHWIG & FILS, INC.

(Sub. of Kravet, Inc.)
75 Virginia Rd
White Plains, NY 10603-2201
Tel.: (914) 684-5800
Fax: (914) 684-6140
Toll Free: (800) 538-1880
E-mail: staff@brunschwig.com
Web Site: www.brunschwig.com
Approx. Number Employees: 50
Year Founded: 1925
Business Description:
Piece Goods & Other Fabrics; Woven Textiles; Wallcoverings; Furniture; Lamps & Tables
S.I.C.: 5131; 5198
N.A.I.C.S.: 424310; 424950
Import Export
Media: 2-4-6-7-11
Distr.: Direct to Consumer; Intl.; Natl.; Reg.
Budget Set: Sept.
Personnel:
Olivier Peardon *(Owner, Pres & CEO)*
Dawn Carlson *(VP-Purchasing & Sls)*
Brands & Products:
AURORA
B & F
BELMONT
BRUNSCHWIG & FILS
CHECQUER
DIRECTOIRE
GOOD DESIGN IS FOREVER
HAMPTON
LANCASTER
LUDWIG
MADELEINE
PIEDMONTE
RESTON
ROXY
THE VINCENT
WESTCHESTER
WHITEHALL
Advertising Agency:
Chillingworth/Radding Inc.
1133 Broadway Ste 1615
New York, NY 10010
Tel.: (212) 674-4700
Fax: (212) 979-0125
(Fabric, Wallpaper, Trimming, Etc.)

BURKE INDUSTRIES, INC.

(Sub. of Mannington Mills, Inc.)
2250 S 10th St
San Jose, CA 95112-4114
Tel.: (408) 297-3500
Fax: (408) 280-0699
Toll Free: (800) 669-7010
E-mail: info@burkeindustries.com
Web Site: www.burkeind.com
Approx. Sls.: $50,000,000
Approx. Number Employees: 250
Year Founded: 1942
Business Description:
Rubber Floor Tile, Stair Treads & Custom Molded Rubber Products; Flexible Membranes for Liners & Covers; Single-Ply Roofing Systems Mfr
S.I.C.: 3996; 2821
N.A.I.C.S.: 326192; 325211
Media: 2-4-7-10-21
Distr.: Natl.
Budget Set: Oct.
Personnel:
Robert Pitman *(Pres & CEO)*
Dan Kelly *(Dir-Sls)*
Joe Walker *(Dir-Sls)*
Brands & Products:
BURKEBASE
BURKELINE ROOFING SYSTEMS
BURKEMERCER
LINEAR
MIRROR FINISH
NATURAL ILLUSIONS
ROULEAU
STEP BOND TAPE

BUSH INDUSTRIES INC.

1 Mason Dr
Jamestown, NY 14701-9265
Tel.: (716) 665-2000
Fax: (716) 665-6090
Toll Free: (800) 727-2874
E-mail: consumerservice@bushindustries.com
Web Site: www.bushfurniture.com
Approx. Number Employees: 2,750
Year Founded: 1959
Business Description:
Ready-To-Assemble Office & Home Furniture Mfr & Designer
S.I.C.: 2511; 2521

Key to Media (For complete agency information see *The Advertising Red Books-Agencies* edition):
1. Bus. Publs. 2. Cable T.V. 3. Catalogs & Directories. 4. Co-op Adv. 5. Consumer Mags. 6. D.M. to Bus. Estab.7. D.M. to Consumers 8. Daily Newsp. 9. Exhibits/Trade Shows 10. Foreign 11. Infomercial 12. Internet Adv.13. Multimedia 14. Network Radio 15. Network T.V. 16. Newsp. Distr. Mags. 17. Other 18. Outdoor (Posters, Transit) 19. Point of Purchase20. Premiums, Novelties 21. Product Samples 22. Special Events Mktg. 23. Spot Radio 24. Spot T.V. 25. Weekly Newsp. 26. Yellow Page Adv.

Bush Industries Inc. — (Continued)

N.A.I.C.S.: 337122; 337211
Import Export
Media: 2-4-10-13-16
Distr.: Intl.
Personnel:
James L. Sherbert, Jr. *(CEO)*
Jim Garde *(CFO)*
Steven Thaelan *(Exec VP-Sls & Mktg)*
Jim Schmidt *(VP-Mktg & Mdsg)*
Brands & Products:
AUBURN MAPLE
BEECH
BELIZE
BIRMINGHAM
BUSH BUSINESS FURNITURE
BUSH FURNITURE
CENTRA
CHARLESTOWN
CITIZEN
COBRA
CONFERENCE
CONTOURS
DENALI
ERIC MORGAN
FAIRVIEW
GENESIS
HALLMARK
HANSEN CHERRY
HARVEST TAN
JAGGER
JAMESTOWN
KINGSTON
LIGHT OAK
MAHOGANY
MIDNIGHT MIST
MILANO
MISSION POINTE
MOCHA CHERRY
NAT CHERRY
NATURAL CHERRY
NEWPORT COVE
NORTHFIELD
OFFICE REVOLUTION
ORION
PEWTER
PLATINUM MIST
PROPANEL
REFLECTIONS
SARATOGA EXECUTIVE
SAVANNAH COLLECTION
SEGMENTS
SLATE
SOMERSET
SONOMA
STANFORD
STONINGTON
STRATOS
TACOMA
TAUPE
TECHNO
TUXEDO
UNIVERSAL
VANTAGE
VERONA
VISIONS
WEST
WESTON

BUSINESS FURNISHINGS LLC
4102 Meghan Beeler Ct
South Bend, IN 46628-8408
Tel.: (574) 243-3255
Fax: (574) 243-3266
E-mail: info@business-furnishings.net
Web Site: www.business-furnishings.net
Approx. Number Employees: 12
Year Founded: 1996
Business Description:
Furniture Retailer
S.I.C.: 5021; 5712
N.A.I.C.S.: 423210; 442110
Import Export
Media: 4
Personnel:
Mike McGann *(Principal)*

BUSINESS INTERIORS OF SEATTLE NORTH WEST INC.
10848 E Marginal Way S
Seattle, WA 98168
Tel.: (206) 762-8818
Fax: (206) 763-4078
E-mail: info@binw.com
Web Site: www.binw.com
Sales Range: $10-24.9 Million
Approx. Number Employees: 125
Year Founded: 1982
Business Description:
Full Service Office Furniture Dealership
S.I.C.: 5712
N.A.I.C.S.: 442110
Import Export
Media: 2-4-7-8-10-13-18-25-26
Personnel:
Sean O'Brien *(Pres)*
Richard Lacher *(CEO)*
Don King *(VP-Sls)*
Cindy Chesbro *(Coord-IT & Mktg)*

BUTLER CARPET COMPANY INC.
(d/b/a Bob's Carpet Mart)
10815 US Hwy 19 N
Clearwater, FL 33764
Tel.: (727) 571-9998
Fax: (727) 571-3727
Toll Free: (800) 228-BOBS
Web Site: www.bobscarpet.com
Approx. Number Employees: 150
Year Founded: 1975
Business Description:
Carpets & Hardwood Floors
S.I.C.: 5713; 5023
N.A.I.C.S.: 442210; 423220
Media: 8-24
Personnel:
Robert H. Butler, III *(Pres)*
Advertising Agency:
Independent Floorcoverings Dealers of America, Inc.
110 Miramont Lake Dr
Woodstock, GA 30189
Tel.: (770) 592-5858
Fax: (770) 592-5508
Toll Free: (888) 261-4332

CARLISLE WIDE PLANK FLOORS, INC.
(Holding of JMH Capital)
1676 Rte 9
Stoddard, NH 03464
Tel.: (603) 283-6599
Fax: (603) 446-3540
Toll Free: (800) 595-9663
E-mail: info@wideplankflooring.com
Web Site: www.wideplankflooring.com
Sales Range: $1-9.9 Million
Approx. Number Employees: 45
Year Founded: 1966
Business Description:
Wooden Plank Flooring Mfr & Retailer
S.I.C.: 5211; 1752
N.A.I.C.S.: 444110; 238330
Media: 6-8-10-13
Personnel:
Don Carlisle *(Founder)*
Kerry Carlisle *(Owner)*
Dean Marcarelli *(Dir-Bus Dev)*
Brands & Products:
CARLISLE

CARPENTER CO.
5016 Monument Ave
Richmond, VA 23230-3620
Mailing Address:
PO Box 27205
Richmond, VA 23261-7205
Tel.: (804) 359-0800
Fax: (804) 358-9716
E-mail: contact@carpenter.com
Web Site: www.carpenter.com
Sales Range: $1-4.9 Billion
Approx. Number Employees: 5,900
Year Founded: 1948
Business Description:
Chemicals, Polyurethane & Polyester Fiber Battings, Expanded Polystyrene & Carpet Cushions Mfr
S.I.C.: 3086; 2211; 2297; 2821; 2823
N.A.I.C.S.: 326150; 313210; 313230; 325211; 325221
Import Export
Media: 2-7-10
Personnel:
Stanley F. Pauley *(CEO)*
Michael Lowery *(CFO)*
Brands & Products:
AMBIENT
CARPENTER
CARPOL
COMFORT COIL
DAISY
DREAM COIL
HYPERSOFT
ISOTONIC
OMALON
PROTECH
QUALATEX
RICHFOAM
SLEEP BETTER
SPILLGUARD
VISCOLUX
WE BRING COMFORT TO YOUR LIFE.

CARPET FAIR, INC.
(d/b/a Bill's Carpet Fair)
7100 Rutherford Rd
Baltimore, MD 21244-2702
Tel.: (410) 298-5800
Fax: (410) 298-5049
Toll Free: (800) 296-3247
E-mail: contact@billscarpetfair.com
Web Site: www.billscarpetfair.com
Approx. Number Employees: 110
Business Description:
Carpet Retailer
S.I.C.: 5713; 5023
N.A.I.C.S.: 442210; 423220
Media: 4-6-9-20-23-24-25
Distr.: Natl.
Budget Set: June
Personnel:
Rubin Schechman *(Pres)*

CC INDUSTRIES, INC.
(Sub. of Henry Crown & Company)
222 N La Salle St Ste 1000
Chicago, IL 60601
Tel.: (312) 855-4000
Fax: (312) 236-7074
Approx. Number Employees: 5,000
Year Founded: 1948
Business Description:
Holding Company; Home Furnishings, Paper Products, Outdoor & Casual Furniture; Owns, Develops & Manages Real Estate
S.I.C.: 2392; 2514
N.A.I.C.S.: 314129; 337124
Import Export
Media: 2-5-6-8-9-10-17-19-20-25-26
Distr.: Natl.
Budget Set: Nov.
Personnel:
Lester Crown *(Chm)*
William H. Crown *(Pres & CEO)*
Leonard Canino *(VP-HR)*
John Merritt *(Dir-HR)*

CENTURY FURNITURE INDUSTRIES
(Sub. of CV Industries Inc.)
401 11th St NW
Hickory, NC 28601
Mailing Address:
PO Box 608
Hickory, NC 28603-0608
Tel.: (828) 328-1851
Fax: (828) 328-2176
Toll Free: (800) 852-5552
E-mail: webcs04@centuryfurniture.com
Web Site: www.centuryfurniture.com
Sales Range: $150-199.9 Million
Approx. Number Employees: 1,500
Year Founded: 1947
Business Description:
Furniture Mfr
S.I.C.: 2512; 2511
N.A.I.C.S.: 337121; 337122
Import
Advertising Expenditures: $1,000,000
Media: 2-4-6-7-8-10-13
Distr.: Intl.; Natl.
Personnel:
Eric S. Schenk *(CEO & Pres)*
Alex Shuford, III *(VP-Sls & Mktg)*
Brands & Products:
BRITISH OPEN
THE CASA COLLECTION
CASPIAN
CENTURY
CITATION
CLARIDGE
COEUR DE FRANCE
CONSULATE
OMNI
SAVOY
SILK ROAD
SUN VALLEY
TOWN & COUNTRY
VENICE

CENTURY SUPPLY CO. INC.
747 E Roosevelt Rd
Lombard, IL 60148-4742
Tel.: (630) 873-8200
Fax: (630) 495-8645
Toll Free: (888) TILE-YOU
Web Site: www.century-tile.com
Approx. Number Employees: 250
Year Founded: 1947

Key to Media (For complete agency information see *The Advertising Red Books-Agencies* edition):
1. Bus. Publs. 2. Cable T.V. 3. Catalogs & Directories. 4. Co-op Adv. 5. Consumer Mags. 6. D.M. to Bus. Estab.7. D.M. to Consumers 8. Daily Newsp. 9. Exhibits/Trade Shows 10. Foreign 11. Infomercial 12. Internet Adv.13. Multimedia 14. Network Radio 15. Network T.V. 16. Newsp. Distr. Mags. 17. Other 18. Outdoor (Posters, Transit) 19. Point of Purchase20. Premiums, Novelties 21. Product Samples 22. Special Events Mktg. 23. Spot Radio 24. Spot T.V. 25. Weekly Newsp. 26. Yellow Page Adv.

Business Description:
Floor Covering Stores
S.I.C.: 5713; 5023
N.A.I.C.S.: 442210; 423220
Import Export
Media: 10-13-18
Personnel:
Bob Kobliska *(CFO)*
Advertising Agency:
CSA Advertising, Inc.
430 W Roosevelt Rd
Wheaton, IL 60187
Tel.: (630) 462-0919

CENTURY WINDOW FASHION INC.
213 Nesbitt Dr
Seaford, DE 19973
Tel.: (302) 990-6800
Fax: (302) 629-5674
Toll Free: (800) 819-2898
Web Site:
www.centurywindowfashion.com
Business Description:
Window Coverings Mfr & Distr
S.I.C.: 5714
N.A.I.C.S.: 442291
Media: 7-10
Personnel:
Yvonne Yip *(Pres)*

CHARLES H. BECKLEY, INC.
749 E 137th St
Bronx, NY 10454-3402
Tel.: (718) 665-2218
Fax: (718) 402-3386
E-mail: admin@chbeckley.com
Web Site: www.chbeckley.com
E-Mail For Key Personnel:
Sales Director: sales@chbeckley.com
Approx. Number Employees: 25
Year Founded: 1931
Business Description:
Custom Bedding, Daybeds, & Headboards
S.I.C.: 2515; 2511
N.A.I.C.S.: 337910; 337122
Media: 2
Distr.: Reg.
Budget Set: Jan.
Personnel:
Tim Marsky *(Dir-Mktg)*
Brands & Products:
ASHTON INNERSPRING
BRISTOL HAIR
BUNKIE BOARDS
CHB
DAYBEDS
DIVAN
DRAWER BEDS
LAMBS WOOL
PILLOW TOPS
TRUNDLE BEDS
YORK INNERSPRING

CHF INDUSTRIES, INC.
1 Park Ave
New York, NY 10016
Tel.: (212) 951-7800
Fax: (212) 951-8001
Toll Free: (800) 243-7090
E-mail: customerservice@chfindustries.com
Web Site: www.chfindustries.com
Sales Range: $100-124.9 Million
Approx. Number Employees: 1,200
Year Founded: 1927
Business Description:
Curtains, Draperies, Bedding & Bath Products
S.I.C.: 5023; 2511
N.A.I.C.S.: 423220; 337122
Import Export
Media: 2
Distr.: Natl.
Budget Set: Oct.
Personnel:
Frank M. Foley *(Pres & CEO)*
Camillo Faraone *(CFO)*
Brands & Products:
B.SMITH
CAMEO
CHF
CHF & YOU
THE GO-TO PLACE FOR THE NEXT GREAT IDEA
KIM PARKER HOME
LOFT STYLE
LYNN CHASE
MY ROOM
NICK MUNRO BATH
OCEAN PACIFIC
PERI HOMEWORKS COLLECTION

CHILD CRAFT INDUSTRIES, INC.
1010 Keller Dr
New Salisbury, IN 47161
Tel.: (812) 206-2200
Fax: (812) 206-6225
E-mail: mjscci@aol.com
Web Site:
www.childcraftindustries.com
Approx. Sls.: $40,000,000
Approx. Number Employees: 80
Year Founded: 1911
Business Description:
Mfr. of Wooden Infant Furniture
S.I.C.: 2511; 5712
N.A.I.C.S.: 337122; 442110
Import Export
Advertising Expenditures: $200,000
Media: 2-4-6-7-8-13
Distr.: Natl.
Budget Set: Apr. -May
Personnel:
William S. Suvak *(Pres)*
Mark Suvak *(CFO)*
Rhonda Geralde *(Reg Mgr-Sls)*
Brands & Products:
CHILD CRAFT
CHILD-CRAFT
LEGACY

CHITTENDEN & EASTMAN CO.
100 New Rand Rd
Sweet Springs, MO 65351-9399
Tel.: (319) 753-2811
Toll Free: (800) 553-5626
Sales Range: $25-49.9 Million
Approx. Number Employees: 80
Year Founded: 1866
Business Description:
Mfr. of Mattresses
S.I.C.: 2515
N.A.I.C.S.: 337910
Import
Media: 2-5
Distr.: Natl.
Budget Set: Monthly
Brands & Products:
AIRELOOM
CHIROPRACTOR'S CARE
EASTMAN HOUSE
ENCASED COIL INNERSPRING COLLECTION
THE RENAISSANCE LATEX FOAM COLLECTION

CHROMCRAFT CORPORATION
(Sub. of Chromcraft Revington, Inc.)
1 Quality Ln
Senatobia, MS 38668
Mailing Address:
PO Box 126
Senatobia, MS 38668-0126
Tel.: (662) 562-8203
Fax: (662) 336-1651
Web Site: www.chromcraftcorp.com
E-Mail For Key Personnel:
Sales Director: contsales@chromcraftcorp.com
Sales Range: $125-149.9 Million
Approx. Number Employees: 400
Year Founded: 1946
Business Description:
Mfr. of Casual Dining Room Furniture, Contract Seating & Office Furniture
S.I.C.: 2511; 2514
N.A.I.C.S.: 337122; 337124
Import Export
Advertising Expenditures: $800,000
Media: 2-4-6-7-8-13-15
Distr.: Intl.; Natl.
Budget Set: Nov.
Brands & Products:
EDGE
GENESIS
GUARDSMAN
PYRAMID
ULTIMA II

C.L. BARNES FURNITURE CO.
6717 B Spring Mall Rd
Springfield, VA 22150
Tel.: (703) 780-7444
Fax: (703) 997-3206
E-mail: comments@clbarnes.com
Web Site: www.barnesfurniture.com
Approx. Number Employees: 250
Year Founded: 1943
Business Description:
Furniture Retailer
S.I.C.: 5712
N.A.I.C.S.: 442110
Media: 2-6-13-25
Personnel:
Renny Barnes *(Owner & CEO)*

CLARIN
(Div. of Greenwich Industries LP)
927 N Shore Dr
Lake Bluff, IL 60044
Tel.: (847) 295-2200
Fax: (847) 234-9001
Toll Free: (800) 323-9062
E-mail: sales@clarinseating.com
Web Site: www.clarinseating.com
E-Mail For Key Personnel:
Sales Director: sales@clarinseating.com
Approx. Number Employees: 90
Year Founded: 1925
Business Description:
Folding & Stacking Chairs Mfr & Distr
S.I.C.: 2531; 3537
N.A.I.C.S.: 337127; 333924
Import Export
Advertising Expenditures: $200,000
Media: 2-4-5-7-10-21
Distr.: Intl.; Natl.
Budget Set: Mar.
Personnel:
Roger Schoenfeld *(COO)*
Brands & Products:
CLARIN CHAIRS

CLAYTON-MARCUS COMPANY, INC.
(Sub. of Rowe Furniture)
166 Teague Town Rd
Hickory, NC 28601-8579
Tel.: (828) 495-2200
Fax: (828) 495-2260
E-mail: info@claytonmarcus.com
Web Site: www.claytonmarcus.com
Approx. Number Employees: 350
Year Founded: 1960
Business Description:
Upholstered Furniture Mfr
S.I.C.: 2512
N.A.I.C.S.: 337121
Media: 2-4-5-6-10-19
Distr.: Natl.

CLEVELAND CHAIR COMPANY
(Div. of Jackson Furniture Industries)
PO Box 159
Cleveland, TN 37364
Tel.: (423) 476-8544
Fax: (423) 961-7343
Web Site: www.jackson.com
Business Description:
Reclining Chairs Mfr
S.I.C.: 2512
N.A.I.C.S.: 337121
Advertising Expenditures: $200,000
Media: 2-6-7-9-10-19
Distr.: Direct to Consumer; Natl.
Budget Set: Jan.
Personnel:
W. Ronald Jackson *(CEO)*
Keith Jackson *(SR VP-Sls & Mktg)*
Brands & Products:
CATNAPPER

CLOSETMAID CORPORATION
(Sub. of Emerson Electric Co.)
650 SW 27th Ave
Ocala, FL 34471-2034
Mailing Address:
PO Box 4400
Ocala, FL 34478-4400
Tel.: (352) 401-6000
Fax: (352) 867-8583
E-mail: info@closetmaid.com
Web Site: www.closetmaid.com
Sales Range: $550-599.9 Million
Approx. Number Employees: 1,300
Year Founded: 1965
Business Description:
Vinyl-Coated Steel Rod Shelving & Storage
S.I.C.: 3496; 2542
N.A.I.C.S.: 332618; 337215
Media: 8-10-13-18-21-22-26
Personnel:
Robert Clements *(Pres)*
Debra Charles *(VP-Fin)*
Craig Moeller *(VP-Mktg)*
Brands & Products:
CABINET MAID
CASTEEL
CLASSIC
CLOSETMAID
KEIJE
MASTERSUITE
STACK-A-SHELF

Key to Media (For complete agency information see *The Advertising Red Books-Agencies* edition):
1. Bus. Publs. 2. Cable T.V. 3. Catalogs & Directories. 4. Co-op Adv. 5. Consumer Mags. 6. D.M. to Bus. Estab.7. D.M. to Consumers 8. Daily Newsp. 9. Exhibits/Trade Shows 10. Foreign 11. Infomercial 12. Internet Adv.13. Multimedia 14. Network Radio 15. Network T.V. 16. Newsp. Distr. Mags. 17. Other 18. Outdoor (Posters, Transit) 19. Point of Purchase20. Premiums, Novelties 21. Product Samples 22. Special Events Mktg. 23. Spot Radio 24. Spot T.V. 25. Weekly Newsp. 26. Yellow Page Adv.

ClosetMaid Corporation — (Continued)

Advertising Agency:
Clarke Advertising
401 N Cattlemen Rd Ste 200
Sarasota, FL 34232-6439
Tel.: (941) 365-2710
Fax: (941) 366-4940
Toll Free: (800) 724-0289

CLOSETS BY DESIGN
11319 Grooms Rd
Cincinnati, OH 45242
Tel.: (513) 469-6130
Fax: (513) 469-7900
Web Site: closetsbysdesign.com
Year Founded: 1982
Personnel:
Glen Grosser *(Owner)*
Lynne Hakes *(Coord-Mktg)*
Advertising Agency:
Killerspots
463 Ohio Pke Ste 102
Cincinnati, OH 45255
Tel.: (800) 639-9728
Fax: (513) 672-0161
Agency of Record

COCHRANE FURNITURE CO., INC.
(Sub. of Chromcraft Revington, Inc.)
190 Cochrane Rd
Lincolnton, NC 28092-7299
Tel.: (704) 732-1151
Fax: (704) 745-2299
Telex: 704-745-2258
Web Site: www.cochrane-furniture.com
Sales Range: $10-24.9 Million
Year Founded: 1905
Business Description:
Mfr. of Bedroom, Dining Room & Upholstered Furniture
S.I.C.: 2511; 2512
N.A.I.C.S.: 337122; 337121
Media: 2-4-6-7-8-10-13
Distr.: Natl.
Personnel:
Beverly Smith *(CFO, Sec & VP)*

COLUMBIA MANUFACTURING INC.
1 Cycle St
Westfield, MA 01085-4447
Mailing Address:
PO Box 1230
Westfield, MA 01086-1230
Tel.: (413) 562-3664
Tel.: (413) 562-5140
Fax: (413) 568-5345
E-mail: custserv@columbiamfginc.com
Web Site: www.columbiamfginc.com
Approx. Number Employees: 125
Year Founded: 1992
Business Description:
Mfr. of Bicycles & School Furniture
S.I.C.: 2531; 5091
N.A.I.C.S.: 337127; 423910
Import Export
Media: 4-7-10-19
Distr.: Natl.
Budget Set: Oct. -Nov.
Personnel:
Don Bieker *(Pres)*
Brands & Products:
COLUMBIA
COMFORT
COMFORT FLEX
IMPULSE
INTRUDER
OMNIA
POWER PORT
SIERRA
SPEC-FLEK
THRUST

THE COMMERCIAL FURNITURE GROUP
(Joint Venture of Oaktree Capital Management, L.P. & Whippoorwill Associates, Inc.)
(d/b/a CFGroup)
10650 Gateway Blvd
Saint Louis, MO 63304-1102
Tel.: (314) 991-9200
Fax: (314) 991-9262
Toll Free: (800) 873-3252
Web Site: www.commercialfurnituregroup.com
Sales Range: $50-74.9 Million
Approx. Number Employees: 800
Year Founded: 1958
Business Description:
Pedestal Table Bases, Table Tops, Metal & Wood Chairs, Booths, Millwork & Casegoods, Wire Shelving Systems & other Wire Metal Kitchen Equipment Mfr
S.I.C.: 2531; 2522
N.A.I.C.S.: 337127; 337214
Import Export
Advertising Expenditures: $210,000
Media: 2-4-7-10-11
Distr.: Intl.; Natl.
Personnel:
Seamus Bateson *(CEO)*
Neal R. Restivo *(CFO & VP-Fin)*
Stephen E. Cohen *(VP-Sls & Mktg)*
Brands & Products:
CASCADE
CHARLOTTE
CITRUS
DRUM
ELISSA
EPIC
FALCON
HOWE FURNITURE
IRIS
JANE
JOHNSON TABLES
KD CONTEXT
LATTICE
MATS
METRA
MIOS
PHILLOCRAFT
PROVENANCE
SHELBY WILLIAMS
SYMPHONY
THONET
TINA
TUFF
TWIST
ZETA

CONCRETE TECHNOLOGY INCORPORATED
8770 133rd Ave
Largo, FL 33773
Tel.: (727) 535-4651
Fax: (727) 536-8273
Toll Free: (800) 447-6573
E-mail: info@flycti.com
Web Site: www.flycti.com
Sales Range: $1-9.9 Million
Approx. Number Employees: 25
Business Description:
Concrete Products
S.I.C.: 3272
N.A.I.C.S.: 327390
Media: 2-6
Personnel:
Kevin Rosenberger *(Founder & Pres)*

CONESTOGA WOOD SPECIALTIES CORP.
245 Reading Rd
East Earl, PA 17519-9549
Mailing Address:
PO Box 158
East Earl, PA 17519-0158
Tel.: (717) 445-6701
Fax: (717) 445-3409
Toll Free: (800) 964-3667
E-mail: executive@conestogawood.com
Web Site: www.conestogawood.com
E-Mail For Key Personnel:
President: AHahn@conestogawood.com
Marketing Director: jeichenseer@conestogawood.com
Sales Range: $125-149.9 Million
Approx. Number Employees: 2,000
Year Founded: 1964
Business Description:
Decorative Wood Doors, Drawers & Components for the Kitchen & Bath Industry Mfr
S.I.C.: 2431; 2521
N.A.I.C.S.: 321911; 337211
Import Export
Media: 4-7-10-11-20
Distr.: Intl.; Natl.
Personnel:
Norman Hahn *(Chm)*
Anthony Hahn *(Pres & CEO)*
Jeff Eichenseer *(Dir-Mktg)*
Brands & Products:
BARCELONA
BERKLEY
CHURCHILL
CONESTOGA
COTTAGE
COUNTRY FRENCH
CRAFTSMAN
DOUGLASS
FRANKLIN
HALF CIRCLE
HANCOCK
LAFAYETTE
LARGE COVE
MONACO
MONARCH SQ
MONROE
NORMANDIE
PIONEER
PRESIDENTIAL
PRESTIGE
PROVENCE
QUEEN ANNE
STAFFORDSHIRE
TULIP

CONGOLEUM CORPORATION
(Sub. of American Biltrite Inc.)
3500 Quaker Bridge Rd
Mercerville, NJ 08619
Mailing Address:
PO Box 3127
Mercerville, NJ 08619-0127
Tel.: (609) 584-3000
Fax: (609) 584-3522
Toll Free: (800) 234-8811
Web Site: www.congoleum.com
Approx. Sls.: $134,917,000
Approx. Number Employees: 523
Year Founded: 1886
Business Description:
Resilient Sheet Vinyl Flooring
S.I.C.: 3842; 3081; 3082; 3996; 5713
N.A.I.C.S.: 339113; 326113; 326121; 326192; 442210
Export
Advertising Expenditures: $300,000
Media: 2-4-9-20
Distr.: Natl.
Budget Set: Oct.
Personnel:
Roger S. Marcus *(Chm, Pres & CEO)*
Howard N. Feist, III *(CFO & VP-Fin)*
Dennis P. Jarosz *(Sr VP-Sls & Mktg)*
Sidharth Nayar *(Sr VP-Fin)*
John L. Russ, III *(Sr VP-Ops)*
Thomas A. Sciortino *(Sr VP-Admin)*
Doreen Trager *(Dir-Creative Svcs)*
Brands & Products:
ADVANTAGE
BRIGHTLIFE
CAREFREE
CONCEPT
DESIGNER CAREFREE
DESIGNER INLAID
DURACERAMIC
DURASTONE
DURASTONE CLASSIC
DURASTONE HPF
EVOLUTION
FLOR-EVER
FORUM PLANK
FORUM SOLIDS
HIGHLIGHT
INTRIGUE
MAJESTIC
PACESETTER
PRELUDE
REFLECTION
REGAL PLANK
ROOMVISION
SPECIAL EFFECTS
ULTIMA
UTOPIA
VALUFLOR
Advertising Agency:
Red Flannel
218 Schanck Rd 2nd Fl
Freehold, NJ 07728
Tel.: (732) 761-8998
Fax: (732) 761-9424
Creative

CONKLIN BROS
2250 Almaden Expy
San Jose, CA 95125
Tel.: (408) 266-2250
Fax: (408) 266-0151
Toll Free: (800) 750-2250
Web Site: www.conklinbrothers.com
Approx. Number Employees: 45
Year Founded: 1880
Business Description:
Floor Coverings & Carpet Distr
S.I.C.: 5713
N.A.I.C.S.: 442210
Media: 26
Personnel:
Rick Oderio *(Pres & CEO)*
Barbara Zibell *(CFO)*
Robin Morales *(Mgr-Fin)*

Key to Media (For complete agency information see *The Advertising Red Books-Agencies* edition):
1. Bus. Publs. 2. Cable T.V. 3. Catalogs & Directories. 4. Co-op Adv. 5. Consumer Mags. 6. D.M. to Bus. Estab.7. D.M. to Consumers 8. Daily Newsp. 9. Exhibits/Trade Shows 10. Foreign 11. Infomercial 12. Internet Adv.13. Multimedia 14. Network Radio 15. Network T.V. 16. Newsp. Distr. Mags. 17. Other 18. Outdoor (Posters, Transit) 19. Point of Purchase20. Premiums, Novelties 21. Product Samples 22. Special Events Mktg. 23. Spot Radio 24. Spot T.V. 25. Weekly Newsp. 26. Yellow Page Adv.

Brands & Products:
ABBEY CARPETS
CONKLIN BROS

CORT BUSINESS SERVICES CORPORATION
(Sub. of Wesco Financial Corporation)
11250 Waples Mill Rd Ste 500
Fairfax, VA 22030
Tel.: (703) 968-8500
Fax: (703) 968-8502
Fax: (703) 968-8503
Toll Free: (800) 962CORT
Toll Free: (800) 669CORT
E-mail: cs@cort.net
Web Site: www.cort.com
E-Mail For Key Personnel:
Sales Director: sales@cort.net
Approx. Rev.: $396,169,984
Approx. Number Employees: 2,450
Year Founded: 1972
Business Description:
Relocation Services & Home & Office Furniture Rental & Leasing
S.I.C.: 7359; 2741
N.A.I.C.S.: 532299; 516110; 532310
Media: 4-10-13
Personnel:
Paul N. Arnold *(Pres & CEO)*
Hal Hardy *(VP-Mktg)*
Advertising Agency:
YP Assistants
173 Chestnut Ridge Rd
Bethel, CT 06801
Tel.: (203) 748-8198

COST PLUS, INC.
200 4th St
Oakland, CA 94607-4312
Tel.: (510) 893-7300
Fax: (510) 893-3681
Toll Free: (877) 967-5362
Web Site:
www.costplusworldmarket.com
Approx. Sls.: $916,564,000
Approx. Number Employees: 1,951
Year Founded: 1958
Business Description:
Retailer of Casual Home Decorating & Entertaining Products
S.I.C.: 5021; 5712; 5713
N.A.I.C.S.: 423210; 442110; 442210
Import
Advertising Expenditures: $49,500,000
Media: 1-3-8-9-10-16-18-23-24-25
Distr.: Natl.
Personnel:
Barry J. Feld *(CEO & Pres)*
Jeffrey A. Turner *(CIO & Exec VP-Ops)*
Joan S. Fujii *(Exec VP-HR)*
Laura Sites-Reynolds *(Sr VP-Inventory Mgmt)*
Matt Gee *(VP & Gen Mgr)*
Cliff A. March *(VP-IT)*
Advertising Agency:
Formula PR
810 Parkview Dr N
El Segundo, CA 90245
Tel.: (310) 578-7050
Fax: (310) 578-7077

COUNTRY CURTAINS RETAIL INC.
(Sub. of Fitzpatrick Companies Inc.)
705 Pleasant St
Lee, MA 01238
Mailing Address:
PO Box 955
Stockbridge, MA 01262
Tel.: (413) 243-1474
Fax: (413) 243-1067
Toll Free: (800) 937-1237
Web Site: www.countrycurtains.com
Approx. Rev.: $7,400,000
Approx. Number Employees: 185
Business Description:
Drapery & Upholstery Stores
S.I.C.: 5719; 2299
N.A.I.C.S.: 442299; 313312
Media: 4-6-8-10-13
Personnel:
John Fitzpatrick *(Founder)*

COUNTRY ROAD ASSOCIATES, LTD.
63 Frnt St
Millbrook, NY 12545
Tel.: (845) 677-6041
Fax: (845) 677-6532
E-mail: info@countryroadassociates.com
Web Site:
www.countryroadassociates.com
Sales Range: Less than $1 Million
Approx. Number Employees: 2
Business Description:
Antique Flooring & Furniture Mfr
S.I.C.: 5712
N.A.I.C.S.: 442110
Media: 6
Personnel:
Dave Dunning *(Owner)*

COURISTAN INC.
2 Executive Dr Ste 400
Fort Lee, NJ 07024-3308
Tel.: (201) 585-8500
Fax: (201) 585-8552
Toll Free: (800) 223-6186
E-mail: info@couristan.com
Web Site: www.couristan.com
Sales Range: $50-74.9 Million
Approx. Number Employees: 200
Year Founded: 1926
Business Description:
Oriental Design Rugs & Fine Broadloom Mfr & Importer
S.I.C.: 2273; 5023
N.A.I.C.S.: 314110; 423220
Import
Advertising Expenditures: $300,000
D.M. to Consumers: $150,000;
Exhibits/Trade Shows: $150,000
Distr.: Natl.
Budget Set: May-Oct.
Personnel:
Ronald J. Couri *(Pres & CEO)*
Steve Codella *(Sr VP-Sls)*
Larry Mahurter *(VP-Mktg & Adv)*
Brands & Products:
ACCENTS
ALAMGIR
ALLURE
ANDROS
ANTIGUA
APOLLO
ARUBA
AUTUMN LEAF
BALMORAL
BALMORAL COLORS
BARBADOS
BARCELONA
BEAUFORT
BELLACERE
BRAVADA
BURBER/CORD
BURBER/KNIT
CABANA
CABO STRIPE
CALCUTTA
CANTERBURY
CARESS
CAREZZA
CENTAURI
CHATEAU DE BALLEROY
CHINESE SPLENDOUR
CHOBI
CLASSICS
CO-ORDINATES
COCO BEACH
CONFETTI
CORFU
CORSICA
COUNTRY ACCENTS
COURISTAN
EL DORADO
ELBA
EMERALD
ENCHANTED GARDEN
ESSENCE
ESTATES
EVEREST
FERNWOOD
FESTIVA
FINESSE
FLORAL MAJESTIC
FLORETTE
FONTENAY
GARDEN BOUQUET
GEM
GOLD COAST
GRANDEURA
HAMPTON PLAID
HARMONY
HERITAGE
HIGHLAND
HIMALAYA
IBIZA
ILLUSIONS
IMPERIAL VELOUR
INDO-NATURAL
INDO-PERSIAN
INTERLOCKEN
INTERPRETATIONS
IZMIR
KABLE
KALAHARI
KASHIMAR
KATHMANDU
KENSINGTON
KENWICK GARDENS
KNOB HILL
LA JOLLA
LABYRINTH
LAHORE
LARENSTAN
LAVAR
LE JARDIN
LEGACY
LIVING THE LIFE LOVING MY COURISTAN
LUXURIA
MAJORCA
MANHATTAN CLASSICS
MARCO ISLAND
MASTERPIECE
METROPOLIS
MIRADA
MIRAGE
MONTEREY
MYCONOS
MYSTIQUE
NANTUCKET
NATURAL ELEGANCE
NATURESQUE
NEW JAMESTOWN
NEW KASHIMAR
NEWPORT
NORTHERN LIGHTS
NOUVEAU
OASIS
ORISSA
PALM BEACH
PALM SPRINGS
PALMYRA
PALOMAR
PAPYRUS
PARADISE
PARALLEX
PASTILLE FRIEZE
PATRA
PELICAN BAY
PETIT-POINT CLASSICS
PHOENICIAN
PHOENICIAN COLORS
PLANTATION
POKHARA
PORTOFINO
PRESTIGE
PROGRESSIONS
QUINTESSENCE
RECIFE
RHINEBECK
RHODOS
RIO
ROCOCO
ROSE MEDLEY
ROYAL CORD
ROYAL DAMASK
ROYAL FRIEZE
ROYAL IMPERIAL
ROYAL KASHIMAR
ROYAL OPERA
ROYAL SUEDE II
ROYALAX
RUBY
SAFARI
SAMOS
SANTA FE
SANTORINI
SAPPHIRE
SARDINIA
SCALA
SERENADE
SERENGETI
SEVILLE
SHAHISTAN
SHERPA
SHIRAZ
SILKEN TREASURES
SIMPLICITY
SISAL WOOL
SOHO
SONOMA
SORRENTO
SOUTH BEACH
SPECTRA POINT
SPLASH
STARDUST
STRATFORD
SULTAN
SUMMA-SINO
SUPER INDO-COLORS
SUPER INDO-NATURAL
SUPER NATURAL
TAJ MAHAL
TAMERLANE
TAORMINA

Key to Media (For complete agency information see *The Advertising Red Books-Agencies* edition):
1. Bus. Publs. 2. Cable T.V. 3. Catalogs & Directories. 4. Co-op Adv. 5. Consumer Mags. 6. D.M. to Bus. Estab.7. D.M. to Consumers
8. Daily Newsp. 9. Exhibits/Trade Shows 10. Foreign 11. Infomercial 12. Internet Adv.13. Multimedia 14. Network Radio
15. Network T.V. 16. Newsp. Distr. Mags. 17. Other 18. Outdoor (Posters, Transit) 19. Point of Purchase20. Premiums, Novelties
21. Product Samples 22. Special Events Mktg. 23. Spot Radio 24. Spot T.V. 25. Weekly Newsp. 26. Yellow Page Adv.

Couristan Inc. — (Continued)

TIBET
TIBURON
TOLEDO
TOPAZ
TRADITIONAL CLASSICS
TUSCANY
ULTRA BOUCLE
ULTRAESSENCE
UMBRIA
VALENCIA
VARANASI
VERONA
VICTORIA
VISIONS
VOGUE
WILD ASIA
WOOL SQUARES
WOOL TONES

CRAFTMATIC INDUSTRIES, INC.
2500 Interplex Dr
Trevose, PA 19053-6943
Tel.: (215) 639-1310
Fax: (215) 639-9941
E-mail: info@craftmatic.com
Web Site: www.craftmatic.com
Approx. Number Employees: 250
Business Description:
Adjustable Beds Mfr
S.I.C.: 5712; 5021
N.A.I.C.S.: 442110; 423210
Media: 3-4-5-6-8-9-11-12-13-15-23-24-25
Distr.: Direct to Consumer; Intl.; Natl.
Budget Set: Monthly
Personnel:
Stanley A. Kraftsow *(Chm & Pres)*
Brands & Products:
CRAFTMATIC

CRATE & BARREL HOLDINGS, INC.
(Sub. of Otto GmbH & Co KG)
1250 Techny Rd
Northbrook, IL 60062
Tel.: (847) 272-2888
Web Site: www.crateandbarrel.com
Approx. Number Employees: 5,800
Year Founded: 1962
Business Description:
Catalog & Store Home Merchandise Retailer
S.I.C.: 5719; 5961
N.A.I.C.S.: 442299; 454111; 454113
Personnel:
Barbara A. Turf *(Pres & CEO)*
John Seebeck *(Sr Dir-Mktg)*
Advertising Agency:
Bluedot Communications
2174 NW Aspen Ave
Portland, OR 97210
Tel.: (503) 702-6811

CREATIVE BRANCH
7246 Wynnwood Ln
Houston, TX 77008
Tel.: (713) 861-5551
Fax: (713) 861-3311
Toll Free: (877) 396-1842
E-mail: info@creativebranch.com
Web Site: www.creativebranch.com
Sales Range: Less than $1 Million
Approx. Number Employees: 14
Business Description:
Silk Floral, Tree, Greenery & Christmas Designs Mfr
S.I.C.: 7389
N.A.I.C.S.: 541490
Media: 4
Personnel:
Blaine Stacy *(Co-Owner & Mgr-Production)*
Melinda Conley *(Artistic Dir)*

CROWN CRAFTS INFANT PRODUCTS, INC.
(Sub. of Crown Crafts, Inc.)
711 W Walnut St
Compton, CA 90220
Tel.: (562) 295-1999
Telex: 362 882
Web Site:
www.crowncraftsinfantproducts.com
Sales Range: $25-49.9 Million
Approx. Number Employees: 75
Year Founded: 1970
Business Description:
Infant Bedding & Accessories Mfr
S.I.C.: 2211; 2299; 2339; 2389; 2392; 2393; 2512; 2515; 3991
N.A.I.C.S.: 313210; 314129; 314911; 314999; 315212; 315999; 337121; 337910; 339994
Import Export
Media: 4-6-10-20
Distr.: Natl.
Personnel:
Nanci Freeman *(Pres & CEO)*
Susan Christensen *(VP-Sls)*
Brands & Products:
BABYSLING
NOJO
PILLOW BUDDIES

DECKER ROSS INTERIORS, INC.
1445 Ct St
Clearwater, FL 33756
Tel.: (727) 442-9996
Fax: (727) 442-1935
E-mail: info@deckerross.com
Web Site: www.deckerross.com
Sales Range: $10-24.9 Million
Approx. Number Employees: 10
Business Description:
Interior Designer Services
S.I.C.: 7389
N.A.I.C.S.: 541410
Media: 6
Personnel:
Suzan Decker Ross *(Owner & Pres)*

DESIGN OPTIONS
5202 Eagle Trl Dr
Tampa, FL 33634-1295
Mailing Address:
PO Box 151777
Tampa, FL 33684-1777
Tel.: (813) 885-4950
Fax: (813) 885-2994
Toll Free: (800) 877-3560
Web Site: www.designoptions.com
E-Mail For Key Personnel:
President: jmesserman@designoptions.com
Sales Director: tbursh@designoptions.com
Approx. Number Employees: 100
Year Founded: 1981
Business Description:
Office Furniture Mfr
S.I.C.: 2521; 2522
N.A.I.C.S.: 337211; 337214
Media: 4-7-8-10-22
Distr.: Natl.
Personnel:
Pat Verble *(Pres-Ops)*
Brands & Products:
DESIGN OPTIONS
FREEDOM FOR YOUR ENVIRONMENT

DESIGN WITHIN REACH, INC.
(Sub. of JH Partners LLC)
225 Bush St 20th Fl
San Francisco, CA 94104
Tel.: (415) 676-6500
Fax: (415) 676-6871
Toll Free: (800) 944-2233
Web Site: www.dwr.com
Approx. Sls.:
Approx. Number Employees: 423
Year Founded: 1998
Business Description:
European-Style Home Furnishings Distr
S.I.C.: 7389; 1799; 5021
N.A.I.C.S.: 541410; 238390; 423210
Advertising Expenditures: $12,000,000
Media: 4-5-8
Personnel:
Glenn J. Krevlin *(Chm)*
John Edelman *(Pres & CEO)*
Theodore R. Upland, III *(CFO & VP)*
John McPhee *(COO)*
Vincent Barriero *(CIO)*
Sandra Hansel *(VP-Sls)*
Michael Sainato *(VP-Creative & Mktg)*
Kari Woldum *(VP-Mdsg)*

DIAL A MATTRESS USA
31-10 48th Ave
Long Island City, NY 11101-3035
Tel.: (718) 472-1200
Fax: (718) 472-1310
Toll Free: (800) MATTRESS
Web Site: www.mattress.com
Approx. Number Employees: 300
Year Founded: 1976
Business Description:
Mattress Delivery Service
S.I.C.: 2515
N.A.I.C.S.: 337910
Export
Advertising Expenditures: $6,150,000
Media: 23-24
Distr.: Natl.; Reg.
Personnel:
Napoleon Barragan *(Founder & CEO)*
Joseph Vicens *(Exec VP & Gen Mgr)*
Tom Pirrone *(Dir-Adv)*
Brands & Products:
1-800-MATTRESS
DIAL A MATTRESS
MATTRESS.COM

DIRECTIONAL FURNITURE
(Div. of Tomlinson/Erwin-Lambeth, Inc.)
201 E Hollyhill Rd
Thomasville, NC 27360
Tel.: (336) 472-5005
Fax: (336) 476-8745
Approx. Number Employees: 80
Business Description:
Furniture Mfr
S.I.C.: 2512
N.A.I.C.S.: 337121
Advertising Expenditures: $200,000
Media: 2-4-9-25
Distr.: Natl.
Personnel:
Tom Powell *(Pres)*
Richard Lambeth *(Mgr-Mfg)*

DMI FURNITURE, INC.
(Sub. of Flexsteel Industries, Inc.)
1 Oxmoor Pl 101 Bullitt Ln Ste 205
Louisville, KY 40222
Tel.: (502) 426-4351
Fax: (502) 429-6285
Web Site: www.dmifurniture.com
E-Mail For Key Personnel:
President: ddreher@dmifurniture.com
Marketing Director: dkunz@dmifurniture.com
Sales Director: sales@dmifurniture.com
Sales Range: $75-99.9 Million
Approx. Number Employees: 240
Year Founded: 1911
Business Description:
Bedroom Furniture, Residential Desks & Office Furniture Mfr & Importer
S.I.C.: 2511; 5021
N.A.I.C.S.: 337122; 423210
Import Export
Media: 2-4-7-10-19
Distr.: Natl.
Budget Set: Nov.
Personnel:
Donald D. Dreher *(Pres, CEO & Sr VP)*
Marc Abrams *(VP-Sls)*
Tracy Long *(Dir-Customer Svc)*
Karen L. Moore *(Mgr-Adv)*
Brands & Products:
CAROLINA DESK COMPANY
DMI OFFICE FURNITURE
HOMESTYLES
WYNWOOD

DOLLY INC.
320 N 4th St
Tipp City, OH 45371-1803
Tel.: (937) 667-5711
Fax: (937) 667-5328
Web Site: www.dolly.com
Approx. Number Employees: 100
Year Founded: 1923
Business Description:
Wall Decor, Nursery Lamps, Mobiles & Diaper Bags Mfr
S.I.C.: 3944; 2393
N.A.I.C.S.: 339932; 314911
Import Export
Media: 10
Distr.: Intl.; Natl.
Budget Set: Oct.
Personnel:
Dennis J. Sullivan *(Pres & CEO)*
Brands & Products:
DOLLY

DOOR GALLERY MFG. INC.
545 N Midland Ave
Saddle Brook, NJ 07663
Tel.: (201) 794-9050
Fax: (201) 794-1607
Web Site: www.doorgallery.com
Approx. Sls.: $4,000,000
Business Description:
Steel Doors & Window Products Mfr & Sales
S.I.C.: 3442; 5211

Key to Media (For complete agency information see *The Advertising Red Books-Agencies* edition):
1. Bus. Publs. 2. Cable T.V. 3. Catalogs & Directories. 4. Co-op Adv. 5. Consumer Mags. 6. D.M. to Bus. Estab.7. D.M. to Consumers 8. Daily Newsp. 9. Exhibits/Trade Shows 10. Foreign 11. Infomercial 12. Internet Adv.13. Multimedia 14. Network Radio 15. Network T.V. 16. Newsp. Distr. Mags. 17. Other 18. Outdoor (Posters, Transit) 19. Point of Purchase20. Premiums, Novelties 21. Product Samples 22. Special Events Mktg. 23. Spot Radio 24. Spot T.V. 25. Weekly Newsp. 26. Yellow Page Adv.

N.A.I.C.S.: 332321; 444110
Media: 3-8-13-26
Personnel:
Andreas Parneros *(Pres)*

DOREL JUVENILE GROUP, INC.

(Sub. of Dorel Industries, Inc.)
2525 State St
Columbus, IN 47201-7443
Tel.: (812) 372-0141
Fax: (812) 372-2154
Fax: (800) 207-8182
Toll Free: (800) 544-1108
Web Site: www.djgusa.com
Approx. Number Employees: 1,100
Year Founded: 1935
Business Description:
Step Stools, Bars, Counter Stools, Carts, Baby Products & Baby Furniture Mfr
S.I.C.: 3089; 3069
N.A.I.C.S.: 326199; 326299
Import Export
Media: 1-2-4-6-7-8-10-19-20
Distr.: Intl.; Natl.
Budget Set: Nov.
Personnel:
Dave Taylor *(Pres & CEO)*
Hani Basile *(Pres-Juvenile Grp)*
Ted Kelley *(Exec VP-Sls & Gen Mgr)*
Richard Glover *(VP-Product Dev)*
Brands & Products:
ALPHA OMEGA
AUTO TRAC
BIG STEP
BOTTOMS UP
COMFORT RIDE
CONTURA
COSCO
DREAM RIDE
EASY REACH STEP STOOL
EXPLORER
GRANDE ENDEVOR
MUSICAL TOILETTE PLUS
OLYMPIAN
OPTIONS 5
QUICK CHANGE
SCRAMPER
TECH STEP
TLC
TOILETTE
TOILETTE PLUS
TRAVEL VEST
TRIAD
TWO STEP
VANGUARD
WORLD GREATEST STEP STOOL & LADDER
Advertising Agencies:
Dorel Juvenile Group/Cosco
2525 State St
Columbus, IN 47201-7443
Tel.: (812) 372-0141
Fax: (812) 372-2154
(Juvenile Products & Furniture; Home Furnishings; Hotel, Restaurant & Medical Products Distribution)

Duffy & Shanley, Inc.
10 Charles St
Providence, RI 02904
Tel.: (401) 274-0001
Fax: (401) 274-3535
Quinny
— Annette Maggiacomo *(Dir-Pub Rel)*

DRAGONFLY GARDEN

730 Broadway Ste 7
Dunedin, FL 34689
Tel.: (727) 734-4900
E-mail: admin@dragonflygardendecor.com
Web Site: www.dragonflygardendecor.com
Business Description:
Garden Decor Services
S.I.C.: 5261
N.A.I.C.S.: 444220
Media: 6-9-13-25-29
Personnel:
Ellen Schwanebeck *(Owner)*

DREAM POLISHERS, INC.

2701 Ivy St
Englewood, FL 34224
Tel.: (941) 473-4180
Fax: (941) 475-5308
Toll Free: (866) 385-9663
E-mail: info@dreampolishers.com
Web Site: www.dreampolishers.com
Sales Range: Less than $1 Million
Approx. Number Employees: 4
Business Description:
Furniture & Cabinet Repair, Restoration & Refurnishing
S.I.C.: 7641
N.A.I.C.S.: 811420
Media: 6-25-26
Personnel:
LaDonna Haywood *(Pres & Mng Partner)*
Troy Parker *(Mgr-Shop)*

DREXEL HERITAGE FURNISHINGS INC.

(Sub. of Furniture Brands International, Inc.)
401 E Main St
Thomasville, NC 27360
Tel.: (336) 313-4599
Fax: (336) 888-4815
Toll Free: (866) 450-3434
Web Site: www.drexelheritage.com
Sales Range: $400-449.9 Million
Approx. Number Employees: 1,600
Year Founded: 1903
Business Description:
Furniture Mfr
S.I.C.: 2512
N.A.I.C.S.: 337121
Import Export
Media: 4-6-7-8-19
Distr.: Natl.
Budget Set: Nov.
Brands & Products:
DH
DREXEL
DREXEL HERITAGE
DREXEL STUDIO
HERITAGE
LILLIAN AUGUST

DURA UNDERCUSHIONS LTD.

8525 Delmeade Road
Montreal, QC H4T 1M1, Canada
Tel.: (514) 737-6561
Fax: (514) 342-7940
Toll Free: (800) 295-4126
E-mail: info@dura-undercushions.com
Web Site: www.duracushion.com
Sales Range: $10-24.9 Million
Approx. Number Employees: 30
Year Founded: 1957
Business Description:
Carpet Cushion Underpadding Mfr
S.I.C.: 2211; 2241; 2281; 2284; 2299; 2389; 2393; 3069; 3842; 3949
N.A.I.C.S.: 313210; 313111; 313113; 313221; 313312; 314911; 314999; 315299; 315999; 326299; 339113; 339920
Import Export
Media: 2-6-26
Distr.: Natl.
Budget Set: July
Personnel:
Michael N. Wilson *(Pres)*
Yves Boudreau *(Gen Mgr)*
Brands & Products:
DURA-SON 3.5 MM
DURA UNDERCUSHIONS
DURACOUSTIC
DURACUSHION
DURALUX
MONOSLAB
PROTECTOR
SUPER DURA

EDELMAN LEATHER, LLC

(Sub. of Knoll, Inc.)
80 Pickett District Rd
New Milford, CT 06776
Tel.: (860) 350-9600
Fax: (860) 350-3231
Toll Free: (800) 886-TEDY
E-mail: info@edelmanleather.com
Web Site: www.edelmanleather.com
Sales Range: $10-24.9 Million
Approx. Number Employees: 36
Business Description:
Leather & Leather Furniture Mfr
S.I.C.: 3111; 3199
N.A.I.C.S.: 316110; 316999
Media: 6-10
Personnel:
Arthur Edelman *(Pres & CEO)*
Echo MacKinzie *(Dir-Mktg)*

EINSTEIN MOOMJY INC.

265 Rt 10 E
Whippany, NJ 07981
Tel.: (973) 575-0895
Fax: (973) 887-1260
Toll Free: (800) 916-1101
E-mail: info@einsteinmoomjy.com
Web Site: www.einsteinmoomjy.com
Sales Range: $10-24.9 Million
Approx. Number Employees: 35
Year Founded: 1955
Business Description:
Retailer of Furniture, Carpets & Other Floor Coverings
S.I.C.: 5713; 5712
N.A.I.C.S.: 442210; 442110
Import
Advertising Expenditures: $2,500,000
Media: 3-5-6-9-12-16
Distr.: Direct to Consumer
Budget Set: July
Personnel:
Andrea Moomjy *(Owner)*
Walter Moomjy *(Chm & Pres)*
Jim Allen *(Dir-Mktg)*
Brands & Products:
ANTIQUE LEGENDS
PERSIAN RENAISSANCE

EKORNES INC.

(Sub. of Ekornes ASA)
615 Pierce St
Somerset, NJ 08873
Tel.: (732) 302-0097
Fax: (732) 868-5412
Web Site: www.ekornes.com/us/about_ekornes/contact_information/
Approx. Number Employees: 44
Business Description:
Nonupholstered Wood Household Furniture Mfr
S.I.C.: 2511
N.A.I.C.S.: 337122
Personnel:
Peter Bjerregaard *(Pres)*
Runar Haugen *(Grp Dir-Mktg)*
John Kane *(Mgr-HR)*
Advertising Agency:
Lennon & Associates
734 N Highland Ave
Los Angeles, CA 90038
Tel.: (323) 465-5104
Fax: (323) 463-6463

EL DORADO FURNITURE CORP.

4200 NW 167th St
Opa Locka, FL 33054
Tel.: (305) 624-9700
Fax: (305) 430-9678
Web Site: www.eldoradofurniture.com
Sales Range: $400-449.9 Million
Approx. Number Employees: 800
Year Founded: 1967
Business Description:
Owner & Operator of Furniture Stores
S.I.C.: 5712
N.A.I.C.S.: 442110
Media: 3-4-8-13-19-23-24
Personnel:
Pedro Capo *(COO)*
Roberto Capo *(VP-Mktg)*
Ivan Trabal *(VP-Fin)*
Luis E. Capo *(Mgr-Visual Display)*

ELDRED WHEELER COMPANY INC.

15 Columbia Rd
Pembroke, MA 02359
Tel.: (781) 826-5700
Toll Free: (800) 779-5310
E-mail: contact@eldredwheeler.com
Web Site: www.eldredwheeler.com
Approx. Number Employees: 50
Business Description:
18th Century American Furniture Mfr & Designer
S.I.C.: 2511; 2512
N.A.I.C.S.: 337122; 337121
Media: 4-6-8-13
Personnel:
David McCaschy *(CEO)*

ELMEN ENTERPRISES

2901 W 11th St
Sioux Falls, SD 57104-2538
Tel.: (605) 338-1800
Fax: (605) 338-9511
Web Site: www.af-rentall.com
Sales Range: $450-499.9 Million
Approx. Number Employees: 250
Year Founded: 1999
Business Description:
Furniture & Appliance Reseller
S.I.C.: 5712
N.A.I.C.S.: 442110
Media: 8-10
Personnel:
Robert C. Elmen *(Pres)*

Key to Media (For complete agency information see *The Advertising Red Books-Agencies* edition):
1. Bus. Publs. 2. Cable T.V. 3. Catalogs & Directories. 4. Co-op Adv. 5. Consumer Mags. 6. D.M. to Bus. Estab.7. D.M. to Consumers
8. Daily Newsp. 9. Exhibits/Trade Shows 10. Foreign 11. Infomercial 12. Internet Adv.13. Multimedia 14. Network Radio
15. Network T.V. 16. Newsp. Distr. Mags. 17. Other 18. Outdoor (Posters, Transit) 19. Point of Purchase20. Premiums, Novelties
21. Product Samples 22. Special Events Mktg. 23. Spot Radio 24. Spot T.V. 25. Weekly Newsp. 26. Yellow Page Adv.

EMPIRE TODAY, LLC
333 NW Ave
Northlake, IL 60164
Tel.: (773) 588-2300
Fax: (847) 675-3181
Web Site: www.empiretoday.com
Sales Range: $25-49.9 Million
Approx. Number Employees: 300
Business Description:
Floor Covering & Window Treatment
S.I.C.: 5713
N.A.I.C.S.: 442210
Media: 8-23-24
Personnel:
Kim Mazdore *(Dir-Media)*
Andrea Lopez *(Dir-Media)*
Brands & Products:
800-588-2300
EMPIRE TODAY

THE ENKEBOLL COMPANY
(d/b/a Enkeboll Designs)
16506 Avalon Blvd
Carson, CA 90746-1096
Tel.: (310) 532-1400
Fax: (310) 532-2042
Toll Free: (800) 745-5507
E-mail: sales@enkeboll.com
Web Site: www.enkeboll.com
E-Mail For Key Personnel:
Sales Director: sales@enkeboll.com
Approx. Number Employees: 107
Year Founded: 1956
Business Description:
Architectural Accents Mfr
S.I.C.: 2541; 3446; 8712
N.A.I.C.S.: 337212; 332323; 541310
Media: 4-6
Personnel:
Steven Dickey *(Pres & COO)*
Kathleen Behun *(Mgr-Sls & Mktg)*

EROOMSYSTEM TECHNOLOGIES, INC.
1072 Madison Ave
Lakewood, NJ 08701
Tel.: (732) 730-0116
Fax: (732) 810-0380
E-mail: investorrelations@eroomsystem.com
Web Site: www.eroomsystem.com
Approx. Rev.: $1,135,719
Approx. Number Employees: 3
Business Description:
Develops In Room Computer Platform & Communications Networks For The Lodging Industry
S.I.C.: 2514; 3577; 3579; 7378
N.A.I.C.S.: 337124; 333313; 334119; 811212
Media: 10-22
Personnel:
David A. Gestetner *(Chm, Pres & CEO)*
Brands & Products:
EROOM SYSTEM
EROOMAINTENANCE
EROOMCASH ADVANCE
EROOMDATA
EROOMENERGY
EROOMPERSONNEL
EROOMSAFE
EROOMSERV
EROOMSYSTEM

E.S. KLUFT & CO.
(Sub. of Chittenden & Eastman Co.)
(d/b/a Aireloom Bedding Co.)
11096 Jersey Blvd Ste 101
Rancho Cucamonga, CA 91730
Tel.: (909) 373-4211
Fax: (909) 937-4212
Web Site: www.aireloom.com
Approx. Number Employees: 17
Year Founded: 1951
Business Description:
Mfr. of Mattresses & Box Springs
S.I.C.: 5712
N.A.I.C.S.: 442110
Advertising Expenditures: $375,000
Media: 2-5-6-7-9-10-13-23-25
Distr.: Reg.
Budget Set: Oct.
Brands & Products:
DESIGNERS CHOICE
KLUFT ROYAL STANDARD
RIP VAN WINKLE
SUPER FEATHERBED
VITAGENIC

ETHAN ALLEN INTERIORS, INC.
Ethan Allen Dr
Danbury, CT 06811
Mailing Address:
PO Box 1966
Danbury, CT 06813-1966
Tel.: (203) 743-8000
Fax: (203) 743-8298
E-mail: plupton@ethanallen.com
Web Site: www.ethanallen.com
Approx. Sls.: $678,960,000
Approx. Number Employees: 4,700
Year Founded: 1932
Business Description:
Holding Company; Fine Furniture, Manufacturing & Retailing Home Furnishings, Vertically Integrated Manufacturer & Retailer
S.I.C.: 2511; 2512
N.A.I.C.S.: 337122; 337121
Import Export
Advertising Expenditures: $20,800,000
Media: 3-4-5-6-8-9-13-14-15-23-24
Distr.: Intl.; Natl.
Budget Set: Mar.
Personnel:
M. Farooq Kathwari *(Chm, Pres & CEO)*
Pamela A. Banks *(Gen Counsel, Sec & VP)*
David R. Callen *(VP-Fin & Treas)*
Corey Whitely *(Exec VP-Ops)*
Vicent T. Nirgo *(VP & Creative Dir-Adv)*
Bridget Depasquale *(VP-Comm & Asst Sec)*
Tracy Paccione *(VP-Mdsg)*
Craig W. Stout *(VP-Prod Dev Case Goods Mfg)*
Lynda W. Stout *(VP-Retail Div)*
Jack Moll *(Gen Mgr-Physical Distr)*
Henry Kapteina *(Dir-Internal Audit)*
Brands & Products:
ADAM
ADISON
ALBERT
AMELIA
AMRITZAR
ANNA
ANTON
ASHTON
ASTOR
AUBUSSON
AUGUSTINE
AVA
AVANTI
AVERY
BALTA
BALUSTRADE
BANJO
BARLEY
BARRISTER
BATIK
BEAUFORD
BEIGE SHANGRILA
BELFIORE
BELIZE
BELLA
BENNETT
BENTLEY
BERMUDA
BERWICK
BISTRO
BOTANICAL
BOUILLOTTE
BRITISH CLASSICS
BROKEN LINE
CALMADY
CAMBRIDGE
CAMEO
CAMERON
CAMILLA
CANYON
CAPITAL
CARA
CASSATT
CATALINA
CENTINALE
CETONIA
CHAMOIS
CHANCELLOR
CHANDLER
CHELSEA
CHINOISERIE
CHIPPENDALE
CINNABAR
CLAIRMONT
CLARKE
CLAUDETTE
COCO
COLETTE
COLLECTORS CLASSICS
COLLIN
COLUMN
CONOR
CONTEMPO
CORBETT
COUNTRY BRIAD
COUNTRY FRENCH
CRANBERRY NEWPORT
CRANE
CREWEL
CRISTAL
CROMWELL
DAFFODIL
DANIELA
DAWSON
DEMILUNE
DEVONSHIRE
DISTANT HORIZONS
DOMINIQUE
DRAKE
DUET
ECHO
ECRU
ELEPHANT
EMMA
ENGLISH
ESSEX
ETHAN ALLEN
EVETTE
FAIRFAX
FAUX TIN
FELICIA
FILM
FIONA
FLORENCE
FLORENTINE
FRANCESCA
FRANKLIN
GAZEBO
GILES
HALEY
HAMPSHIRE
HAMPTON
HARRIS
HARTWELL
HEPBURN
HERRINGBONE
HORIZONS STUDIO
HYACINTH
HYDE
INSPIRATIONAL ORCHARD
INTERSECT JEWEL
ISFAHAN
ITALIAN ROCOCO
J MURPHY BLACKSMITH
JADA
JADEN
JAMAICA
JEFFERSON
JENSEN
JORDAN
JULIETTE
KASHAN
KENSINGTON
LAHORE
LEAF BERRY
LEE
LEWIS
LILY
LOREN
LUCIAN
LYDIA
MADISON
MAHAL
MARCELLE
MARINO
MARRIS
MARSHALL
MATRIX
MERCEDES
MERMAID
METROPOLITAN
MILAN
MILFORD
MINERAL
MITCHELL
MONACO
MONROE
MONTANA
MORGAN
MR. OTTOMAN
NAIVE
NEW COUNTRY
NEWPORT
NICKEL TULIP
OASIS
OATMEAL
OCTAGON
OLIVIA
PALM GROVE
THE PALM HOUSE
PALOMA
PERSIMMON
PRATT
PRESTON
PURITY

Key to Media (For complete agency information see *The Advertising Red Books-Agencies* edition):
1. Bus. Publs. 2. Cable T.V. 3. Catalogs & Directories. 4. Co-op Adv. 5. Consumer Mags. 6. D.M. to Bus. Estab.7. D.M. to Consumers 8. Daily Newsp. 9. Exhibits/Trade Shows 10. Foreign 11. Infomercial 12. Internet Adv.13. Multimedia 14. Network Radio 15. Network T.V. 16. Newsp. Distr. Mags. 17. Other 18. Outdoor (Posters, Transit) 19. Point of Purchase20. Premiums, Novelties 21. Product Samples 22. Special Events Mktg. 23. Spot Radio 24. Spot T.V. 25. Weekly Newsp. 26. Yellow Page Adv.

RADIUS
RAFFIA
REDGRAVE
REILY
RETREAT
RETRO
ROMA
ROMANTIC TAJ
SALINGER
SAROUK
SAVONNIERE
SCONCE
SEAGRASS
SEBAGO
SERENE
SHAKER
SHAWE
SIMONE
SMARTWALL
SOHO
SPICE
STAFFORD
SUFFOLK
SULLIVAN
SUSANNE
SUSSEX
SWEDISH
TANCHOI
TANGO
TERRACOTTA
THOMAS
TOWNHOUSE
TOWNSEND
TRELLIS
TRIAD
TRIBECA
TRIPOD
TUSCANY
VENETIAN
VINTAGE
WATERWITCH
WESTON
WHITFIELD
WHITNEY
WINDHAM
WINDSOR
WOODSTOCK
YOUTH PETITE
ZEBRA
ZEMMOUR
ZIEGLER
ZOE

Advertising Agency:
Media Partnership Corporation
800 Connecticut Ave 3rd Fl N Wing
Norwalk, CT 06854
Tel.: (203) 855-6711
Fax: (203) 855-6705

EUROTECH CABINETRY, INC.

1609 Desoto Rd
Sarasota, FL 34234
Tel.: (941) 351-6557
Fax: (941) 351-3652
Web Site:
www.eurotechcabinetry.com
Approx. Number Employees: 14
Year Founded: 1984
Business Description:
Custom Cabinetry & Furniture Mfr
S.I.C.: 2541
N.A.I.C.S.: 337212
Media: 3-13
Personnel:
David Asher *(Owner)*

EVENFLO COMPANY, INC.

(Holding of Weston Presidio Capital)
1801 Commerce Dr
Piqua, OH 45356
Tel.: (937) 415-3300
Fax: (937) 415-3112
Toll Free: (800) 233-5921
Web Site: www.evenflo.com
Approx. Number Employees: 2,300
Year Founded: 1935
Business Description:
Baby Equipment & Supplies Mfr
S.I.C.: 2519
N.A.I.C.S.: 337125
Import Export
Advertising Expenditures: $1,500,000
Media: 2-4-6-7-8-10-19
Distr.: Natl.
Budget Set: Nov.
Personnel:
Robert S. Matteucci *(CEO)*
Dan Jackson *(VP-Customer Ops)*
Dennis Pregent *(VP-HR)*
Brands & Products:
ACTIVE LEARNING CENTER
AURA
AUTO-FIT
BABYDJ
BABYGO
CARRY RIGHT
COMFORT ANGLE
COMFORT CARE
COMFORT FIRST
COMFORT-GRIP
COMFORT SELECT
COMFORT TOUCH
COMFORT VENT
COMFORTEASE
COMFORTFOLD
COMFORTGLIDE
CONTOURED COMFORT
COOL KIDS
CROSS COUNTRY
CROSS ROADS
CROSS TERRAIN
CUSTOMFLOW
THE DAZZLER
DISCOVERY
DISCRETION
EASY-CLEAN
ELLIPSA
EMBRACE
ENVISION
EVENFLO
EVEREST
EXERCISES BODY & MIND
EXERSAUCER
EXPANSION SWING
GERRY
GLOW 'N' MOTION
GROW WITH ME
HOME DECOR STAIR
INFANT TO TODDLER
JOHNNY JUMP-UP
JOURNEY
JUMP & GO
KEEP-AWAY
MADISON
MEMORY FIT PRESSURE
MICRO AIR VENTS
MY STEP
NATURAL COMFORT
PORTABOUT
POSITION & LOCK PLUS
PRESS'N GO
PRESSURE & SWING
SECURE SOLUTIONS SWING
SECURERIGHT
SENSI-TEMP
SIMPLICITY
SIPRITE
SMART FOLD
SMART SYSTEM ADD-ON PANEL
SMARTSTEPS
SNUGLI
SURE LOCK
SURESIP
SWEET SOUNDS
TOP OF STAIR
TRI-COMFORT
VISUAL LATCH
WHISPER CONNECT
WHISPER CONNECT DUAL
WHISPER CONNECT PRO
WHISPER CONNECT SENSA
WHISPER CONNECT TRIA
WIDE SPACES SWING
Advertising Agency:
WonderGroup
312 Plum St Ste 1000
Cincinnati, OH 45202-2618
Tel.: (513) 357-2950
Fax: (513) 651-1162

F. SCHUMACHER & CO.

79 Madison Ave
New York, NY 10016-7802
Tel.: (212) 213-7900
Fax: (212) 213-7848
E-mail: consumer@fsco.com
Sales Range: $350-399.9 Million
Approx. Number Employees: 1,300
Year Founded: 1889
Business Description:
Home Decorative Fabrics, Wallpaper & Soft Goods Marketer & Mfr
S.I.C.: 5131; 2211
N.A.I.C.S.: 424310; 313210
Import Export
Media: 4-6-7-10-11-23
Distr.: Intl.; Natl.
Budget Set: Jan.
Personnel:
F. Schumacher *(Owner)*
Brands & Products:
DECORATOR'S WALK
F.SCHUMACHER AND CO
GRAMERCY
GREEFF
PATTERSON, FLYNN & MARTIN
ROSECORE
SCHUMACHER
VILLAGE
WAVERLY

THE FANTASY GALLERY

804 W Gray St
Houston, TX 77019-4317
Tel.: (713) 528-6569
Web Site: www.fantasygallery.com
E-Mail For Key Personnel:
President: tcorbett@fantasygallery.com
Year Founded: 1991
Business Description:
Custom Frameshop & Gallery
S.I.C.: 5999
N.A.I.C.S.: 453998
Media: 13-26
Personnel:
Tim Corbett *(Owner)*

F.E. HALE MANUFACTURING COMPANY

120 Benson Pl
Frankfort, NY 13340
Tel.: (315) 894-5490
Fax: (315) 894-5046
Toll Free: (800) 873-4253
E-mail: sales@halebookcases.com
Web Site: www.halesince1907.com
E-Mail For Key Personnel:
Sales Director: sales@halebookcases.com
Approx. Sls.: $9,000,000
Approx. Number Employees: 60
Year Founded: 1907
Business Description:
Wooden Bookcases Mfr
S.I.C.: 2521
N.A.I.C.S.: 337211
Media: 2-4-5-7-10
Distr.: Natl.
Personnel:
Jim Benson *(Pres)*
Mary Harvey *(Mgr-Accts Payable)*
Dan O'Dell *(Mgr-Natl Sls)*
Brands & Products:
HALE
HALE BOOK CASES
LINE PHENIX
MOHAWK
NATURE'S BEAUTY, OUR CRAFTSMANSHIP
PHENIX
SARANAC
SARATOGA
SIGNATURE
Advertising Agency:
The Paige Group
258 Genesee St Ste 204
Utica, NY 13502
Tel.: (315) 733-2313
Fax: (315) 733-1901

FICKS REED

6245 Creek Rd
Cincinnati, OH 45242-4104
Tel.: (513) 985-0606
Fax: (513) 985-9293
E-mail: customerservice@ficksreed.com
Web Site: www.ficksreed.com
Sales Range: $10-24.9 Million
Approx. Number Employees: 25
Year Founded: 1885
Business Description:
Mfr. of Rattan & Wicker Furniture; Designer & Producer of Upholstery
S.I.C.: 2512
N.A.I.C.S.: 337121
Media: 2-4-6-8-10
Distr.: Natl.
Budget Set: Nov.
Personnel:
Eugene L. Saenger, Jr. *(Owner)*
Brands & Products:
FICKSREED

FINGER FURNITURE COMPANY, INC.

4001 Gulf Fwy
Houston, TX 77003-5644
Mailing Address:
PO Box 194
Houston, TX 77001
Tel.: (713) 221-4441
Tel.: (713) 933-1009 (Cust Svc)
Fax: (713) 227-0406

Key to Media (For complete agency information see *The Advertising Red Books-Agencies* edition):
1. Bus. Publs. 2. Cable T.V. 3. Catalogs & Directories. 4. Co-op Adv. 5. Consumer Mags. 6. D.M. to Bus. Estab.7. D.M. to Consumers 8. Daily Newsp. 9. Exhibits/Trade Shows 10. Foreign 11. Infomercial 12. Internet Adv.13. Multimedia 14. Network Radio 15. Network T.V. 16. Newsp. Distr. Mags. 17. Other 18. Outdoor (Posters, Transit) 19. Point of Purchase20. Premiums, Novelties 21. Product Samples 22. Special Events Mktg. 23. Spot Radio 24. Spot T.V. 25. Weekly Newsp. 26. Yellow Page Adv.

Finger Furniture Company, Inc. — (Continued)

Web Site: www.fingerfurniture.com
Approx. Number Employees: 600
Year Founded: 1927
Business Description:
Home Furniture Retailer
S.I.C.: 5712
N.A.I.C.S.: 442110
Media: 4-17-19
Personnel:
Robert Finger *(Pres & CEO)*
Rodney Finger *(Pres & CEO)*
Jim Sperrazzo *(VP-Mktg)*
Martha Schlott *(Mgr-Production)*
Brands & Products:
ASHLEY
LANE
UNIVERSAL
VAUGHN BASSETT

FIRESIDE ANTIQUES

14007 Perkins Rd
Baton Rouge, LA 70810
Tel.: (225) 752-9565
Fax: (225) 751-7603
E-mail: info@firesideantiques.com
Web Site: www.firesideantiques.com
Business Description:
Antiques Dealer
S.I.C.: 5712
N.A.I.C.S.: 442110
Media: 16
Personnel:
Susan Roland *(Owner)*

FLEXSTEEL INDUSTRIES, INC.

3400 Jackson St
Dubuque, IA 52001
Mailing Address:
PO Box 877
Dubuque, IA 52004-0877
Tel.: (563) 556-7730
Fax: (563) 556-8345
Web Site: www.flexsteel.com
Approx. Sls.: $339,426,000
Approx. Number Employees: 1,300
Year Founded: 1893
Business Description:
Upholstered Furniture & Recreational Vehicle Seating Mfr, Designer & Marketer
S.I.C.: 2512; 2329; 2389; 2519; 2759
N.A.I.C.S.: 337121; 315211; 315999; 323113; 337125
Import Export
Advertising Expenditures: $4,100,000
Media: 1-2-6-7-8-9-10-13-19-21-23-24-25-26
Distr.: Natl.
Budget Set: Nov.
Personnel:
L. Bruce Boylen *(Chm)*
Ronald J. Klosterman *(Pres & CEO)*
Timothy E. Hall *(CFO, Treas, Sec & Sr VP-Fin)*
Jeffrey T. Bertsch *(Sr VP-Corp Svcs)*
Thomas D. Burkart *(Sr VP-Vehicle Seating)*
Patrick M. Crahan *(Sr VP-Comml Seating)*
Donald D. Dreher *(Sr VP)*
James E. Gilbertson *(Sr VP-Vehicle Seating)*
James R. Richardson *(Sr VP-Sls & Mktg-Residential)*
Carolyn T.B. Bleile *(VP-Mdsg & Home Furnishings)*
Kevin F. Crahan *(VP-Sls & Mktg Hospitality)*
Lee David Fautsch *(VP-Sls & Residential)*
Michael A. Santillo *(VP-Mktg)*
Justin Mills *(Dir-Adv & Pub Rel)*
Brands & Products:
AIR COIL
ALBANY
ALEXANDRIA
ARROYO GRANDE
BEXLEY
BLUE RIBBON
CAMBRIDGE
CAYMAN
CHICAGO
COMFORT SEATING
DANBURY
DARIEN
DUALFLEX SPRING SYSTEM
ERGO-FLEX
FLEX-LOCK
FLEXSTEEL
GENEVA
HARTFORD
HOME CARE
INDIO
INSTANT BED
JUPITER
KILLARNEY
LAKEWOOD
LAS CRUCES
LATITUDES
MARIETTA
MARSHFIELD
MARTHA
MASQUERADER
NOUVEAU
ORLEANS
OSLO
PACIFIC
POLO
PORT ROYAL
RENO
ROSWELL
SANTE FE
SLEEP HAVEN
SNEAK PREVIEW
SOUTH HAMPTON
SPOKANE
SPRINGFIELD
STUART
TEMECULA
THORNTON
TRITON
VAIL CONVERSATION
VANPAK
WILMINGTON
WRANGLER HOME

FLOOR CONCEPTS INC.

4315 Kirkwood Hwy
Wilmington, DE 19808
Tel.: (302) 994-5002
Business Description:
Prefinished Flooring Needs & Window Blinds
S.I.C.: 1752
N.A.I.C.S.: 238330
Media: 2-9-10-25
Personnel:
Bruce Ball *(Pres)*

FLORENTINE CRAFTSMEN, INC.

12-20 36th Ave
Long Island City, NY 11106
Tel.: (718) 937-7632
Fax: (718) 937-9858
Toll Free: (800) 876-3567
Toll Free: (800) 577-1188
E-mail: info@florentinecraftsmen.com
Web Site: www.florentinecraftsmen.com
Approx. Sls.: $1,000,000
Approx. Number Employees: 12
Year Founded: 1918
Business Description:
Mfr. Art Metal Works & Importers of Marble & Stone Statuaries
S.I.C.: 3299; 3446
N.A.I.C.S.: 327999; 332323
Import Export
Media: 4-6-10-26
Distr.: Direct to Consumer; Natl.

FRAN MURPHY INTERIORS INC.

12800 US Hwy 1
Juno Beach, FL 33408
Tel.: (561) 626-6200
Fax: (561) 626-6233
E-mail: franmurphyint@aol.com
Web Site: www.franmurphyint.com
Approx. Number Employees: 17
Business Description:
Household Furniture Designer & Retailer
S.I.C.: 7389; 5712
N.A.I.C.S.: 541410; 442110
Media: 6-10
Personnel:
Fran Murphy *(Pres)*

FRANK B. RHODES FURNITURE MAKER

535 Morgnec Rd
Chestertown, MD 21620
Tel.: (410) 778-3993
Fax: (410) 778-4846
E-mail: gadroon@crosslink.net
Web Site: www.frankbrhodes.com
Approx. Number Employees: 5
Business Description:
Antique Furniture Reproduction Mfr, Refinishing, Restoring & Upholstering
S.I.C.: 1751; 5712
N.A.I.C.S.: 238350; 442110
Media: 4-22-25
Personnel:
Frank B. Rhodes, Jr. *(Owner)*

FRAN'S WICKER AND RATTAN INC.

295 Rte 10 E
Succasunna, NJ 07876
Tel.: (973) 584-2230
Fax: (973) 584-7446
Toll Free: (800) 372-6799
Web Site: www.franswicker.com
E-Mail For Key Personnel:
Sales Director: sales@franswicker.com
Approx. Sls.: $4,000,000
Approx. Number Employees: 25
Business Description:
Home Furnishings Retailer
S.I.C.: 5719; 5961
N.A.I.C.S.: 442299; 454113
Media: 3-4-6-8-9-13-16-26
Personnel:
David Gruber *(Pres)*
Brands & Products:
FRANS

FURNITURE BRANDS INTERNATIONAL, INC.

1 N Brentwood Blvd
Saint Louis, MO 63105
Tel.: (314) 863-1100
Fax: (314) 863-5306
E-mail: jhastings@furniturebrands.com
Web Site: www.furniturebrands.com
Approx. Sls.: $1,159,934,000
Approx. Number Employees: 6,200
Year Founded: 1921
Business Description:
Residential Furniture Mfr, Distr & Retailer
S.I.C.: 2512; 2511; 5021; 5712
N.A.I.C.S.: 337121; 337122; 423210; 442110
Import Export
Advertising Expenditures: $37,642,000
Media: 3-5-6-8-9-13-15-16-19-22-23-24-25
Personnel:
Ralph P. Scozzafava *(Chm & CEO)*
Steven G. Rolls *(CFO & Sr VP)*
Jim Brenner *(CMO)*
Richard R. Isaak *(Chief Acctg Officer & Controller)*
Daniel Bradley *(Pres-Designer Brands Grp)*
Bruce Burnett *(Pres-Intl Sls)*
Gregory P. Roy *(Pres-Lane Furniture Indus)*
Edward D. Teplitz *(Pres-Drexel Heritage Furniture Indus)*
Mark Wiltshire *(Pres-Canada)*
Jon D. Botsford *(Sr VP & Gen Counsel)*
Raymond J. Johnson *(Sr VP-Global Supply Chain)*
Mary E. Sweetman *(Sr VP-HR)*
John S. Hastings *(VP-Comm & IR)*
Daniel J. Stone *(VP-Strategy & Bus Dev)*
Alex Hodges *(Sr Dir-Corp Innovation Team)*
Cathy Beisel *(Dir-Employee Benefits)*
Rena Peterson *(Dir-Staffing & HR Generalist)*
Lisa Hanly *(Brand Mgr)*
Brands & Products:
BROYHILL
DREXEL HERITAGE
FURNITURE BRANDS
HENREDON
LABARGE
LANE
MAITLAND-SMITH
THOMASVILLE
Advertising Agency:
Rodgers Townsend, LLC
1000 Clark Ave 5th Fl
Saint Louis, MO 63102
Tel.: (314) 436-9960
Fax: (314) 436-9961

GALLERY MODEL HOMES, INC.

(d/b/a Gallery Furniture)
6006 N Fwy
Houston, TX 77076-4029
Tel.: (713) 694-5570

Key to Media (For complete agency information see *The Advertising Red Books-Agencies* edition):
1. Bus. Publs. 2. Cable T.V. 3. Catalogs & Directories. 4. Co-op Adv. 5. Consumer Mags. 6. D.M. to Bus. Estab.7. D.M. to Consumers 8. Daily Newsp. 9. Exhibits/Trade Shows 10. Foreign 11. Infomercial 12. Internet Adv.13. Multimedia 14. Network Radio 15. Network T.V. 16. Newsp. Distr. Mags. 17. Other 18. Outdoor (Posters, Transit) 19. Point of Purchase20. Premiums, Novelties 21. Product Samples 22. Special Events Mktg. 23. Spot Radio 24. Spot T.V. 25. Weekly Newsp. 26. Yellow Page Adv.

Fax: (713) 696-4524
Toll Free: (877) 268-4483
E-mail: info@galleryfurniture.com
Web Site: www.galleryfurniture.com
Approx. Sls.: $150,000,000
Approx. Number Employees: 300
Year Founded: 1981
Business Description:
Home Furnishings & Electronics Retailer
S.I.C.: 5712
N.A.I.C.S.: 442110
Media: 3-8-9-12-13-14-15-18-19-20-22-23-24-26
Personnel:
James McIngvale *(Owner-Gallery Furniture)*
Linda McIngvale *(Treas, Sec & VP)*
Walter Dunnigan *(Dir-IT)*
Advertising Agency:
Love Advertising Inc.
770 S Post Oak Ln Ste 101
Houston, TX 77056-1913
Tel.: (713) 552-1055
Fax: (713) 552-9155
Toll Free: (800) 544-5683
(Retail Furniture)

THE GARDEN COTTAGE COMPANY, INC.

305 B Fairfield Ave
Fairfield, NJ 07004
Tel.: (973) 227-1010
Fax: (973) 425-0054
Toll Free: (866) 263-8325
Web Site: www.gardencottage.com
Approx. Sls.: $2,500,000
Approx. Number Employees: 20
Business Description:
Retailer of Outdoor Furniture & Gifts
S.I.C.: 5712; 5947
N.A.I.C.S.: 442110; 453220
Media: 6-8-13
Personnel:
Eunice Conine *(Pres)*

GBO INC.

274 Duchesnay St
Sainte-Marie, QC G6E 3C2, Canada
Tel.: (418) 387-7723
Tel.: (418) 387-1000
Fax: (418) 387-3904
Toll Free: (800) 463-4044
E-mail: corpo@bocenor.com
Web Site: www.gbo-inc.com
Approx. Rev.: $19,225,133
Approx. Number Employees: 200
Year Founded: 1946
Business Description:
Wood Window & Door Mfr
S.I.C.: 2431
N.A.I.C.S.: 321911
Advertising Expenditures: $452,200
Media: 5-10-13-16-21-22
Personnel:
Christopher M. Wood *(Chm & CEO)*
Danielle Beaudoin *(CFO)*
John Hooker *(VP-Sls & Mktg)*
Robert Couillard *(Mgr-Mktg)*
Brands & Products:
BONNEVILLE
GBO
MULTIVER
POLAR
STROMBUSTER

GIBSON PEWTER

18 E Washington Rd
Hillsboro, NH 03244
Tel.: (603) 464-3410
E-mail: jc@gibsonpewter.com
Web Site: www.gibsonpewter.com
Approx. Number Employees: 1
Year Founded: 1966
Business Description:
Pewter Accessory Mfr
S.I.C.: 3446; 3421
N.A.I.C.S.: 332323; 332211
Media: 4-6-25
Personnel:
Jonathan Gibson *(Owner)*

GRANITE FURNITURE CO

1475 W 90th S
West Jordan, UT 84088
Tel.: (801) 486-3333
Fax: (801) 566-4614
Web Site: www.granitefurniture.com
Approx. Number Employees: 20
Year Founded: 1910
Business Description:
Home Furnishings Retailer
S.I.C.: 5712
N.A.I.C.S.: 442110
Advertising Expenditures: $250,000
Media: 9-13-23-25
Personnel:
John D. Richards, Jr. *(CEO)*
Roger T. Richards *(CFO & Sec)*

THE GREAT AMERICAN HANGER COMPANY INC.

(d/b/a Hangers Direct)
8250 NW 27th St Ste 304
Miami, FL 33122
Tel.: (305) 477-4250
Fax: (305) 477-4254
Toll Free: (800) 400-6680
E-mail: info@hangers.com
Web Site: www.hangers.com
Sales Range: $1-9.9 Million
Approx. Number Employees: 40
Business Description:
Clothes Hanger Mfr & Whslr
S.I.C.: 3496; 2499; 3089; 5023
N.A.I.C.S.: 332618; 321999; 326199; 423220
Media: 4
Personnel:
Devon Rifkin *(Pres)*
Brands & Products:
HANGERS.COM

GROUPE DUTAILIER INC.

299 Rue Chaput
Saint-Pie, QC J0H 1W0, Canada
Tel.: (450) 772-2403
Fax: (450) 772-5055
E-mail: info@dutailier.com
Web Site: www.dutailier.com
Approx. Number Employees: 650
Year Founded: 1976
Business Description:
Children's & Infants' Chairs & Bedroom Furniture Mfr
S.I.C.: 2511
N.A.I.C.S.: 337122
Advertising Expenditures: $1,000,000
Media: 2-5-10
Personnel:
Fernand Fontaine *(Pres)*
David Fontaine *(Mgr-Mktg)*
Brands & Products:
AVANTGLIDE
DUTAILIER
GLIDE-R-MOTION
MATRIX

THE GUNLOCKE COMPANY

(Sub. of HNI Corporation)
1 Gunlocke Dr
Wayland, NY 14572-9515
Tel.: (585) 728-5111
Fax: (585) 728-8353
Toll Free: (800) 828-6300
E-mail: gunlockeweb@gunlocke.com
Web Site: www.gunlocke.com
Sales Range: $200-249.9 Million
Approx. Number Employees: 700
Business Description:
Mfr. of High Quality Office Furniture
S.I.C.: 2521; 2531
N.A.I.C.S.: 337211; 337127
Personnel:
Donald Mead *(Pres)*
Advertising Agency:
Falls Communications
50 Public Sq 25th Fl
Cleveland, OH 44113
Tel.: (216) 696-0229
Fax: (216) 696-0269

HAMILTON LABORATORY WORKSTATIONS

(Sub. of Thermo Fisher Scientific Inc.)
1316 18th St
Two Rivers, WI 54241-3059
Mailing Address:
PO Box 137
Two Rivers, WI 54241-0137
Tel.: (920) 793-1121
Fax: (920) 793-3084
Web Site: www.hamiltonlab.com
Sales Range: $400-449.9 Million
Approx. Number Employees: 1,000
Year Founded: 1880
Business Description:
Laboratory Furniture & Fume Hoods Mfr
S.I.C.: 3821; 2522
N.A.I.C.S.: 339111; 337214
Export
Media: 2-4-10
Distr.: Natl.
Budget Set: Sept.
Personnel:
Steve Goviewski *(Pres)*
Charles Dietrich *(VP-Fin)*
Bill Murphy *(VP-Info Sys)*
Charles Rohlmeier *(VP-HR)*
Brands & Products:
ACCENT
ACCLAIM
BROEN
COLORTECH
CONCEPT
CONTRAST
DURAMAX
MAX/LAB
MAX/MOBILE
MAX/WALL
PIONEER
PRESTIGE
PROFILE
PROVENT
SAFEAIRE
TRADITION
WATERSAVER

HANCOCK & MOORE INC.

166 Hancock & Moore Ln
Hickory, NC 28601
Tel.: (828) 495-8235
Fax: (828) 495-3021
E-mail: service@hancockandmoore.com
Web Site:
www.hancockandmoore.com
Sales Range: $10-24.9 Million
Approx. Number Employees: 200
Business Description:
Couches Sofas & Davenports: Upholstered On Wood Frames
S.I.C.: 2512; 2522
N.A.I.C.S.: 337121; 337214
Personnel:
Jack Glasheen *(Pres & CEO)*
Brands & Products:
ABBEY
ACADEMY
ACROPOLIS
ACTON
ADRON
AIRLIE
ALEXANDER
ANDOVER
APPRENTICE
ARMSTRONG
ARNOLD
ARTHUR
ASHBURN
ATHENS
AUDLEY
AUSTIN
AUTUMN
AVON
BAILEY
BAINBRIDGE
BALDWIN
BALFOUR
BALL AND CLAW
BARCLAY
BARON
BARRETT
BARRISTER
BARTON
BATTIE
BAXTER
BECKLEY
BERKSHIRE
BERWICK
BERWIND
BIRCH
BISHOP
BLAIR
BLAKELY
BLAYLOCK
BOLLINGER
BOUNTY
BOVEY
BOYD
BRADFORD
BRADLEY
BRADSTONE
BRENNER
BRENTWOOD
BRONTE
BRYAN
BUCHANAN
BUCKINGHAM
BURBERRY
BURKE
CAESAR
CAMELBACK
CAMERAE
CAMPAIGN

Hancock & Moore Inc. — (Continued)

CAMPARI
CAMPBELL
CAPTAIN'S
CARA GLIDER
CAREW
CARINTHIA
CARLING
CARRINGTON
CARSON
CASSIDY
CASTLE
CHADSWORTH
CHADWICK
CHALFANT
CHAMBERLAIN
CHANCELLOR
CHARTER
CHATEAU
CHESTERFIELD
CHIPPENDALE
CHURCHILL
CIRRUS
CITIZEN
CITY
CLARINGTON
CLIVEDON
CODINGTON
CODY
COLONNADE
COLUMBIA
CONRAD
CORTINA
CRENSHAW
CROMWELL
CROWE
CUNNINGHAM
DA VINCI
DANIELS
DARCY
DAWSON
DEATON
DELANY
DELEGATE
DELMAR
DESMOND
DICKSON
DILLON
DIOR
DOCKERY
DORSEY
DOWNES
DRAKE
DREW
EAGEN
EASTON
EATON
ECHELON
EDITORIAL
EDMUND
ELKINS
EMBASSY
ENGLISH
EVANS
EVENING
EVERETT
EXTON
FAIRBANKS
FAIRVIEW
FLEMING
FOLIO
FOUNDERS
FOWLER
FOX
FRANKLIN
FREEMAN
FREMONT
GALLAGHER
GARRETT
GEIB
GENTRY
GEORGE III
GEORGETOWN
GLASGOW
GLENDALE
GORDON
GRAFTON
GRAHAM
GREER
GRIGSBY
HAMILL
HAMPTON
HARBISON
HARRIS
HARROD
HEPWORTH
HIGGINS
HIGHLANDS
HILLS
HOLDEN
HOLMES
HOWELL
HOYLE
HUDLOW
IDAHO
INFINITY
IVANHOE
JEFFERSON
JENNINGS
JOCKEY
JOHNSON
JOURNAL
JOURNEY
JUSTICE
KANE
KEARNS
KEITH
KENNEDY
KENNET
KENSINGTON
KENWORTHY
KINGWOOD
KIRKWALL
KODIAK
LANIER
LAREDO
LASALLE
LAUREL
LAWRENCE
LEESBURG
LEGION
LEIGHTON
LENNON
LEOPOLD
LESTER
LIBERTY
LINCOLN
LINLEY
LISBON
LITERARY
LIVINGSTON
LOGAN
LONGFORD
LOWELL
MALONE
MANOR
MARCHANT
MARCO
MARGO
MARINA
MARION
MARQUIS
MARTHA
MARTIAL
MARTIN
MAVERICK
MEADOWS
MELROSE
MERIDIAN
METRO
METROPOLITAN
MIDDLEBURG
MIDLAND
MILLER
MILTON
MONTREAL
MOORE
MORGAN
MURRAY
MYERS
NAUTICAL
NEW ENGLAND
NOLAND
NORFOLD
NORFOLK
NOVEL
OAKLEY
OCTOBER
OLIVER
OXFORD
PARISIAN
PATRIOT
PATTON
PAXTON
PAYNE
PERTH
PIAZZA
PIEDMONT
PIERRE
PILOT
PINGREE
PLANTATIO
POINTE
PORTER
PRATT
PRESTON
PRINCETON
PROFILE
PROSPECT
QUINCY
RALEIGH
RALSTON
RAMSBURY
RANDOLPH
RANGER
RAVEN
RAVENNA
REED
REGENCY
RENFRO
RENOIR
REUNION
RIALTO
RICHMOND
RILEY
RITZ
ROBERTS
ROBINSON
ROGERS
ROSS
ROULEAU
ROYALIST
RUNYON
SACHO
SADLER
SALON
SAMUEL
SARATOGA
SAVANT
SEPTEMBER
SEVILLE
SEYMOUR
SHERWOOD
SINCLAIR
SLOANE
SMITH
SOHO
SOMERSET
SOVEREIGN
SPENCER
STAFFORD
STEWART
STOCKBRIDGE
STOCKHOLM
SULLINS
SULLIVAN
SULTAN
SUMMIT
SUNSET
SWANN
TALAS
TARBORO
TARLETON
TAYLOR
TENNYSON
THEATER
THEORY
THOMAS
THORNHILL
TITUS
TIVOLI
TREATY
TRUFFLE
TRUMAN
URBAN
VALE
VANITY
VARICK
VERSAILLES
VICTOR
VICTORIA
VINCE
VISTA
WALLACE
WALSH
WALTON
WARREN
WARTON
WARWICK
WASHINGTON
WATSON
WATTS
WEATHERBY
WEATHFORD
WEBSTER
WELCH
WELLINGTON
WELSH
WEYMUTH
WHITNEY
WHITTAKER
WILCOX
WILKINSON
WILLIAMSBURG
WINDSOR
WINSTON
WOLFE
WOODSON
WRAY
WRENN
YARMOUTH

Advertising Agency:
Lennon & Associates
734 N Highland Ave
Los Angeles, CA 90038
Tel.: (323) 465-5104
Fax: (323) 463-6463

Key to Media (For complete agency information see *The Advertising Red Books-Agencies* edition):
1. Bus. Publs. 2. Cable T.V. 3. Catalogs & Directories. 4. Co-op Adv. 5. Consumer Mags. 6. D.M. to Bus. Estab.7. D.M. to Consumers
8. Daily Newsp. 9. Exhibits/Trade Shows 10. Foreign 11. Infomercial 12. Internet Adv.13. Multimedia 14. Network Radio
15. Network T.V. 16. Newsp. Distr. Mags. 17. Other 18. Outdoor (Posters, Transit) 19. Point of Purchase20. Premiums, Novelties
21. Product Samples 22. Special Events Mktg. 23. Spot Radio 24. Spot T.V. 25. Weekly Newsp. 26. Yellow Page Adv.

HARDEN FURNITURE INC.
8550 Mill Pond Way
McConnellsville, NY 13401-1800
Tel.: (315) 245-1000
Fax: (315) 245-2884
E-mail: contract@harden.com
Web Site: www.harden.com
Approx. Number Employees: 350
Year Founded: 1844
Business Description:
Mfr of Solid Cherry & Upholstered Household & Office Furniture
S.I.C.: 2511; 2512
N.A.I.C.S.: 337122; 337121
Import Export
Advertising Expenditures: $700,000
Media: 1-2-4-5-6-7-8-9-10-11-13-19-20-21-22-23-25-26
Distr.: Natl.
Budget Set: Sept.
Personnel:
David E. Harden *(Chm)*
Gregory M. Harden *(Pres & CEO)*
Brands & Products:
FROM OUR FORSTS TO YOUR HOME
HARDEN

HARTMANN & FORBES
10655 SW Avery St
Tualatin, OR 97062
Tel.: (503) 692-9313
Fax: (503) 692-9315
Web Site: www.hfshades.com
Approx. Rev.: $5,100,000
Approx. Number Employees: 35
Year Founded: 1998
Business Description:
Custom Manufacturing
S.I.C.: 2519
N.A.I.C.S.: 337125
Personnel:
Michael S. Jones *(Founder & CEO)*
Advertising Agency:
Coates Kokes
34 NW 1st Ave Ste 300
Portland, OR 97209-4016
Tel.: (503) 241-1124
Fax: (503) 241-1326
Window Coverings

HAVERTY FURNITURE COMPANIES, INC.
780 Johnson Ferry Rd Ste 800
Atlanta, GA 30342
Tel.: (404) 443-2900
Fax: (404) 443-4180
Web Site: www.havertys.com
Approx. Sls.: $620,331,000
Approx. Number Employees: 3,100
Year Founded: 1885
Business Description:
Residential Furniture & Accessories Retailer
S.I.C.: 5712; 5722
N.A.I.C.S.: 442110; 443111
Advertising Expenditures: $41,012,000
Media: 4-8-10-13-16
Personnel:
Clarence H. Smith *(Pres & CEO)*
Dennis L. Fink *(CFO & Exec VP)*
J. Edward Clary *(CIO & Sr VP-Distr)*
Allan J. DeNiro *(Chief People Officer & Sr VP)*
Janet E. Taylor *(Gen Counsel & Sr VP)*
Jenny Hill Parker *(Treas, Sec & Sr VP-Fin)*
Steven G. Burdette *(Exec VP-Stores)*
Thomas P. Curran *(Sr VP-Mktg)*
Richard D. Gallagher *(Sr VP-Mdsg)*
Rawson Haverty, Jr. *(Sr VP-Real Estate & Dev)*
Rhonda Wolf *(VP-Mdsg)*
Brands & Products:
HAVERTYS
MAKING IT HOME
MYHAVERTYS
Advertising Agencies:
Bernstein-Rein Advertising, Inc.
4600 Madison Ave Ste 1500
Kansas City, MO 64112-3016
Tel.: (816) 756-0640
Fax: (816) 399-6000
Toll Free: (800) 571-6246

Nurun Inc.
711 De La Commune St W
Montreal, QC H3C 1X6, Canada
Tel.: (514) 392-1900
Fax: (514) 392-0911
Toll Free: (877) 696-1292

HENREDON FURNITURE INDUSTRIES, INC.
(Sub. of Furniture Brands International, Inc.)
400 Henredon Rd
Morganton, NC 28655
Tel.: (341) 863-1100
Fax: (828) 437-5264
Toll Free: (800) 444-3682
Web Site: www.henredon.com
Sales Range: $750-799.9 Million
Approx. Number Employees: 2,700
Year Founded: 1946
Business Description:
Household Furniture Mfr
S.I.C.: 2511; 2512
N.A.I.C.S.: 337122; 337121
Advertising Expenditures: $1,200,000
Media: 4-6-8-10
Distr.: Natl.
Personnel:
Jane Bender *(Mgr-Adv)*
Brands & Products:
HENREDON

HERMAN MILLER, INC.
855 E Main Ave
Zeeland, MI 49464-1366
Mailing Address:
PO Box 302
Zeeland, MI 49464-0302
Tel.: (616) 654-3000
Fax: (616) 654-5234
Toll Free: (888) 443-4357
E-mail: investor@hermanmiller.com
Web Site: www.hermanmiller.com
Approx. Sls.: $1,318,800,000
Approx. Number Employees: 5,460
Year Founded: 1905
Business Description:
Office Systems, Furnishings & Related Services
S.I.C.: 4959; 2521; 7349
N.A.I.C.S.: 562910; 337211; 561790
Import Export
Advertising Expenditures: $2,300,000
Media: 2-4-5-6-7-9-10-19-22
Distr.: Intl.; Natl.
Budget Set: May
Personnel:
Michael A. Volkema *(Chm)*
Brian C. Walker *(Pres & CEO)*
Elizabeth A. Nickels *(Pres-Herman Miller Healthcare)*
Gregory J. Bylsma *(CFO)*
Andrew J. Lock *(Chief Admin Officer & Exec VP)*
John P. Portlock *(Pres-Intl & Exec VP)*
Curtis S. Pullen *(Pres-North American Office/Learning Environ & Exec VP)*
James E. Christenson *(Sec & Sr VP-Legal Svcs)*
Donald D. Goeman *(Exec VP-Res, Design & Dev)*
Kenneth L. Goodson *(Exec VP-Ops)*
Steven C. Gane *(Sr VP-Specialty & Consumer Bus)*
Gregg VanderKooi *(Product Mgr)*
Mary Stevens *(Mgr-Mktg)*
Brands & Products:
AALTO
ABAK
ABOUT FACE
ACTION OFFICE
AERON
AIREWEAVE
AIRIA
AMBI
AO
ARDEA
ARRIO
ASIDE
AVIVE
BABBLE
BASELINE
BOOMERANG
BUBBLETACK
BURDICK
CAPELLI
CAPER
CELESTE
CELLA
CELLE
CELLULAR SUSPENSION
COGNITA
CONVIA
CORNERSTONE
COVEY
EAMES
ENCHORD
EQUA
EQUA CHAIR
ERGON
FLEX-EDGE
FLEXFRONT
FLUTE
FORAY
GEIGER
GOETZ
GREENGERNOMICS
H-ALLOY
HALF-HONEY
HERMAN MILLER
IMT
INTENT
IOTA
KINEMAT
LEAF
LIFEWORK
LIMERICK
LISSOME
LYRIS
MARIMBA
MERIDIAN
MILAFIN
MILCARE
MIRRA
MULTISCRIM
NALA
NELSON
NOGUCHI
OFFICE-IN-A-BOX
OFFICE-IN-A-MINUTE
OPTIC
OVERT
PEDASTOOL
PERCH
PERMEABLE PRIVACY
PRESERVE
PRIVACY WITHOUT WALLS
THE PROMISE
PROPER CHAIR
PROSPECTS
PUZZLE
Q SYSTEM
QUADRANT
RAPUNZEL
REACTION
RECLINE SELECTOR
RESOLVE
ROOMTUNE
SETU
SHELL
STACKABLE
STOA
SUPER ROOM
TD COLLECTION
TEARDROP
TENEO
TRIFLEX
TWIST
UNLIMITED BOUNDARIES
V-WALL
VANISHING POINT
VANTAGE
VARY EASY
VIEWPOINT
VIVO INTERIORS
Advertising Agencies:
mono
(Partially Owned by MDC Partners)
3036 Hennepin Ave
Minneapolis, MN 55408
Tel.: (612) 822-4135
Fax: (612) 454-4950
Furniture

Remedy
121 W Wacker Dr Ste 2250
Chicago, IL 60601
Tel.: (312) 377-3410
Fax: (312) 377-3420
Herman Miller Healthcare (Agency of Record)

HICKORY CHAIR COMPANY
(Sub. of Henredon Furniture Industries, Inc.)
37 9th St SE
Hickory, NC 28602
Mailing Address:
PO Box 2147
Hickory, NC 28603-2147
Tel.: (828) 328-1801
Fax: (828) 328-8954
Web Site: www.hickorychair.com
Sales Range: $10-24.9 Million
Business Description:
Furniture Mfr
S.I.C.: 2512; 2542
N.A.I.C.S.: 337121; 337215
Media: 4-6

Key to Media (For complete agency information see *The Advertising Red Books-Agencies* edition):
1. Bus. Publs. 2. Cable T.V. 3. Catalogs & Directories. 4. Co-op Adv. 5. Consumer Mags. 6. D.M. to Bus. Estab.7. D.M. to Consumers 8. Daily Newsp. 9. Exhibits/Trade Shows 10. Foreign 11. Infomercial 12. Internet Adv.13. Multimedia 14. Network Radio 15. Network T.V. 16. Newsp. Distr. Mags. 17. Other 18. Outdoor (Posters, Transit) 19. Point of Purchase20. Premiums, Novelties 21. Product Samples 22. Special Events Mktg. 23. Spot Radio 24. Spot T.V. 25. Weekly Newsp. 26. Yellow Page Adv.

Hickory Chair Company — (Continued)

Personnel:
Frank J. Reardon *(Pres)*
Cathy Mitchell *(VP-Mdsg)*
Laura Holland *(Dir-Mktg Svcs)*

Brands & Products:
HICKORY CHAIR

HISTORIC HOUSEFITTERS CO., INC.
287 New Milford Tpky
Litchfield, CT 06777
Tel.: (845) 278-2427
Fax: (860) 619-0243
Toll Free: (800) 247-4111
E-mail: david@historichousefitters.com
Web Site:
www.historichousefitters.com
Approx. Number Employees: 4
Business Description:
Reproduction Hardware Mfr
S.I.C.: 5961
N.A.I.C.S.: 454113
Media: 4-6-8-10
Personnel:
David R. Sposato *(Pres)*

HNI CORPORATION
408 E 2nd St
Muscatine, IA 52761-4117
Mailing Address:
PO Box 1109
Muscatine, IA 52761
Tel.: (563) 264-7400
Fax: (563) 264-7655
Telex: 468552
E-mail: investorrelations@hnicorp.com
Web Site: www.honi.com
Approx. Sls.: $1,686,728,000
Approx. Number Employees: 8,000
Year Founded: 1944
Business Description:
Office Furniture & Hearth Products Mfr & Marketer
S.I.C.: 2522
N.A.I.C.S.: 337214
Export
Advertising Expenditures: $54,797,000
Media: 2-7-10-17-21-26
Distr.: Natl.
Budget Set: Oct.
Personnel:
Stanley A. Askren *(Chm, Pres & CEO)*
Kurt A. Tjaden *(CFO & VP)*
Douglas L. Jones *(CIO & VP)*
Steven M. Bradford *(Gen Counsel, Sec & VP)*
Brands & Products:
ALLSTEEL
GUNLOCKE
HEATILATOR
HNI
HOLGA
HON
MAXON
OMNI
PAOLI
PROVISIONS
SENSIBLE SEATING
SOLUTIONS SEATING
STATIONMASTER
Advertising Agency:
Campbell-Ewald
30400 Van Dyke Ave
Warren, MI 48093-2368
Tel.: (586) 574-3400
Fax: (586) 575-9925

HOBBY LOBBY STORES INC.
(Sub. of Hob-Lob Limited Partnership)
7707 SW 44th St
Oklahoma City, OK 73179
Tel.: (405) 745-1100
Web Site: www.hobbylobby.com
Approx. Rev.: $1,470,000,000
Approx. Number Employees: 17,000
Year Founded: 1972
Business Description:
Hobbies, Arts & Crafts Supplies Retailer
S.I.C.: 5945; 5949; 5961
N.A.I.C.S.: 451120; 451130; 454111; 454113
Import Export
Media: 5-8-9-13-16-19
Personnel:
David Green *(CEO)*
John Schumacher *(Asst VP-Adv)*
Advertising Agency:
Producers Playhouse
24 NW 144th Cir Ste D
Edmond, OK 73013
Tel.: (485) 858-0700
Hemispheres TV Spot Production

HOLLANDER HOME FASHIONS CORPORATION
(Holding of Huntsman Gay Global Capital LLC)
6560 W Rogers Cir Ste 19
Boca Raton, FL 33487-2746
Tel.: (561) 997-6900
Fax: (561) 997-8738
Toll Free: (800) Bedrooms
Web Site: www.hollander.com
Sales Range: $250-299.9 Million
Approx. Number Employees: 55
Year Founded: 1953
Business Description:
Household Furnishings Whslr
S.I.C.: 2392; 2258
N.A.I.C.S.: 314129; 313249
Import Export
Personnel:
Jeff Hollander *(Chm)*
John Doherty *(COO)*
Beth Mack *(Chief Mdsg Officer)*
Tim Landers *(VP & Mgr-Bus)*
Jannice Cameron *(VP-Mktg)*
Amy Webster *(VP-Mdsg)*
Louis Smith *(Dir-Brand Mgmt)*
Brands & Products:
BED GLOVE
COUNTESS YORK
CUDDLEBEDS
DREAMSCAPE
HOLLANDER
J.G.HOOK
KAREN NEUBURGER
KOOLFOAM
LAURA ASHLEY
LIVE COMFORTABLY
PARK AVENUE
Advertising Agency:
Middleberg Communications, LLC
317 Madison Ave Ste 1500
New York, NY 10017
Tel.: (212) 812-5663
Tel.: (212) 812-5665
Fax: (212) 202-4118

HOM FURNITURE, INC.
10301 Woodcrest Dr NW
Minneapolis, MN 55433-6519
Tel.: (736) 767-3600
Fax: (763) 767-3762
E-mail: comments@homfurniture.com
Web Site: www.homfurniture.com
Sales Range: $150-199.9 Million
Approx. Number Employees: 1,000
Business Description:
Furniture Retailer
S.I.C.: 5712
N.A.I.C.S.: 442110
Media: 14-15
Personnel:
Rod Johansen *(Pres & CEO)*
Carl Nyberg *(COO)*

HOME MERIDIAN INTERNATIONAL, INC.
(Formerly Pulaski Furniture Corporation)
3980 Premier Dr Ste 310
High Point, NC 27265
Tel.: (336) 819-7200
Fax: (336) 819-7224
Web Site: www.homemeridian.com
Sales Range: $50-74.9 Million
Approx. Number Employees: 2,000
Year Founded: 1955
Business Description:
Holding Company; Furniture Mfr & Whslr
S.I.C.: 6719; 2511; 2512; 2521; 2531; 5021
N.A.I.C.S.: 551112; 337121; 337122; 337127; 337211; 423210
Import
Advertising Expenditures: $600,000
Media: 4-6-9-24
Distr.: Intl.; Natl.
Personnel:
George D. Revington *(CEO)*
Douglas A. Townsend *(CFO)*
Edward Tashjian *(CMO)*
Page Wilson *(Pres-Pulaski Furniture Div)*
Brands & Products:
PULASKI

THE HON COMPANY
(Sub. of HNI Corporation)
200 Oak St
Muscatine, IA 52761-4313
Tel.: (563) 272-7100
Fax: (800) 344-9270
Toll Free: (800) 553-8230
Web Site: www.hon.com
Sales Range: $400-449.9 Million
Approx. Number Employees: 1,200
Year Founded: 1943
Business Description:
Office Furniture Including Chairs, Panel Systems, Desks & Storage Mfr
S.I.C.: 2522; 2521
N.A.I.C.S.: 337214; 337211
Advertising Expenditures: $350,000
Media: 2-7-10-19-21
Distr.: Natl.
Budget Set: Oct.
Personnel:
Jerald K. Dittmer *(Pres)*
Shelley Desilva *(VP-Mktg)*
Brands & Products:
AMP
ANYWHERE CHAIR
ARIEL
CADENCE
CONCENSYS
ENERGY
ENVOY
ESSENTIALS
MIRATI
MOBIUS
NETCONNECT
PENDULUM
PERSONA
RAPTOR
RHAPSODY
SAMBA
SENSIBLE SEATING
SYNCHRONY
TERRACE
TROOPER
VIRAGE
Advertising Agency:
Falls Communications
50 Public Sq 25th Fl
Cleveland, OH 44113
Tel.: (216) 696-0229
Fax: (216) 696-0269

HOOKER FURNITURE CORPORATION
440 E Commonwealth Blvd
Martinsville, VA 24112-1831
Mailing Address:
PO Box 4708
Martinsville, VA 24115-4708
Tel.: (276) 632-2133
Fax: (276) 632-0026
E-mail: investor@hookerfurniture.com
Web Site: www.hookerfurniture.com
Approx. Sls.: $215,429,000
Approx. Number Employees: 688
Year Founded: 1924
Business Description:
Mfr & Importer of Household & Office Furniture
S.I.C.: 2511; 2434; 2512
N.A.I.C.S.: 337122; 337110; 337121
Import Export
Advertising Expenditures: $2,400,000
Media: 2-6-10-19
Distr.: Natl.
Budget Set: Nov.
Personnel:
Paul B. Toms, Jr. *(Chm & CEO)*
Alan Cole *(Pres)*
Paul A. Huckfeldt *(CFO)*
Mike Delgatti *(Pres-Upholstery)*
Robert W. Sherwood *(Treas, Sec & VP-Credit)*
Michael P. Spece *(Exec VP)*
Raymond T. Harm *(Sr VP-Sls)*
Kim D. Shaver *(VP-Mktg Comm)*
Brands & Products:
ABIGAIL
ARION
BEBE
BELLAGIO
BETTY LOU
BONHAM
BRITISH COLONIAL
CARNILLE
CASABLANCA
CHAPMAN
CHLOE
CLOSIERIE
COCO
CONSTANCE
COVINGTON
DALTON

Key to Media (For complete agency information see *The Advertising Red Books-Agencies* edition):
1. Bus. Publs. 2. Cable T.V. 3. Catalogs & Directories. 4. Co-op Adv. 5. Consumer Mags. 6. D.M. to Bus. Estab.7. D.M. to Consumers 8. Daily Newsp. 9. Exhibits/Trade Shows 10. Foreign 11. Infomercial 12. Internet Adv.13. Multimedia 14. Network Radio 15. Network T.V. 16. Newsp. Distr. Mags. 17. Other 18. Outdoor (Posters, Transit) 19. Point of Purchase20. Premiums, Novelties 21. Product Samples 22. Special Events Mktg. 23. Spot Radio 24. Spot T.V. 25. Weekly Newsp. 26. Yellow Page Adv.

DEMILUNE
DOMINIQUE
ETHAN
FENWICK
FIONA
FRENCH QUARTER
GERARD
GISELLE
GUINEVERE
GWENNETH
HARTLEY
HEATHER
HOOKE
JACOBEAN
JAMES
JENNIFER
KNOTTINGHAM
LINGERIE
LISABETH
LOGAN
LONGSTAFFE
PAIGE
PALM BEACH
PENINSULA
PHILIPPA
PIERRE
RADCLIFFE
RANDERS
SABRINA
SARAH
SHERIDAN
SMARTWORKS
TILT SWIVEL
TRIGGER
VERONIQUE
VERSAILLES
VIVI
WYATT
YALE

HOUSE OF NORWAY INC.
491 US Hwy 46
Fairfield, NJ 07004-1905
Tel.: (973) 227-3367
Fax: (732) 254-7577
Web Site: www.houseofnorway.com
Approx. Number Employees: 75
Business Description:
Furniture Stores
S.I.C.: 5712
N.A.I.C.S.: 442110
Media: 23
Personnel:
Odd Frustol *(Pres)*

HOWE FURNITURE CORPORATION
(Joint Venture of Oaktree Capital Management, L.P. & Whippoorwill Associates, Inc.)
10650 Gateway Blvd
Saint Louis, MO 63132
Tel.: (423) 586-7000
Fax: (314) 991-9227
Toll Free: (800) 888-4693
Web Site: www.howefurniture.com
Approx. Number Employees: 12
Year Founded: 1920
Business Description:
Folding & Non-Folding Tables; Flip Top Tables; Computer Support Furniture; Training, Conference & Hospitality Tables
S.I.C.: 2522
N.A.I.C.S.: 337214
Export
Advertising Expenditures: $370,000
Media: 2-4-8-10
Distr.: Intl.; Natl.
Budget Set: Oct.
Personnel:
Harold Howe *(Gen Mgr)*
Brands & Products:
1100/1200 SERIES
200 SERIES
500 II SERIES
ALLIANCE
CONCORDE
DIFFRIENT
FUGUE
GALAXY
HOWE
IMS
RONDO
SPECTRA
STORM
TEMPEST
TUTOR
UTILITY
VARIANT
WAFER

HUB FURNITURE COMPANY, INC.
291 Fore St
Portland, ME 04101-4108
Tel.: (207) 773-1789
Fax: (207) 773-8682
Toll Free: (800) 564-6482
E-mail: info@hubfurnitureco.com
Web Site: www.hubfurnitureco.com
Approx. Number Employees: 15
Year Founded: 1913
Business Description:
Sales of Furniture
S.I.C.: 5712; 5722
N.A.I.C.S.: 442110; 443111
Advertising Expenditures: $250,000
Media: 8-9-16-23-24-25
Personnel:
Sam Novick *(Pres)*
Andrew S. Novick *(VP-Mktg)*

HUMAN TOUCH
3030 Walnut Ave
Long Beach, CA 90807
Tel.: (562) 426-8700
Fax: (562) 426-9690
Toll Free: (800) 742-5493
E-mail: cs@humantouch.com
Web Site: www.humantouch.com
Sales Range: $50-74.9 Million
Approx. Number Employees: 54
Year Founded: 1971
Business Description:
Massage Chair Producer & Marketer
S.I.C.: 5021; 3634; 3639
N.A.I.C.S.: 423210; 335211; 335228
Advertising Expenditures: $524,773
Personnel:
James H. Fordyce *(Chm)*
David Wood *(CEO)*
Brands & Products:
ACU PRODUCTS MASSAGE
ACU-VIBE
EQUALIZER
FOOT SOOTHER
GET-A-WAY
HTT HUMAN TOUCH TEHCNOLOGY
HUMANTOUCH
IJOY
INTERACTIVE HEALTH
MASSAGE SYSTEM
PERFECT
ROBOTIC MASSAGE
TOUCH TECHNOLOGY
WARMAIR
Advertising Agency:
mml inc.
1413 B Abbot Kinney Blvd
Venice, CA 90291
Tel.: (310) 664-0600
Fax: (310) 664-0500

HUNTER DOUGLAS, INC.
(Sub. of Hunter Douglas B.V.)
2 Pkwy Rte 17 S
Upper Saddle River, NJ 07458
Tel.: (201) 327-8200
Fax: (201) 327-5644
Toll Free: (888) 438-4397
E-mail: consumer@hunterdouglas.com
Web Site: www.hunterdouglas.com
Sales Range: $900-999.9 Million
Approx. Number Employees: 100
Year Founded: 1968
Business Description:
Mfr. of Venetian Blinds, Shutters, Vertical Blinds, Pleated Shades, Honeycomb Shades, Window Shadings, Privacy Sheers, Wood Blinds & Roman Shades
S.I.C.: 2591; 3444
N.A.I.C.S.: 337920; 332322
Export
Advertising Expenditures: $8,000,000
Media: 2-3-4-5-6-7-8-10-11-13-16-19-20-21-22-23-26
Distr.: Intl.; Natl.
Personnel:
Marvin B. Hopkins *(Pres & CEO)*
Gordon Kahn *(CFO)*
Robert Meilen *(CIO)*
Scott Smith *(Pres-Fabrication Div)*
Ajit Mehra *(Exec VP)*
James B. Mathews *(Sr VP-Corp Mktg & VP-Corp Mktg)*
Wendell Colson *(Sr VP-R&D)*
James F. Bennett *(VP-Sls)*
Joseph Jankoski *(VP-Mdsg)*
Michelle Watson *(Dir-Product & Brand Mgmt)*
Donna Lobosco *(Dir-Brand Comm)*
Brands & Products:
ALOUETTE
APPLAUSE
BEYOND WOOD
BRILLIANCE
COUNTRY WOODS
DUETTE
HERITANCE
INNERSTYLE
JUBILANCE
LIGHTLINES
LUMINETTE
THE MANHATTAN COLLECTION
MILLENIA
NANTUCKET
PALM BEACH
PROVENANCE
REMEMBRANCE
SILHOUETTE
SILHOUETTE BON SOIR
SILHOUETTE III
VIGNETTE

HUSSEY SEATING CO.
38 Dyer St Ext
North Berwick, ME 03906-6763
Tel.: (207) 676-2271
Fax: (207) 676-9031
Fax: (207) 676-2222
Toll Free: (800) 341-0401
E-mail: info@husseyseating.com
Web Site: www.husseyseating.com
Approx. Sls.: $50,000,000
Approx. Number Employees: 800
Year Founded: 1835
Business Description:
Mfr of Roll-out Gym Seats, Auditorium & Stadium Chairs, Telescopic Bleachers & Platforms
S.I.C.: 2531
N.A.I.C.S.: 337127
Import Export
Advertising Expenditures: $300,000
Media: 2-4-10
Personnel:
Timothy B. Hussey *(Pres & CEO)*
Gary Merrill *(CFO)*
Jack F. Rogers *(VP-Sls & Mktg)*
Chris Robinson *(Dir-Mktg & Comm)*
Mark Beaulieu *(Mgr-Dealer Svc)*
Brands & Products:
FAT-STACK
HUSSEY
LEGEND
MAXAM
MEDALLION
OLYMPIAD
QUATTRO
SENTINEL
YOUR PARTNER FOR SEATING SOLUTIONS

IAC INDUSTRIES, INC.
895 Beacon St
Brea, CA 92821-2926
Tel.: (714) 990-8997
Fax: (714) 990-0557
E-mail: iacind@earthlink.net
Web Site: www.iacindustries.com
Approx. Number Employees: 105
Year Founded: 1971
Business Description:
Industrial Work Benches, Anti-Static Materials & Laminar Flow Work Stations Mfr
S.I.C.: 2531
N.A.I.C.S.: 337127
Media: 2-4-7-10-13-26
Distr.: Natl.
Personnel:
Don Murphy *(Pres)*
Paula McConnell *(Exec VP)*
John Notti *(Dir-Engrg)*
Jerry Sinner *(Mgr-Distr & Sls)*
Jessica Haderer *(Coord-Mktg & Sls)*
Brands & Products:
AIRCLEAN
DIMENSION
DIMENSION 4
EZE WORKMASTER
IAC
ISLES SERIES
OFFICE MATE
OPTIMUM
PRO SERIES
SPACESTATION
TASKMATE
WORKMASTER
Advertising Agency:
Creative Partners Group, Inc.
409 Via Corta
Palos Verdes Estates, CA 90274
Tel.: (310) 378-8043
Fax: (310) 378-8053

Key to Media (For complete agency information see *The Advertising Red Books-Agencies* edition):
1. Bus. Publs. 2. Cable T.V. 3. Catalogs & Directories. 4. Co-op Adv. 5. Consumer Mags. 6. D.M. to Bus. Estab.7. D.M. to Consumers
8. Daily Newsp. 9. Exhibits/Trade Shows 10. Foreign 11. Infomercial 12. Internet Adv.13. Multimedia 14. Network Radio
15. Network T.V. 16. Newsp. Distr. Mags. 17. Other 18. Outdoor (Posters, Transit) 19. Point of Purchase20. Premiums, Novelties
21. Product Samples 22. Special Events Mktg. 23. Spot Radio 24. Spot T.V. 25. Weekly Newsp. 26. Yellow Page Adv.

IKEA NORTH AMERICA SERVICES LLC
(Sub. of Ikea Svenska AB)
420 Alan Wood Rd
Conshohocken, PA 19428
Tel.: (610) 834-0180
Fax: (610) 834-0872
Web Site: www.ikea.com
Approx. Number Employees: 410
Year Founded: 1985
Business Description:
Furniture Stores; Nonresidential Building Operators
S.I.C.: 8742; 5712
N.A.I.C.S.: 541611; 442110
Import Export
Media: 3-4-6-8-11-13-15-24-31
Personnel:
Rich D'Amico *(Reg Mgr-Relationship Mktg)*
Leontyne Green *(Mgr-U.S.-Mktg)*
Brands & Products:
IKEA
Advertising Agencies:
Horizon Print Services Group
75 Varick St
New York, NY 10017
Tel.: (212) 916-8600
Fax: (212) 916-8653

Karmarama
31 Vernon St
London, W14 0RN, United Kingdom
Tel.: (44) 20 7612 1777
Fax: (44) 20 7631 1779

McCann Erickson Worldwide
622 3rd Ave
New York, NY 10017-6707
Tel.: (646) 865-2000
Fax: (646) 487-9610
IKEA Catalogue (Global Agency of Record)

MEC, Global HQ, New York
825 7th Ave
New York, NY 10019-6014
Tel.: (212) 474-0000
Fax: (212) 474-0020
Fax: (212) 474-0003

Ogilvy & Mather
(Sub. of WPP Group plc)
636 11th Ave
New York, NY 10036
Tel.: (212) 237-4000
Fax: (212) 237-5123
General Market
Hispanic Market
— David Carson *(Exec Dir-Creative)*

SCPF
1688 Meridian Ave Ste 200
Miami Beach, FL 33139
Tel.: (305) 674-3222
Fax: (305) 695-2777
Hispanic Market

IMPERIAL WOODWORKS, INC.
7201 Mars Dr
Waco, TX 76712
Tel.: (254) 741-0606
Fax: (254) 741-0736
E-mail: info@imperialww.com
Web Site: www.imperialww.com
Approx. Number Employees: 100
Year Founded: 1960
Business Description:
Mfr. of Church Furniture
S.I.C.: 2531
N.A.I.C.S.: 337127
Media: 4-7
Personnel:
Steve Smith *(Owner)*
Brands & Products:
FOYER
IMPERIAL WOODWORKS
NARTHEX

INTERFACE FLOORING SYSTEMS INC.
(Sub. of Interface, Inc.)
1503 Orchard Hill Rd
Lagrange, GA 30241-1503
Tel.: (706) 882-1891
Fax: (706) 884-5660
Toll Free: (800) 336-0225
E-mail: info@interfacefloor.com
Web Site: www.interfacefloor.com
Sales Range: Less than $1 Million
Approx. Number Employees: 500
Year Founded: 1973
Business Description:
Modular Carpeting & Six Foot Roll Goods for the Commercial Market Mfr
S.I.C.: 2273
N.A.I.C.S.: 314110
Import Export
Advertising Expenditures: $1,000,000
Media: 1-2-4-8-10-20-21-22-26
Distr.: Intl.; Natl.
Budget Set: Sept.
Personnel:
Daniel T. Hendrix *(Pres & CEO)*
Mandy Nolen *(Dir-Interactive Mktg)*
Brands & Products:
INTERFACE

INTERIORS BY STEVEN G INC.
2818 Centre Port Cir
Pompano Beach, FL 33064
Tel.: (954) 735-8223
Fax: (954) 735-7546
E-mail: info@interiorsbysteveng.com
Web Site:
www.interiorsbysteveng.com
Approx. Number Employees: 25
Business Description:
Interior Design Services
S.I.C.: 7389
N.A.I.C.S.: 541410
Media: 6-10
Personnel:
Steven Gurowitz *(Pres)*

INTERKAL, LLC
(Sub. of Kotobuki Corporation)
5981 E Cork St
Kalamazoo, MI 49048
Mailing Address:
PO Box 2017
Kalamazoo, MI 49003-2107
Tel.: (269) 349-1521
Fax: (269) 349-6530
E-mail: info@interkal.com
Web Site: www.interkal.com
Approx. Number Employees: 140
Year Founded: 1981
Business Description:
Telescopic Bleachers, Mass Seating, Movable Stages & Platforms; V.O.S. Gym Seating & Sculpture Seat Contour Seat Module; Stadium Seating Mfr
S.I.C.: 2531
N.A.I.C.S.: 337127
Export
Advertising Expenditures: $350,000
Media: 4-10
Distr.: Intl.; Natl.
Budget Set: Oct.
Brands & Products:
CSM
GDS-FA
GDS-PC
GDS-SC
INTERKAL
SSAR
SSM
VIP

IRWIN SEATING COMPANY INC.
3251 Fruit Rdg Ave NW
Grand Rapids, MI 49544
Tel.: (616) 574-7400
Fax: (616) 574-7411
Toll Free: (866) 464-7946
E-mail: sales@irwinseating.com
Web Site: www.irwinseating.com
E-Mail For Key Personnel:
Sales Director: sales@irwinseating.com
Approx. Number Employees: 400
Year Founded: 1907
Business Description:
Public Seating Mfr & Retailer
S.I.C.: 2531
N.A.I.C.S.: 337127
Import Export
Media: 4-10-22
Personnel:
Earle S. Irwin *(Pres & CEO)*
Ray Vander Kooi *(CFO)*
Bruce Cohen *(Sr VP-Sls & Mktg)*
Brands & Products:
ALLEGRO
AMBASSADOR
AMSTERDAM
CENTURION
CENTURY PAC
CITATION
CRUSADER
DAVIES
E-LINK
EMERSON
EMPIRE
FOREST
GALAXY
GRAND RAPIDS
IMPERIAL
IRWIN SEATING
LOUNGER
MAJESTIC
MARQUEE
METEOR
MILLENNIUM
NEW AMSTERDAM
ORIENTAL
ORPEUM
PARADISE
PATRIOT
RIALTO
SATURN
SENATOR
SIGNATURE
SPRINGFIELD
UNI-LECTA
VIP
VIP SEATING
WINTER GARDEN

J. ROBERT SCOTT INC.
500 N Oak St
Inglewood, CA 90302
Tel.: (310) 680-4200
Fax: (310) 659-4494
Toll Free: (877) 207-5130
Web Site: www.jrobertscott.com
Approx. Sls.: $34,200,000
Approx. Number Employees: 125
Business Description:
Furniture & Woven Textiles
S.I.C.: 5131; 2512
N.A.I.C.S.: 424310; 337121
Media: 4-6-10-11
Personnel:
Bill Holodnak *(Pres)*
Douglas Mann *(Mng Dir-Fin Svcs Practice-New York)*
June Lockhart-Triolo *(Dir-Art & Mgr-Mktg)*
Brands & Products:
ACANTHUS
ADAM
ADELPHI
ADRIANNA
ALLONGD
AMPHORA
ANDROMEDA
ATHENA CHANDELIER
ATHENA WALL SCONCES
BALLETON
BARKLEY
BASKET WEAVE
BEIJING
BETHESDA
BIEDERMEIER FLOOR
BORGHESE
BOSTONIAN
BOXER
BRISTOL
CAMBON
CAMBRIDGE
CANDLESTICK
CANONDA
CAPRI
CAPULET
CHATEAU FAUTEUIL
CHELSEA
CHIARA
CHOSES
CILINDRO
CLAVOS
CLOUD CHEST
COLETTE FLOOR
CORNUCOPIA
CRYSTAL ROD FLOOR
DEANNA
DELTA
DESDEMONA
DIRECTOIRE
DORCHESTER
D'ORSAY
DRUM
EMPIRE DESK
EXXUS
FONTAIN
FORMS
FRENCH
GARBO SETTEE
GEORGES
GEORGIAN
GRAND MARQUIS
GRIFFITH
GUSTAVE BANQUETTE
HALL
HUNTINGTON
IL PRANZARE

Key to Media (For complete agency information see *The Advertising Red Books-Agencies* edition):
1. Bus. Publs. 2. Cable T.V. 3. Catalogs & Directories. 4. Co-op Adv. 5. Consumer Mags. 6. D.M. to Bus. Estab. 7. D.M. to Consumers
8. Daily Newsp. 9. Exhibits/Trade Shows 10. Foreign 11. Infomercial 12. Internet Adv. 13. Multimedia 14. Network Radio
15. Network T.V. 16. Newsp. Distr. Mags. 17. Other 18. Outdoor (Posters, Transit) 19. Point of Purchase 20. Premiums, Novelties
21. Product Samples 22. Special Events Mktg. 23. Spot Radio 24. Spot T.V. 25. Weekly Newsp. 26. Yellow Page Adv.

J. M. SEMANIER
J ROBERT SCOTT
JEFFRY
JONATHAN
JOSEPHINE
LE MIDI
L'HERMITAGE
LIBRA TASK
LISETTE
LITHIC
MANSFIELD
MONDRIAN DESK
ON POINT
PARIS

Advertising Agency:
Iowa Interactive
4212 Glencoe Ave
Marina Del Rey, CA 90292
Tel.: (310) 823-8238
Fax: (310) 823-7108

JAMISON BEDDING, INC.
565 Brick Church Park Dr
Nashville, TN 37207
Mailing Address:
PO Box 681948
Franklin, TN 37068-1948
Tel.: (615) 794-1883
Fax: (615) 794-2254
Toll Free: (800) 255-1883
E-mail: info@jamisonbedding.com
Web Site: www.jamisonbedding.com
Sales Range: $25-49.9 Million
Approx. Number Employees: 200
Year Founded: 1883
Business Description:
Mfr Bedding Products
S.I.C.: 2515; 5712
N.A.I.C.S.: 337910; 442110
Media: 2-5-6-10-26
Distr.: Natl.
Budget Set: Dec.
Personnel:
Frank Gorell *(Pres)*
Thad Pettyjohn *(VP-Sls)*
Kim George *(Dir-Sls & Mktg)*
Brands & Products:
CREST COLLECTION
EQUALIZER
JAMISON
PILLOW TOPPER
SMART COIL
TALALAY LATEX
TRUE BALANCE
VITA PEDIC

JASPER SEATING CO., INC.
225 Clay St
Jasper, IN 47546-2821
Mailing Address:
PO Box 932
Jasper, IN 47547-0932
Tel.: (812) 482-3204
Fax: (812) 482-1548
Toll Free: (800) 622-5661
E-mail: webmaster@jasperseating.com
Web Site: www.jasperseating.com
Approx. Number Employees: 225
Year Founded: 1929
Business Description:
Mfr. of Wood Furniture
S.I.C.: 2521; 2531
N.A.I.C.S.: 337211; 337127
Export
Media: 2-4-6-17
Distr.: Natl.
Personnel:
Mike Elliot *(Pres)*
Brands & Products:
ACCENT
ACCOLADE
ADDISON
ALDEN
AMERICANA
ANTHEM
ARCATA
ARLINGTON
ATHENS
AVALON
BALLAD
BELLE
BISON
BOSTON
BRADBURY
BRADFORD
BROCKTON
BROGAN
CABARET
CADET
CALCULUS
CALLAWAY
CAMBRIDGE
CARRIAGE
CHANCELLOR
CHANDLER
CHARLESTON
CLASS ACT
CLASSMATE
COLLEGIAN
COLONY
CONTEMPO
CORBIN
DEBUT
DEVERAUX
DEXTER
DIMENSION
ELITE
ELLIPSE
EMERSON
ENCORE
FAIRFIELD
FAIRMONT
FINLEY
FLEETWOOD
GALA
GALLERY
GEYSER
GRACE
GUILD
HAMMOND
HAMPTON
HARBOR
HARLEQUIN
HERITAGE
HEROINE
HUDSON
IMPACT
JEFFERSON
KALLY
KELSO
KENDALL
KENNEDY
KEYSTONE
LANCELOT
LAREDO
LAUREL
LEGACY
LINCOLN
LOGAN
MADISON
MANHATTAN
MASTERS
MEDALLION
MELROSE
METRO
MILESTONE
MOTIF
MURPHY
NELSON
NEXUS
OLYMPIA
OVATION
OVERTON
PLATINUM
PLEASANT
PRESTON
PRODIGY
PROFILE
RAVEN
REGAL
SANTA ROSA
SORRELL
SPENCER
STERLING
SULTAN
SUMMIT
SUTTON
TARA
TERRACE
TIERRA
TRIBUTE
TRINITY
ULTIMA
VINTAGE
VISTA
WALKER
WATSON

JBI, INC.
2650 E El Presidio St
Long Beach, CA 90810
Tel.: (310) 537-8200
Fax: (310) 604-3827
E-mail: jbi@jbi-interiors.com
Web Site: www.jbi-interiors.com
Approx. Sls.: $20,000,000
Approx. Number Employees: 175
Year Founded: 1968
Business Description:
Restaurant Furniture Mfr
S.I.C.: 2531; 5046
N.A.I.C.S.: 337127; 423440
Advertising Expenditures: $159,000
Media: 17
Personnel:
Gregg Buchbinder *(CEO)*
Michael Buchbinder *(Co-CEO)*

JENNIFER CONVERTIBLES INC.
(Filed Ch 11 Bankruptcy #10-13779 on 07/20/2010 in U.S. Bankruptcy Ct, Southern Dist of NY)
417 Crossways Park Dr
Woodbury, NY 11797
Tel.: (516) 496-1900
Fax: (516) 496-8638
E-mail: invest@jenniferfurniture.com
Web Site: www.jenniferfurniture.com
Approx. Rev.: $76,305,000
Approx. Number Employees: 417
Year Founded: 1980
Business Description:
Owner & Licensor Sofabed & Leather Specialty Retail Stores
S.I.C.: 5712; 2512; 6794
N.A.I.C.S.: 442110; 337121; 533110
Advertising Expenditures: $10,209,000
Media: 9-10-23-24-25
Distr.: Natl.; Reg.
Budget Set: Monthly
Personnel:
Harley J. Greenfield *(Chm & CEO)*
Rami G. Abada *(Pres, CFO & COO)*
John Dunican *(Sr VP-Sls)*
Leslie Falchook *(Sr VP-Admin)*

JEREMIAH CAMPBELL & COMPANY
1537 Route 1
Cape Neddick, ME 03902-7432
Mailing Address:
PO Box 539
Cape Neddick, ME 03902
Tel.: (207) 363-8499
Fax: (207) 363-8499
E-mail: jeremiahcamp@gwi.net
Web Site:
www.jeremiahcampbell.com
Approx. Number Employees: 2
Business Description:
Antique Reproduction Furniture & Accessories
S.I.C.: 2541
N.A.I.C.S.: 337212
Media: 4-6
Personnel:
Steve Campbell *(Co-Owner)*
Richard Ross *(Co-Owner)*

JOFCO INC.
402 E 13th St
Jasper, IN 47546-2422
Tel.: (812) 482-5154
Fax: (812) 634-2392
Toll Free: (800) 235-6326
E-mail: furniture@jofco.com
Web Site: www.jofco.com
Approx. Number Employees: 270
Year Founded: 1922
Business Description:
Wooden Office Furniture & Seating Mfr
S.I.C.: 2521; 5021
N.A.I.C.S.: 337211; 423210
Import Export
Media: 2-4-7-10-26
Distr.: Natl.
Personnel:
William Rubino *(Pres & CEO)*
Mandy Phillips *(Mgr-Mktg)*
Brands & Products:
ALLOYA
ANNESLEY
APPLICATIONS
ARABESQUE
ASHTON
BEXLEY
BRISTOL
BROADCAST
BUCKINGHAM
CAMBRIDGE
CANDID
CARLTON
CASEWORKS
COLLECTIVE LOUNGE
COLLECTIVE MOTION
COLLECTIVE OFFICE
COLLECTIVE SPACE
COLLECTIVE TABLES
COMPONENTS
CONFIGURATIONS
CONVEX
CONVEX FLEX
FACET
FORMA
FORMA KRISTALL
KENSINGTON

Key to Media (For complete agency information see *The Advertising Red Books-Agencies* edition):
1. Bus. Publs. 2. Cable T.V. 3. Catalogs & Directories. 4. Co-op Adv. 5. Consumer Mags. 6. D.M. to Bus. Estab.7. D.M. to Consumers 8. Daily Newsp. 9. Exhibits/Trade Shows 10. Foreign 11. Infomercial 12. Internet Adv.13. Multimedia 14. Network Radio 15. Network T.V. 16. Newsp. Distr. Mags. 17. Other 18. Outdoor (Posters, Transit) 19. Point of Purchase20. Premiums, Novelties 21. Product Samples 22. Special Events Mktg. 23. Spot Radio 24. Spot T.V. 25. Weekly Newsp. 26. Yellow Page Adv.

Jofco Inc. — (Continued)

LADERA
LEWIS
MADDOX
MAIA
MAIA LOUNGE
MODE
MONTAGE
NEWPORT
OTTO VIENNA
OTTOVIENNA
PALAZZO
PAVILION
PAVILION WOOD
PIVOT
PORTRAIT
PRONTO PROGRAM
PURPOSE
QUICKSHIP PROGRAM
REFLECTIONS
SHELBY
SILVER
SOLARA
SOLARA LOUNGE
TIPER
TRADITIONAL
TREVISO
TRIO PLUS
VANGUARD
WALDEN
WALLSTREET
WALTHAM
WEB SHELVING
WELLINGTON
WESTLAKE
WINDSOR

KANE FURNITURE CORPORATION

5700 70th Ave
Pinellas Park, FL 33781-4238
Tel.: (727) 545-9555
Fax: (727) 541-6960
Web Site: www.kanesfurniture.com
Sales Range: $100-124.9 Million
Approx. Number Employees: 600
Year Founded: 1948
Business Description:
Furniture Stores
S.I.C.: 5712
N.A.I.C.S.: 442110
Import Export
Media: 3-8-9-16-18-23-24-25
Personnel:
Thelma Rothman *(Chm)*
Erwin Novack *(Pres & CEO)*
Wayne Liburdhas *(Dir-MIS)*
Brands & Products:
KANE'S
SAVON

THE KARGES FURNITURE COMPANY, INC.

1501 W Maryland St
Evansville, IN 47719-1831
Tel.: (812) 425-2291
Fax: (812) 425-4016
Toll Free: (800) 252-7437
E-mail: kargesinfo@karges.com
Web Site: www.karges.com
Approx. Number Employees: 95
Year Founded: 1886
Business Description:
Furniture Mfr
S.I.C.: 2511; 2512
N.A.I.C.S.: 337122; 337121
Import Export
Media: 6-7-10
Distr.: Intl.; Natl.
Personnel:
Joan Rogier *(Pres)*
Gretchen Keith *(VP)*
Brands & Products:
KARGES BY HAND

KAYNE & SON CUSTOM HARDWARE INC.

100 Daniel Rdg Rd
Candler, NC 28715
Tel.: (828) 667-8868
Tel.: (828) 665-1988
Fax: (828) 665-8303
E-mail: kaynehdwe@charter.net
Web Site:
www.customforgedhardware.com
Approx. Number Employees: 4
Business Description:
Custom Hardware Mfr
S.I.C.: 0752; 3366
N.A.I.C.S.: 115210; 331525
Media: 6-13
Personnel:
Shirley Kayne *(Owner & Pres)*

KEWAUNEE SCIENTIFIC CORPORATION

2700 W Front St
Statesville, NC 28677-2927
Mailing Address:
PO Box 1842
Statesville, NC 28687-1842
Tel.: (704) 873-7202
Fax: (704) 873-1275
E-mail: marketing@kewaunee.com
Web Site: www.kewaunee.com
Approx. Sls.: $99,093,000
Approx. Number Employees: 578
Year Founded: 1906
Business Description:
Laboratory & Technical Furniture Products Designer, Mfr & Installer
S.I.C.: 3821; 2531
N.A.I.C.S.: 339111; 337127
Export
Advertising Expenditures: $398,000
Media: 4-7-10-13-17
Distr.: Intl.; Natl.
Personnel:
William A. Shumaker *(Chm, Pres & CEO)*
D. Michael Parker *(CFO, Treas, Sec & Sr VP-Fin)*
K. Bain Black *(VP & Gen Mgr-Tech Furniture Grp)*
Dana L. Dahlgren *(VP-Sls & Mktg-Laboratory Products Grp)*
Kurt P. Rindoks *(VP-Engrg & Product Dev)*
Brands & Products:
ADJUSTABENCH
ADVANTAGE
ALPHA SYSTEM
BASIKBENCH
CONTOUR
DISCOVERY
DYNAMIC BARRIER
EARTHLINE
...ENCOURAGING NEW DISCOVERY
EVOLUTION
EXPLORER
FLEXTECH
KEMRESIN
KEWAUNEE SCIENTIFIC CORPORATION
SILHOUTTE
STURDIKWIK
STURDILITE
SUPREME AIR SERIES
TEKRAK
TRADEMARK

KIDCO, INC.

1013 Technology Way
Libertyville, IL 60048
Tel.: (847) 549-8600
Fax: (847) 549-8660
Toll Free: (800) 553-5529
E-mail: information@kidco.com
Web Site: www.kidco.com
Approx. Sls.: $2,800,000
Approx. Number Employees: 30
Business Description:
Home Safety & Baby Products Marketer
S.I.C.: 5021
N.A.I.C.S.: 423210
Media: 6-13
Personnel:
Ken Kaiser *(Chm)*
Carole Childs *(VP-Mktg)*
Brands & Products:
BABYSTEPS
BLINDWINDER
CONFIGUREGATE
ELONGATE
GATEWAY
HEARTHGATE
KIDCO
PEAPOD
PLAYDEN
SHOCK SHIELD
SOFT JAMB

KIMBALL INTERNATIONAL, INC.

1600 Royal St
Jasper, IN 47549-1001
Tel.: (812) 482-1600
Fax: (812) 482-8300
Toll Free: (800) 482-1616
E-mail: webmaster@kimball.com
Web Site: www.ir.kimball.com
Approx. Sls.: $1,202,597,000
Approx. Number Employees: 6,362
Year Founded: 1950
Business Description:
Office & Hospitality Furniture Mfr; Contract Electronics Mfr
S.I.C.: 2521; 3679
N.A.I.C.S.: 337211; 334419
Import Export
Advertising Expenditures: $8,300,000
Media: 2-5-6-7-8-9-10-14-23-26
Distr.: Intl.; Natl.
Budget Set: Feb.
Personnel:
Douglas A. Habig *(Chm)*
James C. Thyen *(Pres & CEO)*
Robert F. Schneider *(CFO & Exec VP)*
Gary W. Schwartz *(CIO & Exec VP)*
Michelle R. Schroeder *(Chief Acctg Officer & VP)*
John H. Kahle *(Gen Counsel, Sec & Exec VP)*
Donald D. Charron *(Exec VP)*
Martin Vaught *(Dir-Pub & IR)*
Brands & Products:
ARTEC
ENVYWORKS
FOCUS
KIMBALL
KIMBALL HOSPITALITY
KIMBALL OFFICE
NATIONAL
REMEDY

KINDEL FURNITURE COMPANY

4047 Eastern Ave SE
Grand Rapids, MI 49508
Tel.: (616) 243-3676
Fax: (616) 243-6248
Web Site: www.kindelfurniture.com
Sales Range: $10-24.9 Million
Approx. Number Employees: 200
Year Founded: 1901
Business Description:
Furniture Mfr
S.I.C.: 2511; 7641
N.A.I.C.S.: 337122; 811420
Media: 2-4-7-8-9-10-13-19-20
Distr.: Natl.
Budget Set: Dec.
Personnel:
Jim Fisher *(CEO)*
Dennis Patterson *(VP-Fin & Ops)*
Amy Wolbert *(Dir-Mktg)*
Brands & Products:
KINDEL

KING KOIL LICENSING COMPANY INC.

7501 S Quincy St Ste 130
Willowbrook, IL 60527
Tel.: (630) 230-9744
Fax: (630) 655-3928
E-mail: contact@kingkoil.com
Web Site: www.comfortsolutions.com
Sales Range: Less than $1 Million
Approx. Number Employees: 15
Year Founded: 1898
Business Description:
Mattress Mfr
S.I.C.: 2515
N.A.I.C.S.: 337910
Media: 1-2-3-5-6-8-9-10-19-23-24
Distr.: Reg.
Budget Set: Jan. -Feb.
Personnel:
Garret Weyand *(Chm)*
Brands & Products:
ADVANTAGELOFT
COMFORT SENSATIONS
COMFORT SOLUTIONS
EVERLAST
KING KOIL
KOOL KIDS
LUXURY ESCAPES
NATURAL RESPONSE
PERFECT CONTOUR
PERFECT CONTOUR EXTRAORDINAIRE
PERFECT SOLUTIONS
SPINE SUPPORT

KINGSDOWN, INC.

126 W Holt St
Mebane, NC 27302
Tel.: (919) 563-3531
Fax: (919) 563-0405
Toll Free: (800) 354-5464
E-mail: customerservice@kingsdown.com
Web Site: www.kingsdown.com
Approx. Number Employees: 300
Year Founded: 1904
Business Description:
Mattress Mfr
S.I.C.: 2515
N.A.I.C.S.: 337910

Key to Media (For complete agency information see *The Advertising Red Books-Agencies* edition):
1. Bus. Publs. 2. Cable T.V. 3. Catalogs & Directories. 4. Co-op Adv. 5. Consumer Mags. 6. D.M. to Bus. Estab.7. D.M. to Consumers 8. Daily Newsp. 9. Exhibits/Trade Shows 10. Foreign 11. Infomercial 12. Internet Adv.13. Multimedia 14. Network Radio 15. Network T.V. 16. Newsp. Distr. Mags. 17. Other 18. Outdoor (Posters, Transit) 19. Point of Purchase20. Premiums, Novelties 21. Product Samples 22. Special Events Mktg. 23. Spot Radio 24. Spot T.V. 25. Weekly Newsp. 26. Yellow Page Adv.

Export
Media: 2-3-5-6-8-9-13-19-20-22-23-24
Distr.: Intl.; Natl.; Reg.
Budget Set: Oct.
Personnel:
W. Eric Hinshaw *(Chm & CEO)*
Pat Flippin *(Pres & COO)*
Thomas I. McLean *(Exec VP)*
Brands & Products:
BODY PERFECT
BODY SYSTEM
CROWN COLLECTION
CROWN COMFORT
CROWN IMPERIAL
DAY MATT
DR. G JUST FOR TEENS
DR. GOODBONES
ECSTASY
FIRM-O-PEDIC
FLEXATRON
FRESH COMFORT
HIGHLAND HOUSE
IMPERIAL COMFORT
KING-O-PEDIC
KINGSDOWN
KINGSDOWN POSTURE
KINGSDOWN TUFF GRIP
NEW EXPERIENCE IV
NEW EXPERIENCE VI
ORIGINAL KINGSDOWN
ORTHOPEDIC SERIES
PARTNER PERFECT
PASSIONS
PLATFORM
PLATFORM PLUS
PLUSH SENSE
QUEENSDOWN
ROYAL KINSDOWN
SCZ
SLEEP COMFORT INTERNATIONAL
SLEEP-IN SOFA
SLEEP-N-LOUNGE
SLEEP TO LIVE
SLEEP TO LIVE WAKE UP TO A BETTER LIFE
SLEEPING BEAUTY
SLEEPING BEAUTY 2000
SLEEPING BEAUTY ELOQUENCE
SLEEPING BEAUTY SOFTIE
SLEEPING BEAUTY SYSTEM
SLEEPING BEAUTY TRADITION
S.O.F. SYSTEM
SOF T-VISION
SPINAL AID
THE STERLING EDITION
STERLING LINE
TRADITION
ULTRA SEVEN
UNIFLEX GRIDS
VARIABLE INCLINING POSITIONS BED
YOUNG AMERICAN

KINGSLEY-BATE, LTD.
7200 Gateway Ct
Manassas, VA 20109-7308
Tel.: (703) 361-7000
Fax: (703) 361-7001
E-mail: teak@kingsleybate.com
Web Site: www.kingsleybate.com
Approx. Number Employees: 12
Business Description:
Teak Outdoor Furniture Mfr
S.I.C.: 2511; 5712
N.A.I.C.S.: 337122; 442110
Media: 4-6-8-10
Personnel:
Chris Kingsley *(Dir)*
Clay Kingsley *(Dir)*
Advertising Agency:
Abrials & Partners
805 King St 2nd Fl
Alexandria, VA 22314
Tel.: (703) 548-2570
Fax: (703) 548-3788

KRAVET FABRICS INC.
225 Central Ave S
Bethpage, NY 11714
Tel.: (516) 293-2000
Fax: (516) 293-1994
Toll Free: (800) 645-9870
E-mail: marketing@kravet.com
Web Site: www.kravet.com
E-Mail For Key Personnel:
President: ckravet@kfi.com
Marketing Director: bgreene@kfi.com
Sales Director: j.dull@kfi.com
Approx. Number Employees: 450
Year Founded: 1918
Business Description:
Whslr of Decorative Fabrics, Furniture, Wallcoverings & Trimming
S.I.C.: 5131; 5198
N.A.I.C.S.: 424310; 424950
Import Export
Media: 4-6-7-8-22
Distr.: Natl.
Personnel:
Cary Kravet *(Pres)*
Jerry Schwartz *(Exec VP & Gen Mgr)*
John Dull *(Exec VP-Sls)*
Beth Greene *(VP-Corp Mktg)*
Anne Felvstein *(Dir-Mktg)*
Brands & Products:
KRAVET
KRAVET BASICS
KRAVET COLLECTIONS
KRAVET CONTRACT
KRAVET DESIGN
KRAVET SOLEIL
KRAVETCOUTURE

KREISS ENTERPRISES INC.
8525 Camino Santa Fe
San Diego, CA 92121
Tel.: (858) 453-6245
Fax: (858) 453-6602
Toll Free: (800) KREISS-1
E-mail: kreiss@kreisshq.com
Web Site: www.kreiss.com
Sales Range: $10-24.9 Million
Approx. Number Employees: 125
Year Founded: 1939
Business Description:
Furniture, Bed Linen & Fabric Designer, Mfr & Retailer
S.I.C.: 5021; 7389
N.A.I.C.S.: 423210; 541410
Import Export
Media: 4-6-8-13
Personnel:
Michael Kreiss *(Pres & CEO)*
Brands & Products:
ALBANY
ANDORA
ARCADIAN CREDENZA
ARES
ASHANTI
AURORA
AVALON
AZTECA
BASSANO
BASTILLE
BELAIR
BORDER
BRIDGEHAMPTON
BRONZE RAINDRUM
BYZANTINE
CALIFORNIA
CAMPAIGN
CARAVELLE
CARMEL
CENTAUR
CHATEAU
CHURCHILL
CLEO
COCO TWIG
COCOSHELL
COLONY
CONCORDE
CONTESSA
CORNICHE
CUBIST
DAKOTA
DARK COCO
DEAUVILLE
DEL MAR
DORCHESTER
DOVER
ECRU
EGGSHELL NESTING
ESPRESSO
ETRUSCAN
FLEUR DE LIS
GALAXY
GATSBY
GIVEMY
GIVERNY
GRECO
GRENOBLE
HAMPTONS
HAMPTONS TRAY
HARTFORD
HEXAGON
IVORY
KHYBER
KLISMOS
KREISS
LACE
LEONARDO
LIBRA
LISBON
LOIRE
LYON
MAGELLAN
MALACCA
MALAYSIAN
MALIBU
MANHATTAN
MARQUESA
MARTINIQUE
MAYAN
MEDICI
MONARCH
MONTANA
MONTEREY
MONTEVIDEO
MONTORO
MONTREAL
MORROCAN
MYKONOS
NAIROBI
NEO CLASSIC
NEPAL
NEPAL COUNTER
PALAZZO
PALERMO
PALMERO
PANAMA
PAVILION
PENINSULA
PICCIONE FLEUR DE LIS
POMPEII
PORTOFINO
PRADO
QUADRO
RANCHO SANTA FE
RANGOON
RENAISSANCE
RICHELIEU
RICHLIEU
ROCOCO
ROMA
SABRE
SAFARI
SALERNO
SAVOY
SCROLL
SCROLL INLAY
SEVILLE
SHERIDAN
SIERRA TOWERS
SOHO
SOLANA
SOMERSET
SONRISA
SOROYA
SPARTA
STOCKHOLM
STRADELLA
STUDY
SUSSEX
THEBES
TORONTO
TORRE
TORTORA
TOSCANA BUREAU
TRADEWINDS
TRAVERTINE
TUXEDO
VENETAIN
VESUVIUS
VICENZA
WESTPORT
WESTPORT ARMLESS
WINDSOR
ZUNIGA

LA-Z-BOY INCORPORATED
1284 N Telegraph Rd
Monroe, MI 48162-5138
Tel.: (734) 242-1444
Fax: (734) 457-2005
E-mail: investorrelations@la-z-boy.com
Web Site: www.lazboy.com
Approx. Sls.: $1,187,143,000
Approx. Number Employees: 7,910
Year Founded: 1927
Business Description:
Furniture Mfr
S.I.C.: 2512; 5712
N.A.I.C.S.: 337121; 442110
Import Export
Advertising Expenditures: $46,300,000
Media: 2-3-6-13-15-16-26
Distr.: Natl.
Budget Set: Feb.
Personnel:
Kurt L. Darrow *(Chm, Pres & CEO)*
Louis M. Riccio, Jr. *(CFO & Sr VP)*
Daniel F. DeLand *(CIO & VP)*
J. Douglas Collier *(CMO)*
Mark S. Bacon, Sr. *(Chief Retail Officer)*

Key to Media (For complete agency information see *The Advertising Red Books-Agencies* edition):
1. Bus. Publs. 2. Cable T.V. 3. Catalogs & Directories. 4. Co-op Adv. 5. Consumer Mags. 6. D.M. to Bus. Estab.7. D.M. to Consumers
8. Daily Newsp. 9. Exhibits/Trade Shows 10. Foreign 11. Infomercial 12. Internet Adv.13. Multimedia 14. Network Radio
15. Network T.V. 16. Newsp. Distr. Mags. 17. Other 18. Outdoor (Posters, Transit) 19. Point of Purchase20. Premiums, Novelties
21. Product Samples 22. Special Events Mktg. 23. Spot Radio 24. Spot T.V. 25. Weekly Newsp. 26. Yellow Page Adv.

La-Z-Boy Incorporated — (Continued)

Rodney D. England *(Pres-Non-Branded Upholstery & Sr VP)*
Otis S. Sawyer *(Pres-Non-Branded Upholstery & Sr VP)*
Steven M. Kincaid *(Pres-Casegoods)*
R. Rand Tucker *(Gen Counsel & VP)*
Paula Hoyas *(VP-Mdsg)*
Steven P. Rindskopf *(Corp VP-HR)*
Matt Targett *(Dir-Interactive Mktg)*

Brands & Products:
ADLER
AMERICAN HOME COLLECTION
ATLAS
BARNETT
BAUHAUS USA
BRADY
BROADWAY
CALLOWAY
CALVIN
CARMEN
CARRINGTON
CHARLOTTE
EVA
GRIFFIN
HALSTEAD
HAMMARY
HARVEY
IRENE
JACKLEY
JULES
JUST YOUR STYLE
KINCAID
LA-Z-BOY
LA-Z-BOY COMFORT STUDIOS
LA-Z-BOY DESIGNER'S CHOICE
LA-Z-BOY FURNITURE GALLERIES
LA-Z-BOY KIDZ
LA-Z-COIL
LA-Z-TOUCH
LAWRENCE
LYLE
MAVERICK
MELANIE
MEMPHIS
MILAN
MONTGOMERY
THE NEW LOOK OF COMFORT
NICHOLAS
ORSON
PROFILE
QUINN
RALEIGH
REESE
REX
RITZ
SARASOTA
SHEFFIELD
SIGNATURE
SKYLER
SOPHIA
SUPREME COMFORT
SYRACUSE
TACOMA
TARLETON
TERRA
TREVORTON
TRISTAN
WINDHAM
ZOE

Advertising Agencies:
Hart Associates, Inc.
1915 Indian Wood Cir
Maumee, OH 43537-4002
Tel.: (419) 893-9600
Fax: (419) 893-9070

L.C. Williams & Associates, LLC
150 N Michigan Ave 38th Fl
Chicago, IL 60601-7558
Tel.: (312) 565-3900
Fax: (312) 565-1770
Toll Free: (800) 837-7123
Pub Rels

RPA
(Rubin Postaer and Associates)
2525 Colorado Ave
Santa Monica, CA 90404
Tel.: (310) 394-4000
Fax: (310) 633-7099

LAMINATE US

4232 NW 120th Ave
Coral Springs, FL 33065
Tel.: (954) 752-4302
Toll Free: (877) 777-3336
Web Site: www.laminateus.com
Sales Range: $10-24.9 Million
Approx. Number Employees: 92
Year Founded: 2001
Business Description:
Laminate Flooring Distr & Installer
S.I.C.: 1752
N.A.I.C.S.: 238330
Advertising Expenditures: $4,000,000

LANE FURNITURE INDUSTRIES

(Sub. of Laneventure, Inc.)
5380 Hwy 145
Tupelo, MS 38801
Mailing Address:
PO Box 1627
Tupelo, MS 38802-1627
Tel.: (662) 566-7211
Fax: (662) 566-3166
Web Site: www.lanefurniture.com
Sales Range: $150-199.9 Million
Approx. Number Employees: 4,000
Year Founded: 1912
Business Description:
Home Furnishings Mfr
S.I.C.: 2512
N.A.I.C.S.: 337121
Media: 3-6-7-10-13-15-16-18-19-20-23-24
Distr.: Natl.
Personnel:
Gregory P. Roy *(Pres)*
Morgan Files *(VP-Mktg)*
Brands & Products:
LANE

LANEVENTURE, INC.

(Div. of Furniture Brands International, Inc.)
205 Workman St
Conover, NC 28601
Mailing Address:
PO Box 849
Conover, NC 28613-0849
Tel.: (828) 328-2352
Fax: (828) 328-6759
Toll Free: (800) 235-3558
Web Site: www.laneventure.com
Sales Range: $75-99.9 Million
Approx. Number Employees: 100
Business Description:
Upholstered Furniture Mfr
S.I.C.: 2512
N.A.I.C.S.: 337121
Media: 6
Personnel:
Gary McCray *(Pres)*
Teresa Beulin *(Mgr-Mktg)*
Mary Harris *(Mgr-Media Rels)*
Brands & Products:
EXCURSIONS
JACQUES PERGAY
TRADEWINDS
WEATHERMASTER
Advertising Agency:
Edelman
101 Marietta St Ste 2900
Atlanta, GA 30303
Tel.: (404) 262-3000
Fax: (404) 264-1431

LARSON-JUHL US LLC

(Sub. of Albecca Inc.)
3900 Steve Reynolds Blvd
Norcross, GA 30093
Tel.: (770) 279-5200
Fax: (770) 279-5297
Toll Free: (800) 886-6126
Web Site: www.larsonjuhl.com
Sales Range: $350-399.9 Million
Approx. Number Employees: 2,070
Business Description:
Custom Frame Designer, Mfr & Distr
S.I.C.: 3999; 3499
N.A.I.C.S.: 339999; 332999
Media: 6-13
Personnel:
Craig A. Ponzio *(Chm)*
Stephen E. McKenzie *(Pres & CEO)*
R. Bradley Goodson *(CFO, Treas, Sec & Sr VP-Fin)*
Greg Perkins *(Mgr-Mktg)*
Brands & Products:
CRAIG PONZIO SIGNATURE COLLECTION
LARSON-JUHL CLASSIC COLLECTION

LEADER'S HOLDING COMPANY

(d/b/a Leader's Casual Furniture)
6303 126th Ave N
Largo, FL 33773
Tel.: (727) 538-5577
Fax: (727) 524-8161
E-mail: leaders@leadersfurniture.com
Web Site: www.leadersfurniture.com
Sales Range: $10-24.9 Million
Approx. Number Employees: 130
Year Founded: 1971
Business Description:
Furniture Stores
S.I.C.: 5712
N.A.I.C.S.: 442110
Media: 9-25
Personnel:
Jerry O. Newton *(Owner & Pres)*
Larry Watt *(CMO)*
Brands & Products:
LEADER'S

LEE JOFA, INC.

(Sub. of Kravet Fabrics Inc.)
201 Central Ave S
Bethpage, NY 11714
Tel.: (516) 752-7600
Fax: (516) 752-7623
Toll Free: (800) 453-3563
E-mail: customer.service@leejofa.com
Web Site: www.leejofa.com
Approx. Number Employees: 100
Year Founded: 1823
Business Description:
Distr of Decorative Fabrics, Furniture, Wall Coverings & Trimmings & Decorative Lighting
S.I.C.: 5021
N.A.I.C.S.: 423210
Import Export
Advertising Expenditures: $650,000
Media: 6-19-22
Distr.: Natl.
Personnel:
Cary Kravet *(Pres)*
Beth Greene *(Head-Mktg)*
Elizabeth McCarthy *(Mgr-Mktg)*
Brands & Products:
COLE & SON
FIRED EARTH
GROUNDWORKS
LEE JOFA
MULBERRY

LEES CARPETS

(Sub. of Mohawk Industries, Inc.)
1975 West Oak Cir
Marietta, GA 30062
Tel.: (770) 792-6300
Fax: (678) 355-5808
Toll Free: (800) 523-5647
Web Site: www.leescarpets.com
Sales Range: $100-124.9 Million
Year Founded: 1846
Business Description:
Carpet & Rug Mfr
S.I.C.: 5713
N.A.I.C.S.: 442210
Import Export
Media: 1-4-5-6-10-11-13-19-20-22
Distr.: Intl.
Budget Set: Aug.
Personnel:
Kurt Topp *(Exec VP-Sls)*
Joe Wallace *(VP & Mgr-Mfg)*
Diann Barbacci *(VP-Mktg, Education & Healthcare)*
Scott Rives *(Dir-Mktg)*
Brands & Products:
ELUMICOLOR
INTEGRATED CUSHION THERMOBOND
LEES SQUARED
METAFLOOR
NEOFLOOR
SELF LOCK
SIMPLEX
UNIBOND
UNIBOND RE
Advertising Agency:
Broach & Company
520 S Elm St
Greensboro, NC 27406
Tel.: (336) 373-0811
Fax: (336) 272-9046
(Commercial Carpeting)

LEGGETT & PLATT, INCORPORATED

1 Leggett Rd
Carthage, MO 64836-9649
Mailing Address:
PO Box 757
Carthage, MO 64836-0757
Tel.: (417) 358-8131
Fax: (417) 358-8449
E-mail: webmaster@leggett.com
Web Site: www.leggett.com

Key to Media (For complete agency information see *The Advertising Red Books-Agencies* edition):
1. Bus. Publs. 2. Cable T.V. 3. Catalogs & Directories. 4. Co-op Adv. 5. Consumer Mags. 6. D.M. to Bus. Estab.7. D.M. to Consumers 8. Daily Newsp. 9. Exhibits/Trade Shows 10. Foreign 11. Infomercial 12. Internet Adv.13. Multimedia 14. Network Radio 15. Network T.V. 16. Newsp. Distr. Mags. 17. Other 18. Outdoor (Posters, Transit) 19. Point of Purchase20. Premiums, Novelties 21. Product Samples 22. Special Events Mktg. 23. Spot Radio 24. Spot T.V. 25. Weekly Newsp. 26. Yellow Page Adv.

Approx. Sls.: $3,359,100,000
Approx. Number Employees: 19,000
Year Founded: 1883
Business Description:
Bedding & Furniture Components, Finished Furniture & Carpet Cushioning; Products Made from Steel, Steel Wire, Aluminum, Foam & Plastic Chemicals, Textile Scrap & Various Woods Mfr & Sales
S.I.C.: 2435; 2434; 2514; 2515; 2519
N.A.I.C.S.: 321211; 337110; 337124; 337125; 337910
Import Export
Media: 1-2-4-6-9-10-20-21-23
Distr.: Natl.
Budget Set: Sept. -Oct.
Personnel:
Richard T. Fisher *(Chm)*
David S. Haffner *(Pres & CEO)*
Matthew C. Flanigan *(CFO & Sr VP)*
Karl G. Glassman *(COO & Exec VP)*
John G. Moore *(Chief Legal Officer, Chief HR Officer, Sec & VP)*
Jack D. Crusa *(Pres-Specialized Products & Sr VP)*
Joseph D. Downes Jr. *(Pres-Indus Matls & Sr VP)*
Paul R. Hauser *(Pres-Residential Furnishings & Sr VP)*
Dennis S. Park *(Pres-Comml Fixturing & Components & Sr VP)*
Arnold E. Berney *(Pres-Asia & VP)*
Scott S. Douglas *(Gen Counsel & VP-Law)*
Daniel R. Hebert *(Sr VP)*
Kenneth W. Purser *(VP & Gen Mgr-Minneapolis Ops)*
Michael W. Blinzler *(VP-IT)*
Peter W. Connelly *(Corp VP-Procurement)*
Vincent Lyons *(VP-Engrg & Tech)*
Karin Pryor *(VP-Mktg)*
Brands & Products:
ADJUSTA-MAGIC
CLASSIC TOUCH
COIL-FLEX
CYCLO-INDEX
EVER-FLEX
FLEX-O-LATORS, INC.
FLEXCORD
GRIBETZ
INNOVATION REDEFINED
INSTAMATIC
L & P
LECTRO-LOK
LOK-FAST, SEMIFLEX, WEBLOK
MIRA-COIL
MIRA-FOAM
MODUCOIL
NO-SAG
NOVA-BOND
NOVA-LOF
OUR PRODUCTS ARE EVERYWHERE
PERMA-EZE
RING-FLEX
SOFA PLUS
WALL HUGGER
WEBLINE
Advertising Agencies:
Leggett & Platt Inc.
1 Leggett Rd
Carthage, MO 64836
Tel.: (417) 358-8131
Fax: (417) 358-8449

LKH&S
54 W Hubbard Ste 100
Chicago, IL 60610
Tel.: (312) 595-0200
Fax: (312) 595-0300

LEN-TEX CORP.

18 Len Tex Ln
North Walpole, NH 03609
Tel.: (603) 445-2342
Fax: (603) 445-5001
Web Site: www.lentexcorp.com
Approx. Number Employees: 97
Business Description:
Wallcovering
S.I.C.: 2672
N.A.I.C.S.: 322222
Personnel:
Donald Lennon *(Pres)*
Advertising Agency:
Signaltree Marketing & Advertising
160 Emerald St Ste 201
Keene, NH 03431
Tel.: (603) 358-5100
Fax: (603) 358-5109

LEON'S FURNITURE LIMITED

45 Gordon MacKay Rd
PO Box 1100
Weston, ON M9L 2R8, Canada
Tel.: (416) 243-7880
Fax: (416) 243-0196
Web Site: www.leons.ca
Approx. Sls.: $688,188,202
Approx. Number Employees: 2,851
Year Founded: 1909
Business Description:
Home Furnishings Mfr & Retailer
S.I.C.: 5712; 2519
N.A.I.C.S.: 442110; 337125
Advertising Expenditures: $27,578,774
Media: 13-16-19-25
Personnel:
Mark J. Leon *(Chm)*
Terrence Thomas Leon *(Pres & CEO)*
Dominic Scarangella *(CFO & VP)*
Edward Florian Leon *(VP-Mdsg)*
Robert J. MacNelly *(VP-Mktg)*

LEXINGTON HOME BRANDS

(Holding of Sun Capital Partners, Inc.)
1300 National Hwy
Thomasville, NC 27360
Tel.: (336) 474-5300
Fax: (336) 474-5450
Toll Free: (800) LEX-INFO
E-mail: info@lexington.com
Web Site: www.lexington.com
Approx. Number Employees: 200
Year Founded: 1901
Business Description:
Home Furnishings Mfr & Whslr
S.I.C.: 2511; 2512
N.A.I.C.S.: 337122; 337121
Import Export
Media: 2-4-6-8-15-19-24
Distr.: Natl.
Personnel:
Philip D. Haney *(Pres & CEO)*
Craig Spooner *(CFO)*
Jim Burke *(Sr VP-Sls)*
Katrina Patton *(VP-Product Dev)*
Robert Stamper *(Dir-Mktg & Comm)*
Brands & Products:
LEXINGTON KIDS
LIVINGSTYLE
NAUTICA
TIMELESS RETREAT
TRAVELER'S RETREAT

LIFETIME PRODUCTS INC.

Freeport Ctr Bldg D 11
Clearfield, UT 84016
Tel.: (801) 776-1532
Fax: (801) 776-4397
Toll Free: (800) 225-3865
E-mail: employment@lifetime.com
Web Site: www.lifetime.com
Approx. Number Employees: 1,600
Year Founded: 1986
Business Description:
Mfr Plastic Tables, Chairs, Picnic Tables & In-Ground Basketball Systems
S.I.C.: 3949; 2519
N.A.I.C.S.: 339920; 337125
Advertising Expenditures: $1,000,000
Media: 4-5-6-10-17
Distr.: Natl.
Personnel:
Richard Hendrickson *(Pres)*
Mark Whiting *(CFO)*
Brands & Products:
ACRYLIC FUSION
ACTION GRIP
ATLAS
ATLAS BASKETBALL EQUIPMENT
BALL HOG
BASELINE
BEST IN THE GAME
COURT TIME
COURTSIDE
DOUBLE SHOT
DUNK ZONE
DURA-TABLE
DURATABLE UTILITY
EASY LIFT
EXTREME
FAST TRACK
FINAL SECOND
FOR THE WAY YOU LIVE.
FREESTYLE
FUSION
HILLCREST
HOOP CHUTE
HOOP TIME
HOOPSTER
IMPACT
IN THE ZONE
KID'S COURT
LANDMARK
LIFETIME
LIFETIME ACCENT
LIFETIME ADVANTAGE
LIFETIME COMPETITION POWERLIFT
MAMMOTH BASKETBALL EQUIPMENT
NAVIGATOR
OPEN COURT
PERSONAL
PICNIC PLUS
POWER LIFT
POWER SHOCK
PRO COURT
PRO GLASS
QUICK ADJUST
QUICK COURT
QUICK LIFT
RAPID-CAM
REACTOR REBOUND
SHOOT CASE
SHOOT CASE & DESIGN
SHOOT-N-SCORE
SLAM-IT
SLAM-IT-GOAL
SLAM-IT PRO
SPEED SHIFT
SPORT TABLE
STOW AWAY
STREET COURT
STRONG MAN
TRANSCOURT
TRANSPORT
TRIPLE DOUBLE
Advertising Agency:
Hunter Public Relations
41 Madison Ave Fl 5
New York, NY 10010-2202
Tel.: (212) 679-6600
Fax: (212) 679-6607

THE LIGHTNING GROUP, INC.

722 N Market St
Duncannon, PA 17020-1716
Tel.: (717) 834-3031
Fax: (717) 834-5561
Sales Range: $1-9.9 Million
Approx. Number Employees: 51
Year Founded: 1904
Business Description:
Antique & Craft Market
S.I.C.: 5932
N.A.I.C.S.: 453310
Export
Media: 10-13
Distr.: Natl.
Personnel:
Norman Rosen *(Owner)*

LISTA INTERNATIONAL CORPORATION

(Sub. of Lista Holding AG)
106 Lowland St
Holliston, MA 01746
Tel.: (508) 429-1350
Fax: (508) 626-0353
Toll Free: (800) 722-3020
E-mail: sales@listaintl.com
Web Site: www.listaintl.com
E-Mail For Key Personnel:
Marketing Director: annesmagorinsky@listaintl.com
Sales Director: sales@listaintl.com
Approx. Number Employees: 204
Year Founded: 1968
Business Description:
Storage System & Workbenches Mfr
S.I.C.: 2531; 2519
N.A.I.C.S.: 337127; 337125
Export
Advertising Expenditures: $500,000
Media: 2-4-10-13
Personnel:
Peter Lariviere *(CEO)*
John Alfieri *(VP-Sls & Mktg)*
Anne Smagorinsky *(Mgr-Mktg Comm)*
Brands & Products:
ALIGN
FLEXWORKS
NEXUS
PREVENTIP
SHELF CONVERTER
STORAGE WALL
Advertising Agency:
Catalyst
275 Promenade St Ste 275
Warwick, RI 02908
Tel.: (401) 732-1886
Fax: (401) 732-5528

Key to Media (For complete agency information see *The Advertising Red Books-Agencies* edition):
1. Bus. Publs. 2. Cable T.V. 3. Catalogs & Directories. 4. Co-op Adv. 5. Consumer Mags. 6. D.M. to Bus. Estab.7. D.M. to Consumers 8. Daily Newsp. 9. Exhibits/Trade Shows 10. Foreign 11. Infomercial 12. Internet Adv.13. Multimedia 14. Network Radio 15. Network T.V. 16. Newsp. Distr. Mags. 17. Other 18. Outdoor (Posters, Transit) 19. Point of Purchase20. Premiums, Novelties 21. Product Samples 22. Special Events Mktg. 23. Spot Radio 24. Spot T.V. 25. Weekly Newsp. 26. Yellow Page Adv.

LOEWEN
77 Hwy 52 W
Steinbach, MB RG5 1B2, Canada
Tel.: (204) 326-6446
Fax: (204) 326-5227
Toll Free: (800) 563-9367
E-mail: info@loewen.com
Web Site: www.loewen.com
Approx. Number Employees: 700
Year Founded: 1905
Business Description:
Doors & Windows Mfr
S.I.C.: 2431
N.A.I.C.S.: 321911
Media: 4-6-10-11
Personnel:
Al Babiuk *(CEO)*
Brands & Products:
STORMFORCE
Advertising Agency:
Direct Focus Marketing Communications Inc.
315 Pacific Ave
Winnipeg, MB MB R3A 0M2, Canada
Tel.: (204) 947-6912
Fax: (204) 947-9136

LOUISVILLE BEDDING COMPANY
10400 Bunsen Way
Louisville, KY 40299
Tel.: (502) 491-3370
Fax: (502) 495-5346
Toll Free: (800) 626-2594
E-mail: custserv@loubed.com
Web Site: www.loubed.com
Approx. Number Employees: 1,000
Year Founded: 1889
Business Description:
Mattress Pads, Dust Ruffles, Tablecloths, Napkins, Placemats & Bed Pillows Mfr
S.I.C.: 2392; 3949
N.A.I.C.S.: 314129; 339920
Media: 4-9-16-19-25-26
Distr.: Natl.
Personnel:
Steve Elias *(Pres & CEO)*
Mary Jo Kissel *(COO & Exec VP)*
Denise Matlack *(VP-Sls & Mktg)*
Mike Seago *(VP-Pur)*
Alice Walter *(VP-HR)*
Brands & Products:
EXPAND-A-GRIP
LOUISVILLE BEDDING

LUXOUT PRODUCTS, INC.
(Div. of Plastic Products Inc.)
3009 Lincoln Ave
Richmond, VA 23228
Tel.: (804) 264-3700
Fax: (888) 644-2356
Toll Free: (800) 676-2055
Web Site: www.luxout.com
Approx. Number Employees: 18
Year Founded: 1948
Business Description:
Stage & Television Studio Curtains Mfr
S.I.C.: 2391
N.A.I.C.S.: 314121
Media: 4-7-10
Distr.: Natl.
Budget Set: June
Brands & Products:
LUXOUT

MANNINGTON MILLS, INC.
75 Mannington Mills Rd
Salem, NJ 08079
Mailing Address:
PO Box 30
Salem, NJ 08079-0030
Tel.: (856) 935-3000
Fax: (856) 339-5948
Web Site: www.mannington.com
Approx. Number Employees: 2,200
Year Founded: 1915
Business Description:
Flooring Mfr
S.I.C.: 3996; 3253
N.A.I.C.S.: 326192; 327122
Media: 1-2-3-4-5-6-8-9-10-11-13-14-15-19-20-21-23-25-26
Distr.: Intl.; Natl.
Budget Set: Dec.
Personnel:
Keith S. Campbell *(Chm)*
Tom Davis *(Pres & CEO)*
Paul Snyder *(CFO & Sr VP)*
Kim Holm *(Pres-Residential Bus Unit)*
Francis J. Norris *(Treas, Sec & Sr VP)*
Edward Duncan *(Sr VP-Mktg)*
Betsy Amoroso *(Mgr-PR)*
Brands & Products:
ADURA
AFFINITY
AURORA
CLEAN GETAWAY
INFINITY
MANNINGTON
NATUREFORM
REVOLUTIONS
ULTRABAC
Advertising Agency:
IMRE
909 Ridgebrook Rd Ste 300
Baltimore, MD 21152
Tel.: (410) 821-8220
Fax: (410) 821-5619
Flooring

MANNINGTON RESILIENT FLOORS
(Sub. of Mannington Mills, Inc.)
75 Mannington Mills Rd
Salem, NJ 08079
Mailing Address:
PO Box 30
Salem, NJ 08079-0030
Tel.: (856) 935-3000
Fax: (856) 339-5875
E-mail: edward_duncan@mannington.com
Web Site: www.mannington.com
Approx. Number Employees: 700
Year Founded: 1915
Business Description:
Flooring Mfr
S.I.C.: 3996; 3253
N.A.I.C.S.: 326192; 327122
Export
Advertising Expenditures: $2,000,000
Media: 1-2-4-5-6-8-9-10-11-14-15-19-20-21-23-25-26
Distr.: Intl.; Natl.
Budget Set: Oct.
Personnel:
Edward Duncan *(VP-Mktg)*
Advertising Agency:
Spencer Advertising and Marketing
3708 Hempland Rd
Mountville, PA 17554
Tel.: (717) 569-6544
Fax: (717) 569-5244

MANNINGTON WOOD FLOORS
(Sub. of Mannington Mills, Inc.)
1327 Lincoln Dr
High Point, NC 27260
Tel.: (336) 884-5600
Fax: (336) 812-4981
Web Site: www.mannington.com
Approx. Number Employees: 250
Year Founded: 1990
Business Description:
Wood Floor Mfr
S.I.C.: 2431; 2435
N.A.I.C.S.: 321918; 321211
Export
Media: 2-3-4-5-6-7-8-9-10-13-19-21-25
Distr.: Natl.

MARC-MICHAELS INTERIOR DESIGN, INC.
720 W Morse Blvd
Winter Park, FL 32789
Tel.: (407) 629-2124
Fax: (407) 629-0910
E-mail: info@marc-michaels.com
Web Site: www.marc-michaels.com
Approx. Number Employees: 75
Year Founded: 1985
Business Description:
Interior Designer
S.I.C.: 7389
N.A.I.C.S.: 541410
Media: 6
Personnel:
Michael J. Abbott *(Co-CEO & CFO)*
S. Marc Thee *(Co-CEO)*
Mark Tremblay *(COO)*
Debbie Maul *(Exec VP)*

MARLO FURNITURE CO., INC.
3300 Marlo Ln
Forestville, MD 20747
Tel.: (301) 735-2000
Fax: (301) 838-2970
E-mail: nglickfield@marlofurniture.com
Web Site: www.marlofurniture.com
Approx. Number Employees: 600
Year Founded: 1955
Business Description:
Furniture Retailer
S.I.C.: 5712
N.A.I.C.S.: 442110
Import
Advertising Expenditures: $18,000,000
Media: 4-6-8-9-14-15-16-18-19-20-22-25
Distr.: Direct to Consumer; Reg.
Personnel:
Neal Glickfield *(Pres)*
David Weinstein *(COO & Exec VP)*
Aquilla Ross *(Dir-HR)*
Brands & Products:
MARLO

MARTIN'S CHAIR, INC.
124 King Ct
New Holland, PA 17557
Tel.: (717) 355-2177
Fax: (717) 355-2351
Toll Free: (877) 519-2724
E-mail: johnm@martinschair.com
Web Site: www.martinschair.com
E-Mail For Key Personnel:
Sales Director: salesinfo@martinschair.com
Approx. Number Employees: 20
Business Description:
Antique Furniture Reproductions
S.I.C.: 2511; 2521
N.A.I.C.S.: 337122; 337211
Media: 4-6
Personnel:
John E. Martin, Jr. *(Owner & Pres)*

MARVIN WINDOWS & DOORS
401 States Ave
Warroad, MN 56763
Tel.: (218) 386-1430
Fax: (218) 386-4207
Toll Free: (888) 537-7828
Web Site: www.marvin.com
Approx. Number Employees: 2,700
Year Founded: 1912
Business Description:
Custom Window & Door Mfr
S.I.C.: 2431; 3442
N.A.I.C.S.: 321911; 332321
Media: 2-6-10
Personnel:
John W. Marvin *(Chm & CEO)*
Frank R. Marvin *(Vice Chm)*
Susan I. Marvin *(Pres)*
Elliot J. Larson *(CFO)*
Duff Marshall *(VP-Sls)*
Brett Boyum *(Dir-Mktg)*
Nicole Welu-Engel *(Mgr-Mktg)*
Brands & Products:
BUILD AROUND YOU
MADE FOR YOU
MARVIN WINDOWS AND DOORS
Advertising Agency:
Martin/Williams Advertising Inc.
(A Member of Omnicom Group)
60 S 6th St Ste 2800
Minneapolis, MN 55402-4428
Tel.: (612) 340-0800
Fax: (612) 342-9700

THE MATTRESS FIRM, INC.
(Holding of J.W. Childs Associates, L.P.)
5815 Gulf Fwy
Houston, TX 77023-5341
Tel.: (713) 923-1090
Fax: (713) 923-1096
Web Site: www.mattressfirm.com
Sales Range: $350-399.9 Million
Approx. Number Employees: 970
Year Founded: 1986
Business Description:
Distr & Retailer of Mattresses & Furniture
S.I.C.: 5712
N.A.I.C.S.: 442110
Personnel:
Steve Stagner *(Pres & CEO)*
Brian Bandarra *(Exec VP-Sls)*
Justin Cassell *(Reg VP-Ops)*
Chris Maloy *(Reg VP-Ops)*
Sam Woods *(Reg VP)*
Dave Brummett *(VP-Product Dev)*
Stephen Leggiero *(VP-Store Ops)*
Craig McAndrews *(VP-Mdsg)*
Jason Starr *(VP-Sls-Central Reg)*
Brands & Products:
SEALY
Advertising Agency:
FKM
1800 W Loop S Ste 2100
Houston, TX 77027

Key to Media (For complete agency information see *The Advertising Red Books-Agencies* edition):
1. Bus. Publs. 2. Cable T.V. 3. Catalogs & Directories. 4. Co-op Adv. 5. Consumer Mags. 6. D.M. to Bus. Estab.7. D.M. to Consumers 8. Daily Newsp. 9. Exhibits/Trade Shows 10. Foreign 11. Infomercial 12. Internet Adv.13. Multimedia 14. Network Radio 15. Network T.V. 16. Newsp. Distr. Mags. 17. Other 18. Outdoor (Posters, Transit) 19. Point of Purchase20. Premiums, Novelties 21. Product Samples 22. Special Events Mktg. 23. Spot Radio 24. Spot T.V. 25. Weekly Newsp. 26. Yellow Page Adv.

Tel.: (713) 862-5100
Fax: (713) 869-6560

MATTRESS GIANT CORPORATION
14665 Midway Rd St 100
Addison, TX 75001-3190
Tel.: (972) 392-2202
Fax: (972) 392-7308
Web Site: www.mattressgiant.com
Approx. Number Employees: 910
Year Founded: 1998
Business Description:
Retail Sales
S.I.C.: 5712
N.A.I.C.S.: 442110
Import Export
Personnel:
Michael Glager *(Pres & CEO)*
Elaine Crowley *(CFO & Exec VP)*
Dan Younkman *(Exec VP-Sls)*
Graeme Gordon *(VP-Adv & Mktg)*
Armando Murillo *(VP-Mdsg)*
Saly Holt *(Dir-HR)*
Brands & Products:
FASHION BED
KINGSDOWN
LEGGETT AND PLATT
MATTRESS GIANT
SERTA
SIMMONS
SPRING AIR
TEMPUR-PEDIC
Advertising Agencies:
Moroch Partners
3625 N Hall St Ste 1100
Dallas, TX 75219-5122
Tel.: (214) 520-9700
Fax: (214) 252-1724

MoToR
215 Ferndale Rd S
Wayzata, MN 55391
Tel.: (612) 234-5520

MATTRESS HOLDING CORP.
(Holding of Sun Capital Partners, Inc.)
5815 Gulf Freeway
Houston, TX 77023
Tel.: (713) 923-1090
Fax: (713) 923-1096
Web Site: www.mattressfirm.com
Sales Range: $150-199.9 Million
Approx. Number Employees: 970
Year Founded: 2002
Business Description:
Holding Company
S.I.C.: 5719; 5712
N.A.I.C.S.: 442299; 442110
Advertising Expenditures: $28,516,413
Personnel:
Michael Marrie *(CEO)*
James R. Black *(CFO)*
Bruce Lewis *(Dir-Real Estate)*
Brands & Products:
MATTRESS FIRM

MATTRESS LAND INC.
4626 N Bendel Ave
Fresno, CA 93722
Tel.: (559) 277-0655
Fax: (559) 277-0659
Web Site: www.mattressland.com
Approx. Number Employees: 56
Business Description:
Beds & Accessories
S.I.C.: 5712
N.A.I.C.S.: 442110
Advertising Agency:
Axis Media
30495 Canwood St
Agoura Hills, CA 91301
Tel.: (818) 264-1555
Fax: (818) 264-1550

MCGUIRE FAMILY FURNITURE MAKERS
239 Main St
Isle La Motte, VT 05440
Mailing Address:
PO Box 218
Isle La Motte, VT 05463-0218
Tel.: (802) 928-4190
Tel.: (802) 796-4337
Web Site: www.mcguirefamilyfurnituremakers.com
Sales Range: Less than $1 Million
Approx. Number Employees: 3
Business Description:
Antique Reproduction Furniture Mfr
S.I.C.: 2511
N.A.I.C.S.: 337122
Media: 4-6
Personnel:
Jack McGuire *(Pres)*

MCSWAIN CARPETS INC.
2430 E Kemper Rd
Cincinnati, OH 45241-1812
Tel.: (513) 771-1400
Fax: (513) 326-4270
Web Site: www.mcswaincarpets.com
Approx. Sls.: $50,000,000
Approx. Number Employees: 155
Year Founded: 1968
Business Description:
Retailer of Carpeting & Flooring
S.I.C.: 5713; 5032
N.A.I.C.S.: 442210; 423320
Personnel:
Jason McSwain *(Pres)*
Gary Pauly *(CFO)*
Barry Wert *(Exec VP-Mktg & Mdsg)*
Matt Gantz *(Dir-Hard Surface)*
Carol Flaherty *(Office Mgr)*
Lou Millspaugh *(Mgr-Installation)*
Advertising Agency:
Krienik Advertising, Inc.
115 W Nineth St
Cincinnati, OH 45202
Tel.: (513) 421-0090
Fax: (513) 421-5329

MEADOWCRAFT, INC.
4700 Pinson Vly Pkwy PO Box 1357
Birmingham, AL 35215
Tel.: (205) 853-2220
Fax: (205) 854-4054
Web Site: www.meadowcraft.com
Approx. Number Employees: 2,500
Year Founded: 1946
Business Description:
Wrought-Iron Outdoor Furniture & Accessories
S.I.C.: 2514; 3999
N.A.I.C.S.: 337124; 339999
Export
Media: 2-4-5-6-7-8-13-19
Distr.: Natl.
Personnel:
Larry York *(VP-HR)*
Brands & Products:
ALEXANDRIA
ATHENS
AUGUSTA
BARCELONA
BERKLEY
BORDEAUX
BRIDGEPORT
CAHABA
CAMBRIDGE
CHARLESTON
CHELSEA
CLASSIC FURNITURE FOR THE GREAT OUTDOORS
CORTEZ
COVENTRY
DEL RIO
DOGWOOD
DURANGO
GENEVA
HANAMINT
MEADOWCRAFT
MERIDIAN
METRO
MILANO
PLANTATION PATTERNS
ROSEMONT
SANNIBEL
SARATOGA
SIERRA
SOLANO
VENETIAN
VERA CRUZ
WYNDHAM

MEGADOOR INC.
(Sub. of Crawford AB)
611 Hwy 74 S
Peachtree City, GA 30269-0957
Tel.: (770) 631-2600
Fax: (770) 631-9086
E-mail: sales@megadoor.com
Web Site: www.megadoor.com
E-Mail For Key Personnel:
Sales Director: sales@megadoor.com
Approx. Number Employees: 23
Business Description:
Industrial & Garage Doors, Wall Systems, Dock Loading Systems, Storage Cabinets & Lockers Mfr
S.I.C.: 5039; 3442
N.A.I.C.S.: 423390; 332321
Media: 10
Personnel:
Ulf Petersson *(Mng Dir)*
Mark Hagl *(Mgr-Svc)*
John Zimmerman *(Mgr-Sls-Americas)*

METRO
(Div. of Coalesse)
7220 Edgewater Dr
Oakland, CA 94621-3004
Tel.: (510) 567-5200
Fax: (510) 562-2915
Web Site: www.metrofurniture.com
Sales Range: $75-99.9 Million
Approx. Number Employees: 210
Year Founded: 1905
Business Description:
Wood Office Furniture Mfr
S.I.C.: 2521; 2522
N.A.I.C.S.: 337211; 337214
Media: 10
Personnel:
Daniel Chong *(Pres & CEO)*
Kevin Owens *(Dir-Sustainability)*
Brands & Products:
BRING LIFE TO WORK
TOPO

METROSTYLE INTERIORS, INC.
(d/b/a Techline Studio New York)
35 E 19th St
New York, NY 10003
Tel.: (212) 674-1813
Fax: (212) 674-1260
E-mail: gavin@techlinestudio.com
Web Site: www.techlinestudio.com
Approx. Number Employees: 16
Business Description:
Furniture Retailer
S.I.C.: 5712; 5021
N.A.I.C.S.: 442110; 423210
Media: 2-6-9-25
Distr.: Natl.
Personnel:
Gavin Bromell *(Dir-Design)*
Brands & Products:
TECHLINE
Advertising Agency:
Pop Labs, Inc
7850 Parkwood Cir Ste B3
Houston, TX 77036
Tel.: (713) 243-4500

MILLER MULTIPLEX DISPLAY FIXTURE CO.
(Sub. of Miller Manufacturing, Inc.)
1610 Design Way
Dupo, IL 62239
Tel.: (636) 343-5700
Fax: (636) 326-1716
Toll Free: (800) 325-3350
E-mail: kathywebster@millermultiplex.com
Web Site: www.millermultiplex.com
Approx. Number Employees: 300
Year Founded: 1903
Business Description:
Custom Store Fixtures Mfr
S.I.C.: 2434
N.A.I.C.S.: 337110
Export
Advertising Expenditures: $250,000
Media: 2-4-7-10
Distr.: Direct to Consumer; Intl.; Natl.
Budget Set: Monthly
Personnel:
Ryandy Cascoe *(Pres)*
Kathy Webster *(Dir-Mktg)*

MITCHELL GOLD & BOB WILLIAMS
(Holding of Wafra Partners LLC)
135 One Comfortable Pl
Taylorsville, NC 28681-6106
Tel.: (828) 632-9200
Fax: (828) 632-2693
E-mail: info@mitchellgold.com
Web Site: www.mitchellgold.com
Approx. Number Employees: 500
Year Founded: 1989
Business Description:
Upholstered Household Furniture & Design
S.I.C.: 2512
N.A.I.C.S.: 337121
Import Export
Media: 6-8-10-11-13
Personnel:
Bob Williams *(Pres-Design)*
Charlie Holt *(VP-Mktg)*

MITY ENTERPRISES, INC.
(Holding of Sorenson Capital Partners)
1301 W 400 N

Key to Media (For complete agency information see *The Advertising Red Books-Agencies* edition):
1. Bus. Publs. 2. Cable T.V. 3. Catalogs & Directories. 4. Co-op Adv. 5. Consumer Mags. 6. D.M. to Bus. Estab.7. D.M. to Consumers
8. Daily Newsp. 9. Exhibits/Trade Shows 10. Foreign 11. Infomercial 12. Internet Adv.13. Multimedia 14. Network Radio
15. Network T.V. 16. Newsp. Distr. Mags. 17. Other 18. Outdoor (Posters, Transit) 19. Point of Purchase20. Premiums, Novelties
21. Product Samples 22. Special Events Mktg. 23. Spot Radio 24. Spot T.V. 25. Weekly Newsp. 26. Yellow Page Adv.

Mity Enterprises, Inc. — (Continued)

Orem, UT 84057-4442
Tel.: (801) 224-0589
Fax: (801) 224-6191
Web Site: www.mitylite.com
E-Mail For Key Personnel:
Sales Director: kevins@mitylite.com
Approx. Sls.: $60,503,000
Approx. Number Employees: 418
Year Founded: 1987
Business Description:
Commercial Furniture Mfr
S.I.C.: 2522; 2531
N.A.I.C.S.: 337214; 337127
Export
Media: 1-2-4-5-7-8-10-26
Distr.: Intl.
Budget Set: Apr.
Personnel:
Randall L. Hales *(Pres & CEO)*
John Dudash *(Exec VP-Sls & Mktg)*
Gregory D. Dye *(VP-HR)*
Kevin W. Stoker *(VP-Sls & Mktg)*
Brands & Products:
BRODA
CENTER CORE
COREL
DOMORE
ELITE
JG SEATING
MITY DELUXE
MITY FLEX
MITY HOST
MITY-LITE
MITY STACK
SERIES SYSTEM 7
SUMMIT LECTURN
SWIFTSET
VERSAFOLD

MOHAWK COMMERCIAL CARPET
(Sub. of Mohawk Industries, Inc.)
1975 W Oak Cir
Marietta, GA 30062-5872
Tel.: (770) 792-6300
Fax: (678) 355-5808
Web Site:
www.mohawkcommercial.com
Sales Range: $25-49.9 Million
Approx. Number Employees: 55
Business Description:
Markets & Sells Carpets
S.I.C.: 2273; 5713
N.A.I.C.S.: 314110; 442210
Export
Advertising Expenditures: $1,500,000
Media: 2-4-7-10
Distr.: Natl.
Budget Set: Dec.
Brands & Products:
BIGELOW
DURKAN
EVERSET
INITIATIVE COLLECTION

MOHAWK HOME
(Div. of Mohawk Industries, Inc.)
3090 Sugar Valley Rd NW
Sugar Valley, GA 30746-5166
Mailing Address:
PO Box 130
Sugar Valley, GA 30746-0130
Tel.: (706) 629-7916
Fax: (706) 625-3544
Toll Free: (800) 843-4473
Approx. Sls.: $15,000,000
Approx. Number Employees: 800
Year Founded: 1984
Business Description:
Mfr of Rugs & Mats
S.I.C.: 2273; 5023
N.A.I.C.S.: 314110; 423220
Export
Advertising Expenditures: $1,550,000
Bus. Publs.: $200,000; Co-op Adv.: $1,000,000; Exhibits/Trade Shows: $200,000; Other: $150,000
Distr.: Natl.
Personnel:
William B. Kilbride *(Pres)*
Kelly Moore *(Gen Mgr-Floor Mat Div)*
Donna Sandy *(Dir-Import Bath Rugs)*
Randy Gardner *(Mgr-Bus)*
Jennifer Palmer *(Specialist-Mktg)*
Brands & Products:
COMFORT MAT
DUO WEAVE
MONTEREY
NATURAL WOOL COLLECTION
WEATHERGUARD MATS

MOHAWK INDUSTRIES, INC.
160 S Industrial Blvd
Calhoun, GA 30701-3030
Mailing Address:
PO Box 12069
Calhoun, GA 30703-7002
Tel.: (706) 629-7721
Fax: (706) 624-3825
Toll Free: (800) 241-4494
E-mail: mohawkind@mohawkind.com
Web Site: www.mohawkind.com
Approx. Sls.: $5,319,072,000
Approx. Number Employees: 26,900
Year Founded: 1988
Business Description:
Flooring Mfr
S.I.C.: 2273; 3253
N.A.I.C.S.: 314110; 327122
Export
Advertising Expenditures: $43,752,000
Media: 3-5-9-15-16-19-21-22
Personnel:
Jeffrey S. Lorberbaum *(Chm & CEO)*
W. Christopher Wellborn *(Pres & COO)*
Frank H. Boykin *(CFO)*
James F. Brunk *(Chief Acctg Officer & Controller)*
Tom Lape *(Pres-Mohawk Residential)*
James T. Lucke *(Gen Counsel & VP)*
Bill Storey *(Sr VP & Gen Mgr-Fashion Brands)*
Keith Gray *(Dir-Tech Mktg)*
Brands & Products:
ALADDIN
AMERICAN OLEAN
AMERICAN RUG CRAFTSMEN
BIGELOW
DAL-TILE
HORIZON
IT'S MORE THAN A FLOOR
KARASTAN
MOHAWK
MOHAWK INDUSTRIES INC
NEWMARK
Advertising Agencies:
Cramer-Krasselt
225 N Michigan Ave
Chicago, IL 60601-7601
Tel.: (312) 616-9600
Fax: (312) 616-3839

Intermark Group, Inc.
101 25th St N
Birmingham, AL 35203
Tel.: (205) 803-0000
Fax: (205) 870-3843
Toll Free: (800) 554-0218

MARC USA Corporate Headquarters
225 W Station Square Dr Ste 500
Pittsburgh, PA 15219-1119
Tel.: (412) 562-2000
Fax: (412) 562-2022

Response Mine
3390 Peachtree Rd Ste 800
Atlanta, GA 30326
Tel.: (404) 233-0370
Fax: (404) 233-0302
Online Marketing

MURPHY BED CO., INC.
42 Central Ave
Farmingdale, NY 11735-6906
Tel.: (631) 420-4330
Fax: (631) 420-4337
Toll Free: (800) 845-2337
E-mail: info@murphybedcompany.com
Web Site:
www.murphybedcompany.com
Sales Range: Less than $1 Million
Approx. Number Employees: 8
Year Founded: 1900
Business Description:
Steel Beds Mfr
S.I.C.: 2514
N.A.I.C.S.: 337124
Import Export
Media: 2-4-6-9-10-26
Distr.: Natl.
Personnel:
Clark W. Murphy *(Founder & Pres)*
Brands & Products:
MURPHY

NATIONAL BEDDING CO.
(Joint Venture of Ontario Teachers' Pension Plan & Ares Management LLC)
(d/b/a Serta Mattress Company)
2600 Forbs Ave
Hoffman Estates, IL 60192
Tel.: (847) 645-0200
Fax: (847) 645-0205
E-mail: info@serta.com
Web Site: www.serta.com
Sales Range: $1-4.9 Billion
Approx. Number Employees: 125
Business Description:
Holding Company; Mattress Mfr & Whslr
S.I.C.: 6719; 2515
N.A.I.C.S.: 551112; 337910
Media: 8-15-16-18-23
Personnel:
Burton Kaplan *(Co-Founder)*
Robert L. Sherman *(Pres)*
Barbara Bradford *(VP-Mktg)*
Kelly Ellis *(Dir-Integrated Mktg-Serta)*
Brands & Products:
SERTA

NATURAL DECORATIONS, INC.
(d/b/a NDI)
777 Industrial Park Dr
Brewton, AL 36426
Tel.: (251) 867-7077
Fax: (251) 867-2525
E-mail: info@ndi.com
Web Site: www.ndi.com
Approx. Number Employees: 110
Year Founded: 1992
Business Description:
Artificial Trees & Flowers
S.I.C.: 3999; 5992
N.A.I.C.S.: 339999; 453110
Media: 4
Personnel:
Carol Faris Gordy *(Owner & CEO)*
Joe Gordy *(Pres)*
Kelly Grosso *(Dir-Mktg)*
Brands & Products:
BALTIMORE ESTATE
GARDENIA
HOLLY PINE
MAGNOLIA
MONET'S GARDEN
NEWLIFE
RAIN FOREST
WILLIAMSBURG

NEMSCHOFF, INC.
(Sub. of Herman Miller, Inc.)
909 N 8th St
Sheboygan, WI 53081-4056
Tel.: (920) 457-7726
Fax: (920) 459-1234
Toll Free: (800) 203-8916
E-mail: sales@nemschoff.com
Web Site: www.nemschoff.com
E-Mail For Key Personnel:
Sales Director: sales@nemschoff.com
Approx. Rev.: $90,000,000
Approx. Number Employees: 300
Year Founded: 1950
Business Description:
Health Care Furniture Mfr
S.I.C.: 2531
N.A.I.C.S.: 337127
Media: 4-10
Distr.: Natl.
Personnel:
Beth Nickels *(Pres)*
Steve Oppeneer *(Treas & Exec VP)*
Pat Keegan *(Exec VP)*
Mary Byrne *(Dir-Matls)*
Jack Morford *(Dir-Project)*
Brands & Products:
ABERDEEN
ABEX
ABINGTON
ABITO
ABRACADABRA
ACADEMIA
ACCOLADE
ACCORD
ACHIEVA
ADOBE
AGAPETOS
AGORA
ALAMO
ALAYA
ALCHEMY
ALDINE
ALESSANDRIA
ALETHOS PLUS
ALHAMBRA
ALICE
ALIGN
ALLEGORY
ALLEGRO
ALMOST PERFECT

Key to Media (For complete agency information see *The Advertising Red Books-Agencies* edition):
1. Bus. Publs. 2. Cable T.V. 3. Catalogs & Directories. 4. Co-op Adv. 5. Consumer Mags. 6. D.M. to Bus. Estab.7. D.M. to Consumers
8. Daily Newsp. 9. Exhibits/Trade Shows 10. Foreign 11. Infomercial 12. Internet Adv.13. Multimedia 14. Network Radio
15. Network T.V. 16. Newsp. Distr. Mags. 17. Other 18. Outdoor (Posters, Transit) 19. Point of Purchase20. Premiums, Novelties
21. Product Samples 22. Special Events Mktg. 23. Spot Radio 24. Spot T.V. 25. Weekly Newsp. 26. Yellow Page Adv.

ALPHA
ALPINE
ALTAIR
ALTERNATIVE
ALTITUDE
ALTRO
AMAZON
AMBER
ANAIS
ANCIENTS
ANDALUSIA
ANDI
ANECDOTE
ANTIGUITY
ANTONIO
ANZEA
APHRODITE
APPLESEED
APROPOS
AQUA
AQUARIUS
ARBOR
ARIA
ARIZONA
AROUND
ARRIVEDERCI
ARROW
ARTESIAN
ARTICLE
ARTIFACT
ARUBA
ASCENT
ASCOT
ASHLEY
ASKEW
ATELIER
ATHENAEUM
ATHENS
ATLAS
ATMOSPHERE
AUTHENTEC
AUTUMN
AUXAL
AVANT GARDE
AVENUE
AVIVA
AVON
AWAKENING
AXIOM
AZTEC
BACK AGAIN
BACK STAGE
BAILEY
BAJA
BAKU
BALANCE
BALLROOM
BALUSTRADE
BAMBOO
BANDEROLE
BANDSTAND
BANGLES
BANQUET
BANYAN
BARENTHAL
BASIL
BATLLO
BAUBLE
BAUHAUS
BAXTER
BEAM
BEANSTALK
BEBOP
BECKON
BEDFORD
BEELINE
BEGUILE
BELENOS
BELLINGHAM
BENCH
BENEFIT
BENNINGTON TOO
BERNHARDT - JUBILEE
BESIDE
BESPOKE STRIPE
BETA
BETSY
BETWIXT
BEVERLY HILLS
BIG BENN
BINARY
BLANCA
BLANKET WRAP
BLUMEN
BLUTO
BOARDWALK
BODRUM
BOLERO
BONNIE
BOOGIE WOOGIE
BOONE
BOREAS
BOSCO
BOSSA NOVA
BOTANY
BOUCLE STRIPE
BOULEVARD
BOUNCE
BOUNTY
BOUQUET
BOURBON STREET
BOUTIQUE
BRAID
BRAVO
BREA
BREE
BREENA
BREEZE
BRIO
BRITESPOT
BRITISH SATEEN
BROADWAY
BROKEN ARROW
BRUNO
BRUSHSTROKE
BUFFETT
BULK
BURKSHIRE
BURNISHED METALS
BURST
BUTTER
CABANA
CABOOSE PLUS
CADENCE
CADENZA
CAINE
CALABASAS
CALAIS
CALCULUS
CALDECOTT
CALENDAR
CALIBER
CALLE
CALVET
CALYPSO
CALYX
CAMDEN TOO
CAMELOT
CAMEO
CANDID
CANOPY
CANTEEN
CANZONE
CAPE COD
CAPE X
CAPELLA
CAPELLA ABC
CARAT
CARDINAL
CARESSA
CARMINE
CARNEGIE
CARNIVALE
CARTEL
CASA
CASANOVA
CASBAH
CASCADIA
CASCO
CASHMERE
CASINO
CATALAN
CATALOGNA
CATHEDRAL
CATWALK
CAVALCADE
CAVIAR
CAYENNE
CELESTE
CELIA
CHAMEA
CHAMOIS
CHANCE
CHANTECLERC
CHAPS
CHAPTER
CHARIOT
CHARISMA PLUSH
CHARLEMAGNE
CHARLESTON
CHARM
CHASER
CHAT
CHATEAU
CHATTERBOX
CHECKER SPLIT
CHECKERS
CHECKMATE
CHEERS
CHELSEA
CHENILLE STITCH
CHEQUE
CHERISH
CHESHIRE
CHEYENNE
CHORUS
CHROMATIC
CIENEGA
CIPHER
CIRCA
CIRCLES
CIRCUIT
CIRCUITBOARD
CIRQUE
CITIES
CLAM DIGGER
CLAREMONT
CLARIDGE
CLARION
CLARITY
CLASSIC REPP
CLASSY
CLAYTON
CLEMATIS
CLEOPATRA
CLINIC
CLIQUE
CLOUD
CLOUT
CLOVIS
CLUBHOUSE
CLUNY
COACH
COBALT
COCO
COLBY
COLLIER
COMET
COMFORT
COMMENT
COMMODITY
COMPACT COMFORT
COMPASS
COMPLIMENTO
CONCERTO
CONFUSION
CONNOISSEUR
CONSIDER
CONTEMPLATE
CONTINUUM
CONVERGENCE
COPA
COPAN
COR-LOC
CORNERSTONE
CORNFLOWER
CORRUGTED
CORSAGE
COSMIC
COSMO
COSMOPOLITAN
COURTYARD
CRACKLE
CRAYON
CRETACEOUS
CRETE
CROCUS
CROQUET
CROSSPATCH
CROSSTOWN
CROWN
CRYPTON TWILL
CUBE
CUMULUS
CURRENTS
CURVY
CYCLADES
DELAUNAY
DELIGHT
DELMONICO
DELPHOS
DENOMINATOR
DETOUR
DIANE
DIVA
DOLCE
DOLPHIN
DOMAIN
DOMINO
DOMINOES
DORSET
DREAMY
DUBLIN
DUET
DULCETTE
DUNE
DUNGAREE
DUOMO
DURALEE
DURANGO
DURASUEDE
DURAWEAVE
DUSK
DWELL
EARLY FALL
EASY
ECHO
ECLIPSE

Key to Media (For complete agency information see *The Advertising Red Books-Agencies* edition):
1. Bus. Publs. 2. Cable T.V. 3. Catalogs & Directories. 4. Co-op Adv. 5. Consumer Mags. 6. D.M. to Bus. Estab.7. D.M. to Consumers
8. Daily Newsp. 9. Exhibits/Trade Shows 10. Foreign 11. Infomercial 12. Internet Adv.13. Multimedia 14. Network Radio
15. Network T.V. 16. Newsp. Distr. Mags. 17. Other 18. Outdoor (Posters, Transit) 19. Point of Purchase20. Premiums, Novelties
21. Product Samples 22. Special Events Mktg. 23. Spot Radio 24. Spot T.V. 25. Weekly Newsp. 26. Yellow Page Adv.

Nemschoff, Inc. — (Continued)

EDEN
ELAN
ELAPSE
ELECTRON
ELEMENTS
ELEPHANT
ELLINGTON
ELLIPTICAL RIB
EMERALD TEAL
ENCAUSTIC
ENCHANTED
ENHANCE
ENIGMA
ENSEMBLE
ENTOURAGE
ENTROPY
ENVIRO
ENVIRONS
EPISODE
ERICA ABC
ERICA JR
ESPACE
ESPERANZA
ESPLANADE
ESSENTIA
ESTATE
ETCHED METALS
ETCHING
ETERNITY
ETON
EUSEBI
EVITA
EVOLVE
EXCALIBUR
EXCELSIOR
EXCHANGE
EXPRESSIONIST
EXPRESSIONS
EXTREME
FACETS
FAIADE
FAIRFIELD
FAITH
FANCY
FANTASIA
FATHOM
FAUVISM
FELIZ
FENIMORE
FERNANDEZ
FESTIVAL
FIAMMA
FIELDS
FIESTA
FIGMENT
FIGURES
FILIGREE
FILMSTRIP
FIORD
FLAMMA
FLAUNT
FLEUR
FLICKER
FLIP-LOC
FLIRTATIOUS
FLOP
FLORA
FLORET
FLOURISH
FLUCTUATE
FOCUS
FOLIO
FORECAST
FORSYTHIA
FORTE
FORTIS
FORTY
FORUM
FOZZY
FRANK
FRANKLIN
FRETWORK
FRIDA
FRIEZE
FRISBEE
FROLIC
FRONTIER
FULCRUM
GABE
GADGET
GALAXY
GALLIARD
GAMBERDINE
GAMBLE
GARDENER
GARNET
GEMINI
GEOLOGY
GEOMETRI
GERTRUDE
GETTY
GIARDINO
GINGER
GINKGO
GINZA
GIORGIO
GIOVANNI
GIZA
GLAM
GLEANINGS
GLENDOWER
GLIMMER
GLITZ
GLOBAL
GLORIA
GLOW
GOLDA
GOSSAMER
GOTHAM
GOUACHE
GRACIA
GRADIENT
GRAFFITI
GRAMERCY
GRANDSTAND
GRAPHIC
GRASS
GRASSLAND
GRAVITY
GREAT PLAINS
GREENBRIAR
GREENHOUSE
GRILLEWORK
GROOVE
GROOVY
GUMBALLS
GUMPTION
HABITAT
HADLEIGH
HADLEY
HAIKU
HAMPSTEAD
HAMPTON
HARRINGTON
HAVANA
HEMISPHERE
HENRY
HERMITAGE
HERMOSA
HIAWATHA
HIDEAWAY
HIGHLANDS
HINT
HONEYCOMB
HONOR PLUS
HOOLA HOOP
HOPSCOTCH
HOT ROD
HUNTER
HUSH
HYDE
HYDRO
I-CHING
IDIOM
IGUANA
ILIAD
ILLUSION
IMPASTO
IMPULSE
INCENTIVE
INCOGNITO
INDIUM
INFLECTION
INFLUENCE
INFUSION
INLAY
INNUENDO
INSIGNIA
INSTANT
INTERLOCHEN
INTERMIX
INTERPOSE
INTERTWINE
INTERVAL
INTUITION
IRIS
ISTANBUL
IVALOO
JAKARTA
JAMESTOWN
JAMMIN
JAUNTY
JAVELIN
JAZZ
JENSEN
JESTER
JETSON
JIGSAW
JINX
JIVE
JUGENDSTIL
JUNIOR
JUNIPER
KABUKI
KALAHARI
KAMIKAZE
KARISMA
KASBAH
KENDO
KENSINGTON
KERNEL
KEYNOTE
KILTER
KIMONO
KNICKERBOCKER
KNOLL
KRAVET
LA SALLE
LABYRINTH
LADDER
LAGOON
LAKE
LALIQUE
LANCASTER
LANDMARK
LARCHMONT
LARIAT
LASSO
LATITUDE
LAVELLE
LEAFAGE
LEAFETTE
LEAFLET
LEDGER
LEGACY
LEGEND
LEONARD
LETTERS
LEVEL
LIBERTY
LILLIAN
LIMBO
LINEA
LINQ
LISMORE
LOCALE
LODEN
LOLA
LONGCHAMP
LORD PAISLEY
LORENZO
LORIEN
LOSETA
LUCIANDO
LUSTRE
LUXE
LUXOR
LYRIC
MABEL
MAGIA
MAJOR
MANDATE
MANGO
MANHATTAN
MANTLE
MARA
MARACAS
MARCO
MARCO GRANDE
MARIANA
MARIPOSA
MARQUEE
MARSACK
MASQUERADE
MASTERTEX
MATINEE
MATISSE
MATRIX
MATSURI
MATTEO
MAURICE
MAVERICK
MAVIN
MAXIM
MAYA
MAYFAIR
MEANDER
MEDALLIONS
MEDIUM
MEDLEY
MELODIE
MELODY
MEMENTO
MEMPHIS
MENA
MENTOR
MERCURY
MERGER
MERLIN
MESH
METALICO
METRIC
METRO
METTA
MEZCLA
MEZZANO
MIDNIGHT

Key to Media (For complete agency information see *The Advertising Red Books-Agencies* edition):
1. Bus. Publs. 2. Cable T.V. 3. Catalogs & Directories. 4. Co-op Adv. 5. Consumer Mags. 6. D.M. to Bus. Estab.7. D.M. to Consumers
8. Daily Newsp. 9. Exhibits/Trade Shows 10. Foreign 11. Infomercial 12. Internet Adv.13. Multimedia 14. Network Radio
15. Network T.V. 16. Newsp. Distr. Mags. 17. Other 18. Outdoor (Posters, Transit) 19. Point of Purchase20. Premiums, Novelties
21. Product Samples 22. Special Events Mktg. 23. Spot Radio 24. Spot T.V. 25. Weekly Newsp. 26. Yellow Page Adv.

MIDTOWN
MIKADO
MILESTONE
MILLERSTRIPE
MILLICENT
MILLIONAIRE
MIMIC
MINERAL
MINT
MINUET
MIRAGE
MIRANDA
MOGUL
MOIRE
MONACO
MONET
MONSOON
MONTAGNA
MONTEZUMA
MOONLIGHT
MOROCCO
MORPHE
MOSAIC
MOSS
MOTIVE
MOTTO
MOUNTAINS
MUIR
MURAL
MUSE
NANCY
NAPOLI
NARRATIVE
NATALIA
NAUGASOFT
NCI
NEBULA
NEMSCHOFF
NEOCHROME
NEWBURY
NEXUS
NICHE
NIKKO
NINFA
NOHO
NOLITA
NOMAD
NONO
NOTION
NOUVEAU
NOVEL
NOVO
NUWEAR
NYLOSUEDE
OAKWOOD
OASIS
OATMEAL
OCEAN
ODALISQUE
ODYSSEY
OKLAHOMA
OLANA
OLIVER
OLIVIA
OLIVIO
OLYMPUS
OODLE
OPORTO
OPTICS
ORISSA
ORNAMENT
ORPHISM
OVATION
OVERLAY
OXEN
OXFORD
OZIO
OZONE
PABLO
PACARO
PACKARD
PAGENT
PAGLIA
PALATINO
PALETTE
PALMOA
PANACHE
PANTHEON
PAPYRUS
PARADISE
PARITY
PARKER
PARLAY
PARTY
PATENT
PATIO
PAVERS
PEACHTREE
PEARCE
PEBBLE BEACH
PEDRERA
PERCEPTION
PERCIVAL
PERFECTION
PERHAPS
PERIWINKLE
PERSPECTIVE
PERSUASION
PERSUEDE
PERU
PESTO
PETALS
PHAROS
PHOENIX
PICCADILLY
PICNIC
PICTOGRAM
PIGMENT
PINEHURST
PINSTRIPE
PINWHEEL
PIPA
PIQUE
PIROUETTE
PISCES
PISTACHIO
PLAINCLOTHESMAN
PLAINVIEW
PLANET
PLAZA
PLUMS
PLURAL
PLUSH
POCONO
POGO
POISE
POLKA
POLO
POMODORO
POMONA
PONG
POTLUCK
PRADO
PRAIRIE
PRANA
PRELUDE
PRESTIGE
PRIMITIVE
PRIMO
PRISM
PRISMATIC
PRISTO
PRIVOT
PUCCI
PUCKER
PUZZLE
QUAD
QUADRANT
QUADRETTI
QUANTUM
QUATREFOIL
QUATTRO
QUEST
RACETRACK
RADIANT
RAFFLES
RAGTIME
RAINDANCE
RAINFOREST
RATTAN
RAVE
REALITY
REBOUND
RECESS
RECOUP
REGENT
REGGAE
REGIS
REGWICK
RELAXED
REMINISCE
REMY
RENAISSANCE
RENATA
RENDEZVOUS
RENDITION
RENNIE
RENOWNED
RESTORATIVE
REVEAL
REVERIE
REVUE
RHOMBUS
RICKSHAW
RIPCORD
RIVA
RIVET
ROADHOUSE
ROSALITA
ROTATION
ROULETTE
ROXY
ROYALTY
RUMBLE
SAFFRAN
SAGRADA
SALON
SALSA
SAMBA
SANDBOX
SAPPHIRE
SARAGASSO
SARANAC
SATURN
SAUCY
SAVANNAH
SAVOY
SAWGRASS
SCHMOOZE
SCOUPE
SCOUT
SEA-SPRAY
SEAGRASS
SEGMENT
SEGUE
SENSE
SEQUENCE
SEQUOIA
SERAPE
SERENADE
SERENDIPITY
SERENITY
SERLING
SHAMMY
SHANE
SHANTUNG
SHEEN
SHIMMER
SHIMMY
SHOREHAM
SHOWBILL
SIGNPOST
SILHOUETTE
SILVERADO
SLEEPOVER
SNAZZY
SOCIALITE
SOCKITTOME
SOPHIA
SOUR APPLE
SOVEREIGN
SPARTACUSA
SPIN
SPRINKLES
STACKS
STARBURST
STARDUST
STRAW
SUNSET
SUPERNOVA
SWAYED
SWIZZLE
SWOON
SYMBOL
SYMMETRY
SYNCOPATION
SYNTHESIS
TABASCO
TACHISME
TACTION
TAFFY
TANGENT
TANGIERS
TANGO
TAPESTRY
TARRAGON
TATAMI
TEAL
TEARDROPS
TEASE
TECHNOCOLOR
TEETER
THEORY
THERMO
THICKET
TIBET
TIDE
TIFFANY
TIGRIS
TILES
TILT-A-WHIRL
TINOS
TOBAGO
TOBOGGAN
TOKEN
TOOSTRIPE
TOPANGA
TOPAS
TOPIARY
TOPOGRAPHY
TORII
TORONTO
TOSCANA
TOTEM
TRACERY
TRADITION
TRAINS
TRANCEPORT

Key to Media (For complete agency information see *The Advertising Red Books-Agencies* edition):
1. Bus. Publs. 2. Cable T.V. 3. Catalogs & Directories. 4. Co-op Adv. 5. Consumer Mags. 6. D.M. to Bus. Estab.7. D.M. to Consumers
8. Daily Newsp. 9. Exhibits/Trade Shows 10. Foreign 11. Infomercial 12. Internet Adv.13. Multimedia 14. Network Radio
15. Network T.V. 16. Newsp. Distr. Mags. 17. Other 18. Outdoor (Posters, Transit) 19. Point of Purchase20. Premiums, Novelties
21. Product Samples 22. Special Events Mktg. 23. Spot Radio 24. Spot T.V. 25. Weekly Newsp. 26. Yellow Page Adv.

Nemschoff, Inc. — (Continued)

TRANSIT
TRANSOM
TRAPEZA
TRAVELOGUE
TRAVERSE
TREETOP
TRELLIS
TRIBE
TRIBUTE
TRYST
TUCKER
TUDOR
TURIN
TURNBERRY
TUSCON
TUSK
TUXEDO
TWEAK
TWEED
TWILIGHT
TWISTER
ULTIMA
UMBRIA
UNHINGED
UNION
UNISOL
UNISON
UNIVERSE
UPBEAT
UPTOWN
UTOPIA
VACATION
VAIL
VALET
VANCANZA
VEGA
VEGAS
VELESE
VENUE
VERANDA
VERDANT
VERMONT
VERSAILLES
VERSE
VESPA
VESUVIO
VIBE
VICTORIA
VIGNETTE
VINETA
VINO
VINTAGE
VIRTUALLY
VISION
VITRERIE
VIVALDI
VOLTAGE
VOLUTE
VORTEX
VOYAGE
WAFFLE
WAINSCOT
WALKWAYS
WALLSAVER
WANDA
WARWICK
WASHI
WATERFRONT
WATERSHED
WEAVERS
WEBSITE
WEIMAR
WESTBURY
WEXFORD
WHIRL
WHIRLWIND
WHISPER
WICKER
WICKERWORK
WINDSOR
WINSLOW
WINTERMINT
WISDOM
WISHBONE
WISHES
WOBBLE
WOOD VIOLET
WORKHORSE
WORLDLY
XANADU
XPRESS
YANAGI
YARN
YORKTOWNE
YOSHE
YUCATAN
ZEBU
ZHIVAGO
ZIPPER
ZOUZOU

NEUTRAL POSTURE, INC.

3904 N Texas Ave
Bryan, TX 77803-0555
Tel.: (979) 778-0502
Fax: (979) 778-0408
Web Site: www.neutralposture.com
Approx. Number Employees: 100
Year Founded: 1989
Business Description:
Mfr, Marketer & Distr of Ergonomic Chairs
S.I.C.: 2522; 2512
N.A.I.C.S.: 337214; 337121
Media: 2-4-7-10-13-23
Personnel:
Rebecca Boenigk *(Chm & CEO)*
David W. Ebner *(Pres)*
Brian Rutherford *(Chief Acctg Officer & VP)*
Jaye E. Congleton *(Sec & Exec VP)*
Brands & Products:
7TH HEAVEN
ABCHAIR
ARTESIAN
ASTRAL
BALANCE
BIG & TALL
CLOUD 9
DICE
ELEMENTAL
EMBRACE
EMBRACE MOTION
FRING
HARMONY
LAPTOP PROP
LIBERTY
MAZING SQUARES
N-DULGENT
N-DURE
N-HANCEMENTS
N-SIDE
N-TUNE
NEUTRAL POSTURE
NEW PERSPECTIVE
NEXTEP
NV
PATRIOT PLUS
RIO
SAHARA
SHARK
SOFTOUCH
STACCATO
STANDUP
TAFT
TERRA

NICHOLS & STONE CO.

1 Stickley Dr
Manlius, NY 13104
Mailing Address:
PO Box 480
Manlius, NY 13104
Tel.: (315) 682-1554
E-mail: info@nicholsandstone.com
Web Site: www.nicholsandstone.com
Sales Range: $10-24.9 Million
Approx. Number Employees: 350
Year Founded: 1857
Business Description:
Chairs, Rockers & Dining Room Furniture Mfr & Distr
S.I.C.: 2511; 5712
N.A.I.C.S.: 337122; 442110
Import Export
Advertising Expenditures: $200,000
Media: 2-4-6-7-10-19
Distr.: Natl.
Budget Set: Apr.-May
Personnel:
Peter Gilbo *(Mgr-Sls & Mktg)*
Brands & Products:
NICHOLS AND STONE

NORRIS FURNITURE INC.

(d/b/a Norris Furniture Interiors)
351 Leonard Blvd N
Fort Myers, FL 33971
Tel.: (239) 433-3633
Fax: (239) 433-3381
Web Site: www.norrisfurniture.com
Approx. Number Employees: 70
Business Description:
Household Furniture Retailer
S.I.C.: 5712
N.A.I.C.S.: 442110
Media: 4-6-8-13-18-24-26

NORWALK CUSTOM ORDER FURNITURE

100 Furniture Pkwy
Norwalk, OH 44857-9587
Tel.: (419) 744-3200
Fax: (419) 668-6223
Toll Free: (800) 837-9002
E-mail: info@norwalkfurniture.com
Web Site: www.norwalkfurniture.com
Sales Range: $10-24.9 Million
Approx. Number Employees: 125
Year Founded: 1902
Business Description:
Mfr. of Upholstered Livingroom Furniture & Tables
S.I.C.: 2512; 5712
N.A.I.C.S.: 337121; 442110
Export
Media: 6
Personnel:
Daniel J. White *(CEO)*
Brands & Products:
ALLISON
APOLLO
ASCOT
ASPEN
BARRYMORE
BASIE
BERKLEY
BOMBAY
BORDEAUX
BROCKTON
BROOKE
BRUBECK
BURGESS
BURTON
CAMBRIDGE
CAMEO
CAMPBELL
CARMEL
CASSANDRA
CENTENNIAL
CHAMBERLAIN
CHARLEVOIX
CHAUCER
CHLOE
CLAIBORNE
CLARKE
COCO
COPA
COPLEY SQUARE
CORONADO
COURTNEY
CYNTHIA
DAWSON
DEBUTANTE
DEL RAY
DEL RIO
DIONNE
DIVA
DREW
DYNO
EMILY
EMPIRE
ESSEX
EVA
EVO
GARBO
GENEVIEVE
GEORGETOWN
GRAHAM
GRAMERCY
GRETCHEN
HAMILTON
HARDWICK
HATHAWAY
HERMOSA
HI ZENO
HIGHLAND
HORIZON
KEATON
KENSINGTON
LAUGHTON
LAWRENCE
LAWSON
LINDSEY
LO ZENO
LOEWY
LOMBARD
LUGANO
MARTHA
MCKENZIE
METRO
MILES
MILFORD
MILFORD SECTIONAL
MIMOSA
MONTAUK
MONTGOMERY
MORGAN
NORWALK
NORWALK FURNITURE
OMNI
ORMOND
PABLO
PAIGE
PARAMOUR
PARIS
PENNINGTON
PERONE
PLAZA

Key to Media (For complete agency information see *The Advertising Red Books-Agencies* edition):
1. Bus. Publs. 2. Cable T.V. 3. Catalogs & Directories. 4. Co-op Adv. 5. Consumer Mags. 6. D.M. to Bus. Estab.7. D.M. to Consumers
8. Daily Newsp. 9. Exhibits/Trade Shows 10. Foreign 11. Infomercial 12. Internet Adv.13. Multimedia 14. Network Radio
15. Network T.V. 16. Newsp. Distr. Mags. 17. Other 18. Outdoor (Posters, Transit) 19. Point of Purchase20. Premiums, Novelties
21. Product Samples 22. Special Events Mktg. 23. Spot Radio 24. Spot T.V. 25. Weekly Newsp. 26. Yellow Page Adv.

PORTLAND
POTTER
POUF
PRESTO
REDGRAVE
REED
SARA
SOTHEBY
STAFFORD
THE STASH
STOWE
SUFFOLK
SUNDANCE
TANNER
TASHA
TEKNO
TIFFANY
TREMONT
TREVOR
TYNDALL
VANESSA
VENTANA
VERANDAH
WATCH HILL
WHEATON
WILSHIRE
WINDERMERE
WINDSOR
WONG

NYDREE FLOORING

1191 Venture Dr
Forest, VA 24551
Tel.: (434) 525-5252
Fax: (434) 525-7437
Toll Free: (800) 682-5698
Web Site: www.nydreeflooring.com/
Approx. Number Employees: 200
Year Founded: 1967
Business Description:
Flooring Products Mfr
S.I.C.: 2431; 3996
N.A.I.C.S.: 321918; 326192
Media: 2-7-13
Personnel:
Barry Brubaker *(Pres & CEO)*
Brands & Products:
GENMAGRAIN
GENUWOOD
GENUWOOD II
PENNTHANE
TIMELESS
TIMELESS SERIES
TIMELESS SERIES 3
ULTRATEC
ULTRATEC 1000
ULTRATEC 2000
ULTRATEC 3000

OAKWOOD & TEXWOOD LIBRARY FURNITURE

1203 Industrial Blvd
Cameron, TX 76520
Tel.: (254) 605-5555
Fax: (254) 605-5516
Toll Free: (888) 878-0000
E-mail: ksmith@texwood.com
Web Site: www.texwood.com
Approx. Number Employees: 100
Year Founded: 1959
Business Description:
Mfr. of Wooden Library Furniture
S.I.C.: 2531
N.A.I.C.S.: 337127
Export
Media: 2-4-10-17-26
Distr.: Natl.
Budget Set: Nov.
Personnel:
Rick Creel *(Pres)*
Brands & Products:
AMERICAN LIBRARY
HOLBROOK EARLY CHILDHOOD FURNITURE

OFFICE RESOURCES INC.

(d/b/a Office Furniture USA)
816 E Broadway
Louisville, KY 40204
Tel.: (502) 589-8400
Fax: (502) 589-8408
E-mail: info@oriusa.com
Web Site: www.oriusa.com
Approx. Number Employees: 50
Business Description:
Office Furniture
S.I.C.: 5021
N.A.I.C.S.: 423210
Personnel:
George Bell *(Pres & CEO)*
Pamela R. Freeman *(CFO, Sec & Treas)*
Advertising Agency:
FUSE/ideas
255 Elm St Ste 201
Somerville, MA 02144
Tel.: (617) 776-5800
Fax: (617) 776-5821

OLSON RUG COMPANY

832 S Central Ave
Chicago, IL 60644-5501
Tel.: (773) 921-1300
Fax: (773) 921-1739
Web Site: www.olsonrug.com
Approx. Number Employees: 100
Year Founded: 1874
Business Description:
Retailer of Carpets & Rugs
S.I.C.: 5713; 5211
N.A.I.C.S.: 442210; 444110
Media: 5-8-23-24-26
Distr.: Reg.
Budget Set: Dec.
Personnel:
Andy Hader *(Pres)*

OLYMPUS FLAG & BANNER

(Private-Parent-Single Location)
9000 W Heather Ave
Milwaukee, WI 53224
Tel.: (414) 355-2010
Web Site: www.olympus-flag.com
Approx. Rev.: $4,300,000
Approx. Number Employees: 80
Year Founded: 1992
Business Description:
Mfg Fabricated Textile Products
S.I.C.: 2299
N.A.I.C.S.: 314999
Advertising Agency:
Blue Horse
309 N Water St Ste 315
Milwaukee, WI 53202
Tel.: (414) 291-7620
Fax: (414) 291-7633

OMEGA NATIONAL PRODUCTS

900 Baxter Ave
Louisville, KY 40204-2047
Tel.: (502) 583-3038
Fax: (502) 584-1022
Toll Free: (800) 228-5276
E-mail: info@omeganationalproducts.com
Web Site:
www.omeganationalproducts.com
Approx. Number Employees: 50
Year Founded: 1946
Business Description:
Home Decor Products Mfr
S.I.C.: 2499; 2452
N.A.I.C.S.: 321999; 321992
Media: 2-3-4-7-10-11-13-21
Distr.: Intl.; Natl.
Budget Set: May
Personnel:
Rod McNerney *(CEO)*
Mike Feusner *(Mgr-Sls)*
Brands & Products:
DECOR
KITCHENMATE
OMEGA NATIONAL PRODUCT
TAMBOUR

ONTARIO WALL COVERINGS

184 Cortland Ave
Concord, ON Canada
Tel.: (905) 669-8909
Fax: (905) 669-8922
Approx. Number Employees: 71
Business Description:
Residential Wall Coverings & Specialty Fabrics Designer, Marketer & Distr
S.I.C.: 2653; 2261; 2675
N.A.I.C.S.: 322211; 313311; 322231
Media: 4
Personnel:
Sidney Ackerman *(Pres)*
Norman G. Maxwell *(CFO & Mgr-Ops)*

PACIFIC DESIGN CENTER

8687 Melrose Ave
West Hollywood, CA 90069-5701
Tel.: (310) 657-0800
Fax: (310) 652-8576
Web Site:
www.pacificdesigncenter.com
Approx. Number Employees: 40
Year Founded: 1975
Business Description:
Furniture, Fabrics, Floor Coverings, Architectural Products, Wallcoverings, Lighting, Kitchen & Bath Products Mfr
S.I.C.: 2519; 2434; 3261; 3262; 3646; 5713; 5714
N.A.I.C.S.: 337125; 327111; 327112; 335122; 337110; 442210; 442291
Media: 2-10-22
Personnel:
Charles Cohen *(Pres)*

PATINA-V

(Sub. of Norlaine Inc.)
15650 Salt Lake Ave
City of Industry, CA 91745
Tel.: (626) 961-2471
Fax: (626) 333-6547
E-mail: info@patinav.com
Web Site: www.patinav.com
Approx. Number Employees: 175
Year Founded: 1908
Business Description:
Mannequins & Display Merchandise Mfr
S.I.C.: 3999; 3993
N.A.I.C.S.: 339999; 339950
Media: 2-13

PEG PEREGO USA INC.

(Sub. of Peg Perego SpA)
3625 Independence Dr
Fort Wayne, IN 46808
Tel.: (260) 482-8191
Fax: (260) 484-2940
Web Site: www.pegperego.com
Approx. Number Employees: 56
Business Description:
Baby Carriages, Strollers & Children's Vehicles Mfr
S.I.C.: 5099; 5092
N.A.I.C.S.: 423990; 423920
Media: 6
Personnel:
Max Well *(VP-Mktg)*

PERLA LICHI DESIGN

7127 N Pine Island Rd
Fort Lauderdale, FL 33321
Tel.: (954) 726-0899
Fax: (954) 720-5828
Toll Free: (877) 869-1122
Web Site: www.perlalichi.com
Approx. Number Employees: 30
Business Description:
Interior Design Services
S.I.C.: 7389
N.A.I.C.S.: 541410
Media: 6-10
Personnel:
Perla Lichi *(Owner)*
Allen Waller *(Mgr-Acctg)*

PIER 1 IMPORTS, INC.

100 Pier 1 Pl
Fort Worth, TX 76102-2600
Mailing Address:
PO Box 961020
Fort Worth, TX 76161-0020
Tel.: (817) 252-8000
Fax: (817) 252-8174
Toll Free: (800) 245-4595
E-mail: mbotto@pier1.com
Web Site: www.pier1.com
Approx. Sls.: $1,396,470,000
Approx. Number Employees: 3,400
Year Founded: 1962
Business Description:
Direct Importer & Retailer of Decorative Home Furnishings & Furniture
S.I.C.: 5712; 5719
N.A.I.C.S.: 442110; 442299
Import
Advertising Expenditures: $55,723,000
Media: 3-4-6-8-9-15
Distr.: Intl.; Natl.
Budget Set: Sept.
Personnel:
Alexander W. Smith *(Pres & CEO)*
Charles H. Turner *(CFO & Exec VP)*
Darla D. Ramirez *(Chief Acctg Officer)*
Michael A. Carter *(Gen Counsel, Sec & Sr VP)*
Catherine David *(Exec VP-Mdsg)*
Gregory S. Humenesky *(Exec VP-HR)*
Sharon M. Leite *(Exec VP-Store Ops)*
Michael Benkel *(Sr VP-Plng & Allocations)*
Laura A. Coffey *(Sr VP-Bus Dev & Strategic Plng Dept)*
Donald L. Kinnison *(Sr VP-Mktg & Visual Mdsg)*
Brands & Products:
PIER 1 IMPORTS
PIER 1 KIDS
PREVIEW THE PLACE TO STOP BEFORE YOU SHOP

Key to Media (For complete agency information see *The Advertising Red Books-Agencies* edition):
1. Bus. Publs. 2. Cable T.V. 3. Catalogs & Directories. 4. Co-op Adv. 5. Consumer Mags. 6. D.M. to Bus. Estab.7. D.M. to Consumers
8. Daily Newsp. 9. Exhibits/Trade Shows 10. Foreign 11. Infomercial 12. Internet Adv.13. Multimedia 14. Network Radio
15. Network T.V. 16. Newsp. Distr. Mags. 17. Other 18. Outdoor (Posters, Transit) 19. Point of Purchase20. Premiums, Novelties
21. Product Samples 22. Special Events Mktg. 23. Spot Radio 24. Spot T.V. 25. Weekly Newsp. 26. Yellow Page Adv.

Pier 1 Imports, Inc. — (Continued)

Advertising Agency:
DDB Canada
33 Bloor Street East Suite 1700
Toronto, ON M4W 3T4, Canada
Tel.: (416) 925-9819
Fax: (416) 925-4180
Public Relations Canada

PLAIN 'N FANCY KITCHENS INC.

(d/b/a Plain & Fancy Custom Cabinetry)
Oak St & Rte 501
Schaefferstown, PA 17088
Tel.: (717) 949-6571
Fax: (717) 949-2114
Toll Free: (800) 447-9006
Web Site: www.plainfancycabinetry.com
Approx. Number Employees: 160
Business Description:
Wood Kitchen Cabinets Mfr
S.I.C.: 2434
N.A.I.C.S.: 337110
Media: 2-4-6-10-25
Personnel:
George Achey *(Pres & CEO)*
Loretta Achey *(CFO)*
Brands & Products:
ALFRESCO KITCHEN
AU NATURAL KITCHEN
BERKSHIRE
CAMBRIDGE
CAMEO
CAMP KITCHEN
CATHEDRAL
CLASSIC REVIVAL KITCHEN
COASTAL KITCHEN
COTTAGE KITCHEN
CULTURES KITCHEN
EASTERN FUSION KITCHEN
GALLOPING GOURMET KITCHEN
GLAZE COLLECTION
KENT
LAKEVIEW
PROVENCAL KITCHEN
SHAKER
SOFTER SPARTAN KITCHEN
SOHO
VINTAGE CREST RAISE
VOGUE

POLIFORM USA, INC.

150 E 58th St
New York, NY 10155
Tel.: (212) 421-1220
Fax: (212) 421-1290
Web Site: www.poliformusa.com
Approx. Sls.: $10,000,000
Approx. Number Employees: 70
Year Founded: 1995
Business Description:
Importer, Retailer & Wholesaler of Furniture
S.I.C.: 5021
N.A.I.C.S.: 423210
Media: 4-6

PULASKI FURNITURE CORPORATION

(Name Changed to Home Meridian International, Inc.)

QUALITY MARBLE, INC.

3860 70th Ave N
Pinellas Park, FL 33781
Tel.: (727) 527-1676
Fax: (727) 527-7317
Toll Free: (800) 527-1676
Web Site: www.qualitymarble.com
Approx. Number Employees: 25
Business Description:
Marble & Granite Importing & Fabrication Services
S.I.C.: 1743; 2519
N.A.I.C.S.: 238340; 337125
Media: 6
Personnel:
Mark West *(Pres)*

RAINBOW INTERNATIONAL RESTORATION & CLEANING

(Sub. of The Dwyer Group, Inc.)
1010 N University Parks Dr
Waco, TX 76707-3854
Tel.: (254) 745-2400
Fax: (254) 754-2516
Toll Free: (800) 583-9100
Web Site: www.rainbowintl.com
Approx. Number Employees: 19
Year Founded: 1981
Business Description:
Specializes in Indoor Restoration & Cleaning Services Ranging from Upholstery & Carpet Cleaning & Deoderization to Furs, Smoke & Water Damage Restoration Services
S.I.C.: 6794
N.A.I.C.S.: 533110
Media: 4-9-14-15-23-24-25

RALPH PUCCI INTERNATIONAL LTD.

44 W 18th St
New York, NY 10011
Tel.: (212) 633-0452
Fax: (212) 633-1058
E-mail: info@ralphpucci.net
Web Site: www.ralphpucci.net
Approx. Number Employees: 30
Business Description:
Furniture, Mannequins, Fine Art & Sculptures
S.I.C.: 5712; 2273; 2299; 2329; 7336
N.A.I.C.S.: 442110; 314110; 314999; 315211; 541430
Media: 6-10
Personnel:
Ralph Pucci *(Pres)*

RAUCH INDUSTRIES, INC.

(Holding of Blackstreet Capital Management, LLC)
2408 Forbes Rd
Gastonia, NC 28053
Mailing Address:
PO Box 609
Gastonia, NC 28053-0609
Tel.: (704) 867-5333
Fax: (704) 865-8260
Web Site: www.rauchindustries.com
Approx. Number Employees: 500
Year Founded: 1952
Business Description:
Mfr. of Christmas Ornaments & Novelties
S.I.C.: 3231; 3999
N.A.I.C.S.: 327215; 339999
Import Export
Advertising Expenditures: $300,000
Media: 4-6-8-9-10-11-13-19
Distr.: Natl.
Brands & Products:
RAUCH

RAYMOUR & FLANIGAN FURNITURE CO.

7248 Morgan Rd
Liverpool, NY 13090
Tel.: (315) 453-2500
Tel.: (315) 453-2510
Fax: (315) 453-2570
Fax: (315) 453-2508
E-mail: sales@raymourflanigan.com
Web Site: www.raymourflanigan.com
E-Mail For Key Personnel:
Marketing Director: SGoldberg@raymourflanigan.com
Sales Director: sales@raymourflanigan.com
Sales Range: $650-699.9 Million
Approx. Number Employees: 3,700
Year Founded: 1947
Business Description:
Furniture Retailer
S.I.C.: 5712
N.A.I.C.S.: 442110
Media: 3-8-18-23-24-25
Distr.: Reg.
Personnel:
Neil Goldberg *(Pres & CEO)*
Steve Goldberg *(Exec VP)*
Lisa King *(Sr VP-Mktg & Dir-Creative)*
Steve Volinsky *(VP-Fin)*
Brands & Products:
FURNISHING YOUR STYLE
RAYMOUR & FLANIGAN
Advertising Agency:
Jay Advertising, Inc.
(A Subsidiary of The Interpublic Group of Companies)
170 Linden Oaks
Rochester, NY 14625-2836
Tel.: (585) 264-3600
Fax: (585) 264-3650
Toll Free: (800) 836-6800

RECONDITIONED SYSTEMS, INC.

2636 S Wilson St Ste 105
Tempe, AZ 85282
Tel.: (480) 968-1772
Fax: (480) 894-1907
Toll Free: (800) 280-5000
E-mail: rsisales@resy.net
Web Site: www.resy.net
E-Mail For Key Personnel:
Sales Director: salesrsi@resy.net
Approx. Sls.: $11,722,286
Approx. Number Employees: 90
Year Founded: 1987
Business Description:
Office Workstations Remanufacturer
S.I.C.: 2522
N.A.I.C.S.: 337214
Import
Media: 26
Personnel:
Scott W. Ryan *(Chm)*
Dirk Anderson *(Pres & CEO)*
Kerrie Janik *(CFO)*
Brands & Products:
HAWORTH
RSI

RED BARON ANTIQUES INCORPORATED

6450 Roswell Rd
Atlanta, GA 30328
Tel.: (404) 252-3770
Fax: (404) 257-0268
E-mail: info@redbaronsantiques.com
Web Site: www.redbaronsantiques.com
Approx. Number Employees: 30
Business Description:
Antiques Seller
S.I.C.: 5932
N.A.I.C.S.: 453310
Media: 4-6

RELAX THE BACK CORPORATION

6 Centerpointe Dr Ste 350
La Palma, CA 90623
Tel.: (714) 523-2870
Fax: (714) 523-2980
Toll Free: (800) 290-2225
E-mail: info@relaxtheback.com
Web Site: www.relaxtheback.com
Approx. Number Employees: 30
Year Founded: 1984
Business Description:
Ergonomic Products Including Chairs, Work Stations, Mattresses, Pillows, & Other Sleep Accessories Mfr & Sales
S.I.C.: 5712; 2515; 2519; 2522
N.A.I.C.S.: 442110; 337125; 337214; 337910
Media: 4-6
Personnel:
Richard Palfreyman *(Pres & CEO)*
Robert McMillan *(CFO & COO)*
Leanne Mattes *(VP-Mktg)*
J.D. Nespoli *(VP-Mdsg)*
Brands & Products:
BACKNOBBER
BACKSAVER
CHILLOW
EQUALIZER PRO
LIFE-FOAM
RELAX THE BACK
SHIATSU
TEMPUR
THERA CANE
THUMPER
VERSAPRO
WONDERFOAM
Advertising Agency:
Specialized Media Services, Inc.
741 Kenilworth Ave Ste 204
Charlotte, NC 28204
Tel.: (704) 333-3111
Fax: (704) 332-7466

RENT-A-CENTER, INC.

5501 Headquarters Dr
Plano, TX 75024
Tel.: (972) 801-1100
Fax: (972) 943-0113
Toll Free: (800) 275-2996
E-mail: media@racenter.com
Web Site: www.rentacenter.com
E-Mail For Key Personnel:
President: mfadel@racenter.com
Marketing Director: adavids@racenter.com
Approx. Rev.: $2,731,632,000
Approx. Number Employees: 18,300
Year Founded: 1986
Business Description:
Rent-to-Own Furniture Store Operator
S.I.C.: 7359
N.A.I.C.S.: 532310
Advertising Expenditures: $78,700,000
Media: 6-8-15-23-26
Personnel:
Mark E. Speese *(Chm & CEO)*
Mitchell E. Fadel *(Pres & COO)*

Key to Media (For complete agency information see *The Advertising Red Books-Agencies* edition):
1. Bus. Publs. 2. Cable T.V. 3. Catalogs & Directories. 4. Co-op Adv. 5. Consumer Mags. 6. D.M. to Bus. Estab.7. D.M. to Consumers
8. Daily Newsp. 9. Exhibits/Trade Shows 10. Foreign 11. Infomercial 12. Internet Adv.13. Multimedia 14. Network Radio
15. Network T.V. 16. Newsp. Distr. Mags. 17. Other 18. Outdoor (Posters, Transit) 19. Point of Purchase20. Premiums, Novelties
21. Product Samples 22. Special Events Mktg. 23. Spot Radio 24. Spot T.V. 25. Weekly Newsp. 26. Yellow Page Adv.

Robert D. Davis *(CFO & Exec VP-Fin)*
Tony F. Fuller *(CIO & Sr VP-IT)*
Ann L. Davids *(CMO, Sr VP-Mktg & Adv)*
Robert W. Rapp, Jr. *(CTO & VP-IT)*
Ronald DeMoss *(Gen Counsel, Sec & Exec VP)*
Theodore V. DeMarino *(Exec VP-Ops)*
Christopher A. Korst *(Exec VP-Ops)*
David E. West *(Exec VP-Operational Svcs)*
Robert Brockman *(Sr VP-HR)*
Dwight Dumler *(Sr VP-Pub Affairs)*
Joel M. Mussat *(Sr VP-Strategic Plng & Dev)*
Bobby R. Pope *(Sr VP-Operational Svcs)*
Ned Villemarette *(Controller & VP-Fin)*
Dawn M. Wolverton *(VP, Assoc Gen Counsel & Asst Sec)*
Andrew Trusevich *(VP & Asst Gen Counsel)*
Joe T. Arnette *(VP-Sls)*
Dan Glasky *(VP-Mdse)*
John D. Gray *(VP-Trng)*
Tim Pitt *(VP-Mktg)*
Maureen Short *(VP-Fin, Analytics & Reporting)*
Kent W. Brown *(Sr Dir-Real Estate)*

Brands & Products:
RAC
RENT-A-CENTER

Advertising Agencies:
Ansira
15851 Dallas Pkwy Ste 725
Addison, TX 75001
Tel.: (972) 663-1100
Fax: (972) 663-1300

OMD Chicago
225 N Michigan Ave 19th Fl
Chicago, IL 60601-7757
Tel.: (312) 324-7000
Fax: (312) 324-8201

RESTONIC MATTRESS CORPORATION

PO Box 755
Antioch, IL 60002
Tel.: (847) 241-1130
Fax: (847) 838-0868
E-mail: cprindle@restonic.com
Web Site: www.restonic.com
Approx. Number Employees: 3
Year Founded: 1938
Business Description:
Mattress Mfr
S.I.C.: 2515
N.A.I.C.S.: 337910
Import Export
Media: 2-9-14-18-19-24-25
Distr.: Intl.; Natl.
Budget Set: Oct.-Nov.
Personnel:
M. Ronald Passaglia *(Pres)*
Brooke Palmieri *(Mgr-Mktg)*

Brands & Products:
CHIROTONIC
COMFORTCARE
CREATIVE EXPRESSIONS
DR. FULLER
FLEXSTEEL
HEALTH REST
MARVELOUS MIDDLE
MODUBAR
PUT YOUR DAY TO REST
RESTONIC
SPIRALOK
SUP-R-POSTURE
SUPER EDGE
VERSALOK

RIO BRANDS, INC.

10981 Decatur Rd
Philadelphia, PA 19154-3210
Tel.: (215) 632-2800
Fax: (215) 824-1172
E-mail: info@riobrands.com
Web Site: www.riobrands.com
Approx. Number Employees: 100
Year Founded: 1950
Business Description:
Mfr of Aluminum Tables, Casual Outdoor Furniture, Folding Beds, Office Chairs, Sand Chairs & Umbrellas
S.I.C.: 2514; 5021
N.A.I.C.S.: 337124; 423210
Import Export
Media: 5-10-17
Distr.: Natl.
Budget Set: Mar.
Personnel:
Warren Cohen *(Pres)*
Ira Cohen *(Exec VP)*
Mark J. Cohen *(Exec VP-Sls & Mktg)*
Garry Mathews *(VP-Pur & Mfg)*

Brands & Products:
AMERICRAFTERS
CAPTURE THE SPIRIT
RIO
SAN ANGELO

ROBB & STUCKY, LTD.

(Filed Ch 11 Bankruptcy #1102801 on 02/18/11 in U.S. Bankruptcy Ct, FL Middle Dist, Tampa)
14550 Plantation Rd
Fort Myers, FL 33912
Tel.: (239) 437-7997
Fax: (239) 437-5950
E-mail: info1@robbstucky.net
Web Site: www.robbstucky.com
Approx. Number Employees: 1,300
Year Founded: 1915
Business Description:
Home Furnishing Services
S.I.C.: 5712; 5713
N.A.I.C.S.: 442110; 442210
Media: 4-6-10-22
Personnel:
Fred Berk *(Pres)*
Clive Lubner *(CEO)*
Brian Crowley *(CFO)*
Leslie Diplacido *(Mgr-Adv Acct)*

ROBERT LIGHTON FURNITURE, INC.

150 E 58 St Fl 3
New York, NY 10155-3450
Tel.: (212) 343-2299
Fax: (212) 343-0485
E-mail: info@robertlighton.com
Web Site: www.robertlighton.com
Sales Range: Less than $1 Million
Approx. Number Employees: 5
Business Description:
Home Furniture & Fixtures
S.I.C.: 2519
N.A.I.C.S.: 337125
Media: 4-6-10
Personnel:
Robert Lighton *(Pres)*

ROCHELLE FURNITURE

(Div. of The Lightning Group, Inc.)
218 E Dowland St
Ludington, MI 49431
Tel.: (231) 845-1263
Fax: (231) 843-9276
E-mail: carrom1700@aol.com
Web Site: www.carrom.com
Approx. Number Employees: 18
Business Description:
Juvenile Furniture Mfr
S.I.C.: 2511
N.A.I.C.S.: 337122
Export
Media: 2-4-7-10
Distr.: Natl.
Personnel:
Norman Rosen *(Pres)*

ROCKAWAY BEDDING INC.

1578 Sussex Tpke
Randolph, NJ 07869
Tel.: (973) 584-2299
Fax: (973) 584-4359
E-mail: rockbed@msn.com
Web Site: www.rockawaybedding.com
Approx. Sls.: $105,000,000
Approx. Number Employees: 400
Business Description:
Bedding & Bedsprings
S.I.C.: 5712
N.A.I.C.S.: 442110
Media: 6-8-13-16-23-24

Advertising Agency:
JL Media, Inc.
1600 Rte 22 E
Union, NJ 07083-3415
Tel.: (908) 687-8700
Fax: (908) 687-9280

THE ROMWEBER COMPANY

4 S Park Ave
Batesville, IN 47006-0191
Tel.: (812) 934-3485
Fax: (812) 934-5042
Web Site: www.romweber.com
Approx. Number Employees: 250
Year Founded: 1879
Business Description:
Mfr. of Furniture
S.I.C.: 2511
N.A.I.C.S.: 337122
Media: 2-4-7-8-10-19-26
Distr.: Natl.
Budget Set: Dec.
Personnel:
Bruce Rippe *(Pres)*

Brands & Products:
ANTHONY W
ASHEVILLE
BRIDGETOWN
CANNES
CHAUMONT
DOVER
GRANT PARK
LANCASTER
MADISON
MANDALAY
MONTREAL
NORTHAMPTON
ROMWEBER
SAN MARTINO
ST. ETIENNE
ST. PIERRE
TORINA
TRADITIONS MADE MODERN
UNION SQUARE
WILLIAMSPORT

ROOMSTORE, INC.

12501 Patterson Ave
Richmond, VA 23233-6414
Tel.: (804) 784-7600
E-mail: websales@roomstore.com
Web Site: www.roomstore.com
Approx. Sls.: $323,421,000
Approx. Number Employees: 1,452
Year Founded: 1992
Business Description:
Retail Furniture Stores
S.I.C.: 5712
N.A.I.C.S.: 442110
Advertising Expenditures: $22,682,000
Media: 8-9-16-22-23-24-25
Personnel:
Robert C. Shaffner *(Chm)*
Curtis C. Kimbrell, III *(Pres & CEO)*
Lewis M. Brubaker *(CFO & Sr VP)*
Ned D. Crosby *(Chief Mdsg & Mktg Officer & Exec VP)*
John M. Hamilton *(Sr VP-HR)*

Brands & Products:
KIDSTORE
ROOMSTORE
WE PUT IT ALL TOGETHER AND SAVE YOU MORE

ROSARIO SALAZAR DESIGN INC.

358 San Lorenzo Ave #3215
Coral Gables, FL 33146
Tel.: (305) 446-6559
Fax: (305) 446-7614
Web Site: www.rosariosalazar.com
Business Description:
Interior Design Services
S.I.C.: 7389
N.A.I.C.S.: 541410
Media: 6
Personnel:
Rosario Salazar *(Pres)*

RTG FURNITURE CORP.

(d/b/a Rooms To Go)
11540 Hwy 92 E
Seffner, FL 33584
Tel.: (813) 623-5400
Fax: (813) 620-1717
E-mail: mkruse@roomstogo.com
Web Site: www.roomstogo.com
Approx. Rev.: $1,760,000,000
Approx. Number Employees: 7,500
Year Founded: 1991
Business Description:
Furniture Retailer
S.I.C.: 5712; 5021
N.A.I.C.S.: 442110; 423210
Media: 3-8-9-10-14-15-18-22-23-24-25
Distr.: Reg.
Personnel:
Stephen R. Buckley *(Pres & COO)*
Jeffrey Seaman *(CEO)*
Lewis Stein *(CFO)*
Russ Rosen *(CIO)*
Gary Cacioppo *(Sr VP)*
Janis Altshuler *(VP-Direct Mktg)*
Martha Kruse *(Sr Dir-Multicultural Mktg)*
Linda Garcia *(Dir-HR)*

Key to Media (For complete agency information see *The Advertising Red Books-Agencies* edition):
1. Bus. Publs. 2. Cable T.V. 3. Catalogs & Directories. 4. Co-op Adv. 5. Consumer Mags. 6. D.M. to Bus. Estab.7. D.M. to Consumers
8. Daily Newsp. 9. Exhibits/Trade Shows 10. Foreign 11. Infomercial 12. Internet Adv.13. Multimedia 14. Network Radio
15. Network T.V. 16. Newsp. Distr. Mags. 17. Other 18. Outdoor (Posters, Transit) 19. Point of Purchase20. Premiums, Novelties
21. Product Samples 22. Special Events Mktg. 23. Spot Radio 24. Spot T.V. 25. Weekly Newsp. 26. Yellow Page Adv.

RTG Furniture Corp. — (Continued)

Advertising Agencies:
ANEW Marketing Group
811 W Jericho Tpke Ste 109E
Smithtown, NY 11787
Tel.: (631) 982-4000
Fax: (631) 434-1129

Response Mine
3390 Peachtree Rd Ste 800
Atlanta, GA 30326
Tel.: (404) 233-0370
Fax: (404) 233-0302

Schawk Retail Marketing
1 N Dearborn Ste 700
Chicago, IL 60602
Tel.: (312) 666-9200
Fax: (312) 260-1970
Toll Free: (888) AMBROSI

Wilen Group
5 Wellwood Ave
Farmingdale, NY 11735-1213
Tel.: (631) 439-5000
Fax: (631) 439-4536
Toll Free: (800) 809-4536

SAUDER MANUFACTURING COMPANY

(Sub. of Sauder Woodworking Co.)
930 W Barre Rd
Archbold, OH 43502-9320
Mailing Address:
PO Box 230
Archbold, OH 43502-0230
Tel.: (419) 446-9384
Fax: (419) 446-3697
Toll Free: (800) 537-1530
E-mail: kelvinfriesen@saudermfg.com
Web Site: www.saudermfg.com
Sales Range: $50-74.9 Million
Approx. Number Employees: 350
Year Founded: 1934
Business Description:
Mfr. of Institutional Office & Church Furniture
S.I.C.: 2531; 5712
N.A.I.C.S.: 337127; 442110
Advertising Expenditures: $75,000
Bus. Publs.: $56,250; Other: $18,750
Distr.: Direct to Consumer; Reg.
Budget Set: Dec.
Personnel:
Maynard Sauder *(Chm)*
Philip Bontrager *(Pres & CEO)*
Kelvin Friesen *(VP-Sls & Mktg)*
Luther Gautsche *(VP-Ops)*
Brands & Products:
DEFINITY SEATING
DESIGNARE
OAKLOK
PLYFOLD
PLYLOK
REGAL
UNITY SEATING
Advertising Agencies:
Hoeck Associates, Inc.
6625 Maplewood Ave.
Sylvania, OH 43560
Tel.: (419) 885-7202
Fax: (419) 885-7096

Lesniewicz Associates
500 E Front St
Perrysburg, OH 43551-2134
Tel.: (419) 873-0500
Fax: (419) 873-0600
Toll Free: (800) 809-3093

SAUDER WOODWORKING CO.

502 Middle St
Archbold, OH 43502-1559
Tel.: (419) 446-2711
Fax: (419) 446-3692
E-mail: sauder@sauder.com
Web Site: www.sauder.com
Sales Range: $700-749.9 Million
Approx. Number Employees: 1,600
Year Founded: 1934
Business Description:
Modular Furniture, Church Furniture & Institutional Seating Mfr
S.I.C.: 2531
N.A.I.C.S.: 337127
Advertising Expenditures: $850,000
Media: 2-4-6-10-19
Distr.: Natl.
Budget Set: Nov.
Personnel:
Kevin Sauder *(Pres & CEO)*
Brent Gingerich *(Exec VP-Mktg & Sls)*
Garrett Tinsman *(Exec VP-Ops)*
Marc Fruth *(VP-HR)*
Myrl Sauder *(VP-Engrng)*
Mike Lambright *(Dir-Mktg)*
Jackie Bowling *(Mgr-Sls Support)*
Brands & Products:
BEGINNINGS
CLOSITS
EZ CUBE
HOT ROD GARAGE
SAUDER
SHELF LIFE

SCALAMANDRE, INC.

(d/b/a Scalamandre Silks)
350 Wireless Blvd
Hauppauge, NY 11788
Tel.: (631) 467-8800
Fax: (631) 467-9448
E-mail: info@scalamandre.com
Web Site: www.scalamandre.com
Approx. Number Employees: 275
Year Founded: 1929
Business Description:
Mfr. of Drapery, Upholstery Fabrics, Trimmings, Wall Coverings, Rugs, Carpets & Furniture
S.I.C.: 2211; 2241
N.A.I.C.S.: 313210; 313221
Import Export
Advertising Expenditures: $250,000
Media: 2-6-8-10-21
Distr.: Natl.
Personnel:
Lou Renzo *(Pres)*
Suzanne Spina *(Dir-Ops)*
Brands & Products:
ADELAIDE
ANNE BOLYN CREWEL
BEEHIVE CUT FRINGE
BLYTHE
BON OEUF
BRINKER
BUDDY
BUTTERFLY
CALIBAN
CARON
CHARLOTTE
CHIYOMI
CLAUDETTE
EDWIN'S
ELVIRA
FERN
FONTANE
FRAGONARD
GIVERNY
GUNGA DIN
HILTON
INGRID
IVEAGH
JESSICA
KANJI
KENMORE
KILKENNY
LANGSTON
LE CTRQUE
LENOX SETTEE
LILABETH'S RIBBON
LOCKSLEY DAMASK
MADAME POMPADOUR
MAGGIE
MELOGRANO
MOULIN
MURIEL
NASHVILLE
NING PO
ORIENTEAUX
OUISTITI
OXLEY
PALMIER
PENELOPE
POTTSGROVE
PRECIOUS CARGO
RANGOON
REDGRAVE
RITWELL
SCALAMANDRE
SHANGHAI
STRATFORD
STRATHMORE
TAIPAN
TIPPERARY
TOBIAS
TOPPER
VOLNAY
YANG TZE

SEAGULL FLOORS INC.

4005 Royal Dr Ste 400
Kennesaw, GA 30144-4611
Tel.: (770) 425-9727
Fax: (770) 425-9715
Toll Free: (800) 929-1770
Web Site: www.seagullfloors.com
Approx. Number Employees: 35
Year Founded: 1989
Business Description:
Sales of Floor Coverings
S.I.C.: 5713; 1752; 3253; 5714
N.A.I.C.S.: 442210; 238330; 327122; 442291
Media: 17-18
Personnel:
Jay Kobrin *(Founder & Pres)*

SEALY CORPORATION

1 Office Pkwy at Sealy Dr
Trinity, NC 27370-9449
Tel.: (336) 861-3500
Fax: (336) 861-3501
Toll Free: (800) 697-3259
E-mail: investors@sealy.com
Web Site: www.sealy.com
Approx. Sls.: $1,219,471,000
Approx. Number Employees: 4,270
Year Founded: 1907
Business Description:
Mattresses, Foundations, Box Springs, Wood Bedroom Furniture, Convertible Sleep Sofas Mfr
S.I.C.: 2515; 3999; 5023; 6794
N.A.I.C.S.: 337910; 339999; 423220; 533110
Advertising Expenditures: $140,400,000
Media: 2-4-6-7-9-17-19-26
Distr.: Intl.; Natl.
Budget Set: Nov.
Personnel:
Lawrence J. Rogers *(Pres & CEO)*
Jeffery C. Ackerman *(CFO & Exec VP)*
Jodi Allen *(CMO)*
Michael Q. Murray *(Gen Counsel, Sec & Sr VP)*
Louis R. Bachicha *(Exec VP-Sls)*
G. Michael Hofmann *(Exec VP-Ops)*
John Deutchki *(Dir-Strategic Projects & Bus Analysis)*
Leo Vogel *(Dir-Global Contract & Export Sls)*
Brands & Products:
ADVANCED GENERATION SEALY POSTUREPEDIC
BASSETT
BEDTIME
CARRINGTON-CHASE
IT'S MADE FOR SLEEP
IT'S MADE FOR SLEEP. IT'S A SEALY.
MEYER
REFLEXION
SAMUEL/LAWRENCE
SEALY
SEALY BACK SAVER
SEALY CORRECT COMFORT
SEALY KIDS
SEALY POSTURE PREMIER
SEALY POSTUREMATIC
SEALY POSTUREPEDIC
SEALY POSTUREPEDIC CROWN JEWEL
SHOCK ABZZORBER
STEARNS & FOSTER
Advertising Agencies:
Cramer-Krasselt Public Relations
225 N Michigan Ave
Chicago, IL 60601-7601
Tel.: (312) 616-9600

Jay Advertising, Inc.
(A Subsidiary of The Interpublic Group of Companies)
170 Linden Oaks
Rochester, NY 14625-2836
Tel.: (585) 264-3600
Fax: (585) 264-3650
Toll Free: (800) 836-6800

Manning Selvage & Lee
222 Merchandise Mart Plz Ste 4-150
Chicago, IL 60654
Tel.: (312) 861-5200
Fax: (312) 861-5252
Brand Awareness
Media
Public Relations Agency of Record
Sealy Posturepedic

SELECT COMFORT CORPORATION

9088 59th Ave N
Minneapolis, MN 55442-3274
Tel.: (763) 551-7000
Fax: (763) 551-7826

Key to Media (For complete agency information see *The Advertising Red Books-Agencies* edition):
1. Bus. Publs. 2. Cable T.V. 3. Catalogs & Directories. 4. Co-op Adv. 5. Consumer Mags. 6. D.M. to Bus. Estab.7. D.M. to Consumers 8. Daily Newsp. 9. Exhibits/Trade Shows 10. Foreign 11. Infomercial 12. Internet Adv.13. Multimedia 14. Network Radio 15. Network T.V. 16. Newsp. Distr. Mags. 17. Other 18. Outdoor (Posters, Transit) 19. Point of Purchase20. Premiums, Novelties 21. Product Samples 22. Special Events Mktg. 23. Spot Radio 24. Spot T.V. 25. Weekly Newsp. 26. Yellow Page Adv.

Toll Free: (800) 548-7231
E-mail: investorrelations@selectcomfort.com
Web Site: www.selectcomfort.com
Approx. Sls.: $605,676,000
Approx. Number Employees: 2,165
Year Founded: 1987
Business Description:
Air Mattresses, Foundations & Accessories Mfr & Retailer
S.I.C.: 2515; 5719
N.A.I.C.S.: 337910; 442299
Advertising Expenditures: $70,200,000
Media: 3-6-8-9-12-13-14-15-19-23-24-25
Personnel:
William R. McLaughlin *(Pres & CEO)*
Wendy L. Schoppert *(CFO)*
Karen R. Richard *(Chief HR Officer & Chief Strategy Officer)*
Mark A. Kimball *(Gen Counsel & Sr VP)*
Shelly R. Ibach *(Exec VP-Sls & Mdsg)*
Kathryn Roedel *(Exec VP-Product & Svc)*
Brands & Products:
ASSURED
CLASSIC PLUSH
DREAMFIT
DUAL-LOFT
EUROLOFT
EXPANDED QUEEN
GRAND KING
GRIDZONE
HYPERSOFT
INTRALUS
LUXLAYER
LUXLOFT
LYOCELL
LYOCELL DOWN
MEMORY FOEM CLASSIC
PRECISION COMFORT
PRIMALOFT
SELECT COMFORT
SELECT COMFORT CREATOR OF THE SLEEP NUMBER BED
SELECT COMFORT SLEEP NUMBER
SLEEP BETTER ON AIR
SLEEP NUMBER
THE SLEEP NUMBER BED BY SELECT COMFORT
THERMO-FOAM
THINSULATE
TRUE SILVER
Advertising Agency:
Fleishman-Hillard Inc.
200 N Broadway
Saint Louis, MO 63102-2730
Tel.: (314) 982-1700
Fax: (314) 982-0586
Sleep Number (PR Agency of Record)

THE SERAPH

420 Main St
Sturbridge, MA 01566
Tel.: (508) 347-2241
Fax: (508) 347-9162
E-mail: info@theseraph.com
Web Site: www.theseraph.com
Approx. Number Employees: 8
Business Description:
Early American Reproduction Furniture & Accessories
S.I.C.: 2512; 2541
N.A.I.C.S.: 337121; 337212
Media: 4-6
Personnel:
Alexandra Pifer *(Owner)*

SERTA, INC.

(Joint Venture of Ontario Teachers' Pension Plan & Ares Management LLC)
(d/b/a Serta International)
2600 Forbs Ave
Hoffman Estates, IL 60192
Tel.: (847) 645-0200
Fax: (847) 645-0205
Toll Free: (888) 557-3782
E-mail: groupreceptionist@serta.com
Web Site: www.serta.com
Approx. Number Employees: 65
Year Founded: 1931
Business Description:
Mattress Mfr
S.I.C.: 2515
N.A.I.C.S.: 337910
Export
Advertising Expenditures: $120,000,000
Media: 8-13-15-22-24-25-26
Distr.: Intl.; Natl.
Personnel:
Jim Nation *(Pres-Bus Dev)*
Andrew Gross *(Sr VP-Mktg)*
Alan Klancnik *(Grp VP)*
Kevin Bayer *(Dir-Acctg)*
Brands & Products:
COUNTINUOUS SUPPORT
FIREBLOCKER
PERFECT NIGHT
PERFECT SLEEPER
WE MAKE THE WORLD'S BEST MATTRESS
Advertising Agency:
Doner
25900 Northwestern Hwy
Southfield, MI 48075
Tel.: (248) 354-9700
Fax: (248) 827-8440

SHAW INDUSTRIES GROUP, INC.

(Holding of Berkshire Hathaway Inc.)
PO Drawer 2128 616 E Walnut Ave
Dalton, GA 30722-2128
Tel.: (706) 278-3812
Fax: (706) 275-3735
Toll Free: (800) 441-7429
E-mail: infocenter@shawinc.com
Web Site: www.shawfloors.com
Sales Range: $5-14.9 Billion
Approx. Number Employees: 28,974
Year Founded: 1967
Business Description:
Carpets, Rugs & Flooring Mfr
S.I.C.: 2273; 2431; 3996
N.A.I.C.S.: 314110; 321918; 326192
Advertising Expenditures: $500,000
Media: 2-6-7-10-13
Personnel:
Randy Merritt *(Pres)*
Vance D. Bell *(CEO)*
Kenneth G. Jackson *(CFO)*
Kathy Young *(Dir-Mktg)*
Brands & Products:
CABIN CRAFTS
PATCRAFT
PHILADELPHIA
QUEEN
SHAWMARK
SUTTON
TUFTEX
Advertising Agency:
Three Atlanta
359 E Paces Ferry Rd Ste 300
Atlanta, GA 30305
Tel.: (404) 266-0899
Fax: (404) 266-3699

SHELBY WILLIAMS INDUSTRIES, INC.

(Joint Venture of Oaktree Capital Management, L.P. & Whippoorwill Associates, Inc.)
5303 E Morris Blvd
Morristown, TN 37813-1138
Tel.: (423) 586-7000
Fax: (423) 587-8266
Toll Free: (800) SEATING
E-mail: swmarketing@commercialfurnituregroup.com
Web Site: www.shelbywilliams.com
Approx. Number Employees: 2,050
Year Founded: 1953
Business Description:
Hotel & Restaurant Upholstered & Wood Office Furniture Mfr; Upholstery Fabrics Mfr & Importer
S.I.C.: 2531; 2672
N.A.I.C.S.: 337127; 322222
Import Export
Advertising Expenditures: $500,000
Media: 2-4-7-10-13-20-21
Distr.: Intl.; Natl.
Budget Set: Dec.
Brands & Products:
CHAIR EXPRESS
SHELBY WILLIAMS
THONET

SIMMONS COMPANY

(Holding of Thomas H. Lee Partners, L.P.)
(d/b/a Simmons Bedding Company)
(Filed Ch 11 Bankruptcy #914037 on 11/16/09 in U.S. Bankruptcy Ct, Dist of DE, Wilmington)
1 Concourse Pkwy Ste 800
Atlanta, GA 30328-6188
Tel.: (770) 512-7700
Fax: (770) 392-2560
Web Site: www.simmons.com
Approx. Sls.: $1,028,700,000
Approx. Number Employees: 1,232
Year Founded: 1870
Business Description:
Bed & Mattress Mfr & Retailer
S.I.C.: 2515; 5712
N.A.I.C.S.: 337910; 442110
Export
Advertising Expenditures: $91,600,000
Media: 2-3-5-6-7-8-9-13-19
Distr.: Intl.; Natl.
Budget Set: Aug.
Personnel:
Stephen G. Fendrich *(Pres & COO)*
Gary T. Fazio *(CEO)*
William S. Creekmuir *(CFO & Exec VP)*
Kristen K. McGuffey *(General Counsel, Corp Sec & Exec VP)*
Dominick A. Azevedo *(Exec VP-Sls)*
Timothy F. Oakhill *(Exec VP-Mktg)*
Kimberly A. Samon *(Exec VP-HR)*
Mark F. Chambless *(Sr VP & Controller)*
Robert M. Carstens *(Sr VP-Technical Svcs)*
Anne Kozel *(Brand Dir)*
Rolf Sannes *(Brand Dir-Beautyrest)*
Brands & Products:
BACKCARE
BACKCARE KIDS
BEAUTYREST
BEAUTYREST BEGINNINGS
BEAUTYREST BLACK
BEAUTYREST FEELINGS
BEAUTYREST STUDIO
BEAUTYSLEEP
BETTER SLEEP THROUGH SCIENCE
COMFORPEDIC
DEEP SLEEP
DREAMWELL
HIDE-A-BED
JOSEPH ABBOUD
LATITUDES
MAXIPEDIC
MOISTURE BAN
NATURAL CARE
POCKETED COIL
RITEHEIGHT
SLUMBER KING
SLUMBER TIME
SPECIALTY SLEEP
WALL-A-BED
Advertising Agencies:
Martin/Williams Advertising Inc.
(A Member of Omnicom Group)
60 S 6th St Ste 2800
Minneapolis, MN 55402-4428
Tel.: (612) 340-0800
Fax: (612) 342-9700

Three Atlanta
359 E Paces Ferry Rd Ste 300
Atlanta, GA 30305
Tel.: (404) 266-0899
Fax: (404) 266-3699
— Christine Foster *(Dir-Pub Rel-Simmons Beautyrest)*
— Katie O'Neill *(Acct Exec-Simmons Beautyrest)*

SIMMONS JUVENILE FURNITURE

(Div. of Delta Enterprise Corporation)
677 commerce Dr
Hortonville, WI 54944
Mailing Address:
PO Box 357
Appleton, WI 54912-0357
Tel.: (920) 982-2140
Fax: (920) 779-4216
E-mail: customerservice@sjfdec.com
Web Site: www.simmonskidsfurniture.com
Approx. Number Employees: 12
Year Founded: 1917
Business Description:
Juvenile Furniture Mfr
S.I.C.: 5712
N.A.I.C.S.: 442110
Media: 2-4-10-17-20
Distr.: Natl.
Budget Set: Aug.
Personnel:
Keith Steve *(Gen Mgr)*

SLEEP COUNTRY USA, INC.

(Sub. of The Sleep Train Inc.)
6705 S 209th St
Kent, WA 98032
Tel.: (866) 683-1923
Fax: (866) 293-5719
Toll Free: (800) 337-2872

Key to Media (For complete agency information see *The Advertising Red Books-Agencies* edition):
1. Bus. Publs. 2. Cable T.V. 3. Catalogs & Directories. 4. Co-op Adv. 5. Consumer Mags. 6. D.M. to Bus. Estab.7. D.M. to Consumers 8. Daily Newsp. 9. Exhibits/Trade Shows 10. Foreign 11. Infomercial 12. Internet Adv.13. Multimedia 14. Network Radio 15. Network T.V. 16. Newsp. Distr. Mags. 17. Other 18. Outdoor (Posters, Transit) 19. Point of Purchase20. Premiums, Novelties 21. Product Samples 22. Special Events Mktg. 23. Spot Radio 24. Spot T.V. 25. Weekly Newsp. 26. Yellow Page Adv.

Sleep Country USA, Inc. — (Continued)

E-mail: customerservice@sleepcountry.com
Web Site: www.sleepcountry.com
Sales Range: $75-99.9 Million
Approx. Number Employees: 200
Year Founded: 1991
Business Description:
Beds & Matresses Whslr
S.I.C.: 5712
N.A.I.C.S.: 442110
Media: 8-9-13-19-22-23-24-25-26
Personnel:
Gina Davis *(Brand Mgr)*
Brands & Products:
WHY BUY A MATTRESS ANYWHERE ELSE
Advertising Agency:
Revolution Public Relations
2345 SE Ivon St
Portland, OR 97202
Tel.: (503) 380-8292
Fax: (503) 233-1452

SLEEPY'S, INC.

1000 S Oyster Bay Rd
Hicksville, NY 11801
Tel.: (516) 844-8800
Fax: (516) 861-8845
Toll Free: (800) 753-3797
E-mail: service@sleepys.com
Web Site: www.sleepys.com
Approx. Number Employees: 1,000
Year Founded: 1957
Business Description:
Mattress & Bedding Retailer
S.I.C.: 5712
N.A.I.C.S.: 442110
Advertising Expenditures: $1,500,000
Media: 2-3-4-5-6-8-9-10-18-19-20-21-23-24-25-26
Distr.: Reg.
Personnel:
Harry Acker *(Chm)*
David Acker *(Pres)*
Joseph Graci *(CFO)*
Jeff Maynard *(CMO)*
Mike Bookbinder *(Exec VP)*
Brands & Products:
THE MATTRESS PROFESSIONALS
SLEEPY'S
Advertising Agency:
Crenshaw Communications
7 West 18th St. 9th Fl
New York, NY 10011
Tel.: (212) 367-9700
Fax: (212) 367-9701
"Sleep Better in 2011"
Public Relations

SPRINGS WINDOW FASHIONS LLC

7549 Graber Rd
Middleton, WI 53562-1001
Tel.: (608) 836-1011
Fax: (608) 831-2184
Toll Free: (800) 221-6352
Web Site:
www.springswindowfashions.com
Approx. Number Employees: 600
Year Founded: 1938
Business Description:
Mfr. of Drapery Rods, Window Shades, Pleated Shades, Horizontal & Vertical Blinds
S.I.C.: 2591
N.A.I.C.S.: 337920
Import Export
Media: 2
Distr.: Intl.; Natl.
Budget Set: Monthly
Personnel:
Scott Fawcett *(Pres & CEO)*
Brands & Products:
BALI
THE BEST EXPERIENCE COMPANY
CASUAL CLASSICS
CRYSTALPLEAT
DESIGN BASICS
DIAMONDCELL
DIFFUSION
GRABER
GRABER SLIDE-VUE
LIGHTBLOCKER
NANIK
NEAT PLEAT
NORTHERN HEIGHTS
PANEL ACCENTS
SHEER ENCHANTMENT
SKYTRACK
SPRINGS WINDOW FASHIONS
TIMBERLINE
TRADEWINDS
VERTICELL
WOOD IMAGES
WOODPLUS

THE STANDARD MATTRESS COMPANY

261 Weston St
Hartford, CT 06120-1209
Tel.: (860) 549-2000
Fax: (860) 527-3101
Toll Free: (800) 873-8498
E-mail: gbmattress@aol.com
Approx. Number Employees: 70
Year Founded: 1899
Business Description:
Mfr. & Distributor of Mattresses, Boxsprings & Related Bedding Products
S.I.C.: 2515; 5021
N.A.I.C.S.: 337910; 423210
Import Export
Advertising Expenditures: $250,000
Consumer Mags.: $125,000; Exhibits/Trade Shows: $62,500; Other: $62,500
Distr.: Natl.; Reg.
Budget Set: Dec.
Personnel:
Robert J. Naboicheck *(Pres & COO)*
Allan Cohen *(CFO)*
Peter M. Naboicheck *(Exec VP)*
Brands & Products:
GOLD BOND
OSTERMOOR

STANLEY FURNITURE CO., INC.

1641 Fairystone Park Hwy
Stanleytown, VA 24168
Mailing Address:
PO Box 30
Stanleytown, VA 24168-0030
Tel.: (276) 627-2000
Fax: (276) 629-5114
E-mail: investor@stanleyfurniture.com
Web Site: www.stanleyfurniture.com
Approx. Sls.: $137,012,000
Approx. Number Employees: 650
Year Founded: 1924
Business Description:
Residential Furniture Mfr
S.I.C.: 2511
N.A.I.C.S.: 337122
Import Export
Advertising Expenditures: $200,000
Media: 2-6-18
Distr.: Natl.
Budget Set: Sept.
Personnel:
Michael P. Haley *(Chm)*
R. Glenn Prillaman *(Pres & CEO)*
Micah S. Goldstein *(CFO, COO, Principal Acctg Officer & Sec)*
Douglas I. Payne *(Sec & Exec VP-Div)*
Kevin Bowman *(VP-Sls)*
Charles Cooley *(VP-Production-Stanleytown Facility)*
Kevin Walker *(VP-Sls)*
Brands & Products:
AMERICAN MODERN
AMERICAN VIEW
BEAU NOUVEAU
COASTAL COTTAGE
COASTAL LIVING
CONTINUUM
CORINTHIA
COTTAGE REVIVAL
ESTATE COLLECTION
HUDSON STREET
LINCOLN PARK
MONTECITO
MOONDANCE
PARADISE VALLEY
PENINSULA
PORTOFINO
SERENITY
SLOANE SQUARE
SOPHIA
TEEN BUNGALOW
TRANSLATION
TRE VENTI
URBAN COMFORT
VENICIA
VILLA ANTICA
WAINWRIGHT
WATER'S EDGE
WINTERHAVEN
YOUNG AMERICA
Advertising Agency:
McNeill Communications Group Inc.
202 Neal Pl
High Point, NC 27262
Tel.: (336) 884-8700
Fax: (336) 884-4141

STANLEY STEEMER INTERNATIONAL, INC.

5500 Stanley Steemer Pkwy
Dublin, OH 43016
Tel.: (614) 764-2007
Fax: (614) 654-7014
Toll Free: (614) 764-1506
Web Site: www.stanleysteemer.com
Sales Range: $250-299.9 Million
Approx. Number Employees: 1,800
Year Founded: 1947
Business Description:
Carpet & Upholstery Cleaning & Related Services
S.I.C.: 7217; 3635
N.A.I.C.S.: 561740; 335212
Advertising Expenditures: $30,000,000
Media: 2-3-4-5-6-7-8-10-13-15-17-18-19-20-21-22-23-24-25-26
Distr.: Natl.
Budget Set: Sept.
Personnel:
Wesley Bates *(CEO)*
Mark Bunner *(CFO & VP)*
Philip P. Ryser *(Gen Counsel & Exec VP)*
Brands & Products:
EZ MOVES PRO
GRANDI GROOM
HANDI BRUSH
HANDI GROOM
LIVING BRINGS IT IN. WE TAKE IT OUT.
ODOR OUT
STANLEY STEEMER
Advertising Agencies:
Empower MediaMarketing (MEDIA THAT WORKS)
1111 Saint Gregory St
Cincinnati, OH 45202
Tel.: (513) 871-9454
Fax: (513) 871-1804

Young & Laramore
407 N Fulton St
Indianapolis, IN 46202
Tel.: (317) 264-8000
Fax: (317) 264-8002
— Brad Bobenmoyer *(Acct Dir-Stanley Steemer)*

STAR FURNITURE COMPANY

(Holding of Berkshire Hathaway Inc.)
16666 Barker Springs Rd
Houston, TX 77084-5032
Mailing Address:
PO Box 219169
Houston, TX 77218
Tel.: (281) 492-6661
Fax: (281) 492-6699
Toll Free: (800) 364-6661
Web Site: www.starfurniture.com
Sales Range: $250-299.9 Million
Approx. Number Employees: 875
Year Founded: 1912
Business Description:
Furniture Stores
S.I.C.: 5712
N.A.I.C.S.: 442110
Media: 3-4-6-8-9-23-24-25-26
Distr.: Reg.
Personnel:
Melvin Lee Wolf *(Chm)*
Bill Ward *(Pres)*
Gary Gibson *(CFO)*
Michael Galloway *(Dir-Adv)*
Advertising Agency:
Yaffe/Deutser
1330 Post Oak Blvd Ste 1350
Houston, TX 77056
Tel.: (713) 212-0700
Fax: (713) 850-2108
Broadcast

STARK CARPET CORPORATION

D&D Bldg 979 3rd Ave Fl 11
New York, NY 10022
Tel.: (212) 752-9000
Fax: (212) 758-4342
E-mail: info@starkcarpet.com
Web Site: www.starkcarpet.com
Sales Range: $100-124.9 Million
Approx. Number Employees: 150
Business Description:
Carpets, Trade Only

Key to Media (For complete agency information see *The Advertising Red Books-Agencies* edition):
1. Bus. Publs. 2. Cable T.V. 3. Catalogs & Directories. 4. Co-op Adv. 5. Consumer Mags. 6. D.M. to Bus. Estab.7. D.M. to Consumers 8. Daily Newsp. 9. Exhibits/Trade Shows 10. Foreign 11. Infomercial 12. Internet Adv.13. Multimedia 14. Network Radio 15. Network T.V. 16. Newsp. Distr. Mags. 17. Other 18. Outdoor (Posters, Transit) 19. Point of Purchase20. Premiums, Novelties 21. Product Samples 22. Special Events Mktg. 23. Spot Radio 24. Spot T.V. 25. Weekly Newsp. 26. Yellow Page Adv.

S.I.C.: 5023; 5131
N.A.I.C.S.: 423220; 424310
Media: 6-7-10-13
Personnel:
Isabelle L'Huillier *(Dir-Sls)*
Arthur Phillips *(Mgr-Wall Coverings)*
Brands & Products:
NEW ORIENTAL
STARK
Advertising Agency:
AGENCYSACKS
345 7th Ave 7th Fl
New York, NY 10001-5006
Tel.: (212) 826-4004
Fax: (212) 593-7824

STEARNS & FOSTER BEDDING COMPANY
(Div. of Sealy Corporation)
1 Office Parkway Rd
Trinity, NC 27370-9449
Tel.: (336) 861-3500
Fax: (336) 861-3501
Web Site: www.stearnsandfoster.com
Approx. Number Employees: 200
Business Description:
Mattresses & Box Springs
S.I.C.: 2515
N.A.I.C.S.: 337910
Import
Advertising Expenditures: $700,000
Media: 5-9-19-23-24-25
Distr.: Natl.
Budget Set: Sept.
Brands & Products:
BASSETT BEDDING
REFLEXION
SEALY
SEALY POSTUREPEDIC
Advertising Agency:
Cramer-Krasselt Public Relations
225 N Michigan Ave
Chicago, IL 60601-7601
Tel.: (312) 616-9600

STONE CREEK FURNITURE INC.
4221 E Raymond St Ste 102
Phoenix, AZ 85040
Tel.: (602) 458-9800
Fax: (602) 437-5126
Toll Free: (800) 515-4221
Web Site:
www.stonecreekfurniture.com
Approx. Number Employees: 100
Business Description:
Furniture Mfr
S.I.C.: 2521
N.A.I.C.S.: 337211
Media: 2-9-10
Personnel:
Ronald Jones *(Pres)*

STOWERS FURNITURE COMPANIES LTD
210 W Rector St
San Antonio, TX 78216
Tel.: (210) 342-9411
Fax: (210) 342-2903
Web Site: www.stowersfurniture.com
Approx. Number Employees: 40
Business Description:
Furniture Stores
S.I.C.: 5712
N.A.I.C.S.: 442110
Personnel:
Walter Harrell Spears *(Pres)*
Johnathan Spears *(Gen Mgr)*
Advertising Agency:
Taylor West Advertising
4040 Broadway St Ste 302
San Antonio, TX 78209-6353
Tel.: (210) 805-0320
Fax: (210) 805-9371

SUBURBAN FURNITURE CORP.
Rte 10 W
Succasunna, NJ 07876
Tel.: (973) 927-1300
Fax: (973) 927-0414
Web Site:
www.suburbanfurniture.com
Approx. Number Employees: 25
Business Description:
Furniture Retailer
S.I.C.: 5712
N.A.I.C.S.: 442110
Media: 8-16-18
Personnel:
Kenneth Luthy *(Pres)*

SUNRISE MEDICAL LONG TERM CARE
(Div. of Sunrise Medical Inc.)
5001 Joerns Dr
Stevens Point, WI 54481-5040
Tel.: (800) 333-4000
Fax: (715) 341-3962
Toll Free: (800) 826-0270
E-mail: info@joerns.com
Web Site: www.joerns.com
Approx. Number Employees: 250
Year Founded: 1889
Business Description:
Hospital & Long Term Care Facilities Beds & Furnishings Mfr
S.I.C.: 5047
N.A.I.C.S.: 423450
Export
Media: 2-4-7-10-17
Distr.: Intl.; Natl.
Brands & Products:
JOERNS

SURE FIT INC.
(Holding of Guardian Capital Partners, LLC)
6575 Snowdrift Rd Ste 101
Allentown, PA 18106-9353
Tel.: (610) 264-7300
Fax: (610) 266-2690
Toll Free: (888) 796-0500
E-mail: customerservice@surefit.com
Web Site: www.surefit.com
Sales Range: $100-124.9 Million
Approx. Number Employees: 500
Year Founded: 1914
Business Description:
Furniture Slipcovers Whslr & Online Retailer
S.I.C.: 5023; 5719; 5961
N.A.I.C.S.: 423220; 442299; 454111
Import
Media: 3-4-6-13
Personnel:
Hugh R. Rovit *(CEO)*
John J. Nucero *(CFO)*
Nancy Cartisano *(Sr VP-Prod Dev)*
George De Sotle *(Sr VP-Sls & Mktg)*
Brands & Products:
SURE FIT

TELESCOPE CASUAL FURNITURE INC.
82 Church St
Granville, NY 12832-1621
Tel.: (518) 642-1100
Fax: (518) 642-2536
Toll Free: (800) 458-3876
E-mail: scampbell@telescopecasual.com
Web Site: www.telescopecasual.com
E-Mail For Key Personnel:
President: HVanderminden@telescopecasual.com
Marketing Director: billvanderminden@telescopecasual.com
Sales Director: AWooten@telescopecasual.com
Approx. Number Employees: 300
Year Founded: 1903
Business Description:
Mfr of Aluminum, Wood & Casual Furniture
S.I.C.: 2514; 2511
N.A.I.C.S.: 337124; 337122
Import Export
Media: 2-4-6-7-10-19-20
Distr.: Natl.
Budget Set: Oct.
Personnel:
Henry Vanderminden, IV *(Pres)*
Kathy Junkett *(CEO)*
Richard Parker *(Pres-New Horizons)*
R. Vanderminden, Jr. *(VP-Production)*
William Vanderminden *(VP-Mktg)*
Dick Vladyka *(VP-Tech & Engrng)*
Adam Vanderminden *(Dir-Adv)*
Brands & Products:
ALFRESCO
ARUBA
BANQUET
BELLA LUCCA
CADIZ
CAPE MAY
CASTLETON
CHESAPEAKE
DIRECTOR
FESTIVAL
FORTIS
GARDENELLA
KEY BISCAYNE
LIGHT 'N EASY
LONG SHOT
MARKET UMBRELLAS
MINI-SUN CHAISES
MOMENTUM
NORTHAMPTON
OCEANSIDE
PRIMERA
ROMANESQUE
SUN & SAND CHAIRS
TELAWEAVE
TELAWEAVE VINYL MESH
TELESCOPE CASUAL FURNITURE
VANESE
VANESE SLING COLLECTION
WINDHAM
WINDHAM SLING
WINDWARD
WORLD-FAMOUS
Advertising Agency:
Telescope Advertising Agency
PO Box 299
Granville, NY 12832
Tel.: (518) 642-1100
Fax: (518) 642-2536

TEMPUR-PEDIC INTERNATIONAL, INC.
1713 Jaggie Fox Way
Lexington, KY 40511-2512
Tel.: (859) 259-0754
Fax: (859) 514-4422
Toll Free: (800) 878-8889
Toll Free: (800) 805-3635 (Investor Rels)
E-mail: customer.service@tempurpedic.com
Web Site: www.tempurpedic.com
Approx. Sls.: $1,105,421,000
Approx. Number Employees: 1,500
Year Founded: 1992
Business Description:
Sales of Swedish Mattresses & Pillows
S.I.C.: 2515; 5021
N.A.I.C.S.: 337910; 423210
Advertising Expenditures: $96,611,000
Media: 1-4-8-10-19-21
Distr.: Intl.; Natl.
Personnel:
Peter Andrews McLane *(Chm)*
Robert B. Trussell, Jr. *(Vice Chm)*
Mark A. Sarvary *(Pres & CEO)*
Dale E. Williams *(CFO & Exec VP)*
Brad Patrick *(Chief HR Officer & Exec VP)*
Bhaskar Rao *(Chief Acctg Officer & Sr VP)*
Richard W. Anderson *(Pres-North America & Exec VP)*
David Montgomery *(Pres-Intl Ops & Exec VP)*
Lou Jones *(Gen Counsel, Sec & Exec VP)*
Matthew D. Clift *(Exec VP-Global Ops)*
Dan Setlak *(VP-Mktg & Direct Sls)*
Brands & Products:
ADVANTAGEBED
AIRFLOW SYSTEM
ALLURABED
BELLAFINA
THE BELLAPILLOW
BELLASONNA
THE BODYPILLOW
CELEBRITYBED
CLASSICBED
CLASSICPILLOW
COMBED
COMFORTPILLOW
COMFORTSLIPPERS
DELUXEDBED
EGYPTIAN
ERGO LEG
FIRM WHERE YOU NEED IT
GRANDBED
GRANDPILLOW
LUMBARCUSHION
NECKPILLOW
NECKSUPPORT
ORIGINALBED
PIMA
PRIMABED
RHAPSODYBED
RHAPSODYPILLOW
SEATCUSHION
SIDEPILLOW
SUPIMA
SYMPHONYPILLOW
TEMPUR
TEMPUR ADVANCED ERGO SYSTEM
TEMPUR-FIT
TEMPUR-FLEX
TEMPUR-HD

Key to Media (For complete agency information see *The Advertising Red Books-Agencies* edition):
1. Bus. Publs. 2. Cable T.V. 3. Catalogs & Directories. 4. Co-op Adv. 5. Consumer Mags. 6. D.M. to Bus. Estab.7. D.M. to Consumers 8. Daily Newsp. 9. Exhibits/Trade Shows 10. Foreign 11. Infomercial 12. Internet Adv.13. Multimedia 14. Network Radio 15. Network T.V. 16. Newsp. Distr. Mags. 17. Other 18. Outdoor (Posters, Transit) 19. Point of Purchase20. Premiums, Novelties 21. Product Samples 22. Special Events Mktg. 23. Spot Radio 24. Spot T.V. 25. Weekly Newsp. 26. Yellow Page Adv.

Tempur-Pedic International, Inc. — (Continued)

TEMPUR-PEDIC
TEMPUR PEDIC
TEMPUR-PEDIC MATTRESS OVERLAY
TRAVELSET
UNIVERSALCUSHION
WELCOME TO BED

Advertising Agency:
PlattForm Advertising
708 3rd Ave 12th Fl
New York, NY 10017
Tel.: (212) 684-4800
Fax: (212) 576-1129
Toll Free: (866) 671-4429

THERAPEDIC ASSOCIATES, INC.

103 College Rd E
Princeton, NJ 08540
Tel.: (609) 720-0700
Fax: (609) 720-0797
Toll Free: (800) 314-4433
E-mail: info@therapedic.com
Web Site: www.therapedic.com
E-Mail For Key Personnel:
President: GBorreggine@therapedic.com
Sales Range: $200-249.9 Million
Approx. Number Employees: 4
Year Founded: 1957
Business Description:
Mfr. of Mattresses
S.I.C.: 2512; 2389; 2393; 2515; 3069; 3842; 3949
N.A.I.C.S.: 337121; 314911; 315299; 315999; 326299; 337910; 339113; 339920
Export
Media: 2-4-6-7-8-9-11-13-19-20-24
Distr.: Intl.; Natl.
Budget Set: Sept.
Personnel:
Norman Rosenblatt *(Chm)*
Gerry Borreggine *(Pres & CEO)*
Brands & Products:
BACK SENSE
INNERGY
LLOYD
LLOYD AND PENFIELD
MEDI-COIL
MEMORYTOUCH
PENEFELD
PERMA GRIP
PURETOUCH
THERAPEDIC
THE TOUCHABLES
TRI-TEC
TRIPLE EDGE

THOMASVILLE FURNITURE INDUSTRIES, INC.

(Sub. of Furniture Brands International, Inc.)
401 E Main St
Thomasville, NC 27360
Tel.: (336) 472-4000
Fax: (336) 472-4071
E-mail: maillist@thomasville.com
Web Site: www.thomasville.com
Sales Range: $650-699.9 Million
Approx. Number Employees: 5,800
Year Founded: 1904
Business Description:
Furniture Mfr
S.I.C.: 2542; 2512
N.A.I.C.S.: 337215; 337121
Export
Advertising Expenditures: $8,000,000
Media: 3-4-6-8-10-24-26
Distr.: Natl.
Personnel:
Edward D. Teplitz *(Pres)*
Terry Bargy *(CIO & VP)*
Shelby McMennamy *(Mgr-Retail Svcs Brand)*
Brands & Products:
THOMASVILLE
Advertising Agency:
The Richards Group, Inc.
8750 N Central Expy Ste 100
Dallas, TX 75231-6430
Tel.: (214) 891-5700
Fax: (214) 265-2933
Thomasville Furniture
— Amanda Carea *(Acct Exec)*

THYBONY WALLCOVERINGS INC.

3445 N Kimball
Chicago, IL 60618
Tel.: (773) 463-3050
Tel.: (773) 561-2275
E-mail: info@thybony.com
Web Site: www.thybony.com
Approx. Number Employees: 120
Year Founded: 1886
Business Description:
Mfr. & Distr. of Wall Coverings
S.I.C.: 5198; 5023
N.A.I.C.S.: 424950; 423220
Advertising Expenditures: $225,000
Media: 2-4-8-10-13-19
Distr.: Natl.
Budget Set: Sept.
Personnel:
James D. Thybony *(Pres)*
Bo Pruski *(VP-Fin)*
Robin Thybony *(VP-Sls)*
Brands & Products:
THYBONY

TOMLINSON/ERWIN-LAMBETH, INC.

201 E Holly Hill Rd
Thomasville, NC 27360-5819
Tel.: (336) 472-5005
Fax: (336) 476-8745
E-mail: tel@northstate.net
Web Site: www.tomlinsonerwinlambeth.com
Approx. Number Employees: 100
Year Founded: 1901
Business Description:
Mfr. of Upholstered Furniture
S.I.C.: 2512
N.A.I.C.S.: 337121
Import Export
Media: 2-4-6-7-10-13
Distr.: Natl.
Budget Set: Oct.
Personnel:
W. R. Lambeth *(Co-owner & CEO)*
Joe Graham *(VP-Mktg)*
Debbie Powell *(Dir-Mktg)*
Brands & Products:
TOMLINSON/ERWIN-LAMBETH

TRANSOLID OKLAHOMA

(Div. of Transolid, Inc.)
1120 Main Pkwy
Catoosa, OK 74015
Tel.: (918) 280-2700
Fax: (918) 280-2701
Fax: (866) 394-5549
Toll Free: (866) 394-8037
E-mail: info@mysterasurfaces.com
Web Site: www.mysterasurfaces.com
Approx. Number Employees: 30
Business Description:
Solid Surface Mfr
S.I.C.: 2434
N.A.I.C.S.: 337110
Media: 2-10
Personnel:
George Saxby *(Pres)*
Curtis Turner *(VP-Mktg)*
Brands & Products:
MYSTERA

TRENDWAY CORPORATION

13467 Quincy St
Holland, MI 49424
Mailing Address:
PO Box 9016
Holland, MI 49422-9016
Tel.: (616) 399-3900
Fax: (616) 399-0668
Toll Free: (800) 748-0234
E-mail: bwitt@trendway.com
Web Site: www.trendway.com
Sales Range: $500-549.9 Million
Approx. Number Employees: 275
Year Founded: 1968
Business Description:
Mfr. of Open Office Furniture Systems, Floor to Ceiling Moveable Partitions & Seating
S.I.C.: 2522; 2521
N.A.I.C.S.: 337214; 337211
Export
Media: 2-5-7-10-13-20-22-26
Distr.: Intl.; Natl.
Personnel:
Don Heeringa *(Chm)*
Bill Bundy *(Pres & CEO)*
Richard Martinus *(CFO)*
Barbara Witt *(Dir-HR)*
Susan Zalnis *(Mgr-Mktg & Comm)*
Brands & Products:
CAMEO
CHOICES
CONTRADA
IN
POWER ARCH
PRELUDE
QUINCY
TRENDWALL
TRENDWAY
TRENDWAY XPRESS
XANTOS

TROPITONE FURNITURE CO., INC.

5 Marconi
Irvine, CA 92618
Tel.: (949) 951-2010
Fax: (949) 951-0716
E-mail: info@tropitone.com
Web Site: www.tropitone.com
Approx. Number Employees: 500
Year Founded: 1954
Business Description:
Furniture Mfr
S.I.C.: 2514
N.A.I.C.S.: 337124
Export
Media: 2-4-10-11-19-20-21-22
Personnel:
Cap Hendrix *(Pres & CEO)*
Randy Danielson *(CFO)*
Victoria Dawson *(Mgr-Fashion Design)*
Brands & Products:
ADD-A-PAD
BALI
BASTA SOLE
CALYPSO
ECHO
EVO WOVEN COLLECTION
EZ SPAN
INDOOR STYLE. OUTDOOR FURNITURE
KAHANA
LA SCALA
LAKESIDE
MILLENNIA
MONTREUX
OPUS
PALLADIAN
PORTICO
PORTOFINO
RADIANCE
SHORELINE
SOMERSET
SPINNAKER
TRANSITIONS
TROPI-KAI
TROPIKANE
TROPITONE

TUFENKIAN IMPORT/EXPORT VENTURES, INC.

919 3rd Ave
New York, NY 10022-3902
Tel.: (212) 475-2475
Fax: (212) 475-2629
Web Site: www.tufenkiancarpets.com
Sales Range: $25-49.9 Million
Approx. Number Employees: 35
Business Description:
Carpets Whslr
S.I.C.: 5023
N.A.I.C.S.: 423220
Media: 6-10
Personnel:
James F. Tufenkian *(Pres)*
Eric Jacobsen *(CFO & COO)*
Katie Dodd *(Coord-Mktg & PR)*

THE TWEED WEASEL PRIMITIVES

633 W Main St
Schaefferstown, PA 17088-0407
Tel.: (717) 949-3883
Web Site: www.thetweedweasel.com
Business Description:
Decorative Rugs, Dolls & Folk Art Mfr & Retailer
S.I.C.: 5947
N.A.I.C.S.: 453220
Media: 4-6-10

UNITED METAL FABRICATORS, INC.

1316 Eisenhower Blvd
Johnstown, PA 15904-3307
Tel.: (814) 266-8726
Fax: (814) 266-1870
Toll Free: (800) 638-5322
E-mail: info@ums.com
Web Site: www.umf-exam.com
Approx. Number Employees: 110
Year Founded: 1955
Business Description:
Physicians & Hospital Furniture Mfr
S.I.C.: 2531; 3444

Key to Media (For complete agency information see *The Advertising Red Books-Agencies* edition):
1. Bus. Publs. 2. Cable T.V. 3. Catalogs & Directories. 4. Co-op Adv. 5. Consumer Mags. 6. D.M. to Bus. Estab.7. D.M. to Consumers 8. Daily Newsp. 9. Exhibits/Trade Shows 10. Foreign 11. Infomercial 12. Internet Adv.13. Multimedia 14. Network Radio 15. Network T.V. 16. Newsp. Distr. Mags. 17. Other 18. Outdoor (Posters, Transit) 19. Point of Purchase20. Premiums, Novelties 21. Product Samples 22. Special Events Mktg. 23. Spot Radio 24. Spot T.V. 25. Weekly Newsp. 26. Yellow Page Adv.

N.A.I.C.S.: 337127; 332322
Import Export
Media: 4-7-10
Distr.: Intl.; Natl.
Personnel:
Ielen Meldin *(Pres)*
Brands & Products:
BARIATRIC
UMF

U.S. HOME SYSTEMS, INC.
405 State Hwy 121 Bypass Bldg A
Ste 250
Lewisville, TX 75067
Tel.: (214) 488-6300
Toll Free: (888) 595-3223
Web Site: www.ushomesystems.com
Approx. Rev.: $145,873,085
Approx. Number Employees: 863
Year Founded: 1980
Business Description:
Kitchen & Bathroom Products & Replacement Windows Mfr & Installer
S.I.C.: 3651; 1799; 2434; 3429; 5031
N.A.I.C.S.: 334310; 238990; 332510; 337110; 423310
Advertising Expenditures: $28,631,000
Media: 2-6-8-10-15-16-19
Personnel:
Murray H. Gross *(Chm, Pres & CEO)*
Robert A. Defronzo *(CFO, Treas & Sec)*
Steven L. Gross *(CMO & Exec VP)*
Richard B. Goodner *(Gen Counsel & VP-Legal Affairs)*

VALLEY FURNITURE SHOP, INC.
20 Stirling Rd
Watchung, NJ 07069
Tel.: (908) 756-7623
Fax: (908) 756-0382
Web Site:
www.valleyfurnitureshop.com
Approx. Number Employees: 20
Year Founded: 1974
Business Description:
Furniture Stores
S.I.C.: 5712
N.A.I.C.S.: 442110
Media: 6-9-23
Personnel:
Joan Kipe *(Pres)*
Skip Kipe *(Mgr-Adv)*

VECTA
(Div. of Coalesse)
1800 S Great SW Pkwy
Grand Prairie, TX 75051-3501
Tel.: (972) 641-2860
Fax: (972) 660-1746
Web Site: www.vecta.com
Sales Range: $100-124.9 Million
Approx. Number Employees: 290
Year Founded: 1959
Business Description:
Office Furniture, Tables & Area Seating Designer & Mfr
S.I.C.: 2522; 2521
N.A.I.C.S.: 337214; 337211
Export
Advertising Expenditures: $350,000
Media: 1-2-4-10-21
Distr.: Natl.
Budget Set: Mar.
Personnel:
Tim Baris *(VP-Fin)*
Brands & Products:
4 O'CLOCK
540 TABLES
AU LAIT
BALLET
BIRA
CONFAIR
DERBY
DISC
E-TABLE
FS
GINKGO BILOBA
GRIP
INDY
KELLY
LOGON
LUCY
MODUS
OPERA BEAM SEATING
PALETTE
RAF SYSTEM
RIZZI ARC
ROCKY
RUNNER
STITZ
TRAIN

VERMONT CLOCK COMPANY
239 Main St
Isle La Motte, VT 05463
Tel.: (802) 928-4190
E-mail: clock@vermontclock.com
Web Site: www.vermontclock.com
Sales Range: Less than $1 Million
Approx. Number Employees: 4
Business Description:
Reproduction Clock Mfr
S.I.C.: 5944; 5999
N.A.I.C.S.: 448310; 453998
Media: 17
Personnel:
Jack McGuire *(Owner)*

VICTORIA LESSER, INC.
1011 Truman Ave
Key West, FL 33040
Mailing Address:
PO Box 78
North Branch, NY 12766-0078
Tel.: (845) 482-5925
E-mail: victoria@victorialesser.com
Web Site: www.victorialesser.com
Business Description:
Interior Designer
S.I.C.: 7389
N.A.I.C.S.: 541410
Media: 10
Personnel:
Victoria Lesser *(Pres)*

VILLAGE AMERICANA, INC.
203 Union St
Occoquan, VA 22125
Tel.: (703) 491-5712
Fax: (703) 491-2588
E-mail: dgivins45@aol.com
Web Site: www.village-americana.com
Approx. Number Employees: 5
Year Founded: 1976
Business Description:
Custom & Reproduction Furniture Sales
S.I.C.: 5712
N.A.I.C.S.: 442110
Media: 6
Personnel:
David Givens *(Pres, CEO & Owner)*
Brands & Products:
VILLAGE AMERICANA

VIRCO MANUFACTURING CORPORATION
2027 Harpers Way
Torrance, CA 90501-1524
Tel.: (310) 533-0474
Fax: (310) 533-6814
Toll Free: (800) 448-4726
E-mail: info@virco.com
Web Site: www.virco.com
Approx. Sls.: $180,995,000
Approx. Number Employees: 1,050
Year Founded: 1950
Business Description:
Furniture Designer, Producer & Distr
S.I.C.: 2531; 2522
N.A.I.C.S.: 337127; 337214
Import Export
Advertising Expenditures: $2,022,000
Media: 2-4-6-7-10-11-20-21
Distr.: Intl.; Natl.
Budget Set: Feb.
Personnel:
Robert A. Virtue *(Chm, Pres & CEO)*
L. L. Swafford *(VP-Legal Affairs & Corp Counsel)*
Robert E. Dose *(Treas, Sec & VP-Fin)*
Douglas A. Virtue *(Exec VP)*
Bassey Yau *(Controller, Asst Treas, Asst Sec & VP-Acctg)*
S. Bell *(VP & Gen Mgr-Conway Div)*
N. Wilson *(VP & Gen Mgr-Torrance Div)*
A. Gamble *(VP-HR)*
Patricia Levine Quinones *(VP-Logistics Mktg Svcs & IT)*
D. R. Smith *(VP-Mktg)*
L. O. Wonder *(VP-Sls)*
Brands & Products:
CLASSIC SERIES
CORE-A-GATOR
FUTURE ACCESS
I.Q.
LUNADA
MARTEST 21
METAPHOR
MOJAVE
PH.D.
PH.D.EXECUTIVE
PLATEAU
TELOS
TEXT
ULTRASTACK
ZUMA
ZUMAFRD

WAREHOUSE HOME FURNISHINGS DISTRIBUTOR, INC.
(d/b/a Farmers' Furniture)
1851 Telfair St
Dublin, GA 31021
Tel.: (478) 275-3150
Fax: (478) 275-6276
E-mail: info@farmersfurniture.com
Web Site: www.farmersfurniture.com
Approx. Number Employees: 1,100
Year Founded: 1949
Business Description:
Farmers Furniture Company; Retail Furniture
S.I.C.: 5712; 5021
N.A.I.C.S.: 442110; 423210
Media: 2-13-16-23
Personnel:
Philip Farrcloth *(Pres)*
Clint Hall *(Sr VP-Field Ops)*
Claudia Peavy *(Dir-HR)*
Robbie Cook *(Mgr-Adv)*
Duane Harrison *(Mgr-Acctg)*
Brands & Products:
FARMERS HOME FURNITURE

WATERLOO INDUSTRIES, INC.
(Sub. of Fortune Brands Home & Security LLC)
100 E Fourth St
Waterloo, IA 50703-4714
Mailing Address:
PO Box 2095
Waterloo, IA 50704-2095
Tel.: (319) 235-7131
Fax: (319) 235-6408
Toll Free: (800) 833-8851
Web Site:
www.waterlooindustries.com/Legal-Statement.jsp
Sales Range: $300-349.9 Million
Approx. Number Employees: 150
Year Founded: 1922
Business Description:
Handboxes, Workbenches, Tool Chests & Cabinets Mfr
S.I.C.: 2531
N.A.I.C.S.: 337127
Import Export
Advertising Expenditures: $500,000
Media: 1-2-4-5-10-11-19-20-21
Distr.: Intl.; Natl.
Personnel:
Brad White *(Sr Mgr-Mktg)*
Brands & Products:
TOOL TOWER
TRAXX
WATERLOO
Advertising Agency:
Hellman Assoc., Inc.
1225 W 4th St PO Box 627
Waterloo, IA 50704-0627
Tel.: (319) 234-7055
Fax: (319) 234-2089
Toll Free: (800) 747-7055
(Tool Storage)

WAVERLY FABRICS
(Sub. of Iconix Brand Group, Inc.)
1450 Broadway 3rd Fl
New York, NY 10018
Tel.: (212) 730-0030
Fax: (212) 391-2057
Web Site: www.waverly.com
Sales Range: $100-124.9 Million
Approx. Number Employees: 80
Business Description:
Fabric & Wallcovering Mfr
S.I.C.: 5131; 2211
N.A.I.C.S.: 424310; 313210
Import Export
Media: 6
Personnel:
Neil Cole *(Pres)*
Warren Clamen *(Exec VP)*
Brands & Products:
GARDEN ROOM
HOME FASHIONS
WAVERLY
Advertising Agency:
Warschawski
1501 Sulgrave Ave Ste 350
Baltimore, MD 21209
Tel.: (410) 367-2700

Key to Media (For complete agency information see *The Advertising Red Books-Agencies* edition):
1. Bus. Publs. 2. Cable T.V. 3. Catalogs & Directories. 4. Co-op Adv. 5. Consumer Mags. 6. D.M. to Bus. Estab.7. D.M. to Consumers 8. Daily Newsp. 9. Exhibits/Trade Shows 10. Foreign 11. Infomercial 12. Internet Adv.13. Multimedia 14. Network Radio 15. Network T.V. 16. Newsp. Distr. Mags. 17. Other 18. Outdoor (Posters, Transit) 19. Point of Purchase20. Premiums, Novelties 21. Product Samples 22. Special Events Mktg. 23. Spot Radio 24. Spot T.V. 25. Weekly Newsp. 26. Yellow Page Adv.

Waverly Fabrics — (Continued)

Fax: (410) 367-2400

WAYNE TILE CO.
2 Doig Rd
Wayne, NJ 07470
Tel.: (973) 883-7962
Fax: (973) 883-7971
Web Site: www.waynetile.com
Approx. Number Employees: 60
Business Description:
Distributors Of Floor Tile
S.I.C.: 5713
N.A.I.C.S.: 442210
Personnel:
Bob Westra, Jr. *(Founder)*
Robert Westra, Sr. *(Founder)*
Advertising Agency:
GWP, Inc.
32 Park Ave
Montclair, NJ 07042
Tel.: (973) 746-0500
Fax: (973) 746-5563

W.C. HELLER & CO.
201 Wabash Ave
Montpelier, OH 43543
Tel.: (419) 485-3176
Fax: (419) 485-8694
E-mail: wcheller@hotmail.com
Web Site: www.wcheller.com
E-Mail For Key Personnel:
Sales Director: sales@wcheller.com
Approx. Number Employees: 10
Year Founded: 1891
Business Description:
Library Furniture & Equipment for Schools, Colleges, Public Libraries & Institutions; Cabinets & Store Equipment for Hardware, Paint & Seed Stores
S.I.C.: 2531
N.A.I.C.S.: 337127
Export
Media: 4-6-7-21
Distr.: Direct to Consumer; Reg.
Personnel:
Robert L. Heller *(Pres)*
Patricia A. Heller *(Treas)*
Andrew M. Heller *(VP-Production & Plant Mgr)*
Robert L. Heller, II *(VP-Sls)*
Brands & Products:
HELLER

W.E. BEDDING CORPORATION
11030 Artesia Blvd
Cerritos, CA 90703-2536
Tel.: (562) 865-6007
Tel.: (562) 865-0294 (Show Rm)
Fax: (562) 402-4123
Toll Free: (800) 734-6784
E-mail: webmaster@orthomattress.com
Web Site: www.orthomattress.com
Approx. Number Employees: 75
Year Founded: 1957
Business Description:
Retail Bedding
S.I.C.: 5719
N.A.I.C.S.: 442299
Export
Media: 9-10-17-19-22-24-26
Distr.: Reg.
Brands & Products:
ADJUSTABLE
BALDWIN
BELMONT
BELSANO
BURGUNDY
CITY
CONFORM
COPPER RIVER MAPLE
CORICA
CORSICA
COUNTOUR
DREAMER
EASTMAN
FENTON
FINLEY
GENTILITY
GRENADA
GRIFFITH
GUARDSMEN
HONOLULU
IMPERIAL MAJESTIC
KYOTO
LANDSCAPE
LANDSDOWNE
LARSON
LOUIS PHILLIPPE
LOVABLE
MARLOW
MEADOW
MONDOCO
NEVIS
NEWPORT
NORLAND
NORMANDY
NOTTINGHILL
NOVONA
ORION
ORTHO
ORTHO CONTOURED
ORTHO MATTRESS
PEMBRIDGE
PROTECT-A-BED
RAKE
RIVIERA
ROCKY
ROYALE
SAIGON
SALEM
SPRING SLEEP
SUMMIT
SUPREME
SURREY
TEMPERED
WALDORF
WHISTLER PINE

WELCOME HOME, INC.
(Sub. of Jordan Industries, Inc.)
309 Raleigh St
Wilmington, NC 28412-6366
Tel.: (910) 791-4312
Fax: (910) 791-4945
Toll Free: (800) 348-4088
E-mail: customerservice@welchome.com
Web Site: www.welcomehomestores.com
Approx. Number Employees: 50
Business Description:
Home Furnishings; Framed Art & Accessories Retailer
S.I.C.: 5947
N.A.I.C.S.: 453220
Media: 7-8-10

WHITE CROSS SLEEP PRODUCTS
(Affil. of Bemco Associates, Inc.)
901 E Lycoming St
Philadelphia, PA 19124-5111
Tel.: (215) 289-5556
Fax: (215) 288-9791
Approx. Sls.: $2,000,000
Approx. Number Employees: 30
Business Description:
Mfr. of Bedding
S.I.C.: 2515
N.A.I.C.S.: 337910
Media: 23-24
Distr.: Reg.
Budget Set: July
Personnel:
Mark Freeman *(Owner)*
Harvey Freeman *(Pres)*

WHITE LOTUS HOME
431 Raritan Ave
Highland Park, NJ 08904
Tel.: (732) 828-2111
Fax: (732) 828-4159
Toll Free: (877) 426-3623
E-mail: info@whitelotus.net
Web Site: www.whitelotus.net
E-Mail For Key Personnel:
Sales Director: sales@whitelotus.net
Approx. Number Employees: 15
Business Description:
Chemical-Free Mattress & Furniture Mfr
S.I.C.: 2511; 2515
N.A.I.C.S.: 337122; 337910
Personnel:
Marlon Pando *(Pres)*
Advertising Agency:
The Soap Group
322 Fore St 3rd Fl
Portland, ME 04101
Tel.: (207) 772-0066
Fax: (207) 772-2066

THE WICKER WORKS
1237 Minnesota St
San Francisco, CA 94107-3407
Tel.: (415) 970-5400
Fax: (415) 970-5410
E-mail: sales@thewickerworks.com
Web Site: www.thewickerworks.com
E-Mail For Key Personnel:
Sales Director: sales@thewickerworks.com
Approx. Number Employees: 25
Year Founded: 1972
Business Description:
Furniture Designer, Mfr, Importer & Wholesaler
S.I.C.: 5023; 2511
N.A.I.C.S.: 423220; 337122
Import
Advertising Expenditures: $200,000
Media: 6-13-17
Distr.: Intl.; Natl.
Budget Set: Mar.
Personnel:
Peter Rocchia *(Founder)*
Phillip France *(Mgr-Ops)*
Thomas Schaub *(Mgr-Sls & Adv)*
Brands & Products:
PIROETTA
TONDA
WICKER WORKS

WILLIAM-WAYNE & COMPANY
850 Lexington Ave & 64th St
New York, NY 10021
Tel.: (212) 737-8934
Tel.: (212) 288-9243
Fax: (212) 288-8915
Toll Free: (800) 318-3435
E-mail: info@william-wayne.com
Web Site: www.william-wayne.com
Year Founded: 1989
Business Description:
Home, Garden & Cottage Furnishings
S.I.C.: 5719
N.A.I.C.S.: 442299
Media: 6
Personnel:
William Meyer *(Pres & Co-Owner)*
Wayne Adler *(VP & Co-Owner)*

WINDOWS AND WALLS UNLIMITED, INC.
375 County Road 39
Southampton, NY 11968
Tel.: (631) 287-1515
Fax: (631) 287-1605
E-mail: info@wwunlimited.com
Web Site: www.wwunlimited.com
Sales Range: $1-9.9 Million
Approx. Number Employees: 5
Year Founded: 1985
Business Description:
Draperies, Blinds, Shutters, Slipcovers & Bed Ensembles Designer & Installer
S.I.C.: 2431; 1721; 2512; 7389
N.A.I.C.S.: 321911; 238320; 337121; 541410
Media: 13
Personnel:
Linda Nuszen *(Owner)*

WINDOWS OF THE WORLD, INC.
1855 Griffin Rd Ste A350
Dania, FL 33004
Tel.: (954) 921-8336
Fax: (954) 921-8557
E-mail: sales@windowsoftheworld.com
Web Site: www.windowsoftheworld.com
E-Mail For Key Personnel:
Sales Director: sales@windowsoftheworld.com
Approx. Number Employees: 11
Year Founded: 1983
Business Description:
Window Treatments, Fabrics & Wallcoverings
S.I.C.: 5023
N.A.I.C.S.: 423220
Export
Media: 6
Personnel:
Sonia R. Najman *(Dir-Windows Treatment Sls)*

WITH HEART & HAND
258 Dedham St Rte 1A
Norfolk, MA 02056
Tel.: (508) 384-6568
Tel.: (508) 384-5740, ext. 10
Fax: (508) 384-0552
E-mail: info@withheartandhand.net
Web Site: www.withheartandhand.net
Business Description:
Country Home Furnishing, Decorations, Fabric & Window Treatments
S.I.C.: 2541; 5023; 5719; 5947
N.A.I.C.S.: 337212; 423220; 442299; 453220
Media: 6-22
Personnel:
Diane Miller *(Owner & Mgr)*
Loretta Menard *(Co-Owner)*

Key to Media (For complete agency information see *The Advertising Red Books-Agencies* edition):
1. Bus. Publs. 2. Cable T.V. 3. Catalogs & Directories. 4. Co-op Adv. 5. Consumer Mags. 6. D.M. to Bus. Estab.7. D.M. to Consumers
8. Daily Newsp. 9. Exhibits/Trade Shows 10. Foreign 11. Infomercial 12. Internet Adv.13. Multimedia 14. Network Radio
15. Network T.V. 16. Newsp. Distr. Mags. 17. Other 18. Outdoor (Posters, Transit) 19. Point of Purchase20. Premiums, Novelties
21. Product Samples 22. Special Events Mktg. 23. Spot Radio 24. Spot T.V. 25. Weekly Newsp. 26. Yellow Page Adv.

WM OHS INC.
5095 Peoria St
Denver, CO 80239
Tel.: (303) 371-6550
E-mail: service@wmohs.com
Web Site: www.wmohs.com
Sales Range: $50-74.9 Million
Approx. Number Employees: 100
Year Founded: 1972
Business Description:
Mfr. of Wood Cabinets
S.I.C.: 2434; 5211
N.A.I.C.S.: 337110; 444190
Media: 4-6-10-13
Personnel:
William Ohs *(Pres)*
Brands & Products:
ARCHITECTURAL SERIES
RENAISSANCE
THEME STYLINGS
TRANSITIONS
WMOHS

WOODARD, LLC
(Sub. of Craftmade International, Inc.)
PO Box 1037
Coppell, TX 75019-1037
Tel.: (972) 393-3800
Fax: (877) 304-1728
Toll Free: (800) 877-2290
E-mail: retail3@woodard-furniture.com
Web Site: www.woodard-furniture.com
Sales Range: $150-199.9 Million
Approx. Number Employees: 400
Year Founded: 1865
Business Description:
Handcrafted Wrought Iron, Aluminum & Steel Furniture
S.I.C.: 5021
N.A.I.C.S.: 423210
Advertising Expenditures: $1,000,000
Media: 2-4-8-9-10-13-25
Distr.: Natl.
Budget Set: Dec.
Brands & Products:
BARBADOS
CARLTON
DEAUVILLE
DELPHI
DEVONSHIRE
EASTON
HERITAGE
LATOUR
MADDOX
MANHATTAN
MODESTO
RAMSGATE
REGENT
RESTON
SHEFFIELD
SOUTH SHORE
TERRACE
TORINO
TRINIDAD
VALENCIA
WINGATE
WOODARD
WYATT

WOVEN LEGENDS INC.
4700 Wissahickon Ave
Philadelphia, PA 19144
Tel.: (215) 849-8344
Fax: (215) 849-8354
E-mail: info@wovenlegends.com
Web Site: www.wovenlegends.com
Approx. Number Employees: 50
Business Description:
Carpets
S.I.C.: 5023; 5713
N.A.I.C.S.: 423220; 442210
Media: 6
Personnel:
N. C. Jevremovic *(CEO)*
Brands & Products:
AKTULU
EUPHRATES
KENTWILLY
RUBIA
SARDIS
STARRY NIGHT
TIGRIS
USKUDAR
WOVEN LEGENDS
YATAK

W.S. BADCOCK CORPORATION
200 N Phosphate Blvd
Mulberry, FL 33860-2328
Tel.: (863) 425-4921
Fax: (863) 425-7591
Toll Free: (800) 223-2625
E-mail: customer.service@badcock.com
Web Site: www.badcock.com
Sales Range: $500-549.9 Million
Approx. Number Employees: 1,200
Year Founded: 1904
Business Description:
Retailer of Home Furnishings, Appliances, Electronics & Floor Coverings
S.I.C.: 5712; 5713
N.A.I.C.S.: 442110; 442210
Media: 3-4-5-6-7-8-9-10-13-14-15-16-18-19-23-24-25-26
Personnel:
Wogan S. Badcock, III *(Chm, Exec VP-Govt & Pub Affairs)*
Michael Ray *(CFO & Sr VP)*
Ben Badcock *(Exec VP)*
Henry C. Badcock *(Exec VP-Strategic Plng)*
William T. Daughtrey *(Exec VP-Mktg)*
William K. Pou, Jr. *(Exec VP-Retail Ops)*
Rob Burnette *(Sr VP)*
Tim Birge *(VP-Mdse)*
Leland Carawan *(VP-Adv)*
Brands & Products:
BADCOCK & MORE
Advertising Agencies:
FKQ Advertising + Marketing
15351 Roosevelt Blvd
Clearwater, FL 33760-3534
Tel.: (727) 539-8800
Fax: (866) 707-6648

Hill & Knowlton, Inc.
201 E Kennedy Blvd Ste 1611
Tampa, FL 33602-5117
Tel.: (813) 221-0030
Fax: (813) 229-2926

YORK WALLCOVERINGS INC.
750 Linden Ave
York, PA 17404-3364
Mailing Address:
PO Box 5166
York, PA 17405-5166
Tel.: (717) 846-4456
Fax: (717) 854-2799
Toll Free: (800) 375-9675
E-mail: intl@yorkwall.com
Web Site: www.yorkwall.com
Approx. Number Employees: 300
Year Founded: 1895
Business Description:
Mfr. of Wall Coverings & Borders
S.I.C.: 2672
N.A.I.C.S.: 322222
Media: 2-10-13
Distr.: Natl.
Personnel:
Carl Vizzi *(Pres)*
Lerue Brown *(Dir-Mktg)*
Brands & Products:
ALDRICH
ANTONINA VELLA DESIGNS
ASIAN TAPESTRY
AVIVA
BRANCH FLORAL
CAREY LIND DESIGNS
THE CARLISLE COMPANY
EMBOSSED
FERN TOSS
GALUCHET
GRASSCLOTH
J. CHESTERFIELD STUDIO
JACOBEAN
KAYLA
MARQUIS
NEOCLASSIC
PIZZAZZ
PLISSE CRINKLE
RONALD REDDING DESIGNS
STAMPED
WATERFORD
WINDEMERE
YORK
YORK WALLCOVERINGS

ZONGKERS CUSTOM FURNITURE, INC.
1717 S 3rd St
Omaha, NE 68108
Tel.: (402) 344-7784
E-mail: info@zongkers.com
Web Site: www.zongkers.com
Approx. Number Employees: 10
Business Description:
Custom Furniture Designer, Engineer, Installer, Builder & Distr
S.I.C.: 2531; 2521
N.A.I.C.S.: 337127; 337211
Media: 13-16
Personnel:
Dan Zongker *(Owner, VP & Furniture Designer)*
Dennis Zongker *(Owner, VP & Furniture Designer)*

Key to Media (For complete agency information see *The Advertising Red Books-Agencies* edition):
1. Bus. Publs. 2. Cable T.V. 3. Catalogs & Directories. 4. Co-op Adv. 5. Consumer Mags. 6. D.M. to Bus. Estab.7. D.M. to Consumers 8. Daily Newsp. 9. Exhibits/Trade Shows 10. Foreign 11. Infomercial 12. Internet Adv.13. Multimedia 14. Network Radio 15. Network T.V. 16. Newsp. Distr. Mags. 17. Other 18. Outdoor (Posters, Transit) 19. Point of Purchase20. Premiums, Novelties 21. Product Samples 22. Special Events Mktg. 23. Spot Radio 24. Spot T.V. 25. Weekly Newsp. 26. Yellow Page Adv.

Games, Toys, Etc.

Coin Operated Games — Dolls — Electrical Toys — Electronic Games & Toys — Hobbies — Kites — Mechanical Toys — Puzzles — Video Games

4KIDS ENTERTAINMENT, INC.
53 W 23rd St
New York, NY 10010
Tel.: (212) 758-7666
Fax: (212) 980-0933
Web Site: www.4kidsent.com
Approx. Rev.: $14,478,000
Approx. Number Employees: 89
Year Founded: 1970
Business Description:
Children's Entertainment Licensing, Marketing & Media Production & Distribution Services
S.I.C.: 7812; 7822
N.A.I.C.S.: 512110; 512120
Import Export
Advertising Expenditures: $523,000
Personnel:
Michael Goldstein *(Chm)*
Bruce R. Foster *(CFO & Exec VP)*
Daniel Barnathan *(Pres-Sls)*
Samuel R. Newborn *(Gen Counsel & Exec VP-Bus Affairs)*
Brian Lacey *(Exec VP-Intl)*
Rosalind C. Nowicki *(Exec VP-Mktg & Licensing)*
Alyssa Tucker *(Sr VP-Licensing & Mktg)*
Matthew Miller *(VP-Ad Sls & Mktg)*
Dave Sharat *(VP-Mktg & Licensing-Asia-Pacific)*
Barry Stagg *(Head-Corp Comm)*
Olivia Mellett *(Exec Dir-Fin & Ops)*
Brands & Products:
4 KIDS ENTERTAINMENT
Advertising Agency:
Dan Klores Communications
(d/b/a dkc)
386 Park Ave S 10th Fl
New York, NY 10016
Tel.: (212) 685-4300
Fax: (212) 685-9024

505 GAMES (US), INC.
5008 Chesebro Rd
Agoura Hills, CA 91301
Tel.: (818) 540-3000
Fax: (818) 865-8546
Web Site: www.505games.com
Business Description:
Video Game Publisher
S.I.C.: 7372
N.A.I.C.S.: 511210
Media: 13

A&A GLOBAL INDUSTRIES INC.
17 Stenersen Ln
Cockeysville, MD 21030
Tel.: (410) 252-1020
Fax: (410) 252-7137
E-mail: info@aaglobalind.com
Web Site: www.aaglobalind.com
Sales Range: $10-24.9 Million
Approx. Number Employees: 200
Year Founded: 1939
Business Description:
Toys, Gifts & Novelties; Coin Operated Vending Machines
S.I.C.: 3312
N.A.I.C.S.: 331111
Import Export
Media: 4-7-10-13
Personnel:
Edward B. Kovens *(Pres)*
Brian S. Kovens *(Exec VP)*
Steven A. Kovens *(Exec VP)*
Phillip A. Brilliant *(VP-Licensing & Mktg)*
Gerry J. Clothier *(VP-Sls)*
Eugene M. Lipman *(VP-Fin & Admin)*

ACTIVISION BLIZZARD, INC.
(Sub. of Vivendi S.A.)
3100 Ocean Park Blvd
Santa Monica, CA 90405
Tel.: (310) 255-2000
Fax: (310) 255-2100
Web Site: www.activision.com
E-Mail For Key Personnel:
Public Relations: pr@activision.com
Approx. Rev.: $4,447,000,000
Approx. Number Employees: 7,600
Year Founded: 2008
Business Description:
Video Game Publisher
S.I.C.: 7372; 7371
N.A.I.C.S.: 511210; 541511
Import Export
Advertising Expenditures: $332,000,000
Media: 3-6-13-19
Distr.: Intl.; Natl.
Budget Set: Mar.
Personnel:
Jean-Bernard Levy *(Co-Chm)*
Michael J. Griffith *(Vice Chm)*
Robert A. Kotick *(CEO)*
Thomas Tippl *(CFO & COO)*
Stephen Wereb *(Chief Acctg Officer & Sr VP)*
Brian Hodous *(Chief Customer Officer)*
George L. Rose *(Chief Pub Policy Officer-Activision Blizzard)*
Eric Hirshberg *(CEO-Publ)*
Amber Mayo *(Dir-Media)*
Aland Failde *(Assoc Product Mgr)*
Brands & Products:
ACTIVISION
ANTHOLOGY
ARENA
BLOODLINES
CALL OF DUTY
DARKNESS
DAY OF DEFEAT
DISNEY'S TARZAN
DREAM WORKS SHARK TALE
EMPIRES
ENTER ELECTRO
EVIL
FANTASTIC FOUR
FINEST HOUR
GUITAR HERO
HELIX-XBOX
INVASION
KELLY SLATER'S PRO SURFER
THE LOST EXPEDITION
MADAGASCAR
MAT HOFFMAN'S PRO BMX
MENACE
MISSIONS
THE MOVIES
MTX: MOTOTRAX
PITFALL
REDEMPTION
SHREK
SNOWBOARDER
SOLDIER OF FORTUNE
SPIDER-MEN
STUART LITTLE
TEAM ARENA
TENCHU
TONY HAWK'S PRO SKATER
TONY HAWK'S UNDERGROUND
TOTAL WAR
ULTIMATE QUAKE
ULTIMATE SPIDER-MAN
UNFORTUNATE EVENTS
UNLEASHED
VAMPIRE
WASTELAND
WOLFENSTEIN
WOLVERINE'S
WORLD
WRATH OF HEAVEN
X-MEN
Advertising Agencies:
72andSunny
6300 Arizona Cir
Los Angeles, CA 90045
Tel.: (310) 215-9009
Fax: (310) 215-9012
Call of Duty

BBDO New York
1285 Ave of the Americas 7th Fl
New York, NY 10019-6028
Tel.: (212) 459-5000

droga5
400 Lafayette 5th Fl
New York, NY 10003
Tel.: (917) 237-8888
Fax: (917) 237-8889

OMD Worldwide
195 Broadway
New York, NY 10007
Tel.: (212) 590-7100
Media
Traditional & Digital Planning & Buying

TBWA Chiat Day Los Angeles
5353 Grosvenor Blvd
Los Angeles, CA 90066
Tel.: (310) 305-5000
Fax: (310) 305-6000

TBWA Chiat Day New York
488 Madison Ave
New York, NY 10022
Tel.: (212) 804-1000
Fax: (212) 804-1200
Creative
Guitar Hero

ALEXANDER DOLL COMPANY, INC.
(Joint Venture of Gefinor S.A.)
615 W 131st St
New York, NY 10027-7922
Tel.: (212) 283-5900
Fax: (212) 283-4263
Toll Free: (800) 229-5192
E-mail: ma@alexdoll.com
Web Site: www.madamealexander.com

Key to Media (For complete agency information see *The Advertising Red Books-Agencies* edition):
1. Bus. Publs. 2. Cable T.V. 3. Catalogs & Directories. 4. Co-op Adv. 5. Consumer Mags. 6. D.M. to Bus. Estab.7. D.M. to Consumers
8. Daily Newsp. 9. Exhibits/Trade Shows 10. Foreign 11. Infomercial 12. Internet Adv.13. Multimedia 14. Network Radio
15. Network T.V. 16. Newsp. Distr. Mags. 17. Other 18. Outdoor (Posters, Transit) 19. Point of Purchase20. Premiums, Novelties
21. Product Samples 22. Special Events Mktg. 23. Spot Radio 24. Spot T.V. 25. Weekly Newsp. 26. Yellow Page Adv.

Approx. Number Employees: 100
Year Founded: 1923
Business Description:
Designer & Mfr. of Madame Alexander Dolls
S.I.C.: 3942
N.A.I.C.S.: 339931
Import
Advertising Expenditures: $300,000
Media: 2-4-7-8-10-13-19
Distr.: Natl.
Personnel:
Gale Jarvis *(Pres)*
David Morgenstern *(Exec VP-Sls-Natl)*
Brands & Products:
CISSY COLLECTION
MADAME ALEXANDER
THE PEEK-A-BOOS

ALFY, INC.

391 Broadway Fl 5
New York, NY 10013
Tel.: (212) 968-0600
Fax: (212) 629-5790
E-mail: info@alfy.com
Web Site: www.alfy.com
E-Mail For Key Personnel:
Sales Director: sales@alfy.com
Approx. Number Employees: 6
Year Founded: 1998
Business Description:
Web Portal for Children
S.I.C.: 7371
N.A.I.C.S.: 541511
Advertising Expenditures: $600,000
Media: 8-10-13
Brands & Products:
ALFY.COM
CLEVERISLAND.COM

AMERICAN GIRL LLC

(Sub. of MATTEL, INC.)
(d/b/a Pleasant Company)
8400 Fairway Pl
Middleton, WI 53562-2548
Tel.: (608) 836-4848
Fax: (608) 836-1999
Toll Free: (800) 360-1861
Web Site: www.americangirl.com
Sales Range: $800-899.9 Million
Approx. Number Employees: 1,500
Year Founded: 1985
Business Description:
Books, Dolls & Accessories Direct Mail Retailer, Publisher & Marketer
S.I.C.: 5961; 2731
N.A.I.C.S.: 454113; 511130
Import
Advertising Expenditures: $500,000
Media: 4-6-8-10-13-22
Distr.: Direct to Consumer; Natl.
Personnel:
Ellen L. Brothers *(Pres)*
Shawn Dennis *(Sr VP)*
Kathy Monetti *(VP-Mktg)*
Brands & Products:
A GIRL'S BEST FRIEND
A SMART GIRL'S GUIDE
ADD-A-GIRL
ADDY
ADDY WALKER
ADDY'S BIRTHDAY TEA
AG FICTION
A.G. GEAR
A.G. MINIS
AGTV
AMERICA AT SCHOOL
AMERICAN GIRL
AMERICAN GIRL ATHLETE
AMERICAN GIRL CAFE
AMERICAN GIRL CLUB
AMERICAN GIRL FASHION SHOW
AMERICAN GIRL GEAR
AMERICAN GIRL ICE CREAM FUN DAY
AMERICAN GIRL LIBRARY
AMERICAN GIRL MAGAZINE
AMERICAN GIRL OF TODAY
AMERICAN GIRL THEATER
AMERICAN GIRL TODAY
AMERICAN GIRLS
THE AMERICAN GIRLS ART STUDIO
THE AMERICAN GIRLS CHRISTMAS
THE AMERICAN GIRLS CLUB
THE AMERICAN GIRLS COLLECTION
THE AMERICAN GIRLS GAME
THE AMERICAN GIRLS HISTORIAN
THE AMERICAN GIRLS NEWS
AMERICAN GIRLS PASTIMES
THE AMERICAN GIRLS POSTCARD COLLECTION
THE AMERICAN GIRLS PREMIERE
THE AMERICAN GIRLS PUZZLE
THE AMERICAN GIRLS REVUE
THE AMERICAN GIRLS SAVINGS GAME
AMERICAN GIRLS SHORT STORIES
THE AMERICAN GIRLS TEA
AMERICAN GIRLS TRADING CARDS
AN AMERICAN GIRLS EVENT
AN AMERICAN GIRLS EXPERIENCE
AN AMERICAN GIRLS LIVING HISTORY PROGRAM
AN AMERICAN GIRLS MUSEUM PROGRAM
ANIMAL PARADE
BITTY BABY
BITTY BABY COLLECTION
BITTY BABY DESIGN
BITTY BEAR
BITTY BEAR'S BUNCH
BITTY BUNNY
BITTY DUCKY
BITTY FROGGY
BITTY KITTY
BITTY LAMBIE
BITTY PIGGY
BITTY PUPPY
BITTY TWINS
CECILE
CELEBRATING GIRL OF YESTERDAY AND TODAY
CELEBRATING GIRLS OF TODAY
CELEBRATING GIRLS OF YESTERDAY
CIRCLE OF FRIENDS-AN AMERICAN GIRLS MUSICAL
COCONUT
DANCING THROUGH TIME: AN AMERICAN GIRLS EVENT
DRESS LIKE YOUR DOLL
ELECTRIC GIRL
EVERYTHING THAT MAKES GIRLS CLICK
FELICITY
FELICITY MERRIMAN
FELICITY'S COLLECTION
GIRLS EXPRESS
GIRLS OF MANY LANDS
GWEN
HALLIE
HISTORY MYSTERIES
HOPSCOTCH HILL SCHOOL
ISABEL
JOSEFINA
JOSEFINA MONTOYA
JOSEFINA'S COLLECTION
JUST LIKE YOU
KAILEY
KATHLEEN
KAYA
KIRSTEN
KIRSTEN LARSON
KIRSTEN'S BIRTHDAY TEA
KIT
KIT KITTREDGE
LEYLA
LICORICE
LINDSEY
LINDSEY BERGMAN
LOGAN
LOOK TO THE PAST-LEARN FOR THE FUTURE
MINI BAG
MINI MAG
MINUK
MISS MANDERLY
MOLLY
MOLLY MCINTIRE
NEELA
PLEASANT COMPANY
PLEASANT COMPANY PRODUCTIONS
PLEASANT COMPANY PUBLICATIONS
PROUD TO BE AN AMERICAN GIRL
SABA
SAMANTHA PARKINGTON
SAMANTHA'S BIRTHDAY TEA
SKYLAR
SPRING PEARL
STAR
TREAT SEAT
WE KNOW GIRLS
WELCOME JOSEFINA
WE'VE MADE AMERICAN GIRLS OUR BUSINESS
WHERE A LOVE FOR LEARNING GROWS
WILD AT HEART

AMERICA'S HOBBY CENTER, INC.

8300 Tonnelle Ave
North Bergen, NJ 07047
Tel.: (201) 662-0777
Fax: (201) 662-1450
Web Site: www.ahc1931.com
Approx. Sls.: $4,000,000
Approx. Number Employees: 32
Year Founded: 1931
Business Description:
Mfr of Radio Control Airplanes, Boats, Cars & Related Accessories
S.I.C.: 5961; 5945
N.A.I.C.S.: 454113; 451120
Export
Media: 3-4-6-8-26
Distr.: Intl.; Natl.
Budget Set: Oct.
Personnel:
Peter R. Winston *(Pres)*
Marshall G. Winston *(Mgr-Retail Sls)*
Brands & Products:
AMERICA'S HOBBY CENTER
DARK THUNDER

ATLUS USA, INC.

(Sub. of Atlus Co. Ltd.)
199 Technology Dr Ste 105
Irvine, CA 92618
Tel.: (949) 788-0455
Fax: (949) 788-0433
E-mail: webmaster@atlus.com
Web Site: www.atlus.com
Approx. Number Employees: 30
Year Founded: 1988
Business Description:
Video Game Publisher
S.I.C.: 3944; 5734
N.A.I.C.S.: 339932; 443120
Media: 6-9-13
Personnel:
Shinichi Suzuki *(Pres & CEO)*
Gail Salamanca *(Mgr-Mktg)*

B. DAZZLE, INC.

500 Meyer Ln
Redondo Beach, CA 90278
Tel.: (310) 374-3000
Fax: (310) 318-6692
E-mail: info@b-dazzle.com
Web Site: www.b-dazzle.com
Sales Range: $1-9.9 Million
Approx. Number Employees: 10
Year Founded: 1993
Business Description:
Puzzles, Games & Gifts Mfr
S.I.C.: 3944
N.A.I.C.S.: 339932
Media: 4-10-13
Personnel:
Kathleen A. Gavin *(Founder, Pres & CEO)*
Marshall P. Gavin *(Exec VP)*
Brands & Products:
5-MINUTE CHALLENGE
B.DAZZLE
MAKERART/COLOR 'N SEEK
SCRAMBLE SQUARES

THE BABY EINSTEIN COMPANY, LLC

(Sub. of The Walt Disney Company)
1201 Grand Central Ave
Glendale, CA 91201
Mailing Address:
PO Box 25020
Glendale, CA 91221
Tel.: (818) 560-1000
Fax: (818) 549-2060
Toll Free: (800) 793-1454
E-mail: webmaster@babyeinstein.com
Web Site: www.babyeinstein.com
Sales Range: $10-24.9 Million
Approx. Number Employees: 5
Year Founded: 1997
Business Description:
Videos & Toys for Children
S.I.C.: 5092
N.A.I.C.S.: 423920
Media: 4-6-10-13
Personnel:
Susan McLain *(Gen Mgr)*
Brands & Products:
BABY BACH
BABY BEETHOVEN
BABY EINSTEIN
BABY GALILEO
BABY MOZART
BABY SANTA'S MUSIC BOX
BABY SHAKESPEARE
BABY VAN GOGH
LANGUAGE NURSERY
NEIGHBORHOOD ANIMALS
WORLD ANIMALS

Key to Media (For complete agency information see *The Advertising Red Books-Agencies* edition):
1. Bus. Publs. 2. Cable T.V. 3. Catalogs & Directories. 4. Co-op Adv. 5. Consumer Mags. 6. D.M. to Bus. Estab.7. D.M. to Consumers 8. Daily Newsp. 9. Exhibits/Trade Shows 10. Foreign 11. Infomercial 12. Internet Adv.13. Multimedia 14. Network Radio 15. Network T.V. 16. Newsp. Distr. Mags. 17. Other 18. Outdoor (Posters, Transit) 19. Point of Purchase20. Premiums, Novelties 21. Product Samples 22. Special Events Mktg. 23. Spot Radio 24. Spot T.V. 25. Weekly Newsp. 26. Yellow Page Adv.

The Baby Einstein Company, LLC —
(Continued)

Advertising Agencies:
Anthem Worldwide
77 Maiden Ln 4th Fl
San Francisco, CA 94108
Tel.: (415) 896-9399
Fax: (415) 896-9387
Web Site

Siltanen & Partners
353 Coral Cir
El Segundo, CA 90245
Tel.: (310) 321-5200
Fax: (310) 321-5270

THE BABY JOGGER COMPANY

(Div. of Dynamic Brands)
1000 8575 Magellan Pkwy
Richmond, VA 23227-1150
Tel.: (804) 726-1327
Fax: (804) 262-6277
Toll Free: (800) 241-1848
E-mail: sales@babyjogger.com
Web Site: www.babyjogger.com
E-Mail For Key Personnel:
Sales Director: sales@babyjogger.com
Approx. Number Employees: 35
Business Description:
Stroller Mfr
S.I.C.: 3751; 3944
N.A.I.C.S.: 336991; 339932
Media: 4-6-10-13
Personnel:
David Boardman *(Pres)*
Brianne Polidori *(Mgr-Sls-Natl)*

BACHMANN INDUSTRIES, INC.

(Sub. of Kader International Limited)
1400 E Erie Ave
Philadelphia, PA 19124
Tel.: (215) 533-1600
Fax: (215) 744-4699
Toll Free: (800) 356-3910
E-mail: sales@bachmanntrains.com
Web Site: www.bachmanntrains.com
E-Mail For Key Personnel:
Marketing Director: marketing@bachmanntrains.com
Sales Director: sales@bachmanntrains.com
Approx. Number Employees: 55
Year Founded: 1833
Business Description:
Scale Model Electrical Train Sets & Accessories Mfr
S.I.C.: 5092; 3944
N.A.I.C.S.: 423920; 339932
Import Export
Advertising Expenditures: $2,000,000
Media: 2-4-5-6-8-10-13-19-21-24
Distr.: Intl.; Natl.
Budget Set: Nov.
Personnel:
Dennis Ting Hok Shou *(Chm)*
Kenneth Ting Woo Shou *(Mng Dir)*
Edwin T. Winter, Jr. *(CFO)*
Doug Blaine *(VP-Mktg & Pub Rel)*
Lee Riley *(Dir-Product Dev)*
Laura Harrif *(Cust Serv Mgr)*
Brands & Products:
ACELA EXPRESS
E-Z COMMAND
E-Z LUBE
E-Z MATE
E-Z TRACK SYSTEM
MCKINLEY EXPLORER
PLASTICVILLE
SILVERTON NORTHERN
THOMAS THE TANK ENGINE
WHITE CHRISTMAS EXPRESS

BANDAI AMERICA INCORPORATED

(Sub. of Bandai Co., Ltd.)
5551 Katella Ave
Cypress, CA 90630
Tel.: (714) 816-9500
Fax: (714) 816-6711
Web Site: www.bandai.com
Approx. Number Employees: 100
Year Founded: 1978
Business Description:
Distr of Toys & Model Kits
S.I.C.: 5092
N.A.I.C.S.: 423920
Advertising Expenditures: $20,000,000
Media: 2-4-6-10-13-15-19-22
Distr.: Intl.; Natl.
Personnel:
Larry Falcon *(Sr VP-Sls)*
Aki Nakanishi *(Sr VP-Pur)*
Danny Satyapan *(Dir)*
Brands & Products:
FUNDAYS
Advertising Agencies:
Dentsu America, Inc.
32 Ave of the Americas 16th Fl
New York, NY 10013
Tel.: (212) 397-3333
Fax: (212) 397-3322
Bandai Toys

Mindshare
2425 Olympic Blvd Ste 220-E
Santa Monica, CA 90404
Tel.: (310) 309-8500
Fax: (310) 309-8595
Media Agency

Rogers Ruder Finn
1875 Century Park E Ste 200
Los Angeles, CA 90067-2504
Tel.: (310) 552-6922
Fax: (310) 552-9052

Vertical Marketing Network LLC
15147 Woodlawn Ave
Tustin, CA 92780
Tel.: (714) 258-2400, ext. 420
Fax: (714) 258-2409

Weber Shandwick-Los Angeles
8687 Melrose Ave 7th Fl
Los Angeles, CA 90069
Tel.: (310) 854-8200
Fax: (310) 854-8201

BLIZZARD ENTERTAINMENT

(Unit of Activision Blizzard, Inc.)
PO Box 18979
Irvine, CA 92623-8979
Tel.: (949) 955-0283
Fax: (949) 737-2000
Toll Free: (800) 953-7669
E-mail: sales@blizzard.com
Web Site: www.blizzard.com
Approx. Rev.: $1,100,000,000
Year Founded: 1991
Business Description:
Entertainment Software Publisher
S.I.C.: 7372
N.A.I.C.S.: 511210
Export
Media: 4-8-11-13
Personnel:
Michael Morhaime *(Pres & CEO)*
Jason Anderson *(Dir-Consumer Insights-Global)*

BRADY GAMES

(Div. of Pearson Technology Group)
199 Pearson Pkwy
Lebanon, IN 46052
Tel.: (212) 366-2000
Fax: (317) 581-3520
Toll Free: (800) 545-5914
Web Site: www.bradygames.com
Approx. Number Employees: 25
Business Description:
Game Strategy Guides Publisher
S.I.C.: 7373
N.A.I.C.S.: 541512
Media: 2-5-6-10-13
Personnel:
David Waybright *(Publr)*
H. Leigh Davis *(Editor-in-Chief)*
David Bartley *(Sr Project Editor)*
Ken Schmidt *(Sr Project Editor)*
Mike Degler *(Dir-Licensing)*
Janet Eshenour *(Mgr-Mktg)*
Tim Cox *(Mgr-Title)*
Tim Fitzpatrick *(Mgr-Title)*
Brands & Products:
BRADYGAMES
TAKE YOUR GAME FURTHER

BUILD-A-BEAR WORKSHOP, INC.

1954 Innerbelt Business Ctr Dr
Saint Louis, MO 63114
Tel.: (314) 423-8000
Fax: (314) 423-8188
Toll Free: (877) 789BEAR
E-mail: Guest.Services@buildabear.com
Web Site: www.buildabear.com
Approx. Rev.: $401,452,000
Approx. Number Employees: 1,200
Year Founded: 1997
Business Description:
Mfr of Make-Your-Own Stuffed Animals
S.I.C.: 5945
N.A.I.C.S.: 451120
Advertising Expenditures: $18,500,000
Personnel:
Maxine Clark *(Founder, Chm & CEO)*
John N. Haugh *(Pres)*
Scott Gower *(Mng Dir-Stores)*
Rick Levine *(Mng Dir-Stores)*
Roger Parry *(Mng Dir-UK)*
Jeff Fullmer *(Mng Dir)*
Tina Klocke *(CFO, COO, Treas & Sec)*
Dave Finnegan *(CIO)*
Teresa Kroll *(CMO)*
Darlene Elder *(Chief HR Officer)*
Eric Fencl *(Gen Counsel)*
Nancy Schwartz *(Dir-Adbeartisement & Intl Mktg)*
Brands & Products:
BEAR BUILDER
BUILD-A-BEAR WORKSHOP
BUILD-A-DINO
BUILD-A-SOUND
BUILDABEARVILLE.COM
CORBEARATE
CUB CONDO
CYBEAR
FIND-A-BEAR
FIND A WORKSHOP
TAKE ME HOME
WHERE BEST FRIENDS ARE MADE
Advertising Agency:
Barkley
1740 Main St
Kansas City, MO 64108
Tel.: (816) 842-1500

CAPCOM USA, INC.

(Sub. of Capcom Co., Ltd.)
800 Concar Dr Ste 300
San Mateo, CA 94402-2649
Tel.: (650) 350-6500
Fax: (650) 350-6655
Web Site: www.capcom.com
Approx. Number Employees: 120
Year Founded: 1985
Business Description:
Mfr of Pinball Machines, Video Games; Operator of Arcades; Consumer Video Games Whslr
S.I.C.: 7993; 3577; 5092; 7372
N.A.I.C.S.: 713120; 334119; 423920; 511210
Advertising Expenditures: $200,000
Media: 3-4-6-15
Distr.: Natl.
Personnel:
Seth Killian *(Dir-Strategic Mktg-Online Community)*

CARROM CO.

(Div. of The Lightning Group, Inc.)
218 E Dowland St
Ludington, MI 49431-2309
Tel.: (231) 845-1263
Fax: (231) 843-9276
E-mail: webmaster@carrom.com
Web Site: www.carrom.com
Approx. Number Employees: 60
Business Description:
Wooden Games & Juvenile Furniture Mfr
S.I.C.: 3944; 2531
N.A.I.C.S.: 339932; 337127
Media: 2-4-7-10
Distr.: Natl.
Personnel:
Kim Asiala *(CFO)*

CARTA MUNDI, INC.

(Sub. of Carta Mundi N.V.)
10444 Wallace Alley St
Kingsport, TN 37663
Tel.: (423) 279-9200
Fax: (423) 279-9201
Toll Free: (800) 892-2782
E-mail: info@cartamundiusa.com
Web Site: www.cartamundiusa.com
Approx. Number Employees: 100
Year Founded: 1995
Business Description:
Playing Cards Mfr
S.I.C.: 5092; 2752; 3944
N.A.I.C.S.: 423920; 323110; 339932
Bus. Publs.: 34%; D.M. to Bus. Estab.: 33%; Exhibits/Trade Shows: 33%
Distr.: Intl.
Personnel:
Chris Doorslaer *(CEO)*
Robert Garity *(VP-Sls)*
Michael Szul *(VP)*
Jon Wiebusch *(VP-Sls)*

COASTAL AMUSEMENTS INC.

1935 Swarthmore Ave
Lakewood, NJ 08701
Tel.: (732) 905-6662

Key to Media (For complete agency information see *The Advertising Red Books-Agencies* edition):
1. Bus. Publs. 2. Cable T.V. 3. Catalogs & Directories. 4. Co-op Adv. 5. Consumer Mags. 6. D.M. to Bus. Estab.7. D.M. to Consumers
8. Daily Newsp. 9. Exhibits/Trade Shows 10. Foreign 11. Infomercial 12. Internet Adv.13. Multimedia 14. Network Radio
15. Network T.V. 16. Newsp. Distr. Mags. 17. Other 18. Outdoor (Posters, Transit) 19. Point of Purchase20. Premiums, Novelties
21. Product Samples 22. Special Events Mktg. 23. Spot Radio 24. Spot T.V. 25. Weekly Newsp. 26. Yellow Page Adv.

Fax: (732) 905-6815
E-mail: sales@coastalamusements.com
Web Site: www.coastalamusements.com
E-Mail For Key Personnel:
Sales Director: sales@coastalamusements.com
Approx. Number Employees: 35
Year Founded: 1988
Business Description:
Mfr. of Coin Operated Redemption Games & Sports Games
S.I.C.: 5099
N.A.I.C.S.: 423990
Media: 10
Personnel:
Leonard Dean *(Pres)*
Walter McInerney *(CFO)*
Sal Mirando *(Exec VP)*
Advertising Agency:
Outside the Box Interactive LLC
150 Bay St Ste 706
Jersey City, NJ 07302
Tel.: (201) 610-0625
Fax: (201) 610-0627

COLLECTOR'S ARMOURY LTD.

PO Box 1050
Lorton, VA 22199
Tel.: (703) 493-9120
Fax: (703) 493-9424
Toll Free: (800) 599-9994
Toll Free: (877) ARMOURY
E-mail: sales@collectorsarmoury.com
Web Site: www.collectorsarmoury.com
E-Mail For Key Personnel:
Marketing Director: jwh@collectorsarmoury.com
Sales Director: sales@collectorsarmoury.com
Approx. Number Employees: 15
Year Founded: 1968
Business Description:
Replica Model Guns, Swords, Knives, Suits of Armour & Miniature Cannons Distr
S.I.C.: 5099
N.A.I.C.S.: 423990
Import Export
Media: 4-10
Distr.: Intl.; Natl.
Budget Set: Aug. -Dec.
Personnel:
Howard Fox *(Pres)*
Advertising Agency:
Alexandria Advertising Associates
9404 Gunston Cove Rd
Lorton, VA 22079
Tel.: (703) 493-9120
Fax: (703) 493-9424

CRANIUM, INC.

(Sub. of Hasbro, Inc.)
2025 1st Ave Ste 600
Seattle, WA 98121
Tel.: (206) 652-9708
Fax: (206) 652-1483
E-mail: jack@playcranium.com
Web Site: www.cranium.com
Sales Range: $25-49.9 Million
Approx. Number Employees: 20
Year Founded: 1998
Business Description:
Board Game Developer & Marketer
S.I.C.: 5092
N.A.I.C.S.: 423920
Media: 5-6-13-15
Personnel:
Mark Stark *(VP-Cranium Brands)*
Brands & Products:
BASEMAN
CRANIUM
CRANIUM BOOSTER BOX
CRANIUM CADOO
CRANIUM COSMO
CRANIUM HOOPLA
PLAY WITH YOUR BRAIN

CRAYOLA CANADA

(Branch of Crayola LLC)
15 Mary Street West
PO Box 120
Lindsay, ON K9V 4R8, Canada
Tel.: (705) 324-6105
Fax: (705) 324-3511
Web Site: www.crayola.com
Approx. Number Employees: 215
Business Description:
Art Materials & Childrens Crafts Distr
S.I.C.: 3952
N.A.I.C.S.: 339942
Import Export
Media: 3-5-10-13-15-16-19-22-24
Distr.: Natl.
Personnel:
Paul Zadorsky *(Gen Mgr)*
John Debois *(Mgr-Acctg & Fin)*

CRAYOLA LLC

(Sub. of Hallmark Cards, Inc.)
1100 Church Ln
Easton, PA 18044
Mailing Address:
PO Box 431
Easton, PA 18044-0431
Tel.: (610) 253-6271
Fax: (610) 250-5768
Telex: 4761084
Web Site: www.crayola.com
Approx. Number Employees: 1,200
Year Founded: 1885
Business Description:
Toys & Artist Materials Mfr
S.I.C.: 3952
N.A.I.C.S.: 339942
Import Export
Media: 1-4-5-6-10-19-21-24
Distr.: Natl.
Personnel:
Sharon Hartley *(Exec VP-Mktg & Product Innovation)*
Stacy Gabrielle *(Mgr-PR & Social Media)*
Brands & Products:
CRAYOLA
INKTANK
LIV CRAYOLA
PORTFOLIO SERIES
SILLY PUTTY
Advertising Agency:
McGarry Bowen, LLC
601 W 26th St Ste 1150
New York, NY 10001
Tel.: (212) 598-2900
Fax: (212) 598-2996

CROSMAN CORPORATION

(Holding of Wellspring Capital Management LLC)
7629 Rtes 5 & 20
Bloomfield, NY 14469
Tel.: (585) 657-6161
Fax: (585) 657-5405
Toll Free: (800) 724-7486
Toll Free: (800) 7-AIRGUN
E-mail: info@crosman.com
Web Site: www.crosman.com
Sales Range: $100-124.9 Million
Approx. Number Employees: 350
Year Founded: 1923
Business Description:
Mfr. of Air Guns, Paint Ball Guns & Accessories
S.I.C.: 3949; 3499
N.A.I.C.S.: 339920; 332999
Media: 4-5-6-10-19
Personnel:
Ken D'Arcy *(Pres & CEO)*
Robert Beckwith *(VP-Fin)*
Bob Hampton *(VP-Mktg)*
Steve Upham *(VP-Sls)*
Dan Gainor *(Mgr-Demand)*
Hal Parker *(Mgr-IT)*
Brands & Products:
BENJAMIN SHERIDAN
CHALLENGER
COPPERHEAD
CROSMAN
VISIBLE IMPACT

DUNCAN TOYS COMPANY

(Sub. of Flambeau Inc)
15981 Valplast St
Middlefield, OH 44062-0005
Tel.: (440) 632-1631
Fax: (440) 632-1581
Toll Free: (800) 356-8396
Web Site: www.yo-yo.com
Approx. Number Employees: 20
Year Founded: 1929
Business Description:
Toy Mfr
S.I.C.: 5945
N.A.I.C.S.: 451120
Export
Media: 4-10-22
Distr.: Intl.; Natl.
Budget Set: May
Personnel:
Jason C. Sauey *(Pres)*
Mike Burke *(Mgr-Natl Sls & Mktg)*
Brands & Products:
DAREDEVIL FOOTBAGS
DUNCAN BUTTERFLY
DUNCAN TETRA TOPS
GLOW IMPERIAL
JUGGLING BALLS
JUGGLING SCARVES
NEO
ROADRUNNER FOOTBAGS
SPIDER FOOTBAGS
WHEELS

EDUCATIONAL INSIGHTS, INC.

(Sub. of Learning Resources, Inc.)
18730 S Wilmington Ave
Rancho Dominguez, CA 90220
Tel.: (310) 884-2000
Fax: (310) 884-2013
Fax: (800) 995-0506
Toll Free: (800) 995-4436
E-mail: info@educationalinsights.com
Web Site: www.educationalinsights.com
Approx. Sls.: $7,500,000
Approx. Number Employees: 100
Year Founded: 1962
Business Description:
Electronic Learning Aids, Games, Activity Books, Science & Nature Products Mfr, Designer & Marketer
S.I.C.: 3999; 3944
N.A.I.C.S.: 339999; 339932
Import Export
Media: 2-4-5-7-8-10-12-19-20-21-23
Distr.: Intl.; Natl.
Budget Set: Nov. -Dec.
Personnel:
Jim Whitney *(Pres)*
Brands & Products:
EDUCATIONAL INSIGHTS
GEOSAFARI
GEOSAFARI PHONICS LAB
GEOSAFARI PHONICS PAD
MATH SAFARI
SEA MONKEYS

EGAMES, INC.

2000 Cabot Blvd W Ste 110
Langhorne, PA 19047-2408
Tel.: (215) 750-6606
Fax: (215) 750-3722
E-mail: tmurphy@egames.com
Web Site: www.egames.com
E-Mail For Key Personnel:
President: gklein@egames.com
Approx. Rev.: $3,602,172
Approx. Number Employees: 11
Year Founded: 1992
Business Description:
PC Software Games Publisher, Marketer & Retailer
S.I.C.: 7372; 7371
N.A.I.C.S.: 334611; 511210; 541511
Media: 4-8-10-13-17-19-21-29
Personnel:
Gerald W. Klein *(Pres & CEO)*
Thomas W. Murphy *(CFO)*
Ellen Pulver Flatt *(Gen Counsel & VP)*
Richard H. Siporin *(VP-Sls & Mktg)*
Brands & Products:
4 ELEMENTS
ANCIENT SECRETS
BEJEWELED TWIST
BLAST THRU
BLOOD TIES
BOWLING MANIA
BURGER ISLAND
CINEMAWARE
CINEMAWARE MARQUEE
CRAZY DRAKE
DRAGON STONE
EGAMES
FAMILY FRIENDLY
FLIPSTER
GALAXY OF GAMES
GALAXY OF HOME OFFICE HELP
GAME MASTER SERIES
HANGMAN WILD WEST II
JEWEL QUEST II
JIGSAW
MAH JONG
MAHJONGG MASTER
MINI GOLF MASTER
MONOPOLY
MUSHROOM AGE
MYSTERY LEGENDS
NINTENDO DS
OUTERBOUND GAMES
PENGUIN PUZZLE
PINBALL MASTER
PLANTS US ZOMBIES
PUZZLE MASTER
RAHJONGG
SCRABBLE RACE ATTACK
SOLITAIRE MASTER 3
SPEEDY EGGBERT
THE TREASURES OF MONTEZUMA

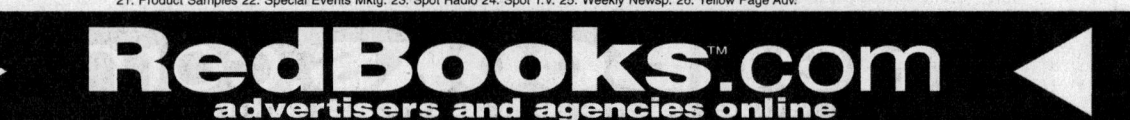

Key to Media (For complete agency information see *The Advertising Red Books-Agencies* edition):
1. Bus. Publs. 2. Cable T.V. 3. Catalogs & Directories. 4. Co-op Adv. 5. Consumer Mags. 6. D.M. to Bus. Estab.7. D.M. to Consumers 8. Daily Newsp. 9. Exhibits/Trade Shows 10. Foreign 11. Infomercial 12. Internet Adv.13. Multimedia 14. Network Radio 15. Network T.V. 16. Newsp. Distr. Mags. 17. Other 18. Outdoor (Posters, Transit) 19. Point of Purchase20. Premiums, Novelties 21. Product Samples 22. Special Events Mktg. 23. Spot Radio 24. Spot T.V. 25. Weekly Newsp. 26. Yellow Page Adv.

eGames, Inc. — (Continued)

WANDERING WILLOWS
WHERE THE E IS FOR EVERYBODY
WII
WORD CONNECT

ELECTRONIC ARTS INC.
209 Redwood Shores Pkwy
Redwood City, CA 94065-1175
Tel.: (650) 628-1500
Fax: (650) 628-1415
E-mail: StockholderCommunications@EA.com
Web Site: www.ea.com
Approx. Rev.: $3,589,000,000
Approx. Number Employees: 7,600
Year Founded: 1982
Business Description:
Interactive Entertainment Software Developer, Publisher & Distr
S.I.C.: 7372; 3944
N.A.I.C.S.: 511210; 339932
Export
Advertising Expenditures: $312,000,000
Media: 3-5-6-8-10-13-15-19-20-22
Distr.: Direct to Retailer
Personnel:
Lawrence F. Probst, III *(Chm)*
John S. Riccitiello *(CEO)*
Eric F. Brown *(CFO & Exec VP)*
Peter Moore *(COO)*
Kenneth A. Barker *(Chief Acctg Officer & Sr VP)*
Greg Zeschuk *(Creative Officer-RPG/MMO Grp)*
Frank D. Gibeau *(Pres-EA Labels)*
Hubert Larenaudie *(Pres-Online-Asia)*
Steve Schnur *(Pres-Artwerk Music Publ)*
Kathy Vrabeck *(Pres-EA Casual Entertainment)*
Stephen G. Bene *(Gen Counsel, Sec & Sr VP)*
Barry Cottle *(Exec VP-EA Interactive)*
Joel Linzner *(Exec VP-Bus & Legal Affairs)*
Bruce E. McMillan *(Exec VP)*
Nancy L. Smith *(Exec VP-Global Publ)*
Gabrielle Toledano *(Exec VP-HR)*
Michael Marchetti *(Sr VP & Gen Mgr-Pogo & Social Games)*
Ray Muzyka *(Sr VP & Gen Mgr)*
Elizabeth Harz *(Sr VP-Media Sls-Global)*
Jon Niermann *(Sr VP-EA)*
Jeff Brown *(VP-Comm)*
Shawn Conly *(VP-Adv)*
Steve Seabolt *(VP-Global Brand Dev)*
Beatrice Spaine *(VP-Publishing-Pogo)*
Aaron Lassila *(Dir-Media Sls-Global)*
Holly Rockwood *(Dir-Corp Comm)*
James Ferris *(Sr Mgr-Global Product)*
Brian G. Kelly *(Sr Mgr-Category)*
Leslie Shinn *(Sr Mgr-Adv)*
Anthony Stevenson *(Sr Mgr-Product)*
Phil Marineau *(Brand Mgr-Dante's Inferno)*
Julian Leong *(Product Mgr)*
Katie Montgomery *(Mgr-Mktg Acq-Pogo)*
Elena Alvarado Peters *(Mgr-Adv & Comm)*
Brands & Products:
THE AFTERMATH
ARMY OF TWO
BATTLEFIELD
BLACK
BOOGIE
BOOM BLOX
BOOM BOOM ROCKET
BURNOUT
COMMAND & CONQUER
COMMAND & CONQUER 3 TIBERIUM WARS
COMMAND & CONQUER RED ALERT
COMMAND & CONQUER RED ALERT COUNTERSTRIKE
COMMAND & CONQUER RENEGADE
COMMAND & CONQUER THE COVERT OPERATION
DANTE'S INFERNO
DEAD SPACE
DOWNTOWN WIRELESS
DRAGON AGE
EA GAMES
EA SPORTS
EA SPORTS ACTIVE
EA SPORTS BIG
ELECTRONIC ARTS
FIRESTORM
IMPERFECTS
MASS EFFECT
MAXIS
MEDAL OF HONOR
MEDAL OF HONOR HEROES
NEED FOR SPEED
PANDEMIC
POGO
POPULOUS
RISE OF THE IMPERFECTS
ROAD RASH
SIMANIMALS
SIMANT
SIMCITY 2000
SIMEARTH
THE SIMS
THE SIMS CARNIVAL
SPORE
THEME PARK
TIBERIAN SUN
ULTIMA
WESTWOOD STUDIOS
WING COMMANDER
YURI'S REVENGE
Advertising Agencies:
Alexander & Tom
3500 Boston St Ste 225
Baltimore, MD 21224-5275
Tel.: (410) 327-7400
Fax: (410) 327-7403

Draftfcb West
1160 Battery St Ste 250
San Francisco, CA 94111
Tel.: (415) 820-8000
Fax: (415) 820-8087
— Jake Slody *(Assoc Dir-Creative)*
— Derrick Ho *(Assoc Dir-Creative)*

Freestyle Interactive
475 Brannon St
San Francisco, CA 94107
Tel.: (415) 541-2700

Heat
Pier 33 S 3rd Fl
San Francisco, CA 94111
Tel.: (415) 477-1999
Fax: (415) 477-1990
EA Sports
— Nei Caetano *(Dir-Creative)*

KemperLesnik
500 Skokie Blvd 4th Fl
Northbrook, IL 60062
Tel.: (847) 850-1818
Fax: (847) 559-0406

TBWA/Manchester
St Paul's 781 Wilmslow Road
Manchester, M20 2RW, United Kingdom
Tel.: (44) 161 908 8600
Fax: (44) 161 908 8601
(eCRM)

Wieden + Kennedy - Amsterdam
Herengracht 258
1015 CJ
Amsterdam, Netherlands
Tel.: (31) 20 712 6500
Fax: (31) 20 712 6699
Harry Potter Video Games

Wieden + Kennedy, Inc.
224 NW 13th Ave
Portland, OR 97209-2953
Tel.: (503) 937-7000
Fax: (503) 937-8000
Bulletstorm
Dante?s Inferno
Family Play
Hellgate Game

ELENCO ELECTRONICS, INC.
150 W Carpenter Ave
Wheeling, IL 60090
Tel.: (847) 541-3800
Fax: (847) 520-0085
E-mail: info@elenco.com
Web Site: www.elenco.com
Approx. Number Employees: 40
Year Founded: 1972
Business Description:
Electronic Toys & Educational Devices
S.I.C.: 8299; 3651; 3663; 3679; 3824; 3825; 3944
N.A.I.C.S.: 611710; 334220; 334310; 334418; 334419; 334514; 334515; 339932
Media: 4-7-13
Personnel:
Arthur F. Seymour *(Pres & CEO)*
Joseph P. Seymour *(CIO & VP)*
Gerald J. Cecchin *(Head-Engrg & VP)*
Jeff Coda *(Mgr-Natl Sls-Elenco Electronics)*
Walter F. Larsen, Jr. *(Mgr-Natl Sls-Toy Div)*

ENVIRONMOLDS, LLC
18 Bank St
Summit, NJ 07901
Tel.: (908) 273-5401
Fax: (908) 273-9256
Toll Free: (866) ARTMOLDS
E-mail: info@environmolds.com
Web Site: www.artmolds.com
Approx. Number Employees: 2
Year Founded: 1997
Business Description:
Sculpture & Lifecasting Kits; Molding & Casting Supplies
S.I.C.: 5945
N.A.I.C.S.: 451120
Media: 3-4-10-13
Personnel:
Ed McCormick *(Founder)*

FACTORY X DISTRIBUTION
2840 Lafayette Rd
Fort Oglethorpe, GA 30742
Tel.: (706) 861-4165
Fax: (706) 861-4164
E-mail: info@factoryx.com
Web Site: www.factoryx.com
Approx. Number Employees: 15
Year Founded: 1994
Business Description:
Toy Mfr & Whslr
S.I.C.: 3942; 3944
N.A.I.C.S.: 339931; 339932
Media: 4-13
Personnel:
Jeff Epperson *(Pres)*

THE FIRST YEARS INC.
(Sub. of RC2 Corporation)
2A 100 Technology Center Dr
Stoughton, MA 02072-4705
Tel.: (781) 341-6250
Fax: (781) 341-6251
Toll Free: (800) 225-0382
Web Site: www.thefirstyears.com
Sales Range: $75-99.9 Million
Approx. Number Employees: 182
Year Founded: 1952
Business Description:
Infant & Toddler Products
S.I.C.: 5092; 5099
N.A.I.C.S.: 423920; 423990
Import Export
Media: 4-5-6-8-9-25
Distr.: Intl.; Natl.
Personnel:
John R. Beals *(CFO, Treas, Controller & Sr VP-Fin)*
Brands & Products:
AIRFLOW
CLEAN AND SIMPLE
THE FIRST YEARS
NATURAL COMFORT
SURE COMFORT
TAKE & TOSS
TUMBLEMATES

FISHER-PRICE, INC.
(Sub. of MATTEL, INC.)
636 Girard Ave
East Aurora, NY 14052
Tel.: (716) 687-3000
Fax: (716) 687-3949
Toll Free: (800) 432-5437
Web Site: www.fisher-price.com
Sales Range: $400-449.9 Million
Approx. Number Employees: 900
Year Founded: 1930
Business Description:
Toys & Juvenile Products Mfr
S.I.C.: 5092; 5021
N.A.I.C.S.: 423920; 423210
Import Export
Advertising Expenditures: $40,000,000
Media: 4-5-6-9-19
Distr.: Intl.; Natl.
Budget Set: Nov.
Personnel:
Kathleen Alfano *(Dir-Res)*
Brenda Andolina *(Dir-PR & Brand Mktg)*
Mary Carson *(Dir-Adv)*

Michele Zimmer *(Mgr-Direct Mktg)*
Harry Mayers *(Assoc Prod Designer)*

Brands & Products:
PIXTER

Advertising Agencies:
Draftfcb New York
100 W 33rd St
New York, NY 10001
Tel.: (212) 885-3000
Fax: (212) 885-3300

Eric Mower and Associates
Key Ctr at Fountain Plz 50 Fountain Plz Ste 1000
Buffalo, NY 14202
Tel.: (716) 842-2233
Fax: (716) 842-6676

Freeman Public Relations
16 Furler St
Totowa, NJ 07512
Tel.: (973) 470-0400
Fax: (973) 470-9036
Blue's Clues
Disney
Winnie the Pooh

FLAMBEAU INC

(Holding of Nordic Group of Companies, Ltd.)
15981 Valplast St
Middlefield, OH 44062-9399
Mailing Address:
PO Box 97
Middlefield, OH 44062-0097
Tel.: (440) 632-1631
Fax: (440) 632-1581
Toll Free: (800) 232-3474
E-mail: info@flambeau.com
Web Site: www.flambeau.com
Sales Range: $150-199.9 Million
Approx. Number Employees: 1,500
Year Founded: 1947
Business Description:
Toys Mfr
S.I.C.: 3944
N.A.I.C.S.: 339932
Export
Media: 1-2-3-4-5-6-7-8-10-11-12-15-16-19-22-24
Distr.: Natl.

Brands & Products:
ART BIN
DUNCAN TOYS
OUTDOORS

FOLKMANIS, INC.

1219 Pk Ave
Emeryville, CA 94608
Tel.: (510) 658-7677
Fax: (513) 742-3355
Toll Free: (800) 654-8922
Web Site: www.folkmanis.com
Approx. Sls.: $2,200,000
Approx. Number Employees: 40
Business Description:
Finger Puppets Mfr & Whslr
S.I.C.: 3999; 3942
N.A.I.C.S.: 339999; 339931
Media: 4-6
Personnel:
Judy Folkmanis *(Co-Owner)*
Atis Folkmanis *(Pres)*
Elaine Folkmanis *(Dir-Mktg)*
John Canelake *(Mgr-Sls)*

Brands & Products:
FOLKMANIS

FORTUNET, INC.

2950 S Highland Dr Ste C
Las Vegas, NV 89109
Tel.: (702) 796-9090
Fax: (702) 796-9069
E-mail: fortunetinfo@fortunet.com
Web Site: www.fortunet.com
Sales Range: $10-24.9 Million
Approx. Number Employees: 50
Business Description:
Electronic Gaming Systems Mfr
S.I.C.: 3944; 5084; 7999
N.A.I.C.S.: 339932; 423830; 713290
Advertising Expenditures: $2,170,270
Personnel:
Yuri Itkis *(Chm, CEO & CFO)*
William R. Jacques, Jr. *(CFO)*
Jack B. Coronel *(CMO & Dir-Compliance/Strategic Dev)*
Boris Itkis *(CTO, Treas, Sec & VP-Engrg)*

Brands & Products:
AIMS
BINGO
BINGOSTAR
COLOR PORTABLE
DO IT YOURSELF
FLASH BOARDS
FORTUNET
LINKED BINGO GAMES
MEGA FORTUNE
MOBIPLAYER
MOBIPLAYER SR
PLUG-N-PLAY
SMART BALL BLOWER
SMART BALLS
SMART DESK
SMART KENO
SMART KIOSK
SMART PACK
SMART SCAN
SMART SIGNS
STATIONARY
TANGO BINGO

FRACTILES, INC.

2525 Arapahoe Ave Ste E4 110
Boulder, CO 80302
Tel.: (303) 541-0930
Fax: (303) 442-7776
Toll Free: (877) 277-3201
E-mail: fractiles@fractiles.com
Web Site: www.fractiles.com
Approx. Number Employees: 10
Year Founded: 1998
Business Description:
Toys
S.I.C.: 3944
N.A.I.C.S.: 339932
Media: 4-13
Personnel:
Beverly Johnson *(Co-Founder & Pres)*

Brands & Products:
FRACTILES

FUN TECHNOLOGIES INC.

(Sub. of Liberty Media LLC)
230 Richmond Street East 2nd Floor
Toronto, ON M5A 1P4, Canada
Tel.: (416) 840-0806
Fax: (416) 840-0818
E-mail: info@funtechnologies.com
Web Site: www.funtechnologies.com
Sales Range: $25-49.9 Million
Approx. Number Employees: 115
Year Founded: 2002
Business Description:
On-Line Games & Fantasy Sports Services
S.I.C.: 7379; 7371; 7372
N.A.I.C.S.: 541519; 334611; 541511
Media: 13
Personnel:
David Goldhill *(Chm)*
James Lanthier *(COO)*
Peter Blacklow *(Pres-Fun Games)*

GAMEFLY, INC.

5340 Alla Rd Ste 110
Los Angeles, CA 90066
Tel.: (310) 664-6400
Toll Free: (888) 986-6400
Web Site: www.gamefly.com
Sales Range: $75-99.9 Million
Approx. Number Employees: 186
Year Founded: 2002
Business Description:
Computer Game Rental Services
S.I.C.: 7841; 7359
N.A.I.C.S.: 532230; 532299
Advertising Expenditures: $15,900,000
Media: 3-6-13-15
Personnel:
Sean Spector *(Co-Founder & Sr VP-Bus Dev & Content)*
David Hodess *(Chm, Pres & CEO)*
Stacey Peterson *(CFO & Sr VP)*
Michael Gimlett *(Sr VP-Mdsg & Logistics)*
Terri Luke *(Sr VP-Ops)*
Nilesh Seth *(Sr VP-Product Dev & Tech)*
Steve Hartmann *(VP-Mktg)*
Scott Paterra *(VP-Adv Sls)*
Rachel Silverstein *(VP-Mktg)*

GAMETECH INTERNATIONAL, INC.

8850 Double Diamond Pkwy
Reno, NV 89521
Tel.: (775) 850-6000
Fax: (775) 850-6090
E-mail: hr@gtiemail.com
Web Site: www.gametech-inc.com
Approx. Rev.: $35,171,000
Approx. Number Employees: 129
Year Founded: 1994
Business Description:
Interactive Electronic Bingo Systems Designer, Developer & Marketer
S.I.C.: 7999
N.A.I.C.S.: 713990; 713290
Advertising Expenditures: $596,000
Media: 2-10-19
Personnel:
William P. Fasig *(Pres, CEO & COO)*
Andy Robinson *(CFO & Sr VP)*
James Robertson *(Gen Counsel & VP)*
Steve Smallman *(Exec VP-Product, Sls & Mktg)*
Justin K. Goodman *(Sr VP-R&D)*
Ellen Droog *(VP-HR)*
Nick Greenwood *(VP-Sls & Mktg-Product Mktg)*
John McCafferty *(VP-Product Mktg)*

Brands & Products:
ALLTRACK2
ALLTRAK
BIG BANG BINGO
DIAMOND ELITE
DIAMOND PRO
DIAMOND VIP
GAMETECH
GAMETECH ELITE
MINI
PAY-N-PLAY
SUPER SIZE
TED
TED 2C
TRACKER
TRAVELER
THE WORLD LEADER IN ELECTRONIC BINGO

GAMEWRIGHT

(Div. of Ceaco Inc.)
70 Ridge St Ste 200
Newton, MA 02458
Tel.: (617) 926-8080
Fax: (617) 969-1758
E-mail: sales@gamewright.com
Web Site: www.gamewright.com
E-Mail For Key Personnel:
Sales Director: sales@gamewright.com
Approx. Number Employees: 25
Year Founded: 1994
Business Description:
Games & Puzzles Mfr & Sales
S.I.C.: 3944
N.A.I.C.S.: 339932
Media: 6-10
Personnel:
Carol J. Glazer *(Pres)*
Allison Yada *(VP-Sls & Mktg)*
Jonathan Panush *(Mgr-Customer Svc)*
Jason Schneider *(Mgr-Product Dev & Mktg)*

Brands & Products:
12 MINUTE GAMES
7 SAFARI
ALIEN HOTSHOTS
BLAST OFF
BZZ OUT
CHECK OUT!
CHOMP!
CLAYMANIA
DISH IT UP!
DOG DICE
EUREKA!
FILL 'ER UP!
FLING!
FOWL PLAY
FROG JUICE
GAMEWRIGHT
GO AWAY MONSTER!
HISSS
HOCUS FOCUS
HONOR OF THE SAMURAI
HORSE SHOW
K-9 CAPERS
KITTY CORNERS
THE LEGEND OF LANDLOCK
LICKETY SPLIT
LILLY'S 3 FOR ALL
LILLY'S PURPLE PLASTIC PURSE COUNTING GAME
LILLY'S PURPLE PLASTIC PURSE GAME
LUCKY CATCH
MAKE IT UP!
MAYA MADNESS
MUMMY RUMMY
PANDAMONIUM
PDQ
PLAY BALL
QUESTS OF THE ROUND TABLE
RAT-A-TAT CAT
THE SCRAMBLED STATES OF AMERICA

Key to Media (For complete agency information see *The Advertising Red Books-Agencies* edition):
1. Bus. Publs. 2. Cable T.V. 3. Catalogs & Directories. 4. Co-op Adv. 5. Consumer Mags. 6. D.M. to Bus. Estab.7. D.M. to Consumers
8. Daily Newsp. 9. Exhibits/Trade Shows 10. Foreign 11. Infomercial 12. Internet Adv.13. Multimedia 14. Network Radio
15. Network T.V. 16. Newsp. Distr. Mags. 17. Other 18. Outdoor (Posters, Transit) 19. Point of Purchase20. Premiums, Novelties
21. Product Samples 22. Special Events Mktg. 23. Spot Radio 24. Spot T.V. 25. Weekly Newsp. 26. Yellow Page Adv.

Gamewright — (Continued)

SHE'S CHARMED & DANGEROUS
SLAMWICH
SNAP
STAMPEDE!
STONE SOUP
SURPRISE!
TARADIDDLE

Advertising Agency:
Aigner Associates PR/Events
214 Lincoln St Ste 300
Allston, MA 02134
Tel.: (617) 254-9500
Fax: (617) 254-3700

GAMING PARTNERS INTERNATIONAL CORPORATION

(d/b/a GPIC)
1700 S Industrial Rd
Las Vegas, NV 89102-2620
Tel.: (702) 384-2425
Fax: (702) 384-1965
Toll Free: (800) PAULSON
E-mail: info@gpigaming.com
Web Site: www.gpigaming.com
Approx. Rev.: $59,875,000
Approx. Number Employees: 642
Year Founded: 1963
Business Description:
Table Game Equipment & Supplies for the Casino Industry
S.I.C.: 3944; 5091; 7999
N.A.I.C.S.: 339932; 423910; 713290; 713990
Advertising Expenditures: $3,768,000
Media: 2-7-10
Distr.: Intl.
Personnel:
Gregory S. Gronau *(Pres & CEO)*
Gerald W. Koslow *(CFO & Treas)*
Laura Mcallister Cox *(Gen Counsel & Exec VP)*
Gay A. Nordfelt *(Corp Sec & Mgr-HR)*
Kirsten Clark *(VP-Global Mktg & Product Mgmt)*
Scott McCarthy *(VP-Sls-Asia)*
Migul Gonglous *(Area Mgr-Sls-Latin America)*
Justin Woodard *(Mgr-Intl Sls & Mktg)*
Advertising Agency:
KCSA Strategic Communications (Kanan, Corbin, Schupak & Aronow, Inc.)
880 3rd Ave 6th Fl
New York, NY 10022
Tel.: (212) 682-6300
Fax: (212) 697-0910
Corp Commun

GLU MOBILE INC.

45 Fremont St Ste 2800
San Francisco, CA 94105
Tel.: (415) 800-6100
E-mail: info@glu.com
Web Site: www.glu.com
Approx. Rev.: $64,345,000
Approx. Number Employees: 369
Year Founded: 2001
Business Description:
Mobile Games Publisher
S.I.C.: 7371; 7372
N.A.I.C.S.: 541511; 511210
Import Export
Advertising Expenditures: $3,184,000
Personnel:
William J. Miller *(Chm)*
Niccolo M. de Masi *(Pres & CEO)*
Eric Ludwig *(CFO, Chief Admin Officer & Sr VP)*
Giancarlo Mori *(Chief Creative Officer)*
Kal Iyer *(Sr VP-R&D)*
Advertising Agency:
Dig Communications
549 W Randolph Ste 201
Chicago, IL 60661
Tel.: (312) 577-1750
Fax: (312) 577-1760

GOLDBERGER DOLL MFG. COMPANY, INC.

36 W 25th St Fl 14
New York, NY 10010
Tel.: (212) 924-1194
Fax: (212) 691-8153
E-mail: goldberger@goldbergerdoll.com
Web Site: www.goldbergerdoll.com
Approx. Number Employees: 50
Year Founded: 1916
Business Description:
Mfr. of Dolls
S.I.C.: 5092
N.A.I.C.S.: 423920
Media: 2-6-10-19
Distr.: Natl.
Budget Set: Oct. -Nov.
Personnel:
Jeff Holtzman *(Owner)*
Brands & Products:
BUNDLE OF JOY
BUNTING BABY
DANCIE
DOLLY DIAPERS
FUZZY FLEECE BABY
GOLDBERGER
LOLLIPALOOZA
SIPPIN SUE
SOFTINA
SOOTHING LAVENDER
SQUEEZE & SQUEAK
UNBELIEVABLY SOFT BABY
ZIP-ITY DO-DOLLY

GRACO CHILDREN'S PRODUCTS INC.

(Sub. of Rubbermaid Home Products)
150 Oaklands Blvd
Exton, PA 19341
Tel.: (610) 884-8000
Fax: (610) 884-8730
Web Site: www.gracobaby.com
Sales Range: $450-499.9 Million
Approx. Number Employees: 1,400
Year Founded: 1946
Business Description:
Mfr. of Baby & Children's Products & Toys
S.I.C.: 3089; 2519; 2531
N.A.I.C.S.: 326199; 337125; 337127
Import Export
Media: 2-4-6-10
Distr.: Natl.
Budget Set: Dec.
Personnel:
Art Gehr *(Dir-Mktg-Travel Sys, Strollers & Car Seats)*
Pancho Gutstein *(Dir-Brand Mktg)*
Brands & Products:
4-IN-1
ASSURA
BEDSIDE BASSINET
BIG KID TRAINER
CENTURY
CUDDLE TUB
FOLD 'N GO
GOTTA GO POTTY
GRACO
HUGGY TUB
KANGA ROCKA ROO
NEXT STEP
NEXUS
OVATION
READY FOR THE ROAD AHEAD
RIGHT FROM THE BEGINNING
RUGGIE BEAR
SMART FIT
SMART MOVE
TRAVELITE
Advertising Agencies:
Graphica
2501 Lyons Road
Miamisburg, OH 45342

LBi
1888 Emery St NW Ste 400
Atlanta, GA 30318
Tel.: (404) 267-7600
Fax: (404) 267-7625

Leapfrog Online
807 Greenwood St
Evanston, IL 60201
Tel.: (847) 492-1968
Fax: (847) 492-1990
(Car Seats, Online Media Buying)

GUND, INC.

(Sub. of Enesco, LLC)
One Runyons Ln
Edison, NJ 08817
Mailing Address:
PO Box 852
Edison, NJ 08818
Tel.: (732) 248-1500
Fax: (732) 248-1968
E-mail: sales@gund.com
Web Site: www.gund.com
E-Mail For Key Personnel:
Sales Director: sales@gund.com
Approx. Number Employees: 230
Year Founded: 1898
Business Description:
Plush Toy Mfr
S.I.C.: 3942; 3944; 5092
N.A.I.C.S.: 339931; 339932; 423920
Advertising Expenditures: $300,000
Media: 4-5-6-10-16-19
Distr.: Natl.
Budget Set: Nov.
Brands & Products:
ARGUS
BABYGUND
BAMBOO
BARKLEY
CARL
CATTITUDES
COMFY COZY
DAWSON
DIDI
DREYFUS
EMMA
EWENICE
FLAPJACK
GOTTA GETTA GUND
GUND
JIMMY
KISSIMEE
KOOKY KREATURES
LIVING PUPPETS
LUKE
MADDY
MANNI
MICKEY
MILKSHAKE
MUTTSY
MVB
NEWTON'S LAW
PERLINA
PIGGSLY
PRINCESS BELLA
ROSE PETALS
SCHLEPP
SLACKER
SNUFFLES
SPUNKY
SQUEAK
TIMBER
TRIXIE
TUTTI FRUTTI
THE WORLD'S MOST HUGGABLE...
THE WORLD'S MOST HUGGABLE SINCE 1898
ZABRINA
Advertising Agency:
Child's Play Communications
135 W 29th St Ste 701
New York, NY 10001
Tel.: (212) 488-2060
Fax: (212) 488-2059

HANDI-CRAFT COMPANY

(Sub. of Swing-A-Way Products)
4433 Fyler Ave
Saint Louis, MO 63116-1803
Tel.: (314) 773-2979
Fax: (314) 773-9273
Toll Free: (800) 778-9001
E-mail: info@handi-craft.com
Web Site: www.handi-craft.com
Approx. Number Employees: 35
Year Founded: 1963
Business Description:
Baby Feeding Products & Children's Toys
S.I.C.: 3085
N.A.I.C.S.: 326160
Media: 4-6-7-10-13
Personnel:
Carl Rhodes *(Pres)*
Jesse Lehnhoff *(Dir-Mktg)*
Brands & Products:
DR. BROWN'S NATURAL FLOW

HANDS-ON MOBILE, INC.

580 California St Ste 600
San Francisco, CA 94104
Tel.: (415) 848-0400
Fax: (415) 399-1966
Web Site: www.handson.com
Business Description:
Mobile Lifestyle, Games & Personalization Products Developer, Publisher & Distr
S.I.C.: 4812
N.A.I.C.S.: 517212
Media: 10
Personnel:
Judy Wade *(Pres & CEO)*
Paul Baldwin *(VP-Distribution & Mktg)*

THE HAPPY COMPANY

(Sub. of Tender Loving Things Inc.)
26203 Production Ave Ste 4
Hayward, CA 94545-3800
Tel.: (510) 300-1260
Fax: (510) 300-1270

Key to Media (For complete agency information see *The Advertising Red Books-Agencies* edition):
1. Bus. Publs. 2. Cable T.V. 3. Catalogs & Directories. 4. Co-op Adv. 5. Consumer Mags. 6. D.M. to Bus. Estab.7. D.M. to Consumers
8. Daily Newsp. 9. Exhibits/Trade Shows 10. Foreign 11. Infomercial 12. Internet Adv.13. Multimedia 14. Network Radio
15. Network T.V. 16. Newsp. Distr. Mags. 17. Other 18. Outdoor (Posters, Transit) 19. Point of Purchase20. Premiums, Novelties
21. Product Samples 22. Special Events Mktg. 23. Spot Radio 24. Spot T.V. 25. Weekly Newsp. 26. Yellow Page Adv.

Web Site: www.thehappycompany.com
Approx. Number Employees: 5
Business Description:
Children's Products Mfr & Sales
S.I.C.: 2844
N.A.I.C.S.: 325620
Media: 4-6-13
Personnel:
Mark Juarez *(Founder & CEO)*
Cindy Souza *(Dir-Ops)*

HASBRO, INC.

1027 Newport Ave
Pawtucket, RI 02861-2539
Mailing Address:
PO Box 1059
Pawtucket, RI 02862-1059
Tel.: (401) 431-8697
Fax: (401) 431-8535
Telex: 92 7-754
E-mail: hi@hasbro.com
Web Site: www.hasbro.com
Approx. Rev.: $4,002,161,000
Approx. Number Employees: 5,800
Year Founded: 1923
Business Description:
Toys, Games, Puzzles & Dolls, Pre-school & Infant Items Mfr & Retailer
S.I.C.: 3944; 3942
N.A.I.C.S.: 339932; 339931
Import Export
Advertising Expenditures: $420,651,000
Media: 3-4-6-10-13-15-17-19-23-24
Distr.: Natl.
Budget Set: Oct.
Personnel:
Alfred J. Verrecchia *(Chm)*
Brian D. Goldner *(Pres & CEO)*
Deborah Thomas Slater *(CFO & Sr VP)*
David D.R. Hargreaves *(COO)*
John A. Frascotti *(CMO)*
Duncan J. Billing *(Chief Dev Officer)*
Stephen J. Davis *(Pres-Hasbro Studios)*
Martin R. Trueb *(Treas & Sr VP)*
Finn Arnesen *(Sr VP-Intl Distr & Dev)*
Lorrie Copeland *(Sr VP-Consumer Insights & Res)*
Jerry Perez *(Sr VP & Global Brand Leader-Preschool)*
Linda Steiner *(Sr VP-Preschool & Girls)*
Kathy Page *(VP-Production)*
Mark Stark *(VP-Global Strategy & Mktg-Core Brands)*
Jeff Taylor *(VP-Mktg)*
Steven Zoltick *(VP-Global IT Ops)*
Lisa Licht *(Gen Mgr-Entertainment & Licensing)*
Greg Lombardo *(Sr Global Brand Dir-Transformers)*
Sarah Hoskin *(Sr Brand Mgr-US Mktg)*
Brands & Products:
1313 DEADEND DRIVE
2-IN-1 TUMMY TIME GYM
ABC SONG GAME
ACQUIRE
ACTION MAN
AGGRAVATION
ANTS IN THE PANTS
ARE YOU SMARTER THAN A 5TH GRADER?
AVALON HILL
AXIS & ALLIES
BAA BAA BLACK SHEEP
BABY ALIVE
THE BACKYARDIGANS
BARREL OF MONKEYS
BART SIMPSON
BATTLE BALL
BATTLE CRY
BATTLEBOTS
BATTLESHIP
BATTLESTAR GALACTICA
BAYBLADE GALEON ATTACKER
BEYBLADE
BIG BEN
BOGGLE
BOGGLE JR.
BOOHBAH
BOP IT
BOUND DEFENDER
BRAIN WARP
BRATZ PASSION
BUG FACTOR LOLLIPOP
BULLS EYE BALL
BULLS-EYE BASEBALL
BUSY BALL POPPER
BUSY BASICS
CANASTA CALIENTE
CANDY LAND
CAT AND THE FIDDLE
CATCH PHRASE
CHARLES WYSOCKI
CHATITUDE
CHUTES & LADDERS
CLASSIC PARCHEES
CLIPO
CLOVERFIELD
CLUE
CLUE FX
CLUE JR.
CONNECT 4
CONNECT FOUR
COOL CREW
COOTIE
COSMIC
COSMIC CATCH
COVER TO COVER
CRANIUM
CROCODILE DENTIST
CROXLEY
DANCE CAM
DESIGNER'S WORLD
DIPLOMACY
DISNEY
DOH DOH'S ISLAND BEACH BUGGY
DOHVILLE
DON'T BREAK THE ICE
DON'T SPILL THE BEANS
DORA THE EXPLORER
DRACIEL
DRACIEL FORTRESS
DRAGON STRIKE
DRAGOON
DREAMTOWN
DRESSY DAISY
DRIGER
DUEL MASTERS
DUNGEONS & DRAGONS
DUNGEONS & DRAGONS MINIATURES
EASY-BAKE OVEN
ELECTRONIC BATTLESHIP
ELECTRONIC CATCH PHRASE
ENGINE GEAR
EPIC DUELS
EXPRESS YOURSELF
THE EYE OF JUDGEMENT
EZ GRASP
FAMILY GAME NIGHT
FANTASTIC 4
FANTASTIC FOUR
FEAR FANG
FOLDIN' ART
FORGOTTEN REALMS
FUN FUNKY FINGERNAILS
FURREAL FRIENDS
GALMAN
GAME OF LIFE
THE GAME OF PERFECTION
THE GAME OF SCATTERGORIES
THE GAME OF THINGS...
GATOR GOLF
GET TOGETHER GAMES
GHOST RIDER
G.I. JOE
GIGA PETS
GIRL TALK
GLIDE 2 RIDE BIKE
GLOWORM
GO-BOTS
GO DIEGO GO!
GO GO MY WALKING PUP
GROOVE IT
GUESS WHERE
GUESS WHO?
GUESSTURES
HALLMARK
HANDS DOWN
HANGMAN
HANNAH MONTANA
HARD METAL SYSTEM
HASBRO
HASBRO GAMES
HEADS UP
HELMET HEROES
HEROSCAPE
HI HO CHERRY-O
HIGH SCHOOL MUSICAL
HITCLIPS
HUNGRY HUNGRY HIPPOS
HYPER SLIDE
I-DOG
I-LIST
IDATEN JUMP
INCREDIBLE HULK
INDIANA JONES
IRON MAN
ITSY BITSY SPIDER
JENGA
JENGA E XTREME
JIVE POD
JUNIOR
KID MOTION
KIM POSSIBLE
KINIGHT DRANZER
LAZER TAG
LIGHTS OUT
LITE-BRITE
LITE-BRITE CUBE
LITTLE EINSTEINS
LITTLE MERMAID
LITTLEST PET SHOP
LUV CUBS
MADE FOR ME
MAGIC SCREEN LEARNING PAL
MAGIC TALKIN' KITCHEN
MAGIC: THE GATHERING
MAGNACORE
MALL MADNESS
MAPLESTORY
MARTIAN MATTER
MASSIVELY MINI MEDIA
MEMORY
MERLIN
MICKEY MOUSE
MIGHTY MUGGS
MILTON BRADLEY
MIO PUP
MISSION: PAINTBALL
THE MOMENT OF TRUTH
MONOPOLY
MOUSE TRAP
MOUSETRAP
MR. MOUTH
MR. POTATO HEAD
MY LITTLE PONY
MYSTERY DATE
NEOPETS
NERF
NET JET
NIBBLE NOTES
NICKELODEON
NITRO XRC
NOODLEBORO
NURSERY RHYME
NUTTY ELEPHANT
OLD MCDONALD HAD A FARM
ORBS
ORIGINAL MEMORY GAME
OUIJA
OUTBURST
OUTBURST JUNIOR
PARCHEESI
PARKER BROTHERS
PARTINI
PASTEL PETS
PAYDAY
PERFECTION
PICTIONARY
PICTIONARY JUNIOR
PICTURE PERFECT
PICTUREKA!
PITCH SIX
PLAIN LAZY
PLAY-DOH
PLAY-DOH DOH DOH ISLAND
PLAYBOX ESSENTIALS
PLAYITNOW
PLAYSKOOL
POP-O-MATIC TONKA
POP-O-MATIC TROUBLE
POP TOPPERS
POW-R-FUEL
POWER TOUR
PRETTY PRETTY PRINCESS
PROJAX
PUZZ 3D
PUZZLE MEDLEY
PUZZLE SHOTS
RACKO
RIDE2ROLL SCOOTER
RISK
RISK 2210 AD
ROLLER ATTACKER
ROLLER COASTER TYCOON BOARD GAME
ROOK
ROOM TECH
ROW ROW ROW YOUR BOAT
RUBIK'S CUBE
SCATTERGORIES
SCRABBLE
SEABORG
SESAME STREET
SHOUT ABOUT MOVIES
SHOWDOWN SPORTS
SILLY SOCCER
SILLY SPORTS
SIMON
THE SIMPSONS
SIT 'N SPIN
SOLITAIRE
SORRY!
SPEEDSTARS

Key to Media (For complete agency information see *The Advertising Red Books-Agencies* edition):
1. Bus. Publs. 2. Cable T.V. 3. Catalogs & Directories. 4. Co-op Adv. 5. Consumer Mags. 6. D.M. to Bus. Estab.7. D.M. to Consumers
8. Daily Newsp. 9. Exhibits/Trade Shows 10. Foreign 11. Infomercial 12. Internet Adv.13. Multimedia 14. Network Radio
15. Network T.V. 16. Newsp. Distr. Mags. 17. Other 18. Outdoor (Posters, Transit) 19. Point of Purchase20. Premiums, Novelties
21. Product Samples 22. Special Events Mktg. 23. Spot Radio 24. Spot T.V. 25. Weekly Newsp. 26. Yellow Page Adv.

Hasbro, Inc. — (Continued)

SPIDER MAN
SPIN POP
SPIROGRAPH
SPONGEBOB SQUAREPANTS
STAR SISTERZ
STEP START WALK N' RIDE
STRATEGO
STRATEGO LEGENDS
SUPER SOAKER
SUPER SOAKER MONSTER ROCKET
SUPERPLEXUS
TABOO
TABOO JUNIOR
THROW ME A BONE
THUMB THING
TIGER ELECTRONICS
TIGER GAMES
TIME FOR US GAMES
TINKERTOYS
TITANIUM SERIES
TJ BEARYTALES
TONKA
TONKA TOUGH TRUCK ADVENTURES
TOOTH TUNES
TOP TRUMPS
TOUGHEST MIGHTY DUMP
TOY STORY
TRANSFORMERS
TRANSFORMERS ARMADA
TRANSFORMERS ENERGON
TRIVIAL PURSUIT
TRIVIAL PURSUIT JUNIOR
TROUBLE
TRYGLE
TRYPIO
TWINKLETWIRLS DANCE STUDIO
TWISTER
TWISTER MOVES
U-DANCE
UPWORDS
VALOR VS. VENOM
VAMPIRE HUNTER
VIDEONOW
WEEBLES
WHAC-A-MOLE
WHEEL OF FORTUNE
WHEEL PALS
WHEELS ON THE BUS
WING DEFENSER
WIZARDS OF THE COAST
WOLBORG
WOODBOARD PUZZLES
YAHTZEE
YAHTZEE GAME FOLIO

Advertising Agencies:
Alcone Marketing Group
(Division of Omnicom Group, Inc.)
4 Studebaker
Irvine, CA 92618-2012
Tel.: (949) 770-4400
Fax: (949) 770-2957

DLB Group USA
848 Brickell Ave 8th Fl
Miami, FL 33131
Tel.: (305) 373-5757
(Agency of Record for Latin America)

Fathom Communications
(Part of Omnicom Group of Companies)
437 Madison Ave
New York, NY 10022
Tel.: (212) 817-6600
Fax: (212) 415-3514

Hunter Public Relations
41 Madison Ave Fl 5
New York, NY 10010-2202
Tel.: (212) 679-6600
Fax: (212) 679-6607

Mediacom Interaction
198 7th Ave
New York, NY 10018
Tel.: (212) 912-5200
Fax: (212) 912-5485

MPG (Media Planning Group)
Roger de Lauria 19
46002
Valencia, Spain
Tel.: (34) 96 353 08 74
Fax: (34) 96 351 15 69

MPG Miami
5301 Blue Lagoon Dr Ste 850
Miami, FL 33126
Tel.: (305) 377-1907
Fax: (305) 337-1906

Renegade, LLC
75 9th Ave 8th Fl
New York, NY 10011
Tel.: (646) 486-7700
Fax: (646) 486-7800

Saatchi & Saatchi
3D River Valley Rd 03-01 Clarke quay
179023
Singapore, Singapore
Tel.: (65) 6339 4733
Fax: (65) 6339 3916

Sarkissian Mason
135 W 26th St 5 Fl
New York, NY 10001
Tel.: (212) 625-8212
Fax: (212) 625-8211

Tribal DDB Europe/London
12 Bishops Bridge Rd
London, W26 AA, United Kingdom
Tel.: (44) 20 7 258 3979
Fax: (44) 20 7258 4253

HEARTHSONG, INC.
(Sub. of 1-800-Flowers.com, Inc.)
7021 Wolftown-Hood Rd
Madison, VA 22727
Tel.: (540) 948-2272
Fax: (540) 948-5022
Toll Free: (800) 533-4397
E-mail: info@hearthsong.com
Web Site: www.hearthsong.com
Sales Range: $50-74.9 Million
Approx. Number Employees: 35
Business Description:
Mail-Order Company For Toys
S.I.C.: 5961; 5945
N.A.I.C.S.: 454113; 451120
Media: 4-8-13

HOBBICO, INC.
2904 Research Rd
Champaign, IL 61822
Tel.: (217) 398-3630
Fax: (217) 356-6608
Web Site: www.hobbico.com
Approx. Number Employees: 700
Year Founded: 1984
Business Description:
Toys, Hobby Goods & Supplies Mfr & Distr
S.I.C.: 5092; 5961
N.A.I.C.S.: 423920; 454113
Import Export
Media: 4-10-13
Personnel:
Bruce Holecek *(Founder)*
Clint Atkins *(Pres)*
Russ Williamson *(Product Mgr)*
Brands & Products:
ACCU-CYCLE
AFTER RUN
COMMAND
DUAL PEAK
DUSTER
HOBBICO
HOBBYLITE
MONOKOTE
PUZZLE GLUE
QUICKPEAK
TOP FLITE

THE HOBBY HUB INC.
15401 Carmenita Rd Ste H
Santa Fe Springs, CA 90670-5667
Fax: (714) 736-0649
Toll Free: (877) 346-2243
E-mail: hobbyhelp@ehobbies.com
Web Site: www.ehobbies.com
Approx. Sls.: $5,000,000
Approx. Number Employees: 7
Year Founded: 2001
Business Description:
Catalog & Mail Order Business
S.I.C.: 5961
N.A.I.C.S.: 454113
Media: 4-8-13-17
Personnel:
Ken Kikkawa *(CEO)*

HOBERMAN DESIGNS, INC.
40 Worth St Ste 1680
New York, NY 10013
Tel.: (212) 349-7919
Fax: (212) 349-7935
E-mail: associates@hoberman.com
Web Site: www.hoberman.com
Approx. Number Employees: 10
Year Founded: 1995
Business Description:
Toys
S.I.C.: 3751; 3944; 5945
N.A.I.C.S.: 336991; 339932; 451120
Media: 4-10-13
Personnel:
Chuck Hoberman *(Pres)*
Brands & Products:
BRAIN TWIST
FLIGHT RING
FLIPOUT
GLITTERGLOBE
HOBERMAN
HOBERMAN SPHERE
MEGA SPHERE
MICRO SPHERE
MINI SPHERE
ORBITER
SONIX FX
SWITCH KICK
SWITCH-O-RING
SWITCH PITCH
TWIDDLESTIX
TWIST-O

ID SOFTWARE, INC.
(Sub. of ZeniMax Media, Inc.)
3819 Towne Crossing Blvd
Mesquite, TX 75150-6123
Tel.: (972) 613-3589
Fax: (972) 686-9288
Toll Free: (800) 434-2637
Web Site: www.idsoftware.com
Approx. Number Employees: 14
Year Founded: 1991
Business Description:
Video Game Studio
S.I.C.: 7371
N.A.I.C.S.: 541511
Media: 6-10-13
Personnel:
Todd Hollenshead *(Co-Owner & CEO)*
John Carmack *(Co-Owner & Dir-Tech)*
Kevin Cloud *(Co-Owner & Artist)*
Tim Willits *(Co-Owner & Lead Designer)*
Donna Jackson *(Office Mgr)*
Brands & Products:
CATACOMBS 3D
COMMANDER KEEN
COMMANDER KEEN GOODBYE GALAXY SET
COMMANDER KEEN INVATION OF THE VORTICONS TRILOGY
COMMANDER KEEN KEEN DREAMS
DOOM
FINAL DOOM
HERETIC
HEXEN
HEXEN II
HOVERTANK 3D
ID SOFTWARE
ORCS AND ELVES
QUAKE
QUAKE 4
QUAKE II
QUAKE III ARENA
QUAKE III GOLD
QUAKE III REVOLUTION
QUAKE III TEAM ARENA
RESCUE ROVER
RETURN TO CASTLE WOLFENSTEIN
SPEAR OF DESTINY
ULTIMATE DOOM
WOLFENSTEIN 3D
Advertising Agency:
Rogers & Cowan
8687 Melrose Ave 7th Fl
Los Angeles, CA 90069
Tel.: (310) 854-8100
Fax: (310) 854-8106
— Wendy Zaas *(VP)*

IMPERIAL TOY CORPORATION
16641 Roscoe Pl
North Hills, CA 91343
Tel.: (818) 536-6500
Fax: (818) 536-6501
Toll Free: (866) 731-1824
E-mail: info@imperialtoy.com
Web Site: www.imperialtoy.com
Approx. Number Employees: 50
Year Founded: 1969
Business Description:
Mfr. of Games, Toys & Childrens Vehicles
S.I.C.: 3944
N.A.I.C.S.: 339932
Import Export
Media: 4-10

Key to Media (For complete agency information see *The Advertising Red Books-Agencies* edition):
1. Bus. Publs. 2. Cable T.V. 3. Catalogs & Directories. 4. Co-op Adv. 5. Consumer Mags. 6. D.M. to Bus. Estab.7. D.M. to Consumers 8. Daily Newsp. 9. Exhibits/Trade Shows 10. Foreign 11. Infomercial 12. Internet Adv.13. Multimedia 14. Network Radio 15. Network T.V. 16. Newsp. Distr. Mags. 17. Other 18. Outdoor (Posters, Transit) 19. Point of Purchase20. Premiums, Novelties 21. Product Samples 22. Special Events Mktg. 23. Spot Radio 24. Spot T.V. 25. Weekly Newsp. 26. Yellow Page Adv.

Personnel:
Peter Tiger *(Pres)*
Brands & Products:
BUDDY L
FUN IN THE SUN
IMPERIAL
JOT.TRON
MIRACLE
MIRACLE BUBBLEMAN
MIRACLE BUBBLES
PETITE MISS
TEC BLUE

INFANTINO, LLC

(Sub. of The Step2 Company LLC)
4920 Carroll Canyon Road, Ste 200
San Diego, CA 92121
Tel.: (858) 457-9797
Fax: (858) 457-0181
Toll Free: (800) 365-8182
Web Site: www.infantino.com
E-Mail For Key Personnel:
Sales Director: sales@infantino.com
Sales Range: $1-9.9 Million
Approx. Number Employees: 45
Business Description:
Juvenile Accessories Whslr
S.I.C.: 5099
N.A.I.C.S.: 423990
Media: 4-10-13
Personnel:
Michael Silberstein *(CEO)*
Wendy Mclean *(VP-Sls)*
Bridget Weiss *(VP-Fin)*
Colette Cosky *(Sr Brand Mgr-Annabel Karmel Line)*
Brands & Products:
6INONERIDER
BUCKET BUDDIES
CART SAFARI
CART TUNES
COZYRIDER
EASYRIDER
EURORIDER
FLUTTERBUG
GIGGLE BALL
GOGORIDER
HAPPY HIPPO GYM
INFANTINO
MOVERSANDSHAKERS
ON THE GO LOUNGER
SHOP AND DINE
SHOPANDPLAY
SLINGRIDER
SMARTRIDER
TUBSIDER
WE THINK LIKE BABIES
ZOOMOBILE

INNOVATIVE USA, INC.

18 Ann St
Norwalk, CT 06854-2202
Tel.: (203) 838-6400
Fax: (203) 855-5582
E-mail: info@innovativekids.com
Web Site: www.innovativekids.com
Sales Range: $25-49.9 Million
Approx. Number Employees: 25
Year Founded: 1989
Business Description:
Educational Toys Retailer; Children's Books Publisher
S.I.C.: 5092; 2731
N.A.I.C.S.: 423920; 511130
Media: 3-4-6-10-18-22-23
Personnel:
Michael Levins *(Owner)*
Shari Kaufman *(Pres)*
Michael O'Keeffe *(CFO)*
Brands & Products:
AMAZING GAME BOARD BOOK
CODE MASTER
GET READY FOR KINDERGARTEN!
IKIDS
INNOVATIVE
INNOVATIVEKIDS
MATH GEAR
NOW I'M READING!
PHONICS COMICS
ROLL-A-RAMA
SHAPE SORTER BOOK
SOFT SHAPES
TOTE-ALONG SOFT SHAPES
WRITE TO SANTA KIT

INTERNATIONAL GAME TECHNOLOGY

9295 Prototype Dr
Reno, NV 89511-8986
Mailing Address:
PO Box 10580
Reno, NV 89510-0580
Tel.: (775) 448-7777
Fax: (775) 448-0719
Toll Free: (866) 296-4232
E-mail: Rick.Sorensen@igt.com
Web Site: www.igt.com
Approx. Rev.: $1,987,200,000
Approx. Number Employees: 4,900
Year Founded: 1981
Business Description:
Computerized Gaming Machines & Systems Products Designer
S.I.C.: 7999; 3999; 7371
N.A.I.C.S.: 713290; 339999; 541511
Export
Advertising Expenditures: $12,400,000
Media: 2-7-9-10-13
Personnel:
Philip G. Satre *(Chm)*
Eric Berg *(Pres)*
Patti S. Hart *(CEO)*
Patrick W. Cavanaugh *(CFO, Treas & Exec VP)*
Eric P. Tom *(COO)*
Robert Melendres *(Chief Legal Officer & Sec)*
Christopher J. Satchell *(CTO, Exec VP-R&D)*
Gideon Bierer *(Exec VP-Interactive)*
T. Rao Coca *(VP-Intellectual Property)*
Aimee Hoyt *(VP-HR)*
Julie W. Brown *(Dir-Mktg)*
Brands & Products:
1 DAY PASS OUT
10 TEN TIMES PAY
100 DEGREES
100 HUNDRED OR NOTHING
100 LADIES
100 PANDAS
100 WOLVES
100X ONE HUNDRED TIMES PAY
10X PAY STRIKE
12 TIMES PAY
18 REELER
21 GAMBLER
2ND CHANCE ROYAL
2ND DRAW ROYAL
2X JACKPOT JEWELS
2X PAY RED WHITE & BLUE
2X3X RED WHITE & BLUE
2X3X4X HOT WIRE
2X3X4X JADE
2X3X4X WHITE PEARL
2X3X4X5X DRAGON
2X3X4X5X LUCKY 7S
2X3X4X5X LUCKY PAYS
2X3X4X5X RED HOT 7S
2X3X4X5X SUPER LUCKY TIMES PAY
3DMETRIX
3X 2X BURNING BARS
3X 777 2X
3X PAY RED WHITE & BLUE
3X TRIPLE JACKPOT 9X
3X2X SUPER 7 SEVENS
3X2X SUPER 7S
4-5 BONUS POKER
4 FOUR TIMES PAY
5 FIVE TIMES PAY
5 WIZARDS
7 STORM
777 SUNSHINE
7777 CLASSIC SEVENS
7X PAY
7X SEVEN TIMES PAY
8 IMMORTALS
9 KOI
9 LIVES
ABRA-CASH-DABRA
ABRACADABRA
ACCORDION REELS
ACE & DEUCE BONUS POKER
ACE INVADERS
ACES DEUCES BONUS POKER
ACRES ADVANTAGE
ACRES BONUSING
ACRES CASHLESS
THE ADAM'S FAMILY
ADVANCED VIDEO PLATFORM
ADVANTAGE BONUSING
ADVANTAGE MATCH PLAY
ADVANTAGE SCAN
ADVENTURE AWARDS
AFRICAN CHIEF
ALL CASH ADVANCE
ALL OR NUT'N KENO
ALL-STAR POKER
ALLEY CAT KENO
AMERICAN BANDSTAND
AMETHYST
ANCIENT ARCADIA
ANCIENT CHINESE SECRET
ANCIENT GOLD
ANDROMEDA
ANIMAL HOUSE
ANTIQUE APPRAISAL
ANYTHING BUT SIX
ANYTHING'S WILD POKER
AQUAMARINE
ARABIAN RICHES
ARCTIC CIRCLE
ARCTIC FOX
ARROWHEAD
AS GOOD AS GOLD
AURORA BOREALIS
AUSTIN POWERS
AUSTRALIA GONE WILD
AUTUMN SUNRISE
AVP
AZTEC PYRAMID
AZTEC TEMPLE
BACCARAT ROYALE
BACK IT UP
BAKER'S DOZEN
BALLOON BARS
BAM
BANK A BIT
BARK AVENUE
BE2
BEAR MOUNTAIN
BENGAL FEVER
BENNY BIG GAME
BETTI THE YETTI
BETTOR BONUS CHANCE
BETTOR CHANCE
BETTOR CHANCE BONUS
BETTOR CHANCE FEATURE
BETTOR CHANCE PAY
BETTOR CHANCE SYMBOL
BETTOR CHANCE WAY
BETTOR CHANCE WIN
BETTOR PAY CHANCE
BETTOR SYMBOL CHANCE
BETTOR WAY CHANCE
BETTOR WIN CHANCE
THE BEVERLY HILLBILLIES
BIDDING FRENZY
BIDDING WILD
BIG 7
BIG BALLS OF CASH
BIG BONES
BIG PICK POKER
BIG PIG
BIG SPLIT POKER
BIG TIME PAYROLL
BIG TIMES DRAW POKER
BIG TIMES PAY
BIG TIMES RED WHITE & BLUE
BIG TIMES WILD CHERRY
BIKINO
BINGO BUGS
BIRDS OF A FEATHER
BITZ & PIZZAS
BLACK CHERRY
BLACK JACK
BLACK MAGIC
BLACK RHINO
BLACK SHEEP
BLACK TIE
BLACK WIDOW
BLACKBEARD'S DOUBLE DOUBLOONS
BLACKBEARD'S GOLD
BLACKOUT PAYS
BLAST OFF
BLUE BLAZES
BLUE DOLPHIN
BOBBLE TIME
BOMBAY
BOMBS AWAY
BON VOYAGE
BONUS BELLS
BONUS ENGINE
BONUS HAND TRIPLE PLAY DRAW POKER
BONUS KING
BONUS POKER
BONUS POKER DELUXE
BONUS SPIN DIAMOND FIVES
BONUS SPIN FIVE TIMES PAY
BONUS SPIN RED WHITE & BLUE
BONUS TIMES PAY
BONZAI
BOOK-END
BOSTON TEA PARTY
BOTTOMS UP
BOWZER'S ROCK N' ROLL PARTY
BRASIL SLINGO
BREW HA HA
BUBBLE UP
BUBBLIN CRUDE
BUCKS AHOY
BUFFET MANIA
BULLS EYE KENO

Key to Media (For complete agency information see *The Advertising Red Books-Agencies* edition):
1. Bus. Publs. 2. Cable T.V. 3. Catalogs & Directories. 4. Co-op Adv. 5. Consumer Mags. 6. D.M. to Bus. Estab.7. D.M. to Consumers 8. Daily Newsp. 9. Exhibits/Trade Shows 10. Foreign 11. Infomercial 12. Internet Adv.13. Multimedia 14. Network Radio 15. Network T.V. 16. Newsp. Distr. Mags. 17. Other 18. Outdoor (Posters, Transit) 19. Point of Purchase20. Premiums, Novelties 21. Product Samples 22. Special Events Mktg. 23. Spot Radio 24. Spot T.V. 25. Weekly Newsp. 26. Yellow Page Adv.

International Game Technology — (Continued)

BUNCO NIGHT
BUT WAIT THERE'S MORE
BUT WAIT! WIN MORE
BY GEORGE
CABLE CAR CASH
CACTUS FLOWER
CAKE WALK
CALYPSO MAGIC
CAMP4CASH
CAPTAIN PAYBACK
CARAVAN
CARD PARTY
CARIBBEAN BLISS
CARIBBEAN BREEZE
CARIBBEAN DREAMS
CARNIVAL OF MYSTERY
CARNIVAL OF MYSTERY MASQUERADE
CASCADA DE DIAMANTES
CASH BALL
CASH COASTER
CASH CONVOY
CASH COVE
CASH DASH
CASH KING CHECKERS
CASH QUEST
CASHBALL
CATCH A WAVE
CATCH THE GREEN
CATS 'N' DOGS
CAVE KING
CAVEMAN KENO
CELEBRATION PRIZES
CHAINSAWS & TOASTERS
CHAMELEON 7S
CHECKMATE
CHERRY ON TOP
CHERRY TREE
THE CHICKEN GAME!
CHINESE ODYSSEY
CHINESE TREASURE
CHU HAN CHESS GOD
CHU HAN CHESS MATCH BONUS
CIGAR
CLAMPETT'S CASH
CLASSIC 7S
CLASSIC COMEDY
CLASSIC SEVENS
CLEOPATRA
CLIPIT
CLOVERS & GOLD
CONNECT LINES
COPS & DONUTS
COPY CATS
CORAL REEF
CORAL ROSE
COUGARLICIOUS
COUNT OF MONTE CRISTO
COUNTRY CASH
COYOTE MOON
CRABMANIA
CRAFTY CARL'S CRABMANIA
CRIBBEAN BLISS
CROWN OF EGYPT
CRYSTAL FIVES
CRYSTAL FIVES BONUS WHEEL
CRYSTAL FORTUNES
CRYSTAL KINGDOM
CRYSTAL ROSE
CRYSTAL SEVENS
CVT
CYRANO
DA VINCI DIAMONDS
DAKOTA THUNDER
DAM LUMBERJACK BEAVERS
DANGEROUS BEAUTY
DAREDEVIL
DATA MANAGEMENT MODULE
DAUB GENIE ON
DAZZLING DIAMONDS
DAZZLING DOLLARS
DEAL WITH THE DEVIL
DEEP POCKETS
DENVER DUCK & THE QUEST FOR THE GOLDEN EGG
DENVER DUCK SLOTS
DESERT MOON
DESERT SPIRIT
DEUCES WILD BONUS POKER
DIABLO DIAMOND
DIAMOND BLAST
DIAMOND CINEMA
DIAMOND FIRE
DIAMOND FIVES
DIAMOND GALAXY
DIAMOND ICE
DIAMOND JACKPOTS
DIAMOND NIGHTS
DIAMOND QUEEN
DIAMOND SPURS
DIAMOND STARS
DIAMOND THIEF
DIAMOND VAULT
DIVOT DIGGER
DOMINO DINERO
DOUBLE 3X4X5X DYNAMITE
DOUBLE 3X4X5X HAYWIRE
DOUBLE 3X4X5X ICE DIAMONDS
DOUBLE 3X4X5X RED HOT 7S
DOUBLE 3X4X5X TIMES PAY
DOUBLE 4X BULLS-EYE
DOUBLE 4X PAY
DOUBLE 4X VOODOO 7S
DOUBLE 4X WILD CHERRY
DOUBLE AMERICAN BEAUTY
DOUBLE BONUS POKER
DOUBLE BUCKS
DOUBLE DESIRE
DOUBLE DIAMOND
DOUBLE DIAMOND 2000
DOUBLE DIAMOND DELUXE
DOUBLE DIAMOND DELUXE BONUS WHEEL
DOUBLE DIAMOND FAST HIT
DOUBLE DIAMOND MINE
DOUBLE DOLLARS
DOUBLE DOWN STUD
DOUBLE GOLD
DOUBLE HEARTS
DOUBLE MYSTICAL MERMAID
DOUBLE PAY SPIN POKER
DOUBLE RED WHITE & BLUE
DOUBLE STRIKE
DOUBLE TEN TIMES PAY
DOUBLE TOP DOLLAR
DOUBLE TRIPLE DIAMOND DELUXE WITH CHEESE
DOUBLE WILD
DOUBLE WILD CHERRY BONUS WHEEL
DOZENS OF DIAMONDS
DRAGON BACCARAT
DRAGON DANCE
DRAGON PHOENIX
DRAGONFLY
DRAGONFLY 7S
DRAGON'S GATE
DRAGONS GOLD
DRAW 6 POKER
DREAM BIG. WIN BIG
DREAM CARD
DUCK STAMPS
DYNAMIC DOLLARS
DYNAMITE BLAST
EARTH QUAKER
EASEL MONEY
EAST & WEST
EASTERN SUN
EASTERN TREASURES
EKEY
EL TORO
ELEPHANT KING
ELVIRA
EMERALD 7S
EMERALD ROSE
EMERALDS & RUBIES
EMPEROR OF ANTARCTICA
EMPEROR'S CHOICE
EMPEROR'S PALACE
ENCHANTED EGYPT
ENCHANTED GARDEN
ENCHANTED ISLAND
ENCHANTED UNICORN
END OF THE RAINBOW
END2END
EUREKA
EXPLODING WILD
EXTRA DRAW KENO
EXTREME WINS
EZ PAY
EZ ROUTE
EZ SAFE
EZ TICKET
EZ-TOUCH
FAME & FORTUNE
FAMILY FEUD
FAMOUS GAMES
FAST ACTION DRAW POKER
FAST MONEY
FENG SHUI
FESTIVAL FANTASTICO
FIDDLER'S GREEN
FIFTH PARTY
FIFTH PARTY LEVEL
FIGARO
FINIAN'S FORTUNE
FIRE BELLS
FIRE DIAMONDS
FIRE GODDESS
FIRE HORSE
FIRE IT UP
FIRE OPALS
FISH FRY
FISH IN A BARREL
FISHIN FOR CASH
FISHING GAME
FIVE ACES POKER
FIVE CARD INSTANT BINGO
FIVE STAR
FIVE TIMES GOLD
FIVE TIMES PAY
FIVE TIMES PAY BONUS WHEEL
FIVE TIMES PAY DELUXE
FLEX PLAY POKER
FORTUNE COOKIE
FOUR TIMES DIAMOND
FOUR TIMES PAY
FOX 'N' HOUND
FREEDOM STARS
FREQUENT FLYER
FRIDAY NIGHT POKER
FROG PRINCESS
FRUIT SLICES WILD-TILES
FRUIT-TASTIC
FULL HOUSE
FUNNY FRUITS
THE GAMBLER
GAME KING
GAME KING PLUS
GARDEN PARTY
GARNET
GEMINI
GEMS WILD-TILES
GEMSTONE 7S
GET EGGCITED
GET NUTS
GET WEALTH SOON
GHOST ISLAND
GHOST WILDS
GIFT OF IMMORTALITY
GIFT POINTS
GLITTER & GOLD
GOING FOR FOURS
GOLD BAR 7'S
GOLD BARS
GOLD CHECKER BONUS
GOLD LEAF
GOLD MOUNTAIN
GOLD SILVER BRONZE
GOLDEN BACCARAT
GOLDEN BLOSSOM
GOLDEN DRAGON
GOLDEN EAGLE
GOLDEN FIRE
GOLDEN GODDESS
GOLDEN KINGDOM
GOLDEN KNIGHT
GOLDEN OPPORTUNITY
GOLDEN TEMPLE
GOLDEN TIGER ETERNAL DRAGON
GOOD TIMES
GOPHER POKER
GOT WHEEL
GRAND MONARCH
GRAND PARTY
GRAND PARTY LEVEL
GRAND PRIZE KENO
GRANDMA'S COOKIE JAR
GREAT PLAINS
GREED IS GOOD
GREENBACK ATTACK
GUARDIAN
GUARDIAN LIONS
GUNSLINGER
HANNIBAL'S MARCH
HAPPY CAMPER
HAUL N CASH
HAWAIIAN SUNSET
HAYWIRE DELUXE
HEART BREAKER
HEART OF TEXAS
HEART OF THE WEST
HEIR TO THE THRONE
HEXBREAKER
HIDDEN ASSETS
HIGH ON THE HOG
HIGHLINER
HOLD 'EM CHALLENGE
HOLEY SMOKES
HOLIDAY IN VENICE
HOLLYWOOD CLASSIC
HOOT LOOT
HOT FLASHES
HOT ICE
HOT PEPPERS
HOT PURSUIT POKER
HOT ROD
HOT TOP DOLLAR
HOT WIRE
HOUSE OF 9 DRAGONS
HOUSE OF JEWELS
HOW LUCKY CAN YOU GET
HULA MOOLAH
HUNDRED OR NOTHING
HUNDRED PLAY DRAW POKER
HYDRA

Key to Media (For complete agency information see *The Advertising Red Books-Agencies* edition):
1. Bus. Publs. 2. Cable T.V. 3. Catalogs & Directories. 4. Co-op Adv. 5. Consumer Mags. 6. D.M. to Bus. Estab.7. D.M. to Consumers
8. Daily Newsp. 9. Exhibits/Trade Shows 10. Foreign 11. Infomercial 12. Internet Adv.13. Multimedia 14. Network Radio
15. Network T.V. 16. Newsp. Distr. Mags. 17. Other 18. Outdoor (Posters, Transit) 19. Point of Purchase20. Premiums, Novelties
21. Product Samples 22. Special Events Mktg. 23. Spot Radio 24. Spot T.V. 25. Weekly Newsp. 26. Yellow Page Adv.

I-CEE DOUBLE
IGAME-PLUS
IGT
IGT ADVANTAGE
IMMORTAL FORTUNE
IMMORTAL JOURNEY
IMMORTAL MOUNTAIN
IMMORTAL POWERS
IMPERIAL DRAGON
IN A BOTTLE
INDIGO SWING
INTERNATIONAL GAME TECHNOLOGY
INTO THE STARS
IRVING THE VIKING
ISABELLA
JACKPOT 7S
JACKPOT BONANZA
JACKPOT HUNTER
JACKPOT JEWELS
JACKPOT JUNGLE
JACKPOT POKER
JACKPOT SEVENS
JACKPOTEERS
JADE GATE
JEKYLL & HYDE
JESTER
JET SETTER
JEWEL OF ARABIA
JEWELS OF ASIA
JEWELS OF INDIA
JOE'S YARD GAMES
JOKER MANIA
JOKER'S GOLD
JOLLY ROGER
JUMPIN' JUNGLE
JUNGLE MAGIC
JUNGLE PRINCESS
KANGAROO CROSSING
KEEPIN' IT HOT
KENO INVADERS
KEY OF BABYLON
KICKIN' KENO
KILIMANJARO
KILLER CASH
KING CASH
KING OF THE GRILL
KING PIN BOWLING
KINGDOM OF GOLD
KITTY GLITTER
KLONDIKE TREASURE
KNIGHT MOVES
KNOCK DOWN
KOOL KAT
KOSSACKS KASH
LADY OF THE LAKE
LATINO MACHINO
LEANING TOWER OF PISA
LEGEND OF THE FIREBIRD
LEGEND OF THE PHOENIX
LEGENDS OF OLYMPIA
LEOPARD CLAW
LEOPARD SPOTS
LIGER LOOT
LIGHTNING BUG
LIGHTNING RICHES
LIL' LADY
LILY OF THE VALLEY
LION DANCE
LION FISH
LITTLE GREEN MEN
LITTLE GREEN MEN FAMILY REUNION
LOUISIANA LOUIE
LUCKY BARS
LUCKY COIN
LUCKY CRICKETS
LUCKY DRAGONFLY
LUCKY FOUR LEAF CLOVER
LUCKY FOX
LUCKY HEARTS
LUCKY JOKERS
LUCKY LARRY'S LOBSTERMANIA
MADAGASCAR
MAG 7
MAGGIE & THE MARTIANS
MAGIC 8 BALL
MAGIC BUTTERFLY
MAGIC CARPET RIDE
MAGIC COIN
MAGIC SPIN
MAGIC WISH
MAGICALLY WILD
MAGNOLIA
MAHARAJA
MAID OF MONEY
MAILBOX MONEY
MAJOR BUCKS AUSSIE ADVENTURE
MAJOR JACKPOTS
MAJORBUCKS
MALTESE FORTUNE
MANHATTAN
MAQUINA LATINA
MARCO POLO
MATA HARI
MATRIX POKER
MEGABUCKS
MEGAJACKPOTS
MIDNIGHT ECLIPSE
MIDNIGHT MATINEE
MIDNIGHT TREASURES
MILLION DOLLAR CHASE
MILLION DOLLAR JEWELS
MILLION DOLLAR MYSTERY
MILLION DOLLAR VOICE
MINIBUCKS
MINIMANIA
MONEY MAD MARTIANS
MONEY MIXER
MONEY STORM
MONEYSTORM
MONSTER KENO
MONSTER MANSION
MOOLAH
MOON WALKER
MOON WARRIORS
MOONSHINE MONEY
MS. LITTLE GREEN MEN
MUCHO DINERO
MULTI-DENOMINATION
MULTI-HAND BLACKJACK
MULTI-STRIKE POKER
MY RICH UNCLE
MYSTICAL MERMAID PARTY
MYSTICAL MERMAIDS
MYSTICAL PRINCESS
MYSTICAL ROSE
MYSTICAL SWORDS
MYSTICAL WIZARD
NEON NIGHTS
NEVADA NICKELS
NEXGEN
NIGHT SKY
NOAH'S ARK
NOBLE KNIGHTS
NORTHERN LIGHTS
NURSE FOLLIES
NUTTIN' TO IT
NYDD
OCEAN PEARL
OKTOBERFEST
OLD HAVANA
ON FIRE
OPPONENT POKER
ORCA
OREGON GOLD
OUTBACK ODYSSEY
PAMPLONA
PANDA PARTY
PARADISE GARDEN
PARISIAN SKY
PARTY ANIMALS
PARTY FANTASTICO
PASSION FLOWERS
PAYROLL
PEACOCK PAYS
PEARL BAY
PEAS IN A POD
PELICAN PAYS
PENNY BARN
PENNY MEGABUCKS
PENNY RICHES
PENNY ROLL
PERFECT CENTS
PERSIAN PRINCESS
PERSONAL LUCKY COIN
PHONE TAG
PINK DIAMOND
PLAYER'S EDGE
PLAYER'S EDGE PLUS
PLAYER'S SUITE
POINT PLAY
PORT ROYALE
POWER KENO
POWER SCORE
PRAIRIE PARTY
PREMONITION
PRICE CHECK
PROGRESSIVE STREAK
PURE PLEASURE
PURE PLEASURE BONUS WHEEL
PURPLE PASSION
PUSH-UP PAYS
PYRAMID
QUACK SHOT
QUAIL RUN
QUARTERMANIA
QUARTERS DELUXE
QUEST
QUEST FOR THE LOST CITY
QUICK QUADS POKER
RACCOONS TO RICHES
RACE FOR MONEY
RAGING 7S
RAINBOW RICHES
RAMPANT REWARDS
RAPID JACKPOT
RAPID RELOAD
RE-SPIN & RE-PAY
RED HOT
RED HOT CHERRY
RED HOT DOUBLE WILD
RED HOT FUSION
RED HOT ICE
RED MANSIONS
RED ROOSTER
RED SIREN 7S
RED SQUARE
RED WHITE & BLUE
RED WHITE & BLUE DELUXE
REEL GOLD
REEL JAZZ
REEL PROFIT
REGIS' CASH CLUB
REMBRANDT RICHES
RENOIR RICHES
RETURNPLAY
RHINO RAMPAGE
RICH GIRL
RINGMASTER RICHES
RISQUE BUSINESS
ROAMIN RHINOS
ROYAL KICKER
ROYAL RICHES
ROYAL TREATMENT
RUMBLING RHINOS
RUN FOR YOUR MONEY
RUSSIAN TREASURE
S2000
SAFARI 7S
SAFARI FLOWERS
SAGUARO
SALE OF THE CENTURY
SAN XING
SAVANNA
SB
SB NEXGEN
SCARLET MOON
SCATTER BUCKS
SCATTERBRAINED
SCATTERPILLAR
SCAVENGER HUNT
SCRAPBOOK PARTY
SEA TREASURES
SEVEN TIMES PAY
SHOOTING GALLERY
SILVER MOON
SIZZLING 7
SIZZLING 7 TIMES PAY
SOARING WINGS
SONG BIRDS
SOUTH PACIFIC
SOUTHERN BELLE
SPACE FOR RENT
SPACE RACE
SPAM
SPELL BINDER
SPIN CYCLE
SPIN FOR CASH
SPIN POKER
SPIN THE WHEEL
SPIRIT BEAR
SPLIT SYMBOLS
SPLITTING HARES
SPOOKY
STACKED WILDS
STATE FAIR
STUDIO ONE
SUGAR & SPICE
SUPER CHERRY
SUPER MAG 7
SUPER SPIN SIZZLING 7
SUPER STARS
SUPER STARS SPIN
SUPER TIMES JACKPOT
SUPER TIMES PAY
SUPER TIMES STRIKE
SUPER WHEEL POKER
SUPER WILD
SURE WIN
SURF CITY
SWEET CHARITY
SWEET DEAL
SWEET GOLD
TABASCO
TABLE TOUCH
TAHITI SUNSET
TAI CHI
TAI PAN
TAILGATE PARTY
TAKE A SHOT
TAKE YOUR PICK
TALES OF HERCULES
TALES OF RICHES
TAMBORA
TARGET KENO
TAVERN KING

Key to Media (For complete agency information see *The Advertising Red Books-Agencies* edition):
1. Bus. Publs. 2. Cable T.V. 3. Catalogs & Directories. 4. Co-op Adv. 5. Consumer Mags. 6. D.M. to Bus. Estab.7. D.M. to Consumers
8. Daily Newsp. 9. Exhibits/Trade Shows 10. Foreign 11. Infomercial 12. Internet Adv.13. Multimedia 14. Network Radio
15. Network T.V. 16. Newsp. Distr. Mags. 17. Other 18. Outdoor (Posters, Transit) 19. Point of Purchase20. Premiums, Novelties
21. Product Samples 22. Special Events Mktg. 23. Spot Radio 24. Spot T.V. 25. Weekly Newsp. 26. Yellow Page Adv.

International Game Technology — (Continued)

TEMPLE OF GOLD
TEMPLE OF TREASURE
TEN PLAY
TEN TIMES GOLD
TEN TIMES PAY
TEN TIMES PAY RED WHITE & BLUE
TEXAS TEA
THAT GIRL
THREE CARD DRAW POKER
THREE TIMES PAY
TOP DOLLAR
TOP DOLLAR DELUXE
TOP DOLLAR LUCKY ROLL
TOP HAT PROGRESSIVES
TOP SECRET SPINS
TOTALLY PUZZLED
TOTALLY RICHIN
TOURNAMENT EDITION
TOURNAMENT KNOCKOUT
TRADE UP POKER
TRAILER PARK PARTY
TRAVELING GNOMES
TRAVELING WILD
TREASURE COVE
TREASURES OF TROY
TREE OF LIFE
TRIPLE BLACK TIE
TRIPLE BONANZA
TRIPLE BUCKS
TRIPLE CASH
TRIPLE CATS 'N' DOGS
TRIPLE CRYSTAL SEVENS
TRIPLE DIAMOND
TRIPLE DIAMOND DELUXE
TRIPLE DIAMOND MINE
TRIPLE DOLLARS
TRIPLE DOUBLE
TRIPLE DOUBLE DIAMOND
TRIPLE DOUBLE DIAMOND SLOT BINGO
TRIPLE DOUBLE DOLLARS
TRIPLE DOUBLE FIVE TIMES PAY
TRIPLE DOUBLE LUCKY 7S
TRIPLE DOUBLE RED WHITE & BLUE
TRIPLE DOUBLE STARS
TRIPLE DOUBLE WILD CHERRY
TRIPLE FIVE TIMES PAY
TRIPLE GOLD BARS
TRIPLE JACKPOT
TRIPLE JACKPOT SLOT BINGO
TRIPLE LUCKY 7S
TRIPLE PLAY
TRIPLE RED WHITE & BLUE
TRIPLE STARS
TRIPLE STRIKE
TRIPLE WILD
TRIPLE ZESTY HOT PEPPERS
TUMBLING REELS
TURBO REELETTE
TURN OF CHANCE
TURN OF FORTUNE
TV HITS
TWICE YOUR HONEY
TWICE YOUR MONKEY
THE TWILIGHT ZONE
TWIN WARRIORS
TWIN WIN
TWIST OF FATE
TWISTED SPINSTER
ULTIMATE SEVENS
ULTIMATE X POKER
UNCLE SAM
UNICORN MAGIC
UNICORN TALES
UNO
USA POKER
USED CARS
VALHALLA
VALLEY OF GOLD
VERSAILLES
VESUVIUS
VIDEO SLOT KING
VISION SERIES
VIVALDI'S SEASONS
VOODOO SPIN
WHEEL OF FORTUNE
WHEEL OF GOLD
WHEELBERT
WHITE HOT ACES
WHITE ICE
WHITE STARS
WILD & LUCKY
WILD BEAR
WILD BEAR SALMON RUN
WILD CHERRY
WILD DIAMONDS
WILD FIVE TIMES PAY
WILD SAPPHIRES
WILD STAR RED WHITE & BLUE
WILD TAXI
WILD THING
WILD-TILES
WILDWOOD
WIN A LATTE
WINE COUNTRY
WINNING TARGET
WINNING TOUCH
WITHCES BROOM
WIZARD GLASS
WORLD OF MAGIC
WU XING SEVENS
XSTATIC
XTRA ACTION
XTRA CREDIT
XTRA LINE
YOKOZUMA
YOUNG FRANKENSTEIN
ZEN GARDEN
ZODIAC RICHES
ZULU KINGDOM

Advertising Agency:
The Glenn Group
50 Washington St
Reno, NV 89503-5603
Tel.: (775) 686-7777
Fax: (775) 686-7750

JADA TOYS, INC.

938 Hatcher Ave
City of Industry, CA 91748
Tel.: (626) 810-8382
Fax: (626) 810-8678
E-mail: info@jadatoys.com
Web Site: www.jadatoysinc.com/
Business Description:
Die-Cast Automotive Toy & Remote Control Toy Mfr
S.I.C.: 3944
N.A.I.C.S.: 339932
Media: 4-13
Personnel:
May Li *(Pres)*
Jack Li *(CEO)*
Bill Simons *(Sr VP)*
Michael Jimenez *(Mgr-Creative Svcs & Mktg)*
Brands & Products:
JADA

JAKKS PACIFIC, INC.

22619 Pacific Coast Hwy Ste 250
Malibu, CA 90265-5080
Tel.: (310) 456-7799
Fax: (310) 317-8527
E-mail: info@jakks.net
Web Site: www.jakks.com
E-Mail For Key Personnel:
President: stephenb@jakks.net
Approx. Sls.: $747,268,000
Approx. Number Employees: 828
Year Founded: 1995
Business Description:
Toys & Related Products Mfr, Developer & Marketer
S.I.C.: 3944; 3751
N.A.I.C.S.: 339932; 336991
Import Export
Advertising Expenditures: $18,400,000
Personnel:
Stephen G. Berman *(Pres & CEO)*
Joel M. Bennett *(CFO & Exec VP)*
Jack McGrath *(COO)*
Jeremy Padawer *(Exec VP-Mktg & Bus Dev)*
Genna Rosenberg *(Sr VP-Comm, IR & Philanthropy)*
Brands & Products:
BIONICAM
CHILD GUIDANCE
COLOR WORKSHOP
CREEPY CRAWLERS
DISCOVERY KIDS SCANOPEDIA
EYECLOPS
FLYING COLORS
FUNNOODLE
GIRL GOURMET
GO FLY A KITE
JAKKS INTERACTIVE
JAKKS PACIFIC
JPI
LASER CHALLENGE
MARBS
NRG PAINTBALL
PENTECH
PLAY ALONG
PLUG IT IN & PLAY TV GAMES
POWER FLYER
REMCO
ROAD CHAMPS
SPA FANTASY
STORM
TOYMAX
TRENDMASTERS

JOSEPH ENTERPRISES, INC.

425 California St Ste 300
San Francisco, CA 94104
Tel.: (415) 397-6992
Fax: (415) 397-0103
E-mail: newidea@jeiusa.com
Web Site: www.chia.com
Approx. Number Employees: 30
Business Description:
General Merchandise Mfr & Retailer
S.I.C.: 3944
N.A.I.C.S.: 339932
Media: 3-6-15
Personnel:
Joseph Pedott *(Pres)*
Brands & Products:
CHIA BART SIMPSON
CHIA BUNNY
CHIA COW
CHIA CROCODILE
CHIA DINOSAUR
CHIA DONKEY
CHIA ELEPHANT
CHIA FROG
CHIA GARFIELD
CHIA GUY
CHIA HEAD
CHIA HIPPO
CHIA HOMER SIMPSON
CHIA KITTEN
CHIA KUNG FU PANDA
CHIA MADAGASCAR ALEX
CHIA MADAGASCAR MARTY
CHIA PET
CHIA PIG
CHIA PROFESSOR
CHIA PUPPY
CHIA SCOOBY - DOO
CHIA SHAGGY
CHIA SHREK
CHIA SNOOZING KITTY CAT
CHIA SYLVESTER & TWEETY CAT
CHIA TAZ
CHIA TWEETY
THE CLAPPER
THE CLAPPER PLUS
CSL
IGNITE-O
JOSEPH ENTERPRISES
THE OVE GLOVE
VCR CO-PILOT
Advertising Agency:
Joseph Pedott Advertising & Marketing, Inc.
425 California St
San Francisco, CA 94104
Tel.: (415) 397-6992
Fax: (415) 397-0103
Toll Free: (800) 345-6992

K&B INNOVATIONS, INC.

N78 W31401 Kilbourne Rd
North Lake, WI 53064
Mailing Address:
PO Box 223
North Lake, WI 53064
Tel.: (262) 966-0305
Fax: (262) 966-0306
E-mail: kbisd@aol.com
Web Site: www.shrinkydinks.com
Year Founded: 1973
Business Description:
Children's Crafts
S.I.C.: 3944
N.A.I.C.S.: 339932
Media: 4-8-13
Personnel:
Betty J. Morris *(Founder & Pres)*
Brands & Products:
SHRINKY DINKS

KID BRANDS, INC.

1800 Valley Rd
Wayne, NJ 07470
Tel.: (201) 405-2400
Fax: (201) 405-7399
Toll Free: (800) 272-7877
Web Site: www.kidbrandsinc.com
Approx. Sls.: $275,777,000
Approx. Number Employees: 304
Year Founded: 1963
Business Description:
Gift, Infant & Juvenile Consumer Products Designer, Importer, Marketer & Distr
S.I.C.: 3942
N.A.I.C.S.: 339931
Import Export
Advertising Expenditures: $900,000
Media: 2-4-5-6-10-19
Distr.: Natl.
Budget Set: Nov.

Key to Media (For complete agency information see *The Advertising Red Books-Agencies* edition):
1. Bus. Publs. 2. Cable T.V. 3. Catalogs & Directories. 4. Co-op Adv. 5. Consumer Mags. 6. D.M. to Bus. Estab.7. D.M. to Consumers 8. Daily Newsp. 9. Exhibits/Trade Shows 10. Foreign 11. Infomercial 12. Internet Adv.13. Multimedia 14. Network Radio 15. Network T.V. 16. Newsp. Distr. Mags. 17. Other 18. Outdoor (Posters, Transit) 19. Point of Purchase20. Premiums, Novelties 21. Product Samples 22. Special Events Mktg. 23. Spot Radio 24. Spot T.V. 25. Weekly Newsp. 26. Yellow Page Adv.

Personnel:
Raphael Benaroya *(Chm & Interim CEO)*
Guy A. Paglinco *(CFO & VP)*
David Sabin *(Pres-Kids Line LLC)*
Marc S. Goldfarb *(Gen Counsel, Sec & Sr VP)*
Brands & Products:
APPLAUSE
COCALO
GIRL POWRR
KIDS LINE
LAJOBI
MAKE SOMEONE HAPPY
MARSHMALLOW
RUSS
RUSS BERRIE
SASSY

KONAMI CORPORATION OF AMERICA INC.

(Sub. of Konami Corporation)
2381 Rosecrans Ave Ste 200
El Segundo, CA 90245-4922
Tel.: (310) 220-8100
Fax: (310) 220-8200
E-mail: koa-info@konami.com
Web Site: www.konami.com
Approx. Number Employees: 130
Year Founded: 1969
Business Description:
Holding Company
S.I.C.: 6719
N.A.I.C.S.: 551112
Media: 3-6-8-10-15-19-20-22-23-24
Distr.: Intl.; Natl.
Personnel:
Kazumi Kitaue *(Sr Mng Exec Officer)*

LEAPFROG ENTERPRISES, INC.

6401 Hollis St Ste 100
Emeryville, CA 94608
Tel.: (510) 420-5000
Fax: (510) 420-5001
E-mail: info@leapfrog.com
Web Site: www.leapfrog.com
Approx. Sls.: $432,564,000
Approx. Number Employees: 511
Year Founded: 1995
Business Description:
Interactive Educational Toy Mfr
S.I.C.: 3944; 3751
N.A.I.C.S.: 339932; 336991
Advertising Expenditures: $49,300,000
Media: 3-4-5-6-9-10-13-15-19
Personnel:
Michael J. Dodd *(Pres & COO)*
John Barbour *(CEO)*
Mark A. Etnyre *(CFO)*
Amy Fitzgerald *(CMO)*
Jean Faulkner *(CTO & Exec VP)*
William K. Campbell *(Pres-Sls & Mktg)*
Michael J. Lorion *(Pres-SchoolHouse Div)*
David Lorie *(Corp Counsel)*
Brands & Products:
2MB MIND STATION
ALPHABET PAL
ALPHAPET EXPLORER
BABY COUNTING PAL
BABY CROKI
THE BACKYARDIGANS
BUSCANDO A NEMO
CLICK START
CRAMMER
DIDJ
DREAMSCAPES
EASY READER
ELECTRONIC FLASH MAGIC
FIX THE MIXI
FLY FUSION
FRIDGE DJ
FRIDGE FARM
FRIDGE PHONICS
FRIDGE TALK
FRIDGE WASH & GO
FRIDGE WORDS
FUN & LEARN
HUG & LEARN
IMAGINATION DESK
LA BOLA EXPLORADORA
LEAP FROG
LEAPFROG SCHOOLHOUSE
LEAPPAD
LEAP'S PHONICS
LEAPSTART
LEAPSTER
LEAPSTER L-MAX
LEAPTRACK
LEARN-ALONG
LEARN & GROOVE
LEARNING BABY TAD
LEARNING BAND
LEARNING FRIEND
LES PETITS
LETTER CRAZY
LETTER FACTORY
LETTERS WITH LULU
LITTLE LEAP
LITTLETOUCH
MAGIC MOMENTS
MATCH UP
MATH CIRCUS
MIND MANIA
MIND STATION
MIND WARS
MY FIRST LEAPPAD
MY OWN LEARNING LEAP
PATITAS
PESCA LETRAS
PHONICS BUS
RADIO LETRAS
READ AND SING
READ-IT-ALL
READY, SET, LEAP!
ROLL & RHYME
SCRIBBLE & WRITE
SEE & LEARN
SEE THE LEARNING.
SHAPES WITH ELLA
SING ALONG READ ALONG
SPIN & SING ALPHABET ZOO
STORYBLOCK
SUPER SAVER
TAG
TALKING WORDS FACTORY
TEXT & LEARN
TOUCH & TUG
TURBO EXTREME
TURBO TWIST
TWIST & SHOUT
WORD WHAMMER
Advertising Agencies:
EVB-Evolution Bureau
55 Union St
San Francisco, CA 94111
Tel.: (415) 281-3950
Fax: (415) 281-3957

Kaplow
19 W 44th St 6th Fl
New York, NY 10036
Tel.: (212) 221-1713
Fax: (212) 768-1960

LEARNING CURVE INTERNATIONAL INC.

(Sub. of RC2 Corporation)
1111 W 22nd St Ste 320
Oak Brook, IL 60523
Tel.: (630) 573-7200
Fax: (630) 573-7575
E-mail: cs@learningcurve.com
Web Site: www.learningcurve.com
Sales Range: $25-49.9 Million
Approx. Number Employees: 100
Year Founded: 1993
Business Description:
Toys, Hobby Goods & Supplies Distr
S.I.C.: 8742
N.A.I.C.S.: 541611
Import Export
Media: 4-6-10
Personnel:
Robert Dodds *(Vice Chm)*
Curtis Stoelting *(CEO)*
Jody L. Taylor *(CFO & Sec)*
Brands & Products:
EDEN
FELTKIDS
LAMAZE

LEGO SYSTEMS, INC.

(Sub. of LEGO A/S)
555 Taylor Rd
Enfield, CT 06082
Tel.: (860) 749-2291
Fax: (860) 763-6623
Web Site: www.lego.com
Approx. Number Employees: 1,300
Year Founded: 1973
Business Description:
Children's Building Sets & Scientific Models Mfr
S.I.C.: 3944; 5092
N.A.I.C.S.: 339932; 423920
Import Export
Media: 1-2-3-4-5-6-7-8-10-13-15-17-19-20-21-22-24-25
Distr.: Natl.
Budget Set: Aug.
Personnel:
Soren Torp Laursen *(Pres)*
Jorgen Vig Knudstorp *(CEO)*
Mads Nipper *(Exec VP)*
Bali Padda *(Exec VP-Global Supply Chain)*
Stig Toftgaard *(Sr VP-Americas)*
Eric Wolfe *(VP-Mktg)*
Charles H. McLeish *(Dir-Mktg)*
Michael McNally *(Dir-Brand Rels)*
Annemarie Munnik *(Brand Mgr)*
Tim Kirchmann *(Sr Brand Mgr-Lego Grp)*
Mike Pratt *(Brand Mgr-Mktg)*
Advertising Agencies:
The Geppetto Group
95 Morton St 8th Fl
New York, NY 10014-3336
Tel.: (212) 462-8140
Fax: (212) 462-8197

Pereira & O'Dell
215 2nd St
San Francisco, CA 94105
Tel.: (415) 284-9916
Fax: (415) 284-9926
The Brick Thief
— Skylar Fogel *(Acct Exec)*

LIFOAM INDUSTRIES INC.

235 Schilling Cir Ste 111
Hunt Valley, MD 21031
Tel.: (410) 889-1023
Fax: (410) 889-0503
Toll Free: (800) 638-1471
Web Site: www.lifoam.com
Approx. Number Employees: 350
Business Description:
Toy & Hobby Product Mfr & Whlsr
S.I.C.: 3944; 5945
N.A.I.C.S.: 339932; 451120
Import Export
Media: 1-5-10-19
Distr.: Intl.; Natl.
Budget Set: Nov.
Personnel:
John Cantlin *(CEO)*
Chris Keller *(CFO & VP-Fin)*
Brands & Products:
DARDA
LIFE-LIKE
LIFE-LIKE RACING
LIFE-LIKE TRAINS
LIFOAM
POWER LOC
PROTO 1000
PROTO 2000

LIONEL LLC

26750 23 Mile Rd
Chesterfield, MI 48051
Tel.: (586) 949-4100
Fax: (586) 949-1013
E-mail: info@lionel.com
Web Site: www.lionel.com
Approx. Number Employees: 100
Year Founded: 1900
Business Description:
Model Electric Trains & Accessories Mfr
S.I.C.: 3944
N.A.I.C.S.: 339932
Import Export
Media: 2-4-6-10-20-22
Distr.: Natl.
Budget Set: Oct.
Personnel:
Scott Turkington *(CFO)*
Judith Munro *(Mgr-Creative Svcs)*
Brands & Products:
ACCESSORY MOTOR CONTROLLER
ACCESSORY SWITCH CONTROLLER
ACTION RECORDER
ACTON RECORDER CONTROLLER
AMERICAN FLYER
BETHLEHEM
BLOCK POWER
BLOCK POWER CONTROLLER
CAB-1
CAMPBELLS
CATERPILLAR
CHOO-CHOO
CONVENTIONAL CLASSICS
CREWTALK
DYNACHUFF
ELECTROCOUPLER
FATBOY
HUSKY STACK
JOSHUA LIONEL COWEN
LEGACY
LIONEL
LIONEL KIDDIE CITY
LIONEL LINES
LIONEL PLAYWORLD

Key to Media (For complete agency information see *The Advertising Red Books-Agencies* edition):
1. Bus. Publs. 2. Cable T.V. 3. Catalogs & Directories. 4. Co-op Adv. 5. Consumer Mags. 6. D.M. to Bus. Estab.7. D.M. to Consumers 8. Daily Newsp. 9. Exhibits/Trade Shows 10. Foreign 11. Infomercial 12. Internet Adv.13. Multimedia 14. Network Radio 15. Network T.V. 16. Newsp. Distr. Mags. 17. Other 18. Outdoor (Posters, Transit) 19. Point of Purchase20. Premiums, Novelties 21. Product Samples 22. Special Events Mktg. 23. Spot Radio 24. Spot T.V. 25. Weekly Newsp. 26. Yellow Page Adv.

Lionel LLC — (Continued)

LIONEL ZW
LIONELVILLE
LIONMASTER
LOCKON
MAGNE-TRACTION
MAGNIVISION
MULTIHORN
MULTIWHISTLE
NESQUIK
NORMAN ROCKWELL
ODYSSEY
OPERATING TRACK CONTROLLER
PH-1 POWERHOUSE
POWERHOUSE
POWERMASTER
POWERSTATION-POWERHOUSE
PULLMOR
RAILSOUNDS
STATIONSOUNDS
TMCC
TOWERCOM
TRACK POWER
TRACK POWER CONTROLLER 300
TRACK POWER CONTROLLER 400
TRAINMASTER
TRAINSOUNDS
WIRELESS TETHER
ZAMBONI

Advertising Agency:
Dan Klores Communications (d/b/a dkc)
386 Park Ave S 10th Fl
New York, NY 10016
Tel.: (212) 685-4300
Fax: (212) 685-9024
(Model Trains)

MAGZ INC.

PO Box 9525
Glendale, CA 91226
Tel.: (626) 398-2000
Fax: (626) 301-0832
Toll Free: (800) 903-MAGZ
E-mail: info@magz.com
Web Site: www.magz.com
Year Founded: 1994
Business Description:
Toy Mfr
S.I.C.: 3944
N.A.I.C.S.: 339932
Media: 4-10-13
Personnel:
Steve Balanchi *(Pres)*
Brands & Products:
MAGZ
MAGZ-X
MAGZPHERE
SKROOZ
WEBZ

MAPLE CITY RUBBER COMPANY

55 Newton St
Norwalk, OH 44857
Mailing Address:
PO Box 587
Norwalk, OH 44857-0587
Tel.: (419) 668-8261
Fax: (419) 668-8261
Toll Free: (800) 841-9434
E-mail: balloons@tuf-tex.net
Web Site: www.maplecityrubber.com
Approx. Number Employees: 85
Business Description:
Toy Balloons Mfr
S.I.C.: 3069
N.A.I.C.S.: 326299
Media: 2-6-8-17
Distr.: Natl.
Budget Set: Dec.
Personnel:
Jeff Tinker *(Pres)*
Paul Bennett *(VP-Production)*
Greg Maxwell *(VP-Production)*
Brands & Products:
TUF-TEX

MARTIN/F. WEBER COMPANY

(Affil. of Martin Universal Design, Inc.)
2727 Southampton Rd
Philadelphia, PA 19154-1293
Tel.: (215) 677-5600
Fax: (215) 677-3336
E-mail: info@weberart.com
Web Site: www.weberart.com
Approx. Number Employees: 35
Year Founded: 1853
Business Description:
Mfr Art Materials
S.I.C.: 3952; 2851
N.A.I.C.S.: 339942; 325510
Export
Media: 6-10-13
Distr.: Natl.
Personnel:
Michael Gorak *(Pres)*
Brands & Products:
BLUE LABEL
BRAQUETTE
DAMAR
FAST FRAME
MATVAR 53
MUSEUM
PERMALBA
PRIMA
RAPIDRY
RES-N-GEL
SALAMANDER
SPHINX
STUDIO VALUE COLLECTION
SUSAN SCHEEWE
SYNVAR
TURPENOID
TURPENOID NATURAL
WINTER HARVEST
Advertising Agency:
Sharlene Yake Advertising
6391 Sherwood Rd.
Philadelphia, PA 19151
Tel.: (215) 477-0729
Fax: (215) 477-0694

MATTEL CANADA, INC.

(Sub. of MATTEL, INC.)
6155 Freemont Blvd
Mississauga, ON L5R 3W2, Canada
Tel.: (905) 501-0404
Fax: (905) 501-6288
Web Site: www.mattel.com
Sales Range: $150-199.9 Million
Year Founded: 1975
Business Description:
Toys Wholesale Distr
S.I.C.: 5945
N.A.I.C.S.: 451120
Personnel:
Geoff Massingberd *(Sr VP-Corp Responsibility)*
Kathleen O'Hara *(Brand Mgr-Entertainment & Games)*
Advertising Agency:
GCI Group-Canada
40 Holly Street Ste 600
Toronto, ON M4S 3C3, Canada
Tel.: (416) 486-7200
Fax: (416) 486-9783

MATTEL GAMES/PUZZLES

(Sub. of MATTEL, INC.)
333 Continental Blvd
El Segundo, CA 90245-5012
Tel.: (310) 252-5548
Fax: (310) 252-2180
Web Site: www.mattel.com
Sales Range: $10-24.9 Million
Approx. Number Employees: 18
Year Founded: 1972
Business Description:
Card, Board, Travel & Action Games Mfr
S.I.C.: 3944; 3942
N.A.I.C.S.: 339932; 339931
Import Export
Media: 1-2-3-4-5-6-7-10-11-15-16-19-20-21-22-23-24-26
Distr.: Natl.
Budget Set: Oct.
Brands & Products:
5 ALIVE
LUCK PLUS
STING
UNO 20 COMMEMORATIVE EDITION
VANTAGE
Advertising Agency:
Ogilvy & Mather
3530 Hayden Ave
Culver City, CA 90232
Tel.: (310) 280-2200
Fax: (310) 280-9473

MATTEL, INC.

333 Continental Blvd
El Segundo, CA 90245-5032
Tel.: (310) 252-2000
Fax: (310) 252-2180
E-mail: service@mattel.com
Web Site: www.mattel.com
Approx. Sls.: $5,856,195,000
Approx. Number Employees: 31,000
Year Founded: 1943
Business Description:
Toy Products Marketer, Designer & Mfr
S.I.C.: 5399; 3942; 3944
N.A.I.C.S.: 452990; 339931; 339932
Import Export
Advertising Expenditures: $647,300,000
Media: 2-3-6-8-9-14-15-18-20-22
Distr.: Intl.; Natl.
Budget Set: Varies
Personnel:
Robert A. Eckert *(Chm & CEO)*
Ronald L. Sargent *(Chm)*
Kevin M. Farr *(CFO)*
Bryan G. Stockton *(COO)*
Alan Kaye *(Chief HR Officer & Exec VP)*
Ellen L. Brothers *(Pres-American Girl Brands)*
Robert Normile *(Gen Counsel, Sec & Sr VP)*
Thomas A. Debrowski *(Exec VP-Worldwide Ops)*
H. Scott Topham *(Sr VP & Controller)*
Chuck Scothon *(Sr VP-Mktg & Gen Mgr)*
Tim Kilpin *(Sr VP & Gen Mgr-Mattel Brands)*
Stephanie Cota *(Sr VP-Mktg-Barbie Brand)*
Geoff Massingberd *(Sr VP-Corp Responsibility)*
Doug Wadleigh *(Sr VP-Entertainment Brands & Partnerships)*
Jim Walter *(Chief Regulatory Officer & Sr VP-Global Product Integrity)*
Cynthia Neiman *(VP-Digital)*
Simon Waldron *(VP-Mktg-Hot Wheels)*
Jill Nordquist *(Sr Dir-Boys Mktg)*
Kitty Pilarz *(Sr Dir-Fisher-Price Product Safety)*
Lauren Bruksch *(Dir-Mktg-Barbie)*
Betsy Burkett *(Dir-Digital Media & Community Mgmt)*
Elizabeth Grampp *(Dir-Mktg)*
Liz Grampp *(Dir-Mktg-Barbie Collector)*
Scott Neitlich *(Dir-Mktg)*
Rosie O'Neill *(Dir-Barbie Mktg)*
Meagan Reay *(Dir-Mktg)*
Susan Russo *(Dir-Game & Play Mktg)*
Heather Miller *(Sr Mgr-Mktg-Hot Wheels)*
Jenny Watson *(Sr Mgr-Mktg)*
Brands & Products:
AMERICAN GIRL
AMERICAN GIRL TODAY
AMERICAN GIRLS COLLECTION
ANNETTE HIMSTEDT
BARBIE
BARBIE GIRLS
BEAR IN THE BIG BLUE HOUSE
BLUE'S CLUES
BOOM-O
CHURCHILL
CLASSICAL CHORUS
DELUXE UNO
DISNEY & PIXAR'S STORY
DISNEY PRINCESSES
DISNEY'S ATLANTIS
DIVA STARZ
ELINA
ELLO
FASHION AVENUE
FISHER-PRICE
GROW TO PRO
HAPPY FAMILY
HILARIUM
HOT WHEELS
HOT WHEELS COLLECTIBLES
HOUSE OF BARBIE
HYDRO STRIKE
IMAGINEXT
JIMMY NEUTRON BOY GENIUS
JUICEBOX
KASEY THE KINDERBOT
KELLY
LEARNING PATTERNS
LI'L MISS DRESS UP
LI'L MISS MAKEUP
LITTLE MOMMY
LITTLE PRETTY
LOONEY TUNES
MAGIC 8 BALL
MAGIC NURSERY
MARY-KATE & ASHLEY
MATCHBOX
MATTEL
MATTEL CLASSIC GAMES
MATTEL GAMES
MICKEY MOUSE
MIND TRAP
MIRACLE BABY

Key to Media (For complete agency information see *The Advertising Red Books-Agencies* edition):
1. Bus. Publs. 2. Cable T.V. 3. Catalogs & Directories. 4. Co-op Adv. 5. Consumer Mags. 6. D.M. to Bus. Estab.7. D.M. to Consumers 8. Daily Newsp. 9. Exhibits/Trade Shows 10. Foreign 11. Infomercial 12. Internet Adv.13. Multimedia 14. Network Radio 15. Network T.V. 16. Newsp. Distr. Mags. 17. Other 18. Outdoor (Posters, Transit) 19. Point of Purchase20. Premiums, Novelties 21. Product Samples 22. Special Events Mktg. 23. Spot Radio 24. Spot T.V. 25. Weekly Newsp. 26. Yellow Page Adv.

MY FIRST UNO
MY SCENE
OTHELLO
OUTBRUST
POWERTOUCH
RAINBOW ADVENTURE
REBOUND
ROCK'EM SOCK'EM ROBOTS
ROCKET POWER
RUGRATS
SCENE IT
SHAKIRA
SHANNEN & SCOOCH
SHIELD BLASTER
SHINING STARS
SKATEBOARD SHANNEN
SKIP-BO
SPELLMASTER
SPONGEBOB SQUAREPANTS
SUPER ELECTRONIC KER PLUNK
THUMBELINA
TIMELESS TREASURES
TIP-IT
TOSS ACROSS
TRAC-BALL
TUFF STUFF
TUMBLIN' MONKEYS
TYCO
UNO
VIDSTER
WHO WANTS TO BE A MILLIONAIRE
WIGGLY WORMS
WILD THORNBERRYS
WINX

Advertising Agencies:
Carat International
Parker Tower 43-49 Parker St
London, WC2B 5PS, United Kingdom
Tel.: (44) 207 430 6000
Fax: (44) 207 430 6299
Media Buying/Planning

Gorilla Nation Media, LLC
5140 W Goldleaf Cir Fl 3
Los Angeles, CA 90056
Tel.: (310) 449-1890
Fax: (310) 449-1891
Online Display Ad Inventory

J-U Carter, Inc.
555 N El Camino Rel St A 462
San Clemente, CA 92672
Tel.: (949) 852-5960
Fax: (949) 852-5960

MEC - NA HQ, New York
825 7th Ave
New York, NY 10019-5818
Tel.: (212) 474-0000
Fax: (212) 474-0003
Media Agency

Ogilvy & Mather
3530 Hayden Ave
Culver City, CA 90232
Tel.: (310) 280-2200
Fax: (310) 280-9473
(Barbie Doll, Small & Large Dolls)

Ogilvy India
14th Floor Commerz International
Business Park Oberoi Garden City
off Western Express Highway
Mumbai, 400 063, India
Tel.: (91) 22 4436 0360
Fax: (91) 22 5034 4370

Razorfish
821 2nd Ave Ste 1800
Seattle, WA 98104-2343
Tel.: (206) 816-8800
Fax: (206) 816-8808
Digital Media Agency of Record

Starcom USA
35 W Wacker Dr
Chicago, IL 60601
Tel.: (312) 220-3535
Fax: (312) 220-6530
American Girl (Media)

Vertical Marketing Network LLC
15147 Woodlawn Ave
Tustin, CA 92780
Tel.: (714) 258-2400, ext. 420
Fax: (714) 258-2409

Y&R
285 Madison Ave
New York, NY 10017-6401
Tel.: (212) 210-3000
Fax: (212) 490-9073
Fax: (212) 370-3796
Fax: (212) 210-5169

MDI ENTERTAINMENT LLC

(Sub. of Scientific Games Corporation)
1500 Bluegrass Lakes Pkwy
Alpharetta, GA 30004
Tel.: (770) 664-3700
Fax: (770) 343-8798
E-mail: webmaster@mediadropin.com
Web Site: www.mdientertainment.com
Sales Range: $10-24.9 Million
Approx. Number Employees: 31
Year Founded: 1986
Business Description:
Marketer of State Lottery Games
S.I.C.: 7373
N.A.I.C.S.: 541512
Advertising Expenditures: $350,000
Media: 2-10
Personnel:
Steven M. Saferin *(Pres)*
Chuck Kline *(Exec VP)*
Ken Przysiecki *(Sr VP-Acctg)*
Don Walsh *(Sr VP-Sls)*
Ron Williams *(Sr Mgr-Integrated Mktg)*
Max Montgomery *(Mgr-Mktg)*

MEGA BRANDS INC.

4505 Hickmore
Montreal, QC H4T 1K4, Canada
Tel.: (514) 333-5555
Fax: (514) 333-8484
Toll Free: (800) 865-6342
E-mail: info_invest@megabrands.com
Web Site: www.megabloks.com
Approx. Sls.: $368,020,000
Approx. Number Employees: 1,300
Year Founded: 1967
Business Description:
Mfr & Marketer of Toys, Stationery & Board Games
S.I.C.: 3944; 2678; 3942
N.A.I.C.S.: 339932; 322233; 339931
Advertising Expenditures: $28,161,000
Media: 4-6-10-11-13-15
Personnel:
Victor J. Bertrand *(Chm)*
Marc Bertrand *(Pres & CEO)*
Peter Ferrante *(CFO & VP)*
Anthony Bazan *(COO & Exec VP)*
Vic Bertrand *(Chief Innovation Officer)*
Lucie Desjardins *(Legal Counsel & Asst Sec)*
Mark Girgis *(Sec & VP-Legal Affairs)*
Sylvain Duval *(Exec VP-Ops)*
Jean-Francois Albert *(VP-Ops-HR)*
Genevieve LeBrun *(VP-Mktg & Bus Dev)*
Joe Marsilii *(VP-Investment & Fin)*
Brands & Products:
ACTIVITY TABLE
BATTLE STRIKER
BIG AIR BANZAI
BLOCK BUDDIES
CITY PURSUIT
CLUBHOUSE
CYCLONE
DECK SLIDE
DRAGONS
DRAIGAR CASTLE
DRAIGAR WAR CHEST
DREAD EYE'S PHANTOM
FIRE FURY
FIRE MOUNTAIN
FLAIR PIPE
GAS N GO
GRIZ-AIR
GYRO
HALO WARS
HELIX
ICOASTER
J-227 QUADWALKER
JUST BUILD
KING ARTHUR
KRYSTAL WARS
MAELSTROM
MAGNEXT
MAN O'WAR
MARAUDER'S CLIFF
MARVEL
MAXI
MEGA
MEGA BLOKS
MEGA BRANDS
MICRO MOTORS
MINI & MICRO
MY MUSICAL FARM
NANO BUILDING SYSTEM
NEO SHIFTERS
NIGHT FORCE OPTIC
NORVAGEN WAR CHEST
PICK TRICK
PLASMA CLASH
RADIX ADVENTURES
RAIL GRIND
RAZORTOOTH
ROSEART
SEA DRAGON
SING ALONG JUKEBLOCKS
SKYCRANE TOWER
SLINGSHOT
SMART BUILDERS
SPINWASH
SPY
STAIR SHRED
STREETZ
STRUXX
TURBO
U-122 STRIKER
U-240 ASSAULT
VERT MADNESS
VORGAN ATTACK
VORGAN STRONGHOLD
VORGAN WAR CHEST
WARRIORS
Advertising Agency:
MPG (Media Planning Group)
11 Great Newport Street
London, WC2H 7JA, United Kingdom
Tel.: (44) 207 393 9000
Fax: (44) 207 393 2525
Media Planning & Buying

MGA ENTERTAINMENT, INC.

16300 Roscoe Blvd Ste 150
Van Nuys, CA 91406
Tel.: (818) 894-2525
Fax: (818) 894-8094
Toll Free: (800) 222-4685
E-mail: service@mgae.com
Web Site: www.mgae.com
Sales Range: $1-9.9 Million
Approx. Number Employees: 1,600
Year Founded: 1979
Business Description:
Toy Developer & Licensor
S.I.C.: 5092
N.A.I.C.S.: 423920
Advertising Expenditures: $15,000,000
Media: 4-6-9-15-24
Distr.: Natl.
Budget Set: Feb.
Personnel:
Isaac Larian *(CEO)*
Dennis R. Jolicoeur *(CFO)*
Eli Makabi *(Exec VP)*
Susan Hale *(Dir-PR)*
Brands & Products:
ALIEN RACERS
COOLECTIBLZ
FAIRIEES
LIL ANGELZ
LITTLE TIKES
MARBLE ODYSSEY
MBR
MGA
MGA ENTERTAINMENT
MICROBLAST RACERS
MUTANT FREAKS
ONE MAN JAM
PLUSH
SPIDERMAN
SUGAR PLANET
Advertising Agency:
Beacon Media Group
1 International Blvd Ste 1110
Mahwah, NJ 07495
Tel.: (201) 335-0032

MICROSOFT GAME STUDIOS

(Sub. of Microsoft Entertainment & Devices Division)
1 Microsoft Way
Redmond, WA 98052-6399
Tel.: (425) 882-8080
Fax: (425) 936-7329
Web Site: www.microsoft.com/games
Sales Range: $50-74.9 Million
Business Description:
Video Games Publisher & Developer
S.I.C.: 3944; 7372
N.A.I.C.S.: 339932; 511210
Media: 1-2-3-4-6-7-8-9-10-11-13-14-15-18-19-20-21-22-23-24-25
Personnel:
William Rhys Dekle *(Dir-Bus Dev)*
Advertising Agency:
McCann Erickson/Los Angeles
5700 Wilshire Blvd Ste 225
Los Angeles, CA 90036
Tel.: (323) 900-7100

Key to Media (For complete agency information see *The Advertising Red Books-Agencies* edition):
1. Bus. Publs. 2. Cable T.V. 3. Catalogs & Directories. 4. Co-op Adv. 5. Consumer Mags. 6. D.M. to Bus. Estab.7. D.M. to Consumers
8. Daily Newsp. 9. Exhibits/Trade Shows 10. Foreign 11. Infomercial 12. Internet Adv.13. Multimedia 14. Network Radio
15. Network T.V. 16. Newsp. Distr. Mags. 17. Other 18. Outdoor (Posters, Transit) 19. Point of Purchase20. Premiums, Novelties
21. Product Samples 22. Special Events Mktg. 23. Spot Radio 24. Spot T.V. 25. Weekly Newsp. 26. Yellow Page Adv.

Microsoft Game Studios — (Continued)

Fax: (323) 900-7111

MUNCHKIN, INC.
16689 Schoenborn St
North Hills, CA 91343-6113
Tel.: (818) 893-5000
Fax: (818) 893-6343
Toll Free: (800) 344-2229
E-mail: cserv@munchkin.com
Web Site: www.munchkin.com
Approx. Number Employees: 50
Year Founded: 1991
Business Description:
Designer, Mfr & Distr of Infant & Toddler Products
S.I.C.: 3085; 3069
N.A.I.C.S.: 326160; 326299
Media: 4-6-10-13
Personnel:
Steven B. Dunn *(Chm & CEO)*
Margaret L. Hardin *(Pres & COO)*
Gary Rolfes *(CFO)*
Andrew Keimach *(Exec VP-Sls)*
Christian Carvelho *(VP-Sls & Mktg-Canada)*
Marc Hayes *(VP-Sls)*
Jeffrey Kaltreider *(VP-Mktg)*
Lucy Wenas *(Mgr-Creative Svcs)*
Brands & Products:
10 SQUIRTIN SEA BUDDIES
BATH DUNKERS
BEAR-WITH-ME
BIG KID
BOBBLE BEE
BUGGIES
CATERPILLAR SPILLERS
COOL FLOW
THE CUPSICLE
DIAPER DUCK
DISCO TUB LIGHTS
DRY WIPES
EARTHLINKS
FOLD 'N GO
FUN ICE
GO DIEGO GO
HEALTHFLOW
ICE COLD CRYSTALS
IT'S THE LITTLE THINGS
JELLY BEAN
MEDICATOR
MIGHTY GRIP
MOZART MAGIC
MOZART MAGIC CUBE
MUDDY PIGS
MUNCHKIN
MY FIRST
NO MORE DRY WIPES
PACIFIER CLEAN 'N GO
PELICAN RINSER
PLAY 'N PAT WATER MAT
RATTLE 'N ROLL
SAFETY SUNBLOCK SHADE
SEA & LEARN
SHAKEY EGGS
SING WITH ME MAGIC CUBE
SNACK 'N SERVE
SNAIL STACKER
SOFT ANIMAL STACKERS
STAY-PUT
STEAM GUARD
SUNBLOCK SHADE
TEETHER BABIES
TEETHER BLANKER BUDDY
TRAVEL BUDDY
TRAVELWARE
TRI-FLOW
TWIST TIGHT
TWISTY FISH
WARM GLOW
WET WHEELS
WHITE HOT

NAVARRE CORPORATION
7400 49th Ave N
New Hope, MN 55428-4258
Tel.: (763) 535-8333
Fax: (763) 533-2156
E-mail: info@navarre.com
Web Site: www.navarre.com
Approx. Sls.: $490,897,000
Approx. Number Employees: 413
Year Founded: 1983
Business Description:
Publisher & Distr of Home Entertainment & Multimedia Software Products
S.I.C.: 5045; 5099; 7372; 7812; 7822
N.A.I.C.S.: 423430; 334611; 423990; 511210; 512110; 512120
Import Export
Advertising Expenditures: $1,700,000
Personnel:
Timothy R. Gentz *(Chm)*
Richard S. Willis *(Pres & CEO)*
J. Reid Porter *(CFO & COO)*
Lina Shurslep *(CIO)*
Joyce Fleck *(Pres-Navarre Distr Svcs)*
Cal Morrell *(Pres-Encore)*
Ward Thomas *(Pres-Bus Svcs & Dev)*
Ryan Urness *(Gen Counsel & Sec)*
John Turner *(Sr VP-Global Logistics)*
Diane D. Lapp *(VP-Fin)*
Margot Mcmanus *(VP-HR)*

NIKKO AMERICA, INC.
(Sub. of NIKKO Co., Ltd.)
2801 Summit Ave
Plano, TX 75074
Tel.: (972) 422-0838
Fax: (972) 578-7059
Toll Free: (800) 776-4556
E-mail: help@nikkoamerica.com
Web Site: www.nikkoamerica.com
Approx. Number Employees: 20
Year Founded: 1984
Business Description:
Electronic Toy Mfr & Whslr
S.I.C.: 3944
N.A.I.C.S.: 339932
Advertising Expenditures: $200,000
Media: 4-13-15
Distr.: Natl.
Budget Set: Monthly
Personnel:
Tom Hirasawa *(COO)*
Brands & Products:
ALIENATOR
DECEPTOR
HERCULES
SCORPION
SHARK HUNTER
STARFISH
THOR
XTENDER
Advertising Agency:
G.S. Schwartz & Co. Inc.
470 Park Ave S 10th Fl S
New York, NY 10016-6819
Tel.: (212) 725-4500
Fax: (212) 725-9188

NINTENDO OF AMERICA, INC.
(Sub. of Nintendo Co., Ltd.)
4600 150th Ave NE
Redmond, WA 98052-5111
Mailing Address:
PO Box 957
Redmond, WA 98073
Tel.: (425) 882-2040
Fax: (425) 882-3585
Toll Free: (800) 633-3236
E-mail: nintendo@noa.nintendo.com
Web Site: www.nintendo.com
Approx. Sls.: $3,175,125,573
Approx. Number Employees: 1,000
Year Founded: 1981
Business Description:
Electronic Games & Home Video Systems Whslr
S.I.C.: 5092
N.A.I.C.S.: 423920
Import
Media: 3-5-8-10-13-15-22-24
Distr.: Natl.
Personnel:
Reggie Fils-Aime *(Pres)*
Mike Fukuda *(Exec VP)*
Scott Moffitt *(Exec VP-Sls & Mktg-Redwood)*
Ingvar Petursson *(Sr VP-Info Svcs)*
Bill Van Zyll *(Gen Mgr-Latin America)*
Kris Rausch *(Dir-Product)*
Ricky Kim *(Mgr-Consumer Promotions)*
Brands & Products:
GAME BOY ADVANCED
GAME BOY COLOR
GAME BOY POCKET
NINTENDO 64
NINTENDO ENTERTAINMENT SYSTEM
NINTENDO GAME CUBE
NINTENDO POWER
SUPER NINTENDO ENTERTAINMENT SYSTEM
Advertising Agencies:
GolinHarris
(Part of the Interpublic Group of Companies)
111 E Wacker Dr 11th Fl
Chicago, IL 60601-4306
Tel.: (312) 729-4000
Fax: (312) 729-4010

Leo Burnett Worldwide, Inc.
35 W Wacker Dr
Chicago, IL 60601-1723
Tel.: (312) 220-5959
Fax: (312) 220-3299
(Super Nintendo Entertainment System, Game Boy, Nintendo Entertainment System)

Starcom MediaVest Group
35 W Wacker Dr
Chicago, IL 60601-1723
Tel.: (312) 220-3535
Fax: (312) 220-6530

Vital Marketing Group LLC
115 E 23rd St 10th Fl
New York, NY 10010
Tel.: (212) 995-9525
Fax: (212) 995-2682
Urban Advertising

NOVELTEX MIAMI, INC.
151 E 10th Ave
Hialeah, FL 33010-5191
Tel.: (305) 887-8191
Fax: (305) 883-7767
E-mail: custcare@noveltexmiami.com
Web Site: www.noveltexmiami.com
E-Mail For Key Personnel:
Marketing Director: anton@noveltexmiami.com
Sales Range: $1-9.9 Million
Approx. Number Employees: 50
Year Founded: 1953
Business Description:
Mfr. of Gifts & Souvenirs
S.I.C.: 3089; 2499
N.A.I.C.S.: 326199; 321999
Import Export
Advertising Expenditures: $500,000
Media: 2-4-6-9-10-11-16-17-20-21-26
Personnel:
Anton Maratos *(VP-Mktg & New Product Dev)*
Dimitris A. Maratos *(VP-Mktg & New Product Dev)*

THE OHIO ART COMPANY, INC.
One Toy St
Bryan, OH 43506-0111
Mailing Address:
PO Box 111
Bryan, OH 43506-0111
Tel.: (419) 636-3141
Fax: (419) 636-7614
Toll Free: (800) 641-6266
E-mail: info@ohioart.com
Web Site: www.ohioart.com
Sales Range: $10-24.9 Million
Approx. Number Employees: 105
Year Founded: 1908
Business Description:
Toys, Games, Sporting Goods & Creativity Products Designer & Mfr
S.I.C.: 3944; 3089
N.A.I.C.S.: 339932; 326199
Import Export
Advertising Expenditures: $1,404,000
Media: 2-3-4-5-6-10-11-19-20-21-22-23-24
Distr.: Intl.
Budget Set: Nov.
Personnel:
William Killgallon *(Chm)*
Larry Killgallon *(Pres & COO)*
Jeff Morris *(CFO-Sls & Ops, Sr VP)*
Martin Killgallon *(Sr VP-Mktg & Product Dev)*
DeDra Walters *(Dir-Domestic Sls)*
Michelle Gibbs *(Mgr-HR)*
Brands & Products:
ATHLETIC BABY
BATH DOLLS
BETTY
BETTY SPAGHETTY
BLOCK N LEARN
BLOCKWAY SHOW
CLASSIC ETCH A SKETCH
CLASSIC MAGNA DOODLE
COLOURFUL BOWLING FRIENDS
DIGITAL ETCH A SKETCH
DOODLE SKETCH
DROP'N GO EMMA
ELECTRONICS ETO
ETCH-A-SKETCH
ETCH A SKETCH FOR IPHONE & IPOD
FOLD'N GO
THE HUNGRY PELICAN
IAM THE BOSS
INCH WORM
JUMBO GO GO GO
K'S KIDS

Key to Media (For complete agency information see *The Advertising Red Books-Agencies* edition):
1. Bus. Publs. 2. Cable T.V. 3. Catalogs & Directories. 4. Co-op Adv. 5. Consumer Mags. 6. D.M. to Bus. Estab.7. D.M. to Consumers
8. Daily Newsp. 9. Exhibits/Trade Shows 10. Foreign 11. Infomercial 12. Internet Adv.13. Multimedia 14. Network Radio
15. Network T.V. 16. Newsp. Distr. Mags. 17. Other 18. Outdoor (Posters, Transit) 19. Point of Purchase20. Premiums, Novelties
21. Product Samples 22. Special Events Mktg. 23. Spot Radio 24. Spot T.V. 25. Weekly Newsp. 26. Yellow Page Adv.

MINI BASEBALL ETCH A SKETCH
MINI BASKETBALL ETCH A SKETCH
MINI FOOTBALL ETCH A SKETCH
MINI SOCCER ETCH A SKETCH
OHIO ART
POCKET DOODLE SKETCH
POCKET ETCH A SKETCH
PULL BACK AUTOS
TRAVEL DOODLE SKETCH
TRAVEL ETCH A SKETCH

OOZ & OZ INC.
3624 46 Ave SW
Seattle, WA 98116
Tel.: (206) 344-3338
Fax: (206) 344-3338
Toll Free: (888) 750-3338
E-mail: info@oozandoz.com
Web Site: www.oozandoz.com
Approx. Number Employees: 5
Business Description:
Educational Toys & Games
S.I.C.: 3944
N.A.I.C.S.: 339932
Media: 4-8-10-13
Personnel:
Myrna Hoffman *(Founder)*
Brands & Products:
MIRROR-ACULOUS
OOZ & OZ

OPTIMAL GROUP INC.
3500 de Maisonneuve Boulevard West
Suite 800
Montreal, QC H3Z 3C1, Canada
Tel.: (514) 738-8885
Fax: (514) 738-8355
E-mail: info@optimalgrp.com
Web Site: www.opmr.com
Approx. Rev.: $66,442,000
Approx. Number Employees: 135
Year Founded: 1984
Business Description:
Electronic Payment & Risk Management Solution Services & Consumer Electronics & Toy Mfr
S.I.C.: 6099; 3944; 7372
N.A.I.C.S.: 522320; 339932; 511210
Export
Advertising Expenditures: $5,072,000
Media: 1-2-6-10-13-17-23-24
Personnel:
Gary S. Wechsler *(CFO & Treas)*
Neil S. Wechsler *(Principal)*
Leon P. Garfinkle *(Gen Counsel, Sec & Sr VP)*
O. Bradley McKenna *(VP-Admin & HR)*
Brands & Products:
OPTIMAL GROUP

PANDEMIC STUDIOS, LLC
(Sub. of Electronic Arts Inc.)
1100 Glendon Ave 19th Fl
Los Angeles, CA 90024
Tel.: (310) 450-5199
Fax: (310) 209-3330
E-mail: info@pandemicstudios.com
Web Site: www.pandemicstudios.com
Sales Range: $25-49.9 Million
Approx. Number Employees: 150
Business Description:
Computer Game Developer
S.I.C.: 7372; 3944
N.A.I.C.S.: 511210; 339932
Media: 6-10
Brands & Products:
PANDEMIC

PARADISE GALLERIES, INC.
PO Box 57086
Irvine, CA 92619
Tel.: (858) 793-4050
Fax: (949) 743-8974
E-mail: cs@paradisegalleries.com
Web Site: www.paradisegalleries.com
Approx. Number Employees: 60
Year Founded: 1991
Business Description:
Doll Retailer
S.I.C.: 5961; 5092
N.A.I.C.S.: 454113; 423920
Media: 4-8-10
Personnel:
Anthony Seutts *(Pres)*
Brands & Products:
BRINGING YOU TOMORROW'S TREASURES TODAY
PARADISE GALLERIES
PARADISE PROMISE
TIMELESS MOMENTS
TREASURY COLLECTION

THE PERFECT PARTS COMPANY
1 N Haven St
Baltimore, MD 21224-1618
Mailing Address:
PO Box 9935
Baltimore, MD 21224-0935
Tel.: (410) 327-3522
Fax: (410) 327-7443
E-mail: sales@perfectpartscompany.com
Web Site:
www.perfectpartscompany.com
E-Mail For Key Personnel:
Sales Director: sales@perfectpartscompany.com
Approx. Sls.: $3,000,000
Approx. Number Employees: 18
Year Founded: 1940
Business Description:
Science Items & Model Railroad Accessories, Hobby Items
S.I.C.: 5945; 3821
N.A.I.C.S.: 451120; 339111
Import Export
Media: 2-4-5-6-7-8-10-19
Distr.: Intl.; Natl.
Budget Set: Nov.
Personnel:
James R. Hudson *(Pres)*
Brands & Products:
THE PERFECT PARTS

PHANTOM ENTERTAINMENT INC.
33 Sherwood Rd
Ridgewood, NJ 07450
Tel.: (201) 560-2500
Fax: (612) 545-4928
E-mail: jlandino@phantom.net
Web Site: www.phantom.net
Sales Range: Less than $1 Million
Approx. Number Employees: 3
Business Description:
Video Game Console Developer
S.I.C.: 7999
N.A.I.C.S.: 713990
Advertising Expenditures: $404,331
Personnel:
Jay Landino *(CEO)*
Brands & Products:
PHANTOM ENTERTAINMENT
PHANTOM LAPBOARD

PIONEER NATIONAL LATEX COMPANY
(Affil. of Continental American Corp.)
246 E 4th St
Ashland, OH 44805-2412
Tel.: (419) 289-3300
Fax: (419) 289-7118
Toll Free: (800) 537-6723
E-mail: masssales@natlatex.com
Web Site: www.natlatex.com
Approx. Number Employees: 100
Year Founded: 1939
Business Description:
Balloons, Play Balls, Punch Balls & Exercise & Therapy Balls Mfr
S.I.C.: 3069; 3944
N.A.I.C.S.: 326299; 339932
Advertising Expenditures: $3,500,000
Media: 2-4-5-7-10-13-19-20-21-26
Distr.: Natl.
Personnel:
Lisa Bennett *(Dir-Mktg)*
Brands & Products:
BALLOON MAGIC
FUNSATIONAL
GROOVY SOAKERS
JUST WRITE
PARTYMATE
PIONEER
QUALATEX
QUALATEX MASTERBOW
SPLASH BASEBALL
WATER GRENADE

PLAYMATES TOYS INC.
(Sub. of Playmates Holdings, Ltd.)
909 N Sepulveda Blvd Ste 800
El Segundo, CA 90245
Tel.: (310) 252-8005
E-mail: toys@playmatestoys.com
Web Site: www.playmatestoys.com
Sales Range: $150-199.9 Million
Approx. Number Employees: 53
Year Founded: 1982
Business Description:
Toys Developer, Marketer & Distr
S.I.C.: 5092
N.A.I.C.S.: 423920
Media: 3-15
Distr.: Natl.
Personnel:
Louis Novak *(Pres)*
Don Sutherland *(CFO & Sr VP)*
Gina Beebe *(Sr VP-Girls Mktg)*
Lori Farbanish-Rotter *(VP-Mktg-Girls Toys)*
Jill Will *(VP-Mktg-Boys Toys)*
Brands & Products:
BABY BRIGHT EYES
INTELLI-TRONIC
PRO-ZONE
Advertising Agency:
Coyne Public Relations
14 Walsh Dr 2nd Fl
Parsippany, NJ 07054
Tel.: (973) 316-1665
Fax: (973) 316-6568
Agency of Record
Hearts for Hearts Girls Brands
Teenage Mutant Ninja Turtles

POKERTEK, INC.
1150 Crews Rd Ste F
Matthews, NC 28105
Tel.: (704) 849-0860
Toll Free: (800) 785-0284
E-mail: info@pokertek.com
Web Site: www.pokertek.com
Approx. Rev.: $5,898,907
Approx. Number Employees: 32
Business Description:
Electronic Poker Tables & Related Software Developer & Marketer
S.I.C.: 7372; 5084; 7999
N.A.I.C.S.: 511210; 423830; 713290
Advertising Expenditures: $2,000
Media: 2-10-13
Personnel:
Gehrig H. White *(Co-Founder)*
Joseph J. Lahti *(Chm)*
James T. Crawford, III *(Pres)*
Mark D. Roberson *(CEO, CFO & Treas)*
Raul Bouchot *(Dir-Sls)*
Brands & Products:
HEADS-UP CHALLENGE
POKERPRO
POKERTEK

POOF-SLINKY INC.
45400 Helm St
Plymouth, MI 48170-6021
Tel.: (734) 454-9552
Fax: (734) 454-9540
E-mail: poof-slinky@poof-slinky.com
Web Site: www.poof-slinky.com
E-Mail For Key Personnel:
Sales Director: sales@poof-slinky.com
Approx. Number Employees: 50
Business Description:
Foam Toys Supplier & Mfr
S.I.C.: 3944
N.A.I.C.S.: 339932
Media: 4-13-15
Personnel:
Douglas Ferner *(COO & Exec VP)*
Brands & Products:
BUKI
CADACO
DEAL
IDEAL
MINI BASKETBALL
POOF
POOF-SLINKY
PUNY PLANE AIRCRAFT CARRIER
RAMROCKET
RX FIRE LITE UP FOOTBALL
SLINKY
SLINKY SCIENCE & MORE

PRESSMAN TOY CORPORATION
7 W 18th St
New York, NY 10010-3302
Tel.: (212) 675-7910
Fax: (212) 645-8512
E-mail: custserv@pressman-toy.com
Web Site: www.pressmantoy.com
E-Mail For Key Personnel:
Sales Director: sales@pressman-toy.com
Sales Range: $10-24.9 Million
Approx. Number Employees: 300
Year Founded: 1922
Business Description:
Mfr. of Toys & Games
S.I.C.: 5092
N.A.I.C.S.: 423920
Import Export
Advertising Expenditures: $500,000
Cable T.V.: $500,000
Distr.: Natl.
Budget Set: Apr.

Key to Media (For complete agency information see *The Advertising Red Books-Agencies* edition):
1. Bus. Publs. 2. Cable T.V. 3. Catalogs & Directories. 4. Co-op Adv. 5. Consumer Mags. 6. D.M. to Bus. Estab.7. D.M. to Consumers 8. Daily Newsp. 9. Exhibits/Trade Shows 10. Foreign 11. Infomercial 12. Internet Adv.13. Multimedia 14. Network Radio 15. Network T.V. 16. Newsp. Distr. Mags. 17. Other 18. Outdoor (Posters, Transit) 19. Point of Purchase20. Premiums, Novelties 21. Product Samples 22. Special Events Mktg. 23. Spot Radio 24. Spot T.V. 25. Weekly Newsp. 26. Yellow Page Adv.

Pressman Toy Corporation — (Continued)

Personnel:
James R. Pressman *(CEO)*

Brands & Products:
HYDROSTRIKE
JUMPIN' MONKEYS
LET'S GO FISHING
MASTERMIND
MILLIONAIRE
OTHELLO
PRESSMAN
PRESSMANTOY
RUMMIKUB
'SMATH
THIN ICE
THINK GAMES
TILT N' TUMBLE
TOPPLE
TRI OMINOS
WEAPONS & WARRIORS

PRIDE PRODUCTS, INC.

5 Slater Dr
Elizabeth, NJ 07206
Tel.: (908) 353-6800
Fax: (908) 353-6974
E-mail: info@prideprod.com
Web Site: www.prideprod.com
Approx. Number Employees: 75
Year Founded: 1982
Business Description:
Household Appliances & Toys Mfr
S.I.C.: 7389
N.A.I.C.S.: 561910
Advertising Expenditures: $200,000
Media: 2-4-10-17-19
Distr.: Natl.
Personnel:
William Yuan *(Chm)*
Brands & Products:
PRIDE PRODUCTS

PRINCESS SOFT TOYS, INC.

7664 W 78th St
Minneapolis, MN 55439-2518
Tel.: (952) 829-7751
Fax: (952) 829-5596
Toll Free: (800) 252-7638
E-mail: princess@princesstoys.com
Web Site: www.princesstoys.com
Sales Range: $10-24.9 Million
Approx. Number Employees: 25
Year Founded: 1965
Business Description:
Stuffed Animals, Puppets & Bean Bags Mfr & Distr
S.I.C.: 3942
N.A.I.C.S.: 339931
Import Export
Media: 2
Personnel:
Sandra Calkins *(Pres & CEO)*
Sarah Powers *(Coord-Mktg & PR)*
Brands & Products:
ABUJA GORILLA
AFTON
ALASKA POLAR BEAR
AMORE
ANCHOR
ANGEL DEVON
ANGELS
ANNAPOLIS CRAB
AUGUSTA LOBSTER
BABY'S BEAR
BAR MITZVAH BEAR
BARK DOG
BATON ROUGE KITTY
BEAR GIFT HUGGER
BEARCROW
BEIJING PANDA
BIG AFTON
BIG BANANA SWIRL
BIG MACAROON
BLOOMER BEAR BROWN
BLUE MAC
BLUEBERRY SWIRL
BOISE BLACK BEAR
BOSTON LADYBUG
BUNNY HOPS
CACKLE BEAR
CARL MOOSE
CARLSBAD DOG
CARLSGOOD BEAR
CATADOODLE
CHARLIE COW
CHEYENNE MOOSE
COLUMBIA DOLPHIN
COLUMBO PEACOCK
COLUMBUS CARDINAL
CONCORD BAT
COWADOODLE
DASH DOLPHIN
DELHI TIGER
DENVER BUFFALO
DEREK
DES MOINES PIG
DIAMOND
DOUGIE DUCK
DOVER DUCK
DUBLIN HEDGEHOG
EVERYWHERE TEDDY BEAR
FARM
FLAG DEREK
FRANKFORT HORSE
FRANKIE FROG
FROGANOODLE
HARBOR LOBSTER
HARMONY
HARRISBURG OWL
HARTFORD PRAYING MANTIS
HENRY
HORSEADOODLE
HOWL WOLF
HUGS AND KISSES PINK
HUMMINGBIRD
I AM LOVED
IN THE MOOED
JACK-O-BEAR
JACKSON TEDDY BEAR
JEFFERSON DOG
JOSHUA BUNNY
KINGSTON PARROT
LANSING WOLF
LARGE ITEMS
LEAP FROG
LIL HONEY
LIL HUGS
LIL HUGS PINK ANGEL
LIL PEEF
LIL WILLOUGHBY
LOME LION
LONDON BULLDOG
LONGFELLOW CAT
LONGFELLOW DOG
LONGFELLOW EMMYPOO
LONGFELLOW JR. BEAR
LONGFELLOWS
MADISON COW
MASKED HALLOWEEN BEAR
MAXWELL SCOTTIE
MEADOW MEDLEYS
MELBOURNE KANGAROO
MICHAEL ANGELO
MIDNIGHT CAT
MISTY ANGEL
MONTEVIDEO MONKEY
MONTGOMERY TURKEY
MONTY MOOSE
MOO COW
NASHVILLE RACCOON
NEIGH PONY
NEW YORK BLUEBIRD
NORTHWOODS MOOSE
OINK PIG
PAPEETE ANGEL FISH
PATRIOTIC
PAULIE PIG
PAULY LOON
PEEF
PENGUIN
PHOENIX FROG
POCKET PEEF
POKEY TURTLE
POUND GORILLA
PRINCESS SOFT TOYS
PROVIDENCE ROOSTER
PUMPKIN AND BOW
PUPADOODLE
PUPPY GIFT HUGGER
RACK MOOSE
RAINBOW BUNNY
RICHMOND FOX
RIO FLAMINGO
ROLLIE RABBIT
ROUNDFELLOW MALLARD
SACRAMENTO SHARK
SAFARI
SALTY BEE
SALUTE
SANTIAGO PENGUIN
SCALES ALLIGATOR
SEA CREATURES
SLOAN
SPOOKERS
SPRINGFIELD BUTTERFLY
STAR OF DAVID BEAR
STRAWBERRY SWIRL
SUPER MACAROON
TALLAHASSEE ALLIGATOR
TIMBER SLIM MOOSE
TOOTH FAIRY BEAR
TOPEKA TURTLE
TRENTON MALLARD
TROPICAL
TROTTER TURKEY
TUCKER
VALENTINE BEAR
VICTORIA PTERANODON
WASHINGTON EAGLE
WASHINGTON WHALE
WAVE WHALE
WEE WHIMSIE
WEEBEANS
WHISPER
WILDIE WOLF
WILDLIFE
WILLOUGHBY
ZOO

PRO-LINE, INC.

201 W Lincoln St
Banning, CA 92220-4933
Tel.: (951) 849-9781
Fax: (951) 922-9311
E-mail: customerservices@pro-lineracing.com
Web Site: www.pro-lineracing.com
Approx. Number Employees: 45
Year Founded: 1982
Business Description:
Mfr of Replacement Parts for Radio Controlled Cars
S.I.C.: 3944
N.A.I.C.S.: 339932
Export
Advertising Expenditures: $300,000
Media: 4-6-8-10-13-20
Distr.: Intl.; Natl.
Budget Set: Oct.
Personnel:
Todd Mattson *(Pres)*
Brands & Products:
BADLANDS
BOW-TIE
CALIBER
CRIME FIGHTER
CROWD PLEAZER
HOLE SHOT
KNUCKLES
MOAB
POWERSTROKE
PRO-LINE
PROTOFORM
RACING TO BRING YOU THE BEST
REVOLVER
VELOCITY

PROFESSIONAL FITNESS CONCEPTS, INC.

521 Vera Ct
Joliet, IL 60436-1895
Tel.: (815) 741-5328
Fax: (815) 741-5352
E-mail: mlyons@pfc-fitness.com
Web Site: www.pfc-fitness.com
Approx. Rev.: $3,700,000
Approx. Number Employees: 10
Year Founded: 2001
Business Description:
Whol Sporting/Recreational Goods
S.I.C.: 5091
N.A.I.C.S.: 423910
Personnel:
Michael Lyons *(Pres)*
Advertising Agency:
JB Chicago
435 N LaSalle Ste 201
Chicago, IL 60654
Tel.: (312) 442-7223
Fax: (312) 264-0138

PUMPKIN MASTERS LLC

(Div. of Rauch Industries, Inc.)
PO Box 609
Gastonia, NC 28053
Tel.: (704) 867-5333
E-mail: info@pumpkinmasters.com
Web Site: www.pumpkinmasters.com
Sales Range: $10-24.9 Million
Business Description:
Creators & Mfr of Pumpkin Carving Kits & Decorative Items
S.I.C.: 5092
N.A.I.C.S.: 423920
Export
Media: 4-8-10-13
Brands & Products:
GLOW IN THE DARK CHALK
JUMBO PUMPKIN CANDLES
KID'S FUN HOUSE
KID'S MONSTER LIGHT
KID'S PUMPKIN HATCHERS
KID'S STICKY SQUISHY PUMPKIN PARTS
LIQUID LAMPS
PUMPKIN INSIDE A PUMPKIN
PUMPKIN MASTERS
PUMPKIN STROBE LIGHT
SAFE PUMPKIN LIGHT

Key to Media (For complete agency information see *The Advertising Red Books-Agencies* edition):
1. Bus. Publs. 2. Cable T.V. 3. Catalogs & Directories. 4. Co-op Adv. 5. Consumer Mags. 6. D.M. to Bus. Estab.7. D.M. to Consumers
8. Daily Newsp. 9. Exhibits/Trade Shows 10. Foreign 11. Infomercial 12. Internet Adv.13. Multimedia 14. Network Radio
15. Network T.V. 16. Newsp. Distr. Mags. 17. Other 18. Outdoor (Posters, Transit) 19. Point of Purchase20. Premiums, Novelties
21. Product Samples 22. Special Events Mktg. 23. Spot Radio 24. Spot T.V. 25. Weekly Newsp. 26. Yellow Page Adv.

SAFE PUMPKIN LIGHT W/COLOR MAGIC
SENSATIONAL SHADOWS
ULTIMATE STROBE LIGHT
XTREME CARVING

RADIO FLYER INC.

6515 W Grand Ave
Chicago, IL 60707
Tel.: (773) 637-7100
Fax: (773) 637-8874
E-mail: info@radioflyer.com
Web Site: www.radioflyer.com
Approx. Number Employees: 100
Year Founded: 1917
Business Description:
Toys & Sporting Goods Mfr
S.I.C.: 3944; 3751
N.A.I.C.S.: 339932; 336991
Media: 2-4-5-6-7
Distr.: Intl.; Natl.
Budget Set: Dec.
Personnel:
Mario Pasin *(Chm)*
Robert Pasin *(CEO)*
Paul Pasin *(CFO & Exec VP)*
Amy Bastuga *(Dir-HR)*
Brands & Products:
BIG FLYER
BIG RED CLASSIC ATW
CLASSIC LIGHTS & SOUNDS TRIKE
CLASSY TINY TRIKE
FOLD 2 GO
GROW 'N GO BIKE
THE INCHWORM
LITTLE RED ROASTER
LITTLE RED SCOOTER
MY 1 SCOOTER
PATHFINDER WAGON
RADIO FLYER
RETRO ROCKER
SCOOT-ABOUT
STEER & STROLL
STEER & STROLL COUPE
TOWN & COUNTRY WAGON
TRAV-LER
TURBO TURTLE
ULTIMATE FAMILY WAGON
VOYAGER
Advertising Agency:
McKinney
(d/b/a McKinney Silver)
318 Blackwell St
Durham, NC 27701
Tel.: (919) 313-0802
Fax: (919) 313-0805
Agency of Record
Branding Campaign
Online Advertising
Point of Sale Collateral
Print
Social Media

RC2 CORPORATION

1111 W 22nd St Ste 320
Oak Brook, IL 60523
Tel.: (630) 573-7200
Fax: (630) 573-7575
E-mail: investor@rc2corp.com
Web Site: www.rc2corp.com
Approx. Sls.: $427,343,000
Approx. Number Employees: 780
Business Description:
Collectibles, Juvenile Toys & Infant Products Designer, Producer & Marketer
S.I.C.: 5945; 3944; 4412; 5091
N.A.I.C.S.: 451120; 339932; 423910; 483111
Advertising Expenditures: $13,200,000
Media: 3-5-6-19
Personnel:
Robert E. Dods *(Chm)*
Peter J. Henseler *(Pres)*
Curtis W. Stoelting *(CEO)*
Peter Nicholson *(CFO)*
Gregory J. Kilrea *(COO)*
Jamie A. Kieffer *(CMO & Sr VP-Mktg)*
Brands & Products:
AMERICAN CHOPPER
AMERICAN MUSCLE
AMT
BOB THE BUILDER
ERTL
THE FIRST YEARS
JOHN DEERE
JOHNNY LIGHTINING
JOYRIDE
JOYRIDE STUDIOS
LAMAZE
LEARNING CURVE
MEMORY LANE
POLAR LIGHTS
PRESS PASS
RC2
THOMAS AND FRIENDS
WILLIAM BRITAIN
Advertising Agency:
Kidvertisers
1133 Broadway Ste 1000
New York, NY 10010
Tel.: (212) 966-2345
Fax: (212) 966-2770

REEVES INTERNATIONAL, INC.

14 Indus Rd
Pequannock, NJ 07440-1920
Tel.: (973) 694-5006
Fax: (973) 694-5213
Web Site: www.breyerhorses.com
Approx. Number Employees: 87
Year Founded: 1947
Business Description:
Importer of Toys
S.I.C.: 3944; 5092
N.A.I.C.S.: 339932; 423920
Advertising Expenditures: $500,000
Media: 2-4-5-6-7-8-10-19
Distr.: Natl.
Budget Set: Sept.
Personnel:
Anthony Fleischmann *(Pres)*
Art Minnocci *(CFO)*
Stephanie Macejko *(VP-Mktg & Product Dev)*
Brands & Products:
THE BIG DIG
BOSUN
BREYER
CLASSICS
JAH MAGAZINE
MINI WHINNIES
PADDOCK PALS
PONY GALS
STABLEMATES
TRADITIONAL
WIND DANCERS

RELIABLE TOY CORPORATION

(Sub. of Allied Plastic Skylight)
1655 DuPont Street
Toronto, ON M6P 3T1, Canada
Tel.: (416) 762-1111
Fax: (416) 762-0889
E-mail: info@viceroyrubber.com
Web Site: www.reliabletoy.com
Approx. Number Employees: 50
Year Founded: 1920
Business Description:
Toys Mfr
S.I.C.: 3944
N.A.I.C.S.: 339932
Media: 2-4-7-10-13-17-18-26
Distr.: Natl.
Budget Set: Oct. -Dec.
Personnel:
Tod Bruhm *(Gen Mgr & Adv Mgr)*
Brands & Products:
RELIABLE

REVELL-MONOGRAM, LLC

1850 Howard St Unit A
Elk Grove Village, IL 60007
Tel.: (847) 758-3200
Fax: (847) 758-3201
Toll Free: (800) 833-3570
E-mail: requests@revell-monogram.com
Web Site: www.revell-monogram.com
Sales Range: $75-99.9 Million
Approx. Number Employees: 200
Year Founded: 1945
Business Description:
Mfr. of Model Kits & Die-Cast Collectibles
S.I.C.: 3944
N.A.I.C.S.: 339932
Import Export
Media: 1-2-4-5-6-7-10-11-13-19
Distr.: Intl.; Natl.
Budget Set: Sept. -Oct.
Personnel:
Jim Foster *(Pres)*
Brands & Products:
COLLECTIBLE CHEVY
COMPLETE KITS
EVERYTHING'S INCLUDED
HOT TRUCKIN'
MONOGRAM
MONOGRAM CLASSICS
PROFINISH
PROMODELER
RAT RODS
REVELL
REVELL METAL BODY
SNAP TITE
THUNDER SQUADRON
WHEELS OF FIRE

ROLLER DERBY SKATE CORP.

311 W Edwards St
Litchfield, IL 62056
Mailing Address:
PO Box 930
Litchfield, IL 62056-0930
Tel.: (217) 324-3961
Fax: (217) 324-2213
E-mail: info@rollerderby.com
Web Site: www.rollerderby.com
Approx. Number Employees: 100
Year Founded: 1939
Business Description:
Roller Skates, Ice Skates & Skateboards; Protective Equipment; Wheels & Bearings Mfr
S.I.C.: 5091; 3949
N.A.I.C.S.: 423910; 339920
Import Export
Media: 2-4-19
Distr.: Natl.
Personnel:
Edwin C. Seltzer *(Pres)*
David N. Kennedy *(CFO & VP)*
Walter Frazier *(VP-Mktg)*
Brands & Products:
ATA 990
ATS
BIG SPIN
CITY LIGHTS
CLASSIC 300
COYOTE
FIRE STAR
FORMULA Z 7
FORMULA Z 90
GS 3000
HYBRID G800
HYBRID G900
LABEDA
LASER 7.9 MX
PROLINE 900
RD ROLLER DERBY
REVERT
ROLLER DERBY
ROLLER STAR 350
ROLLER STAR 550
RTS 400
SPARTAN Z
STINGRAY
TRAC STAR
TRACER
V500
VENOM GT
VIPER M1
WEB STINGER
WORKS Z 4

SAFARI LTD.

1400 NW 159th St
Miami, FL 33169
Tel.: (305) 621-1000
Fax: (800) 598-9866
Toll Free: (800) 554-5414
E-mail: info@safariltd.com
Web Site: www.safariltd.com
Approx. Number Employees: 70
Year Founded: 1979
Business Description:
Toy Distr.
S.I.C.: 3751; 3944
N.A.I.C.S.: 336991; 339932
Export
Media: 4-7-8-10-11-13
Personnel:
Ramona Pariente *(Pres)*

SASSY, INC.

(Sub. of Kid Brands, Inc.)
2305 Breton Indus Pk Dr SE
Grand Rapids, MI 49508
Tel.: (616) 243-0767
Fax: (616) 243-1042
Web Site: www.sassybaby.com
Approx. Sls.: $22,000,000
Approx. Number Employees: 110
Business Description:
Toddler Toys & Products Mfr
S.I.C.: 3944
N.A.I.C.S.: 339932
Personnel:
Dean F. Robinson *(Pres)*
Richard F. Schaub *(Pres-LaJobi Nursery Furniture Bus)*
Brands & Products:
SASSY
Advertising Agency:
Crossbow Group, LLC
136 Main St
Westport, CT 06880
Tel.: (203) 222-2244
Fax: (203) 226-7838

Key to Media (For complete agency information see *The Advertising Red Books-Agencies* edition):
1. Bus. Publs. 2. Cable T.V. 3. Catalogs & Directories. 4. Co-op Adv. 5. Consumer Mags. 6. D.M. to Bus. Estab.7. D.M. to Consumers 8. Daily Newsp. 9. Exhibits/Trade Shows 10. Foreign 11. Infomercial 12. Internet Adv.13. Multimedia 14. Network Radio 15. Network T.V. 16. Newsp. Distr. Mags. 17. Other 18. Outdoor (Posters, Transit) 19. Point of Purchase20. Premiums, Novelties 21. Product Samples 22. Special Events Mktg. 23. Spot Radio 24. Spot T.V. 25. Weekly Newsp. 26. Yellow Page Adv.

Sassy, Inc. — (Continued)

Social Media & Direct Agency of Record

SEGA OF AMERICA INC.
(Sub. of Sega Corporation)
350 Rhode Island St
San Francisco, CA 94103
Tel.: (415) 701-6000
Fax: (415) 701-6011
E-mail: privacy@sega.com
Web Site: www.sega.com
Sales Range: $125-149.9 Million
Approx. Number Employees: 100

Business Description:
Video Games Mfr & Distr
S.I.C.: 5045; 5092
N.A.I.C.S.: 423430; 423920
Media: 3-4-5-6-7-8-10-15-18-19-23-24
Distr.: Intl.; Natl.

Personnel:
Rob Lightner *(Sr VP-Publishing & Content)*
Rick Naylor *(Dir-Mktg)*

Advertising Agencies:
Hauser Advertising Inc.
309 Bellino Dr
Pacific Palisades, CA 90272
Tel.: (310) 459-5911
Fax: (310) 459-5919

JVST
835 Terry Fancois Blvd 2nd Fl
San Francisco, CA 94158
Tel.: (415) 358-1900
Fax: (415) 358-1901

SHUFFLE MASTER, INC.
1106 Palms Airport Dr
Las Vegas, NV 89119-3730
Tel.: (702) 897-7150
Fax: (702) 897-2284
E-mail: shfl@shufflemaster.com
Web Site: www.shufflemaster.com
Approx. Rev.: $201,302,000
Approx. Number Employees: 705
Year Founded: 1983

Business Description:
Automatic Shuffling Equipment & Gaming Products Developer, Mfr & Marketer
S.I.C.: 3999; 3589
N.A.I.C.S.: 339999; 333319
Advertising Expenditures: $2,207,000
Media: 4-7-10-13

Personnel:
Garry W. Saunders *(Chm & Mng Dir)*
Michael Gavin Isaacs *(CEO)*
Linster W. Fox *(CFO, Exec VP & Corp Sec)*
David Lopez *(COO & Exec VP)*
Louis Castle *(Chief Strategy Officer)*
Roger Snow *(Exec VP, Chm-Corp Product Group)*
Katie Lever *(Gen Counsel & Exec VP)*
Julia Boguslawski *(VP-IR & Corp Comm)*
Georg Fekete *(Product Dir-Live Gaming)*
Wolfgang Scheidl *(Product Dir-Electronic Gaming)*
Donald Bauer *(Dir-Sls)*
Alexander Grohs *(Dir-Sls & Mktg)*
Dawn Hinman *(Asst Gen Counsel)*

Brands & Products:
ACE
BAD BEAT TEXAS HOLD'EM
BIG RAISE HOLD 'EM
BLACKJACK PRESS
BLOODHOUND
CARIBBEAN STUD
CASINO WAR
CHIPPER C
CRAZY 4 POKER
DAKOTA STUD
DECK MATE
DRAGON BONUS
EASY CHIPPER
EASY CHIPPER C
FORTUNE BLACKJACK
FORTUNE PAI GOW POKER
FOUR CARD POKER
FOUR CARD POKER & DESIGN
HI-LO STUD POKER
HIT & RUN
I-DEAL
I-SCORE
I-SHOE
I-SHOE AUTO
I-TABLE
INTELLIGGENT TABLE SYSTEM
IS-B1
ISHOE
ITABLE
JACK MAGIC
JACKPOT BACCARAT
JACKPOT PAI GOW POKER
KING
THE KING
LET IT RIDE
LET IT RIDE BONUS
LET IT RIDE THE TOURNAMENT
LIGHTNING POKER
MD1
MD2
MD2 WORKSTATION
MISSISSIPPI STUD
MULTISHIFT DROP BOX
ONE2SIX
PROGRESSIVE JACKPOT PAI GOW POKER
RAPID TABLE GAMES
ROLL YOUR OWN BLACKJACK
ROYAL MATCH
ROYAL MATCH 21
SHARP SHOOTER
SHUFFLE MASTER
STREAK SHOOTER
TABLE ID
TABLE MASTER
TEXAS HOLD'EM BONUS
THREE CARD POKER
ULTIMATE TEXAS HOLD'EM
VEGAS STAR

SMALL WORLD TOYS
(Sub. of Rivenrock Capital LLC)
1451 W Knox St
Torrance, CA 90745
Tel.: (310) 645-9680
Fax: (310) 410-9606
Toll Free: (866) 310-1717
E-mail: info@smallworldtoys.com
Web Site: www.smallworldtoys.com
Approx. Rev.: $28,330,000
Approx. Number Employees: 60
Year Founded: 1962

Business Description:
Specialty Toys
S.I.C.: 5092
N.A.I.C.S.: 423920
Advertising Expenditures: $137,000
Media: 2-6-7-8-10-13-19-20-21-22-23-24

Personnel:
David Adams *(CFO)*
John Matise *(COO)*

Brands & Products:
BANK ON IT
COMMUNITY VEHICLES
FAVORITE TOYS
FIRST FRIENDS CAROUSEL
GERTIE
GIRAFFE GERTIE
HIGH FIVE
IQ BABY
IQ PRESCHOOL
LITTLE DRIVER
LITTLE FRIENDS ROCKER
LIVING
LOOPIES LARGE
LOOPIES MEDIUM
LOOPIES SMALL
MAJESTIC CASTLE & MIGHTY KNIGHTS
MY LIFE & TIMES
MY-OH-MY OCTOPI
NEUROSMITH
POUND-A-BALL
PUZZIBILITIES
PUZZLE PARADE
RIP ROLLING FUN
ROLLER BALL
RYANS ROOM
SAFARI ANIMALS
SCHOOL BUS
SNAPSHOT PUZZLE
SOUNDS ON THE FARM
SOUNDS ON THE GO
SPINNING FIRST FRIENDS
TIGER GERTIE
VROOM VROOM VEHICLES
WHAT AM I
ZEBRA GERTIE

Advertising Agency:
Crier Communications
9507 Santa Monica Blvd Ste 300
Beverly Hills, CA 90210
Tel.: (310) 274-1072
Fax: (310) 274-0611

SONY COMPUTER ENTERTAINMENT OF AMERICA INC.
(Div. of Sony Electronics, Inc.)
919 E Hillsdale Blvd
Foster City, CA 94404-4247
Tel.: (650) 655-8000
Fax: (650) 655-8001
Web Site: www.us.playstation.com
Approx. Number Employees: 1,000

Business Description:
Electronic Games & Accessories Mfr
S.I.C.: 5092; 3944
N.A.I.C.S.: 423920; 339932
Media: 15-24

Personnel:
Jack Tretton *(Pres & CEO)*
Shuhei Yoshida *(Pres-Studios-Worldwide)*
Timothy Bender *(Sr VP-Sls)*
Peter Dille *(Sr VP-Mktg & PlayStation Network)*
Philip Rosenberg *(Sr VP)*
Scott A. Steinberg *(VP-Product Mktg)*
Susan Nourai *(Dir-Mktg)*
John Koller *(Mgr-Mktg)*

Brands & Products:
PLAYSTATION

Advertising Agencies:
Deutsch LA
5454 Beethoven St
Los Angeles, CA 90066-7017
Tel.: (310) 862-3000
Fax: (310) 862-3100
PlayStation

Marketing Werks, Inc.
130 E Randolph St Ste 2400
Chicago, IL 60601
Tel.: (312) 228-0800
Fax: (312) 228-0801
Toll Free: (800) 694WERK

SOUTHPEAK INTERACTIVE CORPORATION
2900 Polo Pkwy
Midlothian, VA 23113
Tel.: (804) 378-5100
Web Site: www.southpeakgames.com
Approx. Rev.: $40,299,139
Approx. Number Employees: 53
Year Founded: 2005

Business Description:
Interactive Entertainment Software Developer, Publisher & Marketer
S.I.C.: 7372
N.A.I.C.S.: 511210
Advertising Expenditures: $6,327,304
Media: 1-3-5-6-8-10-13-17-18-19-23-24

Personnel:
Terry M. Phillips *(Chm)*
Melanie Mroz *(Pres & CEO)*

SPIN MASTER LTD.
450 Front St W
Toronto, ON M5V 1B6, Canada
Tel.: (416) 364-6002
Fax: (416) 364-8005
E-mail: pr@spinmaster.com
Web Site: www.spinmaster.com
Sales Range: $400-449.9 Million
Approx. Number Employees: 450
Year Founded: 1994

Business Description:
Toys & Entertainment Mfr & Distr
S.I.C.: 5092
N.A.I.C.S.: 423920
Media: 13-15-21-22-24

Personnel:
Ronnen Harary *(Chm & CEO)*
Anton Rabie *(Pres & CEO)*
Gaston A. Tano *(CFO & Exec VP)*
Iain Kennedy *(COO)*
Chris Beardall *(Exec VP-Sls)*
Mark Sullivan *(Exec VP-Mktg & Design)*
Ben Varadi *(Exec VP)*
Harold Chizick *(VP-Comm & Promos-Global)*
Donna MacNeil *(Sr Dir-Retail Mktg, Events & Promos)*
Dale Gago *(Coord-PR)*

Brands & Products:
AIR HOGS
AQUA DOODLE
BAKUGAN
BATTLEGROUND
BELLA DANCERELLA
BOUNCE ROUND
BUBBLE MANIA
BUGVILLE
DROP POPZ
FLICK TRIX
FOGO SPORTS
FOOD ACTIVITIES

Key to Media (For complete agency information see *The Advertising Red Books-Agencies* edition):
1. Bus. Publs. 2. Cable T.V. 3. Catalogs & Directories. 4. Co-op Adv. 5. Consumer Mags. 6. D.M. to Bus. Estab.7. D.M. to Consumers
8. Daily Newsp. 9. Exhibits/Trade Shows 10. Foreign 11. Infomercial 12. Internet Adv.13. Multimedia 14. Network Radio
15. Network T.V. 16. Newsp. Distr. Mags. 17. Other 18. Outdoor (Posters, Transit) 19. Point of Purchase20. Premiums, Novelties
21. Product Samples 22. Special Events Mktg. 23. Spot Radio 24. Spot T.V. 25. Weekly Newsp. 26. Yellow Page Adv.

FUR BURRIES
GIRL CRUSH
I-TATOO
KID KLEEN
MICRO TERRAIN TITANS
MOON SAND
PIXOS
SPIN MASTER
STORM HAWKS
SWITCHPLAY
SWYPEOUT
TECH DECK
TINI PUPPINI
YO GABBA GABBA

SPORTS LINE DISTRIBUTORS, INC.

1600 Leider Ln
Buffalo Grove, IL 60089
Tel.: (847) 656-0300
Fax: (847) 613-1017
Toll Free: (800) 833-2386
Web Site: www.sportslined.com
Approx. Number Employees: 30
Business Description:
Sports Cards, Gaming Cards, Bobble Heads, Action Figures, Die-Cast Vehicles & Licensed Sports Products
S.I.C.: 3751; 3363; 3942; 3944; 5941; 5945
N.A.I.C.S.: 336991; 331521; 339931; 339932; 451110; 451120
Media: 4-13
Personnel:
Marty Fairerstain *(Founder, Co-Owner & Shareholder)*
Bill Gausselin *(Pres)*
Rob Corona *(Mgr)*

SRAM CORPORATION

1333 N Kingsbury St No 4
Chicago, IL 60622-2641
Tel.: (312) 664-8800
Fax: (312) 664-8826
E-mail: ramusa@ram.com
Web Site: www.sram.com
Sales Range: $450-499.9 Million
Approx. Number Employees: 1,787
Year Founded: 1987
Business Description:
Mfr of Bicycle Gear Mechanisms
S.I.C.: 3751; 5941
N.A.I.C.S.: 336991; 451110
Media: 22
Personnel:
Stanley R. Day, Jr. *(Pres)*
F. K. Day *(Exec VP)*
Mike Herr *(VP-Fin)*
Brands & Products:
ATTACK
BOXXER
BRAKECRAWLER
CENTERA
CHAIN
DUALDRIVE
ESP
GRIP SHIFT
I-BRAKE
MRX
NIGHTCRAWLER
POWERCHAIN
POWERGLIDE
POWERLINK
REBA
ROCKET
SPARC
SRAM
SRS
TWINDRIVE

STRAT-O-MATIC GAME CO., INC.

46 Railroad Ave
Glen Head, NY 11545
Tel.: (516) 671-6566
Toll Free: (800) 645-3455
E-mail: corporateinfo@strat-o-matic.com
Web Site: www.strat-o-matic.com
Approx. Rev.: $1,000,000
Approx. Number Employees: 10
Year Founded: 1962
Business Description:
Sports Simulation Games Producer
S.I.C.: 5961; 5945
N.A.I.C.S.: 454113; 451120
Personnel:
Harold Richman *(Pres)*
Advertising Agency:
Drotman Communications
368 Veterans Memorial Hwy Ste 8
Commack, NY 11725
Tel.: (631) 462-1198
Fax: (631) 462-2257

STUFFED ANIMAL HOUSE LTD.

27527 51st A Ave
Langley, BC Canada
Tel.: (604) 857-0086
Fax: (604) 857-5036
Fax: (888) 222-8993
Toll Free: (800) 387-5874
E-mail: info@stuffedanimalhouse.com
Web Site:
www.stuffedanimalhouse.com
Approx. Number Employees: 30
Year Founded: 1984
Business Description:
Stuffed Animals Mfr & Distr
S.I.C.: 3942
N.A.I.C.S.: 339931
Media: 4-10-13-26
Personnel:
Russ Iwanson *(Pres)*
Brands & Products:
THE HOUSE OF QUALITY
STUFFED ANIMAL HOUSE

SWINGSET & TOY WAREHOUSE INC.

318 Rte 202
Flemington, NJ 08822-1634
Tel.: (908) 237-0899
Fax: (908) 788-4299
Toll Free: (800) 794-6473
E-mail: info@swingsetwarehouse.com
Web Site:
www.swingsetwarehouse.com
Approx. Sls.: $1,000,000
Approx. Number Employees: 14
Year Founded: 1984
Business Description:
Playground Sets Retailer
S.I.C.: 5945; 5941
N.A.I.C.S.: 451120; 451110
Media: 5-8
Personnel:
Peter Glynos *(Pres)*
Brands & Products:
ALLEYOOP DOUBLEBOUNCE
POWER BOUNCE
STAGEDBOUNCE
SWINGSET & TOY WAREHOUSE
VARIABLE BOUNCE

THE TESTOR CORPORATION

(Sub. of RPM Consumer Holding Co.)
440 Blackhawk Ave
Rockford, IL 61104
Tel.: (815) 962-6654
Fax: (815) 962-7401
Toll Free: (800) 962-6654
E-mail: testors@testors.com
Web Site: www.testors.com
Sales Range: $100-124.9 Million
Approx. Number Employees: 260
Year Founded: 1928
Business Description:
Model Paints, Adhesives, Tools & Plastic Kits Mfr
S.I.C.: 2851; 2891
N.A.I.C.S.: 325510; 325520
Advertising Expenditures: $500,000
Media: 1-4-5-6-8-9-10-12-13-19-21
Distr.: Intl.; Natl.
Budget Set: Oct.
Personnel:
Tracy Tryboski *(Brand Mgr)*
Scott Anderson *(Mgr-Ops)*
Brands & Products:
AZTEK
FLOQUIL
MODEL MASTER
MODEL MASTER FS
PACTRA
POLLY SEALE
TESTOR

THINKWAY TOYS

(Div. of Thinkway Trading Corporation)
8885 Woodbine Ave
Markham, ON L3R 5G1, Canada
Tel.: (905) 470-8883
Fax: (905) 470-8308
Toll Free: (800) 535-5754
E-mail: custserv@thinkwaytoys.com
Web Site: www.thinkwaytoys.com
Approx. Number Employees: 16
Business Description:
Toys Mfr & Distr
S.I.C.: 5945; 3751; 3942; 3944
N.A.I.C.S.: 451120; 336991; 339931; 339932
Media: 10-11-13
Personnel:
Albert Chan *(CEO)*
John Barton *(Sr VP)*

THQ INC.

29903 Agoura Rd
Agoura Hills, CA 91301-2513
Mailing Address:
5016 N Pkwy Ste 100
Calabasas, CA 91302
Tel.: (818) 871-5000
Fax: (818) 871-7400
E-mail: thq@thq.com
Web Site: www.thq.com
E-Mail For Key Personnel:
Public Relations: lpieri@thq.com
Approx. Sls.: $665,258,000
Approx. Number Employees: 1,750
Year Founded: 1990
Business Description:
Interactive Entertainment Software Developer, Publisher & Distr
S.I.C.: 7372
N.A.I.C.S.: 334611; 511210
Advertising Expenditures: $78,000,000
Media: 3-6-7-8-9-10-11-13-14-15-18-22-23-24-25
Personnel:
Brian J. Farrell *(Chm, Pres & CEO)*
Paul J. Pucino *(CFO & Exec VP)*
Teri J. Manby *(Chief Acctg Officer & VP)*
Edward L. Kaufman *(Sec & Exec VP-Bus & Legal Affairs)*
Danny Bilson *(Exec VP-Core Games)*
Ian Curran *(Exec VP-Global Publ)*
Martin J. Good *(Exec VP-Kids, Family, Casual Games & Global Online Svcs)*
Doug Clemmer *(Sr VP)*
Steve Dauterman *(Sr VP-Online)*
Angela Emery *(VP-Corp Comm)*
Colin Bell *(Gen Mgr-THQ Digital UK)*
David Schwartz *(Gen Mgr)*
Brands & Products:
50 CENT
AGE OF EMPIRES
ALL STAR CHEER SQUAD
AMERICAN GIRL
ARE YOU SMARTER THAN A 5TH GRADER?
AVATAR: THE BURNING EARTH
AVATAR: THE LAST AIRBENDER
BACK AT THE BARNYARD
BAJA: EDGE OF CONTROL
BARNYARD
BATTLE OF THE BANDS
BIG BEACH SPORTS
BRATZ
CARS
CARS RACE-O-RAMA
CHOP SUSHI!
COMPANY OF HEROES
COMPANY OF HEROES:TALES OF VALOR
CONAN
DARKSIDER
DE BLOB
DEADLY CREATURES
DESKTOP TOWER DEFENSE
DESTROY ALL HUMANS!
DESTROY ALL HUMANS! BIG WILLY UNLEASHED
DESTROY ALL HUMANS! PATH OF THE FURON
DRAKE & JOSH: TALENT SHOWDOWN
DRAWN TO LIFE
DREAM DAY
DROPCAST
ELEMENTS OF DESTRUCTION
FRONTLINES: FUEL OF WAR
GALLOP & RIDE!
HOMEFRONT
JUICED
MARVEL
MX UNLEASHED
MX VS. ATV ON THE EDGE
MX VS. ATV UNLEASHED
MX VS. ATV UNTAMED
THE OUTFIT
PASS THE PIGS
PAWS & CLAWS: PET RESORT
RATATOUILLE
RED FACTION
RED FACTION: GUERRILLA
SAINT ROW
SPRINT CARS ROAD TO KNOXVILLE
S.T.A.L.K.E.R. SHADOW OF CHERNOBYL
STUNTMAN: IGNITION
SUMMONER
SUPREME COMMANDER
THQ

Key to Media (For complete agency information see *The Advertising Red Books-Agencies* edition):
1. Bus. Publs. 2. Cable T.V. 3. Catalogs & Directories. 4. Co-op Adv. 5. Consumer Mags. 6. D.M. to Bus. Estab.7. D.M. to Consumers
8. Daily Newsp. 9. Exhibits/Trade Shows 10. Foreign 11. Infomercial 12. Internet Adv.13. Multimedia 14. Network Radio
15. Network T.V. 16. Newsp. Distr. Mags. 17. Other 18. Outdoor (Posters, Transit) 19. Point of Purchase20. Premiums, Novelties
21. Product Samples 22. Special Events Mktg. 23. Spot Radio 24. Spot T.V. 25. Weekly Newsp. 26. Yellow Page Adv.

THQ Inc. — (Continued)

TITAN QUEST
TITAN QUEST: IMMORTAL THORNE
UFC 2009 UNDISPUTED
UP
WALL-E
WARHAMMER 40,000: DAWN OF WAR - DARK CRUSADE
WARHAMMER 40,000: SPACE MARINES
WARHAMMER 40,000: SQUAD COMMAND
WORLD OF ZOO
WORMS OPEN WARFARE
WWE LEGENDS OF WRESTLEMANIA
WWE SMACKDOWN VS. RAW
ZOO TYCOON 2
ZOO TYCOON DS

Advertising Agency:
Conill Advertising, Inc.
3501 Sepulveda Blvd
Torrance, CA 90505-2538
Tel.: (310) 214-6400
Fax: (310) 214-6409

TIGER ELECTRONICS, LTD.

(Div. of Hasbro, Inc.)
1027 Newport Ave
Pawtucket, RI 02861
Tel.: (401) 431-8697
Fax: (401) 727-5099
Web Site: www.hasbro.com
Sales Range: $350-399.9 Million
Approx. Number Employees: 1,000
Business Description:
Electronic Toys, Learning Aids & Video Software Mfr
S.I.C.: 3944
N.A.I.C.S.: 339932
Media: 4-6-9-10-13-15-19-20-21-24
Distr.: Natl.
Budget Set: Nov.
Personnel:
Wayne Charness *(Sr VP-Corp Comm)*
Gary Serby *(VP-Corp Comm)*
Charlie Zakin *(Dir-Media & Adv)*

Brands & Products:
TIGER

Advertising Agencies:
Grey New York
777 3rd Ave
New York, NY 10017-1401
Tel.: (212) 546-2000
Fax: (212) 546-1495

Litzky Public Relations
320 Sinatra Dr
Hoboken, NJ 07030
Tel.: (201) 222-9118
Fax: (201) 222-9418

TONNER DOLL COMPANY, INC.

301 Wall St
Kingston, NY 12401
Tel.: (845) 339-9537
Fax: (845) 339-1259
Web Site: www.tonnerdoll.com
Approx. Number Employees: 18
Business Description:
Dolls Designer & Distr
S.I.C.: 3942
N.A.I.C.S.: 339931
Media: 4-6-10-13
Personnel:
Robert Tonner *(Chm & Pres)*

Brands & Products:
AGNES DREARY
ANTOINETTE
BELIEVE IN THE POWER OF PLAY
DEEANNA DENTON
DENTON CHEWING GUM
THE DEVEREAUX SISTERS
ELLOWYNE WILDE
EVANGELINE GHASTLY
KICKITS
MATT O'NEILL
MONICA MERRILL
PEGGY HARCOURT
RE-IMAGINATION
SINISTER CIRCUS
SISTER DREARY
SYDNEY CHASE
TONNER CHARACTER FIGURES
TONNER DOLL
TYLER WENTWORTH
VIKTOR DREARY

TOYS "R" US, INC.

(Joint Venture of Vornado Realty Trust, KKR & CO. L.P. & Bain Capital, LLC)
1 Geoffrey Way
Wayne, NJ 07470
Tel.: (973) 617-3500
Fax: (973) 617-4004
Web Site: www.toysrus.com
Approx. Sls.: $13,864,000,000
Approx. Number Employees: 71,000
Year Founded: 1948
Business Description:
Holding Company; Toys, Games & Children's Clothing Retailer; Owned by Vornado Realty Trust (33%), Bain Capital, LLC (33%) & Kohlberg Kravis Roberts & Co. (33%)
S.I.C.: 6719; 5641; 5945; 5961
N.A.I.C.S.: 551112; 448130; 451120; 454111
Import
Advertising Expenditures: $445,000,000
Media: 3-4-6-8-9-13-14-15-22-23-24-25-26
Distr.: Natl.
Personnel:
Gerald L. Storch *(Chm & CEO)*
Clay F. Creasey, Jr. *(CFO & Exec VP)*
Deborah M. Derby *(Chief Admin Officer & Exec VP)*
Karen Dodge *(Chief Mdsg Officer & Sr VP)*
Neil B. Friedman *(Pres-United States & Exec VP)*
Antonio Urcelay *(Pres-Continental Europe)*
David J. Schwartz *(Gen Counsel, Corp Sec & Exec VP)*
Francesca L. Brockett *(Exec VP-Strategic Plng & Bus Devel)*
Daniel Caspersen *(Exec VP-HR)*
Jon W. Kimmins *(Exec VP-Bus Dev)*
Greg Ahearn *(Sr VP-Mktg & Ecommerce)*
Michael C. Jacobs *(Sr VP-Logistics)*
Len Hostetter *(VP-Mktg)*
Alyssa Brondander *(Assoc Mgr-Social Media)*

Brands & Products:
BABIES "R" US
ETOYS.COM
FAO SCHWARZ
GEOFFREY
KIDSWORLD
TOYS "R" US
TOYSRUS.COM

Advertising Agency:
GSI Commerce, Inc.
935 1st Ave
King of Prussia, PA 19406
Tel.: (610) 491-7000
Fax: (610) 491-7366

UNEEDA DOLL COMPANY, LTD.

227 Red Bud Cir
Henderson, NC 27536
Tel.: (252) 438-6888
Fax: (252) 438-6808
E-mail: uneedadoll@aol.com
Web Site: www.uneedadoll.com
Sales Range: $1-9.9 Million
Approx. Number Employees: 50
Year Founded: 1917
Business Description:
Mfr. & Distr. of Dolls
S.I.C.: 5092
N.A.I.C.S.: 423920
Import
Media: 2-4-7-10
Distr.: Natl.
Budget Set: Jan.-Feb.

Brands & Products:
COSMIC BABIES
FRUIT BABIES
GIGGLE KIDS
GIRLIE GIRLZ
GOT MILK
HAT DOLLZ
KENYA
KISSUMS
SPECIAL SECRET SUE
SWEETUMS
UNEEDA

THE UNITED STATES PLAYING CARD COMPANY

(Sub. of Jarden Branded Consumables)
300 Gap Way
Erlanger, KY 41018
Tel.: (513) 396-5700
Fax: (866) 781-5866
E-mail: consumerrelations@usplayingcard.com
Web Site: www.usplayingcard.com
Sales Range: $125-149.9 Million
Approx. Number Employees: 600
Year Founded: 1926
Business Description:
Playing Cards, Games & Playing Cards Accessories Mfr
S.I.C.: 3944
N.A.I.C.S.: 339932
Media: 5-10-22
Distr.: Intl.; Natl.
Budget Set: July
Personnel:
Marc Hill *(Pres)*

Brands & Products:
AVIATOR
BEE
BICYCLE
HOYLE
KEM
MAVERICK

Advertising Agencies:
Empower MediaMarketing (MEDIA THAT WORKS)
1111 Saint Gregory St
Cincinnati, OH 45202
Tel.: (513) 871-9454
Fax: (513) 871-1804
Media Buying & Planning

French/West/Vaughan, Inc.
112 E Hargett St
Raleigh, NC 27601
Tel.: (919) 832-6300
Fax: (919) 832-6360
Bicyle

UNIVERSITY GAMES CORPORATION

2030 Harrison St
San Francisco, CA 94110-1310
Tel.: (415) 503-1600
Fax: (415) 503-0085
Toll Free: (800) 347-4818
E-mail: info@ugames.com
Web Site: www.ugames.com
Sales Range: $10-24.9 Million
Approx. Number Employees: 40
Year Founded: 1985
Business Description:
Mfr. of Games & Toys
S.I.C.: 3944
N.A.I.C.S.: 339932
Media: 4-5-6-9-10-15-20-24-25
Personnel:
A. Robert Moog *(Founder)*

Brands & Products:
20 QUESTIONS
BEAT THE EXPERTS
BEPUZZLED
BRAIN QUEST
COLORFORMS
COLORFORMS. IT'S TIME TO PLAY.
EVEN MORE FUN TODAY THAN WHEN WE WERE KIDS!
FLIPFAZE
GLOMINITE
GREAT EXPLORATIONS
GREAT X
KIDS ON STAGE
MURDER MYSTERY PARTY
RAINTREE PUZZLES AND GAMES
SPINNER BOOKS
STICK-ONS
SUDOKU WORLD
TOPLINE TOYS
TOTALLY GROSS
TOY CREATOR

Advertising Agency:
Ocean Bridge Group
1714 16th St
Santa Monica, CA 90404
Tel.: (310) 392-3200

THE UPPER DECK COMPANY, LLC

5909 Sea Otter Pl
Carlsbad, CA 92010
Tel.: (760) 929-6500
Fax: (760) 929-6559
Fax: (760) 929-8563
Toll Free: (800) 873-7332
Web Site: www.upperdeck.com
Approx. Number Employees: 90
Year Founded: 1988
Business Description:
Mfr. of Sports & Non-Sports Trading Cards, Posters
S.I.C.: 2752; 5947
N.A.I.C.S.: 323110; 453220
Media: 4-6-7-15-17-18-19-22-23-24
Distr.: Natl.
Personnel:
Richard McWilliam *(CEO)*
Jason Masherah *(VP-Mktg & Bus Dev)*

Key to Media (For complete agency information see *The Advertising Red Books-Agencies* edition):
1. Bus. Publs. 2. Cable T.V. 3. Catalogs & Directories. 4. Co-op Adv. 5. Consumer Mags. 6. D.M. to Bus. Estab.7. D.M. to Consumers
8. Daily Newsp. 9. Exhibits/Trade Shows 10. Foreign 11. Infomercial 12. Internet Adv.13. Multimedia 14. Network Radio
15. Network T.V. 16. Newsp. Distr. Mags. 17. Other 18. Outdoor (Posters, Transit) 19. Point of Purchase20. Premiums, Novelties
21. Product Samples 22. Special Events Mktg. 23. Spot Radio 24. Spot T.V. 25. Weekly Newsp. 26. Yellow Page Adv.

Jodi Wasserman *(Dir-Mktg)*
Josh Zusman *(Brand Mgr-Hockey)*
Chris Carlin *(Mgr-Sports Mktg & Social Media)*

Brands & Products:
UPPER DECK
UPPER DECK AUTHENTICATED
WEBPASS

U.S. TOY CO., INC.

13201 Arrington Rd
Grandview, MO 64030-2886
Tel.: (816) 761-5900
Fax: (816) 761-9295
Toll Free: (800) 832-0224
E-mail: ustoy@ustoyco.com
Web Site: www.ustoy.com
Approx. Number Employees: 130
Year Founded: 1951
Business Description:
Carnival, Party & Seasonal Decorations, Novelty Toys, Stuffed Animals & Balloons Whslr
S.I.C.: 5049; 5092
N.A.I.C.S.: 423490; 423920
Import Export
Media: 4-8-13
Personnel:
Michael Klein *(Chm)*
Jonathan Freiden *(Pres & CEO)*
Seth Freiden *(Co-CEO)*
Brands & Products:
CONSTRUCTIVE PLAYTHINGS
U.S. TOY

THE VERMONT TEDDY BEAR COMPANY

(Holding of The Mustang Group, LLC)
6655 Shelburne Rd
Shelburne, VT 05482-6500
Mailing Address:
PO Box 965
Shelburne, VT 05482-0965
Tel.: (802) 985-3001
Fax: (802) 985-1382
Toll Free: (800) 829BEAR
Toll Free: (800) 988-8277
E-mail: comments@vtbear.com
Web Site: www.vtbear.com
E-Mail For Key Personnel:
President: ERobert@vtbear.com
Sales Range: $50-74.9 Million
Approx. Number Employees: 352
Year Founded: 1981
Business Description:
Customized Teddy Bear Mfr & Retailer
S.I.C.: 3942; 5947; 5961
N.A.I.C.S.: 339931; 453220; 454113
Import Export
Advertising Expenditures: $14,195,000
Media: 4-8-9-13-14-16-18-22-23-24-26
Distr.: Natl.
Personnel:
Bob Crowley *(Chm)*
John Gilbert *(Pres & CEO)*
Scott Smith *(CFO)*
Liz LaVallee *(Dir-Mktg Mgr)*
Cathy Carlisle *(Dir-Mfg)*
Laura Fitzgerald *(Mgr-Digital Mktg)*
Katie Camardo *(Mgr-Retail Store)*
Mark J. Sleeper *(Asst Controller)*
Brands & Products:
ACME CARTOON COMPANY
THE ACME MOVING PICTURE GROUP
ALL-AMERICAN TEDDY BEAR
BEAR ANIMALS
BEAR BOTTOMS
BEAR COUNSELORS
BEAR-GRAM
CALYX & COROLLA
COFFEE CUB
THE GREAT AMERICAN TEDDY BEAR
MAKE A FRIEND FOR LIFE
PAJAMAGRAM
RACER TED
THE TASTYGRAM COMPANY
TEDDY BEAR-GRAM
TEDDY TOGS
TEDDY TREATS
TEDDYGRAMS
VERMONT BABY BEAR
VERMONT BEAR-GRAM
THE VERMONT TEDDY BEAR COMPANY
Advertising Agency:
FUSE/ideas
255 Elm St Ste 201
Somerville, MA 02144
Tel.: (617) 776-5800
Fax: (617) 776-5821

VTECH ELECTRONICS NORTH AMERICA, LLC

(Sub. of VTech Holdings Ltd.)
1155 W Dundee Rd Ste 130
Arlington Heights, IL 60004
Tel.: (847) 400-3600
Fax: (847) 400-3601
Toll Free: (800) 521-2010 (Consumer Services)
E-mail: vtechkids@vtechkids.com
Web Site: www.vtechkids.com
Approx. Number Employees: 50
Year Founded: 1976
Business Description:
Educational Electronic Toys Sales & Marketing
S.I.C.: 5092
N.A.I.C.S.: 423920
Import
Media: 3-4-5-6-10-13-15-19-22-24
Distr.: Natl.
Personnel:
William To *(Pres)*
Rod Kasinck *(CIO)*
Matt Ramage *(Sr VP-Product Mgmt)*
Tom McClure *(VP-Mktg)*
Brands & Products:
ALPHABERT'S LEARN-TO-READ SYSTEM
LEARNING ADVENTURES
PLAY SMART
READY, SET, SCHOOL
SMART SENSATIONS
VOYAGER ADVENTURE SYSTEM
V.SMILE
XL SERIES
Advertising Agencies:
Daniel J. Edelman, Inc.
(d/b/a Edelman)
200 E Randolph St Fl 63
Chicago, IL 60601-6705
Tel.: (312) 240-3000
Fax: (312) 240-2900

Energy BBDO
410 N Michigan Ave
Chicago, IL 60611-4213
Tel.: (312) 337-7860
Fax: (312) 337-6871

Leagas Delaney Group Limited
1 Alfred Place
London, WC1E 7EB, United Kingdom
Tel.: (44) 207 758 1758
Fax: (44) 207 758 1760

Ogilvy PR
350 W Mart Ctr Dr 11th Fl
Chicago, IL 60654
Tel.: (312) 397-6000
Fax: (312) 397-8841
Electronics Learning Products
PR Agency of Record

WABA FUN, LLC

5883 Lockheed Ave
Loveland, CO 80538
Mailing Address:
PO Box 74
Loveland, CO 80538
Tel.: (970) 278-0468
Fax: (970) 667-7395
E-mail: info@superstructs.com
Web Site: www.superstructs.com
Approx. Number Employees: 9
Year Founded: 1978
Business Description:
Construction Toys
S.I.C.: 3944; 5945
N.A.I.C.S.: 339932; 451120
Media: 4-13
Personnel:
David McCloskey *(Founder-Product Dev & Ops)*
Brands & Products:
SUPERSTRUCTS

WHAM-O, INC.

5903 Christie Ave
Emeryville, CA 94608
Tel.: (510) 653-8847
Toll Free: (888) 942-6650
E-mail: info@wham-o.com
Web Site: www.wham-o.com
Approx. Rev.: $50,000,000
Approx. Number Employees: 45
Year Founded: 1948
Business Description:
Toy Mfr
S.I.C.: 3944; 5092
N.A.I.C.S.: 339932; 423920
Media: 4-5-6-15-18-24
Distr.: Natl.
Budget Set: Dec.
Personnel:
Mojde Esfandiari *(Pres & CEO)*
Blake Wong *(Asst Controller)*
Brands & Products:
AIR DARTS
AIR HOCKEY
ALIEN SPLASH ATTACH
ALL SPORT
BACKYARD OBSTACLE COURSE
BATTLE BOOGIE
BIG SPLASH
BIRDIE GOLF
BUMPER GOLF
COASTER
CROQUET GOLF
DELUXE PINBALL SOCCER
FREESTYLE
FRISBEE
FRISBEE CLASSIC
FRISBEE DOG
FRISBEE TOSS
GLOWZONE HOCKEY
GOLF 150G
HACKY SACK
HEATWAVE
HEAVYWEIGHT
IMPACT
INFINITY
LAWN FISHING
MAX FLIGHT
MOONLIGHTER
PRO CLASSIC
SLIM LINE HOCKEY
SLIM LINE SOCCER
SLIP 'N SLIDE
SOCCER BILLIARDS
SOFT SHOT
SOUND SWING BAT & BALL
SPLASH DUNK
SPLASH PASS
SPLASH TANGLE
SPLATTER UP
STRIKER
SUPERBALL
SUPERSTAR
TIDAL WAVE
TRACBALL
WATER BLAST SPEEDWAY
WATER JUMP ROPE
WAVE RIDER
WHAM-O
Advertising Agency:
The Pollack PR Marketing Group
1901 Ave of the Stars Ste 1040
Los Angeles, CA 90067
Tel.: (310) 556-4443
Fax: (310) 286-2350
60th Anniversary
Toys

WHITE WOLF PUBLISHING, INC.

2075 West Park Pl Blvd Suite G
Stone Mountain, GA 30087
Tel.: (404) 292-1819
Fax: (678) 382-3883
Toll Free: (800) 454WOLF
E-mail: retail@white-wolf.com
Web Site: www.white-wolf.com
Approx. Number Employees: 55
Year Founded: 1991
Business Description:
Publisher of Games & Fiction
S.I.C.: 2731
N.A.I.C.S.: 511130
Export
Media: 4-5-6-8-10-11-13-22
Distr.: Intl.
Personnel:
Robert Goudie *(Chm)*
Stewart Wieck *(Publr)*
Dean Burnham *(VP-Sls & Mktg)*
Ryan Dancey *(Mktg Dir)*
Mike Krause *(Sls Dir)*
Brands & Products:
BOREALIS
CHANGELING: THE LOST
CHANGELING:THE DREAMING
CLANBOOK ASSAMITE
CLANBOOK CAPPADOCIAN
CLANBOOK RAVNOS
CLANBOOK TREMERE
CLANBOOK VENTRUE
DARK INFLUENCES
EVE
EXALTED
HUNTER: THE VIGIL EXALTED
HUNTER:THE RECKONING
KINDRED OF THE EAST
LONG LIVE THE KING
MAGE: THE AWAKENING

Key to Media (For complete agency information see *The Advertising Red Books-Agencies* edition):
1. Bus. Publs. 2. Cable T.V. 3. Catalogs & Directories. 4. Co-op Adv. 5. Consumer Mags. 6. D.M. to Bus. Estab.7. D.M. to Consumers
8. Daily Newsp. 9. Exhibits/Trade Shows 10. Foreign 11. Infomercial 12. Internet Adv.13. Multimedia 14. Network Radio
15. Network T.V. 16. Newsp. Distr. Mags. 17. Other 18. Outdoor (Posters, Transit) 19. Point of Purchase20. Premiums, Novelties
21. Product Samples 22. Special Events Mktg. 23. Spot Radio 24. Spot T.V. 25. Weekly Newsp. 26. Yellow Page Adv.

White Wolf Publishing, Inc. — (Continued)

MAGE:THE ASCENSION
MAGE:THE SORCERERS CRUSADE
MIND'S EYE THEATRE
MONSTER MAYHEM
MUMMY:THE RESURRECTION
MURDER CITY
MWAHAHAHA
PIMP: THE BACKHANDING
PRINCE OF THE CITY
PROMETHEAN: THE CREATED
SAS
SCION
TECHNOCRACY PROGENITORS
TRINITY
TRINITY:BATTLEGROUND
VAMPIRE: THE ETERNAL STRUGGLE
VAMPIRE: THE MASQUERADE
VAMPIRE: THE REQUIEM
VAMPIRE:THE DARK AGES
VTES
WEREWOLF: THE FORSAKEN
WEREWOLF:THE APOCALYPSE
WEREWOLF:THE WILD WEST
WHITE WOLF
WORLD OF DARKNESS
WRAITH:THE GREAT WAR

Advertising Agency:
Lead Dog Productions
104 Dogwood Ave
Richmond Hill, GA 31324
Tel.: (912) 756-2231

WILD PLANET ENTERTAINMENT, INC.

225 Bush St #13
San Francisco, CA 94114
Tel.: (415) 705-8300
Fax: (415) 705-8311
Toll Free: (800) 247-6570
E-mail: marketing@wildplanet.com
Web Site: www.wildplanet.com
Approx. Sls.: $3,000,000
Approx. Number Employees: 50
Year Founded: 1993
Business Description:
Toys Mfr
S.I.C.: 3944; 5092
N.A.I.C.S.: 339932; 423920
Media: 6-10
Personnel:
Daniel Grossman *(CEO)*
Drew Stevenson *(Sr VP-Sls-Worldwide)*
Grew Stevenson *(Sr VP-Sls-Worldwide)*
Brands & Products:
A PIRATE'S LIFE
ANIMAL SCRAMBLE
CRAYON TOWN
DINO-MAGIC
HYPER DASH
HYPER GAMES
LITEFORMZ
MERMAID SURPRISE
OFF THE MAP
OUTDOOR ANTICS
ROOM GEAR
SKELEFLEX
SMART STEP
SPY GEAR
UNDERCOVER GIRL
WATER BABIES
WATERBALL
WILD PLANET
ZOOM CAM

Advertising Agency:
Digital Brewing Company
720 Market St 3rd Fl
San Francisco, CA 94102
Tel.: (415) 398-1333
Fax: (415) 398-2266

WIN STUFF LLC

4700 33rd St
Long Island City, NY 11101
Tel.: (718) 937-3333
Fax: (718) 937-1037
Web Site: www.winstuff.com
Approx. Sls.: $50,000,000
Approx. Number Employees: 28
Business Description:
Novelty Vending Machines; Toys & Sporting Goods
S.I.C.: 5962; 5092
N.A.I.C.S.: 454210; 423920
Media: 4-13
Personnel:
David Chazen *(Pres)*
Sidney Bannon *(CEO)*
Raura Allen *(CFO)*
Brands & Products:
BETTY BOOP
BOZO THE CLOWN
CASPER
GUMBY
HOWDY DOODY
LOONEY TUNES
OAKMONT
PINK PANTHER
POPEYE
POWER RANGERS
PREMIER
TOYS
WIN STUFF
WOODY WOODPECKER

WINNING MOVES GAMES, INC.

75 Sylvan St Ste C-104
Danvers, MA 01923
Tel.: (978) 777-7464
Fax: (978) 739-4847
Toll Free: (800) 664-7788
E-mail: info@winning-moves.com
Web Site: www.winning-moves.com
Sales Range: $1-9.9 Million
Approx. Number Employees: 11
Year Founded: 1995
Business Description:
Mfr & Marketer of Games
S.I.C.: 3944
N.A.I.C.S.: 339932
Media: 2-6-7-10-19-22
Personnel:
Tom Kremer *(Chm)*
Phil E. Orbanes *(Part Owner, Pres)*
Darlene Duggan *(VP-Fin & Ops)*
Mike Meyers *(VP-DP, HR & Mfg)*
Joe Sequino *(VP-Mktg)*
Brands & Products:
BOX OF BUNCO
CHARLIE & THE CHOCOLATE FACTORY
CHEESY PARCHEESY
CHOCOLATE FACTORY
CLASSIC, RETRO, COOL & FUN
CLASSIC WATERWORKS
CODA
CROCODILE DENTIST
DELUXE CANASTA CALIENTE
DELUXE PASS THE PIG
DELUXE PIT
DELUXE ROOK
FLINCH
FORBIDDEN
GAME OF THE STATES
GO TO THE HEAD OF THE CLASS
INSTANT INSANITY
KINGS CRIBBAGE
MILLE BORNES
MONOPOLY THE CARD GAME
NO STRESS CHESS
PASS THE PIGS
PAY DAY
PENTE
PIT
PLAY ON WORDS
PRINCESS & THE PEA
ROLLER BOWL
SOLITAIRE TILES
SUPER SCRABBLE
TRIVIAL PURSUIT
ULTIMATE STRATEGO
UNCLE WIGGILY
WATERWORKS
WINNING MOVES GAMES

WIZARDS OF THE COAST, INC.

(Sub. of Hasbro, Inc.)
1600 Lind Ave SW
Renton, WA 98055-4068
Mailing Address:
PO Box 707
Renton, WA 98057-0707
Tel.: (425) 226-6500
Fax: (425) 204-5918
Web Site: www.wizards.com
Sales Range: $100-124.9 Million
Approx. Number Employees: 400
Year Founded: 1990
Business Description:
Game Mfr & Distr
S.I.C.: 3944
N.A.I.C.S.: 339932
Media: 13-19-20
Personnel:
Loren Greenwood *(Pres & CEO)*
Mike Mayhew *(CFO)*
Monty Ashley *(Mng Editor)*
Elaine Chase *(Brand Dir)*
Aaron Forsythe *(Dir-R&D)*
Laura Tommervik *(Sr Mgr-Brand Mktg)*
Lisa J Stevens *(Brand Mgr)*
Elizabeth Sidiratos *(Mktg Mgr-APAC)*
Brands & Products:
ADVANCED DUNGEONS & DRAGONS
AMAZING STORIES
D&D MINIATURES
D20
D20 MODERN
DRAGON
DUNGEONS & DRAGONS
EBERRON
FORGOTTEN REALMS
GREYHAWK

THE WORLD OF MINIATURE BEARS, INC.

8011 NW 64th St
Miami, FL 33166
Tel.: (305) 592-7970
Fax: (305) 592-7971
Fax: (800) 398-4155
Toll Free: (800) 363-7897
E-mail: mail@minibear.com
Web Site: www.minibear.com
Approx. Number Employees: 5
Business Description:
Stuffed Bears Mfr & Distr
S.I.C.: 3942
N.A.I.C.S.: 339931
Media: 2-4-10-13
Personnel:
Theresa Yang *(Founder)*

WORLDWISE, INC.

(Holding of Mistral Equity Partners LLC)
160 Mitchell Blvd
San Rafael, CA 94903-3343
Mailing Address:
PO Box 3360
San Rafael, CA 94912-3360
Tel.: (415) 721-7400
Fax: (415) 721-7418
Toll Free: (800) WORLDWISE
E-mail: customerservice@worldwise.com
Web Site: www.worldwise.com
Sales Range: $50-74.9 Million
Approx. Number Employees: 50
Business Description:
Environmentally Safe Pet Toys,Treats & Accessories Mfr
S.I.C.: 3999; 5199
N.A.I.C.S.: 339999; 424990
Media: 6-10-13
Personnel:
Matt Turnbull *(CEO)*
Christina Gray *(Mgr-Mktg Comm)*
Brands & Products:
BARKLOUNGER
BIRDBOING
BLAZINBALLS
CATCHAISE
CATNIPCOVERALL
CATNIPMIST
CHICKADEECHIRP
COMFYCORNERS
COZYCLAMSHELL
CUDDLECLOUD
CURLUPCUP
DURABARREL
DURAPLANTER
ECOREST
FLICKERBALL
FUZZBUGS
LEAPS'NBOUNDS
LOCO!LASER
LOCO!MOTION
LUXURYLINER
MIX'NSCRATCH SYSTEM
PET THROW
POOCHPLANET
RUNAWAYRASCAL
SCRATCHNOT SPRAY
SCRATCHNOT TAPE
SMARTYKAT
SMARTYKAT BENEFITBITZ
SMARTYKAT BOBBLEBOPS
SMARTYKAT BONKERBALLS
SMARTYKAT BOUNCYMOUSE
SMARTYKAT BUBBLENIP
SMARTYKAT BUNGEEBOUNCER
SMARTYKAT BUNGEEBUDDY
SMARTYKAT CARPETCURE
SMARTYKAT CATNIPCONVERTIBLE
SMARTYKAT CATNIPLOUNGER
SMARTYKAT CATRUSTLER
SMARTYKAT COZYCLAMSHELL
SMARTYKAT CRACKLECHUTE
SMARTYKAT DEEPERSLEEPER
SMARTYKAT FEATHERMOUSE
SMARTYKAT FLUTTERBALLS
SMARTYKAT FUZZYFINS
SMARTYKAT JUTEBRUTE
SMARTYKAT KITTYKARNIVAL
SMARTYKAT SASSYSOFA

Key to Media (For complete agency information see *The Advertising Red Books-Agencies* edition):
1. Bus. Publs. 2. Cable T.V. 3. Catalogs & Directories. 4. Co-op Adv. 5. Consumer Mags. 6. D.M. to Bus. Estab.7. D.M. to Consumers
8. Daily Newsp. 9. Exhibits/Trade Shows 10. Foreign 11. Infomercial 12. Internet Adv.13. Multimedia 14. Network Radio
15. Network T.V. 16. Newsp. Distr. Mags. 17. Other 18. Outdoor (Posters, Transit) 19. Point of Purchase20. Premiums, Novelties
21. Product Samples 22. Special Events Mktg. 23. Spot Radio 24. Spot T.V. 25. Weekly Newsp. 26. Yellow Page Adv.

SMARTYKAT SCRATCHPOD
SMARTYKAT SHRIMPNIP
SMARTYKAT SKITTERCRITTERS
SMARTYKAT SUPERSCRATCHER
SMARTYKAT SUPERSCRATCHER+
SMARTYKAT SWEETGREENS
SMARTYKAT TWEETYTWIRLER
SMARTYKAT WIGGLYWAVER
SMARTYKAT WILDSTREAK
SURFACESAVER
WILDSPIN
WISEGUIDE
WORLDWISE

XBOX
(Sub. of Microsoft Entertainment & Devices Division)
1 Microsoft Way
Redmond, WA 98052-6399
Tel.: (425) 882-8080
Fax: (425) 936-7329
Web Site: www.xbox.com
Sales Range: $50-74.9 Million
Business Description:
Video Game Console Mfr & Magazine Publisher
S.I.C.: 3944; 2721
N.A.I.C.S.: 339932; 511120
Media: 1-2-3-4-6-7-8-9-10-11-13-14-15-18-19-20-21-22-23-24-25
Personnel:
Todd Holmdahl *(Corp VP-Product Grp)*
Paul Evans *(Head-Media, EMEA)*
Cameron Ferroni *(Gen Mgr-Xbox Software Platform)*
Mike Fischer *(Gen Mgr-US Mktg)*
Craig Davison *(Sr Dir-Mktg)*
Steve Beinner *(Dir-Mktg-Global)*
Caroline McNiel *(Dir-Media-Global)*
Gustavo Alvarado *(Sr Mgr-Media)*
Jeremy Hinton *(Mgr-Mktg-Xbox)*
Chuck Frizelle *(Product Mgr-New Media)*

XTC PRODUCTS, INC.
7A Morse Dr
Essex Junction, VT 05452-2811
Tel.: (802) 878-8900
Toll Free: (800) 332-7840
E-mail: sales@peacetoys.com
Web Site: www.peacetoys.com
E-Mail For Key Personnel:
Sales Director: sales@peacetoys.com
Sales Range: Less than $1 Million
Approx. Number Employees: 6
Year Founded: 1982
Business Description:
Toys, Soft Fabric Globes, Map Related Products & Organic Cotton Garments
S.I.C.: 3944; 5092
N.A.I.C.S.: 339932; 423920
Media: 8-10-13-17
Distr.: Intl.; Natl.
Budget Set: Jan. -Feb.
Personnel:
Robert Forenza *(Pres)*
Brands & Products:
EARTH POCKET
EARTHTOY
FOUNDLINGS
HUGG-A-PLANET
HUGG-A-STAR
HUGG AMERICA
PEACE ON EARTH OUR EARTH IN ONE PIECE
POCKET PLANET

ZANER-BLOSER, INC.
(Sub. of Highlights for Children, Inc.)
1201 Dublin Rd
Columbus, OH 43215
Tel.: (614) 486-0221
Fax: (614) 487-2699
Web Site: www.zaner-bloser.com
Year Founded: 1888
Business Description:
Children's Educational Materials
S.I.C.: 5192; 5049
N.A.I.C.S.: 424920; 423490
Media: 7-8-10-13
Personnel:
Robert Page *(Pres)*
Brad Onken *(Sr VP-Strategic Mktg & Bus Dev)*

Key to Media (For complete agency information see *The Advertising Red Books-Agencies* edition):
1. Bus. Publs. 2. Cable T.V. 3. Catalogs & Directories. 4. Co-op Adv. 5. Consumer Mags. 6. D.M. to Bus. Estab.7. D.M. to Consumers
8. Daily Newsp. 9. Exhibits/Trade Shows 10. Foreign 11. Infomercial 12. Internet Adv.13. Multimedia 14. Network Radio
15. Network T.V. 16. Newsp. Distr. Mags. 17. Other 18. Outdoor (Posters, Transit) 19. Point of Purchase20. Premiums, Novelties
21. Product Samples 22. Special Events Mktg. 23. Spot Radio 24. Spot T.V. 25. Weekly Newsp. 26. Yellow Page Adv.

Gasoline & Lubricants

Gasoline — Gasoline Plants — Graphites — Greases — Lubricants — Lubricating Systems — Motor Oils — Petroleum Exploration & Production

ABENGOA BIOENERGY CORP.
(Sub. of Abengoa S.A.)
16150 Main Cricle Dr Ste 300
Chesterfield, MO 63017
Tel.: (636) 728-0508
Fax: (636) 728-1148
E-mail: info@abengoabioenergy.com
Web Site:
www.abengoabioenergy.com
Approx. Number Employees: 200
Year Founded: 1980
Business Description:
Producer of Ethanol
S.I.C.: 2869
N.A.I.C.S.: 325193
Export
Advertising Expenditures: $250,000
Media: 2-4-7-8-9-10-12-20-22-23-24-26
Distr.: Reg.
Budget Set: June
Personnel:
Javier Salgado *(Chm, Pres & CEO)*
Ignacio Garcia *(CFO)*
Gerson Santos-Leon *(Exec VP-New Technologies)*
Christopher Standlee *(Exec VP-Institutional Relationships & Govt Affairs)*
Joaquin Alarcon *(Dir-Corp Dev)*
David Weber *(Dir-Ethanol Sls)*

AGNICO-EAGLE MINES LIMITED
145 King Street East Suite 400
Toronto, ON M5C 2Y7, Canada
Tel.: (416) 947-1212
Fax: (416) 367-4681
Toll Free: (888) 822-6714
E-mail: info@agnico-eagle.com
Web Site: www.agnico-eagle.com
E-Mail For Key Personnel:
President: sboyd@agnico-eagle.com
Public Relations: blanden@agnico-eagle.com
Approx. Rev.: $1,422,521,000
Approx. Number Employees: 3,243
Year Founded: 1972
Business Description:
Gold Exploration & Mining Services
S.I.C.: 1041
N.A.I.C.S.: 212221
Personnel:
James D. Nasso *(Chm)*
Sean Boyd *(Vice Chm & CEO)*
Eberhard Scherkus *(Pres & COO)*
Ammar Al-Joundi *(CFO & Sr VP-Fin)*
R. Gregory Laing *(Gen Counsel, Sec & Sr VP-Legal)*
Donald G. Allan *(Sr VP-Corp Dev)*
Alain Blackburn *(Sr VP-Exploration)*
Louise Grondin *(Sr VP-Environment & Sustainable Dev)*
Tim Haldane *(Sr VP-Latin America)*
Daniel Racine *(Sr VP-Ops)*
Jean Robitaille *(Sr VP-Tech Svcs)*
David L. Smith *(Sr VP-IR)*
Patrice Gilbert *(VP-HR)*
Advertising Agency:
Renmark Financial Communications, Inc.
1550 Metcalfe Ste 502
Montreal, QC H3A 1X6, Canada
Tel.: (514) 939-3989
Fax: (514) 939-3717

ALBERTA STAR DEVELOPMENT CORP.
506-675 West Hastings St
Vancouver, BC V6B1N2, Canada
Tel.: (604) 488-0860
Tel.: (604) 681-3131
Fax: (604) 408-3884
E-mail: astar@telus.net
Web Site: www.alberta-star.com
Approx. Rev.: $378,252
Business Description:
Oil & Natural Gas Resource Exploration & Development
S.I.C.: 1381
N.A.I.C.S.: 213111
Advertising Expenditures: $73,465
Media: 17
Personnel:
Tim Coupland *(Pres & CEO)*
Gordon Steblin *(CFO)*

ALON USA ENERGY, INC.
(Sub. of Alon Israel Oil Company Ltd.)
7616 Lyndon B Johnson Fwy Ste 300
Dallas, TX 75251-1100
Tel.: (972) 367-3600
Web Site: www.alonusa.com
Approx. Sls.: $4,030,743,000
Approx. Number Employees: 2,821
Business Description:
Oil & Gas Refining; Marketing Services
S.I.C.: 2911; 4612; 5541
N.A.I.C.S.: 324110; 447110; 486110
Media: 2-5
Personnel:
David Wiessman *(Chm)*
Jeff D. Morris *(Vice Chm)*
W. Paul Eisman *(Pres & CEO)*
Shai Even *(CFO & Sr VP)*
Joseph Israel *(COO)*
Joseph A. Concienne *(Sr VP-Refining)*
Claire A. Hart *(Sr VP)*
Alan Moret *(Sr VP-Supply)*
Brands & Products:
TOPEIN
Advertising Agency:
Krause Advertising
5307 E Mockingbird Ln Ste 250
Dallas, TX 75206
Tel.: (214) 823-5100
Fax: (214) 823-5108

AMERICAN GREASE STICK CO.
2651 Hoyt St
Muskegon Heights, MI 49444-2141
Mailing Address:
PO Box 729
Muskegon, MI 49443-0729
Tel.: (231) 733-2101
Fax: (231) 733-1784
Toll Free: (800) 253-0403
E-mail: info@agscompany.com
Web Site: www.agscompany.com
Sales Range: $50-74.9 Million
Approx. Number Employees: 35
Year Founded: 1931
Business Description:
Mfr. of Specialized Lubricants
S.I.C.: 2992; 5013
N.A.I.C.S.: 324191; 423120
Advertising Expenditures: $200,000
Media: 2-5-10
Distr.: Natl.
Budget Set: Jan.
Personnel:
Logan Pitts *(Pres)*
Christian Byar *(Mgr-Mktg)*
Brands & Products:
AGS
BELT-EASE
BELT-MAGIC
BRITE BULB
CUT-EASE
DOOR-EASE
DRILL-EASE
EZ-SEAL
GREASE-A-BEARING
HYPOID 90
KABLE-EASE
LITH-EASE
LOCK-EASE
MATCH-UP
MR. OIL
MR. PENETRANT
MR. ZIP
MR. ZIP GRAPHITE
MR. ZIP KABLE-EASE
QUICK-LIFT
RUFF-LITE
RUGLYDE
RYNO-WELD
SIL-GLYDE
STOP OIL LEAKS
STORE-IT START-IT
SUPER CONCENTRATE
SUPRA GLUE
TAP-EASE
THREAD-MAGIC
TRIM-EASE
TUFF-LITE

THE AMERICAN LUBRICANTS COMPANY
1227 Deeds Ave
Dayton, OH 45404-1238
Tel.: (937) 222-2851
Fax: (937) 461-7729
Toll Free: (800) 543-9720
Approx. Sls.: $4,000,000
Approx. Number Employees: 10
Year Founded: 1933
Business Description:
Mfr. of Asphalt Roof Coatings, Building Maintenance Materials, Heavy Duty Lubricants & Industrial Oils
S.I.C.: 2992; 2899
N.A.I.C.S.: 324191; 325998
Import Export
Advertising Expenditures: $250,000
Distr.: Intl.; Natl.
Budget Set: Nov. -Jan.
Personnel:
Robert G. Read *(Pres & Dir-Mktg)*
Lavonne Wilcox *(VP-Mktg)*
Brands & Products:
ALUBCO
BISON
SUPER STURDY
TIFFANY

Key to Media (For complete agency information see *The Advertising Red Books-Agencies* edition):
1. Bus. Publs. 2. Cable T.V. 3. Catalogs & Directories. 4. Co-op Adv. 5. Consumer Mags. 6. D.M. to Bus. Estab.7. D.M. to Consumers 8. Daily Newsp. 9. Exhibits/Trade Shows 10. Foreign 11. Infomercial 12. Internet Adv.13. Multimedia 14. Network Radio 15. Network T.V. 16. Newsp. Distr. Mags. 17. Other 18. Outdoor (Posters, Transit) 19. Point of Purchase20. Premiums, Novelties 21. Product Samples 22. Special Events Mktg. 23. Spot Radio 24. Spot T.V. 25. Weekly Newsp. 26. Yellow Page Adv.

AMIWORLD, INC.
60 E 42nd St Ste 1225
New York, NY 10165
Tel.: (212) 557-0223
Fax: (212) 557-0073
E-mail: info@amiworld.com
Web Site: www.amiworld.com
Approx. Rev.: $64,185,207
Approx. Number Employees: 136
Year Founded: 1998
Business Description:
Holding Company; Biodiesel, Petroleum Diesel Production, Fuel Brokerage & Shipping Services
S.I.C.: 6719; 2999; 4731; 5172; 5989
N.A.I.C.S.: 551112; 324199; 424720; 454319; 488510
Advertising Expenditures: $523,967
Media: 17
Personnel:
Mamoru Saito *(Chm, CEO & Sec)*
Takahito Sakagami *(Pres)*
David Garin *(CFO, Principal Acctg Officer & Treas)*
Luis Martinez *(Dir)*

AMSOIL INC.
925 Tower Ave
Superior, WI 54880
Tel.: (715) 392-7101
Fax: (715) 392-5225
E-mail: info@amsoil.com
Web Site: www.amsoil.com
Approx. Number Employees: 200
Year Founded: 1973
Business Description:
Lubricating Oils & Greases Mfr
S.I.C.: 2992; 3589
N.A.I.C.S.: 324191; 333319
Export
Media: 2-4-5-6-13-18-19-22-26
Personnel:
Alan Amatuzio *(COO & Exec VP)*
Dean Alexander *(Exec VP & Gen Mgr)*
Ed Newman *(Dir-Adv)*
Brands & Products:
AMS-OILER
AMSOIL
THE FIRST IN SYNTHETICS
POWERCORE
POWERSTROKE
SEVERE GEAR
VORTEC

ANADARKO PETROLEUM CORPORATION
1201 Lake Robbins Dr
The Woodlands, TX 77380
Tel.: (832) 636-1000
Fax: (832) 636-8220
Toll Free: (800) 800-1101
Telex: 765353
E-mail: investor@anadarko.com
Web Site: www.anadarko.com
Approx. Rev.: $10,984,000,000
Approx. Number Employees: 4,400
Year Founded: 1959
Business Description:
Exploration, Production & Pipeline Transportation of Natural Gas & Petroleum; Operator of Mineral Mines
S.I.C.: 1311; 1321; 1389; 1474; 3299; 4924
N.A.I.C.S.: 211111; 211112; 212391; 213112; 221210; 327999
Media: 2-10
Personnel:
James T. Hackett *(Chm & CEO)*
R. A. Walker *(Pres & COO)*
Robert G. Gwin *(CFO & Sr VP-Fin)*
Mario M. Coll *(CIO & VP-Info Tech Svcs)*
Robert K. Reeves *(Chief Admin Officer, Gen Counsel & Sr VP)*
M. Cathy Douglas *(Chief Acctg Officer & VP)*
Bruce W. Busmire *(Treas & VP-Fin)*
David L. Siddall *(Sec, VP & Deputy Gen Counsel)*
Robert P. Daniels *(Sr VP-Worldwide Exploration)*
Charles A. Meloy *(Sr VP-Worldwide Ops)*
David C. Bretches *(VP-Mktg & Minerals)*
John M. Colglazier *(VP-IR & Comm)*
Julia A. Struble *(VP-HR)*
John Christiansen *(Mgr-External Comm)*
Phillip R. Loader *(Mgr-North America Frontier Exploration)*

APPROACH RESOURCES INC.
6500 W Freeway Ste 800
Fort Worth, TX 76116
Tel.: (817) 989-9000
Fax: (817) 989-9001
E-mail: office@approachresources.com
Web Site: www.approachresources.com
E-Mail For Key Personnel:
Public Relations: mbrown@approachresources.com
Approx. Rev.: $57,581,000
Approx. Number Employees: 55
Year Founded: 2002
Business Description:
Natural Gas & Oil Properties Exploration, Development, Exploitation, Production & Acquisition
S.I.C.: 1311
N.A.I.C.S.: 211111
Personnel:
Bryan H. Lawrence *(Chm)*
J. Ross Craft *(Pres & CEO)*
Steven P. Smart *(CFO & Exec VP)*
J. Curtis Henderson *(Gen Counsel & Exec VP)*
Ralph P. Manoushagian *(Exec VP-Land)*
Qingming Yang *(Exec VP-Bus Dev & Geosciences)*
William S. Buckler, III *(VP-Engrg)*
Scott Sabatka *(Mgr-Exploitation)*
Gerry Trichel *(Mgr-Drilling)*
Advertising Agency:
GCG Advertising
1612 Summit Ave Ste 410
Fort Worth, TX 76102-5916
Tel.: (817) 332-4600
Fax: (817) 877-4616

ASHLAND INC.
50 E RiverCenter Blvd
Covington, KY 41012
Tel.: (859) 815-3333
Fax: (859) 815-5053
E-mail: investor_relations@ashland.com
Web Site: www.ashland.com
E-Mail For Key Personnel:
Public Relations: MCJohnson@ashland.com
Approx. Sls.: $9,012,000,000
Approx. Number Employees: 14,500
Year Founded: 1927
Business Description:
Holding Company; Specialty Chemicals, Automotive Chemicals & Water Treatment Products Mfr & Distr
S.I.C.: 6719; 2819; 2821; 2869; 2899; 2911; 2992; 2999; 5162; 5169; 5172
N.A.I.C.S.: 551112; 324110; 324191; 324199; 325188; 325199; 325211; 325998; 424610; 424690; 424720
Import Export
Advertising Expenditures: $70,000,000
Media: 2-3-7-8-9-10-14-15-22-23-24-25
Distr.: Natl.
Personnel:
James J. O'Brien *(Chm & CEO)*
Lamar M. Chambers *(CFO & Sr VP)*
Theodore L. Harris *(Pres-Global Supply Chain/Environ, Health & Safety/IT & VP)*
Samuel J. Mitchell, Jr. *(Pres-Ashl& Consumer Markets & VP)*
John E. Panichella *(Pres-Aqualon Functional Ingredients & VP)*
Paul C. Raymond, III *(Pres-Hercules Water Tech & VP)*
David L. Hausrath *(Gen Counsel & Sr VP)*
Linda L. Foss *(Sec & Asst Gen Counsel)*
Susan B. Esler *(VP-HR & Comm)*
Kristy J. Folkwein *(VP-Info Tech)*
Scott Hoertz *(Dir-Mktg)*
Mark Adamovits *(Sr Product Mgr)*
John F. Guldig *(Auditor)*
Brands & Products:
AEROCARB
AME
AMERCOR
AMERFLOC
AMERFLON
AMEROID
AMERPACK
AMERSCENT
AMERSTAT
ARIMAX
AROCURE
AROFENE
AROGUARD
AROMELT
AROMETRICS
AROPOL
AROSET
AROTRAN
ASHLAND
BIOSPERSE
BUCKET-FREE
CAR BRITE
CARBOFLEX
CHARGEPAC
CLEANROOM
DERAKANE
DREW
DREWCLEAN
DREWFAX
DREWFLOC
DREWGARD
DREWPLUS
DREWRAD
DREWSPERSE
DREWZYME
DURABLEND
EAGLE ONE
EDGE
EMABOND
ENGUARD
ENVIREZ
ENVIROCARE
ENVIROPLUS
ENZYBATE
EXPRESS CARE
HANDS OFF
HETRON
HEXAKLEAN
IG-LO
INSTINT
ISO-FAST
ISOCURE
ISOGRIP
ISOMAX
ISOMELT
ISOSEAL
ISOSET
ISOTUBE
LAC
LIQUI PASTE
MAX LIFE
MAXGUARD
MEKOR
MILLSPERSE
MODAR
MY GLOVEBOX
NANO-POLISH
NANO-PROTECTANT
NANOCLEAN
NANOWAX
NOVASET
OPTIMUM CHOICE
P-U-L-S-E
PEP SET
PERFORMAX
PERFORMAX MILLENNIUM
PHASE ALPHA
PHASE EPSILON
PLIOBOND
PLIODECK
PLIOGRIP
POLARIS
POWER2CLEAN
PRAESTOL
PRELAM
PRODETAILER
PURELAM
PYROIL
SONOXIDE
STA-HOT
SURFCHEM
SYNPOWER
TC4
V VALVOLINE
V VALVOLINE RACING
VALVOLINE
VALVOLINE INSTANT OIL CHANGE
VELVAPLAST
VPC
WAX AS-U-DRY
XPRESS-IT
ZEREX
ZIP-SLIP
Advertising Agencies:
Godfrey Advertising
40 N Christian St
Lancaster, PA 17602
Tel.: (717) 393-3831
Fax: (717) 393-1403

Northlich Public Relations
720 E Pete Rose Way Ste 120
Cincinnati, OH 45202-3579

Key to Media (For complete agency information see *The Advertising Red Books-Agencies* edition):
1. Bus. Publs. 2. Cable T.V. 3. Catalogs & Directories. 4. Co-op Adv. 5. Consumer Mags. 6. D.M. to Bus. Estab.7. D.M. to Consumers 8. Daily Newsp. 9. Exhibits/Trade Shows 10. Foreign 11. Infomercial 12. Internet Adv.13. Multimedia 14. Network Radio 15. Network T.V. 16. Newsp. Distr. Mags. 17. Other 18. Outdoor (Posters, Transit) 19. Point of Purchase20. Premiums, Novelties 21. Product Samples 22. Special Events Mktg. 23. Spot Radio 24. Spot T.V. 25. Weekly Newsp. 26. Yellow Page Adv.

Ashland Inc. — (Continued)

Tel.: (513) 421-8840
Fax: (513) 287-1858

ASHLAND INC.
(Sub. of Ashland Consumer Markets (Valvoline))
(d/b/a/ The Valvoline Company)
3499 Blazer Pkwy
Lexington, KY 40509-1850
Mailing Address:
PO Box 14000
Lexington, KY 40512-4000
Tel.: (859) 357-7777
Fax: (859) 357-7733
Toll Free: (800) 354-9061
Web Site: www.valvoline.com
Sales Range: $1-4.9 Billion
Approx. Number Employees: 4,500
Year Founded: 1866
Business Description:
Automotive & Industrial Lubricants, Rust Preventives, Automotive Chemicals & Filters, Automotive Refrigerants, Quick Oil Change Service & Appearance Products Mfr & Marketer
S.I.C.: 2992
N.A.I.C.S.: 324191
Export
Media: 2-3-4-6-7-9-10-11-13-14-15-16-18-19-20-21-22-23-24-25-26
Distr.: Intl.
Budget Set: July
Personnel:
James J. O'Brien *(Chm & CEO)*
Anne T. Schumann *(CIO, Chief Admin Svcs Officer & VP)*
Samuel J. Mitchell, Jr. *(Pres-Ashl & Consumer Markets, VP)*
John E. Panichella *(VP, Pres-Ashl & Aqualon Functional Ingredients)*
Paul C. Raymond *(VP, Pres-Ashl & Hercules Water Technologies)*
Karen L. Evans *(Asst Treas)*
M. Ray Pace *(Asst Treas)*
Blair Boggs *(VP-Brands-Global)*
Joseph R. Broce *(Asst Treas)*
Thomas F. Davis *(Asst Sec)*
Frederick M. Greenwood *(Chief Tax Counsel & Asst Gen Counsel)*
Timothy S. Kavanaugh *(Asst Sec)*
Steven L. Spalding *(Asst Sec)*
Advertising Agency:
Critical Mass Inc.
225 N Michigan Ave Ste 2050
Chicago, IL 60601-7757
Tel.: (312) 288-2500
Fax: (312) 288-2501

A.T. WILLIAMS OIL COMPANY
(d/b/a WilcoHess, LLC)
5446 University Pkwy
Winston Salem, NC 27105-1366
Tel.: (336) 767-6280
Fax: (336) 767-6283
Toll Free: (800) 642-0945
E-mail: webmaster@wilcousa.com
Web Site: www.wilcousa.com
Sales Range: $10-24.9 Million
Approx. Number Employees: 2,000
Year Founded: 1963
Business Description:
Gasoline Service Stations
S.I.C.: 6719
N.A.I.C.S.: 551112
Import Export
Advertising Expenditures: $300,000
Media: 13-22
Personnel:
Arthur T. Williams, Jr. *(Founder)*

BARDAHL MANUFACTURING CORPORATION
1400 NW 52nd St
Seattle, WA 98127-5131
Tel.: (206) 783-4851
Fax: (206) 784-3219
Toll Free: (888) BARDAHL
E-mail: customerservice@bardahl.com
Web Site: www.bardahl.com
Approx. Number Employees: 35
Year Founded: 1939
Business Description:
Mfr. of Auto Additives & Lubricants
S.I.C.: 2992; 2911
N.A.I.C.S.: 324191; 324110
Export
Media: 1-2-4-5-6-9-10-20-24-26
Distr.: Intl.; Natl.
Budget Set: Aug.
Personnel:
Evelyn Bardahl McNeil *(Chm)*
Richard Ross *(VP-Sls)*
Brands & Products:
ALL-U-NEED
AMERICAN CLASSIC
B2
BARDAHL
EVERYTHING RUNS BETTER WITH BARDAHL
KIWAMI
KNOCK-OUT
NO SMOKE
RING-EEZE
SLUDGE GUARD
STOP LEAK

BEL-RAY COMPANY, INC.
Bowman Ave
Wall, NJ 07719
Tel.: (732) 938-2421
Fax: (732) 938-4232
E-mail: employment@belray.com
Web Site: www.belray.com
Approx. Number Employees: 120
Year Founded: 1946
Business Description:
Specialty Lubricants Mfr
S.I.C.: 2992
N.A.I.C.S.: 324191
Export
Media: 4-7-10-17-21-22
Distr.: Natl.
Personnel:
Daryl Brosnan *(CEO)*
Annie Bren *(Mgr-Mktg)*
Brands & Products:
BEL-RAY
BIO-BEL H1R
EXL
HVI
THE LUBE-RARY
NO-TOX

BLUE DOLPHIN ENERGY COMPANY
801 Travis St Ste 2100
Houston, TX 77002-5705
Tel.: (713) 568-4725
Fax: (713) 227-7626
E-mail: scantu@blue-dolphin.com
Web Site: www.blue-dolphin.com
E-Mail For Key Personnel:
President: mjacobson@blue-dolphin.com
Approx. Rev.: $2,741,571
Approx. Number Employees: 5
Year Founded: 1986
Business Description:
Oil & Gas Pipeline Transportation; Oil & Gas Exploration Services
S.I.C.: 1311; 1389; 4612; 4922
N.A.I.C.S.: 211111; 213112; 486110; 486210
Media: 7
Personnel:
Ivar Siem *(CEO, Pres & Sec)*
T. Scott Howard *(Treas & Asst Sec)*

BP AMERICA INC.
(Group of BP plc)
501 Westlake Park Blvd
Houston, TX 77079-2604
Tel.: (281) 366-2000
Web Site: www.bp.com/us
Approx. Number Employees: 7,500
Business Description:
US Headquarters; Oil Exploration & Production; Gas & Power & Alternative Energy Businesses
S.I.C.: 1311; 1381; 1389; 6719
N.A.I.C.S.: 211111; 213111; 213112; 551114
Personnel:
H. Lamar McKay *(Chm & Pres)*
Derek Anthony *(CIO-Gulf of Mexico)*
David Nagel *(Exec VP)*
Geoff Morrell *(Head-Comm)*
Brian Sullivan *(Mgr-IR)*
Advertising Agency:
Ogilvy Public Relations Worldwide
1111 19th St NW 10th Fl
Washington, DC 20036
Tel.: (202) 729-4000
Fax: (202) 729-4001

BP CORPORATION NORTH AMERICA INC.
(Branch of BP Corporation North America Inc.)
28301 Ferry Rd
Warrenville, IL 60555-3018
Tel.: (630) 821-2222
Approx. Number Employees: 100
Business Description:
Petroleum Products Distr
S.I.C.: 5172
N.A.I.C.S.: 424720
Advertising Expenditures: $40,000,000
Media: 2-6-7-8-9-10-14-15-18-19-20-23-24
Distr.: Natl.
Budget Set: Dec.
Personnel:
Mukta Tandon *(Brand Comm Mgr-Americas)*
Advertising Agency:
Ogilvy & Mather
350 W Mart Ctr Dr Ste 1100
Chicago, IL 60654-1866
Tel.: (312) 856-8200
Fax: (312) 856-8207

BP EXPLORATION (ALASKA) INC.
(Sub. of BP Oil Co.)
900 E Benson Blvd
Anchorage, AK 99508-4254
Mailing Address:
PO Box 196612
Anchorage, AK 99519-6612
Tel.: (907) 561-5111
Fax: (907) 564-4920
E-mail: info@bp.com
Web Site: www.bp.com
Approx. Number Employees: 1,692
Business Description:
Oil & Gas Exploration & Production
S.I.C.: 1311
N.A.I.C.S.: 211111
Advertising Expenditures: $500,000
Media: 4-9-17-25
Distr.: Natl.
Budget Set: Nov.
Personnel:
John Minge *(Pres)*
Don Kaneckfer *(VP & Dir-External Affairs)*
Advertising Agencies:
Nerland Agency Worldwide Partners
808 E St
Anchorage, AK 99501-3532
Tel.: (907) 274-9553
Tel.: (907) 274-9549 (Marketing)
Fax: (907) 274-9990

Northwest Strategies
431 W Seventh Ave Ste 101
Anchorage, AK 99501
Tel.: (907) 563-4881
Fax: (907) 562-2570
(Petroleum)

Thompson & Co. Public Relations
445 W 9th Ave
Anchorage, AK 99501
Tel.: (907) 561-4488
Fax: (907) 563-3223

BP LUBRICANTS USA INC.
(Sub. of Castrol North America Inc.)
9300 Pulaski Hwy
Baltimore, MD 21220-2418
Tel.: (410) 574-5000
Fax: (410) 682-9408
Web Site: www.bp.com/genericformsdisplay.do?formId=60300328
Approx. Number Employees: 95
Year Founded: 1987
Business Description:
Commercial Lubricant Mfr & Distr
S.I.C.: 2992; 5172
N.A.I.C.S.: 324191; 424720
Export
Advertising Expenditures: $1,000,000
Media: 2-4-6-7-10-11-13-18-20-21-23-25
Distr.: Natl.
Budget Set: Aug. -Sept.
Personnel:
Marci Drand *(Pres)*
Brands & Products:
AERIAL LIFT
AGRI GEAR PLUS
AGRI GREASE ULTRA
AGRI HYDRAULIC PLUS
AGRI POWER PLUS
AGRI TRANS PLUS
ANVOL SWX FM
ASSURON
BLUE HYDRAULIC PLUS
CARELUBE HTG
CONTRACTORS SPECIAL
DRYDENE TEC II
DUAL RANGE HV
ELIXION
ESGL

Key to Media (For complete agency information see *The Advertising Red Books-Agencies* edition):
1. Bus. Publs. 2. Cable T.V. 3. Catalogs & Directories. 4. Co-op Adv. 5. Consumer Mags. 6. D.M. to Bus. Estab.7. D.M. to Consumers 8. Daily Newsp. 9. Exhibits/Trade Shows 10. Foreign 11. Infomercial 12. Internet Adv.13. Multimedia 14. Network Radio 15. Network T.V. 16. Newsp. Distr. Mags. 17. Other 18. Outdoor (Posters, Transit) 19. Point of Purchase20. Premiums, Novelties 21. Product Samples 22. Special Events Mktg. 23. Spot Radio 24. Spot T.V. 25. Weekly Newsp. 26. Yellow Page Adv.

FIFTH WHEEL GREASE
HD LITHIUM
HYPURON S
ISOLUBE
ISOLUBE EP
LT HYDRAULIC OIL
MP DEXRON - III/MERCON
MULTI-MIX 3
OPEN GEAR 800
PARADENE AW
PARADENE R&O
PYROPLEX BLUE
PYROPLEX GOLD
SFG
SHL
SHL 00
SYNCOM
SYNGEAR
SYNGEAR CD-50
TECTION EXTRA
TECTION S
TRANS-C
TRANSYND
TRANSYND RD
UTF

BP PRODUCTS NORTH AMERICA INC.
(Sub. of BP America Inc.)
150 W Warrenville Rd
Naperville, IL 60563-8473
Tel.: (630) 420-4300
E-mail: linda.bartman@bp.com
Approx. Number Employees: 200
Business Description:
Petroleum Products Distr
S.I.C.: 2911; 4613
N.A.I.C.S.: 324110; 486910
Advertising Agency:
GolinHarris
(Part of the Interpublic Group of Companies)
111 E Wacker Dr 11th Fl
Chicago, IL 60601-4306
Tel.: (312) 729-4000
Fax: (312) 729-4010
(US Fuels)

CASTROL NORTH AMERICA INC.
(Sub. of BP America Inc.)
1500 Valley Rd
Wayne, NJ 07470-2040
Tel.: (973) 633-2200
Fax: (973) 633-9867
E-mail: webmaster@castrolna.com
Web Site: www.castrolusa.com
Approx. Number Employees: 200
Year Founded: 1954
Business Description:
Lubricant & Oil Mfr & Distr
S.I.C.: 2992
N.A.I.C.S.: 324191
Advertising Expenditures: $30,000,000
Media: 1-3-5-15-23
Distr.: Natl.
Budget Set: Sept.

CCS CORPORATION
1800 140 10 Ave SE
Calgary, AB T2G 0R1, Canada
Tel.: (403) 233-7565
Fax: (403) 261-5612
E-mail: info@ccscorporation.ca
Web Site: www.ccscorporation.ca
Sales Range: $1-4.9 Billion
Approx. Number Employees: 3,000
Year Founded: 1993
Business Description:
Energy Resource Development & Marketing, Oil Well Servicing, Waste Treatment & Disposal
S.I.C.: 1311; 1381; 2911; 4953
N.A.I.C.S.: 211111; 213111; 324110; 562211
Media: 10-17-26
Personnel:
David P. Werklund *(Founder, Chm, Pres & CEO)*
Marshall L. McRae *(CFO)*
Jim Coughlan *(VP-Mktg)*
William P. Faubel *(VP-Mktg & Strategic Acct Mgmt)*
David Fulton *(VP-HR)*
Michael Williams *(VP-HR)*
Ramin Bogzaran *(Dir-Bus Dev)*

CENTURION ENERGY INTERNATIONAL INC.
(Sub. of Dana Gas PJSC)
Ste 1700 Bow Valley Square II
Calgary, AB T2P 2V7, Canada
Tel.: (403) 263-6002
Fax: (403) 263-5998
Sales Range: $75-99.9 Million
Approx. Number Employees: 140
Business Description:
Petroleum & Natural Gas Exploration, Development, Drilling & Extraction
S.I.C.: 1311; 1321; 1389
N.A.I.C.S.: 211111; 211112; 213112
Export
Media: 2-7-11
Personnel:
Said S. Arrata *(Chm & CEO)*
David H. Thomas *(Pres & COO)*
Barry W. Swan *(CFO & Sr VP)*
Paul McDougall *(Treas & VP-Fin)*
M. N. Zayat *(VP-Exploration & Gen Mgr-Calgary)*
A.D. Anton *(VP-Engrg, Production & Dir-Special Projects)*
Philip Beck *(VP-Engrg)*
Darren Moulds *(Controller-Fin)*

CGGVERITAS SERVICES (U.S.) INC.
(Sub. of Compagnie Generale de Geophysique-Veritas)
10300 Town Park Dr
Houston, TX 77072-5236
Tel.: (832) 351-8300
Fax: (832) 351-8701
Web Site: www.cggveritas.com
Approx. Number Employees: 1,000
Business Description:
Geophysical Services & Mfr of Geophysical Equipment
S.I.C.: 1389; 8713
N.A.I.C.S.: 213112; 541360
Media: 2-10
Personnel:
Dennis S. Baldwin *(CFO, Treas & Exec VP)*
Stephane-Paul Frydman *(Exec VP-Fin & Strategy)*
Thierry Le Roux *(Exec VP-Bus Dev)*
Colin Murdoch *(Exec VP-Processing, Imaging & Reservoir Div)*
Stephen Hallows *(Sr VP-SD & QHSE)*
Scott Smith *(Sr VP-HR)*
Gary Wilson *(VP-HR)*
Robert Brunck *(Dir)*

CH ENERGY GROUP, INC.
284 South Ave
Poughkeepsie, NY 12601
Tel.: (845) 452-2000
Fax: (845) 486-5465
Web Site: www.centralhudson.com
Approx. Rev.: $972,305,000
Approx. Number Employees: 728
Year Founded: 1999
Business Description:
Holding Company for Electricity, Natural Gas, Propane, Fuel Oil & Petroleum Products
S.I.C.: 4939; 4911; 4924; 4931; 6719
N.A.I.C.S.: 221111; 221119; 221122; 221210; 551112
Advertising Expenditures: $700,000
Personnel:
Steven V. Lant *(Chm & CEO)*
Christopher M. Capone *(CFO & Exec VP)*
John E. Gould *(Gen Counsel & Exec VP)*
James P. Laurito *(Exec VP)*

CHEM-TREND LIMITED PARTNERSHIP
(Div. of Freudenberg Chemical Specialties KG)
1445 McPherson Park Dr
Howell, MI 48843-3947
Tel.: (517) 546-4520
Fax: (517) 548-6710
Toll Free: (800) 727-7730
Web Site: www.chemtrend.com
Approx. Number Employees: 340
Business Description:
Mold Releases Mfr for the Plastic & Rubber Industries; Die Lubricants, Quench Compounds, Plunger Lubricants, Tire Releasants Mfr
S.I.C.: 2992; 2869
N.A.I.C.S.: 324191; 325199
Advertising Expenditures: $700,000
Media: 1-2-4-10-11-17
Distr.: Intl.; Natl.
Personnel:
Devanir Moraes *(Pres & CEO)*
Carl Posluszny *(VP-Fin)*
Brands & Products:
CHEMLEASE
MONO-COAT
MONO-LUBE
POWER-LUBE
PURA
SAFETY-LUBE
SAFETY-LUBE-SUPER

CHEVRON CORPORATION
6001 Bollinger Canyon Rd
San Ramon, CA 94583
Tel.: (925) 842-1000
E-mail: comment@chevron.com
Web Site: www.chevron.com
Approx. Rev.: $204,928,000,000
Approx. Number Employees: 62,000
Year Founded: 1879
Business Description:
Exploration, Production Manufacturing, Marketing, Transportation, Chemicals Manufacturing & Sales, Geothermal & Power Generation, Renewables & Advanced Technologies for the Oil & Natural Gas Industries
S.I.C.: 2911; 1389
N.A.I.C.S.: 324110; 213112
Import Export
Advertising Expenditures: $55,000,000
Media: 2-3-6-9-13-16-17-18-23-24-26
Distr.: Reg.
Budget Set: Aug.
Personnel:
John S. Watson *(Chm & CEO)*
George L. Kirkland *(Vice Chm & Exec VP-Global Upstream & Gas)*
John D. Gass *(Pres & Corp VP-Chevron Global Gas)*
Patricia E. Yarrington *(CFO & VP)*
Gary P. Luquette *(Pres-Chevron North America Exploration & Prod & VP)*
Paul K Siegele *(Pres-Chevron Energy Tech)*
R. Hewitt Pate *(Gen Counsel & VP)*
C. N. Macfarlane *(Gen Counsel-Tax)*
John E. Bethancourt *(Exec VP)*
Charles A. James *(Exec VP-Tech & Svcs)*
Michael K. Wirth *(Exec VP-Global Downstream & Chemicals)*
Rhonda I. Zygocki *(Exec VP-Policy & Plng)*
Matthew J. Foehr *(VP & Comptroller)*
Joe W. Laymon *(VP-HR, Medical & Security)*
Libby Estell *(Assoc Editor-Chevron.com)*
Katie Winter *(Mgr-Comm-Americas Products)*
Brands & Products:
CALTEX
CHEVRON
EXTRAMILE
HAVOLINE
HUMAN ENERGY
ORONITE
ORONITE ALKANE
REVTEX
RPM
STAR MART
STARCARD
TECHRON
TEXACO
URSA
VORTEX
XPRESS LUBE
Advertising Agency:
McGarry Bowen, LLC
601 W 26th St Ste 1150
New York, NY 10001
Tel.: (212) 598-2900
Fax: (212) 598-2996

CIMAREX ENERGY, INC.
(Sub. of Cimarex Energy, Inc.)
Ste 1400 5215 N O'Connor Blvd
Irving, TX 75039-3785
Tel.: (972) 401-0752
Fax: (972) 401-3110
Web Site: www.cimarex.com/locations.html
Sales Range: $450-499.9 Million
Approx. Number Employees: 30
Business Description:
Oil & Natural Gas Producer
S.I.C.: 1389
N.A.I.C.S.: 213112
Media: 10-11
Personnel:
Manette Martina *(Office Mgr)*

CITGO PETROLEUM CORPORATION
(Sub. of Petroleos de Venezuela S.A.)
6100 S Yale

Key to Media (For complete agency information see *The Advertising Red Books-Agencies* edition):
1. Bus. Publs. 2. Cable T.V. 3. Catalogs & Directories. 4. Co-op Adv. 5. Consumer Mags. 6. D.M. to Bus. Estab.7. D.M. to Consumers
8. Daily Newsp. 9. Exhibits/Trade Shows 10. Foreign 11. Infomercial 12. Internet Adv.13. Multimedia 14. Network Radio
15. Network T.V. 16. Newsp. Distr. Mags. 17. Other 18. Outdoor (Posters, Transit) 19. Point of Purchase20. Premiums, Novelties
21. Product Samples 22. Special Events Mktg. 23. Spot Radio 24. Spot T.V. 25. Weekly Newsp. 26. Yellow Page Adv.

Citgo Petroleum Corporation — (Continued)

Tulsa, OK 74136
Tel.: (918) 495-4000
Fax: (918) 495-4511
E-mail: info@citgo.com
Web Site: www.citgo.com
Approx. Number Employees: 4,000
Year Founded: 1900
Business Description:
Refining, Marketing & Transportation of Petroleum
S.I.C.: 2911; 2992
N.A.I.C.S.: 324110; 324191
Advertising Expenditures: $11,000,000
Media: 1-2-3-7-8-9-10-16-17-18-19-20-22-23-24-26
Distr.: Natl.
Personnel:
Alejandro Granado *(Chm, Pres & CEO)*
Brian O'Kelly *(VP-Fin)*
Gustavo Velasquez *(VP-Supply & Mktg)*
Fernando Garay *(Mgr-Pub Affairs)*
Brands & Products:
CELEBRITY CARD
MYSTIK
SUPERGARD
SUPERGARD ULTRALIFE
Advertising Agency:
Carmichael Lynch
110 N 5th St
Minneapolis, MN 55403
Tel.: (612) 334-6000
Fax: (612) 334-6090

CLEAN ENERGY FUELS CORP.

3020 Old Ranch Pkwy Ste 200
Seal Beach, CA 90740
Tel.: (562) 493-2804
Fax: (562) 493-4532
Web Site: www.cleanenergyfuels.com
Approx. Rev.: $125,867,000
Approx. Number Employees: 710
Business Description:
Vehicular Natural Gas Supplier
S.I.C.: 4924
N.A.I.C.S.: 221210
Advertising Expenditures: $985,000
Personnel:
Andrew J. Littlefair *(Pres & CEO)*
Richard R. Wheeler *(CFO)*
Mitchell W. Pratt *(COO)*
James N. Harger *(CMO)*
Harrison Clay *(Gen Counsel & VP-Renewable Fuels)*
Barclay F. Corbus *(Sr VP-Strategic Dev)*
Peter Grace *(Sr VP-Sls)*
Denis C.K. Ding *(VP-Engrg & Construction)*
Michael Eaves *(Asst VP-Tech Advancement)*
Brian Powers *(Asst VP-Ops)*
Chad Lindholm *(Gen Mgr)*
Todd Campbell *(Dir-Pub Policy)*
Greg Roche *(Dir-Bus Dev-Ports)*
John A. Somers *(Dir-Bus Dev-Transit)*
Sean Wine *(Mgr-Bus Dev & Acct Mgr)*
Doug Cameron *(Mgr-Bus Dev)*
Ben Deal *(Mgr-Bus Dev)*
Shaunt Hartounian *(Mgr-Bus Dev-Ports & Reg Trucking)*
Sheree Jeanes *(Mgr-Bus Dev-Transit-Northeast)*
Blake Littauer *(Mgr-Bus Dev-Transit)*
Les Stinson *(Mgr-Real Estate)*
Derek Turbide *(Mgr-Bus Dev)*

THE CLOROX COMPANY-GLOBAL AUTO CARE BUSINESS

(Div. of The Clorox Company)
1221 Broadway
Oakland, CA 94612-1837
Tel.: (510) 271-2270
Web Site: www.stp.com
Sales Range: $300-349.9 Million
Approx. Number Employees: 160
Year Founded: 1954
Business Description:
Mfr of Oil Treatments, Oil & Air Filters & Engine Cleaners
S.I.C.: 2992
N.A.I.C.S.: 324191
Advertising Expenditures: $12,000,000
Media: 2-3-5-6-9-10-11-15-18-19-20-21-23-24-25
Distr.: Natl.
Budget Set: Monthly
Brands & Products:
ARMOR ALL
CAR BUDDY
OOMPH!
SON OF A GUN
STP
TUFF STUFF
Advertising Agency:
DDB San Francisco
555 Market St 5th Fl
San Francisco, CA 94105
Tel.: (415) 732-3600
Fax: (415) 732-3636

COMPLEX CHEMICALS COMPANY, INC.

177 Complex Chemical Rd PO Box 1352
Tallulah, LA 71284
Tel.: (318) 574-0382
Fax: (318) 574-0816
Approx. Number Employees: 40
Year Founded: 1974
Business Description:
Lubricating Oil Mfr
S.I.C.: 2992; 2899
N.A.I.C.S.: 324191; 325998
Media: 2
Personnel:
Jerry Melton *(Owner & Pres)*

CONOCOPHILLIPS

600 N Dairy Ashford Rd
Houston, TX 77079-1100
Tel.: (281) 293-1000
Fax: (281) 293-2819
Web Site: www.conocophillips.com
Approx. Rev.: $198,655,000,000
Approx. Number Employees: 29,700
Year Founded: 1917
Business Description:
Petroleum Products, Natural Gas & Chemicals Explorer, Refiner & Marketer
S.I.C.: 2911; 1311; 4924; 5541
N.A.I.C.S.: 324110; 211111; 221210; 447190
Import Export
Advertising Expenditures: $66,000,000
Media: 2-3-5-6-9-10-13-19-22-23-24
Distr.: Natl.; Reg.
Budget Set: Sept.
Personnel:
James J. Mulva *(Chm & CEO)*
John A. Carrig *(Pres & COO)*
Jeffrey Wayne Sheets *(CFO & Sr VP-Fin)*
Gene L. Batchelder *(Chief Admin Officer & Sr VP)*
Stephen R. Barham *(Pres-Transportation)*
Christopher W. Conway *(Pres-Global Trading)*
Darren C. Jones *(Pres-Global Gas, Strategic Plng & Bus Dev)*
A. Roy Lyons *(Pres-Latin America)*
Donald Evert Wallette, Jr. *(Pres-Asia-Pacific)*
Paul C. Warwick *(Pres-Europe & West Africa)*
John D. Wright *(Pres-Global Supply)*
Larry M. Ziemba *(Pres-Global Refining)*
Janet Langford Kelly *(Gen Counsel, Sec & Sr VP-Legal)*
Larry E. Archibald *(Sr VP-Exploration & Bus Dev)*
Rand C. Berney *(Sr VP-Corp Shared Svcs)*
Stephen R. Brand *(Sr VP-Tech)*
Red Cavaney *(Sr VP-Govt, Pub Affairs & Comm)*
Willie C.W. Chiang *(Sr VP-Refining, Transportation & Mktg)*
Greg C. Garland *(Sr VP-Exploration & Production-Americas)*
Alan J. Hirshberg *(Sr VP-Plng & Strategy)*
Ryan M. Lance *(Sr VP-Exploration & Production-Intl)*
Luc J. Messier *(Sr VP-Project Dev & Procurement)*
Kevin J. Mitchell *(VP-Strategy, Admin & Tech Svcs-Exploration & Production)*
Carin S. Knickel *(VP-HR)*
Edward Walters *(Head-Strategy & Res-Corp Affairs)*
Eric Brandt *(Mgr-Sls)*
Brian Mandell *(Mgr-NGL Trading)*
R Scott Nickel *(Mgr-Compensation & Benefits)*
Mike Schwartje *(Mgr-Propane Mktg)*
Glenn E. Simpson *(Mgr-Americas Crude Supply)*
Matthew Taylor *(Mgr-Assets & Bd)*
Brands & Products:
76
CONOCO
CONOCOPHILLIPS
ENERGY FOR TOMORROW
JET
K-RESIN
KENDALL
LIQUIDPOWER
PHILLIPS
PHILLIPS 66
POWER-D
PROCLEAN
PURE PERFORMANCE
ROYAL TRITON
RYTON
TROPARTIC
Advertising Agencies:
Acento Advertising, Inc.
2254 S Sepulveda Blvd
Los Angeles, CA 90064
Tel.: (310) 943-8300
Fax: (310) 943-8310

Barnett Cox & Associates
711 Tank Farm Rd Ste 210
San Luis Obispo, CA 93401
Tel.: (805) 545-8887
Fax: (805) 545-0860

Digitas Inc.
33 Arch St
Boston, MA 02110
Tel.: (617) 867-1000
Fax: (617) 867-1111

Earthbound Media Group
14988 Sand Canyon Ave Studio 5
Irvine, CA 92618
Tel.: (949) 857-4000
Fax: (949) 857-4004
Toll Free: (866) 623-2784

KSL Media, Inc.
15910 Ventura Blvd 9th Fl
Los Angeles, CA 91436
Tel.: (818) 461-5900
Fax: (818) 461-1373

Southwest Media Group
2100 Ross Ave Ste 3200
Dallas, TX 75201
Tel.: (214) 561-5543
Fax: (214) 744-1086

COUNTRYMARK COOPERATIVE, INC.

225 SE St Ste 44
Indianapolis, IN 46202-4002
Tel.: (317) 692-8500
Fax: (317) 692-7185
Toll Free: (800) 808-3170
E-mail: spindler@countrymark.com
Web Site: www.countrymark.com
Approx. Number Employees: 275
Year Founded: 1938
Business Description:
Petroleum Products for Agriculture Mfr
S.I.C.: 5172
N.A.I.C.S.: 424720
Export
Advertising Expenditures: $1,000,000
Media: 1-2-5-7-10-13-18-19-20-23-25
Distr.: Reg.
Budget Set: June
Personnel:
Charles Smith *(CEO)*
John Deaton *(Sr VP)*
Jim O'Conor *(Dir-Corp Svcs)*

CROSSTEX ENERGY, L.P.

(Affil. of Crosstex Energy, Inc.)
2501 Cedar Springs Rd Ste 100
Dallas, TX 75201-7684
Tel.: (214) 953-9500
Fax: (214) 953-9501
E-mail: allysia.emerson@crosstexenergy.com
Web Site: www.crosstexenergy.com
Year Founded: 1996
Business Description:
Energy & Gas Related Services
S.I.C.: 1311; 1321; 4922
N.A.I.C.S.: 211111; 211112; 486210
Media: 2-18-24
Personnel:
Rhys J. Best *(Chm)*
Barry E. Davis *(Pres & CEO)*

Key to Media (For complete agency information see *The Advertising Red Books-Agencies* edition):
1. Bus. Publs. 2. Cable T.V. 3. Catalogs & Directories. 4. Co-op Adv. 5. Consumer Mags. 6. D.M. to Bus. Estab.7. D.M. to Consumers 8. Daily Newsp. 9. Exhibits/Trade Shows 10. Foreign 11. Infomercial 12. Internet Adv.13. Multimedia 14. Network Radio 15. Network T.V. 16. Newsp. Distr. Mags. 17. Other 18. Outdoor (Posters, Transit) 19. Point of Purchase20. Premiums, Novelties 21. Product Samples 22. Special Events Mktg. 23. Spot Radio 24. Spot T.V. 25. Weekly Newsp. 26. Yellow Page Adv.

Michael Garberding *(CFO & Sr VP)*
William W. Davis *(COO & Exec VP)*
Joe A. Davis *(Gen Counsel & Exec VP)*

CROWN CENTRAL LLC
(Sub. of Rosemore Inc.)
1 N Charles St Ste 2100
Baltimore, MD 21201-3740
Mailing Address:
PO Box 1168
Baltimore, MD 21203-1168
Tel.: (410) 539-7400
Fax: (410) 659-4778
Toll Free: (800) 992-7686
Telex: 7102341677
E-mail: info@crowncentral.com
Web Site: www.crowncentral.com
E-Mail For Key Personnel:
Public Relations: customerservice@crowncentral.com
Approx. Number Employees: 2,600
Year Founded: 1930
Business Description:
Petroleum Products & Petrochemicals Refiner & Marketer
S.I.C.: 2911; 5171
N.A.I.C.S.: 324110; 424710
Media: 1-3-5-8-18-19-20-22-23-24
Distr.: Direct to Consumer; Reg.
Budget Set: Dec.
Personnel:
Henry A. Rosenberg, Jr. *(Chm)*
Paul J. Ebner *(Pres)*
Andrew Lapayowker *(Gen Counsel & Sec)*
Randall M. Trembly *(Exec VP)*
William A. Wolters *(Sr VP-Supply)*
Brands & Products:
CROWN
FAST FARE
ZIPPY MART

CRYSTAL FLASH PETROLEUM CORP.
(Sub. of Heritage Group)
5221 Ivy Tech Dr
Indianapolis, IN 46268-1016
Mailing Address:
PO Box 684
Indianapolis, IN 46206-0684
Tel.: (317) 879-2849
Fax: (317) 879-2855
Toll Free: (800) 886-3835
E-mail: info@crystalflash.com
Web Site: www.crystalflash.com
Approx. Number Employees: 350
Year Founded: 1930
Business Description:
Gasoline Stations & Convenience Stores Operator
S.I.C.: 5541; 5411
N.A.I.C.S.: 447110; 445110
Media: 8-9-18-19-20-23-24-26
Distr.: Direct to Consumer; Reg.
Personnel:
Tom Fehsenfeld *(Pres)*
Bill Stough *(CEO)*
Brands & Products:
CRYSTAL FLASH
CRYSTAL POWER

D-A LUBRICANT COMPANY
1340 W 29th St
Indianapolis, IN 46208-4943
Tel.: (317) 923-5321
Fax: (317) 941-2134
Toll Free: (800) 645-5823
E-mail: dalube@dalube.com
Web Site: www.dalube.com
Sales Range: $50-74.9 Million
Approx. Number Employees: 120
Year Founded: 1919
Business Description:
Lubricating Oils & Greases Whslr
S.I.C.: 2992; 5065
N.A.I.C.S.: 324191; 423690
Media: 10
Personnel:
Mike Protogere *(Owner)*
Gisela M. Miller *(Pres)*
Gloria Comstock *(Dir-Comm)*
Brands & Products:
BLUE FLAME GEO
CHEMGUARD
D-A LUBRICANT
MOLY5
PERMAPLEX
PROPLEX
REDPLEX
RELIANT
SUPERPLEX TC
SYNSURE

DEJOUR ENTERPRISES LTD.
999 Canada Place Suite 598
Vancouver, BC V6C 2X4, Canada
Tel.: (604) 638-5050
Fax: (604) 638-5051
Toll Free: (866) 888-8230
E-mail: investor@dejour.com
Web Site: www.dejour.com
Approx. Rev.: $6,641,318
Approx. Number Employees: 16
Year Founded: 1968
Business Description:
Oil & Gas Property Acquisition & Exploration Services
S.I.C.: 1311; 1094
N.A.I.C.S.: 211111; 212291
Personnel:
Robert L. Hodgkinson *(Co-Chm, Pres & CEO)*
Stephen R. Mut *(Co-Chm)*
Mathew H. Wong *(CFO)*
Phil Bretzloff *(Gen Counsel & VP)*
Lori Kozub *(Dir-Mktg)*
Ricardo Salazar *(Mgr-Ops)*
Advertising Agency:
Porter Levay & Rose, Inc.
7 Penn Plz Ste 810
New York, NY 10001
Tel.: (212) 564-4700
Fax: (212) 244-3075

DELEK US HOLDINGS, INC.
(Sub. of Delek Petroleum Ltd.)
7102 Commerce Way
Brentwood, TN 37027
Tel.: (615) 771-6701
Tel.: (615) 224-1121
Fax: (615) 771-8098
Fax: (615) 224-1186
Web Site: www.delekus.com
Approx. Sls.: $3,755,600,000
Approx. Number Employees: 3,395
Year Founded: 2001
Business Description:
Holding Company
S.I.C.: 1311; 5171; 6719
N.A.I.C.S.: 211111; 424710; 551112
Advertising Expenditures: $2,900,000
Personnel:
Ezra Uzi Yemin *(Pres & CEO)*
Joane Walker *(Chief Acctg Officer & VP)*
Frederec Green *(Pres/COO-Delek Refining & Exec VP)*
Mark B. Cox *(CFO-Delek US Holdings & Exec VP)*
Kent Thomas *(Gen Counsel & Sec)*
Assi Ginzburg *(Exec VP)*
Lynwood Gregory *(Sr VP)*
Noel Ryan *(Dir-IR, Exec Head-IR & Corp Comm)*
Brands & Products:
DISCOUNT FOOD MART
EAST COAST
FAST FOOD & FUEL
FAVORITE MARKETS
GRILLE MARX
MAPCO EXPRESS
MAPCO MART
Advertising Agencies:
Arad Communications Group
72 Pinchas Rosen St
Tel Aviv, 69512, Israel
Tel.: (972) 3 7693303
Tel.: (972) 3 7693313
Fax: (972) 3 7693334

Lovell Communications
(Single Location)
964 Lake Rd
Lake Forest, IL 60045-2223
Tel.: (847) 234-8296

DEVON ENERGY CORPORATION
20 N Broadway
Oklahoma City, OK 73102-8296
Tel.: (405) 235-3611
Fax: (405) 552-4550
Web Site: www.devonenergy.com
E-Mail For Key Personnel:
Public Relations: zack.hager@dvn.com
Approx. Rev.: $9,940,000,000
Approx. Number Employees: 5,000
Year Founded: 1971
Business Description:
Petroleum & Natural Gas Explorer, Extractor & Distr
S.I.C.: 1311; 1381; 4922; 5172
N.A.I.C.S.: 211111; 213111; 424720; 486210
Export
Personnel:
J. Larry Nichols *(Chm & CEO)*
John Richels *(Pres & CEO)*
Jeff A. Agosta *(CFO & Exec VP)*
Danny J. Heatly *(Chief Acctg Officer & VP-Acctg)*
Lyndon C. Taylor *(Gen Counsel & Exec VP)*
K. Earl Reynolds *(Sr VP-Strategic Plng & Gen Mgr-Intl Div)*
David A. Hager *(Exec VP-Exploration & Production)*
Frank W. Rudolph *(Exec VP-HR)*
Bradley A. Foster *(Sr VP & Gen Mgr-Central Div)*
Gregory T. Kelleher *(Sr VP & Gen Mgr-Southern Div)*
Chris Seasons *(Sr VP & Gen Mgr-Canada Div)*
William A. Van Wie *(Sr VP & Gen Mgr-Exploration)*
Tony D. Vaughn *(Sr VP & Gen Mgr-Gulf Div)*
Don D. DeCarlo *(Sr VP-Western Div)*
Darryl G. Smette *(Sr VP-Mktg & Midstream)*
Vincent W. White *(Sr VP-IR)*
William F. Whitsitt *(Sr VP-Pub Affairs)*
Terrence L. Ruder *(VP & Gen Mgr-Mktg & Midstream Div)*
Zack Hager *(Mgr-IR)*
Brands & Products:
DEVON
WISE EYES
Advertising Agency:
Cole & Weber United
221 Yale Ave N Ste 600
Seattle, WA 98109
Tel.: (206) 447-9595
Fax: (206) 233-0178

DEVON ENERGY CORPORATION
(Div. of Devon Energy Corporation)
1200 Smith St Ste 3300
Houston, TX 77002-4400
Tel.: (405) 235-3611
Fax: (713) 265-8008
Web Site: www.devonenergy.com
Sales Range: $1-4.9 Billion
Approx. Number Employees: 950
Year Founded: 1973
Business Description:
Petroleum & Natural Gas Explorer, Extractor & Distr
S.I.C.: 1311; 1381; 4922
N.A.I.C.S.: 211111; 213111; 486210
Media: 2-7-10-17
Distr.: Natl.
Budget Set: Nov.
Personnel:
J. Larry Nichols *(Chm & CEO)*
Darryl G. Smette *(Exec VP-Mktg & Midstream)*
Don D. DeCarlo *(Sr VP-Western Div)*
Vincent White *(Sr VP-IR)*
Gregory T. Kelleher *(VP & Gen Mgr)*
Brian Engel *(Mgr-Pub Affairs)*

DYNEGY, INC.
1000 Louisiana St Ste 5800
Houston, TX 77002
Mailing Address:
PO Box 4777
Houston, TX 77002
Tel.: (713) 507-6400
Fax: (713) 507-3871
Toll Free: (877) DYNEGY9
E-mail: ir@dynegy.com
Web Site: www.dynegy.com
Approx. Rev.: $2,323,000,000
Approx. Number Employees: 1,519
Business Description:
Power Plant Operation & Management Services
S.I.C.: 4911; 4931; 4939
N.A.I.C.S.: 221122; 221119
Media: 2-7-26
Distr.: Natl.
Budget Set: Oct.
Personnel:
Patricia A. Hammick *(Chm)*
Robert C. Flexon *(Pres & CEO)*
Charles C. Cook *(Interim CFO)*
Catherine B. Callaway *(Gen Counsel & Exec VP)*
Carolyn J. Stone *(Treas & Sr VP)*
Lynn A. Lednicky *(Exec VP-Ops)*
Kent R. Stephenson *(Sr VP)*
Norelle V. Lundy *(VP-IR & PR)*
David Byford *(Sr Dir-PR)*

ECU SILVER MINING INC.
1116 Ave Granada

Key to Media (For complete agency information see *The Advertising Red Books-Agencies* edition):
1. Bus. Publs. 2. Cable T.V. 3. Catalogs & Directories. 4. Co-op Adv. 5. Consumer Mags. 6. D.M. to Bus. Estab.7. D.M. to Consumers
8. Daily Newsp. 9. Exhibits/Trade Shows 10. Foreign 11. Infomercial 12. Internet Adv.13. Multimedia 14. Network Radio
15. Network T.V. 16. Newsp. Distr. Mags. 17. Other 18. Outdoor (Posters, Transit) 19. Point of Purchase20. Premiums, Novelties
21. Product Samples 22. Special Events Mktg. 23. Spot Radio 24. Spot T.V. 25. Weekly Newsp. 26. Yellow Page Adv.

ECU Silver Mining Inc. — (Continued)
Rouyn-Noranda, QC J9Y 1G9, Canada
Tel.: (819) 797-1210
Fax: (819) 797-1214
Web Site: www.ecu.ca
Approx. Int. Income: $56,089
Approx. Number Employees: 200
Business Description:
Silver Mining Services
S.I.C.: 1044
N.A.I.C.S.: 212222
Personnel:
Michel Roy *(Chm & CEO)*
Stephen J. Altmann *(Pres)*
Dwight Walker *(CFO)*
Armando Lujan Acuna *(Pres-Mexican Subsidiaries)*
Jorge Lujan Acuna *(Mgr-Mine)*
Ruben Montiel Rodriguez *(Mgr-Mill)*
Advertising Agency:
CHF Investor Relations
90 Adelaide St W Ste 600
Toronto, ON M5H 3V9, Canada
Tel.: (416) 868-1079
Fax: (416) 868-6198

EGPI FIRECREEK, INC.
6564 Smoke Tree Ln
Scottsdale, AZ 85253
Tel.: (480) 948-6581
Fax: (480) 443-1403
Web Site: www.egpifirecreek.com
Approx. Rev.: $15,705
Business Description:
Holding Company; Oil & Gas Production
S.I.C.: 6719; 1389; 6289
N.A.I.C.S.: 551112; 213112; 523999
Advertising Expenditures: $22,158
Media: 17
Personnel:
Dennis R. Alexander *(Chm, CEO & CFO)*
Melvena Alexander *(Sec/Comptroller & Co-Treas)*
David H. Ray *(Treas, Exec VP & Dir)*
Brandon D. Ray *(Exec VP-Fin)*
Larry W. Trapp *(Exec VP)*

ENCANA CORP.
855 2nd Street SW Suite 1800
Box 2850
Calgary, AB T2P 2S5, Canada
Tel.: (403) 645-2000
Fax: (403) 645-3400
E-mail: investor.relations@encana.com
Web Site: www.encana.com
Approx. Rev.: $8,870,000,000
Approx. Number Employees: 4,169
Year Founded: 1973
Business Description:
Oil & Gas Exploration, Production, Gas Storage & Processing
S.I.C.: 1311
N.A.I.C.S.: 211111
Export
Media: 2-7-11
Distr.: Intl.
Personnel:
David P. O'Brien *(Chm)*
Randall K. Eresman *(Pres & CEO)*
Sherri A. Brillon *(CFO & Exec VP)*
Michael M. Graham *(Pres-Canadian Div & Exec VP)*
Jeff E. Wojahn *(Pres-US & Exec VP)*
Gerald T. Ince *(Asst Treas)*
R. William Oliver *(Chief Corp Officer & Exec VP)*
Florence Murphy *(VP-Pub & Community Rels)*
Alan Boras *(Mgr-Media Rels)*
Leanne Deighton *(Grp Coord-Brand Mgmt)*
Susan Grey *(Mgr-IR)*
Brands & Products:
ENCANA
ENERGY FOR PEOPLE

ENERGY PARTNERS, LTD.
(Filed Ch 11 Bankruptcy #932957 on 05/01/09 in U.S. Bankruptcy Ct, Southern Dist of TX, Houston)
201 St Charles Ave Ste 3400
New Orleans, LA 70170-3400
Tel.: (504) 569-1875
Fax: (504) 569-1874
E-mail: investorrelations@eplweb.com
Web Site: www.eplweb.com
Approx. Rev.: $239,909,000
Approx. Number Employees: 100
Year Founded: 1998
Business Description:
Oil & Natural Gas Exploration & Production
S.I.C.: 1311; 1389
N.A.I.C.S.: 211111; 213112
Media: 2-25
Personnel:
Marc McCarthy *(Chm)*
Gary C. Hanna *(CEO)*
Tiffany J. Thom *(CFO, Treas & Sr VP)*
David P. Cedro *(Chief Acctg Officer, Sr VP & Controller)*
John H. Peper *(Gen Counsel, Sec & Exec VP)*
Chad E. Williams *(Sr VP-Production)*
Dennis L. Legendre *(VP-HR)*

ENERNOC, INC.
101 Federal St Ste 1100
Boston, MA 02110
Tel.: (617) 224-9900
Fax: (617) 224-9910
E-mail: info@enernoc.com
Web Site: www.enernoc.com
Approx. Rev.: $280,157,000
Approx. Number Employees: 484
Year Founded: 2001
Business Description:
Energy Demand Response & Management Solutions
S.I.C.: 4939; 4911; 4931
N.A.I.C.S.: 221122; 221119
Media: 10-13-17
Personnel:
Timothy G. Healy *(Co-Founder, Chm & CEO)*
David B. Brewster *(Co-Founder & Pres)*
Timothy Weller *(CFO & Treas)*
Kevin J. Bligh *(Chief Acctg Officer)*
David M. Samuels *(Exec VP)*
Gregg Dixon *(Sr VP-Mktg & Sls)*
Hugh Scandrett *(VP-Engrg)*
Terrence E. Sick *(VP-Product Dev & Engrg)*
Sarah McAuley *(Dir-Mktg Comm)*

ENERPLUS CORPORATION
(Formerly Enerplus Resources Fund)
The Dome Tower 3000 333 7th Ave SW
Calgary, AB T2P 2Z1, Canada
Tel.: (403) 298-2200
Fax: (403) 298-2211
Toll Free: (800) 319-6462
E-mail: investorrelations@enerplus.com
Web Site: www.enerplus.com
Approx. Rev.: $1,104,397,318
Approx. Number Employees: 709
Year Founded: 1986
Business Description:
Oil & Gas Refining
S.I.C.: 1311
N.A.I.C.S.: 211111
Advertising Expenditures: $100,000
Media: 2-7-10-24-25
Personnel:
Douglas R. Martin *(Chm)*
Gordon J. Kerr *(Pres & CEO)*
Robert J. Waters *(CFO & Sr VP)*
Ian C. Dundas *(COO & Exec VP)*
Dana Johnson *(Pres-USA)*
David A. Mccoy *(Gen Counsel, Sec & VP)*
Ray Daniels *(Sr VP-Ops)*
Eric Le Dain *(Sr VP-Strategic Plng, Reserves & Mktg)*
Rodney D. Gray *(VP-Fin)*
Scott Walsh *(VP-Info Sys)*
Jodine J. Jenson Labrie *(Controller-Fin)*
Dennis Sundgaard *(Sr Project Mgr-Oil Sands Project)*

ENERPLUS RESOURCES FUND
(Name Changed to Enerplus Corporation)

ENGLEFIELD OIL COMPANY
447 James Pkwy
Heath, OH 43056-1030
Tel.: (740) 928-8215
Fax: (740) 928-1531
Web Site: www.englefieldoil.com
Approx. Number Employees: 1,300
Year Founded: 1961
Business Description:
Operator of Gas Stations & Convenience Stores
S.I.C.: 5541; 5171
N.A.I.C.S.: 447190; 424710
Media: 9-25
Distr.: Reg.
Personnel:
Bill Englefield, III *(Chm)*
Ben B. Englefield *(Pres)*
Bill Englefield, IV *(Pres-Englefield Inc)*
Frank McManus *(VP-HR & Real Estate)*
John Tomlinson *(Asst VP)*
Barb Meckley *(Office Mgr)*

ENTERPRISE PRODUCTS PARTNERS L.P.
1100 Louisiana St 10th Fl
Houston, TX 77002
Mailing Address:
PO Box 4324
Houston, TX 77210-4324
Tel.: (713) 381-6500
Fax: (713) 381-6668
Toll Free: (866) 230-0745 (Investor Relations)
Web Site: www.epplp.com
Approx. Rev.: $33,739,300,000
Approx. Number Employees: 6,570
Year Founded: 1968
Business Description:
Natural Gas Liquids & Petrochemical Processing, Mfg, Transport & Storage
S.I.C.: 4922; 1311; 4924
N.A.I.C.S.: 486210; 211111; 221210
Media: 7
Personnel:
Michael A. Creel *(Pres & CEO)*
W. Randall Fowler *(CFO & Exec VP)*
A. J. Teague *(COO & Exec VP)*
Richard H. Bachmann *(Chief Legal Officer, Sec & Exec VP)*
Michael J. Knesek *(Principal Acctg Officer, Sr VP & Controller)*
Stephanie C. Hildebrandt *(Gen Counsel, Sec & Sr VP)*
Bryan F. Bulawa *(Treas & Sr VP)*
William Ordemann *(Exec VP)*
Lynn L. Bourdon, III *(Sr VP)*
James A. Cisarik *(Sr VP)*
James M. Collingsworth *(Sr VP)*
Terry L. Hurlburt *(Sr VP)*
Mark A. Hurley *(Sr VP)*
Rudy A. Nix *(Sr VP)*
Gil H. Radtke *(Sr VP-Gas Processing)*
Thomas M. Zulim *(Sr VP)*

EPRODUCTION SOLUTIONS, INC.
(Sub. of Weatherford International Ltd.)
22001 N Park Dr
Kingwood, TX 77339
Tel.: (281) 348-1000
Fax: (281) 348-1280
E-mail: info@ep-solutions.com
Web Site: www.ep-solutions.com
Sales Range: $250-299.9 Million
Approx. Number Employees: 600
Year Founded: 2001
Business Description:
Control Systems & Production Automation for Oil & Gas Industry
S.I.C.: 5084; 3491
N.A.I.C.S.: 423830; 332911
Advertising Expenditures: $200,000
Media: 2-7-10-13
Personnel:
Dharmesh Mehta *(Pres)*
Laurence Ormerod *(Mng Dir-Product)*
Karl Sakoscius *(VP-Mktg)*
Brenda Jones *(Mgr-HR)*
Brands & Products:
AXESS
CAC PRODUCTS
CS7X
EPAC
EPIC
EPRO
EPRODUCTION SOLUTIONS
IBEAM
IESP
MPOD
SPOD

ERGON, INC.
2829 Lakeland Dr
Jackson, MS 39232
Mailing Address:
PO Box 1639
Jackson, MS 39215-1639
Tel.: (601) 933-3000
Fax: (601) 933-3350
E-mail: jim.temple@ergon.com
Web Site: www.ergon.com

Key to Media (For complete agency information see *The Advertising Red Books-Agencies* edition):
1. Bus. Publs. 2. Cable T.V. 3. Catalogs & Directories. 4. Co-op Adv. 5. Consumer Mags. 6. D.M. to Bus. Estab.7. D.M. to Consumers 8. Daily Newsp. 9. Exhibits/Trade Shows 10. Foreign 11. Infomercial 12. Internet Adv.13. Multimedia 14. Network Radio 15. Network T.V. 16. Newsp. Distr. Mags. 17. Other 18. Outdoor (Posters, Transit) 19. Point of Purchase20. Premiums, Novelties 21. Product Samples 22. Special Events Mktg. 23. Spot Radio 24. Spot T.V. 25. Weekly Newsp. 26. Yellow Page Adv.

Approx. Number Employees: 2,500
Year Founded: 1954
Business Description:
Petroleum & Natural Gas Extractor, Refiner & Distr; Asphalt & Emulsion Products Mfr; Modular Computer Products Mfr; Product Transportation & Terminaling Services; Real Estate Acquisition & Leasing Services
S.I.C.: 2911; 1311; 2951; 3613; 3672; 4213; 4412; 4449; 6519; 6531
N.A.I.C.S.: 324110; 211111; 324121; 334412; 335313; 483111; 483211; 484230; 531190; 531390
Media: 2-10-13-26
Personnel:
Leslie B. Lampton, Sr. *(Chm)*
A. Patrick Busby *(CFO)*
Jim Temple *(Dir-Comm)*
Brands & Products:
ERGON

EXTERRAN HOLDINGS, INC.

16666 Northchase Dr
Houston, TX 77060
Tel.: (281) 836-7000
E-mail: investorrelations@exterran.com
Web Site: www.exterran.com
Approx. Rev.: $2,461,533,000
Approx. Number Employees: 10,100
Year Founded: 1992
Business Description:
Petroleum & Natural Gas Processing Equipment & Facilities Design, Engineering, Construction & Maintenance Services
S.I.C.: 1389; 1541; 3559; 5084; 7389; 7699; 8711
N.A.I.C.S.: 213112; 236210; 333298; 423830; 541330; 541420; 811310
Media: 2-7
Personnel:
Ernie L. Danner *(Pres & CEO)*
J. Michael Anderson *(CFO & Sr VP)*
D. Bradley Childers *(Pres-Ops-North America)*
Donald C. Wayne *(Gen Counsel, Sec & Sr VP)*
Steven W. Muck *(Sr VP-Global HR)*
Kenneth R. Bickett *(VP-Fin & Acctg)*
Brands & Products:
EXTERRAN

EXXON MOBIL CORPORATION

5959 Las Colinas Blvd
Irving, TX 75039-2298
Tel.: (972) 444-1000
Fax: (972) 444-1348
Toll Free: (800) 252-1800
Web Site: www.exxon.mobil.com
Approx. Rev.: $383,221,000,000
Approx. Number Employees: 83,600
Year Founded: 1882
Business Description:
Holding Company; Petroleum & Natural Gas Explorer, Extractor, Refiner & Distr & Petroleum Products Mfr
S.I.C.: 1311; 1321; 1381; 1389; 2099; 2813; 2819; 2869; 2899; 2911; 2992; 2999; 3533; 4922; 4924; 5171; 5172; 5541
N.A.I.C.S.: 211111; 211112; 213111; 213112; 221210; 311942; 324110; 324191; 324199; 325110; 325120; 325188; 325199; 325998; 333132; 424710; 424720; 447110; 447190; 486210
Import Export
Advertising Expenditures: $49,060,000
Media: 2-3-6-9-17-18-23-24
Distr.: Natl.
Budget Set: Sept.
Personnel:
Rex W. Tillerson *(Chm & CEO)*
Robert S. Franklin *(Pres-ExxonMobil Upstream Ventures & VP)*
Neil W. Duffin *(Pres-ExxonMobil Dev Co)*
S. J. Balagia *(Gen Counsel & VP)*
Donald D. Humphreys *(Treas & Sr VP)*
Mark W. Albers *(Sr VP)*
Michael J. Dolan *(Sr VP)*
A. P. Swiger *(Sr VP)*
L. J. Cavanaugh *(VP-HR)*
O. K. Owen *(VP-Safety, Security, Health & Environment)*
Michael DeMarco *(Mgr-Global Mktg Support)*
Brands & Products:
EXXON
EXXONMOBIL
MOBIL
MOBIL 1
ON THE RUN
SPEEDPASS
TAKING ON THE WORLD'S TOUGHEST ENERGY CHALLENGES.
Advertising Agencies:
Bergman Group
4880 Sadler Rd Ste 220
Glen Allen, VA 23060
Tel.: (804) 225-0600
Fax: (804) 225-0900

DDB Worldwide Communications Group Inc.
(Sub. of Omnicom Group, Inc.)
(Corporate Headquarters)
437 Madison Ave 5nd Fl
New York, NY 10022-7001
Tel.: (212) 415-2000
Fax: (212) 415-3414
(Global Fuel Marketing)

Denneen & Company
222 Berkeley St Ste 1200
Boston, MA 02116
Tel.: (617) 236-1300
Fax: (617) 267-5001

McCann Erickson Worldwide
622 3rd Ave
New York, NY 10017-6707
Tel.: (646) 865-2000
Fax: (646) 487-9610

MPG
(Div. of HAVAS)
195 Broadway 12th Fl
New York, NY 10007
Tel.: (646) 587-5000
Fax: (646) 587-5005
— Scott Suky *(Sr VP & Grp Acct Dir)*

FERRELLGAS PARTNERS, L.P.

7500 College Blvd Ste 1000
Overland Park, KS 66210
Tel.: (913) 661-1500
E-mail: info@ferrellgas.com
Web Site: www.ferrellgas.com
Approx. Rev.: $2,423,215,000
Approx. Number Employees: 3,588
Year Founded: 1939
Business Description:
Propane Gas Retailer
S.I.C.: 5984; 4924
N.A.I.C.S.: 454312; 221210
Import
Advertising Expenditures: $3,200,000
Media: 1-2-7-8-26
Distr.: Natl.
Personnel:
James E. Ferrell *(Chm)*
Stephen L. Wambold *(Pres & CEO)*
J. Ryan VanWinkle *(CFO & Sr VP)*
Patrick J. Walsh *(CIO & Sr VP)*
George L. Koloroutis *(Pres-Ferrell North America & Sr VP)*
Tod D. Brown *(Sr VP)*
Jennifer A. Boren *(VP-IT)*
Scott Brockelmeyer *(VP-Comm & Mktg)*
Brands & Products:
BLUE RHINO
FERRELL NORTH AMERICA
FERRELLGAS
SMARTFILL

FISKE BROTHERS REFINING COMPANY

129 Lockwood St
Newark, NJ 07105
Tel.: (973) 589-9150
Fax: (973) 589-4432
Toll Free: (800) 733-4755
E-mail: info@lubriplate.com
Web Site: www.lubriplate.com
Approx. Number Employees: 110
Year Founded: 1871
Business Description:
Mfr. of Cutting Oils, Drawing Compounds & Other Metal Working Lubricants
S.I.C.: 2992
N.A.I.C.S.: 324191
Advertising Expenditures: $200,000
Media: 2-4-6-10-21
Distr.: Intl.; Natl.
Budget Set: Jan.
Personnel:
Richard T. McCluskey *(Pres & CEO)*
Michael McCluskey *(CFO)*
Jim Girard *(VP & Gen Mgr)*
Steve Morrow *(VP-Sls)*
Brands & Products:
LUBRIPLATE
Advertising Agency:
Graphic Persuasion, Inc.
169 Tequesta Dr Ste 31E
Tequesta, FL 33469
Tel.: (561) 746-2422
Fax: (561) 746-2204
(Lubriplate Division)

FJ MANAGEMENT, INC.

(Formerly Flying J Inc.)
1104 Country Hills Dr
Ogden, UT 84403-2400
Mailing Address:
PO Box 150310
Ogden, UT 84415-0310
Tel.: (801) 624-1000
Fax: (801) 624-1463
E-mail: info@fjmgt.com
Web Site: www.fjmgt.com
E-Mail For Key Personnel:
Public Relations: virginia.parker@flyingj.com
Sales Range: $15-24.9 Billion
Approx. Number Employees: 16,000
Year Founded: 1968
Business Description:
Holding Company; Petroleum Explorer, Refiner, Pipeline Transportation & Distr; Retail Gasoline Stations Owner & Operator
S.I.C.: 6719; 2911; 4613; 5171; 5541
N.A.I.C.S.: 551112; 324110; 424710; 447110; 486910
Media: 10-13-18
Personnel:
Crystal Call Maggelet *(Chm, Pres & CEO)*
Bron McCall *(CIO)*
John R. Boken *(Chief Restructuring Officer)*
Richard Peterson *(Sr VP-Supply, Distr & Petroleum Mktg)*
James Baker *(Sr VP-Highway Hospitality)*
J.J. Singh *(VP-Fin Svcs)*
Virginia Parker *(Dir-Mktg)*
Brands & Products:
COUNTRY MARKET
FREQUENT FUELER
R.V. REAL VALUE
TOUREWARDS

G-P GYPSUM CORPORATION

(Sub. of Dixie Products Group)
133 Peach Tree St Fl 8
Atlanta, GA 30303
Tel.: (404) 652-4000
Fax: (404) 230-1674
Toll Free: (800) 225-6119
Web Site: www.gp.com
Approx. Number Employees: 2,000
Business Description:
Gypsum Products Mfr
S.I.C.: 3275
N.A.I.C.S.: 327420
Personnel:
Brent Paugh *(Pres)*
Brands & Products:
DENSDECK
DENSGLASS GOLD
DENSSHIELD
TOUGHROCK
Advertising Agency:
BBDO Atlanta
3500 Lenox Rd NE Ste 1900
Atlanta, GA 30326-4232
Tel.: (404) 231-1700
Fax: (404) 841-1893

GARY-WILLIAMS ENERGY CORPORATION

370 17th St Ste 5300
Denver, CO 80202-5653
Tel.: (303) 628-3800
Fax: (303) 628-3834
Web Site: www.gwec.com
Approx. Number Employees: 275
Business Description:
Refining & Gas Processing Services
S.I.C.: 2911
N.A.I.C.S.: 324110
Media: 2-4-7-10
Distr.: Natl.
Personnel:
Samuel Gary *(Chm)*
Ronald Williams *(Pres & CEO)*

Key to Media (For complete agency information see *The Advertising Red Books-Agencies* edition):
1. Bus. Publs. 2. Cable T.V. 3. Catalogs & Directories. 4. Co-op Adv. 5. Consumer Mags. 6. D.M. to Bus. Estab.7. D.M. to Consumers 8. Daily Newsp. 9. Exhibits/Trade Shows 10. Foreign 11. Infomercial 12. Internet Adv.13. Multimedia 14. Network Radio 15. Network T.V. 16. Newsp. Distr. Mags. 17. Other 18. Outdoor (Posters, Transit) 19. Point of Purchase20. Premiums, Novelties 21. Product Samples 22. Special Events Mktg. 23. Spot Radio 24. Spot T.V. 25. Weekly Newsp. 26. Yellow Page Adv.

Gary-Williams Energy Corporation — (Continued)

David Younggren *(CFO & Sr VP)*
Tom Brufkotter *(Sr VP-Mktg)*
Phil Waters *(VP-Prod Supply & Mktg)*
Dave DiPaolo *(Mgr-Acctg)*

GEOKINETICS INC.

1500 City West Blvd Ste 800
Houston, TX 77042
Tel.: (713) 850-7600
Fax: (713) 850-7330
Web Site: www.geokinetics.com
Approx. Rev.: $549,116,000
Approx. Number Employees: 5,200
Business Description:
Oil & Gas Operations
S.I.C.: 1311; 1389
N.A.I.C.S.: 211111; 213112
Advertising Expenditures: $1,045,000
Media: 17
Personnel:
William R. Ziegler *(Chm)*
Richard F. Miles *(Pres & CEO)*
Gary L. Pittman *(CFO & Exec VP)*
Diana S. Moore *(Chief Acctg Officer & VP)*
M. Lee Bell *(Pres-Processing & Interpretation)*
William L. Moll, Jr. *(Gen Counsel, Sec & VP)*
Lee Parker *(Exec VP-Ops)*
Scott M. Zuehlke *(Dir-IR)*

GETTY PETROLEUM MARKETING INC.

(Sub. of Lukoil Americas Holding Limited)
1500 Hempstead Tpke
East Meadow, NY 11554-1558
Tel.: (516) 542-4900
Fax: (516) 832-8632
Telex: 175061 GETTY
E-mail: webmaster@getty.com
Web Site: www.getty.com
Approx. Number Employees: 600
Year Founded: 1996
Business Description:
Independent Marketer & Wholesale Distr of Gasoline, Heating Oil & Petroleum Products
S.I.C.: 5172; 5171
N.A.I.C.S.: 424720; 424710
Import
Advertising Expenditures: $1,500,000
Media: 2-5-7-9-10-11-13-18-20-23-25
Distr.: Natl.
Budget Set: Oct.
Personnel:
Vadim Gluzman *(Chm & CEO)*
Vincent J. DeLaurentis *(Pres)*
Michael K. Hantman *(CFO & Sr VP)*
Patty Bobeck *(Mgr-Adv & Promos)*
Brands & Products:
GETTY
PETRO USA

GLEN ROSE PETROLEUM CORPORATION

22762 Westheimer Pkwy Ste 515
Katy, TX 77450
Tel.: (832) 437-0329
E-mail: info@GlenRosePetroleum.com
Web Site: www.glenrosepetroleum.com
Approx. Rev.: $124,815
Approx. Number Employees: 8
Year Founded: 1981
Business Description:
Crude Petroleum & Natural Gas Production
S.I.C.: 1311
N.A.I.C.S.: 211111
Advertising Expenditures: $36,803
Media: 17
Personnel:
Andrew Taylor-Kimmins *(Chm & Pres)*
Theodore D. Williams *(CFO)*
Ruben Alba *(COO)*

GREEN PLANET GROUP, INC.

33747 N Scottsdale Rd Ste 130
Scottsdale, AZ 85266
Tel.: (480) 222-6222
Fax: (480) 222-6225
E-mail: pnelson@greenplanetgroup.com
Web Site: www.emtacorp.com
Approx. Rev.: $57,380,667
Year Founded: 1978
Business Description:
Eco-Friendly Gasoline, Oil & Diesel Additives Developer, Researcher & Mfr
S.I.C.: 2992; 8733
N.A.I.C.S.: 324191; 541710
Advertising Expenditures: $46,967
Media: 7-8-9-13-19-22-23-24-25
Personnel:
Edmond Lonergan *(Chm, Pres & CEO)*
James Marshall *(CFO & Dir)*
Kevin Kush *(Sr VP-Res & Dev)*

GULF OIL LIMITED PARTNERSHIP

(Joint Venture of Cumberland Farms, Inc. & Catamount Petroleum)
90 Everett Ave
Chelsea, MA 02150-2337
Mailing Address:
PO Box 9151
Chelsea, MA 02150-9151
Tel.: (617) 889-9000
Fax: (617) 884-0637
Web Site: www.gulfoil.com
Sales Range: $1-4.9 Billion
Approx. Number Employees: 350
Business Description:
Oil Marketing & Storage Terminals
S.I.C.: 5171; 5172
N.A.I.C.S.: 424710; 424720
Media: 2-7-8-11-13-15
Personnel:
Ron Sabia *(Pres & COO)*
Joseph H. Petrowski *(CEO)*
Jayne Conway *(CFO & Sr VP)*
Rick Dery *(Sr VP-Branded Mktg & Sls)*
Advertising Agency:
Warner Communications
41 Raymond St
Manchester, MA 01944
Tel.: (978) 526-1960
Fax: (978) 526-8206

H&H GAS CORPORATION

80 N Main St
Windsor, NJ 08561
Tel.: (609) 448-3232
Fax: (609) 448-8061
E-mail: hhgas@aol.com
Web Site: www.hhgas.com
Approx. Number Employees: 42
Year Founded: 1951
Business Description:
Provider of Propane Gas & Appliances
S.I.C.: 5984; 5722
N.A.I.C.S.: 454312; 443111
Personnel:
Dave Gabrielski *(General Mgr)*
Advertising Agency:
Hollyrock/Miller Marketing Communications
117 Rockingham Row
Princeton, NJ 08540
Tel.: (609) 919-9292
Fax: (609) 919-9299

HALLIBURTON COMPANY

3000 N Sam Houston Pkwy E
Houston, TX 77032
Tel.: (281) 871-2699
E-mail: investors@halliburton.com
Web Site: www.halliburton.com
Approx. Rev.: $17,973,000,000
Approx. Number Employees: 58,000
Year Founded: 1919
Business Description:
Holding Company; Oil Field Services & Products; Engineering & Construction Services
S.I.C.: 1381; 1389; 1629; 6719; 8711
N.A.I.C.S.: 213111; 213112; 237990; 541330; 551112
Import Export
Media: 10
Personnel:
David J. Lesar *(Chm, Pres & CEO)*
Mark A. McCollum *(CFO & Exec VP)*
Sherry D. Williams *(Chief Compliance Officer, Chief Ethics Officer & Sr VP)*
Lawrence J. Pope *(Chief HR Officer & Exec VP-Admin)*
Evelyn M. Angelle *(Chief Acctg Officer & Sr VP)*
James S. Brown *(Pres-Geographical)*
Ahmed H.M. Lotfy *(Pres-Eastern Hemisphere)*
Timothy J. Probert *(Pres-Strategy & Corp Dev)*
Albert O. Cornelison, Jr. *(Gen Counsel & Exec VP)*
Craig W. Nunez *(Treas & Sr VP)*
Marc Edwards, *(Exec VP)*
Joseph F. Andolino *(Sr VP-Tax)*
Peter C. Bernard *(Sr VP)*
Christian Garcia *(Sr VP-IR)*
Susan Ponce *(Chief Ethics & Compliance Officer & Sr VP)*
Cathy G. Mann *(Dir-Corp Affairs)*
Laura Schilling *(Mgr-IR)*
Teresa Wong *(Mgr-PR)*
Bruce A. Metzinger *(Asst Sec)*

HALOCARBON PRODUCTS CORPORATION

887 Kinderkamack Rd
River Edge, NJ 07661-2307
Tel.: (201) 262-8899
Fax: (201) 262-0019
E-mail: info@halocarbon.com
Web Site: www.halocarbon.com
Approx. Number Employees: 150
Year Founded: 1950
Business Description:
Fluorochemicals, Inert Lubricants & Inhalation Anesthetics Mfr
S.I.C.: 2899
N.A.I.C.S.: 325998
Export
Media: 2-4-7-10-11-13-21-22
Distr.: Intl.
Budget Set: Oct. -Nov.
Personnel:
Ronald M. Epstein *(Dir-Sls)*
Meg Rubinstein *(Sr Mgr-Sls, Mktg, Pharma & Inhalation Anesthetics)*
Brands & Products:
BIOGRADE
BISPHENOL AF
ETHYL TRIFLUOROACETATE
HALOCARBON
HALOTHANE
HALOVAC
HEXAFLUOROISOPROPANOL
ISOFLURANE
TRIFLUOROACETIC ACID
TRIFLUOROACETIC ACID-BIOGRADE
TRIFLUOROACETIC ANHYDRIDE
TRIFLUOROACETYL CHLORIDE
TRIFLUOROETHANOL

HEADWATERS INCORPORATED

10653 S River Front Pkwy Ste 300
South Jordan, UT 84095
Tel.: (801) 984-9400
Fax: (801) 984-9410
E-mail: smadden@headwaters.com
Web Site: www.headwaters.com
Approx. Rev.: $654,699,000
Approx. Number Employees: 2,860
Year Founded: 1987
Business Description:
Construction Materials & Energy Industry Products & Services
S.I.C.: 5172; 2869; 2999; 3281; 5032
N.A.I.C.S.: 424720; 324199; 325110; 327991; 423320
Advertising Expenditures: $5,400,000
Personnel:
Kirk A. Benson *(Chm & CEO)*
James A. Herickhoff *(Vice Chm)*
Donald P. Newman *(CFO)*
Harlan M. Hatfield *(Gen Counsel, Sec & VP)*
Harvey North *(VP-HR)*

HESS CORPORATION

1185 Ave of the Americas
New York, NY 10036
Tel.: (212) 997-8500
Fax: (212) 536-8593
E-mail: investorrelations@hess.com
Web Site: www.hess.com
Approx. Rev.: $34,613,000,000
Approx. Number Employees: 13,800
Year Founded: 1920
Business Description:
Crude Oil & Gas Exploration, Production & Refining Services
S.I.C.: 1389; 1311; 2911; 2992; 4924; 5171
N.A.I.C.S.: 213112; 211111; 221210; 324110; 324191; 424710
Export
Advertising Expenditures: $9,000,000
Media: 2-7-8-11-13-14-15-18
Distr.: Intl.; Natl.
Budget Set: Nov.
Personnel:
John B. Hess *(Chm & CEO)*
Jeffery L. Steinhorn *(CIO & VP)*
Marc Othersen *(Chief Info Security Officer)*
Gregory P. Hill *(Exec VP & Pres-Worldwide Exploration & Production)*
F. Borden Walker *(Pres-Mktg & Refining & Exec VP)*

Key to Media (For complete agency information see *The Advertising Red Books-Agencies* edition):
1. Bus. Publs. 2. Cable T.V. 3. Catalogs & Directories. 4. Co-op Adv. 5. Consumer Mags. 6. D.M. to Bus. Estab. 7. D.M. to Consumers 8. Daily Newsp. 9. Exhibits/Trade Shows 10. Foreign 11. Infomercial 12. Internet Adv. 13. Multimedia 14. Network Radio 15. Network T.V. 16. Newsp. Distr. Mags. 17. Other 18. Outdoor (Posters, Transit) 19. Point of Purchase 20. Premiums, Novelties 21. Product Samples 22. Special Events Mktg. 23. Spot Radio 24. Spot T.V. 25. Weekly Newsp. 26. Yellow Page Adv.

R. Gordon Shearer *(CEO-Hess LNG & Sr VP)*
Timothy B. Goodell *(Gen Counsel & Sr VP)*
Christopher Baldwin *(Sr VP-Mktg-Retail & Energy)*
Gary Boubel *(Sr VP-Global Dev)*
William Drennen, III *(Sr VP-Global Exploration & New Ventures)*
John A. Gartman *(Sr VP-Energy Mktg)*
Scott M. Heck *(Sr VP-Global Production & Tech)*
Lawrence H. Ornstein *(Sr VP-Mktg, Refining Supply & Fin Controls)*
Howard Paver *(Sr VP-Global New Bus Dev)*
John J. Scelfo *(Sr VP-Fin & Corp Dev)*
John V. Simon *(Sr VP-Global Production)*
Darius Sweet *(Sr VP-Terminals & Refining)*
Michael R. Turner *(Sr VP-Global Production)*
Mykel J. Ziolo *(Sr VP-HR)*
Richard J. Lawlor *(VP-Sls & Retail Mktg)*
Jon L. Pepper *(VP-Corp Comm)*
Nicholas P. Brountas *(Deputy Gen Counsel & Asst Sec)*
Christopher S. Colman *(Deputy Gen Counsel-Environ & Asst Sec)*
John Y. Christopher *(Asst Sec)*
Kevin G. Daley *(Asst Controller)*
Eric Fishman *(Asst Treas)*
Erin K. Macher *(Asst Treas)*
Randy J. Pharr *(Asst Sec)*
Brands & Products:
HESS
HESS EXPRESS
Advertising Agency:
Grey New York
777 3rd Ave
New York, NY 10017-1401
Tel.: (212) 546-2000
Fax: (212) 546-1495

HKN, INC.

180 State St Ste 200
Southlake, TX 76092
Mailing Address:
PO Box 843502
Houston, TX 77284-3502
Tel.: (817) 424-2424
Tel.: (281) 504-4000
Fax: (281) 504-4100
E-mail: info@hkninc.com
Web Site: www.hkninc.com
Approx. Rev.: $12,904,000
Approx. Number Employees: 16
Year Founded: 1979
Business Description:
Oil & Gas Exploration, Extraction, Production & Distribution
S.I.C.: 1311; 1389; 4924; 5172
N.A.I.C.S.: 211111; 213112; 221210; 424720
Media: 2-4-7-17
Distr.: Natl.
Personnel:
Mikel D. Faulkner *(CEO)*
Anna M. Williams *(CFO & Sr VP)*
Elmer A. Johnston *(Gen Counsel, Sec & VP)*

HMT INC.

(Holding of Berkshire Partners LLC)
2002 Timberloch Pl Ste 550
The Woodlands, TX 77380
Tel.: (281) 681-7000
Fax: (281) 351-8589
Toll Free: (800) 394-4684
E-mail: info@hmttank.com
Web Site: www.hmttank.com
Sales Estimate: $20-39 Million
Approx. Number Employees: 800
Year Founded: 1978
Business Description:
Maintenace of Oil Storage Tanks
S.I.C.: 3444
N.A.I.C.S.: 332322
Media: 7-10
Personnel:
Millard H. Jones *(Pres & CEO)*
Brands & Products:
SEAL KING

HUNT REFINING COMPANY INC.

(Sub. of Hunt Oil Company)
1855 Fairlawn Rd
Tuscaloosa, AL 35401
Tel.: (205) 391-3300
Fax: (205) 345-8769
Web Site: www.huntrefining.com
Approx. Number Employees: 200
Year Founded: 1946
Business Description:
Provider of Petroleum Refining Services
S.I.C.: 2911
N.A.I.C.S.: 324110
Personnel:
John Matson *(Chm & Pres)*
Advertising Agency:
TotalCom Marketing, Inc.
922 20th Ave
Tuscaloosa, AL 35401-2307
Tel.: (205) 345-7363
Fax: (205) 345-7373

HUNTING COMPANY, US OFFICE

(Sub. of Hunting Energy Services L.P.)
2 Northpoint Dr Ste 400
Houston, TX 77060
Tel.: (281) 820-3838
Fax: (281) 931-2450
Toll Free: (800) 231-PIPE
Toll Free: (800) 877-2636
Web Site: www.hunting-intl.com
Approx. Number Employees: 400
Year Founded: 1874
Business Description:
Oil Field Services; Distr of Oil Field Tubular Products & Completions Assemblies
S.I.C.: 1389; 8742
N.A.I.C.S.: 213112; 541611
Import Export
Media: 4-7-10-26
Distr.: Intl.; Natl.
Personnel:
Nigel Richardson *(Mng Dir)*
Rob Davie *(Sec & Fin Dir)*
Elmer Campbell *(Exec Dir)*
Kk Ho *(Exec Dir)*
Jim Johnson *(Exec Dir)*
Sam Mcclements *(Exec Dir-Intl)*
John Feuerstein *(Mgr-Mktg)*

HYDROTEX PARTNERS LTD.

12920 Senlac Dr Ste 190
Farmers Branch, TX 75234-9237
Tel.: (972) 389-8500
Fax: (800) 333-8461
Toll Free: (800) 527-9439
Web Site: www.hydrotexlube.com
Approx. Sls.: $12,004,000
Approx. Number Employees: 35
Year Founded: 1936
Business Description:
Mfr & Distr of Lubricants & Fuel Improver Solutions
S.I.C.: 2992
N.A.I.C.S.: 324191
Media: 22
Personnel:
John Beasley *(Pres & CEO)*
Bill Dewberry *(VP-IT)*
Dwight Gleaves *(VP-Sls-Pupil Transportation)*
Alan Harding *(VP-Sls-Food Processing)*
Brian Higgins *(VP-Sls)*
Mike Smith *(Dir-Admin)*
Beverly Brunner *(Mgr-Partner Support)*

HYPERDYNAMICS CORPORATION

12012 Wickchester Ln #475
Houston, TX 77079
Tel.: (713) 353-9400
Fax: (713) 353-9421
E-mail: info@hyperdynamics.com
Web Site: www.hypd.com
Approx. Rev.: $2,229,000
Approx. Number Employees: 20
Year Founded: 1996
Business Description:
Oil & Gas Exploration Services
S.I.C.: 1311
N.A.I.C.S.: 211111
Personnel:
Ray Leonard *(Pres & CEO)*
Paul C. Reinbolt *(CFO & Exec VP)*
Jason D. Davis *(Dir-Fin & Treas)*
Harry J. Briers *(Exec VP)*
James R. Spear *(Exec VP-Exploration & Production)*
Michael W. Palmer *(Sr VP-Ops)*
Curtis Jackson *(VP-Drilling & Tech)*
Tahera Khan *(Dir-HR)*
Bonnie Milne-Andrews *(Mgr-Geological Ops)*
Edward Shaw *(Mgr-Exploration)*
Advertising Agency:
Roher Public Relations
427 Bedford Rd Ste 360
Pleasantville, NY 10570
Tel.: (914) 741-2256
Fax: (914) 741-2246
PR

IMPERIAL OIL LIMITED

(Sub. of Exxon Mobil Corporation)
5th Ave Place 237 4th Ave SW
PO Box 2480 Station M
Calgary, AB T2P 3M9, Canada
Tel.: (403) 237-2710 (Media Rels)
Fax: (403) 237-4017
Toll Free: (800) 567-3776
Telex: 65-24255
Web Site: www.imperialoil.ca
Approx. Rev.: $24,557,038,560
Approx. Number Employees: 4,970
Year Founded: 1880
Business Description:
Exploration, Producing, Refining, Marketing of Petroleum Products, Petrochemicals & Minerals
S.I.C.: 2819; 1311; 2911
N.A.I.C.S.: 325188; 211111; 324110
Import Export
Media: 8-18-19-23-24
Distr.: Natl.
Budget Set: May
Personnel:
Bruce H. March *(Chm, Pres & CEO)*
Brian W. Livingston *(Gen Counsel, Sec & VP)*
Paul J. Masschelin *(Treas, Sr VP-Fin & Admin)*
T. Glenn Scott *(Sr VP-Resources Div)*
Brands & Products:
ESSO
TIGER EXPRESS
Advertising Agencies:
Harling Marketing Inc.
6611 Innovator Drive
Mississauga, ON L5T 2J3, Canada
Tel.: (905) 670-9383
Fax: (905) 670-9410

OMD Canada
67 Richmond St W 2nd Fl
Toronto, ON M5H 1Z5, Canada
Tel.: (416) 681-5600
Fax: (416) 681-5620

IRVING OIL CORPORATION

(Sub. of Ocean Investments Corporation)
190 Commerce Way
Portsmouth, NH 03801
Tel.: (603) 559-8736
Fax: (207) 941-7500
Web Site: www.irvingoil.com
Approx. Number Employees: 100
Year Founded: 1986
Business Description:
Petroleum Products
S.I.C.: 5172; 5541
N.A.I.C.S.: 424720; 447190
Import Export
Media: 14-15
Personnel:
Arthur L. Irving *(Owner & Chm)*

ITW ROCOL NORTH AMERICA

(Sub. of Illinois Tool Works Inc.)
3624 W Lk Ave
Glenview, IL 60026
Tel.: (847) 657-5278
Fax: (800) 952-5823
Toll Free: (800) 452-5823
E-mail: info@rocolnorthamerica.com
Web Site: www.rocolnorthamerica.com
E-Mail For Key Personnel:
Marketing Director: cfuhr@itwfpg.com
Approx. Sls.: $12,000,000
Approx. Number Employees: 25
Year Founded: 1896
Business Description:
Mfr of Metalworking Lubricants & Equipment, Coolants, Tapping Fluids & MRO Products
S.I.C.: 2999
N.A.I.C.S.: 324199
Export
Media: 2-4-5-7-8-10-13-19-21
Distr.: Intl.; Natl.
Budget Set: Nov.
Personnel:
Dave Foley *(Gen Mgr)*
Catherine Fuhr *(Gen Mgr)*
Brands & Products:
ACCU-LUBE
CEDAR LUBRICANTS
DARACLEAN
ROCOL

Key to Media (For complete agency information see *The Advertising Red Books-Agencies* edition):
1. Bus. Publs. 2. Cable T.V. 3. Catalogs & Directories. 4. Co-op Adv. 5. Consumer Mags. 6. D.M. to Bus. Estab.7. D.M. to Consumers 8. Daily Newsp. 9. Exhibits/Trade Shows 10. Foreign 11. Infomercial 12. Internet Adv.13. Multimedia 14. Network Radio 15. Network T.V. 16. Newsp. Distr. Mags. 17. Other 18. Outdoor (Posters, Transit) 19. Point of Purchase20. Premiums, Novelties 21. Product Samples 22. Special Events Mktg. 23. Spot Radio 24. Spot T.V. 25. Weekly Newsp. 26. Yellow Page Adv.

ITW Rocol North America — (Continued)

RUSTLICK
SAFETAP
TRI-LOGIC

J.D. STREETT & CO., INC.
144 Weldon Pkwy
Maryland Heights, MO 63043-3102
Tel.: (314) 432-6600
Fax: (314) 432-1258
Toll Free: (800) 678-6600
E-mail: info@jdstreett.com
Web Site: www.jdstreett.com
Approx. Number Employees: 225
Year Founded: 1884
Business Description:
Petroleum Products Producer & Retailer
S.I.C.: 5171
N.A.I.C.S.: 424710
Import Export
Media: 2-7
Distr.: Intl.
Budget Set: Nov. -Dec.
Personnel:
Newell A. Baker, Sr. *(Chm)*
Newell A. Baker, Jr. *(Pres & CEO)*
Jim Schuering *(CFO)*
Joyce Spizzirri *(Gen Mgr-Retail)*
William Starbuck *(Gen Mgr)*
Stewart Dahlberg *(Mgr-Intl Sls)*
Tom Irwin *(Mgr-Sls-Lube & Anti-Freeze)*
Chuck Whelehon *(Mgr-Sls)*
Brands & Products:
J.D STREETT & COMPANY, INC.
PROFORCE
ZEPHYR
ZX

JIG-A-WORLD
1100 Conde
Montreal, QC Canada
Tel.: (514) 768-2867
Fax: (514) 768-4177
E-mail: info@jigaloo.com
Web Site: www.jigaloo.com
Business Description:
Lubricant Mfr
S.I.C.: 2992
N.A.I.C.S.: 324191
Media: 2-6-19-21
Personnel:
David Gilmour *(Pres & CEO)*
Jean-Loup Barbeau *(Dir-Sls)*
Brands & Products:
ECONOGREEN
GRAPHITE EXTREME
JIG-A-CLEAN
JIG-A-LOO
JIG-A-PATCH
Advertising Agencies:
Driven Media Communications
41593 winchester Rd Ste 110
Temecula, CA 92590
Tel.: (951) 461-2429
Fax: (951) 587-9243

Maximum Exposure P.R. & Media
50 Tice Blvd
Woodcliff Lake, NJ 07677-7654
Tel.: (201) 573-0300
Fax: (201) 573-0376

JIM WALTER RESOURCES, INC.
(Div. of Walter Energy, Inc.)
16243 Hwy 216
Brookwood, AL 35444
Tel.: (205) 554-6150
Fax: (205) 554-6969
Web Site: www.walterenergy.com
Approx. Sls.: $323,184,000
Approx. Number Employees: 1,300
Business Description:
Coal Mining; Methane Gas
S.I.C.: 1222; 1311
N.A.I.C.S.: 212112; 211111
Personnel:
Greg Dean *(CFO & VP)*
Michael T. Madden *(Sr VP-Mktg)*
Richard A. Donnelly *(VP-Engrg)*
Advertising Agency:
TotalCom Marketing, Inc.
922 20th Ave
Tuscaloosa, AL 35401-2307
Tel.: (205) 345-7363
Fax: (205) 345-7373

KL ENERGY CORPORATION
306 E Saint Joseph St Ste 200
Rapid City, SD 57701
Tel.: (605) 718-0372
Fax: (605) 718-1372
E-mail: hr@klenergycorp.com
Web Site: www.klenergycorp.com
Approx. Rev.: $4,069,026
Approx. Number Employees: 13
Year Founded: 2007
Business Description:
Cellulose-Based Ethanol Production & Distribution Services
S.I.C.: 2813; 1389; 4924
N.A.I.C.S.: 325120; 213112; 221210
Advertising Expenditures: $71,000
Media: 17
Personnel:
Thomas Schueller *(Chm)*
Peter Gross *(CEO)*
Thomas J. Bolan *(Acting CFO)*
David B. Litzen *(CTO & VP-Engrg)*

KOCH-GLITSCH, LP
(Sub. of Koch Chemical Technology Group, LLC)
4111 E 37th St N
Wichita, KS 67220
Mailing Address:
PO Box 8127
Wichita, KS 67208-0127
Tel.: (316) 828-5110
Fax: (316) 828-5263
Telex: 16-3544
Web Site: www.koch-glitsch.com
Approx. Number Employees: 1,171
Year Founded: 1997
Business Description:
Mass Transfer Equipment Mfr
S.I.C.: 3443; 3914
N.A.I.C.S.: 332313; 339912
Export
Advertising Expenditures: $500,000
Media: 2-4-7-10-13-17-20
Personnel:
Bob DiFulgentiz *(Pres)*
Brands & Products:
BI-FRAC
CASCADE MINI-RINGS
FLEXIGRID
FLEXIPAC
FLEXIPAC HC
FLEXISADDLE
KG-TOWER
MAX-FRAC
SUPERFRAC
ULTRA-FRAC
VARIOFLEX
Advertising Agency:
Koch Chem Tech Marketing
2703 Telecom Pkwy., Ste. #150A
Richardson, TX 75082
Tel.: (972) 773-2223

KRONOS INTERNATIONAL, INC.
(Sub. of Kronos Worldwide, Inc.)
5430 LBJ Freeway Ste 1700
Dallas, TX 75240-2697
Tel.: (972) 233-1700
Fax: (972) 448-1490
Web Site: www.kronostio2.com
Approx. Sls.: $952,900,000
Approx. Number Employees: 2,000
Business Description:
Chemical Products Mfr & Sales
S.I.C.: 2851; 2899; 5169
N.A.I.C.S.: 325510; 325998; 424690
Advertising Expenditures: $7,000,000
Personnel:
Tim C. Hafer *(Principal Acctg Officer, VP & Controller)*
Gregory M. Swalwell *(Principal Fin Officer & VP-Fin)*
Advertising Agencies:
Boomm! Marketing & Communications
17 N Catherine Ave
La Grange, IL 60525
Tel.: (708) 352-9700
Fax: (708) 352-9701

Lois Paul & Partners
515 Congress Ave Ste 2150
Austin, TX 78701
Tel.: (512) 638-5300
Fax: (512) 638-5310

Mechanica
75 Water St Level 2
Newburyport, MA 01950
Tel.: (978) 499-7871
Fax: (978) 499-7876

KRONOS WORLDWIDE, INC.
(Holding of Valhi, Inc.)
5430 LBJ Freeway Ste 1700
Dallas, TX 75240-2697
Tel.: (972) 233-1700
E-mail: info@kronos.com
Web Site: www.kronostio2.com
Approx. Sls.: $1,449,700,000
Approx. Number Employees: 2,440
Business Description:
Specialty Coating Pigments, Rheological Additives & Titanium Dioxide Pigments Producer & Marketer
S.I.C.: 2851; 2816; 5169
N.A.I.C.S.: 325510; 325131; 424690
Advertising Expenditures: $1,000,000
Personnel:
Harold C. Simmons *(Chm, Pres & CEO)*
Steven L. Watson *(Vice Chm & CEO)*
Gregory M. Swalwell *(CFO & VP)*
Peter C. George *(CTO & Sr VP-Products & Tech)*
Laura L. Vaughan *(VP-Worldwide Sls)*

THE LACLEDE GROUP, INC.
720 Olive St
Saint Louis, MO 63101
Tel.: (314) 342-0500
Fax: (314) 421-1979
E-mail: information@lacledegas.com
Web Site: www.thelacledegroup.com
Approx. Rev.: $1,735,029,000
Approx. Number Employees: 1,749
Year Founded: 2001
Business Description:
Holding Company; Natural Gas Distr
S.I.C.: 4924; 4922
N.A.I.C.S.: 221210; 486210
Advertising Expenditures: $50,000
Media: 4-7-8-10-13-18-20-21-22-23-24-26
Personnel:
Douglas H. Yaeger *(Chm, Pres & CEO)*
Mark D. Waltermire *(CFO & Sr VP)*
Mary Caola Kullman *(Sec & Chief Governance Officer)*
Mark C. Darrell *(Gen Counsel)*
Lynn D. Rawlings *(Treas & Asst Sec)*
Brands & Products:
LACLEDE
LG

LEFFLER ENERGY
(Sub. of Petroleum Heat & Power Co. Inc.)
15 Mount Joy St
Mount Joy, PA 17552
Mailing Address:
PO Box 302
Mount Joy, PA 17552
Tel.: (717) 653-1411
Fax: (717) 653-2302
Toll Free: (800) 984-1411
E-mail: info@lefflerenergy.com
Web Site: www.lefflerenergy.com
Sales Range: $200-249.9 Million
Approx. Number Employees: 390
Year Founded: 1865
Business Description:
Wholesale & Retail Petroleum
S.I.C.: 5541; 5983
N.A.I.C.S.: 447190; 454311
Media: 2-4-6-7-8-10
Distr.: Natl.

LUBRIPLATE LUBRICANTS
(Div. of Fiske Brothers Refining Company)
129 Lockwood St
Newark, NJ 07105
Tel.: (973) 589-9150
Fax: (973) 589-4432
Toll Free: (800) 733-4755
E-mail: info@lubriplate.com
Web Site: www.lubriplate.com
Approx. Number Employees: 20
Business Description:
Producer of Lubricants
S.I.C.: 2992
N.A.I.C.S.: 324191
Media: 2-4-6-10-21
Distr.: Intl.; Natl.
Budget Set: Jan.
Personnel:
Michael McCluskey *(CFO)*
James Girard *(CMO & VP)*
Brands & Products:
AERO
HIGH-TEMP
LOW-TEMP
LUBRIPLATE
MAG-1
PURE TAC
SFGO ULTRA
SYN-LUBE

Key to Media (For complete agency information see *The Advertising Red Books-Agencies* edition):
1. Bus. Publs. 2. Cable T.V. 3. Catalogs & Directories. 4. Co-op Adv. 5. Consumer Mags. 6. D.M. to Bus. Estab.7. D.M. to Consumers 8. Daily Newsp. 9. Exhibits/Trade Shows 10. Foreign 11. Infomercial 12. Internet Adv.13. Multimedia 14. Network Radio 15. Network T.V. 16. Newsp. Distr. Mags. 17. Other 18. Outdoor (Posters, Transit) 19. Point of Purchase20. Premiums, Novelties 21. Product Samples 22. Special Events Mktg. 23. Spot Radio 24. Spot T.V. 25. Weekly Newsp. 26. Yellow Page Adv.

SYNAC
SYNCOOL
Advertising Agency:
Graphic Persuasion, Inc.
169 Tequesta Dr Ste 31E
Tequesta, FL 33469
Tel.: (561) 746-2422
Fax: (561) 746-2204
(Lubrications, Oils, Greases)

LYONDELLBASELL INDUSTRIES
(Sub. of LYONDELLBASELL INDUSTRIES N.V.)
1221 McKinney St
Houston, TX 77010
Tel.: (713) 652-7200
Fax: (713) 309-7799
Web Site: www.lyondell.com
Approx. Sls.: $28,603,000,000
Approx. Number Employees: 7,340
Year Founded: 1985
Business Description:
Chemical & Polymer Mfr & Refiner
S.I.C.: 2819; 2869
N.A.I.C.S.: 325188; 325199
Export
Media: 2-7-10-11
Personnel:
Craig Glidden *(Chief Legal Officer & Exec VP)*
Brands & Products:
ACRYFLOW
ARCONATE
ARCOPLUS
ARCOPURE
ARCOSOLV
CREATING BASIC ELEMENTS FOR LIFE
ETHARCY
IMPRESS
MPDIOL
T-HYDRO
TEBOL

M-I L.L.C.
(Sub. of Smith International, Inc.)
(d/b/a M-I SWACO)
5950 N Course Dr
Houston, TX 77072
Tel.: (713) 739-0222
Fax: (832) 295-2537
Web Site: www.miswaco.com
Sales Range: $1-4.9 Billion
Approx. Number Employees: 1,600
Business Description:
Oil & Gas Services
S.I.C.: 1389; 2992
N.A.I.C.S.: 213112; 324191
Advertising Expenditures: $1,500,000
Media: 2-4-10-13-20
Distr.: Intl.
Budget Set: July
Personnel:
Chris Rivers *(Pres & CEO)*
John Kelly *(Sr VP-Production Tech)*
John Oliver *(Sr VP-South America)*
Brands & Products:
BEM-600
DIPRO
DRILPLEX
ENVIROCENTER
FAZEPRO
MONGOOSE
PRESSPRO RT
RHELIANT
SPEEDWELL
SUPER AUTOCHOKE
ULTRADRIL
VERTI-G
Advertising Agency:
Integral Creative Solutions
5225 Cornish St Unit 4
Houston, TX 77007
Tel.: (713) 880-1533

MAGELLAN PETROLEUM CORPORATION
7 Custom House St 3rd Fl
Portland, ME 04101
Tel.: (207) 619-8500
E-mail: magadmin@magpet.com
Web Site: www.magpet.com
Approx. Rev.: $18,176,877
Approx. Number Employees: 42
Year Founded: 1957
Business Description:
Petroleum & Natural Gas Exploration, Development, Extraction & Marketing
S.I.C.: 1311; 1389
N.A.I.C.S.: 211111; 213112
Media: 2-7-17
Distr.: Intl.; Natl.
Personnel:
J. Robinson West *(Chm)*
J. Thomas Wilson *(Pres & CEO)*
Antoine J. Lafargue *(CFO & Treas)*

MARATHON OIL CANADA CORPORATION
(Sub. of Marathon Oil Corporation)
Ste 2400 440 2nd Ave SW
T2P 5E9
Calgary, AB Canada
Tel.: (403) 233-1700
Fax: (403) 296-0122
E-mail: info@marathonoil.com
Web Site: www.marathonoil.com
Approx. Rev.: $927,212,800
Approx. Number Employees: 40
Business Description:
Crude Oil Production
S.I.C.: 1381; 1311
N.A.I.C.S.: 213111; 211111
Advertising Expenditures: $132,454,000
Personnel:
Steve D.L. Reynish *(Pres)*

MARATHON OIL CORPORATION
5555 San Felipe Rd
Houston, TX 77056-2723
Tel.: (713) 629-6600
Fax: (713) 296-2952
E-mail: ptijerina@marathonoil.com
Web Site: www.marathon.com
Approx. Rev.: $73,621,000,000
Approx. Number Employees: 29,677
Year Founded: 1901
Business Description:
Petroleum & Natural Gas Explorer, Developer, Extractor, Marketer & Distr
S.I.C.: 2911; 1311; 1381; 4612; 4613; 4922
N.A.I.C.S.: 324110; 211111; 213111; 486110; 486210; 486910
Import Export
Media: 5-7-11-13
Personnel:
Clarence P. Cazalot, Jr. *(Pres & CEO)*
Janet F. Clark *(CFO & Exec VP)*
David E. Roberts, Jr. *(COO & Exec VP)*
Thomas K. Sneed *(CIO)*
Sylvia J. Kerrigan *(Gen Counsel, Sec & VP)*
Gary R. Heminger *(Exec VP)*
Annell R. Bay *(Sr VP-Exploration)*
Clifford C. Cook *(Sr VP-Supply, Distr & Plng)*
Thomas M. Kelley *(Sr VP-Mktg)*
Garry L. Peiffer *(Sr VP-Fin & Comml Svcs)*
Mary Ellen Peters *(Sr VP-Transportation & Logistics)*
Jerry C. Welch *(Sr VP-Refinng)*
Patrick J. Kuntz *(VP-Sls-Natural Gas & Crude Oil)*
Rodney P. Nichols *(VP-HR & Admin Svcs)*
Robert Sovine *(VP-HR)*
Chris C. Phillips *(Mgr-IR)*
Advertising Agency:
Wyse
668 Euclid Ave
Cleveland, OH 44114
Tel.: (216) 696-2424
Fax: (216) 736-4425

MARATHON PETROLEUM COMPANY LLC
(Sub. of Marathon Oil Corporation)
539 S Main St
Findlay, OH 45840
Mailing Address:
PO Box 1
Findlay, OH 45839
Tel.: (419) 422-2121
Fax: (419) 425-7040
E-mail: webmaster@marathonpetroleum.com
Web Site: www.mapllc.com
Sales Range: $1-4.9 Billion
Approx. Number Employees: 1,700
Year Founded: 1998
Business Description:
Crude Oil & Petroleum Products Refiner, Transporter & Marketer
S.I.C.: 2911; 4612; 4613; 5171
N.A.I.C.S.: 324110; 424710; 486110; 486910
Media: 5-8-19-20-23-24
Distr.: Reg.
Budget Set: Nov. -Dec.
Personnel:
Gary R. Heminger *(Pres)*
Donald C. Templin *(CFO & Sr VP)*
Don Wehrly *(CIO)*
J. Michael Wilder *(Gen Counsel & Sec)*
Timothy T. Griffith *(Treas & VP-Fin)*
Thomas M. Kelley *(Sr VP-Mktg)*
Garry L. Peiffer *(Sr VP-Fin & Comml Svcs)*
Mary Ellen Peters *(Sr VP-Mktg)*
Rodney P. Nichols *(VP-HR & Admin Svcs)*
Jay Heintschel *(Dir-Downstream Bus Dev)*
Mike Arthur *(Product Mgr)*
Chris Boyer *(Product Mgr)*
Matt Garrity *(Product Mgr)*
Scott Larkey *(Product Mgr)*
Mark Matson *(Product Mgr)*
Howard Beverly, Jr. *(Mgr-Wholesale Mktg-Retired)*
Gary Hewitt *(Mgr-Asphalt Mktg)*
Bill McCleave *(Mgr-Brand Mktg)*
Harold Rinehart *(Mgr-Mtkg, Environ Safety & Security)*
Paul Smith *(Mgr-Real Estate)*
Ronda Tendam *(Mgr-Brand Div Sls)*
Craig Weigand *(Mgr-Adv)*
Lisa Buess *(Specialist-Adv)*

MARKWEST ENERGY PARTNERS, L.P.
1515 Arapahoe St Tower 2 Ste 700
Denver, CO 80202
Tel.: (303) 925-9200
Fax: (303) 290-8769
Toll Free: (800) 730-8388
E-mail: irelations@markwest.com
Web Site: www.markwest.com
E-Mail For Key Personnel:
President: jfox@markwest.com
Approx. Rev.: $1,241,563,000
Approx. Number Employees: 590
Year Founded: 1988
Business Description:
Natural Gas Services
S.I.C.: 1321; 1311; 4924
N.A.I.C.S.: 211112; 211111; 221210
Media: 10-22
Personnel:
Frank M. Semple *(Chm, Pres & CEO)*
Nancy K. Buese *(CFO & Sr VP)*
John C. Mollenkopf *(COO & Sr VP)*
Randy S. Nickerson *(Chief Comml Officer & Sr VP)*
C. Corwin Bromley *(Gen Counsel, Sec & Sr VP)*
Russ Moran *(VP-Mktg)*
Andrew L. Schroeder *(VP-Fin)*

MARTIN LP GAS INC.
(Sub. of Martin Resource Management Corporation)
2606 N Longview St
Kilgore, TX 75662
Tel.: (903) 984-0781
Fax: (903) 986-3519
Toll Free: (800) 256-6644
Web Site: www.martin-gas.com
Approx. Number Employees: 10
Business Description:
Propane Gas Distr
S.I.C.: 5984
N.A.I.C.S.: 454312
Media: 7-8-10-13-23-24-26
Distr.: Reg.
Budget Set: June
Personnel:
Donald R. Neumeyer *(COO & Exec VP)*
Jerry Sullivan *(Mgr)*

MATHESON VALLEY
(Formerly Valley National Gases LLC)
(Sub. of Matheson Tri-Gas, Inc.)
6500 Rockside Rd Ste 200
Independence, OH 44131
Tel.: (216) 573-9909
Fax: (216) 573-9969
Web Site: www.mathesongas.com/
E-Mail For Key Personnel:
Public Relations: bsullivan@matheson-trigas.com
Sales Range: $200-249.9 Million
Approx. Number Employees: 760
Business Description:
Industrial, Medical & Specialty Gases, Welding Equipment & Propane Distr
S.I.C.: 5169; 5084; 5085; 5984
N.A.I.C.S.: 424690; 423830; 423840; 454312
Media: 4-8-13
Personnel:
Howard Hubert *(Pres & COO)*

Key to Media (For complete agency information see *The Advertising Red Books-Agencies* edition):
1. Bus. Publs. 2. Cable T.V. 3. Catalogs & Directories. 4. Co-op Adv. 5. Consumer Mags. 6. D.M. to Bus. Estab.7. D.M. to Consumers 8. Daily Newsp. 9. Exhibits/Trade Shows 10. Foreign 11. Infomercial 12. Internet Adv.13. Multimedia 14. Network Radio 15. Network T.V. 16. Newsp. Distr. Mags. 17. Other 18. Outdoor (Posters, Transit) 19. Point of Purchase20. Premiums, Novelties 21. Product Samples 22. Special Events Mktg. 23. Spot Radio 24. Spot T.V. 25. Weekly Newsp. 26. Yellow Page Adv.

MDU RESOURCES GROUP, INC.
1200 W Century Ave PO Box 5650
Bismarck, ND 58506-5650
Tel.: (701) 530-1000
Tel.: (701) 530-1013
Toll Free: (800) 437-8000
E-mail: investor@mduresources.com
Web Site: www.mdu.com
Approx. Rev.: $3,909,695,000
Approx. Number Employees: 7,895
Year Founded: 1924
Business Description:
Holding Company; Energy Resource Production, Utility Distribution, Construction Materials & Contracting Services
S.I.C.: 6719; 1429; 1442; 1622; 1623; 1629; 3273; 4911; 4924; 4939
N.A.I.C.S.: 551112; 212319; 212321; 221112; 221122; 221210; 237120; 237130; 237310; 237990; 327320
Export
Advertising Expenditures: $3,900,000
Personnel:
Harry Jonathan Pearce *(Chm)*
Terry D. Hildestad *(Pres & CEO)*
Doran N. Schwartz *(CFO & VP)*
Craig Keller *(COO)*
Nicole A. Kivisto *(Chief Acctg Officer, VP & Controller)*
Paul K. Sandness *(Gen Counsel & Sec)*
Douglass A. Mahowald *(Treas & Asst Sec)*
Mark A. Del Vecchio *(VP-HR)*
Rick Matteson *(Dir-Comm & PR)*
Phyllis A. Rittenbach *(Dir-IR)*

MEENAN HOLDINGS OF NEW YORK, INC.
(Sub. of Star Gas Partners, L.P.)
520 Broadhollow Rd
Melville, NY 11747
Tel.: (516) 809-2100
Tel.: (516) 783-1000
Web Site: www.meenan.com
Sales Range: $350-399.9 Million
Approx. Number Employees: 800
Year Founded: 1933
Business Description:
Petroleum Products Whslr
S.I.C.: 5983; 5171
N.A.I.C.S.: 454311; 424710
Media: 1-4-5-7-8-9-13-16-23-25-26
Personnel:
Elena Zazzera *(Gen Mgr)*

MFA OIL COMPANY
1 Ray Young Dr
Columbia, MO 65201
Mailing Address:
PO Box 519
Columbia, MO 65205-0519
Tel.: (573) 442-0171
Fax: (573) 876-0442
E-mail: admin@mfaoil.com
Web Site: www.mfaoil.com
Approx. Number Employees: 1,500
Year Founded: 1929
Business Description:
Fuel & Lubrication Products Mfr; Petroleum & Propane Refiner; Convenience Store Operator
S.I.C.: 5171; 5541
N.A.I.C.S.: 424710; 447190
Media: 6-8-9-10-19-20-23-24-25
Distr.: Reg.
Budget Set: Aug.
Personnel:
Benny Farrell *(Chm)*
Jerome Taylor *(Pres)*
Jim Belcher *(Sr VP-Corp Svcs)*
Brands & Products:
BREAK TIME
THE COMPANY THAT LIVES WHERE YOU DO
MFA OIL
PDFPLUS
PETRO-CARD 24
SOY PLUS
Advertising Agency:
True Media
29 S 9th St Ste 201
Columbia, MO 65201
Tel.: (573) 443-8783
Fax: (573) 443-8784

MOBILE GAS SERVICE CORPORATION
(Sub. of Sempra Pipelines & Storage Corp.)
2828 Dauphin St
Mobile, AL 36606
Tel.: (251) 476-2720
Fax: (251) 478-5817
Web Site: www.mobile-gas.com
Sales Range: $50-74.9 Million
Approx. Number Employees: 150
Year Founded: 1836
Business Description:
Natural Gas Distr
S.I.C.: 4924
N.A.I.C.S.: 221210
Media: 3-5-8-9-10-13-15-20-22-23-24-25-26
Personnel:
James Michael Fine *(Pres)*
LaBarron N. McClendon *(VP-Mktg, HR & Community Affairs)*

MURPHY OIL CORPORATION
200 Peach St
El Dorado, AR 71730
Mailing Address:
PO Box 7000
El Dorado, AR 71731-7000
Tel.: (870) 862-6411
Fax: (870) 864-6373
Telex: 53-6210
E-mail: murphyoil@murphyoilcorp.com
Web Site: www.murphyoilcorp.com
Approx. Rev.: $23,345,071,000
Approx. Number Employees: 3,460
Year Founded: 1950
Business Description:
Explorer & Producer of Crude Oil & Natural Gas; Refining Crude Oil & Sales of Petroleum Products
S.I.C.: 2911; 1311
N.A.I.C.S.: 324110; 211111
Import Export
Advertising Expenditures: $84,600,000
Media: 1-2-5-6-7-8-9-10-17-18-19-20-23-25-26
Distr.: Reg.
Budget Set: Sept.
Personnel:
William C. Nolan, Jr. *(Chm)*
David M. Wood *(Pres & CEO)*
Kevin G. Fitzgerald *(CFO & Sr VP)*
Walter K. Compton *(Gen Counsel & Sr VP)*
John A. Moore *(Sec & Mgr-Law)*
Thomas McKinlay *(Exec VP-Worldwide Downstream Ops)*
Bill Stobaugh *(Sr VP-Plng)*
W. Patrick Olson *(VP-Production)*
N. Allison Parker *(Dir-Admin Svcs)*
Sandy Hostetler *(Mgr-Domestic Crude Oil Pur)*
Michael Johnson *(Mgr-Product Supply & Wholesale Mktg)*
Brands & Products:
MURCO
MURPHY
MURPHY USA
SPUR

NALCO ENERGY SERVICES, L.P.
(Joint Venture of Nalco Co.)
7705 Hwy 90 A
Sugar Land, TX 77478
Tel.: (281) 263-7000
Fax: (281) 263-7900
Web Site: www.nalco.com
Sales Range: $200-249.9 Million
Approx. Number Employees: 1,500
Year Founded: 1994
Business Description:
Specialty Chemicals & Programs for the Oilfield, Refining & Chemical Process Industries & Additives for Gasoline & Diesel Fuel
S.I.C.: 2899; 2911
N.A.I.C.S.: 325998; 324110
Advertising Expenditures: $250,000
Media: 2-7-11-13
Personnel:
Antoine Marcos *(VP-Fin-Bus Ops)*

NATIONAL FUEL GAS COMPANY
6363 Main St
Williamsville, NY 14221
Tel.: (716) 857-7000
Fax: (716) 857-7856
Toll Free: (800) 634-5440
Web Site: www.nationalfuelgas.com
Approx. Rev.: $1,760,503,000
Approx. Number Employees: 1,859
Year Founded: 1902
Business Description:
Integrated Energy Company
S.I.C.: 4924; 1311; 1321
N.A.I.C.S.: 221210; 211111; 211112
Media: 2-5-6-7-8-9-10-14-15-18-19-22-25
Distr.: Reg.
Personnel:
David F. Smith *(Chm & CEO)*
Ronald J. Tanski *(Pres & COO)*
Sarah Mugel *(Gen Counsel & Asst VP)*
Matthew D. Cabell *(Sr VP)*
James D. Ramsdell *(Sr VP)*
Julie Coppola Cox *(Asst Gen Mgr)*
James C. Welch *(Dir-IR)*
Advertising Agency:
Travers Collins & Company
726 Exchange St Ste 500
Buffalo, NY 14210-1495
Tel.: (716) 842-2222
Fax: (716) 842-6424

NEWMARKET CORPORATION
330 S 4th St
Richmond, VA 23219-4350
Mailing Address:
PO Box 2189
Richmond, VA 23218-2189
Tel.: (804) 788-5000
Fax: (804) 788-5688
E-mail: corpcom@ethyl.com
Web Site: www.newmarket.com
Approx. Rev.: $1,797,392,000
Approx. Number Employees: 1,527
Year Founded: 1921
Business Description:
Petroleum Additives for Fuels, Lubricants & Tetraethyl Lead Antiknock Compounds Mfr & Retailer
S.I.C.: 2999; 2869; 5169
N.A.I.C.S.: 324199; 325199; 424690
Import Export
Media: 2-4-10-16-20
Distr.: Intl.; Natl.
Budget Set: Sept.
Personnel:
Bruce C. Gottwald *(Chm)*
Thomas E. Gottwald *(Pres & CEO)*
David A. Fiorenza *(CFO)*
C.S. Warren Huang *(Pres-Afton Chemical Corp)*
Steven M. Edmonds *(Gen Counsel & VP)*
Alexander McLean *(Sr VP-Afton Chemical Corp)*
Brands & Products:
HITEC
NEWMARKET

NEWPARK RESOURCES, INC.
2700 Research Forest Dr Ste 100
The Woodlands, TX 77381
Tel.: (281) 362-6800
Fax: (281) 362-6801
Web Site: www.newpark.com
Approx. Rev.: $715,954,000
Approx. Number Employees: 1,001
Year Founded: 1932
Business Description:
Oilfield & Environmental Services for Oil & Gas Exploration; Industrial Waste Removal Services
S.I.C.: 1389; 1623
N.A.I.C.S.: 213112; 237120
Advertising Expenditures: $250,000
Media: 7-10
Distr.: Direct to Consumer; Natl.
Budget Set: Dec.
Personnel:
Jerry W. Box *(Chm)*
Paul L. Howes *(Pres & CEO)*
Jeffery L. Juergens *(Pres & VP)*
James E. Braun *(CFO & VP)*
David Bock *(CIO)*
Mark J. Airola *(Chief Admin Officer, Gen Counsel, Sec & VP)*
Gregg S. Piontek *(Chief Acctg Officer, VP & Controller)*
Bruce C. Smith *(Pres-Fluids Sys & VP-Engrg)*
Joe L. Gocke *(Treas & VP-Fin)*
William D. Moss *(VP-Corp Strategy & Dev)*
Advertising Agency:
Foster Marketing Communications
3909-F Ambassador Caffrey
Lafayette, LA 70503
Tel.: (337) 235-1848
Fax: (337) 237-7246

NSTAR
800 Boylston St
Boston, MA 02199-8003
Tel.: (617) 424-2000
Fax: (781) 441-8886
E-mail: ir@nstar.com

Key to Media (For complete agency information see *The Advertising Red Books-Agencies* edition):
1. Bus. Publs. 2. Cable T.V. 3. Catalogs & Directories. 4. Co-op Adv. 5. Consumer Mags. 6. D.M. to Bus. Estab.7. D.M. to Consumers 8. Daily Newsp. 9. Exhibits/Trade Shows 10. Foreign 11. Infomercial 12. Internet Adv.13. Multimedia 14. Network Radio 15. Network T.V. 16. Newsp. Distr. Mags. 17. Other 18. Outdoor (Posters, Transit) 19. Point of Purchase20. Premiums, Novelties 21. Product Samples 22. Special Events Mktg. 23. Spot Radio 24. Spot T.V. 25. Weekly Newsp. 26. Yellow Page Adv.

Web Site: www.nstar.com
Approx. Rev.: $2,916,921,000
Approx. Number Employees: 3,000
Year Founded: 1999
Business Description:
Holding Company; Electric & Natural Gas Distr
S.I.C.: 6719; 4911; 4922; 4924; 4939
N.A.I.C.S.: 551112; 221111; 221112; 221122; 221210; 486210
Advertising Expenditures: $306,000,000
Personnel:
Thomas J. May *(Chm, Pres & CEO)*
James J. Judge *(CFO & Sr VP)*
Robert J. Weafer Jr. *(Chief Acctg Officer, VP & Controller)*
Douglas S. Horan *(Gen Counsel, Sec & Sr VP-Strategy, Law & Policy)*
Christine M. Carmody *(Sr VP-HR)*
Joseph R. Nolan Jr. *(Sr VP-Customer & Corp Rels)*
Larry Gelbien *(VP-Engrg)*
Geoffrey O. Lubbock *(VP)*
Don Anastasia *(Asst Treas)*
Rich Morrison *(Asst Sec)*

OCCIDENTAL OIL & GAS CORPORATION
(Sub. of Occidental Petroleum Corporation)
5 E Greeway Plz Ste 110
Houston, TX 77046
Tel.: (713) 215-7000
Fax: (310) 443-6690
E-mail: information@oxy.com
Web Site: www.oxy.com
Sales Range: $250-299.9 Million
Approx. Number Employees: 1,700
Year Founded: 1920
Business Description:
Explorer & Producer of Worldwide Oil & Gas
S.I.C.: 1311
N.A.I.C.S.: 211111
Media: 2-9-17-25
Distr.: Natl.
Budget Set: Nov.
Personnel:
Ray R. Irani *(Chm)*
Stephen I. Chazen *(Pres & CEO)*

OMEGA FLEX, INC.
(Sub. of Mestek, Inc.)
451 Creamery Way
Exton, PA 19341
Tel.: (610) 524-7272
Fax: (610) 524-7282
E-mail: info@omegaflex.com
Web Site: www.omegaflex.com
Approx. Sls.: $46,875,000
Approx. Number Employees: 107
Business Description:
Flexible Gas Piping Systems Mfr
S.I.C.: 1522; 3492; 3498; 5074
N.A.I.C.S.: 236220; 332912; 332996; 423720
Advertising Expenditures: $510,000
Personnel:
John E. Reed *(Chm)*
Edward J. Trainor *(Vice Chm)*
Kevin R. Hoben *(Pres & CEO)*
Paul Kane *(CFO, Principal Acctg Officer & Controller)*
Mark F. Albino *(COO & Exec VP)*
Brands & Products:
AUTOFLARE
COUNTERSTRIKE
HYPERLINK
OMEGAFLEX
QUAL-E-FLEX
TRACLINE
TRACPIPE

ONEOK, INC.
100 W 5th St
Tulsa, OK 74103-4240
Mailing Address:
PO Box 871
Tulsa, OK 74102-0871
Tel.: (918) 588-7000
Fax: (918) 588-7960
E-mail: oneok@oneok.com
Web Site: www.oneok.com
Approx. Rev.: $13,030,051,000
Approx. Number Employees: 4,839
Year Founded: 1906
Business Description:
Natural Gas Extraction, Processing, Transport, Storage & Marketing
S.I.C.: 4922; 1321; 4924
N.A.I.C.S.: 486210; 211112; 221210
Media: 7
Personnel:
David L. Kyle *(Chm)*
John W. Gibson *(Vice Chm, Pres & CEO)*
Robert F. Martinovich *(CFO, Treas & Sr VP)*
Pierce H. Norton, II *(COO)*
Caron A. Lawhorn *(Pres-Distr Companies)*
John R. Barker *(Gen Counsel, Sr VP & Asst Sec)*
Terry K. Spencer *(Exec VP-Natural Gas Liquids)*
Charles Kelley *(Sr VP-ONEOK Energy Svcs)*
Robert S. Mareburger *(Sr VP-Corp Plng & Dev)*
David E. Roth *(Sr VP-Admin Svcs)*
Advertising Agency:
Jordan Associates
3201 Quail Springs Pkwy Ste 100
Oklahoma City, OK 73134-2611
Tel.: (405) 840-3201
Fax: (405) 840-4149

OUTLOOK RESOURCES INC.
40 King Street West Ste 3100 Scotia Plz
Toronto, ON M5H 3Y2, Canada
Tel.: (647) 296-1270
Toll Free: (888) 355-5507
E-mail: info@outlookresources.com
Web Site: www.outlookresources.com
Approx. Rev.: $159,139
Year Founded: 1984
Business Description:
Ferilizers & Biological Products Mfr
S.I.C.: 2875; 2836
N.A.I.C.S.: 325314; 325414
Personnel:
Errol Farr *(CFO)*
William R. Johnstone *(Sec & Legal Counsel)*
Advertising Agency:
CHF Investor Relations
90 Adelaide St W Ste 600
Toronto, ON M5H 3V9, Canada
Tel.: (416) 868-1079
Fax: (416) 868-6198

PACIFIC ETHANOL, INC.
400 Capitol Mall St 2060
Sacramento, CA 95814
Tel.: (919) 403-2123
Fax: (916) 446-3937
E-mail: investorrelations@pacificethanol.net
Web Site: www.pacificethanol.net
Approx. Sls.: $328,332,000
Approx. Number Employees: 145
Business Description:
Ethanol Mfr
S.I.C.: 2869; 4931; 5169
N.A.I.C.S.: 325199; 221119; 325193; 424690
Advertising Expenditures: $84,000
Media: 7-10
Personnel:
William L. Jones *(Founder & Chm)*
Neil M. Koehler *(Pres & CEO)*
Bryon T. McGregor *(CFO)*
Christopher W. Wright *(Gen Counsel & VP)*
Greg Dibiase *(VP-Ethanol Supply & Mktg)*

PARKER DRILLING COMPANY
5 Greenway Plz Ste 100
Houston, TX 77046
Tel.: (281) 406-2000
Fax: (281) 406-2001
E-mail: rose.maltby@parkerdrilling.com
Web Site: www.parkerdrilling.com
Approx. Rev.: $659,475,000
Approx. Number Employees: 2,011
Year Founded: 1934
Business Description:
Barge & Off-Shore Drilling, Work-Over Services, International Land Drilling & Specialized Oil Tool Rentals
S.I.C.: 1389; 1381; 7353
N.A.I.C.S.: 213112; 213111; 532412
Export
Advertising Expenditures: $500,000
Media: 2-7-11-17
Distr.: Intl.; Natl.
Budget Set: Nov.
Personnel:
Robert L. Parker, Jr. *(Chm)*
David C. Mannon *(Pres & CEO)*
W. Kirk Brassfield *(CFO & Sr VP)*
Jon-Al Duplantier *(Gen Counsel & VP)*
Denis J. Graham *(VP-Engrg)*
Joey Husband *(Gen Mgr-Alaska Bus Unit)*
David McCann *(Dir-Bus Dev)*
Tom Horton *(Sr Mgr-Bus Dev)*
Rose Maltby *(Mgr-PR)*
Brands & Products:
AT-2000
HELI-HOIST
OIME
PARCO
PARKER DRILLING
PARTECH
TBA

PARKLAND INCOME FUND
Riverside Ofc Plz Ste 236 59th
Red Deer, AB T4N 6C9, Canada
Tel.: (403) 357-6400
Fax: (403) 346-3015
E-mail: corpinfo@parkland.ca
Web Site: www.parkland.ca
Approx. Sls.: $2,968,250,564
Approx. Number Employees: 1,600
Year Founded: 1977
Business Description:
Open-Ended Mutual Fund Trust
S.I.C.: 6722; 6733
N.A.I.C.S.: 525910; 523991
Media: 2-5-8-9-10-18-19-20-22-23-25
Personnel:
Jim Pantelidis *(Chm)*
Bob Espey *(Pres & CEO)*
Mike Lambert *(CFO & Sr VP)*
Donna Strating *(CIO & VP-IT)*
William Sanford *(Pres-Parkland Comml Fuel)*
Bob Fink *(Gen Counsel & Sec)*
Dean MacKey *(Sr VP-HR & Admin)*
Bradley Williams *(Sr VP-Comml Bus Grp)*
Andrew Cruickshank *(VP-Fin)*
Brands & Products:
ESSO
FAS GAS
LITRE LOG
PARKLAND INCOME FUND
RACE TRAC

PENGROWTH ENERGY CORP.
(Formerly Pengrowth Energy Trust)
222 Third Avenue SW Suite 2100
Calgary, AB T2P 0B4, Canada
Tel.: (403) 233-0224
Fax: (403) 265-6251
Toll Free: (800) 223-4122
E-mail: pengrowth@pengrowth.com
Web Site: www.pengrowth.com
Approx. Sls.: $1,324,431,006
Approx. Number Employees: 582
Year Founded: 1988
Business Description:
Petroleum & Natural Gas Properties Operator
S.I.C.: 1311
N.A.I.C.S.: 211111
Media: 22
Personnel:
James S. Kinnear *(Chm)*
Derek W. Evans *(Pres & CEO)*
Christopher Webster *(CFO)*
Marlon McDougall *(COO)*
Gordon M. Anderson *(VP-Fin)*
Gillian Basford *(VP-HR)*
James E. A. Causgrove *(VP-Production & Ops)*
Grant A. Henschel *(VP-Engrg)*
James Macdonald *(Dir-East Coast Ops)*

PENGROWTH ENERGY TRUST
(Name Changed to Pengrowth Energy Corp.)

PENRECO
(Sub. of Penreco)
138 Petrolia St
Karns City, PA 16041-9222
Tel.: (724) 756-0110
Fax: (724) 756-1050
Toll Free: (800) 245-3952
Web Site: www.penreco.com
Sales Range: $50-74.9 Million
Approx. Number Employees: 170
Year Founded: 1878
Business Description:
Specialty Chemical & Petroleum Mfr
S.I.C.: 2899; 2911
N.A.I.C.S.: 325998; 324110
Export
Media: 2-4-7-10-11-13-20-21
Distr.: Intl.; Natl.
Budget Set: Nov.
Brands & Products:
2251
CONOSOL

Key to Media (For complete agency information see *The Advertising Red Books-Agencies* edition):
1. Bus. Publs. 2. Cable T.V. 3. Catalogs & Directories. 4. Co-op Adv. 5. Consumer Mags. 6. D.M. to Bus. Estab.7. D.M. to Consumers
8. Daily Newsp. 9. Exhibits/Trade Shows 10. Foreign 11. Infomercial 12. Internet Adv.13. Multimedia 14. Network Radio
15. Network T.V. 16. Newsp. Distr. Mags. 17. Other 18. Outdoor (Posters, Transit) 19. Point of Purchase20. Premiums, Novelties
21. Product Samples 22. Special Events Mktg. 23. Spot Radio 24. Spot T.V. 25. Weekly Newsp. 26. Yellow Page Adv.

Penreco — (Continued)

DRAKEOL
DRAKESOL
PAROL
PENETECK
PENN DRAKE PETROSUL
PENRECO
SONTEX
VERSAGELS

PETRO-CANADA

(Sub. of Suncor Energy Inc.)
150 6th Ave SW
PO Box 2844
Calgary, AB T2P 3E3, Canada
Tel.: (403) 296-8000
Fax: (403) 296-3030
E-mail: investor@petro-canada.ca
Web Site: www.petro-canada.ca
Sales Range: $15-24.9 Billion
Approx. Number Employees: 6,088
Year Founded: 1976
Business Description:
Oil & Gas Refining Sales
S.I.C.: 2911; 5541
N.A.I.C.S.: 324110; 447190
Advertising Expenditures: $95,866,400
Media: 1-2-3-4-5-6-7-8-9-10-11-14-15-16-18-19-20-21-22-23-24-25-26
Distr.: Natl.
Budget Set: Sept.
Personnel:
Thomas Edward Kierans *(Chm)*
Ron A. Brenneman *(Pres & CEO)*
E.F.H. Roberts *(CFO & Exec VP)*
Boris J. Jackman *(Exec VP)*
Peter S. Kallos *(Exec VP)*
Neil J. Camarta *(Sr VP-Oil Sands)*
Gordon Carrick *(Sr VP-Ops-Tech)*
Youssef Ghoniem *(Sr VP-Ops-Germany)*
Brant G. Sangster *(Sr VP)*
Kathleen E. Sendall *(Sr VP-Natural Gas-North America)*
Andrew Stephens *(Sr VP-Corp Rel)*
Philip Churton *(VP-Mktg)*
Gerhard Kinast *(VP-Fin)*
Frederick Scharf *(VP-Retail Sls Svc-Ops)*
Helen Wesley *(VP & Fin IBU)*
Brands & Products:
CERTIGARD
CYCLOFLEX
PARAFLEX
PETRO-CANADA
PETRO-PASS
PUREDRILL HT-40
PUREDRILL IA-35LV

PETROKAZAKHSTAN INC.

(Joint Venture of China National Petroleum Corporation & JSC National Company KazMunayGas)
Sun Life Plz N Tower
Calgary, AB T2P 3N3, Canada
Tel.: (403) 221-8435
Fax: (403) 221-8425
Web Site: www.petrokazakhstan.com
E-Mail For Key Personnel:
Public Relations: ihor.wasylkiw@petrokazakhstan.com
Sales Range: $1-4.9 Billion
Year Founded: 1986
Business Description:
Oil & Gas Exploration, Acquisition & Refinement: Owned 67% by China National Petroleum Corporation & 33% by JSC KazMunayGas Exploration
S.I.C.: 1311; 1389
N.A.I.C.S.: 211111; 213112
Media: 17-18
Personnel:
Zhongcai Wang *(Pres)*

PILOT CORPORATION

5508 Lonas Rd
Knoxville, TN 37909-3221
Mailing Address:
PO Box 10146
Knoxville, TN 37939-0146
Tel.: (865) 588-7487
Fax: (865) 450-2800
Toll Free: (800) 562-6210
Web Site: www.pilotcorp.com
Sales Range: $1-4.9 Billion
Approx. Number Employees: 7,710
Year Founded: 1958
Business Description:
Truck Stops & Convenience Stores Operator
S.I.C.: 5541; 5411
N.A.I.C.S.: 447190; 445120
Import
Advertising Expenditures: $200,000
Personnel:
James A. Haslam, III *(CEO)*
Mitch Steenrod *(CFO)*
Mark A. Hazelwood *(Exec VP-Direct Sls & Devel)*
Ed Leddy *(Dir-Mktg)*

PLACID HOLDING COMPANY

1601 Elm St Ste 3400
Dallas, TX 75201-7201
Tel.: (214) 880-8479
Fax: (214) 880-8478
Approx. Number Employees: 3
Year Founded: 1983
Business Description:
Petroleum Refining
S.I.C.: 2911; 6719
N.A.I.C.S.: 324110; 551112
Import Export
Media: 20-22
Personnel:
Petro Hunt *(Owner)*
Eric Belvaux *(Mgr)*
Brands & Products:
CARATARC
CARATAUT
CARATBOU
CARATDUP
CARATFAC
CARATFEX
CARATFOL
CARATLOG
CARATMAP
CARATNEC
CARATNOS
CARATPOS
CARATREM
CARATSEC
PENNFIELD FARMS

PLAINS ALL AMERICAN PIPELINE, L.P.

333 Clay St Ste 1600
Houston, TX 77002-4000
Tel.: (713) 646-4100
Fax: (713) 646-4572
Toll Free: (800) 564-3036
E-mail: info@paalp.com
Web Site: www.paalp.com
Approx. Rev.: $25,893,000,000
Approx. Number Employees: 3,500
Year Founded: 1998
Business Description:
Crude Oil, Refined Petroleum & Natural Gas Transportation, Storage & Marketing
S.I.C.: 5088; 1623; 4612; 4613; 4922; 5172
N.A.I.C.S.: 423860; 237120; 424720; 486110; 486210; 486910
Import Export
Media: 2-7-11-13
Personnel:
Greg L. Armstrong *(Chm & CEO)*
Harry N. Pefanis *(Pres & COO)*
Allan Swanson *(CFO & Exec VP)*
Chris Herbold *(Chief Acctg Officer & VP-Acctg)*
W. David Duckett *(Pres-PMC)*
Tim Moore *(Gen Counsel, Sec & VP)*
Lawrence J. Dreyfuss *(VP, Asst Sec & Gen Counsel-Comml & Litigation)*
Phillip D. Kramer *(Exec VP)*
John R. Rutherford *(Exec VP)*
Mark J. Gorman *(Sr VP-Ops & Bus Dev)*
Alfred A. Lindseth *(Sr VP-Tech, Process & Risk Mgmt)*
John P. Von Berg *(Sr VP-Comml Activities)*
Roger D. Everett *(VP-HR)*
Daniel J. Nerbonne *(VP-Engrg)*
Roy I. Lamoreaux *(Dir-IR)*
Michael C. Mcmanus *(Dir-Internal Audit)*

POWER SERVICE PRODUCTS, INC.

513 Peaster Hwy
Weatherford, TX 76086
Tel.: (817) 599-9486
Fax: (817) 599-4893
Toll Free: (800) 643-9089
E-mail: psp@powerservice.com
Web Site: www.powerservice.com
Approx. Number Employees: 45
Year Founded: 1956
Business Description:
Fuel Additives Mfr
S.I.C.: 2911; 2899
N.A.I.C.S.: 324110; 325998
Media: 2-10-19-23-26
Personnel:
Ed M. Kramer *(Pres & CEO)*
Bob Sellers *(VP-Sls)*
Mandy Kramer *(Dir-Mktg)*
Brands & Products:
AGRI POWER
ARCTIC EXPRESS
BIO KLEEN
CETANE BOOST
CONTAINS SLICKDIESEL
DIESEL 911
DIESEL ADDITIVES
DIESEL FUEL SUPPLEMENT
DIESEL KLEEN
DIESEL LUBE
POWE SERVICE
POWER SERVICE
PREMIUM ARCTIC EXPRESS
SLICKDIESEL
SLIME-X
URBAN EMISSIONS

QUESTAR CORPORATION

180 E 100 S
Salt Lake City, UT 84145-0433
Mailing Address:
PO Box 45433
Salt Lake City, UT 84145-0433
Tel.: (801) 324-5000
Fax: (801) 324-5483
E-mail: martin.craven@questar.com
Web Site: www.questarcorp.com
Approx. Rev.: $1,123,600,000
Approx. Number Employees: 1,705
Year Founded: 1935
Business Description:
Holding Company
S.I.C.: 6719; 1389; 4924
N.A.I.C.S.: 551112; 213112; 221210
Media: 2-3-5-6-7-8-9-10-16-18-20-23-24-25-26
Distr.: Direct to Consumer; Natl.
Budget Set: July
Personnel:
Keith O. Rattie *(Chm)*
Ronald W. Jibson *(Pres & CEO)*
Kevin W. Hadlock *(CFO & Exec VP)*
Shahab Saeed *(COO & VP)*
Thomas C. Jepperson *(Gen Counsel, Corp Sec & Exec VP)*
Martin H. Craven *(Treas & Dir-IR)*
Jay B. Neese *(Exec VP)*
Advertising Agency:
Penna Powers Brian Haynes
1706 S Major St
Salt Lake City, UT 84115
Tel.: (801) 487-4800
Fax: (801) 487-0707
Toll Free: (800) 409-9346

QUICKSILVER RESOURCES INC.

801 Cherry St Ste 3700 Unit 19
Fort Worth, TX 76102
Tel.: (817) 665-5000
Fax: (817) 665-5004
Toll Free: (877) 665-8600
E-mail: quicksilver@qrinc.com
Web Site: www.qrinc.com
Approx. Rev.: $928,331,000
Approx. Number Employees: 452
Year Founded: 1963
Business Description:
Crude Oil & Natural Gas Properties Acquisition, Development & Production
S.I.C.: 1311; 1321; 1389
N.A.I.C.S.: 211111; 211112; 213112
Media: 2-10
Personnel:
Thomas F. Darden *(Chm)*
Glenn M. Darden *(Pres & CEO)*
Philip W. Cook *(CFO & Sr VP)*
John C. Regan *(Chief Acctg Officer, VP & Controller)*
John C. Cirone *(Gen Counsel, Sec & Sr VP)*
Jeff Cook *(Exec VP-Ops)*
Stan G. Page *(Sr VP-US Ops)*
John Hinton *(VP-Fin)*
Chris M. Mundy *(VP-Engrg)*
Anne Darden Self *(VP-HR)*
Brands & Products:
QUICKSILVER RESOURCES
Advertising Agency:
Abernathy MacGregor Group, Inc.
501 Madison Ave 13th Fl
New York, NY 10022-5617
Tel.: (212) 371-5999
Fax: (212) 371-7097

Key to Media (For complete agency information see *The Advertising Red Books-Agencies* edition):
1. Bus. Publs. 2. Cable T.V. 3. Catalogs & Directories. 4. Co-op Adv. 5. Consumer Mags. 6. D.M. to Bus. Estab.7. D.M. to Consumers 8. Daily Newsp. 9. Exhibits/Trade Shows 10. Foreign 11. Infomercial 12. Internet Adv.13. Multimedia 14. Network Radio 15. Network T.V. 16. Newsp. Distr. Mags. 17. Other 18. Outdoor (Posters, Transit) 19. Point of Purchase20. Premiums, Novelties 21. Product Samples 22. Special Events Mktg. 23. Spot Radio 24. Spot T.V. 25. Weekly Newsp. 26. Yellow Page Adv.

RACETRAC PETROLEUM, INC.
3225 Cumberland Blvd S Ste 100
Atlanta, GA 30339-6408
Tel.: (770) 431-7600
Fax: (770) 563-8129
Toll Free: (800) 388-8035
E-mail: info@racetrac.com
Web Site: www.racetrac.com
Sales Range: $1-4.9 Billion
Approx. Number Employees: 3,962
Year Founded: 1959
Business Description:
Gas Stations & Convenience Stores
S.I.C.: 5541; 5171; 5172
N.A.I.C.S.: 447110; 424710; 424720; 447190
Advertising Expenditures: $375,000
Media: 10-13
Personnel:
Carl Bolch, Jr. *(Chm & CEO)*
Max V. Lenker *(Pres)*
Robert J. Dumbacher *(CFO & Treas)*
Allison Moran *(Sr VP)*
Brands & Products:
RACETRAC
RACEWAY
Advertising Agencies:
BrightWave Marketing
1718 Peachtree St Ste 1090
Atlanta, GA 30309
Tel.: (404) 253-3797

Fitzgerald+CO
3060 Peachtree Rd NW
Atlanta, GA 30305
Tel.: (404) 504-6900
Fax: (404) 239-0548

RAE SYSTEMS, INC.
3775 N 1st St
San Jose, CA 95134-1708
Tel.: (408) 952-8200
Fax: (408) 952-8480
Fax: (408) 752-0724
Toll Free: (877) 723-2878
Toll Free: (888) 723-4800
E-mail: raesales@raesystems.com
Web Site: www.raesystems.com
E-Mail For Key Personnel:
Sales Director: raesales@raesystems.com
Approx. Sls.: $87,053,000
Approx. Number Employees: 1,255
Year Founded: 1991
Business Description:
Gas, Chemical & Radiation Detection & Monitoring Services
S.I.C.: 3812; 3824
N.A.I.C.S.: 334511; 334514
Advertising Expenditures: $80,000
Media: 17
Personnel:
Robert I. Chen *(Chm, Pres & CEO)*
Randall Gausman *(CFO)*
Ming-Ting Tang *(Exec VP-Ops)*
Hong Tao Sun *(VP-Engrg)*
Ryan Watson *(VP-Sls-Americas)*
Brands & Products:
AREARAE
AREARAE GAMMA
AREARAE STEEL
AUTORAE
AUTORAE LITE
BADGERAE
BAE CHEMSENTRY
CHEMRAE
COLORIMETRIC GAS
ENTRYRAE
FMC 2000
GAMMARAE
GAMMARAE II R
HAZRAE
HUMIDITY FILTERING II
LIFESHIRT
MESHGUARD
MINIRAE
MINIRAE 3000
MINIRAE LITE
MULLTIRAE IR
MULTIRAE PLUS
NEUTRONRAE II
PLUMERAE
PPBRAE
PPBRAE PLUS
PRORAE
PRORAE REMOTE
PRORAE STUDIO
PRORAE SUITE
QRAE
QRAE II DIFFUSION
QRAE II PUMP
QRAE PLUS
RAE SYSTEMS
RAEGUARD
RAEGUARD EC
RAEGUARD LEL
RAEGUARD PID
RAELINK
RAELINK2
RAELINK3
RDK DETECTOR KIT
RDK HOST CONTROLLER KIT
RDK SYSTEM PACKAGE
SAFER HOMELAND RESPONDER
SAMPLERAE
SENSORRAE
SENTRY RAE
SENTRY RAE STEEL
SMITHS APD-2000
SOLARRAE
TOXIRAE
TOXIRAE 3
TOXIRAE II
TOXIRAE PLUS PID
ULTRARAE
ULTRARAE 3000
VRAE
WEATHERPAK

REEF CHEMICAL CO., INC.
7906 W Hwy 80
Midland, TX 79706
Mailing Address:
PO Box 11347
Midland, TX 79702
Tel.: (432) 560-5600
Fax: (432) 556-0563
Toll Free: (800) 299-8105
Web Site: www.reefcorp.com
Approx. Number Employees: 115
Year Founded: 1976
Business Description:
Oil Field Chemicals Whslr
S.I.C.: 1389
N.A.I.C.S.: 213112
Media: 2-7-10
Personnel:
Clay Baten *(CEO)*

RENEWABLE ENERGY GROUP, INC.
416 S Bell Ave PO Box 888
Ames, IA 50010
Tel.: (515) 239-8000
Fax: (515) 239-8009
E-mail: alicia.clancy@regfuel.com
Web Site: www.regfuel.com
Approx. Rev.: $216,455,000
Approx. Number Employees: 170
Business Description:
Renewable Energy Services
S.I.C.: 1311
N.A.I.C.S.: 211111
Advertising Expenditures: $80,000
Media: 17
Personnel:
Jeffrey Stroburg *(Chm & CEO)*
Daniel Oh *(Pres & COO)*
Chad Stone *(CFO)*
Patrick Hammen *(CIO)*
Myron Danzer *(VP-Customer & Tech Svc)*
Gary Haer *(VP-Sls & Mktg)*
Sara Taylor *(Exec Dir-Corp Affairs)*
Don Nelson *(Dir-Natl Sls)*
Jon Scharingson *(Dir-Sls)*
Alicia Clancy *(Mgr-Corp Affairs)*
Adam Sander *(Mgr-Supply Chain & Transportation)*
Brands & Products:
REG
REG-9000
REG-9000 BIOHEAT

REX ENERGY CORPORATION
476 Rolling Ridge Dr Ste 300
State College, PA 16801
Tel.: (814) 278-7267
Fax: (814) 278-7286
E-mail: investorrelations@rexenergycorp.com
Web Site: www.rexenergy.com
Approx. Rev.: $68,763,000
Approx. Number Employees: 191
Business Description:
Oil & Gas Production, Exploration & Development
S.I.C.: 1311
N.A.I.C.S.: 211111
Advertising Expenditures: $20,000
Personnel:
Lance T. Shaner *(Chm)*
Patrick M. McKinney *(Pres & COO)*
Thomas C. Stabley *(CEO & CFO)*
Bryan J. Clayton *(Sr VP & Reg Mgr-Illinois Basin)*
David Pratt *(Sr VP & Mgr- Exploration)*
Advertising Agency:
The JLS Agency
255 Alhambra Cir Ste 415
Coral Gables, FL 33134
Tel.: (786) 472-5933

ROWAN COMPANIES, INC.
2800 Post Oak Blvd Ste 5450
Houston, TX 77056-6127
Tel.: (713) 621-7800
Fax: (713) 960-7660
E-mail: ir@rowancompanies.com
Web Site: www.rowancompanies.com
Approx. Rev.: $1,819,207,000
Approx. Number Employees: 5,217
Year Founded: 1923
Business Description:
Offshore & Land Drilling Services
S.I.C.: 4432; 1381
N.A.I.C.S.: 483113; 213111
Media: 10-16
Personnel:
Henry E. Lentz, Jr. *(Chm)*
W. Matt Ralls *(Pres & CEO)*
William H. Wells *(CFO, Treas & Sr VP)*
Thomas P. Burke *(COO)*
Lisa Gauthier *(CIO & VP)*
Melanie M. Trent *(Chief Admin Officer, Sec & Sr VP)*
George C. Jones *(Compliance Officer)*
John L. Buvens *(Exec VP-Legal)*
Mark A. Keller *(Exec VP-Bus Dev)*
David P. Russell *(Exec VP-Drilling Ops)*
J. Kevin Bartol *(Sr VP-Corp Dev)*
Michael J. Dowdy *(VP-Engrg)*
Terry D. Woodall *(VP-HR)*
Susan McLeod *(Dir-IR)*

ROYALE ENERGY, INC.
7676 Hazard Ctr Dr Ste 1500
San Diego, CA 92108-4503
Tel.: (619) 881-2800
Fax: (619) 881-2899
Toll Free: (800) 447-8505 (Investor Relations)
E-mail: ir@royl.com
Web Site: www.royl.com
Approx. Rev.: $11,598,440
Approx. Number Employees: 22
Year Founded: 1986
Business Description:
Oil & Gas Exploration & Production
S.I.C.: 1311; 1389
N.A.I.C.S.: 211111; 213112
Advertising Expenditures: $2,061,689
Media: 10
Personnel:
Harry E. Hosmer *(Chm)*
Stephen M. Hosmer *(Co-CEO, CFO & Co-Pres)*
Donald H. Hosmer *(Co-Pres & Co-CEO)*
Mohamed Abdel-Rahman *(VP-Exploration & Production)*
Ronald Lipnick *(VP-Fin)*

RPC, INC.
2801 Buford Hwy Ste 520
Atlanta, GA 30329
Tel.: (404) 321-2140
Fax: (404) 321-5483
E-mail: irdept@rpc.net
Web Site: www.rpc.net
Approx. Rev.: $1,096,384,000
Approx. Number Employees: 2,500
Year Founded: 1984
Business Description:
Holding Company: Oilfield Services Consisting of Equipment Rental, Well Completion, Control Services & Transportation, Storage & Inspection Services for Oilfield Tubular Goods
S.I.C.: 1389; 7359
N.A.I.C.S.: 213112; 532299
Advertising Expenditures: $1,065,000
Personnel:
R. Randall Rollins *(Chm)*
Richard A. Hubbell *(Pres & CEO)*
Brands & Products:
CHAPARRAL BOATS

SASOL NORTH AMERICA INC.
(Affil. of Sasol Chemie GmbH)
900 Threadneedle Ste 100
Houston, TX 77079-2990
Mailing Address:
PO Box 19029
Houston, TX 77224-9029
Tel.: (281) 588-3000
Fax: (281) 588-3888
Fax: (281) 588-3144
E-mail: info@us.sasol.com

Key to Media (For complete agency information see *The Advertising Red Books-Agencies* edition):
1. Bus. Publs. 2. Cable T.V. 3. Catalogs & Directories. 4. Co-op Adv. 5. Consumer Mags. 6. D.M. to Bus. Estab.7. D.M. to Consumers 8. Daily Newsp. 9. Exhibits/Trade Shows 10. Foreign 11. Infomercial 12. Internet Adv.13. Multimedia 14. Network Radio 15. Network T.V. 16. Newsp. Distr. Mags. 17. Other 18. Outdoor (Posters, Transit) 19. Point of Purchase20. Premiums, Novelties 21. Product Samples 22. Special Events Mktg. 23. Spot Radio 24. Spot T.V. 25. Weekly Newsp. 26. Yellow Page Adv.

Sasol North America Inc. — (Continued)

Web Site:
www.sasolnorthamerica.com
Approx. Number Employees: 100
Year Founded: 1984
Business Description:
Mfr. of Industrial Chemicals
S.I.C.: 2821; 2869
N.A.I.C.S.: 325211; 325199
Export
Media: 2-4-6-7-8-10
Distr.: Intl.; Natl.
Budget Set: Aug.
Personnel:
Pat Jernigan *(Pres)*
John P. Stokes *(Dir-Sls)*
Jeff Fenton *(Bus Mgr-Alumina)*
Mark R. Chamberlin *(Mgr-Sls & Mktg)*
Alberto Farnos *(Mgr-Market Sls)*
Michael P. Keung *(Mgr-Sls & Mktg)*
Joseph S. Lopez *(Mgr-Sls)*
Janette Slavens *(Supvr-Mktg)*
Brands & Products:
ALFONIC
NALKYLENE
NOVEL

SHARP ENERGY, INC.
(Sub. of Chesapeake Utilities Corporation)
648 Ocean Hwy
Pocomoke City, MD 21851
Tel.: (410) 957-0422
Fax: (410) 957-0716
Web Site: www.sharpenergy.com
Sales Range: $25-49.9 Million
Approx. Number Employees: 20
Business Description:
Distributors of Propane Products
S.I.C.: 5984
N.A.I.C.S.: 454312
Personnel:
Ralph J. Adkins *(Chm)*
S. Robert Zola *(Pres)*
Advertising Agency:
Warschawski
1501 Sulgrave Ave Ste 350
Baltimore, MD 21209
Tel.: (410) 367-2700
Fax: (410) 367-2400

SHELL CANADA LIMITED
(Sub. of Shell Investments Limited)
400 4th Ave SW
Calgary, AB T2P 0J4, Canada
Mailing Address:
PO Box 100 Station M
Calgary, AB T2P 2H5, Canada
Tel.: (403) 691-3111
Fax: (403) 269-7462
Toll Free: (800) 661-1600
E-mail: questions@shell.com
Web Site: www.shell.ca
Sales Range: $5-14.9 Billion
Approx. Number Employees: 4,500
Year Founded: 1911
Business Description:
Oil & Natural Gas Producer
S.I.C.: 1311
N.A.I.C.S.: 211111
Media: 2-4-6-8-9-11-13-14-15-18-19-20-22-23-24-26
Distr.: Intl.; Natl.
Personnel:
Lorraine Mitchelmore *(Pres & Country Chair)*
Brian E. Straub *(CEO)*
Advertising Agency:
JWT Company Ltd.
160 Bloor St E
Toronto, ON M4W 3P7, Canada
Tel.: (416) 926-7300
Fax: (416) 926-7389

SHELL CHEMICAL LP
(Sub. of The Shell Petroleum Co. Ltd.)
910 Louisiana St
Houston, TX 77002
Mailing Address:
PO Box 2463
Houston, TX 77252
Tel.: (713) 241-6161
Fax: (713) 241-4044
E-mail: info@shellchemicals.com
Web Site: www.shellchemicals.com
Approx. Number Employees: 5,000
Business Description:
Petrochemical Mfr & Marketer
S.I.C.: 2899
N.A.I.C.S.: 325998
Media: 7-11-13
Personnel:
Stacy Methvin *(Former VP-Base Chemicals Americas & CEO)*

SHELL LUBRICANTS - CANADA
(Formerly Pennzoil-Quaker State Canada, Inc.)
(Sub. of Shell Lubricants)
1101 Blair Road
Burlington, ON L7M 1T3, Canada
Tel.: (905) 335-5577
Fax: (905) 332-6406
Telex: 61-8499
Web Site: www.shell.ca/home/content/can-en/products_services/solutions_for_businesses/shell_lubricants_tpkg/
Approx. Number Employees: 100
Business Description:
Oil Products Whslr
S.I.C.: 5172
N.A.I.C.S.: 424720
Media: 2-5-7-8-18-24-26
Personnel:
Tim Holmes *(Mgr)*

SHELL OIL COMPANY
(Sub. of The Shell Petroleum Co. Ltd.)
1 Shell Plz 910 Louisiana
Houston, TX 77002
Mailing Address:
PO Box 2463
Houston, TX 77252
Tel.: (713) 241-6161
Fax: (713) 241-4044
Telex: 762248
Web Site: www.shell.com
Approx. Number Employees: 11,600
Business Description:
Lubricants, Fuel Oils, Oils & Greases, Coke, Asphalts & Asphalt Emulsions, Road Oils, Diesel Fuels, Industrial Chemical & Petroleum Products Mfr & Retailer
S.I.C.: 2999; 5172
N.A.I.C.S.: 324199; 424720
Media: 1-3-4-5-6-8-9-10-14-15-18-19-20-23-24-26
Distr.: Intl
Budget Set: Apr.
Personnel:
William C. Lowrey *(Gen Counsel, Corp Sec & Sr VP)*
Rick Altizer *(Gen Mgr-Shell Retail Mktg-North America)*
Marvin E. Odum *(Dir-Upstream-Americas)*
Gerardo Amado *(Brand Mgr-Shell V-Power)*
Advertising Agencies:
Lopez Negrete Communications, Inc.
3336 Richmond Ave Ste 200
Houston, TX 77098
Tel.: (713) 877-8777
Fax: (713) 877-8796
Spanish Language Advertising

MediaCom
498 7th Ave
New York, NY 10018
Tel.: (212) 912-4200
Fax: (212) 508-4386

SHERRITT INTERNATIONAL CORPORATION
1133 Yonge Street
Toronto, ON M4T 2Y7, Canada
Tel.: (416) 924-4551
Tel.: (416) 935-2468 (IR)
Fax: (416) 924-5015
Toll Free: (800) 704-6698
E-mail: info@sherritt.com
Web Site: www.sherritt.com
Approx. Rev.: $1,804,432,102
Approx. Number Employees: 6,800
Year Founded: 1927
Business Description:
Oil & Natural Gas, Metal Ore & Coal Mining
S.I.C.: 1311; 1021; 1099; 1221
N.A.I.C.S.: 211111; 212111; 212234; 212299
Personnel:
Ian W. Delaney *(Chm, Pres & CEO)*
David Pathe *(CFO & Sr VP-Fin)*
Dean R. Chambers *(COO & Sr VP)*
Robert Reid *(Sr VP-Oil, Gas & Power & Country Mgr-Cuba)*
Michael E. Chalkley *(Sr VP-Tech)*
Greg Fuhr *(Sr VP)*
Mark Plamondon *(Sr VP-Coal)*
Elvin Saruk *(Sr VP-Construction-Ambatovy)*
Brian Tiessen *(Sr VP-Metals)*
Advertising Agency:
BarnesMcInerney Inc.
120 Adelaide St W Ste 910
Toronto, ON M5H 3L5, Canada
Tel.: (416) 367-5000
Fax: (416) 367-5390

SINCLAIR OIL CORPORATION
550 E S Temple PO Box 30825
Salt Lake City, UT 84102-1005
Tel.: (801) 524-2700
Fax: (801) 524-2880
E-mail: webmaster@sinclairoil.com
Web Site: www.sinclairoil.com
Approx. Number Employees: 7,000
Year Founded: 1916
Business Description:
Petroleum Refiner; Service Stations, Convenience Stores, Ski Resorts & Hotels Owner & Operator
S.I.C.: 2911; 4612; 5541; 7011; 7999
N.A.I.C.S.: 324110; 447110; 447190; 486110; 713990; 721110
Advertising Expenditures: $650,000
Personnel:
Robert Earl Holding *(Pres & CEO)*
Charles Barlow *(Treas & VP-Fin)*
Brands & Products:
GRAND AMERICA
LITTLE AMERICA
SINCLAIR
SNOWBASIN
SUN VALLEY
THE WESTGATE HOTEL

SOUTHWEST GAS CORPORATION
5241 Spring Mountain Rd
Las Vegas, NV 89146
Mailing Address:
PO Box 98512
Las Vegas, NV 89193-8512
Tel.: (702) 876-7011
Fax: (702) 364-3045
Web Site: www.swgas.com
Approx. Rev.: $1,830,371,000
Approx. Number Employees: 2,349
Year Founded: 1931
Business Description:
Natural Gas Purchaser, Transporter & Distr
S.I.C.: 1311; 4922; 4924
N.A.I.C.S.: 211111; 221210; 486210
Media: 8-9-25
Distr.: Reg.
Personnel:
James J. Kropid *(Chm)*
James P. Kane *(Pres)*
Jeffrey W. Shaw *(CEO)*
Roy R. Centrella *(CFO & Sr VP)*
Gregory J. Peterson *(Chief Acctg Officer, VP & Controller)*
Thomas R. Sheets *(Gen Counsel & Sr VP-Legal Affairs)*
Kenneth J. Kenny *(Treas & VP-Fin)*
George C. Biehl *(Exec VP)*
James F. Wunderlin *(Sr VP & Engr)*
John P. Hester *(Sr VP)*
Edward A. Janov *(Sr VP-Fin)*
Christina A. Palacios *(Sr VP-Southern Arizona Div)*
Edward Zub *(Sr VP)*
Marilyn McGinnis *(Mgr)*
Advertising Agency:
E.B. Lane
733 W McDowell Rd
Phoenix, AZ 85007-1727
Tel.: (602) 258-5263
Fax: (602) 257-8128

SPEEDWAY LLC
(Formerly Speedway SuperAmerica LLC)
(Sub. of Marathon Petroleum Company LLC)
500 Speedway Dr
Enon, OH 45323
Tel.: (937) 864-3000
Fax: (937) 863-6722
E-mail: info@speedway.com
Web Site: www.speedway.com
Approx. Number Employees: 18,257
Business Description:
Operator of Gasoline Stations, Convenience Stores & Truck Stops
S.I.C.: 5541
N.A.I.C.S.: 447110; 447190
Media: 3-5-8-9-18-19-22-23-24
Distr.: Reg.
Personnel:
Doug Couch *(VP-IT)*
Brands & Products:
RICH OIL
SPEEDWAY
SUPERAMERICA

Key to Media (For complete agency information see *The Advertising Red Books-Agencies* edition):
1. Bus. Publs. 2. Cable T.V. 3. Catalogs & Directories. 4. Co-op Adv. 5. Consumer Mags. 6. D.M. to Bus. Estab.7. D.M. to Consumers 8. Daily Newsp. 9. Exhibits/Trade Shows 10. Foreign 11. Infomercial 12. Internet Adv.13. Multimedia 14. Network Radio 15. Network T.V. 16. Newsp. Distr. Mags. 17. Other 18. Outdoor (Posters, Transit) 19. Point of Purchase20. Premiums, Novelties 21. Product Samples 22. Special Events Mktg. 23. Spot Radio 24. Spot T.V. 25. Weekly Newsp. 26. Yellow Page Adv.

SPEEDWAY SUPERAMERICA LLC
(Name Changed to Speedway LLC)

STALLION OILFIELD SERVICES, INC.
950 Corbindale Rd Ste 300
Houston, TX 77024
Mailing Address:
PO Box 1486
Houston, TX 77251-1486
Tel.: (713) 528-5544
Fax: (713) 528-1276
Web Site: www.stallionoilfield.com
Sales Range: $200-249.9 Million
Approx. Number Employees: 1,344
Business Description:
Oil Production Wellsite Support & Construction Logistics Services
S.I.C.: 1381; 1389
N.A.I.C.S.: 213111; 213112
Advertising Expenditures: $387,000
Personnel:
Gene I. Davis *(Chm)*
Craig M. Johnson *(Pres & CEO)*
David S. Schorlemer *(CFO & VP)*
Hill Dishman *(COO & VP)*
Douglas Stewart *(Gen Counsel, Sec & VP)*
Michael Moore *(VP-Sls & Mktg)*

STAR GAS PARTNERS, L.P.
Clearwater House 2187 Atlantic St
Stamford, CT 06902-6880
Tel.: (203) 328-7300
Fax: (203) 328-7422
Toll Free: (800) 966-9827
E-mail: service@star-gas.com
Web Site: www.star-gas.com
Approx. Sls.: $1,212,776,000
Approx. Number Employees: 2,729
Year Founded: 1903
Business Description:
Home Heating Fuel Distr
S.I.C.: 5984; 5983
N.A.I.C.S.: 454311
Advertising Expenditures: $9,600,000
Media: 2-5-7-8-9-10-17-18-23-26
Distr.: Direct to Consumer; Reg.
Personnel:
Daniel P. Donovan *(CEO)*
Richard F. Ambury *(CFO)*
Brands & Products:
STAR GAS
Advertising Agency:
Darrow Associates, Inc.
273 Walt Whitman Rd Ste 280
Melville, NY 11746
Tel.: (631) 367-1866

STEWART & STEVENSON, LLC
1000 Louisiana Ste 5900
Houston, TX 77002
Tel.: (713) 751-2600
Tel.: (713) 751-2700
Fax: (713) 868-7692
Web Site:
www.stewartandstevenson.com
Approx. Sls.: $861,234,000
Approx. Number Employees: 2,300
Year Founded: 1902
Business Description:
Oil & Gas Equipment Mfr, Sales & Rental Services
S.I.C.: 3533; 1389; 7353
N.A.I.C.S.: 333132; 213112; 532412
Advertising Expenditures: $1,700,000
Personnel:
Hushang Ansary *(Chm)*
Frank C. Carlucci *(Vice Chm)*
Robert L. Hargrave *(Vice Chm)*
Mark Whitman *(Pres)*
Steve Fulgham *(CEO)*
John B. Simmons *(CFO)*
Andrew M. Cannon *(Chief Acctg Officer)*
David C. Sulkis *(Gen Counsel)*
David E. Christensen *(Sr VP-Mfg & Engrg)*
Charles T. Hatcher *(VP-HR)*
Jack L. Pieper *(VP-Fin Ops)*
Kenneth W. Simmons *(VP-Domestic Sls & Aftermarket)*

STONER INC.
1070 Robert Fulton Hwy
Quarryville, PA 17566
Tel.: (717) 786-7355
Fax: (717) 786-9088
E-mail: timesaver@stonersolutions.com
Web Site: www.stonersolutions.com
Approx. Sls.: $10,200,000
Approx. Number Employees: 45
Business Description:
Lubricating Oils
S.I.C.: 2992; 2842
N.A.I.C.S.: 324191; 325612
Media: 6-13
Personnel:
Robert Ecklin *(Founder & Pres)*
Rob Marchalonis *(CEO)*
Jon Farrell *(VP-Fin)*
Brands & Products:
BEAD MAX
FABPROTEX
GUST
INVISIBLE GLASS
MORE SHINE FOR TIRES
SPEED BEAD
TARMINATOR
TRIM SHINE
XENIT

SUNCOR ENERGY INC.
150 6 Avenue SW
PO Box 2844
Calgary, AB T2P 3E3, Canada
Tel.: (403) 296-8000
Fax: (403) 296-3030
Toll Free: (866) SUNCOR-1
E-mail: invest@suncor.com
Web Site: www.suncor.com
Approx. Rev.: $34,350,000,000
Approx. Number Employees: 12,076
Year Founded: 1919
Business Description:
Natural Gas Production, Exploration & Refining Services; Synthetic Crude Oil Sands Mining & Processing Services; Refined Products Distr & Marketer
S.I.C.: 1311; 1389; 2911; 4924; 5172
N.A.I.C.S.: 211111; 213112; 221210; 324110; 424720
Media: 7-22
Personnel:
John T. Ferguson *(Chm)*
Richard L. George *(Pres & CEO)*
Bart W. Demosky *(CFO)*
Steven W. Williams *(COO)*
Janice B. Odegaard *(Gen Counsel & Sr VP)*
Kevin D. Nabholz *(Exec VP-Major Projects)*
Jay Thornton *(Exec VP-Energy Supply)*
Sue Lee *(Sr VP-HR & Comm)*
Advertising Agency:
Scott Peyron & Associates, Inc.
209 Main St Ste 200
Boise, ID 83702
Tel.: (208) 388-3800
Fax: (208) 388-8898

SUNOCO INC.
1818 Market St Ste 1500
Philadelphia, PA 19103
Tel.: (215) 977-3000
Tel.: (215) 977-6082 (Investor Rels)
Fax: (215) 977-3409
Toll Free: (800) 786-6261
E-mail: shareholderrelations@sunocoinc.com
Web Site: www.sunocoinc.com
Approx. Rev.: $37,489,000,000
Approx. Number Employees: 10,200
Year Founded: 1886
Business Description:
Petroleum Refining & Marketing, Synthetic Crude Oil Production & Natural Gas Production
S.I.C.: 2911; 1311; 5541
N.A.I.C.S.: 324110; 211111; 447110; 447190
Import Export
Media: 2-5-6-7-8-9-18-19-20-23-24
Distr.: Reg.
Budget Set: Jan.
Personnel:
Lynn Laverty Elsenhans *(Chm, Pres & CEO)*
Michael J. Thomson *(Pres & Sr VP)*
Brian P. MacDonald *(CFO & Sr VP)*
Dennis Zeleny *(Chief HR Officer & Sr VP)*
Stacy L. Fox *(Gen Counsel, Sec & Sr VP)*
Anne-Marie Ainsworth *(Sr VP-Refining)*
Frederick A. Henderson *(Sr VP)*
Robert W. Owens *(Sr VP-Mktg)*
Joseph P. Krott *(Comptroller)*
Andrew Kabakoff *(Mgr-Natl Category)*
Brands & Products:
SUNOCO
Advertising Agency:
LevLane Advertising/PR/Interactive
100 Penn Sq E
Philadelphia, PA 19107
Tel.: (215) 825-9600
Fax: (215) 809-1900

SUSSER HOLDINGS CORPORATION
4525 Ayers St
Corpus Christi, TX 78415
Tel.: (361) 884-2463
Fax: (361) 884-2494
Toll Free: (800) 569-3585
E-mail: contactus@susser.com
Web Site: www.susser.com
Approx. Rev.: $3,930,630,000
Approx. Number Employees: 5,660
Year Founded: 1938
Business Description:
Convenience Store & Gas Station Owner, Operator & Franchisor
S.I.C.: 5541; 5999
N.A.I.C.S.: 447110; 453998
Advertising Expenditures: $5,500,000
Personnel:
Sam L. Susser *(Pres & CEO)*
Mary E. Sullivan *(CFO, Treas & Exec VP)*
Steve C. DeSutter *(Pres/CEO-Retail)*
Rocky B. Dewbre *(Pres/COO-Wholesale)*
E. V. Bonner *(Gen Counsel & Exec VP)*
Richard Sebastian *(Sr VP-Retail Ops)*
Rod Martin *(VP-Mktg)*
Otis Peaks *(VP-HR)*
M. David Wishard *(VP-Bus Dev-Retail)*
Craig Scotton *(Sr Dir-Petroleum Svcs)*
Stephen Blume *(Dir-Internal Audit)*
Michael R. Choate *(Dir-Construction)*
Ella Cunningham *(Dir-Retail Acctg)*
Chrissy Garcia *(Dir-Fin Reporting)*
Ben Scott, Jr. *(Dir-Maintenance)*
Dee Suarez *(Dir-HR)*
Jeff Turner *(Dir-Environ & Compliance)*
Ray Brysch *(Mgr-Midland & Odessa)*
Brands & Products:
STRIPES
SUSSER

TENNECO, INC.
500 N Field Dr
Lake Forest, IL 60045-2595
Tel.: (847) 482-5000
Fax: (847) 482-5940
Toll Free: (800) 777-9564
E-mail: jostrander@tenneco.com
Web Site: www.tenneco.com
Approx. Rev.: $5,937,000,000
Approx. Number Employees: 22,000
Year Founded: 1943
Business Description:
Mfr., Designer & Marketer of Emission Control & Ride Control Products & Systems
S.I.C.: 3714; 3711
N.A.I.C.S.: 336322; 336211; 336330; 336399
Import Export
Advertising Expenditures: $7,000,000
Media: 2-6-10-13-14-15-18
Distr.: Natl.
Budget Set: Oct.
Personnel:
Gregg M. Sherrill *(Chm & CEO)*
Kenneth R. Trammell *(CFO & Exec VP)*
Hari N. Nair *(COO)*
H. William Haser *(CIO & VP)*
Timothy E. Jackson *(CTO & Sr VP)*
Paul Schultz *(Sr VP-Global Supply Chain Mgmt)*
Neal A Yanos *(Exec VP-North America)*
Brent J. Bauer *(Sr VP & Gen Mgr-North American Original Equipment)*
Josep Fornos *(Sr VP-Europe, South America & India)*
Richard P. Schneider *(Sr VP-Global Admin)*
Enrique Orta *(VP & Gen Mgr-European Original Equipment Emission Control)*
Karel Van Bael *(VP & Gen Mgr-Europe Original Equipment Ride Control)*
Jane Ostrander *(Exec Dir-Global Comm)*
Carri Irby *(Brand Mgr)*

Key to Media (For complete agency information see *The Advertising Red Books-Agencies* edition):
1. Bus. Publs. 2. Cable T.V. 3. Catalogs & Directories. 4. Co-op Adv. 5. Consumer Mags. 6. D.M. to Bus. Estab.7. D.M. to Consumers 8. Daily Newsp. 9. Exhibits/Trade Shows 10. Foreign 11. Infomercial 12. Internet Adv.13. Multimedia 14. Network Radio 15. Network T.V. 16. Newsp. Distr. Mags. 17. Other 18. Outdoor (Posters, Transit) 19. Point of Purchase20. Premiums, Novelties 21. Product Samples 22. Special Events Mktg. 23. Spot Radio 24. Spot T.V. 25. Weekly Newsp. 26. Yellow Page Adv.

Tenneco, Inc. — (Continued)

Brands & Products:
AXIOS
CLEVITE
CLEVITE ELASTOMERS
DNX
DYNOMAX
FONOS
FRIC-ROT
GILLET
HYDROELASTIC
KINETIC
LUKEY
MARZOCCHI
MONROE
RANCHO
TENNECO
THRUSH
WALKER
Advertising Agency:
Pinnacle Communications Group
3153 Mayfield Rd
Silver Lake, OH 44224-3144
Tel.: (330) 688-3500
Pub Rels
Monroe, Walker

TESORO HAWAII CORPORATION

(Sub. of Tesoro Corporation)
91-325 Komohana St
Kapolei, HI 96707
Mailing Address:
PO Box 3379
Honolulu, HI 96842-0001
Tel.: (808) 547-3111
Fax: (808) 547-3849
Web Site: www.tsocorp.com
Sales Range: $150-199.9 Million
Approx. Number Employees: 240
Year Founded: 1904
Business Description:
Petroleum Refining
S.I.C.: 2911
N.A.I.C.S.: 324110
Import Export
Media: 2-7-17
Distr.: Intl.; Natl.
Budget Set: Nov.
Brands & Products:
GAS EXPRESS

TETRA TECHNOLOGIES, INC.

24955 I 45 N
The Woodlands, TX 77380
Tel.: (281) 367-1983
Fax: (281) 364-4306
Toll Free: (800) 327-7817
E-mail: corp@tetratec.com
Web Site: www.tetratec.com
Approx. Rev.: $872,678,000
Approx. Number Employees: 2,923
Year Founded: 1981
Business Description:
Specialty Organic Chemical Products, Services & Process Technologies
S.I.C.: 2816; 1389; 1623; 2819
N.A.I.C.S.: 325131; 213112; 237120; 325188
Import Export
Advertising Expenditures: $200,000
Media: 17
Personnel:
Ralph S. Cunningham *(Chm)*
Stuart M. Brightman *(Pres & CEO)*
Joseph M. Abell, III *(CFO & Sr VP)*
Bass C. Wallace, Jr. *(Gen Counsel & Sec)*
Bruce A. Cobb *(Treas & VP-Fin)*
Philip N. Longorio *(Sr VP)*
Dennis R. Mathews *(Sr VP)*
Michael Lobin *(VP-IT)*
Eileen Price *(Mgr-IR)*

TEXAS REFINERY CORP.

1 Refinery Pl 840 N Main St
Fort Worth, TX 76106
Mailing Address:
PO Box 711
Fort Worth, TX 76101-0711
Tel.: (817) 332-1161
Fax: (817) 336-8441
Toll Free: (800) 827-0711
E-mail: trc711@texasrefinery.com
Web Site: www.texasrefinery.com
Sales Range: $10-24.9 Million
Approx. Number Employees: 120
Year Founded: 1922
Business Description:
Protective Roof Coatings & Lubricants Mfr; Big Red Industrial Cleaner
S.I.C.: 2992; 2952
N.A.I.C.S.: 324191; 324122
Export
Media: 2-7-9-10-11-20-21-25
Distr.: Direct to Consumer; Natl.
Budget Set: July
Personnel:
A.M. Pate, III *(Chm)*
Jerry W. Hopkins *(Pres)*
Patrick Walsh *(VP & Gen Mgr)*
Dennis Parks *(VP & Mgr-Sls)*
Miguel Vivar *(Asst VP & Mgr-Export Div Sls)*
Patty Collins *(Asst VP)*
Brands & Products:
880 CROWN & CHASSIS GREASE
ALUMINUM SHIELD SYSTEM II
BIG RED
BIO-KLEAN
DE-GEL SUPREME
DZL-LENE XL/10
DZL-PEP ARCTIC
GLAS-WEB
GREASE GOBBLER
MAGI-MELT
MAGI-PATCH
MIGHTYPLATE
MIGHTYPLY
MOLY PRO-SPEC
MULTI-KLEAN
NEW ONE-ELEVEN
NU-FLOOR FLEX-JOINT
PARAGON 3000
PERMA-STRIPE
POLY-MAT
POWER CLEANSE
PRO-SPEC
QUADRA-KLEAN
RED MAX
RIG WASH
SAFETY SOLVENT
SAFETYSOLVE II
SUPER BIG RED
SURE-STEP
SURESTA
TEXTRANS
TIRESEAL
TRC
TROXYMITE

TRANSAMMONIA, INC.

320 Park Ave 10th Fl
New York, NY 10022-6022
Tel.: (212) 223-3200
Fax: (212) 759-1410
E-mail: newyork@transammonia.com
Web Site: www.transammonia.com
Approx. Rev.: $8,300,000,000
Approx. Number Employees: 330
Year Founded: 1965
Business Description:
Ammonia, Fertilizers, Liquid Petroleum Gases, Petrochemicals & Petroleum Products Trader & Merchandiser
S.I.C.: 5172
N.A.I.C.S.: 424720
Import Export
Media: 2-4-7-13
Personnel:
Ronald P. Stanton *(Chm & CEO)*
Edward G. Weiner *(CFO)*
Benjamin Tan *(CIO)*
James Benfield *(Treas & Sr VP-Fin)*
Fred M. Lowenfels *(Sr VP)*
Marguerite Harrington *(Dir-HR)*

TRANSMONTAIGNE, INC.

(Sub. of Morgan Stanley & Co. Commodities)
1670 Broadway Ste 3100
Denver, CO 80202
Tel.: (303) 626-8200
Fax: (303) 626-8228
E-mail: mservices@transmontaigne.com
Web Site: www.transmontaigne.com
Sales Range: $5-14.9 Billion
Approx. Number Employees: 727
Business Description:
Crude Oil, Petroleum Products & Natural Gas
S.I.C.: 1623; 1311; 4612; 4924
N.A.I.C.S.: 237120; 211111; 221210; 486110
Media: 7
Personnel:
Charles L. Dunlap *(Pres & CEO)*
Frederick W. Boutin *(CFO)*
Erik B. Carlson *(Exec VP)*
Richard C. Eaton *(Exec VP)*
Rodney R. Hilt *(Exec VP)*
Chee Ooi *(Exec VP-TPSI)*

TRI STAR ENERGY, LLC

1740 Ed Temple Blvd
Nashville, TN 37208-1850
Tel.: (615) 313-3600
Fax: (615) 254-7657
E-mail: email@tri-starenergy.com
Web Site: www.tri-staris.com
Approx. Number Employees: 500
Year Founded: 1958
Business Description:
Petroleum Products Producer & Retailer; Convenience Stores Operator
S.I.C.: 5172
N.A.I.C.S.: 424720
Media: 18-20-23-24
Distr.: Reg.
Personnel:
John B. Jewell, III *(Pres)*
Mark Cole *(CFO)*
John Jewell, IV *(VP-Opers)*
J.R. Lenear, III *(VP-Retail Grp)*

TXCO RESOURCES INC.

(Filed Ch 11 Bankruptcy #951807 on 05/17/2009 in U.S. Bankruptcy Ct, Western Dist of TX, San Antonio)
777 E Sonterra Blvd Ste 350
San Antonio, TX 78258
Tel.: (210) 496-5300
Fax: (210) 496-3232
E-mail: txco@txco.com
Web Site: www.txco.com
Sales Range: $125-149.9 Million
Approx. Number Employees: 121
Business Description:
Onshore Domestic Oil & Gas Reserves Exploration, Development & Production; Oil & Gas Whslr
S.I.C.: 1311; 1389
N.A.I.C.S.: 211111; 213112
Advertising Expenditures: $278,000
Media: 2
Personnel:
Albert S. Conly *(Pres, CEO, CFO, COO, Chief Acctg Officer & Sec)*
Robert E. Lee, Jr. *(Mgr-Land)*
Advertising Agency:
EnerCom, Inc.
633 17th St Ste 1645
Denver, CO 80202
Tel.: (303) 296-8834
Fax: (303) 293-9904

UNITED REFINING COMPANY

(Sub. of United Refining Inc.)
15 Bradley St
Warren, PA 16365-3224
Tel.: (814) 723-1500
Fax: (814) 726-4603
E-mail: webmaster@urc.com
Web Site: www.urc.com
Approx. Sls.: $2,654,401,000
Approx. Number Employees: 1,920
Year Founded: 1902
Business Description:
Petroleum Products Refiner & Marketer
S.I.C.: 2911; 5172; 5541
N.A.I.C.S.: 324110; 424720; 447190
Advertising Expenditures: $300,000
Media: 5
Personnel:
John A. Catsimatidis *(Chm & CEO)*
Myron L. Turfitt *(Pres & COO)*
James E. Murphy *(CFO & VP)*
Ashton L. Ditka *(Sr VP-Mktg)*

UNITED STATES OIL & GAS CORPORATION

11782 Jollyville Rd Ste 211B
Austin, TX 78759
Tel.: (512) 464-1225
Fax: (512) 628-6880
E-mail: investor.relations1@usaoilandgas.com
Web Site: www.usaoilandgas.com
Approx. Sls.: $24,684,110
Approx. Number Employees: 11
Year Founded: 1988
Business Description:
Oil & Gas Investment Services
S.I.C.: 6289; 1389
N.A.I.C.S.: 523999; 213112
Advertising Expenditures: $20,581
Media: 17
Personnel:
Alex Tawse *(Pres, CEO, CFO & Treas)*

VALERO ENERGY CORPORATION

1 Valero Way
San Antonio, TX 78249
Mailing Address:
PO Box 696000
San Antonio, TX 78269
Tel.: (210) 345-2000

Key to Media (For complete agency information see *The Advertising Red Books-Agencies* edition):
1. Bus. Publs. 2. Cable T.V. 3. Catalogs & Directories. 4. Co-op Adv. 5. Consumer Mags. 6. D.M. to Bus. Estab.7. D.M. to Consumers 8. Daily Newsp. 9. Exhibits/Trade Shows 10. Foreign 11. Infomercial 12. Internet Adv.13. Multimedia 14. Network Radio 15. Network T.V. 16. Newsp. Distr. Mags. 17. Other 18. Outdoor (Posters, Transit) 19. Point of Purchase20. Premiums, Novelties 21. Product Samples 22. Special Events Mktg. 23. Spot Radio 24. Spot T.V. 25. Weekly Newsp. 26. Yellow Page Adv.

Fax: (210) 345-2646
Toll Free: (800) 531-7911
E-mail: investorrelations@valero.com
Web Site: www.valero.com

Approx. Rev.: $82,233,000,000
Approx. Number Employees: 20,313
Year Founded: 1980

Business Description:
Petroleum Products Refiner & Marketer
S.I.C.: 2911; 4613; 5172; 5541
N.A.I.C.S.: 324110; 424720; 447110; 447190; 486910
Import Export

Media: 1-7-8-9-10-13-22-23-24
Distr.: Natl.; Reg.

Personnel:
William Klesse *(Chm, Pres & CEO)*
Mike Ciskowski *(CFO & Exec VP)*
Gene Edwards *(Chief Dev Officer & Exec VP-Dev)*
Joe Gorder *(Chief Comml Officer & Exec VP)*
Steve Gilbert *(Disclosure/Compliance Officer & Asst Sec)*
Kim Bowers *(Gen Counsel & Exec VP)*
Jay Browning *(Sec & Sr VP-Corp Law)*
Clay Killinger *(Sr VP & Controller)*
Gary Arthur, Jr. *(Sr VP-Retail Mktg)*
Bob Beadle *(Sr VP-Crude & Feedstock Supply & Trading)*
Mike Crownover *(Sr VP-HR)*
Dave Parker *(Sr VP-Product Supply & Wholesale Mktg)*
Eric Fisher *(VP-Investor & Corp Comm)*
Jerry McVicker *(VP-East Coast Mktg)*
Curt Benefield *(Dir-Asphalt Product-Tech Dev)*
Curtis Bissonnette *(Dir-Branded Mktg)*
Bill Day *(Dir-Corp Comm)*
Doug McClure *(Dir-Mid-Continent Asphalt Mktg)*
Andrea Palsulich *(Dir)*
Carolyn Allen *(Sr Mgr-Wholesale Brands)*
David Goodrum *(Sr Mgr-Wholesale Mktg)*
John Murphy *(Sr Mgr-Area Sls)*
Kiplen Zigmond *(Sr Mgr-Branded Customer Support Svcs)*
Gevan Alford *(Reg Sls Mgr-Gulf Coast Reg)*
Stephen Annunziata *(Sls Mgr-Great Lakes Reg)*
Al Christian *(Sls Mgr-Great Lakes Reg)*
Michael Katz *(Sls Mgr-Northern CA)*
Gene Land *(Sls Mgr-SouthWest)*
Lisa Shaner *(Sls Mgr-Accts)*
Bill Stillwell *(Sls Mgr-Great Lakes Reg)*
Mark Westrick *(Sr Sls Mgr-Great Lakes Reg)*
Jay Bailey *(Mgr-Mktg)*
Kent Bell *(Mgr-Wholesale Capital Projects)*
Tracy Carty *(Mgr-Sls)*
Pat Diemer *(Mgr-Sls)*
Anthony Gavin *(Mgr-Unbranded Sls)*
Bill Glassner *(Mgr-Mktg Support)*
Johnie Goodman *(Mgr-Area Sls)*
Don Goss *(Mgr-Product Tech Svc)*
Sidney Pujol *(Mgr-Area Sls)*
Richard Rodgers *(Mgr-Area Sls)*
Kyle Walker *(Mgr-Area Sls)*

Brands & Products:
BEACON
CORNER STORE
DIAMOND SHAMROCK
SHAMROCK
STOP N GO
ULTRAMAR
VALERO

VERASUN ENERGY CORPORATION

110 N Minnesota Ave Ste 300
Sioux Falls, SD 57104
Tel.: (605) 978-7000
Fax: (605) 696-7250
E-mail: info@verasun.com
Sales Range: $800-899.9 Million
Approx. Number Employees: 496
Year Founded: 2001

Business Description:
Ethanol Mfr
S.I.C.: 2869
N.A.I.C.S.: 325193
Advertising Expenditures: $1,275,000

Personnel:
D. Duane Gilliam *(Chm)*
Matthew K.R. Janes *(COO)*
Bryan D. Meier *(Chief Acctg Officer & VP)*
Mark Dickey *(Gen Counsel & Sr VP)*
Robert L. Antoine Jr. *(Sr VP-HR)*
Paul J. Caudill *(Sr VP-Ops)*
Bill Honnef *(Sr VP-Strategic Initiatives)*
Barry P. Schaps *(Sr VP-Sls & Logistics)*

Brands & Products:
AMERICA'S SOURCE FOR RENEWABLE FUELS
VE85
VERASUN

VULCAN ENERGY CORPORATION

333 Clay St Ste 1600
Houston, TX 77002-4804
Tel.: (713) 646-4100
Fax: (713) 646-4313
Toll Free: (800) 934-6083
Sales Range: $10-24.9 Million
Approx. Number Employees: 95
Year Founded: 1976

Business Description:
Energy Production Services
S.I.C.: 5172; 1311; 5171
N.A.I.C.S.: 424720; 211111; 424710
Advertising Expenditures: $15,000,000
Media: 1-2-8-9-13-17-25
Distr.: Natl.

Personnel:
Tim Moore *(Gen Counsel, Sec & VP)*
James Roberts *(Reg Dir)*

THE WILLIAMS COMPANIES, INC.

1 Williams Ctr
Tulsa, OK 74172
Tel.: (918) 573-2000
Fax: (918) 573-6714
Toll Free: (800) 945-5426
Telex: 910-845-2325
E-mail: ann.oliver@williams.com
Web Site: www.williams.com
Approx. Rev.: $9,616,000,000
Approx. Number Employees: 5,022
Year Founded: 1908

Business Description:
Natural Gas Exploration, Extraction, Processing, Pipeline Transportation, Distribution & Marketing
S.I.C.: 4922; 1321; 4924
N.A.I.C.S.: 486210; 211112; 221210
Media: 26
Distr.: Intl.; Natl.
Budget Set: Oct.

Personnel:
Frank T. MacInnis *(Chm)*
Alan S. Armstrong *(Pres & CEO)*
Donald R. Chappel *(CFO & Sr VP)*
Ted T. Timmermans *(Chief Acctg Officer, VP & Controller)*
Randall L. Barnard *(Pres-Gas Pipeline)*
William E. Hobbs *(Pres-Power)*
Rory Lee Miller *(Pres-Midstream Gathering & Processing)*
Phillip D. Wright *(Pres-Gas Pipeline)*
James J. Bender *(Gen Counsel & Sr VP)*
Frank Ferazzi *(VP-Customer Svc & Rates)*
Melissa Casey *(Dir)*
Lou Hayden *(Dir-Federal Legislative Affairs)*
Rodney J. Sailor *(Dir-Govt Affairs)*
Barbara Shaull *(Dir)*
Scott Turkington *(Dir)*

Brands & Products:
INGENUITY TAKES ENERGY
WILLIAMS

WYNN OIL COMPANY

(Sub. of Illinois Tool Works Inc.)
1050 W 5th St
Azusa, CA 91702
Mailing Address:
PO Box 9526
Azusa, CA 91702-9526
Tel.: (626) 334-0231
Fax: (626) 334-1456
Toll Free: (800) 989-8363
E-mail: wynns_ppdcustservice@wynnsusa.com
Web Site: www.wynnsusa.com
E-Mail For Key Personnel:
Marketing Director:
wynns_marketing@wynnsusa.com
Sales Range: $75-99.9 Million
Approx. Number Employees: 135
Year Founded: 1939

Business Description:
Specialty Chemical Products Marketer
S.I.C.: 2992; 2899
N.A.I.C.S.: 324191; 325998
Import Export
Media: 1-2-4-5-6-7-9-10-19-20-21-23-24
Distr.: Intl.; Natl.
Budget Set: Aug.

Personnel:
Gerry Miles *(Gen Mgr)*
Tohru Hattori *(Mgr)*

Brands & Products:
DU ALL
ENVIROPURGE
POWER FLUSH
TRANSERVE II
WYNN'S

ZECOL INC.

(Sub. of Twinco Automotive Warehouse, Inc.)
4635 Willow Dr
Hamel, MN 55340-9528
Mailing Address:
PO Box 12
Hamel, MN 55340
Tel.: (763) 478-2360
Fax: (763) 478-3411
Toll Free: (800) 682-3800
Web Site: www.twincoromax.com/zecol.htm
Approx. Sls.: $2,000,000
Approx. Number Employees: 15
Year Founded: 1932

Business Description:
Mfr. of Polishing Wax for Autos, Automotive & Industrial Chemicals, Sootout & Lubaid Diesel Additive
S.I.C.: 5013
N.A.I.C.S.: 423120
Media: 17
Distr.: Natl.
Budget Set: Jan.

Brands & Products:
ZECOL

ZION OIL & GAS, INC.

6510 Abrams Rd Ste 300
Dallas, TX 75231
Tel.: (214) 221-4610
Fax: (214) 221-6510
E-mail: dallas@zionoil.com
Web Site: www.zionoil.com
Approx. Int. Income: $18,000
Approx. Number Employees: 19
Year Founded: 2000

Business Description:
Oil & Gas Exploration Services
S.I.C.: 1311
N.A.I.C.S.: 211111
Advertising Expenditures: $207,000

Personnel:
John M. Brown *(Founder & Chm)*
William L. Ottaviani *(Pres & COO)*
Richard J. Rinberg *(CEO)*
Ilan Sheena *(CFO)*
Martin M. Van Brauman *(Chief Legal Officer)*
Patricia J. Beals *(Chief Acctg Officer & VP-Compliance)*
Victor G. Carrillo *(Exec VP)*
John McKenney *(Project Mgr-Ops)*
Stephen E. Pierce *(Mgr-Exploration)*

Key to Media (For complete agency information see *The Advertising Red Books-Agencies* edition):
1. Bus. Publs. 2. Cable T.V. 3. Catalogs & Directories. 4. Co-op Adv. 5. Consumer Mags. 6. D.M. to Bus. Estab.7. D.M. to Consumers 8. Daily Newsp. 9. Exhibits/Trade Shows 10. Foreign 11. Infomercial 12. Internet Adv.13. Multimedia 14. Network Radio 15. Network T.V. 16. Newsp. Distr. Mags. 17. Other 18. Outdoor (Posters, Transit) 19. Point of Purchase20. Premiums, Novelties 21. Product Samples 22. Special Events Mktg. 23. Spot Radio 24. Spot T.V. 25. Weekly Newsp. 26. Yellow Page Adv.

Government & State Agencies

Boards of Trade — Federal, State & Local Governments & Agencies — Lotteries

ALABAMA BUREAU OF TOURISM & TRAVEL
401 Adams Ave Ste 126
Montgomery, AL 36104-4325
Tel.: (334) 242-4169
Fax: (334) 242-4554
Toll Free: (800) ALABAMA
E-mail: info@tourism.alabama.gov
Web Site: www.touralabama.org
Approx. Number Employees: 63
Year Founded: 1951
Business Description:
State Travel & Tourism Administration Services
S.I.C.: 7389
N.A.I.C.S.: 561591
Advertising Expenditures: $3,000,000
Media: 1-2-3-4-5-6-7-9-11-13-17-22-23-24-25
Distr.: Reg.
Budget Set: Sept. -Oct.
Personnel:
Grey Brennan *(Dir-Mktg)*
Lee Sentell *(Dir)*
Rosemary Judkins *(Mgr-Grp Travel)*
Frances Smiley *(Mgr-Welcome Ctrs)*
Marilyn Jones Stamps *(Mgr-Publications)*
Advertising Agency:
Luckie & Company
600 Luckie Dr Ste 150
Birmingham, AL 35223-2429
Tel.: (205) 879-2121
Fax: (205) 877-9855

ALASKA DEPARTMENT OF COMMUNITY & ECONOMIC DEVELOPMENT
PO Box 110800
Juneau, AK 99811-0801
Tel.: (907) 465-2500
Fax: (907) 465-5442
Web Site: www.dced.state.ak.us
Approx. Number Employees: 550
Business Description:
Alaska Tourism Promoter
S.I.C.: 9611
N.A.I.C.S.: 926110
Advertising Expenditures: $500,000
Media: 2-4-13
Personnel:
Susan Bell *(Commissioner)*

ALBUQUERQUE CONVENTION & VISITORS BUREAU
20 First Plz NW Ste 601
Albuquerque, NM 87102
Tel.: (505) 842-9918
Fax: (505) 247-9101
Toll Free: (800) 284-2282
E-mail: info@itsatrip.org
Web Site: www.itsatrip.org
Approx. Number Employees: 39
Year Founded: 1980
Business Description:
Travel & Tourism Promoter
S.I.C.: 8611
N.A.I.C.S.: 813910
Advertising Expenditures: $1,000,000
Media: 2-3-4-6-13-18-22-23-24
Personnel:
Dale Lockett *(CEO)*
Joni O. Thompson *(COO)*
Tania Armenta *(VP-Mktg, Comm & Tourism)*
Larry Atchison *(Sr Dir-Sls)*
Dan Ballou *(Dir-Sports Mktg)*
Cecilia Padilla-Quillen *(Dir-Convention Svcs)*
Don Griego *(Sr Mgr-Natl Sls)*
Anita Sahi *(Sr Mgr-Natl Sls)*
Megan Mayo *(Mgr-Comm & Tourism)*
Brands & Products:
IT'S A TRIP
WELCOME TO ALBUQUERQUE-IT'S A TRIP
Advertising Agency:
McKee Wallwork Cleveland
1030 18th St NW
Albuquerque, NM 87104
Tel.: (505) 821-2999
Fax: (505) 821-0006
Toll Free: (888) 821-2999

ANAHEIM/ORANGE COUNTY VISITOR & CONVENTION BUREAU
800 W Katella Ave
Anaheim, CA 92802-3415
Tel.: (714) 765-8888
Fax: (714) 991-8963
E-mail: visitorinfo@anaheimoc.org
Web Site: www.anaheimoc.org
E-Mail For Key Personnel:
President: cahlers@anaheimoc.org
Sales Director: jkissinger@anaheimoc.org
Public Relations: ecali@anaheimoc.org
Approx. Number Employees: 50
Year Founded: 1961
Business Description:
Visitor & Convention Services
S.I.C.: 7389
N.A.I.C.S.: 561591
Advertising Expenditures: $820,000
Media: 2-4-5-6-7-10
Distr.: Natl.
Budget Set: July
Personnel:
Charles Ahlers *(Pres)*
Mindy Abel *(Sr VP-Convention Sls)*
Elaine Cali *(VP-Comm)*
John McClure *(Assoc VP-Convention Sls)*
Colleen Cornett *(Dir-Convention Housing)*
Elisa Jaworski *(Dir-Northeastern Sls)*
Barbara Kenney *(Dir-Eastern Sls)*
Kim Lord *(Dir-Eastern Sls)*
Carol McNaul *(Dir-Convention Sls)*
Gina McQuade *(Dir-Convention Sls)*
Carolyn Pesenti-Green *(Dir-Convention Svcs)*
Cassie Pressentin *(Dir-Midwestern Sls)*
Lora Stanley *(Dir-Midwestern Sls)*
Tony Toth *(Dir-Convention Sls)*
Kathy Wilmes *(Dir-Convention Sls)*
Juan Flores *(Mgr-Comm)*
Sheri Abadi *(Mgr-Mktg)*
Julie Freund *(Mgr-Membership Sls)*
Kelly Grass *(Mgr-Membership Svcs)*
Phil Hannes *(Mgr-Tourism Dept)*
Kevin Halpin *(Webmaster)*

ARIZONA LOTTERY
4740 E University Dr
Phoenix, AZ 85034-7400
Tel.: (480) 921-4400
Fax: (480) 921-4512
E-mail: feedback@lottery.state.az.us
Web Site: www.arizonalottery.com
Approx. Number Employees: 150
Year Founded: 1981
Business Description:
State Lottery
S.I.C.: 9311
N.A.I.C.S.: 921130
Media: 2-3-6-9-17-18-19-22-23-24-25
Distr.: Direct to Consumer; Reg.
Budget Set: July
Personnel:
Jeff Hatch-Miller *(Exec Dir)*
Karen Emery *(Dir-Game Design)*
Graham Bennett *(Mgr-Acct)*
Ivy Gilio *(Mgr-Game Dev)*
Brands & Products:
2BY2
ARIZONA LOTTERY
FANTASY 5
FAST PLAY
THE PICK
PICK 3
POWERBALL
SCRATCHERS
Advertising Agency:
E.B. Lane
733 W McDowell Rd
Phoenix, AZ 85007-1727
Tel.: (602) 258-5263
Fax: (602) 257-8128
Agency of Record

ARIZONA OFFICE OF TOURISM
1110 W Washington Ste 155
Phoenix, AZ 85007
Tel.: (602) 364-3700
Fax: (602) 364-3702
Toll Free: (877) 476-4123
E-mail: advertisng@azot.gov
Web Site: www.arizonaguide.com
Approx. Number Employees: 37
Business Description:
Tourism Promoter
S.I.C.: 9611; 7389
N.A.I.C.S.: 926110; 561591
Advertising Expenditures: $7,000,000
Media: 5-6-9-22-23-24
Distr.: Intl.; Natl.
Budget Set: Dec.
Personnel:
Sherry Henry *(Dir-Tourism)*
Mary Rittmann *(Dir-Travel Industry Mktg)*
Advertising Agency:
Moses Anshell, Inc.
20 W Jackson St
Phoenix, AZ 85003
Tel.: (602) 254-7312
Fax: (602) 324-1222
(Tourism in Arizona)
— Lauri Klefos *(Acct Exec)*

Key to Media (For complete agency information see *The Advertising Red Books-Agencies* edition):
1. Bus. Publs. 2. Cable T.V. 3. Catalogs & Directories. 4. Co-op Adv. 5. Consumer Mags. 6. D.M. to Bus. Estab.7. D.M. to Consumers 8. Daily Newsp. 9. Exhibits/Trade Shows 10. Foreign 11. Infomercial 12. Internet Adv.13. Multimedia 14. Network Radio 15. Network T.V. 16. Newsp. Distr. Mags. 17. Other 18. Outdoor (Posters, Transit) 19. Point of Purchase20. Premiums, Novelties 21. Product Samples 22. Special Events Mktg. 23. Spot Radio 24. Spot T.V. 25. Weekly Newsp. 26. Yellow Page Adv.

ARKANSAS DEPARTMENT OF ECONOMIC DEVELOPMENT
900 W Capitol Ste 400
Little Rock, AR 72201-1049
Tel.: (501) 682-1121
Fax: (501) 682-7394
Toll Free: (800) ARKANSAS
E-mail: lmiesner@arkansasedc.com
Web Site: www.arkansasedc.com
Approx. Number Employees: 90
Year Founded: 1955
Business Description:
State Economic Development Agency
S.I.C.: 9611
N.A.I.C.S.: 926110
Advertising Expenditures: $550,000
Media: 1-2-5-9-10-11-13-20-22-25
Distr.: Intl.; Natl.
Budget Set: June
Personnel:
Maria Haley *(Exec Dir)*
Joe Holmes *(Dir-Mktg & Comm)*
Kurt Naumann *(Asst Dir-Strategic Plng)*
Advertising Agency:
Stone Ward
225 E Markham St Ste 450
Little Rock, AR 72201-1629
Tel.: (501) 375-3003
Fax: (501) 375-8314
All Media

ARKANSAS DEPARTMENT OF PARKS & TOURISM
1 Capitol Mall 4A 900
Little Rock, AR 72201-1049
Tel.: (501) 682-7777
Fax: (501) 682-2523
Toll Free: (800) NATURAL
E-mail: info@arkansas.com
Web Site: www.arkansas.com
Approx. Number Employees: 500
Year Founded: 1951
Business Description:
State Tourism & Parks Administration Services
S.I.C.: 9621; 7999
N.A.I.C.S.: 926120; 712190
Advertising Expenditures: $6,500,000
Media: 2-4-6-13-23-24
Personnel:
Dena Woerner *(Officer-Public Information)*
Greg Butts *(Exec Dir)*
Joe David Rice *(Dir-Tourism)*
Brands & Products:
ARKANSAS
THE NATURAL STATE
Advertising Agency:
Cranford Johnson Robinson Woods
303 W Capitol Ave
Little Rock, AR 72201-3531
Tel.: (501) 975-6251
Fax: (501) 975-4241
Toll Free: (888) 383-2579
(Creative, Media Placement & Public Relations)
— Karen Mullikin *(Acct. Exec.)*

ARMY NATIONAL GUARD
1411 Jefferson Davis Hwy Ste 3200
Arlington, VA 22202
Tel.: (703) 607-5836
Fax: (703) 607-3628
Web Site: www.arng.army.mil
Year Founded: 1973
Business Description:
National Guard Recruiter
S.I.C.: 9711
N.A.I.C.S.: 928110
Personnel:
Scott Savage *(Exec Officer)*
Roger C. Schultz *(Dir)*
Advertising Agency:
LM&O Advertising
2000 N 14th St 8th Fl
Arlington, VA 22201-2573
Tel.: (703) 875-2193
Fax: (703) 875-2199

ATLANTA CONVENTION & VISITORS BUREAU
233 Peachtree St NE Ste 1400
Atlanta, GA 30303-1553
Tel.: (404) 521-6600
Fax: (404) 584-6331
Toll Free: (800) ATLANTA
Web Site: www.atlanta.net
Approx. Number Employees: 27
Year Founded: 1913
Business Description:
Tourism & Convention Administration
S.I.C.: 7389
N.A.I.C.S.: 561591
Advertising Expenditures: $500,000
Media: 4-8-10-13
Personnel:
Ken Bernhardt *(Chm)*
Spurgeon Richardson *(Pres & CEO)*
Gregory Pierce *(CFO, Chief Admin Officer & Exec VP)*
Mark Vaughan *(Chief Sls Officer & Exec VP)*
W. B. Baldwin *(Sr VP-Corp Dev)*
Kathleen Bertrand *(Sr VP-Community & Govt Affairs)*
Charles Jeffers *(VP-Tech)*
Bob Schuler *(VP-Sls & Convention Svcs)*
Brandon Barnes *(Dir-Mktg & Sls-Intl)*
Anne Fleck *(Dir-Mktg)*
Lauren Jarrell *(Dir-Comm)*
David McAuley *(Dir-Washington, DC Area Office)*
Mark Sussman *(Dir-Trade Show Sls)*
Sheretha Bell *(Sr Mgr-Sls & Mktg)*
Amanda Dyson *(Sr Mgr-Sls)*
Jesus Garcia *(Mgr-Intl Sls)*
Monica Green *(Mgr-Sls & National Accts)*
Cindy Hall *(Mgr-Natl Sls)*
Pholeta Sanders *(Mgr-Tech & Web Presence)*
Advertising Agency:
ATCOMM Publishing
3423 Piedmont Road
Atlanta, GA 30305
Tel.: (404) 249-1750

AUGUSTA METROPOLITAN CONVENTION & VISITORS BUREAU, INC.
1450 Greene St Ste 110
Augusta, GA 30901
Mailing Address:
PO Box 1331
Augusta, GA 30903
Tel.: (706) 823-6600
Fax: (706) 823-6609
Toll Free: (800) 726-0243
E-mail: info@ugustaga.org
Web Site: www.augustaga.org
Approx. Number Employees: 14
Year Founded: 1980
Business Description:
Convention & Visitors Bureau
S.I.C.: 7389
N.A.I.C.S.: 561591
Media: 5-6-10
Personnel:
Barry White *(Pres & CEO)*
Jennifer Bowen *(VP-Product Dev)*
Peggy Seigler *(VP-Sales & Mktg)*
Trent Snyder *(VP-Fin & Admin)*
Michelle Bovian *(Mgr-Convention Sls)*
Stacy McEleveen *(Mgr-Convention Sls)*
Toni Seals Johnson *(Mgr-Visitor Center)*
Advertising Agency:
SMITH
321 Arch St
Fayetteville, NC 28301
Tel.: (910) 222-5071
Fax: (910) 484-6063
Toll Free: (800) 421-1973

AUSTRALIAN TRADE COMMISSION
(Div. of Australian Trade Commission)
(d/b/a Austrade New York)
150 E 42nd St 34th Fl
New York, NY 10017
Tel.: (212) 351-6560
Fax: (212) 867-7710
E-mail: newyork@austrade.gov.au
Web Site: www.austrade.gov.au/usa
Approx. Number Employees: 15
Business Description:
Australian Trade Promoter
S.I.C.: 9611
N.A.I.C.S.: 926110
Export
Media: 10
Distr.: Natl.
Personnel:
Anjali Jain *(Sr Dir-US Market Dev)*
Prashanti Kanagasabai *(Sr Dir)*
Mary Landsfield *(Sr Mgr-Bus Dev)*
Beth Goslin *(Mgr-Bus Dev-Food)*
David Howard *(Mgr-Austrade State)*

BATON ROUGE AREA CONVENTION & VISITORS BUREAU
359 Third St
Baton Rouge, LA 70801
Mailing Address:
PO Box 4149
Baton Rouge, LA 70821
Tel.: (225) 383-1825
Fax: (225) 346-1253
Toll Free: (800) 527-6843
E-mail: linda@visitbatonrouge.com
Web Site: www.visitbatonrouge.com
E-Mail For Key Personnel:
President: lmaisel@bracvb.com
Marketing Director: parrigo@bracvb.com
Sales Director: nbrouss@bracvb.com
Approx. Number Employees: 25
Year Founded: 1972
Business Description:
Convention & Visitors Bureau
S.I.C.: 7389
N.A.I.C.S.: 561591
Advertising Expenditures: $300,500
Media: 5-6-8-13-20-22
Distr.: Intl.; Natl.
Budget Set: Oct.
Personnel:
Paul Arrigo *(Pres & CEO)*
Renee Areng *(Exec VP-Sls & Mktg)*
Philipa Blair *(Dir-Destination Svcs)*
Geraldine Bordelon *(Dir-Destination Sls)*
Thersa Overby *(Dir-Comm)*
Regina Porter *(Sr Mgr-Sls)*
Jennye Snider *(Sr Mgr-Sls)*

BERKSHIRE VISITORS BUREAU
3 Hoosac St
Adams, MA 01220
Tel.: (413) 743-4500
Fax: (413) 743-4560
Toll Free: (800) 237-5747
E-mail: bvb@berkshires.org
Web Site: www.berkshires.org
Approx. Number Employees: 14
Year Founded: 1938
Business Description:
Vistors Bureau
S.I.C.: 7389
N.A.I.C.S.: 561591
Advertising Expenditures: $249,000
Media: 5-6-8-9-10-16
Distr.: Natl.
Budget Set: June
Personnel:
Ray Smith *(CEO)*
Dara Kaufman *(Dir-Member Svcs)*

BERMUDA DEPARTMENT OF TOURISM
675 3rd Ave 20th Fl
New York, NY 10017
Tel.: (212) 818-9800
Fax: (212) 983-5289
Toll Free: (800) BERMUDA
Web Site: www.bermudatourism.com
E-Mail For Key Personnel:
Sales Director: sales@bermudatourism.com
Sales Estimate: $5-9.9 Million
Approx. Number Employees: 18
Year Founded: 1950
Business Description:
Tourist Programs Administration
S.I.C.: 4724
N.A.I.C.S.: 561510
Advertising Expenditures: $10,000,000
Media: 1-2-6-8-9-10-11-19-23-24
Distr.: Intl.; Natl.
Budget Set: June
Personnel:
Calworth L. Furbert *(VP & Gen Mgr)*
Robin C. Danes *(Dir-Sls Canada)*
Donna Douglas *(Sr Mgr-Bus Dev)*
Karin Darrell *(Mgr-Partnership Worldwide)*
Gina Luna *(Mgr-Office)*
Advertising Agencies:
GlobalHue
Ste 1600 4000 Town Ctr
Southfield, MI 48076
Tel.: (248) 223-8900
Fax: (248) 304-8877

J. Walter Thompson Company
(d/b/a JWT)
466 Lexington Ave
New York, NY 10017-3140
Tel.: (212) 210-7000
Fax: (212) 210-7299
(Tourism for Bermuda)

Key to Media (For complete agency information see *The Advertising Red Books-Agencies* edition):
1. Bus. Publs. 2. Cable T.V. 3. Catalogs & Directories. 4. Co-op Adv. 5. Consumer Mags. 6. D.M. to Bus. Estab.7. D.M. to Consumers 8. Daily Newsp. 9. Exhibits/Trade Shows 10. Foreign 11. Infomercial 12. Internet Adv.13. Multimedia 14. Network Radio 15. Network T.V. 16. Newsp. Distr. Mags. 17. Other 18. Outdoor (Posters, Transit) 19. Point of Purchase20. Premiums, Novelties 21. Product Samples 22. Special Events Mktg. 23. Spot Radio 24. Spot T.V. 25. Weekly Newsp. 26. Yellow Page Adv.

BROADCASTING BOARD OF GOVERNORS
330 Independence Ave SW
Washington, DC 20237
Tel.: (202) 203-4545
Tel.: (202) 203-4161 (Mktg)
Fax: (202) 203-4568
E-mail: info@bbg.gov
Web Site: www.bbg.gov
Sales Range: $10-24.9 Million
Approx. Number Employees: 25
Business Description:
Broadcasting Organization
S.I.C.: 9721
N.A.I.C.S.: 928120
Media: 1-2-3-4-6-7-8-9-11-13-14-15-17-18-22-23-24-25
Personnel:
Joaquin F. Blaya *(Chm)*
Andre Mendes *(CIO, CTO & Dir-Tech, Svcs & Innovation)*
Oanh Tran *(Special Projects Officer)*
Jeffery Trimble *(Exec Dir)*
Bruce Sherman *(Dir-Strategic Plng)*
Paul Kollmer-Dorsey *(Deputy Gen Counsel)*
Susan Andross *(Coord-Congressional)*

CALIFORNIA DEPARTMENT OF CONSERVATION
801 K St MS 24-01
Sacramento, CA 95814
Tel.: (916) 322-1080
Fax: (916) 445-0732
E-mail: webmaster@consrv.ca.gov
Web Site: www.conservation.ca.gov
Approx. Number Employees: 530
Year Founded: 1965
Business Description:
Government Agency Providing Conservation Services & Information for the State of California
S.I.C.: 9512
N.A.I.C.S.: 924120
Personnel:
Tom Gibbs *(Dir)*
Advertising Agency:
Riester
802 N 3rd Ave
Phoenix, AZ 85003
Tel.: (602) 462-2200
Fax: (602) 307-5811
(Recycling Program)

CALIFORNIA DEPARTMENT OF CONSUMER AFFAIRS
1625 N Market Blvd
Sacramento, CA 95834
Tel.: (916) 445-1254
Toll Free: (800) 952-5210
E-mail: dca@dca.ca.gov
Web Site: www.dca.ca.gov
Approx. Number Employees: 2,000
Year Founded: 1971
Business Description:
State Department of Consumer Protection & Regulatory Services
S.I.C.: 9611
N.A.I.C.S.: 926110
Advertising Expenditures: $5,000,000
Media: 2-3-7-8-9-10-18-19-20-22-23-24-25
Personnel:
Denise Brown *(Chief Deputy Dir)*
Carrie Lopez *(Dir-DCA)*
Brian Stiter *(Dir-DCA)*
Advertising Agency:
IW Group, Inc.
(An IPG Co.)
8687 Melrose Ave Ste G540
West Hollywood, CA 90069
Tel.: (310) 289-5500
Fax: (310) 289-5501

CALIFORNIA DEPARTMENT OF HEALTH SERVICES
1501 Capitol Ave St 1501
Sacramento, CA 95814
Mailing Address:
PO Box 997413
Sacramento, CA 95899-7413
Tel.: (916) 440-7400
Fax: (916) 440-7404
E-mail: intadmin@dhs.ca.gov
Web Site: www.dhs.ca.gov
Approx. Rev.: $30,739,135
Approx. Number Employees: 5,000
Business Description:
State Administration of Health Services
S.I.C.: 9431
N.A.I.C.S.: 923120
Media: 9-17-23-24
Personnel:
Toby Douglas *(Dir-Health Care Programs)*
Advertising Agencies:
ES Advertising
6222 Wilshire Blvd Ste 302
Los Angeles, CA 90048
Tel.: (323) 964-9001
Fax: (323) 964-9801

IW Group, Inc.
(An IPG Co.)
8687 Melrose Ave Ste G540
West Hollywood, CA 90069
Tel.: (310) 289-5500
Fax: (310) 289-5501

Rogers Ruder Finn
1875 Century Park E Ste 200
Los Angeles, CA 90067-2504
Tel.: (310) 552-6922
Fax: (310) 552-9052

CALIFORNIA LOTTERY
598 N 10th St
Sacramento, CA 95811
Tel.: (916) 830-0292
Fax: (916) 322-6768
Toll Free: (800) 345-4275
E-mail: info@calottery.com
Web Site: www.calottery.com
Approx. Rev.: $2,973,975,717
Approx. Number Employees: 312
Year Founded: 1984
Business Description:
State Lottery Operator
S.I.C.: 9311
N.A.I.C.S.: 921130
Advertising Expenditures: $36,797,516
Media: 1-3-4-6-9-18-19-20-22-23-24-25
Distr.: Reg.
Personnel:
Ed Fong *(COO-Prod Dev & Mktg)*
Leticia Saldivar *(COO-Consumer Mktg & Adv)*
Jim Hasegawa *(Dir)*
Norma Minas *(Mgr-Retailer Comm)*
Brands & Products:
CALOTTERY
DAILY 3
DAILY DERBY
DIAMOND DAZZLER
DIAMOND MINE
FANTASY 5
HOT SPOT
IN THE LINE OF DUTY
JINGLE BUCKS
LEMON TWIST
LUCKY BUG
SCRATCHERS
SUPER LOTTO PLUS
WB RECORDS
X-WORD
YEAR OF THE OX
Advertising Agencies:
David & Goliath
909 N Sepulveda Blvd Ste 700
El Segundo, CA 90245
Tel.: (310) 445-5200
Fax: (310) 445-5201
Advertising/Creative
— Phil Covitz *(Dir-Art & Assoc Dir-Creative)*

Initiative
1 Dag Hammarskjold Plz
New York, NY 10017
Tel.: (212) 605-7000
Fax: (917) 305-4003
Media

CALIFORNIA TRAVEL & TOURISM COMMISSION
980 9th St Ste 480
Sacramento, CA 95814
Tel.: (916) 444-4429
Fax: (916) 444-0410
Toll Free: (800) 862-2543
E-mail: info@cttc1.com
Web Site: www.visitcalifornia.com
Approx. Rev.: $18,250,000
Approx. Number Employees: 25
Year Founded: 1978
Business Description:
State Travel & Tourism Promoter
S.I.C.: 4724
N.A.I.C.S.: 561510
Advertising Expenditures: $4,000,000
Media: 1-3-5-6-9-10-11-13-15-22-24
Distr.: Intl.; Natl.
Budget Set: June
Personnel:
Caroline Beteta *(Pres, CEO & Deputy Sec)*
Sue Coyle *(Dir-Pub Affairs)*
Jennifer Montero *(Dir-Mktg-Latin America & Canada)*
Advertising Agencies:
Carat North America Inc.
150 E 52nd St
New York, NY 10017
Tel.: (212) 252-0050
Fax: (212) 252-1250
Media Assignment

MeringCarson
1010 S Coast Hwy 101 Ste 105
Encinitas, CA 92024
Tel.: (760) 635-2100
Fax: (760) 635-2106

CAPE COD CHAMBER OF COMMERCE, CVB
Junction Rte 6 & Rte 132
Hyannis, MA 02601
Tel.: (508) 362-3225
Fax: (508) 362-3698
Toll Free: (888) 33CAPECOD
E-mail: info@capecodchamber.org
Web Site: www.capecodchamber.org
E-Mail For Key Personnel:
President: wendy@capecodchamber.com
Approx. Rev.: $2,300,000
Approx. Number Employees: 23
Year Founded: 1921
Business Description:
Commercial Operations & Tourism Regulation & Administration Services
S.I.C.: 9651
N.A.I.C.S.: 926150
Advertising Expenditures: $300,000
Brands & Products:
CAPE COD
Advertising Agencies:
Franklin Advertising Associates, Inc.
441 Main St
Yarmouth Port, MA 02675
Tel.: (508) 362-7472
Fax: (508) 362-5975

Pierce-Cote Advertising
911 Main St
Osterville, MA 02655-2015
Tel.: (508) 420-5566
Fax: (508) 420-3314

THE CENTER FOR DISEASE CONTROL & PREVENTION
1600 Clifton Rd NE
Atlanta, GA 30333
Tel.: (404) 639-3311
Tel.: (404) 639-3534 (Media Rels)
Toll Free: (800) 311-3435
E-mail: inquiry@cdc.gov
Web Site: www.cdc.gov
Approx. Rev.: $7,000,000,000
Approx. Number Employees: 8,500
Business Description:
Disease Identification, Research & Prevention Services
S.I.C.: 9431
N.A.I.C.S.: 923120
Advertising Expenditures: $125,000,000
Media: 6
Personnel:
Barbara Harris *(CFO & Deputy Dir-Acctg & Fin)*
Marsha Vanderford *(Assoc Dir-Comm Science)*
Advertising Agencies:
Brandtrust
John Hancock Bldg 875 N Michigan Ave Ste 2945
Chicago, IL 60611
Tel.: (312) 440-1833
Fax: (312) 440-9987

Captains of Industry
21 Union St
Boston, MA 02108
Tel.: (617) 725-1959
Fax: (617) 725-0089

JMH Education
75 Broad St 33rd Fl
New York, NY 10010
Tel.: (212) 924-2944
Fax: (212) 924-3052

Ogilvy Public Relations Worldwide
1111 19th St NW 10th Fl
Washington, DC 20036
Tel.: (202) 729-4000

Key to Media (For complete agency information see *The Advertising Red Books-Agencies* edition):
1. Bus. Publs. 2. Cable T.V. 3. Catalogs & Directories. 4. Co-op Adv. 5. Consumer Mags. 6. D.M. to Bus. Estab.7. D.M. to Consumers
8. Daily Newsp. 9. Exhibits/Trade Shows 10. Foreign 11. Infomercial 12. Internet Adv.13. Multimedia 14. Network Radio
15. Network T.V. 16. Newsp. Distr. Mags. 17. Other 18. Outdoor (Posters, Transit) 19. Point of Purchase20. Premiums, Novelties
21. Product Samples 22. Special Events Mktg. 23. Spot Radio 24. Spot T.V. 25. Weekly Newsp. 26. Yellow Page Adv.

Fax: (202) 729-4001
Choose Respect Initiative

Porter Novelli
(Sub. of Omnicom Group, Inc.)
75 Varick St 6th Fl
New York, NY 10013
Tel.: (212) 601-8000
Fax: (212) 601-8101

Saatchi & Saatchi New York
375 Hudson St
New York, NY 10014-3660
Tel.: (212) 463-2000
Fax: (212) 463-9855

Vox Medica Inc.
601 Walnut St Ste 250-S
Philadelphia, PA 19106-3514
Tel.: (215) 238-8500
Fax: (215) 238-0881

CENTERS FOR MEDICARE & MEDICAID SERVICES

7500 Security Blvd
Baltimore, MD 21244-1849
Toll Free: (877) 267-2323
Web Site: www.cms.hhs.gov
Business Description:
Government Health Program Administration
S.I.C.: 9431
N.A.I.C.S.: 923120
Advertising Expenditures: $35,000,000
Personnel:
Gary G. Christoph *(Deputy Dir & CIO)*
Marsha Davenport *(Dir)*

CERC

805 Brook St Bldg 4
Rocky Hill, CT 06067
Tel.: (860) 571-7136
Fax: (860) 571-7150
Toll Free: (800) 392-2122
E-mail: solutions@cerc.com
Web Site: www.cerc.com
E-Mail For Key Personnel:
Marketing Director: JNally@cerc.com
Approx. Number Employees: 30
Year Founded: 1993
Business Description:
Nonprofit Company Specializing in Economic Development & Marketing for Local, Regional, State & Utility Economic Development Entities
S.I.C.: 8748
N.A.I.C.S.: 541690
Media: 2-4-7-9-10-13-20-22-26
Distr.: Natl.
Budget Set: Sept.
Personnel:
Martha Hunt *(Pres & CEO)*
C. Stephen MacKenzie *(Sr VP-Bus Dev)*
Kristiana Sullivan *(VP-Mktg)*
Paul Ward *(VP-Fin)*
Elliot Cyr *(Dir-Info Tech)*
Gretchen Deans *(Dir-Admin)*
Michael Macionus *(Dir-GIS)*
James Nally *(Dir-Sls & Mktg)*
MaryAnn Simkewicz *(Supvr-Mktg Acct)*
Brands & Products:
CERC
DATAFINDER
PROGRAMFINDER
SITEFINDER

CHICAGO CONVENTION & TOURISM BUREAU

2301 S Lake Shore Dr
Chicago, IL 60616-1419
Tel.: (312) 567-8500
Fax: (312) 567-8533
Toll Free: (877) 244-2226
E-mail: info@choosechicago.com
Web Site: www.choosechicago.com
E-Mail For Key Personnel:
Sales Director: sales@choosechicago.com
Sales Range: $25-49.9 Million
Approx. Number Employees: 80
Year Founded: 1943
Business Description:
State Convention & Tourism Administrative Services
S.I.C.: 7389
N.A.I.C.S.: 561591
Media: 1-2-4-5-6-7-10-11-13-20-23-24
Personnel:
Warren Wilkinson *(Sr VP-Mktg & Comm)*
Harvey Morris *(Dir-Digital Mktg & Social Media)*
Joleen Domaracki *(Asst Dir)*
Maria Alvarez *(Coord-Sls)*
Sandra Becerra *(Coord-Sls)*
Advertising Agency:
Davis Harrison Dion, Inc.
333 N Michigan Ave Ste 2300
Chicago, IL 60601-4109
Tel.: (312) 332-0808
Fax: (312) 332-4260

CITY OF CHICAGO-DEPARTMENT OF PLANNING & DEVELOPMENT

121 N LaSalle St Rm 1111
Chicago, IL 60602-1250
Tel.: (312) 744-6300
Fax: (312) 744-7676
E-mail: planning@cityofchicago.org
Web Site: www.cityofchicago.org
Approx. Number Employees: 220
Year Founded: 1981
Business Description:
Economic Development Programs, Physical Planning & Urban Development in Chicago
S.I.C.: 9611; 9532
N.A.I.C.S.: 926110; 925120
Media: 2-4-6-9-10-13-23-25
Distr.: Natl.
Budget Set: Oct.
Personnel:
Chris Raguso *(Commissioner)*
Leonard Obilor *(Dir-Fin)*

COLORADO LOTTERY

210 212 W 3rd St
Pueblo, CO 81003-3227
Tel.: (303) 759-3552
Fax: (303) 759-6847
Web Site: www.coloradolottery.com
Sales Range: $50-74.9 Million
Approx. Number Employees: 130
Year Founded: 1983
Business Description:
State Lottery
S.I.C.: 9311
N.A.I.C.S.: 921130
Advertising Expenditures: $8,000,000
Media: 3-9-13-18-19-20-22-23-24-25
Distr.: Retail Outlets
Budget Set: Apr.
Personnel:
Jack Boehm *(Dir)*
Tom Kitts *(Dir)*

COLORADO TOURISM OFFICE

1625 Broadway Ste 2700
Denver, CO 80202-4725
Tel.: (303) 892-3885
Fax: (303) 892-3848
Toll Free: (800) COLORADO
E-mail: industry@colorado.com
Web Site: www.colorado.com
Sales Range: Less than $1 Million
Approx. Number Employees: 4
Year Founded: 2000
Business Description:
State Tourism Administrative Services
S.I.C.: 7389
N.A.I.C.S.: 561591
Media: 1-3-5-6-9-10-20-23-24
Distr.: Natl.
Budget Set: Annually
Brands & Products:
COLORADO
LET'S TALK COLORADO
Advertising Agency:
MMG Worldwide
4601 Madison Ave
Kansas City, MO 64112
Tel.: (816) 472-5988
Fax: (816) 471-5395

CONNECTICUT LOTTERY CORPORATION

777 Brook St
Rocky Hill, CT 06067
Tel.: (860) 713-2000
Fax: (860) 713-2805
E-mail: clc@po.state.ct.us
Web Site: www.ctlottery.org
Approx. Sls.: $837,500,000
Approx. Number Employees: 120
Year Founded: 1973
Business Description:
State Lottery
S.I.C.: 9311
N.A.I.C.S.: 921130
Advertising Expenditures: $4,395,000
Cable T.V.: $160,000; Daily Newsp.: $75,000; Network Radio: $2,000,000; Network T.V.: $1,000,000; Other: $200,000; Outdoor (Posters, Transit): $350,000; Point of Purchase: $560,000; Premiums, Novelties: $50,000
Distr.: Reg.
Budget Set: June
Personnel:
John Ramadei *(CFO)*
Brands & Products:
CASH 5
CLASSIC LOTTO
CT LOTTERY
LUCKY-4-LIFE
POWERBALL
Advertising Agency:
Cashman & Katz Integrated Communications
76 Eastern Blvd
Glastonbury, CT 06033
Tel.: (860) 652-0300
Fax: (860) 652-0308

CRIME PREVENTION INC.

(d/b/a CPI Security Systems)
4200 Sandy Porter Rd
Charlotte, NC 28273
Tel.: (704) 527-4070
Fax: (704) 527-4158
Web Site: www.cpisecurity.com
Sales Range: $10-24.9 Million
Approx. Number Employees: 320
Year Founded: 1976
Business Description:
Alarm Signal Systems Designing, Installing & Monitoring
S.I.C.: 7382; 5063
N.A.I.C.S.: 561621; 423610
Personnel:
Kenneth J. Gill *(Pres)*
Advertising Agency:
Specialized Media Services, Inc.
741 Kenilworth Ave Ste 204
Charlotte, NC 28204
Tel.: (704) 333-3111
Fax: (704) 332-7466

DALLAS CONVENTION & VISITORS BUREAU

325 N Saint Paul St Ste 700
Dallas, TX 75201
Tel.: (214) 571-1000
Fax: (214) 571-1008
Toll Free: (800) 232-5527
E-mail: info@visitdallas.com
Web Site: www.visitdallas.com
E-Mail For Key Personnel:
Public Relations: RCrusemann@dallascvb.com
Sales Range: $25-49.9 Million
Approx. Number Employees: 65
Business Description:
Convention & Visitors Bureau
S.I.C.: 7389; 8611
N.A.I.C.S.: 561591; 813910
Media: 4-10-13
Personnel:
J. Peter Kline *(Chm)*
Phillip Jones *(Pres & CEO)*
Ross Crusemann *(Sr VP-Mktg)*
Ann C. Murray *(Reg Dir-Sls-Chicago)*
Deborah Burleson *(Dir-Accts-Natl)*
Kevin Owens *(Dir-Accts-Natl)*
Monica Paul *(Dir-Sports Mktg)*
Alan Sims *(Dir-Sls)*
Veronica Torres *(Dir-Social Media)*
Patti Towell *(Dir-Sls)*
Dena Rambo *(Assoc Dir-Sls)*
Heather Walker-Lovato *(Mgr-Svcs)*
Petre White *(Mgr-Svcs)*
Brands & Products:
DALLAS
LIVE LARGE. THINK BIG
Advertising Agency:
Richards Partners
8750 N Central Expy Ste 1100
Dallas, TX 75231-6430
Tel.: (214) 891-5700
Fax: (214) 891-5230

DAYTONA BEACH RESORT AREA CONVENTION & VISITORS BUREAU

126 E Orange Ave
Daytona Beach, FL 32114-4406
Tel.: (386) 255-0415
Fax: (386) 255-5478
Toll Free: (800) 854-1234
E-mail: info@daytonabeach.com
Web Site: www.daytonabeach.com
Approx. Number Employees: 25
Year Founded: 1987
Business Description:
Convention & Visitors Bureau

Key to Media (For complete agency information see *The Advertising Red Books-Agencies* edition):
1. Bus. Publs. 2. Cable T.V. 3. Catalogs & Directories. 4. Co-op Adv. 5. Consumer Mags. 6. D.M. to Bus. Estab.7. D.M. to Consumers 8. Daily Newsp. 9. Exhibits/Trade Shows 10. Foreign 11. Infomercial 12. Internet Adv.13. Multimedia 14. Network Radio 15. Network T.V. 16. Newsp. Distr. Mags. 17. Other 18. Outdoor (Posters, Transit) 19. Point of Purchase20. Premiums, Novelties 21. Product Samples 22. Special Events Mktg. 23. Spot Radio 24. Spot T.V. 25. Weekly Newsp. 26. Yellow Page Adv.

Daytona Beach Resort Area Convention & Visitors Bureau — (Continued)

S.I.C.: 7389
N.A.I.C.S.: 561591
Media: 6-9-15-23-24-25
Distr.: Intl.; Natl.
Budget Set: Aug.
Personnel:
Roxanne Olsen *(Dir-Membership, Promos & Sr Mgr-Industry Partner)*
Lori Campbell-Baker *(Dir-Comm)*
Kay Galloway *(Dir-Adv)*
Advertising Agency:
Halifax Area Advertising Authority (House Agency)
126 E Orange Ave
Daytona Beach, FL 32114
Tel.: (904) 255-0415
Fax: (904) 255-5478
Toll Free: (800) 321-9308 (Tourism)

D.C. LOTTERY & CHARITABLE GAMES CONTROL BOARD
2101 Martin Luther King Jr Ave SE
Washington, DC 20020-5731
Tel.: (202) 645-8000
Fax: (202) 645-7987
E-mail: info@dclottery.com
Web Site: www.dclottery.com
Sales Range: $75-99.9 Million
Approx. Number Employees: 100
Year Founded: 1982
Business Description:
Lottery & Public Gaming
S.I.C.: 7999
N.A.I.C.S.: 713290
Advertising Expenditures: $6,000,000
Media: 8-9-13-25
Personnel:
William Robinson *(Head-Fin)*
Buddy Roogow *(Exec Dir)*
Kevin Johnson *(Dir-Mktg)*
Brands & Products:
BETTY BOOP
BIG BANG BUCKS
BINGO NIGHT
CASH FIESTA
CRAZY CASH
DC-4
DC KENO
D.C. LOTTERY & CHARITABLE GAMES
EXTREME FROSTY
FUNKY 5'S
HOT FIVE
JR. JUMBO BUCKS
LINE 'EM UP
LOTTO SOUL
LUCKY NUMBERS
POWERBALL
THE PRICE IS RIGHT
ROLLING CASH 5
SUNNY MONEY
TIC TAC SNOW

DELAWARE LOTTERY
1575 McKee Rd Ste 102
Dover, DE 19904-1903
Tel.: (302) 739-5291
Fax: (302) 739-7586
Toll Free: (800) 338-6200
Web Site: www.delottery.com
Approx. Rev.: $674,048,792
Approx. Number Employees: 56
Year Founded: 1975
Business Description:
State Lottery
S.I.C.: 9311; 7999
N.A.I.C.S.: 921130; 713290
Advertising Expenditures: $1,560,000
Internet Adv.: $130,000; Network Radio: $470,000; Network T.V.: $337,000; Other: $53,000; Outdoor (Posters, Transit): $370,000; Point of Purchase: $200,000
Distr.: Direct to Consumer; Reg.
Personnel:
Brian Peters *(Dir-Sls & Mktg)*
Brands & Products:
ALL THE MARBLES
BLACK CHERRY DOUBLER
CASH COUNTDOWN
CASH XPLOSION
DELAWARE LOTTERY GAMES
KACHING
MULTI WIN LOTTO
PAIR IT TO WIN
PLAY 3
PLAY 4
POWERBALL
POWERPLAY
VACATION CASH
VIDEO LOTTERY
Advertising Agencies:
Star Group Communications, Inc. (d/b/a The Star Group)
220 Laurel Rd
Voorhees, NJ 08043
Tel.: (856) 782-7000
Fax: (856) 782-5699

StarShipley
135 S West St
Wilmington, DE 19801
Tel.: (302) 434-8700
Fax: (302) 434-8701

DELAWARE TOURISM OFFICE
99 Kings Hwy
Dover, DE 19901
Tel.: (302) 739-4271
Fax: (302) 739-5749
Toll Free: (866) 284-7483
E-mail: linda.parkowski@state.de.us
Web Site: www.visitdelaware.com
Approx. Number Employees: 11
Year Founded: 1943
Business Description:
Travel & Tourism Promoter
S.I.C.: 9611
N.A.I.C.S.: 926110
Advertising Expenditures: $130,000,000
Media: 2-5-6-10-16
Distr.: Direct to Consumer; Natl.
Budget Set: Aug.
Personnel:
Linda Parkowski *(Dir-Tourism)*
Brands & Products:
IT'S GOOD BEING FIRST

DENVER METRO CONVENTION & VISITORS BUREAU
1555 California St Ste 300
Denver, CO 80202-4200
Tel.: (303) 892-1112
Fax: (303) 892-1636
Toll Free: (800) 645-3446
Web Site: www.visitdenver.com
Sales Estimate: $10-19 Million
Approx. Number Employees: 55
Year Founded: 1909
Business Description:
Tourism & Convention Services
S.I.C.: 7389
N.A.I.C.S.: 561591
Advertising Expenditures: $500,000
Media: 1-4-6-10-20-26
Distr.: Natl.
Budget Set: Monthly
Personnel:
Richard Scharf *(Pres & CEO)*
Rachel Benedick *(VP-Sls)*
Justin Bresler *(VP-Mktg)*
Richard Grant *(Dir-Comm)*
Vikki Valencia Kelly *(Dir-Convention Svcs)*
Toni Kosaris *(Dir-Sls)*
Tim Litherland *(Dir-Sports & Grp Sls)*
Lisa Bruening *(Sr Mgr-Tourism Sls)*
Gysela Fillingham *(Mgr-Sls)*
Lisa Hagen *(Mgr-Svcs)*
Kate Maestas *(Mgr-Convention Sls)*
Tinisha Manns *(Mgr-Acctg)*
Advertising Agency:
Karsh & Hagan Communications, Inc.
2399 Blake St Ste 160
Denver, CO 80205-2108
Tel.: (303) 296-8400
Fax: (303) 296-2015

DEPARTMENT OF COMMERCE MONTANA TOURISM PROMOTION DIVISION
301 S Park Ave
Helena, MT 59620-0533
Tel.: (406) 841-2870
Fax: (406) 841-2871
Toll Free: (800) 847-4868
Web Site: www.visitmt.com
Approx. Number Employees: 25
Year Founded: 1987
Business Description:
Travel Promoter
S.I.C.: 9199
N.A.I.C.S.: 921190
Advertising Expenditures: $2,505,900
Media: 3-5-6-8-11-23-24
Distr.: Natl.
Budget Set: June
Brands & Products:
BIG SKY COUNTRY
Advertising Agency:
Wendt
106 1st Ave South
Great Falls, MT 59401
Tel.: (406) 454-8500
Fax: (406) 771-0603
Tourism & Travel

DOMINICAN REPUBLIC TOURIST BOARD
136 E 57th St Ste 805
New York, NY 10022-2969
Tel.: (212) 588-1012
Fax: (212) 588-1015
Toll Free: (888) 374-6361
E-mail: drtourizonboardny@verizon.net
Web Site: www.godominicanrepublic.com
Approx. Number Employees: 5
Business Description:
Tourism Promoter
S.I.C.: 7389
N.A.I.C.S.: 561591
Media: 1-6-9-10-20-22-23-25-26
Distr.: Reg.
Budget Set: Various
Personnel:
Lucein Lechazarria *(Dir)*
Advertising Agency:
BVK
250 W Coventry Ct #300
Milwaukee, WI 53217-3972
Tel.: (414) 228-1990
Fax: (414) 228-7561
Toll Free: (888) 347-3212

EASTERN STATES EXPOSITION
1305 Memorial Ave
West Springfield, MA 01089-3525
Tel.: (413) 737-2443
Fax: (413) 787-0127
E-mail: info@thebige.com
Web Site: www.thebige.com
Approx. Number Employees: 35
Year Founded: 1916
Business Description:
Not-for-Profit Event Organizer & Promoter for Agriculture, Education, Industry & Family Entertainment
S.I.C.: 8399; 7999
N.A.I.C.S.: 813319; 713990
Advertising Expenditures: $600,000
Media: 2-3-4-6-7-8-9-10-14-15-18-20-23-24-25-26
Distr.: Direct to Consumer; Natl.
Budget Set: Nov.
Personnel:
Wayne Mccary *(Pres)*
Noreen P. Tassinari *(Dir-Mktg)*
Brands & Products:
THE BIG E
Advertising Agency:
Mascola Advertising
434 Forbes Ave
New Haven, CT 06512-1932
Tel.: (203) 469-6900
Fax: (203) 467-8558

EMPIRE STATE DEVELOPMENT-DIVISION OF TOURISM
(Sub. of Empire State Development Corporation)
633 3rd Ave
New York, NY 10017-6706
Tel.: (212) 803-2200
Fax: (212) 803-2279
Web Site: www.iloveny.com
Business Description:
Tourism Services
S.I.C.: 4729; 9532
N.A.I.C.S.: 561599; 925120
Advertising Expenditures: $20,000,000
Media: 9-14-15
Personnel:
Dennia Mullen *(Chm)*
Frances Walton *(CFO)*
Advertising Agency:
Lou Hammond & Associates, Inc.
39 E 51st St
New York, NY 10022-5916
Tel.: (212) 308-8880
Fax: (212) 891-0200

ENTERPRISE FLORIDA, INC.
800 N Magnolia Ave Ste 1100
Orlando, FL 32803
Tel.: (407) 956-5600
Fax: (407) 956-5599
E-mail: information@eflorida.com
Web Site: www.eflorida.com

Key to Media (For complete agency information see *The Advertising Red Books-Agencies* edition):
1. Bus. Publs. 2. Cable T.V. 3. Catalogs & Directories. 4. Co-op Adv. 5. Consumer Mags. 6. D.M. to Bus. Estab.7. D.M. to Consumers 8. Daily Newsp. 9. Exhibits/Trade Shows 10. Foreign 11. Infomercial 12. Internet Adv.13. Multimedia 14. Network Radio 15. Network T.V. 16. Newsp. Distr. Mags. 17. Other 18. Outdoor (Posters, Transit) 19. Point of Purchase20. Premiums, Novelties 21. Product Samples 22. Special Events Mktg. 23. Spot Radio 24. Spot T.V. 25. Weekly Newsp. 26. Yellow Page Adv.

Approx. Rev.: $14,100,000
Approx. Number Employees: 333
Year Founded: 1996
Business Description:
Economic Development Promoter
S.I.C.: 8611
N.A.I.C.S.: 813910
Advertising Expenditures: $1,600,000
Media: 2-5-7-10-12-13-14-16-18-20-22
Personnel:
Ken Wright *(Chm)*
Andy Hyltin *(Vice Chm)*
Gray Swoope *(Pres & CEO)*
John Adam *(CEO)*
Louis Laupsther *(COO)*
Chris Corr *(Exec VP & Chief Strategy Officer)*
Sena Black *(Sr VP)*
Brands & Products:
EFLORIDA
HOSPITALAR
INNOVATION HUB OF THE AMERICAS

ENTERTAINMENT SOFTWARE RATING BOARD

317 Madison Ave 22nd Fl
New York, NY 10017
Tel.: (212) 759-0700
Fax: (212) 759-2223
Web Site: www.esrb.org
Approx. Number Employees: 30
Year Founded: 1994
Business Description:
Computer Games Regulator
S.I.C.: 7819
N.A.I.C.S.: 512191
Media: 3-6-9-13-14-15-23-24-25
Personnel:
Patricia E. Vance *(Pres)*

ESTES PARK CONVENTION & VISITORS BUREAU

500 Big Thompson Ave
Estes Park, CO 80517-9649
Mailing Address:
PO Box 1200
Estes Park, CO 80517-1818
Tel.: (970) 577-9900
Fax: (970) 586-6336
Toll Free: (800) 443-7837
Web Site: www.estesparkcvb.com
Approx. Number Employees: 6
Year Founded: 1923
Business Description:
Tourism & Business Services
S.I.C.: 9651
N.A.I.C.S.: 926150
Advertising Expenditures: $500,000
Media: 6-9-22-24
Distr.: Intl.; Natl.
Budget Set: Aug.
Personnel:
Suzy Blackhurst *(Officer-Comm)*
Advertising Agency:
Turner Public Relations
44 Cook St Ste 650
Denver, CO 80206
Tel.: (303) 333-1402
Fax: (303) 333-4390

FIRST 5 CALIFORNIA

2389 Gateway Oaks Dr Ste 260
Sacramento, CA 95833
Tel.: (916) 263-1050
Fax: (916) 263-1360
E-mail: info@ccfc.ca.gov
Web Site: www.ccfc.ca.gov
Approx. Rev.: $120,000,000
Approx. Number Employees: 45
Year Founded: 1998
Business Description:
Early Childhood Development Information Services
S.I.C.: 8351; 9441
N.A.I.C.S.: 624410; 923130
Media: 7-18-22-23-24-25
Personnel:
Molly Munger *(Vice Chm)*
Kris Perry *(Exec Dir)*
Diane Levin *(Dir)*
Advertising Agency:
Rogers Ruder Finn
1875 Century Park E Ste 200
Los Angeles, CA 90067-2504
Tel.: (310) 552-6922
Fax: (310) 552-9052

FLORIDA DEPARTMENT OF AGRICULTURE & CONSUMER SERVICES - DIVISION OF MARKETING & DEVELOPMENT

Mayo Bldg M9 407 S Calhoun St
Tallahassee, FL 32399-0800
Tel.: (850) 488-4031
Fax: (850) 922-2861
Web Site: www.florida-agriculture.com
Approx. Number Employees: 3,814
Business Description:
Agriculture & Consumer Services Promoter
S.I.C.: 9199; 7319; 7389; 9641
N.A.I.C.S.: 921190; 541870; 561439; 561499; 561990; 926140
Media: 3-10-16-20-22
Personnel:
Nelson L. Mongiovi *(Dir-Mktg)*
Kerry Flack *(Asst Dir)*
Donald Coker *(Chief-State Farmers' Market)*

FLORIDA DEPARTMENT OF HEALTH

Administration 4052 Bald Cypress Way
Tallahassee, FL 32399
Tel.: (850) 245-4443
E-mail: info@doh.state.fl.us
Web Site: www.doh.state.fl.us
Year Founded: 1889
Business Description:
Public Health Regulator
S.I.C.: 9431
N.A.I.C.S.: 923120
Media: 2-8-13-18-22-23-24
Personnel:
Georgia Murphy *(Dir-Art)*
Advertising Agencies:
Anson-Stoner Inc.
111 E Fairbanks Ave
Winter Park, FL 32789-7004
Tel.: (407) 629-9484
Fax: (407) 629-9480

Kidd Group
2074 Centre Point Blvd Ste 200
Tallahassee, FL 32308
Tel.: (850) 878-5433
Fax: (850) 878-6745
Toll Free: (800) 323-4869

THE FLORIDA LOTTERY

250 Marriott Dr
Tallahassee, FL 32399-4000
Tel.: (850) 487-7777
Fax: (850) 487-7796
E-mail: floridalottery@dol.state.fl.us
Web Site: www.flalottery.com
Approx. Number Employees: 355
Year Founded: 1988
Business Description:
State Lottery
S.I.C.: 9311; 7999
N.A.I.C.S.: 921130; 713290
Advertising Expenditures: $32,000,000
Media: 3-9-18-19-22-23-24-25
Distr.: Direct to Consumer; Reg.
Budget Set: July -June
Personnel:
Margarita Delgado *(Pres)*
Patricia Koop *(CMO)*
Brands & Products:
CASH 3
FANTASY 5
FLORIDA LOTTERY
MEGA MONEY
PLAY 4
POWERBALL
Advertising Agency:
Machado/Garcia-Serra Publicidad, Inc.
(d/b/a MGSCOMM)
1790 Coral Way
Miami, FL 33145
Tel.: (305) 444-4647
Fax: (305) 856-2687

FRENCH GOVERNMENT TOURIST OFFICE

825 3rd Ave
New York, NY 10022-6954
Tel.: (212) 838-7800
Fax: (212) 838-7855
Web Site: www.franceguide.com
Sales Estimate: $10-19 Million
Approx. Number Employees: 27
Year Founded: 1946
Business Description:
Government Tourism Administrative Services
S.I.C.: 7389; 4724
N.A.I.C.S.: 561591; 561510
Advertising Expenditures: $700,000
Media: 2-6-9-13-18-19-22
Distr.: Natl.
Personnel:
Corinne Foulquier *(Dir-Mktg)*
Marion Fourestier *(Dir-Comm)*
Daniella Jorge *(Mgr-Niche Mktg)*
Anouk Thiebaut *(Mgr-Mktg-Corp)*
Advertising Agency:
REFLEXADVERTISING
20 W 20th St Ste 900
New York, NY 10001
Tel.: (212) 366-4540
Fax: (212) 243-3320

GEORGIA DEPARTMENT OF ECONOMIC DEVELOPMENT

(Formerly Georgia Department of Industry, Trade & Tourism)
Ste 1200 75 5th St NW
Atlanta, GA 30308-1020
Tel.: (404) 962-4000
Fax: (404) 651-9063
Web Site: www.georgia.org
Approx. Number Employees: 200
Year Founded: 1949
Business Description:
State Tourism Promotion, Industrial Development & International Trade Administrative Services
S.I.C.: 9611
N.A.I.C.S.: 926110
Export
Advertising Expenditures: $8,500,000
Media: 2-4-5-6-7-8-9-10-11-13-20-24-25
Distr.: Intl.; Natl.
Budget Set: June-July
Personnel:
Jim Ewing *(Dir-Indus Dev)*
Jeff Farr *(Dir-Tourism)*
Fred Huff *(Dir-Georgia Tourism Foundation)*
Jennifer Nelson *(Reg Mgr-Project)*
Susie Haggard *(Sr Mgr-Project)*
Kathy Oxford *(Sr Mgr-Intl Trade)*
Daniel Skahen *(Mgr-Mktg)*
Peggy Smith *(Mgr-Customer Svc)*
Brands & Products:
GEORGIA
Advertising Agencies:
GolinHarris
1575 Northside Dr NW Bldg 200 Ste 200
Atlanta, GA 30318
Tel.: (404) 880-4600
Fax: (404) 523-3483

McCrae Communications
107 Stonewall Ave
Fayetteville, GA 30214
Tel.: (770) 460-7277

GEORGIA DEPARTMENT OF INDUSTRY, TRADE & TOURISM

(Name Changed to Georgia Department of Economic Development)

GEORGIA LOTTERY CORPORATION

250 Williams St NW #3000
Atlanta, GA 30303
Tel.: (404) 215-5000
Fax: (404) 215-8871
E-mail: media@galottery.org
Web Site: www.galottery.com
Sales Range: $1-4.9 Billion
Approx. Number Employees: 250
Year Founded: 1992
Business Description:
Lottery Operation
S.I.C.: 7999; 9311
N.A.I.C.S.: 713290; 921130
Media: 8-9-13-24-25
Personnel:
Margaret R. DeFrancisco *(Pres & CEO)*
J. B. Landroche *(VP-Comm)*
Tandi Reddick *(Mgr-Media Rels)*
Brands & Products:
CASH 3
CASH 4
FANTASY 5
GEORGIA LOTTERY
KENO
POWERBALL
WIN FOR LIFE
Advertising Agency:
BBDO Atlanta
3500 Lenox Rd NE Ste 1900
Atlanta, GA 30326-4232
Tel.: (404) 231-1700
Fax: (404) 841-1893

Key to Media (For complete agency information see *The Advertising Red Books-Agencies* edition):
1. Bus. Publs. 2. Cable T.V. 3. Catalogs & Directories. 4. Co-op Adv. 5. Consumer Mags. 6. D.M. to Bus. Estab.7. D.M. to Consumers 8. Daily Newsp. 9. Exhibits/Trade Shows 10. Foreign 11. Infomercial 12. Internet Adv.13. Multimedia 14. Network Radio 15. Network T.V. 16. Newsp. Distr. Mags. 17. Other 18. Outdoor (Posters, Transit) 19. Point of Purchase20. Premiums, Novelties 21. Product Samples 22. Special Events Mktg. 23. Spot Radio 24. Spot T.V. 25. Weekly Newsp. 26. Yellow Page Adv.

GOVERNOR'S OFFICE OF ECONOMIC DEVELOPMENT & TOURISM
221 E 11th St 4th Fl
Austin, TX 78701
Tel.: (512) 936-0100
Tel.: (512) 936-0101
Fax: (512) 936-0450
E-mail: info@governor.state.tx.us
Web Site: www.governor.state.tx.us
Approx. Number Employees: 100
Year Founded: 1997
Business Description:
Texas Tourism Services
S.I.C.: 9611
N.A.I.C.S.: 926110
Export
Media: 1-3-4-5-6-7-8-9-10-11-13-18-22
Distr.: Intl.; Natl.
Budget Set: Aug. -Sept.
Personnel:
Mike Chrobak *(CFO & Dir-Economic Dev)*
Keith Graf *(Dir-Aerospace)*
Tim Fennell *(Mgr-Adv & Tourism)*
Matt Jensen *(Mgr-Mktg)*
Brands & Products:
TEXAS WIDE OPEN FOR BUSINESS
Advertising Agency:
McCann Erickson Southwest
700 Lavaca St Ste 1505
Austin, TX 78701
Tel.: (512) 794-4703

GREATER AUSTIN CHAMBER OF COMMERCE
210 Barton Springs Rd Ste 400
Austin, TX 78704
Tel.: (512) 478-9383
Fax: (512) 478-6389
Toll Free: (800) 856-5602
E-mail: info@austinchamber.com
Web Site: www.austinchamber.com
Approx. Number Employees: 30
Year Founded: 1877
Business Description:
Economic Development Promoter
S.I.C.: 9651
N.A.I.C.S.: 926150
Media: 2-4-7-13-22-23-24
Distr.: Direct to Consumer; Natl.
Budget Set: Sept.
Personnel:
Mike Rolin *(Chm)*
Gary Farmer *(Vice Chm-Economic Devel)*
Michael W. Rollins *(Pres)*
Jan Riepen *(CFO & Sr VP)*
Jeremy Martin *(Sr VP-Govt Rels)*
Nan Matthews *(Sr VP-Comm)*
Susan Davenport *(Sr VP)*
Rebecca Martin *(Sr VP)*
Dave Porter *(Sr VP-Economic Dev)*
Drew Scheberle *(Sr VP)*
Tony Schum *(Dir-Economic Dev)*
Terri Bolin *(Mgr-Lobby Ops)*
Valerie Ferguson *(Mgr-Acctg)*

GREATER BOSTON CONVENTION & VISITORS BUREAU INC.
2 Copley Pl Ste 105
Boston, MA 02116-6501
Tel.: (617) 536-4100
Tel.: (617) 867-8231 (Pub Rels)
Fax: (617) 954-3326
Toll Free: (888) SEE-BOSTON
E-mail: mail@bostonusa.com
Web Site: www.bostonusa.com
Approx. Number Employees: 40
Business Description:
Convention & Visitors Bureau
S.I.C.: 7389
N.A.I.C.S.: 561591
Advertising Expenditures: $300,000
Media: 4-13
Personnel:
Patrick Moscaritolo *(Pres & CEO)*
Cathy Doran *(Sr VP)*
Larry Meehan *(VP-Media & Tourism)*
Brenda Anderson *(Dir-Mktg)*
Diane Dinunzio *(Dir-Visitor Svcs)*
Stacy Shressler *(Coord-Media Rels)*

THE GREATER BOSTON FOOD BANK
70 S Bay Ave
Boston, MA 02118-2701
Tel.: (617) 427-5200
Fax: (617) 427-0146
E-mail: communications@gbfb.org
Web Site: www.gbfb.org
Approx. Rev.: $37,657,554
Approx. Number Employees: 58
Year Founded: 1979
Business Description:
Non-Profit Charitable Organization
S.I.C.: 8641
N.A.I.C.S.: 813410
Advertising Expenditures: $552,627
Media: 9-18-23-24-25
Personnel:
Kip Tiernan *(Founder & Co-Dir)*
Catherine D'Amato *(Pres & CEO)*
David Noymer *(CFO)*
Carol Tienken *(COO)*
Stephanie Nichols *(Mgr-PR)*
Kelly Sajous *(Supvr-Reclamation)*

GREATER CINCINNATI CONVENTION & VISITORS BUREAU
Ste 1500 525 Vine St
Cincinnati, OH 45202
Tel.: (513) 621-2142
Fax: (513) 621-5020
Toll Free: (800) CINCY-USA
E-mail: hr@cincyusa.com
Web Site: www.cincyusa.com
E-Mail For Key Personnel:
Public Relations: JEricksonFolmar@cincyusa.com
Approx. Number Employees: 25
Year Founded: 1945
Business Description:
Convention & Visitors Bureau
S.I.C.: 7389
N.A.I.C.S.: 561591
Media: 2-4-6-7-8-10-13
Personnel:
John T. Taylor *(Chm)*
Nicholas J. Vehr *(Chm)*
Ban Lincoln *(Pres & CEO)*
Julie Calvert *(VP-Comm & Strategic Initiatives)*
Cindi Flick *(VP-Fin & Admin)*
Julie Harrison Calvert *(VP-Commun)*
Leslie Spencer *(Exec Dir-Greater Cincinnati Sports Corp)*
Randi Adam *(Dir-Mktg)*
Sandy Clore *(Dir-Convention Svcs)*
Pam Boeing *(Mgr-Convention Svcs)*
Ross Czarnik *(Mgr-Mktg)*
Windy Darepp *(Mgr-Housing)*
Jessie Erickson Folmar *(Mgr-Mktg & Comm)*
Venus Kent *(Mgr-Sls)*
Sherry Stieritz *(Mgr-HR)*
Brands & Products:
CINCINNATI USA

GREATER HOUSTON CONVENTION & VISITORS BUREAU
901 Bagby St
Houston, TX 77002
Tel.: (713) 437-5200
Toll Free: (800) 4HOUSTON
E-mail: houstongde@aol.com
Web Site: www.visithoustontexas.com
Sales Range: $10-24.9 Million
Approx. Number Employees: 100
Year Founded: 1963
Business Description:
Convention & Visitors Bureau
S.I.C.: 7389
N.A.I.C.S.: 561591
Advertising Expenditures: $200,000
Media: 4-10-13
Personnel:
Greg Ortale *(CEO)*
Karen Williams *(VP-Fin & Gen Mgr)*
Rick Ferguson *(VP & Dir-Film Commission)*
Wayne Chappell *(VP-Tradeshow Rels)*
Holly Clapham *(VP-Mktg)*
Lindsey Brown *(Dir-Mktg & PR)*

GREATER MIAMI CONVENTION & VISITORS BUREAU
701 Brickell Ave Ste 2700
Miami, FL 33131-2847
Tel.: (305) 539-3000
Tel.: (305) 539-3031 (Mktg)
Fax: (305) 539-3113
Toll Free: (800) 933-8448
E-mail: marketing@miamiandbeaches.com
Web Site:
www.miamiandbeaches.com
Approx. Number Employees: 75
Year Founded: 1985
Business Description:
Convention & Visitors Bureau
S.I.C.: 7389
N.A.I.C.S.: 561591
Media: 1-2-5-6-7-9-10-11-13-14-18-25
Distr.: Intl.; Natl.
Personnel:
Adolfo Henriques *(Chm)*
William D. Talbert, III *(Pres & CEO)*
Rolando Aedo *(Sr VP-Mktg & Tourism)*
Ita Moriarty *(Sr VP-Convention Sls)*
Stephen Sonnabend *(Sr VP)*
Nina Cohen *(VP-Mktg)*
Ileana Castillo *(Assoc VP-Convention Sls)*
Mike Carr *(Dir-Mktg)*
Diana Sierra *(Dir-Mktg)*
Ramon Antelo *(Dir-Sls-Mktg)*
Sandra Daley-Francois *(Dir-Sls)*
Peter Moss *(Dir-Sls-Europe & Asia)*
Miguel Southwell *(Dir-Deputy Aviation)*
Linda Stilmann *(Dir-Sls)*
Larissa Valero *(Dir-Sls)*
Joseph McCray *(Mgr-Convention Sls)*
Lisa Murphy *(Mgr-Convention Sls)*
Advertising Agency:
Turkel
2871 Oak Ave
Coconut Grove, FL 33133-5207
Tel.: (305) 476-3500
Fax: (305) 448-6691
(Convention Center)

GREATER MILWAUKEE CONVENTION & VISITORS BUREAU
(d/b/a VISIT Milwaukee)
648 N Plankinton Ave Ste 425
Milwaukee, WI 53203-2501
Tel.: (414) 273-3950
Fax: (414) 273-5596
Toll Free: (800) 231-0903
E-mail: info@visitmilwaukee.org
Web Site: www.visitmilwaukee.org
E-Mail For Key Personnel:
Public Relations: MCasey@milwaukee.org
Approx. Number Employees: 45
Business Description:
Travel & Tourism Promoter
S.I.C.: 8611; 9199
N.A.I.C.S.: 813910; 921190
Advertising Expenditures: $250,000
Media: 2-4-5-6-7-8-9-10-13-20-25-26
Personnel:
Brent Foerster *(VP-Sls & Mktg)*
Maria Brondyke *(Dir-Sls)*
Dana Jones *(Dir-Fin & Admin)*
Dave Larson *(Dir-Convention Svcs)*
Rachel Oliver *(Dir-Mktg)*
Christine Celley *(Mgr-Convention Sls)*
Fran Jackson *(Mgr-Membership Sls)*
Kelly Langenecker *(Mgr-Convention Sls)*
Robert Moore *(Mgr-Convention Svcs)*
Jeanine Sherman *(Mgr-PR)*
Margaret Casey *(Coord-Pub Rels)*
Advertising Agency:
Stir Advertising & Integrated Marketing
252 E Highland Ave
Milwaukee, WI 53202
Tel.: (414) 278-0040
Fax: (414) 278-0390

GREATER NAPLES CHAMBER OF COMMERCE
2390 Tamiami Trl N Ste 210
Naples, FL 34103-4484
Tel.: (239) 262-6376
Tel.: (239) 262-6141
Fax: (239) 262-8374
E-mail: info@napleschamber.org
Web Site: www.napleschamber.org
Approx. Number Employees: 12
Business Description:
Economic Development Promoter
S.I.C.: 9651
N.A.I.C.S.: 926150
Media: 6-10-13-22
Personnel:
Lou Vlasho *(Vice Chm)*
Michael Reagen *(Pres & CEO)*
Patrick O'Connor *(Sr VP-Programs)*
Brenda Borchadt *(Sr VP-Programs)*
Sandy Schoepfer *(Dir-Commun)*
Kathy Swank *(Sr Acct Exec)*

GREATER PHOENIX CHAMBER OF COMMERCE
Chase Tower 201 N Central Ave 27th Fl
Phoenix, AZ 85004
Tel.: (602) 254-5521
Fax: (602) 495-8913
E-mail: info@phoenixchamber.com
Web Site: www.phoenixchamber.com
E-Mail For Key Personnel:

Key to Media (For complete agency information see *The Advertising Red Books-Agencies* edition):
1. Bus. Publs. 2. Cable T.V. 3. Catalogs & Directories. 4. Co-op Adv. 5. Consumer Mags. 6. D.M. to Bus. Estab.7. D.M. to Consumers 8. Daily Newsp. 9. Exhibits/Trade Shows 10. Foreign 11. Infomercial 12. Internet Adv.13. Multimedia 14. Network Radio 15. Network T.V. 16. Newsp. Distr. Mags. 17. Other 18. Outdoor (Posters, Transit) 19. Point of Purchase20. Premiums, Novelties 21. Product Samples 22. Special Events Mktg. 23. Spot Radio 24. Spot T.V. 25. Weekly Newsp. 26. Yellow Page Adv.

President: vmanning@phoenixchamber.com
Public Relations: MRill@phoenixchamber.com
Approx. Number Employees: 30
Year Founded: 1888
Business Description:
Economic Development Promoter & Retention, Public Affairs & Membership Services
S.I.C.: 9651
N.A.I.C.S.: 926150
Media: 2-4-6-7-8-10
Distr.: Reg.
Budget Set: July
Personnel:
Todd Sanders *(Pres & CEO)*
Ron McElhaney *(VP-Fin & Ops)*
Daniel Ayala *(Dir-BidSource)*
Debbie Drotar *(Dir-Bus Dev)*
Loraine LaMorder *(Coord-Info)*

GREATER RALEIGH CONVENTION & VISITORS BUREAU
421 Fayetteville St Mall Ste 1505
Raleigh, NC 27601-2946
Mailing Address:
PO Box 1879
Raleigh, NC 27602
Tel.: (919) 834-5900
Fax: (919) 831-2887
Toll Free: (800) 849-8499
E-mail: visit@raleighcvb.org
Web Site: www.visitraleigh.com
E-Mail For Key Personnel:
President: dheinl@raleighcvb.org
Marketing Director: RSmith@visitraleigh.com
Sales Director: stucker@raleighcvb.org
Sales Range: $25-49.9 Million
Approx. Number Employees: 28
Business Description:
Convention & Visitors Bureau
S.I.C.: 7389
N.A.I.C.S.: 561591
Advertising Expenditures: $1,000,000
Media: 2-3-4-6-7-8-9-10-13-18-20-22-23-24-25
Personnel:
R. Doyle Parrish *(Chm)*
Dennis Edward *(Pres & CEO)*
Loren J. Gold *(Exec VP)*
Kumi Anzalone *(Reg Dir-Natl Accts)*
Linda Bonine *(Dir-Ops)*
Jana R. Oliver *(Dir-Sls)*
Ryan Smith *(Dir-Comm)*
Vimal Vyas *(Dir-IT)*
Malinda Pettaway *(Assoc Dir-Convention Sls)*
Stephen Jackson *(Mgr-Sls-Natl)*
Theresa Tyler *(Mgr-Sports Svcs)*
Loretta Yingling *(Mgr-Sls-Natl)*
Advertising Agency:
MRPP
201 W Chatham St Ste 202
Cary, NC 27511
Tel.: (919) 468-1000
Fax: (919) 468-1956

GREATER TAMPA CHAMBER OF COMMERCE
201 N Franklin St Ste 201
Tampa, FL 33602
Tel.: (813) 228-7777
Fax: (813) 223-7899
Fax: (813) 229-7855
Fax: (813) 221-6095
Toll Free: (800) 298-2672
E-mail: info@tampachamber.com
Web Site: www.tampachamber.com
Approx. Number Employees: 38
Year Founded: 1894
Business Description:
Economic Development Services
S.I.C.: 9651
N.A.I.C.S.: 926150
Media: 7-10-20
Distr.: Intl.; Natl.
Budget Set: Sept. -Oct.
Personnel:
Bob Rohrlack *(Pres & CEO)*
Howard Volland *(Mgr-Fin Svcs Project)*
Wendy Wiemert *(Mgr-Database)*
Michelle Montgomery *(Coord-Events)*

THE GREATER VANCOUVER CONVENTION & VISITOR BUREAU
200 Burrard St Ste 210
Vancouver, BC Canada
Tel.: (604) 682-2222
Fax: (604) 682-1717
E-mail: info@tourismvancouver.com
Web Site: www.tourismvancouver.com
Approx. Rev.: $8,076,970
Approx. Number Employees: 100
Year Founded: 1902
Business Description:
Convention & Visitors Bureau
S.I.C.: 7389
N.A.I.C.S.: 561591
Media: 2-6-9-13-25
Personnel:
Rick Antonson *(Pres & CEO)*
Ted Lee *(CFO & VP-Vistor Svcs)*
James E. Terry *(Exec VP)*
Paul Vallee *(Exec VP)*
Walt Judas *(VP-Mktg Comm & Member Svcs)*
Dayna Miller *(Dir-Sls)*
Patti Smolen *(Dir-Indus Rels)*
Emily Armstrong *(Mgr-Travel Media Rels-N America)*
Wendy Underwood *(Mgr-Travel Media Rels-Trade & Intl)*
Candice Gibson *(Mgr-Mktg)*
Brands & Products:
VANCOUVER SPECTACULAR BY NATURE

GREEK NATIONAL TOURIST ORGANIZATION
(Sub. of Greek National Tourist Organization)
645 5th Ave 9th Fl
New York, NY 10022-5910
Tel.: (212) 421-5777
Fax: (212) 826-6940
E-mail: info@greektourism.com
Web Site: www.gnto.gr
Sales Range: Less than $1 Million
Sales Estimate: $1-4.9 Million
Approx. Number Employees: 10
Business Description:
Travel Information & Services
S.I.C.: 7389
N.A.I.C.S.: 561591
Media: 2-5-6-9-10-25
Distr.: Intl.; Natl.
Budget Set: Sept. -Oct.
Personnel:
Dimy Chryssanthou *(Dir-Adv)*
Fay Georgousis *(Dir-Pub Rels & Mktg)*

GREENSBORO CONVENTION & VISITORS BUREAU
2200 Pinecroft Rd Ste 200
Greensboro, NC 27407
Tel.: (336) 274-2282
Fax: (336) 230-1183
Toll Free: (800) 344-2282
E-mail: gso@visitgreensboronc.com
Web Site: www.visitgreensboronc.com
E-Mail For Key Personnel:
President: hfourrier@greensboronc.org
Marketing Director: gmurphy@greensboronc.org
Sales Director: apope@greensboronc.org
Approx. Rev.: $4,000,000
Approx. Number Employees: 20
Year Founded: 1985
Business Description:
Travel & Tourism in Greensboro Promoter
S.I.C.: 7389
N.A.I.C.S.: 561591
Advertising Expenditures: $750,000
Media: 2-4-6-7-8-10-13-18-22-26
Personnel:
Henri Fourrier *(Pres & CEO)*
Ava Pope *(Dir-Sls)*
Bonita Fleming *(Mgr-Sls)*
Karen Robertson *(Mgr-State Sls)*
James V. Watterson *(Mgr-Admin & Sys)*
Maggie Wilson *(Mgr-Sls-Natl)*

HAMPTON ROADS ECONOMIC DEVELOPMENT ALLIANCE
500 E Main St Ste 1300
Norfolk, VA 23510-2206
Tel.: (757) 627-2315
Fax: (757) 623-3081
Toll Free: (800) 423-5068
E-mail: info@hreda.com
Web Site: www.hreda.com
E-Mail For Key Personnel:
Marketing Director: knorden@fhrpo.hrccva.com
Approx. Number Employees: 15
Year Founded: 1984
Business Description:
Regional Marketing & Business Recruitment - Virginia's Hampton Roads; Economic Development
S.I.C.: 9532; 9611
N.A.I.C.S.: 925120; 926110
Media: 2-7-22
Personnel:
Darryl Gosnell *(Pres & CEO)*
Amy N. Parkhurst *(Sr VP)*
Sarah E. Cavanaugh *(Dir-Investor Dev)*

HAWAII DEPARTMENT OF BUSINESS, ECONOMIC DEVELOPMENT & TOURISM
250 S Hotel St
Honolulu, HI 96813
Mailing Address:
PO Box 2359
Honolulu, HI 96804
Tel.: (808) 586-2355
Fax: (808) 586-2790
E-mail: library@dbedt.hawaii.gov
Web Site: www.hawaii.gov
Sales Range: $100-124.9 Million
Approx. Number Employees: 225
Business Description:
Economic Development
S.I.C.: 9611
N.A.I.C.S.: 926110
Media: 1-2-7-9-10-22-24-25
Distr.: Natl.

HAWAII VISITORS & CONVENTION BUREAU
2270 Kalakaua Ave Ste 801
Honolulu, HI 96815
Tel.: (808) 923-1811
Fax: (808) 924-0290
Toll Free: (800) GO-HAWAII
E-mail: infoof@hvcb.org
Web Site: www.gohawaii.com
E-Mail For Key Personnel:
President: tvericella@hvcb.org
Approx. Number Employees: 75
Year Founded: 1902
Business Description:
Convention & Visitors Bureau
S.I.C.: 7389
N.A.I.C.S.: 561591
Media: 3-5-6-9-13-15-17-22-23-24
Distr.: Intl.; Natl.
Budget Set: Apr.
Personnel:
John Monahan *(Pres & CEO)*
Jay Talwar *(Sr VP-Mktg)*
Mike Murray *(VP-Sls & Mktg)*
George Applegate *(Exec Dir)*
Sue Kanoho *(Exec Dir)*
Kara Imai *(Sr Dir-Online Mktg)*
Christina Aldanese *(Reg Dir)*
Jennifer Cabasag *(Reg Dir-Eastern Reg)*
Kathy Dever *(Reg Dir)*
Joe Nagle *(Reg Dir)*
Meredith Parkins *(Reg Dir)*
Patricia Tarnutzer *(Reg Dir-Accts)*
Eric Dutro *(Sls Dir)*
Keli'i Brown *(Dir-PR)*
Gina Chun *(Dir-Consumer Mktg)*
Darlene Morikawa *(Dir-PR & Comms)*
Jaci Murakami *(Mgr-Online Mktg)*
Brands & Products:
HAWAII
HAWAII, THE ISLANDS OF ALOHA
Advertising Agency:
MVNP
999 Bishop St 21th Fl
Honolulu, HI 96813-4429
Tel.: (808) 536-0881
Fax: (808) 529-6208

HOT SPRINGS CONVENTION & VISITORS BUREAU
134 Convention Blvd
Hot Springs National Park, AR 71901-4135
Tel.: (501) 321-2277
Fax: (501) 321-2136
Toll Free: (800) 543-2284
E-mail: hscvb@hotsprings.org
Web Site: www.hotsprings.org
Approx. Number Employees: 70
Year Founded: 1974
Business Description:
Convention & Visitors Bureau
S.I.C.: 7389
N.A.I.C.S.: 561591
Advertising Expenditures: $1,500,000
Media: 1-2-6-7-8-9-10-11-13-18-23-24

Hot Springs Convention & Visitors Bureau — (Continued)

Distr.: Natl.
Budget Set: Dec.
Personnel:
Charlie Moore *(Chm)*
Steve Arrison *(CEO)*

IDAHO DEPARTMENT OF COMMERCE

700 W State St 2nd Fl
Boise, ID 83720-0093
Tel.: (208) 334-2470
Fax: (208) 334-2631
Toll Free: (800) 635-7820
Toll Free: (800) VISITID
E-mail: info@visitid.org
Web Site: www.visitid.org
Approx. Number Employees: 52
Year Founded: 1982
Business Description:
State Economic Development
Administrative Services
S.I.C.: 9651; 9611
N.A.I.C.S.: 926150; 926110
Advertising Expenditures: $800,000
Media: 4-5-6-10-24
Distr.: Intl.; Natl.
Budget Set: July
Personnel:
Melonie Bartolome *(CFO)*
Karen Ballard *(Dir-Tourism Mktg)*
Don Dietrich *(Dir)*
Peg Owens *(Mgr-Film & Tourism Mktg)*
Julie Howard *(Coord-Mktg)*
Advertising Agency:
Drake Cooper Inc.
416 S 8th 3rd Fl
Boise, ID 83702-5471
Tel.: (208) 342-0925
Fax: (208) 342-0635
(Tourism)

IDAHO LOTTERY

1199 Shoreline Ln Ste 100
Boise, ID 83702
Tel.: (208) 334-2600
Fax: (208) 334-2610
E-mail: info@idaholottery.com
Web Site: www.idaholottery.com
Sales Range: $125-149.9 Million
Approx. Number Employees: 47
Year Founded: 1986
Business Description:
State Lottery
S.I.C.: 9311; 7999
N.A.I.C.S.: 921130; 713290
Advertising Expenditures: $2,300,000
Media: 9-13-19-23-24-25
Distr.: Direct to Consumer; Reg.
Budget Set: June
Personnel:
Amber French *(Dir-Security)*
Mike Helppie *(Dir-Sls & Mktg)*
Sherie Moody-St Clair *(Dir-Creative Svcs)*
Kim Mathison *(Mgr-Key Accts)*
Lynn Craven *(Coord-Charitable Gaming)*
Brands & Products:
BEACH BLANKET SLINGO
BLACK CHERRY DOUBLER
BONUS CASHWORD
CHERRY JAM
COIN CAPER
CRAZY WILD 10S
DOUBLE CHERRY BELLS
DOUBLE PLAY DAILY
ELECTRIC 7'S
FAT PAYDAY
GOIN' GREEN
GOLD BAR BINGO
GOLD RUSH
HOOK, LINE & SINKER
IDAHO LOTTERY
IDAHO PICK 3
LIBERTY BARS
ON A ROLL
PALMS
RED DIAMOND BLUE
REELIN' IN THE DOUGH
SCRABBLE
SCRATCH GAMES
SHAKE RATTLE & DOUGH
SILVER BULLET
SLEIGH RIDE
SLINGO MAGIC
SLINGO TRIO
SLOTS OF GOLD
SMOKIN' HOT 9'S
SPEED 7'S
SPICE HOT CASH
SUPER LUCKY LINES
TIC TAC TURKEY
TRIPLE DYNAMITE 777
WILD CARD 2
WILD CHERRY CASHWORD
WILD THING
WINTER DOUBLE DOUBLER
WOOH!
THE WORKS
YO-YO DOUGH

ILLINOIS BUREAU OF TOURISM

100 W Randolph St Ste 3-400
Chicago, IL 60601-3219
Tel.: (312) 814-4733
Fax: (312) 814-6175
Toll Free: (800) 226-6632
Web Site: www.enjoyillinois.com
Sales Range: $10-24.9 Million
Approx. Number Employees: 18
Year Founded: 1963
Business Description:
State Travel & Tourism Administrative Services
S.I.C.: 7389; 9199
N.A.I.C.S.: 561591; 921190
Advertising Expenditures: $12,000,000
Media: 4-6-9-10-13-16-23-25
Distr.: Reg.
Budget Set: July
Personnel:
Jan Kemmerling *(Mgr-Local Tourism Div)*
Jan Kostner *(Dir-State Travel)*
Jack Lavin *(Dir-Commerce)*
Elisa Marcus *(Mgr-Mktg-Intl)*
Brad Strauss *(Mgr-PR-Domestic)*

ILLINOIS DEPARTMENT OF COMMERCE AND ECONOMIC OPPORTUNITY

620 E Adams St
Springfield, IL 62701-1615
Tel.: (217) 782-7500
Tel.: (312) 814-2354 (Adv)
Fax: (217) 524-0864
Web Site: www.commerce.state.il.us
Sales Estimate: $60-79 Million
Approx. Number Employees: 420
Year Founded: 1979
Business Description:
State Agency For Economic, Community, Business & Industrial Development
S.I.C.: 9611; 9111
N.A.I.C.S.: 926110; 921110
Media: 2-3-4-5-6-7-9-10-11-13-14-15-16-18-20-22-23-24-25
Distr.: Natl.
Budget Set: July
Personnel:
Warren Rively *(Mgr-Bus Devel)*
Brands & Products:
RIGHT HERE. RIGHT NOW.
Advertising Agency:
Energy BBDO
410 N Michigan Ave
Chicago, IL 60611-4213
Tel.: (312) 337-7860
Fax: (312) 337-6871

ILLINOIS STATE LOTTERY

100 W Randolph Ste 7-901
Chicago, IL 60601
Tel.: (312) 793-3026
Fax: (312) 951-7204
E-mail: lottery.info@isl.state.il.us
Web Site: www.illinoislottery.com
Approx. Rev.: $1,590,000,000
Year Founded: 1974
Business Description:
State Lottery
S.I.C.: 9311; 7999
N.A.I.C.S.: 921130; 713290
Media: 1-6-8-9-18-19-23-24
Distr.: Direct to Consumer; Reg.
Budget Set: July
Personnel:
Sarah Cummins *(Dir-Mktg)*
Brands & Products:
BOO BUCKS
CHESTNUT CHANGE
DAY AT THE FAIR
DETOUR DOUBLER
HAVE A BALL!
ILLINOIS LOTTERY
LITTLE LOTTO
LOTTO
MEGA MILLIONS
MILLIONAIRE RAFFLE
NUMBERS NOW
PICK 3
PICK 4
PINK PANTHER
RAINY DAY CHANGE
TANGERINE TRIPLER
TURKEY TRIPLER
WIN IT ALL
Advertising Agency:
Energy BBDO
410 N Michigan Ave
Chicago, IL 60611-4213
Tel.: (312) 337-7860
Fax: (312) 337-6871
(Creative)

INDIA TOURISM

1270 Ave of the Americas Ste 303 fl3
New York, NY 10020-1801
Tel.: (212) 586-4901
Fax: (212) 582-3274
E-mail: ny@itonyc.com
Web Site: www.incredibleindia.org
Approx. Number Employees: 7
Year Founded: 1954
Business Description:
Tourism Promoter
S.I.C.: 4724
N.A.I.C.S.: 561510
Media: 2-6-7-8-9-10-18-23-25
Distr.: Natl.
Personnel:
Narendra Kothiyal *(Mgr-Mktg)*

INDIANA OFFICE OF TOURISM DEVELOPMENT

1 N Capitol Ave Ste 600
Indianapolis, IN 46204-2040
Tel.: (317) 232-8860
Fax: (317) 233-6887
Toll Free: (888) ENJOYIN
E-mail: webmaster@enjoyindiana.com
Web Site: www.visitindiana.com
E-Mail For Key Personnel:
Public Relations: cbrantingham@visitindiana.com
Approx. Number Employees: 8
Business Description:
Tourism Services
S.I.C.: 7389
N.A.I.C.S.: 561499
Advertising Expenditures: $1,500,000
Media: 1-3-4-6-7-8-9-13-18-20-23-24
Distr.: Reg.
Budget Set: July
Personnel:
Amy Vaughan *(Exec Dir)*
Advertising Agency:
Hirons & Company
422 E New York St
Indianapolis, IN 46202
Tel.: (317) 977-2206
Fax: (317) 977-2208
(Agency of Record for Tourism & Film Development & Business Development Divisions)

INDIANAPOLIS CONVENTION & VISITORS ASSOCIATION

30 S Meridian St Ste 410
Indianapolis, IN 46204
Tel.: (317) 639-4282
Fax: (317) 639-5273
Toll Free: (800) 958-INDY
E-mail: icva@visitindy.com
Web Site: www.visitindy.com
E-Mail For Key Personnel:
Sales Director: dbennett@indianapolis.org
Public Relations: mhuggard@indianapolis.org
Approx. Number Employees: 60
Year Founded: 1923
Business Description:
Convention & Visitors Bureau
S.I.C.: 7389
N.A.I.C.S.: 561591
Advertising Expenditures: $450,000
Media: 4-10-13-26
Personnel:
Leonard Hoops *(Pres & CEO)*
Advertising Agency:
Young & Laramore
407 N Fulton St
Indianapolis, IN 46202
Tel.: (317) 264-8000
Fax: (317) 264-8002

IOWA DEPARTMENT OF ECONOMIC DEVELOPMENT

200 E Grand Ave
Des Moines, IA 50309
Tel.: (515) 725-3000

Key to Media (For complete agency information see *The Advertising Red Books-Agencies* edition):
1. Bus. Publs. 2. Cable T.V. 3. Catalogs & Directories. 4. Co-op Adv. 5. Consumer Mags. 6. D.M. to Bus. Estab.7. D.M. to Consumers 8. Daily Newsp. 9. Exhibits/Trade Shows 10. Foreign 11. Infomercial 12. Internet Adv.13. Multimedia 14. Network Radio 15. Network T.V. 16. Newsp. Distr. Mags. 17. Other 18. Outdoor (Posters, Transit) 19. Point of Purchase20. Premiums, Novelties 21. Product Samples 22. Special Events Mktg. 23. Spot Radio 24. Spot T.V. 25. Weekly Newsp. 26. Yellow Page Adv.

Fax: (515) 725-3010
Toll Free: (800) 245-IOWA
E-mail: communications@iowa.gov
Web Site: www.iowalifechanging.com
Approx. Number Employees: 125
Year Founded: 1984
Business Description:
Economic, Business, Tourism & Communication Programs Developer for the State of Iowa
S.I.C.: 9611
N.A.I.C.S.: 926110
Advertising Expenditures: $2,000,000
Media: 2-5-9-10-11-22
Distr.: Reg.
Budget Set: May
Personnel:
Bob Bocken *(Chm)*
Kay Snyder *(Dir-Comm)*
Kanan Kappelman *(Mgr-Mktg)*
Kay Snider *(Mgr-Mktg)*
Lane Palmer *(Coord-Devel Resources)*
Brands & Products:
COME BE OUR GUEST
IOWALIFECHANGING
SMART CAREER MOVE
Advertising Agency:
The Integer Group-Midwest
2633 Fleur Dr
Des Moines, IA 50321-1753
Tel.: (515) 288-7910
Fax: (515) 288-8439
Toll Free: (800) 752-2633
(Business Development & Tourism)

IOWA LOTTERY
2323 Grand Ave
Des Moines, IA 50312
Tel.: (515) 281-7900
Fax: (515) 281-7882
E-mail: web.master@ilot.state.ia.us
Web Site: www.ialottery.com
Approx. Sls.: $209,920,000
Approx. Number Employees: 125
Year Founded: 1985
Business Description:
State Lottery Services
S.I.C.: 9311
N.A.I.C.S.: 921130
Media: 3-9-13-18-19-20-22-23-24
Distr.: Reg.
Budget Set: May
Personnel:
Ken Brickman *(Acting CEO)*
Larry Loss *(VP-Sls)*
Teri Wood TeBockhorst *(VP-Mktg)*
Brands & Products:
ACE'S WILD
ANTE UP
CASH COW
CASH SPLASH
CASINO SPIN
CORN CRAZE
DUBBLE BUBBLE
EZ GRAND
FANTASTIC FORTUNES
THE FREEDOM ROCK
FREEPLAY REPLAY
INSTANT TICKETS
IOWA LOTTERY
IOWA'S $100,000 CASH GAME
IOWA'S POWERBALL
LAND OF LIBERTY
LOOT PURSUIT
MILK IT!
PICK 3
REEL IN THE MONEY
ROLL OUT THE BARREL
SPICE IT UP
SUDOKU
SUPERSTAR CASH
TEE ONE UP
TWISTER
Advertising Agencies:
The Integer Group-Midwest
2633 Fleur Dr
Des Moines, IA 50321-1753
Tel.: (515) 288-7910
Fax: (515) 288-8439
Toll Free: (800) 752-2633

Strategic America
6600 Westown Pkwy Ste 100
West Des Moines, IA 50266-7708
Tel.: (888) 898-6400
Fax: (515) 224-4181
(Lottery Games)

IRVING CONVENTION & VISITORS BUREAU
222 W Las Colinas Blvd Ste 1550
Irving, TX 75039
Tel.: (972) 252-7476
Fax: (972) 257-3153
Toll Free: (800) 2IRVING
E-mail: icvb@airmail.net
Web Site: www.irvingtexas.com
E-Mail For Key Personnel:
Marketing Director: mgast@ci.irving.tx.us
Approx. Number Employees: 26
Year Founded: 1972
Business Description:
Convention & Visitors Bureau
S.I.C.: 7389
N.A.I.C.S.: 561591
Advertising Expenditures: $1,200,000
Media: 2-4-5-6-7-9-14-16-20-22
Distr.: Direct to Bus.; Natl.
Budget Set: Aug.
Personnel:
Mark Thompson *(Exec Dir-Mktg)*
Maura Gast *(Exec Dir)*
Jane Kilburn *(Exec Dir-Admin)*
Lori Fojtasek *(Dir-Sls)*
Diana Pfaff *(Dir-Comm)*
Bob Berry *(Mgr-Customer Svcs)*
Advertising Agency:
Maloney Strategic Communications
11520 N Central Expwy Ste 236
Dallas, TX 75243
Tel.: (214) 342-8385
Fax: (214) 342-8386
— John Maloney *(Chief Exec. Officer)*

ISRAEL MINISTRY OF TOURISM INFORMATION CENTER
800 2nd Ave
New York, NY 10017-4709
Tel.: (212) 499-5660
Fax: (212) 499-5645
Fax: (212) 499-5665
Toll Free: (888) 77ISRAEL
Toll Free: (800) 514-1188
E-mail: info@goisrael.com
Web Site: www.goisrael.com
Sales Estimate: $10-19 Million
Approx. Number Employees: 50
Year Founded: 1948
Business Description:
Israeli Tourism Information
S.I.C.: 7389
N.A.I.C.S.: 561591
Export
Advertising Expenditures: $4,000,000
Media: 1-4-10
Distr.: Natl.
Personnel:
Anat Levi *(Dir-Mktg)*

ITALIAN GOVERNMENT TOURIST BOARD-NORTH AMERICA
630 5th Ave Ste 1565
New York, NY 10111
Tel.: (212) 245-4822
Tel.: (212) 245-5618
Fax: (212) 586-9249
E-mail: enitny@italiantourism.com
Web Site: www.italiantourism.com
Approx. Number Employees: 12
Year Founded: 1916
Business Description:
Government Tourism Administrative Services
S.I.C.: 7389
N.A.I.C.S.: 561591
Export
Media: 1-6-7-8-10-11-13-15
Distr.: Intl.; Natl.
Budget Set: July
Personnel:
Marzia Bortolin *(Press Officer)*
Riccardo Strano *(Dir-North America)*
Francisco Brazzini *(Mgr-Mktg)*

JAMAICA TOURIST BOARD
5201 Blue Lagoon Dr Ste 670
Miami, FL 33126-7016
Tel.: (305) 665-0557
Fax: (305) 666-7239
Toll Free: (800) 233-4582
E-mail: info@visitjamaica-usa.com
Web Site: www.visitjamaica.com
Approx. Number Employees: 12
Year Founded: 1955
Business Description:
Tourism to Jamaica Promoter
S.I.C.: 7389; 4724
N.A.I.C.S.: 561591; 561510
Media: 6-9-17-22-24
Distr.: Natl.
Personnel:
Donald Dawson *(Dir-Sls)*
Diana Willis *(Mgr-Media Rels)*
Brands & Products:
JAMAICA
ONCE YOU GO. YOU KNOW.
Advertising Agency:
The Ruder Finn Group
301 E 57th St
New York, NY 10022-2900
Tel.: (212) 593-6400
Fax: (212) 593-6397

JAPAN NATIONAL TOURIST ORGANIZATION
11 W 42nd St 19th Fl
New York, NY 10036
Tel.: (212) 757-5640
Fax: (212) 307-6754
E-mail: visitjapan@jntonyc.org
Web Site: www.japantravelinfo.com
Approx. Number Employees: 9
Business Description:
Tourism Promotion Services
S.I.C.: 7389; 7319
N.A.I.C.S.: 561591; 541870
Media: 6-7-8-9-10-11-13
Distr.: Natl.
Budget Set: Apr.
Personnel:
Shuichi Kameyama *(Exec Dir)*

KANSAS CITY CONVENTION & VISITORS ASSOCIATION
1100 Main St Ste 2200
Kansas City, MO 64105
Tel.: (816) 221-5242
Fax: (816) 691-3805
Toll Free: (800) 767-7700
E-mail: info@visitkc.com
Web Site: www.visitkc.com
E-Mail For Key Personnel:
President: rhughes@visitkc.com
Marketing Director: LJahn@visitkc.com
Approx. Number Employees: 50
Year Founded: 1918
Business Description:
Convention & Visitors Bureau
S.I.C.: 7389
N.A.I.C.S.: 561591
Advertising Expenditures: $200,000
Media: 4-13-16-24
Personnel:
Richard L. Hughes *(Pres & CEO)*
Bill Bohde *(VP-Sls)*
Alan Carr *(VP-Mktg & Comm)*
Janet Ziegler *(VP-Fin & Admin)*
Denise DeJulio *(Exec Dir-Convention Sls)*
Carl Leonard *(Dir-IT)*
Brandon Billings *(Sr Mgr-Online Mktg)*
Becky Addleman *(Mgr-Accts-Natl)*
Janette Barron *(Mgr-HR)*
Susan Blanco *(Sr Convention, Visitor Svcs & Mgr-Special Events)*
Deanie Blansett *(Mgr-Graphic Design)*
Kim Dooley *(Mgr-Accts-Natl)*
Geralyn Krist *(Mgr-Natl Accts)*
Rod Sanchez *(Mgr-Accts-Natl)*
Vada Taylor *(Mgr-Housing)*
Jerome Toson *(Coord-Acctg)*

KANSAS DEPARTMENT OF COMMERCE
1000 SW Jackson St Ste 100
Topeka, KS 66612
Tel.: (785) 296-3481
Fax: (785) 296-3665
Telex: 785-296-3487
Web Site:
www.kansascommerce.com
E-Mail For Key Personnel:
Marketing Director: cstratton@kdoch.state.ks.us
Approx. Number Employees: 125
Year Founded: 1936
Business Description:
Promoter of Tourism & Industrial & Community Development
S.I.C.: 9651
N.A.I.C.S.: 926150
Advertising Expenditures: $1,000,000
Media: 2-4-6-7-8-10-11-19-20-22
Distr.: Intl.; Natl.
Budget Set: Aug.
Personnel:
John Watson *(Pres & Dir)*
Caleb Asher *(Dir-Mktg)*
Jeff Montague *(Dir-HR)*
Richard Smalley *(Mgr-Mktg)*
Cindee Stratton *(Mgr-Mktg)*
Advertising Agency:
Callahan Creek, Inc.
805 New Hampshire St
Lawrence, KS 66044-2739

Kansas Department of Commerce — (Continued)

Tel.: (785) 838-4774
Fax: (785) 838-4033

KANSAS LOTTERY
128 N Kansas Ave
Topeka, KS 66603
Tel.: (785) 296-5700
Fax: (785) 296-5712
Fax: (785) 296-5722
E-mail: lotteryinfo@kslottery.com
Web Site: www.kslottery.com
Approx. Sls.: $206,900,000
Approx. Number Employees: 90
Year Founded: 1987
Business Description:
State Lottery Services
S.I.C.: 9311
N.A.I.C.S.: 921130
Media: 3-13-18-23-24
Personnel:
Ed Van Petten *(Exec Dir)*
Gail Kennedy *(Dir-HR)*
Colleen O'Neil *(Dir-Mktg)*
Brands & Products:
2BY2
BETTY BOOP
CASH COW
CASH HAPPY
CHIPS AND SALSA
COOL CAT
CRUISIN AND CASH
DOLLAR GRILLS
DOUBLE DOG DARE
HAR-MONEY
HOT LOTTO
JACKPOT JUNGLE
KANSAS LOTTERY
KEEP THE CHANGE
KENO
MILITARY TICKET
MOVIE MONEY
PICK 3
POWERBALL
THE REEL DEAL
ROYAL TREASURE
SPICY HOT CASH
SUNFLOWER STATE GAMES
SUPER KANSAS
VETERANS CELEBRATION
VETERANS GAME
WILD BILL
WILD TURKEYS
WIZARD OF OZ
YAHTZEE

KENTUCKY DEPARTMENT OF TOURISM
500 Mero St 22 Fl
Frankfort, KY 40601
Tel.: (502) 564-4930
Fax: (502) 564-5695
Toll Free: (800) 225-8747
E-mail: travel@mail.state.ky.us
Web Site: www.kentuckytourism.com
E-Mail For Key Personnel:
President: Cheryl.Hatcher@mail.state.ky.us
Sales Range: $10-24.9 Million
Approx. Number Employees: 35
Business Description:
State Tourism Administrative Services
S.I.C.: 7389
N.A.I.C.S.: 561591
Media: 3-5-6-8-9-10-11-13-16-18-23-24-25
Distr.: Natl.
Personnel:
Mike Cooper *(Commissioner)*
Kevin Marie Nuss *(Dir-Mktg & Adv)*
Wayne Cusick *(Asst Dir-Welcome Centers)*
Kathy Yount *(Asst Dir)*

KENTUCKY LOTTERY CORPORATION
1011 W Main St
Louisville, KY 40202
Tel.: (502) 560-1500
Fax: (502) 560-1531
Toll Free: (800) 937-8946
E-mail: custsrvs@kylottery.com
Web Site: www.kylottery.com
Approx. Sls.: $673,500,000
Approx. Number Employees: 150
Year Founded: 1989
Business Description:
State Lottery
S.I.C.: 9311; 7999
N.A.I.C.S.: 921130; 713290
Advertising Expenditures: $8,000,000
Media: 6-8-9-17-18-19-23-24-25
Distr.: Direct to Consumer; Reg.
Budget Set: July
Personnel:
Arthur L. Gleason *(Pres & CEO)*
Howard B. Kline *(CFO, Sr VP-Fin & Admin)*
Margaret Gibbs *(COO & Exec VP)*
Mary Harville *(Gen Counsel, Sec & Sr VP)*
Steve Casebeer *(Sr VP-Mktg-Sls)*
Bill Hickerson *(Sr VP-Security)*
Gale Vessels *(Sr VP-Internal Audit & Info Security)*
Rick Kelley *(VP-Fin)*
Kate Leverette *(VP-Mktg)*
Bob Little *(VP-Sls)*
Chip Polston *(VP-Comm, Govt & PR)*
Church Saufley *(VP-HR)*
Larry Newby *(Dir-Plng & Res)*
Larry Smith *(Dir-Ops)*
Darrell Wilson *(Dir-Pur)*
Edie Frakes *(Mgr-Mktg)*
Brands & Products:
ANNIVERSARY CASH
ANTE UP
AZTEC GOLD
BANKROLL DOUBLER
BEDAZZLED - 2
BEE LUCKY
BIG BLAZIN' BUCKS
BIG MONEY
BIG MONEY DOUBLER
BINGO II
BIRTHSTONES
BLAZIN' BUCKS
BLAZIN' HOT BUCKS
BLAZIN' RED HOT BUCKS
BLING ME THE MONEY
BLOCKBUSTER CASH
BLUE MOON BUCKS
BREAK THE BANK
CASH CELEBRATION
CASH EXTRAVAGANZA
CASINO RICHES
CHERRY TRIPLER
COOKOUT CASH
COOL CASH DOUBLER
DIGGIN' FOR DOLLARS
DREAMIN' FOR DOLLARS
DUCK BILLS
FABULOUS FORTUNE
GOLD BAR BONANZA
HAND ME THE MONEY
HOLIDAY TREATS
IN THE MONEY
KENTUCKY CASHBALL
KENTUCKY LOTTERY
LINE 'EM UP
LUCKY NUMBERS
MEGA CASH II
MERRY WOOFMAS
MOO-LAH MONEY
PIRATE'S GOLD
POCKET FOLDING MONEY
THE PRICE IS RIGHT
RUBY RICHES
SAFE CRACKER
SHAMROCK SHUFFLE
SLEIGH ME THE MONEY
TREASURE TREE

KISSIMMEE-ST. CLOUD CONVENTION & VISITORS BUREAU
1925 E Irlo Bronson Memorial Hwy
Kissimmee, FL 34744-4413
Tel.: (407) 742-8200
Fax: (407) 742-8226
Toll Free: (800) 831-1844
E-mail: media@floridakiss.com
Web Site: www.visitkissimmee.com
Sales Range: $10-24.9 Million
Approx. Number Employees: 32
Business Description:
Convention & Visitors Bureau
S.I.C.: 7389
N.A.I.C.S.: 561591
Advertising Expenditures: $7,000,000
Media: 2-3-4-6-7-8-9-10-13-15-18-20-22-25
Personnel:
Shelly Maccini *(Dir)*

LAS VEGAS CONVENTION & VISITORS AUTHORITY
3150 Paradise Rd
Las Vegas, NV 89109
Tel.: (702) 892-0711
Fax: (702) 892-2824
E-mail: visitors@lasvegas.com
Web Site: www.lvcva.com
Approx. Rev.: $168,352,692
Approx. Number Employees: 400
Year Founded: 1955
Business Description:
Convention & Visitors Bureau
S.I.C.: 7389
N.A.I.C.S.: 561591
Advertising Expenditures: $59,059,994
Media: 2-3-5-6-7-9-10-11-13-14-15-16-18-20-22-23-24
Distr.: Intl.; Natl.
Budget Set: May
Personnel:
Rossi T. Ralenkotter *(Pres & CEO)*
Terry Jicinsky *(Sr VP-Ops)*
Cathy Tull *(Sr VP-Mktg)*
Vince Alberta *(VP-PR)*
Chris Meyer *(VP-Sls)*
Brig Lawson *(Dir-Bus Partnerships)*
Advertising Agencies:
R&R Partners
900 S Pavilion Center Dr
Las Vegas, NV 89144
Tel.: (702) 228-0222
Fax: (702) 939-4383
Las Vegas Tourism
What Happens Here, Stays Here Campaign
— Billy Vassiliadis *(Pres.)*
— Rob Dondero *(Acct. Supvr.)*

Rooster Creative
The Chandlery 50 Westminster Bridge Rd
London, SE1 7QY, United Kingdom
Tel.: (44) 20 7953 8774
Fax: (44) 20 7953 8780
Consumer Public Relations

LIBRARY OF CONGRESS
101 Independence Ave SE
Washington, DC 20540
Tel.: (202) 707-5000
Tel.: (202) 707-2905 (Pub Affairs)
Fax: (202) 707-1714
E-mail: pao@loc.gov
Web Site: www.loc.gov
Approx. Rev.: $607,800,000
Approx. Number Employees: 5,000
Business Description:
Federal Library
S.I.C.: 8231
N.A.I.C.S.: 519120
Media: 9-10-23-25
Personnel:
James H. Billington *(CEO & Corp Librarian)*
Advertising Agency:
Adworks, Inc.
1225 19th St NW Ste 500
Washington, DC 20036
Tel.: (202) 342-5585
Fax: (202) 739-8201

LOS ANGELES CONVENTION & VISITORS BUREAU
333 S Hope St 18th Fl
Los Angeles, CA 90071
Tel.: (213) 624-7300
Fax: (213) 624-9746
Toll Free: (800) 228-2452
Web Site: www.lacvb.com
Sales Estimate: $20-39 Million
Approx. Number Employees: 75
Business Description:
Convention & Visitors Bureau
S.I.C.: 7389
N.A.I.C.S.: 561591
Media: 2-4-6-9-10-13-18-20-22-23-24-25
Distr.: Natl.
Budget Set: June
Personnel:
Mark S. Liberman *(Pres & CEO)*
Stefan J. Dietrich *(CFO & Sr VP)*
Michael Collins *(Exec VP)*
Patti MacJennett *(Sr VP-Mktg)*
Diane G. Krueger *(VP-HR)*
Robert Thibault *(VP-Mktg)*

LOUISIANA DEPARTMENT OF ECONOMIC DEVELOPMENT
Capitol Annex 1051 N 3rd St
Baton Rouge, LA 70802
Mailing Address:
PO Box 94185
Baton Rouge, LA 70804-9185
Tel.: (225) 342-3000
Fax: (225) 342-5389
Toll Free: (800) 450-8115
E-mail: webmaster@lded.state.la.us
Web Site: www.lded.state.la.us
Sales Estimate: $20-39 Million
Approx. Number Employees: 100

Key to Media (For complete agency information see *The Advertising Red Books-Agencies* edition):
1. Bus. Publs. 2. Cable T.V. 3. Catalogs & Directories. 4. Co-op Adv. 5. Consumer Mags. 6. D.M. to Bus. Estab.7. D.M. to Consumers 8. Daily Newsp. 9. Exhibits/Trade Shows 10. Foreign 11. Infomercial 12. Internet Adv.13. Multimedia 14. Network Radio 15. Network T.V. 16. Newsp. Distr. Mags. 17. Other 18. Outdoor (Posters, Transit) 19. Point of Purchase20. Premiums, Novelties 21. Product Samples 22. Special Events Mktg. 23. Spot Radio 24. Spot T.V. 25. Weekly Newsp. 26. Yellow Page Adv.

Year Founded: 1996
Business Description:
Promoter of Commercial & Industrial Development in the State of Louisiana
S.I.C.: 9611
N.A.I.C.S.: 926110
Advertising Expenditures: $1,200,000
Media: 2-11-23
Distr.: Intl.; Natl.
Budget Set: Oct.
Personnel:
Larry Collins *(Dir-Intl Svcs)*
Skip Smart *(Dir-Community Dev)*
Melissa Lambert *(Mgr-Digital Mktg)*

LOUISIANA LOTTERY CORPORATION
555 Laurel St
Baton Rouge, LA 70801
Tel.: (225) 297-2000
Fax: (225) 297-2222
Web Site: www.louisianalottery.com
Approx. Rev.: $308,547,873
Approx. Number Employees: 145
Year Founded: 1991
Business Description:
State Lottery
S.I.C.: 9311; 7999
N.A.I.C.S.: 921130; 713290
Advertising Expenditures: $7,000,000
Media: 1-2-3-9-14-15-18-19-20-23-24-25
Distr.: Reg.
Personnel:
Rose J. Hudson *(Pres & CEO)*
John Carruth *(Gen Counsel & Sr VP)*
Charles Armstrong *(VP-Security)*
Bonny Botts *(VP-Mktg & PR)*
Brian Darouse *(VP-MIS)*
Jimmy Goodrum *(VP-Fin)*
Kimberly Chopin *(Mgr-Comm)*
Brands & Products:
5-STAR
BEE LUCKY
CASH BLOCKBUSTER
CASH QUEST
CASH STASH
COOL 7'S
CRAWFISH CASH
DIAMOND DASH
FAST JACKS
HOT SPOT SUMMER
IN THE CHIPS
JESTER'S WILD
LEMON TWIST
LOTTO
LOUISIANA LOTTERY
NEON 9'S
PICK 3
PICK 4
POWERBALL
POWERBALL INSTANT MILLIONAIRE
SUPER-DUPER CROSSWORD
Advertising Agency:
The Graham Group
11505 Perkins Rd Bldg 3 Ste 3
Baton Rouge, LA 70810
Tel.: (225) 767-8520
Fax: (225) 761-0870
(Media Placement)

LOUISIANA OFFICE OF TOURISM
1051 N 3rd St
Baton Rouge, LA 70802
Tel.: (225) 342-8100
Tel.: (225) 342-8119
Fax: (225) 342-1051
Toll Free: (800) 677-4082
E-mail: freeinfo@crt.state.la.us
Web Site: www.louisianatravel.com
E-Mail For Key Personnel:
Marketing Director: ibabin@crt.state.la.us
Public Relations: bmorgan@crt.state.la.us
Approx. Number Employees: 27
Business Description:
State Tourism Board
S.I.C.: 9621; 9611
N.A.I.C.S.: 926120; 926110
Advertising Expenditures: $500,000
Media: 6-9-13-15-23-24
Distr.: Intl.
Personnel:
Ira Babin *(Dir-Mktg)*
Seth Harving *(Dir-Commun)*
Janis LeBourgeois *(Mgr-Admin)*
Jack Warner *(Asst Sec)*
Advertising Agencies:
bozeken, LLC
110 W Lancaster Ave Ste 130
Wayne, PA 19087
Tel.: (610) 293-2200
Fax: (610) 293-2201

GMc+Company
365 Canal St Ste 2950
New Orleans, LA 70130
Tel.: (504) 524-8117
Fax: (504) 523-7068

LOUISVILLE CONVENTION & VISITORS BUREAU
(Formerly Greater Louisville Convention & Visitors Bureau)
401 W Main St Ste 2300
Louisville, KY 40202
Tel.: (502) 584-2121
Fax: (502) 561-3120
Toll Free: (800) 626-5646
E-mail: info@gotolouisville.com
Web Site: www.gotolouisville.com
Approx. Number Employees: 60
Year Founded: 1968
Business Description:
Convention & Visitors Bureau
S.I.C.: 7389
N.A.I.C.S.: 561591
Advertising Expenditures: $500,000
Media: 1-2-3-4-6-9-10-18-20-23-25
Distr.: Natl.
Budget Set: Oct.
Personnel:
James Wood *(Pres & CEO)*
Karen Williams *(Exec VP)*
Chris Kipper *(VP-Fin & Admin)*
Stacey Yates *(VP-Mktg Comm)*
Randy James *(Dir-IT)*
Cinnamon Jawor *(Dir-Convention Svcs)*
Peggy Riley *(Dir-Multicultural Sls)*
Nichole Twigg *(Dir-Tourism)*
Angi Van Berg *(Dir-Convention Dev)*
Robin Vanzant *(Dir-Fin & Admin)*
Karen Wallace *(Dir-Housing Svcs)*
Susan Sauer *(Sr Mgr-Religious Sls)*
Joanie Allgeier *(Mgr-Adv Sls)*
Susan Dallas *(Mgr-Comm)*
Rita Edmonds *(Mgr-Registration Svcs)*
Lisa LeCompte *(Mgr-Natl Sls)*
Connie Phelps *(Mgr-Fin & Admin)*
Nancy A. Stephen *(Mgr-Comm)*
Harry Young *(Mgr-Housing Svcs)*
Advertising Agencies:
Bandy Carroll Hellige Advertising
307 W Muhammad Ali Blvd
Louisville, KY 40202
Tel.: (502) 589-7711
Fax: (502) 589-0390

Red7e
637 W Main St
Louisville, KY 40202-2987
Tel.: (502) 585-3403
Fax: (502) 582-2043
Toll Free: (800) 656-7272

MAINE BUREAU OF ALOCHOLIC BEVERAGES & LOTTERY OPERATIONS
(d/b/a Maine State Lottery)
10 Water St
Hallowell, ME 04347
Tel.: (207) 287-3721
Fax: (207) 287-6769
Toll Free: (800) 452-8777
E-mail: info@mainelottery.com
Web Site: www.mainelottery.com
Sales Range: $200-249.9 Million
Approx. Number Employees: 23
Year Founded: 1974
Business Description:
State Lottery & Alcohol Regulation Administrative Services
S.I.C.: 9311; 7999; 9651
N.A.I.C.S.: 921130; 713290; 926150
Advertising Expenditures: $2,600,000
Media: 19-22-23-24
Distr.: Direct to Consumer; Reg.
Budget Set: June
Personnel:
Lisa Rodrique *(Dir-Adv)*
Rich Sperlazzi *(Mgr-Mktg)*
Advertising Agency:
NL Partners
20 York St Ste 201
Portland, ME 04101
Tel.: (207) 775-5251
Fax: (207) 775-3389

MAINE DEPARTMENT OF ECONOMIC & COMMUNITY DEVELOPMENT
59 State House Sta
Augusta, ME 04333-0059
Tel.: (207) 624-9800
Fax: (207) 287-8461
E-mail: biz.growth@state.me.us
Web Site: www.econdevmaine.com
Approx. Number Employees: 47
Year Founded: 1987
Business Description:
State Economic & Commercial Development Administrative Services
S.I.C.: 9611
N.A.I.C.S.: 926110
Media: 2-3-4-5-6-7-8-9-10-13-18-19-20-22-23-24-25
Distr.: Natl.
Budget Set: July -Aug.
Personnel:
Lea Girardin *(Dir-Maine Film Office)*
Advertising Agency:
Nancy Marshall Communications
20 W Ave PO Box 317
Augusta, ME 04332
Tel.: (207) 623-4177
Fax: (207) 623-4178

MAINE OFFICE OF TOURISM
59 State House Sta
Augusta, ME 04333-0059
Tel.: (207) 287-5711
Fax: (207) 287-8070
Toll Free: (888) 624-6345
E-mail: info@visitmaine.com
Web Site: www.visitmaine.com
Approx. Number Employees: 10
Business Description:
Tourism Promotion
S.I.C.: 9611
N.A.I.C.S.: 926110
Advertising Expenditures: $1,800,000
Media: 3-5-6-9-10-15-18-23-24-25
Distr.: Natl.; Reg.
Personnel:
Pat Eltman *(Dir-Tourism)*
Brands & Products:
IT MUST BE MAINE
MAINE
THERE'S MORE TO MAINE
Advertising Agency:
Nancy Marshall Communications
20 W Ave PO Box 317
Augusta, ME 04332
Tel.: (207) 623-4177
Fax: (207) 623-4178

MANATEE CHAMBER OF COMMERCE
222 10th St W
Bradenton, FL 34206
Tel.: (941) 748-3411
Fax: (941) 745-1877
E-mail: info@manateechamber.com
Web Site: www.manateechamber.com
Sales Range: $25-49.9 Million
Approx. Number Employees: 20
Business Description:
Commercial Administrative Services
S.I.C.: 9651
N.A.I.C.S.: 926150
Media: 2-7-10-22-24
Personnel:
Bob Bartz *(Pres)*
Cheryl Richert *(Controller-Fin)*
Karen Jones *(Dir-Comm)*
Jahna Leinhauser *(Mgr-Commity Dev)*
Tina West *(Mgr-Better Bus Council)*

MARYLAND OFFICE OF TOURISM DEVELOPMENT
World Trade Ctr 401 Pratt St
Baltimore, MD 21202
Tel.: (410) 767-3400
Fax: (410) 333-6643
Toll Free: (800) MDISFUN
E-mail: info@mdisfun.org
Web Site: www.mdisfun.org
Approx. Number Employees: 59
Business Description:
Tourism Promoter
S.I.C.: 9611; 4729; 9199
N.A.I.C.S.: 926110; 561599; 921190
Advertising Expenditures: $2,820,642
Media: 3-4-5-6-13-17-22-24
Personnel:
Liz Fitzsimmons *(Exec Dir)*
Denise Konopacki *(Asst Dir)*
Marci Ross *(Asst Dir)*
Rich Gilbert *(Sr Mgr-Sls & Mktg)*
Anne Kyle *(Mgr-Product Dev)*
Kat Evans *(Coord-Traffic)*

MARYLAND STATE LOTTERY
1800 Washington Blvd Ste 330
Baltimore, MD 21230

Key to Media (For complete agency information see *The Advertising Red Books-Agencies* edition):
1. Bus. Publs. 2. Cable T.V. 3. Catalogs & Directories. 4. Co-op Adv. 5. Consumer Mags. 6. D.M. to Bus. Estab.7. D.M. to Consumers 8. Daily Newsp. 9. Exhibits/Trade Shows 10. Foreign 11. Infomercial 12. Internet Adv.13. Multimedia 14. Network Radio 15. Network T.V. 16. Newsp. Distr. Mags. 17. Other 18. Outdoor (Posters, Transit) 19. Point of Purchase20. Premiums, Novelties 21. Product Samples 22. Special Events Mktg. 23. Spot Radio 24. Spot T.V. 25. Weekly Newsp. 26. Yellow Page Adv.

Maryland State Lottery — (Continued)

Tel.: (410) 230-8990
Tel.: (410) 230-8790
Fax: (410) 230-8727
Toll Free: (800) 388-1333
E-mail: paffairs@msla.state.md.us
Web Site: www.mdlottery.com
Approx. Sls.: $1,395,000,000
Approx. Number Employees: 150
Year Founded: 1973
Business Description:
State Lottery Services
S.I.C.: 9311
N.A.I.C.S.: 921130
Media: 3-5-8-9-18-19-23-24-25
Distr.: Reg.
Personnel:
Frank Bonaventure *(Chm)*
Patrick Morton *(Mgr)*
Brands & Products:
CASH BLAST
DEUCES ARE WILD
FILL 'ER UP
GOLDEN GLITTER
KISSES & CASH
LIVIN' LUCKY
MARYLAND STATE LOTTERY
MEGA MILLIONS
MERRY MILLIONS
MULTI-MATCH
ONE-EYED JACKS
PICK 3
PICK 4
PLATINUM REWARDS
POKER ROYALE
RACETRAX
SCRATCH-OFFS
SET FOR LIFE 2
SUNNY MONEY
TIC TAC WILD
WINTER WONDERLAND
YEAR OF THE OX
Advertising Agency:
TBC Inc.
900 S Wolfe St
Baltimore, MD 21231
Tel.: (410) 347-7500
Fax: (410) 986-1299
— Jodi Marsico *(Acct. Exec.)*

MASSACHUSETTS DEPARTMENT OF PUBLIC HEALTH
250 Washington St
Boston, MA 02108
Tel.: (617) 624-6000
Fax: (617) 624-6001
E-mail: john.aurbch@state.ma.us
Web Site: www.state.ma.us
Business Description:
State Health Programs Administrative Services
S.I.C.: 9431
N.A.I.C.S.: 923120
Media: 10-13
Personnel:
John Auerbach *(Commissioner)*
Advertising Agency:
Geovision
75 N Beacon St
Watertown, MA 02472
Tel.: (617) 926-5454
Fax: (617) 925-5411

MASSACHUSETTS OFFICE OF TRAVEL & TOURISM
10 Pk Plz Ste 4510
Boston, MA 02116
Tel.: (617) 973-8500
Fax: (617) 973-8525
Toll Free: (800) 227-MASS
E-mail: vacationinfo@state.ma.us
Web Site: www.massvacation.com
E-Mail For Key Personnel:
Marketing Director: jonathan.hyde@state.ma.us
Sales Range: $10-24.9 Million
Approx. Number Employees: 12
Business Description:
State Tourism Administrative Services
S.I.C.: 7389
N.A.I.C.S.: 561591
Media: 2-5-6-7-9-10-20-23-24-25
Budget Set: June -July
Personnel:
Betsy Wall *(Exec Dir)*
Phillis Cahaly *(Dir-Domestic Mktg)*
Brands & Products:
IT'S ALL HERE
MASSACHUSETTS
WHAT'S HOT FROM MOTT
Advertising Agency:
Connelly Partners
46 Waltham St Fl 4
Boston, MA 02118
Tel.: (617) 956-5050
Fax: (617) 956-5054

MASSACHUSETTS STATE LOTTERY
60 Columbian St
Braintree, MA 02184-7342
Tel.: (781) 849-5555
Fax: (781) 849-5509
E-mail: webmaster@masslottery.com
Web Site: www.masslottery.com
Approx. Sls.: $4,482,911,000
Approx. Number Employees: 420
Year Founded: 1971
Business Description:
State Lottery Services
S.I.C.: 9311
N.A.I.C.S.: 921130
Advertising Expenditures: $1,079,000
Media: 1-3-5-9-19-20-23-24-25
Distr.: Reg.
Budget Set: July
Personnel:
Mark Cavanagh *(Exec Dir)*
Brands & Products:
BAH HUMBUCKS
BREAK THE BANK
CAESARS PALACE
CASH BLIZZARD
CASH EXPRESS
CASH ROULETTE
CASH WINFALL
CLOVER CASH
DECK THE HALLS
DUBLIN DOLLARS
FROSTY THE DOUGHMAN
FROSTY'S FORTUNE
HALLO-WIN
HEARTS ARE WILD
JINGLE BELL CASH
JUMBO BUCKS
KENO
MAGIC MONEY
MASS CASH
MAX A MILLION
MEGA MILLIONS
MEGABUCKS
MISTLEDOUGH DOUBLER
MONEY BAGS
MONEY MINE
ONE-EYED JACK
PHAROAH'S GOLD
PHOTO FINISH
PINBALL WIZARD
PLATINUM PAYOUT
SET FOR LIFE
SHOOTING STAR
SILVER BELLS
STRIKE IT RICH
SWEETHEART CASH
WILD MILLIONS
WINNER GREEN
WINNER TAKE ALL
Advertising Agency:
Hill Holliday
53 State St
Boston, MA 02109
Tel.: (617) 366-4000

METRO ATLANTA CHAMBER OF COMMERCE
235 Andrew Young International Blvd NW
Atlanta, GA 30303
Mailing Address:
PO Box 1740
Atlanta, GA 30301-1740
Tel.: (404) 880-9000
Fax: (404) 586-8497
Web Site: www.metroatlantachamber.com
Approx. Number Employees: 80
Business Description:
Economic Development Services
S.I.C.: 9651
N.A.I.C.S.: 926150
Advertising Expenditures: $1,000,000
Media: 2-7-11-24
Distr.: Intl.; Natl.
Budget Set: Jan.
Personnel:
Tom Bell *(Chm)*
Sam A. Williams *(Pres)*
Gary Stokan *(Pres-Sports Council)*
Michael Johns *(Exec VP-Health)*
Renay Blumenthal *(Sr VP-Quality Life)*
Esther E. Campi *(Sr VP-Comm)*
Hans Gant *(Sr VP)*
Janice Rys *(Sr VP)*
Matt Garvey *(VP-Comm)*
David Hartnett *(VP-Economic Dev)*
Tanya Dunne *(Dir-Comm)*
Ricardo E. Hubler *(Dir-Global Bus Growth)*
Matthew Patterson *(Sr Bus Dev Mgr)*
Karen Holladay *(Project Mgr-Global Commerce)*
Chanta Seymore Waller *(Coord-Comm)*

METROPOLITAN TUCSON CONVENTION & VISITORS BUREAU
100 S Church Ave
Tucson, AZ 85701-1631
Tel.: (520) 624-1817
Fax: (520) 884-7804
Toll Free: (800) 638-8350
E-mail: info@visittucson.org
Web Site: www.visittucson.org
Sales Range: Less than $1 Million
Approx. Number Employees: 40
Year Founded: 1982
Business Description:
Convention & Visitors Bureau
S.I.C.: 7389
N.A.I.C.S.: 561591
Advertising Expenditures: $250,000
Media: 2-3-4-5-6-7-8-9-10-13-15-18-22-23-24-25
Distr.: Natl.
Budget Set: July
Personnel:
Jonathan Walker *(Pres & CEO)*
Vicki Doyle *(VP-Partner Dev & Visitor Svcs)*
Richard Vaughan *(Sr VP-Sls-Mktg)*
Jose Felipe Garcia *(VP-Community Affairs & Mktg-Mexico)*
Shelli Hall *(Dir-Film Office)*
April Bourie *(Mgr-Tourism Sls)*
Joy Johnson *(Mgr-Sls-Natl)*
Martha Tadlock *(Mgr-Mexico Mktg)*
Pamela Traficanti *(Mgr-Natl Sls-Arizona, Nevada, New Mexico & Western Texas)*
Laurie J. White *(Mgr-Partner Svcs)*

MEXICAN GOVERNMENT TOURISM OFFICES
375 Park Ave Ste 1905
New York, NY 10152
Tel.: (212) 308-2110
Fax: (212) 308-9060
Toll Free: (800) 446-3942
E-mail: newyork@visitmexico.com
Web Site: www.visitmexico.com
Sales Estimate: $5-9.9 Million
Approx. Number Employees: 10
Year Founded: 1930
Business Description:
Tourism Administrative Services
S.I.C.: 7389
N.A.I.C.S.: 561591
Media: 1-2-6-8-18-22-23-24-26
Distr.: Intl.; Natl.
Personnel:
Gabriela Ibarra *(Dir)*

MEXICO TOURISM BOARD
(Branch of Mexican Government Tourism Offices)
2401 W 6th St
Los Angeles, CA 90057
Tel.: (213) 739-6336
Fax: (213) 739-6340
Toll Free: (800) 44-MEXICO
E-mail: losangeles@visitmexico.com
Web Site: www.visitmexico.com
E-Mail For Key Personnel:
Marketing Director: CRamirez@visitmexico.com
Sales Director: HNajera@visitmexico.com
Sales Estimate: $1-4.9 Million
Approx. Number Employees: 3
Business Description:
Tourism Administrative Services
S.I.C.: 7389
N.A.I.C.S.: 561591
Media: 6-9-23-24
Budget Set: Oct. -Nov.
Personnel:
Jorge Gamboa *(Dir)*
Laura Lopez *(Dir-Media)*
Clara Torres Marquez *(Dir-PR)*

Key to Media (For complete agency information see *The Advertising Red Books-Agencies* edition):
1. Bus. Publs. 2. Cable T.V. 3. Catalogs & Directories. 4. Co-op Adv. 5. Consumer Mags. 6. D.M. to Bus. Estab.7. D.M. to Consumers 8. Daily Newsp. 9. Exhibits/Trade Shows 10. Foreign 11. Infomercial 12. Internet Adv.13. Multimedia 14. Network Radio 15. Network T.V. 16. Newsp. Distr. Mags. 17. Other 18. Outdoor (Posters, Transit) 19. Point of Purchase20. Premiums, Novelties 21. Product Samples 22. Special Events Mktg. 23. Spot Radio 24. Spot T.V. 25. Weekly Newsp. 26. Yellow Page Adv.

THE MICHIGAN ECONOMIC DEVELOPMENT CORPORATION, TOURISM & MARKETING

300 N Washington Sq
Lansing, MI 48913
Tel.: (517) 373-9808
Fax: (517) 373-0059
Toll Free: (888) 522-0103
E-mail: travelmichigan@state.mi.us
Web Site: www.michigan.org
Approx. Number Employees: 28
Year Founded: 1973
Business Description:
Michigan Vacation Travel Advertising & Promotion
S.I.C.: 9611
N.A.I.C.S.: 926110
Advertising Expenditures: $8,000,000
Media: 4-6-9-10-19-24
Distr.: Reg.
Personnel:
Gregory Main *(Pres & CEO)*
Minesh Mody *(CFO)*
Douglas Parks *(Sr VP-New Market Dev)*
Jeff Mason *(Sr VP)*
Elizabeth Parkinson *(Sr VP-Mktg & Comm)*
Donald E. Snider *(Sr VP-Urban Economic Dev)*
Joseph Serwach *(Dir-Comm)*
Harry C. Whalen *(Dir-Bus Dev-Intl)*
Robert Yakushi *(Dir-Product Safety)*

MICHIGAN STATE LOTTERY BUREAU

101 E Hillsdale
Lansing, MI 48933-0001
Tel.: (517) 335-5600
Fax: (517) 335-5651
E-mail: milottery@Michigan.com
Web Site: www.michigan.gov
Approx. Sls.: $2,000,000,000
Approx. Number Employees: 190
Year Founded: 1972
Business Description:
State Lottery Services
S.I.C.: 9311; 7999
N.A.I.C.S.: 921130; 713290
Advertising Expenditures: $18,000,000
Media: 2-9-14-15-16-18-19-20-22-23-25
Distr.: Reg.
Budget Set: Oct.
Personnel:
Tom Weber *(Dir-Mktg)*
Brands & Products:
BETTY BOOP
THE BIG KAHUNA
BONE SHAKIN' RICHES
CINEMA CASH
CLASSIC LOTTO 47
DAILY 3
DAILY 4
DOUBLE WHAMMY
FANTASY 5
GAMES GALORE
GRAND GIVEAWAY
HOLLY JOLLY
KENO
MEGA MILLIONS
MICHIGAN LOTTERY
THE THREE STOOGES
UNO, DOS, SCRATCH
VEGAS BOULEVARD
ZODIAC CASHWORD
Advertising Agency:
Simons Michelson Zieve, Inc.
900 Wilshire Dr Ste 102
Troy, MI 48084-1634
Tel.: (248) 362-4242
Fax: (248) 362-2014
Michigan State Lottery Bureau
— Pam Renusch *(VP & Mngmt Supvr)*

MINNESOTA DEPARTMENT OF EMPLOYMENT AND ECONOMIC DEVELOPMENT

332 Minnesota St Ste E200
Saint Paul, MN 55101-1351
Tel.: (651) 297-4222
Tel.: (651) 297-1291
Fax: (651) 296-3555
Toll Free: (800) 657-3858
E-mail: deed.customerservice@state.mn.us
Web Site: www.positivelyminnesota.com
Approx. Number Employees: 25
Year Founded: 1983
Business Description:
International Trade & Investment
S.I.C.: 9611
N.A.I.C.S.: 926110
Media: 2-9-10-22-26
Distr.: Intl.; Natl.
Budget Set: June
Personnel:
Dan McElroy *(Pres & CEO-Hospitality Minnesota)*
Kirsten Morrell *(Dir-Commun)*

MINNESOTA OFFICE OF TOURISM

100 Metro Sq 121 7th Pl E
Saint Paul, MN 55101
Tel.: (651) 296-5029
Fax: (651) 296-7095
Toll Free: (800) 657-3700
E-mail: explore@state.mn.us
Web Site: www.exploreminnesota.com
Approx. Number Employees: 40
Business Description:
Tourism Promotion
S.I.C.: 9611
N.A.I.C.S.: 926110
Advertising Expenditures: $3,000,000
Media: 1-3-4-5-6-8-9-10-23-24
Distr.: Natl.
Personnel:
Leann Kispert *(Sr Mgr-Mktg & Res)*
Bob Erler *(Mgr-Adv & Tourism Mktg)*
Brands & Products:
EXPLORE MINNESOTA

MINNESOTA STATE LOTTERY

2645 Long Lk Rd
Roseville, MN 55113-2533
Tel.: (651) 635-8100
Fax: (651) 297-7496
E-mail: lottery@mnlottery.com
Web Site: www.mnlottery.com
Approx. Number Employees: 180
Year Founded: 1989
Business Description:
State Lottery Services
S.I.C.: 9311
N.A.I.C.S.: 921130
Advertising Expenditures: $7,550,392
Media: 9-18-19-23-24
Personnel:
John Mellein *(Dir-Mktg & Sls)*
Brands & Products:
$100,000 TREASURE HUNT
$200,000 MEGA SLOTS
$500,000 CASH BLOWOUT
$500,000 CASH EXPLOSION
$500,000 HIGH ROLLER
BORDER BATTLES
CASH FIREWORKS
DAILY 3
DOGGIE DOUGH DOUBLER
DOUBLE BONUS CROSSWORD
FISHIN' FOR FORTUNE
GOPHER 5
HIT THE JACKPOT
HOT HAND
HOT LOTTO
LUCKY LINES
MEGA MONOPOLY
MINNESOTA STATE LOTTERY
MINNESOTA TWINS
NORTHSTAR CASH
PINK PANTHER
POWER PLAY
POWERBALL
POWERBALL INSTANT MILLIONAIRE
PRINT-N-PLAY
PRINT-N-PLAY TEE IT UP
SAPPHIRE BLUE 5'S
SCRATCH GAMES
SPICY 7'S
WPT TEXAS HOLD 'EM
Advertising Agency:
OLSON
1625 Hennepin Ave
Minneapolis, MN 55403
Tel.: (612) 215-9800
Fax: (612) 215-9801

MISSISSIPPI DEVELOPMENT AUTHORITY

501 NW St
Jackson, MS 39201-1008
Tel.: (601) 359-3449
Fax: (601) 359-2832
Toll Free: (800) 222-8311
Toll Free: (800) 647-2290
E-mail: info@mississippi.org
Web Site: www.mississippi.org
Approx. Number Employees: 600
Year Founded: 1936
Business Description:
State Economic & Community Development Agency
S.I.C.: 9611; 9532
N.A.I.C.S.: 926110; 925120
Advertising Expenditures: $200,000
Media: 1-2-3-4-6-8-9-10-11-12-18-20-22-23-24-25
Distr.: Intl.; Natl.
Budget Set: July
Personnel:
Joseph P. Deason *(CFO)*
Melissa Medley *(CMO)*
Stacey Morrison *(Creative Dir)*
Sandy Bynum *(Dir-Adv)*
Whit Hughes *(Dir-Economic Dev)*
Cindy McKey *(Dir-HR)*
Barbara Pepper *(Dir-Ops Div)*
Craig Ray *(Dir-Tourism Dev)*
Griff Salmon *(Dir-Global Bus Div)*
Richard Speights *(Dir-Minority & Small Bus Dev)*
Bill Webb *(Reg Mgr)*
Taunya Smith *(Sr Mgr-Fin)*
Ken Johnston *(Project Mgr)*
Gena Lentz *(Project Mgr)*
Hal Sibley *(Project Mgr)*
Sheron Anderson *(Mgr-Property & Records)*
Valerie Crout *(Mgr-Existing Industry & Bus)*
Jack Curry *(Mgr-Indus Assistance)*
Marsha Hamilton *(Mgr-Intl Rep)*
Carol Harris *(Mgr-Minority & Small Bus Dev)*
Lucy Hetrick *(Assoc Mgr-Sr Adv Publications)*
Dana Jones *(Assoc Mgr-Fin)*
Michael Jones *(Program Mgr-Outdoor)*
Janet Leach *(Program Mgr-Sports Golf Mktg)*
Joey Roberts *(Mgr-Bureau)*
Brands & Products:
HOMETOWN MISSISSIPPI RETIREMENT
MISSISSIPPI
MISSISSIPPI. FEELS LIKE COMING HOME
Advertising Agencies:
Frontier Strategies LLC
529 Pear Orchard Rd Ste C
Ridgeland, MS 39157
Tel.: (601) 856-1544
Fax: (601) 856-1625

The Ramey Agency
1322 Hardwood Trail
Cordova, TN 38016
Tel.: (901) 761-3685
Fax: (901) 761-3688

The Ramey Agency LLC
3100 N State St Ste 300
Jackson, MS 39216
Tel.: (601) 898-8900
Fax: (601) 898-8999
Toll Free: (800) 594-0754
(Business/Industry Location, Travel & Tourism Retirement)

MISSOURI LOTTERY

1823 Southridge Dr
Jefferson City, MO 65109-5645
Tel.: (573) 751-4050
Fax: (573) 751-5188
E-mail: webmail@molottery.com
Web Site: www.molottery.com
E-Mail For Key Personnel:
President: scrogi@exec.molot.com
Marketing Director: halla@mkt.molot.com
Sales Director: stockm@mkt.molot.com
Public Relations: gondeg@molottery.com
Sales Range: $25-49.9 Million
Approx. Number Employees: 160
Year Founded: 1985
Business Description:
State Lottery Services
S.I.C.: 9311; 7999
N.A.I.C.S.: 921130; 713290
Advertising Expenditures: $8,249,500
Daily Newsp.: $300,500; Other: $1,743,000; Outdoor (Posters, Transit): $291,000; Spot Radio: $2,334,000; Spot T.V.: $3,581,000
Distr.: Direct to Consumer; Reg.
Personnel:
Gary Gonder *(Dir-Integrated Svcs)*
Nancy Rollins *(Mgr-Mktg)*

Key to Media (For complete agency information see *The Advertising Red Books-Agencies* edition):
1. Bus. Publs. 2. Cable T.V. 3. Catalogs & Directories. 4. Co-op Adv. 5. Consumer Mags. 6. D.M. to Bus. Estab.7. D.M. to Consumers 8. Daily Newsp. 9. Exhibits/Trade Shows 10. Foreign 11. Infomercial 12. Internet Adv.13. Multimedia 14. Network Radio 15. Network T.V. 16. Newsp. Distr. Mags. 17. Other 18. Outdoor (Posters, Transit) 19. Point of Purchase20. Premiums, Novelties 21. Product Samples 22. Special Events Mktg. 23. Spot Radio 24. Spot T.V. 25. Weekly Newsp. 26. Yellow Page Adv.

Missouri Lottery — (Continued)

Brands & Products:
100 MILLION DOLLAR BLOCKBUSTER
$100,000 PAYDAY
$100,000 RICHES
$100,000 VEGAS MONEY
$200,000 A YEAR FOR LIFE
24K
$25,000 BANKROLL
$25,000 CASH VAULT
$250,000 MEGA CASH
$300,000 CASH SPECTACULAR
$300,000 CASINO NIGHTS
$300,000 CASINO THRILLS
$300,000 CLUB CASINO
$300,000 FORTUNE
$300,000 MEGA MONEY
$300,000 PAYOUT
4 MILLION DOLLAR CASH BONANZA
$500,000 CASH SPECTACULAR
5X LUCKY
7-11-21
ACE IN THE HOLE
AMAZING 8'S
BIG MONEY
CASH EXPLOSION
CASH ON THE SPOT
CLUB KENO
COOL CASH
CRAZY 8'S
CROSSWORD
DEUCES WILD
DIAMOND BINGO
DIAMOND DOLLARS
DOUBLE DOLLARS
DOUBLING 8'S
DREAM STAKES
EMERALD GREEN 8'S
FAST CASH
FISTFUL OF $50S
FISTFUL OF DOLLARS
HIGH STAKES
HOLIDAY JACK
HOT SLOTS
JINGLE BELL BINGO
LEPRECHAUN LUCK
LIFETIME RICHES
LOST TREASURE ADVENTURE
LOTS OF LUCK
LOTTO
LUCKY 7S
LUCKY 7S BINGO
LUCKY BUCKS
LUCKY DOG
LUCKY DOUGH
LUCKY GOLD
LUCKY HEARTS
MEGA MONOPOLY
MERRY MONEY
MISSOURI LOTTERY
MONEY STACK
MONTE CARLO
NIFTY $50'S
PICK 3
PICK 4
PICTURE PERFECT BINGO
POWERBALL
PULL-TABS
QUICK 7S
RED HOT CASH
RED HOT CHERRIES
RING IN THE HOLIDAYS
SAPPHIRE BLUE 7S
SCARY CASH
SCARY MONEY
SCRATCHERS
SHOW ME 5 PAYDOWN
SHOW ME CASH
SIZZLIN' 7'S
SPICY 7'S
STARS AND STRIPES
SUPER 7'S
SUPER CASH
SUPER MONOPOLY
SUPER RUBY RED 7S
TAX PAID 20 GRAND
TIC TAC DOUGH
TRIPLE BANKROLL
TRIPLE BINGO
TRIPLE CASH
TRIPLE DOUGH
TRIPLE FORTUNE
TRIPLE MONEYBAGS
TRIPLE WIN
VIVA LAS VEGAS
WEEKLY $1000 PAYDAY
WILD 8'S

MONTANA LOTTERY

2525 N Montana Ave
Helena, MT 59601-0511
Tel.: (406) 444-5825
Fax: (406) 444-5830
E-mail: montanalottery@mail.com
Web Site: www.montanalottery.com
Sales Range: $25-49.9 Million
Approx. Number Employees: 33
Year Founded: 1987
Business Description:
State Lottery
S.I.C.: 9311; 7999
N.A.I.C.S.: 921130; 713290
Advertising Expenditures: $400,000
Media: 9-17-18-19-23-24-25
Distr.: Direct to Consumer; Reg.
Personnel:
Robert L. Crippen *(Chm)*
Jeri Duran *(Dir-Sls & Mktg)*
John Tarr *(Asst Dir-Security)*
Laurie Felch *(Mgr-Online & Creative Svcs)*
Brands & Products:
FOR THE FUN OF IT
HOT LOTTO
MONTANA CASH
MONTANA LOTTERY
POWERBALL
SCRATCH
WILD CARD
Advertising Agency:
Banik Communications
121 4th St N Ste 1B
Great Falls, MT 59401
Tel.: (406) 454-3422
Fax: (406) 771-1418
Toll Free: (800) 823-3388

NATIONAL AERONAUTICS & SPACE ADMINISTRATION (NASA)

300 E St SW
Washington, DC 20024-3210
Tel.: (202) 358-0000
Fax: (202) 358-4331
Fax: (202) 358-3493
Web Site: www.nasa.gov
Approx. Number Employees: 17,700
Year Founded: 1958
Business Description:
Government Agency for the Adminstration of Space Programs & Aeronautic Research
S.I.C.: 9661
N.A.I.C.S.: 927110
Media: 7-10-22
Personnel:
Terry Bowie *(Acting CFO)*
Deborah Diaz *(Deputy CIO)*
Bryan D. O'Connor *(Chief Safety & Mission Assurance Officer)*
Adena Williams Loston *(Chief Education Officer)*
Gregory D. Blaney *(Dir-Independent Verification & Validation Program-Fairmont)*
Heather Rarick *(Dir-ISS Flight)*
Ron Spencer *(Dir-Flight)*
Michael Ryschkewitsch *(Engr)*

NATIONAL PARK FOUNDATION

1201 Eye St Ste 550B
Washington, DC 20005
Tel.: (202) 354-6460
Fax: (202) 371-2066
Toll Free: (800) 434-9330
E-mail: ask-npf@nationalparks.org
Web Site: www.nationalparks.org
Approx. Number Employees: 37
Year Founded: 1967
Business Description:
National Parks Conservation & Administrative Services
S.I.C.: 7999; 9512
N.A.I.C.S.: 712190; 924120
Media: 6
Personnel:
Neil Mulholland *(Pres & CEO)*
Seleste Regan *(CFO)*
Karen Davis *(Sr VP-Dev)*
Jeniffer Romero *(Coord-Donor Rels)*
Brands & Products:
EGOPARKS
NATIONAL PARK FOUNDATION
Advertising Agency:
BlinnPR
39 W 14th St Ste 506
New York, NY 10011
Tel.: (212) 675-4777
Fax: (212) 675-5557
Public Relations

NEBRASKA DEPARTMENT OF ECONOMIC DEVELOPMENT

301 Centenial Mall S 4th Fl
Lincoln, NE 68509-4666
Tel.: (402) 471-3111
Fax: (402) 471-3778
Toll Free: (800) 426-6505
Web Site: www.neded.org
E-Mail For Key Personnel:
President: rbaier@neded.org
Approx. Number Employees: 75
Year Founded: 1967
Business Description:
Economic Expansion & Tourism for Nebraska
S.I.C.: 9611
N.A.I.C.S.: 926110
Media: 1-2-4-6-9-10-13-14-15-16-18
Distr.: Intl.; Natl.
Budget Set: Oct.
Personnel:
Patricia Wood *(Dir-Mktg & PR)*
Brands & Products:
NEBRASKA
POSSIBILITIES...ENDLESS
Advertising Agency:
Snitily Carr
300 S 68th St Pl
Lincoln, NE 68510
Tel.: (402) 489-2121
Fax: (402) 489-2727

NEBRASKA LOTTERY

1800 O St Ste 101
Lincoln, NE 68508
Tel.: (402) 471-6100
Fax: (402) 471-6108
E-mail: lottery@nelottery.com
Web Site: www.nelottery.com
Sales Range: $10-24.9 Million
Approx. Number Employees: 30
Year Founded: 1993
Business Description:
State Lottery Services
S.I.C.: 7999; 9311
N.A.I.C.S.: 713290; 921130
Advertising Expenditures: $2,500,000
Media: 3-8-9-13-14-15-18-19-20-22-23-24-25
Distr.: Reg.
Budget Set: Mar.
Personnel:
Brian Rockey *(Dir-Lottery Mktg)*
Tom Johnson *(Mgr-Media & Events)*
Jill Marshall *(Mgr-Key Accts)*
Brands & Products:
NEBRASKA 2 BY 2
NEBRASKA LOTTERY
NEBRASKA PICK 3
NEBRASKA PICK 5
POWERBALL
SCRATCH GAMES
Advertising Agency:
Ayres Kahler + Sacco
6800 Normal Blvd
Lincoln, NE 68506-2814
Tel.: (402) 450-7530
Fax: (402) 441-4739
(All)

NETHERLANDS BOARD OF TOURISM

355 Lexington Ave 19th Fl
New York, NY 10017-6603
Tel.: (212) 370-7360
Fax: (212) 370-9507
Toll Free: (888) 464-6552
E-mail: information@holland.com
Web Site: www.holland.com
Sales Estimate: $5-9.9 Million
Approx. Number Employees: 16
Year Founded: 1999
Business Description:
Non-Profit Tourism Promotional & Administrative Services
S.I.C.: 7389
N.A.I.C.S.: 561591
Advertising Expenditures: $100,000
Media: 5-6-7-8-9-10-13-18-22-25
Distr.: Intl.; Natl.
Budget Set: June
Personnel:
Frits Bosch *(Mng Dir-Solutions)*
Hans Driem *(Mng Dir)*
Conrad Van Tiggelen *(Dir-North America)*
Bianca Helderman *(Mgr-Mktg)*
Brigitta Kroon-Fiorita *(Mgr-Media Rels)*
Lex Weststrate *(Mgr-HR)*
Advertising Agency:
cdp-travissully
(A Dentsu Company)
9 Lower John St
London, W1F 9DZ, United Kingdom
Tel.: (44) 207 437 4224
Fax: (44) 207 437 5445

Key to Media (For complete agency information see *The Advertising Red Books-Agencies* edition):
1. Bus. Publs. 2. Cable T.V. 3. Catalogs & Directories. 4. Co-op Adv. 5. Consumer Mags. 6. D.M. to Bus. Estab.7. D.M. to Consumers
8. Daily Newsp. 9. Exhibits/Trade Shows 10. Foreign 11. Infomercial 12. Internet Adv.13. Multimedia 14. Network Radio
15. Network T.V. 16. Newsp. Distr. Mags. 17. Other 18. Outdoor (Posters, Transit) 19. Point of Purchase20. Premiums, Novelties
21. Product Samples 22. Special Events Mktg. 23. Spot Radio 24. Spot T.V. 25. Weekly Newsp. 26. Yellow Page Adv.

NEVADA COMMISSION ON TOURISM

401 N Carson St
Carson City, NV 89701
Tel.: (775) 687-4322
Fax: (775) 687-6779
Toll Free: (800) NEVADA-8
E-mail: ncot@travelnevada.com
Web Site: www.travelnevada.com
Sales Range: $10-24.9 Million
Approx. Number Employees: 30
Year Founded: 1983
Business Description:
Promoter of Tourism to Nevada
S.I.C.: 9199
N.A.I.C.S.: 921190
Advertising Expenditures: $1,200,000
Media: 2-4-6-8-9-18-20-23-24-25-26
Distr.: Natl.
Budget Set: May
Personnel:
Brian K. Krolicki *(Chm)*
Ferenc B. Szony *(Vice Chm)*
Chuck Bowling *(Commissioner)*
Lorraine T. Hunt-Bono *(Commissioner)*
Ellen Oppenheim *(Commissioner)*
Steve Woodbury *(Chief Deputy Officer)*
Jolyn Laney *(Deputy Dir-Mktg)*
Brands & Products:
NEVADA
Advertising Agency:
R&R Partners
615 Riverside Dr
Reno, NV 89503-5601
Tel.: (775) 323-1611
Fax: (775) 323-9021
Public Relations
— Kathy Detwiler *(Dir-Pub Rel)*

NEW HAMPSHIRE LOTTERY COMMISSION

14 Integra Dr
Concord, NH 03301-5102
Mailing Address:
PO Box 1208
Concord, NH 03302-1208
Tel.: (603) 271-3391
Fax: (603) 271-1160
E-mail: webmaster@lottery.nh.gov
Web Site: www.nhlottery.com
Approx. Number Employees: 50
Year Founded: 1963
Business Description:
State Lottery Services
S.I.C.: 9311; 7999
N.A.I.C.S.: 921130; 713290
Media: 23-24-25
Distr.: Reg.
Budget Set: June
Personnel:
Georges Roy *(CFO)*
Kassie Strong *(Accountant)*
Brands & Products:
BONUS SOLITAIRE
BOSTON RED SOX
CASHOLINE
CLOSE TO HOME
FOOTBALL FEVER
HAUNTED FORTUNE
MEGABUCKS
NHLOTTERY
PICK 3
PICK 4
POWERBALL
Advertising Agency:
Griffin York & Krause
121 River Front Dr
Manchester, NH 03102
Tel.: (603) 625-5713
Fax: (603) 222-2329
— Patrick W. Griffin *(Exec. V.P.)*

NEW JERSEY STATE LOTTERY

1 Lawrence Park Complex Brunswick Ave Cir
Lawrenceville, NJ 08648
Tel.: (609) 599-5800
Fax: (609) 599-5935
E-mail: publicinfo@lotterey.state.nj.us
Web Site: www.state.nj.us/lottery/home.shtml
Approx. Sls.: $2,500,000,000
Sales Estimate: $40-59 Million
Approx. Number Employees: 140
Business Description:
State Lottery Commission
S.I.C.: 9311; 7999
N.A.I.C.S.: 921130; 713290
Advertising Expenditures: $7,200,000
Media: 3-8-10-14-15-18-19-20-23-24
Distr.: Reg.
Budget Set: July
Personnel:
Foster Krupa *(Dir-Mkgt)*
Regina Arcuri *(Mgr-Events & Promos)*
Brands & Products:
BEAT THE HEAT
BIG GAME
DOUBLE IT
GIVE YOUR DREAMS A CHANCE
IT'S A WONDERFUL LIFE
JERSEY CASH 5
LOTZEE
LUCKY HEARTS
MATRI-MONEY
NEW JERSEY LOTTERY
PAC-MAN
PICK-3
PICK-4
PICK-6 LOTTO
SUPER PAYDAY
TAIL GATOR
VIP CLUB
X-TREME WINNINGS
YOGI BERRA CASH
ZODIAC
Advertising Agency:
BRUSHfire, Inc.
2 Wing Dr
Cedar Knolls, NJ 07927
Tel.: (973) 871-1700
Fax: (973) 871-1717

NEW MEXICO ECONOMIC DEVELOPMENT DEPARTMENT

1100 St Francis Dr PO Box 20003
Santa Fe, NM 87505-4147
Tel.: (505) 827-0300
Fax: (505) 827-0328
Toll Free: (800) 374-3061
Web Site:
www.newmexicodevelopment.com
E-Mail For Key Personnel:
Public Relations: rorie.hanrahan@edd.state.nm.us
Approx. Number Employees: 70
Business Description:
State Economic Development Administrative Services
S.I.C.: 9611
N.A.I.C.S.: 926110
Media: 5-7-10-13-20-22-23-24
Distr.: Natl.
Budget Set: May -June

NEW MEXICO TOURISM DEPARTMENT

491 Old Santa Fe Trl
Santa Fe, NM 87501-0001
Tel.: (505) 827-7400
Fax: (505) 827-7402
Toll Free: (800) 545-2070
E-mail: enchantment@newmexico.org
Web Site: www.newmexico.org
Approx. Number Employees: 45
Business Description:
Tourism Promoter; New Mexico Magazine Publisher
S.I.C.: 7389; 9611
N.A.I.C.S.: 561591; 926110
Advertising Expenditures: $1,810,700
Bus. Publs.: $53,000; Co-op Adv.: $594,700; Consumer Mags.: $783,000; Daily Newsp.: $85,000; Foreign: $25,000; Spot Radio: $55,000; Spot T.V.: $215,000
Distr.: Natl.
Personnel:
Ethel Hess *(Publisher-New Mexico Magazine)*
Bryan Nicklas *(Dir-Mktg)*
Martin Leger *(Mgr-Adv)*
Brands & Products:
LAND OF ENCHANTMENT
NEW MEXICO

NEW ORLEANS TOURISM MARKETING CORPORATION

365 Canal St Ste 1120
New Orleans, LA 70130-1112
Tel.: (504) 524-4784
Fax: (504) 524-4780
E-mail: info@notmc.com
Web Site: www.neworleansonline.com
Approx. Number Employees: 6
Year Founded: 1991
Business Description:
Promotes Tourism & Business Development
S.I.C.: 9611; 4725
N.A.I.C.S.: 926110; 561520
Advertising Expenditures: $400,000
Media: 6-13-22-23-24-25
Personnel:
Mark Romig *(CEO)*
Advertising Agency:
Peter A. Mayer Advertising, Inc.
324 Camp St
New Orleans, LA 70130-2804
Tel.: (504) 581-7191
Fax: (504) 581-3009
— Mark A. Mayer *(Pres.)*

NEW SMYRNA BEACH AREA VISITORS BUREAU

2238 State Rd 44
New Smyrna Beach, FL 32168
Tel.: (386) 428-1600
Fax: (386) 428-9922
Toll Free: (800) 541-9621
E-mail: nsbinfo@nsbfla.com
Web Site: www.nsbfla.com
Sales Range: Less than $1 Million
Approx. Number Employees: 10
Business Description:
Visitors Bureau
S.I.C.: 7389
N.A.I.C.S.: 561591
Media: 2-6-9-14-18-25
Personnel:
Deborah Boyd *(CEO)*
Debbie Ledbetter *(Dir-Mktg)*

NEW YORK CITY DEPARTMENT OF CITY WIDE ADMINISTRATIVE SERVICES

The Municipal Bldg 1 Centre St 17th Fl S
New York, NY 10007
Tel.: (212) 669-7070
Tel.: (212) 669-7000
Fax: (212) 669-7076
E-mail: ahebert@nyc.gov
Web Site: www.nyc.gov
Approx. Number Employees: 1,700
Year Founded: 1996
Business Description:
Central Urban Agency Administrative Services
S.I.C.: 8742
N.A.I.C.S.: 541611
Advertising Expenditures: $10,000,000
Media: 1-2-4-7-8-10-11-16-18-19-20-23
Distr.: Natl.
Personnel:
Martha K. Hirst *(Commissioner)*
Amy Hebert *(Dir-HR & Trng)*

NEW YORK CITY ECONOMIC DEVELOPMENT CORPORATION

110 William St
New York, NY 10038
Tel.: (212) 312-3600
Tel.: (212) 312-3523 (Pub Affairs)
Tel.: (212) 619-5000
Fax: (212) 312-3909
Toll Free: (888) NYC-0100
E-mail: info@nycedc.com
Web Site: www.nycedc.com
Approx. Number Employees: 325
Business Description:
Urban Economic Development Administrative Services
S.I.C.: 9611; 9532
N.A.I.C.S.: 926110; 925120
Media: 10-22
Personnel:
Seth W. Pinsky *(Chm)*

NEW YORK STATE DEPARTMENT OF HEALTH

Corning Tower Empire State Plz
Albany, NY 12237
Tel.: (518) 474-7354
Tel.: (518) 474-2011 (Commissioner)
Fax: (518) 474-7356
Fax: (518) 473-7071
E-mail: nyhealth@health.state.ny.us
Web Site: www.nyhealth.gov
Approx. Number Employees: 2,000
Business Description:
New York State Agency for Promotion of & Assistance Health Related Issues
S.I.C.: 9431
N.A.I.C.S.: 923120
Media: 2-3-18-20-22-23-24
Personnel:
Christine A. Salmon *(Dir-Bureau of Health, Mktg & Media)*
Brian Y. Scott *(Dir-Info Sys & Health Statistics)*
Kathleen Shure *(Dir-Managed Care)*

Key to Media (For complete agency information see *The Advertising Red Books-Agencies* edition):
1. Bus. Publs. 2. Cable T.V. 3. Catalogs & Directories. 4. Co-op Adv. 5. Consumer Mags. 6. D.M. to Bus. Estab.7. D.M. to Consumers
8. Daily Newsp. 9. Exhibits/Trade Shows 10. Foreign 11. Infomercial 12. Internet Adv.13. Multimedia 14. Network Radio
15. Network T.V. 16. Newsp. Distr. Mags. 17. Other 18. Outdoor (Posters, Transit) 19. Point of Purchase20. Premiums, Novelties
21. Product Samples 22. Special Events Mktg. 23. Spot Radio 24. Spot T.V. 25. Weekly Newsp. 26. Yellow Page Adv.

New York State Department of Health — (Continued)

Mark F. Yanulavich *(Dir-Bureau of Comm Production Svcs)*
Robert Reed *(Supvr-Sys Programming)*
Brands & Products:
CHILD HEALTH PLUS
NEWYORKSTATE
Advertising Agency:
HN Media & Marketing
275 Madison Ave Ste 2200
New York, NY 10016
Tel.: (212) 490-1300
Fax: (212) 490-0777

NEW YORK STATE LOTTERY

1 Broadway Ctr
Schenectady, NY 12305
Mailing Address:
PO Box 7500
Schenectady, NY 12301-7500
Tel.: (518) 388-3300
Fax: (518) 388-3403
Web Site: www.nylottery.org
Approx. Sls.: $6,270,000,000
Approx. Number Employees: 330
Year Founded: 1967
Business Description:
New York State Lottery Games
S.I.C.: 9311
N.A.I.C.S.: 921130
Media: 1-3-5-8-9-10-13-18-19-20-22-23-24-25
Distr.: Direct to Consumer; Reg.
Budget Set: Apr.
Personnel:
Debbie Hewitt *(Mgr-Mktg)*
Brands & Products:
150,000,000 PRIZE PAYOUT BONANZA
$500 A WEEK FOR LIFE
8 OVER 8
ALL THE MONEY
BEST OF 7'S
BINGO
BIRTHDAY BLOWOUT
CASHTACTIC
CASHWORD
CHERRY TWIST
COSMIC CASH
CRUISIN' CASH
DOUBLE DOLLARS
FORTUNE COOKIE
GREEN AND GOLD
GREEN MACHINE
LOOSE CHANGE
LOTTA LUCK
LUCKY 7'S
MAKE-A-CASHWORD
MEGA MILLIONS
MONEY MAZE
MONEY TREE
MONOPOLY
MOO-LA-MILLIONS
NEW YORK LOTTERY
NUMBERS
PANDA-MONEY-UM
PICK 10
QUICK DRAW
RAISING BILLIONS TO EDUCATE MILLIONS!
RUN THE TABLE
SET FOR LIFE
SHOP 'TIL YOU DROP
STACKS OF CASH
STINKIN' RICH
TAKE FIVE
TICKLED PINK
WHITE ICE 8S
WIN 1,000 A WEEK FOR LIFE
WIN 4

NORTH CAROLINA DEPARTMENT OF COMMERCE DIVISION OF TOURISM, FILM & SPORTS DEVELOPMENT

301 N Wilmington St
Raleigh, NC 27601
Mailing Address:
4324 Mail Service Ctr
Raleigh, NC 27699-4324
Tel.: (919) 733-4151
Tel.: (919) 733-4171
Fax: (919) 733-8582
Toll Free: (800) VISITNC
Web Site: www.visitnc.com
Approx. Number Employees: 100
Year Founded: 1937
Business Description:
Tourism & Travel Services
S.I.C.: 9611
N.A.I.C.S.: 926110
Media: 2-3-5-6-9-13-23
Distr.: Reg.
Budget Set: Apr.
Personnel:
David Rhodes *(Mgr-Mktg)*
Brands & Products:
VISITNC.COM
Advertising Agency:
Loeffler Ketchum Mountjoy (LKM)
6115 Park S Dr Ste 350
Charlotte, NC 28210
Tel.: (704) 364-8969
Fax: (704) 364-8470
Toll Free: (800) 851-8436
(Travel & Tourism for North Carolina)

NORTH DAKOTA DEPARTMENT OF COMMERCE TOURISM DIVISION

1600 E Century Ave Ste 2
Bismarck, ND 58503-2057
Tel.: (701) 328-2525
Fax: (701) 328-4878
Toll Free: (800) 435-5663
Toll Free: (800) HELLO-ND
E-mail: tourism@nd.com
Web Site: www.ndtourism.com
E-Mail For Key Personnel:
Marketing Director: HLeMoine@state.nd.us
Sales Range: $10-24.9 Million
Approx. Number Employees: 13
Year Founded: 1962
Business Description:
State Tourism Promotion Services
S.I.C.: 9611
N.A.I.C.S.: 926110
Advertising Expenditures: $1,500,000
Media: 1-2-3-6-7-9-10-11-15-16-18-20-23-24
Distr.: Reg.
Budget Set: June
Personnel:
Deanne Felshle *(Mgr-Grp Travel Mktg)*
Heather LeMoine *(Mgr-Mktg)*
Kim Schmidt *(Mgr-Media & PR)*
Fred Walker *(Mgr-Mktg-Intl)*
Tammy Backhaus *(Project Coord)*
Brands & Products:
NORTH DAKOTA LEGENDARY
Advertising Agency:
Odney
1400 W Century Ave
Bismarck, ND 58503
Tel.: (701) 222-8721
Fax: (701) 222-8172
Toll Free: (888) 500-8721

NORTH DAKOTA STATE SEED DEPARTMENT

1313 18th St N PO Box 5257
Fargo, ND 58105-5257
Tel.: (701) 231-5400
Fax: (701) 231-5401
E-mail: kbertsch@state-seed.ndsu.nodak.edu
Web Site: www.state.nd.us
Approx. Number Employees: 35
Year Founded: 1935
Business Description:
Certified Seed, Grain & Potatoes
S.I.C.: 9641
N.A.I.C.S.: 926140
Media: 2-10-18-23-25
Distr.: Natl.
Budget Set: Various
Personnel:
Kris Steussy *(Officer-Admin)*
Mark Hafdahl *(Mgr-Seed Laboratory)*
Joe Magnusson *(Mgr-Regulatory Program)*
Kris Nicklay *(Mgr-Admin Svcs)*
Jeff Prischmann *(Mgr-Diagnostic Laboratory)*

NYC & COMPANY, INC.

810 7th Ave
New York, NY 10019
Tel.: (212) 484-1200
Fax: (212) 245-5943
Toll Free: (800) NYC-VISIT
E-mail: nymedia@nycgo.com
Web Site: www.nycgo.com
Approx. Rev.: $14,100,000
Approx. Number Employees: 100
Year Founded: 1999
Business Description:
Local Urban Tourism Promotional & Administrative Services
S.I.C.: 7389
N.A.I.C.S.: 561591
Media: 2-3-4-6-7-10-16
Distr.: Intl.; Natl.
Personnel:
Jonathan M. Tisch *(Chm)*
George Fertitta *(CEO)*
Jane Reiss *(CMO)*
Brands & Products:
THE BIG APPLE
NYC
Advertising Agency:
BBH New York
32 Avenue of the Americas 19th Fl
New York, NY 10013
Tel.: (212) 812-6600
Fax: (212) 242-4110
Agency of Record

OHIO DEPARTMENT OF DEVELOPMENT

77 S High St
Columbus, OH 43215
Tel.: (614) 466-5355
Fax: (614) 644-0745
Toll Free: (800) 848-1300
E-mail: webmaster@development.ohio.gov
Web Site: www.development.ohio.gov
Sales Range: $10-24.9 Million
Approx. Number Employees: 525
Year Founded: 1970
Business Description:
Economic & Community Development, Travel & Tourism, International Trade, Small & Minority Business Assistance, Technology Assistance & Business Financing
S.I.C.: 9441
N.A.I.C.S.: 923130
Advertising Expenditures: $89,250
Media: 2-3-4-5-6-7-9-10-11-18-24-25
Distr.: Intl.; Natl.
Budget Set: June
Advertising Agencies:
DigiKnow
3615 Superior Ave Bldg 44 4th Fl
Cleveland, OH 44114
Tel.: (216) 325-1800
Fax: (216) 325-1801

Fahlgren Mortine
4030 Easton Station Ste 300
Columbus, OH 43219
Tel.: (614) 383-1500
Fax: (614) 383-1501

OHIO LOTTERY COMMISSION

615 W Superior Ave
Cleveland, OH 44113-1897
Tel.: (216) 787-3200
Fax: (216) 787-5215
Toll Free: (800) 589-6446
E-mail: Jenie.Roberts@olc.state.oh.us
Web Site: www.ohiolottery.com
Approx. Sls.: $1,919,000,000
Approx. Number Employees: 344
Year Founded: 1974
Business Description:
State Lottery Services
S.I.C.: 9311; 7999
N.A.I.C.S.: 921130; 713290
Advertising Expenditures: $9,872,354
Multimedia: $59,908; Bus. Publs.: $15,799; Consumer Mags.: $64,532; Daily Newsp.: $173,432; Other: $103,421; Outdoor (Posters, Transit): $852,457; Point of Purchase: $283,249; Premiums, Novelties: $14,262; Special Events Mktg.: $28,236; Spot Radio: $1,689,947; Spot T.V.: $6,253,562; Weekly Newsp.: $333,549
Distr.: Reg.
Budget Set: Nov. -Dec.
Personnel:
Dennis Berg *(Dir-Finance)*
Michael Petro *(Dir-Info Tech Div)*
Jenie Robets *(Dir-Comml)*
Gwen Tenn *(Dir-Product Dev)*
Carol Brown *(Supvr-Internal Audit)*
Brands & Products:
100,000 BONUS BINGO
25,000 HOLD 'EM POKER
35 MILLION SPECTACULAR
500,000 PAYDAY
9S IN A LINE
AMAZING 8S
BIG BANG BUCKS
BINGO
BLAZING BUCKS
BONUS CASHWORD
BREAK THE BANK
BUCKEYE 5
CASH BLOWOUT

Key to Media (For complete agency information see *The Advertising Red Books-Agencies* edition):
1. Bus. Publs. 2. Cable T.V. 3. Catalogs & Directories. 4. Co-op Adv. 5. Consumer Mags. 6. D.M. to Bus. Estab.7. D.M. to Consumers 8. Daily Newsp. 9. Exhibits/Trade Shows 10. Foreign 11. Infomercial 12. Internet Adv.13. Multimedia 14. Network Radio 15. Network T.V. 16. Newsp. Distr. Mags. 17. Other 18. Outdoor (Posters, Transit) 19. Point of Purchase20. Premiums, Novelties 21. Product Samples 22. Special Events Mktg. 23. Spot Radio 24. Spot T.V. 25. Weekly Newsp. 26. Yellow Page Adv.

CASH BONUS DOUBLE PLAY
CASH EXPLOSION DOUBLE PLAY
CASH FOR LIFE
CASH OUT
CASHWORD
CASINO ROYALE
DEAL OR NO DEAL
DOUBLE DOUBLER
DOUBLING DOLLARS
DOUBLING STAR CASHWORD
EXTREME GREEN
EZ MONEY
FAST CASH
FAT CAT TRIPLER
FIRE-N-ICE
FOOTBALL FEVER
GO FOR THE GREEN
HAPPY BIRTHDAY
HAPPY GO LUCKY
IGT SLOTS
INSTANT KENO
INSTANT MONOPOLY
INSTANT PAYDAY
JUST A BUCK
THE KICKER
LIFETIME RICHES
LUCK OF THE IRISH
LUCKY CHARM BINGO
LUCKY DOG DOUBLER
LUCKY TIMES TEN
LUCKY TIMES TEN JR.
MAGIC 8 BALL
MATCH & WIN
MONEY FOR LIFE
THE MONEY GAME
MONEY MONEY MONEY
MONEY ROLL
MOTHER'S DAY
NBA INSTANT GAME
OHIO LOTTERY
PICK 3 NUMBERS
PICK 4 NUMBERS
PINBALL WIZARD
PLATINUM PAYOUT
POKER FACE
THE PRICE IS RIGHT
SAPPHIRE 7S
SLOTS OF LUCK
SPRING FLING
STACKS OF CASH
SUPER DOUBLE DOUBLER
SUPER LOTTO PLUS
SUPER SLOTS
SUPERCASH
THANKS A 1,000,000
TRIPLE DOUBLE CASH
VALENTINE'S DAY DOUBLER
WHEEL OF FORTUNE
WILD NUMBER BINGO
WIN FOR LIFE
YANKEE DOODLE DOLLARS

Advertising Agencies:
Hart Associates, Inc.
1915 Indian Wood Cir
Maumee, OH 43537-4002
Tel.: (419) 893-9600
Fax: (419) 893-9070

Marcus Thomas LLC
24865 Emery Rd
Cleveland, OH 44128
Tel.: (216) 292-4700
Fax: (216) 378-0396
Toll Free: (888) 482-4455

Northlich
Sawyer Point Bldg 720 Pete Rose Way
Cincinnati, OH 45202
Tel.: (513) 421-8840
Fax: (513) 455-4749
Agency of Record

Stern Advertising, Inc.
29125 Chagrin Blvd
Cleveland, OH 44122-4622
Tel.: (216) 464-4850
Fax: (216) 464-7859

OKLAHOMA CITY CONVENTION & VISITORS BUREAU

189 W Sheridan Ave
Oklahoma City, OK 73102-9208
Tel.: (405) 297-8912
Fax: (405) 297-8888
Toll Free: (800) 225-5652
E-mail: okccvb@okccvb.org
Web Site: www.okccvb.org
E-Mail For Key Personnel:
Sales Director: sprice@okccvb.org
Approx. Number Employees: 18
Business Description:
Travel & Tourism in Oklahoma City
S.I.C.: 7389
N.A.I.C.S.: 561591
Advertising Expenditures: $300,000
Media: 4-13
Personnel:
Sandy Price *(Dir-Tourism Sls)*
Alan Sims *(Dir-Sls)*

OKLAHOMA DEPARTMENT OF COMMERCE

900 N Stiles Ave
Oklahoma City, OK 73104-3234
Tel.: (405) 815-6552
Fax: (405) 815-5317
Toll Free: (800) 879-6552
E-mail: info@odoc.state.ok.us
Web Site: www.okcommerce.gov
Approx. Number Employees: 145
Year Founded: 1987
Business Description:
Economic & Workforce Development in the State of Oklahoma
S.I.C.: 9651
N.A.I.C.S.: 926150
Media: 1-2-7-11-20
Distr.: Intl.; Natl.
Budget Set: July
Personnel:
Jonna Kirschner *(Dir & Gen Counsel)*
Norma Noble *(Dir-Workforce Dev)*
Sandy Pratt *(Dir)*
Brands & Products:
EDGE
OKLAHOMA'S
OKLAHOMA'S ADVANTAGE
Advertising Agency:
Third Degree Advertising
100 E Main St Ste 200
Oklahoma City, OK 73104
Tel.: (405) 235-3020
Fax: (405) 235-3021

OKLAHOMA TOURISM & RECREATION DEPARTMENT

Ste 600 120 N Robinson Ave
Oklahoma City, OK 73102-7802
Tel.: (405) 230-8400
Fax: (405) 230-8600
Toll Free: (800) 652-6552
E-mail: information@travelok.com
Web Site: www.travelok.com
E-Mail For Key Personnel:
Marketing Director: jennifer@travelok.com
Public Relations: Sandy@TravelOK.com
Sales Estimate: $100-119 Million
Approx. Number Employees: 842
Year Founded: 1937
Business Description:
State Tourism & Recreation Marketer
S.I.C.: 7389
N.A.I.C.S.: 561591
Import
Advertising Expenditures: $4,500,000
Media: 1-3-5-6-9-10-11-14-15-16-17-18-22-23-24
Distr.: Intl.
Budget Set: July
Personnel:
Hardy Watkins *(Exec Dir)*
Keli Clark *(Dir-Mktg)*
Jennifer Kalkman *(Dir-Mktg)*
Kris Marek *(Dir-Dev)*
Lindfay Vidirne *(Dir-Pub Rels)*
Brands & Products:
OKLAHOMA NATIVE AMERICA
OKLAHOMA TODAY MAGAZINE
TRAVELOK.COM

OREGON STATE LOTTERY

500 Airport Rd SE
Salem, OR 97301
Tel.: (503) 540-1000
Fax: (503) 540-1329
E-mail: lottery.webcenter@state.or.us
Web Site: www.oregonlottery.org
Approx. Sls.: $815,000,000
Approx. Number Employees: 430
Year Founded: 1984
Business Description:
State Lottery
S.I.C.: 9311
N.A.I.C.S.: 921130
Advertising Expenditures: $6,200,000
Media: 9-17-20-23-24-25
Distr.: Direct to Consumer; Reg.
Personnel:
Dale Penn *(Dir)*
Carole Hardy *(Asst Dir-Mktg)*
Brands & Products:
BREAKOPENS
IT DOES GOOD THINGS
THE MOVE SCRATCH-ITS
OREGON LOTTERY
RAFFLE
Advertising Agency:
Borders Perrin Norrander Inc
808 SW 3rd Ave 8th Fl
Portland, OR 97204-2400
Tel.: (503) 227-2506
Fax: (503) 227-4827

OREGON TOURISM COMMISSION

(d/b/a Travel Oregon)
670 Hawthorne SE Ste 240
Salem, OR 97301-1282
Tel.: (503) 378-8850
Fax: (503) 378-4574
Toll Free: (800) 547-7842
E-mail: info@traveloregon.com
Web Site: www.traveloregon.com
Sales Range: $25-49.9 Million
Approx. Number Employees: 27
Year Founded: 1995
Business Description:
Tourism Marketing Services
S.I.C.: 9111
N.A.I.C.S.: 921110
Advertising Expenditures: $2,000,000
Media: 2-6-7-8-11-13-23
Distr.: Natl.; Western Editions
Budget Set: July
Personnel:
Todd Davidson *(CEO)*
Scott West *(Chief Strategy Officer)*
Kevin Wright *(Dir-Mktg)*
Michelle Godfrey *(Mgr-PR)*
Mo Sherifdeen *(Mgr-Interactive Mktg)*
Brands & Products:
OREGON. WE LOVE DREAMERS
TRAVEL OREGON
Advertising Agencies:
Maxwell PR
1600 SE Bybee Blvd Ste 202
Portland, OR 97202
Tel.: (503) 231-3086
Fax: (503) 231-3089
(Public Relations)

Wieden + Kennedy, Inc.
224 NW 13th Ave
Portland, OR 97209-2953
Tel.: (503) 937-7000
Fax: (503) 937-8000
(Tourism)

ORLANDO/ORANGE COUNTY CONVENTION & VISITORS BUREAU, INC.

6700 Forum Dr Ste 100
Orlando, FL 32821-8017
Tel.: (407) 363-5800
Fax: (407) 370-5018
Toll Free: (800) 972-3304
E-mail: media@orlandocvb.com
Web Site: www.orlandoinfo.com
E-Mail For Key Personnel:
Public Relations: danielle.courtenay@orlandocvb.com
Approx. Number Employees: 150
Year Founded: 1984
Business Description:
Convention & Visitors Bureau
S.I.C.: 7389
N.A.I.C.S.: 561591
Advertising Expenditures: $7,000,000
Media: 2-3-4-5-6-7-8-9-10-11-13-15-18-23-24-25
Distr.: Intl.; Natl.
Personnel:
Gary Sain *(Pres & CEO)*
Danielle Saba Courtenay *(CMO)*
Karen Soto *(VP-HR)*
Chris Bare *(Dir-Adv)*
Advertising Agency:
22Squared
401 E Jackson St Fl 36
Tampa, FL 33602-5225
Tel.: (813) 202-1200
Fax: (813) 202-1261

PALM BEACH COUNTY CONVENTION & VISITORS BUREAU

1555 Palm Beach Lakes Blvd Ste 800
West Palm Beach, FL 33401
Tel.: (561) 233-3000
Fax: (561) 233-3009
Web Site: www.palmbeachfl.com
Approx. Number Employees: 50

Palm Beach County Convention & Visitors Bureau — (Continued)

Business Description:
Convention & Visitors Bureau
S.I.C.: 7389
N.A.I.C.S.: 561591
Media: 2-6-11-18-22
Personnel:
Jorge Pesquera *(CEO)*
Bill Vervaeke *(VP-Mktg)*
Dave Anderson *(Gen Mgr)*
Sophia Gaeta *(Sr Dir-Sls)*
Connie Hunter *(Sr Dir-Sls)*
Richard Haller *(Dir-Airport Mktg)*
Nancy Spoto *(Dir-Partnership Mktg)*
Eda Ruddock *(Mgr-Tourism Mktg)*
Advertising Agencies:
Bohan
124 12th Ave S
Nashville, TN 37203
Tel.: (615) 327-1189
Fax: (615) 327-8123

Lou Hammond & Associates, Inc.
39 E 51st St
New York, NY 10022-5916
Tel.: (212) 308-8880
Fax: (212) 891-0200

PALM SPRINGS DESERT RESORTS CONVENTION & VISITORS AUTHORITY

70-100 Hwy 111
Rancho Mirage, CA 92270-2853
Tel.: (760) 770-9000
Fax: (760) 770-9001
Toll Free: (800) 967-3767
E-mail: info@palmspringsusa.com
Web Site: www.palmspringsusa.com
Approx. Number Employees: 38
Year Founded: 1985
Business Description:
Convention & Visitors Bureau
S.I.C.: 7389
N.A.I.C.S.: 561591
Advertising Expenditures: $2,000,000
Media: 1-2-4-6-7-8-9-10-13-18-19-20
Distr.: Intl.; Natl.
Budget Set: Aug.
Personnel:
Mark Graves *(Exec Dir-Mktg-Comm)*
Jim LaBay *(Dir-Graphic Comm)*
Tammy Bucklin *(Assoc Dir-Sls)*
Joanne Yanovick *(Mgr-Sls)*
Advertising Agency:
The Jones Agency
303 N Indian Canyon Dr
Palm Springs, CA 92262-6015
Tel.: (760) 325-1437
Fax: (760) 778-0320
(Travel Destination)

PENINSULA COUNCIL FOR WORKFORCE DEVELOPMENT

11820 Fountain Way Ste 301
Newport News, VA 23606
Tel.: (757) 826-3327
Fax: (757) 826-6706
E-mail: mail@pcfwd.org
Web Site: www.pcfwd.org
Approx. Number Employees: 12
Year Founded: 1946
Business Description:
Regional Workforce & Economic Development Administrative Services
S.I.C.: 9611
N.A.I.C.S.: 926110
Export
Advertising Expenditures: $300,000
Media: 1-2-7-10-11
Distr.: Intl.; Natl.
Budget Set: Oct.
Personnel:
Sybil Wheatley *(Chm)*
Matthew James *(Pres & CEO)*
Jeanne Smith *(Dir-Community Svs)*
Mary Dunnigan *(Mgr-Workforce Dev)*

PENNSYLVANIA DEPARTMENT OF COMMUNITY & ECONOMIC DEVELOPMENT

400 N St 4th Fl Commonwealth Keystone Bldg
Harrisburg, PA 17120-0225
Tel.: (717) 787-3405
Fax: (717) 772-4559
Web Site: www.newpa.com
E-Mail For Key Personnel:
President: bchaffee@state.pa.us
Marketing Director: dbowman@state.pa.us
Public Relations: mneuhard@state.pa.us
Approx. Number Employees: 350
Year Founded: 1939
Business Description:
Statewide Community & Economic Development Administrative Services
S.I.C.: 9611; 9532
N.A.I.C.S.: 926110; 925120
Advertising Expenditures: $7,000,000
Media: 1-5-6-7-9-10-11-12-13-14-15-22-23-24
Distr.: Natl.
Budget Set: July
Advertising Agencies:
BarkleyREI
2840 Liberty Ave Ste 100
Pittsburgh, PA 15222
Tel.: (412) 683-3700
Fax: (412) 683-1610
— Todd Harris *(Acct Dir)*

Mullen
The Crane Bldg 40 24th St
Pittsburgh, PA 15222-4600
Tel.: (412) 402-0200
Fax: (412) 402-0160

PENNSYLVANIA STATE LOTTERY

1200 Fulling Mill Rd Ste 1
Middletown, PA 17057
Tel.: (717) 702-8000
Fax: (717) 702-8024
Toll Free: (877) 282-4639
E-mail: emahlman@lottery.state.pa.us
Web Site: www.palottery.state.pa.us
Approx. Rev.: $3,099,693,945
Approx. Number Employees: 320
Year Founded: 1971
Business Description:
State Lottery Services
S.I.C.: 9311
N.A.I.C.S.: 921130
Media: 1-2-3-4-8-14-15-18-19-20-22-23-24
Distr.: Reg.
Budget Set: July
Personnel:
Edward Trees *(Exec Dir)*
Edward Mahlman *(Exec Dir)*
Tom Blaskiewicz *(Deputy Dir-Field Ops)*
Bill Powell *(Dir-Product Delivery)*
Kara Sparks *(Mgr-Instant Product)*
Brands & Products:
BIG 4
CASH 5
THE DAILY NUMBER
MIX & MATCH
PENNSYLVANIA LOTTERY
POWERBALL
SUPER 6 LOTTO
TREASURE HUNT

PENSACOLA BAY AREA CONVENTION & VISITORS BUREAU

1401 E Gregory St
Pensacola, FL 32502
Tel.: (850) 434-1234
Fax: (850) 432-8211
Toll Free: (800) 874-1234
E-mail: information@visitpensacola.com
Web Site: www.visitpensacola.com
Approx. Number Employees: 13
Year Founded: 1962
Business Description:
Convention & Visitors Bureau
S.I.C.: 7389
N.A.I.C.S.: 561591
Advertising Expenditures: $316,200
Media: 2-3-4-6-9-13-18-23-24-25
Distr.: Natl.
Budget Set: Jan. -Dec.
Personnel:
Michael Bersabal *(Mgr-e-Commerce & Internet Mktg)*
Lori Coppels *(Mgr-Sls-Grp Tour)*
Larry Orvis *(Mgr)*

PHILADELPHIA CONVENTION & VISITORS BUREAU

1700 Market St Ste 3000
Philadelphia, PA 19103-1920
Tel.: (215) 636-3300
Fax: (215) 636-3327
Toll Free: (800) CALLPHL
E-mail: webmaster@pcvb.org
Web Site: www.pcvb.org
Approx. Number Employees: 52
Year Founded: 1941
Business Description:
Convention & Visitors Bureau
S.I.C.: 7389
N.A.I.C.S.: 561591
Import
Media: 1-2-6-7-9-10-11-17-20-25
Distr.: Reg.
Budget Set: July
Personnel:
Nicholas DeBenedictis *(Chm)*
Jack Ferguson *(Pres & CEO)*
Wanda Paul *(Sr VP-Fin & Admin)*
Danielle Cohn *(VP-Mktg & Comm)*
Kathlene Titus *(Dir-Tourism)*
Brands & Products:
PHILADELPHIA
THE PLACE THAT LOVES YOU BACK

PINELLAS COUNTY ECONOMIC DEVELOPMENT

Ste 1-200 13805 58th St N
Clearwater, FL 33760-3716
Tel.: (727) 464-7332
Fax: (727) 464-7053
E-mail: econddev@pinellascounty.org
Web Site: www.pced.org
Sales Range: Less than $1 Million
Approx. Number Employees: 12
Business Description:
Economic Development Promoter
S.I.C.: 9611
N.A.I.C.S.: 926110
Media: 2-3-7-13-22
Personnel:
John Morroni *(County Commissioner)*
Mike Meidel *(Dir-Economic Devel)*
Suzanne Christman *(Sr Mgr-Bus Devel)*
Cynthia Johnson *(Sr Mgr-Bus Assistance)*
Stacey Swank *(Mgr-Special Projects)*

PORTLAND BUSINESS ALLIANCE

200 SW Market St Ste 150
Portland, OR 97201-5718
Tel.: (503) 224-8684
Fax: (503) 323-9186
E-mail: info@portlandalliance.com
Web Site: www.portlandalliance.com
E-Mail For Key Personnel:
Marketing Director: CWahrgren@pdxchamber.org
Sales Director: CWahrgren@pdxchamber.org
Approx. Number Employees: 30
Year Founded: 1870
Business Description:
Business Association
S.I.C.: 8611
N.A.I.C.S.: 813910
Media: 6-10-13-22
Distr.: Reg.
Personnel:
Sandra McDonough *(Pres & CEO)*
Karen Riley-Cummings *(Dir-HR)*
Christine Gatlin *(Mgr-Membership Events)*
Brands & Products:
ALLIANCE ENEWSLETTER
LEADING THE WAY
PORTLAND BUSINESS ALLIANCE

POSITIVELY CLEVELAND

100 Public Sq 3100 Terminal Tower
Cleveland, OH 44113-2290
Tel.: (216) 621-4110
Fax: (216) 621-5967
Toll Free: (800) 321-1001
E-mail: cvb@positivelycleveland.com
Web Site: www.positivelycleveland.com
Approx. Number Employees: 50
Business Description:
Convention & Visitors Bureau
S.I.C.: 7389
N.A.I.C.S.: 561591
Advertising Expenditures: $600,000
Media: 1-4-13
Personnel:
Kelly Brewer *(VP-Sls)*
Tamera Brown *(VP-Mktg)*
Tom Fadeley *(Dir-MIS)*
Amanda Bonvechio *(Mgr-Convention Svcs & Housing)*
Tamara Dyer *(Mgr-Convention Svcs & Events)*
Mark Schutte *(Mgr-Publ)*
Michelle Sperber *(Mgr-Bus Dev)*
Richard Jarvis *(Coord-Guest Svcs)*
Joyce Noss *(Coord-Visitor Center Project)*

Key to Media (For complete agency information see *The Advertising Red Books-Agencies* edition):
1. Bus. Publs. 2. Cable T.V. 3. Catalogs & Directories. 4. Co-op Adv. 5. Consumer Mags. 6. D.M. to Bus. Estab.7. D.M. to Consumers 8. Daily Newsp. 9. Exhibits/Trade Shows 10. Foreign 11. Infomercial 12. Internet Adv.13. Multimedia 14. Network Radio 15. Network T.V. 16. Newsp. Distr. Mags. 17. Other 18. Outdoor (Posters, Transit) 19. Point of Purchase20. Premiums, Novelties 21. Product Samples 22. Special Events Mktg. 23. Spot Radio 24. Spot T.V. 25. Weekly Newsp. 26. Yellow Page Adv.

PUERTO RICO TOURISM COMPANY
Princes Bulding Number 2 Princes Work Way
San Juan, PR 00902-3960
Mailing Address:
PO Box 9023960
San Juan, PR 00902-3960
Tel.: (787) 721-2400
Fax: (787) 722-6238
Toll Free: (800) 866-7827
Web Site: www.gotopuertorico.com
Sales Range: $250-299.9 Million
Approx. Number Employees: 600
Year Founded: 1970
Business Description:
Tourist Products & Services
S.I.C.: 4725
N.A.I.C.S.: 561520
Advertising Expenditures: $11,000,000
Media: 1-2-3-4-5-6-9-10-11-13-14-15-17-18-20-22-23-24-25
Distr.: Natl.
Budget Set: July
Personnel:
Nydza Irizarry *(Dir-Legal)*
Brands & Products:
PUERTO RICO
PUERTO RICO DOES IT BETTER
SOUNDS OF PUERTO RICO
Advertising Agency:
Lopito, Ileana & Howie, Inc.
Metro Office Park #13 First St
Guaynabo, PR 00968
Tel.: (787) 783-1160
Fax: (787) 783-2273

RHODE ISLAND ECONOMIC DEVELOPMENT CORPORATION
315 Iron Horse Way Ste 101
Providence, RI 02908
Tel.: (401) 278-9100
Fax: (401) 273-8270
Telex: 6814132
E-mail: info@riedc.com
Web Site: www.riedc.com
Approx. Number Employees: 100
Year Founded: 1995
Business Description:
Economic Development & Tourism Promoter for Rhode Island
S.I.C.: 9611
N.A.I.C.S.: 926110
Media: 1-2-4-5-6-7-9-10-13
Distr.: Natl.
Budget Set: May
Personnel:
John Riendeau *(Head-Defense Industry Sector)*
J. Michael Saul *(Interim Exec Dir)*
Keith Stokes *(Exec Dir)*
Mark Brodeur *(Dir-Tourism)*
Katharine Flynn *(Dir-Bus Dev)*
Denise Javery *(Dir-HR)*
Maureen Mezei *(Dir-Intl Trade)*
William Parsons *(Deputy Dir-Community & Govt Rels)*
Victor Barros *(Mgr-Urban Devel)*
Sherri Lynn Carrera *(Mgr-Small Bus Svcs)*
Paul Harden *(Mgr-Marine, Green Energy, Bus & Workforce Dev)*
Dorothy Reynolds *(Mgr-PTAC Program)*
Melissa Chambers *(Coord-Sr Comm & Market Dev)*

RHODE ISLAND LOTTERY
1425 Pontiac Ave
Cranston, RI 02920-4454
Tel.: (401) 463-6500
Fax: (401) 463-5008
Web Site: www.rilot.com
Sales Range: $1-4.9 Billion
Approx. Number Employees: 55
Year Founded: 1974
Business Description:
State Lottery
S.I.C.: 9311; 7999
N.A.I.C.S.: 921130; 713290
Media: 9-18-23-24-25
Distr.: Direct to Consumer; Reg.
Budget Set: Dec.
Personnel:
Gerald S. Aubin *(Exec Dir)*
Donald Cataldi *(Mgr-Mktg)*
Daniel Sarro *(Mgr-Fin- & Admin)*
Brands & Products:
DESERT GOLD
KENO
KENO PLUS
MONEY MANIA
NEON 9'S
SPICY CASH
SUNNY CASH UP
WILD MONEY

SAN ANTONIO CONVENTION & VISITORS BUREAU
203 S Saint Marys St 2nd Fl
San Antonio, TX 78205
Tel.: (210) 207-6700
Fax: (210) 207-6768
Toll Free: (800) 447-3372
E-mail: sacvb@sanantoniocvb.com
Web Site: www.visitsanantonio.com
Approx. Number Employees: 70
Year Founded: 1968
Business Description:
Convention & Visitors Bureau
S.I.C.: 7389
N.A.I.C.S.: 561591
Media: 4-13
Personnel:
Kari Eustace *(Dir-Svcs)*
Felicia Madison *(Dir-Sls)*
Dee Dee Poteete *(Dir-Comm)*
Robert Salluce *(Dir-Community Rels & Strategic Initiatives)*
Frances Ortiz Schultschik *(Dir-Strategic Dev, PR-Mexico & Latin America)*
Ronnie Price *(Asst Exec Dir-Sls & Mktg)*
Advertising Agency:
Bromley Communications
401 E Houston St
San Antonio, TX 78205-2615
Tel.: (210) 244-2000
Fax: (210) 244-2442

SAN ANTONIO ECONOMIC DEVELOPMENT FOUNDATION
602 E Commerce St
San Antonio, TX 78205
Mailing Address:
PO Box 1628
San Antonio, TX 78296
Tel.: (210) 226-1394
Fax: (210) 223-3386
Toll Free: (800) 552-3333
E-mail: edf@sanantonioedf.com
Web Site: www.sanantonioedf.com
E-Mail For Key Personnel:
President: marioh@dcci.com
Approx. Number Employees: 7
Year Founded: 1975
Business Description:
Economic Development Administrative Services
S.I.C.: 9611; 9532
N.A.I.C.S.: 926110; 925120
Advertising Expenditures: $200,000
Media: 2-4-7-9-13
Distr.: Natl.
Budget Set: Aug.
Personnel:
Mario Hernandez *(Pres)*
Advertising Agency:
Anderson Marketing Group
7420 Blanco Rd Ste 200
San Antonio, TX 78216
Tel.: (210) 223-6233
Fax: (210) 223-9692

SAN DIEGO CONVENTION & VISITORS BUREAU
2215 India St
San Diego, CA 92101-1725
Tel.: (619) 232-3101
Fax: (619) 696-9371
E-mail: sdinfo@sandiego.org
Web Site: www.sandiego.org
E-Mail For Key Personnel:
Marketing Director: shimo@sdcvb.org
Sales Director: KKamenzind@sdcvb.org
Public Relations: jtimko@sdcvb.org
Approx. Number Employees: 85
Business Description:
Convention & Visitors Bureau
S.I.C.: 7389
N.A.I.C.S.: 561591
Advertising Expenditures: $5,000,000
Media: 2-3-5-6-7-9-11-13-14-15-18-23-24
Distr.: Direct to Consumer; Intl.; Natl.
Budget Set: July
Personnel:
Kerri Verbeke Kapich *(Sr VP-Mktg)*
Sue Mason *(Dir-Visitor Svcs)*
Joe Timko *(Dir-PR)*
Dale Vandergaw *(Dir-Worldwide Military & Defense Affairs)*
Robert Arends *(Mgr-PR)*
Advertising Agency:
MeringCarson
1010 S Coast Hwy 101 Ste 105
Encinitas, CA 92024
Tel.: (760) 635-2100
Fax: (760) 635-2106
Agency of Record

SAN FRANCISCO CONVENTION & VISITORS BUREAU
(Name Changed to San Francisco Travel Association)

SAN FRANCISCO TRAVEL ASSOCIATION
(Formerly San Francisco Convention & Visitors Bureau)
201 3rd St Ste 900
San Francisco, CA 94103-3143
Tel.: (415) 974-6900
Fax: (415) 227-2602
Web Site: www.sanfrancisco.travel/
Approx. Number Employees: 80
Year Founded: 1909
Business Description:
Convention & Visitors Bureau
S.I.C.: 7389
N.A.I.C.S.: 561591
Advertising Expenditures: $3,825,000
Media: 2-3-5-6-10-14-23
Distr.: Reg.
Budget Set: Feb.
Personnel:
Joe D'Alessandro *(Pres & CEO)*
Tina Wu *(CFO & Exec VP)*
Matt Stiker *(CMO & Exec VP)*
John Reyes *(Chief Customer Officer & Exec VP)*
Tom Kiely *(Exec VP-Tourism)*
Kathryn Horton *(Sr Dir-Convention Events & Svcs)*
Kenley Moy *(Sr Dir-Natl Sls Office)*
Laurie Armstrong *(Dir-Media Rels-US & Canada)*
Lynn Bruni *(Dir-Consumer Mktg)*
Lisa Cleveland *(Dir-Member Svcs)*
Tom Florek *(Dir-IT)*
Hubertus Funke *(Dir-Intl Tourism-Europe & Latin America)*
Cindy Hu *(Dir-Editorial Svcs)*
Angela Jackson *(Dir-Media Rels Intl)*
Deirdre Lewis *(Dir-Citywide Accounts)*
Helen Tsui *(Dir-Intl Tourism-Asia Pacific)*
Leonie Patrick *(Assoc Dir-Sls)*
Ernie Garcia *(Sr Mgr-Corp & Incentive Sls)*
Beth Melanson *(Sr Mgr-Convention Sls & Eastern Region)*
Oleg Nakonechny *(Sr Mgr-Convention Svcs)*
Jason Wolterstorff *(Sr Mgr-Convention Sls)*
Tanya Houseman *(Mgr-PR)*
Anita Hung *(Mgr-Natl Sls)*
Leticia Lucero *(Mgr-Convention Sls)*
John Plain *(Mgr-Web Svcs)*
Wendy Ramirez *(Mgr-Natl Sls)*
Marco Rodriguez *(Mgr-Convention Sls)*
Robynne Weaver *(Mgr-Convention Svcs)*
Phillip Huff *(Coord-Ops)*

SAN JOSE CONVENTION/ VISITORS BUREAU
408 Almaden Blvd
San Jose, CA 95110
Tel.: (408) 295-9600
Fax: (408) 277-3535
Toll Free: (800) SANJOSE
E-mail: concierge@sanjose.org
Web Site: www.sanjose.org
E-Mail For Key Personnel:
President: DFenton@sanjose.org
Sales Range: $10-24.9 Million
Approx. Number Employees: 45
Year Founded: 1985
Business Description:
Convention & Visitors Bureau
S.I.C.: 7389
N.A.I.C.S.: 561591
Advertising Expenditures: $100,000
Media: 1-2-6-8-9-10-13-16
Distr.: Natl.
Budget Set: Jan.
Personnel:
Daniel N. Fenton *(Pres & CEO)*
Dan Cunningham *(CFO)*
Diana Ponton *(VP-Sls & Mktg)*
Dave Costain *(Dir-Client Svcs)*
Regina Urquidez *(Sr Mgr)*

San Jose Convention/Visitors Bureau — (Continued)

Todd Dibs *(Mgr-Sls-Natl)*
Narith Keo *(Mgr-Info Sys)*
Cheryl Little *(Mgr-Sls-Natl)*
Kim Speziale-Waters *(Mgr-Acctg)*

SARASOTA CONVENTION & VISITORS BUREAU

766 Hudson Ave Ste A
Sarasota, FL 34236
Tel.: (941) 955-0991
Fax: (941) 951-2956
Toll Free: (800) 522-9799
E-mail: info@sarasotafl.org
Web Site: www.sarasotafl.org
Sales Range: $10-24.9 Million
Approx. Number Employees: 14
Business Description:
Convention & Visitors Bureau
S.I.C.: 7389
N.A.I.C.S.: 561591
Media: 6-8-10-13
Personnel:
Virginia Haley *(Pres)*
Stephanie Grosskreutz *(Mng Dir)*
Erin Duggan *(Dir-PR)*
Brands & Products:
FLORIDA'S CULTURAL COAST
OFFICIAL VISITORS GUIDE
SARASOTA

SARASOTA COUNTY HEALTH DEPARTMENT

2200 Ringling Blvd
Sarasota, FL 34237-6102
Tel.: (941) 861-2900
Web Site: www.sarasotahealth.org
Business Description:
Community Health Services
S.I.C.: 9431
N.A.I.C.S.: 923120
Media: 6-9-10-13-22-23-24-25
Personnel:
Barbara Laidlaw *(Interim Dir)*
Dianne Shipley *(Mgr-Media)*

SCOTTISH DEVELOPMENT INTERNATIONAL

(Sub. of Scottish Development International)
28 State St Ste 2300
Boston, MA 02109
Tel.: (617) 621-3034
Fax: (617) 725-2897
Web Site:
www.scottishdevelopmentinternational.com
Approx. Number Employees: 10
Business Description:
American Corporate Investment in Scotland
S.I.C.: 8732
N.A.I.C.S.: 541910
Advertising Expenditures: $200,000
Media: 1-2-9-10-25
Distr.: Intl.; Natl.
Budget Set: Mar.
Personnel:
Dennis Gillings *(Chm/CEO-Quintiles)*
Carol Decker *(Asst VP)*
Geoff Hatton *(Gen Mgr-Systems)*
Simon Foster *(Gen Mgr-Sys)*
Nathan Elia *(Reg Mgr)*
Iain Forrest *(Customer Svcs Mgr)*
Howard Jang *(Mgr-Opers-Korea)*
Yasutsune Kanatani *(Sr Acct Exec)*

SEATTLE CONVENTION & VISITORS BUREAU

One Convention Pl 701 Pike St Ste 800
Seattle, WA 98101-4042
Tel.: (206) 461-5800
Tel.: (206) 461-5840
Fax: (206) 461-5855
E-mail: visinfo@visitseattle.org
Web Site: www.visitseattle.org
Approx. Number Employees: 50
Year Founded: 1956
Business Description:
Convention & Visitors Bureau
S.I.C.: 7389
N.A.I.C.S.: 561591
Media: 4-10-13
Personnel:
Tom Norwalk *(Pres & CEO)*
Kris Cromwell *(VP-Fin)*
Elias Calderon *(Dir-Mktg & Creative Svcs)*
Adriane Fridman *(Dir-Svcs)*
Brad Jones *(Dir-Tourism Dev-UK, Europe & Australia)*
Michael Kurtz *(Dir-Tourism Dev-Asia & Latin America)*
Ralph Morton *(Dir-Sports Commission)*
Brands & Products:
METRONATURAL
PORTAL TO THE FUTURE

SOUTH AFRICAN TOURISM

500 5th Ave 20th Fl Ste 2040
New York, NY 10110-2099
Tel.: (212) 730-2929
Fax: (212) 764-1980
Toll Free: (800) 822-5368
Toll Free: (800) 593-1318
E-mail: info.us@southafrica.net
Web Site: www.southafrica.net
Sales Range: Less than $1 Million
Approx. Number Employees: 10
Year Founded: 1983
Business Description:
National Tourism Bureau of the Republic of South Africa
S.I.C.: 7389; 4729
N.A.I.C.S.: 561591; 561599
Media: 2-5-6-8-13-18
Distr.: Intl.; Natl.
Budget Set: Mar.
Personnel:
Sthu Zungu *(Pres)*
Thandiwe January-McLean *(CEO)*
David DiGregorio *(Mgr-Mktg & Comm)*
Advertising Agencies:
BCA (Brian Cronin & Associates Inc.)
315 Madison Ave Ste 702
New York, NY 10017-6503
Tel.: (212) 286-9300
Fax: (212) 286-9736

Portfolio Management Group
110 2nd Ave Fl 3
New York, NY 10022
Tel.: (212) 715-1612
Public Relations

THE SOUTH CAROLINA EDUCATION LOTTERY

1333 Main St 4th Fl
Columbia, SC 29201
Mailing Address:
PO Box 11949
Columbia, SC 29211-1949
Tel.: (803) 737-2002
Fax: (803) 737-2005
E-mail: questions@sceducationlottery.com
Web Site:
www.sceducationlottery.com
Approx. Rev.: $953,162,647
Approx. Number Employees: 137
Year Founded: 2001
Business Description:
Operator of Lottery in South Carolina
S.I.C.: 9311
N.A.I.C.S.: 921130
Media: 3-6-9-13-18-20-22-23-24-26
Personnel:
Tim Madden *(Chm)*
Anthony S. Cooper *(COO)*
William Hogan Brown *(Dir-Legal Ser)*
Thomas R. Marsh *(Dir-Security)*
Dale M. Rhodes *(Dir-Fin)*
Ann Scott *(Dir-Sls & Retailer Rels)*
Brands & Products:
CANDY CANE CASH
CAROLINA 5
CAROLINA CASH
CASH 5
MEGA MATCH
PICK 4
SOUTH CAROLINA EDUCATION LOTTERY

SOUTH CAROLINA PARKS RECREATION & TOURISM

1205 Pendleton St Ste 110
Columbia, SC 29201-3731
Tel.: (803) 734-1700
Fax: (803) 734-1409
Toll Free: (800) SCSMILE
Web Site:
www.discoversouthcarolina.com
Sales Range: $250-299.9 Million
Approx. Number Employees: 450
Year Founded: 1967
Business Description:
Department of Tourism; Encourages Travel to South Carolina
S.I.C.: 9199
N.A.I.C.S.: 921190
Advertising Expenditures: $5,000,000
Media: 3-5-6-9-11-13-18-23-24
Distr.: Natl.; Reg.
Budget Set: July -May
Personnel:
Beverly Shelley *(Dir-Mktg & Sls)*
Tammy Strawbridge *(Dir-Adv)*
Brands & Products:
SMILING FACES. BEAUTIFUL PLACES
SOUTH CAROLINA
Advertising Agency:
Rawle Murdy Associates, Inc.
2 Beaufain St
Charleston, SC 29401
Tel.: (843) 577-7327
Fax: (843) 722-3960
Media Placement

SOUTH DAKOTA LOTTERY

207 E Capitol Ave
Pierre, SD 57501
Mailing Address:
PO Box 7107
Pierre, SD 57501-7107
Tel.: (605) 773-5770
Fax: (605) 773-5786
E-mail: lottery@state.sd.us
Web Site: www.sdlottery.org
Sales Range: $200-249.9 Million
Approx. Number Employees: 33
Year Founded: 1987
Business Description:
South Dakota State Lottery
S.I.C.: 9311
N.A.I.C.S.: 921130
Advertising Expenditures: $800,000
Media: 8-13-19-20-22-23-24
Distr.: Direct to Consumer; Reg.
Budget Set: July
Personnel:
Mike Mueller *(Dir-Pub Rels & Dir-Adv)*
Joe Willingham *(Dir-Sls & Mktg)*
Brands & Products:
14 KARAT CASH
CORVETTE SUMMER
DAKOTA CASH
LINE EM UP
PHEASANTS FOREVER
SOUTH DAKOTA LOTTERY
WILDCARD2
Advertising Agency:
Media One Advertising/Marketing
3918 S Western Ave
Sioux Falls, SD 57105
Tel.: (605) 339-0000
Fax: (605) 332-8211
(Instant Lottery Tickets, Powerball, Dakota Cash, Wild Card 2, Rolldown)
— Greg Blomberg *(Pres. & Creative Dir.)*

SOUTH DAKOTA'S DEPARTMENT OF TOURISM

711 E Wells Ave
Pierre, SD 57501-3369
Tel.: (605) 773-3301
Fax: (605) 773-3256
Toll Free: (800) SDAKOTA
E-mail: sdinfo@state.sd.us
Web Site: www.travelsd.com
Approx. Number Employees: 25
Year Founded: 1985
Business Description:
Tourism
S.I.C.: 9611
N.A.I.C.S.: 926110
Import
Advertising Expenditures: $6,300,000
Media: 2-4-6-8-9-10-13-14-15-20-22-23-24-25
Distr.: Natl.
Budget Set: July -July
Personnel:
Thad Friedeman *(Mgr-Creative Strategies)*
Wanda Goodman *(Mgr-Media & PR)*
Kirk Hulstein *(Mgr-Res)*
Brands & Products:
GREAT FACES. GREAT PLACES.
SOUTH DAKOTA
Advertising Agency:
Lawrence & Schiller, Inc.
3932 S Willow Ave
Sioux Falls, SD 57105-6234
Tel.: (605) 338-8000
Fax: (605) 338-8892
Toll Free: (888) 836-6224

SOUTHEAST TOURISM SOCIETY

3400 Peachtree Rd NE Ste 725
Atlanta, GA 30326
Tel.: (404) 364-9847
Fax: (404) 262-9518

Key to Media (For complete agency information see *The Advertising Red Books-Agencies* edition):
1. Bus. Publs. 2. Cable T.V. 3. Catalogs & Directories. 4. Co-op Adv. 5. Consumer Mags. 6. D.M. to Bus. Estab.7. D.M. to Consumers 8. Daily Newsp. 9. Exhibits/Trade Shows 10. Foreign 11. Infomercial 12. Internet Adv.13. Multimedia 14. Network Radio 15. Network T.V. 16. Newsp. Distr. Mags. 17. Other 18. Outdoor (Posters, Transit) 19. Point of Purchase20. Premiums, Novelties 21. Product Samples 22. Special Events Mktg. 23. Spot Radio 24. Spot T.V. 25. Weekly Newsp. 26. Yellow Page Adv.

E-mail: sts@southeasttourism.org
Web Site: www.southeasttourism.org
Approx. Number Employees: 4
Year Founded: 1983
Business Description:
Tourism Promoter
S.I.C.: 7389; 7319
N.A.I.C.S.: 711310; 541870; 561439; 561499; 561990; 711320
Media: 5-6-8-10-13-23
Personnel:
William T. Hardman *(Pres & CEO)*
Neville Bhada *(VP-Comm & PR)*
Charles E. Bonelli *(VP-Mktg)*

ST. AUGUSTINE, PONTE VEDRA & THE BEACHES VISITORS & CONVENTION BUREAU
29 Old mission Ave
Saint Augustine, FL 32084
Tel.: (904) 829-1711
Fax: (904) 829-6149
E-mail: jvoorhees@getaway4florida.com
Web Site: www.getaway4florida.com
Approx. Rev.: $5,000,000
Approx. Number Employees: 12
Year Founded: 1995
Business Description:
Convention & Visitors Bureau
S.I.C.: 7389
N.A.I.C.S.: 561591
Advertising Expenditures: $3,000,000
Media: 6-8-10-13-18-22-23-24
Personnel:
Richard Goldman *(Exec Dir)*
Jay Humphreys *(Dir-Comm)*
Evelyn Vazquez *(Dir-Sls)*
Carey Cramer *(Mgr-Tourist Dev)*
Kristi Hansman *(Mgr-Sls (Conference))*
Stacey Sather *(Mgr-Adv & Creative)*
Jaya Larkin *(Coord-Sls)*
Advertising Agency:
The Zimmerman Agency
1821 Miccosukee Commons Dr
Tallahassee, FL 32308-5433
Tel.: (850) 668-2222
Fax: (850) 656-4622
— Emily Fish *(Acct Exec)*

ST. LOUIS CONVENTION & VISITORS COMMISSION
701 Convention Plz Ste 300
Saint Louis, MO 63101
Tel.: (314) 421-1023
Fax: (314) 421-0039
Toll Free: (800) 325-7962
E-mail: webmaster@explorestlouis.com
Web Site: www.explorestlouis.com
Approx. Number Employees: 125
Year Founded: 1909
Business Description:
Convention & Visitors Bureau
S.I.C.: 7389
N.A.I.C.S.: 561591
Advertising Expenditures: $300,000
Media: 2-4-7-10-13
Personnel:
Kathleen Ratcliffe *(Pres)*
Neil Palacios *(CFO)*
Brian Hall *(CMO)*
Steve Stickford *(Sr VP-Convention Industry Rels)*
Joe Ruggeri *(Gen Mgr)*
Donna Andrews *(Dir-PR)*
Bruce Arnold *(Dir-Sls)*
Melanie Donnelly *(Dir-Labor Rels)*
Jennifer Hollenkamp *(Dir-Mktg)*
Paulette Koons *(Dir-Membership)*
Karen Meirink *(Dir-Visitor & Volunteer Svcs)*
Leo H. Ming, Jr. *(Dir-Community Rels)*
Doug Ross *(Dir-IT)*
Gary Schurk *(Dir-Sports Sls)*
Kathy Steffen *(Dir-Convention Svcs)*
Patricia Barnett *(Exec Sls Mgr-Meetings)*
Matt Brinkmann *(Mgr-Convention Svcs)*
Robert Olson *(Mgr-Natl Convention Sls)*
Lori Rockwell *(Mgr-Special Projects)*
Linda Schuette *(Mgr-Convention Sls-Natl)*
Nancy Ulrich *(Mgr-Housing)*
Steve Wood *(Mgr-Creative Svcs)*
Advertising Agency:
Rodgers Townsend, LLC
1000 Clark Ave 5th Fl
Saint Louis, MO 63102
Tel.: (314) 436-9960
Fax: (314) 436-9961

THE STATE LOTTERY COMMISSION OF INDIANA
(d/b/a Hoosier Lottery)
Pan Am Plaza 201 S Capitol Ave Ste 1100
Indianapolis, IN 46225-1096
Mailing Address:
PO Box 6124
Indianapolis, IN 46206-6124
Tel.: (317) 264-4800
Fax: (317) 264-4630
Toll Free: (800) 95-LOTTO
E-mail: playersupport@hoosierlottery.com
Web Site: www.hoosierlottery.com
Approx. Number Employees: 225
Year Founded: 1989
Business Description:
Lottery Operator
S.I.C.: 7999
N.A.I.C.S.: 713290
Advertising Expenditures: $8,000,000
Media: 3-9-13-14-15-18-19-20-22-23-24-25-26
Distr.: Reg.
Budget Set: June
Personnel:
W. Edward Benton *(CFO & Deputy Dir)*
Andrew J. Klinger *(Gen Counsel)*
Kathryn A. Densborn *(Exec Dir)*
Jeff Glock *(Dir-IT)*
Susan Golightly *(Dir-Mktg)*
Irene Lange *(Dir-Sls)*
Brands & Products:
DAILY 3
DAILY 4
HOOSIER LOTTO
LUCKY 5
MIX & MATCH
QUICK DRAW

STATE OF FLORIDA DEPARTMENT OF CITRUS
1115 E Memorial Blvd
Lakeland, FL 33801-2021
Tel.: (863) 537-3999
Fax: (863) 499-2500
Web Site: www.floridajuice.com
Sales Range: $100-124.9 Million
Approx. Number Employees: 50
Year Founded: 1935
Business Description:
State Citrus Industry Marketing, Research & Regulation Government Agency
S.I.C.: 9641
N.A.I.C.S.: 926140
Advertising Expenditures: $18,200,000
Media: 2-6-8-9-14-15-19-20-23-24
Distr.: Natl.
Budget Set: June
Personnel:
Debbie Funkhouser *(Comptroller)*
Leigh Killeen *(Deputy Exec Dir-Mktg & PR)*
Robert P. Norberg *(Dir-Res)*
Advertising Agency:
GolinHarris
(Part of the Interpublic Group of Companies)
111 E Wacker Dr 11th Fl
Chicago, IL 60601-4306
Tel.: (312) 729-4000
Fax: (312) 729-4010

STATE OF MISSOURI DIVISION OF TOURISM
Truman State Ofc Bldg 301 W High St Rm 290
Jefferson City, MO 65101
Mailing Address:
PO Box 1055
Jefferson City, MO 65102-1055
Tel.: (573) 751-4133
Fax: (573) 751-5160
Toll Free: (800) 519-2300
E-mail: tourism@ded.mo.gov
Web Site: www.visitmo.com
E-Mail For Key Personnel:
Public Relations: lsimms@mail.state.mo.us
Approx. Number Employees: 22
Year Founded: 1967
Business Description:
Travel & Tourism Promoter
S.I.C.: 7011
N.A.I.C.S.: 721199
Media: 2-3-5-6-7-9-10-16-18-23-24-25
Distr.: Natl.
Budget Set: Mar.
Personnel:
Raeanne Presley *(Chm)*
Bob Smith, III *(Deputy Dir-Mktg)*
Brands & Products:
MISSOURI NIGHTS
WHERE THE RIVERS RUN
Advertising Agencies:
Hughes
1141 S 7th St
Saint Louis, MO 63104
Tel.: (314) 571-6300

MMG Worldwide
4601 Madison Ave
Kansas City, MO 64112
Tel.: (816) 472-5988
Fax: (816) 471-5395

SWITZERLAND TOURISM
608 5th Ave 49th St
New York, NY 10020-2303
Tel.: (212) 757-5944
Fax: (212) 262-6116
Toll Free: (877) SWITZERLAND
E-mail: info.usa@switzerland.com
Web Site: www.myswitzerland.com
Approx. Number Employees: 15
Year Founded: 1917
Business Description:
Tourist Promotion to Switzerland
S.I.C.: 7389
N.A.I.C.S.: 561591
Media: 6-8-13

TAHITI TOURISME NORTH AMERICA, INC.
300 Continental Blvd Ste 160
El Segundo, CA 90245
Tel.: (310) 414-8484
Fax: (310) 414-8490
Toll Free: (877) GO-TAHITI
E-mail: info@tahiti-tourisme.com
Web Site: www.tahiti-tourisme.com
Approx. Number Employees: 10
Year Founded: 1992
Business Description:
Tourism Services for Tahiti
S.I.C.: 4724
N.A.I.C.S.: 561510
Media: 2-3-5-6-9-18-23-24-25
Distr.: Natl.
Personnel:
Al Keahi *(Mng Dir)*
Tina Karimi *(Mgr-Comm)*
Brands & Products:
TAHITI TOURISME
Advertising Agency:
The Phelps Group
901 Wilshire Blvd
Santa Monica, CA 90401-1854
Tel.: (310) 752-4400
Fax: (310) 752-4444
(Tahiti)

TAMPA BAY & CO.
401 E Jackson St Ste 2100
Tampa, FL 33602
Tel.: (813) 223-1111
Fax: (813) 229-6616
Toll Free: (800) 826-8358
Web Site: www.visittampabay.com
Approx. Number Employees: 60
Business Description:
Convention & Visitors Bureau
S.I.C.: 7389
N.A.I.C.S.: 561591
Media: 2-3-5-6-7-10-11-13-22-23-24
Personnel:
Paul Catoe *(Pres & CEO)*
Greg Orchard *(CFO)*
Steve Hayes *(Exec VP)*
Dianne Jacob *(Sr VP-Mktg)*
Shari Bailey *(Dir-Leisure Sls)*
Delia Quiroz *(Dir-Leisure Sls)*
Susan Williams *(Dir-Svcs & Special)*
Holly Coger *(Sr Mgr-Housing Svcs)*
Lisa Chamberlain *(Mgr-Natl Sls)*
Jennifer Friday *(Mgr-Natl Sls)*
Natalie Bryant *(Mgr-Visitor Info Center)*
Tammy Lamm *(Mgr-Natl Sls)*
Advertising Agency:
Moore, Epstein, Moore
442 W Kennedy Blvd Ste 200
Tampa, FL 33606
Tel.: (813) 286-6500
Fax: (813) 286-6501

TENNESSEE DEPARTMENT OF TOURIST DEVELOPMENT
Tennessee Twr 2 Rosa Middle l'Parks Ave 25th Fl

Key to Media (For complete agency information see *The Advertising Red Books-Agencies* edition):
1. Bus. Publs. 2. Cable T.V. 3. Catalogs & Directories. 4. Co-op Adv. 5. Consumer Mags. 6. D.M. to Bus. Estab.7. D.M. to Consumers 8. Daily Newsp. 9. Exhibits/Trade Shows 10. Foreign 11. Infomercial 12. Internet Adv.13. Multimedia 14. Network Radio 15. Network T.V. 16. Newsp. Distr. Mags. 17. Other 18. Outdoor (Posters, Transit) 19. Point of Purchase20. Premiums, Novelties 21. Product Samples 22. Special Events Mktg. 23. Spot Radio 24. Spot T.V. 25. Weekly Newsp. 26. Yellow Page Adv.

Tennessee Department of Tourist Development — (Continued)

Nashville, TN 37243
Tel.: (615) 741-2159
Tel.: (615) 741-9001 (Commissioner)
Fax: (615) 741-9071
Toll Free: (800) GO2TENN
E-mail: tourdev@ten.gov
Web Site: www.tnvacation.com
Approx. Rev.: $11,000,000,000
Approx. Number Employees: 150
Business Description:
Tourism Development for the State of Tennessee
S.I.C.: 9611
N.A.I.C.S.: 926110
Import Export
Media: 3-5-6-23-24
Distr.: Reg.
Budget Set: July
Brands & Products:
THE STAGE IS SET FOR YOU TENNESSEE
THE VACATION GUIDE
Advertising Agency:
The Brand Squad
6000 Poplar Ave Ste 250
Memphis, TN 38119
Tel.: (901) 866-9402
Fax: (901) 261-5411

TEXAS LOTTERY COMMISSION

611 E 6th St
Austin, TX 78701
Mailing Address:
PO Box 16630
Austin, TX 78761-6630
Tel.: (512) 344-5000
Fax: (512) 344-5080
Fax: (512) 344-5142
Toll Free: (800) 375-6886
E-mail: customer.service@lottery.state.tx.us
Web Site: www.txlottery.org
Approx. Number Employees: 335
Year Founded: 1992
Business Description:
Lottery Gaming & Charitable Bingo Licensing in the State of Texas
S.I.C.: 9311; 7999
N.A.I.C.S.: 921130; 713290
Personnel:
Mary Ann Williamson *(Chm)*
Robert Tirloni *(Product Mgr-Mktg)*
Ray Page *(Mgr-Adv & Promos)*
Brands & Products:
CASH 5
DAILY 4
LOTTO TEXAS
MEGA MILLIONS
PICK 3
TEXAS LOTTERY
TEXAS TWO STEP
Advertising Agencies:
The King Group
1801 Northhampton Ste 410
Desoto, TX 75115
Tel.: (214) 720-9046
Fax: (214) 720-1435

The Ward Group
15400 Knoll Trl Ste 335
Dallas, TX 75248
Tel.: (972) 818-4050
Fax: (972) 818-4151

Toll Free: (800) 807-3077

THOUSAND ISLAND REGIONAL TOURISM DEVELOPMENT CORP

43373 Collins Landing
Alexandria Bay, NY 13607
Tel.: (315) 482-2520
Fax: (315) 482-5906
Toll Free: (800) 847-5263
E-mail: info@visit1000islands.com
Web Site: www.visit1000islands.com
Approx. Number Employees: 6
Year Founded: 1957
Business Description:
Promoter of Tourism
S.I.C.: 8743
N.A.I.C.S.: 541820
Advertising Expenditures: $300,000
Media: 2-3-6-8-9-10-18-23-24
Distr.: Intl.; Natl.
Budget Set: Nov.
Personnel:
Gary Deyoung *(Dir)*
Advertising Agencies:
Ad Workshop
44 Hadjis Way
Lake Placid, NY 12946
Tel.: (518) 523-3359
Fax: (518) 523-0255

River Side Media Group
507 Riverside Dr
Clayton, NY 13624
Tel.: (315) 686-4955
Fax: (315) 686-4957

TORONTO CONVENTION & VISITORS ASSOCIATION

(d/b/a Tourism Toronto)
207 Queens Quay W
PO Box 126
Toronto, ON Canada
Tel.: (416) 203-2600
Fax: (416) 203-6753
E-mail: toronto@torcvb.com
Web Site: www.torontotourism.com
Approx. Number Employees: 75
Business Description:
Convention & Visitors Bureau
S.I.C.: 7389
N.A.I.C.S.: 561591
Media: 2-4-10-13
Personnel:
David Ogilvie *(Chm)*
David Whitaker *(Pres & CEO)*
Joel Peters *(CMO & Sr VP)*
Heidi Wallace *(Dir-Mktg)*
Advertising Agency:
Starcom MediaVest Group
175 Bloor St E N Tower 10th Fl
Toronto, ON M4W 3R9, Canada
Tel.: (416) 928-3636
Fax: (416) 927-3202

TOURISM AUSTRALIA

6100 Ctr Dr Ste 1150
Los Angeles, CA 90045
Tel.: (310) 695-3200
Fax: (310) 695-3201
E-mail: tra@tourism.australia.com
Web Site: www.tourism.australia.com
Sales Estimate: $10-19 Million
Approx. Number Employees: 24
Year Founded: 1985
Business Description:
Promoter of Australian Tourism
S.I.C.: 8743
N.A.I.C.S.: 541820
Advertising Expenditures: $5,200,000
Media: 3-6-13
Distr.: Intl.; Natl.
Personnel:
Andrew McEvoy *(Mng Dir)*
Richard Beere *(Exec Gen Mgr-East)*
Nick Baker *(Gen Mgr-Mktg)*
Frances-Anne Callaghan *(Exec Gen Mgr-West)*
Kim Portrate *(Gen Mgr-Consumer Mktg)*
Lisa Wooldridge *(Dir-Mktg-The Americas)*
Kimberly Ozawa *(Mgr-Digital Mktg)*
Advertising Agencies:
Carat Mumbai
12 Mittal Chambers
Mumbai, 400021, India
Tel.: (91) 22 5660 8088
Fax: (91) 22 5660 8089

DDB Sydney Pty. Ltd.
46-52 Mountain Street Level 3
Ultimo, NSW 2007, Australia
Tel.: (61) 2 8260 2222
Fax: (61) 2 8260 2444

Ketchum
340 Main St Ste 200
Venice, CA 90291-2524
Tel.: (310) 584-8300
Fax: (310) 584-8304
International Media Hosting Program
Public Relations Agency of Record
Social Media
Strategic Media Partnerships

TOURISM IRELAND

345 Park Ave 17th Fl
New York, NY 10154
Tel.: (212) 418-0800
Fax: (212) 371-9052
Toll Free: (800) 223-6470
Telex: 422234
E-mail: corporate.usa@tourismireland.com
Web Site: www.tourismireland.com
Approx. Number Employees: 20
Year Founded: 2001
Business Description:
Ireland Tourism Promoter
S.I.C.: 4729; 9199
N.A.I.C.S.: 561599; 921190
Advertising Expenditures: $4,000,000
Media: 2-6-9-13-23-24
Distr.: Intl.; Natl.
Budget Set: Oct.
Personnel:
Orla Carey *(Mgr-Adv, Direct Mktg & E-Mktg)*
Brands & Products:
TOURISM IRELAND
Advertising Agency:
Mindshare
498 7th Ave
New York, NY 10018
Tel.: (212) 297-7000
Fax: (212) 297-7001

TOURISM NEW ZEALAND

(Branch of Tourism New Zealand)
501 Santa Monica Blvd Ste 300
Santa Monica, CA 90401
Tel.: (310) 395-7480
Fax: (310) 395-5453
Toll Free: (800) 388-5494
Web Site: www.tourisminfo.govt.nz
Approx. Number Employees: 10
Business Description:
Promoter of Tourism to New Zealand
S.I.C.: 9111; 7999
N.A.I.C.S.: 921110; 712190
Advertising Expenditures: $3,000,000
Media: 3-6-8-9-10-22-23-24-25
Distr.: Intl.; Natl.

TOURIST OFFICE OF SPAIN

666 5th Ave 35th Fl
New York, NY 10103-0001
Tel.: (212) 265-8822
Fax: (212) 265-8864
E-mail: oetny@tourspain.es
Web Site: www.spain.info
Approx. Number Employees: 15
Year Founded: 1977
Business Description:
Non-Profit Government Organization Promoting American Tourism to Spain
S.I.C.: 7389
N.A.I.C.S.: 561591
Advertising Expenditures: $1,500,000
Media: 2-4-5-6-9-10-16-19-22-23-24-25
Distr.: Natl.
Budget Set: Jan.

TRAVEL PORTLAND

1000 SW Broadway Ste 2300
Portland, OR 97205
Tel.: (503) 275-9750
Fax: (503) 275-9284
Toll Free: (800) 962-3700
E-mail: info@travelportland.com
Web Site: www.travelportland.com
Approx. Number Employees: 50
Business Description:
Visitors Bureau
S.I.C.: 7389
N.A.I.C.S.: 561591
Media: 4-10-13
Personnel:
Jeff Miller *(Pres & CEO)*
Carol Lentz *(Exec VP)*
Brian McCartin *(Exec VP-Sls-Convention & Tourism)*
Greg Newland *(Exec VP-Mktg & PR)*
Megan Donway *(VP-Comm & PR)*
Karen Martwick *(Editor)*
Christina Anderson *(Dir-Tourism Adv)*
Karla Nutt *(Mktg Mgr)*
Kristine Danzer-Becker *(Mgr-Convention Sls)*
Kitty Jones *(Mgr-Ops)*
Cathy Kretz *(Mgr-Sls)*
Advertising Agency:
Grady Britton
808 SW 3rd Ave #700
Portland, OR 97204
Tel.: (503) 222-0626
Fax: (503) 222-0154

TULSA METRO CHAMBER

2 W 2nd St Williams Center Tower 2 Ste 150
Tulsa, OK 74103
Tel.: (918) 585-1201
Fax: (918) 585-8016
Toll Free: (800) 558-3311
E-mail: tulsacvb@tulsachamber.com
Web Site: www.tulsachamber.com
E-Mail For Key Personnel:
Sales Director: maryking@tulsachamber.com
Approx. Number Employees: 50
Business Description:
Tulsa Tourism Promoter

Key to Media (For complete agency information see *The Advertising Red Books-Agencies* edition):
1. Bus. Publs. 2. Cable T.V. 3. Catalogs & Directories. 4. Co-op Adv. 5. Consumer Mags. 6. D.M. to Bus. Estab.7. D.M. to Consumers 8. Daily Newsp. 9. Exhibits/Trade Shows 10. Foreign 11. Infomercial 12. Internet Adv.13. Multimedia 14. Network Radio 15. Network T.V. 16. Newsp. Distr. Mags. 17. Other 18. Outdoor (Posters, Transit) 19. Point of Purchase20. Premiums, Novelties 21. Product Samples 22. Special Events Mktg. 23. Spot Radio 24. Spot T.V. 25. Weekly Newsp. 26. Yellow Page Adv.

S.I.C.: 9532; 8611
N.A.I.C.S.: 925120; 813910
Media: 2-6-10
Personnel:
Mike Neal *(Pres & CEO)*
Matt Pivarnik *(Exec VP)*
Susan Harris *(Sr VP)*
Sheila A. Curley *(VP-Comm)*
Karen Humphrey *(Dir-Resource Campaign & Affinity Programs)*
Rusty Linker *(Dir-Mktg, Economic Dev)*
Bob Ball *(Mgr-Economic Res)*
Don Sibley *(Mgr-Creative Svcs)*
Elaine Walsh *(Mgr-Member Events)*

THE UNITED STATES AIR FORCE
9038 Mansfield Rd
Shreveport, LA 71118
Tel.: (318) 687-4174
Fax: (318) 689-3219
Web Site: www.airforce.com
Approx. Number Employees: 3
Business Description:
Military Service
S.I.C.: 9711
N.A.I.C.S.: 928110
Media: 31
Advertising Agencies:
GSD&M
828 W 6th St
Austin, TX 78703-5420
Tel.: (512) 242-4736
Fax: (512) 242-4700
— Tim Gilmore *(Acct Dir)*

Image Media Services, Inc.
1521 W Branch Dr Ste 650
McLean, VA 22102-3328
Tel.: (703) 893-8080
Fax: (703) 893-9480

UNITED STATES AIR FORCE RECRUITING SERVICE
550 D St W Ste 1
Randolph AFB, TX 78150-4527
Tel.: (210) 565-4678
Tel.: (210) 565-0535 (Adv)
Tel.: (210) 652-5993
Fax: (210) 565-4690
Toll Free: (800) 423USAF
E-mail: afrspaweb@rs.af.mil
Web Site: www.af.mil
Approx. Number Employees: 23
Business Description:
Recruitment of Personnel for U.S. Air Force
S.I.C.: 9711
N.A.I.C.S.: 928110
Advertising Expenditures: $61,200,000
Media: 1-6-8-13-15-18-20-22-23-25
Distr.: Natl.
Personnel:
Christa D'Andrea *(Dir-Pub Affairs)*
Advertising Agency:
GSD&M
828 W 6th St
Austin, TX 78703-5420
Tel.: (512) 242-4736
Fax: (512) 242-4700
(Recruitment Advertising)
— Travis Scroggins *(Acct Supvr)*

UNITED STATES ARMY
1500 Army Pentagon
Washington, DC 20310-1500
Tel.: (703) 697-2564
Tel.: (703) 697-0050 (Dept Pub Affairs)
Fax: (703) 697-2159
Toll Free: (800) 342-9647
E-mail: tina.m.kitts@us.army.mil
Web Site: www.army.mil
Approx. Number Employees: 12,000,000
Business Description:
Military Branch of the United States
S.I.C.: 9711
N.A.I.C.S.: 928110
Media: 31
Personnel:
Bruce Jasurda *(CMO)*
B.G. Lewis Boone *(Officer-Pub Affairs)*
Stephanie L. Hoehne *(Deputy Chief & Principal)*
Advertising Agencies:
Alloy, Inc.
151 W 26th St 11th Fl
New York, NY 10001-6810
Tel.: (212) 244-4307
Fax: (212) 244-4311
Toll Free: (877) 360-9688

Beanstalk
220 E 42nd St 15th Fl
New York, NY 10017
Tel.: (212) 421-6060
Fax: (212) 421-6388

Carol H. Williams Advertising
1120 6th Ave 4th Fl
New York, NY 10017
Tel.: (646) 865-3888
Fax: (212) 626-6602

Ignited
2221 Park Pl
El Segundo, CA 90245
Tel.: (310) 773-3100
Fax: (310) 773-3101

Inter/Media Advertising
15760 Ventura Blvd 1st Fl
Encino, CA 91436
Tel.: (818) 995-1455
Fax: (818) 995-7115
Toll Free: (800) TIMEBUY

Momentum
444 N Michigan Ave Ste 1700
Chicago, IL 60611
Tel.: (312) 245-3500
Fax: (312) 245-3550

MRM Worldwide
622 3rd Ave
New York, NY 10017-6707
Tel.: (646) 865-6230
Fax: (646) 865-6264
(Online Creative)

R3:JLB
500 N Michigan Ave Ste 300
Chicago, IL 60611
Tel.: (312) 396-4155

Vital Marketing Group LLC
115 E 23rd St 10th Fl
New York, NY 10010
Tel.: (212) 995-9525
Fax: (212) 995-2682

Weber Shandwick-Minneapolis
8000 Norman Ctr Dr Ste 400
Minneapolis, MN 55437
Tel.: (952) 832-5000
Fax: (952) 831-8241

UNITED STATES ARMY ACCESSIONS COMMAND MARKETING DIRECTORATE
232 Old Ironsides Avenue
Fort Knox, KY 40121-2726
Tel.: (502) 626-0141
E-mail: webmaster@usaac.army.mil
Web Site: www.usaac.army.mil
Approx. Number Employees: 54
Business Description:
Advertising & Marketing Services for the Recruitment of U.S. Army & Army Reserve Personnel
S.I.C.: 7319; 9711
N.A.I.C.S.: 541890; 928110
Advertising Expenditures: $254,000,000
Media: 3-6-8-9-10-13-14-15-20-22-23-24
Distr.: Natl.
Budget Set: Oct.
Personnel:
Bruce Jasurda *(CMO)*
Derik Crotts *(Dir-Adv COL)*
John Myers *(Deputy Dir-Adv)*

UNITED STATES COAST GUARD
2100 Second St SW
Washington, DC 20593
Tel.: (202) 372-4620
Fax: (202) 372-4985
Web Site: www.uscg.mil
Approx. Number Employees: 100
Business Description:
Military Branch of the United States
S.I.C.: 6799
N.A.I.C.S.: 523910
Media: 31
Advertising Agency:
Paskill Stapleton & Lord
1 Roberts Ave
Glenside, PA 19038-3497
Tel.: (215) 572-7938
Fax: (215) 572-7937

UNITED STATES DEPARTMENT OF DEFENSE - UNDER SECRETARY OF DEFENSE PERSONNEL & READINESS
1400 Defense Pentagon
Washington, DC 20301
Tel.: (703) 428-0711
Tel.: (703) 692-2000
Tel.: (703) 695-5525
Fax: (703) 695-1149
E-mail: media@defenselink.mil
Web Site: www.defenselink.mil/prhome
Approx. Number Employees: 23,000
Business Description:
Defense Recruiting
S.I.C.: 9711; 7371
N.A.I.C.S.: 928110; 541511
Personnel:
Larry Di Rita *(Acting Deputy Sec-Pub Affairs)*
Advertising Agency:
Mullen
40 Broad St
Boston, MA 02109
Tel.: (617) 226-9000
Fax: (617) 226-9100
(Joint Recruitment Advertising Program)

UNITED STATES DEPARTMENT OF ENERGY
1000 Independence Ave SW
Washington, DC 20585-0001
Tel.: (202) 586-5000
Tel.: (202) 586-5575 (Pub Affairs)
Tel.: (202) 586-5806 (Media)
Fax: (202) 586-4403
Fax: (202) 586-5823 (Media)
Web Site: www.energy.gov
Business Description:
Energy Conservation Promotion
S.I.C.: 9111
N.A.I.C.S.: 921110
Media: 2-6-9-25
Distr.: Natl.
Personnel:
Steven Isakowitz *(CFO)*
Jeanne Lopatto *(Dir-Pub Affairs)*

UNITED STATES DEPARTMENT OF STATE
2201 C St NW
Washington, DC 20520-0001
Tel.: (202) 647-4000
Tel.: (202) 647-2492 (Press Rels)
Fax: (202) 261-8577
E-mail: askpublicaffairs@state.gov
Web Site: www.state.gov
Business Description:
Government Department for the Administration of Foreign Policy
S.I.C.: 9721
N.A.I.C.S.: 928120
Media: 6-23-24
Personnel:
Bruce Morrison *(Acting CIO)*
Richard A. Boucher *(Asst Sec-Bureau of Pub Affairs)*

UNITED STATES DEPARTMENT OF THE INTERIOR
1849 C St NW
Washington, DC 20240-0001
Tel.: (202) 208-3100
Fax: (202) 208-5048
E-mail: webteam@ios.doi.gov
Web Site: www.doi.gov
Sales Range: $300-349.9 Million
Approx. Number Employees: 1,000
Business Description:
Preservation of More than 700 Million Acres of Public Lands
S.I.C.: 9512
N.A.I.C.S.: 924120
Media: 2-9-17-25
Distr.: Natl.

UNITED STATES DEPARTMENT OF THE TREASURY
1500 Pennsylvania Ave NW
Washington, DC 20220
Tel.: (202) 622-2000
Tel.: (202) 622-2960 (Press)
Fax: (202) 622-6415
Web Site: www.treas.gov
Year Founded: 1789
Business Description:
Government Treasurer's Office
S.I.C.: 9311
N.A.I.C.S.: 921130
Media: 2-6-7-8-9-13-14-15-17-18-23-24-25
Distr.: Natl.
Personnel:
Ira L. Hobbs *(CIO)*

Key to Media (For complete agency information see *The Advertising Red Books-Agencies* edition):
1. Bus. Publs. 2. Cable T.V. 3. Catalogs & Directories. 4. Co-op Adv. 5. Consumer Mags. 6. D.M. to Bus. Estab.7. D.M. to Consumers
8. Daily Newsp. 9. Exhibits/Trade Shows 10. Foreign 11. Infomercial 12. Internet Adv.13. Multimedia 14. Network Radio
15. Network T.V. 16. Newsp. Distr. Mags. 17. Other 18. Outdoor (Posters, Transit) 19. Point of Purchase20. Premiums, Novelties
21. Product Samples 22. Special Events Mktg. 23. Spot Radio 24. Spot T.V. 25. Weekly Newsp. 26. Yellow Page Adv.

United States Department of the Treasury — (Continued)

Arthur A. Garcia *(Dir-Community Devel & Fin Institutions Fund)*

UNITED STATES ENVIRONMENTAL PROTECTION AGENCY

Ariel Rios Bldg 1200 Pennsylvania Ave NW
Washington, DC 20460-0001
Tel.: (202) 272-0167
Fax: (202) 501-1450
Web Site: www.epa.gov
Approx. Rev.: $8,265,851,000
Approx. Number Employees: 18,000
Business Description:
Agency for the Protection of the Environment in the United States
S.I.C.: 9511
N.A.I.C.S.: 924110
Media: 2-7-8-13
Advertising Agencies:
Black & Veatch Corporate Marketing & Branding
11401 Lamar Ave
Overland Park, KS 66211
Tel.: (913) 458-2000
Fax: (913) 458-2934

Geovision
75 N Beacon St
Watertown, MA 02472
Tel.: (617) 926-5454
Fax: (617) 925-5411

UNITED STATES MARINE CORPS

(Branch of United States Navy)
172008 Ste 201 Elliot Rd
Quantico, VA 22134-5030
Tel.: (703) 784-3941
Fax: (703) 784-5792
Approx. Number Employees: 5
Business Description:
Military Branch of the United States
S.I.C.: 9711
N.A.I.C.S.: 928110
Media: 31
Personnel:
Deloris Smith *(HR-Mgr)*
Brands & Products:
THE FEW THE PROUD
Advertising Agencies:
JWT U.S.A., Inc.
10 B Glenlake Pkwy NE N Twr 4th Fl
Atlanta, GA 30328
Tel.: (404) 365-7300
Fax: (404) 365-7333
USMC/UFC Integrated Campaign

Uniworld Group, Inc.
1 Metro Center N 11th Fl
Brooklyn, NY 11201
Tel.: (212) 219-1600
Fax: (212) 219-6395

UNITED STATES MARINE CORPS RECRUITING

3280 Russell Rd
Quantico, VA 22134-5143
Tel.: (703) 784-9400
Tel.: (703) 784-9434
Fax: (703) 784-9854
Toll Free: (800) MARINES
Web Site: www.usmc.mil
Approx. Number Employees: 200
Year Founded: 1775
Business Description:
Recruitment of Personnel
S.I.C.: 9711
N.A.I.C.S.: 928110
Media: 1-2-3-4-5-6-8-9-10-13-14-15-17-18-20-22-23-24-25
Distr.: Natl.
Advertising Agency:
JWT U.S.A., Inc.
10 B Glenlake Pkwy NE N Twr 4th Fl
Atlanta, GA 30328
Tel.: (404) 365-7300
Fax: (404) 365-7333
(Recruiting Advertising)

UNITED STATES NAVY

5722 Integrity Dr Bldg 784
Millington, TN 38054
Tel.: (901) 874-9198
Toll Free: (866) 827-5672
Web Site: www.navy.mil
Business Description:
Military Branch of the United States
S.I.C.: 9711
N.A.I.C.S.: 928110
Media: 31
Personnel:
Robert J. Carey *(CIO)*
John L. Lussier *(Deputy CIO-Policy & Integration)*
Aaron Bedy *(Officer-Pub Affairs)*
Brands & Products:
ALL HANDS
Advertising Agencies:
Accentmarketing
La Puerta Del Sol Ste 100 800 Douglas Rd
Coral Gables, FL 33134
Tel.: (305) 461-1112
Fax: (305) 461-0071
AOR Hispanic Advertising

Campbell-Ewald
30400 Van Dyke Ave
Warren, MI 48093-2368
Tel.: (586) 574-3400
Fax: (586) 575-9925
AOR Creative

GlobalHue
Ste 1600 4000 Town Ctr
Southfield, MI 48076
Tel.: (248) 223-8900
Fax: (248) 304-8877
AOR African American & Asian Advertising

UNITED STATES NAVY RECRUITING COMMAND

Bldg 784 5722 Integrity Dr Bldg 784
Millington, TN 38054-5028
Tel.: (901) 874-9388
Tel.: (901) 874-9048 (Pub Affairs)
Fax: (901) 874-9398
Web Site: www.cnrc.navy.mil
Approx. Number Employees: 200
Business Description:
U.S. Navy Recruiting
S.I.C.: 9711
N.A.I.C.S.: 928110
Advertising Expenditures: $100,000,000
Media: 1-3-6-8-9-13-14-15-18-19-23-25
Distr.: Natl.
Personnel:
John Hamilton *(Mgr)*
Brands & Products:
BUILDING OUR NAVY'S FUTURE, ONE SAILOR AT A TIME!
LIFE ACCELERATOR
LIFE, LIBERTY & THE PURSUIT OF ALL WHO THREATEN IT
NAVY, ACCELERATE YOUR LIFE
Advertising Agency:
Campbell-Ewald
30400 Van Dyke Ave
Warren, MI 48093-2368
Tel.: (586) 574-3400
Fax: (586) 575-9925
(Enlistment)

UNITED STATES POSTAL SERVICE

475 L'Enfant Plz SW
Washington, DC 20260-0004
Tel.: (202) 268-2000
Fax: (202) 268-5211
Toll Free: (800) 275-8777
Web Site: www.usps.com
Approx. Sls.: $68,090,000,000
Approx. Number Employees: 663,238
Year Founded: 1775
Business Description:
Postal Service for the United States
S.I.C.: 4311
N.A.I.C.S.: 491110
Advertising Expenditures: $75,000,000
Media: 1-2-3-6-7-8-9-10-13-14-15-18-19-22-23-24-25-26
Distr.: Direct to Consumer; Natl.
Budget Set: Oct.
Personnel:
Paul Vogel *(Pres & CMO)*
Patrick R. Donahoe *(CEO & Postmaster Gen)*
Joseph Corbett *(CFO & Exec VP)*
Megan J. Brennan *(COO & Exec VP)*
Ellis Burgoyne *(CIO & Exec VP)*
Anthony J. Vegliante *(Chief HR Officer & Exec VP)*
Mary Anne Gibbons *(Gen Counsel & Exec VP)*
Thomas G. Day *(Sr VP-Intelligent Mail & Address Quality)*
John T. Edgar *(VP-IT)*
Stephen J. Masse *(VP-Fin & Plng)*
Susan Plonkey *(VP-Sls)*
Samuel M. Pulcrano *(VP-Corp Comm)*
David Failor *(Exec Dir-Stamp Svcs)*
Joyce Carrier *(Dir-Adv)*
Bob Krause *(Mgr)*
William J. Brown *(Coord & Specialist-HR)*
Brands & Products:
AUTOMATED POSTAL CENTERS
CARRIER PICKUP
CERTIFICATE OF MAILING
CERTIFIED MAIL
CLICK 2 MAIL
CLICK-N-SHIP
COLLECT ON DELIVERY
DELIVERY CONFIRMATION
EBILL-PAY
EXPRESS MAIL
EXPRESS MAIL INTERNATIONAL
FIRST-CLASS MAIL
GLOBAL EXPRESS GUARANTEED
GLOBAL PRIORITY MAIL
INSURED MAIL
LIBRARY MAIL
LOCATE A POST OFFICE
LOOK UP A ZIP CODE
MEDIA MAIL
PARCEL POST
PARCEL SELECT
PC POSTAGE
PICKUP ON DEMAND
POSTALONE
PREMIUM POSTCARD
PRIORITY MAIL
PRIORITY MAIL INTERNATIONAL
REDRESS
REGISTERED MAIL
RETURN TO SENDER
SIGNATURE CONFIRMATION
STANDARD MAIL
UNITED STATES POSTAL SERVICE
Advertising Agencies:
AKQA, Inc.
3299 K St NW 5th Fl
Washington, DC 20007
Tel.: (202) 551-9900
Fax: (202) 337-2573

Campbell-Ewald
30400 Van Dyke Ave
Warren, MI 48093-2368
Tel.: (586) 574-3400
Fax: (586) 575-9925
Agency of Record
Al the Letter Carrier Campaign
Fully Integrated Communications

Draftfcb
101 E Erie St
Chicago, IL 60611
Tel.: (312) 425-5000
Fax: (312) 425-5010

o2kl
10 W 18th St 6th Fl
New York, NY 10011
Tel.: (646) 829-6239
Fax: (646) 839-6254

RealTime Media, Inc.
1060 1st Ave Ste 201
King of Prussia, PA 19406
Tel.: (610) 337-3600
Fax: (610) 337-2300

U.S. DEPARTMENT OF HOUSING & URBAN DEVELOPMENT

451 7th St SW
Washington, DC 20410
Tel.: (202) 708-1112
Web Site: www.hud.gov
Business Description:
Government Housing & Community Assistance Services
S.I.C.: 9199
N.A.I.C.S.: 921190
Media: 6-7-8
Personnel:
Marcell E. Belt *(CEO)*
Lisa Schlosser *(CIO)*
Roy A. Bernardi *(Deputy Sec)*

UTAH TOURISM OFFICE

Council Hall 300 N State
Salt Lake City, UT 84114
Tel.: (801) 538-1030
Fax: (801) 538-1399
Toll Free: (800) 200-1160
E-mail: travel@utah.gov
Web Site: www.utah.travel
E-Mail For Key Personnel:

Key to Media (For complete agency information see *The Advertising Red Books-Agencies* edition):
1. Bus. Publs. 2. Cable T.V. 3. Catalogs & Directories. 4. Co-op Adv. 5. Consumer Mags. 6. D.M. to Bus. Estab.7. D.M. to Consumers 8. Daily Newsp. 9. Exhibits/Trade Shows 10. Foreign 11. Infomercial 12. Internet Adv.13. Multimedia 14. Network Radio 15. Network T.V. 16. Newsp. Distr. Mags. 17. Other 18. Outdoor (Posters, Transit) 19. Point of Purchase20. Premiums, Novelties 21. Product Samples 22. Special Events Mktg. 23. Spot Radio 24. Spot T.V. 25. Weekly Newsp. 26. Yellow Page Adv.

Marketing Director: kkraus@travel.state.ut.us
Approx. Number Employees: 25
Year Founded: 1953
Business Description:
Travel & Tourism Promoter
S.I.C.: 7389; 7319
N.A.I.C.S.: 561591; 541870
Media: 1-3-5-6-7-8-10-13-18-20-23-24
Distr.: Intl.; Natl.
Brands & Products:
THE GREATEST SNOW ON EARTH
LIFE ELEVATED
UTAH

VERMONT DEPARTMENT OF TOURISM & MARKETING

1 National Life Dr 6th Fl
Montpelier, VT 05620
Tel.: (802) 828-3237
Tel.: (802) 828-0528
Fax: (802) 828-3233
Toll Free: (800) VERMONT
E-mail: info@vermontvacation.com
Web Site: www.vermontvacation.com
E-Mail For Key Personnel:
Public Relations: Erica.Houskeeper@state.vt.us
Approx. Number Employees: 12
Year Founded: 1970
Business Description:
Tourism Promoter & Marketer
S.I.C.: 9611
N.A.I.C.S.: 926110
Advertising Expenditures: $1,500,000
Media: 1-4-5-6-8-9-10-13-22-24
Distr.: Natl.; State Government
Budget Set: May
Personnel:
Bruce Hyde *(Commissioner)*

VERMONT LOTTERY COMMISSION

1311 US Rt 302 Berlin Ste 100
Barre, VT 05641
Tel.: (802) 479-5686
Fax: (802) 479-4294
Toll Free: (800) 322-8800 (VT Only)
E-mail: staff@vtlottery.com
Web Site: www.vtlottery.com
Approx. Rev.: $92,300,000
Approx. Number Employees: 20
Year Founded: 1977
Business Description:
State Lottery
S.I.C.: 9311
N.A.I.C.S.: 921130
Advertising Expenditures: $1,500,000
Media: 6-9-13-16-18-19-20-22-23-24-25
Distr.: Direct to Consumer; Reg.
Budget Set: July
Personnel:
Frank Cioffi *(Chm)*
Arthur Ristau *(Vice Chm)*
Alan R. Yandow *(Exec Dir)*
Mary Cassani *(Dir-Bus Ops)*
Mark Cayia *(Mgr-Sls & Mktg)*
Brands & Products:
GOOD. CLEAN. FUN
TRI-STATE HEADS OR TAILS
TRI-STATE MEGABUCKS
TRI-STATE PICK 3
TRI-STATE PICK 4
VERMONT LOTTERY
Advertising Agency:
NL Partners
20 York St Ste 201
Portland, ME 04101
Tel.: (207) 775-5251
Fax: (207) 775-3389
— Catherine Palm *(Acct Rep)*
— Chris Nichols *(Pres)*

VIRGINIA ECONOMIC DEVELOPMENT PARTNERSHIP

901 E Byrd St
Richmond, VA 23219
Mailing Address:
PO Box 798
Richmond, VA 23218-0798
Tel.: (804) 545-5600
Tel.: (804) 545-5805 (Media Rels)
Fax: (804) 545-5641
Web Site: www.yesvirginia.org
E-Mail For Key Personnel:
Marketing Director: rrichardson@vedp.state.va.us
Sales Director: g.mclaren@vedp.state.va.us
Approx. Number Employees: 150
Business Description:
Industrial Development Services
S.I.C.: 9611
N.A.I.C.S.: 926110
Media: 2-10-13-14-15-23-24
Budget Set: June
Personnel:
Jeffrey M. Anderson *(Pres & CEO)*
Jerry Giles *(Mng Dir)*
Sandra McNinch *(Gen Counsel)*
Vince Barnett *(Dir-Comm & Promos)*
Paul Grossman *(Dir-Intl Trade & Investment)*
Rob McClintock *(Dir-Res)*
John Mehfoud *(Dir-IT)*
Liz Povar *(Dir-Bus Dev)*
Rick Richardson *(Dir-Comm & Promos)*
Christie Miller *(Mgr-Comm)*
Advertising Agency:
Barber Martin Agency
7400 Beaufont Springs Dr Ste 201
Richmond, VA 23225-5519
Tel.: (804) 320-3232
Fax: (804) 320-1729
Commonwealth of Virginia

VIRGINIA STATE LOTTERY DEPARTMENT

900 E Main St
Richmond, VA 23219-3548
Tel.: (804) 692-7000
Fax: (804) 692-7102
Toll Free: (800) 243-5825
E-mail: webmaster@valottery.com
Web Site: www.valottery.com
Approx. Rev.: $1,135,700,000
Approx. Number Employees: 300
Year Founded: 1988
Business Description:
State Lottery
S.I.C.: 9311; 7999
N.A.I.C.S.: 921130; 713290
Advertising Expenditures: $15,000,000
Media: 3-9-10-13-18-19-20-22-23-24-25
Distr.: Direct to Consumer; Reg.
Budget Set: Mar.
Personnel:
John Miutz *(Editor-Play Back)*
Rob Wesley *(Dir-Sls)*
Mark Hoerath *(Mgr-Adv)*
Advertising Agency:
Qorvis Communications
1201 Connecticut Ave NW Ste 500
Washington, DC 20036
Tel.: (202) 496-1000
Fax: (202) 496-1300

VIRGINIA TOURISM AUTHORITY

(d/b/a Virginia Tourism Corporation)
901 E Byrd St
Richmond, VA 23219-4052
Tel.: (804) 545-5500
Fax: (804) 545-5501
Toll Free: (800) VISITVA
E-mail: vatour@virginia.org
Web Site: www.vatc.org
Approx. Number Employees: 40
Year Founded: 1999
Business Description:
Tourism to Virginia Promoter
S.I.C.: 7389; 8611
N.A.I.C.S.: 561591; 813910
Advertising Expenditures: $3,000,000
Media: 1-2-3-6-8-9-10-11-15-18-20-22-23-24-25
Distr.: Direct to Consumer; Intl.; Natl.; Reg.
Budget Set: July
Personnel:
Alisa L. Bailey *(Pres & CEO)*
Diane Bechamps *(VP-Mktg)*
Beth Campion *(VP-Sls & Mktg)*
Rita D. McClenny *(VP-Customer Svc & Indus Rels)*
Wirt S. Confroy *(Dir-Partnerships & Outreach)*
Heidi Johannesen *(Dir-Intl Mktg)*
Carol N. Torricelli *(Dir-Sls)*
Rebecca Beckstoffer *(Mgr-Mktg)*
Brands & Products:
VIRGINIA IS FOR LOVERS

VISIT FLORIDA INC.

2540 W Executive Ctr Cir Ste 200
Tallahassee, FL 32301
Tel.: (850) 488-5607
Fax: (850) 201-6901
Web Site: www.visitflorida.org
Approx. Number Employees: 65
Business Description:
Tourism Marketing Services
S.I.C.: 4724; 8743
N.A.I.C.S.: 561510; 541820
Media: 6-8-10-11-13-14-15-18-20-22
Personnel:
Christopher Thompson *(Pres & CEO)*
Vangie McCorvey *(CFO)*
Will Seccombe *(CMO)*
Eileen Forrow *(VP-Sls & Mktg)*
Jeffrey S. Brewer *(Dir-IT)*
Meredith M. DaSilva *(Dir-Exec Ops)*
Kimberly Faulk *(Dir-Bus Dev)*
Kimberly Hineman *(Dir-HR)*
Christi McCray *(Dir-Promos)*
Joyce Stillwell *(Dir-Sls)*
Vicki Allen *(Mgr-Res)*
Steven Bonda *(Mgr-Meetings & Conventions Sls)*
Damien Raimondi *(Mgr-Creative Svcs)*
Kathy Torian *(Mgr-Corp Comm)*
Brands & Products:
FLORIDA VACATION GUIDE
VISIT FLORIDA
Advertising Agency:
DDB Miami
770 S Dixie Hwy
Coral Gables, FL 33146
Tel.: (305) 529-4300
Fax: (305) 662-3166

VOICE OF AMERICA

330 Independence Ave SW
Washington, DC 20237-0001
Tel.: (202) 203-4959
Tel.: (202) 203-4164 (Mktg)
Fax: (202) 203-4960
E-mail: askvoa@voanews.com
Web Site: www.voanews.com
Approx. Number Employees: 1,149
Year Founded: 1942
Business Description:
Multimedia Broadcasting of News & U.S. Policy Outside the United States
S.I.C.: 9721
N.A.I.C.S.: 928120
Advertising Expenditures: $166,000,000
Media: 1-2-3-4-6-7-8-9-10-11-13-14-15-18-22-23-24-25
Brands & Products:
A TRUSTED SOURCE OF NEWS AND INFORMATION
VOICE OF AMERICA

WASHINGTON, D.C. CONVENTION & TOURISM CORP.

901 7th St NW 4th Fl
Washington, DC 20001
Tel.: (202) 789-7000
Fax: (202) 789-7037
Web Site: www.washington.org
Approx. Number Employees: 64
Year Founded: 2001
Business Description:
Convention & Visitors Bureau
S.I.C.: 7389
N.A.I.C.S.: 561591
Advertising Expenditures: $500,000
Media: 4-10-13
Personnel:
Elliott Ferguson, II *(Pres & CEO)*
Victoria Isley *(Sr VP-Mktg & Comm)*
John Kim *(VP-Fin & Admin)*
Robin McClain *(Dir-Comm)*
Rebecca Pawlowski *(Dir-Comm)*
Melissa Riley *(Dir-Convention Sls)*
Dianna Waldroup *(Dir-Convention Svcs)*
George Cooley *(Mgr-Sls-Domestic Tourism)*

WASHINGTON STATE DEPARTMENT OF COMMUNITY, TRADE & ECONOMIC DEVELOPMENT

128 10th Ave SW
Olympia, WA 98504-2525
Tel.: (360) 725-4177
Fax: (360) 586-0873
E-mail: tourism@cted.wa.gov
Web Site: www.experiencewashington.com
E-Mail For Key Personnel:
President: peterm@cted.wa.gov
Marketing Director: betsyg@cted.wa.gov
Public Relations: carriew@cted.wa.gov
Approx. Number Employees: 42
Year Founded: 1950

Key to Media (For complete agency information see *The Advertising Red Books-Agencies* edition):
1. Bus. Publs. 2. Cable T.V. 3. Catalogs & Directories. 4. Co-op Adv. 5. Consumer Mags. 6. D.M. to Bus. Estab.7. D.M. to Consumers
8. Daily Newsp. 9. Exhibits/Trade Shows 10. Foreign 11. Infomercial 12. Internet Adv.13. Multimedia 14. Network Radio
15. Network T.V. 16. Newsp. Distr. Mags. 17. Other 18. Outdoor (Posters, Transit) 19. Point of Purchase20. Premiums, Novelties
21. Product Samples 22. Special Events Mktg. 23. Spot Radio 24. Spot T.V. 25. Weekly Newsp. 26. Yellow Page Adv.

Washington State Department of Community, Trade & Economic Development — (Continued)

Business Description:
State Economic & Community Development Administrative Services
S.I.C.: 9611; 9532
N.A.I.C.S.: 926110; 925120
Advertising Expenditures: $600,000
Media: 6
Distr.: Natl.
Budget Set: July
Personnel:
Marsha Massey *(Exec Dir)*
Rogers Weed *(Dir-Dept of Commerce)*
Michelle Campbell *(Mgr-Product Dev)*
Betsy Gabel *(Mgr-Mktg)*
Brands & Products:
EXPERIENCEWA.COM
Advertising Agency:
Edelman
International Sq 1875 Eye St NW Ste 900
Washington, DC 20006-5422
Tel.: (202) 371-0200
Fax: (202) 371-2858

WASHINGTON STATE LOTTERY

814 4th Ave E
Olympia, WA 98504
Tel.: (360) 664-4720
Fax: (360) 664-2630
E-mail: director@walottery.com
Web Site: www.walottery.com
Sales Estimate: $20-39 Million
Approx. Number Employees: 150
Business Description:
State Lottery
S.I.C.: 9311
N.A.I.C.S.: 921130
Advertising Expenditures: $4,500,000
Media: 3-9-14-15-18-23-24-25
Personnel:
Jacque Coe *(Dir-Comm)*
Jim Warick *(Dir-Mktg)*
Advertising Agencies:
Cole & Weber United
221 Yale Ave N Ste 600
Seattle, WA 98109
Tel.: (206) 447-9595
Fax: (206) 233-0178

Publicis West
424 2nd Ave W
Seattle, WA 98119-4013
Tel.: (206) 285-2222
Fax: (206) 273-4219

WEST VIRGINIA DEVELOPMENT OFFICE

1900 Kanawha Blvd E State Capitol Complex Bldg 6 Rm 553
Charleston, WV 25305
Tel.: (304) 558-2234
Fax: (304) 558-0449
Toll Free: (800) 982-3386
Web Site: www.wvdo.org
Approx. Number Employees: 149
Business Description:
Industrial & Community Development
S.I.C.: 9532
N.A.I.C.S.: 925120
Advertising Expenditures: $471,500
Multimedia: $5,000; Bus. Publs.: $150,000; Catalogs & Directories: $50,000; D.M. to Bus. Estab.: $50,000; Daily Newsp.: $4,000; Exhibits/Trade Shows: $80,000; Foreign: $20,000; Premiums, Novelties: $30,000; Special Events Mktg.: $75,000; Weekly Newsp.: $7,500
Distr.: Natl.
Budget Set: July
Personnel:
Kim Harbour *(Dir-Mktg & Comm)*
Bobby Lewis *(Dir-Community Dev Div)*
Helen Watts *(Office Mgr)*

WEST VIRGINIA LOTTERY

312 MacCorkle Ave SE
Charleston, WV 25314-1143
Tel.: (304) 558-0500
Fax: (304) 558-3321
Toll Free: (800) 982-2274
E-mail: info@wvlottery.com
Web Site: www.wvlottery.com
Approx. Number Employees: 110
Year Founded: 1985
Business Description:
State Lottery
S.I.C.: 9311
N.A.I.C.S.: 921130
Advertising Expenditures: $7,000,000
Media: 8-9-13-14-15-19-23-24-25
Distr.: Direct to Consumer; Reg.
Personnel:
John C. Musgrave *(Pres-North America & Dir-West Virginia Lottery)*
John D. Melton *(Gen Counsel)*
Nikki Orcutt *(Dir-Mktg)*
John Myers *(Asst Dir)*
Brands & Products:
BAA BAA BUCKS
CASH25
CREEPY CRAWLY CASH
FAT CAT TRIPLER
HOT LOTTO
HOW SWEET IT IS
KENO BONUS
WEST VIRGINIA LOTTERY
Advertising Agencies:
Charles Ryan Associates Inc.
300 Summers St Ste 1100
Charleston, WV 25301-1631
Tel.: (304) 342-0161
Fax: (304) 342-1941

Fahlgren Mortine
4030 Easton Station Ste 300
Columbus, OH 43219
Tel.: (614) 383-1500
Fax: (614) 383-1501

WISCONSIN DELLS VISITOR & CONVENTION BUREAU

115 La Crosse St
Wisconsin Dells, WI 53965
Tel.: (608) 254-8088
Fax: (608) 254-4293
Toll Free: (800) 223-3557
E-mail: info@wisdells.com
Web Site: www.wisdells.com
E-Mail For Key Personnel:
Public Relations: patty@wisdells.com
Approx. Number Employees: 20
Year Founded: 1949
Business Description:
Convention & Visitors Bureau
S.I.C.: 7389
N.A.I.C.S.: 561591
Media: 7-13-23-24
Distr.: Reg.
Budget Set: Oct. -Nov.
Personnel:
Jill Diehl *(Pres)*
Romy A. Snyder *(Exec Dir)*
Larry Dalka *(Dir-IT)*
Advertising Agency:
Boelter + Lincoln Marketing Communications
1 N Pinckey St
Madison, WI 53703-2800
Tel.: (608) 251-3381
Fax: (608) 251-7979

WISCONSIN DEPARTMENT OF AGRICULTURE, TRADE & CONSUMER PROTECTION

2811 Agriculture Dr
Madison, WI 53718-6777
Tel.: (608) 224-5012
Fax: (608) 224-5034
Web Site: www.datcp.state.wi.us
Sales Estimate: $120-149 Million
Approx. Number Employees: 600
Business Description:
Utilization & Promotion of All Wisconsin Farm Products
S.I.C.: 9199
N.A.I.C.S.: 921190
Advertising Expenditures: $200,000
Media: 2-6-9-10-13-19-21
Distr.: Intl.; Natl.
Budget Set: July
Personnel:
Andrew Diercks *(Chm)*
Janet Jenkins *(Dir-Trade)*
Brands & Products:
SOMETHING SPECIAL FROM WISCONSIN

WISCONSIN DEPARTMENT OF TOURISM

201 W Washington Ave
Madison, WI 53703
Tel.: (608) 266-2161
Tel.: (608) 266-7621
Fax: (608) 266-3403
Toll Free: (800) 432-8747
E-mail: tourinfo@travelwisconsin.com
Web Site: www.travelwisconsin.com
Approx. Number Employees: 23
Year Founded: 1996
Business Description:
Tourism Promoter
S.I.C.: 4725
N.A.I.C.S.: 561520
Media: 3-5-6-8-9-10-11-13-14-15-18-22-23-24-25-26
Distr.: Natl.
Budget Set: July
Personnel:
Sarah Klavas *(Brand Mgr)*
Glenn Aumann *(Mgr-Acctg)*

WYOMING BUSINESS COUNCIL

214 W 15th St
Cheyenne, WY 82002
Tel.: (307) 777-2800
Fax: (307) 777-2837
Toll Free: (800) 262-3425
Web Site: www.wyomingbusiness.org
Sales Range: $25-49.9 Million
Approx. Number Employees: 60
Year Founded: 1998
Business Description:
Economic Development for State of Wyoming
S.I.C.: 9532
N.A.I.C.S.: 925120
Advertising Expenditures: $1,265,000
Media: 1-2-5-6-8-10-13-20-22-23-24
Distr.: Natl.
Personnel:
Bob Jensen *(CEO)*
Diane Moser *(CFO)*
Julie Reis *(Chief Support Svcs Officer)*
Cindy Garretson-Weibel *(Dir-AgriBus Div)*
Diane Shober *(Dir-Travel & Tourism)*
Julie Kozlowski *(Program Mgr)*
Kim Porter *(Program Mgr-Agribusiness Education & Diversification)*
Chuck Coon *(Mgr-Media Rels)*
Michell Howard *(Mgr-Film)*
Paul Howard *(Mgr-Bus Permit Program)*
Advertising Agency:
Barnhart
1732 Champa St
Denver, CO 80202-1233
Tel.: (303) 626-7200
Fax: (303) 626-7252

YBOR CITY CHAMBER OF COMMERCE

1800 E 9th Ave
Tampa, FL 33605-3818
Tel.: (813) 248-3712
Fax: (813) 247-1764
E-mail: info@ybor.org
Web Site: www.ybor.org
Approx. Number Employees: 7
Year Founded: 1930
Business Description:
Urban Commercial Regulative & Administrative Services
S.I.C.: 9651
N.A.I.C.S.: 926150
Media: 7-9-22-25
Personnel:
Beth Drummond *(Chm)*
Thomas P. Keating *(Pres)*
Rose T. Barbie *(Mgr-Visitor Info Center)*
Anna Ramos *(Coord-Events)*

Key to Media (For complete agency information see *The Advertising Red Books-Agencies* edition):
1. Bus. Publs. 2. Cable T.V. 3. Catalogs & Directories. 4. Co-op Adv. 5. Consumer Mags. 6. D.M. to Bus. Estab. 7. D.M. to Consumers 8. Daily Newsp. 9. Exhibits/Trade Shows 10. Foreign 11. Infomercial 12. Internet Adv. 13. Multimedia 14. Network Radio 15. Network T.V. 16. Newsp. Distr. Mags. 17. Other 18. Outdoor (Posters, Transit) 19. Point of Purchase 20. Premiums, Novelties 21. Product Samples 22. Special Events Mktg. 23. Spot Radio 24. Spot T.V. 25. Weekly Newsp. 26. Yellow Page Adv.

Hardware

Bearings — Casters — Chain Saws — Cutlery — Hardware — Hoses — Lawn Mowers — Lawn Trimmers — Locks — Razors — Scales — Valves

ABBOTT BALL COMPANY
19 Railroad Pl
West Hartford, CT 06110-0100
Tel.: (860) 236-5901
Fax: (860) 233-1069
E-mail: mruubel@abbotball.com
Web Site: www.abbottball.com
Approx. Number Employees: 82
Year Founded: 1909
Business Description:
Stainless Steel, Carbon Steel & Specialty Ball Mfr
S.I.C.: 3312
N.A.I.C.S.: 331111
Advertising Expenditures: $200,000
Media: 2-4-7-26
Distr.: Natl.
Budget Set: Jan.
Personnel:
Craig Bond *(Pres)*
Roger A.L. Bond *(CEO)*
Irina Juhasz *(Mgr)*
Brands & Products:
ABBOTTBALL
CELCON
DELRIN

ACE HARDWARE & BUILDING CENTER
4344 Old Hwy 76
Blue Ridge, GA 30513
Tel.: (706) 632-8002
Fax: (706) 632-5521
E-mail: aceware@tds.net
Web Site: www.blueridgeace.com
Sales Range: $10-24.9 Million
Approx. Number Employees: 100
Business Description:
Hardware Stores
S.I.C.: 5251; 5031
N.A.I.C.S.: 444130; 423310
Personnel:
Lamar Lance *(Pres)*
Advertising Agency:
GSD&M
828 W 6th St
Austin, TX 78703-5420
Tel.: (512) 242-4736
Fax: (512) 242-4700

ACE HARDWARE CORPORATION
2200 Kensington Ct
Oak Brook, IL 60523-2100
Tel.: (630) 990-6600
Fax: (630) 990-1742
E-mail: media@acehardware.com
Web Site: www.acehardware.com
Sales Range: $1-4.9 Billion
Approx. Number Employees: 1,000
Year Founded: 1924
Business Description:
Dealer-Owned Hardware Cooperative
S.I.C.: 5072; 5198
N.A.I.C.S.: 423710; 424950
Import Export
Advertising Expenditures: $116,227,000
Media: 2-3-5-6-8-10-12-15-16-17-18-19-22-23-24-26
Distr.: Direct to Ace Dealers; Natl.
Budget Set: Aug.
Personnel:
David S. Ziegler *(Chm)*
Ray A. Griffith *(Pres & CEO)*
Rita D. Kahle *(Exec VP)*
John Venhuizen *(Exec VP)*
Jimmy Alexander *(VP-HR)*
Michael G. Elmore *(VP-IT)*
Rick Whitson *(VP-Retail Support)*
Jeff Gooding *(Dir-Consumer Mktg)*
Brands & Products:
ACE
ACE BEST BUYS
ACE HARDWARE
ACE HARDWARE AND GARDEN CENTER
ACE HARDWARE COMMITTED TO A QUALITY ENVIRONMENT
ACE IS THE PLACE
ACE IS THE PLACE WITH THE HELPFUL HARDWARE FOLKS
ACE PRO
ACE-THE HELPFUL PLACE
ACENET
ASK ACE
COLORS FOR YOUR LIFE
HARDWARE UNIVERSITY
THE HELPFUL HARDWARE FOLKS
PACE
PAINT POD
THE PAINTIN' PLACE
Advertising Agencies:
GSD&M
828 W 6th St
Austin, TX 78703-5420
Tel.: (512) 242-4736
Fax: (512) 242-4700

Revolucion
22 W 23rd St 3rd Fl
New York, NY 10010
Tel.: (212) 229-0700
Fax: (212) 229-0770

Weber Shandwick
(Sub. of The Interpublic Group of Companies)
919 3rd Ave
New York, NY 10022
Tel.: (212) 445-8000
Fax: (212) 445-8001

ACME UNITED CORPORATION
60 Round Hill Rd
Fairfield, CT 06824-5172
Tel.: (203) 254-6060
Fax: (203) 254-6019
Toll Free: (800) 835-2263
E-mail: info@acmeunited.com
Web Site: www.acmeunited.com
Approx. Sls.: $63,148,933
Approx. Number Employees: 132
Year Founded: 1867
Business Description:
Cutting, Measuring & Safety Product Mfr & Distr
S.I.C.: 3423; 3421; 3541
N.A.I.C.S.: 332212; 332211; 333512
Import Export
Advertising Expenditures: $1,039,302
Media: 2-4-6-9-10-19
Distr.: Natl.
Budget Set: Jan.
Personnel:
Walter C. Johnsen *(Chm & CEO)*
Brian S. Olschan *(Pres & COO)*
Paul G. Driscoll *(CFO, Treas, Sec & VP)*
David Farnworth *(VP-Mktg-Westcott, Sr Dir-Mktg & Dir-Mktg)*
Larry H. Buchtmann *(VP-Ops & Tech)*
Evelyn Jennings *(VP-Sls-Comml)*
Brands & Products:
ACME UNITED
BLOOMS
CLAUSS
CRAFT KIDS BARRACUTTER
CRAFT KIDS HIPPOSCISSIUS
CRAFT KIDS RHINOSCISSOR
CRAFT KIDS SCISSAGATOR
CRAFT KIDS SCISSAMANDER
CRAFT KIDS SCISSISAURUS
CRAFTKIDS
CRAFTWORKS
CRITTERS
EXTREMEDGE TITANIUM
FEATHERLITE
FOR THOSE WHO LIVE THEIR CRAFT
GALLERIA
GRIP & RIP
IPOINT
IZONE
KLEENCUT
KLEENEARTH
KUMFY-GRIP
NEW ELITE
NEW WESTCOTT
PHYSICIANS CARE
PREFERRED
SAF-T-CUT
SMOOTHGRIP
SPEEDPAK
SURESET
TAGIT!
TI FLEX BOW
TIGERSHARP
TITANIUM BONDED
TITANIUM TI2
TRUE PROFESSIONAL
ULTRAFLEX
VALUE
WESTCOTT
WILD ONES
WRAP & RIBBON
ZIGZAGZ

ACO HARDWARE, INC.
23333 Commerce Dr
Farmington Hills, MI 48335-2727
Tel.: (248) 471-0100
Fax: (248) 615-2696
Toll Free: (800) 275-4226
Web Site: www.acohardware.com
Approx. Number Employees: 1,400
Year Founded: 1946
Business Description:
Retail Hardware Stores
S.I.C.: 5251
N.A.I.C.S.: 444130
Media: 8-16-18-19-25-26
Distr.: Natl.

ACS INDUSTRIES, INC.
1 New England Way
Lincoln, RI 02865
Mailing Address:
PO Box 1010
Woonsocket, RI 02895-0801

Key to Media (For complete agency information see *The Advertising Red Books-Agencies* edition):
1. Bus. Publs. 2. Cable T.V. 3. Catalogs & Directories. 4. Co-op Adv. 5. Consumer Mags. 6. D.M. to Bus. Estab.7. D.M. to Consumers 8. Daily Newsp. 9. Exhibits/Trade Shows 10. Foreign 11. Infomercial 12. Internet Adv.13. Multimedia 14. Network Radio 15. Network T.V. 16. Newsp. Distr. Mags. 17. Other 18. Outdoor (Posters, Transit) 19. Point of Purchase20. Premiums, Novelties 21. Product Samples 22. Special Events Mktg. 23. Spot Radio 24. Spot T.V. 25. Weekly Newsp. 26. Yellow Page Adv.

ACS Industries, Inc. — (Continued)

Tel.: (401) 769-4700
Fax: (401) 333-6088
Toll Free: (800) 227-1939
E-mail: acsind@acsindustries.com
Web Site: www.acsindustries.com
Sales Range: $150-199.9 Million
Approx. Number Employees: 50
Year Founded: 1939
Business Description:
Automotive & Industrial Wire Mesh Products Mfr
S.I.C.: 3496
N.A.I.C.S.: 332618
Import Export
Media: 2-4-7-10-20-21
Distr.: Natl.
Personnel:
Steven Buckler *(Pres)*
Brands & Products:
CELL-U-FOAM
INCONEL
MIST-MASTER
MISTERMESH
MISTXPERT
MONEL
PLATE-PAK
SCRUBBLE
US FIBER OPTICS

ACUMENT GLOBAL TECHNOLOGIES INC.
(Holding of Platinum Equity, LLC)
840 W Long Lake Rd Ste 450
Troy, MI 48098
Tel.: (248) 813-6300
Fax: (248) 813-6372
E-mail: info@acument.com
Web Site: www.acument.com
Approx. Sls.: $1,800,000,000
Approx. Number Employees: 9,000
Year Founded: 1922
Business Description:
Mechanical Fastener Mfr
S.I.C.: 3452
N.A.I.C.S.: 332722
Import Export
Media: 2-4-7-10-19-20-21
Distr.: Natl.
Budget Set: June
Personnel:
Patrick Paige *(Pres & CEO)*
Martin Schnurr *(VP & Gen Mgr)*
Timothy G. Weir *(Dir-Corp Comm & Pub Affairs)*
Brands & Products:
DAND-O-LINE
DRIL-FLEX
GOLD+
GUY-A-WIRE
STALGARD
TAPDEK
WEATHERMASTER
WOODMASTER
ZER-LON

ADAMS RITE AEROSPACE INC.
(Sub. of TransDigm Inc.)
4141 N Palm St
Fullerton, CA 92835
Tel.: (714) 278-6500
Fax: (714) 278-6510
E-mail: jhanson@ar-aero.com
Web Site:
www.adamsriteaerospace.com
E-Mail For Key Personnel:
Sales Director: kmchenry@ar-aero.com
Sales Range: $50-74.9 Million
Approx. Number Employees: 200
Year Founded: 1946
Business Description:
Aircraft Interior Hardware, Flight Controls, Fluid Hardware & Systems & Life Support Products Mfr
S.I.C.: 3625; 3743
N.A.I.C.S.: 335314; 336510
Media: 1-4-10-13
Distr.: Intl.; Natl.
Budget Set: Mar.
Personnel:
John Leary *(Pres)*
Kevin McHenry *(Dir-Sls)*
Aleem Shaikh *(Reg Mgr)*
Tom Busschaert *(Mgr-Quality)*

AGI-VR/WESSON INC
2673 NE 9th Ave
Cape Coral, FL 33909
Tel.: (239) 573-5132
Fax: (239) 573-5137
Web Site: www.agivrwesson.com
Approx. Sls.: $5,000,000
Approx. Number Employees: 30
Year Founded: 1950
Business Description:
Carbide Cutting Tool Products Mfr
S.I.C.: 3545; 3541
N.A.I.C.S.: 333515; 333512
Export
Advertising Expenditures: $500,000
Media: 2-4-5-7-13
Distr.: Direct to Consumer; Natl.
Personnel:
Tom Fliss *(Pres & CEO)*
Steve Scott *(VP-Sls)*
Brands & Products:
EDG-PREP
TANTUNG
VR/WESSON

AIR-LEC INDUSTRIES, INC.
3300 Commercial Ave
Madison, WI 53714-1458
Tel.: (608) 244-4754
Fax: (608) 246-7676
E-mail: info@air-lec.com
Web Site: www.air-lec.com
E-Mail For Key Personnel:
President: john.lunenschloss@air-lec.com
Marketing Director: harold.clute@air-lec.com
Approx. Number Employees: 8
Year Founded: 1921
Business Description:
Door Operating Equipment & Accessories Mfr
S.I.C.: 3429; 3531
N.A.I.C.S.: 332510; 333120
Export
Media: 2-4-7-10
Distr.: Natl.
Budget Set: Dec.
Personnel:
John T. Lunenschloss *(Pres & Treas)*
Harold Clute *(Dir-Sls & Mktg)*
Brands & Products:
AIR-LEC
ZEPHYR

A.L. HANSEN MANUFACTURING CO.
701 Pershing Rd
Waukegan, IL 60085-4079
Tel.: (847) 244-8900
Fax: (847) 244-7222
E-mail: info@alhansen.com
Web Site: www.alhansen.com
Approx. Number Employees: 100
Year Founded: 1920
Business Description:
Mfr. of Commercial Body & Industrial Hardware
S.I.C.: 3429; 3714
N.A.I.C.S.: 332510; 336399
Export
Media: 2-4-7-8-10-11-20-21-22
Distr.: Intl.; Natl.
Budget Set: Jan.
Personnel:
William Hansen, II *(Pres)*
Colt Fitzgerald *(VP-Sls & Mktg)*

ALASKA INDUSTRIAL HARDWARE INC.
2192 Viking Dr
Anchorage, AK 99501-1731
Tel.: (907) 276-7201
Fax: (907) 258-3054
Toll Free: (800) 478-7201
E-mail: info@aihalaska.com
Web Site: www.aihalaska.com
Approx. Number Employees: 200
Year Founded: 1959
Business Description:
Industrial Hardware Supplier
S.I.C.: 5072; 5251
N.A.I.C.S.: 423710; 444130
Media: 2-4-8-13-16-19-22-25-26
Distr.: Direct to Consumer; Natl.
Budget Set: Dec.
Personnel:
Terry Shurtleff *(CFO)*
Rob Whitmore *(Mgr-Adv)*
Mary Ann Hartzog *(Co-Coord)*
Advertising Agency:
Bradley Reid & Associates
900 W 5th Ave Ste 100
Anchorage, AK 99501
Tel.: (907) 276-6353
Fax: (907) 276-1042
(Hardware & Power Tools)

ALBION INC.
(Sub. of Colson Associates, Inc.)
800 N Clark St
Albion, MI 49224
Tel.: (517) 629-9441
Fax: (517) 629-9501
Toll Free: (800) 835-8911
E-mail: email@albioninc.com
Web Site: www.albioninc.com
Approx. Number Employees: 80
Business Description:
Casters & Wheels
S.I.C.: 3429; 3559
N.A.I.C.S.: 332510; 333298
Media: 4-10
Personnel:
Bill Winslow *(Pres)*
Brands & Products:
ALBION

ALLEGHENY SURFACE TECHNOLOGY
(Sub. of Allegheny Bradford Corporation)
14 Egbert Ln
Lewis Run, PA 16738
Tel.: (814) 368-4465
Fax: (814) 368-7011
Toll Free: (866) 266-9293
E-mail: sales_ast@alleghenybradford.com
Web Site:
www.alleghenysurfacetech.com
E-Mail For Key Personnel:
Sales Director: sales_ast@alleghenybradford.com
Approx. Number Employees: 20
Business Description:
Stainless Steel Finishing Services to Pharmaceutical, Biotechnical, Medical, Food, Dairy & Marine Industries
S.I.C.: 5083; 3471
N.A.I.C.S.: 423820; 332813
Media: 10-13

ALLFAST FASTENING SYSTEMS, INC.
15200 Don Julian Rd
City of Industry, CA 91745
Tel.: (626) 968-9388
Fax: (626) 968-9393
E-mail: sales@allfastinc.com
Web Site: www.allfastinc.com
E-Mail For Key Personnel:
Sales Director: sales@allfastinc.com
Approx. Number Employees: 140
Year Founded: 1966
Business Description:
Mfr. of Aerospace Solid & Blind Rivets
S.I.C.: 3429; 3452
N.A.I.C.S.: 332510; 332722
Export
Advertising Expenditures: $75,000
Bus. Publs.: $40,000; Catalogs & Directories: $15,000; Exhibits/Trade Shows: $20,000
Distr.: Natl.
Budget Set: Nov.
Personnel:
Jim Randall *(Pres)*
Sam Cooperstein *(VP-Sls & Mktg)*
Ralph Luhm *(VP-Engrg)*
Brands & Products:
A CODE
AB CODE RIVET
ALLMAX
ALLMAX RIVET
BRILES
BULB RIVET
FASTACK
FASTACK RIVET
MAXMATIC
RV14GD
RV15GA
RV2000
RV3000 MAXMATIC
RV30GD
RV50GB
RV51GA
SUPER MAX
SUPERMAX
TACKBOLT
TACKBOLT RIVET

ALLIED SECURITY INNOVATIONS, INC.
1709 Rte 34 Ste 2
Farmingdale, NJ 07727
Tel.: (732) 751-1115
Fax: (732) 751-1050
E-mail: mhernandez@cgm-ast.com
Web Site: www.ddsi-cpc.com

Key to Media (For complete agency information see *The Advertising Red Books-Agencies* edition):
1. Bus. Publs. 2. Cable T.V. 3. Catalogs & Directories. 4. Co-op Adv. 5. Consumer Mags. 6. D.M. to Bus. Estab.7. D.M. to Consumers 8. Daily Newsp. 9. Exhibits/Trade Shows 10. Foreign 11. Infomercial 12. Internet Adv.13. Multimedia 14. Network Radio 15. Network T.V. 16. Newsp. Distr. Mags. 17. Other 18. Outdoor (Posters, Transit) 19. Point of Purchase20. Premiums, Novelties 21. Product Samples 22. Special Events Mktg. 23. Spot Radio 24. Spot T.V. 25. Weekly Newsp. 26. Yellow Page Adv.

Approx. Sls.: $3,597,653
Approx. Number Employees: 14
Year Founded: 1986
Business Description:
Indicative & Barrier Security Seals, Security Tapes & Related Packaging Security Systems & Protective Security Products Mfr & Distr
S.I.C.: 2671; 7382
N.A.I.C.S.: 322221; 561621
Advertising Expenditures: $105,746
Media: 17
Personnel:
Anthony Shupin *(Pres & CEO)*
Michael J. Pellegrino *(CFO & Sr VP)*
Brands & Products:
ACTIVEX/32
COMPU-CAPTURE/32
COMPU-SCENE
COMPU-SKETCH
SECURE T.R.A.C.
SUPERSEAL

ALLMETAL SCREW PRODUCTS CORP.
94A E Jefryn Blvd
Deer Park, NY 11729
Tel.: (631) 243-5200
Fax: (631) 243-5307
E-mail: thewebmaster@allmetalcorp.com
Web Site: www.allmetalcorp.com
Sales Range: $1-9.9 Million
Approx. Number Employees: 20
Year Founded: 1929
Business Description:
Stainless Steel Fastener Distr
S.I.C.: 5072; 5085
N.A.I.C.S.: 423710; 423840
Import Export
Media: 4-10
Distr.: Natl.
Personnel:
William Campbell *(Pres)*
Brands & Products:
ALLMETAL

ALPHA INNOTECH CORP.
(Sub. of Cell Biosciences, Inc.)
2401 Merced St
San Leandro, CA 94577
Tel.: (510) 483-9620
Fax: (510) 483-3227
Toll Free: (800) 795-5556
E-mail: info@alphainnotech.com
Web Site: www.alphainnotech.com
Approx. Rev.: $17,608,494
Approx. Number Employees: 51
Year Founded: 1992
Business Description:
Digital Imaging & Detection Systems
S.I.C.: 3826; 3812
N.A.I.C.S.: 334516; 334511
Advertising Expenditures: $110,779
Media: 17
Personnel:
Mark Allen *(Mng Partner)*

A.M. ANDREWS CO.
4621 SW Beaverton-Hillsdale Hwy
Portland, OR 97221
Tel.: (503) 244-1163
Fax: (503) 244-1245
E-mail: amandrews@firstlink.net
Web Site: www.amandrews.com
Sales Range: Less than $1 Million
Approx. Number Employees: 4
Year Founded: 1945
Business Description:
Sprinkler Hoses & Repair Kits Mfr
S.I.C.: 3052
N.A.I.C.S.: 326220
Export
Media: 4-5-7-10
Distr.: Intl.; Natl.
Brands & Products:
ANDREWS

AMATOM ELECTRONIC HARDWARE, INC.
5 Pasco Hill Rd
Cromwell, CT 06416-1093
Tel.: (860) 828-0847
Fax: (860) 828-0381
Toll Free: (800) 243-6032
Web Site: www.amatom.com
Approx. Sls.: $15,000,000
Approx. Number Employees: 125
Year Founded: 1989
Business Description:
Electronic Hardware, Time Recording Equipment & Hydraulic & Pneumatic Valves
S.I.C.: 3429; 3625
N.A.I.C.S.: 332510; 335314
Import Export
Advertising Expenditures: $350,000
Media: 2-4
Distr.: Intl.; Natl.
Budget Set: Jan. -Feb.
Personnel:
John Cary *(Pres)*
Brands & Products:
AMATOM
GAR-KENYON

AMERICAN JEBCO CORPORATION
11330 W Melrose Ave
Franklin Park, IL 60131-1367
Tel.: (847) 455-3150
Fax: (847) 455-0208
E-mail: peotes@jebcoscrew.com
Web Site: www.americanjebco.com
Sales Range: $25-49.9 Million
Approx. Number Employees: 100
Year Founded: 2001
Business Description:
Rivets & Cold-Headed Special Fasteners Mfr
S.I.C.: 3452; 3451
N.A.I.C.S.: 332722; 332721
Import Export
Media: 2-4-7-10-11
Distr.: Intl.; Natl.
Personnel:
Matthew Connor *(Pres, Treas & Sec)*

AMERICAN LAWN MOWER COMPANY
2100 N Granville Ave
Muncie, IN 47303-2153
Mailing Address:
PO Box 369
Shelbyville, IN 46176-0369
Tel.: (765) 288-6624
Fax: (765) 284-5263
E-mail: sales@reelin.com
Web Site: www.reelin.com
E-Mail For Key Personnel:
Sales Director: sales@reelin.com
Approx. Sls.: $5,000,000
Approx. Number Employees: 60
Business Description:
Mfr. of Hand Lawn Mowers, Reel Power Mowers & Gang Mowers
S.I.C.: 3524
N.A.I.C.S.: 333112
Media: 4-6-10-19
Distr.: Natl.
Personnel:
R.E. Kersey *(Pres & Gen Mgr)*
J.W. Hewitt *(VP-Sls & Mktg)*
Brands & Products:
AMERICAN LAWN MOWER
GREAT STATES

AMERICAN LOCKER GROUP INCORPORATED
815 S Main St
Grapevine, TX 76051-5535
Tel.: (817) 329-1600
Fax: (817) 421-8618
Toll Free: (800) 828-9118
E-mail: info@americanlocker.com
Web Site: www.americanlocker.com
Approx. Sls.: $12,099,012
Approx. Number Employees: 103
Year Founded: 1958
Business Description:
Coin, Key & Electronically Controlled Security Lockers & Locks; Plastic Centralized Mail & Parcel Distibution Lockers
S.I.C.: 2542; 2519; 3429
N.A.I.C.S.: 337215; 332510; 337125
Export
Advertising Expenditures: $134,000
Media: 2-4-7-8-10-13-17
Distr.: Intl.; Natl.
Budget Set: Oct.
Personnel:
Paul M. Zaidins *(Pres, CFO & COO)*
Allen D. Tilley *(CEO)*
Chris Reed *(Mgr-Sls)*
Brands & Products:
AMBASSADOR
AMERICAN
COMPU-LOK
E-CBU
ENVOY
GOPOD
KARY KART
LOK-ALL
MINI-CHECK
STATESMAN
STATESMAN JUNIOR
VERIKEY

AMERICAN LOCKER SECURITY SYSTEMS, INC.
(Sub. of American Locker Group Incorporated)
815 S Main St
Grapevine, TX 76051-5535
Tel.: (817) 329-1600
Fax: (817) 421-8618
Toll Free: (800) 828-9118
E-mail: info@americanlocker.com
Web Site: www.americanlocker.com
Sales Range: $25-49.9 Million
Approx. Number Employees: 88
Year Founded: 1931
Business Description:
Coin Operated Checking Lockers, Mini-Check Valuables Lockers, Police Evidence Lockers, Law Enforcement Pistol Lockers, Computer Print-Out Lockers, Parcel Post & Hotel Lockers
S.I.C.: 2542
N.A.I.C.S.: 337215
Export
Media: 2-7-8-10-13-26
Distr.: Intl.; Natl.
Budget Set: Oct.
Brands & Products:
BANK-LOK
COIN-LOK
COMPU-LOK
E-CBU
LOK-ALL
PUSH BUTTON PICKUP BOX

AMERICAN MACHINE & TOOL COMPANY, INC.
(Sub. of The Gorman-Rupp Company)
400 Springs St
Royersford, PA 19468-0070
Mailing Address:
PO Box 70
Royersford, PA 19468-0070
Tel.: (610) 948-3800
Fax: (610) 948-5300
E-mail: sales@amtpump.com
Web Site: www.amtpump.com
E-Mail For Key Personnel:
Sales Director: sales@amtpump.com
Sales Range: $25-49.9 Million
Approx. Number Employees: 32
Year Founded: 1928
Business Description:
Mfr. of Centrifugal Pumps
S.I.C.: 3561
N.A.I.C.S.: 333911
Import Export
Media: 4
Personnel:
Keith Bearde *(VP & Gen Mgr)*
Brands & Products:
AMT

AMEROCK CORPORATION
(Div. of Levolor Home Fashions)
3 Glenlake Pkwy
Atlanta, GA 30328
Tel.: (704) 987-4555
Toll Free: (800) 435-6959
Web Site: www.amerock.com
Approx. Sls.: $200,000,000
Approx. Number Employees: 1,500
Year Founded: 1928
Business Description:
Cabinet Hardware, Functional Hardware, Hinges, Storage & Convenience Products Mfr
S.I.C.: 3499
N.A.I.C.S.: 332999
Import Export
Media: 2-4-5-7-19-20-21
Distr.: Intl.; Natl.
Budget Set: Nov.
Brands & Products:
ACCENT'Z
AMEROCK

AROTECH CORPORATION
1229 Oak Valley Dr
Ann Arbor, MI 48108
Tel.: (734) 761-5836
Fax: (212) 258-3281
Toll Free: (800) 344-1707
E-mail: info@arotech.com
Web Site: www.arotech.com
Approx. Rev.: $73,741,478
Approx. Number Employees: 418
Year Founded: 1994
Business Description:
Mfr. of Zinc-Air Batteries & Vehicle Armor; Multimedia & Interactive Digital Training Systems
S.I.C.: 5084; 8733

Key to Media (For complete agency information see *The Advertising Red Books-Agencies* edition):
1. Bus. Publs. 2. Cable T.V. 3. Catalogs & Directories. 4. Co-op Adv. 5. Consumer Mags. 6. D.M. to Bus. Estab.7. D.M. to Consumers 8. Daily Newsp. 9. Exhibits/Trade Shows 10. Foreign 11. Infomercial 12. Internet Adv.13. Multimedia 14. Network Radio 15. Network T.V. 16. Newsp. Distr. Mags. 17. Other 18. Outdoor (Posters, Transit) 19. Point of Purchase20. Premiums, Novelties 21. Product Samples 22. Special Events Mktg. 23. Spot Radio 24. Spot T.V. 25. Weekly Newsp. 26. Yellow Page Adv.

Arotech Corporation — (Continued)

N.A.I.C.S.: 423830; 541710
Import Export
Advertising Expenditures: $161,459
Media: 2-10
Personnel:
Robert S. Ehrlich *(Chm & CEO)*
Thomas J. Paup *(CFO & VP-Fin)*
Steven Esses *(COO & Exec VP)*
Yaakov Har-Oz *(Gen Counsel, Sec & VP)*
Jonathan Whartman *(Sr VP)*
Brands & Products:
AROTECH
Advertising Agency:
TTC Group
100 Maiden Ln Ste 2001
New York, NY 10038
Tel.: (646) 290-6400
Pub Rels

ARROW FASTENER COMPANY, INC.

(Sub. of Masco Corporation)
271 Mayhill St
Saddle Brook, NJ 07663-5303
Tel.: (201) 843-6900
Fax: (201) 843-3911
Web Site: www.arrowfastener.com
E-Mail For Key Personnel:
Sales Director: sales@arrowfastener.com
Sales Range: $200-249.9 Million
Approx. Number Employees: 600
Year Founded: 1929
Business Description:
Hand Tools & Related Products
S.I.C.: 3546; 3423
N.A.I.C.S.: 333991; 332212
Import Export
Media: 2-3-4-5-6-10-11-15-16-17-19-24
Distr.: Intl.; Natl.
Budget Set: Aug. -Sept.
Personnel:
Ed Wieczerzak *(CFO & VP-Fin)*
Bill Sokol *(VP-Mktg)*
Marie Bostrom *(Dir-Adv)*
Brands & Products:
105
107C
ARROW
THE ATTACKER
B1000
B120
B160
B250
B25G
B25T
B25Y
B300
B30Y
B500
B7200
THE BRUTE
CTR600
DC25
DC66
DT700
ET100
ET125
ET150
ET200
ET2025
ET50
ETC50
ETF50
ETF50BN
ETF50PBN
ETN50
JT21
MIGHTY MO
NAIL MASTER
P22
P35
P66
POWERSHOT
PROSHOT 1
PROSHOT 2
T18
T2025
T27
T30
T32
T37
T50
T55
T59
T75
TOMAHAWK
TWISTER
X MACHINE

ASCO SINTERING CO.

2750 Garfield Ave
Los Angeles, CA 90040
Tel.: (323) 725-3550
Fax: (323) 888-9968
E-mail: info@ascosintering.com
Web Site: www.ascosintering.com
Approx. Number Employees: 110
Business Description:
Hardware
S.I.C.: 3429; 3566
N.A.I.C.S.: 332510; 333612
Personnel:
Patrick Schuster *(Pres & CEO)*
Robert LeBrun *(CFO)*
Advertising Agency:
Cresta Group
1050 N State St
Chicago, IL 60610
Tel.: (312) 944-4700
Fax: (312) 944-1582

ASSA ABLOY DOOR SECURITY SOLUTIONS

(Sub. of Assa Abloy AB)
110 Sargent Dr
New Haven, CT 06511-5918
Tel.: (203) 624-5225
Fax: (203) 777-9042
Web Site: www.assaabloydss.com
Approx. Sls.: $450,000,000
Approx. Number Employees: 3,400
Year Founded: 1991
Business Description:
Mfr & Distr of Industrial & Technical Products, Locking Systems
S.I.C.: 7382; 3442
N.A.I.C.S.: 561621; 332321
Import Export
Media: 2-4-10-17-21
Distr.: Natl.
Budget Set: Oct.
Personnel:
Thansis Molokotos *(Pres & CEO)*
David Amborosini *(CFO)*

ATIS GROUP INC.

1111 St Charles West Suite 952 East Tower
Longueuil, QC J4K 5G4, Canada
Tel.: (450) 928-0101
Fax: (450) 928-7352
E-mail: info@atisgroup.ca
Web Site: www.atisgroup.ca
Approx. Sls.: $178,269,498
Approx. Number Employees: 1,600
Year Founded: 2004
Business Description:
Doors & Windows Developer, Mfr, Distr & Installer
S.I.C.: 3442; 1799
N.A.I.C.S.: 332321; 238990
Advertising Expenditures: $380,903
Personnel:
Leland Lewis *(Chm)*
Robert Doyon *(Pres & CEO)*
Andre Parent *(Treas, Sec & VP-Fin)*
Alain Langis *(Corp VP & Gen Mgr)*

ATLAS BOLT & SCREW COMPANY

(Sub. of Marmon Industrial Companies LLC)
1628 Troy Rd State Rte 511 N
Ashland, OH 44805
Tel.: (419) 289-6171
Fax: (419) 289-2564
Toll Free: (800) 321-6977
E-mail: webmaster@atlasfasteners.com
Web Site: www.atlasfasteners.com
Sales Range: $50-74.9 Million
Approx. Number Employees: 75
Year Founded: 1896
Business Description:
Steel Fasteners Mfr
S.I.C.: 3452; 5085
N.A.I.C.S.: 332722; 423840
Import Export
Media: 2-4-5-10
Personnel:
Becki Antonides *(Coord-Sls & Mktg)*
Brands & Products:
CON-MATE
PERMA-TITE
ULTIMATE
ULTRA Z
VERSAVENT

ATT HOLDING CO.

(Sub. of Griffon Corporation)
(d/b/a Ames True Temper)
465 Railroad Ave
Camp Hill, PA 17001
Tel.: (717) 737-1500
Fax: (717) 730-2550
E-mail: info@ames-truetemper.com
Web Site: www.amestruetemper.com
Sales Range: $450-499.9 Million
Approx. Number Employees: 2,048
Year Founded: 1774
Business Description:
Lawn & Garden Equipment Mfr & Distr
S.I.C.: 3423; 3524; 5083
N.A.I.C.S.: 332212; 333112; 423820
Advertising Expenditures: $15,430,000
Personnel:
John K. Castle *(Chm)*
Daniel Yurovich *(Sr VP-Operation)*
Larry Baab *(VP-Mktg & Product Dev)*
Geoff Brownrigg *(VP-Sls & Bus Dev)*
Chris Ebling *(VP-HR)*
Christopher Frew *(VP-Sls)*
Joseph Wersosky *(VP-Sls & Bus Dev)*
Advertising Agency:
Fahlgren Mortine
4030 Easton Station Ste 300
Columbus, OH 43219
Tel.: (614) 383-1500
Fax: (614) 383-1501

AVENUE INDUSTRIAL SUPPLY CO. LTD.

(Sub. of TAKKT AG)
331 Alden Rd
Markham, ON L3R 3L4, Canada
Tel.: (905) 946-8174
Fax: (905) 946-8435
E-mail: nelson@avenuesupply.com
Web Site: www.avenuesupply.com
Approx. Number Employees: 70
Business Description:
Industrial Products Distr
S.I.C.: 5169
N.A.I.C.S.: 424690
Media: 4
Personnel:
Nelson Rivers *(Pres)*

B&T METALS CO.

425 W Town St
Columbus, OH 43215
Tel.: (614) 228-5411
Fax: (614) 228-0078
Approx. Sls.: $2,500,000
Approx. Number Employees: 2
Business Description:
Trim & Rims for Walls & Floors; Industrial, Commercial & Architectural Aluminum Extrusions, Fabrication & Anodizing
S.I.C.: 3471; 2431
N.A.I.C.S.: 332813; 321918
Media: 2-4
Distr.: Natl.
Budget Set: Jan.
Personnel:
James Whitaker *(CFO)*
Brands & Products:
CHROMEDGE

BALDWIN HARDWARE CORPORATION

(Sub. of Stanley Black & Decker, Inc.)
841 E Wyomissing Blvd
Reading, PA 19611-1759
Tel.: (610) 777-7811
Fax: (610) 796-4493
E-mail: intlInquiry@baldwinhq.com
Web Site: www.baldwinhardware.com
Sales Range: $100-124.9 Million
Approx. Number Employees: 200
Year Founded: 1946
Business Description:
Decorative Brass Accessories, Bath Accessories & Lighting Mfr
S.I.C.: 3429; 3499
N.A.I.C.S.: 332510; 332999
Import Export
Advertising Expenditures: $1,000,000
Media: 1-4-5-6-10-18-19-22-26
Distr.: Natl.
Budget Set: Nov.
Personnel:
Rob Empfield *(Brand Mgr)*
Brands & Products:
BALDWIN BRASS
Advertising Agency:
White Good & Co. Advertising
226 N Arch St Ste 1
Lancaster, PA 17603
Tel.: (717) 396-0200
Fax: (717) 396-9483
Keyless Access Control Product
— Danielle Floyd *(Account Exec-PR)*

Key to Media (For complete agency information see *The Advertising Red Books-Agencies* edition):
1. Bus. Publs. 2. Cable T.V. 3. Catalogs & Directories. 4. Co-op Adv. 5. Consumer Mags. 6. D.M. to Bus. Estab.7. D.M. to Consumers
8. Daily Newsp. 9. Exhibits/Trade Shows 10. Foreign 11. Infomercial 12. Internet Adv.13. Multimedia 14. Network Radio
15. Network T.V. 16. Newsp. Distr. Mags. 17. Other 18. Outdoor (Posters, Transit) 19. Point of Purchase20. Premiums, Novelties
21. Product Samples 22. Special Events Mktg. 23. Spot Radio 24. Spot T.V. 25. Weekly Newsp. 26. Yellow Page Adv.

BERNARD WELDING
(Sub. of Illinois Tool Works Inc.)
449 W Corning Rd
Beecher, IL 60401-3127
Mailing Address:
PO Box 667
Beecher, IL 60401-0667
Tel.: (708) 946-2281
Fax: (708) 946-6726
Toll Free: (800) 946-2281
E-mail: info@bernardwelds.com
Web Site: www.bernardwelds.com
Sales Range: $50-74.9 Million
Approx. Number Employees: 80
Year Founded: 1946
Business Description:
MIG Welding Guns, Consummables & Electrode Holders Mfr
S.I.C.: 3548; 3531
N.A.I.C.S.: 333992; 333120
Export
Advertising Expenditures: $200,000
Media: 4-7-10
Distr.: Intl.; Natl.
Budget Set: Sept.
Personnel:
John Winek *(Gen Mgr)*
Brands & Products:
BERNARD
CENTERFIRE
CUSTOMSELECT
K&K WELDING
OXO

BLACK & DECKER
(Sub. of Black & Decker Canada Inc.)
3980 North Fraser Way
Burnaby, BC V5J 5K5, Canada
Tel.: (604) 419-4300
Fax: (604) 419-4385
Toll Free: (800) 501-9471
E-mail: penny.eggie@bdhhi.com
Web Site: www.weiserlock.ca
Sales Range: $25-49.9 Million
Approx. Number Employees: 35
Year Founded: 1952
Business Description:
Mfr. of Door Locks
S.I.C.: 3429
N.A.I.C.S.: 332510
Import Export
Advertising Expenditures: $1,600,000
Media: 1-2-5-6-10-13-15-19-24-26
Distr.: Natl.
Budget Set: Sept.
Personnel:
Mark Wallace *(Sr Mgr-Mktg Grp-HHI Canada)*
Winfield Gene *(Mgr-CS & DC Support)*

BLACK & DECKER CANADA INC.
(Sub. of The Black & Decker Corporation)
125 Mural St
Richmond Hill, ON L4B 1M4, Canada
Tel.: (905) 886-9511
Fax: (905) 764-4630
Web Site: www.blackanddecker.com
Sales Range: $50-74.9 Million
Approx. Number Employees: 80
Business Description:
Sales & Distribution of Tools
S.I.C.: 5251
N.A.I.C.S.: 444130
Media: 4-5-6-9-14-19-23-24-25-26
Distr.: Natl.

Personnel:
Dave Howe *(Pres)*

BLOUNT INTERNATIONAL, INC.
(Joint Venture of Reinet Investments SCA & Trilantic Capital Management LLC)
4909 SE International Way
Portland, OR 97222-4679
Tel.: (503) 653-8881
Fax: (503) 653-4612
Toll Free: (800) 223-5168
Web Site: www.blount.com
Approx. Rev.: $611,480,000
Approx. Number Employees: 3,600
Year Founded: 1946
Business Description:
Industrial & Outdoor Power Cutting Equipment Mfr
S.I.C.: 3489; 3524; 3545; 3553; 3559
N.A.I.C.S.: 332995; 333112; 333210; 333298; 333515
Import Export
Advertising Expenditures: $7,300,000
Media: 2-3-4-5-6-7-9-10-11-13-19-22-25
Distr.: Direct to Comsumer; Reg.
Budget Set: Dec. -Dec.
Personnel:
Joshua L. Collins *(Chm & CEO)*
David A. Willmott *(Pres & COO)*
Calvin E. Jenness *(CFO & Sr VP)*
Richard H. Irving, III *(Gen Counsel, Sec & Sr VP)*
Brands & Products:
CTR
FABTEK
GEAR
HYDRO-AX
OREGON
PRENTICE
TEL-STIK
WINDSOR

BOBRICK WASHROOM EQUIPMENT, INC.
11611 Hart St
North Hollywood, CA 91605-5882
Tel.: (818) 764-1000
Fax: (818) 765-2700
E-mail: customerservicela@bobrick.com
Web Site: www.bobrick.com
E-Mail For Key Personnel:
Marketing Director: agettelman@bobrick.com
Approx. Number Employees: 500
Year Founded: 1906
Business Description:
Commercial Hand Dryers, Soap Dispensers & Washroom Accessories Mfr
S.I.C.: 3431; 3499; 3564
N.A.I.C.S.: 332998; 332439; 333412
Import Export
Media: 1-2-4-7-10-21
Distr.: Intl.; Natl.
Budget Set: Oct.
Personnel:
Mark Louchheim *(Pres)*
William S. Louchheim, Jr. *(Partner & Mng officer)*
Alan Gettelman *(VP-Mktg)*
Chet Webb *(VP-Sls)*
Brands & Products:
AIRCRAFT
AIRGUARD
AIRPRO
ANYTHING LESS COSTS MORE
BOBRICK
CLASSIC SERIES
COMBAT SERIES
COMPACDRYER
CONTURA SERIES
CUB
DESIGNER SERIES
DURALINE SERIES
ECLIPSE
FRP SERIES
KOALA KARE
LIQUID MATE
MATRIX SERIES
POWDER MATE
QUICK SHIP
RAPID RESPONSE
SIERRA
SOAPER SHELF
SUREFLO
TRIMLINE SERIES
Advertising Agency:
Klein Mickaelian Partners
5670 Wilshire Blvd Ste 1590
Los Angeles, CA 90036-5633
Tel.: (310) 556-0500
Fax: (310) 556-0949
(Architectural Products)

BOMMER INDUSTRIES, INC.
19810 Asheville Hwy
Landrum, SC 29356-9027
Tel.: (864) 457-3301
Fax: (877) 426-1039
Toll Free: (800) 334-1654
E-mail: digit@bommer.com
Web Site: www.bommer.com
Approx. Number Employees: 200
Year Founded: 1876
Business Description:
Lavatory Hardware, Spring Hinges & Mail Receptacles
S.I.C.: 3429; 5072
N.A.I.C.S.: 332510; 423710
Media: 2-4-10-13
Distr.: Natl.
Budget Set: Oct.
Personnel:
Charles A. Martin *(Pres & Treas)*
Brands & Products:
BOMMER
FIREPINS

BON L CANADA, INC.
(Sub. of Signature Aluminum Canada, Inc.)
500 Edward Ave
Richmond Hill, ON L4C 4Y9, Canada
Tel.: (905) 884-9161
Fax: (905) 884-9784
Toll Free: (800) 323-0140
E-mail: GeneralCanada@bonlalum.com
Web Site:
www.signaturealuminum.com
Sales Range: $150-199.9 Million
Year Founded: 1998
Business Description:
Aluminum Extrusions & Ladders Mfr
S.I.C.: 3354
N.A.I.C.S.: 331316
Media: 10-19
Distr.: Natl.
Budget Set: Jan.
Personnel:
Jon Louch *(Bus Mgr-Ladders)*

BRASSCRAFT MANUFACTURING COMPANY
(Sub. of Masco Corporation)
39600 Orchard Hill Pl
Novi, MI 48375
Tel.: (248) 305-6000
Fax: (248) 305-6011
E-mail: customerservice@brasscraft.com
Web Site: www.brasscraft.com
Sales Range: $75-99.9 Million
Approx. Number Employees: 137
Year Founded: 1946
Business Description:
Water Supplies & Gas Plumbing Products Mfr & Distr
S.I.C.: 3494; 3432
N.A.I.C.S.: 332919; 332913
Media: 4-7-10
Personnel:
James Whiteherse *(Sr VP-Sls)*
Tom Carey *(VP-Sls)*
Jeff Jollay *(VP-Mktg & Product Dev)*
Jack Allen *(Reg Mgr-Western)*
Debra Lewis *(Product Mgr)*
Brands & Products:
COPPER-FLEX
PROCOAT
SAFETY+PLUS
SPEEDI PLUMB
SPEEDI PLUMB PLUS
SPEEDWAY

BROCK-MCVEY COMPANY
(Sub. of A.Y. McDonald Manufacturing Co.)
1100 Brock McVey Dr
Lexington, KY 40509-4116
Mailing Address:
PO Box 55487
Lexington, KY 40555-5487
Tel.: (859) 255-1412
Fax: (859) 233-4387
E-mail: brock@brockmcvey.com
Web Site: www.brockmcvey.com
Sales Range: $50-74.9 Million
Approx. Number Employees: 96
Year Founded: 1935
Business Description:
Wholesale Distr of Plumbing, Heating, Cooling, Light Fixtures, Kitchen Cabinets, Industrial & Electrical Products
S.I.C.: 5075; 5074
N.A.I.C.S.: 423730; 423720
Advertising Expenditures: $80,000
Catalogs & Directories: $40,000; Other: $28,000; Premiums, Novelties: $12,000
Distr.: Natl.
Personnel:
John McDonald, III *(Chm & CEO)*
Reggie Hickman *(Pres & COO)*
Brenda Holdren *(Dir-Fin & Admin)*

BROOKS UTILITY PRODUCTS GROUP
(Sub. of Tyden Group Inc.)
23847 Industrial Pk Dr
Farmington Hills, MI 48335-2860
Tel.: (248) 477-0250
Fax: (248) 477-2583
Web Site: www.ekstrom-metering.com
Approx. Number Employees: 50
Year Founded: 1955
Business Description:
Metering Equipment Mfr
S.I.C.: 3829

Key to Media (For complete agency information see *The Advertising Red Books-Agencies* edition):
1. Bus. Publs. 2. Cable T.V. 3. Catalogs & Directories. 4. Co-op Adv. 5. Consumer Mags. 6. D.M. to Bus. Estab.7. D.M. to Consumers 8. Daily Newsp. 9. Exhibits/Trade Shows 10. Foreign 11. Infomercial 12. Internet Adv.13. Multimedia 14. Network Radio 15. Network T.V. 16. Newsp. Distr. Mags. 17. Other 18. Outdoor (Posters, Transit) 19. Point of Purchase20. Premiums, Novelties 21. Product Samples 22. Special Events Mktg. 23. Spot Radio 24. Spot T.V. 25. Weekly Newsp. 26. Yellow Page Adv.

Brooks Utility Products Group — (Continued)

N.A.I.C.S.: 334519
Import Export
Media: 10
Distr.: Natl.
Personnel:
Michael E. Lewis *(Mgr-Mktg)*

C&H DISTRIBUTORS, LLC
(Sub. of TAKKT AG)
770 S 70th St
Milwaukee, WI 53214
Mailing Address:
PO Box 04499
Milwaukee, WI 53214
Tel.: (414) 443-1700
Fax: (414) 443-2700
Fax: (800) 336-1331
Toll Free: (800) 558-9966
Web Site: www.chdist.com
Approx. Number Employees: 200
Year Founded: 1937
Business Description:
Distributor of Industrial Supplies
S.I.C.: 5084; 5113
N.A.I.C.S.: 423830; 424130
Media: 4-13
Personnel:
David McKeon *(Pres)*

CAPITOL MANUFACTURING CO.
(Sub. of Phoenix Forging Company, Inc.)
1125 Capitol Rd
Crowley, LA 70526
Tel.: (337) 783-8626
Fax: (337) 783-5360
Telex: 245455
E-mail: sales@capitolcamco.com
Web Site: www.capitolcamco.com
E-Mail For Key Personnel:
Sales Director: sales@capitolcamco.com
Approx. Number Employees: 219
Year Founded: 1923
Business Description:
Industrial Pipe Fittings
S.I.C.: 3498
N.A.I.C.S.: 332996
Export
Advertising Expenditures: $205,000
Bus. Publs.: $30,000; Cable T.V.: $20,000; Catalogs & Directories: $15,000; Consumer Mags.: $110,000; D.M. to Consumers: $15,000; Exhibits/Trade Shows: $10,000; Premiums, Novelties: $5,000
Distr.: Intl.; Natl.
Budget Set: Sept.
Personnel:
Rodney Dean *(Mgr-Sls)*

CAREFREE OF COLORADO
(Div. of The Scott Fetzer Company)
2145 W 6th Ave
Broomfield, CO 80020-1656
Tel.: (303) 469-1152
Fax: (303) 469-4742
Toll Free: (800) 622-3230
E-mail: contact@carefreeofcolorado.com
Web Site: www.carefreeofcolorado.com
E-Mail For Key Personnel:
Public Relations: humanresources@carefreeofcolorado.com
Sales Range: $100-124.9 Million
Approx. Number Employees: 200
Year Founded: 1972
Business Description:
Accessories for RV's & Motor Homes, Awnings & Canopies Mfr, Marine Accessories & Residential Sun & Shade Accessories
S.I.C.: 2394
N.A.I.C.S.: 314912
Import Export
Advertising Expenditures: $183,000
Media: 2-4-6-7-8-10-11-13-19
Distr.: Natl.
Budget Set: Nov.
Personnel:
Jeff Rutherford *(Pres)*
Brands & Products:
CAMPOUT
CAREFREE ADD-A-ROOM
ECLIPSE
FIESTA
FREEDOM
GUARDIAWN
THE MARQUEE OVER-THE-DOOR
THE MARQUEE WINDOW
MIRAGE
OMEGA II
ONE-TOUCH
POWER PACK
SIDE BLOCKER
SIDEOUT
SIDEOUT KOVER
SIDEVISOR
SIMPLICITY
SL WINDOW AWNING
SLIDE-OUT SUMMIT
SMARTVISOR
SPIRIT
SUN BLOCKER
SUNSHADE
SUPERSPORT
THIN LITE
TRAVEL'R

CASH ACME INC.
(Sub. of IMI plc)
2400 7th Ave SW
Cullman, AL 35055-0295
Tel.: (256) 775-8200
Fax: (256) 775-8149
Toll Free: (800) 879-2042
E-mail: infosystems@cashacme.com
Web Site: www.cashacme.com
E-Mail For Key Personnel:
Sales Director: jbrill@cashacme.com
Approx. Sls.: $26,000,000
Approx. Number Employees: 135
Year Founded: 1921
Business Description:
Mfr. of Automatic Valves
S.I.C.: 3491
N.A.I.C.S.: 332911
Import Export
Advertising Expenditures: $413,000
Multimedia: $3,000; Bus. Publs.: $135,000; Catalogs & Directories: $150,000; Co-op Adv.: $3,000; D.M. to Bus. Estab.: $15,000; Exhibits/Trade Shows: $70,000; Other: $10,000; Point of Purchase: $5,000; Premiums, Novelties: $20,000; Product Samples: $2,000
Distr.: Intl.; Natl.
Budget Set: Monthly
Brands & Products:
CASH ACME

CASHCO, INC.
607 W 15th St
Ellsworth, KS 67439
Mailing Address:
PO Box 6
Ellsworth, KS 67439-0006
Tel.: (785) 472-4461
Fax: (785) 472-3539
Web Site: www.cashco.com
Approx. Number Employees: 155
Year Founded: 1920
Business Description:
Mfr. of Self-Contained Regulators & Control Valves; Spare Parts for Coal Pulverizing Systems Used in Power Plants
S.I.C.: 3491; 3531
N.A.I.C.S.: 332911; 333120
Export
Advertising Expenditures: $209,000
Bus. Publs.: $10,000; Catalogs & Directories: $20,000; Co-op Adv.: $5,000; Consumer Mags.: $80,000; D.M. to Bus. Estab.: $5,000; D.M. to Consumers: $12,000; Exhibits/Trade Shows: $60,000; Internet Adv.: $2,000; Product Samples: $15,000
Distr.: Intl.; Natl.
Budget Set: Oct.
Personnel:
Clint Rogers *(Exec VP-Sls, Mktg & Engrg)*
Randy Helus *(Asst Controller)*
Brands & Products:
CASHCO
PREMIER
RANGER QCT
Advertising Agency:
Brush Art
709 E. Commercial
Downs, KS 67437
Tel.: (785) 454-3383
(Control Valves & Regulators)

CHAMPLAIN CABLE CORP.
(Affil. of Huber + Suhner AG)
175 Hercules Dr
Colchester, VT 05446-5925
Tel.: (802) 654-4200
Fax: (802) 654-4224
Toll Free: (800) 451-5162
E-mail: sales@champcable.com
Web Site: www.champcable.com
E-Mail For Key Personnel:
Sales Director: sales@champcable.com
Sales Range: $10-24.9 Million
Approx. Number Employees: 100
Year Founded: 1955
Business Description:
High Temperature Insulated Wires & Cables Mfr
S.I.C.: 3496
N.A.I.C.S.: 332618
Import Export
Advertising Expenditures: $300,000
Media: 2-4-7-10-13-21
Distr.: Natl.
Budget Set: Oct.
Personnel:
Richard Hall *(Pres)*
Dick Kruger *(VP-Sls & Mktg)*

CHANNELLOCK, INC.
1306 S Main St
Meadville, PA 16335-3035
Tel.: (814) 724-8700
Fax: (814) 337-3616
Toll Free: (800) 724-3018
E-mail: pliers@channellock.com
Web Site: www.channellock.com
Approx. Number Employees: 400
Year Founded: 1886
Business Description:
Mfr. of Hand Tools
S.I.C.: 3423
N.A.I.C.S.: 332212
Export
Advertising Expenditures: $2,000,000
Media: 2-4-5-6-9-10-13-15-16-17-18-19-20-22-25
Distr.: Natl.
Budget Set: Aug.
Personnel:
William S. DeArment *(Pres & CEO)*
Ryan DeArment *(Mgr-Mktg)*
Brands & Products:
CHANNELLOCK
CHANNELLOCK BLUE
THE CRIMPER
GRIPLOCK
HOLD-E-ZEE
INCH NUTBUSTER
LITTLE CHAMP
MICRO CHAMP
NUTBUSTER
PERMALOCK
SAFE-T-STOP
TOG-L-LOK
WIDEAZZ
WIREMASTER
Advertising Agency:
SBC Advertising
333 W Nationwide Blvd
Columbus, OH 43215
Tel.: (614) 891-7070
Fax: (614) 255-2600
Toll Free: (866) 891-7001

CHARLOTTE PIPE & FOUNDRY COMPANY
2109 Randolph Rd
Charlotte, NC 28207
Tel.: (704) 372-5030
Fax: (800) 553-1605
E-mail: info@charlottepipe.com
Web Site: www.charlottepipe.com
Approx. Sls.: $177,300,000
Approx. Number Employees: 200
Business Description:
Iron & Plastics Pipe & Pipe Fittings Mfr
S.I.C.: 3084; 3317
N.A.I.C.S.: 326122; 331210
Personnel:
Roddey Dowd *(Pres)*
Frank W. Dowd, IV *(CEO)*
William Hutaff *(CFO & Sr VP)*
Dewey Manus *(Mgr-Tech Svcs-Cast Iron & Plastics)*
Brands & Products:
CHARLOTTE
CHEMDRAIN
FLOWGUARD GOLD
YOU CAN'T BEAT THE SYSTEM
Advertising Agency:
Eric Mower and Associates
1001 Morehead Sq Dr 5th Fl
Charlotte, NC 28203
Tel.: (704) 375-0123
Fax: (704) 375-0222
Toll Free: (800) 968-0682
— Angela Duerr *(Acct Exec)*

Key to Media (For complete agency information see *The Advertising Red Books-Agencies* edition):
1. Bus. Publs. 2. Cable T.V. 3. Catalogs & Directories. 4. Co-op Adv. 5. Consumer Mags. 6. D.M. to Bus. Estab.7. D.M. to Consumers
8. Daily Newsp. 9. Exhibits/Trade Shows 10. Foreign 11. Infomercial 12. Internet Adv.13. Multimedia 14. Network Radio
15. Network T.V. 16. Newsp. Distr. Mags. 17. Other 18. Outdoor (Posters, Transit) 19. Point of Purchase20. Premiums, Novelties
21. Product Samples 22. Special Events Mktg. 23. Spot Radio 24. Spot T.V. 25. Weekly Newsp. 26. Yellow Page Adv.

THE CHICAGO FAUCET COMPANY
(Sub. of Geberit AG)
2100 S Clearwater Dr
Des Plaines, IL 60018-1918
Tel.: (847) 803-5000
Fax: (847) 803-5454
Toll Free: (800) 325-5060
Web Site: www.chicagofaucets.com
Approx. Number Employees: 80
Year Founded: 1901
Business Description:
Mfr. of Faucets & Brass Plumbing Fittings for Residential & Commercial Use
S.I.C.: 3432
N.A.I.C.S.: 332913
Export
Media: 1-2-4-5-7-10-13-19-20-21
Distr.: Intl.; Natl.
Budget Set: July
Personnel:
Bob Gilbert *(CFO & VP)*
Pat Kimener *(Sr VP-Sls)*
Brands & Products:
CONTROL-A-FLO
EAGLE EYE
ECONO-FLO
EXPRESSIONS
ILLUSIONS
LEGACY
MARATHON
MVP
QUATURN
REACT
SOFT-FLO
STEDI-FLO
TEMPSHIELD
Advertising Agency:
Brandtrust
John Hancock Bldg 875 N Michigan Ave Ste 2945
Chicago, IL 60611
Tel.: (312) 440-1833
Fax: (312) 440-9987

COMPX INTERNATIONAL INC.
(Holding of NL Industries, Inc.)
5430 LBJ Fwy Ste 1700
Dallas, TX 75240
Tel.: (972) 448-1400
Fax: (972) 448-1445
Web Site: www.compxnet.com
Approx. Sls.: $135,264,000
Approx. Number Employees: 828
Business Description:
Ergonomic Computer Support Systems, Ball Bearing Slides & Locks Mfr
S.I.C.: 3341; 3421; 3429
N.A.I.C.S.: 331314; 332211; 332510
Advertising Expenditures: $369,000
Personnel:
Glenn R. Simmons *(Chm)*
David A. Bowers *(Vice Chm, Pres & CEO)*
Darryl R. Halbert *(CFO)*
Brands & Products:
COMPX
STOCK LOCKS

COMPX NATIONAL, INC.
(Sub. of CompX International Inc.)
200 Old Mill Rd
Mauldin, SC 29662-2043
Mailing Address:
PO Box 200
Mauldin, SC 29662-0200
Tel.: (864) 297-6655
Fax: (864) 297-9987
Web Site: www.compxnet.com
Approx. Number Employees: 300
Year Founded: 1903
Business Description:
Security Hardware
S.I.C.: 3429
N.A.I.C.S.: 332510
Export
Media: 2-4-7-10
Distr.: Natl.
Budget Set: Jan.-Dec.
Personnel:
Scott James *(Pres)*
Brands & Products:
STOCK LOCKS

COOPER B-LINE, INC.
(Sub. of Cooper Industries plc)
509 W Monroe St
Highland, IL 62249
Tel.: (618) 654-2184
Fax: (618) 654-5907
Fax: (800) 356-1438
Toll Free: (800) 851-7415
E-mail: blineus@cooperindustries.com
Web Site: www.cooperbline.com
Sales Range: $75-99.9 Million
Approx. Number Employees: 427
Year Founded: 1956
Business Description:
Enclosures for Electronic Products Mfr
S.I.C.: 3441; 3443
N.A.I.C.S.: 332312; 332313
Media: 2-10
Distr.: Intl.; Natl.
Budget Set: Sept. -Oct.
Personnel:
Kevin C. Kissling *(Pres)*
Joe Klein *(VP-Mktg)*
Laura May *(Product Mgr)*
Brands & Products:
B-LINE
Advertising Agency:
Hughes
1141 S 7th St
Saint Louis, MO 63104
Tel.: (314) 571-6300

CRANE RESISTOFLEX/ INDUSTRIAL
(Sub. of Crane Fluid Handling)
1 Quality Way
Marion, NC 28752
Tel.: (828) 724-4000
Fax: (828) 724-9469
Web Site: www.resistoflex.com
Sales Range: $50-74.9 Million
Approx. Number Employees: 132
Year Founded: 1937
Business Description:
Plastic-Lined Pipes & Fittings Mfr
S.I.C.: 3084; 3498
N.A.I.C.S.: 326122; 332996
Export
Media: 2-4-7-10-11-13-21-26
Personnel:
Strom James *(VP & Sls Mgr)*
Brands & Products:
CONQUEST
MULTI-AXIS

CREATIVE VISTAS INC.
2100 Forbes Street Unit 8-10
Whitby, ON L1N 9T3, Canada
Tel.: (905) 666-8676
Fax: (905) 666-9795
E-mail: info@creativevistasinc.com
Web Site: www.creativevistasinc.com
Approx. Rev.: $39,866,485
Approx. Number Employees: 447
Year Founded: 1983
Business Description:
Electronic Security & Surveillance Products & Solutions
S.I.C.: 7382; 3679
N.A.I.C.S.: 561621; 334419
Advertising Expenditures: $40,000
Media: 17
Personnel:
Sayan Navaratnam *(Chm)*
Dominic Burns *(Pres & CEO)*
Heung Hung Lee *(CFO & Sec)*

DANAHER CORPORATION
2099 Pennsylvania Ave NW 12th Fl
Washington, DC 20006-1813
Tel.: (202) 828-0850
Fax: (202) 828-0860
E-mail: investor.relations@danaher.com
Web Site: www.danaher.com
Approx. Sls.: $13,202,602,000
Approx. Number Employees: 48,200
Year Founded: 1982
Business Description:
Professional Instrumentation Products & Industrial Technologies Tools & Components Mfr
S.I.C.: 3823; 3423; 3545; 3546; 3559; 3585; 3589; 3625; 3822; 3824; 3825
N.A.I.C.S.: 334513; 332212; 332410; 333220; 333295; 333298; 333319; 333415; 333515; 333991; 334512; 334514; 334515; 335314
Media: 1-2-4-5-7-10-20
Distr.: Intl.; Natl.
Personnel:
Steven M. Rales *(Chm)*
H. Lawrence Culp, Jr. *(Pres & CEO)*
Daniel L. Comas *(CFO & Exec VP)*
Robert S. Lutz *(Chief Acctg Officer & VP)*
Linda S. Cheever *(Pres-Asia Pacific)*
Jonathan P. Graham *(Gen Counsel & Sr VP)*
William K. Daniel, II *(Exec VP)*
Thomas P. Joyce Jr. *(Exec VP)*
James A. Lico *(Exec VP)*
James H. Ditkoff *(Sr VP-Fin & Tax)*
William H. King *(Sr VP-Strategic Dev)*
Daniel A. Raskas *(Sr VP-Corp Dev)*
Henk van Duijnhoven *(Sr VP-Dental Segment)*
Kevin A. Klau *(VP-HR)*
Eric A. McAllister *(VP-HR)*
Craig L. Overhage *(Mgr)*
Brands & Products:
ALLEN
ALLTEC
AMERICAN SIGMA
ANATEL
ANDERSON
ARMSTRONG TOOLS
ARTUS
BAUTZ
BUHLER MONTEC
CALZONI S.R.L.
CURRENT TECHNOLOGY
DANAHER CONTROLS
DELTA CONSOLIDATED INDUSTRIES
ELE
ELECTRO-KINETICS
ENERGETIC MATERIALS
FISHER PIERCE
FLUKE
FLUKE NETWORKS
GEMS SENSORS
GENDEX
GILBARCO
GLI
GUARDIAN VOTING SYSTEMS
HACH
HAROWE
HART SCIENTIFIC
HECON
HENGSTLER GMBH
HENNESSY INDUSTRIES
HOLO-KROME
HYDROLAB
INMOTION
ISELI
JACOBS CHUCK MANUFACTURING
JACOBS VEHICLE SYSTEMS
JENNINGS TECHNOLOGY
JOSLYN
JOSLYN CLARK
JOSLYN HI-VOLTAGE
K-D TOOLS
KAVO
KISTLER MORSE
KOLLMORGEN
KOLLMORGEN ELECTRO-OPTICAL
LACHAT INSTRUMENTS
MATCO TOOLS
MCCROMETER
MICRON
NAMCO JENNER
NEAT
ORBISPHERE
PACIFIC SCIENTIFIC ATG
PARTLOW WEST
POLYMETRON
PORTESCAP
RADIOMETER
RADIOMETER ANALYTICAL
RAYTEK
RED JACKET
ROBIN ELECTRONICS
SATA
SECO
SETRA
SPLINE GAUGES
SUNBANK
SUPERIOR ELECTRIC
THOMSON
THOMSON TOLLO
UNITED POWER
VEEDER ROOT
VIDEOJET TECHNOLOGIES
WEST INSTRUMENTS
WILLETT
Advertising Agencies:
BMWW
17 Governors Ct Ste 150
Baltimore, MD 21244-2713
Tel.: (410) 298-0390
Fax: (410) 298-8716

eXubrio Group LLC
1321 Millersport Hwy Ste 204
Williamsville, NY 14221
Tel.: (716) 830-5219

Key to Media (For complete agency information see *The Advertising Red Books-Agencies* edition):
1. Bus. Publs. 2. Cable T.V. 3. Catalogs & Directories. 4. Co-op Adv. 5. Consumer Mags. 6. D.M. to Bus. Estab.7. D.M. to Consumers
8. Daily Newsp. 9. Exhibits/Trade Shows 10. Foreign 11. Infomercial 12. Internet Adv.13. Multimedia 14. Network Radio
15. Network T.V. 16. Newsp. Distr. Mags. 17. Other 18. Outdoor (Posters, Transit) 19. Point of Purchase20. Premiums, Novelties
21. Product Samples 22. Special Events Mktg. 23. Spot Radio 24. Spot T.V. 25. Weekly Newsp. 26. Yellow Page Adv.

DANFOSS HAGO INC.
(Sub. of Danfoss Burner Components Division)
1120 Globe Ave
Mountainside, NJ 07092
Tel.: (908) 232-8687
Fax: (908) 232-7246
Toll Free: (800) 710-4246
E-mail: sales@hagonozzles.com
Web Site: www.hago.danfoss.com
E-Mail For Key Personnel:
Sales Director: sales@hagonozzles.com
Sales Range: $10-24.9 Million
Approx. Number Employees: 60
Business Description:
Mfr of Oil Burner Nozzles
S.I.C.: 3433; 3492
N.A.I.C.S.: 333414; 332912
Media: 4-10

DARNELL-ROSE
(Div. of Evans Industries, Inc.)
17915 Railroad St
City of Industry, CA 91748
Tel.: (626) 912-1688
Fax: (626) 912-3765
Toll Free: (800) 327-6355
E-mail: info@casters.com
Web Site: www.casters.com
Approx. Number Employees: 30
Year Founded: 1921
Business Description:
Casters, Wheels & Rubber Bumpers & Industrial Truck Couplers Mfr & Distributor
S.I.C.: 3499; 3069; 5072
N.A.I.C.S.: 332999; 326299; 423710
Export
Media: 4-6-7-10-17
Distr.: Natl.
Budget Set: Jan.
Personnel:
Brent Barger *(Pres)*
Brands & Products:
DARNELL-ROSE
DR

DE-STA-CO INDUSTRIES
(Sub. of Dover Industrial Products, Inc.)
1025 Doris Rd
Auburn Hills, MI 48326
Tel.: (248) 836-6700
Fax: (248) 836-6740
Toll Free: (888) -DESTACO
Web Site: www.destaco.com
Approx. Sls.: $20,000,000
Approx. Number Employees: 100
Year Founded: 1915
Business Description:
Robotic Tooling & Flexible Industrial Automation Solutions
S.I.C.: 3593; 3495
N.A.I.C.S.: 333995; 332612
Import Export
Advertising Expenditures: $710,000
Bus. Publs.: $213,000; Catalogs & Directories: $71,000; Consumer Mags.: $106,500; Daily Newsp.: $177,500; Exhibits/Trade Shows: $142,000
Distr.: Direct to Consumer; Natl.
Budget Set: Oct.-Nov.
Personnel:
John Podczerwinski *(Pres)*
John Bubnikovich *(Mktg Dir-Segment Strategy)*
Brands & Products:
CLAMP MASTER
DE-STA-CO

DECO PRODUCTS CO.
506 Sanford St
Decorah, IA 52101
Tel.: (563) 382-4264
Fax: (563) 382-9845
Toll Free: (800) 327-9751
E-mail: deco@decoprod.com
Web Site: www.decoprod.com
E-Mail For Key Personnel:
Sales Director: jraptes@decoprod.com
Approx. Number Employees: 275
Year Founded: 1960
Business Description:
Mfr. of Zinc Die Castings, Mechanical Assemblies, Machining, Powder Coating & Hose Clamps
S.I.C.: 3364; 3429
N.A.I.C.S.: 331522; 332510
Export
Media: 2-17
Distr.: Natl.
Personnel:
Chris Storlie *(Asst Gen Mgr)*
Lew Storlie *(Gen Mgr)*
Jim Raptes *(Mgr-Sls-Custom)*
Gary Timp *(Mgr-Sls-Windows & Doors)*
Brands & Products:
DECO
SASH LOCK

DETECTO SCALE COMPANY
(Div. of Cardinal Scale Manufacturing Co.)
203 E Daugherty St
Webb City, MO 64870-1929
Mailing Address:
PO Box 151
Webb City, MO 64870-0151
Tel.: (417) 673-4631
Fax: (417) 673-5001
Toll Free: (800) 641-2008
E-mail: detecto@cardet.com
Web Site: www.detectoscale.com
Approx. Number Employees: 350
Year Founded: 1900
Business Description:
Beam & Digital Clinical Scales Mfr
S.I.C.: 3596; 5065
N.A.I.C.S.: 333997; 423690
Export
Media: 2-4-7-10
Distr.: Natl.
Budget Set: July
Personnel:
David H. Perry *(Pres)*
Charles Masters *(CFO)*
Fred Cox *(VP-Sls)*
Jonathan Sabo *(Mgr-Adv)*

DISTRIBUTION AMERICA, INC.
2700 S River Rd Ste 300
Des Plaines, IL 60018-4107
Tel.: (847) 296-7000
Fax: (847) 296-8217
Web Site: www.daonline.com
Approx. Number Employees: 28
Year Founded: 1991
Business Description:
Wholesale Hardware Co-Operative
S.I.C.: 5072; 5198
N.A.I.C.S.: 423710; 424950
Media: 1-2-4-5-7-8-9-10-16-19-20-25
Distr.: Natl.
Budget Set: Sept.
Personnel:
Kenneth R. Beauvais *(Chm & Pres)*
David W. Christmas *(Pres & CEO)*
Brands & Products:
DISTRIBUTION AMERICA
THE DISTRIBUTION SERVICES COMPANY
GOLDEN RULE
MINUTEMAN
RPM
SENTRY
TRUSTWORTHY
VAL-U-LINE

DIXON VALVE & COUPLING COMPANY
800 High St
Chestertown, MD 21620
Tel.: (410) 778-2000
Fax: (410) 778-4702
Toll Free: (800) 355-1991
E-mail: sales@dixonvalve.com
Web Site: www.dixonvalve.com
E-Mail For Key Personnel:
Sales Director: sales@dixonvalve.com
Approx. Number Employees: 900
Year Founded: 1916
Business Description:
Valve & Hose Coupling Mfr
S.I.C.: 3492; 5085
N.A.I.C.S.: 332912; 423840
Export
Media: 2-4-7-10-11-13-20
Distr.: Natl.
Budget Set: Nov.
Personnel:
Richard L. Goodall *(CEO)*
Jim Canalichio *(CFO & Sr VP)*
Louis F. Farina *(Sr VP)*
Scott Jones *(VP-Sls & Mktg)*
John E. Myers *(Mgr-Acctg)*
Brands & Products:
AIR CHIEF
AIR KING
DUAL LOCK
EZ BOSS LOCK
KALREZ
THE RIGHT CONNECTION
T-BOLT
TUFF-LITE
Advertising Agency:
Mullin/Ashley Associates, Inc.
306 Canon St
Chestertown, MD 21620
Tel.: (410) 778-2184
Fax: (410) 778-6640
Toll Free: (888) 662-4558

DO IT BEST CORP.
6502 Nelson Rd
Fort Wayne, IN 46803-1920
Tel.: (260) 748-5300
Fax: (260) 493-1245
E-mail: mail@doitbest.com
Web Site: www.doitbestcorp.com
Approx. Sls.: $3,100,000,000
Approx. Number Employees: 1,550
Year Founded: 1945
Business Description:
Distr of Lumber, Building Materials & Hardware
S.I.C.: 5072; 5031
N.A.I.C.S.: 423710; 423310
Import Export
Media: 2-3-4-5-7-8-9-10-13-23-25-26
Distr.: Natl.
Personnel:
Robert N. Taylor *(Pres & CEO)*
David Haist *(COO & Exec VP)*
Dan Starr *(Gen Counsel & VP-HR)*
Jay Brown *(VP-Retail Dev)*
Mike Alton Door *(VP-Info Tech)*
Tim Miller *(VP-Mktg)*
Brands & Products:
ADPAK
DO IT
DO IT BEST ALL ACROSS AMERICA
DO IT BEST CROP
DO IT BEST GIFT CARD
DO IT BEST HOME
DO IT BEST INTELLIPC
DO IT CENTER
DO IT EXPRESS
HWI
INCOM
INCOM DISTRIBUTOR SUPPLY
INFO-PLUS
Advertising Agencies:
Asher Agency, Inc.
535 W Wayne St
Fort Wayne, IN 46802-2123
Tel.: (260) 424-3373
Fax: (260) 424-0848
Fax: (260) 420-2615 (Media)
Toll Free: (800) 900-7031

Ferguson Advertising Inc.
803 S Calhoun St 6th Fl
Fort Wayne, IN 46802-2319
Tel.: (260) 426-4401
Fax: (260) 422-6417
Agency of Record
Creative
Marketing
Public Relations
Strategic Planning

DORCY INTERNATIONAL INC.
2700 Port Rd
Columbus, OH 43217-1136
Tel.: (614) 497-5830
Fax: (614) 497-5822
Toll Free: (800) 837-8558
E-mail: support@dorcy.com
Web Site: www.dorcy.com
Sales Range: $10-24.9 Million
Approx. Number Employees: 50
Business Description:
Mfr & Distr of Flashlights, Lanterns & Batteries
S.I.C.: 5063
N.A.I.C.S.: 423610
Import Export
Media: 2-4-7-10-19-20-21
Distr.: Intl.; Natl.
Budget Set: Nov.
Personnel:
Tom Beckett *(Pres & CEO)*
Marvin Corns *(VP & Dir-Ops)*
Mike Riley *(VP-Sls & Mktg)*
Kathy Verhoeven *(VP-Fin & Admin)*
Brands & Products:
ADVENTURE
BOSS
DORCY
EXCELL
FAILSAFE
FROST BRITE
LUMINATOR
MASTERCELL
SIGNAL WAND
SPYDER

Key to Media (For complete agency information see *The Advertising Red Books-Agencies* edition):
1. Bus. Publs. 2. Cable T.V. 3. Catalogs & Directories. 4. Co-op Adv. 5. Consumer Mags. 6. D.M. to Bus. Estab.7. D.M. to Consumers 8. Daily Newsp. 9. Exhibits/Trade Shows 10. Foreign 11. Infomercial 12. Internet Adv.13. Multimedia 14. Network Radio 15. Network T.V. 16. Newsp. Distr. Mags. 17. Other 18. Outdoor (Posters, Transit) 19. Point of Purchase20. Premiums, Novelties 21. Product Samples 22. Special Events Mktg. 23. Spot Radio 24. Spot T.V. 25. Weekly Newsp. 26. Yellow Page Adv.

SUPER HEAVY DUTY

DREMEL
(Div. of Robert Bosch Tool Corp)
4915 21st St
Racine, WI 53406-5028
Tel.: (262) 554-1390
Fax: (262) 554-7654
Toll Free: (800) 437-3635
Web Site: www.dremel.com
Approx. Number Employees: 30
Year Founded: 1934
Business Description:
Mfr. of Rotary Tools, Multi Purpose Saws & Electric Engraving Tools
S.I.C.: 3429; 5085
N.A.I.C.S.: 332510; 423840
Export
Advertising Expenditures: $600,000
Media: 2-3-5-6-10-23-24
Distr.: Intl.; Natl.
Budget Set: June
Brands & Products:
ADVANTAGE ROTARY SAW
MINI-MITE
MULTIPRO ROTARY TOOLS
VERSATIP

DRIV-LOK, INC.
1140 Pk Ave
Sycamore, IL 60178-2927
Tel.: (815) 895-8161
Fax: (815) 895-6909
E-mail: driv-lok@driv-lok.com
Web Site: www.driv-lok.com
Approx. Number Employees: 80
Year Founded: 1933
Business Description:
Press Fit Fasteners Mfr
S.I.C.: 3429
N.A.I.C.S.: 332510
Export
Media: 2-4-7-10-13-20
Distr.: Intl.; Natl.
Budget Set: Sept.
Personnel:
Gary Seegers *(Pres-Owner)*
Brands & Products:
BARB-LOK
DRIV-LOK
ENGINOMICS
HARDENED LOK-DOWELS
LOK-DOWEL
SHEARPROOF
VENT DOWELS

DUO-FAST CORPORATION
(Sub. of Illinois Tool Works Inc.)
2400 Galvin Dr
Elgin, IL 60123-7883
Tel.: (847) 783-5500
Fax: (847) 783-5501
Toll Free: (888) DUO-FAST
Web Site: www.duo-fast.com
Sales Range: $50-74.9 Million
Approx. Number Employees: 100
Year Founded: 1937
Business Description:
Nailers, Staplers, Tackers, Nails & Staples Mfr
S.I.C.: 3423; 3312; 3315; 3316; 3341; 3471; 3496
N.A.I.C.S.: 332212; 331111; 331221; 331222; 331314; 331423; 331492; 332618; 332813
Media: 1-2-4-7-10-11-13-16-20-26
Distr.: Intl.; Natl.
Budget Set: Oct.
Brands & Products:
DUO-BOND
DUO-FAST
MAINFRAME
SLAPSHOT
SURESHOT

EAO SWITCH CORPORATION
(Sub. of EAO AG)
98 Washington St
Milford, CT 06460-3670
Tel.: (203) 877-4577
Fax: (203) 877-3694
E-mail: info@eaoswitch.com
Web Site: www.eaoswitch.com
Approx. Number Employees: 27
Year Founded: 1978
Business Description:
General Purpose Pushbutton Switches, Keypads, Indicators, Membranes & Custom Front Panels Mfr
S.I.C.: 5063
N.A.I.C.S.: 423610
Import
Media: 2-4-7-10-11-13-21
Distr.: Natl.
Budget Set: Nov.
Personnel:
Joseph Torzillo *(VP-Sls)*
Dan Digioia *(Mgr-Mktg)*

EASTMAN INDUSTRIES
(Sub. of Eastman Industries)
410 Riverside St
Portland, ME 04103
Tel.: (207) 878-5353
Fax: (207) 878-9109
E-mail: info@eastmanind.com
Web Site: www.eastmanind.com
Approx. Number Employees: 65
Year Founded: 1983
Business Description:
Mfr. of Lawn & Garden Equipment
S.I.C.: 3524
N.A.I.C.S.: 333112
Export
Media: 2-3-6-7-17-19
Distr.: Natl.
Personnel:
Linda Thompson *(Mgr-Natl Sls)*
Brands & Products:
EASTMAN INDUSTRIES
HOWERMOWER

EBERHARD MANUFACTURING DIVISION
(Div. of The Eastern Company)
21944 Drake Rd
Strongsville, OH 44149
Mailing Address:
PO Box 368012
Cleveland, OH 44136-9712
Tel.: (440) 238-9720
Fax: (440) 572-2732
E-mail: ebermark@eberhard.com
Web Site: www.eberhard.com
Sales Range: $75-99.9 Million
Approx. Number Employees: 150
Business Description:
Industrial Truck Body Trailer & Custom Hardware Mfr
S.I.C.: 3429; 3452
N.A.I.C.S.: 332510; 332722
Advertising Expenditures: $400,000
Media: 4-6-10-21
Distr.: Natl.
Budget Set: Nov.
Personnel:

ECHO INCORPORATED
(Sub. of Kioritz Corporation)
400 Oakwood Rd
Lake Zurich, IL 60047-1561
Tel.: (847) 540-8400
Fax: (847) 540-9670
Web Site: www.echo-usa.com
Approx. Number Employees: 675
Year Founded: 1972
Business Description:
Outdoor Power Equipment Distr
S.I.C.: 3524
N.A.I.C.S.: 333112
Import Export
Media: 1-2-4-7-10-15-19-22-24
Distr.: Natl.
Budget Set: June
Personnel:
Yoshi Nagao *(Pres)*
Craig Van Balen *(Dir-HR)*
Barbara Gora *(Mgr-Mktg)*
Brands & Products:
CLOROX
POWER EDGERS
POWER PRUNER
PRO ATTACHMENT SERIES
PRO-FIRE
PROLITE
PROPADDLE
PROSWEEP
PROTHATCH
QUIET 1
QUIKVENT
SHRED "N" VAC
VITON
Advertising Agency:
Cramer-Krasselt
246 E Chicago St
Milwaukee, WI 53202
Tel.: (414) 227-3500
Fax: (414) 276-8710
Agency of Record
Creative Assignment
Media Assignment

ELECTRO-OPTIX, INC.
2181 N Powerline Rd Ste 1
Pompano Beach, FL 33069
Tel.: (954) 973-2800
Fax: (954) 973-3951
Toll Free: (800) 779-2801
E-mail: info@electro-optix.com
Web Site: www.electro-optix.com
Sales Range: $10-24.9 Million
Approx. Number Employees: 15
Year Founded: 1970
Business Description:
Mfr of Illuminated Magnifiers, Travel Mirrors, Ball Pens with Flashlights, Reading Magnifiers & Outdoor Thermometers
S.I.C.: 3827; 3823; 3873
N.A.I.C.S.: 333314; 334513; 334518
Media: 2-4-5-7-10-18-19-20-21
Distr.: Natl.
Personnel:
Chris Schoenjohn *(Owner)*
Brands & Products:
ELECTROOPTIX
KLEAR TEMP
MAGI MIRROR
NITEWRITER

ELECTRON BEAM TECHNOLOGIES, INC.
1275 Harvard Dr
Kankakee, IL 60901-9471
Tel.: (815) 935-2211
Fax: (815) 935-8605
E-mail: ebt@electronbeam.com
Web Site: www.electronbeam.com
E-Mail For Key Personnel:
Sales Director: sales@electronbeam.com
Approx. Number Employees: 50
Year Founded: 1963
Business Description:
OEM Composite Welding Cables & Bulk Electrode Accessories Mfr
S.I.C.: 3548; 3541
N.A.I.C.S.: 333992; 333512
Export
Media: 2-4-7-10-13
Distr.: Intl.; Natl.
Personnel:
Paul M. Wlos *(Pres)*
Valgene E. Raloff *(Mgr-Product)*
Brands & Products:
BIG BLUE PE
BLUE PE
DURA DOME
DURA-DOMES
ERC
FAST 'N EASY
POLY-XL
QCC
STRAIGHT 'N EASY

ELYRIA FOUNDRY COMPANY
120 Filbert St
Elyria, OH 44035
Tel.: (440) 322-4657
Fax: (440) 323-1101
E-mail: bwright@elyriafoundry.com
Web Site: www.elyriafoundry.com
Approx. Number Employees: 500
Year Founded: 1905
Business Description:
Mfr of Gray & Ductile Iron Castings
S.I.C.: 3321; 3369
N.A.I.C.S.: 331511; 331528
Export
Media: 2-4-7-10
Distr.: Natl.
Personnel:
Bruce Smips *(CEO)*
Brian Wright *(VP-Sls & Mktg)*
Denise A. Sprague *(Dir-HR)*
Sherry L. Bouch *(Coord-Inside Sls)*

EMERY-WATERHOUSE COMPANY
7 Rand Rd
Portland, ME 04104
Mailing Address:
PO Box 659
Portland, ME 04104-0659
Tel.: (207) 775-2371
Fax: (207) 775-5206
Toll Free: (800) 283-0236
Web Site: www.emeryonline.com
Sales Range: $100-124.9 Million
Approx. Number Employees: 300
Year Founded: 1842
Business Description:
Hardware, Tools, Plumbing & Ventilation Components, Electrical Components, Paint, Housewares, Motor Vehicle Supplies, Industrial Supplies, Lawn & Garden Supplies Distr

Key to Media (For complete agency information see *The Advertising Red Books-Agencies* edition):
1. Bus. Publs. 2. Cable T.V. 3. Catalogs & Directories. 4. Co-op Adv. 5. Consumer Mags. 6. D.M. to Bus. Estab.7. D.M. to Consumers 8. Daily Newsp. 9. Exhibits/Trade Shows 10. Foreign 11. Infomercial 12. Internet Adv.13. Multimedia 14. Network Radio 15. Network T.V. 16. Newsp. Distr. Mags. 17. Other 18. Outdoor (Posters, Transit) 19. Point of Purchase20. Premiums, Novelties 21. Product Samples 22. Special Events Mktg. 23. Spot Radio 24. Spot T.V. 25. Weekly Newsp. 26. Yellow Page Adv.

Emery-Waterhouse Company — (Continued)

S.I.C.: 5072; 5013; 5023; 5049; 5063; 5074; 5083; 5085; 5198
N.A.I.C.S.: 423710; 423120; 423220; 423490; 423610; 423720; 423820; 423840; 424950
Exhibits/Trade Shows: 100%
Budget Set: Nov.
Personnel:
Charles L. Hildreth *(Chm)*
Stephen M. Frawley *(Pres & CEO)*
Joan Walsh *(CFO)*
Jim Cook *(Dir-Sls)*
Brands & Products:
EMERY-WATERHOUSE
ON THE LEVEL. EVERY DAY.
RETAILRIGHT

EMERY WINSLOW SCALE COMPANY
(Sub. of The A.H. Emery Company)
73 Cogwheel Ln
Seymour, CT 06483
Tel.: (203) 881-9333
Fax: (203) 881-9477
E-mail: homeoffice@emerywinslow.com
Web Site: www.emerywinslow.com
Approx. Number Employees: 60
Year Founded: 1868
Business Description:
Mfr. & Distr of Scales
S.I.C.: 3596
N.A.I.C.S.: 333997
Media: 10
Personnel:
Dave Young *(Chm)*
William Fisher *(Pres)*
Rudy Baisch *(VP-Sls)*

ENERGY & PROCESS CORP.
(Sub. of Ferguson Enterprises, Inc.)
2146 B Flintstone Dr
Tucker, GA 30084-5008
Mailing Address:
PO Box 125
Tucker, GA 30085-0125
Tel.: (770) 934-3101
Fax: (770) 938-8903
Toll Free: (800) 241-9460
E-mail: contact@energyandprocess.com
Web Site:
www.energyandprocess.com
Approx. Number Employees: 40
Year Founded: 1966
Business Description:
Whslr of Pipe Valves & Fittings
S.I.C.: 5085
N.A.I.C.S.: 423840
Media: 2-9-17
Distr.: Natl.
Budget Set: Sept.
Personnel:
Mark Capallo *(Chm)*

ENGINEERED MATERIALS SOLUTIONS
(Sub. of Engineered Materials Solutions Inc.)
600 Vly Rd
Hamburg, PA 19526-8387
Tel.: (610) 562-3841
Fax: (610) 562-5800
Toll Free: (800) 494-4841
Approx. Number Employees: 115
Year Founded: 1970
Business Description:
Clad Metal Products Mfr
S.I.C.: 3499
N.A.I.C.S.: 332999
Import Export
Media: 2-4-7-10
Distr.: Intl.; Natl.
Budget Set: Oct. -Nov.

E.R. WAGNER CASTERS AND WHEELS DIV.
(Div. of E.R. Wagner Manufacturing Co.)
331 Riverview Dr
Hustisford, WI 53034
Tel.: (920) 349-3271
Fax: (920) 349-3487
Toll Free: (800) 558-0117
E-mail: cw.sales@erwagner.com
Web Site: www.erwagner.com
Approx. Number Employees: 60
Business Description:
Custom Hinges, Engineered Stampings, Casters, Wheels & Tubular Products Mfr
S.I.C.: 3429
N.A.I.C.S.: 332510
Media: 2-4
Distr.: Natl.
Budget Set: Oct.
Personnel:
Wade Fletcher *(Pres)*

FARREY'S WHOLESALE HARDWARE CO., INC.
1850 NE 146th St
Miami, FL 33181
Mailing Address:
PO Box 619500
Miami, FL 33261-9500
Tel.: (305) 947-5451
Fax: (305) 940-0157
Toll Free: (888) 854-5483
E-mail: info@farreys.com
Web Site: www.farreys.com
Sales Range: $25-49.9 Million
Approx. Number Employees: 150
Year Founded: 1924
Business Description:
Lighting, Kitchen & Bath Fixtures, Ceiling Fans & Other Hardware Retailer & Whslr
S.I.C.: 5719; 5023; 5072; 5251
N.A.I.C.S.: 442299; 423220; 423710; 444130
Media: 16-29
Personnel:
John F. Farrey *(Founder)*
Frank X. Farrey, Jr. *(CFO & Sr VP)*
Paige Farrey *(Dir-Mktg)*
Kevin Farrey *(Dir-Internet Sls)*

FEDERAL HOSE MANUFACTURING INC.
(Sub. of The Crawford Group Inc.)
25 Florence Ave
Painesville, OH 44077-1103
Tel.: (440) 352-8927 .
Fax: (440) 352-8926
Toll Free: (800) 346-4673
Web Site: www.federalhose.com
Approx. Number Employees: 25
Year Founded: 1921
Business Description:
Mfr. of Flexible Metal Hose & Distributor of Silicone Hose
S.I.C.: 3499; 5085
N.A.I.C.S.: 332999; 423840
Export
Media: 2-4-7-10-17
Distr.: Intl.; Natl.
Personnel:
Dave Lally *(VP-Sls)*
Brands & Products:
FLOMASTER
GALVAFLEX
SUPERFLEX

THE FERRY CAP & SET SCREW COMPANY
(Sub. of Doncasters Group Ltd.)
13300 Bramley Ave
Lakewood, OH 44107
Tel.: (216) 771-2533
Tel.: (216) 649-7400
Fax: (216) 861-6747
Web Site: www.ferrycap.com
Year Founded: 1906
Business Description:
Cold-Headed Industrial Fasteners Mfr
S.I.C.: 3452
N.A.I.C.S.: 332722
Media: 10
Distr.: Natl.
Personnel:
Joe McAuliffe *(Pres)*
Donald E. Johnson *(VP-Sls)*
Jerry Mullin *(Controller)*

FIKE CORPORATION
704 SW 10th St
Blue Springs, MO 64015
Tel.: (816) 229-3405
Fax: (816) 228-9277
E-mail: info@fike.com
Web Site: www.fike.com
Sales Range: $150-199.9 Million
Approx. Number Employees: 350
Year Founded: 1945
Business Description:
Rupture Discs, Flanges, Pressure Relief Devices, Explosive Vents, Fire Extinguishing Systems & Components & Metal Fabrication Explosion Suppression Systems Mfr
S.I.C.: 3494; 3569
N.A.I.C.S.: 332919; 333999
Export
Advertising Expenditures: $425,000
Media: 2-4-7-10-13-17
Distr.: Natl.
Budget Set: Jan.
Personnel:
Lester L. Fike, Jr. *(Chm)*
Chuk Kopoulus *(Pres & CEO)*
David Wiseman *(Treas & Dir)*
Marvin Griffey *(Sr VP-Quality Assurance)*
Jim Morgan *(Dir-Mktg)*
Brands & Products:
AXIUS
AXIUS SC
CHEETAH
CHEETAH SYSTEM
CHEETAH XI
CYBERCAT
ECARO-25
ELEGUARD
ELEQUENCH
ELEVEX
EPACO
FIKE
FIKEGUARD
FIRERASER
FLAMQUENCH
FLAMQUENCH II
GATORPRO
LASERCOMPACT
LASERPLUS
MICORE
MICROMIST
MICROMIST SYSTEM
POLY-SD
PROINERT
S3
SHARK
SHP-PRO
SITEPRO
TRI-CLOVER
VALVEGUARD
VESDA
VESDA LASERPLUS

FISCHER PRECISE USA
(Sub. of Fischer AG Prazisionsspindeln)
3715 Blue River Ave
Racine, WI 53405-4131
Mailing Address:
PO Box 085000
Racine, WI 53408-5000
Tel.: (262) 632-6173
Fax: (262) 632-6730
Toll Free: (800) 333-6173
E-mail: info@fischerprecise.com
Web Site: www.fischerprecise.com
Approx. Number Employees: 40
Year Founded: 1941
Business Description:
High Speed Spindle Systems for Precision Milling, Drilling & Grinding Applications
S.I.C.: 3423
N.A.I.C.S.: 332212
Import Export
Media: 1-2-10-13
Distr.: Intl.; Natl.
Budget Set: Mar.-Apr.
Personnel:
Ryan Brath *(Pres)*
John Easley *(VP-Sls & Mktg)*
Advertising Agency:
Brown & Martin Inc.
21001 Watertown Rd.
Waukesha, WI 53186
Tel.: (262) 789-1565
Fax: (262) 789-1569

THE FORD METER BOX COMPANY, INC.
775 Manchester Ave
Wabash, IN 46992
Tel.: (260) 563-3171
Fax: (260) 563-0167
Fax: (800) 826-3487
E-mail: info@fordmeterbox.com
Web Site: www.fordmeterbox.com
Approx. Sls.: $15,000,000
Approx. Number Employees: 1,000
Year Founded: 1898
Business Description:
Mfr. of Water Meter Setting & Testing Equipment, Valves & Fittings for Water Utility Industry
S.I.C.: 3432; 3829
N.A.I.C.S.: 332913; 334519
Import Export
Advertising Expenditures: $200,000
Media: 1-2-5-7-10-26
Distr.: Natl.
Budget Set: Nov.

Key to Media (For complete agency information see *The Advertising Red Books-Agencies* edition):
1. Bus. Publs. 2. Cable T.V. 3. Catalogs & Directories. 4. Co-op Adv. 5. Consumer Mags. 6. D.M. to Bus. Estab.7. D.M. to Consumers 8. Daily Newsp. 9. Exhibits/Trade Shows 10. Foreign 11. Infomercial 12. Internet Adv.13. Multimedia 14. Network Radio 15. Network T.V. 16. Newsp. Distr. Mags. 17. Other 18. Outdoor (Posters, Transit) 19. Point of Purchase20. Premiums, Novelties 21. Product Samples 22. Special Events Mktg. 23. Spot Radio 24. Spot T.V. 25. Weekly Newsp. 26. Yellow Page Adv.

Personnel:
Steve Ford *(Pres)*
Carl Doran *(Sr VP)*
Charles Chapman *(Mgr-Adv)*

Brands & Products:
FORD BRASS
FORD METER BOX
UNI-FLANGE

FOXWORTH-GALBRAITH LUMBER COMPANY

17111 Waterview Pkwy
Dallas, TX 75252-8005
Tel.: (972) 437-6100
Fax: (972) 454-4238
E-mail: info@foxgal.com
Web Site: www.foxgal.com
Sales Range: $500-549.9 Million
Approx. Number Employees: 2,500
Year Founded: 1901
Business Description:
Lumber & Building Materials Retailer & Whslr
S.I.C.: 5031
N.A.I.C.S.: 423310
Advertising Expenditures: $255,000
Media: 9-18-23-24-25
Distr.: Reg.
Personnel:
Walter L. Foxworth *(Chm)*
Rich Perkins *(CFO)*
Jack Foxworth *(COO)*
Grant Foxworth *(Exec VP)*
H.S. Galbraith *(Exec VP)*
Daniel Brunson *(Sr VP-Ops)*
Dan Orona *(VP-Mktg)*
Dana Christian *(Mgr-Adv)*

Brands & Products:
FOXWORTH-GALBRAITH
GO WITH THE PROS

GABRIEL TECHNOLOGIES CORPORATION

4538 S 140th St
Omaha, NE 68137
Tel.: (402) 614-0258
Fax: (402) 614-0498
E-mail: info@gabrieltechnologies.com
Web Site: www.gabrieltechnologies.com
Sales Range: $10-24.9 Million
Approx. Number Employees: 19
Business Description:
Locking Systems Used for Securing Truck Trailers, Railcars & Shipping Containers
S.I.C.: 7382
N.A.I.C.S.: 561621
Media: 2-7
Personnel:
George Tingo, Jr. *(Pres & CEO)*

Brands & Products:
GABRIEL TECHNOLOGIES
WAR-LOK

GARDEN ART INTERNATIONAL

(Formerly Jardinier Alternative Irrigation Systems, Inc.)
2840 W 1st St
Santa Ana, CA 92703
Tel.: (714) 541-4200
Fax: (714) 541-3700
Toll Free: (800) 366-7166
E-mail: info@gardenartinc.com
Web Site: www.gardenartint.com/
Approx. Sls.: $1,200,000
Approx. Number Employees: 10
Year Founded: 1988
Business Description:
Mfr. of Sub Irrigation Growing Containers; Interior-Exterior Sub Irrigation Systems; Automated Systems
S.I.C.: 4941
N.A.I.C.S.: 221310
Import Export
Advertising Expenditures: $150,000
Media: 5-6-10-19-20-21
Distr.: Natl.
Budget Set: Various
Personnel:
Harry Hodgins *(Interim CEO)*

Brands & Products:
ASIS
DR. JARDINIER'S ONCE A MONTH PLANT WATERING SYSTEM
ECO CAPILLARY SOIL
JARDINIER
MAKE EVERY DROP COUNT
SURFACEFLOW

GENERAL TOOLS MANUFACTURING COMPANY, LLC

80 White St
New York, NY 10013-3527
Tel.: (212) 431-6100
Fax: (212) 431-6499
E-mail: gentools@generaltools.com
Web Site: www.generaltools.com
Approx. Number Employees: 40
Year Founded: 1922
Business Description:
Mfr. of Hand & Precision Tools, Measuring Devices, Magnets, Magnetic Tools
S.I.C.: 3423
N.A.I.C.S.: 332212
Import Export
Advertising Expenditures: $600,000
Media: 2-6-10-11-20
Distr.: Intl.; Natl.
Budget Set: Nov.
Personnel:
Gerald Weinstein *(Chm)*
Jerome Ennis *(Pres)*
Jeff Arbeit *(CFO)*
Peter Harper *(VP-Strategic Mktg)*
Paul Schlesinger *(Controller)*

Brands & Products:
GENERAL
PICKUP STICK
SPEED-CHUCK
TORX
ULTRA RULE
ULTRATEST

GERDAU AMERISTEEL JOLIET STEEL MILL

(Sub. of Gerdau Ameristeel Corporation)
1 Industry Ave
Joliet, IL 60435-2653
Tel.: (815) 723-9335
Fax: (815) 740-4907
Web Site: www.gerdauameristeel.com
Sales Range: $50-74.9 Million
Approx. Number Employees: 200
Year Founded: 1986
Business Description:
Hot Rolled Steel Bar & Rebar Mfr
S.I.C.: 3312; 3316
N.A.I.C.S.: 331111; 331221
Media: 8
Distr.: Natl.
Budget Set: Oct.
Personnel:
Chuck Graves *(Gen Mgr)*
Chuck Boyd *(Mgr-Sls & Mktg)*
Chuck Lamar *(Mgr-Quality Assurance)*

Advertising Agency:
Schifino Lee Advertising
511 W Bay St Ste 400
Tampa, FL 33606
Tel.: (813) 258-5858
Fax: (813) 254-1146
Communications
Rebranding

GERDAU AMERISTEEL SAND SPRINGS STEEL MILL

(Sub. of Gerdau Ameristeel Corporation)
2300 S Hwy 97
Sand Springs, OK 74063-7914
Mailing Address:
PO Box 218
Sand Springs, OK 74063-0218
Tel.: (918) 245-1335
Fax: (918) 245-9343
Web Site: www.gerdau.com/longsteel/
Approx. Sls.: $296,659,000
Approx. Number Employees: 672
Year Founded: 1929
Business Description:
Mfr of Hot Rolled Steel Bar Products
S.I.C.: 3316; 3312
N.A.I.C.S.: 331221; 331111
Media: 2-7
Personnel:
Robert L. Bullard *(VP & Gen Mgr)*
Tyler Berry *(Mgr-HR)*
Brett Blackburn *(Mgr-Safety)*
Mike Lawrence *(Mgr-Warehouse & Transportation)*
Ron Phillips *(Mgr-Metallurgical Svcs)*
Doug Strickland *(Mgr-Environ)*
Jon Heath *(Plant Engineer)*

GIBBS WIRE & STEEL COMPANY, INC.

Metals Dr PO Box 520
Southington, CT 06489
Tel.: (860) 621-0121
Fax: (860) 628-7780
Toll Free: (800) 800-GIBB
Web Site: www.gibbswire.com
E-Mail For Key Personnel:
Sales Director: sales@gibbswire.com
Sales Range: $50-74.9 Million
Approx. Number Employees: 170
Year Founded: 1956
Business Description:
Distr & Processor of Metal
S.I.C.: 5051
N.A.I.C.S.: 423510
Export
Media: 4-7-11-13
Distr.: Intl.; Natl.
Personnel:
C. Wayne Gibbs *(Chm)*
William Torres *(Pres & CEO)*
Mario Izzo *(CFO & Treas)*
Robert Iorio *(VP-Sls-Eastern Reg)*
Tom Molnar *(VP)*
Calvin Goodman *(Dir & Mgr-Quality)*
John Mintun *(Dir-Wire Products)*
Mike Sullivan *(Dir-Mfg)*
Patricia Wright *(Dir-MIS)*
Robert Burrell *(Mgr-Quality & Project)*
Vern Guetens *(Mgr-Quality)*
Dick Lane *(Sr Project Mgr & Sr Advisor)*

Brands & Products:
GIBBS
INCONEL 600
INCONEL X750
PRECO

GORILLA GLUE CO.

4550 Red Bank Expy
Cincinnati, OH 45227
Tel.: (513) 271-3300
Fax: (513) 527-3742
Toll Free: (800) 966-3458
E-mail: info@gorillaglue.com
Web Site: www.gorillaglue.com
Approx. Sls.: $4,000,000
Approx. Number Employees: 100
Business Description:
Glue Distr
S.I.C.: 3423
N.A.I.C.S.: 332212
Media: 6-19
Personnel:
Peter Ragland *(Pres)*
Jake Ragland *(VP-Sls)*
Lauren Connley *(Dir-Mktg)*

Brands & Products:
FOR THE TOUGHEST JOBS ON PLANET EARTH
GORILLA GLUE
IMPACT-TOUGH

GREENLEE TEXTRON INC.

(Sub. of Textron Inc.)
4455 Boeing Dr
Rockford, IL 61109-2932
Tel.: (815) 397-7070
Fax: (815) 397-1865
Toll Free: (800) 435-0786
E-mail: info@greenlee.textron.com
Web Site: www.greenlee.textron.com
Sales Range: $250-299.9 Million
Approx. Number Employees: 900
Year Founded: 1862
Business Description:
Wire & Cable Installation Tools
S.I.C.: 3496; 3469; 3537
N.A.I.C.S.: 332618; 332214; 333924
Import Export
Media: 2-4-5-7-10-13-17-19
Distr.: Intl.; Natl.
Budget Set: June
Personnel:
J. Scott Hall *(Pres-Textron Indus Segment & Greenlee)*
Chera Ellis *(VP & Gen Mgr)*
Ed Certisimo *(VP-Fin)*
Martha Kness *(VP-Mktg & Customer Svc)*
Stan Noble *(VP-HR)*
Joel Smith *(Reg Mgr)*
Neil Burns *(Mgr-Canadian Natl Sls & Mgr-N/E USA Sls)*
Scott Swift *(Mgr-Accts-Original Equipment Mfr)*

Brands & Products:
CIRCUIT SEEKER
D'VERSIBIT
EASY TUGGER
FLEX SPLITTER
GATOR
GREENLEE
KWIK CYCLE
KWIK STEPPER
KWIK STRIPPER

Key to Media (For complete agency information see *The Advertising Red Books-Agencies* edition):
1. Bus. Publs. 2. Cable T.V. 3. Catalogs & Directories. 4. Co-op Adv. 5. Consumer Mags. 6. D.M. to Bus. Estab.7. D.M. to Consumers
8. Daily Newsp. 9. Exhibits/Trade Shows 10. Foreign 11. Infomercial 12. Internet Adv.13. Multimedia 14. Network Radio
15. Network T.V. 16. Newsp. Distr. Mags. 17. Other 18. Outdoor (Posters, Transit) 19. Point of Purchase20. Premiums, Novelties
21. Product Samples 22. Special Events Mktg. 23. Spot Radio 24. Spot T.V. 25. Weekly Newsp. 26. Yellow Page Adv.

Greenlee Textron Inc. — (Continued)

L'IL FISHER
LIMB-LOPPER
LITTLE KICKER
MARKER MATE
MIGHTY MOUSER
NAIL EATERS
OMNI MARKER
QUICK DRAW
SITE RITE
SLUG-BUSTER
SLUG SPLITTER
SMART BENDER
SPEED BENDER
SUPER TUGGER
THERE WITH YOU
TRADESMAN
TUGGER
ULTRA CABLE FEEDER
ULTRA TUGGER
UNI MARKER

Advertising Agency:
Eric Mower and Associates
211 West Jefferson St.
Syracuse, NY 13202
Tel.: (315) 466-1000
Fax: (315) 466-2000

GRIPNAIL CORPORATION
97 Dexter Rd
East Providence, RI 02914-2045
Tel.: (401) 431-1791
Fax: (401) 438-8520
Toll Free: (800) 474-7624
E-mail: gripnail@gripnail.com
Web Site: www.gripnail.com
Approx. Sls.: $4,000,000
Approx. Number Employees: 50
Year Founded: 1966
Business Description:
Fasteners, Fastening Equipment & Hvac Supplies Mfr
S.I.C.: 3429; 3452
N.A.I.C.S.: 332510; 332722
Export
Media: 4-10
Distr.: Natl.
Personnel:
Peter Hallock *(Chm)*
David Ashton *(Pres)*
Cris Ryding *(COO)*
Brands & Products:
AMTAK
GRIPNAIL
INSUL-TACKS
POWER PINNER
POWERPOINT WELD PINS

GROHE AMERICA, INC.
(Sub. of Grohe AG)
241 Covington Dr
Bloomingdale, IL 60108-3109
Tel.: (630) 582-7711
Fax: (630) 582-7722
E-mail: info@groheamerica.com
Web Site: www.groheamerica.com
Approx. Number Employees: 100
Business Description:
Distributor of Faucets & Shower Heads
S.I.C.: 3432; 5074
N.A.I.C.S.: 332913; 423720
Media: 6
Personnel:
Franz Droege *(Pres & CEO)*

GROOV-PIN CORPORATION
331 Farnum Pike
Smithfield, RI 02917
Tel.: (401) 232-3377
Tel.: (201) 933-8302 (Sls & Mktg)
Fax: (401) 232-3253
Fax: (401) 231-5505
E-mail: info@groov-pin.com
Web Site: www.groov-pin.com
Approx. Number Employees: 100
Year Founded: 1926
Business Description:
Mfr. of Metal Fasteners & Precision Turned Components
S.I.C.: 3452; 3429
N.A.I.C.S.: 332722; 332510
Export
Advertising Expenditures: $300,000
Media: 2-10
Distr.: Direct To OEM; Natl.
Budget Set: May
Personnel:
Scot Jones *(Pres & CEO)*
Mark Ciuba *(Mgr-Sls)*
Brands & Products:
BARB-SERT
GROOV-PIN
SPEEDSERT
TAP-LOK
VIBRA-SERT

HAMMOND VALVE CORP.
(Sub. of Milwaukee Valve Company, Inc.)
16550 W Stratton Dr
New Berlin, WI 53151
Tel.: (262) 432-2702
Fax: (262) 432-2703
E-mail: info@hammondvalve.com
Web Site: www.hammondvalve.com
Approx. Number Employees: 200
Business Description:
Plumbing & Heating; Industrial Bronze; Iron; Ball & Butterfly; Cast Carbon & Stainless Steel Valves
S.I.C.: 3494; 3492
N.A.I.C.S.: 332919; 332912
Import Export
Media: 2-4-7-9-10-20
Distr.: Natl.
Budget Set: May -June
Personnel:
Rich Giannini *(Pres)*
Tom Laguardia *(VP-Sls & Mktg)*
Advertising Agency:
KW Advertising
333 Bishops Way Ste 148
Brookfield, WI 53005-6209
Tel.: (262) 786-4402
Fax: (262) 786-7236

HAYS FLUID CONTROLS
(Div. of Romac Industries, Inc.)
114 Eason Rd PO Box 580
Dallas, NC 28034
Mailing Address:
PO Box 580
Dallas, NC 28034-0580
Tel.: (704) 922-9565
Fax: (704) 922-9595
Toll Free: (800) 354-4297
E-mail: info@haysfluidcontrols.com
Web Site: www.haysfluidcontrols.com
Approx. Number Employees: 65
Year Founded: 1865
Business Description:
Mfr. of Flow Control Products, Brass & Stainless Steel Solenoid Valves, Brass Flow Control & Balancing Valves, Brass Flow Switches, Brass & Iron Plug Valves, Pulse, Nickel Plated, Brass, Epoxy Coated Iron & PVC Meters, Reed Switch Sensors
S.I.C.: 3824; 3494
N.A.I.C.S.: 334514; 332919
Import Export
Advertising Expenditures: $350,000
Media: 2-4-10
Distr.: Natl.
Budget Set: Oct.
Personnel:
Tom Kokolis *(Mgr-Natl Sls & Mktg)*
Brands & Products:
ELECTRO-STEAM
ELECTROFLO
ELECTROMITE
MARFAID
MESURFLO
SHURFLO
Y-BALL MESURFLO SYSTEM

HAYWARD POOL PRODUCTS
620 Division St
Elizabeth, NJ 07207
Tel.: (908) 351-5400
Fax: (908) 351-5675
Web Site: www.haywardnet.com
Approx. Number Employees: 1,700
Year Founded: 1923
Business Description:
Holding Company; Swimming Pool Equipment & Parts Mfr
S.I.C.: 6719; 3569
N.A.I.C.S.: 551112; 333999
Media: 1-2-4-5-6-7-8-10-19-20
Distr.: Natl.
Personnel:
Oscar Davis *(Chm)*
Robert Davis *(Pres & CEO)*
Andrew Diamond *(CFO & VP-Fin)*
Mike Massa *(VP-Sls)*
Kevin Potucek *(VP-Product Mgmt)*
Bruce Porter *(Dir-Mktg Comm)*
Brands & Products:
AQUA LOGIC
AQUA POD
AQUA RITE
AQUA TROL
ASTROLITE
COLORLOGIC
DIVER DAVE
ELITE
GOLDLINE
HAYWARD
HEATPRO
MAX-FLO
NAVIGATOR
NORTHSTAR
PHANTOM
POOL VAC ULTRA
POWER-FLO II
POWER-FLO LX
POWERFLO MATRIX
SUPER
SWIMCLEAR
TOTALLY HAYWARD
VIPER
WANDA THE WHALE
XSTREAM
Advertising Agency:
Scales Advertising
2303 Wycliff St
Saint Paul, MN 55114
Tel.: (651) 641-0226
Fax: (651) 641-1031

HENKEL CORPORATION
(Sub. of Henkel AG & Co. KGaA)
1001 Trout Brook Crossing 1 Hanco Way
Rocky Hill, CT 06067-3582
Tel.: (860) 571-5100
Fax: (860) 571-5465
Toll Free: (800) LOCTITE
Web Site: www.henkelna.com
Approx. Number Employees: 470
Year Founded: 1953
Business Description:
Coatings, Adhesives & Sealants For Locking, Sealing, Retaining, Bonding & Protecting Mfr
S.I.C.: 2891; 3677
N.A.I.C.S.: 325520; 334416
Advertising Expenditures: $800,000
Media: 1-2-3-4-7-10-12-15-19-20-21-22-24
Distr.: Intl.; Natl.
Budget Set: Oct.
Personnel:
Julian Colquitt *(Pres-Adhesive Tech-North America)*
Joseph D. DeBiase *(Sr VP & Gen Mgr)*
Greg A. Tipsord *(Sr VP & Gen Mgr)*
Ed Capasso *(Sr VP)*
Eric Schwartz *(VP-Mktg)*
Marshall Kearns *(Dir-HR)*
Brands & Products:
BIG FOOT
C5-A
CLOVER
DURABOND
ENCAP
FIXMASTER
FLASHCURE
HENKEL
NORDBAK
VIBRA-SEAL
Advertising Agency:
Martino & Binzer
270 Farmington Ave Ste 128
Farmington, CT 06032
Tel.: (860) 678-4300
Fax: (860) 678-4301
(Trade Magazines)

HENRY PRATT COMPANY
401 S Highland Ave
Aurora, IL 60506-5580
Tel.: (630) 844-4000
Fax: (630) 844-4124
Toll Free: (877) 436-7977
E-mail: customerservice@henrypratt.com
Web Site: www.henrypratt.com
Approx. Number Employees: 300
Year Founded: 1901
Business Description:
Butterfly & Ball Valves & Various Valve Operators & Control Systems Mfr
S.I.C.: 3491
N.A.I.C.S.: 332911
Export
Advertising Expenditures: $200,000
Media: 2-4-5-7-9-10-11-20-21
Distr.: Intl.; Natl.
Budget Set: Sept.
Personnel:
Steve Sharp *(VP & Gen Mgr)*
Tim Fallon *(Mgr-Product-Mktg)*
Brands & Products:
CHECK-MATE
DIVINER
DURA-CYL
E-LOK

ELECTRO-CHECK
GROUNDHOG
HP250II
MONOFLANGE
POSITAC
POSITRON
PRATT
RD-SERIES
SA-SERIES
TRITON HP-250
TRITON XL
TRITON XR-70
VALVES FOR THE 21ST CENTURY

HINDLEY MANUFACTURING COMPANY, INC.
9 Havens St
Cumberland, RI 02864
Tel.: (401) 722-2550
Fax: (401) 722-3083
Toll Free: (800) 323-9031
E-mail: hindley@hindley.com
Web Site: www.hindley.com
Sales Range: $1-9.9 Million
Approx. Number Employees: 80
Year Founded: 1897
Business Description:
Mfr. of Wire Hardware, Cotter Pin & Plumbing Accessories, Special Wire Forms & Peg Hooks
S.I.C.: 3452; 3496
N.A.I.C.S.: 332722; 332618
Import Export
Media: 2-4-7-10-13-26
Distr.: Natl.
Budget Set: Apr.
Personnel:
C.J. Hindley, Jr. *(Owner)*
Roy Medeiros *(CFO)*
Scott A. Hindley *(VP-Sls & Mktg)*
Brands & Products:
HINDLEY
PIC-PAK
THE SHAPES OF THINGS TO COME
STOR-ALL
STOR-PAK

HITACHI KOKI USA, LTD.
(Div. of Hitachi Koki USA, Ltd.)
85 S Holland Dr
Pendergrass, GA 30567
Tel.: (706) 693-4860
Fax: (706) 693-4859
Toll Free: (800) 488-8540
E-mail: hku-usa@hitachi-powertools.com
Web Site: www.hitachipowertools.com
Approx. Sls.: $31,500,000
Approx. Number Employees: 175
Year Founded: 1981
Business Description:
Sales of Electric Power Tools, Line Printers & Scientific Instruments
S.I.C.: 5084; 3541
N.A.I.C.S.: 423830; 333512
Import Export
Media: 2-4-5-6-7-10-17-19-20-21
Distr.: Intl.; Natl.
Budget Set: July
Personnel:
Shoji Matsushima *(VP-Fin)*
Abby Bradford *(Mgr-Mktg Commun)*
Advertising Agencies:
Creative Brand Advertising
333 NE 24th St
Miami, FL 33137
Tel.: (305) 573-2661
Hispanic Advertising

Huey & Partners
812 - A Lambert Dr
Atlanta, GA 30324
Tel.: (404) 541-9990
Fax: (404) 541-9991
Creative

HOCHIKI AMERICA CORPORATION
(Sub. of Hochiki Corporation)
7051 Village Dr Ste 100
Buena Park, CA 90621
Tel.: (714) 522-2246
Fax: (714) 522-2268
Toll Free: (800) 845-6692
E-mail: sales@hochiki.com
Web Site: www.hochiki.com
E-Mail For Key Personnel:
Sales Director: sales@hochiki.com
Approx. Number Employees: 140
Year Founded: 1972
Business Description:
Mfr of Industrial & Commercial Fire Safety Devices
S.I.C.: 5063; 3669
N.A.I.C.S.: 423610; 334290
Import Export
Media: 2-4-6-8-10-11-13
Distr.: Natl.
Personnel:
Hisham Harake *(Pres)*
Ivy Kiyumura *(Mgr-Mktg)*

THE HOME DEPOT, INC.
2455 Paces Ferry Rd NW
Atlanta, GA 30339-4024
Tel.: (770) 433-8211
Fax: (770) 384-2356
E-mail: public_relations@homedepot.com
Web Site: www.homedepot.com
Approx. Sls.: $67,997,000,000
Approx. Number Employees: 321,000
Year Founded: 1978
Business Description:
Holding Company; Home Improvement Products Retailer
S.I.C.: 6719; 5211
N.A.I.C.S.: 551112; 444110
Import Export
Advertising Expenditures: $864,000,000
Media: 2-3-4-5-6-7-8-9-12-13-15-18-19-22-23-24-25-26
Distr.: Natl.
Budget Set: Nov.
Personnel:
Francis S. Blake *(Chm & CEO)*
Carol B. Tome *(CFO & Exec VP-Corp Svcs)*
Matt Carey *(CIO & Exec VP)*
Trish Mueller *(CMO)*
Jim Kane *(Pres-Northern Div)*
Joseph McFarland, III *(Pres-Western Div)*
Ricardo Saldivar *(Pres-The Home Depot-Mexico)*
Annette M. Verschuren *(Pres-Canada & Asia)*
Teresa Wynn Roseborough *(Gen Counsel, Sec & Exec VP)*
Timothy M. Crow *(Exec VP-HR)*
Marvin R. Ellison *(Exec VP-US Stores)*
Craig A. Menear *(Exec VP-Mdsg)*
Kelly Barrett *(Sr VP-Enterprise Program Mgmt)*
Diane Dayhoff *(Sr VP-IR)*
Mark Holifield *(Sr VP-Supply Chain)*
Ron Jarvis *(Sr VP-Mdse)*
Brad Shaw *(Sr VP-Corp Comm & External Affairs)*
Ron DeFeo, Sr. *(Dir-Pub Rel)*
Paula Drake *(Sr Mgr-Corp Comm)*
Brands & Products:
HOME DECORATORS COLLECTION
THE HOME DEPOT
YOU CAN DO IT. WE CAN HELP.
Advertising Agencies:
Carat
150 E 42nd St
New York, NY 10017
Tel.: (212) 689-6800
Fax: (212) 689-6005
Media Buying
Media Planning

IMRE
909 Ridgebrook Rd Ste 300
Baltimore, MD 21152
Tel.: (410) 821-8220
Fax: (410) 821-5619
Media Relations Only

JLA
3494 Sheridan Ste 1
Marietta, GA 30067
Tel.: (770) 988-0440
Fax: (800) 783-8168

Marketing Support, Inc.
200 E Randolph Dr Ste 5000
Chicago, IL 60601
Tel.: (312) 565-0044
Fax: (312) 946-6100

Moxie Interactive Inc.
The Northyards 384 Northyards Blvd NW Ste 290
Atlanta, GA 30313-2440
Tel.: (404) 601-4500
Fax: (404) 601-4505

Point B Communications
750 N Orleans Ste 600
Chicago, IL 60654
Tel.: (312) 867-7750
Fax: (312) 867-7751

PointRoll Inc.
951 E Hector St
Conshohocken, PA 19428
Tel.: (267) 558-1300
Fax: (267) 285-1141
Toll Free: (800) 203-6956

Response Media, Inc.
3155 Medlock Bridge Rd
Norcross, GA 30071-1423
Tel.: (770) 451-5478
Fax: (770) 451-4929

The Richards Group, Inc.
8750 N Central Expy Ste 100
Dallas, TX 75231-6430
Tel.: (214) 891-5700
Fax: (214) 265-2933
Creative
Broadcast
— Scott Crockett *(Principal)*

Richards/Lerma
8750 N. Central Expwy
Dallas, TX 75231-6437
Tel.: (214) 891-5700
Hispanic Agency of Record

Uniworld Group, Inc.
1 Metro Center N 11th Fl
Brooklyn, NY 11201
Tel.: (212) 219-1600
Fax: (212) 219-6395

HOME HARDWARE STORES LIMITED
34 Henry St W
Saint Jacobs, ON N0B 2N0, Canada
Tel.: (519) 664-2252
Fax: (519) 664-2865
Web Site: www.homehardware.com
Sales Range: $1-4.9 Billion
Approx. Number Employees: 2,000
Year Founded: 1906
Business Description:
Hardware, Building Supply & Furniture Stores
S.I.C.: 5211
N.A.I.C.S.: 444110
Media: 8
Personnel:
Walter Hachborn *(Pres)*
Paul Straus *(CEO)*

HOMELAND SECURITY CAPITAL CORPORATION
1005 N Glebe Rd Ste 550
Arlington, VA 22201
Tel.: (703) 528-7073
Fax: (703) 528-0956
E-mail: info@hscapcorp.com
Web Site: www.hscapcorp.com
Approx. Rev.: $97,899,868
Approx. Number Employees: 476
Year Founded: 1997
Business Description:
Specialized Technology-Based Radiological, Nuclear, Environmental, Disaster Relief & Security Solutions to Government & Commercial Customers
S.I.C.: 7382; 9711
N.A.I.C.S.: 561621; 928110
Advertising Expenditures: $278,298
Personnel:
C. Thomas McMillen *(Chm & CEO)*
Christopher P. Leichtweis *(Pres)*
Michael T. Brigante *(VP-Mktg)*

HUBERT COMPANY
(Sub. of TAKKT AG)
9555 Dry Fork Rd
Harrison, OH 45030
Mailing Address:
PO Box 631642
Cincinnati, OH 45263-1642
Tel.: (513) 367-8600
Fax: (513) 367-8603
Toll Free: (866) 482-4357
E-mail: info@hubert.com
Web Site: www.hubert.com
Approx. Number Employees: 308
Business Description:
Mail Order Services for Equipment & Supplies for the Food Service Industry & General Retail
S.I.C.: 5046; 5023
N.A.I.C.S.: 423440; 423220
Advertising Expenditures: $9,000,000
Catalogs & Directories: $9,000,000
Brands & Products:
PRODUCTS & IDEAS THAT CREATE COMPETITIVE ADVANTAGE

HYER INDUSTRIES INC.
(d/b/a Thayer Scale)
91 Schoosett St

Key to Media (For complete agency information see *The Advertising Red Books-Agencies* edition):
1. Bus. Publs. 2. Cable T.V. 3. Catalogs & Directories. 4. Co-op Adv. 5. Consumer Mags. 6. D.M. to Bus. Estab.7. D.M. to Consumers 8. Daily Newsp. 9. Exhibits/Trade Shows 10. Foreign 11. Infomercial 12. Internet Adv.13. Multimedia 14. Network Radio 15. Network T.V. 16. Newsp. Distr. Mags. 17. Other 18. Outdoor (Posters, Transit) 19. Point of Purchase20. Premiums, Novelties 21. Product Samples 22. Special Events Mktg. 23. Spot Radio 24. Spot T.V. 25. Weekly Newsp. 26. Yellow Page Adv.

Hyer Industries Inc. — (Continued)

Pembroke, MA 02359
Mailing Address:
PO Box 669
Pembroke, MA 02359-0669
Tel.: (781) 826-8101
Fax: (781) 826-7944
E-mail: mail@thayerscale.com
Web Site: www.thayerscale.com
E-Mail For Key Personnel:
Sales Director: sales@thayerscale.com
Approx. Number Employees: 50
Year Founded: 1949
Business Description:
Mfr of Weight Belt, Loss-in-Weight Feeders, Belt Scales, Bridge Breakers & Bin Flow Aid Devices
S.I.C.: 3596
N.A.I.C.S.: 333997
Export
Advertising Expenditures: $200,000
Media: 2-6-7-8-10-13
Distr.: Natl.
Budget Set: Sept.
Personnel:
Frank S. Hyer *(Pres)*
Bruce G. Atwood *(CFO)*
Tom Picone *(VP-Sls & Mktg)*
Brands & Products:
BRIDGE BREAKER
CABOSIL
POWDER FEEDER
POWER WALL
THAYER

IDEAL INDUSTRIES, INC.

1 Becker Pl
Sycamore, IL 60178-2420
Tel.: (815) 895-5181
Fax: (815) 895-4800
Toll Free: (800) 435-0705
E-mail: ideal_industries@idealindustries.com
Web Site: www.idealindustries.com
Approx. Number Employees: 600
Year Founded: 1916
Business Description:
Mfr. of Tools & Supplies for Electricians
S.I.C.: 3825; 3643
N.A.I.C.S.: 334515; 335931
Export
Media: 1-2-4-5-7-8-10-11-13-19-20-21
Distr.: Intl.; Natl.
Budget Set: Oct.
Personnel:
D.W. Juday *(Chm)*
Jim James *(Pres & CEO)*
James Pfotenhauer *(VP-Fin)*
Joe Saganowich *(VP-Sls)*
David DiDonato *(Gen Mgr)*
Tom Peterson *(Dir-Sls-Mktg)*
Tim Deed *(Product Mgr)*
Jim Gregorec *(Mgr-Bus Unit)*
John Spencer *(Mgr-Strategic Accounts)*
Brands & Products:
AQUA-GEL
AUTO-LOCK
B-CAP
BUCHANAN
BUCHANAN TERMEND
BUYRATE
CLEARGLIDE
DIGISNAP
E-Z CHECK
ERGO-ELITE
GILBERT-ULTRASEAL
GOLD FISH
GREENIE
GRIP-N-STRIP
IDEAL
IN-SURE
KINETIC REFLEX
KINETIC SUPER
NM CABLE T
NOALOX
NUTMASTER
OEM WIRE-NUT
PLATINUMPRO
POLE MEGGER
POWERBLADE
POWR-CONNECT
POWR-CONNECTOR
POWR-FISH
POWR-GLO
PREMIUM
PRO-MET
PRO-PULL
QUICKJAW
RAPID-PAK
S-CLASS
SAFE-T-GRIP
SMART-GRIP
STAT-GARD
STRIPMASTER
SUPER T
SURE TEST
SUREGRIP
SWIVEL-BLADE T
TAPE-PAK
TELEWIRE-DIGICON-S
TERM-A-NUT
TEST-GLO
TEST-PRO
THERMO-SHRINK
THUMB WINDER
TUFF-GRIP
TUFF-ROD
TWISTER
TWISTER DB PLUS
TWISTER PRO
UNDERGROUND
VOL-CON
VOL-TEST XL
WEATHERPROOF
WING NUT
WINGTWIST
WIRE LUBE
WIRE-NUT
WIRE TWIST
WRAP-CAP
YELLOW 77
ZOOM
Advertising Agency:
Davis Harrison Dion, Inc.
333 N Michigan Ave Ste 2300
Chicago, IL 60601-4109
Tel.: (312) 332-0808
Fax: (312) 332-4260
(Products for Electrical Industry)

IMPULSE NC, INC.

(Sub. of Marmon Industrial Companies LLC)
100 IMPulse Way
Mount Olive, NC 28365-8691
Tel.: (919) 658-2200
Fax: (919) 658-2268
Web Site: www.impulsenc.com
Sales Range: $10-24.9 Million
Approx. Number Employees: 150
Year Founded: 1998
Business Description:
Overhead Contact System Hardware Designer & Mfr
S.I.C.: 3612
N.A.I.C.S.: 335311
Media: 4
Personnel:
Jeff Wharton *(Gen Mgr)*
Brands & Products:
IMPROCON
SUBSTATIONS

INGERSOLL-RAND SECURITY TECHNOLOGIES

(Div. of Ingersoll-Rand Company)
11819 N Pennsylvania St
Carmel, IN 46032-5643
Tel.: (317) 810-3700
Web Site:
www.securitytechnologies.ingersollrand.com
Approx. Number Employees: 450
Business Description:
Security Systems Mfr
S.I.C.: 7382
N.A.I.C.S.: 561621
Media: 1-2-4-5-6-7-10-11-19-20-23-24
Personnel:
John Conover *(Pres)*
Brands & Products:
PROVEN SOURCE. PROVEN SOLUTIONS

INTERLINE BRANDS, INC.

701 San Marco Blvd
Jacksonville, FL 32207
Tel.: (904) 421-1400
Fax: (904) 358-2486
E-mail: irinfo@interlinebrands.com
Web Site: www.interlinebrands.com
Approx. Sls.: $1,086,989,000
Approx. Number Employees: 3,485
Year Founded: 1978
Business Description:
Repair, Maintenance & Operations Products Marketer & Distr
S.I.C.: 1711; 5063; 5072; 5074; 5211
N.A.I.C.S.: 238220; 423610; 423710; 423720; 444190
Import Export
Advertising Expenditures: $2,500,000
Media: 1-4-5-7-10-16-26
Personnel:
Michael J. Grebe *(Chm & CEO)*
Kenneth D. Sweder *(Pres & COO)*
John A. Ebner *(CFO)*
Lucretia Doblado *(CIO)*
David C. Serrano *(Chief Acctg Officer & Controller)*
Fred Bravo *(VP-Field Sls)*
Annette Ricciuti *(VP-HR)*
Brands & Products:
AF LIGHTING
BARNETT
HARDWARE EXPRESS
INTERLINE BRANDS
LERAN
MAINTENANCE USA
SEXAUER
SUNSTAR
U.S. LOCK
WILMAR

IONBOND LLC

(Sub. of IonBond AG)
1823 E Whitcomb Ave
Madison Heights, MI 48071-1413
Tel.: (248) 398-9100
Fax: (248) 398-2110
E-mail: infous@ionbond.com
Web Site: www.ionbond.com
Approx. Number Employees: 50
Business Description:
Coating Equipment
S.I.C.: 2851
N.A.I.C.S.: 325510
Media: 10-22

IRRITROL SYSTEMS

(Sub. of The Toro Company Irrigation Products)
5825 Jasmine St
Riverside, CA 92504
Mailing Address:
PO Box 489
Riverside, CA 92502-0489
Tel.: (951) 688-9221
Fax: (951) 359-1870
Toll Free: (800) 444-2734
Web Site: www.irritrolsystems.com
Sales Range: $75-99.9 Million
Approx. Number Employees: 200
Business Description:
Mfr. of Drip & Agricultural Irrigation Systems & Commercial Turf Sprinklers
S.I.C.: 6141
N.A.I.C.S.: 522291
Export
Advertising Expenditures: $750,000
Media: 1-2-4-5-6-7-8-10-16-19-21-25
Distr.: Intl.; Natl.
Budget Set: Mar.
Brands & Products:
CR500 SERIES
GUIDED PROGRAMMING
IBOC PLUS
IRRITROL
KWIKDIAL
MC PLUS
OMNI-REG
RAIN DIAL
RAIN DIAL PLUS
SHOWERS OF DIAMONDS
SLIM DIAL
TOTAL CONTROL

ITT INDUSTRIES-RULE

(Div. of ITT Fluid Technology Corporation)
Cape Ann Industrial Pk 1 Kendolin Rd
Gloucester, MA 01930
Tel.: (978) 281-0440
Fax: (978) 283-2619
Web Site: www.rule-industries.com
E-Mail For Key Personnel:
Marketing Director: stilders@fluids.ittind.com
Sales Director: gcragin@fluids.ittind.com
Sales Range: $75-99.9 Million
Approx. Number Employees: 180
Year Founded: 1963
Business Description:
Mfr. of Marine Submersible Pumps, Compasses & Anchors, Chemicals, Sealants & Powered Winches
S.I.C.: 3561; 2851
N.A.I.C.S.: 333911; 325510
Import Export
Media: 1-2-4-6-7-10
Distr.: Intl.; Natl.
Budget Set: June
Personnel:
Steve Tilders *(Dir-Marine Sls)*
William Gell *(Product Mgr)*
Jeff Schopperle *(Mgr-Innovation Lab)*

Key to Media (For complete agency information see *The Advertising Red Books-Agencies* edition):
1. Bus. Publs. 2. Cable T.V. 3. Catalogs & Directories. 4. Co-op Adv. 5. Consumer Mags. 6. D.M. to Bus. Estab.7. D.M. to Consumers 8. Daily Newsp. 9. Exhibits/Trade Shows 10. Foreign 11. Infomercial 12. Internet Adv.13. Multimedia 14. Network Radio 15. Network T.V. 16. Newsp. Distr. Mags. 17. Other 18. Outdoor (Posters, Transit) 19. Point of Purchase20. Premiums, Novelties 21. Product Samples 22. Special Events Mktg. 23. Spot Radio 24. Spot T.V. 25. Weekly Newsp. 26. Yellow Page Adv.

Brands & Products:
RULE
SUDBURY

ITW BUILDEX
(Sub. of Illinois Tool Works Inc.)
1349 W Bryn Mawr Ave
Itasca, IL 60143-1313
Tel.: (630) 595-3500
Fax: (630) 595-3549
Toll Free: (800) BUILDEX
E-mail: info@itwbuildex.com
Web Site: www.itwbuildex.com
Sales Range: $50-74.9 Million
Approx. Number Employees: 100
Year Founded: 1967
Business Description:
Fasteners & Building Products Mfr
S.I.C.: 3965; 2952; 3452; 3542
N.A.I.C.S.: 339993; 324122; 332722; 333513
Media: 4-7-10-13
Personnel:
Ramunas Venclovas *(Gen Mgr)*
Brands & Products:
ACCUDRIVE
ACCUTRAC
AUTOTRAXX
BUILDING IDEAS THAT WORK
BX 900
BX12
BX14
CLIMASEAL
DEK-CAP
DEKSTRIP
DRIV-TRU
EYE-HOOK
FLASHDEK
GRIDMASTER
GRIDMATE
HEXTRA
HTZ
LOW PROFILE GEARLOK
MAXLOAD
NAILCON
REEL-FAST
ROOFGRIP
SAMMY XPRESS
SCOTS
SPEX
TEKS
TRUGRIP
UNIDEK

ITW SWITCHES
(Sub. of Illinois Tool Works Inc.)
2550 Millbrook Dr
Buffalo Grove, IL 60089-4694
Tel.: (847) 876-9400
Fax: (847) 876-9440
Toll Free: (800) 544-3354
E-mail: customer_service@itwswitches.com
Web Site: www.itwswitches.com
Sales Range: $75-99.9 Million
Approx. Number Employees: 250
Year Founded: 1954
Business Description:
Electrical Switches Mfr
S.I.C.: 3679; 3643
N.A.I.C.S.: 334419; 335931
Export
Media: 2-4-5-7-10-11-13
Distr.: Intl.; Natl.
Budget Set: Oct.
Personnel:
Brian Truesdale *(Gen Mgr)*

ITW WORKHOLDING GROUP
(Sub. of Illinois Tool Works Inc.)
2002 Stephenson Hwy
Troy, MI 48083-2151
Tel.: (248) 743-4400
Fax: (248) 743-4401
Toll Free: (800) 544-3823
Telex: 810-232-1507
E-mail: sales@itwchucks.com
Web Site: www.itwworkholding.com
E-Mail For Key Personnel:
Sales Director: sales@itwchucks.com
Sales Range: $100-124.9 Million
Approx. Number Employees: 75
Year Founded: 1939
Business Description:
Work-Holding Equipment, Machine Tools, Chucks, Jigs, Arbors & Inspection Tools, Tool Holders, Quick Changes Mfr
S.I.C.: 3423; 3541; 3544
N.A.I.C.S.: 332212; 333512; 333514
Import Export
Advertising Expenditures: $250,000
Media: 2-4-7-8-21-26
Distr.: Direct to Consumer; Intl.; Natl.
Budget Set: Sept.
Personnel:
Chris Brown *(Reg Mgr)*
Brands & Products:
ECC
TORK-LOK
ZERO-C
Advertising Agency:
Kracoe Szykula & Townsend Inc.
2950 W Square Lake Rd Ste 207
Troy, MI 48098-5725
Tel.: (248) 641-7500
Fax: (248) 641-4779

JAMES HARDIE BUILDING PRODUCTS INC.
(Sub. of James Hardie Industries N.V.)
26300 La Alameda Ste 250
Mission Viejo, CA 92691-6380
Tel.: (949) 348-1800
Fax: (949) 367-1294
E-mail: info@jameshardie.com
Web Site: www.jameshardie.com
Approx. Sls.: $1,144,800,000
Approx. Number Employees: 1,809
Business Description:
Fibre Cement Building Products Mfr & Distr
S.I.C.: 3299; 3241
N.A.I.C.S.: 327999; 327310
Advertising Expenditures: $15,000,000
Media: 1-13-14-16-23-24-25
Personnel:
Nigel Rigby *(VP & Gen Mgr-Northern Div)*
Prashant Panchal *(Head-Mktg)*
Advertising Agencies:
KSL Media, Inc.
367 Park Ave S 4th Fl
New York, NY 10016
Tel.: (212) 352-5800
Fax: (212) 352-5935

Vertical Marketing Network LLC
15147 Woodlawn Ave
Tustin, CA 92780
Tel.: (714) 258-2400, ext. 420
Fax: (714) 258-2409

JARCO/U.S. CASTINGS
4407 Park Ave
Union City, NJ 07087
Tel.: (201) 271-0003
Fax: (201) 271-0009
Toll Free: (800) 433-1494
E-mail: info@jarcousa.com
Web Site: www.jarcousa.com
Approx. Number Employees: 52
Year Founded: 1945
Business Description:
Mfr. of Pocket & Purse Flashlights, Metal, Marble & Stone Desk Accessories, Key Chains, Award Medals, Stone Product & Building Replicas & Lapel Pins
S.I.C.: 7311
N.A.I.C.S.: 541810
Import Export
Advertising Expenditures: $200,000
Media: 2-4-10-21-22
Distr.: Natl.
Personnel:
Mario Herrera *(Owner & Pres)*
Chuck Marsh *(Dir-Mktg)*
Brands & Products:
EXPLORE THE POSSIBILITIES
JARCO

JARDINIER ALTERNATIVE IRRIGATION SYSTEMS
(Name Changed to Garden Art International)

JELD-WEN, INC.
401 Harbor Isles Blvd
Klamath Falls, OR 97601
Tel.: (541) 882-3451
Fax: (541) 885-7454
Fax: (541) 884-2231 (Sales)
Toll Free: (800) 877-9482
Web Site: www.jeld-wen.com
Approx. Sls.: $1,877,500,000
Approx. Number Employees: 20,000
Year Founded: 1960
Business Description:
Windows, Doors, Millwork, Building Products, Metal Doors, Wood Pallets, Sash & Trim Mfr & Distr
S.I.C.: 2499; 5031
N.A.I.C.S.: 321999; 423310
Media: 2-3-4-6-9-10-13-14-15-16-18-19-20-21-22-23-24-26
Personnel:
Roderick C. Wendt *(Pres & CEO)*
Neil Stewart *(CFO & Exec VP)*
Steve Wynne *(CMO)*
Rick Hetherington *(Sr VP)*
Robert Turner *(Sr VP)*
Teri Cline *(Dir-Comm)*
Ken Hart *(Product Mgr)*
Kelly Reynolds *(Product Mgr)*
Brands & Products:
ALTERNAPLUS
AURALAST
AURORA
CARADCO
CARRIAGE HOUSE SERIES
CONTOURS
ENERGY SAVER
FINISHIELD
GLADIATOR
IWP
JELD-WEN
MAGNAFRAME
NORCO
POZZI
RELIABILITY FOR REAL LIFE
SUMMIT
WEN-LOCK
WILLMAR
YAKIMA DOOR
Advertising Agency:
CMD
1631 NW Thurman St
Portland, OR 97209-2558
Tel.: (503) 223-6794
Fax: (503) 223-2430
— Jeff Brown *(Acct Dir)*

JOHN HASSALL, INC.
609-1 Cantiague Rock Rd
Westbury, NY 11590
Tel.: (516) 334-6200
Fax: (516) 222-1911
Web Site: www.hassall.com
Approx. Number Employees: 100
Year Founded: 1850
Business Description:
Mfr Custom Pins, Rivets & Threaded Fasteners
S.I.C.: 3452; 3496
N.A.I.C.S.: 332722; 332618
Media: 1-2-4-10
Distr.: Intl.; Natl.
Budget Set: Dec.
Personnel:
Theodore B. Smith, III *(Pres)*
Walter J. Morley *(CFO & Treas)*
Thomas Matura *(VP-Sls)*
Brands & Products:
JOHN HASSALL
Advertising Agency:
Wynet Communications
6 Bayview Ave 3rd Fl
Northport, NY 11768
Tel.: (631) 612-2660

K-TEL INTERNATIONAL, INC.
2491 Xenium Ln N
Plymouth, MN 55441
Tel.: (763) 559-5566
Fax: (763) 559-5505
E-mail: info@k-tel.com
Web Site: www.ktel.com
Sales Range: $1-9.9 Million
Approx. Number Employees: 10
Year Founded: 1968
Business Description:
Music Recordings Licensor, Mfr & Distr; Miscellaneous Consumer Products Retailer
S.I.C.: 2741; 3652; 8999
N.A.I.C.S.: 512230; 512210; 512220
Import Export
Advertising Expenditures: $123,000
Media: 15-19-23-24
Distr.: Natl.
Budget Set: Monthly
Personnel:
Philip Kives *(Founder)*
Steve Wilson *(Product Mgr)*
Brands & Products:
K-TEL
K-TEL DRUG MART

KABA ILCO ACCESS CONTROL
(Sub. of Kaba Holding AG)
2941 Indiana Ave
Winston Salem, NC 27105
Tel.: (336) 725-1331
Fax: (336) 725-8814
Toll Free: (800) 849-8324

Key to Media (For complete agency information see *The Advertising Red Books-Agencies* edition):
1. Bus. Publs. 2. Cable T.V. 3. Catalogs & Directories. 4. Co-op Adv. 5. Consumer Mags. 6. D.M. to Bus. Estab.7. D.M. to Consumers
8. Daily Newsp. 9. Exhibits/Trade Shows 10. Foreign 11. Infomercial 12. Internet Adv.13. Multimedia 14. Network Radio
15. Network T.V. 16. Newsp. Distr. Mags. 17. Other 18. Outdoor (Posters, Transit) 19. Point of Purchase20. Premiums, Novelties
21. Product Samples 22. Special Events Mktg. 23. Spot Radio 24. Spot T.V. 25. Weekly Newsp. 26. Yellow Page Adv.

Kaba Ilco Access Control — (Continued)

E-mail: info@kws.kaba.com
Web Site: www.kaba-ilco.com
Approx. Number Employees: 250
Year Founded: 1964
Business Description:
Electronic & Pushbutton Locks Mfr
S.I.C.: 3429
N.A.I.C.S.: 332510
Media: 2-4-5-6-7-10-13
Personnel:
Mark Allan *(VP-Mktg)*

KABA ILCO CORP.

(Sub. of Kaba Holding AG)
400 Jeffreys Rd
Rocky Mount, NC 27804
Mailing Address:
PO Box 2627
Rocky Mount, NC 27802-2627
Tel.: (252) 446-3321
Fax: (252) 446-4702
Toll Free: (800) 334-1381
Web Site: www.kaba-ilco.com
Approx. Number Employees: 500
Year Founded: 1973
Business Description:
Access Control Systems Mfr
S.I.C.: 3429
N.A.I.C.S.: 332510
Import Export
Media: 1-2-4-6-7-10-11-13-18-19
Distr.: Intl.; Natl.
Budget Set: June
Personnel:
Chuck Murray *(Gen Mgr)*
Karen Blount *(Mgr-Creative Svcs)*
Brands & Products:
4000 SERIES
E-PLEX 5000
PEAKS
POWERLEVER PROX 9000
UNICAN

KENNAMETAL INC.

1600 Technology Way
Latrobe, PA 15650-4647
Mailing Address:
PO Box 231
Latrobe, PA 15650-0231
Tel.: (724) 539-5000
Fax: (724) 539-7835
E-mail: investor.relations@kennametal.com
Web Site: www.kennametal.com
Approx. Sls.: $2,403,493,000
Approx. Number Employees: 11,612
Year Founded: 1938
Business Description:
Metal-Cutting Tools, Industrial Metal Components & Specialty Metal Products Mfr
S.I.C.: 3541; 2542; 3398; 3423; 3429; 3494; 3499; 3532; 3545
N.A.I.C.S.: 333512; 332117; 332212; 332439; 332510; 332811; 332919; 332999; 333131; 333515; 337215
Import Export
Advertising Expenditures: $4,000,000
Media: 1-2-4-5-7-10-13-19-20-22
Distr.: Intl.; Natl.
Budget Set: Apr. -May
Personnel:
Carlos M. Cardoso *(Chm, Pres & CEO)*
Frank P. Simpkins *(CFO & VP)*
Steven R. Hanna *(CIO & VP)*
John H. Jacko, Jr. *(CMO & VP)*
John R. Tucker *(Pres-Bus Grp & VP)*
Kevin G. Nowe *(Gen Counsel, Sec & VP)*
Martha A. Bailey *(VP-Fin & Controller)*
Brands & Products:
BASSETT
BORIDE
CARBIDIE
CARMET
CHICAGO-LATROBE
CIRCLE
CLAPPDICO
CLEVELAND
DIAL SET
EASY-PULL
ERICKSON
GREENFIELD
HANITA
KENBORE
KENCAST
KENCLAW
KENCOAT
KENDEX
KENFACE
KENLOC
KENNA-LOK
KENNAMETAL
KENNAMETAL CAMCO
KENNAMETAL SINTEE
KENNAMETAL TRICON
KEZIZ
KM
KYON
METAL REMOVAL
METCUT
MILCLAW
PRO-POINT
RTW
RUBIG
TENTHSET
TOOLBOSS
TOP NOTCH
VAN KEUREN
VERMONT
WIDIA
WIDIA CIRCLE
WIDIA CLAPPDICO
WIDIA GTD
WIDIA HANITA
WIDIA MANCHESTER
WIDIA RUBIG
WINTOMS
Advertising Agency:
Levy MG
Four Smithfield St
Pittsburgh, PA 15222-2222
Tel.: (412) 201-1900
Fax: (412) 201-1410

KENNEY MANUFACTURING COMPANY

1000 Jefferson Blvd
Warwick, RI 02886
Tel.: (401) 739-2200
Fax: (401) 821-4240
Toll Free: (800) 7-KENNEY
E-mail: info@kenney.com
Web Site: www.kenney.com
Approx. Number Employees: 350
Year Founded: 1914
Business Description:
Household Consumer Products Mfr & Distr
S.I.C.: 2591; 5023
N.A.I.C.S.: 337920; 423220
Import Export
Media: 2-4-6
Distr.: Intl.; Natl.
Budget Set: Nov.
Personnel:
Dickson Kenney *(Chm)*
Leslie M. Kenney *(Pres)*
Joseph T. Assad *(Exec VP)*
Brands & Products:
A WORLD OF CAPABILITIES
KENNEY

KLEIN TOOLS INC.

450 Bond St
Lincolnshire, IL 60069-0350
Mailing Address:
PO Box 1418
Lincolnshire, IL 60069-1418
Tel.: (847) 821-5500
Fax: (847) 677-4476
Toll Free: (800) 553-4676 (customer svc)
Web Site: www.kleintools.com
Approx. Sls.: $170,000,000
Approx. Number Employees: 1,100
Year Founded: 1857
Business Description:
Hand Tools & Occupational Protective Equipment Mfr
S.I.C.: 3423; 3199
N.A.I.C.S.: 332212; 316999
Media: 2-4-10-11-19-22-23
Distr.: Intl.; Natl.
Budget Set: Aug.-Sept.
Personnel:
Mathias A. Klein, III *(Chm)*
Thomas R. Klein *(Pres)*
Verne Tuite *(CFO)*
John J. McDevitt *(Exec VP-Sls & Mktg)*
Mark Klein *(Dir-Sls-North America)*
Abby Ceppos *(Assoc Dir-Mktg)*
Vince Kendzierski *(Mgr-Mktg)*
Brands & Products:
2000 SERIES
BENDER
BULL DRIVER
CHICAGO
GRIP IT
GRIZZLY
JOURNEYMAN
KLEIN-BENFIELD
KLEIN-FLEX
KLEIN HAVEN'S GRIP
KLEIN KLEANERS
KLEIN-KURVE
KLEIN-LITE
KLEIN TOOLS
NYLON-CORDURA
POWERLINE
POWERLINE SERIES
PROFILATED
RAPI-DRIV
SPEEDWAY
TORX
ULTRA-HYDE

KNAPE & VOGT MANUFACTURING COMPANY

(Holding of Wind Point Partners)
2700 Oak Industrial Dr NE
Wyoming, MI 49505-3408
Tel.: (616) 459-3311
Fax: (616) 459-3467
Toll Free: (800) 253-1561
E-mail: steve.beckwith@kv.com
Web Site: www.knapeandvogt.com
Sales Range: $150-199.9 Million
Approx. Number Employees: 591
Year Founded: 1898
Business Description:
Mfr of Shelving Hardware, Drawer Slides & Storage Products
S.I.C.: 2542; 3429
N.A.I.C.S.: 337215; 332510
Import Export
Advertising Expenditures: $1,305,000
Media: 2-4-5-7-10-19
Distr.: Intl.; Natl.
Budget Set: Mar. -Apr.
Personnel:
Bill Denton *(Chm)*
Peter Martin *(Pres & CEO)*
Rick McQuigg *(CFO, Treas & Sec)*
Steve Beckwith *(Sr Mgr-Mktg Svcs)*
Bill Larsen *(Mktg Mgr-Drawer Slides & Related Hardware)*
Robert Livingston *(Product Mgr-Decorative & Utility Shelving & Specialty Hardware)*
Miles Mullins *(Product Mgr-Kitchen & Bath Products)*
Derek Timm *(Mgr-Tech Svcs-Ergonomic Products)*
Brands & Products:
IDEA @ WORK
JOHN STERLING
KNAPE AND VOGT
KV
REAL SOLUTIONS FOR REAL LIFE
WORKRITE

KRAFT HARDWARE, INC.

315 E 62nd St
New York, NY 10065
Tel.: (212) 838-2214
Fax: (212) 644-9254
E-mail: info@kraft-hardware.com
Web Site: www.kraft-hardware.com
Approx. Sls.: $4,000,000
Approx. Number Employees: 18
Year Founded: 1936
Business Description:
Mfr of Brass Cabinet & Door Hardware
S.I.C.: 5072; 5023
N.A.I.C.S.: 423710; 423220
Import
Media: 2-4-7
Distr.: Natl.
Personnel:
Stan Alloiger *(Pres)*

KRAFTMAID CABINETRY, INC.

(Sub. of Masco Cabinetry, LLC)
15535 S State Ave
Middlefield, OH 44062
Mailing Address:
PO Box 1055
Middlefield, OH 44062-1055
Tel.: (440) 632-5333
Fax: (440) 632-5648
E-mail: comment@kraftmaid.com
Web Site: www.kraftmaid.com
Sales Range: $25-49.9 Million
Approx. Number Employees: 400
Business Description:
Wooden Cabinets Mfr
S.I.C.: 2434; 2542
N.A.I.C.S.: 337110; 337215
Media: 4-10-15
Personnel:
Tom Fenton *(Mgr-Product Mktg)*
Brands & Products:
KRAFTMAID
KRAFTMAID IDEA BOOK
PASSPORT SERIES

Advertising Agency:
OLSON
1625 Hennepin Ave
Minneapolis, MN 55403
Tel.: (612) 215-9800
Fax: (612) 215-9801

KWIKSET CORPORATION
(Sub. of Stanley Black & Decker, Inc.)
19701 Da Vinci
Lake Forest, CA 92610
Tel.: (949) 672-4000
Fax: (949) 672-4001
Toll Free: (800) 327-LOCK
E-mail: kwikhelp@bdhhi.com
Web Site: www.kwikset.com
Sales Range: $450-499.9 Million
Approx. Number Employees: 2,000
Year Founded: 1945
Business Description:
Locksets & Security Products Mfr
S.I.C.: 3429
N.A.I.C.S.: 332510
Advertising Expenditures: $3,000,000
Media: 2-3-4-5-6-7-10-11-13-19-21-23
Distr.: Intl.; Natl.
Budget Set: Sept.
Advertising Agency:
VITRO
(An MDC Partners Company)
625 Broadway Fl 4
San Diego, CA 92101-5403
Tel.: (619) 234-0408
Fax: (619) 234-4015

LAMPERT YARDS, INC.
1850 Como Ave
Saint Paul, MN 55108
Tel.: (651) 695-3600
Fax: (651) 695-3601
E-mail: lamperts@lampertyards.com
Web Site: www.lampertyards.com
E-Mail For Key Personnel:
Marketing Director: pleier@lampertyards.com
Sales Director: began@lampertyards.com
Sales Range: $150-199.9 Million
Approx. Number Employees: 633
Year Founded: 1887
Business Description:
Retailer of Lumber & Building Materials
S.I.C.: 5031; 1521
N.A.I.C.S.: 423310; 236115
Import
Advertising Expenditures: $2,400,000
Media: 2-6-7-8-9-10-18-19-22-23-24-25-26
Distr.: Reg.
Budget Set: Nov.
Personnel:
Pam R. Leier *(VP-Mktg)*
Brian Stoen *(VP-Pur)*
Brands & Products:
LAMPERT LEGEND

LASALLE BRISTOL CORP.
(Sub. of Heywood Williams Group plc)
601 County Rd 17
Elkhart, IN 46516
Mailing Address:
PO Box 98
Elkhart, IN 46516
Tel.: (574) 295-4400
Fax: (574) 295-5290
Web Site: www.lasallebristol.com
Approx. Sls.: $165,000,000
Approx. Number Employees: 650
Year Founded: 1947
Business Description:
Plumbing Products Mfr & Distr
S.I.C.: 2519; 2511; 2512; 2514; 2517
N.A.I.C.S.: 337125; 337121; 337122; 337124; 337129
Import Export
Advertising Expenditures: $500,000
Media: 4-7-10-11-26
Distr.: Natl.
Budget Set: Nov.
Personnel:
Larry Campbell *(Pres-Distr)*

LAVELLE INDUSTRIES INC.
665 McHenry St
Burlington, WI 53105
Tel.: (262) 763-2434
Fax: (262) 763-5607
Web Site: www.lavelle.com
E-Mail For Key Personnel:
Sales Director: kturke@lavelle.com
Approx. Number Employees: 250
Year Founded: 1912
Business Description:
Mfr Rubber & Plastic Molded Parts for the OEM & Plumbing Industries
S.I.C.: 3069; 3061
N.A.I.C.S.: 326299; 326291
Export
Advertising Expenditures: $30,000
Bus. Publs.: $18,000; D.M. to Consumers: $6,000; Exhibits/Trade Shows: $6,000
Distr.: Natl.
Budget Set: Annually
Personnel:
Rhonda Sullivan *(Pres)*
Kathryn Turke *(VP-Sls)*
Chris Kurth *(Mgr-Tech Sls)*
Brands & Products:
CHLORAZONE
EASYFIX
EASYSORT
KORKY
KORKY PLUS
KORKY QUIETFILL
LAVELLE
Advertising Agency:
Design North, Inc.
8007 Douglas Ave
Racine, WI 53402
Tel.: (262) 639-2080
Tel.: (262) 898-1090
Fax: (262) 639-5230
Toll Free: (800) 247-8494

LAWRENCE PLUMBING SUPPLY CO.
(Sub. of Wolseley plc)
31 SW 57th Ave
Miami, FL 33144
Tel.: (305) 266-1571
Fax: (305) 264-8775
Web Site: www.lpsco.com
Approx. Number Employees: 4
Business Description:
Plumbing & Hydronic Heating Supplies
S.I.C.: 5074; 1711
N.A.I.C.S.: 423720; 238220
Media: 4
Personnel:
Romi Robau *(Mgr)*
Brands & Products:
LAWRENCE

LEATHERMAN TOOL GROUP, INC.
12106 NE Ainsworth Cir
Portland, OR 97220-9001
Tel.: (503) 253-7826
Fax: (503) 253-7830
Toll Free: (800) 847-8665
E-mail: mktg@leatherman.com
Web Site: www.leatherman.com
Approx. Number Employees: 450
Year Founded: 1983
Business Description:
Mfr. of Tools
S.I.C.: 3423
N.A.I.C.S.: 332212
Media: 6
Personnel:
Tim Leatherman *(Founder)*
Roger Bjorklund *(VP-Mktg & Intl Sls)*
Norm Henry *(VP-Fin)*
Brands & Products:
BLAST
CHARGE
CRUNCH
FLAIR
FUSE
JUICE
KICK
LEATHERMAN
MICRA
MINI-TOOL
PST
PST II
PULSE
SIDECLIP
SQUIRT
SUPER TOOL
SUPER TOOL 200
WAVE

LENOX
(Sub. of Newell Rubbermaid Inc.)
301 Chestnut St
East Longmeadow, MA 01028-5601
Tel.: (413) 525-3961
Fax: (413) 525-5890
E-mail: info@lenoxtools.com
Web Site: www.lenoxtools.com
Sales Range: $125-149.9 Million
Approx. Number Employees: 700
Year Founded: 1915
Business Description:
Mfr. of Band Saw Blades, Power Tool Accessories, Hand Tools & Related Products
S.I.C.: 3425
N.A.I.C.S.: 332213
Import Export
Media: 4-10
Distr.: Natl.
Personnel:
Bill Burke *(Pres)*
Rich Wuerthele *(Pres-Indus Products & Svcs)*
Myra Lee *(Dir-Mktg Comm)*
Brands & Products:
ARMOR
BAND-ADE
CONTESTOR GT
DEMOLITION
DIEMASTER
FLEX BACK
HACKMASTER
LAZER
LENOX
MASTER-GRIT
MICRONIZER
ONE TOOTH
PROTOOL LUBE
SST CARBIDE
TRI-MASTER
VARI-BIT
Advertising Agency:
Eric Mower and Associates
211 West Jefferson St.
Syracuse, NY 13202
Tel.: (315) 466-1000
Fax: (315) 466-2000

LOCK-MAN LOCKSMITHS
6236 Park Blvd
Pinellas Park, FL 33781
Tel.: (727) 544-1824
Web Site: www.lockmanlocksmiths.com
Business Description:
Locksmith
S.I.C.: 7699
N.A.I.C.S.: 561622
Media: 8-13
Personnel:
Claude Hensley *(Owner)*

LONG-LOK FASTENERS CORP.
10630 Chester Rd
Cincinnati, OH 45215
Tel.: (513) 772-1880
Fax: (513) 772-1888
Toll Free: (800) LONG-LOK
Web Site: www.longlok.com
E-Mail For Key Personnel:
President: randy@longlok.com
Marketing Director: juanita@longlok.com
Approx. Number Employees: 40
Year Founded: 1957
Business Description:
Self-Locking Fasteners & Self-Sealing Fasteners Mfr
S.I.C.: 3452
N.A.I.C.S.: 332722
Export
Media: 2-4-7-10-13-21
Distr.: Intl.; Natl.
Budget Set: Aug.
Personnel:
Randy Ammon *(Pres)*
Margret Figueroa *(Mgr-Customer Svc)*
Brands & Products:
DUAL-LOK
DYNA-THRED
DYNA-THRED II
LONG-LOK
LONG-LOK FASTENER
OMNI-LOK
POLY-LOK
SELF-SEAL
T-SERT
TEK-LOK

LOWELL CORPORATION
65 Hartwell St
West Boylston, MA 01583-2407
Mailing Address:
PO Box 158
Worcester, MA 01613-0158
Tel.: (508) 835-2900
Fax: (508) 835-2944
Toll Free: (800) 456-9355
E-mail: customerservice@lowellcorp.com
Web Site: www.lowellcorp.com
Approx. Number Employees: 26
Year Founded: 1869

Key to Media (For complete agency information see *The Advertising Red Books-Agencies* edition):
1. Bus. Publs. 2. Cable T.V. 3. Catalogs & Directories. 4. Co-op Adv. 5. Consumer Mags. 6. D.M. to Bus. Estab.7. D.M. to Consumers 8. Daily Newsp. 9. Exhibits/Trade Shows 10. Foreign 11. Infomercial 12. Internet Adv.13. Multimedia 14. Network Radio 15. Network T.V. 16. Newsp. Distr. Mags. 17. Other 18. Outdoor (Posters, Transit) 19. Point of Purchase20. Premiums, Novelties 21. Product Samples 22. Special Events Mktg. 23. Spot Radio 24. Spot T.V. 25. Weekly Newsp. 26. Yellow Page Adv.

Lowell Corporation — (Continued)

Business Description:
Ratchet, Wrench & Clutch Designer, Retailer & Mfr
S.I.C.: 3423
N.A.I.C.S.: 332212
Import Export
Advertising Expenditures: $225,000
Media: 1-2-4-7-8-9-10-11-26
Distr.: Direct to Bus. Estab.; Intl.; Natl.
Budget Set: Nov.
Personnel:
David S. Cummings *(Pres)*
Brands & Products:
A TURN FOR THE BETTER
LOWELL WRENCH
Advertising Agency:
Duncan Kendall & Company, Inc.
10 Abbott Park Place
Providence, RI 02903
Tel.: (508) 336-0725
(Industrial Tools)

LOWE'S COMPANIES, INC.

1000 Lowe's Blvd
Mooresville, NC 28117
Tel.: (704) 758-1000
Toll Free: (800) 445-6937
Telex: 510-922-5737
E-mail: investorrelations@lowes.com
Web Site: www.lowes.com
Approx. Sls.: $48,815,000,000
Approx. Number Employees: 161,000
Year Founded: 1946
Business Description:
Building Materials & Related Products for the Do-It-Yourself Home Improvement & Home Construction Markets
S.I.C.: 5211; 5031
N.A.I.C.S.: 444110; 423310
Advertising Expenditures: $790,000,000
Media: 2-3-4-5-6-8-9-10-12-13-14-15-16-18-19-20-22-23-24-25-26
Distr.: Reg.
Personnel:
Robert A. Niblock *(Chm & CEO)*
Larry D. Stone *(Pres & COO)*
Robert F. Hull Jr. *(CFO & Exec VP)*
Michael K. Brown *(CIO & Exec VP)*
Gaither M. Keener Jr. *(Chief Compliance Officer, Gen Counsel, Sec & Exec VP)*
Matthew V. Hollifield *(Chief Acctg Officer & Sr VP)*
Michael K. Menser *(Pres-Global Sourcing & Sr VP-Product Dev)*
Alan Huggins *(Pres-Canada)*
Gregory M. Bridgeford *(Exec VP-Bus Dev)*
Robert J. Gfeller, Jr. *(Exec VP-Mdsg)*
Joseph M. Mabry, Jr. *(Exec VP-Logistics & Distr)*
M. Lee Reeves *(Sr VP, Asst Sec & Deputy Gen Counsel)*
Maureen K. Ausura *(Sr VP-HR)*
Cedric T. Coco *(Sr VP-Learning & Organizational Effectiveness)*
Ronnie E. Damron *(Sr VP-Store Plng & Environment)*
Clinton T. Davis *(Sr VP & Gen Mdsg Mgr-Kitchen & Bath)*
William W. Edwards *(Sr VP-Store Ops-South Central Div)*
James M. Frasso *(Sr VP-Store Ops-Northeast Div)*
Robert Ihrie, Jr. *(Sr VP-Employee Rewards & Svcs)*
Brent G. Kirby *(Sr VP-Store Ops-North Central Div)*
Dennis R. Knowles *(Sr VP-Store Ops-West Div)*
Thomas J. Lamb *(Sr VP-Mtkg & Adv)*
Richard D. Maltsbarger *(Sr VP-Strategy)*
N.Brian Peace *(Sr VP-Corp Affairs)*
K. Scott Plemmons *(Sr VP-Specialty Sls)*
Patricia M. Price *(Sr VP & Gen Mdsg Mgr-Home Decor)*
William Doug Robinson *(Sr VP-Customer Support Svcs)*
Kelly D. Ross *(Sr VP-Fin Plng & Analysis)*
Eric D. Sowder *(Sr VP & Gen Mdsg Mgr-Outdoor Living)*
Stephen J. Szilagyi *(Sr VP-Distr)*
Robert F. Wagner *(Sr VP-Specialty Sls & Store Ops Support)*
Gary E. Wyatt *(Sr VP-Real Estate, Engrg & Construction)*
Bruce Ballard *(VP-Mdsg)*
Kevin M. Cleary *(Dir-Media Svcs)*
Kendra Shillington *(Dir-Online Art)*
Holly Beeson *(Mktg Mgr)*
Jodi Laffoon *(Mgr-Studio)*
Brands & Products:
BASIC BLINDZ
BRAND NAMES YOU KNOW AND TRUST
CLOSETMAID
CREATIVE IDEAS FOR HOME AND GARDEN
GERM
HUNTER
IDYLIS
IMPROVING HOME IMPROVEMENT
LET'S BUILD SOMETHING TOGETHER
LOWE'S
LOWE'S DELIVERS
WHIRLPOOL
Advertising Agencies:
BBDO Worldwide Inc.
(Sub. of Omnicom Group, Inc.)
1285 Ave of the Americas
New York, NY 10019-6028
Tel.: (212) 459-5000
Fax: (212) 459-6645

Campbell-Ewald
30400 Van Dyke Ave
Warren, MI 48093-2368
Tel.: (586) 574-3400
Fax: (586) 575-9925

JohnsonRauhoff
2525 Lake Pines Dr
Saint Joseph, MI 49085
Tel.: (269) 428-9212
Fax: (269) 428-3312
Toll Free: (800) 572-3996

Nova Marketing
300 Crown Colony Dr
Quincy, MA 02169
Tel.: (617) 770-0304
Fax: (617) 770-1821

OMD-USA
195 Broadway
New York, NY 10007
Tel.: (212) 590-7100

Summit Marketing
Three Cityplace Dr Ste 350
Saint Louis, MO 63141-7091
Tel.: (314) 569-3737
Fax: (314) 569-0037
Toll Free: (866) 590-6000

TPN Inc.
9400 N Central Expwy Ste 1500
Dallas, TX 75231-5044
Tel.: (214) 692-1522
Fax: (214) 692-8316

L.R. NELSON CORPORATION

1 Sprinkler Ln
Peoria, IL 61615
Tel.: (309) 690-2200
Fax: (309) 692-5847
E-mail: info@lrnelson.com
Web Site: www.lrnelson.com
Approx. Number Employees: 425
Year Founded: 1911
Business Description:
Mfr of Sprinklers & Sprinkler Controllers, Valves & Hoses
S.I.C.: 3432; 3494
N.A.I.C.S.: 332913; 332919
Import Export
Media: 2-5-6-10-19-23-24-26
Distr.: Intl.; Natl.
Budget Set: May
Personnel:
Dave Ransburg *(Chm & CEO)*
Ingrid Baker *(VP-HR)*
Brands & Products:
ALL YOUR YARDS
DIAL-5
DIAL-A-TIME
EASY CLIK
EASY-SET 3
EASYSET 1
FAN SPRAY
FRONT TRIGGER
GRIP-N-SPRAY
GRIPGUARD
GRIPMASTER
INDUSTRIAL
MAN'S BEST FRIEND
NELSON
OCEAN SHELL
PINCH-SET
POPPY
POUND OF RAIN
QUICK-SET
RAINMISER
RAINPULSE
RAINSWIRL
RAINTRAIN
ROTOR
ROTOR GEAR DRIVE
SIMPLE SOAKER
SNAP-N-RAIN
SPOT RAIN
TOUCH-SET
TRIPLE SPRAY
TURBOHEART
TWIST
WHIZ HEAD

MAC-IT CORPORATION

275 E Liberty St
Lancaster, PA 17602
Tel.: (717) 397-3535
Fax: (717) 392-1843
E-mail: info@macit.com
Web Site: www.macit.com
Approx. Number Employees: 25
Year Founded: 1911
Business Description:
Specialty Fasteners Mfr
S.I.C.: 3451; 3452
N.A.I.C.S.: 332721; 332722
Media: 2-4-26
Distr.: Natl.
Budget Set: Oct.
Personnel:
Rob Stillman *(VP-Sls & Mktg)*

MAKITA CANADA, INC.

(Sub. of Makita Corporation)
1950 Forbes St
Whitby, ON L1N 7B7, Canada
Tel.: (905) 571-2200
Fax: (905) 571-7434
E-mail: info@makita.com
Web Site: www.makita.ca
Sales Range: $100-124.9 Million
Approx. Number Employees: 150
Year Founded: 1973
Business Description:
Portable Electric & Cordless Power Tools Mfr
S.I.C.: 3546
N.A.I.C.S.: 333991
Import Export
Advertising Expenditures: $1,000,000
Media: 2-4-5-6-9-10-19-20-23-24
Distr.: Natl.
Budget Set: Sept. -Nov.
Personnel:
Mack Tokui *(Pres)*

MASONITE INTERNATIONAL CORPORATION

(Sub. of Masonite Inc.)
1820 Matherson Blvd Unit B4
Mississauga, ON L4W 1J2, Canada
Tel.: (905) 670-6500
Fax: (905) 219-2950
Toll Free: (800) 663DOOR
E-mail: questions@premdor.com
Web Site: www.masonite.com
Year Founded: 1955
Business Description:
Door, Door Component & Door Entry System Mfr
S.I.C.: 2431
N.A.I.C.S.: 321911
Media: 2-4-7-10-22
Distr.: Natl.; Reg.
Budget Set: Oct. -Dec.
Personnel:
Lawrence P. Repar *(COO & Exec VP)*
Christopher A. Virostek *(Sr VP-Corp Dev)*
Brands & Products:
ARTEK
BALMORAL
BARRINGTON
BELLAGIO
BELLEVILLE
BUCKINGHAM
CAPRI
CASTLEGATE
CELCO
CROWN
DECOR
DECORLINE
EKEM
ENTERGY
EVERGREEN
FASTFIT
FLORAL
FONMARTY
FRAME-FINDER

Key to Media (For complete agency information see *The Advertising Red Books-Agencies* edition):
1. Bus. Publs. 2. Cable T.V. 3. Catalogs & Directories. 4. Co-op Adv. 5. Consumer Mags. 6. D.M. to Bus. Estab.7. D.M. to Consumers 8. Daily Newsp. 9. Exhibits/Trade Shows 10. Foreign 11. Infomercial 12. Internet Adv.13. Multimedia 14. Network Radio 15. Network T.V. 16. Newsp. Distr. Mags. 17. Other 18. Outdoor (Posters, Transit) 19. Point of Purchase20. Premiums, Novelties 21. Product Samples 22. Special Events Mktg. 23. Spot Radio 24. Spot T.V. 25. Weekly Newsp. 26. Yellow Page Adv.

HAMPTON
IMPRESSIONIST SERIES
INNOVA
JOHNSON
MAGRI
MASON SERIES
MIAMI
MIROIR
MOHAWK
MONNERIE
MULTYPANEL
OAKCRAFT
PALAZZO
PORTES BELHUMEUR
PREMDOR
PREMDOR ADAPT-A-FIT
PREMDOR CROSBY
PREMWOOD
RADIATA
RENOVATOR
RIVIERA
ROYAL MAHOGANY
SAFE' N SOUND
SET-RITE
SPAN-RITE
SPECIALTY
STANLEY DOOR
STORMPROOF
TIFFANY
VITRE ART
WOODLANDS MILLWORK

Advertising Agency:
Meadwell
4310 Sherwoodtowne Blvd Ste 302
Mississauga, ON L4Z 4C4, Canada
Tel.: (905) 897-1717
Fax: (905) 897-1625

MASTER APPLIANCE CORP.

2420 18th St
Racine, WI 53403
Tel.: (262) 633-7791
Fax: (262) 633-9745
Toll Free: (800) 558-9413
E-mail: sales@masterappliance.com
Web Site: www.masterappliance.com
E-Mail For Key Personnel:
Sales Director: sales@masterappliance.com
Approx. Number Employees: 50
Year Founded: 1958
Business Description:
Heat Tools & Soldering Irons Mfr
S.I.C.: 3699
N.A.I.C.S.: 335999
Import Export
Media: 2-4-5-10-11-16-19-21-26
Distr.: Intl.; Natl.
Budget Set: Monthly
Personnel:
Scott Radwill *(Pres & CEO)*
John Brott *(Dir-Sls)*
Brands & Products:
ECOHEAT
ECONOIRON
ECONOLRON
GG-100K PORTAPRO
MASTER AND VARITEMP
MASTER APPLIANCE
MASTER FLOW
MASTER GT
MASTER HEAT
MASTER HEAT GUN
MASTER MICROPRO
MASTER-MITE
MASTER-MITE ESD
MASTER PROSEAL
MASTERFLOW
MICROPRO
MICROPRO BT-30
MICROTORCH
MT-11 MICROTORCH
MT-11K MICROTORCH
MULTISEAL
PORTAPRO
PROFEAL
PROHEAT
PROSEAL
SOLDERSEAL
ULTRATANE
ULTRATANE BUTANE
ULTRATIP
ULTRATORCH
VARIAIR
VARITEMP

MASTER LOCK COMPANY LLC

(Sub. of Fortune Brands Home & Security LLC)
137 W Forrest Hills Ave
Oak Creek, WI 53154
Tel.: (414) 571-5625
Fax: (414) 766-6335
Toll Free: (800) 558-5528
E-mail: hr@mlock.com
Web Site: www.masterlock.com
Sales Range: $450-499.9 Million
Approx. Number Employees: 1,300
Year Founded: 1921
Business Description:
Padlocks & Security Products Mfr
S.I.C.: 3429; 3462
N.A.I.C.S.: 332510; 332111
Import Export
Media: 2-3-4-5-6-7-9-10-11-13-14-15-16-18-19-20-21-22-23-24-25
Distr.: Natl.
Personnel:
John N. Heppner *(Pres & COO)*
David J. Love *(VP & Gen Mgr-Retail)*
Franco Daino *(VP-Comml Mktg & Prod Dev)*
Brands & Products:
AURA
BARBELL
COMBO LOCKER
CORROZEX
EX SERIES
FORTRESS
GUNLOCK
IACCESS
IMASTER
LOCK & LOAD
MAGNUM
MASTER
MASTER BLOCK
MASTER LOCK
MASTER PRO
NIGHTWATCH
PRO SERIES
PRO SPORT
PYTHON
SELECT ACCESS
SPHERO
STREET CUFF
STREET LINKS
TRIUMPH
WEATHER TOUGH
X-TREME
Advertising Agency:
The Ungar Group
333 N Michigan Ave Ste 2234
Chicago, IL 60601
Tel.: (312) 541-0000
Fax: (312) 541-0010

MATCO TOOLS CORPORATION

(Joint Venture of Cooper Industries plc & Danaher Corporation)
4403 Allen Rd
Stow, OH 44224
Tel.: (330) 929-4949
Fax: (330) 926-5323
Toll Free: (866) BUY-TOOL
Web Site: www.matcotools.com
Sales Range: $350-399.9 Million
Approx. Number Employees: 200
Year Founded: 1946
Business Description:
Automotive Tools, Toolboxes & Equipment Mfr & Distr
S.I.C.: 3423; 3429; 3499; 5072
N.A.I.C.S.: 332212; 332510; 332999; 423710
Media: 4-6-10-13
Personnel:
Thomas N. Willis *(Pres)*
Ernest C. Lauber *(Sr VP-Sls)*
John C. Green *(VP-Mktg & eCommerce)*
Tom Hill *(VP-Fin)*
Jeffrey J. Peterson *(VP-Comml Sls & Customer Svc)*
Michael K. Smith *(VP-Matls, Engrg & Quality)*
Tony D. Stohlmeyer *(VP-HR)*

MCCOY'S BUILDING SUPPLY CENTERS

1350 N Interstate 35
San Marcos, TX 78666-7118
Tel.: (512) 353-5400
Fax: (512) 395-6608
E-mail: info@mccoys.com
Web Site: www.mccoys.com
Approx. Sls.: $30,000,000
Approx. Number Employees: 2,250
Year Founded: 1966
Business Description:
Retail of Lumber & Other Building Materials
S.I.C.: 5031; 5251
N.A.I.C.S.: 423310; 444130
Personnel:
Brian McCoy *(Pres & CEO)*
G. Richard Neal *(CFO)*
Chuck Churchwell, III *(Exec VP)*
Dan Stauffer *(VP-Mktg)*
Brands & Products:
MCCOY'S BUILDING SUPPLY
Advertising Agency:
nFusion Group
5000 Plz on the Lake Ste 200
Austin, TX 78746
Tel.: (512) 716-7000
Fax: (512) 716-7001

MEDCASTER

(Sub. of Colson Associates, Inc.)
800 N Clark St
Albion, MI 49224
Tel.: (866) 462-9700
Fax: (517) 686-1072
Toll Free: (866) 462-9700
E-mail: info@medcaster.com
Web Site: www.medcaster.com
Business Description:
Medical & Pharmaceutical Casters
S.I.C.: 3842; 3499
N.A.I.C.S.: 339113; 332999
Media: 4
Personnel:
Brian Denisty *(Pres)*

MEDECO HIGH SECURITY LOCKS, INC.

(Sub. of Assa Abloy AB)
3625 Alleghany Dr
Salem, VA 24153
Mailing Address:
PO Box 3075
Salem, VA 24153-0330
Tel.: (540) 380-5000
Fax: (800) 421-6615
Toll Free: (800) 675-7558
E-mail: comments@medeco.com
Web Site: www.medeco.com
Approx. Number Employees: 350
Year Founded: 1968
Business Description:
High Security Mechanical & Electronic Locks Mfr
S.I.C.: 3429
N.A.I.C.S.: 332510
Export
Advertising Expenditures: $1,360,000
Media: 1-2-4-5-6-7-8-9-10-19-20-21-22
Distr.: Natl.
Budget Set: Sept.
Personnel:
Tom Kaika *(Pres)*
Ann McCrady *(Mgr-Mktg)*
Brands & Products:
BIAXIAL
COMMERCIAL MAXUM
DURACAM
DURACAM II R/C
EMBASSY
KEYMARK
MVP
NEXGEN
SEGAL
SITEKEY
SITELINE
SPRINGLATCH
STEELGUARD

MEEK'S BUILDING CENTERS

1311 E Woodhurst Dr
Springfield, MO 65804-4282
Tel.: (417) 521-2801
Fax: (417) 521-2868
E-mail: contact@meeklumber.com
Web Site: www.meeklumber.com
Approx. Sls.: $300,000,000
Approx. Number Employees: 50
Year Founded: 1919
Business Description:
Home Improvement Centers
S.I.C.: 5031
N.A.I.C.S.: 423310
Media: 3-8-15-16-18-19-20-22-23-24
Distr.: Reg.
Personnel:
Terry O. Meek *(Pres)*
Kent May *(CFO)*
Charlie Meek *(Gen Mgr)*
Advertising Agency:
Young & Company
1615-C S Ingram Mill
Springfield, MO 65804
Tel.: (417) 866-3366
Fax: (417) 866-3689

MELNOR, INC.

3085 Shawnee Dr
Winchester, VA 22601-4205
Tel.: (540) 722-5600

Key to Media (For complete agency information see *The Advertising Red Books-Agencies* edition):
1. Bus. Publs. 2. Cable T.V. 3. Catalogs & Directories. 4. Co-op Adv. 5. Consumer Mags. 6. D.M. to Bus. Estab.7. D.M. to Consumers 8. Daily Newsp. 9. Exhibits/Trade Shows 10. Foreign 11. Infomercial 12. Internet Adv.13. Multimedia 14. Network Radio 15. Network T.V. 16. Newsp. Distr. Mags. 17. Other 18. Outdoor (Posters, Transit) 19. Point of Purchase20. Premiums, Novelties 21. Product Samples 22. Special Events Mktg. 23. Spot Radio 24. Spot T.V. 25. Weekly Newsp. 26. Yellow Page Adv.

Melnor, Inc. — (Continued)

Fax: (540) 722-1131
E-mail: info@melnor.com
Web Site: www.melnor.com
Approx. Number Employees: 90
Year Founded: 1947
Business Description:
Lawn & Garden Watering Products & Accessories Mfr
S.I.C.: 3524; 3634
N.A.I.C.S.: 333112; 335211
Import Export
Advertising Expenditures: $675,000
D.M. to Consumers: $337,500;
Exhibits/Trade Shows: $337,500
Distr.: Intl.; Natl.
Budget Set: Oct.
Personnel:
Juergen Nies *(Pres & CEO)*
Richard Boyle *(VP-Sls & Mktg)*
Brands & Products:
AQUA-GAUGE
AQUA-GUN
AQUA SENTRY
AUTOMATIC RAIN MOTOR
BE-WATERWISE
GENTLE RAIN
HERITAGE EDITION
MELNOR
TIME-A-MATIC

MENARD, INC.
5101 Menard Dr
Eau Claire, WI 54703-9604
Tel.: (715) 876-5911
Fax: (715) 876-2868
Web Site: www.menards.com
Sales Range: $5-14.9 Billion
Approx. Number Employees: 35,000
Year Founded: 1972
Business Description:
Retail Home Improvement Stores
S.I.C.: 5031; 2452
N.A.I.C.S.: 423310; 321992
Advertising Expenditures: $30,000,000
Media: 8-9-15-23-24-25
Distr.: Reg.
Personnel:
John R. Menard, Jr. *(Pres)*
Earl R. Rasmussen *(CFO & Treas)*
Charlie Menard *(COO)*
Dave Wagner *(CIO)*
Ed Archibald *(VP-Mdsg)*
Jamie Radabaugh *(Dir-Sls & Licensing)*
John VanDerGeest *(Project Mgr-Construction)*
Terri Jain *(Mgr-Payroll)*
John Leonauskas *(Mgr-Mktg)*
Scott Nuttelman *(Mgr)*
Tom O'Neil *(Mgr-Real Estate Acq)*
Brands & Products:
DEDICATED TO SERVICE AND QUALITY
MENARDS

METABO CORPORATION
1231 Wilson Dr
West Chester, PA 19380-4243
Tel.: (610) 436-5900
Fax: (610) 638-2261
Fax: (610) 436-9072
Toll Free: (800) 638-2264
E-mail: info@metabousa.com
Web Site: www.metabousa.com
Sales Range: $10-24.9 Million
Approx. Number Employees: 50
Business Description:
Mfr of Industrial Hand Tools
S.I.C.: 5072
N.A.I.C.S.: 423710
Export
Media: 2-4-7-10-13
Distr.: Natl.
Budget Set: Nov.
Personnel:
Martin Cross *(Pres)*
Brands & Products:
ELEKTRA BECKUM
LUREM
METABO
ORIGINAL SLICER
WORK. DON'T PLAY.
Advertising Agency:
The Simon Group, Inc.
1506 Old Bethlehem Pike
Sellersville, PA 18960-1427
Tel.: (215) 453-8700
Fax: (215) 453-1670

METTLER-TOLEDO INC.
(Sub. of Mettler-Toledo International Inc.)
1900 Polaris Pkwy
Columbus, OH 43240
Tel.: (614) 438-4511
Fax: (614) 438-4900
Toll Free: (800) 523-5123
Web Site: www.mettlertoledo.com
Approx. Number Employees: 100
Year Founded: 1901
Business Description:
Electronic Scales, Industrial Software & Weighing Systems Mfr
S.I.C.: 3596; 5049
N.A.I.C.S.: 333997; 423490
Export
Media: 2-4-5-7-10-20-22
Distr.: Intl.

MG BUILDING MATERIALS
2651 SW Military Dr
San Antonio, TX 78224-1048
Tel.: (210) 924-8604
Fax: (210) 924-6082
E-mail: mgonline@mgbuildingmaterials.com
Web Site: www.mgbuildingmaterials.com
Approx. Number Employees: 300
Year Founded: 1972
Business Description:
Building Materials & Home Improvement Supplies Retailer
S.I.C.: 5031
N.A.I.C.S.: 423310
Media: 8
Distr.: Reg.
Personnel:
Alan Grothues *(Co-Pres)*
David Grothues *(Co-Pres)*
Thomas Grothues *(Co-Pres)*
Larry Grothues *(Partner)*

MICRO STAMPING CORP.
140 Belmont Dr
Somerset, NJ 08873-1204
Tel.: (732) 302-0800
Fax: (732) 302-0436
Web Site: www.microstamping.com
E-Mail For Key Personnel:
Sales Director: sales@microstamping.com
Sales Range: $50-74.9 Million
Approx. Number Employees: 150
Year Founded: 1945
Business Description:
Metal Stampings Mfr
S.I.C.: 3469; 3841
N.A.I.C.S.: 332116; 339112
Import Export
Personnel:
Tonya Reivich *(Dir-HR)*
Advertising Agency:
Briechle-Fernandez Marketing Services Inc.
265 Industrial Way W Ste 7
Eatontown, NJ 07724
Tel.: (732) 982-8222
Fax: (732) 982-8223

MIDWEST FASTENER CORPORATION
9031 Shaver Rd
Kalamazoo, MI 49024-6164
Tel.: (269) 327-6917
Fax: (269) 327-9798
Toll Free: (800) 444-7313
Web Site: www.mwf.net
Approx. Sls.: $32,000,000
Approx. Number Employees: 85
Year Founded: 1975
Business Description:
Distributor of Hardware & Fasteners
S.I.C.: 5072
N.A.I.C.S.: 423710
Personnel:
Henry De Vries *(Pres & CFO)*
Advertising Agency:
Sonnhalter
633 W Bagley Rd
Berea, OH 44017-1356
Tel.: (440) 234-1812
Fax: (440) 234-1890

MILLERS FORGE INC.
1411 Capital Ave
Plano, TX 75074-8119
Tel.: (972) 422-2145
Fax: (972) 881-0639
Toll Free: (800) 527-3474
E-mail: info@millersforge.com
Web Site: www.millersforge.com
Approx. Sls.: $5,000,000
Approx. Number Employees: 3
Business Description:
Mfr of Manicure Cutlery, Surgical Tools, Pet Grooming Tools & Scissors
S.I.C.: 5199; 5047
N.A.I.C.S.: 424990; 423450
Import Export
Advertising Expenditures: $100,000
Media: 2-10-19
Distr.: Intl.; Natl.
Personnel:
Ted Hughes *(Pres & COO)*
Mike Engels *(Dir-Mktg & Adv)*
Brands & Products:
CUTI CLIP
DUBL DUCK
MILLERS FORGE
NAILAID
PREMIER
VISTA

MILWAUKEE ELECTRIC TOOL CORP.
(Sub. of Techtronic Industries Co., Ltd.)
13135 W Lisbon Rd
Brookfield, WI 53005-2550
Tel.: (262) 781-3600
Fax: (262) 783-8279
Web Site: www.milwaukeetool.com
Approx. Number Employees: 350
Year Founded: 1924
Business Description:
Portable Electric Power Tools Mfr
S.I.C.: 3546; 3425
N.A.I.C.S.: 333991; 332213
Import Export
Media: 2-4-7-10-18-19-20-26
Distr.: Natl.
Budget Set: Jan.
Personnel:
Steven P. Richman *(Pres)*
Eric Hanson *(Dir-IT)*
Brands & Products:
44 MAGNUM
THE AX
BODY GRIP
DYMORIG
EAGLE
ENDURANCE
FAT PACK
GRIP-LOK
THE HATCHET
HAWG WASH
HAWK
HEX GRIP
HOLE HAWG
HOLE SHOOTERS
LOK-TOR
MAGNUM
MILWAUKEE
MOSSY OAK
NOTHING BUT HEAVY DUTY
QUIK-LOK CORD
SAWZALL
SAWZALL PLUS
SCREW-SHOOTERS
SHARP-FIRE
SMART START
STEEL HAWG
SUPER HAWG
SUPER SAWZALL
SUPER SHARP
SUPER-TOUGH
THUNDERBOLT
THUNDERMAX
TILT-LOK
THE TORCH
U.S. 1
VAC-U-RIG

MITEK, INC.
(Holding of Berkshire Hathaway Inc.)
14515 N Outer Forty Rd Ste 300
Chesterfield, MO 63017
Tel.: (314) 434-1200
Fax: (314) 434-9110
Toll Free: (800) 325-8075
Web Site: www.mii.com
Approx. Sls.: $175,000,000
Approx. Number Employees: 200
Year Founded: 1955
Business Description:
Steel Fasteners, Hydraulic & Pneumatic Presses & Construction Product Mfr
S.I.C.: 3965; 3429; 3441; 3531
N.A.I.C.S.: 339993; 332312; 332510; 333120
Export
Media: 2-7-10-19-20-21
Distr.: Natl.
Personnel:
Eugene M. Toombs *(Chm & CEO)*

Key to Media (For complete agency information see *The Advertising Red Books-Agencies* edition):
1. Bus. Publs. 2. Cable T.V. 3. Catalogs & Directories. 4. Co-op Adv. 5. Consumer Mags. 6. D.M. to Bus. Estab.7. D.M. to Consumers
8. Daily Newsp. 9. Exhibits/Trade Shows 10. Foreign 11. Infomercial 12. Internet Adv.13. Multimedia 14. Network Radio
15. Network T.V. 16. Newsp. Distr. Mags. 17. Other 18. Outdoor (Posters, Transit) 19. Point of Purchase20. Premiums, Novelties
21. Product Samples 22. Special Events Mktg. 23. Spot Radio 24. Spot T.V. 25. Weekly Newsp. 26. Yellow Page Adv.

Ron Burkhardt *(CFO & Exec VP)*
Terry Nicholson *(Sr VP-Global Software & Tech)*
Nicholson Terry *(Sr VP-Software & Tech-Global)*
Gene Toombs, IV *(Sr VP-Ops)*
Gunnar Isaacson *(Dir-Product Mgmt)*
Terry McGrath *(Accountant)*
Brands & Products:
ELIMINATOR
MITEK 2000
PLANX
POSI-STRUT
ULTRA-SPAN

MKT FASTENING, LLC

1 Gunnebo Dr
Lonoke, AR 72086
Tel.: (501) 676-2222
Fax: (501) 676-2524
Toll Free: (800) 336-1640
Web Site: www.mktfastening.com
E-Mail For Key Personnel:
President: bert@mktfastening.com
Marketing Director: mike@mktfastening.com
Approx. Number Employees: 40
Year Founded: 1947
Business Description:
Mfr Anchoring Devices & Allied Products
S.I.C.: 3462; 3546
N.A.I.C.S.: 332111; 333991
Import Export
Media: 4-10-13-20
Distr.: Intl.; Natl.
Budget Set: Sept.
Personnel:
Bert Mayer *(Pres)*
Ron Brooks *(VP-Fin)*
Mike Irvin *(VP-Sls & Mktg)*
Jim Ellis *(Mgr-DP)*
Cindy Gladish *(Mgr-Cust Svcs)*
Cheri Henderson *(Mgr-Pur)*
Brands & Products:
A SOLID CONNECTION
CONSET
FORWAY
HOLLY
KEYSTONE
MKT
SUP-R-CAULK
SUP-R-DROP
SUP-R-LAG
SUP-R-LEAD
SUP-R-SHORTY
SUP-R-SLEEVE
SUP-R-SPLIT
SUP-R-STUD
SUP-R-TOGGLE
TAPER BOLT
UNI-TAP
UNISET
USE DIAMOND
VERSA-TOGGLE
ZAP-IT

MOEN INCORPORATED

(Sub. of Fortune Brands Home & Security LLC)
25300 Al Moen Dr
North Olmsted, OH 44070-8022
Tel.: (440) 962-2000
Fax: (440) 962-2770
Toll Free: (800) 321-8809
E-mail: webmail@moen.com
Web Site: www.moen.com
Approx. Sls.: $100,000,000
Approx. Number Employees: 3,200
Year Founded: 1937
Business Description:
Bathroom & Kitchen Plumbing Fixture Mfr
S.I.C.: 3432; 3431
N.A.I.C.S.: 332913; 332998
Import Export
Media: 1-2-3-4-5-7-10-11-13-15-16-19-20-22-24-26
Distr.: Intl.; Natl.
Budget Set: Aug.
Personnel:
David B. Lingafelter *(Pres)*
Mike Bauer *(Pres-US Bus)*
Nancy E. Uridil *(Sr VP)*
Todd Teter *(VP & Gen Mgr-Wholesale Bus Unit)*
Tim McDonough *(VP Global Brand Marketing)*
Michael Pickett *(VP Global Brand Dev)*
Charles J. Bluhm *(VP-Sys)*
Gary Gajewski *(VP-Fin)*
Kevin Campbell *(Sr Dir-Mktg-Wholesale Bus Unit)*
Kathy Flinn *(Dir-Adv & Brand)*
Ginny Long *(Dir-Online & Direct Mktg)*
Jerry Capasso *(Product Mgr)*
Brands & Products:
ABERDEEN
ASCERI
BAMBOO
BUY IT FOR LOOKS. BUY IT FOR LIFE
CASA
CASTLEBY
CHATEAU
COLONNADE
DELUXE
EVA
EXECTTEMP
EXTENSA
FELICITY
FINA
HOME CARE
INSPIRATIONS
INTEGRA
KINGSLEY
LANCELOT
LEGEND
MANNERLY
MEDORA
MOEN
MOENSTONE
MONTICELLO
ONETOUCH
ORGANIC
POSI-TEMP
PURETOUCH
PURETOUCH AQUASUITE
PURETOUCH CLASSIC
PURETOUCH EURO
PURETOUCH PROFESSIONAL
ROTHBURY
SALORA
SHOWHOUSE
SOLACE
SOPHISTICATE
TRADITIONAL
TRES CHIC
VESTIGE
VILETTA
WATERHILL
WATERSENSE
WOODMERE
Advertising Agencies:
Critical Mass Inc.
402 11th Ave SE
Calgary, AB T2G 0Y4, Canada
Tel.: (403) 262-3006
Fax: (403) 262-7185
Digital Agency of Record

Falls Communications
50 Public Sq 25th Fl
Cleveland, OH 44113
Tel.: (216) 696-0229
Fax: (216) 696-0269
Pub Rels
— Jennifer Allanson *(Acct Exec)*

MARC USA Corporate Headquarters
225 W Station Square Dr Ste 500
Pittsburgh, PA 15219-1119
Tel.: (412) 562-2000
Fax: (412) 562-2022

Marketing Directions, Inc.
28005 Clemens Rd
Cleveland, OH 44145
Tel.: (440) 835-5550
Fax: (440) 892-9195

Wyse
668 Euclid Ave
Cleveland, OH 44114
Tel.: (216) 696-2424
Fax: (216) 736-4425

MORRIS COUPLING COMPANY

2240 W 15th St
Erie, PA 16505
Tel.: (814) 459-1741
Fax: (814) 453-5155
Toll Free: (800) 426-1579
E-mail: sales@morriscoupling.com
Web Site: www.morriscoupling.com
E-Mail For Key Personnel:
Sales Director: sales@morriscoupling.com
Approx. Number Employees: 250
Year Founded: 1941
Business Description:
Mfr. of Piping Components for the Pneumatic Conveying Industry
S.I.C.: 6029; 3498; 3568
N.A.I.C.S.: 522110; 332996; 333613
Export
Advertising Expenditures: $175,000
Media: 2-4-7-10-13
Distr.: Intl.; Natl.
Budget Set: Nov.
Personnel:
Robert Shreve *(VP-Sls & Mktg)*
John McUmber *(Reg Mgr-Sls-Midwest)*
Brands & Products:
CERAM-BACK-ELBOW
EVER-TITE
GRIPPER
HELI-GROOVE
MORR-CLEAR
MORR-LITE
MORR-THANE
MORR-TITE
MORR-TUFF
MORRIS
MORRIS HELI-GROOVE
QUICKON II
QUICKON II COUPLER
TOUGH-TITE
Advertising Agency:
Core Creative
231 W. Seventh St..
Erie, PA 16501
Tel.: (814) 455-7866
(Couplings, Pipe & Tubing, Cam & Groove Couplings)

MR. ROOTER CORPORATION

(Sub. of The Dwyer Group, Inc.)
1010 N University Parks Dr
Waco, TX 76707-3854
Tel.: (254) 745-2400
Fax: (254) 745-2501
Web Site: www.mrrooter.com
Approx. Number Employees: 15
Business Description:
Plumbing Services
S.I.C.: 1711; 7519
N.A.I.C.S.: 238220; 532120
Advertising Expenditures: $2,000,000
Media: 4-6-9-14-15-23-24-25
Personnel:
Mary Kennedy Thompson *(Pres)*

MSC INDUSTRIAL DIRECT CO., INC.

75 Maxess Rd
Melville, NY 11747
Tel.: (516) 812-2000
Fax: (516) 349-1301
Toll Free: (800) 645-7270
Web Site: www1.mscdirect.com
Approx. Sls.: $1,692,041,000
Approx. Number Employees: 4,173
Year Founded: 1995
Business Description:
Tool & Industrial Products Distr
S.I.C.: 5084; 5085
N.A.I.C.S.: 423830; 423840
Advertising Expenditures: $17,578,000
Media: 4-7-8
Personnel:
David K. Sandler *(Pres & CEO)*
Jeffrey Kaczka *(CFO & Exec VP)*
Erik David Gershwind *(COO & Exec VP)*
Douglas Jones *(Exec VP-Global Supply Chain Ops)*
Eileen Mcguire *(Sr VP-HR)*
Shelley Boxer *(VP-Fin)*
Thomas Cox *(VP-Sls)*
Cindy Nardella *(Bus Mgr)*
Brands & Products:
MSC
Advertising Agency:
dgs Marketing Engineers
10100 Lantern Rd Ste 225
Fishers, IN 46037
Tel.: (317) 813-2222
Fax: (317) 813-2233

MSP INDUSTRIES CORPORATION

(Sub. of American Axle & Manufacturing, Inc.)
45 W Oakwood Rd
Oxford, MI 48371-1631
Tel.: (248) 628-4150
Fax: (248) 628-9710
Web Site: www.msp.com
Sales Range: $75-99.9 Million
Approx. Number Employees: 170
Year Founded: 1981
Business Description:
Mfr of Forgings of Ferrous & Non-Ferrous Materials

Key to Media (For complete agency information see *The Advertising Red Books-Agencies* edition):
1. Bus. Publs. 2. Cable T.V. 3. Catalogs & Directories. 4. Co-op Adv. 5. Consumer Mags. 6. D.M. to Bus. Estab.7. D.M. to Consumers
8. Daily Newsp. 9. Exhibits/Trade Shows 10. Foreign 11. Infomercial 12. Internet Adv.13. Multimedia 14. Network Radio
15. Network T.V. 16. Newsp. Distr. Mags. 17. Other 18. Outdoor (Posters, Transit) 19. Point of Purchase20. Premiums, Novelties
21. Product Samples 22. Special Events Mktg. 23. Spot Radio 24. Spot T.V. 25. Weekly Newsp. 26. Yellow Page Adv.

MSP Industries Corporation — (Continued)

S.I.C.: 3462
N.A.I.C.S.: 332111
Export
Advertising Expenditures: $200,000
Media: 1-2-4-7-8-10-21
Distr.: Intl.; Natl.
Budget Set: Jan.
Personnel:
Lisa Smith *(Mgr)*

MTD PRODUCTS, INC.

5965 Grafton Rd
Valley City, OH 44280
Tel.: (330) 225-2600
Fax: (330) 273-4617
E-mail: iparts@mtdproducts.com
Web Site: www.mtdproducts.com
Sales Range: $550-599.9 Million
Approx. Number Employees: 6,600
Year Founded: 1932
Business Description:
Outdoor Power Equipment Designer & Mfr
S.I.C.: 5083; 3524
N.A.I.C.S.: 423820; 333112
Export
Media: 2-3-4-5-6-8-9-10-13-19-24-26
Distr.: Intl.; Natl.
Budget Set: July
Personnel:
Curtis E. Moll *(Chm)*
Heidi Ketvertis *(Dir-Mktg Comm-Mass Retail Group)*
Brands & Products:
BOLENS
CUB CADET
CUB CADET COMMERCIAL
RYOBI
TROY-BILT
WHITE OUTDOOR
YARD MACHINES
YARD-MAN
Advertising Agencies:
Brunner
11 Stanwix St 5th Fl
Pittsburgh, PA 15222-1312
Tel.: (412) 995-9500
Fax: (412) 995-9501
Cub Cadet
Cub Heating Bill POP

Marketing Directions, Inc.
28005 Clemens Rd
Cleveland, OH 44145
Tel.: (440) 835-5550
Fax: (440) 892-9195

NATIONAL DETROIT, INC.

1590 Northrock Ct
Rockford, IL 61103-1234
Mailing Address:
PO Box 2285
Loves Park, IL 61131-0285
Tel.: (815) 877-4041
Fax: (815) 877-4050
Toll Free: (866) 800-9900
E-mail: sales@nationaldetroit.com
Web Site: www.nationaldetroit.com
E-Mail For Key Personnel:
Sales Director: sales@nationaldetroit.com
Approx. Number Employees: 20
Year Founded: 1939
Business Description:
Pneumatic Portable Sanding Machines Mfr
S.I.C.: 3546; 3553
N.A.I.C.S.: 333991; 333210
Export
Media: 2-4-10
Distr.: Intl.; Natl.
Budget Set: Jan.
Brands & Products:
DUAL ACTION
MITY MIDGET
NATIONAL DETROIT

NATIONAL-STANDARD CO.

(Sub. of Heico Companies, LLC)
1631 Lake St
Niles, MI 49120
Tel.: (269) 683-8100
Fax: (269) 683-6249
Toll Free: (800) 777-1618
E-mail: webmaster@nationalstandard.com
Web Site: www.nationalstandard.com
Approx. Sls.: $200,000,000
Approx. Number Employees: 1,000
Year Founded: 1907
Business Description:
Tire Bead Wire, Fine & Specialty Wire, Welding Wire, Wire Cloth
S.I.C.: 5063
N.A.I.C.S.: 423610
Import Export
Advertising Expenditures: $500,000
Media: 1-4-6-8-10-20-22
Distr.: Direct to Consumer; Intl.; Natl.
Budget Set: Aug.
Brands & Products:
FIBREX
SATIN GLIDE
TRIGGER-TRAC
TRU-TRAC

NEW HAMPSHIRE BALL BEARINGS, INC.

(Sub. of Minebea Co., Ltd.)
175 Jaffrey Rd
Peterborough, NH 03458-1767
Tel.: (603) 924-4100
Fax: (603) 524-9025
E-mail: info@nhbb.com
Web Site: www.nhbb.com
Approx. Number Employees: 450
Year Founded: 1946
Business Description:
Precision Bearings & Bearing Products Mfr
S.I.C.: 3562
N.A.I.C.S.: 332991
Import Export
Advertising Expenditures: $300,000
Media: 2-4-8-10-26
Distr.: Intl.; Natl.
Budget Set: Sept.
Personnel:
Gary C. Yomantas *(Pres)*

NEWAGE TESTING INSTRUMENTS, INC.

(Sub. of AMETEK Electronic Instruments Group)
820 Pennsylvania Blvd
Feasterville Trevose, PA 19053
Tel.: (215) 526-2200
Fax: (215) 354-1803
Toll Free: (800) 806-3924
E-mail: newage.info@ametek.com
Web Site: www.hardnesstesters.com/
Sales Range: $10-24.9 Million
Approx. Number Employees: 37
Year Founded: 1954
Business Description:
Hardness Testers Mfr
S.I.C.: 3829
N.A.I.C.S.: 334519
Import Export
Media: 2-4-7-10
Distr.: Direct to Consumer; Natl.
Budget Set: Sept. -Oct.
Personnel:
Alex Cosenza *(Reg Mgr-Sls)*
Rich Wismer *(Reg Mgr-Sls)*
Brands & Products:
B.O.S.S.
DATAVIEW
EXACTA
HILIGHT
INDENTRON
INSTRON
ME-2
MITUTOYO
PIN BRINELL
ROCKMAN
ROCKMATE
SHIMADZU
VERSITRON
WILSON

NICKERSON LUMBER COMPANY

15 Main St
Orleans, MA 02653-2442
Tel.: (508) 255-0200
Fax: (508) 760-4492
Web Site: www.midcape.net
Approx. Number Employees: 250
Year Founded: 1895
Business Description:
Sawmill Products, Structural Lumber, Prefabricated Homes, Kitchen & Bath Appliances Sales
S.I.C.: 5031
N.A.I.C.S.: 423310
Media: 2-6-9-22-25
Distr.: Reg.
Personnel:
Joshua A. Nickerson *(Chm)*
Robert Labrie *(Sr VP)*

NORWALK POWDERED METALS, INC.

1100 Boston Ave Bldg 3
Bridgeport, CT 06610-2654
Tel.: (203) 338-8000
Fax: (203) 338-8011
E-mail: sales@norwalkpm.com
Web Site: www.norwalkpm.com
E-Mail For Key Personnel:
Sales Director: sales@norwalkpm.com
Approx. Sls.: $20,000,000
Approx. Number Employees: 100
Year Founded: 1958
Business Description:
Powdered Metals & Engineered Components Mfr
S.I.C.: 3316
N.A.I.C.S.: 331221
Export
Advertising Expenditures: $400,000
Media: 7
Distr.: Direct to Consumer; Reg.
Budget Set: Oct.
Personnel:
Thomas A. Blumenthal *(Pres)*
Ann Blumenthal *(COO)*
Peter Sedelnik *(Mgr-Sls & Mktg)*

NU-WOOD DECORATIVE MILLWORK

1722 N Eisenhower Dr
Goshen, IN 46526
Tel.: (574) 534-1192
Fax: (574) 534-0218
Toll Free: (800) 526-1278
E-mail: nuwood@bnin.net
Web Site: www.nu-wood.com
Approx. Number Employees: 40
Year Founded: 1989
Business Description:
Interior & Exterior Urethane Decorative Moldings Mfr
S.I.C.: 3086; 3089
N.A.I.C.S.: 326150; 326199
Media: 4-13
Personnel:
Len Morris *(Pres)*
Sam Korenstra *(Gen Mgr)*

ORBEL CORPORATION

2 Danforth Dr
Easton, PA 18045
Tel.: (610) 829-5000
Fax: (610) 829-5050
E-mail: customerservice@orbel.com
Web Site: www.orbel.com
E-Mail For Key Personnel:
President: kmarino@orbel.com
Approx. Number Employees: 50
Year Founded: 1961
Business Description:
Photo Chemical Milling, Chemical Etching, Electroplating & Precision Metal Parts Mfr
S.I.C.: 3471
N.A.I.C.S.: 332813
Media: 2-4-7-10-17
Distr.: Intl.; Natl.
Personnel:
Kenneth Marino *(Pres)*

ORCHARD SUPPLY HARDWARE STORES CORP.

(Sub. of Sears, Roebuck & Co.)
6450 Via Del Oro
San Jose, CA 95119-1208
Mailing Address:
PO Box 49027
San Jose, CA 95161-9027
Tel.: (408) 281-3500
Fax: (408) 365-2690
Web Site: www.osh.com
Sales Range: $800-899.9 Million
Approx. Number Employees: 7,000
Year Founded: 1931
Business Description:
Hardware Store Services
S.I.C.: 5251; 5261
N.A.I.C.S.: 444130; 444220
Personnel:
William Crowley *(Chm)*
Mark Baker *(Pres & CEO)*
Steve Olsen *(Chief Strategy Officer & Sr VP)*
Steve Mahurin *(Chief Mdsg Officer & Exec VP)*
John Beasley *(Sr VP-Ops)*
Mark A. Bussard *(Sr VP-Ops)*
Advertising Agency:
PRx, Inc.
991 W Hedding St Ste 201
San Jose, CA 95126
Tel.: (408) 287-1700
Fax: (408) 556-1487

Key to Media (For complete agency information see *The Advertising Red Books-Agencies* edition):
1. Bus. Publs. 2. Cable T.V. 3. Catalogs & Directories. 4. Co-op Adv. 5. Consumer Mags. 6. D.M. to Bus. Estab.7. D.M. to Consumers 8. Daily Newsp. 9. Exhibits/Trade Shows 10. Foreign 11. Infomercial 12. Internet Adv.13. Multimedia 14. Network Radio 15. Network T.V. 16. Newsp. Distr. Mags. 17. Other 18. Outdoor (Posters, Transit) 19. Point of Purchase20. Premiums, Novelties 21. Product Samples 22. Special Events Mktg. 23. Spot Radio 24. Spot T.V. 25. Weekly Newsp. 26. Yellow Page Adv.

OUTWATER PLASTIC INDUSTRIES, INC.
(Sub. of Foga System International AB)
24 River Rd
Bogota, NJ 07603
Tel.: (973) 340-1040
Fax: (201) 498-8751
Toll Free: (888) 688-9283
E-mail: outwater@outwater.com
Web Site: www.outwater.com
Approx. Number Employees: 150
Year Founded: 1971
Business Description:
Hardware & Decorative Trim Plastic Mouldings
S.I.C.: 5072
N.A.I.C.S.: 423710
Media: 2-4-6-7
Personnel:
Susan Molnar *(VP-Sls)*
Joey Shimm *(VP-Mktg & Adv)*

OXO INTERNATIONAL INC.
(Sub. of Helen of Troy Limited)
601 W 26th St 10th Fl St 1050
New York, NY 10011
Tel.: (212) 242-3333
Fax: (212) 242-3336
Fax: (877) 523-7186
Toll Free: (800) 545-4411
E-mail: info@oxo.com
Web Site: www.oxo.com
E-Mail For Key Personnel:
Sales Director: intlsales@oxo.com
Sales Range: $25-49.9 Million
Approx. Number Employees: 50
Business Description:
Kitchenware, Cleaning Supplies & Hardware Mfr
S.I.C.: 3429
N.A.I.C.S.: 332510
Media: 6-19
Personnel:
Alex Lee *(Pres)*
Larry Witt *(VP-Mktg)*
Brands & Products:
GOOD GRIPS
GRIND IT
SOFTWORKS
STEEL

PALMGREN STEEL PRODUCTS, INC.
(Sub. of Colovos Company)
4444 Ohio St
Chicago, IL 60624
Tel.: (773) 265-5700
Fax: (773) 265-5740
Toll Free: (800) 621-6145
E-mail: sales@palmgren.com
Web Site: www.palmgren.com
E-Mail For Key Personnel:
Sales Director: sales@palmgren.com
Approx. Number Employees: 26
Year Founded: 1919
Business Description:
Machine Vises, Milling Attachments & Tables, Rotary Tables, Cable Connectors & Weld Gauges Mfr
S.I.C.: 3545
N.A.I.C.S.: 333515
Import Export
Advertising Expenditures: $200,000
Media: 2-4
Distr.: Intl.
Budget Set: Dec.
Personnel:
Robert Eakins *(Exec VP)*
Brands & Products:
PALMGREN

PANAVISE PRODUCTS, INC.
7540 Colbert Dr
Reno, NV 89511-1225
Tel.: (775) 850-2900
Fax: (775) 850-2929
Toll Free: (800) 759-7535
E-mail: webmaster@panavise.com
Web Site: www.panavise.com
E-Mail For Key Personnel:
President: grichter@panavise.com
Approx. Sls.: $6,000,000
Approx. Number Employees: 42
Year Founded: 1956
Business Description:
Precision Vises, Circuit Board Holders & Specialty Mounts Mfr
S.I.C.: 3542
N.A.I.C.S.: 333513
Export
Media: 2-4-5-6-10-11-19-20
Distr.: Intl.; Natl.
Personnel:
Gary Richter *(Pres, Mgr-Asian Mfg)*
Eric Richter *(Dir-Internet, OEM Sls & Mktg)*
Tom Simpkins *(Dir-Sls & Mktg)*
Rosselle Hasegawa *(Mgr-Acctg)*
Amado Puga *(Supvr-Production)*
Brands & Products:
INDASH
PANAPRESS
PANAVISE
PORTAGRIP
PORTAGRIP 2000
POSI-STOP
PV JR
SLIMLINE
SLIMLINE 2000
STAYPUT
UNIFLEX
VISE BUDDY
WINDOWGRIP
Advertising Agency:
Alder & Associates
3218 E Oak Cliff Drive
Salt Lake City, UT 84124
Tel.: (801) 274-1522
(Work Hold Devices, Cellular Phone Holders & Mounts, Speaker Mounts, Laptop Mounts)

PASLODE
(Sub. of Illinois Tool Works Inc.)
888 Forest Edge Dr
Vernon Hills, IL 60061-3105
Tel.: (847) 634-1900
Fax: (847) 634-6602
Toll Free: (800) 682-3428
Toll Free: (800) 222-6990
E-mail: webmaster@paslode.com
Web Site: www.paslode.com
E-Mail For Key Personnel:
Sales Director: tech@paslode.com
Approx. Sls.: $100,000,000
Approx. Number Employees: 800
Year Founded: 1935
Business Description:
Pneumatic & Cordless Fastening Systems Mfr & Marketer
S.I.C.: 3965; 3429
N.A.I.C.S.: 339993; 332510
Export
Advertising Expenditures: $1,200,000
Media: 1-2-4-5-7-10-13-19-20-26
Distr.: Intl.; Natl.
Budget Set: Sept.
Personnel:
Jacek Romanski *(Product Mgr)*
Pat Talano *(Product Mgr)*
John Courtney *(Mgr-Mktg)*
Brands & Products:
FLOORGRIP
GUN-NAILER
IMPULSE
PASLODE
POSITIVE PLACEMENT
POWER MASTER
PROSTRIP
ROOFER'S CHOICE
ROUNDRIVE
SPEED FRAME
TLN
TRIM MASTER
WOOD-TO-STEEL
Advertising Agencies:
Marketing Resources, Inc.
945 Oaklawn Ave
Elmhurst, IL 60126
Tel.: (630) 530-0100
Fax: (630) 530-0134
Toll Free: (888) 220-4238

Stiegler, Wells, Brunswick & Roth, Inc.
(d/b/a SWB&R)
3865 Adler Pl
Bethlehem, PA 18017-9000
Tel.: (610) 866-0611
Fax: (610) 866-8650

PAYSON CASTERS, INC.
2323 N Delany Rd
Gurnee, IL 60031
Tel.: (847) 336-6200
Fax: (847) 336-6542
Toll Free: (800) 323-4552
Web Site: www.paysoncasters.com
Approx. Number Employees: 80
Year Founded: 1873
Business Description:
Caster & Wheel Mfr
S.I.C.: 3562; 3568
N.A.I.C.S.: 332991; 333613
Import
Media: 4-16-19
Distr.: Natl.
Budget Set: Sept.
Personnel:
Harold Sullivan, III *(Pres)*
Brands & Products:
PAYSON
Advertising Agency:
Tannahill Advertising
4025 Tannahill Dr
Gurnee, IL 60031
Tel.: (847) 336-6280
Fax: (847) 336-6542
(Casters & Wheels)

PCC SPS FASTENER DIVISION
(Div. of Precision Castparts Corp.)
301 Highland Ave
Jenkintown, PA 19046
Tel.: (215) 572-3000
Fax: (215) 572-3790
E-mail: spshq@spstech.com
Web Site: www.spstech.com
Approx. Sls.: $1,520,000,000
Approx. Number Employees: 4,200
Year Founded: 1903
Business Description:
Fasteners, Rivets, Washers & Precision Components Mfr
S.I.C.: 3452
N.A.I.C.S.: 332722
Media: 2-4-7-10-13-21
Distr.: Intl.; Natl.
Budget Set: Oct.
Personnel:
Kevin Stein *(Pres)*
James J. Costello *(VP-Aerospace Sls & Mktg-Global)*
Thomas S. Cross *(VP-HR)*
Joe Digiacomo *(Product Line Mgr-OEM Sls)*
Nick Leszcynski *(Product Line Mgr)*
Rich McVaugh *(Product Line Mgr-Nuts)*
David Patterson *(Mgr-Sls)*
Alan Waeltz *(Product Line Mgr-Bolts)*

PDS ASSOCIATES INC.
(d/b/a Waterworks)
(Filed Ch 11 Bankruptcy #950875 on 05/03/09 in U.S. Bankruptcy Ct, Dist of CT, Bridgeport)
60 Backus Ave
Danbury, CT 06810
Tel.: (203) 546-6000
Fax: (203) 546-6001
Web Site: www.waterworks.com
Approx. Sls.: $22,700,000
Approx. Number Employees: 45
Business Description:
Plumbing Fittings & Supplies
S.I.C.: 5074; 5999
N.A.I.C.S.: 423720; 453998
Media: 4-6
Personnel:
Robert Sallick *(Co-Founder & VP-Engrg)*
Barbara Sallick *(Co-Founder & VP-Design)*
Advertising Agency:
Meter Industries
41 E 11th Street 11th Floor
New York, NY 10003
Tel.: (212) 699-6490

PENN ENGINEERING & MANUFACTURING CORP.
(Holding of Tinicum Incorporated)
5190 Old Easton Rd Bldg 3
Danboro, PA 18916
Mailing Address:
PO Box 1000
Danboro, PA 18916-1000
Tel.: (215) 766-8853
Fax: (215) 766-7366
Toll Free: (800) 237-4736
E-mail: penn-eng@penn-eng.com
Web Site: www.penn-eng.com
Sales Range: $75-99.9 Million
Approx. Number Employees: 1,202
Year Founded: 1942
Business Description:
Specialty Fastener Mfr
S.I.C.: 3452; 3429; 3621
N.A.I.C.S.: 332722; 332510; 335312
Import Export
Advertising Expenditures: $500,000
Media: 2-4-7-9-10-11-13-20-21
Distr.: Intl.; Natl.
Budget Set: Sept.
Personnel:
Charles W. Grigg *(Chm)*
Mark Petty *(Pres & CEO)*
Richard Davies *(Treas & Asst Sec)*

Key to Media (For complete agency information see *The Advertising Red Books-Agencies* edition):
1. Bus. Publs. 2. Cable T.V. 3. Catalogs & Directories. 4. Co-op Adv. 5. Consumer Mags. 6. D.M. to Bus. Estab.7. D.M. to Consumers 8. Daily Newsp. 9. Exhibits/Trade Shows 10. Foreign 11. Infomercial 12. Internet Adv.13. Multimedia 14. Network Radio 15. Network T.V. 16. Newsp. Distr. Mags. 17. Other 18. Outdoor (Posters, Transit) 19. Point of Purchase20. Premiums, Novelties 21. Product Samples 22. Special Events Mktg. 23. Spot Radio 24. Spot T.V. 25. Weekly Newsp. 26. Yellow Page Adv.

Penn Engineering & Manufacturing Corp. — (Continued)

Brands & Products:
ATLAS
AUTOSPEC
BLU-COAT
BUSBAR
ELCOM
ELCOM II
FOILGARD
HYBRID
LO-COG
PEM
PEMFLEX
PEMHEX
PEMSERT
PEMSERTER
PENNENGINEERING
R'ANGLE
SI
SNAP-TOP
STICKSCREW
WAVEGARD

PENNENGINEERING FASTENING TECHNOLOGIES

(Div. of Penn Engineering & Manufacturing Corp.)
5190 Old Easton Rd
Danboro, PA 18916
Tel.: (215) 766-8853
Fax: (215) 766-0143
E-mail: info@pemnet.com
Web Site: www.pemnet.com
Sales Range: $125-149.9 Million
Approx. Number Employees: 800
Business Description:
Self-Clinching Fasteners Mfr
S.I.C.: 3429
N.A.I.C.S.: 332510
Import Export
Media: 2-4-7-9-10-11-13-20-21
Distr.: Intl.; Natl.
Budget Set: Sept.
Personnel:
Mark Petty *(CEO)*
Leon Attarian *(Dir-Mktg)*
Brands & Products:
CONNECT'R WARE
PEMSERTER 2000
PEMSERTER LT4
PEMSERTER MICROMATE
PEMSERTER PLUS
PEMSERTER SERIES 4
PEMSERTER SERIES B49
PEMSERTER SERIES P3
PEMSERTER TNT618
PEMSERTER TRU-MOTION
PFS
PFT
PK-100
TY-D
Advertising Agency:
Hammerhead Advertising
720 Monroe St Ste E308
Hoboken, NJ 07030
Tel.: (201) 610-1313
Fax: (201) 610-0109

PENNSYLVANIA SCALE COMPANY

(Sub. of The A.H. Emery Company)
1042 New Holland Ave
Lancaster, PA 17601
Tel.: (717) 295-6935
Fax: (717) 295-6941
Toll Free: (800) 233-0473
E-mail: rsw@pascale.com
Web Site: www.pascale.com
Approx. Sls.: $6,000,000
Approx. Number Employees: 12
Year Founded: 1908
Business Description:
Mfr. of Scales
S.I.C.: 3596
N.A.I.C.S.: 333997
Import Export
Media: 2-4-5-7-10-13-16-20-21
Distr.: Intl.; Natl.
Personnel:
Rob Woodward *(VP & Gen Mgr)*
Brands & Products:
PENNSYLVANIA SCALE
SOFTWEIGHER

PERGO INC.

(Sub. of Pergo AB)
3128 Highwoods Blvd
Raleigh, NC 27604-1018
Tel.: (919) 773-6000
Fax: (919) 773-6004
E-mail: info@pergo.com
Web Site: www.pergo.com
Approx. Rev.: $269,451,584
Approx. Number Employees: 550
Business Description:
Laminated Flooring
S.I.C.: 3996; 5023
N.A.I.C.S.: 326192; 423220
Personnel:
Lee Osborne *(VP-Fin)*
David Small *(Dir-Mktg)*
Advertising Agency:
Fitzgerald+CO
3060 Peachtree Rd NW
Atlanta, GA 30305
Tel.: (404) 504-6900
Fax: (404) 239-0548

POWERS FASTENERS INC.

2 Powers Ln
Brewster, NY 10509
Tel.: (914) 235-6300
Fax: (914) 235-3289
E-mail: info@powers.com
Web Site: www.powers.com
Approx. Number Employees: 300
Year Founded: 1921
Business Description:
Mfr. of Anchoring Systems
S.I.C.: 3545; 3089
N.A.I.C.S.: 333515; 326199
Export
Media: 1-2-4-7-10-19-20-21-26
Distr.: Natl.
Budget Set: Apr.
Personnel:
Christopher W. Powers *(Chm & CEO)*
Frederic B. Powers, III *(Pres)*
Jeffrey R. Powers *(CEO)*
Robert Diana *(CFO & VP-Fin)*
Lenny Colasuonno *(VP-Sls & Mktg)*
Mike Fergus *(VP-Pur)*
Mark Ziegler *(Dir-Engrg)*
Brands & Products:
AC100 PLUS
AC100+ GOLD
BALLISTIC POINT
BANG-IT
BANTAM PLUG
BLACK TRIGGERFOAM
CALIBER SAFETY STRIPS
CALK-IN
CHEM-STUD
DECK SCREWS
DOUBLE
DRIVE
DROPIN
FIBERPLUG
FOIL-FAST
HAMMER-CAPSULE
HELI-PIN
HOLLOW-SET
ITW RAMSET
LAG SHIELD
LEGS
LOK-BOLT
LOUIE LOOP
MINI DROPIN
NYLON NAILIN
PE1000+
PERMA-SEAL
POLLY
POLY-TOGGLE
POP-TOGGLE
POWER-BOLT
POWER-FAST
POWER-STUD
POWERFOAM
POWERLITE
POWERS FASTENER
POWERSTICK
QUATRO
RAWL-BOLT
RAWL-STUD
RAWLDRILL
RAWLITE
RAWLPLUG
RAWLY
ROOFING SPIKE
S-4 PLUS
SABER-TOOTH
SCRU-LEAD
SDS-MAX
SET-BOLT
SINGLE
SNAKE
SPIKE
STEEL DROPIN
STRAP-TOGGLE
TAPPER
TILT WALL WEDGE-BOLT
TRAK-IT
TRI-CUTTER
TRIGGERFOAM
VERTIGO
WALL-DOG
WEDGE-BOLT
WOOD-KNOCKER
WOODIE
ZAMAC HAMMER-SCREW
ZAMAC NAILIN
ZIP-IT
ZIP-TOGGLE

PRECISION VALVE CORPORATION

700 Nepperhan Ave
Yonkers, NY 10703
Tel.: (914) 969-6500
Fax: (914) 966-4428
Web Site: www.precision-valve.com
E-Mail For Key Personnel:
President: jabplanalp@precision-valve.com
Sales Director: dminogue@precision-valve.com
Approx. Number Employees: 2,000
Year Founded: 1949
Business Description:
Mfr of Aerosol Valves
S.I.C.: 3499; 5085
N.A.I.C.S.: 332999; 423840
Export
Advertising Expenditures: $310,000
Bus. Publs.: $75,000; Catalogs & Directories: $10,000; Consumer Mags.: $100,000; Exhibits/Trade Shows: $50,000; Foreign: $75,000
Distr.: Intl.; Natl.
Budget Set: Mar.
Personnel:
John P. Abplanalp *(Pres & CEO)*
Ron Schulman *(CFO)*
Ian Tyler *(VP-Sls)*
Brands & Products:
ACC-U-SOL
BALSA
CARAT
CORTES
FRISCO
JASON
KONTOUR
KOSMOS
LAGO
MACH
MARQUESA
MEDINA
MERLIN
MONTEFRISCO
MONTICELLO
PRECISION
REINA
SEGURA
SPRAYMATE
VULKAN

PREMIERE LOCK COMPANY

(d/b/a Weslock)
8301 E 81st St
Tulsa, OK 74133
Tel.: (918) 294-8179
Fax: (918) 294-3869
Toll Free: (800) 575BOLT
Telex: 69-0420
Web Site: www.weslock.com
Sales Range: $10-24.9 Million
Approx. Number Employees: 30
Year Founded: 1933
Business Description:
Mfr of Residential Door Locks & Related Hardware
S.I.C.: 3429
N.A.I.C.S.: 332510
Export
Media: 2-4-7-8-10-11-20-21
Distr.: Intl.; Natl.
Budget Set: Aug.
Personnel:
Clint Brumble *(Pres)*
Mike Driggers *(CFO)*
Brands & Products:
ACCESS
BALL
BARRINGTON
BORDEAU
CALAIS
COLONIAL
ELEGANTI
IMPRESA
LEXINGTON
OVAL
PROVENCE
SAVANNAH
SONIC
UNIGARD
WESLOCK

PRICE PFISTER, INC.

(Sub. of Stanley Black & Decker, Inc.)
19701 Da Vinci

Key to Media (For complete agency information see *The Advertising Red Books-Agencies* edition):
1. Bus. Publs. 2. Cable T.V. 3. Catalogs & Directories. 4. Co-op Adv. 5. Consumer Mags. 6. D.M. to Bus. Estab.7. D.M. to Consumers 8. Daily Newsp. 9. Exhibits/Trade Shows 10. Foreign 11. Infomercial 12. Internet Adv.13. Multimedia 14. Network Radio 15. Network T.V. 16. Newsp. Distr. Mags. 17. Other 18. Outdoor (Posters, Transit) 19. Point of Purchase20. Premiums, Novelties 21. Product Samples 22. Special Events Mktg. 23. Spot Radio 24. Spot T.V. 25. Weekly Newsp. 26. Yellow Page Adv.

Foothill Ranch, CA 92610-2622
Tel.: (949) 672-4000
Fax: (949) 672-4001
Toll Free: (800) 414-2200
Web Site: www.pricepfister.com
Sales Range: $100-124.9 Million
Approx. Number Employees: 500
Year Founded: 1910
Business Description:
Decorative Faucets Mfr
S.I.C.: 3432; 3369
N.A.I.C.S.: 332913; 331528
Import Export
Media: 2-4-5-6-7-10-11-13-19-20-21-22
Distr.: Natl.
Personnel:
Diane Whitmer *(Brand Mgr-Mktg)*
Brands & Products:
PFRESHEST IDEAS IN PFAUCETS

PRIMESOURCE BUILDING PRODUCTS, INC.
(Sub. of PrimeSource Building Products, Inc.)
11700 NW 100th Rd
Medley, FL 33178-1033
Tel.: (972) 999-8500
Fax: (305) 884-1714
Toll Free: (800) 653-4846
Web Site: www.primesourcebp.com
Approx. Number Employees: 300
Year Founded: 1947
Business Description:
Mfr. of Nails, Screws, Fasteners, Fence Products & Wire Products
S.I.C.: 5051; 5031
N.A.I.C.S.: 423510; 423310
Media: 2-4-7-10-17-20
Distr.: Natl.
Budget Set: Nov.
Personnel:
Linda Braziano *(Dir-Mktg)*
Brands & Products:
GRIP-RITE
GRIP-RITE FAS'NERS
GRIP-RITE GRIP-CAP
GRIP-RITE PRIMEGUARD PLUS
PRO-TWIST

THE PRODUCTO MACHINE CO.
(Sub. of PMT Group Inc)
800 Union Ave
Bridgeport, CT 06607-1137
Mailing Address:
PO Box 4088
Bridgeport, CT 06607-0906
Tel.: (203) 367-8675
Fax: (203) 367-0418
Toll Free: (800) 243-9898
E-mail: custserv@producto.com
Web Site: www.producto.com
E-Mail For Key Personnel:
President: nmarsilius@pmt-group.com
Sales Director: krchnavy@producto.com
Approx. Number Employees: 500
Year Founded: 1928
Business Description:
Mfr. of Tooling Components
S.I.C.: 3541; 3545
N.A.I.C.S.: 333512; 333515
Import Export
Media: 2-4-10
Distr.: Natl.
Budget Set: Mar.
Personnel:
Newman M. Marsilius *(Pres & CEO)*
Brands & Products:
MOORE
PRODUCTO
RING

THE RENOVATOR'S SUPPLY, INC.
Renovators Old Mill
Millers Falls, MA 01349
Tel.: (413) 423-3559
Fax: (413) 423-3800
Toll Free: (800) 659-0203 (Catalog)
Toll Free: (800) 659-2211 (Cust Svs)
E-mail: csm1@renovatorssupply.com
Web Site: www.rensup.com
Sales Range: $25-49.9 Million
Approx. Number Employees: 120
Year Founded: 1978
Business Description:
Mail Order Internet Services: Hardware, Plumbing & Lighting
S.I.C.: 3429; 3645
N.A.I.C.S.: 332510; 335121
Import
Advertising Expenditures: $300,000
Media: 2-4-6-8-10-13
Distr.: Natl.
Budget Set: Jan.
Personnel:
Claude Jeanloz *(Pres)*
Mike Gordon *(Mgr-Mfg)*
Brands & Products:
RENOVATOR'S SUPPLY
YIELD HOUSE
Advertising Agency:
Old Mill Marketing
Renovators Old Mill
Millers Falls, MA 01349
Tel.: (413) 423-3569
Fax: (413) 423-3800

REPUBLIC FASTENER PRODUCTS CORP.
1827 Waterview Dr
Great Falls, SC 29055-8929
Tel.: (803) 482-2500
Fax: (803) 482-2526
Toll Free: (800) 386-1949
E-mail: vicky@repfast.com
Web Site: www.repfast.com
E-Mail For Key Personnel:
Sales Director: sales@repfast.com
Approx. Number Employees: 15
Year Founded: 1949
Business Description:
Mfr. of Fasteners, Tools, Cutters, Hooks & Special Wire Forms
S.I.C.: 3965; 3546
N.A.I.C.S.: 339993; 333991
Export
Media: 2-4-7-8-13
Distr.: Intl.; Natl.
Budget Set: Jan.
Personnel:
Richard A. Barnes *(Pres & COO)*
Daniel F. Barnes *(CEO)*
Brands & Products:
SQUEEZ-KLIP

RESTORATION HARDWARE, INC.
(Holding of Catterton Partners)
15 Koch Rd Ste J
Corte Madera, CA 94925-1231
Tel.: (415) 924-7910
Fax: (415) 927-9133
Toll Free: (877) 777-7059
Web Site: www.restorationhardware.com
Sales Range: $700-749.9 Million
Approx. Number Employees: 1,900
Year Founded: 1979
Business Description:
Home Furnishings, Functional & Decorative Hardware & Related Merchandise Retailer; Owned by Catterton Partners & Three Towers Partners LLC
S.I.C.: 5712; 2434; 5072; 5719
N.A.I.C.S.: 442110; 337110; 423710; 442299
Advertising Expenditures: $40,200,000
Media: 4-6-9-13-17
Personnel:
Carlos Alberini *(Co-CEO)*
Gary G. Friedman *(CEO)*
Jim Stewart *(CFO)*
Ken Dunaj *(COO & Exec VP)*
Ian B. Sears *(CMO & Gen Mgr)*
Bonnie Orofino *(Chief Mdsg Officer)*
Advertising Agency:
Resource Interactive
343 N Front St
Columbus, OH 43215-2219
Tel.: (614) 621-2888
Fax: (614) 621-2873
Toll Free: (800) 550-5815

REV-A-SHELF
(Sub. of Jones Plastic & Engineering Company, LLC)
2409 Plantside Dr
Louisville, KY 40299-2527
Mailing Address:
PO Box 99585
Jeffersontown, KY 40269-0585
Tel.: (502) 499-5835
Fax: (502) 491-2215
Toll Free: (800) 626-1126
E-mail: info@rev-a-shelf.com
Web Site: www.rev-a-shelf.com
Sales Range: $25-49.9 Million
Approx. Number Employees: 155
Business Description:
Storage Organizing Products Mfr
S.I.C.: 3429
N.A.I.C.S.: 332510
Advertising Expenditures: $12,000,000
Media: 2-6-8-10-16-19
Distr.: Intl.; Natl.
Personnel:
David P. Noe *(Gen Mgr)*
Rob Jenkins *(Dir-Mktg & Consumer Sls)*
Shari McPeek *(Mgr-Mktg)*
Brands & Products:
ARTISAN COLLECTION
RAS
RAS HOME OFFICE
TOT-LOK
WOOD CLASSICS

RICHCO, INC.
8145 River Dr
Morton Grove, IL 60053
Tel.: (773) 539-4060
Fax: (773) 539-6770
Toll Free: (800) 466-8301
E-mail: customerservice@richco-inc.com
Web Site: www.richco-inc.com
Approx. Number Employees: 300
Year Founded: 1954
Business Description:
Plastic Installation Hardware Mfr
S.I.C.: 3089; 3496
N.A.I.C.S.: 326199; 332618
Import Export
Media: 2-4-10
Distr.: Intl.; Natl.; Reg.
Personnel:
Samantha Richardson *(Owner & Chm)*
Jim Fegen *(Vice Chm)*
Rick Streicher *(Pres & CEO)*
Steve Poulsen *(VP-Fin)*
Bob Reisel *(VP-Tech)*
Diane Vleck *(VP-HR)*
David Decker *(Dir-Worldwide Mfg)*
Cheryl Cummins *(Sr Mgr-Product)*
Brands & Products:
GLOBAL PRESENCE WITH LOCAL SUPPORT!
RICHCO

RICHELIEU HARDWARE LTD.
7900 W Henri Bourassa Blvd
Ville Saint Laurent, QC H4S 1V4, Canada
Tel.: (051) 433-64144
Fax: (051) 433-66896
Fax: (514) 832-4002
Toll Free: (800) 619-5446 (in US)
Toll Free: (800) 361-6000 (in Canada)
E-mail: info@richelieu.com
Web Site: www.richelieu.com
Approx. Sls.: $455,374,844
Approx. Number Employees: 1,500
Business Description:
Veneer Sheets & Edgebanding Products Mfr, Panels & Specialty Boards Distr & Importer of Specialty Hardware
S.I.C.: 2435; 3429
N.A.I.C.S.: 321211; 332510
Media: 2-4-7-8-10-13
Personnel:
Robert Chevrier *(Chm)*
Richard Lord *(Pres & CEO)*
Alain Giasson *(CFO & VP)*
Normand Guindon *(VP & Gen Mgr-Ops)*
Guy Grenier *(VP-Sls & Mktg-Indus Hardware)*
Christian Ladouceur *(VP-Sls & Mktg-Hardware)*
Eric Daignault *(Gen Mgr)*
Marion Kloibhofer *(Gen Mgr-Central Canada)*
John Statton *(Gen Mgr-Western Canada)*
Charles White *(Gen Mgr-USA)*
Christian Dion *(Mgr-HR)*
Genevieve Quevillon *(Mgr-Supply Chain & Logistics)*

ROBERT BOSCH TOOL CORP
(Sub. of Robert Bosch GmbH Power Tools Division)
1800 W Central Rd
Mount Prospect, IL 60056
Tel.: (224) 232-2000
Fax: (224) 232-3169
Web Site: www.bosch.us/content/language1/html/955.htm
Approx. Number Employees: 4,000
Year Founded: 1924
Business Description:
Power Tools Mfr
S.I.C.: 3546; 3545

Key to Media (For complete agency information see *The Advertising Red Books-Agencies* edition):
1. Bus. Publs. 2. Cable T.V. 3. Catalogs & Directories. 4. Co-op Adv. 5. Consumer Mags. 6. D.M. to Bus. Estab.7. D.M. to Consumers 8. Daily Newsp. 9. Exhibits/Trade Shows 10. Foreign 11. Infomercial 12. Internet Adv.13. Multimedia 14. Network Radio 15. Network T.V. 16. Newsp. Distr. Mags. 17. Other 18. Outdoor (Posters, Transit) 19. Point of Purchase20. Premiums, Novelties 21. Product Samples 22. Special Events Mktg. 23. Spot Radio 24. Spot T.V. 25. Weekly Newsp. 26. Yellow Page Adv.

Robert Bosch Tool Corp — (Continued)

N.A.I.C.S.: 333991; 333515
Advertising Expenditures: $1,000,000
Media: 2-3-4-5-6-9-10-15-19-20-24
Personnel:
Manfred Seitz *(Chm, Pres & CEO)*
John Surane *(Pres-Skil Power Tool)*
Gregg Mangialardi *(Product Mgr-Skilsaws)*
Georgia Mitchell *(Mgr-PR & Internal Comm)*
Brands & Products:
SKIL
SKILSAW
Advertising Agencies:
Cramer-Krasselt
246 E Chicago St
Milwaukee, WI 53202
Tel.: (414) 227-3500
Fax: (414) 276-8710
Creative
Media Buying
Media Planning
SKIL Power Tools Agency of Record

Fountainhead Communications
817 Elm St #206
Winnetka, IL 60093
Tel.: (847) 446-2244

JSH&A Public Relations
2 TransAm Plz Dr Ste 450
Oakbrook Terrace, IL 60181
Tel.: (630) 932-4242
Fax: (630) 932-1418
Skil Power Tools
Traditional & Social Media

ROBINSON HOME PRODUCTS INC.
2615 Walden Ave
Buffalo, NY 14225-0550
Tel.: (716) 685-6300
Fax: (716) 685-4916
E-mail: customerservice@robinsonus.com
Web Site: www.robinsonus.com
E-Mail For Key Personnel:
Sales Director: sales@robinsonusa.com
Approx. Number Employees: 50
Year Founded: 1921
Business Description:
Scissors, Shears & Travel Accessories Wholesale Distr
S.I.C.: 5023
N.A.I.C.S.: 423220
Media: 2-4-6-9-23
Distr.: Natl.
Personnel:
Jim Walsh *(Pres)*
John Fancher *(CFO)*
Brands & Products:
AMERICA COOKS
CHIP CLIP
NEON

ROCKY MOUNTAIN HARDWARE INC.
1030 Airport Way
Hailey, ID 83333
Mailing Address:
PO Box 4108
Hailey, ID 83333
Tel.: (208) 788-2013
Fax: (208) 788-2577
Toll Free: (888) 788-2013
E-mail: info@rockymountainhardware.com
Web Site: www.rockymountainhardware.com
Approx. Sls.: $25,000,000
Approx. Number Employees: 75
Business Description:
Furniture & Other Household Hardware Mfr
S.I.C.: 3429
N.A.I.C.S.: 332510
Media: 2-4-6-10
Personnel:
Mark Nickum *(Owner)*
Christine Kirby *(Dir-Mktg)*
Brands & Products:
ROCKY MOUNTAIN
ROCKY MOUNTAIN HARDWARE

ROGERS TOOL WORKS, INC.
(Sub. of Kennametal Advanced Materials Solutions Group)
(d/b/a Kennametal)
205 N 13th St
Rogers, AR 72756-3551
Mailing Address:
PO Box 9
Rogers, AR 72757-0009
Tel.: (479) 636-1515
Fax: (479) 636-7638
E-mail: us.rtwsupport@kennametal.com
Web Site: www.rtwcarbide.com
Sales Range: $25-49.9 Million
Approx. Number Employees: 60
Year Founded: 1952
Business Description:
Carbide & Carbide Tipped Cutting Tools Mfr
S.I.C.: 3545; 3532
N.A.I.C.S.: 333515; 333131
Advertising Expenditures: $500,000
Media: 2-4-7-10
Distr.: Intl.; Natl.
Budget Set: Jan.

ROHL LLC
3 Parker
Irvine, CA 92618
Tel.: (714) 557-1933
Fax: (714) 557-8635
Toll Free: (800) 777-9762
E-mail: rohlinfo@rohlhome.com
Web Site: www.rohlhome.com
Approx. Sls.: $8,500,000
Approx. Number Employees: 40
Year Founded: 1982
Business Description:
Luxury Faucets for Kitchen & Bath Mfr & Distr
S.I.C.: 5074
N.A.I.C.S.: 423720
Media: 2-6-10
Personnel:
Kenneth S. Rohl *(Owner)*
Paul Satkin *(CFO)*
Greg Rohl *(Pres-Western Div)*
Skip Johnson *(VP-Mktg)*
Brands & Products:
AUTHENTIC LUXURY FOR KITCHEN AND BATH
CISAL
THE EXPERIENCE OF AUTHENTIC LUXURY
MICHAEL BERMAN
PERRIN & ROWE
ROHL
VINCENT

ROMAC INDUSTRIES, INC.
21919 20th Ave SE Ste 100
Bothell, WA 98021-4446
Tel.: (425) 951-6200
Fax: (425) 951-6201
Toll Free: (800) 426-9341
E-mail: sales@romacindustries.com
Web Site: www.romac.com
E-Mail For Key Personnel:
Sales Director: sales@romacindustries.com
Approx. Number Employees: 230
Year Founded: 1969
Business Description:
Mfr of Pipe Fittings; Valves & Tools for the Water Works Industry
S.I.C.: 3494; 3541
N.A.I.C.S.: 332919; 333512
Export
Media: 1-2-4-7-10-13-16
Distr.: Natl.
Personnel:
James J. Larkin *(Pres)*
James M. Treinen *(CFO)*
Brands & Products:
B-TOO
FLEXIJOINT
GRIPRING
INSERTAVALVE
QUICKVALVE
RIDGID
ROMAGRIP
SEAL
TAPMATE

RYOBI TECHNOLOGIES, INC.
(Sub. of Techtronic Industries Co., Ltd.)
1428 Pearman Dairy Rd
Anderson, SC 29625-2000
Mailing Address:
PO Box 1207
Anderson, SC 29622-1207
Tel.: (864) 226-6511
Fax: (864) 261-9435
Toll Free: (800) 323-4615
Web Site: www.tti.com
Approx. Number Employees: 500
Year Founded: 1988
Business Description:
Power Tools & Vacuum Cleaners Distr
S.I.C.: 5251; 5085
N.A.I.C.S.: 444130; 423840
Import Export
Advertising Expenditures: $400,000
Media: 2-5-6-10-13-19-21
Distr.: Natl.
Budget Set: July
Personnel:
Adrian Gutierrez *(Mgr-Multicultural Mktg)*
Brian Stearns *(Mgr-Mktg)*
Brands & Products:
CRAFTSMAN
PRO FEATURES. AFFORDABLE PRICES.
Advertising Agency:
IMRE
909 Ridgebrook Rd Ste 300
Baltimore, MD 21152
Tel.: (410) 821-8220
Fax: (410) 821-5619

SANYO ENERGY (U.S.A.) CORPORATION
(Sub. of Sanyo Electric Co., Ltd.)
2055 Sanyo Ave
San Diego, CA 92154-6297
Tel.: (619) 661-4888
Fax: (619) 661-6743
Web Site: www.sanyo.com
Approx. Number Employees: 150
Year Founded: 1987
Business Description:
Mfr. & Sales of Dry Cell & Rechargable Batteries
S.I.C.: 3692; 5999
N.A.I.C.S.: 335912; 453998
Media: 4-5-10-13-19-22
Brands & Products:
DOMECHARGER
GE/SANYO
OMNICHARGER
OMNIPACK
RECHARGACELL
Advertising Agency:
Quantum Communications
221 Pawnee St.
San Marcos, CA 92069
Tel.: (760) 736-7045
Fax: (760) 736-7051
(OEM)

SARGENT & GREENLEAF, INC.
(Sub. of Stanley Security Solutions, Inc.)
1 Security Dr
Nicholasville, KY 40356-2159
Mailing Address:
PO Box 930
Nicholasville, KY 40340-0930
Tel.: (859) 885-9411
Fax: (859) 885-3063
Toll Free: (800) 826-7652
Web Site: www.sglocks.com
Sales Range: $50-74.9 Million
Approx. Number Employees: 130
Year Founded: 1857
Business Description:
Mechanical & Electronic Locks Mfr
S.I.C.: 3429
N.A.I.C.S.: 332510
Media: 1-2-4-7-10-20
Distr.: Intl.; Natl.
Budget Set: Sept.
Personnel:
Bill Dempsey *(Pres & COO)*
Phil Pitt *(Dir-Mktg)*
Brands & Products:
ADJUSTA-LOCK
BRUTE
CENTI-SPLINE
MP LOCKS
SPY-PROOF
TIMEBINATION
Advertising Agency:
Strata-G Communications
830 Main St 10th Fl
Cincinnati, OH 45202
Tel.: (513) 381-8855
Fax: (513) 381-0385
Toll Free: (800) 540-6986
(Locks and Security Systems)

SARGENT MANUFACTURING COMPANY
(Sub. of McKinney Products Company)
100 Sargent Dr
New Haven, CT 06511-5918
Mailing Address:
PO Box 9725
New Haven, CT 06536-0915
Tel.: (203) 562-2151
Fax: (203) 776-5992
Fax: (888) 863-5054

Key to Media (For complete agency information see *The Advertising Red Books-Agencies* edition):
1. Bus. Publs. 2. Cable T.V. 3. Catalogs & Directories. 4. Co-op Adv. 5. Consumer Mags. 6. D.M. to Bus. Estab.7. D.M. to Consumers 8. Daily Newsp. 9. Exhibits/Trade Shows 10. Foreign 11. Infomercial 12. Internet Adv.13. Multimedia 14. Network Radio 15. Network T.V. 16. Newsp. Distr. Mags. 17. Other 18. Outdoor (Posters, Transit) 19. Point of Purchase20. Premiums, Novelties 21. Product Samples 22. Special Events Mktg. 23. Spot Radio 24. Spot T.V. 25. Weekly Newsp. 26. Yellow Page Adv.

E-mail: webmaster@sargentlock.com
Web Site: www.sargentlock.com
Approx. Number Employees: 900
Year Founded: 1864
Business Description:
Mfr of High Quality Architectural Hardware, Locks, Door Closers & Exit Devices
S.I.C.: 3429
N.A.I.C.S.: 332510
Import Export
Advertising Expenditures: $400,000
Media: 1-2-4-10-20-21
Distr.: Intl.; Natl.
Budget Set: Oct.
Personnel:
Thanasis Molokotos *(Pres)*
Dave Ambrosini *(CFO)*
Al Leites *(Gen Mgr-Systems)*
D. Ortiz *(Mgr-Adv Production)*
Brands & Products:
SARGENT

SCHILLER-PFEIFFER, INC.
1028 St Rd
Southampton, PA 18966-4227
Tel.: (215) 357-5110
Fax: (215) 357-1071
Web Site: www.littlewonder.com
Approx. Number Employees: 125
Year Founded: 1935
Business Description:
Mfr. & Marketer of Lawn & Garden Power Equipment
S.I.C.: 3524; 5083
N.A.I.C.S.: 333112; 423820
Import Export
Advertising Expenditures: $200,000
Media: 2-3-5-6-7-8-9-10-13-19-21-22-25
Distr.: Natl.
Budget Set: Nov.
Personnel:
Pat Cappuci *(Pres & COO)*
Howard Kaplan *(Dir-Mktg Svcs)*
Steve Lepera *(Dir-Sls & Mktg-Mantis)*
Linda Beattie *(Mgr-Mktg & PR)*
Brands & Products:
LITTLE WONDER
MANTIS
PROFESSIONALS DEMAND LITTLE WONDER. SHOULDN'T YOU?

SCHLAGE LOCK COMPANY
(Div. of Ingersoll-Rand Security Technologies)
11819 N Pennsylvania St
Carmel, IN 46032
Tel.: (317) 810-3700
E-mail: info@schlage.com
Web Site: www.schlage.com
Approx. Number Employees: 2,712
Business Description:
Locks & Door Hardware Mfr
S.I.C.: 3429; 2542; 3452; 3494; 3499; 3536; 3714
N.A.I.C.S.: 332510; 332439; 332722; 332919; 333923; 336399; 337215
Media: 2-4-5-6-7-10-11-19-23-24
Distr.: Intl.; Natl.
Budget Set: Oct.
Personnel:
Chris Casazza *(VP-Exits, Closers & Doors)*
Henry Lardie *(Mgr-Mktg)*

THE SCOTT FETZER COMPANY
(Sub. of BHSF, Inc.)
28800 Clemens Rd
Westlake, OH 44145-1197
Tel.: (440) 892-3000
Fax: (440) 892-3060
Sales Range: $1-4.9 Billion
Approx. Number Employees: 4,889
Year Founded: 1914
Business Description:
Consumer & Commercial Appliances Mfr
S.I.C.: 3563; 2731; 3621; 3635; 3711; 5162
N.A.I.C.S.: 333912; 335212; 335312; 336120; 424610; 511130
Advertising Expenditures: $3,217,050
Media: 2-8-20-21
Distr.: Direct to Consumer; Natl.
Budget Set: Nov.
Personnel:
Kenneth J. Semelsberger *(Chm)*
Robert McBride *(Pres & CEO)*
William Stephens *(CFO, Treas & VP)*
Vince Nardy *(COO & Dir-Merger & Acq)*
Brands & Products:
CLEVELAND WOOD PRODUCTS
CWP
MERIAM
SCOT LABORATORIES
SFZ
STAHL
SUPER PAL
UCFS
WAYNE
WBFI
WESTERN ENTERPRISES

SENECA WIRE & MANUFACTURING COMPANY
319 S Vine St
Fostoria, OH 44830-1843
Tel.: (419) 435-9261
Fax: (419) 435-9265
Toll Free: (800) 537-9537
E-mail: info@senecawire.com
Web Site: www.senecawire.com
Approx. Number Employees: 300
Year Founded: 1905
Business Description:
Mfr of Steel Wire, Industrial & Insect Screening
S.I.C.: 3315; 3355
N.A.I.C.S.: 331222; 331319
Import Export
Media: 2-4-7-10-11-13
Distr.: Intl.; Natl.
Budget Set: May -June
Personnel:
Steve Wray *(Pres)*
Kevin Shumaker *(CFO & VP)*
Doug Stearns *(VP-Sls & Mktg)*
Brands & Products:
SENECA WIRE
SSW

SETCO SALES COMPANY
(Sub. of Holden Industries, Inc.)
5880 Hillside Ave
Cincinnati, OH 45233-1524
Tel.: (513) 941-5110
Fax: (513) 941-6913
Toll Free: (800) 543-0470
E-mail: sales@setcousa.com
Web Site: www.setcousa.com
E-Mail For Key Personnel:
Sales Director: sales@setcousa.com
Sales Range: $900-999.9 Million
Approx. Number Employees: 75
Year Founded: 1912
Business Description:
Mfr of Machine Tool Components, Spindles & Slides
S.I.C.: 3541; 5084
N.A.I.C.S.: 333512; 423830
Export
Advertising Expenditures: $380,000
Multimedia: $25,000; Bus. Publs.: $100,000; Catalogs & Directories: $100,000; Co-op Adv.: $10,000; D.M. to Bus. Estab.: $10,000; D.M. to Consumers: $5,000; Exhibits/Trade Shows: $100,000; Internet Adv.: $10,000; Product Samples: $5,000; Special Events Mktg.: $15,000
Distr.: Natl.
Personnel:
Jeff Clark *(Pres)*
Craig Rath *(CFO)*
Eric Bilodeau *(CIO)*
Dominic Iannarino *(Mgr-Acctg)*
Gary Renner *(Mgr-Mktg)*
Brands & Products:
AIRSHIELD
FLEXCENTER
GOLD LINE
MASTER
MCS
POPE
PROMETRIX
SENTRY
SETCO
TCT GOLD LINE
WHITNON

SFS INTEC, INC.
(Sub. of SFS Holding AG)
Spring St & Van Reed Rd
Wyomissing, PA 19610
Mailing Address:
PO Box 6326
Wyomissing, PA 19610-0326
Tel.: (610) 376-5751
Fax: (610) 376-8551
Toll Free: (800) 234-4533
Web Site:
www.constructionfasteners.com
Approx. Rev.: $100,000,000
Approx. Number Employees: 200
Year Founded: 1956
Business Description:
Bolts, Nuts, Rivets & Washers
S.I.C.: 3452
N.A.I.C.S.: 332722
Import Export
Media: 10
Personnel:
Michael A. Mullen *(Pres)*
David J. Hebert *(VP-Sls & Mktg-Automotive/Indus Products)*
Tom Van Kirk *(VP-Sls & Mktg)*
Scott Carpenter *(Dir-Sls-Flat Roof Products)*
Scott Hutchings *(Dir-Sls-Building Fasteners)*
Ken Deck *(Reg Mgr-Sls-Southeast)*
Joel Farley *(Reg Mgr-Indus Products)*
Bill Jones *(Reg Mgr-Sls-Southwest)*
Roy Bieber *(Mgr-Bus Dev)*
Jeff Bornschlegl *(Mgr-Sls-Midwest-District)*
Donn Couch *(Mgr-Sls-Southeast-District)*
Bob Lammers *(Mgr-Sls)*
Ted Maack *(Mgr-Northeast-District)*
Brands & Products:
DEKFAST
EXTRUDE-TITE
IMPAX
REMFORM
TAPTITE
TIMBERWORK
WEATHERGARD
WOODGRIP
ZAC

THE SHELBURNE CORPORATION
6221 Shelburne Rd
Shelburne, VT 05482
Mailing Address:
PO Box 158
Shelburne, VT 05482-0307
Tel.: (802) 985-3321
Fax: (802) 985-2233
Approx. Number Employees: 150
Year Founded: 1950
Business Description:
Builders & Replacement Hardware, Ski Racks, Poles & Products Mfr
S.I.C.: 3469
N.A.I.C.S.: 332116
Media: 2-3-4-6-10-19
Distr.: Natl.
Budget Set: Various
Personnel:
Mark H. Snelling *(Pres)*
Brands & Products:
HUSKY

SHERMAN & REILLY, INC.
400 W 33rd St
Chattanooga, TN 37410-1039
Mailing Address:
PO Box 11267
Chattanooga, TN 37401
Tel.: (423) 756-5300
Fax: (423) 756-2947
Toll Free: (800) 251-7780
E-mail: sales@sherman-reilly.com
Web Site: www.sherman-reilly.com
E-Mail For Key Personnel:
Sales Director: sales@sherman-reilly.com
Approx. Number Employees: 85
Year Founded: 1927
Business Description:
Mfr. of Overhead & Underground Electrical Power Lines, Equipment, Tools & Hardware, Deployment of Fiber-Optic Telecommunication Cables
S.I.C.: 3644
N.A.I.C.S.: 335932
Export
Media: 2-4-7-10-11-13-17
Distr.: Intl.; Natl.
Personnel:
James W. Reilly *(Chm & CEO)*
Robert E. Orr *(VP)*
Brands & Products:
CABLEJET
FIGARINO
FIGARO
FIGARONE
HYDRAULIC DAWG UDH-70-T
HYDRAULIC SUPERJET
PNEUMATIC SUPERJET
XS-100-B

Key to Media (For complete agency information see *The Advertising Red Books-Agencies* edition):
1. Bus. Publs. 2. Cable T.V. 3. Catalogs & Directories. 4. Co-op Adv. 5. Consumer Mags. 6. D.M. to Bus. Estab.7. D.M. to Consumers 8. Daily Newsp. 9. Exhibits/Trade Shows 10. Foreign 11. Infomercial 12. Internet Adv.13. Multimedia 14. Network Radio 15. Network T.V. 16. Newsp. Distr. Mags. 17. Other 18. Outdoor (Posters, Transit) 19. Point of Purchase20. Premiums, Novelties 21. Product Samples 22. Special Events Mktg. 23. Spot Radio 24. Spot T.V. 25. Weekly Newsp. 26. Yellow Page Adv.

SIGMUND COHN CORP.

121 S Columbus Ave
Mount Vernon, NY 10553
Tel.: (914) 664-5300
Fax: (914) 664-5377
E-mail: info@sigmundcohn.com
Web Site: www.sigmundcohn.com
Approx. Number Employees: 90
Year Founded: 1901
Business Description:
Precision Metals Mfr
S.I.C.: 3356; 3496
N.A.I.C.S.: 331491; 332618
Media: 2-7-10
Distr.: Natl.
Budget Set: Jan.
Personnel:
Thomas Cohn *(Pres)*
Mike O'Shaughnessy *(Product Mgr)*

Brands & Products:
MEDWIRE
PT 385
PYROFUZE
SIGMUND COHN

SIMPSON STRONG-TIE (QUIK DRIVE FACTORY)

(Plant of Simpson Strong-Tie Co., Inc.)
375 N Veldere
Gallatin, TN 37066
Tel.: (615) 230-8788
Fax: (615) 451-9806
Toll Free: (888) 487-7845
E-mail: info@quickdrive.com
Web Site: www.quikdrive.com
Sales Range: $25-49.9 Million
Approx. Number Employees: 100
Business Description:
Fasteners & Auto-feed Fastener Driving Systems Mfr
S.I.C.: 3965
N.A.I.C.S.: 339993
Media: 10

SIOUX TOOLS, INC.

(Sub. of Snap-on Tools)
250 Snap On Dr
Murphy, NC 28906
Tel.: (828) 835-9765
Fax: (828) 835-9685
Toll Free: (800) 722-7290
E-mail: siouxtoolstechsupport@snapon.com
Web Site: www.siouxtools.com
Sales Range: $50-74.9 Million
Approx. Number Employees: 200
Year Founded: 1914
Business Description:
Mfr. of Portable Air, Electric & Cordless Power Tools; Valve & Valve Seat Reconditioning Equipment
S.I.C.: 5072
N.A.I.C.S.: 423710
Import Export
Media: 2-4-10
Distr.: Intl.; Natl.
Personnel:
Brian Spikes *(Gen Mgr)*

Brands & Products:
SIOUX TOOLS

Advertising Agency:
Rock Solid Inc.
705 Douglas St #238
Sioux City, IA 51101
Tel.: (712) 293-0126

SK HAND TOOL CORPORATION

3535 W 47th St
Chicago, IL 60632
Tel.: (708) 485-4574
Fax: (800) 752-2434
Toll Free: (800) 752-7263
E-mail: marketing@skhandtool.com
Web Site: www.skhandtool.com
Approx. Number Employees: 350
Year Founded: 1921
Business Description:
Hand Tools Designer & Mfr
S.I.C.: 3423
N.A.I.C.S.: 332212
Import Export
Advertising Expenditures: $250,000
Media: 1-2-4-7-10-11-19-20-21
Distr.: Intl.; Natl.
Budget Set: Sept.
Personnel:
Claude Fuger *(Pres & CEO)*
Leonard D. O'Connell *(VP-HR)*
Karen Medina *(Mgr-Export Sls)*

Brands & Products:
FACOM
MICRO TECH
OGV
PROFESSIONAL
S-K
S K SUPERSETS
SUPERKROME
SUPERSETS
SUREGRIP
TUFF 1
VSE 1000 VOLT

SLOAN VALVE COMPANY

10500 Seymour Ave
Franklin Park, IL 60131
Tel.: (847) 671-4300
Fax: (847) 671-6944
Toll Free: (800) 9VALVE9
E-mail: info.411@sloanvalve.com
Web Site: www.sloanvalve.com
E-Mail For Key Personnel:
Marketing Director: skennedy@sloanvalve.com
Sales Range: $125-149.9 Million
Approx. Number Employees: 750
Year Founded: 1906
Business Description:
Plumbing Systems, Hand Dryers, Wall Paneling, Vacuum Breakers & Non-Ferrous Brass Coatings Mfr & Whslr
S.I.C.: 3494; 3261
N.A.I.C.S.: 332919; 327111
Import Export
Media: 2-10
Distr.: Intl.; Natl.
Budget Set: Nov. -Dec.
Personnel:
Charles S. Allen *(Pres & CEO)*
Steve Connaughton *(Mgr-Product Line)*

Brands & Products:
ACT-O-MATIC
AQUS
CONTINENTAL
CROWN
CROWN II
DOLPHIN
EASY ACCESS
G2 OPTIMA PLUS
GEM
HEALTHMINDER
HYDRAULIC REGAL
LUMINO
MICROPLUMB
NAVAL
NAVAL OPTIMA SMO
OPTIMA
OPTIMA PLUS
OPTIMA ROYAL
OPTIMA ROYAL II
OPTISHIELD
PERMEX
POLARIS
PRISON
REGAL
REGAL OPTIMA SMO
REGAL PRO
REGAL PRO OPTIMA
REGAL PRO OPTIMA SMO
REVIT
ROYAL
ROYAL G2 OPTIMA PLUS
ROYAL HYDRAULIC
ROYAL HYDRAULIC PRISON
ROYAL II
ROYAL OPTIMA
ROYAL OPTIMA SMO
ROYAL PRISON
ROYAL PRISON REGAL
ROYAL SLIMLINE HYDRAULIC
SLIMLINE
SLIMLINE OPTIMA PLUS
SLOAN
SLOAN OPTIMA
SLOAN STONE
SLOANSTONE
SMOOTH
SOLIS
TRIM PLATE
XLERATOR

Advertising Agency:
Interline Creative Group, Inc
553 North Court, Ste. 160
Palatine, IL 60067
Tel.: (847) 358-4848
(Sloan Royal Regal, Showerheads & Optima Product Lines)

SNAP-ON INCORPORATED

2801 80th St
Kenosha, WI 53143
Mailing Address:
PO Box 1410
Kenosha, WI 53141-1410
Tel.: (262) 656-5200
Fax: (262) 656-5577
Web Site: www.snapon.com
E-Mail For Key Personnel:
Public Relations: public.relations@snapon.com
Approx. Sls.: $2,619,200,000
Approx. Number Employees: 11,300
Year Founded: 1920
Business Description:
Hand & Power Tools, Diagnostics & Shop Equipment & Tool Storage Units Mfr, Developer & Whslr
S.I.C.: 5072; 3423; 3546
N.A.I.C.S.: 423710; 332212; 333991
Import Export
Advertising Expenditures: $41,100,000
Media: 1-2-4-6-8-10-11-18-19-20-22
Distr.: Intl.; Natl.
Budget Set: Oct.
Personnel:
Nicholas T. Pinchuk *(Chm, Pres & CEO)*
Thomas L. Kassouf *(Pres & Sr VP)*
Aldo J. Pagliari *(CFO & Sr VP-Fin)*
Jeanne M. Moreno *(CIO & VP)*
Thomas J. Ward *(Pres-Repair Sys, Info Grp & Sr VP)*
Anup Banerjee *(Pres-Comml Grp)*
Donald E. Broman *(Pres-Indul Worldwide)*
Richard V. Caskey *(Pres-Mdse Products)*
Tim Chambers *(Pres-Snap-on Bus & Equipment Solutions)*
Michael Gentile *(Pres-Hand Tools)*
Andrew R. Ginger *(Pres-Indus)*
Barrie Young *(Pres-Sls & Franchising)*
Eugenio Amador *(VP & Gen Mgr-SNA Europe)*
David E. Cox *(VP-Equipment Sls)*

Brands & Products:
ATI
BLACKHAWK
BLUE POINT
BREWCO
CDI
DIESELKARE
ELECTROTORK
ETHOS
FISH & HOOK
FLANK DRIVE
HEIN-WERNER
HOFMANN
IRIMO
JOHN BEAN
LINDSTROM
MITCHELL REPAIR
MODIS
PALMERA
PRADINES
SANDFLEX
SCANBAY
SHOPKEY
SIOUX
SNAP-LINK
SNAP-ON
SOLUS
SOLUS PRO
SUNPRO
TECH
TRANSMISSION TROUBLESHOOTER
VANTAGE
VANTAGE PRO
VERUS
WHEELTRONIC
WILLIAMS

Advertising Agencies:
Design North, Inc.
8007 Douglas Ave
Racine, WI 53402
Tel.: (262) 639-2080
Tel.: (262) 898-1090
Fax: (262) 639-5230
Toll Free: (800) 247-8494

Group 4
147 Simsbury Rd
Avon, CT 06001
Tel.: (860) 678-1570
Fax: (860) 678-0783

Tempo Creative, Inc.
15955 N Dial Blvd Ste 1B
Scottsdale, AZ 85260
Tel.: (480) 659-4100
Fax: (480) 659-9180

SNAP-ON TOOLS

(Div. of Snap-on Incorporated)
2801 80th St

Key to Media (For complete agency information see *The Advertising Red Books-Agencies* edition):
1. Bus. Publs. 2. Cable T.V. 3. Catalogs & Directories. 4. Co-op Adv. 5. Consumer Mags. 6. D.M. to Bus. Estab.7. D.M. to Consumers 8. Daily Newsp. 9. Exhibits/Trade Shows 10. Foreign 11. Infomercial 12. Internet Adv.13. Multimedia 14. Network Radio 15. Network T.V. 16. Newsp. Distr. Mags. 17. Other 18. Outdoor (Posters, Transit) 19. Point of Purchase20. Premiums, Novelties 21. Product Samples 22. Special Events Mktg. 23. Spot Radio 24. Spot T.V. 25. Weekly Newsp. 26. Yellow Page Adv.

Kenosha, WI 53143-5656
Tel.: (262) 656-5200
Fax: (262) 656-5577
Web Site: www.snapon.com/international/exportsales.asp
Sales Range: $150-199.9 Million
Business Description:
Provides Tools & Equipment to Automotive Technicians & Shop Owners
S.I.C.: 3423; 3546
N.A.I.C.S.: 332212; 333991
Personnel:
Blaine A. Metzger *(Sr VP-Fin & Acctg)*
Nicholas Loffredo *(VP-Sls)*
Advertising Agency:
Design North, Inc.
8007 Douglas Ave
Racine, WI 53402
Tel.: (262) 639-2080
Tel.: (262) 898-1090
Fax: (262) 639-5230
Toll Free: (800) 247-8494

SNAPPER, INC.
(Div. of Simplicity Manufacturing, Inc.)
535 Macon St
McDonough, GA 30253
Tel.: (770) 954-2500
Fax: (770) 954-2533
E-mail: info@snapper.com
Web Site: www.snapper.com
Sales Range: $200-249.9 Million
Approx. Number Employees: 600
Year Founded: 1951
Business Description:
Lawn & Garden Equipment Mfr
S.I.C.: 3524; 3537
N.A.I.C.S.: 333112; 333924
Export
Advertising Expenditures: $8,000,000
Media: 1-2-3-4-5-7-9-10-14-15-16-18-19-20-23-24-25-26
Personnel:
Shane Sumners *(Pres)*
Brands & Products:
SNAPPER

SNYDER-DIAMOND
1399 Olympic Blvd
Santa Monica, CA 90404-3730
Tel.: (310) 450-1000
Fax: (310) 452-7259
E-mail: diamond@snyderdiamond.com
Web Site: www.snyderdiamond.com
Sales Range: $10-24.9 Million
Approx. Number Employees: 110
Year Founded: 1949
Business Description:
Plumbing Fixtures & Supplies, Appliances, Decorative Hardware & Kitchen Appliances Sales
S.I.C.: 5999; 5722
N.A.I.C.S.: 453998; 443111
Import
Media: 4-8
Personnel:
Russell Diamond *(Pres & COO)*
Patricia Limon *(CFO)*
Advertising Agency:
Fry Communications Inc.
800 W Church Rd
Mechanicsburg, PA 17055-3179
Tel.: (717) 766-0211
Fax: (717) 691-0341
Toll Free: (800) 334-1429
Marketing Agency

SODISCO-HOWDEN GROUP, INC.
(Sub. of CanWel Building Materials Ltd.)
465 McGill Street 8th Floor
Montreal, QC H2Y 2H4, Canada
Tel.: (514) 286-8986
Fax: (514) 286-2911
Approx. Number Employees: 500
Year Founded: 1882
Business Description:
Hardware & Home Renovation Products Distr
S.I.C.: 1531
N.A.I.C.S.: 236118
Media: 7

SOLIDSCAPE, INC.
(Sub. of Stratasys, Inc.)
316 Daniel Webster Hwy
Merrimack, NH 03054
Tel.: (603) 429-9700
Fax: (603) 424-1850
E-mail: precision@solid-scape.com
Web Site: www.solid-scape.com
Business Description:
Modelmaking Hardware & Software Mfr
S.I.C.: 3429
N.A.I.C.S.: 332510
Media: 10
Personnel:
Michael Varanka *(Pres & COO)*
David Bothwell *(CEO)*

SOUTHCO, INC.
210 N Brinton Lk Rd
Concordville, PA 19331
Tel.: (610) 459-4000
Fax: (610) 459-4012
E-mail: info@southco.com
Web Site: www.southco.com
Approx. Number Employees: 1,500
Year Founded: 1899
Business Description:
Latching Systems & Hardware Mfr. & Designer
S.I.C.: 3965
N.A.I.C.S.: 339993
Import Export
Media: 2-4-7-10-20-21
Personnel:
Brian McNeill *(Pres & CEO)*
Michael McPhilmy *(VP-HR)*
Brands & Products:
CLICK
DOORKEEPERS
FLUSH
GRABBER
LIFT AND TURN
LINK LOCK
MCCOY
MOBELLA
NEW VISE ACTION
NOVIBRA
OFFSHORE
OMNI
OMNI POCKET
PARROT
PIN LATCH
ROTO LOCK
SECURE
SNAPPY
SOUTHCO
STRIKERS
SUNDECKER
TALON
VERSA-LATCH
VISE ACTION

SOUTHERN FOLGER DETENTION EQUIPMENT COMPANY
(Sub. of Phelps Tointon Inc.)
4634 S Presa St PO Box 2021
San Antonio, TX 78223
Tel.: (210) 240-3086
Fax: (210) 533-2211
Toll Free: (800) 966-6739
Web Site: www.southernfolger.com
Approx. Number Employees: 170
Year Founded: 1905
Business Description:
Prison Locks & Hardware Installers
S.I.C.: 3429
N.A.I.C.S.: 332510
Export
Media: 2-4-6-7-9-10-20-21
Personnel:
Don Halloran *(Pres)*

SOUTHWIRE COMPANY
1 Southwire Dr
Carrollton, GA 30119
Mailing Address:
PO Box 1000
Carrollton, GA 30119-0002
Tel.: (770) 832-4242
Fax: (770) 832-4929
Toll Free: (800) 444-1700
E-mail: webmaster@southwire.com
Web Site: www.southwire.com
Approx. Number Employees: 4,180
Year Founded: 1950
Business Description:
Aluminum & Copper Electrical Wire & Cable Mfr
S.I.C.: 3355; 3351; 3357
N.A.I.C.S.: 331319; 331421; 331422
Export
Advertising Expenditures: $250,000
Media: 2-4-17
Personnel:
Roy Richards, Jr. *(Chm)*
Stuart Thorn *(Pres & CEO)*
J. Guyton Cochran *(CFO & Exec VP)*
Jack Carlson *(Pres-Electrical Div & Exec VP)*
Charlie Murrah *(Pres-Energy Div & Exec VP)*
Will Berry *(Pres-SCR Div & Sr VP)*
Stanley Tate *(Chief Environmental Officer, Gen Counsel & Exec VP)*
Jeff Herrin *(Exec VP-Ops)*
Michael Wiggins *(Exec VP-HR)*
Norman Adkins *(Sr VP-Sls Electrical Div)*
Vince Kruse *(Sr VP-R&D)*
Phil Tuggle *(Sr VP-Mktg, Bus Dev & Electrical Div)*
Gary Leftwich *(Dir-Corp Comm)*
Brands & Products:
ALFLEX
ARMORLITE
DATA-FLEX
DURACLAD
GALFLEX
GLO-PLUG
RED ALERT
ROMEX
SHOCK TRAP
SIMPULL
SLINKY-FLEX
SOUTHWIRE
SURESEAL
ULTRATITE
Advertising Agency:
Eric Mower and Associates
1001 Morehead Sq Dr 5th Fl
Charlotte, NC 28203
Tel.: (704) 375-0123
Fax: (704) 375-0222
Toll Free: (800) 968-0682

SPRAYING SYSTEMS CO.
N Ave at Schmale Rd
Wheaton, IL 60188
Mailing Address:
PO Box 7900
Wheaton, IL 60189-7900
Tel.: (630) 665-5000
Fax: (630) 260-0842
E-mail: info@spray.com
Web Site: www.spray.com
Approx. Number Employees: 1,000
Year Founded: 1937
Business Description:
Spray Nozzles & Spray Guns Mfr
S.I.C.: 5084
N.A.I.C.S.: 423830
Export
Media: 2-4-7-10-26
Distr.: Intl.; Natl.
Budget Set: Oct.
Personnel:
James E. Bramsen *(CEO)*
Frank Bramsen *(Dir-Indus Sls, Adv & Mktg-US)*
Brands & Products:
ACCUCOAT
AUTOJET
CASTERJET
CLIP-EYELET
CONEJET
DIRECTOVALVE
DISCJET
DISTRIBOJET
DRIP FREE
EXPERTS IN SPRAY TECHNOLOGY
FLATJET
FLOMAX
FLOODJET
FOGJET
FULLJET
GAST
GUNJET
HOLLOWJET
ISPRAY
MULTEEJET
PLASTIC FOAMJET
PROMAX
PULSAJET
QUICK TEEJET
QUICKJET
QUICKMIST
ROTOCLEAN
SNOWJET
SPIRALJET
SPRAYCHECK
SPRAYDRY
SPRAYING SYSTEMS CO
SPRAYLOGIC
SPRAYWARE
SPRIRALJET
STREAMJET
TEEJET
TEEVALVE
ULTRASTREAM
UNIJET
VEEJET
WASHJET

Key to Media (For complete agency information see *The Advertising Red Books-Agencies* edition):
1. Bus. Publs. 2. Cable T.V. 3. Catalogs & Directories. 4. Co-op Adv. 5. Consumer Mags. 6. D.M. to Bus. Estab.7. D.M. to Consumers
8. Daily Newsp. 9. Exhibits/Trade Shows 10. Foreign 11. Infomercial 12. Internet Adv.13. Multimedia 14. Network Radio
15. Network T.V. 16. Newsp. Distr. Mags. 17. Other 18. Outdoor (Posters, Transit) 19. Point of Purchase20. Premiums, Novelties
21. Product Samples 22. Special Events Mktg. 23. Spot Radio 24. Spot T.V. 25. Weekly Newsp. 26. Yellow Page Adv.

Spraying Systems Co. — (Continued)

WHIRLJET
WINDJET

STANLEY BLACK & DECKER, INC.

1000 Stanley Dr
New Britain, CT 06053
Tel.: (860) 225-5111
Tel.: (860) 827-3966
Fax: (860) 826-3213
Telex: 99289
Web Site:
www.stanleyblackanddecker.com/
Approx. Sls.: $8,409,600,000
Approx. Number Employees: 36,700
Year Founded: 1843
Business Description:
Industrial Hardware, Power & Hand Tools, Door Accessories, Garage Door Operating Equipment, Storage Systems, Fasteners, Hinges & Builders' Products Mfr & Distr
S.I.C.: 1791; 3423; 3429; 3546
N.A.I.C.S.: 238120; 332212; 332510; 333991
Advertising Expenditures: $120,700,000
Media: 2-4-5-6-7-8-9-10-11-13-15-16-17-18-20-21-22-23-24-25
Distr.: Natl.
Budget Set: Sept.
Personnel:
Nolan D. Archibald *(Chm)*
John F. Lundgren *(Pres & CEO)*
Donald Allan, Jr. *(CFO & Sr VP)*
James M. Loree *(COO & Exec VP)*
Hubert W. Davis, Jr. *(CIO & Sr VP)*
Jeff Hung-Tse Chen *(Pres-Asia & VP)*
Jim Cannon *(Pres-Indus & Automotive Repair-North America)*
Jaime Ramirez *(Pres-Latin America)*
Bhupinder S. Sihota *(Pres-Emerging Markets-Pacific Grp)*
William Scott Taylor *(Pres-Prof Power Tools & Products)*
Michael A. Tyll *(Pres-Engineered Fastening)*
John H.A. Wyatt *(Pres-Construction & DIY-EMEA)*
Bruce H. Beatt *(Gen Counsel, Sec & Sr VP)*
Jeffery D. Ansell *(Sr VP, Grp Exec-Construction & DIY)*
D. Brett Bontrager *(Sr VP & Grp Exec-Convergent Security Solutions)*
Justin C. Boswell *(Sr VP & Grp Exec-Mechanical Access Solutions)*
Mark J. Mathieu *(Sr VP-HR)*
Scott Bannell *(VP-Brand Mktg)*
Stephen Subasic *(VP-HR-CDIY)*
Tim Perra *(Dir-Global Comm)*
Kate White *(Dir-IR)*
Jonathan Sullivan *(Sr Mgr-Digital Mktg-CDIY)*
Kelly Dolan *(Mgr-Interactive Mktg-Stanley Tools & Stanley Bostitch)*
Brands & Products:
ACCUSCAPE
ATRO
BALDWIN
BEST
BLACK & DECKER
BLACKHAWK
BLICK
BOST PASTORINO
BOSTITCH
BRITOOL
CJ RUSH
COBOTICS
CONTACT EAST
CONTRACTOR GRADE
CST
DATEL
DAVID WHITE
DEWALT
DYNAGRIP
EMHART
FACOM
FATMAX
FRISCO BAY
FUBAR
GOLDBLATT
HARMONY
HARTCO
HUSKY
INNERSPACE
INTELLITOOLS
ISR
JENSEN
KWIKSET
LABOUNTY
MAC
MAKE SOMETHING GREAT
MAXGRIP
PAC
PORTER-CABLE
POWERLOCK
PRICE PFISTER
PROTO
QLINE
ROLATAPE
SAFEMASTER
SARGENT AND GREENLEAF
SENIOR TECHNOLOGIES
SPACETRAX
SPENAX
STANLEY
STANVISION
SYKES PICAVENT
USAG
VIDMAR
WANDERGUARD
ZAG
Advertising Agencies:
Fitzgerald+CO
3060 Peachtree Rd NW
Atlanta, GA 30305
Tel.: (404) 504-6900
Fax: (404) 239-0548

Keiler & Company
304 Main St
Farmington, CT 06032-2985
Tel.: (860) 677-8821
Fax: (860) 676-8164
(Stanley Hardware & Corporate Projects)

Mullen
40 Broad St
Boston, MA 02109
Tel.: (617) 226-9000
Fax: (617) 226-9100
(Corporate Branding)
FuBar

STARRETT

(Formerly Evans Rule Co., Inc.)
(Div. of The L.S. Starrett Company)
5965 Core Ave Ste 618
North Charleston, SC 29406-4909
Mailing Address:
PO Box 40309
Charleston, SC 29423-0309
Tel.: (843) 797-2500
Fax: (843) 747-7913
Toll Free: (800) 772-3649
Web Site: www.starrett.com
Sales Range: $25-49.9 Million
Approx. Number Employees: 17
Year Founded: 1972
Business Description:
Folding Rulers, Steel Measuring Tapes, Chalkline Reels, Utility Knives & Key Caddies Mfr
S.I.C.: 3423; 3829
N.A.I.C.S.: 332212; 334519
Export
Media: 3-8-10-14-15-16-18-22-23-24
Distr.: Intl.; Natl.
Budget Set: Aug.
Personnel:
Tim McCarty *(Gen Mgr)*

STERLING SUPPLY COMPANY, INC.

4900 Lincoln Ave
Lisle, IL 60532-2197
Tel.: (630) 969-8600
Fax: (630) 969-3271
Toll Free: (800) 391-5890
E-mail: contact@sterling-supply.com
Web Site: www.sterling-supply.com
E-Mail For Key Personnel:
President: roger@sterling-supply.com
Public Relations: victoria@sterling-supply.com
Approx. Number Employees: 42
Year Founded: 1948
Business Description:
Wholesaler of Plumbing Supplies
S.I.C.: 5074
N.A.I.C.S.: 423720
Media: 20-26
Distr.: Natl.
Budget Set: Jan.
Personnel:
Bernice Samson *(Chm & Pres)*
Roger Samson *(Exec VP-Personnel)*

STIHL, INC.

(Sub. of Andreas Stihl AG & Co.)
536 Viking Dr
Virginia Beach, VA 23452
Tel.: (757) 486-9100
Fax: (757) 631-5745
Toll Free: (800) 467-8445
Web Site: www.stihlusa.com
Approx. Number Employees: 2,000
Year Founded: 1974
Business Description:
Mfr of Chain Saws, Grass Trimmers, Leaf Blowers, Grass Edgers & Augers
S.I.C.: 3546; 3398
N.A.I.C.S.: 333991; 332811
Export
Advertising Expenditures: $4,000,000
Media: 1-2-3-4-5-6-7-8-9-10-14-15-19-20-21-22-23-24-26
Distr.: Natl.
Budget Set: Sept.
Personnel:
Fred J. Whyte *(Pres)*
Peter Mueller *(Exec VP-Ops)*
Peter Burton *(VP-Sls & Mktg)*
Kent Hall *(Product Mgr)*
Adam Hanks *(Product Mgr)*
Jackson D'Armond *(Mgr-Mktg Commun)*
Steve Hagen *(Mgr-Applications & Trng)*
Roger Phelps *(Mgr-Promoal Comm)*
Randy Scully *(Mgr-Product Svc)*
Tom Trebi *(Mgr-Product)*
Brands & Products:
STIHL
Advertising Agencies:
D&S Creative Communications Inc.
140 Park Ave E
Mansfield, OH 44902-1830
Tel.: (419) 524-4312
Fax: (419) 524-6494

The Meridian Group
575 Lynnhaven Pkwy 3rd Fl
Virginia Beach, VA 23452-7350
Tel.: (757) 340-7425
Fax: (757) 340-8379
Toll Free: (800) 294-3840
(Trade Media & Public Relations)

SULZER METCO (WESTBURY) INC.

(Sub. of Sulzer Metco AG)
1101 Prospect Ave
Westbury, NY 11590-2724
Tel.: (516) 334-1300
Fax: (516) 338-2414
E-mail: info@sulzermetco.com
Web Site: www.sulzermetco.com
Sales Range: $100-124.9 Million
Approx. Number Employees: 300
Year Founded: 1933
Business Description:
Mfr. of Thermal Spray Equipment, Supplies & Accessories
S.I.C.: 3316; 3479
N.A.I.C.S.: 331221; 332812
Import Export
Bus. Publs.: 40%; D.M. to Bus. Estab.: 5%; D.M. to Consumers: 0%; Exhibits/Trade Shows: 50%; Premiums, Novelties: 5%
Distr.: Natl.
Budget Set: Dec.
Personnel:
Bruno Gerig *(Exec VP-HR)*
Thomas Gutzwiller *(Exec VP-Components)*
Friedrich Herold *(Exec VP-Materials)*
Markus Heusser *(Exec VP)*
Michael Corr *(Mgr-Acctg)*
Brands & Products:
BRAINWARE
BRAZBOND
CHROMCOAT
THE COATINGS COMPANY
ELDIM
ELECTRO-PLASMA
HOSP
LINTRAV
LPPS
LVPS
METAPLAS IONON
METCO
METCOLITE
MULTICOAT
PLASMA-TECHNIK
PROTAL
ROTACLEAN
SMARTARC
SPRABRASS
SPRAYSENTRY
SPRAYWIZARD
SULZER METCO
THERMOSPRAY
VALUARC
VALUPLAZ

Key to Media (For complete agency information see *The Advertising Red Books-Agencies* edition):
1. Bus. Publs. 2. Cable T.V. 3. Catalogs & Directories. 4. Co-op Adv. 5. Consumer Mags. 6. D.M. to Bus. Estab.7. D.M. to Consumers 8. Daily Newsp. 9. Exhibits/Trade Shows 10. Foreign 11. Infomercial 12. Internet Adv.13. Multimedia 14. Network Radio 15. Network T.V. 16. Newsp. Distr. Mags. 17. Other 18. Outdoor (Posters, Transit) 19. Point of Purchase20. Premiums, Novelties 21. Product Samples 22. Special Events Mktg. 23. Spot Radio 24. Spot T.V. 25. Weekly Newsp. 26. Yellow Page Adv.

SUMMIT TOOL COMPANY
768 E North St
Akron, OH 44305
Mailing Address:
PO Box 9320
Akron, OH 44305
Tel.: (330) 535-7177
Fax: (330) 535-1345
Web Site:
www.summittoolcompany.com
Sales Range: $25-49.9 Million
Approx. Number Employees: 100
Year Founded: 1932
Business Description:
Tire Changing Tools Mfr
S.I.C.: 3423; 3714
N.A.I.C.S.: 332212; 336399
Import Export
Media: 2-4-10
Distr.: Natl.
Budget Set: Nov.
Personnel:
Alexander Pendleton *(Chm & CEO)*
Brands & Products:
BEADEZE
CARICA
CHALLENGER
DETECTO MIST
KEN-TOOL
OLDFORGE
RESHAPING THE WAY TIRES ARE CHANGED
SERPENT

SUPPLY TECHNOLOGIES LLC
(Sub. of Park-Ohio Industries, Inc.)
6065 Parkland Blvd
Cleveland, OH 44124
Tel.: (440) 947-2100
Fax: (440) 947-2299
Toll Free: (800) 695-8650
E-mail: marketing@supplytechnologies.com
Web Site:
www.supplytechnologies.com
Sales Range: $900-999.9 Million
Approx. Number Employees: 1,500
Year Founded: 1845
Business Description:
Supply Chain Management Services
S.I.C.: 5085; 3452; 8742
N.A.I.C.S.: 423840; 332722; 541611; 541614
Import Export
Media: 1-2-4-10-16-20-26
Distr.: Natl.
Budget Set: Jan.
Personnel:
A. A. Arena *(Pres)*
Michael Justice *(COO & Sr VP)*

SWAGELOK COMPANY
29500 Solon Rd
Solon, OH 44139-3449
Tel.: (440) 248-4600
Fax: (440) 349-5970
E-mail: publicrelations@swagelok.com
Web Site: www.swagelok.com
Sales Range: $1-4.9 Billion
Approx. Number Employees: 3,000
Year Founded: 1947
Business Description:
Mfr. of Tube Fittings, Valves, Welding Systems, Tubing, Weld & Pipe Fittings
S.I.C.: 3494; 3491
N.A.I.C.S.: 332919; 332911
Media: 2-4-9-17-26
Distr.: Natl.
Personnel:
Arthur F. Anton *(Pres & CEO)*
Frank J. Roddy *(CFO)*
Matthew P. LoPiccolo *(CIO & VP)*
Michael R. Butkovic *(VP-Mktg)*
Franziska H. Dacek *(VP-Corp Comm)*
James L. Francis *(VP-HR)*
David E. O'Connor *(VP-Customer Svc)*
Paul Bachman *(Dir-Mfg Strategy)*
Edward Bayer *(Dir-Sustainability)*
Harsha Bhojraj *(Dir-Valves Group)*
Patricia A. Carlson *(Dir-Corp Comm)*
Jim Cavoli *(Dir-Strategic Accts)*
Andy Curtiss *(Dir-Customer Svc)*
Eric Eber *(Dir-Application Dev-Info Svcs Org)*
Dave Krabill *(Dir-Customer Svc)*
David Lucarelli *(Dir-HR Ops)*
Kennan J. Malec *(Dir-Engrg)*
Michelle Massey *(Dir-Fin Reporting & Acctg)*
Jay Nordholt *(Dir-Ops Fittings Svc Group)*
Greg S. Shaw *(Dir-Tech Dev)*
Robert Sitzwohl *(Dir-Valve Svcs Grp)*
Neil Smith *(Dir-Quality & Continuous Improvement)*
Sally Turner *(Dir-HR Svcs)*
Jill Whelan *(Dir-Outbound Supply Chain)*
Brands & Products:
BRINGING OUR STAINLESS REPUTATION TO PLASTICS
CAJON
FERRULE-PAK
KENMAC
MICRO-FIT
NUPRO
SNOOP
SWAGELOK
SWAGELOK.COM
VCR
WHITEY

TECKNIT INCORPORATED
(Sub. of Parker Chomerics)
129 Dermody St
Cranford, NJ 07016-3217
Tel.: (908) 272-5500
Fax: (908) 276-4916
E-mail: hr@tecknit.com
Web Site: www.tecknit.com
Sales Range: $10-24.9 Million
Approx. Number Employees: 250
Year Founded: 1958
Business Description:
Mfr. of EMI Shielding & Conductive Materials
S.I.C.: 3496
N.A.I.C.S.: 332618
Advertising Expenditures: $300,000
Media: 2-4-8-10-21
Distr.: Natl.
Budget Set: Sept.
Personnel:
David Hill *(Pres)*
Brands & Products:
CONMAX
CONSIL
CONSIL-A
CONSIL-C
CONSIL-E
CONSIL-II
CONSIL-N
CONSIL-R
DUOGASKETS
DUOLASTIC
DUOSIL
DUOSTRIPS
ECTC WINDOW
ECTC WINDOWS
ELASTO-BOND
ELASTOFOAM
ELASTOMET
FUZZ BUTTON
FUZZ BUTTONS
NC-CONSIL
SC-CONSIL
TECKAIRE
TECKBOND
TECKCELL
TECKFELT
TECKFILM
TECKMASK TAPE
TECKNIT
TECKSCREEN
TECKSHIELD
TECKSOF
TECKSPAN
TECKSTRIP

THERMWELL PRODUCTS CO., INC.
420 Rte 17 S
Mahwah, NJ 07430
Tel.: (201) 684-4400
Fax: (201) 684-1214
Toll Free: (800) 526-5265
E-mail: support@frostking.com
Web Site: www.frostking.com
Approx. Number Employees: 1,000
Year Founded: 1910
Business Description:
Do-It-Yourself Packaged Consumer Products Mfr
S.I.C.: 2672; 2671
N.A.I.C.S.: 322222; 322221
Advertising Expenditures: $450,000
Media: 2-3-4-6-9-10-11-19-23-24-25-26
Distr.: Intl.
Budget Set: Jan. -June
Personnel:
David B. Gerstein *(Pres & CEO)*
Mel Gerstein *(Treas & Dir-Mktg, Adv & PR)*
Brands & Products:
FROST KING
MORTITE
REGENT TAPE
Advertising Agency:
Linder Marketing Co.
1500 Palisade Ave.
Fort Lee, NJ 07024
Tel.: (201) 461-1250
(Frost King Weatherstripping, Insulation, Drop Cloths, Tapes)

THE TORO COMPANY
8111 Lyndale Ave S
Bloomington, MN 55420-1196
Tel.: (952) 888-8801
Fax: (952) 887-8258
Toll Free: (800) 348-2424
E-mail: companyinfo@thetorocompany.com
Web Site: www.toro.com
E-Mail For Key Personnel:
Public Relations: pr@toro.com
Approx. Sls.: $1,690,378,000
Approx. Number Employees: 4,609
Year Founded: 1914
Business Description:
Outdoor Care & Maintenance Products Mfr
S.I.C.: 3524; 3423; 3645
N.A.I.C.S.: 333112; 332212; 335121
Export
Advertising Expenditures: $39,281,000
Media: 5-7-8-9-18-19-23-24-25
Distr.: Intl.; Natl.
Budget Set: Aug.
Personnel:
Michael J. Hoffman *(Chm & CEO)*
Renee J. Peterson *(CFO & VP-Fin)*
Michael D. Drazan *(CIO-Contractor Bus & VP)*
Timothy P. Dordell *(Gen Counsel, Sec & VP)*
Peter M. Ramstad *(VP-HR & Bus Dev)*
Lisa Howard *(Mgr-Mktg Comm)*
Brands & Products:
COUNT ON IT.
EXMARK
IRRITROL SYSTEMS
LAWN-BOY
LAWN GENIE
TORO
TORO WHEEL HORSE
Advertising Agency:
The Falls Agency
2550 Blaisdell Ave S
Minneapolis, MN 55404
Tel.: (612) 872-6372
Fax: (612) 872-1018
Toll Free: (800) 339-1119

THE TORO COMPANY IRRIGATION PRODUCTS
(Sub. of The Toro Company)
5825 Jasmine St
Riverside, CA 92504-1144
Mailing Address:
PO Box 489
Riverside, CA 92502-0489
Tel.: (951) 688-9221
Fax: (951) 359-1870
E-mail: info@toro.com
Web Site: www.toro.com
Sales Range: $100-124.9 Million
Approx. Number Employees: 300
Business Description:
Irrigation Sprinkler Systems Mfr
S.I.C.: 4941
N.A.I.C.S.: 221310
Media: 2-4-5-6-7-8-9-10-11-18-19-20-21-23-24-26
Distr.: Intl.; Natl.

TOTO USA, INC.
(Sub. of Toto Ltd.)
1155 Southern Rd
Morrow, GA 30260-2917
Tel.: (770) 282-8686
Fax: (770) 282-8697
Toll Free: (888) 295-8134
E-mail: marketing@totousa.com
Web Site: www.totousa.com
Approx. Number Employees: 1,500
Year Founded: 1996
Business Description:
Plumbing Supplies Mfr
S.I.C.: 5074
N.A.I.C.S.: 423720
Advertising Expenditures: $300,000
Media: 2-4-5-6-7-8-10-18-19-20-22
Personnel:
D. J. Nogata *(Pres)*
Miles Casaday *(CFO)*

Key to Media (For complete agency information see *The Advertising Red Books-Agencies* edition):
1. Bus. Publs. 2. Cable T.V. 3. Catalogs & Directories. 4. Co-op Adv. 5. Consumer Mags. 6. D.M. to Bus. Estab.7. D.M. to Consumers
8. Daily Newsp. 9. Exhibits/Trade Shows 10. Foreign 11. Infomercial 12. Internet Adv.13. Multimedia 14. Network Radio
15. Network T.V. 16. Newsp. Distr. Mags. 17. Other 18. Outdoor (Posters, Transit) 19. Point of Purchase20. Premiums, Novelties
21. Product Samples 22. Special Events Mktg. 23. Spot Radio 24. Spot T.V. 25. Weekly Newsp. 26. Yellow Page Adv.

Toto USA, Inc. — (Continued)
Lenora Campos *(Sr Mgr-PR & Corp Spokesperson)*
Virginia Guillian *(Mgr-Mktg)*

TRUE VALUE COMPANY

8600 W Bryn Mawr Ave
Chicago, IL 60631-3579
Tel.: (773) 695-5000
Fax: (773) 695-6516
E-mail: international@truserv.com
Web Site: www.truevaluecompany.com
Sales Range: $200-249.9 Million
Approx. Number Employees: 500
Year Founded: 1948
Business Description:
Hardware, Lumber, Building Materials & Related Merchandise Distr; Paint & Paint Applicators Mfr
S.I.C.: 5251; 5083
N.A.I.C.S.: 444130; 444210
Advertising Expenditures: $44,817,000
Media: 2-3-4-5-6-8-9-10-13-14-15-16-18-19-20-22-23-24-26
Distr.: Natl.
Personnel:
Brian A. Webb *(Chm)*
Lyle G. Heidemann *(Pres & CEO)*
David A. Shadduck *(CFO & Sr VP)*
Cathy Anderson *(Gen Counsel, Sec & Sr VP-HR)*
Michael Clark *(Chief Mdsg Officer & Sr VP)*
Carol Wentworth *(VP-Mktg)*
Brands & Products:
COAST TO COAST HARDWARE
COMMERCIAL SALES
E-Z KARE
EASY COLOR
HELP IS JUST AROUND THE CORNER
HOME & GARDEN SHOWPLACE
INDUSERVE SUPPLY
SERVISTAR HARDWARE
SUMMER IS JUST AROUND THE CORNER
TAYLOR RENTAL
TRU-TEST
TRUE VALUE HARDWARE STORES
WEATHERALL
Advertising Agency:
MARC USA Corporate Headquarters
225 W Station Square Dr Ste 500
Pittsburgh, PA 15219-1119
Tel.: (412) 562-2000
Fax: (412) 562-2022
— Vanessa Mackey *(Sr Acct Exec)*

TRUTH HARDWARE CORP.

(Sub. of Melrose PLC)
700 W Bridge St
Owatonna, MN 55060
Tel.: (507) 451-5620
Fax: (507) 451-5655
Toll Free: (800) 866-7884
E-mail: truthsal@truth.com
Web Site: www.truth.com
Approx. Number Employees: 1,200
Business Description:
Residential & Commercial Door & Window Hardware Mfr
S.I.C.: 3429
N.A.I.C.S.: 332510
Advertising Expenditures: $200,000
Media: 2-4-7-10-13
Personnel:
Ron Foy *(Pres & CEO)*
Patti Siegfried *(CFO)*
Steve Groves *(Sr VP-Sls & Mktg)*
Matt Kottke *(Mgr-Mktg Support)*

THE TURNER & SEYMOUR MANUFACTURING COMPANY

100 Lawton St
Torrington, CT 06790-6715
Mailing Address:
PO Box 358
Torrington, CT 06790-0358
Tel.: (860) 489-9214
Fax: (860) 482-3197
Toll Free: (800) 733-9214
E-mail: info@turnerseymour.com
Web Site: www.turnerseymour.com
E-Mail For Key Personnel:
Sales Director: sales@turnerseymour.com
Approx. Number Employees: 50
Year Founded: 1848
Business Description:
Chains, Upholstery, Nails & Tacks & Furniture Glides Mfr
S.I.C.: 3496; 3321
N.A.I.C.S.: 332618; 331511
Import Export
Advertising Expenditures: $35,000
Media: 2-9
Distr.: Natl.
Budget Set: Nov.
Personnel:
Allen M Sperry *(Chm)*
Paul Ayub *(Pres)*
Carol Soliani *(VP-HR)*
Brands & Products:
TURNER & SEYMOUR
Advertising Agency:
Thomas Industrial Network Advertising
5 Penn Plz
New York, NY 10001
Tel.: (212) 629-2100
Fax: (212) 290-7362
Toll Free: (888) 734-4662

TWIN CITY DIE CASTINGS CO.

1070 SE 33rd Ave
Minneapolis, MN 55414-2707
Tel.: (651) 645-3611
Fax: (651) 645-0724
E-mail: sales@tcdcinc.com
Web Site: www.tcdcinc.com
E-Mail For Key Personnel:
Sales Director: sales@tcdcinc.com
Approx. Number Employees: 100
Year Founded: 1919
Business Description:
Aluminum, Zinc & Magnesium Die Castings Mfr
S.I.C.: 3363; 3364
N.A.I.C.S.: 331521; 331522
Export
Advertising Expenditures: $600,000
Media: 2-4-7-10
Distr.: Natl.
Personnel:
Douglas Harmon *(CEO)*

TYCO VALVES & CONTROLS, INC.

(Div. of Tyco Valves & Controls, Inc.)
3950 Greenbriar Dr
Stafford, TX 77477-3919
Mailing Address:
PO Box 944
Stafford, TX 77497-0944
Tel.: (281) 274-4400
Fax: (281) 240-1800
Telex: 0775219 AGCO VALVE HOU
E-mail: info@tycovalves.com
Web Site: www.tycovalves.com
Approx. Number Employees: 1,000
Year Founded: 1947
Business Description:
Pressure Relief Valves, Manifolds, Hand Valves, Check Valves, Regulators, Nuclear & Fossil Fuel Power Plant Valves, Rupture Discs Mfr
S.I.C.: 3491; 5084
N.A.I.C.S.: 332911; 423830
Import Export
Media: 1-2-4-8-10-11-13-21-26
Distr.: Intl.; Natl.
Budget Set: Aug.
Personnel:
John Ward *(Gen Mgr)*
Carl Hyltin *(Mgr-Reg Sls-Power Generation)*
Brands & Products:
YARWAY

TYDENBROOKS SECURITY PRODUCTS GROUP

(Sub. of Tyden Group Inc.)
8 Microlab Rd
Livingston, NJ 07039-1602
Tel.: (973) 597-2900
Fax: (973) 597-2939
Toll Free: (800) 458SEAL
E-mail: sales@tydenbrooks.com
Web Site: www.tydenbrooks.com
Sales Range: $25-49.9 Million
Approx. Number Employees: 300
Year Founded: 1873
Business Description:
Plastic/Metal Security Seals & Locking Devices Mfr
S.I.C.: 3429
N.A.I.C.S.: 332510
Import Export
Media: 2-4-7-8-10-11-20-21-26
Distr.: Intl.
Budget Set: Jan.
Personnel:
Michael Abatemarco *(VP & Gen Mgr)*
Ralph Mallozzi *(VP-Sls)*
Brands & Products:
BROOKS
CABLE SEAL 2000
ECHOPOINT
EDURO SEAL
E.J. BROOKS
GRIPLOCK
INTERMODAL
MORE CHOICES. MORE SOLUTIONS
NIFTY-LOK
POLY-LOK II
RING-PULL
ROTO-SEAL
SECUR-HASP II
SECUR-PULL
SECURE-GRIP
SPRING-LOK
SPRING-LOK STRINGING RING

UNIVERSAL INDUSTRIAL PRODUCTS CO.

1 Coreway Dr
Pioneer, OH 43554-0628
Mailing Address:
PO Box 628
Pioneer, OH 43554-0628
Tel.: (419) 737-2324
Fax: (419) 737-2130
Toll Free: (800) 922-6957
E-mail: hinges@soss.com
Web Site: www.soss.com
Approx. Rev.: $6,000,000
Approx. Number Employees: 30
Year Founded: 1941
Business Description:
Universal Mower Blades, Construction Hinges, Stamping & Precision Grinding Metal Parts Mfr
S.I.C.: 3469; 3429
N.A.I.C.S.: 332116; 332510
Import Export
Media: 2-4-5-6-7-10-19-21
Distr.: Intl.; Natl.
Budget Set: June
Personnel:
Neil Marko *(Owner)*
Randy Herriman *(CFO)*
Brands & Products:
SOSS
ULTRALATCH

UNIVERSAL THREAD GRINDING COMPANY

30 Chambers St
Fairfield, CT 06825
Tel.: (203) 336-1849
Fax: (203) 366-1326
E-mail: sales@universal-thread.com
Web Site: www.universal-thread.com
E-Mail For Key Personnel:
Sales Director: sales@universal-thread.com
Approx. Number Employees: 20
Year Founded: 1946
Business Description:
Precision Lead Screws Mfr
S.I.C.: 3452
N.A.I.C.S.: 332722
Media: 2-4-7-10-13
Distr.: Natl.
Personnel:
William H. Everett, Jr. *(Pres)*
Brian Elliott *(Sr VP-Experience Architect)*
Advertising Agency:
Technell, Inc.
81 Nutmeg Ln
Stamford, CT 06905
Tel.: (203) 609-9065
Fax: (203) 609-9065

VANCE INDUSTRIES, INC.

230 Sievert Ct
Bensenville, IL 60106-1190
Tel.: (630) 694-8500
Fax: (630) 694-8501
E-mail: sales@vanceind.com
Web Site: www.vanceind.com
E-Mail For Key Personnel:
President: jschleiter@vanceind.com
Sales Director: sales@vanceind.com
Approx. Number Employees: 18
Year Founded: 1949
Business Description:
Mfr. of Stainless Steel Sinks, Brass Bar Sinks, Sink Frames, Tempered Glass Food Preparation Surfaces & Assorted Kitchen Accessories & Plastic & Wood Kitchen Products
S.I.C.: 3231; 3431
N.A.I.C.S.: 327215; 332998
Advertising Expenditures: $328,000
Bus. Publs.: $48,000; Catalogs & Directories: $50,000; Consumer

Key to Media (For complete agency information see *The Advertising Red Books-Agencies* edition):
1. Bus. Publs. 2. Cable T.V. 3. Catalogs & Directories. 4. Co-op Adv. 5. Consumer Mags. 6. D.M. to Bus. Estab.7. D.M. to Consumers
8. Daily Newsp. 9. Exhibits/Trade Shows 10. Foreign 11. Infomercial 12. Internet Adv.13. Multimedia 14. Network Radio
15. Network T.V. 16. Newsp. Distr. Mags. 17. Other 18. Outdoor (Posters, Transit) 19. Point of Purchase20. Premiums, Novelties
21. Product Samples 22. Special Events Mktg. 23. Spot Radio 24. Spot T.V. 25. Weekly Newsp. 26. Yellow Page Adv.

Mags.: $15,000; D.M. to Bus. Estab.: $30,000; Exhibits/Trade Shows: $45,000; Other: $10,000; Point of Purchase: $100,000; Product Samples: $30,000
Distr.: Intl.; Natl.
Budget Set: Nov.
Brands & Products:
EZ SLIDE 'N STOR
PERFECT-FIT
SINK UNDERMOUNTER
SPICE DRAWER INSERT
SPICE-STEPS CABINET
SURFACE SAVERS
TRIM-FIT
VANCE INDUSTRIES
VANSEAL SINK CLAMP

VAUGHAN & BUSHNELL MANUFACTURING COMPANY, INC.

11414 Maple Ave PO Box 390
Hebron, IL 60034
Tel.: (815) 648-2446
Fax: (815) 648-4300
E-mail: vaughanmfg@aol.com
Web Site: www.vaughanmfg.com
Approx. Number Employees: 550
Year Founded: 1869
Business Description:
Tools Mfr
S.I.C.: 3423; 2499
N.A.I.C.S.: 332212; 321999
Import Export
Media: 2-5-6
Distr.: Natl.
Budget Set: Oct.
Personnel:
Charles Vaughan *(Pres & COO)*
Ron Miller *(VP-Fin)*
Robert Bachta *(Mgr-Mktg)*
Brands & Products:
999
BEAR CLAW
BEARSAW
BLUE MAX
BOWJAK
CALIFORNIA FRAMER
CARPENTER'S PRIDE
DOUBLE DUTY
E-Z SWING
EAGLE
GROUNDBREAKERS
HEADSTART
HEAVY HITTERS
LITTLE PRO
LIVING WEDGE
PRO-16
PRO-GRIP
PRO-ROCKER
SHOCK-BLOK
STEEL EAGLE
SUB-ZERO
SUPERBAR
SUPERSTEEL
SURE-LOCK
TI-TECH
TOUGH-FIBRE
V&B
VAUGHAN

VENNERBECK, STERN, LEACH

4 Carrol Dr
Lincoln, RI 02865-0486
Mailing Address:
PO Box 486
Lincoln, RI 02865
Tel.: (401) 333-1450
Fax: (401) 333-1721
Web Site: www.sternleach.com/contact.aspx
Approx. Sls.: $11,000,000
Approx. Number Employees: 35
Business Description:
Mfr. of Gold Filled & Rolled Gold Plate, Carat Gold & Silver Sheet Stock, Wire & Solders
S.I.C.: 3339
N.A.I.C.S.: 331419
Advertising Expenditures: $200,000
Media: 2
Distr.: Natl.
Brands & Products:
VSL

VERTEX DISTRIBUTION

523 Pleasant St Bldg 10
Attleboro, MA 02703
Tel.: (508) 431-1120
Fax: (508) 431-1114
E-mail: sales@vertexdistribution.com
Web Site: www.vertexdistribution.com
E-Mail For Key Personnel:
Sales Director: sales@vertexdistribution.com
Approx. Number Employees: 100
Business Description:
High Carbon Steel, Stainless Steel & Special Alloy Bolts, Studs & Other Threaded Fastening Devices
S.I.C.: 3452
N.A.I.C.S.: 332722
Media: 2-4-7-8-10-20-21
Distr.: Natl.
Personnel:
Mark Alperin *(Pres)*
Mark Klosek *(Exec VP)*
Brands & Products:
VERTEX

VICTAULIC COMPANY

4901 Kesslersville Rd
Easton, PA 18044-0031
Mailing Address:
PO Box 31
Easton, PA 18044-0031
Tel.: (610) 559-3300
Fax: (610) 250-8817
Toll Free: (800) 742-5842
E-mail: victaulic@victaulic.com
Web Site: www.victaulic.com
Approx. Number Employees: 2,500
Year Founded: 1925
Business Description:
Pipe Couplings, Fittings, Valves, Tools & Sprinkler Heads Mfr
S.I.C.: 3494; 3491
N.A.I.C.S.: 332919; 332911
Import Export
Media: 1-2-4-7-10-11-13-20-21
Distr.: Intl.; Natl.
Budget Set: June
Personnel:
Gary Moore *(Exec VP)*
Mark Gilbert *(VP & Gen Mgr-EMEA & India)*
Chuck Wilk *(Product Mgr)*
Scott J. Frey *(Mgr-Mktg Commun)*
Scott Moll *(Supvr-Market Res)*
Brands & Products:
AQUAMINE
COASTLINE
DEPEND-O-LOK
DUO-LOCK
ENDSEAL
FIRE-R
FIREBALL
FIRELOCK
FIRELOCK EZ
FIT
FLUSHSEAL
MECHANICAL-T
MOVER
PIPECO
PLAINLOCK
PRESSFIT
ROUST-A-BOUT
SNAP-JOINT
SNAP-LET
SWINGER
SYSTEM II
TESTMASTER
VIC
VIC-ADJUSTABLE
VIC-BALL
VIC-BOLTLESS
VIC-EASY
VIC-FLANGE
VIC-FLEX
VIC-GROOVER
VIC-LET
VIC-O-WELL
VIC-PLUG
VIC-PRESS 304
VIC-STRAINER
VIC-TAP
ZERO-FLEX

WATER MASTER COMPANY

13 S 3rd Ave
Highland Park, NJ 08904-2509
Mailing Address:
PO Box 1186
New Brunswick, NJ 08903-1186
Tel.: (732) 247-1900
Approx. Number Employees: 5
Year Founded: 1947
Business Description:
Toilet Tank Balls, Flapper Tank Balls, Toilet Plungers & Metal Polish Mfr
S.I.C.: 3069; 3471
N.A.I.C.S.: 326299; 332813
Advertising Expenditures: $300,000
Media: 2-6-9
Distr.: Natl.
Budget Set: Oct.
Brands & Products:
TARNITE
TOILAFLEX
WATER MASTER
WATER MASTER FLAPPER

WATERWISE INC.

3608 Pkwy Blvd
Leesburg, FL 34748
Tel.: (352) 787-5008
Fax: (352) 787-8123
Fax: (866) 329-8123
Toll Free: (800) 874-9028
Web Site: www.waterwise.com
E-Mail For Key Personnel:
Sales Director: sales@waterwise.com
Approx. Number Employees: 30
Year Founded: 1977
Business Description:
Water Distillation & Filtration Products
S.I.C.: 5074; 5722
N.A.I.C.S.: 423720; 443111
Media: 4-6-13
Personnel:
Jack Barber *(Pres)*
Greg Barber *(VP-Sls & Mktg)*
Brands & Products:
WATERWISE

W.E. AUBUCHON CO., INC.

95 Aubuchon Dr
Westminster, MA 01473-1470
Tel.: (978) 874-0521
Fax: (978) 874-2096
Toll Free: (800) 282-4393
E-mail: help@aubuchon.com
Web Site: www.aubuchon.com
Approx. Number Employees: 1,100
Year Founded: 1908
Business Description:
Hardware Store
S.I.C.: 5251; 5031
N.A.I.C.S.: 444130; 423310
Media: 3-4-8-9-13-16-17-23-24-26
Distr.: Direct to Consumer; Reg.
Personnel:
William E. Aubuchon, III *(Chm & CEO)*
Marcus M. Moran *(Pres & Treas)*
Danny Aubuchon *(VP-HR)*
Ken Moore *(VP-Sls & Mktg)*
Jeff Aubuchon *(Dir-Fin)*
Michael Mattson *(Dir-Adv & PR)*
Brands & Products:
AUBUCHON
WE'LL FIX YOU RIGHT UP

WEJ-IT FASTENING SYSTEMS

10541 E Ute St
Tulsa, OK 74116-1522
Tel.: (918) 743-1030
Fax: (918) 749-3726
Toll Free: (800) 343-1264
E-mail: info@wejit.com
Web Site: www.wejit.com
Sales Range: $75-99.9 Million
Approx. Number Employees: 100
Year Founded: 1952
Business Description:
Concrete Masonry Anchors Mfr
S.I.C.: 3452; 3531
N.A.I.C.S.: 332722; 333120
Import Export
Media: 1-2-4-6-7-8-10-11-19-20-21-26
Distr.: Natl.
Budget Set: Oct.-Nov.
Personnel:
Dave Gentry *(VP-Sls)*
Harold Kalich *(Gen Mgr)*
Brands & Products:
ANKR-TITE
AT II
FRICTION-FIT
INJECT-TITE
POWER-DROP
POWER-SERT
POWER-SET
SLAM-TITE
WEJ-IT

WELDON TOOL COMPANY

(Sub. of Talbot Holdings Inc.)
200 Front St
Millersburg, PA 17061
Tel.: (717) 692-2113
Fax: (717) 692-5270
Toll Free: (800) 622-7742
Web Site: www.weldontool.com
Sales Range: $1-9.9 Million
Approx. Number Employees: 130
Year Founded: 1918

Weldon Tool Company — (Continued)

Business Description:
Mfr. of End Mills & Holders, Counter Bores, Deburring & Cutting Tools, Relieving Fixtures, Sinks & Sharpening Fixtures
S.I.C.: 3541; 5084
N.A.I.C.S.: 333512; 423830
Import Export
Media: 4-7-10-20
Distr.: Intl.; Natl.
Budget Set: Mar.
Personnel:
Bill Coyle *(Pres)*
Brands & Products:
AMERICUT
BULLDOG
CREST-KUT
SKI-CARB
SKI-KUT
TU-LIP
ULTRA-KUT
UNI-LEAD
WELDON

WESTLAKE ACE HARDWARE, INC.

(Holding of Goldner Hawn Johnson & Morrison Inc.)
14000 Marshall Dr
Lenexa, KS 66215
Tel.: (913) 888-0808
Fax: (913) 888-2153
Toll Free: (800) 848-4307
E-mail: comments@westlakehardware.com
Web Site: www.westlakehardware.com
Approx. Sls.: $210,000,000
Approx. Number Employees: 1,500
Year Founded: 1905
Business Description:
Operator of Hardware & Building Material Stores
S.I.C.: 5251
N.A.I.C.S.: 444130
Advertising Expenditures: $4,000,000
Media: 5-6-13-17-18-19-20-21-22-23-24-25-26
Distr.: Natl.
Personnel:
George Smith, Sr. *(Pres & CEO)*
George Shadid *(CFO & Exec VP)*
Rob Easley *(COO & Exec VP)*
Tara Denman *(Sr VP & HR Officer)*
Brands & Products:
WESTLAKE
Advertising Agency:
Bozell
1022 Leavenworth St
Omaha, NE 68102
Tel.: (402) 965-4434
Fax: (402) 965-4399

Key to Media (For complete agency information see *The Advertising Red Books-Agencies* edition):
1. Bus. Publs. 2. Cable T.V. 3. Catalogs & Directories. 4. Co-op Adv. 5. Consumer Mags. 6. D.M. to Bus. Estab.7. D.M. to Consumers 8. Daily Newsp. 9. Exhibits/Trade Shows 10. Foreign 11. Infomercial 12. Internet Adv.13. Multimedia 14. Network Radio 15. Network T.V. 16. Newsp. Distr. Mags. 17. Other 18. Outdoor (Posters, Transit) 19. Point of Purchase20. Premiums, Novelties 21. Product Samples 22. Special Events Mktg. 23. Spot Radio 24. Spot T.V. 25. Weekly Newsp. 26. Yellow Page Adv.

Heating & Air Conditioning

Air Conditioners — Boilers — Dehumidifiers — Furnaces — Heating Appliances — Kerosene Heaters — Oil Burners — Ovens — Portable Heaters — Radiators — Stokers — Ventilators — Water Heaters

AAF INTERNATIONAL
(Sub. of O.Y.L. Industries Bhd.)
10300 Ormsby Pk Pl Ste 600
Louisville, KY 40223
Mailing Address:
PO Box 35690
Louisville, KY 40232-5690
Fax: (502) 637-0452
Toll Free: (888) 223-2003
Web Site: www.aafintl.com
E-Mail For Key Personnel:
Marketing Director: druss@aafintl.com
Approx. Sls.: $880,000,000
Approx. Number Employees: 200
Year Founded: 1982
Business Description:
Commercial, Industrial & Institutional Heating, Ventilating, Air-Conditioning, Filtration & Air Pollution Control Products, Systems & Controls
S.I.C.: 3585; 5075
N.A.I.C.S.: 333415; 423730
Export
Advertising Expenditures: $2,000,000
Bus. Publs.: $200,000; Catalogs & Directories: $100,000; D.M. to Bus. Estab.: $600,000; Exhibits/Trade Shows: $600,000; Other: $400,000; Point of Purchase: $100,000
Distr.: Intl.; Natl.
Budget Set: Dec.
Personnel:
Rich Lancaster *(CIO)*
Brands & Products:
AAF
AMERICANAIRFILTER
BETTER AIR IS OUR BUSINESS
MCQUAY

AAON, INC.
2425 S Yukon Ave
Tulsa, OK 74107-2728
Tel.: (918) 583-2266
Fax: (918) 583-6094
E-mail: investor@aaon.com
Web Site: www.aaon.com
Approx. Sls.: $244,552,000
Approx. Number Employees: 1,394
Business Description:
Mfr & Marketer of Rooftop Air Conditioning, Heating & Heat Recovery Systems
S.I.C.: 3585; 1711
N.A.I.C.S.: 333415; 238220
Export
Advertising Expenditures: $877,000
Media: 2
Personnel:
Norman H. Asbjornson *(Chm, Pres & CEO)*
Sam Neale *(Mgr-Mktg)*
Brands & Products:
AAON
AAONAIRE
AAONECAT
AAONECAT32
CELEBRITY 1

ABLE ENERGY, INC.
198 Green Pond Rd
Rockaway, NJ 07866
Tel.: (973) 588-9866
Fax: (973) 586-9866
Sales Range: $200-249.9 Million
Approx. Number Employees: 501
Business Description:
Heating Oil & Other Fuels Distr
S.I.C.: 5983; 5989
N.A.I.C.S.: 454311; 454319
Advertising Expenditures: $908,000
Media: 2-3-10-13-23-26
Personnel:
Richard A. Mitstifer *(Pres)*
John F. O'Brien *(CFO)*
William Roger Roberts *(COO)*
Brands & Products:
ABLE

ACCO ENGINEERED SYSTEMS
6265 San Fernando Rd
Glendale, CA 91201-2214
Tel.: (818) 244-6571
Fax: (818) 247-6533
Toll Free: (800) 998-2266
Web Site: www.accoes.com
Approx. Number Employees: 1,450
Year Founded: 1934
Business Description:
Heating, Ventilating & Air Conditioning Systems Designer & Mfr
S.I.C.: 1711; 7699
N.A.I.C.S.: 238220; 811412
Media: 2-4-9
Distr.: Reg.
Personnel:
John Aversano *(Co-Pres & CEO)*
Ronald Krassensky *(Co-Pres & COO)*
John G. Petersen *(CFO)*
Peter H. Narbonne *(Exec VP-Southern Div)*
Charles K. Richter *(Exec VP-Corp Dev)*
Kenneth B. Westphal *(Exec VP-Building Svcs Div)*
Milton L. Goodman *(Sr VP-Construction)*
John W Hansen *(Sr VP-Project Mgmt-Northern California)*
Jeffrey R. Marrs *(Sr VP-Project Mgmt-Southern California)*
Steven J. Smith *(Sr VP-Building Svcs)*
Robert P. Vlick *(Sr VP-Special Projects)*
Richard D. Yates *(Sr VP-Project Mgmt)*

AERCO INTERNATIONAL INC.
159 Paris Ave
Northvale, NJ 07647-2029
Tel.: (201) 768-2400
Fax: (201) 768-7789
Toll Free: (800) 526-0288
E-mail: reception@aerco.com
Web Site: www.aerco.com
Approx. Number Employees: 168
Year Founded: 1949
Business Description:
Mfr. of Heat Exchangers; Control Valves; Steam Generators; Heat Recovery Systems; Heaters & Boilers
S.I.C.: 3443; 3492
N.A.I.C.S.: 332313; 332912
Import Export
Advertising Expenditures: $500,000
Media: 2-10-16-21-26
Distr.: Natl.
Budget Set: Sept.
Personnel:
Basem Hishmeh *(Chm)*
Fred W. Depuy *(CEO)*
Tony Laraia *(VP-Engrng & Ops)*
Neil Pilaar *(VP-Sls)*
Dan Quigley *(VP-Mktg)*
Marc Croce *(Dir-Mktg)*
Brands & Products:
AERCO
BENCHMARK
C-MORE
HEAT YOU CAN BANK ON
KC 1000
LOADALERT
MODULEX
SMARTPLATE
WATERWIZARD

AEROFIN CORP.
(Sub. of Ampco-Pittsburgh Corporation)
4621 Murray Pl
Lynchburg, VA 24502-2235
Mailing Address:
PO Box 10819
Lynchburg, VA 24506-0819
Tel.: (434) 845-7081
Fax: (434) 528-6242
Web Site: www.aerofin.com
Sales Range: $100-124.9 Million
Approx. Number Employees: 215
Year Founded: 1923
Business Description:
Heating & Cooling Coils Mfr
S.I.C.: 3585; 3443
N.A.I.C.S.: 333415; 332313
Export
Media: 2-4-10-13-26
Distr.: Natl.
Budget Set: Oct.
Personnel:
Gavin Divers *(Pres)*
Brands & Products:
AEROFIN

AIRMASTER FAN COMPANY
1300 Falahee Rd
Jackson, MI 49203-3554
Tel.: (517) 764-2300
Fax: (517) 764-3838
Toll Free: (800) 255-3084
E-mail: sales@airmasterfan.com
Web Site: www.airmasterfan.com
E-Mail For Key Personnel:
Sales Director: sales@airmasterfan.com
Approx. Number Employees: 75
Year Founded: 1975
Business Description:
Air Circulators, Exhaust Fans, Ceiling Fans & Roof Ventilators
S.I.C.: 3564
N.A.I.C.S.: 333412
Import Export
Media: 2-5-7-8-10-19
Distr.: Intl.; Natl.
Budget Set: Varies
Personnel:
Richard Stone *(Pres & CEO)*
Michael Pignataro *(Dir-Sls)*
Brands & Products:
AIRMASTER
MANCOOLER

Key to Media (For complete agency information see *The Advertising Red Books-Agencies* edition):
1. Bus. Publs. 2. Cable T.V. 3. Catalogs & Directories. 4. Co-op Adv. 5. Consumer Mags. 6. D.M. to Bus. Estab.7. D.M. to Consumers 8. Daily Newsp. 9. Exhibits/Trade Shows 10. Foreign 11. Infomercial 12. Internet Adv.13. Multimedia 14. Network Radio 15. Network T.V. 16. Newsp. Distr. Mags. 17. Other 18. Outdoor (Posters, Transit) 19. Point of Purchase20. Premiums, Novelties 21. Product Samples 22. Special Events Mktg. 23. Spot Radio 24. Spot T.V. 25. Weekly Newsp. 26. Yellow Page Adv.

Airmaster Fan Company — (Continued)

TURBO
WASHDOWN FAN

AJAX ELECTRIC CO.
60 Tomlinson Rd
Huntingdon Valley, PA 19006
Tel.: (215) 947-8500
Fax: (215) 947-6757
E-mail: jabber@ajaxelectric.com
Web Site: www.ajaxelectric.com
Approx. Sls.: $3,500,000
Approx. Number Employees: 45
Year Founded: 1931
Business Description:
Electric & Gas Fired Salt Bath Heat Treating Furnaces, Atmosphere Conveyor Furnaces, Custom Designed Salt Reclamation Systems; Electronic, Pneumatic & Hydraulic Control Panels & Integrated Control Systems
S.I.C.: 3567; 3613
N.A.I.C.S.: 333994; 335313
Export
Media: 2-4-10
Distr.: Direct to Consumer; Natl.
Budget Set: Nov. -Dec.
Personnel:
John A. Barry *(Pres)*
Donna Stelman *(VP)*
Joe Bauer *(Mgr-Engrg)*
Paul Sweger *(Mgr-Pur)*
Brands & Products:
AJAX
AJAX ELECTRIC
BACL2EAN
CONVEY-O-QUENCH
ECONOSAL
UNI-HOIST
WHEN YOU NEED A BATH

AJAX TOCCO MAGNETHERMIC CORPORATION
(Sub. of Park-Ohio Industries, Inc.)
1745 Overland Ave NE
Warren, OH 44483-2860
Tel.: (330) 372-8511
Fax: (330) 372-8641
Toll Free: (800) 547-1527
Web Site: www.ajaxtocco.com
Sales Range: $100-124.9 Million
Approx. Number Employees: 350
Year Founded: 1948
Business Description:
Mfr. of Induction Heating & Melting Equipment for Metal Working Industry
S.I.C.: 3567; 3612
N.A.I.C.S.: 333994; 335311
Advertising Expenditures: $286,000
Media: 2-4-10-20-26
Distr.: Natl.
Budget Set: Oct.
Personnel:
Jerald Jackson *(VP-Sls)*
Brands & Products:
AJAXOMATIC
DYNAPOUR
JET-FLOW
PACER
PACHYDYNE
POWERFLEX
ULTR-CASE

ALUMA SHIELD INDUSTRIES, INC.
(Sub. of Metec Inc.)
725 Summerhill Dr
Deland, FL 32724
Tel.: (386) 626-6789
Fax: (386) 734-3289
Toll Free: (888) 882-5862
E-mail: mail@alumashield.com
Web Site: www.alumashield.com
Approx. Number Employees: 234
Year Founded: 1952
Business Description:
Mfr. of Insulated Panels & Doors
S.I.C.: 3585
N.A.I.C.S.: 333415
Import Export
Media: 2-4-7-10
Distr.: Natl.
Budget Set: Aug.
Brands & Products:
HERCULES
MAX-R

AMERICAN DG ENERGY INC.
45 1st Ave
Waltham, MA 02451
Tel.: (781) 522-6000
Tel.: (781) 622-1120
Fax: (781) 522-6050
Fax: (781) 622-1027
E-mail: info@americandg.com
Web Site: www.americandg.com
Approx. Sls.: $5,634,765
Approx. Number Employees: 14
Year Founded: 2001
Business Description:
Energy Saving Device Distr & Operator
S.I.C.: 4939; 1711; 4911
N.A.I.C.S.: 221122; 238220
Media: 10
Personnel:
George N. Hatsopoulos *(Chm)*
Barry J. Sanders *(Pres & COO)*
John N. Hatsopoulos *(CEO)*
Anthony S. Loumidis *(CFO & Treas)*
Advertising Agency:
Winsper Inc.
77 Summer St
Boston, MA 02110
Tel.: (617) 695-2900
Fax: (617) 696-2910
CRM
Digital Advertising
Marketing
Strategic Counsel
Website Development

AMETEK ROTRON
(Unit of AMETEK Aerospace & Defense Division)
55 Hasbrouck Ln
Woodstock, NY 12498-1807
Tel.: (845) 679-2401
Fax: (845) 679-7080
E-mail: milinquiry@ametek.com
Web Site: www.rotron.com
Sales Range: $100-124.9 Million
Approx. Number Employees: 300
Year Founded: 1948
Business Description:
Cooling Equipment Mfr
S.I.C.: 3564
N.A.I.C.S.: 333412
Media: 2-4-7-10-21
Distr.: Intl.; Natl.
Budget Set: Oct.
Personnel:
Tom Gates *(Mgr-Mktg)*
Brands & Products:
AMETEK
Advertising Agency:
Lefton Company
100 Independence Mall W
Philadelphia, PA 19106-2399
Tel.: (215) 923-9600
Fax: (215) 351-4298

AMOT CONTROLS CORPORATION
(Sub. of Roper Industries, Inc.)
8824 Fallbrook Dr
Houston, TX 77064
Tel.: (281) 940-1800
Fax: (281) 688-8802
E-mail: sales@amotusa.com
Web Site: www.amotusa.com
E-Mail For Key Personnel:
Sales Director: sales@amotusa.com
Approx. Sls.: $25,000,000
Approx. Number Employees: 100
Year Founded: 1947
Business Description:
Mfr. of Thermostatic Valves, Switches, Electronics, Engine Controls, Panels & Sensors
S.I.C.: 3823; 3491
N.A.I.C.S.: 334513; 332911
Export
Media: 2-4-7-10-21
Distr.: Intl.; Natl.
Budget Set: Sept.
Personnel:
Eric Schellenberger *(Pres)*
John Simmons *(Dir-Sls & Mktg)*

ARMSTRONG INTERNATIONAL, INC.
816 Maple St
Three Rivers, MI 49093-2345
Tel.: (269) 273-1415
Fax: (269) 278-6555
E-mail: marketing@armstronginternational.com
Web Site: www.armstrong-intl.com
Approx. Number Employees: 550
Year Founded: 1907
Business Description:
Steam Traps; Steam Humidifiers; Purgers for Refrigeration; Pipe Line Strainers; Air Vents; Fishing & Marine Equipment Mfr
S.I.C.: 3491; 3321
N.A.I.C.S.: 332911; 331511
Import Export
Media: 2-4-7-8-10-26
Distr.: Intl
Budget Set: July
Personnel:
Tom Morris *(Gen Counsel)*
Tom Henry *(Dir-Mktg-Global)*
Brands & Products:
ARMSTRONG
ARMSTRONG SERVICE
DURAMIX
FLO-DIRECT
FLO-RITE-TEMP
HUMID-A-WARE
HUMIDICLEAN
INTELLIGENT SYSTEM SOLUTIONS
POSI-PRESSURE
RADA
STEAM-A-WARE
STEAMEYE
STEAMIX
STEAMSTAR
TRAPALERT

BABCOCK & WILCOX POWER GENERATION GROUP, INC.
(Unit of The Babcock & Wilcox Company)
20 S Van Buren Ave
Barberton, OH 44203-0351
Mailing Address:
PO Box 351
Barberton, OH 44203-0351
Tel.: (330) 753-4511
Fax: (330) 860-1886
E-mail: info@babcock.com
Web Site: www.babcock.com
Approx. Number Employees: 8,000
Business Description:
Fossil Power Generation & Equipment
S.I.C.: 4939; 3559
N.A.I.C.S.: 221112; 332410
Import Export
Advertising Expenditures: $100,000
Bus. Publs.: $20,000; Catalogs & Directories: $10,000; D.M. to Bus. Estab.: $10,000; Exhibits/Trade Shows: $60,000
Distr.: Intl.; Natl.
Budget Set: Feb. -Mar.
Personnel:
Richard L. Killion *(Pres)*
Michael P. Dickerson *(VP & Officer-IR)*
Advertising Agency:
SmileyHanchulak Marketing Communications
47 N Cleveland Massillon Rd
Akron, OH 44333-2420
Tel.: (330) 666-0868
Fax: (330) 666-5762

BAKER & SONS AIR CONDITIONING INC.
164 Sarasota Center Blvd
Sarasota, FL 34240
Tel.: (941) 377-3602
Web Site: www.bakerandsonsac.com
Business Description:
Heating & Air Conditioning Services
N.A.I.C.S.: 238220
Media: 8-10-13-16
Personnel:
Bill Baker *(Pres)*

BALTIMORE AIRCOIL COMPANY
(Div. of AMSTED Industries Incorporated)
7600 Dorsey Run Rd
Jessup, MD 20794-9323
Mailing Address:
PO Box 7322
Baltimore, MD 21227-0322
Tel.: (410) 799-6200
Fax: (410) 799-6416
E-mail: Inco@baltimoreaircoil.com
Web Site: www.baltimoreaircoil.com
Approx. Number Employees: 1,200
Year Founded: 1938
Business Description:
Mfr. of Cooling Water Recovery Systems, Cooling Towers, Evaporative Condensers, Closed Circuit Cooling Towers, Thermal Storage Units & Heat Exchangers Thermal Storage
S.I.C.: 3585; 3559
N.A.I.C.S.: 333415; 332410

Key to Media (For complete agency information see *The Advertising Red Books-Agencies* edition):
1. Bus. Publs. 2. Cable T.V. 3. Catalogs & Directories. 4. Co-op Adv. 5. Consumer Mags. 6. D.M. to Bus. Estab.7. D.M. to Consumers 8. Daily Newsp. 9. Exhibits/Trade Shows 10. Foreign 11. Infomercial 12. Internet Adv.13. Multimedia 14. Network Radio 15. Network T.V. 16. Newsp. Distr. Mags. 17. Other 18. Outdoor (Posters, Transit) 19. Point of Purchase20. Premiums, Novelties 21. Product Samples 22. Special Events Mktg. 23. Spot Radio 24. Spot T.V. 25. Weekly Newsp. 26. Yellow Page Adv.

Export
Media: 2-4-10
Distr.: Intl.; Natl.
Budget Set: Oct.
Personnel:
Steven S. Duerwachter *(Pres)*
Timothy P. Facius *(VP-Global Mktg)*
Rob Landstra *(VP-Fin)*
Michael D. Pugh *(Dir-Sls-Americas)*
Brands & Products:
AR AIRCOIL
B.A.C.
BACOUNT
BACROSS
B.A.C.ULOGIC
BALTIBOND
BALTIDRIVE
EASY CLEAN
EASY CONNECT
ENERGY MISER
HIGH-K
ICE CHILLER
ICE-LOGIC
IOBIO

BARD MANUFACTURING COMPANY
1914 Randolph Dr
Bryan, OH 43506-2253
Mailing Address:
PO Box 607
Bryan, OH 43506-0607
Tel.: (419) 636-1194
Fax: (419) 636-2640
E-mail: bard@bardhvac.com
Web Site: www.bardhvac.com
Approx. Sls.: $69,928,208
Approx. Number Employees: 300
Year Founded: 1914
Business Description:
Gas-Oil Heating Equipment, Air to Air & Water to Air Heat Pumps & Air Conditioning Equipment Mfr
S.I.C.: 3585; 3433
N.A.I.C.S.: 333415; 333414
Export
Advertising Expenditures: $300,000
Media: 2-5-10-18-22
Distr.: Intl.; Natl.
Personnel:
Bill Steel *(Chm, Pres & CEO)*
Robert S. Hood *(COO & VP-Mfg)*
John V. Briggs *(VP-Pur)*
Irvin L. Derks *(VP-Engrg)*
Brands & Products:
BARD
Q-TEC
WALL-MOUNT

BELL & GOSSETT/DOMESTIC PUMP
(Div. of ITT Fluid Technology Corporation)
8200 N Austin Ave
Morton Grove, IL 60053-3205
Tel.: (847) 966-3700
Fax: (847) 966-9052
E-mail: rcw.webmaster@itt.com
Web Site: www.bellgossett.com
Sales Range: $300-349.9 Million
Approx. Number Employees: 850
Year Founded: 1970
Business Description:
Hydronic Specialties; Centrifugal Pumps; Heat Transfer Equipment; Steam Traps, Regulators & Valves; Boiler Controls; Liquid Level Controls; Flow Switches; Valves
S.I.C.: 3561; 3443
N.A.I.C.S.: 333911; 332313
Export
Advertising Expenditures: $2,000,000
Media: 1-2-4-5-7-10-11-20-26
Distr.: Natl.
Budget Set: Sept.
Personnel:
Karl Buscher *(VP-Mktg)*
Robert Byron *(Mgr-Domestic Product)*
Donna Lutter *(Mgr-Mktg, Comm, & Adv)*
Brands & Products:
CHECK-TROL
DOMESTIC PUMP
ESP-PARTS
ESP-PLUS
HOFFMAN SPECIALTY
MCDONNELL & MILLER
THERMOFLOW

THE BETHLEHEM CORPORATION
25th & Lennox Sts
Easton, PA 18045
Tel.: (610) 258-7111
Fax: (610) 258-8154
E-mail: info@bethcorp.com
Web Site: www.bethcorp.com
Sales Range: $1-9.9 Million
Approx. Number Employees: 15
Year Founded: 1856
Business Description:
Materials Processing Equipment Mfr
S.I.C.: 3589; 3567
N.A.I.C.S.: 333319; 333994
Export
Advertising Expenditures: $60,000
Media: 1-2-4-7-10-20-26
Distr.: Intl.; Natl.
Budget Set: Mar.
Brands & Products:
PORCUPINE
THERMAL DISC

BRADFORD-WHITE CORPORATION
725 Talamore Dr
Ambler, PA 19002-1815
Tel.: (215) 641-9400
Fax: (215) 641-1612
Toll Free: (800) 523-2931
E-mail: info@bradfordwhite.com
Web Site: www.bradfordwhite.com
Sales Range: $10-24.9 Million
Approx. Number Employees: 1,100
Year Founded: 1881
Business Description:
Water Heaters For Residential, Commercial & Industrial Applications; Available In Gas, Electric, Oil & Solar Power Mfr
S.I.C.: 3433; 1711
N.A.I.C.S.: 333414; 238220
Media: 2-4-7-10-12-19-20
Distr.: Intl.; Natl.
Personnel:
A. R. Carnevale *(Chm & CEO)*
N. J. Giuffre *(Pres & COO)*
Eric Lannes *(Gen Mgr)*
F. D. Vattimo *(Dir-Mktg)*
Brands & Products:
ADVANCED SCREENLOK
BRADFORD WHITE
COMBICOR
DEFENDER ENERGY SAVER
EVERHOT
HYDROJET
JETGLAS
MAGNUM
POWERCOR
POWERFUL COMPACT
THROUGH-THE-WALL
TTW1
TTW2
TURBO-STATIC DISC
ULTRACOIL
VITRAGLAS
Advertising Agency:
Marketing Group
880 Louis Dr
Warminster, PA 18974
Tel.: (215) 259-1500
Fax: (215) 259-0290
(Bradford-White Water Heaters)
— Kirk Zucal *(Acct. Exec.)*

BROAN-NUTONE LLC
(Sub. of Nortek, Inc.)
926 W State St
Hartford, WI 53027-0140
Mailing Address:
PO Box 140
Hartford, WI 53027-0140
Tel.: (262) 673-4340
Fax: (262) 673-8709
Toll Free: (800) 558-1711
E-mail: info@broan.com
Web Site: www.broan-nutone.com
Approx. Number Employees: 3,200
Year Founded: 1932
Business Description:
Residential Ventilation Systems Mfr & Distr
S.I.C.: 3634; 3564; 3585; 3699
N.A.I.C.S.: 335211; 333412; 333415; 335999
Import Export
Media: 1-2-3-4-6-7-8-10-16-19-20-22-23-24-26
Distr.: Natl.
Personnel:
David L. Pringle *(Pres & CEO)*
John Pendergast *(CFO)*
Stephen Swenerton *(Sr VP-Mktg & Sls)*
Joseph Podawiltz *(Grp VP-HR)*
Karen Collins *(Mgr-Mktg & Comm)*
Brands & Products:
ALLURE
BEST BY BROAN
BIG HEAT
BROAN
BROAN-NUTONE
ECLIPSE
EUROPA
GUARDIAN PLUS
LOSONE
PRESSRITE
RANGEMASTER
SENSAIRE
SENSONIC
SOLITAIRE
Advertising Agency:
Cramer-Krasselt
225 N Michigan Ave
Chicago, IL 60601-7601
Tel.: (312) 616-9600
Fax: (312) 616-3839

BUHLER AEROGLIDE
(Sub. of Buhler AG)
100 Aeroglide Dr
Cary, NC 27511-6900
Mailing Address:
PO Box 29505
Raleigh, NC 27626-0505
Tel.: (919) 851-2000
Fax: (919) 851-6029
Telex: 579421
E-mail: sales@aeroglide.com
Web Site: www.aeroglide.com
E-Mail For Key Personnel:
Sales Director: sales@aeroglide.com
Sales Range: $50-74.9 Million
Approx. Number Employees: 220
Year Founded: 1940
Business Description:
Designer & Mfr of Industrial Drying & Cooling Equipment
S.I.C.: 3556; 3585
N.A.I.C.S.: 333294; 333415
Export
Advertising Expenditures: $350,000
Media: 2-4-10-11-13
Distr.: Intl.; Natl.
Budget Set: Nov.
Personnel:
J. Frederick Kelly, Jr. *(Pres & CEO)*
Michael Williams *(CFO & VP)*
Tom Mix *(Sr VP-Sls-Worldwide)*
Tom Barber *(Reg Dir-Americas)*
Brands & Products:
AEROGLIDE
FEC

BURNHAM HOLDINGS, INC.
1241 Harrisburg Pike
Lancaster, PA 17603
Mailing Address:
PO Box 3245
Lancaster, PA 17604-3245
Tel.: (717) 397-4700
Fax: (717) 293-5816
E-mail: info@burnham.com
Web Site: www.burnhamholdings.com
Approx. Rev.: $189,707,000
Approx. Number Employees: 1,000
Year Founded: 1856
Business Description:
Holding Company; Heating Boilers, Radiation & Gray-Iron Castings
S.I.C.: 3433; 3559; 6719
N.A.I.C.S.: 333414; 332410; 551112
Import Export
Advertising Expenditures: $1,000,000
Media: 2-4-5-6-7-8-10-19-22
Distr.: Natl.
Personnel:
Albert Morrison, III *(Chm, Pres & CEO)*
Douglas B. Springer *(CFO & VP)*
Stephan P. Amicone *(COO & Exec VP)*
Douglas S. Brossman *(Gen Counsel & VP)*
Brands & Products:
BRYAN BOILERS
BRYAN STEAM
BURNHAM
CROWN BOILER
GOVERNALE
INVESTING IN THE FUTURE
NEW YORKER
THERMAL SOLUTIONS
THERMO PRIDE
U.S BOILERS COMPANY

CAMFIL FARR, INC.
(Sub. of Camfil AB)
2121 E Paulhan St
Compton, CA 90220-6433
Tel.: (310) 668-6300

Key to Media (For complete agency information see *The Advertising Red Books-Agencies* edition):
1. Bus. Publs. 2. Cable T.V. 3. Catalogs & Directories. 4. Co-op Adv. 5. Consumer Mags. 6. D.M. to Bus. Estab.7. D.M. to Consumers 8. Daily Newsp. 9. Exhibits/Trade Shows 10. Foreign 11. Infomercial 12. Internet Adv.13. Multimedia 14. Network Radio 15. Network T.V. 16. Newsp. Distr. Mags. 17. Other 18. Outdoor (Posters, Transit) 19. Point of Purchase20. Premiums, Novelties 21. Product Samples 22. Special Events Mktg. 23. Spot Radio 24. Spot T.V. 25. Weekly Newsp. 26. Yellow Page Adv.

Camfil Farr, Inc. — (Continued)

Fax: (310) 608-2268
Toll Free: (800) 333-7320
Web Site: www.camfilfarr.com/cou_us/
Sales Range: $300-349.9 Million
Approx. Number Employees: 500
Year Founded: 1937
Business Description:
Mfr. of Air Filtration Equipment, (HVAC) Engine Air Cleaners & Dust Collection Systems
S.I.C.: 3564
N.A.I.C.S.: 333411
Import Export
Advertising Expenditures: $610,000
Bus. Publs.: $100,000; Catalogs & Directories: $300,000; Exhibits/Trade Shows: $150,000; Premiums, Novelties: $25,000; Yellow Page Adv.: $35,000
Distr.: Intl.; Natl.
Budget Set: Sept.
Personnel:
John Johnston *(Pres)*
Brands & Products:
30/30
ABSOLUTE
AEROPAC
AEROPLEAT
CITYSORB
DETERMINATOR
DURAFIL
DYNAVANE
FILTRA 2000
GOLD SERIES FILTERS
HI-FLO
HP 100
HP 200
MICRETAIN
OPTI-PAC
RIGA-FLO
RIGA-SORB
SNAP-SEAL
TENKAY
TM-33
UHD
ULTRA-PAC
ULTRASOLVE
ZEPHYR II

CARRIER CORPORATION
(Group of United Technologies Corporation)
1 Carrier Pl
Farmington, CT 06032-4015
Tel.: (860) 674-3000
Fax: (860) 674-3139
Toll Free: (800) CARRIER
Web Site: www.carrier.com
Sales Range: $5-14.9 Billion
Approx. Number Employees: 32,400
Year Founded: 1915
Business Description:
Air Conditioning, Heating & Refrigeration Products
S.I.C.: 3585
N.A.I.C.S.: 333415
Import Export
Advertising Expenditures: $10,000,000
Media: 2-4-5-6-7-8-9-10-11-15-16-18-19-20-23-24-26
Distr.: Natl.
Budget Set: July
Personnel:
Geraud Darnis *(Pres)*
Robert J. McDonough *(Pres-Residential & Light Comml Sys-North America)*
Kelly Romano *(Pres-Building Sys & Svcs)*
Rajan Goel *(VP-Strategic Plng, Mktg & Comm)*
Patrick Preux *(VP-HR)*
Elizabeth Young *(Mgr-Comm & PR)*
Brands & Products:
CARRIER
INFINITY
PAYNE

CFM CORPORATION
(Holding of Teachers' Private Capital)
2695 Meadowvale Blvd
Mississauga, ON L5N 8A3, Canada
Tel.: (905) 819-4777
Tel.: (905) 858-8010
Fax: (905) 670-7915
Fax: (905) 858-9121
Fax: (905) 858-1165
E-mail: cfm@cfmcorp.com
Sales Range: $500-549.9 Million
Approx. Number Employees: 2,700
Year Founded: 1987
Business Description:
Home Products & Related Accessories Mfr
S.I.C.: 3433
N.A.I.C.S.: 333414
Import
Media: 4-5-6-10
Personnel:
Charles E. Csiszar *(CMO)*
Brands & Products:
DYNA-GLO
GREENWAY
INSTA-FLAME
KINDER
MAJESTIC
MESINA
NORTHERN FLAME
PYROMASTER
TIMBERLINE
VERMONT CASTINGS
VICTORIAN GARDEN

CHARLES A. HONES, INC.
607 Albany Ave
Amityville, NY 11701-0518
Tel.: (631) 842-8886
Fax: (631) 842-9300
E-mail: info@charlesahones.com
Web Site: www.charlesahones.com
Approx. Number Employees: 8
Year Founded: 1911
Business Description:
Mfr. of Buzzer Gas Burners & Furnaces & Industrial Process Gas Equipment
S.I.C.: 3567
N.A.I.C.S.: 333994
Export
Advertising Expenditures: $250,000
Media: 2-4-10-11-16-26
Distr.: Intl.; Natl.
Personnel:
Robert Michael Hones *(Pres)*
Susan Elaine Hones *(Mgr)*
Brands & Products:
BASO
BUZZER
CHARLES A. HONES

CHROMALOX, INC.
(Holding of Sentinel Capital Partners LLC)
103 Gamma Dr
Pittsburgh, PA 15238-2919
Tel.: (412) 967-3800
Fax: (412) 967-5148
Toll Free: (800) 443-2640
E-mail: info@chromalox.com
Web Site: www.chromalox.com
Sales Range: $150-199.9 Million
Approx. Number Employees: 1,450
Year Founded: 2001
Business Description:
Industrial Electric Heating Equipment & Temperature Control System Mfr
S.I.C.: 3433; 3679
N.A.I.C.S.: 333414; 334419
Import Export
Advertising Expenditures: $1,450,000
Catalogs & Directories: $700,000; Co-op Adv.: $70,000; D.M. to Bus. Estab.: $30,000; D.M. to Consumers: $30,000; Exhibits/Trade Shows: $80,000; Internet Adv.: $20,000; Point of Purchase: $45,000; Premiums, Novelties: $40,000; Product Samples: $400,000; Yellow Page Adv.: $35,000
Distr.: Intl.; Natl.
Budget Set: Oct.
Personnel:
Scott Dysert *(CEO)*
Brands & Products:
CHROMALOX
MAXPAC
MINIMAX
VERSATHERM

C.I. HAYES
(Sub. of Gasbarre Products Inc.)
33 Freeway Dr
Cranston, RI 02920
Tel.: (401) 467-5200
Fax: (401) 467-2108
E-mail: cihayesinfo@cihayes.com
Web Site: www.cihayes.com
Sales Range: $10-24.9 Million
Approx. Number Employees: 120
Year Founded: 1905
Business Description:
Heat Treating Solutions
S.I.C.: 3567; 3433; 3585
N.A.I.C.S.: 333994; 333414; 333415
Media: 2-4-10-11-13
Distr.: Natl.
Budget Set: Oct.
Personnel:
P. Parker *(Mgr-Replacement Parts Sls)*
Bob Brodeur *(Engr)*
Matthew Marzullo *(Engr-Sls)*
R. O'Neill *(Engr)*
Brands & Products:
C.I. HAYES

CINCINNATI SUB-ZERO PRODUCTS, INC.
12011 Mosteller Rd
Cincinnati, OH 45241-1528
Tel.: (513) 772-8810
Fax: (513) 772-9119
Toll Free: (800) 989-7373
E-mail: cszinc@cszinc.com
Web Site: www.cszinc.com
E-Mail For Key Personnel:
Marketing Director: yelton@cszinc.com
Approx. Number Employees: 200
Year Founded: 1940
Business Description:
Production Chilling Chambers; Environmental Test Equipment; Cryogenic Equipment; Hyperthermia & Hypothermia Equipment; Disposable Blankets & Pads Mfr
S.I.C.: 3823; 3841
N.A.I.C.S.: 334513; 339112
Export
Media: 2-4-10-21
Distr.: Direct to Rep; Intl.
Personnel:
Steve Berke *(Pres & CEO)*
Kristal Yelton *(Mgr-Mktg)*
Brands & Products:
BLANKETROL
BLANKETROL II
COOLTEMP
CSZ
DISPOSA-COVERS
ECMO
ELECTRI-COOL
FILTEREDFLO
GELLI-ROLL
HEMOTHERM
HOT/ICE
KOOL-KIT
MAXI-THERM
MICRO-TEMP
MICROCLIMATE
MINI-TEMP
NEURO-COOL
NORM-O-TEMP
PLASTIPAD
STERIPROBE
TEMP-PAD
THERMA-TEMP
TROPI-COOL
WARM AIR
WARMING TUBE

COMAIR HOLDINGS CORP.
2675 Customhouse Ct Ste F
San Diego, CA 92154-7651
Tel.: (619) 661-6688
Fax: (619) 661-6057
Fax: (619) 661-1757
E-mail: sales@comairrotron.com
Web Site: www.comairrotron.com
E-Mail For Key Personnel:
Sales Director: sales@comairrotron.com
Sales Range: $50-74.9 Million
Approx. Number Employees: 1,400
Year Founded: 1996
Business Description:
Blowers & Fans
S.I.C.: 3564
N.A.I.C.S.: 333412
Import Export
Personnel:
Steve Pellegrini *(Pres)*
Melissa Johnson *(CIO & VP-IT)*
Advertising Agency:
Northlich
Sawyer Point Bldg 720 Pete Rose Way
Cincinnati, OH 45202
Tel.: (513) 421-8840
Fax: (513) 455-4749

CROWN ANDERSEN INC.
1015 Tyrone Rd Ste 410
Tyrone, GA 30290-2456
Tel.: (770) 486-2000
Fax: (770) 487-5066
E-mail: tom.vanremmen@and2k.com
Web Site: www.crownandersen.com

Key to Media (For complete agency information see *The Advertising Red Books-Agencies* edition):
1. Bus. Publs. 2. Cable T.V. 3. Catalogs & Directories. 4. Co-op Adv. 5. Consumer Mags. 6. D.M. to Bus. Estab.7. D.M. to Consumers
8. Daily Newsp. 9. Exhibits/Trade Shows 10. Foreign 11. Infomercial 12. Internet Adv.13. Multimedia 14. Network Radio
15. Network T.V. 16. Newsp. Distr. Mags. 17. Other 18. Outdoor (Posters, Transit) 19. Point of Purchase20. Premiums, Novelties
21. Product Samples 22. Special Events Mktg. 23. Spot Radio 24. Spot T.V. 25. Weekly Newsp. 26. Yellow Page Adv.

Sales Range: $1-9.9 Million
Approx. Number Employees: 3
Year Founded: 1971
Business Description:
Industrial Pollution Control, Air Handling, Heat Recovery & Disposal Systems Mfr & Installer
S.I.C.: 3564
N.A.I.C.S.: 333412; 333411
Export
Media: 4-7-10-11-13
Personnel:
Randall Morgan *(CFO)*
Brands & Products:
CHEAF
HEAF
SUBDEW

DESA LLC
(Holding of H.I.G. Capital, LLC)
2701 Industrial Dr
Bowling Green, KY 42101-4065
Mailing Address:
PO Box 90004
Bowling Green, KY 42102-9004
Tel.: (270) 781-9600
Fax: (270) 781-9400
Fax: (800) 991-3372
Toll Free: (866) 672-6040
E-mail: cschaut@desaint.com
Web Site: www.desaint.com
Approx. Number Employees: 1,100
Business Description:
Heating Equipment, Portable Chain Saws, Security Lighting Door Bells & Specialty Tools Mfr
S.I.C.: 3433; 3965
N.A.I.C.S.: 333414; 339993
Media: 2-3-4-5-10-19
Personnel:
Mike Briggs *(CEO & COO)*
Augusto Millan *(Pres-Intl Bus)*
Samir Barudhi *(VP-Engrg)*
Ralph Pratt *(Mgr-Quality Control)*
Brands & Products:
COMFORT GLOW
DESA
POWERFAST
REDDY HEATER
VANGUARD

DESPATCH INDUSTRIES
8860 207th St W
Lakeville, MN 55044
Tel.: (952) 469-5424
Fax: (952) 469-4513
Toll Free: (800) 828-9903
E-mail: info@despatch.com
Web Site: www.despatch.com
Approx. Number Employees: 250
Year Founded: 1902
Business Description:
Mfr. of Standard, Custom Batch & Continuous Industrial Ovens, Furnaces & Fully Integrated Continuous Thermal Processing Solutions for Electronic Component, Pharmaceutical, Semiconductor, Metal & Other Material Applications
S.I.C.: 3567; 3821
N.A.I.C.S.: 333994; 339111
Import Export
Media: 17-26
Distr.: Intl.; Natl.
Budget Set: Nov.
Personnel:
Patrick J. Peyton *(Chm & CEO)*
Kevin Rowekamp *(CFO)*
Ellen Cheng *(Gen Mgr-Despatch Industries Taiwan, Ltd.)*
Ernie Serrano *(Reg Mgr-Latin America)*
Erik Anderson *(Product Mgr-Solar)*
Brad Rohlf *(Product Mgr)*
Brands & Products:
CACTAS
DESPATCH
DIGITRONIC
MOJAVE
PCO2-14
PRIORITY LINE
PROTOCOL MANAGER
PROTOCOL PLUS
RANSCO

DETROIT STOKER CO.
1510 E 1st St
Monroe, MI 48161-1915
Mailing Address:
PO Box 732
Monroe, MI 48161
Tel.: (734) 241-9500
Fax: (734) 241-7126
Toll Free: (800) STOKER4
Web Site: www.detroitstoker.com
E-Mail For Key Personnel:
Sales Director: sales@detroitstoker.com
Sales Range: $25-49.9 Million
Approx. Number Employees: 350
Year Founded: 1898
Business Description:
Industrial Stokers Mfr
S.I.C.: 3433
N.A.I.C.S.: 333414
Export
Media: 2-4-7-10-11
Distr.: Direct to Consumer; Natl.
Budget Set: Dec.
Personnel:
Thomas Giaier *(Pres)*
Brands & Products:
DETROIT
DSC
HYDROGRATE
RECIPROGRATE
ROTOGRATE
ROTOSTOKER VCG
VACPAK
WOODPAK

DIAMOND POWER INTERNATIONAL, INC.
(Sub. of Babcock & Wilcox Power Generation Group, Inc.)
2600 E Main St
Lancaster, OH 43130-8490
Mailing Address:
PO Box 415
Lancaster, OH 43130-0415
Tel.: (740) 687-6500
Fax: (740) 687-4229
Web Site: www.diamondpower.com
Sales Range: $75-99.9 Million
Approx. Number Employees: 1,600
Year Founded: 1903
Business Description:
Mfr. of Boiler Cleaning Equipment, Ash Handling Equipment, Boiler Drum Level Gauges & Indicators, Boiler Cleaning Controls & Diagnostics
S.I.C.: 3559
N.A.I.C.S.: 333298
Export
Advertising Expenditures: $200,000
Media: 2-4-6-7-8-9-10
Distr.: Intl.; Natl.
Budget Set: Nov.
Personnel:
Eileen Competti *(Pres)*
William Powers *(Controller)*
R.M. Dortch *(Gen Mgr-Ops)*
Charlie C. England *(Gen Mgr)*
D. R. Gibbs *(Gen Mgr-Bus Dev & Mktg)*
R. M. Randal *(Gen Mgr-Ops)*
M.A. Bunton *(Gen Mgr-Engrg)*
T.E. Moskal *(Dir-Mktg)*
James Craft *(Dir-HR)*
Mike Dowling *(Mgr-Mktg)*

DOMETIC CORPORATION
(Sub. of Dometic International AB)
2320 Industrial Pkwy
Elkhart, IN 46515
Mailing Address:
PO Box 490
Elkhart, IN 46515-0490
Tel.: (574) 294-2511
Fax: (574) 293-9686
E-mail: dometic@usa.com
Web Site: www.dometicusa.com
Approx. Number Employees: 1,500
Year Founded: 1956
Business Description:
Air Conditioners Mfr, Refrigeration Products & Awnings Mfr
S.I.C.: 3585
N.A.I.C.S.: 333415
Media: 2-6-9-10-19
Distr.: Natl.
Budget Set: Nov.
Personnel:
Doug Whyte *(Pres)*
Rutger Wachtmeister *(Exec VP-Mktg-Sls)*
Advertising Agency:
TaigMarks Inc.
223 S Main St Ste 100
Elkhart, IN 46516
Tel.: (574) 294-8844
Fax: (574) 294-8855

DRESSER-RAND
(Div. of Dresser-Rand Group Inc.)
299 Lincoln St
Worcester, MA 01527-8000
Tel.: (508) 595-1700
Fax: (508) 595-1780
Web Site: www.tuthill.com
Approx. Sls.: $60,000,000
Approx. Number Employees: 300
Year Founded: 1909
Business Description:
Steam Turbines, Blowers, Exhausters & Marine Ventilators Mfr
S.I.C.: 3511; 3564
N.A.I.C.S.: 333611; 333412
Import Export
Media: 1-2-4-5-7-8-10-11-13-21-22-26
Distr.: Intl.; Natl.
Budget Set: Sept.
Personnel:
Gordon Duncan *(VP-Sls)*
Tom Levis *(Mgr-Mktg)*
Brands & Products:
CADET
DOUBLE DUTY
FANMIX
HEAT KILLER
JECTAIR
PORT-AIRE
VANO
VENTAIR

ECODYNE HEAT EXCHANGERS, INC.
(Sub. of Marmon Water Treatment)
8203 Market St Rd
Houston, TX 77029
Tel.: (713) 675-3511
Fax: (713) 675-7922
E-mail: info@ecodynehx.com
Web Site: www.ecodynehx.com
Sales Range: $50-74.9 Million
Approx. Number Employees: 100
Year Founded: 1987
Business Description:
Aircooler Equipment & Tubing Mfr
S.I.C.: 3585; 3433
N.A.I.C.S.: 333415; 333414
Media: 4
Personnel:
Larry Arndt *(VP-Fin)*
Greg Cash *(VP-Sls)*
John Zarafonetis *(Aftermarket Engr)*

ECR INTERNATIONAL - OLSEN DIVISION
(Div. of ECR International, Inc.)
6800 Base Line
Wallaceburg, ON N8A 5E5, Canada
Tel.: (519) 627-0791
Fax: (519) 627-4719
E-mail: oosinfo@ecrinternational.com
Web Site: www.olsenhvac.com
Approx. Number Employees: 40
Year Founded: 1963
Business Description:
Heating, Cooling & Refrigeration Equipment Whslr
S.I.C.: 3433
N.A.I.C.S.: 333414
Media: 10
Personnel:
David Morgan *(Mgr)*

EDD HELMS GROUP, INC.
17850 NE 5th Ave
Miami, FL 33162-1008
Tel.: (305) 653-2520
Fax: (305) 651-5527
Toll Free: (800) 329-2520
E-mail: info@eddhelms.com
Web Site: www.eddhelms.com
Sales Range: $10-24.9 Million
Approx. Number Employees: 140
Year Founded: 1975
Business Description:
Electrical Contracting, Air Conditioning & Data Communications
S.I.C.: 1731; 1711; 4813
N.A.I.C.S.: 238210; 238220; 517110
Advertising Expenditures: $493,651
Media: 3-7-10-13-18-23-26
Personnel:
L. Wade Helms *(Pres & CEO)*
Dean A. Goodson *(CFO)*
Joe Kelly *(Gen Mgr-Electrical)*
Bob Roberts *(Gen Mgr-HVAC)*
Joni Alonso *(Mgr-Trade Shows)*
Sherrie Helms *(Mgr-Westin Diplomat Events)*
Luis Morales *(Mgr-Building Controls Div)*

EFM SALES COMPANY
(Sub. of BCS Managment Company)
302 S 4th St
Emmaus, PA 18049-3853
Tel.: (610) 965-9041
Fax: (610) 967-6593
E-mail: efmsalescompany@enter.net

Key to Media (For complete agency information see *The Advertising Red Books-Agencies* edition):
1. Bus. Publs. 2. Cable T.V. 3. Catalogs & Directories. 4. Co-op Adv. 5. Consumer Mags. 6. D.M. to Bus. Estab.7. D.M. to Consumers
8. Daily Newsp. 9. Exhibits/Trade Shows 10. Foreign 11. Infomercial 12. Internet Adv.13. Multimedia 14. Network Radio
15. Network T.V. 16. Newsp. Distr. Mags. 17. Other 18. Outdoor (Posters, Transit) 19. Point of Purchase20. Premiums, Novelties
21. Product Samples 22. Special Events Mktg. 23. Spot Radio 24. Spot T.V. 25. Weekly Newsp. 26. Yellow Page Adv.

EFM Sales Company — (Continued)

Web Site: www.efmheating.com
Approx. Number Employees: 3
Year Founded: 1922
Business Description:
Mfr of Automatic Heating Equipment
S.I.C.: 3433; 1711
N.A.I.C.S.: 333414; 238220
Advertising Expenditures: $200,000
Media: 1-2-3-4-5-10-13-23-26
Brands & Products:
ELECTRIC FURNACE-MAN

EMBASSY INDUSTRIES, INC.

(Sub. of Mestek, Inc.)
315 Oser Ave
Hauppauge, NY 11788
Tel.: (631) 694-1800
Fax: (631) 694-1832
E-mail: sales@embassyind.com
Web Site: www.embassyind.com
E-Mail For Key Personnel:
Sales Director: sales@embassyind.com
Approx. Sls.: $12,000,000
Approx. Number Employees: 6
Year Founded: 1966
Business Description:
Baseboard & Radiant Floor Heating Equipment Mfr
S.I.C.: 3433; 1711
N.A.I.C.S.: 333414; 238220
Import Export
Advertising Expenditures: $200,000
Media: 2-4-7-10
Distr.: Natl.
Brands & Products:
COMMERCIAL-PAK
HIDE-A-VECTOR2
PANEL-TRACK
SYSTEM6

EMCOR SERVICES NORTHEAST COMMAIR/ BALCO

(Sub. of EMCOR Group, Inc.)
80 Hawes Way
Stoughton, MA 02072
Tel.: (781) 573-1700
Fax: (781) 341-3337
Toll Free: (800) 252-2526
Web Site: www.commairbalco.com
Sales Range: $150-199.9 Million
Approx. Number Employees: 250
Year Founded: 1941
Business Description:
Commercial Facility Heating, Ventilation, Air-Conditioning, Plumbing & Fire Protection Systems Contractor
S.I.C.: 1711; 1731; 9224
N.A.I.C.S.: 238220; 238210; 922160
Media: 2-4-7-10-18-23-26
Distr.: Reg.
Personnel:
Phillip C. Megna *(Pres)*
Tom Ritchie *(VP-Fin & Admin)*

EMERSON AIR COMFORT PRODUCTS

(Div. of Emerson Electric Co.)
8100 W Florissant Ave Bldg T2
Saint Louis, MO 63136-1417
Tel.: (314) 553-5000
Tel.: (314) 553-5230
Fax: (314) 553-5311
Toll Free: (800) 237-6511
E-mail: info@emersonsans.com
Sales Range: $10-24.9 Million
Approx. Number Employees: 25
Year Founded: 1898
Business Description:
Ceiling Fans Mfr
S.I.C.: 3824
N.A.I.C.S.: 334514
Import Export
Advertising Expenditures: $3,000,000
Media: 2-4-5-10-19-20

EMERSON NETWORK POWER

(Sub. of Emerson Network Power Liebert)
610 Exec Campus Dr
Westerville, OH 43082-8871
Tel.: (614) 888-0246
Fax: (614) 841-6362
Web Site: www.emersonnetworkpower.com
Sales Range: $100-124.9 Million
Approx. Number Employees: 210
Business Description:
Computer Peripheral Equipment
S.I.C.: 7378; 5731; 5734
N.A.I.C.S.: 811212; 443112; 443120
Personnel:
Phil Arlinghaus *(VP-HR)*
Dale Reed *(VP-Sls-North America)*
Robert Rohde *(VP-Fin)*
Lauri Turevon *(VP-Sls)*
Advertising Agency:
Emerging Marketing
29 W 3rd Ave
Columbus, OH 43201
Tel.: (614) 923-6000
Fax: (614) 424-6200

EMERSON NETWORK POWER LIEBERT

(Formerly Liebert Corporation)
(Div. of Emerson Network Power)
1050 Dearborn Dr
Columbus, OH 43085
Tel.: (614) 888-0246
Fax: (614) 841-6022
Telex: LIEBERT WOGN
Web Site: www.liebert.com
Sales Range: $1-4.9 Billion
Approx. Number Employees: 5,000
Year Founded: 1964
Business Description:
Power & Environmental Control Systems Mfr
S.I.C.: 3613; 3585
N.A.I.C.S.: 335313; 333415
Import Export
Media: 1-2-4-5-7-10-11-13-20-21-22-26
Distr.: Intl.; Natl.
Budget Set: July -Aug.
Personnel:
Robert P. Bauer *(Pres-Liebert, Grp VP-Emerson)*
John Carey *(Sr VP-Ops)*
Steve Madara *(VP & Gen Mgr-Liebert Precision Cooling Bus)*
Jeff Blind *(VP-Fin)*
Fred Stack *(VP-Mktg-Cooling)*
Bill Campbell *(Sr Mgr-Product)*
Bill Barcus *(Product Mgr-Liebert AC Power)*
Ron Spangler *(Mgr-Product Mktg)*
Brands & Products:
COMMSURE
DATAWAVE
MINI-MATE2
NPOWER
X-TREME DENSITY SYSTEMS

EMERSON RETAIL SERVICES, INC.

(Sub. of Emerson Climate Technologies)
3240 Townpoint Dr Ste 100
Kennesaw, GA 30144
Tel.: (770) 425-6232
Fax: (770) 425-9319
E-mail: sales@ersus.com
Web Site: www.ersus.com
E-Mail For Key Personnel:
Sales Director: sales@ersus.com
Sales Range: $25-49.9 Million
Approx. Number Employees: 100
Year Founded: 1999
Business Description:
Climate Control Engineering & Consulting Services
S.I.C.: 8711; 3821; 3824; 3829; 3873; 8299; 8748
N.A.I.C.S.: 541330; 334514; 334518; 334519; 339111; 541618; 611710
Media: 7-10-11
Personnel:
Tom Parrish *(Mgr-Mktg)*
Brands & Products:
E-COMMISSIONING
N-COMMISSIONING
PROACT CB
VERIFRESH

EMERSON WHITE-RODGERS

(Formerly White-Rodgers)
(Div. of Emerson Climate Technologies)
8100 W Florissant Ave
Saint Louis, MO 63136
Tel.: (314) 553-3600
Web Site: www.emersonclimate.com/en-us/brands/white_rodgers/pages/white_rodgers.aspx
Sales Range: $50-74.9 Million
Approx. Number Employees: 150
Year Founded: 1937
Business Description:
Thermostat Mfr
S.I.C.: 3822; 3625
N.A.I.C.S.: 334512; 335314
Export
Media: 1-2-4-5-7-10-19-20
Distr.: Intl.; Natl.
Budget Set: Oct.
Personnel:
Mark J. Bulanda *(Pres)*
Ron Miles *(VP-Sls & Mktg Distr)*
John Black *(Dir-Mktg Svcs)*
Brands & Products:
70 SERIES
80 SERIES
90 SERIES
COMFORT-SET
COMFORTPLUS
HOT SURFACE IGNITION
INTELL-IGNITION
Advertising Agency:
Marketing Support, Inc.
200 E Randolph Dr Ste 5000
Chicago, IL 60601
Tel.: (312) 565-0044
Fax: (312) 946-6100

EVERGREEN ELECTRIC, INC.

59 Frog Hollow Rd
Califon, NJ 07830-3212
Tel.: (908) 832-5454
Fax: (908) 832-5500
E-mail: general@evergreenelectric.com
Web Site: www.evergreenelectric.biz
Approx. Number Employees: 3
Year Founded: 1975
Business Description:
Electrical Contractor
S.I.C.: 1731
N.A.I.C.S.: 238210
Export
Media: 4-7-26
Personnel:
Dave M. Como *(Pres)*

FAFCO INC.

435 Otterson Dr
Chico, CA 95928
Tel.: (530) 332-2100
Fax: (530) 332-2109
Toll Free: (800) 994-7652
E-mail: clazzaretto@fafco.com
Web Site: www.fafco.com
Approx. Number Employees: 97
Year Founded: 1969
Business Description:
Solar Heaters & Collectors
S.I.C.: 3433
N.A.I.C.S.: 333414
Advertising Expenditures: $2,547,200
Media: 10
Personnel:
Freeman A. Ford *(Chm)*
Robert W. Leckinger *(Pres)*
Nancy Garvin *(VP-Fin)*
Brands & Products:
FAFCO
ICESTOR
REVOLUTION
SUNSAVER

FIELD CONTROLS LLC

(Div. of Pettibone, LLC)
2630 Airport Rd
Kinston, NC 28504-7319
Tel.: (252) 522-3031
Fax: (252) 522-0214
E-mail: sales@fieldcontrols.com
Web Site: www.fieldcontrols.com
E-Mail For Key Personnel:
Sales Director: sales@fieldcontrols.com
Sales Range: $25-49.9 Million
Approx. Number Employees: 100
Year Founded: 1927
Business Description:
HVAC Products Mfr
S.I.C.: 3829; 3433; 3564; 3585
N.A.I.C.S.: 334519; 333412; 333414; 333415
Import Export
Media: 2-4-9-10-12
Distr.: Intl.; Natl.
Budget Set: Dec.
Personnel:
Patrick Holleran *(Pres)*
Tony Schrank *(VP-Engrg)*
Steve Guzorek *(Engr-Mechanical)*
Brands & Products:
AIRBOOT
CLEAR WAVE
THE ELIMINATOR
EVENAIR
EVENMIST
FAN-IN-A-CAN
FRESHMIST 90
STAR-KAP
THERMO-MIST
WATER SENTRY

Key to Media (For complete agency information see *The Advertising Red Books-Agencies* edition):
1. Bus. Publs. 2. Cable T.V. 3. Catalogs & Directories. 4. Co-op Adv. 5. Consumer Mags. 6. D.M. to Bus. Estab.7. D.M. to Consumers 8. Daily Newsp. 9. Exhibits/Trade Shows 10. Foreign 11. Infomercial 12. Internet Adv.13. Multimedia 14. Network Radio 15. Network T.V. 16. Newsp. Distr. Mags. 17. Other 18. Outdoor (Posters, Transit) 19. Point of Purchase20. Premiums, Novelties 21. Product Samples 22. Special Events Mktg. 23. Spot Radio 24. Spot T.V. 25. Weekly Newsp. 26. Yellow Page Adv.

Advertising Agency:
Carney & Co.
1653 N Winstead Ave
Rocky Mount, NC 27804-7398
Tel.: (252) 451-0060
Fax: (252) 451-0660
Toll Free: (800) 849-7547

FILTERTEK INC.
(Sub. of Illinois Tool Works Inc.)
11411 Price Rd
Hebron, IL 60034-8936
Tel.: (815) 648-2416
Fax: (815) 648-2929
Toll Free: (800) 248-2461
E-mail: sales@filtertek.com
Web Site: www.filtertek.com
E-Mail For Key Personnel:
Sales Director: sales@filtertek.com
Sales Range: $250-299.9 Million
Approx. Number Employees: 900
Year Founded: 1965
Business Description:
Custom Filters & Filtration Equipment Designer & Mfr
S.I.C.: 3569
N.A.I.C.S.: 333999
Import Export
Media: 2-7-10-11-13
Distr.: Natl.
Budget Set: July
Personnel:
David F. Atkinson *(Pres)*

FLEXFAB HORIZONS INTERNATIONAL, LLC
1699 W M43 Hwy
Hastings, MI 49058-9629
Tel.: (269) 945-2433
Fax: (269) 945-4802
Toll Free: (800) 331-0003
E-mail: sales@flexfab.com
Web Site: www.flexfab.com
E-Mail For Key Personnel:
President: ddecamp@flexfab.com
Sales Director: sales@flexfab.com
Approx. Number Employees: 400
Year Founded: 1961
Business Description:
Flexible Non-Metallic Hoses & Ducting Mfr
S.I.C.: 3569; 3052
N.A.I.C.S.: 333999; 326220
Export
Media: 2-4-7-10-11-13-21
Distr.: Intl.
Personnel:
Matthew DeCamp *(Pres & CEO)*
Jeff Weiden *(CFO & VP-Fin)*
David Brown *(VP-Sls & Mktg-Global)*
Bob Snow *(Dir-Quality & Bus Sys)*
Dave Anderson *(Mgr-Matls)*
Steve Egleston *(Mgr-Tech Dev)*
John Haines *(Mgr-Quality)*
Bill Haywood *(Program Mgr-Global Aerospace)*
Bill Morrissey *(Mgr-Sls & Mktg)*
Brands & Products:
FLEXFAB
INSULFAB
MARATHON MILKER
NEOFAB
NEOFAB-1
NOMEX
SILFAB
SILFAB-1
VENTFAB

Advertising Agency:
Hurst Advertising & Public Relations
2138 Lombard St Ste 4A
Philadelphia, PA 19146
Tel.: (610) 725-9600

FOSTORIA INDUSTRIES, INC.
1200 N Main St
Fostoria, OH 44830-1911
Tel.: (419) 435-9201
Fax: (419) 435-0842
Toll Free: (800) 495-4525
E-mail: email@fostoriaindustries.com
Web Site: www.fostoriaindustries.com
Approx. Number Employees: 160
Year Founded: 1917
Business Description:
Industrial Lighting; Industrial Ovens; Industrial, Commercial & Residential Heating
S.I.C.: 3585; 3567
N.A.I.C.S.: 333415; 333994
Import Export
Media: 2-4-7-8-10-21
Distr.: Intl.; Natl.
Budget Set: Oct. -Sept.
Personnel:
Larry E. Dunlap *(Pres & CEO)*
Mark Abell *(Reg VP)*
Brands & Products:
FOSTORIA
LOCALITE
MITEY MIDGET
PROMETAL

FRIEDRICH AIR CONDITIONING CO.
4200 N Pan Am Expy PO Box 1540
San Antonio, TX 78295-5212
Tel.: (210) 357-4400
Fax: (210) 357-4480
Toll Free: (800) 541-6645
Web Site: www.friedrich.com
Sales Range: $10-24.9 Million
Approx. Number Employees: 500
Year Founded: 1883
Business Description:
Mfr. of Air Conditioners & Heat Pumps, Electronic Air Cleaners & Ductless Split Systems
S.I.C.: 3585; 1711
N.A.I.C.S.: 333415; 238220
Export
Media: 2-4-5-6-8-9-10-11-19-20-22-23-26
Distr.: Intl
Personnel:
George Vanhoomisen *(CEO)*
Chuck Campbell *(VP-Mktg & Sls)*
Ronald L. Koehler *(Sr Mgr-Mktg)*
Jane Deming *(Mgr-Mktg Comm)*
Robert Gonzales *(Creative Svcs Mgr)*
Brands & Products:
CASEMENT
FRIEDRICH
HAZARDGARD
KP
MONEYSAVER
QUIETMASTER
QUIETMASTER DELUXE
QUIETMASTER HEAVY DUTY
SP
TWIN TEMP
UNI-FIT
VERT-I-PAK
WALLMASTER
X-STAR
Z-STAR

GEA FES, INC.
(Sub. of Royal GEA Grasso Holding NV-Refrigeration Division)
3475 Board Rd
York, PA 17406-9414
Tel.: (717) 767-6411
Fax: (717) 764-3627
Toll Free: (800) 888-4337
E-mail: sales.fes@geagroup.com
Web Site: www.geafes.com
E-Mail For Key Personnel:
Sales Director: sales.fes@geagroup.com
Approx. Number Employees: 260
Year Founded: 1949
Business Description:
Industrial Refrigeration Equipment Mfr
S.I.C.: 3585
N.A.I.C.S.: 333415
Media: 2-4-7
Personnel:
Ronald Eberhard *(Pres)*
Dennis Halsey *(VP-Sls & Mktg)*
Greg Klidonas *(VP-Engrg)*
Glenn Miller *(VP-Fin)*
Ash Bhadsavle *(Product Mgr-Heat Exchangers)*
Jim Nesbitt *(Product Mgr-Standard Compressor Packages)*
Jim Rohrbaugh *(Product Mgr-Controls)*
Art Stipanovic *(Product Mgr-Custom Engineered Sys)*
Jeff Cook *(Mgr-Mktg)*
Jeff Hoch *(Mgr-Quality Control)*
Brands & Products:
COMMENT
LITELINK
MICRO III

GENERAL FILTERS, INC.
43800 Grand River Ave
Novi, MI 48375-1115
Tel.: (248) 476-5100
Fax: (248) 349-2366
E-mail: sales@generalfilters.com
Web Site: www.generalfilters.com
E-Mail For Key Personnel:
Sales Director: sales@generalfilters.com
Approx. Number Employees: 49
Year Founded: 1937
Business Description:
Mfr. of Filters for Heating Fuel, Hydraulic & Lubricating Oils, Residential Humidifiers, Air Filters & Accessories
S.I.C.: 3585; 3564
N.A.I.C.S.: 333415; 333411
Import Export
Advertising Expenditures: $330,000
Media: 2-7-10-19
Distr.: Intl.; Natl.
Budget Set: Nov.
Personnel:
Robert R. Redner *(Pres)*
Carl Redner *(VP-Engrg)*
Brands & Products:
GENERAL AIRE
GENERAL FILTERS

GOODMAN GROUP, INC.
(Holding of Hellman & Friedman LLC)
5151 San Felipe Ste 500
Houston, TX 77056
Tel.: (713) 861-2500
Fax: (713) 861-4701
E-mail: customerservice@goodmanmfg.com
Web Site: www.goodmanmfg.com
Approx. Sls.: $1,851,186,000
Approx. Number Employees: 4,331
Year Founded: 1975
Business Description:
Air-Conditioners & Heating Units Mfr
S.I.C.: 3585
N.A.I.C.S.: 333415
Advertising Expenditures: $1,900,000
Personnel:
David Swift *(Pres & CEO)*
Lawrence M. Blackburn *(CFO & Exec VP)*
Terrance M. Smith *(CIO & Sr VP)*
James L. Mishler *(Pres-Company Owned Distr)*
Ben D. Campbell *(Gen Counsel, Sec & Exec VP)*
Peter H. Alexander *(Sr VP)*
Samuel G. Bikman *(Sr VP-Logistics & Bus Dev)*
Gary L. Clark *(Sr VP-Mktg)*
Karilee A. Durham *(Sr VP-HR)*
William L. Topper *(Sr VP-Ops)*
Neelkanth S. Gupte *(VP-Engrg)*
Brands & Products:
COPELAND
FRANKLIN
GOODMAN
QUIETFLEX

THE GRIEVE CORPORATION
500 Hart Rd
Round Lake, IL 60073-2835
Tel.: (847) 546-8225
Fax: (847) 546-9210
E-mail: sales@grievecorp.com
Web Site: www.grievecorp.com
E-Mail For Key Personnel:
Sales Director: sales@grievecorp.com
Approx. Number Employees: 80
Year Founded: 1949
Business Description:
Mfr of Industrial & Laboratory Ovens & Furnaces
S.I.C.: 3567; 3821
N.A.I.C.S.: 333994; 339111
Import Export
Media: 2-4-10-11-13-26
Distr.: Intl.; Natl.
Budget Set: Oct. -Nov.
Personnel:
D. V. Grieve *(Pres)*
Brands & Products:
GRIEVE
Advertising Agency:
Bernard & Company
1540 E Dundee Rd Ste 250
Palatine, IL 60074-8320
Tel.: (847) 934-4500
Fax: (847) 934-4720
(Ovens & Furnaces)

HEAT CONTROLLER, INC.
1900 Wellworth
Jackson, MI 49203-6428
Mailing Address:
PO Box 1089
Jackson, MI 49204-1089
Tel.: (517) 787-2100
Fax: (517) 787-9341
Web Site: www.heatcontroller.com
Approx. Number Employees: 250
Year Founded: 1933
Business Description:
Air Conditioning & Heating Equipment Mfr; OEM

Key to Media (For complete agency information see *The Advertising Red Books-Agencies* edition):
1. Bus. Publs. 2. Cable T.V. 3. Catalogs & Directories. 4. Co-op Adv. 5. Consumer Mags. 6. D.M. to Bus. Estab.7. D.M. to Consumers 8. Daily Newsp. 9. Exhibits/Trade Shows 10. Foreign 11. Infomercial 12. Internet Adv.13. Multimedia 14. Network Radio 15. Network T.V. 16. Newsp. Distr. Mags. 17. Other 18. Outdoor (Posters, Transit) 19. Point of Purchase20. Premiums, Novelties 21. Product Samples 22. Special Events Mktg. 23. Spot Radio 24. Spot T.V. 25. Weekly Newsp. 26. Yellow Page Adv.

Heat Controller, Inc. — (Continued)

S.I.C.: 3585
N.A.I.C.S.: 333415
Import Export
Advertising Expenditures: $1,000,000
Media: 1-2-5-7-10-16-18-19-20
Distr.: Intl.; Natl.
Budget Set: Nov.
Personnel:
Donald Peck *(Pres & CEO)*
Dave Duane *(VP-Fin)*
David Lamb *(Dir-Pur)*
Brenda Paul *(Mgr-Credit)*
LeeAnne Perkins *(Mgr-Adv)*
Jim Wilenius *(Natl Svc Mgr)*
Brands & Products:
CENTURY
COMFORT-AIRE
COMPACT-AIRE
CONQUEST 80
CONQUEST 90
ENERGY KNIGHT
HEAT CONTROLLER
PATRIOT 80
PORTABLE-AIRE
POWER-AIRE
SUPER POWER-AIRE

HEAT-TIMER CORPORATION

20 New Dutch Ln
Fairfield, NJ 07004
Tel.: (973) 575-4004
Fax: (973) 575-4052
E-mail: support@heat-timer.com
Web Site: www.heat-timer.com
Approx. Sls.: $4,000,000
Approx. Number Employees: 50
Year Founded: 1938
Business Description:
Electronic Heating Controls, Motorized Valves, Smoke Alarms, Electro-Hydronic Heating Systems & Tempering Valves Mfr
S.I.C.: 3822
N.A.I.C.S.: 334512
Advertising Expenditures: $250,000
Media: 2-4-7-10
Distr.: Natl.
Personnel:
Michael Pitonyak *(Owner)*
Vincent Clerico *(VP-Sls)*
Brands & Products:
DIGI-SPAN
HEAT-TIMER
HEAT-TROL
INJECTEMP
NOTIFACT
VARIVALVE

HENRY TECHNOLOGIES, INC.

(Holding of Hendricks Holding Company, Inc.)
(d/b/a Henry Technologies Group)
655 3rd St Ste 100
Beloit, WI 53511
Tel.: (608) 361-4400
Web Site: www.henrytech.com
Sales Range: $10-24.9 Million
Approx. Number Employees: 250
Year Founded: 1914
Business Description:
Commercial & Industrial Heating, Ventilation, Air Conditioning & Refrigeration Valve & Component Mfr & Distr
S.I.C.: 3491; 3494; 3559; 3585; 5075; 5078
N.A.I.C.S.: 332911; 332410; 332919; 333415; 423730; 423740
Import Export
Media: 4-10-11
Personnel:
Michael Giordano *(Pres & CEO)*
Christian J. Garver *(CFO)*
Brands & Products:
A-1 COMPONENTS
AC & R
CHIL-CON
HENRY TECHNOLOGIES
HENRY VALVE COMPANY

HILL PHOENIX INC.

(Sub. of Dover Engineered Systems, Inc.)
709 Sigman Rd
Conyers, GA 30013
Tel.: (770) 285-3100
Fax: (770) 285-3071
Web Site: www.hillphoenix.com
Sales Range: $450-499.9 Million
Approx. Number Employees: 1,700
Year Founded: 1994
Business Description:
Refrigeration Condensing Systems Mfr
S.I.C.: 3585
N.A.I.C.S.: 333415
Media: 2-4-7-10
Distr.: Natl.
Personnel:
John Guerrieri *(VP-Sls-Central Reg)*
Brad Roche *(VP-Mktg)*
Raymond Downes *(Mgr-Dealer Grp)*
Brands & Products:
COOLGENIX
ORIGIN2
POWERCENTER
POWERPLUS
POWERWALL
PRESTIGE

HONEYWELL ENVIRONMENTAL & COMBUSTION CONTROLS

(Div. of Honeywell Automation & Control Solutions)
1985 Douglas Dr N
Golden Valley, MN 55422
Tel.: (763) 950-5500
Web Site: yourhome.honeywell.com
Sales Range: $100-124.9 Million
Business Description:
Heating, Ventilation, Air Purification & Lighting Control System Developer & Mfr
S.I.C.: 3822
N.A.I.C.S.: 334512
Advertising Agency:
Waldbillig & Besteman, Inc.
8001 Excelsior Dr Ste 110
Madison, WI 53717-1956
Tel.: (608) 829-0900
Fax: (608) 829-0901
Toll Free: (800) 395-4767

HUDSON TECHNOLOGIES, INC.

1 Blue Hill Plz PO Box 1541
Pearl River, NY 10965
Tel.: (845) 512-6000
Fax: (845) 512-6070
Fax: (845) 359-4718
Toll Free: (800) 501-HDSN
Toll Free: (800) 501-4376
E-mail: info@hudsontech.com
Web Site: www.hudsontech.com
Approx. Rev.: $37,273,000
Approx. Number Employees: 77
Year Founded: 1991
Business Description:
Heating, Ventilating & Air Conditioning Specializing in Refrigerant Contaminant Cleanup
S.I.C.: 7699; 1711; 1796; 5078
N.A.I.C.S.: 811310; 238220; 238290; 423740
Media: 2-7-13
Personnel:
Kevin J. Zugibe *(Chm & CEO)*
Brian F. Coleman *(Pres & COO)*
James R. Buscemi *(CFO)*
Charles F. Harkins Jr. *(VP-Legal & Regulatory)*
Stephen P. Mandracchia *(VP-Legal & Regulatory)*
George Dinsmore *(Dir-Bus Dev)*
Joseph Longo *(Dir-Engrg)*
Riyaz Papar *(Dir-Energy Assets & Optimization)*
Nancy Overman *(Mgr-Refrigerant Sls)*
Brands & Products:
CHILLER CHEMISTRY
CHILLSMART
FLUID CHEMISTRY
HUDSON TECHNOLOGIES
REFRIGERANTSIDE
ZUGIBEAST

HUSSMANN CANADA INC.

(Sub. of Hussmann International, Inc.)
5 Cherry Blossom Rd Bldg 1 Unit 3
PO Box 550
Cambridge, ON N3H 4R7, Canada
Tel.: (519) 653-9980
Fax: (519) 653-1805
Web Site: www.hussmann.com
Approx. Number Employees: 30
Year Founded: 1906
Business Description:
Sales of Refrigeration Equipment
S.I.C.: 5078
N.A.I.C.S.: 423740
Import Export
Advertising Expenditures: $625,000
Media: 2-4-7-10-11
Distr.: Intl.; Natl.
Budget Set: June
Brands & Products:
IMPACT
PROTOCOL

INTERNATIONAL COMFORT PRODUCTS CORPORATION

(Sub. of Carrier Corporation)
650 Heil Quaker Ave
Lewisburg, TN 37091-2135
Mailing Address:
PO Box 128
Lewisburg, TN 37091-0100
Tel.: (931) 359-3511
Fax: (931) 270-4255
E-mail: info@icpusa.com
Web Site: www.icpusa.com
Approx. Rev.: $600,000,000
Approx. Number Employees: 200
Business Description:
Electric, Oil & Gas Furnaces; Central Air Conditioning; Heating & Cooling Products
S.I.C.: 3433; 3585
N.A.I.C.S.: 333414; 333415
Export
Media: 1-2-4-5-6-7-9-10-15-18-19-20-23-24-25-26
Distr.: Natl.
Budget Set: Dec.
Personnel:
Lisa Townley *(Mgr-ICP Brand Mktg)*
Brands & Products:
AIRQUEST
ARCO AIRE
COMFORTMAKER
HEIL
INTERNATIONAL COMFORT PRODUCTS
TEMPSTAR
Advertising Agency:
Gish, Sherwood & Friends, Inc. (d/b/a GS&F)
4235 Hillsboro Pike
Nashville, TN 37215-3344
Tel.: (615) 385-1100
Fax: (615) 783-0500

INVENSYS CLIMATE CONTROLS

(Sub. of Invensys Process Systems)
8115 US Route 42 N
Plain City, OH 43064
Tel.: (614) 873-9200
Fax: (614) 873-9332
Web Site: www.icca.invensys.com/
Approx. Number Employees: 2,000
Year Founded: 1978
Business Description:
Temperature & Pressure Controls, Valves, Humidity & Automatic Controls & Control Systems Mfr
S.I.C.: 3822; 3714
N.A.I.C.S.: 334512; 336322
Advertising Expenditures: $1,000,000
Media: 2-4-10-21
Distr.: Intl.; Natl.
Budget Set: Oct.
Brands & Products:
RENCO

IPSEN INTERNATIONAL, INC.

(Sub. of Ipsen International Holding GmbH)
984 Ipsen Rd
Cherry Valley, IL 61016
Mailing Address:
PO Box 6266
Rockford, IL 61125-1266
Tel.: (815) 332-4941
Fax: (815) 332-4995
Toll Free: (800) 727-7625
E-mail: sales@abaripsen.com
Web Site: www.ipsenusa.com
E-Mail For Key Personnel:
Sales Director: sales@abaripsen.com
Approx. Number Employees: 300
Year Founded: 1948
Business Description:
Mfr of Production Heat Treating & Brazing Equipment, Vacuum Furnaces; Industrial Furnaces; Parts & Service
S.I.C.: 3567
N.A.I.C.S.: 333994
Export
Advertising Expenditures: $200,000
Media: 2-6-7-10-11-13
Distr.: Intl.
Budget Set: Nov.
Personnel:
Geoffrey Somary *(Pres & CEO)*

Key to Media (For complete agency information see *The Advertising Red Books-Agencies* edition):
1. Bus. Publs. 2. Cable T.V. 3. Catalogs & Directories. 4. Co-op Adv. 5. Consumer Mags. 6. D.M. to Bus. Estab.7. D.M. to Consumers 8. Daily Newsp. 9. Exhibits/Trade Shows 10. Foreign 11. Infomercial 12. Internet Adv.13. Multimedia 14. Network Radio 15. Network T.V. 16. Newsp. Distr. Mags. 17. Other 18. Outdoor (Posters, Transit) 19. Point of Purchase20. Premiums, Novelties 21. Product Samples 22. Special Events Mktg. 23. Spot Radio 24. Spot T.V. 25. Weekly Newsp. 26. Yellow Page Adv.

Mark Heninger *(Product Mgr)*
Roger Anderson *(Mgr-Mktg Svcs Grp)*
Fred Roth *(Mgr-Engineered Components)*

Brands & Products:
AVAC
CARB-O-PROF
GLOBAL VR
METALMASTER
MULTIMASTER
TOOLTREATER
TURBOTREATER
VARIOCLEAN

JOHN ZINK COMPANY LLC

(Sub. of Koch-Glitsch, LP)
11920 E Apache
Tulsa, OK 74116-1309
Tel.: (918) 234-1800
Fax: (918) 234-2700
Toll Free: (800) 421-9242
E-mail: info@johnzink.com
Web Site: www.johnzink.com
Approx. Number Employees: 1,100
Year Founded: 1929
Business Description:
Pollution Control Equipment Mfr
S.I.C.: 3444
N.A.I.C.S.: 332322
Export
Media: 2-10-22
Distr.: Intl.

Brands & Products:
GORDON-PIATT
JOHN ZINK
JZ
KALDAIRE
TODD
VARIFLAME II
ZEUS

Advertising Agency:
Procom Marketing
108 W Main
Haskell, OK 74436
Tel.: (918) 482-4216
— Chad Engler *(Acct Exec)*

JOHNSON CONTROLS, INC.

(Branch of Johnson Controls Building Efficiency Group)
631 S Richland Ave
York, PA 17403-3445
Mailing Address:
PO Box 1592
York, PA 17405-1592
Tel.: (717) 771-7890
Fax: (717) 771-7238
Web Site: www.johnsoncontrols.com
Sales Range: $200-249.9 Million
Approx. Number Employees: 700
Year Founded: 1874
Business Description:
Heating, Ventilating, Air Conditioning & Refrigeration Products Mfr
S.I.C.: 3585
N.A.I.C.S.: 333415
Import Export
Advertising Expenditures: $27,500,000
Media: 6
Personnel:
Joseph Villani *(Mgr-Software Engrg)*

Brands & Products:
YORK

KADANT JOHNSON INC.

(Sub. of KADANT INC.)
805 Wood St
Three Rivers, MI 49093
Tel.: (269) 278-1715
Fax: (269) 279-5980
E-mail: info@kadantjohnson.com
Web Site: www.kadantjohnson.com
Sales Range: $75-99.9 Million
Approx. Number Employees: 120
Year Founded: 1933
Business Description:
Mfr. of Rotary Joints, Syphons, Condensate Systems, Cylinder & Solenoid Valves, Vacuum Breakers, Separators & Sight Flow Indicators
S.I.C.: 3494; 3568
N.A.I.C.S.: 332919; 333613
Media: 1-2-4-7-10-11-13-21
Distr.: Intl.; Natl.
Budget Set: Oct.
Personnel:
Greg Wedel *(Pres)*
Wesley Martz *(VP-Mktg)*
Dennis Moon *(Dir-Fin)*

Brands & Products:
CARB
JOCO
JOHNSON DMS
JOHNSON SYSTEM
LIQUI-MOVER
LUBRIMATE
TURBULATOR
TURBULATOR TUBE

KIDDE-FENWAL, INC.

(Sub. of Kidde Residential & Commercial Division)
400 Main St
Ashland, MA 01721-2150
Tel.: (508) 881-2000
Fax: (508) 881-6729
Toll Free: (800) 872-6527
Telex: 94-8421
E-mail: info@kidde-fenwal.com
Web Site: www.kidde-fenwal.com
Sales Range: $75-99.9 Million
Approx. Number Employees: 500
Year Founded: 1991
Business Description:
Temperature Controls & Fire & Explosion Protection Systems & Repair Kits Mfr
S.I.C.: 9224; 3823
N.A.I.C.S.: 922160; 334513
Advertising Expenditures: $675,000
Multimedia: $15,000; Bus. Publs.: $200,000; Catalogs & Directories: $175,000; D.M. to Bus. Estab.: $35,000; Exhibits/Trade Shows: $125,000; Premiums, Novelties: $15,000; Yellow Page Adv.: $110,000
Distr.: Natl.
Budget Set: Oct.
Personnel:
John Sullivan *(Pres)*
Joe McCadden *(CFO)*
Gerry Conley *(VP-Sls)*

Brands & Products:
ANALASER
CARDOX
CHEMETRON
CHEMETRONICS
DELTA PAC
DETECT-A-FIRE
FENWAL CONTROLS
FIREPAC 360
SEAL N PLACE
SMARTONE
THERMOSWITCH
X-PAC

KYSOR/WARREN

(Unit of The Manitowoc Company, Inc.)
5201 Transport Blvd
Columbus, GA 31907
Tel.: (706) 568-1514
Fax: (706) 568-8990
Toll Free: (800) 866-5596
E-mail: solutions@kysorwarren.com
Web Site: www.kysorwarren.com
Sales Range: $150-199.9 Million
Approx. Number Employees: 150
Year Founded: 1882
Business Description:
Commercial Refrigeration Equipment Mfr
S.I.C.: 3556
N.A.I.C.S.: 333294
Export
Media: 1-2-4-5-7-10
Distr.: Intl.; Natl.
Budget Set: Jan.
Personnel:
Charles Eaves *(Mgr)*

LENNOX INTERNATIONAL INC.

2140 Lake Park Blvd
Richardson, TX 75080
Tel.: (972) 497-5000
Fax: (972) 497-5292
E-mail: investor@lennoxintl.com
Web Site: www.lennoxinternational.com
Approx. Sls.: $3,096,400,000
Approx. Number Employees: 11,800
Year Founded: 1895
Business Description:
Climate Control Solutions
S.I.C.: 3585; 3621
N.A.I.C.S.: 333415; 335312
Advertising Expenditures: $59,500,000
Media: 5-15-23-24
Personnel:
Richard L. Thompson *(Chm)*
Todd M. Bluedorn *(CEO)*
Robert W. Hau *(CFO)*
Prakash Bedapudi *(CTO & Exec VP)*
John D. Torres *(Chief Legal Officer)*
Daniel M. Sessa *(Chief HR Officer & Exec VP)*
Roy A. Rumbough *(Chief Acctg Officer, VP & Controller)*
Harry J. Bizios *(Pres/COO-Comml Heating, Cooling & Exec VP)*
Michael J. Blatz *(Pres/COO-Svc Experts & Exec VP)*
David W. Moon *(Pres/COO-Worldwide Refrigeration & Exec VP)*
Douglas L. Young *(Pres/COO-Residential Heating/Cooling & Exec VP)*
Christopher Peel *(VP & Gen Mgr-Worldwide Refrigeration-Americas)*
Manuel E. Molera, Jr. *(VP-HR)*
Ozzie Buckler *(Dir-Comm & PR)*
Victor Gonzalez-Maertens *(Dir-Product Mgmt & Mktg)*
Rob Lytton *(Dir-IT Bus Sys)*
Bill Carlson *(Mgr-Retail Natl Accounts)*

Brands & Products:
ADVANCED DISTRIBUTOR PRODUCTS
AIR-EASE
AIRE-FLO
AIREASE
ARMSTRONG
ARMSTRONG AIR
BOHN
CLIMATE CONTROL
COMPLETEHEAT
CONCORD
DUCANE
ELITE
FRIGA-BOHN
HEATCRAFT
JANKA
LARKIN
LENNOX
LENNOX INTERNATIONAL
MAGIC-PAK
SERVICE EXPERTS

Advertising Agencies:
GSD&M
828 W 6th St
Austin, TX 78703-5420
Tel.: (512) 242-4736
Fax: (512) 242-4700

Power Creative
11701 Commonwealth Dr
Louisville, KY 40299-2358
Tel.: (502) 267-0772
Fax: (502) 267-1727

LESLIE CONTROLS, INC.

(Sub. of CIRCOR International, Inc.)
12501 Telecom Dr
Tampa, FL 33637
Tel.: (813) 978-1000
Fax: (813) 978-0984
Toll Free: (800) 800-2LESLIE
E-mail: sales@lesliecontrols.com
Web Site: www.leslie-controls.com
E-Mail For Key Personnel:
Sales Director: sales@lesliecontrols.com
Sales Range: $150-199.9 Million
Business Description:
Mfr of Regulators, Control Valves, Control Instrumentation, Steam Water Heaters & Air Whistles
S.I.C.: 3491; 3433
N.A.I.C.S.: 332911; 333414
Import Export
Advertising Expenditures: $400,000
Media: 1-2-4-7-10-11-13-19
Distr.: Intl.; Natl.
Budget Set: Feb. -Mar.

Brands & Products:
CONSTANTEMP
CONSTANTEMP SKIDDED
CPC-CRYOLAB
FIRE-CIDE
LES SERIES

LINDBERG

(Div. of Thermal Product Solutions)
3827 Riverside Rd
Riverside, MI 49084
Tel.: (269) 849-2700
Fax: (269) 849-3021
E-mail: tpsinfo@tps.spx.com
Web Site: www.heat-treat.com
Sales Range: $10-24.9 Million
Approx. Number Employees: 50
Year Founded: 1912
Business Description:
Furnace Solutions
S.I.C.: 3821; 3567
N.A.I.C.S.: 339111; 333994
Import Export
Advertising Expenditures: $500,000
Media: 1-2-4-7-8-10

Key to Media (For complete agency information see *The Advertising Red Books-Agencies* edition):
1. Bus. Publs. 2. Cable T.V. 3. Catalogs & Directories. 4. Co-op Adv. 5. Consumer Mags. 6. D.M. to Bus. Estab.7. D.M. to Consumers 8. Daily Newsp. 9. Exhibits/Trade Shows 10. Foreign 11. Infomercial 12. Internet Adv.13. Multimedia 14. Network Radio 15. Network T.V. 16. Newsp. Distr. Mags. 17. Other 18. Outdoor (Posters, Transit) 19. Point of Purchase20. Premiums, Novelties 21. Product Samples 22. Special Events Mktg. 23. Spot Radio 24. Spot T.V. 25. Weekly Newsp. 26. Yellow Page Adv.

Lindberg — (Continued)

Distr.: Intl.; Natl.
Budget Set: Jan.
Personnel:
Joel Shingledecker *(Mgr)*
Brands & Products:
MEGAMISER
PACEMAKER
PACEMAKER SL

LOCHINVAR CORPORATION
300 Maddox Simpson Pkwy
Lebanon, TN 37090
Tel.: (615) 889-8900
Fax: (615) 547-1000
E-mail: lochinvar@lochinvar.com
Web Site: www.lochinvar.com
Approx. Number Employees: 350
Year Founded: 1919
Business Description:
Mfr. of Residential & Commercial Water Heaters
S.I.C.: 3639; 3559
N.A.I.C.S.: 335228; 332410
Import Export
Media: 2-4-7-10-11-17
Distr.: Intl.; Natl.
Personnel:
Bill Vallett *(Pres)*
Jeff Vallett *(Exec VP)*
Mike Lahti *(VP-Sls)*
Bob Lancaster *(VP-HR)*
John Wyatt *(VP-Info Tech)*
Stirling Boston *(Dir-Mktg)*
Tim Bray *(Mgr-Facility)*
Mike Juhnke *(Mgr-Mktg)*
Joining Lochinvar *(Mgr)*
Lee Poplin *(Mgr-Quality Assurance)*
Jim Smelcer *(Mgr-Engrg)*
James Williams *(Mgr-Facility)*
Brands & Products:
COPPER-FIN
COPPER-FIN II
COPPER-PAK
EFFICIENCY
EFFICIENCY +
EFFICIENCY-PAC
ENERGYRITE
HARMONY
HI-POWER
INTELLI-FIN
LOCHINVAR
LOCK-TEMP
MINI-FIN
POWER-FIN
TURBOCHARGER

LYTRON INCORPORATED
55 Dragon Ct
Woburn, MA 01801
Tel.: (781) 933-7300
Fax: (781) 935-4529
E-mail: info@lytron.com
Web Site: www.lytron.com
E-Mail For Key Personnel:
Sales Director: dvoorhes@lytron.com
Approx. Number Employees: 180
Year Founded: 1958
Business Description:
Cold Plates, Cooling Systems & Heat Exchangers Mfr
S.I.C.: 3585
N.A.I.C.S.: 333415
Export
Media: 10-13
Distr.: Intl.; Natl.
Personnel:
Charles Carswell *(Pres)*
Dave Voorhes *(VP-Sls & Mktg)*
Tracy Barber *(Mgr-Mktg Commun)*
Brands & Products:
ASPEN
CAJON
EXTENDED SURFACE
EXTENDED SURFACE I
EXTENDED SURFACE II
HASTELLOY
HIGH PERFORMANCE
KODIAK
LYTRON
PRESS-LOCK
PRESSLOCK I
PRESSLOCK II
THERMAL SOLUTIONS
THERMOCUBE
THERMOCUBE CHILLER
TOTAL THERMAL SOLUTIONS

MANNING & LEWIS ENGINEERING COMPANY
675 Rahway Ave
Union, NJ 07083
Tel.: (908) 687-2400
Fax: (908) 687-2404
E-mail: sales@manninglewis.com
Web Site: www.manninglewis.com
E-Mail For Key Personnel:
Sales Director: sales@manninglewis.com
Sales Range: $1-9.9 Million
Approx. Number Employees: 60
Year Founded: 1937
Business Description:
Shell & Tube Heat Exchangers Mfr
S.I.C.: 3559
N.A.I.C.S.: 332410; 333298
Import Export
Media: 2-10-13
Distr.: Natl.
Budget Set: Apr.
Personnel:
Kurt Nelson *(Pres & CEO)*
Kevin Elwood *(Mgr-Adv & Sls)*

MARLEY ENGINEERED PRODUCTS
(Div. of SPX Cooling Technologies)
470 Beauty Spot Rd
Bennettsville, SC 29512
Tel.: (843) 479-4006
Fax: (843) 479-8912
Web Site: www.marleymep.com
Sales Range: $150-199.9 Million
Approx. Number Employees: 330
Year Founded: 1986
Business Description:
Residential, Commercial & Light Industrial Heating & Ventilating Solutions
S.I.C.: 5075; 1711
N.A.I.C.S.: 423730; 238220
Export
Media: 2-8-10
Distr.: Natl.
Budget Set: Jan. -Feb.
Personnel:
Jim Garrigus *(Dir-Mktg)*
Brands & Products:
BERKO
FAHRENHEAT
LEADING EDGE
MARLEY BUILDER'S PRODUCTS
MARLEY INDUSTRIAL PRODUCTS
QMARK

MCQUAY INTERNATIONAL
(Sub. of O.Y.L. Industries Bhd.)
13600 Industrial Park Blvd
Minneapolis, MN 55441
Tel.: (763) 553-5330
Fax: (763) 553-5177
Toll Free: (800) 432-1342
Web Site: www.mcquay.com
Approx. Number Employees: 250
Year Founded: 1872
Business Description:
Heating, Ventilating & Air Conditioning Equipment Mfr, Retailer & Servicer
S.I.C.: 3585; 5064
N.A.I.C.S.: 333415; 423620
Export
Media: 1-2-4-10-13-20-26
Distr.: Intl.; Natl.
Budget Set: Nov. -Dec.
Personnel:
Chris Sachrison *(COO)*
Ron Hanlon *(Reg VP)*
John Kampbell *(Reg VP)*
Mark McNeil *(Product Mgr)*
Brands & Products:
MCQUAY
Advertising Agency:
Creative Communications Consultants, Inc.
111 3rd Ave S Ste 390
Minneapolis, MN 55401-2553
Tel.: (612) 338-5098
Fax: (612) 338-1398

MEASUREMENT SPECIALTIES/ YSI TEMPERATURE
(Sub. of Measurement Specialties Inc.)
2670 Indian Ripple Rd
Dayton, OH 45440
Tel.: (937) 427-1231
Fax: (937) 427-1640
Toll Free: (800) 747-5367 (US Only)
Web Site: www.ysi.com
Sales Range: $10-24.9 Million
Approx. Number Employees: 45
Year Founded: 1942
Business Description:
Mfr. of Thermistors, Varistors & Thinsistors for the Military & Medical Industries
S.I.C.: 3826; 3823
N.A.I.C.S.: 334516; 334513
Import Export
Media: 2-4-10-21
Distr.: Intl.; Natl.
Budget Set: Sept.
Personnel:
Bobert K. Hurst *(VP & Gen Mgr)*
Brian Ream *(Mgr-Medical Products Applications Engrng)*
Brands & Products:
TEMPHART
THINSISTOR
UNICHIP

MESTEK, INC.
260 N Elm St
Westfield, MA 01085-1614
Tel.: (413) 568-9571
Fax: (413) 568-2969
Web Site: www.mestek.com
Approx. Sls.: $303,541,000
Approx. Number Employees: 2,600
Year Founded: 1946
Business Description:
Holding Company; Heating, Ventilation & Air Conditioning Products, Coil Handling Equipment, Extruded Aluminum Products & Computer Information Systems Mfr
S.I.C.: 6719; 3354; 3433; 3585; 3677; 5075
N.A.I.C.S.: 551112; 331316; 333414; 333415; 334416; 423730
Import Export
Advertising Expenditures: $4,774,000
Media: 1-10
Personnel:
John E. Reed *(Chm & CEO)*
R. Bruce Dewey *(Pres)*
Stephen M. Shea *(CFO)*
Stewart B. Reed *(COO & Exec VP)*
William S. Rafferty *(Exec VP)*
David R. DeBell *(VP-HR)*
Brands & Products:
ALTON
APPLIED AIR
ARROW
BEACON/MORRIS
CWP
DYNAFORCE
FLOORLEVEL
HEATRIM
HYDROTHERM
IFB
KOLDWAVE
MESTEK
MULTIPULSE
MULTITEMP
NESBITT
PETITE 7
PHILLIPS AIRE
ROWE
SELECTEMP
SERVOMATIC
SERVOMAX
SPACEPAK
STERLING
STERLING RADIATOR
TWIN-FLO
VIFB
VULCAN
WING
Advertising Agency:
RDW Group Inc.
125 Holden St
Providence, RI 02908-4919
Tel.: (401) 521-2700
Fax: (401) 521-0014

MEYER HEATING & AIR CONDITIONING, INC.
1300 SW Washington St
Peoria, IL 61602-1706
Tel.: (309) 673-6351
Fax: (309) 673-6358
Approx. Sls.: $2,000,000
Approx. Number Employees: 10
Business Description:
HVAC Products, Heating & Air Conditioning Equipment Mfr
S.I.C.: 1711
N.A.I.C.S.: 238220
Media: 1-4-5-9-10-16-19-20-21-22-23-25-26
Distr.: Reg.
Budget Set: Dec.

MFRI INC.
7720 N Lehigh Ave
Niles, IL 60714
Tel.: (847) 966-1000

Fax: (847) 966-8563
E-mail: webmaster@mfri.com
Web Site: www.mfri.com
Approx. Sls.: $218,598,000
Approx. Number Employees: 1,123
Year Founded: 1993
Business Description:
Holding Company
S.I.C.: 3564; 3498
N.A.I.C.S.: 333411; 332996; 333412
Media: 2-7-10
Distr.: Natl.
Personnel:
David Unger *(Chm & CEO)*
Bradley E. Mautner *(Pres & COO)*
Michael D. Bennett *(CFO, Treas, Sec & VP)*
Stephen C. Buck *(Pres-Thermal Care)*
Fati A. Elgendy *(Pres-Perma)*
Avin Gidwani *(Pres-Perma-Pipe Middle East FZC)*
Timothy P. Murphy *(VP-HR)*

MIDCO INTERNATIONAL, INC.
4140 W Victoria St
Chicago, IL 60646
Tel.: (773) 604-8700
Fax: (773) 604-4070
E-mail: info@midcointernational.com
Web Site:
www.midcointernational.com
E-Mail For Key Personnel:
Marketing Director: judith@midco-intl.com
Sales Director: sales@midco-intl.com
Approx. Number Employees: 50
Year Founded: 1941
Business Description:
Power Gas Burners Mfr
S.I.C.: 3433; 3567
N.A.I.C.S.: 333414; 333994
Export
Media: 2-4-5-10-20-21
Distr.: Intl.; Natl.
Budget Set: Jan.
Personnel:
Terry Stanger *(Pres)*
Brands & Products:
ECONOMITE
EMBER-GLO
INCINOMITE
MAKE UP AIR
MIDCO
UNIPOWER

MODINE MANUFACTURING COMPANY
1500 DeKoven Ave
Racine, WI 53403-2552
Tel.: (262) 636-1200
Fax: (262) 636-1424
E-mail: info@modine.com
Web Site: www.modine.com
E-Mail For Key Personnel:
Public Relations: invest@modine.com
Approx. Sls.: $1,448,235,000
Approx. Number Employees: 6,497
Year Founded: 1916
Business Description:
Heat Transfer & Heat Storage Products Mfr for the Vehicular, Industrial, Commercial & Building HVAC Markets
S.I.C.: 3714; 3585
N.A.I.C.S.: 336399; 333415; 336391
Import Export
Media: 2-4-5-7-10
Distr.: Intl.; Natl.
Budget Set: Jan.
Personnel:
Thomas A. Burke *(Pres & CEO)*
Michael B. Lucareli *(CFO, Treas & VP-Fin)*
Margaret C. Kelsey *(Gen Counsel, Sec & VP-Corp Dev)*
Scott L. Bowser *(Reg VP-Americas)*
Klaus A. Feldmann *(Reg VP-Europe)*
Matthew J. McBurney *(Dir-Comml Products NA)*
Brands & Products:
ALBRAZE
ALFUSE
APPLIED THERMAL INNOVATON
HOT DAWG
MODINE
PF
Advertising Agencies:
Core Creative, Inc.
126 N Jefferson St Ste 250
Milwaukee, WI 53202
Tel.: (414) 291-0912
Fax: (414) 291-0932

KW Advertising
333 Bishops Way Ste 148
Brookfield, WI 53005-6209
Tel.: (262) 786-4402
Fax: (262) 786-7236

N&M COOL TODAY, INC.
6143 Clark Center Ave
Sarasota, FL 34238
Tel.: (941) 548-4011
Fax: (941) 923-3642
Web Site: www.nmcool.com
Business Description:
Air Conditioning, Heating & Plumbing Contractor
S.I.C.: 1711
N.A.I.C.S.: 238220
Media: 3-6-8-9-13-14-15-18-22-25-26
Personnel:
Jaime DiDomenico *(Owner & Pres)*
Charles Blum *(Mgr-Svc & Indoor Air Quality)*
Kathleen Ell *(Mgr-Sls & Mktg)*

NAO, INC.
1284 E Sedgley Ave
Philadelphia, PA 19134
Tel.: (215) 743-5300
Fax: (215) 743-3018
Toll Free: (800) 523-3495
E-mail: sales@nao.com
Web Site: www.nao.com
E-Mail For Key Personnel:
Sales Director: sales@nao.com
Approx. Number Employees: 50
Year Founded: 1912
Business Description:
Mfr of Industrial Oil & Gas Burners, Furnace Equipment & Flare Burners for Anti-Pollution
S.I.C.: 3823
N.A.I.C.S.: 334513
Export
Advertising Expenditures: $125,000
Media: 1-2-4-10-20
Distr.: Intl.; Natl.
Budget Set: Nov.
Personnel:
John F. Straitz, III *(Pres)*
Cor N. Knook *(Mgr-Sls)*
Brands & Products:
AIROCOOL
AIROVENT
COMBUSTOR
FIREWALL
FLUIDIC SEAL
FLUIDIC VENT TIP
GLOWALL
HEXAD
HOT DOG TIPS
HYDROCOOL
JET MIX
JET MIX VORTEX
LINEAR
MULTI EXTERNAL COANDA
MULTI JET MIX
NAO
POPULATED AREA COMBUSTORS
TANDEM

NIAGARA BLOWER COMPANY
673 Ontario St
Buffalo, NY 14207
Tel.: (716) 875-2000
Fax: (716) 875-1077
Toll Free: (800) 426-5169
Web Site: www.niagarablower.com
E-Mail For Key Personnel:
Sales Director: sales@niagrablower.com
Approx. Number Employees: 48
Year Founded: 1904
Business Description:
Mfr of Process Equipment for Industry & Heat Transfer
S.I.C.: 3585; 1711
N.A.I.C.S.: 333415; 238220
Import Export
Media: 2-4-7
Distr.: Intl.; Natl.
Budget Set: Oct.
Personnel:
Peter Demakos *(Pres)*
Brands & Products:
AERO
HYGROL
NIAGARA
NIAGARA NO-FROST
NO-FROST
WET SURFACE
WSAC

NOOTER/ERIKSEN, INC.
(Sub. of Nooter Corporation)
1509 Ocello Dr
Fenton, MO 63026
Tel.: (636) 651-1000
Fax: (636) 651-1501
E-mail: info@ne.com
Web Site: www.ne.com
Approx. Number Employees: 200
Business Description:
Supplies Heat Recovery Systems Designed to Conserve Energy & Improve Plant Efficiency
S.I.C.: 8742
N.A.I.C.S.: 541611
Media: 4-17
Personnel:
Don Lange *(Pres)*

NORDYNE INC.
(Sub. of Nortek, Inc.)
8000 Phoenix Pkwy
O Fallon, MO 63368
Tel.: (636) 561-7300
Fax: (636) 561-7399
Toll Free: (888) 667-4822
Web Site: www.nordyne.com
E-Mail For Key Personnel:
Public Relations: bakerc@nordyne.com
Approx. Number Employees: 200
Year Founded: 1939
Business Description:
Oil, Gas & Electric Furnaces, Air Conditioning Systems, Heat Pumps, Water Heaters & Fireplaces Mfr
S.I.C.: 3585; 5064
N.A.I.C.S.: 333415; 423620
Export
Advertising Expenditures: $2,553,000
Multimedia: $35,000; Bus. Publs.: $150,000; Catalogs & Directories: $20,000; Co-op Adv.: $1,200,000; Consumer Mags.: $30,000; D.M. to Bus. Estab.: $40,000; D.M. to Consumers: $60,000; Daily Newsp.: $300,000; Exhibits/Trade Shows: $200,000; Infomercial: $2,000; Network Radio: $10,000; Newsp. Distr. Mags.: $19,000; Other: $30,000; Outdoor (Posters, Transit): $10,000; Point of Purchase: $22,000; Premiums, Novelties: $35,000; Product Samples: $25,000; Special Events Mktg.: $30,000; Spot Radio: $250,000; Spot T.V.: $35,000; Weekly Newsp.: $10,000; Yellow Page Adv.: $40,000
Distr.: Intl.; Natl.
Budget Set: Oct.
Personnel:
David J. La Grand *(Pres & CEO)*
Doug Jones *(VP-Mktg & Sls)*
Alan Reisel *(VP-Engrng)*
Brands & Products:
FRIGIDAIRE
GIBSON
INTERTHERM
KELVINATOR
MILLER
PHILCO
TAPPAN

OCEAN STATE HEATING & AIR
1476 Atlantic Blvd
Neptune Beach, FL 32266-2565
Tel.: (904) 249-8251
Fax: (904) 249-8949
Web Site: www.oceanstateac.com
Business Description:
Installation & Maintenance for Home Air Quality & ComfortEquipment
S.I.C.: 5075
N.A.I.C.S.: 423730
Media: 13-17
Personnel:
James Jones *(Pres)*

P&F INDUSTRIES, INC.
445 Broadhollow Rd Ste 100
Melville, NY 11747
Tel.: (631) 694-9800
Fax: (631) 694-9804
E-mail: info@pfina.com
Web Site: www.pfina.com
Approx. Rev.: $50,609,000
Approx. Number Employees: 133
Year Founded: 1959
Business Description:
Heating Equipment & Air Powered Hand Tools & Hardware Mfr
S.I.C.: 3546; 3433; 3559
N.A.I.C.S.: 333991; 333298; 333414

Key to Media (For complete agency information see *The Advertising Red Books-Agencies* edition):
1. Bus. Publs. 2. Cable T.V. 3. Catalogs & Directories. 4. Co-op Adv. 5. Consumer Mags. 6. D.M. to Bus. Estab.7. D.M. to Consumers
8. Daily Newsp. 9. Exhibits/Trade Shows 10. Foreign 11. Infomercial 12. Internet Adv.13. Multimedia 14. Network Radio
15. Network T.V. 16. Newsp. Distr. Mags. 17. Other 18. Outdoor (Posters, Transit) 19. Point of Purchase20. Premiums, Novelties
21. Product Samples 22. Special Events Mktg. 23. Spot Radio 24. Spot T.V. 25. Weekly Newsp. 26. Yellow Page Adv.

P&F Industries, Inc. — (Continued)

Import Export
Advertising Expenditures: $890,000
Media: 2-4-7-10-20-26
Distr.: Natl.
Personnel:
Richard A. Horowitz *(Chm, Pres & CEO)*
Joseph A. Molino Jr. *(CFO & COO)*
Richard B. Goodman *(Gen Counsel)*
George Aronson *(VP-Fin & Acctg)*

PEIRCE-PHELPS, INC.

2000 N 59th St
Philadelphia, PA 19131-3031
Tel.: (215) 879-7000
Fax: (215) 879-5427
Web Site: www.peirce.com
Approx. Number Employees: 300
Year Founded: 1926
Business Description:
Consumer Electronics & Home Appliance Products; Heating & Air Conditioning Products Distr
S.I.C.: 5075; 5064
N.A.I.C.S.: 423730; 423620
Import
Advertising Expenditures: $200,000
Media: 2-4-7-10
Distr.: Natl.
Personnel:
Brian Peirce *(CEO)*
Robert P. Subranni *(CFO & VP)*
Brands & Products:
PEIRCE MARKET SHARP

PENNBARRY

(Joint Venture of Onex Corporation & Canada Pension Plan Investment Board)
605 Shiloh Rd
Plano, TX 75074
Tel.: (972) 212-4700
Telex: 83-4545
E-mail: pennbarrysales@pennbarry.com
Web Site: www.pennbarry.com
Approx. Number Employees: 550
Year Founded: 1928
Business Description:
Ventilators & Air-Moving Equipment Mfr
S.I.C.: 3585
N.A.I.C.S.: 333415
Advertising Expenditures: $200,000
Media: 2-4-7-10
Distr.: Natl.
Budget Set: Nov.
Brands & Products:
PENN

PRECISION BOILERS, INC.

(Holding of Source Capital LLC)
5727 Superior Dr
Morristown, TN 37814-1075
Tel.: (423) 587-9390
Fax: (423) 581-7749
Toll Free: (800) 448-2301
E-mail: sales@precisionboilers.com
Web Site: www.precisionboilers.com
Approx. Number Employees: 98
Year Founded: 1942
Business Description:
Gas Boilers, Electric & Gas Hot Water Heaters Mfr
S.I.C.: 3559
N.A.I.C.S.: 332410
Export
Advertising Expenditures: $200,000
Media: 2-4-6-7-10
Distr.: Intl.; Natl.
Budget Set: June
Brands & Products:
COMPAC
COPPER COAT
PRECISION BOILERS
THERMOGENETIC

PREFERRED UTILITIES MANUFACTURING CORPORATION

(Sub. of PUMC Holding Corporation)
31 35 South St
Danbury, CT 06810-8147
Tel.: (203) 743-6741
Fax: (203) 798-7313
E-mail: info@preferred-mfg.com
Web Site: www.preferred-mfg.com
Approx. Number Employees: 82
Year Founded: 1920
Business Description:
Combustion Equipment; Combustion Controls & Data Acquisition Systems; Fuel Oil Handling Equipment, Pump Sets, Day Tanks Filtration Systems & Oil & Gas Burners Mfr
S.I.C.: 3829; 3433
N.A.I.C.S.: 334519; 333414
Import Export
Media: 4-7-10-11
Distr.: Intl.
Personnel:
Robert G. Bohn *(Chm & CEO)*
David G. Bohn *(Pres)*
Charles White *(Exec VP-Engrg & Mfg)*
Ben DeFazio *(VP-Engrg)*
Ronald Scattolini *(VP-Pur)*
Brands & Products:
PCC III
SCADA
THERMO-PAK

PREMIER POWER RENEWABLE ENERGY, INC.

4961 Windplay Dr Ste 100
El Dorado Hills, CA 95762
Tel.: (916) 939-0400
Fax: (916) 939-0490
E-mail: info@premierpower.com
Web Site: www.premierpower.com
Approx. Rev.: $86,787,000
Approx. Number Employees: 65
Year Founded: 2006
Business Description:
Solar Power Equipment Design, Integration & Installation Services
S.I.C.: 4931; 3612
N.A.I.C.S.: 221119; 335311
Advertising Expenditures: $800,000
Media: 2-6-10-13-23
Personnel:
Miguel De Anquin *(Pres)*
Dean R. Marks *(CEO)*
Frank Sansone *(CFO)*
Stephen H. Clevett *(COO)*
Ken Baker *(Dir-Engrg)*
Rob Hichborn *(Dir-Sls)*
Don Peek *(Mgr-Sys Integration)*

PROAIR, LLC

(Sub. of KODA Specialty Products Group)
28731 County Rd 6
Elkhart, IN 46514-9512
Tel.: (574) 264-5494
Fax: (574) 264-2194
Web Site: www.proairllc.com
Approx. Number Employees: 80
Year Founded: 1997
Business Description:
Air Conditioning & Heating Equipment
S.I.C.: 3585; 5075
N.A.I.C.S.: 336391; 423730
Import Export
Media: 4
Personnel:
Dave Lavine *(Exec VP)*
Brands & Products:
PROAIR

PURE N NATURAL SYSTEMS, INC.

5836 Lincoln Ave Ste 100
Morton Grove, IL 60053
Tel.: (847) 470-1652
Tel.: (847) 470-1653
Fax: (847) 470-1686
Toll Free: (800) 237-9199
Web Site: www.purennatural.com
Approx. Number Employees: 6
Year Founded: 1989
Business Description:
Home Environmental Protection Solutions
S.I.C.: 3564
N.A.I.C.S.: 333411
Media: 6-13
Personnel:
Joseph Roy *(Pres)*

RAY BURNER COMPANY

401 Parr Blvd
Richmond, CA 94801
Tel.: (510) 236-4972
Tel.: (510) 948-3649
Fax: (510) 236-4083
Toll Free: (800) RAY-BURNER
E-mail: rayburner@rayburner.com
Web Site: www.rayburner.com
Approx. Number Employees: 25
Year Founded: 1872
Business Description:
Oil, Gas & Combination Burners, Solid Fuel Boilers & Water Boilers Mfr For Shipboard
S.I.C.: 3433; 3443
N.A.I.C.S.: 333414; 332313
Import Export
Media: 2-4-7-8-10-26
Distr.: Intl.; Natl.
Budget Set: Nov.
Personnel:
Russ Westover *(Pres)*
Brands & Products:
RAY
WAY WOLFF

RAYPAK, INC.

(Sub. of Rheem Manufacturing Company)
2151 Eastman Ave
Oxnard, CA 93030-5194
Tel.: (805) 278-5300
Fax: (805) 278-5468
E-mail: info@raypak.com
Web Site: www.raypak.com
Approx. Number Employees: 350
Year Founded: 1947
Business Description:
Water Heating Equipment Mfr
S.I.C.: 3433; 3634
N.A.I.C.S.: 333414; 335211
Media: 2-9-25
Distr.: Natl.
Budget Set: Oct.
Personnel:
Michael Sentovich *(Pres)*
Brands & Products:
ADVANCED DESIGN BOILER
E-4 BOILER ALARM ANNUNCIATOR
ECONOMASTER II
HI DELTA
THE HOT WATER MANAGEMENT EXPERTS
RAYTHERM

REAL GOODS SOLAR, INC.

(Sub. of Gaiam, Inc.)
833 W South Boulder Rd
Louisville, CO 80027-2452
Tel.: (303) 222-8400
Toll Free: (888) 507-2561
Web Site: www.realgoodssolar.com
Approx. Rev.: $77,324,000
Approx. Number Employees: 263
Business Description:
Solar Power System Installation Services
S.I.C.: 1799
N.A.I.C.S.: 238990
Advertising Expenditures: $2,200,000
Media: 4-5-8-10-13-23
Personnel:
Jirka Rysavy *(Chm)*
John Schaeffer *(Pres)*
Kent Halliburton *(VP-Sls)*

RESEARCH PRODUCTS CORPORATION

1015 E Washington Ave
Madison, WI 53703-2938
Mailing Address:
PO Box 1467
Madison, WI 53701
Tel.: (608) 257-8801
Fax: (608) 257-4357
Web Site: www.aprilaire.com
Approx. Number Employees: 300
Year Founded: 1938
Business Description:
Heating, Air-Conditioning & Air Purification Equipment
S.I.C.: 3585; 3564
N.A.I.C.S.: 333415; 333411
Import Export
Media: 1-2-3-4-5-6-7-8-10-13-18-19-23-24-26
Distr.: Natl.
Budget Set: Nov.
Personnel:
Larry A. Olsen *(Pres & CEO)*
P. M. Graham *(Sr VP)*
Tom Ruse *(Mgr-Mktg Comm)*
Brands & Products:
APRILAIRE
COOLPAK
DETECTAGAS
EZ KLEEN
FRESH IDEAS FOR INDOOR AIR
KLEEN-GARD
PERFECTAIRE
PERFECTEMP
RP
RPEZ-KLEEN
SPACE-GARD
SUPER E Z KLEEN
TRIM-TO-SIZE
ZONED COMFORT CONTROL

Key to Media (For complete agency information see *The Advertising Red Books-Agencies* edition):
1. Bus. Publs. 2. Cable T.V. 3. Catalogs & Directories. 4. Co-op Adv. 5. Consumer Mags. 6. D.M. to Bus. Estab.7. D.M. to Consumers 8. Daily Newsp. 9. Exhibits/Trade Shows 10. Foreign 11. Infomercial 12. Internet Adv.13. Multimedia 14. Network Radio 15. Network T.V. 16. Newsp. Distr. Mags. 17. Other 18. Outdoor (Posters, Transit) 19. Point of Purchase20. Premiums, Novelties 21. Product Samples 22. Special Events Mktg. 23. Spot Radio 24. Spot T.V. 25. Weekly Newsp. 26. Yellow Page Adv.

RHEEM MANUFACTURING - AIR CONDITIONING DIV
(Div. of Rheem Manufacturing Company)
5600 Old Greenwood Rd
Fort Smith, AR 72908-6586
Mailing Address:
PO Box 17010
Fort Smith, AR 72917-7010
Tel.: (479) 646-4311
Fax: (479) 648-4812
Web Site: www.rheemac.com
Approx. Number Employees: 2,000
Year Founded: 1924
Business Description:
Mfr. of Air Conditioning Equipment & Supplies
S.I.C.: 3433; 3585
N.A.I.C.S.: 333414; 333415
Export
Advertising Expenditures: $300,000
Media: 2-5-6-9-18-20
Distr.: Natl.
Budget Set: Oct.
Personnel:
J. R. Jones *(Pres & CEO)*
Bill Hanesworth *(VP & Gen Mgr)*
W. A. Lux *(VP International)*
Ed Raniszeski *(Dir-Mktg)*

RHEEM MANUFACTURING COMPANY
(Sub. of Paloma Industries Limited)
1100 Abernathy Rd Ste 1400
Atlanta, GA 30328
Tel.: (770) 351-3000
Fax: (770) 351-3003
E-mail: info@rheem.com
Web Site: www.rheem.com
Approx. Number Employees: 40
Year Founded: 1927
Business Description:
Mfr. of Water Heaters & Residential & Commercial Heating & Air-Conditioning
S.I.C.: 3585; 3433
N.A.I.C.S.: 333415; 333414
Import Export
Advertising Expenditures: $300,000
Media: 2-4-6-7-9-10-11-13-14-18-20-23
Distr.: Natl.
Budget Set: Oct.
Personnel:
J.R. Jones *(CEO)*
Chris Peel *(COO & Sr VP)*
Peter Reynolds *(VP & Gen Mgr-Water Heating)*
Joseph A. Fristik *(Corp VP-Natl Accts & Mktg)*
Ed Raniszeski *(Dir-Mktg)*
Tommy Olsen *(Sr Product Mgr)*
Brands & Products:
ENERGY MISER
MARATHON
PROZONE
RAYPAK
RHEEM
RICHMOND
RUUD

RHEEM WATER HEATER
(Div. of Rheem Manufacturing Company)
101 Bell Rd
Montgomery, AL 36117-4305
Tel.: (334) 260-1500
Fax: (334) 262-1332
Web Site: www.rheem.com
Approx. Number Employees: 1,500
Business Description:
Residential & Commercial Water Heaters Mfr
S.I.C.: 3585
N.A.I.C.S.: 333415
Media: 2-4-10-19
Distr.: Natl.

RINNAI AMERICA CORP.
(Sub. of Rinnai Corporation)
103 Intl Dr
Peachtree City, GA 30269-1911
Tel.: (678) 829-1700
Fax: (678) 829-1666
Web Site: www.rinnai.us
Sales Range: $10-24.9 Million
Approx. Number Employees: 50
Business Description:
Wholesale Gas Appliances
S.I.C.: 5075
N.A.I.C.S.: 423730
Media: 7-10-14-22
Personnel:
Yuzo Yoshida *(Pres)*
Brad Sweet *(VP-Mktg)*
James York *(VP-Engrg)*
Phil Weeks *(Gen Mgr)*
Carmella Ross *(Dir-HR)*
Brands & Products:
RINNAI
Advertising Agency:
The Titan Agency
5 Concourse Pkwy
Atlanta, GA 30328
Tel.: (678) 332-5200
Fax: (678) 332-5221

ROBERTS-GORDON INC.
1250 William St
Buffalo, NY 14206
Tel.: (716) 852-4400
Fax: (716) 852-0854
Toll Free: (800) 828-7450
Web Site: www.rg-inc.com
Approx. Sls.: $80,000,000
Approx. Number Employees: 100
Year Founded: 1923
Business Description:
Mfr of Infrared Heating Equipment & Vented Infrared Gas Heating Systems
S.I.C.: 3433; 1711
N.A.I.C.S.: 333414; 238220
Export
Media: 2-4-5-6-7-9-10-19-23-25-26
Distr.: Natl.
Budget Set: Feb.
Personnel:
Mark J. Dines *(COO)*
Madonna Courtney *(VP-Corp Mktg)*
Stephan Richter *(VP-Engrg)*
Richard Jasiura *(Accountant)*
Brands & Products:
CARIBE
CORAYVAC
GORDONGLO
GORDONRAY
ROBERTS GORDON
ULTRAVAC
VANTAGE

SCHWANK INC.
PO Box 798
Waynesboro, GA 30830-0988
Tel.: (706) 554-6191
Fax: (706) 554-9390
Web Site: www.schwankgroup.com
Approx. Number Employees: 5
Year Founded: 1882
Business Description:
Infrared Heaters
S.I.C.: 3433; 3585
N.A.I.C.S.: 333414; 333415
Advertising Expenditures: $200,000
Media: 2-5-10-19-21-24
Distr.: Natl.
Budget Set: Oct.
Brands & Products:
PERFECTION
PERFECTION/SCHWANK INFRA-RED

SECO/WARWICK CORPORATION
180 Mercer St
Meadville, PA 16335-3618
Tel.: (814) 332-8400
Fax: (814) 724-1407
E-mail: info@secowarwick.com
Web Site: www.secowarwick.com
Approx. Number Employees: 75
Year Founded: 1984
Business Description:
Industrial Heat Treating Furnaces & Systems; Melting & Holding Equipment for Nonferrous Metals; Incinerator Systems Mfr
S.I.C.: 3567; 5084
N.A.I.C.S.: 333994; 423830
Export
Media: 2-4-7-10-17
Distr.: Intl.; Natl.
Budget Set: Aug.-Sept.
Personnel:
Keith Boeckenhauer *(Pres)*
Art Russo *(CFO & Treas)*
Janusz Kowalewski *(Gen Mgr)*
Brands & Products:
ACCUBRAZE
AMMOGAS
CASEMASTER
CUPROBRAZE
ENDOGAS
EXOGAS
FINECARB
METAL MINUTES
SCRAP MANAGER
SECO/WARWICK
WHIRL-A-WAY
Advertising Agency:
Altman-Hall Associates
235 W 7th St
Erie, PA 16501-1601
Tel.: (814) 454-0158
Fax: (814) 454-3266

SEELEY INTERNATIONAL AMERICAS
(Sub. of Seeley International)
1202 N 54th Ave Bldg 2 Ste 117
Phoenix, AZ 85043
Tel.: (602) 353-8066
Fax: (602) 353-8070
Toll Free: (800) 926-6824
E-mail: msculley@seeleyinternational.com
Web Site: www.convaircooler.com
Approx. Number Employees: 30
Year Founded: 1986
Business Description:
Evaporative Coolers Mfr
S.I.C.: 5075
N.A.I.C.S.: 423730
Import Export
Advertising Expenditures: $770,000
Bus. Publs.: $308,000; D.M. to Bus. Estab.: $77,000; Exhibits/Trade Shows: $231,000; Other: $154,000
Distr.: Reg.
Budget Set: Aug.
Brands & Products:
ARCTIC BREEZE
AWARD
BREEZAIR
CONVAIR
CONVAIR 3 IN 1
COOL WIND
DESINGLINE
MILLENIA
PRESTIGE
WESTWIND

SELAS HEAT TECHNOLOGY COMPANY LLC
130 Keystone Dr
Montgomeryville, PA 18936-8375
Tel.: (215) 646-6600
Fax: (215) 646-3536
Toll Free: (800) 523-6500
Telex: 24-4472
E-mail: sales@selas.com
Web Site: www.selas.com
E-Mail For Key Personnel:
Sales Director: sales@selas.com
Approx. Number Employees: 50
Year Founded: 1930
Business Description:
Combustion & Thermal Processing Equipment Mfr
S.I.C.: 3559
N.A.I.C.S.: 333298
Export
Media: 2-4-7-10
Distr.: Natl.
Budget Set: Oct. -Nov.
Personnel:
David Bovenizer *(CEO)*
Brands & Products:
DURADIANT
FLO-SCOPE
FLOTRONICS
GRADIATION
THE HEAT TECHNOLOGY COMPANY
KARBO-MATIC
LIQUI-JECTOR
MINI-MULE
NOZ-L-MIX
POSI-MIX
QUAL-O-RIMETER
SELAS
TEMPUTER
TRIM BLEND
VACU-DRAW
VERTA-FLAME

SELKIRK CANADA CORPORATION
(Joint Venture of Onex Corporation & Canada Pension Plan Investment Board)
375 Green Rd
Stoney Creek, ON L8E 4A5, Canada
Tel.: (905) 662-6600
Fax: (905) 662-5352
Toll Free: (888) 735-5475
E-mail: info@selkirkcanada.com
Approx. Number Employees: 30
Business Description:
Chimney Pipes, Venting & Fireplace Mfr
S.I.C.: 3272

Key to Media (For complete agency information see *The Advertising Red Books-Agencies* edition):
1. Bus. Publs. 2. Cable T.V. 3. Catalogs & Directories. 4. Co-op Adv. 5. Consumer Mags. 6. D.M. to Bus. Estab.7. D.M. to Consumers 8. Daily Newsp. 9. Exhibits/Trade Shows 10. Foreign 11. Infomercial 12. Internet Adv.13. Multimedia 14. Network Radio 15. Network T.V. 16. Newsp. Distr. Mags. 17. Other 18. Outdoor (Posters, Transit) 19. Point of Purchase20. Premiums, Novelties 21. Product Samples 22. Special Events Mktg. 23. Spot Radio 24. Spot T.V. 25. Weekly Newsp. 26. Yellow Page Adv.

Selkirk Canada Corporation — (Continued)

N.A.I.C.S.: 327390
Media: 10
Personnel:
John Vukanovich *(Pres-Mktg)*

SELKIRK CORPORATION

(Joint Venture of Onex Corporation & Canada Pension Plan Investment Board)
1301 W President Bush Hwy Ste 330
Richardson, TX 75080
Mailing Address:
PO Box 831950
Richardson, TX 75083-1950
Tel.: (972) 943-6100
Fax: (972) 943-6137
Toll Free: (800) 992-8368
E-mail: sales@selkirkinc.com
Web Site: www.selkirkinc.com
Approx. Number Employees: 1,200
Business Description:
Chimneys & Venting Products Mfr
S.I.C.: 5074
N.A.I.C.S.: 423720
Media: 10
Personnel:
Curt Monhart *(Exec VP-Sls & Mktg)*
Tim Rothgeb *(VP-Sls)*
Gary Light *(Mgr-Natl Retail Sls)*
Fred Pierce *(Mgr-Natl Sls-Comml, Indus & Hearth Division)*
Brands & Products:
METALBESTOS
SELKIRK

SIEMENS WATER TECHNOLOGIES

(Unit of Siemens Water Technologies)
1901 S Prairie Ave
Waukesha, WI 53189-7360
Mailing Address:
PO Box 1604
Waukesha, WI 53187-1604
Tel.: (262) 547-0141
Fax: (262) 547-4120
Toll Free: (800) 524-4120
Web Site: www.industry.siemens.com
Approx. Number Employees: 220
Business Description:
Waste Water Treatment Equipment Mfr
S.I.C.: 4953
N.A.I.C.S.: 562219
Advertising Expenditures: $200,000
Media: 2-7-10-17
Distr.: Intl.; Natl.
Personnel:
Anselmo Teixeira *(Sr VP)*
Michael Quick *(Mgr-Mktg Comm)*
Brands & Products:
CANNIBAL
GRIT-TREAT
LINK-BELT
REX

SIEMENS WATER TECHNOLOGIES

(Unit of Siemens Water Technologies)
13100 Gregg St Ste B
Poway, CA 92064-7150
Tel.: (858) 486-8500
Fax: (858) 486-8501
E-mail: information.water@siemens.com
Web Site: www.industry.siemens.com
Approx. Number Employees: 35
Year Founded: 1997
Business Description:
Air Purification Equipment Mfr
S.I.C.: 3564; 5074
N.A.I.C.S.: 333411; 423720
Media: 4-10-20
Brands & Products:
ODOR CONTROL SYSTEM

SLANT/FIN CORPORATION

100 Forest Dr
Greenvale, NY 11548
Tel.: (516) 484-2600
Fax: (516) 484-5921
E-mail: info@slantfin.com
Web Site: www.slantfin.com
Approx. Number Employees: 600
Year Founded: 1949
Business Description:
Climate Control Equipment & Devices & Optical Instruments Mfr & Retailer
S.I.C.: 3433; 3585
N.A.I.C.S.: 333414; 333415
Export
Advertising Expenditures: $500,000
Media: 1-2-3-4-5-7-10-11-18-19-20-21-23-24
Distr.: Natl.
Budget Set: June
Personnel:
Melvin Dubin *(Chm)*
Adam Dubin *(Pres)*
Robert Flanagan *(VP)*
Brands & Products:
BASE/LINE
CARAVAN
FAST/FLEX
FINE/LINE
FUTURA
GALAXY
HEPA-CLEAR
HOFFMAN MODULATION CONTRAST SYSTEM
HYDRO-TITE
INTREPID
LIBERTY
MODULATION OPTICS
MONITRON
MULTI/PAK
OPTIC RULE
PURI-CLEAR
SENTINEL
SENTRY
SLANT/FIN
VICTORY
XL-2000

SPIRAX SARCO, INC.

(Sub. of Spirax-Sarco Engineering plc)
1150 Northpoint Blvd
Blythewood, SC 29016
Tel.: (803) 714-2000
Fax: (803) 714-2224
Web Site: www.spiraxsarco.com/us/
E-Mail For Key Personnel:
Sales Director: sales@spirax.com
Approx. Number Employees: 230
Year Founded: 1910
Business Description:
Steam Traps, Temperature Controls, Heating Specialties, Strainers, Condensate Return Systems, Pumps, Pressure Reducing Valves, Boiler Controls, Flowmeters Mfr
S.I.C.: 3491; 3494
N.A.I.C.S.: 332911; 332919
Import Export
Advertising Expenditures: $250,000
Media: 2-4-10-20-21-26
Distr.: Natl.
Budget Set: Nov.
Personnel:
Don Harrison *(CFO)*
Bruce Moninghoff *(VP-Mktg)*
Justin C. O'Dowd *(Gen Mgr)*
Brands & Products:
SARCO
SPIRAX SARCO
STMS
THERMO-DYNAMIC
TSS
Advertising Agency:
Forge Marketing Communications
4283 Chestnut St 1st Fl
Emmaus, PA 18049
Tel.: (610) 928-3333
Fax: (610) 928-3340

SPORLAN VALVE COMPANY

(Div. of Parker Hannifin Climate & Industrial Controls Group)
206 Lange Dr
Washington, MO 63090-1040
Tel.: (636) 239-1111
Fax: (636) 239-9130
Web Site: www.parker.com
Sales Range: $125-149.9 Million
Approx. Number Employees: 600
Year Founded: 1934
Business Description:
Refrigeration & Air Conditioning Controls & Components Mfr
S.I.C.: 3491; 3822
N.A.I.C.S.: 332911; 334512
Import Export
Advertising Expenditures: $400,000
Media: 1-2-4-7-10-13-19-20-21
Distr.: Intl.; Natl.
Budget Set: Dec.
Personnel:
Patrick Donoban *(Pres)*
Andy Schoen *(Sr Mgr-Product)*
Brands & Products:
CATCH-ALL
LEVEL MASTER
SEE-ALL
SPORLAN
SPORLAN VALVE

S.T. JOHNSON CO.

925 Stanford Ave
Oakland, CA 94608
Tel.: (510) 652-6000
Fax: (510) 652-4302
E-mail: info@johnsonburners.com
Web Site: www.johnsonburners.com
Sales Range: $10-24.9 Million
Approx. Number Employees: 20
Year Founded: 1903
Business Description:
Mfr. of Gas, Oil & Combination Gas & Oil Burners & Control Systems For Commercial & Industrial Applications
S.I.C.: 3433; 1711
N.A.I.C.S.: 333414; 238220
Export
Media: 2-4-7-10-26
Distr.: Intl.; Natl.
Budget Set: Jan.
Personnel:
Antonio de la O *(Pres)*
Todd Cole *(Gen Mgr)*
Reed Cole *(Mgr-Pur)*
Brands & Products:
JOHNSON
NOXMATIC

SURFACE COMBUSTION, INC.

1700 Indian Wood Cir
Maumee, OH 43537-4005
Tel.: (419) 891-7150
Fax: (419) 891-7151
Toll Free: (800) 537-8980
E-mail: info@surfacecombustion.com
Web Site: www.surfacecombustion.com
Approx. Number Employees: 150
Year Founded: 1915
Business Description:
Thermal Processing Systems; Heat Treating Furnaces; Gas Generators for Metallurgical, Food & Chemical Industries Mfr
S.I.C.: 3567; 8733
N.A.I.C.S.: 333994; 541710
Export
Media: 2-4-7-10-11
Distr.: Intl.; Natl.
Personnel:
W. J. Bernard *(Pres & CEO)*
Daniel E. Goodman *(VP-Production)*
M. Hoetzl *(VP-Tech)*
T. C. McClain *(VP-Fin & Admin)*
Lori Lingle *(Mgr-Pur)*
Brands & Products:
AG
AIR JET QUENCH
ALLCASE
ASRX
ATMOSPHERE GAS
ATMOTROL
ATP/CASEMATE
AUTOCARB
AX
BALCO
BATCHMASTER
BATHMASTER
BELTMATE
CASEMATE
CG
CHAR-GAS
CHARMO
CONJECTO
DATAVAC
DX
ECONOMATIC
ENDOQUENCH
ENERGY RADIANT TUBE
ERT
ESA
EUTECTROL
EXTENDED REACH
FORC-AIRE
GAS PROCESSING SYSTEM
GPS
HEAT TREAT MANAGEMENT
HNX
HTM
HX
HYDROGEN ATMOSPHERE
INTRA-KOOL
IONPRO
IRX
LOADTRAC
MAX
MDX
METALINE
METALINED
MRX
MULTIBAR
MX

Key to Media (For complete agency information see *The Advertising Red Books-Agencies* edition):
1. Bus. Publs. 2. Cable T.V. 3. Catalogs & Directories. 4. Co-op Adv. 5. Consumer Mags. 6. D.M. to Bus. Estab.7. D.M. to Consumers 8. Daily Newsp. 9. Exhibits/Trade Shows 10. Foreign 11. Infomercial 12. Internet Adv.13. Multimedia 14. Network Radio 15. Network T.V. 16. Newsp. Distr. Mags. 17. Other 18. Outdoor (Posters, Transit) 19. Point of Purchase20. Premiums, Novelties 21. Product Samples 22. Special Events Mktg. 23. Spot Radio 24. Spot T.V. 25. Weekly Newsp. 26. Yellow Page Adv.

NITROGEN ATMOSPHERE
NX
ONEROW
P/M UNI-DRAW
POWER CONVECTION
PROCESSTRAC
PROLECTRIC
PYROBATCH
PYROTHERM
RADICATOR
RX
SHUTTLETRAC
SLCMATE
SLIDING BED
SMALLCASE
SOFTVAC
SRX
SURFACE
SURVAC
SYSTEM #1
SYSTEM #2
SYSTEM #3
TAL
TEMPMATE
THRIFT OVENS
TREND ALARM LOG
TRIDENT
TRINIDING
ULTRACASE
UNI-BLUE
UNI-DRAW
UNI-DROP
VACCASE
VACUDRAW
VRINGCARB
VX
WIN-RECIPE
XO

TACO INCORPORATED

1160 Cranston St
Cranston, RI 02920-7335
Tel.: (401) 942-8000
Fax: (401) 942-2360
E-mail: timsmi@taco-hvac.com
Web Site: www.taco-hvac.com
Approx. Number Employees: 500
Year Founded: 1920
Business Description:
Pumping, Heat Transfer, Hydronic Control & Solar Equipment Mfr
S.I.C.: 3433; 3561
N.A.I.C.S.: 333414; 333911
Import Export
Media: 1-2-4-5-10-19-21-22
Distr.: Intl.; Natl.
Budget Set: Oct. -Nov.
Personnel:
John H. White, Jr. *(Pres)*
Glenn Graham *(Treas & Sr VP-Fin)*
Chris Integlia *(Exec VP-residential Div)*
Kyle Adamonis *(Sr VP-HR)*
Candy Castaldi *(Sr VP-Circulator Division)*
Todd Facey *(Sr VP-Residential Sls & Mktg)*
Joe Gaul *(Sr VP-Comml Pump Div)*
Tom Lawrence *(Sr VP-Sls & Mktg)*
Robert Lee *(Sr VP-Heat Transfer Div)*
Tim Smith *(Dir-Mktg)*
Rae Aldrich *(Coord-Mktg)*
Brands & Products:
AIR SCOOPS
D'MAND
DO IT ONCE. DO IT RIGHT.
FREEDOM FLANGES
HY-VENTS
IN-LINE
IT'S ALL ABOUT YOU
LOADMATCH
PLUMB N' PLUG
SOLAR X-PUMP BLOCK
TACO
TWIN-TEE
VORTECH
X-PUMP BLOCK
Advertising Agency:
Sheppard Leger Nowak Inc.
1 Richmond Sq
Providence, RI 02906-5139
Tel.: (401) 276-0233
Fax: (401) 276-0230

TD INDUSTRIES, INC.

13850 Diplomat Dr
Dallas, TX 75234-8812
Tel.: (972) 888-9500
Fax: (972) 888-9482
E-mail: info@tdindustries.com
Web Site: www.tdindustries.com
Sales Range: $300-349.9 Million
Approx. Number Employees: 1,000
Year Founded: 1946
Business Description:
Air Conditioning, Heating, Plumbing & Refrigeration Supplies Whslr
S.I.C.: 1711; 7699
N.A.I.C.S.: 238220; 811412
Advertising Expenditures: $75,000
Media: 2-18-22
Personnel:
Harold McDull *(CEO)*
Mike Fitzpatrick *(CFO)*
Brands & Products:
TD MECHANICAL
TD SERVICE
TEMPO MECHANICAL

THERMEX-THERMATRON, LP

10501 Bunsen Way Ste 102
Louisville, KY 40299
Tel.: (502) 493-1299
Fax: (502) 493-4013
E-mail: sales@thermex-thermatron.com
Web Site: www.thermex-thermatron.com/
E-Mail For Key Personnel:
Sales Director: sales@thermex-thermatron.com
Year Founded: 1942
Business Description:
Dielectric Heat Sealing Equipment Mfr
S.I.C.: 3567
N.A.I.C.S.: 333994
Export
Media: 2-4-7-10-21
Distr.: Natl.
Brands & Products:
DELTA SERIES
QUANTUM SERIES
THERMATRON
THERMEX
THERMEX-THERMATRON
TRIMBOND SERIES

THERMO KING CORPORATION

(Sub. of Ingersoll-Rand Company)
314 W 90th St
Bloomington, MN 55420-3630
Tel.: (952) 887-2200
Fax: (952) 887-2615
E-mail: tkwebmaster@thermoking.com
Web Site: www.thermoking.com
Approx. Number Employees: 600
Year Founded: 1938
Business Description:
Mfr. of Mechanical Refrigeration Systems for Trucks, Trailers & Rail Cars; Bus Air Conditioning
S.I.C.: 3585
N.A.I.C.S.: 333415
Export
Advertising Expenditures: $2,500,000
Media: 1-2-4-5-6-7-8-9-10-11-15-18-19-20-21-23-26
Distr.: Intl.; Natl.
Budget Set: Sept.-Oct.
Personnel:
Tom Kampf *(Mgr-Product)*
Brands & Products:
THERMO KING
Advertising Agency:
Noble
33 W Monroe St Ste 300
Chicago, IL 60603
Tel.: (312) 670-2900
Fax: (312) 670-7420
Toll Free: (800) 986-6253

THERMON AMERICAS INC.

(Sub. of Thermon Group Holdings, Inc.)
100 Thermon Dr
San Marcos, TX 78666-5947
Mailing Address:
PO Box 609
San Marcos, TX 78667-0609
Tel.: (512) 396-5801
Fax: (512) 396-3627
Toll Free: (800) 820-4328
E-mail: sales@thermon.com
Web Site: www.thermon.com
E-Mail For Key Personnel:
Sales Director: sales@thermon.com
Approx. Number Employees: 200
Year Founded: 1954
Business Description:
Electrical, Mechanical & Instrument Heat Tracing Products & Services
S.I.C.: 3643; 3612
N.A.I.C.S.: 335931; 335311
Export
Advertising Expenditures: $300,000
Media: 1-2-4-5-7-10-11-13-20-21
Distr.: Intl.
Budget Set: Jan.
Personnel:
Rodney Bingham, *(CEO)*
Brands & Products:
CELLEX
COMPUTRACE
ECOTRACE
EFS
FIBREFORM
FLEXIPANEL
GAGECASE
THE HEAT TRACING SPECIALISTS
HEETSHEET
LEVEL GAGECASE
LEXAN
MIQ
RTF FLEXIPANEL
SADDLETRACE
SAFETRACE
SELF-REGULATING
SHADECASE
SNAP TRACE
SNOTRACE
SX
TEK
TERMINATOR
THERM TRAC
THERMASEAM
THERMOCASE
THERMOMOUNT
THERMON
THERMON FIBREFORM
THERMOSTAT
THERMOTUBE
THERMTRAC
TRACEPLUS
TRACEVIEW
TUBETRACE
VERSASTAND
WARMTRACE

THOMAS & BETTS REZNOR DIVISION

(Div. of Thomas & Betts Corporation)
8155 T & B Blvd
Memphis, TN 38125-8888
Tel.: (901) 682-7766
Fax: (901) 252-5000
Toll Free: (800) 695-1901
Web Site: www.tnb.com
Sales Range: $200-249.9 Million
Approx. Number Employees: 650
Year Founded: 1888
Business Description:
Mfr. of Heating & Ventilating Products
S.I.C.: 3643; 3678
N.A.I.C.S.: 335931; 334417
Export
Advertising Expenditures: $1,000,000
Media: 1-2-4-5-7-8-10-13-19-20-26
Distr.: Intl.; Natl.
Budget Set: Aug.
Personnel:
John Garavelli *(Mgr-Comm)*
Brands & Products:
INFRA-REZ
V3
VENTURION

TRENT, INC.

201 Leverington Ave
Philadelphia, PA 19127
Tel.: (215) 482-5000
Fax: (215) 482-9389
Toll Free: (800) 544-TRENT
E-mail: trentheat@aol.com
Web Site: www.trentheat.com
Sales Range: $10-24.9 Million
Approx. Number Employees: 25
Year Founded: 1927
Business Description:
Heated Industrial Equipment, Folded & Formed Electric Elements Mfr
S.I.C.: 3567; 3634
N.A.I.C.S.: 333994; 335211
Export
Advertising Expenditures: $100,000
Media: 2-10
Distr.: Direct to Consumer; Natl.
Brands & Products:
F&F
FOLDED & FORMED
TRENT
TRENTKNIT
Advertising Agency:
Howard Miller Associates, Inc.
32-E Roseville Rd
Lancaster, PA 17601
Tel.: (717) 581-1919
Fax: (717) 581-1972
(All Trent Products)

Key to Media (For complete agency information see *The Advertising Red Books-Agencies* edition):
1. Bus. Publs. 2. Cable T.V. 3. Catalogs & Directories. 4. Co-op Adv. 5. Consumer Mags. 6. D.M. to Bus. Estab.7. D.M. to Consumers
8. Daily Newsp. 9. Exhibits/Trade Shows 10. Foreign 11. Infomercial 12. Internet Adv.13. Multimedia 14. Network Radio
15. Network T.V. 16. Newsp. Distr. Mags. 17. Other 18. Outdoor (Posters, Transit) 19. Point of Purchase20. Premiums, Novelties
21. Product Samples 22. Special Events Mktg. 23. Spot Radio 24. Spot T.V. 25. Weekly Newsp. 26. Yellow Page Adv.

TURBINE ENGINE COMPONENTS TECHNOLOGIES CORP.
(Unit of Stony Point Group)
1211 Old Albany Rd
Thomasville, GA 31792
Tel.: (229) 228-8910
Fax: (229) 228-8949
Web Site: www.tectcorp.com
Approx. Number Employees: 1,400
Year Founded: 1981
Business Description:
Mfr of Fan Blades, Vanes & Structural Components
S.I.C.: 3511
N.A.I.C.S.: 333611
Personnel:
Robert S. Cohen *(Pres & CEO)*
Doug Cochran *(Mgr-Major Acct)*
Larry Friesen *(Mgr-Accts)*
Advertising Agency:
Sullivan Higdon & Sink Incorporated
255 N Mead St
Wichita, KS 67202-2707
Tel.: (316) 263-0124
Fax: (316) 263-1084
Toll Free: (800) 577-5684

VILTER MANUFACTURING LLC
(Sub. of Emerson Climate Technologies)
5555 S Packard Ave
Cudahy, WI 53110-2658
Tel.: (414) 744-0111
Fax: (414) 744-3483
E-mail: vilter@execpc.com
Web Site: www.emersonclimate.com/en-US/brands/vilter/Pages/Vilter.aspx
Sales Range: $150-199.9 Million
Approx. Number Employees: 340
Year Founded: 1867
Business Description:
Mfr of Industrial Refrigeration, Heat Exchange & Air Conditioning Equipment
S.I.C.: 3585; 3443; 3559
N.A.I.C.S.: 333415; 332313; 332410; 332420
Export
Advertising Expenditures: $100,000
Media: 1-2-4-7-10-11-13-22
Distr.: Intl.; Natl.
Budget Set: Oct.
Personnel:
Ronald Prebish *(Pres, CEO & COO)*
Siem Gladis *(Exec VP-Sls & Mktg)*
Mark Stencel *(VP-Sls & Mktg)*
Shawn Goggins *(Mgr-North America)*
Andrew Gurney *(Mgr-Sls)*
Shelley Nichols *(Mgr-Credit)*
Dan Nunn *(Mgr)*
Brands & Products:
COOL COMPRESSION
PARALLEX
TECOFROST
TRI-MICRO
VANTAGE
VILTER
VISSION
VISTA
VSG

VISHAY SPECTROL
(Sub. of Vishay Intertechnology, Inc.)
4051 Greystone Dr
Ontario, CA 91761-3100
Tel.: (909) 923-3313
Fax: (909) 923-6765
Toll Free: (800) 624-8902
E-mail: robert.leon@vishay.com
Web Site: www.spectrol.com
E-Mail For Key Personnel:
Sales Director: sales@spectrol.com
Sales Range: $25-49.9 Million
Approx. Number Employees: 90
Year Founded: 1956
Business Description:
Variety of Potentiometers & Encoders, Components for Aerospace & Industrial Applications Producer
S.I.C.: 3612
N.A.I.C.S.: 335311
Import Export
Advertising Expenditures: $500,000
Media: 1-2-4-5-10-20
Budget Set: Oct.
Personnel:
George Kanelas *(Mgr-Mktg)*
Robert Leon *(Mgr-Ops)*
Brands & Products:
SPECTROL

VULCAN ELECTRIC COMPANY
28 Endfield St
Porter, ME 04068-3502
Tel.: (207) 625-3231
Fax: (207) 625-8938
Toll Free: (800) 922-3027
E-mail: sales@vulcanelectric.com
Web Site: www.vulcanelectric.com
E-Mail For Key Personnel:
Sales Director: sales@vulcanelectric.com
Sales Range: $125-149.9 Million
Approx. Number Employees: 140
Year Founded: 1927
Business Description:
Mfr. of Electric Heating Units, Thermostats & Controls
S.I.C.: 3567
N.A.I.C.S.: 333994
Export
Advertising Expenditures: $100,000
Media: 2-4-5-6-7-10-11-13-26
Distr.: Intl.; Natl.
Personnel:
Michael Quick *(Pres & CEO)*
Brands & Products:
ARMORWALL
THUNDERBOLT
VULCAN CAL-STAT

WATLOW ELECTRIC MANUFACTURING COMPANY
12001 Lackland Rd
Saint Louis, MO 63146
Tel.: (314) 878-4600
Toll Free: (800) 4-WATLOW
E-mail: info@watlow.com
Web Site: www.watlow.com
E-Mail For Key Personnel:
President: PDesloge@watlow.com
Marketing Director: LMorrison@watlow.com
Sales Director: SSked@watlow.com
Approx. Number Employees: 2,500
Year Founded: 1922
Business Description:
Mfr. & Designer of Electric Heating Units, Temperature Controls & Sensors, Power Switching Devices & Controls for Industrial & Commercial Machinery & Equipment
S.I.C.: 3567; 3822
N.A.I.C.S.: 333994; 334512
Import Export
Advertising Expenditures: $1,500,000
Media: 1-2-4-7-10-11-13-21
Distr.: Intl.; Natl.
Budget Set: Aug.
Personnel:
Peter Desloge *(Chm, Pres & CEO)*
Stephen Desloge *(CFO)*
John A. Penning *(Gen Counsel, Sec & VP)*
Ray Feller *(Gen Mgr)*
Craig Dennis *(Product Mgr)*
Tony Foster *(Product Mgr)*
Brands & Products:
ALCRYN
ANASOFT
ANAWIN
BETTER THERMAL SOLUTIONS...FASTER
CONTROL CONFIDENCE
DIN-A-MITE
E-SAFE
EZ-ZONE
FIREBAR
FIREROD
FREEFLEX
INCOLOY
INCONEL
K-RING
KAPTON
LOGICPRO
MICROCOIL
MICRODIN
MINICHEF
MINICHEF 2000
MINITEMP
MODULE-MOUNT
ON-LINE KITCHEN
PROPLUS
RAPID RESPONSE
RAYMAX
SERV-RITE
ST PRO
STRETCH-TO-LENGTH
THERMOPOLYMER
THINBAND
THINBAND BARREL HEATERS
TRU-TUNE
TUBULAR
ULTRAMIC
WATCONNECT
WATLOW
WATLOW.COM
WATTS CURRENT
WATVIEW
XACTEMP
XACTPAK

WATSCO INC.
2665 S Bayshore Dr Ste 901
Coconut Grove, FL 33133
Tel.: (305) 714-4100
Fax: (305) 858-4492
Web Site: www.watsco.com
Approx. Rev.: $2,844,595,000
Approx. Number Employees: 4,000
Year Founded: 1945
Business Description:
Climate Control Components & Related Products Distr
S.I.C.: 5075; 3585
N.A.I.C.S.: 423730; 333415
Export
Advertising Expenditures: $26,646,000
Media: 2-4-7-8-9-10-16-25-26
Distr.: Intl.; Natl.
Budget Set: Jan.
Personnel:
Albert H. Nahmad *(Pres & CEO)*
Barry S. Logan *(Sec & Sr VP)*

WATTS WATER TECHNOLOGIES, INC.
815 Chestnut St
North Andover, MA 01845-6098
Tel.: (978) 688-1811
Fax: (978) 794-1848
Telex: 947460 WATTS REG LAW
Web Site: www.wattswater.com
Approx. Sls.: $1,274,600,000
Approx. Number Employees: 5,400
Year Founded: 1874
Business Description:
Plumbing & Heating Controls, Safety Devices, Backflow Preventers, Ball Valves, Butterfly Valves Mfr
S.I.C.: 3084; 3479; 3491; 3494; 5074
N.A.I.C.S.: 326122; 332812; 332911; 332919; 423720
Import Export
Advertising Expenditures: $500,000
Media: 1-2-4-6-7-10-13-18-19-20-21-22
Distr.: Intl.; Natl.
Budget Set: June
Personnel:
John K. McGillicuddy *(Chm)*
David J. Coghlan *(Pres & CEO)*
J. Dennis Cawte *(Grp Mng Dir-Europe)*
William C. McCartney *(CFO & Treas)*
Michael P. Flanders *(Pres-Asia)*
Kenneth R. Lepage *(Gen Counsel, Sec & Exec VP-Admin)*
Ernest E. Elliott *(Exec VP-Mktg)*
Chad LaCroix *(Mgr-Natl Market-Watts Brand Brass & Tubular Products)*
Brands & Products:
INNOVATIVE WATER SOLUTIONS
UNDERSINK GUARDIAN
WATTS

WEIL-MCLAIN
(Unit of SPX Corporation)
500 Blaine St
Michigan City, IN 46360-2388
Tel.: (219) 879-6561
Fax: (219) 877-0556
Web Site: www.weil-mclain.com
Sales Range: $200-249.9 Million
Approx. Number Employees: 600
Year Founded: 1881
Business Description:
Residential & Commercial Heating Boilers Mfr
S.I.C.: 3433; 1711; 1731; 1799
N.A.I.C.S.: 333414; 238210; 238220; 238910
Import Export
Advertising Expenditures: $500,000
Media: 1-2-3-4-5-6-7-8-10-13-14-16-18-19-20-21-22-26
Distr.: Natl.
Budget Set: Oct.
Personnel:
Tom Blashill *(Pres)*
Brands & Products:
EASY-FIT
GOLD GV
GOLD OIL
GOLD PLUS
H.E.A.T.
PLUS
ULTRA

Key to Media (For complete agency information see *The Advertising Red Books-Agencies* edition):
1. Bus. Publs. 2. Cable T.V. 3. Catalogs & Directories. 4. Co-op Adv. 5. Consumer Mags. 6. D.M. to Bus. Estab.7. D.M. to Consumers 8. Daily Newsp. 9. Exhibits/Trade Shows 10. Foreign 11. Infomercial 12. Internet Adv.13. Multimedia 14. Network Radio 15. Network T.V. 16. Newsp. Distr. Mags. 17. Other 18. Outdoor (Posters, Transit) 19. Point of Purchase20. Premiums, Novelties 21. Product Samples 22. Special Events Mktg. 23. Spot Radio 24. Spot T.V. 25. Weekly Newsp. 26. Yellow Page Adv.

YORK UNITARY PRODUCTS GROUP
(Div. of Johnson Controls Building Efficiency Group)
5005 York Dr
Norman, OK 73069
Tel.: (405) 364-4040
Fax: (405) 419-6545
Toll Free: (877) 874-7378
E-mail: upg.consumer.relations@york.com
Web Site: www.yorkupg.com
Sales Range: $1-4.9 Billion
Approx. Number Employees: 3,000
Business Description:
Mfr of Residential & Light Commercial Air Conditioning, Furnaces & Heat Pumps
S.I.C.: 5149
N.A.I.C.S.: 424490
Export
Media: 1-2-3-4-5-6-7-8-10-15-18-19-20-23
Distr.: Natl.
Personnel:
R. Bruce Mcdonald *(CFO & Exec VP)*
Colin Boyd *(CIO & VP-Info Tech)*
Beda Bolzenius *(Pres-Automotive Experience & VP)*
Alex A. Molinaroli *(Pres-Power Solutions & VP)*
Susan F. Davis *(Exec VP-HR)*
Jeffrey S. Edwards *(Grp VP-Asia OEMs Japan & Korea Ops)*
Advertising Agency:
Godfrey Advertising
40 N Christian St
Lancaster, PA 17602
Tel.: (717) 393-3831
Fax: (717) 393-1403

YOUNG REGULATOR COMPANY
7100 Krick Rd
Walton Hills, OH 44146
Tel.: (440) 232-9700
Fax: (440) 232-8266
Web Site: www.youngregulator.com
Approx. Number Employees: 18
Year Founded: 1930
Business Description:
Dampers, Regulators & Accessories, Air Distribution Heating Controls, Ventilating & Air Conditioning Systems Mfr
S.I.C.: 3822; 1711
N.A.I.C.S.: 334512; 238220
Import Export
Media: 4-6-10-13
Distr.: Intl.; Natl.
Personnel:
Michael Mcguigan *(Pres)*
Rick Spiner *(Gen Mgr)*
Brands & Products:
BOWDEN CABLE CONTROLS
VALCALOX
VENTGARD
YR

Key to Media (For complete agency information see *The Advertising Red Books-Agencies* edition):
1. Bus. Publs. 2. Cable T.V. 3. Catalogs & Directories. 4. Co-op Adv. 5. Consumer Mags. 6. D.M. to Bus. Estab.7. D.M. to Consumers
8. Daily Newsp. 9. Exhibits/Trade Shows 10. Foreign 11. Infomercial 12. Internet Adv.13. Multimedia 14. Network Radio
15. Network T.V. 16. Newsp. Distr. Mags. 17. Other 18. Outdoor (Posters, Transit) 19. Point of Purchase20. Premiums, Novelties
21. Product Samples 22. Special Events Mktg. 23. Spot Radio 24. Spot T.V. 25. Weekly Newsp. 26. Yellow Page Adv.

Hotels, Resorts & Real Estate

Chambers of Commerce — Community Developers — Industrial Developments — Real Estate Agents & Brokers

ABOOD WOOD-FAY REAL ESTATE GROUP
95 Merrick Way Ste 380
Coral Gables, FL 33134
Tel.: (305) 446-0011
Fax: (305) 446-1907
Web Site: www.aboodwoodfay.com
Sales Range: $50-74.9 Million
Approx. Number Employees: 48
Business Description:
Real Estate Services
S.I.C.: 6531
N.A.I.C.S.: 531210
Media: 6
Personnel:
Carol Ellis-Cutler *(Partner & Sr VP)*
Donna Abood *(CEO-Colliers Abood Wood-Fay)*

ACCOR ECONOMY LODGING
(Div. of Accor North America, Inc.)
4001 International Pkwy
Carrollton, TX 75007
Tel.: (972) 360-9000
Fax: (972) 360-2821
Web Site: www.accor-na.com
Approx. Number Employees: 22,800
Year Founded: 1962
Business Description:
Operator of Motels & Franchise Properties
S.I.C.: 7011
N.A.I.C.S.: 721110
Advertising Expenditures: $31,715,000
Cable T.V.: $4,000,000; Catalogs & Directories: $5,000,000; Consumer Mags.: $500,000; D.M. to Consumers: $100,000; Exhibits/Trade Shows: $50,000; Network Radio: $4,500,000; Network T.V.: $4,500,000; Newsp. Distr. Mags.: $500,000; Outdoor (Posters, Transit): $4,000,000; Premiums, Novelties: $35,000; Spot Radio: $4,000,000; Spot T.V.: $4,500,000; Yellow Page Adv.: $30,000
Distr.: Natl.
Budget Set: Nov.
Personnel:
Olivier Poirot *(CEO)*
Lance Miceli *(Exec VP & CMO-Motel 6)*
Bernard Rudler *(Exec VP-Franchising)*
Dean Savas *(Sr VP-Franchising)*
Advertising Agency:
The Richards Group, Inc.
8750 N Central Expy Ste 100
Dallas, TX 75231-6430
Tel.: (214) 891-5700
Fax: (214) 265-2933
(Motel 6)

ACCOR NORTH AMERICA, INC.
(Sub. of Accor S.A.)
4001 International Pkwy
Carrollton, TX 75007
Tel.: (972) 360-9000
Fax: (972) 360-2545
Web Site: www.accor-na.com
Approx. Number Employees: 300
Business Description:
Holding Company; Hotel & Restaurant Operator
S.I.C.: 7011
N.A.I.C.S.: 721110
Personnel:
Olivier Poirot *(CEO)*
Jeffrey Palmer *(CMO)*
Robert Moore *(Exec VP-Tech Svcs & New Construction)*
Kristin Taylor *(Exec VP-Technical Svcs-Real Estate & Dev)*
Laura Rojo-Eddy *(Dir-Corp Comm)*
Advertising Agency:
TM Advertising
1717 Main St Ste 2000
Dallas, TX 75201
Tel.: (972) 556-1100
Fax: (972) 830-2619
Motel 6

ADAM'S MARK HOTELS & RESORTS
(Div. of HBE Corporation)
11330 Olive Blvd
Saint Louis, MO 63141
Tel.: (314) 567-9000
Fax: (314) 567-0602
Web Site: www.adamsmark.com
Sales Range: $250-299.9 Million
Approx. Number Employees: 758
Business Description:
Designer, Builder, Owner & Operator of Hotels
S.I.C.: 7011; 6552
N.A.I.C.S.: 721110; 237210
Media: 6
Brands & Products:
ADAM'S MARK

ADVANCE REALTY GROUP, LLC
1430 Hwy 206 Ste 100
Bedminster, NJ 07921
Tel.: (908) 719-3000
Fax: (908) 719-9444
E-mail: infoadvance@advancerealtygroup.com
Web Site: www.advancerealtygroup.com
Approx. Number Employees: 100
Year Founded: 1979
Business Description:
Commercial Real Estate Services
S.I.C.: 6531
N.A.I.C.S.: 531210
Media: 2
Personnel:
Peter J. Cocoziello *(Pres & CEO)*
David J. Fisher *(Sr VP & Reg Mng Dir-Washington-DC)*
Lisa Becher *(Dir-Mktg Svcs)*
Nadine Golis *(Sr Mgr-Mktg)*

AIMCO PROPERTIES, L.P.
(Sub. of Apartment Investment and Management Company)
4582 S Ulster St Pkwy Ste 1100
Denver, CO 80237
Tel.: (303) 757-8101
Fax: (303) 759-3226
E-mail: info@aimco.com
Web Site: www.aimco.com
Year Founded: 1994
Business Description:
Residential Real Estate Acquisition, Development & Property Management Services
S.I.C.: 6531; 6513
N.A.I.C.S.: 531311; 531110; 531390
Advertising Expenditures: $25,000,000
Personnel:
Terry Trust Considine *(Chm & CEO)*
Ernest M. Freedman *(CFO & Exec VP)*
Paul Beldin *(Chief Acctg Officer & Sr VP)*

ALBANESE DEVELOPMENT CORPORATION
1050 Franklin Ave Ste 200
Garden City, NY 11530
Tel.: (516) 746-6000
Fax: (516) 746-0580
E-mail: info@albanesedev.com
Web Site: www.albanesedev.com
Approx. Number Employees: 40
Year Founded: 1949
Business Description:
Real Estate Developer
S.I.C.: 6552; 6531
N.A.I.C.S.: 237210; 531390
Media: 2-7
Personnel:
Anthony A. Albanese *(Chm)*
Russell Albanese *(Vice Chm)*
James Polcari *(CFO)*
Advertising Agency:
Harrison Leifer DiMarco, Inc.
100 Merrick Rd
Rockville Centre, NY 11570-4800
Tel.: (516) 536-2020
Fax: (516) 536-2641
Toll Free: (888) 571-2500

ALEXANDER & BALDWIN, INC.
822 Bishop St
Honolulu, HI 96813-3924
Mailing Address:
PO Box 3440
Honolulu, HI 96801-3440
Tel.: (808) 525-6611
Fax: (808) 525-6652
Web Site: www.alexanderbaldwin.com
Approx. Rev.: $1,646,000,000
Approx. Number Employees: 2,300
Year Founded: 1870
Business Description:
Ocean Transportation, Sugar Production & Property Management Services
S.I.C.: 4731; 4412
N.A.I.C.S.: 488510; 483111
Import Export
Media: 9-16
Distr.: Intl.; Natl.
Budget Set: Oct.
Personnel:
Walter A. Dods, Jr. *(Chm)*
Stanley M. Kuriyama *(Pres & CEO)*
Christopher J. Benjamin *(CFO, Treas & Sr VP)*
Nelson N.S. Chun *(Chief Legal Officer & Sr VP)*
Alyson J. Nakamura *(Sec & Asst Gen Counsel)*
Meredith J. Ching *(Sr VP-Govt & Community Rels)*
Paul K. Ito *(VP, Controller & Asst Treas)*
Son-Jai Paik *(VP-HR)*

Key to Media (For complete agency information see *The Advertising Red Books-Agencies* edition):
1. Bus. Publs. 2. Cable T.V. 3. Catalogs & Directories. 4. Co-op Adv. 5. Consumer Mags. 6. D.M. to Bus. Estab.7. D.M. to Consumers
8. Daily Newsp. 9. Exhibits/Trade Shows 10. Foreign 11. Infomercial 12. Internet Adv.13. Multimedia 14. Network Radio
15. Network T.V. 16. Newsp. Distr. Mags. 17. Other 18. Outdoor (Posters, Transit) 19. Point of Purchase20. Premiums, Novelties
21. Product Samples 22. Special Events Mktg. 23. Spot Radio 24. Spot T.V. 25. Weekly Newsp. 26. Yellow Page Adv.

Allan Darling *(Dir-Internal Audit)*
Suzy Hollinger *(Dir-IR)*
Karalynn Uchimura *(Mgr-Internal Audit)*

Brands & Products:
HC&S
KAUAI COFFEE
MATSON
MAUI
MAUI MALL

Advertising Agency:
MVNP
999 Bishop St 21th Fl
Honolulu, HI 96813-4429
Tel.: (808) 536-0881
Fax: (808) 529-6208
(Food, Property Acquisition)

AMB PROPERTY CORPORATION

Pier 1 Bay 1
San Francisco, CA 94111
Tel.: (415) 394-9000
Fax: (415) 394-9001
E-mail: webmaster@amb.com
Web Site: www.amb.com
Approx. Rev.: $633,500,000
Approx. Number Employees: 521
Business Description:
Industrial Real Estate Investment Trust
S.I.C.: 6798
N.A.I.C.S.: 525930
Personnel:
Hamid R. Moghadam *(Chm & CEO)*
Thomas S. Olinger *(CFO)*
Nina A. Tran *(Chief Acctg Officer)*
Guy F. Jaquier *(Pres-Europe & Asia & Pres-Private Capital)*
Eugene F. Reilly *(Pres-North America)*
Nathan Paine *(COO-Japan, Korea & Singapore & Sr VP)*
Tamra D. Browne *(Gen Counsel, Sec & Sr VP)*
Bruce Freedman *(Exec VP-Real Estate Ops)*
Martina Malone *(Sr VP-Client Rels)*
Hideaki Matsunami *(Sr VP-Bus Dev)*
Tracy Ward *(VP-IR & Corp Comm)*
Lillian Li *(Dir-Bus Dev)*
Chiquita McCullough *(Dir-Property Mgmt)*

Advertising Agency:
Holton Sentivan and Gury
7 E Skippack Pike
Ambler, PA 19002
Tel.: (215) 619-7600
Fax: (215) 619-7621
(Global Print Campaign)

AMERICAN CAMPUS COMMUNITIES, INC.

12700 Hill Country Blvd Ste T-200
Austin, TX 78738
Tel.: (512) 732-1000
Fax: (512) 732-2450
E-mail: info@studenthousing.com
Web Site: www.studenthousing.com
Approx. Rev.: $344,991,000
Approx. Number Employees: 2,334
Year Founded: 1993
Business Description:
Real Estate Investment Trust
S.I.C.: 6798; 6531; 6552
N.A.I.C.S.: 525930; 237210; 531210
Advertising Expenditures: $8,400,000
Personnel:
R. D. Burck *(Chm)*
William C. Bayless, Jr. *(Pres & CEO)*
Jonathan A. Graf *(CFO, Sec, Treas & Exec VP)*
Greg A. Dowell *(COO & Sr Exec VP)*
Daniel Perry *(Exec VP-Capital Markets)*
James C. Hopke, Jr. *(Exec VP-Project Mgmt & Construction)*
William W. Talbot *(Exec VP-Investments)*
James E. Wilhelm, III *(Exec VP-Pub Private Transactions)*
Kim K. Voss *(Sr VP & Controller)*
Jennifer Beese *(Sr VP-Leasing Admin)*
Clint Braun *(Sr VP-Construction Mgmt)*
Steve Crawford *(Sr VP-Mgmt Svcs)*
Jorge De De Cardenas *(Sr VP-IT)*
James R. Sholders *(Sr VP-Mgmt Svcs)*
Jason R. Wills *(Sr VP-On-Campus Dev)*
Brian Winger *(Sr VP-Transactions)*
Victor Young *(Sr VP-Project Mgmt & Construction)*

AMERICAN EXPRESS TRAVEL RELATED SERVICES COMPANY, INC.

(Sub. of American Express Company)
200 Vesey St
New York, NY 10285
Tel.: (212) 640-2000
Web Site: axptravel.americanexpress.com/consumertravel/travel.do
Sales Range: $100-124.9 Million
Business Description:
Travel Related Services
S.I.C.: 4729
N.A.I.C.S.: 561599
Personnel:
Kenneth I. Chenault *(CEO)*

Advertising Agency:
ISM
745 Boylston St 7th Fl
Boston, MA 02116
Tel.: (617) 353-1822
Fax: (617) 266-1890

AMERICAN RESIDENTIAL SERVICES L.L.C.

(Holding of CI Capital Partners LLC)
965 Ridge Lake Blvd Ste 201
Memphis, TN 38120-9421
Tel.: (901) 271-9700
Web Site: www.ars.com
Approx. Number Employees: 200
Business Description:
Building Maintenance & Related Services
S.I.C.: 7699; 6794
N.A.I.C.S.: 562991; 533110
Personnel:
Donald Karnes *(CEO)*

Advertising Agency:
PUSH
101 Ernestine St
Orlando, FL 32801-2317
Tel.: (407) 841-2299
Fax: (407) 841-0999

AMERICAN TRADING & PRODUCTION CORPORATION

10 E Baltimore St Ste 1600
Baltimore, MD 21202
Tel.: (410) 347-7100
Fax: (410) 347-7151
Web Site: www.atapco.com
Approx. Number Employees: 25
Year Founded: 1931
Business Description:
Owner & Operator of Real Estate Properties
S.I.C.: 6531
N.A.I.C.S.: 531210
Import Export
Media: 2-4-6-7-8-10-19-21
Distr.: Intl.; Natl.
Personnel:
Daniel B. Hirschhorn *(Chm)*

AMON INVESTMENTS, LLC

211 E International Speedway Blvd
Daytona Beach, FL 32118
Tel.: (386) 257-0240
E-mail: info@amonsales.com
Web Site: www.amoninvestments.com
Approx. Sls.: $1,300,000,000
Business Description:
Real Estate Developer, Sales & Investment Services
S.I.C.: 1522; 6289; 6531
N.A.I.C.S.: 236116; 523999; 531390
Media: 6

AMREP CORPORATION

300 Alexander Park Ste 204
Princeton, NJ 08540
Tel.: (609) 716-8200
Fax: (609) 716-8255
Web Site: www.amrepcorp.com
Approx. Rev.: $96,837,000
Approx. Number Employees: 1,230
Year Founded: 1961
Business Description:
Land Developer & Magazine Distr
S.I.C.: 6552; 1531; 5192
N.A.I.C.S.: 237210; 236117; 424920
Advertising Expenditures: $800,000
Media: 2-4-6-10
Distr.: Natl.
Personnel:
Edward B. Cloues, II *(Chm)*
Nicholas G. Karabots *(Vice Chm)*
Theodore J. Gaasche *(Pres & CEO)*
Peter M. Pizza *(CFO, Treas & VP)*
Irving Needleman *(Gen Counsel, Sec & VP)*

AMURCON CORPORATION

30215 Southfield Rd Ste 200
Southfield, MI 48076-1361
Tel.: (248) 646-0202
Fax: (248) 646-0482
Toll Free: (800) 649-3777
Telex: 352-0725
E-mail: amurcon@amurcorp.com
Web Site: www.amurcorp.com
Approx. Number Employees: 350
Year Founded: 1971
Business Description:
Property Management Services
S.I.C.: 6531
N.A.I.C.S.: 531210
Media: 2-4-6-7-8
Distr.: Reg.

APARTMENT INVESTMENT AND MANAGEMENT COMPANY

(d/b/a AIMCO)
4582 S Ulster St Ste 1100
Denver, CO 80237
Tel.: (303) 757-8101
Fax: (303) 759-3226
Toll Free: (888) 789-8600
E-mail: investor@aimco.com
Web Site: www.aimco.com
Approx. Rev.: $1,144,934,000
Approx. Number Employees: 3,100
Business Description:
Real Estate Investment Trust
S.I.C.: 6798
N.A.I.C.S.: 525930
Advertising Expenditures: $14,200,000
Media: 2-4-7
Personnel:
Terry Trust Considine *(Chm & CEO)*
Ernest M. Freedman *(CFO & Exec VP)*
Richard Brennan *(CIO)*
Miles Cortez *(Chief Admin Officer & Exec VP)*
Lisa R. Cohn *(Gen Counsel, Sec & Exec VP)*
Patti K. Fielding *(Treas, Exec VP-Securities & Debt)*
Lance J. Graber *(Exec VP-Transactions-East)*
Stephen D. Crane *(Sr VP)*
Melanie G. French *(Sr VP)*
Terri C. Heredia *(Sr VP-Talent)*
Becky Holeman *(Sr VP)*
Martha L. Long *(Sr VP-Partnership Transactions)*
Leeann Morein *(Sr VP-Performance Mgmt)*
Patti Shwayder *(Sr VP)*
H. Lynn Stanfield *(Sr VP-Tax)*
Cynthia Duffy *(Dir-Corp Comm)*

Advertising Agency:
Mason & Kichar Recruitment Advertising
260 Amity Rd
Woodbridge, CT 06525
Tel.: (203) 392-0252
Fax: (203) 392-0255

ARAMARK HARRISON LODGING

(Sub. of ARAMARK Corporation)
135 New Rd
Madison, CT 06443
Tel.: (203) 318-2102
Web Site: www.aramarkharrisonlodging.com
Year Founded: 2002
Business Description:
Operator of Conference Centers, Corporate Training Centers & Specialty Hotels
S.I.C.: 5812; 7218
N.A.I.C.S.: 722310; 812332
Media: 2-6-9-10-13-17
Personnel:
Bruce W. Fears *(Pres)*
Abigail Charpentier *(VP-HR)*
Gregory Wier *(Asst VP-Ops-Higher Education Grp)*
Brian Murphy *(Gen Mgr)*

ARCHON CORPORATION

2200 Casino Dr
Laughlin, NV 89029
Tel.: (702) 732-9120
Fax: (702) 732-9465
Approx. Rev.: $26,580,277
Approx. Number Employees: 321
Year Founded: 1982
Business Description:
Holding Company; Hotels & Casinos
S.I.C.: 7999; 5812; 7011; 7997

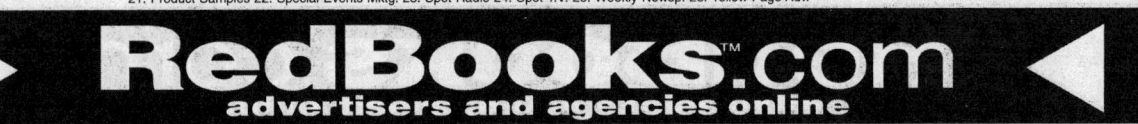

Key to Media (For complete agency information see *The Advertising Red Books-Agencies* edition):
1. Bus. Publs. 2. Cable T.V. 3. Catalogs & Directories. 4. Co-op Adv. 5. Consumer Mags. 6. D.M. to Bus. Estab.7. D.M. to Consumers 8. Daily Newsp. 9. Exhibits/Trade Shows 10. Foreign 11. Infomercial 12. Internet Adv.13. Multimedia 14. Network Radio 15. Network T.V. 16. Newsp. Distr. Mags. 17. Other 18. Outdoor (Posters, Transit) 19. Point of Purchase20. Premiums, Novelties 21. Product Samples 22. Special Events Mktg. 23. Spot Radio 24. Spot T.V. 25. Weekly Newsp. 26. Yellow Page Adv.

Archon Corporation — (Continued)

N.A.I.C.S.: 713990; 713910; 721120; 722110
Advertising Expenditures: $100,000
Media: 2-6-8-9-18-20-22-25-26
Distr.: Local
Budget Set: Sept.
Personnel:
Paul W. Lowden *(Chm, Pres & CEO)*
Suzanne Lowden *(Treas, Sec & Exec VP)*
Chris Lowden *(Dir-Design & Devel)*
Bernadette Miller *(Mgr-Tax)*

ARDEN REALTY, INC.
(Sub. of GE Capital Real Estate)
11601 Wilshire Blvd 4th Fl
Los Angeles, CA 90025-1740
Tel.: (310) 966-2600
Fax: (310) 966-2699
Web Site: www.ardenrealty.com
Sales Range: $400-449.9 Million
Approx. Number Employees: 300
Year Founded: 1996
Business Description:
Real Estate Investment Trust
S.I.C.: 6798
N.A.I.C.S.: 525930
Media: 10
Personnel:
Joaquin de Monet *(Pres & CEO)*
Derric DuBourdieu *(Sr Mgr-Portfolio Leasing)*
Don Trapani *(Sr Mgr-Portfolio Leasing)*
Michael Pollack *(Sr Portfolio Leasing Mgr)*

ARLINGTON HOSPITALITY, INC.
(Sub. of Sunburst Hospitality Corporation)
2355 S Arlington Heights Rd Ste 400
Arlington Heights, IL 60005
Tel.: (847) 228-5400
Fax: (847) 228-5409
E-mail: info@arlingtonhospitality.com
Web Site: www.arlingtonhospitality.com
Sales Range: $50-74.9 Million
Approx. Number Employees: 889
Year Founded: 1989
Business Description:
Hotel Developer, Owner & Operator
S.I.C.: 7011
N.A.I.C.S.: 721110
Advertising Expenditures: $1,117,000
Media: 13-18
Personnel:
James Dale *(CFO & Sr VP-Fin)*
Rick A. Gerhart *(Sr VP-Ops)*

ASSOCIATED ESTATES REALTY CORPORATION
1 AEC Pkwy
Richmond Heights, OH 44143-1467
Tel.: (216) 261-5000
Fax: (216) 289-9600
Toll Free: (800) 440-2372
E-mail: ir@aecrealty.com
Web Site: www.aecrealty.com
Approx. Rev.: $153,715,000
Approx. Number Employees: 390
Year Founded: 1993
Business Description:
Real Estate Investment Trust
S.I.C.: 6798
N.A.I.C.S.: 525930
Advertising Expenditures: $1,500,000
Media: 7-8-10-13-18-19
Personnel:
Jeffrey I. Friedman *(Chm, Pres & CEO)*
Lou Fatica *(CFO, Treas & VP)*
Bradley A. van Auken *(Gen Counsel, Sec & VP)*
John T. Shannon *(Sr VP-Ops)*
Daniel E. Gold *(VP-HR)*

ATLAS HOTELS, INC.
500 Hotel Cir N
San Diego, CA 92108-3005
Tel.: (619) 291-2232
Fax: (619) 291-4097
Approx. Number Employees: 1,000
Year Founded: 1953
Business Description:
Holding Company; Hotel, Restaurant & Resort Owner & Operator
S.I.C.: 6719; 5812; 7011
N.A.I.C.S.: 551112; 721110; 722110
Media: 2-4-5-6-7-8-9-10-11-18-20-24-25
Distr.: Natl.
Budget Set: Oct.
Personnel:
Jim Oddo *(COO & Exec VP)*
C. Terry Brown *(Pres-Atlas Dev Corp)*
Nikki Barker *(Mgr-Pur)*
Brands & Products:
ATLAS
Advertising Agency:
Hotel Marketing Group
814 Morena Blvd., Ste 210
San Diego, CA 92110
Tel.: (619) 295-8080
(Hotel & Restaurant)

ATLIFIC INC.
(Affil. of Ocean Properties, Ltd.)
(d/b/a Atlific Hotels & Resorts)
250 Saint-Antoine
Montreal, QC H2Y 0A3, Canada
Tel.: (514) 403-1000
Fax: (514) 403-2332
Toll Free: (888) 285-4342
E-mail: info@atlific.com
Web Site: www.atlific.com
E-Mail For Key Personnel:
Marketing Director: john.dunn@atlific.com
Approx. Number Employees: 3,000
Year Founded: 1959
Business Description:
Hotel Management Services
S.I.C.: 7011
N.A.I.C.S.: 721110
Media: 4-7-8-9-10-14-20
Distr.: Intl.; Natl.
Budget Set: Oct. -Nov.
Personnel:
Michael Walsh *(Pres)*
Robert Chartrand *(CFO & Exec VP)*
Richard Ade *(Exec VP)*
Philippe Gadbois *(Sr VP-Sls & Mktg)*
Carolyn Glen *(Dir-Mktg-Natl)*
Arlene Wray *(Dir-Sls-Western Canada)*

AUBERGE RESORTS, LLC
591 Redwood Hwy Ste 3150
Mill Valley, CA 94941
Tel.: (415) 380-3460
Fax: (415) 380-3461
Toll Free: (866) 282-3743
Web Site: www.aubergeresorts.com
Approx. Number Employees: 7
Year Founded: 1999
Business Description:
Resort & Spa Management Services
S.I.C.: 7011
N.A.I.C.S.: 721110
Media: 8-13-22
Personnel:
Robert Harmon *(Chm & Principal)*
Claude Rouas *(Vice Chm & Principal)*
Mark Harmon *(CEO & Principal)*
Lorraine Scherer *(CFO)*
Eric Calderon *(COO & Principal)*
Grant Harmon *(Principal & Gen Counsel)*
Caroline MacDonald *(Principal & Sr VP-Mktg)*
Tracy Lee *(Principal & VP-Spa Dev)*
George Goeggel *(Principal & Dir)*
Tim Harmon *(Principal & Dir)*
Rick Graves *(VP-Tech & Dir-Dev)*
Laura Manzano *(VP-Sls)*
Ursula Zopp *(VP-HR)*
Advertising Agency:
Murphy O'Brien, Inc.
(d/b/a Murphy O'Brien Public Relations)
1630 Stewart St Ste 140
Santa Monica, CA 90404
Tel.: (310) 453-2539
Fax: (310) 264-0083

AVALONBAY COMMUNITIES, INC.
671 N Glebe Rd Ste 800
Arlington, VA 22203
Tel.: (703) 329-6300
Fax: (703) 329-1459
Web Site: www.avalonbay.com
Approx. Rev.: $895,266,000
Approx. Number Employees: 1,993
Year Founded: 1998
Business Description:
Real Estate Investment Trust
S.I.C.: 6798
N.A.I.C.S.: 525930
Personnel:
Bryce Blair *(Chm & CEO)*
Thomas J. Sargeant *(CFO)*
Keri A. Shea *(Treas & VP-Fin)*
Sean J. Breslin *(Exec VP-Investments & Asset Mgmt)*
William M. McLaughlin *(Exec VP-Dev & Construction-Northeast)*
Suzanne Jakstavich *(VP-HR)*
Alaine S. Walsh *(Sr Dir)*
Brands & Products:
AVALON
AVALONBAY
AVALONBAY COMMUNITIES
EXCELLENT EXECUTION...
TIME WELL SPENT
Advertising Agencies:
Blue Bug Digital
1828 L St NW Ste 240
Washington, DC 20036
Tel.: (202) 349-4000
Fax: (202) 333-4515
Social Media Agency of Record

Stein Rogan + Partners
432 Park Ave S
New York, NY 10016-8013
Tel.: (212) 213-1112
Fax: (212) 779-7305

AVATAR HOLDINGS INC.
201 Alhambra Cir
Coral Gables, FL 33134-5107
Tel.: (305) 442-7000
Fax: (305) 448-9927
E-mail: juanita_kerrigan@avatarholdings.com
Web Site: www.avatarhomes.com
Approx. Rev.: $59,138,000
Approx. Number Employees: 243
Year Founded: 1970
Business Description:
Holding Company; Residential Community Development & Housing Construction Services
S.I.C.: 6719; 1531; 6531
N.A.I.C.S.: 551112; 236117; 531390
Advertising Expenditures: $1,342,000
Media: 1-2-4-6-7-8-9-10-11-13-14-15-18-20-22-23-25
Distr.: Intl.; Natl.
Personnel:
Joshua Lionel Nash *(Chm)*
Gerald D. Kelfer *(Vice Chm)*
Jon M. Donnell *(Pres & CEO)*
Tina Johnston *(CFO, Chief Acctg Officer & VP)*
Patricia Kimball Fletcher *(Gen Counsel & Exec VP)*
Joseph Carl Mulac, III *(Exec VP)*
Brands & Products:
AVATAR
BELLALAGO
POINCIANA
SOLIVITA
TERRALARGO

AVATAR RETIREMENT COMMUNITIES, INC.
(Sub. of Avatar Holdings Inc.)
201 Alhambra Cir 12 Fl
Coral Gables, FL 33134-5107
Tel.: (305) 442-7000
Fax: (305) 567-0682
Web Site: www.solivita.com
Sales Range: $50-74.9 Million
Approx. Number Employees: 200
Year Founded: 1997
Business Description:
Adult Communities Developer
S.I.C.: 8361
N.A.I.C.S.: 623312
Media: 6-22
Personnel:
Gerald D. Kelfer *(Vice Chm)*
Richard P. Weida *(Asst VP-Tax)*
Brands & Products:
SOLIVITA

BABCOCK & BROWN RESIDENTIAL, INC.
(Sub. of Babcock & Brown LP)
301 S College St Ste 3850
Charlotte, NC 28202-6024
Tel.: (704) 944-0100
Fax: (704) 334-3437
E-mail: investor.relations@bnp-residential.com
Web Site: www.babcockbrownresidential.com
Sales Range: $50-74.9 Million
Approx. Number Employees: 240
Year Founded: 1987
Business Description:
Real Estate Investment Trust
S.I.C.: 6798; 6531
N.A.I.C.S.: 525930; 531311
Advertising Expenditures: $758,000
Media: 8-22
Personnel:
Philip S. Payne *(Chm & CEO)*

Pamela B. Bruno *(CFO, Treas & VP)*
Eric Rohm *(Gen Counsel, Sec & VP)*

BALLY'S PARK PLACE, INC.
(Joint Venture of Apollo Advisors, L.P. & TPG Capital, L.P.)
(d/b/a Bally's Atlantic City)
Park Pl & Boardwalk
Atlantic City, NJ 08401
Tel.: (609) 340-2000
Fax: (609) 340-4713
Toll Free: (800) 542-7724
E-mail: info@ballysac.com
Web Site: www.ballysac.com
Approx. Number Employees: 5,000
Year Founded: 1977
Business Description:
Hotel & Casino
S.I.C.: 7011; 7999
N.A.I.C.S.: 721120; 713290; 713990
Personnel:
Erin Chamberlin *(VP-Mktg-Caesars Atlantic City and Bally's Atlantic City)*
John Katapodis *(Dir-Hotel Operations)*
Advertising Agencies:
Kolber Enterprises
500 Easton Rd
Willow Grove, PA 19090-0648
Tel.: (215) 657-4600
Fax: (215) 657-8192

TracyLocke
1999 Bryan St Ste 2800
Dallas, TX 75201
Tel.: (214) 259-3500
Fax: (214) 259-3550

BARONA VALLEY RANCH RESORT & CASINO
1932 Wildcat Canyon Rd
Lakeside, CA 92040
Tel.: (619) 443-2300
Fax: (619) 443-2300
Toll Free: (888) 722-7662
Web Site: www.barona.com
Approx. Number Employees: 3,600
Year Founded: 1932
Business Description:
Hotel & Casino
S.I.C.: 7011
N.A.I.C.S.: 721120
Media: 1-4-7-8-10-13-20-22
Brands & Products:
BARONA
CLUB BARONA
Advertising Agency:
NYCA
1010 S Coast Hwy Ste 101
Encinitas, CA 92024
Tel.: (760) 436-7033
Fax: (760) 436-7047

BARRATT GROUP
2055 Corte del Nogal
Carlsbad, CA 92011
Tel.: (760) 842-6565
Fax: (760) 579-0170
E-mail: admin@barratt.com
Web Site: www.barratt.com
Sales Range: $300-349.9 Million
Approx. Number Employees: 66
Year Founded: 1980
Business Description:
House & Apartment Complex Developer & Builder
S.I.C.: 1522; 6552
N.A.I.C.S.: 236116; 237210
Media: 1-10-22
Personnel:
Robert Cummings *(Pres)*
Michael Pattinson *(CEO & Principal)*
J. Michael Armstrong *(Principal & Gen Counsel)*

BAY WALK
(Sub. of The Sembler Company)
Ste 310 146 2nd St N
Saint Petersburg, FL 33701-3361
Tel.: (727) 824-8888
Web Site: www.baywalkstpete.com
Business Description:
Shopping Complex
S.I.C.: 5999; 5731
N.A.I.C.S.: 453910; 443112
Media: 9-22-25

BAYOU GOLF CLUB
(Holding of Fore Golf Services, LP)
7979 Bayou Club Blvd
Largo, FL 33777-3040
Tel.: (727) 399-1000
Fax: (727) 398-4364
E-mail: Manager7979@BayouClubGolf.com
Web Site: www.bayouclubgolf.com
Year Founded: 1991
Business Description:
Golf Club Operations
S.I.C.: 7997
N.A.I.C.S.: 713910
Media: 6-22
Personnel:
Chad Boyd *(Dir-Membership)*
Scott Gray *(Dir-Golf)*
Jim King *(Dir-Instruction)*
Kari Perkey *(Mgr-Food & Beverage & Coord-Special Events)*

BEAZER HOMES USA, INC.
1000 Abernathy Rd Ste 1200
Atlanta, GA 30328
Tel.: (770) 829-3700
Fax: (770) 481-2808
Toll Free: (866) 457-3678
E-mail: lkratcos@beazer.com
Web Site: www.beazer.com
Approx. Rev.: $1,009,841,000
Approx. Number Employees: 883
Year Founded: 1985
Business Description:
Single-Family Housing Construction
S.I.C.: 1521
N.A.I.C.S.: 236115
Import Export
Advertising Expenditures: $11,400,000
Media: 6
Personnel:
Allan P. Merrill *(Pres & CEO)*
Robert L. Salomon *(CFO & Exec VP)*
Michael H. Furlow *(COO & Exec VP)*
Cindy B. Tierney *(CIO)*
Kathi James *(CMO)*
Tony L. Callahan *(Chief Procurement Officer)*
Kenneth F. Khoury *(Gen Counsel & Exec VP)*
Peggy J. Caldwell *(Sr VP & Deputy Gen Counsel)*
Fred Fratto *(Sr VP-HR)*
Carey Phelps *(Dir-IR & Corp Comm)*
Advertising Agencies:
Brunner
11 Stanwix St 5th Fl
Pittsburgh, PA 15222-1312
Tel.: (412) 995-9500
Fax: (412) 995-9501
(Creative, Strategic Planning, Media Buying/Planning, Digital, Direct)

IMRE
909 Ridgebrook Rd Ste 300
Baltimore, MD 21152
Tel.: (410) 821-8220
Fax: (410) 821-5619
Single-Family Homes

BEHRINGER HARVARD HOLDINGS, LLC
15601 Dallas Pkwy Ste 600
Addison, TX 75001
Tel.: (214) 655-1600
Fax: (214) 655-1610
Web Site: www.behringerharvard.com
Approx. Number Employees: 200
Business Description:
Holding Company
S.I.C.: 6719
N.A.I.C.S.: 551112
Personnel:
Robert M. Behringer *(Founder, Owner & CEO)*
Robert S. Aisner *(Pres & Co-COO)*
Gary S. Bresky *(CFO, Treas & Exec VP)*
Samuel A. Gillespie *(Co-COO & Exec VP)*
Kent Barner *(CIO)*
M. Jason Mattox *(Chief Admin Officer)*
Scott Fordham *(Chief Acctg Officer & Sr VP)*
Gerald J. Reihsen, III *(Sec, Exec VP-Corp Dev & Legal)*
Robert Franklin Muller, Jr. *(Exec VP & Head-Distr)*
Jon Dooley *(Exec VP-Real Estate)*
Andrew J. Bruce *(Sr VP-Capital Markets)*
Margaret M. Daly *(Sr VP-Multifamily Property Mgmt)*
Gerald D. Oliver, Jr. *(Sr VP-Comml Property Mgmt.)*
Kelleen Richter *(Sr VP-Mktg)*
Michael Stricker *(Sr VP-Investment Svcs)*
Stewart P. Yee *(Dir-IR)*
Lisa Harris *(Reg Mgr)*
Advertising Agency:
The Richards Group, Inc.
8750 N Central Expy Ste 100
Dallas, TX 75231-6430
Tel.: (214) 891-5700
Fax: (214) 265-2933

BENCHMARK HOSPITALITY INTERNATIONAL INC.
4 Waterway Sq Ste 300
The Woodlands, TX 77380
Tel.: (281) 367-5757
Fax: (281) 367-1407
Toll Free: (888) 846-6338
E-mail: bhi@benchmarkmanagement.com
Web Site: www.benchmarkhospitality.com
Sales Range: $1-9.9 Million
Approx. Number Employees: 6,300
Business Description:
Management & Marketing Services for Resorts, Conference Centers, Conference Hotels & Golf Clubs
S.I.C.: 8742; 7011; 7997
N.A.I.C.S.: 541611; 541613; 713910; 721110; 721199
Media: 2
Personnel:
Burt Cabanas *(Chm & CEO)*
Greg Champion *(COO)*
Dennis Blyshak *(Chief Corp Officer)*
Alex Cabanas *(Pres-Bus Dev & Fin)*
Bruce Burkhalter *(Sr VP-Technical Svcs)*
Ted Davis *(Sr VP-Sls & Mktg)*
Greg Parsons *(Sr VP-Ops)*
Ellen Sinclair *(Sr VP-Ops)*
John Davies *(VP-Mktg)*
Rodney Thiel *(VP-IT)*
Todd M. Felsen *(Gen Mgr-Cheyenne Mountain Resort)*
Michael J. Taylor *(Gen Mgr-Transitions)*
Katsuhito Sugaya *(Dir-Intl Sls)*

BEST WESTERN INTERNATIONAL, INC.
6201 N 24th Pkwy
Phoenix, AZ 85016-2023
Tel.: (602) 957-4200
Toll Free: (800) 780-7234
Telex: 165743
Web Site: www.bestwestern.com
Approx. Number Employees: 1,200
Year Founded: 1946
Business Description:
Lodging Chain Motor Inns, Hotels, Resorts
S.I.C.: 4729; 7311
N.A.I.C.S.: 561599; 541810
Media: 1-2-3-5-6-10-11-13-15-18-19-20-21-22-23-24-26
Distr.: Intl.; Natl.
Budget Set: Sept.
Personnel:
David Kong *(Pres & CEO)*
Ron Borges *(Mng Dir & Controller)*
Mark Straszynski *(CFO & VP-Fin)*
Lawrence Cuculic *(Gen Counsel & Sr VP)*
Dorothy Dowling *(Sr VP-Mktg & Sls)*
Karmela Gaffney *(Mng Dir-eCommerce, Adv & Creative Svcs)*
Renee Ryan *(VP-Mktg)*
Jamie Daer *(Dir-Communication & Specialist-Adv)*
Mike Durazo *(Dir-Online Client Solutions)*
Johannes Jahns *(Dir-Ops-Asia)*
Tiffany Tchida *(Dir-eCommerce)*
David Trumble *(Dir-External Commun)*
Lori Polhemus *(Reg Mgr-Mktg)*
Judy? Sprott *(Mgr-Internet Mktg)*
Brands & Products:
BEST BUSINESS WORLDWIDE
BEST REQUESTS
BEST WESTERN
BEST WESTERN BEST RATES
BEST WESTERN PREMIER
BEST WESTERN TRAVEL CARD
BESTCHEQUE
BESTWESTERN.COM
BUSINESS PLUS
THE WORLD'S LARGEST HOTEL CHAIN
Advertising Agencies:
Allison & Partners
410 N 44th St Ste 1100
Phoenix, AZ 85008
Tel.: (480) 966-0100
Fax: (480) 966-0111

Gotham Incorporated
150 E 42nd St 12th Fl

Key to Media (For complete agency information see *The Advertising Red Books-Agencies* edition):
1. Bus. Publs. 2. Cable T.V. 3. Catalogs & Directories. 4. Co-op Adv. 5. Consumer Mags. 6. D.M. to Bus. Estab.7. D.M. to Consumers 8. Daily Newsp. 9. Exhibits/Trade Shows 10. Foreign 11. Infomercial 12. Internet Adv.13. Multimedia 14. Network Radio 15. Network T.V. 16. Newsp. Distr. Mags. 17. Other 18. Outdoor (Posters, Transit) 19. Point of Purchase20. Premiums, Novelties 21. Product Samples 22. Special Events Mktg. 23. Spot Radio 24. Spot T.V. 25. Weekly Newsp. 26. Yellow Page Adv.

Best Western International, Inc. — (Continued)

New York, NY 10017
Tel.: (212) 414-7000
Fax: (212) 414-7095

Initiative Los Angeles
5700 Wilshire Blvd Ste 400
Los Angeles, CA 90036-3648
Tel.: (323) 370-8000
Fax: (323) 370-8950
Media Placement

BEVERLY-HANKS & ASSOCIATES INC.

300 Executive Park
Asheville, NC 28801
Tel.: (828) 254-7221
Fax: (828) 255-8994
Web Site: www.beverly-hanks.com
Approx. Number Employees: 55
Year Founded: 1976
Business Description:
Real Estate Brokers & Agents
S.I.C.: 6531
N.A.I.C.S.: 531210
Media: 6-9-17-18-20-25
Personnel:
Neal Hanks, Jr. *(Pres)*
Bob Boettcher *(VP & Mng Broker)*
Sharon Montague *(Dir-Education & Trng)*
Larry Zapf *(Dir-Relocation & Bus Dev)*

THE BEVERLY HILLS HOTEL

(Sub. of Dorchester Group Ltd.)
9641 Sunset Blvd
Beverly Hills, CA 90210-2938
Tel.: (310) 276-2251
Fax: (310) 887-2887
Toll Free: (800) 283-8885
Telex: 188586
E-mail: concierge@thebeverlyhillshotel.com
Web Site: www.thebeverlyhillshotel.com
E-Mail For Key Personnel:
Sales Director: sales@thebeverlyhillshotel.com
Approx. Number Employees: 400
Year Founded: 1912
Business Description:
Hotels
S.I.C.: 7011; 5812
N.A.I.C.S.: 721110; 722110
Media: 2-11
Distr.: Direct to Consumer; Reg.
Personnel:
Alberto del Hoyo *(Gen Mgr)*
Tracy Koven *(Sr Dir-Catering Sls)*
Janet Jacobs *(Reg Dir-Fin)*
Darlene Adams *(Dir-Sls & Mktg)*
Timthy Gustie *(Dir-Food & Beverage)*
Ron Howard *(Dir-Sls-Middle East)*
Kayal Moore *(Dir-Room Reservations)*
Wendy Schnee *(Dir-Pub Rels)*
Ava White *(Dir-HR)*
Advertising Agency:
Gordon Gelfond Associates Inc.
PO Box 17818
Beverly Hills, CA 90219
Tel.: (310) 203-9982

BINSWANGER CORPORATION

2 Logan Sq
Philadelphia, PA 19103
Tel.: (215) 448-6000
Fax: (215) 448-6238
E-mail: fgbiii@binswanger.com
Web Site: www.binswanger.com
E-Mail For Key Personnel:
Marketing Director: eweiss@cbb.com
Approx. Number Employees: 5,200
Year Founded: 1931
Business Description:
Full Service International Real Estate Services
S.I.C.: 6531
N.A.I.C.S.: 531210
Media: 1-2-4-5-7-9-11-13-18-19-25-26
Distr.: Intl.; Natl.
Budget Set: Dec.
Personnel:
John K. Binswanger *(Chm)*
John J. Dues *(Vice Chm)*
Clive Mendelow *(Vice Chm)*
David R. Binswanger *(Pres)*
Beth Ganss *(CFO)*
Frank G. Binswanger, III *(Pres-Binswanger Intl)*
Walter K. Evans *(Pres-Mgmt Svcs)*
Christopher J. Hall *(Pres-Appraisal)*
Larry M. Spinelli *(Pres-Natl Grp)*
Daniel Cullen *(Gen Counsel & Sr VP)*
Steven R. Baron *(Exec VP-Tenant Representation & Transaction Svcs)*
J. Holmes Davis, IV *(Sr VP)*
Eric Dienstbach *(Sr VP-Realty Grp)*
Martha A. Fisher *(Sr VP-HR)*
Andrew Harris *(Sr VP-Advisory Svcs)*
Gerald Norton *(Sr VP)*
Charles S. Pawlak *(Sr VP-Tech)*
Marc Policarpo *(Sr VP)*
Ruth Sansom *(Sr VP-Mgmt Svcs)*
Frank W. Truesdell *(Sr VP)*
W. Alexis Lambeth *(VP-Sls-Dallas)*
Advertising Agency:
Rittenhouse Marketing Associates
2 Logan Sq 4th Fl
Philadelphia, PA 19103-2719
Tel.: (215) 448-6000
Fax: (215) 448-6238
(Real Estate Services)

BLACK GAMING, LLC

950 W Mesquite Blvd
Mesquite, NV 89027
Tel.: (702) 346-4000
Fax: (702) 346-6860
Toll Free: (800) 346-7721
Web Site: www.itsmesquite.com
Sales Range: $150-199.9 Million
Approx. Number Employees: 1,700
Business Description:
Holding Company; Casino Hotels & Resorts Owner & Operator
S.I.C.: 7011; 6719
N.A.I.C.S.: 721120; 551112
Advertising Expenditures: $4,500,000
Personnel:
Robert R. Black, Sr. *(CEO)*
Anthony Toti *(COO)*
Brands & Products:
CASABLANCA HOTEL
OASIS RESORT HOTEL & CASINO
VIRGIN RIVER HOTEL

BLACK HAWK GAMING & DEVELOPMENT CO. INC.

(Sub. of Jacobs Entertainment, Inc.)
Ste 250 17301 W Colfax Ave
Golden, CO 80401-4800
Tel.: (303) 582-1117
Tel.: (303) 215-5200
Fax: (303) 582-0239
Web Site: www.thelodgecasino.com
Year Founded: 1991
Business Description:
Owner & Operator of Casino & Hotels
S.I.C.: 7011; 6552
N.A.I.C.S.: 721120; 237210
Media: 7
Personnel:
Brett Kramer *(VP-Fin)*
Meera Rosser *(Dir-Mktg)*

BLUEGREEN CORPORATION

4960 Conference Way N Ste 100
Boca Raton, FL 33431-4490
Tel.: (561) 912-8000
Fax: (561) 912-8100
E-mail: tony.puleo@bluegreencorp.com
Web Site: www.bluegreencorp.com
Approx. Rev.: $365,677,000
Approx. Number Employees: 3,825
Business Description:
Residential Land & Timeshare Properties Acquirer, Developer & Seller
S.I.C.: 8699; 6513; 6531; 6552
N.A.I.C.S.: 813990; 237210; 531110; 531390
Advertising Expenditures: $50,000,000
Media: 7-8-9-10-13-18-19-22-23-24-25
Personnel:
Alan B. Levan *(Chm)*
John E. Abdo *(Vice Chm)*
John M. Maloney Jr. *(Pres & CEO)*
Daniel C. Koscher *(Pres, CEO-Bluegreen Communities & Sr VP)*
Anthony M. Puleo, Jr. *(CFO, Treas & Sr VP)*
Raymond S. Lopez *(Chief Acctg Officer & Sr VP)*
Susan J. Saturday *(Chief HR Officer & Sr VP)*
Gary Byrd *(Chief Hospitality Officer)*
David L. Pontius *(Pres-Bluegreen Resorts & Sr VP)*
David A. Bidgood *(Pres-Field Sls & Mktg)*
Allan J. Herz *(Sr VP-Mortgage Ops & Asst Treas)*
Laurel M. Liber *(Sr VP-Owner Rels)*
Paul Humphrey *(VP-Fin & Capital Markets)*

BOOMTOWN, LLC

(Sub. of Pinnacle Entertainment, Inc.)
(d/b/a Boomtown-Reno)
PO Box 399
Verdi, NV 89439-0399
Tel.: (775) 345-6000
Fax: (775) 345-8665
Toll Free: (800) 648-3790
E-mail: jeff.babinski@boomtownmail.com
Web Site: www.boomtownreno.com
Sales Range: $200-249.9 Million
Approx. Number Employees: 400
Business Description:
Hotel & Casino
S.I.C.: 7999; 7011
N.A.I.C.S.: 713290; 721120
Media: 3-6-8-9-18-23-24
Distr.: Natl.

BORGATA HOTEL CASINO & SPA

(Joint Venture of Boyd Gaming Corporation & MGM Resorts International)
1 Borgata Way
Atlantic City, NJ 08401
Tel.: (609) 317-1000
Fax: (609) 347-1000
E-mail: customercare@theborgata.com
Web Site: www.theborgata.com
Sales Range: $200-249.9 Million
Approx. Number Employees: 6,000
Business Description:
Hotel & Casino; Owned by Boyd Gaming Corporation & Tracinda Corporation
S.I.C.: 7011
N.A.I.C.S.: 721120
Media: 6-18-20-22-23-24
Personnel:
Dave Coskey *(VP-Mktg)*
John Forelli *(VP-IT)*
Advertising Agencies:
Lerner Enterprises, Inc.
13 Melissa Ln
Old Bethpage, NY 11804
Tel.: (516) 752-7557
Fax: (516) 752-7557
Toll Free: (866) LERNER1

Nancy J. Friedman Public Relations, Inc.
35 E 21st St 8th Fl
New York, NY 10010
Tel.: (212) 228-1500
Fax: (212) 228-1517

SK+G Advertising
8912 Spanish Ridge Ave
Las Vegas, NV 89148
Tel.: (702) 478-4000
Fax: (702) 478-4001

Visions Advertising Media, LLC
426 Shore Rd Ste B
Atlantic City, NJ 08401
Tel.: (609) 926-6358
Fax: (609) 926-6358

BOYD GAMING CORPORATION

3883 Howard Hughes Pkwy 9th Fl
Las Vegas, NV 89169
Tel.: (702) 792-7200
Fax: (702) 792-7313
E-mail: robstillwell@boydgaming.com
Web Site: www.boydgaming.com
Approx. Rev.: $2,494,724,000
Approx. Number Employees: 21,300
Year Founded: 1974
Business Description:
Casino & Entertainment Hotels Owner & Operator
S.I.C.: 7999; 7011
N.A.I.C.S.: 713290; 721120
Advertising Expenditures: $31,800,000
Media: 2-3-4-5-6-8-9-10-16-18-20-22-23-24-25-26
Distr.: Natl.
Budget Set: Jan.
Personnel:
William S. Boyd *(Chm)*
Marianne Boyd Johnson *(Vice Chm, Chief Diversity Officer & Exec VP)*
Keith E. Smith *(Pres & CEO)*

Key to Media (For complete agency information see *The Advertising Red Books-Agencies* edition):
1. Bus. Publs. 2. Cable T.V. 3. Catalogs & Directories. 4. Co-op Adv. 5. Consumer Mags. 6. D.M. to Bus. Estab.7. D.M. to Consumers 8. Daily Newsp. 9. Exhibits/Trade Shows 10. Foreign 11. Infomercial 12. Internet Adv.13. Multimedia 14. Network Radio 15. Network T.V. 16. Newsp. Distr. Mags. 17. Other 18. Outdoor (Posters, Transit) 19. Point of Purchase20. Premiums, Novelties 21. Product Samples 22. Special Events Mktg. 23. Spot Radio 24. Spot T.V. 25. Weekly Newsp. 26. Yellow Page Adv.

Josh Hirsberg *(CFO)*
Paul J. Chakmak *(COO & Exec VP)*
Robert L. Boughner *(Chief Bus Dev Officer & Exec VP)*
Ellie J. Bowdish *(Chief Acctg Officer & VP)*
Brian A. Larson *(Gen Counsel, Sec & Exec VP)*
Christopher R. Gibase *(Sr VP-Ops, Midwest & South Region)*
William J. Noonan *(Sr VP-Admin)*
Stephen S. Thompson *(Sr VP-Ops-Nevada Region)*
Rob Meyne *(VP-Corp Comm)*
Dan Stark *(VP-Corp Mktg)*
Brian Best *(Dir-E-Commerce)*
James Mao *(Mgr-Internet Mktg)*

Brands & Products:
BLUE CHIP HOTEL & CASINO
BOYDGAMING
CALIFORNIA HOTEL & CASINO
DELTA DOWNS RACE TRACK & CASINO
ELDORADO CASINO
FREMONT HOTEL & CASINO
JOKERS WILD CASINO
MAIN STREET STATION HOTEL, CASINO & BREWERY
PAR-A-DICE HOTEL & CASINO
SAMS TOWN TUNICA HOTEL & GAMBLING HALL
TREASURE CHEST CASINO

Advertising Agencies:
Boyd Creative Services
4500 W Tropicana Ave
Las Vegas, NV 89103
Tel.: (702) 365-7135
Fax: (702) 365-7525

JMPR, Inc.
5850 Canoga Ave Ste 300
Woodland Hills, CA 91367
Tel.: (818) 992-4353
Fax: (818) 992-0543

Nuevo Advertising Group, Inc.
677 N Washington Blvd
Sarasota, FL 34236
Tel.: (941) 752-4433
Fax: (941) 752-1114

BOYNE USA RESORTS INC.

1 Boyne Mountain Rd
Boyne Falls, MI 49713-9642
Tel.: (231) 549-6040
Fax: (231) 549-6094
Toll Free: (800) GOBOYNE
E-mail: info@boyne.com
Web Site: www.boyneresorts.com
E-Mail For Key Personnel:
Marketing Director: jard@boyne.com
Sales Director: MHomuth@boyne.com
Approx. Number Employees: 3,000
Year Founded: 1947
Business Description:
Operator of Ski & Golf Resorts
S.I.C.: 7011
N.A.I.C.S.: 721110
Advertising Expenditures: $500,000
Media: 1-2-3-5-6-7-8-9-10-11-13-18-19-23-24-25-26
Distr.: Direct to Consumer; Natl.
Budget Set: Dec. -Aug.
Personnel:
Stephen Kircher *(Owner & Pres-Eastern Ops)*
John Kircher *(Pres-Western Ops)*
Julie Ard *(Dir-Mktg)*
Mark Homuth *(Dir-Sls)*
Barbara Elliott *(Mgr-Natl Acct Sls)*
Erin Ernst *(Mgr-PR)*
Don Marszalec *(Mgr-Sls)*
Trisha Olach *(Mgr-Sls-Natl Accts)*
Leah Pierce *(Mgr-Sls-Natl Accts)*
Tracy Russold *(Mgr-Sls)*
Brands & Products:
BAVARIAN VILLAGE
BOYNE
BOYNE RESORTS
EXPERIENCE THE LIFESTYLE

THE BOZZUTO GROUP

(Sub. of Bozzuto & Associates Inc.)
(d/b/a Buzzuto and Assoc., Inc)
7850 Walker Dr Ste 400
Greenbelt, MD 20770
Tel.: (301) 220-0100
Fax: (301) 220-3738
E-mail: frontdesk@bozzuto.com
Web Site: www.bozzuto.com
Approx. Rev.: $3,300,000
Approx. Number Employees: 250
Business Description:
Single-Family Housing Construction
S.I.C.: 1521; 6163
N.A.I.C.S.: 236115; 522310
Personnel:
Rick Mostin *(Co-Owner, Founding Partner, COO & Principal)*
John Slidell *(Vice Chm & Pres)*
Thomas S. Bozzuto *(CEO)*
Jamie Gorski *(Sr VP-Corp Mktg)*
Advertising Agency:
Crosby Marketing Communications
705 Melvin Ave Ste 200
Annapolis, MD 21401-1540
Tel.: (410) 626-0805
Fax: (410) 269-6547

BRESLER & REINER, INC.

Ste 502 11200 Rockville Pike
Rockville, MD 20852-7105
Tel.: (301) 945-4300
Fax: (301) 945-4301
Web Site: www.breslerandreiner.com
Sales Range: $75-99.9 Million
Approx. Number Employees: 16
Business Description:
Operators of Apartment Buildings, Office Buildings, Shopping Centers, Real Estate Development Management
S.I.C.: 6513; 6512
N.A.I.C.S.: 531110; 531120
Media: 8-13
Personnel:
Sidney M. Bresler *(CEO)*

BRIDGESTREET WORLDWIDE INC.

(Sub. of Sorrento Asset Management Ltd.)
4501 N Fairfax Dr
Arlington, VA 22203
Tel.: (703) 387-3600
Fax: (703) 387-3601
Toll Free: (800) 278-7338
Telex: 888-428-0600
E-mail: info@bridgestreet.com
Web Site: www.bridgestreet.com
Sales Range: $125-149.9 Million
Approx. Number Employees: 500
Year Founded: 1996
Business Description:
Extended Stay & Relocation Services to Corporations & Professional Firms in the United States, Canada & the United Kingdom
S.I.C.: 7299
N.A.I.C.S.: 812990
Media: 2-4-7-13-18
Personnel:
H. Lee Curtis *(Pres)*
Sean Worker *(CEO)*
Dale Gingrich *(Sr VP-Fin)*
Max Thorne *(Sr VP-Dev)*
Natalie Hickernell *(VP-HR)*
Jo Layton *(VP-Sls & Mktg-EMEA)*
Liz Warnes *(VP-Fin-EMEA)*

BROADMOOR HOTEL, INC.

1 Lk Ave
Colorado Springs, CO 80906-4254
Tel.: (719) 634-7711
Tel.: (719) 577-5718 (Pub Rels)
Fax: (719) 577-5741
Toll Free: (800) 634-7711
E-mail: info@broadmoor.com
Web Site: www.broadmoor.com
Sales Range: $50-74.9 Million
Approx. Number Employees: 1,700
Year Founded: 1918
Business Description:
Resort Hotel & Spa
S.I.C.: 7011
N.A.I.C.S.: 721110
Advertising Expenditures: $850,000
Media: 2-4-5-6-8-9-10-13-22-23-24-25
Distr.: Intl.; Natl.
Budget Set: Oct.
Personnel:
Stephan Bartolin *(Pres & CEO)*
DennisV Lesko *(VP-Mktg)*
John Washko *(VP-Sls)*
Terry McHale *(Dir-Facilities)*
Russ Miller *(Dir-Golf)*
Sarah B. Knowlton *(Mgr-Mktg & Pub Rel)*
Jeff Yeager *(Mgr)*
Brands & Products:
THE BROADMOOR
Advertising Agency:
Vladimir Jones
6 N Tejon St 4 Fl
Colorado Springs, CO 80903-1509
Tel.: (719) 473-0704
Fax: (719) 473-0754

BROOKFIELD FINANCIAL PROPERTIES, INC.

(Sub. of BROOKFIELD PROPERTIES CORPORATION)
3 World Financial Ctr 200 Vesey St 11Fl
New York, NY 10281
Tel.: (212) 417-7000
Fax: (212) 417-7214
Fax: (212) 417-7196
Web Site: www.brookfield.com/contact/
Approx. Number Employees: 100
Business Description:
Real Estate Development & Management
S.I.C.: 6512; 6552
N.A.I.C.S.: 531120; 237210
Advertising Expenditures: $200,000
Media: 2-6-17
Distr.: Natl.
Budget Set: Oct.
Personnel:
John E. Zuccotti *(Chm)*
Dennis Friedrich *(Pres & CEO-US Property Ops)*
Paul Schulman *(COO)*
Kathleen G. Kane *(Sr VP-Property Ops & Gen Counsel-Property Ops)*
Lawrence F. Graham *(Exec VP-Property Ops-United States)*
Edward F. Beisner *(Sr VP-Property Ops & Controller-Property Ops)*
Jeremiah B. Larkin *(Sr VP-Property Ops & Dir-Leasing-Property Ops)*
Joshua J. Sirefman *(Sr VP-US Dev)*

BROOKFIELD GLOBAL RELOCATION SERVICES

(Unit of GMAC Home Services LLC)
900 S Frontage Rd Ste 200
Woodridge, IL 60517
Tel.: (630) 972-2250
Fax: (630) 972-2287
Toll Free: (866) 465-0323
Web Site: www.brookfieldgrs.com
Approx. Number Employees: 70
Year Founded: 2000
Business Description:
Global Relocation & Assignment Management Services
S.I.C.: 7361
N.A.I.C.S.: 541612
Media: 4
Personnel:
Rick E. Schwartz *(Pres)*
Maggie Ryan *(Exec VP-Global Ops)*
Scott T. Sullivan *(Exec VP-Global Sls & Mktg)*
Eric M. Stern *(Sr VP-Global Ops-EMEA & APAC)*
Jill Taylor *(VP-Consulting Svcs)*
Paige Bearce-Beery *(Dir-Global Bus Dev)*
Tom Smat *(Dir-Global Ops)*
Brands & Products:
THE WORLD IS OUR HOMETOWN

BRUTGER EQUITIES, INC.

100 4th Ave S
Saint Cloud, MN 56301
Tel.: (320) 252-6262
Fax: (320) 529-2801
Web Site: www.brutgerequities.com
Approx. Number Employees: 15
Year Founded: 1990
Business Description:
Operation of Apartments & Hotels
S.I.C.: 7011; 6513
N.A.I.C.S.: 721110; 531110
Advertising Expenditures: $750,000
Media: 4-5-6-7-9-18-25-26
Distr.: Natl.
Personnel:
Larry Brutger *(Pres & CEO)*
Laura Pfenstein *(CFO)*
Tom S. Etienne *(VP-HR)*

C. BREWER & CO. LTD.

26-238 Hawaii Belt Rd
Hilo, HI 96720
Tel.: (808) 969-1826
Fax: (808) 969-8150
Approx. Number Employees: 3
Year Founded: 1826
Business Description:
Agriculture & Real Estate
S.I.C.: 0173; 0133

Key to Media (For complete agency information see *The Advertising Red Books-Agencies* edition):
1. Bus. Publs. 2. Cable T.V. 3. Catalogs & Directories. 4. Co-op Adv. 5. Consumer Mags. 6. D.M. to Bus. Estab.7. D.M. to Consumers 8. Daily Newsp. 9. Exhibits/Trade Shows 10. Foreign 11. Infomercial 12. Internet Adv.13. Multimedia 14. Network Radio 15. Network T.V. 16. Newsp. Distr. Mags. 17. Other 18. Outdoor (Posters, Transit) 19. Point of Purchase20. Premiums, Novelties 21. Product Samples 22. Special Events Mktg. 23. Spot Radio 24. Spot T.V. 25. Weekly Newsp. 26. Yellow Page Adv.

C. Brewer & Co. Ltd. — (Continued)

N.A.I.C.S.: 111335; 111930
Export
Media: 2-9-23-24
Personnel:
John W.A. Buyers *(Chm)*
J. Alan Kugle *(CEO-Real Estate)*

CAESARS ENTERTAINMENT CORPORATION

(Formerly Harrah's Entertainment, Inc.)
(Joint Venture of Apollo Advisors, L.P. & TPG Capital, L.P.)
1 Caesars Palace Dr
Las Vegas, NV 89109
Tel.: (702) 407-6000
Fax: (702) 407-6307
Web Site: www.caesars.com
Approx. Rev.: $8,818,600,000
Approx. Number Employees: 69,000
Year Founded: 1937
Business Description:
Holding Company; Casinos & Casino Hotels Owner & Operator; Owned by Apollo Global Management, LLC & TPG Capital, L.P.
S.I.C.: 6719; 5812; 5813; 7011; 7999
N.A.I.C.S.: 551112; 713210; 721120; 722110; 722410
Advertising Expenditures: $199,700,000
Media: 3-10-15-18-20-22
Distr.: Natl.
Personnel:
Gary W. Loveman *(Chm, Pres & CEO)*
Jonathan S. Halkyard *(CFO & Sr VP)*
David W. Norton *(CMO & Sr VP)*
Katrina R. Lane *(CTO & Sr VP)*
Diane E. Wilfong *(Chief Acctg Officer & VP)*
Tom M. Jenkin *(Pres-Western Div)*
Donald P. Marrandino *(Pres-Eastern Div)*
John Payne *(Pres-Central Div)*
Timothy R. Donovan *(Gen Counsel & Sr VP)*
John W. Baker *(Sr VP-Enterprise Effectiveness)*
Janis L. Jones *(Sr VP-Comm & Govt Rels)*
Mary H. Thomas *(Sr VP-HR)*
Veronica Smiley *(VP-Natl Promos, Strategic Partnerships & Total Experiences)*
Patrick Espinoza *(Dir-Sls-Central Div)*
Ed Coffey *(Dir-Sls-Western Reg)*
Marty Turman *(Dir-Multicultural Mktg)*
Eric Petersen *(Mgr-Social Mktg Strategy)*
Leslie Thuet *(Mgr-PR)*
Brands & Products:
BALLY'S
BILL'S
BLUFF'S RUN
CAESARS
CAESARS PALACE
FLAMINGO
GRAND CASINO
HARRAH'S
HARVEYS
HORSESHOE
LOUISIANA DOWNS
PARIS
REWARD CREDITS
RIO
SEVEN STARS
SHOWBOAT
TOTAL REWARDS
WINNERS CIRCLE
WORLD SERIES OF POKER
Advertising Agencies:
BBDO West
555 Market St 17th Fl
San Francisco, CA 94105
Tel.: (415) 808-6200
Fax: (415) 808-6221
Penn & Teller Live Performance

BKV Inc.
10561 Barkley St Ste 200
Overland Park, KS 66212
Tel.: (913) 648-8333
Fax: (913) 648-5024

Euro RSCG EDGE
915 SW Stark St 2nd Fl
Portland, OR 97205-3017
Tel.: (503) 228-5555
Fax: (503) 228-0560

G2 USA
200 5th Ave
New York, NY 10010
Tel.: (212) 537-3700
Fax: (212) 537-3737

Leo Burnett Worldwide, Inc.
35 W Wacker Dr
Chicago, IL 60601-1723
Tel.: (312) 220-5959
Fax: (312) 220-3299
Caesars

PHD Los Angeles
10960 Wilshire Blvd
Los Angeles, CA 90024
Tel.: (310) 405-8700
Fax: (310) 405-8797

SCA Promotions, Inc.
3030 LBJ Freeway Ste 300
Dallas, TX 75234
Tel.: (214) 860-3700
Fax: (214) 860-3723
Toll Free: (888) 860-3700

Walton / Isaacson
4250 Wilshre Blvd
Los Angeles, CA 90010
Tel.: (323) 456-1100
Fax: (323) 456-1139
Hispanic

Zenith Media Services
(Regional Headquarters for ZenithOptimedia, the Americas)
299 W Houston St 10th Fl
New York, NY 10014-4806
Tel.: (212) 859-5100
Fax: (212) 727-9495
(Media Planning & Buying)

CAESARS NEW JERSEY, INC.

(Joint Venture of Apollo Advisors, L.P. & TPG Capital, L.P.)
(d/b/a Caesars Atlantic City)
2100 Pacific Ave
Atlantic City, NJ 08401-6612
Tel.: (609) 348-4411
Fax: (609) 343-2892
Web Site: www.caesarsac.com
Approx. Number Employees: 4,291
Business Description:
Hotel & Casino
S.I.C.: 7011; 7999
N.A.I.C.S.: 721120; 713290
Media: 8-9-13-18
Personnel:
Alex Figueras *(CFO)*

CAFRITZ COMPANY

1825 K St Ste 1200
Washington, DC 20006
Tel.: (202) 862-6800
Year Founded: 1925
Personnel:
Carlton Diehl *(COO)*
Advertising Agency:
Axis Communications
1250 H St NW Ste 1101
Washington, DC 20005
Tel.: (202) 347-0060
Fax: (202) 347-5331

CALDWELL WATSON REAL ESTATE GROUP

7904 N Sam Houston Pkwy W 4th Fl
Houston, TX 77064
Tel.: (713) 690-0000
Fax: (713) 690-0490
Toll Free: (877) 527-SALE
E-mail: info@caldwellcos.com
Web Site: www.caldwellcos.com
Approx. Number Employees: 50
Year Founded: 1997
Business Description:
Real Estate Development
S.I.C.: 6531
N.A.I.C.S.: 531210
Media: 17
Personnel:
Fred F. Caldwell *(Pres & CEO)*
Brad Fishman *(Chief Admin Officer, Gen Counsel & Sr VP)*
Ron Roberson *(Exec VP)*
Advertising Agencies:
4 Guys Interactive
8203 S Willow Pl Ste 230
Houston, TX 77070
Tel.: (281) 807-4344
Fax: (281) 807-4384

Steward Marketing, LLC
9595 Six Pines Ste 8210
The Woodlands, TX 77380
Tel.: (832) 955-1056
Fax: (832) 442-5842
Toll Free: (877) 541-2718

CALIFORNIA COASTAL COMMUNITIES, INC.

6 Executive Cir Ste 250
Irvine, CA 92614-6732
Tel.: (949) 250-7700
Fax: (949) 261-6550
E-mail: info@hearthside-homes.com
Web Site: www.californiacoastalcommunities.com/
Approx. Rev.: $47,200,000
Approx. Number Employees: 33
Business Description:
Residential Land Development & Home Building
S.I.C.: 1522; 1521; 1531
N.A.I.C.S.: 236220; 236115; 236117
Media: 6-7-8-9-16-18-25
Personnel:
Sandra G. Sciutto *(CFO)*

CALPROP CORPORATION

1784 La Costa Meadows Dr Ste 106
San Marcos, CA 92078
Tel.: (760) 471-1500
Fax: (760) 471-0105
E-mail: info@clpo.com
Web Site: www.clpo.com
Sales Range: $10-24.9 Million
Approx. Number Employees: 7
Year Founded: 1961
Business Description:
Real Estate Development
S.I.C.: 1522; 1521; 1531; 1541; 6513; 6531; 8699
N.A.I.C.S.: 236220; 236115; 236117; 236118; 236210; 531110; 531210; 531311; 531312; 531320; 531390; 813990
Advertising Expenditures: $340,000
D.M. to Consumers: $20,000; Daily Newsp.: $200,000; Internet Adv.: $5,000; Newsp. Distr. Mags.: $15,000; Outdoor (Posters, Transit): $30,000; Special Events Mktg.: $30,000; Spot Radio: $20,000; Weekly Newsp.: $20,000
Distr.: Direct to Consumer; Natl.

CAMDEN SUMMIT, INC.

(Sub. of Camden Property Trust)
309 E Morehead St Ste 200
Charlotte, NC 28202-0001
Tel.: (704) 334-3000
Fax: (704) 334-4496
Web Site: www.summitproperties.com
Sales Range: $200-249.9 Million
Approx. Number Employees: 450
Year Founded: 1994
Business Description:
Real Estate Investment Trusts
S.I.C.: 6798; 6513
N.A.I.C.S.: 525930; 531110
Import Export
Advertising Expenditures: $2,800,000

CANDY SWICK & COMPANY

2063 Main St
Sarasota, FL 34237
Tel.: (941) 954-9000
Fax: (941) 955-7169
Web Site: www.candyswick.com
Approx. Number Employees: 8
Business Description:
Real Estate Services
S.I.C.: 6531
N.A.I.C.S.: 531210
Media: 6
Personnel:
Cornelia S. Swick *(Pres)*
Lisa M. Yoder *(Dir-Mktg)*

CANYON RANCH MANAGEMENT, LLC

8600 E Rockcliff Rd
Tucson, AZ 85750
Tel.: (520) 749-9000
Tel.: (520) 749-9655
Fax: (720) 749-1646
Toll Free: (800) 742-9000
Toll Free: (800) 742-6494
E-mail: tucsonguestservices@canyonranch.com
Web Site: www.canyonranch.com
Approx. Number Employees: 700
Year Founded: 1978
Business Description:
Resort
S.I.C.: 7011
N.A.I.C.S.: 721199; 721110
Media: 6-8-22

Key to Media (For complete agency information see *The Advertising Red Books-Agencies* edition):
1. Bus. Publs. 2. Cable T.V. 3. Catalogs & Directories. 4. Co-op Adv. 5. Consumer Mags. 6. D.M. to Bus. Estab.7. D.M. to Consumers 8. Daily Newsp. 9. Exhibits/Trade Shows 10. Foreign 11. Infomercial 12. Internet Adv.13. Multimedia 14. Network Radio 15. Network T.V. 16. Newsp. Distr. Mags. 17. Other 18. Outdoor (Posters, Transit) 19. Point of Purchase20. Premiums, Novelties 21. Product Samples 22. Special Events Mktg. 23. Spot Radio 24. Spot T.V. 25. Weekly Newsp. 26. Yellow Page Adv.

Personnel:
Richard H. Carmona *(Vice Chm & CEO-Health Div)*
Jerry Cohen *(CEO)*
Roxanne Housley *(VP-Sls & Mktg)*
Brands & Products:
CANYONRANCH
THE POWER OF POSSIBILITY
SPACLUB
YOUR TRANSFORMATION
Advertising Agencies:
Susan Magrino Agency
641 Lexington Ave 28th Fl
New York, NY 10022
Tel.: (212) 957-3005
Fax: (212) 957-4071
Agency of Record

Tom, Dick & Harry Advertising
350 W Erie 2nd Fl
Chicago, IL 60654
Tel.: (312) 327-9500
Fax: (312) 327-9501

CAPITAL SENIOR LIVING CORPORATION

14160 Dallas Pkwy Ste 300
Dallas, TX 75240-4383
Tel.: (972) 770-5600
Fax: (972) 770-5666
E-mail: main@capitalsenior.com
Web Site: www.capitalsenior.com
Approx. Rev.: $211,929,000
Approx. Number Employees: 2,178
Year Founded: 1988
Business Description:
Owner, Manager & Developer of Senior Living Communities
S.I.C.: 8059; 8249
N.A.I.C.S.: 623110; 611519; 623311
Advertising Expenditures: $6,500,000
Personnel:
Keith N. Johannessen *(Pres & COO)*
Lawrence A. Cohen *(CEO)*
Ralph A. Beattie *(CFO & Exec VP)*
Brands & Products:
CAPITAL SENIOR LIVING
QUALITY AFFORDABLE RETIREMENT LIVING

CARLSON COMPANIES INC.

701 Carlson Pkwy
Minnetonka, MN 55305-8212
Mailing Address:
PO Box 59159
Minneapolis, MN 55459-8212
Tel.: (763) 212-4000
Fax: (763) 212-2219
E-mail: carlsonpublicrelations@carlson.com
Web Site: www.carlson.com
Sales Range: $25-49.9 Billion
Approx. Number Employees: 57,000
Year Founded: 1938
Business Description:
Holding Company; Owner of Hotels, Inns, Resorts, Trading Stamps, Premium Promotions, Restaurants, Real Estate & Travel Agencies
S.I.C.: 7011; 4724; 5812; 6719
N.A.I.C.S.: 721110; 551112; 561510; 722110
Import Export
Media: 2-6-9-10-11-18-25-26
Distr.: Intl.; Natl.
Personnel:
Marilyn Carlson Nelson *(Chm)*
Hubert Joly *(Pres & CEO)*
Jeffrey A. Balagna *(Pres, CEO-Mktg & Exec VP)*
Trudy A. Rautio *(CFO & Exec VP)*
William A. Van Brunt *(Gen Counsel & Exec VP)*
Jim Porter *(Exec VP-HR & Comm)*
Brands & Products:
CARLSON
CARLSON DESTINATION MARKETING SERVICES
CARLSON LEISURE TRAVEL SERVICES
CARLSON MARKETING
COUNTRY INNS & SUITES BY CARLSON
CRUISE HOLIDAYS
CW GOVERNMENT TRAVEL
GOLD POINTS REWARD NETWORK
PARK INN
PARK PLAZA
PEPPERS & ROGERS GROUP
PICK UP STIX
RADISSON
REGENT
RESULTS TRAVEL
SEAMASTER CRUISES
SINGLESCRUISE.COM
T.G.I. FRIDAY'S

CARLSON REAL ESTATE COMPANY

(Sub. of Carlson Companies Inc.)
301 Carlson Pkwy Ste 100
Minnetonka, MN 55305-5358
Tel.: (952) 404-5000
Fax: (952) 404-5001
E-mail: crcmninfo@carlson.com
Web Site: www.carlsonrealestate.org
Approx. Number Employees: 40
Business Description:
Commercial Industrial Real Estate & Investment Services
S.I.C.: 6531
N.A.I.C.S.: 531210
Media: 2-9-18-25-26
Distr.: Natl.
Personnel:
Matt Van Slooten *(Pres)*
Mark G. Herreid *(CFO & Sr VP)*
Debra Altschuler *(Corp Counsel)*
Mark Schlitter *(VP-Fin)*
Nataly Baig *(Dir-Fin & Acctg)*
Tim Kuharski *(Dir-Fin & Acctg)*
Christy Taylor *(Mgr-Acctg)*
Advertising Agencies:
Geoffrey Carlson Gage, LLC
(d/b/a Geoffrey Carlson Gage Brand Solutions)
500 Lake St Ste 100
Excelsior, MN 55331-2010
Tel.: (952) 401-7658
Fax: (952) 401-7662

LaBreche
500 Washington Ave S Ste 2020
Minneapolis, MN 55415
Tel.: (612) 338-0901
Fax: (612) 338-0921

CB RICHARD ELLIS GROUP, INC.

11150 Santa Monica Blvd Ste 1600
Los Angeles, CA 90025
Tel.: (310) 405-8900
Fax: (310) 203-9624
E-mail: info@cbre.com
Web Site: www.cbre.com
Approx. Rev.: $5,115,316,000
Approx. Number Employees: 31,000
Year Founded: 1971
Business Description:
Real Estate Investment Services
S.I.C.: 6531; 6159; 6552
N.A.I.C.S.: 531390; 237210; 522292
Import Export
Advertising Expenditures: $27,500,000
Personnel:
Richard C. Blum *(Chm)*
Robert E. Sulentic *(Pres)*
W. Brett White *(CEO)*
Carol Bell *(Mng Dir)*
Timothy J. Brauer *(Mng Dir)*
Enrique Cabrera *(Mng Dir)*
J. Martin Mitchell *(Mng Dir)*
Kenneth M. Murawski *(Mng Dir)*
Gil Borok *(CFO)*
Donald B. Goldstein *(CIO-Global)*
Arlin E. Gaffner *(Chief Acctg Officer)*
Robert Blain *(Chm/CEO-Asia Pacific)*
E. M. Blake Hutcheson *(Pres-Canada & Latin America)*
Calvin W. Frese, Jr. *(Pres-Global Svcs)*
Douglas Haney *(Pres-Valuation & Advisory Svcs)*
Michael J. Lafitte *(Pres-Americas)*
Tony Long *(Leader-Asset Svcs)*
Christopher R. Ludeman *(Pres-Americas Brokerage & Capital Markets)*
Vance G. Maddocks *(Pres-Strategic Partners US)*
James A. Reid *(Pres-Eastern Div)*
Mitchell E. Rudin *(Pres-Tri-State Region)*
Brian F. Stoffers *(Pres-Capital Markets)*
Pauline Goh *(CEO-Singapore & South East Asia)*
Laurence Midler *(Gen Counsel & Exec VP)*
Sacha M. Zarba *(Sr VP)*
Barbara L. Emmons *(Exec VP)*
Tony Kepano *(Exec VP)*
Peter C. Larkin *(Exec VP-Pub Institutions & Education Solution Team)*
Michael B. McShea *(Exec VP-Brokerage Svcs-Washington)*
Silvio Petriello *(Exec VP)*
John Porter *(Exec VP)*
Andy Ratner *(Exec VP)*
Robert Stillman *(Exec VP)*
James C. Ackerson *(Sr VP)*
Cody Armbrister *(Sr VP)*
John F. Boyd *(Sr VP)*
Sean M. Cahill *(Sr VP)*
Seth Kelly *(Sr VP-Global Corp Svcs Grp)*
Nick Kormeluk *(Sr VP-IR)*
Richard P. Levine *(Sr VP)*
Nicholas P. Matt *(Sr VP-Debt & Equity Fin-Pittsburgh)*
Brandon D. Megal *(Sr VP-LEED AP)*
Brad Needleman *(Sr VP)*
Jennifer Pierson *(Sr VP-Investment Properties-Dallas)*
Andrew Sussman *(Sr VP)*
Douglas Lehman *(First VP)*
William S. Mooney *(First VP)*
James E. Rodriguez *(First VP)*
Erik W. Schwetje *(First VP)*
David Sours *(First VP)*
Jena L. Hollensteiner *(VP-Mktg-Americas)*
Hajimu Taguchi *(Sr Dir-Global Corp Svcs-Minato-ku)*
Drew Robinson *(Dir-Mktg & Res)*
Jim Clement *(Dir-Asset Svcs)*
Maureen Ehrenberg *(Dir-Facilities Mgmt-Global)*
Lisa Jesmer *(Dir-Asset Svcs-South Florida Reg)*
Andrew Johnston *(Assoc Dir)*
Peter J. Williams *(Assoc Dir-Property Asset Mgmt)*
Rosana Watts *(Mgr-Real Estate)*
Raymond Torto *(Chief Economist-Global Ops)*
Advertising Agencies:
Active International (Europe) S.A.R.L.
27 rue Nicolo
75116
Paris, France
Tel.: (33) 1 45 04 32 90
Fax: (33) 1 40 72 66 16

Active International (Japan) Co. Ltd.
Fujistar Bldg 10/F 105 11-8 Nihonbashi
Tokyo, 103-0011, Japan
Tel.: (81) 356235800
Fax: (81) 356235808

Burson-Marsteller, S.A.
Avenida Diagonal 545 4th Fl 1st Door
08029
Barcelona, Spain
Tel.: (34) 93 201 1028
Fax: (34) 93 414 3390

WordWrite Communications
10475 Perry Hwy Ste 104
Wexford, PA 15090
Tel.: (724) 935-7580
Fax: (724) 935-7808

CB RICHARD ELLIS, INC.

(Sub. of CB Richard Ellis, Inc.)
200 Park Ave
New York, NY 10166-0005
Tel.: (212) 984-8000
Fax: (212) 984-8040
Web Site: www.cbre.com
Sales Range: $400-449.9 Million
Approx. Number Employees: 300
Business Description:
Commercial Real Estate Services
S.I.C.: 6531
N.A.I.C.S.: 531210
Media: 2-7-25
Personnel:
Mary Ann Tighe *(CEO)*
Brian F. Stoffers *(Pres-Capital Markets)*
Laurence Midler *(Gen Counsel & Exec VP)*
Eric S. Yarbro *(Sr VP)*

CBSHOME REAL ESTATE

(Sub. of HomeServices of America, Inc.)
14769 California St
Omaha, NE 68154
Tel.: (402) 964-4600
Fax: (402) 964-4640
E-mail: webmaster@cbshome.com
Web Site: www.cbshome.com
Sales Range: $50-74.9 Million
Approx. Number Employees: 100
Business Description:
Real Estate

CBSHOME Real Estate — (Continued)

S.I.C.: 6531
N.A.I.C.S.: 531210
Media: 2-4-8-9-13-25
Personnel:
Joseph J. Valenti *(Pres & CEO)*
Larry Melichar *(Exec VP & Gen Mgr)*
Monica Humpal *(Dir-Career Opportunities)*

CENTRAL FLORIDA INVESTMENTS INC.
(d/b/a Westgate Resorts)
5601 Windhover Dr
Orlando, FL 32819-7914
Tel.: (407) 351-3350
Fax: (407) 352-7233
Web Site: www.westgateresorts.com
Sales Range: $400-449.9 Million
Approx. Number Employees: 10,000
Year Founded: 1970
Business Description:
Subdividers & Developers; Timeshare Services
S.I.C.: 6552; 7011
N.A.I.C.S.: 237210; 721110; 721120
Media: 4-6-8-10-12-13-18-26
Personnel:
David A. Siegel *(Founder, Pres & CEO)*
Tom Dugan *(CFO)*
David Crabtree *(COO-Sales & Mktg)*
Mark Waltrip *(COO)*
Barry W. Siegel *(Exec VP-Sls)*
Jim Gissy *(VP-Mktg)*
Brands & Products:
WESTGATE RESORTS

CENTURY 21 REAL ESTATE LLC
(Sub. of Realogy Corporation)
1 Campus Dr
Parsippany, NJ 07054
Tel.: (973) 407-5296
Fax: (973) 407-5495
Web Site: www.century21.com
Approx. Rev.: $41,300,000
Approx. Number Employees: 155
Year Founded: 1971
Business Description:
Franchisor of Real Estate Agencies
S.I.C.: 6794; 6531
N.A.I.C.S.: 533110; 531210
Media: 5-13-14-15-24
Distr.: Intl.; Natl.
Budget Set: Jan. -June
Personnel:
Rick Davidson *(Pres & CEO)*
Beverly Thorne *(CMO)*
Anju Chellani *(Sr Dir-Digital Mktg)*
Brands & Products:
CENTURY 21 CONNECTIONS
CENTURY 21 FINE HOMES & ESTATES
CENTURY 21 MATURE MOVES
CENTURY 21 NEW CONSTRUCTION
CENTURY 21 RECREATIONAL PROPERTIES
Advertising Agencies:
Mediacom Interaction
198 7th Ave
New York, NY 10018
Tel.: (212) 912-5200
Fax: (212) 912-5485
(Media)

MRM Gillespie
(A McCann-Erickson World Group Company)
3450 Princeton Pike
Lawrenceville, NJ 08648
Tel.: (609) 895-0200
Fax: (609) 895-0222

Mullen
40 Broad St
Boston, MA 02109
Tel.: (617) 226-9000
Fax: (617) 226-9100

Sky Advertising, Inc.
14 E 33 St 8th Fl
New York, NY 10016
Tel.: (212) 677-2500
Fax: (212) 677-2791
Toll Free: (888) 752-9664

CHAMPION REALTY INC.
(Sub. of HomeServices of America, Inc.)
5418 Baltimore Annapolis Blvd
Severna Park, MD 21146-3934
Tel.: (410) 975-3000
Fax: (410) 544-0137
Toll Free: (800) 640-0630
E-mail: webmaster@championrealty.com
Web Site: www.championrealty.com
Sales Range: $10-24.9 Million
Approx. Number Employees: 50
Year Founded: 1970
Business Description:
Real Estate Agents & Managers
S.I.C.: 6531
N.A.I.C.S.: 531210
Media: 2-4-8-9-13-25
Personnel:
Jonathan R.M. Coile *(Pres & CEO)*
Advertising Agency:
Peterson Milla Hooks
1315 Harmon Pl
Minneapolis, MN 55403-1926
Tel.: (612) 349-9116
Fax: (612) 349-9141

CHATTANOOGA CHOO-CHOO HOLIDAY INN
(Sub. of Choo Choo Partners L.P.)
1400 Market St
Chattanooga, TN 37402-4429
Tel.: (423) 266-5000
Fax: (423) 265-4635
Toll Free: (800) TRACK29
E-mail: frontdesk@choochoo.com
Web Site: www.choochoo.com
Approx. Number Employees: 400
Year Founded: 1989
Business Description:
Operator of Hotel & Railroad Museum with HO Gauge Model Railroad
S.I.C.: 7011; 5812
N.A.I.C.S.: 721110; 722110
Media: 2-3-4-5-6-7-8-9-10-12-13-15-16-18-20-22-23-24-25-26
Distr.: Direct to Consumer; Reg.
Budget Set: Nov.
Personnel:
Jim Bambrey *(Gen Mgr)*
Julie Dodson *(Dir-Mktg)*
Annie Still *(Dir-Sls)*
Joy Nolan *(Asst Dir-Sls)*

CHOICE HOTELS INTERNATIONAL, INC.
10750 Columbia Pike
Silver Spring, MD 20901
Tel.: (301) 592-5000
Fax: (301) 592-6157
Telex: 800-228-3323
E-mail: investor_relations@choicehotels.com
Web Site: www.choicehotels.com
Approx. Rev.: $596,076,000
Approx. Number Employees: 1,524
Year Founded: 1939
Business Description:
Hotel & Motel Franchising Services
S.I.C.: 7011; 8742
N.A.I.C.S.: 721110; 541611
Advertising Expenditures: $81,300,000
Distr.: Intl.; Natl.
Budget Set: Dec.
Personnel:
Stewart Bainum, Jr. *(Chm)*
Charles A. Ledsinger, Jr. *(Vice Chm)*
Stephen P. Joyce *(Pres & CEO)*
David L. White *(CFO)*
Ronald D. Parisotto *(Gen Counsel, Sec & Sr VP)*
Bruce N. Haase *(Exec VP-Global Brands, Mktg & Ops)*
Patrick Pacious *(Exec VP-Global Strategy, Distr & Tech)*
William Carlson *(Sr VP-Performance Analytics)*
Patrick Cimerola *(Sr VP-HR & Admin)*
Alexandra Jaritz *(Sr VP-Brand Strategy & Mktg)*
Anne C. Madison *(Sr VP-Corp Comm)*
Michael Murphy *(Sr VP-Cambria Suites)*
Mark Laurence Pearce *(Sr VP-InterNatl Div)*
David A. Pepper *(Sr VP-Global Dev)*
Anne Hendrick *(VP-HR)*
Christine Lynn *(VP-Mktg Svcs)*
Kelly Poling *(VP-Mktg & Distr Strategy)*
Kelly Kane *(Sr Dir-Corp Comm)*
David Peikin *(Sr Dir-Corp Comm)*
Bret Limage *(Asst Sec & Asst Gen Counsel)*
Brands & Products:
ASCEND COLLECTION
CAMBRIA SUITES
CHOICE HOTELS
CHOICE PRIVILEGES
CLARION
COMFORT INN
COMFORT SUITES
ECONO LODGE
MAINSTAY SUITES
QUALITY
RODEWAY INN
SLEEP INN
SUBURBAN
Advertising Agencies:
Doner Direct
25900 Northwestern Hwy
Southfield, MI 48075-1067
Tel.: (248) 354-9700
Fax: (248) 827-0880
Promotions Lead

Leo Burnett Worldwide, Inc.
35 W Wacker Dr
Chicago, IL 60601-1723
Tel.: (312) 220-5959
Fax: (312) 220-3299
Creative Advertising Lead

MMG Worldwide
4601 Madison Ave
Kansas City, MO 64112
Tel.: (816) 472-5988
Fax: (816) 471-5395

Ypartnership
423 S Keller Rd Ste 100
Orlando, FL 32810-6121
Tel.: (407) 875-1111
Fax: (407) 875-1115

CIRCUS CIRCUS CASINOS, INC.
(Sub. of MGM Resorts International)
(d/b/a Circus Circus Hotel & Casino-Las Vegas)
2880 Las Vegas Blvd S
Las Vegas, NV 89109-1138
Tel.: (702) 792-4810
Fax: (702) 794-3816
Toll Free: (877) 224-7287
Web Site: www.circuscircus.com
Sales Range: $200-249.9 Million
Approx. Number Employees: 4,500
Year Founded: 1968
Business Description:
Gambling Casinos
S.I.C.: 7011
N.A.I.C.S.: 721120
Media: 1-3-6-8-9-13-15-16-18-20-23-24-25
Distr.: Direct to Consumer
Budget Set: Oct.
Personnel:
Jackie Zlatanovski *(VP-Mktg)*
Tom Nolan *(Dir-Theme Park)*

CLAYTON HOMES, INC.
(Holding of Berkshire Hathaway Inc.)
500 Alcoa Trl
Maryville, TN 37804-5550
Tel.: (865) 380-3000
Fax: (865) 380-3750
E-mail: info@clayton.net
Web Site: www.clayton.net
E-Mail For Key Personnel:
Public Relations: recruiting@clayton.com
Sales Range: $1-4.9 Billion
Approx. Number Employees: 1,400
Year Founded: 1968
Business Description:
Manufactured Homes Mfr & Developer
S.I.C.: 2451; 2452; 5271
N.A.I.C.S.: 321991; 321992; 453930
Media: 2-6-8-9-13-23-25
Distr.: Natl.
Budget Set: June
Personnel:
Kevin T. Clayton *(Pres & CEO)*
Mark Ezzo *(VP-Engrg)*
Chris Nicely *(VP-Mktg)*
Brands & Products:
CLAYTON
CREST
GOLDEN WEST
MARLETTE
OAKWOOD
SHULT

THE CLIFFS COMMUNITIES, INC.
3598 Hwy 11
Travelers Rest, SC 29690
Tel.: (864) 371-1000

Key to Media (For complete agency information see *The Advertising Red Books-Agencies* edition):
1. Bus. Publs. 2. Cable T.V. 3. Catalogs & Directories. 4. Co-op Adv. 5. Consumer Mags. 6. D.M. to Bus. Estab.7. D.M. to Consumers 8. Daily Newsp. 9. Exhibits/Trade Shows 10. Foreign 11. Infomercial 12. Internet Adv.13. Multimedia 14. Network Radio 15. Network T.V. 16. Newsp. Distr. Mags. 17. Other 18. Outdoor (Posters, Transit) 19. Point of Purchase20. Premiums, Novelties 21. Product Samples 22. Special Events Mktg. 23. Spot Radio 24. Spot T.V. 25. Weekly Newsp. 26. Yellow Page Adv.

Toll Free: (866) 435-5123
Web Site: www.cliffscommunities.com
Sales Range: $100-124.9 Million
Approx. Number Employees: 600
Year Founded: 1991
Business Description:
Hotel, Golf Course & Spa Owner & Operator
S.I.C.: 7011; 7231; 7997
N.A.I.C.S.: 721110; 713910; 812112
Media: 6-9-22
Personnel:
Jim Anthony *(Founder)*
Geoffrey Carey *(Exec VP)*
Kristopher Clark *(Sr Dir-Ops)*
Laurie Kent *(Mgr-Mktg)*

THE CLUB AT EAGLEBROOKE

1300 Eaglebrooke Blvd
Lakeland, FL 33813
Tel.: (863) 701-0101
Fax: (863) 701-0313
E-mail: info@eaglebrooke.com
Web Site: www.eaglebrooke.com
Sales Range: $1-9.9 Million
Approx. Number Employees: 120
Business Description:
Member-Only Country Club & Golf Course
S.I.C.: 7997
N.A.I.C.S.: 713910
Media: 6-22
Personnel:
Dale Jacobs *(Pres)*

CLUBCORP, INC.

(Holding of KSL Capital Partners, LLC)
3030 Lyndon B Johnson Fwy Ste 600
Dallas, TX 75234-7763
Tel.: (972) 243-6191
E-mail: info@clubcorp.com
Web Site: www.clubcorp.com
Sales Range: $900-999.9 Million
Approx. Number Employees: 16,000
Year Founded: 1957
Business Description:
Holding Company; Private Clubs, Resorts & Golf Courses Owner & Operator
S.I.C.: 6719; 7997
N.A.I.C.S.: 551112; 713910
Advertising Expenditures: $200,000
Personnel:
Eric L. Affeldt *(Pres & CEO)*
Daniel T. Tilley *(CIO & Exec VP)*
Ingrid Keiser *(Gen Counsel, Sec & Exec VP-People Strategy)*
Mark Burnett *(Exec VP-Golf & Country Club Div)*
Jamie Walters *(Exec VP-Sls)*
David B. Woodyard *(Exec VP)*
William T. Walden *(Sr VP-Pur)*
Brands & Products:
CLUBCORP

COAST HOTELS & CASINOS

(Sub. of Boyd Gaming Corporation)
4000 W Flamingo Rd
Las Vegas, NV 89103-5420
Tel.: (702) 367-7111
Fax: (702) 367-1897
Web Site: www.goldcoastcasino.com
Sales Range: $25-49.9 Million
Approx. Number Employees: 400
Year Founded: 1996
Business Description:
Hotel & Motel Services
S.I.C.: 7011
N.A.I.C.S.: 721120
Advertising Expenditures: $720,000

COASTAL CONSTRUCTION GROUP OF SOUTH FLORIDA INC.

Ste 200 5959 Blue Lagoon Dr
Miami, FL 33126-2052
Tel.: (305) 559-4900
Fax: (305) 221-5005
Web Site:
www.coastalconstruction.com
Approx. Sls.: $75,000,000
Approx. Number Employees: 55
Year Founded: 1997
Business Description:
Single-Family Housing Construction Services
S.I.C.: 1521; 1522
N.A.I.C.S.: 236115; 236220
Import Export
Media: 6
Personnel:
Thomas P. Murphy, Jr. *(Chm & CEO)*
Dan Whiteman *(Pres)*
Ken Alderman *(CFO, Treas & Sec)*

THE COEUR D'ALENE RESORT

(Sub. of Hagadone Hospitality Inc.)
115 S 2nd St
Coeur D'Alene, ID 83814
Tel.: (208) 765-4000
Fax: (208) 664-7276
Toll Free: (800) 688-5253
Web Site: www.cdaresort.com
Year Founded: 1986
Business Description:
Resort, Golf Course & Spa Operations
S.I.C.: 7011; 7231; 7997
N.A.I.C.S.: 721110; 713910; 812112
Media: 6-22
Personnel:
Jerry Jaeger *(Pres & Co-Owner)*
William T. Reagan *(Gen Mgr)*
Advertising Agency:
Murphy O'Brien, Inc.
(d/b/a Murphy O'Brien Public Relations)
1630 Stewart St Ste 140
Santa Monica, CA 90404
Tel.: (310) 453-2539
Fax: (310) 264-0083

COLDWELL BANKER MID PLAZA

PO Box 290714
Brooklyn, NY 11229
Tel.: (718) 887-6200
Fax: (718) 775-3356
Approx. Number Employees: 50
Business Description:
Real Estate Services
S.I.C.: 6531
N.A.I.C.S.: 531210
Media: 1-8-9-13-23-24-25
Personnel:
Tony VanderBeek *(Exec VP)*

COLDWELL BANKER REAL ESTATE LLC

(Sub. of Realogy Corporation)
1 Campus Dr
Parsippany, NJ 07054-3826
Tel.: (973) 407-5296
Toll Free: (800) 932-4677
Web Site: www.coldwellbanker.com
Approx. Number Employees: 200
Year Founded: 1971
Business Description:
Real Estate Services
S.I.C.: 6531
N.A.I.C.S.: 531210
Advertising Expenditures: $6,125,000
Consumer Mags.: $100,000; D.M. to Consumers: $1,000,000; Daily Newsp.: $2,000,000; Exhibits/Trade Shows: $125,000; Premiums, Novelties: $100,000; Special Events Mktg.: $2,000,000; Weekly Newsp.: $800,000
Distr.: Reg.
Personnel:
Budge Huskey *(Pres & COO)*
James R. Gillespie *(CEO)*
Michael Fischer *(CMO)*
Advertising Agencies:
FD Kinesis
26 Washington St
Morristown, NJ 07960
Tel.: (973) 206-1021

MSLGROUP
1675 Broadway 9th Floor
New York, NY 10019-5865
Tel.: (212) 468-4200
Fax: (212) 468-3007
Public Relations

o2kl
10 W 18th St 6th Fl
New York, NY 10011
Tel.: (646) 829-6239
Fax: (646) 839-6254
Marketing Communications

Siltanen & Partners
353 Coral Cir
El Segundo, CA 90245
Tel.: (310) 321-5200
Fax: (310) 321-5270
Creative Agency of Record

COLDWELL BANKER RESIDENTIAL BROKERAGE

(Sub. of NRT Inc.)
52 2nd St 3 Fl
Waltham, MA 02451
Tel.: (781) 684-6300
Fax: (781) 684-6398
Web Site:
www.newenglandmoves.com
Approx. Number Employees: 125
Year Founded: 1973
Business Description:
Real Estate Services
S.I.C.: 6531
N.A.I.C.S.: 531210
Media: 8-13-19
Personnel:
Rick Loughlin *(Pres)*
Bill McIntire *(CFO & COO)*
Michael Fischer *(CMO)*
Christopher Bernier *(Reg VP-West Boston MA)*
Richard Burbine *(Reg VP-Maine & New Hampshire)*
Michael Jewell *(Reg VP-North Shore MA)*
Mary Leahey *(Reg VP-Rhode Island & Western MA)*
Robert Shortsleeve *(Reg VP-Greater Boston MA)*
Pat Villani *(Reg VP-Southern Massachusetts)*
Advertising Agency:
Henson Consulting
111 W Wesley Ste 5
Wheaton, IL 60187
Tel.: (630) 933-9477

COLLIERS MEREDITH & GREW

(Sub. of Colliers International Property Consultants, Inc.)
(d/b/a Colliers International - Boston)
160 Federal St
Boston, MA 02110-1700
Tel.: (617) 330-8000
Fax: (617) 330-8130
Web Site: www.m-g.com
Approx. Number Employees: 150
Year Founded: 1875
Business Description:
Commercial Real Estate Services
S.I.C.: 6531; 6163
N.A.I.C.S.: 531210; 522310
Media: 2-6-7-9-18-25-26
Distr.: Intl.
Personnel:
Thomas J. Hynes, Jr. *(Co-Chm & CEO)*
Kevin C. Phelan *(Co-Chm)*
Ronald K. Perry *(Pres)*
Lisa M. Campoli *(Mng Partner & Exec VP)*
David M. Douvadjian *(Mng Partner & Exec VP)*
James L. Elcock *(Mng Partner & Exec VP)*
Joseph F. Flaherty *(Mng Partner & Exec VP)*
Dennis F. Callahan *(Exec VP)*
Theodore J. Chryssicas *(Exec VP)*
Francis Durand *(Exec VP)*
John P. O'Hearn, Jr. *(Exec VP)*
Daniel R. Quinn *(Exec VP-Dev & Advisory Svcs)*
Kristin E. Blount *(Sr VP)*
Roger W. Breslin *(Sr VP)*
John A. Carroll, III *(Sr VP)*
John A. Carroll, Jr. *(Sr VP)*
Gintaras P. Cepas *(Sr VP)*
Robert E. Cronin *(Sr VP)*
Matthew J. Daniels *(Sr VP)*
Sandra J. Driscoll *(Sr VP)*
Lawrence T. Epstein *(Sr VP)*
David L. Francis *(Sr VP)*
Leigh L. Freudenheim *(Sr VP)*
Tucker L. Hansen *(Sr VP)*
Stephen M. Horan *(Sr VP)*
Neil J. Hurley *(Sr VP)*
Mary Kelly *(Sr VP-Mktg & Res)*
Robert P. LaPorte, Jr. *(Sr VP)*
Theodore A. Lee *(Sr VP)*
Edward J. Lowney *(Sr VP-Property & Asset Mgmt Svcs)*
Patrick J. Paladino, Jr. *(Sr VP)*
Thomas D. Robinson *(Sr VP)*
Lynn S. Scarbo *(Sr VP)*
Yanni K. Tsipis *(Sr VP)*
Thomas F. Welch *(Sr VP)*
Adam M. Coppola *(Asst VP)*
Elizabeth A. Davis *(Asst VP)*
Bonnie Lombardo *(Asst VP)*
Advertising Agency:
Oliveri & Associates
104 Pleasant Valley Rd
Westwood, MA 02090
Tel.: (718) 320-9090
Fax: (718) 320-9020

Key to Media (For complete agency information see *The Advertising Red Books-Agencies* edition):
1. Bus. Publs. 2. Cable T.V. 3. Catalogs & Directories. 4. Co-op Adv. 5. Consumer Mags. 6. D.M. to Bus. Estab.7. D.M. to Consumers 8. Daily Newsp. 9. Exhibits/Trade Shows 10. Foreign 11. Infomercial 12. Internet Adv.13. Multimedia 14. Network Radio 15. Network T.V. 16. Newsp. Distr. Mags. 17. Other 18. Outdoor (Posters, Transit) 19. Point of Purchase20. Premiums, Novelties 21. Product Samples 22. Special Events Mktg. 23. Spot Radio 24. Spot T.V. 25. Weekly Newsp. 26. Yellow Page Adv.

COLONY RESORTS LVH ACQUISITIONS, LLC
(Affil. of Colony Capital, LLC)
3000 Paradise Rd
Las Vegas, NV 89109
Tel.: (702) 732-5111
Fax: (702) 732-5988
Toll Free: (888) 732-7117
Web Site: www.lvhilton.com
Approx. Rev.: $210,984,000
Approx. Number Employees: 1,900
Year Founded: 2003
Business Description:
Hotel & Casino Operator
S.I.C.: 7011
N.A.I.C.S.: 721120
Advertising Expenditures: $4,700,000
Personnel:
Thomas Joseph Barrack, Jr. *(Chm)*
Nicholas L. Ribis *(Vice Chm)*
David J. Monahan *(CEO & Gen Mgr)*
Kenneth M. Ciancimino *(Exec VP-Admin)*
Robert Schaffhauser *(Exec VP-Fin)*
Gavin Mealisse *(VP-Sls)*
Idalia Sandoval *(Exec Dir-Latin Mktg)*
Patricia Schiralli *(Exec Dir-Slot Mktg)*
Nancy Briggs *(Dir-Asian Mktg)*
Brands & Products:
HILTON
RESORTS INTERNATIONAL CLUB CARD
RESORTS INTERNATIONAL PLAYER'S CLUB
SUPERNOVA

COMMERCIAL REALTY & RESOURCES CORP.
(Sub. of NJR Energy Holdings Corporation)
1415 Wyckoff Rd
Wall, NJ 07719
Mailing Address:
PO Box 1468
Wall, NJ 07719-1468
Tel.: (732) 938-1111
Fax: (732) 938-6735
E-mail: jlishak@njresources.com
Sales Range: $25-49.9 Million
Approx. Number Employees: 2
Year Founded: 1981
Business Description:
Real Estate Development & Management
S.I.C.: 6512
N.A.I.C.S.: 531120
Media: 7
Distr.: Reg.
Budget Set: Aug.
Personnel:
John Lishak, Jr. *(Pres)*

COMSTOCK HOMEBUILDING COMPANIES, INC.
11465 Sunset Hills Rd Ste 510
Reston, VA 20190
Tel.: (703) 883-1700
Fax: (703) 760-1520
Web Site:
www.comstockhomebuilding.com
Approx. Rev.: $23,851,000
Approx. Number Employees: 26
Year Founded: 1985
Business Description:
Residential Real Estate Developer
S.I.C.: 6531; 1521; 1522; 8322
N.A.I.C.S.: 531390; 236115; 236116; 624229
Advertising Expenditures: $47,000
Media: 17
Personnel:
Christopher Clemente *(Owner)*
Gregory M. Benson *(Pres)*
Joseph M. Squeri *(CFO)*
Jubal R. Thompson *(Gen Counsel)*
Brands & Products:
COMSTOCK HOMES
WORTHY OF THE INVESTMENT

CONCORD PACIFIC GROUP
(Sub. of Adex Securities, Inc.)
1095 W Pender St 9th Fl
Vancouver, BC V6E 2M6, Canada
Tel.: (604) 681-8882
Fax: (604) 895-8296
E-mail: info@concordpacific.com
Web Site: www.concordpacific.com
Approx. Number Employees: 40
Business Description:
Urban Residential Real Estate Developer
S.I.C.: 6531
N.A.I.C.S.: 531210
Media: 6-10
Personnel:
Terence Hui *(Pres & CEO)*
Dennis Au-Yeung *(CFO & VP)*

CONSOLIDATED-TOMOKA LAND CO.
1530 Cornerstone Blvd Ste 100
Daytona Beach, FL 32117
Mailing Address:
PO Box 10809
Daytona Beach, FL 32120-0809
Tel.: (386) 274-2202
Fax: (386) 274-1223
E-mail: ctlc@consolidatedtomoka.com
Web Site: www.ctlc.com
Approx. Rev.: $3,059,921
Approx. Number Employees: 21
Year Founded: 1902
Business Description:
Real Estate, Income Properties & Golf Operations
S.I.C.: 6531; 6519; 6552; 7997
N.A.I.C.S.: 531390; 237210; 531190; 713910
Media: 18
Personnel:
Jeffry B. Fuqua *(Chm)*
William H. McMunn *(Pres & CEO)*
Bruce W. Teeters *(Treas & Sr VP-Fin)*
Gisele Found *(Mgr-Land Holdings)*
Tammy Girvin *(Mgr-Land Info)*
Andrew Young *(Mgr-Real Estate Investment)*

CORCORAN SUNSHINE MARKETING GROUP
(Div. of The Corcoran Group)
888 7th Ave
New York, NY 10106
Tel.: (212) 355-3550
Fax: (212) 752-8634
E-mail: info@corcoransunshine.com
Web Site: www.corcoran.com
Approx. Number Employees: 60
Business Description:
Property Developer & Marketer
S.I.C.: 6531
N.A.I.C.S.: 531390; 531210
Media: 13-17
Personnel:
Kelly Kennedy Mack *(Pres-Corcoran Sunshine Marketing Group)*
Patricia Hayes Cole *(Exec VP)*
Christina Lowris *(Exec VP-Mktg & Adv)*
Selma Nasser *(Dir-PR & Adv)*

CORNISH & CAREY COMMERCIAL INC.
2804 Mission College Blvd Ste 120
Santa Clara, CA 95054-1803
Tel.: (408) 970-9990
Fax: (408) 988-6340
Toll Free: (800) 540-9669
Web Site: www.ccarey.com
Approx. Number Employees: 70
Year Founded: 1935
Business Description:
Provider of Real Estate Agency Services
S.I.C.: 6531
N.A.I.C.S.: 531210
Import Export
Personnel:
Scott T. Carey *(Chm & Gen Counsel)*
Charles E. Seufferlein *(Pres & CEO)*
Meredith Kern *(Partner-Portfolio Solutions Grp)*
Erik Doyle *(Exec Mng Dir-Capital Group)*
Jay R. Belquist *(CFO)*
Jay Phillips *(Sr VP)*
Michael R. Brand *(Exec VP)*
Howard E. Dallmar *(Exec VP)*
Mark C. Davis *(Exec VP)*
C. Bradley Lyman *(Exec VP)*
Philip A. Mahoney *(Exec VP)*
R. Randolph Scott *(Exec VP)*
Jack Troedson *(Exec VP)*
Kevin S. Manning *(Sr VP & Dir-Global Corp Svcs)*
Thomas J. Fehr *(Sr VP & Sls Mgr-Walnut Creek)*
Bryan Courson *(Sr VP & Mgr-Sls)*
Nick Slonek *(Sr VP & Mgr-Sls)*
John C. Yandle *(Sr VP & Mgr)*
Joe Hamilton *(Sr VP-Strategic Plng & Advisory Svcs)*
Tom Sweeney *(Sr VP)*
Advertising Agency:
Creative Search Media
5615 Scotts Valley Dr Ste 105
Scotts Valley, CA 95066
Tel.: (831) 588-5198
Toll Free: (877) 944-9444

COUNTRY WIDE REALTY INC.
1234 Castle Hill Ave
Bronx, NY 10462-4810
Tel.: (718) 863-2900
Fax: (718) 863-3389
Approx. Number Employees: 12
Year Founded: 1990
Business Description:
Real Estate Services
S.I.C.: 6531
N.A.I.C.S.: 531210
Advertising Expenditures: $200,000
Media: 4-8-9-25
Distr.: Natl.
Personnel:
Harry Sanichara *(Pres & Gen Mgr)*
Richie Singh *(Mgr & Assoc-Licensed Real Estate)*

COUSINS PROPERTIES INCORPORATED
191 Peachtree St NE Ste 3600
Atlanta, GA 30303
Tel.: (404) 407-1000
Fax: (404) 407-1002
E-mail: information@cousinsproperties.com
Web Site:
www.cousinsproperties.com
Approx. Rev.: $228,506,000
Approx. Number Employees: 320
Year Founded: 1958
Business Description:
Real Estate Development & Investment Services
S.I.C.: 6798; 6159; 6531
N.A.I.C.S.: 525930; 522292; 531210
Media: 2-7-9-10-18-20-21-22-23-25
Personnel:
Lawrence L. Gellerstedt, III *(Pres & CEO)*
Gregg D. Adzema *(CFO & Exec VP)*
Craig B. Jones *(Chief Investment Officer & Exec VP)*
John D. Harris Jr. *(Chief Acctg Officer, Sr VP & Asst Sec)*
Robert M. Jackson *(Gen Counsel, Sec & Sr VP)*
William I. Bassett *(Exec VP & Dir-Dev-Retail Div)*
Jeffrey S Quinn *(Sr VP & Gen Mgr-Callaway & Blalock)*
Pamela F Roper *(Sr VP, Assoc Gen Counsel & Asst Corp Sec)*
Thad Goff *(Sr VP-Dev)*
Claude G Winstead, III *(Sr VP-Dev)*
Dennis A Granger *(VP-Info Sys)*
Brands & Products:
A
THE AVENUE
THE AVENUE OF THE PENINSULA
THE AVENUE PEACHTREE CITY
THE AVENUE WEST COBB
COUSINS

CRESA PARTNERS LLC
(Affil. of ATISreal)
100 Pk Ave 24th Fl
New York, NY 10017
Tel.: (212) 758-3131
Fax: (212) 980-1977
E-mail: info@cresapartners.com
Web Site: www.cresapartners.com
Approx. Number Employees: 25
Business Description:
Real Estate & Foreign Trade Consulting
S.I.C.: 8742; 6531
N.A.I.C.S.: 541611; 531210
Media: 2
Personnel:
Jessica Mogilka *(Dir-Intl Svcs)*

CRESCENT REAL ESTATE EQUITIES LP
(Joint Venture of Barclays PLC & Goff Capital Partners, L.P.)
777 Main St Ste 2100
Fort Worth, TX 76102-5304
Tel.: (817) 321-1456
Fax: (817) 321-2002
E-mail: jsweek@crescent.com
Web Site: www.crescent.com
Approx. Rev.: $928,696,000
Approx. Number Employees: 748
Year Founded: 1994

Key to Media (For complete agency information see *The Advertising Red Books-Agencies* edition):
1. Bus. Publs. 2. Cable T.V. 3. Catalogs & Directories. 4. Co-op Adv. 5. Consumer Mags. 6. D.M. to Bus. Estab.7. D.M. to Consumers
8. Daily Newsp. 9. Exhibits/Trade Shows 10. Foreign 11. Infomercial 12. Internet Adv.13. Multimedia 14. Network Radio
15. Network T.V. 16. Newsp. Distr. Mags. 17. Other 18. Outdoor (Posters, Transit) 19. Point of Purchase20. Premiums, Novelties
21. Product Samples 22. Special Events Mktg. 23. Spot Radio 24. Spot T.V. 25. Weekly Newsp. 26. Yellow Page Adv.

Business Description:
Real Estate Investment & Management Services; Owned by Goff Capital Partners, L.P. & Barclays Capital
S.I.C.: 6798
N.A.I.C.S.: 525930
Advertising Expenditures: $4,407,000
Media: 2-10-20-22
Personnel:
John C. Goff *(Chm & CEO)*
Suzanne M. Stevens *(CFO & Mng Dir)*
David M. Dean *(Mng Dir-Law & Sec)*
Robert H. Boykin, Jr. *(Mng Dir)*
Michael S. Lewis *(Mng Dir)*
James H. Wilson *(Mng Dir)*
John L. Zogg, Jr. *(Mng Dir)*
Jason E. Anderson *(COO)*
Jason Phinney *(Sr VP & Controller)*
John P. Albright *(Sr VP-Fin)*
Joseph Pitchford *(Sr VP-Dev)*
Connie Angelot *(VP & Asst Controller)*

CRESTED BUTTE MOUNTAIN RESORT, INC.

(Holding of Triple Peaks, LLC)
17 Emmons Loop
Crested Butte, CO 81225
Mailing Address:
PO Box 5700
Crested Butte, CO 81225
Tel.: (970) 349-2333
Fax: (970) 349-2250
Toll Free: (800) 810-7669
Web Site: www.skicb.com
Approx. Number Employees: 700
Year Founded: 1961
Business Description:
Ski Resort
S.I.C.: 7011
N.A.I.C.S.: 721110
Advertising Expenditures: $200,000
Media: 6-7-8-10-23
Distr.: Natl.; Reg.
Budget Set: Apr.
Brands & Products:
CRESTED BUTTE
Advertising Agency:
Art + Logic Interactive
1209 Pearl St Ste 9-11
Boulder, CO 80302
Tel.: (303) 442-9301
Fax: (303) 442-9302

CRESTLINE HOTELS & RESORTS, INC.

(Sub. of Barcelo Crestline Corporation)
3950 University Dr Ste 301
Fairfax, VA 22030
Tel.: (571) 529-6100
Fax: (571) 529-6095
Web Site: www.crestlinehotels.com
Approx. Number Employees: 65
Business Description:
Hotel Management
S.I.C.: 7011
N.A.I.C.S.: 721110
Media: 7
Personnel:
James Carroll *(Pres & CEO)*
Pierre Donahue *(Gen Counsel & Sr VP)*
Edward Hoganson *(Exec VP-Fin & Bus Dev)*
Vicki Denfeld *(Sr VP-Sls & Mktg)*
Shaun Kirby *(Sr VP-Ops)*
Jerry Galindo *(VP-IT)*
Deanne Johnson-Anderson *(VP-HR)*
Carolee Ettline Moore *(VP-Sls)*
Eddie Andre *(Gen Mgr-Hilton Checkers Los Angeles)*
John L. Daw *(Gen Mgr)*
Duane Gauthier *(Gen Mgr-Sheraton Virginia Beach Oceanfront Hotel)*
Richard Johnson *(Gen Mgr-Hilton Garden Inn)*
David Kipfmiller *(Gen Mgr-The Hilton Garden Inn Downtown Detroit)*
Jean-Pierre Lamarre *(Gen Mgr-Courtyard-Marriott Baltimore Inner Harbor)*
Frank Leone *(Gen Mgr-Silversmith Hotel & Suites)*
Andrea J. Mayer *(Gen Mgr-Hilton Garden Inn Chicago Downtown)*
Justin J. Presnol *(Gen Mgr)*
David Ragland *(Gen Mgr)*
Hans J. Schmitt *(Gen Mgr-Hotel Derek-Houston)*
Damon Strickland *(Gen Mgr-Staybridge Suites)*
Doreen M. Turgeon *(Gen Mgr)*
Scott M. Weber *(Gen Mgr-Renaissance Portsmouth Hotel & Conference Center)*
Jack Zimmerman *(Gen Mgr-Crowne Plaza)*
Gina L. Worobel *(Dir-Sls & Mktg-Hilton Singer Island Oceanfront Resort)*
Michelle Bland *(Dir-Sls-Hilton Garden Inn BWI Airport-Maryland)*
Connie Brewer *(Dir-Sls)*
Linda Cahue *(Dir-Sls & Mktg-Wyndham Palm Springs Hotel)*
Cathryn Giff *(Dir-Sls)*
Ryan Hymel *(Dir-Fin & Bus Dev)*
Amy Johnson *(Dir-Sls-Courtyard by Marriott Carolina Beach)*
Donna Lewis *(Dir-Sls & Mktg-Hilton Checkers Los Angeles)*
Pamela McDonald *(Dir-Sls-The Hilton Garden Inn Downtown Detroit)*
Katherine A. Saad *(Dir-Sls & Mktg)*
Patricia Scott *(Dir-Sls-Courtyard by Marriott & Residence Inn)*
Douglas C. Varsano *(Dir-Sls & Mktg-Hilton Parsippany & Hampton Inn Parsippany)*
Colleen Wolfe *(Dir-Sls)*
Sherri Griffin Wright *(Dir-Sls-Courtyard-Marriott & Residence Inn Hotels)*
David Shapiro *(Sr Mgr-Bus Dev)*

THE CROWNE PLAZA TIMES SQUARE MANHATTAN

1605 Broadway
New York, NY 10019-7406
Tel.: (212) 977-4000
Fax: (212) 333-7393
Web Site:
www.manhattan.crowneplaza.com
Approx. Number Employees: 500
Year Founded: 1987
Business Description:
Provider of Hotel & Motel Services
S.I.C.: 7011
N.A.I.C.S.: 721110
Brands & Products:
CROWNE PLAZA
Advertising Agency:
Fallon Minneapolis
901 Marquette Ave Ste 2400
Minneapolis, MN 55402
Tel.: (612) 758-2345
Fax: (612) 758-2346
Toll Free: (866) 758-2345

CUSHMAN & WAKEFIELD, INC.

(Sub. of EXOR S.p.A.)
1290 Avenue of the Americas
New York, NY 10104
Tel.: (212) 841-7500
Fax: (212) 841-5002
Web Site:
www.cushmanwakefield.com
Approx. Rev.: $1,565,623,100
Approx. Number Employees: 11,000
Year Founded: 1917
Business Description:
Real Estate Brokerage & Property Management Services
S.I.C.: 6531
N.A.I.C.S.: 531210; 531390
Media: 1-2-7-9-10-11-23-25
Personnel:
John C. Cushman, III *(Chm)*
Glenn J. Rufrano *(Pres & CEO)*
John Busi *(Exec Mng Dir)*
Robert Ortiz *(Exec Mng Dir)*
Carolyn F. Sessa *(Exec Mng Dir-Global HR)*
Janice Stanton *(Sr Mng Dir-Analytics)*
Robert P. Rozek *(CFO & Exec VP)*
Joseph Harbert *(COO-New York Metro Reg)*
John C. Santora *(Pres/CEO-Client Solutions)*
Paul Bacon *(CEO-EMEA)*
Bryan Laxton *(CEO-UK)*
John B. Coppedge, III *(Exec VP-Intl Ops)*
Brian R. Corcoran *(Exec VP & Global Head-Valuation Svcs)*
Bruce Ficke *(Exec VP)*
Frank P. Liantonio *(Exec VP)*
Kenneth Lipper *(Exec VP)*
Michael Rotchford *(Exec VP)*
Kenneth P. Singleton *(Exec VP & Global Gen Counsel)*
Thomas Bomba *(Head-Global Bus Consulting)*
Kirill Popov *(Exec Dir)*
Rupert Dodson *(Sr Dir)*
Al Mirin *(Sr Dir)*
Advertising Agencies:
Heffner Graphics
33-5 Chase Ct
Ossining, NY 10562
Tel.: (914) 923-0083
Fax: (914) 945-0175

Miller Advertising Agency Inc.
71 5th Ave 5th Fl
New York, NY 10003-3004
Tel.: (212) 929-2200
Fax: (212) 727-4734
Toll Free: (800) 229-6574

MRM Gillespie
(A McCann-Erickson World Group Company)
3450 Princeton Pike
Lawrenceville, NJ 08648
Tel.: (609) 895-0200
Fax: (609) 895-0222

Munroe Creative Partners
1435 Walnut St Ste 600
Philadelphia, PA 19102-3219
Tel.: (215) 563-8080
Fax: (215) 563-1270

Posner Advertising
30 Broad St 33rd Fl
New York, NY 10004
Tel.: (212) 867-3900
Fax: (212) 480-3440
Toll Free: (800) 664-3817

CUSHMAN & WAKEFIELD OF FLORIDA, INC.

(Sub. of Cushman & Wakefield, Inc.)
200 S Biscayne Blvd Ste 2800
Miami, FL 33131-2662
Tel.: (305) 371-4411
Fax: (305) 375-0056
Web Site: www.cushwake.com
Approx. Number Employees: 45
Year Founded: 1968
Business Description:
Real Estate Services
S.I.C.: 6531
N.A.I.C.S.: 531210
Media: 6
Personnel:
Anna Rossie *(Dir & Mgr-Ops)*

CYPRESS EQUITIES

(Sub. of SRS Real Estate Partners)
8343 Douglas Ave Ste 300
Dallas, TX 75225
Tel.: (214) 561-8800
Fax: (214) 283-1600
Toll Free: (800) 203-2244
Web Site: www.cypressequities.com
Sales Range: $10-24.9 Million
Approx. Number Employees: 55
Year Founded: 1995
Business Description:
Real Estate Development
S.I.C.: 6531
N.A.I.C.S.: 531390
Personnel:
Chris Maguire *(CEO)*
Brian Parro *(CFO)*
Advertising Agency:
AMG Worldwide
900 SW 8th St Ste C 2
Miami, FL 33130
Tel.: (305) 856-8004
Fax: (305) 856-8650

DANIEL DECARO REAL ESTATE AUCTIONS, INC.

29 Ave of the Flowers
Longboat Key, FL 34228
Tel.: (941) 504-3555
Toll Free: (800) 332-3767
E-mail: elliott@decaroauctions.com
Web Site: www.decaroauctions.com
Approx. Number Employees: 6
Business Description:
Real Estate Services
S.I.C.: 6531
N.A.I.C.S.: 531390
Media: 6-10
Personnel:
Daniel DeCaro *(Pres)*

DAYS INNS WORLDWIDE, INC.

(Sub. of Wyndham Hotel Group, LLC)
1 Sylvan Way
Parsippany, NJ 07054-3887
Tel.: (973) 428-9700
Fax: (973) 496-7658
Toll Free: (800) 329-7466
Web Site: www.daysinn.com

Key to Media (For complete agency information see *The Advertising Red Books-Agencies* edition):
1. Bus. Publs. 2. Cable T.V. 3. Catalogs & Directories. 4. Co-op Adv. 5. Consumer Mags. 6. D.M. to Bus. Estab.7. D.M. to Consumers 8. Daily Newsp. 9. Exhibits/Trade Shows 10. Foreign 11. Infomercial 12. Internet Adv.13. Multimedia 14. Network Radio 15. Network T.V. 16. Newsp. Distr. Mags. 17. Other 18. Outdoor (Posters, Transit) 19. Point of Purchase20. Premiums, Novelties 21. Product Samples 22. Special Events Mktg. 23. Spot Radio 24. Spot T.V. 25. Weekly Newsp. 26. Yellow Page Adv.

Days Inns Worldwide, Inc. — (Continued)

Sales Range: $10-24.9 Million
Approx. Number Employees: 43
Year Founded: 1970
Business Description:
Franchiser of Hotels & Motels
S.I.C.: 7011
N.A.I.C.S.: 721110
Media: 2-3-6-8-10-13-14-15-20-26
Distr.: Intl.; Natl.
Budget Set: Oct.
Personnel:
Clyde Guinn *(Pres)*
Brands & Products:
DAYS BUSINESS PLACE
DAYS HOTELS
DAYS INN
DAYS SUITES
DAYSTOP
Advertising Agency:
Decker Creative Marketing
99 Citizens Dr
Glastonbury, CT 06033-1262
Tel.: (860) 659-1311
Fax: (860) 659-3062
Toll Free: (800) 777-3677
(Radio & Print Campaign)

DELAWARE NORTH COMPANIES, INC.

40 Fountain Plz
Buffalo, NY 14202-2229
Tel.: (716) 858-5000
Fax: (716) 858-5125
E-mail: info@delawarenorth.com
Web Site: www.delawarenorth.com
Sales Range: $1-4.9 Billion
Approx. Number Employees: 430,000
Year Founded: 1915
Business Description:
Holding Company; Airport & Sporting Facilities Food Service; Inflight Catering; Sports Concessions, Recreation & Hospitality, National Parks, Hotel Ownership, Gaming & Entertainment
S.I.C.: 5812; 7011
N.A.I.C.S.: 722310; 721120
Advertising Expenditures: $1,000,000
Media: 2-9-10-22
Personnel:
Jeremy M. Jacobs, Sr. *(Chm & CEO)*
Charles E. Moran, Jr. *(Pres & COO)*
Kevin Quinlivan *(CIO)*
William J. Bissett *(Pres-Gaming & Entertainment)*
Charles Jacobs *(Principal)*
Jeremy M. Jacobs, Jr. *(Principal)*
Louis M. Jacobs *(Principal)*
Bryan J. Keller *(Gen Counsel, Sec & VP)*
Hugh Lombardi *(Sr VP & Gen Mgr)*
Jeffrey Hess *(VP-Retail)*
Eileen Morgan *(VP-HR)*
Wendy A. Watkins *(VP-Corp Comm & PR)*
Steven Werner *(Mgr-Loss Prevention-Corp Security Dept)*
Gwen Clinkscales *(Assoc Supvr-Svc Center)*
Brands & Products:
DNC
GREENPATH
GUESTPATH

DELTIC TIMBER CORPORATION

210 E Elm St
El Dorado, AR 71731-7200
Mailing Address:
PO Box 7200
El Dorado, AR 71731-7200
Tel.: (870) 881-9400
Fax: (870) 881-6454
E-mail: ir@deltic.com
Web Site: www.deltic.com
Approx. Sls.: $141,623,000
Approx. Number Employees: 454
Year Founded: 1950
Business Description:
Timber & Land Management; Lumber Manufacturing & Marketing; Real Estate Development
S.I.C.: 2421; 0139
N.A.I.C.S.: 321113; 111998
Advertising Expenditures: $987,000
Media: 4-16-22
Personnel:
Robert C. Nolan *(Chm)*
Ray C. Dillon *(Pres & CEO)*
Kenneth D. Mann *(CFO, Treas & VP)*
Jim F. Andrews, Jr. *(Gen Counsel, Sec & VP)*

THE DELTONA CORPORATION

8014 SW 135th St Rd
Ocala, FL 34473-6807
Tel.: (352) 347-2322
Fax: (352) 347-2340
Toll Free: (800) 935-6378
E-mail: corporate@deltona.com
Web Site: www.deltona.com
Sales Range: $10-24.9 Million
Approx. Number Employees: 42
Year Founded: 1962
Business Description:
Community Developer, Commercial Operations
S.I.C.: 6552; 7997
N.A.I.C.S.: 237210; 713910
Media: 1-2-5-6-8-9-10-18-19-23-25
Distr.: Intl.; Natl.
Budget Set: Sept.
Personnel:
Antony Gram *(Owner)*
Sharon J. Hummerhielm *(Exec VP)*
Beth Fisher *(Mgr-Marion Oaks)*
Brands & Products:
DELTONA

DENIHAN HOSPITALITY GROUP, LLC

551 Fifth Ave
New York, NY 10176
Tel.: (212) 465-3700
Fax: (212) 465-3511
Web Site: www.denihan.com
Business Description:
Hotels Owner & Operator
S.I.C.: 7011
N.A.I.C.S.: 721110
Personnel:
Brook Barrett *(Co-CEO)*
Patrick Benjamin Denihan *(Co-CEO)*
John Moser *(Chief Brand Officer & CMO)*
Brands & Products:
AFFINIA HOTELS
THE BENJAMIN
DHG
THE JAMES
Advertising Agency:
TwentySix2 Marketing
1123 Zonolite Rd Ste 4
Atlanta, GA 30306
Tel.: (404) 541-9780
Fax: (404) 541-9784
Search Engine Optimization

DETROIT ENTERTAINMENT, LLC

(Sub. of MGM Resorts International)
2901 Grand River Ave
Detroit, MI 48201
Tel.: (866) 752-9622
Web Site: www.motorcitycasino.com
Sales Range: $300-349.9 Million
Approx. Number Employees: 2,700
Business Description:
Entertainment Groups Management
S.I.C.: 7999
N.A.I.C.S.: 713290
Personnel:
Gregg Solomon *(CEO)*
Jacci Woods *(Dir-Pub Rel)*
Advertising Agency:
SK+G Advertising
8912 Spanish Ridge Ave
Las Vegas, NV 89148
Tel.: (702) 478-4000
Fax: (702) 478-4001

DEVELOPERS DIVERSIFIED REALTY CORPORATION

3300 Enterprise Pkwy
Beachwood, OH 44122
Tel.: (216) 755-5500
Fax: (216) 755-1500
Toll Free: (877) CALLDDR
E-mail: sschroeder@ddrc.com
Web Site: www.ddrc.com
E-Mail For Key Personnel:
President: DHurwitz@ddrc.com
Approx. Rev.: $803,069,000
Approx. Number Employees: 682
Year Founded: 1993
Business Description:
Real Estate Investment Trust
S.I.C.: 6798
N.A.I.C.S.: 525930
Advertising Expenditures: $250,000
Media: 2-13
Personnel:
Daniel B. Hurwitz *(Pres & CEO)*
David J. Oakes *(CFO & Sr Exec VP)*
John S. Kokinchak *(Chief Admin Officer & Sr Exec VP)*
Mark Bratt *(Chief Investment Officer & Exec VP)*
Christa A. Vesy *(Chief Acctg Officer & Sr VP)*
David E. Weiss *(Gen Counsel & Exec VP)*
R. Christopher Salata *(Asst Gen Counsel-Corp)*
Francine J. Glandt *(Treas & Sr VP-Capital Markets)*
Joan U. Allgood *(Exec VP)*
Richard E. Brown *(Exec VP-Intl)*
Timothy J. Bruce *(Exec VP-Dev)*
Robin R. Walker *(Exec VP-Leasing)*
Erik Christopher *(Sr VP)*
David J. Favorite *(Sr VP-Property Mgmt)*
Marc H. Feldman *(Sr VP-New Bus Dev)*
Paul Freddo *(Sr VP-Leasing & Dev)*
Marc A. Hayss *(Sr VP-Leasing-Intl & Specialty Centers)*
Timothy J. Lordan *(Sr VP-Fund Mgmt)*
Craig A. Schultz *(Sr VP-Tax)*
Kenneth L. Stern *(Sr VP-Peripheral Dev)*
Bryan P. Zabell *(Sr VP-Leasing-Anchor Store Redev)*
Dawn M. Lecklikner *(Reg VP-Shopping Center Mktg)*
Edward T. Sullivan *(Reg VP-Property Mgmt-Eastern)*
John Potts *(VP-Internal Audit)*
Michael Olsen *(Dir-Leasing-Anchor Store Redevelopment)*
Laura Skiver *(Mgr-Bus Dev)*
Brands & Products:
DEVELOPERS DIVERSIFIED REALTY
TOGETHER WE BREAK NEW GROUND EVERYDAY
Advertising Agency:
Cohn Marketing
2881 N Speer Blvd
Denver, CO 80211
Tel.: (303) 839-1415
Fax: (303) 839-1511

DIAMOND JO, LLC

3rd St Ice Harbor PO Box 1750
Dubuque, IA 52004-1683
Tel.: (319) 583-7005
Web Site: www.diamondjo.com/
Approx. Rev.: $286,280,000
Approx. Number Employees: 1,540
Business Description:
Casino Operator
S.I.C.: 7999
N.A.I.C.S.: 713210
Advertising Expenditures: $2,800,000
Personnel:
Michael S. Luzich *(Pres & Sec)*
Brent Stevens *(CEO)*
Natalie A. Schramm *(CFO)*
Jonathan Swain *(COO)*
James Adams *(VP-Legal Affairs)*
Karen Greene *(VP-Adv)*
Dustin Manternach *(VP-Corp Fin)*
Brian Adkins *(Corp Dir-Performance Analytics)*
Lori Nelson *(Corp Dir-Fin Reporting)*

DISNEY VACATION CLUB

(Sub. of Walt Disney Parks & Resorts)
1390 Celebration Blvd
Celebration, FL 34747
Tel.: (407) 566-3000
Fax: (407) 566-3333
E-mail: info@disneyvacationclub.com
Web Site:
www.disneyvacationclub.com
Sales Range: $1-9.9 Million
Approx. Number Employees: 418
Year Founded: 1990
Business Description:
Resort Hotel
S.I.C.: 7011
N.A.I.C.S.: 721110; 721199
Personnel:
Jim Lewis *(Pres)*
Cherie George (Rogers) *(Mgr-Member Mktg)*
Maggie Varnadoe *(Mgr-Member Mktg)*
Advertising Agency:
GoConvergence
4545 36th St
Orlando, FL 32811
Tel.: (407) 235-3210
Fax: (407) 299-9907

Key to Media (For complete agency information see *The Advertising Red Books-Agencies* edition):
1. Bus. Publs. 2. Cable T.V. 3. Catalogs & Directories. 4. Co-op Adv. 5. Consumer Mags. 6. D.M. to Bus. Estab.7. D.M. to Consumers 8. Daily Newsp. 9. Exhibits/Trade Shows 10. Foreign 11. Infomercial 12. Internet Adv.13. Multimedia 14. Network Radio 15. Network T.V. 16. Newsp. Distr. Mags. 17. Other 18. Outdoor (Posters, Transit) 19. Point of Purchase20. Premiums, Novelties 21. Product Samples 22. Special Events Mktg. 23. Spot Radio 24. Spot T.V. 25. Weekly Newsp. 26. Yellow Page Adv.

DISNEYLAND HOTELS
(Div. of Walt Disney Resorts)
1150 Magic Way
Anaheim, CA 92802-2247
Tel.: (714) 778-6600
Fax: (714) 956-6597
Web Site: www.disneyland.disney.go.com
Sales Range: $200-249.9 Million
Approx. Number Employees: 2,000
Year Founded: 1955
Business Description:
Guest Rooms, Convention Facilities, Meeting Rooms & Resort Hotel
S.I.C.: 7011; 5812
N.A.I.C.S.: 721110; 722110
Media: 1-2-4-5-6-7-8-9-10-11-13-20-21-23-24-25-26
Distr.: Intl.; Natl.
Advertising Agency:
Starcom MediaVest Group
35 W Wacker Dr
Chicago, IL 60601-1723
Tel.: (312) 220-3535
Fax: (312) 220-6530

DIVI HOTELS, INC.
6320 Quadrangle Dr Ste 210
Chapel Hill, NC 27517
Tel.: (919) 419-3484
Fax: (919) 419-2076
Toll Free: (800) 367-3484
E-mail: comments@diviresorts.com
Web Site: www.diviresorts.com
Approx. Number Employees: 55
Business Description:
Hotel Timeshare & Casino Services
S.I.C.: 7011; 7999
N.A.I.C.S.: 721110; 713290
Media: 2-4-5-6-8-10-11-13-23-24
Personnel:
Mike Walsnovich *(CFO)*
Mark Stewart *(Dir-Mktg)*
Brands & Products:
DIVI RESORTS

DON CESAR RESORT HOTEL LTD.
(Sub. of Loews Hotels Holding Corporation)
3400 Gulf Blvd
Saint Petersburg, FL 33706-4015
Tel.: (727) 360-1881
Fax: (727) 363-5041
Toll Free: (866) 728-2206
Web Site: www.doncesar.com
Sales Range: $25-49.9 Million
Approx. Number Employees: 300
Year Founded: 1928
Business Description:
Hotel & Motel Services
S.I.C.: 7011; 5812
N.A.I.C.S.: 721110; 722110
Import Export
Media: 8
Personnel:
John Marks *(Gen Mgr)*
Heather Buss *(Dir-Accounts-Natl)*
Patty Metcalf-Sobczak *(Dir-Accounts-Natl)*
Advertising Agency:
The Zimmerman Agency
1821 Miccosukee Commons Dr
Tallahassee, FL 32308-5433
Tel.: (850) 668-2222
Fax: (850) 656-4622
Public Relations

D.R. HORTON, INC.
301 Commerce St Ste 500
Fort Worth, TX 76102
Tel.: (817) 390-8200
Fax: (817) 436-6717
Web Site: www.drhorton.com
Approx. Rev.: $4,309,700,000
Approx. Number Employees: 3,214
Year Founded: 1978
Business Description:
Residential Home Builder
S.I.C.: 1531; 1521
N.A.I.C.S.: 236117; 236115
Advertising Expenditures: $39,300,000
Media: 2-9-10-13-18-21-23-24-25
Personnel:
Donald J. Tomnitz *(Vice Chm, Pres & CEO)*
Bill W. Wheat *(CFO & Exec VP)*
Ted Ira Harbour *(Chief Legal Officer)*
David Auld *(Pres-East Reg)*
Chris Chambers *(Pres-West Reg)*
Donald R. Horton *(Pres-South Reg)*
Richard L. Horton *(Pres-South Reg)*
Randy Present *(Pres-Fin Svcs)*
George Seagraves *(Pres-North Reg)*
Stacey H. Dwyer *(Treas & Exec VP-IR)*
Advertising Agency:
McCullough Communications & Marketing
4590 MacArthur Blvd Ste 500
Newport Beach, CA 92660-2028
Tel.: (949) 833-1135
Fax: (949) 833-1244

D.R. HORTON, INC./SCHULER HOMES LLC
(Sub. of D.R. Horton, Inc.)
828 Fort St Mall 4th Fl
Honolulu, HI 96813-4321
Tel.: (808) 521-5661
Fax: (808) 538-1476
Sales Range: $50-74.9 Million
Approx. Number Employees: 100
Business Description:
Designs, Builds & Sells Single-Family Houses, Townhomes & Condominiums to Entry-Level & First-Time Homebuyers
S.I.C.: 6552
N.A.I.C.S.: 237210
Advertising Expenditures: $59,300,000
Media: 2-17
Personnel:
James K. Schuler *(Chm & CEO)*
Michael T. Jones *(Pres)*
Mary Flood *(VP-Sls)*
Galen Lee *(VP-Fin)*

DRAPER & KRAMER RETIREMENT PROPERTY SERVICES
(Sub. of DKH Incorporated)
33 W Monroe St Fl 19
Chicago, IL 60603
Tel.: (312) 346-8600
Fax: (312) 346-2177
Web Site: www.draperandkramer.com
Approx. Rev.: $480,000
Approx. Number Employees: 100
Business Description:
Real Estate Managers
S.I.C.: 6531
N.A.I.C.S.: 531210
Media: 6
Personnel:
Forrest D. Bailey *(Pres & CEO)*

EDUCATION REALTY TRUST, INC.
530 Oak Court Dr Ste 300
Memphis, TN 38117
Tel.: (901) 259-2500
Fax: (901) 259-2547
Web Site: www.educationrealty.com
Approx. Rev.: $119,580,000
Approx. Number Employees: 1,138
Business Description:
Ownership, Development & Management of Student Housing
S.I.C.: 7021; 6733; 6798
N.A.I.C.S.: 721310; 523991; 525930
Advertising Expenditures: $2,473,000
Media: 9-10-13-25
Personnel:
Paul O. Bower *(Chm)*
Randall L. Churchey *(Pres & CEO)*
Randall H. Brown *(CFO, Treas, Sec & Exec VP)*
Thomas Trubiana *(Chief Investment Officer & Exec VP)*
J.Drew Koester *(Chief Acctg Officer, VP & Asst Sec)*
Thomas J. Hickey *(Sr VP)*
Christine D. Richards *(Sr VP-Property Ops)*
Wallace L. Wilcox *(Sr VP-Construction & Engrg)*
Susan B. Arrison *(VP-HR)*

ELVIS PRESLEY ENTERPRISES, INC.
(Sub. of CKX, Inc.)
3734 Elvis Presley Blvd
Memphis, TN 38116
Tel.: (901) 332-3322
Fax: (901) 345-8511
Toll Free: (800) 238-2010
Toll Free: (800) 238-2000
E-mail: graceland@elvis.com
Web Site: www.elvis.com
Sales Range: $75-99.9 Million
Approx. Number Employees: 350
Business Description:
Restaurant & Hotel Owner; Tour Operator; Gift & Novelty Sales
S.I.C.: 8412; 5947
N.A.I.C.S.: 712110; 453220
Media: 1-2-3-4-6-8-9-10-11-12-13-14-15-18-20-22-23-24-25-26
Personnel:
Lisa Marie Presley *(Chm)*
Jack Soden *(Pres & CEO)*
Gary Hovey *(Exec VP-Entertainment & Music Publ)*
Scott Williams *(VP-Mktg)*
Brands & Products:
ELVIS PRESLEY
ELVIS PRESLEY'S MEMPHIS
GRACELAND
HEARTBREAK HOTEL

EMBASSY SUITES HOTELS
(Div. of Hilton Worldwide, Inc.)
7930 Jones Branch Dr
McLean, TN 22102
Tel.: (703) 883-1000
Web Site: www.hiltonworlwide.com
Sales Range: Less than $1 Million
Approx. Number Employees: 50
Business Description:
Hotels
S.I.C.: 7011
N.A.I.C.S.: 721110
Personnel:
Jim Holthouser *(Sr VP-Brand Mngmt)*
Advertising Agency:
Emanate
711 3rd Ave 12th Fl
New York, NY 10017
Tel.: (212) 805-8000
Fax: (212) 805-8098
Agency of Record

EMPIRE RESORTS, INC.
c/o Monticello Casino & Raceway Rte 17B
Monticello, NY 12701
Tel.: (845) 807-0001
E-mail: cdegliomini@empireresorts.com
Web Site: www.empireresorts.com
Approx. Rev.: $68,545,000
Approx. Number Employees: 310
Year Founded: 1993
Business Description:
Gaming & Hospitality Services
S.I.C.: 7999; 7011
N.A.I.C.S.: 713990; 713290; 721110; 721120
Advertising Expenditures: $1,400,000
Media: 8-9-24
Personnel:
Emanuel R. Pearlman *(Chm)*
Joseph A. D'Amato *(CEO)*
Laurette J. Pitts *(CFO)*
Clifford A. Ehrlich *(Pres/Gen Mgr-Monticello Raceway Mgmt)*
Charles A. Degliomini *(Exec VP-Govt Rels & Corp Comm)*
Brands & Products:
EMPIRE RESORTS
MIGHTY M
Advertising Agency:
RPM Advertising
222 S Morgan St
Chicago, IL 60610
Tel.: (312) 455-8600
Fax: (312) 455-8617
Toll Free: (800) 475-2000

EQUITY LIFESTYLE PROPERTIES, INC.
2 N Riverside Plz Ste 800
Chicago, IL 60606
Tel.: (312) 279-1400
Fax: (312) 279-1710
Fax: (312) 454-0614 (Investor Rels)
Toll Free: (800) 247-5279 (Investor Rels)
E-mail: information@mhchomes.com
Web Site: www.mhchomes.com
Approx. Rev.: $511,361,000
Approx. Number Employees: 3,600
Year Founded: 1992
Business Description:
High Quality Resort Communities Owner & Operator
S.I.C.: 7011; 6798
N.A.I.C.S.: 721199; 525930
Media: 6
Personnel:
Samuel Zell *(Chm)*
Howard Walker *(Vice Chm)*
Thomas P. Heneghan *(Pres & CEO)*
Michael Berman *(CFO & Exec VP)*
Ellen Kelleher *(Exec VP-Property Mgmt)*
Roger Maynard *(Exec VP-Asset Mgmt)*

Key to Media (For complete agency information see *The Advertising Red Books-Agencies* edition):
1. Bus. Publs. 2. Cable T.V. 3. Catalogs & Directories. 4. Co-op Adv. 5. Consumer Mags. 6. D.M. to Bus. Estab.7. D.M. to Consumers 8. Daily Newsp. 9. Exhibits/Trade Shows 10. Foreign 11. Infomercial 12. Internet Adv.13. Multimedia 14. Network Radio 15. Network T.V. 16. Newsp. Distr. Mags. 17. Other 18. Outdoor (Posters, Transit) 19. Point of Purchase20. Premiums, Novelties 21. Product Samples 22. Special Events Mktg. 23. Spot Radio 24. Spot T.V. 25. Weekly Newsp. 26. Yellow Page Adv.

Equity LifeStyle Properties, Inc. — (Continued)

Marguerite Nader *(Exec VP-New Bus Dev)*
Seth Rosenberg *(Sr VP-Sls & Mktg)*

ERA FRANCHISE SYSTEMS LLC
(Sub. of Realogy Corporation)
113 Parsippany Rd
Parsippany, NJ 07054
Tel.: (973) 887-1560
Fax: (973) 887-8106
Toll Free: (800) 869-1260
Web Site: www.era.com
E-Mail For Key Personnel:
President: Brenda.Casserly@asera.com
Year Founded: 1971
Business Description:
International Residential Franchise Brokerage Services; Home Warranties, Referral & Relocations Services; Sellers Security & Buyers Protection Plan
S.I.C.: 6794
N.A.I.C.S.: 533110
Advertising Expenditures: $10,000,000
Media: 1-2-4-6-7-8-9-10-11-13-15-18-23-24-26
Distr.: Direct to Consumer; Intl.; Natl.; Reg.
Personnel:
Brenda W. Casserly *(Pres & CEO)*
Advertising Agency:
Clean Design, Inc.
10 Laboratory Dr Bldg 2 Ste 200
Research Triangle Park, NC 27709
Tel.: (919) 544-2193
Fax: (919) 473-2200

ERICKSON RETIREMENT COMMUNITIES LLC
701 Maiden Choice Ln
Catonsville, MD 21228-3738
Tel.: (410) 242-2880
Fax: (410) 737-8854
E-mail: info@ericksonretirement.com
Web Site: www.ericksonretirement.com
Approx. Number Employees: 300
Year Founded: 1979
Business Description:
Developer of Retirement Communities
S.I.C.: 6552
N.A.I.C.S.: 237210
Personnel:
Rick Grindrod *(Pres)*
Debra Doyle *(Exec VP-Ops)*
Mel Tansil *(Mgr-Pub Affairs)*
Brands & Products:
ANN'S CHOICE
ASHBY PONDS
BROOKSBY VILLAGE
CEDAR CREST
CHARLESTOWN
EAGLE'S TRACE
ERICKSON
ERICKSON ADVANTAGE
ERICKSON HEALTH
ERICKSON LIVING
FOX RUN
GREENSPRING
HENRY FORD VILLAGE
HICKORY CHASE
HIGHLAND SPRINGS
INFORM.INSPIRE.INVOLVE
LINDEN PONDS
MARIS GROVE
MONARCH LANDING
OAK CREST
RIDERWOOD
SEABROOK
SEDGEBROOK
TALLGRASS CREEK
WIND CREST
Advertising Agencies:
BBDO Atlanta
3500 Lenox Rd NE Ste 1900
Atlanta, GA 30326-4232
Tel.: (404) 231-1700
Fax: (404) 841-1893

Ketchum
2000 L St NW Ste 300
Washington, DC 20036-4923
Tel.: (202) 835-8800
Fax: (202) 835-8879

PHD Chicago
225 N Michigan Ave Ste 800
Chicago, IL 60601
Tel.: (312) 595-2800
Fax: (312) 467-0977

ESSEX PROPERTY TRUST, INC.
925 E Meadow Dr
Palo Alto, CA 94303-4233
Tel.: (650) 494-3700
Fax: (650) 494-8743
E-mail: accounting@essexpropertytrust.com
Web Site: www.essexproperties.com
Approx. Rev.: $415,732,000
Approx. Number Employees: 1,039
Year Founded: 1994
Business Description:
Real Estate Investment Trust
S.I.C.: 6798
N.A.I.C.S.: 525930
Advertising Expenditures: $3,842,000
Personnel:
George M. Marcus *(Chm)*
Michael J. Schall *(Pres & CEO)*
Keith R. Guericke *(Pres)*
Michael T. Dance *(CFO & Exec VP)*
Bryan G. Hunt *(Chief Acctg Officer & VP)*
Jordan E. Ritter *(Gen Counsel & Sr VP)*
John F. Burkart *(Exec VP-Asset Mgmt)*
John D. Eudy *(Exec VP-Dev)*
Craig K. Zimmerman *(Exec VP-Acq)*
Erik J. Alexander *(Sr VP & Div Mgr)*
Mark J. Mikl *(Sr VP-Asset Mgmt)*
Gerald Kelly *(First VP)*
Bruce Knoblock *(First VP-Dev)*
Maura Lederer *(First VP)*
Bryan Meyer *(First VP-Acq)*
Jeff Rowerdink *(First VP-Acq)*
Jamie Williams *(First VP-Info Sys)*
Suzanne M. Golden *(VP-HR)*
Lisa Burton *(Dir-Fin)*

ESSLINGER-WOOTEN-MAXWELL REALTORS, INC.
(Sub. of HomeServices of America, Inc.)
1360 S Dixie Hwy
Coral Gables, FL 33146
Tel.: (305) 667-8871
Fax: (305) 662-5646
Web Site: www.ewm.com
Sales Range: $1-4.9 Billion
Approx. Number Employees: 950
Year Founded: 1964
Business Description:
Real Estate Services
S.I.C.: 6531; 6163
N.A.I.C.S.: 531210; 522310
Media: 2-4-8-9-10-13-25
Personnel:
Al Harper *(Chm)*
Ron Shuffield *(Pres)*
Hena M. Aguirre *(CFO)*
Patrick O'Connell *(Sr VP-Dev Svcs)*
Sherrie Jones-Porter *(Sr VP & Gen Mgr-Sls)*
Lourdes Diego *(Creative Dir)*
Cristina Allen *(Asst Mgr)*
Susie Friedman *(Mgr-Mktg)*
Lisa Silva *(Mgr-Corp Svcs)*
Marta Toledo *(Mgr-HR)*

EXCLUSIVE RESORTS, LLC
(Holding of Revolution, LLC)
1515 Arapahoe Carver St Ste 300
Denver, CO 80202
Tel.: (303) 226-4900
Fax: (303) 474-6990
Toll Free: (866) 863-2688
E-mail: info@exclusiveresorts.com
Web Site: www.exclusiveresorts.com
Approx. Number Employees: 150
Year Founded: 2003
Business Description:
Resort Operator
S.I.C.: 7011
N.A.I.C.S.: 721110
Media: 4-6-13
Personnel:
Brad Handler *(Co-Founder)*
Stephen M. Case *(Chm)*
Jeff Potter *(CEO)*
Robert E. Parsons, Jr. *(CFO & Exec VP)*
Adam Wegner *(Gen Counsel & Exec VP)*
David Kallery *(Exec VP-Acquisation & HR)*
Todd Harris *(Sr VP-Hospitality & Member Svcs)*
Charles Livingston *(Sr VP-Tech)*
Cathy Ross *(Sr VP-Real Estate Ops)*
Ian Authur *(Dir-Commun)*
Karen Fields *(Dir-Mktg)*
Anne Griebling *(Mgr-Comm)*
Brands & Products:
EXCLUSIVE RESORTS
Advertising Agency:
DDB Seattle
1000 2nd Ave Ste 1000
Seattle, WA 98104
Tel.: (206) 442-9900
Fax: (206) 223-6309

EXIT REALTY CENTRAL
870 N Military Hwy
Norfolk, VA 23502
Tel.: (757) 466-1009
Fax: (757) 466-3694
Web Site: www.exitcentralhr.com
Approx. Number Employees: 67
Business Description:
Real Estate Services
S.I.C.: 6531
N.A.I.C.S.: 531210
Media: 13
Personnel:
Kimberly Plourde *(Owner & Broker)*

EXTENDED STAY HOTELS LLC
(Joint Venture of The Blackstone Group L.P. & Centerbridge Partners, L.P.)
(Filed Ch 11 Bankruptcy #913764 on 06/15/09 in U.S. Bankruptcy Ct, Southern Dist of NY, NY)
100 Dunbar St
Spartanburg, SC 29306
Tel.: (864) 573-1600
Fax: (864) 573-1695
Toll Free: (800) EXT-STAY
Toll Free: (800) 804-3724
E-mail: extstay@extstay.com
Web Site: www.extstay.com
Sales Range: $550-599.9 Million
Approx. Number Employees: 7,600
Year Founded: 1995
Business Description:
Hotel Chain Developer, Owner & Operator; Owned by Centerbridge Partners, L.P. & The Blackstone Group L.P.
S.I.C.: 7011
N.A.I.C.S.: 721110
Media: 8-9-13-18
Personnel:
Gary A. Delapp *(Pres & CEO)*
David Kim *(CIO & Exec VP-Fin)*
Mike Haaf *(CMO)*
Jon Wohlfert *(Exec VP-Sls)*
Mark Mahoney *(VP-Sls)*
Brands & Products:
CROSSLAND ECONOMY STUDIOS
EXTENDED STAY AMERICA
EXTENDED STAY AMERICA EFFICIENCY STUDIOS
STUDIOPLUS
STUDIOPLUS DELUXE STUDIOS

EXTRA SPACE STORAGE, INC.
2795 E Cottonwood Pkwy Ste 400
Salt Lake City, UT 84121
Tel.: (801) 562-5556
Toll Free: (888) 586-9658
E-mail: info@extraspace.com
Web Site: www.extraspace.com
Approx. Rev.: $281,497,000
Approx. Number Employees: 2,125
Year Founded: 1977
Business Description:
Real Estate Investment Trust
S.I.C.: 6798; 4225
N.A.I.C.S.: 525930; 531130
Advertising Expenditures: $6,430,000
Media: 8-13-26
Personnel:
Spencer F. Kirk *(Chm & CEO)*
Kent W. Christensen *(CFO & Exec VP)*
Karl T. Haas *(COO & Exec VP)*
Charles L. Allen *(Chief Legal Officer, Sec & Exec VP)*
David L. Rasmussen *(Gen Counsel, VP & Asst Sec)*
P. Scott Stubbs *(Sr VP-Fin & Acctg)*
Richard S. Tanner *(Sr VP-Dev & Construction)*
Advertising Agency:
Thunder Factory
27 Maiden Ln Ste 525
San Francisco, CA 94108
Tel.: (415) 992-3276
Fax: (415) 956-0604

EYCHNER ASSOCIATES, INC.
10 Christopher St
New York, NY 10014

Key to Media (For complete agency information see *The Advertising Red Books-Agencies* edition):
1. Bus. Publs. 2. Cable T.V. 3. Catalogs & Directories. 4. Co-op Adv. 5. Consumer Mags. 6. D.M. to Bus. Estab.7. D.M. to Consumers 8. Daily Newsp. 9. Exhibits/Trade Shows 10. Foreign 11. Infomercial 12. Internet Adv.13. Multimedia 14. Network Radio 15. Network T.V. 16. Newsp. Distr. Mags. 17. Other 18. Outdoor (Posters, Transit) 19. Point of Purchase20. Premiums, Novelties 21. Product Samples 22. Special Events Mktg. 23. Spot Radio 24. Spot T.V. 25. Weekly Newsp. 26. Yellow Page Adv.

Tel.: (212) 807-0700
Fax: (212) 807-1823
E-mail: contact@eychner.com
Web Site: www.eychner.com
Approx. Number Employees: 30
Year Founded: 1986
Business Description:
Real Estate Services
S.I.C.: 6531
N.A.I.C.S.: 531210
Media: 2-6
Personnel:
Robert Eychner *(Pres)*

FAIRFIELD RESORTS, INC.
(Name Changed to Wyndham Vacation Ownership)

FAIRMONT HOTELS & RESORTS INC.
(Joint Venture of Colony Capital, LLC & Kingdom Hotels International)
Canadian Pacific Tower
TD Centre PO Box 40
Toronto, ON M5K 1B7, Canada
Tel.: (416) 874-2600
Fax: (416) 874-2601
Toll Free: (866) 627-0642
E-mail: communications@fairmont.com
Web Site: www.fairmont.com
Sales Range: $800-899.9 Million
Approx. Number Employees: 30,000
Business Description:
Luxury Hotels & Resorts Owner & Operator
S.I.C.: 7011
N.A.I.C.S.: 721110
Media: 2-6
Personnel:
Peter Cowperthwaite Godsoe *(Chm)*
Chris J. Cahill *(Pres & COO)*
William R. Fatt *(CEO)*
Diana Ee-Tan *(Exec VP-Asia Pacific)*
Michael F. Glennie *(Exec VP-Real Estate)*
Jeff Senior *(Exec VP)*
Kevin Frid *(Sr VP-Ops-North America)*
Mark Huntley *(Reg VP)*
Brian Richardson *(VP-Brand Mktg & Comm)*
Matthew Smith *(VP-HR-Europe, Africa, Middle East & Asia Pacific)*
Philip Barnes *(Regional VP-United Arab Emirates & Gen Mgr-Fairmont Dubai)*
David Doucette *(Exec Dir-Internet Mktg)*
Roger Gwynn *(Dir-Global Accts)*
Michael Innocentin *(Dir-Internet Mktg)*
Edward Flaherty *(Mgr-Sls)*
Blair French *(Mgr)*
Brands & Products:
DELTA HOTELS
FAIRMONT HOTELS & RESORTS
RAFFLES HOTELS & RESORTS

THE FAIRMONT SONOMA MISSION INN & SPA
100 Boyes Blvd
Sonoma, CA 95476
Tel.: (707) 938-9000
Fax: (707) 938-4250
Toll Free: (800) 862-4945
E-mail: smi.reservations@fairmont.com
Web Site: www.fairmont.com
Approx. Number Employees: 500
Year Founded: 1985
Business Description:
Resort & Spa
S.I.C.: 7011
N.A.I.C.S.: 721110
Advertising Expenditures: $250,000
Bus. Publs.: $5,000; Catalogs & Directories: $5,000; Consumer Mags.: $10,000; D.M. to Consumers: $75,000; Daily Newsp.: $75,000; Spot Radio: $80,000
Distr.: Natl.
Budget Set: Nov.
Personnel:
Kelley Cosgrove *(Gen Mgr)*
David Burt *(Dir-Mktg & Sls)*

FAMILY INNS OF AMERICA, INC.
3124 Tammy King Rd
Pigeon Forge, TN 37863-3335
Mailing Address:
PO Box 10
Pigeon Forge, TN 37868-0010
Tel.: (865) 453-4988
Toll Free: (800) 472-1188
E-mail: kart@kmsfia.com
Web Site:
www.familyinnsofamerica.com/pigeonforge.html
Sales Range: $25-49.9 Million
Approx. Number Employees: 750
Year Founded: 1972
Business Description:
Motels, Restaurants & Lounges Owner & Operator
S.I.C.: 6794; 7011
N.A.I.C.S.: 533110; 721110
Media: 1-2-3-4-5-6-7-8-9-10-13-14-15-16-18-19-20-22-23-24-25-26
Distr.: Natl.
Budget Set: Jan.
Brands & Products:
FAMILY INNS OF AMERICA

FELCOR LODGING TRUST INCORPORATED
545 E John Carpenter Fwy Ste 1300
Irving, TX 75062-8124
Tel.: (972) 444-4900
Fax: (972) 444-4949
E-mail: information@felcor.com
Web Site: www.felcor.com
Approx. Rev.: $928,311,000
Approx. Number Employees: 68
Year Founded: 1991
Business Description:
Hotel Real Estate Investment Trust
S.I.C.: 6798; 7011
N.A.I.C.S.: 525930; 721110
Advertising Expenditures: $103,807,000
Personnel:
Thomas J. Corcoran Jr. *(Chm)*
Richard A. Smith *(Pres & CEO)*
Andrew J. Welch *(CFO & Exec VP)*
Troy A. Pentecost *(COO & Exec VP)*
Michael A. Denicola *(CIO & Exec VP)*
Lester C. Johnson *(Chief Acctg Officer & Sr VP)*
Jonathan H. Yellen *(Gen Counsel, Sec & Exec VP)*
Robert P. Carl *(Sr VP & Dir-Design & Construction)*
Eric U. Nylen *(Sr VP-Dev-Capital Transactions Grp)*
Michael C. Hughes *(VP-Fin)*
Stephen A. Schafer *(VP-IR & Media Rels)*
Larry Mundy *(Deputy Gen Counsel)*

FIRST REALTY/GMAC REAL ESTATE
(Sub. of HomeServices of America, Inc.)
3501 Westown Pkwy
West Des Moines, IA 50266
Tel.: (515) 453-6222
Fax: (515) 453-5786
Web Site: www.firstrealtyhomes.com
Sales Range: $10-24.9 Million
Approx. Number Employees: 50
Business Description:
Real Estate Services
S.I.C.: 6531
N.A.I.C.S.: 531210
Media: 2-4-8-9-13-25
Personnel:
R.M. Knapp *(Pres & CEO)*

FISHER AUCTION COMPANY, INC.
351 S Cypress Rd Ste 210
Pompano Beach, FL 33060
Tel.: (954) 942-0917
Fax: (954) 782-8143
Toll Free: (800) 331-6620
E-mail: info@fisherauction.com
Web Site: www.fisherauction.com
Approx. Number Employees: 20
Year Founded: 1967
Business Description:
Consulting Services & Real Estate Auctioneers
S.I.C.: 5961
N.A.I.C.S.: 454112
Advertising Expenditures: $800,000
Media: 2-3-4-6-7-8-9-10-11-18-23-24-25-26
Distr.: Natl.
Personnel:
Louis B. Fisher, Jr. *(Founder & Chm)*
Andre Labauve *(CFO)*

THE FLATLEY COMPANY
Bldg 35 Braintree Hill Office Pk
Braintree, MA 02184
Tel.: (781) 848-2000
Fax: (781) 849-4440
Web Site: flatleyco.com/
Sales Range: $1-9.9 Million
Approx. Number Employees: 40
Business Description:
Cooperative Industrial Buildings, Shopping Centers & Commercial Property Developers
S.I.C.: 6531; 1541
N.A.I.C.S.: 531210; 236210
Advertising Expenditures: $500,000
Media: 2-4-6-7-10-18-20-22-23
Distr.: Reg.
Personnel:
John J. Roche *(CEO)*

FOREST CITY ENTERPRISES, INC.
50 Public Sq Terminal Tower Ste 1100
Cleveland, OH 44113-2203
Tel.: (216) 621-6060
Fax: (215) 267-3925
E-mail: stationsquareoffice@fceinc.com
Web Site: www.fceinc.com
Approx. Rev.: $1,177,661,000
Approx. Number Employees: 2,571
Year Founded: 1921
Business Description:
Commercial & Residential Real Estate Properties Owner, Developer & Manager
S.I.C.: 6512; 1522; 1531; 6513; 7389
N.A.I.C.S.: 531120; 236116; 236118; 236220; 531110; 711310
Import
Media: 2-22-25
Distr.: Natl.
Budget Set: Oct.
Personnel:
Charles A. Ratner *(Chm)*
Bruce C. Ratner *(Vice Chm & CEO)*
James A. Ratner *(Vice Chm & CEO)*
David J. LaRue *(Pres & CEO)*
Robert G. O'Brien *(CFO & Exec VP)*
Linda M. Kane *(Chief Admin Officer, Chief Acctg Officer & Sr VP)*
John S. Lehigh *(Pres-Forest City Stapleton)*
Geralyn Presti *(Gen Counsel, Sec & Sr VP)*
Andrew Passen *(Exec VP-HR)*
Brian J. Ratner *(Exec VP)*
Ronald A. Ratner *(Exec VP)*
Nancy W. McCann *(Sr VP-Mktg & Pub Rel)*
Allan C. Krulak *(VP & Dir-Community Affairs)*
Joyce Mihalik *(Dir-Energy Mgmt)*
Thomas T. Kmiecik *(Asst Treas)*
Advertising Agencies:
Cohn Marketing
2881 N Speer Blvd
Denver, CO 80211
Tel.: (303) 839-1415
Fax: (303) 839-1511
The Orchard Town Center

Dix & Eaton Incorporated
200 Public Sq Ste 1400
Cleveland, OH 44114
Tel.: (216) 241-0405
Fax: (216) 241-3070

FOUR SEASONS HOTELS INC.
(Holding of Cascade Investment LLC)
1165 Leslie Street
Toronto, ON M3C 2K8, Canada
Tel.: (416) 449-1750
Fax: (416) 441-4374
Web Site: www.fshr.com
Sales Range: $200-249.9 Million
Approx. Number Employees: 33,280
Year Founded: 1960
Business Description:
Hotels Owner & Operator
S.I.C.: 7011
N.A.I.C.S.: 721110
Media: 2-4-6-7-8-10-16-26-30
Distr.: Intl.
Budget Set: Nov. -Dec.
Personnel:
Isadore Sharp *(Founder & Chm)*
Kathleen P. Taylor *(Pres)*
John Davison *(CFO)*
Antoine Corinthios *(Pres-EMEA)*
James FitzGibbon *(Pres-Worldwide Hotel Ops)*
Randolph Weisz *(Gen Counsel & Exec VP-Bus Admin)*
Susan J. Helstab *(Exec VP-Mktg)*
Nicholas Mutton *(Exec VP)*
Scott Woroch *(Exec VP-Worldwide Dev)*

Key to Media (For complete agency information see *The Advertising Red Books-Agencies* edition):
1. Bus. Publs. 2. Cable T.V. 3. Catalogs & Directories. 4. Co-op Adv. 5. Consumer Mags. 6. D.M. to Bus. Estab.7. D.M. to Consumers
8. Daily Newsp. 9. Exhibits/Trade Shows 10. Foreign 11. Infomercial 12. Internet Adv.13. Multimedia 14. Network Radio
15. Network T.V. 16. Newsp. Distr. Mags. 17. Other 18. Outdoor (Posters, Transit) 19. Point of Purchase20. Premiums, Novelties
21. Product Samples 22. Special Events Mktg. 23. Spot Radio 24. Spot T.V. 25. Weekly Newsp. 26. Yellow Page Adv.

Four Seasons Hotels Inc. — (Continued)

Royal Rowe *(Gen Mgr)*
David Miller *(Dir-Mktg & Sls)*
Shoshana Weinberg *(Dir-Spa-Hong Kong)*

Brands & Products:
FOUR SEASONS

Advertising Agencies:
Bates 141 Asia Pacific
(Bates Asia Headquarters)
33F Tower 1 Times Square
Causeway Bay, China (Hong Kong)
Tel.: (852) 21036333
Fax: (852) 25274086

ISM
745 Boylston St 7th Fl
Boston, MA 02116
Tel.: (617) 353-1822
Fax: (617) 266-1890
(Tactical Advertising)

FOUR WINDS CASINO RESORT

11111 Wilson Rd
New Buffalo, MI 49117
Toll Free: (866) 494-6371
Web Site: www.fourwindscasino.com
Business Description:
Casino Hotel
S.I.C.: 7011
N.A.I.C.S.: 721120
Media: 3-8-9-18-22-23-24-25
Personnel:
Matthew Harkness *(Gen Mgr)*
Advertising Agency:
Dresner Corporate Services
20 N Clark St Ste 3550
Chicago, IL 60602
Tel.: (312) 780-7211
Fax: (312) 726-7448
Toll Free: (800) 373-7637
— Joshua Taustien *(Acct Exec)*

FRANK HARDY, INC.

417 Park St
Charlottesville, VA 22902
Tel.: (434) 296-0134
Fax: (434) 296-9730
E-mail: info@farmandestate.com
Web Site: www.farmandestate.com
Approx. Number Employees: 40
Business Description:
Real Estate Services
S.I.C.: 6531
N.A.I.C.S.: 531210
Media: 2-6-9
Personnel:
R. Franklin Hardy *(Owner & Photographer)*

GAL-TEX HOTEL CORPORATION

2302 Post Ofc St Ste 500
Galveston, TX 77550-1936
Mailing Address:
PO Box 59
Galveston, TX 77553-0059
Tel.: (409) 763-8536
Fax: (409) 763-5304
Sales Range: $550-599.9 Million
Approx. Number Employees: 3,000
Year Founded: 1940
Business Description:
Holding Company; Hotel Owner & Operator
S.I.C.: 6719; 7011
N.A.I.C.S.: 551112; 721110
Media: 2-4-6-7-8-9-10-16-18-23-24-25
Distr.: Natl.
Budget Set: Mar.
Personnel:
Eugene Lucas *(Pres)*
Advertising Agency:
MH&T Advertising Agency
1227 Tremont
Galveston, TX 77550
Tel.: (409) 765-7144
Fax: (409) 763-5304
(Hotels)
— Pat Welsh *(Acct Exec)*

GALAXY HOTEL SYSTEMS LLC

(Sub. of Starwood Hotels & Resorts Worldwide, Inc.)
15621 Red Hill Ave Ste 100
Tustin, CA 92780-7322
Tel.: (714) 258-5800
Fax: (714) 258-5880
Toll Free: (800) 624-2953
E-mail: sales@galaxyhotelsystems.com
Web Site:
www.galaxyhotelsystems.com
E-Mail For Key Personnel:
Sales Director: sales@galaxyhotelsystems.com
Sales Range: Less than $1 Million
Approx. Number Employees: 60
Year Founded: 1969
Business Description:
Computer Software Solutions for the Hotel Industry
S.I.C.: 7011
N.A.I.C.S.: 721110
Media: 2-7-8-10
Personnel:
Dan Hogan *(Gen Mgr-Galaxy Hotel Systems)*
Brands & Products:
GALAXY/GH
GALAXY LIGHTSPEED
GALAXY/UX

GARDEN CITY HOTEL INC.

45 7th St
Garden City, NY 11530
Tel.: (516) 747-3000
Fax: (516) 747-1414
Toll Free: (800) 547-0400
E-mail: info@gchotel.com
Web Site: www.gardencityhotel.com
Approx. Sls.: $16,000,000
Approx. Number Employees: 475
Year Founded: 1874
Business Description:
Owner & Operator of Hotel
S.I.C.: 7011
N.A.I.C.S.: 721110
Media: 2
Personnel:
Catherine Nelkin Miller *(Pres)*

GARRIGAN & ASSOCIATES REALTY, INC.

1954 Alternate 19 S
Tarpon Springs, FL 34689
Tel.: (727) 942-1111
Toll Free: (800) 393-1517
E-mail: dgarri8167@aol.com
Web Site:
www.garriganandassociates.com
Approx. Number Employees: 9
Business Description:
Real Estate Services
S.I.C.: 6531
N.A.I.C.S.: 531210
Media: 6
Personnel:
Debbie Garrigan *(Owner & Broker)*

GAYLORD ENTERTAINMENT COMPANY

1 Gaylord Dr
Nashville, TN 37214
Tel.: (615) 316-6000
Fax: (615) 316-6555
E-mail: information@gaylordentertainment.com
Web Site:
www.gaylordentertainment.com
Approx. Rev.: $769,961,000
Approx. Number Employees: 6,634
Year Founded: 1991
Business Description:
Hospitality & Attraction Services
S.I.C.: 7011; 7999
N.A.I.C.S.: 721110; 713990
Import Export
Advertising Expenditures: $25,600,000
Media: 2-4-10-14-15-18-22-23-24
Distr.: Reg.
Personnel:
Colin V. Reed *(Chm & CEO)*
David C. Kloeppel *(Pres & COO)*
Mark Fioravanti *(CFO & Sr VP)*
Richard A Maradik *(CMO & Sr VP)*
Kemp Gallineau *(Chief Sls Officer & Sr VP)*
Carter R. Todd *(Gen Counsel, Sec & Exec VP)*
John A. Imaizumi *(Sr VP & Gen Mgr-Gaylord Texan Resort & Convention Ctr)*
Johann Krieger *(Sr VP & Gen Mgr-Gaylord Palms Resort & Convention Center)*
Stephen G. Buchanan *(Sr VP-Media & Entertainment)*
Gara Pryor *(Sr VP-HR)*
Bennett D. Westbrook *(Sr VP-Dev, Design & Construction)*
Mike Wainwright *(VP-Sls & Mktg-Gaylord Palms Resort)*
Advertising Agencies:
JA Integrated Thinking
104 Continental Pl Ste 300
Brentwood, TN 37027-4645
Tel.: (615) 377-9111
Fax: (615) 377-9197

Sloane & Company LLC
(d/b/a Sloane & Company)
7 Times Sq Tower 17th Fl
New York, NY 10036
Tel.: (212) 486-9500
Fax: (212) 486-9094

TBC Public Relations
900 S Wolfe St
Baltimore, MD 21231
Tel.: (410) 347-7500
Fax: (410) 986-1322

GE CAPITAL REAL ESTATE

(Div. of General Electric Capital Corporation)
901 Main Ave
Norwalk, CT 06902
Tel.: (203) 750-2900
Toll Free: (888) 433-4778
Web Site: www.gerealestate.com
Sales Range: $1-4.9 Billion
Approx. Number Employees: 5,400
Business Description:
Commercial Real Estate Services
S.I.C.: 6798
N.A.I.C.S.: 525930
Media: 2-4-7-9-10-25
Distr.: Natl.
Personnel:
Ronald R. Pressman *(Pres & CEO)*
Stewart Koenigsberg *(CFO)*
Hank Zupnick *(CIO-Real Estate)*
Jayne Day *(Sr VP & Chief Risk Officer)*
Alec Burger *(Pres-Notth America)*
Jonathan Kern *(Pres-Global Investment Mgmt)*
Michael Rowan *(Pres-Global Asset Mgmt)*
Eileen Brumback *(Gen Counsel & Sr VP)*
Kathleen Carey *(Sr VP)*
Bernard Garrigues *(Sr VP-HR-Global)*
Tony Kinnel *(Sr VP-Sourcing)*
Alexandre Sieber *(VP & Gen Mgr-Bus Property Div)*
Grace Chang *(Gen Mgr-Asia-Pacific)*
Thierry Leleu *(Gen Mgr-EMEA)*

GENERAL GROWTH PROPERTIES, INC.

110 N Wacker Dr
Chicago, IL 60606-1511
Tel.: (312) 960-5000
Fax: (312) 960-5475
E-mail: corporateinfo@generalgrowth.com
Web Site: www.generalgrowth.com
Year Founded: 1954
Business Description:
Real Estate Investment Trust
S.I.C.: 6798
N.A.I.C.S.: 525930
Advertising Expenditures: $35,797,000
Media: 7-17
Personnel:
Sandeep Mathrani *(CEO)*
Steven James Douglas *(CFO & Exec VP)*
Edmund Hoyt *(Sr VP & Chief Acctg Officer)*
Andrew J. Perel *(Gen Counsel & Exec VP)*
Michael H. McNaughton *(Exec VP-Asset Mgmt)*
Richard S. Pesin *(Exec VP-Anchors, Dev & Construction)*
Cathie Hollowell *(Sr VP-HR)*
Marvin Levine *(Sr VP-Real Estate Svcs)*
Mark Pfeifer *(Sr VP-Mktg)*
Advertising Agencies:
David Saint Germain LLC
580 County Rd B2 East
Saint Paul, MN 55117
Tel.: (952) 210-6962
Fax: (651) 244-9583

Haworth Marketing & Media Company
TCF Tower 10th Fl 121 S 8th St
Minneapolis, MN 55402
Tel.: (612) 677-8900
Fax: (612) 677-8901

Woodruff Sweitzer, Inc.
501 Fay St Ste 110
Columbia, MO 65201

Key to Media (For complete agency information see *The Advertising Red Books-Agencies* edition):
1. Bus. Publs. 2. Cable T.V. 3. Catalogs & Directories. 4. Co-op Adv. 5. Consumer Mags. 6. D.M. to Bus. Estab.7. D.M. to Consumers 8. Daily Newsp. 9. Exhibits/Trade Shows 10. Foreign 11. Infomercial 12. Internet Adv.13. Multimedia 14. Network Radio 15. Network T.V. 16. Newsp. Distr. Mags. 17. Other 18. Outdoor (Posters, Transit) 19. Point of Purchase20. Premiums, Novelties 21. Product Samples 22. Special Events Mktg. 23. Spot Radio 24. Spot T.V. 25. Weekly Newsp. 26. Yellow Page Adv.

Tel.: (573) 875-7917
Fax: (573) 874-7979
Toll Free: (888) 300-7485

GH III MANAGEMENT LLC
(d/b/a Prudential Gary Green Realtors)
10575 Katy Fwy Ste 100
Houston, TX 77024
Tel.: (713) 465-6644
Fax: (713) 465-9823
Toll Free: (800) 231-0707
Web Site: www.garygreene.com
Sales Range: $1-4.9 Billion
Approx. Number Employees: 1,000
Year Founded: 1975
Business Description:
Real Estate Brokerage Services
S.I.C.: 6531
N.A.I.C.S.: 531210
Media: 3-9-14-15-18-23-24-25
Personnel:
Marilyn Eiland *(Partner)*
Mark Woodroof *(Partner)*
Lynn Breedlove *(Dir-Relocation)*
Tracy Bogiel *(Branch Mgr)*
Sharon Teusink *(Mgr)*
Brands & Products:
PRUDENTIAL GARY GREENE, REALTORS

GILA RIVER GAMING ENTERPRISES, INC.
5040 W Wild Horse Pass Blvd
Chandler, AZ 85246
Mailing Address:
PO Box 6790
Chandler, AZ 85246
Tel.: (520) 796-4452
Web Site: www.wingilariver.com
Business Description:
Hotel & Casino
N.A.I.C.S.: 721120
Media: 13-23-24-29
Personnel:
Kenneth Manuel *(Pres)*
Melody Hudson *(Mgr-PR)*
Advertising Agency:
Touchpoints Marketing, LLC
2550 Belle Chasse Hwy Ste 220
Gretna, LA 70053
Tel.: (504) 361-1804

GLACIER PARK, INC.
(Div. of Viad Corp.)
PO Box 2025
Columbia Falls, MT 59912
Tel.: (406) 892-2525
Fax: (406) 892-1375
E-mail: info@glacierparkinc.com
Web Site: www.glacierparkinc.com
Sales Range: Less than $1 Million
Approx. Number Employees: 50
Year Founded: 1981
Business Description:
Hotel Management Services
S.I.C.: 7011
N.A.I.C.S.: 721110
Media: 4-6-18-22
Personnel:
Alicia Thompson *(Exec VP-Sls & Mktg)*

GLIMCHER REALTY TRUST
180 E Broad St
Columbus, OH 43215
Tel.: (614) 621-9000
Fax: (614) 621-9311
E-mail: grtinfo@glimcher.com
Web Site: www.glimcher.com
Approx. Rev.: $274,772,000
Approx. Number Employees: 652
Year Founded: 1959
Business Description:
Real Estate Investment Trust
S.I.C.: 6798
N.A.I.C.S.: 525930
Advertising Expenditures: $4,577,000
Personnel:
Michael P. Glimcher *(Chm & CEO)*
Marshall A. Loeb *(Pres & COO)*
Mark E. Yale *(CFO & Exec VP)*
George A. Schmidt *(CIO & Exec VP)*
Kim A. Rieck *(Gen Counsel, Sec & Sr VP)*
Thomas J. Drought, Jr. *(Exec VP & Dir-Leasing)*
Melissa A. Indest *(Sr VP-Fin & Acctg)*
Armand Mastropietro *(Sr VP-Property Mgmt)*
Grace E. Schmitt *(VP-HR)*

GLORIA NILSON GMAC REAL ESTATE
(Sub. of Residential Capital, LLC)
350 Route 35
Middletown, NJ 07748
Mailing Address:
PO Box 214
Middletown, NJ 07748
Tel.: (732) 450-2300
Fax: (732) 450-2308
E-mail: info@glorianilson.com
Web Site: www.glorianilson.com
Approx. Number Employees: 25
Year Founded: 2000
Business Description:
Real Estate Brokers & Agents
S.I.C.: 6531
N.A.I.C.S.: 531210
Media: 7-8
Personnel:
Pat Bell *(Pres & CEO)*
Gary Foulks *(Reg VP)*
Sharon DiMonaco *(Mgr-Mktg)*
Cathy Eakle *(Mgr-Technical Trng Dev)*

GOLD STRIKE CASINO RESORT
(Sub. of MGM Resorts International)
1010 Casino Ctr Dr
Robinsonville, MS 38664
Mailing Address:
PO Box 459
Robinsonville, MS 38664
Tel.: (662) 357-1111
Fax: (662) 357-1306
Toll Free: (888) 24K-PLAY
Web Site:
www.goldstrikemississippi.com
Sales Range: $350-399.9 Million
Approx. Number Employees: 2,000
Business Description:
Hotel & Casino
S.I.C.: 7999
N.A.I.C.S.: 713290
Media: 8-13-20
Personnel:
George Corchis *(Pres)*
Sandra Stokes *(Dir-Hotel Ops)*

GREAT WOLF RESORTS, INC.
525 Junction Rd Ste 6000 S
Madison, WI 53717
Tel.: (608) 662-4700
Fax: (608) 662-4281
E-mail: info@greatwolfresorts.com
Web Site: corp.greatwolf.com
Approx. Rev.: $284,206,000
Approx. Number Employees: 2,800
Business Description:
Resort Operator
S.I.C.: 7011; 7996; 7999
N.A.I.C.S.: 721110; 713110; 713990
Advertising Expenditures: $17,982,000
Personnel:
Joseph V. Vittoria *(Chm)*
Kimberly K. Schaefer *(CEO)*
James A. Calder *(CFO)*
Rajiv Castellino *(CIO)*
Luke Schneider *(CEO-Creative Kingdoms LLC)*
Timothy D. Black *(Exec VP-Ops)*
Nikki Donofrio *(Sr VP-Strategic Brand Mktg)*
Julie Stokes *(Sr VP-Sls)*
Derrek Kinzel *(Reg VP-Ops)*
Scott Maupin *(Reg VP-Ops)*
Valerie McGee *(VP-Mdsg)*
Rodney S. Jones *(Sr Dir-Engrg & Construction)*
Steve Shattuck *(Dir-Comm)*
Advertising Agencies:
Doner
25900 Northwestern Hwy
Southfield, MI 48075
Tel.: (248) 354-9700
Fax: (248) 827-8440

Hill Holliday
53 State St
Boston, MA 02109
Tel.: (617) 366-4000
Account Management
Agency of Record
Brand Management
Creative Development
Data Analytics
Great Wolf Lodge
Marketing Communications
Media Planning & Purchasing

GREEKTOWN CASINO HOTEL
555 E Lafayette Blvd
Detroit, MI 48226
Tel.: (313) 223-2655
Fax: (313) 961-5805
Web Site:
www.greektowncasinohotel.com
Business Description:
Casino Hotel
S.I.C.: 7011
N.A.I.C.S.: 721120
Personnel:
Michael Puggi *(CEO)*
Advertising Agencies:
Duffey Petrosky
39303 Country Club Dr Ste A18
Farmington Hills, MI 48331-3482
Tel.: (248) 489-8300
Fax: (248) 994-1600
Agency of Record

Preferred Public Relations & Marketing
2630 S Jones Blvd
Las Vegas, NV 89146
Tel.: (702) 254-5704
Fax: (702) 242-1205

GREEN BUILDERS, INC.
8121 Bee Cave Rd
Austin, TX 78746
Tel.: (512) 732-0932
Fax: (512) 732-0959
E-mail: cwilson@greenbuildersinc.com
Web Site: www.greenbuildersinc.com
Approx. Rev.: $14,516,436
Approx. Number Employees: 13
Year Founded: 2005
Business Description:
Land Acquirer & Residential Communities Developer
S.I.C.: 6531; 1522
N.A.I.C.S.: 531390; 236116
Advertising Expenditures: $167,000
Media: 4-8-13-17-18
Personnel:
Clark N. Wilson *(Pres & CEO)*
Clay Thornton *(Dir-Construction Ops)*
Brands & Products:
GREEN BUILDERS

THE GREENBRIER
(Sub. of CSX Corporation)
300 W Main St
White Sulphur Springs, WV 24986-2414
Tel.: (304) 536-1110
Fax: (304) 536-7893
Toll Free: (800) 624-6070
E-mail: the_greenbrier@greenbrier.com
Web Site: www.greenbrier.com
E-Mail For Key Personnel:
Sales Director: ann_walker@greenbrier.com
Public Relations: lynn_swann@greenbrier.com
Sales Range: $150-199.9 Million
Approx. Number Employees: 1,600
Year Founded: 1778
Business Description:
Hotel Operator
S.I.C.: 7011; 7991
N.A.I.C.S.: 721110; 713940
Media: 2-4-6-7-8-9-10-13-20-23-24-25
Distr.: Direct to Consumer; Natl.
Budget Set: Sept.
Personnel:
Todd Gillespie *(VP-Sls)*
Patricia Jenkins *(Dir-Svc Quality)*
Lynn Swann *(Dir-PR)*

THE GRIFFIN GROUP, INC.
11150 Olympic Blvd Ste 1080
Los Angeles, CA 90064
Tel.: (310) 385-2700
Fax: (424) 208-8852
E-mail: customer_feedback@griffgroup.com
Approx. Number Employees: 20
Year Founded: 1958
Business Description:
Casino Hotel & Resort Owner
S.I.C.: 7011
N.A.I.C.S.: 721120
Media: 3-4-5-8-9-18-19-25-26
Distr.: Direct to Consumer; Reg.
Budget Set: Sept.-Oct.
Personnel:
Rick Sullivan *(VP-Fin-Treas)*
Advertising Agency:
The Griffin Group West
130 el Camino Dr
Beverly Hills, CA 90212-2705
Tel.: (310) 385-2700
Fax: (310) 858-7956

GROSSE POINTE DEVELOPMENT COMPANY, INC.
15065 McGregor Blvd
Fort Myers, FL 33908
Tel.: (239) 437-5007
Fax: (239) 437-5010
E-mail: rkeltner@gpdevelopment.com
Web Site: www.gpdevelopment.com
Approx. Number Employees: 6
Year Founded: 1995
Business Description:
Real Estate Developer
S.I.C.: 6552; 6531
N.A.I.C.S.: 237210; 531210
Media: 4-6
Personnel:
Robert D. Hensley *(CEO)*
Glenn P. Oorlog *(CFO)*
Jim Crumbie *(Exec VP)*

GRUBB & ELLIS COMPANY
1551 N Tustin Ave Ste 300
Santa Ana, CA 92705
Tel.: (714) 667-8252
Fax: (714) 667-6860
Toll Free: (800) 877-9066
E-mail: corporatecommunications@grubb-ellis.com
Web Site: www.grubb-ellis.com
Approx. Rev.: $575,457,000
Approx. Number Employees: 4,500
Year Founded: 1957
Business Description:
Holding Company; Real Estate Brokerage, Property Management & Consulting Services
S.I.C.: 6719; 6512; 6519; 6531
N.A.I.C.S.: 551112; 531120; 531190; 531210; 531390
Media: 2-7-9-10-20-22-25-26
Distr.: Natl.
Personnel:
C. Michael Kojaian *(Chm)*
Thomas P. D'Arcy *(Pres & CEO)*
Michael Allen *(Exec Mng Dir)*
Michael J. Rispoli *(CFO & Exec VP)*
Jack Van Berkel *(COO, Pres-Real Estate Svcs & Exec VP)*
Jack Berkel *(COO & Pres-Real Estate)*
Glendon Esnard *(Pres-Capital Markets)*
Mathieu B. Streiff *(Gen Counsel, Sec & Exec VP)*
Matthew A. Engel *(Exec VP-Fin)*
Jeffrey T. Hanson *(Exec VP)*
Jay P. Leupp *(Exec VP)*
David Susoreny *(Exec VP)*
Andrew J. Banister *(Sr VP-Investment Svcs Grp)*
Daniel Dobric *(Sr VP-Office Grp)*
Janice McDill *(Sr VP-Mktg & Comm)*
Scott Smith *(Sr VP-Facilities Mgmt)*
Robin Newton *(VP-Retail Grp)*
Donald Schmidt *(Assoc Dir)*
Brands & Products:
FROM INSIGHT TO RESULTS
GRUBB & ELLIS

GUNSTOCK RECREATION AREA
719 Cherry Valley Rd
Gilford, NH 03249
Tel.: (603) 293-4341
Fax: (603) 293-4318
Toll Free: (800) GUNSTOCK
E-mail: gunstock@gunstock.com
Web Site: www.gunstock.com
E-Mail For Key Personnel:
Marketing Director: marketing@gunstock.com
Sales Range: $10-24.9 Million
Approx. Number Employees: 35
Year Founded: 1936
Business Description:
Ski Area & Resort
S.I.C.: 7011
N.A.I.C.S.: 721110
Advertising Expenditures: $600,000
Media: 1-2-3-4-5-7-8-9-10-14-18-19-20-22-23-24-25-26
Distr.: Reg.
Budget Set: May
Personnel:
Gregg Goddard *(Gen Mgr)*
Bill Quigley *(Dir-Mktg & Sls)*
Brands & Products:
GUNSTOCK
MOUNTAIN MAGIC

HANNAH-BARTOLETTA CONSTRUCTION
(d/b/a Hannah-Bartoletta Homes)
19001 Sunlake Blvd
Lutz, FL 33558
Tel.: (813) 909-1245
Tel.: (813) 909-1200
Fax: (813) 909-1205
Web Site: www.hbh.info
Approx. Sls.: $24,093,370
Approx. Number Employees: 20
Business Description:
Single-Family Houses Construction Services
S.I.C.: 1531; 1521
N.A.I.C.S.: 236118; 236115
Media: 6

HARD ROCK CAFE INTERNATIONAL LAS VEGAS
(Sub. of Hard Rock Cafe Foundation, Inc.)
4455 Paradise Rd
Las Vegas, NV 89169-6574
Tel.: (702) 693-5000
Fax: (702) 693-5021
Toll Free: (800) HRDROCK
E-mail: info@hrhvegas.com
Web Site: www.hardrock.com
Sales Range: $1-9.9 Million
Approx. Number Employees: 200
Year Founded: 1990
Business Description:
Full Service Theme Restaurant
S.I.C.: 5812; 5813
N.A.I.C.S.: 722110; 722211; 722410
Personnel:
Patrick Manion *(Chief HR Officer & VP)*
Darci Byers *(Dir-Ops)*
Jessica Harman *(Mgr-Sls & Mktg)*
Advertising Agency:
Dan Klores Communications
(d/b/a dkc)
386 Park Ave S 10th Fl
New York, NY 10016
Tel.: (212) 685-4300
Fax: (212) 685-9024
— Marissa Mastellone *(Acct Exec)*

HARRAHS ENTERTAINMENT, INC.
(Name Changed to Caesars Entertainment Corporation)

HARRY NORMAN REALTORS
(Sub. of HomeServices of America, Inc.)
532 E Paces Ferry Rd Ste 300
Atlanta, GA 30305
Tel.: (404) 504-7300
Toll Free: (800) 552-8608
E-mail: CorpOffice@harrynorman.com
Web Site: www.harrynorman.com/
Sales Range: $1-9.9 Million
Approx. Number Employees: 35
Business Description:
Real Estate Services
S.I.C.: 6531
N.A.I.C.S.: 531210
Media: 2-4-8-9-13-25
Personnel:
Dan Parmer *(Pres & CEO)*
Martha Hayhurst *(Pres)*
Ron Minick *(CFO & Sr VP)*
Scott Bennett *(VP-IT)*
Marianna Barton *(Dir-Mktg & Comm)*
Chris Burell *(Dir-Career Svcs)*
Lisa Martin *(Dir-HR)*

HELMSLEY ENTERPRISES, INC.
230 Pk Ave
New York, NY 10169
Tel.: (212) 679-3600
Fax: (212) 953-2810
E-mail: frontdesk@helmsleyhotels.com
Web Site: www.helmsleyhotels.com
Approx. Number Employees: 2,800
Business Description:
Owner & Operator of Lodging, Restaurants, Food Service, Real Estate Development & Management
S.I.C.: 6512; 6513
N.A.I.C.S.: 531120; 531110
Advertising Expenditures: $5,000,000
Media: 2-4-6-7-8-9-10-20-23-24-25
Distr.: Natl.
Budget Set: Oct.
Personnel:
Abe Wolf *(CFO)*
George Barameda *(Dir-Mktg)*

HERSHA HOSPITALITY TRUST
44 Hersha Dr
Harrisburg, PA 17102
Tel.: (717) 236-4400
Fax: (717) 774-7383
Web Site: www.hersha.com
E-Mail For Key Personnel:
President: hasu@hersha.com
Public Relations: ashish@hersha.com
Approx. Rev.: $282,775,000
Approx. Number Employees: 28
Year Founded: 1998
Business Description:
Hotel Real Estate Investment Trust
S.I.C.: 6798; 7011
N.A.I.C.S.: 525930; 721110
Advertising Expenditures: $143,000
Media: 17
Personnel:
Hasu P. Shah *(Chm)*
Neil H. Shah *(Pres & COO)*
Jay H. Shah *(CEO)*
Ashish R. Parikh *(CFO)*
Michael R. Gillespie *(Chief Acctg Officer)*

Advertising Agency:
Mason & Kichar Recruitment Advertising
260 Amity Rd
Woodbridge, CT 06525
Tel.: (203) 392-0252
Fax: (203) 392-0255

HERSHEY ENTERTAINMENT & RESORTS COMPANY
27 W Chocolate Ave
Hershey, PA 17033-0860
Tel.: (717) 534-3131
Fax: (717) 534-3324
Toll Free: (800) 437-7439
E-mail: info@hersheypa.com
Web Site: www.hersheypa.com
Approx. Number Employees: 2,000
Year Founded: 1927
Business Description:
Theme Parks, Hotels & Recreational Facilities
S.I.C.: 7996; 7011
N.A.I.C.S.: 713110; 721110
Advertising Expenditures: $4,000,000
Media: 3-5-6-7-8-9-10-13-18-20-22-23-24-25
Distr.: Natl.
Budget Set: Oct.
Personnel:
William F. Simpson, Jr. *(Pres & COO)*
David P. Lavery *(CFO, Treas & Sec)*
Kimberly K. Schaller *(CMO & Exec VP)*
Nathan D. Douty *(VP-HR)*
William Liedholm *(Gen Mgr-Hershey Lodge)*
Advertising Agencies:
MayoSeitz Media
532 E. Township Line Rd
Blue Bell, PA 19422
Tel.: (215) 641-8700
Fax: (215) 641-8712

Nasuti + Hinkle Creative Thinking
7768 Woodmont Ave Ste 202
Bethesda, MD 20814
Tel.: (301) 222-0010

HILTON INTERNATIONAL CO.
(Sub. of Hilton Worldwide, Inc.)
5201 Blue Lagoon Dr
Miami, FL 33126
Tel.: (305) 444-3444
Fax: (305) 774-3895
Sales Range: Less than $1 Million
Approx. Number Employees: 35
Year Founded: 1967
Business Description:
International Hotel Management
S.I.C.: 7011
N.A.I.C.S.: 721110
Media: 1-2-4-5-6-7-8-9-11-25
Distr.: Intl.; Natl.
Personnel:
Ted Ratcliff *(Sr VP-Ops-East)*
Magdy Metwally *(Gen Mgr-Hilton Sharm Dreams Resort-Egypt)*

HILTON WORLDWIDE, INC.
(Holding of The Blackstone Group L.P.)
7930 Jones Branch Dr Ste 1100
McLean, VA 22102
Tel.: (703) 883-1000
E-mail: kathy_shepard@hilton.com
Web Site: www.hiltonworldwide.com
Approx. Rev.: $8,090,000,000
Approx. Number Employees: 135,000
Year Founded: 1917

Key to Media (For complete agency information see *The Advertising Red Books-Agencies* edition):
1. Bus. Publs. 2. Cable T.V. 3. Catalogs & Directories. 4. Co-op Adv. 5. Consumer Mags. 6. D.M. to Bus. Estab.7. D.M. to Consumers
8. Daily Newsp. 9. Exhibits/Trade Shows 10. Foreign 11. Infomercial 12. Internet Adv.13. Multimedia 14. Network Radio
15. Network T.V. 16. Newsp. Distr. Mags. 17. Other 18. Outdoor (Posters, Transit) 19. Point of Purchase20. Premiums, Novelties
21. Product Samples 22. Special Events Mktg. 23. Spot Radio 24. Spot T.V. 25. Weekly Newsp. 26. Yellow Page Adv.

Business Description:
Holding Company; Hotels & Resorts Operator
S.I.C.: 6719; 7011
N.A.I.C.S.: 551112; 721110
Media: 2-4-5-6-8-9-10-11-13-15-18-19-20-21-23-24-26-30
Distr.: Natl.
Budget Set: June -Aug.
Personnel:
Christopher J. Nassetta *(Pres & CEO)*
Thomas C. Kennedy *(CFO & Exec VP)*
Robert J Webb *(CIO)*
Matthew W. Schuyler *(Chief HR Officer & Exec VP)*
Paul J. Brown *(Pres-Global Brands & Comml Svcs)*
Ian R. Carter *(Pres-Global Ops & Dev)*
Kristin A. Campbell *(Gen Counsel & Exec VP)*
Kevin J. Jacobs *(Treas & Sr VP-Corp Strategy)*
James T. Harvey *(Exec VP-Global Distr Svcs)*
Dottie Brienza *(Sr VP-Global Talent Mgmt)*
Jeff Diskin *(Sr VP-Global Customer Mktg)*
Ellen Gonda *(Sr VP-Global Corp Comm)*
William F. Kornegay, Jr. *(Sr VP-Hilton Supply Mgmt)*
Barry Lewin *(Sr VP-Hotel Ops)*
Robert Allegrini *(VP-Corp Comm)*
Andrew Flack *(VP-Strategic Sourcing Trasition)*
Aaron C. Radelet *(VP-Global Comm & PR)*
Carla Raynor *(VP-Sls & MktguHomewood Suites-Hilton & Home2 Suites)*
John T.A. Vanderslice *(Global Head-Luxury & Lifestyle Brands)*
Celina Low *(Sr Dir-Corp Comm-Asia Pacific)*
Cynthia Rankin *(Reg Dir-Corp Comm)*
Silvie Alric *(Dir-Reg Mktg)*
Emma Corcoran *(Dir-Corp Comm-Middle East & Africa)*
Pierre Dorrell *(Dir-Reg Mktg)*
Nicola Mcshane *(Dir-Comm)*
Jason Morros *(Dir-Media Strategy & Plng)*
Dasha Ross *(Dir-Global Corp Comm)*
Terry Tilea *(Dir-Mktg-Home2 Suites)*
Ellen Burke Van Slyke *(Dir-Restaurant Dev-Americas Reg)*
Tom Muldoon *(Mgr-Acctg)*
Brands & Products:
CONRAD
DOUBLETREE
DOUBLETREE GUEST SUITES
EMBASSY SUITES
EVERYTHING. RIGHT WHERE YOU NEED IT.
GARDEN SLEEP SYSTEM
HAMPTON
HAMPTON INN
HAMPTON INNS & SUITES
HILTON
HILTON GARDEN INN
HILTON GRAND VACATION CLUB
HILTON GRAND VACATIONS COMPANY
HILTON HAWAIIAN VILLAGE BEACH RESORT & SPA
HILTON HONORS
HILTON HOTELS
HOME2SUITES
HOMEWOOD SUITES BY HILTON
PAVILION PANTRY
TAKE ME TO THE HILTON
WALDORF ASTORIA
WE LOVE HAVING YOU HERE
YOU BRING THE FAMILY AND WE'LL PACK THE FUN
YOUR PERFECT SECOND HOME
Advertising Agencies:
Absolute Media Solutions
208 Lee Ln
Horwich, Lancashire BL6 7JF, United Kingdom
Tel.: (44) 1204 669 566
Fax: (44) 1204 667 246

BBDO Atlanta
3500 Lenox Rd NE Ste 1900
Atlanta, GA 30326-4232
Tel.: (404) 231-1700
Fax: (404) 841-1893
(Embassy Suites)

Cramer-Krasselt
225 N Michigan Ave
Chicago, IL 60601-7601
Tel.: (312) 616-9600
Fax: (312) 616-3839
Agency of Record

DGWB
217 N Main St Ste 200
Santa Ana, CA 92701
Tel.: (714) 881-2300
Fax: (714) 881-2442
Garden Inn

Geile Leon Marketing Communications
130 S Bemiston Ste 800
Saint Louis, MO 63105
Tel.: (314) 727-5850
Fax: (314) 727-5819

MMG Worldwide
4601 Madison Ave
Kansas City, MO 64112
Tel.: (816) 472-5988
Fax: (816) 471-5395

Murphy O'Brien, Inc.
(d/b/a Murphy O'Brien Public Relations)
1630 Stewart St Ste 140
Santa Monica, CA 90404
Tel.: (310) 453-2539
Fax: (310) 264-0083
Public Relations Agency of Record

OMD Los Angeles
5353 Grosvenor Blvd
Los Angeles, CA 90066
Tel.: (310) 301-3600
Fax: (646) 278-8000
Homewood Suites
Media Buying

OMD-USA
195 Broadway
New York, NY 10007
Tel.: (212) 590-7100
(Embassy Suites, Media Planning & Buying)

Organic, Inc.
2600 S Telegraph Rd Ste 100
Bloomfield Hills, MI 48302
Tel.: (248) 454-4000
Fax: (248) 454-3370
Digital
Homewood Suites

Publicis New York
4 Herald Sq 950 6th Ave
New York, NY 10001
Tel.: (212) 279-5550
Fax: (212) 279-5560
Creative
Homewood Suites

rbb Public Relations
355 Alhambra Cir Ste 800
Miami, FL 33134
Tel.: (305) 448-7450
Fax: (305) 448-5027
Homewood Suites
Public Relations

Red Moon Marketing
4100 Coca-Cola Plz Ste 215
Charlotte, NC 28211
Tel.: (704) 366-1147
Fax: (704) 366-2283

Swafford & Company Advertising
10390 Santa Monica Blvd Ste 230
Los Angeles, CA 90025-5093
Tel.: (310) 553-0611
Fax: (310) 553-9639
Garden Inn

Zehnder Communications, Inc.
650 Poydras St Ste 2450
New Orleans, LA 70130
Tel.: (504) 558-7778
Fax: (504) 558-7779
Toll Free: (877) 558-7778

HOBE SOUND GOLF CLUB, INC.
11671 SE Plandome Dr
Hobe Sound, FL 33455
Tel.: (772) 546-4600
Web Site:
www.hobesoundgolfclub.com
Sales Range: $1-9.9 Million
Approx. Number Employees: 60
Business Description:
Golf Club Operations
S.I.C.: 7997
N.A.I.C.S.: 713910
Media: 6-22
Personnel:
Richard C. Maloof *(Pres)*

HOME PROPERTIES INC.
850 Clinton Sq
Rochester, NY 14604-1730
Tel.: (585) 546-4900
Fax: (585) 546-5433
E-mail: yvonnew@homeproperties.com
Web Site: www.homeproperties.com
Approx. Rev.: $516,579,000
Approx. Number Employees: 1,100
Year Founded: 1967
Business Description:
Real Estate Investment Trust; Owner, Developer & Manager of Apartment Communities
S.I.C.: 6798; 6513
N.A.I.C.S.: 525930; 531110
Advertising Expenditures: $4,606,000
Media: 9-13-25
Personnel:
Nelson B. Leenhouts *(Co-Chm)*
Norman P. Leenhouts *(Co-Chm)*
Edward J. Pettinella *(Pres & CEO)*
David P. Gardner *(CFO & Exec VP)*
Johanna A. Falk *(CIO, Chief Admin Officer & Sr VP)*
John E. Smith *(Chief Investment Officer & Sr VP)*
Robert J. Luken *(Chief Acctg Officer, Treas & Sr VP)*
Ann M. McCormick *(Gen Counsel, Sec & Exec VP)*
Lisa M. Critchley *(Sr VP-HR)*
Scott A. Doyle *(Sr VP-Strategic Property Mgmt)*
Rosemary Cook-Manely *(Dir-Mktg)*
Brands & Products:
HOME PROPERTIES
WHERE COURTESY & COMFORT COUNT

HOME REAL ESTATE INC.
(Sub. of HomeServices of America, Inc.)
3355 Orwell St Ste 102
Lincoln, NE 68516
Tel.: (402) 436-3310
E-mail: webmaster@homerealestate.com
Web Site: www.homerealestate.com
Sales Range: $1-9.9 Million
Approx. Number Employees: 35
Business Description:
Real Estate Services
S.I.C.: 6531
N.A.I.C.S.: 531210
Media: 2-4-8-9-13-25

HOMESERVICES OF AMERICA, INC.
(Holding of Berkshire Hathaway Inc.)
Ste 2700 333 S 7th St
Minneapolis, MN 55402-2438
Tel.: (952) 928-5900
Fax: (952) 928-5572
Toll Free: (888) 485-0018
Web Site: www.homeservices.com
Sales Range: $650-699.9 Million
Approx. Number Employees: 3,228
Year Founded: 1998
Business Description:
Real Estate Brokerage Services
S.I.C.: 6531
N.A.I.C.S.: 531210
Media: 13
Personnel:
Ronald J. Peltier *(Chm & CEO)*
Robert R. Moline *(Pres & COO)*
R. Michael Knapp *(Pres & CEO-Iowa Realty)*
Advertising Agency:
Peterson Milla Hooks
1315 Harmon Pl
Minneapolis, MN 55403-1926
Tel.: (612) 349-9116
Fax: (612) 349-9141

THE HOMESTEAD
(Holding of KSL Resorts)
1766 Homestead Dr
Hot Springs, VA 24445
Mailing Address:
PO Box 2000
Hot Springs, VA 24445-2000
Tel.: (540) 839-1766
Fax: (540) 839-7670

Key to Media (For complete agency information see *The Advertising Red Books-Agencies* edition):
1. Bus. Publs. 2. Cable T.V. 3. Catalogs & Directories. 4. Co-op Adv. 5. Consumer Mags. 6. D.M. to Bus. Estab.7. D.M. to Consumers
8. Daily Newsp. 9. Exhibits/Trade Shows 10. Foreign 11. Infomercial 12. Internet Adv.13. Multimedia 14. Network Radio
15. Network T.V. 16. Newsp. Distr. Mags. 17. Other 18. Outdoor (Posters, Transit) 19. Point of Purchase20. Premiums, Novelties
21. Product Samples 22. Special Events Mktg. 23. Spot Radio 24. Spot T.V. 25. Weekly Newsp. 26. Yellow Page Adv.

The Homestead — (Continued)

Toll Free: (800) 838-1766
Web Site: www.thehomestead.com
Sales Range: $50-74.9 Million
Approx. Number Employees: 1,000
Year Founded: 1766
Business Description:
Hotel & Resort Operator
S.I.C.: 7011; 5812; 7997
N.A.I.C.S.: 721110; 713910; 722110
Media: 2-4-6-7-8-9-13-23-26
Distr.: Natl.
Budget Set: Mar.
Personnel:
Peter Faraone *(VP & Gen Mgr)*
Phil Norman *(Dir-HR)*
Brands & Products:
THE HOMESTEAD

HOMEVESTORS OF AMERICA, INC.

6500 Greenville Ave Ste 400
Dallas, TX 75206
Tel.: (972) 761-0046
Fax: (972) 761-9022
Web Site: www.homevestors.com
Sales Range: $10-24.9 Million
Approx. Number Employees: 20
Year Founded: 1989
Business Description:
Real Estate Services
S.I.C.: 6289
N.A.I.C.S.: 523999
Advertising Expenditures:
$18,000,000
Media: 8-9-15-18-23-24-25-26
Personnel:
C. Burley *(Vice Chm)*
Ken Channell *(Co-Pres)*
June Marie London *(Dir-Media)*
Scott Bowling *(Mgr-Bus Dev)*
Brands & Products:
HOMEVESTORS
UG BUYS UGLY HOUSES
UGLY'S OK
Advertising Agencies:
BizCom Associates
16301 Quorum Dr #150 A
Addison, TX 75001
Tel.: (972) 490-0903
Fax: (972) 692-5451
Public Relations
— Scott White *(Pres & Partner)*

Phids, Inc.
(D/B/A Acquirgy)
877 Executive Ctr Dr W Ste 300
Saint Petersburg, FL 33702-2474
Tel.: (727) 576-6630
Fax: (727) 576-4864

HOMEWOOD CORPORATION

2700 E Dublin Granville Rd Ste 300A
Columbus, OH 43231-4078
Tel.: (614) 898-7200
Fax: (614) 898-7708
E-mail: customerservice@homewood-homes.com
Web Site: www.homewood-homes.com
Approx. Rev.: $80,000,000
Approx. Number Employees: 165
Year Founded: 1963
Business Description:
Builder of Single Family Houses, Multi-Family Dwellings & Apartment Buildings
S.I.C.: 1531
N.A.I.C.S.: 236117
Media: 2-8-9-13-25
Personnel:
George A. Skestos *(Pres)*
John H. Bain *(CEO)*

HONOURS GOLF COMPANY, LLC

1960 Stonegate Dr
Birmingham, AL 35242
Tel.: (205) 298-0001
Fax: (205) 970-0304
Toll Free: (866) HONOURS
E-mail: info@honoursgolf.com
Web Site: www.honoursgolf.com
Sales Range: $1-9.9 Million
Approx. Number Employees: 60
Business Description:
Golf Course Owner & Operator
S.I.C.: 7997
N.A.I.C.S.: 713910
Media: 6-22
Personnel:
Robert E. Julian *(Chm)*
Robert L. Schultz *(Pres)*
Robert B. Barrett *(CEO)*
Gary D. Spivey *(CFO & VP)*
Kelly Olshove *(Dir-Mktg Svcs)*
Phil Oakes *(Dir-HR)*

HOST HOTELS & RESORTS, INC.

6903 Rockledge Dr Ste 1500
Bethesda, MD 20817
Tel.: (240) 744-1000
Fax: (240) 744-5125
Toll Free: (800) 774-4678
E-mail: ir@hosthotels.com
Web Site: www.hosthotels.com
Approx. Rev.: $4,437,000,000
Approx. Number Employees: 203
Year Founded: 1993
Business Description:
Hotels & Resorts Owner & Operator
S.I.C.: 6798; 6531; 7011
N.A.I.C.S.: 525930; 531390; 721110
Media: 4-7-8
Personnel:
Richard E. Marriott *(Chm)*
W. Edward Walter *(Pres & CEO)*
Larry K. Harvey *(CFO & Exec VP)*
James F. Risoleo *(Chief Investment Officer & Exec VP)*
Elizabeth A. Abdoo *(Gen Counsel, Sec & Exec VP)*
Minaz Abji *(Exec VP-Asset Mgmt)*
Gregory J. Larson *(Exec VP-Corp Strategy & Fund Mgmt)*
Brian G. Macnamara *(Sr VP & Controller)*
Jeffrey S. Clark *(Sr VP-Tax)*
Rogerio Miranda de Souza *(Sr VP-Acq-Rio de Janeiro)*
Gerard E. Haberman *(Sr VP-Dev, Design & Construction)*
Pamela K. Wagoner *(Sr VP)*

HOTEL MAX

620 Stewart St
Seattle, WA 98101
Tel.: (206) 728-6299
Fax: (206) 443-5754
Toll Free: (866) 833-6299
E-mail: frontdesk@hotelmaxseattle.com
Web Site: www.hotelmaxseattle.com
Sales Range: $50-74.9 Million
Approx. Number Employees: 70
Year Founded: 2005
Business Description:
Hotel
S.I.C.: 7011
N.A.I.C.S.: 721110
Media: 13-17
Personnel:
Jim Chittenden *(Gen Mgr)*
Advertising Agency:
Anvil Media, Inc.
310 NE Failing St.
Portland, OR 97212
Tel.: (503) 595-6050
Fax: (503) 223-1008

HOTEL ROUGE

(Sub. of LaSalle Hotel Properties)
1315 16th St NW
Washington, DC 20036-2205
Tel.: (202) 232-8000
Fax: (202) 667-9827
E-mail: info@rougehotel.com
Web Site: www.rougehotel.com
Sales Range: $1-9.9 Million
Approx. Number Employees: 100
Business Description:
Hotels
S.I.C.: 7011
N.A.I.C.S.: 721110
Media: 7-8-9-13-25
Distr.: Direct to Consumer; Reg.
Personnel:
Mark Jennings *(Gen Mgr)*
Advertising Agency:
Lipman
408 W 14th St 3rd Fl
New York, NY 10014
Tel.: (212) 684-1100
Fax: (212) 929-7330
(Hotels)

HOULIHAN/LAWRENCE INC.

4 Valley Rd
Bronxville, NY 10708
Tel.: (914) 337-7700
Fax: (914) 337-0447
E-mail: corporate@houlihanlawrence.com
Web Site: www.houlihanlawrence.com
Approx. Sls.: $2,500,000,000
Approx. Number Employees: 900
Year Founded: 1888
Business Description:
Real Estate Brokers & Agents
S.I.C.: 6531
N.A.I.C.S.: 531210
Media: 3-4-6-8-13-18-22-26
Personnel:
Nancy Seaman *(Chm)*
Stephen R. Meyers *(CEO)*
Christopher Meyers *(COO)*
Anthony Cutugno *(Sr VP, Broker-Licensed Assoc & Dir-Luxury Country Properties)*
Debra Dalton *(Sr VP)*
Bobbie Egan *(Dir-Mktg)*
Advertising Agency:
Firelight Group
PO Box 2407
Madison, WI 53701
Tel.: (608) 441-3473
Fax: (914) 397-0815

HOVNANIAN ENTERPRISES, INC.

110 W Front St
Red Bank, NJ 07701
Mailing Address:
PO Box 500
Red Bank, NJ 07701-0500
Tel.: (732) 747-7800
Fax: (732) 747-7159
E-mail: ir@khov.com
Web Site: www.khov.com
Approx. Rev.: $1,371,842,000
Approx. Number Employees: 1,629
Year Founded: 1959
Business Description:
Holding Company; New Housing Operative Builder & Marketer
S.I.C.: 6719; 1531
N.A.I.C.S.: 551112; 236117
Advertising Expenditures:
$18,200,000
Media: 1-2-4-5-6-7-8-9-10-11-13-14-16-18-19-20-22-23-25-26
Distr.: Reg.
Personnel:
Ara K. Hovnanian *(Chm, Pres & CEO)*
J. Larry Sorsby *(CFO & Exec VP)*
Thomas J. Pellerito *(COO)*
Nicholas R. Colisto *(CIO)*
Brad G. O'Connor *(Chief Acctg Officer, VP & Controller)*
Peter S. Reinhart *(Gen Counsel & Sr VP)*
David G. Valiaveedan *(Treas & VP-Fin)*
Robyn T. Mingle *(Sr VP-HR)*
Laura C. Dempsey *(VP-HR)*
Dawn Boggio Korbelak *(Dir-Architect Design)*
Jeffrey T. O'Keefe *(Dir-IR)*
Brands & Products:
FORECAST HOMES
IF YOU'RE NOT 55 YEARS OLD...YOU'LL WISH YOU WERE
K. HOVNANIAN
K. HOVNANIAN HOMES
K. HOVNANIAN'S FOUR SEASONS
MATZEL & MUMFORD
Advertising Agency:
PACE Advertising
(Sub. of WPP Group PLC)
1065 Ave of the Americas
New York, NY 10018
Tel.: (212) 818-0111
Fax: (212) 818-0120
(New Homes)
— Holly Kingsley *(Acct Exec)*

HOWARD JOHNSON INTERNATIONAL, INC.

(Sub. of Wyndham Hotel Group, LLC)
22 Sylvan Way
Parsippany, NJ 07054
Tel.: (973) 753-6000
Toll Free: (800) 544-9881
Web Site: www.howardjohnson.com
Sales Range: $250-299.9 Million
Business Description:
Hotel Franchisor
S.I.C.: 6794
N.A.I.C.S.: 533110
Personnel:
Rui Barros *(Sr VP-Brand)*
Brands & Products:
GO ANYWHERE. STAY HERE.
HOWARD JOHNSON
HOWARD JOHNSON HOME OFFICE

Key to Media (For complete agency information see *The Advertising Red Books-Agencies* edition):
1. Bus. Publs. 2. Cable T.V. 3. Catalogs & Directories. 4. Co-op Adv. 5. Consumer Mags. 6. D.M. to Bus. Estab.7. D.M. to Consumers 8. Daily Newsp. 9. Exhibits/Trade Shows 10. Foreign 11. Infomercial 12. Internet Adv.13. Multimedia 14. Network Radio 15. Network T.V. 16. Newsp. Distr. Mags. 17. Other 18. Outdoor (Posters, Transit) 19. Point of Purchase20. Premiums, Novelties 21. Product Samples 22. Special Events Mktg. 23. Spot Radio 24. Spot T.V. 25. Weekly Newsp. 26. Yellow Page Adv.

Advertising Agencies:
Decker Creative Marketing
99 Citizens Dr
Glastonbury, CT 06033-1262
Tel.: (860) 659-1311
Fax: (860) 659-3062
Toll Free: (800) 777-3677

OnTap
99 Citizens Dr
Glastonbury, CT 06033-1262
Tel.: (860) 659-1311
Fax: (860) 659-3062

HYATT HOTELS CORPORATION

71 S Wacker Dr
Chicago, IL 60606-3414
Tel.: (312) 750-1234
Fax: (312) 750-8550
E-mail: concierge@hyatt.com
Web Site: www.hyatt.com
Approx. Rev.: $3,527,000,000
Approx. Number Employees: 45,000
Year Founded: 1957
Business Description:
Hotel Owner, Operator & Franchiser
S.I.C.: 7011
N.A.I.C.S.: 721110
Media: 2-3-4-6-8-18
Personnel:
Thomas J. Pritzker *(Chm)*
Mark S. Hoplamazian *(Pres & CEO)*
Harmit J. Singh *(CFO)*
John Wallis *(CMO & Global Head-Mktg & Brand Strategy)*
Jeff Semenchuk *(Chief Innovation Officer)*
Rena Hozore Reiss *(Gen Counsel & Sec)*
Stephen G. Haggerty *(Exec VP & Global Head-Real Estate & Dev)*
Rene Mizwicki *(Sr Dir-Mktg)*
Brands & Products:
HYATT
Advertising Agencies:
BBDO New York
1285 Ave of the Americas 7th Fl
New York, NY 10019-6028
Tel.: (212) 459-5000
(Corporate Branding)

PHD
(An Omnicom Company)
220 E 42nd 7th Fl
New York, NY 10017
Tel.: (212) 894-6600
Fax: (212) 894-4100
(Media Buying/Planning)

HYATT REGENCY LAKE TAHOE RESORT & CASINO

(Sub. of Hyatt Hotels Corporation)
111 Country Club Dr
Incline Village, NV 89451
Tel.: (775) 832-1234
Fax: (775) 831-2171
Toll Free: (888) 899-5019
E-mail: info@haytt.com
Web Site: www.laketahoe.hyatt.com
Sales Range: $75-99.9 Million
Approx. Number Employees: 850
Business Description:
Resort Hotel & Casino
S.I.C.: 7011
N.A.I.C.S.: 721120
Advertising Expenditures: $1,100,000
Media: 2-3-6-7-8-9-10-13-14-18-22-23-24-25-26
Distr.: Reg.
Personnel:
Mark Pardue *(Gen Mgr)*
Nate Hardesty *(Dir-Sls & Mktg)*
Advertising Agency:
Smith & Jones
880 Northwood Blvd.
Incline Village, NV 89451
Tel.: (775) 831-6262
Fax: (775) 831-9172
(Gaming & Hotel Services)

ICAHN ENTERPRISES L.P.

767 5th Ave Ste 4700
New York, NY 10153
Tel.: (212) 702-4300
Fax: (212) 750-5841
Toll Free: (800) 255-2737 (Investor Relations)
E-mail: ir@ielp.com
Web Site: www.icahnenterprises.com
Approx. Rev.: $9,119,000,000
Approx. Number Employees: 26
Year Founded: 1987
Business Description:
Holding Company; Investment Services
S.I.C.: 6719; 6289; 6512; 6531; 7011
N.A.I.C.S.: 551112; 523999; 531120; 531390; 721110; 721120
Advertising Expenditures: $169,700,000
Personnel:
Carl Celian Icahn *(Chm)*
Daniel A. Ninivaggi *(Pres)*
Dominick Ragone *(CFO)*

INNKEEPERS USA TRUST

(Sub. of Grand Prix Holdings LLC)
(Filed Ch 11 Bankruptcy #10-13794 on 07/26/2010 in U.S. Bankruptcy Ct, Southern Dist of NY)
340 Royal Poinciana Way Ste 306
Palm Beach, FL 33480
Tel.: (561) 835-1800
Fax: (561) 835-0457
E-mail: info@innkeepersusa.com
Web Site: www.innkeepersusa.com
Sales Range: $250-299.9 Million
Approx. Number Employees: 36
Year Founded: 1994
Business Description:
Hotel Real Estate Investment Trust
S.I.C.: 6798
N.A.I.C.S.: 525930
Import Export
Advertising Expenditures: $8,323,000
Media: 4-7
Personnel:
Tim Walker *(Pres & CEO)*
Nathan Cook *(CFO)*
Marc Beilinson *(Chief Restructuring Officer)*
Mark A. Murphy *(Gen Counsel & Sec)*

INNSUITES HOSPITALITY TRUST

InnSuites Hotel Ctr 1625 E Northern Ave Ste 105
Phoenix, AZ 85020
Tel.: (602) 944-1500
Fax: (602) 678-0281
E-mail: mberg@innsuites.com
Web Site: www.innsuitestrust.com
Approx. Rev.: $15,740,427
Approx. Number Employees: 368
Year Founded: 1971
Business Description:
Real Estate Investment Trust
S.I.C.: 7011; 6798
N.A.I.C.S.: 721110; 525930
Advertising Expenditures: $788,000
Personnel:
James F. Wirth *(Chm & Pres)*
Anthony B. Waters *(CFO)*
Robert R. Mazakis *(Chief Acctg Officer & Controller)*
Marc E. Berg *(Exec VP)*
James D. Green *(Dir-Ops)*
Brands & Products:
INNSUITES
YOUR SUITE CHOICE

INTERCONTINENTAL HOTELS CORPORATION

(Sub. of InterContinental Hotels Group PLC)
(d/b/a InterContinental Hotels Group - Americas)
3 Ravinia Drive Ste 100
Atlanta, GA 30346
Tel.: (770) 604-2000
Fax: (770) 604-2107
E-mail: americas.development@ichotelsgroup.com
Web Site: www.ichotelsgroup.com
Approx. Sls.: $8,000,000
Approx. Number Employees: 2,000
Business Description:
Hotel Franchisor & Operator
S.I.C.: 7011; 6794
N.A.I.C.S.: 721110; 533110
Media: 6-9-17-25-26
Distr.: Intl.; Natl.
Personnel:
Angela Brav *(COO)*
Eric Pearson *(CMO-Americas)*
Joel Eisemann *(Chief Dev Officer-Americas & Sr VP)*
Kirk Kinsell *(Pres-Americas)*
Bob Gunkel *(CFO-Americas & Sr VP)*
Steven W. Smith *(Gen Counsel-Americas & Sr VP)*
James F. Anhut *(Sr VP-Brand Mgmt-Americas)*
Kevin Kowalski *(Sr VP-Global Brand Mgmt)*
Lynne Zappone *(Sr VP-Global Learning & HR-Americas)*
Jenifer Zeigler *(Sr VP-Global Brand Mngmt)*
Heather Balsley *(VP-Strategy-Americas)*
Robert Chitty *(VP-Tax & Treasury)*
Mike Fegley *(VP-Sls)*
Mike Higgins *(VP-Upscale Brand Dev-Americas Reg)*
Ricardo Lopez *(VP-Sls & Mktg-Latin America & Caribbean)*
Francie Schulwolf *(VP-Corp Comm)*
Steve Ekdahl *(Dir-Leisure Travel)*
Brands & Products:
FORUM
Advertising Agencies:
Blue Sky Agency
950 Lowery Blvd Ste 30
Atlanta, GA 30318
Tel.: (404) 876-0202
Fax: (404) 876-0212

Fitzgerald+CO
3060 Peachtree Rd NW
Atlanta, GA 30305
Tel.: (404) 504-6900
Fax: (404) 239-0548

J.R. Stacy & Associates
413 Ringwood Circle
Winter Springs, FL 32708
Tel.: (407) 660-1919
Fax: (407) 660-1935

McCann Erickson/New York
622 3rd Ave
New York, NY 10017
Tel.: (646) 865-2000
Fax: (646) 487-9610
Creative
Holiday Inn
Holiday Inn Express

OgilvyInteractive
636 11th Ave
New York, NY 10036
Tel.: (212) 237-4000
Fax: (212) 237-5123
Global Digital Assignement

OgilvyOne
111 Sutter St 10th Fl
San Francisco, CA 94104
Tel.: (415) 782-4700
Fax: (415) 782-4800
Global Digital Assignment

ZAAZ
414 Olive Way Ste 500
Seattle, WA 98101
Tel.: (206) 341-9885
Fax: (206) 749-9868
Crowne Plaza
Holiday Inn
Indigo
InterContinental
Social Media Strategy

INTOWN SUITES MANAGEMENT, INC.

Ste 2-1200 2727 Paces Ferry Rd SE
Atlanta, GA 30339-6143
Tel.: (770) 799-5000
Web Site: www.intownsuites.com
Approx. Number Employees: 50
Business Description:
Budget Extended-Stay Hotel Owner & Operator
S.I.C.: 7011
N.A.I.C.S.: 721110
Media: 2-9-13-26
Personnel:
Scott Griffith *(Pres & CEO)*
Douglas N. Wells *(Pres)*
Dennis Cassel *(CFO)*

INTRAWEST ULC

(Holding of Fortress Investment Group LLC)
200 Burrard Street Suite 300
Vancouver, BC V6C 3L6, Canada
Tel.: (604) 695-8200
Fax: (604) 669-0605
E-mail: intrainfo@intrawest.com
Web Site: www.intrawest.com
Approx. Rev.: $936,116,000
Approx. Number Employees: 22,000
Year Founded: 1976
Business Description:
Resort Developer & Operator
S.I.C.: 7011; 7999

Key to Media (For complete agency information see *The Advertising Red Books-Agencies* edition):
1. Bus. Publs. 2. Cable T.V. 3. Catalogs & Directories. 4. Co-op Adv. 5. Consumer Mags. 6. D.M. to Bus. Estab.7. D.M. to Consumers
8. Daily Newsp. 9. Exhibits/Trade Shows 10. Foreign 11. Infomercial 12. Internet Adv.13. Multimedia 14. Network Radio
15. Network T.V. 16. Newsp. Distr. Mags. 17. Other 18. Outdoor (Posters, Transit) 19. Point of Purchase20. Premiums, Novelties
21. Product Samples 22. Special Events Mktg. 23. Spot Radio 24. Spot T.V. 25. Weekly Newsp. 26. Yellow Page Adv.

Intrawest ULC — (Continued)

N.A.I.C.S.: 713920; 713990; 721110
Media: 6-13-20-26
Personnel:
Joe S. Houssian *(Chm)*
William Jensen *(CEO)*
Kevin R. Smith *(CFO & Exec VP)*
Stephen Richards *(Chief Legal Officer & Sr VP)*
Michael F. Coyle *(Chief Strategy Officer)*
Mara Pagotto *(Chief People Officer & Sr VP)*
Daniel O. Jarvis *(Chief Corp Dev Officer)*
Catharine Johnston *(Exec VP-Bus & Organizational Excellence)*
Hugh R. Smythe *(Sr VP-Intrawest Mountain Resorts)*
Marke Dickson *(Mktg Mgr)*
Brands & Products:
CLUB INTRAWEST
PLAYGROUND

INTUIT REAL ESTATE SOLUTIONS INC.
(Name Changed to MRI Software, LLC)

INVESTORS REAL ESTATE TRUST
3015 16th St SW, Ste 100
Minot, ND 58701
Mailing Address:
PO Box 1988
Minot, ND 58702-1988
Tel.: (701) 837-4738
Fax: (701) 838-7785
Toll Free: (888) 478-4738
E-mail: info@iret.com
Web Site: www.iret.com
Approx. Rev.: $237,407,000
Approx. Number Employees: 305
Year Founded: 1970
Business Description:
Real Estate Investment Trust
S.I.C.: 6798
N.A.I.C.S.: 525930
Advertising Expenditures: $956,852
Personnel:
Jeffrey L. Miller *(Chm)*
Stephen L. Stenehjem *(Vice Chm)*
Timothy P. Mihalick *(Pres & CEO)*
Diane K. Bryantt *(CFO & Sr VP)*
Thomas A. Wentz, Jr. *(COO & Sr VP)*
Thomas A. Wentz, Sr. *(CIO & Sr VP)*
Michael A. Bosh *(Gen Counsel, Sr VP & Asst Sec)*
Charles Greenberg *(Sr VP-Asset Management Grp)*
Ted E. Holmes *(Sr VP-Fin)*
Andrew Martin *(Sr VP-Residential Property Mgmt)*

IOWA REALTY CO., INC.
(Sub. of HomeServices of America, Inc.)
3501 Westown Pkwy
West Des Moines, IA 50266
Tel.: (515) 224-6222
Web Site: www.iowarealty.com
Sales Range: $300-349.9 Million
Business Description:
Real Estate Services
S.I.C.: 6531
N.A.I.C.S.: 531210
Media: 2-4-8-9-13-18-25-26

Personnel:
Mike Knapp *(CEO)*

THE IRVINE COMPANY INC.
550 Newport Ctr Dr
Newport Beach, CA 92660-7011
Tel.: (949) 720-2000
Fax: (949) 720-2501
E-mail: webmaster@irvinecompany.com
Web Site: www.irvinecompany.com
Approx. Number Employees: 3,200
Year Founded: 1894
Business Description:
Real Estate Investment Services
S.I.C.: 6552; 6531
N.A.I.C.S.: 237210; 531210
Advertising Expenditures: $5,000,000
Media: 2-5-6-7-9-17-25
Distr.: Reg.
Personnel:
Donald Bren *(Chm)*
Marc Ley *(CFO & Grp Sr VP)*
Richard I. Gilchrist *(Pres-Investment Properties Grp)*
Robert Elliott *(Sr VP-Urban Plng & Design Grp)*
Nicole Conniff *(VP-Mktg)*

JACKSON HOLE MOUNTAIN RESORT
3395 W Cody Dr
Teton Village, WY 83025
Tel.: (307) 733-2292
Fax: (307) 733-2660
Toll Free: (888) DEEPSNO
E-mail: info@jacksonhole.com
Web Site: www.jacksonhole.com
E-Mail For Key Personnel:
Public Relations: olson@jacksonhole.com
Approx. Number Employees: 200
Year Founded: 1963
Business Description:
Mountain Resort Owner & Operator
S.I.C.: 7991; 6552
N.A.I.C.S.: 713940; 237210
Advertising Expenditures: $250,000
Media: 1-3-4-5-6-9-11-22-23-24-25-26
Distr.: Natl.
Budget Set: Apr. -May
Personnel:
John L. Kemmerer *(Chm)*
Jerry M. Blann *(Pres)*
Matt McCreedy *(CFO)*
Scott Horn *(Chief Admin Officer)*
Tom Spangler *(VP & Gen Mgr)*
Bill Lewkowitz *(Dir-Bus Dev)*
Anna Olson *(Dir-Brands)*
Richard Ray *(Dir-IT)*
William Schreiber *(Dir-Plan & Engrg)*
Shawn Daus *(Mgr-Sls)*
Spencer Long *(Mgr-Sls)*
Advertising Agency:
Richter7
280 S 400 W Ste 200
Salt Lake City, UT 84101
Tel.: (801) 521-2903
Fax: (801) 359-2420
(Ski Packages)

JACOBSEN MANUFACTURING, INC.
(d/b/a Jacobsen Homes)
600 Packard Ct
Safety Harbor, FL 34695-3001
Tel.: (727) 726-1138
Fax: (727) 726-7019
Toll Free: (800) 282-5389
Web Site: www.jachomes.com
Approx. Number Employees: 175
Year Founded: 1959
Business Description:
Mfr. of Mobile Homes
S.I.C.: 2451; 3448
N.A.I.C.S.: 321991; 332311
Advertising Expenditures: $250,000
Media: 6
Personnel:
William R. Jacobsen *(Owner)*
Dusty Rhodes *(Pres)*
Janet Weis *(Dir-Mktg)*
Brands & Products:
THE CAPTIVA 2
CLASSIC III
THE GRAND ISLAND
JACOBSEN HOMES
THE JASPER
THE MARGATE
THE MULBERRY
THE OAK HILL
THE OXFORD
THE SIESTA KEY
THE VENICE

JAMESON INNS, INC.
(Sub. of Park Management Group)
4770 S Atlanta Rd
Smyrna, GA 30080
Tel.: (404) 350-9990
Fax: (404) 601-6106
E-mail: webmaster@jamesoninns.com
Web Site: www.jamesoninns.com
Sales Range: $75-99.9 Million
Approx. Number Employees: 1,750
Year Founded: 1987
Business Description:
Economy & Mid-Scale Inns Owner, Operator & Franchisor
S.I.C.: 1522; 7011
N.A.I.C.S.: 721191; 236220; 721110
Advertising Expenditures: $3,000,000
Media: 3-7-8-9-10-13-17-18-20-22-25
Personnel:
Steven Curlee *(Gen Counsel)*
Brands & Products:
COMBINED INNS
JAMESON INN
SIGNATURE INN

JAY PEAK, INC.
(Sub. of Mont Saint-Sauveur International, Inc.)
4850 VT Rte 242
Jay Peak, VT 05859
Tel.: (802) 988-2611
Fax: (802) 988-4049
Toll Free: (800) 451-4449
E-mail: info@jaypeakresort.com
Web Site: www.jaypeakresort.com
E-Mail For Key Personnel:
President: bstenger@jaypeakresort.com
Approx. Number Employees: 440
Year Founded: 1955
Business Description:
All Seasons Resort Operator
S.I.C.: 7011; 6552
N.A.I.C.S.: 721199; 237210
Advertising Expenditures: $200,000
Media: 2-4-5-6-8-9-10-11-13-16-18-19-20-24-25-26
Distr.: Reg.
Budget Set: June
Personnel:
Bill Stenger *(Owner)*
Steve Wright *(VP-Sls & Mktg)*
Advertising Agency:
Almighty
300 Western Ave
Boston, MA 02134
Tel.: (617) 782-1511
Fax: (617) 782-1611

J.E. ROBERT COMPANY
1650 Tysons Blvd Ste 1600
McLean, VA 22102
Tel.: (703) 714-8000
Fax: (703) 714-8100
Web Site: www.jer.com
Approx. Sls.: $22,000,000
Approx. Number Employees: 120
Business Description:
Real Estate & Asset Management
S.I.C.: 6531
N.A.I.C.S.: 531210
Personnel:
Joseph E. Robert Jr. *(Chm)*
Andy O'Brien *(Mng Dir)*
Barden N. Gale *(CEO-JER Partners)*
Advertising Agency:
Mason & Kichar Recruitment Advertising
260 Amity Rd
Woodbridge, CT 06525
Tel.: (203) 392-0252
Fax: (203) 392-0255

JETPADS, INC.
650 S Hill St J-4
Los Angeles, CA 90014
Tel.: (310) 728-6579
Toll Free: (877) 538-7717
Web Site: www.jetpadhomes.com
Approx. Rev.: $83,568
Year Founded: 2008
Business Description:
Luxury Homes & Condominiums Developer, Owner, Operator & Franchisor
S.I.C.: 1531; 6531
N.A.I.C.S.: 531390; 236117; 531210
Advertising Expenditures: $45,698
Media: 17
Personnel:
Robert Kanaat *(Chm, Pres & CEO)*

JIM WILSON & ASSOCIATES, INC.
Ste 100 2660 Eastchase Ln
Montgomery, AL 36117-7024
Tel.: (334) 260-2500
Fax: (334) 260-2533
E-mail: info@jwamalls.com
Web Site: www.jwamalls.com
Approx. Number Employees: 35
Year Founded: 1975
Business Description:
Property Manager & Developer
S.I.C.: 6531; 6552
N.A.I.C.S.: 531210; 237210
Media: 2-4-6-7-10-13-20-22
Distr.: Natl.
Budget Set: Mar.
Personnel:
Will Wilson *(Pres)*
Carl Bartlett *(Sr VP)*
Woody Rush *(Sr VP-Leasing)*

JMB REALTY CORPORATION
900 N Michigan Ave Ste 1500
Chicago, IL 60611-1542

Key to Media (For complete agency information see *The Advertising Red Books-Agencies* edition):
1. Bus. Publs. 2. Cable T.V. 3. Catalogs & Directories. 4. Co-op Adv. 5. Consumer Mags. 6. D.M. to Bus. Estab.7. D.M. to Consumers
8. Daily Newsp. 9. Exhibits/Trade Shows 10. Foreign 11. Infomercial 12. Internet Adv.13. Multimedia 14. Network Radio
15. Network T.V. 16. Newsp. Distr. Mags. 17. Other 18. Outdoor (Posters, Transit) 19. Point of Purchase20. Premiums, Novelties
21. Product Samples 22. Special Events Mktg. 23. Spot Radio 24. Spot T.V. 25. Weekly Newsp. 26. Yellow Page Adv.

Tel.: (312) 440-4800
Fax: (312) 915-2310
Sales Range: $1-4.9 Billion
Approx. Number Employees: 1,000
Business Description:
Real Estate Investment Firm, Syndicator & Developer
S.I.C.: 6289; 6552
N.A.I.C.S.: 523999; 237210
Media: 1-2-9-10-17-18-22-23-24-25
Distr.: Natl.
Personnel:
Judd Malkin *(Co-Founder & Chm)*
Neil G. Bluhm *(Founder & Pres)*
Steve Lovelett *(CFO)*
Rigel Barbec *(COO)*

JOHN BUCK COMPANY
1 N Wacker Dr Ste 2400
Chicago, IL 60606
Tel.: (312) 993-9800
Fax: (312) 993-0857
E-mail: info@tjbc.com
Web Site: www.tjbc.com
Approx. Number Employees: 108
Business Description:
Real Estate Agents & Managers
S.I.C.: 6512
N.A.I.C.S.: 531120
Personnel:
John A. Buck *(Chm & CEO)*
Greg Gerber *(Principal)*
Advertising Agency:
Slack Barshinger & Partners, Inc.
233 N Michigan Ave Ste 3050
Chicago, IL 60601
Tel.: (312) 970-5800
Fax: (312) 970-5850
Toll Free: (800) 888-6197
Real Estate

JOHN Q. HAMMONS HOTELS INC.
300 S John Q Hammons Pkwy Ste 900
Springfield, MO 65806
Tel.: (417) 864-4300
Fax: (417) 873-3540
Web Site: www.jqhhotels.com
Approx. Rev.: $430,780,000
Approx. Number Employees: 5,800
Business Description:
Hotel Owner & Operator
S.I.C.: 7011
N.A.I.C.S.: 721110
Advertising Expenditures: $35,289,000
Personnel:
John Q. Hammons *(Founder & Chm)*
Justin Harris *(Gen Counsel & Sr VP)*
Jacqueline A. Dowdy *(Exec VP-Fin)*
Steven E. Minton *(Sr VP-Architecture)*
Joe Morrissey *(Sr VP-Ops)*
Christopher Smith *(Sr VP-Admin & Control)*
Joseph F. Kelly *(Reg VP)*
Phill Burgess *(VP-Sls & Revenue Mgmt)*
Kent Foster *(VP-HR)*
Micheal Morgan *(VP-IT)*
Douglas Drake *(Asst Gen Mgr-Food & Beverage Div)*

KENNEDY-WILSON, INC.
(Sub. of Kennedy-Wilson Holdings, Inc.)
9701 Wilshire Blvd Ste 700
Beverly Hills, CA 90212
Tel.: (310) 887-6400
Fax: (310) 887-3410
Toll Free: (800) 522-6664
E-mail: info@kennedywilson.com
Web Site: www.kennedywilson.com
Sales Range: $75-99.9 Million
Approx. Number Employees: 50
Year Founded: 1977
Business Description:
Real Estate Property Management & Investment Services
S.I.C.: 6531; 6282; 6512; 6519
N.A.I.C.S.: 531312; 523920; 531120; 531190; 531210; 531390
Media: 6-7-8-9-11-25
Distr.: Intl.
Personnel:
William J. McMorrow *(Chm & CEO)*
John C. Prabhu *(Pres)*
Naoki Oshima *(Exec Mng Dir)*
Barbara Montes *(Sr Mng Dir)*
Joseph Winkler *(Sr Mng Dir)*
Richard Drottz *(Sr Mng Dir)*
Stephen Pyhrr *(Sr Mng Dir)*
Douglas Hause *(Mng Dir)*
Ross Crowe *(Mng Dir)*
Mary Jacobs *(Mng Dir)*
Peter G. Lawson *(Mng Dir)*
Freeman A. Lyle *(CFO & Exec VP)*
Robert Hart *(Pres/CEO-KW Multifamily Mgmt Grp)*
Stuart Cramer *(Pres-Residential Investments)*
James A. Rosten *(Pres-KW Properties)*
Donald J. Herrema *(Exec Vice Chm & CEO-KW Capital Markets Grp)*
Mary L. Ricks *(Exec Vice Chm & CEO-KW Comml Investment Grp)*
Clifford Smith *(Sr VP)*
James Ozello *(Sr Mng Dir-HR)*
Rob Hannan *(Mng Dir-Investment Sls)*
Tim Jones *(Reg VP)*
Teri A. Anodide *(VP-Fin & Controller)*
Lennard Coplin *(Sr Dir-Mktg)*
Shirley Finney *(Sr Mgr-Property)*
Brigitte Boudress *(Office Mgr)*

KEYSTONE RESORT PROPERTY MANAGEMENT COMPANY
(Sub. of Vail Resorts, Inc.)
0175 Summit County Rd 8
Keystone, CO 80435-0038
Mailing Address:
PO Box 38 K-19
Keystone, CO 80435-0038
Tel.: (970) 496-4155
Fax: (970) 496-4277
Web Site: www.keystoneresort.com
Sales Range: $25-49.9 Million
Approx. Number Employees: 150
Business Description:
Resorts
S.I.C.: 5812
N.A.I.C.S.: 722110
Personnel:
Rob Katz *(Chm & CEO)*
Advertising Agency:
Cultivator Advertising & Design
2737 Larimer St Ste B
Denver, CO 80205
Tel.: (303) 444-4134
Fax: (800) 783-4152

KIAWAH RESORT ASSOCIATES LP
1 Kiawah Is Pkwy
Kiawah Island, SC 29455
Tel.: (843) 768-3400
Fax: (843) 768-5204
Toll Free: (800) 277-7008
Web Site: www.kiawahisland.com
Approx. Number Employees: 500
Year Founded: 1987
Business Description:
Hotel Operators
S.I.C.: 7011
N.A.I.C.S.: 721110
Media: 2
Personnel:
Charles P. Darby, III *(CEO)*
Townsend Clarkson *(COO)*
Leonard L. Long, Jr. *(Exec VP)*

KILROY REALTY CORPORATION
12200 W Olympic Blvd Ste 200
Los Angeles, CA 90064
Tel.: (310) 481-8400
Fax: (310) 481-6580
E-mail: investorrelations@kilroyrealty.com
Web Site: www.kilroyrealty.com
E-Mail For Key Personnel:
Public Relations: investorrelations@kilroyrealty.com
Approx. Rev.: $301,980,000
Approx. Number Employees: 141
Year Founded: 1997
Business Description:
Nonresidential Building Operators
S.I.C.: 6159; 6512; 6798
N.A.I.C.S.: 522292; 525930; 531120
Media: 5
Personnel:
John B. Kilroy, Sr. *(Chm)*
John B. Kilroy, Jr. *(Pres & CEO-Kilroy Realty Corp.)*
Tyler H. Rose *(CFO & Exec VP)*
Jeffrey C. Hawken *(COO & Exec VP)*
Eli Khouri, III *(Chief Investment Officer & Exec VP)*
Heidi Roth *(Sr VP & Controller)*
John T. Fucci *(Sr VP-Asset Mgmt)*
Steven R. Scott *(Sr VP-San Diego)*
Justin W. Smart *(Sr VP-Dev)*
Michelle Ngo *(Dir-Corp Fin)*

KIMPTON HOTEL & RESTAURANT GROUP LLC.
222 Kearny St Ste 200
San Francisco, CA 94108
Tel.: (415) 397-5572
Fax: (415) 296-8031
Web Site: www.kimptongroup.com
Sales Range: $50-74.9 Million
Approx. Number Employees: 4,000
Year Founded: 1982
Business Description:
Hotels & Restaurants Operations & Management Services
S.I.C.: 7011; 5812; 8741
N.A.I.C.S.: 721110; 561110; 722110
Personnel:
Michael A. Depatie *(CEO)*
Ben Rowe *(CFO & Exec VP)*
Niki Leondakis *(COO & Pres-Hotels & Restaurants)*
Joseph Long *(Chief Investment Officer & Exec VP-Dev)*
Judy Miles *(Gen Counsel & Exec VP)*
Mike DeFrino *(Sr VP-Hotel Ops)*
Troy Furbay *(Sr VP-Acq & Dev)*
John Inserra *(Sr VP-Restaurant Ops)*
Steve Pinetti *(Sr VP-Sls & Mktg)*
Ken Reynolds *(Sr VP-Construction)*
David Sussman *(Sr VP-Hotel Devel & Design)*
Vanessa Bortnick *(VP-Comm)*
Stacey Ellis *(Sr Dir-PR)*
Jamie Law *(Mgr-Media Rels & Special Events)*
Advertising Agencies:
Baltz & Company
49 W 23rd St
New York, NY 10010
Tel.: (212) 982-8300
Fax: (212) 982-8302

Ink & Co.
446 Broadway 4th Fl
New York, NY 10013
Tel.: (212) 334-3168
Fax: (212) 334-3167
Agency of Record

Porter Novelli-Bay Area-San Francisco
550 3rd St
San Francisco, CA 94107
Tel.: (415) 975-2200
Fax: (415) 975-2201

KITCHELL CORPORATION
1707 E Highland Ste 100
Phoenix, AZ 85016
Tel.: (602) 264-4411
Fax: (602) 631-9112
E-mail: info@kitchell.com
Web Site: www.kitchell.com
E-Mail For Key Personnel:
Marketing Director: mleyva@kitchell.com
Approx. Number Employees: 700
Year Founded: 1950
Business Description:
Holding Company; Industrial & Public Construction Manager; Luxury Custom Home Builder; Real Estate Developer
S.I.C.: 1522; 1541
N.A.I.C.S.: 236220; 236210
Media: 2-6-10
Distr.: Natl.; Reg.
Personnel:
William C. Schubert *(Chm)*
Maria Leyva *(Dir-Mktg)*

KOENIG & STREY GMAC REAL ESTATE
(Sub. of HomeServices of America, Inc.)
3201 Old Glenview Rd
Wilmette, IL 60091
Tel.: (847) 853-5000
Fax: (847) 853-5005
E-mail: info@ksgmac.com
Web Site: www.ksgmac.com
Sales Range: $250-299.9 Million
Approx. Number Employees: 900
Business Description:
Real Estate Brokers & Agents
S.I.C.: 6163
N.A.I.C.S.: 522310
Media: 7-8
Personnel:
Doug Ayers *(Pres)*
Michael Mazzei *(Sr VP)*
Constance Conway *(VP & Dir-Risk Mgmt)*

Key to Media (For complete agency information see *The Advertising Red Books-Agencies* edition):
1. Bus. Publs. 2. Cable T.V. 3. Catalogs & Directories. 4. Co-op Adv. 5. Consumer Mags. 6. D.M. to Bus. Estab.7. D.M. to Consumers 8. Daily Newsp. 9. Exhibits/Trade Shows 10. Foreign 11. Infomercial 12. Internet Adv.13. Multimedia 14. Network Radio 15. Network T.V. 16. Newsp. Distr. Mags. 17. Other 18. Outdoor (Posters, Transit) 19. Point of Purchase20. Premiums, Novelties 21. Product Samples 22. Special Events Mktg. 23. Spot Radio 24. Spot T.V. 25. Weekly Newsp. 26. Yellow Page Adv.

Koenig & Strey GMAC Real Estate — (Continued)

Robert Sheridan *(Dir-Mktg Dev)*
Tere Proctor *(Dir-Sls Trump Tower Chicago)*

KRAVCO SIMON COMPANY
234 Mall Blvd
King of Prussia, PA 19406
Tel.: (610) 768-6300
Fax: (610) 768-6444
E-mail: kravco@kravcosimon.com
Web Site: www.kravco.com
E-Mail For Key Personnel:
President: jpowell@kravcosimon.com
Approx. Number Employees: 40
Business Description:
Shopping Center, Property Operation Only
S.I.C.: 6512; 6552
N.A.I.C.S.: 531120; 237210
Personnel:
Arthur L. Powell *(Chm)*
Jon R. Powell *(Pres)*
Lisa Fair Pliskin *(Gen Counsel & VP-Legal)*
Robert C. Birkbeck *(VP-Acctg & Fin)*
Lori Pumo *(Mgr-Tech Svcs)*
Advertising Agency:
Furia Rubel Communications
2 Hidden Ln Bldg 2
Doylestown, PA 18901
Tel.: (215) 340-0480
Fax: (215) 340-0580
Montgomery Mall

KSL RESORTS
(Sub. of KSL Capital Partners, LLC)
50-905 Avenida Bermudas
La Quinta, CA 92253
Tel.: (760) 564-8000
Fax: (760) 564-8004
Web Site: www.kslresorts.com
Approx. Number Employees: 50
Year Founded: 1992
Business Description:
Resort Management Services
S.I.C.: 8742; 7011
N.A.I.C.S.: 541611; 721110
Media: 6
Personnel:
Scott M. Dalecio *(Pres & CEO)*
James Struthers *(CFO & VP)*
Bryan Wright *(Gen Counsel & VP)*
Arthur L. Berg *(VP-Mktg)*
Peter Corsa *(VP-Retail)*
Michael E. Erickson *(VP-Sls)*
Jason Kycek *(Dir-Travel Travel Industry Sls & Mktg)*
Advertising Agency:
Middleton & Gendron, Inc.
1065 Ave of the Americas 7th Fl
New York, NY 10018
Tel.: (212) 980-9060
Fax: (212) 759-6521

LA QUINTA CORPORATION
(Holding of The Blackstone Group L.P.)
909 Hidden Ridge Ste 600
Irving, TX 75038
Tel.: (214) 492-6600
Toll Free: (800) 531-5900
E-mail: dguest@lq.com
Web Site: www.lq.com
Sales Range: $550-599.9 Million
Approx. Number Employees: 9,130
Year Founded: 1968
Business Description:
Hotel Owner & Operator
S.I.C.: 7011; 8741
N.A.I.C.S.: 721199; 561110
Advertising Expenditures: $18,100,000
Media: 15
Personnel:
Wayne B. Goldberg *(Pres & CEO)*
Temple H. Weiss *(CFO & Exec VP)*
Angelo J. Lombardi *(COO & Exec VP)*
Julie Cary *(CMO & Exec VP)*
Rajiv K. Trivedi *(Chief Dev Officer & Exec VP-Franchising)*
Mark Chloupek *(Gen Counsel & Exec VP)*
Murry Cathlina *(Exec VP-Design & Construction)*
Feliz P. Jarvis *(Exec VP-Sls)*
David Wilner *(Sr VP-Corp Dev-Dallas)*
Derek Blake *(VP-Mktg)*
Teresa Ferguson *(Dir-PR & Comm)*
Nicolas Petrone *(Dir-Franchise Dev-La Quinta Inns & Suites-Southeast)*
Brands & Products:
BUDGETEL
LA QUINTA
LA QUINTA INN & SUITES
LA QUINTA INNS
WOODFIELD SUITES
Advertising Agencies:
IgnitionOne
32 Ave of the Americas 5th Fl
New York, NY 10013
Toll Free: (888) 744-6483

Mullen
101 N Cherry St Ste 600
Winston Salem, NC 27101-4035
Tel.: (336) 765-3630
Fax: (336) 774-9550

LA QUINTA INNS, INC.
(Sub. of La Quinta Corporation)
909 Hidden Ridge Ste 600
Irving, TX 75038
Tel.: (214) 492-6600
Telex: 203496
Web Site: www.lq.com
Sales Range: $10-24.9 Million
Year Founded: 1968
Business Description:
Hotel Owner & Operator
S.I.C.: 7011; 8741
N.A.I.C.S.: 721199; 561110
Media: 2-4-8-9-18-23
Distr.: Direct to Consumer; Natl.
Budget Set: Apr.
Personnel:
Wayne B. Goldberg *(Pres & CEO)*
Mike Case *(VP-Mktg & Sr Loyalty Officer)*
Fran Wagner *(Dir-Dev-Mid Atlantic Reg)*
Advertising Agencies:
Definition 6
2115 Monroe Dr Ste 100
Atlanta, GA 30324
Tel.: (404) 870-0323
Fax: (404) 897-1258

Red Door Interactive, Inc.
350 10th Ave Set 1100
San Diego, CA 92101
Tel.: (619) 398-2670
Fax: (619) 398-2671

LAGO MAR PROPERTIES, INC.
1700 S Ocean Ln
Fort Lauderdale, FL 37316
Tel.: (954) 523-6511
Fax: (954) 524-6627
Toll Free: (800) LAGOMAR
E-mail: reservations@lagomar.com
Web Site: www.lagomar.com
Approx. Number Employees: 225
Business Description:
Hotel & Resort
S.I.C.: 7011; 5812
N.A.I.C.S.: 721110; 722110
Media: 6-8
Personnel:
Walter Banks *(Pres)*

LAKE AUSTIN SPA RESORT
1705 S Quinlan Pk Rd
Austin, TX 78732
Tel.: (512) 372-7300
Fax: (512) 372-7370
Toll Free: (800) 847-5637
E-mail: info@lakeaustin.com
Web Site: www.lakeaustin.com
Sales Range: $1-9.9 Million
Approx. Number Employees: 115
Business Description:
Resort & Spa
S.I.C.: 7011
N.A.I.C.S.: 721199; 721110
Media: 6-8
Personnel:
Mike McAdams *(Co-Owner)*
William W. Rucks, IV *(Co-Owner)*
Tracy York *(Gen Mgr)*
Robbie Hudson *(Dir-Programming)*
Trisha Shirey *(Dir-Flora & Fauna)*
Megan Hair *(Mgr-Mktg)*

LAKE TAHOE HORIZON CASINO RESORT
50 Hwy 50
Stateline, NV 89449
Tel.: (775) 588-6211
Fax: (775) 586-4048
Toll Free: (800) 648-3322
E-mail: reservations@horizoncasino.com
Web Site: www.horizoncasino.com
E-Mail For Key Personnel:
Sales Director: rturner@horizoncasino.com
Approx. Number Employees: 1,500
Year Founded: 1965
Business Description:
Casino & Resort Owner & Operator
S.I.C.: 7011
N.A.I.C.S.: 721120
Advertising Expenditures: $1,100,000
Media: 6-9-14-18-23-26
Distr.: Direct to Consumer
Personnel:
William J. Yung *(Pres)*
John Sedilla *(Gen Mgr-Casino)*
Drew Welsheimer *(Dir-Sls)*

LANCASTER HOST RESORT & CONFERENCE CENTER
2300 Lincoln Hwy E
Lancaster, PA 17602
Tel.: (717) 299-5500
Fax: (717) 295-5116
Toll Free: (800) 233-0121
Web Site: www.lancasterhost.com
Approx. Number Employees: 300
Year Founded: 1966
Business Description:
Hotel & Conference Center Owner & Operator
S.I.C.: 7011
N.A.I.C.S.: 721199; 721110
Advertising Expenditures: $300,000
Media: 1-2-3-4-5-6-7-8-9-10-13-14-16-17-18-19-20-21-22-23-25-26
Distr.: Direct to Consumer; Reg.
Budget Set: Sept.

LAND PROPERTIES INC.
255 E Cheyenne Mtn Blvd Ste 200
Colorado Springs, CO 80906
Tel.: (719) 226-7977
Fax: (719) 226-7981
E-mail: info@landproperties.com
Web Site: www.landproperties.com
Sales Range: $25-49.9 Million
Approx. Number Employees: 35
Year Founded: 1981
Business Description:
Real Estate Marketer
S.I.C.: 6531
N.A.I.C.S.: 531210
Advertising Expenditures: $400,000
Media: 2-6-9-13-25
Distr.: Natl.
Personnel:
David Martin *(Pres)*
Randy Lanosga, Jr. *(CFO)*

THE LANDBANK GROUP, INC.
(Sub. of The Shaw Group Inc.)
9201 E Dry Creek Rd
Centennial, CO 80112
Tel.: (303) 763-8500
Fax: (303) 763-5700
Web Site: www.landbank.net
Sales Range: $1-9.9 Million
Approx. Number Employees: 5
Year Founded: 1995
Business Description:
Distressed Land, Buildings & Operating Facilities Acquirer, Restorer & Redeveloper
S.I.C.: 8711
N.A.I.C.S.: 541330
Media: 2-10

LAS VEGAS SANDS CORP.
3355 Las Vegas Blvd S
Las Vegas, NV 89109
Tel.: (702) 414-1000
Fax: (702) 414-4884
E-mail: comments@venetian.com
Web Site: www.lasvegassands.com
Approx. Rev.: $6,853,182,000
Approx. Number Employees: 34,000
Business Description:
Casinos, Hotels, Resorts & Convention Space Owner & Operator
S.I.C.: 7999; 7011
N.A.I.C.S.: 721120; 713210; 721110
Advertising Expenditures: $56,700,000
Media: 2-6-8-9-13-15-18-23-24
Personnel:
Sheldon Gary Adelson *(Chm & CEO)*
Michael A. Leven *(Pres & COO)*
Kenneth J. Kay *(CFO & Exec VP)*
Manjit Singh *(CIO)*
Michael Alan Quartieri *(Chief Acctg Officer)*
John Caparella *(Pres-Venetian, Palazzo & Sands Expo Center)*
Robert G. Goldstein *(Pres-Global Gaming Ops)*

Key to Media (For complete agency information see *The Advertising Red Books-Agencies* edition):
1. Bus. Publs. 2. Cable T.V. 3. Catalogs & Directories. 4. Co-op Adv. 5. Consumer Mags. 6. D.M. to Bus. Estab.7. D.M. to Consumers 8. Daily Newsp. 9. Exhibits/Trade Shows 10. Foreign 11. Infomercial 12. Internet Adv.13. Multimedia 14. Network Radio 15. Network T.V. 16. Newsp. Distr. Mags. 17. Other 18. Outdoor (Posters, Transit) 19. Point of Purchase20. Premiums, Novelties 21. Product Samples 22. Special Events Mktg. 23. Spot Radio 24. Spot T.V. 25. Weekly Newsp. 26. Yellow Page Adv.

Gayle M. Hyman *(Gen Counsel & Sr VP)*
Ron Reese *(VP-Comm)*
Advertising Agency:
Strategic Moves
20 Ayer Rajah Crescent #08-26
Singapore, 139964, Singapore
Tel.: (65) 6324 0662
Fax: (65) 6324 0422

THE LEADING HOTELS OF THE WORLD, LTD.
99 Park Ave
New York, NY 10016-1601
Tel.: (212) 515-5600
Fax: (212) 515-5899
E-mail: info@lhw.com
Web Site: www.lhw.com
Approx. Number Employees: 150
Business Description:
Hotel Operator
S.I.C.: 7011; 8611
N.A.I.C.S.: 721110; 813910
Media: 1
Personnel:
Ted Teng *(Pres & CEO)*
Paul M. McManus *(Pres)*
Daniel Neumann *(CFO & Sr VP)*
Claudia Kozma Kaplan *(Sr VP-Mktg & Comm)*
Phil Koserowski *(VP-Interactive Mktg)*
Advertising Agency:
Didit
55 Maple Ave 1st Fl
Rockville Centre, NY 11570
Tel.: (516) 255-0500
Fax: (516) 255-0509
Toll Free: (800) 932-7761

LEDIC MANAGEMENT GROUP
2650 Thousand Oaks Blvd Ste 3100
Memphis, TN 38118
Tel.: (901) 761-9300
Fax: (901) 435-7701
E-mail: contact@ledic.com
Web Site: www.ledic.com
Approx. Sls.: $10,000,000
Approx. Number Employees: 500
Business Description:
Real Estate Managers
S.I.C.: 7389
N.A.I.C.S.: 561499
Personnel:
Pierce Ledbetter *(Pres & CEO)*
Scott Ledbetter *(CEO)*
Justin D. Towner *(Sr VP-Opers)*
Nelda Jones *(Reg VP)*
Advertising Agency:
The Brand Squad
6000 Poplar Ave Ste 250
Memphis, TN 38119
Tel.: (901) 866-9402
Fax: (901) 261-5411

LEFRAK ORGANIZATION INC.
40 W 57th St
New York, NY 10019
Tel.: (212) 708-6600
Fax: (212) 708-6600
E-mail: info@lefrak.com
Web Site: www.lefrak.com
Sales Range: $1-4.9 Billion
Approx. Number Employees: 16,200
Year Founded: 1901
Business Description:
Real Estate Owner & Manager
S.I.C.: 6513; 6512
N.A.I.C.S.: 531110; 531120
Advertising Expenditures: $500,000
Media: 7-8
Personnel:
Richard S. LeFrak *(Chm, Pres & CEO)*
Harrison LeFrak *(Vice Chm)*
James LeFrak *(Vice Chm)*
Richard Papert *(CFO & Exec VP)*
Edward Cortese *(Sr VP-Mktg & PR)*
Advertising Agency:
Miller Advertising Agency Inc.
71 5th Ave 5th Fl
New York, NY 10003-3004
Tel.: (212) 929-2200
Fax: (212) 727-4734
Toll Free: (800) 229-6574

LENNAR CORPORATION
700 NW 107th Ave Ste 400
Miami, FL 33172-3139
Tel.: (305) 559-4000
Fax: (305) 228-8383
Toll Free: (800) 741-4663
E-mail: feedback@lennar.com
Web Site: www.lennar.com
Approx. Rev.: $3,074,022,000
Approx. Number Employees: 4,087
Year Founded: 1954
Business Description:
Single-Family Home Development & Construction Services
S.I.C.: 1521; 1531; 6552
N.A.I.C.S.: 236115; 236117; 237210
Advertising Expenditures: $40,200,000
Media: 6-9-16-18-22-26
Distr.: Direct to Consumer; Intl.
Personnel:
Stuart A. Miller *(Pres & CEO)*
Bruce E. Gross *(CFO & VP)*
John R. Nygard, III *(CIO)*
Todd Jones *(Pres-Atlanta Div)*
David J. Kaiserman *(Pres-Lennar Ventures)*
Mark Sustana *(Gen Counsel & Sec)*
Richard Beckwitt *(Exec VP)*
Kay L. Howard *(Dir-Comm)*
Brands & Products:
EVERYTHING YOU WANT.EVERYTHING YOU NEED LENNAR
THATS THE LOGIC OF LENNAR
Advertising Agency:
Beber Silverstein Group
3361 SW 3rd Ave
Miami, FL 33145-3911
Tel.: (305) 856-9800
Fax: (305) 854-7686

LENNAR HOMES, INC.
(Sub. of Lennar Corporation)
700 Northwest 107th Ave Ste 400
Miami, FL 33172-3139
Tel.: (305) 559-4000
Fax: (305) 227-7115
Web Site: www.lennar.com
Sales Range: $400-449.9 Million
Approx. Number Employees: 600
Year Founded: 1954
Business Description:
Single-Family Housing Construction Services
S.I.C.: 1522; 1521; 1531; 1541
N.A.I.C.S.: 236220; 236115; 236117; 236118; 236210
Media: 6-8-9-11-18-20-23
Personnel:
Stuart A. Miller *(CEO)*
Bruce E. Gross *(CFO & VP)*
Jonathan M. Jaffe *(COO & VP)*
Mark Sustana *(Gen Counsel & Sec)*
Kay L. Howard *(Dir-Comm)*
Advertising Agencies:
In Place Marketing
410 S Cedar Ave
Tampa, FL 33606
Tel.: (813) 933-1810
Fax: (813) 932-8512

Zimmerman Advertising
2200 W Commercial Blvd Ste 300
Fort Lauderdale, FL 33309-3064
Tel.: (954) 644-4000
Fax: (954) 731-2977
Toll Free: (800) 248-8522

LIBERTY GROUP OF COMPANIES
13577 Feather Sound Dr Ste 520
Clearwater, FL 33762
Tel.: (727) 866-7999
Fax: (727) 865-6407
E-mail: contact@libertyg.com
Web Site: www.libertyg.com
Sales Range: $10-24.9 Million
Approx. Number Employees: 55
Year Founded: 1981
Business Description:
Condominium Developer
S.I.C.: 1521
N.A.I.C.S.: 236115
Media: 6
Personnel:
Punit R. Shah *(Pres & COO)*
Raxit N. Shah *(CEO)*
Ketki Shah *(Treas)*
Patrick Shine *(VP-Mktg & Bus Dev)*

THE LIGHTSTONE GROUP, LLC
505 Park Ave 5th Fl
New York, NY 10022
Tel.: (212) 616-9969
Fax: (212) 751-2494
Web Site: www.lightstonegroup.com
Approx. Number Employees: 1,200
Year Founded: 1988
Business Description:
Real Estate Holding Company
S.I.C.: 6531; 6719
N.A.I.C.S.: 531210; 531390; 551112
Personnel:
David Lichtenstein *(Chm & CEO)*
Peyton H. Owen, Jr. *(Pres & COO)*
Michael M. Schurer *(CFO)*
David Kim *(Chief Investment Officer & Exec VP-Fin)*
Joseph E. Teichman *(Gen Counsel & Exec VP)*
Adriana Peters *(Asst Gen Counsel)*
Arvind K. Bajaj *(Exec VP-Investments)*
Joshua Kornberg *(Sr VP & Dir-Acq)*
Bruno de Vinck *(Sr VP-Special Projects)*
Sam Moerman *(Sr VP-Property Mgmt)*
Jeffrey Dash *(VP-Retail Leasing)*
Bill Murphy *(Dir-Utility)*
Advertising Agency:
Beckerman Public Relations
One University Plz Ste 507
Hackensack, NJ 07601
Tel.: (908) 781-6420
Fax: (201) 465-8040

THE LITCHFIELD COMPANY
14240 Ocean Hwy 17
Pawleys Island, SC 29585-0097
Tel.: (843) 237-4000
Fax: (843) 237-9509
Toll Free: (800) 476-2861
E-mail: realestatesales@thelitchfieldcompany.com
Web Site: www.thelitchfieldcompany.com
Approx. Number Employees: 100
Year Founded: 1956
Business Description:
Real Estate Services
S.I.C.: 6531
N.A.I.C.S.: 531390; 531210
Import Export
Media: 6
Personnel:
Royce King *(Pres)*

LODGIAN INC.
(Holding of Lone Star Funds)
3445 Peachtree Rd NE Ste 700
Atlanta, GA 30326
Tel.: (404) 364-9400
Fax: (404) 364-0088
E-mail: corphq@lodgian.com
Web Site: www.lodgian.com
Approx. Rev.: $188,544,000
Approx. Number Employees: 1,686
Year Founded: 1998
Business Description:
Hotel Owner & Operator
S.I.C.: 7011; 8741
N.A.I.C.S.: 721199; 561110; 721110
Advertising Expenditures: $9,328,000
Personnel:
Daniel E. Ellis *(Gen Counsel, Sec & Exec VP)*

LOEWS HOTELS HOLDING CORPORATION
(Sub. of Loews Corporation)
667 Madison Ave
New York, NY 10065
Tel.: (212) 521-2000
Fax: (212) 545-2525
Telex: 14
Web Site: www.loewshotels.com
Sales Range: $200-249.9 Million
Approx. Number Employees: 2,000
Business Description:
Hotel & Resort Operator
S.I.C.: 7011
N.A.I.C.S.: 721110
Advertising Expenditures: $3,000,000
Media: 2-6-8-9-19-23-25-30
Distr.: Natl.
Budget Set: Nov.
Personnel:
Jonathan M. Tisch *(Chm & CEO)*
Jack S. Adler *(Pres & COO)*
Vince Dunleavy *(CFO & Exec VP-Fin)*
Troy Furbay *(Exec VP-Acq & Dev)*
Sherrie Laveroni *(Exec VP-Ops)*
Felicia Fisher *(Sr VP-Sls & Strategic Plng)*
Nancy Mendelson *(Sr VP-Branding & Comm)*
Lark-Marie Anton *(VP-PR)*
Emily Goldfischer *(VP-PR)*
Alan Momeyer *(VP-HR)*
Marian Succoso *(VP-Adv & Creative)*
Ellen Gale *(Reg Dir-PR)*
Jen Duffy *(Dir-PR)*
Jennifer Hodges *(Dir-PR)*
Sarah Murov *(Dir-PR)*
Steven R. Spivak *(Dir-Sls & Mtkg)*
Anne Stephany *(Dir-PR)*

Key to Media (For complete agency information see *The Advertising Red Books-Agencies* edition):
1. Bus. Publs. 2. Cable T.V. 3. Catalogs & Directories. 4. Co-op Adv. 5. Consumer Mags. 6. D.M. to Bus. Estab.7. D.M. to Consumers
8. Daily Newsp. 9. Exhibits/Trade Shows 10. Foreign 11. Infomercial 12. Internet Adv.13. Multimedia 14. Network Radio
15. Network T.V. 16. Newsp. Distr. Mags. 17. Other 18. Outdoor (Posters, Transit) 19. Point of Purchase20. Premiums, Novelties
21. Product Samples 22. Special Events Mktg. 23. Spot Radio 24. Spot T.V. 25. Weekly Newsp. 26. Yellow Page Adv.

Loews Hotels Holding Corporation — (Continued)

Brands & Products:
LOEWS

Advertising Agency:
Agency212, LLC
(The Tucker Partnership, Inc. (Parent Company))
112 W 20th St 7th Fl
New York, NY 10011
Tel.: (212) 994-6700
Fax: (212) 994-6699

LOEWS LE CONCORDE

(Sub. of Loews Hotels Holding Corporation)
1225 Cours Du General De Montcalm
Quebec, QC G1R 4W6, Canada
Tel.: (418) 647-2222
Fax: (418) 647-4710
Toll Free: (800) 463-5256
E-mail: loewsleconcordeinfo@loewshotels.com
Web Site: www.loewshotels.com
Sales Range: $10-24.9 Million
Approx. Number Employees: 450
Business Description:
Operator of Hotels
S.I.C.: 7011
N.A.I.C.S.: 721110
Media: 30
Personnel:
Renee Gosselin *(Gen Dir)*

Advertising Agency:
Amalgame
580 Grand Allee Est, Bureau 250
Quebec, QC G1R 2K2, Canada
Tel.: (418) 529-1414
Fax: (418) 529-3894

LONG REALTY COMPANY

(Sub. of HomeServices of America, Inc.)
900 E River Rd
Tucson, AZ 85718-5600
Tel.: (520) 888-8844
Fax: (520) 887-3681
E-mail: info@longrealty.com
Web Site: www.longrealty.com
Sales Range: $50-74.9 Million
Approx. Number Employees: 90
Business Description:
Real Estate Company
S.I.C.: 6531
N.A.I.C.S.: 531210
Media: 2-4-8-9-13-25
Personnel:
Kip Longan *(Pres-Long Realty Co-Tucson Tanque Verde)*
Rosey Koberlein *(CEO-Long Companies Home Office)*
Jerome King *(Exec Dir & Broker-Designated)*
Chris Patterson *(Branch Mgr)*
Ken Ryan *(Branch Mgr-Tucson-Houghton)*
Jim Vernon *(Branch Mgr-Tucson-Northwest Catalina)*
Linda Casey *(Mgr-Sls)*
Alvaro Fragoso *(Mgr-Douglas)*
Dick Wroldson *(Mgr-Tucson Foothills)*

THE LUSK COMPANY

16592 Hale Ave
Irvine, CA 92606
Mailing Address:
PO Box 1174
Corona Del Mar, CA 92625-6174
Tel.: (949) 757-6100
Fax: (949) 493-7760
Sales Estimate: $10-19 Million
Approx. Number Employees: 28
Year Founded: 1954
Business Description:
Holding Company; Real Estate Developer
S.I.C.: 6519
N.A.I.C.S.: 531190
Advertising Expenditures: $500,000
Media: 2-7
Distr.: Reg.
Personnel:
John Halo *(Owner)*

THE MACERICH COMPANY

401 Wilshire Blvd Ste 700
Santa Monica, CA 90401
Mailing Address:
PO Box 2172
Santa Monica, CA 90407-2172
Tel.: (310) 394-6000
Fax: (310) 395-2791
E-mail: macerich@macerich.com
Web Site: www.macerich.com
Approx. Rev.: $758,559,000
Approx. Number Employees: 2,658
Year Founded: 1965
Business Description:
Real Estate Investment Trusts; Owner, Operator & Developer of Retail Properties
S.I.C.: 6798; 6531
N.A.I.C.S.: 525930; 531312
Media: 4-7-13
Personnel:
Arthur M. Coppola *(Chm & CEO)*
Dana K. Anderson *(Vice Chm)*
Edward C. Coppola *(Pres)*
Thomas E O'Hern *(CFO, Chief Acctg Officer, Treas & Sr Exec VP)*
J.P. Jones *(CIO & Sr VP)*
Richard A. Bayer *(Chief Legal Officer, Sec & Sr Exec VP)*
Stephen L. Spector *(Gen Counsel & Sr VP)*
Randy L. Brant *(Exec VP-Real Estate)*
John M. Genovese *(Exec VP-Dev)*
Tracey P. Gotsis *(Exec VP-Dev & Mktg)*
Eric Salo *(Exec VP)*
Christopher Zecchini *(Sr VP & Controller)*
Chet Cramin *(Sr VP & Assoc Gen Counsel)*
Michael J. Busenhart *(Sr VP-Acq)*
Doug Healy *(Sr VP-Leasing)*
Mark A. Jacoby *(Sr VP-Internal Audit)*
Scott Kingsmore *(Sr VP-Fin)*
Genene M. Kruger *(Sr VP-HR)*
Charles A. Mcphee *(Sr VP-Dev)*
Michael Nevins *(Sr VP-Leasing)*
Madonna R. Shannon *(Sr VP & Sr Corp Counsel)*
David M. Short *(Sr VP-Asset Mgmt)*
Dane F. Smith *(Sr VP)*
Tom Unis *(Sr VP-Natl Leasing Svcs & Retailer Rels)*
Ken Volk *(Sr VP-Dev)*
Traci Weber *(Sr VP-Strategic Mktg)*
Robert Williams *(Sr VP-Dev Leasing)*
Lamont Ewell *(Mgr)*
Dawn Simon *(Mgr-Mktg)*

Brands & Products:
MACERICH

Advertising Agency:
Lovell Public Relations, Inc.
8080 N Central Expwy Ste 1410
Dallas, TX 75026-1817
Tel.: (972) 788-4511
Fax: (972) 788-4322

MACK-CALI REALTY CORPORATION

343 Thornall St
Edison, NJ 08837-2206
Mailing Address:
PO Box 7817
Edison, NJ 08818-7817
Tel.: (732) 590-1000
Fax: (732) 205-8237
E-mail: investorrelations@mack-cali.com
Web Site: www.mack-cali.com
Approx. Rev.: $787,480,000
Approx. Number Employees: 390
Year Founded: 1949
Business Description:
Real Estate Investment Services
S.I.C.: 6798
N.A.I.C.S.: 525930
Advertising Expenditures: $65,000
Media: 2-7-9-10-13-25
Personnel:
William L. Mack *(Chm)*
Mitchell E. Hersh *(Pres & CEO)*
Barry Lefkowitz *(CFO & Exec VP)*
Roger W. Thomas *(Gen Counsel, Sec & Exec VP)*
Michael A. Grossman *(Exec VP)*
John J. Crandall *(Sr VP-Dev)*
Anthony Krug *(Sr VP-Fin)*
Gabe Sasso *(Sr VP)*
Dean Cingolani *(First VP-Property Mgmt-Northern NJ)*
Anthony P. DeCaro, Jr. *(First VP-Property Mgmt-Central NJ)*
Daniel Wagner *(VP, Sr Assoc Gen Counsel & Asst Sec)*
William Fitzpatrick *(VP-Treasury)*
Nicholas Mitarotonda, Jr. *(VP-Info Sys)*
Janice H. Torchinsky *(VP-HR)*
Brian Decillis *(Sr Dir-Leasing)*

Brands & Products:
MACK-CALI
MOVE IN GET MORE

Advertising Agency:
Rubenstein Associates, Inc.
1345 Ave of the Americas Fl 30
New York, NY 10105-0109
Tel.: (212) 843-8000
Fax: (212) 843-9200
Pub Rels

MAGNUSON CORPORATION

100 Parnell St
Merritt Island, FL 32953
Tel.: (321) 449-9501
Fax: (321) 449-9504
Approx. Number Employees: 33
Business Description:
Real Estate Developer
S.I.C.: 6552; 6531
N.A.I.C.S.: 237210; 531210
Media: 1-11
Distr.: Natl.
Personnel:
John Moynahan *(Pres)*

MAMMOTH MOUNTAIN SKI AREA

(Sub. of Starwood Capital Group Global LLC)
1 Minaret Rd
Mammoth Lakes, CA 93546
Mailing Address:
PO Box 24
Mammoth Lakes, CA 93546
Tel.: (760) 934-2571
Fax: (760) 934-0603
Toll Free: (800) MAMMOTH
Web Site:
www.mammothmountain.com
E-Mail For Key Personnel:
Public Relations: dvanderhouwen@mammoth-mtn.com
Approx. Number Employees: 800
Business Description:
Ski Resort Services
S.I.C.: 7999; 7011
N.A.I.C.S.: 713920; 721110
Personnel:
Rusty Gregory *(Chm & CEO)*
Joani Lynch *(Dir-Comm)*
Josh Chauvet *(Brand Mgr-Action Sports)*

Advertising Agencies:
Colle+McVoy
400 1st Ave N Ste 700
Minneapolis, MN 55401-1954
Tel.: (612) 305-6000
Fax: (612) 305-6500
Agency of Record
Creative
Strategy

Initiative San Diego
4747 Executive Dr Ste 1080
San Diego, CA 92131
Tel.: (858) 877-2705
Fax: (858) 877-2701
(Media Buying)

MANDALAY CORP.

(Sub. of MGM Resorts International)
(d/b/a Mandalay Bay Resort & Casino)
3950 Las Vegas Blvd S
Las Vegas, NV 89119
Tel.: (702) 632-7777
Fax: (702) 632-7234
Web Site: www.mandalaybay.com
Sales Range: $350-399.9 Million
Approx. Number Employees: 7,000
Business Description:
Hotel & Casino Operator
S.I.C.: 7011; 7999
N.A.I.C.S.: 721120; 713290
Personnel:
Renee West *(Pres & COO)*
Randy Boynton *(Exec Dir-Mktg)*
Mark Cherry *(Assoc Dir-Sls)*
Jennifer Muna *(Assoc Dir-Tradeshow Sls)*
Daniel Rush *(Assoc Dir-Sls)*
Kathy Perlsweig *(Sr Mgr-Natl Sls)*
Rosalyn Putnam *(Natl Sls Mgr-Northeast)*

Advertising Agency:
MMG Worldwide
4601 Madison Ave
Kansas City, MO 64112
Tel.: (816) 472-5988
Fax: (816) 471-5395

MARCUS & MILLICHAP REAL ESTATE INVESTMENT COMPANY

16830 Ventura Blvd Ste 352
Encino, CA 91436
Tel.: (818) 907-0600
Fax: (818) 212-2710

Key to Media (For complete agency information see *The Advertising Red Books-Agencies* edition):
1. Bus. Publs. 2. Cable T.V. 3. Catalogs & Directories. 4. Co-op Adv. 5. Consumer Mags. 6. D.M. to Bus. Estab.7. D.M. to Consumers
8. Daily Newsp. 9. Exhibits/Trade Shows 10. Foreign 11. Infomercial 12. Internet Adv.13. Multimedia 14. Network Radio
15. Network T.V. 16. Newsp. Distr. Mags. 17. Other 18. Outdoor (Posters, Transit) 19. Point of Purchase20. Premiums, Novelties
21. Product Samples 22. Special Events Mktg. 23. Spot Radio 24. Spot T.V. 25. Weekly Newsp. 26. Yellow Page Adv.

Web Site: www.marcusmillichap.com
Sales Range: $600-649.9 Million
Approx. Number Employees: 850
Year Founded: 1971
Business Description:
Real Estate Services
S.I.C.: 6531
N.A.I.C.S.: 531210
Media: 4-9-10-25
Personnel:
George M. Marcus *(Chm)*
William A. Millichap *(Co-Chm)*
John K. Kerin *(Pres & CEO)*
Stuart E. Kaiser *(Mng Dir & CFO)*
Paul S. Mudrich *(Mng Dir, Chief Legal Officer & Sr VP)*
Hessam Nadji *(Sr VP & Mng Dir-Res & Advisory Svcs)*
David A. Wetta *(Mng Dir & Sr VP)*
Bernard Haddigan *(Mng Dir & Sr VP)*
William T. Hughes *(Mng Dir & Sr VP)*
Gary R. Lucas *(Mng Dir & Sr VP)*
Linwood C. Thompson *(Mng Dir & Sr VP)*
Richard Peltz *(CIO & Sr VP)*
Donald A. Lorenz *(Chief Investment Officer)*
Gene A. Berman *(Exec VP)*
Jonathan Weiss *(Sr VP)*
Jerry Goldstein *(First VP-Investments)*
Bill Rose *(Dir-Natl Retail Grp)*

THE MARCUS CORPORATION
100 E Wisconsin Ave Ste 1900
Milwaukee, WI 53202-4125
Tel.: (414) 905-1000
Fax: (414) 905-2879
E-mail: joanvoelzke@marcuscorp.com
Web Site: www.marcuscorp.com
Approx. Rev.: $377,004,000
Approx. Number Employees: 6,200
Year Founded: 1935
Business Description:
Owner & Operator of Hotels, Motels & Theaters
S.I.C.: 7011; 7832
N.A.I.C.S.: 721110; 512131
Advertising Expenditures: $19,608,000
Media: 5-8-9-18-19-23-24-25-26
Distr.: Natl.
Personnel:
Stephen H. Marcus *(Chm)*
Gregory S. Marcus *(Pres & CEO)*
Douglas A. Neis *(CFO & Treas)*
Jane Durment *(CIO)*
Thomas F. Kissinger *(Gen Counsel, Sec & VP)*
J. David Merritt *(Sr VP-Dev)*
Bruce J. Olson *(Sr VP)*
Bruce Hoffmann *(Sr Dir-Fin & Asst Treas)*
Diane Marcus Gershowitz *(Dir-Real Estate Investment & Mgmt)*
Karen Y. Spindler *(Dir-HR)*
Joan Voelzke *(Mgr-IR)*
Brands & Products:
BAYMONT INNS AND SUITES
BIG SCREEN BISTRO
BUDGETEL INN
GUEST OVATIONS
HOT ZONE
THE MARCUS CORPORATION
MARCUS THEATERS
WOODFIELD SUITES
ZAFFIRO'S

MARI VESCI REALTORS, INC.
9000 Gulf Shore Dr
Naples, FL 34108
Tel.: (239) 566-8989
Fax: (239) 594-9440
Toll Free: (800) 24-VESCI
E-mail: vesci@vesci.com
Web Site: www.vesci.com
Approx. Number Employees: 30
Year Founded: 1998
Business Description:
Real Estate Services
S.I.C.: 6531
N.A.I.C.S.: 531210
Media: 6
Personnel:
Mari Vesci *(Owner)*

MARKET LEADER, INC.
11332 NE 122nd Way
Kirkland, WA 98034-6916
Tel.: (425) 952-5500
E-mail: info@marketleader.com
Web Site: www.marketleader.com/
Approx. Rev.: $24,430,000
Approx. Number Employees: 186
Year Founded: 1999
Business Description:
Real Estate & Mortgage Lead Generation
S.I.C.: 6531; 2741; 7311
N.A.I.C.S.: 531320; 516110; 531210; 531390; 541810
Advertising Expenditures: $11,032,000
Media: 7-13-15-22-23-24
Personnel:
Frank M. Higgins *(Chm)*
Ian Morris *(Pres & CEO)*
Jacqueline L. Davidson *(CFO)*
Robert Bill *(VP & Gen Mgr-Broker Svcs)*
Scott Smith *(VP-Sls & Bus Strategy)*
Sue Iverson *(Sr Dir-HR)*
Mark Lamb *(Dir-IR)*
Brands & Products:
GROWTHLEADER.COM
HOUSEVALUES
JUSTLISTED.COM
MARKETLEADER
REALTYGENERATOR.COM
TEAMLEADER.COM

MARRIOTT INTERNATIONAL, INC.
10400 Fernwood Rd
Bethesda, MD 20817
Mailing Address:
1 Marriott Dr
Washington, DC 20058
Tel.: (301) 380-3000
Fax: (301) 380-3969
Telex: 89597
E-mail: investorrelations@marriott.com
Web Site: www.marriott.com
Approx. Rev.: $11,691,000,000
Approx. Number Employees: 129,000
Year Founded: 1927
Business Description:
Hotels & Related Lodging Facilities Operation & Franchise Services
S.I.C.: 7011
N.A.I.C.S.: 721110
Export
Media: 2-3-6-9-14-15-18-22-23-24
Distr.: Intl.; Natl.
Personnel:
J. Willard Marriott, Jr. *(Chm & CEO)*
John W. Marriott, III *(Vice Chm)*
Arne M. Sorenson *(Pres & COO)*
Carl T. Berquist *(CFO & Exec VP)*
Carl Wilson *(CIO & Exec VP)*
R. Lee Cunningham *(Exec VP & Chief Bus Officer-Marriott Vacation Club Intl)*
Edwin D. Fuller *(Pres/Mng Dir-Lodging Intl Ops)*
Amy C. McPherson *(Pres/Mng Dir-Europe)*
David J. Grissen *(Pres-Americas Div)*
Robert J. McCarthy Jr. *(Pres-North American Lodging Ops & Global Brand Mgmt)*
Stephen P. Weisz *(Pres-Marriott Vacation Club)*
Edward A. Ryan *(Gen Counsel & Exec VP)*
A. Bradford Bryan *(Exec VP-Architecture & Construction)*
Tony G. Capuano *(Exec VP-Global Dev)*
Michael E. Dearing *(Exec VP-Project Fin)*
Paul Foskey *(Exec VP-Lodging Dev-Asia Pacific)*
Geoffrey Garside *(Exec VP-Loding Ops-Asia Pacific)*
Carolyn B. Handlon *(Exec VP-Fin & Global Treas)*
Richard S. Hoffman *(Exec VP-Mergers, Acq & Bus Dev)*
Herve Humler *(Exec VP-Intl Ops)*
Kevin P. Kearney *(Exec VP-EMEA)*
Brendan M. Keegan *(Exec VP-HR)*
Charles Kelley *(Exec VP-Lodging Ops-Caribbean & Latin America)*
Kevin M. Kimball *(Exec VP-Fin Marriott Lodging)*
Kathleen Matthews *(Exec VP-Global Comm & Pub Affairs)*
Scott E. Melby *(Exec VP-Dev Plng & Feasibility)*
M. Lester Pulse, Jr. *(Exec VP-Taxes)*
David A. Rodriguez *(Exec VP-Global HR)*
Craig Smith *(Exec VP-Asia-Pacific)*
Tim Miller *(Sr VP & Mng Dir-Edition Hotels)*
Nancy C. Lee *(Sr VP & Deputy Gen Counsel)*
Steven M. Goldman *(Sr VP & Assoc Gen Counsel)*
W. David Mann *(Sr VP & Assoc Gen Counsel)*
Tina Edmundson *(Sr VP-Lifestyle Brands & Renaissance Ops)*
Deborah Fell *(Sr VP-Mktg Strategy)*
James C. Fisher *(Sr VP-Franchise Svcs)*
Deborah Marriott Harrison *(Sr VP-Govt Affairs)*
Brian King *(Sr VP)*
Stephanie Coleman Linnartz *(Sr VP-Sls-Global)*
Jimmie Walton Paschall *(Sr VP-External Affairs & Global Diversity Officer)*
Laura E. Paugh *(Sr VP-IR)*
Susan Thronson *(Sr VP-Mktg-Global)*
Peggy Fang Roe *(VP-Global Brand Mgmt)*
Leigh Anne Ambrose *(Sr Dir-Global Incentives & Gift Cards)*
Ganesh Bala *(Sr Dir-Mktg Measurement & Analysis)*
Matthew Carroll *(Sr Dir-Dev Mktg & Franchise Svcs)*
Michelle Lapierre *(Sr Dir-Customer Relationship Mktg)*
Jackie McAllister *(Mktg Dir-Strategy & Programs)*
Mike Burns *(Dir-Mktg Activation)*
Todd Castor *(Dir-Vacation Packaging Products)*
Dan Dillon *(Dir-Loss Prevention & Shipping Marriott O'Hare)*
Debra Schacher *(Reg Mgr-Mktg & Ecommerce)*
Allyson Musci *(Mgr-Mktg Strategy)*
Bruce Rohr *(Mgr-Sls & Mktg Svcs)*
Kelly Snyder *(Mgr-Email Mktg)*
Brands & Products:
BULGARI
COURTYARD BY MARRIOTT
COURTYARD CLUB
EXECUSTAY
FAIRFIELD INN
GRAND RESIDENCES
HORIZONS BY MARRIOTT
JW MARRIOTT
MARRIOTT
MARRIOTT VACATION CLUB
RAMADA
RENAISSANCE
RESIDENCE INN
RITZ-CARLTON
SPRINGHILL SUITES
TOWNEPLACE SUITES
TRAVEL PLAZAS BY MARRIOTT
Advertising Agencies:
22squared
1170 Peachtree St NE 15th Fl
Atlanta, GA 30309-7649
Tel.: (404) 347-8700
Fax: (404) 347-8800
Courtyard
Fairfield Inn
JW Marriott
Marriott Hotels & Resorts
Renaissance
Residence Inn
SpringHill Suites
TownPlace Suites

Acxiom Digital
1051 Hillsdale Blvd Ste 400
Foster City, CA 94404
Tel.: (650) 356-3400
Fax: (650) 356-3410

Alison Brod Public Relations
373 Park Ave S 4th Fl
New York, NY 10016
Tel.: (212) 230-1800
Fax: (212) 230-1161
U.S. Agency of Record

Carat
150 E 42nd St
New York, NY 10017
Tel.: (212) 689-6800
Fax: (212) 689-6005

McGarry Bowen, LLC
601 W 26th St Ste 1150
New York, NY 10001
Tel.: (212) 598-2900
Fax: (212) 598-2996

Publicis Hong Kong
23/F 1063 Kings Road
Hong Kong, China (Hong Kong)

Key to Media (For complete agency information see *The Advertising Red Books-Agencies* edition):
1. Bus. Publs. 2. Cable T.V. 3. Catalogs & Directories. 4. Co-op Adv. 5. Consumer Mags. 6. D.M. to Bus. Estab.7. D.M. to Consumers
8. Daily Newsp. 9. Exhibits/Trade Shows 10. Foreign 11. Infomercial 12. Internet Adv.13. Multimedia 14. Network Radio
15. Network T.V. 16. Newsp. Distr. Mags. 17. Other 18. Outdoor (Posters, Transit) 19. Point of Purchase20. Premiums, Novelties
21. Product Samples 22. Special Events Mktg. 23. Spot Radio 24. Spot T.V. 25. Weekly Newsp. 26. Yellow Page Adv.

Marriott International, Inc. — (Continued)

Tel.: (852) 2590 5888
Fax: (852) 2856 9905

Rosetta
3700 Park East Dr Ste 300
Cleveland, OH 44122
Tel.: (216) 896-8900
Fax: (216) 896-8991

MATRIX DEVELOPMENT GROUP INC.

Forsgate Dr CN 4000
Cranbury, NJ 08512
Tel.: (732) 521-2900
Fax: (609) 395-8289
E-mail: hbudny@matrixcompanies.com
Web Site: www.matrixcompanies.com
Approx. Number Employees: 60
Year Founded: 1979
Business Description:
Real Estate Investor & Developer
S.I.C.: 6552
N.A.I.C.S.: 237210
Media: 2
Personnel:
Joseph S. Taylor *(Pres & CEO)*
Donald M. Epstein *(CFO)*
Richard Johnson *(Sr VP)*

MCGRATH RENTCORP

5700 Las Positas Rd
Livermore, CA 94551
Tel.: (925) 606-9200
Fax: (925) 453-3200
Toll Free: (800) 352-2900
E-mail: information@mgrc.com
Web Site: www.mgrc.com
Approx. Rev.: $291,374,000
Approx. Number Employees: 655
Year Founded: 1979
Business Description:
Relocatable Modular Office & Classroom Space & Electronic Test Equipment Mfr, Retailer & Renter
S.I.C.: 7359
N.A.I.C.S.: 532490; 532210; 532310
Media: 7-10-18-26
Distr.: Natl.
Budget Set: Apr.
Personnel:
Ronald H. Zech *(Chm)*
Dennis C. Kakures *(Pres & CEO)*
Keith E. Pratt *(CFO)*
Joseph F. Hanna *(COO & Sr VP)*
Randle F. Rose *(Chief Admin Officer & Sr VP)*
Phil B. Hawkins *(VP & Div Mgr)*
Kay Dashner *(VP-HR)*
Brands & Products:
MCGRATH
MOBILE MODULAR
TRS ENVIRONMENTAL
TRSRENTELCO
WE'RE TALKING RENTS

MCLEAN FAULCONER INC.

503 Faulconer Dr Ste 5
Charlottesville, VA 22903
Tel.: (434) 295-1131
Fax: (434) 293-7377
E-mail: homes@mcleanfaulconer.com
Web Site: www.mcleanfaulconer.com
Approx. Sls.: $486,000,000
Approx. Number Employees: 14
Year Founded: 1980
Business Description:
Real Estate Services
S.I.C.: 6531
N.A.I.C.S.: 531210
Media: 6-9-13-25-26
Personnel:
James W. Faulconer, Jr. *(Owner & Principal Broker)*
Stephen T. McLean *(Pres)*

MCO PROPERTIES INC.

(Sub. of MAXXAM Property Company)
13620 N Sagaro Blvd Ste 200
Fountain Hills, AZ 85268
Tel.: (480) 837-9660
Fax: (480) 837-1677
E-mail: info@mcoproperties.com
Web Site: www.mcoproperties.com
Sales Range: $10-24.9 Million
Approx. Number Employees: 10
Business Description:
Land Development Services
S.I.C.: 6531; 6513; 8699
N.A.I.C.S.: 531210; 531110; 531311; 531312; 531320; 531390; 813990
Advertising Expenditures: $500,000
Media: 3-6-8-9-10-18-20-25
Distr.: Natl.
Personnel:
Jeremy Hall *(Pres)*
Shelly Johnson *(Dir-Mktg & PR)*

M.D.C. HOLDINGS, INC.

4350 S Monaco St Ste 500
Denver, CO 80237
Tel.: (303) 773-1100
Fax: (303) 741-4134
Web Site: www.mdcholdings.com
Approx. Rev.: $958,655,000
Approx. Number Employees: 1,119
Year Founded: 1971
Business Description:
Homebuilding & Financial Services
S.I.C.: 1531; 1521; 6159; 6289
N.A.I.C.S.: 236117; 236115; 522292; 523999
Advertising Expenditures: $8,000,000
Media: 6-8-9-10-13-18-23-25
Personnel:
Larry A. Mizel *(Chm & CEO)*
David D. Mandarich *(Pres & COO)*
Zane DeHerrera *(CMO & VP-Mktg)*
Vilia Valentine *(Chief Acctg Officer, VP-Fin & Controller)*
Joseph H. Fretz *(Sec & Corp Counsel)*
Michael Touff *(Gen Counsel & Sr VP)*
John J. Heaney *(Treas & Sr VP)*
Ed Gwynn *(VP-Fin & Controller)*
Shelley Casagrande *(VP-Internal Audit)*
Robert N. Martin *(VP-Fin & Bus Dev)*
Advertising Agency:
Enlighten
3027 Miller Rd
Ann Arbor, MI 48103
Tel.: (734) 668-6678
Fax: (734) 668-1883

MERRITT PROPERTIES, LLC

(Sub. of Merritt Management Corporation)
2066 Lord Baltimore Dr
Baltimore, MD 21244
Tel.: (410) 298-2600
Business Description:
Commercial & Industrial Building Operation
S.I.C.: 6512; 6513; 6531
N.A.I.C.S.: 531120; 531110; 531311
Personnel:
Leroy Merritt, Sr. *(Founder)*
Advertising Agency:
Planit
500 E Pratt St 10th Fl
Baltimore, MD 21202
Tel.: (410) 962-8500
Fax: (410) 962-8508
Interactive
Public Relations

MGM GRAND HOTEL, LLC

(Sub. of MGM Resorts International)
(d/b/a MGM Grand Hotel & Casino)
3799 Las Vegas Blvd S
Las Vegas, NV 89109-4319
Tel.: (702) 891-1111
Fax: (702) 891-3036
Toll Free: (800) 929-1111
Web Site: www.mgmgrand.com
Sales Range: $700-749.9 Million
Approx. Number Employees: 9,300
Year Founded: 1989
Business Description:
Hotel, Casino & Entertainment
S.I.C.: 7011
N.A.I.C.S.: 721120
Media: 4-6
Personnel:
Gamal Aziz *(Pres)*
Michael Neubecker *(CFO)*
Gary Jacobs *(Gen Counsel, Sec, Exec VP & Dir)*
Alan Feldman *(Sr VP-Pub Affairs)*
Cynthia Murphey *(Sr VP-HR)*
Teresa Fry-Drew *(Dir-Adv & Mktg)*
Michelle White *(Dir-Sls)*
Advertising Agency:
Barkley
1740 Main St
Kansas City, MO 64108
Tel.: (816) 842-1500

MGM RESORTS INTERNATIONAL

3600 Las Vegas Blvd S
Las Vegas, NV 89109-4303
Tel.: (702) 693-7120
Fax: (702) 693-8626
Web Site: www.mgmmirage.com
Approx. Rev.: $6,652,761,000
Approx. Number Employees: 45,000
Year Founded: 1986
Business Description:
Holding Company; Casino, Casino Hotel & Resort Owner & Operator
S.I.C.: 6719; 7011; 7997; 7999
N.A.I.C.S.: 551112; 713210; 713910; 721120
Advertising Expenditures: $123,000,000
Media: 6-9-11-13-14-15-18-19-21-22
Personnel:
James J. Murren *(Chm & CEO)*
Cynthia Kiser Murphey *(Pres & COO)*
Daniel J. D'Arrigo *(CFO)*
Corey I. Sanders *(COO)*
William J. Hornbuckle *(CMO)*
Aldo Manzini *(Chief Admin Officer & Exec VP)*
Robert C. Selwood *(Chief Acctg Officer & Exec VP)*
Robert H. Baldwin *(Chief Design Officer & Chief Construction Officer)*
Ken Rosevear *(Pres-Dev)*
Jeff Pryor *(Exec VP)*
Alan Feldman *(Sr VP-Pub Affairs)*
Phyllis A. James *(Sr VP & Sr Counsel)*
Shawn T. Sani *(Sr VP-Tax)*
Jennifer Michaels *(VP-PR)*
Lou Ragg *(VP-Internet Ops & Mktg)*
Stacy Hamilton *(Dir- Pub Rels)*
Michael Weiss *(Dir-Internet Mktg)*
Brands & Products:
MGM GRAND
MGM GRAND HOTEL
NEW YORK, NEW YORK
Advertising Agencies:
David & Goliath
909 N Sepulveda Blvd Ste 700
El Segundo, CA 90245
Tel.: (310) 445-5200
Fax: (310) 445-5201
(Monte Carlo Resort & Casino, New York Hotel & Casino)

Masterminds
6727 Delilah Rd
Egg Harbor Township, NJ 08234
Tel.: (609) 484-0009
Fax: (609) 484-1909

MGM MIRAGE Advertising, Inc.
3260 Industrial Rd
Las Vegas, NV 89109-1132
Tel.: (702) 792-4990
Fax: (702) 792-4940

MICHAEL SAUNDERS & COMPANY

100 S Washington Blvd
Sarasota, FL 34236
Tel.: (941) 951-6650
Fax: (941) 342-8528
Toll Free: (888) 552-5228
Web Site: www.michaelsaunders.com
Approx. Sls.: $2,000,000,000
Approx. Number Employees: 300
Year Founded: 1976
Business Description:
Real Estate Services
S.I.C.: 6531
N.A.I.C.S.: 531210
Advertising Expenditures: $4,000,000
Media: 1-3-4-6-9-13-15-25
Personnel:
Michael Saunders *(Founder & CEO)*
Drayton Saunders *(Pres)*
Eileen Lyle *(Exec Dir-Sls)*
Amy Drake *(Dir-New Homes & Condominiums)*
JoAnne Whalen *(Mgr-Relocation-Corp Mgmt Svcs Div)*

THE MILLS PROPERTIES

(Sub. of Simon Property Group, Inc.)
5425 Wisconsin Ave Ste 500
Chevy Chase, MD 20815
Tel.: (301) 968-6000
Web Site: www.simon.com
Sales Range: $650-699.9 Million
Approx. Number Employees: 1,150
Year Founded: 1967
Business Description:
Real Estate Investment Trust; Regional Retail & Entertainment Projects Owner, Developer, Manager & Marketer
S.I.C.: 6798; 6552
N.A.I.C.S.: 525930; 237210
Advertising Expenditures: $5,000,000
Media: 3-6-9-18-21-23-24-25
Distr.: Intl.; Natl.; Reg.
Budget Set: Dec.

Key to Media (For complete agency information see *The Advertising Red Books-Agencies* edition):
1. Bus. Publs. 2. Cable T.V. 3. Catalogs & Directories. 4. Co-op Adv. 5. Consumer Mags. 6. D.M. to Bus. Estab.7. D.M. to Consumers
8. Daily Newsp. 9. Exhibits/Trade Shows 10. Foreign 11. Infomercial 12. Internet Adv.13. Multimedia 14. Network Radio
15. Network T.V. 16. Newsp. Distr. Mags. 17. Other 18. Outdoor (Posters, Transit) 19. Point of Purchase20. Premiums, Novelties
21. Product Samples 22. Special Events Mktg. 23. Spot Radio 24. Spot T.V. 25. Weekly Newsp. 26. Yellow Page Adv.

Personnel:
Gary Duncan *(Exec VP-Leasing)*
Paul C. Fickinger *(Exec VP-Property Mgmt)*
Rob Mercer *(Exec VP-Dev)*
Kelly Mikesell *(Mktg Dir)*
Brands & Products:
EXPAND RETAIL BOUNDARIES
THE MILLS

MIRAGE RESORTS INCORPORATED

(Sub. of MGM Resorts International)
3400 Las Vegas Blvd S
Las Vegas, NV 89109-8923
Mailing Address:
PO Box 7777
Las Vegas, NV 89177-0777
Tel.: (702) 791-7111
Fax: (702) 792-7676
Toll Free: (800) 477-5110
E-mail: support@mirageresorts.com
Web Site: www.mirageresorts.com
Sales Range: $300-349.9 Million
Approx. Number Employees: 7,000
Year Founded: 1946
Business Description:
Gaming Casinos & Resorts
S.I.C.: 7011
N.A.I.C.S.: 721120
Advertising Expenditures: $5,000,000
Media: 2-3-4-6-7-8-9-10-11-13-18-22-23-24-25-26
Distr.: Direct to Consumer; Reg.
Budget Set: Nov. -Dec.
Personnel:
Scott Sibella *(Pres)*
Lora Lee *(VP-HR)*
Tyler Shook *(VP-Mktg)*
Brands & Products:
BEAU RIVAGE RESORTS
BELLAGIO RESORTS
GOLDEN NUGGET
MIRAGE

MIRAVAL RESORT

5000 E Via Estancia Miraval
Catalina, AZ 85739
Tel.: (520) 825-4000
Fax: (520) 818-5870
Toll Free: (800) 232-3969
Web Site: www.miravalresort.com
Approx. Number Employees: 200
Business Description:
Resort & Hotel
S.I.C.: 7011; 7231
N.A.I.C.S.: 721110; 812112
Media: 6-10-23-24
Personnel:
Wyatt Webb *(Dir-Equine Programs)*
Dana Mohaupt Wendell *(Mgr-Mktg)*
Brands & Products:
LIFE IN BALANCE
MIRAVAL

MISSION INN RESORTS INC.

10400 County Rd 48
Howey in the Hills, FL 34737
Tel.: (352) 324-3101
Tel.: (352) 324-2024 (Mktg & Pub Rels)
Fax: (352) 324-2636
E-mail: frontoffice@missioninnresort.com
Web Site: www.missioninnresort.com
E-Mail For Key Personnel:
Marketing Director: marketing@missioninnresort.com
Sales Director: sales@missioninnresort.com
Public Relations: publicrelations@missioninnresort.com
Sales Range: $10-24.9 Million
Approx. Number Employees: 200
Business Description:
Golf Course, Hotel & Resort Owner & Operator
S.I.C.: 7997; 7011; 7999
N.A.I.C.S.: 713910; 713990; 721110
Media: 6-22
Personnel:
Robert Beucher *(Pres)*
Chuck Kelset *(Dir-Sls)*

MORGANS HOTEL GROUP CO.

475 10th Ave
New York, NY 10018
Tel.: (212) 277-4100
Fax: (212) 277-4260
Web Site:
www.morganshotelgroup.com
Approx. Rev.: $236,370,000
Approx. Number Employees: 4,600
Year Founded: 1984
Business Description:
Hotel Owner & Operator
S.I.C.: 7011
N.A.I.C.S.: 721110
Advertising Expenditures: $10,400,000
Media: 6-7-8-9-13-22-23-24-25
Personnel:
David T. Hamamoto, II *(Chm)*
Michael Jonathan Gross *(CEO)*
Richard Szymanski *(CFO)*
Daniel R. Flannery *(COO)*
Scott S. Williams *(Chief Insight Officer)*
David Smail *(Gen Counsel & Exec VP)*
Joseph A. Magliarditi *(Exec VP-Gaming)*
David Weidlich *(Exec VP-Ops)*
M. Thomas Buoy *(Sr VP-Customer Mktg & Revenue Mgmt)*
Brian Jones *(Sr VP-Sls)*
David Freiberger *(VP-Guest Experience)*
Fernando Cerna *(Dir-Global Sls)*
Kim Walker *(Dir-Creative)*
Advertising Agency:
Joele Frank, Wilkinson Brimmer Katcher
140 E 45th St 37th Fl
New York, NY 10017
Tel.: (212) 355-4449
Fax: (212) 355-4554

MOTEL 6

(Sub. of Accor Economy Lodging)
4001 International Pkwy
Carrollton, TX 75007
Tel.: (972) 360-9000
Fax: (972) 360-5995
Web Site: www.motel6.com
Approx. Number Employees: 400
Year Founded: 1962
Business Description:
Motels
S.I.C.: 7011
N.A.I.C.S.: 721110
Media: 14-15-17-18
Personnel:
Jim Amorosia *(Pres & COO)*
Olivier Poirot *(CEO)*
Lance Miceli *(CMO-Motel 6 & Studio 6)*

MRI SOFTWARE, LLC

(Formerly Intuit Real Estate Solutions, Inc.)
(Holding of Vista Equity Partners LLC)
20800 Harvard Rd
Cleveland, OH 44122
Tel.: (216) 464-3225
Fax: (216) 464-5488
Toll Free: (800) 321-8770
Web Site: www.mrisoftware.com
E-Mail For Key Personnel:
Sales Director: sales@mrisoftware.com
Sales Range: $75-99.9 Million
Approx. Number Employees: 340
Year Founded: 1971
Business Description:
Property Management Software
S.I.C.: 7372; 6531; 7374
N.A.I.C.S.: 511210; 518210; 531390
Media: 10
Personnel:
David Post *(CEO)*
John Ensign *(Gen Counsel)*
Andrew Rains *(VP-Mktg)*
Parrish Snyder *(VP-Global Sls)*
Adam Wallace *(VP-Product Dev)*
Advertising Agency:
Richards Communications
3201 Enterprise Pkwy Ste 400
Beachwood, OH 44122
Tel.: (216) 514-7800
Fax: (216) 514-7801

NAPLES BEACH HOTEL & GOLF CLUB

851 Gulf Shore Blvd N
Naples, FL 34102
Tel.: (239) 261-2222
Fax: (239) 261-7380
Toll Free: (800) 455-1546
E-mail: m.marsee@naplesbeachhotel.com
Web Site:
www.naplesbeachhotel.com
Approx. Number Employees: 360
Business Description:
Hotel & Resort
S.I.C.: 7011; 7997
N.A.I.C.S.: 721110; 713910
Media: 2-6
Personnel:
Jason Parsons *(Gen Mgr)*
Claudia Jonsson *(Mgr-Sls)*
Advertising Agency:
Chisano Marketing Group, Inc.
2170 W State Rd 434 Ste 280
Longwood, FL 32779-4993
Tel.: (407) 788-7070
Fax: (407) 788-7090
Public Relations

NAPLES GRANDE RESORT AND CLUB

(Sub. of Boca Resorts, Inc.)
475 Seagate Dr
Naples, FL 34103
Tel.: (239) 597-3232
Fax: (239) 594-6310
Toll Free: (800) 247-9810
Web Site:
www.naplesgranderesort.com
Sales Range: $125-149.9 Million
Business Description:
Resort
S.I.C.: 7011
N.A.I.C.S.: 721110
Media: 2-4-6-8-13

NEVADA GOLD & CASINOS, INC.

50 Briar Hollow Ln Ste 500W
Houston, TX 77027
Tel.: (713) 621-2245
Fax: (713) 627-6919
E-mail: info@nevadagold.com
Web Site: www.nevadagold.com/
Approx. Rev.: $24,843,876
Approx. Number Employees: 481
Business Description:
Gaming Facilities & Lodging Owner & Operator
S.I.C.: 7011; 7999
N.A.I.C.S.: 721120; 713210
Advertising Expenditures: $1,612,000
Media: 17
Personnel:
William J. Sherlock *(Chm)*
Robert B. Sturges *(Pres & CEO)*
James Kohn *(CFO & Sr VP)*

NEWMAN-DAILEY RESORT PROPERTIES, INC.

12815 Hwy 98 W Ste 100
Destin, FL 32550
Mailing Address:
PO Box 1779
Destin, FL 32540
Tel.: (850) 837-1071
Fax: (850) 654-1932
Toll Free: (800) 225-7652
E-mail: info@destinsales.com
Web Site: www.destinsales.com
E-Mail For Key Personnel:
Sales Director: sales@ndrp.com
Approx. Number Employees: 47
Year Founded: 1985
Business Description:
Real Estate Owner
S.I.C.: 6531
N.A.I.C.S.: 531210
Media: 6-8-13
Personnel:
Jeanne Dailey *(Pres & Co-Founder)*

NORTHAMPTON GROUP INC.

2601 Matheson Blvd E Ste 212
Mississauga, ON L4W 5A8, Canada
Tel.: (905) 629-9992
Fax: (905) 629-9636
E-mail: admin@nhgi.com
Web Site: www.nhgi.com
Approx. Rev.: $25,114,915
Approx. Number Employees: 6
Year Founded: 1974
Business Description:
Hotel Operator
S.I.C.: 7011
N.A.I.C.S.: 721199; 721110
Personnel:
Vinod N. Patel *(Pres & CEO)*
Narendra C. Patel *(CFO & VP)*
Advertising Agency:
Fallon Worldwide
901 Marquette Ave Ste 2400
Minneapolis, MN 55402
Tel.: (612) 758-2345
Fax: (612) 758-2346
(Holiday Inn Express)

Key to Media (For complete agency information see *The Advertising Red Books-Agencies* edition):
1. Bus. Publs. 2. Cable T.V. 3. Catalogs & Directories. 4. Co-op Adv. 5. Consumer Mags. 6. D.M. to Bus. Estab.7. D.M. to Consumers
8. Daily Newsp. 9. Exhibits/Trade Shows 10. Foreign 11. Infomercial 12. Internet Adv.13. Multimedia 14. Network Radio
15. Network T.V. 16. Newsp. Distr. Mags. 17. Other 18. Outdoor (Posters, Transit) 19. Point of Purchase20. Premiums, Novelties
21. Product Samples 22. Special Events Mktg. 23. Spot Radio 24. Spot T.V. 25. Weekly Newsp. 26. Yellow Page Adv.

NTS DEVELOPMENT COMPANY
10172 Linn Sta Rd Ste 200
Louisville, KY 40223
Tel.: (502) 426-4800
Fax: (502) 426-4994
Web Site: www.ntsdevelopment.com
Approx. Sls.: $65,000,000
Approx. Number Employees: 350
Year Founded: 1968
Business Description:
Subdivider & Developer Services
S.I.C.: 6552; 6531
N.A.I.C.S.: 237210; 531210
Media: 2-6-8-10-13-18-22-25-26
Personnel:
Brian F. Lavin *(Pres & CEO)*
Ellen Lamb *(Dir-Corp Mktg)*

OCEAN PROPERTIES, LTD.
1001 Atlantic Ave
Delray Beach, FL 33444-1146
Tel.: (561) 279-9900
Fax: (561) 276-1563
Approx. Number Employees: 5,500
Year Founded: 1975
Business Description:
Hotel Management & Commercial Land Development Services
S.I.C.: 7011
N.A.I.C.S.: 721110
Advertising Expenditures: $1,100,000
Media: 2-4-9-17-18-25-26
Distr.: Natl.
Budget Set: Oct.
Personnel:
Linda Haserot *(VP-Sls & Mktg)*
Advertising Agencies:
The Boner Group, Inc.
440 Columbia Dr Ste 105
West Palm Beach, FL 33409-1801
Tel.: (561) 688-2880
Fax: (561) 688-2780
Multi Media & Promotions

S.R. Video Pictures, Ltd.
23 S Route 9W
Haverstraw, NY 10927
Tel.: (845) 429-1116
Fax: (845) 429-1117

OJAI VALLEY INN & SPA
905 Country Club Rd
Ojai, CA 93023
Tel.: (805) 646-1111
Fax: (805) 646-7969
E-mail: info@ojairesort.com
Web Site: www.ojairesort.com
Sales Range: $25-49.9 Million
Approx. Number Employees: 600
Business Description:
Resort, Spa & Golf Course
S.I.C.: 7011; 7231; 7997
N.A.I.C.S.: 721110; 713910; 812112
Media: 6
Personnel:
Stephen Crown *(Owner)*
Allison Kneubuhl *(Dir-Sls & Mktg)*
Veronica Cole *(Mgr-PR)*

OMNI HOTELS CORPORATION
(Sub. of TRT Holdings Inc.)
420 Decker Dr
Irving, TX 75062-3988
Tel.: (972) 730-6664
Fax: (972) 871-5665
Toll Free: (800) THEOMNI
E-mail: recruiting@omnihotels.com
Web Site: www.omnihotels.com
Approx. Sls.: $400,000,000
Approx. Number Employees: 8,100
Year Founded: 1958
Business Description:
Hotel, Restaurant & Lounge Ownership & Management
S.I.C.: 7011
N.A.I.C.S.: 721110
Media: 2-3-5-6-8-9-10-11-15-18-19-23-24-25
Distr.: Intl.; Natl.
Budget Set: Sept. -Oct.
Personnel:
Michael J. Deitemeyer *(Pres)*
James D. Caldwell *(CEO)*
Tom Santora *(CMO & Sr VP-Sls)*
Michael G. Smith *(Gen Counsel & Sr VP)*
Paul Dietzler *(Exec VP-Asset Mgmt)*
Stephen Rosenstock *(Sr VP-Food, Beverage & Brand Standards)*
Joy Rothschild *(Sr VP-HR)*
Tom Faust *(VP-Sls & Distr)*
Caryn Kboudi *(VP-Corp Comm)*
Brad Frazier *(Dir-Global Bus Travel Sls)*
Brands & Products:
BERKSHIRE PLACE
EXECUTIVE SERVICE PLAN
KOKACHIN
THE LAST HURRAH
OMNI
OMNI EXPRESS
OMNI INTERNATIONAL
OMNILINK
PARKER HOUSE
POPPIES
PUMP ROOM
THE ROYAL ORLEANS
THE SHOREHAM
Advertising Agencies:
Affect Strategies
989 Ave of the Americas 6th Fl
New York, NY 10018
Tel.: (212) 398-9680
Fax: (212) 504-8211
New Media

Asher Media, Inc.
15303 Dallas Pkwy Ste 1300
Addison, TX 75001
Tel.: (972) 732-6464

Avrea Foster
1999 Bryan St Ste 1850
Dallas, TX 75201
Tel.: (214) 855-1400
Fax: (214) 259-3670
Advertising Agency of Record
Branding
Luxury Hotel Brand
Marketing Strategy
Mokara Hotel & Spa
Omni Dallas Hotel
Promotional Activities
Social Media

TracyLocke
1999 Bryan St Ste 2800
Dallas, TX 75201
Tel.: (214) 259-3500
Fax: (214) 259-3550

O'NEILL PROPERTIES GROUP
2701 Renaissance Blvd 4th Fl
King of Prussia, PA 19406
Tel.: (610) 337-5560
Fax: (610) 337-5599
Web Site: www.oneillproperties.com
Approx. Number Employees: 100
Business Description:
Real Estate Developer
S.I.C.: 6531
N.A.I.C.S.: 531210
Personnel:
Brian O'Neill *(Founder & Chm)*
Advertising Agency:
Gregory FCA
27 W Athens Ave Ste 200
Ardmore, PA 19003
Tel.: (610) 642-8253
Fax: (610) 642-1258
Fax: (610) 649-9029
Toll Free: (800) 499-4734

ORANGE COUNTY NATIONAL GOLF CENTER & LODGE
16301 Phil Ritson Way
Winter Garden, FL 34787
Tel.: (407) 656-2626
Fax: (407) 656-4045
Toll Free: (888) PAR-3672
E-mail: info@ocngolf.com
Web Site: www.ocngolf.com
Sales Range: $10-24.9 Million
Approx. Number Employees: 150
Year Founded: 1994
Business Description:
Golf Course & Club Owner & Operator
S.I.C.: 7997
N.A.I.C.S.: 713910
Media: 6-22
Personnel:
Terri Nobles *(Controller & Dir-HR)*
Bruce Gerlander *(Gen Mgr)*
Jimmy Bell *(Dir-Sls-Mktg)*
Charles Kinard *(Dir-Info Sys)*
Alan Walker *(Dir-Golf)*
Derek Piazza *(Mgr-Lodge)*

ORIENT-EXPRESS HOTELS INC.
(Sub. of Orient-Express Hotels Ltd.)
1114 Avenue of The Americas 38th Fl
New York, NY 10036-2711
Tel.: (212) 302-5055
Fax: (212) 302-5203
Web Site: www.orient-expresshotels.com
Approx. Number Employees: 23
Year Founded: 1969
Business Description:
Hotel & Tourist Train Operations
S.I.C.: 7011; 4013
N.A.I.C.S.: 721110; 488210
Distr.: Direct to Consumer; Intl.; Natl.
Budget Set: Jan.
Personnel:
David C. Williams *(VP-Sls & Mktg)*
Advertising Agency:
Geto & deMilly Inc.
276 5th Ave Ste 806
New York, NY 10001
Tel.: (212) 686-4551
Fax: (212) 213-6850

OUTRIGGER ENTERPRISES, INC.
(d/b/a Outrigger Hotels & Resorts)
2375 Kuhio Ave
Honolulu, HI 96815-2939
Tel.: (808) 921-6600
Fax: (808) 921-6975
Toll Free: (800) 688-7444
E-mail: reservations@outrigger.com
Web Site: www.outrigger.com
E-Mail For Key Personnel:
President: david.carey@outrigger.com
Marketing Director: rob.solomon@outrigger.com
Sales Range: $100-124.9 Million
Approx. Number Employees: 260
Year Founded: 1947
Business Description:
Family Owned Resort Hotels
S.I.C.: 7011; 4724
N.A.I.C.S.: 721110; 561510
Media: 2-4-6-8-9-13-23-26
Budget Set: July
Personnel:
Danny Ojiri *(Chm)*
W. David Carey *(Pres & CEO)*
Melvyn Wilinsky *(CFO & Exec VP)*
Mel Kaneshige *(Exec VP-Real Estate)*
Barry Wallace *(Exec VP-Hospitality Svcs)*
Sam Hoffman *(Dir-Mktg)*
Roy Cordeiro *(Dir-Sls & Mktg)*
Nancy Daniels *(Dir-Pub Rels)*
Lisa Tojo *(Dir-Interactive Commerce)*
Kieran Yap *(Dir-Corp Tax)*

OVERTON MOORE PROPERTIES
19300 S Hamilton Ave Ste 200
Gardena, CA 90248-4337
Tel.: (310) 323-9100
Fax: (310) 608-7997
E-mail: info@omprop.com
Web Site: www.omprop.com
E-Mail For Key Personnel:
President: ttecimer@omprop.com
Approx. Number Employees: 16
Year Founded: 1973
Business Description:
Real Estate Developers
S.I.C.: 1531
N.A.I.C.S.: 236117
Media: 2-18
Personnel:
Timur Tecimer *(Pres & COO)*
Stanley A. Moore *(CEO)*
Gaye Tomita *(CFO)*

OXFORD REALTY, INC.
4700 Millenia Blvd Ste 175
Orlando, FL 32839
Tel.: (407) 629-1222
Fax: (407) 370-2699
Toll Free: (800) 858-0230
E-mail: sales@oxfordrealty.com
Web Site: www.oxfordrealty.com
E-Mail For Key Personnel:
Sales Director: sales@oxfordrealty.com
Sales Range: $10-24.9 Million
Approx. Number Employees: 35
Business Description:
Real Estate Services
S.I.C.: 6531
N.A.I.C.S.: 531210
Media: 6-8-9
Personnel:
Carol Ann Hewitt *(Owner)*

PACIFICA HOTEL COMPANY
(Sub. of Pacifica Real Estate Group, LLC)
1933 Cliff Dr Ste 1
Santa Barbara, CA 93109
Tel.: (805) 957-0095

Key to Media (For complete agency information see *The Advertising Red Books-Agencies* edition):
1. Bus. Publs. 2. Cable T.V. 3. Catalogs & Directories. 4. Co-op Adv. 5. Consumer Mags. 6. D.M. to Bus. Estab.7. D.M. to Consumers
8. Daily Newsp. 9. Exhibits/Trade Shows 10. Foreign 11. Infomercial 12. Internet Adv.13. Multimedia 14. Network Radio
15. Network T.V. 16. Newsp. Distr. Mags. 17. Other 18. Outdoor (Posters, Transit) 19. Point of Purchase20. Premiums, Novelties
21. Product Samples 22. Special Events Mktg. 23. Spot Radio 24. Spot T.V. 25. Weekly Newsp. 26. Yellow Page Adv.

Fax: (805) 899-2426
E-mail: info@pacificahotels.com
Web Site: www.pacificahotelco.com
Business Description:
Hotel Management
S.I.C.: 6531; 7011
N.A.I.C.S.: 531210; 721110
Personnel:
Dale J. Marquis *(Chm, Pres & CEO)*
Advertising Agency:
Point B Communications
750 N Orleans Ste 600
Chicago, IL 60654
Tel.: (312) 867-7750
Fax: (312) 867-7751

PALM HARBOR HOMES, INC.
15303 Dallas Pkwy Ste 800
Addison, TX 75001-4600
Tel.: (972) 991-2422
Fax: (972) 991-5949
E-mail: email@palmharbor.com
Web Site: www.palmharbor.com
Approx. Sls.: $298,371,000
Approx. Number Employees: 1,700
Year Founded: 1977
Business Description:
Mobile & Manufactured Construction Homes & Services
S.I.C.: 2452; 5211
N.A.I.C.S.: 321992; 444190
Media: 4-6-7-8-10-13-16
Personnel:
Larry H. Keener *(Chm, Pres & CEO)*
Brian Cejka *(Chief Restructuring Officer)*
Joe Kesterson *(Pres-Retail)*
Colleen Rogers *(VP-Branding & Adv)*
Jennifer Burkhart *(Dir-HR)*
Susan Bouscher *(Mgr-Fin Reporting)*

PARADIGM PROPERTIES, INC.
220 N Main St
Gainesville, FL 32601
Tel.: (352) 375-2152
Fax: (352) 374-4344
E-mail: ppmtmail@teamparadigm.com
Web Site: www.teamparadigm.com
Approx. Rev.: $7,600,000
Approx. Number Employees: 300
Year Founded: 1998
Business Description:
Apartment Building Operators
S.I.C.: 6513
N.A.I.C.S.: 531110
Media: 13-17

PARK PLACE HOTEL
300 E State St
Traverse City, MI 49684
Tel.: (231) 946-5000
Fax: (231) 946-2772
Toll Free: (800) 748-0133
Web Site: www.park-place-hotel.com
Approx. Number Employees: 150
Year Founded: 1930
Business Description:
Hotel Owner & Operator
S.I.C.: 7011
N.A.I.C.S.: 721110
Media: 7-8-9-13-18-20-23-25
Personnel:
Amy Parker *(Gen Mgr)*
Mike Ruede *(Dir-Food & Beverage)*

PATRICK STRACUZZI REAL ESTATE TEAM
2895 SE Ocean Blvd
Stuart, FL 34996
Tel.: (772) 283-9991
Fax: (772) 288-4620
Toll Free: (800) 889-0917
Web Site: www.stracuzzi.com
Approx. Number Employees: 30
Business Description:
Real Estate Services
S.I.C.: 6531
N.A.I.C.S.: 531210
Media: 6-9-25
Personnel:
Jan Sorokowski *(Dir-First Impressions)*
Brands & Products:
LUXURY REAL ESTATE EXPERT
PATRICK STRACUZZI

PEABODY HOTEL GROUP, INC.
(Sub. of Belz Enterprises)
5118 Park Ave Ste 245
Memphis, TN 38117
Tel.: (901) 762-5400
Fax: (901) 762-5464
Web Site: www.peabodyhotelgroup.com
Approx. Number Employees: 200
Business Description:
Hotel Franchise
S.I.C.: 7011; 6519
N.A.I.C.S.: 721110; 531190
Advertising Expenditures: $400,000
Media: 1-4-5-7-8-9-10-11-17-18-19-20-22-25-26
Distr.: Intl.
Budget Set: Sept.
Personnel:
Martin S. Belz *(Chm & Pres)*
Michael K. Craft *(CFO & Exec VP)*
Merilyn G. Mangum *(Chief Admin Officer & Exec VP)*
Alan C. Villaverde *(Exec VP-Ops)*
Maureen Gonzalez *(Dir-PR)*
Lisa Massa *(Sr Mgr-Sls)*
Brands & Products:
MEMPHIS PEABODY
PEABODY LITTLE ROCK
PEABODY ORLANDO
PHG
Advertising Agency:
Bohan
124 12th Ave S
Nashville, TN 37203
Tel.: (615) 327-1189
Fax: (615) 327-8123

PEBBLE BEACH COMPANY
(d/b/a Pebble Beach Resorts)
2700 17 Mile Dr
Pebble Beach, CA 93953
Tel.: (831) 647-7500
Fax: (831) 622-3603
Toll Free: (800) 654-9300
E-mail: customerservice@pebblebeach.com
Web Site: www.pebblebeach.com
Sales Range: $50-74.9 Million
Approx. Number Employees: 1,800
Year Founded: 1992
Business Description:
Hotels & Motels
S.I.C.: 7011; 7997
N.A.I.C.S.: 721110; 713910
Import Export
Personnel:
Cody Plott *(Pres & COO)*
William L. Perocchi *(CEO)*
David Heuck *(CFO & Exec VP)*
Mark Stilwell *(Gen Counsel & Exec VP)*
Paul Spengler *(Exec VP)*
David Stivers *(Exec VP-Brand Mgmt)*
Steve Aitchison *(Sr VP-Capital Svcs)*
R. J. Harper *(Sr VP-Golf)*
Susan Merfeld *(VP-HR)*
Tim Ryan *(VP-Sls)*
Don Tkachenko *(Dir-Security)*
Brands & Products:
PEBBLE BEACH
Advertising Agency:
Hoffman/Lewis
1725 Montgomery St
San Francisco, CA 94111-1030
Tel.: (415) 434-8500
Fax: (415) 434-8484

PEDDLER'S VILLAGE, INC.
Rt 202 & 263
Lahaska, PA 18931
Tel.: (215) 794-4000
E-mail: info@peddlersvillage.com
Web Site: www.peddlersvillage.com
Approx. Number Employees: 50
Business Description:
Lodging & Restaurants
S.I.C.: 7011; 5812
N.A.I.C.S.: 721199; 721110; 722110
Media: 4-10-18-22-24
Personnel:
Eve Gelman *(Mgr-PR & Digital Comm)*

PELICAN MARSH GOLF CLUB
(Sub. of WCI Communities, Inc.)
1810 Persimmon Dr
Naples, FL 34109
Tel.: (239) 597-3000
Web Site: www.pelicanmarshgc.com
Business Description:
Golf Club Operations
S.I.C.: 7997
N.A.I.C.S.: 713910
Media: 6-22
Personnel:
Doug Young *(Gen Mgr)*
David May *(Mgr-Club)*

PHILLIPS DEVELOPMENT & REALTY, LLC
142 W Platt St
Pampa, FL 33606
Tel.: (919) 954-1700
Web Site: www.pdrllc.com
Sales Range: $1-9.9 Million
Approx. Number Employees: 10
Business Description:
Real Estate Developer & Realtor
S.I.C.: 6531; 1522
N.A.I.C.S.: 236116; 236220; 531210; 531390
Media: 6
Personnel:
Donald Phillips *(Mng Dir)*
Amy Jacobs *(Mgr-Property)*

POCONO MANOR GOLF RESORT & SPA
1 Manor Dr
Pocono Manor, PA 18349
Tel.: (570) 839-7111
Fax: (570) 839-0708
Toll Free: (800) 233-8150
E-mail: info@poconomanor.com
Web Site: www.poconomanor.com
Sales Range: $1-9.9 Million
Approx. Number Employees: 200
Year Founded: 1902
Business Description:
Resort Hotel Facility; Other Related Convention Facilities
S.I.C.: 7011
N.A.I.C.S.: 721110
Media: 4-5-6-7-8-10-22-26
Distr.: Reg.
Personnel:
Charles Brush *(Gen Mgr)*

PORTSMOUTH SQUARE, INC.
(Sub. of Santa Fe Financial Corporation)
10940 Wilshire Blvd Ste 2150
Los Angeles, CA 90024
Tel.: (310) 889-2500
Fax: (310) 889-2525
Approx. Rev.: $32,680,000
Approx. Number Employees: 3
Business Description:
Commercial Real Estate Brokerage & Management
S.I.C.: 6531
N.A.I.C.S.: 531210; 531390
Advertising Expenditures: $278,000
Personnel:
John V. Winfield *(Chm, Pres & CEO)*
Michael G. Zybala *(Gen Counsel, Sec & VP)*

POST APARTMENT HOMES, L.P.
(Sub. of Post Properties, Inc.)
4401 Northside Pkwy NW Ste 800
Atlanta, GA 30327
Tel.: (404) 846-5000
Fax: (404) 846-6171
E-mail: info@postproperties.com
Web Site: www.postproperties.com
Business Description:
Real Estate Developer, Owner & Manager
S.I.C.: 6513; 6531
N.A.I.C.S.: 531110; 531210; 531390
Media: 2-8-13-22
Personnel:
Robert C. Goddard, III *(Chm)*
Douglas Crocker, II *(Vice Chm)*
David P. Stockert *(Pres & CEO)*
Christopher J. Papa *(CFO & Exec VP)*
Arthur J. Quirk *(Chief Acctg Officer & Sr VP)*

POST PROPERTIES, INC.
4401 Northside Pkwy Ste 800
Atlanta, GA 30327-3057
Tel.: (404) 846-5000
Fax: (404) 504-9369
E-mail: polly.butler@postproperties.com
Web Site: www.postproperties.com
Approx. Rev.: $285,138,000
Approx. Number Employees: 597
Year Founded: 1984
Business Description:
Developers & Operators of Upscale Multi-Family Apartment Communities in the Southeastern & Southwestern United States
S.I.C.: 6798
N.A.I.C.S.: 525930
Media: 4-6
Personnel:
Robert C. Goddard, III *(Chm)*

Post Properties, Inc. — (Continued)

Douglas Crocker, II *(Vice Chm)*
David P. Stockert *(Pres & CEO)*
Christopher J. Papa *(CFO & Exec VP)*
Arthur J. Quirk *(Chief Acctg Officer & Sr VP)*
Sherry W. Cohen *(Sec & Exec VP)*
Todd T. Tibbitts *(Sr VP-Corp Svcs)*
Jeffrey W. Harris *(Exec VP & Reg Investment Dir-Southeast Reg)*
Charles A. Konas *(Exec VP-Construction & Property Svcs)*
Jamie Teabo *(Exec VP)*
David C. Ward *(Exec VP & Reg Investment Dir-Southwest Reg)*
Linda J. Ricklef *(Sr VP-HR & Exec Dir-Post HOPE Foundation)*
Kathleen M. Mason *(Sr VP-Taxation)*
Glen P. Smith *(Sr VP-Legal)*
Laura J. Vanloh *(Sr VP-Property Mgmt)*
Orlala Icenberger *(Gen Mgr)*
Wallace Hitt *(Reg Dir-Sls-Mktg)*
Lori Hoogland *(Dir-Bus Dev)*
Dwayne Prosser *(Dir-Security)*

Brands & Products:
POST
POST STORY
POSTECOACTIVE
POSTHOPE

PREFERRED HOTELS GROUP

311 S Wacker Dr Ste 1900
Chicago, IL 60606-6676
Tel.: (312) 913-0400
Fax: (312) 913-0444
Toll Free: (800) 323-7500
E-mail: info@preferredhotels.com
Web Site: www.preferredhotels.com
E-Mail For Key Personnel:
President: JUeberroth@preferredhotels.com
Approx. Number Employees: 100
Year Founded: 1968
Business Description:
Independent Luxury Hotels & Resorts
S.I.C.: 8611
N.A.I.C.S.: 813910
Advertising Expenditures: $1,975,000
Bus. Publs.: $400,000; Catalogs & Directories: $240,000; Consumer Mags.: $1,000,000; D.M. to Consumers: $200,000; Foreign: $100,000; Premiums, Novelties: $35,000
Distr.: Intl.; Natl.
Budget Set: May
Personnel:
John A. Ueberroth *(Chm & CEO)*
Gail Ueberroth *(Pres)*
Lindsey Ueberroth *(Pres)*
Bob Van Ness *(Exec Mng Dir-Global)*
Rob Cornell *(Sr VP-Global Dev)*
Marshall Calder *(VP-Mktg-Global)*
Michelle Woodley *(VP-Reservations & Distr)*
Shannon Reid *(Dir-Mktg-EMEA)*

Brands & Products:
PREFERRED HOTELS & RESORTS
STERLING HOTELS & RESORTS
SUMMIT HOTELS & RESORTS

PROLOGIS

4545 Airport Way
Denver, CO 80239
Tel.: (303) 567-5000
Fax: (303) 567-5605
Toll Free: (800) 566-2706
E-mail: info@prologis.com
Web Site: www.prologis.com
Approx. Rev.: $909,155,000
Approx. Number Employees: 1,100
Year Founded: 1991
Business Description:
Real Estate Investment Trust; Owner, Operator, Developer & Manager of Distribution Facilities
S.I.C.: 6798
N.A.I.C.S.: 525930
Media: 2-10
Personnel:
Stephen L. Feinberg *(Chm & CEO)*
Ted R. Antenucci *(Pres & Chief Investment Officer)*
William E. Sullivan *(CFO)*
Luck Lands *(CIO)*
Charles E. Sullivan *(Chief Admin Officer)*
Lori A. Palazzolo *(Chief Acctg Officer & Sr VP)*
John R. Rizzo *(Chief Sustainability Officer)*
Larry H. Harmsen *(Pres-United States & Canada)*
Walter C. Rakowich *(CEO-ProLogis)*
Edward S. Nekritz *(Gen Counsel, Head-Global Strategic Risk Mgmt & Sec)*
Melissa Marsden *(Sr VP-IR & Corp Comm)*
Robin Woodbridge *(Sr VP-Dev)*

Brands & Products:
PROLOGIS

Advertising Agency:
90octane
518 17th St Ste 1400
Denver, CO 80202
Tel.: (720) 904-8169
Fax: (303) 295-1577

PRUDENTIAL CALIFORNIA REALTY

(Sub. of HomeServices of America, Inc.)
2365 Northside Dr Ste 200
San Diego, CA 92108
Tel.: (619) 294-3113
Fax: (619) 521-0100
E-mail: contactus@prudentialcal.com
Web Site: www.prudentialcal.com
Sales Range: $50-74.9 Million
Approx. Number Employees: 100
Business Description:
Real Estate Services
S.I.C.: 6531
N.A.I.C.S.: 531210
Media: 2-4-8-9-13-25
Personnel:
Mark Johnson *(VP-Mktg & Tech)*
Carol Cianfarani *(Mgr)*

PRUDENTIAL FLORIDA WCI REALTY

(Sub. of Prudential Financial, Inc.)
1150 S US Hwy 1
Jupiter, FL 33477
Tel.: (954) 693-0100
Fax: (954) 693-0112
Toll Free: (800) 386-1554
Web Site: www.prudentialfloridawcirealty.com
Sales Range: $750-799.9 Million
Year Founded: 1999
Business Description:
Real Estate Services
S.I.C.: 6531; 6513; 8699
N.A.I.C.S.: 531210; 531110; 531311; 531312; 531320; 531390; 813990
Advertising Expenditures: $3,000,000
Media: 2-6-8-13-25
Personnel:
David Fry *(Pres & CEO)*
Rei Mesa *(Pres-Florida Real Estate Services)*
Stacy Benedict *(VP-ECommerce & Mktg)*
Raul Rodriguez *(VP-Fin, Real Estate Svcs)*
Rosalie Palmer *(Dir-Internal Ops)*

PRUDENTIAL NEW JERSEY PROPERTIES

220 Davidson Ave
Somerset, NJ 08873
Tel.: (732) 627-8400
Fax: (732) 627-9626
Toll Free: (800) 548-3466
E-mail: dottiewinhold@prudentialnewjersey.com
Web Site: www.prunewjersey.com
Approx. Number Employees: 500
Business Description:
Real Estate Services
S.I.C.: 6531
N.A.I.C.S.: 531210
Media: 6-7-8-9-13-25
Personnel:
Bill Keleher *(Chm & CEO)*
Nancy Litwin *(Vice Chm)*
Seymour Litwin *(Vice Chm)*
Steve Janett *(COO)*
Christopher Brown *(Gen Mgr-Sls & Exec VP)*
Michele Giordano *(VP & Dir-Mktg)*
Bruce Graham *(VP & Director-Career Dev)*

PRUDENTIAL REAL ESTATE AFFILIATES, INC.

(Sub. of Prudential Financial, Inc.)
3333 Michelson Dr Ste 1000
Irvine, CA 92612-1690
Tel.: (949) 794-7900
Fax: (949) 794-7039
Toll Free: (800) 666-6634
Toll Free: (800) 999-1120
Web Site: www.prea.prudential.com
Sales Range: $1-4.9 Billion
Approx. Number Employees: 43,000
Year Founded: 1987
Business Description:
Real Estate Services
S.I.C.: 6531; 6513; 8699
N.A.I.C.S.: 531210; 531110; 531311; 531312; 531320; 531390; 813990
Media: 1-2-3-5-6-8-13-15-19-21-23-24
Distr.: Natl.
Budget Set: Nov.
Personnel:
Steven McSkimming *(VP-Mktg & Client Svcs)*
Doniel Sutton *(Mgr-HR)*

PS BUSINESS PARKS, INC.

701 Western Ave
Glendale, CA 91201-2349
Tel.: (818) 244-8080
Fax: (818) 242-0566
E-mail: info@psbusinessparks.com
Web Site: www.psbusinessparks.com
Approx. Rev.: $279,089,000
Approx. Number Employees: 142
Business Description:
Real Estate Investment Trust; Commercial Properties Owner & Lessor
S.I.C.: 6798; 6512; 6531
N.A.I.C.S.: 525930; 531120; 531312
Media: 6
Personnel:
Ronald L. Havner, Jr. *(Chm)*
Edward A. Stokx *(CFO & Exec VP)*
John Petersen *(COO & Exec VP)*
Maria R. Hawthorne *(Exec VP-East Coast)*
Eddie F. Ruiz *(VP & Dir-Facilities)*
Andrew Mircovich *(Reg Mgr)*
Eugene Uhlman *(Reg Mgr-Maryland)*

PUEBLO BONITO HOTELS & RESORTS

4350 La Jolla Village Dr Ste 460
San Diego, CA 92122
Tel.: (858) 642-2050
Fax: (858) 642-2052
E-mail: admin@pueblobonito.com
Web Site: www.pueblobonito.com
Approx. Number Employees: 14
Year Founded: 1987
Business Description:
Hotel Owner & Operator
S.I.C.: 7011
N.A.I.C.S.: 721110
Media: 6
Personnel:
Ernesto Coppel *(Owner)*

Advertising Agency:
Novom Marketing
8033 Sunset Blvd Ste 863
Hollywood, CA 90046
Tel.: (323) 882-8333
Fax: (323) 882-8310
— Charlotte Novom *(Acct Exec)*

PULTEGROUP, INC.

100 Bloomfield Hills Pkwy Ste 300
Bloomfield Hills, MI 48304
Tel.: (248) 647-2750
Fax: (248) 433-4598
Toll Free: (866) 785-8325
E-mail: mark.marymee@pulte.com
Web Site: www.pulte.com/pulteinc
Approx. Rev.: $4,569,290,000
Approx. Number Employees: 4,363
Year Founded: 1950
Business Description:
Holding Company; New Housing Operative Builder, Real Estate Brokerage, Sales & Mortgage Services
S.I.C.: 6719; 1531; 6141; 6163; 6531; 6552
N.A.I.C.S.: 551112; 236117; 237210; 522220; 522310; 531210
Advertising Expenditures: $54,900,000
Media: 2-6-8-9-10-11-13-18-22-25
Budget Set: Jan. -Dec.
Personnel:
Richard J. Dugas, Jr. *(Chm, Pres & CEO)*
Timothy R. Eller *(Vice Chm)*
William J. Pulte *(Mng Partner)*
Robert T. O'Shaughnessy *(CFO & Exec VP)*
Jerry R. Batt *(CIO & VP)*
Deborah W. Meyer *(CMO & Sr VP)*
Kevin Meuth *(Pres-Houston)*
Harmon Smith *(Pres-Gulf Coast)*
Steven M. Cook *(Gen Counsel, Sec & Sr VP)*

Key to Media (For complete agency information see *The Advertising Red Books-Agencies* edition):
1. Bus. Publs. 2. Cable T.V. 3. Catalogs & Directories. 4. Co-op Adv. 5. Consumer Mags. 6. D.M. to Bus. Estab.7. D.M. to Consumers 8. Daily Newsp. 9. Exhibits/Trade Shows 10. Foreign 11. Infomercial 12. Internet Adv.13. Multimedia 14. Network Radio 15. Network T.V. 16. Newsp. Distr. Mags. 17. Other 18. Outdoor (Posters, Transit) 19. Point of Purchase20. Premiums, Novelties 21. Product Samples 22. Special Events Mktg. 23. Spot Radio 24. Spot T.V. 25. Weekly Newsp. 26. Yellow Page Adv.

James R. Ellinghausen *(Exec VP-HR)*
Gregory M. Nelson *(VP & Asst Sec)*
Steven A. Burch *(VP-Natl Strategic Mktg)*
Janice M. Jones *(VP-Mdsg)*
Brands & Products:
HOME SCIENCES
HOMEOWNER FOR LIFE
MYPULTE
PULTE
PULTE HOMES
PULTE MASTER BUILDER
PULTE MORTGAGE
Advertising Agencies:
Barrie D'Rozario Murphy
400 1st Ave N Ste 220
Minneapolis, MN 55401
Tel.: (612) 279-1500
Fax: (612) 332-9995

Enlighten
3027 Miller Rd
Ann Arbor, MI 48103
Tel.: (734) 668-6678
Fax: (734) 668-1883

GSD&M
828 W 6th St
Austin, TX 78703-5420
Tel.: (512) 242-4736
Fax: (512) 242-4700
Lead Agency

PURCELL CO., INC.
4401 E Aloha Dr
Diamondhead, MS 39525-3303
Tel.: (228) 255-7773
Fax: (228) 255-7830
Sales Range: $50-74.9 Million
Approx. Number Employees: 200
Year Founded: 1969
Business Description:
Real Estate Development; Resort, Municipal & Commercial Operations
S.I.C.: 1521
N.A.I.C.S.: 236115
Advertising Expenditures: $275,000
Media: 2-8-9-25
Distr.: Natl.
Budget Set: Sept. -Oct.
Personnel:
Bill Alexander *(CFO & VP-Fin)*
Carl H. Joffe *(Gen Counsel & Sec)*
George M. McCook *(VP-Mktg & Sls)*

QUAIL WEST LTD.
(Sub. of SEGRO plc)
6289 Burnham Rd
Naples, FL 34119
Tel.: (239) 593-4100
Toll Free: (800) 742-8885
Web Site: www.quailwest.com
Approx. Number Employees: 170
Business Description:
Resort
S.I.C.: 7997
N.A.I.C.S.: 713910
Media: 6-8

RADISSON HOTELS & RESORTS
(Div. of Carlson Hotels Worldwide)
701 Carlson Pkwy
Minnetonka, MN 55305
Mailing Address:
PO Box 59159
Minneapolis, MN 55459-8204
Tel.: (763) 212-1000
Fax: (763) 212-3400
Toll Free: (800) 333-3333
E-mail: creation@radisson.com
Web Site: www.radisson.com
Approx. Number Employees: 5,000
Year Founded: 1967
Business Description:
Hotel Chain
S.I.C.: 7011; 6531
N.A.I.C.S.: 721110; 531210
Media: 1-2-3-6-8-9-11-15-22
Distr.: Natl.
Budget Set: Nov. -Dec.
Personnel:
Nancy Johnson *(Chief Dev Officer & Exec VP)*
John Reynolds *(Gen Mgr)*
Craig Bollman *(Dir-Sls-Radisson Hotel Pittsburgh Green Tree)*
Frank Colega *(Dir-Catering)*
Tonia Noonan *(Dir-Sls/Mktg-Radiisson Plaza Lord Baltimore)*
Tina Seebaran *(Dir-Sls/Mktg-Radisson Hotel Central Dallas)*
Sharon Tietjens *(Dir-Sls & Mktg)*
Valerie DeMatteo *(Mgr-Sls-Radisson Hotel Pittsburgh Green Tree)*
Mary Ann Mathews *(Mgr-Catering Sls/ Wedding Specialist-Radisson Hotel Pittsburgh Gre)*
Kathy McLewis *(Mgr-Catering Sls)*
Debbie Kleespies *(Mgr-Convention Svcs)*

RAMADA WORLDWIDE INC.
(Sub. of Wyndham Hotel Group, LLC)
22 Sylvan Way
Parsippany, NJ 07054
Tel.: (973) 753-6000
Toll Free: (800) 2RAMADA
Web Site:
www.ramadainternational.com
Sales Range: $10-24.9 Million
Business Description:
Hotels & Resorts
S.I.C.: 7011; 5813
N.A.I.C.S.: 721110; 722410
Personnel:
Keith Pierce *(Pres)*
Advertising Agencies:
Decker Creative Marketing
99 Citizens Dr
Glastonbury, CT 06033-1262
Tel.: (860) 659-1311
Fax: (860) 659-3062
Toll Free: (800) 777-3677

OnTap
99 Citizens Dr
Glastonbury, CT 06033-1262
Tel.: (860) 659-1311
Fax: (860) 659-3062

RE/MAX ALLEGIANCE
6084 Franconia Rd Ste A
Alexandria, VA 22310
Tel.: (703) 971-5555
Fax: (703) 971-8566
E-mail: vanrmax@yahoo.com
Web Site:
www.myallegiancehome.com/
Approx. Sls.: $547,000,000
Approx. Number Employees: 60
Business Description:
Real Estate Agent, Commercial
S.I.C.: 6531
N.A.I.C.S.: 531210
Media: 6-8-13-14-15-22-23
Personnel:
Judy Austin *(Owner)*

RE/MAX INTERNATIONAL, INC.
5075 S Syracuse St
Denver, CO 80237
Tel.: (303) 770-5531
Fax: (303) 796-3599
Toll Free: (800) 525-7452
E-mail: webmaster@remax.com
Web Site: www.remax.com
E-Mail For Key Personnel:
Public Relations: echols@remax.net
Sales Range: $250-299.9 Million
Approx. Number Employees: 250
Year Founded: 1973
Business Description:
Franchiser of Real Estate, Relocation & Asset Management Services
S.I.C.: 7389
N.A.I.C.S.: 561990
Media: 1-2-3-4-5-7-10-13-15-16-22
Distr.: Intl.; Natl.
Budget Set: Dec.
Personnel:
Dave Liniger *(Co-Founder & Chm)*
Gail Liniger *(Co-Founder & Vice Chm)*
Vinnie Tracey *(Pres)*
Margaret Kelly *(CEO)*
Geoff Lewis *(Chief Legal Officer & Sr VP)*
Jack Kreider *(Exec VP-Reg Svcs)*
Bill Soteroff *(Exec VP-US & Intl Reg Dev)*
Bruce Benham *(Sr VP-Office of the Chm)*
Mike Reagan *(Sr VP-Brand Mktg)*
Nick Bailey *(Reg VP)*
Ricardo Cardenas *(Reg VP)*
Kevin Northrup *(Reg VP-Pacific Northwest)*
Kerron Stokes *(Reg VP)*
Shaun White *(VP-Corp Comm)*
Brands & Products:
ABOVE THE CROWD
THE BEST JUST KEEP GETTING BETTER
HOME OF THE BEST AGENTS
THE HOMETOWN EXPERTS WITH A WORLD OF EXPERIENCE
MIRACLE HOME
OUT IN FRONT
OUTSTANDING AGENTS. OUTSTANDING RESULTS.
PREMIER MARKET PRESENCE
RE/MAX
THE REAL ESTATE LEADERS
THE REAL ESTATE SUPERSTARS
THE SIGN THAT BRINGS YOU HOME
SOLD FOR THE CURE
WHEN YOU GET THE FACTS...IT'S RE/MAX!
WHERE DO YOU WANT TO BE?

REALOGY CORPORATION
(Holding of Apollo Management, L.P.)
1 Campus Dr
Parsippany, NJ 07054
Tel.: (973) 407-2000
Fax: (973) 407-7188
E-mail: investor.relations@realogy.com
Web Site: www.realogy.com
E-Mail For Key Personnel:
Public Relations: mark.panus@realogy.com
Approx. Rev.: $4,090,000,000
Approx. Number Employees: 10,500
Year Founded: 2006
Business Description:
Real Estate & Relocation Services
S.I.C.: 6531
N.A.I.C.S.: 531390; 531210
Advertising Expenditures: $161,000,000
Media: 13
Personnel:
Richard A. Smith *(Pres & CEO)*
Anthony E. Hull *(CFO, Treas & Exec VP)*
David J. Weaving *(Chief Admin Officer & Exec VP)*
Dea Benson *(Chief Acctg Officer, Sr VP & Controller)*
Marilyn Wasser *(Gen Counsel, Corp Sec & Exec VP)*
Mark Panus *(Sr VP-Corp Comm)*
Chris Sears *(Sr VP-Procurement & Preferred Alliance)*
Greg Sexton *(Sr VP)*
Kathy Borruso *(Sr Dir-Corp Comm)*
Brands & Products:
CARTUS
CENTURY 21
COLDWELL BANKER
COLDWELL BANKER COMMERCIAL
ERA
SOTHEBY'S INTERNATIONAL REALTY
TRG

REALTYSOUTH
(Sub. of HomeServices of America, Inc.)
2501 20th Pl S Ste 400
Birmingham, AL 35223-1744
Tel.: (205) 322-7500
Fax: (205) 715-0350
Web Site: www.realtysouth.com
Sales Range: $25-49.9 Million
Approx. Number Employees: 80
Year Founded: 1998
Business Description:
Real Estate Agency
S.I.C.: 6531
N.A.I.C.S.: 531210
Media: 2-4-8-9-13-25
Personnel:
Ty Dodge *(Pres & CEO)*
Richard Grimes *(Sr VP)*
Dawn Reeves *(VP-Mktg)*
Janet Whitney *(Dir-HR)*

RECTOR-HAYDEN REALTORS
(Sub. of HomeServices of America, Inc.)
2100 Nicholasville Rd
Lexington, KY 40503
Tel.: (859) 276-4811
Fax: (859) 277-5513
Web Site: www.rhr.com
Sales Range: $125-149.9 Million
Approx. Number Employees: 220
Business Description:
Real Estate Services
S.I.C.: 6531; 8611
N.A.I.C.S.: 531210; 813910
Media: 2-4-8-9-13-25

RED LION HOTELS CORP.
201 W North River Dr Ste 100
Spokane, WA 99201-2262
Tel.: (509) 459-6100
Fax: (509) 325-7324

Key to Media (For complete agency information see *The Advertising Red Books-Agencies* edition):
1. Bus. Publs. 2. Cable T.V. 3. Catalogs & Directories. 4. Co-op Adv. 5. Consumer Mags. 6. D.M. to Bus. Estab.7. D.M. to Consumers 8. Daily Newsp. 9. Exhibits/Trade Shows 10. Foreign 11. Infomercial 12. Internet Adv.13. Multimedia 14. Network Radio 15. Network T.V. 16. Newsp. Distr. Mags. 17. Other 18. Outdoor (Posters, Transit) 19. Point of Purchase20. Premiums, Novelties 21. Product Samples 22. Special Events Mktg. 23. Spot Radio 24. Spot T.V. 25. Weekly Newsp. 26. Yellow Page Adv.

Red Lion Hotels Corp. — (Continued)

E-mail: info@redlion.com
Web Site: www.westcoasthotels.com
Approx. Rev.: $163,494,000
Approx. Number Employees: 2,463
Year Founded: 1937
Business Description:
Owner, Manager & Franchisor of Hotels & Motels
S.I.C.: 7011; 5812
N.A.I.C.S.: 721110; 722110
Import Export
Advertising Expenditures: $3,500,000
Media: 8-13-17
Personnel:
Jon E. Eliassen *(Pres & CEO)*
Julie Shiflett *(CFO & Exec VP)*
George H. Schweitzer *(COO & Exec VP-Hotel Ops)*
David Barbieri *(CIO & Sr VP)*
Donald K. Barbieri *(CIO & Sr VP)*
Thomas L. Mckeirnan *(Gen Counsel, Sec & Sr VP)*
Harry G. Sladich *(Exec VP-Sls & Mktg)*
Richard P. Carlson *(Sr VP-Lodging Dev)*
Krisann Hatch *(Sr VP-HR)*
Barry Hughes *(Sr VP-Distr & Mktg)*
Mike Castro *(Dir-Brand Svcs)*
Pam Scott *(Dir-Corp Comm)*
Julie Langenheim *(Mgr-Asset & Corp Svcs)*
Brands & Products:
G & B
NET4GUESTS
RED LION
STAY COMFORTABLE
TICKETSWEST
WESTAWARDS
WESTCOAST
Advertising Agency:
HVS Marketing Communications
369 Willis Ave
Mineola, NY 11501
Tel.: (516) 248-8828
Fax: (516) 742-3059

RED ROOF INNS, INC.
(Joint Venture of Citigroup Inc. & Westmont Hospitality Group)
The Red Roof Bldg 605 S Front St
Columbus, OH 43215
Tel.: (614) 744-2600
Fax: (614) 224-9724
Toll Free: (800) REDROOF
E-mail: info@redroof.com
Web Site: www.redroof.com
Approx. Rev.: $345,600,000
Approx. Number Employees: 6,500
Year Founded: 1972
Business Description:
Economy Lodging Business
S.I.C.: 7011
N.A.I.C.S.: 721199
Media: 3-9-14-15-20
Distr.: Natl.
Personnel:
Andrew Alexander *(Pres, Gen Counsel & Sr VP)*
Robert Wallace *(Exec VP-Brand Ops & Franchising)*
Larry Daniel *(Sr VP-Distr Svcs)*
Randy Fox *(Sr VP-Ops)*
Marina MacDonald *(Sr VP-Sls & Mktg)*
Brands & Products:
REDICARD

Advertising Agency:
The Richards Group, Inc.
8750 N Central Expy Ste 100
Dallas, TX 75231-6430
Tel.: (214) 891-5700
Fax: (214) 265-2933

REECE & NICHOLS REALTORS
(Sub. of HomeServices of America, Inc.)
11500 Granada Ln
Shawnee Mission, KS 66211
Tel.: (913) 491-1001
Fax: (913) 491-0930
E-mail: webmaster@reeceandnichols.com
Web Site: www.reeceandnichols.com
Sales Range: $75-99.9 Million
Approx. Number Employees: 110
Business Description:
Real Estate Services
S.I.C.: 6531
N.A.I.C.S.: 531210
Media: 2-4-8-9-13-25
Personnel:
Linda Vaughan *(Pres)*
Jerry Reece *(CEO)*
Mike Frazier *(CFO)*
Sandy Green *(Pres-Reece & Nichols Alliance)*
Kent Shelman *(Pres-Kansas City Title)*
Christian Kelly *(VP & Gen Counsel)*

THE RELATED COMPANIES, L.P.
60 Columbus Cir
New York, NY 10023
Tel.: (212) 421-5332
Fax: (212) 801-1003
Web Site: www.related.com
Approx. Sls.: $24,100,000
Approx. Number Employees: 400
Business Description:
Holding Company; Residential & Commercial Real Estate Properties Acquisition, Development & Management Services
S.I.C.: 6719; 6512; 6513; 6531; 6552
N.A.I.C.S.: 551112; 237210; 531110; 531120; 531311; 531312; 531390
Personnel:
Bruce L. Warwick *(Vice Chm)*
Kenneth P. Wong *(Vice Chm)*
Jeff Blau *(Pres)*
Stephen Millard Ross *(Pres)*
Michael J. Brenner *(CFO & Exec VP)*
Bruce A. Beal, Jr. *(Exec VP)*
Ronald W. Wackrow *(Exec VP)*
Nicki Berlyn *(Dir-Mktg)*
Advertising Agency:
SSG, LLC
333 Parkland Plaza
Ann Arbor, MI 48103
Tel.: (734) 998-1340
Fax: (734) 998-1326
Real Estate Development

RELATED FLORIDA, INC.
(d/b/a The Related Group of Florida)
315 S Biscayne
Miami, FL 33131
Tel.: (305) 460-9900
Fax: (305) 460-9911
E-mail: info@relatedgroup.com
Web Site: www.relatedgroup.com
Approx. Rev.: $3,200,000,000
Approx. Number Employees: 400
Year Founded: 1979

Business Description:
Real Estate Services
S.I.C.: 6552; 6513
N.A.I.C.S.: 237210; 531110
Personnel:
Jorge M. Perez *(Founder, Chm & CEO)*
Jordan C. Paul *(Sr Mng Dir-Related Investment Fund)*
Advertising Agency:
BGT Partners
2627 NE 203rd St Ste 202
Miami, FL 33180
Tel.: (305) 438-1800
Fax: (305) 438-1560

THE RENEW INSTITUTE MEDICAL SPA
27343 Wesley Chapel Blvd State Rd 54
Wesley Chapel, FL 33543
Tel.: (813) 991-7144
Fax: (813) 907-2395
Web Site: www.fmcrenewinstitute.com
Business Description:
Medical Spa
S.I.C.: 8011
N.A.I.C.S.: 621491
Media: 9-13-25
Personnel:
Joseph Cozzolino *(Dir-Medical)*

THE RESORT AT LONGBOAT KEY CLUB
301 Gulf of Mexico Dr
Longboat Key, FL 34228
Tel.: (941) 383-8821
Fax: (941) 383-5396
Toll Free: (800) 237-8821
Web Site: www.longboatkeyclub.com
Approx. Number Employees: 500
Business Description:
Resort & Hotel
S.I.C.: 6531; 6552
N.A.I.C.S.: 531210; 237210
Media: 2-6-9
Personnel:
Mary Ryan *(Dir-Mktg & Comm)*
Advertising Agency:
Chisano Marketing Group, Inc.
2170 W State Rd 434 Ste 280
Longwood, FL 32779-4993
Tel.: (407) 788-7070
Fax: (407) 788-7090

RESORTQUEST INTERNATIONAL, INC.
(Holding of Leucadia National Corporation)
546 Mary Esther Cut-Off NW Ste 3
Fort Walton Beach, FL 32548
Tel.: (850) 275-5000
Fax: (850) 267-0613
Toll Free: (888) 909-6857
E-mail: info@resortquest.com
Web Site: www.resortquest.com
Sales Range: $150-199.9 Million
Approx. Number Employees: 4,000
Year Founded: 1998
Business Description:
Vacation Condominium & Home Sales & Rentals; Property Management Services
S.I.C.: 6531
N.A.I.C.S.: 531390
Media: 2-6-8-13
Personnel:
Cheryl Spezia *(VP-Mktg)*

RESORTS ATLANTIC CITY
(Holding of Colony Capital, LLC)
1133 Boardwalk
Atlantic City, NJ 08401
Tel.: (609) 340-6756
Fax: (609) 340-7751
Toll Free: (800) 336-6378
E-mail: info@resortsac.com
Web Site: www.resortsac.com
Approx. Number Employees: 3,500
Year Founded: 1978
Business Description:
Casino Hotel
S.I.C.: 5812
N.A.I.C.S.: 722110
Advertising Expenditures: $3,500,000
Media: 6-8-9-18-22-23-25
Distr.: Reg.
Budget Set: Aug.
Personnel:
Eric Fiocco *(Sr VP-Mktg & Casino Ops)*
Brian Cahill *(Exec Dir-Adv & Media Rels-Resorts Intl)*

REYNOLDS PLANTATION
100 Linger Longer Rd
Greensboro, GA 30642
Toll Free: (888) 298-3119
Web Site: www.reynoldsplantation.com
Approx. Number Employees: 50
Year Founded: 1986
Business Description:
Resort Community; Golf & Country Club
S.I.C.: 7011
N.A.I.C.S.: 721110
Advertising Expenditures: $500,000
Media: 2-6-8-9-13-18-19
Distr.: Direct to Consumer; Reg.
Personnel:
Mercer Reynolds *(Chm)*
Jamie Reynolds *(Vice Chm)*
Gino Marasco *(Dir-Sls & Mktg)*

RIDGEWOOD LAKES GOLF & COUNTRY CLUB INC.
200 Eagle Ridge Dr
Davenport, FL 33837
Tel.: (863) 424-8688
Fax: (863) 424-9198
Toll Free: (800) 684-8800
E-mail: jdewildt@rlgolf.com
Web Site: www.ridgewoodlakesgolf.com
Sales Range: $1-9.9 Million
Approx. Number Employees: 40
Business Description:
Golf Course & Country Club Owner & Operator
S.I.C.: 7997
N.A.I.C.S.: 713910
Media: 6-22
Personnel:
Jason DeWildt *(Gen Mgr)*

THE RITZ-CARLTON CHICAGO
(Sub. of Four Seasons Hotels Inc.)
160 E Pearson St at Water Tower Pl
Chicago, IL 60611-2308
Tel.: (312) 266-1000
Fax: (312) 266-9498
E-mail: guest.rcchicago@fourseasons.com
Web Site: www.fourseasons.com/chicagorc
Approx. Number Employees: 650

Key to Media (For complete agency information see *The Advertising Red Books-Agencies* edition):
1. Bus. Publs. 2. Cable T.V. 3. Catalogs & Directories. 4. Co-op Adv. 5. Consumer Mags. 6. D.M. to Bus. Estab.7. D.M. to Consumers
8. Daily Newsp. 9. Exhibits/Trade Shows 10. Foreign 11. Infomercial 12. Internet Adv.13. Multimedia 14. Network Radio
15. Network T.V. 16. Newsp. Distr. Mags. 17. Other 18. Outdoor (Posters, Transit) 19. Point of Purchase20. Premiums, Novelties
21. Product Samples 22. Special Events Mktg. 23. Spot Radio 24. Spot T.V. 25. Weekly Newsp. 26. Yellow Page Adv.

Business Description:
Hotel Services
S.I.C.: 7011
N.A.I.C.S.: 721110
Media: 2-7-8-9-11-13-20-22-25
Personnel:
Susan Maier *(Dir-PR)*

THE RITZ-CARLTON HOTEL COMPANY LLC

(Sub. of Marriott International, Inc.)
4445 Willard Ave Ste 800
Chevy Chase, MD 20815
Tel.: (301) 547-4700
Fax: (301) 547-4740
Web Site: www.ritzcarlton.com
Sales Range: $700-749.9 Million
Approx. Number Employees: 25,000
Year Founded: 1983
Business Description:
Hotel Management Company
S.I.C.: 7011; 6552
N.A.I.C.S.: 721110; 237210
Media: 2-6-7-8-9-16
Distr.: Intl.
Budget Set: Aug.
Personnel:
Herve Humler *(Pres & COO)*
Chris Gabaldon *(Chief Sls & Mtkg Officer)*
Kenneth Rehmann *(Exec VP-Ops)*
Kathleen O. Smith *(Sr VP-HR)*
Lisa Poppen *(Sr Dir-Mktg)*
Jorian Weiner *(Mgr-PR)*
Advertising Agency:
Team One
(Sub. of Saatchi & Saatchi Advertising Worldwide)
1960 E Grand Ave
El Segundo, CA 90245-5059
Tel.: (310) 615-2000
Fax: (310) 322-7565

RIVERPOINT LANDING MARINA

4950 Buckley Cove Way
Stockton, CA 95219
Tel.: (209) 951-4144
Fax: (209) 951-0372
Toll Free: (800) 550-4144
E-mail: info@riverpointlanding.com
Web Site: www.riverpointlanding.com
Approx. Rev.: $1,200,000
Approx. Number Employees: 5
Year Founded: 1974
Business Description:
RV Resort & Marina Operator
S.I.C.: 4493; 4226
N.A.I.C.S.: 713930; 493190
Media: 4-6-16-26
Distr.: Natl.
Budget Set: Sept.
Personnel:
Richard Dunn *(Pres)*

ROCKEFELLER GROUP, INC.

(Sub. of Mitsubishi Estate Co., Ltd.)
1221 Ave of The Americas
New York, NY 10020-1001
Tel.: (212) 282-2100
Fax: (212) 282-2142
Toll Free: (800) 699-9199
Web Site: www.therockefellergroup.com
E-Mail For Key Personnel:
Public Relations: vsilves@rockgrp.com
Approx. Number Employees: 120
Business Description:
Telecommunications Services
S.I.C.: 4899
N.A.I.C.S.: 517910
Media: 2-4-7-10-17
Distr.: Intl.; Natl.
Personnel:
Vincent E Silvestri *(COO)*
Brands & Products:
RGTS

ROGER SMITH HOTELS CORP.

501 Lexington Ave
New York, NY 10017-2008
Tel.: (212) 755-1400
Fax: (212) 319-9130
Toll Free: (800) 445-0277
E-mail: reservations@rogersmith.com
Web Site: www.rogersmith.com
Sales Range: $10-24.9 Million
Approx. Number Employees: 85
Year Founded: 1929
Business Description:
Hotel & Restaurant Services
S.I.C.: 7011; 5813
N.A.I.C.S.: 721110; 722410
Advertising Expenditures: $230,000
Media: 2-4-6-7-8-9-11-13-19-20
Distr.: Direct to Consumer; Reg.
Budget Set: Dec.
Personnel:
James Knowles *(Pres)*
Fred England *(Comptroller)*

ROSEWOOD HOTELS & RESORTS LLC

(Div. of The Rosewood Corporation)
500 Crescent Ct Ste 300
Dallas, TX 75201
Tel.: (214) 880-4200
Fax: (214) 880-4201
Web Site: www.rosewoodhotels.com
Approx. Number Employees: 55
Year Founded: 1979
Business Description:
Hotel Owner & Operator
S.I.C.: 7011
N.A.I.C.S.: 721110
Media: 2-6-20-23-24
Personnel:
Stephen Sands *(Chm)*
John M. Scott, III *(Pres & CEO)*
Robert Boulogne *(COO)*
Susan Aldridge *(Gen Counsel & Sr VP-Legal)*
Alex Alt *(Sr VP-Global Dev & Strategy)*
Jim Brackensick *(Sr VP-Pur)*
Ernest Glidden *(Sr VP-Fin)*
Ralph Aruzza *(VP-Sls & Mktg)*
Advertising Agency:
Nike Communications, Inc.
75 Broad St Ste 510
New York, NY 10004
Tel.: (212) 529-3400
Fax: (212) 353-0175

ROYAL PALM COMMUNITIES

2500 N Military Trl Ste 400
Boca Raton, FL 33431
Tel.: (561) 998-8100
Fax: (561) 998-7558
E-mail: info@royalpalmhomes.com
Web Site: www.royalpalmhomes.com
Approx. Number Employees: 90
Year Founded: 1978
Business Description:
Real Estate Developer
S.I.C.: 6531
N.A.I.C.S.: 531210
Media: 6
Personnel:
Daniel Kodsi *(CEO)*
Advertising Agency:
GHR Advertising
1761 W Hillsboro Blvd Ste 203
Deerfield Beach, FL 33442
Tel.: (954) 785-4444
Fax: (954) 785-7991

THE RYLAND GROUP, INC.

24025 Park Sorrento Ste 400
Calabasas, CA 91302-4009
Tel.: (818) 223-7500
Fax: (818) 598-1930
Toll Free: (800) 638-1768
Toll Free: (800) 267-0998
E-mail: investors@ryland.com
Web Site: www.ryland.com
Approx. Rev.: $1,063,892,000
Approx. Number Employees: 991
Year Founded: 1967
Business Description:
Homebuilding, Attached & Detached, Mortgage & Finance
S.I.C.: 1531; 6163
N.A.I.C.S.: 236117; 522310
Advertising Expenditures: $5,300,000
Media: 2-3-6-9-23-24-25
Distr.: Natl.
Budget Set: Nov.
Personnel:
William L. Jews *(Chm)*
Larry T. Nicholson *(Pres & CEO)*
Gordon Milne *(CFO & Exec VP)*
Craig McSpadden *(CIO & VP)*
David L. Fristoe *(Chief Acctg Officer, Sr VP & Controller)*
Daniel G. Schreiner *(Pres-Ryland Fin Svcs & Sr VP-The Ryland Group)*
Peter G. Skelly *(Pres-Ryland Homebuilding)*
Timothy J. Geckle *(Gen Counsel, Sec & Sr VP)*
Robert J. Cunnion, III *(Sr VP-HR)*
Eric E. Elder *(Sr VP-Mktg & Comm)*
Steven M. Dwyer *(VP-Pur)*
Charles W. Jenkins *(VP-Sls Trng)*
Brands & Products:
LIVE LIFE.EVEN BETTER
MY STYLE
RYLAND
Advertising Agencies:
5th Gear Advertising
8695 W Washington Blvd
Culver City, CA 90232
Tel.: (310) 567-3234
Fax: (310) 841-5064

Marcel Media
445 W Erie Ste 211
Chicago, IL 60654
Tel.: (312) 255-8044
Fax: (866) 643-7506

SADDLEBROOK RESORTS, INC.

(Sub. of Saddlebrook Holdings, Inc.)
5700 Saddlebrook Way
Wesley Chapel, FL 33543-4499
Tel.: (813) 973-1111
Fax: (813) 973-1312
Toll Free: (800) 729-8383
E-mail: griehle@saddlebrookresort.com
Web Site: www.saddlebrookresort.com
Approx. Rev.: $26,790,225
Approx. Number Employees: 525
Year Founded: 1979
Business Description:
Hotel Resort Operator
S.I.C.: 7011; 7997
N.A.I.C.S.: 721110; 713910
Import Export
Advertising Expenditures: $374,000
Personnel:
Thomas L. Dempsey *(Chm & CEO)*
Gregory R. Riehle *(Exec VP & Gen Mgr)*
Maureen Dempsey *(Exec VP)*
Sean Dempsey *(VP & Dir-Sls)*
Diane L. Riehle *(VP & Asst Sec)*
Al Martinez-Fonts, Jr. *(Dir-Mktg & Adv)*
Brands & Products:
SADDLEBROOK

SALAMANDER INNISBROOK, LLC

36750 US 19 N
Palm Harbor, FL 34684
Tel.: (727) 942-2000
Approx. Rev.: $32,140,525
Approx. Number Employees: 354
Year Founded: 2007
Business Description:
Resort Operator
S.I.C.: 7011
N.A.I.C.S.: 721110
Advertising Expenditures: $389,536
Personnel:
Dale Pelletier *(CFO)*

SANDALS RESORTS INTERNATIONAL

4950 SW 72nd Ave
Miami, FL 33155-5533
Tel.: (305) 284-1300
Fax: (305) 668-2798
Toll Free: (800) SANDALS
Toll Free: (800) BEACHES
E-mail: info@sandals.com
Web Site: www.sandals.com
Approx. Number Employees: 300
Year Founded: 1981
Business Description:
Travel Representatives
S.I.C.: 7011; 4725; 8741
N.A.I.C.S.: 721110; 561110; 561520
Advertising Expenditures: $1,500,000
Media: 2-3-5-6-7-8-9-10-11-13-15-18-24-25
Personnel:
Kevin Froemming *(Pres)*
Warren Cohen *(VP-Tour Operator Mktg)*
Brands & Products:
BEACHES
FAMILYMOONS
LUXURY INCLUDED
ROYAL PLANTATION
SANDALS
WEDDINGMOON
Advertising Agencies:
Hunter Hammer Smith
725 NE 125th St
Miami, FL 33161
Tel.: (305) 895-8430
Fax: (305) 892-9611
(Travel)

ID Media-Chicago

Key to Media (For complete agency information see *The Advertising Red Books-Agencies* edition):
1. Bus. Publs. 2. Cable T.V. 3. Catalogs & Directories. 4. Co-op Adv. 5. Consumer Mags. 6. D.M. to Bus. Estab.7. D.M. to Consumers 8. Daily Newsp. 9. Exhibits/Trade Shows 10. Foreign 11. Infomercial 12. Internet Adv.13. Multimedia 14. Network Radio 15. Network T.V. 16. Newsp. Distr. Mags. 17. Other 18. Outdoor (Posters, Transit) 19. Point of Purchase20. Premiums, Novelties 21. Product Samples 22. Special Events Mktg. 23. Spot Radio 24. Spot T.V. 25. Weekly Newsp. 26. Yellow Page Adv.

Sandals Resorts International — (Continued)

633 N Saint Clair 18th Fl
Chicago, IL 60611
Tel.: (312) 799-6900
Fax: (312) 799-6950
Online Media Buying/Planning

SANDESTIN GOLF & BEACH RESORT

9300 Emerald Coast Pkwy W
Destin, FL 32550
Tel.: (850) 267-8000
Fax: (850) 267-6843
Toll Free: (800) 277-0800
Web Site: www.sandestin.com
Sales Range: $125-149.9 Million
Business Description:
Resort Operator
S.I.C.: 7011
N.A.I.C.S.: 721110
Media: 6
Personnel:
Nancy Wilkerson *(Reg Dir-Sls)*
Angela Gaff *(Mgr-Special Events-Finz Beachside Grille)*
Advertising Agency:
MMG Worldwide
4601 Madison Ave
Kansas City, MO 64112
Tel.: (816) 472-5988
Fax: (816) 471-5395

SB HEALTH & BEAUTY SPA

116 S Oregon Ave
Tampa, FL 33606
Tel.: (813) 259-3606
Fax: (813) 259-3607
Web Site: www.sbspa.com
Approx. Number Employees: 10
Business Description:
Health & Beauty Spa
S.I.C.: 7231
N.A.I.C.S.: 812112
Personnel:
Bianca Diaz *(Owner)*
Bianca Menzorotolo *(Gen Mgr)*
Advertising Agency:
Nitesol
1121 N Miles Ave
Orlando, FL 32803
Toll Free: (877) 648-3765

THE SCHULTZ ORGANIZATION

900 US Hwy 9 N
Woodbridge, NJ 07095
Tel.: (732) 855-0001
Fax: (732) 855-0034
Web Site: www.schultznet.com
Approx. Sls.: $5,000,000
Approx. Number Employees: 60
Year Founded: 1990
Business Description:
Real Estate Services
S.I.C.: 6531
N.A.I.C.S.: 531210
Media: 2
Personnel:
Harvey Schultz *(Chm)*
Jonathan Schultz *(Pres & CEO)*
Samuel J. Giordano *(CFO)*

SCOTTSDALE COMPANY

(d/b/a Lutgert Companies)
4200 Gulf Shore Blvd N
Naples, FL 34103
Tel.: (239) 261-6100
Fax: (239) 262-6315
E-mail: barbaras@lutgert.com
Web Site: www.lutgert.com
Approx. Number Employees: 45
Business Description:
Speculative Builder, Multi-Family Dwellings
S.I.C.: 1522
N.A.I.C.S.: 236116; 236220
Media: 4-6-18
Personnel:
Scott Lutgert *(Chm)*
Howard B. Gutman *(Pres)*

SEA ISLAND COMPANY

100 Salt Marsh
Sea Island, GA 31561
Tel.: (912) 638-3611
Fax: (912) 638-5191
Toll Free: (800) 732-4752
E-mail: media@seaisland.com
Web Site: www.seaisland.com
Approx. Number Employees: 2,500
Year Founded: 1928
Business Description:
Provider of Real Estate Development, Resort & Landscape Operations
S.I.C.: 7011; 7997
N.A.I.C.S.: 721110; 713910
Media: 6-8-9-10-18
Distr.: Natl.
Budget Set: Oct.
Personnel:
Alfred W. Jones III *(Chm & CEO)*
Ron Roberts *(CFO)*
Merry Tipton *(Dir-Corp Comm)*
Carla Spears *(Reg Mgr-Sls-NE)*
Brands & Products:
THE CLOISTER
SEA ISLAND

SEA PINES RESORT, LLC

(Holding of The Riverstone Group, LLC)
32 Greenwood Dr
Hilton Head Island, SC 29928-4510
Mailing Address:
PO Box 7000
Hilton Head Island, SC 29938-7000
Tel.: (843) 785-3333
Fax: (843) 842-1475
E-mail: info@seapines.com
Web Site: www.seapines.com
Approx. Number Employees: 375
Year Founded: 1987
Business Description:
Resort, Hotel & Recreational Facility
S.I.C.: 7011; 7997
N.A.I.C.S.: 721110; 713910
Media: 2-4-6-7-8-9-17-24-26
Distr.: Natl.
Budget Set: Sept.
Personnel:
Steven Birdwell *(Pres & CEO)*
Cary Corbitt *(Dir-Sports & Ops)*
Brands & Products:
SEA PINES
Advertising Agency:
Rawle Murdy Associates, Inc.
2 Beaufain St
Charleston, SC 29401
Tel.: (843) 577-7327
Fax: (843) 722-3960

SEASIDE PROPERTIES GROUP, INC.

2100 N Ocean Blvd Ste 402
Fort Lauderdale, FL 33305
Tel.: (954) 828-1858
Fax: (954) 563-8180
Toll Free: (888) 242-4422
E-mail: info@seasidepropertiesgroup.com
Web Site:
www.seasidepropertiesgroup.com
Approx. Number Employees: 5
Business Description:
Real Estate Services
S.I.C.: 6531
N.A.I.C.S.: 531210
Media: 6-13
Personnel:
Niki Higgins *(Pres)*
Allison Hardison *(Art Dir)*
Dana Armellini *(Mgr-Office)*
Advertising Agency:
Mark Berlin & Associates
PO Box 56576
Jacksonville, FL 32241
Tel.: (904) 880-2940

SEMONIN REALTORS

(Sub. of HomeServices of America, Inc.)
4967 US Hwy 42 Ste 100
Louisville, KY 40222
Tel.: (502) 425-4760
Fax: (502) 339-8950
E-mail: clientcare@semonin.com
Web Site: www.semonin.com
Sales Range: $1-4.9 Billion
Approx. Number Employees: 750
Business Description:
Real Estate Services
S.I.C.: 6531
N.A.I.C.S.: 531210
Media: 2-4-8-9-13-17-26
Personnel:
Brad Devries *(Pres & CEO)*
Brands & Products:
SEMONIN REALTOR

SHAPELL INDUSTRIES, INC.

8383 Wilshire Blvd Ste 700
Beverly Hills, CA 90211-2406
Tel.: (323) 655-7330
Fax: (323) 651-4349
Web Site: www.shapell.com
Sales Range: $10-24.9 Million
Approx. Number Employees: 250
Year Founded: 1955
Business Description:
Real Estate Developer & Builder
S.I.C.: 1531
N.A.I.C.S.: 236117
Advertising Expenditures: $200,000
Consumer Mags.: $60,000; Exhibits/Trade Shows: $80,000; Other: $60,000
Distr.: Natl.
Personnel:
Max Webb *(Co-Founder)*
David Shapell *(Exec VP)*
Brands & Products:
SHAPELL

THE SHERATON CORPORATION

(Sub. of Starwood Hotels & Resorts Worldwide, Inc.)
(d/b/a Sheraton Hotels & Resorts)
1111 Westchester Ave
White Plains, NY 10604
Tel.: (914) 640-8100
Fax: (914) 640-8310
Toll Free: (800) 325-3535
E-mail: info@sheraton.com
Web Site: www.sheraton.com
Sales Range: $1-4.9 Billion
Approx. Number Employees: 104,000
Year Founded: 1937
Business Description:
Hotels & Inns
S.I.C.: 7011; 8741
N.A.I.C.S.: 721110; 561110
Media: 2-3-6-7-8-9-10-13-15-20-24-25
Distr.: Natl.
Personnel:
Javier Benito *(CMO)*
Hoyt H. Harper *(Sr VP-Sheraton Grp)*
Brands & Products:
SWEET SLEEPER
Advertising Agencies:
Deutsch, Inc.
(A Lowe & Partners Company)
111 8th Ave 14th Fl
New York, NY 10011-5201
Tel.: (212) 981-7600
Fax: (212) 981-7525
(Creative & Media)

The Kaplan Thaler Group
825 8th Ave 34th Fl
New York, NY 10019
Tel.: (212) 474-5000
Fax: (212) 474-5702

Razorfish New York
1440 Broadway 19th Fl
New York, NY 10018
Tel.: (212) 798-6600
Fax: (212) 798-6601

Zapwater Communications
1165 N Clark St Ste 313
Chicago, IL 60610
Tel.: (312) 771-1271
Tel.: (312) 943-0333
Fax: (312) 943-0852
(Sheraton Chicago Northbrook Hotel)

THE SHIDLER GROUP

841 Bishop St Ste 1700
Honolulu, HI 96813-4789
Tel.: (808) 531-3000
Fax: (808) 528-7127
Web Site: www.theshidlergroup.com
Approx. Number Employees: 185
Year Founded: 1971
Business Description:
Real Estate Investment
S.I.C.: 6289
N.A.I.C.S.: 523999
Media: 2-4-5-9-11-16-25
Distr.: Natl.
Personnel:
Rob Holman *(Partner)*
Stan Mattison *(Partner)*
Jim Reynolds *(Partner)*
Jay H. Shidler *(Partner)*
Edwina Takasaki *(Dir-Mktg)*
Brands & Products:
SHIDLER

SILVERLEAF RESORTS, INC.

1221 River Bend Dr Ste 120
Dallas, TX 75247-4919
Tel.: (214) 631-1166
Fax: (204) 637-0585
E-mail: info@silverleafresorts.com
Web Site: www.silverleafresorts.com
Approx. Rev.: $226,011,000
Approx. Number Employees: 1,983
Year Founded: 1988

Key to Media (For complete agency information see *The Advertising Red Books-Agencies* edition):
1. Bus. Publs. 2. Cable T.V. 3. Catalogs & Directories. 4. Co-op Adv. 5. Consumer Mags. 6. D.M. to Bus. Estab.7. D.M. to Consumers
8. Daily Newsp. 9. Exhibits/Trade Shows 10. Foreign 11. Infomercial 12. Internet Adv.13. Multimedia 14. Network Radio
15. Network T.V. 16. Newsp. Distr. Mags. 17. Other 18. Outdoor (Posters, Transit) 19. Point of Purchase20. Premiums, Novelties
21. Product Samples 22. Special Events Mktg. 23. Spot Radio 24. Spot T.V. 25. Weekly Newsp. 26. Yellow Page Adv.

Business Description:
Timeshare Resorts Developer, Operator & Marketer
S.I.C.: 6531; 7011
N.A.I.C.S.: 531210; 531311; 721110
Media: 8-18-21
Personnel:
Robert E. Mead *(CEO)*
Harry J. White, Jr. *(CFO)*
Joe W. Conner *(COO-Fin, Dev & Resort Ops)*
Michael D. Jones *(CIO)*
Edward L. Lahart *(COO-Mktg & Fin Svcs)*
David T. O'Connor *(Sr Exec VP-Sls)*
Thomas J. Morris *(Exec VP-Capital Markets & Strategic Plng)*
Phillip B. Davis *(VP-Fin)*
Barbara L. Lewis *(VP-Fin Svcs)*

SIMON PROPERTY GROUP, INC.
225 W Washington St
Indianapolis, IN 46204
Mailing Address:
PO Box 7033
Indianapolis, IN 46207-7033
Tel.: (317) 636-1600
Fax: (317) 263-2318
Fax: (317) 685-7270 (Investor Relations)
Toll Free: (800) 461-3439
E-mail: ircontact@simon.com
Web Site: www.simon.com
Approx. Rev.: $3,957,630,000
Approx. Number Employees: 3,500
Year Founded: 1960
Business Description:
Real Estate Investment Trust; Shopping Malls Owner & Operator
S.I.C.: 6798; 5999; 6159; 6512; 6531
N.A.I.C.S.: 525930; 453998; 522292; 531120; 531312
Advertising Expenditures: $93,565,000
Media: 1-2-3-8-10-18-19-20-22-23-24
Distr.: Direct to Consumer
Budget Set: Oct.
Personnel:
David E. Simon *(Chm & CEO)*
Richard S. Sokolov *(Pres & COO)*
Stephen E. Sterrett *(CFO & Exec VP)*
David Schacht *(CIO & Sr VP)*
Mikael Thygesen *(CMO & Pres-Simon Brand Ventures)*
John Rulli *(Chief Admin Officer, Pres-Simon Mgmt Group & Exec VP)*
John Dahl *(Chief Acctg Officer)*
Gary M. Lewis *(Pres-Leasing & Sr Exec VP)*
James M. Barkley *(Gen Counsel & Sec)*
Andrew A. Juster *(Treas & Exec VP)*
James H. Allen *(Exec VP-Local Leasing)*
David Bloom *(Exec VP)*
Timothy G. Earnest *(Exec VP-Simon Mgmt Grp)*
Vicki Hanor *(Exec VP-Leasing)*
Michael E. McCarty *(Exec VP-Dev Ops)*
Barney Quinn *(Exec VP-Leasing)*
Thomas J. Schneider *(Exec VP)*
Bruce Tobin *(Exec VP-Leasing)*
David Campbell *(Sr VP-Fin-Operating Properties)*
Andy Lugo *(Sr VP-Simon Construction Grp)*
Shari Simon *(Sr VP-Corp Mktg)*
Cathi Weiner *(Sr VP-Simon Brand Ventures)*
Holly Carpenter *(Gen Mgr)*
Kathryn Middleton *(Dir-Mall Mktg)*
Megan Phillips *(Dir-Mktg & Bus Dev-Galleria Dallas)*
Kathy Burnett *(Dir-Parking Svcs)*
Tina Musico *(Dir-Mktg)*
Kelly White *(Dir-Mktg & Bus Dev)*
Mark Gianquitti *(Mgr)*
Alison Griffith *(Mgr-Guest Svcs-Cordova Mall)*
Brands & Products:
THE MILLS
MORE CHOICES
PREMIUM OUTLET CENTERS
SIMON
SIMON GIFTACCOUNT
SIMON GIFTCARD
Advertising Agency:
Bitner Goodman
701 W Cypress Creek Rd Ste 204
Fort Lauderdale, FL 33309-2045
Tel.: (954) 730-7730
Fax: (954) 730-7130
Florida Malls, Outlets & Lifestyle Centers

SIMON PROPERTY GROUP, L.P.
(Sub. of Simon Property Group, Inc.)
225 W Washington St
Indianapolis, IN 46204
Tel.: (317) 636-1600
E-mail: info@simon.com
Web Site: www.simon.com
Approx. Number Employees: 2,500
Business Description:
Real Estate Investment Trust
S.I.C.: 6798
N.A.I.C.S.: 525930
Advertising Expenditures: $61,814,000
Personnel:
David E. Simon *(Chm & CEO)*

SKI ROUNDTOP OPERATING CORP.
(Sub. of Snow Time, Inc.)
925 Roundtop Rd
Lewisberry, PA 17339-9762
Tel.: (717) 432-9631
Fax: (717) 432-2949
E-mail: skiroundtop@skiroundtop.com
Web Site: www.skiroundtop.com
Approx. Number Employees: 800
Year Founded: 1964
Business Description:
Ski Resort
S.I.C.: 7011
N.A.I.C.S.: 721199
Media: 3-6-8-10-17-23-24
Distr.: Direct to Consumer; Reg.
Personnel:
Chris Dudding *(Dir-Mktg)*
Jim Garling *(Mgr)*
Brands & Products:
SKI ROUNDTOP

SKYLINE EQUITIES REALTY, LLC
800 Brickell Ave Ste 201
Miami, FL 33131
Tel.: (305) 285-7272
Tel.: (312) 595-4886
Fax: (305) 285-7277
E-mail: info@skylineequitiesrealty.com
Web Site: www.skylineequitiesrealty.com
Approx. Number Employees: 6
Business Description:
Real Estate Services
S.I.C.: 6531
N.A.I.C.S.: 531210
Media: 2-6
Personnel:
Evangeline Gouletas *(Chm & CEO)*
Hugh Wiedman *(COO)*
Isos Y. Stamelos-Monroe *(VP-Sls & Licensed Mng Broker)*
Stylianos G. Vayanoas *(VP-Mktg & Sls)*

SMITH MANAGEMENT CO., INC.
5101 Monkhouse Dr
Shreveport, LA 71109-6509
Mailing Address:
PO Box 3853
Shreveport, LA 71133
Tel.: (318) 861-1994
Fax: (318) 674-2999
Approx. Number Employees: 243
Business Description:
Motels Management & Development
S.I.C.: 6513
N.A.I.C.S.: 531110
Media: 2-5-7-8-17-18-20-26
Distr.: Reg.
Budget Set: Nov.
Personnel:
Harrison W. Smith *(Pres)*

SNOW KING RESORT, INC.
400 E Snow King Ave
Jackson, WY 83001
Mailing Address:
PO Box SKI
Jackson, WY 83001
Tel.: (307) 733-5200
Fax: (307) 733-4086
Toll Free: (800) 522-5464
E-mail: info@snowking.com
Web Site: www.snowking.com
Approx. Number Employees: 200
Year Founded: 1976
Business Description:
Ski Resort
S.I.C.: 7011
N.A.I.C.S.: 721110
Media: 2-5-6-8-9-10-25-26
Distr.: Natl.
Personnel:
Manuel B. Lopez *(Pres)*
Dana Ahrensberg *(Gen Mgr)*
Jackie Bradford *(Mgr-Natl Sls)*
Adam Shankland *(Mgr-Mountain Ops)*

SNOWMASS VILLAGE RESORT ASSOCIATION
130 Kearns Rd
Snowmass Village, CO 81615
Mailing Address:
PO Box 5566
Snowmass Village, CO 81615-5566
Tel.: (970) 923-2000
Fax: (970) 923-5466
Toll Free: (800) 598-2006
E-mail: info@tosv.com
Web Site: www.snowmassmeetings.com
E-Mail For Key Personnel:
Marketing Director: bhuske@snowmassvillage.com
Sales Director: sales@tosv.com
Sales Range: Less than $1 Million
Approx. Number Employees: 12
Business Description:
Central Reservation Services
S.I.C.: 8611
N.A.I.C.S.: 813910
Media: 3-5-6-8-9-13-18-22-23
Distr.: Natl.
Budget Set: Aug.
Personnel:
Susan Hamley *(Dir-Snowmass Tourism Office)*
Karla Baker *(Mgr-Natl Sls)*
Jim O'Leary *(Mgr-Natl Sls)*
Kiesha Techau *(Coord-Grp)*
Brands & Products:
SNOW MASS

SONESTA INTERNATIONAL HOTELS CORPORATION
116 Huntington Ave 9th Fl
Boston, MA 02116
Tel.: (617) 421-5400
Fax: (617) 421-5402
Toll Free: (800) SONESTA
E-mail: info@sonesta.com
Web Site: www.sonesta.com
E-Mail For Key Personnel:
President: president@sonesta.com
Approx. Rev.: $74,684,000
Approx. Number Employees: 718
Year Founded: 1940
Business Description:
Owner & Operator of Resorts & Hotels
S.I.C.: 7011
N.A.I.C.S.: 721110
Advertising Expenditures: $7,204,000
Media: 1-2-4-5-6-7-8-9-10-11-13-14-16-18-19-22-23-25-26
Distr.: Direct to Consumer; Intl.; Natl.
Budget Set: Nov.-Dec.
Personnel:
Peter J. Sonnabend *(Chm)*
Stephanie Sonnabend *(Pres & CEO)*
John DePaul *(Exec VP-Dev)*
Jacqueline Sonnabend *(Exec VP & Sr Quality Officer)*
Kathy Sonnabend Rowe *(Sr VP-Food & Beverage)*
Stephen Sonnabend *(Sr VP)*
Carol Campbell Beggs *(VP-Tech)*
Curtis J. Crider *(Gen Mgr)*
Tasia Fatone *(Exec Dir-Reg Sls-Sonesta Collection Brand)*
Dennis Hatch *(Dir-HR)*
Tom Sonnabend *(Dir-Reg Sls)*
Patti Sonnabend Wagner *(Dir-Corp Acctg)*
Mark Wilson *(Dir-Mktg)*
Liliana Penaranda *(Bus Travel-Sls Mgr)*
Antonella Sacchero *(Sls Mgr-Euro)*
Brands & Products:
BEGUES
NILE CRUISES
SONESTA HOTELS & RESORTS
Advertising Agency:
Point B Communications
750 N Orleans Ste 600
Chicago, IL 60654
Tel.: (312) 867-7750
Fax: (312) 867-7751

Key to Media (For complete agency information see *The Advertising Red Books-Agencies* edition):
1. Bus. Publs. 2. Cable T.V. 3. Catalogs & Directories. 4. Co-op Adv. 5. Consumer Mags. 6. D.M. to Bus. Estab.7. D.M. to Consumers 8. Daily Newsp. 9. Exhibits/Trade Shows 10. Foreign 11. Infomercial 12. Internet Adv.13. Multimedia 14. Network Radio 15. Network T.V. 16. Newsp. Distr. Mags. 17. Other 18. Outdoor (Posters, Transit) 19. Point of Purchase20. Premiums, Novelties 21. Product Samples 22. Special Events Mktg. 23. Spot Radio 24. Spot T.V. 25. Weekly Newsp. 26. Yellow Page Adv.

SOTHEBY'S INTERNATIONAL REALTY, INC.
(Sub. of NRT Inc.)
38 E 61st St
New York, NY 10065
Tel.: (212) 606-7660
Fax: (212) 606-7661
Web Site: www.sothebysrealty.com
Approx. Number Employees: 110
Year Founded: 1976
Business Description:
Residential Real Estate Brokerage Firm
S.I.C.: 6531
N.A.I.C.S.: 531210
Media: 2-4-6-9-17-25-26
Distr.: Natl.
Budget Set: Dec.
Personnel:
Kathryn A. Korte *(Pres & CEO)*
Frank G. Symons *(COO-Western & Exec VP)*
Clayton Andrews *(Exec VP & COO-Mountain)*
George Ballantyne *(Exec VP-New England Reg)*
Ellie Johnson *(Sr VP & Brokerage Mgr)*
Richard Moeser *(Sr VP-Southeast)*
Zackary W. Wright *(Sr VP-West)*
Bill Kirk *(VP & Mgr-Palm Beach Brokerage)*
Cynthia Frasher *(Asst VP-Southampton Brokerage)*
Martin Schiller *(Dir-Australia Brokerage)*
Lew Geffen *(Mgr-S Africa Brokerage)*
Lori Thorton *(Mgr-Mktg)*

SOUTH BEND CLINIC LLP
(d/b/a Medical Arts Pharmacy)
211 N Eddy St
South Bend, IN 46617
Tel.: (574) 234-8161
Fax: (574) 239-1489
E-mail: info@southbendclinic.com
Web Site: www.southbendclinic.com
Sales Range: $75-99.9 Million
Approx. Number Employees: 575
Business Description:
Real Estate Managers
S.I.C.: 8011
N.A.I.C.S.: 621111
Personnel:
Paul Meyer *(Exec Dir)*
Advertising Agency:
Villing & Company, Inc.
5909 Nimtz Pkwy
South Bend, IN 46628
Tel.: (574) 277-0215
Fax: (574) 277-5513

SOUTHWOOD GOLF CLUB
(Sub. of The St. Joe Company)
3750 Grove Park Dr
Tallahassee, FL 32311
Tel.: (850) 942-4653
Fax: (850) 671-6162
Web Site: www.southwoodgolf.com
Sales Range: $10-24.9 Million
Approx. Number Employees: 85
Business Description:
Golf Club Operations
S.I.C.: 7997
N.A.I.C.S.: 713910
Media: 6-22
Personnel:
Beth Murphy *(Gen Mgr)*

SPA FINDER, INC.
257 Park Ave S 10th Fl
New York, NY 10010
Tel.: (212) 924-6800
Fax: (212) 924-7240
E-mail: info@spafinder.com
Web Site: www.spafinder.com
Year Founded: 1996
Business Description:
Spa, Travel & Marketing Services Connecting Consumers Via Publishing, Internet & Corporate Incentive Programs
S.I.C.: 2721; 2741; 5961; 7389; 8742
N.A.I.C.S.: 511120; 454111; 454113; 516110; 519190; 541613
Media: 4-6-13
Personnel:
Susie Ellis *(Pres)*
Sallie Fraenkel *(COO)*
Neil Kurlander *(Chief Admin Officer & Gen Counsel)*
Daniel Lizio-Katzen *(Mng Dir-Spa Booker)*
Advertising Agency:
RBI Communications, Los Angeles
6311 Romaine St
Hollywood, CA 90038
Tel.: (323) 960-1360

SRS REAL ESTATE PARTNERS
(Sub. of Jones Lang LaSalle Incorporated)
8343 Douglas Ave Ste 200
Dallas, TX 75225
Tel.: (214) 560-3200
Fax: (214) 560-6900
Toll Free: (888) 213-1110
E-mail: dallas@srsre.com
Web Site: www.srsre.com
E-Mail For Key Personnel:
Marketing Director: Diane.Gillas@staubach.com
Sales Range: $200-249.9 Million
Approx. Number Employees: 1,181
Year Founded: 1977
Business Description:
Commercial Real Estate
S.I.C.: 6531
N.A.I.C.S.: 531390
Import Export
Media: 2-7-9-10-22-25
Personnel:
Chris Maguire *(Chm & CEO)*
Hugh Kelly *(Mng Principal-Northeast Reg)*
Jimmy Dockal *(CFO)*
Drew Kiesling *(COO)*
Matthew Ramsey *(CIO)*
Matthew Alexander *(Exec VP & Mng Principal-Northwest)*
Steve Dawkins *(Exec VP)*
Stan Heller *(Exec VP)*
Mark Newman *(Exec VP)*
Mark Reeder *(Exec VP)*
Scott Riddles *(Exec VP & Market Leader)*
Ray Uttenhove *(Exec VP)*
John Artope *(Sr VP & Market Leader)*
John Rischard *(Sr VP-Fin & Admin)*
Daniel Taylor *(Sr VP)*

ST. BARTH PROPERTIES, INC.
693 E Central St Ste 201
Franklin, MA 02038
Tel.: (508) 528-7727
Fax: (508) 528-7789
Toll Free: (800) 421-3396
E-mail: info@stbarth.com
Web Site: www.stbarth.com
Sales Range: $1-9.9 Million
Approx. Number Employees: 8
Year Founded: 1989
Business Description:
Real Estate Services
S.I.C.: 6531
N.A.I.C.S.: 531390
Media: 6-11
Personnel:
Margaret Walsh *(Pres)*
Kathryn Schlitzer *(Dir-Client Svcs)*

STARWOOD HOTELS & RESORTS WORLDWIDE, INC.
1111 Westchester Ave
White Plains, NY 10604
Tel.: (914) 640-8100
Fax: (914) 640-8310
Web Site: www.starwood.com
Approx. Rev.: $5,071,000,000
Approx. Number Employees: 145,000
Year Founded: 1969
Business Description:
Hotels Owner & Operator
S.I.C.: 7011
N.A.I.C.S.: 721199; 721110
Advertising Expenditures: $132,000,000
Media: 2-3-5-6-8-9-10-11-13-14-15-18-20-22-23-24-25
Personnel:
Lynne Dougherty *(Sr VP & Owner-Rels & Franchise)*
Miguel Ko *(Chm & Pres-Asia Pacific)*
Vasant M. Prabhu *(Vice Chm, CFO & Exec VP)*
Bruce W. Duncan *(Pres & CEO)*
Frits D. van Paasschen *(Pres & CEO)*
Kenneth S. Siegel *(Chief Admin Officer & Gen Counsel)*
Jeff Cava *(Chief HR Officer & Exec VP)*
Tad G. Wampfler *(Chief Supply Chain Officer)*
Matthew E. Avril *(Pres-Hotel Grp)*
Denise Coll *(Pres-North America Div)*
Osvaldo V. Librizzi *(Pres-Latin America)*
Simon Turner *(Pres-Global Dev)*
Roeland Vos *(Pres-Europe, Africa & Middle East Div)*
Phil McAveety *(Chief Brand Officer & Exec VP)*
Eva Ziegler *(Sr VP & Head-Brands-W Hotels & Le Meridien)*
Christie Hicks *(Sr VP-Sls-Global)*
Brian McGuinness *(Sr VP-Specialty Select Brands)*
Tim Roby *(Sr VP-Sls North Amercia)*
Mike Tiedy *(Sr VP-Global Brand & Innovation)*
Shane Hodges *(Mng Dir-Global Corp Sls)*
Flavio Bucciarelli *(Mgr-Northern France & Gen Mgr-Le Meridien Etoile-Paris)*
Thomas Meding *(Gen Mgr-SLS Hotel)*
Helen Horsham-Bertels *(Sr Dir-Consumer Affairs)*
Alyssa Waxenberg *(Sr Dir-Emerging Platforms)*
Chloe Hampton *(Assoc Dir)*
Abbey Reider *(Assoc Dir-Search Mktg, Affiliate & Social Media Strategy-Global)*
Paul James *(Global Brand Mgr)*
Sewar Sawalha *(Mgr-Pub Rel-LeMeridien Amman Hotel)*
Brands & Products:
ALOFT
ELEMENT
FOUR POINTS
FOUR POINTS BY SHERATON
HEAVENLY
LE MERIDIEN
THE LUXURY COLLECTION
THE PHOENICIAN
SHERATON
SPG
ST. REGIS
STARPOINTS
STARWOOD
STARWOOD PREFERRED GUEST
W HOTELS
WESTIN
Advertising Agencies:
Alison Brod Public Relations
373 Park Ave S 4th Fl
New York, NY 10016
Tel.: (212) 230-1800
Fax: (212) 230-1161

Davie Brown Entertainment
4721 Alla Rd
Marina Del Rey, CA 90292
Tel.: (310) 979-1980
Fax: (310) 754-1783
Westin

Deutsch, Inc.
(A Lowe & Partners Company)
111 8th Ave 14th Fl
New York, NY 10011-5201
Tel.: (212) 981-7600
Fax: (212) 981-7525
(Creative & Media for Westin & Sheraton Brands)

MMG Worldwide
4601 Madison Ave
Kansas City, MO 64112
Tel.: (816) 472-5988
Fax: (816) 471-5395

Razorfish New York
1440 Broadway 19th Fl
New York, NY 10018
Tel.: (212) 798-6600
Fax: (212) 798-6601
— Pierre Odendaal *(Grp Dir-Creative)*

STEAMBOAT SKI & RESORT CORPORATION
(Sub. of Intrawest ULC)
2305 Mount Werner Cir
Steamboat Springs, CO 80487-9023
Tel.: (970) 879-6111
Fax: (970) 879-7844
Fax: (970) 879-4757
Toll Free: (877) 237-2628
E-mail: info@steamboat.com
Web Site: www.steamboat.com
Sales Range: $125-149.9 Million
Approx. Number Employees: 250
Year Founded: 1963
Business Description:
Year-Round Resort Featuring Skiing & All Summer Activities
S.I.C.: 5941; 7999
N.A.I.C.S.: 451110; 487990
Media: 2-5-6-7-8-9-10-11-13-16-18-22-23-24-25
Distr.: Direct to Consumer; Natl.

Key to Media (For complete agency information see *The Advertising Red Books-Agencies* edition):
1. Bus. Publs. 2. Cable T.V. 3. Catalogs & Directories. 4. Co-op Adv. 5. Consumer Mags. 6. D.M. to Bus. Estab.7. D.M. to Consumers 8. Daily Newsp. 9. Exhibits/Trade Shows 10. Foreign 11. Infomercial 12. Internet Adv.13. Multimedia 14. Network Radio 15. Network T.V. 16. Newsp. Distr. Mags. 17. Other 18. Outdoor (Posters, Transit) 19. Point of Purchase20. Premiums, Novelties 21. Product Samples 22. Special Events Mktg. 23. Spot Radio 24. Spot T.V. 25. Weekly Newsp. 26. Yellow Page Adv.

Budget Set: May
Personnel:
Chris Diamond *(Pres & CEO)*
Andy Wirth *(Sr VP-Mktg & Sls)*
Mike Lane *(Dir-PR)*
Loryn Kasten *(Mgr-PR)*
Brands & Products:
STEAMBOAT

STILES CORPORATION
300 SE 2nd St
Fort Lauderdale, FL 33301-1923
Tel.: (954) 627-9300
Fax: (954) 627-9386
E-mail: info@stiles.com
Web Site: www.stiles.com
E-Mail For Key Personnel:
Public Relations: pr@stiles.com
Sales Range: $250-299.9 Million
Approx. Number Employees: 300
Year Founded: 1951
Business Description:
Developer of Office, Industrial & Retail Projects; Mixed-use Residential Construction; Real Estate Brokers; Landscaping Contractors; Architectural Services; Property Management
S.I.C.: 1541; 1522
N.A.I.C.S.: 236210; 236220
Media: 2-4-7-9-10-13-17-20-22-25-26
Distr.: Reg.
Budget Set: Sept.
Personnel:
Terry W. Stiles *(Chm & CEO)*
Doug Eagon *(Pres)*
Stephen R. Palmer *(COO)*
Robert Esposito *(Chief Admin Officer & Chief Acctg Officer)*
James W. Stine *(Chief Investment Officer)*
Thomas R. Kates *(Pres-Stiles Realty Company)*
Doug Watt *(VP-Construction & VP-Mktg)*

STOWE AREA ASSOCIATION, INC.
51 Main St
Stowe, VT 05672
Tel.: (802) 253-7321
Fax: (802) 253-6628
Toll Free: (877) GOSTOWE
E-mail: askus@gostowe.com
Web Site: www.gostowe.com
Approx. Number Employees: 26
Business Description:
Visitor Information Services
S.I.C.: 8611; 4729
N.A.I.C.S.: 813910; 561599
Advertising Expenditures: $200,000
Media: 5-6-8-9-10-13-18-19-20-22-23
Distr.: Natl.
Personnel:
Ed Stahl *(Exec Dir)*
Jasmine Bigelow *(Dir-Mktg)*

STRATOSPHERE CORPORATION
(Holding of Icahn Enterprises L.P.)
2000 Las Vegas Blvd S
Las Vegas, NV 89104-2507
Tel.: (702) 380-7777
Fax: (702) 383-4733
Toll Free: (800) 998-6937
Web Site: www.stratospherehotel.com
E-Mail For Key Personnel:
Public Relations: pr@stratospherehotel.com
Approx. Rev.: $142,000,000
Approx. Number Employees: 3,000
Year Founded: 1993
Business Description:
Owner & Operator of Hotel & Casino
S.I.C.: 7011; 7999
N.A.I.C.S.: 721120; 713990
Import Export
Advertising Expenditures: $2,300,000
Media: 8-13-22
Personnel:
Ned Martin *(CFO)*
Barbara Aalberts *(Mgr-Adv)*
Brands & Products:
STRATOSPHERE CASINO, HOTEL & TOWER

STRATTON MOUNTAIN RESORT
(Sub. of Intrawest ULC)
RR 1 Box 145
Stratton Mountain, VT 05155
Tel.: (802) 297-4000
Fax: (802) 297-4300
Toll Free: (800) STRATTON
E-mail: infostratton@intrawest.com
Web Site: www.stratton.com
Sales Range: $100-124.9 Million
Business Description:
Ski Resort
S.I.C.: 7011; 7999
N.A.I.C.S.: 721110; 713990; 721199
Media: 3-4-6-8-10-13-18-22-23-24-25
Distr.: Direct to Consumer; Reg.
Budget Set: Apr.
Personnel:
Michael Cobb *(VP-Mktg & Sls)*
Myra Foster *(Sr Mgr-Mktg & Comm)*

STRATUS ASSET MANAGEMENT, LLC
(Formerly Boca Developers, Inc.)
321 E Hillsboro Blvd
Deerfield Beach, FL 33441
Tel.: (954) 418-0208
Fax: (954) 418-0207
Web Site: www.stratusam.com
Approx. Number Employees: 50
Business Description:
Business Development & Management
S.I.C.: 6552; 6513
N.A.I.C.S.: 541611
Media: 2-4-6-13
Personnel:
Brian Street *(Pres)*
Jeffrey Scott DiBartolo *(CFO)*
Theodore R. Stotzer *(Gen Counsel & Exec VP)*
Joe Fairleigh *(VP-Sls)*

STRATUS PROPERTIES, INC.
212 Lavaca St Ste 300
Austin, TX 78701
Tel.: (512) 478-5788
Fax: (512) 478-6356
Toll Free: (800) 690-0315
E-mail: investors@stratusproperties.com
Web Site: www.stratusproperties.com
Approx. Rev.: $9,123,000
Approx. Number Employees: 35
Business Description:
Real Estate Development Services
S.I.C.: 6552; 6531
N.A.I.C.S.: 237210; 531210
Advertising Expenditures: $100,000
Media: 17
Personnel:
William H. Armstrong, III *(Pres & Chm)*
Eric D. Pickens *(CFO & Sr VP)*
Kenneth N. Jones *(Gen Counsel)*

SUMMER BAY RESORT
25 Town Ctr Blvd Ste C
Clermont, FL 34714
Tel.: (352) 242-1100
Fax: (352) 242-2669
Toll Free: (888) 742-1100, ext. 7417
E-mail: arodriguez@summerbayresort.com
Web Site: www.summerbayresort.com
Approx. Number Employees: 310
Business Description:
Resort & Hotel
S.I.C.: 7011; 5947
N.A.I.C.S.: 721110; 453220
Media: 6-13
Personnel:
Joe H. Scott, Sr. *(Pres)*

SUN COMMUNITIES, INC.
The American Center 27777 Franklin Rd Ste 200
Southfield, MI 48034
Tel.: (248) 208-2500
Web Site: www.suncommunities.com
Approx. Sls.: $263,140,000
Approx. Number Employees: 747
Year Founded: 1975
Business Description:
Real Estate Investment Trusts
S.I.C.: 6798; 6531
N.A.I.C.S.: 525930; 531390
Advertising Expenditures: $2,200,000
Personnel:
Gary A. Shiffman *(Chm, Pres & CEO)*
Karen J. Dearing *(CFO, Treas, Sec & Exec VP)*
John B. McLaren *(COO & Exec VP)*
Jonathan M. Colman *(Exec VP)*

SUN VALLEY COMPANY
(Sub. of Grand America Hotels & Resorts)
1 Sun Valley Rd
Sun Valley, ID 83353
Tel.: (208) 622-4111
Tel.: (208) 622-2001
Fax: (208) 622-2082
Toll Free: (800) 786-8259
Web Site: www.sunvalley.com
Business Description:
Hotels & Resorts
S.I.C.: 7011
N.A.I.C.S.: 721110
Personnel:
Tim Silva *(Gen Mgr)*
Dick Andersen *(Dir-Hotel Ops)*
Brent Gillette *(Dir-Sls-Sun Valley Resort)*
Kelly Mitchell *(Dir-Retail & Buyer)*
Rob Prew *(Dir-IT)*
Jack Sibbach *(Dir-Sls, Mktg & PR)*
Peter Stearns *(Dir-Race Dept)*
Mike Federko *(Mgr-Mountain)*
Rick Hickman *(Mgr-Resort Night)*
Doug Horn *(Mgr-Catering)*
Jennifer Uhrig *(Mgr-Ticket Sls)*
Brands & Products:
THE AMERICAN ORIGINAL
Advertising Agencies:
Drake Cooper Inc.
416 S 8th 3rd Fl
Boise, ID 83702-5471
Tel.: (208) 342-0925
Fax: (208) 342-0635

Eleven Inc.
445 Bush St 8th Fl
San Francisco, CA 94108
Tel.: (415) 707-1111
Fax: (415) 707-1100

SUNBURST HOSPITALITY CORPORATION
10770 Columbia Pike Ste 200
Silver Spring, MD 20901-4448
Tel.: (301) 592-3800
Fax: (301) 592-3830
E-mail: info@sunbursthospitality.com
Web Site: www.sunbursthospitality.com
Approx. Number Employees: 2,500
Year Founded: 1997
Business Description:
Owner & Operator of Extended-Stay Hotels
S.I.C.: 7011; 8741
N.A.I.C.S.: 721110; 561110
Media: 13-18-23
Personnel:
Kevin P. Hanley *(Pres & CEO)*
Charles G. Warczak, Jr. *(CFO, Treas & Sr VP)*
Joe Smith *(CFO, Treas & VP)*
Pamela M. Williams *(Chief Admin Officer, Gen Counsel & Exec VP)*
Mark Elbaum *(VP-Info Sys)*
Julie Thompson *(VP-Sls & Mktg)*
Brands & Products:
SUNBURST HOSPITALITY CORPORATION

SUNCOR DEVELOPMENT COMPANY
(Sub. of Pinnacle West Capital Corporation)
80 E Real Salado Pkwy Ste 410
Tempe, AZ 85281
Tel.: (480) 317-6800
Fax: (480) 317-6800
Fax: (480) 317-6934
Web Site: www.suncoraz.com
Sales Range: $200-249.9 Million
Approx. Number Employees: 60
Year Founded: 1986
Business Description:
Land Development & Resort Management
S.I.C.: 6552; 6513; 6531; 8699
N.A.I.C.S.: 237210; 531110; 531210; 531311; 531312; 531320; 531390; 813990
Advertising Expenditures: $2,500,000
Media: 2-3-6-7-8-9-13-18-20-22-23-24-25-26
Distr.: Reg.
Budget Set: Aug. -Sept.
Brands & Products:
CORAL CANYON
GOLDEN HERITAGE HOMES
HIDDEN HILLS
PALM VALLEY
RANCHO VIEJO
SEDONA GOLF RESORT
STONERIDGE
SUNCOR

Key to Media (For complete agency information see *The Advertising Red Books-Agencies* edition):
1. Bus. Publs. 2. Cable T.V. 3. Catalogs & Directories. 4. Co-op Adv. 5. Consumer Mags. 6. D.M. to Bus. Estab.7. D.M. to Consumers
8. Daily Newsp. 9. Exhibits/Trade Shows 10. Foreign 11. Infomercial 12. Internet Adv.13. Multimedia 14. Network Radio
15. Network T.V. 16. Newsp. Distr. Mags. 17. Other 18. Outdoor (Posters, Transit) 19. Point of Purchase20. Premiums, Novelties
21. Product Samples 22. Special Events Mktg. 23. Spot Radio 24. Spot T.V. 25. Weekly Newsp. 26. Yellow Page Adv.

SUNSTONE HOTEL INVESTORS, INC.
120 Vantis Ste 350
Aliso Viejo, CA 92656
Tel.: (949) 369-4000
Fax: (949) 369-3134
Web Site: www.sunstonehotels.com
Approx. Rev.: $643,090,000
Approx. Number Employees: 35
Year Founded: 1994
Business Description:
Real Estate Investment Trust
S.I.C.: 6798; 6289; 7011
N.A.I.C.S.: 525930; 523999; 721110
Advertising Expenditures: $33,182,000
Personnel:
Lewis N. Wolff *(Co-Chm)*
Kenneth E. Cruse *(Pres)*
John V. Arabia *(CFO & Exec VP-Corp Strategy)*
Lindsay N. Monge *(Treas & Sr VP)*
Bryan Giglia *(Sr VP-Corp Fin)*
Marc A. Hoffman *(Sr VP-Asset Mgmt)*
Guy Lindsey *(Sr VP-Design & Construction)*
David Sloan *(VP-Legal)*
Brands & Products:
SUNSTONE

SUNSTREAM, INC.
(d/b/a SunStream Hotels & Resorts)
6231 Estero Blvd
Fort Myers Beach, FL 33931
Tel.: (239) 765-4111
Fax: (239) 765-5755
Toll Free: (888) 627-1595
E-mail: info@sunstream.com
Web Site: www.sunstream.com
Approx. Number Employees: 250
Year Founded: 1986
Business Description:
Hotels & Condo Resorts Owner & Operator
S.I.C.: 7011
N.A.I.C.S.: 721110
Media: 6-8-22-24
Personnel:
David A. Lawrence *(Pres)*
Brands & Products:
BELLASERA
DIAMONDHEAD BEACH RESORT
GREENLINKS GOLF RESORT
GULLWING BEACH RESORT
PARK SHORE RESORT
POINTE ESTERO BEACH RESORT
SANTA MARIA HARBOUR RESORT

SYZYGY ENTERTAINMENT, LTD.
The Rotunda 4201 Congress St Ste 145
Charlotte, NC 28209
Tel.: (704) 366-5122
Web Site: www.syzygyent.com/
Approx. Rev.: $4,150,305
Approx. Number Employees: 42
Business Description:
Casino Operator
S.I.C.: 7999
N.A.I.C.S.: 713210
Advertising Expenditures: $132,569
Media: 17
Personnel:
S. Gregory Smith *(Pres & CEO)*

TANGER FACTORY OUTLET CENTERS, INC.
3200 Northline Ave Ste 360
Greensboro, NC 27408-7612
Tel.: (336) 292-3010
Fax: (336) 852-2096
E-mail: tangermail@tangeroutlet.com
Web Site: www.tangeroutlet.com
Approx. Rev.: $276,303,000
Approx. Number Employees: 197
Year Founded: 1993
Business Description:
Real Estate Investment Trusts
S.I.C.: 6531; 6798
N.A.I.C.S.: 531210; 525930
Import Export
Advertising Expenditures: $18,978,000
Personnel:
Steven B. Tanger *(Pres & CEO)*
Frank C. Marchisello, Jr. *(CFO, Sec & Exec VP)*
Thomas E. McDonough *(COO)*
Virginia R. Summerell *(Treas, VP & Asst Sec)*
James F. Williams *(Sr VP & Controller)*
Kevin M. Dillon *(Sr VP-Construction & Site Selection)*
Lisa J. Morrison *(Sr VP-Leasing)*
Carrie A. Warren *(Sr VP-Mktg)*
Laura M. Atwell *(VP-Mktg)*
Rick Farrar *(VP-IT)*
Mary Williams *(VP-HR)*
Mike Buescher *(Dir-PR)*
Brands & Products:
TANGER

TANGER PROPERTIES LIMITED PARTNERSHIP
(Sub. of Tanger Factory Outlet Centers, Inc.)
3200 Northline Ave Ste 360
Greensboro, NC 27408-7612
Tel.: (336) 292-3010
Fax: (336) 852-7954
E-mail: info@tangeroutlet.com
Web Site: www.tangeroutlet.com
Business Description:
Property Management Services
S.I.C.: 6798; 6531
N.A.I.C.S.: 525930; 531312
Advertising Expenditures: $18,978,000
Media: 8-9-13-17-23-24-25
Personnel:
Stanley K. Tanger *(Founder & Chm)*
Steven B. Tanger *(Pres & CEO)*
Frank C. Marchisello, Jr. *(CFO & Exec VP)*
Virginia R. Summerell *(Treas, VP & Asst Sec)*
Thomas E. McDonough *(Exec VP-Ops)*
James F. Williams *(Sr VP & Controller)*
Lisa J. Morrison *(Sr VP-Leasing)*
Carrie A. Warren *(Sr VP-Mktg)*

TANNER REALTY OF NORTHWEST FLORIDA INC.
421 E Zaragoza St
Pensacola, FL 32502
Tel.: (850) 435-9007
Fax: (850) 435-7248
Toll Free: (866) TANNER1
E-mail: funtanner@aol.com
Web Site: www.kathytanner.com
Approx. Number Employees: 7
Business Description:
Real Estate Services
S.I.C.: 6531
N.A.I.C.S.: 531210
Media: 6-9-25
Personnel:
Kathy Tanner *(Owner)*

TAOS SKI VALLEY, INC.
116 Sutton Pl
Taos Ski Valley, NM 87525-0090
Tel.: (575) 776-2291
Fax: (505) 776-8596
E-mail: tsv@skitaos.org
Web Site: www.skitaos.org
Approx. Number Employees: 600
Year Founded: 1954
Business Description:
Ski Area Operations; Ski Shop; Ski School; Ski-Rental; Restaurants; Bar; Package Liquor Sales; Resort-Related Activities & Services
S.I.C.: 7999; 5941
N.A.I.C.S.: 487990; 451110
Advertising Expenditures: $500,000
Media: 1-4-5-6-8-9-10-15-18-20-23-24-25-26
Distr.: Intl.; Natl.
Budget Set: Apr.
Personnel:
John A. Mitchell *(Chm)*
Michael H. Blake *(Pres)*
Gordon Briner *(COO)*
Seth Bullington *(Mgr-Mktg)*
Brands & Products:
TAOS
TAOS SKI & BOOT
TSV
Advertising Agency:
McKee Wallwork Cleveland
1030 18th St NW
Albuquerque, NM 87104
Tel.: (505) 821-2999
Fax: (505) 821-0006
Toll Free: (888) 821-2999

TARRAGON CORPORATION
423 W 55th St 12th Fl
New York, NY 10019-1903
Tel.: (212) 949-5000
Fax: (212) 949-8001
Toll Free: (888) 525-2216
Web Site: www.tarragonmanagement.com/
Sales Range: $100-124.9 Million
Approx. Number Employees: 499
Year Founded: 1973
Business Description:
Real Estate Investment Services
S.I.C.: 6798
N.A.I.C.S.: 525930
Advertising Expenditures: $911,000
Personnel:
Robert P. Rothenberg *(Pres & COO)*
William S. Friedman *(CEO)*
Kathryn Mansfield *(Gen Counsel)*
Jamie Helman *(Exec VP)*

TAUBMAN CENTERS, INC.
200 E Long Lake Rd Ste 300
Bloomfield Hills, MI 48304-2324
Tel.: (248) 258-6800
Fax: (248) 258-7697
E-mail: bbaker@taubman.com
Web Site: www.taubman.com
Approx. Rev.: $654,558,000
Approx. Number Employees: 582
Year Founded: 1950
Business Description:
Real Estate Investment Trust
S.I.C.: 6159; 6798
N.A.I.C.S.: 522292; 525930
Personnel:
Robert S. Taubman *(Chm, Pres & CEO)*
Lisa A. Payne *(Vice Chm & CFO)*
William S. Taubman *(COO)*
Robert R. Reese *(Chief Admin Officer & Sr VP)*
Esther R. Blum *(Chief Acctg Officer, Sr VP & Controller)*
Chris B. Heaphy *(Gen Counsel, Sec & Sr VP)*
Steven E. Eder *(Treas & Sr VP)*
Denise Anton *(Sr VP-Center Ops)*
Steven J. Kieras *(Sr VP-Dev)*
David T. Weinert *(Sr VP-Leasing)*
Lori McGhee *(Reg Dir-Specialty Leasing)*
Karen Macdonald *(Dir-Comm)*
Emily Dewolfe *(Mgr-Interactive Mktg)*
Advertising Agency:
Simons Michelson Zieve, Inc.
900 Wilshire Dr Ste 102
Troy, MI 48084-1634
Tel.: (248) 362-4242
Fax: (248) 362-2014

TAYLOR MORRISON
(Sub. of Taylor Morrison Inc.)
8430 Enterprise Cir
Bradenton, FL 34202
Tel.: (941) 554-2000
Fax: (941) 554-3005
Web Site: www.taylormorrison.com
Approx. Number Employees: 70
Business Description:
Home Construction & Development Services
S.I.C.: 6531
N.A.I.C.S.: 531390
Media: 6
Personnel:
Brian Watson *(VP-Fin)*
Jill Hoffman Meeks *(Mgr-Sls-West Florida)*

T.C. GROUP LLC
121 Triple Diamond Blvd Unit 8
North Venice, FL 34275
Tel.: (941) 486-0068
Business Description:
Real Estate Services
S.I.C.: 1531
N.A.I.C.S.: 236118
Media: 6

THOMPSON REALTY CORPORATION
(Sub. of The Thompson Company)
1701 N Collins Blvd Ste 2500
Richardson, TX 75082
Tel.: (972) 644-2400
Fax: (972) 644-2411
Web Site: www.thompson-realty.com
Approx. Number Employees: 240
Year Founded: 1957
Business Description:
Commercial Construction
S.I.C.: 1521; 5122
N.A.I.C.S.: 236115; 424210
Import Export
Personnel:
W. T. Field *(Pres & CEO)*
Todd Radford *(Treas & VP-Fin)*

Key to Media (For complete agency information see *The Advertising Red Books-Agencies* edition):
1. Bus. Publs. 2. Cable T.V. 3. Catalogs & Directories. 4. Co-op Adv. 5. Consumer Mags. 6. D.M. to Bus. Estab.7. D.M. to Consumers 8. Daily Newsp. 9. Exhibits/Trade Shows 10. Foreign 11. Infomercial 12. Internet Adv.13. Multimedia 14. Network Radio 15. Network T.V. 16. Newsp. Distr. Mags. 17. Other 18. Outdoor (Posters, Transit) 19. Point of Purchase20. Premiums, Novelties 21. Product Samples 22. Special Events Mktg. 23. Spot Radio 24. Spot T.V. 25. Weekly Newsp. 26. Yellow Page Adv.

Advertising Agency:
Pugliese Creative
9330 Amberton Pkwy Ste 1260
Dallas, TX 75243
Tel.: (214) 916-5667
Fax: (214) 575-0064
Toll Free: (877) 295-3826

TIMELESS LASER REJUVENATION CENTER

3206 Hillsdale Ln
Kissimmee, FL 34741
Tel.: (407) 933-8004
Fax: (407) 846-3261
Web Site: www.timelesslaser.com
Approx. Number Employees: 10
Business Description:
Medical Spa
S.I.C.: 7032
N.A.I.C.S.: 721214
Media: 13
Personnel:
Alanna McDonald *(Pres)*

TISHMAN SPEYER PROPERTIES LP

45 Rockseller Plz
New York, NY 10111
Tel.: (212) 715-0300
Fax: (212) 319-1745
E-mail: info@tishmanspeyer.com
Web Site: www.tishmanspeyer.com
Sales Range: $50-74.9 Million
Approx. Number Employees: 700
Year Founded: 1978
Business Description:
Subdividers & Developers/Real Estate & Acquisitions
S.I.C.: 6531; 6552
N.A.I.C.S.: 531210; 237210
Import Export
Personnel:
Jerry I. Speyer *(Chm & Co-CEO)*
Robert Speyer *(Pres & Co-CEO)*
Russell Makowsky *(Sr Mng Dir & CFO)*
Michael Benner *(Sr Mng Dir & Gen Counsel)*
Paul A. Galiano *(Sr Mng Dir & Co-Head-Acq, Dispositions, Capital Markets)*
Steven R. Wechsler *(Sr Mng Dir & Co-Head-Acq, Dispositions, Equity Capital Markets)*
John R. Miller, III *(Sr Mng Dir & Reg Dir-West Coast)*
Eric Adler *(Sr Mng Dir)*
Charles A. DeBenedittis *(Sr Mng Dir)*
Casey Wold *(Sr Mng Dir)*
Advertising Agency:
Landis Communications Inc.
1388 Sutter St Ste 901
San Francisco, CA 94109
Tel.: (415) 561-0888
Fax: (415) 561-0778
(Property Development, The Infinity)

TOWNE PROPERTIES

1055 St Paul Pl
Cincinnati, OH 45202-6042
Tel.: (513) 381-8696
Fax: (513) 345-6971
E-mail: info@tp1.com
Web Site: www.towneproperties.com
Approx. Sls.: $60,000,000
Approx. Number Employees: 557
Year Founded: 1961
Business Description:
Real Estate Development & Management
S.I.C.: 6531
N.A.I.C.S.: 531210
Media: 2-7-8-13-22
Personnel:
Robert Wahlke *(Pres)*
Neil K. Bortz *(Partner)*
Phil Montanus *(Partner)*
Marvin Rosenberg *(Partner)*
Janet Chiarella *(VP-Mktg & Trng)*

TRADEWINDS ISLANDS RESORTS ON SAINT PETE BEACH

(Sub. of Resort Inns of America Inc.)
5500 Gulf Blvd
Saint Pete Beach, FL 33706
Tel.: (727) 363-2215
Fax: (727) 363-2221
E-mail: info@tradewindsresort.com
Web Site: www.tradewindsresort.com
Approx. Number Employees: 600
Business Description:
Hotel & Dining Services
S.I.C.: 7011
N.A.I.C.S.: 721110
Media: 4-6-8-9-13-22-24-25
Personnel:
Tim Bogott *(CEO)*
George Bentley *(Dir-Catering & Convention Svcs)*
Brands & Products:
ISLAND GRAND
JUST LET GO
SANDPIPER

TRAMMELL CROW COMPANY

(Sub. of CB Richard Ellis Group, Inc.)
2001 Ross Ave Ste 3400
Dallas, TX 75201-2966
Tel.: (214) 863-4101
Tel.: (214) 863-3000
Fax: (214) 863-3138
Fax: (214) 863-3125
E-mail: info@trammellcrow.com
Web Site: www.trammellcrow.com
Sales Range: $500-549.9 Million
Approx. Number Employees: 6,200
Year Founded: 1948
Business Description:
Commercial Real Estate Development, Property Management, Brokerage & Retail Services
S.I.C.: 6552; 6512; 6519
N.A.I.C.S.: 237210; 531120; 531190
Media: 2-6-7-8
Distr.: Natl.
Personnel:
Danny Queenan *(CEO)*
Mark Allyn *(Sr Mng Dir)*
Stan Erwin *(Sr Mng Dir)*
Richard Fletcher *(Mng Dir & Chief Acq Officer)*
Eric Fischer *(Mng Dir)*
Jeffrey Holcomb *(Mng Dir)*
Scott Krikorian *(Mng Dir)*
Adam Saphier *(Mng Dir)*
Chris Kirk *(COO)*
James Groch *(Officer-Global Strategy & CI)*
T. Christopher Roth *(Pres-Northeast Ops)*
John A. Stirek *(Pres-Western Ops)*
Matthew S. Khourie *(CEO-CBREI)*
Scott A. Dyche *(Principal & Gen Counsel)*
Matt Hill *(Principal)*
Galen Johnson *(Principal)*
Kenneth Krasnow *(Exec VP & Dir-Brokerage Svcs)*
Douglas C. Holowink *(Sr VP-Strategic Advisory Svcs)*
David Stahl *(Sr VP)*
Cynthia Langhorst *(Sr Dir)*
Opal Taylor *(Mgr-Accts)*

TRANSCONTINENTAL LENDING GROUP

401 Fairway Dr
Deerfield Beach, FL 33441
Tel.: (954) 489-0800
Fax: (954) 489-0650
Web Site:
www.transconlendinggroup.com
Approx. Sls.: $70,000,000
Approx. Number Employees: 55
Business Description:
Provider of Mortgage Services
S.I.C.: 6163
N.A.I.C.S.: 522310
Media: 5-17
Personnel:
Earl S. Wiley *(Pres)*

TRAVELODGE HOTELS, INC.

(Sub. of Wyndham Hotel Group, LLC)
22 Sylvan Way
Parsippany, NJ 07054
Tel.: (973) 753-6000
Toll Free: (800) 835-2424
Web Site: www.travelodge.com
Sales Range: $125-149.9 Million
Business Description:
Hotels & Resorts
S.I.C.: 7011
N.A.I.C.S.: 721110
Personnel:
Grant Hearn *(Chm)*
Ken Greene *(Pres)*
Rui Barros *(Sr VP-Brand)*
Advertising Agencies:
Carat International
Parker Tower 43-49 Parker St
London, WC2B 5PS, United Kingdom
Tel.: (44) 207 430 6000
Fax: (44) 207 430 6299

Decker Creative Marketing
99 Citizens Dr
Glastonbury, CT 06033-1262
Tel.: (860) 659-1311
Fax: (860) 659-3062
Toll Free: (800) 777-3677

OnTap
99 Citizens Dr
Glastonbury, CT 06033-1262
Tel.: (860) 659-1311
Fax: (860) 659-3062

Swordfish Communications
5 Stoneleigh Dr
Laurel Springs, NJ 08021
Tel.: (856) 767-7772
Fax: (866) 801-7772

TROPICANA CASINOS & RESORTS, INC.

(Name Changed to TROPICANA ENTERTAINMENT INC.)

TROPICANA ENTERTAINMENT INC.

(Formerly Tropicana Casinos & Resorts, Inc.)
3930 Howard Hughes Pkwy 4th Fl
Las Vegas, NV 89169
Tel.: (702) 589-3900
E-mail: investorrelations@tropicanaent.com
Web Site: www.tropicanacasinos.com
Approx. Rev.: $604,038,000
Approx. Number Employees: 7,200
Year Founded: 1990
Business Description:
Holding Company; Riverboat Casinos & Casino Hotel Resorts Owner & Operator
S.I.C.: 6719; 7011; 7999
N.A.I.C.S.: 551112; 713210; 721120
Personnel:
Carl Celian Icahn *(Chm)*
Daniel A. Ninivaggi *(Interim Pres & Interim CEO)*
Lance J. Millage *(CFO & Exec VP)*
Trent Dang *(Dir-Corp Mktg)*
Brands & Products:
AZTAR
CASINO AZTAR
HORIZON
MONTBLEU
THE QUARTER
RIVER PALMS
TROP
TROP PARK
TROPICANA
Advertising Agency:
Kolber Enterprises
500 Easton Rd
Willow Grove, PA 19090-0648
Tel.: (215) 657-4600
Fax: (215) 657-8192

TRUMP ENTERTAINMENT RESORTS, INC.

1000 Boardwalk at Virginia Ave
Atlantic City, NJ 08401
Tel.: (609) 449-5534
Fax: (609) 449-6586
Toll Free: (877) 777-1177
Web Site: www.trumpcasinos.com
Sales Range: $1-4.9 Billion
Approx. Number Employees: 5,500
Year Founded: 1995
Business Description:
Holding Company; Casino Hotels Owner & Operator
S.I.C.: 6719; 7011
N.A.I.C.S.: 551112; 721120
Advertising Expenditures: $9,129,000
Media: 1-13-18-22
Personnel:
Marc Lasry *(Chm & CEO)*
Robert F. Griffin *(CEO)*
David R. Hughes *(CFO & Exec VP)*
Robert M. Pickus *(Gen Counsel)*
Joseph A. Fusco *(Exec VP-Govt Affairs)*
Richard M. Santoro *(Exec VP-Asset Protection & Risk Mgmt)*
Eric L. Hausler *(Sr VP-Dev)*
Kathleen McSweeney *(Sr VP-Mktg)*
Brands & Products:
TRUMP
TRUMP MARINA
TRUMP ONE
TRUMP PLAZA
TRUMP TAJ MAHAL

Key to Media (For complete agency information see *The Advertising Red Books-Agencies* edition):
1. Bus. Publs. 2. Cable T.V. 3. Catalogs & Directories. 4. Co-op Adv. 5. Consumer Mags. 6. D.M. to Bus. Estab.7. D.M. to Consumers
8. Daily Newsp. 9. Exhibits/Trade Shows 10. Foreign 11. Infomercial 12. Internet Adv.13. Multimedia 14. Network Radio
15. Network T.V. 16. Newsp. Distr. Mags. 17. Other 18. Outdoor (Posters, Transit) 19. Point of Purchase20. Premiums, Novelties
21. Product Samples 22. Special Events Mktg. 23. Spot Radio 24. Spot T.V. 25. Weekly Newsp. 26. Yellow Page Adv.

Trump Entertainment Resorts, Inc. — (Continued)

Advertising Agency:
The 7th Art, LLC
120 Wooster St 6th Fl
New York, NY 10012
Tel.: (212) 431-8289
Fax: (212) 431-8492

THE TRUMP ORGANIZATION, LLC
725 5th Ave
New York, NY 10022
Tel.: (212) 832-2000
Fax: (212) 935-0141
Web Site: www.trump.com
Approx. Sls.: $10,400,000,000
Approx. Number Employees: 15,000
Business Description:
Real Estate Holding Company
S.I.C.: 6719; 6531
N.A.I.C.S.: 551112; 531210
Advertising Expenditures: $20,000,000
Media: 1-2-6-8-9-17-25
Distr.: Natl.
Budget Set: Jan.
Personnel:
Donald J. Trump *(CEO)*
Allen Weisselberg *(CFO & Exec VP)*
Mathew F. Calamari *(Exec VP-Ops)*
George Ross *(Exec VP)*
Donald J. Trump, Jr. *(Exec VP)*
Ivanka M. Trump *(Exec VP-Dev & Acq)*
Andrew Weiss *(Exec VP)*
Brian A Winston *(VP-Sls & Mktg, Trump Hotel Collection)*
Advertising Agency:
Ocean Bridge Group
1714 16th St
Santa Monica, CA 90404
Tel.: (310) 392-3200

U-STORE-IT TRUST
460 E Swedesford Rd Ste 3000
Wayne, PA 19087
Tel.: (610) 293-5700
Toll Free: (800) 800-1717
Web Site: www.u-store-it.com
Approx. Rev.: $216,826,000
Approx. Number Employees: 1,172
Year Founded: 2004
Business Description:
Owner & Operator of Self-Storage Facilities; Real Estate Investment Trust
S.I.C.: 6798; 4225
N.A.I.C.S.: 525930; 493110; 531130
Advertising Expenditures: $4,500,000
Personnel:
William M. Diefenderfer, III *(Chm)*
William M. Diefenderfer, III *(Trustees:)*
Dean Jernigan *(CEO)*
Timothy M. Martin *(CFO)*
Ajai Nair *(CIO)*
Dean Jernigan *(Trustees)*
Jeffrey P. Foster *(Chief Legal Officer & Sr VP)*
Steve Hartman *(Sr VP-Mktg)*

ULTIMATE ESCAPES, INC.
(Filed Ch 11 Bankruptcy #10-12915 on 9/20/10 in U.S. Bankruptcy Court, Dist of DE, Wilmington)
3501 W Vine St Ste 225
Kissimmee, FL 34741
Tel.: (407) 483-1900
Fax: (407) 483-1935
Web Site: www.ultimateescapes.com
Approx. Rev.: $37,011,000
Approx. Number Employees: 88
Year Founded: 2007
Business Description:
Luxury Destination Club Services
S.I.C.: 7011; 6531; 7999
N.A.I.C.S.: 721110; 531390; 713990; 721199
Advertising Expenditures: $1,231,000
Personnel:
Ted Curtis *(CMO & Chief Sls Officer)*

UMH PROPERTIES, INC.
3499 Rt 9 N Ste 3-C
Freehold, NJ 07728
Tel.: (732) 577-9997
Fax: (732) 577-9980
E-mail: umh@umh.com
Web Site: www.umh.com
Approx. Rev.: $37,408,059
Approx. Number Employees: 130
Year Founded: 1968
Business Description:
Pre-fabricated Homes Mfr
S.I.C.: 6519; 2451; 6798
N.A.I.C.S.: 531190; 321991; 525930
Media: 10-18
Personnel:
Eugene W. Landy *(Owner)*
Samuel A. Landy *(Pres & CEO)*
Anna T. Chew *(VP & CFO)*
Michael P. Landy *(Exec VP)*

UNITED, INC.
(d/b/a United Communities)
808 4th Avenue Southwest Ste 200
Calgary, AB T2P 3E8, Canada
Tel.: (403) 265-6180
Fax: (403) 265-6270
E-mail: inquiriescgy@unitedcommunities.com
Web Site: www.unitedcommunities.com
Approx. Number Employees: 28
Business Description:
Real Estate Development & Services
S.I.C.: 6531
N.A.I.C.S.: 531390
Media: 6-7-9-10-18
Personnel:
Donald J. Douglas *(Pres & CEO)*
B. Paul Simpson *(CFO & Exec VP)*
Chris M. Kolozetti *(COO & Exec VP)*
Donna Bygrave *(Mgr-Mktg)*
Brands & Products:
UNITEDCOMMUNITIES

UNITED STATES REALTY & INVESTMENT COMPANY
450 7th Ave 45th Fl
New York, NY 12123
Tel.: (212) 244-6650
Fax: (212) 244-6651
E-mail: dbraka@aetnarealty.com
Web Site: www.aetnarealty.com
Sales Range: $200-249.9 Million
Year Founded: 1896
Business Description:
Investment Properties
S.I.C.: 6531
N.A.I.C.S.: 531210
Media: 2-6-9-11-25-26
Distr.: Direct to Consumer; Reg.
Personnel:
Ivor Braka *(Pres)*
Gerald J. Valerius *(VP & Dir-Real Estate)*

VAGABOND FRANCHISE SYSTEM, INC.
3101 S Figueroa
Los Angeles, CA 90007
Tel.: (213) 746-1531
Toll Free: (800) 522-1555
Web Site: www.vagabondinn.com
Approx. Number Employees: 650
Year Founded: 1998
Business Description:
Owner & Manager of Hotels
S.I.C.: 7011
N.A.I.C.S.: 721110
Media: 4-6-7-8-9-13-18-20-23-26
Distr.: Natl.
Budget Set: Nov.
Personnel:
Juan Sanchez-Llaca *(Chm)*
Bruce Weitzman *(Pres & CEO)*
Les Biggins *(CFO)*
Jim Apostolis *(VP-Info Sys)*
Erica Munguia *(Dir-Guest Rels)*
Sandy Valentino *(Dir-HR)*
Brands & Products:
GOOD VALUE. FRIENDLY PEOPLE.
VAGABOND INN
VAGABOND INN EXECUTIVE

VAIL RESORTS, INC.
390 Interlocken Crescent Ste 1000
Broomfield, CO 80021
Mailing Address:
PO Box 7
Vail, CO 81658
Tel.: (303) 404-1800
Tel.: (970) 845-2500
Fax: (970) 845-5728
Toll Free: (888) 222-9324
E-mail: comments@vailresorts.com
Web Site: www.vailresorts.com
Approx. Rev.: $1,167,046,000
Approx. Number Employees: 5,100
Year Founded: 1977
Business Description:
Hotel & Resort Owner & Operator
S.I.C.: 7011; 7997
N.A.I.C.S.: 721110; 713910
Advertising Expenditures: $18,800,000
Media: 4-6-8-20
Personnel:
Robert A. Katz *(Chm & CEO)*
Jeffrey W. Jones *(Co-Pres & CFO)*
Blaise T. Carrig *(Co-Pres)*
John McD. Garnsey *(Co-Pres)*
Robert N. Urwiler *(CIO & Exec VP)*
Kirsten A. Lynch *(CMO & Exec VP)*
Mark R. Gasta *(Chief People Officer & Exec VP)*
Mark L. Schoppet *(Chief Acctg Officer, Sr VP & Controller)*
Jen Brown *(Pres-Lodging Div)*
Patricia A. Campbell *(COO-Breckenridge Ski Resort & Sr VP)*
Christopher E. Jarnot *(COO-Vail Mountain Resort & Sr VP)*
Fiona E. Arnold *(Gen Counsel & Exec VP)*
Heidi Kercher-Pratt *(VP-Corp Mktg)*
Kelly Ladyga *(VP-Corp Comm)*
John Buhler *(Gen Mgr-Keystone Resort)*
Pete Sonntag *(Gen Mgr-Heavenly Mountain Resort)*
Amy Kemp *(Dir-Comm)*
Michelle Lang *(Dir-Fin & IR)*
Russ Pecoraro *(Dir-Commun)*
Kate Lessman *(Sr Mgr-Comm)*
Kristen Petitt *(Sr Mgr-Intl Comm)*
Brands & Products:

BBDO West
555 Market St 17th Fl
San Francisco, CA 94105
Tel.: (415) 808-6200
Fax: (415) 808-6221
Creative
Heavenly Mountain Resort

E.B. Lane
733 W McDowell Rd
Phoenix, AZ 85007-1727
Tel.: (602) 258-5263
Fax: (602) 257-8128

Jackson Integrated
5804 Churchman Bypass
Indianapolis, IN 46203-6109
Tel.: (317) 791-9000
Fax: (317) 791-9800
Toll Free: (888) JACKSON

Kelley & Company
1050 Winter St Ste 1000
Waltham, MA 02451
Tel.: (781) 239-8092
Fax: (781) 239-8093

VORNADO REALTY TRUST
888 7th Ave
New York, NY 10019
Tel.: (212) 894-7000
Fax: (201) 587-0600
E-mail: information@vno.com
Web Site: www.vno.com
Approx. Rev.: $2,779,727,000
Approx. Number Employees: 4,780
Year Founded: 1981
Business Description:
Real Estate Investment Trust; Owns, Leases, Develops, Redevelopes & Manages Office & Retail Properties Primarily in the New York & Washington DC Metro Areas
S.I.C.: 6798
N.A.I.C.S.: 525930
Media: 4-5-9-18-20-23-24-25
Distr.: Reg.
Budget Set: Nov.
Personnel:
Steven Roth *(Chm)*
Steven Roth *(Trustees:)*
Michael D. Fascitelli *(Pres & CEO)*
Joseph Macnow *(CFO, Exec VP-Fin & Admin)*
David R. Greenbaum *(Pres-New York Office Div)*
Christopher G. Kennedy *(Pres-Mdse Mart Div)*
Mitchell N. Schear *(Pres-Charles E. Smith LP)*
Michelle Felman *(Exec VP-Acq)*
Wendy Silverstein *(Exec VP-Capital Markets)*
Advertising Agency:
One Source Visual Marketing Solution
108 W 39th St 2nd Fl
New York, NY 10018
Tel.: (212) 398-0444

Key to Media (For complete agency information see *The Advertising Red Books-Agencies* edition):
1. Bus. Publs. 2. Cable T.V. 3. Catalogs & Directories. 4. Co-op Adv. 5. Consumer Mags. 6. D.M. to Bus. Estab.7. D.M. to Consumers
8. Daily Newsp. 9. Exhibits/Trade Shows 10. Foreign 11. Infomercial 12. Internet Adv.13. Multimedia 14. Network Radio
15. Network T.V. 16. Newsp. Distr. Mags. 17. Other 18. Outdoor (Posters, Transit) 19. Point of Purchase20. Premiums, Novelties
21. Product Samples 22. Special Events Mktg. 23. Spot Radio 24. Spot T.V. 25. Weekly Newsp. 26. Yellow Page Adv.

Toll Free: (877) 398-0444

W HOTELS REAL ESTATE, LLC

(Sub. of Starwood Hotels & Resorts Worldwide, Inc.)
75 Varick St 10th Fl
New York, NY 10013
Tel.: (212) 380-4000
Web Site: www.starwoodhotels.com/whotels/index.html
Sales Range: Less than $1 Million
Approx. Number Employees: 20
Business Description:
Hotel Operator
S.I.C.: 7011
N.A.I.C.S.: 721110
Personnel:
Eva Ziegler *(Head-W Hotels Brand-Worldwide)*
Arnaud Champenois *(Brand Dir-W Hotels Worldwide-Asia Pacific)*
Advertising Agency:
Chandelier
611 Broadway Ph
New York, NY 10012
Tel.: (212) 620-5252
Fax: (212) 620-5329

WCI COMMUNITIES, INC.

24301 Walden Ctr Dr Ste 300
Bonita Springs, FL 34134
Tel.: (239) 498-8200
Fax: (239) 498-8338
Toll Free: (800) WCI-4005
E-mail: wci@wcicommunities.com
Web Site: www.wcicommunities.com
Sales Range: $550-599.9 Million
Approx. Number Employees: 1,450
Business Description:
Retirement Communities Developer; Real Estate Services
S.I.C.: 1531; 6531; 6552
N.A.I.C.S.: 236117; 237210; 531390
Advertising Expenditures: $9,718,000
Media: 7-8-9-18-23-24-25
Personnel:
Carl Celian Icahn *(Chm)*
David L. Fry *(Pres & CEO)*
Russell Devendorf *(CFO & Sr VP)*
Vivien N. Hastings *(Gen Counsel & Sr VP)*
Paul Erhardt *(Sr VP-Community Dev & Ops)*
Dan Callender *(Gen Mgr-Bay Club-Westshore Yacht Club)*
Brands & Products:
ARTESIA
AVERSANA
CAMBRIA
CAPE MARCO
CASA AT CASTELLA
CENTREX
THE COLONY AT PELICAN LANDING
COSTA VERANO
CREATING LASTING LIFESTYLES
THE EXPERIENCE IS EVERYTHING
FLORIDA LIFE, YOUR STYLE
GATEWAY
HARBOUR ISLES
HERON BAY
HERON ISLES
IT'S GOOD TO BE GREEN
LA SCALA
LET GO. CATCH LIFE.
LIVE THE EXPERIENCE. ADMIRE THE VIEW.
LOST KEY
MOSAIC
NOBODY
NOBODY DOES IT BETTER
OLD PALM GOLF CLUB
ON THE MARK HOSPITALITY CONCIERGE PROGRAM
ONE BAL HARBOUR
PARKLAND GOLF & COUNTRY CLUB
PELICAN BAY NAPLES FLORIDA
PELICAN LANDING
PELICAN SOUND
THE PENTHOUSE COLLECTION
THE RESORT AT SINGER ISLAND
SERANO
SIGNATURE SERVICES CONCIERGE
SKY HOMES
SUN CITY CENTER
TARPON BAY
TIBURON
TIBURON NAPLES
TREVISO
VENTANAS
VENTIAN GOLD & RIVER CLUBS
WATERLEFE
WCI
WCI COMMUNITIES,INC
WCI LIFESTYLES BEYOND EXPECTATIONS
WESTSHORE YACHT CLUB
WHERE FLORIDA LIVES
WHERE FLORIDA LIVES & PLAYS
WILDCAT RUN
Advertising Agency:
Gibson Roscoe Owens
658 W Indiantown Rd Ste 209
Jupiter, FL 33458-7535
Tel.: (561) 741-1441
Fax: (561) 741-1455

WEBDIGS, INC.

3433 W Broadway St NE Ste 501
Minneapolis, MN 55413
Tel.: (612) 332-7371
Fax: (866) 397-8103
Toll Free: (888) 932-3447
E-mail: info@webdigs.com
Web Site: www.webdigs.com
Approx. Rev.: $468,152
Approx. Number Employees: 3
Year Founded: 2007
Business Description:
Real Estate Brokerage Services
S.I.C.: 6531
N.A.I.C.S.: 531210
Advertising Expenditures: $20,638
Media: 17
Personnel:
Robert A. Buntz, Jr. *(Chm, Pres & CEO)*
Edward P. Wicker *(CFO)*

WECOSIGN, INC.

3400 W MacArthur Blvd Ste I
Santa Ana, CA 92704
Tel.: (714) 556-6800
Fax: (714) 556-6803
Toll Free: (877) 556-6807
E-mail: jbennington@wecosign.com
Web Site: www.wecosign.com
Approx. Rev.: $142,820
Approx. Number Employees: 7
Year Founded: 2007
Business Description:
Real Estate Rental Services
S.I.C.: 6531; 6371
N.A.I.C.S.: 531390; 525990
Advertising Expenditures: $31,823
Media: 17
Personnel:
Frank Jakubaitis *(Chm)*
Carlos Padilla, III *(CIO)*
Jamie Derderian *(VP-Customer Svc)*
Maryann Cerami *(Reg Mgr-West)*
Brands & Products:
WECOSIGN

WEICHERT REALTORS

1625 State Rte 10
Morris Plains, NJ 07950-2905
Tel.: (973) 267-7777
Fax: (973) 539-1249
E-mail: questions@weichert.com
Web Site: www.weichert.com
Approx. Number Employees: 1,500
Year Founded: 1969
Business Description:
Full Service Real Estate Services
S.I.C.: 6531
N.A.I.C.S.: 531210
Media: 6-8-9-11-13-14-15-25-26
Distr.: Intl.; Natl.
Personnel:
Jim Weichert *(Founder & Pres)*
Jim Weichert, Jr. *(Founder & Pres)*
Mary Banen *(VP-Trng & Dev)*
Larry Muller *(VP-Mktg)*
Brands & Products:
WEICHERT REALTORS
Advertising Agencies:
Media Network Advertising (House Agency)
1625 State Highway 10
Morris Plains, NJ 07950
Tel.: (973) 267-7777

Star Group Communications, Inc. (d/b/a The Star Group)
220 Laurel Rd
Voorhees, NJ 08043
Tel.: (856) 782-7000
Fax: (856) 782-5699

WEICHERT RELOCATION RESOURCES INC.

(Affil. of Weichert Realtors)
1625 Rte 10
Morris Plains, NJ 07950-2905
Tel.: (973) 397-3500
Toll Free: (800) 648-3303
E-mail: marketing@wrii.com
Web Site: www.wrii.com
Sales Range: $1-4.9 Billion
Approx. Number Employees: 400
Business Description:
Corporate Relocation Consultants
S.I.C.: 8742; 4731
N.A.I.C.S.: 541614; 488510
Media: 2-4-7-10-13-19-20-22-26
Personnel:
Jim Schneider *(Exec VP)*
Kelly Reiss *(Reg VP)*
Ellie Sullivan *(Dir-Mktg & Consulting)*

WELLS REAL ESTATE FUNDS, INC.

6200 the Corners Pkwy Ste 250
Norcross, GA 30092
Tel.: (770) 449-7800
Fax: (770) 243-8199
E-mail: info@wellsref.com
Web Site: www.wellsref.com
Sales Range: $550-599.9 Million
Approx. Number Employees: 300
Business Description:
Real Estate Investment Trust
S.I.C.: 6798
N.A.I.C.S.: 525930
Personnel:
Leo Wells *(Pres)*
Robert McCullough *(CFO)*
Mike Dobbs *(CMO)*
Advertising Agency:
Rubenstein Associates, Inc.
1345 Ave of the Americas Fl 30
New York, NY 10105-0109
Tel.: (212) 843-8000
Fax: (212) 843-9200

WESTIN PREMIER, INC.

(Sub. of Starwood Hotels & Resorts Worldwide, Inc.)
(d/b/a Westin Hotels & Resorts)
1111 Westchester Ave
White Plains, NY 10604-3520
Tel.: (914) 640-8100
Fax: (914) 640-8388
Toll Free: (800) 937-8461
Web Site: www.westin.com
Sales Range: $150-199.9 Million
Approx. Number Employees: 1,500
Year Founded: 1930
Business Description:
Hotel Operation
S.I.C.: 7011
N.A.I.C.S.: 721199; 721110
Media: 2-6-7-8-9-10-13-20-24-25
Advertising Agencies:
Deutsch, Inc.
(A Lowe & Partners Company)
111 8th Ave 14th Fl
New York, NY 10011-5201
Tel.: (212) 981-7600
Fax: (212) 981-7525
(Creative & Media)

Hollyrock/Miller Marketing Communications
117 Rockingham Row
Princeton, NJ 08540
Tel.: (609) 919-9292
Fax: (609) 919-9299

WIGWAM RESORT

(Sub. of Kabuto International Phoenix Inc.)
300 E Wigwam Blvd
Litchfield Park, AZ 85340
Tel.: (623) 935-3811
Fax: (623) 535-4995
Toll Free: (800) 327-0396
E-mail: wigwam@luxurycollection.com
Web Site: www.wigwamresort.com
Approx. Number Employees: 800
Year Founded: 1929
Business Description:
Resort
S.I.C.: 7011
N.A.I.C.S.: 721110
Media: 25
Distr.: Natl.
Personnel:
Frank Ashmore *(Dir-Mktg)*

WOODFIN SUITE HOTELS

(Sub. of Hardage Investments, Inc.)
Ste 300 12671 High Bluff Dr
San Diego, CA 92130-3018
Tel.: (858) 794-2338
Fax: (858) 794-2348
E-mail: customerservice@woodfinsuites.com

Key to Media (For complete agency information see *The Advertising Red Books-Agencies* edition):
1. Bus. Publs. 2. Cable T.V. 3. Catalogs & Directories. 4. Co-op Adv. 5. Consumer Mags. 6. D.M. to Bus. Estab.7. D.M. to Consumers 8. Daily Newsp. 9. Exhibits/Trade Shows 10. Foreign 11. Infomercial 12. Internet Adv.13. Multimedia 14. Network Radio 15. Network T.V. 16. Newsp. Distr. Mags. 17. Other 18. Outdoor (Posters, Transit) 19. Point of Purchase20. Premiums, Novelties 21. Product Samples 22. Special Events Mktg. 23. Spot Radio 24. Spot T.V. 25. Weekly Newsp. 26. Yellow Page Adv.

Woodfin Suite Hotels — (Continued)

Web Site:
www.woodfinsuitehotels.com
Approx. Number Employees: 700
Business Description:
Hotel Management & Franchising Services
S.I.C.: 7011
N.A.I.C.S.: 721110
Personnel:
Samuel A. Hardage *(Founder & Chm)*
Brands & Products:
CHASE SUITE HOTELS
WOODFIN SUITE HOTELS
Advertising Agency:
Bailey Gardiner Inc.
444 W. Beech St Ste 400
San Diego, CA 92101
Tel.: (619) 295-8232
Fax: (619) 295-8234

WOODS BROS REALTY, INC.

(Sub. of HomeServices of America, Inc.)
3355 Orwell St Ste 102
Lincoln, NE 68516
Tel.: (402) 434-3700
Fax: (402) 434-3704
E-mail: webmaster@woodsbros.com
Web Site: www.woodsbros.com
Sales Range: $350-399.9 Million
Approx. Number Employees: 280
Year Founded: 1889
Business Description:
Real Estate Services
S.I.C.: 6531
N.A.I.C.S.: 531210
Media: 2-4-8-9-13-25
Personnel:
Jan Tucknott *(Dir-Relocation)*

WYNDHAM VACATION OWNERSHIP

(Formerly Fairfield Resorts, Inc.)
(Sub. of Wyndham Vacation Ownership, Inc.)
8427 S Park Cir Ste 500
Orlando, FL 32819-9054
Tel.: (407) 370-5200
Fax: (407) 370-5280
Toll Free: (800) 251-8736
Web Site: www.wyndham.com
Sales Range: $1-4.9 Billion
Approx. Number Employees: 1,200
Year Founded: 1969
Business Description:
Vacation Resort Properties Developer, Marketer & Operator
S.I.C.: 6531; 6141
N.A.I.C.S.: 531210; 522220
Export
Media: 4-6-8-10-11-13
Personnel:
Franz S. Hanning *(Pres & CEO)*
Larry Kinsolving *(Gen Counsel)*
Brands & Products:
FAIRSHARE
FAIRSHARE PLUS
LEISUREPLAN

WYNDHAM WORLDWIDE CORPORATION

22 Sylvan Way
Parsippany, NJ 07054
Tel.: (973) 753-6000
Fax: (973) 496-7658
Web Site:
www.wyndhamworldwide.com
Approx. Rev.: $3,851,000,000
Approx. Number Employees: 26,400
Year Founded: 1981
Business Description:
Hotel & Resort Services
S.I.C.: 6798; 7011
N.A.I.C.S.: 525930; 721110
Advertising Expenditures: $77,000,000
Media: 13-14-15-16
Personnel:
Stephen P. Holmes *(Chm & CEO)*
Thomas G. Conforti *(CFO & Exec VP)*
Mary R. Falvey *(Chief HR Officer & Exec VP)*
Nicola Rossi *(Chief Acctg Officer & Sr VP)*
Scott G. McLester *(Gen Counsel & Exec VP)*
Thomas F. Anderson *(Chief Real Estate Dev Officer & Exec VP)*
Margo C. Happer *(Sr VP-IR)*
Barbara Eskin *(Sr Dir-Mktg, Retention & Loyalty)*
Sharleen Hoehler *(Sr Dir-Mktg)*
Brands & Products:
AMERIHOST INN
BAYMONT INN & SUITES
DAYS INN
HAWTHORN SUITES
HOWARD JOHNSON
KNIGHTS INN
MICROTEL INNS & SUITES
RAMADA
SUPER 8
TRAVELODGE
TRIP REWARDS
WINGATE
WINGATE INN
WYNDHAM HOTELS & RESORTS
WYNDHAM WORLDWIDE
Advertising Agencies:
Berlin Cameron United
100 Ave of the Americas 2nd Fl
New York, NY 10013
Tel.: (212) 824-2000
Fax: (212) 268-8454
Super 8
Howard Johnson
Travelodge

Buntin Out-of-Home Media
1001 Hawkins St
Nashville, TN 37203-4758
Tel.: (615) 244-5720
Fax: (615) 244-6511

EastWest Marketing Group
401 5th Ave 4th Fl
New York, NY 10016
Tel.: (212) 951-7220
Fax: (212) 951-7201
Travelodge
Howard Johnson

Interlex Communications Inc.
4005 Broadway Ste B
San Antonio, TX 78209-6311
Tel.: (210) 930-3339
Fax: (210) 930-3383
Toll Free: (866) 430-3339

S3
718 Main St
Boonton, NJ 07005
Tel.: (973) 257-5533
Fax: (973) 257-5543

WYNN LAS VEGAS, LLC

(Sub. of Wynn Resorts Limited)
3131 Las Vegas Blvd S
Las Vegas, NV 89109
Tel.: (702) 770-7000
Tel.: (702) 770-7555
Fax: (702) 770-1500
Toll Free: (877) 321-WYNN
Web Site: www.wynnlasvegas.com
Approx. Rev.: $1,296,556,000
Approx. Number Employees: 9,405
Business Description:
Casino Hotel & Resort Operator
S.I.C.: 7011; 6531; 7999
N.A.I.C.S.: 721120; 531312; 713290; 713990
Advertising Expenditures: $17,300,000
Personnel:
Stephen A. Wynn *(Chm)*
Marilyn Winn Spiegel *(Pres)*
Scott Peterson *(CFO & Sr VP)*
Linda Chen *(Pres-Intl Mktg)*
Callie de Quevedo *(Dir-PR & Brand)*
Lori Kobashigawa *(Dir-Interactive Mktg)*
Kari Hoffman *(Mgr-Internet Adv)*
Advertising Agency:
Korey Kay & Partners
130 5th Ave
New York, NY 10011-4306
Tel.: (212) 620-4300
Fax: (212) 620-7055
Fax: (212) 620-7149

WYNN RESORTS LIMITED

3131 Las Vegas Blvd S
Las Vegas, NV 89109
Tel.: (702) 770-7000
Toll Free: (877) 321-WYNN
E-mail: investorrelations@wynnresorts.com
Web Site: www.wynnresorts.com
Approx. Rev.: $4,184,698,000
Approx. Number Employees: 16,405
Year Founded: 2002
Business Description:
Casino Hotels & Resorts Designer, Developer & Operator
S.I.C.: 1522; 6531; 7011; 7997
N.A.I.C.S.: 721120; 236220; 531390; 713910; 721110
Advertising Expenditures: $20,400,000
Personnel:
Stephen A. Wynn *(Chm & CEO)*
Kazuo Okada *(Vice Chm)*
Matt Maddox *(CFO & Treas)*
John Strzemp *(Chief Admin Officer & Exec VP)*
Kim Sinatra *(Gen Counsel, Sec & Sr VP)*
Chris Wilcock *(Dir-Enterprise Mktg)*
Allison Aprile *(Brand Mgr-Web & Digital Media)*
Brands & Products:
ENCORE
WYNN
WYNN LAS VEGAS
WYNN MACAU
Advertising Agency:
Korey Kay & Partners
130 5th Ave
New York, NY 10011-4306
Tel.: (212) 620-4300
Fax: (212) 620-7055
Fax: (212) 620-7149

ZIPREALTY, INC.

2000 Powell St Ste 300
Emeryville, CA 94608
Tel.: (510) 735-2600
Fax: (510) 735-2850
Toll Free: (800) CALLZIP
E-mail: team@ziprealty.com
Web Site: www.ziprealty.com
Approx. Rev.: $118,696,000
Approx. Number Employees: 159
Year Founded: 1999
Business Description:
Residential Real Estate Brokerage Services
S.I.C.: 6531; 7374
N.A.I.C.S.: 531210; 518210
Advertising Expenditures: $1,586,000
Media: 2-8-9-10-13-18-25
Personnel:
Charles C. Baker *(Pres & CEO)*
David A. Rector *(CFO)*
Joseph Trifoglio *(CIO & VP)*
Samantha Harnett *(Gen Counsel, Sec & Sr VP)*
Genni Combes *(Sr VP-Tech & Operational Strategy)*
Joan Burke *(VP-HR)*
Brands & Products:
YOUR HOME IS WHERE OUR HEART IS
ZIPAGENT
ZIPNOTIFY
ZIPREALTY
Advertising Agency:
Allison & Partners
505 Sansome St 7th Fl
San Francisco, CA 94111-3310
Tel.: (415) 217-7500
Fax: (415) 217-7503

Key to Media (For complete agency information see *The Advertising Red Books-Agencies* edition):
1. Bus. Publs. 2. Cable T.V. 3. Catalogs & Directories. 4. Co-op Adv. 5. Consumer Mags. 6. D.M. to Bus. Estab.7. D.M. to Consumers 8. Daily Newsp. 9. Exhibits/Trade Shows 10. Foreign 11. Infomercial 12. Internet Adv.13. Multimedia 14. Network Radio 15. Network T.V. 16. Newsp. Distr. Mags. 17. Other 18. Outdoor (Posters, Transit) 19. Point of Purchase20. Premiums, Novelties 21. Product Samples 22. Special Events Mktg. 23. Spot Radio 24. Spot T.V. 25. Weekly Newsp. 26. Yellow Page Adv.

Housewares

Aluminum Ware — Baskets — Blankets — Bottle Caps — China — Cooking — Utensils — Crockery — Curtains — Cut Glass — Earthenware — Enameled Ware — Fire Extinguishers — Fireless Cookers — Fruit Jars & Rings — Giftwares — Glassware — Household Paper — Kitchen Utensils — Linens — Matches — Metal Ware — Mops & Polish — Pillows — Silverware

ALL-CLAD METALCRAFTERS LLC
(Sub. of Groupe SEB)
424 Morganza Rd
Canonsburg, PA 15317-5707
Tel.: (724) 745-8300
Fax: (724) 746-5035
E-mail: info@allclad.com
Web Site: www.allclad.com
Approx. Number Employees: 400
Business Description:
Metal Cookware Mfr
S.I.C.: 3316; 3469
N.A.I.C.S.: 331221; 332214
Media: 4-6-8-10-13-22
Personnel:
Martin Armstrong *(VP-Sls)*
Chris Hubbuch *(Dir-Sls & Mktg)*
Lori Brodak *(Mgr-Natl Acct)*
Advertising Agency:
Chillingworth/Radding Inc.
1133 Broadway Ste 1615
New York, NY 10010
Tel.: (212) 674-4700
Fax: (212) 979-0125

ALNO USA
(Sub. of ALNO AG)
1 Design Ctr Pl Ste 643
Boston, MA 02210-2335
Tel.: (617) 896-2700
Fax: (617) 896-2799
E-mail: EMarkowksi@daliakitchens.com
Web Site: www.alno.com
Approx. Number Employees: 14
Business Description:
Distributors of Alno Kitchen Cabinetry
S.I.C.: 5031
N.A.I.C.S.: 423310
Advertising Agency:
JB Cumberland PR
135 W 27th St Tenth Fl
New York, NY 10001
Tel.: (646) 230-6940
Fax: (646) 230-6935
Kitchens

ALSONS CORPORATION
(Sub. of Masco Corporation)
3010 W Mechanic St
Hillsdale, MI 49242-1095
Mailing Address:
PO Box 282
Hillsdale, MI 49242-0282
Tel.: (517) 439-1411
Fax: (517) 439-9644
Toll Free: (800) 421-0001
E-mail: info@alsons.com
Web Site: www.alsons.com
E-Mail For Key Personnel:
Marketing Director: cmistovich@alsons.com
Public Relations: cmistovich@alsons.com
Sales Range: $100-124.9 Million
Approx. Number Employees: 220
Year Founded: 1956
Business Description:
Bathroom Shower Fixtures & Accessories
S.I.C.: 3431; 3432
N.A.I.C.S.: 332998; 332913
Import Export
Media: 1-2-4-5-10-23-24
Distr.: Intl.; Natl.
Personnel:
Al Marandola *(VP-Fin & Ops)*
Chuck Mistovich *(Dir-Mktg)*
Brands & Products:
BRILLIANCE
DELUGE
DOWNPOUR RAIN SHOWER
INCREDIBLE HEAD
INCREDIBLE HEAD ELITE
INCREDIBLE HEAD GALAXY
LADY ALSONS
MIXET
SHOWER SPA
TROPICAL RAIN

ANCHOR HOCKING COMPANY
(Holding of Monomoy Capital Partners, L.P.)
519 N Pierce Ave
Lancaster, OH 43130
Tel.: (740) 687-2111
Toll Free: (800) 562-7511
Web Site: www.anchorhocking.com
Sales Range: $200-249.9 Million
Approx. Number Employees: 1,300
Year Founded: 1905
Business Description:
Glassware Products Mfr
S.I.C.: 3229; 3089
N.A.I.C.S.: 327212; 326199
Media: 2
Personnel:
Mark R. Eichhorn *(CEO)*
Bert Filice *(Sr VP-Sls & Mktg)*
Joe Sundberg *(Sr VP)*
Barbara Wolf *(Sr Mgr-Mktg Comm)*

ARCTIC PRODUCTS, INC.
1412 Creek Trail Dr
Jefferson City, MO 65109-9238
Mailing Address:
PO Box 104293
Jefferson City, MO 65110-4293
Tel.: (573) 636-9678
Fax: (573) 635-6777
Toll Free: (800) 801-1951
E-mail: arcinfo@arcticproducts.com
Web Site: www.arcticproducts.com
Sales Range: $1-9.9 Million
Approx. Number Employees: 15
Year Founded: 1996
Business Description:
Portable Outdoor Fireplaces, Bar-B-Que Grills, Mosquito Killing Machines, Umbrellas, Chimenea & Gazebos Mfr
S.I.C.: 5191
N.A.I.C.S.: 424910
Import Export
Media: 2-7-10
Distr.: Intl.; Natl.
Personnel:
Floyd C. Hoffmann *(Pres)*
Brands & Products:
ARCTIC
ARCTIC PAVILION
ARCTIC SHADE
ARCTIC SUN
BON FIRE
BON FLAME
CHINOOK 150
CHINOOK 250
FIRE RING
THE GREAT OUTDOORS JUST GOT BETTER.
LAWN & GARDEN
LIL ARCTIC SUN
LIL BON FIRE
LIL BON FLAME
LIL CAMPER
LIL KETTLE
MOSQUITO KILLING SYSTEM
MOSQUITO SHIELD
PAGODA
PATIO HEARTH
PATIO HEARTH PRO
PATIO PIT
PAVILION
SS PATIO HEARTH

BACCARAT, INC.
(Holding of Baccarat SA)
36 Mayfield Ave
Edison, NJ 08837-3821
Tel.: (732) 225-9600
Fax: (732) 225-1336
Approx. Number Employees: 40
Business Description:
Home Furnishings Importer & Distr
S.I.C.: 5719; 5023
N.A.I.C.S.: 442299; 423220
Advertising Expenditures: $1,500,000
Media: 5-6-7-8
Distr.: Natl.

BEACON LOOMS, INC.
411 Alfred Ave
Teaneck, NJ 07666
Tel.: (201) 833-1600
Fax: (201) 833-4053
E-mail: info@beaconlooms.com
Web Site: www.beaconlooms.com
Approx. Number Employees: 33
Business Description:
Mfr. of Curtains, Comforters, Comforter Covers & Piece Goods
S.I.C.: 2391; 2299
N.A.I.C.S.: 314121; 314999
Import Export
Media: 4-7-9-19-21
Distr.: Intl.; Natl.
Budget Set: Jan.
Personnel:
S. Sadinoff *(CEO)*
Brands & Products:
ALESSANDRA
AUSTIN
BEACON LOOMS
COLONIAL GARDENS
DAKOTA
ELEGANTE
FOLIAGE
GATHERINGS
HARMONY
PORTOFINO
PORTOFOLIO
ROCKLEIGH
SERENGETI
TEMPO
TRULON
VARIATIONS

BED BATH & BEYOND INC.
650 Liberty Ave
Union, NJ 07083

Key to Media (For complete agency information see *The Advertising Red Books-Agencies* edition):
1. Bus. Publs. 2. Cable T.V. 3. Catalogs & Directories. 4. Co-op Adv. 5. Consumer Mags. 6. D.M. to Bus. Estab.7. D.M. to Consumers 8. Daily Newsp. 9. Exhibits/Trade Shows 10. Foreign 11. Infomercial 12. Internet Adv.13. Multimedia 14. Network Radio 15. Network T.V. 16. Newsp. Distr. Mags. 17. Other 18. Outdoor (Posters, Transit) 19. Point of Purchase20. Premiums, Novelties 21. Product Samples 22. Special Events Mktg. 23. Spot Radio 24. Spot T.V. 25. Weekly Newsp. 26. Yellow Page Adv.

Bed Bath & Beyond Inc. — (Continued)

Tel.: (908) 688-0888
Fax: (908) 688-6483
Toll Free: (800) 462-3966
E-mail: customer.service@bedbath.com
Web Site: www.bedbathandbeyond.com
Approx. Sls.: $8,758,503,000
Approx. Number Employees: 45,000
Year Founded: 1971
Business Description:
Domestic Merchandise & Home Furnishings Retailer
S.I.C.: 5719; 5712; 5722
N.A.I.C.S.: 442299; 442110; 443111
Import
Advertising Expenditures: $198,300,000
Media: 5-6-8-9-13-15-16-18-19-24-25
Personnel:
Warren Eisenberg *(Co-Chm)*
Leonard Feinstein *(Co-Chm)*
Arthur Stark *(Pres & Chief Mdsg Officer)*
Steven H. Temares *(CEO)*
Eugene A. Castagna *(CFO & Treas)*
Ronald Curwin *(CFO)*
Robert Claybrook *(CIO & VP)*
Richard C. McMahon *(Chief Strategy Officer & VP-Corp Ops)*
Michael J. Callahan *(Corp Counsel & VP)*
Allan N. Rauch *(Gen Counsel & VP-Legal)*
Matthew Fiorilli *(Sr VP-Stores)*
Charles E. Arnold *(Reg VP)*
Salvatore J. Dimino *(Reg VP)*
Dana Pelan *(Reg VP)*
Nancy J. Katz *(VP & Gen Mdse Mgr)*
Farley S. Nachemin *(VP, Gen Mdse Mgr-Bath & Seasonal)*
Scott Hames *(VP-Mktg & Analytics)*
Susan E. Lattmann *(VP-Fin)*
Rita Little *(VP-Mktg)*
Hank Reinhart *(VP-Customer Svc & Bridal & Gift Registry)*
Robert A. Roe *(VP-IT)*
Louis M. Sepe *(VP-Mdsg Sys & Bus Intelligence)*
Concetta Van Dyke *(VP-HR)*
Kevin M. Wanner *(VP-Tech & Ops)*
Alan J. Natowitz *(Gen Mgr-Mdse)*
Bari Fagin *(Dir-PR)*
Catherine Gentile *(Mgr-PR)*
Advertising Agency:
Wilen Press
3333 SW 15th St
Deerfield Beach, FL 33442
Tel.: (954) 246-5000
Fax: (954) 246-3333

BETRAS USA, INC.

2525 Chesnee Hwy
Spartanburg, SC 29307-4121
Mailing Address:
PO Box 6325
Spartanburg, SC 29304-6325
Tel.: (864) 599-0855
Fax: (864) 599-9138
Toll Free: (800) 845-7188
E-mail: betras@betras.com
Web Site: www.betras.com
Approx. Number Employees: 200
Year Founded: 1983
Business Description:
Mfr of Promotional Plastic Drinkware, Thermos Mugs & Sports Bottles
S.I.C.: 3089; 2759
N.A.I.C.S.: 326199; 323119
Advertising Expenditures: $500,000
Media: 2-4-7-10-13
Distr.: Natl.
Personnel:
Joe Betras *(Pres & CEO)*
Henya Betras *(Exec VP)*
Brandi Ligon *(Mgr- Mktg-Customer Svc)*
Brands & Products:
BETRAS USA

BLENKO GLASS COMPANY

9 Boill Blenko Dr
Milton, WV 25541
Tel.: (304) 743-9081
Fax: (304) 743-0547
E-mail: blenko@usa.net
Web Site: www.blenkoglass.com
Approx. Number Employees: 50
Year Founded: 1922
Business Description:
Glassware
S.I.C.: 3229; 3211
N.A.I.C.S.: 327212; 327211
Import Export
Media: 1-2-4-7-10-13-17-26
Distr.: Intl.; Natl.
Personnel:
W.H. Blenko, Jr. *(Chm)*
Brands & Products:
BLENKO GLASS
BLENKO HANDCRAFT
CONFETTI
EBONY
FADE
GALLERY
KIWI
MARDI
MILLE FLEUR
OPAQUE
TANGERINE
TEQUILA SUNRISE

BRIGHT OF AMERICA, INC.

300 Greenbrier Rd
Summersville, WV 26651-1826
Tel.: (304) 872-3000
Fax: (304) 872-3033
Approx. Rev.: $6,780,000
Approx. Number Employees: 84
Year Founded: 1961
Business Description:
Mfr. of Placemats, Candles, Home Fragrance Products & Educational Products
S.I.C.: 2392; 3999
N.A.I.C.S.: 314129; 339999
Import Export
Advertising Expenditures: $550,000
Media: 4-5-8-10-20-21
Distr.: Intl.; Natl.
Budget Set: Jan.
Brands & Products:
EARTH SCENTS

BURLINGTON BASKET CO.

1404 W Mt Pleasant Rd
West Burlington, IA 52655
Tel.: (319) 754-6508
Fax: (319) 754-5991
Toll Free: (800) 553-2300
E-mail: burlingtonbasketinfo@burlingtonbasket.com
Web Site: www.burlingtonbasket.com
Approx. Sls.: $12,000,000
Approx. Number Employees: 75
Year Founded: 1888
Business Description:
Fiber Products & Household Accessories Mfr
S.I.C.: 2519
N.A.I.C.S.: 337125
Media: 2-6
Distr.: Natl.
Budget Set: Nov.
Personnel:
Rick Thompson *(CEO)*
Brands & Products:
HAWKEYE

BURNES GROUP

(Holding of Cerberus Capital Management, L.P.)
21 Cypress Blvd Ste 1010
Round Rock, TX 78665
Tel.: (512) 257-6500
Fax: (512) 257-6530
Toll Free: (877) 643-7263
Web Site: www.burnesofboston.com/ContentPages/AboutUs.aspx?AspxAutoDetectCookieSupport=1
Sales Range: $150-199.9 Million
Approx. Number Employees: 2,500
Business Description:
Mfr of Picture Frames & Photo Albums
S.I.C.: 3499; 3999
N.A.I.C.S.: 332999; 339999
Media: 4-5-7-10-19
Distr.: Natl.
Budget Set: Dec.
Brands & Products:
BURNES ALBUMS
BURNES OF BOSTON
CARR
INTERCRAFT
PANODIA
RAREWOODS
TERRAGRAFICS
Advertising Agency:
Ellen Miller
75 Capwell Ave
Pawtucket, RI 02860
Tel.: (401) 724-3773
— Ellen Miller *(Owner)*

BUSH EQUITIES

(d/b/a Cuddledown Inc)
312 Canco Rd
Portland, ME 04103-4223
Tel.: (207) 761-0201
Fax: (207) 761-1948
Toll Free: (800) 323-6793
E-mail: letter@cuddledown.com
Web Site: www.cuddledown.com
E-Mail For Key Personnel:
President: ceo@cuddledown.com
Approx. Number Employees: 95
Year Founded: 1973
Business Description:
Mfr. & Retailer of Bedding & Home Furnishings
S.I.C.: 5961; 5719
N.A.I.C.S.: 454113; 442299
Import Export
Media: 4-8-13-17-22-24
Personnel:
Chris Bradley *(CEO)*
Brands & Products:
ACANTHUS
ACORN
ANGUILLA
ANGUILLA CANE
ATELIER
BATISTE
BAY
BLOSSOM VINE
BRISTOL CHERRY
CALIDA
CALLA LILY VOILE
CARAVANSERAI
CENTURION
CHRYSANTHEMUM
CLARION
CLASSIC SEERSUCKER
CONTEMPORARY
CROSSROADS
CUDDLEDOWN
DAISY
DETATCHABLE
DOT PALAZZO
DUAL WARMTH COMFORTER
EVA
FIORE BELLO
FLORALIA
FRENCH EYELET
GARDEN
GUINEVERE
HEIRLOOM
HEMSTITCH
ISTANBUL
JERSEY
JERSEY KNIT
JEWEL BOUQUET
JEWEL LEAF
JOIE DE VIVRE
KIMONO
KINGSBRIDGE
LATTICE
LUXURE
MAGNOLIA
MARSEILLES
MEDALLION
MEDITERRANEAN
MELON CANOPY
MERRY
MESA
MONET
NEWBURY
PENNSYLVANIA
PERLE DE JARDIN
PETRA
PICCADILLY
PIQUE
PROVENCAL
RAINBOW
ROSALINDA
SCOTTY
SCOTTY DOGS
SHERATON
SOHO
SOLID
TAILORED
TAPESTRY
TARTAN
TERRAZZO
THISTLE
TIGER MAPLE
TIKI TOILE
TIVI PERCALE
TRUNDLE
TUSCAN ROSE
URBANO
URBANO CHERRY
VICTORIAN
VIOLA
YUMA

Key to Media (For complete agency information see *The Advertising Red Books-Agencies* edition):
1. Bus. Publs. 2. Cable T.V. 3. Catalogs & Directories. 4. Co-op Adv. 5. Consumer Mags. 6. D.M. to Bus. Estab.7. D.M. to Consumers
8. Daily Newsp. 9. Exhibits/Trade Shows 10. Foreign 11. Infomercial 12. Internet Adv.13. Multimedia 14. Network Radio
15. Network T.V. 16. Newsp. Distr. Mags. 17. Other 18. Outdoor (Posters, Transit) 19. Point of Purchase20. Premiums, Novelties
21. Product Samples 22. Special Events Mktg. 23. Spot Radio 24. Spot T.V. 25. Weekly Newsp. 26. Yellow Page Adv.

CALIFORNIA CEDAR PRODUCTS COMPANY
1340 W Washington St
Stockton, CA 95203
Tel.: (209) 944-5800
Fax: (209) 944-9072
E-mail: sales@calcedar.com
Web Site: www.calcedar.com
E-Mail For Key Personnel:
Sales Director: sales@calcedar.com
Approx. Number Employees: 250
Year Founded: 1929
Business Description:
Cedar Pencil Slats, Wood/Wax Fire Logs, Siding & Deck Products Mfr
S.I.C.: 2499
N.A.I.C.S.: 321999
Export
Media: 2-3-5-6-8-9-10-18-19-21-23-24-25-26
Distr.: Intl.; Natl.
Budget Set: Mar.
Brands & Products:
CALCEDAR
CALIFORNIA CEDAR PRODUCTS
CALIFORNIA REPUBLIC
ECOSLAT
FORESTCHOICE
FRONTIER
INCENSE-CEDAR
SHASTINA
SLAT SELECTOR

CALIFORNIA FAUCETS INC.
5231 Argosy Ave
Huntington Beach, CA 92649
Tel.: (714) 891-7797
Fax: (714) 891-2478
E-mail: info@calfaucets.com
Web Site: www.calfaucets.com
Approx. Sls.: $10,000,000
Approx. Number Employees: 70
Business Description:
Faucets & Spigots, Metal & Plastic
S.I.C.: 3432; 3431
N.A.I.C.S.: 332913; 332998
Personnel:
Jeff Silverstein *(Pres)*
Fred Silverstein *(CEO)*
Noah Taft *(Sr VP-Mktg & Sls)*
Brands & Products:
ALISO
AVALON
BALBOA
CALIFORNIA FAUCETS
CAMARILLO
CARDIFF
CARMEL
CATALINA
CLASSIC MODERNE
CORONADO
CRYSTAL COVE
DECO MODERNE
DEL MAR
DOHENY
EMPIRE MODERNE
ENCINITAS
HERMOSA
HUMBOLDT
HUNTINGTON
JALAMA
LA JOLLA
MALIBU
MANHATTAN
MENDOCINO
MONTARA
MONTECITO
PALOS VERDES
REDONDO
SALINAS
SAN CLEMENTE
SAN SIMEON
SANTA BARBARA
SANTA MONICA
SAUSALITO
SOLANA
STYLEDRAIN
SUNSET
SWAROVSKI
TIBURON
TOPANGA
VENICE
Advertising Agency:
Purdie Rogers, Inc.
5447 Ballard Ave NW
Seattle, WA 98107
Tel.: (206) 628-7700
Fax: (206) 628-2818

CALPHALON CORPORATION
(Div. of Rubbermaid Home Products)
3rd D St
Perrysburg, OH 43551
Mailing Address:
PO Box 583
Toledo, OH 43697
Tel.: (419) 666-8700
Fax: (419) 666-2859
Toll Free: (800) 809-7267
Web Site: www.calphalon.com
Sales Range: $75-99.9 Million
Approx. Number Employees: 300
Year Founded: 1963
Business Description:
Mfr. of Gourmet Cookware & Related Products
S.I.C.: 3365; 3469
N.A.I.C.S.: 331524; 332116
Export
Media: 2-4-5-6-7-10-15-19-21-24
Distr.: Natl.
Budget Set: Jan.
Personnel:
Kristie Juster *(Pres)*
Jim Poppens *(VP-Mktg)*
Brands & Products:
CALPHALON COLORS
CALPHALON COMMERCIAL NON-STICK
CALPHALON COMMERCIAL TRI-PLY
PROFESSIONAL BAKEWARE FROM CALPHALON
PROFESSIONAL NONSTICK FROM CALPHALON
PROFESSIONAL STAINLESS FROM CALPHALON

CBK LTD.
(Sub. of Blyth, Inc.)
600 E Sherwood Dr
Union City, TN 38261
Tel.: (731) 885-7836
Fax: (731) 885-3857
Toll Free: (800) 394-4225
E-mail: customerservice@cbkltd.com
Web Site: www.cbkhome.com
Sales Range: $100-124.9 Million
Approx. Number Employees: 165
Year Founded: 1979
Business Description:
Decorative Products Whslr
S.I.C.: 5199; 5023
N.A.I.C.S.: 424990; 423220
Media: 4-6
Personnel:
Ric Conceno *(Pres)*
Brands & Products:
CBK

CHEF'S CATALOGUE, INC.
(Sub. of JH Partners LLC)
5070 Centennial Blvd
Colorado Springs, CO 80919-2402
Tel.: (719) 272-2700
Fax: (719) 272-2601
Toll Free: (800) 884CHEF
Web Site: www.chefscatalog.com
Approx. Number Employees: 200
Year Founded: 1979
Business Description:
Online & Mail Order Kitchen Equipment
S.I.C.: 5961
N.A.I.C.S.: 454113
Media: 4-8-13
Personnel:
Tim Littleton *(Pres & CEO)*

CHICOPEE INC.
(Sub. of Polymer Group, Inc.)
9335 Harris Corners Pkwy Ste 300
Charlotte, NC 28269
Tel.: (704) 697-5100
Toll Free: (888) 835-2442
E-mail: chixsales@pginw.com
Sales Range: $25-49.9 Million
Approx. Number Employees: 100
Year Founded: 1827
Business Description:
Towel & Wiping Products Mfr
S.I.C.: 2297; 2392
N.A.I.C.S.: 313230; 314129
Import Export
Advertising Expenditures: $750,000
Media: 2-4-7-10-13-19-20-21-26
Distr.: Intl
Budget Set: Sept.
Brands & Products:
CHIX

COAST CUTLERY COMPANY
8033 NE Holman St
Portland, OR 97218-4019
Tel.: (503) 234-4545
Fax: (503) 234-4422
Toll Free: (800) 426-5858
E-mail: consumer.help@coastportland.com
Web Site: www.coastportland.com
Approx. Number Employees: 40
Year Founded: 1919
Business Description:
Mfr. of Kitchen Cutlery, Sportsman & Recreational Knives
S.I.C.: 5072
N.A.I.C.S.: 423710
Media: 2-4-6
Distr.: Natl.
Personnel:
David C. Brands *(Pres)*
Kelsey Omlin *(Mgr-Special Mktg)*
Brands & Products:
ADVANCED FOCUS SYSTEM
BACK PACKER
BANTAM
BUDDY
COAST
DUKE
EARL
GRANDPA
HOBBYTEC
HUNTER'S PAL
KRAYTON
MAJOR
MICRO STAG
MINI TAC
NANO TAC
ONE-HANDED SPEED-FOCUS
PILOT
POWER TAC
PRINCE
QUICK-CYCLE SWITCH SYSTEM
RAMBLER
SCOUT
SKINNER
SPORTEC
THUYA
V2 MINI MOON
V2 TRIPLEX
WHITEHUNTER

CORNING INCORPORATED
1 Riverfront Plz
Corning, NY 14831-0001
Tel.: (607) 974-9000
Fax: (607) 974-5927
Fax: (607) 974-8091
E-mail: Inquiries@corning.com
Web Site: www.corning.com
Approx. Sls.: $6,632,000,000
Approx. Number Employees: 26,200
Year Founded: 1851
Business Description:
Specialty Glass & Ceramic Products Mfr
S.I.C.: 3229; 3264; 3297; 3357; 3496; 3827
N.A.I.C.S.: 327212; 327113; 327125; 331422; 332618; 333314; 335921; 335929
Import Export
Advertising Expenditures: $556,200,000
Media: 2-4-10-13-26
Distr.: Natl.
Personnel:
Wendell P. Weeks *(Chm & CEO)*
Alan T. Eusden *(Chm, Pres-Corning Display Technologies-Taiwan)*
James B. Flaws *(Vice Chm & CFO)*
Kirk P. Gregg *(Chief Admin Officer & Exec VP)*
Joseph A. Miller, Jr. *(CTO & Exec VP)*
Clark Kinlin *(Pres/CEO-Corning Cable Sys)*
Eric S. Musser *(CEO-Corning Greater China)*
Mark Rogus *(Treas & Sr VP)*
Lawrence D. Mcrae *(Exec VP-Strategy & Corp Dev)*
Pamela C. Schneider *(Exec VP & Chief of Staff-Ops)*
R. Tony Tripeny *(Sr VP & Corp Controller)*
Mark A. Beck *(Sr VP & Gen Mgr-Environmental Tech)*
Kimberly Seymour Hartwell *(Sr VP)*
Jean-Pierre Mazeau *(Sr VP-Corp Prod & Process Dev)*
Christine M. Pambianchi *(Sr VP-HR)*
Richard Eglen *(VP & Gen Mgr-Life Sciences Bus Segment)*
Vincent P. Hatton *(VP & Dir-Legal)*
Dan Collins *(VP-Corp Comm)*
Lisa Burns *(Mgr-Corp Comm)*
Monica Sofio *(Mgr-Mktg Comm)*
Brands & Products:
12-PETTE
8-PETTE

Key to Media (For complete agency information see *The Advertising Red Books-Agencies* edition):
1. Bus. Publs. 2. Cable T.V. 3. Catalogs & Directories. 4. Co-op Adv. 5. Consumer Mags. 6. D.M. to Bus. Estab.7. D.M. to Consumers 8. Daily Newsp. 9. Exhibits/Trade Shows 10. Foreign 11. Infomercial 12. Internet Adv.13. Multimedia 14. Network Radio 15. Network T.V. 16. Newsp. Distr. Mags. 17. Other 18. Outdoor (Posters, Transit) 19. Point of Purchase20. Premiums, Novelties 21. Product Samples 22. Special Events Mktg. 23. Spot Radio 24. Spot T.V. 25. Weekly Newsp. 26. Yellow Page Adv.

Corning Incorporated — (Continued)

ALTOS
CELCOR
CELLBIND
CELLCUBE
CELLSTACK
CGW
CHEMCOR
CONEC
CORMETECH
CORNING
COY
CPC
CY-BET
CYLINDERMASTER
DCM
DENSEPAK
DESK-LINK
DFX
DNA-BIND
DUALCOM
DURATRAP
EAGLE
EAGLE 2000
ECLIPSE
EPIC
EVOLANT
EZ-TERM
FDC
FREEDM
FUSELITE
FUTUREWAY
G2
GMS
GPO
GPPO
GUIDELINES
HPFS
HYPERFLASK
INFINICOR
LANSCAPE
LCG
LCGX
LEAF
LID-SYSTEM
M-CAT
M-STAR
MACBETH
MACOR
MAXI-BUNDLE
MC
METROCOR
MFP
MIC
MINIMASS
MPC
MTP
NANOSPOT
NETWELL
NEXCOR
OCTAPETTE
OPTIFIT
OPTIFOCUS
OPTISHEATH
OPTOCERAMIC
OPTOCOMMERCE
PBX
PGII
PGX
PHOTOBROWN
PHOTOBROWN EXTRA
PHOTOGRAY
PHOTOGRAY EXTRA
PYREX
PYREX PORTABLES
PYREXPLUS
PYROCERAM
QUANTUMFOCUS
ROBOFLASK
ROTAFLO
SABRE
SC-DC
SC-QC
SCHOLAR
SEARCHLITE
SEROCLUSTER
SHORTIES
SILHOUETTE
SMF-28
SMF-28E
SMF-28E+
SMOOTHLINE
SOLO
SPIN-X
STEUBEN
STRANTERM
STRIPETTE
SUNSENSORS
TBII
THERMOWELL
THETAFORM
TRANSPLATE
TRANSTAR-96
TRANSWELL
TROPEL
TUBESTAR
ULE
ULTRAEASE
ULTRARANGE
ULTRASEAL
UNICAM
UNIDEX
VASCADE
VERSABLOCK
VISTACOR
VYCOR
WARE
XS

Advertising Agency:
Brodeur Partners
855 Boylston St 2nd Fl
Boston, MA 02116-2622
Tel.: (617) 587-2800
Fax: (617) 587-2828

CRESCENT MANUFACTURING COMPANY

1310 Majestic Dr
Fremont, OH 43420-9142
Tel.: (419) 332-6484
Fax: (419) 332-6564
Toll Free: (800) 537-1330
E-mail: sales@crescentblades.com
Web Site: www.crescentblades.com
E-Mail For Key Personnel:
Sales Director: sales@crescentblades.com
Approx. Number Employees: 130
Year Founded: 1898
Business Description:
Mfr. of Precision Disposable Industrial Blades
S.I.C.: 3421; 3425
N.A.I.C.S.: 332211; 332213
Import Export
Media: 2-4-6-8-13
Distr.: Intl.; Natl.
Budget Set: Nov.
Personnel:
Jeff Miller *(Dir-Sls & Mktg)*
Brands & Products:
CRESCENT
DURAEDGE
ENCORE

CROSCILL, INC.

(Holding of Patriarch Partners, LLC)
295 5th Ave
New York, NY 10016
Tel.: (212) 689-7222
Fax: (212) 481-8656
E-mail: croscill@croscill.com
Web Site: www.croscill.com
Approx. Sls.: $309,000,000
Approx. Number Employees: 1,500
Year Founded: 1945
Business Description:
Textile Home Furnishings; Window Treatments & Bed Coverings Mfr
S.I.C.: 2391; 2392
N.A.I.C.S.: 314121; 314129
Import Export
Advertising Expenditures: $5,000,000
Media: 4-6-9-16-17
Distr.: Natl.
Brands & Products:
410 COLLECTION
ADLER POPPIES COLOR KHAKI
ALEXANDRIA
ALICIA
ALLISON EMBROIDERY
ALPINE
ANNETTE
ANTIQUE ROSE SHEER
ARABELLA
ARBOR MIST
ASHLEY
ASIAN GOLD
AUSTIN
BAMBOO
BEACH GLASS
BEACH HAVEN
BEACH MEMORIES
BEADS
BEADS TERRY
BELLA
BELLAVISTA
BENGAL ROAD
BIG SKY
BIJOU
BLUE BELL
BRITISH COLONIAL
CAITLYN
CAMELOT
CAPRI SATIN
CARLISLE
CARLISLE SHOWER
CARLISLE STRIPE
CAROLENA SHEER
CARRARA MARBLE
CARRINGTON STRIPE
CASCADE
CASINO
CASSANDRA
CASSARINA
CENTRUM
CHAMBORD
CHAMPAGNE POPPIES
CHARLESTON
CHARLOTTE
CHEETAH
CHEVRON CHENILLE
CHINOISERIE
CLASSICO
CLAUDIA
CROSCILL
DAVINCI COLOR NATURAL
DAZZLE
DRIFTWOOD
DUNE
EDGE
EFFERVESCENCE
ELECTRA
EVERGREEN
FANDANGO
FAUX SUEDE
FIGARO
FILIGREE
FIONA
FIORE
FLORENTINE
FORGET ME NOT
FUJI
GLOBAL FUSION
GRAND CAYMAN
GREEN GARDAN
GROOMIN
HERITAGE CREWEL
HIGHLAND
JAZZ
JUNO
KALIHARI
KAUAI
LARIAT
LAVISH
LEDERA
LOVE LETTER
LVY
MACRAME
MARTINIQUE
MAYURI
MERCURY
METRO
MIRABEAU SHEER
NAVIGATOR
NICOLETTE
OCEANVIEW
OLIVIA
OPULENCE
ORCHIDS AND NARCISSUS
ORLEANS
OSLO
PEBBLE
PLATINUM LEAF
PORT OF CALL
PORTICO MACRAME
POSITANO
PRIMROSE
PRINCESS
RAINIER
RICE PAPER
ROMANZA
ROMERO
ROSE GARDEN
ROSELYN STRIPE
ROYAL PAISLEY
SAHARA
SANDSTONE
SARA CLIP
SAVOIR FAIRE
SAXONY
SHAVED ICE
SHEER MIST
SHOJI
SIGNATURE LAQUERWARE
SILK BLOSSOMS
SPA GLASS
SPA LEAF
SPATTERWARE
STRATA
SYNERGY
TATAMI
TORINO
TOWNHOUSE
TRIOMPHE
TULIPS
WATERFALL
WISTERIA

Key to Media (For complete agency information see *The Advertising Red Books-Agencies* edition):
1. Bus. Publs. 2. Cable T.V. 3. Catalogs & Directories. 4. Co-op Adv. 5. Consumer Mags. 6. D.M. to Bus. Estab.7. D.M. to Consumers
8. Daily Newsp. 9. Exhibits/Trade Shows 10. Foreign 11. Infomercial 12. Internet Adv.13. Multimedia 14. Network Radio
15. Network T.V. 16. Newsp. Distr. Mags. 17. Other 18. Outdoor (Posters, Transit) 19. Point of Purchase20. Premiums, Novelties
21. Product Samples 22. Special Events Mktg. 23. Spot Radio 24. Spot T.V. 25. Weekly Newsp. 26. Yellow Page Adv.

CUISINART INC.
(Div. of Conair Corporation)
1 Cummings Point Rd
Stamford, CT 06902-7901
Tel.: (203) 351-9000
Fax: (203) 975-4660
Fax: (203) 351-9180
E-mail: info@cuisinart.com
Web Site: www.cuisinart.com
Approx. Number Employees: 300
Business Description:
Cooking Equipment Mfr & Retailer
S.I.C.: 5719; 3262
N.A.I.C.S.: 442299; 327112
Import
Advertising Expenditures: $5,000,000
Media: 2-3-4-6-9-10-13-15-19-20-21-22-24
Distr.: Natl.
Personnel:
Ron Diamond *(Pres)*
Mary Rodgers *(Dir-Mktg Comm)*
Ken Rosi *(Dir-Art)*
Joyce Varrone *(Dir-Media Svcs)*
Melissa Abbazia *(Supvr-Creative)*
Brands & Products:
CUISINART
FLAVOR DUO
LITTLE PRO
SAVOR THE GOOD LIFE

CUTCO CORPORATION
1116 E State St
Olean, NY 14760-3814
Tel.: (716) 372-3111
Fax: (716) 790-7160
Fax: (716) 373-6145
Toll Free: (800) 282-0130
Web Site: www.cutco.com
Sales Range: $75-99.9 Million
Approx. Number Employees: 700
Year Founded: 1982
Business Description:
Cutlery Whslr
S.I.C.: 3421; 5023
N.A.I.C.S.: 332211; 423220
Import Export
Media: 4-10-13-22
Personnel:
James E. Stitt *(CEO)*
Brent A. Driscoll *(Exec VP-Admin & Fin)*
Kathleen Donovan *(Coord-PR)*
Brands & Products:
CUTCO
THE WORLD'S FINEST CUTLERY

DECOLAV, INC.
424 SW 12th Ave
Deerfield Beach, FL 33442
Tel.: (561) 274-2110
Fax: (561) 274-2016
E-mail: info@decolav.com
Web Site: www.decolav.com
Sales Range: $10-24.9 Million
Approx. Number Employees: 60
Year Founded: 2000
Business Description:
Bathroom Fixtures
S.I.C.: 3431
N.A.I.C.S.: 332998
Advertising Expenditures: $1,500,000
Media: 4-6-10-13-17-19-22
Personnel:
Robert H. Mayer *(Pres & CEO)*
David Neustein *(COO & Gen Counsel)*
Brain Bringham *(Sr Dir-Mktg)*
Brands & Products:
A PERFECT CHISEL
CHANGING THE WAY YOU VIEW THE BATHROOM
DECOLAV
SIMPLY STAINLESS
TRANSLUCENCE
Advertising Agency:
Jennings & Company
436 Woodland Dr
Sarasota, FL 34234
Tel.: (941) 351-1005
Fax: (941) 351-0846
Pub Rels
— Linda Jennings *(Founder)*

DECORATOR INDUSTRIES, INC.
10011 Pines Blvd Ste 201
Pembroke Pines, FL 33024
Tel.: (954) 436-8909
Fax: (954) 436-1778
E-mail: sales@decoratorindustries.com
Web Site: www.decoratorindustries.com
E-Mail For Key Personnel:
Sales Director: sales@decoratorindustries.com
Approx. Sls.: $18,600,358
Approx. Number Employees: 200
Year Founded: 1953
Business Description:
Interior Furnishing Products Mfr
S.I.C.: 2392; 2261; 2391; 2843
N.A.I.C.S.: 314129; 313311; 314121; 325613
Import
Advertising Expenditures: $243,886
Personnel:
William A. Bassett *(Chm)*
William A. Johnson *(Pres & CEO)*
Diana Hinton *(Head-HR)*
Brands & Products:
DI

DEXTER-RUSSELL INC.
(Sub. of Hyde Manufacturing Company)
44 River St
Southbridge, MA 01550
Tel.: (508) 765-0201
Fax: (508) 764-2897
E-mail: info@dexter-russell.com
Web Site: www.dexter-russell.com
Approx. Number Employees: 250
Year Founded: 1818
Business Description:
Mfr of Professional & Industrial Cutlery
S.I.C.: 3421; 3423
N.A.I.C.S.: 332211; 332212
Import Export
Advertising Expenditures: $200,000
Media: 2-4-5-7-10-13-19-21
Distr.: Intl.; Natl.
Personnel:
Kevin Clark *(VP-Sls)*
Jim Bellerose *(Mgr-Mktg)*
Brands & Products:
CONNOISSEUR
DEXTER
DEXTER/RUSSELL
LIMELITE
RUSSELL GREEN RIVER
RUSSELL INTERNATIONAL
SANI-SAFE
SANI-SATIONS
SOFGRIP
V-LO

DIVERSEY, INC.
(Sub. of Diversey Holdings Inc.)
8310 16th St
Sturtevant, WI 53177-0902
Mailing Address:
PO Box 902
Sturtevant, WI 53177
Tel.: (262) 631-4001
Fax: (262) 631-4282
Web Site: www.johnsondiversey.com
Year Founded: 1997
Business Description:
Industrial Hygienic Products Mfr
S.I.C.: 2842; 2841
N.A.I.C.S.: 325612; 325611
Advertising Expenditures: $1,665,000
Personnel:
Helen P. Johnson-Leipold *(Chm)*
Edward F. Lonergan *(Pres & CEO)*
Norman Clubb *(CFO & Exec VP)*
Brent W. Hoag *(CIO & VP)*
Scott D. Russell *(Chief Compliance Officer, Gen Counsel, Corp Sec & Exec VP)*
Christopher J. Slusar *(Chief Acctg Officer)*
Moreno G. Dezio *(Reg Pres-Europe)*
Pedro Chidichimo *(Pres-Global Customer Solutions & Innovation)*
Gregory F. Clark *(Chief Process Officer & Sr VP)*
James W. Larson *(Sr VP-Global HR)*
John W. Matthews *(Sr VP-Corp Affairs)*
Clive A. Newman *(VP-Fin-EMEA)*
Mark Goldman *(Sr Dir-Global Comm)*
Kathleen Powers *(Dir-Global Treasury)*
Brands & Products:
ENDUROPOWER
J-FLEX
SOFT CARE
SUMA
TASKI

DOUGLAS/QUIKUT
(Div. of The Scott Fetzer Company)
118 E Douglas Rd
Walnut Ridge, AR 72476-0029
Tel.: (870) 886-6774
Fax: (870) 886-9162
Toll Free: (800) 982-5233
E-mail: sales@quikut.com
Web Site: www.quikut.com
E-Mail For Key Personnel:
Sales Director: sales@quikut.com
Sales Range: $25-49.9 Million
Approx. Number Employees: 250
Year Founded: 1923
Business Description:
Soaps & Specialty Cleaners; Electric & Manual Fillet Knives, Cutlery & Cutting Boards; Camping Products & Sporting Goods Mfr
S.I.C.: 3421; 3635
N.A.I.C.S.: 332211; 335212
Import
Media: 1-3-4-5-6-8-9-10-11-19-20-21-23-24-25
Distr.: Natl.
Budget Set: Aug.
Brands & Products:
AMERICAN ANGLER
GINSU
QUIKUT
READIVAC
ULTRA SHARP

DURAFLAME, INC.
PO Box 1230
Stockton, CA 95201-1230
Tel.: (209) 461-6600
Fax: (209) 462-9412
E-mail: info@duraflame.com
Web Site: www.duraflame.com
Approx. Number Employees: 30
Year Founded: 1972
Business Description:
Fireplace Logs Mfr & Distr
S.I.C.: 5099
N.A.I.C.S.: 423990
Export
Media: 2-3-5-6-8-10-13-14-18-19-20-23-24
Distr.: Natl.
Budget Set: Mar.
Personnel:
Crystal Whole *(Brand Mgr)*
Sarah Salori *(Mgr-Brand)*
Brands & Products:
ANYTIME
CRACKLEFLAME
DURAFLAME
EASYTIME
FIRESTART
FLUE-RENEW
FRESH LIGHT
HEARTH ESSENTIALS
INSTA-MATCH
OPEN AIR
QUICK COALS
QUICK START
XTRATIME
Advertising Agency:
CPC Marketing, Inc.
(House Agency)
PO Box 1230
Stockton, CA 95201
Tel.: (209) 461-6600
(In-House Media Buying)

DURAND GLASS MANUFACTURING CO.
(Sub. of ARC International North America Inc.)
901 S Wade Blvd
Millville, NJ 08332
Mailing Address:
PO Box 5012
Millville, NJ 08332-5012
Tel.: (856) 327-4800
Fax: (856) 691-1245
Web Site: www.arc-intl.com
Approx. Number Employees: 1,000
Year Founded: 1982
Business Description:
Glassware Mfr & Distr
S.I.C.: 3229; 3221; 3231; 3262
N.A.I.C.S.: 327212; 327112; 327213; 327215
Import Export
Media: 2-5-10-11
Distr.: Natl.
Personnel:
Fred Dohn *(CFO)*
Tom Reed *(VP-HR)*
Brands & Products:
ARCOFLAM
ARCOPAL
ARCUISINE
CRISTAL DE FLANDRE
CRISTAL J. G. DURAND
J.G. DURAND
SALVIATI

Key to Media (For complete agency information see *The Advertising Red Books-Agencies* edition):
1. Bus. Publs. 2. Cable T.V. 3. Catalogs & Directories. 4. Co-op Adv. 5. Consumer Mags. 6. D.M. to Bus. Estab.7. D.M. to Consumers 8. Daily Newsp. 9. Exhibits/Trade Shows 10. Foreign 11. Infomercial 12. Internet Adv.13. Multimedia 14. Network Radio 15. Network T.V. 16. Newsp. Distr. Mags. 17. Other 18. Outdoor (Posters, Transit) 19. Point of Purchase20. Premiums, Novelties 21. Product Samples 22. Special Events Mktg. 23. Spot Radio 24. Spot T.V. 25. Weekly Newsp. 26. Yellow Page Adv.

D'VONTZ
7208 E 38th St
Tulsa, OK 74145
Tel.: (918) 622-3600
Fax: (918) 622-3649
E-mail: info@dvontz.com
Web Site: www.dvontz.com
Approx. Number Employees: 100
Business Description:
Fashion Plumbing Products Designer & Mfr
S.I.C.: 3432
N.A.I.C.S.: 332913
Media: 4-13

DWYER PRODUCTS CORPORATION
Ste F 1226 N Michael Dr
Wood Dale, IL 60191-1056
Tel.: (219) 874-5236
Toll Free: (800) 348-8508
Web Site: www.dwyerkitchens.com
Approx. Number Employees: 75
Year Founded: 1926
Business Description:
Compact Kitchens, Custom Wet Bars & Under Counter Refrigerators Mfr
S.I.C.: 2514; 2434
N.A.I.C.S.: 337124; 337110
Export
Media: 1-2-4-5-7-10-17
Distr.: Intl.; Natl.
Budget Set: Oct.
Personnel:
Emily Rudolph *(Mgr-Mktg)*
Brands & Products:
DWYER COMPACT KITCHENS
METRO
SIGNATURE
Advertising Agency:
LEC
12 E Ohio St
Chicago, IL 60611-5311
Tel.: (312) 670-0077
Fax: (312) 670-4477
Toll Free: (800) 731-6171
— Laurie Cairns *(Pres.)*

EDLUND COMPANY, INC.
159 Indus Pkwy
Burlington, VT 05401-5437
Tel.: (802) 862-9661
Fax: (802) 862-4822
Toll Free: (800) 772-2126
E-mail: customerservice@edlundco.com
Web Site: www.edlundco.com
Approx. Number Employees: 100
Year Founded: 1926
Business Description:
Mfr. of Can Openers & Can Opening Systems, Scales & Stainless Steel Food Service Equipment
S.I.C.: 3423; 3556
N.A.I.C.S.: 332212; 333294
Import Export
Media: 2-4-6-7-11-13
Distr.: Intl.; Natl.
Budget Set: Dec.
Personnel:
Peter Nordell *(Pres)*
Brands & Products:
350 XL SERIES
CROWN PUNCH
EDLUND
WE'RE IN YOUR KITCHEN

E.L. MUSTEE & SONS, INC.
5431 W 164th St
Cleveland, OH 44142
Tel.: (216) 267-3100
Fax: (216) 267-9997
E-mail: info@mustee.com
Web Site: www.mustee.com
Approx. Number Employees: 70
Year Founded: 1932
Business Description:
Shower Stalls, Floors & Enclosures, Bathtub Walls, Laundry/Utility Tubs, Laundry Cabinets, Utility Sinks, Mop Service Basins, Washer and Water Heater Pans & Easy-Access Showers Mfr
S.I.C.: 3088; 3432
N.A.I.C.S.: 326191; 332913
Media: 2-4-10-19
Distr.: Natl.
Personnel:
Robert J. Mustee *(Pres)*
Kevin Mustee *(VP-Mktg)*
Brands & Products:
3060 SHOWERTUB
ADA
CAREGIVER
COPOLYPURE
DURABASE
DURAGUARD
DURAPAN
DURASTALL
DURASTONE
DURATRIM
DURATUB
DURAWALL
HANDIFLO
IAPMO
MUSTEE
SHOWERTUB
STARBURST
STYLEMATE
UTILATUB
UTILATWIN

ELEGANZA INTERNATIONAL INC.
1630 E Hallandale Beach Blvd
Hallandale, FL 33009-4610
Tel.: (954) 454-7731
Fax: (954) 454-0871
Toll Free: (888) 486-4221
E-mail: eleganza@bellsouth.net
Approx. Number Employees: 4
Year Founded: 1939
Business Description:
Gifts Importer
S.I.C.: 5099
N.A.I.C.S.: 423990
Import
Media: 2-4-8-10-26
Distr.: Natl.
Budget Set: Jan.

ENESCO, LLC
(Holding of Tinicum Incorporated)
225 Windsor Dr
Itasca, IL 60143-1200
Tel.: (630) 875-5300
Fax: (630) 875-5350
Toll Free: (800) 436-3726
E-mail: caffairs@enesco.com
Web Site: www.enesco.com
Sales Range: $200-249.9 Million
Approx. Number Employees: 1,182
Year Founded: 2007
Business Description:
Fine Gifts, Collectibles & Home Decor Accessories Mfr
S.I.C.: 3262; 5199; 5947
N.A.I.C.S.: 327112; 424990; 453220
Import Export
Advertising Expenditures: $600,000
Media: 2-9-10-25
Distr.: Natl.
Personnel:
Matthew Bousquette *(Chm)*
Thomas G. Bowles *(CEO)*
Anthony G. Testolin *(Chief Acctg Officer)*
Michael Griffith *(Sr VP-Sls-US)*
Liz Wain *(Dir-Design & Bus Dev)*
Brands & Products:
BLOOMING WILD
BORDER FINE ARTS
CAROL ROWAN
CHERISHED TEDDIES
CHILDREN OF THE INNER LIGHT
CIRCLE OF LOVE
DEBORAH LEWIS
ENDA-BUG
ENESCO
ENESCO BABY BRANDS
FOUNDATIONS
GROWING UP GIRLS
HEARTWOOD CREEK BY JIM SHORE
HOME & GARDEN
JULIE UELAND
MAHOGANY PRINCESS
MARY ENGELBREIT
MARYS MOO MOOS
MY LITTLE KITCHEN FAIRIES
RANDY OUZTS
ROS WALSH
STANDING OVATIONS
TERRA COPPER
THAT'S MY GIRL
TREASURED MEMORIES
UNMISTAKABLE
VALENTINA
Advertising Agencies:
Carlsson & Company Inc.
29710 Whitley Collins Dr
Rancho Palos Verdes, CA 90275
Tel.: (310) 377-7582
Fax: (888) 415-2101

Herbert Krug & Associates, Inc.
500 Davis St Ste 508
Evanston, IL 60201-4643
Tel.: (847) 864-0550
Fax: (847) 864-0575

EUROMARKET DESIGNS, INC.
(Sub. of Otto GmbH & Co KG)
(d/b/a Crate & Barrel Stores)
1250 Techny Rd
Northbrook, IL 60062-2349
Tel.: (847) 272-2888
Fax: (847) 272-2938
Web Site: www.crateandbarrel.com
Approx. Number Employees: 600
Year Founded: 1962
Business Description:
Home Furnishings Retailer
S.I.C.: 5719; 5947
N.A.I.C.S.: 442299; 453220
Import
Media: 4-6-9-18-23-25
Distr.: Reg.
Budget Set: Jan.
Personnel:
Barbara Turf *(CEO)*
Ed Rennemann *(CIO)*
Barb Reimann *(Sr VP-Ops)*
Michelle Levy *(Dir-Mktg)*
Brands & Products:
CRATE & BARREL

THE EVERCARE COMPANY
3440 Preston Rdg Rd Ste 650
Alpharetta, GA 30005
Tel.: (770) 570-5000
Fax: (770) 570-5001
Toll Free: (800) 521-5856
Toll Free: (800) 435-6223
Web Site: www.evercare.com
Approx. Number Employees: 200
Year Founded: 1956
Business Description:
Mfr. of Lint Pic-Up Adhesive Rollers & Refills, Lint Brushes, Battery Operated Fuzz Shaver, Sweater Brushes, Pet Hair Pic-Up Adhesive Rollers, Spot Remover, Shoe Shapers & Shoe Horns, Travel Organizers
S.I.C.: 2393; 3991
N.A.I.C.S.: 314911; 339994
Import Export
Media: 1-2-3-4-5-6-7-9-10-11-13-16-19-20-21-24-25
Distr.: Intl.; Natl.
Personnel:
Mike Ortale *(VP-Sls)*
Terry Snider *(VP-Sls)*
Brands & Products:
BRAWNY
EVERCARE
EVERCARE PET
EVERCARE PROFESSIONAL
EVERCARE VETERINARIAN
LINT PIC-UP
LITTLE THINGS - BIG DIFFERENCES
MAGIK BRUSH
STAIN ERASER
SWEEP 'N CLEAN
WOOLITE
Advertising Agency:
Trevelino/Keller Communications Group
949 W Marietta St NW Ste X106
Atlanta, GA 30318-5275
Tel.: (404) 214-0722
Fax: (404) 214-0729

FARIBAULT MILLS
1500 2nd Ave NW
Faribault, MN 55021-3018
Tel.: (507) 334-6444
Fax: (507) 332-2936
Toll Free: (800) 448-9665
E-mail: info@faribaultmills.com
E-Mail For Key Personnel:
Public Relations: rwallace@fairbowool.com
Approx. Number Employees: 130
Year Founded: 1865
Business Description:
Mfr. of Corn Fiber, Wool, Cotton & Acrylic Blankets & Afghan Throws
S.I.C.: 2211
N.A.I.C.S.: 313210
Export
Advertising Expenditures: $200,000
Media: 1-6-7-8-10-13-18
Distr.: Natl.
Budget Set: June

Key to Media (For complete agency information see *The Advertising Red Books-Agencies* edition):
1. Bus. Publs. 2. Cable T.V. 3. Catalogs & Directories. 4. Co-op Adv. 5. Consumer Mags. 6. D.M. to Bus. Estab.7. D.M. to Consumers 8. Daily Newsp. 9. Exhibits/Trade Shows 10. Foreign 11. Infomercial 12. Internet Adv.13. Multimedia 14. Network Radio 15. Network T.V. 16. Newsp. Distr. Mags. 17. Other 18. Outdoor (Posters, Transit) 19. Point of Purchase20. Premiums, Novelties 21. Product Samples 22. Special Events Mktg. 23. Spot Radio 24. Spot T.V. 25. Weekly Newsp. 26. Yellow Page Adv.

Personnel:
Mike Harris *(CEO)*
Dennis Melchert *(COO)*
Brands & Products:
BABY HEARTS
BACNIC BACK PAK
BUCKING BRONCO
CAMPUS PAK-A-ROBE
COMMANDER PAK-A-ROBE
COURIER ROLL-UP
CRUISER ROLL-UP
DEER LODGE
EMBROIDERED THROW
ETERNITY THROW
EVERGREEN
EXPLORER PAK-A-ROBE
FARIBAULT MILLS
FARIBO
FRONTIER
GLOBETROTTER PAK-A-ROBE
LIFESTYLES PAK-A-ROBE
LULLABYE
NATURES CHOICE
PAK-A-ROBE
SOLITAIRE SCARF
STATESMAN PAK-A-ROBE
TOWN & COUNTRY SCARF
TRADITIONS ROLL-UP
VOYAGER PAK-A-ROBE
WE BLANKET THE WORLD SINCE 1865

THE FENTON ART GLASS COMPANY

700 Elizabeth St
Williamstown, WV 26187-1028
Tel.: (304) 375-6122
Fax: (304) 375-7833
Toll Free: (800) 933-6766
E-mail: askfenton@fentonartglass.com
Web Site: www.fentonartglass.com
E-Mail For Key Personnel:
President: gfenton@fentonartglass.com
Approx. Number Employees: 130
Year Founded: 1905
Business Description:
Mfr. of Handmade Glassware
S.I.C.: 3229; 3231
N.A.I.C.S.: 327212; 327215
Import Export
Advertising Expenditures: $100,000
Media: 2-4-6-7-9-10-18-20-21-24
Distr.: Natl.
Budget Set: Dec.
Personnel:
Pat Gollinger *(Chm)*
George W. Fenton *(Pres)*
Scott Fenton *(VP-Sls)*
Brands & Products:
FENTON
FENTON ART GLASS
Advertising Agency:
GGG Brand Marketing & Design
140 Gross St
Marietta, OH 45750
Tel.: (304) 485-8990
Fax: (304) 464-4220
Toll Free: (800) 628-8521

FISKARS BRANDS, INC.

(Sub. of Fiskars Oyj Abp)
2537 Daniels St
Madison, WI 53718
Tel.: (608) 259-1649
Fax: (608) 294-4798
Toll Free: (866) 348-5661
E-mail: socconsumeraffairs@fiskars.com
Web Site: www.fiskarsbrands.com
Approx. Number Employees: 250
Business Description:
Scissors, Cutlery, Sporting Goods & Garden Shears Mfr
S.I.C.: 3421; 3423
N.A.I.C.S.: 332211; 332212
Media: 2-4-5-6-9-10-19-20-21-23
Distr.: Natl.
Budget Set: Dec.
Personnel:
Chad Vincent *(Pres)*
Jay Gillespie *(VP-Mktg-Brand)*
Rich Walker *(VP-HR)*
Kelly A. Newbold *(Mgr-Category Mktg)*

FORSHAW OF ST. LOUIS

825 S Lindbergh Blvd
Saint Louis, MO 63131
Tel.: (314) 993-5570
Fax: (314) 993-5593
Toll Free: (800) FORSHAW
E-mail: jforshaw@forshaws.com
Web Site: www.forshaws.com
Approx. Sls.: $2,500,000
Approx. Number Employees: 50
Year Founded: 1871
Business Description:
Patio Furniture, Wood Stoves, Fireplace & Barbecue Equipment Distr
S.I.C.: 5712; 5023
N.A.I.C.S.: 442110; 423220
Advertising Expenditures: $250,000
Media: 4-8-23-24-25
Distr.: Natl.; Reg.
Budget Set: Dec.
Personnel:
Joseph Forshaw, IV *(Pres)*
Rick Forshaw *(CEO)*
Phillip Chamberlin *(Mgr-Natl Sls)*

FREUDENBERG HOUSEHOLD PRODUCTS LP

(Sub. of Freudenberg & Co. Kommanditgesellschaft)
505 N Rail Rd Ave
Northlake, IL 60164
Tel.: (708) 452-4100
Fax: (630) 270-1600
Toll Free: (800) 543-8105
E-mail: info@ocedar.com
Web Site: www.ocedar.com
E-Mail For Key Personnel:
President: ron.tillery@fhp-ww.com
Marketing Director: tim.molek@fhp-ww.com
Sales Director: jim.castetter@fhp-ww.com
Approx. Number Employees: 45
Business Description:
Mfr. of Mops, Sponge Mops & Refills, Brooms & Dust Mops
S.I.C.: 3991
N.A.I.C.S.: 339994
Import Export
Media: 3-8-11-12-13-15-19-24
Distr.: Natl.
Budget Set: Nov.
Personnel:
Jim Castetter *(VP-Sls)*
Tim Molek *(Gen Mgr)*
Brands & Products:
EXSTATIC
O-CEDAR
PERFORMER
ROLL-O-MATIC
SCRUNGE SCRUBBER SPONGES
VILEDA

GARLAND COMMERCIAL RANGES, LTD.

(Sub. of Manitowoc Foodservice Companies, Inc.)
1177 Kamato Road
Mississauga, ON L4W 1X4, Canada
Tel.: (905) 624-0260
Fax: (905) 624-5669
Web Site: www.garland-group.com
Sales Range: $75-99.9 Million
Approx. Number Employees: 300
Year Founded: 1952
Business Description:
Commercial Cooking & Ventilation Equipment Mfr
S.I.C.: 3589
N.A.I.C.S.: 333319
Export
Media: 2-4-5-10-16-19-20-26
Distr.: Natl.
Budget Set: Nov.-Dec.
Personnel:
Jacques Seguin *(Pres-Garland Grp)*
Mary Chiarot *(VP-Sls, Mktg)*
Larry Gammon *(VP-Procurement & Tech-Manitowoc Food Svc)*
Steve Sharples *(Sr Mgr-Products)*
Larry Orton *(Mgr-Distributed Brands)*

GRAYLINE HOUSEWARES, INC.

(Sub. of Panacea Products Corporation)
2711 International St
Columbus, OH 43228
Tel.: (614) 850-7000
Fax: (614) 850-7111
Toll Free: (800) 543-0031
E-mail: graylne@aol.com
Web Site: www.graylinehousewares.com
Approx. Sls.: $19,000,000
Approx. Number Employees: 250
Year Founded: 1947
Business Description:
Houseware Mfr
S.I.C.: 3089
N.A.I.C.S.: 326199
Export
Media: 2-5-6-10
Distr.: Intl.; Natl.
Budget Set: Nov.
Personnel:
Fred K. Rosen *(Pres)*
Brands & Products:
GRAYLINE
Advertising Agency:
Advertising & Promotional Services, Inc. (Adpro, Inc.)
(d/b/a ADPRO, INC)
6 S 503 Wildwood Dr
Aurora, IL 60506
Tel.: (630) 801-9900
Fax: (630) 801-9663
Toll Free: (866) 895-2535

THE HALL CHINA COMPANY

1 Anna St
East Liverpool, OH 43920-3675
Tel.: (330) 385-2900
Fax: (330) 385-6185
Toll Free: (800) 837-4950
E-mail: custserv@hallchina.com
Web Site: www.hallchina.com
E-Mail For Key Personnel:
President: jgs@hallchina.com
Public Relations: natlacct@hallchina.com
Approx. Number Employees: 60
Year Founded: 1903
Business Description:
Mfr. of Ceramic Products for the Food Service Industry; Fireproof Cooking China
S.I.C.: 3262; 3421
N.A.I.C.S.: 327112; 332211
Export
Media: 4-6-10-21
Distr.: Intl.; Natl.
Budget Set: Nov.
Brands & Products:
HALL
SUPER EXPRESS SERVICE
Advertising Agency:
Hybrid Marketing
1220 W 6th St Ste 200
Cleveland, OH 44113
Tel.: (216) 774-9274

HAMMACHER SCHLEMMER & CO., INC.

9307 N Milwaukee Ave
Niles, IL 60714
Tel.: (847) 581-8600
Fax: (847) 966-3121
Toll Free: (800) 321-1484
E-mail: info@hammacher.com
Web Site: www.hammacher.com
Approx. Number Employees: 200
Year Founded: 1848
Business Description:
Housewares & Giftware Retailer
S.I.C.: 5961; 5399
N.A.I.C.S.: 454113; 452990
Import Export
Media: 4-5-8-10-13-16
Distr.: Direct to Consumer; Natl.
Budget Set: Monthly
Personnel:
Richard W. Tinberg *(Pres & CEO)*
Heather Zdan *(VP-Mktg)*
Fred Berns *(Gen Mgr-Direct Mktg Exec)*
Robert Bohlin *(Dir-Mdsg)*
Brands & Products:
HAMMACHER SCHLEMMER

HOME CARE INDUSTRIES INC.

1 Lisbon St
Clifton, NJ 07013
Tel.: (973) 365-1600
Fax: (973) 365-1770
Web Site: www.homecareind.com
Sales Range: $75-99.9 Million
Approx. Number Employees: 187
Business Description:
Vacuum Cleaner Bags: Made From Purchased Materials
S.I.C.: 2674; 2393
N.A.I.C.S.: 322224; 314911
Personnel:
Thomas W. Arenz *(Chm)*
Robert Logemann *(Pres & CEO)*
Tony Gigante *(CFO)*
Brands & Products:
ALFCO
CLEAN-SEAL
ELECTRAFLO
MICRO-AIR
MICRO-LINER
QUINTEX

Key to Media (For complete agency information see *The Advertising Red Books-Agencies* edition):
1. Bus. Publs. 2. Cable T.V. 3. Catalogs & Directories. 4. Co-op Adv. 5. Consumer Mags. 6. D.M. to Bus. Estab.7. D.M. to Consumers
8. Daily Newsp. 9. Exhibits/Trade Shows 10. Foreign 11. Infomercial 12. Internet Adv.13. Multimedia 14. Network Radio
15. Network T.V. 16. Newsp. Distr. Mags. 17. Other 18. Outdoor (Posters, Transit) 19. Point of Purchase20. Premiums, Novelties
21. Product Samples 22. Special Events Mktg. 23. Spot Radio 24. Spot T.V. 25. Weekly Newsp. 26. Yellow Page Adv.

Home Care Industries Inc. — (Continued)

SYNTECH

Advertising Agency:
Manhattan Marketing Ensemble
443 Park Ave S 4th Fl
New York, NY 10016-7322
Tel.: (212) 779-2233
Fax: (212) 779-0825

HOME PRODUCTS INTERNATIONAL, INC.

(Holding of Third Avenue Management LLC)
4501 W 47th St
Chicago, IL 60632-4451
Tel.: (773) 890-1010
Fax: (773) 890-0523
Toll Free: (800) 327-3534
E-mail: homzinfo@homz.biz
Web Site: www.homzproducts.com
Sales Range: $350-399.9 Million
Approx. Number Employees: 375
Year Founded: 1952
Business Description:
Mfr of Home Organizational Products
S.I.C.: 5023
N.A.I.C.S.: 423220
Advertising Expenditures: $15,098,000
Media: 5-19-20
Personnel:
George Hamilton *(CEO)*
Dennis Dohney *(CFO)*
Jaci Volles *(Exec VP-Sls & Mktg)*
John Pugh, Jr. *(VP-HR)*
Rita Taylor *(Mgr-Intl Accts)*
Brands & Products:
CORDLOCK
COUNTERPRO
COUNTERTOP
CRYSTAL CLEAR
DRAWCORD
DURA-CHROME STEEL
DURA-COATED STEEL
DURABILT
EASYBOARD
ELITE GOLD
FLIP 'N FRESH
FOUR N' ONE DRY
HAIR TRAPPER
HANG-A-HAMPER
HOMZ
IRONINGPRO
IRONMATE
KIDTIVITY
KLEAR POR
KLEAR STOR
LIL' HELPERS
LOC-LEGS
MEDIUM GRIPPER
MERCHANDISERS
NEOCHROME
PEEL N' STICK
POP-TOP STORABLES
POW'R-GRIP
READYPRESS
REVERSIFIT
SAFETYSTATION
SCORCHSHIELD
SELFIX
SEWINGHELPER
SIMITRE
SLIDE-LOC
SNAPLOCK
SOFT GRIPS
SPACEWORKS
SPACEWORKS FOR BATH
STABLETABLE
STACKER
STAINGUARD
STEAMPRESS
STEEL BATH HARDWARE
STOWAWAYS
STRETCH AND FIT
SUCTION-LOCK SHOWER ORGANIZERS
SUCTIONLOCK
SUNGFIT
SUPERGRIP
SUREFOOT
SUREGRIP
SURELOCK
TAILORED ULTRAFIT
TAMOR
TIDY KIDS
TOWEL GRIP-ITS
TUFF LIL' SQUIRTZ
TWIST AND HOLD
ULTRATHICK
WET N' SET
THE WORKPLACE ROLLING STORAGE

HOMEGOODS, INC.

(Sub. of The TJX Companies, Inc.)
770 Cochituate
Framingham, MA 01701
Tel.: (508) 390-1000
Web Site: www.homegoods.com/press-fact-sheet.asp
Sales Range: $25-49.9 Million
Approx. Number Employees: 100
Year Founded: 1992
Business Description:
Off Price Home Furnishing
S.I.C.: 5719
N.A.I.C.S.: 442299
Advertising Expenditures: $200,000
Distr.: Reg.
Personnel:
Nan Stutz *(Pres)*
Katherine Beede *(VP-Mktg)*
Mary Brogdon *(Mgr-Mktg)*
Advertising Agency:
kirshenbaum bond senecal + partners
160 Varick St 4th Fl
New York, NY 10013
Tel.: (212) 633-0080
Fax: (212) 463-8643
(Creative)

THE HOMER LAUGHLIN CHINA COMPANY

672 Fiesta Dr
Newell, WV 26050-1067
Tel.: (304) 387-1300
Fax: (304) 387-0593
Toll Free: (800) 452-4462
E-mail: hlc@hlchina.com
Web Site: www.hlchina.com
Approx. Number Employees: 1,100
Year Founded: 1871
Business Description:
Mfr. of Lead Free Vitreous China Dinnerware for Hotel, Restaurant, Health Care & Retail Markets
S.I.C.: 3262; 5719
N.A.I.C.S.: 327112; 442299
Export
Media: 2-5-7-8-9-10-18-19-21
Distr.: Intl.; Natl.
Personnel:
Joseph M. Wells, III *(Pres)*
Dave Conley *(Dir-Retail Sls & Mktg)*
Judi Noble *(Dir-Art)*
Ann Culler *(Office Mgr)*
Brands & Products:
ACCENT
ALEXA
ALPENA
ALPHALAIN
AMERICAN ROSE
AMERIWHITE
AMETHYST
AQUA MATE
ARCADIA
ARNO
ATLANTIS
AVILA
BEDFORD
BEST CHINA
BRIGHTON
CALYPSO
CAMBRIDGE
CANYON
CHECKMATE
CHEVRONE
CONFETTI
CONNECTIONS
CORNFLOWER
DESERT WINDS
DYNAMICS
ENERGY
EXPRESSIONS
FABRIQUE
FAIRVIEW
FIESTA
FRENCH VIOLETS
GALA
GENUINE FIESTA ACCESSORIES
GIZA
GOTHIC
HANOVER
HASTINGS
HEARTLAND
HURON
IMPERIA
INDIGO
INVERNESS
JADE
JOSIE
KALAHARI
KAVIR
KELLY
KENSINGTON
KNOSSOS
KOKOPELLIS
LA COSTA
LAME
LEXINGTON
LYDIA
LYRICA
MARLBROUGH
MARTIQUES
MAYFAIR
MELODY
MEMPHIS
MESA
MIKADO
MILFORD
MOCHA
MOJAVE
MONTE CARLO
MONTEREY
MYSTIQUE
NEWPORT
OASIS
OZONE
PARKERTON
PATIO
PESTO
PHOENIX
PINK VIOLETS
PISA
POMPEII
PORTABELLO
PRIME
PRISTINE
PUEBLA
PYRAMID
RENAISSANCE
RIVER MARSH
ROMAN
ROSEMALING
ROSS
ROYALE
SAHARA
SALERNO
SAN REMO
SANTA FE
SARA
SARDINIA
SCRIBBLE
SEA SHELLS
SEVILLE
SHELLS
SILHOUETTE
SIMPLICITY ROSE
SONORAN
SOVONA
ST. TROPEZ
STEPPING OUT
SWEET PEA
THAR
TONES
TOULON
TROPIC SEAS
UNITY
UPTOWN
VICTORIAN VIOLETS
VINEYARD
VINO
VOLLETTA
WESTMINSTER
WOODSTOCK
Advertising Agency:
Benghiat Marketing & Communications
23240 Chagrin Blvd Ste 445
Beachwood, OH 44122
Tel.: (216) 831-8580
Fax: (216) 831-4240

HYDE MANUFACTURING COMPANY

54 Eastford Rd
Southbridge, MA 01550-3604
Tel.: (508) 764-4344
Fax: (508) 765-5250
Toll Free: (800) 872-4933
E-mail: info@hydetools.com
Web Site: www.hydetools.com
Approx. Number Employees: 150
Year Founded: 1917
Business Description:
Mfr. & Distributor of Hand Tools for the Paint, Drywall, Flooring, Masonry & Industrial Knife Markets
S.I.C.: 3423; 3421
N.A.I.C.S.: 332212; 332211
Import Export
Media: 2-4-5-6-10-13
Distr.: Intl.; Natl.
Budget Set: Sept.
Personnel:
Richard B. Hardy *(CEO)*
Robert Scoble *(VP-Sls & Mktg)*

Key to Media (For complete agency information see *The Advertising Red Books-Agencies* edition):
1. Bus. Publs. 2. Cable T.V. 3. Catalogs & Directories. 4. Co-op Adv. 5. Consumer Mags. 6. D.M. to Bus. Estab.7. D.M. to Consumers
8. Daily Newsp. 9. Exhibits/Trade Shows 10. Foreign 11. Infomercial 12. Internet Adv.13. Multimedia 14. Network Radio
15. Network T.V. 16. Newsp. Distr. Mags. 17. Other 18. Outdoor (Posters, Transit) 19. Point of Purchase20. Premiums, Novelties
21. Product Samples 22. Special Events Mktg. 23. Spot Radio 24. Spot T.V. 25. Weekly Newsp, 26. Yellow Page Adv.

Brands & Products:
BLACK & SILVER
CAULK-AWAY PRO
CAULK-RITE PRO
CORNER EASE
FOR A BETTER FINISH, START WITH HYDE.
HAMMER HEAD
HYDE
MAXXGRIP PRO
PAINT MISER
PAINTER'S PYRAMID
RVT
WET & SET

Advertising Agency:
I.P. Hyde
(House Agency)
54 Eastford Rd.
Southbridge, MA 01550
Tel.: (508) 764-4344
(Black & Silver Putty Knives & Scrapers)

IGLOO PRODUCTS CORPORATION
(Sub. of Westar Capital LLC)
777 Igloo Rd
Katy, TX 77494
Mailing Address:
PO Box 19322
Houston, TX 77224-9322
Tel.: (713) 584-6800
Fax: (713) 935-7702
Toll Free: (800) 324-2653
Web Site: www.igloocoolers.com
Sales Range: $200-249.9 Million
Approx. Number Employees: 1,000
Year Founded: 1947
Business Description:
Seat Top Beverage Coolers & Ice Chests, Industrial Plastic & Metal Water Coolers & Heavy-Duty Utility Containers Mfr
S.I.C.: 3086
N.A.I.C.S.: 326140
Import Export
Advertising Expenditures: $1,000,000
Media: 2-4-5-6-7-8-10-19-21
Distr.: Intl.; Natl.
Budget Set: July
Personnel:
James Roberts *(Pres & CEO)*
Sue Miller Payton *(Dir-Mktg)*
Linda Baltus *(Product Mgr)*
Brands & Products:
BAG IT
BUILT FOR THE REAL WORLD
CARGO
COOL CARGO
COOL ROLLER
COOL SACK
COOL SACK DELUXE
DUFFEL COOL
FUNMATE
HAUL ICE
IGLOO
IGLOO BEVERAGE CUBE
IGLOO LUNCH & MUNCH
KOOL KIT
KOOL KLASSIC
KOOL MATE
KOOL SIPPER
LEGEND
LEGEND SIX-PACKER
LITTLE LUNCHMATE
LITTLE PLAYMATE
LUNCH EXPRESS
LUNCHMATE
MARINE ROLLER
MAXCOLD
MESSENGER LUNCH
MINIMATE
PLAYMATE ELITE
PLAYMATE PLUS
PLENTIKOOL
POLARMATE
POP-TOP LUNCH KIT
QUICK & COOL
S'COOLMATE
SOFEMATE
SPACEMATE
TWIN LUNCH KIT
TWO COOL
ULTRATHERM
WHEELIE COOL

THE IRONEES COMPANY
207 Barclay Cir
Cheltenham, PA 19012-1001
Tel.: (215) 782-1516
Fax: (215) 634-8678
Approx. Sls.: $4,000,000
Approx. Number Employees: 140
Year Founded: 1962
Business Description:
Mfr. of Housewares & Domestics
S.I.C.: 2392; 3499
N.A.I.C.S.: 314129; 332999
Media: 2-5-6-8-10-15-20
Distr.: Natl.
Budget Set: Nov.
Brands & Products:
IRONEES
LAUNDRYWARE

JARDEN HOME BRANDS
(Sub. of Hearthmark, LLC)
1800 Cloquet Ave
Cloquet, MN 55720-2141
Tel.: (218) 879-6700
Fax: (800) 777-7943
Toll Free: (800) 777-7942
E-mail: info@diamondbrands.com
Web Site: www.diamondbrands.com
Sales Range: $250-299.9 Million
Approx. Number Employees: 800
Year Founded: 1986
Business Description:
Matches, Barbecue Starters, Toothpicks, Ice Cream & Corn Dog Sticks, Plastic Cutlery & Citronella Mfr
S.I.C.: 3221
N.A.I.C.S.: 327213
Import Export
Media: 1-2-4-6-7-10
Distr.: Natl.
Personnel:
Bill Olson *(CFO)*
Tom Fry *(COO)*
Craig P. Goguen *(Sr VP)*
Brands & Products:
DIAMOND
FORSTER

JOHN BOOS & CO.
(Sub. of JBC Holding Co.)
315 S 1st St
Effingham, IL 62401
Mailing Address:
PO Box 609
Effingham, IL 62401
Tel.: (217) 347-7701
Fax: (217) 347-7705
E-mail: sales@johnboos.com
Web Site: www.johnboos.com
E-Mail For Key Personnel:
Sales Director: sales@johnboos.com
Approx. Number Employees: 110
Year Founded: 1887
Business Description:
Wood Butcher Blocks, Counter Tops & Stainless Steel Kitchen Products Mfr
S.I.C.: 2499; 2421; 2434; 2514; 2531; 3431
N.A.I.C.S.: 321999; 321912; 332998; 337110; 337124; 337127
Import Export
Media: 2-6-10-15
Distr.: Natl.
Budget Set: Nov.
Personnel:
Joseph A. Emmerich *(Pres)*
Brands & Products:
BOOS BLOCKS
CUCINA AMERICANA
PRO-CHEF
TABLE TAILORS

KATY INDUSTRIES, INC.
305 Rock Industrial Park Dr
Bridgeton, MO 63044
Tel.: (314) 656-4321
E-mail: janiecs@concico.com
Web Site: www.katyindustries.com
Approx. Sls.: $141,000,000
Approx. Number Employees: 607
Year Founded: 1968
Business Description:
Household Products Mfr
S.I.C.: 3559; 5063; 5065
N.A.I.C.S.: 332410; 423610; 423690
Import Export
Advertising Expenditures: $600,000
Media: 2-4-5-7-8-10
Distr.: Intl.; Natl.
Budget Set: Dec.
Personnel:
William F. Andrews *(Chm)*
David J. Feldman *(Pres & CEO)*
Robert A. Gail *(Pres-Continental Comml Products)*
Samuel P. Frieder *(Co-Mng Partner)*
Christopher Lacovara *(Co-Mng Partner)*
Christopher Anderson *(Partner)*
Shant Mardirossian *(Partner)*
James W. Shaffer *(CFO, Treas, Sec & VP)*
Edward D. Carter *(VP-Sls & Mktg)*
Joseph E. Mata *(VP-HR)*
Robert Libon *(Mgr-Sls)*
Brands & Products:
BORAXO
BRILLO
KATY
KLEENFAST
LOCKERSTAR
SERVING THE NEEDS OF COMMERCIAL CUSTOMERS
YELLOW JACKET

KENNEDY BROTHERS, INC.
11 N Main St
Vergennes, VT 05491
Tel.: (802) 877-2975
Fax: (802) 877-2977
E-mail: info@kennedy-brothers.com
Web Site: www.kennedy-brothers.com
Approx. Number Employees: 9
Year Founded: 1937
Business Description:
Retailer of Woodenware & Early American Household Accessories
S.I.C.: 6512; 5947
N.A.I.C.S.: 531120; 453220
Export
Media: 2-4-7-9-25
Distr.: Intl.; Natl.
Budget Set: Mar.
Personnel:
Edwin R. Grant *(Pres)*

THE KINGSFORD PRODUCTS COMPANY
(Sub. of The Clorox Company)
1221 Broadway
Oakland, CA 94612-1837
Tel.: (510) 271-7000
Fax: (510) 271-7218
Fax: (510) 832-1463
Web Site: www.kingsford.com
Sales Range: $1-4.9 Billion
Approx. Number Employees: 2,000
Business Description:
Charcoal Briquets, Barbecue Products & Food Products Mfr
S.I.C.: 2861; 2099
N.A.I.C.S.: 325191; 311942
Media: 3-5-6-8-15-18-19-22-23-24
Distr.: Natl.
Brands & Products:
GLAD
KINGSFORD
MATCH LIGHT

KIRK & MATZ LTD.
3390 Denver Dr
Denver, NC 28037
Tel.: (704) 489-8490
Fax: (704) 489-8493
Toll Free: (800) 525-6238
E-mail: awards@kirk-matz.com
Web Site: www.kirk-matz.com
E-Mail For Key Personnel:
Sales Director: sales@kirk-matz.com
Sales Range: $10-24.9 Million
Approx. Number Employees: 15
Year Founded: 1946
Business Description:
Trophies & Awards Whslr
S.I.C.: 5099; 5094
N.A.I.C.S.: 423990; 423940
Import
Media: 4-7-10
Distr.: Intl.; Natl.
Personnel:
Victor Matz *(Pres)*
Brands & Products:
K&M

KIRKLAND'S INC.
2501 McGavock Pike Ste 1000
Nashville, TN 37214
Tel.: (615) 872-4800
Web Site: www.kirklands.com
Approx. Rev.: $415,300,000
Approx. Number Employees: 3,948
Year Founded: 1966
Business Description:
Gift Store Owner & Operator
S.I.C.: 5947; 5999
N.A.I.C.S.: 453220; 453998
Import
Advertising Expenditures: $4,000,000
Media: 6-8
Personnel:
R. Wilson Orr, III *(Chm)*

Key to Media (For complete agency information see *The Advertising Red Books-Agencies* edition):
1. Bus. Publs. 2. Cable T.V. 3. Catalogs & Directories. 4. Co-op Adv. 5. Consumer Mags. 6. D.M. to Bus. Estab.7. D.M. to Consumers 8. Daily Newsp. 9. Exhibits/Trade Shows 10. Foreign 11. Infomercial 12. Internet Adv.13. Multimedia 14. Network Radio 15. Network T.V. 16. Newsp. Distr. Mags. 17. Other 18. Outdoor (Posters, Transit) 19. Point of Purchase20. Premiums, Novelties 21. Product Samples 22. Special Events Mktg. 23. Spot Radio 24. Spot T.V. 25. Weekly Newsp. 26. Yellow Page Adv.

Kirkland's Inc. — (Continued)

Robert E. Alderson *(CEO)*
W. Michael Madden *(CFO & Sr VP)*
Lowell E. Pugh, II *(Gen Counsel, Sec & VP)*
Michelle R. Graul *(Sr VP-HR & Stores)*
Todd A. Weier *(Sr VP-Logistics, Mdse Plng & Allocations)*
Karla Calderon *(VP-Mdsg)*
Adam Holland *(VP-Fin)*
Deborah McDonald *(VP-Mdsg Ops)*

Brands & Products:
KIRKLAND'S
NO BARE WALLS

Advertising Agency:
Communications Associates Marketing, LLC
7051 Hwy 70 S Ste 340
Nashville, TN 37221
Tel.: (615) 662-2999
Fax: (615) 662-2444

LALIQUE NORTH AMERICA

(Affil. of Lalique S.A.)
25 Branca Rd
East Rutherford, NJ 07073
Tel.: (201) 939-4199
Fax: (201) 939-4492
Toll Free: (800) 993-2580
E-mail: info@lalique.com
Web Site: www.cristallalique.fr/v2/
Approx. Number Employees: 60
Year Founded: 1954
Business Description:
French Crystal Distr
S.I.C.: 5023; 5099
N.A.I.C.S.: 423220; 423990
Import
Advertising Expenditures: $1,500,000
Bus. Publs.: $450,000; Catalogs & Directories: $225,000; Consumer Mags.: $375,000; Daily Newsp.: $150,000; Exhibits/Trade Shows: $300,000
Distr.: Natl.
Budget Set: Nov.
Personnel:
George Bonifacio *(Dir-Ops)*

LENOX CORPORATION

(Holding of Clarion Capital Partners, LLC)
1414 Radcliffe St
Bristol, PA 19007-0806
Mailing Address:
PO Box 2006
Bristol, PA 19007-0806
Tel.: (267) 525-7800
Toll Free: (800) 223-4311
Web Site: www.lenox.com
Sales Range: $150-199.9 Million
Approx. Number Employees: 295
Year Founded: 1889
Business Description:
Fine China, Crystal, Flatware, Tableware, Glassware & Giftware Mfr, Distr & Retailer
S.I.C.: 3262; 3229; 5023; 5961
N.A.I.C.S.: 327112; 327212; 423220; 454111
Media: 7-8-9-18
Distr.: Intl.; Natl.
Budget Set: Feb.
Personnel:
Peter Cameron *(CEO)*

Brands & Products:
DANSK
GORHAM
LENOX

LEVOLOR HOME FASHIONS

(Sub. of Newell Rubbermaid Inc.)
3 Glenlake Pkwy NE
Atlanta, GA 30328
Tel.: (678) 404-3300
Fax: (336) 881-5838
Web Site: www.levolor.com
Sales Range: $50-74.9 Million
Approx. Number Employees: 175
Business Description:
Mfr. of Vertical Blinds
S.I.C.: 2591
N.A.I.C.S.: 337920
Personnel:
Kristie Juster *(Pres)*

Advertising Agencies:
Corder Philips, Inc.
508 W 5th St Ste 100
Charlotte, NC 28202
Tel.: (704) 333-3924
Fax: (704) 358-0134
Media Buying

Woodbine
210 S Cherry St
Winston Salem, NC 27101-5231
Tel.: (336) 724-0450
Fax: (336) 724-6725

LIBBEY, INC.

300 Madison Ave
Toledo, OH 43604
Mailing Address:
PO Box 10060
Toledo, OH 43699-0060
Tel.: (419) 325-2100
Tel.: (419) 325-2445
Fax: (419) 325-2793
E-mail: info@libbey.com
Web Site: www.libbey.com
Approx. Rev.: $801,584,000
Approx. Number Employees: 7,005
Year Founded: 1888
Business Description:
Mfr & Marketer of Glass Tableware, Metal Flatware & Ceramic Dinnerware
S.I.C.: 3262; 3229; 3421
N.A.I.C.S.: 327112; 327212; 332211
Advertising Expenditures: $200,000
Media: 4-5-20-21
Personnel:
John F. Meier *(Chm & CEO)*
Richard I. Reynolds *(CFO & Exec VP)*
Scott M. Sellick *(Chief Acctg Officer & VP)*
Susan A. Kovach *(Gen Counsel & VP)*
Roberto Rubio Barnes *(VP-Mfg & Engrg-Global)*
Daniel P. Ibele *(VP-Sls & Mktg-Global)*

Brands & Products:
LIBBEY

Advertising Agency:
Marcus Thomas LLC
24865 Emery Rd
Cleveland, OH 44128
Tel.: (216) 292-4700
Fax: (216) 378-0396
Toll Free: (888) 482-4455

LIFETIME BRANDS, INC.

1000 Stewart Ave
Garden City, NY 11530
Tel.: (516) 683-6000
Fax: (516) 683-6116
Web Site: www.lifetimebrands.com
Approx. Sls.: $443,171,000
Approx. Number Employees: 1,040
Year Founded: 1983
Business Description:
Household Cutlery, Kitchenware, Cutting Board, Pantryware & Bakeware Designer, Marketer & Distr
S.I.C.: 3469; 3421; 5023; 5072
N.A.I.C.S.: 332214; 332211; 423220; 423710
Import Export
Advertising Expenditures: $775,000
Media: 2-4-6-8-9-11-20-26
Distr.: Natl.
Personnel:
Ronald Shiftan *(Vice Chm)*
Jeffrey Siegel *(Pres & CEO)*
Laurence Winoker *(CFO)*
Evan Miller *(Pres-Sls & Exec VP)*
Robert Reichenbach *(Pres-Cutlery/ Cutting Boards/Bakeware-At-Home Entert Div & Exec VP)*
Jeffrey M. Berman *(Pres-Retail Direct)*
Larry Sklute *(Pres-Kitchenware)*
Craig Phillips *(Sr VP-Distr)*
Heather Scholl *(VP-Mktg)*

Brands & Products:
CASAMODA
FARBERWARE
HOFFRITZ
LIFETIME BRANDS
MIKASA
PFALTZGRAFF
TRISTAR

LINCOLN FOODSERVICE PRODUCTS, LLC

(Sub. of Manitowoc Foodservice USA)
1111 N Hadley Rd
Fort Wayne, IN 46804-5540
Mailing Address:
PO Box 1229
Fort Wayne, IN 46801-1229
Tel.: (260) 459-8200
Fax: (260) 436-0735
E-mail: mfincher@lincolnfp.com
Web Site: www.lincolnfp.com
Approx. Sls.: $57,000,000
Approx. Number Employees: 330
Year Founded: 1957
Business Description:
Commercial Food Service Aluminum Cookware, Slicers, Dicers, Wedgers & Air Impingement Ovens Mfr
S.I.C.: 3556
N.A.I.C.S.: 333294
Import Export
Advertising Expenditures: $650,000
Media: 2-4-10
Distr.: Intl.; Natl.
Personnel:
Gary Dykstra *(VP & Gen Mgr-Lincoln Foodservice)*
Derek Walz *(VP-Engrg)*
Sandy Hyndman *(Mgr-Mktg)*

Brands & Products:
CAN MASTER
CENTURION
CHEESE BLOCKER
CUBE KING
FRESH-O-MATIC
GRILL TENDER
IMPINGER
INSTA-BLEND
INSTA-BLOOM
INSTA-SLICE
KING KUTTER
LETTUCE KING I
LETTUCE KING IV
LINCOLN
LOBSTER KING
ONION KING
OYSTER KING
REDCO
TATER KING
TOMATO KING
TOMATO PRO
WEAREVER
WEDGEMASTER

THE LONGABERGER COMPANY

1500 E Main St
Newark, OH 43055-8847
Tel.: (740) 322-5000
Fax: (740) 322-5240
E-mail: info@longaberger.com
Web Site: www.longaberger.com
Sales Range: $900-999.9 Million
Approx. Number Employees: 7,300
Year Founded: 1973
Business Description:
Handcrafted Baskets, Pottery & Home Decor Items Mfr & Marketer
S.I.C.: 2499; 3262
N.A.I.C.S.: 321999; 327112
Media: 8-10-22
Personnel:
Tami Longaberger *(Chm & CEO)*
David K. Bishop *(Exec Dir-Digital Mktg)*

Brands & Products:
AMERICAN CELEBRATIONS
AMERICAN HOME
BOTANICAL FIELDS
BOTANICAL WEAVE LARGE BOARDWALK
COLLECTORS CLUB
COLLECTORS CLUB TAMI LONGABERGER HERITAGE SERIES
FLORA
JOHN DEERE
LARGE BOARDWALK
LARGE DESKTOP
LARGE RECIPE
LONGABERGER
LONGABERGER TO GO
MASTER'S STUDIO FLARE
SMALL OVAL GATHERING
SPRING
TALL TISSUE
TV TIME
VANITY
WOODCRAFTS
WORK-A-ROUND
WOVEN TRADITIONS

LTL HOME PRODUCTS, INC.

125 Rt 61 S
Schuylkill Haven, PA 17972
Tel.: (570) 385-5470
Fax: (570) 385-5475
E-mail: customer.service@ltlhomeproducts.com
Web Site: www.ltlhomeproducts.com
Approx. Sls.: $24,000,000
Approx. Number Employees: 65
Year Founded: 1989

Key to Media (For complete agency information see *The Advertising Red Books-Agencies* edition):
1. Bus. Publs. 2. Cable T.V. 3. Catalogs & Directories. 4. Co-op Adv. 5. Consumer Mags. 6. D.M. to Bus. Estab.7. D.M. to Consumers 8. Daily Newsp. 9. Exhibits/Trade Shows 10. Foreign 11. Infomercial 12. Internet Adv.13. Multimedia 14. Network Radio 15. Network T.V. 16. Newsp. Distr. Mags. 17. Other 18. Outdoor (Posters, Transit) 19. Point of Purchase20. Premiums, Novelties 21. Product Samples 22. Special Events Mktg. 23. Spot Radio 24. Spot T.V. 25. Weekly Newsp. 26. Yellow Page Adv.

Business Description:
Home Products Mfr & Distr
S.I.C.: 5031; 5072
N.A.I.C.S.: 423310; 423710
Media: 4-13
Personnel:
Malcolm Groff *(Pres)*
Brands & Products:
ANCHOR SYSTEM
EXPRESS ONE
EXPRESS ONE PLUS
GROUNDMASTER
GROUNDTECH
INNOVATIVE IDEAS FOR EASIER LIVING
LTL
PINECROFT
SPECTRUM
TUFFSPIKE
WALLSCAPES

MACK MILLER CANDLE CO., INC.

202 Sheridan Rd
Liverpool, NY 13090
Tel.: (315) 453-9665
Toll Free: (800) 522-6353
E-mail: mackmiller98@verizon.net
Web Site: mysite.verizon.net/vzeecmkb/
Approx. Number Employees: 4
Year Founded: 1898
Business Description:
Ecclesiastical Candles, Accessories & Liquid Paraffin Retailer
S.I.C.: 5199
N.A.I.C.S.: 424990
Media: 7
Distr.: Reg.
Budget Set: June

MAGLA PRODUCTS, LLC

159 S St
Morristown, NJ 07960
Mailing Address:
PO Box -1934
Morristown, NJ 07962-1934
Tel.: (973) 984-7998
Fax: (973) 984-2382
Toll Free: (800) 247-5281
E-mail: jglatt@magla.com
Web Site: www.magla.com
E-Mail For Key Personnel:
Marketing Director: sgolub@magla.com
Sales Range: $25-49.9 Million
Approx. Number Employees: 18
Year Founded: 1950
Business Description:
Cleaning Accessories Mfr
S.I.C.: 5722
N.A.I.C.S.: 443111
Media: 2-7-10
Distr.: Intl.; Natl.
Budget Set: Sept.
Personnel:
Herbert Glatt *(Founder)*
Jordan Glatt *(Owner)*
Alison Carpinello *(CFO & VP)*
Steve Golub *(VP-Mktg)*
Brands & Products:
ANTIVIBE
EASY WIPES
EXTRA HANDS
HAND HELPERS
ICLEAN
LOVING HANDS
MAGLA
MAGLA TOUCH
NYPLEX
PUT YOUR HANDS IN OUR BRANDS

MEADWESTVACO CALMAR

(Unit of MeadWestvaco Corporation)
11901 Grandview Rd
Grandview, MO 64030
Mailing Address:
PO Box 1203
La Puente, CA 91749-1203
Tel.: (816) 986-6027
Tel.: (816) 986-6000
Fax: (816) 986-6010
Toll Free: (800) 599-2124
E-mail: calmar@meadwestvaco.com
Web Site: www.calmar.com
Sales Range: $400-449.9 Million
Approx. Number Employees: 1,600
Year Founded: 1942
Business Description:
Sprayers & Dispensers for Liquid Dispensing Systems Mfr
S.I.C.: 3089
N.A.I.C.S.: 326199
Import Export
Advertising Expenditures: $450,000
Media: 2-4-5-6-7-9-10-11-18-19-20-21-23-24
Distr.: Intl.; Natl.
Budget Set: June -Aug.
Personnel:
John McKernan *(Pres)*
Francois Gilbert *(CFO)*
Mark Frey *(VP-Sls & Mktg)*
Earl Trout *(Dir-Mktg, Personal & Beauty Care)*
Becky Harner *(Product Mgr)*
Bob Bakas *(Mgr-Mktg)*
Brands & Products:
DISPLAY SAFE
SHIPSAFE

MICHAELS STORES, INC.

(Joint Venture of The Blackstone Group L.P. & Bain Capital, LLC)
8000 Bent Branch Dr
Irving, TX 75234
Mailing Address:
PO Box 619566
Dallas, TX 75261-9566
Tel.: (972) 409-1300
Fax: (972) 409-1556
Toll Free: (800) 642-4235
E-mail: custhelp@michaels.com
Web Site: www.michaels.com
Approx. Sls.: $4,031,000,000
Approx. Number Employees: 10,900
Year Founded: 1984
Business Description:
Arts & Crafts, Frames & Floral Items Retailer
S.I.C.: 5949; 5945; 5999
N.A.I.C.S.: 451130; 451120; 453998
Import
Advertising Expenditures: $172,000,000
Media: 6-8-9-16-23-24-25
Distr.: Intl.; Natl.
Budget Set: July
Personnel:
John Bruce Menzer *(CEO)*
Charles M. Sonsteby *(CFO & Chief Admin Officer)*
Michael J. Jones *(CIO)*
Paula A. Puleo *(CMO)*
Michael J. Veitenheimer *(Gen Counsel, Sec & Sr VP)*
Nicholas E. Crombie *(Exec VP-Store Ops)*
Thomas C. DeCaro *(Exec VP-Supply Chain)*
Philo T. Pappas *(Exec VP-Mdsg)*
Weizhong Zhu *(Exec VP-Private Brands & Global Sourcing)*
Shawn E. Hearn *(Sr VP-HR)*
Richard S. Jablonski *(Controller & VP-Fin)*
Anthony Price *(Sr Dir-Digital Mktg & PR)*
Robert Freeman *(Mgr-Digital Mktg, PR & Social Media)*
Brands & Products:
THE ARTS AND CRAFTS STORE
MICHAEL'S
VILLAGE CRAFTS BY MICHAELS
Advertising Agencies:
American Communications Group, Inc.
21311 Madrona Ave Ste 101
Torrance, CA 90503
Tel.: (310) 530-4100
— Christopher Cope *(Acct Exec)*
— Bill Gamble *(Acct Exec)*

Empower MediaMarketing
(MEDIA THAT WORKS)
1111 Saint Gregory St
Cincinnati, OH 45202
Tel.: (513) 871-9454
Fax: (513) 871-1804
— Laura Nix *(Acct Exec)*

MILWAUKEE DUSTLESS BRUSH COMPANY

6247 Randolph St
Los Angeles, CA 90040-3514
Tel.: (323) 724-7777
Fax: (323) 724-1111
Toll Free: (800) 632-3220
E-mail: sales@milwaukeedustless.com
Web Site:
www.milwaukeedustless.com
E-Mail For Key Personnel:
Sales Director: sales@milwaukeedustless.com
Approx. Sls.: $5,000,000
Approx. Number Employees: 50
Year Founded: 1897
Business Description:
Mfr of Floor Brushes, Custom Built Industrial Brushes & Street Sweeper Brooms
S.I.C.: 3991
N.A.I.C.S.: 339994
Import Export
Media: 2-4-7-10-17-19
Distr.: Direct to Consumer; Natl.
Budget Set: Nov.
Personnel:
Bill Loitz *(Mgr)*
Kenneth Rakusin *(Mgr)*
Brands & Products:
FLEX SQUEEGY
PERMA POLY
SCRUB TEX
SPEED SQUEEGY
SPEED SWEEP
SPEED WASH
SPEEDY CORN
SPEEDY MOP

MUENCH-KREUZER CANDLE COMPANY

617 E Hiawaatha
Syracuse, NY 13221-4969
Tel.: (315) 471-4515
Fax: (315) 471-4581
Toll Free: (800) 448-7884
Approx. Number Employees: 100
Year Founded: 1925
Business Description:
Mfr & Distr of Church Products
S.I.C.: 3999
N.A.I.C.S.: 339999
Media: 2-4-7-10-13-17-21-25
Distr.: Natl.
Budget Set: Feb.
Personnel:
John P. Brogan *(Chm)*
Roland Devore *(Pres & Mgr-Mktg)*
Renee Roy *(VP-Sls)*
Brands & Products:
ABBEY BRAND
EMKAY
MORGAN

MW MANUFACTURERS INC.

(Sub. of Ply Gem Industries, Inc.)
433 N Main St PO Box 559
Rocky Mount, VA 24151
Tel.: (540) 483-0211
Fax: (540) 484-6392
Toll Free: (800) 999-8400
E-mail: info@mwwindows.com
Web Site: www.mwwindows.com
Approx. Number Employees: 1,200
Year Founded: 1939
Business Description:
Windows, Doors & Building Materials Mfr
S.I.C.: 2431; 3442
N.A.I.C.S.: 321911; 332321
Media: 2-4-6-10-19-20-21
Distr.: Natl.
Budget Set: Oct.
Personnel:
Lynn Morstad *(Pres)*
Brands & Products:
FREEDOM
JEFFERSON
TWINSEAL
V WOOD

NATIONAL PRESTO INDUSTRIES, INC

3925 N Hastings Way
Eau Claire, WI 54703-0485
Tel.: (715) 839-2121
Fax: (715) 839-2122
E-mail: inventions@gopresto.com
Web Site: www.gopresto.com
Approx. Sls.: $479,000,000
Approx. Number Employees: 1,053
Year Founded: 1905
Business Description:
Housewares & Related Products
S.I.C.: 3433; 3556; 3634
N.A.I.C.S.: 333414; 333294; 335211
Import Export
Advertising Expenditures: $9,000
Media: 3-13-15-19
Distr.: Natl.
Budget Set: Apr.
Personnel:
Maryjo Cohen *(Pres)*
Randy F. Lieble *(CFO, Treas & VP)*
Donald E. Hoeschen *(VP-Sls)*
Larry Teinor *(VP-Engrg)*

Key to Media (For complete agency information see *The Advertising Red Books-Agencies* edition):
1. Bus. Publs. 2. Cable T.V. 3. Catalogs & Directories. 4. Co-op Adv. 5. Consumer Mags. 6. D.M. to Bus. Estab.7. D.M. to Consumers 8. Daily Newsp. 9. Exhibits/Trade Shows 10. Foreign 11. Infomercial 12. Internet Adv.13. Multimedia 14. Network Radio 15. Network T.V. 16. Newsp. Distr. Mags. 17. Other 18. Outdoor (Posters, Transit) 19. Point of Purchase20. Premiums, Novelties 21. Product Samples 22. Special Events Mktg. 23. Spot Radio 24. Spot T.V. 25. Weekly Newsp. 26. Yellow Page Adv.

National Presto Industries, Inc — (Continued)

Brands & Products:
ABOVEALL
CONTROL MASTER
COOLDADDY
DIAMONDCOAT
DUALDADDY
EVERNU
EVERSHARP
FRYBABY
FRYDADDY
GRANPAPPY
GRILL-N-LITE
HEATDISH
KITCHEN KETTLE
LIDDLE GRIDDLE
MIXER TOO SALADSHOOTER
ORIGINAL SALADSHOOTER
PIZZAZZ
POPCORNNOW
POPLITE
POWERBASE
POWERCRISP
POWERCUP
POWERPOP
PRESTO
PRESTO ORVILLE REDENBACHER
PRESTO PRIDE
PRESTOBURGER
PROFESSIONAL SALADSHOOTER PLUS
PROFRY
SAPPHIRITE
SCANDINAVIAN DESIGN
SLOWCOOK'NMORE

NEWELL RUBBERMAID INC.

3 Glenlake Pkwy
Atlanta, GA 30328
Tel.: (770) 418-7000
Fax: (770) 407-3970
Web Site:
www.newellrubbermaid.com
Approx. Sls.: $5,759,200,000
Approx. Number Employees: 19,400
Year Founded: 1902
Business Description:
Housewares, Hardware, Home Furnishings, Juvenile Products, Hair Products & Office Products Mfr
S.I.C.: 3089; 3082; 3423; 3631
N.A.I.C.S.: 326199; 326121; 332212; 335221
Export
Advertising Expenditures: $152,900,000
Media: 2-3-4-5-6-7-10-15-20-24
Distr.: Natl.
Budget Set: Dec.
Personnel:
Michael T. Cowhig *(Chm)*
Michael B. Polk *(CEO)*
Juan R. Figuereo *(CFO & Exec VP)*
Gordon C. Steele *(CIO & Sr VP-Program Mgmt)*
Theodore W. Woehrle *(CMO & Sr VP)*
Hartley D. Blaha *(Pres-Corp Dev)*
Paul G. Boitmann *(Pres-Global Sls Ops)*
William A Burke, III *(Pres-Tools, Hardware & Comml Products)*
Jay D. Gould *(Pres-Home & Family)*
G. Penny McIntyre *(Pres-Office Products)*
J. Eduardo Senf *(Pres-International)*
John Stipancich *(Gen Counsel, Sec & Sr VP)*
James M. Sweet *(Exec VP-HR)*
Robert Block *(VP-Res, Design & Tech)*
Joe Ketter *(VP-Corp HR)*
Alisha Pennix *(Sr Mgr-IR)*
Christin Hartsfield *(Brand Mgr)*

Brands & Products:
AMEROCK
BERNZOMATIC
BLUE ICE
BRANDS THAT MATTER
BRUTE
BULLDOG
CALPHALON
CARDSCAN
DYMO
ENDICIA
EXPO
GOODY
GRACO
KIRSCH
LENOX
LEVOLOR
MARATHON
MIMIO
PAPER MATE
PARKER
PELOUZE
QUICK-GRIP
ROLODEX
ROUGHNECK
RUBBERMAID
SANFORD
SHARPIE
SHUR-LINE
STAIN SHIELD
TAKEALONGS
TOUGH TOOLS
VISE-GRIP
WATERMAN

Advertising Agencies:
Draftfcb
101 E Erie St
Chicago, IL 60611
Tel.: (312) 425-5000
Fax: (312) 425-5010

Ketchum
(Part of Omnicom)
1285 Ave of the Americas
New York, NY 10019
Tel.: (646) 935-3900
Fax: (646) 935-4482
Public Relations AOR for Technology Global Business Unit

McCann Erickson Worldwide
622 3rd Ave
New York, NY 10017-6707
Tel.: (646) 865-2000
Fax: (646) 487-9610
Creative AOR for Technology Global Business Unit

NORTHLAND ALUMINUM PRODUCTS INC.

5005 County Rd 25
Minneapolis, MN 55416-2274
Tel.: (952) 920-2888
Fax: (952) 924-8530
Toll Free: (800) 328-4310
Web Site: www.nordicware.com
Approx. Sls.: $17,000,000
Approx. Number Employees: 200
Year Founded: 1946
Business Description:
Cookware, Bakeware, Barbecue & Microwave Accessories Mfr
S.I.C.: 3089; 3365
N.A.I.C.S.: 326199; 331524
Import Export
Advertising Expenditures: $2,000,000
Media: 1-2-3-4-5-6-7-8-9-10-11-13-16-19-20-23-24-25
Distr.: Intl.; Natl.
Personnel:
H. David Dalquist, Jr. *(Pres & CEO)*
Wayne Adriaenn *(Dir-Mktg)*
Reed Winter *(Mgr-Mktg)*
Brands & Products:
BUNDT
GEMSTONE
MICRO-GO-ROUND
MICROWARE
NORDIC WARE
OVEN ESSENTIALS
SIZZLIN' SKILLET

OLFA NORTH AMERICA

(Sub. of World Kitchen LLC)
5500 North Pearl St Ste 400
Rosemont, IL 60018
Tel.: (847) 233-8656 (Mktg)
Fax: (800) 685-3950
Toll Free: (800) 962-6532
E-mail: olfainfo@worldkitchen.com
Web Site: www.olfa.com
Sales Range: $10-24.9 Million
Approx. Number Employees: 39
Year Founded: 1967
Business Description:
Mfr. & Distr of Utility Knives, Specialty Cutters & Blades
S.I.C.: 5719
N.A.I.C.S.: 442299
Import Export
Advertising Expenditures: $180,000
Media: 4-6-8-9-14-16-17-19-23-24-25
Distr.: Intl.; Natl.
Personnel:
Joe Mallof *(CEO)*
Sarah Meltzer *(Assoc Brand Mgr)*
Brands & Products:
BEST MADE CUTTING TOOLS IN THE WORLD
FLEX-GUARD
HANDSAVER
OLFA
OLO
PRO-LOAD

ONEIDA LTD

163-181 Kenwood Ave
Oneida, NY 13421
Tel.: (315) 361-3000
Fax: (315) 361-3700
Web Site: www.oneida.com
Approx. Rev.: $350,819,000
Approx. Number Employees: 690
Year Founded: 1880
Business Description:
Flatware, Crystal Giftware & Stemware, Cutlery & China Dinnerware Mfr & Distr
S.I.C.: 3421; 3231; 3262; 3911; 3914
N.A.I.C.S.: 332211; 327112; 327215; 339911; 339912
Import Export
Advertising Expenditures: $862,000
Media: 2-4-5-7-8-10-11-15-19-20-25
Distr.: Intl.; Natl.
Budget Set: Jan.
Personnel:
James E. Joseph *(Pres & CEO)*
Andrew G. Church *(COO)*
Foster Sullivan *(Pres-Foodservice Div)*
Catherine H. Suttmeier *(Gen Counsel)*
Paul E. Gebhardt *(Sr VP-Design & Adv)*
Bill Grannis *(Sr VP-Global Procurement)*
Brands & Products:
1881
ACT I
AFFECTION
AMERICAN HARMONY
ANASTASIA
APOLLO
AQUARIUS
ARBOR ROSE
ARIA
ASTRAGAL
ASTRID
AUSTERE
AXIS
BELCOURT
BELLINI
BIRMINGHAM
BUFFALO
CANTATA
CAPELLO
CENTIGRADE
CHATEAU
COLONIAL BOSTON
COLOSSEUM
COMMUNITY
CORELLI
CORONATION
DANUBE
DELCO
DELMONICO
DI VINCI
DICKINSON
DISTINCTION
DONIZETTI
DOVER
EASTON
EMERY
EQUATOR
ETAGE
FLIGHT
FLORENCE
FORTE
FROST
GRAND MAJESTY
HEIRLOOM
HYANNIS
IMPLUSE
INTERLUDE
ISLET
JUILLIARD
JULIET
KENSINGTON
KENWOOD
KING JAMES
LOUISIANA
MAJESTICWARE
MARQUETTE
MASCAGNI
MERCUTIO
METROPOLIS
MICHAELANGELO
MIDNIGHT
MIDTOWNE
MODERNE
OBELUS
OLYMPIA
ONEIDA

Key to Media (For complete agency information see *The Advertising Red Books-Agencies* edition):
1. Bus. Publs. 2. Cable T.V. 3. Catalogs & Directories. 4. Co-op Adv. 5. Consumer Mags. 6. D.M. to Bus. Estab.7. D.M. to Consumers 8. Daily Newsp. 9. Exhibits/Trade Shows 10. Foreign 11. Infomercial 12. Internet Adv.13. Multimedia 14. Network Radio 15. Network T.V. 16. Newsp. Distr. Mags. 17. Other 18. Outdoor (Posters, Transit) 19. Point of Purchase20. Premiums, Novelties 21. Product Samples 22. Special Events Mktg. 23. Spot Radio 24. Spot T.V. 25. Weekly Newsp. 26. Yellow Page Adv.

ONEIDAWARE
OTHENIA
PARADOX
PAUL REVERE
PERPETUA
PLATINUM PLUME
POPPY
POST ROAD
PROSE
PUCCINI
QUANTUM
RADIUS
RAYAL MANOR
RCR
REFLECTIONS
ROGERS
SAINT ANDREA
SAKURA
SAND DUNE
SANT' ANDREA
SATIN ACCENT
SATIN CAMBER
SATIN CANTATA
SATIN DOVER
SATIN DRIFTWOOD
SATIN ETAGE
SATIN LINEA
SATIN ROSSINI
SATIN SAXON
SATIN SCOOP
SATIN TAHITA
SATIN TRIBECA
SATIN WOODCREST
SATINIQUE
SCARLATTI
SCHOTT
SESTINA
SHERATON
SONNET
SP
SPINELLE
SPIRO
ST. MORITZ
STILETTO
STRAUSS
SWING
TARAZA
TORSADA
TORSADE
TRIBECA
UNITY
VECTRA
VERDI

Advertising Agencies:
Jay Advertising, Inc.
(A Subsidiary of The Interpublic Group of Companies)
170 Linden Oaks
Rochester, NY 14625-2836
Tel.: (585) 264-3600
Fax: (585) 264-3650
Toll Free: (800) 836-6800

Kenwood Advertising Inc.
Kenwood Station
Oneida, NY 13421
Tel.: (315) 361-3000

PITCO FRIALATOR INC.
(Sub. of Blodgett Oven Company Inc)
509 Route 3A
Bow, NH 03304-3102
Mailing Address:
PO Box 501
Concord, NH 03302-0501
Tel.: (603) 225-6684
Fax: (603) 225-8472
Toll Free: (800) 258-3708
E-mail: info@pitco.com
Web Site: www.pitco.com
Sales Range: $75-99.9 Million
Approx. Number Employees: 200
Year Founded: 1918
Business Description:
Commercial Frying Systems Mfr
S.I.C.: 3589
N.A.I.C.S.: 333319
Export
Media: 1-2-4-8-10-17
Distr.: Natl.
Brands & Products:
PITCO FRIALATOR
SOLSTICE

POLAR WARE COMPANY
502 Hwy 67
Kiel, WI 53042
Tel.: (920) 458-3561
Fax: (920) 894-7029
Toll Free: (800) 237-3655
E-mail: customerservice@polarware.com
Web Site: www.polarware.com
Approx. Number Employees: 150
Year Founded: 1907
Business Description:
Mfr. of Stainless Steel Utensils & Deep Drawn Stainless Steel Components
S.I.C.: 3469; 3431
N.A.I.C.S.: 332116; 332998
Import Export
Advertising Expenditures: $200,000
Consumer Mags.: $100,000; Other: $100,000
Distr.: Intl.; Natl.
Budget Set: Oct.
Personnel:
Walter Vollrath, III *(CEO)*
Tom Dinolfo *(CFO)*
Brands & Products:
ADVANTEDGE
THE EDGE
GRIP-N-LIFT
POLAR WARE

PORTLAND WILLAMETTE
(Sub. of Portland Willamette)
6800 NE 59th Pl
Portland, OR 97218-2714
Tel.: (503) 288-7511
Fax: (503) 288-8655
Toll Free: (800) 288-7511
Web Site: www.portwill.com
Approx. Number Employees: 125
Year Founded: 1946
Business Description:
Fireplace Equipment
S.I.C.: 3429
N.A.I.C.S.: 332510
Import Export
Advertising Expenditures: $350,000
Consumer Mags.: $140,000; D.M. to Bus. Estab.: $70,000; Exhibits/Trade Shows: $140,000
Distr.: Intl.; Natl.
Budget Set: Oct.
Personnel:
John L. Boire *(Gen Mgr)*
Brands & Products:
AMPLIFIRE
GLASSFYRE
MODERNSCREEN
PORTLAND GLASS FIRESCREEN
ULTRA FYRE GAS INSERTS
ULTRA FYRE GAS LOGS

RCLC, INC.
3 Ronson Rd
Woodridge, NJ 07095
Tel.: (732) 636-2430
Tel.: (732) 469-8300
Fax: (732) 563-2246
Fax: (800) 839-6904
Toll Free: (888) 5-RONSON
E-mail: info@ronsoncorp.com
Web Site: www.ronsoncorp.com
Approx. Number Employees: 91
Year Founded: 1895
Business Description:
Holding Company; Lighter Accessories Mfr; Aircraft Repair & Maintenance
S.I.C.: 6719; 2899; 3429; 3499; 5162
N.A.I.C.S.: 551112; 325998; 332439; 332510; 424610
Import Export
Advertising Expenditures: $104,000
Media: 4-6-7-13-19
Distr.: Natl.
Budget Set: Sept.
Personnel:
Louis V. Aronson, II *(Pres & CEO)*
Daryl K. Holcomb *(CFO)*
Erwin M. Ganz *(Treas & Asst Sec)*
Brands & Products:
AERO TORCH
AMEROFLAME
AMEROLITE
COMET
EURO LITE
JETLITE
KLEENOL
MULTI-FILL
MULTI-LUBE
RONII
RONSON
RONSONOL
STARDUST
TECH TORCH
WINDII
WINDLITE
THE WORLD'S GREATEST LIGHTER

RECKITT BENCKISER INC.
(Sub. of Reckitt Benckiser plc)
Morris Corp Ctr IV 399 Interpace Pkwy
Parsippany, NJ 07054
Mailing Address:
PO Box 225
Parsippany, NJ 07054-0225
Tel.: (973) 404-2600
Fax: (973) 404-5700
Toll Free: (800) 333-3899
Web Site: www.reckittbenckiser.com
Approx. Number Employees: 400
Business Description:
Mfr & Distr of Food & Household Consumer Products
S.I.C.: 2842; 2035
N.A.I.C.S.: 325612; 311941
Import Export
Media: 2-3-6-9-15-17-18-23-24
Distr.: Natl.
Budget Set: Aug.
Personnel:
Bart Becht *(CEO)*
Freddy Caspers *(Exec VP-Developing Markets)*
Robert de Groot *(Exec VP-North America & Australia)*
Alex Whitehouse *(VP-Mktg)*
Jiri Kulik *(Gen Mgr-Household Mktg)*
Matthew Leung *(Dir-Adv)*
David J. Long *(Dir)*
Alan Cheung *(Brand Mgr-Lysol-Hand Hygiene)*
David Bernardino *(Sr Brand Mgr)*
Ashwini Dumaswala *(Sr Brand Mgr-Veet)*
Advertising Agency:
Euro RSCG Worldwide
350 Hudson St
New York, NY 10014-4504
Tel.: (212) 886-2000
Fax: (212) 886-2016
Toll Free: (800) 937-0233
(French's Mustard)

RED GOAT DISPOSERS - UNITED SERVICE EQUIPMENT
(Div. of Standex Food Service Equipment Group)
914 Ridgely Rd
Murfreesboro, TN 37129
Mailing Address:
PO Box 20428
Murfreesboro, TN 37129-0428
Tel.: (615) 893-8432
Fax: (877) 876-9665
Toll Free: (800) 251-4232
E-mail: rginfo@useco.com
Web Site: www.redgoat.com
Sales Range: $10-24.9 Million
Approx. Number Employees: 6
Year Founded: 1939
Business Description:
Mfr. of Commercial Food Processors, Choppers, Grinders, Food Waste Disposers, Food Mixers & Slicers
S.I.C.: 5033
N.A.I.C.S.: 423330
Media: 2-5-10-20
Distr.: Intl.; Natl.
Budget Set: May-June
Brands & Products:
GENERAL SLICING
USCO

REED & BARTON CORPORATION
144 W Britannia St
Taunton, MA 02780-1634
Tel.: (508) 824-6611
Fax: (508) 822-7269
Toll Free: (800) 343-1383
Telex: 753535
E-mail: information@reedbarton.com
Web Site: www.reedbarton.com
Approx. Number Employees: 488
Year Founded: 1824
Business Description:
Manufactures Silverware
S.I.C.: 3914; 5094
N.A.I.C.S.: 339912; 423940
Import
Advertising Expenditures: $1,980,000
Catalogs & Directories: $200,000; Co-op Adv.: $1,300,000; Consumer Mags.: $100,000; D.M. to Consumers: $200,000; Exhibits/Trade Shows: $60,000; Point of Purchase: $100,000; Weekly Newsp.: $20,000
Distr.: Natl.
Budget Set: Nov.
Brands & Products:
THE CLASSIC AMERICAN SILVER
MILLER/ROGASKA
R AND B EVERYDAY
REED & BARTON HANDCRAFTED CHESTS

Key to Media (For complete agency information see *The Advertising Red Books-Agencies* edition):
1. Bus. Publs. 2. Cable T.V. 3. Catalogs & Directories. 4. Co-op Adv. 5. Consumer Mags. 6. D.M. to Bus. Estab.7. D.M. to Consumers 8. Daily Newsp. 9. Exhibits/Trade Shows 10. Foreign 11. Infomercial 12. Internet Adv.13. Multimedia 14. Network Radio 15. Network T.V. 16. Newsp. Distr. Mags. 17. Other 18. Outdoor (Posters, Transit) 19. Point of Purchase20. Premiums, Novelties 21. Product Samples 22. Special Events Mktg. 23. Spot Radio 24. Spot T.V. 25. Weekly Newsp. 26. Yellow Page Adv.

REGAL WARE, INC.
1675 Reigle Dr
Kewaskum, WI 53040-8923
Tel.: (262) 626-2121
Fax: (262) 626-8565
E-mail: cookware@regalware.com
Web Site: www.regalware.com
Sales Range: $50-74.9 Million
Approx. Number Employees: 800
Year Founded: 1945
Business Description:
Cookware, Kitchen Accessories & Home Water & Air Filters Mfr
S.I.C.: 3634; 3469
N.A.I.C.S.: 335211; 332214
Import Export
Advertising Expenditures: $317,000
Multimedia: $5,500; Bus. Publs.: $15,000; Catalogs & Directories: $75,000; Exhibits/Trade Shows: $200,000; Foreign: $10,000; Point of Purchase: $10,000; Premiums, Novelties: $1,500
Distr.: Direct to Consumer; Intl.; Natl.
Budget Set: July-Aug.
Personnel:
Jeffrey A. Reigle *(Pres & CEO)*
Jerry Koch *(CFO & Sr VP)*
Dennis L. Schmidt *(COO & Exec VP)*
Douglas J. Reigle *(COO)*
David A. Anderson *(Exec VP-Opers)*
Joseph A. Swanson *(Sr VP-Ops)*
Brands & Products:
INTEGRITY, DEDICATION, PERFORMANCE, PRIDE.
MARCUS
REGAL WARE
REGAL WARE WORLDWIDE
WEST BEND

RELIABLE AUTOMATIC SPRINKLER CO., INC.
103 Fairview Pk Dr
Elmsford, NY 10523
Tel.: (914) 586-4242
Fax: (914) 668-0804
Toll Free: (800) 431-1588
E-mail: info@reliablesprinkler.com
Web Site: www.reliablesprinkler.com
E-Mail For Key Personnel:
Marketing Director: mfee@reliablesprinkler.com
Sales Director: SWhite@reliablesprinkler.com
Sales Range: $50-74.9 Million
Approx. Number Employees: 550
Year Founded: 1918
Business Description:
Automatic Fire Sprinklers & Sprinkler System Control Equipment Mfr
S.I.C.: 3569; 4941
N.A.I.C.S.: 333999; 221310
Media: 2-4-7-10-11
Distr.: Intl.
Personnel:
Frank J. Fee, III *(Pres)*
Kevin T. Fee *(Exec VP)*
Michael R. Fee *(VP-Mktg & Sls Opers)*
John McNamara *(VP-Sls)*
David Asplund *(Dir-Tech Svcs)*
Bob Eagle *(Dir-Sls)*
Michael Racanello *(Dir-Sls Ops)*
Floyd Thomas *(Dir-Sls)*
J. Todd Bresnahan *(Reg Mgr-Sls)*
William Cook *(Reg Mgr-Sls)*
Bruce Gachne *(Reg Mgr-Sls)*
Berny Holden *(Reg Mgr-Sls-Western Europe)*
Bob Poulton *(Reg Mgr-Sls)*
David J. Rosso *(Reg Mgr-Sls)*
Matt Squirell *(Reg Mgr)*
Mick Taylor *(Reg Mgr-Sls)*
Scott R. White *(Reg Mgr-Sls)*
Hartmut Winkler *(Reg Mgr-Sls)*
Dan Forsberg *(Reg Sls Mgr)*
Steve Yeung *(Sls Mgr)*
Mark A. Connor *(Mgr-Sls)*
Guy Devillers *(Mgr-Ops)*
Ron Duke *(Mgr-Ops)*
Chuck Gallagher *(Mgr-Tech Svcs)*
Jerry Holowak *(Mgr-Ops)*
Sal Izzo *(Mgr-Tech Svcs)*
James A. Mikkila *(Mgr-Tech Svcs)*
Edward R. Smith *(Mgr-Western Reg)*
Brands & Products:
HANDISHAPES
LDX
PEMKOHINGE
PREPAK
RELIABLE
SIDEWALL CONCEALER
SURE-OFF

REPLACEMENTS, LTD.
1089 Knox Rd
McLeansville, NC 27301-9228
Mailing Address:
PO Box 26029
Greensboro, NC 27420-6029
Tel.: (336) 697-3000
Fax: (336) 697-3100
Toll Free: (800) 737-5223
E-mail: inquire@replacements.com
Web Site: www.replacements.com
Approx. Number Employees: 700
Year Founded: 1981
Business Description:
Mail Order House Distr of Discontinued China, Crystal & Flatware
S.I.C.: 5961
N.A.I.C.S.: 454113
Import Export
Advertising Expenditures: $7,413,643
Catalogs & Directories: $137,000; Consumer Mags.: $532,000; D.M. to Bus. Estab.: $135,000; D.M. to Consumers: $3,000,000; Daily Newsp.: $94,750; Internet Adv.: $3,371,160; Outdoor (Posters, Transit): $143,733
Distr.: Direct to Consumer; Natl.
Personnel:
Bob Page *(Founder & Owner)*
Scott Fleming *(Pres)*
Kelly Smith *(CFO)*
Jack Whitley *(Sr VP-E-Commerce)*
Anne Embry *(VP-Sls)*
Keith Winkler *(Product Mgr-Mktg)*
Mark Donahue *(Coord-Media)*
Brands & Products:
REPLACEMENTS
REPLACEMENTS, LTD.
WE REPLACE THE IRREPLACEABLE
Advertising Agency:
Replacements, Ltd.
1089 Knox Rd
McLeansville, NC 27301
Tel.: (336) 697-3100
Fax: (336) 697-3100
(China, Crystal, Silver & Collectibles)

REYNOLDS PACKAGING GROUP
(Holding of Reynolds Group Holdings Limited)
6641 W Broad St
Richmond, VA 23230-1723
Tel.: (804) 281-2000
Fax: (804) 281-2041
Approx. Number Employees: 200
Year Founded: 1919
Business Description:
Flexible Packaging, Aluminum Foil & Food Container Mfr
S.I.C.: 2671; 2673; 3089; 3353; 3497
N.A.I.C.S.: 322221; 322223; 322225; 326199; 331315
Export
Advertising Expenditures: $7,000,000
Media: 1-3-15-24
Distr.: Natl.
Personnel:
Jeff Kellar *(Pres)*
Matthew Greenshields *(Dir-Market Res)*
J. Douglas Mickle *(Grp Dir-Adv & Mktg Svcs)*
Charles Kinsolving *(Sr Brand Mgr-Reynolds Wrap Foil)*
Brands & Products:
REYNOLDS
REYNOLDS CUT RITE WAX PAPER
REYNOLDS GRILL BUDDIES
REYNOLDS HOT BAGS
REYNOLDS OVEN BAGS
REYNOLDS POT LUX
REYNOLDS WRAP
REYNOLDS WRAP RELEASE
REYNOLDS WRAPPERS
Advertising Agencies:
Bromley Communications
401 E Houston St
San Antonio, TX 78205-2615
Tel.: (210) 244-2000
Fax: (210) 244-2442
Reynolds Wrap Aluminum Foil

Saatchi & Saatchi New York
375 Hudson St
New York, NY 10014-3660
Tel.: (212) 463-2000
Fax: (212) 463-9855
(Reynolds Plastic Wrap & Reynolds Aluminum Foil)

ROSENTHAL U.S.A. LIMITED
(Sub. of Rosenthal GmbH)
355 Michele Pl
Carlstadt, NJ 07072-2304
Tel.: (201) 804-8000
Fax: (201) 842-9195
E-mail: info@rosenthalchina.com
Web Site: www.rosenthalchina.com
Approx. Number Employees: 25
Year Founded: 1962
Business Description:
Marketer of Fine China, Stemware, Crystal & Porcelain & Stainless Flatware
S.I.C.: 5023
N.A.I.C.S.: 423220
Import
Media: 4-6-10-19
Distr.: Natl.
Budget Set: Oct.
Personnel:
Andrea Viinello *(Pres)*
Brands & Products:
ROSENTHAL CLASSIC
ROSENTHAL STUDIO-LINE
THOMAS BY ROSENTHAL

THE ROYAL CHINA & PORCELAIN COMPANIES INC.
(Sub. of Spode Limited)
1265 Glen Ave
Moorestown, NJ 08057-1111
Tel.: (856) 866-2900
Fax: (856) 866-2499
E-mail: info@royalchina.com
Web Site: www.royalchina.com
Approx. Rev.: $30,000,000
Approx. Number Employees: 100
Year Founded: 1750
Business Description:
Distr of Fine Bone China, Porcelain & Oven-to-Tableware; Fine Stone China & Earthenware & Giftware Products
S.I.C.: 3914; 5714
N.A.I.C.S.: 339912; 442291
Import
Advertising Expenditures: $1,500,000
Media: 2-4-5-6-8
Distr.: Intl.; Natl.
Budget Set: Sept.-Oct.
Personnel:
Nancy Seymour *(Coord-Consumer Affairs)*
Brands & Products:
RCPC
ROYAL WORCESTER

ROYAL DOULTON USA INC.
(Sub. of WWRD USA, LLC)
PO Box 1454
Wall, NJ 07719
Tel.: (732) 356-7880
Fax: (732) 764-4974
Toll Free: (800) 682-4462
E-mail: usa@royal-doulton.com
Web Site: www.royaldoulton.com/US/Home
Sales Range: $1-9.9 Million
Approx. Number Employees: 176
Year Founded: 1945
Business Description:
Fine China, Casual Tableware, Crystal, Glassware & Ceramic Ornaments Distr & Retailer
S.I.C.: 5023; 5947; 5961
N.A.I.C.S.: 423220; 453220; 454111
Import
Advertising Expenditures: $500,000
Media: 4-5-6-10-13-16-22-23
Distr.: Natl.
Budget Set: Sept.

ROYAL PRESTIGE OF NEW YORK
(Sub. of Hy Cite Corporation)
10309 37th Ave
Flushing, NY 11368-1940
Tel.: (718) 507-4568
Fax: (718) 898-1138
Web Site: www.royalprestige.com
Approx. Number Employees: 6
Year Founded: 1986
Business Description:
Cookware Supplier
S.I.C.: 5023; 5046
N.A.I.C.S.: 423220; 423440
Personnel:
Miguel Angel Gonzales *(VP-Sls & Latino Mktg)*

Key to Media (For complete agency information see *The Advertising Red Books-Agencies* edition):
1. Bus. Publs. 2. Cable T.V. 3. Catalogs & Directories. 4. Co-op Adv. 5. Consumer Mags. 6. D.M. to Bus. Estab.7. D.M. to Consumers 8. Daily Newsp. 9. Exhibits/Trade Shows 10. Foreign 11. Infomercial 12. Internet Adv.13. Multimedia 14. Network Radio 15. Network T.V. 16. Newsp. Distr. Mags. 17. Other 18. Outdoor (Posters, Transit) 19. Point of Purchase20. Premiums, Novelties 21. Product Samples 22. Special Events Mktg. 23. Spot Radio 24. Spot T.V. 25. Weekly Newsp. 26. Yellow Page Adv.

Advertising Agency:
The San Jose Group
233 N Michigan Ave 24 Fl
Chicago, IL 60601
Tel.: (312) 565-7000
Fax: (312) 565-7500

RUBBERMAID CANADA INC.
(Holding of Rubbermaid Home Products)
2562 Stanfield Rd
Mississauga, ON L4Y 1S5, Canada
Tel.: (905) 279-1010
Fax: (905) 279-1054
Web Site: www.rubbermaid.com
Sales Range: $25-49.9 Million
Approx. Number Employees: 94
Year Founded: 1950
Business Description:
Mfr. & Marketer of Plastic Products
S.I.C.: 3089
N.A.I.C.S.: 326199
Media: 6-8-10-14-19-23
Distr.: Natl.
Budget Set: Aug.

RUBBERMAID HOME PRODUCTS
(Div. of Newell Rubbermaid Inc.)
3320 W Market St
Fairlawn, OH 44333-3306
Tel.: (330) 869-7100
Tel.: (330) 264-6464
Fax: (330) 202-5392
Web Site: www.rubbermaid.com
Sales Range: $550-599.9 Million
Approx. Number Employees: 6,000
Year Founded: 1920
Business Description:
Mfr & Distr of Rubber & Plastic Products for the Consumer & Institutional Markets
S.I.C.: 3089
N.A.I.C.S.: 326199
Import Export
Advertising Expenditures: $2,000,000
Media: 1-2-3-4-5-6-10-14-15-19-20
Distr.: Intl.
Budget Set: May
Brands & Products:
2-IN-1 WAGON
ACTIONPACKER
ANYTHING GOES
ARTCRAFT
ASPIRA
BETTER WORKSPACE FOR THE WORK PLACE
BOUNCER III
BUBBLES THE WHALE
BUSTER THE TORTOISE
COMFORT TREAD
CON-TACT
CONTENTS
CONTOURS
COZY COTTAGE
COZY COUPE
DAVSON
DELTAMAT
DRAINTAINER
DUST FORCE
EASY RIDER
EASYVUE
ELDON CRESTMONT
ELEGANCE
EURO BLUE
EVERYTHING RUBBERMAID
EXPRESSIONS
EZ TOPPS
EZMT
FABRICRAFT
FRESH TOPS
FUN THAT LASTS
GRAND MANSION
GRAND MANSION COLLECTIBLES
GRIP LINER
HIP HUGGER
HOMEWORKS
HUMPRHEY THE DINOSAUR
ICE DESIGNS
KID BUILDERS
KIDSSCAPE
LIFT'N TOSS
LI'L ROUGHNECK
LITTERLESS
LUNCH BREAK
MOBILEMANAGER
MUNCHETTES
OFFICEWORKS
OMNI
PAD/DOCK
PEEK-A-BOO ACTIVITY TUNNEL
PENINSULA TABLE
PROFESSIONAL PLUS
PROSERIES
PUSH'N RIDE
ROADSTER
ROUGH RIDER
RUBBERMAID TOYS THAT LAST
SAFETY STRIPES
SERVIN' SAVER
SIGN(WARE)
SIMPLIFILE
SLIDE N'STACK
TIKES PEAK
TODDLE TOTS
TOTEWHEELS
UFO-USER FRIENDLY OFFICE
WEE WAFFLE
WORK MANAGER
WRAP'N CRAFT
Advertising Agencies:
Ketchum
(Part of Omnicom)
1285 Ave of the Americas
New York, NY 10019
Tel.: (646) 935-3900
Fax: (646) 935-4482
Public Relations AOR for Technology Global Business Unit

McCann Erickson Worldwide
622 3rd Ave
New York, NY 10017-6707
Tel.: (646) 865-2000
Fax: (646) 487-9610
Creative AOR for Technology Global Business Unit

THE RUBINET FAUCET COMPANY LIMITED
10 Corstate Ave
Concord, ON L4K 4X2, Canada
Tel.: (905) 851-6781
Fax: (905) 851-8031
Toll Free: (800) 461-5901
E-mail: customer_service@rubinet.com
Web Site: www.rubinet.com
E-Mail For Key Personnel:
President: domenic@rubinet.com
Sales Director: aldo@rubinet.com
Approx. Sls.: $8,000,000
Approx. Number Employees: 30
Year Founded: 1982
Business Description:
Decorative Faucets & Bath China & Matching Bath Accessories Mfr
S.I.C.: 3432; 3494
N.A.I.C.S.: 332913; 332919
Import Export
Media: 4-5-10-13-17
Distr.: Natl.
Personnel:
Dominic Luisi *(Owner)*
Aldo Marchesi *(Mgr-Mktg & Sls)*
Brands & Products:
ETRUSCAN
FLEMISH
HEXIS
ROMANESQUE
RUBINET

SALADMASTER
(Div. of Regal Ware, Inc.)
230 W White Pl Ste 101
Arlington, TX 76018
Tel.: (817) 633-3555
Fax: (817) 633-5544
E-mail: info@saladmaster.com
Web Site: www.saladmaster.com
Approx. Number Employees: 20
Year Founded: 1947
Business Description:
Mfr. of Cookware & Crockery
S.I.C.: 3631
N.A.I.C.S.: 335221
Media: 2-7-9-10-15-20
Distr.: Direct to Consumer; Intl.; Natl.
Budget Set: Sept.
Personnel:
Joe Trevino *(Dir-Dealer & Consumer Svcs)*
Brands & Products:
SALADMASTER

SERVER PRODUCTS INC.
3601 Pleasant Hill Rd
Richfield, WI 53076
Tel.: (262) 628-5600
Fax: (262) 628-5110
E-mail: pumps@execpc.com
Web Site: www.server-products.com
Approx. Number Employees: 100
Business Description:
Commercial Cooking & Foodwarming Equipment
S.I.C.: 3589
N.A.I.C.S.: 333319
Personnel:
Paul Wickesberg *(Owner)*
Jean-Francois Versele *(Mng Dir)*
Brent Henschel *(Coord-Mktg)*
Brands & Products:
CRYOVAC
HOLDCOLD
IN-COUNTER
INNOVATION IS SERVED
MIX-N-SERVE
SEASON2TASTE
SERVE-A-CUP
SERVER EXPRESS
SERVER PRODUCTS
SERVER SIMPLICITY
SERVER SOLUTION
SIGNATURE TOUCH
SUPREME
Advertising Agency:
Scott, Inc. of Milwaukee
(dba Scott Advertising)
1031 N Astor St
Milwaukee, WI 53202-3324
Tel.: (414) 276-1080
Fax: (414) 276-3327

SHEEX, INC.
1237 Gadsden St Ste 200E
Columbia, SC 29201
Tel.: (803) 820-9220
Web Site: www.sheex.com
Business Description:
Bedding Products Mfr & Distr
S.I.C.: 2515; 2392; 5023
N.A.I.C.S.: 337910; 314129; 423220
Media: 13-17-21-22
Personnel:
Michelle Marciniak *(Founder)*
Susan Walvius *(Founder)*

SMITH-LEE CO., INC.
537 Fitch St
Oneida, NY 13421-1515
Tel.: (315) 363-2500
Fax: (315) 363-9573
Toll Free: (800) 448-3363
Web Site: www.smith-lee.com
Approx. Number Employees: 100
Year Founded: 1898
Business Description:
Paper, Lace & Linen Place Mats, Doilies, Napkins & Tray Covers; Bath Mats; Packaged Merchandise & Paper Plates
S.I.C.: 2679; 2676
N.A.I.C.S.: 322299; 322291
Media: 9-23-25
Distr.: Natl.
Budget Set: Dec.
Personnel:
Milt Napper *(VP-Sls & Mktg)*
Marty Burger *(Dir-Mktg)*
Pam Laube *(Mgr-Acctg)*
Brands & Products:
SERV-EASE

SPRINGS INDUSTRIES, BEDDING DIVISION
(Div. of Springs Global, Inc.)
205 N White St
Fort Mill, SC 29715-1654
Tel.: (803) 547-1500
Fax: (803) 547-1579
Web Site: www.springs.com
Approx. Number Employees: 800
Business Description:
Comforters & Rugs, Specialty Mats, Sheets, Pillow Cases & Bed Tents
S.I.C.: 2211; 2273
N.A.I.C.S.: 313210; 314110
Media: 2-4-6-10-19-23-24
Distr.: Intl.; Natl.
Budget Set: Oct.
Brands & Products:
GARDEN ROOM
JCPENNEY HOME COLLECTION
SPRINGMAID
WAMSUTTA
WAVERLY

STANLEY ROBERTS, INC.
185 Garibaldi 2nd Fl
Lodi, NJ 07644-0686
Tel.: (973) 778-5900
Fax: (973) 778-8542
Approx. Number Employees: 7
Year Founded: 1871
Business Description:
Mfr. of Stainless Flatware, Cutlery & Gold Flatware
S.I.C.: 5023; 5072

Key to Media (For complete agency information see *The Advertising Red Books-Agencies* edition):
1. Bus. Publs. 2. Cable T.V. 3. Catalogs & Directories. 4. Co-op Adv. 5. Consumer Mags. 6. D.M. to Bus. Estab.7. D.M. to Consumers 8. Daily Newsp. 9. Exhibits/Trade Shows 10. Foreign 11. Infomercial 12. Internet Adv.13. Multimedia 14. Network Radio 15. Network T.V. 16. Newsp. Distr. Mags. 17. Other 18. Outdoor (Posters, Transit) 19. Point of Purchase20. Premiums, Novelties 21. Product Samples 22. Special Events Mktg. 23. Spot Radio 24. Spot T.V. 25. Weekly Newsp. 26. Yellow Page Adv.

Stanley Roberts, Inc. — (Continued)

N.A.I.C.S.: 423220; 423710
Media: 6-9
Distr.: Natl.
Personnel:
Edward Pomeranz *(Pres)*
Brands & Products:
MASTERGUILD
ROGERS
STANLEY ROBERTS
Advertising Agency:
Burton-Miles Advertising, Inc.
171 Madison Ave
New York, NY 10016-5110
Tel.: (212) 683-5660
Fax: (212) 481-0327

STERILITE CORPORATION

30 Scales Ln
Townsend, MA 01469-1010
Mailing Address:
PO Box 8001
Townsend, MA 01469-1010
Tel.: (978) 597-1100
Fax: (978) 597-1195
Web Site: www.sterilite.com
Sales Range: $25-49.9 Million
Approx. Number Employees: 650
Business Description:
Mfr. of Plastic Kitchenware, Tableware, Houseware & Storage Products
S.I.C.: 3089; 4226
N.A.I.C.S.: 326199; 493190
Media: 6-9-13-15-17-24
Personnel:
Albert Stone *(Chm)*
David Stone *(Pres & COO)*
Steven L. Stone *(Exec VP)*
Richard Ahern *(VP-Mktg)*
Philip Dimarzio *(VP-Sls)*
Brands & Products:
CLEARVIEW
COLANDER
FLIPTOP
OMNIBOX
RUGGED ULTRA
SHOWOFFS
STERILITE
SWING-TOP
TOUCH-TOP
ULTRA
ULTRASEAL

STERLING CUT GLASS COMPANY, INC.

3233 Mineola Pke
Erlanger, KY 41018-1027
Tel.: (859) 283-2333
Fax: (859) 283-2434
Toll Free: (800) 543-1317
E-mail: info@sterlingcutglass.com
Web Site: www.sterlingcutglass.com
Sales Range: $10-24.9 Million
Approx. Number Employees: 100
Year Founded: 1902
Business Description:
Mfr. of Etched & Cut Glassware
S.I.C.: 5023; 3993
N.A.I.C.S.: 423220; 339950
Import
Advertising Expenditures: $300,000
Media: 2-4-6-7-10-13-17
Distr.: Natl.
Personnel:
Michael W. Dyas *(Pres)*
Leslie Dyas *(Exec VP)*

SUMMER INFANT, INC.

1275 Park East Dr
Woonsocket, RI 02895
Tel.: (401) 671-6550
E-mail: customerservice@summerinfant.com
Web Site: www.summerinfant.com
Approx. Sls.: $194,485,000
Approx. Number Employees: 218
Business Description:
Retailer of Infant Health, Safety & Wellness Products
S.I.C.: 6719
N.A.I.C.S.: 551112
Advertising Expenditures: $15,445,000
Personnel:
Jason P. Macari *(Pres & CEO)*
Joseph Driscoll *(CFO & Treas)*
Jeffrey L. Hale *(COO)*
Denis z Horton *(Exec VP-Intl)*
Mark C. Strozik *(VP-HR)*
Cynthia Barlow *(Dir-Comm)*
Paulette Polidoro *(Dir-Packaging)*

SWISS ARMY BRANDS, INC.

(Sub. of Victorinox AG)
7 Victoria Dr
Monroe, CT 06484
Mailing Address:
PO Box 874
Shelton, CT 06484-6226
Tel.: (203) 929-6391
Fax: (203) 925-2988
Fax: (800) 243-4006
Toll Free: (800) 442-2706
E-mail: web.orders@swissarmy.com
Web Site: www.swissarmy.com
Approx. Number Employees: 150
Year Founded: 1855
Business Description:
Cutlery & Pocket Knives, Watches, Apparel, Luggage & Travel Accessories Distr & Marketer
S.I.C.: 5072; 5023
N.A.I.C.S.: 423710; 423220
Import Export
Media: 2-3-4-5-6-7-9-11-15-19-20-23
Distr.: Intl.; Natl.
Budget Set: Dec.
Personnel:
Thomas M. Lupinski *(CFO, Treas, Sec & Sr VP)*
Marc Gold *(Sr VP-Fin)*
Kristin DiCunzolo *(VP-Mktg & Comm)*
Brands & Products:
R.H. FORSCHNER
SWISS ARMY
VICTORINOX
VICTORINOX CUTLERY
VICTORINOX MEN'S APPAREL
Advertising Agency:
Mullen
40 Broad St
Boston, MA 02109
Tel.: (617) 226-9000
Fax: (617) 226-9100

TOWNECRAFT, INC.

1 De Boer Dr
Glen Rock, NJ 07452-3301
Tel.: (201) 445-9700
Fax: (201) 445-3108
E-mail: customerservice@townecraft.com
Web Site: www.townecraft.com
Approx. Number Employees: 300
Year Founded: 1944
Business Description:
Cookware Distr
S.I.C.: 5023
N.A.I.C.S.: 423220
Media: 4-6-7-9-10-24
Distr.: Direct to Consumer; Natl.
Budget Set: Mar.
Personnel:
E. H. Barbaris *(Pres)*
Paul J. Ando *(VP-Mktg & Adv)*
John Dimaria *(VP-Sls)*
Brands & Products:
CHEFCO
CHEF'S WARE
TOWNECRAFT

TUPPERWARE BRANDS CORPORATION

14901 S Orange Blossom Trl
Orlando, FL 32837-6600
Mailing Address:
PO Box 2353
Orlando, FL 32802-2353
Tel.: (407) 826-5050
Fax: (407) 826-8268
Web Site: www.tupperware.com
Approx. Sls.: $2,300,400,000
Approx. Number Employees: 13,500
Year Founded: 1942
Business Description:
Direct Retailer & Marketer of Storage & Serving Containers, Toys & Beauty Supplies
S.I.C.: 7389; 3082; 3089
N.A.I.C.S.: 541420; 326121; 326199
Import Export
Advertising Expenditures: $23,100,000
Media: 4-6-8-24
Distr.: Intl.; Natl.
Personnel:
E. V. Goings *(Chm & CEO)*
Simon C. Hemus *(Pres & COO)*
Michael S. Poteshman *(CFO & Exec VP)*
Thomas M. Roehlk *(Chief Legal Officer, Sec & Exec VP)*
Lillian D. Garcia *(Pres-Fuller Argentina & Exec VP)*
R. Glenn Drake *(Pres-Europe, Africa & Middle East Grp)*
Jose R. Timmerman *(Exec VP-Supply Chain & Worldwide)*
Josef Hajek *(Sr VP-Tax & Govt Affairs)*
Rashit Ismail *(Sr VP-Global Mktg Strategies)*
Christian E. Skroeder *(Sr VP-Worldwide Market Dev)*
Carl Benkovich *(VP-Sls-US & Canada)*
Brands & Products:
ARMAND DUPREE
AVROY SHALIN
BREAD SMART
CHEESE SMART
CHEF SERIES
CRYSTALWAVE
DREAMWORKS
FLATOUT
FRIDGESMART
FULLER
KUNG-FU PANDA
MADAGASCAR 2
MIX-N-STOR
MODULAR MATES
NATURECARE
NUTRIMETICS
NUVO
ONE TOUCH
QUICK CHEF
ROCK 'N SERVE
SHAPE-O
SQUARE-A-WAY
STUFFABLES
SWISSGARDE
TUPPERCARE
TUPPERKIDS
TUPPERWARE
TUPPERWAVE
WONDERLIER
Advertising Agencies:
DeVries Public Relations
30 E 60th St 14th Fl
New York, NY 10022
Tel.: (212) 891-0400
Fax: (212) 644-0291

EMG - Ethnic Marketing Group, Inc.
26074 Ave Hall Ste 20
Valencia, CA 91355
Tel.: (661) 295-5704
Fax: (661) 295-5771

VECTOR MARKETING CORPORATION

(Sub. of CUTCO Corporation)
1116 E State St
Olean, NY 14760-3814
Tel.: (716) 373-6141
Fax: (716) 790-7091
Web Site: www.cutco.com
Approx. Number Employees: 100
Year Founded: 1985
Business Description:
Direct Selling Establishments
S.I.C.: 5963; 5023
N.A.I.C.S.: 454390; 423220
Export
Media: 7
Personnel:
John W. Whelpley *(Pres & COO)*
Mark D. Heister *(CFO)*
Albert T. DiLeonardo *(Pres/CEO-Vector East)*
Bruce S. Goodman *(Pres/CEO-Vector West)*
Amar Dave *(Exec VP-Eastern Reg)*
Deborah Keenan *(Mgr-Product & Internet Mktg)*
Brands & Products:
CUTCO CUTLERY

VILLEROY & BOCH TABLEWARE, LTD.

(Sub. of Villeroy & Boch AG)
5 Vaughn Dr Ste 303
Princeton, NJ 08540-6313
Tel.: (609) 578-4300
Fax: (609) 734-7840
Toll Free: (800) 845-5376
E-mail: info@villeroybochtableware.com
Web Site: www.villeroy-boch.com
Approx. Number Employees: 35
Business Description:
Mfr. of Ceramics & Dinnerware
S.I.C.: 3262
N.A.I.C.S.: 327112
Export
Catalogs & Directories: 80%;
Consumer Mags.: 20%
Distr.: Intl.; Natl.
Personnel:
Bernard Reuter *(Pres)*

Key to Media (For complete agency information see *The Advertising Red Books-Agencies* edition):
1. Bus. Publs. 2. Cable T.V. 3. Catalogs & Directories. 4. Co-op Adv. 5. Consumer Mags. 6. D.M. to Bus. Estab.7. D.M. to Consumers
8. Daily Newsp. 9. Exhibits/Trade Shows 10. Foreign 11. Infomercial 12. Internet Adv.13. Multimedia 14. Network Radio
15. Network T.V. 16. Newsp. Distr. Mags. 17. Other 18. Outdoor (Posters, Transit) 19. Point of Purchase20. Premiums, Novelties
21. Product Samples 22. Special Events Mktg. 23. Spot Radio 24. Spot T.V. 25. Weekly Newsp. 26. Yellow Page Adv.

Danis Biggis *(VP-Retail)*
Michael Coggins *(VP-Sls & Mktg)*
Jean Esposito *(Mgr-Mktg)*

VITA-MIX CORPORATION

8615 Usher Rd
Cleveland, OH 44138-2199
Tel.: (440) 235-4840
Fax: (440) 235-3726
E-mail: household@vitamix.com
Web Site: www.vitamix.com
Sales Range: $75-99.9 Million
Approx. Number Employees: 240
Year Founded: 1921
Business Description:
Housewares Mail Order & Mfr
S.I.C.: 3631; 5961
N.A.I.C.S.: 335221; 454111; 454113
Media: 6-10
Personnel:
Jodi Berg *(Pres)*
Anthony Ciepiel *(VP-Sls & Mktg)*
Advertising Agency:
Rosetta
3700 Park East Dr Ste 300
Cleveland, OH 44122
Tel.: (216) 896-8900
Fax: (216) 896-8991
Content Strategy
Creative Design
Interactive Agency of Record
Marketing
Search Engine Optimization
Website Development

THE VOLLRATH COMPANY LLC

1236 N 18th St
Sheboygan, WI 53081-3201
Tel.: (920) 457-4851
Fax: (920) 459-6570
E-mail: vollrathfs@vollrathco.com
Web Site: www.vollrathco.com
Approx. Number Employees: 800
Year Founded: 1874
Business Description:
Mfr. of Stainless Steel Smallware, Utensils & Equipment, Plastic Serving Utensils, Medical Products & Deep-Drawn Components
S.I.C.: 3914; 3365
N.A.I.C.S.: 339912; 331524
Import Export
Media: 2-4-7-10-11-19-20
Distr.: Intl.; Natl.
Personnel:
Paul Bartelt *(Pres & CEO)*
Martin Crneckiy, Jr. *(Treas & Exec VP)*
Cathy Fitzgerald *(Dir-Mktg Comm)*
David Hogan *(Mgr-Sls-Central Reg)*
Brands & Products:
AFFORDABLE PORTABLE
BIG-MOUTH SERVERS
BLACK SPOODLE
CATERACK
CAYENNE
CLASSIC
CLASSIC SELECT
COLONIAL KETTLE
CONTINENTAL CHAFER
DAKOTA
ELEGANT REFLECTIONS
ERGOGRIP
ESQUIRE
GRIP N SERV
GRIP N'SERV SPOODLE II
INTRIGUE
KOOL-TOUCH
KOOL-TOUCH COVERS
KOOL-TOUCH LADLES
LE TONG
LEMON DROP
MAXIMILLIAN
MILESTONE
MIRAMAR
NY NY
ODYSSEY
ORION
PANACEA
PANAMAX
PULLTAP
QUEEN ANNE
ROYAL CREST
ROYAL CREST CHAFER
SERVEWELL
SETTING THE STANDARD
SIGNATURE SERVER
SOFTSPOON
SPOODLE
SUPER PAN
SUPER PAN 3
SUPER PAN II
SWIRL SERVE
THORNHILL
TILT & POUR
TOTE N STORE
TRIBUTE
TRIENNIUM
VALHALLA
VOLLRATH
WINDWAY
YORKSHIRE
Advertising Agency:
Marketing Support, Inc.
200 E Randolph Dr Ste 5000
Chicago, IL 60601
Tel.: (312) 565-0044
Fax: (312) 946-6100
— Thea Rooks *(Acct Supvr)*

WESTPOINT HOME, INC.

(Holding of WestPoint International, Inc.)
28 E 28th St 8th Fl
New York, NY 10016
Tel.: (212) 930-2000
Toll Free: (800) 435-1199 (Customer Svc)
Toll Free: (800) 533-8229 (Consumer Affairs)
E-mail: consumeraffairs@wphome.com
Web Site: www.westpointhome.com
Sales Range: $1-4.9 Billion
Approx. Number Employees: 13,886
Year Founded: 1880
Business Description:
Bed Linens & Towels Mfr
S.I.C.: 2392; 2211; 2299
N.A.I.C.S.: 314129; 313210; 313312
Advertising Expenditures: $11,100,000
Media: 2-4-6-7-8-9-10-14-16-18-20-21-23-24-25
Distr.: Natl.
Brands & Products:
ATELIER MARTEX
CHATHAM
GLYNDA TURLEY
GRAND PATRICIAN
LADY PEPPERELL
LUXOR
MARTEX
PATRICIAN
STEVENS
UTICA
VELLUX
Advertising Agency:
Chillingworth/Radding Inc.
1133 Broadway Ste 1615
New York, NY 10010
Tel.: (212) 674-4700
Fax: (212) 979-0125

WILL & BAUMER

100 Buckley Rd
Liverpool, NY 13088-6602
Tel.: (315) 451-1000
Fax: (315) 451-0120
Toll Free: (800) 733-7337
E-mail: info@will-baumer.com
Web Site: www.willbaumer.com
Approx. Number Employees: 50
Year Founded: 1855
Business Description:
Mfr of Religious Candles & Accessories
S.I.C.: 3999; 2842; 8661
N.A.I.C.S.: 339999; 325612; 813110
Import Export
Media: 2-4-5-7-10-20-21
Distr.: Natl.
Budget Set: Apr.
Personnel:
Marshall Ciccone *(Exec VP-Fin)*
Brands & Products:
ALTAR
ALTAR BRAND
BRITE-LITE
GENUINE VIGIL LIGHT
GLEAMLIGHTS
IMAGE OF SAINTS
LIQUID LITE
MAGIC MOOD
OFFERLIGHTS
POLAR
POLAR BRAND
PURE BEESWAX
TORCH CANDLE
TRU-FIL
TWINKLE T-LITES
VERSA-STAND
VIGIL LIGHT
VOTICANDLES
WILL & BAUMER

WILLERT HOME PRODUCTS, INC.

4044 Pk Ave
Saint Louis, MO 63110-2320
Tel.: (314) 772-2822
Fax: (314) 772-3506
E-mail: whp@willert.com
Web Site: www.willert.com
E-Mail For Key Personnel:
Marketing Director: spatrick@willert.com
Approx. Number Employees: 300
Year Founded: 1952
Business Description:
Mfr. of Household Insecticides & Deodorants
S.I.C.: 2879; 2869
N.A.I.C.S.: 325320; 325199
Media: 2-3-4-5-10-13-15-19-20-22
Distr.: Natl.
Budget Set: Oct.
Personnel:
William D. Willert *(Owner & Pres)*
Brian Warner *(CFO)*
Shelly Patrick *(Mgr-Mktg)*
Brands & Products:
BOWL FRESH
CONCERTO
ENOZ
REEFER GALLER
SCENTED GARDEN
SPIRITUAL SKY
WILLERT

WILLIAMS-SONOMA, INC.

3250 Van Ness Ave
San Francisco, CA 94109-1012
Tel.: (415) 421-7900
Fax: (415) 616-8359
Web Site: www.williams-sonomainc.com
Approx. Rev.: $3,504,158,000
Approx. Number Employees: 6,200
Year Founded: 1956
Business Description:
Cookware, Tableware & Related Equipment Retailer
S.I.C.: 5999; 2514; 5712; 5961
N.A.I.C.S.: 453998; 337124; 442110; 454113
Import
Advertising Expenditures: $293,623,000
Media: 4-6-8-9-13-22
Distr.: Natl.
Budget Set: Mar. -Apr.
Personnel:
Charles E. Williams *(Founder & Dir Emeritus)*
Adrian D. P. Bellamy *(Chm)*
Laura J. Alber *(Pres & CEO)*
Sharon L. McCollam *(CFO, COO & Exec VP)*
Patrick J. Connolly *(CMO & Exec VP)*
Dean Miller *(Chief Supply Chain Officer)*
Seth R. Jaffe *(Gen Counsel & Sr VP)*
Martha Benson *(Sr VP-Strategy & Bus Dev)*
Christina Nicholson *(Dir-Sustainable Dev)*
Keren Sachs *(Mgr-Creative)*
Brands & Products:
PB TEEN
POTTERY BARN KIDS
WEST ELM
WILLIAMS-SONOMA
WILLIAMS-SONOMA HOME
Advertising Agencies:
iCrossing Los Angeles
12910 Culver Blvd Ste B
Los Angeles, CA 90066
Tel.: (480) 282-6058
Fax: (310) 302-6001

Silverlign Group Inc.
54 N Central Ave Ste 200
Campbell, CA 95008
Tel.: (408) 792-3010
Fax: (408) 792-3014

Xenophon Strategies
1625 Eye St NW 6th Fl Ste 610
Washington, DC 20006
Tel.: (202) 289-4001
Fax: (202) 777-2030

Xenophon Strategies
215 Western Ave Ste A
Petaluma, CA 94952
Tel.: (707) 781-9170
Fax: (707) 781-9182

WILTON PRODUCTS, INC.
(Holding of GTCR Golder Rauner, LLC)
2240 W 75th St
Woodridge, IL 60517-2333
Tel.: (630) 963-1818
Fax: (630) 963-7177
Toll Free: (800) 794-5866
E-mail: info@wilton.com
Web Site: www.wilton.com
Approx. Number Employees: 700
Year Founded: 1929
Business Description:
Mfr., Distr & Importer of Consumer Products; Baking & Decorating Cookware & Kitchenware & Picture Frames
S.I.C.: 5023; 2731
N.A.I.C.S.: 423220; 511130
Import Export
Media: 2-4-6-8-10-13-24
Distr.: Direct to Consumer; Intl.; Natl.
Budget Set: Mar.
Personnel:
Mary Merfield *(Pres)*
Steven Fraser *(CEO)*
Eric Erwin *(Exec VP-Mktg & Product Dev)*
Jeremy T. Steele *(Asst Gen Counsel)*
Brands & Products:
COPCO
ROWOCO
THE WESTON GALLERIES
WILTON
WILTON ENTERPRISES
WOVO

WITT INDUSTRIES, INC.
(Div. of The Armor Group, Inc.)
4600 N Mason-Montgomery Rd
Mason, OH 45040
Tel.: (513) 923-5631
Fax: (877) 891-8200
Toll Free: (800) 543-7417
E-mail: sales@witt.com
Web Site: www.witt.com
E-Mail For Key Personnel:
President: timh@witt.com
Sales Director: billa@witt.com
Approx. Number Employees: 165
Year Founded: 1887
Business Description:
Waste Receptacle Mfr
S.I.C.: 3499
N.A.I.C.S.: 332999
Import Export
Advertising Expenditures: $200,000
Media: 2-5-7-10-20-21-26
Distr.: Natl.
Budget Set: Jan.
Personnel:
Patty Richardson *(Mgr-Inside Sls)*
Brands & Products:
DISPENSE-A-LINER
SAFETY STEP
STADIUM SERIES
WITT

WMF OF AMERICA, INC.
(Sub. of WMF Wurttembergische Metallwarenfabrik AG)
3512 Faith Church Rd
Indian Trail, NC 28079
Tel.: (704) 882-3898
Fax: (704) 893-2198
Toll Free: (800) 999-6347
Web Site: www.wmf-usa.com
Sales Range: $10-24.9 Million
Approx. Number Employees: 30
Year Founded: 1960
Business Description:
Stainless Steel Tableware, China Dinnerware, Giftware, Glassware, Cookware, Cutlery & Kitchen Tools Whslr
S.I.C.: 5023
N.A.I.C.S.: 423220
Import
Advertising Expenditures: $100,000
Media: 10
Distr.: Natl.
Personnel:
Markus Glueck *(Pres & CEO)*
Brands & Products:
SPIEGELAU
WMF/USA

WORLD KITCHEN LLC
(Sub. of WKI Holding Company, Inc.)
5500 N Pearl St Ste 400
Rosemont, IL 60018
Tel.: (847) 678-8600
Fax: (847) 233-8902
Toll Free: (800) 367-3526
E-mail: careers@worldkitchen.com
Web Site: www.worldkitchen.com
Approx. Number Employees: 5,200
Business Description:
Kitchen & Barbeque Tools, Bar Accessories, Bathroom Fittings, Closet Hardware, Tableware, Household Tinware & Microwave Accessories Mfr
S.I.C.: 3469
N.A.I.C.S.: 332214
Import Export
Advertising Expenditures: $3,000,000
Media: 2-6-9-10-24-25
Distr.: Natl.
Budget Set: Feb.
Personnel:
Terry R. Peets *(Chm)*
Joseph T. Mallof *(Pres & CEO)*
John Conklin *(Grp VP & CIO)*
Debbie Paskin *(Chief Legal Officer, Gen Counsel, Sec & Sr VP)*
Raymond J. Kulla *(Gen Counsel, Sec & Sr VP)*
Courtney Marsala *(Brand Mgr)*
Carl Cottrell *(Mgr-Accounts-Natl-OLFA-North Americe Div)*
Brands & Products:
CHICAGO CUTLERY
CORNINGWARE
MAGNALITE
OLFA
Advertising Agencies:
Cramer-Krasselt
225 N Michigan Ave
Chicago, IL 60601-7601
Tel.: (312) 616-9600
Fax: (312) 616-3839
Corelle
CorningWare
Pyrex

Marketing Support, Inc.
200 E Randolph Dr Ste 5000
Chicago, IL 60601
Tel.: (312) 565-0044
Fax: (312) 946-6100

W.R. CASE & SONS CUTLERY COMPANY
(Sub. of Zippo Manufacturing Company, Inc.)
PO Box 4000 Owens Way
Bradford, PA 16701
Tel.: (814) 368-4123
Fax: (814) 368-1736
Toll Free: (800) 523-6350
E-mail: consumer-relations@wrcase.com
Web Site: www.wrcase.com
Approx. Rev.: $38,000,000
Approx. Number Employees: 370
Year Founded: 1889
Business Description:
Pocket Knives, Hunting & Sporting Knives, Household Cutlery, Shears & Accessories Mfr
S.I.C.: 3421
N.A.I.C.S.: 332211
Export
Advertising Expenditures: $2,000,000
Media: 4-5-6-18-20-21
Distr.: Natl.
Personnel:
Tom Arrowsmith *(Pres)*
Edward J. Jessup, Jr. *(VP-Mktg & Sls)*
Brands & Products:
ZIPPO

ZENITH PRODUCTS CORPORATION
(Holding of Charlesbank Capital Partners, LLC)
400 Lukens Dr
New Castle, DE 19720-2728
Tel.: (302) 326-8200
Fax: (302) 326-8400
Toll Free: (800) 892-3986
E-mail: customerservice@zenith-products.com
Web Site: www.zenith-products.com
Approx. Number Employees: 630
Year Founded: 1946
Business Description:
Bathroom Furniture & Storage Product Mfr
S.I.C.: 3089; 3432
N.A.I.C.S.: 326199; 332913
Import Export
Media: 2-4-5-7-10-19-21
Distr.: Natl.
Budget Set: July
Personnel:
Joseph Mahon *(CEO)*
Brands & Products:
TWIST TIGHT

ZEPHYR MANUFACTURING COMPANY INC.
200 Mitchell Rd
Sedalia, MO 65301-2114
Tel.: (660) 827-0352
Fax: (660) 827-0713
E-mail: info@zephyrmfg.com
Web Site: www.zephyrmfg.com
Approx. Sls.: $5,000,000
Approx. Number Employees: 50
Year Founded: 1927
Business Description:
Brooms, Mops, Dust Mops & Mopheads; Wax Appliers; Broomsticks Mfr
S.I.C.: 3991
N.A.I.C.S.: 339994
Import Export
Media: 2-4-10-21
Distr.: Natl.
Personnel:
John A. Lindstrom *(Pres)*
R. J. Lindstrom *(Pres)*
Brands & Products:
DOVER
YOUR ONE STOP SOURCE FOR QUALITY CLEANING PRODUCTS
ZEPHYR

Key to Media (For complete agency information see *The Advertising Red Books-Agencies* edition):
1. Bus. Publs. 2. Cable T.V. 3. Catalogs & Directories. 4. Co-op Adv. 5. Consumer Mags. 6. D.M. to Bus. Estab.7. D.M. to Consumers 8. Daily Newsp. 9. Exhibits/Trade Shows 10. Foreign 11. Infomercial 12. Internet Adv.13. Multimedia 14. Network Radio 15. Network T.V. 16. Newsp. Distr. Mags. 17. Other 18. Outdoor (Posters, Transit) 19. Point of Purchase20. Premiums, Novelties 21. Product Samples 22. Special Events Mktg. 23. Spot Radio 24. Spot T.V. 25. Weekly Newsp. 26. Yellow Page Adv.

Industrial Chemicals

Acids — Aerosols — Carbons — Cellulose — Dyes — Explosives — Gases — Metals — Pigments — Plastics — Resins — Solvents — Sulphur — Synthetics

3M COMPANY
3M Center
Saint Paul, MN 55144-1000
Tel.: (651) 733-1110
Fax: (651) 733-9973
Toll Free: (888) 364-3577
Web Site: www.solutions.3m.com
Approx. Sls.: $26,662,000,000
Approx. Number Employees: 80,057
Year Founded: 1902
Business Description:
Aerospace, Automotive, Communications Arts, Construction & Maintenance, Consumer, Dental, Health Care, Industrial, Marine, Media, Office, Packaging, Pharmaceutical, Safety & Security, Telecommunications, Transportation & Transportation Safety Products Mfr
S.I.C.: 2891; 2821; 2899; 5085; 5113
N.A.I.C.S.: 325520; 325211; 325998; 423840; 424130
Import Export
Advertising Expenditures: $512,000,000
Media: 1-2-4-6-7-8-9-10-11-13-14-15-16-17-18-19-20-21-22-23-24-25-26
Distr.: Intl.; Natl.
Budget Set: Jan.
Personnel:
George W. Buckley *(Chm, Pres & CEO)*
Patrick D. Campbell *(CFO & Sr VP)*
Inge G. Thulin *(COO)*
Frederick J. Palensky *(CTO & Exec VP-R & D)*
Nicholas C. Gangestad *(Chief Acctg Officer, VP & Controller)*
David W. Meline *(Chief Acctg Officer)*
Stefan Gabriel *(Pres-New Ventures)*
Marschall I. Smith *(Gen Counsel & Sr VP-Legal Affairs)*
Gregg M. Larson *(Deputy Gen Counsel & Sec)*
Joaquin Delgado *(Exec VP-Electro & Comm Bus)*
Michael A. Kelly *(Exec VP-Display & Graphics Bus)*
Jean Lobey *(Exec VP-Safety, Security & Protection Svcs Bus)*
Brad T. Sauer *(Exec VP-Health Care Bus)*
Hak Cheol Shin *(Exec VP-Indus & Transportation Bus)*
Michael G. Vale *(Exec VP-Consumer & Office Bus)*
Roger H. D. Lacey *(Sr VP-Strategy & Corp Dev)*
Angela S. Lalor *(Sr VP-HR)*
Robert D. MacDonald, III *(Sr VP-Sls & Mktg)*
John K. Woodworth *(Sr VP-Corp Supply Chain Ops)*
Thomas A. Boardman *(VP & Deputy Gen Counsel)*
Tomi Jacobson *(Sr Brand Mgr)*
Michelle Gebbie *(Mgr-Mktg Comm)*
Sandra Kelly *(Mgr-Market Res)*
Steven J. Beilke *(Asst Sec)*
Brands & Products:
3M
3M-MATIC
ACCENTRIM
ACCUGLIDE
ADPER
AIR CEL
AIR-MATE
ALGAE BLOCK
AMESEAL
APLICAP
AVAGARD
BETWEEN COATS
BLENDERM
BODY SCHUTZ
BREATH-O-PRENE
BUF-PUF
BUMPON
CAVILON
CAVIRINSE
CAVIT
CAVITYSHIELD
CEM APLICAP
CEREC
CLARITY
CLEARTEK
CLINPRO
COBAN
CODEFINDER
COMPUBLEND
CONCEPT
CONTROLRX
CORNERSTONE
CUSHION-MOUNT
DIAMOND GRADE
DOBIE
DOODLEBUG
DRGFINDER
DUAL LOCK
DUAL-TAC
DUO-GLASS
DURAPREP
DURELON
DYNATEL
ELECTROCUT
ELIPAR
EMPORE
EQUISPORT
ESPE
EVENRUN
EXPRESS
FABRICUT
FAST 'N FIRM
FASTBOND
FIBRLOK
FILTEK
FILTRETE
FILTRON
FINESSE-IT
FIREDAM
FLEXIBLE CLEAR
FLEXICLEAR
FLEXOMOUNT
FLIP-FRAME
FLOSS N TOSS
FLOSSRX
FLUORAD
FLUORINERT
FREEZE WATCH
FUR FIGHTER
GARANT
GENTLE PAPER
GREEN CORPS
GREPTILE
HAND-MASKER
HIGHLAND
HOLDFAST
HOOKIT
IMPERIAL
IMPREGUM
IMPRINT
INDAG
JET-WELD
JUST FOR KIDS
JUST LIKE WOOD
KETAC
KETAC-BOND
KETAC-FIL
KETAC-SILVER
KLEEN-TEAM
LATITUDE
LAVA
LEAP
LITE LOFT
LITTMANN
MAXICAP
MBT
MEDIPORE
METPAK
MICROFOAM
MICROTOUCH
MOLAR APLICAP
MONITORMARK
MS2
NAILSAVER
NEVER RUST
NEXCARE
NEXCARE ACTIVE
NEXTEL
NIAGARA
NOMAD
NOVEC
O-CEL-O
OPTICLUDE
ORTHOWASH
PAINT BUSTER
PANAFLEX
PANAGRAPHICS
PANELSAFE
PAPER TAPER
PARADIGM
PENTA
PENTAMIX
PERFECT-IT
PERMADYNE
PETRIFILM
PHOTAC
PHOTO MOUNT
PLUS APLICAP
POLYCUT
POLYGUN
POST-IT
PRESS-ON
PRIMACAST
PRIVACYTOUCH
PRO-PAD
PRODUCTION
PROMPT L-POP
PROTEMP
RAMITEC
REGAL
REGALITE
RELYX
RESTON
ROCATEC
ROCKER GARD
ROTOMIX
SAFE-RELEASE
SAFE-TIGUE
SAFEST STRIPPER

Key to Media (For complete agency information see *The Advertising Red Books-Agencies* edition):
1. Bus. Publs. 2. Cable T.V. 3. Catalogs & Directories. 4. Co-op Adv. 5. Consumer Mags. 6. D.M. to Bus. Estab.7. D.M. to Consumers
8. Daily Newsp. 9. Exhibits/Trade Shows 10. Foreign 11. Infomercial 12. Internet Adv.13. Multimedia 14. Network Radio
15. Network T.V. 16. Newsp. Distr. Mags. 17. Other 18. Outdoor (Posters, Transit) 19. Point of Purchase20. Premiums, Novelties
21. Product Samples 22. Special Events Mktg. 23. Spot Radio 24. Spot T.V. 25. Weekly Newsp. 26. Yellow Page Adv.

3M Company — (Continued)

SAFETY-WALK
SANDBLASTER
SATIN
SBS
SCIENTIFIC ANGLERS
SCOTCH
SCOTCH-BRITE
SCOTCH-MOUNT
SCOTCH-SEAL
SCOTCH-WELD
SCOTCHAL
SCOTCHBLOK
SCOTCHBOND
SCOTCHBRICK
SCOTCHCAL
SCOTCHCAST
SCOTCHCODE
SCOTCHFIL
SCOTCHGARD
SCOTCHKOTE
SCOTCHLITE
SCOTCHLOK
SCOTCHMARK
SCOTCHMATE
SCOTCHPAD
SCOTCHPRO
SCOTCHRAP
SCOTCHTINT
SHARPSHOOTER
SHIPPING-MATE
SINFONY
SLIC
SMARTCLIP
SOF-LEX
SOFT SCOUR!
SOFTBACK
SPANGLE
SPEEDGLAS
SPRAY-MOUNT
STAMARK
STANCE
STAYFRESH
STELLAR
STERI-DRAPE
STERI-GAS
STERI-LOK
STERI-STRIP
STERI-VAC
STERIGAGE
STIKIT
STOMASEAL
SUPER 77
SUPERBUFF
SUPREME
SURFACE SAVER
TARNI-SHIELD
TARTAN
TATTLE-TAPE
TATTOO
TEGAGEN
TEGAPORE
TEGASORB
TEMFLEX
TEMPA-DOT
TEXTOOL
THERMALOG
THINSULATE
TOUCHPEN
TOUGHTOUCH
TRIZACT
TROUBLESHOOTER
TWIST-LOK
TWIST 'N FILL
ULTRA
ULTRAFINA
ULTRAPRO
ULTRATHON
UNDERSEAL
UNITEK
VF-45
VIKUITI
VISIO
VITREBOND
VITREMER
VITROTRIM
VOLITION
WALLSAVER
WEATHERBAN
WET CEL
WET TIP
WETORDRY
WINDO-WELD
XODUST
Z-LIGHT SPHERES
Z100
ZEEOSPHERES

Advertising Agencies:

Cohn & Wolfe
200 Fifth Ave
New York, NY 10010
Tel.: (212) 798-9700
Fax: (212) 329-9900

GoConvergence
4545 36th St
Orlando, FL 32811
Tel.: (407) 235-3210
Fax: (407) 299-9907

Hunter Public Relations
41 Madison Ave Fl 5
New York, NY 10010-2202
Tel.: (212) 679-6600
Fax: (212) 679-6607
(Nexcare First-Aid Products)

Interbrand Corporation
(Part of Omnicom Group Inc.)
130 5th Ave
New York, NY 10011-4306
Tel.: (212) 798-7500
Fax: (212) 798-7501

Martin/Williams Advertising Inc.
(A Member of Omnicom Group)
60 S 6th St Ste 2800
Minneapolis, MN 55402-4428
Tel.: (612) 340-0800
Fax: (612) 342-9700
(Commercial Graphics, Commercial Office Supply, Dental Products, Consumer Stationery, Sports & Leisure Products, Consumer Health Care)

Riley Hayes Advertising
333 S First St
Minneapolis, MN 55401
Tel.: (612) 338-7161
Fax: (612) 338-7344
(TacFast Carpet Systems; Scotchtint)
— Tom Hayes *(Acct. Exec.)*

Scales Advertising
2303 Wycliff St
Saint Paul, MN 55114
Tel.: (651) 641-0226
Fax: (651) 641-1031

A BRITE COMPANY

3217 Wood Dr
Garland, TX 75041
Tel.: (214) 291-0400
Fax: (214) 291-0300
Web Site: www.abrite.com
Approx. Number Employees: 20
Year Founded: 1982
Business Description:
Mfr. & Marketer of Chemicals for Metal Finishing & Envrionmental Industries
S.I.C.: 3559; 5084
N.A.I.C.S.: 333298; 423830
Media: 2-7-10-13
Personnel:
Frank Dunigan *(Owner)*
Scott Dunigan *(Pres)*
Les Winkler *(COO)*
Dan Dunigan *(Mgr-Mktg)*
Brands & Products:
ALDEOX
ALKLEEN
ALUMA ETCH
AQUAKLEEN
BANANA SPLIT
BRITEGUARD
BRITEGUARD PITCHBLACK
CHROME PLUS
ENBRITE
ENVIROBRITE
ENVIROLLOY
GALAXIE
MY-T-KLEEN
NIBLACK
NIBRITE
NIDEX
PENTASTAR ONE
PHOSHIELD
PICKLEEN
QUASAR
SATINIQUE
SPARKLEEN
STRIPRITE
SUPERKOTE
ZNBRITE

A. SCHULMAN, INC.

3550 W Market St
Akron, OH 44333-2658
Tel.: (330) 666-3751
Fax: (330) 668-7204
Toll Free: (800) 547-3746
Toll Free: (800) 54-RESIN
Telex: 6874422
E-mail: info@aschulman.com
Web Site: www.aschulman.com
Approx. Sls.: $1,590,443,000
Approx. Number Employees: 2,900
Year Founded: 1928
Business Description:
Mfr. & Supplier of Plastic Resins & Compounds
S.I.C.: 2824; 2821; 5162
N.A.I.C.S.: 325222; 325211; 424610
Import Export
Advertising Expenditures: $200,000
Media: 2-4-10-20-25-26
Distr.: Intl.; Natl.
Budget Set: Sept.
Personnel:
Joseph M. Gingo *(Chm, Pres & CEO)*
Joseph J. Levanduski *(CFO, Treas & VP)*
Bernard Rzepka *(COO & Gen Mgr-Europe)*
John B. Broerman *(CIO & VP)*
Paul R. Boulier *(CMO & VP)*
Donald B. McMillan *(Chief Acctg Officer & Controller)*
Derek R. Bristow *(Gen Mgr)*
Gustavo Perez *(Gen Mgr)*
Jennifer Beeman *(Dir-Corp Comm & IR)*
Thomas R. Rice *(Dir-HR-Americas)*
Patrick Speek *(CFO EMEA & Dir-Fin)*
Liu Hao *(Sls Mgr-China)*
Todd Nichols *(Sls Mgr-Engineered Plastics-North America)*
Mannar Mannan Shanmugam *(Sls Mgr-India)*
Alice Chan *(Mgr-Masterbatch Asia Bus Unit)*
R. J. Schoger *(Mgr-Fin Reporting)*
Sanja Valentic *(Mgr-Corp Mktg & Bus Dev)*
Malia Gelfo *(Asst Controller)*
Brands & Products:
A SCHULMAN
AQUALOY
AQUASOL
CLARIX
COMALLOY
COMPOUNDING YOUR SUCCESS
COMSHIELD
COMTUF
FORMION
HILOY
INVISION
LUBRILON
PAPERMATCH
POLYAXIS
POLYBATCH
POLYBATCH COLOR
POLYBATCH FILM
POLYBLAK
POLYETHELENE
POLYFABS
POLYFLAM
POLYFORT
POLYLUX
POLYMAN
POLYPROPYLENE
POLYPUR
POLYSTAT
POLYSTYRENE
POLYTROPE
POLYVIN
SCHULABLEND
SCHULADUR
SCHULAFLEX
SCHULAFORM
SCHULAMID
SCHULATEC
SCHULINK
SUNFROST
SUNPRENE
SUPERLINEAR
TEMPALLOY
THERMEX
VINIKA
VOLOY
Advertising Agency:
Dix & Eaton Incorporated
200 Public Sq Ste 1400
Cleveland, OH 44114
Tel.: (216) 241-0405
Fax: (216) 241-3070

AAPER ALCOHOL AND CHEMICAL COMPANY

1101 Isaac Shelby Dr
Shelbyville, KY 40065
Tel.: (502) 232-7600
Fax: (502) 633-0594
Toll Free: (800) 456-1017
E-mail: contact@aaper.com
Web Site: www.aaper.com
Approx. Number Employees: 100
Year Founded: 1979
Business Description:
Ethyl Alcohol Mfr & Sales

Key to Media (For complete agency information see *The Advertising Red Books-Agencies* edition):
1. Bus. Publs. 2. Cable T.V. 3. Catalogs & Directories. 4. Co-op Adv. 5. Consumer Mags. 6. D.M. to Bus. Estab.7. D.M. to Consumers 8. Daily Newsp. 9. Exhibits/Trade Shows 10. Foreign 11. Infomercial 12. Internet Adv.13. Multimedia 14. Network Radio 15. Network T.V. 16. Newsp. Distr. Mags. 17. Other 18. Outdoor (Posters, Transit) 19. Point of Purchase20. Premiums, Novelties 21. Product Samples 22. Special Events Mktg. 23. Spot Radio 24. Spot T.V. 25. Weekly Newsp. 26. Yellow Page Adv.

S.I.C.: 2869; 5169
N.A.I.C.S.: 325199; 424690
Media: 2-10-13
Personnel:
Paul Drmarco *(Pres)*
Brands & Products:
AAPER

ACCURATE CHEMICAL & SCIENTIFIC CORPORATION
300 Shames Dr
Westbury, NY 11590-1736
Tel.: (516) 333-2221
Fax: (516) 997-4948
Toll Free: (800) 645-6264
E-mail: info@accuratechemical.com
Web Site: www.accuratechemical.com
Approx. Sls.: $5,000,000
Approx. Number Employees: 22
Year Founded: 1974
Business Description:
Organic & Inorganic Chemicals & Biochemicals
S.I.C.: 5169
N.A.I.C.S.: 424690
Import Export
Advertising Expenditures: $400,000
Media: 2-4-7-8-10-20-21-22
Distr.: Direct to Consumer; Natl.
Budget Set: Oct.
Personnel:
Rudy Rosenberg *(Pres)*
Brands & Products:
ACCURATE
AXELL
ITS MORE THAN A MAN ITS A PROMISE
THOMAFLUID

ACETO CORPORATION
4 Tri Harbor Court
Port Washington, NY 11050
Tel.: (516) 627-6000
Fax: (516) 627-6093
Telex: 6859146
E-mail: aceto@aceto.com
Web Site: www.aceto.com
Approx. Sls.: $412,428,000
Approx. Number Employees: 238
Year Founded: 1947
Business Description:
Health & Industrial Chemical Distr
S.I.C.: 5169; 2869
N.A.I.C.S.: 424690; 325199
Import Export
Media: 2-9
Personnel:
Albert L. Eilender *(Chm & CEO)*
Vincent G. Miata *(Pres & COO)*
Douglas Roth *(CFO, Treas & Asst Sec)*
Frank DeBenedittis *(Exec VP)*
Nicholas Shackley *(Sr VP-Intl-Active Pharmaceutical Ingredients)*
Roger Weaving, Jr. *(Sr VP-Specialty Chemicals Bus Segment)*
Charles Alaimo *(VP-HR)*
Edward Kelly *(Controller & Asst VP)*
Amy Tam Rogers *(Asst VP & Dir-Transportation)*
Peter Tomasino *(Asst VP-Nutritional Chemicals)*
Theodore Ayvas *(Dir-Corp Comm & IR)*

ACHESON INDUSTRIES, INC.
(Sub. of Henkel AG & Co. KGaA)
1600 Washington Ave
Port Huron, MI 48060-3456
Tel.: (810) 984-5581
Fax: (810) 984-3135
Toll Free: (800) 255-1908
Web Site: www.achesonindustries.com
Approx. Number Employees: 750
Business Description:
Specialty Lubricants, Chemicals & Spray Equipment Mfr.
S.I.C.: 2899; 3644
N.A.I.C.S.: 325998; 335932
Export
Media: 7-8-10-11
Personnel:
Christine Haas *(Mgr-Mktg)*

ACL INCORPORATED
(d/b/a Staticide)
840 W 49th Pl
Chicago, IL 60609
Tel.: (847) 981-9212
Fax: (847) 981-9278
Toll Free: (800) 782-8420
E-mail: info@aclstaticide.com
Web Site: www.aclstaticide.com
Approx. Number Employees: 10
Year Founded: 1969
Business Description:
Anti-Static Products & Office & Computer Cleaning & Maintenance Products Mfr & Marketer
S.I.C.: 2819; 3825
N.A.I.C.S.: 325188; 334515
Media: 10
Brands & Products:
DUALMAT
STATICIDE

ACTON TECHNOLOGIES, INC.
100 Thompson St
Pittston, PA 18640
Tel.: (570) 654-0612
Fax: (570) 654-2810
E-mail: usa@actontech.com
Web Site: www.actontech.com
Approx. Number Employees: 50
Year Founded: 1985
Business Description:
Specialty Chemicals Processor & Mfr
S.I.C.: 3081; 2843
N.A.I.C.S.: 326113; 325613
Export
Media: 2-7-10-11-13
Personnel:
Kevin G. Nelson *(Chm)*
Terrence Neville *(Pres)*
Bill Scott *(Dir-Sls & Mktg-Global)*
Brands & Products:
ACLON
ACTON TECHNOLOGIES
BUILDING TECHNOLOGY FOR TOMORROW
FLUOROETCH
HGX
WAXCUT

ADM TRONICS UNLIMITED, INC.
224 Pegasus Ave
Northvale, NJ 07647
Tel.: (201) 767-6040
Fax: (201) 784-0620
E-mail: sales@admtronics.com
Web Site: www.admtronics.com
E-Mail For Key Personnel:
Sales Director: sales@admtronics.com
Approx. Rev.: $1,166,591
Approx. Number Employees: 15
Year Founded: 1969
Business Description:
Chemical Products, Resins, Medical Electronic Devices Mfr & Sales
S.I.C.: 2821; 2844; 2891; 2899; 3841; 3845
N.A.I.C.S.: 325211; 325520; 325620; 325998; 334510; 339112
Advertising Expenditures: $12,975
Media: 4-7
Personnel:
Andre A. DiMino *(Pres)*

AFFYMETRIX
(Formerly USB Corporation)
(Sub. of Affymetrix, Inc.)
26111 Miles Rd
Cleveland, OH 44128
Tel.: (216) 765-5000
Fax: (216) 464-5075
Toll Free: (800) 321-9322
Web Site: www.affymetrix.com
Sales Range: $25-49.9 Million
Sales Estimate: $80-99 Million
Approx. Number Employees: 67
Year Founded: 1999
Business Description:
Biochemicals & Molecular Biology Product Retailer
S.I.C.: 2834; 2833
N.A.I.C.S.: 325412; 325411
Media: 7-13-20
Personnel:
Camellia Ngo *(Sr VP-HR)*
Brands & Products:
LIGATE-IT
OPTIKINASE

AIR LIQUIDE AMERICA CORPORATION
(Sub. of Air Liquide S.A.)
2700 Post Oak Blvd Ste 1800
Houston, TX 77056-5797
Mailing Address:
PO Box 460229
Houston, TX 77056-8229
Tel.: (713) 624-8000
Fax: (713) 624-8030
Toll Free: (800) 820-2522
Web Site: www.airliquide.com
Approx. Number Employees: 600
Year Founded: 1969
Business Description:
Supplier of Industrial Gases
S.I.C.: 2813; 3533
N.A.I.C.S.: 325120; 333132
Import Export
Advertising Expenditures: $3,000,000
Media: 2
Distr.: Natl.
Brands & Products:
AIRLIQUIDE

AIR LIQUIDE AMERICA SPECIALTY GASES LLC
(Sub. of Air Liquide America Corporation)
6141 Easton Rd PO Box 310
Plumsteadville, PA 18949-0310
Mailing Address:
PO Box 310
Plumsteadville, PA 18949
Tel.: (215) 766-8861
Tel.: (215) 766-8860
Fax: (215) 766-0320
Toll Free: (800) 21SCOTT
Web Site: www.scottgas.com
Sales Range: $75-99.9 Million
Approx. Number Employees: 450
Year Founded: 1960
Business Description:
Pure Gases, Gas Mixtures, Pure & Mixed Gases In Disposable Containers, Gas Handling Equipment & Services
S.I.C.: 2813; 5084
N.A.I.C.S.: 325120; 423830
Import Export
Advertising Expenditures: $200,000
Media: 2-4-6-7-8-10-11-13-17-20-26
Distr.: Intl.
Budget Set: July
Brands & Products:
ACUBLEND
ACULIFE
ACUPHASE
CEM DAILY STANDARDS
CONTINUUM
ESCOTT
FOLIO
GLOBAL CROSS REFERENCE SERVICE
GRAVSTAT
MICROGRAV
PROTOCOL ELEVEN
SCOTTY TRANSPORTABLES
TECHNIGAS
TECHNIMATE
Advertising Agency:
Timmons & Company, Inc.
3795 Rte 202
Doylestown, PA 18901
Tel.: (215) 340-9090
Fax: (215) 340-5861
(Specialty Gases & Gas Handling Equipment)

AIR PRODUCTS AND CHEMICALS, INC.
7201 Hamilton Blvd
Allentown, PA 18195-1526
Tel.: (610) 481-4911
Fax: (610) 481-5900
E-mail: info@airproducts.com
Web Site: www.airproducts.com
Approx. Sls.: $9,026,000,000
Approx. Number Employees: 17,900
Year Founded: 1940
Business Description:
Industrial, Medical & Specialty Gases, Intermediate Chemicals & Performance Processing Equipment Mfr & Distr
S.I.C.: 5169; 2813; 2869
N.A.I.C.S.: 424690; 325120; 325199
Import Export
Advertising Expenditures: $4,600,000
Media: 2-4-7-8-10-11-14-18-21
Distr.: Intl.; Natl.
Budget Set: June
Personnel:
John E. McGlade *(Chm, Pres & CEO)*
Paul E. Huck *(CFO & Sr VP)*
Richard Boocock *(CIO & VP-IT)*
John Stanley *(Gen Counsel & Sr VP)*
Robert D. Dixon *(Sr VP & Gen Mgr-Merchant Gases)*
Stephen J. Jones *(Sr VP & Gen Mgr-Tonnage Gases, Equipment & Energy)*
Scott A. Sherman *(Sr VP, Gen Mgr-Strategy & Execution)*
John W. Marsland *(Sr VP-Supply Chain)*

Key to Media (For complete agency information see *The Advertising Red Books-Agencies* edition):
1. Bus. Publs. 2. Cable T.V. 3. Catalogs & Directories. 4. Co-op Adv. 5. Consumer Mags. 6. D.M. to Bus. Estab.7. D.M. to Consumers 8. Daily Newsp. 9. Exhibits/Trade Shows 10. Foreign 11. Infomercial 12. Internet Adv.13. Multimedia 14. Network Radio 15. Network T.V. 16. Newsp. Distr. Mags. 17. Other 18. Outdoor (Posters, Transit) 19. Point of Purchase20. Premiums, Novelties 21. Product Samples 22. Special Events Mktg. 23. Spot Radio 24. Spot T.V. 25. Weekly Newsp. 26. Yellow Page Adv.

Air Products and Chemicals, Inc. — (Continued)

Lynn C. Minella *(Sr VP-HR & Comm)*
Corning F. Painter *(Sr VP-Corp Strategy & Tech)*
Howard Castle-Smith *(Reg VP-Tonnage Gases-Europe & Middle East)*
Jeffry L. Byrne *(VP & Gen Mgr-Tonnage Gases)*
Bruce C. Hargus *(VP & Gen Mgr-Sls & Ops-Electronics Div)*
Patricia A. Mattimore *(VP & Gen Mgr-Performance Matls Div)*
Elizabeth L. Klebe *(VP-Corp Comm)*
John R. Dodds *(Dir-Global Brand & Mktg Comm)*
Simon R. Moore *(Dir-IR)*
Julie O'Brien *(Mgr-Corp Sustainability)*

Brands & Products:
ABSOLUTE
ACT
ADURA
AIR PRODUCTS
AIRBOND
AIRFLEX
AMICURE
ANCAMIDE
ANCAMINE
ANCAREZ
ANCHOR
ANQUAMINE
ANQUAWHITE
APACHI
APCOS
ASCEND
CCAR
CHEMGUARD
CLEANCAST
CLEANFIRE
COPE
CRYO-CONDAP
CRYO-GRIND
CRYO-QUICK
CUPRASELECT
CUREZOL
CURITHANE
CYRO-TRIM
DABCO
DEMS
DICYANEX
DYNOL
ENVIROGEM
EPILINK
EPODIL
EXTREMA
EZ-FIRE
FLEXBOND
FLEXCRYL
FLEXTHANE
FLONASE
FRESHPAK
GASGUARD
HRI
HYBRIDUR
ICEFLY
IMICURE
JETBOX
KEEPCOLD
LEAM
LK
LONZACURE
MDOT
MEGASYS
METACURE
MULTIFLUOR
NOURYBOND
OPTIPATTERN
OPTIRINSE
OPTIYIELD
OXPRO OR
OXYRICH
PDEMS
POLYCAT
PRIMAX
PRISM
PURIFIRE
QMAC
RAPIDFIRE
RILEE
SCHUMACHER
SELECTFLUOR
STABILIFE
SUR-WET
SURFYNOL
SYTON
TELALERT
TRANS-LC
V MDOT
VALBOND
VALTAC
VERSATHANE
VINAC
WAVE
Z3MS
Z4MS
ZTOMCATS

Advertising Agency:
Carton Donofrio Partners, Inc.
100 N Charles St 15th Fl
Baltimore, MD 21201
Tel.: (410) 576-9000
Fax: (410) 528-8809
(Industrial Gases and Chemicals, Environmental and Energy Systems)

AIRGAS, INC.

259 N Radnor-Chester Rd Ste 100
Radnor, PA 19087-5283
Mailing Address:
PO Box 6675
Radnor, PA 19087-8675
Tel.: (610) 687-5253
Fax: (610) 225-2165
Toll Free: (800) 255-2165
E-mail: investor@airgas.com
Web Site: www.airgas.com
Approx. Sls.: $4,251,467,000
Approx. Number Employees: 14,000
Year Founded: 1982
Business Description:
Industrial, Specialty & Medical Gases & Equipment Distr & Producer; Welding Equipment & Safety Products Distr
S.I.C.: 5169; 2899
N.A.I.C.S.: 424690; 325998
Media: 2-4-7-10-13-20-22-26
Personnel:
Peter McCausland *(Chm & CEO)*
Robert M. McLaughlin *(CFO & Sr VP)*
Michael L. Molinini *(COO & Exec VP)*
Robert A. Dougherty *(CIO & Sr VP)*
Max Hooper *(Pres-Western Div)*
Robert H. Young, Jr. *(Gen Counsel & Sr VP)*
Andrew R. Cichocki *(Sr VP-Distr Ops & Bus Process Improvement)*
Leslie J. Graff *(Sr VP-Corp Dev)*
Michael E. Rohde *(Sr VP)*
Ronald J. Stark *(Sr VP-Sls & Mktg)*
Thomas S. Thoman *(Sr VP)*
Dwight T. Wilson *(Sr VP-HR)*
Frederick E. Manley *(VP-Tech & Svcs Markets)*
R. Jay Worley *(VP-Comm & IR)*
E. David Coyne *(Dir-Internal Audit)*
Barry Strzelec *(Dir-IR)*
Drew Wiess *(Dir-HR Programs)*
Dan Meddaugh *(Product Mgr-Radnor)*
Earlene Shillingford *(Product Mgr-Specialty Gases & Process Chemicals)*
Skip Olson *(Mgr-Welding Products)*

Brands & Products:
AIRGAS
RADNOR
YOU'LL FIND IT WITH US.

Advertising Agency:
Backe Digital Brand Marketing
35 Cricket Ter Ctr
Ardmore, PA 19003-2203
Tel.: (610) 896-9260
Fax: (610) 896-9242

AKZO NOBEL INC.

(Sub. of Akzo Nobel N.V.)
525 W Van Buren St 14,15,16 Fl
Chicago, IL 60607
Tel.: (312) 544-7000
Fax: (312) 544-6901
Web Site: www.akzonobel.com
Approx. Number Employees: 300
Year Founded: 1969
Business Description:
Mfr. of Healthcare Products, Coatings & Chemicals
S.I.C.: 2869; 2851
N.A.I.C.S.: 325199; 325510
Import Export
Media: 2-6-9-10-25
Distr.: Natl.
Personnel:
Philip E. Radtke *(Pres)*
Alain Mimeault *(Dir-Pur-Solvents-Global)*
Eric Stasiowski *(Dir-Comm)*

ALBEMARLE CORPORATION

Baton Rouge Twr 451 Florida St
Baton Rouge, LA 70801
Tel.: (225) 388-8011
Fax: (225) 388-7686
Toll Free: (800) 535-3030
Web Site: www.albemarle.com
Approx. Sls.: $2,362,764,000
Approx. Number Employees: 4,020
Year Founded: 1994
Business Description:
Highly-Engineered Specialty Chemicals & Services Developer, Mfr & Marketer
S.I.C.: 2821; 2834
N.A.I.C.S.: 325211; 325412
Media: 4-10-11
Personnel:
Mark C. Rohr *(Chm)*
Luther C. Kissam, IV *(CEO)*
Scott A. Tozier *(CFO & Sr VP)*
John M. Steitz *(COO & Exec VP)*
Nicole C. Daniel *(VP, Chief Compliance Officer, Asst Gen Counsel, Corp Sec)*
William B. Allen, Jr. *(Chief Acctg Officer, VP & Corp Controller)*
David W. Clary *(Chief Sustainability Officer & VP)*
Karen G. Narwold *(Gen Counsel & Sr VP)*
William H. Dumas *(VP-Pur & Logistics)*
Darian K. Rich *(VP-HR)*
Lorin Crenshaw *(Dir-IR & Comm)*
William Pickrell *(Dir-Global Bus)*

Brands & Products:
ABZOL
ADMA
ALBEMARLE
ALBLEND
ALBROM
ANTIBLAZE
ASUR
BRIGHTSUN
COMPALOX
DAMA
ETHACURE
ETHANOX
ETHAPHOS
EZA
FIRSTCURE
GO-ULTRA
HITEC
MAGNIFIN
MARTIFILL
MARTIFIN
MARTIGLOSS
MARTINAL
MARTOXID
MARTOXIN
NCENDX
PERGOPAK
PYRO-CHEK
SANIBROM
SAYTEX
STABROM
WELLBROM
WELLFORM
WELLGUARD
XTRABROM

ALCO INDUSTRIES, INC.

820 Adams Ave Ste 130
Norristown, PA 19403
Tel.: (610) 666-0930
Fax: (610) 666-0752
E-mail: webmaster@alcoind.com
Web Site: www.alcoind.com
Approx. Number Employees: 1,973
Year Founded: 1983
Business Description:
Chemical, Rubber, Plastic & Metal Products Mfr
S.I.C.: 2879; 2821; 2822; 2851; 2873; 2899; 3494
N.A.I.C.S.: 325320; 325211; 325212; 325311; 325510; 325998; 332919
Media: 7-10
Distr.: Natl.

ALDRICH CHEMICAL COMPANY, INC.

(Sub. of Sigma-Aldrich Corporation)
6000 N Teutonie Ave
Milwaukee, WI 53209
Tel.: (414) 438-3850
Fax: (414) 438-2199
E-mail: aldrich@sial.com
Web Site: www.sigma-aldrich.com
Sales Range: $250-299.9 Million
Approx. Number Employees: 500
Business Description:
Mfr. of Fine Chemicals & Related Products for Research & Industry
S.I.C.: 2869; 2819
N.A.I.C.S.: 325199; 325188
Advertising Expenditures: $300,000
Bus. Publs.: $255,000; Exhibits/Trade Shows: $45,000
Distr.: Intl.; Natl.
Budget Set: Oct.

Key to Media (For complete agency information see *The Advertising Red Books-Agencies* edition):
1. Bus. Publs. 2. Cable T.V. 3. Catalogs & Directories. 4. Co-op Adv. 5. Consumer Mags. 6. D.M. to Bus. Estab.7. D.M. to Consumers
8. Daily Newsp. 9. Exhibits/Trade Shows 10. Foreign 11. Infomercial 12. Internet Adv.13. Multimedia 14. Network Radio
15. Network T.V. 16. Newsp. Distr. Mags. 17. Other 18. Outdoor (Posters, Transit) 19. Point of Purchase20. Premiums, Novelties
21. Product Samples 22. Special Events Mktg. 23. Spot Radio 24. Spot T.V. 25. Weekly Newsp. 26. Yellow Page Adv.

Personnel:
Joe Porwal *(Pres)*
Bill Seitz *(Mgr)*

ALTAIR NANOTECHNOLOGIES INC.
204 Edison Way
Reno, NV 89502-2306
Tel.: (775) 856-2500
Fax: (775) 856-1619
E-mail: marketing@altairnano.com
Web Site: www.altairnano.com
Approx. Rev.: $7,830,000
Approx. Number Employees: 99
Year Founded: 1973
Business Description:
Titanium Dioxide Particle Producer
S.I.C.: 2816; 2899
N.A.I.C.S.: 325131; 325998
Media: 2-7
Personnel:
Pierre Lortie *(Chm)*
H. Frank Gibbard *(Pres & CEO)*
Stephen B. Huang *(CFO & VP)*
Stephen A. Balogh *(VP-HR)*
Toni Bondi *(Dir-Acctg)*
Brands & Products:
ALTAIR NANOTECHNOLOGIES
ALTAIRNANO
HYDROCHLORIDE PIGMENT PROCESS
NANOCHECK
RENAZORB
TINANO
Advertising Agency:
Investor Relation Resources, LLC
2865 East Coast Hwy Ste 311
Corona, CA 92625
Tel.: (949) 566-9860

AMCOL INTERNATIONAL CORPORATION
2870 Forbs Ave
Hoffman Estates, IL 60192
Tel.: (847) 851-1500
Fax: (847) 506-6199
Toll Free: (800) 426-5564
E-mail: invest@amcol.com
Web Site: www.amcol.com
Approx. Sls.: $852,538,000
Approx. Number Employees: 2,383
Year Founded: 1927
Business Description:
Minerals Producer, Mfr & Marketer
S.I.C.: 1459; 1481; 5032
N.A.I.C.S.: 212325; 213115; 423320
Import Export
Advertising Expenditures: $8,948,807
Media: 2-4-10
Distr.: Intl.
Personnel:
John Hughes *(Chm)*
Ryan F. McKendrick *(Pres & CEO)*
Donald W. Pearson *(CFO & Sr VP)*
Jeff Gathe *(CIO & VP)*
Gary L. Castagna *(Pres-Global Minerals & Matls)*
Brands & Products:
ACCOCARB
ACCOFORM
ACCOPURE
ACCOSORB
ADDITROL
AGGRECOR
AGRO GEL S
AGRO LIG
BENTOMAT
BLACK HILLS
CARE FREE KITTY
CAST-RITE
CAT TAILS
CELLFLO
CLAYMAX
COPE ROPE
DRILL GEL
DUCKSBACK
ENERSOL-X
FLO-CARB
HECTABRITE
HECTALITE
HEVI-SAND
HYDROSHIELD
IMPERM
KRYSTAL-KLEAN
KWK
MACROBEAD
MAGNABRITE
MAGNASPERSE
MPC 220
NANOMAX
NANOMER
ORGANO-GRO
PAMPER KAT
PANTHER CREEK
PELBEN
POLARGEL
POLY-PORE
POLY-SPHERE
POLYSEC
PREMIUM CHOICE
PROBENT
PROBOND
PROGEL
REELI-KLEAN
RETAIN
RHEOSPAN
RIPPLES
SEFRONITE
SPV
STRONGSEAL
SUPER TREAT
VIRISORB
VOLCARB
VOLCLAY
WATERSTOP-RX

AMERICAN CHEMET CORPORATION
740 Waukegan Rd Ste 202
Deerfield, IL 60015-4374
Tel.: (847) 948-0800
Fax: (847) 948-0811
E-mail: sales@chemet.com
Web Site: www.chemet.com
E-Mail For Key Personnel:
Sales Director: sales@chemet.com
Approx. Number Employees: 104
Year Founded: 1946
Business Description:
Mfr. & Marketer of Cuprous Oxide, Copper Powder, Cupric Oxide, Zinc Oxide, Dispersion Strengthened Copper & Copper-Based Agricultural Fungicides
S.I.C.: 2819; 2816
N.A.I.C.S.: 325188; 325131
Import Export
Advertising Expenditures: $250,000
Media: 2-7-10-13
Personnel:
W.W. Shropshire, Jr. *(Chm)*
Skip Klatt *(VP-Sls)*
Brands & Products:
AMERICAN CHEMET
CHEMET CDC
CHEMET DSC
CHEN COPP
LOLO TINT
PURPLE COPP
RED PREMIUM
ULTRAFINE
ZINOX 350

AMERICAN GAS & CHEMICAL CO., LTD.
220 Pegasus Ave
Northvale, NJ 07647-1904
Tel.: (201) 767-7300
Fax: (201) 767-1741
Toll Free: (800) 288-3647
Telex: 135151
E-mail: contact@amgas.com
Web Site: www.amgas.com
E-Mail For Key Personnel:
Marketing Director: mkershaw@amgas.com
Sales Range: $125-149.9 Million
Approx. Number Employees: 30
Year Founded: 1953
Business Description:
Leak Testing & Gas Monitoring Products Mfr
S.I.C.: 2819; 3829
N.A.I.C.S.: 325188; 334519
Import Export
Advertising Expenditures: $300,000
Media: 2-4-5-6-7-10-11-19-20-21-26
Distr.: Intl.; Natl.
Budget Set: Nov. -Dec.
Personnel:
Gerald L. Anderson *(Pres & CEO)*
Melanie Kershaw *(VP-Mktg)*
Brands & Products:
AMGAS
CGT-501
CGT-701
FLUORO-FINDER III
IMMERSIT
LEAK-TEC
MICRO 550
MICRO 750
MICRO PAC
MUD-DUCK
PINPOINT
SBG-200
SONIC 3000
TSI-301

ANACHEMIA CANADA, INC.
255 Norman
Lachine, QC H8R 1A3, Canada
Tel.: (514) 489-5711
Fax: (514) 363-5281
E-mail: info@anachemia.com
Web Site: www.anachemia.com
Approx. Number Employees: 100
Year Founded: 1942
Business Description:
Laboratory Grade Chemicals Mfr & Laboratory Supplies & Equipment Distr
S.I.C.: 2899
N.A.I.C.S.: 325998
Import Export
Media: 10
Personnel:
Ivoj Kudrnac *(Chm)*
Martin Robinson *(Pres)*
Russell Lavigne *(VP & Gen Mgr)*
Doug Crossman *(VP-Sls)*
Carol Haley *(VP-Sls & Mktg)*
Chris Jorgensen *(VP-IT)*
Barry Yee *(VP-Fin-Admin)*
Peter Cavender *(Dir-Mining-North America)*
Bill Clifford *(Dir-Mining & Sls-Intl)*
Roy Hogarth *(Dir-New Projects)*
Lorraine Jobin *(Dir-Customer Support Sys)*
Del MacNeil *(Dir-Bus Dev)*
Dan Paradis *(Dir-Sls)*
Ninder Mann *(Office Mgr)*
Vicki Turco *(Office Mgr)*

ANDERSON DEVELOPMENT COMPANY
(Sub. of Mitsui Chemicals America, Inc.)
1415 E Michigan St
Adrian, MI 49221-3499
Tel.: (517) 263-2121
Fax: (517) 263-1000
Web Site: www.andersondevelopment.com
Year Founded: 1988
Business Description:
Specialty Chemicals Mfr & Sales
S.I.C.: 2899
N.A.I.C.S.: 325998
Media: 10
Personnel:
Joseph D. Greulich *(Pres & CEO)*

ANGUS CHEMICAL COMPANY
(Sub. of THE DOW CHEMICAL COMPANY)
1500 E Lk Cook Rd
Buffalo Grove, IL 60089-6553
Tel.: (847) 215-8600
Fax: (847) 215-8626
Toll Free: (800) 362-2580
Telex: 275422 ANGUS UR
Web Site: www.angus.com
Sales Range: $25-49.9 Million
Approx. Number Employees: 100
Year Founded: 1982
Business Description:
Nitroparaffin-Based Chemicals & Derivatives Mfr & Marketer
S.I.C.: 2869; 2899
N.A.I.C.S.: 325199; 325998
Export
Media: 2-4-7-10-11-17
Distr.: Intl.; Natl.
Personnel:
Alan Whetten *(Dir-Res & Dev)*
John Berryman *(Sr Mgr-Fin)*
Liam Doherty *(Mgr-Global Mtkg)*
Tina Frattaroli *(Mgr-Global Mtkg)*
Susan Jiang *(Mgr-Bus Comm)*
Jerry Konst *(Mgr-Global Product Mtkg)*
Dwayne J. Roark *(Mgr-Global Bus Comm)*

ANSUL, INCORPORATED
(Sub. of Tyco Fire & Security)
1 Stanton St
Marinette, WI 54143-2542
Tel.: (715) 735-7411
Fax: (715) 732-3469
Toll Free: (800) 862-6785
Web Site: www.ansul.com
Sales Range: $200-249.9 Million
Approx. Number Employees: 650
Year Founded: 1939
Business Description:
Fire Suppression & Control Products Mfr
S.I.C.: 9224

Key to Media (For complete agency information see *The Advertising Red Books-Agencies* edition):
1. Bus. Publs. 2. Cable T.V. 3. Catalogs & Directories. 4. Co-op Adv. 5. Consumer Mags. 6. D.M. to Bus. Estab.7. D.M. to Consumers 8. Daily Newsp. 9. Exhibits/Trade Shows 10. Foreign 11. Infomercial 12. Internet Adv.13. Multimedia 14. Network Radio 15. Network T.V. 16. Newsp. Distr. Mags. 17. Other 18. Outdoor (Posters, Transit) 19. Point of Purchase20. Premiums, Novelties 21. Product Samples 22. Special Events Mktg. 23. Spot Radio 24. Spot T.V. 25. Weekly Newsp. 26. Yellow Page Adv.

Ansul, Incorporated — (Continued)

N.A.I.C.S.: 922160
Export
Advertising Expenditures: $750,000
Media: 2-4-10-20-26
Distr.: Intl.; Natl.
Budget Set: Sept.
Personnel:
Dennis Moraros *(VP-Fin)*
David A. Pelton *(Dir-Global Mktg)*
Jim Cox *(Sr Mgr-Mktg Comm)*
Bob Kroll *(Product Mgr-Vehicle & Indus Sys-Americas)*
Mark Neumann *(Mgr-Mktg-Restaurant Sys-Americas)*
Steve W. Hansen *(Mktg Mgr-Foam Products & Engred Sys)*
Mike Stromberg *(Product Mgr-Portable Products-Americas)*
Randy Bero *(Mgr-Quality Engrg)*
Marie R. Engman *(Mgr-Customer Svcs-US)*
Sally Falkenberg *(Mgr-Publ & Distr)*
Julie Overman *(Mgr-Customer Svcs-Intl)*
Rich Seaberg *(Mgr-Quality Assurance)*
David Seikel *(Mgr-Govt Sls)*
Mary Lieburn *(Coord-Quality Svcs)*
Brands & Products:
A-101
ANSUL
AUTOPULSE
CHECKFIRE
CLEANGUARD
FORAY
IND-X
INERGEN
K-GUARD
LVS
MAGNUM
MET-L-X
PIRANHA
PLUS-FIFTY
R-102
RED LINE
SAPPHIRE
SENTRY
SILV-EX
SPILL-X
TARGET-7
VESDA

ARCH CHEMICALS, INC.
501 Merritt 7
Norwalk, CT 06851
Mailing Address:
PO Box 5204
Norwalk, CT 06856-5204
Tel.: (203) 229-2900
Fax: (203) 229-3652
E-mail: mefaford@archchemicals.com
Web Site: www.archchemicals.com
Approx. Sls.: $1,377,400,000
Approx. Number Employees: 2,504
Year Founded: 1999
Business Description:
Specialty Chemicals Mfr
S.I.C.: 2899; 2812; 2819; 2869
N.A.I.C.S.: 325998; 325181; 325188; 325199
Advertising Expenditures: $12,000,000
Media: 2-3-6-7-10-20-21-23-24
Personnel:
Michael E. Campbell *(Chm, Pres & CEO)*
Steven C. Giuliano *(CFO & Sr VP)*
Sarah A. O'Connor *(Chief Legal Officer & Sr VP-Strategic Dev)*
Joseph H. Shaulson *(Exec VP-Personal Care, Indus Biocides & Performance Products)*
Michael Cook *(Sr VP-HTH Water Products)*
Rick Walden *(Sr VP-Indus Biocides, Performance Products & Asia Pacific)*
Mark E. Faford *(VP-IR & Corp Comm)*
Brands & Products:
ACQUA-BIOMIN
ARCH
BAQUACIL
BAQUASPA
BETAVERA
BIO-OIL
BIO-PLEX
BIO-POL
THE BIOCIDES COMPANY
BIODYNES
BIOMIN
BIOPLEX RNA
BIOVERT
BOROCIDE P
BROOKOSOME
BROOKSWAX
CCH
CHRONOSPHERE
CONSTANT CHLOR
COSMOCIL
DENSIL
DRICON
DRYTEC
DURATION
FOAM-COLL
FROM GOOD CHEMISTRY COMES GOOD INNOVATIONS
GENTI-FOL
GLB
HTH
J3
LEISURE TIME
LINEA BLU
LIQUIWAX
LOTUS ZYMBIOZOME
MIKROKILL
NATURAL SELECT
NON-COM
OMACIDE
OMADINE
OUTDOOR
PACE
PEPTAMIDE
PHYTOKERATIN
PLANELL
PLANELL OIL
POLY-A
POLY-G
POOLIFE
PROXEL
PULSAR
PURISTA
REPUTAIN
REPUTEX
RESIDENTIAL OUTDOOR
SAYERLACK
SOCK IT
SOY ZYMBIOZOME
SPIRAPLEX
SUPER SOCK
SUPER SOCK IT
TANALISED
TANALITH
TRIADINE
ULTRA PURE
VACSOL
VANQUISH
VANTOCIL
VITAZYME
WAYHIB
WOLMAN
WOLMANIZED
Advertising Agencies:
Brownstein Group
215 S Broad St 9th Fl
Philadelphia, PA 19107-5325
Tel.: (215) 735-3470
Fax: (215) 735-6298

Summit Marketing
Three Cityplace Dr Ste 350
Saint Louis, MO 63141-7091
Tel.: (314) 569-3737
Fax: (314) 569-0037
Toll Free: (866) 590-6000

ARCH CHEMICALS, INC.
(Sub. of Arch Chemicals, Inc.)
5660 New Northside Dr 1100
Atlanta, GA 30328
Tel.: (678) 627-2000
Fax: (678) 627-2093
Fax: (866) 705-0465
Toll Free: (800) 523-7391
E-mail: info@wolmanizedwood.com
Web Site: www.wolmanizedwood.com
Sales Range: $75-99.9 Million
Approx. Number Employees: 200
Business Description:
Preservatives & Additives for Pressure Treated Wood Mfr
S.I.C.: 2899; 2861
N.A.I.C.S.: 325998; 325191
Export
Media: 2-4-7-9-10-13-19-20
Distr.: Intl.; Natl.
Budget Set: Sept.
Personnel:
Huck Devenzio *(Mgr-Mktg Comm)*
Brands & Products:
ANTIBLU
CELCURE
CLEAR GUARD
ENVIRO-PROCESSED
EXTRA
FRX
SILLBOR

ARIZONA CHEMICAL CO.
(Holding of American Securities LLC)
4600 Touchton Rd Ste 500
Jacksonville, FL 32246-4402
Mailing Address:
PO Box 550850
Jacksonville, FL 32255-0850
Tel.: (904) 928-8700
Fax: (904) 928-8779
Toll Free: (800) 526-5294
Telex: 441695
Web Site: www.arizonachemical.com
Approx. Number Employees: 1,400
Year Founded: 1930
Business Description:
Pine Tree-Based Chemical Mfr
S.I.C.: 2861
N.A.I.C.S.: 325191
Import Export
Advertising Expenditures: $200,000
Media: 2-4-10
Distr.: Intl.; Natl.
Budget Set: Dec.
Personnel:
Cornelis Kees Verhaar *(Pres & CEO)*
Frederic Jung *(CFO & VP)*
Dick Stuyfzand *(Gen Counsel & VP)*
Dave Cowfer *(VP-HR & Comm)*
Brands & Products:
AQUATAC
CENTURY
CENWAX
SYLFAT
SYLVABLEND
SYLVACLEAR
SYLVACOTE
SYLVAGEL
SYLVAGUM
SYLVALITE
SYLVAPINE
SYLVAPRINT
SYLVARES
SYLVAROS
SYLVATAC
SYLVATAL
UNI-KYD
UNI-REZ
UNI-TAC
UNICLEAR
UNIDYME
UNIFLEX
UNITOL
XR 4286
ZONATAC

ARKEMA INC.
(Sub. of Arkema S.A.)
2000 Market St
Philadelphia, PA 19103-3231
Tel.: (215) 419-7000
Fax: (215) 419-7591
Toll Free: (800) 225-7788
Web Site: www.arkema-inc.com
Sales Range: $1-4.9 Billion
Approx. Number Employees: 800
Year Founded: 2000
Business Description:
Producer & Marketer of Commodity Chemicals, Chemical Intermediates, Specialties & Agrichemicals Including Plastics, Specialized Process Equipment & Health Products Consisting of Ethical & Proprietary Drugs
S.I.C.: 2899
N.A.I.C.S.: 325998
Import Export
Media: 2-4-5-6-7-8-10-11-15-19-20-21-26
Distr.: Intl.; Natl.
Budget Set: Nov.
Personnel:
George Cornelius *(Pres & CEO)*
Patricia McCarthy *(CFO & Sr VP)*
Mike Keough *(CIO)*
Richard Rowe *(Pres-Additives Grp)*
William Hamel *(Gen Counsel & VP)*
Bernard Leconte *(Sr VP-Mfg & Regulatory Svcs)*
Chris Giangrasso *(VP-HR & Comm)*
Jim Bell *(Dir-Comm)*
Amy Bosshardt *(Mgr-Comm)*
Olivier Griperay *(Mgr-Market)*
Brands & Products:
FLEXJOINT
FORANE
FURALAC
KRYOCIDE
PENNTROWEL
PLATAMID
VOLTALEF

Key to Media (For complete agency information see *The Advertising Red Books-Agencies* edition):
1. Bus. Publs. 2. Cable T.V. 3. Catalogs & Directories. 4. Co-op Adv. 5. Consumer Mags. 6. D.M. to Bus. Estab.7. D.M. to Consumers 8. Daily Newsp. 9. Exhibits/Trade Shows 10. Foreign 11. Infomercial 12. Internet Adv.13. Multimedia 14. Network Radio 15. Network T.V. 16. Newsp. Distr. Mags. 17. Other 18. Outdoor (Posters, Transit) 19. Point of Purchase20. Premiums, Novelties 21. Product Samples 22. Special Events Mktg. 23. Spot Radio 24. Spot T.V. 25. Weekly Newsp. 26. Yellow Page Adv.

Advertising Agency:
Chletcos/Gallagher Inc.
63 Greene St Ste 602
New York, NY 10012
Tel.: (212) 334-2455
Fax: (212) 334-2463

ARLON, INC.
(Sub. of Bairnco Corporation)
2811 S Harbor Blvd
Santa Ana, CA 92704-0260
Mailing Address:
PO Box 5260
Santa Ana, CA 92704-5805
Tel.: (714) 540-2811
Fax: (714) 540-7190
Toll Free: (800) 854-0361
E-mail: webmaster@arlon.com
Web Site: www.arlon.com
Approx. Number Employees: 160
Business Description:
Mfr. of Electronics Materials, Tape & Pressure Sensitive Materials
S.I.C.: 3089; 3081
N.A.I.C.S.: 326199; 326113
Import Export
Media: 2-7-10-17
Personnel:
Ron Hopkins *(Pres)*
Brands & Products:
COLORKOTE
DURALON
FLEXFACE
GLASSKOTE
PLASTIPRINT
SUPERGLASSKOTE

ARMAND PRODUCTS COMPANY
(Joint Venture of Church & Dwight Co., Inc. & Occidental Petroleum Corporation)
469 N Harrison St
Princeton, NJ 08540-3510
Tel.: (609) 683-7090
Fax: (609) 497-7176
E-mail: info@armandproducts.com
Web Site: www.armandproducts.com
Sales Range: $150-199.9 Million
Approx. Number Employees: 350
Year Founded: 1986
Business Description:
Potassium Carbonate & Bicarbonate Products Mfr; Owned by Church & Dwight Co., Inc. & Occidental Chemical Corporation
S.I.C.: 2819
N.A.I.C.S.: 325188
Media: 2-7-13
Personnel:
W. Patrick Fiedler *(Pres)*

ASHLAND PERFORMANCE MATERIALS
(Sub. of Ashland Services B.V.)
5200 Blazer Pkwy
Dublin, OH 43017-5309
Mailing Address:
PO Box 2219
Columbus, OH 43216-2219
Tel.: (614) 790-3333
Fax: (614) 790-3823
Toll Free: (888) ASHCHEM
Web Site: www.ashchem.com
Sales Range: $1-4.9 Billion
Approx. Number Employees: 8,000
Year Founded: 1967
Business Description:
Specialty Chemicals Supplier for Construction, Packaging & Converting, Transportation & Marine & Metal Casting; High Performance Adhesives & Specialty Resins Mfr
S.I.C.: 2899; 2819; 2821; 2869; 2891
N.A.I.C.S.: 325998; 325188; 325199; 325211; 325520
Import Export
Media: 1-2-4-7-10-11-13-15-26
Distr.: Intl.; Natl.
Personnel:
Jane O'Brien *(Pres)*
Bob Moffit *(Product Mgr-Building & Construction)*
Brands & Products:
ASHLAND

ASSOCIATED CHEMISTS, INC.
(d/b/a ACI)
4401 SE Johnson Creek Blvd
Portland, OR 97222-9218
Tel.: (503) 659-1708
Fax: (503) 653-0409
Toll Free: (800) 535-5053
E-mail: info@achemists.com
Web Site: www.achemists.com
Sales Range: Less than $1 Million
Approx. Number Employees: 12
Year Founded: 1929
Business Description:
Specialty Chemicals Mfr
S.I.C.: 2869
N.A.I.C.S.: 325199
Media: 2-10
Personnel:
Steve Brown *(Pres)*

ATLAS REFINERY, INC.
142 Lockwood St
Newark, NJ 07105-4719
Tel.: (973) 589-2002
Fax: (973) 589-7377
E-mail: info@atlasrefinery.com
Web Site: www.atlasrefinery.com
Approx. Number Employees: 36
Year Founded: 1887
Business Description:
Specialty Chemicals, Lubricants, Emulsifiers, Wetting Agents & Surfactants Mfr
S.I.C.: 2843; 2899
N.A.I.C.S.: 325613; 325998
Import Export
Advertising Expenditures: $300,000
Media: 4-13
Distr.: Intl.; Natl.
Personnel:
Steven B. Schroeder *(Owner)*
Brands & Products:
ATLAS
ATLAS LEATHER OIL
ATLAS REFINERY
ATLASENE
ATLASOL
ATLASTAN
EUREKA

AUSTIN POWDER COMPANY
(Sub. of Davis Mining & Manufacturing Inc.)
25800 Science Park Dr 3rd Fl Ste 300
Cleveland, OH 44122-7311
Tel.: (216) 464-2400
Fax: (216) 464-4418
E-mail: humanresources@austinpowder.com
Web Site: www.austinpowder.com
Approx. Number Employees: 1,000
Year Founded: 1833
Business Description:
Mfr & Distr of Industrial Explosives
S.I.C.: 2892
N.A.I.C.S.: 325920
Export
Media: 2-7-11-13
Budget Set: Oct. -Nov.
Personnel:
David M. Gleason *(Pres & CEO)*
David TRUE *(Pres)*
Michael Gleason *(COO)*
Thomas Cochran *(Dir-Adv)*
Advertising Agency:
SmileyHanchulak Marketing Communications
47 N Cleveland Massillon Rd
Akron, OH 44333-2420
Tel.: (330) 666-0868
Fax: (330) 666-5762

AVANTOR PERFORMANCE MATERIALS, INC.
(Formerly Mallinckrodt Baker, Inc.)
(Holding of New Mountain Capital, LLC)
222 Red School Ln
Phillipsburg, NJ 08865
Tel.: (908) 859-2151
Fax: (908) 859-9318
Toll Free: (800) 582-2537
E-mail: info@avantormaterials.com
Web Site: www.avantormaterials.com
Sales Range: $400-449.9 Million
Approx. Number Employees: 100
Year Founded: 1904
Business Description:
High Purity Chemicals Mfr & Marketer
S.I.C.: 2819
N.A.I.C.S.: 325188
Import Export
Media: 2-7-10
Distr.: Natl.
Budget Set: June
Personnel:
Raj Gupta *(Chm)*
Robert Harrer *(CFO, Chief Admin Officer & Exec VP)*
Jean-Marc Gilson *(CEO-Avantor Performance Matls)*
Allison Hosak *(Dir-Corp Comm)*
Russell Thorpe *(Dir-Mktg)*
Advertising Agency:
SGW
219 Changebridge Rd
Montville, NJ 07045-9514
Tel.: (973) 299-8000
Fax: (973) 299-7937
Toll Free: (800) SSDWIMC

BAKER PETROLITE CORPORATION
(Sub. of Baker Hughes Incorporated)
12645 W Airport Blvd
Sugar Land, TX 77478-6120
Mailing Address:
PO Box 5050
Sugar Land, TX 77487-5050
Tel.: (281) 276-5400
Fax: (281) 275-7395
Telex: 44-899
E-mail: info@bakerpetrolite.com
Web Site: www.bakerpetrolite.com
Sales Range: $250-299.9 Million
Approx. Number Employees: 489
Year Founded: 1918
Business Description:
Chemical Technology Solutions
S.I.C.: 2899; 2869
N.A.I.C.S.: 325998; 325199
Advertising Expenditures: $400,000
Media: 2-4-7-10-17
Distr.: Intl.; Natl.
Budget Set: Oct.
Personnel:
John A. O'Donnell *(VP & Pres-Western Hemisphere Ops)*
Jerry Basconi *(VP & Gen Mgr-Downstream Indus Grp)*
Greg Baker *(VP-HR)*
Susan Bourgain *(Mgr-Mktg)*
Brands & Products:
AURACOR
EXCALIBUR
PETROCARE
PREPARED TO RESPOND
TOLAD
VISTEC

BAMBERGER POLYMERS, INC.
2 Jericho Plz
Jericho, NY 11753-1658
Tel.: (516) 622-3600
Fax: (516) 622-3610
Toll Free: (800) 888-8959
E-mail: nesales@bapoly.com
Web Site: www.bambergerpolymers.com
Sales Range: $250-299.9 Million
Approx. Number Employees: 112
Year Founded: 1967
Business Description:
Plastic Resins Distr
S.I.C.: 5162
N.A.I.C.S.: 424610
Import Export
Media: 2-4-10-13
Personnel:
Lawrence Ubertini *(Chm & CEO)*
Steven Goldberg *(Pres)*
Paul Coco *(CFO)*
Chris Hessenius *(Reg Mgr-Sls)*

BARTON MINES COMPANY LLC
6 SIF Warren St
Lake George, NY 12801-3438
Tel.: (518) 798-5462
Fax: (518) 798-5728
Toll Free: (800) 792-5462
E-mail: info@barton.com
Web Site: www.barton.com
Approx. Number Employees: 300
Year Founded: 1878
Business Description:
Garnet Abrasives Mfr
S.I.C.: 1499; 3291
N.A.I.C.S.: 212399; 327910
Import Export
Media: 2-4-7-10
Distr.: Natl.
Personnel:
C. H. Bracken *(Chm)*
R. Randolph Rapple *(Pres)*
Joseph Ahrberg *(VP-Sls)*
Steve Lemay *(Mgr-Outbound Logistics)*

BASF CATALYSTS LLC
(Div. of BASF Corporation)
25 Middlesex Essex Tpke

Key to Media (For complete agency information see *The Advertising Red Books-Agencies* edition):
1. Bus. Publs. 2. Cable T.V. 3. Catalogs & Directories. 4. Co-op Adv. 5. Consumer Mags. 6. D.M. to Bus. Estab.7. D.M. to Consumers 8. Daily Newsp. 9. Exhibits/Trade Shows 10. Foreign 11. Infomercial 12. Internet Adv.13. Multimedia 14. Network Radio 15. Network T.V. 16. Newsp. Distr. Mags. 17. Other 18. Outdoor (Posters, Transit) 19. Point of Purchase20. Premiums, Novelties 21. Product Samples 22. Special Events Mktg. 23. Spot Radio 24. Spot T.V. 25. Weekly Newsp. 26. Yellow Page Adv.

BASF Catalysts LLC — (Continued)

Iselin, NJ 08830-0770
Mailing Address:
PO Box 770
Iselin, NJ 08830-0770
Tel.: (732) 205-5000
Fax: (732) 906-0337
Toll Free: (800) 458-9823
E-mail: info-ec@basf.com
Web Site: www.catalysts.basf.com
Approx. Number Employees: 7,100
Year Founded: 1981
Business Description:
Material Science Technology & Precious Metal Services
S.I.C.: 5169; 2816; 2819
N.A.I.C.S.: 424690; 325131; 325188
Import Export
Media: 2-4-7-8-10-11-18-20-22-26
Distr.: Intl.; Natl.
Personnel:
Wayne T. Smith *(Pres)*
Rui-Artur Goerck *(Grp VP-Mobile Emissions Catalysts)*
Hans-Peter Neumann *(Grp VP-Process Catalyst & Tech)*
Brands & Products:
ACTIMET
ACTYSSE
ALSIBRONZ
ANSILEX
APPLICAT
ARISTALOY
ART
ARTCAT
ASEPTROL
ASP
ATTACLAY
ATTACOTE
ATTAFLOW
ATTAGEL
ATTAPULGITE
ATTASORB
AURASPERSE
AURORA
BACKLITE
BI-LITE
BIJU
BLACK OLIVE
BLEACHAID
CAMET
CATEZOMES
CELLINI
CHAMELEON
CHARCAT
CHROMA-LITE
CLEANOX
CMX
COCAT
CONVERTER
CYCLO
DELINK
DEOXO
DESERT REFLECTIONS
DESICCITE
DIGITEX
DPX
DRYGUARD
DURACAT
DYNACOLOR
ECLIPSE
ECONO-TAPE
EMCAT-30
EMCOR
ENCLAD
ENGALOY
EQUISTAT
ESCAT
ETX
EXACTUS
EXCALIBER
EXSILON
EZ FLOW
FASTNET
FIREMIST
FLEX-TEC
GEN
GERMAZIDE
HFZ
HI-TEMP
HPN
HT
HYDRONEAL
HZ-1
HZ-PLUS
KALSITEX
KWW
LITECOTE
LOSLIP
LUMINA
LUSOIL
LYNX
LYNX 1000
MAGNASIV
MEARLIN
MEARLITE
MEGNAPEARL
MELARREST
META MAX PA
METAMEX
METEOR
MICROSORB
MIRAFILM
MIRAGLOSS
MIRANA
MOLECULAR GATE
NAPHTHAMAX
NEVERGREEN
NITRONEAL
NOVASIL PLUS
NOXCAT
NUCLAY
NYSOFACT
NYSOSEL
OCTAFINING
OCTISIV
OPTIONS
ORALIUM
OXYCLEAN
PHARMASORB
PHARMOLIN
PREMAIR
PRESORB
PROCAT
PTX
RIGHTFIT
S-22
S-23
SANSURF
SATINGLO 30
SATINTONE
SELECT Z
SELECTRA
SILVA-BRITE
SILVALOY
SOLAREASE
SORBEAD
SOXCAT
SPECTROPURE
SPEEDI-DRI-OIL
SPRAY SATIN
SURROUND
SYNERGY
TRANSLINK
ULTRA COTE
ULTRA GLOSS 90
ULTRA WHITE 90
ULTREX
UNISOIL
VOCAT
Advertising Agency:
J. Hunter Advertising Inc.
(Division of J. Hunter Group)
1111 Broadhollow Rd Ste 211
Farmingdale, NY 11735
Tel.: (631) 777-3331
Fax: (631) 393-6788

BASF CORPORATION

(Sub. of BASF SE)
100 Campus Dr
Florham Park, NJ 07932
Tel.: (973) 245-6000
Fax: (973) 245-6714
Toll Free: (800) 526-1072
Web Site: www2.basf.us/corporate/index.html
Sales Range: $15-24.9 Billion
Approx. Number Employees: 15,000
Year Founded: 1986
Business Description:
Holding Company; North America Regional Managing Office
S.I.C.: 6719
N.A.I.C.S.: 551112; 551114
Import Export
Advertising Expenditures: $78,000,000
Media: 1-2-3-4-5-6-7-9-10-15-18-19-20-21-22-24-26
Distr.: Intl.; Natl.
Budget Set: Sept.
Personnel:
Kurt Bock *(Chm & CEO)*
Wayne T. Smith *(Pres)*
Fried-Walter Munstermann *(CFO & Exec VP)*
Frank A Bozich *(Pres-Global Catalysts Div)*
Norman H. Maas *(Principal)*
David Stryker *(Gen Counsel & Sr VP)*
Joseph C. Breunig *(Exec VP)*
Christopher Toomey *(Sr VP-Procurement)*
Gerry P. Podesta *(Grp VP-Performance Chemicals)*
Thomas Droege *(Dir-Global Mktg)*
Mark Miller *(Bus Dir-Care Chemicals, Home & Personal Care, I&I-North America)*
Laura Troha *(Product Mgr-Tonalin CLA-Human Nutrition)*
Advertising Agencies:
Universal McCann
100 33rd St 8th Fl
New York, NY 10001
Tel.: (212) 883-4700

Wieden + Kennedy-New York
150 Varick St Fl 7
New York, NY 10013-1218
Tel.: (917) 661-5200
Fax: (917) 661-5500

BAYER CROPSCIENCE

(Unit of Bayer CropScience LP)
8400 Hawthorne Rd
Kansas City, MO 64120-2301
Tel.: (816) 242-2000
Fax: (816) 242-2830
E-mail: gail.rothrock@bayercropscience.com
Web Site: www.bayercropscience.com
Business Description:
Insecticides & Herbicides Distr
S.I.C.: 2879
N.A.I.C.S.: 325320
Advertising Agency:
Rhea + Kaiser
Naperville Financial Ctr 400 E Diehl Rd Ste 500
Naperville, IL 60563-1342
Tel.: (630) 505-1100
Fax: (630) 505-1109

BERRYMAN PRODUCTS, INC.

3800 E Randol Mill Rd
Arlington, TX 76011-5437
Tel.: (817) 640-2376
Fax: (817) 640-4850
Toll Free: (800) 433-1704
E-mail: info@berrymanproducts.com
Web Site: www.berrymanproducts.com
E-Mail For Key Personnel:
President: tblankenship@berrymanproducts.com
Sales Range: $50-74.9 Million
Approx. Number Employees: 50
Year Founded: 1918
Business Description:
Automotive Chemicals, Fuel Conditioners, Carburetor Cleaner, Parts Cleaners, Degreasers, Aerosol Lubricants & Tire Sealers
S.I.C.: 5169
N.A.I.C.S.: 424690
Export
Media: 2-4-5-18
Distr.: Natl.
Budget Set: Jan. -Sept.
Brands & Products:
ALL PURPOSE CLEAN-R
B-12 CHEMTOOL
B-33
B-7 CHEMSEAL
BERRYMAN
CHEM-DIP
DEXRON
GREEN STUFF
MERCON
MMT+ OCTANE
POWER STEERING FLUID
SURE SHOT
TIRE SEAL-R
TITE GRIP
TOTAL LUBE

BIOSAFE SYSTEMS, LLC

22 Meadow St
East Hartford, CT 06108
Tel.: (860) 290-8890
Fax: (860) 290-8802
E-mail: info@biosafesystems.com
Web Site: www.biosafesystems.com
Approx. Sls.: $7,932,600
Approx. Number Employees: 30
Business Description:
Biodegradeable Disease-Control Products Mfr; Owned 40% by Consulier Engineering, Inc.
S.I.C.: 2879; 2869; 2899
N.A.I.C.S.: 325320; 325199; 325998
Media: 10
Personnel:
Robert Larose *(Pres & CEO)*
Donna Bishel *(Dir-Tech)*

Key to Media (For complete agency information see *The Advertising Red Books-Agencies* edition):
1. Bus. Publs. 2. Cable T.V. 3. Catalogs & Directories. 4. Co-op Adv. 5. Consumer Mags. 6. D.M. to Bus. Estab.7. D.M. to Consumers 8. Daily Newsp. 9. Exhibits/Trade Shows 10. Foreign 11. Infomercial 12. Internet Adv.13. Multimedia 14. Network Radio 15. Network T.V. 16. Newsp. Distr. Mags. 17. Other 18. Outdoor (Posters, Transit) 19. Point of Purchase20. Premiums, Novelties 21. Product Samples 22. Special Events Mktg. 23. Spot Radio 24. Spot T.V. 25. Weekly Newsp. 26. Yellow Page Adv.

Vijay Choppakatla *(Dir-Res)*
Tammy Raymond *(Dir-Mktg & PR)*
Noel Raymong *(Engr-Product & IT)*

BIRKO CORPORATION
9152 Yosemite St
Henderson, CO 80640
Tel.: (303) 289-1090
Fax: (303) 289-1190
E-mail: info@birkocorp.com
Web Site: www.birkocorp.com
Sales Range: $10-24.9 Million
Approx. Number Employees: 60
Year Founded: 1953
Business Description:
Inorganic Chemicals
S.I.C.: 2819; 5169
N.A.I.C.S.: 325188; 424690
Media: 7-10
Personnel:
Florence S. Powers *(Founder)*
Kelly Heffer *(VP & Gen Mgr)*
Brett Burrough *(Dir-Pur)*
Jerry Oates *(Dir-Midwest Reg Sls)*
Fred Gonzales *(Mgr-IT)*
Brands & Products:
AC TEC 100
ACID BRITE NO 2
ACID KLEEN
ACTO 140
ANLC 1
BI-QUAT
BI TEC 77H
BIG RED
BIRKO
BIRKO ANTIFOAM 10
BIRKO ANTIFOAM 100
BIRKO D FOAM
BIRKODYNE
BIRKOSIDE
BLANCO
BRILLO
BRU-R-EZ
CHALLENGE
CHAMELEON
CHLOROFOAM
CHLOROMATIC
CHLOROMATIC NO 3
CIR-Q-LATE
CIR SCALD
CIRTEC CLQR
CLEAN FRONT IODINE BLOCKS
CON-TACT-IT
DENATURANT G
DIACTOLATE
DOUBLE X LON
EMERALD
FASHUN
FD&C RED CONCENTRATE
FOM-BLOC
FOMACID
GC-161
GLACIAL ACETIC ACID
HAND E SAN
HARD SCALD LIQUID
HD OIL
HYDROLUBE
LIQ. SMOKEHOUSE CLEANER
LIQUIK
LIQUIK 250
LIQUIK CHAR
LIQUILON
LON CHLOR
META-TEC
META TEC 2C
MONLAUN
MONLAUN #3
NEUTRA-FOAM
NEUTRA-SOL
NU SCALD
OXYSTIX
PATCOTE
PRONTO
PT-103
QUADRA-QUAT
RUSTEC
SANI-CLEAN
SHINE-A-LINE
SLIP-PIN
S.P.D.E. 33
SYNCHLOROZENE
TROLLEZE
TURKLEEN
ULTRA-QUAT
ULTRALUBE
XLERATOR

B.J. ALAN COMPANY
(d/b/a Phantom Fireworks)
555 Martin Luther King Jr Blvd
Youngstown, OH 44502-1102
Tel.: (330) 746-4129
Fax: (330) 746-4410
Toll Free: (800) 777-1699
E-mail: info@bjalanco.com
Web Site: www.fireworks.com
Approx. Number Employees: 500
Year Founded: 1977
Business Description:
Consumer Fireworks Retailer
S.I.C.: 5092
N.A.I.C.S.: 423920
Advertising Expenditures: $1,000,000
Media: 2-3-4-6-8-9-13-14-15-17-18-23-24-25-26
Distr.: Natl.
Personnel:
Bruce J. Zoldan *(Pres & CEO)*
William Weimer *(Gen Counsel & VP)*
Alan L. Zoldan *(Exec VP)*
Jerry Bostocky *(VP-Sls)*
Christian Fodor *(Mgr-Mktg)*
Brands & Products:
FIREWORKS.COM
GRUCCI
PHANTOM
WOLF PACK

BLASTGARD INTERNATIONAL INC.
2451 McMullen Booth Rd Ste 242
Clearwater, FL 33759
Tel.: (727) 592-9400
Fax: (727) 592-9402
E-mail: info@blastgardintl.com
Web Site: www.blastgardintl.com
Approx. Sls.: $87,994
Approx. Number Employees: 2
Business Description:
Explosives Mitigation Materials Mfr
S.I.C.: 2892
N.A.I.C.S.: 325920
Advertising Expenditures: $110,971
Media: 1-7
Personnel:
James F. Gordon *(Co-Founder & Dir)*
Michael J. Gordon *(CFO, VP-Corp Admin & Board Member)*
Brands & Products:
BLASTGARD
BLASTWRAP

BOSTIK INC.
(Sub. of Bostik)
211 Boston St
Middleton, MA 01949-2128
Tel.: (978) 777-0100
Fax: (978) 750-7802
Toll Free: (800) 726-7845
E-mail: info@bostik-us.com
Web Site: www.bostik-us.com
Approx. Number Employees: 1,600
Year Founded: 1890
Business Description:
Adhesives, Sealants & Lubricants Mfr & Distr
S.I.C.: 2891
N.A.I.C.S.: 325520
Export
Media: 1-2-4-5-7-10-13-19-21-26
Distr.: Direct to OEM; Natl.
Budget Set: Jan.
Personnel:
Scott Banda *(Bus Mgr-Leed AP-Consumer Products Grp)*
Brands & Products:
CHEM CALK
DRI COTE
NEVER-SEEZ
SUPER GRIP 2000
SUPER TAK
THERMOGRIP
TOP COTE
Advertising Agency:
Haslimann Taylor Public Relations
1 Wrens Ct 53 Lowr Queen St
Birmingham, B72 1RT, United Kingdom
Tel.: (44) 121 355 3446
Fax: (44) 121 355 3393

BOSTIK INC.
(Sub. of Bostik)
11320 Watertown Plank Rd
Wauwatosa, WI 53226-3413
Tel.: (414) 774-2250
Fax: (414) 774-8075
E-mail: bostik@bostik-us.com
Web Site: www.bostik-us.com
Approx. Sls.: $250,000,000
Approx. Number Employees: 160
Year Founded: 1911
Business Description:
Mfr. & Distribution of Adhesives, Sealants & Lubricants
S.I.C.: 2891
N.A.I.C.S.: 325520
Import Export
Media: 2-4-6-7-8
Distr.: Natl.
Personnel:
Mike Klonne *(Pres & CEO)*
Brands & Products:
CHEM-CALK
SYL-A-POCKET

BOULDER SCIENTIFIC COMPANY
598 3rd St
Mead, CO 80542
Tel.: (970) 535-4494
Fax: (970) 535-4584
E-mail: info@bouldersci.com
Web Site: www.bouldersci.com
E-Mail For Key Personnel:
Sales Director: sales@bouldersci.com
Approx. Number Employees: 90
Year Founded: 1972
Business Description:
Organic Chemical Products Mfr
S.I.C.: 2869; 3826
N.A.I.C.S.: 325199; 334516
Media: 2-4-10-13
Personnel:
John M. Birmingham *(Founder)*
Scott Birmingham *(Founder)*
Roy Isiminger *(CFO)*

BP CHEMICALS, INC.
(Sub. of BP America Inc.)
150 W Warrenville Rd B6
Naperville, IL 60563-8473
Tel.: (630) 420-4300
Fax: (630) 961-7920
Toll Free: (877) 701-2726
E-mail: chem_americas@bp.com
Approx. Number Employees: 800
Business Description:
Industrial Chemical Mfr; Holding Company
S.I.C.: 2869; 2873
N.A.I.C.S.: 325199; 325311
Advertising Expenditures: $1,800,000
Media: 2-4-5-6-7-8-9-10-14-18-19-20-21-23-25
Distr.: Natl.
Budget Set: Nov.

BRADKEN
(Sub. of Bradken Ltd.)
400 S 4th St
Atchison, KS 66002
Tel.: (913) 367-2121
Fax: (913) 367-2155
Web Site: www.bradken.com
Sales Range: $300-349.9 Million
Approx. Number Employees: 1,275
Year Founded: 1991
Business Description:
Steel, Iron & Non-Ferrous Castings & Forgings
S.I.C.: 3325; 3321
N.A.I.C.S.: 331513; 331511
Import Export
Media: 1-7-10
Personnel:
Kevin T. McDermott *(CFO & VP)*
Roy Roux *(VP-Sls)*
Wayne Braun *(Corp Dir-Mktg)*

BREEZE INDUSTRIAL PRODUCTS CORPORATION
(Holding of Wind Point Partners)
3582 Tunnelton Rd
Saltsburg, PA 15681-9593
Tel.: (724) 639-3571
Fax: (724) 639-3020
Telex: 86-6294
Approx. Sls.: $20,000,000
Approx. Number Employees: 266
Business Description:
Gear-Driven Fasteners & Tachometers & Related Equipment; Crane Accessories & Other Construction-Related Equipment
S.I.C.: 3429
N.A.I.C.S.: 332510
Media: 4
Personnel:
Brian Long *(Gen Mgr)*
Brands & Products:
BREEZE
HOSECRAMS

BREWER SCIENCE, INC.
2401 Brewer Dr
Rolla, MO 65401-7003
Tel.: (573) 364-0300
Fax: (573) 368-3318
E-mail: info@brewerscience.com

Key to Media (For complete agency information see *The Advertising Red Books-Agencies* edition):
1. Bus. Publs. 2. Cable T.V. 3. Catalogs & Directories. 4. Co-op Adv. 5. Consumer Mags. 6. D.M. to Bus. Estab. 7. D.M. to Consumers 8. Daily Newsp. 9. Exhibits/Trade Shows 10. Foreign 11. Infomercial 12. Internet Adv. 13. Multimedia 14. Network Radio 15. Network T.V. 16. Newsp. Distr. Mags. 17. Other 18. Outdoor (Posters, Transit) 19. Point of Purchase 20. Premiums, Novelties 21. Product Samples 22. Special Events Mktg. 23. Spot Radio 24. Spot T.V. 25. Weekly Newsp. 26. Yellow Page Adv.

Brewer Science, Inc. — (Continued)

Web Site: www.brewerscience.com
Approx. Number Employees: 300
Year Founded: 1981
Business Description:
Thin Film Polymer Coatings Supplier with Tailored Optical, Mechanical & Electrical Properties; Custom Designed Coating & Bake Equipment Supplier for the Micro-Electronics & Opto-Electronics Industries
S.I.C.: 2851; 8733
N.A.I.C.S.: 325510; 541710
Import Export
Media: 2-4-7-10-13-21-23-26
Personnel:
Terry Brewer *(Pres)*
Russ Pagel *(Mgr-Global Security)*
Loretta Wallis *(Mgr-Corp Rels)*
Brands & Products:
ANTI-REFLECTIVE COATING
ARC
BARC
BREWER SCIENCE
CEE
CON-TACT
DARC
OPTINDEX
PIRL
PROTEK
PSC
PSK
T-POLYM
TALON

BRUSH WELLMAN INC.
(Sub. of BRUSH ENGINEERED MATERIALS INC.)
6070 Parkland Blvd
Mayfield Heights, OH 44124-2602
Tel.: (216) 486-4200
Fax: (216) 383-4091
Web Site: www.brushwellman.com
Sales Range: $50-74.9 Million
Approx. Number Employees: 123
Year Founded: 1931
Business Description:
High Performance Engineered Materials
S.I.C.: 3351; 3356
N.A.I.C.S.: 331421; 331491
Import Export
Media: 2-4-7-10
Distr.: Natl.
Budget Set: Oct.
Personnel:
Richard J. Hipple *(Pres & CEO)*
John Grampa *(CFO & Sr VP)*
Michael D. Anderson *(Pres-BE PRoducts)*
Stephen Freeman *(Pres-Brush Intl)*
Glenn Maxwell *(Pres-Alloy Products)*
Daniel Skoch *(Sr VP-Admin)*
Joe Szafraniec *(VP-HR)*
David C. Deubner *(Dir-Corp Medical)*
Brands & Products:
BRUSH WELLMAN
Advertising Agency:
FLS Marketing
405 Madison Ave Ste 1550
Toledo, OH 43604-1226
Tel.: (419) 241-1244
Fax: (419) 241-5210

BUCKEYE TECHNOLOGIES INC.
1001 Tillman St
Memphis, TN 38112-2038
Mailing Address:
PO Box 80407
Memphis, TN 38108-0407
Tel.: (901) 320-8100
E-mail: info@bkitech.com
Web Site: www.bkitech.com
Approx. Sls.: $905,273,000
Approx. Number Employees: 1,400
Year Founded: 1993
Business Description:
Mfr of Cellulose for Chemical & Papermaking Applications, Wood & Cotton Linter Market Pulp
S.I.C.: 2676; 2611
N.A.I.C.S.: 322291; 322110
Export
Advertising Expenditures: $100,000
Media: 2-4-7-8-10-21-22
Distr.: Intl.
Budget Set: Oct.
Personnel:
John B. Crowe *(Chm & CEO)*
Kristopher J. Matula *(Pres & COO)*
Steven G. Dean *(CFO & Sr VP)*
Elizabeth J. Welter *(Chief Acctg Officer & VP)*
Sheila Jordan Cunningham *(Gen Counsel, Sec & Sr VP)*
Charles S. Aiken *(Sr VP-Energy & Sustainability)*
Jeffery T. Cook *(Sr VP)*
Douglas L. Dowdell *(Sr VP-Specialty Fibers)*
William M. Handel *(Sr VP-Lean Enterprise)*
Paul N. Horne *(Sr VP-Product & Market Dev)*
Marko M. Rajamaa *(Sr VP-Nonwovens)*
F. Gray Carter *(VP-Pur & Logistics)*
Dan R. Moore *(VP-Process Tech)*
Terrence M. Reed *(VP-HR)*
Anne Grosvenor *(Mgr-Mktg)*
Advertising Agency:
The Ransom Group
3674 Canada Rd
Arlington, TN 38002
Tel.: (901) 383-1200
Fax: (901) 383-1035

BUCKMAN
(Formerly Buckman Laboratories Inc.)
(Sub. of Bulab Holdings, Inc.)
1256 N Mclean Blvd
Memphis, TN 38108-1241
Tel.: (901) 278-0330
Fax: (901) 276-5343
Toll Free: (800) BUCKMAN
Web Site: www.buckman.com
Approx. Sls.: $310,000,000
Approx. Number Employees: 1,300
Year Founded: 1945
Business Description:
Mfr. of Specialty Chemicals for Use Industrial, Agricultural & Human Environmental Use
S.I.C.: 2869; 2819
N.A.I.C.S.: 325199; 325188
Import Export
Media: 2-4-7-10-13-20
Distr.: Natl.
Budget Set: Oct.

Personnel:
Patricia Browning *(VP-Strategic Plng)*
Michael Alpert *(Dir-Sls Ops)*
Lela Gerald *(Dir-Global Mktg Comm)*
Brands & Products:
BRD
BUFLOC
BUSAN
BUSPERSE
NEOTERIC

BURGESS PIGMENT COMPANY
187 Pierce Ave
Macon, GA 31204-2821
Tel.: (478) 746-5658
Fax: (478) 746-4882
E-mail: info@burgesspigment.com
Web Site: www.burgesspigment.com
Approx. Number Employees: 162
Year Founded: 1948
Business Description:
Processor of Kaolin & Alumina
S.I.C.: 3295; 2819; 2899
N.A.I.C.S.: 327992; 325998; 331311
Import Export
Media: 2-4-7-10
Personnel:
Malcolm S. Burgess *(Founder)*
Robert S. Burgess *(Exec VP)*
Tom Adrien *(VP-Sls & Mktg)*
Brands & Products:
BURGESS BSC-SD
BURGESS HC-77
BURGESS ICECAP K
BURGESS ICECAP KSF
BURGESS NO. 10
BURGESS NO. 17
BURGESS NO. 20
BURGESS NO. 28
BURGESS NO. 40
BURGESS NO. 50
BURGESS NO. 60
BURGESS NO. 80
BURGESS NO. 86
BURGESS NO. 97
BURGESS NO. 98
BURGESS OPTIPOZZ
BURGESS PIGMENT
BURGESS POLYCLAY
BURGESS THERMOGLACE H
ICEBERG
OPTIWHITE
OPTIWHITE MX
OPTIWHITE P
Advertising Agency:
Haynes Marketing Network, Inc.
721-B Walnut St
Macon, GA 31201
Tel.: (478) 742-5266
Fax: (478) 742-5334
(Clay)

CABOT CORPORATION
2 Seaport Ln Ste 1300
Boston, MA 02210-2019
Tel.: (617) 345-0100
Fax: (617) 342-6103
Telex: 6817525
E-mail: info@cabot-corp.com
Web Site: www.cabot-corp.com
Approx. Sls.: $2,893,000,000
Approx. Number Employees: 3,900
Year Founded: 1882

Business Description:
Carbon Black, Fumed Metal Oxides, Inkjet Colorants, Tantalum & Related Products Mfr
S.I.C.: 2895; 2816; 3081; 5169
N.A.I.C.S.: 325182; 325131; 326113; 424690
Import Export
Media: 2-4-7-10-11-21
Distr.: Intl.; Natl.
Budget Set: Aug.
Personnel:
Patrick M. Prevost *(Pres & CEO)*
Eduardo E. Cordeiro *(CFO & Exec VP)*
Douglas A. Church *(CIO & VP)*
Brian A. Berube *(Gen Counsel & VP)*
David A. Miller *(Exec VP & Gen Mgr-Core Segment & Americas Reg)*
Friedrich von Gottberg *(VP & Gen Mgr-New Bus Segment)*
Xinsheng Zhang *(VP & Gen Mgr-Asia & Pacific Reg)*
Robby Sisco *(VP-HR)*
Christina Bramante *(Dir-Product Support & Toxicology)*
Erica McLaughlin *(Dir-IR)*
Joshua Preneta *(Mgr-Segment-Global)*
Karen Abrams *(Asst Sec)*
John F. Fox *(Asst Treas)*
Brands & Products:
BLACK PEARLS
CAB-O-JET
CAB-O-SIL
CAB-O-SPERSE
CABELEC
CABOT
CEC
CRX
CSX
ECOBLACK
ELFTEX
ELFTEX 3
EMPEROR
K-PLUS
MOGUL
MONARCH
NANOGEL
PLASADD
PLASBLAK
PLASGREY
PLASWITE
RAINBOW
REGAL
SPHERON
STERLING
UNITED
VULCAN
Advertising Agency:
Adam Friedman Associates
11 E 44 St 5th Fl
New York, NY 10017
Tel.: (212) 981-2529
Fax: (212) 981-8174

CABOT MICROELECTRONICS CORPORATION
870 N Commons Dr
Aurora, IL 60504-7963
Tel.: (630) 375-6631
Fax: (630) 499-2666
Toll Free: (800) 811-2756
Web Site: www.cabotcmp.com
Approx. Rev.: $408,201,000
Approx. Number Employees: 933
Year Founded: 2000

Key to Media (For complete agency information see *The Advertising Red Books-Agencies* edition):
1. Bus. Publs. 2. Cable T.V. 3. Catalogs & Directories. 4. Co-op Adv. 5. Consumer Mags. 6. D.M. to Bus. Estab.7. D.M. to Consumers 8. Daily Newsp. 9. Exhibits/Trade Shows 10. Foreign 11. Infomercial 12. Internet Adv.13. Multimedia 14. Network Radio 15. Network T.V. 16. Newsp. Distr. Mags. 17. Other 18. Outdoor (Posters, Transit) 19. Point of Purchase20. Premiums, Novelties 21. Product Samples 22. Special Events Mktg. 23. Spot Radio 24. Spot T.V. 25. Weekly Newsp. 26. Yellow Page Adv.

Business Description:
Mfr of Polishing Compounds & Pads Used in Manufacture of Semiconductors
S.I.C.: 3674
N.A.I.C.S.: 334413
Media: 2
Personnel:
William P. Noglows *(Chm, Pres & CEO)*
William S. Johnson *(CFO)*
H. Carol Bernstein *(Gen Counsel, Sec & VP)*
Carmelina M. Stoklosa *(Dir-Fin & Treas)*
Stephen R. Smith *(VP-Mktg)*
Daniel S. Wobby *(VP-Global Sls)*
Amy Ford *(Dir-IR)*
John McMahon *(Dir-Global Quality)*
Lisa Polezol *(Mgr-HR)*
Brands & Products:
CABOT MICROELECTRONICS
ICUE
SEMI-SPERSE

CALGON CARBON CORPORATION
400 Calgon Carbon Dr
Pittsburgh, PA 15205
Mailing Address:
PO Box 717
Pittsburgh, PA 15230-0717
Tel.: (412) 787-6700
Fax: (412) 787-4511
Toll Free: (800) 4CARBON
Telex: 6711837 CCC
E-mail: info@calgoncarbon.com
Web Site: www.calgoncarbon.com
E-Mail For Key Personnel:
Public Relations: gerono@calgoncarbon.com
Approx. Sls.: $482,341,000
Approx. Number Employees: 1,070
Year Founded: 1942
Business Description:
Producer & Marketer of Activated Carbons & Related Products & Services
S.I.C.: 2899; 5169; 7629
N.A.I.C.S.: 325998; 424690; 811219
Import Export
Media: 2-10-13-21
Personnel:
John S. Stanik *(Chm, Pres & CEO)*
Stevan R. Schott *(CFO & VP)*
C.H.S. Majoor *(Exec VP-Europe & Asia)*
Robert P. O Brien *(Exec VP-Americas)*
Gail A. Gerono *(VP-HR, IR & Corp Comm)*
Brands & Products:
ALLGONE
AMMONASORB
APOLLO
BPL
BREATHESAFE
CADRE
CAL
CALGO CARBON
CALMEDIA
CALRES
CARBSORB
C(CUBE)150
C(CUBE)500
CENTAUR
CSEP
CYCLESORB
DISPOSORB
FCA
FILTRASORB
FLEXZORB
FLOWSORB
FLUEPAC
FORMASORB
GEMINI
HERCULES
HGR
HGR LH
HGR-P
HIGH FLOW
HIGH-FLOW VENTSORB
ISEP
MINI-PHOENIX
MINOTAUR
PEROX-PURE
PHOENIX
PREZERVE
PROTECT
PURRFECTLY FRESH
RAYOX
REVOLVER-Z
SENTINEL
SGL
SORBAMINE
SULFUSORB
SWEETSTREET
SWEETVENT
TITAN
VAPOR PAC
VENTSORB
ZORFLEX

CAMERON INTERNATIONAL
(Formerly NATCO Group Inc.)
(Sub. of Cameron International Corporation)
11210 Equity Dr Ste 100
Houston, TX 77041
Tel.: (713) 849-7500
Fax: (713) 849-8973
Toll Free: (877) 288-6270
Web Site: www.c-a-m.com
Approx. Rev.: $657,404,000
Approx. Number Employees: 2,522
Year Founded: 1988
Business Description:
Oil & Gas Field Machinery Services
S.I.C.: 3533
N.A.I.C.S.: 333132
Import Export
Media: 10
Personnel:
Les Hiller *(Pres-Process Sys)*
Greg Dodson *(VP-Tech & Product Mgmt-Process Sys)*
George Siller *(VP-Fin-Process Sys)*
Brands & Products:
BTEX BUSTER
CYCLONE
DESI-DRI
DFX
DOX
DUAL FREQUENCY
DUAL POLARITY
EDD ELECTRO-DYNAMIC
ELECTROMAX
FLOSPLITTER
FLUIDSEP
GLYMINE
HIPERFILTER
HIPERSCREEN
HIPERSTRIP
HIPERVAC
JEWEL T
LTX
MISTTRAP
MOZLEY SANDSPIN
MOZLEY WELLSPIN
NATCO-LESCER
OILSPIN
PERFORMAX
PORTA-TEST REVOLUTION
PORTA-TEST WHIRLYSCRUB
PORTA-TEST WHIRLYSCRUB I
POWERCLEAN
SFX
SHV
SULFATREAT
SURETRAP
TRIDAIR
TRIDAIR HYDRAULIC
TRIDAIR MECHANICAL
TRIGRID
TRIGRIDMAX
TRIPACK
TRIVOLT
TRIVOLTMAX
VERSAFLO
VFHRM
VFX

CARBOLINE CO.
(Sub. of RPM Industrial Holding Co.)
2150 Schuetz Rd
Saint Louis, MO 63146
Tel.: (314) 644-1000
Fax: (314) 644-4617
Toll Free: (800) 848-4645
E-mail: carbolineusa@carboline.com
Web Site: www.carboline.com
Sales Range: $100-124.9 Million
Approx. Number Employees: 300
Year Founded: 1947
Business Description:
Protective Coatings Mfr
S.I.C.: 2851
N.A.I.C.S.: 325510
Export
Media: 2-4-8-10-11-20-21-22-26
Distr.: Intl.; Natl.
Budget Set: Jan.
Personnel:
Richard Wilson *(Pres)*
Doug Moore *(Dir-Mktg)*
Brands & Products:
CARBO ZINC
CARBOCRYLIC
CARBOGUARD
CARBOMASTIC
NULLFIRE
PHENOLINE
PYROCRETE

CARUS CORPORATION
(d/b/a Carus Chemical Company)
315 5th St
Peru, IL 61354-2859
Tel.: (815) 223-1500
Fax: (815) 224-6697
Toll Free: (800) 435-6856
E-mail: drinkingwater@caruscorporation.com
Web Site: www.caruscorporation.com
Approx. Number Employees: 250
Year Founded: 1915
Business Description:
Chemical Mfr; Potassium Permanganate & Industrial & Municipal Water Treatment Chemicals
S.I.C.: 2819
N.A.I.C.S.: 325188
Import Export
Media: 2-10
Personnel:
Inga Carus *(Pres & CEO)*
J. C. Wilkes *(VP-HR)*
Joseph Sigmund *(Mgr-Market Specialty-Global)*
Brands & Products:
AQUA MAG
AQUA MAG DP
AQUOX
CAIROX
CAIROX-CR
CARULITE
CARUS
CARUS ORTHOPHOS
CARUS UPZ
CARUSEL
CARUSMATIC
CARUSOL
CYCLE-BIN
ECONOX
LIQUOX
MOBILOX
REMOX
RESPONSIBLE CARE
TPC 427
VIRCHEM

CENTRAL RESEARCH LABORATORIES
(Sub. of Dover Industrial Products, Inc.)
3965 Pepin Ave
Red Wing, MN 55066
Tel.: (651) 388-3565
Fax: (651) 385-2109
E-mail: info@centres.com
Web Site: www.centres.com
Sales Range: $25-49.9 Million
Approx. Number Employees: 55
Year Founded: 1945
Business Description:
Remote Handling of Toxic & Dangerous Materials
S.I.C.: 4953
N.A.I.C.S.: 562211
Media: 4
Distr.: Intl.; Natl.
Budget Set: Sept. -Oct.
Personnel:
Lawton Cain *(Gen Mgr)*
Advertising Agency:
Preston Kelly
222 First Ave NE
Minneapolis, MN 55413
Tel.: (612) 843-4000
Fax: (612) 843-3900
(Dexterous Maneuvers Through Teleoperation)

CERAC, INC.
(Sub. of Materion Microelectronics & Services)
407 N 13th St
Milwaukee, WI 53233
Tel.: (414) 289-9800
Fax: (414) 289-9805
E-mail: info@cerac.com
Web Site: www.cerac.com
Sales Range: $10-24.9 Million
Approx. Number Employees: 150
Year Founded: 1964
Business Description:
Mfr of Specialty Inorganic Materials & Physical Vapor Deposition Materials
S.I.C.: 2819
N.A.I.C.S.: 325188
Media: 2-7-10

Key to Media (For complete agency information see *The Advertising Red Books-Agencies* edition):
1. Bus. Publs. 2. Cable T.V. 3. Catalogs & Directories. 4. Co-op Adv. 5. Consumer Mags. 6. D.M. to Bus. Estab.7. D.M. to Consumers 8. Daily Newsp. 9. Exhibits/Trade Shows 10. Foreign 11. Infomercial 12. Internet Adv.13. Multimedia 14. Network Radio 15. Network T.V. 16. Newsp. Distr. Mags. 17. Other 18. Outdoor (Posters, Transit) 19. Point of Purchase20. Premiums, Novelties 21. Product Samples 22. Special Events Mktg. 23. Spot Radio 24. Spot T.V. 25. Weekly Newsp. 26. Yellow Page Adv.

CERAC, Inc. — (Continued)

Personnel:
Dick Sager *(Pres)*
Bart Ott *(VP-Sls & Mktg)*
E. J. Strother *(VP-Mktg & New Bus Dev)*
Alan Devaney *(Mgr-Product Mktg)*

Brands & Products:
CERAC

CHASE CORPORATION

Bethany House 26 Summer St
Bridgewater, MA 02324-2626
Tel.: (508) 279-1789
Fax: (508) 697-6419
E-mail: pmyers@chasecorp.com
Web Site: www.chasecorp.com
Approx. Rev.: $118,743,000
Approx. Number Employees: 305
Year Founded: 1941
Business Description:
Protective Materials for Electrical Cables, Steel Highway Bridges, Underground Pipelines & Printed Circuitry & Conformal Coatings for Electronics Systems
S.I.C.: 3699; 3069; 3089; 3479; 3496; 3644; 5063
N.A.I.C.S.: 335999; 326199; 326299; 332618; 332812; 335932; 423610
Import Export
Media: 10-17
Personnel:
George M. Hughes *(Founder, Principal-Associates Corp Sec)*
Peter R. Chase *(Chm & CEO)*
Adam P. Chase *(Pres & COO)*
Kenneth L. Dumas *(CFO & Treas)*

Brands & Products:
CEVA
CHASE & SONS
CHASE BLH2OCK
CHASE FACILE
EVA-POX
GREENLINE
HUMISEAL
PAPER TYGER
ROSPHALT
ROYSTON
TAPECOAT
ZOO MIX

CHEMETALL FOOTE CORPORATION

(Sub. of Rockwood Specialties Group, Inc.)
348 Holiday Inn Dr
Kings Mountain, NC 28086-3615
Tel.: (704) 734-2797
Fax: (704) 734-0208
E-mail: foote.lithium@chemetall.com
Sales Range: $25-49.9 Million
Approx. Number Employees: 130
Year Founded: 1982
Business Description:
Lithium Chemicals, Metals & Chloride Brine, Flouride Powder & Butyllithium Polmerization Catalysts Mfr
S.I.C.: 1479
N.A.I.C.S.: 212393
Import Export
Media: 2-8-10-11-16-20-25
Distr.: Natl.
Budget Set: Oct.
Personnel:
R.A. France *(Pres)*
Gary Otwell *(Mgr-Mktg)*

Brands & Products:
CRYSTAL GUARD
NAFTOCIT
NAFTONOX
NAFTOZIN

CHEMISPHERE CORPORATION

2101 Clifton Ave
Saint Louis, MO 63139
Tel.: (314) 644-1300
Fax: (314) 644-1425
Fax: (314) 644-7194
Toll Free: (800) 844-1301
E-mail: mpclote@chemispherecorp.com
Web Site: www.chemispherecorp.com
E-Mail For Key Personnel:
Marketing Director: mpclote@chemispherecorp.com
Approx. Number Employees: 34
Year Founded: 1974
Business Description:
Industrial Chemicals Whslr
S.I.C.: 5169
N.A.I.C.S.: 424690
Media: 2-10
Personnel:
Robert F. Schwent *(Pres)*
Michael Clote *(VP & Gen Mgr)*

CHEMTURA CORPORATION

199 Benson Rd
Middlebury, CT 06749
Tel.: (203) 573-2000
Fax: (203) 573-3711
Toll Free: (877) 948-2660
Web Site: www.chemtura.com
Approx. Sls.: $2,760,000,000
Approx. Number Employees: 4,200
Year Founded: 2005
Business Description:
Chemical Additives Mfr
S.I.C.: 5169; 2821; 2843; 2869; 2891; 2899
N.A.I.C.S.: 424690; 325199; 325211; 325520; 325613; 325998
Import Export
Media: 2-7-10-13-14
Distr.: Intl.; Natl.
Personnel:
Craig A. Rogerson *(Chm, Pres & CEO)*
Stephen C. Forsyth *(CFO & Exec VP)*
Raymond E. Dombrowski *(Chief Restructuring Officer)*
Billie S. Flaherty *(Gen Counsel, Corp Sec & Sr VP)*
Chet H. Cross *(Grp Pres-Engineered Products & Exec VP)*
Kevin V. Mahoney *(Sr VP & Controller)*
Alan M. Swiech *(Sr VP-HR)*
Keith Dupont *(VP-Procurement)*
Lloyd N. Moon *(VP-Global Govt Affairs & Comm)*
Jon Amdursky *(Dir-Mktg Comm)*
John D. Dennerlein *(Dir-Bus-Global)*

Brands & Products:
ACRAMITE
ACTAFOAM
ACTAFOAM R-3
ADEPT
ADIPRENE
ADIPRENE BL16
ADIPRENE EXTREME
ADIPRENE L 200
ADIPRENE L100
ADIPRENE L167
ALANAP
ALKANOX
AMINOX
ANOX
ARANOX
AXION
AZUB
B-NINE
B-NINE WSG
BA-59P
BC-52
BC-58
BE-51
BIK OT
BLE
BLENDEX
BLIZZARD
BOMAG
BOMAG-A
BUTAZATE
BUTRALIN
CALCINATE
CASORON
CASORON 4G
CAYTUR
CD-75P
CELOGEN
CHEMTURA
COMITE
DE-83R
DELAC
DIMLIN
DP-45
DRAPEX
DURAZONE
ESPERAL
ESPEROX
ETHACURE
ETHAZATE
EURECEN
EURENOR
EXPANDEX
FAZOR
FF-680
FIREMASTER
FIRESHIELD
FIRESTORM
FLEXAMINE
FLEXZONE
FLORAMITE
FLUPRO
FOMREZ
FYREBLOC
GENOX
GRANUFLO
HARVADE
HEPTEEN BASE
HYBASE
HYSTRENE
INDUSTRENE
INTERLOY
KAYDOL
KEMAMIDE
KEMAMINE
KEMESTER
KEMSTRENE
KRONITOX
LAUREX
LEAFLESS
LINTPLUS
LIQUAZINC
LOBASE
LOWILITE
LOWINOX
LUBRAZINC
MARK
MARK OBS
MARKLEAR
MARKLUBE
MARKSCREEN
MARKSTAT
METHAZATE
MICROFINE
MICROMITE
MOLDPRO
NAUGALUBE
NAUGARD
NAUGAWHITE
NAUGEX
NOVAZONE
OCTAMINE
OFF-SHOOT T
OMITE
ONCOR
ONGARD
OPEX
OPEX 80
ORNAMITE
PACZOL
PEDESTAL
PETCAT
PETRONATE
PLANTVAX
POLYBOND
POLYGARD
POLYLITE
POLYWET
PROCURE
PYROBLOC
REMOL
REOFOS
REOGARD
RESPONSIBLE CARE
RETARDER
RIMON
ROYAL MH
ROYALAC
ROYALEDGE
ROYALENE
ROYALTAC
ROYALTHERM
ROYALTUF
SMOKEBLOC
SPITFIRE
SUNOLITE
SUNPROOF
SURCHEM
SYNTON
TEMPRANO
TERRACLOR
TERRAGUARD
TERRAMASTER
TERRAZOLE
THERMOGUARD
TIMONOX
TONOX
TRILENE
TRIMENE
TRUTINT
TUEX
TURFCIDE
ULTRAFINE
ULTRANOX
UNICURE
UNIROYAL CHEMICAL
VIBRACURE
VIBRATHANE
VITAVAX
VITICURE
WESTON
WITCO
WITCOBOND
WITCOTHANE
WYTOX

Key to Media (For complete agency information see *The Advertising Red Books-Agencies* edition):
1. Bus. Publs. 2. Cable T.V. 3. Catalogs & Directories. 4. Co-op Adv. 5. Consumer Mags. 6. D.M. to Bus. Estab.7. D.M. to Consumers
8. Daily Newsp. 9. Exhibits/Trade Shows 10. Foreign 11. Infomercial 12. Internet Adv.13. Multimedia 14. Network Radio
15. Network T.V. 16. Newsp. Distr. Mags. 17. Other 18. Outdoor (Posters, Transit) 19. Point of Purchase20. Premiums, Novelties
21. Product Samples 22. Special Events Mktg. 23. Spot Radio 24. Spot T.V. 25. Weekly Newsp. 26. Yellow Page Adv.

Advertising Agency:
Shaw & Todd, Inc.
95 Mt Bethel Rd 1st Fl
Warren, NJ 07059
Tel.: (908) 668-1106
Fax: (908) 668-1107

CHICAGO WHITE METAL CASTING, INC.

Rte 83 & Fairway Dr
Bensenville, IL 60106
Tel.: (630) 595-4424
Fax: (630) 595-4474
E-mail: sales@cwmtl.com
Web Site: www.cwmdiecast.com
E-Mail For Key Personnel:
Sales Director: sales@cwmtl.com
Approx. Number Employees: 150
Year Founded: 1937
Business Description:
Custom Die Castings & Subassemblies Mfr
S.I.C.: 3363; 3364
N.A.I.C.S.: 331521; 331522
Media: 2-4
Distr.: Natl.
Budget Set: Dec.
Personnel:
Walter G. Treiber, Jr. *(Chm)*
Eric Treiber *(Pres & COO)*
Anthony Lo Coco *(CFO & Exec VP)*
Mike Dimitroff *(VP-Sls & Mktg)*
John Stocker *(VP-Engrng)*

CHURCH & DWIGHT CO., INC.

469 N Harrison St
Princeton, NJ 08543-5297
Tel.: (609) 683-5900
Fax: (609) 497-7269
E-mail: info@churchdwight.com
Web Site: www.churchdwight.com
Approx. Sls.: $2,589,220,000
Approx. Number Employees: 3,600
Year Founded: 1846
Business Description:
Household Deodorizing & Cleaning, Laundry & Personal Care Products & Specialty Inorganic Chemicals Mfr & Marketer
S.I.C.: 2842; 1474; 2819; 2835; 2841; 3069; 3843
N.A.I.C.S.: 325612; 212391; 325188; 325413; 325611; 326299; 339114
Import Export
Advertising Expenditures: $41,100,000
Media: 3-5-6-8-10-13-15-19-21-22-23-24
Distr.: Natl.
Budget Set: Oct.
Personnel:
James R. Craigie *(Chm & CEO)*
Matthew T. Farrell *(CFO & Exec VP)*
Bruce F. Fleming *(CMO & Exec VP)*
Adrian J. Huns *(Exec VP, Pres-Intl Consumer Products)*
Joseph A. Sipia, Jr. *(Exec VP, Pres-Specialty Products Div)*
Susan E. Goldy *(Gen Counsel, Sec & Exec VP)*
Jacquelin J. Brova *(Exec VP-HR)*
Mark G. Conish *(Exec VP-Global Ops)*
Steven P. Cugine *(Exec VP-Global New Products Innovation)*
Paul A. Siracusa *(Exec VP-Global R&D)*
Louis H. Tursi, Jr. *(Exec VP-Domestic Consumer Sls-USA)*
Roger A. Madden *(VP & Gen Mgr)*
Stacey Feldman *(VP-Mktg-Women's Health & Personal Care)*
Joe Kossow *(Dir-Mktg)*
Steve Bolkan *(Dir-R&D)*
Bryan Harpine *(Dir-Global New Products)*
Craig Sheehan *(Mgr-Product-Fabric Care)*
Brands & Products:
AIM
ANSWER
ARM & HAMMER
ARM & HAMMER DENTAL CARE
ARM & HAMMER ESSENTIALS
ARM & HAMMER ORALCARE
ARM & HAMMER SUPER SCOOP
ARM & HAMMER VACUUM FREE
ARMAKLEEN
ARMEX BLAST MEDIA
ARRID
BRILLO
CAMEO
CARTER'S
CLEAN SHOWER
ELEXA
FIRST RESPONSE
KABOOM
LADY'S CHOICE
LAMBERT KAY
MENTADENT
NAIR
NAIR FOR MEN
NAIR PRETTY
NAIR SENSITIVE FORMULA COLLECTION
NATURALAMB
ORANGE GLO
OXICLEAN
PEARL DROPS
PEPSODENT
RIGIDENT
SCRUB FREE
SNO BOL
STRIP & SHINE
TROJAN
XTRA
XTRA NICE'N FLUFFY
Advertising Agencies:
Becker Guerry
107 Tindall Rd
Middletown, NJ 07748-2321
Tel.: (732) 671-6440
Fax: (732) 671-4350

Edelman
250 Hudson St
New York, NY 10013
Tel.: (212) 768-0550
Fax: (212) 704-0128
(Arm & Hammer Essentials)

Ferrara & Company
29 Airpark Rd
Princeton, NJ 08540
Tel.: (609) 924-4932
Fax: (609) 945-8700
(Arm & Hammer Essentials)

The Joey Company
45 Main St Ste 632
Brooklyn, NY 11201
Tel.: (718) 852-7730
Fax: (718) 412-3498
Nair

The Kaplan Thaler Group
825 8th Ave 34th Fl
New York, NY 10019
Tel.: (212) 474-5000
Fax: (212) 474-5702
Trojan

L.C. Williams & Associates, LLC
150 N Michigan Ave 38th Fl
Chicago, IL 60601-7558
Tel.: (312) 565-3900
Fax: (312) 565-1770
Toll Free: (800) 837-7123
Arm & Hammer
— Laura Bohacz *(Acct Exec-Arm & Hammer)*

CHURCH & DWIGHT SPECIALTY PRODUCTS DIVISION

(Div. of Church & Dwight Co., Inc.)
469 N Harrison St
Princeton, NJ 08543-5297
Tel.: (609) 683-5900
Fax: (609) 497-7176
Toll Free: (800) 221-0453
Web Site: www.ahspecialty.com
Approx. Sls.: $220,293,000
Business Description:
Sodium Bicarbonate, Ammonium Bicarbonate & Potassium Carbonate Products Mfr
S.I.C.: 2819; 2899
N.A.I.C.S.: 325188; 325998
Media: 2-7-10-13-19-20
Personnel:
Joseph A. Sipia, Jr. *(Pres & COO-Specialty Products Division)*
Brands & Products:
ARMEX
K MINUS
MEGALAC
MEGALAC PLUS
THE NORMALIZER
SQ-810

CLARIANT CORPORATION

(Div. of Clariant International AG)
4000 Monroe Rd
Charlotte, NC 28205
Tel.: (704) 331-7000
Fax: (704) 377-1063
E-mail: info@clariant-northamerica.com
Web Site: www.clariant-northamerica.com
Approx. Number Employees: 3,700
Year Founded: 1919
Business Description:
Specialty Chemicals Mfr
S.I.C.: 2869; 2865
N.A.I.C.S.: 325199; 325132
Import Export
Media: 1-2-4-7-9-10-20
Distr.: Intl.; Natl.
Budget Set: Sept.
Personnel:
Kenneth Golder *(CEO)*
Connie Knight *(Dir-Corp Comm)*

CLARIANT-MASTERBATCHES DIVISION

(Div. of Clariant International AG)
85 Industrial Dr
Holden, MA 01520
Tel.: (508) 829-6321
Fax: (508) 829-6230
Web Site: www.clariant.masterbatches.com
Approx. Number Employees: 3,500
Year Founded: 1948
Business Description:
Color & Additive Masterbatches & Specialty Compounding
S.I.C.: 3087; 2816
N.A.I.C.S.: 325991; 325131
Export
Media: 1-2-4-7-10-11-16-17-20-26
Distr.: Natl.
Budget Set: Sept.
Personnel:
Jeff Sager *(Mgr-Mktg)*
Brands & Products:
CESA
GLOBAL COLORWORKS
HYDROCEROL
NATURAL PLUS
OMNICOLOR
REMAFIN
RENOL

CLAYTON CORPORATION

866 Horan Dr
Fenton, MO 63026-2416
Tel.: (636) 349-5333
Fax: (636) 349-5335
Toll Free: (800) 729-8220
Web Site: www.claytoncorp.com
Approx. Number Employees: 150
Year Founded: 1945
Business Description:
Mfr. of Aerosol Valves & Accessories; Consumer Energy Saving Sealant Products Sold to Retail Trade; Tamper Evident Closures & Covers
S.I.C.: 3491; 3086
N.A.I.C.S.: 332911; 326150
Import Export
Advertising Expenditures: $1,000,000
Media: 2-4-6-7-8-10-13-19-20-21-23-24-26
Personnel:
Byron R. Lapin *(Pres)*
Gene Lapin *(VP-Pur)*
Dave Orf *(VP-HR)*
Larry Pennock *(VP-Mktg)*
Brands & Products:
CLAYTON
TOUCH 'N FOAM
TOUCH 'N SEAL
TOUCH 'N STICK

CODEXIS, INC.

200 Penobscot Dr
Redwood City, CA 94063
Tel.: (650) 421-8100
Fax: (650) 421-8102
E-mail: info@codexis.com
Web Site: www.codexis.com
Approx. Rev.: $107,104,000
Approx. Number Employees: 291
Year Founded: 2002
Business Description:
Biocatalytic Chemical Processes Developer
S.I.C.: 2899; 2834; 8733
N.A.I.C.S.: 325998; 325412; 541710
Advertising Expenditures: $55,000
Media: 17
Personnel:
Thomas R. Baruch *(Chm)*
Alan Shaw *(Pres & CEO)*
Robert J. Lawson *(CFO & Sr VP)*
David L. Anton *(CTO & Sr VP-Process Dev & Mfg)*

Key to Media (For complete agency information see *The Advertising Red Books-Agencies* edition):
1. Bus. Publs. 2. Cable T.V. 3. Catalogs & Directories. 4. Co-op Adv. 5. Consumer Mags. 6. D.M. to Bus. Estab.7. D.M. to Consumers
8. Daily Newsp. 9. Exhibits/Trade Shows 10. Foreign 11. Infomercial 12. Internet Adv.13. Multimedia 14. Network Radio
15. Network T.V. 16. Newsp. Distr. Mags. 17. Other 18. Outdoor (Posters, Transit) 19. Point of Purchase20. Premiums, Novelties
21. Product Samples 22. Special Events Mktg. 23. Spot Radio 24. Spot T.V. 25. Weekly Newsp. 26. Yellow Page Adv.

CODEXIS, INC. — (Continued)

Joseph J. Sarret *(Pres-Pharmaceuticals/Enzyme Products & Chief Bus Officer)*
Douglas T. Sheehy *(Gen Counsel, Sec & Sr VP)*
John H. Grate *(Chief Science Officer & Sr VP-Science & Innovation)*
Peter Strumph *(Sr VP-Comml Ops)*
Michael J. Knauf *(VP & Gen Mgr-Bioindustrials)*
Jacques Beaudry-Losique *(VP-Corp Dev & Strategy)*
Lynn Marcus-Wyner *(VP-Intellectual Property)*
Achilles Antonio Clement *(Dir-Latin America)*

Brands & Products:
CODEXIS

COEUR D'ALENE MINES CORPORATION

(d/b/a Coeur, The Precious Metals Co.)
505 Front Ave
Coeur D'Alene, ID 83814
Mailing Address:
PO Box I
Coeur D'Alene, ID 83816-0316
Tel.: (208) 667-3511
Fax: (208) 667-2213
Toll Free: (800) 624-2824
E-mail: coeurir@coeur.com
Web Site: www.coeur.com
Approx. Sls.: $515,457,000
Approx. Number Employees: 1,471
Year Founded: 1928
Business Description:
Precious Metal Mining Services
S.I.C.: 3339; 1041; 1044
N.A.I.C.S.: 331419; 212221; 212222
Advertising Expenditures: $100,000
Media: 2-9-10-23-25
Distr.: Direct to Consumer; Intl.; Natl.
Budget Set: Nov. -Dec.
Personnel:
Dennis E. Wheeler *(Chm)*
Mitchell J. Krebs *(Pres & CEO)*
Frank L. Hanagarne, Jr. *(CFO & Sr VP)*
K. Leon Hardy *(COO & Sr VP)*
Kelli C. Kast *(Chief Admin Officer, Gen Counsel & Sr VP)*
Thomas T. Angelos *(Chief Compliance Officer & Sr VP)*
Donald J. Birak *(Sr VP-Exploration)*
Alfredo Cruzat *(Sr VP-Exploration CDE)*
Larry A. Nelson *(VP-HR)*
John Blue *(Dir-IR-Australia & Asia)*
Tony Ebersole *(Dir-Corp Comm)*
Loni Knepper *(Mgr-Fin Reporting)*

COGNIS CORPORATION

(Sub. of Cognis GmbH)
5051 Estecreek Dr
Cincinnati, OH 45232-1447
Tel.: (513) 482-3000
Fax: (513) 482-5503
Toll Free: (800) 254-1029
Approx. Number Employees: 2,000
Business Description:
Specialty Chemicals
S.I.C.: 2819
N.A.I.C.S.: 325188
Media: 2-4-7-10
Distr.: Natl.
Personnel:
Joe Boroden *(Dir-Ops)*
Raquel Ark *(Sr Mgr-Comm)*

COHESANT, INC.

23400 Commerce Park
Beachwood, OH 44122
Tel.: (216) 910-1700
Web Site: www.cohesant.com
Approx. Sls.: $10,880,739
Year Founded: 1931
Business Description:
Specialized Spray Finishing & Coating Application Equipment & Specialty Coating Products Designer, Developer & Mfr
S.I.C.: 3559; 2851; 3563; 3569
N.A.I.C.S.: 333298; 325510; 333912; 333999
Advertising Expenditures: $919,471
Media: 2-4-7-10
Personnel:
Brian LeMaire *(Founder, Chm & Sr VP)*
Morris H. Wheeler *(Chm, Pres & CEO)*
Robert W. Pawlak *(CFO & Exec VP-Fin)*
Jack Prause *(Pres-CuraFlo & VP)*
Steve Goden *(Sr VP-Admin)*
Brands & Products:
AQUATAPOXY
COHESANT
CURAFLO
CURAPOXY
PROBLER P2
RAVEN
SUPER MAXI

COMPASS MINERALS INTERNATIONAL, INC.

9900 W 109th St Ste 600
Overland Park, KS 66210
Tel.: (913) 344-9200
Fax: (913) 345-0309
E-mail: InvestorRelations@compassminerals.com
Web Site: www.compassminerals.com
Approx. Sls.: $1,068,900,000
Approx. Number Employees: 1,776
Business Description:
Producer of Rock Salt, General Trade Salt & Sulfate of Potash
S.I.C.: 1474; 1479; 1499; 2819
N.A.I.C.S.: 212391; 212393; 212399; 325188
Export
Advertising Expenditures: $250,000
Media: 2-6-19-20-23-26
Distr.: Reg.
Personnel:
Angelo C. Brisimitzakis *(Pres & CEO)*
Rodney L. Underdown *(CFO, Treas & Sec)*
Jerry Smith *(CIO & VP)*
Ronald Bryan *(VP & Gen Mgr-Great Salt Lake Minerals & Compass Minerals UK)*
Jerry Bucan *(VP & Gen Mgr-Consumer-Indus Bus)*
Keith E. Clark *(VP & Gen Mgr-North America Highway)*
Dennis Bergeson *(VP-Supply Chain & Tech)*
Victoria Heider *(VP-HR)*
Brands & Products:
AMERICAN STOCKMAN
COMPASS MINERALS

CONSOL ENERGY INC.

CNX Center 1000 CONSOL Energy Dr
Canonsburg, PA 15317-4000
Tel.: (724) 485-4000
Web Site: www.consolenergy.com
Approx. Rev.: $5,236,021,000
Approx. Number Employees: 8,630
Year Founded: 1860
Business Description:
Coal & Coalbed Methane Producer
S.I.C.: 1221; 1222
N.A.I.C.S.: 212111; 212112
Export
Advertising Expenditures: $5,000,000
Media: 2-11-17
Personnel:
J. Brett Harvey *(Chm & CEO)*
John L. Whitmire, III *(Vice Chm)*
Nicholas J. Deluliis *(Pres)*
William J. Lyons *(CFO & Exec VP)*
P. Jerome Richey *(Chief Legal Officer, Sec & Exec VP-Corp Affairs)*
Robert P. King *(Exec VP-Bus Advancement & Support Svcs)*
Robert F. Pusateri *(Exec VP-Energy Sls & Transportation Svcs)*
Tommy Johnson *(Sr VP-External Affairs)*
Brandon R. Elliott *(VP-IR & PR)*
Joseph A. Cerenzia *(Dir-Pub Rel)*
Brands & Products:
AMERICA'S ON SWITCH
CONSOLENERGY
Advertising Agency:
Brunner
11 Stanwix St 5th Fl
Pittsburgh, PA 15222-1312
Tel.: (412) 995-9500
Fax: (412) 995-9501

COOKSON ELECTRONICS ASSEMBLY MATERIALS GROUP

(Div. of Cookson America Inc.)
109 Corporate Blvd
South Plainfield, NJ 07080
Tel.: (814) 940-6740
Tel.: (908) 791-3000
Fax: (201) 434-7508
Fax: (908) 791-3090
E-mail: alphausa@cooksonelectronics.com
Web Site: www.alphametals.com
Approx. Sls.: $75,000,000
Approx. Number Employees: 150
Year Founded: 1880
Business Description:
Solder, Soldering Chemicals, Anodes, Solder Stampings & Special Alloys Mfr
S.I.C.: 3356; 3341
N.A.I.C.S.: 331491; 331492
Import Export
Advertising Expenditures: $300,000
Media: 2-4-7-10
Distr.: Intl.; Natl.
Budget Set: Sept.
Personnel:
Steve Adase *(VP-Fin)*
Brands & Products:
AQUALINE
CLEANLINE
GUIDELINE

CORAL CHEMICAL COMPANY

135 LeBaron St
Waukegan, IL 60085
Tel.: (847) 246-6666
Fax: (847) 246-6667
Toll Free: (800) 228-4646
Web Site: www.coral.com
Approx. Number Employees: 30
Year Founded: 1953
Business Description:
Industrial Chemical Products Mfr
S.I.C.: 2842; 2812
N.A.I.C.S.: 325612; 325181
Media: 2-10
Personnel:
Mike Stark *(COO & CFO)*
Peter Dority *(VP-Sls & Mktg)*
Brands & Products:
CORAL
CORAL ECO-TREAT
CORALUBE
GL CONTROL SYSTEMS
GUARDIAN SERIES
YELLOW OUT

CP KELCO

(Div. of CP Kelco)
8225 Aero Dr
San Diego, CA 92123-1718
Tel.: (858) 292-4900
Fax: (858) 292-4901
Toll Free: (800) 535-2656
E-mail: solutions@cpkelco.com
Web Site: www.cpkelco.com
E-Mail For Key Personnel:
President: Thomas.Lamb@cpkelco.com
Sales Director: Edmund.Liu@cpkelco.com
Public Relations: cindy.palerno@cpkelco.com
Approx. Number Employees: 1,300
Year Founded: 2000
Business Description:
Specialty Hydrocolloids Mfr
S.I.C.: 2099
N.A.I.C.S.: 311999
Import Export
Media: 1-2-4-7-10-11-20-21
Distr.: Intl.
Personnel:
Thomas B. Lamb *(Chm, Pres & CEO)*
Edward Castorina *(Gen Counsel & VP)*
Thomas K. Johnson *(VP-HR)*

CYANOTECH CORPORATION

73-4460 Queen Kaahumanu Hwy Ste 102
Kailua Kona, HI 96740
Tel.: (808) 326-1353
Fax: (808) 329-4533
E-mail: info@cyanotech.com
Web Site: www.cyanotech.com
Approx. Sls.: $16,827,000
Approx. Number Employees: 71
Year Founded: 1983
Business Description:
Microalgae Products Researcher, Developer & Mfr
S.I.C.: 2833
N.A.I.C.S.: 325411
Export
Advertising Expenditures: $235,000
Media: 4-13-17-21
Personnel:
Michael A. Davis *(Chm)*
Brent Bailey *(Pres & CEO)*

Key to Media (For complete agency information see *The Advertising Red Books-Agencies* edition):
1. Bus. Publs. 2. Cable T.V. 3. Catalogs & Directories. 4. Co-op Adv. 5. Consumer Mags. 6. D.M. to Bus. Estab.7. D.M. to Consumers 8. Daily Newsp. 9. Exhibits/Trade Shows 10. Foreign 11. Infomercial 12. Internet Adv.13. Multimedia 14. Network Radio 15. Network T.V. 16. Newsp. Distr. Mags. 17. Other 18. Outdoor (Posters, Transit) 19. Point of Purchase20. Premiums, Novelties 21. Product Samples 22. Special Events Mktg. 23. Spot Radio 24. Spot T.V. 25. Weekly Newsp. 26. Yellow Page Adv.

Jole Deal *(CFO, Treas, Sec & VP-Fin)*
Gerald R. Cysewski *(Chief Scientific Officer & Exec VP)*
Robert J. Capelli *(VP-Sls)*

Brands & Products:
BIOASTIN
NATUROSE NATURAL ASTAXANTHIN
SPIRULINA PACIFICA

Advertising Agencies:
Media Relations, Inc.
350 W Burnsville Pkwy Ste 350
Burnsville, MN 55337
Tel.: (612) 798-7200
Fax: (612) 798-7272

Russell Communications Group
6176 Bristol Pkwy.
Culver City, CA 90230
Tel.: (310) 216-1414
Fax: (310) 216-1223

CYTEC INDUSTRIES, INC.

5 Garret Mountain Plz
West Paterson, NJ 07424-3317
Tel.: (973) 357-3100
Fax: (973) 357-3065
E-mail: info@cytec.com
Web Site: www.cytec.com
Approx. Sls.: $2,748,300,000
Approx. Number Employees: 6,000
Year Founded: 1993
Business Description:
Specialty Chemicals & Materials Developer, Marketer & Mfr
S.I.C.: 5136; 2299; 2821; 2851; 2899
N.A.I.C.S.: 424320; 313312; 325211; 325510; 325998
Import Export
Media: 2-4-10
Personnel:
Shane D Fleming *(Chm, Pres & CEO)*
David M. Drillock *(CFO & VP)*
William N. Avrin *(Pres-Building Block Chemicals, VP-Corp & Bus Dev)*
Frank Aranzana *(Pres-Cytec Specialty Chemicals)*
William Wood *(Pres-Engineered Matls)*
Roy Smith *(Gen Counsel, Sec & VP)*

Brands & Products:
ACCO-PHOS
ACORGA
ADDITOL
AERO
AERODRI
AEROFLOAT
AEROFLOC
AEROFROTH
AEROMINE
AEROPHINE
AEROSOL
AEROSPRAY
AEROTEX
AEROTIL
AVIMID
BECKOPOX
BR
CARBOFORM
COMPLEMIX
CONACURE
CONAP
CONAPOXY
CONATHANE
CRYLCOAT
CY-EX
CY-TEMP
CYANAMER
CYANATROL
CYANEX
CYANOX
CYASORB
CYASORB THT
CYASTAT
CYBOND
CYBREAK
CYCAT
CYCOM
CYDRIL
CYDROTHANE
CYFLOC
CYFORM
CYLINK
CYMEL
CYPAN
CYPHOS
CYPLY
CYQUEST
CYREZ
CYSEP
CYTHANE
CYTOP
CYTOX
DAOTAN
DAPCO
DECLAR
DIPEB
DURATOOL
DUROFTALT
DUROXYN
EASYPOXY
EBECRYL
ECO2FUME
FM
GELVA
MACRYNAL
MAX HT
MELURAC
METLBOND
MODAFLOW
MULTIFLOW
OREPREP
PHENODUR
POWDERLINK
PYROSET
RAYLOK
RESAMIN
RESYDROL
SANTOSOL
SOLUCRYL
SOLUSOL
SUPERFLOC
SYNTHACRYL
TECHNOLOGY AHEAD OF ITS TIME
THERMALGRAPH
THORNEL
TMI
TMXDI
TOOL/RITE
UCECOAT
UCECRYL
UVECOAT
UVEKOL
VAPORPH3OS
VIACRYL
VIALKYD

Advertising Agencies:
Pratt & Buehl
3390 Peachtree Rd Ste 500
Atlanta, GA 30326
Tel.: (404) 231-2311
Fax: (404) 231-0543

The SPI Group LLC
165 Passaic Ave Ste 410
Fairfield, NJ 07004
Tel.: (973) 244-9191
Fax: (973) 244-9193

DAUBERT INDUSTRIES, INC.

1333 Burr Rdg Pkwy Ste150
Burr Ridge, IL 60527-0833
Tel.: (630) 203-6800
Fax: (630) 203-6900
Toll Free: (800) 535-3535
Web Site: www.daubert.com
Approx. Number Employees: 200
Year Founded: 1935
Business Description:
Holding Company; Manufacturer of Non-Rust Volatile Corrosion Inhibitor (VCI) Protective Packaging for Metal Surfaces; Auto Armor Rust Protection, Paint Protection & Interior Protection Packaged Systems; Rust Preventive Wax, Grease & Oil Coatings; Cutting Fluids; Specialty Metalworking Compounds; Daubond, Laminating, Hot Melt & Structural Adhesives; Specialty Formulated Bonding Systems
S.I.C.: 5169; 2891
N.A.I.C.S.: 424690; 325520
Export
Advertising Expenditures: $270,000
Media: 2-5-10-20-21
Distr.: Intl.; Natl.
Budget Set: Aug.
Personnel:
Peter Fischer *(Chm)*
Fritz Fischer *(Vice Chm)*

Brands & Products:
ALUMITEX
AUTO ARMOR
AUTOARMOR
CLEAR PAK
COOL-FORM
COOL-SPEED
COPPERTEX
DAUBERT
DAUBOND
DAUBRITE
EVAPO-RUST
FERRO-FILM
FERRO-GALV
METAL-GUARD
MILITARY APPROVED FERRO-FILM
NOX-RUST
PLATINUM
PREMIUM METAL-GUARD
PROFITS IN EVERY DEPARTMENT
THE PROTECTOR
PROTEK WRAP
SILVER-GUARD
SILVER SAVER
TECTYL
UNIWRAP
V-DAMP
VAPOR WRAPPER
VERSIL-PAK

DEEPWATER CHEMICALS, INC.

(Sub. of Toyota Tsusho America, Inc.)
1210 Airpark Rd
Woodward, OK 73801-9568
Tel.: (580) 256-0500
Fax: (580) 256-0575
Toll Free: (800) 854-4064
Web Site: www.deepwaterchemicals.com
Approx. Number Employees: 50
Year Founded: 1931
Business Description:
Chemical Products Mfr
S.I.C.: 2819; 2899
N.A.I.C.S.: 325188; 325998
Import Export
Media: 2-10
Distr.: Intl.; Natl.
Personnel:
Pamela S. Clem *(Mgr-Sls)*
William V. Stanley *(Mgr-Regulatory)*

DELTA FOREMOST CHEMICAL CORPORATION

3915 Air Pk St
Memphis, TN 38118-6007
Tel.: (901) 363-4340
Fax: (901) 375-3600
Toll Free: (800) 238-5150
E-mail: sales@deltaforemost.com
Web Site: www.deltaforemost.com
E-Mail For Key Personnel:
Sales Director: sales@deltaforemost.com
Sales Range: $25-49.9 Million
Approx. Number Employees: 175
Year Founded: 1947
Business Description:
Industrial Cleaning Chemical Mfr
S.I.C.: 2842; 5087
N.A.I.C.S.: 325612; 423850
Media: 2-4-7-10-13
Distr.: Natl.
Personnel:
Ronald Cooper *(Pres & CEO)*
John Trobaugh *(CFO & Treas)*
Steve Cole *(Mgr-Adv)*

Brands & Products:
ACTI-ZYME
ALUMI-BRITE
ANTI-SLIP
BUG BUSTER
BUG OFF!
CIP PLUS
CITRAFECT
CITRI-KOTE PLUS
CONSEAL
DE-STAIN
DEL-GUARD
DELTA FOREMOST
DEO-MIST
DRI 'N LUBE
DUO
DUST-A-WAY
DUST COMMAND
DYNA-KLEEN
EZY CLEANER
FLOW AWAY
FOAM-N-KLEEN
GREASE-A-WAY
GRILL BRITE
GRIME-X
GRIT BLITZ
HANDY-SAN
HI-TECK
ICE-CHASER
INSECT-O-FOG
INSECTI-MIST
JET SPRAY CLEAN
KLEER SEAL
KOIL BRITE
KOIL MASTER
LECTRO-SOLV
MASK-A-WAY
MASK OFF
MEASUR-MIST
MICROZORB

Key to Media (For complete agency information see *The Advertising Red Books-Agencies* edition):
1. Bus. Publs. 2. Cable T.V. 3. Catalogs & Directories. 4. Co-op Adv. 5. Consumer Mags. 6. D.M. to Bus. Estab.7. D.M. to Consumers 8. Daily Newsp. 9. Exhibits/Trade Shows 10. Foreign 11. Infomercial 12. Internet Adv.13. Multimedia 14. Network Radio 15. Network T.V. 16. Newsp. Distr. Mags. 17. Other 18. Outdoor (Posters, Transit) 19. Point of Purchase20. Premiums, Novelties 21. Product Samples 22. Special Events Mktg. 23. Spot Radio 24. Spot T.V. 25. Weekly Newsp. 26. Yellow Page Adv.

Delta Foremost Chemical Corporation — (Continued)

MISTI-CIDE
NU CON SEAL
NU-SURFACE
OVERSPRAY AWAY
PREP POWER
QUAD-DIS PLUS
RED RAGE
SANI-FOAM
SANI-FOG
SCRUBMASTER
SHOCK-LESS
SHOW-OFF
SLEDGE HAMMER
SLIX
SMOKEATER
STRIP-A-WAY
SUDS-N-KLEEN
SUPER BRITE
SUPER FERRO-KLEEN
SUPER-GUARD
SUPER KLEEN
SUPER SAFE SOLV
SUPER-SOLV
SURE STEP
TOWER TREET
TRAILER-BRITE
WEED ZAPPER
WEEDZOUT
WINTER-SLIX
WONDER CLEANER
ZIP POWER
ZORBITALL

Advertising Agency:
APR Associates, Inc.
3915 Air Park St
Memphis, TN 38118-6007
Tel.: (901) 363-5904
Fax: (901) 375-3600
Toll Free: (800) 238-5182
(Engineered Cleaners for Industry)

DENISON MINES CORP.

Atrium on Bay 595 Bay St Ste 402
Toronto, ON M5G 2C2, Canada
Tel.: (416) 979-1991
Fax: (416) 979-5893
Toll Free: (888) 689-7842
E-mail: info@denisonmines.com
Web Site: www.denisonmines.com
Approx. Rev.: $128,320,000
Approx. Number Employees: 348
Business Description:
Uranium Recycling & Mining Services
S.I.C.: 1241; 1094
N.A.I.C.S.: 213113; 212291
Personnel:
James R. Anderson *(Owner)*
Ron F. Hochstein *(Pres & CEO)*
Harold R. Roberts *(Exec VP-US Ops)*
Curt D. Steel *(VP-Mktg & Sls)*
Advertising Agency:
W.S. Adamson & Associates, Inc.
175 West 200 South Ste 3003 First Commerce Ctr
Salt Lake City, UT 84101
Tel.: (801) 532-5322
Fax: (801) 532-5324
Toll Free: (877) 532-5344

DETREX CORPORATION

24901 Northwestern Hwy Ste 410
Southfield, MI 48075-2209
Tel.: (248) 358-5800
Fax: (248) 799-7192
Toll Free: (800) 525-1496
Web Site: www.detrex.com
E-Mail For Key Personnel:
President: tmark@detrex-hq.com
Approx. Sls.: $93,664,728
Approx. Number Employees: 203
Year Founded: 1920
Business Description:
Industrial Chemical Specialties, Lubricant Additives & PVC Pipes Mfr
S.I.C.: 2899; 1321; 2816; 2819; 2992; 3084
N.A.I.C.S.: 325998; 211112; 324191; 325131; 325188; 326122
Export
Advertising Expenditures: $200,000
Media: 2-4-7-10
Distr.: Direct to Consumer; Natl.
Budget Set: Dec.
Personnel:
William C. King *(Chm)*
Thomas E. Mark *(Pres & CEO)*
Robert M. Currie *(Gen Counsel, Treas, Sec & VP)*
Brands & Products:
DETREX
HARVEL PLASTICS
LXT
PERM-A-CLOR
ULTRAMAX

DIAGNOSTIC CHEMICALS LIMITED

70 Watts Ave W Royalty Industrial Pk
Charlottetown, PE C1E 2B9, Canada
Tel.: (902) 566-1396
Fax: (902) 628-6504
Toll Free: (800) 565-0265
E-mail: sales@dclchem.com
Web Site: www.dclchem.com
E-Mail For Key Personnel:
Sales Director: sales@dclchem.com
Approx. Number Employees: 200
Year Founded: 1970
Business Description:
Diagnostic Chemical Producer
S.I.C.: 2899
N.A.I.C.S.: 325998
Media: 7-10
Personnel:
J. Regis Duffy *(Chm & Pres)*
Gordon Rogers *(CFO, VP-Fin & Corp Sys)*
Lee Lipski *(Dir-Mktg & Sls-N America)*
Bob Fredrickson *(Dir-Res & New Tech Devel)*
Julien Gaudin *(Dir-Diagnostic Mfg Opers)*
Valerie Taylor *(Dir-HR)*

DOBER CHEMICAL CORP.

14461 Waverly Ave
Midlothian, IL 60445-2939
Tel.: (708) 388-7700
Fax: (708) 388-9344
Toll Free: (800) 323-4983
E-mail: ddobrez@dober-group.com
Web Site: www.dober-group.com
Approx. Number Employees: 175
Year Founded: 1957
Business Description:
Industrial Chemicals Mfr
S.I.C.: 2899; 2842
N.A.I.C.S.: 325998; 325612
Media: 2-6-7-8
Distr.: Natl.
Personnel:
John G. Dobrez *(Pres & CEO)*
Jim Harper *(CFO)*
Dan Dobrez *(Exec VP)*
Chris Dobrez *(VP-Mktg)*
Brands & Products:
DOBER

DOVER CHEMICAL CORPORATION

(Sub. of ICC Industries, Inc.)
3676 Davis Rd NW
Dover, OH 44622-0040
Tel.: (330) 343-7711
Fax: (330) 364-1579
Toll Free: (800) 321-8805
Web Site: www.doverchem.com
Sales Range: $100-124.9 Million
Approx. Number Employees: 160
Business Description:
Chemicals Mfr
S.I.C.: 2819; 2869
N.A.I.C.S.: 325188; 325199
Media: 2-7-10
Distr.: Natl.
Budget Set: Oct.
Personnel:
Dwain Colvin *(Pres)*
Jack Teat *(Exec VP)*
Chuck Fletcher *(VP-Sls & Mktg)*
Tom Kelley *(Dir-Global Sls)*
Mark Harr *(Reg Mgr-Sls-Midwest)*
Chad McGlothlin *(Reg Mgr-Sls-Midwest)*
Curtis Lege *(Bus Mgr-Lubricants Additives)*
Wendy Finch *(Mgr-Customer Svc)*
Rob Hendriks *(Mgr-Sls-Southwest)*
Tom Slam *(Mgr-Mktg)*
Damon S. Stevenson *(Mgr-Sls)*
James D. Williamson *(Mgr-Sls-Northeast Reg)*
Brands & Products:
CHLOREZ
CHLOROWAX
DOVERLUBE
DOVERNOX
DOVERPHOS
DOVERSPERSE
HORDARESIN
PAROIL
PHOSBOOSTER

DOW AGROSCIENCES LLC

(Sub. of Mycogen Corporation)
9330 Zionsville Rd
Indianapolis, IN 46268-1053
Tel.: (317) 337-3000
Fax: (317) 337-4542
Toll Free: (800) 258-3033
Web Site: www.dowagroscience.com
Approx. Sls.: $3,400,000,000
Approx. Number Employees: 5,500
Business Description:
Agricultural Chemicals Mfr
S.I.C.: 2879; 5191
N.A.I.C.S.: 325320; 424910
Personnel:
Antonio Galindez *(Pres & CEO)*
Christy Randolph *(Brand Mgr-Enlist Weed Control System)*
Brands & Products:
AGROMEN
BRODBECK
CLINCHER
DAIRYLAND
DELEGATE
DITHANE
FORTRESS
GARLON
GLYPHOMAX
GRANITE
HERCULEX
KEYSTONE
LAREDO
LONTREL
LORSBAN
MILESTONE
MUSTANG
MYCOGEN
NEXERA
PHYTOGEN
PROFUME
RENZE
SENTRICON
SIMPLICITY
STARANE
TELONE
TORDON
TRACER NATURALYTE
TRIUMPH
VIKANE
WIDESTRIKE
Advertising Agency:
Bader Rutter & Associates, Inc.
13845 Bishops Dr
Brookfield, WI 53005
Tel.: (262) 784-7200
Fax: (262) 938-5595
Toll Free: (888) 742-2337

DOW CHEMICAL CANADA INC.

(Sub. of THE DOW CHEMICAL COMPANY)
450 First St SW Ste 2100
Calgary, AB T2P 5H1, Canada
Tel.: (403) 267-3500
Fax: (403) 267-3597
Telex: 64-76172
E-mail: info@dow.com
Web Site: www.dow.com
Sales Range: $1-4.9 Billion
Approx. Number Employees: 25
Year Founded: 1942
Business Description:
Industrial Chemicals & Plastics Mfr & Sales
S.I.C.: 5169
N.A.I.C.S.: 424690
Export
Media: 2-4-7-10-20-21
Distr.: Natl.

THE DOW CHEMICAL COMPANY

2030 Dow Ctr
Midland, MI 48674-0001
Tel.: (989) 636-1000
Fax: (989) 638-1740
Toll Free: (800) 258-2436
E-mail: dowshareholders@bankofny.com
Web Site: www.dow.com
Approx. Sls.: $53,674,000,000
Approx. Number Employees: 49,505
Year Founded: 1897
Business Description:
Holding Company; Various Chemicals, Petrochemicals, Agricultural Chemicals, Plastics, Specialty Coatings & Products Mfr & Whslr
S.I.C.: 6719; 2819; 2821; 2869; 2879; 2891; 2899; 3081; 3086; 3089; 3479; 5162; 5169
N.A.I.C.S.: 551112; 325110; 325188; 325199; 325211; 325320; 325520; 325998; 326113; 326140; 326150; 326199; 332812; 424610; 424690

Key to Media (For complete agency information see *The Advertising Red Books-Agencies* edition):
1. Bus. Publs. 2. Cable T.V. 3. Catalogs & Directories. 4. Co-op Adv. 5. Consumer Mags. 6. D.M. to Bus. Estab.7. D.M. to Consumers
8. Daily Newsp. 9. Exhibits/Trade Shows 10. Foreign 11. Infomercial 12. Internet Adv.13. Multimedia 14. Network Radio
15. Network T.V. 16. Newsp. Distr. Mags. 17. Other 18. Outdoor (Posters, Transit) 19. Point of Purchase20. Premiums, Novelties
21. Product Samples 22. Special Events Mktg. 23. Spot Radio 24. Spot T.V. 25. Weekly Newsp. 26. Yellow Page Adv.

Import Export
Advertising Expenditures:
$30,000,000
Media: 2-3-6-9-13-15-16-17-24
Distr.: Direct to Consumer; Natl.
Budget Set: July -Oct.

Personnel:

Andrew N. Liveris *(Chm & CEO)*
Jose Maria Bermudez *(Pres & Gen Mgr-North Reg Latin America)*
William H. Weideman *(CFO & Exec VP)*
David E. Kepler, II *(CIO, Exec VP-Bus Svcs & Chief Sustainability Officer)*
William F. Banholzer *(CTO & Exec VP-Ventures, New Bus Dev & Licensing)*
Heinz Haller *(Chief Comml Officer & Exec VP)*
William L. Curry *(Chief Tax Officer & Asst Sec)*
James R. Fitterling *(Pres-Corp Dev & Hydrocarbons, Exec VP)*
Joseph E. Harlan *(Pres-Performance Products & Performance Sys Div & Exec VP)*
Geoffery E. Merszei *(Pres-Dow Europe, Middle East and Africa & Exec VP)*
Pat D. Dawson *(Pres-Asia Pacific)*
Peter Sykes *(Pres-Greater China)*
Carol Williams *(Pres-Chemicals & Energy Div & Grp Sr VP-The Dow Chemical Company)*
Charles J. Kalil *(Gen Counsel, Corp Sec & Exec VP-Law & Govt Affairs)*
Gregory M. Freiwald *(Exec VP-HR, Corp Affairs & Aviation)*
Michael R. Gambrell *(Exec VP-Mfg & Engrg Ops)*
Jerome A. Peribere *(Exec VP)*
James D. McIlvenny *(Sr VP-Performance Products & Meg Projects)*
Guillermo Novo *(Grp VP-Dow Coatings Matls)*
Mark Henning *(Gen Mgr-Dow Microbial Control)*
Jonathan J. Hastings *(Sr Dir-Strategy & New Bus Dev)*
Chuck Carn *(Mktg Mgr)*
Douglas J. Anderson *(Corp Auditor)*
Warren Michael McGuire *(Asst Sec)*
Amy Wilson *(Asst Sec)*

Brands & Products:

ACRYSOL
ACUDYNE
ACULYN
ACUMER
ACUPLANE
ADCOTE
AFFINITY
AFFIRM
AG BOARD
AGILITY
AGMATE
AIM
AMBERLITE
AMBITROL
AMICAL
AMILOX
AMINE CS-1135
AMINE CS-1246
AMINE MANAGEMENT
AMP-90
AMP-95
AMP-REGULAR
AMP-ULTRA
AMPLIFY
AQUA-LAM
AQUASET
AQUCAR
AR
ASOS
ASPUN
ATTANE
AUROLECTROLESS
AUTOMATT
AUTOTHANE
AVANSE
BETACLEAN
BETADAMP
BETAFOAM
BETAGUARD
BETAGUN
BETAPRIME
BIOAQUEOUS
BIOBALANCE
BIOCARE
BLUE
BLUEBOARD
BLUEBOARD DIGEST
BLUECOR
BLUEPRINTS
BONARIL
BOROL
BRINER'S CHOICE
BUNA
CALIBRE
CANGUARD
CARBITOL
CARBOWAX
CAVITYMATE
CELEX
CELLOSIZE
CELLOSOLVE
CHANNELMATE
CHELAMED
CHEMAWARE
CHEMIPALOOZA
CLADMATE
COASOL
COMBOTHERM
CONTINUUM
COPPER GLEAM
CORRGUARD
CORSAF
COVELLE
CRANIUM PALLADIUM
CURRITHANE
CYCLOTENE
CYRACURE
DALPAD
DAXAD
D.E.H.
DELTA THERM
DEMTROL
D.E.N.
D.E.R.
DIANTOL
DISPURSA
DMAMP-80
DOMAMATE
DOW
DOW XLA
DOWANOL
DOWCAL
DOWCLENE
DOWCLOR
DOWEX
DOWEX OPTIPORE
DOWEX QCAT
DOWFAX
DOWFLAKE
DOWFROST
DOWICIDE
DOWLEX
DOWPER
DOWPHARMA
DOWTHERM
DOXIMER
DRYTECH
DURALAST
DURAMATE
DURAMOULD
DURAPOSIT
DURAVELLE
DYNATHANE
ECHELON
ECOPANE
ECOSOFT
ECOSURF
EFFECTIONS
ELASTENE
ELIMINATOR
ELITE
EMERGE
EMKADIXOL
ENDURANCE
ENERBOND
ENERBOND BA
ENERBOND DW
ENERBOND SF
ENERFOAM
ENFORCER
ENGAGE
ENHANCER
THE ENHANCER
ENLIGHT
ENLITE
ENSEMBLE
ENVELON
ENVISION
EPIC
EQUIFOAM
ESSEX ARGOSY
ESSEXPAK
ESTASOL
ESTICLEAN
ESTILUBE
ESTIMOL
ETHACALC
ETHAFOAM
ETHOCEL
EVANACID
EVIDENCE
EVOCAR
EXTRAMATE
FIBRANCE
FIEXOMER
FILL & SEAL
FILMTEC
FLEXOL
FLEXOMER
FLOORMATE
FLUENT-BRAKE
FLUENT-CANE
FLUENT-FAX
FLUENT-LUB
FLUENT-MAT
FLUIDFILE
FOAM CALC
FOAM CRETE
FOAM PLUS
FOAM SULATE
FORTEFIBER
FORTEGRA
FOUNDATIONS
THE FREEDOM FIBER
FROTH-PAK
FUELSAVER
FUNGI-BLOCK
GEOMATE
GREAT GRIP
GREAT STUFF
HALPACLEAN
HALPANAL
HALPASOL
HAMPSHIRE
HARVEST
HI-TRI
HPL
HYPERKOTE
HYPERLAST
HYPOL
ILEC
IMMOTUS
INCLOSIA
INDEX
INFOBLEU
INFUSE
INSITE
INSPIRE
INSTA FLO
INSTA-GRIP
INSTA SEAL
INSTA-STIK
INSTEP
INSTILL
INTEGRAL
INTERVIA
INVERT
IPN
ISOBIND
ISOCAST
ISOFORM
ISONATE
ISONOL
ISOPLAST
JENIUS
KASTEL
KYTAMER
LAMDEX
LDLA
LIFESPAN
LIGHTER
LIGHTER AQUAFONTIS
LIQUIDOW
LITEFEIL
LITHOJET
LP OXO
MAESTRO
MAGNUM
MAXICHECK
MAXISTAB
MECTHENE
MEGARAD
MERIDIAN
METAL SIGNATURE
METEOR
METGARD
METHOCEL
MIRATHEN
MONOTHANE
MOR-FREE
MORLEX DEEA
MORTRACE
MULTIFIT
N-SERVE
NEOCAR
NEOLYTICA
NEPD
NEU-TRI
NIPAR
NITROFUEL
NORDEL
NORKOOL
NYLOPAK

Key to Media (For complete agency information see *The Advertising Red Books-Agencies* edition):
1. Bus. Publs. 2. Cable T.V. 3. Catalogs & Directories. 4. Co-op Adv. 5. Consumer Mags. 6. D.M. to Bus. Estab.7. D.M. to Consumers 8. Daily Newsp. 9. Exhibits/Trade Shows 10. Foreign 11. Infomercial 12. Internet Adv.13. Multimedia 14. Network Radio 15. Network T.V. 16. Newsp. Distr. Mags. 17. Other 18. Outdoor (Posters, Transit) 19. Point of Purchase20. Premiums, Novelties 21. Product Samples 22. Special Events Mktg. 23. Spot Radio 24. Spot T.V. 25. Weekly Newsp. 26. Yellow Page Adv.

THE DOW CHEMICAL COMPANY — (Continued)

ONE
OPTICALC
OPTICITE
OPTIM
OPTIML
OPTISOL
OPTOGRADE
OPULYN
OUTREACH
OXABAN
OXILUBE
PANELINE
PANELMATE
PAPI
PARABIS
PECOBACK
PELADOW
PELASPAN
PELLETHANE
PERIMATE
PIMIC
PIROR
PITAPANE
PKWF
POLYOX
POLYPHOBE
POLYSLIP
POWERHOUSE
PREVAIL
PRIMACOR
PRIMAL
PRINTOSOL
PRINTOVISC
PROCITE
PROGLYDE
PROMATCH
PROPE
PROPEL
PULSE
QBIS
QUASH
QUATRISOFT
QUESTRA
QUIKCHAR
RAP
REDI-LINK
RENUVA
RETAIN
REZILUBE
RHOPLEX
ROBOND
ROKLITE
ROOFMATE
ROOFPAK
ROOMLAC
ROPAQUE
ROTAKOTE
SABRE
SAFE-TAINER
SAFECHEM
SARAN
SARANEX
SATISFIT
SCAN
SCONAPOR
SELEXOL
SERFENE
SHAC
SHAPEMATE
SI-LINK
SILK
SIMUSOLV
SLOPER
SOLIMATE
SOLTERRA
SOLTEX
SPECFIL
SPECFLEX
SPECTRIM
STATURE
STRANDFOAM
STUCCOMATE
STYROACE
STYROFOAM
STYRON
STYRON A-TECH
SUMP BUDDY
SYLTHERM
SYNALOX
SYNERGY
SYNTEGRA
TANKLITE
TECHMATE
TECTOR
TERGITOL
TERRALOX
TERRAQUENCH
TERRASURF
THERMAX
THERMODRY
THERMOPROOF
THIXOMAG
TILE BOND
TONE
TRAFFIDECK
TRBRITE
TRENCHCOAT
TRIS NITRO
TRITON
TRYCITE
TRYMER
TUFLIN
TULOPAN
TYDEX
TYMOR
TYRIL
TYRIN
UCAR
UCARCIDE
UCARHIDE
UCARKLEAN
UCARMAG
UCARSAN
UCARSEP
UCARSOL
UCARTHERM
UCAT
UCON
UCONALL
UCONEX
UNICARB
UNIGARD
UNIPURGE
UNIVAL
UNOXOL
UPCORE
URETHANE
UTILI-FOAM
UTILITY FIT
VERDISEAL
VERSABACS
VERSENATE
VERSENE
VERSENEX
VERSENOL
VERSIFY
VISCOPHOBE
VIVYPAK
VORACOR
VORACTIV
VORALAST
VORALIFE
VORALUX
VORAMER
VORANATE
VORANOL
VORASTAR
VORASURF
VORATEC
VORATRON
WALLMATE
WALOCEL
WALSRODER
WEATHERMATE
WOODSTALK
X-TENSE
X-TUNE
XPOGRAPH
ZETABON

Advertising Agencies:

Alexander Marketing
801 Broadway Ave Ste 300
Grand Rapids, MI 49504
Tel.: (616) 957-2000
Fax: (616) 957-3514

Bader Rutter & Associates, Inc.
13845 Bishops Dr
Brookfield, WI 53005
Tel.: (262) 784-7200
Fax: (262) 938-5595
Toll Free: (888) 742-2337
(Agricultural Products)

Draftfcb
101 E Erie St
Chicago, IL 60611-2812
Tel.: (312) 425-5000
Fax: (312) 425-5010
Dow Solar Solutions (Agency of Record)
Human Element Campaign

Fitzgerald+CO
3060 Peachtree Rd NW
Atlanta, GA 30305
Tel.: (404) 504-6900
Fax: (404) 239-0548

GolinHarris
(Part of the Interpublic Group of Companies)
111 E Wacker Dr 11th Fl
Chicago, IL 60601-4306
Tel.: (312) 729-4000
Fax: (312) 729-4010

The Quest Business Agency, Inc.
2150 W 18th St Ste 202
Houston, TX 77008
Tel.: (713) 956-6569
Fax: (713) 956-2593

The Scott & Miller Group
816 S Hamilton St
Saginaw, MI 48602-1516
Tel.: (989) 799-1877
Fax: (989) 799-6115
Toll Free: (888) 791-1876

DOW CORNING CORPORATION

(Joint Venture of Corning Incorporated & THE DOW CHEMICAL COMPANY)
2200 W Salzburg Rd
Midland, MI 48686
Mailing Address:
PO Box 994
Midland, MI 48686-0994
Tel.: (989) 496-4400
Fax: (989) 496-1886
Web Site: www.dowcorning.com
Approx. Sls.: $5,500,000,000
Approx. Number Employees: 10,000
Year Founded: 1943
Business Description:
Silicone-Based Products, Adhesives, Lubricants & Insulating Materials Mfr; Joint Venture of The Dow Chemical Company (50%) & Corning Incorporated (50%)
S.I.C.: 2819; 2821
N.A.I.C.S.: 325188; 325211
Export
Media: 22
Distr.: Direct to Indus. Customers; Natl.
Personnel:
Stephanie A. Burns *(Chm)*
Robert D. Hansen *(Pres & CEO)*
Joseph D. Sheets *(CFO & Exec VP)*
Kristy Folkwein *(CIO & Exec Dir)*
Brian Chermside *(CMO & VP)*
Alan Hubbart *(Chief HR Officer)*
John D. Lyon *(Pres-Central & Eastern Europe)*
Sue K. McDonnell *(Corp Sec, Sr VP & Gen Counsel)*
Thomas H. Cook *(Sr VP & Gen Mgr-Specialty Chemicals Bus)*
James R. Whitlock *(Sr VP & Gen Mgr-Core Bus)*
Kenneth P. Kaufman *(VP-Mfg, Engrg & Global Ops)*
Scott E. Fuson *(Exec Dir-Mktg & Sls)*
Linda D. Kennan *(Exec Dir-Corp Stewardship)*
Randall Rozin *(Dir-Brand Mgmt & Mktg Comm-Global)*
Karen Heenan-Davies *(Mgr-Comm & E-Bus & Life Sciences)*
Brands & Products:
561
BIO-PSA
BIO-RELEASE
CAPTUREPLUS
DOW CORNING
DYMASIL
EVOLUTION
FOX
HIPEC
HSC
LUBOLID
MD7-4502
MD7-4602
MG-0153/PA-0153
MG-0560/PA 0560
MG-0580/PA-0580
MG-0607/PA-0607
MG-0610/PA-0610
MOLYKOTE
OPTIGARD
ORTHOLOC
PENE-LUBE
PULPAID
S
SIGHT SAVERS
SILASTIC
SILSOFT
SS
SYL-OFF
SYLGARD
TRADE MATE
TRSIV
WE HELP YOU INVENT THE FUTURE

Key to Media (For complete agency information see *The Advertising Red Books-Agencies* edition):
1. Bus. Publs. 2. Cable T.V. 3. Catalogs & Directories. 4. Co-op Adv. 5. Consumer Mags. 6. D.M. to Bus. Estab.7. D.M. to Consumers
8. Daily Newsp. 9. Exhibits/Trade Shows 10. Foreign 11. Infomercial 12. Internet Adv.13. Multimedia 14. Network Radio
15. Network T.V. 16. Newsp. Distr. Mags. 17. Other 18. Outdoor (Posters, Transit) 19. Point of Purchase20. Premiums, Novelties
21. Product Samples 22. Special Events Mktg. 23. Spot Radio 24. Spot T.V. 25. Weekly Newsp. 26. Yellow Page Adv.

XIAMETER
Z3MS

Advertising Agencies:
BLUE Interactive Marketing
245 Park Ave 39th Fl
New York, NY 10167
Tel.: (212) 672-1930
Fax: (212) 792-4001

Brunner
260 Peachtree St NW Ste 1100
Atlanta, GA 30303
Tel.: (404) 479-2200
Fax: (404) 479-9850

Draftfcb
101 E Erie St
Chicago, IL 60611
Tel.: (312) 425-5000
Fax: (312) 425-5010

Slack Barshinger & Partners, Inc.
233 N Michigan Ave Ste 3050
Chicago, IL 60601
Tel.: (312) 970-5800
Fax: (312) 970-5850
Toll Free: (800) 888-6197

DUPONT PERFORMANCE ELASTOMERS LLC

(Joint Venture of THE DOW CHEMICAL COMPANY & E.I. du Pont de Nemours & Company)
300 Bellevue Pkwy Ste 300
Wilmington, DE 19809
Tel.: (302) 792-4000
Fax: (302) 792-4450
Toll Free: (800) 853-5515
Web Site:
www.dupontelastomers.com
Sales Range: $350-399.9 Million
Approx. Number Employees: 1,500
Year Founded: 1996
Business Description:
Specialty Elastomers Supplier; 50% Owned by The Dow Chemical Company & 50% by E.I. duPont de Nemours & Company
S.I.C.: 3089
N.A.I.C.S.: 326199
Media: 10-11
Personnel:
Francine C. Shawl *(Pres, CEO & Exec VP)*

DYNAMITE PLANT FOOD

(Sub. of Florikan E.S.A.)
PO Box 190
Oxford, FL 34484
Tel.: (800) 447-3304
Fax: (352) 748-4310
Approx. Number Employees: 40
Business Description:
Agricultural Products Mfr & Distr
S.I.C.: 2879
N.A.I.C.S.: 325320
Media: 2-3-4-10-13-22
Personnel:
Mas Wade *(Owner)*

EASTMAN CHEMICAL COMPANY

200 S Wilcox Dr
Kingsport, TN 37660
Mailing Address:
PO Box 511
Kingsport, TN 37662-0431
Tel.: (423) 229-2000
Fax: (423) 229-2145
Toll Free: (800) 327-8626
E-mail: eastman1@eastman.com
Web Site: www.eastman.com
Approx. Sls.: $5,842,000,000
Approx. Number Employees: 10,000
Year Founded: 1920
Business Description:
Fine Chemicals Mfr
S.I.C.: 2899; 2821
N.A.I.C.S.: 325998; 325211
Import Export
Advertising Expenditures: $10,000,000
Bus. Publs.: $5,000,000; Catalogs & Directories: $100,000; D.M. to Bus. Estab.: $500,000; Exhibits/Trade Shows: $2,000,000; Foreign: $2,000,000; Internet Adv.: $300,000; Premiums, Novelties: $100,000
Distr.: Intl.; Natl.
Budget Set: Sept. -Oct.
Personnel:
James P. Rogers *(Chm, Pres & CEO)*
Mark J. Costa *(CMO & Exec VP-Specialty Polymers, Coatings, Adhesives)*
Theresa K. Lee *(Chief Legal Officer, Chief Admin Officer & Sr VP)*
Ronald C. Lindsay *(Exec VP-Performance Chemicals, Intermediates & Ops Support)*
Curtis E. Espeland *(Sr VP)*
Richard L. Johnson *(Sr VP-Fibers & Global Supply Chain)*
Norris P. Sneed *(Sr VP)*
Brad Lich *(VP & Gen Mgr-CASPI)*
Randy Roberts *(VP-Pub Rels)*
Damon Warmack *(VP-Corp Dev & Strategy)*
Gregory Riddle *(Dir-IR)*
Karen Parsons *(Mgr-Mktg Comm)*
Brands & Products:
ABALYN
ABITOL
AQUASTAB
BIOEXTEND
CADENCE
CELLOLYN
CHROMSPUN
DRESINATE
DURASTAR
DYMEREX
EASTACRYL
EASTALLOY
EASTAPURE
EASTAR
EASTMAN
EASTMAN AQ
EASTMAN AQUA PET
EASTMAN G
EASTMAN NPG
EASTMAN PET
EASTMAN TXIB
EASTOBRITE
EASTOFLEX
EASTONE
EASTOTAC
ECDEL
EMBRACE
ENDEX
EPOLENE
ESTROBOND
ESTRON
FORAL-E
FORALYN
THE GLASS POLYMER
HEATWAVE
INTEGREX
KELVX
KRISTALEX
METALYN
NEOSTAR
NUTRIENE
NUTRILAYER
OPTIFILM
PAMOLYN
PARASTAR
PENTALYN
PERMALYN
PICCO
PICCOLASTIC
PICCOTAC
PICCOTEX
PLASTOLYN
POLY-PALE
PROVISTA
REGALITE
REGALREZ
SOLUS
SPECTAR
STAYBELITE-E
SUSTANE SAIB
TACOLYN
TECSOL
TENITE
TENOX
TEXANOL
TIGLAZE
TMPD
TRITAN
VITIVA PET
Advertising Agencies:
Bader Rutter & Associates, Inc.
13845 Bishops Dr
Brookfield, WI 53005
Tel.: (262) 784-7200
Fax: (262) 938-5595
Toll Free: (888) 742-2337
Eastman Tritan Copolyester

The Tombras Group
630 Concord St
Knoxville, TN 37919-3305
Tel.: (865) 524-5376
Fax: (865) 524-5667

E.I. DU PONT DE NEMOURS & COMPANY

(d/b/a DuPont)
1007 Market St
Wilmington, DE 19898-0001
Tel.: (302) 774-1000
Fax: (302) 999-4399
Toll Free: (800) 441-7515
Telex: 835420
E-mail: info@usa.dupont.com
Web Site: www2.dupont.com
Approx. Rev.: $32,733,000,000
Approx. Number Employees: 60,000
Year Founded: 1802
Business Description:
Chemical Products Mfr
S.I.C.: 2821; 2879; 2899
N.A.I.C.S.: 325211; 325320; 325998
Import Export
Media: 2-5-6-7-8-10-11-13-14-15-23-24
Distr.: Natl.
Personnel:
Ellen J. Kullman *(Chm & CEO)*
Nicholas C. Fanandakis *(CFO & Exec VP)*
Phuong Tram *(CIO & VP-IT)*
Scott Coleman *(CMO, Chief Sls Officer & VP-Corp Mktg & Sls)*
Douglas W. Muzyka *(Chief Tech Officer, Sr VP & Chief Science Officer)*
Linda J. Fisher *(Chief Sustainability Officer & VP-Safety, Health & Environ)*
Uma Chowdhry *(Chief Science Officer)*
Craig F. Binetti *(Pres-Nutrition & Health)*
Diane H. Gulyas *(Pres-Performance Polymer)*
William J. Harvey *(Pres-Pkg & Indus Polymers)*
David B. Miller *(Pres-Electronic & Comm Tech)*
Thomas G. Powell *(Pres-Protection Tech)*
Paul E. Schickler *(Pres-Pioneer Hi-Bred)*
Gary W. Spitzer *(Pres-Chemicals & Fluoroproducts)*
Eduardo W. Wanick *(Pres-Latin America)*
James R. Weigand *(Pres-DuPont Sustainable Solutions)*
Mary E. Bowler *(Sec & Corp Counsel)*
Thomas L. Sager *(Sr VP-Legal & Gen Counsel)*
Susan M. Stalnecker *(Treas & VP-Fin)*
James C. Borel *(Exec VP)*
Thomas M. Connelly, Jr. *(Exec VP & Chief Innovation Officer)*
Jeffrey L. Keefer *(Exec VP)*
Mark P. Vergnano *(Exec VP)*
David G. Bills *(Sr VP-Corp Strategy)*
Benito Cachinero-Sanchez *(Sr VP-HR)*
Jeffrey A. Coe *(Sr VP-Integrated Ops & Engrg)*
Richard C. Olson *(Sr VP-DuPont Corp Productivity & Bus Process Simplification)*
Hinton J. Lucas, Jr. *(VP & Asst Gen Counsel)*
Martha L. Rees *(VP & Asst Gen Counsel)*
Harry Parker *(VP)*
Maritza J. Poza-Grise *(VP-HR)*
Steven Wolf *(Gen Mgr-Stone, Tile & Carpet Care)*
Dawn Rittenhouse *(Dir-Sustainable Dev)*
Pam Pryor *(Mgr-Licensing & Mktg)*
Carlito C. Galleta *(Grp Sls Mgr)*
Curtis Orrben *(Natl Sls Mgr)*
Carl Festre *(Mgr-EMEA Energy Mgmt)*
Brenda Franke *(Mgr-Global Mktg)*
Rosanne Miller *(Mgr-Global Comm)*
Clay W. Scherer *(Mgr-Product Dev)*
Nancy Schwartz *(Mgr-Mktg)*
Charles Silcox *(Mgr-Global Product Dev)*
Roger Wicks *(Mgr-Global Tech Mktg)*
Brands & Products:
ACCENT
ACELEPRYN
ACSIUM
ACTUREL
ADOX
ADVION
AFFINITY
AGILITY
ALESTA
ALLY
ALTACOR
ANTHIUM DIOXCIDE

Key to Media (For complete agency information see *The Advertising Red Books-Agencies* edition):
1. Bus. Publs. 2. Cable T.V. 3. Catalogs & Directories. 4. Co-op Adv. 5. Consumer Mags. 6. D.M. to Bus. Estab.7. D.M. to Consumers
8. Daily Newsp. 9. Exhibits/Trade Shows 10. Foreign 11. Infomercial 12. Internet Adv.13. Multimedia 14. Network Radio
15. Network T.V. 16. Newsp. Distr. Mags. 17. Other 18. Outdoor (Posters, Transit) 19. Point of Purchase20. Premiums, Novelties
21. Product Samples 22. Special Events Mktg. 23. Spot Radio 24. Spot T.V. 25. Weekly Newsp. 26. Yellow Page Adv.

E.I. du Pont de Nemours & Company — (Continued)

APPEEL
AQUA EC
ARACON
ARTISTRI
ASANA
ASSURE
AUTOGRAPH
AVAUNT
AVITEX
BASIS
BAX
BELCO
BIASILL
BIODEGRADABLE STAKES
BIRD NETTING
BIROX
BOOSTER
BREAKFREE
BUTACITE
BYNEL
CANOPY
CAPSTONE
CARNEBON
CENTARI
CERENOL
CHINEX
CHROMALUSION
CHROMASYSTEM
CIMARRON
CINCH
CLASSIC
COMFORMAX
CONPOL
COOL-GUARD
COOL2GO
COOLAM
CORAGEN
CORIAN
CORLAR
CORMAX
CRASTIN
CROMACHECK
CROMALIN
CROMANET
CROMAPRINT
CROMAPRO
CROMAX
CROMAX PRO
CRONAR
CROP COVER WITH DUPONT XAVAN
CRYOCIDE
CRYSTAR
CURZATE
CYREL
DEER NETTING
DELRIN
DIGITAL DYLUX
DIREX
DRYLOX
DUPONT
DUPONT TEIJIN FILMS
DYLUX
DYMEL
DYMETROL
ELVALOY
ELVAMIDE
ELVANOL
ELVAX
ENDIMAL
ENERGAIN
ENLITE
ENTIRA
ENVIVE
ESCORT
EXPRESS
FERMASURE
FINESSE
FIRSTSHOT
FLAMERESIST
FLEXWRAP
FLUOROGUARD
FM-200
FODEL
FORAFAC
FORMACEL
FREON
FROST BLANKET
FUSABOND
GARDEN PRODUCTS
GLEAN
GLYPURE
GREEN TAPE
GREENVISTA
GRIPPER
HARMONY
HEROX
HOTHUES
HYDROLOGY
HYPALON
HYTREL
HYVAR
IMAGEMASTER
IMRON
INTERRA
INTRUDER
INVAROX
ISCEON
ISOCLEAN
ISOLATIONWEAR
ISOTHERMING
IZON
K-4
KALREZ
KAPTON
KELDAX
KEVLAR
KEVLAR XP
KOCIDE
KRENITE
KROVAR
KRYTOX
LANDMARK
LANNATE
LAYBY
LINEX
LIQUI-BOX
LOROX
LUXPRINT
MANEX
MANKOCIDE
MANZATE
MATRIX
MAZIN
MELINEX
MINI-SIP
MINLON
THE MIRACLES OF SCIENCE
MYLAR
NAFION
NAP-GARD
NASON
NEOPRENE
NFPA COMPLIANT TYCHEM
NOMEX
NUCREL
NUFAB
OASIS
OPTILON
OREL
OUST
OUSTAR
OXONE
OXYCHLOR
PARTICLEAR
PERMX
PIONEER
PLANTEX
PRO-COTE
PROBOX
PROCLEAN
PROSHIELD
PROTECT
PROTERA
PUNCH
PYRALUX
RELYON
REQUIRE
RESOLVE
RIBOPRINTER
RISTON
RPS VANTAGE
RYNITE
SEED GERMINATION BLANKET
SELAR
SENTRYGLAS
SIERRA
SIMPLICITY
SINBAR
SOFTESSE
SOLAE
SOLAMET
SONTARA
SONTARA AC
SONTARA FS
SONTARA PC
SORONA
SPALLSHIELD
SPIES HECKER
STANDOX
STAPLE
STARBLAST
STATMEDIA
STEADFAST
STEWARD
STONETECH
STOP
STORMROOM
STOUT
STRAIGHTFLASH
STRATCO
STREET SMART
STS
SUMMUS
SUPRASHIELD
SUPREL
SURESTEP
SURLYN
SURLYN REFLECTION SERIES
SUVA
SYNCHRONY
SYTON
TANOS
TEDLAR
TEFLON
TEFZEL
TEIJIN
TEIJIN TETORON
TELAR
TEMPRO
TEONEX
THERMOMAN
THERMX
THROTTLE
TI-PURE
TI-SELECT
TRANXIT
TRASYS
TYCHEM
TYNEX
TYPAR
TYVEC ATTICWRAP
TYVEK
TYVEK ASURON
TYVEK BRILLION
TYVEK COMMERCIAL WRAP
TYVEK DRAINWRAP
TYVEK HOMEWRAP
TYVEK STUCCOWRAP
TYVEK THERMAWRAP
TYZOR
UPBEET
UPPERCUT
VACREL
VAMAC
VAZO
VELPAR
VERTAK
VERTEX
VERTREL
VESPEL
VIRKON
VITON
VOLATEX
VOLTRON
VYDATE
WATERPROOF
WEDGE
WESTAR
YIELDMASTER
ZEMDRAIN
ZENITE
ZODIAQ
ZONYL
ZYRON
ZYTEL

Advertising Agencies:
Koncordia Group
2417 Lancaster Ave
Wilmington, DE 19805
Tel.: (302) 427-8606
Fax: (302) 427-8545

Mindshare
498 7th Ave
New York, NY 10018
Tel.: (212) 297-7000
Fax: (212) 297-7001

ELKEM METALS COMPANY
(Sub. of Elkem ASA)
Airport Office Pk Bldg 2 400 Rouser Rd
Moon Township, PA 15108-2749
Mailing Address:
PO Box 266
Pittsburgh, PA 15230-0266
Tel.: (412) 299-7200
Fax: (412) 299-7225
Web Site: www.elkem.com
Approx. Number Employees: 16
Business Description:
Silicon Metal & Calcium Carbide Mfr
S.I.C.: 3365
N.A.I.C.S.: 331524
Personnel:
Mark Nilsen *(Pres)*
Advertising Agency:
Robert N. Pyle & Associates
1223 Potomac St NW
Washington, DC 20007
Tel.: (202) 333-8190
Fax: (202) 337-3809

EMD CHEMICALS INC.
(Sub. of Merck KGaA)
7 Skyline Dr

Key to Media (For complete agency information see *The Advertising Red Books-Agencies* edition):
1. Bus. Publs. 2. Cable T.V. 3. Catalogs & Directories. 4. Co-op Adv. 5. Consumer Mags. 6. D.M. to Bus. Estab.7. D.M. to Consumers
8. Daily Newsp. 9. Exhibits/Trade Shows 10. Foreign 11. Infomercial 12. Internet Adv.13. Multimedia 14. Network Radio
15. Network T.V. 16. Newsp. Distr. Mags. 17. Other 18. Outdoor (Posters, Transit) 19. Point of Purchase20. Premiums, Novelties
21. Product Samples 22. Special Events Mktg. 23. Spot Radio 24. Spot T.V. 25. Weekly Newsp. 26. Yellow Page Adv.

Hawthorne, NY 10532-2156
Tel.: (914) 592-4660
Fax: (914) 592-9469
Web Site: www.emindustries.com
Approx. Number Employees: 70
Business Description:
Mfr. of Chemical Products & Pigments
S.I.C.: 5169
N.A.I.C.S.: 424690
Media: 7-8-19-20-21-22
Personnel:
Clifford Pettinelli *(Mgr)*
Brands & Products:
COLORONA

EMERALD PERFORMANCE MATERIALS, LLC

(Holding of Sun Capital Partners, Inc.)
2020 Front St Ste 100
Cuyahoga Falls, OH 44221
Tel.: (330) 916-6700
Fax: (330) 916-6734
E-mail: corporate@emeraldmaterials.com
Web Site: www.emeraldmaterials.com
Approx. Rev.: $400,000,000
Approx. Number Employees: 600
Business Description:
Mfr of Chemical Additives & Polymers
S.I.C.: 2899
N.A.I.C.S.: 325998
Personnel:
Candace M. Wagner *(Pres & CFO)*
James M. Donnelly *(Pres-Emerald Specialties Grp)*
Edward T. Gotch *(Pres-Emerald Kalama Chemicals Div)*
Thomas J. Nelson *(VP-HR)*
Peter M. Fielder *(Gen Mgr-Rubber Chemicals & Nitrile Latex)*
James E. Davis *(Bus Dir-Emerald Carolina Chemical)*
Walter Getzinger *(Dir-Bus-Emerald Polymer Additives)*
Thomas Penny *(Mgr-Technical Sls)*
Advertising Agency:
Falls Communications
50 Public Sq 25th Fl
Cleveland, OH 44113
Tel.: (216) 696-0229
Fax: (216) 696-0269

EMERSON & CUMING

(Sub. of Henkel AG & Co. KGaA)
46 Manning Rd
Billerica, MA 01821-3916
Tel.: (978) 436-9700
Fax: (978) 436-9701
Toll Free: (800) 832-4929
E-mail: info@emersoncuming.com
Web Site: www.emersoncuming.com
Approx. Number Employees: 210
Year Founded: 1948
Business Description:
Polymer Designer & Mfr
S.I.C.: 2819
N.A.I.C.S.: 325188
Export
Media: 2-7-10-11-16
Distr.: Intl.; Natl.
Budget Set: Oct.
Brands & Products:
AMICON
ECCOBOND
ECCOCOAT
MINICO
STYCAST

ENTHONE INC.

(Sub. of Cookson America Inc.)
350 Frontage Rd
West Haven, CT 06516-4130
Tel.: (203) 934-8611
Fax: (203) 799-1513
Web Site: www.enthone.com
Approx. Number Employees: 200
Year Founded: 1934
Business Description:
High-Performance Speciality Chemicals & Coatings
S.I.C.: 2899; 5084
N.A.I.C.S.: 325998; 423830
Media: 2-10-13
Distr.: Intl.; Natl.
Personnel:
David Crimp *(Exec VP-Europe)*
Amy Tsang *(Dir-Mktg & Performance)*
Barry Lee Cohen *(Dir-Mktg & Comm-Global)*
Jim Meade *(Mgr-Global Mktg-Electronics Matls)*
Brands & Products:
ACHROLYTE
ACTANE
ALUMON
ANKOR
BLACK PEARL
CLASSIC
CLEARLYTE
CROMYLITE
CUPRALITE
DIMENSION
DUR NI
EBONOL
ELPELYT
ENBOND
ENFINITY
ENLOY
ENPLATE
ENPREP
ENSEAL
ENSTRIP
ENTEK
ENTHOBRITE
ENTHOX
HI STEP
IMMUNOX
INFINITY
MONOLITH
NIRON
PEARLBRITE
PERMA PASS
STRIPPER
TRI NI
TRICOLYTE
UBAC
UDIQUE
ZERO-MIST
ZINCROLYTE
Advertising Agency:
Mason, Inc.
23 Amity Rd
Bethany, CT 06524-3417
Tel.: (203) 393-1101
Fax: (203) 393-2813
(Chemicals)

EP MANAGEMENT CORP.

(Formerly EaglePicher Corporation)
(Holding of Tennenbaum Capital Partners, LLC)
5850 Mercury Dr Ste 250
Dearborn, MI 48126
Tel.: (313) 749-6100
Fax: (313) 749-6150
Web Site: www.epcorp.com
Sales Range: $125-149.9 Million
Year Founded: 1867
Business Description:
Diversified Manufacturing Services
S.I.C.: 3714; 3691
N.A.I.C.S.: 336340; 335911; 336399
Import Export
Media: 2-4
Distr.: Intl.; Natl.
Personnel:
Donald L. Runkle *(Chm)*
David L. Treadwell *(Pres & CEO)*
Patrick S. Aubry *(CFO)*
Scott Koepke *(Pres-Wolverine Advanced Matls)*
Benjamin DePompei *(VP-HR)*

EQUISTAR CHEMICALS, LP

(Sub. of LyondellBasell Industries)
1221 McKinney St Ste 700
Houston, TX 77010
Mailing Address:
PO Box 3646
Houston, TX 77253-3646
Tel.: (713) 652-7200
Fax: (713) 652-4151
Sales Range: $10-24.9 Million
Business Description:
Polyethylene & Special Polymers & Chemicals Mfr
S.I.C.: 2899; 2821; 2869
N.A.I.C.S.: 325998; 325110; 325211
Media: 2-9
Distr.: Natl.
Budget Set: Nov.
Brands & Products:
ACRYTHENE
ALATHON
FLEXATHENE
MICROTHENE
PETROTHENE
PETROTHENE XL
PLEXAR
PUNCTILIOUS
ULTRATHENE
VYNATHENE

ERCO WORLDWIDE

(Div. of Superior Plus, Inc.)
302 The East Mall Suite 200
Toronto, ON M9B 6C7, Canada
Tel.: (416) 239-7111
Fax: (416) 239-0235
E-mail: info@ercoworldwide.com
Web Site: www.ercoworldwide.com
Approx. Number Employees: 420
Year Founded: 1896
Business Description:
Sodium Chlorate & Sodium Chlorite Mfr; Chlorine Dioxide Generation Systems Supplier
S.I.C.: 2899
N.A.I.C.S.: 325998
Export
Advertising Expenditures: $200,000
Bus. Publs.: $40,000; Exhibits/Trade Shows: $160,000

E.T. HORN COMPANY INC.

16141 Heron Ave
La Mirada, CA 90638-5516
Tel.: (714) 523-8050
Fax: (714) 670-6851
Toll Free: (800) 442-4676
E-mail: ethorn@ethorn.com
Web Site: www.ethorn.com
Approx. Sls.: $65,000,000
Approx. Number Employees: 63
Year Founded: 1961
Business Description:
Supplier of Chemicals, Raw Materials & Allied Products
S.I.C.: 5169
N.A.I.C.S.: 424690
Personnel:
Gene Alley *(Chm)*
Jeff Martin *(Pres)*
Bob Ahn *(Pres-Indus Grp)*
Kevin Salerno *(Pres-Nutraceutical Grp)*
Lisa Alley-Zarkades *(VP-Sls-Animal Wellness)*
Jim Berg *(VP-Sls-FoodTech Grp)*
Jim Calkin *(VP-Mktg)*
Frank Reilly *(VP-Innovation Tech)*
Julie Wubbena *(VP-Fin & Ops)*
Tim Costello *(Sr Mgr-Acct-Advanced Matls Div)*
Arsine Aboolian *(Mgr-Acct)*
Eva O'Keefe *(Mgr-Strategic Acct)*
Advertising Agency:
Marcomm Associates
595 Tamarack Ave Ste E
Brea, CA 92821
Tel.: (714) 255-0700
Fax: (714) 255-0900

EUREKA CHEMICAL COMPANY

234 Lawrence Ave
South San Francisco, CA 94080-6817
Mailing Address:
PO Box 2205
South San Francisco, CA 94080
Tel.: (650) 761-3536
Fax: (650) 589-1943
Toll Free: (888) 387-3523
E-mail: info@eurekafluidfilm.com
Web Site: www.eurekafluidfilm.com
Approx. Sls.: $4,500,000
Approx. Number Employees: 14
Year Founded: 1940
Business Description:
Chemical Corrosion Control Systems & Fluid Film Mfr
S.I.C.: 2899
N.A.I.C.S.: 325998
Import Export
Media: 2-7
Distr.: Intl.; Natl.
Budget Set: Sept.
Personnel:
Anna F. Stanton *(CEO)*
D. Thomas Stanton, Jr. *(Pres)*
Jeff Wilson *(Dir-Sls)*
Dan Williams *(Product Mgr)*
Brands & Products:
FLUID FILM

E.V. ROBERTS & ASSOCIATES, INC.

18027 Bishop Ave
Carson, CA 90746
Mailing Address:
PO Box 2999
Phoenix, AZ 85062-2999
Tel.: (310) 204-6159
Fax: (310) 202-7247
Toll Free: (800) 374EVRA
Web Site: www.evroberts.com
Approx. Number Employees: 50
Year Founded: 1938

Key to Media (For complete agency information see *The Advertising Red Books-Agencies* edition):
1. Bus. Publs. 2. Cable T.V. 3. Catalogs & Directories. 4. Co-op Adv. 5. Consumer Mags. 6. D.M. to Bus. Estab.7. D.M. to Consumers 8. Daily Newsp. 9. Exhibits/Trade Shows 10. Foreign 11. Infomercial 12. Internet Adv.13. Multimedia 14. Network Radio 15. Network T.V. 16. Newsp. Distr. Mags. 17. Other 18. Outdoor (Posters, Transit) 19. Point of Purchase20. Premiums, Novelties 21. Product Samples 22. Special Events Mktg. 23. Spot Radio 24. Spot T.V. 25. Weekly Newsp. 26. Yellow Page Adv.

E.V. Roberts & Associates, Inc. — (Continued)

Business Description:
Adhesives, Sealants, Potting & Encapsulation Compounds Supplier & Mfr
S.I.C.: 5162; 2821
N.A.I.C.S.: 424610; 325211
Export
Media: 4-7-8-10-13-20-21-22
Distr.: Natl.

Personnel:
Ronald E. Cloud *(CEO)*
Carlos Rubalcava *(Mgr-Acctg)*

EVANS ADHESIVE CORPORATION, LTD.

925 Old Henderson Rd
Columbus, OH 43220-3722
Tel.: (614) 451-2665
Fax: (614) 451-1373
E-mail: orders@evansadhesive.com
Web Site: www.evansadhesive.com
Sales Range: $75-99.9 Million
Approx. Number Employees: 65
Year Founded: 1900

Business Description:
Mfr. of Industrial & Commercial Adhesives & Related Products
S.I.C.: 2891; 6519
N.A.I.C.S.: 325520; 531190
Export
Media: 2-4-7-10-18-20
Distr.: Natl.

Personnel:
Arthur E. Loos *(Chm)*
Rusty Thompson *(Pres & CEO)*
Tambera Schueler *(CFO)*
Jean Hollo *(VP-Sls)*

Brands & Products:
BILL TITE

EVONIK CYRO LLC

(Sub. of Evonik Rohm GmbH)
379 Interpace Pkwy
Parsippany, NJ 07054
Tel.: (973) 541-8000
Fax: (973) 541-8445
Toll Free: (800) 631-5384
Telex: 5105 008106
Web Site: www.cyro.com
Approx. Number Employees: 700
Year Founded: 1976

Business Description:
Acrylic Sheets & Films & Methyl Methacrylates Producer
S.I.C.: 2821; 3083
N.A.I.C.S.: 325211; 326130
Export
Media: 2-4-7-10-20-21-22
Distr.: Intl.; Natl.

Personnel:
John Rolando *(Pres & CEO)*
Robert S. Wurst *(VP-Fin & Bus Svcs)*
Gail J. Wood *(Sr Mgr-Mktg Commun)*

Brands & Products:
ACRYLITE
CYREX
CYROLITE
CYROVU HP2
EUROPLEX
VU-STAT
XT POLYMER

EVONIK DEGUSSA CORPORATION

(Sub. of Evonik Degussa GmbH)
379 Interpace Pkwy
Parsippany, NJ 07054-1115
Mailing Address:
PO Box 677
Parsippany, NJ 07054-0677
Tel.: (973) 541-8230
Fax: (973) 541-8161
Toll Free: (877) 202-3463
E-mail: industrialchemicals@evonik.com
Web Site: www.degussa-bk.com
Approx. Number Employees: 7,000

Business Description:
Specialty Chemicals Mfr
S.I.C.: 2869; 2819
N.A.I.C.S.: 325199; 325188
Import Export
Advertising Expenditures: $1,669,000
Multimedia: $78,000; Bus. Publs.: $797,000; Catalogs & Directories: $315,000; D.M. to Bus. Estab.: $60,000; Daily Newsp.: $60,000; Exhibits/Trade Shows: $217,000; Internet Adv.: $25,000; Premiums, Novelties: $117,000
Distr.: Intl.; Natl.
Budget Set: Aug. -Sept.

Personnel:
Thomas Bates *(Pres)*
Guenter Hoelken *(VP-Procurement & Logistics-North America)*
Jonathan Evens *(Dir-Commun)*

Advertising Agencies:
Briechle-Fernandez Marketing Services Inc.
265 Industrial Way W Ste 7
Eatontown, NJ 07724
Tel.: (732) 982-8222
Fax: (732) 982-8223
(All)
— Lorenzo Fernandez *(Exec. V.P.)*

Davis Harrison Dion, Inc.
333 N Michigan Ave Ste 2300
Chicago, IL 60601-4109
Tel.: (312) 332-0808
Fax: (312) 332-4260

EVONIK GOLDSCHMIDT CORPORATION

(Sub. of Evonik Goldschmidt GmbH)
914 E Randolph Rd
Hopewell, VA 23860
Mailing Address:
PO Box 1299
Hopewell, VA 23860-1299
Tel.: (804) 541-8658
Fax: (804) 452-0476
Web Site: www.degussa-nafta.com
Approx. Number Employees: 200
Year Founded: 1991

Business Description:
Industrial Organic Chemicals Mfr
S.I.C.: 2869; 2819
N.A.I.C.S.: 325199; 325188

Personnel:
Reinhold Brand *(Pres)*
David Del Guercio *(Dir-Bus-Textile Care)*
Barry Dubois *(Dir-HR)*
Russell Mait *(Dir-Environ Health, Safety & Quality)*
Philip Munson *(Mgr)*

Advertising Agency:
Briechle-Fernandez Marketing Services Inc.
265 Industrial Way W Ste 7
Eatontown, NJ 07724
Tel.: (732) 982-8222
Fax: (732) 982-8223

EXXONMOBIL CHEMICAL COMPANY INC.

(Branch of ExxonMobil Chemical Company)
37567 Interchange Dr
Farmington Hills, MI 48335
Tel.: (248) 350-6500
Web Site: www.exxonmobilchemical.com/Public_Siteflow/WorldwideEnglish/SalesOffices/NA_GlobalChemsBasicSalesOffice.asp
Sales Range: $50-74.9 Million
Approx. Number Employees: 50

Business Description:
Automotive Lubricants
S.I.C.: 1311
N.A.I.C.S.: 211111

Brands & Products:
EXXON SUPER FLO
MOBIL 1
MOBIL DRIVE CLEAN

Advertising Agency:
Brewer Associates Marketing Communications
39555 Orchard Hill Pl Ste 600
Novi, MI 48375
Tel.: (734) 458-7180

FERRO CORPORATION

1000 Lakeside Ave E
Cleveland, OH 44114-1117
Mailing Address:
PO Box 7000
Cleveland, OH 44114
Tel.: (216) 641-8580
Fax: (216) 875-7205
Telex: 98-0165
E-mail: postmaster@ferro.com
Web Site: www.ferro.com
Approx. Sls.: $2,101,865,000
Approx. Number Employees: 5,034
Year Founded: 1919

Business Description:
Technology-Based Performance Materials & Chemicals Mfr
S.I.C.: 2851
N.A.I.C.S.: 325510
Import Export
Media: 2-4-7-10-11-13

Personnel:
James F. Kirsch *(Chm, Pres & CEO)*
Thomas R. Miklich *(CFO, VP & Principal Acctg Officer)*
Mark H. Duesenberg *(Gen Counsel, Sec & VP)*
Ann E. Killian *(VP-HR)*
Mary Abood *(Dir-Corp Comm)*
David Longfellow *(Dir-IR)*

Brands & Products:
ADVANCED POLYMER ALLOYS
ALCRYN
ALOX
AMERICAL
AMERICAL PLUS
APC
AQUAREALEASE
AULTRA-THIN
AZURICO
BARNESITE
CATA-CHEK
CE-RITE
CERDECOAT
CERDECOLOR
CERDECOR
CERMARK
CHECK MARK
CHEK-MATE
COLORGUARD
CONDUCTROX
COOL COLORS
COPPERCLAD
CORDOBOND
COVEROHM
CYCLESAVER
DRAKENFELD
DRAKOTHERM
DURACYN
DURAGRIP
ECLIPSE
EVOLUTION
FANTASIE
FERRENE
FERREX
FERRO
FERRO-PERC
FERROCON
FERROFLEX
FERROFLO
FERROPAK
FIESTA
GAPEX
GAPEX HT
GEODE
HYVEX
IMPRESSIONPLUS
INDIO
INSTANTCOLOR
ISO-OHM
KARLEX
KEMLEX
KERAJET
KINEMAX
LIBERTY COAT
LT COLOURS
MICRO-CHEK
MICRONAL
MINERALOX
MIRAMAX
MULTIFIRE
NIMEX
NYBEX
OPTUM
OTTASEPT
OXI-CHEK
OXUS BLACK
PALETTE
PARTILOK
PDI
PERC
PERMYL
PETRAC
PLAS-CHEK
POWEROHM
PURFICTPURGE
REALEASE
ROTOCOAT
RXLOY
SAMBAPLUS
SANTICIZER
SATINAL
SENSOHM
SILICA-SEAL
SKYPLUS
SPECTRAFLO
SPECTRULITE

Key to Media (For complete agency information see *The Advertising Red Books-Agencies* edition):
1. Bus. Publs. 2. Cable T.V. 3. Catalogs & Directories. 4. Co-op Adv. 5. Consumer Mags. 6. D.M. to Bus. Estab.7. D.M. to Consumers 8. Daily Newsp. 9. Exhibits/Trade Shows 10. Foreign 11. Infomercial 12. Internet Adv.13. Multimedia 14. Network Radio 15. Network T.V. 16. Newsp. Distr. Mags. 17. Other 18. Outdoor (Posters, Transit) 19. Point of Purchase20. Premiums, Novelties 21. Product Samples 22. Special Events Mktg. 23. Spot Radio 24. Spot T.V. 25. Weekly Newsp. 26. Yellow Page Adv.

SPRINGTIME II
SUNSHINE
SUPER CE-RITE
SUPERSHIELD
SYN-CHEK
SYNKAD
SYNPRO
THERM-CHEK
TICON
TIZOX
ULTRA
ULTRASHIELD
UV-CHEK
VIBROXIDE
VITR-AU-LESS
VYBEX
ZOX

Advertising Agency:
Arnold Communications Co.
3311 Oak Knoll Dr
Beachwood, OH 44122
Tel.: (216) 464-7503
Fax: (216) 464-0524

FIBER GLASS SYSTEMS L.P.
(Sub. of Fiberglass Systems)
2700 W 65th St
Little Rock, AR 72209
Tel.: (501) 568-4010
Fax: (501) 568-6440
Web Site: www.smithfibercast.com
Sales Range: $25-49.9 Million
Approx. Number Employees: 185
Year Founded: 1961
Business Description:
Fiberglass Piping Products Mfr
S.I.C.: 3498
N.A.I.C.S.: 332996
Export
Media: 2-5-6-10
Personnel:
Rick Heindinger *(VP-Sls & Mktg)*
David Meehan *(Mgr-Market, Marine & Offshore)*

Brands & Products:
GREEN THREAD
RED THREAD
SILVER STREAK

THE FLAMEMASTER CORPORATION
13576 Desmond St
Pacoima, CA 91331
Tel.: (818) 890-1401
Fax: (818) 890-6001
E-mail: information@flamemaster.com
Web Site: www.flamemaster.com
Sales Range: $10-24.9 Million
Approx. Number Employees: 31
Year Founded: 1942
Business Description:
Mfr. of Flame Retardant Coatings & Heat Resistant Systems
S.I.C.: 2891; 2899
N.A.I.C.S.: 325520; 325998
Export
Media: 2
Distr.: Natl.
Budget Set: Oct.
Personnel:
Joseph Mazin *(Pres & CEO)*
Linda Smith *(Mgr-Customer Rels)*

Brands & Products:
CHEM SEAL
FLAMEMASTER
FLAMEMASTIC 77

FLEXIBLE SOLUTIONS INTERNATIONAL, INC.
615 Discovery Street
Victoria, BC V8T 5G4, Canada
Tel.: (250) 477-9969
Fax: (250) 477-9912
Toll Free: (800) 661-3560
E-mail: info@flexiblesolutions.com
Web Site: www.flexiblesolutions.com
E-Mail For Key Personnel:
Sales Director: sales@flexiblesolutions.com
Approx. Sls.: $11,491,401
Approx. Number Employees: 33
Business Description:
Water & Energy Conservation Chemicals & Products Developer, Mfr & Marketer
S.I.C.: 2899; 3089; 5169
N.A.I.C.S.: 325998; 326199; 424690
Advertising Expenditures: $92,051
Media: 17
Personnel:
Daniel B. O'Brien *(Pres & CEO)*
Jason Bloom *(VP-Corp Comm)*

Brands & Products:
COVER AND CONSERVE
ECOSAVR
FLEXIBLE SOLUTIONS
HEATSAVR
WATERSAVR

FLINT GROUP, INC.
(Sub. of Flint Group Germany GmbH)
14909 N Beck Rd
Plymouth, MI 48170-2411
Tel.: (734) 781-4600
Tel.: (734) 622-6000
Fax: (734) 622-6131
Fax: (734) 781-4699
E-mail: info@na.flintgrp.com
Web Site: www.flintgrp.com
E-Mail For Key Personnel:
President: mgannon@flintink.com
Public Relations: rconrad@flintink.com
Sales Range: $1-4.9 Billion
Approx. Number Employees: 8,350
Year Founded: 1920
Business Description:
Ink & Coating Mfr
S.I.C.: 2893
N.A.I.C.S.: 325910
Export
Media: 2-4-7-10
Personnel:
Russell Joyce *(Pres-Narrow Web)*
William B. Miller *(Pres-Americas)*
Thomas Telser *(Pres-Flexographic Products)*
Mike Green *(VP/Gen Mgr-Publication Inks)*

FLORIKAN E.S.A.
1579 Barber Rd
Sarasota, FL 34240
Tel.: (941) 377-8666
Fax: (941) 377-3633
Toll Free: (800) 322-8666
Web Site: www.florikan.com
Business Description:
Agricultural Products Mfr & Distr
S.I.C.: 2879
N.A.I.C.S.: 325320
Media: 2-3-4-10-13-22
Personnel:
Eric Rosenthal *(Dir-Sls & Mktg)*
John Rosenthal *(Dir-Bus Devel)*

FMC CORPORATION
1735 Market St
Philadelphia, PA 19103-7501
Tel.: (215) 299-6000
Fax: (215) 299-5998
Toll Free: (800) 3211FMC
Web Site: www.fmc.com
Approx. Rev.: $3,116,300,000
Approx. Number Employees: 4,900
Year Founded: 1885
Business Description:
Holding Company; Diversified Chemicals Producer
S.I.C.: 6719; 2869; 2879; 2899
N.A.I.C.S.: 551112; 325199; 325320; 325998
Import Export
Media: 2-4-6-7-8-9-10-11-13-15-23-24-25
Distr.: Intl.; Natl.
Budget Set: Sept.
Personnel:
Pierre R. Brondeau *(Chm, Pres & CEO)*
William Kim Foster *(CFO & Exec VP)*
Mark A. Douglas *(Pres-Indus Chemicals Grp)*
Milton Steele *(Pres-Agricultural Products Grp)*
D. Michael Wilson *(Pres-Specialty Chemicals Grp)*
Andrea E. Utecht *(Gen Counsel, Sec & Exec VP)*
Theodore H. Laws, Jr. *(Dir-Tax & Asst Treas)*
Kenneth R. Garrett *(Exec VP-HR & Corp Comm)*

Brands & Products:
AC-DI-SOL
ADVACOR
ADVAGUARD
AQUACOAT
ARIA
ASTRO
AUTHORITY ASSIST
AUTHORITY FIRST DF
AUTHORITY MTZ
AVICEL
BRIGADE 2EC
BRIGADE WSB
BRIGADIER
CADET
CAPTURE
CAPTURE LFR
CAPTURE LIQUIDREADY SYSTEM
COMMAND
COMMAND 3ME
CYNOFF
DRAGNET
FIRSTLINE
FLUORGUARD
FMC
FURADAN
FURADAN 4F
GAUNTLET
GELCARIN
GELSTAR
HERO
HERO EW
INITIALI
KONJAC
LACTARIN
LATTICE
LECTRO
LIFETECH
LIFETIME
LIMIT
LUSTRECLEAR
MUSTANG
MUSTANG MAX
MUSTANG MAX EC
MUSTANG MAX EW
NILYN
NOVAGEL
ONYX
PERMEOX
PREVAIL
PROTACID
QUICKSILVER
RAGE
RAGE D-TECH
RENEW
S-CARB
SEAKEM
SESQUI
SHARK
SHARK EW
SHARK H2O
SPARTAN
SPARTAN ADVANCE
SPARTAN CHARGE
SUMMON
TALSTAR
TALSTARONE
VIGOROX
VISCARIN

Advertising Agency:
dgs Marketing Engineers
10100 Lantern Rd Ste 225
Fishers, IN 46037
Tel.: (317) 813-2222
Fax: (317) 813-2233

FMC LITHIUM DIVISION
(Sub. of FMC Corporation)
Ste 300 2801 Yorkmont Rd
Charlotte, NC 28208-7377
Tel.: (704) 426-5300
Fax: (704) 426-5370
Toll Free: (888) LITHIUM
E-mail: lithium_info@fmc.com
Web Site: www.fmclithium.com
Sales Range: $50-74.9 Million
Approx. Number Employees: 40
Business Description:
Chemical Mfr
S.I.C.: 1479; 1321; 2816; 2819; 2899
N.A.I.C.S.: 212393; 211112; 325131; 325188; 325998
Media: 1-2-4-7-10-11-20-21-22
Personnel:
George Sandor *(Dir-Global Organics-Americas Sls & Dev)*
Anthony DiMaggio *(Mgr-Sls & Bus Dev)*
Claudio E. Manissero *(Mgr-Sls & Mktg)*
David B. Stokes *(Mgr-Concrete Technologies)*
Bruce M. Urban *(Mgr-Bus Devel-Primaries & SI)*

FOAMEX INNOVATIONS, INC.
(Name Changed to FXI)

FREEPORT-MCMORAN COPPER & GOLD, INC.
333 N Central Ave
Phoenix, AZ 85004
Tel.: (602) 366-8100
Toll Free: (800) 535-7094
E-mail: fms_communications@fmi.com
Web Site: www.fcx.com

Key to Media (For complete agency information see *The Advertising Red Books-Agencies* edition):
1. Bus. Publs. 2. Cable T.V. 3. Catalogs & Directories. 4. Co-op Adv. 5. Consumer Mags. 6. D.M. to Bus. Estab.7. D.M. to Consumers
8. Daily Newsp. 9. Exhibits/Trade Shows 10. Foreign 11. Infomercial 12. Internet Adv.13. Multimedia 14. Network Radio
15. Network T.V. 16. Newsp. Distr. Mags. 17. Other 18. Outdoor (Posters, Transit) 19. Point of Purchase20. Premiums, Novelties
21. Product Samples 22. Special Events Mktg. 23. Spot Radio 24. Spot T.V. 25. Weekly Newsp. 26. Yellow Page Adv.

Freeport-McMoRan Copper & Gold, Inc. — (Continued)

Approx. Rev.: $18,982,000,000
Approx. Number Employees: 29,700
Year Founded: 1913
Business Description:
Copper, Gold & Molybdenum Mining Services
S.I.C.: 1021; 1041; 1099
N.A.I.C.S.: 212234; 212221; 212299
Export
Media: 2-9-25
Distr.: Intl.; Natl.
Personnel:
James R. Moffett *(Chm)*
B. M. Rankin, Jr. *(Vice Chm)*
Richard C. Adkerson *(Pres & CEO)*
Kathleen L. Quirk *(CFO, Treas & Exec VP)*
Michael J. Arnold *(Chief Admin Officer & Exec VP)*
W. Russell King *(Sr VP-Intl, Rels & Federal Affairs)*
William L. Collier, III *(VP-Comm)*
David Joint *(Dir-IR)*
Eric Kinneberg *(Dir-External Comm)*

FULL VISION, INC.

3017 Full Vision Dr
Newton, KS 67114-9750
Tel.: (316) 283-3344
Fax: (316) 283-3350
E-mail: sales@full-vision.com
Web Site: www.full-vision.com
E-Mail For Key Personnel:
Sales Director: sales@full-vision.com
Approx. Number Employees: 65
Year Founded: 1958
Business Description:
Mfr. & Designer of Volume Metal Fabricated Products & Components for Industry Applications
S.I.C.: 3537; 3531
N.A.I.C.S.: 333924; 333120
Export
Media: 2-4-7-10-17-20
Distr.: Natl.
Personnel:
Peter Benson *(Chm & Pres)*
Brands & Products:
FULL VISION
INTEGRA STRENGTH
Advertising Agency:
Van Sickle & Associates
358 Laura
Wichita, KS 67208
Tel.: (316) 264-1277
Fax: (316) 264-0819
(OEM Contract Manufacturing)

FXI

(Formerly Foamex Innovations, Inc.)
(Joint Venture of Black Diamond Capital Holdings, LLC & MatlinPatterson Global Advisers LLC)
Rose Tree Corporate Center II 1400 Providence Rd Ste 2000
Media, PA 19063-2076
Tel.: (610) 744-2300
Toll Free: (800) 355-3626
Web Site: www.fxi.com
Sales Range: $600-649.9 Million
Approx. Number Employees: 2,000
Year Founded: 1921
Business Description:
Foam Product Mfr
S.I.C.: 3086
N.A.I.C.S.: 326150; 326140
Personnel:
John G. Johnson, Jr. *(Pres & CEO)*
David J. Prilutski *(COO & Exec VP)*
Alvaro Vaselli *(Sr VP)*
Vincent A. Bonaddio *(Sr VP)*
Andrew R. Prusky *(Sr VP-Legal)*
Frederick P. Rullo *(Sr VP-Sls)*
Chiu Chan *(VP-Tech)*
Robert W. Clark *(Dir-Bus)*
Harold J. Earley *(CFO)*
Brands & Products:
AERUS
AQUAZONE
DRIFAST
ENERGIA
PILLOWFLEX
QUILTFLEX
REFLEX
REFLEX BOUNCE
REFLEX CORE
REFLEX MEMORY
REFLEX PLUS
REFLEX WRAP
RESILITEX
SENSUS
VENUS
Advertising Agency:
Sard Verbinnen & Co.
630 3rd Ave 9th Fl
New York, NY 10017
Tel.: (212) 687-8080
Fax: (212) 687-8344

GAGE PRODUCTS COMPANY

(Sub. of Gage Corporation)
821 Wanda St
Ferndale, MI 48220
Tel.: (248) 541-3824
Fax: (248) 541-0643
E-mail: ashley@gageproducts.com
Web Site: www.gageproducts.com
Approx. Number Employees: 60
Business Description:
Solvents, Organic
S.I.C.: 2869; 2842
N.A.I.C.S.: 325199; 325612
Advertising Agency:
AutoCom Associates
74 W Long Lk Rd Ste 103
Bloomfield Hills, MI 48304-2770
Tel.: (248) 647-8621
Fax: (248) 642-2110

GDF SUEZ ENERGY NORTH AMERICA, INC.

(Sub. of GDF SUEZ Energy International)
1990 Post Oak Blvd Ste 1900
Houston, TX 77056-4499
Tel.: (713) 636-0000
Fax: (713) 636-1344
Web Site: www.suezenergyna.com
Approx. Rev.: $39,600,000
Approx. Number Employees: 2,000
Year Founded: 1994
Business Description:
Development & Operation of Electricity & Cogeneration Facilities; Distribution of Liquefied Natural Gas
S.I.C.: 4931; 4924
N.A.I.C.S.: 221119; 221210
Media: 6
Personnel:
Zin Smati *(Pres & CEO)*
Geert Peeters *(CFO & Exec VP)*
Bart Clark *(Gen Counsel & Sr VP)*
Paul Cavicchi *(Exec VP-Bus Dev)*
Karim Barbir *(Sr VP-Strategy, Risk & Portfolio Mgmt)*
Mike Thompson *(Sr VP-HR)*
Advertising Agency:
Litos Strategic Communication
684 Warren Ave
East Providence, RI 02914
Tel.: (401) 435-8900
Fax: (401) 435-5858

GENCORP INC.

Hwy 50 & Aerojet Rd
Rancho Cordova, CA 95670
Mailing Address:
PO Box 537012
Sacramento, CA 95853-7012
Tel.: (916) 355-4000
Fax: (916) 351-8668
E-mail: comments@gencorp.com
Web Site: www.gencorp.com
E-Mail For Key Personnel:
Public Relations: Linda.Cutler@gencorp.com
Approx. Sls.: $857,900,000
Approx. Number Employees: 3,135
Year Founded: 1915
Business Description:
Holding Company; Mechanical & Automotive Rubber Goods; Chemicals, Molded & Extruded Plastics
S.I.C.: 3764; 3053; 3061; 3069
N.A.I.C.S.: 336415; 326291; 326299; 339991
Export
Media: 17
Distr.: Natl.
Budget Set: Dec. -Nov.
Personnel:
James R. Henderson *(Chm)*
Scott J. Seymour *(Pres & CEO)*
Kathleen E. Redd *(CFO, Sec & VP)*
Robert G. Hall *(Asst Sec)*
Advertising Agency:
KP Public Relations
1201 K St Ste 800
Sacramento, CA 95814
Tel.: (916) 448-2162
Fax: (916) 448-4923

GENERAL MAGNAPLATE CORPORATION

1331 US Rte 1
Linden, NJ 07036
Tel.: (908) 862-6200
Fax: (908) 862-6110
Toll Free: (800) 441-6173
E-mail: info@magnaplate.com
Web Site: www.magnaplate.com
Sales Range: $10-24.9 Million
Approx. Number Employees: 130
Year Founded: 1952
Business Description:
Mfr. of High-Technology Composite Coatings For Industrial Metal Parts
S.I.C.: 3479; 3471
N.A.I.C.S.: 332812; 332813
Media: 2-4-7-10-11-13-17
Distr.: Intl.; Natl.
Budget Set: Apr.
Personnel:
Edmund V. Aversenti *(Pres & COO)*
Candida C. Aversenti *(CEO)*
Susan Neri *(CFO)*
Valerie Corigliano *(Coord-Mktg)*
Brands & Products:
CANADIZE
CMPT
DYNALOY
GOLDENEDGE
HI-T-LUBE
LECTROFLUOR
MAGNADIZE
MAGNAGOLD
MAGNAPLATE HCR
MAGNAPLATE HMF
MAGNAPLATE HTR
MAGNAPLATE TNS
NEDOX
PLASMADIZE
TUFRAM

GEO SPECIALTY CHEMICALS, INC.

401 S Earl Ste 3A
Lafayette, IN 47904
Tel.: (765) 448-9412
Fax: (765) 448-6728
Web Site: www.geosc.com
Sales Range: $150-199.9 Million
Approx. Number Employees: 420
Business Description:
Dispersant Specialty Chemicals Mfr
S.I.C.: 2899
N.A.I.C.S.: 325998
Personnel:
Kenneth Ghazey *(Pres & CEO)*
William P. Eckman *(CFO & Exec VP)*
Brands & Products:
LOMAR DISBURSEMENTS
TRIMET POLYOLS
VULVUP PEROXIDES
Advertising Agency:
Richards Communications
3201 Enterprise Pkwy Ste 400
Beachwood, OH 44122
Tel.: (216) 514-7800
Fax: (216) 514-7801

GFS CHEMICALS, INC.

3041 Home Rd
Powell, OH 43065
Tel.: (740) 881-5501
Fax: (740) 881-9408
Toll Free: (877) 534-0795
E-mail: sales@gfschemicals.com
Web Site: www.gfschemicals.com
E-Mail For Key Personnel:
Sales Director: sales@gfschemicals.com
Approx. Number Employees: 90
Year Founded: 1928
Business Description:
Fine & Specialty Chemicals Mfr
S.I.C.: 2819; 3821
N.A.I.C.S.: 325188; 339111
Export
Media: 2-4-10-13
Personnel:
J.S. Hutchinson *(Owner & Pres)*
David Baust *(Gen Mgr-Organic Chemical Mfg Div)*
Liza Tallon *(Dir-Mktg & Sls)*
Brands & Products:
AMCO CLEAR
AQUALINE
AQUASTAR
GFSELECT
HYDRANAL
IN-SPEC
WATERMARK

Key to Media (For complete agency information see *The Advertising Red Books-Agencies* edition):
1. Bus. Publs. 2. Cable T.V. 3. Catalogs & Directories. 4. Co-op Adv. 5. Consumer Mags. 6. D.M. to Bus. Estab.7. D.M. to Consumers
8. Daily Newsp. 9. Exhibits/Trade Shows 10. Foreign 11. Infomercial 12. Internet Adv.13. Multimedia 14. Network Radio
15. Network T.V. 16. Newsp. Distr. Mags. 17. Other 18. Outdoor (Posters, Transit) 19. Point of Purchase20. Premiums, Novelties
21. Product Samples 22. Special Events Mktg. 23. Spot Radio 24. Spot T.V. 25. Weekly Newsp. 26. Yellow Page Adv.

GLOBE SPECIALTY METALS INC.

One Penn Plz Ste 2514
New York, NY 10119
Tel.: (212) 798-8100
Tel.: (212) 798-8122
Fax: (212) 798-8185
E-mail: info@glbsm.com
Web Site: www.glbsm.com
Approx. Sls.: $472,658,000
Approx. Number Employees: 464
Business Description:
Silicon Metal & Silicon-Based Alloys Producer
S.I.C.: 3313; 3469
N.A.I.C.S.: 331112; 332116
Advertising Expenditures: $8,687,000
Personnel:
Alan Kestenbaum *(Chm)*
Jeff K. Bradley *(CEO & COO)*
Stephen Lebowitz *(Chief Legal Officer)*

GLS CORPORATION

(Sub. of PolyOne Corporation)
833 Ridgeview Dr
McHenry, IL 60050
Tel.: (815) 385-8500
Fax: (815) 385-8533
Toll Free: (800) 457-8777
E-mail: info@glscorp.com
Web Site: www.glstpes.com
Sales Range: $125-149.9 Million
Approx. Number Employees: 200
Year Founded: 1940
Business Description:
Thermoplastic Elastomer Compound Developer & Mfr
S.I.C.: 3089
N.A.I.C.S.: 326199
Media: 2-10
Personnel:
Sandy Wagner *(Mgr-Mktg Comm)*
Brands & Products:
DYNAFLEX
GLS
VERSAFLEX
VERSALLOY
VERSOLLAN
Advertising Agency:
Johnson Marketing Group Inc.
15255 S 94th Ave Ste 600
Orland Park, IL 60462
Tel.: (708) 403-4004
Fax: (708) 403-4111

GSE LINING TECHNOLOGY, INC.

(Sub. of Gundle/SLT Environmental, Inc.)
19103 Gundle Rd
Houston, TX 77073
Tel.: (281) 443-8564
Fax: (281) 875-6010
Toll Free: (800) 435-2008
E-mail: gse@gseworld.com
Web Site: www.gseworld.com
E-Mail For Key Personnel:
Sales Director: JNguyen@gseworld.com
Approx. Number Employees: 700
Year Founded: 1984
Business Description:
Geomembrane Liners Mfr & Whslr
S.I.C.: 3081
N.A.I.C.S.: 326113
Media: 2-4-7-10-21-26
Personnel:
Gerald E. Hersh *(VP & Gen Mgr-Installation Svcs)*
Jacky Nguyen *(VP-Sls-Mktg)*
Boyd J. Ramsey *(VP-Tech-North American)*
Ed Zimmel *(VP-Engrg & Quality Control-North American)*
Don Bohac *(Dir-Mfg-Americas)*
Brands & Products:
GSE WHITE CONDUCTIVE
GUNDSEAL

GUNDLE/SLT ENVIRONMENTAL, INC.

(Sub. of GEO Holdings Corp.)
19103 Gundle Rd
Houston, TX 77073
Tel.: (281) 443-8564
Fax: (281) 875-6010
Toll Free: (800) 435-2008
E-mail: gse@gseworld.com
Web Site: www.gseworld.com
Approx. Sls.: $373,318,000
Approx. Number Employees: 928
Year Founded: 1986
Business Description:
Polyethylene Lining Products Mfr
S.I.C.: 4952; 1799; 3081
N.A.I.C.S.: 221320; 238990; 326113
Export
Media: 2-4-7-10-11-13-21-26
Personnel:
Richard E. Goodrich *(Pres & CEO)*
C. Wayne Case *(Gen Counsel, Sec & VP)*
Brands & Products:
BENTOFIX
FABRINET
GSE
GSE CONDUCTIVE
GSE CURTAIN WALL
GSE FABRINET
GSE HD
GSE HYPERNET
GSE NW
GSE PROFLEX
GSE STUDLINER
GSE TUNNELLINER
GSE ULTRAFLEX
GSE WHITE
GUNDSEAL
HYPERNET
THERMAL LOCK

HARRINGTON & KING PERFORATING COMPANY, INC.

5655 W Fillmore St
Chicago, IL 60644-5504
Tel.: (773) 626-1800
Fax: (773) 261-1686
Toll Free: (800) 621-3869
Toll Free: (800) 251-6026
E-mail: sales@hkperf.com
Web Site: www.hkperf.com
E-Mail For Key Personnel:
Sales Director: sales@hkperf.com
Approx. Number Employees: 145
Year Founded: 1883
Business Description:
Mfr. of Perforated Metal Sheets & Coils; Plates; Plastics
S.I.C.: 3469; 3089
N.A.I.C.S.: 332116; 326199
Import Export
Media: 1-2-4-5-10-13-17-20-21-22-24-26
Distr.: Natl.
Budget Set: Nov.
Personnel:
John Lovaas *(Chm, Pres, CEO, Treas & Gen Mgr)*
Andrew Lovaas *(VP-Quality & Mktg)*
V. Ponni *(Mgr-Sls)*
Brands & Products:
H&K
Advertising Agency:
Reed Advertising
13 Emory Pl
Knoxville, TN 37917
Tel.: (865) 523-4075
Fax: (865) 523-4824
(Perforated Materials)

HARWICK STANDARD DISTRIBUTION CORPORATION

60 S Seiberling St
Akron, OH 44305-4217
Mailing Address:
PO Box 9360
Akron, OH 44305-0360
Tel.: (330) 798-9300
Fax: (330) 798-0214
Toll Free: (800) 899-4412
Web Site: www.harwickstandard.com
E-Mail For Key Personnel:
Sales Director: jpatterson@harwickstandard.com
Approx. Number Employees: 100
Year Founded: 1932
Business Description:
Supplier of Raw Materials to the Rubber & Plastic Industries
S.I.C.: 5169; 5162
N.A.I.C.S.: 424690; 424610
Import Export
Media: 2-4-5-7-10-21
Distr.: Intl.; Natl.
Budget Set: Oct. -Nov.
Personnel:
Ernest Pouttu *(Pres & CEO)*
Jim Houston *(CFO & VP -Fin)*
Kurt Nygaard *(VP-Sls)*
David Schultz *(Dir-Technical)*
Advertising Agency:
WhiteSpace Creative
24 N High St Ste 200
Akron, OH 44308
Tel.: (330) 762-9320
Fax: (330) 763-9323
(Raw Materials for Rubber & Plastic Industries)

HAVILAND ENTERPRISES INC.

421 Ann St NW
Grand Rapids, MI 49504-2019
Tel.: (616) 361-6691
Fax: (616) 361-9772
E-mail: chemicalexperts@havilandusa.com
Web Site: www.havilandusa.com
Approx. Number Employees: 150
Year Founded: 1934
Business Description:
Mfr. & Distributor of Chemical Products for Home & Industry
S.I.C.: 5169
N.A.I.C.S.: 424690
Export
Media: 2-4-6-7-9-10-16-18-19-20-26
Distr.: Intl.; Natl.
Budget Set: Nov.
Personnel:
E. Bernard Haviland *(CEO)*
Marie Haviland *(Dir-Comm & Credit Mgr)*
Brands & Products:
ANO-KLEEN
DUROCHOLOR
HAVABLACK
HAVABOND
HAVASOL
HAVASTRIP
HAVILAND ENTERPRISES
Advertising Agency:
The Imagination Factory
648 Monroe NW Ste 118
Grand Rapids, MI 49503
Tel.: (616) 356-2545
Fax: (616) 356-2546

HAWKINS, INC.

3100 E Hennepin Ave
Minneapolis, MN 55413-2922
Tel.: (612) 331-6910
Fax: (612) 331-5304
Toll Free: (800) 328-5460
E-mail: ir@hawkinsinc.com
Web Site: www.hawkinschemical.com
Approx. Sls.: $297,641,000
Approx. Number Employees: 321
Year Founded: 1938
Business Description:
Bulk Specialty Chemicals Processor & Distr
S.I.C.: 5169; 5084; 5191
N.A.I.C.S.: 424690; 423830; 424910
Media: 10
Personnel:
John S. McKeon *(Chm)*
Patrick H. Hawkins *(Pres & CEO)*
Kathleen P. Pepski *(CFO, Treas & VP)*
Richard G. Erstad *(Gen Counsel, Sec & VP)*
Daniel E. Soderlund *(Gen Mgr-Pharmaceutical Grp)*
Fritz J. Wagner *(Bus Mgr-Manufactured Products & Specialty Chemicals)*
Brands & Products:
CHEESE-PHOS
CITRAFLO
HAWKIINS
SIMPLGEL 30
TOMMYGEL

H.B. FULLER COMPANY

1200 Willow Lake Blvd
Saint Paul, MN 55110-5146
Mailing Address:
PO Box 64683
Saint Paul, MN 55164-0683
Tel.: (651) 236-5900
Fax: (651) 236-5165
Toll Free: (800) 214-2523
Web Site: www.hbfuller.com
E-Mail For Key Personnel:
Public Relations: keralyn.groff@hbfuller.com
Approx. Rev.: $1,356,161,000
Approx. Number Employees: 3,300
Year Founded: 1887
Business Description:
Mfr & Marketer of Adhesives, Sealants, Coatings, Paints & Other Chemical Products
S.I.C.: 2891; 2851
N.A.I.C.S.: 325520; 325510
Export
Media: 1-2-4-5-6-7-10-13-19-20-21-26

Key to Media (For complete agency information see *The Advertising Red Books-Agencies* edition):
1. Bus. Publs. 2. Cable T.V. 3. Catalogs & Directories. 4. Co-op Adv. 5. Consumer Mags. 6. D.M. to Bus. Estab.7. D.M. to Consumers
8. Daily Newsp. 9. Exhibits/Trade Shows 10. Foreign 11. Infomercial 12. Internet Adv.13. Multimedia 14. Network Radio
15. Network T.V. 16. Newsp. Distr. Mags. 17. Other 18. Outdoor (Posters, Transit) 19. Point of Purchase20. Premiums, Novelties
21. Product Samples 22. Special Events Mktg. 23. Spot Radio 24. Spot T.V. 25. Weekly Newsp. 26. Yellow Page Adv.

H.B. Fuller Company — (Continued)

Distr.: Natl.
Budget Set: Aug.
Personnel:
James J. Owens *(Pres & CEO)*
James R. Giertz *(CFO & Sr VP)*
Timothy J. Keenan *(Gen Counsel, Corp Sec & VP)*
Steven Kenny *(Sr VP-EMEA & India)*
Ann Parriott *(VP-HR)*
Keralyn Groff *(Dir-PR & Community Affairs)*
Brands & Products:
ADVANTRA
AIRSPERSE
AQUA-MELT
CLARITY
COR-WELD
EVERYDAY
FABU-LAS
FASTSET
FLEXTRA
FOSTER
FULL-POUR
FULL-PROOF
FULLBOR
H.B. FULLER
HYDROFLEX
HYDROLOCK
INSUL-DRI
LAMIN8
LIQUILOC
MAX-WELD
MONOLAR
OPTIMA
OPTIMELT
PADLOCK
PLYABLE
PROPEL
RAKOLL
RAPIDEX
SOLARCURE
SPARK-FAS
TACKTILE
TILE PERFECT
ZEROPACK
Advertising Agency:
Tribu/Nazca Saatchi & Saatchi
150 Sur del Gimnasio Nacional
San Jose, Costa Rica
Tel.: (506) 2209 7700
Fax: (506) 209 7900

HEATBATH CORPORATION
107 Frnt St
Indian Orchard, MA 01151-1124
Tel.: (413) 452-2000
Fax: (413) 543-2378
E-mail: info@heatbath.com
Web Site: www.heatbath.com
Approx. Number Employees: 99
Year Founded: 1923
Business Description:
Heat Treating Salts & Quenchants & Metal Finishing Chemical Products Mfr
S.I.C.: 2819; 5169
N.A.I.C.S.: 325188; 424690
Media: 2-7-10-26
Personnel:
Ernest Walen *(Pres)*
Gerald Krywicki *(VP-Sls)*
Thomas Walen *(Mgr-Mktg)*
Brands & Products:
ACIDALL
ALCHROME
ALU-KLEEN
ALUM-ETCH
ARICID
AUS-QUENCH
BATHMINDER
CARTECSAL
CHROMLIFT
CU-BRITE
CU-STRIP L
CUPRAKOTE
DEOXIDE
DERUSTAL
DRAW BLACK
DRYLUBE
DURACOAT
DURASTRIP
ELECTRO-KLEEN
HEATBATH
HIGH SPEED
KWIK-BLAK
LUSTRA-CAD
LUSTRA-TIN
LUSTRA-TIN SN
LUSTRA-ZINC
MARQUENCH
MORPHOS
MULTI-KLEEN
NICKEL PENTRATE
NISTRIP
NIT-OFF
NITEC
NO-CARB
NU-SAL
OXICOAT
PARCURE
PARK
PARK KASE
PARKO
PARQUENCH
PARTHERM
PEN DIP
PEN KARB
PENTRATE
PERMIC
PHOS DIP
PHOSEAL
PLASTIQUENCH
POLYQUENCH
PX
RINSE KLEEN
SCALE KLEEN
SLUDGE DEVIL
STA-HARD
THERMO-QUENCH
UNI-HARD
UNI KLEEN
WATERSHED
WETAID
ZI-BLAK
ZINOL

HENKEL CORPORATION
(Sub. of Henkel AG & Co. KGaA)
2200 Renaissance Blvd
Gulph Mills, PA 19406
Tel.: (610) 270-8100
Fax: (610) 270-8102
Web Site: www.henkelcorp.com
Approx. Number Employees: 2,500
Year Founded: 1876
Business Description:
Industrial Chemicals, Adhesives, Resins & Fatty Acids, Resins Derivatives, Water Treatment Polymers Retailer & Mfr
S.I.C.: 2869; 2843
N.A.I.C.S.: 325199; 325613
Import Export
Advertising Expenditures: $3,000,000
Multimedia: $100,000; Bus. Publs.: $950,000; Catalogs & Directories: $750,000; D.M. to Bus. Estab.: $950,000; Exhibits/Trade Shows: $200,000; Product Samples: $50,000
Distr.: Direct to Consumer; Natl.
Budget Set: July
Personnel:
Jeffrey C. Piccolomini *(Pres)*
Julian Colquitt *(Pres-Adhesive Technologies-North America)*
Brands & Products:
ALAMAC
ALAMINE
ALCORD
ALIQUAT
ALUMINALL
AVIROL
CARBOXANE
COTTOSINT
COVI-OX
COVITOL
DDI
DERIPHAT
DIAM
EMULLO
FINNALINE
FONDO
FOSTERGE
FOSTEX
G-CRYL
G-CURE
GENAMID
GENEROL
GENLECO
GUARTEC
KEP-DRI
KEP-TITE
KEPECO
KEPOLAC
LEVELTONE
LIOFOL
LIX REAGENTS
LOCTITE
MACROMELT
MACROPLAST
NITRENE
NY-WHITE
OMNIFIT
PRESTO
QUATRENE
RETARDINE
SICOMET
STANAX
STANDAFIN
STANDAPHOS
STANDAPOL
STANDAPON
STANFIX
STANFLAKE
STANSOFT
STANTEX
SULFOBETAINE
SULFOTEX
TEXTAMER
TEXTAMINE
TEXTAMINE OXIDE
TEXTERGE
TEXTOFOAM
VELVETEX
VERSADYME
VERSALON
VERSAMID
VERSATRYME
Advertising Agency:
Cramer-Krasselt
246 E Chicago St
Milwaukee, WI 53202
Tel.: (414) 227-3500
Fax: (414) 276-8710
Loctite
Out of Home
Point of Sale
Print
TV
Web Site

HENKEL CORPORATION
(Sub. of Henkel AG & Co. KGaA)
32100 Stephenson Hwy
Madison Heights, MI 48071-5514
Tel.: (248) 583-9300
Fax: (248) 583-2976
Web Site:
www.automotive.henkel.com
Approx. Number Employees: 700
Business Description:
Adhesive Sealants & Surface Treatments Mfr
S.I.C.: 2899; 2869
N.A.I.C.S.: 325998; 325199
Export
Advertising Expenditures: $350,000
Media: 2-4-7-10-13-18-20-21-22
Distr.: Intl.; Natl.
Budget Set: Oct.
Personnel:
John Knudson *(Pres, CEO & Chief Admin Officer)*
Keena Toth *(Mgr-Comm)*
Brands & Products:
ALODINE
AUTOPHORETIC
BONDBRITE
CUPRODINE
DEOXIDINE
GRANODINE
LINEGUARD
PARIO CLEANERS
PARIOLENE
RIDOLINE
RODINE

HENSLEY INDUSTRIES, INC.
(Sub. of Komatsu Ltd.)
2108 Joe Field Rd
Dallas, TX 75229-3255
Mailing Address:
PO Box 29779
Dallas, TX 75229-0779
Tel.: (972) 241-2321
Fax: (972) 241-0915
E-mail: webmaster@hensleyind.com
Web Site: www.hensleyind.com
Approx. Number Employees: 500
Year Founded: 1947
Business Description:
Mfr. of Steel Foundry Construction Equipment, Mining Teeth, Adapters, Buckets & Ground Engaging Tool Wear Parts
S.I.C.: 3325; 3531
N.A.I.C.S.: 331513; 333120
Export
Media: 1-2-4-7-10-11-13-19-20-22-26
Distr.: Intl.; Natl.
Personnel:
Kerry Tatsumikawa *(Pres & COO)*
John F. Fiedler *(CFO & VP-Corp Plng)*
Ralph Huebner *(Exec VP & VP-Sls & Mktg)*
Tom McCormack *(Gen Mgr-Gen Affairs, HR, Komatsu Way & Compliance)*
Terry Noto *(Gen Mgr-Sls & Mktg)*

Key to Media (For complete agency information see *The Advertising Red Books-Agencies* edition):
1. Bus. Publs. 2. Cable T.V. 3. Catalogs & Directories. 4. Co-op Adv. 5. Consumer Mags. 6. D.M. to Bus. Estab.7. D.M. to Consumers 8. Daily Newsp. 9. Exhibits/Trade Shows 10. Foreign 11. Infomercial 12. Internet Adv.13. Multimedia 14. Network Radio 15. Network T.V. 16. Newsp. Distr. Mags. 17. Other 18. Outdoor (Posters, Transit) 19. Point of Purchase20. Premiums, Novelties 21. Product Samples 22. Special Events Mktg. 23. Spot Radio 24. Spot T.V. 25. Weekly Newsp. 26. Yellow Page Adv.

Wayne Shamblin *(Gen Mgr-Attachments)*
Rick Campbell *(Prod Mgr-Attachments Sls)*
Wes Martin *(Product Mgr-Mining & Laminite Sls)*
Steve Smith *(Product Mgr-Comml Metals Sls)*

Brands & Products:
ABRASION ACE
BLADESAVER
HENSLEY
LAMINITE
PARABOLIC

H.E.R.C. PRODUCTS INCORPORATED

155 W 35th St Ste C
National City, CA 91950
Tel.: (619) 427-0776
Fax: (619) 427-0063
E-mail: info@hercprod.com
Web Site: www.hercprod.com
Sales Range: $10-24.9 Million
Approx. Number Employees: 70
Year Founded: 1986
Business Description:
Chemical Mfr & Engineering Technology
S.I.C.: 2899; 5169; 7349
N.A.I.C.S.: 325998; 424690; 561790
Media: 2-4-7-10
Personnel:
S. Steven Carl *(Chm & CEO)*
Brands & Products:
HERC
LINE-OUT
MICONTROL
PIPE-KLEAN
PIPE-KOAT
WELL-KLEAN
WELL-KLEAN II

HERCULES CLOROBEN CORP.

(Sub. of Hercules Chemical Co., Inc.)
111 S St
Passaic, NJ 07055-7901
Tel.: (973) 778-5000
Fax: (973) 777-4115
Toll Free: (800) 631-8550
E-mail: cloro@herchem.com
Web Site: www.herculeschem.com
Approx. Sls.: $7,000,000
Year Founded: 1915
Business Description:
Mfr. of Drain Cleaning Products
S.I.C.: 2899; 3241
N.A.I.C.S.: 325998; 327310
Export
Media: 2-4-5-7-10-19-20-21
Distr.: Natl.
Personnel:
David Siegal *(Pres & CEO)*
Brands & Products:
CLORO-DOSER
CLOROBEN DE

HERCULES INCORPORATED

(Group of Ashland Inc.)
(d/b/a/ Ashland Hercules Water Technologies)
1313 N Market St
Wilmington, DE 19894-0001
Tel.: (302) 594-5000
Telex: 83-5479
Web Site: ppd.herc.com/
Approx. Sls.: $2,136,200,000
Approx. Number Employees: 4,660
Year Founded: 1912
Business Description:
Specialty Chemical Supplier; Papermaking, Commercial, Institutional, Food & Beverage, Mining & General Manufacturing Chemicals
S.I.C.: 2861; 2819; 2869; 2899
N.A.I.C.S.: 325191; 325188; 325199; 325998
Import Export
Media: 2-4-7-10-17
Distr.: Natl.
Personnel:
Paul C. Raymond, III *(Pres)*
Brands & Products:
ADMIRAL
ADVANTAGE
AEROWHIP
AMBERGUM
AMYLOTEX
AQUAFLO
AQUAFLOW
AQUALON
AQUAPAC
AQUAPEL
AQUASORB
BENECEL
BLANOSE
BONDWELL
CREPETROL
CULMINAL
DE-AIREX
DELFLOC
DELSETTE
DRESINATE
FIBERVISIONS
GALACTASOL
HERCOBOND
HERCOFLEX
HERCOLUBE
HERCON
HERCOSET
INFINITY
KLUCEL
KYBREAK
KYMENE
LIBERTY
MICROLUBE
N-HANCE
NATROSOL
NATURALLY, A BETTER SOLUTION
NEXTON
PARACOL
PERFORM
PINOVA
POLYCUP
POLYSURF
PRECIS
PREQUEL
PRIMAFLO
PROSOFT
REZOSOL
SCRIPSET
SILIPON
SILIPUR
SPECTRUM
SUPERCOL
VINSOL
ZENIX

HERMES ABRASIVES LTD.

(Sub. of Hermes Schleifmittel GmbH & Co. KG)
524 Viking Dr
Virginia Beach, VA 23452
Mailing Address:
PO Box 2389
Virginia Beach, VA 23450
Tel.: (757) 486-6623
Fax: (757) 431-2370
Fax: (800) 243-7637
Toll Free: (800) 464-8314
E-mail: marketing@hermesabrasives.com
Web Site: www.hermesabrasives.com
Approx. Sls.: $50,000,000
Approx. Number Employees: 230
Year Founded: 1970
Business Description:
Coated Abrasive Products
S.I.C.: 3291
N.A.I.C.S.: 327910
Media: 10

HEXION SPECIALTY CHEMICALS INC.

(Name Changed to Momentive Specialty Chemicals Inc.)

HILL & GRIFFITH COMPANY

1085 Summer St
Cincinnati, OH 45204-2037
Tel.: (513) 921-1075
Fax: (513) 244-9180
Toll Free: (800) 543-0425
E-mail: sales@hillandgriffith.com
Web Site: www.hillandgriffith.com
E-Mail For Key Personnel:
Sales Director: sales@hillandgriffith.com
Approx. Number Employees: 26
Year Founded: 1896
Business Description:
Mfr. of Foundry Sand Additives & Release Agents for Concrete
S.I.C.: 3295; 5085
N.A.I.C.S.: 327992; 423840
Export
Advertising Expenditures: $50,000
Media: 2-4-7-10
Distr.: Natl.
Personnel:
David Greek, Jr. *(COO & Exec VP)*
Dale P. Welsh *(VP-Fin)*
Brands & Products:
AQUAPART
CARBONITE
CONCOTE
DILUCO
DRYCOLUBE
GREEN HORNET
GRIFCOTE
GRIFLUBE
KWIK MULL
PLUNGER LUBE
PREMIX
SHURSTIK
SLIKEASE
VEIN AWAY
Advertising Agency:
Lohre & Associates, Incorporated
126A W 14th St 2nd Floor
Cincinnati, OH 45202
Tel.: (513) 961-1174
Fax: (513) 961-1192

HOUGHTON INTERNATIONAL INC.

(Holding of AEA Investors LP)
Madison & Van Buren Ave
Valley Forge, PA 19482
Mailing Address:
PO Box 930
Valley Forge, PA 19482-0930
Tel.: (610) 666-4000
Fax: (610) 666-5689
Web Site: www.houghtonintl.com
Sales Range: $300-349.9 Million
Approx. Number Employees: 150
Year Founded: 1865
Business Description:
Industrial Specialty Chemicals
S.I.C.: 2869; 2992
N.A.I.C.S.: 325199; 324191
Import
Advertising Expenditures: $400,000
Media: 4-7-10-20-21
Distr.: Natl.
Budget Set: Nov.
Personnel:
Paul DeVivo *(CEO)*
David H. Hays *(CFO & VP)*
Thaddeus L. Piatkowski *(Pres-Houghton Metal Finishing & Exec VP)*
Chung Y. Lai *(VP-North Asia Reg & Pres-Houghton China)*
Richard R. Lovely *(VP-HR-Global)*
Wesley D. Warner *(VP-HR)*
John M. Burke *(Dir-Engrg Svcs)*
Hank Limper *(Mgr-Mktg)*
Jim McMahon *(Mgr-Sls-Natl)*
Brands & Products:
AQUA-QUENCH
BIO-QUENCH
CERFA-KLEEN
CINDOL
HOCUT
HOUGHTO-DRAW
HOUGHTO-QUENCH
HOUGHTO-SAFE
HOUGHTON
HYDROLUBRIC
MAR-TEMP
MICROSURFACE
QUENCHCARE
VIBRA-KLEEN
Advertising Agency:
Schubert Communications, Inc.
112 Schubert Dr
Downingtown, PA 19335-3382
Tel.: (610) 269-2100
Fax: (610) 269-2275

HUBBARD-HALL, INC.

563 S Leonard St
Waterbury, CT 06708-4316
Tel.: (203) 756-5521
Fax: (203) 756-9017
Toll Free: (800) 648-3412
E-mail: info@hubbardhall.com
Web Site: www.hubbardhall.com
E-Mail For Key Personnel:
President: askipp@hubbardhall.com
Approx. Number Employees: 121
Year Founded: 1849
Business Description:
Metal Finishing & Industrial Chemicals, Semi-Conductor & Microelectronic Chemicals; Specialty Chemicals, Rust Inhibitors & Black Oxides Mfr & Distr
S.I.C.: 5169; 3471
N.A.I.C.S.: 424690; 332813
Export
Advertising Expenditures: $500,000
Media: 2-4-7-10-20-21-26
Personnel:
Charles T. Kellogg *(Chm & CFO)*
Andrew K. Skipp *(Pres & CEO)*
Jeff Davis *(CMO & Sr VP)*
W. Brent Burleson *(Sr VP)*

Key to Media (For complete agency information see *The Advertising Red Books-Agencies* edition):
1. Bus. Publs. 2. Cable T.V. 3. Catalogs & Directories. 4. Co-op Adv. 5. Consumer Mags. 6. D.M. to Bus. Estab.7. D.M. to Consumers
8. Daily Newsp. 9. Exhibits/Trade Shows 10. Foreign 11. Infomercial 12. Internet Adv.13. Multimedia 14. Network Radio
15. Network T.V. 16. Newsp. Distr. Mags. 17. Other 18. Outdoor (Posters, Transit) 19. Point of Purchase20. Premiums, Novelties
21. Product Samples 22. Special Events Mktg. 23. Spot Radio 24. Spot T.V. 25. Weekly Newsp. 26. Yellow Page Adv.

Hubbard-Hall, Inc. — (Continued)

Janice Crelan *(Controller & Asst Treas)*
Tony Sacco *(Gen Mgr-W Springfield)*
Robbie Stack *(Mgr-Mktg)*
Brands & Products:
ACHOPHOS
ACID BRITE
AQUAEASE
AQUAPURE
BLACK MAGIC
CLEANER
DIE BRITE
ELECTROPOLISH
HALLSTRIP
LASER
LUSTERCLEAN
METAL GUARD
MI-CLEAN
MI-TIQUE
SUNBRITE
ULTRASOAK

HUNTSMAN CORPORATION

500 Huntsman Way
Salt Lake City, UT 84108
Tel.: (801) 584-5700
Fax: (801) 584-5781
Toll Free: (800) 421-2411
Telex: 759496
Web Site: www.huntsman.com
Approx. Rev.: $9,250,000,000
Approx. Number Employees: 12,000
Year Founded: 1982
Business Description:
Holding Company; Chemical Products Mfr & Whslr
S.I.C.: 6719; 2816; 2819; 2843; 2851; 2865; 2869; 2899; 3086; 5169
N.A.I.C.S.: 551112; 325110; 325131; 325132; 325188; 325199; 325510; 325613; 325998; 326150; 424690
Import Export
Media: 2-4-7-10
Distr.: Natl.
Personnel:
Jon M. Huntsman, Sr. *(Chm)*
Peter R. Huntsman *(Pres & CEO)*
Anthony P. Hankins *(CEO, Pres-Asia Pacific, Div & Polyurethanes)*
J. Kimo Esplin *(CFO & Exec VP)*
Maria Csiba-Womersley *(CIO & VP)*
Andre Genton *(Pres-Advanced Materials Div)*
Paul G. Hulme *(Pres-Textile Effects Div)*
Stewart Monteith *(Pres-Performance Products Div)*
Simon Turner *(Pres-Pigments Div)*
James R. Moore *(Gen Counsel, Sec & Exec VP)*
Russell R. Stolle *(Sr VP & Deputy Gen Counsel)*
Ronald W. Gerrard *(Sr VP-Environmental, Health, Safety & Mfg Excellence)*
Brian V. Ridd *(Sr VP-Pur)*
R. Wade Rogers *(Sr VP-HR-Global)*
John R. Heskett *(VP-Treasury & Plng)*
Brands & Products:
ACCUMIX
ACTIVE
AGO RAPID
AGOMET
AGOMET TWIN
AGOREX
AIROUT
ALGENE
ALKADET
ALKANATE
ARA
ARACAST
ARADUR
ARAFAST
ARAFLOOR
ARALDIT
ARALDIT RAPID
ARALDITE
ARALDITE BUILDER
ARALDITE BUILDER BARRIER KOAT
ARALDITE BUILDER INTEGRA
ARALDITE BUILDER KLAD-X
ARALDITE BUILDER RENOVA
ARALDITE FUSION
ARASEAL
ARATHAN
ARATHANE
ARATHERM
ARATRONIC
ARAVITE
AROCY
ATLAS
ATLAS-AGO-INFRA
ATLAS-AGO-RAPID
AZYRAL
BIONIC
CAST-IT
CEMTRONIC
DEFOAMER
DEHSCOFIX
DEHSCOTEX
DELTIO
DIPLAST
ECCONDO
ECOTERIC
ELTESOL
EMPICOL
EMPIGEN
EMPIMIN
EMPIPHOS
EMPIWAX
ENRICHING LIVES THROUGH INNOVATION
ENRICHING LIVES THROUGH INNOVATON
ENTERION
EPIBOND
EPOCAST
EPOSERT
EPOX-E-SEAL
EURELON
EUREMELT
EURETEK
EXACTOMER
EXATRON
FUSION
HARTASIST
HUNTSMAN
HYDRAPOL
HYDROL
IROGRAN
JEFFAMINE
JEFFCAT
JEFFCOOL
JEFFOL
JEFFSOL
KERIMID
KINEL
KNITTEX
KRYSTALFLEX
KRYSTALGRAN
LANACRON
LANASET
LANASOL
LAUREX
LYOPRINT
MARCHON
MATRIMID
MAXILON
MEGASOFT
MIRALAN
MISTRALE
MITIN
MORMATE
NANSA
NEOLAN
NOVACRON
NOVASOL
OXAMIN
PARTSINMINUTES
PHOBOL
PHOBOTEX
PHOBOTONE
POGOL
POLAR
POLYFROTH
POLYSIL
PYROVATEX
PYROVATIM
QUATREX
RENCAST
RENGEM
RENLAM
RENPASTE
RENPIM
RENSHAPE
REXTAC
RUBIFLEX
RUBINATE
SAPAMINE
SHADEFACTORY
SILVATOL
SMARTLITE
SOLOPHENYL
STABILON
SUPRASEC
SURFOL
SURFONAMIDE
SURFONAMINE
SURFONIC
SYNCOL
TACTIX
TECTILON
TERASIL
TERATOP
TERIC
TERMUL
TERSPERSE
TERWET
TESCOL
THERMACOL
TINEGAL
TIOXIDE
TURPEX
ULTRAPHIL
ULTRATEX
ULTRAVON
UNIFLOT
UNIMAX
UNIVADINE
URALANE
UV-FAST
UV-SUN
UVITEX
VICOL
ZEROSTAT

HURST CHEMICAL COMPANY

231 W Pedegosa St
Santa Barbara, CA 93101
Tel.: (323) 223-4121
Fax: (800) 723-2005
Toll Free: (800) 723-2004
E-mail: info@hurstchemical.com
Web Site: www.hurstchemical.com
Approx. Number Employees: 25
Year Founded: 1958
Business Description:
Graphic Art Chemicals & Printing Press Supplies Mfr & Distr
S.I.C.: 5169
N.A.I.C.S.: 424690
Media: 2-7-10-13-21
Personnel:
Joanne Hirsh *(Pres)*
Brands & Products:
BLACK PLATE
ENCO
EPSON
FUJI
HURST GRAPHICS
IMATION
ITEK
MEAD
MEGA
MEGALITH
POLYCHROME
SCAN-PRINT
SILVERMASTER
SMARTPLATE
ULTRAPRECISE
VALU LINE
VALULINE

IKONICS CORPORATION

4832 Grand Ave
Duluth, MN 55807-2743
Tel.: (218) 628-2217
Fax: (218) 628-3245
Toll Free: (800) 328-4261
E-mail: info@ikonics.com
Web Site: www.ikonics.com
Approx. Sls.: $16,517,338
Approx. Number Employees: 72
Year Founded: 1952
Business Description:
Mfr, Developer & Marketer of Petrochemical Imaging Products
S.I.C.: 3861; 3555
N.A.I.C.S.: 325992; 333293
Advertising Expenditures: $100,000
Media: 2-10-13
Personnel:
William C. Ulland *(Chm, Pres & CEO)*
Jon Gerlach *(CFO & VP-Fin)*
Claude Piguet *(Exec VP)*
Parnell Thill *(VP-Mktg)*
Mike Skrbich *(Mgr-Chromaline)*
Brands & Products:
CHROMA/FILL
CHROMALINE
CRYSTALBLAST
IKONICS
IKONMETAL

INOLEX CHEMICAL COMPANY

(Sub. of Inolex Group Inc.)
2101 S Swanson St
Philadelphia, PA 19148
Tel.: (215) 271-0800
Fax: (215) 271-2621
Toll Free: (800) 521-9891
E-mail: cheminfo@inolex.com
Web Site: www.inolex.com
Year Founded: 1892
Business Description:
Raw Materials to Industrial & Cosmetic Applications
S.I.C.: 2821; 2865
N.A.I.C.S.: 325211; 325132
Advertising Expenditures: $1,000,000

Key to Media (For complete agency information see *The Advertising Red Books-Agencies* edition):
1. Bus. Publs. 2. Cable T.V. 3. Catalogs & Directories. 4. Co-op Adv. 5. Consumer Mags. 6. D.M. to Bus. Estab.7. D.M. to Consumers 8. Daily Newsp. 9. Exhibits/Trade Shows 10. Foreign 11. Infomercial 12. Internet Adv.13. Multimedia 14. Network Radio 15. Network T.V. 16. Newsp. Distr. Mags. 17. Other 18. Outdoor (Posters, Transit) 19. Point of Purchase20. Premiums, Novelties 21. Product Samples 22. Special Events Mktg. 23. Spot Radio 24. Spot T.V. 25. Weekly Newsp. 26. Yellow Page Adv.

Media: 2-4-7-10-13
Distr.: Intl.; Natl.
Budget Set: June
Personnel:
Noelle Giletto *(CFO)*

INOLEX GROUP INC.

Jackson and Swanson Sts
Philadelphia, PA 19148
Tel.: (215) 271-0800
Fax: (215) 271-2621
Toll Free: (800) 521-9891
E-mail: cheminfo@inolex.com
Web Site: www.inolex.com
Approx. Number Employees: 100
Year Founded: 1892
Business Description:
Mfr. of Plastic Materials & Resins
S.I.C.: 2821; 2869
N.A.I.C.S.: 325211; 325199
Import Export
Media: 2-4-7-13
Personnel:
Conrad A. Plimpton *(Chm & Owner)*
Reb Heimz *(Pres)*
Tyler Housel *(Dir-Applications)*
Daniel Winn *(Mgr-Mktg)*
Brands & Products:
INOLEX
LEXAMINE
LEXATE
LEXFEEL
LEXGARD
LEXOREZ
LEXQUAT

INTERCAT INC.

(Sub. of Johnson Matthey PLC)
2399 Hwy 34 Bldg C1
Manasquan, NJ 08736-1500
Tel.: (732) 223-4644
Fax: (732) 223-3447
Toll Free: (800) 346-5425
E-mail: info@intercat.com
Web Site: www2.intercatinc.com
Approx. Number Employees: 150
Year Founded: 1986
Business Description:
Fluid Cracking Catalyst Additives Mfr & Developer
S.I.C.: 2819
N.A.I.C.S.: 325188
Import Export
Advertising Expenditures: $400,000
Media: 4-7-13
Personnel:
Regis B. Lippert *(Pres & CEO)*
Brands & Products:
BCA
CAT-AID
CAT-AID V
COP
COP-NP
HI-Y
INTERCAT
ISOCAT
ISOCAT HP
LGS
NOXGETTER
OCTAMAX
OCTAMAX HP
PENTA-CAT
PENTA-CAT HP
PENTA-CAT PLUS
SOXGETTER
SUPER SOXGETTER
SUPER Z
ULTRA LO-SOX
Z-CAT HP
Z-CAT PLUS
ZMX

INTERCHEM CORPORATION

120 Rte 17 N
Paramus, NJ 07653-1579
Mailing Address:
PO Box 1579
Paramus, NJ 07653
Tel.: (201) 261-7333
Fax: (201) 261-7339
E-mail: sales@interchem.com
Web Site: www.interchem.com
E-Mail For Key Personnel:
President: joe@interchem.com
Marketing Director: tkelly@interchem.com
Sales Director: sales@interchem.com
Approx. Number Employees: 50
Year Founded: 1981
Business Description:
Supplier of Fine Chemicals, Intermediates & Bulk Actives
S.I.C.: 5122; 5169
N.A.I.C.S.: 424210; 424690
Media: 2
Personnel:
Ron Mannino *(Owner)*
Joseph M. Pizza *(Pres & CEO)*
Theresa Kelly *(Sr VP)*

INTERNATIONAL ABSORBENTS, INC.

(Holding of Kinderhook Industries, LLC)
1569 Dempsey Rd
North Vancouver, BC V7K 1S8, Canada
Tel.: (604) 681-6181
Fax: (604) 904-4105
Toll Free: (866) 514-6559
E-mail: info@internationalabsorbents.com
Web Site: www.absorbent.com
Approx. Sls.: $34,575,000
Approx. Number Employees: 112
Year Founded: 1983
Business Description:
Biodegradable Absorption Products Mfr, Developer & Marketer
S.I.C.: 5199; 2048; 2823; 5093
N.A.I.C.S.: 424990; 311119; 325221; 423930
Advertising Expenditures: $478,000
Personnel:
Gordon L. Ellis *(Chm & Pres)*
David H. Thompson *(CFO & Sec)*
Brands & Products:
CAREFRESH
HEALTHY PET
INTERNATIONAL ABSORBENTS
SUPER SHAVIN'S

INTERNATIONAL DIOXIDE, INC.

(Sub. of E.I. du Pont de Nemours & Company)
40 Whitecap Dr
North Kingstown, RI 02852-4220
Tel.: (401) 295-8800
Fax: (401) 295-7108
Toll Free: (800) 477-6071
Telex: 642-582 PROLINE
Web Site: www.idiclo2.com
Sales Range: $10-24.9 Million
Approx. Number Employees: 30
Year Founded: 1956
Business Description:
Anthium Dioxide & Stabilized Chlorine Dioxide Germicide, Chlorine Dioxide Generators, Sodium Chlorite Mfr & Whslr
S.I.C.: 2812; 2819
N.A.I.C.S.: 325181; 325188
Advertising Expenditures: $200,000
Media: 2-8-9-10-19-20-21-26
Distr.: Intl.; Natl.
Brands & Products:
ADOX
ANTHIUM
CARNEBON
CRYOCIDE
ENDIMAL
OXYCHLOR

INTERNATIONAL SPECIALTY PRODUCTS, INC.

1361 Alps Rd
Wayne, NJ 07470
Tel.: (973) 628-4000
Tel.: (973) 872-4339 (HR)
Fax: (973) 628-3311
Toll Free: (800) 622-4423
E-mail: info@ispcorp.com
Web Site: www.ispcorp.com
E-Mail For Key Personnel:
President: skumar@ispcorp.com
Sales Director: solsen@ispcorp.com
Sales Range: $1-4.9 Billion
Approx. Number Employees: 3,120
Business Description:
Holding Company; Chemicals & Mineral Products Mfr & Supplier
S.I.C.: 6719; 2899
N.A.I.C.S.: 551112; 325998
Media: 2-4-7-10-13-21
Distr.: Direct to Consumer; Intl.; Natl.
Budget Set: Jan.
Personnel:
Samuel J. Heyman *(Chm)*
Gregg Kam *(CFO & Sr VP)*
Roger J. Cope *(Sr VP-Devel & Strategy)*
Larry Grenner *(Sr VP-Res)*
Catherine Joy *(Sr VP)*
Dan Andrews *(VP-Engrng)*
Ken Morris *(VP-IT For IST)*
Carlos Restrepo *(VP-Indus)*
Mary Anne Spencer *(VP-HR-Global)*
Paul Taylor *(Sr Dir-Tech & Ops)*
Walt Galacki *(Dir-Environ)*
John Bozza *(Sr Mgr-Personal Care Div-Southeast Reg)*
Mark Dailey *(Sr Mgr- Sls)*
Brands & Products:
2-PYROL
ADVANTAGE
AGRIMAX
AGRIMER
AGRISYNTH
AGSOLEX
ALGINADE
ALGINATES
ALLANTOIN
ALLIANZ
ANTARA
AQUAFLEX
AQUAZOL
BIOTREND
BUTOXYNE
CAVAMAX
CERAPHYL
CERASYNT
CHROMABOND
CONDITIONEZE
CONFETTI
COS-KELP
DARILOID
DISINTEX
DOSE-MAP
EASY-SPERSE
EMULSYNT
ESCALOL
FERRONYL
FOAMFLUSH
FUNGITROL
GAFCHROMIC
GAFFIX
GAFQUAT
GANEX
GANTREZ
GERMABEN
GERMALL
INTEGRA
INTEGRA 44
ISP CAPTIVATES
ISP COLORFLOW
KELACID
KELCOLOID
KELCOSOL
KELGIN
KELMAR
KELSET
KELTONE
KELTOSE
KELVIS
LACTICOL
LIQUAPAR
LUBRAJEL
LUBRASIL
M-PYROL
MANUCOL
MANUGEL
MANUTEX
MICROFLEX
MICROPOWDER
MICROPURE
NUOCIDE
NUOSEPT
OMNIREZ
OPTIPHEN
OPTIPHENTM
ORCHID COMPLEX
PERM
PEROXYDONE
PHARMASOLVE
PLASDONE
PLEXAJEL
POLECTRON
POLYCLAR
POLYPLASDONE
PROLIPID
RAD-SURE
RAPI-CURE
RAPITHIX
SHIPSHAPE
SI-TEC
SOREZ
STABILEZE
STERIN
STYLEZE
SURFADONE
SUTTOCIDE
TEXTUREZE
V-CAP
V-PYROL
VITAL ET
VIVIPRINT
X-TEND

Key to Media (For complete agency information see *The Advertising Red Books-Agencies* edition):
1. Bus. Publs. 2. Cable T.V. 3. Catalogs & Directories. 4. Co-op Adv. 5. Consumer Mags. 6. D.M. to Bus. Estab.7. D.M. to Consumers 8. Daily Newsp. 9. Exhibits/Trade Shows 10. Foreign 11. Infomercial 12. Internet Adv.13. Multimedia 14. Network Radio 15. Network T.V. 16. Newsp. Distr. Mags. 17. Other 18. Outdoor (Posters, Transit) 19. Point of Purchase20. Premiums, Novelties 21. Product Samples 22. Special Events Mktg. 23. Spot Radio 24. Spot T.V. 25. Weekly Newsp. 26. Yellow Page Adv.

INTERPLASTIC CORPORATION
1225 Willow Lk Blvd
Saint Paul, MN 55110-5145
Tel.: (651) 481-6860
Fax: (651) 481-9836
Toll Free: (800) 736-5497
E-mail: webmaster@interplastic.com
Web Site: www.interplastic.com
E-Mail For Key Personnel:
Marketing Director: RLazzara@ interplastic.com
Approx. Number Employees: 500
Year Founded: 1959
Business Description:
Synthetic Resins & Companion Items; Sheet Molding Compound Mfr & Sales
S.I.C.: 2821; 5169
N.A.I.C.S.: 325211; 424690
Import Export
Media: 2-10
Distr.: Reg.
Personnel:
James D. Wallenfelsz *(CEO)*
Robert DeRoma *(Sr VP)*
John Wilcox *(VP & Bus Mgr)*
David Dana *(VP-Res & Tech)*
David Engelsgaard *(VP-Fin)*
Bobbi Jenson *(VP-Mktg)*
David Herzog *(Dir-Res)*
Lou Ross *(Dir-Res)*
Peter Surmak *(Bus Mgr-Vinyl Esters & Engineered Resins)*
Daryl Francis *(Bus Mgr)*
Steve Wetzel *(Mgr-Natl Sls)*
Bobbi Jensen *(Mgr-Mktg Comm)*
Brands & Products:
COR-TITE
COREZYN
INTERPLASTIC CORPORATION
SILMAR

INVISTA B.V.
(Sub. of Koch Industries, Inc.)
4123 E 37th St N
Wichita, KS 67220
Tel.: (316) 828-1000
Fax: (316) 828-1801
Toll Free: (877) 446-8478
E-mail: invistainfo@invista.com
Web Site: www.invista.com
Approx. Sls.: $7,200,000,000
Approx. Number Employees: 18,000
Business Description:
Textile & Polymer Mfr
S.I.C.: 2821; 2296
N.A.I.C.S.: 325211; 314992
Import Export
Media: 4-7-10-11
Personnel:
Jeff Gentry *(CEO)*
Dave Trerotola *(Pres-Performance Fibers)*
Steve Kromer *(Sr VP)*
Diane O'Sullivan *(Dir-Mktg-Global)*
Cindy McNaull *(Brand Mgr-Cordura-Global)*
Brands & Products:
ADI-PURE
ANTRON
AVANTIGE
AVORA
C12
COOLMAX
CORDURA
DYTEK
ESP
LYCRA
POLARGUARD
STAINMASTER
SUPPLEX
TACTEL
TERATHANE
THERMOLITE
Advertising Agency:
Howard, Merrell & Partners, Inc.
8521 Six Forks Rd 4th Fl
Raleigh, NC 27615-5278
Tel.: (919) 848-2400
Fax: (919) 848-2420
Cordura

IRT, INC.
(d/b/a Immediate Response Technologies)
7100 Holladay Tyler Rd
Glenn Dale, MD 20769
Tel.: (301) 352-8800
Fax: (301) 352-8818
Toll Free: (800) 598-9711
E-mail: sales@imresponse.com
Web Site: www.imresponse.com
Sales Range: $25-49.9 Million
Approx. Number Employees: 205
Business Description:
Decontamination Systems Mfr
S.I.C.: 3564; 2394; 3812
N.A.I.C.S.: 333411; 314912; 334511
Advertising Expenditures: $387,000
Personnel:
Mark N. Hammond *(Co-Chm)*
Todd L. Parchman *(Co-Chm)*
Harley A. Hughes *(Pres & CEO)*
Sherri S. Voelkel *(CFO, Exec VP & Sec)*
John P. McMullen *(COO & Exec VP)*
Donald C. Yount, Jr. *(COO & Exec VP)*
Sean R. Hunt *(Gen Counsel, Sec & Sr VP)*
Brands & Products:
1500 CHEM/BIO
1500 HEPA
400 CHEM/BIO
400 HEPA
C420 PAPR SYSTEM
INTELLIJET
MOBILITY,RESPONSE,PROTECTION
PUREAIR BIO RESPONSE KIT
PUREAIR PAPR C8
PUREAIR PAPR K7
TVI CORPORATION

ITRONICS INC.
6490 S McCarren Blvd Bldg C Ste 23
Reno, NV 89509
Tel.: (775) 677-6049
Fax: (775) 689-7691
E-mail: investor@itronics.com
Web Site: www.itronics.com
Sales Range: $1-9.9 Million
Approx. Number Employees: 23
Year Founded: 1987
Business Description:
Chemicals & Fertilizers Mfr; Recycler of Photo Processing Waste; Refiner of Silver; Resource Consulting Services
S.I.C.: 8733; 4953; 8742
N.A.I.C.S.: 541710; 541611; 562920
Advertising Expenditures: $309,014
Personnel:
Gregory S. Skinner *(Exec Officer)*
Brands & Products:
A CREATIVE CLEANTECH COMPANY
A CREATIVE ENVIRONMENTAL TECHNOLOGY COMPANY
GOLD'N GRO
INSIDEMETALS
ITRONICS

ITW DYMON
(Sub. of Illinois Tool Works Inc.)
805 E Old 56 Hwy
Olathe, KS 66061-4914
Mailing Address:
PO Box 340
Olathe, KS 66051-0340
Tel.: (913) 397-8704
Fax: (913) 397-8707
Toll Free: (800) 443-9536
Toll Free: (800) 224-4860
Web Site: www.dymon.com
Sales Range: $25-49.9 Million
Approx. Number Employees: 100
Year Founded: 1998
Business Description:
Specialty Chemicals & Marking Systems Mfr
S.I.C.: 2899; 3953
N.A.I.C.S.: 325998; 339943
Media: 2-4-7
Personnel:
Christine Froth *(Mgr-Mktg)*
Brands & Products:
ACTION MARKER
BRITE-MARK
CLEAR REFLECTIONS
DALO
DO-IT-ALL
DRY BREEZE
DYKEM
THE ELIMINATOR
LIQUID ALIVE
MECHANIC'S FRIEND
MEDAPHENE
NATURAL FORCE
SCRUBS
SOLAR GUARD
STEEL BLUE
TEXPEN

ITW PLEXUS
(Sub. of Illinois Tool Works Inc.)
30 Endicott St
Danvers, MA 01923
Tel.: (978) 777-1100
Fax: (978) 774-0516
E-mail: info@itwplexus.com
Web Site: www.itwplexus.com
Sales Range: $25-49.9 Million
Approx. Number Employees: 100
Business Description:
Adhesive & Sealant Mfr
S.I.C.: 2891
N.A.I.C.S.: 325520
Media: 10
Brands & Products:
FUSIONMATE
PLEXUS

JARCHEM INDUSTRIES, INC.
414 Wilson Ave
Newark, NJ 07105
Tel.: (973) 344-0600
Fax: (973) 344-5743
E-mail: info@jarchem.com
Web Site: www.jarchem.com
Approx. Number Employees: 45
Year Founded: 1978
Business Description:
Mfr. of Pharmaceutical Preservatives & Acetate Salts for Food, Textile, Photographic & Chemical Processing Industries
S.I.C.: 2869
N.A.I.C.S.: 325199
Import Export
Media: 2-4-7-10-11-13-17
Distr.: Intl.; Natl.
Personnel:
Arnold Stern *(Pres)*
Stephen Winer *(Dir-Mktg)*
Brands & Products:
GLYCINE
JARBROM
JARBROM I-16
JARCHLOR
JARCHLOR I-16
JARCOAL
JARCOL
JARESTER
JARGRIP
JARIC 22U
JARIC I-12
JARLC
JARPOL
JARTHERM
LIPEX CELLECT
SHEA STICK 3000

J.M. HUBER CORPORATION
333 Thornall St
Edison, NJ 08837-2220
Tel.: (732) 549-8600
Fax: (732) 549-7256
E-mail: webmaster@huber.com
Web Site: www.huber.com
Sales Range: $1-4.9 Billion
Approx. Number Employees: 4,500
Year Founded: 1890
Business Description:
Specialty Additives & Thickeners Mfr
S.I.C.: 2819
N.A.I.C.S.: 325188
Import Export
Media: 2-4-10
Distr.: Natl.
Personnel:
Robert Currie *(VP)*
Louis Capello *(Dir-Risk Mngmt)*
Brands & Products:
HUBER
HUBERCARB
KELTROL
NYLOK
POLYFIL
ZEOTHIX

JOHNSON MANUFACTURING COMPANY
114 Lost Grove Rd
Princeton, IA 52768
Tel.: (563) 289-5123
Fax: (563) 289-3825
E-mail: johnsonmfg@aol.com
Web Site: www.johnsonmfg.com
Approx. Number Employees: 50
Year Founded: 1909
Business Description:
Developer, Mfr & Retailer Lead-Free Solders & Fluxes
S.I.C.: 2899; 5085
N.A.I.C.S.: 325998; 423840
Media: 2-4-10-13
Personnel:
Alan Gickler *(Pres)*

Key to Media (For complete agency information see *The Advertising Red Books-Agencies* edition):
1. Bus. Publs. 2. Cable T.V. 3. Catalogs & Directories. 4. Co-op Adv. 5. Consumer Mags. 6. D.M. to Bus. Estab.7. D.M. to Consumers
8. Daily Newsp. 9. Exhibits/Trade Shows 10. Foreign 11. Infomercial 12. Internet Adv.13. Multimedia 14. Network Radio
15. Network T.V. 16. Newsp. Distr. Mags. 17. Other 18. Outdoor (Posters, Transit) 19. Point of Purchase20. Premiums, Novelties
21. Product Samples 22. Special Events Mktg. 23. Spot Radio 24. Spot T.V. 25. Weekly Newsp. 26. Yellow Page Adv.

Brands & Products:
ALLEN'S SAL-AMMONIAC
HEALTHWATCH
JOHNSON

JOHNSON MATTHEY INC.
(Sub. of Johnson Matthey Noble Metals)
435 Devon Park Dr Ste 600
Wayne, PA 19087
Tel.: (610) 971-3000
Fax: (610) 971-3191
Telex: 6851052
Web Site: www.jmusa.com
Approx. Number Employees: 1,400
Year Founded: 1901
Business Description:
Refines & Fabricates Platinum Group Metals; Platinum Chemicals, Catalysts, Lab Apparatus, Wire, Sheet, Automotive Converters, Transfers & Colors Mfr
S.I.C.: 3499
N.A.I.C.S.: 332999
Import Export
Advertising Expenditures: $300,000
Media: 2-4-7
Distr.: Natl.
Budget Set: Feb.
Personnel:
Robert M. Talley *(Gen Counsel & Sec)*

JONES-HAMILTON CO.
30354 Tracy Rd
Walbridge, OH 43465-9775
Tel.: (419) 666-9838
Fax: (419) 666-1817
E-mail: info@jones-hamilton.com
Web Site: www.jones-hamilton.com
Approx. Number Employees: 93
Year Founded: 1951
Business Description:
Chemicals & Compounds Producer, Packager & Distr
S.I.C.: 2819
N.A.I.C.S.: 325188
Media: 13
Personnel:
J. Kern Hamilton *(Co-Founder & Co-Chm)*
Robert L. James *(Pres & CEO)*
Brands & Products:
JH
PHASE
PLT
PWT

JPS INDUSTRIES, INC.
55 Beattie Pl Ste 1510
Greenville, SC 29601-2146
Tel.: (864) 239-3900
Fax: (864) 271-9939
Toll Free: (800) 288-0577
E-mail: twoodlee@jpsglass.com
Web Site: www.jpsglass.com
Sales Range: $25-49.9 Million
Approx. Number Employees: 600
Year Founded: 1982
Business Description:
Extruded Eurethanes, Polypropylenes & Mechanically Formed Glass Substrates Mfr
S.I.C.: 2211; 3081
N.A.I.C.S.: 313210; 326113
Advertising Expenditures: $600,000
Media: 10
Personnel:
Michael L. Fulbright *(Chm, Pres & CEO)*
Chuck R. Tutterow *(CFO, Sec & Exec VP)*
Monnie L. Broome *(VP-HR)*
William E. Jackson *(VP-Fin & Admin)*
Joan Kirby *(Mgr-Customer Svc)*
Brands & Products:
GORILLA-MESH
HI-TUFF
HI-TUFF PLUS
INDUSTRO-QUARTZ
JPS
TEMPRATEX
VERSAFLEX

KANEKA AMERICA LLC
(Sub. of Kaneka Corporation)
546 5th Ave 21st Fl
New York, NY 10036
Tel.: (212) 705-4340
Fax: (212) 705-4350
E-mail: fiberinfo@kaneka.com
Web Site: www.kaneka.com
Approx. Number Employees: 20
Business Description:
Synthetic Fiber, Pharmaceutical Intermediate & Heat Resistant Resin Marketer & Retailer
S.I.C.: 8743; 8732
N.A.I.C.S.: 541820; 541910
Advertising Expenditures: $200,000
Media: 4-5-6-7-8-9-10-20-21
Distr.: Intl.; Natl.
Budget Set: Apr. -Oct.
Personnel:
Atsushi Ikenaga *(Pres)*
Shinji Ige *(Sr VP)*
Brands & Products:
APICAL
EPERAN
KANE ACE
KANEKA CPVC
KANEKALON
LIPOSORBER
MS POLYMER
PROTEX
SIBSTAR

KENNECOTT UTAH COPPER CORPORATION
(Sub. of Rio Tinto Copper)
8362 W 10200 S
Bingham Canyon, UT 84006-0351
Mailing Address:
PO Box 6001
Magna, UT 84044-6001
Tel.: (801) 569-6700
Fax: (801) 569-6797
E-mail: info@kennecott.com
Web Site: www.kennecott.com
Approx. Number Employees: 1,700
Year Founded: 1936
Business Description:
Copper & Lead Ore Mining
S.I.C.: 1021; 1031
N.A.I.C.S.: 212234; 212231
Media: 2-10-11-17
Distr.: Intl.; Natl.
Budget Set: Oct.
Personnel:
Kelly Sanders *(Pres & CEO)*
Patrick Keenan *(CFO)*
Clayton Walker *(COO)*
Lynn Cardey-Yates *(VP-Legal)*
James Cowley *(VP-Mktg-Sls)*
Diana Wood *(Sr Sls Acct Exec)*

KIDDE FIRE FIGHTING
(Sub. of Kidde Residential & Commercial Division)
180 Sheree Blvd Ste 3900
Exton, PA 19341
Mailing Address:
PO Box 695
Exton, PA 19341-0695
Tel.: (610) 363-1400
Fax: (610) 524-9073
E-mail: webmaster@kidde-fire.com
Web Site: www.kidde-fire.com
Sales Range: $125-149.9 Million
Approx. Number Employees: 150
Business Description:
Fire Extinguishers, Fire Suppression Foam, Fire Hose & Fire Fighting Equipment Mfr
S.I.C.: 3569; 2899; 3052; 3492; 9224
N.A.I.C.S.: 333999; 325998; 326220; 332912; 922160
Import Export
Media: 1-2-4-10-11-26
Distr.: Intl.; Natl.
Budget Set: Sept.
Personnel:
Rob Lane *(Gen Mgr)*
Ed Keenan *(Reg Mgr-Sales-Southeastern)*
Roger McCardell *(Reg Mgr-Sales-Northeastern)*
Austin Offutt *(Reg Mgr-Sales-Industrial Channel)*
Mark Rafalzik *(Reg Mgr-Sales-Central/ Western)*
Bill Drake *(Mgr-Sls National)*
Brands & Products:
AER-O-WATER
ALCOSEAL
CHEMICOIL
GLADIATOR
KNOCKDOWN
NATIONAL
RED ALERT
SERVO COMMAND
SMARTFLOW
SURFZONE 850
TERMINATOR
TERRA FOAM
UNIVERSAL

KILGORE FLARES
(Sub. of Chemring Group plc)
155 Kilgore Rd
Toone, TN 38381-7850
Tel.: (731) 658-5231
Fax: (731) 658-4173
Telex: 53-4446
E-mail: info@kilgoreflares.com
Web Site: www.kilgoreflares.com
Approx. Number Employees: 300
Business Description:
Mfr of Military & Commercial Flares & Pyrotechnics
S.I.C.: 3728; 2899
N.A.I.C.S.: 336413; 325998
Import Export
Media: 2-10-11
Distr.: Intl.; Natl.
Budget Set: Aug.
Personnel:
Chris Watt *(Pres)*
Bill Heinsohn *(Dir-Mktg)*
Brands & Products:
KILGORE FLARES

KOPPERS HOLDINGS INC.
436 7th Ave
Pittsburgh, PA 15219-1800
Tel.: (412) 227-2001
Fax: (412) 227-2333
Toll Free: (800) 321-9876
E-mail: investorrelations@koppers.com
Web Site: www.koppers.com
Approx. Sls.: $1,245,500,000
Approx. Number Employees: 575
Year Founded: 2004
Business Description:
Holding Company: Integrated Producer of Chemicals, Carbon Compounds, & Treated Wood Products for Various Industries
S.I.C.: 2819; 2491; 2821; 2861; 2865; 2895; 2899; 6289
N.A.I.C.S.: 325188; 321114; 325132; 325182; 325191; 325211; 325998; 523999
Advertising Expenditures: $100,000
Media: 2-10
Personnel:
David M. Hillenbrand *(Chm)*
Walter W. Turner *(Pres & CEO)*
Leroy M. Ball *(CFO & VP)*
Steven R. Lacy *(Gen Counsel, Sec & Sr VP-Admin)*
Thomas D. Loadman *(VP & Gen Mgr-Railroad Products & Svcs)*
Michael W. Snyder *(Dir-IR)*
Brands & Products:
ARCH
CP-POLY
FLASH-ON 441
GLASFAB
GLASSCOAT
GLASSFAB
HIGH-PEN PRIMER 452
HYDROSHIELD 451
JUTE
KFOAM
KOP-KLAD
KOP-R
KOPPERS
ONYX
PERLITE
TAR GLAS
U.F. MAT
Advertising Agency:
WordWrite Communications
10475 Perry Hwy Ste 104
Wexford, PA 15090
Tel.: (724) 935-7580
Fax: (724) 935-7808

KRAFT CHEMICAL COMPANY
1975 N Hawthorne Ave
Melrose Park, IL 60160
Tel.: (708) 345-5200
Fax: (708) 345-0761
Toll Free: (800) 345-5200
E-mail: salesinfo@kraftchemical.com
Web Site: www.kraftchemical.com
E-Mail For Key Personnel:
Sales Director: salesinfo@kraftchemical.com
Approx. Number Employees: 30
Year Founded: 1932
Business Description:
Chemical Coatings Supplier
S.I.C.: 5169
N.A.I.C.S.: 424690
Media: 10-13

Key to Media (For complete agency information see *The Advertising Red Books-Agencies* edition):
1. Bus. Publs. 2. Cable T.V. 3. Catalogs & Directories. 4. Co-op Adv. 5. Consumer Mags. 6. D.M. to Bus. Estab.7. D.M. to Consumers 8. Daily Newsp. 9. Exhibits/Trade Shows 10. Foreign 11. Infomercial 12. Internet Adv.13. Multimedia 14. Network Radio 15. Network T.V. 16. Newsp. Distr. Mags. 17. Other 18. Outdoor (Posters, Transit) 19. Point of Purchase20. Premiums, Novelties 21. Product Samples 22. Special Events Mktg. 23. Spot Radio 24. Spot T.V. 25. Weekly Newsp. 26. Yellow Page Adv.

Kraft Chemical Company — (Continued)

Personnel:
Rick Kraft *(Pres)*
Kathleen Barth *(Gen Mgr)*
Jerry Planek *(Mgr-Sls)*

KUEHNE CHEMICAL COMPANY, INC.

86 N Hackensack Ave
Kearny, NJ 07032
Tel.: (973) 589-0700
Fax: (973) 589-4866
Web Site: www.kuehnecompany.com
Approx. Number Employees: 200
Year Founded: 1919
Business Description:
Mfr. of Industrial Inorganic Chemicals
S.I.C.: 2819; 7389
N.A.I.C.S.: 325188; 561910
Import Export
Media: 13

KYANITE MINING CORPORATION

30 Willis Mtn Ln
Dillwyn, VA 23936
Mailing Address:
PO Box 486
Dillwyn, VA 23936-0486
Tel.: (434) 983-2085
Fax: (434) 983-5178
E-mail: info@kyanite.com
Web Site: www.kyanite.com
E-Mail For Key Personnel:
President: guydixon@kyanite.com
Sales Director: hankjamerson@kyanite.com
Approx. Number Employees: 150
Year Founded: 1932
Business Description:
Refractory/Ceramic Additives; Kyanite & Mullite
S.I.C.: 1459
N.A.I.C.S.: 212325
Export
Media: 2-4-5-6-7-8-9-10-11-16-17-19-20-21
Distr.: Intl.; Natl.
Budget Set: Mar.
Personnel:
Guy B. Dixon *(Pres & Gen Mgr)*
Dilip C. Jain *(VP-Tech & Asia Sls)*
Hank Jamerson *(VP-Sls & Mktg)*
John R. Snoddy *(Dir-Dimensional Stone Dept)*
Lakshmi Bertram *(Mgr-HR)*

LA-CO INDUSTRIES MARKAL CO., INC.

1201 Pratt Blvd
Elk Grove Village, IL 60007
Tel.: (847) 956-7600
Fax: (847) 956-9885
Toll Free: (800) 621-4025
E-mail: customer_service@laco.com
Web Site: www.laco.com
Approx. Number Employees: 112
Year Founded: 1934
Business Description:
Plumbing Chemicals & Supplies Mfr
S.I.C.: 2899; 2891
N.A.I.C.S.: 325998; 325520
Import Export
Advertising Expenditures: $300,000
Media: 2-7-8-10-20-21-22-24-25
Distr.: Natl.
Budget Set: Nov. -Dec.
Personnel:
Dan Kleiman *(Chm & CEO)*
John Hardin *(Pres)*
Brands & Products:
ALERT
BALL PAINT MARKER
BLOC-IT
COOL GEL
DURA-BALL
DURA-INK
E-Z BREAK
EPOXY-STIK
EPOXY-TAB
EZ-BREAK
FAST
FLUX-RITE
FLUX-RITE 90
HEAT-SEAL STIK
KRAK STIK
LA-CO
LA-CO BRITE
LACQUER-STIK
LEAK-TITE
LIFTER
LOC
LUBRI-JOINT
OXYTITE
OYLTITE-STIK
PAINTSTIK
PIERCE
PIPETITE
PIPETITE-STIK
PLASTO-JOINT STIK
PLUMBSET
PRO-EX
PRO-LINE
PRO-MAX
PROVEN EVERYDAY // PROVEN EVERYWHERE
QUIK STIK
RED-RITER
RUST BUSTER
SCAN-IT
SCAN-IT PLUS
SILVER-STREAK
SLIC-TITE
SOLDER BRITE
SURE-CHEK
SWEATIN' FLUX
T-O-T
THERMOMELT
TRADES
TRADES MARKER
TYRE MARQUE
ULTIMATE
VALVE ACTION
VISU-GLOW
ZOOM SPOUT
Advertising Agency:
Marketing Support, Inc.
200 E Randolph Dr Ste 5000
Chicago, IL 60601
Tel.: (312) 565-0044
Fax: (312) 946-6100

LANDA WATER CLEANING SYSTEMS

(Sub. of C-Tech Industries)
4275 NW Pacific Rim Blvd
Camas, WA 98607
Tel.: (360) 833-9100
Fax: (360) 833-9200
Toll Free: (800) 547-8672
Toll Free: (800) 526-3248
E-mail: info@karcherna.com
Web Site: www.karcherna.com
Sales Range: $50-74.9 Million
Approx. Number Employees: 300
Year Founded: 1969
Business Description:
Industrial Pressure Washers & Water Cleaning Systems Mfr
S.I.C.: 3589; 7359
N.A.I.C.S.: 333319; 532490
Import
Advertising Expenditures: $50,000
Media: 4-7-10-13-18-19-20
Distr.: Intl.
Budget Set: Dec.
Personnel:
Elliot Younessian *(CEO)*
Brands & Products:
BUCKSHOT
COMMANDO SERIES
DYNA-MIGHT
HARD DRIVE
HBE SERIES
HBG SERIES
HYPER DRIVE
INTERFACE
LAZERWASH
NOVA
REBEL WASH
RESPONSE
SJ-10
SJ-15
SJ-350
SUPER NOVA
WATER BLAZE
WB SERIES

LINDE GAS NORTH AMERICA LLC

(Sub. of Linde AG - Gases Division)
6055 Rockside Woods Blvd
Independence, OH 44131
Mailing Address:
PO Box 94737
Cleveland, OH 44101-4737
Tel.: (216) 642-6600
Fax: (216) 642-8516
Toll Free: (800) 4AGAGAS
Web Site: www.agagas.com
Approx. Number Employees: 160
Year Founded: 1978
Business Description:
Industrial Gases & Welding Products Mfr
S.I.C.: 3548
N.A.I.C.S.: 333992
Import Export
Advertising Expenditures: $1,000,000
Media: 2-4-7-10-26
Distr.: Reg.
Budget Set: Sept.
Personnel:
Patrick F. Murphy *(Pres & CEO)*
Brands & Products:
AGA
GRYO STACK

LIPO CHEMICALS INC.

207 19th Ave
Paterson, NJ 07504
Tel.: (973) 345-8600
Fax: (973) 345-8365
Web Site: www.lipochemicals.com
E-Mail For Key Personnel:
Marketing Director: salesandmarketing@lipochemicals.com
Sales Director: salesandmarketing@lipochemicals.com
Approx. Number Employees: 100
Year Founded: 1962
Business Description:
Industrial Organic Chemical Mfr & Distr
S.I.C.: 2869
N.A.I.C.S.: 325199
Media: 2-10-13
Personnel:
Joseph Carloto *(CFO)*
Chris Humberstone *(Exec VP)*
Caren Dres-Hajeski *(Dir-Mktg)*
Steven Richards *(Dir-Sls-North America)*
Brands & Products:
GORGONIAN EXTRACT
HYPAN
LIPAMIDE
LIPO
LIPO CD
LIPO POLYGLYCOL
LIPOBEAD
LIPOBRITE
LIPOBRONZE
LIPOCAPSULE
LIPOCARE
LIPOCOL
LIPODERMA
LIPOLAN
LIPOLIGHT
LIPOMIC
LIPOMULSE
LIPONATE
LIPONIC
LIPONYL
LIPOPEARL
LIPOPEG
LIPOQUAT
LIPOSATIN
LIPOSCRUB
LIPOSERVE
LIPOSILT
LIPOSORB
LIPOSPHERE
LIPOTHIX
LIPOVOL
LIPOWAX
PERSEA BUTTER
POLYTEX

LITTLE FALLS ALLOYS, INC.

171-191 Caldwell Ave
Paterson, NJ 07501
Tel.: (973) 278-1666
Fax: (973) 278-7345
Toll Free: (888) LFAWIRE
E-mail: info@lfawire.com
Web Site: www.lfawire.com
Approx. Number Employees: 28
Year Founded: 1943
Business Description:
Producer of Non-Ferrous Wire
S.I.C.: 3351; 3496
N.A.I.C.S.: 331421; 332618
Export
Media: 2-4-7-10-17-26
Distr.: Natl.
Personnel:
James Sacco *(Pres)*
Orlando P. Veltri *(CFO)*
Jim Dolan *(Dir-Adv)*
Tara Bash *(Mgr-Acctg)*
Brands & Products:
AMZIRC
LFA
Advertising Agency:
James Dolan Advertising
463 Is Rd

Key to Media (For complete agency information see *The Advertising Red Books-Agencies* edition):
1. Bus. Publs. 2. Cable T.V. 3. Catalogs & Directories. 4. Co-op Adv. 5. Consumer Mags. 6. D.M. to Bus. Estab.7. D.M. to Consumers
8. Daily Newsp. 9. Exhibits/Trade Shows 10. Foreign 11. Infomercial 12. Internet Adv.13. Multimedia 14. Network Radio
15. Network T.V. 16. Newsp. Distr. Mags. 17. Other 18. Outdoor (Posters, Transit) 19. Point of Purchase20. Premiums, Novelties
21. Product Samples 22. Special Events Mktg. 23. Spot Radio 24. Spot T.V. 25. Weekly Newsp. 26. Yellow Page Adv.

Ramsey, NJ 07446
Tel.: (201) 934-7795
Fax: (201) 825-3760

LOCKHART COMPANY
2873 W Hardies Rd
Gibsonia, PA 15044
Tel.: (724) 444-1900
Fax: (724) 444-1919
E-Mail For Key Personnel:
Sales Director: sales@lockhartchem.com
Approx. Number Employees: 70
Year Founded: 1972
Business Description:
Surface Protection Technologies
S.I.C.: 2819; 8733
N.A.I.C.S.: 325188; 541710
Export
Media: 2-4-7
Distr.: Natl.
Budget Set: Sept.
Personnel:
Thomas J. Gillespie, Jr. *(Chm, Pres & CEO)*
Raj Minhas *(Pres & COO)*

LONZA INC.
(Sub. of Lonza Group Ltd.)
90 Boroline Rd
Allendale, NJ 07401-1613
Tel.: (201) 316-9200
Fax: (201) 785-9973
Telex: 475-4539
E-mail: contact.allendale@lonza.com
Web Site: www.lonza.com
Approx. Number Employees: 160
Year Founded: 1969
Business Description:
Mfr, Marketer & Retailer of Organic & Fine Chemicals, Performance Chemicals, Plastics & Inorganics
S.I.C.: 2899; 2869
N.A.I.C.S.: 325998; 325199
Import Export
Advertising Expenditures: $1,000,000
Media: 2-4-6-10-11-13-20
Distr.: Natl.
Personnel:
Jeanne Thoma *(Head-Microbial Control & Pres)*
Brands & Products:
ACRAWAX C
ALDO
ALKAWET
AMPHOTERGE
BARDAC
BARDAC-22
BARLOX
BARQUAT/HYAMINE 3500
BARQUAT/UNIQUAT
BIO GENTLE
BIOSURF
CARSOQUAT
DANTOBROM
DANTOCHLOR
DANTOGARD
DANTOGARD PLUS
DANTOGARD PLUS LIQUID
GLYCOLUBE
GLYCON
GLYCOSPERSE
GLYCOSTAT
GLYCOWAX
GLYDANT
GLYDANT PLUS
GLYDANT PLUS LIQUID
GLYTEX
HYAMINE 1622
ISOCIL
LONZABAC-12
LONZABAC-4
LONZACURE
LONZAMONE
LONZEST143-S
PEGOSPERSE
POLYALDO
PRIMASET
UNIHIB
VINYLUBE

LSB INDUSTRIES, INC.
16 S Pennsylvania Ave
Oklahoma City, OK 73107-7024
Mailing Address:
PO Box 754
Oklahoma City, OK 73101-0754
Tel.: (405) 235-4546
Fax: (405) 235-5067
E-mail: info@lsb-okc.com
Web Site: www.lsb-okc.com
Approx. Sls.: $609,905,000
Approx. Number Employees: 1,780
Year Founded: 1968
Business Description:
Diversified Holding Company; Mfr & Marketer of Chemicals, Pumps & Climate Control Products
S.I.C.: 6719; 1321; 2816; 2819; 2873; 2899; 3561; 3594; 5169
N.A.I.C.S.: 551112; 211112; 325131; 325188; 325311; 325998; 333911; 333996; 424690
Advertising Expenditures: $5,915,000
Personnel:
Jack E. Golsen *(Founder, Chm & CEO)*
Barry H. Golsen *(Vice Chm, Pres & Pres-Climate Control Bus)*
Tony M. Shelby *(CFO)*
David M. Shear *(Sr VP & Gen Counsel)*
David R. Goss *(Exec VP)*
Brands & Products:
CLIMATEMASTER
INTERNATIONAL ENVIRONMENTAL
LSB INDUSTRIES

THE LUBRIZOL CORPORATION
29400 Lakeland Blvd
Wickliffe, OH 44092-2298
Tel.: (440) 943-4200
Fax: (440) 943-5337
Telex: 980520
E-mail: investor.relations@lubrizol.com
Web Site: www.lubrizol.com
Approx. Rev.: $5,417,800,000
Approx. Number Employees: 6,900
Year Founded: 1928
Business Description:
Lubricant & Fuel Additive Mfr
S.I.C.: 2869; 2899; 5169
N.A.I.C.S.: 325199; 325998; 424690
Import Export
Media: 1-2-4-10-11-20
Distr.: Intl.
Budget Set: Dec.
Personnel:
James L. Hambrick *(Chm, Pres & CEO)*
Charles P. Cooley *(CFO & Sr VP)*
Stephen F. Kirk *(COO & Sr VP)*
Jeffrey A. Vavruska *(Chief Tax Officer)*
Eric R. Schnur *(Pres-Advanced Matls & Corp VP)*
Daniel L. Sheets *(Pres-Additives & Corp VP)*
Julian M. Steinberg *(COO-Lubrizol Advanced Materials & Sr VP)*
Joseph W. Bauer *(Gen Counsel & VP)*
Mark W. Meister *(Corp VP-HR)*
Gregory D. Taylor *(Corp VP-Corp Strategy, Dev & Comm)*
James S. Baldwin *(Dir-Comm-Global)*
Melanie Bingham *(Dir-HR-Advanced Matls)*
Mark Sutherland *(Dir-IR)*
Julie S. Young *(Dir-Corp Comm)*
David L. Cowen *(Mgr-Pub Affairs)*
Terry Pacifico *(Mgr-Creative Ops & Comm)*
Brands & Products:
ADEX
AMPS
ANGLAMOL
BLAZEMASTER
CARBOPOL
CARBOSPERSE
CORZAN
ESTANE
FBC
FLOWGUARD
FLOWGUARD GOLD
IRCOGEL
ISOPLAST
LUBRIZOL
NOVEON
PELLETHANE
PEMULEN
RHEORANGER
SENSIMAP
SKYTHANE
TEMPRITE
THERMEDICS
Advertising Agencies:
The Arras Group
Terminal Tower Ste 444 50 Public Sq
Cleveland, OH 44113
Tel.: (216) 621-1601
Fax: (216) 377-1919

Dix & Eaton Incorporated
200 Public Sq Ste 1400
Cleveland, OH 44114
Tel.: (216) 241-0405
Fax: (216) 241-3070
(Additives for Lubricants & Fuels)

LUSTER-ON PRODUCTS, INC.
54 Waltham Ave
Springfield, MA 01109-3335
Mailing Address:
PO Box 90247
Springfield, MA 01139-0247
Tel.: (413) 739-2541
Fax: (413) 731-5549
Toll Free: (800) 888-2541
E-mail: sales@luster-on.com
Web Site: www.luster-on.com
E-Mail For Key Personnel:
Sales Director: sales@luster-on.com
Approx. Sls.: $5,000,000
Approx. Number Employees: 25
Year Founded: 1969
Business Description:
Metal Finishing Products Mfr & Distr
S.I.C.: 2899; 5084
N.A.I.C.S.: 325998; 423830
Import Export
Media: 2-10-13-14
Distr.: Direct to Consumer; Natl.
Budget Set: Oct.
Personnel:
Alexander J. Price *(Pres)*
Brands & Products:
LUSTER-FLOC
LUSTER-FOS
LUSTER-ON

LUVATA BUFFALO, INC.
(Sub. of Luvata Oy)
70 Sayre St
Buffalo, NY 14207
Mailing Address:
PO Box 981
Buffalo, NY 14240-0981
Tel.: (716) 879-6700
Fax: (716) 879-6735
Web Site: www.luvata.com
Approx. Number Employees: 650
Year Founded: 1920
Business Description:
Copper & Copper Alloy Sheet, Strip & Tube Mfr
S.I.C.: 3351
N.A.I.C.S.: 331421
Import Export
Advertising Expenditures: $250,000
Media: 10-21
Distr.: Intl.; Natl.
Budget Set: Oct.
Personnel:
Todd Heusner *(VP-Mktg & Sls)*
Brad Groff *(Gen Mgr-Sls-Mktg)*
Ray Mercer *(GM-Production)*

MACDERMID, INC.
(Joint Venture of Weston Presidio Capital & Court Square Capital Partners, L.P.)
1401 Blake St
Denver, CO 80202
Tel.: (720) 479-3060
Fax: (720) 479-3087
E-mail: corpinfo@macdermid.com
Web Site: www.macdermid.com
Approx. Sls.: $817,609,000
Approx. Number Employees: 2,500
Year Founded: 1922
Business Description:
Mfr & Retailer of Specialty Chemicals for Electronics & Metal Finishing Markets & Polymer Resins & Compounds
S.I.C.: 5162; 2842; 2899
N.A.I.C.S.: 424610; 325612; 325998
Import Export
Advertising Expenditures: $800,000
Media: 1-2-4-10-17
Distr.: Intl.
Personnel:
Mark R. Hollinger *(Pres)*
Daniel H. Leever *(CEO)*
Frank Monterio *(CFO & Sr VP)*
John L. Cordani *(Gen Counsel)*
Brands & Products:
AQUA MER
ELIMINATOR
MACSTAN
MACUSPEC
MICROTRACE
MULTIBOND
MULTIPREP
STANTEK
STERLING
ULTRA ETCH
ULTRASTRIP

MACE SECURITY INTERNATIONAL, INC.
240 Gibraltar Rd Ste 220
Horsham, PA 19044
Tel.: (267) 317-4009
Fax: (215) 672-8900
E-mail: info@mace.com
Web Site: www.mace.com
Approx. Rev.: $18,395,000
Approx. Number Employees: 197
Year Founded: 1993
Business Description:
Security Products Mfr & Distr; Digital Media Marketing Services; Car Wash Operator
S.I.C.: 7382; 5961; 7542; 8742
N.A.I.C.S.: 561621; 454111; 454113; 541613; 811192
Advertising Expenditures: $513,400
Media: 2-4-10-13-20
Personnel:
John C. Mallon *(Chm)*
Dennis R. Raefield *(Pres & CEO)*
Gregory M. Krzemien *(CFO & Treas)*
Ron Gdovic *(Pres-Digital Media & Mktg Div)*
Steve Rolley *(Controller & Dir-Fin Reporting)*
Brands & Products:
BEAR PEPPER SPRAY
BIG JAMMER
EASY WATCH
INDUSTRIAL VISION SOURCE
IRONCLAD
JAMMERS
KINDERGARD
MACE
MAGNUM MACE
MICHIGAN FORMULA
MUZZLE
MUZZLE CANINE
OBSERVISION
OFF DUTY
PEPPER
PEPPER GEL
PEPPER MACE
PEPPER SPRAY
PEPPERGARD
PROTECTITNOW!
SCREECHER
SECURITYANDMORE
SMARTCHOICE
SUPER BRIGHT
TAKEDOWN
TG GUARD
TRIPLE ACTION
VIPER
WISCONSIN FORMULA

MALCO PRODUCTS, INC.
361 Fairview Ave
Barberton, OH 44203
Tel.: (330) 753-0361
Fax: (330) 753-2025
Toll Free: (800) 253-2526
E-mail: sales@malcopro.com
Web Site: www.malcopro.com
E-Mail For Key Personnel:
Sales Director: sales@malcopro.com
Approx. Number Employees: 300
Year Founded: 1953
Business Description:
Chemical Specialty Product Mfr, Packager & Marketer
S.I.C.: 2842; 8742
N.A.I.C.S.: 325612; 541613
Import Export
Media: 2-4-6-9-10-14-18-19-20-21-23-25-26
Distr.: Natl.
Budget Set: Oct.
Personnel:
Stuart Glauberman *(Pres)*
Mike Strick *(CFO)*
Patricia Doyle *(Dir-Mktg)*
Rebeca Korwin *(Dir-Tech)*
Brands & Products:
CONQUEST
MALCO
MALCO PRODUCTS
WHIZ

MALLINCKRODT BAKER INC.
(Name Changed to Avantor Performance Materials, Inc.)

MASTER BOND INC.
154 Hobart St
Hackensack, NJ 07601
Tel.: (201) 343-8983
Fax: (201) 343-2132
E-mail: main@masterbond.com
Web Site: www.masterbond.com
Approx. Number Employees: 25
Year Founded: 1976
Business Description:
Adhesives, Sealants & Coatings Mfr & Retailer
S.I.C.: 2891; 2851
N.A.I.C.S.: 325520; 325510
Media: 2-13
Personnel:
Walter Brenner *(Dir-Technical)*
James Brenner *(Mgr-Mktg)*
Brands & Products:
EP21HT
EP31
SUPREME 10HT
SUPREME 11F
SUPREME 3HTND-2GT
UV15-7LRI

MASTER SILICON CARBIDE INDUSTRIES, INC.
558 Lime Rock Rd
Lakeville, CT 06039
Tel.: (860) 435-7000
Approx. Rev.: $12,948,096
Approx. Number Employees: 365
Year Founded: 2007
Business Description:
Silicon Carbide Mfr & Sales
S.I.C.: 2895; 5169
N.A.I.C.S.: 325182; 424690
Advertising Expenditures: $66,525
Media: 17
Personnel:
John Douglas Kuhns *(Chm, Pres & CEO)*
Lin Han *(CFO)*
Mary E. Fellows *(Sec & Exec VP)*

MAYS CHEMICAL COMPANY
5611 E 71st St
Indianapolis, IN 46220-3920
Tel.: (317) 842-8722
Fax: (317) 576-9630
Web Site: www.mayschem.com
Sales Range: $200-249.9 Million
Approx. Number Employees: 165
Year Founded: 1980
Business Description:
Distributor of Industrial Chemicals
S.I.C.: 5169; 8741
N.A.I.C.S.: 424690; 561110
Import Export
Media: 2-4-7-10-13-18-22-26
Personnel:
William G. Mays *(Pres & CEO)*

MCGEAN-ROHCO, INC.
(d/b/a McGean)
2910 Harvard Ave
Cleveland, OH 44105
Tel.: (216) 441-4900
Fax: (216) 441-1377
Toll Free: (800) 932-7006
E-mail: info@mcgean.com
Web Site: www.mcgean.com
Approx. Number Employees: 50
Year Founded: 1929
Business Description:
Chemical Mfr
S.I.C.: 2899; 2819
N.A.I.C.S.: 325998; 325188
Media: 7-10-13-21
Distr.: Natl.
Budget Set: Sept.
Personnel:
Dickson L. Whitney *(Chm, Pres & CEO)*
Kerry H. May *(CFO)*
Brands & Products:
CEE-BEE
ECO TRU
HONEY BEE
HONEY-BEE
INTEX
MCGEAN
MET-L-CHEK
NORTEX
SUPER BEE
Advertising Agency:
Detrow & Underwood
12 W Main St
Ashland, OH 44805-2218
Tel.: (419) 289-0265
Fax: (419) 289-3390
(Plating, Cleaning, Phospating, Metalworking & Waste Treatment Markets)

MCINTYRE GROUP, LTD.
(Sub. of Rhodia S.A.)
24601 Governors Hwy
University Park, IL 60466-4127
Tel.: (708) 534-6200
Fax: (708) 534-6216
Toll Free: (800) 645-6457
E-mail: info@mcintyregroup.com
Web Site: www.mcintyregroup.com
Approx. Sls.: $146,000,000
Approx. Number Employees: 200
Year Founded: 1974
Business Description:
Specialty Cleaning Surfactants Mfr
S.I.C.: 2843; 2899
N.A.I.C.S.: 325613; 325998
Media: 2-4-10-13-21
Personnel:
William McIntyre *(Chm)*
John Kennedy *(Mgr-Supply Chain)*
Brands & Products:
MACKADET
MACKALENE
MACKAM
MACKAMIDE
MACKAMINE
MACKANATE
MACKAZOLINE
MACKCONDITIONER
MACKERNIUM
MACKESTER
MACKINE
MACKOL
MACKPEARL
MACKPRO
MACKSTAT
MCINTYRE
PARAGON
PHENAGON

MERICHEM COMPANY
5455 Old Spanish Trl
Houston, TX 77024
Tel.: (713) 428-5100
Fax: (713) 921-4604
E-mail: jmarroquin@merichem.com
Web Site: www.merichem.com
Approx. Number Employees: 450
Year Founded: 1945
Business Description:
Mfr of Industrial Chemicals & Licensing & Fabricating of Proprietary Technology
S.I.C.: 2869; 2819
N.A.I.C.S.: 325199; 325188
Advertising Expenditures: $400,000
Media: 2-10
Personnel:
Kenneth F. Currie *(CEO)*
Bruce D. Upshaw *(CFO & Sr VP)*
Brands & Products:
MERICHEM

MILLER-STEPHENSON CHEMICAL COMPANY, INC.
George Washington Hwy
Danbury, CT 06813
Tel.: (203) 743-4447
Fax: (203) 791-8702
E-mail: ct.sales@miller-stephenson.com
Web Site: www.miller-stephenson.com
Approx. Number Employees: 50
Year Founded: 1955
Business Description:
Supplier of High Purity Chemicals
S.I.C.: 2842; 2821
N.A.I.C.S.: 325612; 325211
Media: 2-4-7-8-10-13
Personnel:
George M. Stephenson *(Founder & Pres)*
Bob Wilcox *(Mgr-Mktg)*
Brands & Products:
AERO-DUSTER
AERODUSTER
ANCAMINE
CAB-O-SIL
CARDURA
CLEANER PLUS
COBRA
CONTACT RE-NU
ECO-CRYL
EPI-CURE
EPI-REZ
EPONEX
EPONOL
HELOXY
MS
NOVOLAC
PLEXIGLAS
QUIK-FREEZE
RE-NU
VITON

Key to Media (For complete agency information see *The Advertising Red Books-Agencies* edition):
1. Bus. Publs. 2. Cable T.V. 3. Catalogs & Directories. 4. Co-op Adv. 5. Consumer Mags. 6. D.M. to Bus. Estab.7. D.M. to Consumers 8. Daily Newsp. 9. Exhibits/Trade Shows 10. Foreign 11. Infomercial 12. Internet Adv.13. Multimedia 14. Network Radio 15. Network T.V. 16. Newsp. Distr. Mags. 17. Other 18. Outdoor (Posters, Transit) 19. Point of Purchase20. Premiums, Novelties 21. Product Samples 22. Special Events Mktg. 23. Spot Radio 24. Spot T.V. 25. Weekly Newsp. 26. Yellow Page Adv.

Advertising Agency:
Miller-Stephenson Chemical Co.
George Washington Hwy
Danbury, CT 06810
Tel.: (203) 743-4447
Fax: (203) 791-8702

THE MISTRAL INC.
7910 Woodmont Ave Ste 820
Bethesda, MD 20814
Tel.: (301) 913-9366
Fax: (301) 913-9369
E-mail: webmaster@mistralgroup.com
Web Site: www.mistralgroup.com
Approx. Number Employees: 20
Year Founded: 1988
Business Description:
Turnkey Solutions for Buyers of Industrial, Defense & Security Products
S.I.C.: 3728; 3764
N.A.I.C.S.: 336413; 336415
Media: 13
Personnel:
Eyal Banai *(Owner)*
Jack Yohe *(Sr VP)*
Roey Bahat *(Dir-Mktg)*
Robert Koren *(Mgr-Intl)*
Arkadi Kolodkin *(Engineer)*

MITSUI CHEMICALS AMERICA, INC.
(Sub. of Mitsui Chemicals, Inc.)
800 Westchester Ave Ste N607
Rye Brook, NY 10573
Tel.: (914) 253-0777
Fax: (914) 253-0790
E-mail: info@mitsuichem.com
Web Site: www.mitsuichemicals.com
Approx. Number Employees: 35
Year Founded: 1997
Business Description:
Chemical Products & Plastics Developer & Mfr
S.I.C.: 2899
N.A.I.C.S.: 325998
Media: 10
Personnel:
Jennifer Giuliano *(Mgr-Corp Mktg)*

MOHAWK FINISHING PRODUCTS, INC.
(Sub. of RPM Consumer Holding Co.)
22 S Ctr St PO Box 535414
Hickory, NC 28602
Mailing Address:
PO Box 22000
Hickory, NC 28603-0220
Tel.: (828) 261-0325
Fax: (800) 721-1545
Toll Free: (800) 545-0047
E-mail: info@mohawk-finishing.com
Web Site: www.mohawk-finishing.com
Sales Range: $75-99.9 Million
Approx. Number Employees: 190
Year Founded: 1948
Business Description:
Wood, Metal & Vinyl Substrates Repair Products Mfr
S.I.C.: 2851; 5072
N.A.I.C.S.: 325510; 423710
Media: 4-10
Personnel:
Renee Webb *(Dir-Sls Plng, Mktg & Customer Svc)*

Brands & Products:
BLENDAL STICKS
DURACOAT
E-Z VINYL
ULTRA CLEAR
ULTRA WHITE
VERSACLAD
VERSALAC
WIPING WOOD

MOMENTIVE SPECIALTY CHEMICALS INC.
(Formerly Hexion Specialty Chemicals, Inc.)
(Sub. of Momentive Performance Materials Holdings LLC)
180 E Broad St
Columbus, OH 43215
Tel.: (614) 225-4000
Fax: (614) 225-4357
Web Site: www.hexion.com
Approx. Sls.: $4,818,000,000
Approx. Number Employees: 6,000
Year Founded: 1899
Business Description:
Industrial Chemical Mfr
S.I.C.: 2869; 2821
N.A.I.C.S.: 325199; 325211
Import Export
Media: 7-11-13
Personnel:
Craig O. Morrison *(Chm, Pres & CEO)*
Marvin O. Schlanger *(Vice Chm)*
Willaim H. Carter *(CFO & Exec VP)*
Joseph P. Bevilaqua *(Pres-Phenolic & Forest Product Resins & Exec VP)*
Mary Ann Jorgenson *(Gen Counsel & Exec VP)*
George F. Knight *(Treas & Sr VP-Fin)*
Nathan E. Fisher *(Exec VP-Global Procurement)*
Kevin W. McGuire *(Exec VP-Bus Processes & IT)*
Richard L. Monty *(Exec VP-Environ Health & Safety)*
Judith A. Sonnett *(Exec VP-HR)*
John Kompa *(Dir-IR)*
Brands & Products:
BAKELITE
BETASET
BORDEN
CARDURA
EPIKOTE
EPIKURE
EPON
FASKURE FT
LAWTER
PLASTISAND
SHAKE-FREE
SIGMA SAND
SUPER F
SUPER FII
VEOVA

MONSANTO COMPANY
800 N Lindbergh Blvd
Saint Louis, MO 63167
Tel.: (314) 694-1000
Fax: (314) 694-8394
E-mail: queries.media@monsanto.com
Web Site: www.monsanto.com
E-Mail For Key Personnel:
Public Relations: queries.media@monsanto.com
Approx. Sls.: $10,502,000,000
Approx. Number Employees: 21,400
Year Founded: 2000
Business Description:
Crop Protection Chemicals, Herbicide Products & Genetically-Altered Crop Seeds Mfr
S.I.C.: 2879; 0139; 5191
N.A.I.C.S.: 325320; 111998; 424910
Export
Advertising Expenditures: $59,000,000
Media: 2-4-15
Distr.: Intl.; Natl.
Budget Set: Sept.
Personnel:
Hugh Grant *(Chm, Pres & CEO)*
Pierre Courduroux *(CFO & Sr VP)*
Robert T. Fraley *(CTO & Exec VP)*
Brett D. Begemann *(Chief Comml Officer & Exec VP)*
David F. Snively *(Gen Counsel, Sec & Sr VP)*
Steven C. Mizell *(Exec VP-HR)*
Gerald A. Steiner *(Exec VP-Corp Affairs & Sustainability)*
Janet M. Holloway *(Sr VP & Chief-Staff-Community Rels)*
Kerry J. Preete *(Sr VP-Global Strategy)*
Mark Halton *(VP-Global Corp Mktg)*
Ruben Mella *(Dir-IR)*
Laura Meyer *(Dir-IR)*
Kathleen McAleenan *(Mgr-Global Mktg)*
Brands & Products:
AGRIPRO
AGROCERES
ANTHEM
AQUAMASTER
ASGROW
BOLLGARD
BOLLGARD II
CAMPAIGN
CERTAINTY
CHOICE GENETICS
DE RUITER
DEGREE
DEKALB
DEKALB CHOICE GENETICS
DELTAPINE
ENVIRO-CHEM
HARNESS
HARTZ
HOLDENS FOUNDATION SEEDS
IMAGINE
LASSO
LEADER
MAVERICK
MONITOR
MONSOY
NEWLEAF
OUTRIDER
PETOSEED
QUIKPRO
ROUNDUP
ROUNDUP PRO
ROUNDUP PRODRY
ROUNDUP READY
ROUNDUP READY 2 YIELD
ROYAL SLUIS
SEMINIS
SUNDANCE
VISTIVE
YIELDGARD
YIELDGARD VT
Advertising Agency:
Osborn & Barr Communications
Cupples Sta 914 Spruce St
Saint Louis, MO 63102
Tel.: (314) 726-5511
Fax: (314) 726-6350
Toll Free: (800) 666-1765
Toll Free: (888) BELIEF-2

MONTELLO, INC.
6106 E 32 Pl Ste 100
Tulsa, OK 74135
Tel.: (918) 665-1170
Fax: (918) 665-1480
Toll Free: (800) 331-4628
E-mail: call@montelloinc.com
Web Site: www.montelloinc.com
Approx. Number Employees: 5
Year Founded: 1957
Business Description:
Oilfield Products & Chemical Products Mfr
S.I.C.: 2899; 2869
N.A.I.C.S.: 325998; 325199
Media: 2-10
Personnel:
Allen Johnson *(Pres)*
Brands & Products:
HME ENERGIZER
MON PAC
MON PAC ULTRA LO

MULTICHEM, INC.
(Sub. of Unipex Group Inc.)
1570 Rue Ampere Ste 106
Boucherville, QC J4B 7L4, Canada
Tel.: (450) 449-6363
Fax: (450) 449-5280
Toll Free: (877) 230-4156
E-mail: info@multichem.ca
Web Site: www.multichem.ca
Approx. Number Employees: 30
Year Founded: 1985
Business Description:
Chemical Distr
S.I.C.: 5169
N.A.I.C.S.: 424690
Media: 2
Personnel:
Bernard Vinet *(VP-Fin & Admin)*
Jean-Pierre Pelchat *(Bus Unit Mgr-Indus Chemicals)*
Mario Marceau *(Product Mgr)*

NACCO INDUSTRIES, INC.
5875 Landerbrook Dr
Mayfield Heights, OH 44124-4017
Tel.: (440) 449-9600
Fax: (440) 449-9607
E-mail: ir@naccoind.com
Web Site: www.nacco.com
Approx. Rev.: $2,687,500,000
Approx. Number Employees: 5,000
Year Founded: 1913
Business Description:
Holding Company; Coal Mining, Materials Handling Equipment, Portable Electric Appliances, Retail Kitchenware
S.I.C.: 5084; 3499; 3537; 3634; 5722
N.A.I.C.S.: 423830; 332439; 333924; 335211; 443111
Import Export
Advertising Expenditures: $15,600,000
Media: 2-5-7
Personnel:
Alfred Marshall Rankin, Jr. *(Chm, Pres & CEO)*
Charles A. Bittenbender *(Gen Counsel, Sec & VP)*

NACCO Industries, Inc. — (Continued)

Mary D. Maloney *(Asst Sec & Asst Gen Counsel)*
Suzanne S. Taylor *(Asst Sec & Asst Gen Counsel)*
Brands & Products:
HYSTER
NACCO INDUSTRIES,INC.
YALE
Advertising Agency:
Dix & Eaton Incorporated
200 Public Sq Ste 1400
Cleveland, OH 44114
Tel.: (216) 241-0405
Fax: (216) 241-3070

NALCO CO.

(Sub. of Nalco Holding Company)
1601 W Diehl Rd
Naperville, IL 60563-1198
Tel.: (630) 305-1000
Fax: (630) 305-2900
Toll Free: (800) 288-0879
Web Site: www.nalco.com
Sales Range: $700-749.9 Million
Approx. Number Employees: 1,000
Year Founded: 1928
Business Description:
Chemicals & Services for Water Treatment, Pollution Control, Papermaking, Energy Conservation, Oil Production & Refining, Steelmaking, Metalworking & Other Industrial Processes
S.I.C.: 2899; 2992
N.A.I.C.S.: 325998; 324191
Import Export
Advertising Expenditures: $500,000
Media: 2-7-10-17
Distr.: Natl.
Budget Set: Sept.
Personnel:
Erik J. Fyrwald *(Chm & CEO)*
Mary Manupella *(VP-HR)*
Laurie Marsh *(VP-HR)*

NANOPHASE TECHNOLOGIES CORPORATION

1319 Marquette Dr
Romeoville, IL 60446-4055
Tel.: (630) 771-6700
Tel.: (630) 771-6708
Fax: (630) 771-0825
E-mail: investor-relations@nanophase.com
Web Site: www.nanophase.com
E-Mail For Key Personnel:
Sales Director: sales@nanophase.com
Approx. Rev.: $9,461,184
Approx. Number Employees: 49
Year Founded: 1980
Business Description:
Nanocrystalline Materials Developer for Advanced Materials Technology
S.I.C.: 3339
N.A.I.C.S.: 331419
Media: 10
Personnel:
Donald S. Perkins *(Chm)*
Jess A. Jankowski *(Pres & CEO)*
Frank Cesario *(CFO)*
David W. Nelson *(VP-Sls & Mktg)*
Nancy Baldwin *(Dir-HR & IT)*
Brands & Products:
NANOARC
NANODUR
NANOGARD
NANOPHASE
NANOSHIELD
NANOTEK
WE MAKE NANOTECHNOLOGY WORK!

NARCHEM CORPORATION

3800 W 38th St
Chicago, IL 60632
Tel.: (773) 376-8666
Fax: (773) 376-8932
Toll Free: (800) 458-1057
E-mail: info@narchem.com
Web Site: www.narchem.com
Approx. Number Employees: 10
Year Founded: 1984
Business Description:
Contract Chemical Research & Development for the Pharmaceutical Industry
S.I.C.: 8733
N.A.I.C.S.: 541720
Media: 4-10
Brands & Products:
NARCHEM

NCH CORPORATION

2727 Chemsearch Blvd
Irving, TX 75062-6454
Tel.: (972) 438-0211
Fax: (972) 438-0707
E-mail: webmaster@nch.com
Web Site: www.nch.com
Sales Range: $650-699.9 Million
Approx. Number Employees: 6,500
Year Founded: 1919
Business Description:
Chemical & Maintenance Specialties, Industrial Fasteners, Welding Equipment, Replacement Plumbing
S.I.C.: 2842; 2899
N.A.I.C.S.: 325612; 325998
Advertising Expenditures: $400,000
Media: 2-7
Distr.: Intl.; Natl.
Budget Set: Oct.
Personnel:
Irvin L. Levy *(Chm)*
Lester A. Levy *(Exec VP)*
Brands & Products:
NCH

NEVILLE CHEMICAL COMPANY

2800 Neville Rd
Pittsburgh, PA 15225-1408
Tel.: (412) 331-4200
Fax: (412) 777-4234
Fax: (412) 771-0226
Toll Free: (877) 704-4200
E-mail: customerservice@nevchem.com
Web Site: www.nevchem.com
Approx. Number Employees: 250
Year Founded: 1925
Business Description:
Mfr of Resins & Plastic Products
S.I.C.: 2821; 2869
N.A.I.C.S.: 325211; 325199
Advertising Expenditures: $750,000
Media: 2-4-10-13
Distr.: Intl.; Natl.
Budget Set: Oct. -Nov.
Personnel:
L.V. Van Dauler, Jr. *(Chm)*
Thomas F. McKnight *(Pres & CEO)*
Louis Benvenuti *(Mgr-Mktg)*
Brands & Products:
AG-12-28
CUMAR
DERMULSENE
LX-1035
LX-105
LX-1082
LX-1122
LX-1127
LX-1144
LX-1200
LX-125
LX-130
LX-1314
LX-135
LX-2000
LX-2600
LX-270
LX-280
LX-685
LX-782
LX-830
LX-961
NEVAILLAC
NEVASTAIN
NEVCHEM
NEVEX
NEVILLAC
NEVILLE
NEVOXY
NEVPENE
NEVROZ
NEVTAC
NP-10
NP-25
PERMATAC
SUPER NEVTAC
VERSADIL

NEWPORT ADHESIVES & COMPOSITES, INC.

(Holding of Mitsubishi Rayon America Inc)
1822 Reynolds Ave
Irvine, CA 92614-5714
Tel.: (949) 253-5680
Fax: (949) 253-5692
Web Site: www.newportad.com
Approx. Number Employees: 130
Year Founded: 1978
Business Description:
Adhesives & Carbon Fiber Composites Producer & Retailer
S.I.C.: 2891; 2951
N.A.I.C.S.: 325520; 324121
Media: 2-7-10-21
Personnel:
Takahiro Ono *(VP-Sls)*
David Knapp *(Mgr-Marine Bus)*
Mike Pierce *(Mgr-Sls)*

NEXEN INC.

801 7th Avenue SW
Calgary, AB T2P 3P7, Canada
Tel.: (403) 699-4000
Fax: (403) 699-5800
E-mail: investor_relations@nexeninc.com
Web Site: www.nexeninc.com
Approx. Rev.: $5,701,789,680
Approx. Number Employees: 3,925
Year Founded: 1971
Business Description:
Diversified Energy & Chemical Services
S.I.C.: 1311
N.A.I.C.S.: 211111
Media: 10-13-22
Personnel:
Francis M. Saville *(Chm)*
Marvin F. Romanow *(Pres & CEO)*
Kevin J. Reinhart *(CFO & Exec VP)*
Eric B. Miller *(Gen Counsel, Sec & VP)*
Matt Fox *(Exec VP-Intl Oil & Gas)*
Gary H. Nieuwenburg *(Exec VP-Canada)*
Jim Arnold *(Sr VP-Synthetic Crude)*
Una M. Power *(Sr VP-Corp Plng & Bus)*
Catherine Hughes *(VP-Ops Svcs & Tech)*
Randy J. Jahrig *(VP-HR & Corp Svc)*
Doug Brennan *(Mgr-HR-Canada)*
Carla Yuill *(Mgr)*

NL INDUSTRIES, INC.

(Holding of Valhi, Inc.)
5430 LBJ Fwy
Dallas, TX 75240-2697
Tel.: (972) 233-1700
Fax: (972) 448-1445
Web Site: www.nl-ind.com
Approx. Sls.: $135,264,000
Approx. Number Employees: 3,268
Year Founded: 1891
Business Description:
Holding Company; Precision Ball Bearing Slides, Security Products & Ergonomic Computer Support Systems Mfr; Titanium Dioxide Pigments Producer & Marketer
S.I.C.: 2865; 2522; 2812; 2816; 2899; 3356; 3562; 5169; 6719; 7373
N.A.I.C.S.: 325132; 325131; 325181; 325998; 331491; 332991; 337214; 424690; 541512; 551112
Advertising Expenditures: $40,000
Media: 2-4-7-10-20-21
Distr.: Intl.; Natl.
Budget Set: Aug.
Personnel:
Harold C. Simmons *(Chm, Pres & CEO)*
Gregory M. Swalwell *(CFO & VP-Fin)*

NOAH TECHNOLOGIES CORPORATION

1 Noah Park
San Antonio, TX 78249-3419
Tel.: (210) 691-2000
Fax: (210) 691-2600
E-mail: sales@noahtech.com
Web Site: www.noahtech.com
E-Mail For Key Personnel:
Sales Director: sales@noahtech.com
Approx. Number Employees: 100
Year Founded: 1978
Business Description:
High Purity Inorganic Chemicals Mfr
S.I.C.: 2819; 2899
N.A.I.C.S.: 325188; 325998
Media: 2-10
Personnel:
Sonya Blumenthal *(Pres)*
Diane Milner *(Mgr-Mktg)*

NORMAN, FOX & CO.

5511 S Boyle Ave
Los Angeles, CA 90058-3932
Tel.: (323) 837-7400
Fax: (323) 837-7474
Toll Free: (800) 632-1777
E-mail: norfox@worldatt.att.net
Web Site: www.norfoxx.com
Approx. Number Employees: 50

Key to Media (For complete agency information see *The Advertising Red Books-Agencies* edition):
1. Bus. Publs. 2. Cable T.V. 3. Catalogs & Directories. 4. Co-op Adv. 5. Consumer Mags. 6. D.M. to Bus. Estab.7. D.M. to Consumers 8. Daily Newsp. 9. Exhibits/Trade Shows 10. Foreign 11. Infomercial 12. Internet Adv.13. Multimedia 14. Network Radio 15. Network T.V. 16. Newsp. Distr. Mags. 17. Other 18. Outdoor (Posters, Transit) 19. Point of Purchase20. Premiums, Novelties 21. Product Samples 22. Special Events Mktg. 23. Spot Radio 24. Spot T.V. 25. Weekly Newsp. 26. Yellow Page Adv.

Year Founded: 1971
Business Description:
Distributor of Specialty Chemicals, Soaps & Detergents
S.I.C.: 5169; 2841
N.A.I.C.S.: 424690; 325611
Media: 2-10
Brands & Products:
NORFOX

THE NORTH AMERICAN COAL CORPORATION

(Sub. of NACCO Industries, Inc.)
14785 Preston Rd Ste 1100
Dallas, TX 75254
Tel.: (972) 239-2625
Fax: (972) 387-1031
Web Site: www.nacoal.com
E-Mail For Key Personnel:
Marketing Director: mike.gregory@nacoal.com
Sales Range: $250-299.9 Million
Approx. Number Employees: 53
Year Founded: 1913
Business Description:
Coal Mining
S.I.C.: 1221; 1222
N.A.I.C.S.: 212111; 212112
Advertising Expenditures: $230,000
Media: 10-17
Distr.: Natl.
Budget Set: Nov.
Personnel:
Bob D. Carlton *(CFO & VP)*
Thomas Andrew Koza *(VP, Asst Sec & Sr Counsel)*

NOVA CHEMICALS CORPORATION

(Sub. of International Petroleum Investment Company)
1000 7th Ave SW
PO Box 2518
Calgary, AB T2P 5C6, Canada
Tel.: (403) 750-3600
Fax: (403) 269-7410
E-mail: public@novachem.com
Web Site: www.novachem.com
E-Mail For Key Personnel:
Public Relations: public@novachem.com
Approx. Rev.: $4,576,000,000
Approx. Number Employees: 2,445
Year Founded: 1998
Business Description:
Plastics & Chemicals Production & Marketing
S.I.C.: 2869; 2819; 2899; 5169
N.A.I.C.S.: 325110; 325188; 325199; 325998; 424690
Export
Media: 2-4-9-10-11-16-22
Distr.: Intl.
Budget Set: Sept.
Personnel:
Khadem Al Qubaisi *(Chm)*
Mohamed Al Mehairi *(Vice Chm)*
Randy Woelfel *(CEO)*
Todd Karran *(CFO & Sr VP)*
William Mitchell *(Gen Counsel & VP)*
Lawrence A. Macdonald *(Sr VP)*
Brands & Products:
ARCEL
COSMO
DYLARK
DYLENE
DYLITE
ELEMIX
EPS SILVER
IMX
INNOLAST
ISOPACK
ISOPACK PREMIUM
ISOPOL
NAS
NOVA
NOVACAT
NOVAPOL
OCTYLENES
PETROCARB
QINNEX
RESPONSIBLE CARE
SCLAIR
SCLAIRCOAT
SCLAIRTECH
STYROSUN
SURPASS
ULTRA LOW
UPES
ZYLAR
ZYNTAR

NUCO2 INC.

(Holding of Aurora Capital Group L.P.)
2800 SE Market Pl
Stuart, FL 34997-4965
Tel.: (772) 221-1754
Fax: (772) 781-3500
Toll Free: (800) 472-2855
E-mail: info@nuco2.com
Web Site: www.nuco2.com
Approx. Rev.: $156,125,000
Approx. Number Employees: 786
Year Founded: 1990
Business Description:
Bulk Carbon Dioxide for the Food Services & Hospitality Industries
S.I.C.: 2899; 5169
N.A.I.C.S.: 325998; 424690
Import Export
Personnel:
Michael E. DeDomenico *(Chm & CEO)*
J. Robert Vipond *(CFO & Exec VP)*
Robert Vipond *(Exec VP & CFO)*
Eric M. Wechsler *(Gen Counsel & Sec)*
Randy Gold *(Sr VP-Sls & Customer Svc)*
Keith Gordon *(Sr VP-Mktg & Bus Dev)*
Victoria Strauss *(Sr VP-Ops)*
Jeffrey S. Gilheney *(VP-HR)*
Brands & Products:
NUCO2
Advertising Agency:
Burdette Ketchum
1023 Kings Ave
Jacksonville, FL 32207
Tel.: (904) 645-6200
Fax: (904) 645-6080

OCCIDENTAL CHEMICAL CORPORATION

(Sub. of Occidental Petroleum Corporation)
5005 Lyndon B Johnson Fwy
Dallas, TX 75244-6100
Mailing Address:
PO Box 809050
Dallas, TX 75380-9050
Tel.: (972) 404-3800
Fax: (972) 404-3669
Toll Free: (800) 578-8880
E-mail: info@oxy.com
Web Site: www.oxychem.com
Sales Range: $1-4.9 Billion
Approx. Number Employees: 600
Year Founded: 1902
Business Description:
Chemicals, Chlorine & Caustic Soda, PVC & Specialty Chemicals Mfr
S.I.C.: 2812; 2869
N.A.I.C.S.: 325181; 325110
Export
Media: 1-2-4-7-10-20-22
Distr.: Intl.; Natl.
Personnel:
James M. Lienert *(CFO & Exec VP-Fin)*
B. Chuck Anderson *(Pres-Occidental Chemical Corporation)*
Brands & Products:
ACL
AQUA CLEAR
DECHLORANE
FERROPHOS
FLUOROLUBES
HALSO
NGO
OXSOL
OXYCHEM

OCCIDENTAL PETROLEUM CORPORATION

10889 Wilshire Blvd
Los Angeles, CA 90024-4201
Tel.: (310) 208-8800
Fax: (310) 443-6690
E-mail: investorrelations_newyork@oxy.com
Web Site: www.oxy.com
Approx. Rev.: $19,157,000,000
Approx. Number Employees: 11,000
Year Founded: 1920
Business Description:
Crude Oil & Natural Gas Explorer, Developer, Producer & Marketer; Basic Chemicals Marketer & Mfr
S.I.C.: 1311; 2819
N.A.I.C.S.: 211111; 325188
Media: 2-7-8-9-10-11-16-19-20
Distr.: Intl.; Natl.
Personnel:
Ray R. Irani *(Chm)*
Stephen I. Chazen *(Pres & CEO)*
James M. Lienert *(CFO & Exec VP)*
Donald P. De Brier *(CIO & VP)*
Edward A. Lowe *(Pres- Oxy Oil, Gas-Intl Production-Occidental Oil & Gas Co, VP)*
Anita Powers *(Exec VP-Worldwide Exploration-Oxy Oil & Gas & VP)*
Richard S. Kline *(VP-Comm & Pub Affairs)*
Rich Venn *(Mgr-Interactive Comm)*
Brands & Products:
OCCIDENTAL PETROLEUM CORPORATION
OXY
OXYVINYLS

OKON, INC.

(Sub. of Zinsser Co., Inc.)
173 Belmont Dr
Somerset, NJ 08875
Tel.: (732) 469-8100
Fax: (303) 321-7880
Toll Free: (800) 237-0565
E-mail: info@okoninc.com
Web Site: www.okoninc.com
Sales Range: $10-24.9 Million
Approx. Number Employees: 12
Year Founded: 1972
Business Description:
Water Repellant Sealer Mfr
S.I.C.: 2891; 2899
N.A.I.C.S.: 325520; 325998
Media: 2-4-10-13
Brands & Products:
OKON DECK STAIN
OKON FINAL SHIELD
OKON GRAFFITI SOLUTIONS REMOVER
OKON GRAFFITI SOLUTIONS SEAL COAT
OKON GRAFFITI SOLUTIONS WIPES
OKON NATURAL CHOICE
OKON PLUGGER
OKON PLUS COLOR
OKON SAFETY GRIP
OKON SEAL & FINISH
OKON STUCCO SEALER
OKON W-1
OKON W-2
OKON WATERPROOF SEALER
OKON WATERSTOPPER
OKON WEATHER PRO
OKON WOOD CLEANER
PAINTBOOSTER

OLD WORLD INDUSTRIES, INC.

4065 Commercial Ave
Northbrook, IL 60062-1828
Tel.: (847) 559-2000
Fax: (847) 559-2100
E-mail: chemicals@oldworldind.com
Web Site: www.oldworldind.com
Approx. Sls.: $500,000,000
Approx. Number Employees: 200
Year Founded: 1968
Business Description:
Automotive & Industrial Chemicals & Accessories Mfr
S.I.C.: 2899; 2992
N.A.I.C.S.: 325998; 324191
Import Export
Media: 2-3-4-6-7-8-10-11-15-16-19-20-21-22-23
Distr.: Direct to Consumer; Natl.
Budget Set: Monthly
Personnel:
Tom Hurvis *(Chm)*
Richard Jago *(Pres-Auto Div)*
Jerry T. Riccioni *(VP-Retail & Intl Sls)*
Karen Hoban *(Dir-Art)*
Susan Sperling *(Mgr-Mktg)*
Brands & Products:
BIG SPARK
DO-IT-YOURSELF
FLEET CHARGE
HERCULINER
PEAK
SIERRA
SMARTBLADE
SPLITFIRE
Advertising Agencies:
Heisler Gordon & Associates
1643 N Milwaukee Ave
Chicago, IL 60647
Tel.: (773) 342-9900
Fax: (773) 342-8020
Fax: (177) 334-2132

Noble
33 W Monroe St Ste 300
Chicago, IL 60603
Tel.: (312) 670-2900
Fax: (312) 670-7420
Toll Free: (800) 986-6253

Key to Media (For complete agency information see *The Advertising Red Books-Agencies* edition):
1. Bus. Publs. 2. Cable T.V. 3. Catalogs & Directories. 4. Co-op Adv. 5. Consumer Mags. 6. D.M. to Bus. Estab.7. D.M. to Consumers 8. Daily Newsp. 9. Exhibits/Trade Shows 10. Foreign 11. Infomercial 12. Internet Adv.13. Multimedia 14. Network Radio 15. Network T.V. 16. Newsp. Distr. Mags. 17. Other 18. Outdoor (Posters, Transit) 19. Point of Purchase20. Premiums, Novelties 21. Product Samples 22. Special Events Mktg. 23. Spot Radio 24. Spot T.V. 25. Weekly Newsp. 26. Yellow Page Adv.

OLIN CORPORATION
190 Carondelet Plz Ste 1530
Clayton, MO 63105
Tel.: (314) 480-1400
Fax: (203) 750-3292
Fax: (314) 862-7406
E-mail: olincorpinfo@olin.com
Web Site: www.olin.com
Approx. Sls.: $1,585,900,000
Approx. Number Employees: 3,700
Year Founded: 1892
Business Description:
Metal Products, Chlorine & Sporting Ammunition Mfr
S.I.C.: 1474; 2812; 2821; 3351
N.A.I.C.S.: 212391; 325181; 325211; 331421
Export
Media: 2-4-5-6-7-8-9-10-19-20-21-25-26
Distr.: Intl.; Natl.
Budget Set: Nov.
Personnel:
Joseph D. Rupp *(Chm, Pres & CEO)*
John L. McIntosh *(Pres)*
Richard M. Hammett *(Pres-Winchester Div)*
Larry P. Kromidas *(Dir-IR & Asst Treas)*
Brands & Products:
FINEWELD
HYDROLIN
OLIN
POSIT-BOND
REDUCTONE
WINCHESTER

OMNOVA SOLUTIONS INC
175 Ghent Rd
Fairlawn, OH 44333-3330
Tel.: (330) 869-4200
Fax: (330) 869-4410
E-mail: inforequest@omnova.com
Web Site: www.omnova.com
Approx. Sls.: $846,200,000
Approx. Number Employees: 2,430
Year Founded: 1999
Business Description:
Specialty Chemicals & Decorative & Functional Surfaces Used in Commercial & Industrial Applications
S.I.C.: 2899; 2295; 3069
N.A.I.C.S.: 325998; 313320; 326299
Advertising Expenditures: $1,000,000
Media: 2-4-7-10-20-21
Personnel:
Kevin M. McMullen *(Chm, Pres & CEO)*
Michael E. Hicks *(CFO & Sr VP)*
Douglas E. Wenger *(CIO & Sr VP)*
James J. Hohman *(Pres-Performance Chemicals & Corp VP)*
Robert H. Coleman *(Pres-Decorative Products)*
James C. LeMay *(Gen Counsel & Sr VP-Bus Dev)*
Kristine Syrvalin *(Sec, Asst Gen Counsel, VP-HR & Admin)*
Sandi Noah *(Dir-Comm)*
Brands & Products:
ACRYGEN
AVANT
BOLTA
BOLTAFLEX
BOLTASOFT
BREASE
DESIGN4
DIVERSIWALL
ECORE
ENDURION
ESSEX
GENCAL
GENCEAL
GENCRYL
GENCRYL PT
GENFLEX
GENFLO
GENGLAZE
GENON
GENTAC
GUARD
HARMONY COLLECTION
LANARK
LIFELINES
MEMERASE
MEMERASE II
MOR-FLO
MOR-GLO
MOR-SHINE
MUREK
MYKON
MYKOSIL
MYKOSOFT
NAUTOLEX
NOVACRYL
NOVAGREEN
NOVANE
OMNABLOC
OMNAGLIDE
OMNAGLO
OMNAPEL
OMNATUF
OMNOVA
PERMAFRESH
POLYFOX
PREEMPT
PREFIXX
PREVAILL
RADIANCE
RADIANT ELEMENT
REACTOPAQUE
RECORE
RENDURA
SCION
SECOAT
SECRYL
SEQUABOND
SEQUAFLOW
SEQUAPEL
SEQUAREZ
STYLECOAT
SUNBOND
SUNCRYL
SUNKEM
SUNKOTE
SUNREZ
SURF (X)
TOWER
UNIQ-PRINT
VIEWNIQUE
WEBCORE
X-CAPE
XQUEST
Advertising Agency:
Dix & Eaton Incorporated
200 Public Sq Ste 1400
Cleveland, OH 44114
Tel.: (216) 241-0405
Fax: (216) 241-3070

P. KAY METAL SUPPLY INC.
2448 E 25th St
Los Angeles, CA 90058
Tel.: (323) 585-5058
Fax: (323) 585-1380
E-mail: inquiries@pkaymetal.com
Web Site: www.pkaymetal.com
Approx. Number Employees: 28
Year Founded: 1978
Business Description:
Global Mfr of Solders & Fluxes
S.I.C.: 5051; 2899
N.A.I.C.S.: 423510; 325998
Export
Media: 2-4-7-10-11
Personnel:
Larry Kay *(Pres)*

PACE INTERNATIONAL LLC
1201 3rd Ave Ste 5450
Seattle, WA 98101
Toll Free: (800) 936-6750
E-mail: webmaster@paceint.com
Web Site: www.paceint.com
E-Mail For Key Personnel:
President: georgel@paceint.com
Approx. Number Employees: 60
Year Founded: 1950
Business Description:
Supplier of Commercial Agricultural Products
S.I.C.: 2842; 2879
N.A.I.C.S.: 325612; 325320
Export
Media: 2-10-26
Distr.: Intl.; Natl.
Budget Set: Nov.
Personnel:
George Lobisser *(Pres & CEO)*
Selynn Vong *(Mgr-Mktg)*
Brands & Products:
CITRASHINE
DEADLINE
HINDER
LEFFIINGWELL
NATURAL SHINE
OPTI-CAL
PRIMAFRESH
SHIELD-BRITE

PBI/GORDON CORPORATION
1217 W 12th St
Kansas City, MO 64101-1407
Tel.: (816) 421-4070
Fax: (816) 474-0462
Toll Free: (800) 821-7925
E-mail: webmaster@pbigordon.com
Web Site: www.pbigordon.com
Sales Range: $125-149.9 Million
Approx. Number Employees: 200
Year Founded: 1947
Business Description:
Agricultural Chemicals & Lawn & Garden Chemicals Mfr
S.I.C.: 2879; 6512
N.A.I.C.S.: 325320; 531120
Import Export
Advertising Expenditures: $600,000
Media: 2-10-13-21-23
Personnel:
William E. Mealman *(Chm)*
Richard E. Martin *(Pres & CEO)*
Tom Hoffman *(Mgr)*
Brands & Products:
ALL-SEASON BRUSH-NO-MORE
AMINE
AQUACURE
AQUEOUS
ATRIMMEC
AZATROL
BARRIER
BENSUMEC
BLADE
BOV-A-MURA
BRUSHKILLER
BRUSHMASTER
BUG-NO-MORE
CLEANOUT
DORMANT
DURA-DUST
DURA-SPRAY
DYMEC
EMBARK
EMT
FERROMEC
FOCUS
FORMEC
GARDEN GUARD
GLYPHOMATE
GRUB-NO-MORE
HI-DEP
IMIDIPRO
JUMP-SHOT
LAUNCH
LICE-NO-MORE
LIQUID GARDEN GUARD
MALATHION
MECOMEC
ORCHARDMASTER
ORNAMEC
PASTURE PRO
PBI/GORDON CORPORATION
PONDMASTER
POWERZONE
PRE-SAN
PRONTO
PRONTO BIG N' TUF
Q4
SPEEDZONE
SPRED-RITE
STRONGHOLD
SUPER TRIMEC
SUPERBRUSH
SURGE
TEREMEC
TRANSFILM
TRIMEC
TRIMEC ENCORE
TRIPLE-10
TUPERSAN
TUPERSCAN
VAPONA
VEGEMEC
WEED-NO-MORE

PEABODY ENERGY CORPORATION
701 Market St
Saint Louis, MO 63101
Tel.: (314) 342-3400
Fax: (314) 342-7799
E-mail: pr@peabodyenergy.com
Web Site: www.peabodyenergy.com
Approx. Rev.: $6,860,000,000
Approx. Number Employees: 7,200
Year Founded: 1883
Business Description:
Coal Mining & Processing Services
S.I.C.: 1221; 1222
N.A.I.C.S.: 212111; 212112
Export
Media: 2-4
Distr.: Intl.; Natl.
Budget Set: Jan.
Personnel:
Gregory H. Boyce *(Chm & CEO)*
Richard A. Navarre *(Pres & Chief Comml Officer)*
Michael C. Crews *(CFO & Exec VP)*
Eric Ford *(COO & Exec VP)*
Alexander C. Schoch *(Chief Legal Officer, Sec & Exec VP-Law)*

Key to Media (For complete agency information see *The Advertising Red Books-Agencies* edition):
1. Bus. Publs. 2. Cable T.V. 3. Catalogs & Directories. 4. Co-op Adv. 5. Consumer Mags. 6. D.M. to Bus. Estab.7. D.M. to Consumers
8. Daily Newsp. 9. Exhibits/Trade Shows 10. Foreign 11. Infomercial 12. Internet Adv.13. Multimedia 14. Network Radio
15. Network T.V. 16. Newsp. Distr. Mags. 17. Other 18. Outdoor (Posters, Transit) 19. Point of Purchase20. Premiums, Novelties
21. Product Samples 22. Special Events Mktg. 23. Spot Radio 24. Spot T.V. 25. Weekly Newsp. 26. Yellow Page Adv.

Sharon D. Fiehler *(Chief Admin Officer & Exec VP)*
Kenneth L. Wagner *(Chief Compliance Officer, VP & Asst Gen Counsel)*
Christopher J. Hagedorn *(Sr VP-Global Sls & Trading Support)*
Erik L. Ludtke *(Pres-Sls, Mktg & Trading)*
Zhenchun Shi *(Pres-Asia)*
L. Brent Stottlemyre *(Sr VP & Controller)*
Carlton B. Adams *(Sr VP-Supply Chain Mgmt)*
Terry L. Bethel *(Sr VP-Resource Mgt)*
Rick Bowen *(Sr VP)*
Charles A. Burggraf *(Sr VP-Global Safety)*
Walter L. Hawkins *(Sr VP-Fin)*
Delbert Lee Lobb *(Sr VP-Mongolian Ops)*
Fredrick D. Palmer *(Sr VP-Govt Rels)*
Robert L. Reilly *(Sr VP-Bus Dev)*
Richard Robison *(Sr VP)*
Victor P. Svec *(Sr VP-IR & Corp Comm)*
Lina A. Young *(Sr VP-IT)*
Charles Meintjes *(Group VP-Midwest & Colorado)*
Kemal Williamson *(Grp VP-Ops)*
Mary L. Frontczak *(VP & Asst Gen Counsel)*
Edward L. Sullivan *(VP & Asst Gen Counsel)*
Gary R. Kalbfleisch *(VP-IT)*
Amy B. Schwetz *(VP-Fin & Capital Plng)*
Morry C. Davis *(Dir-Govt Rels)*
Thomas A. Benner *(Dir-Underground Mining)*
Carl Consalus *(Dir-Design & Construction Engrg)*
Christina A. Morrow *(Dir-IR)*

PENFORD CORPORATION

7094 S Revere Pkwy
Centennial, CO 80112-3952
Tel.: (303) 649-1900
Fax: (303) 649-1700
Toll Free: (800) 204PENX
Toll Free: (888) 317-2013
E-mail: IR@penx.com
Web Site: www.penx.com

Approx. Sls.: $254,274,000
Approx. Number Employees: 330
Year Founded: 1984

Business Description:
Specialty Carbohydrates & Synthetic Polymer Chemicals Mfr; Specialty Food Ingredients & Agricultural Nutrition Supplements Producer & Marketer
S.I.C.: 2046; 2041
N.A.I.C.S.: 311221; 311211

Media: 2-7
Distr.: Intl.; Natl.

Personnel:
Paul H. Hatfield *(Chm)*
Thomas D. Malkoski *(Pres & CEO)*
Wallace H. Kunerth *(Chief Science Officer & VP)*
Timothy M. Kortemeyer *(Pres-Penford Products Co & VP)*
John R. Randall *(Pres-Penford Food Ingredients & VP)*
Steven O. Cordier *(CFO, Sr VP & Asst Sec)*
Margaret Von Der Schmidt *(Controller & Asst Sec)*
Michael J. Friesema *(Dir-Bus Dev)*

Brands & Products:
APOLLO
ASTRO GUM 21
ASTRO GUMS
ASTRO X
ASTROCOTE 75
CALENDER SIZE 2283
CANTAB
CARRIDEX
CLEARSOL GUMS
CREATED BY NATURE ADVANCED THROUGH SCIENCE
CROWN THIN BOILING
DOUGLAS-COOKER
DOUGLAS-ENZYME
EMCOSOY
EMVELOP
FIELDCLEER
LIQUISIZE
LUBRITAB
MAPS
MAZACA
NATURE. SCIENCE. SOLUTIONS.
PENBIND
PENCLING
PENFLEX
PENFORD
PENGLOSS
PENPLUS
PENSIZE
PRUV
SOLUDEX
TOPCAT

PERMABOND ENGINEERING ADHESIVES

(Sub. of National Starch & Chemical Co.)
20C World's Fair Dr
Somerset, NJ 08873
Mailing Address:
PO Box 6500
Bridgewater, NJ 08807-0500
Tel.: (732) 868-1372
Fax: (732) 868-0267
Toll Free: (800) 714-0170
E-mail: info.americas@permabond.com
Web Site: www.permabond.com
Business Description:
Adhesives & Sealants Mfr for Industrial & Consumer Application
S.I.C.: 2851; 2821
N.A.I.C.S.: 325510; 325211
Media: 2-5-10-21-26
Distr.: Natl.
Brands & Products:
PERMABOND

PETROFERM INC.

(Holding of H.I.G. Capital, LLC)
402 Center St Ste A
Fernandina Beach, FL 32034
Tel.: (904) 277-5247
Tel.: (904) 261-8286
E-mail: Customerservice@petroferm.com
Web Site: www.petroferm.com
Year Founded: 1983
Business Description:
Specialty Chemicals
S.I.C.: 2899
N.A.I.C.S.: 325998
Export
Advertising Expenditures: $100,000
Media: 2-4-7-10-11-13-20-21
Personnel:
Robert Drennan *(CEO)*
Kampta Gupta *(Reg Mgr-South Asia Sls)*
Bill Johnson *(Reg Mgr-Western Sls)*
Jack Lam *(Reg Mgr-Great China Sls)*
Jose Zapata *(Reg Mgr-Latin American Sls)*
Jonathan Tomassetti *(Reg Mgr-Asia Pacific Sls)*
Mike Savidakis *(Mktg Mgr-Electronics)*
Jeff Beard *(Mgr-Sls-North American)*
Sandra Gates *(Mgr-Sls Reg)*
Brands & Products:
AXAREL
BIOACT
HYDREX
LAMBENT
LENIUM
MEGASOLV NOC
RE-ENTRY

PHIBROCHEM

65 Challenger Rd 3rd Fl
Ridgefield Park, NJ 07660
Tel.: (201) 329-7300
Fax: (201) 329-7399
Toll Free: (800) 223-0434
Web Site: www.pahc.com
Approx. Number Employees: 1,500
Year Founded: 1947
Business Description:
Industrial & Agricultural Chemicals
S.I.C.: 5169; 5191
N.A.I.C.S.: 424690; 424910
Import Export
Media: 7-10
Distr.: Intl.
Personnel:
Gerald K. Carlson *(CEO)*
George Moffett *(Mng Dir)*
Richard Johnson *(CFO)*
Michael Giambalvo *(Pres-PhibroChem)*
Dean Warras *(Pres-Prince Agri Products)*
Daniel G. Welch *(Sr VP-HR)*
Yehuda Markovitz *(Gen Mgr-Koffolk)*
Brands & Products:
AVIAX
BANMINTH
BLOAT GUARD
MECADOX
NEO-TERRAMYCIN
NICARB
RUMATEL
STAFAC
TERRAMYCIN
V-MAX

PLASTOMER TECHNOLOGIES

(Unit of Plastomer Technolgies)
1600 Industry Rd
Hatfield, PA 19440
Tel.: (215) 855-9916
Fax: (800) 618-4717
Toll Free: (800) 618-4701
E-mail: info@porterprocess.com
Web Site: www.plastomertech.com
Sales Range: $10-24.9 Million
Approx. Number Employees: 30
Year Founded: 1969
Business Description:
Mfr of Joint & Thread Sealants, Fine Powder Compounds, PTFE Fiber & Specialty Tapes
S.I.C.: 3053
N.A.I.C.S.: 339991
Media: 2-4-7-10-11-26

PMC GLOBAL, INC.

12243 Branford St
Sun Valley, CA 91352-1010
Tel.: (818) 896-1101
Fax: (818) 897-0180
Toll Free: (800) 423-5632
E-mail: info@pmcglobalinc.com
Web Site: www.pmcglobalinc.com
Sales Range: $25-49.9 Million
Approx. Number Employees: 3,600
Year Founded: 1971
Business Description:
Piping, Plastic Products, Soaps, Chemicals & Equipment Mfr
S.I.C.: 3086; 3674
N.A.I.C.S.: 326150; 334413
Import Export
Media: 10
Personnel:
Philip E. Kamins *(CEO)*

POLYONE CORPORATION

33587 Walker Rd
Avon Lake, OH 44012
Tel.: (440) 930-1000
Fax: (440) 930-3064
Web Site: www.polyone.com
Approx. Sls.: $2,621,900,000
Approx. Number Employees: 4,000
Year Founded: 2000
Business Description:
Specialty Ink, Polymer & Elastomer Developer, Mfr & Distr
S.I.C.: 2821; 3086; 3089
N.A.I.C.S.: 325211; 326150; 326199
Export
Media: 2-7-10-20-26
Personnel:
Stephen D. Newlin *(Chm, Pres & CEO)*
Robert M. Patterson *(CFO & Exec VP)*
Michael E. Kahler *(Chief Comml Officer & Sr VP)*
Cecil C. Chappelow *(Chief Innovation Officer & VP-Innovation & Sustainability)*
Craig Nikrant *(Pres-Specialty Engineered Matls & Sr VP)*
Willie Chien *(Pres-Asia & VP)*
Bernard Baert *(Pres-Europe & Intl)*
Robert M. Rosenau *(Pres-Performance Products & Solutions)*
John V. Van Hulle *(Pres-Global Color)*
Michael L. Rademacher *(Sr VP & Gen Mgr-Distr)*
Thomas J. Kedrowski *(Sr VP-Supply Chain & Ops)*
Julie A. McAlindon *(VP-Mktg)*
David Honeycutt *(Dir-Mktg Comm)*
Marc Imowitz *(Dir-Strategic Pricing)*
Amanda Marko *(Dir-Corp Comm)*
Brands & Products:
AQUAMIX
BERGADUR
BERGAMID
COMPETE
DURACAP
ECC0H
ECOMASS
EDGEGLO
EDGETEK
EDGETEK XT
ELASTAMAX
FAST MARK
FIBERLOC

Key to Media (For complete agency information see *The Advertising Red Books-Agencies* edition):
1. Bus. Publs. 2. Cable T.V. 3. Catalogs & Directories. 4. Co-op Adv. 5. Consumer Mags. 6. D.M. to Bus. Estab.7. D.M. to Consumers 8. Daily Newsp. 9. Exhibits/Trade Shows 10. Foreign 11. Infomercial 12. Internet Adv.13. Multimedia 14. Network Radio 15. Network T.V. 16. Newsp. Distr. Mags. 17. Other 18. Outdoor (Posters, Transit) 19. Point of Purchase20. Premiums, Novelties 21. Product Samples 22. Special Events Mktg. 23. Spot Radio 24. Spot T.V. 25. Weekly Newsp. 26. Yellow Page Adv.

PolyOne Corporation — (Continued)

FIRECON
FORPRENE
GEON 120
GEON 130
GEON 140
GEON 170
GEON 180
GEON 210
GEON CPVC
GEON DURACAP
GEON FIBERLOC
GEON HC
GEON HTX
GEON HTX ULTRA
GEON SPECIALTY SUSPENSION
GEON VINYL CELLULAR
GEON VINYL DRY BLEND
GEON VINYL FITTINGS
GEON VINYL FLEXIBLE
GEON VINYL PACKAGING
GEON VINYL RIGID EXTRUSION
GEON VINYL RIGID MOLDING
GEON VINYL WIRE & CABLE
GRAVI-TECH
HANNA FX
HOLOFLAKE
LUBRI-TECH
LUBRIONE
MAXXAM
MAXXAM FR
MULTI-PURGE
NANOBLEND
NITEBRITE
NYMAX
ONCAP
ONCOLOR
ONCOLOR COMPETE
ONFORCE LFT
OXYPURGE
PLAST-O-MERIC
PLASTONE
POLYONE
POLYTRON
PPROTINT
QUANTUMONE
SMARTBATCH
SPEEDECOLOR
STAN-TONE
STAT-TECH
SYNCURE
SYNPLAST
SYNPRENE
THERMA-TECH
TRILLIANT HC
WHERE SPEED & SOLUTIONS ARE THE DIFFERENCE
WILFLEX

Advertising Agency:
Bader Rutter & Associates, Inc.
13845 Bishops Dr
Brookfield, WI 53005
Tel.: (262) 784-7200
Fax: (262) 938-5595
Toll Free: (888) 742-2337

POTASH CORP.
(Sub. of Potash Corporation of Saskatchewan Inc.)
1101 Skokie Blvd Ste 400
Northbrook, IL 60062-4123
Tel.: (847) 849-4200
Fax: (847) 849-4695
Toll Free: (800) 241-6908
E-mail: info@potashcorp.com
Web Site: www.potashcorp.com
Approx. Number Employees: 200
Year Founded: 1905
Business Description:
Phosphate Fertilizer Materials, Potash, Sulphur, Sulphuric Acid & Feed Ingredients
S.I.C.: 2874; 1474
N.A.I.C.S.: 325312; 212391
Export
Advertising Expenditures: $400,000
Media: 1-2-4-7-8-9-10-20-21-23-24-25
Distr.: Natl.
Personnel:
Will Barrett *(Sr Dir-Customer Svc)*
Tom Pasztor *(Sr Dir-Corp & Govt Relations)*
Tim Henning *(Dir-Nitrogen Mktg)*
John Hewson *(Mgr-Sustainability)*
Brands & Products:
HI GREEN
SUPER-49

PPG AEROSPACE
(Div. of PPG Industries, Inc.)
12780 San Fernando Rd
Sylmar, CA 91342
Tel.: (818) 362-6711
Fax: (818) 362-0603
Telex: 67-4208
Web Site: www.corporate.ppg.com/PPG/Aerospace/default.htm
Sales Range: $800-899.9 Million
Approx. Number Employees: 1,200
Year Founded: 1945
Business Description:
Aerospace Coatings, Sealants & Aircraft Windshield Mfr
S.I.C.: 2851; 3728
N.A.I.C.S.: 325510; 336413
Export
Advertising Expenditures: $250,000
Media: 2-4-10-11-13-21-26
Distr.: Natl.
Budget Set: July
Personnel:
Ralph Dyba *(CFO)*
Mark Cancilla *(Dir-Global Platform-Transparencies)*
Brian Roberson *(Dir-Global Platform-Coatings)*
Brands & Products:
DESOTO
PERMAPOL
PRC
PRO-SEAL
PRORECO
RUBBER CALK
SEMCO
SEMKIT
SEMPAK
WHERE SMART SOLUTIONS TAKE FLIGHT

PPG CANADA INC.
(Sub. of PPG Industries, Inc.)
2301 Royal Windsor Dr
Mississauga, ON L5J 1K5, Canada
Tel.: (905) 823-1100
Fax: (905) 823-7618
Web Site: corporateportal.ppg.com/PPG/worldwide/NA_Canada.htm
Approx. Sls.: $660,000,000
Approx. Number Employees: 2,100
Year Founded: 1984
Business Description:
Flat Glass, Coatings & Chemicals Mfr
S.I.C.: 3211
N.A.I.C.S.: 327211
Import Export
Advertising Expenditures: $200,000
Media: 2-17
Distr.: Natl.
Personnel:
Jean-Guy Rosa *(Dir-Refinish)*
Mark Shoemaker *(Mgr-Fin & HR)*

PQ CORPORATION
(Holding of The Carlyle Group, LLC)
1200 W Swedesford Rd
Berwyn, PA 19312-1077
Mailing Address:
PO Box 840
Valley Forge, PA 19482-0840
Tel.: (610) 651-4200
Fax: (610) 651-4504
Web Site: www.pqcorp.com
E-Mail For Key Personnel:
President: stan.silverman@pqcorp.com
Approx. Number Employees: 1,600
Year Founded: 1831
Business Description:
Sodium Silicate Mfr
S.I.C.: 2819; 1481; 1499; 3231; 3299
N.A.I.C.S.: 325188; 212399; 213115; 327215; 327999
Export
Media: 2-4-7-10
Distr.: Natl.
Budget Set: Aug.
Personnel:
Michael R. Boyce *(Chm & CEO)*
Alan McIlroy *(CFO & VP)*
Brands & Products:
ADVERA
AGSIL
B-W
BALLOTINI
BJ
BRITESIL
BRITESORB
CONDUCTO-O-FIL
KASIL
KASIL SS
KASOLV
LUXIL
MAGNABRITE
MAGNAGROW
METSO
METSO BEADS
METSO PENTABEAD
PENTABEAD
Q-CEL
RU
SIL-MATRIX
SPHERICEL
SPHERIGLASS
SS
STAR
STARSO
STIXSIL
STIXSO
VALFOR
VISIBEAD
VISIGUN

PRAXAIR, INC.
39 Old Ridgebury Rd
Danbury, CT 06810
Tel.: (203) 837-2000
Tel.: (716) 879-4077
Fax: (800) 772-9985
Fax: (716) 879-2040
Toll Free: (800) 772-9247
E-mail: info@praxair.com
Web Site: www.praxair.com
Approx. Sls.: $10,116,000,000
Approx. Number Employees: 26,261
Year Founded: 1907
Business Description:
Industrial Gases
S.I.C.: 3251; 2813; 3569; 5169
N.A.I.C.S.: 327121; 325120; 333999; 424690
Export
Personnel:
Stephen F. Angel *(Chm, Pres & CEO)*
James S. Sawyer *(CFO & Exec VP)*
M. Melissa Buckwalter *(CIO)*
Raymond P. Roberge *(CTO & Sr VP)*
Murilo Barros De Melo *(Pres-Praxair Mexico & Central America)*
Mark F. Gruninger *(Pres-Praxair Surface Technologies, Inc)*
Daniel H. Yankowski *(Pres-Global Hydrogen Praxair, Inc.)*
James T. Breedlove *(Gen Counsel, Sec & Sr VP)*
Ricardo S. Malfitano *(Exec VP)*
Scott E. Telesz *(Sr VP)*
Randy S. Kramer *(Grp VP-Sls)*
Sunil Mattoo *(VP-Strategic Plng & Mktg)*
Nigel D. Muir *(VP-Comm)*
Sally A. Savoia *(VP-HR)*
Brands & Products:
PRAXAIR
Advertising Agencies:
Adkins Design Visual Communications LLC
35 Corporate Drive Suite 1090
Trumbull, CT 06614
Tel.: (203) 375-2887
Fax: (203) 386-1203

Farago+Partners
71 Broadway
New York, NY 10006
Tel.: (212) 344-9472
Fax: (212) 243-1682

LeadGenesys
Pacific Stock Exchange Bldg 155
Sansome St 6th Fl
San Francisco, CA 94104
Tel.: (415) 392-0333
Fax: (415) 963-4041

Mintz & Hoke Communications Group
40 Tower Ln
Avon, CT 06001-4222
Tel.: (860) 678-0473
Fax: (860) 679-9850

Re:Think Group
700 Canal St 5th Fl
Stamford, CT 06902
Tel.: (203) 357-9004
Fax: (203) 357-9006

Travers Collins & Company
726 Exchange St Ste 500
Buffalo, NY 14210-1495
Tel.: (716) 842-2222
Fax: (716) 842-6424

PRENTISS INCORPORATED
3600 Mansell Rd Ste 350
Alpharetta, GA 11001-2714
Mailing Address:
CB 2000
Floral Park, NY 11002-2000
Tel.: (770) 552-8072

Key to Media (For complete agency information see *The Advertising Red Books-Agencies* edition):
1. Bus. Publs. 2. Cable T.V. 3. Catalogs & Directories. 4. Co-op Adv. 5. Consumer Mags. 6. D.M. to Bus. Estab.7. D.M. to Consumers 8. Daily Newsp. 9. Exhibits/Trade Shows 10. Foreign 11. Infomercial 12. Internet Adv.13. Multimedia 14. Network Radio 15. Network T.V. 16. Newsp. Distr. Mags. 17. Other 18. Outdoor (Posters, Transit) 19. Point of Purchase20. Premiums, Novelties 21. Product Samples 22. Special Events Mktg. 23. Spot Radio 24. Spot T.V. 25. Weekly Newsp. 26. Yellow Page Adv.

Fax: (770) 552-8076
Toll Free: (800) 645-1911
E-mail: info@prentiss.com
Web Site: www.prentiss.com
E-Mail For Key Personnel:
President: jmiller@prentiss.com
Sales Director: sales@prentiss.com
Approx. Number Employees: 38
Year Founded: 1919
Business Description:
Agricultural Pesticides
S.I.C.: 2879
N.A.I.C.S.: 325320
Import Export
Media: 2-7-10-11-13
Distr.: Intl.; Natl.
Budget Set: Oct.
Brands & Products:
MEELIUM
NOXFISH
NUSYN-NOXFISH
PBO-8
PRENFISH
PRENTOX
PYRONYL
SYNPREN-FISH

PVS CHEMICALS, INC.

10900 Harper Ave
Detroit, MI 48213-3364
Tel.: (313) 921-1200
Fax: (313) 921-1378
Toll Free: (800) 624-5787
E-mail: info@pvschemicals.com
Web Site: www.pvschemicals.com
Approx. Number Employees: 350
Year Founded: 1945
Business Description:
Industrial Chemicals Production
S.I.C.: 5169
N.A.I.C.S.: 424690
Export
Media: 10
Personnel:
James B. Nicholson *(Pres & CEO)*
Allan A. Schlumberger *(Grp VP)*
Brands & Products:
CARBITOL
NIAPROOF
PLURAFAC
PLURONIC
PVS CHEMICALS

QUADRANT ENGINEERING PLASTIC PRODUCTS

(Sub. of Quadrant AG)
2120 Fairmont Ave
Reading, PA 19605-3041
Mailing Address:
PO Box 14235
Reading, PA 19612-4235
Tel.: (610) 320-6600
Fax: (610) 320-6868
Toll Free: (800) 366-0300
Web Site: www.quadrantepp.com
Sales Range: $100-124.9 Million
Approx. Number Employees: 350
Year Founded: 1946
Business Description:
Mfr. of Basic Shapes from High-Grade Engineering Plastics & Articles
S.I.C.: 2824; 3082
N.A.I.C.S.: 325222; 326121
Import Export
Media: 2-7-8-10-22-26
Distr.: Intl.; Natl.
Budget Set: Nov.
Personnel:
Fred Sanford *(Sr Dir-Sls, Mktg, R & D)*
Richard Campbell *(Dir-Product Dev)*
Kress Schwartz *(Mgr-Mktg & Comm)*

QUAKER CHEMICAL CORP.

1 Quaker Pk 901 Hector St
Conshohocken, PA 19428-0809
Tel.: (610) 832-4000
Fax: (610) 832-8682
E-mail: info@quakerchem.com
Web Site: www.quakerchem.com
E-Mail For Key Personnel:
President: joe_bauer@quakerchem.com
Approx. Sls.: $544,063,000
Approx. Number Employees: 1,385
Year Founded: 1918
Business Description:
Custom-Formulated Chemical Specialty Products & Fluid Management Services for the Steel, Automotive & Can Industries
S.I.C.: 2869; 2819; 2899
N.A.I.C.S.: 325199; 325188; 325998
Import Export
Media: 2-4-10-21
Distr.: Intl.; Natl.
Personnel:
Michael F. Barry *(Chm, Pres & CEO)*
Mark A. Featherstone *(CFO, Treas & VP)*
D. Jeffry Benoliel *(Gen Counsel, Corp Sec & VP-Global Strategy)*
Frank R. Olah *(Gen Counsel-Tax & Tax Officer)*
Irene M. Kisleiko *(Asst Corp Sec & Mgr-IR)*
Brands & Products:
CHEMTRAQ
DELIVERING EVERYTHING, THE BEST FROM ANYWHERE.
ENVIRO-SCRUB
ENVIRO-TEK
EPMAR
FERROCOTE
FLEXIBLE SEAL
KEMIKO
MINETECH
OXY-SHIELD
QUACAST
QUAKER
QUAKER DRYCOTE
QUAKER FORMULA
QUAKER QUAKEROL
QUAKERAL
QUAKERCLEAN
QUAKERCOOL
QUAKERCUT
QUAKERDRAW
QUINTOLUBRIC
QWERL
RAPID ARMOUR
RAPIDSHIELD
REMBRANDT
RINSEAID
SCRUB-IT
STA CRETE
STA-NATURAL
SYNDECK
VULCHUR

RAYONIER INC.

1301 Riverplace Blvd
Jacksonville, FL 32207
Tel.: (904) 357-9100
Fax: (904) 357-9101
Toll Free: (800) 243-2890
Telex: 996472
E-mail: webmaster@rayonier.com
Web Site: www.rayonier.com
Approx. Sls.: $1,315,233,000
Approx. Number Employees: 1,800
Year Founded: 1926
Business Description:
Timber, Performance Fiber & Wood Products; Real Estate Investment Trust
S.I.C.: 6798; 2421; 2671; 2861
N.A.I.C.S.: 525930; 321912; 325191; 326112
Export
Media: 1-2-7-9-10-25
Distr.: Intl.; Natl.
Personnel:
Lee M. Thomas *(Chm & CEO)*
Paul G. Boynton *(Pres & COO)*
Hans E. Vanden Noort *(CFO & Sr VP)*
W. Edwin Frazier, III *(Chief Admin Officer, Sec & Sr VP)*
Michael R. Herman *(Gen Counsel & VP)*
Timothy H. Brannon *(Sr VP-Forest Resources)*
Carl E. Kraus *(Sr VP-Fin)*
Charles Margiotta *(Sr VP-Real Estate)*
Jay Posze *(VP-HR)*
Helen C. Rowan *(VP-Strategic Plng & Comm)*

READING ANTHRACITE COMPANY

200 Mahantongo St
Pottsville, PA 17901-7200
Tel.: (570) 622-5150
Fax: (570) 622-2612
E-mail: pnrpete@readinganthracite.com
Web Site: www.readinganthracite.com
Sales Range: $25-49.9 Million
Approx. Number Employees: 100
Year Founded: 1871
Business Description:
Mining, Processing & Sale of Anthracite Coal & Associated Products
S.I.C.: 1231
N.A.I.C.S.: 212113
Export
Media: 10-13-21-23
Distr.: Intl.; Natl.
Budget Set: Jan.
Personnel:
John W. Rich *(Chm)*
Brian R. Rich *(Pres)*
Frank Derrick *(Gen Mgr)*
Jeff A. Gliem *(Dir-Ops)*
Ricardo Muntone *(Dir-Safety)*
Joseph Brennan *(Mgr)*
Brands & Products:
FAMOUS READING ANTHRACITE
MOTHER NATURE'S CLEAN COAL
PHILTERKOL
READING ANTHRACITE

REICHHOLD, INC.

Research Triangle Park 2400 Ellis Rd
Durham, NC 27703
Mailing Address:
PO Box 13582
Research Triangle Park, NC 27709
Tel.: (919) 990-7500
Fax: (919) 990-7749
Toll Free: (800) 448-3482
Web Site: www.reichhold.com
Approx. Number Employees: 1,400
Year Founded: 1927
Business Description:
Synthetic Resins, Coatings Resins, Latex Polymers & Adhesives Mfr
S.I.C.: 2821; 2822
N.A.I.C.S.: 325211; 325212
Import Export
Advertising Expenditures: $2,000,000
Media: 2-7-10-11-13-20-24
Distr.: Intl.; Natl.
Budget Set: Oct.
Personnel:
John Gaither *(Pres & CEO)*
Roger Willis *(CFO)*
Edward R. Leydon *(Gen Counsel)*
Mitzi A. Van Leeuwen *(Sr VP-Corp Svcs)*

RENOSOL CORPORATION

1512 Woodland Dr
Saline, MI 48176-1632
Tel.: (734) 557-3814
Fax: (734) 429-5351
E-mail: info@renosol.com
Web Site: www.renosol.com
E-Mail For Key Personnel:
President: larry.adkisson@renosol.com
Approx. Number Employees: 400
Year Founded: 1981
Business Description:
Polyurethane Systems, Molded Seating & Interior Trim Products Mfr
S.I.C.: 3089; 3087
N.A.I.C.S.: 326199; 325991
Import Export
Media: 4-10
Personnel:
Douglas E. Peck *(Chm)*
Larry Adkisson *(Pres)*
Toby Huff *(Sls Mgr)*
Bethany Freeland *(Mgr-Mktg & Corp Dev)*
Brands & Products:
RENOSOL
VORANOL

RENTECH, INC.

10877 Wilshire Blvd Ste 710
Los Angeles, CA 90024
Tel.: (310) 571-9800
Fax: (310) 571-9799
E-mail: ir@rentk.com
Web Site: www.rentechinc.com
Approx. Rev.: $130,624,000
Approx. Number Employees: 252
Year Founded: 1981
Business Description:
Owner & Operator of Chemical Facilities that Convert Synthesis Gas into Liquid Hydrocarbons
S.I.C.: 2851; 2899
N.A.I.C.S.: 325510; 325998
Media: 2-7-13
Personnel:
Dennis L. Yakobson *(Chm)*
D. Hunt Ramsbottom, Jr. *(Pres & CEO)*
Dan J. Cohrs *(CFO & Exec VP)*
Tom Samson *(Chief Dev Officer & Exec VP)*
Harold A. Wright *(CTO & Sr VP)*
Eileen Ney *(Chief Acctg Officer & VP)*
Colin M. Morris *(Gen Counsel, Sec & VP)*
Douglas M. Miller *(Exec VP-Project Dev)*
John H. Diesch *(Sr VP-Ops)*

Key to Media (For complete agency information see *The Advertising Red Books-Agencies* edition):
1. Bus. Publs. 2. Cable T.V. 3. Catalogs & Directories. 4. Co-op Adv. 5. Consumer Mags. 6. D.M. to Bus. Estab.7. D.M. to Consumers 8. Daily Newsp. 9. Exhibits/Trade Shows 10. Foreign 11. Infomercial 12. Internet Adv.13. Multimedia 14. Network Radio 15. Network T.V. 16. Newsp. Distr. Mags. 17. Other 18. Outdoor (Posters, Transit) 19. Point of Purchase20. Premiums, Novelties 21. Product Samples 22. Special Events Mktg. 23. Spot Radio 24. Spot T.V. 25. Weekly Newsp. 26. Yellow Page Adv.

Rentech, Inc. — (Continued)

Richard J. Wesolowski *(Sr VP-HR)*
Julie Dawoodjee *(VP-IR & Comm)*
Robert L. Freerks *(Dir-Prod Dev)*

REUNION INDUSTRIES, INC.

11 Stanwix St Ste 1400
Pittsburgh, PA 15222-1312
Tel.: (412) 281-2111
Fax: (412) 281-4747
E-mail: info@reunionindustries.com
Web Site: www.reunionindustries.com
Sales Range: $25-49.9 Million
Approx. Number Employees: 354
Year Founded: 1989
Business Description:
Pneumatic Cylinders Mfr
S.I.C.: 3084; 3089; 3443
N.A.I.C.S.: 326122; 326199; 332313
Media: 2-4-7-9-13-25
Personnel:
Kimball J. Bradley *(Chm, Pres & CEO)*
Brands & Products:
CP INDUSTRIES CYLINDERS
HANNA CYLINDERS
ORC PLASTICS
REUNION
STEELCRAFT LEAF SPRINGS

RHODIA INC.

(Sub. of Rhodia S.A.)
8 Cedar Brook Dr
Cranbury, NJ 08512-7500
Tel.: (609) 860-4000
Fax: (609) 860-4990
E-mail: rhodiac@us.rhodia.com
Web Site: www.rhodia.us
Approx. Sls.: $3,000,000,000
Approx. Number Employees: 400
Business Description:
Herbicides, Insecticides, Fungicides, Animal Health Products & Feed Additives, Organic Intermediates, Aroma Chemicals, Silicones, Rare Earths, Aluminas, Plastics, Packaging Film Mfr
S.I.C.: 2819; 2812
N.A.I.C.S.: 325188; 325181
Import Export
Media: 2-6-7-8-18-23-24
Distr.: Natl.
Personnel:
James Harton *(Pres)*
Mark Dahlinger *(CFO)*
Michel Audoin *(Pres-Acetow Enterprise)*
Kenji Takahashi *(Dir-Mktg)*
James Hathaway *(Dir-Medical)*
Frederic Jacquin *(Mktg Project Dir)*
Jean-Francois Mayer *(Dir-Comml)*
David Klucsik *(Mgr-Comm)*
Steve Krenzke *(Mgr-Regulatory Affairs)*
Advertising Agency:
Red Flannel
218 Schanck Rd 2nd Fl
Freehold, NJ 07728
Tel.: (732) 761-8998
Fax: (732) 761-9424

ROCK VALLEY OIL & CHEMICAL COMPANY

1911 Windsor Rd
Loves Park, IL 61111
Tel.: (815) 654-2400
Fax: (815) 654-2428
Web Site: www.rockvalleyoil.com
Approx. Number Employees: 40
Year Founded: 1971
Business Description:
Supplier of Industrial Lubricants, Solvents & Chemicals
S.I.C.: 2992; 5169
N.A.I.C.S.: 324191; 424690
Media: 2-10
Personnel:
Roger L. Schramm *(Pres)*
Tom Wieland *(CFO & VP)*
Jim Lang *(Mgr-Mktg)*
Brands & Products:
ALIPHATIC NAPHTHAS
AROMATIC
CAVALIER
HD
HUSKIE
HUSKIE HD
PTO
REGENT
ROCKCUT
ROCKFORM
ROCKQUENCH
ROCKSPIN
ROCKWAY
SPARTAN
SPARTAN AW
TITAN
TROJAN
TROJAN ALL-SEASON
TROJAN AW
TROJAN TURBINE
VALRUST
VISCOOL
VISCOR

ROHM & HAAS COMPANY

(Sub. of THE DOW CHEMICAL COMPANY)
100 Independence Mall W
Philadelphia, PA 19106-2399
Tel.: (215) 592-3000
Fax: (215) 592-3377
E-mail: camartin@rohmhaas.com
Web Site: www.rohmhaas.com
Approx. Sls.: $8,897,000,000
Approx. Number Employees: 15,710
Year Founded: 1909
Business Description:
Industrial Plastics, Polymers, Resins & Monomers, PVC, Lubricants, Paper & Resins for Leather, Salt, Adhesives & Sealants; Electronic Materials Mfr
S.I.C.: 2821; 2851; 2899
N.A.I.C.S.: 325211; 325510; 325998
Import Export
Advertising Expenditures: $8,500,000
Media: 1-2-4-8-9-10-11-13-19-20-26
Distr.: Intl.; Natl.
Budget Set: Oct.
Personnel:
Jacques M. Croisetiere *(CFO, Chief Strategy Officer & Exec VP)*
Anne M. Wilms *(CIO, Exec VP & Dir-HR)*
Ruby R. Chandy *(CMO & VP)*
William F. Banholzer *(CTO & Exec VP-New Bus Dev & Licensing)*
Geoffery E. Merszei *(Chm-Dow Europe, Chm-Dow Europe & Exec VP-Dow Chemical Company)*
Sam Shoemaker *(Pres-CMPT)*
Robert A. Lonergan *(Gen Counsel, Corp Sec & Exec VP)*
Carlos Festa *(VP & Dir-Latin America)*
Neil Carr *(Gen Mgr-Coating Materials North America)*
Martin Sutcliffe *(Gen Mgr-Europe, Middle East & Africa)*
Joe Cavallaro *(Dir-HR-Dow Coating Matls)*
Barry Crawford *(Dir-Global Mfg-Dow Coating Matls)*
John Klier *(Dir-Global R&D)*
Margaret Mccarvill *(Dir-Global Supply Chain Dow Coating Matls)*
Kim Ann Mink *(Dir-Global Bus)*
Brands & Products:
ACIMA
ACRYJET
ACRYSOL
ACTRONAL
ACUBRIGHT
ACUMER
ADCOTE
ADVALUBE
ADVASTAB
ALUPREP
AMBERCHROM
AMBEREDGE
AMBERJET
AMBERLITE
AMBERLYST
AMBERSYNTH
AMBERZYME
AQUA-LAM
AQUACOAT
AURALL
AUTOMATE
BESTER
BLO-PRUF
BOROL
BRITEBOND
CATAPOSIT
CELEXIS
CHROMACLEAR
CIRCUPOSIT
COSEAL
CUPOSIT
CVD SILICONE CARBIDE
DIAGRID
DUOLITE
DURAGLOW
DURAPREP
ELASTENE
ELASTOMAG
ERIDEN
ETHYLBLOC
EVERON
HYDRHOLAC
IMAC
INSITE
INTERVIA
KATHON
KLEBOSOL
LAMAL
LATITUDE
LEUKOTAN
LIGHTLINK
LUBRITAN
LUCIDENE
LUCIWAX
MARINCO
MASTER WORKS
MEGUM
METAL ORGANICS
METAMARE
MICROFILL
MIRAGLOSS
MOR-AD
MOR-ESTER
MOR-FLOCK
MOR-FREE
MOR-MELT
MOR-PRIME
MOR-QUIK
MOR-TRIM
MORCRYL
MOREZ
MORLIFE
MORSTIK
MORTON
MORTRACE
NALCO
NEOLONE
NICULOY
NIPLATE
NIPOSIT
NOVA
OMNISHIELD
OROPON
PARALOID
PAVE
PAVE BOND
PAVECRYL
PENTAPHAN
PHENOL
PHOTOPOSIT
POLITEX PRIMA
POLYCO
POLYFLOCK
POLYGLAS
POLYGRIP
POLYLUBE
POLYMOLD
PRIMAL
PRIMENE
PULVERLAC
REGISTAR
RETAN
RHOPLEX
ROBOND
ROCRYL
RODEL
RODERM
ROHM-CHROME
ROHMIN
ROLEASE
RONACLEAN
ROPAQUE
ROSEAL
ROSLIP
SEA GUARD
SEA-NINE
SERFENE
SHIPLEY
SOLDERMASK
SPARKLON
SPECTRACE
STRATA
SUBA
SUGAR CURE
SURFACESTRIP
TAMOL
TENDER QUICK
THIXON
TYMOR
UNIFLUX
UNIOIL
VALU-SOFT
VENMAT
VENPURE
VERSAMAG
VITRIDE
WEATHERSLIP
WHITE CRYSTAL
WINDSOR
WINDSOR SALT
XAD
XMATE

Key to Media (For complete agency information see *The Advertising Red Books-Agencies* edition):
1. Bus. Publs. 2. Cable T.V. 3. Catalogs & Directories. 4. Co-op Adv. 5. Consumer Mags. 6. D.M. to Bus. Estab.7. D.M. to Consumers 8. Daily Newsp. 9. Exhibits/Trade Shows 10. Foreign 11. Infomercial 12. Internet Adv.13. Multimedia 14. Network Radio 15. Network T.V. 16. Newsp. Distr. Mags. 17. Other 18. Outdoor (Posters, Transit) 19. Point of Purchase20. Premiums, Novelties 21. Product Samples 22. Special Events Mktg. 23. Spot Radio 24. Spot T.V. 25. Weekly Newsp. 26. Yellow Page Adv.

Advertising Agencies:
K I Lipton Inc.
132 Welsh Rd Ste 120
Horsham, PA 19044
Tel.: (267) 893-5671
Fax: (267) 893-5681
(Agricultural, Polymers, Resins, Monomers, Water Treatment)

Lefton Company
100 Independence Mall W
Philadelphia, PA 19106-2399
Tel.: (215) 923-9600
Fax: (215) 351-4298
(Agricultural, Polymers, Resins, Monomers, Water Treatment)

Loomis Group
345 Spear St Ste 110
San Francisco, CA 94105
Tel.: (415) 882-9494
Fax: (415) 882-7209

Reese, Tomases & Ellick, Inc. (RT&E)
1105 Market St Ste 100
Wilmington, DE 19801
Tel.: (302) 652-3211
Fax: (302) 428-3920
Toll Free: (888) 720-7561

Sam Brown Inc.
7 Maplewood Dr
Newtown Square, PA 19073
Tel.: (610) 353-4545
Fax: (610) 353-5462

ROHM AND HAAS ELECTRONIC MATERIALS LLC

(Sub. of Rohm & Haas Company)
(d/b/a Dow Advanced Materials)
455 Forest St
Marlborough, MA 01752
Tel.: (508) 481-7950
Fax: (508) 485-9113
Toll Free: (800) 832-6200
E-mail: fglwend@dow.com
Web Site:
www.electronicmaterials.rohmhaas.com

Approx. Sls.: $1,000,000,000
Approx. Number Employees: 700

Business Description:
Specialty Materials & Process Technology Solutions for Semiconductor & Electronics Mfr
S.I.C.: 3679; 3674
N.A.I.C.S.: 334419; 334413

Media: 2-7
Distr.: Natl.
Budget Set: Sept. -Oct.

Personnel:
David E. Kepler *(CIO, Chief Sustainability Officer & Exec VP-Bus Svcs)*
William F. Banholzer *(CTO & Exec VP-New Bus Dev, Licensing)*
James R. Fitterling *(Pres-Corp Dev, Hydrocarbons & Exec VP-The Dow Chemical)*
Charles J. Kalil *(Gen Counsel, Corp Sec & Exec VP-Law, Govt Affairs)*
Gregory M. Freiwald *(Exec VP-HR, Corp Affairs & Aviation)*
Michael R. Gambrell *(Exec VP-Mfg & Engrg Ops)*
W. Michael McGuire *(Asst Sec)*

ROLLINS, INC.

2170 Piedmont Rd NE
Atlanta, GA 30324-4135
Mailing Address:
PO Box 647
Atlanta, GA 30301-0647
Tel.: (404) 888-2000
Fax: (404) 888-2662
E-mail: investorrelations@rollinscorp.com
Web Site: www.rollinscorp.com
Approx. Rev.: $1,136,890,000
Approx. Number Employees: 10,300
Year Founded: 1948
Business Description:
Pest Control Services
S.I.C.: 7342; 7349
N.A.I.C.S.: 561710; 561790
Advertising Expenditures: $43,693,000
Media: 2-10-18-23-26
Distr.: Direct to Consumer; Intl.; Natl.
Budget Set: Aug.
Personnel:
R. Randall Rollins *(Chm)*
Harry J. Cynkus *(CFO)*
Kevin Smith *(CMO)*
Martha Craft *(VP-PR)*
Rob Crigler *(VP-Global Digital Strategy & Integrated Mktg)*
Ruby Swann *(Dir-Recruiting & Talent Mgmt)*
Shelby Beal *(Mgr-Mktg)*
Gary W. Rollins *(Mgr-Svc Dept)*
Brands & Products:
THE LEADER IN PEST CONTROL
ORKIN
ROLLINS
Advertising Agencies:
Mindshare
3340 Peachtree Rd NE Ste 300
Atlanta, GA 30326
Tel.: (404) 832-3400
Fax: (404) 832-3430

The Richards Group, Inc.
8750 N Central Expy Ste 100
Dallas, TX 75231-6430
Tel.: (214) 891-5700
Fax: (214) 265-2933

ROYAL ADHESIVES & SEALANTS

(Branch of Royal Adhesives & Sealants LLC)
600 Cortlandt St
Belleville, NJ 07109-3328
Tel.: (973) 751-3000
Fax: (973) 751-8407
Toll Free: (888) 442-7362
Web Site: www.royaladhesives.com
Sales Range: $10-24.9 Million
Approx. Number Employees: 75
Business Description:
Mfr. of Epoxy & Elastomeric Compounds, Butyl Rubbers, Sealants, Molding Compounds, Urethanes, DPR & Acrylweld
S.I.C.: 2821; 3586
N.A.I.C.S.: 325211; 333913
Export
Advertising Expenditures: $340,000
Media: 2-4-7-10-21
Distr.: Intl.; Natl.
Budget Set: Dec.
Personnel:
Joan Stein *(Mgr-Customer Svc)*

ROYAL ADHESIVES & SEALANTS LLC

(Holding of Arsenal Capital Partners, Inc.)
2001 Washington St
South Bend, IN 46628-2032
Tel.: (574) 246-5000
Fax: (574) 246-5425
Toll Free: (800) 999-GLUE
Web Site: www.royaladhesives.com
Approx. Number Employees: 65
Year Founded: 1980
Business Description:
Industrial Adhesives & Sealants, Commercial Roofing Adhesives & Mirror Mastics Mfr & Marketer
S.I.C.: 2891
N.A.I.C.S.: 325520
Media: 2-4-7-10
Personnel:
Bill Ward *(Pres)*
Ted Clark *(CEO)*
Gary Stenke *(CFO)*
Steven Zens *(VP-Sls & Mktg)*
Sarah Harkleroad *(Head-Mktg)*
Jim Gagen *(Mgr-Natl Sls)*
Manny Nerantzoulis *(Mgr-R&D)*
John Schlacter *(Mgr-Eastern Reg Sls)*
Jamie Wenger *(Mgr-Central Reg)*
Brands & Products:
EXTRA/BUILD
GUNTHER MIRROR & MORE CLEANER
GUNTHER PREMIERE
GUNTHER PRIME-N-SEAL
HYDRA FAST-EN
ROYAL ADHESIVES & SEALANTS
SILAPRENE
ULTRA/BOND

R.T. VANDERBILT COMPANY, INC.

30 Winfield St
Norwalk, CT 06855-1329
Tel.: (203) 853-1400
Fax: (203) 853-1452
Toll Free: (800) 243-6064
Web Site: www.rtvanderbilt.com
E-Mail For Key Personnel:
Sales Director: sales@rtvanderbilt.com
Sales Range: $200-249.9 Million
Approx. Number Employees: 700
Year Founded: 1916
Business Description:
Whslr of Industrial Minerals & Chemicals
S.I.C.: 5169; 2869
N.A.I.C.S.: 424690; 325199
Export
Advertising Expenditures: $500,000
Media: 2-4-10-11-13-20-21
Distr.: Natl.
Budget Set: Nov.
Personnel:
Hugh Vanderbilt, Jr. *(Chm & CEO)*
Roger K. Price *(Pres & COO)*
Joseph Denaro *(CFO, Treas & VP)*
Kenneth H. Kelly *(VP, Gen Mgr-Sls & Mktg)*
A. S. Flores *(VP-Sls & Mktg Svcs)*
Steve Donnelly *(Global Bus Mgr-Petroleum)*
Arthur Delgrosso *(Mgr-Sls Dev)*
Brands & Products:
ACTIV-8
AGERITE
ALTAX
BUTYL EIGHT
BUTYL NAMATE
CAPTAX
DARVAN
DIAK
ETHYL TUADS
ISOBUTYL NICLATE
LEEGEN
NYTAL
OCTOATE Z
PROPYL ZITHATE
PYRAX
R.T. VANDERBILT COMPANY
SETSIT
UNADS
VANAX
VANCHEM
VANCIDE
VANFRE
VANPLAST
VANSIL
VANTALC
VANWAX
VEEGUM
ZETAX

RUSSEL METALS INC.

1900 Minnesota Ct Ste 210
Mississauga, ON L5N 3C9, Canada
Tel.: (905) 819-7777
Fax: (905) 819-7409
E-mail: info@russelmetals.com
Web Site: www.russelmetals.com
Approx. Rev.: $2,216,341,028
Approx. Number Employees: 2,300
Year Founded: 1929
Business Description:
Metals Distr & Processing Services
S.I.C.: 5051; 3499
N.A.I.C.S.: 423510; 332999
Import Export
Advertising Expenditures: $500,000
Media: 2-4-7-11
Distr.: Natl.
Personnel:
Anthony Frear Griffiths *(Chm)*
Brian R. Hedges *(Pres & CEO)*
Marion E. Britton *(CFO, Sec & VP)*
Lesley M. S. Coleman *(VP, Controller & Asst Sec)*
David J. Halcrow *(VP-Pur & Inventory Mgmt)*
Maureen A. Kelly *(VP-Info Sys)*
Sherri Mooser *(Asst Sec)*
Brands & Products:
10-MAR
ACCURLOY
AJF
B&T STEEL
BI
COMCO
CONCRETE
DRUMMOND MCCALL
E-Z BRAZE
FEDMET TUBULARS
FUSION BOND
JMS RUSSEL METALS CORP.
LEROUX
LILLY 2040
MANGABRAZE
MCCABE STEEL
MEGANTIC METAL
METAUX RUSSEL
MILSPEC
NICHROLOY
PIONEER PIPE
POWERCRETE

Key to Media (For complete agency information see *The Advertising Red Books-Agencies* edition):
1. Bus. Publs. 2. Cable T.V. 3. Catalogs & Directories. 4. Co-op Adv. 5. Consumer Mags. 6. D.M. to Bus. Estab.7. D.M. to Consumers 8. Daily Newsp. 9. Exhibits/Trade Shows 10. Foreign 11. Infomercial 12. Internet Adv.13. Multimedia 14. Network Radio 15. Network T.V. 16. Newsp. Distr. Mags. 17. Other 18. Outdoor (Posters, Transit) 19. Point of Purchase20. Premiums, Novelties 21. Product Samples 22. Special Events Mktg. 23. Spot Radio 24. Spot T.V. 25. Weekly Newsp. 26. Yellow Page Adv.

Russel Metals Inc. — (Continued)

PRITEC
RUSSEL DRILLING & INDUSTRIAL SUPPLY
RUSSEL METALS SPECIALTY PRODUCTS
RUSSEL METALS WILLIAMS BAHCALL
SPARTAN
SUNBELT
SYNERGY
TGFIII
TRIUMPH TUBULAR
TUFFBRAZE
V-MAX
VANTAGE LASER CUTTING
WIRTH
X-TRU
YORK-ENNIS
ZAP-LOK

SACHEM INC.

821 E Woodward St
Austin, TX 78704
Tel.: (817) 641-3803
Fax: (512) 445-5066
E-mail: info@sacheminc.com
Web Site: www.sacheminc.com
E-Mail For Key Personnel:
President: jmooney@sacheminc.com
Approx. Number Employees: 75
Year Founded: 1950
Business Description:
Chemical Products Mfr
S.I.C.: 2869; 2899
N.A.I.C.S.: 325199; 325998
Import Export
Media: 2-4-7-10-13
Personnel:
John Mooney *(Pres)*
Ron Morse *(CFO)*
Thomas J. Mooney *(Pres-Asia)*
John Mattson *(Dir-Process Tech)*
Armin Buhling *(Mgr-Mktg)*
Rosemary Hoffmann *(Mgr-Mktg-Life Sciences)*
Mark Stasney *(Mgr-Asia Ops)*
Brands & Products:
AVANTA AC
CATASAIL
ENVURE
EXPELL
ISOLIS
MARISAIL
MISSION. CRITICAL. CHEMISTRY
MOBIUS SYSTEM
PROPELL
SACHEM
SBS
TERRASAIL
Advertising Agency:
Milkshake Media LP
600 W 7th St
Austin, TX 78701
Tel.: (512) 474-7777

SAFETY-KLEEN HOLDCO, INC.

5360 Legacy Dr Cluster II Bldg 2 Ste 100
Plano, TX 75024
Tel.: (972) 265-2000
Fax: (972) 265-2990
Toll Free: (800) 669-5740
E-mail: info@safety-kleen.com
Web Site: www.safety-kleen.com
Sales Range: $100-124.9 Million
Approx. Number Employees: 4,500
Business Description:
Holding Company; Industrial & Hazardous Waste Management Services
S.I.C.: 4953; 6719
N.A.I.C.S.: 562211; 551112; 562219
Media: 2-7-10
Personnel:
Ronald W. Haddock *(Chm)*
Robert M. Craycraft, II *(Pres & CEO)*
Jeff Richard *(CFO & Exec VP)*
Curtis C. Knapp *(Sr VP & CMO)*
Virgil Duffie *(Chief Compliance Officer & Sr VP)*
Steve Grimshaw *(Exec VP-West Grp)*
Dave Sprinkle *(Exec VP-Oil Re-Refining)*
Rodney Walker *(Dir-Technical-Oil Re-Refining)*
Brands & Products:
AEROSOLV
AMERICA'S CHOICE
ARMAKLEEN
FIRST RECOVERY
FLUIDKEEN
LITE-DRI
OIL-ONLY 4 IN 1
SAFETY-KLEEN
TOTAL ENVIRONMENTAL ACTIVITY MANAGEMENT
WE CARE

SAINT-GOBAIN ABRASIVES, INC. - PHILADELPHIA

(Sub. of Saint-Gobain Abrasives, Inc)
200 Commerce Dr
Montgomeryville, PA 18936-9640
Mailing Address:
PO Box 505
Montgomeryville, PA 18936
Tel.: (215) 855-4300
Fax: (215) 362-3809
Toll Free: (800) 331-8837
E-mail: moyco@moycotech.com
Web Site: www.moycotech.com
Sales Range: $1-9.9 Million
Approx. Number Employees: 55
Business Description:
Abrasive Materials Mfr
S.I.C.: 3291
N.A.I.C.S.: 327910
Advertising Expenditures: $336,831
Media: 7-10-13
Personnel:
Alexander Pecora *(Mgr-Site & Product-US)*
Brands & Products:
COLSIL
GIGASIL
SUPERSIL
TRACTION PLUS
ULTRACEROX
ULTRALAP

SECURITY PLASTICS DIVISION/NMC LLC

(Div. of National Molding Corporation)
14427 NW 60th Ave
Miami Lakes, FL 33014-2806
Tel.: (305) 823-5440
Fax: (305) 557-1431
Toll Free: (800) 327-3787
E-mail: contactus@securityplastics.com
Web Site: www.nationalmolding.com
Approx. Number Employees: 900
Year Founded: 1955
Business Description:
Custom Injection Molder of Engineered Components, Thermoplastic Components & Mechanical & Decorative Secondary Ops Supplied to the E/E, Automotive & Telecommunications Markets
S.I.C.: 3089
N.A.I.C.S.: 326199
Export
Media: 2-4-7-10-13
Distr.: Natl.
Budget Set: Nov.
Personnel:
Joseph Anscher *(Pres)*
Brands & Products:
HETERO-CAVITY

SENSIENT COLORS INC.

(Sub. of Sensient Technologies Corporation)
2515 N Jefferson Ave
Saint Louis, MO 63106
Tel.: (314) 286-7160
Fax: (314) 658-7318
Fax: (314) 658-7314
Toll Free: (800) 325-8110
E-mail: sfc@sensient-tech.com
Web Site: www.sensient-tech.com
Approx. Rev.: $8,999,000
Approx. Number Employees: 300
Year Founded: 1904
Business Description:
Food Colors & Organic Pigments Mfr
S.I.C.: 2087
N.A.I.C.S.: 311930
Media: 1-2-4-7-10-13-20-21-22-26
Distr.: Intl.; Natl.
Budget Set: Oct.
Personnel:
Paul Manning *(Pres-Color Grp)*
Brands & Products:
ATLAS WHITE
COLOR PAK
DUST MASTER
EXTRUCLEAN
HERCULES
KOWET
LAKOLENE
MASTERCOTE
THE NATURAL RESOURCE
RED SEAL SPECTRABLEND CLEAR
RED SEAL SPECTRACOAT
RED SEAL SPECTRASPRAY
ULTRABIX

SEQUA CORPORATION

(Holding of The Carlyle Group, LLC)
200 Park Ave
New York, NY 10166
Tel.: (212) 986-5500
Fax: (212) 370-1969
Web Site: www.sequa.com
Approx. Sls.: $2,183,816,000
Approx. Number Employees: 10,155
Year Founded: 1929
Business Description:
Aerospace Components, Metal Coatings & Aerospace Products Mfr
S.I.C.: 9661; 3479; 3764; 5084; 7539
N.A.I.C.S.: 927110; 332812; 336415; 423830; 811118
Import Export
Advertising Expenditures: $5,303,000
Media: 17
Distr.: Intl.; Natl.
Budget Set: Jan.
Personnel:
Armand Lauzon, Jr. *(CEO)*
Donna M. Costello *(CFO)*
Gerard M. Dombek *(Pres-Precoat Metals)*
Steven R. Lowson *(Gen Counsel, Sec & VP)*
Robert F. Ellis *(Sr VP)*
John J. Bollman *(VP-HR)*
Robert D. DeVito *(VP-Corp Dev & Strategy)*
Andrew Farrant *(VP-Mktg & Corp Comm)*

SGS U.S. TESTING COMPANY INC.

(Sub. of SGS North America Inc.)
291 Fairfield Ave
Fairfield, NJ 07004-3833
Tel.: (973) 575-5252
Fax: (973) 575-7175
Fax: (963) 656-0636
Telex: 7607729 USTC-UR
E-mail: sgsisi.us@sgs.com
Web Site: www.ustesting.sgsna.com
Approx. Number Employees: 150
Year Founded: 1880
Business Description:
Specializes in the Testing Certification & Inspections of Industrial & Consumer Products
S.I.C.: 8733; 8734
N.A.I.C.S.: 541710; 541380
Advertising Expenditures: $200,000
Media: 2-4-7-10-13-20
Distr.: Natl.
Budget Set: Sept.
Brands & Products:
SGS
UNITED STATES TESTING COMPANY
USTC

SI GROUP, INC.

2750 Ball Gown Rd
Schenectady, NY 12309
Tel.: (518) 370-4200
Fax: (518) 370-3105
Fax: (518) 346-3111
E-mail: info@siigroup.com
Web Site: www.siigroup.com
E-Mail For Key Personnel:
Sales Director: productinfo@siigroup.com
Approx. Number Employees: 2,200
Year Founded: 1906
Business Description:
Insulating Varnishes, Magnet Wire Enamels, Coatings & Alkylphenols Mfr
S.I.C.: 2869; 3087
N.A.I.C.S.: 325110; 325991
Media: 2-4-7-8-10
Distr.: Intl.; Natl.
Budget Set: Nov.
Personnel:
Wallace A. Graham *(Chm)*
Stephen J. Large *(Pres & CEO)*
John C. Obst *(CFO & Sr VP-Fin)*
Heather Ward *(Sec & Dir-Global Plng)*
Paul Tilley *(Sr VP)*
Traci Hockstra *(VP-Global HR)*
Milan Knezevic *(Exec Dir-Global R & D)*
Frank Hert *(Mgr-Acctg)*
Brands & Products:
ALKYLPHENOLS
ECORAD
ISOCOAT

Key to Media (For complete agency information see *The Advertising Red Books-Agencies* edition):
1. Bus. Publs. 2. Cable T.V. 3. Catalogs & Directories. 4. Co-op Adv. 5. Consumer Mags. 6. D.M. to Bus. Estab.7. D.M. to Consumers 8. Daily Newsp. 9. Exhibits/Trade Shows 10. Foreign 11. Infomercial 12. Internet Adv.13. Multimedia 14. Network Radio 15. Network T.V. 16. Newsp. Distr. Mags. 17. Other 18. Outdoor (Posters, Transit) 19. Point of Purchase20. Premiums, Novelties 21. Product Samples 22. Special Events Mktg. 23. Spot Radio 24. Spot T.V. 25. Weekly Newsp. 26. Yellow Page Adv.

ISOLITE
ISONOX
ISORAD
REZICURE
RIBETAK

SIEMENS WATER TECHNOLOGIES

(Unit of Siemens Water Technologies)
1828 Metcalf Ave
Thomasville, GA 31792-6845
Mailing Address:
PO Box 1419
Thomasville, GA 31799-1419
Tel.: (229) 226-5733
Fax: (229) 228-0312
Web Site: www.usfilter.com
Approx. Number Employees: 200
Business Description:
Water & Sewage Distribution & Treatment Products
S.I.C.: 4953
N.A.I.C.S.: 562219
Import Export
Advertising Expenditures: $200,000
Media: 1-2-4-7-26
Distr.: Natl.
Budget Set: Mar.
Personnel:
Dwight Smith *(Product Mgr)*
Brands & Products:
DRAGON DRYER

SIGMA-ALDRICH CORPORATION

3050 Spruce St
Saint Louis, MO 63103-2530
Tel.: (314) 771-5765
Fax: (314) 286-5757
Toll Free: (800) 521-8956
E-mail: sig-ald@sial.com
Web Site: www.sigmaaldrich.com
Approx. Sls.: $2,271,000,000
Approx. Number Employees: 7,890
Year Founded: 1975
Business Description:
Biochemicals & Organic Chemicals Developer, Mfr & Distr
S.I.C.: 2899; 2836; 2869
N.A.I.C.S.: 325998; 325199; 325414
Export
Media: 1-2-4-7-8-10-13-16-20-21-22
Distr.: Intl.; Natl.
Budget Set: Jan.
Personnel:
Barrett A. Toan *(Chm)*
Rakesh Sachdev *(Pres & CEO)*
Magnus Borg *(CIO & VP)*
Gilles A. Cottier *(Pres-SAFC)*
David A. Smoller *(Pres-Res Biotech)*
Franklin D. Wicks, Jr. *(Pres-Res Specialties & Res Essentials)*
George Miller *(Gen Counsel, Sec & Sr VP)*
Karen J. Miller *(VP-Strategy & Corp Dev)*
Douglas W. Rau *(VP-HR)*
Gerrit J. C. Van Den Dool *(VP-Sls)*
Josef Vihlman *(VP-Mktg)*
Jeff Broadway *(Mgr-Mktg Comm)*
Kelley Euchner *(Coord-Mktg)*
Brands & Products:
ALDRICH
BIOTINTAG
EXTRAVIDIN
FLUKA
FLUOROTAG
GENELUTE
IMMUNOPROBE
PROTEOQWEST
RIEDEL-DE HAEN
SIGMA
SIGMA-ALDRICH
SIGMA HYBRI MAX
SUPELCO
Advertising Agency:
College Hill Life Sciences
The Registry Royal Mint Court
London, EC3N 4QN, United Kingdom
Tel.: (44) 20 7457 2020
Fax: (44) 20 7866 7900

SLIDE PRODUCTS, INC.

430 Wheeling Rd
Wheeling, IL 60090-4742
Mailing Address:
PO Box 156
Wheeling, IL 60090-0156
Tel.: (847) 541-7220
Fax: (847) 541-7986
Fax: (800) 756-7986
Toll Free: (800) 323-6433
E-mail: info@slideproducts.com
Web Site: www.slideproducts.com
Approx. Sls.: $4,000,000
Approx. Number Employees: 16
Year Founded: 1954
Business Description:
Industrial Aerosols, Lubricants, Mold Releases, Cleaners & Coatings Mfr
S.I.C.: 2813; 2992
N.A.I.C.S.: 325120; 324191
Export
Media: 2-4-5-7-10-11-21
Distr.: Intl.; Natl.
Budget Set: Dec.
Brands & Products:
ECONOMIST
ECONOSPRAY
NO-RUST
PENETRANT PLUS
QUICK
SLIDE
VERI-KLEEN

SOLUTIA INC.

575 Maryville Ctr Dr
Saint Louis, MO 63141-5813
Tel.: (314) 674-1000
Fax: (314) 674-1585
E-mail: info@solutia.com
Web Site: www.solutia.com
Approx. Sls.: $1,950,000,000
Approx. Number Employees: 3,300
Year Founded: 1997
Business Description:
Detergent, Rubber, Specialty Chemicals, Man-Made Fibers, Plastics, Resins, Elastomers, Pharmaceuticals & Fabricated Products
S.I.C.: 2821; 2824; 5122
N.A.I.C.S.: 325211; 325222; 424210
Export
Media: 2-7-10-11-13
Personnel:
Jeffrey N. Quinn *(Chm, Pres & CEO)*
James M. Sullivan *(CFO, Treas & Exec VP)*
James R. Voss *(COO & Exec VP)*
Paul J. Berra, III *(Chief Admin Officer, Gen Counsel & Sr VP-Legal & Governmental)*
Greta N. Senn *(Pres/Gen Mgr-Technical Specialties)*
Robert T. DeBolt *(Sr VP-Bus Ops)*
Nadim Z. Quereshi *(VP-Corp Dev & Strategy)*
Timothy J. Wessel *(Pres/Gen Mgr-Advanced Interlayers)*
Emily Bealke Parenteau *(Dir-Corp Branding)*
Brands & Products:
6QDI
ACRILAN
ADVANCED SOLUTIONS FOR GLASS
AGS
ALPHOX
AMINES
ASCEND
BOUNCE-BACK
BUTVAR
CLEAN MACHINE
CLEAR PASS
COKE
COURTGARD
CPFILMS
CRYSTEX
DURASCRAPE
DURASPUN
DURATREK
DYENAMIX
E-BUSINESS
FLEXSYS
FORMALIN
GILOTHERM
HB-40
HYDRAWAY
KEEPSAFE
KEEPSAFE GLASS & DESIGN
KEEPSAFE MAXIMUM
KOOL-LITE
LIQUA SHIELD
LITTER BUSTER
LITTER BUTLER
LOCKED-IN STAINBLOCKER
LXI
MCS
MEALMAID
MINERAL BLUE
NANO-CERAMIC
NO-SHOCK
PET HAIR ELIMINATOR
PHOSGARD
REMEMBER
RENEW
SAFLEX
SANTOCHLOR
SANTONYL
SANTOSOL
SANTOTAC MRS
SANTOWAX
SC50
SKYDROL
SKYKLEEN
THE SMART YARNS
SOLUTIA
SOLUTIA & INFINITY
SOLUTIONS FOR A BETTER LIFE
SOLUTIONS FOR IMPROVED PERFORMANCE
SOUND PRO
SPEC THIS
SPRAY GUARD
SUREBASE
TETRATHAL
THERMA SEALED
THERMINOL
ULTRON
UVSHIELD
VANCEVA
VANCEVA COLOR
VOCOL
VYDYNE
WEAR-DATED
ZEACRIMP

SOUTHERN AGRICULTURAL INSECTICIDES, INC.

7600 Bayshore Rd
Palmetto, FL 34221-8363
Tel.: (941) 722-3285
Fax: (941) 723-2974
E-mail: sales@southernag.com
Web Site: www.southernag.com
E-Mail For Key Personnel:
Sales Director: sales@southernag.com
Approx. Sls.: $43,000,000
Approx. Number Employees: 86
Year Founded: 1930
Business Description:
Agricultural Chemicals; Agricultural & Household Pesticides
S.I.C.: 5191; 2879
N.A.I.C.S.: 424910; 325320
Advertising Expenditures: $40,000
Media: 2-4-7-10-13-26
Personnel:
Darrin Diem *(Mgr-Mktg)*
Brands & Products:
CONSERVE
DURSBAN
LIVESTOCK DUST
MALATHION
PAYBACK
SA-50
SEVIN
SOUTHERN AG
VANTAGE
WEED PRO

SPECTRUM CHEMICALS & LABORATORY PRODUCTS, INC.

14422 S San Pedro St
Gardena, CA 90248-2027
Tel.: (310) 516-8000
Fax: (310) 516-9843
Toll Free: (800) 772-8786
E-mail: sales@spectrumchemical.com
Web Site: www.spectrumchemical.com
E-Mail For Key Personnel:
Sales Director: sales@spectrumchemical.com
Approx. Number Employees: 280
Year Founded: 1971
Business Description:
Laboratory & Research Chemicals & Laboratory Equipment & Supplies Mfr & Distr
S.I.C.: 2899; 2834
N.A.I.C.S.: 325998; 325412
Media: 2-4-7-8-10-13
Personnel:
Rodica Burg *(Owner)*
Paul Burg *(Chm)*
Sheldon Zhang *(Gen Mgr)*
Larry Hilton *(Dir-Bus)*
Brands & Products:
AMBERLITE
AQUAPHOR
AQUASTAR
ARISTOWAX
ASCARITE
ATLAS G
BIOSOLV

Key to Media (For complete agency information see *The Advertising Red Books-Agencies* edition):
1. Bus. Publs. 2. Cable T.V. 3. Catalogs & Directories. 4. Co-op Adv. 5. Consumer Mags. 6. D.M. to Bus. Estab.7. D.M. to Consumers 8. Daily Newsp. 9. Exhibits/Trade Shows 10. Foreign 11. Infomercial 12. Internet Adv.13. Multimedia 14. Network Radio 15. Network T.V. 16. Newsp. Distr. Mags. 17. Other 18. Outdoor (Posters, Transit) 19. Point of Purchase20. Premiums, Novelties 21. Product Samples 22. Special Events Mktg. 23. Spot Radio 24. Spot T.V. 25. Weekly Newsp. 26. Yellow Page Adv.

Spectrum Chemicals & Laboratory Products, Inc. — (Continued)

BLUE-TEN
BRIJ
CHROMACLEAN
CIRRASOL
CITRANOX
COOMASSIE
DAVISIL
DRIERITE
FERROZINE
GCSOLV
GCSOLY
HEXANICITE
HYDRANAL
HYDRION
IMPAQ
INDICATORPHIAL
IQEPAL
LIQUINOX
LUXOL
MICRO
MOISTURE-GONE
MYRI
N-POINT
NADIC
NONIDET
NORIT
OMNIPURE
OMNISOLV
OPTIFIX
PESTISOLV
PYCAL
RED-FOUR
RENEX
SPECTROSOLV
SPECTRUM
TERATHANE
TERGITOL
TIRON
TREVIGEL
TRISMAT
TRITON
ULTRACLEAN
UNISOLV
VITRIDE
WELCH DIRECTORR
XTRACLEAN
YELLOW-SEVEN

SPURRIER CHEMICAL COMPANIES, INC.

1200 E Central Ave
Wichita, KS 67214
Tel.: (316) 265-9491
Fax: (316) 265-9518
Toll Free: (800) 835-1059
E-mail: info@spurrierchemical.com
Web Site: www.spurrierchemical.com
Approx. Number Employees: 45
Year Founded: 1932
Business Description:
Mfr. of Cleaning Products
S.I.C.: 2869; 5087
N.A.I.C.S.: 325199; 423850
Media: 2-10
Personnel:
Robert Spurrier *(Pres)*
Donald Ryel *(Sr VP)*

STEMCO INC

(Sub. of EnPro Industries, Inc.)
300 Industrial Dr
Longview, TX 75602-4720
Mailing Address:
PO Box 1989
Longview, TX 75606-1989
Tel.: (903) 758-9981
Fax: (903) 232-3530
E-mail: info@stemco.com
Web Site: www.stemco.com
Sales Range: $150-199.9 Million
Approx. Number Employees: 400
Business Description:
Wheel Lubrication Systems
S.I.C.: 3714
N.A.I.C.S.: 336399
Personnel:
Jay A. Johnston *(Chm)*
Jon Cox *(Pres)*
Dan Gregurich *(VP-Fin)*
Morie Myers *(VP-Sls)*
John Rickers *(VP-HR)*
Jeff Pond *(Reg Mgr-Sls)*
Todd Heim *(Product Mgr-Brake Products Grp)*
Alan Matsumoto *(Mgr-Natl Svc)*
Advertising Agency:
Stiegler, Wells, Brunswick & Roth, Inc.
(d/b/a SWB&R)
3865 Adler Pl
Bethlehem, PA 18017-9000
Tel.: (610) 866-0611
Fax: (610) 866-8650

STEPAN COMPANY

Edens & Winnetka Rd
Northfield, IL 60093
Tel.: (847) 446-7500
Fax: (847) 501-2100
E-mail: jhurlbutt@stepan.com
Web Site: www.stepan.com
Approx. Sls.: $1,431,122,000
Approx. Number Employees: 1,768
Year Founded: 1932
Business Description:
Basic & Intermediate Chemicals & Surfactants Mfr
S.I.C.: 2899; 2821; 2841; 2843; 5122
N.A.I.C.S.: 325998; 325211; 325611; 325613; 446120
Import Export
Media: 2-4-7-10-13
Distr.: Direct to Consumer; Intl.; Natl.
Budget Set: Oct.
Personnel:
F. Quinn Stepan, Sr. *(Chm)*
F. Quinn Stepan, Jr. *(Pres & CEO)*
James E. Hurlbutt *(CFO & VP)*
Frank Pacholec *(VP-R&D & Corp Sustainability Officer)*
H. Edward Wynn *(Gen Counsel, Sec & VP)*
John Hall *(VP & Gen Mgr-Asia Pacific Surfactants)*
John V. Venegoni *(VP & Gen Mgr-Surfactants)*
Robert J. Wood *(VP & Gen Mgr-Polymers)*
Robert S. Mangold *(VP-Mfg & Engrg)*
Arthur W. Mergner *(VP-Procurement)*
Gregory Servatius *(VP-HR)*
Kathleen O. Sherlock *(Asst Sec & Asst Gen Counsel)*
Brands & Products:
ACCOSOFT
ALPHA FOAMER
ALPHA-STEP
AMMONYX
AMPHOSOL
BIO-SOFT
BIO-TERGE
BIOBLOX
CEDEPAL
CEDEPHOS
DREWMULSE
DREWPLAST
DREWPOL
EMULPHOPAL
EMULPHOR
G-3300
HALLCOMID
IGEPAL
LATHANOL
MAKON
MAPROSY
MERPOL
MICRO-STEP
NACCONOL
NEOBEE
NEUTRONYX
NINATE
NINEX
NINOL
NIPOL
NUTRAPON
ONAMER
ONYXIDE
PETROSTEP
PHTHALIC ANHYDRIDE
PLASTICIZER
POLYSTEP
SECOMIX
SECOSOL
SO/SAN
STEOL
STEP-FLOW
STEPAN
STEPAN-MILD
STEPAN S
STEPANATE
STEPANFOAM
STEPANFORM
STEPANOL
STEPANPOL
STEPANQUAT
STEPANTAN
STEPANTEX
STEPFAC
STEPOSOL
STEPSPERSE
STEPWET
SULFONIC
TOXIMUL
WECOBEE
ZELEC
Advertising Agency:
L.C. Williams & Associates, LLC
150 N Michigan Ave 38th Fl
Chicago, IL 60601-7558
Tel.: (312) 565-3900
Fax: (312) 565-1770
Toll Free: (800) 837-7123

THE STIMPSON COMPANY, INC.

1515 sw 13th Ct
Pompano Beach, FL 33069
Tel.: (954) 946-3500
Fax: (954) 545-7440
Toll Free: (877) 765-0748
E-mail: customer_service@stimpson.com
Web Site: www.stimpson.com
Approx. Number Employees: 500
Business Description:
Metal Stampings Mfr
S.I.C.: 3965; 3452
N.A.I.C.S.: 339993; 332722
Advertising Expenditures: $200,000
Media: 4-7-10-11
Distr.: Intl.
Personnel:
Scott Thomas *(Pres)*
Bill Rauss *(VP-Mktg & Sls)*
Brands & Products:
CE
STIMPSON
STIMPSON GS

STONETECH PROFESSIONAL

(Sub. of DuPont Safety & Protection)
370 N Wiget Ln Ste 200
Walnut Creek, CA 94598
Tel.: (925) 295-9700
Fax: (925) 295-9701
Toll Free: (877) 786-6383
E-mail: info@stonetechpro.com
Web Site: www.stonetechpro.com
Sales Range: $1-9.9 Million
Approx. Number Employees: 22
Year Founded: 1997
Business Description:
Protective Chemicals & Care Products for Natural Stone, Ceramic Tile, Grout & Masonry Surfaces Mfr & Whslr
S.I.C.: 5169
N.A.I.C.S.: 424690
Media: 4-6-10-26
Brands & Products:
BULLETPROOF
ENHANCER PRO
IMPREGNATOR PRO
KLENZALL
RESTORE
REVITALIZER
STONETECH PROFESSIONAL

SUD-CHEMIE INC.

(Sub. of Sud-Chemie AG)
1600 W Hill St
Louisville, KY 40210-1750
Mailing Address:
PO Box 32370
Louisville, KY 40232-2370
Tel.: (502) 634-7200
Fax: (502) 637-3732
Telex: 204190
Telex: 204239
E-mail: webmaster@sud-chemieinc.com
Web Site: www.sud-chemieinc.com
Approx. Number Employees: 750
Year Founded: 1977
Business Description:
Catalyst & Specialty Chemical Mfr
S.I.C.: 2819; 3295
N.A.I.C.S.: 325188; 327992
Import Export
Advertising Expenditures: $350,000
Consumer Mags.: $70,000; D.M. to Consumers: $105,000; Exhibits/Trade Shows: $175,000
Distr.: Intl.; Natl.
Budget Set: Dec.
Personnel:
John A. Ray *(CEO)*
Charles Maisch *(VP-HR)*
Jill Parman *(Mgr-Mktg)*

SULZER CHEMTECH USA, INC.

(Sub. of Sulzer Chemtech AG)
4106 New W Dr
Pasadena, TX 77507
Tel.: (281) 604-4100
Fax: (281) 291-0207
E-mail: p-merry@spencer-ind.com
Web Site: www.sulzerchemtech.com
Approx. Number Employees: 40

Key to Media (For complete agency information see *The Advertising Red Books-Agencies* edition):
1. Bus. Publs. 2. Cable T.V. 3. Catalogs & Directories. 4. Co-op Adv. 5. Consumer Mags. 6. D.M. to Bus. Estab.7. D.M. to Consumers 8. Daily Newsp. 9. Exhibits/Trade Shows 10. Foreign 11. Infomercial 12. Internet Adv.13. Multimedia 14. Network Radio 15. Network T.V. 16. Newsp. Distr. Mags. 17. Other 18. Outdoor (Posters, Transit) 19. Point of Purchase20. Premiums, Novelties 21. Product Samples 22. Special Events Mktg. 23. Spot Radio 24. Spot T.V. 25. Weekly Newsp. 26. Yellow Page Adv.

Business Description:
Provider of Chemical Technology Services in Mass Transfer
S.I.C.: 3441
N.A.I.C.S.: 332312
Advertising Agency:
AMP Agency
295 Devonshire St
Boston, MA 02110
Tel.: (617) 542-5587
Fax: (617) 896-1311

SUMMIT CORPORATION OF AMERICA
1430 Waterbury Rd
Thomaston, CT 06787-2029
Tel.: (860) 283-4391
Fax: (860) 283-4010
E-mail: sales@scact.com
Web Site: www.scact.com
E-Mail For Key Personnel:
Sales Director: sales@scact.com
Approx. Number Employees: 100
Business Description:
Electroplating
S.I.C.: 3471; 3479
N.A.I.C.S.: 332813; 332812
Media: 13
Personnel:
Harry Skoble *(Pres)*
Dave Smith *(Dir-Sls & Mktg)*
Michael Montana *(Mgr-Inside Sls & Estimating)*

SUN CHEMICAL INK
(Div. of Sun Chemical Corporation)
135 W Lake St
Northlake, IL 60164
Tel.: (708) 562-0550
Fax: (708) 562-0580
Toll Free: (800) 933-7863
Web Site: www.sunchemicalink.com
Approx. Number Employees: 4,000
Year Founded: 1928
Business Description:
General Printing Inks Mfr
S.I.C.: 2893
N.A.I.C.S.: 325910
Advertising Expenditures: $2,000,000
Media: 2-4-7-10-13-20-26
Distr.: Intl.; Natl.
Personnel:
Susan Guerin *(CFO)*
Greg Lawson *(Pres-Sun Chemical Latin America)*
Corey Soeldner *(Dir-Pur & Supply Chain-N America)*
Brands & Products:
SUNCHEMCIAL

SUNOCO CHEMICALS
(Sub. of Sunoco Inc.)
1735 Market St
Philadelphia, PA 19103-1699
Tel.: (215) 977-3000
Fax: (215) 977-3470
Toll Free: (877) 481-7840
E-mail: info@sunocochem.com
Web Site: www.sunocochemicals.com
Approx. Sls.: $1,000,000,000
Approx. Number Employees: 939
Year Founded: 1986
Business Description:
Industrial Chemicals, Dibasic Acids & Alcohol, Plasticizers, Acrylic Sheet; Polypropylene Mfr
S.I.C.: 2869; 2899
N.A.I.C.S.: 325110; 325998
Export
Media: 1-2-4-7-9-10-21
Distr.: Natl.
Budget Set: Dec.
Personnel:
Bruce G. Fischer *(Sr VP)*
Robert Owens *(Sr VP-Mktg)*

SUPER GLUE CORPORATION
9420 Santa Anita Ave
Rancho Cucamonga, CA 91730-6117
Tel.: (909) 987-0550
Fax: (909) 987-0490
Toll Free: (800) 538-3091
E-mail: info@supergluecorp.com
Web Site: www.supergluecorp.com
Approx. Number Employees: 113
Year Founded: 1982
Business Description:
Mfr & Supplier of Glues, Epoxies & Other Adhesives for Household, Office & Consumer Applications
S.I.C.: 2891; 3089
N.A.I.C.S.: 325520; 326199
Import Export
Media: 2-4-5-6-10-13-14-19-21-22-26
Personnel:
Ronald T. Gravette *(Pres)*
Brands & Products:
ANCHOR-TITE
BLUE XS
BONDINI
COPPER XS
FUTURE GLUE
PACER
PACER TECH INDUSTRIAL
PRO-LOK
PRO SEAL
PRO WELD
SUPER GLUE
ZAP
Advertising Agency:
Nuffer Smith Tucker, Inc.
707 Broadway 19th Fl
San Diego, CA 92101
Tel.: (619) 296-0605
Fax: (619) 296-8530

SYMRISE, INC.
(Sub. of Symrise AG)
300 N St
Teterboro, NJ 07608-1204
Tel.: (201) 288-3200
Fax: (201) 462-2250
Toll Free: (800) 422-1559
Web Site: www.symrise.com
Year Founded: 1997
Business Description:
Mfr. & Sell Flavors, Fragrances & Aroma Chemicals Used in Foods, Perfumery, Cosmetics & Other Consumer Products
S.I.C.: 2869
N.A.I.C.S.: 325199
Import Export
Advertising Expenditures: $200,000
Media: 2-6-10-16
Distr.: Intl.; Natl.
Budget Set: Sept. -Oct.
Personnel:
Arlene Kobos *(VP-Sls)*
Brands & Products:
CREMOGEN
DARITEEN
FRESCOLAT
MENTHOL H & R
NEOHELIOPAN
OPTAMINT
OPTAROME
Advertising Agency:
Delfino Marketing Communications, Inc.
400 Columbus Ave Ste 120S
Valhalla, NY 10595-1396
Tel.: (914) 747-1400
Fax: (914) 747-1430
(Flavors, Fragrances, Aroma Chemicals)

SYNGENTA PROFESSIONAL PRODUCTS
(Sub. of Syngenta AG)
PO Box 18300
Greensboro, NC 27419
Tel.: (336) 632-6107
Fax: (336) 632-2290
Toll Free: (866) 796-4368
Web Site:
www.syngentaprofessionalproducts.com
Business Description:
Turf, Vegetation & Pest Management Gardening Products
S.I.C.: 2879
N.A.I.C.S.: 325320
Personnel:
Steve Spain *(Head-Sls)*
Margaret Bell *(Sr Mgr-Mktg Comm)*
Advertising Agencies:
Martin/Williams Advertising Inc.
(A Member of Omnicom Group)
60 S 6th St Ste 2800
Minneapolis, MN 55402-4428
Tel.: (612) 340-0800
Fax: (612) 342-9700
Syngenta Crop Protection
Syngenta Seeds

Trone Inc.
4035 Piedmont Pkwy
High Point, NC 27265-9402
Tel.: (336) 886-1622
Fax: (336) 886-2174
(Lawn & Garden, Home Care Products)

TECH SPRAY, L.P.
(Sub. of Illinois Tool Works Inc.)
1001 NW 1st
Amarillo, TX 79107
Tel.: (806) 372-8523
Fax: (806) 372-8750
Toll Free: (800) 858-4043
E-mail: tsales@techspray.com
Web Site: www.techspray.com
E-Mail For Key Personnel:
Sales Director: Maurer@techspray.com
Sales Range: $100-124.9 Million
Approx. Number Employees: 44
Year Founded: 1968
Business Description:
Chemical Cleaners & Anti-Static Solutions
S.I.C.: 5169; 8733
N.A.I.C.S.: 424690; 541710
Advertising Expenditures: $300,000
Media: 1-2-4-5-7-10-13-19-21
Distr.: Intl.; Natl.
Budget Set: July
Personnel:
David Boysen *(Gen Mgr)*
Ken Caskey *(Dir-Sls)*
Steve Cook *(Dir-Product Tech)*
Kevin Marion *(Reg Mgr-Midwest & Canada)*
Brands & Products:
ADVANEX
AXAREL
BLUE SHOWER
BLUE STUFF
C/D-SOLV
CONTACT CLEANER
EASY PULL
ECOLINE
ECOLUBE
ECONLINE
ENVI-RO-TECH
EQUINOX GOLD
FD PLUS
FINE-L-KOTE
FLUX REMOVER
G3
GENESOLV
KLEEN-IT
LICRON
NO CLEAN FLUX REMOVER
PENETRATOR
PRECISION DUSTER
PRO WICK
PROSHIELD
PURWIPE
QUICK TEST
RID-OX
SLIC
SMT
STATIC SENSITIVE BRUSHES
STRATUS
TECH BRUSHES
TECH HOLD
TECHBRUSH
TECHCLEAN
TECHROLL
TECHSPRAY
TECHSWABS
TRACE TECHNOLOGIES
TSNET
VORTEX
WONDERMAS
WONDERMASK
ZERO CHARGE

TECHNIC INCORPORATED
1 Spectacle St
Cranston, RI 02910-1032
Mailing Address:
PO Box 9650
Providence, RI 02940-9650
Tel.: (401) 781-6100
Fax: (401) 781-2890
E-mail: info@technic.com
Web Site: www.technic.com
Approx. Number Employees: 500
Year Founded: 1945
Business Description:
Mfr. of Chemical & Metallurgical Products
S.I.C.: 2899; 3559
N.A.I.C.S.: 325998; 333298
Import Export
Media: 1-2-7-10-11-20-21-22-26
Distr.: Intl.
Personnel:
Peter Ribbons *(Dir-Mktg & Adv)*
Bob Sheeren *(Mgr-Mktg)*
Brands & Products:
ACR
COTE D'OR
CY-LESS
DECOR
GOLD-CLAD
NICKEL STRIPPER
OROCLAD
OROMERSE

Key to Media (For complete agency information see *The Advertising Red Books-Agencies* edition):
1. Bus. Publs. 2. Cable T.V. 3. Catalogs & Directories. 4. Co-op Adv. 5. Consumer Mags. 6. D.M. to Bus. Estab.7. D.M. to Consumers 8. Daily Newsp. 9. Exhibits/Trade Shows 10. Foreign 11. Infomercial 12. Internet Adv.13. Multimedia 14. Network Radio 15. Network T.V. 16. Newsp. Distr. Mags. 17. Other 18. Outdoor (Posters, Transit) 19. Point of Purchase20. Premiums, Novelties 21. Product Samples 22. Special Events Mktg. 23. Spot Radio 24. Spot T.V. 25. Weekly Newsp. 26. Yellow Page Adv.

Technic Incorporated — (Continued)

OROSENE
OROTEMP
OROTHERM
PALLABAR
PALLADIUM-NICKEL
PALLAMERSE
PALLASPEED
PLATINUM AP
PLATINUM TP
RHODIUM S-LESS
TARNIBAN
TECHNI ACTIVATING
TECHNI COPPER
TECHNI EN
TECHNI ENVIROSTRIP AG
TECHNI FB BRIGHT ACID COPPER
TECHNI-GOLDCLAD
TECHNI NF COPPER
TECHNI NICKEL JB
TECHNI RESIST STRIP
TECHNI-RHODIUM
TECHNI SBZ CONDITIONER
TECHNI-SILVER
TECHNI-SOLDER
TECHNI STRIP AU
TECHNI-TIN
TECHNI X-CELL
TECHNIC ACID DESCALER BC
TECHNIC BUFF SOLV
TECHNIC-COPPER
TECHNIC DIE GLO-ZN
TECHNIC-LAB
TECHNIC NICKEL
TECHNIC TEC
TECHNIC ZAMAK BRITE DIP
TECHNIGOLD
TECHNISPEED G
TECHNISPEED VG
TRUSHADE

TECK RESOURCES LIMITED

550 Burrard Street Suite 3300
Vancouver, BC V6C 0B3, Canada
Tel.: (604) 699-4000
Fax: (604) 699-4750
E-mail: info@teck.com
Web Site: www.teckcominco.com
Approx. Rev.: $9,139,892,520
Approx. Number Employees: 9,100
Year Founded: 1906
Business Description:
Mineral & Metal Ore Exploration, Mining, Smelting & Refining Services
S.I.C.: 1031; 1021; 1041; 1081; 1222; 1241; 3331; 3339; 5052
N.A.I.C.S.: 212231; 212112; 212221; 212234; 213113; 213114; 331411; 331419; 423520
Import Export
Advertising Expenditures: $10,000,000
Media: 6-9-10
Distr.: Intl.
Budget Set: Sept. -Nov.
Personnel:
Norman B. Keevil *(Chm)*
Donald Richard Lindsay *(Pres & CEO)*
Ronald A. Millos *(CFO & Sr VP-Fin)*
G. Leonard Manuel *(Gen Counsel & Sr VP)*
Mike Agg *(Sr VP-Zinc)*
Roger Higgins *(Sr VP-Copper)*
Douglas H. Horswill *(Sr VP-Sustainability & External Affairs)*
Boyd Payne *(Sr VP-Coal)*
Peter C. Rozee *(Sr VP-Comml & Legal Affairs)*
Robert G. Scott *(Sr VP-Operating Excellence)*
Ronald J. Vance *(Sr VP-Corp Dev)*
Timothy C. Watson *(Sr VP-Project Dev)*
Michael J. Allan *(VP-Engrg)*
Anne J. Chalmers *(VP-Risk & Security)*
John F.H. Thompson *(VP-Tech & Dev)*
James A. Utley *(VP-HR)*
Catherine Hart *(Mgr-Public Affairs, Coal & Energy)*
Anthony A. Zoobkoff *(Asst Sec & Sr Counsel)*
Brands & Products:
BATH MANAGER
BRITEPLUS
CRX
DEAL
GALVA-GUARD
PAL
TECK
Advertising Agency:
Edelman
214 King Street W Suite 600
Toronto, ON M5H 3S6, Canada
Tel.: (416) 979-1120
Fax: (416) 979-0176

TEKRA CORPORATION

16700 W Lincoln Ave
New Berlin, WI 53151-2728
Tel.: (262) 784-5533
Fax: (262) 797-3276
Toll Free: (800) 448-3572
Telex: 880393 TEKRA UD
E-mail: info@tekra.com
Web Site: www.tekra.com
Approx. Number Employees: 185
Year Founded: 1938
Business Description:
Wholesale Distr & Converter of Plastic Films, Adhesive Tapes, Laminating Adhesives, Hardcoated Plastics & Printable Topcoated Films
S.I.C.: 3089; 3081
N.A.I.C.S.: 326199; 326113
Import Export
Media: 2-7-10-13-26
Distr.: Natl.
Personnel:
Andrew Tully *(Pres & CEO)*
Harry Whepley *(COO & Exec VP)*
Mike Drehobl *(VP)*
Mark Mawer *(VP-Sls & Mktg)*
Andy Danihel *(Mgr-Digital Adv)*
Julie Levins *(Mgr-Market Dev)*
Kevin Suino *(Mgr-Market Dev)*
Jason Wichmann *(Mgr-R & D)*
Brands & Products:
BAYFOL
DURA-GO
DURAKOTE
DURAVIEW
MAKROFOL
MARNOT
MELINEX
MYLAR
PROTEK
TEIJIN
TEONEX
TERRAPIN
TETORON
TYVEK

THEOCHEM LABORATORIES, INC.

7373 Rowlett Pk Dr
Tampa, FL 33610
Tel.: (813) 237-6463
Fax: (813) 237-2059
Toll Free: (800) 237-2591
E-mail: webmaster@theochem.com
Web Site: www.theochem.com
E-Mail For Key Personnel:
President: johnt@theochem.com
Approx. Number Employees: 150
Year Founded: 1963
Business Description:
Cleaning & Maintenance Products Including Aerosols, Automotive Chemicals, Acid Cleaners, Bowl Cleaners, Carpet Cleaners, Dishwashing Chemicals, Floor Finishers & Sealers, Laundry Products & Rust Removers Mfr
S.I.C.: 2842; 2841
N.A.I.C.S.: 325612; 325611
Import Export
Media: 2-4-5-7-10-18-21-22-26
Distr.: Intl.; Natl.
Budget Set: May
Personnel:
John S. Theofilos *(Pres & CEO)*
Steve Morrison *(VP-Sls & Market Dev)*
Brands & Products:
AIREZE
MOLDSTAT
SOLUTIONS FOR A CLEANER WORLD
THEOCHEM LABORATORIES

TITANIUM METALS CORPORATION

(d/b/a Timet)
5430 LBJ Fwy Ste 1700
Dallas, TX 75240
Tel.: (972) 934-5300
Fax: (972) 934-5343
E-mail: investor.relations@timet.com
Web Site: www.timet.com
Approx. Sls.: $1,151,500,000
Approx. Number Employees: 2,385
Business Description:
Titanium Metal Products Mfr
S.I.C.: 3341; 3339; 3356
N.A.I.C.S.: 331423; 331419; 331491
Import Export
Media: 1-2-4-7-8-10-21
Distr.: Intl.; Natl.
Budget Set: Nov.
Personnel:
Harold C. Simmons *(Chm)*
Steven L. Watson *(Vice Chm)*
Bobby D. O'Brien *(Pres & CEO)*
Christopher Armstrong *(Exec VP)*
Robert D. Graham *(Exec VP)*
James R. Pieron *(Exec VP-Global Ops & Logistics)*
Kelly D. Luttmer *(VP & Dir-Tax)*
Brands & Products:
CODEROLL
CODEWELD
TIMET
TIMETAL

TOHO TENAX AMERICA, INC.

(Sub. of Toho Tenax Co., Ltd.)
121 Cardiff Vly Rd
Rockwood, TN 37854
Tel.: (865) 354-8408
Fax: (865) 354-8409
Toll Free: (800) 252-3001
E-mail: info@tohotenaxamerica.com
Web Site: www.tohotenaxamerica.com
Approx. Number Employees: 150
Business Description:
Carbon Fiber Mfr
S.I.C.: 2824
N.A.I.C.S.: 325222
Import Export
Media: 7-10
Distr.: Natl.
Budget Set: Nov.
Personnel:
Robert Klawonn *(Pres)*
David L. Lacy *(Mgr-Sls)*
Brands & Products:
ACRYLOX
FORTAFIL
UNIWEB

TOR MINERALS INTERNATIONAL INC.

722 Burleson St
Corpus Christi, TX 78402-1344
Mailing Address:
PO Box 2544
Corpus Christi, TX 78403-2544
Tel.: (361) 882-5175
Fax: (361) 883-7619
E-mail: info@torminerals.com
Web Site: www.torminerals.com
Approx. Sls.: $31,016,000
Approx. Number Employees: 146
Year Founded: 1973
Business Description:
Mineral Products, Pigments & Pigment Extenders for Use in Paints, Industrial Coatings & Plastics Mfr
S.I.C.: 1479; 2816; 5169
N.A.I.C.S.: 212393; 325131; 424690
Import Export
Media: 2-4-7-10-17
Distr.: Intl.; Natl.
Personnel:
Bernard A. Paulson *(Chm)*
Olaf Karasch *(Pres, CEO & Mng Dir)*
Barbara Russell *(CFO)*
Mark Schomp *(Exec VP-Sls & Mktg)*
Lance Silstorf *(Mgr-Sls & Mktg-North America)*
Brands & Products:
ALUPREM
BARTEX
HALTEX
HITOX
TIOPREM
TITOX
Advertising Agency:
Morehead, Dotts & Associates
2767 Santa Fe
Corpus Christi, TX 78404
Tel.: (361) 883-6327

TOTAL PETROCHEMICALS USA, INC.

(Sub. of Total Petrochemicals)
1201 Louisiana St Ste 1800
Houston, TX 77002
Mailing Address:
PO Box 674411
Houston, TX 77267-4411
Tel.: (713) 483-5000
Fax: (713) 483-5466
Telex: 730316
E-mail: publicaffairs@total.com

Key to Media (For complete agency information see *The Advertising Red Books-Agencies* edition):
1. Bus. Publs. 2. Cable T.V. 3. Catalogs & Directories. 4. Co-op Adv. 5. Consumer Mags. 6. D.M. to Bus. Estab.7. D.M. to Consumers 8. Daily Newsp. 9. Exhibits/Trade Shows 10. Foreign 11. Infomercial 12. Internet Adv.13. Multimedia 14. Network Radio 15. Network T.V. 16. Newsp. Distr. Mags. 17. Other 18. Outdoor (Posters, Transit) 19. Point of Purchase20. Premiums, Novelties 21. Product Samples 22. Special Events Mktg. 23. Spot Radio 24. Spot T.V. 25. Weekly Newsp. 26. Yellow Page Adv.

Web Site: www.totalpetrochemicalsusa.com
Sales Range: $1-4.9 Billion
Approx. Number Employees: 1,700
Year Founded: 1956
Business Description:
Mfr. of Polypropylene, Polyethylene & Polystyrene, Styrene, Base Chemicals & Transportation Fuels
S.I.C.: 2869; 3086
N.A.I.C.S.: 325110; 326140
Import Export
Advertising Expenditures: $3,400,000
Media: 1-2-3-5-7-8-9-10-15-16-18-19-20-22-23-24
Distr.: Reg.
Budget Set: Nov.
Personnel:
Bertrand De La Noue *(CFO)*
Geoffroy Petit *(Sr VP-Strategy & Svcs)*
Karyn Grace *(Mgr-Pub Affairs & Corp Comm)*

TRIMAX BUILDING PRODUCTS
(Sub. of American Pacific Financial Corporation)
(Filed for Ch.11 Bankruptcy, 7/23/2004)
2600 W Roosevelt Rd
Chicago, IL 60608
Tel.: (312) 491-2500
Fax: (312) 491-2501
Toll Free: (866) 987-4629
E-mail: info@trimaxbp.com
Web Site: www.trimaxbp.com
Sales Range: $25-49.9 Million
Approx. Number Employees: 449
Year Founded: 2006
Business Description:
Plastic Lumber Products Mfr
S.I.C.: 2821
N.A.I.C.S.: 325211
Advertising Expenditures: $880,000
Media: 2-7-10
Brands & Products:
CARFREE XTERIORS
DURAWOOD HDPE
RECYCLE DESIGN
TRIMAX STRUCTURE

TROY CORPORATION
8 Vreeland Rd
Florham Park, NJ 07932-0955
Tel.: (973) 443-4200
Fax: (973) 443-0258
E-mail: troyusa@troycorp.com
Web Site: www.troycorp.com
E-Mail For Key Personnel:
Marketing Director: marketing@troycorp.com
Approx. Number Employees: 100
Year Founded: 1950
Business Description:
Mfr. of Industrial Fungicides, Bactericides, Specialty Chemicals for Paints, Inks, Adhesives, Caulks, Sealants, Textiles & Metal Working Fluids
S.I.C.: 2869; 2992
N.A.I.C.S.: 325199; 324191
Import Export
Media: 7-10-22
Distr.: Intl.; Natl.
Budget Set: July
Personnel:
Daryl D. Smith *(Chm & CEO)*
Mark C. Gwillim *(Pres & COO)*
Ismael Colon *(Mng Dir & VP)*
Gordon P. Andrews *(Gen Counsel)*
Donald A. Shaw *(Gen Mgr & VP-Dev)*
David E. Faherty, Jr. *(VP-Sls & Mktg)*
Alexander M. Gerardo *(VP-HR & Admin)*
Brands & Products:
B-F
CM TESTER
GROTAN
MERGAL
MICROPEL
POLYPHASE
POWDERMATE
TROY
TROY UNIFILM
TROYCHEM
TROYKYD
TROYMAX
TROYSAN
TROYSHIELD
TROYSOL
TROYSPERSE
TROYTHIX
WOCOSEN

UNETTE CORPORATION
88 N Main St
Wharton, NJ 07885-1607
Tel.: (973) 328-6800
Fax: (973) 328-0500
E-mail: info@unette.com
Web Site: www.unette.com
Sales Range: $10-24.9 Million
Approx. Number Employees: 80
Year Founded: 1955
Business Description:
Tube & Pouch Filling & Contract Filling of Liquids & Creams
S.I.C.: 3089
N.A.I.C.S.: 326199
Import Export
Media: 2-4-10-13-21-22-26
Distr.: Intl.; Natl.
Budget Set: Nov.
Personnel:
Joseph R. Hark *(Pres)*
Chris Doscher *(VP-Fin)*
Brands & Products:
COPICAP
DRUMCAP
PRISMAPAK
UNETTE

UNITED-GUARDIAN, INC.
230 Marcus Blvd
Hauppauge, NY 11788-3731
Mailing Address:
PO Box 18050
Hauppauge, NY 11788-8850
Tel.: (631) 273-0900
Fax: (631) 273-0858
Toll Free: (800) 645-5566
E-mail: pgc@u-g.com
Web Site: www.u-g.com
Approx. Sls.: $13,723,074
Approx. Number Employees: 36
Year Founded: 1942
Business Description:
Drugs, Organic Laboratory Reagents, Fine & Specialty Chemicals, Healthcare & Specialty Products & Cosmetic Bases Mfr
S.I.C.: 2841; 2834; 2844; 2899
N.A.I.C.S.: 325611; 325412; 325620; 325998
Import Export
Advertising Expenditures: $8,800
Media: 2-4-6-7-8-9-10-21-26
Distr.: Intl.
Budget Set: Mar.
Personnel:
Kenneth H. Globus *(Chm, Pres & Gen Counsel)*
Robert S. Rubinger *(CFO, Treas, Sec & Exec VP)*
Charles W. Castanza *(Sr VP & Dir-Plant Ops)*
Joseph J. Vernice *(VP & Dir-Tech Svcs & Mgr-R&D)*
Peter A. Hiltunen *(VP & Mgr-Production)*
Brands & Products:
ACUAJEL
DERMA-SURE SKIN BARRIER
SUPER TI POWDER
UNITED-GUARDIAN

UNIVAR INC.
(Corporate Headquarters of Univar N.V.)
17425 NE Union Hill Rd
Redmond, WA 98052
Mailing Address:
PO Box 34325
Seattle, WA 98124-1325
Tel.: (425) 889-3400
Fax: (425) 889-4100
Web Site: www.univarcorp.com
Sales Range: $1-4.9 Billion
Approx. Number Employees: 3,950
Year Founded: 1924
Business Description:
Holding Company; Chemicals Distr
S.I.C.: 6719; 5169
N.A.I.C.S.: 551112; 424690
Import Export
Advertising Expenditures: $300,000
Media: 2-4-10
Distr.: Intl.; Natl.
Budget Set: Oct.
Personnel:
Gary E. Pruitt *(Chm)*
John J. Zillmer *(Pres & CEO)*
Steven M. Nielsen *(CFO & Exec VP)*
Mark J. Byrne *(COO & Exec VP)*
Edward A. Evans *(Chief HR Officer & Exec VP)*
Terry Hill *(Pres-Emerging Markets & Exec VP-Indus Rels)*
Randy D. Craddock *(Pres-Canada)*
David M. Strizzi *(Pres-US)*
Peter D. Heinz *(Gen Counsel, Sec & VP)*
John Ederer *(VP-Global Comm & IR)*
Jane Wells *(VP-Mktg)*
Beth Warren *(Dir-Mktg-Food Ingredients)*
Karen Weber-Millstein *(Dir-Corp Comm)*
Advertising Agency:
CitySavvy Ltd.
39 King Street
London, WC2E 8JS, United Kingdom
Tel.: (44) 20 7395 1000
Fax: (44) 20 7395 1001

U.S. PUMICE COMPANY
20219 Bahama St
Chatsworth, CA 91311-6204
Tel.: (818) 882-3888
Fax: (818) 882-9643
Toll Free: (800) 423-3037
Web Site: www.uspumice.com
Approx. Number Employees: 15
Year Founded: 1941
Business Description:
Block Pumice Mining & Block Pumice Products Producers
S.I.C.: 1499; 3299
N.A.I.C.S.: 212399; 327999
Media: 2-4-5-6-7-8-10-19-21-26
Distr.: Natl.
Budget Set: Oct.
Personnel:
Eric L. Anderson *(Pres)*
Brands & Products:
FEATHEROCK
GRILLMASTER
LADY'S AIDE
POOL BLOK
PUMIE
UNITED STATES PUMICE COMPANY
Advertising Agency:
Sierra Advertisers
20219 Bahama St
Chatsworth, CA 91311
Tel.: (818) 882-3888
Fax: (818) 882-9643

U.S. SILICA COMPANY
(Holding of Golden Gate Capital)
2496 Hancock Rd
Berkeley Springs, WV 25411
Mailing Address:
PO Box 187
Berkeley Springs, WV 25411
Tel.: (304) 258-2500
Fax: (304) 258-8295
Toll Free: (800) 243-7500
E-mail: sales@ussilica.com
Web Site: www.u-s-silica.com
E-Mail For Key Personnel:
Marketing Director: guttmann@ussilica.com
Sales Director: sales@ussilica.com
Approx. Number Employees: 700
Year Founded: 1987
Business Description:
Industrial Minerals Supplier
S.I.C.: 1446; 1455
N.A.I.C.S.: 212322; 212324
Export
Media: 2-4-7-9-10-11-16-19-20-21-26
Distr.: Natl.
Budget Set: Sept.
Personnel:
Wayne Webber *(Gen Mgr)*
David A. Hadigian *(Dir-Customer Svc)*
Matthew J. Lyman *(Dir-Technical)*
George I. Dodson *(Mgr-Building Products)*
John F. Miller *(Mgr-Natl Accts)*
Brands & Products:
APLITE
FILPRO
FLORISIL
LIGHTHOUSE
MIN-U-SIL
MYSTIC WHITE
Q-ROK
Q-ROK 1
Q-ROK 2
Q-ROK 3
SIL-CO-SIL
SILURIAN
SNOW*TEX
STANDARD MELT
U.S. SILICA
Advertising Agency:
Three Marketeers Advertising
1305 Jefferson Blvd
Hagerstown, MD 21742

Key to Media (For complete agency information see *The Advertising Red Books-Agencies* edition):
1. Bus. Publs. 2. Cable T.V. 3. Catalogs & Directories. 4. Co-op Adv. 5. Consumer Mags. 6. D.M. to Bus. Estab.7. D.M. to Consumers 8. Daily Newsp. 9. Exhibits/Trade Shows 10. Foreign 11. Infomercial 12. Internet Adv.13. Multimedia 14. Network Radio 15. Network T.V. 16. Newsp. Distr. Mags. 17. Other 18. Outdoor (Posters, Transit) 19. Point of Purchase20. Premiums, Novelties 21. Product Samples 22. Special Events Mktg. 23. Spot Radio 24. Spot T.V. 25. Weekly Newsp. 26. Yellow Page Adv.

U.S. Silica Company — (Continued)
Tel.: (301) 791-6555

VALHI, INC.
(Holding of Contran Corporation)
5430 LBJ Fwy Ste 1700
Dallas, TX 75240
Tel.: (972) 233-1700
Fax: (972) 448-1445
Web Site: www.valhi.net
Approx. Rev.: $1,651,200,000
Approx. Number Employees: 3,412
Year Founded: 1932
Business Description:
Holding Company; Chemicals, Refined Sugar, Integrated Forest Products, Fast Food & Hardware Products
S.I.C.: 2816; 2899; 5169; 6719
N.A.I.C.S.: 325131; 325998; 424690; 551112
Import Export
Advertising Expenditures: $1,000,000
Media: 7
Distr.: Intl.; Natl.
Personnel:
Harold C. Simmons *(Chm)*
Glenn R. Simmons *(Vice Chm)*
John Mark Hollingsworth *(Gen Counsel, VP & Asst Sec)*
William J. Lindquist *(Sr VP)*

VELSICOL CHEMICAL CORPORATION
(Holding of Arsenal Capital Partners, Inc.)
10400 W Higgins Rd Ste 700
Rosemont, IL 60018-3713
Tel.: (847) 813-7888
Fax: (847) 768-3227
Toll Free: (877) 847-8350
E-mail: distributioninfo@velsicol.com
Web Site: www.velsicol.com
E-Mail For Key Personnel:
Public Relations: comms@velsicol.com
Approx. Number Employees: 400
Year Founded: 1931
Business Description:
Specialty Chemicals Mfr
S.I.C.: 2819
N.A.I.C.S.: 325188
Import Export
Media: 2-4
Distr.: Intl.; Natl.
Personnel:
Dennis T. Leu *(Pres)*
Brands & Products:
VELSICOL

VERTELLUS PERFORMANCE MATERIALS INC.
(Sub. of Vertellus Performance Materials Inc.)
40 Ave A
Bayonne, NJ 07002-5265
Tel.: (201) 858-7900
Fax: (201) 437-2728
Toll Free: (800) 227-2436
Web Site: www.eaton.com
Approx. Number Employees: 156
Year Founded: 1857
Business Description:
Castor Oil Refinery
S.I.C.: 2869; 2079
N.A.I.C.S.: 325199; 311225
Advertising Expenditures: $150,000
Bus. Publs.: $37,500; D.M. to Bus. Estab.: $30,000; Daily Newsp.: $45,000; Other: $37,500
Brands & Products:
CASTOR WAX
POLYCIN
STANTIV OMA-1
VORITE

VERTELLUS SPECIALTIES INC.
(Holding of Wind Point Partners)
201 N Illinois St Ste 1800
Indianapolis, IN 46204
Tel.: (317) 247-8141
Fax: (317) 247-6472
E-mail: info@vertellus.com
Web Site: www.vertellus.com
Sales Range: $500-549.9 Million
Approx. Number Employees: 700
Year Founded: 2006
Business Description:
Specialty Chemicals Mfr
S.I.C.: 2869; 2899
N.A.I.C.S.: 325199; 325998
Import Export
Advertising Expenditures: $545,000
Media: 2-4-7-10-13-21
Distr.: Intl
Budget Set: Oct.
Personnel:
Rich Preziotti *(Pres & CEO)*
Bentley Park *(Pres-Agriculture & Nutrition Bus)*
James Keay *(Bus Dir)*
Brands & Products:
DI-PIP
DI-PYR
EASY-FLO
HAP
PDHP
POLYCIN
REILLCAT
REILLEX
ZEMAC
ZEPURE

WALL COLMONOY CORPORATION
101 W Girard
Madison Heights, MI 48071
Tel.: (248) 585-6400
Fax: (248) 585-7960
E-mail: wcc@wallcolmonoy.com
Web Site: www.wallcolmonoy.com
Approx. Number Employees: 300
Year Founded: 1938
Business Description:
Mfr. of Hard Surfacing Alloys
S.I.C.: 3398; 3316
N.A.I.C.S.: 332811; 331221
Import Export
Media: 2-4-7-10-17-20
Distr.: Intl.
Budget Set: Oct.
Personnel:
Craig Johnson *(VP-Alloy Products Grp & Gen Mgr)*
Marianne Huesing *(Mgr-HR)*
Brands & Products:
COLMONOY
COLSPRAY
FUSEWELDER
NICROBRAZ
NICROCRAFT
NICROSPRAY
SOLOCOAT
SPRAYWELDER

WATER TECHNOLOGIES CORPORATION
(Sub. of Waters Corporation)
Gautier Benitez Ave 230 Ste 20
Caguas, PR 00725
Tel.: (787) 747-8445
Fax: (787) 747-8448
Web Site: www.waters.com/waters/home.htm?locale=en_US
Sales Range: $25-49.9 Million
Approx. Number Employees: 32
Business Description:
High Performance Liquid Chromatography (HPLC), Thermal Analysis & Mass Spectrometry (MS) Instruments, Columns & Related Services Mfr & Distr
S.I.C.: 5049
N.A.I.C.S.: 423490
Media: 11-13-17
Distr.: Natl.
Personnel:
Carlos Hernandez *(Svc Dir)*
Julio Acededo *(Mgr-Fin-Admin)*
Culeo Acevedo *(Mgr-Fin-Admin)*
Diane Luque *(Mgr-Mktg)*

WESTLAKE CHEMICAL CORPORATION
2801 Post Oak Blvd Ste 600
Houston, TX 77056-6105
Tel.: (713) 960-9111
Fax: (713) 963-1590
E-mail: mediarelations@westlake.com
Web Site: www.westlake.com
Approx. Sls.: $3,171,787,000
Approx. Number Employees: 1,873
Year Founded: 1986
Business Description:
Chemicals, Polymers, Vinyls & Fabricated Products Mfr
S.I.C.: 2821; 2869; 2899
N.A.I.C.S.: 325199; 325110; 325211; 325998
Media: 13-16
Personnel:
James Y. Chao *(Chm)*
Albert Y. Chao *(Pres & CEO)*
M. Steven Bender *(CFO & Sr VP)*
George J. Mangieri *(Chief Acctg Officer & VP)*
Stephen Wallace *(Gen Counsel, Sec & VP)*
Robert F. Buesinger *(Sr VP-Vinyls)*
Donald M. Condon, Jr. *(Sr VP-Olefins & Corp Bus Dev)*
David R. Hansen *(Sr VP-Admin)*
Jeffrey L. Taylor *(Sr VP-Polyethylene)*
Brands & Products:
HDPE
LDPE
LLDPE
WESTLAKE
WESTLAKE CHEMICAL
Advertising Agency:
Savage
4203 Montrose Blvd.
Houston, TX 77006
Tel.: (713) 522-1555
Fax: (713) 522-1582
Public Relations

WHITFORD WORLDWIDE COMPANY
47 Park Ave
Elverson, PA 19520
Tel.: (610) 286-3500
Fax: (610) 286-3510
Web Site: www.whitfordww.com
E-Mail For Key Personnel:
Sales Director: sales@whitfordww.com
Approx. Number Employees: 315
Year Founded: 1989
Business Description:
Mfr of Fluoropolymer Coatings
S.I.C.: 2891
N.A.I.C.S.: 325520
Import Export
Media: 2-7-10-13-20-21
Personnel:
David P. Willis, Jr. *(Founder, Pres & CEO)*
Brian Kilty *(CFO)*
Joan Eberhardt *(Chief Admin Officer)*
Mike Miller *(Mgr-Technical)*
Brands & Products:
DYKOR
ECLIPSE
EXCALIBUR
QUANTANIUM
QUANTUM
QUANTUM2
SUAVE
ULTRALON
WHITFORD
XYLAC
XYLAN
XYLAR

WILBUR-ELLIS COMPANY
345 California St 27th Fl
San Francisco, CA 94104-2644
Tel.: (415) 772-4000
Fax: (415) 772-4011
E-mail: contactus@wecon.com
Web Site: www.wilburellis.com
Sales Range: $1-4.9 Billion
Approx. Number Employees: 2,500
Year Founded: 1921
Business Description:
Marketing, Distribution, & Formulation of Agricultural Products, Industrial Specialty Chemicals & Raw Materials
S.I.C.: 5191; 5169
N.A.I.C.S.: 424910; 424690
Export
Media: 2-4-6-7-9-10-11-13-19-20-23
Distr.: Natl.
Personnel:
Herbert B. Tully *(Chm)*
Carter P. Thacher *(Vice Chm)*
John Thacher *(Pres & CEO)*
Dan Vradenburg *(Pres-Agribusiness)*
Dick Barrett *(Dir-Branded Products)*
Rick Cahoon *(Dir-Enterprise Support)*
Anne Cleary *(Dir-HR)*
Brands & Products:
BIVERT
CERANO
DESPERADO
H2OK
IDEAS TO GROW WITH
KUTTER
REGUARD
RENEGADE
TWICER
VENDETTA
Advertising Agency:
Paulsen Marketing Communications, Inc.
(d/b/a Paulsen AgriBranding)
3510 S 1st Ave Cir

Key to Media (For complete agency information see *The Advertising Red Books-Agencies* edition):
1. Bus. Publs. 2. Cable T.V. 3. Catalogs & Directories. 4. Co-op Adv. 5. Consumer Mags. 6. D.M. to Bus. Estab.7. D.M. to Consumers
8. Daily Newsp. 9. Exhibits/Trade Shows 10. Foreign 11. Infomercial 12. Internet Adv.13. Multimedia 14. Network Radio
15. Network T.V. 16. Newsp. Distr. Mags. 17. Other 18. Outdoor (Posters, Transit) 19. Point of Purchase20. Premiums, Novelties
21. Product Samples 22. Special Events Mktg. 23. Spot Radio 24. Spot T.V. 25. Weekly Newsp. 26. Yellow Page Adv.

Sioux Falls, SD 57105-5807
Tel.: (605) 336-1745
Fax: (605) 336-2305

THE WILLAMETTE VALLEY COMPANY
(d/b/a Wilvaco)
1075 Arrowsmith St
Eugene, OR 97402
Tel.: (541) 484-9621
Fax: (541) 484-1987
Toll Free: (800) 333-9826
E-mail: info@wilvaco.com
Web Site: www.wilvaco.com
Approx. Number Employees: 350
Year Founded: 1952
Business Description:
Synthetic Patch, Polyurethane Fillers, Epoxies, Adhesive Fillers & Extenders Mfr; Equipment Mfr for Wood Products Industry
S.I.C.: 5085; 2851
N.A.I.C.S.: 423840; 325510
Media: 2-10-13
Personnel:
John Harrison *(Pres)*
Brands & Products:
SPIKEFAST
WVCO

WOOD WYANT, INC.
(Sub. of Sani-Marc inc.)
3025 Joseph Armand Bombardier
Laval, QC H7P 6C5, Canada
Tel.: (450) 680-9700
Fax: (450) 680-9735
Toll Free: (800) 724-0130
E-mail: wwlachine@woodwyant.com
Web Site: www.woodwyant.com
Approx. Number Employees: 60
Year Founded: 1997
Business Description:
Janitorial Chemicals, Disinfectants, Floorcare Products, Soaps & Deodorizers
S.I.C.: 2841
N.A.I.C.S.: 325611
Media: 4-10
Personnel:
Patrick Couture *(Dir-Mktg)*
Herve Girard *(Dir-Bus Dev)*
Yvon Jacques *(Natl Mgr-Credit)*
Brands & Products:
WOOD WYANT

Key to Media (For complete agency information see *The Advertising Red Books-Agencies* edition):
1. Bus. Publs. 2. Cable T.V. 3. Catalogs & Directories. 4. Co-op Adv. 5. Consumer Mags. 6. D.M. to Bus. Estab.7. D.M. to Consumers
8. Daily Newsp. 9. Exhibits/Trade Shows 10. Foreign 11. Infomercial 12. Internet Adv.13. Multimedia 14. Network Radio
15. Network T.V. 16. Newsp. Distr. Mags. 17. Other 18. Outdoor (Posters, Transit) 19. Point of Purchase20. Premiums, Novelties
21. Product Samples 22. Special Events Mktg. 23. Spot Radio 24. Spot T.V. 25. Weekly Newsp. 26. Yellow Page Adv.

Insurance

Brokers — Fidelity & Surety Bonds — Health Care Plans — Reinsurance

21ST CENTURY INSURANCE GROUP
(Sub. of Farmers Group, Inc.)
3 Beaver Valley Rd
Wilmington, DE 19803
Tel.: (302) 252-2000
Fax: (302) 252-2452
Toll Free: (800) 211-7283
E-mail: inetcorpinfo@21st.com
Web Site: www.21st.com
Approx. Premiums: $3,600,000,000
Approx. Number Employees: 2,900
Year Founded: 1958
Business Description:
Holding Company; Auto, Home & Life Insurance Carrier
S.I.C.: 6719; 6311; 6331; 6361; 6399
N.A.I.C.S.: 551112; 524113; 524126; 524127; 524128
Advertising Expenditures: $74,900,000
Media: 5-6-8-9-13-18-22-23-24-26
Distr.: Reg.
Personnel:
Tony Desantis *(Pres)*
Steven P. Erwin *(CFO & Sr VP)*
John L. Ingersoll *(VP)*
MIke Boyd *(Asst VP-Brand & Creative Dev)*
Advertising Agencies:
Baker Street Partners
2410 Baker St
San Francisco, CA 94123
Tel.: (415) 659-3900
Fax: (415) 659-3903

DonatWald+Haque
1316 Third St Ste 301
Santa Monica, CA 90401
Tel.: (310) 394-1717
Fax: (310) 394-1716
Agency of Record
Broadcast
Creative
Digital Advertising

Glyphix Advertising
6964 Shoup Ave
West Hills, CA 91307
Tel.: (818) 704-3994
Fax: (818) 704-8850

Mindshare
498 7th Ave
New York, NY 10018
Tel.: (212) 297-7000
Fax: (212) 297-7001
U.S. Media Planning & Buying

AAA AUTO CLUB SOUTH
(Affil. of American Automobile Association)
1515 N Westshore Blvd
Tampa, FL 33607
Mailing Address:
PO Box 31087
Tampa, FL 33607
Tel.: (813) 289-5000
Fax: (813) 289-1475
Toll Free: (800) 222-1134
E-mail: editorial@goingplaces.com
Web Site: www.aaasouth.com
Approx. Number Employees: 300
Business Description:
Insurance & Travel Services
S.I.C.: 4729; 4724
N.A.I.C.S.: 561599; 561510
Media: 8
Personnel:
Robert R. Sharp *(Chm)*
John Tomlin *(Pres & CEO)*
Amy Stracke *(Mng Dir)*
Robert A. McKee *(CFO, Chief Acctg Officer & Sr VP)*
Larry Patrick *(Sr VP)*
Mike Petrilli *(Sr VP-IS & ECommerce)*
Sandy Klim *(Editor-in-Chief-GoingPlaces)*
Yoli Buss *(Dir-Driver Improvement)*
Mike Kiral *(Mgr-Safety)*

AAA PUBLIC ADJUSTING GROUP, INC.
1926 Hollywood Blvd Ste 100
Hollywood, FL 33020
Tel.: (954) 894-0043
Fax: (954) 894-0201
E-mail: slcleansconsultants@yahoo.com
Web Site:
www.slcleansconsultant.com
Approx. Rev.: $603,007
Approx. Number Employees: 4
Business Description:
Holding Company; Insurance Adjusting Services
S.I.C.: 6719; 6411
N.A.I.C.S.: 551112; 524291; 524298
Advertising Expenditures: $11,815
Media: 6-8-9-24-25
Personnel:
Christopher Lombardi *(Pres & CEO)*

ACCEPTANCE INSURANCE COMPANIES, INC.
300 W Broadway Ste 1600
Council Bluffs, IA 51503
Tel.: (712) 329-3600
Fax: (712) 329-3812
Toll Free: (800) 228-7217
E-mail: lcrum@aicins.com
Web Site: www.aicins.com
Sales Range: $1-9.9 Million
Approx. Number Employees: 23
Year Founded: 1968
Business Description:
Insurance Services
S.I.C.: 6331
N.A.I.C.S.: 524126
Media: 2-5-7-8-9-14-24
Distr.: Natl.
Budget Set: Jan.
Personnel:
John E. Martin *(Pres & CEO)*
William R. Baxter *(Treas & Sr VP-Fin)*

AEGON USA, INC.
(Branch of AEGON USA, Inc.)
2 E Chase St
Baltimore, MD 21202
Tel.: (410) 685-2900
Telex: 464414
Web Site: www.aegonins.com
Business Description:
Insurance Holding Company
S.I.C.: 6311
N.A.I.C.S.: 524113
Advertising Expenditures: $250,000
Media: 5-6-8-9-16-24-25
Personnel:
Eric Goodman *(Chief Investment Officer)*
James A. Beardsworth *(Treas, Sr VP & Corp Dev Exec)*

AETNA INC.
151 Farmington Ave
Hartford, CT 06156-0001
Tel.: (860) 273-0123
Fax: (860) 273-3971
Toll Free: (800) 872-3862
Web Site: www.aetna.com
Approx. Rev.: $34,246,000,000
Approx. Number Employees: 34,000
Year Founded: 1850
Business Description:
Health Maintenance Organization
S.I.C.: 6321
N.A.I.C.S.: 524114
Media: 2-6-9-10-14-18-23-24
Distr.: Natl.; Reg.
Personnel:
Mark T. Bertolini *(Chm, Pres & CEO)*
Joseph M. Zubretsky *(CFO & Sr Exec VP)*
Michael G. Mathias *(CIO & VP)*
Rajan Parmeswar *(Chief Acctg Officer, VP & Controller)*
Michael J. Guyette *(Pres-Natl Accts)*
Anne Rote *(CEO-Texas Medicaid)*
William J. Casazza *(Gen Counsel & Sr VP)*
Margaret M. McCarthy *(Exec VP)*
Robert M. Mead *(Sr VP-Mktg, Product & Comm)*
Elease E. Wright *(Sr VP-HR)*
Jill Griffiths *(VP-Market, Clinical & Corp Comm)*
Charles D. Saunders *(Head-Strategic Diversification)*
Michael S. Elliott *(Gen Mgr-Asia Pacific-Aetna Intl)*
Edmund J. Pezalla *(Dir-Natl Medical Pharmacy Mgmt-Aetna Health Plans)*
Wayne Rawlins *(Dir-Medical-Natl)*
Melissa Jones *(Mgr-Mktg-Northeast & Massachusetts)*
Bill Shaughnessy *(Mgr-Mktg)*
Brian Kelly *(Engr-Info Security)*
Brands & Products:
AETNA
AETNA EZCONNECT
AETNA EZENROLL
AETNA EZLINK
AETNA NAGIVATOR
AETNA RX HOME DELIVERY
DOCFIND
EASY QUOTE
PRODUCER WORLD
WE WANT YOU TO KNOW
Advertising Agencies:
Arnold Worldwide
101 Huntington Ave
Boston, MA 02199-7603
Tel.: (617) 587-8000
Fax: (617) 587-8004
Lead Creative Agency
Social Media
Traditional Advertising

Key to Media (For complete agency information see *The Advertising Red Books-Agencies* edition):
1. Bus. Publs. 2. Cable T.V. 3. Catalogs & Directories. 4. Co-op Adv. 5. Consumer Mags. 6. D.M. to Bus. Estab.7. D.M. to Consumers
8. Daily Newsp. 9. Exhibits/Trade Shows 10. Foreign 11. Infomercial 12. Internet Adv.13. Multimedia 14. Network Radio
15. Network T.V. 16. Newsp. Distr. Mags. 17. Other 18. Outdoor (Posters, Transit) 19. Point of Purchase20. Premiums, Novelties
21. Product Samples 22. Special Events Mktg. 23. Spot Radio 24. Spot T.V. 25. Weekly Newsp. 26. Yellow Page Adv.

eTargetMedia.com, Inc.
6810 Lyons Technology Circle Ste 160
Coconut Creek, FL 33073
Tel.: (954) 480-8470
Fax: (954) 480-8489
Toll Free: (888) 805-3282

G2 Worldwide
200 5th Ave
New York, NY 10010
Tel.: (212) 537-3700
Fax: (212) 546-2425
Direct Marketing Assignment

Harmelin Media
525 Righters Ferry Rd
Bala Cynwyd, PA 19004-1315
Tel.: (610) 668-7900
Fax: (610) 668-9548
Media Planning & Buying

Mediacom Interaction
2301 Platt Rd Ste 400
Ann Arbor, MI 48104
Tel.: (734) 677-8000
Fax: (734) 677-8001

AFFINITY HEALTH PLAN

2500 Halsey St
Bronx, NY 10461
Tel.: (718) 794-7700
Fax: (718) 794-7800
E-mail: webadmin@affinityplan.org
Web Site: www.affinityplan.org
Business Description:
Health Insurance Services
S.I.C.: 6321
N.A.I.C.S.: 524114
Personnel:
Maura Bluestone *(Pres & CEO)*
Mark Corcoran *(CFO & Exec VP)*
Advertising Agency:
Brian Kearney, Inc.
314 W Broadway Ste 200
Salt Lake City, UT 84101
Tel.: (801) 322-1140
Fax: (801) 322-0522

AFLAC INCORPORATED

1932 Wynnton Rd
Columbus, GA 31999-0001
Tel.: (706) 323-3431
Fax: (706) 324-6330
Toll Free: (800) 992-3522
E-mail: fieldservices@aflac.com
Web Site: www.aflac.com
E-Mail For Key Personnel:
Sales Director: fieldservices@aflac.com
Approx. Rev.: $20,732,000,000
Approx. Number Employees: 7,919
Year Founded: 1973
Business Description:
Holding Company; Supplemental Life & Health Insurance
S.I.C.: 6311
N.A.I.C.S.: 524113
Advertising Expenditures: $228,000,000
Media: 2-3-11-14-15-18
Distr.: Intl.; Natl.
Budget Set: Sept.
Personnel:
Daniel P. Amos *(Chm & CEO)*
Kriss Cloninger, III *(Pres, Exec VP, Treas & CFO)*
Paul Shelby Amos, II *(Pres & COO)*
Gerald W. Shields *(CIO & Sr VP)*
Michael W. Zuna *(CMO & Sr VP)*
Eric M. Kirsch *(Global Chief Investment Officer & First Sr VP)*
Jun Isonaka *(Chief Admin Officer & Sr VP)*
June P. Howard *(Chief Acctg Officer & Sr VP-Fin Svcs-IFRS)*
Yuji Arai *(Principal Fin Officer & Sr VP-All Fin, Actuarial, Investment Ops)*
Joey M. Loudermilk *(Gen Counsel)*
Susan R. Blanck *(Exec VP, Corp Actuary & First Sr VP-Aflac Japan)*
Kenneth S. Janke, Jr. *(Exec VP & Deputy CFO)*
Audrey Boone Tillman *(Exec VP-Corp Svcs)*
Teresa White *(Exec VP)*
Phillip J. Friou *(Sr VP & Dir-Governmental Rels)*
Thomas R. Giddens *(Sr VP & Dir-Sls)*
Takaaki Matsumoto *(Sr VP & Dir-Mktg)*
Ronald S. Sanders *(Sr VP & Dir-Aflac Group & Broker Sls)*
William Jeremy Jeffery *(Sr VP-Fixed Income Investments)*
David L. Pringle *(Sr VP-Federal Rels)*
James Wisdom *(Second VP-Integrated Mktg)*
Missy Wood *(2nd VP)*
Kelly Servedio *(Mgr-Market Res Insights)*
Jon Sullivan *(Mgr-Corp Comm)*
Brands & Products:
AFLAC
WE'VE GOT YOU UNDER OUR WING
WITHOUT IT, NO INSURANCE IS COMPLETE
Advertising Agencies:
Digitas Inc.
33 Arch St
Boston, MA 02110
Tel.: (617) 867-1000
Fax: (617) 867-1111
Digital Media Buying & Planning

The Kaplan Thaler Group
825 8th Ave 34th Fl
New York, NY 10019
Tel.: (212) 474-5000
Fax: (212) 474-5702
(General Supplemental Health Insurance Products)

MediaVest USA
1675 Broadway
New York, NY 10019
Tel.: (212) 468-4000
Fax: (212) 468-4110
Traditional Media Planning & Buying

PainePR
19000 MacArthur Blvd 8 Fl
Irvine, CA 92612-1438
Tel.: (949) 809-6700
Fax: (949) 260-1116
Toll Free: (866) PAINEPR
Corporate Communications

Solar Velocity
3300 Highland Pkwy Ste 260
Smyrna, GA 30082
Tel.: (404) 978-2240
Fax: (404) 978-2241

The Zimmerman Agency
1821 Miccosukee Commons Dr
Tallahassee, FL 32308-5433
Tel.: (850) 668-2222
Fax: (850) 656-4622
Movie-Tie in - Toy Story 3
Print
Social Media
Sweepstakes

Zubi Advertising Services, Inc.
355 Alhambra Cir 10th Fl
Coral Gables, FL 33134-5006
Tel.: (305) 448-9824
Fax: (305) 460-6393

AIG LIFE HOLDINGS (US), INC.

(Sub. of American International Group, Inc.)
2929 Allen Pkwy
Houston, TX 77019-7100
Mailing Address:
PO Box 4373
Houston, TX 77253-3247
Tel.: (713) 522-1111
Fax: (713) 523-8531
Web Site: www.aigag.com
Sales Range: $1-4.9 Billion
Approx. Number Employees: 15,900
Year Founded: 1926
Business Description:
Holding Company; Owner of Life Insurance, Retirement Services, Consumer Lending & Investment Management
S.I.C.: 6719; 6311; 6321; 6331; 6411
N.A.I.C.S.: 551112; 524113; 524114; 524126; 524130; 524298; 525190
Media: 1-2-8-9-10-18-19-20-23-24-25-26
Distr.: Natl.
Personnel:
Bob Benmosche *(Pres & CEO)*
Stasa Cushman *(Dir-Comm)*

AIG SUNAMERICA INC.

(Sub. of American International Group, Inc.)
1 SunAmerica Center
Los Angeles, CA 90067-6002
Tel.: (310) 772-6000
E-mail: employment@sunamerica.com
Web Site: www.sunamerica.com
E-Mail For Key Personnel:
Public Relations: mediainfo@sunamerica.com
Sales Range: $1-4.9 Billion
Approx. Number Employees: 2,500
Year Founded: 1957
Business Description:
Financial Services
S.I.C.: 6289; 6282
N.A.I.C.S.: 523999; 523930
Advertising Expenditures: $6,000,000
Media: 2-7-9
Distr.: Natl.
Personnel:
Jay Wintrob *(Pres)*
N. Scott Gillis *(CFO & Sr VP)*
Marc H. Gamsin *(Exec VP)*
Timothy Schiltz *(Sr VP-SunAmerica Fin Group)*
Gail Wright *(VP-Mktg Commun)*
Brands & Products:
THE RETIREMENT SPECIALIST
SUNAMERICA

ALLIANZ LIFE INSURANCE COMPANY OF NORTH AMERICA

(Sub. of Allianz of America, Inc.)
5701 Golden Hills Dr
Minneapolis, MN 55416-1297
Mailing Address:
PO Box 1344
Minneapolis, MN 55416-1344
Tel.: (763) 765-6500
Fax: (763) 765-6403
Toll Free: (800) 950-5872
Telex: 467 393 NO AMER MPS CI
Web Site: www.allianzlife.com
Sales Range: $5-14.9 Billion
Approx. Number Employees: 2,000
Year Founded: 1896
Business Description:
Life Insurance, Annuity Products, Long Term Care Insurance & Broker-Dealer Services
S.I.C.: 6311
N.A.I.C.S.: 524113
Media: 2-4-5-6-7-8-9-10-19-20-25-26
Distr.: Intl.; Natl.
Budget Set: Jan.
Personnel:
Jay Ralph *(Chm)*
Gary C. Bhojwani *(Pres & CEO)*
Giulio Terzariol *(CFO)*
Tom Bauer *(CIO)*
Nancy Jones *(CMO)*
Walter White *(Chief Admin Officer)*
Neil McKay *(Chief Actuary & Sr VP)*
Tom Burns *(Chief Distr Officer)*
Bob Densmore *(Sr VP & Dir-District)*
Carl Adamek *(Sr VP-Acct Mgmt)*
Catherine Mahone *(Sr VP-Enterprise Ops)*
Amanda Brinkman *(VP-Branding & Creative Svcs)*
Andy Dulka *(VP-Infrastructure & Application Maintenance)*
Paul Kelash *(VP-Corp Comm)*
Doug Koenen *(VP-Distr Mktg)*
Heidi Wachholz *(VP-Sls-Northeast)*
Sherri Du Mond *(Head-Distr Trng)*
Karen Gemmill *(Sr Dir-Product Innovation)*
Julia Gutz Moller *(Sr Dir-Mktg-US)*
Jeannee Hoppe *(Sr Dir-Market Mgmt & Product Innovation)*
Debra Repya *(Sr Dir-Advanced Markets)*
Pete Hartley *(Dir-Fin Reporting)*
Wayne Hechanova *(Dir-Distr Mktg)*
Steve Lennick *(Dir-Sls Dev & Trng)*
Andy Mattson *(Dir-Program Mgmt)*
Craig Parker *(Dir-Consumer & Distr Insights)*
Marty Vanderzanden *(Dir-Special Investigations)*
Maureen Phillips *(Chief Counsel & Deputy Gen Counsel)*
Brands & Products:
GENERATION PROTECTOR

ALLIED INSURANCE

(Sub. of Nationwide Mutual Insurance Company)
1100 Locus St
Des Moines, IA 50391-2000
Tel.: (515) 508-4430
Fax: (515) 508-4399
Toll Free: (800) 532-1436
Web Site: www.alliedinsurance.com
Approx. Number Employees: 4,400

Key to Media (For complete agency information see *The Advertising Red Books-Agencies* edition):
1. Bus. Publs. 2. Cable T.V. 3. Catalogs & Directories. 4. Co-op Adv. 5. Consumer Mags. 6. D.M. to Bus. Estab.7. D.M. to Consumers
8. Daily Newsp. 9. Exhibits/Trade Shows 10. Foreign 11. Infomercial 12. Internet Adv.13. Multimedia 14. Network Radio
15. Network T.V. 16. Newsp. Distr. Mags. 17. Other 18. Outdoor (Posters, Transit) 19. Point of Purchase20. Premiums, Novelties
21. Product Samples 22. Special Events Mktg. 23. Spot Radio 24. Spot T.V. 25. Weekly Newsp. 26. Yellow Page Adv.

Allied Insurance — (Continued)

Year Founded: 1929
Business Description:
Insurance Services
S.I.C.: 6311; 6331; 6399
N.A.I.C.S.: 524126; 524113; 524128; 525190
Media: 3-5-7-8-10-20-22-23-24-25-26
Personnel:
Kim Austen *(Pres & COO)*
Susan McGinness *(VP-HR)*
Brands & Products:
ALLIED GROUP
ON YOUR SIDE
Advertising Agency:
Strategic America
6600 Westown Pkwy Ste 100
West Des Moines, IA 50266-7708
Tel.: (888) 898-6400
Fax: (515) 224-4181

ALLIED MUTUAL INSURANCE CO.

(Sub. of Allied Insurance)
1100 Locust St
Des Moines, IA 50391
Tel.: (515) 280-4211
Fax: (515) 538-6811
E-mail: baileyl1@nationwide.com
Web Site: www.alliedinsurance.com
Sales Range: $1-4.9 Billion
Approx. Number Employees: 1,000
Year Founded: 1929
Business Description:
Property Damage Insurance
S.I.C.: 6411
N.A.I.C.S.: 524210
Media: 2-3-5-6-7-9-10-19-20-22-23
Advertising Agency:
Strategic America
6600 Westown Pkwy Ste 100
West Des Moines, IA 50266-7708
Tel.: (888) 898-6400
Fax: (515) 224-4181

THE ALLSTATE CORPORATION

2775 Sanders Rd
Northbrook, IL 60062
Tel.: (847) 402-5000
Fax: (847) 836-3998
E-mail: careers@allstate.com
Web Site: www.allstate.com
Approx. Rev.: $31,400,000,000
Approx. Number Employees: 35,000
Year Founded: 1931
Business Description:
Auto, Fire, Personal Liability, Homeowners, Life & Business Insurance; Financial Services
S.I.C.: 6331; 6311
N.A.I.C.S.: 524126; 524113
Advertising Expenditures: $275,000,000
Media: 2-3-5-6-8-9-13-14-15-16-18-19-22-23-24-26
Distr.: Direct to Consumer; Natl.
Budget Set: Oct.
Personnel:
Thomas J. Wilson, II *(Chm, Pres & CEO)*
Matthew Winter *(Pres & CEO-Allstate Fin)*
Don Civgin *(CFO & Exec VP)*
Mark Raymond LaNeve *(CMO & Exec VP)*
Catherine S. Brune *(Pres-Allstate Protection-South Reg)*
W. Guy Hill, Jr. *(Pres-California & East Reg)*
Joseph P. Lacher, Jr. *(Pres-Allstate Protection)*
Anurag Chandra *(COO-Fin)*
Michele Coleman Mayes *(Gen Counsel & Exec VP)*
Suren Gupta *(Exec VP-Tech & Ops)*
Michael J. Roche *(Exec VP-Claims)*
Joan H. Walker *(Exec VP-Corp Rels)*
James A. Haskins *(Sr VP-Claims-California & East Reg)*
Brands & Products:
ALLSTATE
ALLSTATE FINANCIAL
ALLSTATE INDEMNITY & CASUALTY INSURANCE COMPANY
ALLSTATE INSURANCE COMPANY
ALLSTATE MOTOR CLUB
AMERICAN HERITAGE LIFE
GLENBROOK LIFE
LINCOLN BENEFIT LIFE
NORTHBROOK LIFE
NORTHBROOK PROPERTY & CASUALTY
SURETY LIFE
Advertising Agencies:
Burrell
233 N Michigan Ave Ste 2900
Chicago, IL 60601
Tel.: (312) 297-9600
Fax: (312) 297-9601

Digitas Inc.
33 Arch St
Boston, MA 02110
Tel.: (617) 867-1000
Fax: (617) 867-1111

The Goodness Company
Cornerstone Ofc Ste 820 Baker St
Wisconsin Rapids, WI 54494
Tel.: (715) 423-1255
Fax: (715) 423-1310
Toll Free: (866) 265-1001

Lapiz
35 W Wacker Dr 12th Fl
Chicago, IL 60601
Tel.: (312) 220-5000
Fax: (312) 220-6212

Leo Burnett Worldwide, Inc.
35 W Wacker Dr
Chicago, IL 60601-1723
Tel.: (312) 220-5959
Fax: (312) 220-3299
(Print/Media/Broadcast-Insurance & Financial Services)
Speech

Piranha Kid
222 Merchandise Mart Plz Ste 275
Chicago, IL 60654
Tel.: (312) 255-1200
Fax: (312) 255-3030

PromoGroup
444 N Orleans St Ste 400
Chicago, IL 60610-4494
Tel.: (312) 467-1300
Fax: (312) 467-1311

Siegel+Gale
625 Ave of the Americas 4th Fl
New York, NY 10011
Tel.: (212) 453-0400
Fax: (212) 453-0401

Simple Truth Communication Partners
314 W Superior St Ste 300
Chicago, IL 60654
Tel.: (312) 376-0360
Fax: (312) 376-0366

Starcom MediaVest Group
35 W Wacker Dr
Chicago, IL 60601-1723
Tel.: (312) 220-3535
Fax: (312) 220-6530

Starcom Worldwide
5200 Lankershim Ste 600
North Hollywood, CA 91601
Tel.: (818) 753-7200
Fax: (818) 753-7350

Summit Marketing
Three Cityplace Dr Ste 350
Saint Louis, MO 63141-7091
Tel.: (314) 569-3737
Fax: (314) 569-0037
Toll Free: (866) 590-6000

Tapestry Partners
35 W Wacker Dr
Chicago, IL 60601
Tel.: (312) 220-3535
Fax: (312) 220-6561

Weber Shandwick
(Sub. of The Interpublic Group of Companies)
919 3rd Ave
New York, NY 10022
Tel.: (212) 445-8000
Fax: (212) 445-8001

AMERICAN AUTOMOBILE ASSOCIATION

1000 AAA Dr
Heathrow, FL 32746-5062
Tel.: (407) 444-7000
Fax: (407) 444-7380
Web Site: www.aaa.com
Approx. Number Employees: 41,419
Year Founded: 1902
Business Description:
Travel, Insurance, Financial & Auto Related Services
S.I.C.: 4729; 6331
N.A.I.C.S.: 561599; 524126
Media: 3-6-8-10-20-26
Distr.: Intl.; Natl.
Budget Set: Aug. -Sept.
Personnel:
Robert L. Darbelnet *(Pres & CEO)*
Carol Droessler *(Mng Dir)*
Satish Mahajan *(CIO & VP)*
Mark H. Brown *(Exec VP-Association & Club Svcs)*
Richard D. Rinner *(Exec VP-Admin & Publ)*
Brands & Products:
365
AAA
AAA AUTOEASE
AAA AUTOMAKER
AAA AUTOMANAGER
AAA CAMPBOOK
AAA CITIBOOK
AAA NORTH AMERICAN ROAD ATLAS
AAA TOURBOOK
AAA TRAVELBOOK
AAA TRIPTIK
AUTOGRAPH
AUTOSOLVE
AUTOTEST
CAR AND TRAVEL
CITIMAP
CLUBLINK
CREDITGARD
ENVIRONMENTAL NEWS DIGEST
FIVE DIAMOND
FLYING ALONE
GAS WATCHERS
GOING PLACES
HOLIDAYS NEWS SERVICE
HOSTMARK
MAP-PAK
PETBOOK
RESPONSE LLC
ROAD SERVICE ONLINE
ROUTEMASTER
SMARTSTART
SOUND VALUE
SUPERNUMBER
THREE A
TRAVELMATCH
TRIPASSIST
TRIPCLIK
TRIPLE A
TRIPTIK
VACATION DESTINATION
Advertising Agency:
Ad Club
1304 W Roseburg Ave
Modesto, CA 95350-4855
Tel.: (209) 529-9067
Fax: (209) 529-5265
Toll Free: (800) 333-1228

AMERICAN FAMILY AGENCIES

2260 Gulf to Bay Blvd
Clearwater, FL 33765
Tel.: (727) 669-4777
Fax: (727) 669-8407
E-mail: contact@yourinsurancehome.com
Web Site: www.myinsurancehome.com
Approx. Number Employees: 8
Business Description:
Insurance Agency
S.I.C.: 6411
N.A.I.C.S.: 524210
Media: 13-16
Personnel:
Joe Garcia *(Pres)*

AMERICAN FAMILY INSURANCE COMPANY

(Sub. of American Family Mutual Insurance Company)
6000 American Pkwy
Madison, WI 53783-0001
Tel.: (608) 249-2111
Web Site: www.amfam.com
Approx. Number Employees: 7,750
Year Founded: 1996
Business Description:
Property, Casualty & Health Insurance
S.I.C.: 6311
N.A.I.C.S.: 524113
Personnel:
Jack Salzeedel *(Pres)*
J. Brent Johnson *(Treas & Exec VP-Fin)*
Telisa Yancy *(Dir-Adv)*

Key to Media (For complete agency information see *The Advertising Red Books-Agencies* edition):
1. Bus. Publs. 2. Cable T.V. 3. Catalogs & Directories. 4. Co-op Adv. 5. Consumer Mags. 6. D.M. to Bus. Estab.7. D.M. to Consumers 8. Daily Newsp. 9. Exhibits/Trade Shows 10. Foreign 11. Infomercial 12. Internet Adv.13. Multimedia 14. Network Radio 15. Network T.V. 16. Newsp. Distr. Mags. 17. Other 18. Outdoor (Posters, Transit) 19. Point of Purchase20. Premiums, Novelties 21. Product Samples 22. Special Events Mktg. 23. Spot Radio 24. Spot T.V. 25. Weekly Newsp. 26. Yellow Page Adv.

Advertising Agencies:
commonground
1035 W Lake St Ste 302
Chicago, IL 60607
Tel.: (312) 384-1906
Fax: (312) 633-1906
African American Market

Joule
10 E 40th St 37th Fl
New York, NY 10016
Tel.: (212) 796-8382
Digital

Mindshare
350 W Mart Center Dr Ste 1270
Chicago, IL 60654-1270
Tel.: (312) 242-1100
Fax: (312) 242-1350
Media

Ogilvy & Mather
350 W Mart Ctr Dr Ste 1100
Chicago, IL 60654-1866
Tel.: (312) 856-8200
Fax: (312) 856-8207
Lead Creative Agency

The San Jose Group
233 N Michigan Ave 24 Fl
Chicago, IL 60601
Tel.: (312) 565-7000
Fax: (312) 565-7500
Hispanic Advertising

AMERICAN FAMILY MUTUAL INSURANCE COMPANY

(d/b/a American Family Insurance Group)
6000 American Pkwy
Madison, WI 53783
Tel.: (608) 249-2111
Fax: (608) 243-4921
Web Site: www.amfam.com
Approx. Rev.: $6,321,474,000
Approx. Number Employees: 7,801
Year Founded: 1927
Business Description:
Auto, Home, Health, Life & Business Insurance; Consumer Finance Services
S.I.C.: 6311; 6331
N.A.I.C.S.: 524113; 524126
Advertising Expenditures: $45,000,000
Media: 2-3-5-6-7-8-9-11-13-18-19-20-22-23-24-25-26
Distr.: Reg.
Budget Set: Sept.
Personnel:
David R. Anderson *(Chm & CEO)*
Jack C. Salzwedel *(Pres & COO)*
Daniel R. Schultz *(CFO & Treas)*
Christopher S. Spencer *(Chief Legal Officer, Sec & Sr VP)*
Mark V. Afable *(Exec VP-Claims)*
Gerry W. Benusa *(Exec VP-Comml-Farm & Ranch)*
Bradley J. Gleason *(Exec VP)*
Jerome G. Rekowski *(Exec VP)*
Mary L. Schmoeger *(Exec VP)*
Peter C. Gunder *(Sr VP-Investments)*
Kristin R. Kirkconnell *(Sr VP-Info Svcs)*
Lisa Bacus *(VP-Mktg)*
Michael R. Duran *(VP-Sls-West Reg)*
Rick Fetherston *(VP-PR)*
Carolyn S. Gilb *(VP-Comm-Farm & Ranch)*
David C. Holman *(VP-Corp Legal)*
Daniel J. Kelly *(VP-HR)*
Christopher R. Listau *(VP-Sls-Central Reg)*
Bernard T. McCartan *(VP-Claims Legal)*
Alan E. Meyer *(VP-Life, Variable Products & Health)*
Richard M. Steffen *(VP-Sls-Esat Region)*
Evonne M. Steger *(VP-Corp Strategy & Plng)*
Judy Lowell *(Mgr-Community Rels)*
Brands & Products:
ALL YOUR PROTECTION UNDER ONE ROOF
AMERICAN FAMILY INSURANCE
Advertising Agencies:
Mindshare
498 7th Ave
New York, NY 10018
Tel.: (212) 297-7000
Fax: (212) 297-7001

Ogilvy & Mather
350 W Mart Ctr Dr Ste 1100
Chicago, IL 60654-1866
Tel.: (312) 856-8200
Fax: (312) 856-8207
Creative

AMERICAN GENERAL LIFE & ACCIDENT INSURANCE COMPANY

(Sub. of AGC Life Insurance Company)
American General Ctr
Nashville, TN 37250-0001
Tel.: (615) 749-1000
Fax: (615) 749-1400
Toll Free: (800) 255-2674
E-mail: voluntarybenefits@aigag.com
Web Site: www.agla.com
Sales Range: $800-899.9 Million
Approx. Number Employees: 8,000
Year Founded: 1978
Business Description:
Life & Health Insurance
S.I.C.: 6311
N.A.I.C.S.: 524113
Media: 8-9-10-20-22-25
Distr.: Natl.
Budget Set: Jan. -Dec.
Personnel:
James Mallon *(CEO)*

AMERICAN GENERAL LIFE COMPANIES, LLC

(Sub. of American General Life Insurance Company)
3600 Rte 66 PO Box 1580
Neptune, NJ 07753
Tel.: (732) 922-7000
Fax: (732) 922-7604
Approx. Rev.: $1,800,000,000
Approx. Number Employees: 800
Year Founded: 1966
Business Description:
Insurance-Based Financial Services
S.I.C.: 6311; 6331
N.A.I.C.S.: 524113; 524126
Advertising Expenditures: $4,000,000
Media: 1-2-3-5-7-8-9-14-15-17-20-22-23-24-26
Distr.: Natl.
Budget Set: Oct.
Personnel:
Michael Vivalo *(Reg VP)*
Advertising Agency:
Mintz & Hoke Communications Group
40 Tower Ln
Avon, CT 06001-4222
Tel.: (860) 678-0473
Fax: (860) 679-9850

AMERICAN INTERNATIONAL GROUP, INC.

180 Maiden Ln
New York, NY 10038
Tel.: (212) 770-7000
Fax: (212) 770-6970
E-mail: aig.infoexchange@aig.com
Web Site: www.aigcorporate.com
Approx. Rev.: $77,301,000,000
Approx. Number Employees: 63,000
Year Founded: 1919
Business Description:
Holding Company; Insurance & Financial Services
S.I.C.: 6331; 6311; 6321; 6411; 6719
N.A.I.C.S.: 524126; 524113; 524114; 524210; 524298; 551112
Advertising Expenditures: $200,000,000
Media: 2-4-6-7-8-9-10-11-20-26
Distr.: Intl.; Natl.
Budget Set: Jan. -Dec.
Personnel:
Louis P. Iglesias *(Chm, Pres & CEO-AIG Risk Mgmt, Inc.)*
Win J. Neuger *(Chm & CEO-Investment)*
Robert Steve Miller, Jr. *(Chm)*
Robert H. Benmosche *(Pres & CEO)*
Peter D. Hancock *(CEO)*
David L. Herzog *(CFO & Exec VP)*
Jeffrey M. Farber *(Deputy CFO & Sr VP)*
Monika Machon *(Chief Investment Officer & Sr VP)*
Kevin B. McGinn *(VP & Chief Credit Officer)*
Sid Sankaran *(Chief Risk Officer & Sr VP)*
Charlie Shamieh *(Chief Actuary & Sr VP)*
Russell Johnston *(Pres-Risk Mgmt)*
Thomas A. Russo *(Gen Counsel & Exec VP-Legal, Compliance & Regulatory/Govt Affairs)*
Brian T. Schreiber *(Treas & Exec VP-Treasury & Capital Markets)*
Kathleen Shannon *(Sec & Sr VP)*
William N. Dooley *(Exec VP-Investments & Fin Svcs)*
Rodney O. Martin Jr. *(Exec VP-Life Insurance)*
Kristian P. Moor *(Exec VP-Domestic Gen Insurance)*
Nicholas C. Walsh *(Exec VP-Foreign Gen Insurance)*
Jay S. Wintrob *(Exec VP-SunAmerica Financial Grp)*
Paulette Mullings Bradnock *(Sr VP & Dir-Intenal Audit)*
Jeffrey J. Hurd *(Sr VP-HR & Comm)*
David DeMuro *(Head-Compliance & Regulatory Affairs, VP & Deputy Gen Counsel)*
Tal Kaissar *(VP & Dir-Tax)*
Mark Herr *(VP-Corp Media Rels)*
Peter Juhas *(Head-Strategic Plng)*
Jesus C. Zaragoza *(Deputy Comptroller-Fin Reporting)*
Steve Cherry *(Sr Dir-Mktg)*
Joe Norton *(Dir-Pub Rels)*
Clarissa Potter *(Deputy Dir-Tax)*
Ned Burke *(Asst Dir-IR)*
Jeffrey Malc *(Program Mgr-Direct Mktg)*
Tonia Williams *(Mgr-Funds-AIG Asset Mgmt Grp)*
Brands & Products:
AIG
AIGLIFE
Advertising Agency:
Warner Communications
41 Raymond St
Manchester, MA 01944
Tel.: (978) 526-1960
Fax: (978) 526-8206
AIG Excess Casualty

AMERICAN NATIONAL INSURANCE COMPANY

1 Moody Plz
Galveston, TX 77550-7947
Tel.: (409) 763-4661
Fax: (409) 766-6417
Web Site: www.anico.com
Approx. Rev.: $3,067,088,000
Approx. Number Employees: 3,251
Year Founded: 1905
Business Description:
Individual & Group Life Insurance
S.I.C.: 6311; 6331
N.A.I.C.S.: 524113; 524126
Media: 2-5-9-10-23
Distr.: Natl.
Personnel:
Robert L. Moody, Sr. *(Chm & CEO)*
G. Richard Ferdinandtsen *(Pres & COO)*
John J. Dunn, Jr. *(CFO & Exec VP)*
James E. Pozzi *(Sr Exec VP & Chief Admin Officer)*
Dwain Allen Akins *(Sr VP-Corp Affairs & Chief Compliance Officer)*
Ronald Jay Welch *(Chief Actuary & Chief Corp Risk Mngmt Officer & Sr Exec VP)*
James A. Collura *(Pres/CEO-SM&R, VP & Chief Life Mktg & Ops Officer-Multiple Line)*
Michael W. McCroskey *(Treas & Exec VP)*
David Alan Behrens *(Exec VP-Independent Mktg Grp)*
Bill Joe Garrison *(Exec VP)*
William F. Carlton *(Sr VP & Controller)*
Frank Vincent Broll, Jr. *(Sr VP & Actuary)*
Rex David Hemme *(Sr VP & Actuary)*
Albert Louis Amato, Jr. *(Sr VP-Life Insurance Admin)*
Scott Frank Brast *(Sr VP-Real Estate & Mortgage Loan Investments)*
Gordon Dennis Dixon *(Sr VP-Securities Investments)*
Bernard Stephen Gerwel *(Sr VP & Chief MLEA Admin Officer)*
Bruce Murray LePard *(Sr VP-HR)*
Richard Thomas Crawford *(VP-Gen Acctg & Asst Controller)*
Dwight D. Judy *(VP-Fin & Mktg)*
J. Wayne Cucco *(Asst VP & Dir-Advanced Life Sls)*
James B. McEniry *(Asst VP & Dir-Telecom)*

Key to Media (For complete agency information see *The Advertising Red Books-Agencies* edition):
1. Bus. Publs. 2. Cable T.V. 3. Catalogs & Directories. 4. Co-op Adv. 5. Consumer Mags. 6. D.M. to Bus. Estab.7. D.M. to Consumers
8. Daily Newsp. 9. Exhibits/Trade Shows 10. Foreign 11. Infomercial 12. Internet Adv.13. Multimedia 14. Network Radio
15. Network T.V. 16. Newsp. Distr. Mags. 17. Other 18. Outdoor (Posters, Transit) 19. Point of Purchase20. Premiums, Novelties
21. Product Samples 22. Special Events Mktg. 23. Spot Radio 24. Spot T.V. 25. Weekly Newsp. 26. Yellow Page Adv.

American National Insurance Company — (Continued)

Ronald J. Ostermayer *(Asst VP & Dir-Health System Admin-Security Office)*
Raymond E. Pittman, Jr. *(Asst VP & Dir-Mktg & Career Dev)*
Joseph J. Cantu *(Asst VP & Illustration Actuary)*
Donna L. Daulong *(Asst VP-Gen Acctg)*
Nancy M. Day *(Asst VP-Pension Admin)*
John Ferguson *(Asst VP-Creative Svcs)*
Barbara J. Huerta *(Asst VP-IT Enterprise Svcs)*
Carol Ann Kratz *(Asst VP-HR)*
Katherine S. Meisetschlaeger *(Asst VP-IT Enterprise Sys)*
Michael S. Nimmons *(Asst VP & Assoc Gen Auditor-Home Office)*
Judith L. Regini *(Asst VP-Corp Compliance)*
James A. Tyra *(Asst VP-Life Insurance Sys)*
Jenette E. Cernosek *(Asst Sec)*
Brands & Products:
AMERICAN NATIONAL INSURANCE COMPANY

AMERICAN REPUBLIC INSURANCE COMPANY

(Holding of American Enterprise Mutual Holding Company)
601 6th Ave
Des Moines, IA 50334-0001
Mailing Address:
PO Box 1
Des Moines, IA 50301
Tel.: (515) 245-2000
Fax: (402) 496-8199
Toll Free: (800) 247-2190
E-mail: info@aric.com
Web Site: www.aric.com
Approx. Number Employees: 650
Year Founded: 1929
Business Description:
Comprehensive Health, Life, Cancer, Critical Illness & Long Term Care Insurance
S.I.C.: 6321; 6311; 6331; 6399
N.A.I.C.S.: 524114; 524113; 524128; 525190
Advertising Expenditures: $2,000,000
Media: 6-8
Distr.: Reg.
Budget Set: Nov.
Personnel:
Michael E. Abbott *(Chm, Pres, CEO & CFO)*
Thomas W. Peterson *(COO & Sr VP)*
Mark Stadler *(Sr VP & Sls Dir)*
Brands & Products:
AMERICARE
THE CARE COMPANY
TAILORED PROTECTION
ULTRA CARE
ULTRA COMP

AMERISAFE, INC.

2301 Hwy 190 W
Deridder, LA 70634-6004
Tel.: (337) 463-9052
Fax: (337) 463-7298
E-mail: applications@amerisafe.com
Web Site: www.amerisafe.com
Approx. Rev.: $248,156,000
Approx. Number Employees: 423
Year Founded: 1985
Business Description:
Hazardous Work Compensation Services
S.I.C.: 6331; 6719
N.A.I.C.S.: 525190; 524126; 551112
Import Export
Advertising Expenditures: $444,000
Media: 7-13
Personnel:
C. Allen Bradley, Jr. *(Chm & CEO)*
Geoffrey R. Banta *(Pres & COO)*
G. Janelle Frost *(CFO & Exec VP)*
Brendan Gau *(Chief Investment Officer & Exec VP)*
Todd Walker *(Gen Counsel, Sec & Exec VP)*
Craig P. Leach *(Exec VP-Sls & Mktg)*
Allan E. Farr *(Sr VP-Enterprise Risk Mgmt)*
Vincent Gagliano *(Sr VP-IT)*
Kelly R. Goins *(Sr VP-Underwriting Ops)*
Cynthia P. Harris *(Sr VP-HR & Client Svcs)*
Leon J. Lagneaux *(Sr VP-Safety Ops)*
Henry O. Lestage, IV *(Sr VP-Claims Ops)*
Advertising Agency:
Calzone & Associates
1011 Lee Ave
Lafayette, LA 70502
Tel.: (337) 235-2924
Fax: (337) 237-0556

AMERISURE MUTUAL INSURANCE COMPANY

26777 Halsted Rd
Farmington Hills, MI 48331-3560
Mailing Address:
PO Box 2060
Farmington Hills, MI 48333-2060
Tel.: (248) 615-9000
Fax: (248) 615-8548
Toll Free: (800) 257-1900
Web Site: www.amerisure.com
Sales Range: $550-599.9 Million
Approx. Number Employees: 630
Year Founded: 1912
Business Description:
Casualty & Property Insurance Services
S.I.C.: 6331
N.A.I.C.S.: 524126
Media: 2-3-7-8-9-10-12-13-16-20-22-23-26
Distr.: Reg.
Budget Set: Oct. -Nov.
Personnel:
James B. Nicholson *(Chm)*
John C. Hamann *(Asst VP-Application Svcs)*
Robert Stahl *(Asst VP-Field Claimsa)*
Jack A. Wilson *(Asst VP-Enterprise Architecture)*
Steven M. Hartzler *(Platinum Mktg Underwriter & FMU Mgr)*
Brands & Products:
AMERISURE

AMERITAS LIFE INSURANCE CORP.

(Sub. of UNIFI Mutual Holding Company)
5900 O St
Lincoln, NE 68510
Tel.: (402) 467-1122
Fax: (402) 467-7790
Toll Free: (800) 745-1112
Web Site: www.ameritas.com
E-Mail For Key Personnel:
Public Relations: sstuckey@ameritas.com
Approx. Number Employees: 2,000
Year Founded: 1887
Business Description:
Life Insurance, Retirement Plans & Annuities, Savings & Investment Products & Services
S.I.C.: 6311; 6282; 6331; 6371; 6411; 6722
N.A.I.C.S.: 524113; 523920; 524298; 525110; 525190; 525910
Media: 2-5-6-8-9-20-23-25
Distr.: Direct to Consumer; Wholesaler
Budget Set: Nov.
Personnel:
JoAnn M. Martin *(Chm, Pres & CEO)*
Robert C. Barth *(CFO & Sr VP)*
Nancy A. Dalessio *(CIO & Sr VP)*
Dale D. Johnson *(Sr VP & Chief Actuary)*
Steven J. Valerius *(Pres-Individual Div)*
Kenneth L. VanCleave *(Pres-Grp Div)*
Jan M. Connolly *(Sr VP & Corp Sec)*
William W. Lester *(Exec VP)*
Janet L. Schmidt *(Sr VP & Dir-HR)*
Mary Beth DeSalvo *(Second VP-HR)*
Scott Stuckey *(VP-Corp Comm)*
Brands & Products:
AMERITAS
Advertising Agency:
Bailey Lauerman
1248 O St Ste 900
Lincoln, NE 68508-1460
Tel.: (402) 475-2800
Fax: (402) 475-5115
(Insurance)

AMICA MUTUAL INSURANCE CO.

100 Amica Way
Lincoln, RI 02865
Mailing Address:
PO Box 6008
Providence, RI 02940-6008
Tel.: (401) 334-0108
Toll Free: (800) 992-6422
Web Site: www.amica.com
Approx. Number Employees: 3,200
Year Founded: 1973
Business Description:
Personal Lines Property & Casualty Insurance
S.I.C.: 6331; 6311
N.A.I.C.S.: 524126; 524113
Media: 7-8-9-16-18-20-23-24-26
Distr.: Direct to Consumer; Natl.
Personnel:
Robert DiMuccio *(Pres & CEO)*
Maribeth Williamson *(Sr VP & Controller)*
James E. McDermott, Jr. *(Sr VP-Mktg)*
Craig Phelps *(Asst VP-Comm)*
Advertising Agency:
Cronin & Company, Inc.
50 Nye Rd
Glastonbury, CT 06033-1280
Tel.: (860) 659-0514
Fax: (860) 659-3455

ANTHEM HEALTH PLANS OF VIRGINIA

(Sub. of WellPoint, Inc.)
2015 Staples Mill Rd Ste 1
Richmond, VA 23279-3119
Mailing Address:
PO Box 27401
Richmond, VA 23279-7401
Tel.: (804) 354-7000
Fax: (804) 354-3399
E-mail: tracy.staten@anthem.com
Web Site: www.anthem.com
Sales Range: $1-4.9 Billion
Approx. Number Employees: 3,112
Year Founded: 1935
Business Description:
Managed Healthcare
S.I.C.: 6321
N.A.I.C.S.: 524114
Media: 1-2-3-4-5-6-7-8-9-10-13-18-20-22-23-24-25-26
Distr.: Reg.
Budget Set: Aug.
Personnel:
Wayne Deveydt *(CFO)*
Advertising Agency:
Adworks, Inc.
1225 19th St NW Ste 500
Washington, DC 20036
Tel.: (202) 342-5585
Fax: (202) 739-8201

ANTHEM INSURANCE COMPANIES, INC.

(Sub. of WellPoint, Inc.)
120 Monument Cir
Indianapolis, IN 46204
Tel.: (317) 488-6000
Web Site: www.anthem.com
Sales Range: $500-549.9 Million
Approx. Number Employees: 14,800
Year Founded: 1944
Business Description:
Health Insurance & Benefits
S.I.C.: 6321; 6411
N.A.I.C.S.: 524114; 524298
Media: 17
Personnel:
Wayne Veydt *(CFO)*
Kim E. Gray *(Mgr-District Sls)*

AON CORPORATION

200 E Randolph St
Chicago, IL 60601
Tel.: (312) 381-1000
Fax: (312) 381-6032
E-mail: investors@asc.aon.com
Web Site: www.aon.com
Approx. Rev.: $8,512,000,000
Approx. Number Employees: 59,000
Year Founded: 1979
Business Description:
Insurance Holding Company
S.I.C.: 6331; 6321; 6411; 6719
N.A.I.C.S.: 525190; 524114; 524210; 551112
Media: 8-9-10-18-25
Distr.: Natl.
Personnel:
Gregory C. Case *(Pres & CEO)*
Christa Davies *(CFO & Exec VP)*
Steve Betts *(CIO)*
Kevann M. Cooke *(Chief Governance Officer, Sec & Sr VP)*
Corbette S. Doyle *(Chief Diversity Officer)*
Bernard S.Y Fung *(Chm/CEO-Aon Asia Pacific)*

Key to Media (For complete agency information see *The Advertising Red Books-Agencies* edition):
1. Bus. Publs. 2. Cable T.V. 3. Catalogs & Directories. 4. Co-op Adv. 5. Consumer Mags. 6. D.M. to Bus. Estab.7. D.M. to Consumers
8. Daily Newsp. 9. Exhibits/Trade Shows 10. Foreign 11. Infomercial 12. Internet Adv.13. Multimedia 14. Network Radio
15. Network T.V. 16. Newsp. Distr. Mags. 17. Other 18. Outdoor (Posters, Transit) 19. Point of Purchase20. Premiums, Novelties
21. Product Samples 22. Special Events Mktg. 23. Spot Radio 24. Spot T.V. 25. Weekly Newsp. 26. Yellow Page Adv.

Stephen P. McGill *(Chm/CEO-Aon Risk Solutions)*
Baljit Dail *(CEO-Aon Consulting Global)*
Edouard Merette *(CEO-Consulting-Asia Pacific)*
Peter M. Lieb *(Gen Counsel & Exec VP)*
Karen Mildenhall *(Exec VP & Resident Mng Dir)*
Laurel Meissner *(Sr VP & Controller)*
Judy Bamberger *(Sr VP-Bus Dev-Risk Solutions-Los Angeles)*
Jeanne Herold *(Sr VP)*
Roy C. Keller *(Sr VP-Global Real Estate)*
Yohei Miyamoto *(Sr VP-Real Estate Practice-Southern California)*
David Sult *(Sr VP-Transformation Svcs)*
Richard E. Barry *(VP & Deputy Gen Counsel)*
Robert S. Rivkin *(VP & Deputy Gen Counsel)*
Regis J. Coccia *(Dir-Mktg & Comm)*

Advertising Agencies:
GolinHarris
(Part of the Interpublic Group of Companies)
111 E Wacker Dr 11th Fl
Chicago, IL 60601-4306
Tel.: (312) 729-4000
Fax: (312) 729-4010

KemperLesnik
500 Skokie Blvd 4th Fl
Northbrook, IL 60062
Tel.: (847) 850-1818
Fax: (847) 559-0406
Aon Risk Services
Aon Consulting

AON RISK SERVICES INC.

(Sub. of Aon Corporation)
200 E Randolph St
Chicago, IL 60601
Tel.: (312) 381-1000
Fax: (312) 381-0171
Web Site: www.aon.com
Sales Range: $350-399.9 Million
Approx. Number Employees: 2,000
Business Description:
Insurance Brokers
S.I.C.: 6411; 8111
N.A.I.C.S.: 524210; 541110
Media: 1-2-3-4-5-6-7-8-9-10-11-16-20-22-23-24-25-26
Distr.: Intl.; Natl.
Budget Set: Nov.
Personnel:
Dirk P.M. Verbeek *(Chm & CEO)*

ARBELLA INSURANCE GROUP

1100 Crown Colony Dr
Quincy, MA 02269
Tel.: (617) 328-2800
Fax: (617) 328-2980
Toll Free: (800) ARBELLA
E-mail: info@arbella.com
Web Site: www.arbella.com
Approx. Number Employees: 870
Year Founded: 1988
Business Description:
Fire, Marine & Casualty Insurance
S.I.C.: 8742
N.A.I.C.S.: 541611
Import Export
Personnel:
John Donohue *(Chm, Pres & CEO)*
Francis X. Bellotti *(Vice Chm)*
Robert P. Medwid *(CFO, Treas & Exec VP)*
Janet Corcoran *(COO & Sr VP)*
Thomas S. Carpenter *(Chief Actuary & Exec VP)*
Gail Eagan *(Gen Counsel & VP)*
Beverly T. Tangvik *(Sec & Asst VP)*
John F. Kittel *(Exec VP)*
Christopher E. Hall *(VP-Fin)*
Steven A. Jacobs *(VP-Mktg)*
Gayle O'Connell *(VP-HR & Corp Comm)*
Brands & Products:
ARBELLA
Advertising Agency:
Rasky Baerlein Strategic Communications
70 Franklin St 3rd Fl
Boston, MA 02110
Tel.: (617) 443-9933
Fax: (617) 443-9944
Auto Insurance

ARROWPOINT CAPITAL CORP.

Whitehall Corporate Ctr 3 3600 Arco Corporate Dr
Charlotte, NC 28273
Mailing Address:
PO Box 1000
Charlotte, NC 28201-1000
Tel.: (704) 522-2000
Fax: (704) 522-3200
Web Site:
www.arrowpointcapitalcorp.com
Sales Range: $1-4.9 Billion
Approx. Number Employees: 5,700
Year Founded: 1985
Business Description:
Personal & Commercial Insurance Products & Services
S.I.C.: 6331; 6311; 6411
N.A.I.C.S.: 524126; 524113; 524298
Advertising Expenditures: $1,000,000
Media: 2-7-8-10-13-19-26
Distr.: Independent Insurance Agents
Budget Set: Dec.
Personnel:
John Tighe *(Pres & CEO)*
Sean Beatty *(CFO)*
Dennis Cahill *(COO)*
Mike McLaughlin *(CMO)*
Dave Shumway *(Chief Investment Officer)*
Dan Keddie *(Chief Actuary)*
Julie Fortune *(Chief Claims Officer)*
Andre Lefebvre *(Fin Risk Officer)*
Jim Meehan *(Gen Counsel)*

ASSET MARKETING SYSTEMS INSURANCE SERVICES, LLC

9715 Businesspark Ave
San Diego, CA 92131
Fax: (858) 348-2611
Toll Free: (888) 303-8755
Web Site:
www.assetmarketingsystems.net
Approx. Premiums: $1,600,000,000
Approx. Number Employees: 175
Year Founded: 1996
Business Description:
Annuities & Life Insurance Services
S.I.C.: 6399; 6311; 6371; 6411; 7319; 7389
N.A.I.C.S.: 524128; 524113; 524210; 524291; 524292; 524298; 541870; 561439; 561499; 561990
Media: 2-10
Personnel:
Dee Costa *(Sr VP-Sls & Mktg)*
Louise Erdman *(VP-Mktg)*
Jessica Elliot *(Dir-Mktg)*

ASSURANT HEALTH

(Div. of Assurant, Inc.)
501 W Michigan Ave
Milwaukee, WI 53203-2706
Tel.: (414) 271-3011
Fax: (414) 224-0472
Web Site: www.assuranthealth.com
Approx. Sls.: $729,900,000
Approx. Number Employees: 2,700
Year Founded: 1892
Business Description:
Individual & Group Health Insurance Plans
S.I.C.: 6321
N.A.I.C.S.: 524114
Media: 2-13-24
Distr.: Natl.
Budget Set: Nov.
Personnel:
Mark Berquist *(VP & Chief Actuary)*
Jennifer Kopps-Wagner *(Gen Counsel & Sr VP)*
Howard Miller *(Sr VP-Strategic Initiatives)*
Mike Norderhaug *(Sr VP & Exec Sls Officer-Assurant Health)*
Steve Keller *(VP-Mktg, Media & ECommerce)*
Whitney Smith *(VP-Mktg)*
Jacquie Fossett *(Dir-Self Funded Product Line)*
Kris Wickline *(Dir-Lead Acq & Ecommerce)*
Amy Wargin *(Mgr-Mktg)*
Advertising Agency:
HLB Communications, Inc.
875 N Michigan Ave
Chicago, IL 60611-1896
Tel.: (312) 649-0371
Fax: (312) 649-1119
Pub Rels
— Peter Duckler *(Sr Consultant)*

ASSURANT, INC.

1 Chase Manhattan Plz 41st Fl
New York, NY 10005
Tel.: (212) 859-7000
Fax: (212) 859-5893
E-mail: investor.relations@assurant.com
Web Site: www.assurant.com
Approx. Rev.: $8,527,722,000
Approx. Number Employees: 14,000
Year Founded: 1969
Business Description:
Specialized Insurance & Insurance-Related Products & Services
S.I.C.: 6321; 6311; 6331; 6411
N.A.I.C.S.: 525190; 524113; 524114; 524126; 524210
Media: 7-8-11
Personnel:
John Michael Palms *(Chm)*
Robert B. Pollock *(Pres & CEO)*
Donald Hamm *(CEO)*
Michael J. Peninger *(CFO & Exec VP)*
Bart R. Schwartz *(Chief Legal Officer, Sec & Exec VP)*
Christopher J. Pagano *(Treas & Exec VP)*
Alan Colberg *(Exec VP-Mktg & Bus Dev)*
Sylvia R. Wagner *(Exec VP-HR & Dev)*
Stephen W. Gauster *(Sr VP, Chief Corp Counsel & Asst Sec)*
William D. Greiter *(Sr VP-Corp Dev)*
Melissa Kivett *(Sr VP-IR)*
Ronny B. Lancaster *(Sr VP)*
Richard J. Lauria *(Sr VP)*
Jane Meyer *(Sr VP-HR)*

ASSURITY LIFE INSURANCE COMPANY

(Sub. of Assurity Security Group Inc.)
1526 K St
Lincoln, NE 68508
Mailing Address:
PO Box 82533
Lincoln, NE 68501-2533
Tel.: (402) 476-6500
Fax: (402) 437-4395
Toll Free: (800) 869-0355
E-mail: info@assurity.com
Web Site: www.assurity.com
Sales Range: $400-449.9 Million
Approx. Number Employees: 250
Year Founded: 1890
Business Description:
Life, Annuity & Disability Insurance Services
S.I.C.: 6411; 6311; 6321
N.A.I.C.S.: 524210; 524113; 524114
Media: 1-3-4-5-8-10-13-20-23-25-26
Distr.: Natl.
Budget Set: Oct.
Personnel:
Thomas E. Henning *(Chm, Pres & CEO)*
Marvin P. Ehly *(CFO & VP)*
Susan L. Keisler-Munro *(COO & Sr VP)*
Todd W. Reimers *(CMO & Sr VP)*
William R. Schmeeckle *(Chief Investment Officer & VP)*
David T. Wallman *(Chief Actuary & Sr VP)*
Carol S. Watson *(Gen Counsel, Sec & VP)*
Roseann R. Christensen *(VP-Mktg)*
Janice A. Zoucha *(VP-HR)*
Kevin G. Faltin *(Controller & Sr Dir)*
Kirk J. Spellman *(Dir-Mktg Svcs)*
Brands & Products:
ASSURITY

ATLANTIC MUTUAL COMPANIES

100 Wall St
New York, NY 10005
Tel.: (212) 943-1800
Fax: (212) 428-6566
Web Site: www.atlanticmutual.com
Approx. Number Employees: 1,800
Year Founded: 1842
Business Description:
Property & Casualty Insurance Services
S.I.C.: 6331
N.A.I.C.S.: 524126
Media: 2-5-13
Distr.: Natl.
Budget Set: Sept.
Personnel:
Richard J. Hertling *(CFO & Exec VP)*

Key to Media (For complete agency information see *The Advertising Red Books-Agencies* edition):
1. Bus. Publs. 2. Cable T.V. 3. Catalogs & Directories. 4. Co-op Adv. 5. Consumer Mags. 6. D.M. to Bus. Estab.7. D.M. to Consumers 8. Daily Newsp. 9. Exhibits/Trade Shows 10. Foreign 11. Infomercial 12. Internet Adv.13. Multimedia 14. Network Radio 15. Network T.V. 16. Newsp. Distr. Mags. 17. Other 18. Outdoor (Posters, Transit) 19. Point of Purchase20. Premiums, Novelties 21. Product Samples 22. Special Events Mktg. 23. Spot Radio 24. Spot T.V. 25. Weekly Newsp. 26. Yellow Page Adv.

Atlantic Mutual Companies — (Continued)

Brands & Products:
ATLANTIC MASTER PLAN
ATLANTIC RISK SERVICES
INSUREPOINT
RISKPOINT
WHEN IT COUNTS

ATTO & ASSOCIATES INSURANCE BROKERS, INC.

5660 McAdam Rd Unit A1
Mississauga, ON Canada
Tel.: (905) 890-1412
Fax: (905) 890-1569
Toll Free: (800) 263-9683
E-mail: info@attoinsurance.com
Web Site: www.attoinsurance.com
Approx. Number Employees: 55
Year Founded: 1983
Business Description:
Insurance Brokerage Services
S.I.C.: 6411; 6371
N.A.I.C.S.: 524298; 524210; 524291; 524292
Media: 2-6-9-14-15-22
Distr.: Reg.
Personnel:
John Atto *(Founder)*
Barbara Hubel *(CFO)*

AUTO-OWNERS INSURANCE GROUP

6101 Anacapri Blvd
Lansing, MI 48917
Tel.: (517) 323-1200
Fax: (517) 323-8796
Toll Free: (888) 264-3556
Web Site: www.auto-owners.com
Sales Range: $5-14.9 Billion
Approx. Number Employees: 3,270
Year Founded: 1916
Business Description:
Holding Company; Insurance Products & Services
S.I.C.: 6719; 6331; 6361; 6399; 6411
N.A.I.C.S.: 551112; 524126; 524127; 524128; 524298
Media: 3-5-6-8-9-14-18-20-23-24-25-26
Personnel:
J. Harrold *(Chm & Pres)*
Ron Simon *(CEO & Bd Member)*
Robert Buchanan *(Sr VP)*
Daniel J. Thelen *(Sr VP-Personnel)*
Brands & Products:
AUTO-OWNERS
IN BUSINESS TO WRITE BUSINESS
THE NO PROBLEM PEOPLE
SAFE. SOUND. SECURE

AVEMCO INSURANCE COMPANY

(Sub. of HCC Insurance Holdings, Inc.)
Frederick Municipal Airport 411
Aviation Way
Frederick, MD 21701
Tel.: (301) 694-5700
Fax: (301) 694-4376
Toll Free: (888) 241-7891
Web Site: www.avemco.com
Sales Range: $25-49.9 Million
Approx. Number Employees: 70
Year Founded: 1961
Business Description:
Aviation Insurance & Financial Services
S.I.C.: 6321; 6331
N.A.I.C.S.: 524114; 524126
Advertising Expenditures: $2,000,000
Media: 2-4-5-6-7-8-10-13-19-20-22
Distr.: Direct to Consumer; Natl.
Budget Set: Oct.
Personnel:
James A. Lauerman *(Pres)*
Michael J. Schell *(CEO)*
Lauretta Godbey *(VP-Mktg & Dir-PR)*
Brands & Products:
WINS-FIS

AVERA HEALTH

3900 W Avera Dr
Sioux Falls, SD 57108
Tel.: (605) 322-4700
Fax: (605) 322-4799
E-mail: John@Porter.avera.org
Web Site: www.avera.org
Approx. Number Employees: 100
Year Founded: 1982
Business Description:
Health Care Services
S.I.C.: 6321
N.A.I.C.S.: 524114
Media: 9-13-25
Personnel:
John T. Porter *(Pres & CEO)*
Advertising Agency:
BVK
250 W Coventry Ct #300
Milwaukee, WI 53217-3972
Tel.: (414) 228-1990
Fax: (414) 228-7561
Toll Free: (888) 347-3212

AVIVA USA

(Sub. of Aviva plc)
(d/b/a AmerUs Group Co)
611 5th Ave
Des Moines, IA 50309
Tel.: (515) 362-3600
Fax: (515) 362-3652
Web Site: www.avivausa.com
Approx. Number Employees: 1,190
Year Founded: 1896
Business Description:
Life & Annuity Insurance Services
S.I.C.: 6311
N.A.I.C.S.: 524113
Media: 2-7-8-20-26
Distr.: Natl.
Budget Set: Feb.
Personnel:
Christopher J. Littlefield *(Pres & CEO)*
Charles Preseau *(CFO)*
Joseph W. Wittrock *(Chief Investment Officer)*
Jeff Fitch *(Chief Risk Officer & Sr VP)*
John D. Currier, Jr. *(Chief Actuary)*
Richard C. Cohan *(Gen Counsel & Exec VP)*
Brian J. Clark *(Chief Product Officer & Exec VP)*
Michael H. Miller *(Exec VP-Sls & Distr)*
Christopher R. Welp *(Exec VP-Insurance Ops)*
Rhonda Elming *(Sr VP-Product Mgmt)*
Randy Wadle *(Sr VP-Change Mgmt)*
Advertising Agency:
BBDO Minneapolis
150 S 5th St Ste 3500
Minneapolis, MN 55402-4200
Tel.: (612) 338-8401
Fax: (612) 656-0602

AXA EQUITABLE

(Sub. of AXA)
1290 Ave of the Americas
New York, NY 10104-0101
Tel.: (212) 554-1234
Fax: (212) 315-3141
Web Site: www.axa-financial.com
Approx. Rev.: $13,344,900,000
Approx. Number Employees: 11,350
Year Founded: 1992
Business Description:
Insurance Services
S.I.C.: 6311; 6211; 6282
N.A.I.C.S.: 524113; 523110; 523920
Advertising Expenditures: $3,816,000
Media: 1-2-6-7-8-9-10-15-17-20-22-26
Distr.: Natl.
Budget Set: Sept. -Nov.
Personnel:
Mary Farrell *(Vice Chm, Exec VP Senior Vice President)*
Jean-Rene Fourtou *(Vice Chm)*
Mark Pearson *(Pres & CEO)*
Christopher Mark Condron *(Pres & CEO-Life & Savings Ops)*
Richard S. Dziadzio *(CFO & Sr Exec VP)*
Barbara Goodstein *(Chief Mktg Officer, Chief Innovation Officer & Exec VP)*
Richard Silver *(Chief Admin Officer, Chief Legal Officer & Sr Exec VP)*
Andrew McMahon *(Pres-Fin Protection, Wealth Mgmt Bus & Sr Exec VP)*
James Shepherdson *(Pres-Retirement Savings Bus & Sr Exec VP)*
David Kam *(Sr VP & Head-Annuity Product Devel)*
Alvin H. Fenichel *(Sr VP & Controller)*
Stacy Braun *(Sr VP-Mktg & Adv)*
Brands & Products:
YOUR FUTURE. YOUR WAY.
Advertising Agencies:
Johnston Duffy
2424 E York Rd No 215
Philadelphia, PA 19125
Tel.: (215) 389-2888
Fax: (215) 389-2988

Merkley + Partners
(Sub. of Omnicom Group, Inc.)
200 Varick St
New York, NY 10014-4810
Tel.: (212) 366-3500
Fax: (212) 805-7445

BANKERS LIFE & CASUALTY COMPANY

(Sub. of Bankers Life Holding Corp.)
600 W Chicago Ave
Chicago, IL 60654
Tel.: (312) 396-6000
Fax: (312) 396-5920
Toll Free: (800) 572-5189
Web Site: www.bankerslife.com
Approx. Sls.: $2,254,000,000
Approx. Number Employees: 1,200
Year Founded: 1879
Business Description:
Life Accident & Health Insurance Services
S.I.C.: 6321; 6311
N.A.I.C.S.: 524114; 524113
Advertising Expenditures: $12,000,000
Media: 2-6-8-9-14-15-22-24-26
Distr.: Reg.
Budget Set: Monthly
Personnel:
Scott R. Perry *(Pres)*
Michael J Buckley *(Sr VP-Sls)*
David Nelson *(Sr VP-Sls & Distr)*
John W. Wells *(Sr VP-Opers)*
Scott L. Goldberg *(VP-Strategy & Mktg)*
John Scheil *(Reg Dir & Branch Mgr)*
Ashley Sherwood *(Mgr-Recruiting)*
Brands & Products:
BANKERS HEALTH ADVANTAGE PROGRAM

BB&T - OSWALD TRIPPE & CO.

(Formerly OTCI Acquisition, LLC)
(Unit of BB&T Insurance Services, Inc.)
13515 Bell Twr Dr
Fort Myers, FL 33907-5944
Tel.: (239) 433-4535
Fax: (239) 433-4148
Toll Free: (800) 621-6821
Web Site: insurance.bbt.com/insurance/transition/oswaldtrippe
Sales Range: $25-49.9 Million
Approx. Number Employees: 200
Year Founded: 1981
Business Description:
Insurance Agency
S.I.C.: 6411
N.A.I.C.S.: 524210
Media: 2-7-8
Personnel:
John M. Pollock *(Mgr-Florida)*
Gray G. Davis *(Mgr)*

BERKSHIRE HATHAWAY INC.

3555 Farnam St Ste 1440
Omaha, NE 68131
Tel.: (402) 346-1400
Fax: (402) 346-3375
E-mail: berkshire@berkshirehathaway.com
Web Site: www.berkshirehathaway.com
Approx. Rev.: $136,185,000,000
Approx. Number Employees: 260,000
Business Description:
Holding Company; Property & Casualty Insurance & Reinsurance Services
S.I.C.: 6719; 6289; 6321; 6331; 6411
N.A.I.C.S.: 551112; 523999; 524126; 524130; 524210
Media: 2-3-4-6-7-8-9-10-13-25
Distr.: Natl.
Personnel:
Warren E. Buffett *(Chm & CEO)*
Charles T. Munger *(Vice Chm)*
Rebecca K. Amick *(Dir-Internal Auditing)*
Todd Combs *(Mgr-Investment)*

BERKSHIRE LIFE INSURANCE COMPANY OF AMERICA

(Sub. of The Guardian Life Insurance Company of America)
700 South St
Pittsfield, MA 01201-8212
Tel.: (413) 499-4321
Fax: (413) 499-4831
E-mail: customerservice@berkshirelife.com
Web Site: www.theberkshire.com
Approx. Number Employees: 460
Year Founded: 2001

Key to Media (For complete agency information see *The Advertising Red Books-Agencies* edition):
1. Bus. Publs. 2. Cable T.V. 3. Catalogs & Directories. 4. Co-op Adv. 5. Consumer Mags. 6. D.M. to Bus. Estab.7. D.M. to Consumers
8. Daily Newsp. 9. Exhibits/Trade Shows 10. Foreign 11. Infomercial 12. Internet Adv.13. Multimedia 14. Network Radio
15. Network T.V. 16. Newsp. Distr. Mags. 17. Other 18. Outdoor (Posters, Transit) 19. Point of Purchase20. Premiums, Novelties
21. Product Samples 22. Special Events Mktg. 23. Spot Radio 24. Spot T.V. 25. Weekly Newsp. 26. Yellow Page Adv.

Business Description:
Life Insurance, Disability Income Insurance, Pensions, Annuities & Mutual Fund Services
S.I.C.: 6311
N.A.I.C.S.: 524113
Media: 1-2-6-7-8-9-10-20-25
Distr.: Reg.
Personnel:
Gordon Dinsmore *(Pres)*
Larry Hazzard *(VP-Product & Mktg)*

BITUMINOUS CASUALTY CORPORATION
(Sub. of Bitco Corporation)
320 18th St
Rock Island, IL 61201-8938
Tel.: (309) 786-5401
Fax: (309) 786-3847
Toll Free: (800) 475-4477
E-mail: info@bituminousinsurance.com
Web Site: www.bituminousinsurance.com
E-Mail For Key Personnel:
President: gator@bituminousinsurance.com
Marketing Director: rhervey@bituminousinsurance.com
Sales Range: $350-399.9 Million
Approx. Number Employees: 600
Year Founded: 1917
Business Description:
Property & Liability Insurance Services
S.I.C.: 6331
N.A.I.C.S.: 524126
Media: 2-7-10-26
Distr.: Reg.
Budget Set: Jan.
Personnel:
Greg Ator *(Pres & CEO)*
R. Rainey *(Treas & Sr VP)*
Mark Jorgenson *(Exec VP)*
R. Broderick *(Sr VP-Info Sys)*
Bruce Horack *(Sr VP-Claims)*
Advertising Agency:
Finley Communications Services
PO Box 406 920 15th Ave
East Moline, IL 61244-0406
Tel.: (309) 752-1019

BLUE CROSS & BLUE SHIELD ASSOCIATION
225 N Michigan Ave
Chicago, IL 60601-7601
Tel.: (312) 297-6000
Fax: (312) 297-6609
Web Site: www.bcbs.com
Approx. Number Employees: 850
Year Founded: 1929
Business Description:
Health Insurance Hospital & Medical Plans
S.I.C.: 6794; 6321
N.A.I.C.S.: 533110; 524114
Media: 2-6-14-15-23-24
Distr.: Natl.
Budget Set: Sept.
Personnel:
Dan Loepp *(Chm)*
Scott P. Serota *(Pres & CEO)*
Allan M. Korn *(Chief Medical Officer & Sr VP-Office of Clinical Affairs)*
Roger Wilson *(Gen Counsel, Sr VP & Corp Sec-Legal & Governance)*
William J. Colbourne *(Sr VP-HR & Admin Svcs)*
Steve W. Gammarino *(Sr VP-Natl Programs)*
Mary Nell Lehnhard *(Sr VP-Policy & Representation)*
Maureen E. Sullivan *(Sr VP-Strategic Svcs)*
Bonnie Summers *(Exec Dir)*
Naomi Aronson *(Exec Dir-Tech)*
Kevin D. Shanklin *(Exec Dir)*
Jed Weissberg *(Assoc Exec Dir-Quality)*
Howard Oppenheimer *(Dir-Mktg & Strategic Svcs)*
Claudia Bonnell *(Project Mgr)*
Fernande Georges *(Project Mgr)*
Brands & Products:
BLUE CROSS BLUE SHIELD ASSOCIATION
BLUE DISTINCTION
BLUE DISTINCTION CENTERS FOR BARIATRIC SURGERY
BLUE DISTINCTION CENTERS FOR CARDIAC CARE
BLUE DISTINCTION CENTERS FOR SPINE SURGERY
BLUE DISTINCTION CENTERS FOR TRANSPLANTS
BLUECARD PROGRAM
BLUECARD WORLDWIDE

BLUE CROSS & BLUE SHIELD OF MASSACHUSETTS, INC.
The LandMark Ctr 401 Pk Dr
Boston, MA 02215-3326
Tel.: (617) 246-5000
Fax: (617) 246-4832
Toll Free: (800) 262-2583
Web Site: www.bcbsma.com
E-Mail For Key Personnel:
President: william.vanfaasen@bcbsma.com
Sales Range: $1-4.9 Billion
Approx. Number Employees: 3,575
Year Founded: 1937
Business Description:
Health Insurance Carrier
S.I.C.: 6321; 8742
N.A.I.C.S.: 524114; 541611
Advertising Expenditures: $10,030,000
Bus. Publs.: $300,000; Catalogs & Directories: $250,000; Consumer Mags.: $900,000; D.M. to Bus. Estab.: $200,000; D.M. to Consumers: $200,000; Daily Newsp.: $1,700,000; Exhibits/Trade Shows: $120,000; Outdoor (Posters, Transit): $700,000; Special Events Mktg.: $110,000; Spot Radio: $1,300,000; Spot T.V.: $4,000,000; Weekly Newsp.: $250,000
Distr.: Direct to Consumer; Reg.
Personnel:
William C. Van Faasen *(Chm)*
Paul Guzzi *(Vice Chm)*
Andrew Dreyfus *(Pres & CEO)*
Allen P. Maltz *(CFO & Exec VP)*
Ann S. Anderson *(Chief HR Officer)*
Fredi Shonkoff *(Sr VP-Corp Rels)*

BLUE CROSS & BLUE SHIELD OF MICHIGAN
600 Lafayette E Blvd
Detroit, MI 48226
Tel.: (313) 225-9000
Web Site: www.bcbsm.com
Approx. Rev.: $8,150,600,000
Approx. Number Employees: 8,500
Year Founded: 1930
Business Description:
Health Care Insurance
S.I.C.: 6321
N.A.I.C.S.: 524114
Personnel:
Spencer C. Johnson *(Vice Chm)*
Daniel J. Loepp *(Pres & CEO)*
Mark R. Bartlett *(CFO, Pres-Emerging Markets & Exec VP)*
George F. Francis, III *(Chief Admin Officer & Sr VP)*
Thomas L. Simmer *(Sr VP & Chief Medical Officer)*
J. Paul Austin *(Chief Actuarial Officer & Sr VP)*
Lisa S. DeMoss *(Gen Counsel, Sec & Sr VP)*
Kevin L. Seitz *(Sr VP-Subsidiary Opers)*
R. Andrew Hetzel *(VP-Corp Commun)*
Francine Pegues *(Mktg Dir)*
Advertising Agencies:
Seyferth & Associates Inc.
40 Monroe Ctr NW Ste 202
Grand Rapids, MI 49503
Tel.: (616) 776-3511
Fax: (616) 776-3502
Toll Free: (800) 435-9539

Undertone Networks
270 Madison Ave 19th Fl
New York, NY 10016
Tel.: (212) 685-8000
Fax: (212) 685-8001

BLUE CROSS & BLUE SHIELD OF RHODE ISLAND
500 Exchange St
Providence, RI 02903-3206
Tel.: (401) 459-1000
Fax: (401) 459-0006
Toll Free: (800) 527-7290
E-mail: info@bcbsri.org
Web Site: www.bcbsri.org
Approx. Rev.: $1,604,574,000
Approx. Number Employees: 1,100
Year Founded: 1939
Business Description:
Health Care Insurance
S.I.C.: 6321
N.A.I.C.S.: 524114
Advertising Expenditures: $5,000,000
Cable T.V.: $250,000; Daily Newsp.: $1,250,000; Infomercial: $500,000; Other: $250,000; Outdoor (Posters, Transit): $250,000; Premiums, Novelties: $250,000; Special Events Mktg.: $250,000; Spot Radio: $500,000; Spot T.V.: $1,250,000; Weekly Newsp.: $250,000
Distr.: Reg.
Budget Set: Nov.
Personnel:
Deborah R. Jacobson *(Chm)*
Fredric V. Christian *(Vice Chm)*
Andrus Szaiewicz *(Pres)*
William K. Wray *(CIO & Exec VP)*
Gus Manocchia *(VP & Chief Medical Officer-Provider Rels)*
Mark Waggoner *(Chief Contracting Officer & VP)*
Michele B. Lederberg *(Gen Counsel & Exec VP)*
Shanna Marzilli *(Sr VP-Strategic Transformation & Strategic Plng)*
Eric Gasbarro *(VP-HR)*
Paul Hanlon *(VP-IT)*
Monica Neronha *(VP-IT)*
Brands & Products:
BLUE CROSS BLUE SHIELD OF RHODE ISLAND
BLUE365
BLUECHIP
CLASSIC BLUE
DENTAL DIRECT
HEALTHMATE COAST-TO-COAST
YOUR PLAN FOR LIFE
Advertising Agency:
RDW Group Inc.
125 Holden St
Providence, RI 02908-4919
Tel.: (401) 521-2700
Fax: (401) 521-0014
(All)

BLUE CROSS & BLUE SHIELD OF TENNESSEE
801 Pine St
Chattanooga, TN 37402
Tel.: (423) 535-5600
Fax: (423) 535-5785
Toll Free: (800) 565-9140
E-mail: media@bcbst.com
Web Site: www.bcbst.com
Business Description:
Health Insurance Hospital & Medical Plans
S.I.C.: 6321
N.A.I.C.S.: 524114
Personnel:
Lamar J. Partridge *(Chm)*
William Gracey *(Pres & COO)*
Vicky B. Gregg *(CEO)*
John Giblin *(CFO & Exec VP)*
Mark Austin *(CMO & Sr VP)*
Bill Young *(Gen Counsel, Sr VP-Risk Mngmt & Chief Compliance Officer)*
Bob Worthington *(Sr VP & Chief Strategy Officer)*
David Locke *(VP & Chief Medical Officer)*
Jim Srite *(Chief Actuary & VP)*
Steven Coulter *(Pres-Govt Bus & Exec VP)*
Joan Harp *(Pres-Comml Bus & Established Markets & Exec VP)*
Chris Hunter *(Treas & Sr VP)*
Linda Andreae *(Sr VP-Product Performance)*
Ron Harr *(Sr VP-People Svcs & Pub Affairs)*
Don Lawhorn *(VP-Sls)*
Chris Levan *(VP-Info Svcs)*
Kelly Allen *(Specialist-Comm)*
Advertising Agency:
Katcher Vaughn & Bailey Public Relations, Inc.
(d/b/a KVBPR)
401 Church St Ste 2100
Nashville, TN 37219
Tel.: (615) 248-8202
Fax: (615) 248-8120

BLUE CROSS BLUE SHIELD OF WISCONSIN
(Sub. of WellPoint, Inc.)
(d/b/a Anthem Blue Cross and Blue Shield)
N17 W24340 Riverwood Dr
Waukesha, WI 53118
Tel.: (414) 459-5000

Key to Media (For complete agency information see *The Advertising Red Books-Agencies* edition):
1. Bus. Publs. 2. Cable T.V. 3. Catalogs & Directories. 4. Co-op Adv. 5. Consumer Mags. 6. D.M. to Bus. Estab.7. D.M. to Consumers 8. Daily Newsp. 9. Exhibits/Trade Shows 10. Foreign 11. Infomercial 12. Internet Adv.13. Multimedia 14. Network Radio 15. Network T.V. 16. Newsp. Distr. Mags. 17. Other 18. Outdoor (Posters, Transit) 19. Point of Purchase20. Premiums, Novelties 21. Product Samples 22. Special Events Mktg. 23. Spot Radio 24. Spot T.V. 25. Weekly Newsp. 26. Yellow Page Adv.

Blue Cross Blue Shield of Wisconsin — (Continued)

Web Site: www.anthem.com/health-insurance/home/overview
E-Mail For Key Personnel:
Public Relations: jill.becher@bcbswi.com
Sales Range: $1-4.9 Billion
Approx. Number Employees: 2,200
Year Founded: 1940
Business Description:
Group Life & Disability Insurance
S.I.C.: 6321
N.A.I.C.S.: 524114
Media: 5-6-7-8-9-10-18-20-23-24-25-26
Distr.: Reg.
Budget Set: Sept.-Oct.
Personnel:
Steve Martenet *(Pres & Gen Mgr)*
Craig Steffes *(VP-Fin)*
Jill Becher *(Mgr-Corp Commun)*
Brands & Products:
DENTALBLUE
GET THE POWER OF BLUE WORKING FOR YOU.
LIFESTYLEBLUE

BLUE CROSS OF CALIFORNIA

(Sub. of WellPoint, Inc.)
(d/b/a Anthem Blue Cross)
1 Wellpoint Way
Thousand Oaks, CA 91362-3893
Tel.: (805) 557-6655
Fax: (805) 557-6872
Toll Free: (800) 333-0912
Web Site: www.bluecrossca.com
Sales Range: $1-4.9 Billion
Approx. Number Employees: 10,900
Year Founded: 1937
Business Description:
Health Insurance Products & Related Services
S.I.C.: 6411
N.A.I.C.S.: 524298
Media: 1-2-3-5-6-7-9-10-18-23-24
Personnel:
Leslie A. Margolin *(Pres & Gen Mgr)*
Craig Christenson *(CFO & VP)*
Leslie Porras *(Dir-Pub Rels)*

BLUE SHIELD OF CALIFORNIA

50 Beale St
San Francisco, CA 94105-1808
Tel.: (415) 229-5000
Fax: (415) 229-5730
Web Site: www.blueshieldca.com
Sales Range: $5-14.9 Billion
Approx. Number Employees: 4,800
Year Founded: 1939
Business Description:
Health Care Service Plans
S.I.C.: 6321
N.A.I.C.S.: 524114
Advertising Expenditures: $367,268,000
Media: 2-6-7-8-9-18-23-24-25
Distr.: Direct to Consumer; Reg.
Budget Set: Oct. -Nov.
Personnel:
Bruce Bodaken *(Chm, Pres & CEO)*
Heidi Kunz Fields *(CFO & Exec VP)*
Paul Markovich *(COO & Exec VP)*
Elinor MacKinnon *(CIO & Sr VP)*
Charles Sweeris *(Chief Compliance Officer, Deputy Gen Counsel & VP)*
Ed Cymerys *(Chief Actuary & Sr VP)*
Meredith Mathews *(Chief Medical Officer & Sr VP)*
Mark Gastineau *(CEO-Individual, Small Grp & Govt Bus Unit & Sr VP)*
Tom Brophy *(CFO-Underwriting & Fin-Large Grp Bus Unit & VP)*
John Hedberg *(VP-Fin & Underwriting & CFO-Individual, Small Grp & Govt Bus Unit)*
Seth A. Jacobs *(Gen Counsel, Sec & Sr VP)*
Juan Davila *(Sr VP-Network Mgmt)*
Rob Geyer *(Sr VP-Customer Ops)*
Marianne Jackson *(Sr VP-HR)*
David S. Joyner *(Sr VP-Large Grp & Specialty Benefits Bus Unit)*
Janet Widmann *(Sr VP-Calpers, Labor, Pub & Strategic Accts)*
Duncan Ross *(VP & Gen Mgr-Specialty Benefits)*
Doug Biehn *(VP-Corp Mktg)*
Cindy Bottenhagen *(VP-HR, Customer Svcs & Corp Mktg)*
Karman Chan *(VP-Fin & Underwriting)*
Jim Elliott *(VP-Mid & Large Sector Sls-Southern CA-Large Grp Bus Unit)*
Jeff Hermosillo *(VP-Sls, Acct Mgmt, Labor, Pub & Strategic Accts)*
Thad Roake *(VP-Mid & Large Sector Sls-Northern CA-Large Grp Bus Unit)*
Mike Sears *(VP-Customer Svc)*
Sue deLeeuw *(Brand Dir)*
Elmer Jones *(Dir-Medical-Quality, Disease Mgmt & Behavioral Health)*

BOLLINGER INC.

(Holding of Evercore Capital Partners)
101 JFK Pkwy
Short Hills, NJ 07078
Tel.: (973) 467-0444
Fax: (973) 921-2876
Toll Free: (800) 526-1379
Web Site:
www.bollingerinsurance.com
Sales Range: $100-124.9 Million
Approx. Number Employees: 420
Business Description:
Personal & Commercial Property, Casualty & Life Insurance Services
S.I.C.: 6411; 6311; 6331
N.A.I.C.S.: 524210; 524113; 524126
Media: 2
Personnel:
John A. Windolf *(Chm & CEO)*
Christopher H. Wetzel *(CFO & Exec VP)*
G. Alex Crispo *(Chief Admin Officer)*
Susan Monahan *(Exec VP)*

BOSTON MUTUAL LIFE INSURANCE COMPANY

120 Royall St
Canton, MA 02021-1028
Tel.: (781) 828-7000
Fax: (781) 770-0575
Toll Free: (800) 669-2668
E-mail: Frank_Melo@BostonMutual.com
Web Site: www.bostonmutual.com
Sales Range: $250-299.9 Million
Year Founded: 1891
Business Description:
Insurance Company
S.I.C.: 6311
N.A.I.C.S.: 524113
Advertising Expenditures: $900,000
Media: 2-7-8-19-20-26
Distr.: Natl.
Personnel:
Paul E. Petry *(Pres & CEO)*
Clifford Lange *(CFO, Chief Actuary & VP)*
Howard V. Neff, Jr. *(CIO & VP)*
Frederick C. Thurston *(Chief Compliance Officer & Second VP)*
Walter J. Gorski *(Gen Counsel, Sec & VP)*
Christine T. Coughlin *(Treas & Second VP)*
Susan Gardner *(Second VP & Controller)*
Frank E. Melo *(Second VP-General Audito)*
Philip G. Sullivan *(Dir-Medical)*

BROWN & BROWN, INC.

220 S Ridgewood Ave
Daytona Beach, FL 32114
Mailing Address:
PO Box 2412
Daytona Beach, FL 32115
Tel.: (386) 252-9601
Fax: (386) 239-5729
Toll Free: (800) 877-2769
E-mail: dhudson@bbins.com
Web Site: www.bbinsurance.com
Approx. Rev.: $973,492,000
Approx. Number Employees: 5,286
Year Founded: 1939
Business Description:
Health, Life, Casualty, Property & Surety Insurance Services
S.I.C.: 6411
N.A.I.C.S.: 524298; 524210
Advertising Expenditures: $500,000
Media: 2-5-7-10
Distr.: Direct to Consumer; Natl.
Budget Set: Sept.
Personnel:
J. Hyatt Brown *(Chm)*
J. Powell Brown *(Pres & CEO)*
Cory T. Walker *(CFO, Treas & Sr VP)*
Laurel Grammig *(Gen Counsel, Sec & VP)*
Robert W. Lloyd *(Gen Counsel & VP)*
Kenneth Masters *(Exec VP)*
Anthony Strianese *(Exec VP)*
Thomas M. Donegan, Jr. *(VP & Asst Sec)*
Rob Roth *(Dir-Pro Liability-Wholesale Brokerage Div)*
Vaughn Stoll *(Dir-Acq)*
Brands & Products:
AUTOMOBILE DEALERS PROTECTOR PLAN
BROWN AND BROWN
CALSURANCE
ENVIRONMENTAL PROTECTOR PLAN
LAWYERS PROTECTOR PLAN
THE LAWYERS PROTECTOR PLAN
MANUFACTURERS PROTECTOR PLAN
OPTICAL SERVICES PROTECTOR PLAN
THE OPTOMETRIC PROTECTOR PLAN
OPTOMETRISTS PROTECTOR PLAN
PARCEL INSURANCE PLAN
PHYSICIANS PROTECTOR PLAN
PROFESSIONAL PROTECTOR PLAN
THE PROFESSIONAL PROTECTOR PLAN
PROFESSIONAL SERVICES PLANS
PUBLIC RISK UNDERWRITERS
RAILROAD PROTECTOR PLAN
TITLEPAC
TOWING OPERATORS PROTECTOR PLAN

CALIFORNIA STATE AUTOMOBILE ASSOCIATION

(Affil. of American Automobile Association)
3055 Oak Rd
Walnut Creek, CA 94597
Tel.: (415) 565-2400
Fax: (925) 279-5655
Web Site: www.csaa.com
Approx. Number Employees: 6,000
Business Description:
Automobile Insurance
S.I.C.: 4729; 6411
N.A.I.C.S.: 561599; 524298
Media: 8
Personnel:
Paula F. Downey *(Pres & CEO)*
James R. Pouliot *(CEO)*
Jennifer Mack *(Sr Mgr-Media Rels)*
Advertising Agencies:
B.A.R.C. Communications, Inc.
170 Columbus Ave 5th Fl
San Francisco, CA 94133-5128
Tel.: (415) 772-1989
Fax: (415) 772-8964

Eleven Inc.
445 Bush St 8th Fl
San Francisco, CA 94108
Tel.: (415) 707-1111
Fax: (415) 707-1100

CAREFIRST BLUECROSS BLUESHIELD

(Sub. of CareFirst of Maryland, Inc.)
840 First St NE
Washington, DC 20065-0001
Tel.: (202) 479-8000
Web Site: www.carefirst.com/company/html/Locations.html
Approx. Number Employees: 280
Year Founded: 1942
Business Description:
Not-For-Profit Managed Health Company Which, Along With Its Affiliates & Subsidiaries, Offers A Comprehensive Portfolio of Health Insurance Products, Direct Health Care & Administrative Services
S.I.C.: 6399
N.A.I.C.S.: 524128
Personnel:
Greg Chaney *(CFO & Exec VP)*
Advertising Agency:
Cramer-Krasselt
7 W 22nd 8th Fl
New York, NY 10010
Tel.: (212) 889-6450
Fax: (212) 251-1265

CARELINK HEALTH PLANS INC

(Sub. of Coventry Health Care, Inc.)
500 Virginia St E Ste 400
Charleston, WV 25301-2135
Tel.: (304) 348-2900
Fax: (304) 348-2948
Toll Free: (800) 348-2922
Web Site: www.chccarelink.com
Sales Range: $10-24.9 Million
Approx. Number Employees: 63

Business Description:
HMO
S.I.C.: 8011; 6371
N.A.I.C.S.: 621491; 525120
Media: 7-8-13-16
Brands & Products:
CARELINK HEALTH PLANS

CATALYST HEALTH SOLUTIONS, INC.
800 King Farm Blvd Ste 400
Rockville, MD 20850
Tel.: (301) 548-2900
Fax: (301) 548-2991
Toll Free: (800) 233-3034
Web Site:
www.catalysthealthsolutions.com
Approx. Rev.: $3,764,092,000
Approx. Number Employees: 1,036
Year Founded: 1997
Business Description:
Health & Disability Insurance Benefit Programs Sales
S.I.C.: 6411; 5122
N.A.I.C.S.: 524210; 424210
Media: 2-3-6-7-8-10-24
Personnel:
Edward S. Civera *(Chm)*
Richard A. Bates *(Pres & COO)*
David T. Blair *(CEO)*
Deirdre Kramer *(Interim CFO)*
Mark Noga *(Chief Pharmacy Officer-Govt Svcs)*
Babette Edgar *(Pres-Govt Svcs)*
Richard Keane *(Pres-Employer Segment)*
Bruce F. Metge *(Gen Counsel & Sec)*
Wayne Dix *(Sr VP-Ops & Bus Transformation)*
Chris Myers *(Sr VP-Member Svcs)*

CATHOLIC ORDER OF FORESTERS
355 Shuman Blvd
Naperville, IL 60563
Mailing Address:
PO Box 3012
Naperville, IL 60566-7012
Tel.: (630) 983-4900
Fax: (630) 983-4057
Toll Free: (800) 552-0145
Web Site: www.catholicforester.org
E-Mail For Key Personnel:
Sales Director: cofsales@aol.com
Public Relations: cofpr@aol.com
Sales Range: $100-124.9 Million
Approx. Number Employees: 100
Year Founded: 1883
Business Description:
Fraternal Life Insurance for Catholics
S.I.C.: 6311
N.A.I.C.S.: 524113
Advertising Expenditures: $78,000
Media: 2-7-8-10-25-26
Distr.: Reg.
Budget Set: June
Personnel:
David E. Huber *(Pres)*
Mary Anne File *(Asst VP-Comm)*
Brands & Products:
CATHOLIC FORESTER
CATHOLIC ORDER OF FORESTERS
COF MATCHING FUNDS PROGRAM
COF PHOTO AND POSTER CONTESTS
FIRSTVANTAGE
FIRSTVANTAGE/PATHWAYS PROGRAM
FORESTER FLEX
FORESTER GUARDIAN
FORESTER GUARDIAN PLUS
FORESTER HERITAGE
FORESTER HERITAGE PLUS
FORESTER LEGACY
FORESTER LEVEL TERM TO AGE 35
FORESTER LIFE
FORESTER MEMBERSHIP AND TRAVEL CARE
FORESTER OPTIMIZER
FORESTER TRAVEL CARE
FORESTERBASIC
FORESTERBASIC 10
FORESTERBASIC 15
FRATERNAL BENEFIT POLICY
MODIFIED WHOLE LIFE
REAP
RELIGIOUS EDUCATION ASSISTANCE PROGRAM
STRONG.SOLID.SECURE
TAP

CENTEGRA NORTHERN ILLINOIS MEDICAL CENTER
4201 W Medical Ctr Dr
McHenry, IL 60050-8409
Tel.: (815) 363-2356
Fax: (815) 788-5263
Web Site: www.centegra.org
Approx. Number Employees: 2,477
Year Founded: 1982
Business Description:
Health Services
S.I.C.: 8062
N.A.I.C.S.: 622110
Media: 17
Personnel:
Michael S. Eesley *(CEO)*
Susan Milford *(Sr VP-Mktg)*
Lisa Hughes O'Neil *(Dir-Mktg & Comm)*
Kim Piraino *(Mgr-Sls & Mktg-Centegra Health Bridge Fitness Centers)*

CENTRAL MUTUAL INSURANCE COMPANY
800 S Washington St
Van Wert, OH 45891-2357
Mailing Address:
PO Box 351
Van Wert, OH 45891-0351
Tel.: (419) 238-1010
Fax: (419) 238-7626
Web Site: www.central-insurance.com
Approx. Sls.: $290,500,000
Approx. Number Employees: 550
Year Founded: 1876
Business Description:
Property & Casualty Insurance Services
S.I.C.: 6331
N.A.I.C.S.: 524126
Media: 2-3-5-18-19-20-26
Distr.: Natl.
Budget Set: Oct.
Personnel:
P. W. Purmort *(Chm & Pres)*
Laura Ditto *(Mgr-Mktg Comm)*
Brands & Products:
CENTRAL INSURANCE COMPANIES

THE CHUBB CORPORATION
15 Mountain View Rd
Warren, NJ 07059
Tel.: (908) 903-2000
Fax: (908) 903-2027
Telex: 299719
E-mail: info@chubb.com
Web Site: www.chubb.com
Approx. Rev.: $13,319,000,000
Approx. Number Employees: 10,100
Year Founded: 1882
Business Description:
Holding Company
S.I.C.: 6719; 6331
N.A.I.C.S.: 551112; 524126
Media: 2-22
Personnel:
John D. Finnegan *(Chm, Pres & CEO)*
Richard G. Spiro *(CFO & Exec VP)*
James P. Knight *(CIO-Chubb & Son & Exec VP)*
Ned I. Gerstman *(Co-Chief Investment Officer & Exec VP)*
Harold L. Morrison, Jr. *(Chief Admin Officer, Chief Global Field Officer & Exec VP)*
Sunita Holzer *(Chief HR Officer & Exec VP)*
Maureen A. Brundage *(Chief Ethics Officer, Gen Counsel & Exec VP)*
Paul J. Krump *(Pres-Comml & Specialty Lines, Exec VP)*
Dino E. Robusto *(Pres-Personal Lines & Claims, Exec VP)*
Robert C. Cox *(COO-Chubb Specialty Insurance & Exec VP)*
W. Andrew Macan *(VP, Corp Counsel & Sec)*
John J. Kennedy *(Asst VP)*
Francisco Barajas *(Mgr-Underwriting)*
Lisa Land *(Mgr-Product)*
Brent McAllister *(Mgr-Surety)*
Steve McGuinness *(Mgr-UK & Ireland Pricing)*
Brands & Products:
AGENCY CLAIMVIEW
AGENCY E-LOSS
CHUBB
CLAIMVIEW
RELAX. YOU'VE PLACED YOUR BEST CLIENTS WITH CHUBB.
SURETYPLUS
YACHT PREFERENCE
Advertising Agencies:
Alexander & Richardson
161 Washington Valley Rd Ste 205
Warren, NJ 07059-7121
Tel.: (732) 302-1223
Fax: (732) 356-9574

Creative Insurance Marketing Co.
208 2nd Ave
Belmar, NJ 07719
Tel.: (732) 681-0700
Fax: (732) 681-7102

Miller Advertising Agency Inc.
71 5th Ave 5th Fl
New York, NY 10003-3004
Tel.: (212) 929-2200
Fax: (212) 727-4734
Toll Free: (800) 229-6574

Red Flannel
218 Schanck Rd 2nd Fl
Freehold, NJ 07728
Tel.: (732) 761-8998
Fax: (732) 761-9424

CIGI DIRECT INSURANCE SERVICES, INC.
232 F St
Salida, CO 81201
Tel.: (719) 539-3000
Fax: (719) 539-3133
Toll Free: (800) 876-8007
E-mail: info@eterm.com
Web Site: www.eterm.com
Approx. Number Employees: 120
Year Founded: 1986
Business Description:
Insurance Brokerage
S.I.C.: 6411
N.A.I.C.S.: 524210
Media: 8-13
Personnel:
John Robert Hightower *(Pres)*
Melissa Hightower *(Treas)*
Jim Webster *(Sr VP)*
Bob Thorgeson *(Dir-Internet Mktg)*
Brands & Products:
CIGI DIRECT
E-TERM
ETERM.COM

CIGNA CORPORATION
2 Liberty Pl 1601 Chestnut St
Philadelphia, PA 19192
Tel.: (215) 761-1000
Fax: (215) 761-5515
E-mail: inquiries@cigna.com
Web Site: www.cigna.com
Approx. Rev.: $21,253,000,000
Approx. Number Employees: 30,600
Year Founded: 1982
Business Description:
Insurance, Investment Management, Health Care & Financial Services
S.I.C.: 6321; 6211; 6311; 6371; 6719
N.A.I.C.S.: 524114; 523120; 524113; 525110; 551112
Advertising Expenditures: $125,000,000
Media: 2-3-6-7-9-10-13-15-18-22-26
Distr.: Natl.
Budget Set: Oct. -Dec.
Personnel:
Isaiah Harris, Jr. *(Chm)*
David M. Cordani *(Pres & CEO)*
Ralph J. Nicoletti *(CFO & Exec VP)*
Philip Emond *(CIO & Exec VP-Ops-US)*
Benjamin Karsch *(CMO & Sr VP)*
John M. Murabito *(Chief HR Officer & Exec VP-HR & Svcs)*
Mary T. Hoeltzel *(Chief Acctg Officer & VP)*
Rosanna M. Durruthy *(Chief Diversity Officer)*
C. Daniel Huron *(Pres-Pharmacy Mgmt Unit)*
Matthew G. Manders *(Pres-Svc, Clinical & Specialty-US)*
Bertram L. Scott *(Pres-Comml-US)*
Nicole S. Jones *(Gen Counsel-Bloomfield)*
Thomas A. Croswell *(Sr VP-Medical Mgmt)*
Alfredo Lathrop *(Sr VP-HR)*
Alan M. Muney *(Sr VP-Total Health & Network)*
Mark Parsons *(Sr VP)*
Craig Shumard *(Chief Info Security Officer & Sr VP)*
Thomas A. McCarthy *(VP-Fin)*
Derek Weiss *(VP-Strategy & Mktg)*

Key to Media (For complete agency information see *The Advertising Red Books-Agencies* edition):
1. Bus. Publs. 2. Cable T.V. 3. Catalogs & Directories. 4. Co-op Adv. 5. Consumer Mags. 6. D.M. to Bus. Estab.7. D.M. to Consumers 8. Daily Newsp. 9. Exhibits/Trade Shows 10. Foreign 11. Infomercial 12. Internet Adv.13. Multimedia 14. Network Radio 15. Network T.V. 16. Newsp. Distr. Mags. 17. Other 18. Outdoor (Posters, Transit) 19. Point of Purchase20. Premiums, Novelties 21. Product Samples 22. Special Events Mktg. 23. Spot Radio 24. Spot T.V. 25. Weekly Newsp. 26. Yellow Page Adv.

CIGNA Corporation — (Continued)

Joseph Mondy *(Asst VP)*
Meredith Wagner *(Bus Mgr)*
James Batty *(Mgr-New Bus-NJ)*
Paul Gallenda *(Mgr-Bus)*
Anthony Hidell *(Mgr-New Bus)*
Russ Hyde *(Mgr-New Bus)*
Scott Senci *(Mgr-Sls)*
Mia Walters *(Mgr-Mktg Comm)*

Brands & Products:
A BUSINESS OF CARING
CIGNA
CIGNA DENTAL NETWORK ACCESS
CIGNAFLEX ADVANTAGE
CIGNAPLUS SAVINGS
IT'S TIME TO FEEL BETTER

Advertising Agency:
Hill Holliday
53 State St
Boston, MA 02109
Tel.: (617) 366-4000
Advertising
Agency of Record
B2B Marketing
Media Buying

CITIZENS INC.

400 E Anderson Ln
Austin, TX 78752
Mailing Address:
PO Box 149151
Austin, TX 78714-9151
Tel.: (512) 837-7100
Fax: (512) 836-9785
E-mail: postoffice@citizensinc.com
Web Site: www.citizensinc.com
Approx. Rev.: $191,181,000
Approx. Number Employees: 330
Year Founded: 1977
Business Description:
Holding Company; Insurance & Securities Services
S.I.C.: 6321; 6211; 6311; 6719
N.A.I.C.S.: 524130; 523110; 524113; 551112
Media: 5
Personnel:
Harold E. Riley *(Chm & CEO)*
Rick D. Riley *(Vice Chm & Pres & Chief Corp Officer)*
Kay E. Osbourn *(CFO, Treas & Exec VP)*
Ray A. Riley *(CMO & Exec VP)*
Geoffery M. Kolander *(Gen Counsel, Sec & VP)*
Randall H. Riley *(Dir-Intl Mktg)*

CNA INSURANCE COMPANIES

(Sub. of CNA Financial Corporation)
CNA Ctr 333 S Wabash Ave
Chicago, IL 60604-0001
Tel.: (312) 822-5000
Fax: (312) 822-6419
Web Site: www.cna.com
Approx. Number Employees: 12,000
Year Founded: 1898
Business Description:
Insurance
S.I.C.: 6399; 6331
N.A.I.C.S.: 524128; 524126; 525190
Media: 8
Distr.: Natl.
Budget Set: Oct.
Personnel:
Thomas F. Motamed *(Chm & CEO)*
D. Craig Mense *(CFO & Exec VP)*
Thomas Pontarelli *(Chief Admin Officer & Exec VP)*
Larry A. Haefner *(Exec VP & Chief Actuary)*
Peter W. Wilson *(Pres/COO-CNA Specialty)*
Jonathan David Kantor *(Gen Counsel, Sec & Exec VP)*
George R. Fay *(Exec VP-Worldwide P & C Claim)*
John Angerami *(Sr VP-CNA Select Risk)*
Michael W. Coyne *(Sr VP-Bus Insurance)*
Christopher Mead *(Mng Dir-Mktg)*
Richard Vonesh *(Dir-Claim-Western Svc Center-Denver)*

Brands & Products:
CNA

Advertising Agency:
Magnani Continuum Marketing
200 S Michigan Ave 5th Fl
Chicago, IL 60606-2424
Tel.: (312) 957-0770
Fax: (312) 957-0457

CNO FINANCIAL GROUP, INC.

(Formerly Conseco, Inc.)
11825 N Pennsylvania St
Carmel, IN 46032-4555
Tel.: (317) 817-6100
Fax: (317) 817-2847
Toll Free: (800) 888-4918
Web Site: cnoinc.com/
Approx. Rev.: $4,083,900,000
Approx. Number Employees: 3,680
Year Founded: 1979
Business Description:
Holding Company; Insurance Services
S.I.C.: 6321; 6311; 6719
N.A.I.C.S.: 524114; 524113; 551112
Media: 2-6-8-13-22
Distr.: Natl.
Budget Set: Dec.
Personnel:
Glenn R. Hilliard *(Chm)*
C. James Prieur *(CEO)*
Edward J. Bonach *(CFO & Exec VP)*
Russell M. Bostick *(CIO)*
Eric R. Johnson *(Chief Investment Officer)*
John R. Kline *(Chief Acctg Officer & Sr VP)*
Christopher J. Nickele *(Pres-CNO Bus & Exec VP-Product Mgmt)*
Scott R. Perry *(Pres-Bankers Life & Casualty)*
Matthew J. Zimpfer *(Gen Counsel & Exec VP)*
Susan L. Menzel *(Exec VP-HR)*
Thomas Fineis *(Sr VP-Health Valuation Actuary)*
Thomas Donald Barta *(Sr VP-Fin Plng & Analysis)*
Mark Billingsley *(Sr VP-Valuation & Projections)*
Richard Garner *(Sr VP-Product Mgmt-Health)*
Jerome Lynch *(VP-Bankers Life & Casualty Valuation)*

Advertising Agency:
Summit Marketing
Three Cityplace Dr Ste 350
Saint Louis, MO 63141-7091
Tel.: (314) 569-3737
Fax: (314) 569-0037
Toll Free: (866) 590-6000

THE CO-OPERATORS GROUP LIMITED

130 Macdonell Street
Guelph, ON N1H 6P8, Canada
Tel.: (519) 824-4400
Fax: (519) 823-9944
Toll Free: (800) 363-6442
E-mail: service@cooperators.ca
Web Site: www.cooperators.ca
Sales Range: $1-4.9 Billion
Approx. Number Employees: 4,500
Year Founded: 1945
Business Description:
General Insurer
S.I.C.: 6411
N.A.I.C.S.: 524298
Media: 2-6
Personnel:
Richard Lemoing *(Chm)*
Kathy Bardswick *(Pres & CEO)*
Bruce West *(CEO & Exec VP)*
Vivien Fong *(CIO)*
Dennis Deters *(Exec VP-Member Rels & Corp Svcs)*
Rick McCombie *(Exec VP-Distr & Insurance Ops)*
Martin-Eric Tremblay *(Exec VP-National P & C Product & Pres Quebec Ops)*
Andrew Cartmell *(Reg VP-Central Ontario)*
Brian Gaudette *(Reg VP-Atlantic)*
Terrry McRorie *(Reg VP-West Region)*
Don Viau *(Reg VP)*
Leonard Sharman *(Dir-Media Rels)*
Denise Brown *(Coord-Mktg)*

Brands & Products:
A BETTER PLACE FOR YOU.
THE COOPERATORS

COLONIAL LIFE & ACCIDENT INSURANCE COMPANY

(Sub. of Unum Group)
(d/b/a Colonial Supplemental Insurance Co.)
1200 Colonial Life Blvd W
Columbia, SC 29210-7646
Mailing Address:
PO Box 1365
Columbia, SC 29202-1365
Tel.: (803) 798-7000
Fax: (803) 731-2618
Fax: (800) 880-9325
Toll Free: (800) 325-4368
Web Site: www.coloniallife.com
Approx. Rev.: $2,700,000
Approx. Number Employees: 900
Year Founded: 1939
Business Description:
Personal Accident & Life Insurance
S.I.C.: 6311
N.A.I.C.S.: 524113
Personnel:
Randall C. Horn *(Pres & CEO)*
Tom Gilligan *(Sr VP-Natl Sls-Colonial Life)*
Charles Irick *(Asst VP)*
Don Montgomery *(Asst VP-HR)*
Pam Jenkins *(Product Mgr & Dir-Life Product Dev)*
Mark Kuban *(Reg Mgr-Broker Mktg)*
Chris Holman *(Mgr-Broker Mktg-West Reg)*
Belinda Maffei *(Mgr-Broker Mktg-Southwest Reg)*
Kimsey Shanks *(Mgr-Broker Mktg-Southeast Reg)*

Brands & Products:
REFLEX SM

Advertising Agency:
The VIA Group LLC
34 Danforth St Ste 309
Portland, ME 04101
Tel.: (207) 221-3000
Fax: (207) 761-9422

COLUMBIAN MUTUAL LIFE INSURANCE COMPANY

Vestal Pkwy E
Binghamton, NY 13902
Tel.: (607) 724-2472
Fax: (607) 724-6382
Web Site: www.cfglife.com
Approx. Number Employees: 250
Year Founded: 1882
Business Description:
Life & Health Insurance
S.I.C.: 6411
N.A.I.C.S.: 524210
Media: 2-5-7-10-20-24
Distr.: Natl.; Reg.
Budget Set: Oct.
Personnel:
Thomas Rattmann *(Chm)*
Peggy M. Rubin *(COO & Exec VP)*
Daniel J. Fischer *(Chief Compliance Officer, Gen Counsel, Sec & Sr VP)*
Michael Fosbury *(Chief Investment Officer & Sr VP)*
Gregory J. Nilles *(Treas, VP, Comptroller & Asst Sec)*
August S. Dittemore *(Sr VP-Sls & Mktg)*
Richard Pollard *(Sr VP-Fin)*
Karen W. Amitrano *(Second VP-Underwriting)*
Paul H. Zurawel *(Second VP & Assoc Actuary)*
Alice Cobb *(VP-Mktg & Sls Support)*
Scott Dittemore *(VP Sls)*
Jack Greenberg *(VP-Pricing & Product Dev)*
Gerald J. Hennenhoefer *(VP-Sls)*
James Gross *(Asst VP)*

THE COMMERCE GROUP, INC.

(Sub. of MAPFRE S.A.)
211 Main St
Webster, MA 01570-2249
Tel.: (508) 943-9000
Fax: (508) 949-4921
Toll Free: (800) 922-8276
E-mail: generalcomments@commerceinsurance.com
Web Site:
www.commerceinsurance.com
Approx. Rev.: $1,982,447,000
Approx. Number Employees: 2,373
Year Founded: 1972
Business Description:
Fire, Marine & Casualty Insurance
S.I.C.: 6331
N.A.I.C.S.: 524126
Import Export
Media: 13-26
Personnel:
Gerald Fels *(Chm, Pres & CEO)*
Randall V. Becker *(CFO & Sr VP)*
John W. Hawie *(Chief Investment Officer & Sr VP)*
Debra A. Mann *(Sr VP-Mgmt Info)*
Cathleen M. Moynihan *(Sr VP-HR)*

Key to Media (For complete agency information see *The Advertising Red Books-Agencies* edition):
1. Bus. Publs. 2. Cable T.V. 3. Catalogs & Directories. 4. Co-op Adv. 5. Consumer Mags. 6. D.M. to Bus. Estab.7. D.M. to Consumers 8. Daily Newsp. 9. Exhibits/Trade Shows 10. Foreign 11. Infomercial 12. Internet Adv.13. Multimedia 14. Network Radio 15. Network T.V. 16. Newsp. Distr. Mags. 17. Other 18. Outdoor (Posters, Transit) 19. Point of Purchase20. Premiums, Novelties 21. Product Samples 22. Special Events Mktg. 23. Spot Radio 24. Spot T.V. 25. Weekly Newsp. 26. Yellow Page Adv.

COMMERCIAL TRAVELERS MUTUAL INSURANCE COMPANY
70 Genesee St
Utica, NY 13502
Tel.: (315) 797-5200
Fax: (315) 797-3198
Toll Free: (800) 422-6200
E-mail: comtravl@commercialtravelers.com
Web Site: www.commercialtravelers.com
Approx. Sls.: $28,000,000
Approx. Number Employees: 100
Year Founded: 1883
Business Description:
Mutual Insurance Company; School & College Health & Accident Insurance, Sports Coverage, Small Employer Group Life & Disablity Income
S.I.C.: 6311; 6321
N.A.I.C.S.: 524113; 524114
Media: 8-13
Distr.: Direct to Consumer; Natl.
Budget Set: Nov.
Personnel:
Paul H. Trevvett *(Pres & CEO)*

CONSECO, INC.
(Name Changed to CNO Financial Group, Inc.)

CONSOLIDATED SERVICES GROUP
Brookview Corp Ctr 1240 S Broad St Ste 200
Lansdale, PA 19446
Tel.: (215) 661-0500
Fax: (215) 661-0871
Toll Free: (888) 243-7900
E-mail: marketing@conservgrp.com
Web Site: www.medlogix.com
Sales Range: $10-24.9 Million
Approx. Number Employees: 500
Year Founded: 1980
Business Description:
Medical Claims Management
S.I.C.: 6411
N.A.I.C.S.: 524298
Personnel:
Michael A. Morrone *(Pres & CEO)*
Craig Goldstein *(COO & Exec VP)*
Stan Tomasevich *(CIO & Sr VP)*
Maria Longworth *(Sr VP-Medical Case Mgmt Svcs)*
Advertising Agency:
Creative Marketing Alliance Inc.
191 Clarksville Rd
Princeton Junction, NJ 08550
Tel.: (609) 297-2222
Fax: (609) 799-7032

CORELOGIC, INC.
(Formerly First American Corporation)
4 First American Way
Santa Ana, CA 92707-5913
Tel.: (703) 610-5410
Fax: (703) 610-5040
Toll Free: (800) 426-1466
E-mail: investor@corelogic.com
Web Site: www.corelogic.com
Approx. Rev.: $1,623,272,000
Approx. Number Employees: 10,084
Business Description:
Consumer, Financial & Property Information Services
S.I.C.: 7389; 6531
N.A.I.C.S.: 519190; 531390
Media: 2
Personnel:
Parker S. Kennedy *(Chm)*
Anand K. Nallathambi *(Pres & CEO)*
Frank D. Martell *(CFO)*
Michael Larson *(CIO-Joint Ventures-Natl)*
James Balas *(Chief Acctg Officer, Sr VP & Controller)*
Karen J. Collins *(VP-Community Rels)*
George Livermore *(Pres-Data & Analytics)*
Barry M. Sando *(Pres-Bus & Info Svcs)*
Terry Theologides *(Gen Counsel, Sec & Sr VP)*
Scott Friberg *(Exec VP)*
Jerald L. Hoerauf *(Exec VP-Corp Dev)*
Dan Smith *(Sr VP-Infor Solutions Grp)*
Kevin R. Wall *(Sr VP-Bus & Info Svcs)*
Steve Kendall *(VP-Sls-Client Svcs-First American Real Estate Solutions)*
Bob Frady *(Dir-Sls)*
Brands & Products:
EAGLE 9
EVERYDAY WE HELP PEOPLE
EXCELIS
LIENWATCH
SMART TITLE SOLUTIONS
SMS
Advertising Agencies:
Corporate Communications, Inc.
65 Seavey St
North Conway, NH 03860
Tel.: (603) 356-7011

De Alba Communications
482 San Pablo Ter
Pacifica, CA 94044
Tel.: (650) 557-5711
Fax: (650) 989-6836

SicolaMartin
206 E 9th Ste 1800
Austin, TX 78701
Tel.: (512) 343-0264
Fax: (512) 343-0659

CORVEL CORPORATION
2010 Main St Ste 600
Irvine, CA 92614-7203
Tel.: (949) 851-1473
Fax: (949) 851-1469
Toll Free: (888) 7CORVEL
E-mail: investor_relations@corvel.com
Web Site: www.corvel.com
Approx. Rev.: $380,668,000
Approx. Number Employees: 2,986
Year Founded: 1988
Business Description:
Managed Health Care Services
S.I.C.: 6321; 8748
N.A.I.C.S.: 524114; 541618
Media: 2-10-26
Personnel:
V. Gordon Clemons *(Chm)*
Daniel J. Starck *(Pres, CEO & COO)*
Scott F. McCloud *(CFO)*
Donald C. McFarlane *(CIO)*
Tom Benson *(VP-Info Sys)*
Diane J. Blaha *(VP-Sls)*
Heather Burnham *(VP-Mktg)*
Cathy Casil *(Dir-HR)*
Sharon O'Connor *(Dir-Legal Svcs)*
Brands & Products:
CAREMC
CORCARE
CORCARE RX
CORCASE
CORVEL
CORVEL HEALTHCARD
MEDCHECK
MEDCHECK SELECT

COTTON STATES LIFE INSURANCE COMPANY
(Sub. of COUNTRY Financial)
244 Perimeter Ctr Pkwy NE
Atlanta, GA 30346
Mailing Address:
PO Box 105303
Atlanta, GA 30348
Tel.: (770) 391-8600
Fax: (770) 391-8986
Toll Free: (800) 282-6536
E-mail: corporate@cottonstates.com
Web Site: www.cottonstatesinsurance.com
E-Mail For Key Personnel:
Marketing Director: cook.mike@cottonstates.com
Sales Range: $50-74.9 Million
Approx. Number Employees: 300
Year Founded: 1941
Business Description:
Life Insurance Network
S.I.C.: 6311
N.A.I.C.S.: 524113
Advertising Expenditures: $300,000
Media: 5-8-9-18-20
Personnel:
Paul Bishop *(Sr VP-Sls)*
Steve Denault *(Sr VP-HR & Comm)*
Jeffrey C. Gendron *(Sr VP-Property & Casualty Ops)*
Wade Harrison *(Sr VP-Fin Svcs Ops)*
Alan T. Reiss *(Sr VP-Svc Ops)*
Tim Teagarden *(VP-HR)*
Brands & Products:
COTTON STATES
OUR MOST IMPORTANT POLICY IS TRUST

COUNTRY FINANCIAL
1701 Towanda Ave
Bloomington, IL 61701
Tel.: (309) 821-3000
Fax: (309) 821-5459
Toll Free: (866) 255-7965
Web Site: www.countryfinancial.com
Sales Range: $1-4.9 Billion
Approx. Number Employees: 3,600
Year Founded: 1925
Business Description:
Insurance & Financial Services
S.I.C.: 6411
N.A.I.C.S.: 524210
Advertising Expenditures: $5,500,000
Media: 2-3-5-6-8-9-18-20-23-24
Distr.: Reg.
Budget Set: Sept. -Aug.
Personnel:
John D. Blackburn *(CEO)*
David A. Magers *(CFO)*
Barbara A. Baurer *(COO)*
Doyle J. Williams *(CMO)*
Paul Bishop *(Sr VP-Sls)*
Deanna L. Frautschi *(Sr VP-HR)*
Jeffrey C. Gendron *(Sr VP-Property & Casualty Ops)*
Wade Harrison *(Sr VP-Fin Svcs Ops)*
Alan T. Reiss *(Sr VP-Svc Ops)*
Jean B. Lawyer *(Dir-Corp Comm)*
Natalie Wyse *(Mgr-Property & Casualty Billing Svcs)*
Melinda Zehr *(Mgr-Pub Rels)*
Advertising Agency:
Noble
33 W Monroe St Ste 300
Chicago, IL 60603
Tel.: (312) 670-2900
Fax: (312) 670-7420
Toll Free: (800) 986-6253

CRAWFORD & COMPANY
1001 Summit Blvd
Atlanta, GA 30319
Mailing Address:
PO Box 5047
Atlanta, GA 30302-5047
Tel.: (404) 300-1000
Fax: (404) 300-1005 (Investor Rels)
Toll Free: (800) 241-2541
E-mail: info@us.crawco.com
Web Site: www.crawfordandcompany.com
Approx. Rev.: $1,110,801,000
Approx. Number Employees: 8,678
Year Founded: 1941
Business Description:
Claims Management Solutions
S.I.C.: 6411; 7371
N.A.I.C.S.: 524298; 524210; 524291; 541511
Advertising Expenditures: $3,121,000
Personnel:
Jeffrey T. Bowman *(Pres & CEO)*
W. Bruce Swain, Jr. *(CFO & Exec VP)*
Brian Clark *(COO-Continental EMEA Region)*
Brian S. Flynn *(CIO-Global & Sr VP)*
L. Martin Fagan *(CMO, Sr VP & Chief Bus Dev Officer-US Property & Casualty Segment)*
Allen W. Nelson *(Chief Admin Officer, Gen Counsel & Sec)*
Glenn T. Gibson *(Chief Strategy Officer)*
Alesandra Carillo *(Sr Mktg Exec-London)*
Kevin B. Frawley *(CEO-Property & Casualty-Americas)*
David A. Isaac *(CEO-The Garden City Group, Inc)*
Ian V. Muress *(CEO-Property & Casualty-EMEA & Asia-Pacific)*
Richard J. Martin *(Sr VP & Reg Mng Dir-Asia Pacific)*
Mauricio Alonso *(Mng Dir Latin America & Caribbean & Sr VP)*
Phyllis R. Austin *(Sr VP-HR)*
William L. Beach *(Sr VP)*
Robert J. Cormican *(Sr VP-Compliance, Quality & Trng)*
Douglas F. Dell *(Sr VP-E-Learning Svcs)*
Alice Edwards *(Exec Gen Adjuster & Sr VP-Global Technical Svcs, Bus Dev)*
Philip G. Porter *(Sr VP)*
R. Eric Powers, III *(VP, Asst Sec & Assoc Gen Counsel-Corp)*
Geoffrey J. Evans *(VP-Internal Audit)*
Kara B. Pardini *(VP-Corp Comm)*
Andries G. Willemse *(VP-Strategy, Projects & Dev-Global)*
Valerie Holmes *(Dir-Global Fin Controls-Atlanta)*

Key to Media (For complete agency information see *The Advertising Red Books-Agencies* edition):
1. Bus. Publs. 2. Cable T.V. 3. Catalogs & Directories. 4. Co-op Adv. 5. Consumer Mags. 6. D.M. to Bus. Estab.7. D.M. to Consumers
8. Daily Newsp. 9. Exhibits/Trade Shows 10. Foreign 11. Infomercial 12. Internet Adv.13. Multimedia 14. Network Radio
15. Network T.V. 16. Newsp. Distr. Mags. 17. Other 18. Outdoor (Posters, Transit) 19. Point of Purchase20. Premiums, Novelties
21. Product Samples 22. Special Events Mktg. 23. Spot Radio 24. Spot T.V. 25. Weekly Newsp. 26. Yellow Page Adv.

Crawford & Company — (Continued)

Stephanie Zercher *(Dir-PR)*
Ricardo Ortega *(Mgr-Claim Ops-Brazil)*

CSE INSURANCE GROUP

50 California St Ste 2550
San Francisco, CA 94111-4624
Tel.: (415) 274-7800
Fax: (415) 274-7855
Toll Free: (800) 282-6848
E-mail: infocenter@cse-insurance.com
Web Site: www.cse-insurance.com
E-Mail For Key Personnel:
President: pbize@cseinsurance.com
Sales Range: $25-49.9 Million
Approx. Number Employees: 135
Year Founded: 1951
Business Description:
Insurance Holding Company
S.I.C.: 6331
N.A.I.C.S.: 524126
Advertising Expenditures: $25,000
Media: 2-5-8-10-13-18-20-22-23-26
Distr.: Reg.
Budget Set: Nov.
Personnel:
Pierre Bize *(Pres & CEO)*
Stefan Dobrus *(CFO & Sr VP)*
Frank Querques *(Sr VP-Insurance Ops)*
James Williamson *(Sr VP-Claims)*
F. Lee Baumgartner *(VP-Admin, Info & Tech)*
Brands & Products:
CSE INSURANCE GROUP
CSE SAFEGUARD
WE SERVE THE PEOPLE WHO SERVE THE PEOPLE

DENTAL HEALTH ALLIANCE, L.L.C.

(Holding of Assurant Employee Benefits)
2323 Grand Blvd
Kansas City, MO 64141-6608
Mailing Address:
PO Box 419608
Kansas City, MO 64108
Fax: (816) 474-2638
Toll Free: (800) 522-1313
E-mail: info@dha.com
Web Site: www.dha.com
Sales Range: $1-9.9 Million
Approx. Number Employees: 35
Year Founded: 1994
Business Description:
Group Dental Insurance Services
S.I.C.: 6411
N.A.I.C.S.: 524298
Media: 10-18

DIRECT GENERAL CORPORATION

(Joint Venture of Calera Capital Management Inc. & TPG Capital, L.P.)
1281 Murfreesboro Rd
Nashville, TN 37217
Tel.: (615) 399-4700
Toll Free: (800) 444-4211
Web Site: www.direct-general.com
Approx. Rev.: $532,928,000
Approx. Number Employees: 2,426
Year Founded: 1991
Business Description:
Personal Auto, Life, Hospital Indemnity & Travel Insurance Services; Owned by TPG & Calera Capital
S.I.C.: 6331; 6411
N.A.I.C.S.: 524126; 524210
Personnel:
Robert Sandler *(Chm)*
John W. Mullen *(CEO)*
Brands & Products:
DIRECT
Advertising Agency:
Cramer-Krasselt
7 W 22nd 8th Fl
New York, NY 10010
Tel.: (212) 889-6450
Fax: (212) 251-1265

DISPUTE RESOLUTION MANAGEMENT, INC.

770 E 9000 S Ste A2
Sandy, UT 84094-2051
Tel.: (801) 355-1444
Fax: (801) 568-2410
Toll Free: (800) 516-4359
E-mail: info@drmworld.com
Web Site: www.drmworld.com
Approx. Number Employees: 20
Year Founded: 1996
Business Description:
Insurance & Consulting Services
S.I.C.: 8742
N.A.I.C.S.: 541611
Export
Media: 7-10
Personnel:
Deborah J. Rouse *(Pres)*
Todd B. Duzett *(CFO)*
William C. Lee *(Reg VP)*

THE DOCTORS COMPANY

185 Greenwood Rd
Napa, CA 94558
Tel.: (707) 226-0100
Fax: (707) 226-0111
E-mail: info@thedoctors.com
Web Site: www.thedoctors.com
Approx. Rev.: $573,721,000
Approx. Number Employees: 500
Year Founded: 1976
Business Description:
Medical Malpractice & Liability Insurance Carrier & Services
S.I.C.: 6399; 6411
N.A.I.C.S.: 524128; 524210; 524298
Media: 4-13-16-17
Personnel:
Richard E. Anderson *(Chm & CEO)*
Thomas G. Luffy *(CFO)*
Robert D. Francis *(COO)*
Bryan Lawton *(Chief Governance Officer & Chief Corp Dev Officer)*
David McHale *(Gen Counsel & Sr VP)*
David B. Troxel *(Sec & Dir-Medical)*
Martha A. Martin *(Mgr-Policy)*

EMBLEMHEALTH INC

55 Water St
New York, NY 10001
Tel.: (646) 447-0098
Web Site: www.emblemhealth.com
Business Description:
Health Insurance
S.I.C.: 6321
N.A.I.C.S.: 524114
Personnel:
Ilene Margolin *(Sr VP-Pub Affairs & Comm)*
Advertising Agency:
Hacker Group
1215 4th Ave Ste 2100
Seattle, WA 98161-1018
Tel.: (206) 805-1500
Fax: (206) 805-1599

EMPIRE HEALTHCHOICE ASSURANCE, INC.

(Sub. of Empire Blue Cross & Blue Shield)
11 W 42nd St
New York, NY 10036
Tel.: (212) 476-1000
Fax: (212) 476-1281
Web Site: www.empireblue.com
Approx. Number Employees: 17,036
Year Founded: 1935
Business Description:
Health Care & Travel Protection Insurance Services
S.I.C.: 6321
N.A.I.C.S.: 524114
Advertising Expenditures: $3,000,000
Media: 1-2-4-6-7-8-9-18-20-22-23-25-26
Distr.: Reg.
Budget Set: Nov.
Personnel:
Michael A. Stocker *(Pres & CEO)*
John W. Remshard *(CFO & Sr VP)*
Gloria McCarthy *(COO & Exec VP)*
Grace Messina *(CIO & VP)*
Michael Fedyna *(Chief Actuary & VP)*

EMPLOYERS INSURANCE COMPANY OF NEVADA

(Sub. of Employers Holdings, Inc.)
PO Box 539004
Henderson, NV 89053
Tel.: (775) 327-2700
Fax: (866) 290-5608
E-mail: customersupport@employers.com
Web Site: www.employers.com
Sales Range: $25-49.9 Million
Approx. Number Employees: 120
Business Description:
Worker's Compensation Insurance Services
S.I.C.: 6411
N.A.I.C.S.: 524298
Advertising Agency:
The Glenn Group
50 Washington St
Reno, NV 89503-5603
Tel.: (775) 686-7777
Fax: (775) 686-7750

EMPLOYERS INSURANCE COMPANY OF WAUSAU

(Sub. of Liberty Mutual Group Inc.)
(d/b/a Wausau Insurance Companies)
2000 Westwood Dr
Wausau, WI 54401-7802
Mailing Address:
PO Box 8017
Wausau, WI 54402-8017
Tel.: (715) 845-5211
Toll Free: (800) 826-1661
Approx. Rev.: $700,000,000
Approx. Number Employees: 1,400
Year Founded: 1911
Business Description:
Property, Casualty & Workers Comp Insurance
S.I.C.: 6331; 6311
N.A.I.C.S.: 524126; 524113
Advertising Expenditures: $2,000,000
Media: 2-3-6-9-13-26
Distr.: Natl.
Budget Set: Sept.
Personnel:
Susan M. Doyle *(Exec VP & Gen Mgr)*
Michael L. Parker *(Sr VP & Exec Dir-Broker Relations)*
Scott Kosinski *(Dir-Adv & Mktg)*
Christine Smith *(Product Mgr)*
Jeffrey Kapp *(Mgr-Central Div)*
Brands & Products:
WAUSAU

FACTORY MUTUAL INSURANCE COMPANY

(d/b/a FM Global)
270 Central Ave
Johnston, RI 02919
Tel.: (401) 275-3000
Fax: (401) 275-3029
E-mail: information@fmglobal.com
Web Site: www.fmglobal.com
Approx. Rev.: $3,462,300,000
Approx. Number Employees: 5,000
Year Founded: 1835
Business Description:
Commercial & Industrial Property Insurance Services
S.I.C.: 6331; 6411
N.A.I.C.S.: 524126; 524298
Media: 2-6
Distr.: Intl.; Natl.
Budget Set: Oct.
Personnel:
Shivan S. Subramaniam *(Chm & CEO)*
Ruud H. Bosman *(Vice Chm)*
Jonathan W. Hall *(Exec VP)*
Thomas A. Lawson *(Exec VP)*
Bret N. Ahnell *(Sr VP-Western Div)*
Gerardo L. Alonso *(Sr VP-Claims)*
Carol G. Barton *(Sr VP-Underwriting & Reinsurance)*
Jeffrey A. Burchill *(Sr VP-Fin)*
Brion E. Callori *(Sr VP-Engrg & Res)*
Kenneth W. Davey *(Sr VP-EMEA & Asia Pacific Div)*
Rodney C. Fisher *(Sr VP-Central Div)*
Chris Johnson *(Sr VP-Mktg & Enterprise Learning)*
Paul E. LaFleche *(Sr VP-Investments)*
Jeanne R. Lieb *(Sr VP-Info Svcs)*
John J. Pomeroy *(Sr VP-Law & Governmental Affairs)*
Enzo Rebula *(Sr VP-HR)*
Michael R. Turner *(Sr VP-Eastern Div)*
Kevin S. Ingram *(VP-Fin Svcs)*
William A. Mekrut *(VP-Treasury)*
Brands & Products:
FM GLOBAL
MYRISK
RISKMARK
WORLDREACH

FAIRLANE FINANCIAL CORPORATION

1200 S Pine Island Rd Ste 100
Fort Lauderdale, FL 33324-4469
Tel.: (954) 476-2505
Fax: (954) 476-0051
Toll Free: (888) 324-7526
E-mail: info@888fairlane.com
Web Site: www.888fairlane.com
Approx. Number Employees: 20
Year Founded: 1955
Business Description:
Annuity Distr

Key to Media (For complete agency information see *The Advertising Red Books-Agencies* edition):
1. Bus. Publs. 2. Cable T.V. 3. Catalogs & Directories. 4. Co-op Adv. 5. Consumer Mags. 6. D.M. to Bus. Estab.7. D.M. to Consumers
8. Daily Newsp. 9. Exhibits/Trade Shows 10. Foreign 11. Infomercial 12. Internet Adv.13. Multimedia 14. Network Radio
15. Network T.V. 16. Newsp. Distr. Mags. 17. Other 18. Outdoor (Posters, Transit) 19. Point of Purchase20. Premiums, Novelties
21. Product Samples 22. Special Events Mktg. 23. Spot Radio 24. Spot T.V. 25. Weekly Newsp. 26. Yellow Page Adv.

S.I.C.: 6411; 6371
N.A.I.C.S.: 524298; 524210; 524291; 524292
Media: 2
Personnel:
Samuel R. Lane *(Chm)*

FARMERS GROUP, INC.
(Sub. of Zurich Financial Services AG)
(d/b/a Farmers Insurance Group)
4680 Wilshire Blvd
Los Angeles, CA 90010-3807
Tel.: (323) 932-3200
Fax: (323) 932-3101
Web Site: www.farmersinsurance.com
Approx. Number Employees: 20,000
Year Founded: 1928
Business Description:
Auto, Home & Life Insurance Carrier
S.I.C.: 6411; 6311; 6321; 6331; 6361
N.A.I.C.S.: 524298; 524113; 524114; 524126; 524127
Media: 3-6-15-18-23
Distr.: Reg.
Budget Set: Nov.
Personnel:
Jeff Dailey *(Pres)*
F. Robert Woudstra *(CEO)*
Scott R. Lindquist *(CFO & Exec VP)*
Michael Linton *(CMO)*
Paul Patsis *(Pres-Market Mgmt & Exec VP)*
Mhayse G. Samalya *(Pres-Farmers Bus Insurance & Exec VP)*
Jack Hannigan *(Exec VP)*
David Travers *(Exec VP-Ops)*
Todd Brooks *(Sr VP-Eastern Zone)*
Scott Stice *(Sr VP-Eastern Market Ops)*
Jim Westerman *(Sr VP-Field Ops)*
Luisa Acosta-Franco *(Asst VP-Emerging Markets)*
Jerry Davies *(Dir-Media Rels)*
Advertising Agencies:
Accentmarketing
La Puerta Del Sol Ste 100 800 Douglas Rd
Coral Gables, FL 33134
Tel.: (305) 461-1112
Fax: (305) 461-0071
Hispanic Agency of Record

Glyphix Advertising
6964 Shoup Ave
West Hills, CA 91307
Tel.: (818) 704-3994
Fax: (818) 704-8850

IW Group, Inc.
(An IPG Co.)
8687 Melrose Ave Ste G540
West Hollywood, CA 90069
Tel.: (310) 289-5500
Fax: (310) 289-5501

Mindshare
498 7th Ave
New York, NY 10018
Tel.: (212) 297-7000
Fax: (212) 297-7001

Muse Communications
9543 Culver Blvd 2nd Fl
Culver City, CA 90232
Tel.: (310) 945-4100
Fax: (310) 945-4110

RPA
(Rubin Postaer and Associates)
2525 Colorado Ave
Santa Monica, CA 90404
Tel.: (310) 394-4000
Fax: (310) 633-7099
Critters
University of Farmers

FARMERS MUTUAL HAIL INSURANCE COMPANY OF IOWA
6785 Westown Pkwy
West Des Moines, IA 50266-7727
Tel.: (515) 282-9104
Fax: (515) 282-1220
Toll Free: (800) 247-5248
Web Site: www.fmh.com
Sales Range: $75-99.9 Million
Approx. Number Employees: 200
Year Founded: 1893
Business Description:
Crop Insurance
S.I.C.: 6331
N.A.I.C.S.: 524126
Media: 2-5-10-20-26
Distr.: Reg.
Budget Set: Jan.
Personnel:
Steven C. Rutledge *(Chm)*
Ronald P. Rutledge *(Pres & CEO)*
Scott Rutledge *(Sr VP)*
Kevin A. Johnson *(VP & Mgr-Sls)*
Steve G. Fischer *(VP-HR)*
Ken Liljedahl *(Mgr-Corp Svcs)*
Nick Harris *(Coord-Production Support)*
Brands & Products:
FARMERS MUTUAL HAIL
Advertising Agency:
Lessing-Flynn Advertising Co.
3106 Ingersoll Ave
Des Moines, IA 50312
Tel.: (515) 274-9271
Fax: (515) 274-9283

FEDERATED MUTUAL INSURANCE COMPANY
121 E Pk Sq
Owatonna, MN 55060-3046
Mailing Address:
PO Box 328
Owatonna, MN 55060-0328
Tel.: (507) 455-5200
Fax: (507) 446-4697
Toll Free: (800) 533-0472
E-mail: info@federatedinsurance.com
Web Site:
www.federatedinsurance.com
Approx. Number Employees: 2,750
Year Founded: 1904
Business Description:
Provider of Fire, Casualty, Accident & Health Insurance
S.I.C.: 6331
N.A.I.C.S.: 524126; 525190
Media: 2-3-4-5-7-8-10-13-14-15-18-20-22-25-26
Personnel:
Paul F. Droher *(Exec VP-Opers)*
David W. Ramsey *(Sr VP-Agency Opers)*
Tim Lueck *(Mgr-Adv)*
Brands & Products:
FEDERATED CLICK 2 PAY
FEDERATED DIRECT
FEDERATED HEALTH CHOICE
FEDERATED INSURANCE
IT'S OUR BUSINESS TO PROTECT YOURS
SERVICE PLUS
VALUE DIFFERENCE

FIDELITY MUTUAL LIFE INSURANCE COMPANY
250 King of Prussia Rd
Radnor, PA 19087-5295
Tel.: (610) 964-7000
Fax: (610) 964-1852
Toll Free: (800) 523-4573
Web Site: www.fmlic.com
Approx. Number Employees: 80
Year Founded: 1878
Business Description:
Life Insurance Services
S.I.C.: 6311
N.A.I.C.S.: 524113
Media: 8-9-25
Distr.: Natl.

FINANCIAL BROKERAGE INC.
2238 S 156 Cir
Omaha, NE 68130
Tel.: (402) 697-9998
Fax: (402) 334-6301
Toll Free: (800) 397-9999
Web Site: www.fb-inc.com
Approx. Number Employees: 60
Business Description:
Annuity, Life & Long-Term Care Products Marketer & Distr
S.I.C.: 6399; 6311; 6371; 6411
N.A.I.C.S.: 524128; 524113; 524210; 524291; 524292; 524298
Media: 2-7-22
Personnel:
Joleen K. Misek *(Pres & CEO)*
Ed Wieger *(CFO & Sr VP)*
Kevin Kusleika *(CTO & Sr VP)*
David J. Storck *(Exec VP-Eastern Region)*
Doug Murphy *(VP-Life Mktg)*
Kevin Kibby *(Controller & Asst VP)*
Shelly Whitaker *(Dir-Compliance)*
Advertising Agency:
Ayres Kahler + Sacco
6800 Normal Blvd
Lincoln, NE 68506-2814
Tel.: (402) 450-7530
Fax: (402) 441-4739

FINANCIAL INDEPENDENCE GROUP INC.
19250 W Catawba Ave
Cornelius, NC 28031-6222
Tel.: (704) 895-5606
Fax: (704) 895-5607
Toll Free: (800) 527-1155
E-mail: info@figmarketing.com
Web Site: www.figmarketing.com
Year Founded: 1976
Business Description:
Insurance Services
S.I.C.: 6371; 6411
N.A.I.C.S.: 524298; 524210; 524291; 524292
Media: 2
Personnel:
William H. Cain *(CEO)*
Jim Cooper *(CMO)*
Jo Cain *(Chief Admin Officer)*
Isaiah Smith, II *(Dir-Annuity Mktg)*

FIREMAN'S FUND INSURANCE COMPANY
(Sub. of Allianz SE)
777 San Marin Dr
Novato, CA 94998-0001
Tel.: (415) 899-2000
Fax: (415) 899-3600
Toll Free: (800) 227-1700
Telex: 176 315 fundam nova
Web Site: www.firemansfund.com
Approx. Number Employees: 4,500
Year Founded: 1863
Business Description:
Commercial & Personal Property & Liability Insurance Services
S.I.C.: 6331
N.A.I.C.S.: 524126
Advertising Expenditures: $8,000,000
Bus. Publs.: $800,000; Consumer Mags.: $4,000,000; Other: $1,600,000; Premiums, Novelties: $1,600,000
Distr.: Natl.
Personnel:
Lori Fouche *(Pres & CEO)*
Kevin Walker *(CFO)*
Alexander Bockelmann *(CIO)*
Gregory Tacchetti *(Chief Admin Officer)*
Christian Kortebein *(Chief Actuary & Sr VP)*
Roger M. Nulton, Jr. *(Pres-AgriBus)*
Darryl Page *(Pres-Personal Insurance)*
Greg Meyer *(Sr VP-Product Mgmt-Personal Insurance Div)*
David Zona *(Sr VP-Product Mgmt)*

FIRST ACCEPTANCE CORPORATION
3813 Green Hills Village Dr
Nashville, TN 37215
Tel.: (615) 844-2800
Tel.: (615) 327-4888
Fax: (615) 844-2835
E-mail: webadmin@usauto.cc
Web Site:
www.firstacceptancecorp.com
Approx. Rev.: $210,734,000
Approx. Number Employees: 1,045
Year Founded: 1969
Business Description:
Auto Insurance Services
S.I.C.: 6399
N.A.I.C.S.: 524128
Advertising Expenditures: $8,300,000
Personnel:
Gerald J. Ford *(Chm)*
Mark A. Kelly *(Interim Pres)*
Stephen J. Harrison *(CEO)*
Michael J. Bodayle *(Interim CFO)*
William R. Wilkins *(Chief Actuary & Sr VP)*
John R. Barnett *(Sr VP-Fin)*
Daniel L. Walker *(Sr VP-Ops)*

FIRST AMERICAN CORPORATION
(Name Changed to CoreLogic, Inc.)

FIRST HEALTH GROUP CORP.
(Sub. of Coventry Health Care, Inc.)
3200 Highland Ave
Downers Grove, IL 60515-1223
Tel.: (630) 737-7900
Fax: (630) 719-0076
Web Site: www.firsthealth.com

Key to Media (For complete agency information see *The Advertising Red Books-Agencies* edition):
1. Bus. Publs. 2. Cable T.V. 3. Catalogs & Directories. 4. Co-op Adv. 5. Consumer Mags. 6. D.M. to Bus. Estab.7. D.M. to Consumers
8. Daily Newsp. 9. Exhibits/Trade Shows 10. Foreign 11. Infomercial 12. Internet Adv.13. Multimedia 14. Network Radio
15. Network T.V. 16. Newsp. Distr. Mags. 17. Other 18. Outdoor (Posters, Transit) 19. Point of Purchase20. Premiums, Novelties
21. Product Samples 22. Special Events Mktg. 23. Spot Radio 24. Spot T.V. 25. Weekly Newsp. 26. Yellow Page Adv.

First Health Group Corp. — (Continued)

Sales Range: $800-899.9 Million
Approx. Number Employees: 6,000
Year Founded: 1982
Business Description:
Group Health, Workers' Compensation & Government Medical Services
S.I.C.: 6321
N.A.I.C.S.: 524114
Media: 6-24
Personnel:
Dale B. Wolf *(CEO)*
Brands & Products:
FIRST HEALTH

FORUM NATIONAL INVESTMENTS LTD.
Suite 200 13040 No 2 Road
Richmond, BC V7E 2G1, Canada
Tel.: (778) 588-7780
Tel.: (778) 588-7784 (CFO)
Fax: (604) 684-6139
Fax: (604) 275-8745
Toll Free: (877) 832-3518
E-mail: info@foruminvestments.com
Web Site: www.foruminvestments.com
Approx. Rev.: $4,276,713
Approx. Number Employees: 22
Year Founded: 1995
Business Description:
Holding Company; Investment Services
S.I.C.: 6289; 6411; 6719; 7991
N.A.I.C.S.: 523999; 524298; 551112; 713940
Advertising Expenditures: $13,033
Media: 8-13
Personnel:
Daniel Clozza *(Pres & CEO)*
Martin Tutschek *(CFO)*
Kevin O'Brien *(CMO)*

THE FRANKLIN MUTUAL INSURANCE COMPANY
5 Broad St
Branchville, NJ 07826
Tel.: (973) 948-3120
Fax: (973) 948-7190
Web Site: www.fmiweb.com
Approx. Rev.: $110,201,206
Approx. Number Employees: 100
Year Founded: 1879
Business Description:
Commercial & Residential Insurance Products & Services
S.I.C.: 6331; 6321; 6361; 6411
N.A.I.C.S.: 524126; 524127; 524130; 524298
Personnel:
George H. Guptill Jr. *(Chm)*
James T. Ayers *(Pres)*
Howard Alden *(Mgr-HR)*
Advertising Agency:
Morbelli, Russo & Partners Advertising, Inc.
2 Sylvan Way Ste 302
Parsippany, NJ 07054
Tel.: (973) 644-9663
Fax: (973) 644-9878

FREMONT GENERAL CORPORATION
(Name Changed to Signature Group Holdings, Inc.)

FRENKEL & CO. INC.
1740 Broadway
New York, NY 10019
Tel.: (201) 356-3400
Fax: (212) 488-1800
Web Site: www.frenkel.com
Approx. Premiums: $17,000,000,000
Approx. Number Employees: 250
Year Founded: 1878
Business Description:
Insurance Services
S.I.C.: 6411
N.A.I.C.S.: 524210
Media: 8
Personnel:
Robert E. Shunk *(Chm)*
John F. Kelly *(Pres & CEO)*
Richard Eknoian *(CFO)*
Craig Hasday *(Pres-Life & Employee Benefits Div)*
George Custance *(Exec VP-Mktg)*
Michael Feinstein *(Exec VP-Insurance Broker)*
Jose Irizarry *(Exec VP)*
Joseph Valenza *(Exec VP)*
Frank D'Ambrosio *(Sr VP)*
Ron Kinelski *(Sr VP-Claims)*
Colleen Quiggle *(Sr VP)*
Jeffrey Urbanke *(Sr VP-Comml Accts)*
Donna Casanova-Ricci *(VP-HR)*

GAB ROBINS NORTH AMERICA, INC.
(Holding of Brera Capital Partners, LLC)
9 Campus Dr Ste 7
Parsippany, NJ 07054-4412
Tel.: (973) 993-3400
Fax: (973) 993-9579
Toll Free: (800) 422-4436
Telex: 64-2975 GAB PAPY
E-mail: answers@gabrobins.com
Web Site: www.gabrobinsna.com
Sales Range: $350-399.9 Million
Approx. Number Employees: 3,809
Year Founded: 1872
Business Description:
Property & Casualty Insurance Claims & Adjusting
S.I.C.: 6411
N.A.I.C.S.: 524291
Media: 1-2-4-7-10-13-17-26
Distr.: Natl.
Budget Set: Oct.
Personnel:
Edward G. Troy *(Chm)*
Carl Mussenden *(Sr VP-TPA Ops & Quality & Performance Mgmt)*

GEICO CORPORATION
(Holding of Berkshire Hathaway Inc.)
1 Geico Plz
Washington, DC 20076
Tel.: (301) 986-3000
Fax: (301) 986-2888
Toll Free: (800) 861-8380
E-mail: comments@geico.com
Web Site: www.geico.com
E-Mail For Key Personnel:
Marketing Director: contactmarketing@geico.com
Public Relations: communications@geico.com
Sales Range: $5-14.9 Billion
Approx. Number Employees: 21,390
Year Founded: 1936
Business Description:
Insurance Holding Company
S.I.C.: 6331; 6411; 6719
N.A.I.C.S.: 524126; 524210; 551112
Media: 3-6-8-15
Personnel:
Tony Nicely *(Chm, Pres & CEO)*
Mike Campbell *(CFO & Sr VP)*
Ted Ward *(VP-Mktg)*
Bill Brower *(Dir-Adv)*
Amy Furman *(Dir-Database Mktg)*
Keith Slonski *(Dir-Online Mktg)*
Brands & Products:
GEICO
Advertising Agencies:
Horizon Media, Inc.
75 Varick St
New York, NY 10013
Tel.: (212) 220-5000
Toll Free: (800) 633-4201

The Martin Agency
One Shockoe Plz
Richmond, VA 23219-4132
Tel.: (804) 698-8000
Fax: (804) 698-8001

Red Peg Marketing
727 N Washington St
Alexandria, VA 22314
Tel.: (703) 519-9000
Fax: (703) 519-9290

Response Media, Inc.
3155 Medlock Bridge Rd
Norcross, GA 30071-1423
Tel.: (770) 451-5478
Fax: (770) 451-4929

Sanna Mattson MacLeod, Inc.
811 W Jericho Tpke
Smithtown, NY 11787-3232
Tel.: (631) 265-5160
Fax: (631) 265-5185

Summit Marketing
Three Cityplace Dr Ste 350
Saint Louis, MO 63141-7091
Tel.: (314) 569-3737
Fax: (314) 569-0037
Toll Free: (866) 590-6000

Video Enterprises, Inc.
575 29th St
Manhattan Beach, CA 90266-2211
Tel.: (310) 796-5555
Fax: (310) 546-2921

GEICO GENERAL INSURANCE COMPANY
(Sub. of GEICO Corporation)
5260 Western Ave
Chevy Chase, MD 20815
Mailing Address:
1 GEICO Plz
Washington, DC 20076
Tel.: (301) 986-3000
Fax: (301) 986-3088
Toll Free: (800) 861-8380
E-mail: communications@geico.com
Web Site: www.geico.com
Sales Range: $1-4.9 Billion
Approx. Number Employees: 24,000
Business Description:
Automobile Insurance
S.I.C.: 6331; 6411
N.A.I.C.S.: 524126; 524298
Media: 3-15-20-22-23
Personnel:
Tony Nicely *(Chm, Pres & CEO)*
Donald D. Lyons *(Sr VP)*
Ted Ward *(VP-Mktg)*
Jacqueline Pasley *(Asst VP-Product Mngmt)*
Advertising Agencies:
Black Diamond Media
574 Heritage Rd Ste 201A
Southbury, CT 06488
Tel.: (203) 262-0588
Fax: (203) 262-0589

The Martin Agency
One Shockoe Plz
Richmond, VA 23219-4132
Tel.: (804) 698-8000
Fax: (804) 698-8001

Red Peg Marketing
727 N Washington St
Alexandria, VA 22314
Tel.: (703) 519-9000
Fax: (703) 519-9290

GENAMERICA FINANCIAL CORPORATION
(Sub. of MetLife, Inc.)
13045 Tesson Ferry Rd
Saint Louis, MO 63128
Tel.: (314) 843-8700
Fax: (314) 444-0486
Toll Free: (800) 638-9294
Toll Free: (800) 223-9989
Web Site: www.genamerica.com
E-Mail For Key Personnel:
Public Relations: ammayuga@genam.com
Sales Range: $1-4.9 Billion
Approx. Number Employees: 3,500
Year Founded: 1933
Business Description:
Life Insurance Services
S.I.C.: 6311
N.A.I.C.S.: 524113
Media: 2-6-17-22-23
Distr.: Natl.
Budget Set: Oct.
Brands & Products:
THE CHOICE OF LEADERS

GENWORTH FINANCIAL
(Formerly First Colony Life Insurance Company)
(Sub. of Genworth Financial, Inc.)
700 Main St
Lynchburg, VA 24504
Mailing Address:
PO Box 10716
Lynchburg, VA 24506-0716
Tel.: (434) 845-0911
Fax: (434) 948-5880
Toll Free: (888) 325-5433
Web Site: www.genworth.com
Sales Range: $1-4.9 Billion
Approx. Number Employees: 851
Year Founded: 1955
Business Description:
Life Insurance & Annuity Products
S.I.C.: 6311; 6321
N.A.I.C.S.: 524113; 524114
Media: 2-7
Distr.: Natl.
Personnel:
Thomas L. Creasy *(Mgr-Info Sys)*

GENWORTH LIFE AND ANNUITY INSURANCE COMPANY
(Sub. of Genworth Financial, Inc.)
6610 W Broad St
Richmond, VA 23230
Tel.: (804) 281-6000
Fax: (804) 281-6929
E-mail: al.orendorff@genworth.com
Web Site: www.genworth.com
Approx. Rev.: $1,687,800,000
Year Founded: 1871
Business Description:
Life Insurance & Annuities
S.I.C.: 6311; 6411
N.A.I.C.S.: 524113; 524298
Media: 2-5-6-9-24
Distr.: Natl.
Budget Set: Nov. -Dec.
Personnel:
Pamela S. Schutz *(Pres & CEO)*
Kelly L. Groh *(CFO & Sr VP)*
Ronald P. Joelson *(Chief Investment Officer & Sr VP)*
Paul A. Haley *(Chief Actuary & Sr VP)*
Leon E. Roday *(Gen Counsel, Sec & Sr VP)*
Al Orendorff *(Sr VP-PR)*
Brands & Products:
COMMONWEALTH VA PLUS
DOMINION LIFE
LVPLUS III
SURVIVOR LIFE
Advertising Agency:
OMD-USA
195 Broadway
New York, NY 10007
Tel.: (212) 590-7100

GEOVERA INSURANCE COMPANY INC.
(Joint Venture of Hellman & Friedman LLC & Friedman Fleischer & Lowe, LLC)
4820 Business Center Dr Ste 200
Fairfield, CA 94533
Tel.: (707) 863-3700
Fax: (707) 863-9350
Toll Free: (800) 324-6020
E-mail: info@geovera.com
Web Site: www.geovera.com
Approx. Number Employees: 150
Year Founded: 1993
Business Description:
Insurance Agents, Brokers & Service; Owned by Hellman & Friedman LLC & Friedman Fleischer & Lowe, LLC
S.I.C.: 6411
N.A.I.C.S.: 524210
Import Export
Media: 17
Personnel:
Kevin Nish *(Pres, CEO & Dir)*
Brian Sheekey *(CFO & Sr VP)*
Karen Padovese *(Sr VP-Insurance Ops)*

GERBER LIFE INSURANCE COMPANY
(Sub. of Gerber Products Company)
1311 Mamaroneck Ave
White Plains, NY 10605-5223
Tel.: (914) 272-4000
Fax: (914) 272-4099
E-mail: info@gerberlife.com
Web Site: www.gerberlife.com
Approx. Number Employees: 50
Year Founded: 1967
Business Description:
Life & Health Insurance Carrier
S.I.C.: 6311; 6321
N.A.I.C.S.: 524113; 524114
Media: 5-6-8-9-13-16-19-23-24-25-26
Distr.: Natl.
Budget Set: June
Personnel:
Wesley David Protheroe *(Pres & CEO)*
Keith O'Riley *(CFO & Sr VP)*
George Thacker *(CMO)*
Joseph Pastore *(Dir-HR)*
Michael Bouteneff *(Sr Mgr-Internet Mktg)*
Lisa Bancroft *(Bus Mgr)*
Brands & Products:
GIVE YOUR CHILD AN ADVANTAGE FOR LIFE
GROW-UP PLAN
WE'RE WITH YOU EVERY STEP OF THE WAY

GLOBE LIFE & ACCIDENT INSURANCE COMPANY
(Sub. of Torchmark Corporation)
Globe Life Ctr 204 N Robinson
Oklahoma City, OK 73102
Tel.: (972) 540-6542
Fax: (405) 270-1120
Web Site: www.globeontheweb.com
Sales Range: $250-299.9 Million
Approx. Number Employees: 400
Year Founded: 1951
Business Description:
Life & Health Insurance Services
S.I.C.: 6311; 6321
N.A.I.C.S.: 524113; 524114
Media: 2-3-5-6-8-9-15-24-25
Distr.: Natl.
Budget Set: Sept.
Personnel:
Charles Hudson *(Pres & CEO)*

GREAT AMERICAN LIFE INSURANCE COMPANY
(Sub. of Great American Financial Resources, Inc.)
525 Vine St 7th Fl
Cincinnati, OH 45202
Tel.: (513) 333-5300
Tel.: (513) 357-3300
Toll Free: (888) 497-8556
Web Site: www.gafri.com
Sales Range: $1-4.9 Billion
Approx. Number Employees: 3,400
Year Founded: 1959
Business Description:
Life Insurance; Retirement Annuities
S.I.C.: 6311
N.A.I.C.S.: 524113
Media: 2-8-20-23-24
Distr.: Natl.

GREATER NEW YORK MUTUAL INSURANCE COMPANY
200 Madison Ave
New York, NY 10016
Tel.: (212) 683-9700
Fax: (212) 481-7780
E-mail: kwiseman@gny.com
Web Site: www.gny.com
E-Mail For Key Personnel:
Marketing Director: jturrisi@gny.com
Sales Range: $250-299.9 Million
Approx. Number Employees: 330
Year Founded: 1914
Business Description:
Mutual Holding Company; Property & Casualty Insurance Products & Services
S.I.C.: 6719; 6331
N.A.I.C.S.: 551112; 524126
Media: 2-7-10
Distr.: Natl.
Personnel:
Warren W. Heck *(Chm & CEO)*
Elizabeth Heck *(Pres & COO)*
Thomas Hughes *(Gen Counsel, Sec & Sr VP)*
John Minner *(Treas & Sr VP)*
Margaret Alien *(Sr VP-Legal)*
Gerard Ragusa *(Sr VP-Liability Claims)*
Jeff Turrisi *(Sr VP-Mktg)*
Lawrence Cretella *(Asst VP-Liability Claims)*
William Lancer *(Asst VP-Admin Svcs)*
Kenneth Wiseman *(Asst VP-Admin Svcs)*
Brands & Products:
BRITE UMBRELLA GROUP
GNY

GRINNELL MUTUAL REINSURANCE COMPANY INC.
4215 Hwy 146
Grinnell, IA 50112
Tel.: (641) 236-6121
Fax: (641) 236-2830
Toll Free: (800) 362-2041
E-mail: inquiries@gmrc.com
Web Site: www.gmrc.com
E-Mail For Key Personnel:
President: dagnew@gmrc.com
Sales Range: $300-349.9 Million
Approx. Number Employees: 660
Year Founded: 1909
Business Description:
Fire, Marine & Casualty Insurance
S.I.C.: 6331; 6411
N.A.I.C.S.: 524126; 524210
Import Export
Advertising Expenditures: $500,000
Media: 2-3-18-23-24-26
Personnel:
Stephen R. Crawford *(Pres & CEO)*
Jerry D. Woods *(CFO, Treas & VP-Fin)*
Dennis H. Mehmen *(CIO & VP-Bus Info Svcs)*
Dennis G. Day *(Gen Counsel, VP & Sec)*
W. B. McDonald *(Sr VP-Direct Claims)*
Larry J. Jansen *(Sr VP-Underwriting)*
Barb Baker *(Mgr-Adv & Community Rels)*

GROUP HEALTH SERVICE OF OKLAHOMA, INC.
(Div. of Health Care Service Corporation)
(d/b/a Blue Cross and Blue Shield of Oklahoma)
1215 S Boulder Ave
Tulsa, OK 74119-2827
Mailing Address:
PO Box 3283
Tulsa, OK 74102-3283
Tel.: (918) 560-3500
Fax: (918) 560-7879
Web Site: www.bcbsok.com
Approx. Number Employees: 1,500
Year Founded: 1940
Business Description:
Health & Medical Insurance Carrier
S.I.C.: 6321; 6411
N.A.I.C.S.: 524114; 524298
Media: 2-7-8-9-13-18-20-22-23-24-25-26
Distr.: Direct to Consumer
Personnel:
Bert Marshall *(Pres)*
Advertising Agency:
Jordan Associates
3201 Quail Springs Pkwy Ste 100
Oklahoma City, OK 73134-2611
Tel.: (405) 840-3201
Fax: (405) 840-4149
(Health, Life, Property & Casualty Insurance)

THE GUARDIAN LIFE INSURANCE COMPANY OF AMERICA
7 Hanover Sq
New York, NY 10004-4025
Tel.: (212) 598-8000
Fax: (212) 919-2170
Toll Free: (866) 425-4542
Web Site: www.guardianlife.com
Sales Range: $5-14.9 Billion
Approx. Number Employees: 5,000
Year Founded: 1861
Business Description:
Mutual Life Insurance Company
S.I.C.: 6411; 6282; 6311; 6371; 6399
N.A.I.C.S.: 524298; 523920; 524113; 524128; 524210; 524291; 524292; 525110; 525120; 525990
Media: 2-5-6-7-8-13-18-23-24
Distr.: Natl.
Budget Set: Dec.
Personnel:
Dennis J. Manning *(Chm & CEO)*
Deanna M. Mulligan *(Pres & COO)*
David Turner *(Mng Dir & Head-Private Equity)*
Shelley McIntyre *(CIO & VP-Div)*
Richard C. Jones *(Chief Comml Officer & Sr VP)*
Margaret W. Skinner *(Chief Distr Officer & Exec VP)*
Robert E Broatch *(CFO-Risk & Operational Excellence & Exec VP)*
Tracy Rich *(Gen Counsel, Sec & Exec VP)*
Scott Dolfi *(Exec VP-Bus & Ops)*
John P. McCarthy *(Exec VP-HR)*
John Flannigan *(Sr VP & Controller)*
Dong H. Ahn *(Sr VP-Grp Insurance)*
Eric Jones *(Reg VP)*
Lisa Powell *(VP)*
Philip Eichinger *(Sls Mgr-Natl)*
Jacqueline Kanas *(Mgr-Adv)*
Brands & Products:
GUARDIAN
THE LIVING BALANCE SHEET
Advertising Agencies:
CooperKatz & Company
205 Lexington Ave 5th Fl
New York, NY 10016
Tel.: (917) 595-3030
Fax: (917) 326-8997

Harden Communications Partners
32 Cathy Ln
Oakland, CA 94619
Tel.: (510) 635-4150
Fax: (510) 969-4980

Key to Media (For complete agency information see *The Advertising Red Books-Agencies* edition):
1. Bus. Publs. 2. Cable T.V. 3. Catalogs & Directories. 4. Co-op Adv. 5. Consumer Mags. 6. D.M. to Bus. Estab.7. D.M. to Consumers
8. Daily Newsp. 9. Exhibits/Trade Shows 10. Foreign 11. Infomercial 12. Internet Adv.13. Multimedia 14. Network Radio
15. Network T.V. 16. Newsp. Distr. Mags. 17. Other 18. Outdoor (Posters, Transit) 19. Point of Purchase20. Premiums, Novelties
21. Product Samples 22. Special Events Mktg. 23. Spot Radio 24. Spot T.V. 25. Weekly Newsp. 26. Yellow Page Adv.

GUIDEONE INSURANCE COMPANY
1111 Ashworth Rd
West Des Moines, IA 50265-3544
Tel.: (515) 267-5000
Fax: (515) 267-5546
Toll Free: (877) 448-4331
Web Site: www.guideone.com
Sales Range: $650-699.9 Million
Approx. Number Employees: 1,000
Year Founded: 1947
Business Description:
Property & Casualty Coverage Insurance
S.I.C.: 6371; 6331; 6399; 6411
N.A.I.C.S.: 524298; 524126; 524128; 524210; 524291; 524292; 525190
Media: 2-3-4-5-6-7-8-9-10-13-18-19-20-22-23-24-25-26
Distr.: Natl.
Budget Set: Monthly
Personnel:
Jim Wallace *(Chm, Pres & CEO)*
Scott Reddig *(COO & Exec VP)*
Tom Fischer *(CIO & Sr VP)*
Tom Farr *(Gen Counsel & Sr VP-Claims)*
Jan Beckstrom *(Exec VP)*
Brian Hughes *(Sr VP-Investments)*
Mark Joos *(Sr VP-Fin)*
Sarah Buckley *(VP-Corp Comm & Mktg)*
Cathy Murray *(VP-HR)*
Brands & Products:
GUIDEONE
PLACE YOUR FAITH IN THE EXPERT

HALLMARK FINANCIAL SERVICES, INC.
777 Main St Ste 1000
Fort Worth, TX 76102
Tel.: (817) 348-1600
Fax: (972) 788-0520
Web Site: www.hallmarkgrp.com
Approx. Rev.: $307,060,000
Approx. Number Employees: 351
Business Description:
Property & Casualty Insurance Services
S.I.C.: 6399; 6331; 6411
N.A.I.C.S.: 524128; 524126; 524291
Media: 2-8
Personnel:
Mark J. Morrison *(Pres & CEO)*
Mark E. Schwarz *(Exec Chm & CEO)*
Kevin T. Kasitz *(COO & Exec VP-Comml Lines)*
Gregory P. Birdsall *(CIO)*
Jeffrey R. Passmore *(Chief Acctg Officer & Sr VP)*
Richard N. Gibson *(Chief Actuary)*
Brookland F. Davis *(Pres-Personal Lines & Exec VP)*
James A. Damonte *(Pres-Heath XS)*
Christopher C. Jones *(Pres-Aerospace)*
Donald E. Meyer *(Pres-TGA Insurance)*

THE HANOVER INSURANCE COMPANY
(Sub. of The Hanover Insurance Group, Inc.)
440 Lincoln St
Worcester, MA 01653
Tel.: (508) 855-1000
Fax: (508) 853-6332
Web Site: www.hanover.com/
Sales Range: $1-4.9 Billion
Approx. Number Employees: 5,540
Year Founded: 1852
Business Description:
Property & Casualty Insurance Products & Services
S.I.C.: 6331; 6411
N.A.I.C.S.: 524126; 524291; 524298
Media: 9-10-17-18-19-20-23-25
Distr.: Reg.
Personnel:
Fred Eppinger *(Pres & CEO)*

HARLEYSVILLE GROUP INC.
355 Maple Ave
Harleysville, PA 19438-2297
Tel.: (215) 256-5000
Fax: (215) 256-5799
Toll Free: (800) 523-6344
E-mail: information@harleysvillegroup.com
Web Site: www.harleysvillegroup.com
E-Mail For Key Personnel:
Public Relations: BFlemming@harleysvillegroup.com
Approx. Rev.: $986,272,000
Approx. Number Employees: 1,706
Year Founded: 1979
Business Description:
Holding Company; Multiple Line Insurance Underwriting & Brokerage Services
S.I.C.: 6719; 6411
N.A.I.C.S.: 551112; 524210; 524298
Media: 8-10-22
Personnel:
Michael L. Browne *(Pres & CEO)*
Arthur E. Chandler *(CFO & Sr VP)*
Arne Herenstein *(CIO & Sr VP)*
Robert A. Kauffman *(Chief Compliance Officer, Gen Counsel, Sec & Sr VP)*
Mark R. Cummins *(Chief Investment Officer, Treas & Exec VP)*
Allan R. Becker *(Chief Actuary & Sr VP)*
Kevin M. Toth *(Chief Underwriting Officer & Sr VP)*
Thomas E. Clark *(Sr VP-Field Ops)*
Beth A. Friel *(Sr VP-HR)*
Theodore A. Majewski *(Sr VP-Personal Lines)*
Brian D. Flemming *(VP-Mktg)*
Roger N. Pandel *(Asst VP-Comml Property Underwriting)*
Randy Buckwalter *(Dir-Corp Comm)*
Craig R. Hearl *(Dir-Premium Audit)*
Bob Croll *(Product Mgr)*
L. Shields *(Asst Sec)*
Brands & Products:
COMPUPAK
GOOD PEOPLE TO KNOW
HAR TECH
HARLEYSVILLE
SHIPMATE
SIGNATURE
STARPAK
TIP

THE HARTFORD FINANCIAL SERVICES GROUP, INC.
1 Hartford Plz
Hartford, CT 06155
Tel.: (860) 547-5000
Fax: (860) 547-2680
E-mail: media.relations@thehartford.com
Web Site: www.thehartford.com
Approx. Rev.: $22,383,000,000
Approx. Number Employees: 26,800
Year Founded: 1810
Business Description:
Insurance & Financial Services Holding Company
S.I.C.: 6712; 6311; 6321; 6331; 6411; 6722; 6733
N.A.I.C.S.: 551111; 523991; 524113; 524126; 524130; 524210; 524291; 524298; 525910
Advertising Expenditures: $20,000,000
Media: 3-9-15-17-25
Distr.: Natl.
Budget Set: Oct.
Personnel:
Liam E. McGee *(Chm, Pres & CEO)*
Robert Froehlich *(Sr Mng Dir)*
Christopher J. Swift *(CFO & Exec VP)*
Greg McGreevey *(Chief Investment Officer & Exec VP)*
William Awad *(CTO & Sr VP)*
Christopher Lewis *(Sr VP-Capital Plng & Chief Risk Officer-Property & Casualty Ops)*
Lizabeth H. Zlatkus *(Chief Risk Officer & Exec VP)*
Robert Paiano *(Sr VP & Chief Risk Officer-Enterprise)*
David N. Levenson *(Pres-Wealth Mgmt)*
Andy Napoli *(Pres-Consumer Markets)*
Alan J. Kreczko *(Gen Counsel & Exec VP)*
Ricardo A. Anzaldua *(Sec, Sr VP, Dir-Corp Law & Assoc Gen Counsel)*
Michael Concannon *(Exec VP-Sls & Distr-Property & Casualty)*
James Eckerle *(Exec VP-Strategic Initiatives & Enterprise Tech)*
Brian D. Murphy *(Exec VP-Individual Markets Grp)*
Andrew J. Pinkes *(Exec VP-Claims & Acting Head-Comml Markets)*
Sharon Ritchey *(Exec VP-Retirement Plans Grp)*
Karen C. Tripp *(Exec VP-Mktg & Comm)*
Eileen Whelley *(Exec VP-HR)*
Michael Dandini *(Sr VP & Head-Fin Products Div)*
Rex Sprunger *(Sr VP & Mgr-Western Div)*
Robert Alexander Ingram *(Sr VP)*
Lisa Morgan *(Sr VP-Middle Market Comml Insurance Bus)*
Don MacQuattie *(VP & Dir-Retirement Plans-Healthcare, Education & Tax Exempt Org)*
Ronald A. Williams *(VP & Actuary)*
Stephen Whelan *(VP-Comml & Fin Risks-Fin Products Div)*
Tom Tooley *(Dir-Natl Accts)*
David Williams *(Dir-Medical-Individual Life Insurance Div)*
Brands & Products:
@VENTURE
BOND 1STEP SURETY
CLAIMPLUS
HARTFORD
PREPARE TO LIVE
PRODUCER VIEW
TEAM - WORK
Advertising Agency:
Campbell Mithun, Inc.
Campbell Mithun Tower 222 S 9th St
Minneapolis, MN 55402-3389
Tel.: (612) 347-1000
Fax: (612) 347-1515

HEALTH CARE SERVICE CORPORATION
300 E Randolph St
Chicago, IL 60601-5099
Mailing Address:
PO Box 6
Ellsworth, KS 67439-0006
Tel.: (312) 653-6000
Fax: (312) 819-1628
Web Site: www.hcsc.com
Sales Range: $15-24.9 Billion
Approx. Number Employees: 17,500
Year Founded: 1936
Business Description:
Holding Company; Health & Life Insurance Products & Services
S.I.C.: 6719; 6311; 6321; 6411
N.A.I.C.S.: 551112; 524113; 524114; 524210; 524298
Media: 2-4-7-8-9-10-18-23-25-26
Distr.: Reg.
Budget Set: Nov. -Dec.
Personnel:
Milton Carroll *(Chm)*
Patricia A. Hemingway Hall *(Pres & CEO)*
Denise A. Bujak *(CFO & Sr VP)*
Colleen Reitan *(COO & Exec VP)*
Brian Hedberg *(CIO & Sr VP)*
Deborah Dorman-Rodriguez *(Chief Legal Officer & Sr VP)*
Tom Lubben *(Chief Compliance Officer & Sr VP)*
Kenneth S. Avner *(Chief Actuary & Sr VP)*
Paul B. Handel *(Chief Medical Officer & Sr VP)*
Pat O'Connor *(Chief HR Officer & Sr VP)*
Martin G. Foster *(Pres-Plan Ops & Exec VP)*
Anthony F. Trani *(Pres-Subsidiary Companies)*
Tara Dowd Gurber *(Exec VP-Corp Svcs)*
Joel Farran *(Sr VP-Strategy & Plng)*

HEALTH INSURANCE PLAN OF GREATER NEW YORK
(d/b/a HIP)
55 Water St
New York, NY 10041
Tel.: (212) 630-5000
Toll Free: (800) 447-8255
E-mail: webmaster@hipusa.com
Web Site: www.hipusa.com
Sales Range: $1-4.9 Billion
Approx. Number Employees: 3,000
Year Founded: 1947
Business Description:
Health Management Insurance Services
S.I.C.: 6321
N.A.I.C.S.: 524114
Advertising Expenditures: $26,300,000
Media: 2-24
Personnel:
Anthony L. Watson *(Chm & CEO)*
Daniel T. McGowan *(Pres & COO)*

Key to Media (For complete agency information see *The Advertising Red Books-Agencies* edition):
1. Bus. Publs. 2. Cable T.V. 3. Catalogs & Directories. 4. Co-op Adv. 5. Consumer Mags. 6. D.M. to Bus. Estab.7. D.M. to Consumers
8. Daily Newsp. 9. Exhibits/Trade Shows 10. Foreign 11. Infomercial 12. Internet Adv.13. Multimedia 14. Network Radio
15. Network T.V. 16. Newsp. Distr. Mags. 17. Other 18. Outdoor (Posters, Transit) 19. Point of Purchase20. Premiums, Novelties
21. Product Samples 22. Special Events Mktg. 23. Spot Radio 24. Spot T.V. 25. Weekly Newsp. 26. Yellow Page Adv.

Araksi H. Sarafian *(Chief Pharmacy Officer)*
John Steber *(Exec VP)*
Fred Blickman *(Sr VP-HR)*
Patricia Gillespie *(Dir-Printing)*
Eileen Counihan *(Asst Dir-Gen Pur)*
Edward Reilly *(Asst Mgr-E)*
Diane Davies *(Asst Pur Mgr-Florida Office)*
Eric O'Brien *(Mgr-Print)*

Brands & Products:
HIP

HEALTHPARTNERS, INC.

8170 33rd Ave S
Bloomington, MN 55425
Mailing Address:
PO Box 1309
Minneapolis, MN 55440-1309
Tel.: (952) 883-6000
Tel.: (952) 883-5302 (Corp Commun)
Fax: (952) 883-5633
E-mail: healthpartners@healthpartners.com
Web Site: www.healthpartners.com
E-Mail For Key Personnel:
President: topresident@healthpartners.com
Sales Range: $10-24.9 Million
Approx. Number Employees: 9,200
Year Founded: 1957
Business Description:
Health Plan
S.I.C.: 6321; 8011
N.A.I.C.S.: 524114; 621111
Media: 9-18-23-24-25
Distr.: Reg.
Personnel:
Ann Wynia *(Chm)*
Barbara J. Kaufman *(Vice Chm)*
Mary K. Brainerd *(Pres & CEO)*
Kathy Cooney *(CFO, Chief Admin Officer & Exec VP)*
Andrea Walsh *(CMO & Exec VP)*
George Isham *(Chief Health Officer & Dir-Medical)*
Barb Tretheway *(Gen Counsel & Sr VP)*
Doug Smith *(Sr VP-Sls)*
Breana Mercer *(Product Mgr)*
Diane McGuire *(Mgr-Health & Patient Education & Health Literacy)*
Donna Swartz *(Mgr-Adv & Creative Svcs)*

Brands & Products:
10,000 STEPS
CARECHECK
CARESPAN
CONSUMER CHOICE
HEALTH INVESTMENT
HEALTHPARTNERS
PARTNERINGCARE
YOUR HEALTH. YOUR PARTNER.

HIGHMARK INC.

120 5th Ave
Pittsburgh, PA 15222
Tel.: (412) 544-7000
Fax: (412) 544-8368
E-mail: webmaster@highmark.com
Web Site: www.highmark.com
Sales Range: $50-74.9 Million
Approx. Number Employees: 19,000
Year Founded: 1937
Business Description:
Managed Care & Indemnity Health Care Coverage & Employee Benefits Products & Services
S.I.C.: 6321; 8099
N.A.I.C.S.: 524114; 621999
Media: 2-3-6-8-9-10-18-20-22-23-24-25
Distr.: Reg.
Budget Set: Dec.
Personnel:
J. Robert Baum *(Chm)*
Kenneth R. Melani *(Pres & CEO)*
Nanette DeTurk *(CFO, Chief Admin Officer, Treas & Exec VP)*
Elizabeth A. Farbacher *(Chief Compliance Officer, Chief Auditor Officer & Exec VP)*
Michael A. Romano *(Sr VP)*
David M. O'Brien *(Exec VP-Govt Svcs & External Affairs)*
Aaron A. Walton *(Sr VP-Corp Affairs)*
Aaron Billger *(Dir-PR)*
Jean I. Zellers *(Dir-Adv)*
Bonita Herrle *(Asst Sec)*
Joseph F. Reichard *(Asst Treas)*

Brands & Products:
HIGHMARK

Advertising Agency:
Mullen
The Crane Bldg 40 24th St
Pittsburgh, PA 15222-4600
Tel.: (412) 402-0200
Fax: (412) 402-0160

HINRICHS FLANAGAN FINANCIAL

S Park Twrs 6000 Fairview Rd Ste 400
Charlotte, NC 28210
Tel.: (704) 557-9600
Fax: (704) 557-9670
Toll Free: (800) 289-1846
E-mail: hinrichsflanagan@finsvcs.com
Web Site: www.hinrichsflanagan.com
Approx. Number Employees: 128
Year Founded: 1935
Business Description:
Insurance & Securities Brokerage, Asset Management, Financial Planning & Advisory Services
S.I.C.: 6411; 6211; 6282; 6371; 6733
N.A.I.C.S.: 524210; 523120; 523920; 523930; 523991; 524292
Import Export
Media: 7-10
Personnel:
Timothy Flanagan *(Pres)*

HORACE MANN COMPANIES

1 Horace Mann Plaza
Springfield, IL 62715-0001
Tel.: (217) 789-2500
Fax: (217) 788-5161
Web Site: www.horacemann.com
Approx. Rev.: $937,427,000
Approx. Number Employees: 1,866
Year Founded: 1945
Business Description:
Insurance Holding Company; Markets & Underwrites Personal Line of Property, Casualty & Life Insurance & Retirement Annuities
S.I.C.: 6331; 6311
N.A.I.C.S.: 524126; 524113
Media: 2-7-8-13
Personnel:
Joseph J. Melone *(Chm)*
Peter H. Heckman *(Pres & CEO)*
Dwayne D. Hallman *(Exec VP & CFO)*
Ann M. Caparros *(Gen Counsel, Chief Compliance Officer & Sec)*
Charlton Young *(Asst VP & Asst Gen Counsel-Law Div)*
Thomas C. Wilkinson *(Exec VP-Property & Casualty)*
Bret A. Conklin *(Sr VP & Controller)*
Dave Baumgardner *(VP-Mktg-Strategic Plng-Mktg Div)*
Denise Rice *(VP-IT)*
Eric Tawfall *(Asst VP & Product Mgr)*
Dawn Klintworth *(Asst VP-Web Strategy-Creative Svcs & Comm, Res & Educator Allianc)*
Kevin Leamon *(Asst VP-Acct Mgmt & Writing Svcs)*
Angel Plaza *(Asst VP-Product Mgmt)*
Scott Keeshin *(Asst Gen Counsel)*
Becky Johnson *(Coord-Sls Promotion)*

Brands & Products:
EDUCATOR ADVANTAGE
FOUNDED BY EDUCATORS FOR EDUCATORS
HORACE MANN

HORIZON BLUE CROSS BLUE SHIELD OF NEW JERSEY

3 Penn Plz E
Newark, NJ 07105
Tel.: (973) 466-4000
Web Site: www.horizon-bcbsnj.com
Sales Range: $5-14.9 Billion
Approx. Number Employees: 4,400
Year Founded: 1932
Business Description:
Medical Insurance Plans
S.I.C.: 6321; 6411
N.A.I.C.S.: 524114; 524210
Media: 2-6-8-9-13-18-23-24-25
Personnel:
Emmanuel Kampouris *(Chm)*
Robert A. Marino *(Pres & CEO)*
Robert J. Pures *(CFO, Treas & Sr VP-Admin)*
Philip Bonaparte *(VP-Clinical Affairs & CMO-NJ Health)*
Margaret Johnson *(Chief Pharmacy Officer & VP)*
John W. Campbell *(Gen Counsel, Sec & Sr VP)*
Christy W. Bell *(Sr VP-Healthcare Mgmt)*
Jackie R. Jennifer *(Sr VP-Svc)*
Christopher M. Lepre *(Sr VP-Market Bus Unit)*
Larry Altman *(VP-Corp Mktg & Comm)*
Carol A. Banks *(VP-State Health Benefit Programs)*
Margaret Coons *(VP-HR)*
David R. Huber *(VP-Fin)*
Paul Felice *(Mgr-Mktg & Sls Admin)*
Greg Visicaro *(Mgr-Adv)*

Brands & Products:
BLUECARD
HORIZON
MAKING HEALTHCARE WORK

Advertising Agency:
Bernard Hodes Group
534 Broadhollow Rd Ste 305A
Melville, NY 11747-3620
Tel.: (631) 753-1901
Fax: (631) 753-1914

HORTICA INSURANCE

1 Horticultural Ln
Edwardsville, IL 62025-0428
Tel.: (618) 656-4240
Fax: (618) 656-7581
Toll Free: (800) 851-7740
E-mail: sales@hortica-insurance.com
Web Site: www.hortica-insurance.com
E-Mail For Key Personnel:
Sales Director: sales@hortica-insurance.com
Approx. Premiums: $67,000,000
Approx. Number Employees: 250
Year Founded: 1887
Business Description:
Insurance for the Floral & Horticultural Industry
S.I.C.: 6411
N.A.I.C.S.: 524210
Media: 7-8-9-18-20-26
Distr.: Direct to Consumer; Reg.
Personnel:
Mona B. Haberer *(Pres & CEO)*
Kenneth J. Krieg *(COO)*
Peter H. Fornof *(CIO & Sr VP-Admin)*
Brent Bates *(Sr VP & Dir-Claim)*
John M. Hodapp *(Sr VP-Agency Ops)*
Colleen J. Nelson *(Sr VP)*
Connie J. Turner *(VP-HR)*

Brands & Products:
HORTICA
TO GUIDE AND PROVIDE

HSB GROUP, INC.

(Sub. of Munich Reinsurance America, Inc)
1 State St
Hartford, CT 06103-5024
Tel.: (860) 722-1866
Fax: (860) 722-5106
Web Site: www.hsb.com
Approx. Number Employees: 2,400
Business Description:
Specialty Insurance Products, Engineering Services & Management Consulting
S.I.C.: 6399; 6331; 6371; 6411
N.A.I.C.S.: 524128; 524126; 524210; 524291; 524292; 524298; 525190
Media: 2-7
Personnel:
Saul L. Basch *(Vice Chm, CFO & Treas)*
Greg Barats *(CEO)*
Loren P. Shoemaker *(COO & Sr VP)*
William J. Rucci *(CIO & Sr VP)*
James C. Rowan, Jr. *(Chief Investment Officer)*
Maurice Darbyshire *(Exec VP)*
Nancy Onken *(Gen Counsel, Sec & Exec VP)*
Mike Petruzzello *(Chief Underwriting Officer & Exec VP)*
Anthony J. Trivella *(Exec VP)*
Theodore D. Kmiecik *(Sr VP & Comptroller)*
Joan Mocarski *(Sr VP & Controller-Insurance)*
Roberta A. O'Brien *(Sr VP, Deputy Gen Counsel & Compliance Officer)*
Susan W. Ahearn *(Sr VP-HR)*
Mike Fusselbaugh *(Sr VP-Renewable Energy)*
William MacKay Heckles *(Chief Reinsurance Officer & Sr VP)*
Jeanne B. Merola *(Sr VP)*
Tom Tucker *(Sr VP-Bus Dev)*

Brands & Products:
HSB

Key to Media (For complete agency information see *The Advertising Red Books-Agencies* edition):
1. Bus. Publs. 2. Cable T.V. 3. Catalogs & Directories. 4. Co-op Adv. 5. Consumer Mags. 6. D.M. to Bus. Estab.7. D.M. to Consumers 8. Daily Newsp. 9. Exhibits/Trade Shows 10. Foreign 11. Infomercial 12. Internet Adv.13. Multimedia 14. Network Radio 15. Network T.V. 16. Newsp. Distr. Mags. 17. Other 18. Outdoor (Posters, Transit) 19. Point of Purchase20. Premiums, Novelties 21. Product Samples 22. Special Events Mktg. 23. Spot Radio 24. Spot T.V. 25. Weekly Newsp. 26. Yellow Page Adv.

HSB Group, Inc. — (Continued)

Advertising Agency:
Mintz & Hoke Communications Group
40 Tower Ln
Avon, CT 06001-4222
Tel.: (860) 678-0473
Fax: (860) 679-9850

HUMANA, INC.

The Humana Bldg 500 W Main St
Louisville, KY 40202
Mailing Address:
PO Box 1438
Louisville, KY 40201-1438
Tel.: (502) 580-1000
Fax: (502) 580-3677
Toll Free: (800) 486-2620
Toll Free: (800) 4HUMANA
Toll Free: (800) 992-2551
Toll Free: (800) 457-4708
Web Site: www.humana.com

Approx. Rev.: $33,868,208,000
Approx. Number Employees: 35,200
Year Founded: 1961

Business Description:
Health Insurance Coverage & Related Services
S.I.C.: 6331; 6321; 8011
N.A.I.C.S.: 525190; 524114; 621491

Media: 2-3-4-6-7-8-9-12-13-14-15-16-18-19-20-23-24-25
Distr.: Direct to Consumer; Intl.; Natl.; Reg.
Budget Set: Oct.

Personnel:
Michael B. McCallister *(Chm & CEO)*
James H. Bloem *(CFO, Treas & Sr VP)*
James E. Murray *(COO)*
Bruce J. Goodman *(CIO, Chief Svc Officer & Sr VP)*
Raja Rajamannar *(CMO, Chief Innovation Officer & Sr VP)*
Paul B. Kusserow *(Chief Strategy Officer, Chief Corp Dev Officer & Sr VP)*
Bonita C. Hathcock *(Chief HR Officer & Sr VP)*
Roy Goldman *(Chief Actuary & VP)*
Raymond Vigil *(Chief Learning Officer)*
Tim Love *(Pres-Comml Ops-Florida)*
J. Edward Quinlan *(Pres-Specialty Products-Southern California)*
Dave Reynolds *(Pres-Illinois Comml Market)*
Pattie Dale Tye *(Pres-Market)*
Mark El-Tawil *(CEO-West Comml Reg)*
Linda T. Hummel-McAlpin *(CEO-South Texas Ops)*
Ken Malcolmson *(CEO-West Central Reg)*
Christopher M. Todoroff *(Gen Counsel & Sr VP)*
Thomas J. Liston *(Sr VP-Products)*
Heidi S. Margulis *(Sr VP-Pub Affairs)*
Tom Noland *(Sr VP-Corp Comm)*
Bruce D. Perkins *(Sr VP-Natl Contracting & Puerto Rico Ops)*
Kathleen Pellegrino *(VP & Deputy Gen Counsel)*
Phyllis Anderson *(VP-Mktg)*
Beth Bierbower *(VP-Product Innovation)*
Edward J. Kaleta, III *(Dir-Washington Office)*
Carolyn Karibo-Livingston *(Dir-Humana Active Outlook, Strategy & Plng)*
Melanie Toniazzo *(Dir-Acct Mgmt)*
Stacy Wilson *(Dir-Direct Response Mktg)*
Jeff Blunt *(Mgr-Media Rels-Midwest & Mid-Atlantic)*
Mitch Lubitz *(Mgr-Media Rels-Northeast & Southeast)*
Ross McLerran *(Mgr-Media Rels-West)*
Lindsey Minella *(Mgr-Media Rels-Midwest)*
Marybeth Peters *(Mgr-Direct Response Media Strategy)*
Greg Shafer *(Mgr-Workplace Strategy)*
Steven D. Taylor *(Mgr-Internet Mktg)*
Jim Turner *(Mgr-Corp Media Rels-Natl)*
David Jonovic *(Actuary)*

Brands & Products:
GUIDANCE WHEN YOU NEED IT MOST
HUMANA
HUMANAACCESS
HUMANABEGINNINGS
HUMANAONE
PERSONAL NURSE
PLANPROFESSOR
RIGHTSOURCE
RX CALCULATOR
SMARTSELECT
SMARTSUITE

Advertising Agencies:
Interbrand Corporation
(Part of Omnicom Group Inc.)
130 5th Ave
New York, NY 10011-4306
Tel.: (212) 798-7500
Fax: (212) 798-7501

PHD
(An Omnicom Company)
220 E 42nd 7th Fl
New York, NY 10017
Tel.: (212) 894-6600
Fax: (212) 894-4100
Digital
Media

RAPP
437 Madison Ave 3rd Fl
New York, NY 10022
Tel.: (212) 817-6800
Fax: (212) 590-8400
Lead Creative Agency

H.W. KAUFMAN FINANCIAL GROUP, INC.

30833 NW Hwy Ste 220
Farmington Hills, MI 48334
Mailing Address:
PO Box 707
Southfield, MI 48037-0707
Tel.: (248) 932-9000
Fax: (248) 932-9046
Toll Free: (800) 521-1918
E-mail: info@burnsandwilcox.com
Web Site: www.burnsandwilcox.com
Approx. Number Employees: 200
Year Founded: 1969
Business Description:
General Agents & Brokers of Specialty Insurance Products & Services
S.I.C.: 6141
N.A.I.C.S.: 522220
Advertising Expenditures: $1,000,000
Media: 8-10
Personnel:
Alan Jay Kaufman *(Chm, Pres & CEO)*
Daniel T. Muldowney *(CFO)*
Steven D. Kaufman *(Dir-Mktg, Promos & PR)*
Kendra Corman *(Mgr-Adv)*

INDIANA FARM BUREAU INSURANCE

(Sub. of Indiana Farm Bureau Inc.)
225 SE St
Indianapolis, IN 46202-4058
Mailing Address:
PO Box 1250
Indianapolis, IN 46206-1250
Tel.: (317) 692-7200
Fax: (317) 692-7185
Toll Free: (800) 723-3276
E-mail: crm.customerservice@infarmbureau.com
Web Site: www.infarmbureau.com
E-Mail For Key Personnel:
Marketing Director: tkoopman@farmbureau.com
Approx. Number Employees: 1,200
Year Founded: 1934
Business Description:
Multiple Line Insurance Provider
S.I.C.: 6311; 6411
N.A.I.C.S.: 524113; 524210
Advertising Expenditures: $3,000,000
Media: 3-5-18-22-23-24-26
Distr.: Reg.
Budget Set: Jan. -Dec.
Personnel:
Donald B. Villwock *(Pres)*
Lynn B. Jongleux *(Gen Counsel, Sec & Sr VP)*
Patty Poehler *(Sr VP-Mktg)*
Carl Shepherd *(Sr VP)*
Teresa Koopman *(Mgr-Agency Promos)*
Brands & Products:
SOLUTIONS YOU NEED FROM A COMPANY YOU KNOW

INFINITE INSURANCE COMPANY

(Sub. of Infinity Group Inc.)
5205 N O'Connor Blvd Ste 700
Irving, TX 75039
Tel.: (972) 501-8300
Fax: (972) 532-3379
Toll Free: (877) 953-2337
Sales Range: $100-124.9 Million
Approx. Number Employees: 350
Year Founded: 1872
Business Description:
Property & Casualty Insurance Services
S.I.C.: 6411
N.A.I.C.S.: 524291
Advertising Expenditures: $500,000
Media: 2-7-8-9-25
Distr.: Natl.
Budget Set: Nov.
Personnel:
Tommy Stone *(Pres)*

INFINITY AUTO INSURANCE COMPANY

(Sub. of Infinity Group Inc.)
3700 Colonnade Pkwy
Birmingham, AL 35243
Tel.: (205) 870-4000
Fax: (205) 803-8406
Toll Free: (800) 782-1020
E-mail: customer.service@infinityauto.com
Web Site: www.infinityauto.com
Sales Range: $400-449.9 Million
Approx. Number Employees: 900
Year Founded: 1978
Business Description:
Provider of Property & Casualty Insurance Services
S.I.C.: 6411
N.A.I.C.S.: 524210
Personnel:
James R. Gober *(Chm & CEO)*
Advertising Agency:
Acento Advertising, Inc.
2254 S Sepulveda Blvd
Los Angeles, CA 90064
Tel.: (310) 943-8300
Fax: (310) 943-8310
Hispanic Agency of Record

INFINITY PROPERTY & CASUALTY CORPORATION

3700 Colonnade Pkwy
Birmingham, AL 35243
Tel.: (205) 870-4000
Fax: (205) 803-8231
Toll Free: (800) 782-2040
E-mail: infinity.relations@infinity-insurance.com
Web Site: www.ipacc.com
Approx. Rev.: $961,276,000
Approx. Number Employees: 1,900
Business Description:
Property & Casualty Insurance
S.I.C.: 6331; 6399
N.A.I.C.S.: 524126; 524128
Advertising Expenditures: $10,800,000
Media: 23-24-25
Personnel:
James R. Gober *(Chm, Pres & CEO)*
Roger Smith *(CFO & Exec VP)*
Ralph Gravelle *(CIO & Sr VP)*
Joseph A. Pietrangelo *(Pres-East Reg)*
Samuel J. Simon *(Gen Counsel, Sec & Exec VP)*
Glen N. Godwin *(Sr VP-Bus Dev)*
Scott C. Pitrone *(Sr VP-Product Mgmt)*
James Raley *(VP-Customer Svc)*
Mary Linn Clark *(Asst VP & Asst Treas)*
Troy P. Ballard *(Asst VP-Tax)*
Amy K. Jordan *(Asst VP-IR)*

INSURANCE.COM, INC.

29000 Aurora Rd
Solon, OH 44139
Tel.: (440) 498-0971
Fax: (440) 498-1875
Web Site: www.insurance.com
Approx. Number Employees: 175
Business Description:
Auto Insurance Seller
S.I.C.: 6411
N.A.I.C.S.: 524298
Media: 8-13
Personnel:
Robert Klapper *(CEO)*

INSWEB CORPORATION

11290 Pyrites Way Ste 200
Gold River, CA 95670
Tel.: (916) 853-3300
Fax: (916) 853-3325
Toll Free: (877) 909-4679
E-mail: comments@insweb.com
Web Site: www.insweb.com

Key to Media (For complete agency information see *The Advertising Red Books-Agencies* edition):
1. Bus. Publs. 2. Cable T.V. 3. Catalogs & Directories. 4. Co-op Adv. 5. Consumer Mags. 6. D.M. to Bus. Estab.7. D.M. to Consumers
8. Daily Newsp. 9. Exhibits/Trade Shows 10. Foreign 11. Infomercial 12. Internet Adv.13. Multimedia 14. Network Radio
15. Network T.V. 16. Newsp. Distr. Mags. 17. Other 18. Outdoor (Posters, Transit) 19. Point of Purchase20. Premiums, Novelties
21. Product Samples 22. Special Events Mktg. 23. Spot Radio 24. Spot T.V. 25. Weekly Newsp. 26. Yellow Page Adv.

Approx. Rev.: $42,359,000
Approx. Number Employees: 86
Year Founded: 1995
Business Description:
Insurance Via Internet
S.I.C.: 2741; 6411
N.A.I.C.S.: 516110; 524210
Advertising Expenditures: $15,207,000
Media: 8-13
Personnel:
Hussein A. Enan *(Chm & CEO)*
Kiran Rasaretnam *(CFO & Sr VP)*
John Cadigan *(CTO & Sr VP)*
Steven J. Yasuda *(Chief Acctg Officer)*
L. Eric Loewe *(Gen Counsel & Sec)*
Brad Cooper *(Sr VP-Ops)*
Brands & Products:
AGENTINSIDER
INSWEB
SIMPLIFYING YOUR INSURANCE DECISIONS

INTEGRITY LIFE INSURANCE COMPANY

(Sub. of The Western & Southern Financial Group)
400 Broadway
Cincinnati, OH 45202-3341
Tel.: (513) 362-8000
Fax: (888) 220-2677
Toll Free: (800) 325-8583
E-mail: corpinfo@integritycompanies.com
Web Site: www.integritycompanies.com
Sales Range: $900-999.9 Million
Approx. Number Employees: 225
Year Founded: 1993
Business Description:
Markets Annuities Through Brokers, Financial Planners, Independent Agents & Financial Institutions, Specializes in Long-Term Asset Accumulation & Retirement Savings
S.I.C.: 6311
N.A.I.C.S.: 524113
Media: 2-7-8-13
Personnel:
John R. Lindholm *(Pres & CEO)*
John F. O'Connell *(Sr VP-Broker Dealer Sls Channel)*

JOE MAX GREEN INSURANCE CONCEPTS

(d/b/a Insurance Concepts)
3310 N University Dr
Nacogdoches, TX 75963
Tel.: (936) 564-0221
Fax: (936) 569-6938
Toll Free: (866) 279-0520
E-mail: naco@jmgic.com
Web Site: www.jmgic.com
Approx. Sls.: $11,600,000
Approx. Number Employees: 40
Business Description:
Insurance Agents
S.I.C.: 6411; 6531
N.A.I.C.S.: 524210; 531210
Media: 6-13-16-24
Personnel:
Gary LaFour *(Pres & COO)*
Joe Max Green *(CEO)*
Jack Thompson *(Sr VP)*
Advertising Agency:
Hancock Advertising Agency
PO Box 630010
Nacogdoches, TX 75963-0010
Tel.: (936) 564-9559
Fax: (936) 560-0845

JOHN HANCOCK FINANCIAL SERVICES, INC.

(Sub. of Manulife Financial Corporation)
John Hancock Pl
Boston, MA 02117
Mailing Address:
PO Box 111
Boston, MA 02117-0111
Tel.: (617) 572-6000
Fax: (617) 572-9799
Web Site: www.johnhancock.com
Sales Range: $5-14.9 Billion
Approx. Number Employees: 3,914
Year Founded: 2000
Business Description:
Individual Life, Group & Personal Health Insurance & Specialty Investment Products
S.I.C.: 6311; 6331
N.A.I.C.S.: 524113; 524126
Media: 2-3-4-5-6-7-8-9-10-11-13-20-23-24-26
Distr.: Natl.
Budget Set: Jan.
Personnel:
Marc Costantini *(Pres & Gen Mgr-John Hancock Variable Annuities)*
Steven Finch *(Pres & Gen Mgr-John Hancock Life Insurance)*
Mike Treske *(Pres)*
Allan T. Hackney *(CIO & Sr VP-John Hancock Fin)*
Warren Thomson *(Chief Investment Officer & Exec VP)*
Chris Conkey *(Global Chief Investment Officer-Equities-Manulife Fin Corp)*
Craig Raymond *(Chief Actuary & Chief Risk Officer)*
Keith F. Hartstein *(Pres/CEO-John Hancock Funds)*
Peter R. Gordon *(Pres-John Hancock Fin Network)*
James R. Boyle *(Pres-John Hancock Fin Svcs)*
Robert A. Cook *(Pres-US Insurance Grp)*
Hugh C. McHaffie *(Pres-John Hancock Wealth Mgmt)*
Laura Moore *(Pres-Long Term Care Insurance)*
Jonathan Chiel *(Gen Counsel & Exec VP)*
John Danello *(VP & Chief Counsel-US Wealth Mgmt)*
Robert T. Cassato *(Exec VP--Distr-John Hancock Fin Svcs)*
Brian B. Heapps *(Exec VP-Sls JHFN)*
James P. O'Malley *(Exec VP)*
David Longfritz *(Sr VP & Gen Mgr-Retirement Income/Rollover Solutions)*
Jim Brockelman *(Sr VP)*
Kevin J. Cloherty *(Sr VP & Deputy Chief-Global Compliance)*
Kathy Klinger *(Sr VP-Bus Dev & Mktg-Fin Network)*
Karyn O'Connor *(Sr VP)*
Diana L. Scott *(Sr VP-HR)*
Carey Foran Hoch *(VP & Head-Mktg)*
Tom Mullen *(VP-Mktg-Annuities)*
Joanna Padden *(VP-Adv)*
Laura Vail Wooster *(VP-Mktg)*
Gerry Sullivan *(Asst VP-Web Mktg)*
Brands & Products:
JOHN HANCOCK
Advertising Agency:
Hill Holliday
53 State St
Boston, MA 02109
Tel.: (617) 366-4000
(Insurance & Investment Products Including Mutual Funds)
— Karen Kaplan *(Sr. V.P. & Mngmt. Supvr.)*

KAISER FOUNDATION HEALTH PLAN OF THE MID-ATLANTIC STATES, INC.

(Div. of Kaiser Permanente)
2101 E Jefferson St
Rockville, MD 20852
Tel.: (301) 816-2424
Fax: (301) 816-7478
Toll Free: (800) 777-7902
Web Site: www.kff.org/
Approx. Number Employees: 950
Year Founded: 1980
Business Description:
HMO Plans
S.I.C.: 6321
N.A.I.C.S.: 524114
Personnel:
Marilyn Kawamura *(Pres & CEO)*
Beth Jaeger *(VP-HR)*
Herman Weil *(VP-Sls)*
Keith Montgomery *(Dir-Mktg Commun)*
Susan Ayres *(Mgr-Mktg)*
Beberlie Brinson *(Mgr-Media)*
Amy Wood *(Strategist-Stakeholder Engagement)*
Brands & Products:
KAISER PERMANENTE
Advertising Agency:
Crosby Marketing Communications
705 Melvin Ave Ste 200
Annapolis, MD 21401-1540
Tel.: (410) 626-0805
Fax: (410) 269-6547

KANAWHA INSURANCE COMPANY

(Sub. of KMG America Corporation)
210 S White St 310 S Main St
Lancaster, SC 29720-2560
Tel.: (803) 283-5300
Fax: (803) 283-5350
E-mail: webmaster@kanawha.com
Web Site: www.kanawha.com
Sales Range: $300-349.9 Million
Approx. Number Employees: 250
Year Founded: 1958
Business Description:
Insurance Services
S.I.C.: 6311
N.A.I.C.S.: 524113
Media: 2-7-8-10-13-19
Personnel:
Dale Vaughn *(Chm & CEO)*
Brands & Products:
SCRIPTSAVE

KINGSTONE COMPANIES, INC.

1154 Broadway
Hewlett, NY 11557
Tel.: (516) 374-7600
Fax: (516) 295-7216
E-mail: info@kingstonecompanies.com
Web Site: www.dcapgroup.com
Approx. Rev.: $21,595,931
Approx. Number Employees: 43
Business Description:
Insurance Services
S.I.C.: 6411; 6311
N.A.I.C.S.: 524210; 524113
Advertising Expenditures: $41,000
Media: 17
Personnel:
Barry B. Goldstein *(Chm, Pres, CEO, CFO)*
Victor Brodsky *(CFO & Sec)*
Barry G. Lefkowitz *(VP-Product Dev & Mktg)*

LIBERTY LIFE INSURANCE COMPANY

(Sub. of RBC Insurance Holding Inc.)
2000 Wade Hampton Blvd
Greenville, SC 29615
Mailing Address:
PO Box 789
Greenville, SC 29602
Tel.: (864) 609-8111
Fax: (864) 609-4329
Web Site: www.rbcinsurance.com
Approx. Number Employees: 200
Business Description:
Life, Accident & Health Insurance
S.I.C.: 6311
N.A.I.C.S.: 524113
Media: 1-2-4-7-8-9-10-11-13-19-20-24-25-26
Distr.: Reg.
Budget Set: Sept.
Personnel:
David R. Black *(Pres & CEO)*
Jerry Shaleuly *(Sr VP)*
Alison Denis *(Dir-Mktg-Wilmington)*

LIBERTY MUTUAL GROUP INC.

(Sub. of LMHC Massachusetts Holdings Inc.)
175 Berkeley St
Boston, MA 02117
Tel.: (617) 357-9500
Fax: (617) 350-7648
Toll Free: (800) 225-2390
Web Site: www.libertymutual.com
Sales Range: $15-24.9 Billion
Approx. Number Employees: 2,000
Year Founded: 1912
Business Description:
Fire, Marine, Life & Casualty Insurance Services
S.I.C.: 6331; 6311; 6399
N.A.I.C.S.: 524126; 524113; 524128
Advertising Expenditures: $115,000,000
Media: 6-9-13-14-15-18-23-24
Distr.: Direct to Consumer; Natl.
Budget Set: Sept.
Personnel:
Edmund F. Kelly *(Chm & CEO)*
J. Paul Condrin, III *(Pres-Liberty Mutual Agency Corp & Exec VP)*
Gary R. Gregg *(Pres-Agency Markets & Exec VP)*
David H. Long *(Pres-Liberty Mutual Group)*
Greg Gordon *(Sr VP-Mktg)*
John Cusolito *(VP & Mgr-PR)*
Advertising Agencies:
Hill Holliday
53 State St
Boston, MA 02109
Tel.: (617) 366-4000

Key to Media (For complete agency information see *The Advertising Red Books-Agencies* edition):
1. Bus. Publs. 2. Cable T.V. 3. Catalogs & Directories. 4. Co-op Adv. 5. Consumer Mags. 6. D.M. to Bus. Estab.7. D.M. to Consumers 8. Daily Newsp. 9. Exhibits/Trade Shows 10. Foreign 11. Infomercial 12. Internet Adv.13. Multimedia 14. Network Radio 15. Network T.V. 16. Newsp. Distr. Mags. 17. Other 18. Outdoor (Posters, Transit) 19. Point of Purchase20. Premiums, Novelties 21. Product Samples 22. Special Events Mktg. 23. Spot Radio 24. Spot T.V. 25. Weekly Newsp. 26. Yellow Page Adv.

Liberty Mutual Group Inc. — (Continued)

Ketchum
(Part of Omnicom)
1285 Ave of the Americas
New York, NY 10019
Tel.: (646) 935-3900
Fax: (646) 935-4482

LIBERTY NATIONAL LIFE INSURANCE CO.

(Sub. of Torchmark Corporation)
100 Concourse Pkwy Ste 350
Hoover, AL 35244
Mailing Address:
PO Box 2612
Birmingham, AL 35202-2612
Tel.: (205) 325-2722
Fax: (205) 325-4915
Toll Free: (800) 333-0637
E-mail: customerservice@libnat.com
Web Site: www.libnat.com
Sales Range: $900-999.9 Million
Approx. Number Employees: 1,090
Year Founded: 1900
Business Description:
Life Insurance Services
S.I.C.: 6311
N.A.I.C.S.: 524113
Media: 9-14-15-23-24-25
Personnel:
Wester A. Gray *(CIO & Sr VP)*

LIFE QUOTES, INC.

8205 S Cass Ave Ste 102
Darien, IL 60561
Tel.: (630) 515-0170
Fax: (630) 515-0276
Toll Free: (800) 556-9393
Web Site: www.lifequotes.com
Approx. Rev.: $14,650,203
Approx. Number Employees: 106
Year Founded: 1984
Business Description:
Insurance Agency & Brokerage; Online Consumer Insurance Information Services
S.I.C.: 6411
N.A.I.C.S.: 524210
Advertising Expenditures: $373,967
Media: 2-6
Personnel:
Robert S. Bland *(Chm & CEO)*
Phillip A. Perillo *(CFO)*
William V. Thoms *(COO & Exec VP)*
Richard C. Claahsen *(Gen Counsel, Sec & VP)*
Amy Danise *(Editor)*
Andrew Gregory *(Asst Dir-IT)*

LINCOLN FINANCIAL BENEFIT PARTNERS

(Sub. of Lincoln National Corporation)
8801 Indian Hills Dr
Omaha, NE 68114
Mailing Address:
PO Box 2616
Omaha, NE 68103-2616
Tel.: (402) 361-7300
E-mail: jpf.group@jpfinancial.com
Web Site: www.lfg.com
Sales Range: $50-74.9 Million
Approx. Number Employees: 1,000
Year Founded: 1901
Business Description:
Employee Life, Disability & Dental Insurance Services
S.I.C.: 6411
N.A.I.C.S.: 524210
Media: 2-7-10
Distr.: Reg.
Budget Set: Nov.
Personnel:
Paula Hanson *(Asst VP-Worksite Mktg)*

LINCOLN FINANCIAL GROUP

(Div. of Lincoln National Corporation)
100 N Greene St
Greensboro, NC 27401
Mailing Address:
PO Box 21008
Greensboro, NC 27420-1008
Tel.: (336) 691-3000
Fax: (336) 691-3938
Web Site: www.lfg.com
E-Mail For Key Personnel:
Public Relations: Warren.May@jpfinancial.com
Sales Range: $1-4.9 Billion
Approx. Number Employees: 3,100
Year Founded: 1968
Business Description:
Life Insurance Services
S.I.C.: 6311
N.A.I.C.S.: 524113
Media: 2-3-8
Distr.: Intl.; Natl.
Personnel:
Dennis R. Glass *(CEO)*
Charles Philip Elam, II *(Chief Investment Officer)*
Charles C. Cornelio *(Pres-Defined-Contribution Bus)*
Mark E. Konen *(Pres-Insurance & Retirement Solutions)*
Eric Levy *(Sr VP & Head-Defined Contribution Products)*
Heidi Dross *(VP-New Bus)*
Emily Pachuta *(VP-Mktg)*
Kristin Curtin *(Dir-Large Market Pricing)*
Ray Radikas *(Product Mgr)*
Brands & Products:
JEFFERSON PILOT FINANCIAL
Advertising Agencies:
22squared
1170 Peachtree St NE 15th Fl
Atlanta, GA 30309-7649
Tel.: (404) 347-8700
Fax: (404) 347-8800
Insurance

Emerging Marketing
29 W 3rd Ave
Columbus, OH 43201
Tel.: (614) 923-6000
Fax: (614) 424-6200

THE LINCOLN NATIONAL LIFE INSURANCE CO.

(Sub. of Lincoln National Corporation)
1300 S Clinton St
Fort Wayne, IN 46802
Tel.: (260) 455-2000
Fax: (215) 405-8095
Web Site: www.lfg.com
Sales Range: $1-4.9 Billion
Approx. Number Employees: 1,800
Year Founded: 1905
Business Description:
Life Insurance & Financial Services
S.I.C.: 6311; 6321
N.A.I.C.S.: 524113; 524114
Media: 1-2-4-8-9-15-17-18-20-22-23-25
Distr.: Natl.
Budget Set: Oct. -Nov.
Personnel:
Fred Crawford *(CFO)*

LYNX SERVICES, LLC

(Sub. of Pittsburgh Glass Works, LLC)
6351 Bayshore Rd Ste 18
Fort Myers, FL 33917-3172
Tel.: (239) 479-6000
Web Site: www.lynxservices.com
Approx. Number Employees: 50
Year Founded: 1994
Business Description:
Automotive Glass Insurance Claims Management Services
S.I.C.: 6411
N.A.I.C.S.: 524298
Media: 2-7-10
Personnel:
Gary Eilers *(Pres)*

M FINANCIAL HOLDINGS INC.

1125 NW Couch St Ste 900
Portland, OR 97209
Tel.: (503) 232-6960
Fax: (503) 238-1621
Web Site: www.mfin.com
Sales Range: $400-449.9 Million
Approx. Number Employees: 150
Year Founded: 1978
Business Description:
Holding Company; Insurance, Investment & Executive Benefits
S.I.C.: 6719; 6282
N.A.I.C.S.: 551112; 523930
Media: 2
Personnel:
Fred H. Jonske *(Pres & CEO)*
Randall O'Connor *(CFO & Sr VP)*
Brands & Products:
M FINANCIAL GROUP
Advertising Agency:
BLW + Associates
16625 Pacific Hwy
Lake Oswego, OR 97034
Tel.: (503) 222-3546
Fax: (503) 227-2369

MARKEL CORPORATION

4521 Highwoods Pkwy
Glen Allen, VA 23060-9817
Mailing Address:
PO Box 2009
Glen Allen, VA 23058-2009
Tel.: (804) 747-0136
Fax: (804) 965-1600
Toll Free: (800) 446-6671
E-mail: information@markelcorp.com
Web Site: www.markelcorp.com
Approx. Rev.: $2,225,393,000
Approx. Number Employees: 4,800
Year Founded: 1930
Business Description:
Specialty Insurance Products Underwriter
S.I.C.: 6331; 6411
N.A.I.C.S.: 524126; 524210; 524298
Advertising Expenditures: $15,000,000
Media: 1-2-4-5-6-7-8-9-10-13-16-20-22-25-26
Distr.: Direct to Consumer; Natl.
Budget Set: Nov.
Personnel:
Alan I. Kirshner *(Chm & CEO)*
Anthony F. Markel *(Vice Chm)*
Steven Andrew Markel *(Vice Chm)*
F. Michael Crowley *(Co-Pres & Co-COO)*
Richard R. Whitt, III *(Co-Pres & Co-COO)*
Thomas Sinnickson Gayner *(Co-Pres & Chief Investment Officer)*
Anne G. Waleski *(CFO, Treas & VP)*
David Egbert *(CIO)*
Britton L. Glisson *(Chief Admin Officer)*
Brad Kiscaden *(Chief Corp Actuary)*
John K. Latham *(Pres-Wholesale Div)*
Gerard Albanese, Jr. *(Chief Underwriting Officer & Exec VP)*
Daniel Confalone *(Dir-Mktg)*
Brenda Phillips *(Dir-Mktg)*
Brands & Products:
COVERING YOUR WORLD ONE RISK AT A TIME
MARKEL

MARSH & MCLENNAN COMPANIES INC.

1166 Ave of the Americas
New York, NY 10036-2774
Tel.: (212) 345-5000
Fax: (212) 345-4808
Web Site: www.mmc.com
E-Mail For Key Personnel:
Public Relations: James.Speros@mmc.com
Approx. Rev.: $10,550,000,000
Approx. Number Employees: 51,000
Year Founded: 1871
Business Description:
Risk Management, Insurance, Investment, Human Resource & Consulting Services
S.I.C.: 6411; 6289; 7361; 8742; 8748
N.A.I.C.S.: 524210; 523999; 541611; 541612; 541618
Media: 2-3-9-15-22-25
Distr.: Intl.; Natl.
Personnel:
Brian Duperreault *(Pres & CEO)*
Daniel S. Glaser *(Grp Pres & Grp COO)*
Vanessa Ames Wittman *(CFO & Exec VP)*
Michael A. Petrullo *(COO)*
Ben Allen *(CIO, Chief Innovation Officer & Sr VP)*
James D. Speros *(CMO)*
E. Scott Gilbert *(Chief Risk Officer, Chief Complience Officer & Sr VP)*
John P. Drzik *(Pres/CEO-Oliver Wyman Grp)*
Luciana Fato *(Deputy Gen Counsel & Corp Sec)*
Peter J. Beshar *(Gen Counsel & Exec VP)*
Orlando D. Ashford *(Sr VP-HR)*
Silvia Davi *(VP & Head-Corp Comm)*
Oliver Schneidemann *(VP-Global IT & Shared Svcs)*
Brands & Products:
EXECUTIVE BENEFIT RESTORATION SERVICE
FINPRO
GUY CARPENTER
LIPPINCOTT MERCER
MARSH
MARSH THE WORLD'S #1 RISK SPECIALIST
MERCER DELTA
MERCER HUMAN RESOURCE CONSULTING
MMC CAPITAL

Key to Media (For complete agency information see *The Advertising Red Books-Agencies* edition):
1. Bus. Publs. 2. Cable T.V. 3. Catalogs & Directories. 4. Co-op Adv. 5. Consumer Mags. 6. D.M. to Bus. Estab.7. D.M. to Consumers
8. Daily Newsp. 9. Exhibits/Trade Shows 10. Foreign 11. Infomercial 12. Internet Adv.13. Multimedia 14. Network Radio
15. Network T.V. 16. Newsp. Distr. Mags. 17. Other 18. Outdoor (Posters, Transit) 19. Point of Purchase20. Premiums, Novelties
21. Product Samples 22. Special Events Mktg. 23. Spot Radio 24. Spot T.V. 25. Weekly Newsp. 26. Yellow Page Adv.

MMC ENTERPRISE RISK
RIMSTAR
RISK-ADJUSTED SUPPLY CHAIN MANAGEMENT
RISK MANAGEMENT HIERARCHY

Advertising Agency:
KRT Marketing
3685 Mt Diablo Blvd Ste 255
Lafayette, CA 94549-3776
Tel.: (925) 284-0444
Fax: (925) 284-0448
Recruitment

MASSACHUSETTS MUTUAL LIFE INSURANCE COMPANY

(d/b/a MassMutual Financial Group)
1295 State St
Springfield, MA 01111
Tel.: (413) 788-8411
Fax: (413) 744-6005
Toll Free: (800) 542-6767
Web Site: www.massmutual.com
Sales Range: $15-24.9 Billion
Approx. Number Employees: 27,000
Year Founded: 1851
Business Description:
Life Insurance & Pension Products Sales
S.I.C.: 6371
N.A.I.C.S.: 524292
Media: 2-3-6-7-8-9-10-13-15-20-22-25
Distr.: Natl.
Personnel:
Roger W. Crandall *(Chm, Pres & CEO)*
John Miller, Jr. *(CFO & Sr Mng Dir)*
Anne S. Kandilis *(Mng Dir)*
Michael T. Rollings *(CFO & Exec VP)*
Robert J. Casale *(CIO & Exec VP)*
E. Heather Smiley *(CMO-Retirement Svcs)*
Thomas M. Finke *(Chief Investment Officer & Exec VP)*
Isadore Jermyn *(Chief Actuary & Sr VP)*
Michael R. Fanning *(Chm/CEO-MML Investors Svcs & Exec VP-US Insurance Grp)*
Elaine A. Sarsynski *(Chm/CEO MassMutual International & Exec VP)*
Mark D. Roellig *(Gen Counsel, Sec & Exec VP)*
Sheldon Francis *(VP/Asst Gen Counsel-Investment Law Grp)*
Debra A. Palermino *(Exec VP)*
Elizabeth A. Ward *(Exec VP)*
Matthew Winter *(Exec VP-Individual Insurance)*
Gregory E. Deavens *(Sr VP & Head-Fin-US Insurance Grp)*
Kenneth S. Cohen *(Sr VP & Deputy Gen Counsel)*
Rodney J. Dillman *(Sr VP)*
Melissa Millan *(First Sr VP-Prod Mngmt)*
Hugh O'Toole *(Sr VP-Natl Sls & Distr-Retirement Svcs Div)*
Douglas G. Russell *(Sr VP)*
Trish Walsh *(Sr VP)*
Douglas J. Jangraw *(VP & Actuary)*
Paula Tremblay *(Asst VP-Media Rels)*
Joel Almeida *(Dir-Sls & Bus Dev)*
Dan Kretz *(Dir-Sls & Bus Dev-Mid-Atlantic Reg)*
Jim Lacey *(Dir-Corp Commun)*
Tony Gomes *(Assoc Dir-Enterprise Messaging)*
Scott Buffington *(Natl Sls Mgr-Taft-Hartley Market)*
George Sutherland *(Div Sls Mgr-Institutional Sales)*
Brands & Products:
MASSMUTUAL
YOU CAN'T PREDICT. YOU CAN PREPARE
Advertising Agency:
Mullen
40 Broad St
Boston, MA 02109
Tel.: (617) 226-9000
Fax: (617) 226-9100

MBIA INC.

113 King St
Armonk, NY 10504
Tel.: (914) 273-4545
Fax: (914) 765-3163
Web Site: www.mbia.com
Approx. Rev.: $893,798,000
Approx. Number Employees: 392
Year Founded: 1973
Business Description:
Municipal & Corporate Bond Insurance
S.I.C.: 6331
N.A.I.C.S.: 524126
Media: 17
Personnel:
Daniel P. Kearney *(Chm)*
C. Edward Chaplin *(Co-Pres, CFO & Chief Admin Officer)*
William C. Fallon *(Co-Pres & COO)*
Clifford D. Corso *(Co-Pres & Chief Investment Officer)*
Joseph W. Brown *(CEO)*
Jason Cameron *(Mng Dir)*
David McCollum *(Mng Dir)*
Chris Moros *(Mng Dir)*
Christopher Chafizadeh *(Mng Dir)*
Greg Diamond *(Mng Dir)*
Tom Jordan *(Mng Dir)*
Roger Shields *(Mng Dir)*
Christopher E. Weeks *(Mng Dir)*
Marc D. Morris *(CFO & Mng Dir-Asset Mgmt)*
Ram D. Wertheim *(Chief Legal Officer)*
Mitchell I. Sonkin *(Chief Portfolio Officer)*
Pat Brosnan *(Dir-Comml Securitization Grp)*
Brian Cooney *(Dir-Global Consumer Asset Fin)*
David Wilson *(Dir-Asset Mgmt-Asset Liabilty Grp)*
Advertising Agency:
Bonner & Associates
1101 17th St NW Ste 800
Washington, DC 20036-4716
Tel.: (202) 463-8880
Fax: (202) 833-3584

MEDICA, INC.

401 Carlson Pkwy
Minnetonka, MN 55305
Tel.: (952) 992-2900
Fax: (952) 992-3890
E-mail: info@medica.com
Web Site: www.medica.com
Sales Range: $1-4.9 Billion
Approx. Number Employees: 900
Year Founded: 1994
Business Description:
Insurance Service
S.I.C.: 6321
N.A.I.C.S.: 524114
Import Export
Media: 2-4-7-8-10
Personnel:
John D. Buck *(Chm & CEO-Whitefish Ventures)*
David Tilford *(Pres & CEO)*
Aaron Reynolds *(CFO, Chief Admin Officer & Exec VP)*
Charles Fazio *(Chief Medical Officer & Sr VP)*
Jim Jacobson *(Gen Counsel & Sr VP)*
Glenn E. Andis *(Sr VP-Govt Programs)*
Mark Baird *(Sr VP-Fin & Healthcare Economics)*
Jana L. Johnson *(Sr VP-Ops)*
Deb Knutson *(Sr VP-HR, Learning & Facilities)*
Rob Longendyke *(Sr VP-Mktg & Comm)*
Greg Bury *(Sr Mgr-PR)*
Brands & Products:
BROKERLINK
CENTER FOR HEALTHY AGING
CHOICES FOR LIFE
CUSTOM OPTIONS BY MEDICA
DENTAL EXPLORER
EMEDICA
EVERYONE BENEFITS
FIT CHOICES BY MEDICA
FOCUS ON HEALTH
GETTING FIT JUST GOT EASIER
HEALTH ADVANTAGE BY MEDICA
HEALTHCONNECT
HEALTHY ATTITUDES
HEALTHY AVENUE
IMEDICA
IT'S YOUR HEALTH
LABORCARE
LIVING SMARTER
MEDICA
MEDICA ACCESSABILITY SOLUTION
MEDICA ADVANTAGE SOLUTION
MEDICA BASICS
MEDICA BEHAVIORAL HEALTH
MEDICA CALL LINK
MEDICA CHOICE
MEDICA CHOICE CARE
MEDICA COMPLETE SOLUTION
MEDICA CONNECTIONS
MEDICA DENTALCARE
MEDICA DENTALCHOICE
MEDICA DIRECT
MEDICA DIRECT DENTAL
MEDICA DIRECT FOR INDIVIDUALS
MEDICA DIRECT HSA FOR INDIVIDUALS
MEDICA DIRECT SHORT-TERM FOR INDIVIDUALS
MEDICA DIRECT VALUE FOR INDIVIDUALS
MEDICA DUAL SOLUTION
MEDICA ELECT
MEDICA ELITE SOLUTION
MEDICA ENCORE
MEDICA ESSENTIAL
MEDICA FIT STEPS
MEDICA FOCUS
MEDICA GROUP ADVANTAGE SOLUTION
MEDICA GROUP PRIME SOLUTION
MEDICA GROUP SELECT SOLUTION
MEDICA INDICATORS
MEDICA LINK
MEDICA MEDICARE SOLUTIONS
MEDICA PRIME SOLUTION
MEDICA SELECT SOLUTION
MEDICA SELECTCARE
MEDICA SENIORCARE
MEDICA SENIORDENTAL
MEDICA SOLO
MEDICA.COM
MY HEALTH MANAGER FROM MEDICA
MY MEDICA
MYMEDICA
PASSPORT FROM MEDICA
PATIENT CHOICE INSIGHTS
PREMIUM INSIGHTS
PROVIDE-A-RIDE
SELECTCARE
THE WAY TO BETTER HEALTH

MEDICAL MUTUAL OF OHIO

2060 E 9th St
Cleveland, OH 44115
Tel.: (216) 687-7000
Fax: (216) 687-7001
Toll Free: (800) 700-2583
E-mail: info@medmutual.com
Web Site: www.medmutual.com
Approx. Premiums: $1,500,000,000
Approx. Number Employees: 2,500
Year Founded: 1934
Business Description:
Health Insurance
S.I.C.: 6321
N.A.I.C.S.: 524114
Personnel:
Rick Chiricosta *(Pres & CEO)*
Dennis Jancsy *(CFO & Exec VP)*
Jared Chaney *(CMO & Chief Comm Officer)*
Kenneth Sidon *(Chief Info & Security Officer & Exec VP)*
Susan Tyler *(Chief Experience Officer & Exec VP)*
Mary Novak *(Sr VP-Pub & Multi-Employer Market)*
Don Olson *(Dir-Corp Comm)*
Ezell Underdown *(Dir-Legal Affairs)*
Ann Vickers *(Dir-Mktg & Comm)*
Karen Williams *(Dir-Fin Analysis, Cost & Budget)*
Steve Harry *(Product Mgr)*
Barbara Heilman *(Mgr-Member Appeals)*
Brands & Products:
GET-WELL CARD
MEDICAL MUTUAL
SAVEWELL
SUPERMED CLASSIC
SUPERMED ONE
SUPERMED PLUS
SUPERMED SELECT
SUPERWELL
Advertising Agency:
Wyse
668 Euclid Ave
Cleveland, OH 44114
Tel.: (216) 696-2424
Fax: (216) 736-4425

THE MEDICAL PROTECTIVE COMPANY

(Sub. of Columbia Insurance Co.)
5814 Reed Rd
Fort Wayne, IN 46835
Tel.: (260) 485-9622
Fax: (260) 486-0415
Fax: (800) 398-6726
Toll Free: (800) 463-3776
Web Site: www.medpro.com

Key to Media (For complete agency information see *The Advertising Red Books-Agencies* edition):
1. Bus. Publs. 2. Cable T.V. 3. Catalogs & Directories. 4. Co-op Adv. 5. Consumer Mags. 6. D.M. to Bus. Estab.7. D.M. to Consumers
8. Daily Newsp. 9. Exhibits/Trade Shows 10. Foreign 11. Infomercial 12. Internet Adv.13. Multimedia 14. Network Radio
15. Network T.V. 16. Newsp. Distr. Mags. 17. Other 18. Outdoor (Posters, Transit) 19. Point of Purchase20. Premiums, Novelties
21. Product Samples 22. Special Events Mktg. 23. Spot Radio 24. Spot T.V. 25. Weekly Newsp. 26. Yellow Page Adv.

The Medical Protective Company — (Continued)

Sales Range: $200-249.9 Million
Approx. Number Employees: 350
Year Founded: 1899
Business Description:
Medical Professional Liability Coverage & Risk Services
S.I.C.: 6331
N.A.I.C.S.: 524126
Media: 2-7-8-10
Distr.: Natl.
Budget Set: Oct.
Personnel:
Timothy J. Kenesey *(Pres & CEO)*
Nancy Stahulak *(VP & Mktg Leader)*
Advertising Agency:
Ferguson Advertising Inc.
803 S Calhoun St 6th Fl
Fort Wayne, IN 46802-2319
Tel.: (260) 426-4401
Fax: (260) 422-6417

MERCHANTS GROUP, INC.
(Sub. of American European Group, Inc.)
250 Main St
Buffalo, NY 14202
Tel.: (716) 849-3333
Fax: (716) 849-3222
Fax: (716) 849-3270
Toll Free: (800) 362-3343
E-mail: information@merchantsgroup.com
Web Site: www.merchantsgroup.com
Approx. Rev.: $49,540,000
Approx. Number Employees: 313
Year Founded: 1886
Business Description:
Property & Casualty Insurance Services
S.I.C.: 6331; 6411
N.A.I.C.S.: 524126; 524210
Media: 2-5-9-23-25-26
Distr.: Reg.
Budget Set: Nov.
Personnel:
Robert M. Zak *(Pres & CEO)*
Kennth Wiison *(CFO)*
Lisa Wishman *(Asst VP-Mktg)*
Cammy Belser *(Reg Mgr)*
Samuel Guarnieri *(Reg Mgr)*
Tina Schaedler *(Reg Mgr)*

MERCURY GENERAL CORPORATION
4484 Wilshire Blvd
Los Angeles, CA 90010-3710
Tel.: (323) 937-1060
Fax: (323) 857-7116
Web Site: www.mercuryinsurance.com
Approx. Rev.: $2,775,885,000
Approx. Number Employees: 4,800
Year Founded: 1961
Business Description:
Automobile Insurance
S.I.C.: 6331; 6411
N.A.I.C.S.: 524126; 524210
Advertising Expenditures: $30,000,000
Personnel:
George Joseph *(Chm)*
Gabriel Tirador *(Pres & CEO)*
Theodore R. Stalick *(CFO & VP)*
Allan Lubitz *(CIO & Sr VP)*
Christopher Graves *(Chief Investment Officer & VP)*
Joanna Y. Moore *(Sr VP & Chief Claims Officer)*
Bruce E. Norman *(Sr VP-Mktg)*
John Sutton *(Sr VP-Customer Svc)*

MERCURY INSURANCE COMPANY
(Sub. of Mercury General Corporation)
4484 Wilshire Blvd
Los Angeles, CA 90010
Tel.: (323) 937-1060
Fax: (323) 857-7116
Web Site: www.mercuryinsurance.com
Sales Range: $25-49.9 Million
Approx. Number Employees: 150
Year Founded: 1961
Business Description:
Provider of Automobile Insurance Services
S.I.C.: 8111
N.A.I.C.S.: 541110
Personnel:
George Joseph *(Chm)*
Gabriel Tirador *(Pres & CEO)*
Erik Thompson *(Dir-Adv)*
Advertising Agency:
The MWW Group
660 S Figueroa St Ste 1400
Los Angeles, CA 90017
Tel.: (213) 486-6560
Fax: (213) 486-6501
(Home & Auto Insurance)

METLIFE, INC.
200 Park Ave
New York, NY 10166-0188
Tel.: (212) 578-2211
Fax: (212) 578-3320
Toll Free: (800) 638-5433
E-mail: info@metlife.com
Web Site: www.metlife.com
Approx. Rev.: $52,717,000,000
Approx. Number Employees: 66,000
Business Description:
Holding Company; Insurance & Financial Services
S.I.C.: 6411; 6311; 6321; 6719
N.A.I.C.S.: 524210; 524113; 524114; 551112
Media: 2-3-4-5-6-9-10-14-15-16-18-22-23-24-25-26
Distr.: Direct to Consumer; Natl.
Personnel:
C. Robert Henrikson *(Chm)*
Steven A. Kandarian *(Pres & CEO)*
William J. Wheeler *(CFO & Exec VP)*
Steven J. Goulart *(Chief Investment Officer)*
Frans Hijkoop *(Chief HR Officer & Exec VP)*
Peter M. Carlson *(Chief Acctg Officer)*
William J. Mullaney *(Pres-Bus-US)*
William J. Toppeta *(Pres-Intl)*
Lukasz Kalinowski *(CEO-Life Insurance-Polska & TUnZ)*
Nicholas D. Latrenta *(Gen Counsel & Exec VP)*
Marlene Debel *(Treas & Sr VP)*
Martin Lippert *(Exec VP & Head-Global Tech)*
Maria R. Morris *(Exec VP-Tech & Ops)*
Adam M. Hodes *(Sr VP & Head-Mergers & Acq)*
Beth Hirschhorn *(Sr VP-Global Brand & Mktg Svcs)*
Robert Love *(Sr VP-Grp Benefits Sls)*
Anthony J. Nugent *(Sr VP)*
John J. Calagna *(VP-Corp Comm)*
Chris Smart *(Dir-Sls Dev)*
Brands & Products:
AUTO ADVANTAGE
DEDUCTIBLE SAVINGS BENEFIT
GRANDPROTECT
LIFE ADVICE
METLIFE
METLIFE AUTO & HOME
PREFERENCE PLUS ACCOUNT
TOTAL CONTROL ACCOUNT
Advertising Agencies:
Alexander & Richardson
161 Washington Valley Rd Ste 205
Warren, NJ 07059-7121
Tel.: (732) 302-1223
Fax: (732) 356-9574

Bernstein-Rein Advertising, Inc.
4600 Madison Ave Ste 1500
Kansas City, MO 64112-3016
Tel.: (816) 756-0640
Fax: (816) 399-6000
Toll Free: (800) 571-6246

CP+B
3390 Mary St Ste 300
Coconut Grove, FL 33133
Tel.: (305) 859-2070
Fax: (305) 854-3419
Creative Assignment - Business to Consumer

Mark Berlin & Associates
PO Box 56576
Jacksonville, FL 32241
Tel.: (904) 880-2940

Mass Transmit
453 W17th St
New York, NY 10011
Tel.: (704) 706-2670
Fax: (704) 447-7262

MIDLAND NATIONAL LIFE INSURANCE CO.
(Sub. of Sammons Enterprises, Inc.)
1 Midland Plz
Sioux Falls, SD 57193-0001
Tel.: (605) 335-5700
Fax: (605) 335-3621
Toll Free: (800) 923-3223
E-mail: webmaster@mnlife.com
Web Site: www.mnlife.com
Sales Range: $500-549.9 Million
Approx. Number Employees: 450
Year Founded: 1906
Business Description:
Provider of Life Insurance
S.I.C.: 6311
N.A.I.C.S.: 524113
Media: 10
Personnel:
Steven Palmitier *(Pres & COO)*

MILLENNIUM MARKETING GROUP, LLC
11309 Chicago Cir
Omaha, NE 68154
Tel.: (402) 390-0433
Fax: (402) 390-0450
Toll Free: (877) 333-5558
Web Site: www.mmginsurance.com
Sales Range: Less than $1 Million
Approx. Number Employees: 5
Business Description:
Annuity, Life & Long-Term Care Services
S.I.C.: 6399; 6311; 6371; 6411
N.A.I.C.S.: 524298; 524113; 524128; 524210; 524291; 524292
Media: 2-13
Personnel:
Steve Pennella *(Pres)*

THE MINNESOTA LIFE INSURANCE COMPANY
(Sub. of Securian Financial Group, Inc.)
400 Robert St N
Saint Paul, MN 55101
Tel.: (651) 665-3500
Fax: (651) 665-4488
E-mail: info@minnesotalife.com
Web Site: www.minnesotalife.com
Sales Range: $1-4.9 Billion
Approx. Number Employees: 2,000
Year Founded: 1880
Business Description:
Individual & Group Life Insurance, Group Disability & Pensions; Asset Management Services
S.I.C.: 6311
N.A.I.C.S.: 524113
Media: 17
Distr.: Natl.
Budget Set: Oct.
Personnel:
Robert L. Senkler *(Chm & CEO)*
Randy F. Wallake *(Pres)*
Gregory S. Strong *(CFO & Sr VP)*
Jean Delaney Nelson *(CIO)*
John F. Bruder *(Sr VP-Securian Financial Network)*
James E. Johnson *(Sr VP-Grp Insurance)*
Betty N. Brost *(VP-Strategic Bus Dev)*
Mark B. Hier *(VP-Comm)*
Chris Owens *(Dir-Natl Sls-Individual Life Insurance)*
Brands & Products:
ADVANTUS
MINNESOTA LIFE
SECURIAN FINANCIAL NETWORK

MODERN WOODMEN OF AMERICA
1701 1st Ave
Rock Island, IL 61201-8724
Tel.: (309) 786-6481
Fax: (309) 793-5603
Fax: (309) 793-5547
E-mail: memberservice@modern-woodmen.org
Web Site: www.modern-woodmen.org
Approx. Number Employees: 435
Year Founded: 1883
Business Description:
Fraternal Life Insurance Services
S.I.C.: 6311
N.A.I.C.S.: 524113
Advertising Expenditures: $318,554
Multimedia: $40,000; Bus. Publs.: $47,854; Co-op Adv.: $200,000; Premiums, Novelties: $30,700
Distr.: Natl.
Budget Set: Sept.
Personnel:
Rosemary Costello *(Mgr-HR)*
Brands & Products:
FRATERNAL FINANCIAL
JUNIOR MAX
MAXCL

Key to Media (For complete agency information see *The Advertising Red Books-Agencies* edition):
1. Bus. Publs. 2. Cable T.V. 3. Catalogs & Directories. 4. Co-op Adv. 5. Consumer Mags. 6. D.M. to Bus. Estab.7. D.M. to Consumers 8. Daily Newsp. 9. Exhibits/Trade Shows 10. Foreign 11. Infomercial 12. Internet Adv.13. Multimedia 14. Network Radio 15. Network T.V. 16. Newsp. Distr. Mags. 17. Other 18. Outdoor (Posters, Transit) 19. Point of Purchase20. Premiums, Novelties 21. Product Samples 22. Special Events Mktg. 23. Spot Radio 24. Spot T.V. 25. Weekly Newsp. 26. Yellow Page Adv.

MAXCL PRO
MAXIMIZER
MAXLIFE
MODERN WOODMEN
STEP ONE
TOUCHING LIVES. SECURING FUTURES.

MONUMENTAL LIFE INSURANCE COMPANY

(Sub. of AEGON USA-Monumental Division)
2 E Chase St
Baltimore, MD 21202-2505
Tel.: (410) 685-2900
Fax: (410) 223-4475
Web Site: www.monlife.com/ml
Approx. Number Employees: 1,325
Year Founded: 1906
Business Description:
Life Insurance Services
S.I.C.: 6311
N.A.I.C.S.: 524113
Media: 10-16-19-26
Personnel:
Carol Davies *(CIO & VP)*
Susan Reier *(Chief Admin Officer & VP)*
Steven J. Cammarata *(Chief Actuary & VP)*

MOTORISTS MUTUAL INSURANCE CO.

471 E Broad St Ste 200
Columbus, OH 43215
Tel.: (614) 232-1700
Fax: (866) 790-6431
Toll Free: (888) 876-6542
Web Site: www.motoristsgroup.com
Sales Range: $500-549.9 Million
Approx. Number Employees: 1,144
Year Founded: 1965
Business Description:
Property, Casualty & Life Insurance Services
S.I.C.: 6331
N.A.I.C.S.: 524126
Advertising Expenditures: $800,000
Multimedia: $75,000; Co-op Adv.: $150,000; Consumer Mags.: $170,000; Network Radio: $200,000; Premiums, Novelties: $5,000; Special Events Mktg.: $80,000; Spot Radio: $60,000; Yellow Page Adv.: $60,000
Distr.: Reg.
Budget Set: Nov.
Personnel:
John J. Bishop *(Chm, Pres & CEO)*
Michael L. Wiseman *(CFO & Treas)*

MUTUAL OF AMERICA LIFE INSURANCE COMPANY

320 Pk Ave
New York, NY 10022
Tel.: (212) 224-1600
Fax: (212) 224-2462
Toll Free: (800) 468-3785
Web Site: www.mutualofamerica.com
Approx. Rev.: $1,858,301,336
Approx. Number Employees: 1,000
Year Founded: 1945
Business Description:
Group & Individual Variable Annuities & Pensions & Retirement Services
S.I.C.: 6311; 6331; 6371; 6411
N.A.I.C.S.: 524113; 524210; 525110; 525190; 525990
Personnel:
Thomas J. Moran *(Chm, Pres & CEO)*
Manfred Altstadt *(COO)*
John J. Corrigan *(Exec VP)*
Stephen J. Rich *(Exec VP)*
Joan M. Squires *(Exec VP-Tech)*
Nicole Lanni *(Sr VP-Tech Svcs)*
Advertising Agency:
MCS Advertising
270 Farmington Ave Ste 332
Farmington, CT 06032
Tel.: (860) 676-9090
Fax: (860) 676-9292

MUTUAL OF OMAHA INSURANCE COMPANY

Mutual of Omaha Plz
Omaha, NE 68175
Tel.: (402) 342-7600
Fax: (402) 351-2775
E-mail: webmaster@mutualofomaha.com
Web Site: www.mutualofomaha.com
E-Mail For Key Personnel:
Public Relations: newscenter@mutualofomaha.com
Sales Range: $1-4.9 Billion
Approx. Number Employees: 4,620
Year Founded: 1909
Business Description:
Holding Company; Life Insurance, Annuities, Reinsurance & Other Financial Products & Services
S.I.C.: 6719; 6311; 6321; 6331; 6411
N.A.I.C.S.: 551112; 524113; 524114; 524130; 524298; 525190
Advertising Expenditures: $5,350,000
Bus. Publs.: $100,000; Cable T.V.: $1,100,000; Daily Newsp.: $1,000,000; Other: $100,000; Outdoor (Posters, Transit): $500,000; Premiums, Novelties: $250,000; Special Events Mktg.: $100,000; Spot Radio: $100,000; Spot T.V.: $1,000,000; Weekly Newsp.: $200,000; Yellow Page Adv.: $900,000
Distr.: Natl.
Budget Set: July
Personnel:
Daniel P. Neary *(Chm & CEO)*
Christine Johnson *(Pres)*
David A. Diamond *(CFO, Treas & Exec VP)*
Richard A. Witt *(Chief Investment Officer & Exec VP)*
Richard C. Anderl *(Gen Counsel & Exec VP)*
James T. Blackledge *(Exec VP-Info Svcs)*
Daniel P. Martin *(Exec VP-Grp Benefit Svcs)*
Madeline R. Rucker *(Exec VP-Customer Svc)*
Stacy A. Scholtz *(Exec VP-Corp Svcs)*
Michael C. Weekly *(Exec VP-Individual Fin Svcs)*
Michelle P. Lebens *(Sr VP-BIPM)*
Ryan Bauer *(Dir-Retirement Svcs Mktg)*
Brands & Products:
BEGIN TODAY.
MUTUAL OF OMAHA
SWIMVITATIONAL
WILD KINGDOM
Advertising Agencies:
Horizon Media, Inc.
75 Varick St
New York, NY 10013
Tel.: (212) 220-5000
Toll Free: (800) 633-4201

Skadaddle Media
2658 Bridgeway Ste 203
Sausalito, CA 94965
Tel.: (415) 332-5577
Fax: (415) 332-5544

NATIONAL CLAIMS ADMINISTRATIVE SERVICES

(Sub. of Capital BlueCross Inc.)
(d/b/a NCAS Pennsylvania)
1023 State St
Lemoyne, PA 17043
Tel.: (717) 541-3800
Fax: (717) 541-3850
Toll Free: (800) 635-8832
Approx. Number Employees: 60
Year Founded: 1988
Business Description:
Third-Party Administrator for Self-Funded Employer Groups
S.I.C.: 6411
N.A.I.C.S.: 524210
Media: 7
Personnel:
Robbi Oneglia *(Dir-Accts-Admin Mgmt)*

NATIONAL LIFE INSURANCE COMPANY

1 National Life Dr
Montpelier, VT 05604
Tel.: (802) 229-3333
Fax: (802) 229-9281
Toll Free: (800) 732-8939
Web Site: www.nationallife.com
Sales Range: $1-4.9 Billion
Approx. Number Employees: 900
Year Founded: 1848
Business Description:
Life Insurance, Annuities, Variable Annuities, Mutual Funds & Outside Investment Programs
S.I.C.: 6311; 6321
N.A.I.C.S.: 524113; 524114
Advertising Expenditures: $300,000
Media: 1-2-7-8-13-19-24-25-26
Distr.: Natl.
Budget Set: Oct.
Personnel:
Bob Cotton *(CFO & Sr VP)*
Rich Pedersen *(CIO & Sr VP)*
Michele S. Gatto *(Exec VP-Corp Svcs)*
Edward J. Parry, III *(Exec VP)*
Craig A. Smith *(VP & Actuary)*
Brands & Products:
FPA-FLEXIBLE PREMIUM ANNUITY
GREEN MOUNTAIN ANNUITY SERIES
GREEN MOUNTAIN HERITAGE
GREEN MOUNTAIN LIBERTY
GREEN MOUNTAIN PRIVILEGE
GREEN MOUNTAIN SECURITY 3
GREEN MOUNTAIN SECURITY 5
NATIONAL LIFE GROUP
RETIREMAX FLEX I
RETIREMAX FLEX II
RETIREMAX PREMIER + 1
SECURE PLUS SELECT
SECURE PLUS TSA
SENTINEL ADVANTAGE
SENTINEL FAMILY OF FUNDS
SPIA-SINGLE PREMIUM IMMEDIATE ANNUITY
Advertising Agencies:
Schwartz Public Relations Associates, Inc.
444 Park Ave S 12th Fl
New York, NY 10016-7321
Tel.: (212) 677-8700
Fax: (212) 254-2507

Spike Advertising Inc.
27 Kilburn St
Burlington, VT 05401
Tel.: (802) 951-1700
Fax: (802) 951-1705

THE NATIONAL SECURITY GROUP, INC.

661 E Davis St
Elba, AL 36323
Mailing Address:
PO Box 703
Elba, AL 36323-1621
Tel.: (334) 897-2273
Fax: (334) 897-5694
E-mail: info@nationalsecuritygroup.com
Web Site:
www.nationalsecuritygroup.com
Approx. Rev.: $69,392,000
Approx. Number Employees: 147
Year Founded: 1947
Business Description:
Holding Company
S.I.C.: 6321; 6311; 6331
N.A.I.C.S.: 524130; 524113; 524126
Advertising Expenditures: $113,000
Media: 17
Personnel:
Winfield Baird *(Chm)*
William L. Brunson, Jr. *(Pres & CEO)*
Brian R. McLeod *(CFO, VP-Fin & Ops)*
Brunson L. White *(CIO & VP)*

NATIONAL UNION FIRE INSURANCE COMPANY OF PITTSBURGH, PA.

(Sub. of Chartis, Inc.)
(d/b/a National Union)
175 Water St
New York, NY 10038-4918
Tel.: (212) 770-7000
Fax: (212) 943-1125
Sales Range: $125-149.9 Million
Year Founded: 1921
Business Description:
Liability Products & Services
S.I.C.: 6399; 6331
N.A.I.C.S.: 524128; 524126; 525190
Media: 2-6-9-22-25-26
Distr.: Natl.
Budget Set: Dec.
Personnel:
Scott Meyer *(Pres-Fin Institutions)*
Brands & Products:
CRIMEGUARD

NATIONAL WESTERN LIFE INSURANCE COMPANY

850 E Anderson Ln
Austin, TX 78752-1602
Tel.: (512) 836-1010
Fax: (512) 835-2729
Toll Free: (800) 531-5442
E-mail: bpribyl@nationalwesternlife.com
Web Site:
www.nationalwesternlife.com
E-Mail For Key Personnel:

Key to Media (For complete agency information see *The Advertising Red Books-Agencies* edition):
1. Bus. Publs. 2. Cable T.V. 3. Catalogs & Directories. 4. Co-op Adv. 5. Consumer Mags. 6. D.M. to Bus. Estab.7. D.M. to Consumers 8. Daily Newsp. 9. Exhibits/Trade Shows 10. Foreign 11. Infomercial 12. Internet Adv.13. Multimedia 14. Network Radio 15. Network T.V. 16. Newsp. Distr. Mags. 17. Other 18. Outdoor (Posters, Transit) 19. Point of Purchase20. Premiums, Novelties 21. Product Samples 22. Special Events Mktg. 23. Spot Radio 24. Spot T.V. 25. Weekly Newsp. 26. Yellow Page Adv.

NATIONAL WESTERN LIFE INSURANCE COMPANY — (Continued)

President: rmoody@nationalwesternlife.com
Approx. Rev.: $575,992,000
Approx. Number Employees: 292
Year Founded: 1956
Business Description:
Life Insurance & Annuities
S.I.C.: 6311; 6411
N.A.I.C.S.: 524113; 524298
Media: 2-8-10-20
Distr.: Natl.
Budget Set: Oct.
Personnel:
Robert L. Moody, Sr. *(Chm & CEO)*
Ross R. Moody *(Pres & COO)*
Brian M. Pribyl *(CFO, Treas & Sr VP)*
Patricia L. Scheuer *(CIO)*
S. Christopher Johnson *(CMO & Sr VP)*
Michael P. Hydanus *(Chief Admin Officer & Sr VP)*
Paul D. Facey *(Chief Actuary & Sr VP)*
James P. Payne *(Sec & Sr VP)*
Scott E. Arendale *(Sr VP-Intl Mktg)*
Charles D. Milos *(Sr VP-Mortgage Loans & Real Estate)*
Paul Garofoli *(VP-Mktg)*
Robin Hulsey *(Asst VP)*

NATIONWIDE FINANCIAL NETWORK

(Sub. of Nationwide Financial Services, Inc.)
1000 Chesterbrook Blvd
Berwyn, PA 19312-1181
Mailing Address:
PO Box 1717
Valley Forge, PA 19482-1717
Tel.: (610) 889-1717
Fax: (610) 407-1902
Toll Free: (800) 523-4681
Web Site:
www.nationwideprovident.com
Approx. Number Employees: 70
Year Founded: 1865
Business Description:
Financial Services
S.I.C.: 6211
N.A.I.C.S.: 523120
Advertising Expenditures: $300,000
Media: 1-2-3-5-6-8-10-20-25-26
Distr.: Natl.
Budget Set: Dec.
Personnel:
Richard Waterworth *(Reg VP)*

NATIONWIDE MUTUAL INSURANCE COMPANY

1 Nationwide Plz
Columbus, OH 43215-2220
Tel.: (614) 249-7111
Tel.: (614) 249-6349 (Pub Rels)
Fax: (614) 854-3676
Toll Free: (800) 882-2822
E-mail: havilab@nationwide.com
Web Site: www.nationwide.com
Approx. Rev.: $20,265,000,000
Approx. Number Employees: 36,000
Year Founded: 1925
Business Description:
Insurance, Retirement & Investment Services
S.I.C.: 6331; 6289; 6371
N.A.I.C.S.: 524126; 523999; 525110
Advertising Expenditures:
$15,200,000
Bus. Publs.: $200,000; Cable T.V.: $500,000; Co-op Adv.: $4,100,000; Consumer Mags.: $300,000; D.M. to Consumers: $200,000; Daily Newsp.: $500,000; Internet Adv.: $400,000; Network T.V.: $700,000; Outdoor (Posters, Transit): $200,000; Premiums, Novelties: $500,000; Special Events Mktg.: $100,000; Spot Radio: $500,000; Spot T.V.: $6,000,000; Yellow Page Adv.: $1,000,000
Distr.: Natl.
Budget Set: Sept. -Oct.
Personnel:
Keith W. Eckel *(Chm)*
Stephen Rasmussen *(CEO)*
Lawrence A. Hilsheimer *(CFO & Exec VP)*
Michael Keller *(CIO & Exec VP)*
Patricia R. Hatler *(Chief Legal Officer & Exec VP)*
Terri Hill *(Chief Admin Officer & Exec VP)*
Gail G. Snyder *(Chief Investment Officer & Exec VP)*
David LaPaul *(Treas & Sr VP)*
Tariq Khan *(VP-Market Dev & Diversity)*
Marie Casimir *(Reg Dir-Mktg)*
Stephanie Cotton *(Dir-Mktg)*
Jeff Myer *(Dir-Adv)*
Stephanie Schwartz *(Dir-Media & Promos)*
Patrick Foy *(Mgr-Comml Product)*
Brands & Products:
1-877-ON YOUR SIDE
LIFE COMES AT YOU FAST
NATIONWIDE
NATIONWIDE BLUE RIBBON
NATIONWIDE EAGLE PLUS
NATIONWIDE PLATINUM III
NATIONWIDE PLATINUM V
NATIONWIDE QUATRO SELECT ANNUITY
NATIONWIDE TRIO SELECT+
Advertising Agencies:
McKinney
(d/b/a McKinney Silver)
318 Blackwell St
Durham, NC 27701
Tel.: (919) 313-0802
Fax: (919) 313-0805

Universal McCann
100 33rd St 8th Fl
New York, NY 10001
Tel.: (212) 883-4700
Media Buying (Spot TV, Radio, Print, Out-of-Home)

The VIA Group LLC
34 Danforth St Ste 309
Portland, ME 04101
Tel.: (207) 221-3000
Fax: (207) 761-9422
(Brand Marketing)

Wunderman
(Worldwide Headquarters)
285 Madison Ave
New York, NY 10017
Tel.: (212) 941-3000
Fax: (212) 210-5454

NEIGHBORHOOD HEALTH PLAN INC.

253 Summer St 5th Fl
Boston, MA 02110-1114
Tel.: (617) 772-5500
Fax: (617) 772-5513
Fax: (617) 772-5510
Toll Free: (800) 462-5449
Web Site: www.nhp.org
Approx. Number Employees: 180
Year Founded: 1986
Business Description:
Medical & Health Care Plans
S.I.C.: 6321
N.A.I.C.S.: 524114
Import Export
Media: 13-18
Personnel:
Deborah Enos *(Pres & CEO)*
Advertising Agency:
Yellin/McCarron, Inc.
280 Summer St 4th Fl
Boston, MA 02210
Tel.: (617) 426-9211
Fax: (617) 426-7443

NEW ENGLAND LIFE INSURANCE CO.

(Sub. of MetLife, Inc.)
(d/b/a New England Financial)
501 Boylston St
Boston, MA 02117
Tel.: (212) 578-2211
Fax: (617) 536-2393
Web Site: www.nefn.com
Sales Range: $650-699.9 Million
Approx. Number Employees: 2,400
Year Founded: 1835
Business Description:
Life & Health Insurance Services
S.I.C.: 6311; 6321
N.A.I.C.S.: 524113; 524114
Media: 2-5-6-8-9-10-20-23-24
Distr.: Natl.
Budget Set: Oct.
Personnel:
Robert C. Henrikson *(Chm)*
Brands & Products:
NEW ENGLAND FINANCIAL

NEW JERSEY MANUFACTURERS INSURANCE COMPANY

301 Sullivan Way
West Trenton, NJ 08628
Tel.: (609) 883-1300
Fax: (609) 883-0653
E-mail: careers@njm.com
Web Site: www.njm.com
Sales Range: $900-999.9 Million
Approx. Number Employees: 2,340
Year Founded: 1913
Business Description:
Property & Casualty Insurance
S.I.C.: 6331; 8093
N.A.I.C.S.: 524126; 621420
Media: 6
Personnel:
Bernard Flynn *(Pres & CEO)*
Charles Prall *(CFO)*
Lee Bellarmino *(Pres-Bank, CEO-Insurance & Sr VP-SPHR)*
Patrick Breslin *(Sec & Mgr-Comm)*
Mark Duca *(Sec & Mgr-Workers Compensation Claims)*
William Barrett *(Asst VP-Workers Compensation Claims)*

NEW YORK LIFE INSURANCE COMPANY

51 Madison Ave
New York, NY 10010
Tel.: (212) 576-7000
Fax: (212) 576-8145
Toll Free: (800) 692-3086
Web Site: www.newyorklife.com
Sales Range: $15-24.9 Billion
Approx. Number Employees: 12,650
Year Founded: 1845
Business Description:
Life Insurance; Financial Services & Annuities
S.I.C.: 6311; 6331
N.A.I.C.S.: 524113; 524126
Advertising Expenditures:
$18,000,000
Bus. Publs.: $180,000; Cable T.V.: $3,600,000; Co-op Adv.: $180,000; Consumer Mags.: $3,600,000; D.M. to Consumers: $720,000; Daily Newsp.: $360,000; Internet Adv.: $180,000; Network Radio: $4,680,000; Network T.V.: $4,500,000
Distr.: Natl.
Budget Set: Aug.
Personnel:
Theodore A. Mathas *(Chm, Pres & CEO)*
Gary E. Wendlandt *(Vice Chm & Chief Investment Officer)*
Michael E. Sproule *(CFO & Exec VP)*
Sue Ericksen *(CIO)*
Frank M. Boccio *(Chief Admin Officer & Exec VP)*
Sheila K. Davidson *(Chief Investment Officer)*
Barry Schub *(Chief HR Officer & Sr VP)*
John Y. Kim *(Chm/CEO-New York Life Intl & Exec VP)*
Christine Park *(Pres-NYL Foundation)*
Paul Pasteris *(COO-US Life Insurance & Sr VP)*
Michael A. DeMicco *(Sr VP & Deputy Gen Counsel)*
Dennis Gagnon *(VP & Assoc Gen Counsel)*
Linda M. Reimer *(VP & Assoc Gen Counsel)*
Richard Witterschein *(Treas & First VP)*
Christopher O. Blunt *(Exec VP-Retirement Income Security)*
Mark W Pfaff *(Exec VP-US Life Insurance & Agency)*
John Meyer *(Sr VP & Head-Annuity)*
Benjamin Woloshin *(Sr VP & Head-3rd Party Relationship Mgmt)*
Mark E. Arning *(Sr VP)*
Sara Badler *(Sr VP & Deputy Gen Counsel)*
Katherine O'Brien *(Sr VP & Deputy Gen Counsel)*
Ronald Terry *(Sr VP)*
James T. Bain *(Sr VP)*
Scott Berlin *(Sr VP)*
Alexander A. Burbatsky *(Sr VP)*
John Cassagne *(Sr VP)*
Len Elmer *(Sr VP)*
Thomas F. English *(Chief Insurance Counsel & Sr VP)*
Michael G. Gallo *(Sr VP)*
Solomon Goldfinger *(Sr VP)*
Michael Gordon *(Sr VP-Agency Life Ops)*

Key to Media (For complete agency information see *The Advertising Red Books-Agencies* edition):
1. Bus. Publs. 2. Cable T.V. 3. Catalogs & Directories. 4. Co-op Adv. 5. Consumer Mags. 6. D.M. to Bus. Estab.7. D.M. to Consumers 8. Daily Newsp. 9. Exhibits/Trade Shows 10. Foreign 11. Infomercial 12. Internet Adv.13. Multimedia 14. Network Radio 15. Network T.V. 16. Newsp. Distr. Mags. 17. Other 18. Outdoor (Posters, Transit) 19. Point of Purchase20. Premiums, Novelties 21. Product Samples 22. Special Events Mktg. 23. Spot Radio 24. Spot T.V. 25. Weekly Newsp. 26. Yellow Page Adv.

John Grady *(Sr VP-Corp Fin)*
Robert J. Hebron *(Sr VP)*
Tom Johnson *(Sr VP)*
Angela Kyle *(Sr VP-Retirement Income Svcs)*
Elizabeth McCarthy *(Sr VP-Corp Comm)*
Allyson McDonald *(Sr VP-Retirement Income Security)*
Frank J. Ollari *(Sr VP)*
Robert L. Smith *(Sr VP)*
Robert Rosh *(First VP & Deputy Gen Counsel)*
Richard Taigue *(First VP & Deputy Gen Counsel)*
John A. Natale *(First VP)*
Dottie Rodd *(First VP)*
William Werfelman, Jr. *(First VP)*
Fred T. DeFilippo *(VP-Agency Mktg)*
Daniel O'Brien *(VP-Sls, Mktg & Acct Svcs)*
Christopher J. Sorgie *(Corp VP-Corp Comm)*
Theresa Wolcott *(Asst VP)*
Robert Elias *(Sr Mgr-Web Mktg)*
Jean Sheridan *(Product Mgr)*

Brands & Products:
ASSET PRESERVER
THE COMPANY YOU KEEP
THE FACILITATOR
INSTANT LEGACY
MAINSTAY
NEW YORK LIFE
NYLIFE
TARGET LIFE

Advertising Agency:
Dewitt Media Strategies, Inc.
45 Rockefeller Ctr Ste 2000
New York, NY 10111
Tel.: (212) 332-3272

NORTH CAROLINA MUTUAL LIFE INSURANCE COMPANY

411 W Chapel Hill St
Durham, NC 27701-3616
Tel.: (919) 682-9201
Fax: (919) 682-9934
Fax: (919) 683-1694
Toll Free: (800) 626-1899
E-mail: info@ncmutuallife.com
Web Site: www.ncmutuallife.com
Approx. Number Employees: 80
Year Founded: 1898
Business Description:
Life Insurance Services
S.I.C.: 6311
N.A.I.C.S.: 524113
Media: 8-10
Distr.: Direct to Consumer; Natl.
Budget Set: Nov.
Personnel:
James Herbert Speed, Jr. *(Pres & CEO)*
Richard Hall *(COO & Sr VP)*

NORTHWESTERN MUTUAL LIFE INSURANCE COMPANY

720 E Wisconsin Ave
Milwaukee, WI 53202-4797
Tel.: (414) 271-1444
Fax: (414) 665-7022
Web Site:
www.northwesternmutual.com
Approx. Rev.: $23,109,000,000
Approx. Number Employees: 7,000
Year Founded: 1857
Business Description:
Life & Disability Income Long Term Care Insurance, Annuities & Mutual Funds Services
S.I.C.: 6311; 6211
N.A.I.C.S.: 524113; 523120
Advertising Expenditures: $18,800,000
Cable T.V.: $9,000,000; Co-op Adv.: $1,500,000; Consumer Mags.: $4,000,000; Spot Radio: $1,000,000; Spot T.V.: $3,000,000; Yellow Page Adv.: $300,000
Distr.: Natl.
Budget Set: Dec.
Personnel:
John E. Schlifske *(Chm & CEO)*
Gary A. Poliner *(Pres & Chief Risk Officer)*
Michael G. Carter *(CFO & VP)*
Timothy G. Schaefer *(CIO)*
Marcia Rimai *(Chief Admin Officer, Chief Compliance Officer & Exec VP)*
Mark G. Doll *(Chief Investment Officer & Exec VP)*
David Robert Remstad *(Chief Actuary & VP)*
Raymond J. Manista *(Gen Counsel & Sec)*
Gary Michael Hewitt *(Treas & VP-Treasury & Investment Ops)*
Todd M. Schoon *(Exec VP-Agencies)*
Jean M. Maier *(Exec VP-Enterprise Ops & Tech)*
Gregory C. Oberland *(Exec VP-Insurance & Investment Products)*
Jefferson V. DeAngelis *(Sr VP-Pub Markets)*
David Dennis Clark *(Sr VP-Real Estate)*
Christina H. Fiasca *(Sr VP-Agency Svcs)*
John Mitchell Grogan *(Sr VP-Wealth Mgmt)*
Jeffrey J. Lueken *(Sr VP-Securities)*
Meridee Joy Maynard *(Sr VP-Life Product)*
Joann M. Eisenhart *(VP-HR)*
Kimberley Goode *(VP-Comm)*
Karl Gabriel Gouverneur *(VP-Info Sys)*
Thomas C. Guay *(VP-New Bus)*
Martha M. Valerio *(VP-Info Sys)*
Conrad C. York *(VP-Mktg)*
Rebekah Barsch *(Dir-Strategic Plng & Consulting)*
Steve Iler *(Asst Dir-Mktg Tools)*
Marie Squire *(Mgr-Brand & Adv)*
Brandon Meves *(Specialist-Mktg)*

Brands & Products:
BAIRD
ESTATE STRATEGIES GROUP
FRANK RUSSELL COMPANY
MASON STREET FUNDS
NORTHWESTERN MUTUAL
NORTHWESTERN MUTUAL TRUST CO.
STRATEGIC EMPLOYEE BENEFITS

Advertising Agency:
OLSON
1625 Hennepin Ave
Minneapolis, MN 55403
Tel.: (612) 215-9800
Fax: (612) 215-9801
Agency of Record
Brand Strategy
Marketing

ODYSSEY RE HOLDINGS CORP.

(Sub. of FAIRFAX FINANCIAL HOLDINGS LIMITED)
300 First Stamford Pl
Stamford, CT 06902
Tel.: (203) 977-8000
Fax: (203) 356-0196
Web Site: www.odysseyre.com/
Approx. Rev.: $2,431,257,000
Approx. Number Employees: 721
Business Description:
Reinsurance Services
S.I.C.: 6331; 6321
N.A.I.C.S.: 524126; 524130
Media: 10-17
Personnel:
Vivan Prem Watsa *(Chm)*
James F. Dowd *(Vice Chm)*
Brian D. Young *(Pres & CEO)*
Jan Christiansen *(CFO & Exec VP)*
Robert W. Bennett *(Chief Actuary & Exec VP)*
Lucien Pietropoli *(CEO-EuroAsia Div)*
Peter Lovell *(Gen Counsel, Sec & Sr VP)*
Michael G. Wacek *(Exec VP-Global Risk Strategies)*
Jeffrey M. Rubin *(Sr VP & Dir-Claims-Global)*
Gerard A. Dugan *(Sr VP-Claims)*

Brands & Products:
ODYSSEYRE

Advertising Agency:
McLaughlin, DelVecchio & Casey, Inc.
1 Church St
New Haven, CT 06510-3330
Tel.: (203) 624-4151
Fax: (203) 401-6134

OHIO CASUALTY INSURANCE COMPANY

(Sub. of Liberty Mutual Group Inc.)
9450 Seward Rd
Fairfield, OH 45014-5412
Tel.: (513) 603-2400
Fax: (513) 603-7900
Toll Free: (800) 843-6446
Web Site: www.ocas.com
Sales Range: $1-4.9 Billion
Approx. Number Employees: 2,150
Year Founded: 1919
Business Description:
Property, Casualty & Life Insurance
S.I.C.: 6331
N.A.I.C.S.: 524126
Advertising Expenditures: $500,000
Media: 2-7-13
Distr.: Reg.
Personnel:
Michael A. Winner *(Pres & CEO)*
John S. Kellington *(CTO & Sr VP)*
John E. Bade, Jr. *(Sr VP-Field Mktg)*

Advertising Agency:
Northlich
Sawyer Point Bldg 720 Pete Rose Way
Cincinnati, OH 45202
Tel.: (513) 421-8840
Fax: (513) 455-4749

OHIO FARMERS INSURANCE COMPANY

(d/b/a Westfield Group)
1 Park Cir PO Box 5001
Westfield Center, OH 44251-5001
Tel.: (330) 887-0101
Fax: (330) 887-0840
Web Site:
www.westfieldinsurance.com
Approx. Number Employees: 2,500
Year Founded: 1848
Business Description:
Holding Company; Insurance, Investment & Banking Services
S.I.C.: 6719; 6029; 6211; 6331; 6399; 6411
N.A.I.C.S.: 551112; 522110; 523110; 524126; 524128; 524210; 524298
Media: 22-24
Personnel:
Robert J. Joyce *(Chm & CEO)*
Frank Carrino *(Gen Counsel & Sec)*

Brands & Products:
SHARING KNOWLEDGE. BUILDING TRUST.
WESTFEILD INSURANCE

OLD AMERICAN INSURANCE COMPANY

(Sub. of Kansas City Life Insurance Company)
3520 Broadway St
Kansas City, MO 64111-2502
Tel.: (816) 753-4900
Fax: (816) 753-4902
Toll Free: (800) 733-6242
Web Site: www.oaic.com
Sales Range: $75-99.9 Million
Approx. Number Employees: 135
Year Founded: 1939
Business Description:
Life Insurance
S.I.C.: 6311; 6321
N.A.I.C.S.: 524113; 524114
Advertising Expenditures: $5,715,000
D.M. to Consumers: $5,000,000; Daily Newsp.: $300,000; Spot Radio: $15,000; Spot T.V.: $400,000
Distr.: Natl.
Personnel:
Walter E. Bixby, III *(Pres)*
John Alderton *(VP-Mktg)*

Brands & Products:
GOLDE 50
PARTNERS IN PROGRESS
PEACE OF MIND
SECURITY PLUS

OMNICARE HEALTH PLAN

(Sub. of Coventry Health Care, Inc.)
1333 Gratiot Ave Ste 400
Detroit, MI 48207
Tel.: (313) 465-1500
E-mail: info@cvty.com
Web Site: www.ochp.com
Sales Range: $150-199.9 Million
Approx. Number Employees: 250
Year Founded: 1973
Business Description:
Health Maintenance Organization
S.I.C.: 6321
N.A.I.C.S.: 524114
Advertising Expenditures: $3,000,000
Media: 1-2-3-4-7-8-12-13-14-18-20-23-24-25-26
Distr.: Reg.
Budget Set: Feb.
Personnel:
Thomas McDonough *(Pres)*

Brands & Products:
BUTTERFLY
OMNICARE

Key to Media (For complete agency information see *The Advertising Red Books-Agencies* edition):
1. Bus. Publs. 2. Cable T.V. 3. Catalogs & Directories. 4. Co-op Adv. 5. Consumer Mags. 6. D.M. to Bus. Estab.7. D.M. to Consumers
8. Daily Newsp. 9. Exhibits/Trade Shows 10. Foreign 11. Infomercial 12. Internet Adv.13. Multimedia 14. Network Radio
15. Network T.V. 16. Newsp. Distr. Mags. 17. Other 18. Outdoor (Posters, Transit) 19. Point of Purchase20. Premiums, Novelties
21. Product Samples 22. Special Events Mktg. 23. Spot Radio 24. Spot T.V. 25. Weekly Newsp. 26. Yellow Page Adv.

OmniCare Health Plan — (Continued)

OMNICAREPLUS

OXFORD HEALTH PLANS LLC

(Div. of UnitedHealth Group Incorporated)
48 Monroe Tpke
Trumbull, CT 06611-1341
Tel.: (203) 459-6000
Fax: (203) 459-6464
Toll Free: (800) 889-7658
Web Site: www.oxhp.com
Sales Range: $1-4.9 Billion
Approx. Number Employees: 3,200
Year Founded: 1985
Business Description:
Hospital & Medical Service Plans
S.I.C.: 6321
N.A.I.C.S.: 524114
Media: 7-8-9-17-23-24
Distr.: Reg.
Brands & Products:
ACTIVE PARTNER
FREEDOM PLAN
HEALTHY BONUS
HEALTHY MIND, HEALTHY BODY
HEALTHY MOTHER, HEALTHY BABY
HMO LAUREL
HMO LAUREL SELECT
LIBERTY PLAN
OXFORD CONSUMER OPTIONS SUITE
OXFORD EXCLUSIVE PLAN
OXFORD HEALTH PLANS
OXFORD MYPLAN
OXFORD ON-CALL
OXFORD USA

OXFORD LIFE INSURANCE COMPANY

(Sub. of AMERCO)
2721 N Central Ave
Phoenix, AZ 85004-1121
Tel.: (602) 263-6666
Fax: (602) 277-5901
Web Site: www.oxfordlife.com
Approx. Sls.: $50,000,000
Approx. Number Employees: 65
Business Description:
Insurance Carriers
S.I.C.: 6321
N.A.I.C.S.: 524130; 524114
Media: 10
Personnel:
Mark A. Haydukovich *(Pres & CEO)*
Charle Mayler *(Partner)*
Eric Johansson *(Chief Ops Officer & VP)*
Don Smith *(CMO & VP)*

PACIFIC LIFE INSURANCE COMPANY

(Sub. of Pacific LifeCorp)
700 Newport Ctr Dr
Newport Beach, CA 92660
Mailing Address:
PO Box 9000
Newport Beach, CA 92658-9030
Tel.: (949) 219-3011
Fax: (949) 219-7614
Toll Free: (800) 800-7646
E-mail: info@pacificlife.com
Web Site: www.pacificlife.com
Approx. Number Employees: 200
Year Founded: 1868
Business Description:
Life & Health Insurance Services
S.I.C.: 6311; 6371
N.A.I.C.S.: 524113; 525110
Advertising Expenditures: $12,010,000
Media: 3-9-13-15-18-20-22-26
Distr.: Natl.
Budget Set: Oct.
Personnel:
James T. Morris *(Chm, Pres & CEO)*
Khanh T. Tran *(CFO, Chief Investment Officer & Exec VP)*
Richard J. Schindler *(CMO-Life Insurance Div & Sr VP)*
Chris van Mierlo *(CMO & Sr VP-Sls)*
Edward R. Byrd *(Chief Acctg Officer & Sr VP)*
Sharon A. Cheever *(Gen Counsel & Sr VP)*
Michael Bell *(Exec VP-Life Insurance Div)*
Mary Ann Brown *(Exec VP-Corp Dev)*
Dewey P. Bushaw *(Exec VP-Annuities & Retirement)*
Michael Robb *(Exec VP-Real Estate)*
Todd Nasser *(Sr VP-Investment Mgmt)*
Joseph Celentano *(Sr VP-Prod Mgmt)*
Martha Gates *(Sr VP-Ops, Life Insurance Div)*
Robert Haskell *(Sr VP-Pub Affairs & Brand Mgmt)*
Scott E. Johnson *(Reg VP)*
Christine Tucker *(VP-Mktg & Retirement Solutions Div)*
Brands & Products:
PACIFIC FINANCIAL PRODUCTS
PACIFIC LIFE & ANNUITY COMPANY
PACIFIC LIFECORP
PACIFIC LIFE INSURANCE CO.
Advertising Agencies:
Centra360
1400 Old Country Rd Ste 420
Westbury, NY 11590-5119
Tel.: (516) 997-3147
Fax: (516) 334-7798

Engine Company One
451 Pacific Ave
San Francisco, CA 94133
Tel.: (415) 989-2500
Fax: (415) 732-9535
Creative Agency of Record
Network & Cable Television Campaign

Mediaspot, Inc.
1550 Bayside Dr
Corona Del Mar, CA 92625-1711
Tel.: (949) 721-0500
Fax: (949) 721-0555
Media Buying Agency of Record

PAN-AMERICAN LIFE INSURANCE COMPANY

601 Poydras St
New Orleans, LA 70130-6029
Tel.: (504) 566-1300
Toll Free: (877) 939-4550
Web Site: www.panamericanlife.com
Approx. Number Employees: 600
Year Founded: 1911
Business Description:
Life & Health Insurance, Hospital & Medical Service Plans, Pension Plans & Administration
S.I.C.: 6311; 8111
N.A.I.C.S.: 524113; 541110
Media: 7
Distr.: Natl.
Budget Set: Oct.
Personnel:
Jose S. Suquet *(Chm, Pres & CEO)*
Carlos F. Mickan *(CFO & Exec VP)*
Karen Chauvin *(CIO)*
Rodolfo J. Revuelta *(Chief Investment Officer & Sr VP)*
Gregg M. Schneider *(Sr VP & Chief Actuary)*
Rafael R. Shabetai *(VP & Chief Underwriting Officer)*
Patrick Fraizer *(Gen Counsel & Sr VP-HR)*
Eugenio Magdalena *(Exec VP-Intl Affairs)*
John P. Foley *(Sr VP-Domestic Markets)*
Felix Martinez *(Sr VP-Intl Dollar Sls)*
Bruce Parker *(Sr VP-Global Life Insurance)*
Scott Reitan *(Sr VP-Admin & IT)*
Ronnie Spedale *(Second VP-Worksite Sls)*
Phillip Straub *(Second VP-Individual Sls)*
David M. Cheek *(VP-Sls)*
Marta Reeves *(VP-Corp Mktg)*
Kathleen L. Smith *(VP-Audit)*
Brands & Products:
FAMILY DIGNITY PLAN
PAN AMERICAN LIFE INSURANCE GROUP
PANAMED
TERM LIFE
UNIVERSAL LIFE
WHOLE LIFE
WIREPROTECT
Advertising Agency:
Fleishman-Hillard Inc.
2800 Ponce de Leon Blvd Ste 1400
Coral Gables, FL 33134-5202
Tel.: (305) 520-2000
Fax: (305) 520-2001
100th Anniversary - A Century of Promises Kept
— Isabel Abislaiman *(Sr VP)*

PATRIOT RISK MANAGEMENT, INC.

401 E Las Olas Blvd 9th Fl
Fort Lauderdale, FL 33301
Tel.: (954) 670-2900
Fax: (954) 670-2937
E-mail: investorinfo@prmigroup.com
Web Site: www.prmigroup.com
Approx. Rev.: $55,868,000
Approx. Number Employees: 210
Year Founded: 2003
Business Description:
Insurance & Risk Management Services
S.I.C.: 6411
N.A.I.C.S.: 524210
Media: 2-10
Personnel:
Steven M. Mariano *(Chm, Pres & CEO)*
Michael W. Grandstaff *(CFO & Sr VP)*
Judith L. Haddad *(CIO)*
Michael J. Sluka *(Chief Acctg Officer)*
Theodore G. Bryant *(Sec, Sr VP, Counsel)*
Richard G. Turner *(Exec VP-Alternative Markets)*
Dean Watters *(Sr VP-Bus Dev)*
John D. Brant *(VP-HR, Comm & Community Rels)*

PBC HEALTH BENEFITS SOCIETY

(d/b/a Pacific Blue Cross)
PO Box 7000
Vancouver, BC V6B 4E1, Canada
Tel.: (604) 419-2000
Fax: (604) 419-2990
Toll Free: (888) 275-4672
Web Site: www.pac.bluecross.ca
Sales Range: $750-799.9 Million
Approx. Number Employees: 700
Business Description:
Health & Dental Benefits
S.I.C.: 6321
N.A.I.C.S.: 524114
Personnel:
Kenneth G. Martin *(Pres & CEO)*
Catherine Aczel Boivie *(Sr VP-IT)*
Cindy Bratkowski *(Sr VP-Info Tech & Client Svcs)*
John Crawford *(Sr VP-Fin Svcs)*
Anne Kinvig *(Sr VP-Human)*
Leza Muir *(Sr VP-Claims Svcs)*
Morris Nord *(Sr VP-Mktg & Client Dev)*
Advertising Agencies:
DDB Vancouver
1600-777 Hornby St
Vancouver, BC V6Z 2T3, Canada
Tel.: (604) 687-7911
Fax: (604) 640-4343

OMD Canada
67 Richmond St W 2nd Fl
Toronto, ON M5H 1Z5, Canada
Tel.: (416) 681-5600
Fax: (416) 681-5620
Media Buying

Tribal DDB Vancouver
1600-777 Hornby St
Vancouver, BC V6Z 2T3, Canada
Tel.: (604) 608-4451
Fax: (604) 640-4343

PEMCO MUTUAL INSURANCE CO. INC.

325 Eastlake Ave E
Seattle, WA 98111
Mailing Address:
PO Box 778
Seattle, WA 98111
Tel.: (206) 628-4000
Fax: (206) 268-2735
Web Site: www.pemco.com
Approx. Number Employees: 700
Year Founded: 1948
Business Description:
Provider of Fire, Marine & Casualty Insurance Services
S.I.C.: 6331
N.A.I.C.S.: 524126
Import Export
Personnel:
Stan McNaughton *(Chm, Pres & CEO)*
Rod Brooks *(CMO & VP)*
Advertising Agency:
DNA Brand Mechanics
1301 5th Ave Ste 2600
Seattle, WA 98101-3100
Tel.: (206) 770-9615
Fax: (206) 770-9015
Automobile Insurance

Key to Media (For complete agency information see *The Advertising Red Books-Agencies* edition):
1. Bus. Publs. 2. Cable T.V. 3. Catalogs & Directories. 4. Co-op Adv. 5. Consumer Mags. 6. D.M. to Bus. Estab.7. D.M. to Consumers
8. Daily Newsp. 9. Exhibits/Trade Shows 10. Foreign 11. Infomercial 12. Internet Adv.13. Multimedia 14. Network Radio
15. Network T.V. 16. Newsp. Distr. Mags. 17. Other 18. Outdoor (Posters, Transit) 19. Point of Purchase20. Premiums, Novelties
21. Product Samples 22. Special Events Mktg. 23. Spot Radio 24. Spot T.V. 25. Weekly Newsp. 26. Yellow Page Adv.

PENNSYLVANIA NATIONAL MUTUAL CASUALTY INSURANCE COMPANY
(d/b/a Penn National Insurance)
2 N 2nd St
Harrisburg, PA 17101-1619
Mailing Address:
PO Box 2361
Harrisburg, PA 17105-2361
Tel.: (717) 234-4941
Fax: (717) 255-6850
Fax: (717) 255-6887
Toll Free: (800) 388-4764
E-mail: communications@pnat.com
Web Site: www.pennnationalinsurance.com
E-Mail For Key Personnel:
President: drowe@pnat.com
Sales Range: $500-549.9 Million
Approx. Number Employees: 2,388
Year Founded: 1919
Business Description:
Property & Casualty Insurance Services
S.I.C.: 6331; 6311
N.A.I.C.S.: 524126; 524113
Media: 2-7-8-14
Personnel:
Dennis C. Rowe *(Chm)*
Kenneth R. Shutts *(Pres & CEO)*
Gregory R. Stine *(CFO, Treas & Sr VP)*
Christine Sears *(COO & Exec VP)*
Karen C. Yarrish *(Gen Counsel, Sec & Sr VP-Corp Comm)*
Robert B. Brandon *(Sr VP-Underwriting Ops)*

THE PHOENIX COMPANIES, INC.
1 American Row
Hartford, CT 06102
Mailing Address:
PO Box 5056
Boston, MA 06102-5056
Tel.: (860) 403-5000
Fax: (860) 403-5855
E-mail: pnx.ir@phoenixwm.com
Web Site: www.phoenixwm.phl.com
Approx. Rev.: $2,084,900,000
Approx. Number Employees: 625
Year Founded: 1851
Business Description:
Wealth Management Products & Services
S.I.C.: 6311
N.A.I.C.S.: 524113
Advertising Expenditures: $5,000,000
Media: 2-3-6-9-13-20-24-25
Distr.: Natl.
Budget Set: Aug.
Personnel:
Thomas S. Johnson *(Chm)*
James David Wehr *(Pres & CEO)*
Peter A. Hofmann *(CFO & Sr Exec VP)*
Christopher M. Wilkos *(Chief Investment Officer & Exec VP)*
David R. Pellerin *(Sr VP & Chief Risk Officer)*
Michael E. Hanrahan *(Chief Acctg Officer)*
John T. Mulrain *(Gen Counsel, Sec & Sr VP)*
Edward W. Cassidy *(Exec VP-Distr, The Phoenix)*
John V. LaGrasse *(Exec VP-Alternative Retirement Solutions)*
Bonnie J. Malley *(Exec VP-HR & Corp Svcs)*
Thomas Buckingham *(Sr VP-Product Dev-Life & Annuity)*
Katherine P. Cody *(Sr VP-Alternative Retirement Solutions)*
Michele Urban Farley *(Sr VP)*
Frank T. Gencarelli *(Sr VP-Phoenix Life Solutions)*
Stephen D. Gresham *(Sr VP-Product Mgmt & Mktg-Asset Mgmt Bus)*
Gina Collopy O'Connell *(Sr VP)*
Zafar Rashid *(Sr VP)*
Francis G. Waltman *(Sr VP-Product Dev-Asset Mgmt)*
J. Steven Neamtz *(Head-Retail Distr)*
Brands & Products:
PHOENIX
WHERE EXCELLENCE GROWS

PHYSICIANS MUTUAL INSURANCE CO.
2600 Dodge St
Omaha, NE 68131-2671
Mailing Address:
PO Box 3313
Omaha, NE 68172
Tel.: (402) 633-1000
Fax: (402) 633-1096
Fax: (402) 633-1604
Toll Free: (888) 932-7642
Web Site: www.physiciansmutual.com
Sales Range: $700-749.9 Million
Approx. Number Employees: 1,300
Year Founded: 1902
Business Description:
Life, Accident & Health Insurance Services
S.I.C.: 6331; 6311
N.A.I.C.S.: 525190; 524113
Media: 2-5-6-8-9-10-23-24-25-26
Distr.: Direct to Consumer; Natl.
Personnel:
Robert Reed *(CEO & Interim CIO)*
Melissa J. Crawford *(Sr VP)*
James Juhler *(Sr VP-Acctg)*
Steven Scanlan *(Sr VP)*
Kelly N. LeBlanc *(VP-Customer Svc)*
Michael W. Peterson *(VP-Direct Mktg)*
Rhonda Ahrens *(Asst VP-Actuary)*
Katherine M. Anderson *(Asst VP-Customer Svc)*
Mike Ebeling *(Asst VP-Tele Sls)*
Mark Peters *(Asst VP-Agency)*
Timothy R. Reed *(Asst VP-Market Segmentation)*
Sheri A. Smith *(Asst VP-Internal Audit)*
Debra Walton *(Asst VP-Corp Comm)*
Advertising Agency:
LDMI
13936 Gold Cir
Omaha, NE 68144-2359
Tel.: (402) 334-9446
Fax: (402) 334-9622
Toll Free: (800) 366-7686 (Insurance)

PREMERA BLUE CROSS
7001-220 St SW Bldg 1
Mountlake Terrace, WA 98043
Tel.: (509) 536-4700
Fax: (509) 464-5282
E-mail: jobline@premera.com
Web Site: www.premera.com
Sales Range: $1-4.9 Billion
Approx. Number Employees: 425
Year Founded: 1933
Business Description:
Health Insurance Carrier
S.I.C.: 6321
N.A.I.C.S.: 524114
Import Export
Personnel:
H.R. Brereton Barlow *(Pres & CEO)*
Kent Marquardt *(CFO & Exec VP)*
Kristen Simonitsch *(CIO & Sr VP)*
Yori Milo *(Chief Legal Officer & Exec VP)*
John Pierce *(Gen Counsel & Sr VP)*
Brian Ancell *(Exec VP-Healthcare Svcs & Stategic Dev)*
Karen Bartlett *(Exec VP-Ops)*
Barbara Magusin *(Sr VP-HR)*
Richard Maturi *(Sr VP-Healthcare Delivery Sys)*
Jack McRae *(Sr VP-Congressional/ Legislative Affairs)*
Lisa Spivey *(Mgr-Web Product)*
Rodney Fowler *(Adv Specialist)*
Brands & Products:
PREMERA
Advertising Agency:
Copacino + Fujikado, LLC
101 Yesler Way Ste 500
Seattle, WA 98104
Tel.: (206) 467-6610
Fax: (206) 467-6604

PRESIDENTIAL LIFE CORPORATION
69 Lydecker St
Nyack, NY 10960-2103
Tel.: (845) 358-2300
Fax: (845) 353-0273
Toll Free: (800) 926-7599
Web Site: www.presidentiallife.com
Approx. Rev.: $297,023,000
Approx. Number Employees: 108
Year Founded: 1965
Business Description:
Sales of Life Insurance & Annuities
S.I.C.: 6311
N.A.I.C.S.: 524113
Media: 17
Personnel:
William M. Trust, Jr. *(Chm)*
Donald L. Barnes *(Vice Chm, Pres & CEO)*
Paul B. Pheffer *(CFO, Treas & Sr VP)*
Mark Abrams *(Exec VP)*

PROASSURANCE CORPORATION
100 Brookwood Pl Ste 300
Birmingham, AL 35209-6811
Mailing Address:
PO Box 590009
Birmingham, AL 35259-0009
Tel.: (205) 877-4400
Fax: (205) 868-4073
Toll Free: (800) 282-6242
E-mail: information@proassurance.com
Web Site: www.proassurance.com
E-Mail For Key Personnel:
Public Relations: foneil@proassurance.com
Approx. Rev.: $692,065,000
Approx. Number Employees: 739
Business Description:
Holding Company; Medical Liability Insurance
S.I.C.: 6331; 6411; 6719
N.A.I.C.S.: 524126; 524298; 551112
Advertising Expenditures: $50,000
Media: 2-10
Personnel:
William Stancil Starnes *(Chm & CEO)*
Victor T. Adamo *(Pres)*
Edward L. Rand Jr. *(CFO & Sr VP)*
Jeffrey L. Bowlby *(CMO & Sr VP-Professional Liability Grp)*
Howard H. Friedman *(Chief Underwriting Officer, Chief Actuary & Sr VP)*
Hayes V. Whiteside *(Chief Medical Officer & Sr VP)*
Darryl K. Thomas *(Chief Claims Officer & Sr VP)*
Jeffrey P. Lisenby *(Gen Counsel, Corp Sec & Sr VP)*
Frank B. O'Neil *(Sr VP-Corp Comm & IR)*
Clay Shaw *(VP-HR)*
Brands & Products:
CLAIMS-MADE PLUS
MEDICAL ASSURANCE
PROASSURANCE
PROFESSIONALS GROUP
PRONATIONAL
TREATED FAIRLY

PROASSURANCE CORPORATION
(Sub. of ProAssurance Corporation)
1115 30th St NW
Washington, DC 20007
Tel.: (205) 877-4400
Fax: (202) 969-1881
Toll Free: (800) 613-3615
Web Site: www.proassurance.com
Sales Range: $75-99.9 Million
Approx. Number Employees: 107
Business Description:
Medical Malpractice Insurance & Practice Management Services
S.I.C.: 6411
N.A.I.C.S.: 524210
Media: 7-10
Personnel:
Victor T. Adamo *(Pres)*
Brands & Products:
NCRIC

PROASSURANCE WISCONSIN INSURANCE COMPANY
(Formerly Physicians Insurance Company of Wisconsin Inc.)
(Sub. of ProAssurance Corporation)
1002 Deming Way
Madison, WI 53717
Tel.: (608) 831-8331
Fax: (608) 831-0084
Toll Free: (800) 279-8331
Web Site: www.proassurance.com
Sales Range: $25-49.9 Million
Approx. Number Employees: 75
Year Founded: 1986
Business Description:
Liability Insurance Services
S.I.C.: 6411
N.A.I.C.S.: 524210
Media: 2-7-10-23
Personnel:
David L. Maurer *(COO)*
Carol Moseson *(Specialist-Mktg)*

Key to Media (For complete agency information see *The Advertising Red Books-Agencies* edition):
1. Bus. Publs. 2. Cable T.V. 3. Catalogs & Directories. 4. Co-op Adv. 5. Consumer Mags. 6. D.M. to Bus. Estab.7. D.M. to Consumers 8. Daily Newsp. 9. Exhibits/Trade Shows 10. Foreign 11. Infomercial 12. Internet Adv.13. Multimedia 14. Network Radio 15. Network T.V. 16. Newsp. Distr. Mags. 17. Other 18. Outdoor (Posters, Transit) 19. Point of Purchase20. Premiums, Novelties 21. Product Samples 22. Special Events Mktg. 23. Spot Radio 24. Spot T.V. 25. Weekly Newsp. 26. Yellow Page Adv.

PROFESSIONAL PLANNERS MARKETING GROUP, LLC
5500 Village Blvd Ste 200
West Palm Beach, FL 33407
Tel.: (561) 845-1997
Fax: (561) 845-0366
Toll Free: (800) 330-1997
E-mail: info@ppmg.net
Web Site: www.ppmg.net
Year Founded: 1976
Business Description:
Insurance Marketing Services
S.I.C.: 6371; 6411
N.A.I.C.S.: 524298; 524210; 524291; 524292
Media: 2-22

THE PROGRESSIVE CORPORATION
6300 Wilson Mills Rd
Mayfield Village, OH 44143-2109
Tel.: (440) 461-5000
Fax: (440) 603-4420
Toll Free: (800) 876-6327
Web Site: www.progressive.com
Approx. Rev.: $14,963,300,000
Approx. Number Employees: 24,638
Year Founded: 1937
Business Description:
Holding Company for Property & Casualty Insurance Entities
S.I.C.: 6331; 6719
N.A.I.C.S.: 524126; 551112
Advertising Expenditures: $175,000,000
Media: 3-6-8-10-13-15-16-18-23-24-26
Distr.: Natl.
Budget Set: Oct.
Personnel:
Peter B. Lewis *(Chm)*
Glenn M. Renwick *(Pres & CEO)*
Brian C Domeck *(CFO)*
Raymond M. Voelker *(CIO)*
Jeff Charney *(CMO)*
Charles E. Jarrett *(Chief Legal Officer)*
John A. Barbagallo *(Pres-Comml Lines Grp)*
John P. Sauerland *(Pres-Personal Lines)*
Mariann Wojtkun Marshall *(Asst Sec)*
Brands & Products:
1-800-PROGRESSIVE
GET YOUR HOME & AUTO COVERAGE ALL IN ONE PLACE
IMMEDIATE RESPONSE
PROGRESSIVE
Advertising Agency:
Arnold Worldwide
101 Huntington Ave
Boston, MA 02199-7603
Tel.: (617) 587-8000
Fax: (617) 587-8004
Progressive Direct

PROMUTUAL GROUP, INC.
101 Arch St
Boston, MA 02110
Mailing Address:
PO Box 55178
Boston, MA 02205-9178
Tel.: (617) 330-1755
Fax: (617) 330-1748
Toll Free: (800) 225-6168
E-mail: info@promutualgroup.com
Web Site: www.promutualgroup.com
E-Mail For Key Personnel:
President: rbrewer@promutualgroup.com
Approx. Rev.: $164,997,000
Approx. Number Employees: 160
Year Founded: 1975
Business Description:
Medical Malpractice Insurance
S.I.C.: 6331
N.A.I.C.S.: 524126
Personnel:
Richard W. Brewer *(Pres & CEO)*
Gregg L. Hanson *(COO)*
Donna Miele-Cesario *(CIO)*
Daniel Judson *(Mgr-Compliance)*
Brands & Products:
FINANCIAL INTEGRITY, PHYSICIAN LOYALTY
PROMUTUAL GROUP
Advertising Agency:
Solomon McCown & Company, Inc.
177 Milk St Ste 610
Boston, MA 02109
Tel.: (617) 695-9555
Fax: (617) 695-9505

PROTECTIVE LIFE CORPORATION
2801 Hwy 280 S
Birmingham, AL 35223-2407
Mailing Address:
PO Box 2606
Birmingham, AL 35202-2606
Tel.: (205) 879-9230
Fax: (205) 268-3196
Toll Free: (800) 866-3555
E-mail: web_feedback@protective.com
Web Site: www.protective.com
Approx. Rev.: $2,625,394,000
Approx. Number Employees: 2,315
Year Founded: 1907
Business Description:
Holding Company; Insurance Services
S.I.C.: 6311; 6321
N.A.I.C.S.: 524113; 524114
Media: 9-13-26
Distr.: Reg.
Budget Set: Dec.
Personnel:
John D. Johns *(Chm, Pres & CEO)*
Richard Joseph Bielen *(Vice Chm & CFO)*
R. Stephen Briggs *(Pres)*
Carolyn M. Johnson *(COO & Exec VP)*
David Gutierrez *(CIO)*
Carl S. Thigpen *(Chief Investment Officer & Exec VP)*
Steven G. Walker *(Chief Acctg Officer, Sr VP & Controller)*
D. Scott Adams *(Chief HR Officer & Sr VP)*
Wayne E. Stuenkel *(Chief Actuary & Sr VP)*
John Deremo *(Sr VP)*
Deborah J. Long *(Gen Counsel, Sec & Exec VP)*
Kevin J. Howard *(Chief Product Actuary & Sr VP)*
Brent E. Griggs *(Sr VP-Asset Protection)*
Carolyn King *(Sr VP-Acq & Corp Dev)*
Webster Ray *(Sr VP)*
Judy Wilson *(Sr VP-Stable Value Products)*
Donna Pharo *(Asst VP)*
Sherri Swickard *(Asst VP-Mortgage Acctg & Reporting)*
Brands & Products:
DOING THE RIGHT THING IS SMART BUSINESS.
PROTECTIVE
PROTECTIVE BENEFITS COMMUNICATIONS
PROTECTIVE EQUITY SERVICES
PROTECTIVE FINANCIAL CORPORATION
PROTECTIVE LIFE CORPORATION
PROTECTIVE LIFE INSURANCE COMPANY
Advertising Agency:
Lewis Communications
600 Corporate Pkwy Ste 200
Birmingham, AL 35242
Tel.: (205) 980-0774
Fax: (205) 437-0250

PROTECTIVE LIFE INSURANCE COMPANY
(Sub. of Protective Life Corporation)
2801 Hwy 280 S
Birmingham, AL 35223
Tel.: (205) 879-9230
Fax: (205) 268-3402
Web Site: www.protective.com
Approx. Rev.: $2,936,984,000
Approx. Number Employees: 1,833
Year Founded: 1907
Business Description:
Life & Health Insurance Services
S.I.C.: 6321; 6311
N.A.I.C.S.: 524130; 524113; 524114
Media: 6
Personnel:
John D. Johns *(Chm, Pres & CEO)*
Wayne E. Stuenkel *(Chief Actuary & Sr VP)*
Richard Joseph Bielen *(Vice Chm & CFO)*
Carolyn Johnson *(COO & Exec VP)*
Steven G. Walker *(Chief Acctg Officer, Sr VP & Controller)*
Deborah J. Long *(Gen Counsel, Sec & Exec VP)*
Carolyn King *(Sr VP-Acq & Dev)*
Judy Wilson *(Sr VP-Stable Value Products)*
Brands & Products:
DOING THE RIGHT THING IS SMART BUSINESS

PROTEGRITY HOLDINGS, INC
260 Wekiva Springs Rd
Longwood, FL 32779
Tel.: (407) 788-1717
Fax: (407) 788-0629
Toll Free: (888) 282-1761
Web Site: www.protegrityproperties.com/
Sales Range: $25-49.9 Million
Approx. Number Employees: 325
Year Founded: 1997
Business Description:
Insurance Services
S.I.C.: 6411
N.A.I.C.S.: 524210
Personnel:
D. Gene Roberts *(Pres & CEO)*
Brands & Products:
PROTEGRITY
Advertising Agency:
BlinnPR
39 W 14th St Ste 506
New York, NY 10011
Tel.: (212) 675-4777
Fax: (212) 675-5557

QUALCARE, INC.
30 Knightsbridge Rd
Piscataway, NJ 08854
Tel.: (732) 562-0833
Fax: (732) 562-2833
Toll Free: (800) 992-6613
Toll Free: (800) 254-0130
E-mail: info@qualcareinc.com
Web Site: www.qualcareinc.com
Approx. Number Employees: 400
Year Founded: 1993
Business Description:
Managed Care Organization
S.I.C.: 6321; 6411
N.A.I.C.S.: 524114; 524210
Media: 7-18-22
Personnel:
Annette Catino *(Pres & CEO)*
John J. McSorley *(CFO & Exec VP)*
Sharon Seitzman *(COO & Exec VP)*
Janet Buggle *(VP-Fin & Controller)*
Allison Hofmann *(VP-Mktg & Sls, Natl & Large Grp Accounts)*
Yvonne Attalla *(Asst VP-HR)*
Advertising Agencies:
The MWW Group
1 Meadowlands Plz 6th Fl
East Rutherford, NJ 07073
Tel.: (201) 507-9500
Fax: (201) 507-0092

Promark Direct Inc.
300 N Midland Ave Ste 2
Saddle Brook, NJ 07663-5723
Tel.: (201) 398-9000
Fax: (201) 398-9212
Toll Free: (800) 404-1900

QUINCY MUTUAL FIRE INSURANCE COMPANY
57 Washington St
Quincy, MA 02169
Tel.: (617) 770-5100
Fax: (617) 472-4503
Fax: (800) 899-7790
Toll Free: (800) 899-1116
E-mail: contactus@quincymutual.com
Web Site: www.quincymutual.com
Approx. Number Employees: 220
Year Founded: 1851
Business Description:
Home Owners, Automobile, Commercial Multi-Peril & Business Owners Insurance Services
S.I.C.: 6331; 6411
N.A.I.C.S.: 524126; 524210
Media: 2-5-19
Distr.: Reg.
Budget Set: Jan.
Personnel:
K. Douglas Briggs *(Pres & CEO)*
James J. Moran, Jr. *(Gen Counsel, Sec & Sr VP)*
Thomas A. Harris *(Treas & Sr VP)*
Kevin M. Meskell *(Exec VP)*
Steven H. Briggs *(Sr VP-Claims)*
Mark A. Giuliani *(VP-Info Sys)*
Lu-Ann R. Smith *(VP-HR)*
John P. Murphy *(Asst VP-Claims)*

Key to Media (For complete agency information see *The Advertising Red Books-Agencies* edition):
1. Bus. Publs. 2. Cable T.V. 3. Catalogs & Directories. 4. Co-op Adv. 5. Consumer Mags. 6. D.M. to Bus. Estab.7. D.M. to Consumers 8. Daily Newsp. 9. Exhibits/Trade Shows 10. Foreign 11. Infomercial 12. Internet Adv.13. Multimedia 14. Network Radio 15. Network T.V. 16. Newsp. Distr. Mags. 17. Other 18. Outdoor (Posters, Transit) 19. Point of Purchase20. Premiums, Novelties 21. Product Samples 22. Special Events Mktg. 23. Spot Radio 24. Spot T.V. 25. Weekly Newsp. 26. Yellow Page Adv.

REGENCE BLUECROSS BLUESHIELD OF OREGON
(Sub. of The Regence Group)
100 SW Market St
Portland, OR 97201
Mailing Address:
PO Box 1271
Portland, OR 97207-1271
Tel.: (503) 944-2800
Tel.: (503) 225-5336
Fax: (503) 225-5283
Fax: (503) 225-5274
Toll Free: (800) 452-7278
Web Site: www.regence.com/OR/index.jsp
Approx. Number Employees: 2,475
Year Founded: 1941
Business Description:
Medical, Dental & Life Insurance Products & Services
S.I.C.: 6321; 6311; 6331; 6411
N.A.I.C.S.: 524114; 524113; 524291; 524298; 525190
Media: 8-9-23-24-25
Distr.: Reg.
Budget Set: Jan.
Personnel:
Jared L. Short *(Pres)*
Steve Hooker *(CFO & Sr VP)*
David Clark *(Sr VP-Health Care Svcs)*
Csaba Mera *(Exec Dir-Medical)*
Michael Mudrow *(Dir-Insurance Legal Svcs & Deputy Gen Counsel)*

RELIANCE STANDARD LIFE INSURANCE COMPANY
(Holding of Delphi Financial Group, Inc.)
2001 Market St Ste 500
Philadelphia, PA 19103
Tel.: (610) 994-7800
Tel.: (267) 256-3500
Fax: (610) 994-7809
Fax: (267) 256-3543
Toll Free: (800) 321-2347
Web Site: www.rsli.com
Sales Range: $150-199.9 Million
Approx. Number Employees: 300
Year Founded: 1907
Business Description:
Life Insurance Dental Insurance & General Insurance
S.I.C.: 6311
N.A.I.C.S.: 524113
Personnel:
Lawrence E. Daurelle *(Pres & CEO)*
Robert M. Smith Jr. *(Chief Investment Officer)*
Christopher A. Fazzini *(Exec VP-Sls & Mktg)*
Andrew Orear *(VP-Sls)*
Marie Killian *(Dir-Health & Productivity Mgmt)*
Advertising Agency:
LevLane Advertising/PR/Interactive
100 Penn Sq E
Philadelphia, PA 19107
Tel.: (215) 825-9600
Fax: (215) 809-1900

RICHARDS & SUMMERS INC.
76 Broadway
Denville, NJ 07834-0068
Tel.: (973) 627-0100
Fax: (973) 627-0915
E-mail: info@richsum.com
Web Site: www.richardsandsummers.com
Approx. Sls.: $2,000,000
Approx. Number Employees: 10
Year Founded: 1963
Business Description:
Insurance Agent
S.I.C.: 6411
N.A.I.C.S.: 524210
Media: 2-26
Personnel:
William D. Richards *(Owner)*
Brands & Products:
RICHARDS & SUMMERS

RISK PLANNERS, INC.
(Sub. of Arthur J. Gallagher & Co.)
6533 Flying Cloud Dr Ste 100
Eden Prairie, MN 55344
Mailing Address:
PO Box 240
Minneapolis, MN 55440
Tel.: (800) 328-7475
Fax: (952) 914-5778
Toll Free: (800) 328-7475
E-mail: stephanie.jewett@supervalu.com
Web Site: www.riskplanners.com
Sales Range: $1-9.9 Million
Approx. Number Employees: 35
Year Founded: 1969
Business Description:
Property, Casualty & Life Insurance Services
S.I.C.: 6371; 6411
N.A.I.C.S.: 524298; 524210; 524291; 524292
Media: 8-10-22
Personnel:
Keith D. Cody *(Pres)*
Seth Rogers *(VP-Sls)*
Mark Hageness *(Mgr-Loss Prevention)*
Joel Renner *(Mgr-Acctg)*
Bob Cook *(Sr Acct Exec)*
Kathryn Lessen *(Sr Acct Exec)*
John Barber *(Sr Acct Exec)*

RLI CORP.
9025 N Lindbergh Dr
Peoria, IL 61615
Tel.: (309) 692-1000
Fax: (309) 692-1068
Toll Free: (800) 331-4929
E-mail: inquiries@rlicorp.com
Web Site: www.rlicorp.com
Approx. Rev.: $583,424,000
Approx. Number Employees: 670
Year Founded: 1965
Business Description:
Holding Company; Insurance Services
S.I.C.: 6719; 6321
N.A.I.C.S.: 551112; 524130
Advertising Expenditures: $500,000
Media: 2-4-7-8-9-10-19
Distr.: Natl.
Budget Set: Nov.
Personnel:
Jonathan E. Michael *(Pres & CEO)*
Thomas Brown *(CFO)*
Michael J. Stone *(COO & Pres-RLI & Mt. Hawley Insurance)*
Carol Jeanne Denzer *(CIO & VP)*
John E. Robison *(Chief Investment Officer & Treas)*
Kevin J Brawley *(Pres-RLI Re)*
David A. Dunn *(Pres-RLI Transportation)*
Robert J. Schauer *(Pres-Marine)*
Daniel O'Connor Kennedy *(Gen Counsel, Sec & VP)*
Thomas Carroll *(Exec VP)*
Stephen Clark *(Exec VP)*
James S. Davis *(Exec VP)*
Craig W. Kliethermes *(Sr VP-Risk Svcs)*
Jeffrey S. Wefer *(Sr VP-E & S Property)*
Victor Corso *(VP & Mgr-Global Claims)*
Nima Crotwell *(VP)*
Jeffrey D. Fick *(VP-HR)*
David Williams *(VP-Sls & Mktg)*
Paul Gagliardi *(Asst VP)*
Larry Goodson *(Asst VP-Marine)*
Phil Judson *(Asst VP)*
John Kirchhofer *(Asst VP)*
Cheri Robinson *(Asst VP)*
Sue Whittington *(Asst VP)*
Jim Baalmann *(Dir-Midwest)*
Debra Blighton *(Dir)*
Steve Daugherty *(Dir-Mktg)*
Roger Ecoff *(Dir-Natl Loss Control)*
Eric Hoadley *(Dir-Internet Content)*
Bill Muir *(Dir-Natl-Inland Marine)*
Mike Neubauer *(Dir-Casualty Underwriting)*
Linda Paul *(Dir-Risk Svcs-Property Underwriting)*
Steve Tait *(Dir-Claims)*
Nikki Collazo *(Office Mgr)*
Cindy Dohm *(Mgr-Surety Ops)*
Ed Lewis *(Mgr)*

RODNEY D. YOUNG INSURANCE
4445 W Ledbetter Dr
Dallas, TX 75236
Tel.: (214) 467-8733
Fax: (214) 333-1172
Toll Free: (800) 477-7390
E-mail: ggopinath@tcga.com
Web Site: www.rodneydyoung.com
Approx. Number Employees: 125
Year Founded: 1952
Business Description:
Auto Insurance Company
S.I.C.: 6331
N.A.I.C.S.: 524126
Media: 14-18-26

ROYAL NEIGHBORS OF AMERICA
230 16th St
Rock Island, IL 61201-8608
Tel.: (309) 788-4561
Fax: (309) 788-4561
Web Site: www.royalneighbors.org
Approx. Number Employees: 150
Year Founded: 1895
Business Description:
Life Insurance
S.I.C.: 6311; 6411
N.A.I.C.S.: 524113; 524210
Import Export
Personnel:
Brain Haynes *(CFO & Treas)*
Bruce Peterson *(Gen Counsel & Sec)*
Brands & Products:
ROYAL NEIGHBORS OF AMERICA
Advertising Agency:
HOWECreative!
217 E 2nd St
Davenport, IA 52801
Tel.: (563) 343-5075
Fax: (563) 326-0244

SAFEGUARD HEALTH ENTERPRISES, INC.
(Sub. of MetLife, Inc.)
95 Enterprise Ste 200
Aliso Viejo, CA 92656-2065
Tel.: (949) 425-4300
Fax: (948) 425-4308
Toll Free: (800) 880-1800
E-mail: info@safeguard.net
Web Site: www.safeguard.net
Sales Range: $100-124.9 Million
Approx. Number Employees: 360
Year Founded: 1974
Business Description:
Dental Insurance Benefits
S.I.C.: 6321
N.A.I.C.S.: 524114
Advertising Expenditures: $148,000
Media: 17
Brands & Products:
SAFEGUARD

SAFEWAY INSURANCE COMPANY
790 Pasquinelli Dr
Westmont, IL 60559
Tel.: (630) 887-8300
Fax: (630) 887-9101
Web Site: www.safewayins.com
Sales Range: $75-99.9 Million
Approx. Number Employees: 100
Business Description:
Automobile Insurance
S.I.C.: 6331
N.A.I.C.S.: 524126
Personnel:
William J. Parrillo *(Chm & Pres)*
Robert M. Bordeman *(CEO)*
Advertising Agency:
Glyphix Advertising
6964 Shoup Ave
West Hills, CA 91307
Tel.: (818) 704-3994
Fax: (818) 704-8850

SBLI USA MUTUAL LIFE INSURANCE COMPANY, INC.
460 W 34th St Ste 800
New York, NY 10001-2320
Tel.: (212) 356-0300
Fax: (212) 620-4099
Toll Free: (877) SBLIUSA
Toll Free: (877) 725-4872
E-mail: info@sbliusa.com
Web Site: www.sbliusa.com
E-Mail For Key Personnel:
President: vpryor@sbliusa.com
Public Relations: bfranklin@sbliusa.com
Approx. Number Employees: 250
Year Founded: 1939
Business Description:
Insurance Services
S.I.C.: 6311
N.A.I.C.S.: 524113
Media: 2-4-6-7-8-9-10-13
Distr.: Reg.
Personnel:
Evelyn Murphy *(Chm)*
Robert Damante *(CFO & Exec VP)*
Eric J. Bulis *(CIO & Exec VP-Ops)*
Debra E. Klugman *(Gen Counsel, Sec & Sr VP)*
John Vernaleken *(VP-Tech)*
Brands & Products:
A NAME YOU CAN TRUST FOR LIFE
ACTIVELIFE

Key to Media (For complete agency information see *The Advertising Red Books-Agencies* edition):
1. Bus. Publs. 2. Cable T.V. 3. Catalogs & Directories. 4. Co-op Adv. 5. Consumer Mags. 6. D.M. to Bus. Estab.7. D.M. to Consumers
8. Daily Newsp. 9. Exhibits/Trade Shows 10. Foreign 11. Infomercial 12. Internet Adv.13. Multimedia 14. Network Radio
15. Network T.V. 16. Newsp. Distr. Mags. 17. Other 18. Outdoor (Posters, Transit) 19. Point of Purchase20. Premiums, Novelties
21. Product Samples 22. Special Events Mktg. 23. Spot Radio 24. Spot T.V. 25. Weekly Newsp. 26. Yellow Page Adv.

SBLI USA Mutual Life Insurance Company, Inc. — (Continued)

BE THE DREAM
CASH DELUXE
CENTER OF INFLUENCE
CUSTOMER ADVANTAGE TERM
EASY OPTION ACCOUNT
EVERYTHING'S RIGHT ABOUT THAT
FOR PEOPLE WHO MAKE AMERICA WORK
HE/SHE/THEY'RE COVERED IF YOU'RE COVERED
LIFE INSURANCE FOR PEOPLE THAT MAKE AMERICA WORK
LUMEN
LUMENLIFE
NICKELS AND DIMES IN MASON JARS
THE POWER OF S
SAVINGS. FOR EVERY STAGE OF YOUR LIFE
SBLI USA EASY PAY
SBLI USA FINANCIAL ENPOWERMENT COMPANY
SBLI USA PAYCHECK PROTECTOR
SURVIVING FAMILY FUND
USA EASY PAY
USA FINANCIALEMPOWERMENT STORE
USA LIFE INSURANCE COMPANY
USA SUPERSTORES
YOU CAN
YOU CAN ACHIEVE YOUR DREAM
YOU CAN MAKE A DIFFERENCE
YOU CAN PLAN YOUR LIFE
YOU CAN REALIZE YOUR POWER
YOUR FIRST STEP IN FINANCIAL PLANNING

SEABRIGHT HOLDINGS, INC.

(Formerly SeaBright Insurance Holdings, Inc.)
1501 4th Ave Ste 2600
Seattle, WA 98101
Tel.: (206) 269-8500
Fax: (206) 269-8903
Web Site: www.sbic.com
Approx. Rev.: $298,520,000
Approx. Number Employees: 335
Year Founded: 2003
Business Description:
Insurance Services; Holding Company
S.I.C.: 6331; 6719
N.A.I.C.S.: 524126; 551112
Personnel:
John G. Pasqualetto *(Chm, Pres & CEO)*
Neal A. Fuller *(CFO, Sr VP & Asst Sec)*
Richard J. Gergasko *(COO)*
Marc B. Miller *(Sr VP & Chief Medical Officer)*
D. Drue Wax *(Gen Counsel, Sec & Sr VP)*
Scott H. Maw *(Sr VP)*
Richard W. Seelinger *(Sr VP-Policyholder Svcs)*
Jeffrey C. Wanamaker *(Sr VP-Underwriting)*
M. Philip Romney *(VP-Fin)*
Advertising Agency:
KCSA Strategic Communications
(Kanan, Corbin, Schupak & Aronow, Inc.)
880 3rd Ave 6th Fl
New York, NY 10022
Tel.: (212) 682-6300
Fax: (212) 697-0910

SEABRIGHT INSURANCE HOLDINGS, INC.

(Name Changed to SeaBright Holdings, Inc.)

SECURITY MUTUAL LIFE INSURANCE COMPANY OF NEW YORK

100 Court St
Binghamton, NY 13901
Tel.: (607) 723-3551
Fax: (607) 722-5622
Fax: (607) 772-2114
Toll Free: (800) 346-7171
E-mail: tlord@smlny.com
Web Site: www.smlny.com
E-Mail For Key Personnel:
President: bboyea@smlny.com
Marketing Director: gkozol@smlny.com
Sales Range: $350-399.9 Million
Approx. Number Employees: 350
Year Founded: 1886
Business Description:
Provider of Life & Group Insurance Services
S.I.C.: 6311; 6321
N.A.I.C.S.: 524113; 524114
Media: 2-7-9-26
Distr.: Direct to Consumer; Reg.
Budget Set: Oct.
Personnel:
Bruce W. Boyea *(Chm, Pres & CEO)*
Frederick L. Wortman *(Chief Compliance Officer & Exec VP-Admin)*
James M. Lynch *(Chief Actuary & VP)*
F. David Mistretta *(Gen Counsel, Sec & Exec VP)*
Susan E. Mistretta *(VP & Assoc Gen Counsel & Privacy Officer)*
George B. Kozol *(Sr VP-Mktg)*
Gregory W. Simonelli *(Sr VP-Agency)*
Kennie Lee *(Second VP-Product Dev & Actuary)*
James S. Mellema *(Second VP-Actuary)*
Linda M. Fiacco *(Second VP-Bus Sys)*
Janet M. Vanek *(Second VP-HR)*
Susan A. Inneo *(VP & Asst Gen Counsel)*
Daniel P. Foley *(VP-Mktg & Tech)*
Thomas E. Robbins *(VP-Traditional Worksite Mktg)*
Peter F. Graham *(Reg Dir)*
Michael P. Purvis *(Reg Dir)*

SECURITY PLAN LIFE INSURANCE COMPANY

(Sub. of Citizens Insurance Company of America)
205 Railroad Ave Ste 201
Donaldsonville, LA 70346
Tel.: (225) 473-8654
Fax: (225) 474-9071
E-mail: info@citizeninc.com
Web Site: www.citizeninc.com
Sales Range: $450-499.9 Million
Approx. Number Employees: 700
Year Founded: 1949
Business Description:
Life & Fire Insurance Sales
S.I.C.: 6311; 6331
N.A.I.C.S.: 524113; 524126
Media: 17
Personnel:
Rick Riley *(Pres)*
Scott Buchholtz *(Head-HR)*

THE SEIBELS BRUCE GROUP, INC.

1501 Lady St
Columbia, SC 29201
Tel.: (803) 748-2000
Fax: (803) 748-8420
Toll Free: (800) 525-8835
Web Site: www.seibels.com
Sales Range: $50-74.9 Million
Approx. Number Employees: 264
Year Founded: 1869
Business Description:
Multiple Line Property & Casualty Insurance; Servicing Carrier; Managing General Agent; Brokerage Services
S.I.C.: 6331; 6311
N.A.I.C.S.: 524126; 524113
Media: 2-5-7-8-10-13-19-20-22
Distr.: Natl.
Budget Set: Oct.
Personnel:
Rex Huggins *(Chm & CEO)*
Michael Culbertson *(Pres)*
Bryan D. Rivers *(CFO)*
S. Melinda Hydrick *(VP-IT)*
Alexa Stuart *(Dir-HR)*
Brands & Products:
FLOODXPERT
THE SEIBELS BRUCE GROUP
XSFLOOD

SELECTIVE INSURANCE GROUP, INC.

40 Wantage Ave
Branchville, NJ 07890
Tel.: (973) 948-3000
Fax: (973) 948-0292
Toll Free: (800) OIL-HEAT
E-mail: corporate.governance@selective.com
Web Site: www.selective.com
Approx. Rev.: $1,564,621,000
Approx. Number Employees: 1,900
Year Founded: 1977
Business Description:
Holding Company for Seven Property & Casualty Insurance Companies; Automobile, Property, Workers' Compensation, General Liability Insurance & Fidelity & Surety Bonds & Professional Employer Organization
S.I.C.: 6331; 6411; 6719
N.A.I.C.S.: 524126; 524210; 551112
Media: 2-17-26
Distr.: Reg.
Budget Set: Sept.
Personnel:
Gregory E. Murphy *(Chm, Pres & CEO)*
Dale A. Thatcher *(CFO & Exec VP)*
Ronald St. Clair *(CIO & Exec VP)*
Susan B. Sweeney *(Chief Investment Officer & Sr VP)*
Ronald J. Zaleski *(Chief Actuary & Exec VP)*
Douglas H. Holbrook *(Chief Claim Officer)*
Michael H. Lanza *(Gen Counsel & Exec VP)*
Jennifer DiBerardino *(Treas & Sr VP-IR)*
Steven B. Woods *(Exec VP-HR)*
Brenda Hall *(Sr VP & Dir-Field Ops)*
Anthony D. Harnett *(Sr VP & Controller)*
Andrew S. Becker *(Sr VP, Dir-Comml Pricing & Res)*
Vincent M. Senia *(Sr VP-Actuarial Reserving)*
Bonnie L. Kikkert *(VP & Mgr-Claims Ops)*
Debra A. Maizys *(Asst VP & Mgr-Actuarial)*
W. Scott Crump *(Asst VP-Property Line & Bus Mgr)*
Scott C. Betlesky *(Asst VP & Mgr-Field Ops)*
John J. Vessecchia *(Asst VP & Mgr-Auto Bus)*
Cassie S. Masone *(Mgr-Reinsurance)*
Brands & Products:
E-SELECT
RESPONSE IS EVERYTHING
SELECTIVE
SELECTPAY
Advertising Agencies:
PL Communications
417 Victor St
Scotch Plains, NJ 07076
Tel.: (908) 889-8884
Fax: (908) 889-8886
Toll Free: (800) 569-8882

St. Jacques Marketing
60 Washington St Ste 203
Morristown, NJ 07960
Tel.: (973) 829-0858
Fax: (973) 624-3836
Toll Free: (800) 708-9467

SENIOR MARKET SALES, INC.

8420 W Dodge Rd 5th Fl
Omaha, NE 68114
Tel.: (402) 397-3311
Fax: (402) 397-0455
Toll Free: (800) 786-5566
E-mail: info@seniormarketsales.com
Web Site: www.seniormarketsales.com
Approx. Number Employees: 45
Year Founded: 1982
Business Description:
Insurance & Financial Services
S.I.C.: 6411; 6099; 6371; 7319; 7389
N.A.I.C.S.: 524298; 522320; 524210; 524291; 524292; 541870; 561439; 561499; 561990
Media: 2
Personnel:
Jim Summers *(Pres)*
Milton M. Kleinberg *(CEO)*
Dan C. Drennen *(Dir-Intl Benefits & Travel Insurance)*

SENTRY GROUP

(Sub. of Sentry Insurance)
3 Carlisle Rd
Westford, MA 01886-3601
Mailing Address:
PO Box 584
Westford, MA 01886-0584
Tel.: (978) 392-7000
Fax: (978) 392-7033
Web Site: www.sentry.com
Approx. Number Employees: 200
Business Description:
Insurance Services
S.I.C.: 6411
N.A.I.C.S.: 524298
Media: 10-20-22
Distr.: Direct to Consumer; Reg.

Key to Media (For complete agency information see *The Advertising Red Books-Agencies* edition):
1. Bus. Publs. 2. Cable T.V. 3. Catalogs & Directories. 4. Co-op Adv. 5. Consumer Mags. 6. D.M. to Bus. Estab.7. D.M. to Consumers 8. Daily Newsp. 9. Exhibits/Trade Shows 10. Foreign 11. Infomercial 12. Internet Adv.13. Multimedia 14. Network Radio 15. Network T.V. 16. Newsp. Distr. Mags. 17. Other 18. Outdoor (Posters, Transit) 19. Point of Purchase20. Premiums, Novelties 21. Product Samples 22. Special Events Mktg. 23. Spot Radio 24. Spot T.V. 25. Weekly Newsp. 26. Yellow Page Adv.

Budget Set: Jan.
Personnel:
Dale R. Schuh *(Pres & CEO)*

SENTRY INSURANCE GROUP
1800 Northpoint Dr
Stevens Point, WI 54481
Tel.: (715) 346-6000
Fax: (715) 346-6770
E-mail: sentry-insurance@coredcs.com
Web Site: www.sentry-insurance.com
Approx. Number Employees: 4,000
Year Founded: 1904
Business Description:
Insurance Holding Company
S.I.C.: 6411
N.A.I.C.S.: 524210
Media: 1-2-3-6-7-8-9-18-20-23-24-25-26
Distr.: Natl.
Budget Set: Sept.
Personnel:
William J. Lohr *(Treas & Sr VP)*
Joe Fritzsche *(VP-HR)*
Brands & Products:
PAYBACK
PLAIN TALK
SENTRY INSURANCE
STRENGTH . PROTECTION . VIGILANCE

SHENANDOAH LIFE INSURANCE COMPANY
2301 Brambleton Ave SW
Roanoke, VA 24015
Mailing Address:
PO Box 12847
Roanoke, VA 24029
Tel.: (540) 985-4400
Fax: (540) 985-4444
E-mail: marketing@shenlife.com
Web Site: www.shenlife.com
Sales Range: $150-199.9 Million
Approx. Number Employees: 165
Year Founded: 1914
Business Description:
Annuity, Life & Health Insurance
S.I.C.: 6311
N.A.I.C.S.: 524113
Media: 2-7-8-10-13-22
Brands & Products:
ALTIS
LIVING LEGACY
SAFE CHOICE
SHENANDOAH LIFE INSURANCE
STARPROTECT

SIERRA HEALTH SERVICES, INC.
(Sub. of UnitedHealthcare, Inc.)
(d/b/a United HealthCare of Nevada)
2724 N Tenaya Way
Las Vegas, NV 89128-0424
Mailing Address:
PO Box 15645
Las Vegas, NV 89114-5645
Tel.: (702) 242-7000
Fax: (702) 242-7960
Web Site: www.sierrahealth.com
Approx. Rev.: $1,909,697,000
Approx. Number Employees: 3,000
Year Founded: 1984
Business Description:
Health Maintenance Organization, Life Insurance Company, Multi-Specialty Medical Group, Home Health Care Company, Hospice & Benefits Consulting Service
S.I.C.: 6321
N.A.I.C.S.: 524114
Media: 2-3-5-7-8-9-17-18-20-23-24-25
Distr.: Natl.; Reg.
Personnel:
Tom Giancurfil *(Pres & COO)*
Robert L. Schaich *(CIO & VP-IT)*
Joseph A. Kaufman *(VP-Medical Affairs & Chief Medical Officer)*
William R. Godfrey *(Exec VP-Admin Svcs)*
Marie H. Soldo *(Exec VP-Govt Affairs & Special Projects)*
Donald J. Giancursio *(Sr VP-Sls & Mktg)*
Carmel Fritz *(VP-HR)*
Paul H. Palmer *(Controller & Asst VP)*
Joy Alexander *(Sr Brand Mgr)*
Brands & Products:
SIERRA HEALTH SERVICE INC.

SIGNATURE GROUP HOLDINGS, INC.
(Formerly Fremont General Corporation)
15305 Ventura Blvd Ste 1600
Sherman Oaks, CA 91403
Tel.: (805) 409-4340
Sales Range: $1-9.9 Million
Year Founded: 1963
Business Description:
Financial Holding Company
S.I.C.: 6712; 6029; 6159
N.A.I.C.S.: 522292; 522110; 522298; 551111
Media: 1-2-4-7-8-10-20-22-26
Distr.: Reg.
Budget Set: Oct.
Personnel:
Stephen H. Gordon *(Chm)*
Kyle C. Ross *(Interim CFO & Exec VP)*
David Collett *(Treas & Sr VP)*
David N. Brody *(Sr VP & Sec)*
Ronald J. Nicolas, Jr. *(Exec VP & Dir-Corp Dev)*

SOLERA HOLDINGS, INC.
15030 Ave of Science Ste 100
San Diego, CA 92128
Tel.: (858) 724-1600
Tel.: (925) 866-1100
Toll Free: (888) 776-5372
Toll Free: (888) 7-SOLERA
Web Site: www.soleraInc.com
Approx. Rev.: $631,348,000
Approx. Number Employees: 2,202
Year Founded: 2005
Business Description:
Automobile Insurance Claims Processing Software & Services
S.I.C.: 7372; 6411
N.A.I.C.S.: 511210; 334611; 524291; 524298
Advertising Expenditures: $4,775,000
Personnel:
Tony Aquila *(Founder, Chm & CEO)*
Renato C. Giger *(CFO)*
Jason Brady *(Gen Counsel & Sr VP)*
Doug Linn *(Sr VP-Global HR)*
Kamal Hamid *(Dir-IR)*

SOUTH CAROLINA FARM BUREAU MUTUAL INSURANCE COMPANY
724 Knox Abbott Dr
Cayce, SC 29033-3340
Tel.: (803) 796-6700
Fax: (803) 936-4629
Web Site: www.scfbins.com
Approx. Number Employees: 250
Year Founded: 1955
Business Description:
Provider of Insurance Services
S.I.C.: 6331
N.A.I.C.S.: 524126
Personnel:
Carl Derrick *(VP-Sls)*
Brands & Products:
FARM BUREAU
HELPING YOU IS WHAT WE DO BEST
Advertising Agency:
Jackson Marketing Group
2 Task Ct
Greenville, SC 29607
Tel.: (864) 272-3000
Fax: (864) 272-3040

SOUTHWESTERN LIFE INSURANCE COMPANY
(Sub. of Swiss Reinsurance America Corporation)
8616 Freeport Pkwy
Irving, TX 75063-2575
Tel.: (469) 499-1300
Fax: (803) 333-7833
Toll Free: (800) 792-4368
Approx. Sls.: $250,000,000
Approx. Number Employees: 200
Year Founded: 1903
Business Description:
Life Insurance Company
S.I.C.: 6311
N.A.I.C.S.: 524113
Media: 2-6-7-8-9-20-23-25
Distr.: Natl.
Budget Set: Sept.
Brands & Products:
SOUTHWESTERN

STAHL & ASSOCIATES INSURANCE
110 Carillon Pkwy
Saint Petersburg, FL 33716
Tel.: (727) 391-9791
Fax: (727) 393-5623
Web Site: www.stahlinsurance.com
Approx. Sls.: $9,000,000
Approx. Number Employees: 40
Business Description:
Insurance Brokerage Services
S.I.C.: 6411
N.A.I.C.S.: 524210
Media: 6
Personnel:
Robert Stahl *(Pres)*
Bob Bowles *(Pres-Lake Mary Div)*
Susan Brown *(Sr VP)*
Ken Williams *(Sr VP)*
Chuck Davies *(VP-Sls)*
Sandie Grimes *(VP-Sls)*
Michael A. Pagano *(Asst VP-Sls)*
Debbie Beausoleil *(Mgr-Personal Lines)*

STANDARD INSURANCE COMPANY
(Sub. of StanCorp Financial Group, Inc.)
1100 SW 6th Ave
Portland, OR 97204
Tel.: (971) 321-7000
Fax: (971) 321-6776
E-mail: vtm@standard.com
Web Site: www.standard.com
Sales Range: $1-4.9 Billion
Approx. Number Employees: 2,679
Year Founded: 1906
Business Description:
Life & Disability Insurance; Retirement Plans; Dental Insurance
S.I.C.: 6311; 6321
N.A.I.C.S.: 524113; 524114
Advertising Expenditures: $800,000
Media: 1-2-5-7-8-9-10-16-22-25-26
Distr.: Natl.
Budget Set: Oct.
Personnel:
Gregg Ness *(Chm)*
J. Gregory Ness *(Pres & CEO)*
Floyd F. Chadee *(CFO & Sr VP)*
Michael T. Winslow *(Gen Counsel, Sec & VP)*
Katherine Durham *(VP-Mktg & Comm)*
Karen Weisz *(VP-HR & Corp Svcs)*
Mike Dunst *(Asst VP-Absence Mgmt)*
Julie A. Grandstaff *(Asst VP-Securities)*
Brands & Products:
ADMINEASE
ADVANCED RATE ANNUITY
BALANCED CARE
THE BUSINESS EQUITY PROTECTOR
THE BUSINESS PROTECTOR
CONSOLIDATED DISABILITY
E-CONTRACT DOCUMENTS
ESSENTIALTD
EXECUTIVE BENEFITS INCOME PROTECTION
HELPING PEOPLE GET BACK TO WORK
HIGH/LOW OPTIMA CARE
INTELLIDENT
INTELLIDENT PLUS
MEDICAL EXPENSE BENEFIT
OPTIMACARE
PLAN TODAY FOR A SECURE TOMORROW
PLANNET
PRODUCER HOTLINK
THE PROTECTOR
REPORTS ONLINE
SST
STANCORP MORTGAGE INVESTORS
THE STANDARD. . . IN EMPLOYEE BENEFITS
THE STANDARD CONNECTION
STANDARD INSURANCE COMPANY
THE STANDARD SECURECARD
TRANSITIONAL DUTY PACKAGE
Advertising Agency:
HMH
1800 SW 1st Ave Ste 250
Portland, OR 97201
Tel.: (503) 295-1922
Fax: (503) 295-1938
Toll Free: (800) 350-9355

Key to Media (For complete agency information see *The Advertising Red Books-Agencies* edition):
1. Bus. Publs. 2. Cable T.V. 3. Catalogs & Directories. 4. Co-op Adv. 5. Consumer Mags. 6. D.M. to Bus. Estab.7. D.M. to Consumers 8. Daily Newsp. 9. Exhibits/Trade Shows 10. Foreign 11. Infomercial 12. Internet Adv.13. Multimedia 14. Network Radio 15. Network T.V. 16. Newsp. Distr. Mags. 17. Other 18. Outdoor (Posters, Transit) 19. Point of Purchase20. Premiums, Novelties 21. Product Samples 22. Special Events Mktg. 23. Spot Radio 24. Spot T.V. 25. Weekly Newsp. 26. Yellow Page Adv.

STANDARD LIFE & ACCIDENT INSURANCE COMPANY
(Sub. of American National Insurance Company)
2450 S Shore Blvd
League City, TX 77573
Tel.: (281) 538-3288
Fax: (281) 538-3393
Toll Free: (888) 290-1085
Web Site: www.slaico.com
Sales Range: $25-49.9 Million
Approx. Number Employees: 40
Year Founded: 1976
Business Description:
Life, Accident & Health Insurance
S.I.C.: 6321; 6311
N.A.I.C.S.: 524114; 524113
Media: 2-4-5-6-8-9-10
Distr.: Direct to Consumer; Intl.; Natl.
Budget Set: Oct.
Personnel:
G. Richard Ferdinantsen *(Chm, Pres & COO)*
Debra R. Knowles *(VP-Mktg)*

STANDARD SECURITY LIFE INSURANCE COMPANY OF NEW YORK
(Holding of Independence Holding Company)
485 Madison Ave
New York, NY 10022-5872
Tel.: (212) 355-4141
Fax: (212) 754-3346
E-mail: information@sslicny.com
Web Site: www.sslicny.com
Approx. Number Employees: 350
Year Founded: 1958
Business Description:
Insurance Services
S.I.C.: 6311; 6321
N.A.I.C.S.: 524113; 524114
Advertising Expenditures: $1,200,000
Media: 2-4-5-7-8-9-10-13-20-26
Distr.: Natl.
Budget Set: Oct.
Personnel:
Gary J. Balzofiore *(Sr VP)*

STATE AUTOMOBILE MUTUAL INSURANCE COMPANY
518 E Broad St
Columbus, OH 43215
Tel.: (614) 464-5000
Fax: (888) 999-8095
Toll Free: (800) 444-9950
Web Site: www.stateauto.com
Sales Range: $1-4.9 Billion
Approx. Number Employees: 2,000
Year Founded: 1921
Business Description:
Property & Casualty Insurance
S.I.C.: 6331; 6411
N.A.I.C.S.: 524126; 524210
Advertising Expenditures: $50,000
Media: 17
Distr.: Reg.
Budget Set: Oct.
Personnel:
Robert P. Restrepo, Jr. *(Chm, Pres & CEO)*
Steven E. English *(CFO & VP)*
Clyde H. Fitch, Jr. *(Chief Sls Officer & Sr VP)*
Cynthia A. Powell *(Chief Acctg Officer, Treas & VP)*
Nancy Edwards *(Chief Security Officer-Continuity Plan Officer & VP)*
Richard L. Miley *(Pres-BroadStreet Capital Partners)*
James A. Yano *(Gen Counsel, Sec & VP)*
Doug E. Allen *(VP & Dir-IT)*
Joel E. Brown *(VP & Dir-Personal Insurance)*
David W. Dalton *(VP & Dir-Audit)*
Steven P. Hazelbaker *(VP & Dir-Corp Enterprise Risk Mgmt)*
John B. Melvin *(VP & Dir-Claims)*
Cathy B. Miley *(VP & Dir-Corp Dev)*
Paul E. Nordman *(VP & Dir-Bus Insurance)*
John M. Petrucci *(VP & Dir-Sls)*
Jean Reynolds *(VP & Dir-Mktg)*
Lyle D. Rhodebeck *(VP & Dir-Operational Effectiveness)*
Lorraine Siegworth *(VP & Dir-Strategy)*
Larry D. Williams *(VP & Dir-Middle Market Ops)*
Terrence P. Higerd *(VP & Mgr-Data Center Construction Program)*
Winford L. Logan *(Dir-Corp Comm)*

STATE FARM MUTUAL AUTOMOBILE INSURANCE CO.
1 State Farm Plz
Bloomington, IL 61710-0001
Tel.: (309) 766-2311
Fax: (309) 766-2239
E-mail: info@statefarm.com
Web Site: www.statefarm.com
Approx. Premiums: $32,064,000,000
Approx. Number Employees: 68,000
Year Founded: 1922
Business Description:
Automobile & Fire Insurance; Mutual Funds, Banking & Financial Service Products
S.I.C.: 6331; 6321
N.A.I.C.S.: 524126; 524114
Advertising Expenditures: $200,000,000
Media: 2-3-5-6-9-14-15-23-24-26
Distr.: Direct to Consumer; Natl.
Budget Set: Nov.
Personnel:
Edward B. Rust, Jr. *(Chm, Pres & CEO)*
Vincent J. Trosino *(Vice Chm, Pres & COO)*
James E. Rutrough *(Vice Chm & Chief Admin Officer)*
Michael C. Davidson *(Vice Chm, Chief Agency & Mktg Officer)*
Pam El *(Chief Admin Officer & Exec VP)*
Brian V. Boyden *(Exec VP)*
Willie Brown *(Exec VP)*
Barbara Cowden *(Exec VP)*
Deborah Traskell *(Sr VP)*
Mark Gibson *(Asst VP-Advertising)*
Edward Gold *(Dir-Adv)*
Angela French *(Mgr-Zone Mktg)*
Karen Noel *(Mgr-Adv)*
Jennifer Holland *(Analyst-Mktg)*
Brands & Products:
STATE FARM BANK
STATE FARM INSURANCE
STATEFARM.COM
Advertising Agencies:
Draftfcb
101 E Erie St
Chicago, IL 60611-2812
Tel.: (312) 425-5000
Fax: (312) 425-5010

interTrend Communications, Inc.
555 E Ocean Blvd
Long Beach, CA 90802-5003
Tel.: (562) 733-1888
Fax: (562) 733-1889
Asian

OMD Chicago
225 N Michigan Ave 19th Fl
Chicago, IL 60601-7757
Tel.: (312) 324-7000
Fax: (312) 324-8201
Media

SURVIVAL INSURANCE INC.
600 N Brand Blvd 3rd Fl
Glendale, CA 91203
Tel.: (818) 502-8200
Fax: (323) 908-9655
Toll Free: (888) SURVIVAL
E-mail: public-relations@survivalinsurance.com
Web Site: www.survivalinsurance.com
Approx. Number Employees: 400
Year Founded: 1983
Business Description:
Insurance Services
S.I.C.: 6411
N.A.I.C.S.: 524210
Import Export
Media: 8-24
Personnel:
Susan McFarlane *(Owner)*
Sue Onorato *(Pres)*
Richard J. Acunto *(CEO)*
James E. Owen *(CIO)*

SWISS REINSURANCE AMERICA CORPORATION
(Sub. of Swiss Re America Holding Corp.)
175 King St
Armonk, NY 10504
Tel.: (914) 828-8000
Fax: (914) 828-7000
E-mail: info@swissre.com
Web Site: www.swissre.com
Approx. Number Employees: 1,000
Year Founded: 1923
Business Description:
Insurance Services
S.I.C.: 6331
N.A.I.C.S.: 524126
Media: 2
Distr.: Natl.
Brands & Products:
NORTH AMERICAN REASSURANCE
Advertising Agency:
Marquardt & Roche and Partners
5 High Ridge Pk
Stamford, CT 06905
Tel.: (203) 327-0890
Fax: (203) 353-8487

TEACHERS INSURANCE & ANNUITY ASSOCIATION - COLLEGE RETIREMENT EQUITIES FUND
(d/b/a TIAA-CREF)
730 3rd Ave
New York, NY 10017-3206
Tel.: (212) 490-9000
Fax: (212) 916-4840
Toll Free: (800) 842-2252
Web Site: www.tiaa-cref.org
E-Mail For Key Personnel:
Public Relations: scohenglass@tiaa-cref.org
Approx. Managed Assets: $414,600,000,000
Approx. Number Employees: 7,500
Business Description:
Holding Company; Pensions & Retirement Annuities, Insurance, Investment & Other Financial Services
S.I.C.: 6311; 6371
N.A.I.C.S.: 551112; 523999; 524298; 525110; 525190; 525990
Media: 1-2-3-6-7-8-9-11-13-14-15-18-20-22-25
Distr.: Natl.
Budget Set: Dec.
Personnel:
Roger W. Ferguson, Jr. *(Pres & CEO)*
Annabelle Bexiga *(CIO & Sr Mng Dir)*
Virginia M. Wilson *(CFO & Exec VP)*
Edward D. Van Dolsen *(COO & Exec VP)*
Constance Kruse Weaver *(CMO & Exec VP)*
Brandon C. Becker *(Chief Legal Officer & Exec VP)*
Scott C. Evans *(Exec VP-Asset Mgmt)*
Stephen B. Gruppo *(Exec VP-Risk Mgmt)*
Dermot J. O'Brien *(Exec VP-HR)*
Brian Bohaty *(Sr VP-Institutional & Individual Ops)*
Delia de Lisser *(Exec Dir-Adv & Brand Mgmt)*
Brands & Products:
FINANCIAL SERVICES FOR THE GREATER GOOD
Advertising Agencies:
Digitas, Inc.
355 Park Ave S
New York, NY 10010-1706
Tel.: (212) 610-5000
Fax: (212) 350-7850

KRT Marketing
3685 Mt Diablo Blvd Ste 255
Lafayette, CA 94549-3776
Tel.: (925) 284-0444
Fax: (925) 284-0448
Recruitment

TargetCast tcm
909 3rd Ave 31st Fl
New York, NY 10022
Tel.: (212) 500-6900
Fax: (212) 500-6880

TELETRACK, INC.
(Sub. of First Advantage Corporation)
The Summit at Technology Park
5550-A Peach Tree Pwy Ste 600
Norcross, GA 30092
Tel.: (770) 449-8809
Fax: (770) 449-6647
Toll Free: (800) 729-6981
Web Site: www.teletrack.com
Sales Range: $50-74.9 Million
Approx. Number Employees: 70
Year Founded: 1989
Business Description:
Consumer Credit Information Services
S.I.C.: 7323; 6099; 7319; 7389
N.A.I.C.S.: 561450; 522320; 541870; 561439; 561499; 561990
Media: 2-10

Key to Media (For complete agency information see *The Advertising Red Books-Agencies* edition):
1. Bus. Publs. 2. Cable T.V. 3. Catalogs & Directories. 4. Co-op Adv. 5. Consumer Mags. 6. D.M. to Bus. Estab.7. D.M. to Consumers
8. Daily Newsp. 9. Exhibits/Trade Shows 10. Foreign 11. Infomercial 12. Internet Adv.13. Multimedia 14. Network Radio
15. Network T.V. 16. Newsp. Distr. Mags. 17. Other 18. Outdoor (Posters, Transit) 19. Point of Purchase20. Premiums, Novelties
21. Product Samples 22. Special Events Mktg. 23. Spot Radio 24. Spot T.V. 25. Weekly Newsp. 26. Yellow Page Adv.

Personnel:
Kara Akins *(CFO)*
Terry Theologides *(Gen Counsel, Sec & Sr VP)*
Jerald L. Hoerauf *(Exec VP-Corp Dev)*
Michael A. Rasic *(Sr VP-Fin & Acctg)*
Mark Hutton *(VP-IT)*
Katie Bryson *(Mktg Dir)*

THRIVENT FINANCIAL FOR LUTHERANS
625 4th Ave S
Minneapolis, MN 55415-1624
Tel.: (612) 340-7000
Tel.: (612) 340-7215
Fax: (612) 340-8389
Toll Free: (800) 847-4836
Toll Free: (800) THRIVENT
Web Site: www.thrivent.com
Approx. Rev.: $6,524,745,802
Approx. Number Employees: 3,009
Year Founded: 1917
Business Description:
Life, Disability Income Insurance, Universal Life, Mutual Funds & Variable Universal Life Services
S.I.C.: 6311; 6331
N.A.I.C.S.: 524113; 525190
Advertising Expenditures: $9,470,000
Media: 2-6-8-9-13-20-22-26
Distr.: Natl.
Budget Set: Sept.
Personnel:
Kurt M. Senske *(Chm)*
Bradford L. Hewitt *(CEO)*
Randall L. Boushek *(CFO & Sr VP)*
Holly J. Morris *(CIO, Sr VP-Corp & IT Svcs)*
Jon M. Stellmacher *(Chief Admin Officer & Exec VP)*
Russell W. Swansen *(Chief Investment Officer & Sr VP)*
Teresa J. Rasmussen *(Gen Counsel, Sec & Sr VP)*
Pamela J. Moret *(Exec VP-Strategic Dev)*
James A. Thomsen *(Exec VP)*
Timothy J. Lehman *(Sr VP-Mktg)*
Jennifer H. Martin *(Sr VP)*
Marie A. Uhrich *(Sr VP-Comm)*
Piper Jaffray *(Mng Dir-Comm)*
Mark Anema *(VP-Accumulation & Retirement Income Solutions)*
Stacy Hanley *(Dir-Community Rels)*
Ann Koplin *(Dir-Annuity Product Mktg)*
Beth Larson *(Dir-Strategic Mktg)*
John Vekich *(Dir)*
Matthew Finn *(Sr Mgr-Equity Portfolio)*
David Heupel *(Mgr-Portfolio)*
Connie Posselt *(Trust Mktg Coord)*
Brands & Products:
LET'S THRIVE
LIFEMAP
LUTHERAN BROTHERHOOD
SIMPLY GIVING
THRIVENT FINANCIAL FOR LUTHERANS
THRIVENT MAGAZINE
WHERE VALUES THRIVE

TRANSAMERICA INSURANCE & INVESTMENT GROUP
(Sub. of AEGON N.V.)
1150 S Olive St
Los Angeles, CA 90015-2211
Tel.: (213) 742-2111
Fax: (213) 746-7025
E-mail: tii.customerservice@transamerica.com
Web Site: www.transamerica.com
Approx. Number Employees: 1,500
Year Founded: 1906
Business Description:
All Forms of Life, Accident & Group Insurance; Design, Underwriting, Sales & Service of Life Insurance, Pension Products, Reinsurance, Structured Settlements, Annuities & Investment Products, Long Term Care
S.I.C.: 6411
N.A.I.C.S.: 524210
Media: 1-2-6-7-8-25
Distr.: Intl.; Natl.
Budget Set: July
Personnel:
Bill Tate *(CMO & Exec VP)*
Brands & Products:
TRANSAMERICA PYRAMID
Advertising Agency:
Hauser Advertising Inc.
309 Bellino Dr
Pacific Palisades, CA 90272
Tel.: (310) 459-5911
Fax: (310) 459-5919

TRANSAMERICA LIFE & PROTECTION
(Formerly AEGON Direct Marketing Services, Inc.)
(Sub. of AEGON USA, Inc.)
520 Pk Ave
Baltimore, MD 21201
Tel.: (410) 685-5500
Fax: (410) 209-5902
Web Site: www.aegondms.com
Approx. Number Employees: 405
Business Description:
Life Insurance, Supplemental Health Insurance Products & Fee-Based Programs Direct Marketer
S.I.C.: 6411
N.A.I.C.S.: 524298
Media: 7-8
Personnel:
Marilyn Carp *(CEO)*
Marcia Moore *(Asst VP-Mktg)*
Advertising Agency:
David James Group
1 Trans Am Plz Dr Ste 300
Oakbrook Terrace, IL 60181
Tel.: (630) 305-0003
Fax: (630) 384-1478
Direct Solutions Group
Marketing
Message Development
Sales Collateral
Trade Show Planning & Promotions

THE TRAVELERS COMPANIES, INC.
485 Lexington Ave
New York, NY 10017
Tel.: (917) 778-6000
Toll Free: (800) 328-2189
Web Site: www.travelers.com
Approx. Rev.: $25,112,000,000
Approx. Number Employees: 32,000
Year Founded: 1853
Business Description:
Holding Company; Property & Casualty Insurance; Asset & Risk Management Services
S.I.C.: 6311; 6331
N.A.I.C.S.: 524113; 524126
Media: 2-4-7-9-10-14-26
Distr.: Natl.
Budget Set: Nov.
Personnel:
Jay S. Fishman *(Chm & CEO)*
Jay S. Benet *(Vice Chm & CFO)*
William H. Heyman *(Vice Chm & Chief Investment Officer)*
Charles J. Clarke *(Vice Chm)*
Brian W. MacLean *(Pres & COO)*
Deborah Mochon Zawisza *(Sr VP & CIO-Claim Svcs)*
Anne MacDonald *(CMO & Exec VP)*
Andy F. Bessette *(Chief Admin Officer & Exec VP)*
Alan D. Schnitzer *(Chief Legal Officer)*
Patrick Kinney *(Pres-Field Mgmt)*
Matthew S. Furman *(Sec & Sr VP & Grp Gen Counsel-Corp & Governance)*
Kenneth F. Spence, III *(Gen Counsel & Exec VP)*
Maria Olivo *(Exec VP-Strategic Dev & Treas)*
John J. Albano *(Exec VP)*
Lisa M. Caputo *(Exec VP-Mktg & Comm)*
John P. Clifford *(Exec VP-HR)*
William E. Cunningham, Jr. *(Exec VP-Bus Insurance)*
Doreen Spadorcia *(Exec VP)*
Douglas K. Russell *(Sr VP & Controller)*
Michael F. Klein *(Sr VP-Bus Insurance)*
Advertising Agencies:
Fallon Worldwide
901 Marquette Ave Ste 2400
Minneapolis, MN 55402
Tel.: (612) 758-2345
Fax: (612) 758-2346
Lead Creative Agency

MediaCom
498 7th Ave
New York, NY 10018
Tel.: (212) 912-4200
Fax: (212) 508-4386
Media Buying
Media Planning

PAN Communications
300 Brickstone Sq 7th Fl
Andover, MA 01810
Tel.: (978) 474-1900
Fax: (978) 474-1903

TRAVELERS INSURANCE
(Sub. of The Travelers Companies, Inc.)
385 Washington St
Saint Paul, MN 55102-1309
Tel.: (651) 310-7911
Web Site: www.travelers.com/corporate-info/careers/iwcm/lifeAtTravelers/stpaulDirections.aspx
Year Founded: 1981
Business Description:
Insurance Agents, Brokers & Services
S.I.C.: 6411; 6331; 6371; 6399
N.A.I.C.S.: 524298; 524126; 524128; 524210; 524291; 524292; 525190
Import Export
Personnel:
Jay Fishman *(Chm & CEO)*
Advertising Agency:
Fallon Minneapolis
901 Marquette Ave Ste 2400
Minneapolis, MN 55402
Tel.: (612) 758-2345
Fax: (612) 758-2346
Toll Free: (866) 758-2345

UNICO AMERICAN CORPORATION
23251 Mulholland Dr
Woodland Hills, CA 91364
Tel.: (818) 591-9800
Fax: (818) 591-9822
Web Site: www.crusaderinsurance.com
Approx. Rev.: $37,120,751
Approx. Number Employees: 87
Business Description:
Insurance Holding Company; Property & Casualty Insurance Services
S.I.C.: 6719; 6411
N.A.I.C.S.: 551112; 524210
Media: 2-7-8
Personnel:
Cary L. Cheldin *(Pres)*
Lester A Aaron *(CFO & Treas)*
Terry L. Kinigstein *(Gen Counsel & VP)*

THE UNION CENTRAL LIFE INSURANCE COMPANY
(Sub. of Ameritas Life Insurance Corp.)
1876 Waycross Rd
Cincinnati, OH 45240
Mailing Address:
PO Box 40888
Cincinnati, OH 45240
Tel.: (513) 595-2200
Fax: (513) 595-2918
Toll Free: (800) 825-1551
Web Site: www.unioncentral.com
E-Mail For Key Personnel:
President: jjacobs@unioncentral.com
Sales Range: $500-549.9 Million
Approx. Number Employees: 826
Year Founded: 1867
Business Description:
Life Insurance, Annuities & Disability Income Insurance Products & Services
S.I.C.: 6311; 6331; 6371; 6411
N.A.I.C.S.: 524113; 524298; 525110; 525190
Advertising Expenditures: $150,000
Media: 2-15-17-18-22
Distr.: Natl.
Budget Set: Oct.
Personnel:
Mark Perlman *(Sr VP-Field Sls)*
Dave Shaver *(Assoc VP-Actuary Dept)*

UNITED AMERICAN INSURANCE COMPANY
(Sub. of Torchmark Corporation)
3700 S Stonebridge Dr
McKinney, TX 75070-5934
Tel.: (972) 529-5085
Fax: (972) 569-3709
Web Site: www.unitedamerican.com
Sales Range: $400-449.9 Million
Approx. Number Employees: 630
Business Description:
Medicare Supplement Insurance
S.I.C.: 6311; 6321
N.A.I.C.S.: 524113; 524114
Advertising Expenditures: $1,000,000
Media: 9-14-15-23-24-25
Personnel:
Andrew W. King *(Pres)*

UNITED FIRE & CASUALTY COMPANY
118 2nd Ave SE
Cedar Rapids, IA 52401-1212
Mailing Address:
PO Box 73909
Cedar Rapids, IA 52407-3909
Tel.: (319) 399-5700
Fax: (319) 399-5499
Web Site: www.unitedfiregroup.com
Approx. Rev.: $591,072,000
Approx. Number Employees: 640
Year Founded: 1946
Business Description:
Property, Casualty & Life Insurance Services
S.I.C.: 6399; 6321; 6331
N.A.I.C.S.: 524128; 524114; 524126
Media: 2-10-22-24-26
Personnel:
Jack B. Evans *(Chm)*
John A. Rife *(Vice Chm)*
Randy A. Ramlo *(Pres & CEO)*
Dianne M. Lyons *(CFO & VP)*
Barrie W. Ernst *(Chief Investment Officer & VP)*
David E. Conner *(Chief Claims Officer & VP)*
Neal R. Scharmer *(Gen Counsel & VP)*
Michael T. Wilkins *(Exec VP-Corp Admin)*
Timothy G. Spain *(VP-HR)*
Brad M. Sayre *(Mgr)*

UNITED INSURANCE HOLDINGS CORP.
360 Central Ave Ste 900
Saint Petersburg, FL 33701
Tel.: (727) 895-7737
Web Site: www.upcic.com
Approx. Rev.: $79,991,000
Approx. Number Employees: 46
Year Founded: 2007
Business Description:
Holding Company; Property & Casualty Insurance Products & Services
S.I.C.: 6719; 6331; 6411
N.A.I.C.S.: 551112; 524126; 524291; 524298
Advertising Expenditures: $783,000
Personnel:
Gregory C. Branch *(Chm)*
Gordon G. Pratt *(Vice Chm)*
Donald J. Cronin *(Pres & CEO)*
Nicholas W. Griffin *(CFO)*
Melvin A. Russell, Jr. *(Sec, Chief Underwriting Officer & Sr VP)*

UNITED SERVICES AUTOMOBILE ASSOCIATION
(d/b/a USAA)
9800 Fredericksburg Rd
San Antonio, TX 78288-0001
Tel.: (210) 498-2211
Fax: (800) 531-8877
Toll Free: (800) 531-8722
Web Site: www.usaa.com
Approx. Rev.: $17,946,000,000
Approx. Number Employees: 22,600
Year Founded: 1922
Business Description:
Financial Planning, Insurance, Investment, Banking & Other Services Primarily to Military Personnel
S.I.C.: 6331; 6289; 6311; 8742; 8748
N.A.I.C.S.: 524126; 523999; 524113; 541611; 541618
Personnel:
John H. Moellering *(Chm)*
Josue Robles, Jr. *(Pres & CEO)*
Kristi Matus *(CFO & Exec VP)*
Roger Adams *(CMO)*
Kevin J. Bergner *(Chief Admin Officer & Exec VP)*
Steven A. Bennett *(Gen Counsel, Sec & Exec VP)*
Elizabeth D. Conklyn *(Exec VP-Special Projects)*
Shon Manasco *(Exec VP-People Svcs)*
Wayne Peacock *(Exec VP-Member Experience)*
Stephen M. Speakes *(Exec VP-Enterprise Strategy & Plng)*
Wendi E. Strong *(Exec VP-Corp Comm)*
Advertising Agencies:
Campbell-Ewald
30400 Van Dyke Ave
Warren, MI 48093-2368
Tel.: (586) 574-3400
Fax: (586) 575-9925
(Creative, Media Planning & Buying)

Deutsch, Inc.
(A Lowe & Partners Company)
111 8th Ave 14th Fl
New York, NY 10011-5201
Tel.: (212) 981-7600
Fax: (212) 981-7525

UNITED STATES AIRCRAFT INSURANCE GROUP
(Sub. of General Reinsurance Corporation)
199 Water St
New York, NY 10038-3526
Tel.: (212) 952-0100
Fax: (212) 349-8226
Web Site: www.usau.com
Sales Range: $150-199.9 Million
Approx. Number Employees: 300
Year Founded: 1928
Business Description:
Aviation Insurance
S.I.C.: 6331
N.A.I.C.S.: 524126
Media: 10
Distr.: Natl.
Budget Set: Jan.
Personnel:
Michael L. Sweeney *(Pres & COO)*
Joan Ames *(Dir-Mktg)*
Paul Ratte *(Dir-Aviation Safety Programs)*

UNITEDHEALTH GROUP INCORPORATED
UnitedHealth Group Ctr 9900 Bren Rd E
Minnetonka, MN 55343
Mailing Address:
PO Box 1459
Minneapolis, MN 55440-1459
Tel.: (952) 936-1300
Fax: (952) 936-7430
E-mail: Investor_Relations@uhc.com
Web Site:
www.unitedhealthgroup.com
Approx. Rev.: $94,155,000,000
Approx. Number Employees: 87,000
Year Founded: 1977
Business Description:
Holding Company; Commercial & Individual Health Plans, Insurance & Specialized Care Services
S.I.C.: 6321; 6311; 6719
N.A.I.C.S.: 524114; 524113; 524130; 551112
Media: 2-3-6-7-8-9-10-13-15-17-18-20-22-23-24-26
Distr.: Direct to Consumer; Natl.
Personnel:
Richard T. Burke, Sr. *(Chm)*
Stephen J. Hemsley *(Pres & CEO)*
Kate Rubin *(Pres & VP-Social Responsibility)*
David S. Wichmann *(CEO & Exec VP)*
George L. Mikan, III *(CFO & Exec VP)*
Rich Baer *(Chief Legal Officer & Exec VP)*
Don Nathan *(Chief Comm Officer & Sr VP)*
Reed V. Tuckson *(Chief Medical Affairs Officer & Exec VP)*
Eric S. Rangen *(Chief Acctg Officer & Sr VP)*
Simon Stevens *(Pres-Global Health & Exec VP)*
Gail K. Boudreaux *(CEO-UnitedHealthcare & Exec VP)*
Christopher J. Walsh *(Exec VP & Co-Gen Counsel)*
Mitchell Zamoff *(Exec VP & Co-Gen Counsel)*
William A. Munsell *(Exec VP)*
Larry C. Renfro *(Exec VP)*
Jeannine M. Rivet *(Exec VP)*
Lori K. Sweere *(Exec VP-Human Capital)*
John S. Penshorn *(Sr VP)*
Beth Miller *(Sr Dir-The Carrot Agency)*
Lauren Mihajlov *(Dir-Social Responsibility Comm)*
Kim Mallison Thorson *(Dir-Mktg-Specialty Benefits Vision)*
Brands & Products:
AMERICHOICE
HELPING PEOPLE LIVE HEALTHIER LIVES
INGENIX
OPTUMHEALTH
OVATIONS
THERE'S SOMETHING GREATER AT WORK HERE
UNIPRISE
UNITEDHEALTH GROUP
Advertising Agencies:
Draftfcb New York
100 W 33rd St
New York, NY 10001
Tel.: (212) 885-3000
Fax: (212) 885-3300

HeadQuarters Advertising Inc.
888 Brannan St Ste 380
San Francisco, CA 94103-5607
Tel.: (415) 626-6200
Fax: (415) 626-6273

KRT Marketing
3685 Mt Diablo Blvd Ste 255
Lafayette, CA 94549-3776
Tel.: (925) 284-0444
Fax: (925) 284-0448
Recruitment

Ogilvy & Mather
(Sub. of WPP Group plc)
636 11th Ave
New York, NY 10036
Tel.: (212) 237-4000
Fax: (212) 237-5123

OLSON
1625 Hennepin Ave
Minneapolis, MN 55403
Tel.: (612) 215-9800
Fax: (612) 215-9801
Interactive
— Michael Kraabel *(Creative Dir)*

UNITRIN, INC.
1 E Wacker Dr
Chicago, IL 60601-1802
Tel.: (312) 661-4600
Fax: (312) 494-6995
E-mail: webmaster@unitrin.com
Web Site: www.unitrin.com
Approx. Rev.: $2,743,400,000
Approx. Number Employees: 7,130
Business Description:
Property & Casualty Insurance, Life & Health Insurance & Consumer Finance Services
S.I.C.: 6331
N.A.I.C.S.: 524126
Media: 17
Personnel:
Donald G. Southwell *(Chm, Pres & CEO)*
Richard Roeske *(Chief Acctg Officer & VP)*
Dennis R. Vigneau *(CFO & Sr VP)*
John M. Boschelli *(Chief Investment Officer & VP)*
Scott Renwick *(Gen Counsel, Sec & Sr VP)*
Lisa M. King *(VP-HR)*

UNITY MUTUAL LIFE INSURANCE COMPANY
507 Plumb St PO Box 5000
Syracuse, NY 13250
Tel.: (315) 448-7000
Fax: (315) 448-7100
Toll Free: (800) 836-7100
E-mail: emailus@unity-life.com
Web Site: www.unity-life.com
Sales Range: $50-74.9 Million
Approx. Number Employees: 250
Year Founded: 1903
Business Description:
Life Insurance Services
S.I.C.: 6311
N.A.I.C.S.: 524113
Media: 7-8
Distr.: Reg.
Personnel:
Patrick A. Mannion *(Chm, Pres & CEO)*
Joyce Kopcik *(CFO & VP)*
Jeanne Clarke *(COO & Exec VP)*
Jay Wason *(Gen Counsel, Sec & VP)*
Toni McFadden *(Mgr-Treas-Ops)*
Joseph Masella *(Exec VP)*
Kenneth Freedman *(VP-Sls & Mktg)*
Lynn Wilber *(VP-Audit)*
Beth Keeley *(Asst VP-Sales & Mktg)*
Gregory Sim *(Asst VP-Technical Svcs)*
Neil Strathdee *(Asst VP-Market & Product Analyst)*
Mary Nappa *(Mgr-Program)*

Key to Media (For complete agency information see *The Advertising Red Books-Agencies* edition):
1. Bus. Publs. 2. Cable T.V. 3. Catalogs & Directories. 4. Co-op Adv. 5. Consumer Mags. 6. D.M. to Bus. Estab.7. D.M. to Consumers
8. Daily Newsp. 9. Exhibits/Trade Shows 10. Foreign 11. Infomercial 12. Internet Adv.13. Multimedia 14. Network Radio
15. Network T.V. 16. Newsp. Distr. Mags. 17. Other 18. Outdoor (Posters, Transit) 19. Point of Purchase20. Premiums, Novelties
21. Product Samples 22. Special Events Mktg. 23. Spot Radio 24. Spot T.V. 25. Weekly Newsp. 26. Yellow Page Adv.

UNIVERSAL UNDERWRITERS INSURANCE COMPANY

(Sub. of Zurich Holding Company of America, Inc.)
7045 College Blvd
Overland Park, KS 66211
Tel.: (913) 339-1000
Tel.: (913) 664-4270 (Press)
Fax: (888) 734-6776
Toll Free: (800) 821-7803
E-mail: service.center@zurichna.com
Web Site: www.uuic.com
Approx. Number Employees: 1,900
Year Founded: 1922
Business Description:
Property & Casualty Insurance
S.I.C.: 6331; 6311
N.A.I.C.S.: 524126; 524113
Advertising Expenditures: $1,000,000
Media: 2-4-5-7-8-10
Distr.: Natl.
Budget Set: Nov.
Brands & Products:
UNIVERSAL UNDERWRITERS

UNUM GROUP

1 Fountain Sq
Chattanooga, TN 37402-1307
Tel.: (423) 294-1011
Fax: (423) 755-3962
Toll Free: (866) 679-3054
E-mail: mguenther@unum.com
Web Site: www.unum.com
Approx. Rev.: $10,193,200,000
Approx. Number Employees: 9,500
Year Founded: 1848
Business Description:
Holding Company
S.I.C.: 6719; 6311; 6321
N.A.I.C.S.: 551112; 524113; 524114
Media: 2-3-6-7-13
Distr.: Natl.
Budget Set: Nov.
Personnel:
Jon S. Fossel *(Chm)*
Thomas R. Watjen *(Pres & CEO)*
Richard P. McKenney *(CFO & Exec VP)*
Marco Forato *(CMO)*
Breege A. Farrell *(Chief Investment Officer & Sr VP)*
Al Riggieri *(Chief Actuary & Sr VP)*
Kevin P. McCarthy *(Pres/CEO-Unum US)*
Liston Bishop, III *(Gen Counsel & Exec VP)*
Robert O. Best *(Exec VP-Global Bus Technology, Unum Grp)*
Eileen Farrar *(Sr VP-HR)*
Thomas A.H. White *(Sr VP-IR)*
Jim Sabourin *(VP-Corp Comm)*
Mary Fortune *(Mgr-Corp Comm)*
Brands & Products:
BETTER BENEFITS AT WORK
UNUM
Advertising Agencies:
All Star Incentive Marketing, Inc.
660 Main St
Fiskdale, MA 01518
Tel.: (508) 347-7672
Fax: (508) 347-5404
Toll Free: (800) 526-8629

Verbfactory
1956 Webster St Ste 250
Oakland, CA 94612
Tel.: (415) 359-4906
Fax: (415) 449-6301

USI HOLDINGS CORPORATION

(Holding of GS Capital Partners L.P.)
555 Pleasantville Rd Ste 160 S
Briarcliff Manor, NY 10510
Tel.: (914) 749-8500
Fax: (610) 537-4500
Web Site: www.usi.biz
Sales Range: $500-549.9 Million
Approx. Number Employees: 2,900
Year Founded: 1994
Business Description:
Insurance Services
S.I.C.: 6411; 6371
N.A.I.C.S.: 524210; 524292
Media: 2-13
Personnel:
Michael J. Sicard *(Chm, Pres & CEO)*
Michael Dinkins *(CFO & Exec VP)*
Philip E. Larson, III *(COO)*
Kim van Orman *(Chief HR Officer & Sr VP)*
Ernest J. Newborn, II *(Gen Counsel, Sec & Sr VP)*
Edward J. Bowler *(Sr VP-Corp Dev)*
Robert Reers *(Sr VP-Employee Benefits)*
Brands & Products:
USI

UTG, INC.

5250 S 6th St Rd PO Box 5147
Springfield, IL 62703-5128
Tel.: (217) 241-6300
Fax: (217) 241-6578
E-mail: customer.service@utgins.com
Web Site: www.utgins.com
Approx. Rev.: $38,443,357
Approx. Number Employees: 67
Year Founded: 1994
Business Description:
Life Insurance Holding Company
S.I.C.: 6321; 6311; 6719
N.A.I.C.S.: 524130; 524113; 551112
Media: 2-4-7-10-20
Distr.: Direct to Consumer; Reg.
Personnel:
Jesse Thomas Correll *(Chm & CEO)*
James Patrick Rousey *(Pres)*
Theodore C. Miller *(CFO & Sec)*
Douglas A. Dockter *(VP-IT)*

UTICA MUTUAL INSURANCE COMPANY

(Holding of Utica National Insurance Group)
(d/b/a Utica National Insurance Group)
180 Genesee St
New Hartford, NY 13413-2299
Tel.: (315) 734-2000
Fax: (315) 734-2680
Toll Free: (800) 274-1914
Web Site: www.uticanational.com
Sales Range: $650-699.9 Million
Approx. Number Employees: 1,400
Year Founded: 1914
Business Description:
Multiple-Line Property & Casualty Insurance
S.I.C.: 6331; 6311
N.A.I.C.S.: 524126; 524113
Advertising Expenditures: $800,000
Media: 1-2-10-20-23-24
Distr.: Natl.
Budget Set: Sept.
Personnel:
J. Douglas Robinson *(Chm & CEO)*
Brian P. Lytwynec *(Pres & COO)*
Anthony C. Paolozzi *(CFO, Treas & Exec VP)*
Daniel D. Daly *(Exec VP, Sr Mktg & Profit Center Officer)*
Steven P. Guzski *(Sr VP & Dir-HR)*
Chris Eells *(Sr VP & Mgr-South Central Profit Center)*
Robert F. Manfredo *(Sr VP & Sr Underwriting Officer)*
Michael C. Austin *(VP & Dir-Corp Comm)*
William F. Krause *(Dir-Medical)*
Brands & Products:
HOMEBIZ
INSURANCE THAT STARTS WITH YOU
UTICA/GRAPHIC
UTICA NATIONAL
W.I.S.E.
Advertising Agency:
Utica Advertising Associates (Corp. Communications Dept.)
(House Agency)
Utica Natl. Insurance Grp. 180 Genesee St.
New Hartford, NY 13413
Tel.: (315) 734-2000
(Insurance)

VERISK ANALYTICS, INC.

545 Washington Blvd
Jersey City, NJ 07310-1686
Tel.: (201) 469-2000
Fax: (201) 469-4017
E-mail: info@verisk.com
Web Site: www.verisk.com
Approx. Rev.: $1,138,343,000
Approx. Number Employees: 4,706
Business Description:
Holding Company; Risk Information & Assessment Services
S.I.C.: 6719; 6411; 7389
N.A.I.C.S.: 551112; 519190; 524298
Personnel:
Frank J. Coyne *(Chm & CEO)*
Scott G. Stephenson *(Pres & COO)*
Mark V. Anquillare *(CFO & Exec VP)*
Kenneth E. Thompson *(Gen Counsel, Sec & Exec VP)*
Eva Huston *(Treas, VP-Corp Fin & Head-IR)*
Carole J. Banfield *(Exec VP-Info Svcs & Govt Rel Dept)*
Vincent Cialdella *(Sr VP-ISO)*
Kevin B. Thompson *(Sr VP-Insurance Svcs)*
Advertising Agency:
The MWW Group
1 Meadowlands Plz 6th Fl
East Rutherford, NJ 07073
Tel.: (201) 507-9500
Fax: (201) 507-0092

VERTAFORE INC.

(Formerly AMS Services, Inc.)
(Sub. of Vertafore Inc.)
7 Waterside Crossing
Windsor, CT 06095
Tel.: (860) 602-6000
Fax: (860) 602-6006
Toll Free: (800) 444-6543
E-mail: information@vertafore.com
Web Site: www.vertafore.com
Approx. Number Employees: 200
Year Founded: 1963
Business Description:
Insurance Software
S.I.C.: 7371
N.A.I.C.S.: 541511
Media: 2
Distr.: Natl.
Personnel:
Dave Acker *(VP-Sls & Mktg)*

VETERINARY PET INSURANCE CO.

3060 Saturn St
Brea, CA 92821
Tel.: (714) 989-0555
Fax: (714) 989-0557
Toll Free: (800) USA-PETS
E-mail: mediainfo@petinsurance.com
Web Site: www.petinsurance.com
Sales Range: $75-99.9 Million
Approx. Number Employees: 400
Business Description:
Pet Insurance Services
S.I.C.: 6411; 0752
N.A.I.C.S.: 524210; 115210
Media: 6-10-18
Personnel:
Dennis Drent *(Pres & CEO)*
Jonathon Kass *(VP-Ops & CIO)*
Curtis Steinhoff *(Sr Dir)*
Brent Otey *(Dir-Mktg)*
Brands & Products:
VETERINARY PET INSURANCE

VISION FINANCIAL CORPORATION

17 Church St
Keene, NH 03431-0506
Tel.: (603) 357-1450
Fax: (603) 357-0250
Toll Free: (800) 793-0223
Toll Free: (800) 635-4467
E-mail: info@visfin.com
Web Site: www.visfin.com
Sales Range: $50-74.9 Million
Approx. Number Employees: 65
Year Founded: 1989
Business Description:
Third Party Administrator for Insurance
S.I.C.: 6331
N.A.I.C.S.: 524126
Media: 2-7-8-9-10-19-25
Distr.: Natl.
Budget Set: Oct. -Nov.
Personnel:
James T. Pettapiece *(Pres)*
Corinne Bell *(VP-IT)*
Terri Frigon *(Mgr-Fin Acctg)*
Marion Holloway *(Mgr-Mktg)*
Paul A. Lepage *(Actuary)*
Brands & Products:
PARTNERSHIPS THAT WORK
VISION FINANCIAL

VREELAND INSURANCE INC.

Rockaway 80 Corp Ctr 100 Enterprise Dr Ste 501
Rockaway, NJ 07866
Tel.: (973) 334-7100
Fax: (973) 334-0980
E-mail: info@vreelandinsurance.com
Web Site: www.vreelandinsurance.com
Approx. Number Employees: 15
Year Founded: 1931
Business Description:
Insurance Services
S.I.C.: 6411
N.A.I.C.S.: 524210

Key to Media (For complete agency information see *The Advertising Red Books-Agencies* edition):
1. Bus. Publs. 2. Cable T.V. 3. Catalogs & Directories. 4. Co-op Adv. 5. Consumer Mags. 6. D.M. to Bus. Estab.7. D.M. to Consumers 8. Daily Newsp. 9. Exhibits/Trade Shows 10. Foreign 11. Infomercial 12. Internet Adv.13. Multimedia 14. Network Radio 15. Network T.V. 16. Newsp. Distr. Mags. 17. Other 18. Outdoor (Posters, Transit) 19. Point of Purchase20. Premiums, Novelties 21. Product Samples 22. Special Events Mktg. 23. Spot Radio 24. Spot T.V. 25. Weekly Newsp. 26. Yellow Page Adv.

Vreeland Insurance Inc. — (Continued)

Media: 2-26
Personnel:
Joe Merullo *(Pres)*
Barbara Hayes *(Mgr-Accts)*
Lynn Walker *(Mgr-Accts)*

WASHINGTON NATIONAL INSURANCE CO.
(Sub. of CNO Financial Group, Inc.)
11815 N Pennsylvania St
Carmel, IN 46032
Mailing Address:
PO Box 2003
Carmel, IN 46082-2003
Tel.: (317) 817-6100
Fax: (317) 817-6687
Web Site: www.conseco.com
Sales Range: $100-124.9 Million
Approx. Number Employees: 110
Business Description:
Dental & Disability Insurance
S.I.C.: 6311; 6321; 6331
N.A.I.C.S.: 524113; 524114; 525190
Advertising Expenditures: $1,000,000
Media: 2-5-6-7-8-9-20-22-23-25-26
Distr.: Natl.
Budget Set: Oct.
Personnel:
Steven M. Stecher *(Pres)*

WATTS HEALTH FOUNDATION INC.
(d/b/a UHP Healthcare)
3405 W Imperial Hwy
Inglewood, CA 90303-2219
Tel.: (310) 671-3465
Fax: (310) 412-7129
Toll Free: (800) 847-1222
Approx. Number Employees: 200
Year Founded: 1971
Business Description:
Health Maintenance Organization
S.I.C.: 8011; 8059
N.A.I.C.S.: 621491; 623110
Media: 6-8-9-25
Distr.: Direct to Consumer
Brands & Products:
CREATED JUST FOR CARING
WE BEGIN WITH U

WELCOME FUNDS, INC.
6001 Broken Sound Pkwy Ste 320
Boca Raton, FL 33487
Tel.: (561) 862-0244
Fax: (561) 862-0242
Toll Free: (877) 227-4484
E-mail: info@welcomefunds.com
Web Site: www.welcomefunds.com
Approx. Number Employees: 16
Business Description:
Life Settlement Broker
S.I.C.: 6399; 6311; 7319; 7389
N.A.I.C.S.: 524128; 524113; 541870; 561439; 561499; 561990
Media: 2
Personnel:
John M. Welcom *(Founder, Pres & CEO)*
Daniel Ohman *(COO & VP)*

WELLCARE HEALTH PLANS INC.
8725 Henderson Road Renaissance One
Tampa, FL 33634
Tel.: (813) 290-6200
Fax: (813) 262-2802
Toll Free: (800) 795-3432
Web Site: www.wellcare.com
Approx. Rev.: $5,440,225,000
Approx. Number Employees: 3,300
Year Founded: 1985
Business Description:
Hospital & Medical Plan Services
S.I.C.: 6321; 8011; 9431
N.A.I.C.S.: 524114; 621491; 923120
Import Export
Advertising Expenditures: $7,010,000
Personnel:
Alexander R. Cunningham *(CEO)*
Thomas L. Tran *(CFO & Sr VP)*
Blair W. Todt *(Chief Compliance Officer & Sr VP)*
Walter W. Cooper *(Chief Admin Officer)*
Maurice S. Hebert *(Chief Acctg Officer)*
Lawrence D. Anderson *(Chief HR Officer & Sr VP)*
Michael L. Cotton *(Pres-South Div)*
Marc S. Russo *(Pres-North Div)*
Jesse L. Thomas *(Pres-South Div)*
Timothy S. Susanin *(Gen Counsel, Sec & Sr VP)*
John C. Richter *(VP & Chief Litigation Counsel)*
Lisa G. Iglesias *(VP & Asst Gen Counsel)*
Amy Knapp *(Sr Dir-Corp Comm)*
Advertising Agency:
Schifino Lee Advertising
511 W Bay St Ste 400
Tampa, FL 33606
Tel.: (813) 258-5858
Fax: (813) 254-1146
Lead Generation
Medicare Advantage
Online Enrollment

WELLMARK, INC
636 Grand Ave
Des Moines, IA 50309-2565
Tel.: (515) 376-4500
Web Site: www.wellmark.com
Media: 17-22
Personnel:
John D. Forsyth *(Chm & CEO)*
David N. Southwell *(Exec VP, CFO & Treas)*
Denis J. Roy *(Exec VP & CIO)*
George B. Hanna *(Chief Legal Officer & Exec VP)*
Ellen J. Gaucher *(Chief Admin Officer)*
Keith W. Heckel *(Exec VP-Sls & Mktg)*
Laura Jackson *(Exec VP-Health Care Strategy & Policy)*
Richard C. Anderson *(Sr VP-Fin)*
Michele A. Druker *(VP, Assoc Gen Counsel & Asst Sec)*
Mike Crowley *(VP-Fin & Investments)*
Elaine M. Palmer *(VP-Customer & Provider Service)*
Tim Weber *(VP-Mktg)*

WELLPOINT, INC.
120 Monument Cir
Indianapolis, IN 46204-4906
Tel.: (317) 488-6000
Tel.: (317) 488-6255
Fax: (317) 488-6260
E-mail: wayne.deveydt@wellpoint.com
Web Site: www.wellpoint.com
Approx. Rev.: $58,801,800,000
Approx. Number Employees: 37,500
Year Founded: 1944
Business Description:
Holding Company; Health Insurance Services
S.I.C.: 1522; 6321; 6719
N.A.I.C.S.: 236220; 524114; 551112
Advertising Expenditures: $226,100,000
Media: 2-5-9-23
Personnel:
Angela F. Braly *(Chm, Pres & CEO)*
Wayne S. DeVeydt *(CFO & Exec VP)*
Roy Mellinger *(Chief Info Security Officer & VP-IT Security)*
Kate Quinn *(CMO & Sr VP)*
Marjorie W. Dorr *(Chief Strategy Officer)*
Randy L. Brown *(Chief HR Officer & Exec VP)*
Cynthia S. Miller *(Chief Actuary & Integration Mgmt Officer & Exec VP)*
Samuel R. Nussbaum *(Exec VP-Clinical Health Policy & Chief Medical Officer)*
Linda Jimenez *(Officer-Diversity & VP-Diversity & Inclusion)*
Brian A. Sassi *(Pres/CEO-Consumer Bus & Exec VP)*
Kenneth R. Goulet *(Pres/CEO-Comml Bus Unit)*
John Martie *(Pres/CEO-Natl Accts Bus)*
Rajeev Bal *(Pres-Individual Bus Unit)*
Krista A. Bowers *(Pres-Sr Bus & Consumer Bus Mktg)*
Kevin R. Hayden *(Pres-State Sponsored Bus)*
John M. Cannon, III *(Gen Counsel, Sec & Exec VP)*
Lori Beer *(Exec VP-Enterprise Bus Svcs)*
Bradley M. Fluegel *(Exec VP, Chief Strategy & External Affairs Officer)*
Harlan Levine *(Exec VP-Comprehensive Health Solutions)*
John E. Gallina *(Sr VP)*
Lisa M. Guertin *(Sr VP-Mktg & Product)*
Andrew J. Lang *(Sr VP-Application Dev)*
Douglas J. Wenners *(Sr VP-Provider Engagement & Contracting)*
Craig Christenson *(VP-Fin)*
Charles Kennedy *(VP-Clinical Informatics)*
S. Kristie Hamilton *(Dir-Sls & Mktg Compliance)*
Shelley Patchin *(Dir-Adv)*
Suzanne Appel *(Mgr-Internet Mktg)*
Jennifer Merrick *(Mgr-Digital Mktg)*
Brands & Products:
UNICARE
WELLPOINT
Advertising Agencies:
Deutsch LA
5454 Beethoven St
Los Angeles, CA 90066-7017
Tel.: (310) 862-3000
Fax: (310) 862-3100
(Creative, Design, Interactive)

Engauge Communications
437 Grant St
Pittsburgh, PA 15219
Tel.: (412) 471-5300
Fax: (412) 471-3308
Toll Free: (800) 937-3657

FSG Ad Partners
3 Tobey Pl
East Northport, NY 11731-2726
Tel.: (631) 368-2001
Fax: (631) 980-4040

J-U Carter, Inc.
555 N El Camino Rel St A 462
San Clemente, CA 92672
Tel.: (949) 852-5960
Fax: (949) 852-5960

Publicis & Hal Riney
2001 The Embarcadero
San Francisco, CA 94133-5200
Tel.: (415) 293-2001
Fax: (415) 293-2620

Ricochet Public Relations, Inc.
55 Broadway 7th Fl
New York, NY 10006
Tel.: (212) 679-3300
Fax: (212) 679-3348
Agency of Record

SS&K
88 Pine St 30th Fl
New York, NY 10005
Tel.: (212) 274-9500
Fax: (212) 274-9598
Toll Free: (800) 274-7765

Starcom MediaVest Group
35 W Wacker Dr
Chicago, IL 60601-1723
Tel.: (312) 220-3535
Fax: (312) 220-6530
(Media Planning/Buying)

Xpectrum Marketing Group
1953 Ainsley Rd
San Diego, CA 92123
Tel.: (619) 571-7594
Fax: (858) 277-8857

WEST COAST LIFE INSURANCE COMPANY
(Sub. of Protective Life Corporation)
343 Sansome St
San Francisco, CA 94104-1303
Mailing Address:
PO Box 193892
San Francisco, CA 94119-3892
Tel.: (415) 591-8200
Fax: (415) 433-1372
Toll Free: (800) 366-9378
E-mail: wcl.support@wclife.com
Web Site: www.westcoastlife.com
Sales Range: $50-74.9 Million
Approx. Number Employees: 120
Year Founded: 1906
Business Description:
Life Insurance Services
S.I.C.: 6311; 6321
N.A.I.C.S.: 524113; 524114
Advertising Expenditures: $200,000
Bus. Publs.: $130,000; Exhibits/Trade Shows: $10,000; Other: $10,000; Premiums, Novelties: $50,000
Distr.: Reg.
Budget Set: Oct.
Personnel:
Anil Manji *(Sr VP-Actuary)*

Key to Media (For complete agency information see *The Advertising Red Books-Agencies* edition):
1. Bus. Publs. 2. Cable T.V. 3. Catalogs & Directories. 4. Co-op Adv. 5. Consumer Mags. 6. D.M. to Bus. Estab.7. D.M. to Consumers
8. Daily Newsp. 9. Exhibits/Trade Shows 10. Foreign 11. Infomercial 12. Internet Adv.13. Multimedia 14. Network Radio
15. Network T.V. 16. Newsp. Distr. Mags. 17. Other 18. Outdoor (Posters, Transit) 19. Point of Purchase20. Premiums, Novelties
21. Product Samples 22. Special Events Mktg. 23. Spot Radio 24. Spot T.V. 25. Weekly Newsp. 26. Yellow Page Adv.

THE WESTERN & SOUTHERN FINANCIAL GROUP

400 Broadway
Cincinnati, OH 45202
Tel.: (513) 629-1800
Fax: (513) 629-1220
Toll Free: (800) 333-5222
Toll Free: (800) 936-1212
Web Site: www.westernsouthern.com
E-Mail For Key Personnel:
President: john.barrett@westernsouthernlife.com
Marketing Director: bryan.dunn@westernsouthernlife.com
Public Relations: herb.brown@westernsouthernlife.com
Sales Range: $1-4.9 Billion
Approx. Number Employees: 5,000
Year Founded: 1888
Business Description:
Life, Accident & Health Insurance Services
S.I.C.: 6719
N.A.I.C.S.: 551112
Media: 2-6-9-18-26
Distr.: Natl.
Budget Set: Oct.
Personnel:
John Finn Barrett *(Chm, Pres & CEO)*
Clint D. Gibler *(CIO & Sr VP)*
Nora E. Moushey *(Chief Actuary & Sr VP)*
Bryan C. Dunn *(Pres-W & S Agency Grp)*
Noreen J. Hayes *(Sr VP-HR)*
Edward S. Heenan *(Sr VP)*
Constance M. Maccarone *(Sr VP)*
Robert L. Walker *(Sr VP)*
Jill Ravitz *(Reg VP-Broker & Dealer Channel-W & S Fin Grp Distributors Inc)*
Advertising Agency:
Northlich
Sawyer Point Bldg 720 Pete Rose Way
Cincinnati, OH 45202
Tel.: (513) 421-8840
Fax: (513) 455-4749
Western & Southern Strength

WESTERN NATIONAL MUTUAL INSURANCE CO.

5350 W 78th St
Minneapolis, MN 55439
Tel.: (952) 835-5350
Fax: (952) 921-3163
Web Site: www.wnins.com
Sales Range: $200-249.9 Million
Approx. Number Employees: 350
Business Description:
Property Damage Insurance
S.I.C.: 6331
N.A.I.C.S.: 524126
Advertising Expenditures: $10,000
Media: 10
Personnel:
Stuart Henderson *(Pres & CEO)*
Leon Smith *(CFO)*
Mary Manley *(Sr VP-Corp Affairs & Admin)*
Brands & Products:
AGENTSONLINE
MAINSTREETXPRESS
THE RELATIONSHIP COMPANY
WESTERN NATIONAL
Advertising Agency:
Risdall Marketing Group
550 Main St
New Brighton, MN 55112-3271
Tel.: (651) 286-6700
Fax: (651) 631-2561
Toll Free: (888) RISDALL
— Ted Risdall *(Principal)*

WHITE MOUNTAINS REINSURANCE COMPANY OF AMERICA

(Sub. of White Mountains Re Group)
1 Liberty Plz
New York, NY 10006
Tel.: (212) 312-2500
Fax: (212) 312-2526
Web Site: www.wtmreamerica.com
Approx. Number Employees: 160
Business Description:
Reinsurance Services
S.I.C.: 6321
N.A.I.C.S.: 524130
Media: 2-7
Personnel:
Dwight Evans *(Pres & CEO)*
Robert Freiling *(CFO & Sr VP)*
Daniel J. Wilson *(COO)*
Faith Pipitone *(Sr VP & Chief Actuary)*
Tony Sasso *(Chief Underwriting Officer-Property Treaty)*
Robert Kuehn *(Gen Counsel & Sr VP)*
Peter Hudson *(Sr VP & Mgr-Casualty Treaty)*
Geanie Villomann *(Sr VP-HR)*
Louis Zingone *(Reinsurance Controller & Sr VP)*

WILLIS HRH, INC.

(Div. of Willis North America, Inc.)
200 Liberty St 3rd Fl
New York, NY 10281
Tel.: (212) 915-8888
Fax: (212) 915-8511
Web Site: www.willis.com
Sales Range: $750-799.9 Million
Approx. Number Employees: 4,200
Business Description:
Property, Fire, Marine & Casualty, Accident, Health & Life Insurance Services
S.I.C.: 6411; 6311; 6321; 6331; 6399
N.A.I.C.S.: 524210; 524113; 524114; 524126; 524128
Media: 2-7-10
Distr.: Natl.
Personnel:
Joe Gunn *(Partner-NY Metro Reg)*
John P. Mcgrath *(Partner-Midwest Reg)*
Derek Smyth *(CFO)*
Carolyn Jones *(Treas & Sr VP-IR)*
Les Boughner *(Exec VP)*
Timothy J. Korman *(Exec VP-Mergers & Acq)*
William L. Chaufty *(VP & Reg Dir)*
J. Thomas Stiles *(VP & Reg Dir-Southeast Reg)*
Robert P. Abramson *(VP & Dir-Excess & Surplus Lines)*
Frank H. Beard *(VP & Natl Dir-Property & Casualty)*
Karl E. Manke *(VP & Natl Dir-Select & Personal Lines)*
William C. Widhelm *(VP-Internal Audit)*
Nick Balamaci *(Exec-Internal Comm & Dir)*
Liz Cougot *(Dir-Comm)*
Brands & Products:
HRH
PROBLEM SOLVED

W.R. BERKLEY CORPORATION

475 Steamboat Rd
Greenwich, CT 06830
Tel.: (203) 629-3000
Fax: (203) 629-3073
Web Site: www.wrbc.com
Approx. Rev.: $411,623,000
Approx. Number Employees: 6,253
Year Founded: 1967
Business Description:
Holding Company; Property Casualty Insurance Services
S.I.C.: 6331; 6321
N.A.I.C.S.: 524126; 524130
Media: 2-8-9-23-25
Distr.: Natl.
Budget Set: Oct.
Personnel:
William R. Berkley *(Chm & CEO)*
W. Robert Berkley, Jr. *(Pres & COO)*
Eugene G. Ballard *(CFO & Sr VP)*
Ira S. Lederman *(Gen Counsel, Sec & Sr VP)*
Robert P. Cole *(Sr VP)*
Kevin H. Ebers *(Sr VP-IT)*
Robert W. Gosselink *(Sr VP-Insurance Risk Mgmt)*
Jeffrey M. Hafter *(Sr VP)*
Paul J. Hancock *(Sr VP)*
Robert C. Hewitt *(Sr VP)*
Gillian James *(Sr VP-Enterprise Risk Mgmt)*
Peter L. Kamford *(Sr VP)*
C. Fred Madsen *(Sr VP)*
James W. McCleary *(Sr VP-Underwriting)*
James G. Shiel *(Sr VP-Investments)*
Robert D. Stone *(Sr VP)*
Nelson Tavares *(Sr VP-Claims)*
Steven W. Taylor *(Sr VP)*
Philip S. Welt *(Sr VP)*
Josephine A. Raimondi *(VP & Asst Sec)*
Harry J. Berkley *(VP-IT)*
Karen A. Horvath *(VP-External Fin Comm)*
Joseph M. Pennachio *(VP-HR)*
Raymond J. O'Brien *(Asst VP & Dir-Internal Audit)*
Thomas P. Boyle *(Asst VP-Corp Actuarial)*
Arthur Gurevitch *(Asst VP-Analytics)*
Bryan V. Spero *(Asst VP-Corp Actuary)*
Bruce I. Weiser *(Asst VP)*
Dawn M. Callahan *(Dir-Investment Acctg)*
John S. Navratil *(Asst Dir-Tax)*
Jean P. Milot *(Asst Controller)*
George K. Richardson *(Asst Treas)*
Janet L. Shemanske *(Asst Sec)*

ZENITH MARKETING GROUP, INC.

303 W Main St Ste 200
Freehold, NJ 07728
Tel.: (732) 577-1400
Fax: (732) 577-0111
Toll Free: (800) 733-0054
E-mail: info@zenithmarketing.com
Web Site: www.zenithmarketing.com
Approx. Number Employees: 52
Business Description:
Insurance Brokerage Services
S.I.C.: 6411; 6371
N.A.I.C.S.: 524298; 524210; 524291; 524292
Media: 2-10
Personnel:
Michael Gorlick *(Pres & CEO)*
Barbara Seidel *(Partner)*
James P. Farrell *(VP-Brokerage Sls-Wayne)*
Paul Seidel *(Dir-Mktg)*

ZURICH HOLDING COMPANY OF AMERICA, INC.

(Sub. of Zurich Financial Services AG)
Zurich Towers 1400 American Ln
Schaumburg, IL 60196
Tel.: (847) 605-6000
Fax: (847) 605-6011
Toll Free: (800) 382-2150
E-mail: info_source@zurichna.com
Web Site: www.zurichna.com
Approx. Number Employees: 5,000
Business Description:
Holding Company; Commercial, Personal & Casualty Insurance Services
S.I.C.: 6719; 6331
N.A.I.C.S.: 551112; 524126
Media: 2-7
Distr.: Natl.
Personnel:
Axel P. Lehmann *(CEO)*
Tina Mallie *(Chief Admin Officer)*
Peter Rebrin *(CEO-Latin America)*

Internet/Online

1&1 INTERNET, INC.
(Sub. of United Internet AG)
701 Lee Rd Ste 300
Chesterbrook, PA 19087
Tel.: (610) 560-1500
Fax: (610) 560-1501
Toll Free: (877) GO-1AND1
E-mail: info@1and1.com
Web Site: www.1and1.com
Year Founded: 1992
Business Description:
Internet & Web Hosting Services
S.I.C.: 7375
N.A.I.C.S.: 518111
Media: 6-13
Personnel:
Andreas Gauger *(Chm)*
Oliver Mauss *(CEO)*
Elisabeth Kurek *(Head-Adv)*
Hillary Close *(Dir-Product Mktg)*

10BEST, INC.
9 Legrand Blvd
Greenville, SC 29607-2909
Tel.: (864) 241-0779
Fax: (864) 241-0917
Web Site: www.10best.com
Approx. Sls.: $2,200,000
Approx. Number Employees: 30
Year Founded: 1999
Business Description:
Internet Travel Services
S.I.C.: 7375
N.A.I.C.S.: 518111
Media: 13
Personnel:
Michael Quattlebaum *(CFO)*

123GREETINGS.COM, INC.
(Sub. of IntraSoft Technologies Limited)
1674 Broadway Ste 403
New York, NY 10019
Tel.: (212) 246-0044
Fax: (212) 202-4738
E-mail: support@123greetings.com
Web Site: www.123greetings.com
E-Mail For Key Personnel:
President: vivek@123greetings.com
Approx. Number Employees: 50
Year Founded: 1999
Business Description:
Electronic Greeting Card Service
S.I.C.: 2771
N.A.I.C.S.: 511191
Media: 13
Personnel:
Eddie Marmol *(Mgr-Bus Dev)*

2WIRE, INC.
(Sub. of Pace plc)
(d/b/a Pace Americas-San Jose)
1704 Automation Pkwy
San Jose, CA 95131-1873
Tel.: (408) 428-9500
Fax: (408) 428-9590
Web Site: www.pace.com
Sales Range: $200-249.9 Million
Approx. Number Employees: 475
Year Founded: 1998
Business Description:
Broadband Products & Services for the Residential Marketplace
S.I.C.: 5065; 5045
N.A.I.C.S.: 423690; 423430
Media: 2-4-7-13
Personnel:
Mike Talley *(Exec VP & Gen Mgr)*
Steve Maher *(VP-Engrg)*
Brands & Products:
FULLPASS
GATEWAY MEDIC
GEM AMETHYST
GEM EMERALD
GEM RUBY
GEM SAPPHIRE
GEM TOPAZ
GREENLIGHT
GUESTPASS
HOMEPORTAL
HOMEPORTAL GEM
HYPERG
INID
MEDIAPOINT
MEDIAPORTAL
MEDIASCOUT
OFFICEPORTAL

4NANNIES.COM, INC.
2 Pidgeon Hill Dr Ste 550
Potomac Falls, VA 20165
Tel.: (703) 404-8151
Fax: (703) 404-8155
Toll Free: (800) 810-2611
E-mail: support@4nannies.com
Web Site: www.4nannies.com
Approx. Number Employees: 10
Year Founded: 1998
Business Description:
Nanny & Family Job Matching Services
S.I.C.: 2741; 7361
N.A.I.C.S.: 516110; 561310
Media: 13
Personnel:
Kathleen Webb *(Co-founder & Mng Partner)*

4SURE.COM, INC.
(Sub. of Office Depot, Inc.)
6 Cambridge Dr
Trumbull, CT 06611-4746
Tel.: (203) 615-7000
Fax: (203) 615-7055
E-mail: custcare@4sure.com
Web Site: www.4sure.com
Sales Range: $25-49.9 Million
Approx. Number Employees: 130
Year Founded: 1998
Business Description:
Direct Marketer of Computer & Technology Products to Businesses & Consumers
S.I.C.: 5734; 5045
N.A.I.C.S.: 443120; 423430
Media: 4-7-8
Brands & Products:
COMPUTERS4SURE.COM

A BOOK COMPANY, LLC
(d/b/a ecampus.com)
2415 Palumbo Dr
Lexington, KY 40509-1116
Tel.: (859) 514-5200
Fax: (859) 514-6827
Toll Free: (888) 388-9909
E-mail: eservice@ecampus.com
Web Site: www.ecampus.com
Approx. Number Employees: 65
Year Founded: 2001
Business Description:
Online Retailer of College Textbooks, Trade, Consumer & Other Books & College Related Items
S.I.C.: 5942
N.A.I.C.S.: 451211
Media: 13
Personnel:
Barry Kern *(VP-Partner Svcs)*
Andrew Aquart *(Dir-Product Devel)*

ABOUT, INC.
(Sub. of The New York Times Company)
249 W 17th St
New York, NY 10011
Tel.: (212) 204-4000
Fax: (212) 204-1521
E-mail: work@about.com
Web Site: www.about.com
Sales Range: $75-99.9 Million
Approx. Number Employees: 500
Year Founded: 1997
Business Description:
Internet-Based Information Retrieval & Storage
S.I.C.: 2741; 8999
N.A.I.C.S.: 516110; 518112
Media: 13
Personnel:
Darline Jean *(Pres & CEO)*
Chris Coluzzi *(Sr VP-Ops)*
Mike Daecher *(Sr VP-Content & Guide Ops)*
Frank Minishak *(VP-Sls-Eastern US)*
Evan Minskoff *(VP-Mktg)*
Tracy Raiser *(VP-Sls & Team-West)*
Mary Hartley *(Dir-Nutrition)*
Brands & Products:
ABOUT.COM

ABOVENET, INC.
360 Hamilton Ave 7th Fl
White Plains, NY 10601
Tel.: (914) 421-6700
Fax: (914) 421-6777
Toll Free: (866) 859-6971
E-mail: info@above.net
Web Site: www.above.net
Approx. Rev.: $409,700,000
Approx. Number Employees: 692
Year Founded: 1993
Business Description:
Fiber-Optic Networks Mfr; Internet Hosting Services
S.I.C.: 4813; 7373; 7375; 7379
N.A.I.C.S.: 517110; 517310; 518111; 541512; 541519
Media: 6-8-9-13
Personnel:
William G. LaPerch *(Pres & CEO)*
Joseph P. Ciavarella *(CFO)*
Rajiv Datta *(COO)*
Robert Sokota *(Chief Admin Officer, Gen Counsel, Sec & Sr VP)*
John Jacquay *(Sr VP-Sls & Mktg)*
Douglas M. Jendras *(Sr VP-Ops)*

Key to Media (For complete agency information see *The Advertising Red Books-Agencies* edition):
1. Bus. Publs. 2. Cable T.V. 3. Catalogs & Directories. 4. Co-op Adv. 5. Consumer Mags. 6. D.M. to Bus. Estab.7. D.M. to Consumers
8. Daily Newsp. 9. Exhibits/Trade Shows 10. Foreign 11. Infomercial 12. Internet Adv.13. Multimedia 14. Network Radio
15. Network T.V. 16. Newsp. Distr. Mags. 17. Other 18. Outdoor (Posters, Transit) 19. Point of Purchase20. Premiums, Novelties
21. Product Samples 22. Special Events Mktg. 23. Spot Radio 24. Spot T.V. 25. Weekly Newsp. 26. Yellow Page Adv.

MaryBeth Nance *(Exec Dir-Bus Dev & Mktg)*
Eric Nickla *(Exec Dir-Sls-Central Reg)*
Brian Sheehan *(Dir-Indirect Channel Sls)*

Brands & Products:
ABOVENET
DCXCHANGE
EXPRESSWAVE
JABNET

ACCELA COMMUNICATIONS
(Sub. of Accela Incorporated)
118 Tpke Rd
Southborough, MA 01772-2104
Tel.: (508) 303-9700
Fax: (508) 303-9753
E-mail: privacy@itworld.com
Web Site: www.itworld.com
Approx. Number Employees: 40
Year Founded: 1999
Business Description:
Provider of Information Technology & Broadband Communications
S.I.C.: 7373; 8742
N.A.I.C.S.: 541512; 541611
Advertising Expenditures: $250,000
Media: 10-13-17
Personnel:
Thornton May *(CIO)*
Claire O'Brien *(VP-Sls)*
Ann Roskey *(VP-Mktg & Audience Devel)*

Brands & Products:
ITWORLD.COM

ACD SYSTEMS OF AMERICA INC.
(Sub. of ACD Systems International Inc.)
Waterford Business Pk 9th Fl 5201 Blue Lagoon Dr
Miami, FL 33126
Tel.: (305) 596-5644
Fax: (305) 406-9802
E-mail: sales@deneba.com
Web Site: www.acdcorporate.com
E-Mail For Key Personnel:
Sales Director: sales@deneba.com
Approx. Number Employees: 150
Year Founded: 1986
Business Description:
Integrated Cross-Platform Graphics Software Developer
S.I.C.: 7372; 7371
N.A.I.C.S.: 511210; 541511
Media: 2-8-10-13

ACME PACKET INC.
100 Crosby Dr
Bedford, MA 01730
Tel.: (781) 328-4400
Fax: (781) 425-5077
E-mail: info@acmepacket.com
Web Site: www.acmepacket.com
Approx. Rev.: $231,232,000
Approx. Number Employees: 570
Year Founded: 2000
Business Description:
Interactive Voice, Video & Multimedia Communications
S.I.C.: 3679; 7375
N.A.I.C.S.: 334419; 518111
Advertising Expenditures: $14,969,000
Media: 1-2-4-10-13

Personnel:
Andrew D. Ory *(Co-Founder, Pres & CEO)*
Peter Minihane *(CFO)*
Marianne Budnik *(CMO)*
Robert G. Ory *(Sec & Asst Treas)*
Seamus Hourihan *(Sr VP-Corp Strategy)*
Erin Medeiros *(Sr VP-Pro Svcs)*
Dino Dipalma *(VP-Bus Dev & Sls)*

A.D.A.M., INC.
(Sub. of Ebix Inc.)
10 10th Street NE Ste 525
Atlanta, GA 30309-3848
Tel.: (404) 604-2757
Toll Free: (800) 755-ADAM
E-mail: customersvc@adamcorp.com
Web Site: www.adam.com
E-Mail For Key Personnel:
Marketing Director: jretel@adamcorp.com
Approx. Rev.: $28,161,000
Approx. Number Employees: 97
Year Founded: 1990
Business Description:
Online Health & Medical Information
S.I.C.: 7372; 7379
N.A.I.C.S.: 511210; 519130; 541519
Advertising Expenditures: $34,000
Media: 2-13
Personnel:
Robert S. Cramer, Jr. *(Co-Founder & Chm)*
Mark B. Adams *(Pres & CEO)*
Christopher R. Joe *(CFO)*
Shannon McGuire *(Sr VP & Gen Mgr-Education Solutions)*
Sunny Simpson *(Dir-BenergyOS)*

ADENYO INC.
(Sub. of Motricity, Inc.)
130 Spadina Avenue Ste 606
Toronto, ON M5V 2L4, Canada
Tel.: (416) 363-0060
Fax: (416) 363-1083
E-mail: info@adenyo.com
Web Site: www.adenyo.com
Sales Range: $10-24.9 Million
Business Description:
Mobile Marketing Software & Consulting Services
S.I.C.: 5045; 7372
N.A.I.C.S.: 423430; 511210
Media: 7-10-13-22-27
Personnel:
Tyler Nelson *(Chm & CEO)*
Ghazala Parvez *(CFO)*
Chris Matys *(Chief Analytics Officer)*
Alec Andronikov *(Exec VP & Gen Mgr-Enterprise Bus)*
Steve Eros *(Exec VP & Gen Mgr-Indirect Channels)*

ADVANCED INTERNET TECHNOLOGIES INC.
421 Maiden Ln
Fayetteville, NC 28301
Tel.: (910) 321-1201
Fax: (910) 321-1390
Toll Free: (800) 878-4084
E-mail: cmo@ait.com
Web Site: www.aitcom.net
Approx. Sls.: $30,000,000
Approx. Number Employees: 200
Year Founded: 1996
Business Description:
E-Commerce & Web Hosting Services
S.I.C.: 7375
N.A.I.C.S.: 518111
Export
Media: 2-6-8-11-13
Personnel:
Clarence Briggs *(CEO)*

ADVERTISING.COM, LLC
(Sub. of AOL Advertising Inc.)
1020 Hull St Ivory Bldg
Baltimore, MD 21230
Tel.: (410) 244-1370
Fax: (410) 244-1699
E-mail: privacy@advertising.com
Web Site: www.advertising.com
Sales Range: $125-149.9 Million
Approx. Number Employees: 286
Year Founded: 1998
Business Description:
Online Interactive Advertising Services
S.I.C.: 7313
N.A.I.C.S.: 541840
Media: 10-13-22
Personnel:
Mike Treon *(Dir-Sls-Central Region)*

AEGIS PEOPLESUPPORT, INC.
(Sub. of Aegis Communications, Inc.)
2049 Century Park E Ste 300
Los Angeles, CA 90067
Tel.: (310) 824-6200
Fax: (310) 824-6299
Toll Free: (877) 914-5999
Approx. Rev.: $140,647,000
Approx. Number Employees: 8,550
Business Description:
Global Labor Management Services
S.I.C.: 7361; 8742
N.A.I.C.S.: 561310; 541611
Media: 2-10-13
Personnel:
Lance Rozensweig *(Founder, Chm, Pres, CEO & Sec)*
Caroline Rook *(CFO & Principal Acctg Officer)*
Jesper Rathje *(Chief Acctg Officer)*
Jennifer Sherry *(VP-Global HR)*

AFFINION GROUP, INC.
(Sub. of Affinion Group Holdings, Inc.)
6 High Ridge Park
Stamford, CT 06905
Tel.: (203) 956-1000
Fax: (203) 956-8502
Toll Free: (800) 251-2148
E-mail: todd.smith@affiniongroup.com
Web Site: www.affiniongroup.com
Approx. Rev.: $1,376,300,000
Approx. Number Employees: 3,900
Year Founded: 1973
Business Description:
Holding Company; Consumer Membership, Insurance & Package Enhancement Programs & Services Direct Marketer
S.I.C.: 6719; 5963; 7299; 7389; 8742
N.A.I.C.S.: 551112; 454390; 541613; 561499; 812990
Media: 5-8-13
Personnel:
Nathaniel J. Lipman *(Chm & CEO)*
Lloyd M. Wirshba *(Pres & CEO)*
Brian J. Dick *(Chief Acctg Officer)*
Bill Graham *(Pres-Affinion Intl)*
Steven E. Upshaw *(CEO-Affinion Intl)*
Todd H. Siegel *(Gen Counsel & Exec VP)*
Wayne Conte *(Exec VP-Sls)*
John Kitzie *(Exec VP-Global Ops)*
Mary Rusterholz *(Exec VP-Support Svcs)*

Brands & Products:
AUTOVANTAGE
BUYERS ADVANTAGE
COMPLETEHOME
GREAT FUN
HEALTHSAVER
HOT-LINE
NATIONAL CARD REGISTRY
NETMARKET.COM
PRIVACYGUARD
SHOPPERS ADVANTAGE
TRAVELERS ADVANTAGE

AIR2WEB, INC.
3424 Peachtree Rd NE Ste 400
Atlanta, GA 30326
Tel.: (404) 942-5300
Fax: (404) 815-7708
E-mail: info@air2web.com
Web Site: www.air2web.com
Approx. Number Employees: 50
Year Founded: 1999
Business Description:
Network & Server Software for Delivering Data to Wireless Devices
S.I.C.: 4812
N.A.I.C.S.: 517212
Media: 10-13-20
Personnel:
Sanjay Malik *(Co-Founder & Chm)*
Patrick Klosterman *(CFO)*
Jay Sheth *(Sr VP-Bus Dev)*

Brands & Products:
2CRM
2NOTIFY
2NOTIFY CAMPAIGN MANAGER
AIR2WEB
AIRCARE
CAMPAIGNPRO
DIRECTTEXT
ITEXTER

AJUMP.COM INC.
4435 Enterprise St
Fremont, CA 94538
Tel.: (510) 497-8765
Fax: (510) 497-8698
Toll Free: (877) 692-5867
E-mail: customerservice@ajump.com
Web Site: www.ajump.com
Approx. Number Employees: 5
Year Founded: 2000
Business Description:
Online PC Peripherals, Systems & Software Retailer
S.I.C.: 5734
N.A.I.C.S.: 443120
Media: 4-13
Personnel:
Jerry Shih *(Pres)*
Bernardo Nakata *(Gen Mgr)*

AKAMAI TECHNOLOGIES, INC.
8 Cambridge Ctr
Cambridge, MA 02142
Tel.: (617) 444-3000
Fax: (617) 444-3001
Toll Free: (877) 425-2624
E-mail: media@akamai.com
Web Site: www.akamai.com
Approx. Rev.: $1,023,586,000
Approx. Number Employees: 2,200
Year Founded: 1998

Key to Media (For complete agency information see *The Advertising Red Books-Agencies* edition):
1. Bus. Publs. 2. Cable T.V. 3. Catalogs & Directories. 4. Co-op Adv. 5. Consumer Mags. 6. D.M. to Bus. Estab.7. D.M. to Consumers 8. Daily Newsp. 9. Exhibits/Trade Shows 10. Foreign 11. Infomercial 12. Internet Adv.13. Multimedia 14. Network Radio 15. Network T.V. 16. Newsp. Distr. Mags. 17. Other 18. Outdoor (Posters, Transit) 19. Point of Purchase20. Premiums, Novelties 21. Product Samples 22. Special Events Mktg. 23. Spot Radio 24. Spot T.V. 25. Weekly Newsp. 26. Yellow Page Adv.

Akamai Technologies, Inc. — (Continued)

Business Description:
Application & Content Delivery Products & Services
S.I.C.: 7373
N.A.I.C.S.: 541512
Advertising Expenditures: $700,000
Media: 13

Personnel:
David W. Kenny *(Pres)*
Paul L. Sagan *(CEO)*
J. Donald Sherman *(CFO)*
Robert Wood *(Chief Dev Officer & Sr VP)*
Melanie Haratunian *(Gen Counsel & Sr VP)*
Robert W. Hughes *(Exec VP-Global Sls, Svcs & Mktg)*
Chris Schoettle *(Exec VP-Products)*
Robert Blumofe *(Sr VP-Ops-Networks)*
Debra L. Canner *(Sr VP-HR)*
Harald Prokop *(Sr VP-Engrg)*
Eric Crawley *(Sr Dir-Enterprise Acceleration)*
Jeff Young *(Sr Dir-Corp Comm)*
Suzanne Johnson *(Dir-Mktg, Media & Entertainment)*
Sandy Smith *(Dir-IR)*
Philip Chua *(Reg Mgr-South East Asia)*
Melinda Stackpoole *(Sr Acct Exec-ADS)*

Brands & Products:
AKAMAI
EDGECOMPUTING
EDGECONTROL
EDGEPLATFORM
EDGESCAPE
EDGESUITE
POWERING A BETTER INTERNET
STREAMING
THE TRUSTED CHOICE FOR ONLINE BUSINESS

Advertising Agency:
PJA
12 Arrow St
Cambridge, MA 02138-5105
Tel.: (617) 492-5899
Fax: (617) 661-1530

ALEXA INTERNET, INC.

(Sub. of Amazon.com, Inc.)
Presidio of San Francisco Bldg 37
San Francisco, CA 94129
Mailing Address:
PO Box 29141
San Francisco, CA 94129
Tel.: (415) 561-6900
Fax: (415) 561-6795
E-mail: pr@alexa.com
Web Site: www.alexa.com
Sales Range: $10-24.9 Million
Approx. Number Employees: 25
Year Founded: 1996

Business Description:
Internet-Traffic Measurement Services
S.I.C.: 8732
N.A.I.C.S.: 541910
Media: 13

Personnel:
Dave Sherfesee *(Pres)*
Niall O'Driscoll *(CEO)*
Greger Orelind *(Product Mgr)*

Brands & Products:
ALEXA

ALLDOMAINS INC.

PO Box 821066
Vancouver, WA 98682-0024
Tel.: (360) 253-2210
Fax: (360) 397-8707
E-mail: info@alldomains.com
Web Site: www.alldomains.com
Approx. Number Employees: 20

Business Description:
Domain Name Registration Services
S.I.C.: 7379; 8111
N.A.I.C.S.: 541519; 541110
Media: 13

Brands & Products:
ALLWHOIS
D-CART
D-GEAR
D-TECTIVE
DELTA
DELTA DNS

ALLRECIPES.COM

(Sub. of The Reader's Digest Association, Inc.)
3317 Third Ave S Ste D
Seattle, WA 98134
Tel.: (206) 292-3990
Fax: (206) 292-1793
Web Site: www.allrecipes.com
Approx. Number Employees: 300
Year Founded: 1997

Business Description:
Website Offering Recipes, Cooking Techniques, Menu Ideas & Other Culinary Products & Services
S.I.C.: 2741
N.A.I.C.S.: 516110
Advertising Expenditures: $50,000
Media: 13

Personnel:
Lisa Shaples *(Pres & CEO)*
Amber Dunn *(Sr VP-Sls & integrated Partnerships)*
Esmee Williams *(VP-Mktg)*
Monica Williams *(VP-Fin & Ops)*
Marney Ayers *(Sr Mgr-Mktg)*

AMAZON.COM, INC.

410 Terry Ave N
Seattle, WA 98109-5210
Tel.: (206) 266-1000
Fax: (206) 266-1821
E-mail: feedback@amazon.com
Web Site: www.amazon.com
Approx. Sls.: $34,204,000,000
Approx. Number Employees: 33,700
Year Founded: 1995

Business Description:
Books, CDs, Videos, DVDs, Magazines, Audiotapes, Apparel, Sporting Goods, Toys, Software, Phones, Office Products, Electronics, Garden Equipment & Supplies Online Retailer
S.I.C.: 5735; 5961; 7379
N.A.I.C.S.: 454113; 451220; 454111; 541519
Advertising Expenditures: $890,000,000
Media: 5-6-13-16-31

Personnel:
Jeffrey Preston Bezos *(Chm, Pres & CEO)*
Thomas J. Szkutak *(CFO & Sr VP)*
L. Michelle Wilson *(Gen Counsel, Sec & Sr VP)*
Jeffrey Blackburn *(Sr VP-Bus Dev)*
Sebastian J. Gunningham *(Sr VP-Seller Svcs)*
Andrew Jassy *(Sr VP-Web Svcs)*
Steven Kessel *(Sr VP-Worldwide Digital Media)*
Marc Onetto *(Sr VP-Worldwide Ops)*
Diego Piacentini *(Sr VP-Intl Retail)*
H. Brian Valentine *(Sr VP-Ecommerce Platform)*
Jeffrey A. Wilke *(Sr VP-North America Retail)*
Young Lee *(Dir-Bus Dev)*
Jay Marine *(Dir-Product Mgmt-Amazon Kindle)*
Dan D. Park *(Dir-Consumer Electronics)*
Patrick Teo *(Dir-MP3 Tech)*
Thomas Plaster *(Sr Mgr-Bus Dev)*
Kasi Mout *(Mgr-Mktg)*
Nick Mottet *(Sr Product Mgr)*
John Balotsky *(Mgr-Procurement & Materials)*
Russell Hall *(Mgr-Client Bus-Australia)*
Matthew Scott *(Mgr-Sls-Americas)*

Brands & Products:
AMAZON.COM
CDNOW.COM
KINDLE
NEVER MISS A BEAT

Advertising Agencies:
Berlin Cameron United
100 Ave of the Americas 2nd Fl
New York, NY 10013
Tel.: (212) 824-2000
Fax: (212) 268-8454

Doner
25900 Northwestern Hwy
Southfield, MI 48075
Tel.: (248) 354-9700
Fax: (248) 827-8440
Kindle

ANCESTRY.COM INC.

(Holding of Spectrum Equity Investors)
360 W 4800 North
Provo, UT 84604
Tel.: (801) 705-7000
Fax: (801) 705-7001
Web Site: www.ancestry.com
Approx. Rev.: $300,931,000
Approx. Number Employees: 795
Year Founded: 1983

Business Description:
Genealogy Website Publisher Owner & Operator
S.I.C.: 7375; 2721; 2741
N.A.I.C.S.: 519130
Advertising Expenditures: $43,600,000
Media: 6-11-13-24

Personnel:
Timothy P. Sullivan *(Pres & CEO)*
Howard Hochhauser *(CFO)*
William C. Stern *(Gen Counsel & Sec)*
Joshua Hanna *(Exec VP & Head-Mktg-Intl)*
Ken Chahine *(Sr VP & Gen Mgr-DNA)*
Eric Shoup *(Sr VP-Product)*
Christopher Tracy *(Sr VP-Global Content)*
Jonathan Young *(Sr VP-Tech Ops)*
Nick Cifuentes *(Global Dir-Social Media)*
Sean Pate *(Dir-US PR)*

Brands & Products:
1-2-3 FAMILY TREE
ANCESTRY MAGAZINE
ANCESTRY.COM
FAMILYHISTORY.COM
GENEALOGICAL COMPUTING MAGAZINE
MYFAMILY.COM

Advertising Agency:
Duncan Channon
114 Sansome St 14th Fl
San Francisco, CA 94104
Tel.: (415) 306-9200
Fax: (415) 306-9201
Agency of Recor

ANDALE INC.

300 Ferguson Dr
Mountain View, CA 94043-5227
Tel.: (650) 230-3000
Fax: (650) 230-3090
E-mail: info@andale.com
Web Site: www.andale.com
Approx. Number Employees: 75
Year Founded: 1999

Business Description:
Selling Tools & Management Services for Online Auction Merchants
S.I.C.: 7389
N.A.I.C.S.: 561499
Media: 13

Personnel:
Linda Hayes *(Pres & CEO)*
Timothy Vago *(Dir-Fin)*

Brands & Products:
RESEARCH PRO
WHAT'S HOT

ANGIE'S LIST INC

1030 E Washington St
Indianapolis, IN 46202
Tel.: (317) 297-5478
Fax: (317) 396-0101
Toll Free: (888) 944-5478
Web Site: www.angieslist.com
Approx. Rev.: $34,200,000
Approx. Number Employees: 431
Year Founded: 1995

Business Description:
IOnline Review & Referral Service
S.I.C.: 7389
N.A.I.C.S.: 519190
Media: 3-6-13-14-15

Personnel:
William S. Oesterle *(Co-Founder & CEO)*
Angie Hicks Bowman *(Co-Founder & CMO)*
Robert R. Millard *(CFO)*
Scott A Brenton *(COO)*
Michael M Holt *(Exec VP)*
Gary Rush *(VP-IT)*
Michael Rutz *(VP-Sls)*

ANSWERS CORPORATION

(Holding of Summit Partners L.P.)
237 W 35th St Ste 1101
New York, NY 10001
Tel.: (646) 502-4777
Web Site: www.answers.com
Approx. Rev.: $21,471,000
Approx. Number Employees: 79
Year Founded: 1999

Business Description:
Search Engine Portals
S.I.C.: 7372; 8999
N.A.I.C.S.: 511210; 518112
Advertising Expenditures: $150,000

Key to Media (For complete agency information see *The Advertising Red Books-Agencies* edition):
1. Bus. Publs. 2. Cable T.V. 3. Catalogs & Directories. 4. Co-op Adv. 5. Consumer Mags. 6. D.M. to Bus. Estab.7. D.M. to Consumers
8. Daily Newsp. 9. Exhibits/Trade Shows 10. Foreign 11. Infomercial 12. Internet Adv.13. Multimedia 14. Network Radio
15. Network T.V. 16. Newsp. Distr. Mags. 17. Other 18. Outdoor (Posters, Transit) 19. Point of Purchase20. Premiums, Novelties
21. Product Samples 22. Special Events Mktg. 23. Spot Radio 24. Spot T.V. 25. Weekly Newsp. 26. Yellow Page Adv.

Media: 5-6-7-8-10-13
Personnel:
Robert S. Rosenschein *(Chm, Pres & CEO)*
Mark A. Tebbe *(Vice Chm)*
Steven Steinberg *(CFO)*
Bruce D. Smith *(Chief Strategic Officer)*
Caleb A. Chill *(Gen Counsel, Sec & VP)*
Brands & Products:
1CLICK ANSWERS
ANSWERS.COM
ANSWERTIPS
MOBILE ANSWERS
WIKIANSWERS
WIKIANSWERS.COM

AOL INC.

770 Broadway
New York, NY 10003
Tel.: (212) 206-4400
Web Site: www.aol.com
Approx. Rev.: $2,416,700,000
Approx. Number Employees: 5,860
Year Founded: 1985
Business Description:
Internet Advertising, Entertainment & Information Services; Internet Access Services
S.I.C.: 7375; 2741
N.A.I.C.S.: 518111; 516110
Advertising Expenditures: $79,300,000
Media: 2-3-4-5-6-8-9-10-11-12-13-14-15-16-17-19-22-23-24-25
Personnel:
Timothy M. Armstrong *(Chm & CEO)*
Don Neff *(Sr VP-Internal Audit & Chief Exec-Audit)*
Arthur Minson *(CFO & Chief Admin Officer)*
Doug Horne *(Deputy CFO, Chief Acctg Officer & Controller)*
Ned Brody *(Chief Revenue Officer & Pres-AOL Advertising)*
David Eun *(Pres-Media & Studios)*
Brad Garlinghouse *(Pres-Applications)*
Julie M. Jacobs *(Gen Counsel & Exec VP)*
David Harmon *(Exec VP-HR & Corp Svcs)*
Jon Werther *(Exec VP-Bus Dev)*
Emily Becher *(Sr VP & Gen Mgr-Marketplace)*
Jonathan Dube *(Sr VP, Gen Mgr-News & Info)*
Jennifer Wong *(Sr VP, Gen Mgr-Lifestyle & New Bus)*
Tim Castelli *(Sr VP)*
Ran Harnevo *(Sr VP-Video)*
Chris Heine *(Sr VP-Adv Ops)*
Don Kennedy *(Sr VP-Sls-Advertising.com)*
Wendy MacGregor *(Sr VP)*
Michael Manos *(Sr VP-Tech Ops)*
Mike Maser *(Sr VP-Product Mktg)*
Marty Moe *(Sr VP-Programming)*
Jim Norton *(Sr VP)*
Tim Richards *(Sr VP)*
Maureen Marquess Sullivan *(Sr VP-Mktg & Brand Partnerships)*
Kerry Trainor *(Sr VP-Entertainment)*
Jay Kirsch *(VP & Gen Mgr-Marketplace)*
Mike DeLuca *(Head-Sls-AOL Local)*
Debra J. Menin *(Head-Entertainment Practice)*
Miguel Ferrer *(Gen Mgr)*
Anthony Schinella *(Editor-Local)*
Matt Zarzecki *(Sr Dir-Product, Local & Travel)*
Jonathan Tauber *(Acct Dir-Sls-Natl)*
Bao T. Nguyen *(Dir-Technical-Large Scale Analytics)*
Jay Wardle *(Dir-Sls-AOL Adv)*
Sandro Bellini *(Sr Mgr-Sls Strategy & Entertainment)*
Cathy Brough *(Sr Mgr-Sls Strategy-Import Autos)*
Advertising Agencies:
Brandimage Desgrippes & Laga
990 Skokie Blvd
Northbrook, IL 60062
Tel.: (847) 291-0500
Fax: (847) 291-0516

Heat
Pier 33 S 3rd Fl
San Francisco, CA 94111
Tel.: (415) 477-1999
Fax: (415) 477-1990
— Nei Caetano *(Dir-Creative)*

Maslansky, Luntz & Partners
1101 King St Ste 110
Alexandria, VA 22314
Tel.: (703) 358-0080
Fax: (703) 358-0089

Method Inc.
972 Mission St 2nd Fl
San Francisco, CA 94103
Tel.: (415) 901-6300
Fax: (415) 901-6310
Corporate Site

APPSSAVVY

594 Broadway Ste 207
New York, NY 10012
Tel.: (212) 941-5759
Fax: (212) 253-4019
E-mail: info@appssavvy.com
Web Site: www.appssavvy.com
Approx. Number Employees: 50
Business Description:
Platform that Connects People & Brands Through Social Activity Across the Web, Mobile & Applications
S.I.C.: 7319
N.A.I.C.S.: 541890
Media: 10-27
Personnel:
Michael Burke *(Co-Founder & Pres)*
Chris Cunningham *(Co-Founder & CEO)*
Paul Olliver *(COO)*
Jack Bamberger *(Chief Client Officer)*
Todd Bowman *(Sr VP-Sls)*
Sushene Swenson *(VP-Fin)*
Robert Victor *(VP-Product & Strategy)*
Advertising Agency:
Illuminate PR
2708 44th Ave SW
Seattle, WA 98116
Tel.: (206) 300-9134

APTIMUS, INC.

(Sub. of Apollo Group, Inc.)
199 Fremont St Ste 1800
San Francisco, CA 94105
Tel.: (415) 896-2123
E-mail: john.wade@aptimus.com
Web Site: www.aptimus.com
E-Mail For Key Personnel:
Public Relations: publicrelations@aptimus.com
Sales Range: $10-24.9 Million
Approx. Number Employees: 60
Year Founded: 1997
Business Description:
Internet Advertising & Optimization Platform Services
S.I.C.: 8742
N.A.I.C.S.: 541613
Advertising Expenditures: $205,000
Media: 13
Personnel:
Brad Benz *(Sr VP-BD)*
Michael Mayor *(Sr VP-Sls)*
Michael Sullivan *(Sr VP-Mktg & Media Svcs)*
Lance Nelson *(VP-Tech)*
Brands & Products:
APTIMUS

ARCHIPELAGO LEARNING, INC.

3232 McKinney Ave Ste 400
Dallas, TX 75204
Tel.: (214) 397-0794
Fax: (877) 592-1357
Toll Free: (800) 419-3191
E-mail: press@archipelagolearning.com
Web Site:
www.archipelagolearning.com
Approx. Rev.: $58,650,000
Approx. Number Employees: 355
Year Founded: 2000
Business Description:
Web-Based Educational Software Retailer
S.I.C.: 5961; 5734; 8299
N.A.I.C.S.: 454111; 443120; 611710
Media: 6-8-10-13
Personnel:
Timothy J. McEwen *(Chm, Pres & CEO)*
Mark S. Dubrow *(CFO & Exec VP)*
Ray F. Lowrey *(CTO & Exec VP)*
Donna Regenbaum *(Chief Strategy Officer & Exec VP)*
Julie Huston *(Exec VP-Global Sls)*
Cathy Caldwell *(VP-Product Dev)*
Christy C. Linn *(Dir-IR & Corp Comm)*
Brands & Products:
NORTHSTAR LEARNING
STUDY ISLAND
TEACHERWEB

ARIAL SOFTWARE, LLC

1501 Stampede Ave Ste 3040
Cody, WY 82414
Tel.: (949) 218-3852
Fax: (949) 606-9198
E-mail: info@arialsoftware.com
Web Site: www.arialsoftware.com
Approx. Number Employees: 7
Year Founded: 1993
Business Description:
Personalized E-mail Marketing Software Applications
S.I.C.: 5045; 8732
N.A.I.C.S.: 425110; 541910
Media: 7-13-22
Personnel:
Mike Adams *(Pres & CEO)*
Brands & Products:
ARIAL SOFTWARE
AUTO RESPONDER
CAMPAIGN ENTERPRISE
CAMPAIGN ENTERPRISE FUSION & ARRAY
EMAIL MARKETING DIRECTOR

ARQ TECHNOLOGIES, LLC

Rm 201 415 Market St
Harrisburg, PA 17101-2309
Tel.: (717) 805-0385
Fax: (717) 766-1315
E-mail: info@arqtechnologies.com
Web Site: www.arqtechnologies.com
Approx. Number Employees: 2
Year Founded: 1999
Business Description:
Web Application Development, Web Design & Maintenance Services
S.I.C.: 5045
N.A.I.C.S.: 423430
Media: 13

ARRIN SYSTEMS, INC.

2434 Vineyard Ste 202
Escondido, CA 92029
Tel.: (760) 670-3281
Fax: (760) 735-8043
Toll Free: (888) 257-7177
E-mail: salesinfo@arrin.net
Web Site: www.arrin.net
E-Mail For Key Personnel:
Sales Director: salesinfo@arrin.net
Approx. Number Employees: 15
Year Founded: 1986
Business Description:
Provider of Background & Pre-Employment Checks Services
S.I.C.: 7381
N.A.I.C.S.: 561611
Media: 13
Brands & Products:
ARRIN SYSTEMS

ART & LOGIC, INC.

2 N Lake Ave Ste 1050
Pasadena, CA 91101
Tel.: (818) 500-1933
Fax: (626) 405-9802
Toll Free: (877) 278-5644
E-mail: info@artlogic.com
Web Site: www.artlogic.com
Sales Range: $50-74.9 Million
Approx. Number Employees: 50
Year Founded: 1991
Business Description:
Software Developer
S.I.C.: 7373; 7371
N.A.I.C.S.: 541512; 541511
Media: 10-13
Personnel:
Paul Hershenson *(Co-founder)*
Bob Bajoras *(Mgr-Sls)*

ART TECHNOLOGY GROUP, INC.

(Sub. of Oracle Corporation)
1 Main St
Cambridge, MA 02142
Tel.: (617) 386-1000
Fax: (617) 386-1111
E-mail: pr@atg.com
Web Site: www.atg.com
Sales Range: $150-199.9 Million
Approx. Number Employees: 545
Year Founded: 1991
Business Description:
Online CRM Applications
S.I.C.: 7372
N.A.I.C.S.: 511210
Media: 2-5-7-10-13-22

Key to Media (For complete agency information see *The Advertising Red Books-Agencies* edition):
1. Bus. Publs. 2. Cable T.V. 3. Catalogs & Directories. 4. Co-op Adv. 5. Consumer Mags. 6. D.M. to Bus. Estab.7. D.M. to Consumers
8. Daily Newsp. 9. Exhibits/Trade Shows 10. Foreign 11. Infomercial 12. Internet Adv.13. Multimedia 14. Network Radio
15. Network T.V. 16. Newsp. Distr. Mags. 17. Other 18. Outdoor (Posters, Transit) 19. Point of Purchase20. Premiums, Novelties
21. Product Samples 22. Special Events Mktg. 23. Spot Radio 24. Spot T.V. 25. Weekly Newsp. 26. Yellow Page Adv.

Art Technology Group, Inc. — (Continued)

Personnel:
Dorian Daley *(Pres & CEO)*
Lou Frio *(Sr VP-Svcs)*

Brands & Products:
ATG
ATG DATA ANYWHERE ARCHITECTURE
ATG SCENARIO PERSONALIZATION
DYNAMO
ESTARA
PERSONALIZATION SERVER
SCENARIO SERVER
THE TECHMARK

Advertising Agency:
Matter Communications
50 Water St, Mill #3, The Tannery
Newburyport, MA 01950
Tel.: (978) 499-9250
Fax: (978) 499-9253

ART.COM

2100 Powell St 13th Fl
Emeryville, CA 94608
Tel.: (510) 879-4700
Fax: (510) 588-3930
Toll Free: (800) 952-5592
E-mail: mediarelations@art.com
Web Site: www.art.com
Approx. Number Employees: 150
Year Founded: 1995
Business Description:
Online Posters, Art Prints & Phototgraphs Retailer & Custom Framing
S.I.C.: 5999
N.A.I.C.S.: 453998
Media: 13
Personnel:
Michael Heinstein *(Chm)*
Geoffroy Martin *(CEO)*
Chuck Kurth *(CFO)*
Andrew Wait *(CMO)*
Ivy Ross *(Chief Mdsg Officer)*
Roger Wason *(Product Mgr)*

Brands & Products:
ART.COM
EMBRACE YOUR SPACE

ARTISTDIRECT, INC.

1601 Cloverfield Blvd Ste 400 S
Santa Monica, CA 90404
Tel.: (310) 956-3300
Fax: (310) 956-3301
E-mail: customerservice@artistdirect.com
Web Site: www.artistdirect.com
E-Mail For Key Personnel:
Public Relations: press@artistdirect.com
Approx. Rev.: $12,141,000
Approx. Number Employees: 68
Year Founded: 1996
Business Description:
Online Music Services
S.I.C.: 4311; 2741; 5961
N.A.I.C.S.: 491110; 454111; 454113; 516110
Advertising Expenditures: $527,000
Media: 8-13-17-22
Personnel:
Octavio Herrera *(Pres-MediaDefender)*
Terri Denver *(Sr VP-Sls & Mktg-Worldwide)*
Betsy Murphy *(VP-Sls-Worldwide)*

Brands & Products:
A & DESIGN
ARTIST DIRECT
ARTISTDIRECT
ARTISTDIRECT DIGITAL
IMUSIC
UBL
THE ULTIMATE BAND LIST

ASKANYTHING, INC.

2565 3rd St Ste 304
San Francisco, CA 94107-3152
Mailing Address:
PO Box 150037
San Rafael, CA 94915-0037
Tel.: (415) 225-6030
Fax: (415) 914-2224
Toll Free: (800) 339-6030
E-mail: info@askanything.com
Web Site: www.askanything.com
Sales Range: $25-49.9 Million
Approx. Number Employees: 30
Business Description:
Online Information Exchange
S.I.C.: 7375; 8111
N.A.I.C.S.: 518111; 541110
Advertising Expenditures: $200,000
Media: 13
Personnel:
Stephen Roth *(Pres & CEO)*
Dave Laverne *(Exec VP-Bus Dev)*
Peter Mui *(Dir-Bus Dev & Mktg)*

Brands & Products:
ASKANYTHING
ASKANYTHING WEB
QUESTION & ANSWER ONLINE CUSTOMER SUPPORT SOFTWARE

ASKME CORPORATION

(Sub. of Realcom Inc.)
Ste 220 15395 SE 30th Pl
Bellevue, WA 98007-6535
Tel.: (425) 564-9000
Fax: (425) 564-9200
E-mail: info@askme.com
Web Site: www.askmecorp.com
Approx. Number Employees: 150
Year Founded: 1999
Business Description:
Enterprise Software Solutions
S.I.C.: 7371
N.A.I.C.S.: 541511
Media: 2-7-10-13
Personnel:
Udai Shekawat *(Owner & CEO)*

Brands & Products:
ASKME

AT&T WIRELESS SERVICES

(Formerly Wayport, Inc.)
(Sub. of AT&T Inc.)
4509 Freidrich Ln Bldg III Ste 300
Austin, TX 78744
Tel.: (512) 519-6000
Fax: (512) 519-6450
Toll Free: (877) WAYPORT
Web Site: www.business.att.com/enterprise/Service/network-services/internet-connectivity/wifi-service/
Sales Range: $50-74.9 Million
Approx. Number Employees: 700
Business Description:
Data & Internet Services
S.I.C.: 8748; 7375
N.A.I.C.S.: 541618; 518111
Media: 13-31
Personnel:
Daniel Lowden *(VP-Mktg & Bus Dev)*

Brands & Products:
LAPTOP LANE
WAYPORT

AUDIBLE, INC.

(Sub. of Amazon.com, Inc.)
1 Washington Park
Newark, NJ 07102
Tel.: (973) 820-0400
Fax: (973) 820-0505
Toll Free: (888) 283-5051
E-mail: bizdev@audible.com
Web Site: www.audible.com
Approx. Rev.: $63,237,000
Approx. Number Employees: 172
Year Founded: 1995
Business Description:
Online Audio Book Retailer
S.I.C.: 5961; 2741
N.A.I.C.S.: 454111; 516110
Advertising Expenditures: $6,700,000
Media: 13-22-23
Personnel:
Donald R. Katz *(Founder & CEO)*
William H. Mitchell *(CFO)*
Beth Anderson *(Publr & Exec VP)*
Brian M. Fielding *(Exec VP-Corp Dev)*
Foy C. Sperring, Jr. *(Exec VP-Customer Acquisition)*

Brands & Products:
AUDIBLE
AUDIBLEENTERPRISE
AUDIBLELISTENER
AUDIBLEREADY
AUDIBLEWIRELESS
BASICLISTENER
PREMIUMLISTENER

AUTOBYTEL INC.

18872 MacArthur Blvd
Irvine, CA 92612-1400
Tel.: (949) 225-4500
Fax: (949) 225-4557
Toll Free: (888) 422-8999
E-mail: consumercare@autobytel.com
Web Site: www.autobytel.com
Approx. Rev.: $51,534,000
Approx. Number Employees: 119
Year Founded: 1995
Business Description:
Online Automotive Marketing Services
S.I.C.: 7373; 2741; 7371; 7375
N.A.I.C.S.: 541512; 516110; 518111; 541511
Advertising Expenditures: $900,000
Media: 2-10-13
Personnel:
Michael Fuchs *(Chm)*
Jeffrey H. Coats *(Pres & CEO)*
Lenny Mcginley *(VP-Dealer Sls)*

Brands & Products:
AIC
AUTOAHORROS.COM
AUTOBYTEL.COM
AUTOSITE.COM
AUTOWEB.COM
CAR.COM
CARSMART.COM
CARTV.COM
MYRIDE.COM

Advertising Agencies:
Finn Partners
11400 W Olympic Blvd Ste 850
Los Angeles, CA 90064-1544
Tel.: (310) 479-9929
Fax: (310) 479-9989

RBI Communications, Los Angeles
6311 Romaine St
Hollywood, CA 90038
Tel.: (323) 960-1360

Y&R/LMDA
316 Occidental Ave Ste 200
Seattle, WA 98104
Tel.: (206) 587-0799
Fax: (206) 505-7501

AUTOMATIONDIRECT, INC.

(Sub. of Koyo Electronics Industries Co., Ltd.)
3505 Hutchinson Rd
Cumming, GA 30040-5860
Tel.: (770) 889-2858
Fax: (770) 889-7876
Web Site: www.automationdirect.com
E-Mail For Key Personnel:
Marketing Director: marketing@automationdirect.com
Sales Range: $25-49.9 Million
Approx. Number Employees: 150
Year Founded: 1994
Business Description:
Automation Products Online Sales
S.I.C.: 5084
N.A.I.C.S.: 423830
Import Export
Media: 2-4-6-13
Personnel:
Tim Hohmann *(Pres)*
Tina Crowe *(Dir-Adv)*

Brands & Products:
AUTOMATION DIRECT
DIRECT LOGIC
DIRECT TOUCH
WINPLC

AUTOTRADER.COM LLC

(Sub. of Manheim Auctions, Inc.)
5775 Peachtree Dunwoody Rd Ste A-100
Atlanta, GA 30342
Tel.: (404) 568-8000
Fax: (404) 269-3028
Fax: (404) 269-3060
E-mail: info@autotrader.com
Web Site: www.autotrader.com
Approx. Number Employees: 1,400
Year Founded: 1998
Business Description:
Online Automobile Buying & Selling Services
S.I.C.: 5961
N.A.I.C.S.: 454112
Advertising Expenditures: $500,000
Media: 2-13-23-24
Personnel:
Chip Perry *(Pres & CEO)*
Dallas S. Clement *(CFO)*
Jim Franchi *(COO & Sr VP-Ops)*
Clark Wood *(CMO)*
Matt McKenna *(Sr VP-Natl Accts)*
Alan Smith *(Sr VP-Dealer Sls)*
Dave Amundsen *(VP-Fin)*
David Pyle *(VP-Sls-West Div)*
Rob Huting *(Gen Mgr-AutoTrader Classics)*
Melanie Kovach *(Gen Mgr-Private Seller Svc & Sls)*
Todd Shea *(Sr Dir-IT Dev)*
Scott Tracy *(Dir-Mktg)*

Bryan A. Weston *(Dir-Natl Accts-AutoTrader Classics)*
Dave Braverman *(Sr Mgr-Dealer Adv Products)*
Brett McCarey *(Sr Mgr-Integrated Mktg-Affiliate Brands)*
Mark Scott *(Sr Mgr-PR)*
Jessica Winter *(Sr Mgr-Consumer Mktg)*
Advertising Agencies:
Cellit
213 W Institute Pl Ste 603
Chicago, IL 60610
Tel.: (312) 492-4128
Fax: (866) 856-3936
Toll Free: (800) 790-6597

Doner
25900 Northwestern Hwy
Southfield, MI 48075
Tel.: (248) 354-9700
Fax: (248) 827-8440

Moxie Interactive Inc.
The Northyards 384 Northyards Blvd NW Ste 290
Atlanta, GA 30313-2440
Tel.: (404) 601-4500
Fax: (404) 601-4505

AUTOWEB.COM, INC.
(Sub. of Autobytel Inc.)
18872 MacArthur Blvd
Irvine, CA 92612
Tel.: (949) 225-4500
Fax: (949) 225-4541
Web Site: www.autoweb.com
Sales Range: $50-74.9 Million
Approx. Number Employees: 75
Year Founded: 1998
Business Description:
Online Automotive Information that Helps Consumers Select New or Pre-Owned Vehicles from Member Dealers
S.I.C.: 2741
N.A.I.C.S.: 516110
Advertising Expenditures: $20,600,000
Media: 10-13-16-22
Advertising Agency:
AutoCom Associates
74 W Long Lk Rd Ste 103
Bloomfield Hills, MI 48304-2770
Tel.: (248) 647-8621
Fax: (248) 642-2110

AVVO, INC.
1218 3rd Ave Ste 300
Seattle, WA 98101
Tel.: (206) 734-4111
Fax: (206) 340-6040
Web Site: www.avvo.com
Business Description:
Online Legal Directory
S.I.C.: 2741
N.A.I.C.S.: 511140
Media: 17
Personnel:
Mark Britton *(Founder & CEO)*

AWARDS.COM LLC
1205 Sarah St 171
Altamonte Springs, FL 32750
Tel.: (407) 265-2001
E-mail: info@awards.com
Web Site: www.awards.com
Approx. Sls.: $10,000,000
Approx. Number Employees: 50
Business Description:
Trophies & Plaques
S.I.C.: 5999
N.A.I.C.S.: 453998
Media: 4-7-10-13
Personnel:
Warren Struhl *(Chm)*

B4UTRADE.COM, CORP.
30 Montgomery St Ste 600
Jersey City, NJ 07302
Tel.: (201) 427-9060
Fax: (201) 427-9064
E-mail: info@b4utrade.com
Web Site: www.b4utrade.com
Approx. Number Employees: 15
Year Founded: 1999
Business Description:
Online Stock & Financial Information Services
S.I.C.: 8732
N.A.I.C.S.: 541910
Media: 13-17
Personnel:
Keith Savitz *(Founder & Chm)*
Angie Oaks *(Co-Founder, COO & Exec VP)*
Dennis Cassidy *(CEO)*
Brands & Products:
B4UTRADE.COM
GIVE YOURSELF AN INSTITUTIONAL ADVANTAGE

BABYCENTER, LLC
(Sub. of Johnson & Johnson)
163 Freelon St
San Francisco, CA 94107-1624
Tel.: (415) 537-0900
Fax: (415) 537-0909
Web Site: www.babycenter.com
E-Mail For Key Personnel:
Public Relations: pr@babycenter.com
Sales Range: $25-49.9 Million
Approx. Number Employees: 100
Year Founded: 1996
Business Description:
Baby Products Retailer & Online Information for Expecting Mothers
S.I.C.: 7299; 8733
N.A.I.C.S.: 812990; 541720
Media: 1-4-6-13-20-22
Personnel:
Tina Sharkey *(Chm & Global Pres)*
Colleen Hancock *(COO & Sr VP)*
Scott Kinzie *(CMO)*
Michael Fogarty *(Global Grp Publr & Sr VP)*
Suzanna Skop *(VP-Sls-US)*
Brands & Products:
BABYCENTER
PARENTCENTER

BANKDIRECT
(Div. of Texas Capital Bank)
2000 McKinney Ste 700
Dallas, TX 75201
Tel.: (214) 932-6600
Fax: (214) 939-6881
Toll Free: (877) 839-2737
E-mail: info@bankdirect.com
Web Site: www.bankdirect.com
Sales Range: $25-49.9 Million
Approx. Number Employees: 90
Year Founded: 1998
Business Description:
Internet Based Banking & Financial Services
S.I.C.: 6029
N.A.I.C.S.: 522110
Media: 13
Personnel:
Vince Ackerson *(Exec VP & Chief Lending Officer)*
Brands & Products:
BANKDIRECT

BANKRATE, INC.
(Holding of Apax Partners LLP)
11760 US Hwy 1 Ste 200
North Palm Beach, FL 33408
Tel.: (561) 630-2400
Fax: (561) 625-4540
E-mail: info@bankrate.com
Web Site: www.bankrate.com
Approx. Rev.: $220,598,000
Approx. Number Employees: 360
Year Founded: 1976
Business Description:
Internet Consumer Banking Marketplace
S.I.C.: 6371; 2741; 6029
N.A.I.C.S.: 525990; 516110; 522110
Advertising Expenditures: $4,835,941
Media: 9-10-13-17-23-26
Personnel:
Peter C. Morse *(Chm)*
Thomas R. Evans *(Pres & CEO)*
Edward J. DiMaria *(CFO & Sr VP)*
Bruce J. Zanca *(CMO, Sr VP & Chief Comm Officer)*
Daniel P. Hoogterp *(CTO & Sr VP)*
Donaldson M. Ross *(Sr VP & Chief Revenue Officer)*
Michael J. Ricciardelli *(Sr VP-Bus Dev & Consumer Mktg)*
Beth Planakis *(VP-Corp Mktg & Ad Sls)*
Kayleen J. Keneally *(Sr Dir-Corp Comm)*
Brands & Products:
CONSUMER MORTAGE GUIDE
INTEREST.COM

BARRA, INC.
(Sub. of MSCI Inc.)
(d/b/a MSCI Barra)
2100 Milvia St
Berkeley, CA 94704-1113
Tel.: (510) 548-5442
Fax: (510) 548-4374
E-mail: contactus@mscibarra.com
Web Site: www.mscibarra.com
Sales Range: $150-199.9 Million
Approx. Number Employees: 555
Year Founded: 1975
Business Description:
Risk Management Technology & Decision Support Tools Mfr
S.I.C.: 7371; 7372
N.A.I.C.S.: 541511; 511210
Media: 2-8-10
Personnel:
Henry A. Fernandez *(Chm, Pres & CEO)*
Brands & Products:
BARRA AEGIS
BARRA COSMOS
BARRA CREDIT
BARRA ENTERPRISE PERFORMANCE
BARRA MODELS
BARRA PROFESSIONAL SERVICES
BARRA TOTAL RISK
BARRA WORLD MARKETS MODEL
BARRAONE

BEAUTY.COM, INC.
(Sub. of drugstore.com, inc.)
411 108th Ave NE Ste 1400
Bellevue, WA 98004-4440
Tel.: (425) 372-3200
Fax: (425) 372-3800
Web Site: www.beauty.com
Sales Range: $150-199.9 Million
Approx. Number Employees: 300
Year Founded: 2000
Business Description:
Cosmetics & Beauty Aids, Information & Products
S.I.C.: 5912
N.A.I.C.S.: 446110
Personnel:
Tracey Wright *(CFO)*
Brands & Products:
ASK YOUR BEAUTY EXPERT
BEAUTY.COM
CLINICAL SKIN SOLUTIONS
WHAT EVERY BODY NEEDS
THE WORLD OF BEAUTY ONLINE
THE WORLD OF PRESTIGE BEAUTY
Advertising Agency:
Alison Brod Public Relations
373 Park Ave S 4th Fl
New York, NY 10016
Tel.: (212) 230-1800
Fax: (212) 230-1161

BENJAMIN MICHAEL & ASSOCIATES, INC.
PO Box 609
Smithtown, NY 11787-0609
Tel.: (631) 234-5020
Fax: (631) 234-3487
Toll Free: (877) 411-2900
Web Site: www.benjaminmichaelassociates.com
Sales Range: $10-24.9 Million
Approx. Number Employees: 5
Year Founded: 1998
Business Description:
Debt Collection Services
S.I.C.: 7322
N.A.I.C.S.: 561440
Advertising Expenditures: $250,000
Media: 6-13
Brands & Products:
BMA

BESTTRANSPORT, INC.
400 W Wilson Bridge Rd
Worthington, OH 43085
Tel.: (614) 888-2378
Fax: (614) 433-9748
E-mail: csinfo@besttransport.com
Web Site: www.besttransport.com
Sales Range: $10-24.9 Million
Approx. Number Employees: 20
Year Founded: 1998
Business Description:
Internet Service
S.I.C.: 7375
N.A.I.C.S.: 518111
Advertising Expenditures: $25,000
Media: 7-13
Personnel:
Rick Frio *(Founder)*
Brands & Products:
BESTCARRIERS.COM
BESTSHIPPERS.COM
BESTTRANSPORT
BESTTRANSPORT.COM

Key to Media (For complete agency information see *The Advertising Red Books-Agencies* edition):
1. Bus. Publs. 2. Cable T.V. 3. Catalogs & Directories. 4. Co-op Adv. 5. Consumer Mags. 6. D.M. to Bus. Estab.7. D.M. to Consumers
8. Daily Newsp. 9. Exhibits/Trade Shows 10. Foreign 11. Infomercial 12. Internet Adv.13. Multimedia 14. Network Radio
15. Network T.V. 16. Newsp. Distr. Mags. 17. Other 18. Outdoor (Posters, Transit) 19. Point of Purchase20. Premiums, Novelties
21. Product Samples 22. Special Events Mktg. 23. Spot Radio 24. Spot T.V. 25. Weekly Newsp. 26. Yellow Page Adv.

BEYOND.COM, INC.
1060 1st Ave Ste 100
King of Prussia, PA 19406
Tel.: (610) 878-2800
Fax: (610) 878-2801
E-mail: customerservice@beyond.com
Web Site: www.beyond.com
Sales Range: $10-24.9 Million
Approx. Number Employees: 70
Year Founded: 1998
Business Description:
Online Career Database & Directory
S.I.C.: 7361; 2741
N.A.I.C.S.: 561310; 511140
Personnel:
Marla R. Milgram *(Owner, Gen Counsel & Exec VP)*
Richard P. Milgram *(CEO)*
Mark Karsch *(CFO)*
James John *(COO)*
David M. Brensilber *(Sr VP-Bus Dev)*
Brad Miller *(VP-Mktg & Comm)*
Michael J. Owsiany *(VP-Strategy & Execution)*
Mark Anderson *(Sr Dir-Enterprise Sls)*
Tim Heston *(Dir-Enterprise Sls)*
Advertising Agency:
PAN Communications
300 Brickstone Sq 7th Fl
Andover, MA 01810
Tel.: (978) 474-1900
Fax: (978) 474-1903

BIDZ.COM, INC.
3562 Eastham Dr
Culver City, CA 90232
Tel.: (310) 280-7373
E-mail: customerservice@bidz.com
Web Site: www.bidz.com
Approx. Rev.: $104,772,000
Approx. Number Employees: 177
Year Founded: 1998
Business Description:
Online Jewelry Auctioneer
S.I.C.: 5961; 5094
N.A.I.C.S.: 454112; 423940
Advertising Expenditures: $6,200,000
Media: 13
Personnel:
Peter G. Hanelt *(Chm)*
Leon Kuperman *(Pres & CTO)*
David Zinberg *(CEO)*
Lawrence Y. Kong *(CFO)*
Claudia Y. Liu *(COO)*
Jorge L. Gonzalez *(Mgr-Customer Svc)*
Vilius Zukauskas *(Mgr-Auctions)*

BIKINI.COM
(Sub. of Always Summer LLC)
421 Hudson St Ste 520
New York, NY 10014
Tel.: (305) 932-6655
E-mail: info@bikini.com
Web Site: www.bikini.com
Year Founded: 1997
Business Description:
Website Promoting Beach-Related Merchandise
S.I.C.: 5162; 8742
N.A.I.C.S.: 424610; 541611
Advertising Expenditures: $50,000
Bus. Publs.: $25,000; Exhibits/Trade Shows: $25,000

BIOSPACE, INC.
(Sub. of onTargetjobs, Inc.)
2399 Hwy 34 Bldg A5
Manasquan, NJ 08736-1528
Tel.: (732) 528-3688
Fax: (732) 528-3668
Toll Free: (888) BIOSPACE
E-mail: info@biospace.com
Web Site: www.biospace.com
Sales Range: $1-9.9 Million
Approx. Number Employees: 70
Year Founded: 1985
Business Description:
Online Life Sciences & Career Information Publisher
S.I.C.: 2741; 8743
N.A.I.C.S.: 516110; 541820
Media: 6-7-10-13
Personnel:
Raj Kasuganti *(Dir-Sls-BioCapital)*
Brands & Products:
BIO NC
BIO UK
BIOAUS
BIOCAPITAL
BIOCORRIDOR
BIOCROSSROADS
BIOGARDEN
BIOPENN
BIOTECH BAY
BIOTECH BEACH
GENETOWN
PHARM COUNTRY

BIRDSALL INTERACTIVE, INC.
111 Myrtle St 3rd Fl
Oakland, CA 94607-2525
Tel.: (925) 284-5900
Fax: (510) 433-8909
E-mail: mike@birdsallinteractive.com
Web Site: www.birdsallinteractive.com
Approx. Number Employees: 15
Year Founded: 1991
Business Description:
Web Development, E-Mail Marketing & Flash Demonstrations
S.I.C.: 8999
N.A.I.C.S.: 518112
Media: 6-7-9-13
Personnel:
Maureen Birdsall *(Owner-Creative Force & Social Strategist)*
Mike Birdsall *(Owner)*

BIZLAND INC.
70 Blanchard Rd
Burlington, MA 01803
Tel.: (781) 272-6470
Fax: (781) 272-6550
Toll Free: (866) 599-9964
Toll Free: (866) 788-7483 (Sales)
E-mail: info@bizland-inc.com
Web Site: www.bizland.com
Approx. Number Employees: 50
Business Description:
Web Hosting Services
S.I.C.: 2741
N.A.I.C.S.: 516110
Media: 10-13
Personnel:
Hari Ravichandran *(Founder & CTO)*
Steve Sydness *(CEO)*
Brands & Products:
BIZLAND
SITEDELUX

BIZRATE.COM
12200 W Olympic Blvd Ste 300
Los Angeles, CA 90064
Tel.: (310) 571-1235
Fax: (310) 571-1236
E-mail: help@bizrate.com
Web Site: www.bizrate.com
Sales Range: $100-124.9 Million
Approx. Number Employees: 300
Year Founded: 1996
Business Description:
E-Commerce Search Services
S.I.C.: 8732; 7375
N.A.I.C.S.: 541910; 518111
Media: 13
Personnel:
John Phelps *(Pres-Shopzilla)*
Brad Kates *(CFO)*
Blythe Holden *(Gen Counsel)*
Beth Sterling *(VP-Sls)*
Brands & Products:
BIZRATE
RAISE YOUR SHOPPING I.Q.
SHOPRANK

BLACKBOARD INC.
650 Massachusetts Ave NW
Washington, DC 20001
Tel.: (202) 463-4860
Fax: (202) 463-4863
Toll Free: (800) 424-9299
Web Site: www.blackboard.com
Approx. Rev.: $447,318,000
Approx. Number Employees: 1,780
Year Founded: 1997
Business Description:
Online Educational Software
S.I.C.: 7372
N.A.I.C.S.: 511210
Export
Advertising Expenditures: $5,200,000
Media: 2-7-10-11-13
Personnel:
Matthew L. Pittinsky *(Chm)*
Michael L. Chasen *(Pres & CEO)*
John Kinzer *(CFO)*
C. Russ Carlson *(Pres-Blackboard North America Higher Education)*
David Marr *(Pres-Blackboard Transact)*
Michael J. Stanton *(Treas, Sr VP-IR & Corp Affairs)*
Craig Chanoff *(Sr VP & Gen Mgr-Blackboard Student Svcs)*
Kayvon Beykpour *(VP-Blackboard Mobile)*
Jonathan R. Walsh *(VP-Fin & Acctg)*
Tim Connor *(Dir-Art)*
Brands & Products:
BBONE
BLACKBOARD
BLACKBOARD ACADEMIC SUITE
BLACKBOARD COMMERCE SUITE
BLACKBOARD COMMUNITY SYSTEM
BLACKBOARD CONNECT
BLACKBOARD CONTENT SYSTEM
BLACKBOARD LEARN
BLACKBOARD LEARNING SYSTEM
BLACKBOARD TRANSACT
BLACKBOARD TRANSACTION SYSTEM
INCREASE THE IMPACT. TRANSFORM THE EXPERIENCE.
Advertising Agency:
Pappas Group
671 N Glebe Rd Ste 700
Arlington, VA 22203
Tel.: (703) 738-9012
Fax: (703) 349-7253

BLUE PHOENIX MEDIA
265 Canal St Ste 509
New York, NY 10013
Toll Free: (877) 264-8387
Web Site: www.bluephoenixmedia.com
Business Description:
Customer Acquisition & Interactive Lead Generation Network
S.I.C.: 7319
N.A.I.C.S.: 541890
Media: 10-13
Personnel:
Amy Sheridan *(CEO)*
Malaika Schmidt *(COO)*
Brands & Products:
BLUE PHOENIX

BLUEFLY, INC.
42 W 39th St
New York, NY 10018-3809
Tel.: (212) 944-8000
Fax: (212) 354-3400
E-mail: investorkit@bluefly.com
Web Site: www.bluefly.com
Approx. Sls.: $88,563,000
Approx. Number Employees: 83
Year Founded: 1998
Business Description:
Online Apparel & Home Accessories Retailer
S.I.C.: 5961; 5611; 5621
N.A.I.C.S.: 454111; 448110; 448120
Export
Advertising Expenditures: $2,401,000
Media: 4-5-6-8-13-22
Personnel:
David K. Wassong *(Interim Chm)*
Melissa J. Payner-Gregor *(CEO)*
Kara B. Jenny *(CFO)*
Bradford Matson *(CMO)*
Martin Keane *(Sr VP-E-Commerce)*
Monica Halpert *(Dir-Content & Creative)*
Brands & Products:
BLUEFLY
FABULOUS FASHION. FIERCE PRICES
FLYPAPER
Advertising Agency:
Renegade, LLC
75 9th Ave 8th Fl
New York, NY 10011
Tel.: (646) 486-7700
Fax: (646) 486-7800

BONUS.COM INC.
(Sub. of Appaloosa Interactive Corporation)
2100 Geng Rd Ste 105
Palo Alto, CA 94303-4617
Tel.: (650) 813-0100
Fax: (650) 813-0101
Web Site: www.bonus.com
Sales Range: $10-24.9 Million
Approx. Number Employees: 15
Year Founded: 1997
Business Description:
Online Entertainment
S.I.C.: 7375; 7371
N.A.I.C.S.: 518111; 541511
Media: 4-7-8-13

Key to Media (For complete agency information see *The Advertising Red Books-Agencies* edition):
1. Bus. Publs. 2. Cable T.V. 3. Catalogs & Directories. 4. Co-op Adv. 5. Consumer Mags. 6. D.M. to Bus. Estab.7. D.M. to Consumers
8. Daily Newsp. 9. Exhibits/Trade Shows 10. Foreign 11. Infomercial 12. Internet Adv.13. Multimedia 14. Network Radio
15. Network T.V. 16. Newsp. Distr. Mags. 17. Other 18. Outdoor (Posters, Transit) 19. Point of Purchase20. Premiums, Novelties
21. Product Samples 22. Special Events Mktg. 23. Spot Radio 24. Spot T.V. 25. Weekly Newsp. 26. Yellow Page Adv.

BRANDERS.COM INC.
1850 Gateway Dr Ste 400
San Mateo, CA 94404
Tel.: (650) 292-2752
Fax: (650) 292-2640
Toll Free: (877) 272-6337
E-mail: orders@branders.com
Web Site: www.branders.com
Approx. Sls.: $6,500,000
Approx. Number Employees: 170
Year Founded: 1999
Business Description:
Customizable Promotional Items
S.I.C.: 5961
N.A.I.C.S.: 454113
Media: 13
Personnel:
Jerry McLaughlin *(CEO)*

BRAVOSOLUTION US
(Branch of BravoSolution S.p.A.)
400 Chester Field Pkwy
Malvern, PA 19355
Tel.: (610) 240-0600
Fax: (610) 240-9470
E-mail: info@verticalnet.com
Web Site: www.verticalnet.com
Approx. Rev.: $16,164,000
Approx. Number Employees: 88
Year Founded: 1995
Business Description:
Online Information Resources, Communication Vehicles & E-Commerce Channels Supplier
S.I.C.: 7372
N.A.I.C.S.: 511210
Media: 7-10-13
Personnel:
Luke Schneider *(Sr VP-Ops)*
Jim Wetekamp *(Sr VP-Solution Strategy)*
Brian L. Cupp *(VP-Product Dev)*
Larry Fournier *(VP-Worldwide Mktg)*
Brands & Products:
VERTICALNET

BRIGHTLANE.COM, INC.
(Sub. of TeamStaff, Inc.)
3650 Mansell Rd Ste 200
Alpharetta, GA 30022-3068
Tel.: (678) 385-2820
E-mail: comments@brightlane.com
Web Site: www.brightlane.com
Sales Range: $10-24.9 Million
Approx. Number Employees: 31
Year Founded: 1999
Business Description:
Financial, Management & Administrative Services for Businesses Online
S.I.C.: 7389; 7375
N.A.I.C.S.: 541990; 518111
Media: 13

BRILLIANT DIGITAL ENTERTAINMENT, INC.
14011 Ventura Blvd Ste 501
Sherman Oaks, CA 91423-5233
Tel.: (818) 386-2180
Fax: (818) 386-2179
E-mail: info@b3d.com
Web Site: www.brilliantdigital.com
Sales Range: $1-9.9 Million
Approx. Number Employees: 8
Year Founded: 1996
Business Description:
Entertainment Content, Internet Tools & Technology
S.I.C.: 7372; 2741
N.A.I.C.S.: 334611; 516110
Media: 13
Personnel:
Kevin Bermeister *(Chm, Pres & CEO)*
Tyler Tarr *(CFO)*
Lee Jaffe *(Chief Creative Officer)*
Andrew Wilson *(Dir-New Media)*
Brands & Products:
B3D
BRILLIANT
BRILLIANT DIGITAL

BROADCASTER, INC.
353 Bel Marin Keys Blvd #14
Novato, CA 94949-5641
Tel.: (415) 883-5641
Sales Range: $1-9.9 Million
Approx. Number Employees: 4
Year Founded: 1982
Business Description:
Mobile Entertainment Services
S.I.C.: 4812; 7379; 7999
N.A.I.C.S.: 517212; 541519; 713990
Media: 7-8-13
Personnel:
Martin R. Wade, III *(CEO)*
Blair Mills *(CFO)*

BROADSOFT, INC.
9737 Washingtonian Blvd Ste 350
Gaithersburg, MD 20878
Tel.: (301) 977-9440
E-mail: info@broadsoft.com
Web Site: www.broadsoft.com
Approx. Rev.: $95,623,000
Approx. Number Employees: 372
Year Founded: 1998
Business Description:
VoIP Application Software
S.I.C.: 7372
N.A.I.C.S.: 511210; 517919
Personnel:
Robert P. Goodman *(Chm)*
Michael Tessler *(Pres & CEO)*
James Tholen *(CFO)*
Mary Ellen Seravalli *(Gen Counsel & VP)*
Greg Callanan *(VP-Sls)*
Craig Decker *(VP-Sls-EMEA)*
Leslie Ferry *(VP-Mktg)*
Robert Weidenfeller *(VP-Engrg)*
Advertising Agency:
Strategic Communications Group
1400 Spring St Ste 330
Silver Spring, MD 20910
Tel.: (301) 408-4500
Fax: (301) 408-4506

BRS MEDIA INC.
55 New Montgonery Suit 622
San Francisco, CA 94105
Tel.: (415) 677-4027
Fax: (415) 677-4025
Fax: (888) 418-2782
Toll Free: (888) 697-2860
E-mail: info@brsmedia.fm
Web Site: www.brsmedia.fm
Sales Range: $10-24.9 Million
Approx. Number Employees: 400
Business Description:
Internet E-Commerce
S.I.C.: 7375
N.A.I.C.S.: 518111
Media: 13
Personnel:
George T. Bundy *(CEO-Media)*
Junaid Siddiqui *(Mgr-Ops)*
Brands & Products:
A GREAT SOUNDING WEB ADDRESS ENDS IN DOTFM!
A SOUND WEB ADDRESS.
ASHEARDON.COM
@RADIO.AM
@RADIO.FM
BRS MEDIA INC.
DNAZ.NET
DNS@DOT
DOTAM
DOTFM
DOTRADIO
DOTZCD
DOTZDJ
DOTZLA
DOTZ.MD
DOTZTV
GET A GREAT SOUNDING WEB ADDRESS!
HOSTROCK.NET
IDOTZ.NET
IRRP.NET
PREMIUM DOMAIN FOR TODAY'S BROADCASTING INDUSTRY!
PROGRAMMING ON AIR & ONLINE!
RADIO.AM
RADIO.FM
WEB-RADIO
WEBCASTI AM/FM
WEBCASTI.COM
WEBZ.NET

BUSINESS-SUPPLY.COM, INC.
(Sub. of LoanSource Inc.)
114 Mackenan Dr Ste 300
Cary, NC 27511-7903
Tel.: (919) 465-9661
Fax: (919) 466-7072
Fax: (800) 620-4389
Toll Free: (800) 676-0180
E-mail: support@business-supply.com
Web Site: www.business-supply.com
Approx. Number Employees: 50
Year Founded: 1999
Business Description:
Business-Related Products Online Retailer
S.I.C.: 5961; 5943
N.A.I.C.S.: 454111; 453210
Media: 4-7-10-13-20
Personnel:
Brad King *(Pres)*
David Ryan *(CFO)*
Brad Justun *(Mgr-Mktg)*

BUSINESS.COM, INC.
(Sub. of Resource Nation, Inc.)
2120 Colorado Ave
Santa Monica, CA 90404-3559
Tel.: (310) 586-4111
Fax: (310) 586-4696
Toll Free: (888) 441-4466
E-mail: customerservice@business.com
Web Site: www.business.com
Sales Range: $50-74.9 Million
Approx. Number Employees: 100
Business Description:
Online Business Directory & Search Engine
S.I.C.: 8999; 2741; 7375
N.A.I.C.S.: 518112; 511140; 516110; 518111
Media: 13
Personnel:
Patricia Neuray *(VP-Sls & Mktg)*
John Brown *(Dir-Network Distr)*
Jeff Copeland *(Mgr-Content Product)*
Brands & Products:
BUSINESS.COM
WORK.COM

BUY.COM INC.
(Sub. of Rakuten USA, Inc.)
85 Enterprise Ste 100
Aliso Viejo, CA 92656
Tel.: (949) 389-2000
Fax: (949) 389-2800
Toll Free: (888) 880-1030
Web Site: www.buy.com
E-Mail For Key Personnel:
Marketing Director: marketing@buy.com
Sales Range: $50-74.9 Million
Approx. Number Employees: 140
Year Founded: 1997
Business Description:
Internet Retailer
S.I.C.: 5961
N.A.I.C.S.: 454111
Media: 6-13
Personnel:
Scott Blum *(Founder)*
Neel Grover *(Pres & CEO)*
Greg Giraudi *(COO & Gen Counsel)*
Sathya Jagannathan *(CIO)*
Herb Criscito *(Sr VP-Tech Sls & Mdsg)*
Melissa Salas *(Dir-Mktg)*
Brands & Products:
BUY.COM
BUYMAGAZINE
GO GREEN WITH BUY.COM!
THE INTERNET SUPERSTORE
Advertising Agencies:
GolinHarris
(Part of the Interpublic Group of Companies)
111 E Wacker Dr 11th Fl
Chicago, IL 60601-4306
Tel.: (312) 729-4000
Fax: (312) 729-4010
— Marlene Esqueda *(Acct Exec)*

Walton / Isaacson
4250 Wilshre Blvd
Los Angeles, CA 90010
Tel.: (323) 456-1100
Fax: (323) 456-1139

BUYERZONE.COM LLC
(Joint Venture of Reed Elsevier NV & Reed Elsevier plc)
225 Wyman St
Waltham, MA 02451-1209
Tel.: (617) 868-5757
Fax: (617) 868-6161
Toll Free: (888) 393-5000
E-mail: info@buyerzone.com
Web Site: www.buyerzone.com
Approx. Number Employees: 50
Year Founded: 1992
Business Description:
Business-to-Business Online Marketplace
S.I.C.: 5045; 7389
N.A.I.C.S.: 425110; 561499
Media: 13-14-15-17
Personnel:
Mie-Yun Lee *(Founder & Pres)*
Aaron R. Bailey *(VP-Fin & Ops)*
Anne Kelly *(VP-Sls)*
W. Brian Seymour *(VP-Tech)*

Key to Media (For complete agency information see *The Advertising Red Books-Agencies* edition):
1. Bus. Publs. 2. Cable T.V. 3. Catalogs & Directories. 4. Co-op Adv. 5. Consumer Mags. 6. D.M. to Bus. Estab.7. D.M. to Consumers
8. Daily Newsp. 9. Exhibits/Trade Shows 10. Foreign 11. Infomercial 12. Internet Adv.13. Multimedia 14. Network Radio
15. Network T.V. 16. Newsp. Distr. Mags. 17. Other 18. Outdoor (Posters, Transit) 19. Point of Purchase20. Premiums, Novelties
21. Product Samples 22. Special Events Mktg. 23. Spot Radio 24. Spot T.V. 25. Weekly Newsp. 26. Yellow Page Adv.

BWAY.NET, INC.
568 Broadway Ste 404
New York, NY 10012-3265
Tel.: (212) 982-9800
Fax: (212) 982-5499
Toll Free: (888) 384-3279
E-mail: info@bway.net
Web Site: www.bway.net
Approx. Number Employees: 10
Year Founded: 1995
Business Description:
Internet Dial-Up & Broadband, Web Hosting & Design & Computer Training & Consulting Services
S.I.C.: 7371; 8243
N.A.I.C.S.: 541511; 611420
Advertising Expenditures: $600,000
Media: 13
Personnel:
Ian Stevelman *(Pres)*
Joe Ornellas *(Dir-Mktg)*
George Rosen *(Dir-Sls)*

C I HOST
2300 Valley View Ln
Irving, TX 76021
Tel.: (817) 868-9931
Fax: (817) 868-7203
Toll Free: (877) 4CI-HOST
E-mail: cs@cihost.com
Web Site: www.cihost.com
Approx. Number Employees: 202
Year Founded: 1995
Business Description:
Web Hosting & Related Services
S.I.C.: 7375; 7374
N.A.I.C.S.: 518111; 518210
Media: 2-6-9-13-23-24
Personnel:
Van Stout *(CFO)*

CAFEPRESS.COM, INC.
1850 Gateway Dr Ste 300
San Mateo, CA 94404
Tel.: (650) 655-3000
Fax: (650) 655-3008
Toll Free: (877) 809-1659
E-mail: info@cafepress.com
Web Site: www.cafepress.com
Approx. Number Employees: 80
Year Founded: 1999
Business Description:
Online Service for Designing & Selling Custom Merchandise
S.I.C.: 7375; 5961
N.A.I.C.S.: 518111; 454113
Export
Media: 4-8-13
Personnel:
Fred Durham *(Co-Founder & CEO)*
Bob Marino *(Pres)*
Monica Johnson *(CFO)*
Kara Parsons *(Gen Mgr)*
Brands & Products:
CAFEPRESS
Advertising Agency:
Six Degrees
Old Trinity Church Trinity Rd
Marlow, Buckinghamshire SL7 3AN, United Kingdom
Tel.: (44) 1628 480280
Fax: (44) 1628 480281
Consumer Public Relations

CALLWAVE, INC.
136 W Canon Perdido St Ste C
Santa Barbara, CA 93101
Tel.: (805) 690-4100
Fax: (805) 690-4241
Toll Free: (888) 777-2807
E-mail: info@callwave.com
Web Site: www.callwave.com
Sales Range: $10-24.9 Million
Approx. Number Employees: 49
Year Founded: 1998
Business Description:
Internet-Based Telecommunications Services
S.I.C.: 4813; 7375
N.A.I.C.S.: 517110; 518111
Advertising Expenditures: $2,300,000
Media: 13
Personnel:
Peter V. Sperling *(Co-Founder & Chm)*
Jeffrey Cavins *(Pres & CEO)*
Michael Buday *(Chief Software Architect)*
Alan Lippman *(Exec VP-Advanced Tech)*
Patrick Moran *(VP-Mktg)*
Brands & Products:
CALLWAVE
THE CALLWAVE DESIGN
CALLWAVE JINGLE
FAX2EMAIL
FAXWAVE
THE FAXWAVE DESIGN
THE FUTURE OF FAXING
FUZE
INTERNET ANSWERING MACHINE
IT'S WHAT IS NEXT FOR YOUR CELL PHONE
LIBERTY TELECOM
MOBILE CALL SCREENING
MOBILE CALL TRANSFER
WEBMESSENGER
WEBMESSENGER MOBILE

CALYX & COROLLA, INC.
(Sub. of The Vermont Teddy Bear Company)
6655 Shelburne Rd
Shelburne, VT 05482
Tel.: (802) 985-3001
Fax: (772) 299-1208
Toll Free: (888) 882-2599
Web Site: www.calyxandcorolla.com
E-Mail For Key Personnel:
Public Relations: pr@calyxandcorolla.com
Approx. Number Employees: 30
Year Founded: 1988
Business Description:
Direct Response, Online & Catalog Florists
S.I.C.: 5961
N.A.I.C.S.: 454113
Media: 4-13-14-23
Brands & Products:
THE FLOWER LOVER'S FLOWER COMPANY

CAMBRIDGE SOUNDWORKS, INC.
(Sub. of Creative Technology Ltd.)
100 Brickstone Sq
Andover, MA 01810-1428
Tel.: (978) 623-4400
Fax: (978) 475-7219
Toll Free: (800) 367-4434
E-mail: info@cambridgesoundworks.com
Web Site:
www.cambridgesoundworks.com
Approx. Number Employees: 250
Year Founded: 1988
Business Description:
Online Retailer of Consumer Electronics
S.I.C.: 5731; 5961
N.A.I.C.S.: 443112; 454113
Media: 4-13
Personnel:
Michael Sullivan *(Pres)*
Sam Kennedy *(VP-Sls)*
Brian Shea *(VP-Product Mktg)*
Rob Mainiero *(Gen Mgr)*
Brands & Products:
AMBIANCE
BASSCASE
BASSCUBE
CAMBRIDGE SOUNDWORKS
CAMBRIDGESOUNDWORKS.COM
CENTER CHANNEL II BY HENRY KLOSS
CENTERSTAGE BY HENRY KLOSS
CSW
ENSEMBLE
MEGATHEATER
MEGAWORKS
MICROWORKS
MODEL 88 BY HENRY KLOSS
MODEL 88CD BY HENRY KLOSS
MODEL ELEVEN
MOVIEWORKS
MULTIPOLE
MUSICWORKS
NEODYNE
NEWTON SERIES
THE OUTDOOR
PCWORKS
PLAYDOCK
SELECT CIRCLE
SOUNDWORKS
THE SURROUND
TOWER BY HENRY KLOSS
TOWER II BY HENRY KLOSS
TOWER III BY HENRY KLOSS

CAPITAL ONE AUTO FINANCE INC.
(Sub. of Capital One Financial Corporation)
3905 N Dallas Pkwy
Plano, TX 75093
Tel.: (214) 872-3124
Toll Free: (800) 946-0332
E-mail: comment@capitaloneauto.com
Web Site:
www.capitaloneautofinance.com
Sales Range: $75-99.9 Million
Approx. Number Employees: 250
Year Founded: 1995
Business Description:
Consumer Vehicle Loans Via The Internet
S.I.C.: 6141
N.A.I.C.S.: 522291
Advertising Expenditures: $600,000
Media: 2-8-13
Brands & Products:
BLANK CHECK
PEOPLEFIRST

CARDEAN LEARNING GROUP, LLC
111 N Canal St Ste 455
Chicago, IL 60606-7204
Tel.: (312) 669-5222
Fax: (312) 669-5005
E-mail: info@cardeanlearninggroup.com
Web Site:
www.cardeanlearninggroup.com
Sales Range: $1-9.9 Million
Approx. Number Employees: 110
Year Founded: 1998
Business Description:
Online Business Courses
S.I.C.: 8299
N.A.I.C.S.: 611699
Advertising Expenditures: $500,000
Media: 13
Personnel:
Andrew M. Rosenfield *(Founder)*
Jeffrey Pierne *(CFO)*

CAREERBUILDER, LLC
(Sub. of Gannett Co., Inc.)
200 N LaSalle St Ste 1100
Chicago, IL 60601
Tel.: (773) 527-3600
Toll Free: (866) 638-4212
E-mail: info@careerbuilder.com
Web Site: www.careerbuilder.com
Sales Range: $500-549.9 Million
Approx. Number Employees: 2,000
Year Founded: 1995
Business Description:
Online Recruitment Advertising Services; Owned 50.8% by Gannett Co., Inc., 30.8% by Tribune Company, 14.4% by The McClatchy Company & 4% by Microsoft Corporation
S.I.C.: 2741; 7361
N.A.I.C.S.: 516110; 561310
Advertising Expenditures: $44,000,000
Media: 2-3-6-7-8-9-10-13-15-16-18-23-24-25
Personnel:
Matthew W. Ferguson *(CEO)*
Kevin Knapp *(CFO)*
Richard Castellini *(CMO)*
Brent Rasmussen *(Pres-North America)*
Farhan Yasin *(Pres-Europe, Middle East & Africa)*
Alex Green *(Gen Counsel)*
Rosemary Haefner *(VP-HR)*
Cynthia McIntyre *(VP-Mktg & Comm)*
Jennifer Grasz *(Sr Dir-Corp Comm)*
Brands & Products:
CAREERBUILDER ACHIEVE
CAREERBUILDER NETWORK
MEGA JOB-SEARCH
PERSONAL SEARCH AGENT
PSA
TEAMBUILDER
TEAMBUILDER ONLINE
Advertising Agencies:
CBMedia
200 N LaSalle Ste 1100
Chicago, IL 60601
Tel.: (312) 698-1075
Fax: (888) 718-7099
In-House Agency

Centra360
1400 Old Country Rd Ste 420
Westbury, NY 11590-5119
Tel.: (516) 997-3147
Fax: (516) 334-7798

CAREERMAG.COM
(Sub. of Jameson Publishing Inc.)
1060 First Ave Ste 100
King of Prussia, PA 19406
Tel.: (610) 642-6999
E-mail: sales@careermag.com

Key to Media (For complete agency information see *The Advertising Red Books-Agencies* edition):
1. Bus. Publs. 2. Cable T.V. 3. Catalogs & Directories. 4. Co-op Adv. 5. Consumer Mags. 6. D.M. to Bus. Estab.7. D.M. to Consumers
8. Daily Newsp. 9. Exhibits/Trade Shows 10. Foreign 11. Infomercial 12. Internet Adv.13. Multimedia 14. Network Radio
15. Network T.V. 16. Newsp. Distr. Mags. 17. Other 18. Outdoor (Posters, Transit) 19. Point of Purchase20. Premiums, Novelties
21. Product Samples 22. Special Events Mktg. 23. Spot Radio 24. Spot T.V. 25. Weekly Newsp. 26. Yellow Page Adv.

Web Site: www.careermag.com
E-Mail For Key Personnel:
Sales Director: sales@careermag.com
Approx. Number Employees: 30
Year Founded: 1994
Business Description:
Online Recruiting Agency
S.I.C.: 5023
N.A.I.C.S.: 423220
Media: 13

CARS.COM
(Joint Venture of Gannett Co., Inc., The Washington Post Company, The McClatchy Company, Tribune Employee Stock Ownership Plan & A.H. Belo Corporation)
175 W Jackson Blvd Ste 800
Chicago, IL 60604
Tel.: (312) 601-5000
Fax: (312) 601-5093
Web Site: www.cars.com
Sales Range: $25-49.9 Million
Approx. Number Employees: 100
Year Founded: 1997
Business Description:
Online Automobile Advertising Services
S.I.C.: 7319
N.A.I.C.S.: 519130; 541890
Media: 6-13-15-24
Personnel:
Mitch Golub *(Pres)*
Lisa A. Campbell *(CFO)*
William Swislow *(Sr VP-Product)*
Alex Vetter *(Sr VP-Adv)*
Carolyn Crafts *(VP-Mktg)*
Gregory McGivney *(VP-Strategy & Bus Dev)*
Kathy Kimmel *(Dir-Trng)*
Jonathan Yenkin *(Dir-Consumer Products)*
Lynda Myszkowski *(Sr Mgr-Online Mktg)*
Laurie Foster *(Mgr-Dealer Trng)*
Advertising Agency:
DDB Chicago
200 E Randolph St
Chicago, IL 60601
Tel.: (312) 552-6000
Fax: (312) 552-2370

CARSDIRECT.COM, INC.
(Sub. of Internet Brands, Inc.)
909 N Sepulveda Blvd
El Segundo, CA 90245
Tel.: (310) 280-4000
Fax: (310) 280-5125
Toll Free: (800) 431-2500
Web Site: www.carsdirect.com
Approx. Number Employees: 150
Year Founded: 1998
Business Description:
Online Provider of Automobile Research, Price, Design, Order & Delivery Services
S.I.C.: 2741; 5511; 5521
N.A.I.C.S.: 516110; 441110; 441120
Internet Adv.: 100%

CATCHWIND
1011 Locust St Ste 304
Des Moines, IA 50309
Tel.: (515) 244-5303
Fax: (866) 440-1616
Toll Free: (866) 440-1313
E-mail: info@catchwind.com
Web Site: www.catchwind.com
Business Description:
Mobile Marketing Services
S.I.C.: 2741
N.A.I.C.S.: 516110
Media: 2-6-8-10-13-23-24-27
Personnel:
Brian Hemesath *(CEO)*

CBEYOND, INC.
320 Interstate N Pkwy Ste 500
Atlanta, GA 30339
Tel.: (678) 424-2400
Fax: (678) 424-2500
Toll Free: (866) 424-2600
E-mail: info@cbeyond.net
Web Site: www.cbeyond.net
Approx. Rev.: $451,965,000
Approx. Number Employees: 1,944
Year Founded: 1999
Business Description:
Local, Long Distance Services & Broadband Internet for the Small Business Market
S.I.C.: 4899; 4813; 7375
N.A.I.C.S.: 517910; 517110; 518111
Advertising Expenditures: $3,000,000
Media: 7-13
Personnel:
James F. Geiger *(Founder, Chm, Pres & CEO)*
J. Robert Fugate *(CFO & Exec VP)*
Richard J. Batelaan *(COO)*
Joseph A. Oesterling *(CIO)*
Christopher C. Gatch *(CTO & Sr VP-Svc Mgmt)*
Robert R. Morrice *(Chief People Officer & Exec VP)*
Henry C. Lyon *(Chief Acctg Officer & VP)*
N. Brent Cobb *(Chief Revenue & Customer Officer)*
Brooks A. Robinson *(Pres-Cloud Svcs)*
William H. Weber *(Gen Counsel)*
Kurt J. Abkemeier *(Treas & VP-Fin)*
Joan L. Tolliver *(VP-HR)*
Shana Keith *(Dir-PR)*
Advertising Agency:
Arketi Group
2801 Buford Hwy Druid Chase Ste 375
Atlanta, GA 30329
Tel.: (404) 929-0091
Fax: (404) 321-3397

CBS SPORTSLINE.COM, INC.
(Sub. of CBS Interactive Inc.)
1401 W Cypress Creek Rd
Fort Lauderdale, FL 33309-1825
Tel.: (954) 351-2120
Fax: (954) 351-9175
Web Site: www.cbssports.com
Approx. Number Employees: 275
Year Founded: 1994
Business Description:
Internet-Based Sports Media Services
S.I.C.: 2741
N.A.I.C.S.: 516110
Media: 8-13-14-15
Personnel:
Stephen E. Snyder *(Exec VP & Gen Mgr-Games, Music & Sports)*
Jason Kint *(Gen Mgr & Sr VP-CBS Interactive)*
Alex Riethmiller *(Mgr-Media Rels & Corp Commun)*
Brands & Products:
CBSSPORTSLINE.COM
MVP.COM
NCAASPORTS.COM
NFL.COM
PGATOUR.COM

CBT DIRECT, LLC
25400 US Hwy 19 N 285
Clearwater, FL 33763
Tel.: (727) 724-8994
Fax: (727) 726-6922
Fax: (800) 355-9684 (Sales)
Toll Free: (800) 475-5831
E-mail: support@cbtdirect.com
Web Site: www.cbtdirect.com
Approx. Number Employees: 60
Business Description:
Interactive Education Software Mfr
S.I.C.: 7372
N.A.I.C.S.: 511210
Media: 2-5-7-13-14-23-26
Personnel:
Frank Coleman *(CEO)*
Eric R. Williams *(Mgr-Mktg & Graphic Designer)*
Brands & Products:
CBT DIRECT

CELLFISH MEDIA LLC
215 Lexington Ave Fl 18
New York, NY 10016
Tel.: (212) 767-5200
Fax: (212) 767-5271
E-mail: mfanfan@cellfishmedia.com
Web Site: www.cellfishmedia.com
Sales Range: $100-124.9 Million
Approx. Number Employees: 320
Business Description:
Mobile & Online Media & Entertainment Services
S.I.C.: 4812
N.A.I.C.S.: 517212
Media: 13
Personnel:
Fabrice Sergent *(CEO)*
Brands & Products:
BLINGTONES
CELLFISH MEDIA

CEOEXPRESS COMPANY
1 Broadway 14th Fl
Cambridge, MA 02142
Tel.: (617) 482-1200
Fax: (617) 273-8033
Web Site: www.ceoexpress.com
Approx. Number Employees: 13
Year Founded: 1998
Business Description:
Online Information Service
S.I.C.: 8741
N.A.I.C.S.: 561110
Media: 13
Personnel:
Patricia Pomerleau *(Founder & Pres)*
Brands & Products:
CEOEXPRESS
CEOEXPRESSSELECT

CHANA & ASSOCIATES
(Filed Chapter 11 Bankruptcy Protection 08/31/11)
121 Chanlon Rd
New Providence, NJ 07974
Tel.: (908) 486-6801
Fax: (908) 790-5405
Toll Free: (800) 340-3467
E-mail: info@chanaassociates.com
Approx. Rev.: $201,000
Year Founded: 1988
Business Description:
Direct Marketing
S.I.C.: 7311
N.A.I.C.S.: 541810
Personnel:
Walter A. Chana *(Pres & CEO)*
John Kelly *(CEO)*
Kieran Kerson *(Partner-NY Metro Reg)*
Tanya Hurst *(CFO)*
Ava Adams *(Exec Officer)*
Tim Jones *(CEO-NJ)*
Kelly Hertman *(Treas-Sls, VP & Mktg)*
Tony Herson *(VP & Supvr-Creative)*
T. Abter *(VP-Mktg)*
Tom Jones *(VP-Sls & Mktg)*
Una Wilson *(VP-Mktg)*
Gina Liller *(Deputy Gen Mgr)*
Sarah Silver *(Exec Dir-Creative)*
Billy Elliot *(Sr Dir)*
Alison Apter *(Dir-Media)*
Bob Barlow *(Dir-Art)*
Russ Bernstein *(Dir-Creative)*
Cassie Carson *(Dir-Creative)*
E. Edwards *(Dir-Comml)*
Orin Oloson *(Dir-Mktg)*
J. Smith *(Dir-Media)*
B Burns *(Art Dir)*
Pam Smith *(Sls Dir)*
Alvin Albert *(Dir-Art)*
Henry Black *(Dir-Sls)*
Dara Devins *(Dir-Relationship Mktg)*
H. Smith *(Dir-Mktg)*
Roger Valaard *(Assoc Dir-Media)*
Tina Jones *(Mgr-Mktg)*
Jen Green *(Product Mgr)*
Amy Abrams *(Mgr-Mktg Comm)*
Dennis Diller *(Sr Acct Exec)*
Helen Hilson *(Strategist)*
Jim Johnson *(Strategist-PR)*
Tina Cummings *(Engr)*
Mona Lin *(Engr)*
Jim Long *(Assoc Acct Exec)*
Tina Cummings *(Supervisory Board of Directors)*
Brands & Products:
CHANA CHINA
Advertising Agencies:
Browning Advertising, Inc.
121 Chanlon Rd
New Providence, NJ 07974
Tel.: (908) 464-0000
Fax: (908) 790-5405
— Maggie Arguelles *(Acct Dir)*
— Himanshu Goodluck *(Dir-Creative)*
— J. Jesser *(Mng Acct Svcs Dir)*
— Orville Smith *(Acct Exec)*

Leo Burnett Worldwide, Inc.
35 W Wacker Dr
Chicago, IL 60601-1723
Tel.: (312) 220-5959
Fax: (312) 220-3299

CHANNELINX.COM, INC.
250 Executive Ctr Dr Ste 203
Greenville, SC 29615-4517
Tel.: (864) 527-3500
Fax: (864) 527-3501
Toll Free: (800) 701-8053
E-mail: info@channelinx.com
Web Site: www.channelinx.com
Approx. Number Employees: 12
Year Founded: 1998

Key to Media (For complete agency information see *The Advertising Red Books-Agencies* edition):
1. Bus. Publs. 2. Cable T.V. 3. Catalogs & Directories. 4. Co-op Adv. 5. Consumer Mags. 6. D.M. to Bus. Estab.7. D.M. to Consumers
8. Daily Newsp. 9. Exhibits/Trade Shows 10. Foreign 11. Infomercial 12. Internet Adv.13. Multimedia 14. Network Radio
15. Network T.V. 16. Newsp. Distr. Mags. 17. Other 18. Outdoor (Posters, Transit) 19. Point of Purchase20. Premiums, Novelties
21. Product Samples 22. Special Events Mktg. 23. Spot Radio 24. Spot T.V. 25. Weekly Newsp. 26. Yellow Page Adv.

ChanneLinx.com, Inc. — (Continued)

Business Description:
Electronic Commerce Infrastructure for the Building Materials & Construction Industry
S.I.C.: 6371
N.A.I.C.S.: 525990
Media: 13
Personnel:
Kurt Herwald *(Acting CFO)*

CHARLES SCHWAB
(Formerly CyberTrader, Inc.)
(Sub. of The Charles Schwab Corporation)
12401 Research Blvd Bld 2 Ste 350
Austin, TX 78759
Mailing Address:
PO Box 202890
Austin, TX 78720-2890
Tel.: (512) 320-5444
Fax: (512) 320-1561
Toll Free: (888) 76CYBER
Web Site: www.schwab.com
Sales Range: $50-74.9 Million
Approx. Number Employees: 220
Year Founded: 1995
Business Description:
Electronic Trading Technology & Brokerage Service
S.I.C.: 7371
N.A.I.C.S.: 541511
Media: 13
Personnel:
Dave Lerman *(Assoc Dir-Mktg)*
Randy Frederick *(Dir-Dev)*
Brands & Products:
CYBER X2
Advertising Agency:
Euro RSCG Worldwide
350 Hudson St
New York, NY 10014-4504
Tel.: (212) 886-2000
Fax: (212) 886-2016
Toll Free: (800) 937-0233

CHAZAK VALUE CORP.
75 Rockefeller Plz 16 Fl
New York, NY 10019
Tel.: (212) 265-7013
Web Site: www.chazak.com/
Approx. Sls.: $3,314,000
Approx. Number Employees: 26
Year Founded: 1913
Business Description:
Designs, Develops, Manufactures & Markets Conditional Access & Security Systems, Payment Systems & Data Storage
S.I.C.: 3577; 7382; 8711
N.A.I.C.S.: 334119; 541330; 561621
Media: 2-4-6-9-10-18-20-23-25
Distr.: Natl.
Personnel:
Joseph E. Sarachek *(Pres & CEO)*
Marc B. Ross *(CFO, Treas & Sec)*
Brands & Products:
CHIPNET
CHIPNET QUICKSTART
EASYCARD
SMARTPRINT CENTRAL

CHEMINDUSTRY.COM, INC.
730 E Cypress Ave
Monrovia, CA 91016
Tel.: (626) 930-0808
Fax: (626) 930-0102
E-mail: info@chemindustry.com
Web Site: www.chemindustry.com
Year Founded: 1999
Business Description:
Directory & Search Engine for Chemical & Related Industry Professionals
S.I.C.: 7375
N.A.I.C.S.: 518111
Media: 10-13
Personnel:
Yaron Rapaport *(Founder)*
Daniel Fishman *(CEO)*

CHEMISTRY.COM
(Sub. of Match.Com, L.P.)
8300 Douglas Ave
Dallas, TX 75225
Tel.: (214) 576-9352
Web Site: www.chemistry.com
Sales Range: $50-74.9 Million
Year Founded: 2006
Business Description:
Online Dating Service
S.I.C.: 7299
N.A.I.C.S.: 812990
Advertising Agency:
Hanft Raboy & Partners
205 Hudson St 7th Fl
New York, NY 10013
Tel.: (212) 674-3100
Fax: (212) 228-7679

CHERRYROAD TECHNOLOGIES INC.
301 Gibraltar Dr Ste 2C
Morris Plains, NJ 07950
Tel.: (973) 402-7802
Fax: (973) 402-7808
Toll Free: (877) 402-7804
E-mail: info@cherryroad.com
Web Site: www.cherryroad.com
Sales Range: $50-74.9 Million
Approx. Number Employees: 400
Year Founded: 1983
Business Description:
Technical & Management Consulting Services
S.I.C.: 7373
N.A.I.C.S.: 541512
Media: 2-7
Personnel:
Mike Gulban *(Chm)*
Jeremy Gulban *(Pres & COO)*
Nancy Hirsch Rogerson *(CFO)*
Shari Forster *(Dir-Fin)*
John W. McCartney *(Mgr-Strategic Info Sys)*
Elaine Verrone *(Mgr-Mktg)*
Brands & Products:
CHERRYROAD

CHIPS & BITS, INC.
(Sub. of theglobe.com, inc.)
65 Millet St
Richmond, VT 05477
Tel.: (802) 434-6682
Fax: (802) 329-2135
Toll Free: (800) 699-4263
E-mail: info@chipsbits.com
Web Site: www.chipsbits.com
Sales Range: $1-9.9 Million
Approx. Number Employees: 50
Year Founded: 1990
Business Description:
Computer Games, Console Games & Gaming Related Hardware Retailer
S.I.C.: 5734; 5961
N.A.I.C.S.: 443120; 454113
Media: 6-13

CIQ, INC.
(d/b/a Voisys)
611 Druid Rd Ste 405
Clearwater, FL 33756
Tel.: (727) 608-4040
Fax: (727) 441-2100
Toll Free: (877) 438-8642
Web Site: www.voisys.com
E-Mail For Key Personnel:
Marketing Director: oscar@creditiq.com
Approx. Sls.: $3,200,000
Approx. Number Employees: 30
Year Founded: 1998
Business Description:
Lead Generation Services
S.I.C.: 4899
N.A.I.C.S.: 517910
Media: 2-7-10-13
Personnel:
Nick Spiridellis *(Chm)*
Paul Snider *(Pres & CEO)*
Brands & Products:
CREDITIQ
VOISYS
YOUR COMPLETE LEAD GENERATION EXPERT

CITRIX ONLINE LLC
(Div. of Citrix Systems, Inc.)
6500 Hollister Ave
Goleta, CA 93117
Tel.: (805) 690-6400
Fax: (805) 690-6471
E-mail: info@citrixonline.com
Web Site: www.citrixonline.com
E-Mail For Key Personnel:
Public Relations: Laura.McCormick@citrix.com
Sales Range: $100-124.9 Million
Approx. Number Employees: 500
Year Founded: 1999
Business Description:
Remote Support & Access Technologies
S.I.C.: 7375
N.A.I.C.S.: 518111
Media: 13-22
Personnel:
Klaus Schauser *(Co-Founder & CTO)*
Brett Caine *(Pres)*
Bernardo De Albergaria *(VP & Gen Mgr-Global Mktg & Ecommerce)*
Erin Hintz *(VP-Mktg-Global & Gen Mgr-eCommerce)*
Mike Mansbach *(VP & Gen Mgr-Global Sls)*
Scott Allen *(VP-Fin & Ops)*
Justin Madison *(VP-Engrg & Ops)*
Tina Long *(Dir-Pub Rel)*
Jocelyn Chambers *(Sr Mgr-Media)*
Melissa Leachman *(Sr Mgr-Media)*
Allison Kohn *(Mgr-Corp Comm)*
Brands & Products:
CITRIX
GOTOASSIST
GOTOMEETING
GOTOMYPC
GOTOWEBINAR
Advertising Agencies:
Access Communications, LLC
101 Howard St 2nd Fl
San Francisco, CA 94105
Tel.: (415) 904-7070
Fax: (415) 904-7055
Mediasmith
274 Brannan St Ste 601
San Francisco, CA 94107-2000
Tel.: (415) 252-9339
Fax: (415) 252-9854
Digital
GoToAssist
GoToManage
GoToMeeting
GoToMyPC
GoToTraining
GoToWebinar
Print
Reese
955 Berkshire Blvd
Wyomissing, PA 19610-1229
Tel.: (610) 378-1835
Fax: (610) 378-1676

CLARIA CORPORATION
555 Broadway St
Redwood City, CA 94063
Tel.: (650) 980-1500
Fax: (650) 980-1599
E-mail: info@giftcertificates.com
E-Mail For Key Personnel:
Public Relations: press@claria.com
Approx. Rev.: $90,480,000
Approx. Number Employees: 140
Year Founded: 1998
Business Description:
Services & Software that Facilitates Easier Web Navigation
S.I.C.: 7319; 7311
N.A.I.C.S.: 541870; 541810
Media: 13
Personnel:
Denis Coleman *(Chm)*
Brands & Products:
CLARIA
FEEDBACK RESEARCH
SEARCHSCOUT

CLASSIFIED VENTURES, LLC
(Joint Venture of Gannett Co., Inc., The Washington Post Company, The McClatchy Company, Tribune Employee Stock Ownership Plan & A.H. Belo Corporation)
175 W Jackson Blvd Ste 800
Chicago, IL 60604
Tel.: (312) 601-5000
Fax: (312) 601-5093
Web Site:
www.classifiedventures.com
Sales Range: $25-49.9 Million
Approx. Number Employees: 350
Year Founded: 1997
Business Description:
Online Classified Advertising Services; Owned 28% by Tribune Company, 25.6% by The McClatchy Company, 23.6% by Gannett Co., Inc., 16.5% by The Washington Post Company & 6.3% by A. H. Belo Corporation
S.I.C.: 7319
N.A.I.C.S.: 519130; 541890
Media: 2-7-8-9-10-13-18-20-22-25
Personnel:
Daniel A. Jauernig *(Pres & CEO)*
Bob Gallagher *(CFO & VP)*
Neil Hayes *(Chief Legal Officer & VP)*
Timothy Fagan *(Pres/CEO-Homefindercom)*
Mitch Golub *(Sr VP & Pres-Carscom)*
Kevin Doyle *(Sr VP & Gen Mgr-Apartmentscom)*

Key to Media (For complete agency information see *The Advertising Red Books-Agencies* edition):
1. Bus. Publs. 2. Cable T.V. 3. Catalogs & Directories. 4. Co-op Adv. 5. Consumer Mags. 6. D.M. to Bus. Estab.7. D.M. to Consumers 8. Daily Newsp. 9. Exhibits/Trade Shows 10. Foreign 11. Infomercial 12. Internet Adv.13. Multimedia 14. Network Radio 15. Network T.V. 16. Newsp. Distr. Mags. 17. Other 18. Outdoor (Posters, Transit) 19. Point of Purchase20. Premiums, Novelties 21. Product Samples 22. Special Events Mktg. 23. Spot Radio 24. Spot T.V. 25. Weekly Newsp. 26. Yellow Page Adv.

Richard Burke *(Sr VP-Admin & Corp Dev)*
Doug Breaker *(VP-Product Dev)*
Lee Rosenthal *(VP-Mktg-Apartments.com)*
Mark Tepper *(VP-Bus Dev & Sls)*
Chad Cooper *(Sr Dir-Data Ops & Dev)*
Kirk Musselman *(Dir-HR)*
Shana Sternstein *(Dir-Recruiting)*
Shannon Swierczek *(Dir-Comm)*
Brands & Products:
APARTMENTS.COM
CARS.COM
HOMEFINDER.COM
HOMEGAIN
Advertising Agency:
DDB Chicago
200 E Randolph St
Chicago, IL 60601
Tel.: (312) 552-6000
Fax: (312) 552-2370

CLASSMATES ONLINE, INC.

(Sub. of ClassMates Media Corporation)
333 Elliott Ave W, Ste 500
Seattle, WA 98119
Tel.: (425) 917-5000
Fax: (206) 301-5701
Web Site: www.classmates.com
Sales Range: $50-74.9 Million
Approx. Number Employees: 175
Year Founded: 1995
Business Description:
Online Directory of High School, Workplace & Military Alumni
S.I.C.: 2741
N.A.I.C.S.: 516110
Media: 2-13
Personnel:
Ted Cahall *(COO & Exec VP)*
Rita Spangler *(VP-Mktg)*

CLASSROOM CONNECT

(Div. of Houghton Mifflin Harcourt Learning Technology)
9400 South Park Center Loop
Orlando, FL 32819
Tel.: (407) 345-2000
Toll Free: (800) 638-1639
E-mail: help@classroom.com
Web Site: corporate.classroom.com
Approx. Number Employees: 75
Business Description:
Online Educational Curriculum
S.I.C.: 7371
N.A.I.C.S.: 541511
Media: 2-7
Personnel:
Barry O'Callaghan *(CEO)*
Brian Thomas *(Mgr-Sls)*
Brands & Products:
CONNECTED CONFERENCES
CONNECTED EDUCATOR
CONNECTED NEWSLETTER
CONNECTED TECH
CONNECTED UNIVERSITY
CONNECTED WORKSHOPS

CLBL, INC.

(d/b/a CD Universe)
101 N Plains Indus Rd
Wallingford, CT 06492-2360
Tel.: (203) 294-1648
Fax: (203) 294-0391
Toll Free: (800) 231-7937
E-mail: manager@cduniverse.com
Web Site: www.cduniverse.com
Approx. Number Employees: 20
Year Founded: 1996
Business Description:
Online CD Music Store
S.I.C.: 5961
N.A.I.C.S.: 454113
Media: 13
Personnel:
Charles Beilman *(Pres)*

CLICK2ASIA

1334 Parkview Ave Ste 260
Manhattan Beach, CA 90266-3752
Tel.: (310) 802-8028
E-mail: info@staff.click2asia.com
Web Site: www.click2asia.com
Approx. Number Employees: 30
Year Founded: 1999
Business Description:
Asian Internet Media & News Provider
S.I.C.: 7389
N.A.I.C.S.: 711320
Media: 6-8-13-18-20-22
Personnel:
Pierre Wuu *(Founder)*
Suok Pae *(Pres & CEO)*
Brands & Products:
CLICK2ASIA.COM

CLICK4LOANS.COM

605 Baltimore Ave
Towson, MD 21204
Tel.: (410) 823-4554
Fax: (410) 823-4846
E-mail: keith@click4loans.com
Web Site: www.click4loans.com
E-Mail For Key Personnel:
Marketing Director: keith@click4loans.com
Approx. Sls.: $2,570,000
Approx. Number Employees: 3
Year Founded: 1998
Business Description:
Online Equipment Financing & Commercial Loan Services
S.I.C.: 6163
N.A.I.C.S.: 522310
Advertising Expenditures: $400,000
Media: 13
Personnel:
Keith Plasse *(Owner)*

CLICKER INC.

18952 MacArthur Blvd Ste 210
Irvine, CA 92614
Tel.: (949) 486-3990
Fax: (949) 486-3995
E-mail: info@clickerinc.com
Web Site: www.clickerinc.com
Approx. Rev.: $766,446
Approx. Number Employees: 6
Year Founded: 1984
Business Description:
Internet Publisher & Broadcaster
S.I.C.: 2741
N.A.I.C.S.: 516110
Advertising Expenditures: $56,854
Media: 7-13-17
Personnel:
Lloyd Lapidus *(CEO)*

THE COBALT GROUP, INC.

(Sub. of Automatic Data Processing, Inc.)
2200 1st Ave S Ste 400
Seattle, WA 98134-1452
Tel.: (206) 269-6363
Fax: (206) 269-6350
Toll Free: (888) 620-8816
E-mail: info@cobaltgroup.com
Web Site: www.cobaltgroup.com
Sales Range: $200-249.9 Million
Year Founded: 1995
Business Description:
Information Technology Services for the Automotive Industry
S.I.C.: 7375
N.A.I.C.S.: 518111
Media: 2-7-10
Personnel:
John W.P. Holt *(Chm & CEO)*
Jim Beach *(CFO & Exec VP)*
Scott Mathews *(COO & Exec VP)*
Chris Reed *(CMO & VP)*
Greg Meyer *(Sr VP-Products & Tech)*

COFFEECUP SOFTWARE INC.

165 Courtland St Ste A
Atlanta, GA 30303
Mailing Address:
PO Box 312
Atlanta, GA 30303
Tel.: (678) 495-3480
Fax: (678) 495-3481
E-mail: email@coffeecup.com
Web Site: www.coffeecup.com
Approx. Number Employees: 14
Year Founded: 1996
Business Description:
Software Development & Search Engine Submission
S.I.C.: 7372; 7371
N.A.I.C.S.: 511210; 541511
Media: 13
Personnel:
Hans Top *(CEO)*
Bob Visser *(CFO)*
Brands & Products:
BLUEDOMINO
COFFEECUP
MAKE KILLER FLASH
SUBMITFIRE

COGENCY SOFTWARE, INC.

500 Airport Blvd Ste 200
Burlingame, CA 94010
Tel.: (650) 685-2500
Fax: (650) 655-2515
E-mail: info@cogencysoft.com
Web Site: www.cogencysoft.com
Approx. Sls.: $4,600,000
Approx. Number Employees: 45
Year Founded: 1997
Business Description:
Automated Management Solutions Developer
S.I.C.: 7371
N.A.I.C.S.: 541511
Advertising Expenditures: $600,000
Media: 10-13
Personnel:
Jeffrey Axelrod *(Pres & CEO)*
Brands & Products:
ACCESS UNDERSTAND PROFIT
COGENCY
COGENCY SOFTWARE
COGENCY WISDOM
FUND OF HEDGE FUNDS INSIGHT

COMCAST INTERACTIVE MEDIA, LLC

(Sub. of Comcast Corporation)
1701 JSK Blvd
Philadelphia, PA 19103
Tel.: (215) 665-1700
Fax: (215) 286-7790
E-mail: comcast_fulfillment@cable.comcast.com
Web Site: www.comcast.com
Sales Range: $700-749.9 Million
Approx. Number Employees: 6,000
Business Description:
Online Media Developer
S.I.C.: 2741
N.A.I.C.S.: 516110
Media: 8-13
Personnel:
Amy L. Banse *(Pres-Comcast Interactive Media & Sr VP)*
Chuck Davis *(Exec VP)*
John Najarian *(Exec VP)*
Samuel H. Schwartz *(Exec VP-Strategy & Dev)*
Lee Raftery *(Sr VP-Intl Mktg-Comcast Intl Media Grp)*
Scott Schiller *(Sr VP-Adv Sls)*
Robin? Dagostino *(Sr Mgr-Mktg)*
Corey Wilson *(Mgr-Mktg Solutions)*

COMMERCE SCIENCE CORPORATION

3400 Peachtree Rd NE Ste 630
Atlanta, GA 30326-1189
Tel.: (404) 320-6900
Fax: (404) 442-5641
E-mail: info@commercescience.com
Web Site: www.commercescience.com
Approx. Number Employees: 12
Year Founded: 1999
Business Description:
E-Commerce Services
S.I.C.: 5065
N.A.I.C.S.: 423690
Media: 2-4-5-7-13-18-22

COMMUNISPACE CORPORATION

100 Talcott Ave
Watertown, MA 02472
Tel.: (617) 607-1400
Fax: (617) 923-3446
E-mail: info@communispace.com
Web Site: www.communispace.com
Sales Range: $10-24.9 Million
Approx. Number Employees: 275
Year Founded: 1999
Business Description:
Online Business Support Services
S.I.C.: 7371; 7375
N.A.I.C.S.: 541511; 518111
Personnel:
Diane Hessan *(Pres & CEO)*
Maria Rapp *(Mng Dir)*
Gary Arena *(CFO)*
Howard M. Kogan *(Chief Tech & Strategy Officer)*
Siobhan Dullea *(Sr VP-Client Srvs)*
Julie Wittes Schlack *(Sr VP-Innovation & Design)*
Tom Finocchio *(VP-Fin & Controller)*
Jen Buatti *(VP-Mktg)*
Ginny Churchill *(VP-HR)*
Leslie Forde *(VP-Strategic Alliancev)*
Ken Murray *(VP-Tech)*
Manila Austin *(Dir-Res)*
Susan Cress *(Dir-Strategic Accts)*
Paul Morisson *(Dir-Software Architecture)*
David Rosenberg *(Dir)*
Judy Walklet *(Dir-Strategic Accts)*
Janet Toole *(Office Mgr)*
James Bailey *(Mgr-Mktg)*
Maria Tollefson *(Mgr-HR)*

Key to Media (For complete agency information see *The Advertising Red Books-Agencies* edition):
1. Bus. Publs. 2. Cable T.V. 3. Catalogs & Directories. 4. Co-op Adv. 5. Consumer Mags. 6. D.M. to Bus. Estab.7. D.M. to Consumers
8. Daily Newsp. 9. Exhibits/Trade Shows 10. Foreign 11. Infomercial 12. Internet Adv.13. Multimedia 14. Network Radio
15. Network T.V. 16. Newsp. Distr. Mags. 17. Other 18. Outdoor (Posters, Transit) 19. Point of Purchase20. Premiums, Novelties
21. Product Samples 22. Special Events Mktg. 23. Spot Radio 24. Spot T.V. 25. Weekly Newsp. 26. Yellow Page Adv.

Communispace Corporation — (Continued)

Mike Broderick *(Software Engr)*
Mike Butler *(Software Engr)*
Steven Pollard *(Applications Engr)*
Advertising Agency:
Greenough Communications
9 Harcourt St
Boston, MA 02116
Tel.: (617) 275-6500
Fax: (617) 275-6501
Online Customer Communities

COMMUNITY ISP, INC.
(d/b/a CISP)
3035 Moffat Rd
Toledo, OH 43615-1836
Tel.: (419) 867-6060
Fax: (419) 867-6913
E-mail: info@cisp.com
Web Site: www.cisp.cc
Approx. Sls.: $2,000,000
Approx. Number Employees: 39
Business Description:
Internet Web Hosting & Related Services
S.I.C.: 7375
N.A.I.C.S.: 518111
Advertising Expenditures: $200,000
Media: 13
Personnel:
Dustin Wade *(Pres)*
Jeffrey Klingshirn *(COO)*

COMPUTER MART
4052 Lawrenceville Hwy
Tucker, GA 30084-4621
Tel.: (770) 938-0486
Fax: (770) 934-6164
Toll Free: (877) 938-0486
E-mail: sales@computermart.com
Web Site: www.computermart.com
Approx. Number Employees: 15
Year Founded: 1982
Business Description:
Online Retailer of Computers & Computer Parts
S.I.C.: 5734
N.A.I.C.S.: 443120
Media: 4-13
Personnel:
Dave Carlson *(Owner)*

COMPUTERJOBS.COM, INC.
(Sub. of JobServe Ltd.)
280 Interstate N Pkwy SE Ste 300
Atlanta, GA 30339-2411
Tel.: (770) 850-0045
Fax: (770) 850-0369
Toll Free: (800) 850-0045
E-mail: info@computerjobs.com
Web Site: www.computerjobs.com
E-Mail For Key Personnel:
Marketing Director: marketing@computerjobs.com
Approx. Number Employees: 150
Year Founded: 1995
Business Description:
Online Employment Services for IT Professionals & Employers
S.I.C.: 7361; 7379
N.A.I.C.S.: 561310; 541519
Media: 8-10-13
Brands & Products:
COMPUTERJOBS.COM
WHERE THE BEST PEOPLE AND JOBS CLICK

COMPUTERS4SURE.COM
(Div. of 4SURE.com, Inc.)
6 Cambridge Dr
Trumbull, CT 06611-4746
Tel.: (203) 615-7000
Fax: (212) 497-7005
Toll Free: (800) 266-7883
E-mail: custcare@4sure.com
Web Site: www.computers4sure.com
Sales Range: $25-49.9 Million
Approx. Number Employees: 130
Year Founded: 1998
Business Description:
Internet Based Computer Product Superstore
S.I.C.: 5734; 5045
N.A.I.C.S.: 443120; 423430
Media: 7-8-13

COMSCORE, INC
11950 Democracy Dr Ste 600
Reston, VA 20190
Tel.: (703) 438-2000
Fax: (703) 438-2051
E-mail: press@comscore.com
Web Site: www.comscore.com
Approx. Rev.: $174,999,000
Approx. Number Employees: 920
Year Founded: 1997
Business Description:
Digital Marketing Intelligence Services
S.I.C.: 2741; 8742
N.A.I.C.S.: 516110; 541613
Advertising Expenditures: $220,000
Personnel:
Magid M. Abraham *(Co-Founder, Pres & CEO)*
Gian M. Fulgoni *(Exec Chm & Co-Founder)*
Kenneth J. Tarpey *(CFO)*
Eric Bosco *(COO)*
Gregory T. Dale *(COO)*
Chris Nicotra *(CIO)*
Linda Abraham *(CMO)*
Christiana L. Lin *(Chief Privacy Officer, Gen Counsel & Exec VP)*
Wolfgang Allisat *(Exec VP-Intl Markets)*
Will Hodgman *(Exec VP-Intl)*
Erin Hunter *(Exec VP)*
Bridget O'Toole *(Exec VP)*
Mark Donovan *(Sr VP-Mobile)*
Hugh McGoran *(Sr VP-Sls-Adv Agency-United States)*
Anthony Psacharopoulos *(Sr VP)*
Dan Piech *(Product Mgr)*

COMTEX NEWS NETWORK, INC.
625 N Washington St Ste 301
Alexandria, VA 22314
Tel.: (703) 820-2000
Fax: (703) 820-2005
Toll Free: (800) 266-8399
E-mail: sales@comtex.com
Web Site: www.comtex.com
E-Mail For Key Personnel:
Sales Director: sales@comtex.com
Public Relations: pr@comtexnews.net
Approx. Rev.: $6,401,518
Approx. Number Employees: 26
Year Founded: 1980
Business Description:
Online News Distribution Services
S.I.C.: 7383; 7389
N.A.I.C.S.: 519110; 541990; 561439
Advertising Expenditures: $19,000
Media: 13
Personnel:
C. W. Gilluly *(Chm)*
Chip Brian *(Pres & CEO)*

CONCUR TECHNOLOGIES, INC.
18400 NE Union Hill Rd
Redmond, WA 98052-3332
Tel.: (425) 702-8808
Fax: (425) 702-8828
Toll Free: (877) 426-6287
E-mail: investor_relations@concur.com
Web Site: www.concur.com
Approx. Rev.: $292,936,000
Approx. Number Employees: 1,200
Year Founded: 1993
Business Description:
Workplace E-Commerce Solutions
S.I.C.: 7372; 7371
N.A.I.C.S.: 334611; 511210; 541511
Advertising Expenditures: $8,521,000
Media: 13-17
Personnel:
S. Steven Singh *(Chm & CEO)*
Rajeev Singh *(Pres & COO)*
Frank Pelzer *(CFO)*
Kyle Sugamele *(Chief Legal Officer & Corp Sec)*
Robert Cavanaugh *(Exec VP & Gen Mgr-North America)*
Michael L. Eberhard *(Exec VP & Gen Mgr-Asia Pacific)*
Tom DePasquale *(Exec VP-Strategy)*
Michael W. Hilton *(Exec VP-Worldwide Mktg)*
Michael T. Koetting *(Exec VP-Supplier Mgmt & Adv)*
Meghan Kiernan *(Sr Dir-Adv-Tripit.com & Concur)*
Brands & Products:
CLICK. DONE.
CONCUR
CONCUR AUDIT
CONCUR CLIQBOOK TOOL
CONCUR CLIQBOOK TRAVEL
CONCUR CONNECT
CONCUR EXPENSE
CONCUR INTELLIGENCE
CONCUR INVOICE
CONCUR MOBILE
CONCUR PAY
CONCUR TRAVEL & EXPENSE
ONE TOUCH BUSINESS TRAVEL
SMART EXPENSES
Advertising Agencies:
Oceanos Marketing, Inc.
99 Derby St Ste 305
Hingham, MA 02043
Tel.: (781) 804-1010
Fax: (617) 687-8008

Weber Shandwick-Seattle
605 5th Ave S Ste 900
Seattle, WA 98104
Tel.: (425) 452-5400
Fax: (425) 452-5397

CONDE NAST DIGITAL
(Unit of Conde Nast Publications, Inc.)
1166 Avenue of the Americas 15th Fl
New York, NY 10036
Tel.: (212) 790-5100
Fax: (212) 790-1822
Web Site: www.condenastdigital.com
Approx. Number Employees: 125
Year Founded: 1995
Business Description:
Fashion, Relationship, Food, Travel & Health Web Sites
S.I.C.: 2741
N.A.I.C.S.: 516110
Media: 13
Personnel:
Sarah Chubb *(Pres)*
Debi Chirichella *(COO)*
Drew Schutte *(Chief Revenue Officer & Sr VP)*
Eileen Mulloy *(Publr-Epicurious)*
Amy Junger *(Sr VP-Fin & Plng)*
Ted Nadeau *(Sr VP & Gen Mgr)*
Elizabeth Stafford *(VP-Mktg)*
Richard Glosser *(Exec Dir-Emerging Media)*
Sandor Marik *(Exec Dir-Bus Dev & Performance Mktg)*
Brands & Products:
CONCIERGE.COM
EPICURIOUS.COM
FLIP.COM
MEN.STYLE.COM
NUTRITIONDATA.COM
STYLE.COM

CONNEXUS CORP.
(Name Changed to Epic Media Group Inc.)

CONSUMERREVIEW, INC.
(Div. of Invenda Corporation)
100 Marine Pkwy Ste 550
Redwood Shores, CA 94065
Tel.: (650) 264-4800
Fax: (650) 264-4841
Web Site: www.consumerreview.com
E-Mail For Key Personnel:
Sales Director: jthomas@consumerreview.com
Sales Range: $1-9.9 Million
Approx. Number Employees: 30
Year Founded: 1998
Business Description:
Consumer Product Information Services
S.I.C.: 2741
N.A.I.C.S.: 516110
Media: 10-13
Personnel:
Dadi Akhavan *(Co-Founder, Pres & CMO)*
Francis Cebedo *(Founder & Gen Mgr)*
Michael Foley *(Gen Mgr-Product)*
Jim Thomas *(Mgr-Sls)*

COOKING.COM
4086 Del Rey Ave
Marina Del Rey, CA 90292
Tel.: (310) 450-3270
Fax: (310) 450-0655
E-mail: advertising@cooking.com
Web Site: www.cooking.com
Approx. Number Employees: 75
Year Founded: 1998
Business Description:
Housewares & Cooking Information
S.I.C.: 2741
N.A.I.C.S.: 516110
Media: 4-5-8-13
Personnel:
Tracy Randall *(CEO)*
David Gaeta *(Dir-Online Mktg)*
Laura Walse *(Product Mgr)*
Brands & Products:
COOKING.COM

Key to Media (For complete agency information see *The Advertising Red Books-Agencies* edition):
1. Bus. Publs. 2. Cable T.V. 3. Catalogs & Directories. 4. Co-op Adv. 5. Consumer Mags. 6. D.M. to Bus. Estab.7. D.M. to Consumers
8. Daily Newsp. 9. Exhibits/Trade Shows 10. Foreign 11. Infomercial 12. Internet Adv.13. Multimedia 14. Network Radio
15. Network T.V. 16. Newsp. Distr. Mags. 17. Other 18. Outdoor (Posters, Transit) 19. Point of Purchase20. Premiums, Novelties
21. Product Samples 22. Special Events Mktg. 23. Spot Radio 24. Spot T.V. 25. Weekly Newsp. 26. Yellow Page Adv.

COPERNIC INC.
(Sub. of Harris Computer Systems)
400 Jean-Lesage Blvd
Quebec, QC G1K 8W1, Canada
Tel.: (418) 527-0528
Fax: (418) 527-1751
Toll Free: (888) 725-2271
E-mail: mferland@copernic.com
Web Site: www.copernic.com
Approx. Rev.: $6,052,432
Approx. Number Employees: 25
Year Founded: 1985
Business Description:
Internet Marketing & Information Retrieval Services
S.I.C.: 2741; 7371; 7375
N.A.I.C.S.: 519130; 516110; 518111; 541511
Advertising Expenditures: $100,000
Media: 10-13
Personnel:
Marc Ferland *(Pres & CEO)*
Brands & Products:
COPERNIC AGENT
COPERNIC DESKTOP SEARCH
COPERNIC MEDIA SOLUTIONS
COPERNIC SUMMARIZER
COPERNIC TRACKER
MAMMA.COM
THE MOTHER OF ALL SEARCH ENGINES

CORNERWORLD CORPORATION
12404 Park Central Dr Ste 400
Dallas, TX 75251
Tel.: (214) 224-1081
Web Site: www.cornerworld.com
Approx. Sls.: $11,446,700,000
Approx. Number Employees: 27
Year Founded: 2004
Business Description:
Internet Publishing & Broadcasting
S.I.C.: 2741
N.A.I.C.S.: 516110
Advertising Expenditures: $100,761
Media: 13
Personnel:
Scott Beck *(Chm & CEO)*
V. Chase McCrea, III *(CFO)*
Marc Pickren *(CMO & Pres-Enversa Companies)*
David Fleming *(Dir-Corp Comm)*

COVISTA COMMUNICATIONS, INC.
4803 Hwy 58
Chattanooga, TN 37416-1826
Tel.: (423) 648-9700
Fax: (423) 648-9705
Toll Free: (800) 805-1000
Toll Free: (800) 864-4000
Toll Free: (888) 426-8478
Telex: 423 648 9705
E-mail: support@covista.com
Web Site: www.covista.com
Sales Range: $50-74.9 Million
Approx. Number Employees: 60
Year Founded: 1983
Business Description:
High-Speed Internet Access, Data Networking, International & Domestic Long-Distance Services
S.I.C.: 4813; 7375
N.A.I.C.S.: 517110; 517310; 518111
Media: 3-13-17-22
Personnel:
Henry G. Luken *(Chm)*
Warren Feldman *(Pres & CEO)*

CREDITCARDS.COM, INC.
13809 Research Blvd Ste 906
Austin, TX 78750
Tel.: (512) 996-8663
Web Site: www.creditcards.com
Sales Range: $25-49.9 Million
Approx. Number Employees: 30
Year Founded: 2002
Business Description:
Online Credit Card Marketplace
S.I.C.: 2741; 6141; 6371
N.A.I.C.S.: 516110; 522210; 525990
Advertising Expenditures: $19,800,000
Media: 13
Personnel:
Christopher J. Speltz *(CEO)*
Ben Woolsey *(Dir-Mktg)*
Advertising Agency:
Janine Gordon Associates
11 E 26th St
New York, NY 10010
Tel.: (212) 871-3020
Pub Rels

CRITICAL PATH, INC.
(Holding of General Atlantic LLC)
1215 Bordeaux Dr
Sunnyvale, CA 94085
Tel.: (415) 541-2500
Fax: (415) 520-5737
Toll Free: (877) 441PATH
E-mail: info@criticalpath.net
Web Site: www.criticalpath.net
Sales Range: $25-49.9 Million
Approx. Number Employees: 203
Year Founded: 1997
Business Description:
Internet Messaging Products & Services
S.I.C.: 4899; 2741; 7371; 7372; 7375
N.A.I.C.S.: 517910; 511210; 516110; 518111; 541511
Advertising Expenditures: $648,000
Media: 2-7-10-13-22
Personnel:
Mark J. Ferrer *(Chm)*
Mark E. Palomba *(CEO)*
Tim Noel *(CFO)*
Barry Twohig *(Exec VP-Engrg)*
Brands & Products:
CRITICAL PATH
MEMOVA

CROIX CONNECT
8130 Boone Blvd Ste 240
Vienna, VA 22182
Tel.: (703) 584-0284
Fax: (703) 905-9053
E-mail: sales@croixconnect.com
Web Site: www.croixconnect.com
Sales Range: $1-9.9 Million
Approx. Number Employees: 7
Year Founded: 2001
Business Description:
Internet Information Services
S.I.C.: 7375; 7371
N.A.I.C.S.: 518111; 541511
Media: 13
Personnel:
Brian Roberts *(Founder & CEO)*
Myron Radio *(Exec VP-Mgmt Consulting)*
Donna Weyh Roberts *(Sr VP & Board Member)*
Brands & Products:
CROIX CONNECT
LINKING PEOPLE, IDEAS, AND BUSINESS

CRUCIAL TECHNOLOGY DIV OF MICRON
(Sub. of Micron Technology, Inc.)
3475 Commercial Ct
Meridian, ID 83642-6041
Tel.: (208) 363-5790
Fax: (208) 363-5501
E-mail: crucialgeneralmanager@micron.com
Web Site: www.crucial.com
Sales Range: $125-149.9 Million
Approx. Number Employees: 300
Business Description:
Flash Memory Distr
S.I.C.: 5065
N.A.I.C.S.: 423690
Media: 3-5-6-13-14-15-24-26
Personnel:
Steve R Appleton *(Chm & CEO)*
Rick D'Ambrosio *(Mgr-Mktg)*
Roddy McLean *(Mktg Mgr-Tech)*
Ed Walker *(Mgr-Adv)*
Brands & Products:
BALLISTIX
CRUCIAL
GIZMO!
PCI EXPRESS
RADEON

CRUTCHFIELD CORPORATION
1 Crutchfield Park
Charlottesville, VA 22911
Tel.: (434) 817-1000
Fax: (434) 817-1010
E-mail: media@crutchfield.com
Web Site: www.crutchfield.com
Sales Range: $200-249.9 Million
Approx. Number Employees: 500
Year Founded: 1974
Business Description:
Mail Order & E-Commerce Services
S.I.C.: 5961
N.A.I.C.S.: 454113
Media: 4-5-8-13-23
Personnel:
Bill Crutchfield *(Founder & CEO)*
Rick Souder *(Exec VP-Mdsg)*
Kurt Goodwin *(Sr Dir)*
Chris Lilley *(Sr Dir-HR)*

CYBERPLEX INC.
1255 Bay St 4th Fl
Toronto, ON M5R 2A9, Canada
Tel.: (416) 597-8889
Fax: (416) 597-2345
Toll Free: (888) 597-8889
E-mail: investor@cyberplex.com
Web Site: www.cyberplex.com
Approx. Rev.: $108,874,178
Approx. Number Employees: 192
Business Description:
Provider of Internet Software Development Services
S.I.C.: 7371
N.A.I.C.S.: 541511
Media: 13
Personnel:
Vernon F. Lobo *(Chm)*
Ted Hastings *(Pres)*
Geoffrey Rotstein *(CEO)*
Richard Maisel *(CFO)*
David Katz *(Gen Counsel & Exec VP-Corp Dev)*
David Benoliel *(VP-Sls & Mktg)*
Salim Teja *(VP-Adv Ops)*
Chris Varney *(VP-Publ Ops)*
Brands & Products:
ACTIONS SPEAK LOUDER
CYBERPLEX

CYBERSETTLE, INC.
1700 E Putnam Ave
Old Greenwich, CT 06870
Tel.: (914) 286-5600
Fax: (914) 684-2020
Toll Free: (888) 656-3600
E-mail: support@cybersettle.com
Web Site: www.cybersettle.com
E-Mail For Key Personnel:
Marketing Director: jzissu@cybersettle.com
Sales Range: $1-9.9 Million
Approx. Number Employees: 9
Year Founded: 1996
Business Description:
Software Solutions for the Resolution of Claims Settlements
S.I.C.: 7389
N.A.I.C.S.: 541990
Media: 2-7-10-20-26
Personnel:
MaryAnn Jennings *(Gen Counsel & Sr VP)*
Michael S. Carey *(Sr VP)*
Brands & Products:
CASE CLOSED
CHANGING THE WAY AMERICA SETTLES DISPUTES
CHANGING THE WAY THE WORLD SETTLES DISPUTES
CYBERSETTLE
CYBERSETTLE IT
THE FASTEST WAY TO MAKE A CASE HISTORY
SETTLE DISPUTES AT THE SPEED OF THE INTERNET
SWIFT JUSTICE
WHY SUE WHEN YOU CAN CYBERSETTLE?
THE WORLD'S FIRST INTERNET DISPUTE RESOLUTION SYS
THE WORLD'S FIRST ONLINE CLAIM RESOLUTION SYSTEM

DAS ACQUISITION COMPANY, LLC
12140 Woodcrest Exec Dr Ste 150
Saint Louis, MO 63141
Tel.: (314) 628-2000
Fax: (314) 628-2035
Toll Free: (877) 434-4555
E-mail: uppys@aol.com
Web Site: www.usamortgage.com
Sales Range: $5-14.9 Billion
Approx. Number Employees: 200
Business Description:
Mortgage Loans & Services
S.I.C.: 6163
N.A.I.C.S.: 522310
Media: 6-7-8-13
Personnel:
Douglas Schukar *(Pres & CEO)*
Linda Pring *(Exec VP)*
Stephanie Todd *(Mgr-Mktg)*

Key to Media (For complete agency information see *The Advertising Red Books-Agencies* edition):
1. Bus. Publs. 2. Cable T.V. 3. Catalogs & Directories. 4. Co-op Adv. 5. Consumer Mags. 6. D.M. to Bus. Estab.7. D.M. to Consumers
8. Daily Newsp. 9. Exhibits/Trade Shows 10. Foreign 11. Infomercial 12. Internet Adv.13. Multimedia 14. Network Radio
15. Network T.V. 16. Newsp. Distr. Mags. 17. Other 18. Outdoor (Posters, Transit) 19. Point of Purchase20. Premiums, Novelties
21. Product Samples 22. Special Events Mktg. 23. Spot Radio 24. Spot T.V. 25. Weekly Newsp. 26. Yellow Page Adv.

DELTATHREE, INC.
224 W 35th St
New York, NY 10001
Tel.: (212) 500-4850
Tel.: (212) 500-4836 (Media Rels)
Fax: (212) 500-4888
E-mail: pr@deltathree.com
Web Site: www.deltathree.com
Approx. Rev.: $14,200,000
Approx. Number Employees: 39
Year Founded: 1996
Business Description:
Internet Protocol Network Manager
S.I.C.: 4813; 7375
N.A.I.C.S.: 517310; 517110; 518111
Advertising Expenditures: $4,100,000
Media: 13
Personnel:
Robert Stevanovski *(Chm)*
Efraim Baruch *(CEO)*
Arie Rand *(CFO & Treas)*
Peter Scott Friedman *(Gen Counsel & Sec)*
Todd T. Stone *(VP-Bus Dev & Sls)*
Neta Issacof *(Dir-Mktg)*

DEMAND MEDIA, INC.
1299 Ocean Ave Ste 500
Santa Monica, CA 90401
Tel.: (310) 394-6400
Web Site: www.demandmedia.com
Approx. Rev.: $252,936,000
Approx. Number Employees: 600
Year Founded: 2006
Business Description:
Social Media Content Development & Distribution Services
S.I.C.: 7371; 7372
N.A.I.C.S.: 541511; 511210; 519130
Advertising Expenditures: $2,230,000
Media: 10-13-22
Personnel:
Richard M. Rosenblatt *(Co-Founder, Chm & CEO)*
Shawn Colo *(Co-Founder & Exec VP-Corp Dev)*
Charles S. Hilliard *(Pres & CFO)*
Drew Atherton *(CFO & COO-Platform)*
David E. Panos *(CMO)*
Joanne K. Bradford *(Chief Revenue Officer)*
Matthew P. Polesetsky *(Gen Counsel & Exec VP)*
Will Ballard *(Exec VP-Tech & Engrg)*
Michael L. Blend *(Exec VP-Registrar Svcs)*
Larry D. Fitzgibbon *(Exec VP-Media & Ops)*
Steven Kydd *(Exec VP-Demand Studios)*
Courtney Montpas *(Exec VP-People Ops)*
Justin Newton *(Exec VP-IT Ops)*
Joe Perez *(Exec VP-Product)*
Byron Reese *(Exec VP-Innovation)*
Steve Semelsberger *(Sr VP & Gen Mgr-Social Solutions)*
Crid Yu *(Sr VP-Strategic Partnerships)*
Nicolas Schoenlaub *(VP-HR)*
Dan'l Hewitt *(Dir-Strategic Accounts-EMEA)*

DG FASTCHANNEL, INC.
750 W John Carpenter Fwy Ste 700
Irving, TX 75039-2508
Tel.: (972) 581-2000
Fax: (972) 581-2001
E-mail: info@dgfastchannel.com
Web Site: www.dgfastchannel.com
Approx. Rev.: $247,528,000
Approx. Number Employees: 897
Year Founded: 1991
Business Description:
Digital Technology & Information Distribution Services
S.I.C.: 4899; 2741; 7319; 7374; 7389
N.A.I.C.S.: 561499; 516110; 517410; 517919; 518210; 519190; 541870; 541890
Personnel:
Scott K. Ginsburg *(Chm & CEO)*
Neil H. Nguyen *(Pres & COO)*
Omar A. Choucair *(CFO)*
Pamela Maythenyi *(Sr VP-SourceEcreative)*
Advertising Agency:
Atomic Public Relations
735 Market St 4th Fl
San Francisco, CA 94103
Tel.: (415) 402-0230
Fax: (415) 402-0237
Communications Strategy
Executive Positioning
Media Strategy
Public Relations Agency of Record
Search
Social Media
Video

DGB LUGGAGE & LEATHER LLC
(d/b/a The Luggage Center)
4340 Almaden Expy Ste 100
San Jose, CA 95118
Tel.: (408) 266-5398
Fax: (408) 266-5474
Toll Free: (800) 450-2400
Approx. Number Employees: 175
Year Founded: 1927
Business Description:
Online Luggage, Business Cases & Travel Accessories Retailer
S.I.C.: 5948
N.A.I.C.S.: 448320
Advertising Expenditures: $200,000
Media: 3-5-6-9-23-24-25

DIABETICSUPPLIES.COM, INC.
614 E Main St Ste 103
Vancouver, WA 98604
Tel.: (360) 833-8000
Fax: (360) 833-1674
Toll Free: (877) 787-7543
E-mail: csr@diabeticsupplies.com
Web Site: www.diabeticsupplies.com
Sales Range: $1-9.9 Million
Approx. Number Employees: 8
Business Description:
Diabetic Supplies Online Retailer
S.I.C.: 5961
N.A.I.C.S.: 454111
Media: 6-13
Personnel:
Bryan Luna *(Pres & CEO)*

DIAMOND.COM
(Sub. of ICE.com, Inc.)
4058 Jean Talon W Suite 200
Montreal, QC H4P 1V5, Canada
Tel.: (514) 393-9788
Toll Free: (877) 602-3817
Toll Free: (888) DIAMOND
E-mail: info@diamond.com
Web Site: www.diamond.com
Approx. Number Employees: 100
Year Founded: 1999
Business Description:
Diamonds, Jewelry & Watches Online Retailer
S.I.C.: 5961
N.A.I.C.S.: 454111
Media: 4-8-13
Personnel:
Mayer Gniwisch *(Pres)*
Schmuel Gniwisch *(CEO)*
Michael Krebs *(CFO)*
Moshe Krasnanski *(COO)*
Yona Shtern *(CMO)*
Pinny Ginwisch *(Chief Motivational Officer)*
Susan Galasso *(Sr VP-Brand)*
Pardo Vincelli *(VP-Customer Care)*
Alan Woolff *(VP-Mdsg)*
Julie Schwartz *(Dir-Design)*
Brands & Products:
ASHFORD.COM
DIAMOND.COM
WORLDOFWATCHES.COM

DICE HOLDINGS, INC.
1040 Ave of the Americas 16th Fl
New York, NY 10018
Tel.: (212) 725-6550
Fax: (212) 725-6559
Toll Free: (888) 321-DICE
Web Site: www.dice.com
Approx. Rev.: $128,997,000
Approx. Number Employees: 338
Year Founded: 1994
Business Description:
Online Recruiting Services
S.I.C.: 7361; 7379
N.A.I.C.S.: 561310; 541519
Advertising Expenditures: $20,300,000
Media: 7-8-10-13
Personnel:
Scot W. Melland *(Chm, Pres & CEO)*
Michael P. Durney *(Sr VP-Fin & CFO)*
Constance E. Melrose *(VP-Treasury)*
Thomas M. Silver *(Sr VP-North America)*
Paul C. Melde *(VP-Tech)*
Brands & Products:
CLEARANCEJOBS.COM
DICE
DICE HOLDINGS
DICE.COM
EFINANCIALCAREERS
JOBSINTHEMONEY
TARGETED JOB FAIRS
Advertising Agency:
Publicis Modem
One Selleck St 2nd Fl
Norwalk, CT 06855
Tel.: (203) 295-0615
Fax: (203) 299-7060

DICE.COM
(Sub. of Dice Holdings, Inc.)
4101 NW Urbandale Dr
Urbandale, IA 50322-7928
Tel.: (515) 280-1144
Fax: (515) 280-1452
Toll Free: (877) 386-3323
E-mail: info@dice.com
Web Site: www.dice.com
Sales Range: $25-49.9 Million
Approx. Number Employees: 90
Year Founded: 1990
Business Description:
Online Staffing & Recruitment Services for Computer Professionals
S.I.C.: 7361; 8299
N.A.I.C.S.: 561310; 611430
Media: 13
Brands & Products:
DICE.COM

DIGITAL RIVER, INC.
9625 W 76th St Ste 150
Eden Prairie, MN 55344
Tel.: (952) 253-1234
Fax: (952) 253-8497
E-mail: publicrelations@digitalriver.com
Web Site: www.digitalriver.com
E-Mail For Key Personnel:
Marketing Director: marketing@digitalriver.com
Approx. Rev.: $363,226,000
Approx. Number Employees: 1,280
Year Founded: 1994
Business Description:
Outsourcing Services for Web Commerce & Online Marketing Solutions
S.I.C.: 8742; 7371; 7372
N.A.I.C.S.: 541613; 511210; 541511
Advertising Expenditures: $1,000,000
Media: 7-10-11-13
Personnel:
Thomas M. Donnelly *(Pres)*
Joel A. Ronning *(CEO)*
Stefan B. Schulz *(CFO)*
Kevin L. Crudden *(Gen Counsel & VP)*
Jeff Hemenway *(Grp VP-Games)*
Gerri Dyrek *(Assoc Dir-PR)*
Jennifer Jasinski *(Mgr-Mktg Comm)*
Kristin McKensie *(Mgr-PR)*
Brands & Products:
DIGITAL RIVER

DIGITALWORK, INC.
130 S Jefferson St Ste 100
Chicago, IL 60661
Tel.: (312) 379-5950
Fax: (312) 379-5952
Toll Free: (877) 496-7571
E-mail: customerservice@digitalwork.com
Web Site: www.digitalwork.com
E-Mail For Key Personnel:
Marketing Director: dglines@digitalwork.com
Approx. Number Employees: 15
Year Founded: 1998
Business Description:
Web Site Creation & Hosting for Small Businesses & Entrepreneurs
S.I.C.: 7375
N.A.I.C.S.: 518111
Media: 13
Brands & Products:
DIGITALWORK
I-WORKS
TOTALWEB

DISABOOM, INC.
7730 E Belleview Ave Ste A306
Denver, CO 80111
Tel.: (720) 407-6530
Fax: (720) 407-6531
E-mail: info@disaboom.com
Web Site: www.disaboom.com
Approx. Rev.: $752,152
Approx. Number Employees: 27
Year Founded: 2006

Key to Media (For complete agency information see *The Advertising Red Books-Agencies* edition):
1. Bus. Publs. 2. Cable T.V. 3. Catalogs & Directories. 4. Co-op Adv. 5. Consumer Mags. 6. D.M. to Bus. Estab.7. D.M. to Consumers 8. Daily Newsp. 9. Exhibits/Trade Shows 10. Foreign 11. Infomercial 12. Internet Adv.13. Multimedia 14. Network Radio 15. Network T.V. 16. Newsp. Distr. Mags. 17. Other 18. Outdoor (Posters, Transit) 19. Point of Purchase20. Premiums, Novelties 21. Product Samples 22. Special Events Mktg. 23. Spot Radio 24. Spot T.V. 25. Weekly Newsp. 26. Yellow Page Adv.

Business Description:
Online Services for People With Disabilities
S.I.C.: 2741
N.A.I.C.S.: 516110
Advertising Expenditures: $2,237,000
Media: 1-3-6-10-13-14-15-20-22
Personnel:
J. Glen House *(Chm & Chief Medical Advisor)*
Advertising Agency:
Cowboy
22 E 49th St 7th Flr
New York, NY 10017
Tel.: (212) 999-6557
Fax: (212) 691-6584

DISCOUNT SCHOOL SUPPLY
(Sub. of Excelligence Learning Corp.)
2 Lowr Ragsdale Dr
Monterey, CA 93940-5748
Tel.: (831) 333-2000
Fax: (831) 333-3610
E-mail: customerservice@discountschoolsupply.com
Web Site:
www.discountschoolsupply.com
Approx. Rev.: $10,200,000
Year Founded: 1994
Business Description:
Educational Books, Toys, Games & Software Online Retailer
S.I.C.: 5945
N.A.I.C.S.: 451120
Media: 13
Personnel:
Ron Elliott *(Pres & CEO)*
Kelly Crampton *(VP & Gen Mgr)*
Brands & Products:
COLORATIONS
Advertising Agency:
Child's Play Communications
135 W 29th St Ste 701
New York, NY 10001
Tel.: (212) 488-2060
Fax: (212) 488-2059

DISNEY INTERACTIVE MEDIA GROUP
(Formerly Walt Disney Internet Group)
(Sub. of The Walt Disney Company)
5161 Lankershim Blvd
North Hollywood, CA 91601
Tel.: (818) 623-3200
Fax: (818) 623-3577
Web Site: corporate.disney.go.com/wdig/
Sales Range: $50-74.9 Million
Approx. Number Employees: 200
Year Founded: 1995
Business Description:
Online Family Entertainment Services
S.I.C.: 7996
N.A.I.C.S.: 519130
Media: 13
Personnel:
James Pitaro *(Co-Pres)*
John Pleasants *(Co-Pres)*
Bruce Gordon *(CFO & Sr VP-Disney Interactive)*
Alan N. Braverman *(Sr Exec VP, Gen Counsel & Secretary)*
Larry Shapiro *(Exec VP-Bus Dev & Ops)*
Alex Seropian *(Sr VP & Gen Mgr-Core Games)*
Brooke Chaffin *(Sr VP-Women & Family)*
Brad Davis *(Sr VP-Sls & Mktg-Disney Online Media)*
Dave Dickman *(Sr VP-Digital Ad Sls)*
Mark L. Walker *(Sr VP-Disney.com)*
Sunir Kochhar *(VP-Product Dev & Ops)*
Mitchell Kreuch *(VP-Digital Ad Sls-Eastern Reg)*
Stan Liu *(VP-Product Dev)*
Garry Randall *(VP-HR)*
Brandy Phillips *(Sr Mgr-Comm)*
Ayrie Aranda *(Mgr-Sls & Digital Media-West Coast)*

DOLLARSTORE, INC.
2021 Business Ctr Dr Ste 102
Irvine, CA 92612
Tel.: (949) 261-7488
Fax: (949) 261-6626
Toll Free: (800) 705-5277
E-mail: contact@dollarstore.com
Web Site: www.dollarstore.com
E-Mail For Key Personnel:
President: rex@dollarstore.com
Approx. Sls.: $1,200,000
Approx. Number Employees: 8
Year Founded: 1998
Business Description:
Consumer Retail Store Franchiser Online Services
S.I.C.: 5961
N.A.I.C.S.: 454113
Media: 13
Personnel:
Rex Mehta *(Pres)*

DOTPHOTO, INC.
860 Lower Ferry Rd
West Trenton, NJ 08628
Tel.: (609) 643-0090
E-mail: support@dotphoto.com
Web Site: www.dotphoto.com
Sales Range: $75-99.9 Million
Approx. Number Employees: 25
Year Founded: 1999
Business Description:
Photo Printing & Image & Sound Archiving Services on the Internet
S.I.C.: 7371
N.A.I.C.S.: 541511
Advertising Expenditures: $200,000
Media: 2-6-10-13-19
Personnel:
Peter Macnee *(Pres & CEO)*
Tom Juhamo *(CFO)*
Brandon Lipson *(Dir-Mktg)*
Lisa Jaffee *(Dir-Mktg)*
Brands & Products:
CLICK & DELIVER
DOTPHOTO
MYHOROSCOPES
MYWALLPAPER
PICTAVISION
RINGTALKER
SHARE YOUR LIFE

DOUBLECLICK, INC.
(Sub. of Google Inc.)
111 8th Ave 10th Fl
New York, NY 10011
Tel.: (212) 271-2542
Fax: (212) 287-1203
Web Site: www.doubleclick.com
Approx. Rev.: $300,000,000
Approx. Number Employees: 1,200
Year Founded: 1996
Business Description:
Marketing Software Developer
S.I.C.: 7372; 7311; 7319
N.A.I.C.S.: 511210; 541810; 541890
Media: 7-13
Personnel:
Ruth Kirschner *(Dir-Advertiser Sls-Natl)*
Brands & Products:
DART
DART ENTERPRISE
DART FOR ADVERTISERS
DART FOR PUBLISHERS
DART SALES MANAGER
DART SEARCH
DOUBLECLICK
KLIPMART
MOTIF
PERFORMICS
Advertising Agency:
AKQA, Inc.
175 Varick St 10th Fl
New York, NY 10014
Tel.: (212) 989-2572
Fax: (212) 989-2363

DRUGSTORE.COM, INC.
411 108th Ave NE Ste 1400
Bellevue, WA 98004-8404
Tel.: (425) 372-3200
Fax: (425) 372-3800
E-mail: info@drugstore.com
Web Site: www.drugstore.com
Approx. Sls.: $456,507,000
Approx. Number Employees: 945
Year Founded: 1999
Business Description:
Online Retailer of Drug & Beauty Products
S.I.C.: 5912; 5961
N.A.I.C.S.: 446110; 454111
Advertising Expenditures: $34,200,000
Media: 4-13
Personnel:
Dawn Gould Lepore *(Chm, Pres & CEO)*
Tracy Wright *(CFO & VP)*
David Lonczak *(CMO & VP)*
Robert P. Potter *(Chief Acctg Officer & VP)*
Yukio Morikubo *(Gen Counsel & VP-Strategy)*
Julie Johnston *(VP-Mdsg)*
Brands & Products:
A VERY HEALTHY WAY TO SHOP
DRUGSTORE
DRUGSTORE.COM
EMED ALERT
EPUNCHCARD
FRIENT-TO-FRIEND
QUICK LISTS
RXML
SHOPPER'S UPDATE
THE SIMPLE WAY TO LOOK AND FEEL YOUR BEST
TEST DRIVE
THE UNCOMMON DRUGSTORE
WHAT'S IN STORE
YOUR LIST AND DESIGN

DXSTORM.COM INC.
824 Winston Churchill Blvd
Oakville, ON L6J 7X2, Canada
Tel.: (905) 842-8262
Fax: (905) 842-3255
Toll Free: (877) 397-8676
E-mail: info@dxstorm.com
Web Site: www.dxstorm.com
E-Mail For Key Personnel:
President: zoran@dxstorm.com
Approx. Rev.: $1,750,176
Year Founded: 1993
Business Description:
E-Commerce Solutions
S.I.C.: 7375; 7373; 7379
N.A.I.C.S.: 518111; 541512; 541519
Media: 7-13
Personnel:
Zoran Popovic *(Pres & CEO)*
Keith Pires *(Dir-Sls & Mktg)*
Brands & Products:
DXCART
DXCUSTOM
DXSHOP
DXSTORM
DXSTORM.COM
DXWEB

E! ONLINE, INC.
(Joint Venture of Comcast Corporation & General Electric Company)
5750 Wilshire Blvd
Los Angeles, CA 90036-3697
Tel.: (323) 954-2400
Fax: (323) 954-2660
Fax: (323) 954-2888
E-mail: info@eonline.com
Web Site: www.eonline.com
Sales Range: $400-449.9 Million
Approx. Number Employees: 1,400
Year Founded: 1996
Business Description:
Entertainment News & Celebrity Gossip
S.I.C.: 7375
N.A.I.C.S.: 518111
Media: 3-13
Personnel:
Suzanne Kolb *(Pres-E! Entertainment)*
Jennifer Davis *(VP-West Coast Sls)*
Lisa Working *(Supervisor-Editorial)*
Isabel Faustino Boley *(Exec Dir-Mktg Solutions)*
Gil Snyder *(Mktg Mgr)*
Tim Carroll *(Mgr-Adv)*
Brands & Products:
STLYE
Advertising Agencies:
Ad2One
246 Westminister Bridge Road
London, SE1 7PD, United Kingdom
Tel.: (44) 20 7401 0222
Fax: (44) 20 7401 0366

The1stMovement
1010 E Union St Ste 120
Pasadena, CA 91106
Tel.: (626) 689-4993
Fax: (626) 628-1991

E-REWARDS, INC.
8401 N Central Expy Ste 900 LB-38
Dallas, TX 75225
Tel.: (214) 782-2800
Fax: (214) 782-2900
Toll Free: (888) 203-6245
E-mail: info@e-rewards.com
Web Site: www.e-rewards.com
Sales Range: $150-199.9 Million
Approx. Number Employees: 800
Year Founded: 1999
Business Description:
Online Market Research Services
S.I.C.: 8732
N.A.I.C.S.: 541910

Key to Media (For complete agency information see *The Advertising Red Books-Agencies* edition):
1. Bus. Publs. 2. Cable T.V. 3. Catalogs & Directories. 4. Co-op Adv. 5. Consumer Mags. 6. D.M. to Bus. Estab.7. D.M. to Consumers
8. Daily Newsp. 9. Exhibits/Trade Shows 10. Foreign 11. Infomercial 12. Internet Adv.13. Multimedia 14. Network Radio
15. Network T.V. 16. Newsp. Distr. Mags. 17. Other 18. Outdoor (Posters, Transit) 19. Point of Purchase20. Premiums, Novelties
21. Product Samples 22. Special Events Mktg. 23. Spot Radio 24. Spot T.V. 25. Weekly Newsp. 26. Yellow Page Adv.

e-Rewards, Inc. — (Continued)

Personnel:
Hal Brierley *(Founder)*
Donald J. Carty *(Chm)*
Kurt Knapton *(Pres & CEO)*
Nathan Runnicles *(CFO)*
Bill Russo *(CMO & Exec VP)*
David Mellinger *(Exec VP-Corp Dev)*
Craig Stevens *(Exec VP-Sls-Americas)*
Miles Worne *(Exec VP-Comml)*
Joel Davis *(Sr VP-Tech)*
Steve Myers *(Sr VP-Ops)*
Patty Stone *(Sr VP-HR)*
Bryan Black *(Sr Dir-HR)*

Brands & Products:
E-REWARDS

Advertising Agency:
Brierley & Partners
8401 N Central Expy Ste 1000 LB-37
Dallas, TX 75225-4403
Tel.: (214) 760-8700
Fax: (214) 743-5511

EAGLE:XM

5105 E 41st Ave
Denver, CO 80216-4420
Tel.: (303) 320-5411
Fax: (303) 393-6584
Toll Free: (800) 426-5376
E-mail: extendedmedia@eaglexm.com
Web Site: www.eaglexm.com
Sales Range: Less than $1 Million
Approx. Number Employees: 70
Year Founded: 1956
Business Description:
Online Printing & Direct Marketing Production Services
S.I.C.: 2752; 8742
N.A.I.C.S.: 323110; 541613
Media: 4-7-13-26
Personnel:
Howard J. Harris *(Pres)*
William Schaefer *(COO)*
Joel I. Susel *(Sr VP-Sls & Solution Dev)*
Shell Watt *(VP-IT)*

Brands & Products:
AUTOMATIC MARKETING
BROADBAND INSIGHTS
THE MARKETING RESOURCE CENTER

EARTHCAM, INC.

84 Kennedy St
Hackensack, NJ 07601-5229
Tel.: (201) 488-1111
Fax: (201) 488-1119
E-mail: cammaster@earthcam.com
Web Site: www.earthcam.com
Approx. Number Employees: 20
Year Founded: 1996
Business Description:
Web Portal, Live Streaming Video & Broadcasting Services
S.I.C.: 8743
N.A.I.C.S.: 541820
Media: 13
Personnel:
Brian Cury *(Founder & CEO)*
Jim Kelly *(COO)*
Sean Maloney *(Sr VP & Dir-Sales-Mktg)*
John Patrick *(VP-Technology)*
Paula Matera *(Controller)*
Jim Griffin *(Gen Mgr)*
Justin Camerlengo *(Dir-Mktg)*

Brands & Products:
CONSTRUCTIONCAM
CONSTRUCTIONCAM LITE
CONTROL CENTER 5
EARTHCAM
MEGAPIXELCAM
NOTECAM
SECURITYCAM
TOURISMCAM
TRAFFICCAM

EARTHLINK, INC.

1375 Peachtree St
Atlanta, GA 30309
Tel.: (404) 815-0770
Fax: (404) 892-7616
Toll Free: (800) 395-8410
E-mail: presslink@earthlink.net
Web Site: www.earthlink.net
Approx. Rev.: $955,577,000
Approx. Number Employees: 1,870
Year Founded: 1994
Business Description:
Internet & Network Services
S.I.C.: 7375; 4813; 7371
N.A.I.C.S.: 518111; 517310; 541511
Import
Advertising Expenditures: $13,800,000
Media: 3-4-5-6-7-8-9-10-13-15-18-19-20-22-23-24-25-26
Distr.: Natl.
Personnel:
Rolla P. Huff *(Chm & CEO)*
Joseph M. Wetzel *(Pres & COO)*
Bradley A. Ferguson *(CFO & Exec VP)*
Barbara Dondiego *(CMO & Sr VP)*
Stacie Hagan *(Chief People Officer & Exec VP)*
Vikram Desai *(Pres-Natl Accts)*
Mae Squier-Dow *(Pres-Premier Bus Solutions)*
Samuel R. DeSimone, Jr. *(Gen Counsel, Sec & Exec VP)*
Kevin F. Brand *(Exec VP-Consumer Products & Support)*
Brian Fink *(Exec VP-Managed Svcs)*
James P. O'Brien *(Exec VP-Network Svcs & Customer Ops)*
Cardi M. Prinzi *(Exec VP-Mktg)*
Mark Droege *(Sr VP-Treasury & Corp Svcs)*
Dan Greenfield *(VP-Corp Comm)*
Sean? Cook *(Dir)*

Brands & Products:
EARTHLINK
EARTHLINK DSL
EARTHLINK PROTECTIONBLOG
EARTHLINK REVOLVES AROUND YOU
WE REVOLVE AROUND YOU

Advertising Agencies:
Bennett Kuhn Varner, Inc.
3390 Peachtree Rd 10th Fl
Atlanta, GA 30326
Tel.: (404) 233-0332
Fax: (404) 233-0302

Direct Partners
4755 Alla Rd
Marina Del Rey, CA 90292-6311
Tel.: (310) 482-4200
Fax: (310) 482-4201

Moxie Interactive Inc.
The Northyards 384 Northyards Blvd NW Ste 290
Atlanta, GA 30313-2440
Tel.: (404) 601-4500
Fax: (404) 601-4505

Whitespeed
29672 Zuma Bay Way
Malibu, CA 90265
Tel.: (310) 869-9979
Fax: (310) 899-3199

EASYLINK SERVICES CORPORATION

(Sub. of EasyLink Services International Corporation)
33 Knightsbridge Rd
Piscataway, NJ 08854
Tel.: (732) 652-3500
Fax: (732) 652-3810
Toll Free: (800) 624-5266
E-mail: sales@easylink.com
Web Site: www.easylink.com
E-Mail For Key Personnel:
Sales Director: sales@easylink.com
Approx. Rev.: $74,025,000
Approx. Number Employees: 310
Business Description:
Content & Document Management Software & Information & Records Management Services
S.I.C.: 7371; 4899; 7338
N.A.I.C.S.: 541511; 517910; 561410
Advertising Expenditures: $799,000
Media: 2-10-13

EBAGS, INC.

5500 ST 160
Greenwood Village, CO 80111-4801
Tel.: (303) 694-1933
Tel.: (303) 967-2276 (Pub Rels)
Fax: (303) 694-9491
Toll Free: (800) 725-8229
Toll Free: (800) 820-6126 (Customer Svc)
E-mail: info@ebags.com
Web Site: www.ebags.com
Approx. Number Employees: 68
Year Founded: 1998
Business Description:
Online Retailer of Bags & Accessories for Business, Sports & Travel
S.I.C.: 5948
N.A.I.C.S.: 448320
Advertising Expenditures: $550,000
Media: 4-6-13-25
Personnel:
Peter Cobb *(Co-Founder & Sr VP-Mktg)*
John Nordmark *(Chm, Pres & CEO)*
Vince Jones *(CEO)*
Wanda Gottschalk *(Chief Devel Officer)*
Mike Frazzini *(VP-Tech)*
Bernard Majeau *(Mgr-Product Design)*

Brands & Products:
EBAGS

EBATES.COM

333 Bryant St Ste 250
San Francisco, CA 94107
Tel.: (415) 908-2200
Tel.: (415) 618-0322
Fax: (415) 508-2399
E-mail: customerservice@ebates.com
Web Site: www.ebates.com
E-Mail For Key Personnel:
Marketing Director: marketing@ebates.com
Approx. Number Employees: 60
Year Founded: 1998
Business Description:
Internet Retailer
S.I.C.: 5961
N.A.I.C.S.: 454113
Advertising Expenditures: $250,000
Media: 1-13
Personnel:
Kevin H. Johnson *(CEO)*
Greg Kaplan *(CFO)*

EBAY INC.

2145 Hamilton Ave
San Jose, CA 95125-5905
Tel.: (408) 376-7400
Fax: (408) 376-7401
E-mail: info@ebay.com
Web Site: www.ebay.com
Approx. Rev.: $9,156,274,000
Approx. Number Employees: 17,700
Year Founded: 1995
Business Description:
Web-Based Auctions & Retail Services
S.I.C.: 5961
N.A.I.C.S.: 454112; 454111; 454113
Advertising Expenditures: $808,400,000
Media: 6-13-14-15
Personnel:
Pierre M. Omidyar *(Chm)*
John J. Donahoe *(Pres & CEO)*
Robert H. Swan *(CFO & Sr VP-Fin)*
Richelle Parham *(CMO-NA)*
Mark T. Carges *(CTO & Sr VP-Global Products-Marketplaces)*
Devin Wenig *(Pres-Global eBay Marketplaces Bus Unit)*
Michael R. Jacobson *(Gen Counsel, Sec & Sr VP-Legal Affairs)*
Elizabeth L. Axelrod *(Sr VP-HR)*
Alan Marks *(Sr VP-Corp Comm)*
Miriam Lahage *(VP & Gen Mgr-Fashion)*
Benaifer Reporter *(Head-HR)*
Dean Nelson *(Sr Dir-Global Foundation Svcs)*
Andrea Linett *(Dir-Creative-Fashion)*
Laurie Strangia *(Dir-Internet Mktg & Adv)*
Michael Blais *(Sr Mgr-Interactive Mktg)*
Jonas Klink *(Sr Product Mgr-Search Front-End & Global Accessibility Efforts)*

Brands & Products:
EBAY
EBAY LIVE AUCTIONS
EBAY MOBILE
EBAY MOTORS
EBAY PROFESSIONAL SERVICES
THE EBAY SHOP
EBAY STORE
EBAY TOOLBAR
HALF.COM
MY EBAY
THE WORLD'S ONLINE MARKETPLACE

Advertising Agencies:
BBDO New York
1285 Ave of the Americas 7th Fl
New York, NY 10019-6028
Tel.: (212) 459-5000

Creative Artists Agency

Key to Media (For complete agency information see *The Advertising Red Books-Agencies* edition):
1. Bus. Publs. 2. Cable T.V. 3. Catalogs & Directories. 4. Co-op Adv. 5. Consumer Mags. 6. D.M. to Bus. Estab.7. D.M. to Consumers
8. Daily Newsp. 9. Exhibits/Trade Shows 10. Foreign 11. Infomercial 12. Internet Adv.13. Multimedia 14. Network Radio
15. Network T.V. 16. Newsp. Distr. Mags. 17. Other 18. Outdoor (Posters, Transit) 19. Point of Purchase20. Premiums, Novelties
21. Product Samples 22. Special Events Mktg. 23. Spot Radio 24. Spot T.V. 25. Weekly Newsp. 26. Yellow Page Adv.

2000 Ave of the Stars
Los Angeles, CA 90067
Tel.: (424) 288-2000
Fax: (424) 288-2900

Mekanism, Inc.
640 Second St 3rd Fl
San Francisco, CA 94107
Tel.: (415) 908-4000
Fax: (415) 908-3993

Venables, Bell & Partners
201 Post St Ste 200
San Francisco, CA 94108
Tel.: (415) 288-3300
Fax: (415) 421-3683

EBIX INC.
5 Concourse Pkwy Ste 3200
Atlanta, GA 30328
Tel.: (678) 281-2020
Fax: (678) 281-2019
E-mail: info@ebix.com
Web Site: www.ebix.com
Approx. Rev.: $132,188,000
Approx. Number Employees: 1,179
Year Founded: 1976
Business Description:
Insurance & Financial Software Products & Services
S.I.C.: 7373; 7372; 7379
N.A.I.C.S.: 541512; 511210; 541519
Advertising Expenditures: $973,000
Media: 7-10
Personnel:
Robin Raina *(Chm, Pres & CEO)*
Robert F. Kerris *(CFO)*
Graham Prior *(Sr VP-Intl Bus & Intellectual Property)*
Warren Brinker *(VP-Global CRM Sls)*
Tom Chelston *(VP-Sls-Health Solutions)*
David Greiff *(VP-Sls-Health Solutions)*
Darren Joseph *(Corp VP-HR)*
Jose A. Lopez *(VP-Sls & Corp VP-LATAM)*
Larry Panetta *(VP-Sls-BPO)*
Michael Sladek *(VP-Exchange Sls)*
Brands & Products:
EBIX
EBIX ASP
EBIX.COM

EC OUTLOOK
5555 San Felipe Rd
Houston, TX 77056
Tel.: (713) 773-9922
Fax: (713) 773-9944
Toll Free: (888) 376-1203
E-mail: info@ecoutlook.com
Web Site: www.ecoutlook.com
Approx. Number Employees: 160
Year Founded: 1999
Business Description:
Value Chain Integration Applications Developer
S.I.C.: 7375
N.A.I.C.S.: 518111
Media: 13

ECOMPANYSTORE, INC.
5945 Cabot Pkwy Bldg 200 Ste 150
Alpharetta, GA 30005
Tel.: (678) 942-3100
Fax: (678) 942-3101
Toll Free: (877) 588-8932 (eCustomerCare)
Toll Free: (800) 975-6467 (Sales)
E-mail: info@ecompanystore.com
Web Site: www.ecompanystore.com
Approx. Number Employees: 84
Year Founded: 1998
Business Description:
Internet-Based, Business-to-Enterprise Solutions for the Management & Procurement of Custom Logo Merchandise
S.I.C.: 5961
N.A.I.C.S.: 454111
Advertising Expenditures: $300,000
Media: 13
Personnel:
Campbell B. Lanier, III *(Chm)*
Craig Callaway *(CEO)*
Jeff Camp *(CFO)*
Ann Reda *(Mktg Mgr)*

ECOST.COM, INC.
(Sub. of PC Mall, Inc.)
200 N Sepulveda Blvd Ste 101
El Segundo, CA 90245
Tel.: (310) 658-5000
Toll Free: (877) 888-2678
E-mail: comments@ecost.com
Web Site: www.ecost.com
Sales Range: $150-199.9 Million
Approx. Number Employees: 93
Year Founded: 1999
Business Description:
Retailer of Discounted New, Close-Out & Refurbished Brand-Name Merchandise
S.I.C.: 5961
N.A.I.C.S.: 454111; 454113
Advertising Expenditures: $3,609,000
Media: 8-13
Personnel:
Gary W. Guy *(Pres)*

ECRUSH.COM, INC.
(Sub. of Hearst Magazines Digital Media)
2035 W Wabansia Fl 2
Chicago, IL 60647
Tel.: (773) 384-5131
Fax: (773) 384-5620
E-mail: bizdev@ecrush.com
Web Site: www.ecrush.com
E-Mail For Key Personnel:
President: karen@ecrush.com
Approx. Number Employees: 8
Year Founded: 1996
Business Description:
Teen Social Networking Website Operator
S.I.C.: 2741
N.A.I.C.S.: 519130
Media: 6-13
Brands & Products:
ECRUSH
ESPIN-THE-BOTTLE
SURVEYS4TEENS
TRUTHQUIZ

EDIETS.COM, INC.
1000 Corporate Dr Ste 600
Fort Lauderdale, FL 33334
Tel.: (954) 360-9022
Fax: (954) 360-9095
Toll Free: (800) 265-6170
E-mail: corp@ediets.com
Web Site: www.ediets.com
Approx. Rev.: $23,357,000
Approx. Number Employees: 48
Year Founded: 1996
Business Description:
Subscription-Based Weight-Loss Programs Using Proprietary Software to Generate Customized Diet Programs
S.I.C.: 7299
N.A.I.C.S.: 812990; 812191
Advertising Expenditures: $9,000,000
Media: 8-13-15-17
Personnel:
Kevin A. Richardson, II *(Chm)*
Kevin N. McGrath *(Pres & CEO)*
Thomas Hoyer *(CFO)*
Jennifer Hartnett *(CMO)*
Laura Klein *(Sr VP-Corp Svcs)*
Robert Smedley *(Sr VP-Sls & Member Svcs)*
Lianne de Moya *(Sr Dir-Mktg & Bus Unit Dev)*
Pamela Ofstein *(Dir-Nutrition Svcs)*
Brands & Products:
A WHOLE NEW YOU
DIET SMART
DR. PHIL
EDIETS
EDIETS.COM
THE ZONE
Advertising Agencies:
Imarketing Ltd, Inc.
20 Nassau St Ste 250E
Princeton, NJ 08542
Tel.: (609) 921-0400
Digital Assignment

Karlin+Pimsler
1375 Broadway Ste 1400
New York, NY 10018
Tel.: (212) 779-2111
Tel.: (212) 779-3375
Fax: (212) 779-4154
Direct Response TV - Creative

EDMUNDS, INC.
1620 26th St Ste 400 S Tower
Santa Monica, CA 90404
Tel.: (310) 309-6300
Fax: (310) 309-6400
E-mail: info@edmunds.com
Web Site: www.edmunds.com
Approx. Number Employees: 370
Year Founded: 1966
Business Description:
New & Used Car Online Information Services
S.I.C.: 2741
N.A.I.C.S.: 516110
Media: 6-8-13
Personnel:
Peter Steinlauf *(Chm)*
Avi Steinlauf *(Pres)*
Jeremy P. Anwyl *(CEO)*
Karren Fink *(VP-HR)*
Paul Seredynski *(Exec Editor)*
Warren Clarke *(Editor-Automotive Content)*
John DiPietro *(Editor-Automotive)*
Josh Jacquot *(Editor-Road Test)*
Jay Kavanagh *(Engr Editor)*
Doug Lloyd *(Sr Copy Editor)*
Bryn MacKinnon *(Editor)*
Philip Reed *(Editor-Consumer Advice)*
James Riswick *(Editor-Automotive)*
Brent Romans *(Editor)*
Josh Sadler *(Assoc Editor)*
Mark Takahashi *(Editor)*
Chris Walton *(Chief Road Test Editor)*
Jessica Caldwell *(Dir-Pricing & Indus Analysis)*
Dan Edmunds *(Dir-Vehicle Testing)*
Al Austria *(Engr)*
Mike Schmidt *(Coord-Vehicle Testing)*
Brands & Products:
EDMUNDS
EDMUNDS AUTOOBSERVER
EDMUNDS CARSPACE
EDMUNDS DATA SERVICES
EDMUNDS INSIDE LINE
EDMUNDS.COM
TMV
TRUE COST TO OWN
WHERE SMART CAR BUYERS START

EFAX.COM INC.
(Sub. of J2 Global Communications, Inc.)
6922 Hollywood Blvd 5th Fl
Los Angeles, CA 90028-6128
Tel.: (323) 817-3207
Fax: (650) 327-6003
Toll Free: (800) EFAXCOM
E-mail: advertising@efax.com
Web Site: www.efax.com
Sales Range: $75-99.9 Million
Approx. Number Employees: 200
Year Founded: 1988
Business Description:
Fax-to-Email Service
S.I.C.: 3577
N.A.I.C.S.: 334119
Media: 2-13
Personnel:
Scott Turicchi *(Exec VP)*
Mike Pugh *(VP-Mktg-j2 Global Comm)*
Kyle Flowers *(Dir-Mktg-Fax Products)*
Joe Cervera *(Sr Acct Exec)*
Brands & Products:
E FAX BROADCAST
E FAX CORPORATE
E FAX FREE
E FAX PLUS
EASY FAXING ANYWHERE

EGAIN COMMUNICATIONS CORPORATION
345 E Middlefield Rd
Mountain View, CA 94043
Tel.: (650) 230-7500
Fax: (650) 230-7600
Toll Free: (888) 603-4246
E-mail: pr@egain.com
Web Site: www.egain.com
Approx. Rev.: $29,877,000
Approx. Number Employees: 272
Year Founded: 1997
Business Description:
Customer Communications Solutions for Companies Engaged in E-Commerce
S.I.C.: 7372; 7371
N.A.I.C.S.: 334611; 511210; 541511
Advertising Expenditures: $289,000
Media: 1-6-7-8-10-13-25
Personnel:
Ashutosh Roy *(Co-Founder, Chm & CEO)*
Eric N. Smit *(CFO)*
Andrew Mennie *(Sr VP & Gen Mgr-Europe)*
Promod Narang *(Sr VP-Products & Technologies)*
Thomas Michael Hresko *(Sr VP-Worldwide Sls)*
Charles Jepson *(Sr VP-Bus Dev)*
Sam Hahn *(VP-Engrg)*
Anand Subramaniam *(VP-Mktg)*

Key to Media (For complete agency information see *The Advertising Red Books-Agencies* edition):
1. Bus. Publs. 2. Cable T.V. 3. Catalogs & Directories. 4. Co-op Adv. 5. Consumer Mags. 6. D.M. to Bus. Estab.7. D.M. to Consumers
8. Daily Newsp. 9. Exhibits/Trade Shows 10. Foreign 11. Infomercial 12. Internet Adv.13. Multimedia 14. Network Radio
15. Network T.V. 16. Newsp. Distr. Mags. 17. Other 18. Outdoor (Posters, Transit) 19. Point of Purchase20. Premiums, Novelties
21. Product Samples 22. Special Events Mktg. 23. Spot Radio 24. Spot T.V. 25. Weekly Newsp. 26. Yellow Page Adv.

eGain Communications Corporation — (Continued)

Brands & Products:
AUTHOR ONCE
CONTENT ADAPTER
DATA ADAPTER
EGAIN
EGAIN ADMINISTRATOR
EGAIN ADVISOR
EGAIN AUTOCLASSIFY
EGAIN AUTOWORKFLOW
EGAIN CALL TRACK
EGAIN CAMPAIGN
EGAIN CASEBASE
EGAIN CHAT
EGAIN CHATBOT
EGAIN CIH
EGAIN COBROWSE
EGAIN CONSOLES
EGAIN CTI ADAPTER
EGAIN CUSTOMERS
EGAIN DASHBOARD
EGAIN EMAIL ADAPTER
EGAIN FAX
EGAIN INFERENCE ENGINE
EGAIN INFORM
EGAIN INTERACTIONS
EGAIN IVR
EGAIN KNOWLEDGEAGENT
EGAIN KNOWLEDGEBASE
EGAIN LIVE
EGAIN LIVEWEB
EGAIN MAIL
EGAIN MALL
EGAIN MESSAGE CENTER
EGAIN MONITOR
EGAIN NOTIFY
EGAIN ON-DEMAND
EGAIN REPORTS
EGAIN SECURE MAIL
EGAIN SELF SERVICE
EGAIN SERVICE
EGAIN SERVICEEXPRESS
EGAIN SME
EGAIN SMS
EGAIN SURVEY
EGAIN USERS
EGAIN WEBFORMS
EGAIN WORKFLOW ENGINE
EGAIN WORKFLOWS
ESERVICE
KNOWLEDGEAGENT
ONDEMAND
OUTLOOK PLUGIN
SELFSERVICE
SHAREPOINT
TRUSTED BY LEADERS

EHARMONY.COM, INC.
300 N Lake Ave Ste 1111
Pasadena, CA 91101
Tel.: (626) 795-4814
Fax: (626) 585-4040
E-mail: media@eharmony.com
Web Site: www.eharmony.com
Approx. Number Employees: 130
Year Founded: 1998
Business Description:
Internet Dating Services
S.I.C.: 7299
N.A.I.C.S.: 812990
Media: 3-6-13
Personnel:
Neil Clark Warren *(Chm)*
Greg Steiner *(Pres & COO)*
Steve Carter *(Sr Dir-Res & Dev)*
Lindsey Digrado *(Asst Mgr-Mktg)*
Brands & Products:
EHARMONY
REAL PEOPLE. REAL ADVICE.
Advertising Agencies:
DonatWald+Haque
1316 Third St Ste 301
Santa Monica, CA 90401
Tel.: (310) 394-1717
Fax: (310) 394-1716

OMD Worldwide
195 Broadway
New York, NY 10007
Tel.: (212) 590-7100

EHEALTH, INC.
440 E Middlefield Rd
Mountain View, CA 94043
Tel.: (650) 584-2700
Fax: (650) 961-2153
Toll Free: (877) 456-7180
E-mail: headquarters@ehealth.com
Web Site: www.ehealthinsurance.com
Approx. Rev.: $160,404,000
Approx. Number Employees: 641
Year Founded: 1997
Business Description:
Holding Company; Internet-Based Marketer & Retailer of Health Insurance Products & Services
S.I.C.: 6719; 6321; 6411
N.A.I.C.S.: 524210; 524114; 524298; 551112
Advertising Expenditures: $49,277,000
Media: 7-8-13
Personnel:
Gary L. Lauer *(Chm & CEO)*
Stuart M. Huizinga *(CFO & Sr VP)*
Sheldon X. Wang *(CTO & Exec VP-Tech)*
Samuel C. Gibbs, III *(Pres-eHealth Govt Sys)*
Bruce A. Telkamp *(Exec VP-Bus & Corp Dev)*
Robert S. Hurley *(Sr VP-Carrier Rels)*
Brian Mast *(VP-Comm)*
Nate Purpura *(Dir-PR & Social Media)*
Kate Sidorovich *(Dir-IR)*

THE ELECTRIC MAIL COMPANY
(Sub. of J2 Global Communications, Inc.)
Ste 300 3999 Henning Dr
Burnaby, BC V5C 6P9, Canada
Tel.: (604) 482-1111
Fax: (604) 482-1110
Fax: (888) 735-3631
Toll Free: (800) 419-7463
E-mail: info@electricmail.com
Web Site: www.electricmail.com
Sales Range: $1-9.9 Million
Approx. Number Employees: 23
Year Founded: 1994
Business Description:
Electronic Messaging Services
S.I.C.: 7373; 7379
N.A.I.C.S.: 541512; 541519
Media: 13
Personnel:
John Boyce *(Co-Founder & CTO)*
Ian J. McDonald *(VP-Sls & Gen Mgr)*
Adam Hyde *(Dir-Product Strategy)*
Chris Hyde *(Dir-Dev & Network Ops)*
Brands & Products:
MESSAGING MAESTRO
SPAMSMART

ELEMENT K LLC
(Sub. of NIIT Technologies Limited)
500 Canal View Blvd
Rochester, NY 14623-2800
Tel.: (585) 240-7500
Fax: (585) 240-7760
Toll Free: (800) 456-4677
E-mail: jobs@elementk.com
Web Site: www.elementk.com
Approx. Sls.: $25,000,000
Approx. Number Employees: 800
Year Founded: 1982
Business Description:
Internet-Based Training
S.I.C.: 7373; 7371; 7372; 8243
N.A.I.C.S.: 541512; 511210; 541511; 611420
Media: 2-10-13
Personnel:
Vijay Thadani *(Chm)*
Paul Krause *(Pres & CEO)*
Bill Steinmetz *(CIO)*
Heather Mapstone *(Gen Counsel & VP)*
Daniel Cleveland *(Sr VP)*
Jim Morris *(Sr VP-Sls)*
Donna Maxwell *(VP-HR)*
David Snider *(Sr Dir-Mktg)*
Brands & Products:
CISCO
COMPTIA
EC-COUNCIL
ELEMENT K
GETABSTRACT
KNOWLEDGEHUB
VLAB
VLABS

ELEMICA, INC.
222 Valley Creek Blvd Ste 220
Wayne, PA 19341
Tel.: (610) 786-1200
Fax: (610) 786-1240
Toll Free: (888) 247-8878
E-mail: info@elemica.com
Web Site: www.elemica.com
Sales Range: $25-49.9 Million
Approx. Number Employees: 55
Year Founded: 2000
Business Description:
E-Commerce for the Chemical Industry
S.I.C.: 7375
N.A.I.C.S.: 518111
Media: 10-17
Personnel:
Christoper Michael McGuigan *(CEO)*
Scott Miltenberger *(CFO)*
Bradley Delizia *(Gen Counsel & Sr VP)*
Rich Katz *(Sr VP-Product Mgmt)*
Rob Guerriere *(Mgr-Product Line)*
Brands & Products:
ELEMICA
ELEMICA BUYER DIRECT
ELEMICA CONNECTED SOLUTION
ELEMICA SELLER DIRECT
ELEMICA SUPPLY CHAIN HOSTED SOLUTION
MANAGE YOUR CONNECTION
TRANSLINK

ELITE PARTNER SOLUTIONS LLC
(d/b/a QwikBids.com)
8889 E Bell Rd Ste 102
Scottsdale, AZ 85260
Tel.: (480) 751-1009
Fax: (480) 455-5117
Toll Free: (888) 794-5243
E-mail: info@qwikbids.com
Web Site: www.qwikbids.com
Approx. Number Employees: 10
Business Description:
Web Based Service Linking Consumers to Products & Services
S.I.C.: 7375
N.A.I.C.S.: 518111
Media: 6-10-13
Personnel:
Dave Collins *(Co-Founder)*
Cathy Collins *(COO)*
Advertising Agency:
Ubiquity Public Relations
1840 E Berridge Ln
Phoenix, AZ 85016
Tel.: (602) 268-6849

ELLE.COM
(Unit of Hachette Filipacchi Holdings, Inc.)
1633 Brdwy 44th Fl
New York, NY 10019
Tel.: (212) 767-5800
Tel.: (212) 76-7 5930
Fax: (212) 767-5330
E-mail: elleinteractive@elle.com
Web Site: www.elle.com
Year Founded: 1996
Business Description:
Online Women's Magazine
S.I.C.: 2721
N.A.I.C.S.: 511120
Media: 13-22
Personnel:
Jack Kliger *(Pres & CEO)*
Steve Parr *(CFO & Exec VP)*
Robin Domeniconi *(Sr VP & Chief Brand Officer)*
Kevin Martinez *(Publr-Brand & VP)*
Roberta Myers *(Editor-in-Chief)*
Brands & Products:
ELLE.COM

ELLIE MAE, INC.
4155 Hopyard Rd Ste 200
Pleasanton, CA 94588
Tel.: (925) 227-7000
Fax: (925) 227-9030
Toll Free: (877) 355-4362
E-mail: info@elliemae.com
Web Site: www.elliemae.com
Approx. Rev.: $43,234,000
Approx. Number Employees: 190
Year Founded: 1997
Business Description:
Electronic Mortgage Origination Network; Software Publisher
S.I.C.: 2741; 6163; 7372; 7379
N.A.I.C.S.: 516110; 511210; 522310; 541519
Advertising Expenditures: $211,000
Media: 7-13-17-22
Personnel:
Sigmund Anderman *(Pres & CEO)*
Edgar A. Luce *(CFO & Exec VP-Fin/Admin)*
Jonathan H. Corr *(Chief Strategic Officer & Exec VP-Bus Dev/Product Strategy)*
Joseph H. Langner *(Chief Sls Officer & Exec VP-Sls/Client Implementation)*
Limin Hu *(CTO & Exec VP-Tech/Ops)*
Elisa Lee *(Gen Counsel, Sec & VP)*
Felicia Egan *(Dir-Mktg)*

Key to Media (For complete agency information see *The Advertising Red Books-Agencies* edition):
1. Bus. Publs. 2. Cable T.V. 3. Catalogs & Directories. 4. Co-op Adv. 5. Consumer Mags. 6. D.M. to Bus. Estab.7. D.M. to Consumers
8. Daily Newsp. 9. Exhibits/Trade Shows 10. Foreign 11. Infomercial 12. Internet Adv.13. Multimedia 14. Network Radio
15. Network T.V. 16. Newsp. Distr. Mags. 17. Other 18. Outdoor (Posters, Transit) 19. Point of Purchase20. Premiums, Novelties
21. Product Samples 22. Special Events Mktg. 23. Spot Radio 24. Spot T.V. 25. Weekly Newsp. 26. Yellow Page Adv.

Brands & Products:
CENTERWISE
CONTOUR
ELLIE MAE
ELLIE MAE NETWORK
ENCOMPASS360

EMUSIC.COM, INC.
(Sub. of Dimensional Associates, LLC)
244 5th Ave Ste 2070
New York, NY 10001
Tel.: (212) 201-9240
E-mail: info@emusic.com
Web Site: www.emusic.com
Year Founded: 1998
Business Description:
Digital Music Distr
S.I.C.: 7389; 2741
N.A.I.C.S.: 512290; 516110
Media: 13
Personnel:
Deirdre Stone *(Sr VP-Product Dev)*
Yancey Strickler *(Sr Dir-Editorial & Features)*
Advertising Agencies:
Maloney & Fox
89 5th Ave 4th Fl
New York, NY 10003
Tel.: (212) 243-2000
Fax: (212) 243-5500

MMB
580 Harrison Ave
Boston, MA 02118
Tel.: (617) 670-9700
Fax: (617) 670-9711

Sarkissian Mason
135 W 26th St 5 Fl
New York, NY 10001
Tel.: (212) 625-8212
Fax: (212) 625-8211
Branding

EN POINTE TECHNOLOGIES, INC.
(Sub. of Din Global Corp.)
18701 S Figueroa St
Gardena, CA 90248-4506
Tel.: (310) 337-5200
Fax: (310) 338-4855
E-mail: marketing@enpointe.com
Web Site: www.enpointe.com
Approx. Sls.: $300,462,000
Approx. Number Employees: 1,200
Year Founded: 1993
Business Description:
Computer Products Mfr & Services
S.I.C.: 3572; 5045; 7373
N.A.I.C.S.: 334112; 423430; 541512
Advertising Expenditures: $498,000
Media: 5-7-22-26
Personnel:
Mansoor S. Shah *(Chm)*
Attiazaz Din *(Pres & CEO)*
Javed Latif *(CFO)*
Brands & Products:
ACCESSPOINTE
ACCESSPOINTE PRO
EN POINTE
ENTRENCHED WITH EXPERIENCE, ARMED WITH TECHNOLOGY
SUPPLY ACCESS

EOLAS TECHNOLOGIES, INC.
10 E Ontario St Ste 5106
Chicago, IL 60611
Tel.: (630) 871-3343
Fax: (630) 221-0192
E-mail: info@eolas.com
Web Site: www.eolas.com
Approx. Number Employees: 5
Year Founded: 1994
Business Description:
Information Technology Services
S.I.C.: 7379
N.A.I.C.S.: 541519
Media: 1-2-13-22
Personnel:
Michael D. Doyle *(Chm)*
Mark C. Swords *(CEO)*
Brands & Products:
DARK IRON
EOLAS
INVENTED HERE
METAMAP
MUSART
MUSE
THE SAGA SYSTEM
TICKLE
WEB ROUSER
ZMAP

EOS INTERNATIONAL, INC.
2292 Faraday Ave
Carlsbad, CA 92008-7208
Tel.: (760) 431-8400
Fax: (760) 431-8448
Web Site: www.eosintl.com
E-Mail For Key Personnel:
Sales Director: sales@eosintl.com
Approx. Number Employees: 455
Year Founded: 1999
Business Description:
Holding Company; Consumer Goods
S.I.C.: 5963
N.A.I.C.S.: 454390
Media: 8
Personnel:
William S. Walsh *(Chm)*
Gregory Leiser *(VP-Fin)*
Salvatore Provenza *(VP-Sls & Mktg)*

EPHONAMATION.COM INC.
(d/b/a Ansafone Communications)
145 E Columbine Ave
Santa Ana, CA 92707
Tel.: (714) 560-1000
Fax: (714) 565-1035
Toll Free: (800) 938-9009
E-mail: sales@ansafone.com
Web Site: www.ansafone.com
E-Mail For Key Personnel:
President: rharmat@ansafone.com
Sales Director: sales@ansafone.com
Approx. Number Employees: 90
Year Founded: 1970
Business Description:
Telecommunications Services
S.I.C.: 4899
N.A.I.C.S.: 517910
Media: 10-13-26
Personnel:
Randall J. Harmat *(CEO)*
Robert Martinez *(Mgr-Ops)*
Brands & Products:
ANSAFONE COMMUNICATIONS

EPIC MARKETPLACE
(Sub. of Epic Media Group Inc.)
512 7th Avenue 12th Floor
New York, NY 10018
Tel.: (212) 308-8509
Toll Free: (866) 891-0300
Web Site: www.epicmarketplace.com
E-Mail For Key Personnel:
Sales Director: sales@epicmarketplace.com
Year Founded: 2011
Business Description:
Distribution Platform for Marketers Using Social Media, Mobile, Display, Search, Rich Media & Video
N.A.I.C.S.: 541890
Media: 13
Personnel:
Don Mathis *(CEO & Pres)*
Young Kim *(Exec VP-Fin)*
Charles Nowaczek *(COO)*
Chirs Pirrone *(Exec VP & Gen Mgr)*
Mike Sprouse *(CMO)*

EPIC MARKETPLACE, INC.
(Formerly Traffic Marketplace, Inc.)
(Sub. of Epic Media Group Inc.)
139 Townsend St Ste 250
San Francisco, CA 94107
Tel.: (415) 821-8850
Web Site: www.epicmarketplace.com
E-Mail For Key Personnel:
Sales Director: sales.inquiry@theepicmediagroup.com
Business Description:
Online Advertising Services Including Account Management, Performance Analysis & Media Planning
S.I.C.: 2741
N.A.I.C.S.: 516110
Media: 13
Personnel:
Chris Pirrone *(Exec VP & Gen Mgr-Premium Display, Mobile & Video Adv)*
Lynn D'Alessandro *(Sr VP-Sls)*
Jana Massey *(Sr Dir-Media Ops)*

EPIC MEDIA GROUP INC.
(Formerly Connexus Corp.)
512 7th Ave 12th Fl
New York, NY 10018
Tel.: (646) 315-9595
Web Site:
www.theepicmediagroup.com
Year Founded: 1999
Business Description:
Online Media & Performance-Based Marketing
S.I.C.: 2741
N.A.I.C.S.: 516110
Media: 13
Personnel:
Donald Mathis *(CEO)*
Brands & Products:
SCALE, FLEXIBILITY, AND PERFORMANCE

EPITONIC.COM
(Sub. of Palm Pictures, LLC)
601 W 26th St Ste 1150
New York, NY 10001
Tel.: (212) 320-3624
Fax: (212) 320-3709
E-mail: info@epitonic.com
Web Site: www.epitonic.com
Approx. Number Employees: 3
Year Founded: 1999
Business Description:
Online Digital Music Supplier
S.I.C.: 8743
N.A.I.C.S.: 541820
Media: 8-13
Personnel:
Jesse Ashlock *(Editor)*
Brands & Products:
EPITONIC

EPROJECT, INC.
1008 Western Ave Ste 500
Seattle, WA 98104-1032
Tel.: (206) 341-9117
Fax: (206) 341-9123
E-mail: sales@eproject.com
Web Site: www.eproject.com
E-Mail For Key Personnel:
Sales Director: sales@eproject.com
Approx. Number Employees: 80
Year Founded: 1997
Business Description:
Web-Based Project Management Services
S.I.C.: 7371
N.A.I.C.S.: 541511
Advertising Expenditures: $50,000
Media: 2-7-10-13
Personnel:
Steven Anderson *(COO)*
Chris Lynch *(VP-Engrg)*
Brands & Products:
EPROJECT
EPROJECT ENTERPRISE
EPROJECT EXPRESS
EPROJECT WORKGROUP

EQUITYSTATION, INC.
(Sub. of vFinance, Inc.)
3010 N Military Trl Ste 300
Boca Raton, FL 33431
Tel.: (561) 981-1000
Fax: (561) 422-4158
Toll Free: (888) 451-4545
Web Site: www.equitystation.com
Sales Range: $75-99.9 Million
Approx. Number Employees: 30
Year Founded: 1998
Business Description:
Electronic Securities Trading Systems & Support Services
S.I.C.: 6211
N.A.I.C.S.: 523120
Media: 13
Personnel:
Jonathan C. Rich *(Exec VP)*
Jody Giraldo *(VP)*

ERESEARCH TECHNOLOGY INC.
1818 Market St
Philadelphia, PA 19103-4001
Tel.: (215) 972-0420
Fax: (215) 972-0414
Toll Free: (866) 669-4324
E-mail: eresearch@ert.com
Web Site: www.ert.com
Approx. Rev.: $140,992,000
Approx. Number Employees: 647
Year Founded: 1977
Business Description:
Medical Diagnostic & Testing Web-Based Software & Consulting Services
S.I.C.: 7372; 7379; 8071; 8734; 8748
N.A.I.C.S.: 511210; 541380; 541519; 541690; 621511
Advertising Expenditures: $1,200,000
Media: 2-10-13
Personnel:
Elam M. Hitchner, III *(Chm)*
Jeffrey S. Litwin *(Pres & CEO)*
Keith D. Schneck *(CFO & Exec VP)*
Amy Furlong *(COO & Exec VP)*
Thomas P. Devine *(CIO & Exec VP)*

Key to Media (For complete agency information see *The Advertising Red Books-Agencies* edition):
1. Bus. Publs. 2. Cable T.V. 3. Catalogs & Directories. 4. Co-op Adv. 5. Consumer Mags. 6. D.M. to Bus. Estab.7. D.M. to Consumers 8. Daily Newsp. 9. Exhibits/Trade Shows 10. Foreign 11. Infomercial 12. Internet Adv.13. Multimedia 14. Network Radio 15. Network T.V. 16. Newsp. Distr. Mags. 17. Other 18. Outdoor (Posters, Transit) 19. Point of Purchase20. Premiums, Novelties 21. Product Samples 22. Special Events Mktg. 23. Spot Radio 24. Spot T.V. 25. Weekly Newsp. 26. Yellow Page Adv.

eResearch Technology Inc. — (Continued)

John B. Sory *(Chief Dev Officer & Exec VP)*
John M. Blakeley *(Chief Comml Officer & Exec VP)*
Anna Marie Pagliaccetti *(Gen Counsel)*
Robert S. Brown *(Sr VP-Strategic Mktg, Plng & Partnerships)*
George Tiger *(Sr VP-Global Sls)*
Valerie Mattern *(VP-HR)*
Brands & Products:
EDATA ENTRY
EDATA MANAGEMENT
EDICTIONARY
EHEALTH EDUCATION
ERESEARCH COMMUNITY
ERESNET
ERT
ESAFETY NET
ESITE MONITOR
ESTUDY CONDUCT
EXPERT
EXPERT DIRECT
EXPERT EPRO
GETTING IT DONE. RIGHT.
SUBSCRIPTION MANAGER

ESCHOOLMALL, INC.
2 Walnut Grove Dr Ste 190
Horsham, PA 19044
Tel.: (215) 444-9300
Fax: (215) 444-9200
Toll Free: (877) 969-7246
E-mail: information@eshoolmall.com
Web Site: www.eschoolmall.com
E-Mail For Key Personnel:
Marketing Director: thomasm@eschoolmall.com
Approx. Sls.: $4,000,000
Approx. Number Employees: 36
Year Founded: 1998
Business Description:
Internet-Based Purchasing & Administrative Services for Educators & Schools
S.I.C.: 5049; 2741
N.A.I.C.S.: 423490; 516110
Media: 4-10-13
Personnel:
Harry Goldberg *(VP-Mktg & Bus Dev)*
Brands & Products:
BIMS
EASYBID
EASYFORMS
EASYPAY
EASYPROJECT
EASYPURCHASE
EASYPURCHASE WAREHOUSE
EASYQUOTE
ESCHOOLMALL
SMARTAGENT

ESPIAL GROUP INC.
200 Elgin St Suite 900
Ottawa, ON K2P 1L5, Canada
Tel.: (613) 230-4770
Fax: (613) 230-8498
Toll Free: (888) 437-7425
Web Site: www.espial.com
Approx. Rev.: $11,957,262
Approx. Number Employees: 80
Business Description:
Internet Protocol Television Application Designer
S.I.C.: 7373; 2741
N.A.I.C.S.: 541512; 516110
Media: 10-22
Personnel:
Peter Seeligsohn *(Chm)*
Jaison Dolvane *(Pres & CEO)*
Carl Smith *(CFO)*
Kumanan Yogaratnam *(CTO & VP-Engrg)*
Nemer D. Abourizk *(Gen Counsel)*
Sanjay Mehta *(VP-Engrg)*
Kirk Edwardson *(Dir-Mktg)*

ESSENTIAL GROUP, INC.
1325 Tri-State Pkwy Ste 300
Gurnee, IL 60031-9161
Tel.: (847) 855-7676
Fax: (847) 855-9676
Toll Free: (888) 287-2722
E-mail: sales@essentialgroupinc.com
Web Site: www.essentialgroupinc.com
E-Mail For Key Personnel:
Sales Director: sales@essentialgroupinc.com
Sales Range: $50-74.9 Million
Approx. Number Employees: 87
Business Description:
Online Medical Content
S.I.C.: 8011; 8733
N.A.I.C.S.: 621111; 541720
Media: 2-5-7-13
Personnel:
Pradip K. Banerjee *(Chm)*
Dennis N. Cavender *(CFO & Exec VP)*
Julie A. Ross *(Sr VP-Clinical Ops)*
Brands & Products:
ESSENTIAL
ESSENTIAL NAVIGATION SYSTEM
ESSENTIAL PATIENT RECRUITMENT
EXPERIENCE ESSENTIAL.EXPERIENCE RESULTS.

ESURANCE, INC.
(Sub. of White Mountains Insurance Group, Ltd.)
650 Davis St
San Francisco, CA 94111
Tel.: (415) 875-4500
Fax: (415) 875-4501
Toll Free: (800) ESURANCE
E-mail: info@esurance.com
Web Site: www.esurance.com
Sales Range: $10-24.9 Million
Approx. Number Employees: 26
Year Founded: 1999
Business Description:
Internet-Based Personal Lines Insurance Supplier
S.I.C.: 6411
N.A.I.C.S.: 524210
Media: 2-6-8-9-13
Personnel:
Gary C. Tolman *(Pres & CEO)*
Jonathan Adkisson *(CFO)*
Christopher Henn *(COO)*
Phil Swift *(CIO)*
John Swigart *(CMO)*
Advertising Agency:
Leo Burnett Worldwide, Inc.
35 W Wacker Dr
Chicago, IL 60601-1723
Tel.: (312) 220-5959
Fax: (312) 220-3299
Agency of Record

ETHNICGROCER.COM, INC.
(Div. of Namaste Partners, Ltd.)
1090 Industrial Dr Ste 5
Bensenville, IL 60106
Tel.: (630) 860-1733
Fax: (630) 477-0207
E-mail: Support@EthnicGrocer.com
Web Site: www.ethnicgrocer.com
Sales Range: $25-49.9 Million
Approx. Number Employees: 60
Year Founded: 1998
Business Description:
Specialty Foods Online Retailer
S.I.C.: 5149
N.A.I.C.S.: 424490
Advertising Expenditures: $200,000
Media: 13

ETICA ENTERTAINMENT INC.
PO Box 2064
Escondido, CA 92033
Tel.: (760) 480-8791
Fax: (760) 480-8271
E-mail: support@truepath.com
Web Site: www.truepath.com
Approx. Number Employees: 4
Year Founded: 1997
Business Description:
Holding Company
S.I.C.: 6719
N.A.I.C.S.: 551112
Media: 13
Personnel:
Gil Vidals *(CEO)*

ETRONICS, INC.
(Sub. of Foto Electric Supply Co., Inc.)
216 Maspeth Ave
Brooklyn, NY 11211
Tel.: (212) 475-2450
Fax: (212) 475-3904
Toll Free: (800) 541-1490
E-mail: info@etronics.com
Web Site: www.etronics.com
E-Mail For Key Personnel:
Sales Director: sales@etronics.com
Approx. Number Employees: 50
Year Founded: 1999
Business Description:
Electronic Products, Videos, Music & Games Retailer
S.I.C.: 5731
N.A.I.C.S.: 443112
Advertising Expenditures: $550,000
Media: 2-13
Personnel:
Mayer Balser *(COO)*
Brands & Products:
ETRONICS.COM
SUPREME VIDEO
SUPREMEVIDEO.COM

EVEO INC.
1725 Montgomery St Ste 205
San Francisco, CA 94111
Tel.: (415) 749-6777
Fax: (415) 771-8718
E-mail: sales@eveo.com
Web Site: www.eveo.com
E-Mail For Key Personnel:
Marketing Director: marketing@eveo.com
Sales Director: sales@eveo.com
Approx. Sls.: $5,220,000
Approx. Number Employees: 50
Year Founded: 1999
Business Description:
Rich Media Publication Services
S.I.C.: 7313
N.A.I.C.S.: 541840
Media: 13
Personnel:
Olivier Zitoun *(Founder & CEO)*
Randey Arnold-Kraft *(Dir-HR)*
Brands & Products:
EVEO
RICH MEDIA MADE SIMPLE

EVERYCONTRACTOR, INC.
3600 N Rancho Dr
Las Vegas, NV 89130
Tel.: (702) 851-4730
E-mail: info@everycontractor.com
Web Site: www.everycontractor.com
Approx. Number Employees: 15
Year Founded: 1999
Business Description:
Internet Business Services for the Building & Construction Industry
S.I.C.: 7374
N.A.I.C.S.: 518210
Media: 2-3-4-5-6-7-8-9-10-13-14-15-16-23-24-25
Personnel:
Dave Johnson *(Owner & Pres)*

EVISION INTERNATIONAL, INC.
1888 Sherman St Ste 500
Denver, CO 80203
Tel.: (303) 894-7971
Fax: (303) 860-6001
E-Mail For Key Personnel:
Public Relations: ir@evisionusa.com
Sales Range: Less than $1 Million
Approx. Number Employees: 4
Year Founded: 1995
Business Description:
Financial Investment Group
S.I.C.: 6289; 8742
N.A.I.C.S.: 523999; 541611
Media: 13
Personnel:
Tony T.W. Chan *(CEO)*

EVITE.COM
(Sub. of IAC/InterActiveCorp)
8833 W Sunset Blvd
West Hollywood, CA 90069
Tel.: (310) 360-4500
Tel.: (408) 529-6277 (Pub Rels)
E-mail: marketing@evite.com
Web Site: www.evite.com
Sales Range: $10-24.9 Million
Approx. Number Employees: 26
Year Founded: 1998
Business Description:
Online Invitation Services
S.I.C.: 2741
N.A.I.C.S.: 516110
Media: 13
Advertising Agency:
CarryOn
5670 Wilshire Blvd
Los Angeles, CA 90036
Tel.: (323) 848-4300
Fax: (323) 848-4310
Toll Free: (888) 838-NEWS

EWINWIN, INC.
5334 Primrose Lake Circle
Tampa, FL 33647
Toll Free: (877) 571-2740
Web Site: www.eWinWin.com
Approx. Rev.: $1,800,000
Approx. Number Employees: 21
Year Founded: 2000
Business Description:
Custom Computer Programming Services

Key to Media (For complete agency information see *The Advertising Red Books-Agencies* edition):
1. Bus. Publs. 2. Cable T.V. 3. Catalogs & Directories. 4. Co-op Adv. 5. Consumer Mags. 6. D.M. to Bus. Estab.7. D.M. to Consumers
8. Daily Newsp. 9. Exhibits/Trade Shows 10. Foreign 11. Infomercial 12. Internet Adv.13. Multimedia 14. Network Radio
15. Network T.V. 16. Newsp. Distr. Mags. 17. Other 18. Outdoor (Posters, Transit) 19. Point of Purchase20. Premiums, Novelties
21. Product Samples 22. Special Events Mktg. 23. Spot Radio 24. Spot T.V. 25. Weekly Newsp. 26. Yellow Page Adv.

S.I.C.: 7371
N.A.I.C.S.: 541511
Personnel:
Greg Masaros *(Founder & CEO)*
Advertising Agency:
French/West/Vaughan, Inc.
112 E Hargett St
Raleigh, NC 27601
Tel.: (919) 832-6300
Fax: (919) 832-6360

EWORK
(Formerly eWork Healthcare)
(Sub. of ZeroChaos)
100 Spear St Ste 210
San Francisco, CA 94105
Tel.: (415) 546-4800
Fax: (415) 546-4889
E-Mail For Key Personnel:
Marketing Director: marketing@ework.com
Approx. Number Employees: 60
Year Founded: 1999
Business Description:
Healthcare Staffing Support Services
S.I.C.: 7361
N.A.I.C.S.: 561310
Advertising Expenditures: $500,000
Media: 13
Personnel:
Harold Mills *(CEO)*
Brands & Products:
EWORK
PROSOURCE

EXACTTARGET INC.
20 N Meridian St
Indianapolis, IN 46204
Tel.: (317) 423-3928
Fax: (317) 423-3928
Toll Free: (866) 362-4538
E-mail: info@exacttarget.com
Web Site: www.exacttarget.com
Sales Range: $50-74.9 Million
Approx. Number Employees: 280
Year Founded: 2000
Business Description:
Software Products Mfr
S.I.C.: 7372
N.A.I.C.S.: 511210
Media: 13-24
Personnel:
Scott Dorsey *(Co-Founder & CEO)*
Peter McCormick *(Co-Founder & Gen Mgr)*
Scott McCorkle *(COO)*
Tim Kopp *(CMO)*
Traci Dolan *(CFO-Fin Adm & Exec VP)*
Andy Kofoid *(Exec VP-Global Sls)*
Chip House *(VP-Industry & Relation Mktg Svcs)*
Jeff Rohrs *(VP-Mktg)*
Joel Book *(Dir-eMktg Education)*
Tracy Yeadon *(Dir-Sls Enablement & Sls Dev)*
Ryan Porter *(Sr Mgr-Creativity & Ideation)*
Advertising Agency:
Dittoe Public Relations, Inc.
2815 E 62nd St Ste 300
Indianapolis, IN 46220-2983
Tel.: (317) 202-2280
Fax: (317) 202-2290

EXPEDIA, INC.
333 108th Ave NE
Bellevue, WA 98004
Tel.: (425) 679-7200
Fax: (425) 564-7240
Toll Free: (800) EXPEDIA
E-mail: ir@expedia.com
Web Site: www.expedia.com
Approx. Rev.: $3,348,109,000
Approx. Number Employees: 8,900
Year Founded: 1994
Business Description:
Online Travel, Hotel & Automobile Services
S.I.C.: 4729; 2741
N.A.I.C.S.: 561599; 516110
Advertising Expenditures: $589,000,000
Media: 3-6-8-13-14-15-18-23-24
Personnel:
Barry Diller *(Chm & Sr Exec)*
Victor A. Kaufman *(Vice Chm)*
Dara Khosrowshahi *(Pres & CEO)*
Dhiren Fonseca *(Co-Pres-Partner Svcs)*
Gary Fritz *(Co-Pres-Partner Svcs)*
Michael B. Adler *(CFO & Exec VP)*
Will Daugherty *(Pres-Destination Svcs & Expert-Expedia Local)*
Scott Durchslag *(Pres-Worldwide)*
Robert Greyber *(Pres-Expedia Corp Travel)*
Burke Norton *(Gen Counsel, Sec & Exec VP)*
Stu Haas *(Treas & Sr VP-IR)*
Sean D. Kell *(Sr VP & Gen Mgr-Global Online & Customer Mktg)*
Pamela Keenan Fritz *(Sr VP-Americas-Egencia)*
Connie Symes *(Sr VP-HR)*
Andrew Warner *(Sr Dir-EMEA Mktg)*
Dana Fornasar *(Sr Mgr-Mktg)*
Ingrid Michelsen *(Sr Mgr-PassportAds)*
Brands & Products:
CLASSIC VACATIONS
EGENCIA
EXPEDIA
GO WITH CONFIDENCE
HOTELS.COM
HOTWIRE.COM
TRIPADVISOR
Advertising Agencies:
Fusion Idea Lab
506 N Clark St
Chicago, IL 60654
Tel.: (312) 670-9060
Fax: (312) 670-9061

GWP Brand Engineering
46 Spadina Ave Ste 200
Toronto, ON M5V 2H8, Canada
Tel.: (416) 593-4000
Fax: (416) 593-4001
Expedia.ca

The Martin Agency
One Shockoe Plz
Richmond, VA 23219-4132
Tel.: (804) 698-8000
Fax: (804) 698-8001

Ogilvy & Mather
(Sub. of WPP Group plc)
636 11th Ave
New York, NY 10036
Tel.: (212) 237-4000
Fax: (212) 237-5123
Pan-European

PHD
(An Omnicom Company)
220 E 42nd 7th Fl
New York, NY 10017
Tel.: (212) 894-6600
Fax: (212) 894-4100
European Media Planning & Buying

PointRoll Inc.
951 E Hector St
Conshohocken, PA 19428
Tel.: (267) 558-1300
Fax: (267) 285-1141
Toll Free: (800) 203-6956

Radarworks
1929 3rd Ave Ste 200
Seattle, WA 98101
Tel.: (206) 441-6657
Fax: (206) 441-4107

RealTime Media, Inc.
1060 1st Ave Ste 201
King of Prussia, PA 19406
Tel.: (610) 337-3600
Fax: (610) 337-2300

EXPERIAN CONSUMER DIRECT
(Sub. of Experian Information Solutions, Inc.)
18500 Von Karman Ave Ste 400
Irvine, CA 92612
Tel.: (949) 567-3800
Fax: (949) 222-0582
Toll Free: (888) 888-8553
E-mail: helpconsumerinfo@consumerinfo.com
Web Site: www.consumerinfo.com
Approx. Number Employees: 300
Year Founded: 1995
Business Description:
Credit Report Products & Services
S.I.C.: 7323; 2741
N.A.I.C.S.: 561450; 516110
Media: 13
Personnel:
Gerry Tschopp *(Sr VP-Pub Affairs)*
Dacy Yee *(Sr Dir-Emerging Media & Websites)*
Marcey Smith *(Dir-Adv)*
Jennifer Tan *(Mgr-SEM)*
Advertising Agency:
Doner
25900 Northwestern Hwy
Southfield, MI 48075
Tel.: (248) 354-9700
Fax: (248) 827-8440

FACEBOOK, INC.
156 University Ave
Palo Alto, CA 94301
Tel.: (650) 543-4800
Fax: (650) 543-4801
E-mail: press@facebook.com
Web Site: www.facebook.com
Sales Range: $1-4.9 Billion
Approx. Number Employees: 1,000
Year Founded: 2005
Business Description:
Online Directory Publisher
S.I.C.: 2741
N.A.I.C.S.: 511140; 516110
Media: 31
Personnel:
Mark Zuckerberg *(Founder & CEO)*
Andrew McCollum *(Co-Founder)*
Eduardo Saverin *(Co-Founder)*
Sean N. Packer *(Pres)*
David A. Ebersman *(CFO)*
Sheryl K. Sandberg *(COO)*
Theodore W. Ullyot *(Gen Counsel & VP)*
Tom Arrix *(VP-Sls-US)*
Blake Chandlee *(VP-Sls-Emerging Markets-Eastern Europe & Asia Pacific)*
Lori Goler *(VP-HR & Recruiting)*
Alexandre Hohagen *(VP-Sls-Latin America Reg)*
Joe Lockhart *(VP-Global Comm)*
Mike Murphy *(VP-Global Sls)*
Elliot Schrage *(VP-Comm & Mktg & Public Policy)*
Michael Schroepfer *(VP-Engrg)*
Joanna Shields *(VP-Bus Dev & Sls-Europe)*
Kevin Colleran *(Dir-Sls)*
Josh Rahn *(Dir-Sls)*
Ethan Beard *(Dir-Platfroom Mktg)*
Dan Coughlin *(Dir-Media Sls)*
Mark D'Arcy *(Dir-Global Creative Solutions-Adv Bus)*
Jocelyn Goldfein *(Dir-Engrg)*
Mike Hoefflinger *(Dir-Customer Mktg)*
Ji Lee *(Dir-Creative)*
Sarah Personette *(Dir-Global Agency Relations)*
Amin Zoufonoun *(Dir-Corp Dev)*
Mark Slee *(Mgr-Product)*
David Baser *(Product Mgr-Pages Insights)*
Peter Deng *(Product Mgr)*
Naomi Gleit *(Product Mgr)*
Jared Morgenstern *(Product Mgr-Games & Credits)*
Kate O'Neill *(Product Mgr)*
Blake Ross *(Product Mgr)*
Keith Schacht *(Product Mgr)*
Carl Sjogreen *(Product Mgr-Platform)*
Brian Wheelis *(Mgr-Agency Mgmt Ops)*
Dhiraj Kumar *(Strategist-Mobile, Customer Mktg-Global)*
Kay Madati *(Strategist-Entertainment & Customer Mktg-Global)*
Advertising Agency:
OutCast Communications
123 Townsend St Ste 500
San Francisco, CA 94107
Tel.: (415) 392-8282
Fax: (415) 392-8281

FACTSET RESEARCH SYSTEMS INC.
601 Merritt 7 3rd Fl
Norwalk, CT 06851
Tel.: (203) 810-1000
Fax: (203) 810-1001
E-mail: webmaster@factset.com
Web Site: www.factset.com
Approx. Rev.: $641,059,000
Approx. Number Employees: 4,116
Year Founded: 1978
Business Description:
Online Integrated Financial Information & Analytical Applications for Investment Professionals
S.I.C.: 2741; 6371; 7371; 7374
N.A.I.C.S.: 516110; 518210; 525990; 541511
Media: 2-7-10-13-20
Personnel:
Philip A. Hadley *(Chm & CEO)*
Charles J. Snyder *(Vice Chm)*
Peter G. Walsh *(COO & Exec VP)*

Key to Media (For complete agency information see *The Advertising Red Books-Agencies* edition):
1. Bus. Publs. 2. Cable T.V. 3. Catalogs & Directories. 4. Co-op Adv. 5. Consumer Mags. 6. D.M. to Bus. Estab.7. D.M. to Consumers
8. Daily Newsp. 9. Exhibits/Trade Shows 10. Foreign 11. Infomercial 12. Internet Adv.13. Multimedia 14. Network Radio
15. Network T.V. 16. Newsp. Distr. Mags. 17. Other 18. Outdoor (Posters, Transit) 19. Point of Purchase20. Premiums, Novelties
21. Product Samples 22. Special Events Mktg. 23. Spot Radio 24. Spot T.V. 25. Weekly Newsp. 26. Yellow Page Adv.

FactSet Research Systems Inc. — (Continued)

Townsend Thomas *(Chief Content Officer & Sr VP)*
Michael D. Frankenfield *(Exec VP & Dir-Sls-Global)*
Chris Ellis *(Sr VP & Dir-US Investment Mgmt Sls)*
Kieran M. Kennedy *(Sr VP & Dir-Sls Ops)*
Maurizio Nicolelli *(Principal Fin Officer & Sr VP)*
Steve Greiner *(Dir-Portfolio Risk Res)*

FAIR ISAAC CORPORATION

(d/b/a FICO)
901 Marquette Ave Ste 3200
Minneapolis, MN 55402
Tel.: (612) 758-5200
Fax: (415) 492-5691
Toll Free: (800) 999-2955
E-mail: info@fairisaac.com
Web Site: www.fairisaac.com
E-Mail For Key Personnel:
Marketing Director: marketing@fairisaac.com
Approx. Rev.: $605,643,000
Approx. Number Employees: 1,485
Year Founded: 1956
Business Description:
Decision Management Solutions, Security Software & Credit Scoring Services
S.I.C.: 8733; 6099; 7372; 7389
N.A.I.C.S.: 541710; 511210; 522390; 561499
Export
Advertising Expenditures: $3,000,000
Media: 2-7-10-13-17-22
Personnel:
A. George Battle *(Chm)*
Mark N. Greene *(CEO)*
Michael J. Pung *(CFO & Sr VP)*
Richard S. Deal *(Chief HR Officer & Sr VP)*
Andrew N. Jennings *(Chief Analytics Officer & Sr VP)*
Mark R. Scadina *(Gen Counsel, Sec & Exec VP)*
Charles L. Ill, III *(Exec VP-Sls, Svcs & Mktg)*
Deborah Kerr *(Chief Product Officer & Exec VP)*
Lynn Johnson *(Mgr-Analyst Rels)*
Brands & Products:
BUREAUXLINK
CAPSTONE
THE CONSTRUCTION LENDER
CREDIT CAPACITY INDEX
CREDITDESK
DEBT MANAGER
DYNAMATCH
EXPANSION
FAIR ISAAC
FAIR ISAAC BLAZE ADVISOR
FALCON
FICO
FICO SCORE SIMULATOR
IT'S JUST A SMARTER WAY TO DO BUSINESS
LENSTAR
LIQUIDCREDIT
LSAMS
MARKETSMART DECISION SYSTEM
MASTERCARD
MIRA
MYFICO
NEXTGEN FICO
PAYMENT OPTIMIZER
PLACEMENTSPLUS
PRESCORE
PROPERTY PREDICTR
RECOVERY MANAGEMENT SYSTEM
ROAMEX
SCORENET
SMARTADVISOR
STRATEGY MACHINE
STRATEGYWARE
TELADAPTIVE
TREEVIEW
TRIAD
VECTUS
VISTA

FAMILY EDUCATION NETWORK

(Sub. of Pearson, Inc.)
501 Boylston St Ste 900
Boston, MA 02116-4398
Tel.: (617) 542-6500
Fax: (617) 542-6564
E-mail: salesdevelopment@fen.com
Web Site: www.familyeducation.com
E-Mail For Key Personnel:
Sales Director: salesdevelopment@fen.com
Approx. Number Employees: 100
Year Founded: 1990
Business Description:
Educational Material Online Services
S.I.C.: 7375; 2721
N.A.I.C.S.: 518111; 511120
Media: 1-7-8-13

FARMS.COM LTD.

1790 Dundas St Unit 5
London, ON N5W 3E5, Canada
Tel.: (519) 438-5729
Fax: (519) 438-3152
Toll Free: (877) 438-5729
E-mail: info@farms.com
Web Site: www.farms.com
Sales Range: $25-49.9 Million
Approx. Number Employees: 40
Year Founded: 1995
Business Description:
Online Livestock & Agriculture Market Data
S.I.C.: 9641
N.A.I.C.S.: 926140
Advertising Expenditures: $750,000
Media: 2-7-10-13-18-19-20-21-22
Personnel:
David Gilmour *(Chm)*
Graham Dyer *(Pres & CEO)*
Eric Spell *(Pres-AgCareers)*
Joseph Dales *(Sr VP & Dir)*
Todd Crowe *(Gen Mgr)*
Jack Tichy *(Gen Mgr-PigCHAMP)*
Brands & Products:
AGCAREERS.COM
CYBERCROP.COM
FARMS.COM
PIG CHAMP

FILECONTROL INC.

77 Sugar Creek Center Blvd Ste 200
Sugar Land, TX 77478
Tel.: (713) 355-1111
Fax: (713) 355-1112
Toll Free: (888) 463-4643
E-mail: sales@filecontrol.com
Web Site: www.filecontrol.com
E-Mail For Key Personnel:
Sales Director: sales@filecontrol.com
Approx. Sls.: $2,000,000
Approx. Number Employees: 20
Year Founded: 1997
Business Description:
Document Management Applications & Services
S.I.C.: 7389; 7379
N.A.I.C.S.: 561499; 541519
Media: 13
Personnel:
Ahmad O. Mian *(Founder, Pres & CEO)*

FIRECLICK, INC.

(Div. of Digital River, Inc.)
2355 Northside Dr Ste B-250
San Diego, CA 92108
Tel.: (650) 917-7600
Fax: (650) 887-2983
Toll Free: (800) 364-4656
E-mail: salesinfo@fireclick.com
Web Site: www.fireclick.com
Sales Range: $10-24.9 Million
Approx. Number Employees: 25
Year Founded: 1999
Business Description:
Provider of Web Experience Management Solutions
S.I.C.: 7375
N.A.I.C.S.: 518111
Media: 13

FIRST INTERNATIONAL COMPUTER OF AMERICA, INC.

(Sub. of First International Computer, Inc.)
(d/b/a FICA)
5020 Brandin Ct
Fremont, CA 94538-3140
Tel.: (510) 252-7777
Fax: (510) 252-8888
E-mail: sales@fica.com
Web Site: www.fica.com
E-Mail For Key Personnel:
Marketing Director: mktg@fica.com
Sales Director: sales@fica.com
Approx. Number Employees: 70
Year Founded: 1990
Business Description:
Motherboards & Systems Mfr
S.I.C.: 3577
N.A.I.C.S.: 334119
Advertising Expenditures: $750,000
Media: 2-10-13
Personnel:
Paul Kim *(Mgr-Mktg)*
Brands & Products:
FIC
FIRST MAIN BOARD

FLASHLINE, INC.

1300 E 9th St Ste 1600
Cleveland, OH 44114-1573
Tel.: (216) 861-4000
Fax: (216) 861-1861
Toll Free: (800) 259-1961
E-mail: info@flashline.com
Web Site: www.flashline.com
Approx. Number Employees: 30
Year Founded: 1998
Business Description:
Provider of Software Component Products, Services & Resources for Business Software Systems
S.I.C.: 7375; 8742
N.A.I.C.S.: 518111; 541611
Media: 2-7-10-13
Brands & Products:
FLASHLINE
FLASHLINE REGISTRY
FLASHPACK
FLASHTRAX
REGISTRY
RETURN ON SOFTWARE

FLOWERBUD.COM

155 B Ave Ste 110
Lake Oswego, OR 97034-3233
Tel.: (503) 697-1790
Fax: (503) 697-1791
Toll Free: (877) 524-5400
E-mail: customercare@flowerbud.com
Web Site: www.flowerbud.com
Approx. Number Employees: 9
Year Founded: 1999
Business Description:
Retailer & Online Provider of Flowers
S.I.C.: 5992
N.A.I.C.S.: 453110
Media: 6-13-15-22
Personnel:
Mark Hayes *(CEO)*
Marcy Lepine *(Gen Mgr)*

FOCUS

514 Bryant St
San Francisco, CA 94107
Tel.: (415) 318-7200
Tel.: (415) 318-7208 (Advertising)
Fax: (415) 318-7219
E-mail: info@tippit.com
Web Site: www.tippit.com
Approx. Number Employees: 50
Business Description:
Online Media Services
S.I.C.: 4899
N.A.I.C.S.: 517910
Media: 1-10-13-22
Personnel:
Scott Albro *(Founder & CEO)*

FOLIOFN INVESTMENTS, INC.

8000 Towers Crescent Dr Ste 1500
Vienna, VA 22182-6216
Mailing Address:
PO Box 3068
Merrifield, VA 22116-3068
Tel.: (703) 245-4000
Fax: (703) 245-4800
Toll Free: (888) 973-7890
E-mail: bolieka@foliofn.com
Web Site: www.foliofn.com
Approx. Number Employees: 68
Year Founded: 1998
Business Description:
Online Brokerage Services, Portfolio Management & Trading Technology
S.I.C.: 7375; 6211
N.A.I.C.S.: 518111; 523120
Advertising Expenditures: $200,000
Media: 2-13-24
Personnel:
Steve M.H. Wallman *(Founder & CEO)*
Brands & Products:
FOLIO ADVISOR
FOLIO INVESTING

FORBES.COM LLC

(Div. of Forbes, Inc.)
E 60 5th Ave
New York, NY 10011-5204
Tel.: (212) 620-2200
Fax: (212) 366-8868

Key to Media (For complete agency information see *The Advertising Red Books-Agencies* edition):
1. Bus. Publs. 2. Cable T.V. 3. Catalogs & Directories. 4. Co-op Adv. 5. Consumer Mags. 6. D.M. to Bus. Estab.7. D.M. to Consumers 8. Daily Newsp. 9. Exhibits/Trade Shows 10. Foreign 11. Infomercial 12. Internet Adv.13. Multimedia 14. Network Radio 15. Network T.V. 16. Newsp. Distr. Mags. 17. Other 18. Outdoor (Posters, Transit) 19. Point of Purchase20. Premiums, Novelties 21. Product Samples 22. Special Events Mktg. 23. Spot Radio 24. Spot T.V. 25. Weekly Newsp. 26. Yellow Page Adv.

E-mail: firstname_lastname@forbes.com
Web Site: www.forbes.com
Approx. Number Employees: 200
Year Founded: 2001
Business Description:
Online Business Information Services
S.I.C.: 2741
N.A.I.C.S.: 516110
Media: 6-9-13-25
Personnel:
Michael Smith *(Chm)*
William J. Flatley *(VP & Chief Adv Officer)*
Bruce Rogers *(Chief Brand Officer-Forbes Media)*
Carl Lavin *(Deputy Mng Editor)*
Melanie Scharler *(Dir-Bus Dev)*
Brands & Products:
FORBESTRAVELER.COM
Advertising Agency:
MediaMind Technologies Inc.
135 W 18th St 5th Fl
New York, NY 10011
Tel.: (646) 202-1320
Fax: (212) 686-9208

FORTUNECITY.COM, INC.
322 8th Ave 11th Fl
New York, NY 10001
Tel.: (212) 981-8600
Fax: (212) 981-8125
Toll Free: (866) 638-2489
E-mail: jobs@fortunecity.com
Web Site: www.fortunecity.com
Approx. Rev.: $4,060,904
Approx. Number Employees: 20
Year Founded: 1997
Business Description:
Personal Web Site Publishing Services, Online Photo Sharing, Photo & Gift Merchandise Printing
S.I.C.: 7371; 2741; 7374
N.A.I.C.S.: 541511; 516110; 518210
Media: 13
Personnel:
Jeremy Metcalfe *(Chm)*
Peter Macnee *(Pres & CEO)*
Brands & Products:
FORTUNECITY.COM

FOURSQUARE LABS, INC
36 Cooper Square, 5th Fl
New York, NY 10003
Web Site: www.foursquare.com
Approx. Number Employees: 60
Year Founded: 2008
Business Description:
Social Networking Site
N.A.I.C.S.: 516110
Media: 13
Personnel:
Dennis Crowley *(Co-Founder & CEO)*
Naveen Selvadurai *(Co-Founder)*
William Kurtz *(Pres)*
Evan Cohen *(Gen Mgr)*
Eric Friedman *(Dir-Bus Dev)*
Siobhan Quinn *(Product Mgr)*

FOX INTERACTIVE MEDIA, INC.
(Sub. of News Corporation)
1440 S Sepulveda Blvd
Los Angeles, CA 90025
Tel.: (310) 444-8300
Fax: (310) 444-8180
Web Site: www.fox.com
Sales Range: $100-124.9 Million
Business Description:
Online Site Operator
S.I.C.: 7379
N.A.I.C.S.: 541519
Personnel:
Peer Schneider *(Sr VP & Publr)*
Heidi Browning *(Sr VP-Client Solutions)*
Chris Ellis *(Sr VP-Comml)*
George Blue *(VP-Fox Entertainment Adv Sls)*
Advertising Agency:
Sprokkit
333 S Grand Ave Ste 1600
Los Angeles, CA 90071
Tel.: (213) 626-2076
Fax: (231) 232-3739

FRAGRANCENET.COM, INC.
104 Parkway Dr S
Hauppauge, NY 11788-2012
Tel.: (631) 582-5204
Fax: (631) 582-8433
Toll Free: (800) 727-3867
E-mail: info@fragrancenet.com
Web Site: www.fragrancenet.com
E-Mail For Key Personnel:
President: ja@fragrancenet.com
Sales Range: $25-49.9 Million
Approx. Number Employees: 40
Year Founded: 1997
Business Description:
Online Fragrance Retailer
S.I.C.: 5961; 5122
N.A.I.C.S.: 454111; 446120
Advertising Expenditures: $3,303,000
Media: 6-8-9-10-13-14-15-21-25
Personnel:
Dennis Apfel *(Chm & CEO)*
Jason Apfel *(Pres)*

FREE SPARK, LLC
470 Norristown Rd Ste 201
Blue Bell, PA 19422-2322
Tel.: (888) 653-8098
Fax: (888) 653-8091
E-mail: jfiumara@freespark.com
Web Site: www.freespark.com
Business Description:
E-Commerce Support Services
S.I.C.: 7319
N.A.I.C.S.: 541870
Media: 13
Brands & Products:
NOVA BUYER'S REWARD

FREEREALTIME.COM INC.
22365 El Toro Rd 224
Lake Forest, CA 92630
Tel.: (949) 458-6935
Toll Free: (888) 869-8300
E-mail: bizdev@corp.freerealtime.com
Web Site: www.freerealtime.com
E-Mail For Key Personnel:
Sales Director: sales@corp.freerealtime.com
Approx. Sls.: $2,400,000
Approx. Number Employees: 5
Year Founded: 1996
Business Description:
Online Financial Advice & Market Quotes
S.I.C.: 7299
N.A.I.C.S.: 812990
Media: 13
Personnel:
Michael Neufeld *(Pres & CFO)*
Aleem Rajpar *(Architect-Database)*

FRIENDSTER
800 W El Camino Real Ste 170
Mountain View, CA 94040
Fax: (650) 964-4966
E-mail: help@friendster.com
Web Site: www.friendster.com
Business Description:
Global Online Social Network
S.I.C.: 2741
N.A.I.C.S.: 516110
Personnel:
Richard B. Kimber *(CEO)*
Advertising Agency:
The Hoffman Agency
70 N 2nd St
San Jose, CA 95113-1204
Tel.: (408) 286-2611
Fax: (408) 286-0133

FUSION TELECOMMUNICATIONS INTERNATIONAL, INC.
420 Lexington Ave Ste 1718
New York, NY 10170
Tel.: (212) 201-2400
Fax: (212) 972-7884
Toll Free: (800) 503-3325
E-mail: info@fusiontel.com
Web Site: www.fusiontel.com
Approx. Rev.: $41,763,002
Approx. Number Employees: 56
Year Founded: 1997
Business Description:
Communication & Internet Technologies
S.I.C.: 4812; 4813
N.A.I.C.S.: 517310; 517110; 517212
Advertising Expenditures: $42,704
Media: 17
Personnel:
Marvin S. Rosen *(Co-Founder & Chm)*
Gordon Hutchins, Jr. *(Pres, Acting CFO & COO)*
Matthew D. Rosen *(CEO)*
Eric D. Ram *(Exec VP-Intl)*
Jan Sarro *(Exec VP-Global Sls & Mktg)*
Brands & Products:
EFONICA
FUSION
FUSION TELECOM
FUSION TELECOMMUNICATIONS INTERNATIONAL
ONE WORLD. ONE VISION. ONE VOICE.

FUSIONONE, INC.
(Sub. of Synchronoss Technologies, Inc.)
55 Almaden Blvd 5th Fl
San Jose, CA 95113
Tel.: (408) 282-1200
Fax: (408) 282-2345
E-mail: inquiries@fusionone.com
Web Site: www.fusionone.com
Year Founded: 1998
Business Description:
Premium Data Services for Mobile Phones & Software for Wireless & Mobile Communications
S.I.C.: 7371
N.A.I.C.S.: 541511
Media: 2-6-10-13-17-21
Personnel:
Jay Burrell *(Exec VP)*
Seetharaman Ramasubramani *(Sr VP-Product Ops)*
Mohan Sadashiva *(Sr VP-Mktg)*
Brands & Products:
FUSIONONE
MIGHTYBACKUP
MIGHTYPHONE

GAMESPY INDUSTRIES, INC.
(Sub. of IGN Entertainment, Inc.)
3070 Bristol Street
Costa Mesa, CA 92626
Tel.: (714) 460-6700
Fax: (714) 460-6799
E-mail: info@gamespy.com
Web Site: www.gamespy.com
Sales Range: $10-24.9 Million
Approx. Number Employees: 70
Year Founded: 1995
Business Description:
Publisher of Websites; Provider of Gaming Applications & Technology Development & Publishing Tools
S.I.C.: 7375
N.A.I.C.S.: 518111
Advertising Expenditures: $200,000
Media: 10-13
Personnel:
Kym Nelson *(VP-Game Sls)*
Todd Northcutt *(VP-GameSpy Tech)*
Sean Flinn *(Sr Mgr-Product-GameSpy Technology)*
Brands & Products:
FILEPLANET
GAMESPY
GAMESPY ARCADE

GARAGEBAND.COM
3281 Hackamore Dr
Hayward, CA 94541
Tel.: (415) 704-3432
E-mail: itsonlymoney@garageband.com
Web Site: www.garageband.com
Approx. Number Employees: 29
Year Founded: 1999
Business Description:
Online Services & Information for New Bands & Music
S.I.C.: 2741
N.A.I.C.S.: 516110
Media: 13

GARTNER, INC.
56 Top Gallant Rd
Stamford, CT 06902-7747
Mailing Address:
PO Box 10212
Stamford, CT 06904-2212
Tel.: (203) 964-0096
Fax: (203) 316-6488
Telex: 643528
E-mail: irinfo@gartner.com
Web Site: www.gartner.com
Approx. Rev.: $1,288,454,000
Approx. Number Employees: 4,461
Year Founded: 1979
Business Description:
Supplier of Research & Advisory Services to the Information Technology Industry
S.I.C.: 6719; 8732; 8748
N.A.I.C.S.: 551114; 541618; 541910
Export
Media: 10-11-13-22
Personnel:
Eugene A. Hall *(CEO)*

Key to Media (For complete agency information see *The Advertising Red Books-Agencies* edition):
1. Bus. Publs. 2. Cable T.V. 3. Catalogs & Directories. 4. Co-op Adv. 5. Consumer Mags. 6. D.M. to Bus. Estab.7. D.M. to Consumers
8. Daily Newsp. 9. Exhibits/Trade Shows 10. Foreign 11. Infomercial 12. Internet Adv.13. Multimedia 14. Network Radio
15. Network T.V. 16. Newsp. Distr. Mags. 17. Other 18. Outdoor (Posters, Transit) 19. Point of Purchase20. Premiums, Novelties
21. Product Samples 22. Special Events Mktg. 23. Spot Radio 24. Spot T.V. 25. Weekly Newsp. 26. Yellow Page Adv.

Gartner, Inc. — (Continued)

Christopher J. Lafond *(CFO & Exec VP)*
Darko Hrelic *(CIO & Sr VP)*
Lewis G. Schwartz *(Chief Compliance Officer, Gen Counsel, Sec & Sr VP)*
Kendall B. Davis *(Sr VP-End-User Programs Div)*
Diane Julian *(Sr VP-Strategy)*
Robin B. Kranich *(Sr VP-HR)*
Dale Kutnick *(Sr VP-Exec Programs)*
Timothy T.M.F. Noble *(Sr VP-Global Sls)*
Peter Sondergaard *(Sr VP-Res Content)*
Michael Yoo *(Sr VP-High-Tech & Telecom Programs)*
Andrew Spender *(VP-Corp Comm)*
Tom McCall *(Sr Dir-PR)*
Elise Olding *(Dir-Res)*
Christy Pettey *(Sr Mgr-PR)*

GEEKNET, INC.

11216 Waples Mill Rd Ste 100
Fairfax, VA 22030
Toll Free: (877) 433-5638
Web Site: geeknet.com
Approx. Rev.: $94,619,000
Approx. Number Employees: 122
Year Founded: 1993
Business Description:
Online Media & e-Commerce Solutions
S.I.C.: 7372; 7373
N.A.I.C.S.: 511210; 334611; 541512
Advertising Expenditures: $4,100,000
Media: 10-13
Personnel:
Kenneth Gerald Langone *(Chm)*
Kathryn McCarthy *(CFO & Exec VP)*
Carol A. DiBattiste *(Chief Admin Officer, Gen Counsel & Exec VP)*
Matthew Sweeney *(Chief Revenue Officer)*
Jeffrey Drobick *(Pres/CEO-Media Div)*
Colon Washburn *(Pres/CEO-ThinkGeek, Inc.)*
Deborah Crimmings *(Exec Dir-Sls-Northeast)*
Brands & Products:
FRESH MEAT.NET
SLASHDOT
SOURCEFORGE
SOURCEFORGE.NET
THINK GREEK

GIFTCERTIFICATES.COM

(Holding of Marlin Equity Partners, LLC)
11510 Blondo St
Omaha, NE 68164-3846
Tel.: (402) 445-2300
Fax: (402) 951-4223
Toll Free: (877) 737-0200
E-mail: customerservice@giftcertificates.com
Web Site: www.giftcertificates.com
Sales Range: $75-99.9 Million
Approx. Number Employees: 120
Year Founded: 1997
Business Description:
Online Seller of Gift Certificates from Various Retailers to Consumers & Corporations
S.I.C.: 5963
N.A.I.C.S.: 454390
Media: 2-7-8-9-10-13-20-23-24-25
Personnel:
Ian O'Brien *(CEO)*
Brands & Products:
GIFTCERTIFICATES.COM
SUPERCERTIFICATE

GIFTS.COM

(Sub. of IAC/InterActiveCorp)
8833 Sunset Blvd
West Hollywood, CA 90069
Tel.: (704) 541-5351
Fax: (704) 541-1824
Web Site: www.gifts.com
Sales Range: $150-199.9 Million
Year Founded: 2005
Business Description:
Online Gift Retailer
S.I.C.: 5947
N.A.I.C.S.: 453220
Advertising Agency:
Susan Magrino Agency
641 Lexington Ave 28th Fl
New York, NY 10022
Tel.: (212) 957-3005
Fax: (212) 957-4071

GO DADDY GROUP, INC.

(godaddy.com)
14455 N Hayden Rd Ste 226
Scottsdale, AZ 85260
Tel.: (480) 505-8800
Fax: (480) 505-8844
E-mail: press@godaddy.com
Web Site: www.godaddy.com
Sales Range: $125-149.9 Million
Approx. Number Employees: 899
Business Description:
Domain Name Registration Services
S.I.C.: 7379
N.A.I.C.S.: 541519
Advertising Expenditures: $15,239,000
Media: 2-3-6-7-8-13-14-15-17-23
Personnel:
Bob Parsons *(Founder & CEO)*
Warren J. Adelman *(Pres & COO)*
Michael J. Zimmerman *(CFO & Exec VP)*
Barbara J. Rechterman *(CMO & Sr Exec VP)*
Neil G. Warner *(Chief Info Security Officer & VP-Tech ops)*
Christine N. Jones *(Gen Counsel, Sec & Exec VP)*
Brands & Products:
DOMAINS BY PROXY
GO DADDY
MAKE A.COM NAME WITH US!
QUICK SHOPPING CART
STARFIELD TECHNOLOGIES
THEDOMAINNAMEAFTERMARKET
TRAFFIC BLAZER
WEBSITE TONIGHT
WILD WEST DOMAINS

GO2CALL.COM, INC.

Ste 600 500 Davis St
Evanston, IL 60201-4622
Tel.: (847) 864-4123
Fax: (847) 864-4423
E-mail: info@go2call.com
Web Site: www.go2call.com
Approx. Number Employees: 23
Year Founded: 1998
Business Description:
Internet-Based Telephone Calling
S.I.C.: 8748; 4813
N.A.I.C.S.: 541690; 517310
Media: 10-13

GOINDUSTRY-DOVEBID, INC.

(Sub. of GoIndustry USA, Inc.)
1900 O'Farrell St Ste 325
San Mateo, CA 94403
Tel.: (650) 571-7400
Fax: (650) 356-6700
Toll Free: (800) 665-1042
E-mail: customerservice@dovebid.com
Web Site: www.dovebid.com
Approx. Number Employees: 12
Year Founded: 1937
Business Description:
Webcast & Online Business-to-Business Capital Asset Auctions & Valuation Services
S.I.C.: 5961
N.A.I.C.S.: 454112
Export
Media: 2-7-9-10-11-13-25
Personnel:
Ross M. Dove *(Pres)*
Romie Castelli *(Sr VP-Sls-North America)*

GOLFBALLS.COM, INC.

126 Arnould Blvd
Lafayette, LA 70506
Tel.: (337) 210-4653
Fax: (337) 210-1574
Toll Free: (800) 372-2557
E-mail: info@golfballs.com
Web Site: www.golfballs.com
E-Mail For Key Personnel:
President: tomcox@golfballs.com
Marketing Director: steven@golfballs.com
Approx. Number Employees: 40
Year Founded: 1995
Business Description:
New, Used & Custom Golf Balls, Golf Clubs & Apparel Online Retailer
S.I.C.: 5941
N.A.I.C.S.: 451110
Import Export
Advertising Expenditures: $200,000
Media: 4-8-9-13-18-19-20-21-22-23-24-25-26
Personnel:
Tom Cox *(Pres & CEO)*
Robin Bonin *(Dir-Tech)*
Johnny Cox *(Dir-Ops)*

GOOD TECHNOLOGY, INC.

101 Redwood Shores Pkwy Ste 400
Redwood City, CA 94065-1180
Tel.: (650) 486-6000
Tel.: (650) 486-6022 (Intl)
Fax: (650) 622-9590
Toll Free: (866) 723-4669
E-mail: sales@good.com
Web Site: www.visto.com
E-Mail For Key Personnel:
Sales Director: sales@good.com
Public Relations: pr@corp.visto.com
Approx. Number Employees: 300
Year Founded: 1996
Business Description:
Holding Company; Mobile Telecommunications Network Software Solutions
S.I.C.: 6719; 4812; 7372; 7374
N.A.I.C.S.: 551112; 511210; 517212; 517919; 518210
Media: 13
Personnel:
King R. Lee, III *(Pres & CEO)*
David Russian *(CFO)*
Jean Tripier *(Exec VP)*
Frederic Aries *(Sr VP-Sls-EMEA & Latin America)*
Peter Barker *(Sr VP-Engrg)*
Brian Carr *(Sr VP-Worldwide Sls)*
John Herrema, III *(Sr VP-Corp Strategy)*
Susan Vinci-Lucero *(Sr VP-Mktg & Product Mgmt)*
Neil Hooper *(VP-Sls-North America)*
Adriana Stadecker *(VP-HR)*
Advertising Agency:
The CC Group
Floor 3 Imperium Imperial Way
Reading, Berkshire RG2 0TD, United Kingdom
Tel.: (44) 118 920 7650
Fax: (44) 118 986 7148

GOOGLE INC.

1600 Amphitheatre Pkwy
Mountain View, CA 94043
Tel.: (650) 253-0000
Fax: (650) 253-0001
E-mail: info@google.com
Web Site: www.google.com
Approx. Rev.: $29,321,000,000
Approx. Number Employees: 24,400
Year Founded: 1998
Business Description:
Internet Search Engine, Data Processing, Publishing & Related Services
S.I.C.: 7372; 2741; 7319; 7371; 7374
N.A.I.C.S.: 519130; 511210; 516110; 518210; 541511; 541850
Advertising Expenditures: $772,000,000
Media: 2-7-10-13-20-27
Personnel:
Larry Page *(Co-Founder & CEO)*
Jason Wheeler *(Founder & Entrepreneur-Real Estate)*
Eric E. Schmidt *(Chm)*
Patrick Pichette *(CFO & Sr VP)*
Ben Fried *(CIO)*
David C. Drummond *(Chief Legal Officer & Sr VP-Corp Dev)*
Sergey Brin *(Pres-Tech & Asst Sec)*
Henrique De Castro *(Pres-Global Media, Mobile & Platforms)*
Margo Georgiadis *(Pres-Americas)*
Dave Girouard *(Pres-Enterprise)*
Kent M. Walker *(Gen Counsel & Sr VP)*
Laszlo Bock *(Sr VP-People Ops)*
Shona L. Brown *(Sr VP-Bus Ops)*
William M. Coughran, Jr. *(Sr VP-Engrg)*
Alan Eustace *(Sr VP-Knowledge)*
Jeffrey T. Huber *(Sr VP-Commerce & Local)*
Andy Rubin *(Sr VP-Mobile)*
Susan Wojcicki *(Sr VP-Google & Adv)*
Barry Salzman *(Mng Dir-Media & Platforms-Americas)*
Megan Smith *(VP-New Bus Dev & Gen Mgr)*
Urs Holzle *(VP-Engr)*
Stuart Feldman *(VP-Engrg)*
Mark Fuchs *(VP-Fin & Chief Accountant)*
Vic Gundotra *(VP-Engrg)*
Udi Manber *(VP-Engrg)*
Brian McClendon *(VP-Engrg)*
Cosmos Nicolaou *(VP-Engrg)*
Stephanie Tilenius *(VP-Commerce)*

Key to Media (For complete agency information see *The Advertising Red Books-Agencies* edition):
1. Bus. Publs. 2. Cable T.V. 3. Catalogs & Directories. 4. Co-op Adv. 5. Consumer Mags. 6. D.M. to Bus. Estab.7. D.M. to Consumers
8. Daily Newsp. 9. Exhibits/Trade Shows 10. Foreign 11. Infomercial 12. Internet Adv.13. Multimedia 14. Network Radio
15. Network T.V. 16. Newsp. Distr. Mags. 17. Other 18. Outdoor (Posters, Transit) 19. Point of Purchase20. Premiums, Novelties
21. Product Samples 22. Special Events Mktg. 23. Spot Radio 24. Spot T.V. 25. Weekly Newsp. 26. Yellow Page Adv.

Benjamin Sloss Treynor *(VP-Engrg)*
Linus Upson *(VP-Engrg)*
David Bryant *(Head-Creative)*
Jeff Montgomery *(Head-Retail)*
Allison Mooney *(Head-Trends & Insights, Mktg)*
Keith Coleman *(Dir-Product)*
James Crawford *(Dir-Engrg-Google Books)*
Brett Crosby *(Dir-Product Mktg)*
Rian Liebenberg *(Dir-Engrg)*
Benjamin Ling *(Dir-Product Mgmt & Search Products)*
Patrick Mork *(Dir-Mktg-Mobile Apps)*
Eileen Naughton *(Dir-Media Sls & Ops-Americas)*
Chikai Ohazama *(Dir-Product Mgmt)*
Tom Oliveri *(Dir-Global Mktg, Enterprise & Consumer Applications)*
Peter Scocimara *(Dir-Enterprise Support-Global)*
Joshua Spanier *(Dir-Media)*
Michael Steib *(Dir-Emerging Platforms)*
Tom Stocky *(Dir-Product Mgmt)*
Chris Theodoros *(Dir-Indus Rels)*
Rachel Whetstone *(Dir-Corp Comm)*
Chris Wiggins *(Dir-Creative Digital)*
Brian Zeug *(Dir-Sls-Natl-Display & Video)*
Megan Stack *(Exec Mgr-Comm)*
Stephen Chau *(Sr Mgr-Product-Google Maps)*
Chris Gaither *(Sr Mgr-Corp Comm)*
Josh Cohen *(Mgr-Bus Product)*
Shuman Ghosemajumder *(Bus Product Mgr-Trust & Safety)*
Rajen Sheth *(Grp Product Mgr & Bus Mgr)*
Jessica Ewing *(Product Mgr-iGoogle)*
Alex Kenin *(Mgr-Product Mktg)*
Aaron Brown *(Sr Product Mgr-Google Health)*
Jeff Chin *(Product Mgr-Google Translate)*
John Collins *(Sr Product Mgr-Global Trust)*
Kate Cushing *(Assoc Product Mgr-Google Analytics)*
Greg D'Alesandre *(Sr Product Mgr-App Engine)*
Benoit de Boursetty *(Product Mgr-Google Apps)*
Rishi Dhand *(Product Mgr-Google Apps)*
Daniel Dulitz *(Grp Product Mgr)*
Marc Freed-Finnigan *(Sr Product Mgr-Google Wallet Bus)*
Benjamin Grol *(Product Mgr)*
Jeff Harris *(Product Mgr-Google Docs)*
Richard Hung *(Product Mgr- Google Shopper)*
Scott Johnston *(Grp Product Mgr-Google Docs & Sites)*
Navneet Joneja *(Product Mgr-Google Cloud SQL)*
Paul Joyce *(Product Mgr-Music Beta)*
Sagar Kamdar *(Product Mgr)*
Kei Kawai *(Sr Product Mgr)*
Bill Kee *(Product Mgr-Google Analytics)*
Chang Kim *(Product Mgr)*
Raj Krishnan *(Product Mgr-Sitelinks)*
Pierre Lebeau *(Product Mgr)*
Steve Lee *(Product Mgr-Android)*
Nitin Mangtani *(Grp Product Mgr-Google Commerce)*
Thor Mitchell *(Product Mgr-Google Maps API)*
Shailesh Nalawadi *(Product Mgr-Goggles)*
Christian Oestlien *(Product Mgr)*
Shiva Rajaraman *(Grp Product Mgr)*
Chris Ramsdale *(Product Mgr-Developer Tools)*
Jonathan Rochelle *(Product Mgr)*
Ethan Russell *(Sr Product Mgr)*
Eric Sachs *(Product Mgr-Security)*
Nishit Shah *(Product Mgr-Google Security)*
Dan Shapiro *(Product Mgr-Google Advisor)*
Saurabh Sharma *(Product Mgr-Google Plus)*
Aitan Weinberg *(Sr Product Mgr-Audience Solutions)*
Vince Wu *(Sr Product Mgr-Chrome OS)*
Jon Diorio *(Mgr-Product Mktg)*
Koh Kim *(Assoc Mgr-Product Mktg)*
Rajas Moonka *(Mgr-Product)*
Johanna Wright *(Mgr-Product)*
Elaine Arber *(Sr Acct Exec-Mobile Display)*
Roni Zeiger *(Strategist-Health)*
Deepak Anand *(Engr-Software)*
Robert T. Brennan *(Engr-Software)*
Sridhar Ramaswamy *(Engr-Software)*
Iftah Sneh *(Engr-Software)*
Michael Weiss-Malik *(Engr-Software)*
Hal Varian *(Chief Economist)*

Brands & Products:
AD MANAGER
ADMOB
ADSENSE
ADSENSE FOR CONTENT
ADSENSE FOR PRINT
ADSENSE FOR SEARCH
ADVERTISING ON THE NEIGHBORHOOD WIDE WEB
ADWORDS
ADWORDS AUTHORIZED RESELLERS
ADWORDS EDITOR
ANDROID
BLOGGER
BROADCAST YOURSELF
CITIZENTUBE
CLAIM YOUR CONTENT
CLOSED LOG AVAILS
DALVIK
DMARC
DODGEBALL
FEEDBURNER
FEEDFLARE
GMAIL
GOOG 411
GOOGEL SEARCH APPLIANCE
GOOGLE
GOOGLE AD MANAGER
GOOGLE ADSENSE
GOOGLE ADVERTISING PROFESSIONALS
GOOGLE ADWORDS
GOOGLE ALERTS
GOOGLE ANALYTICS
GOOGLE ANSWERS
GOOGLE APP ENGINE
GOOGLE APPS
GOOGLE AUDIO ADS
GOOGLE BASE
GOOGLE BLOG SEARCH
GOOGLE BLOGGER
GOOGLE BOOK SEARCH
GOOGLE CALENDAR
GOOGLE CATALOGS
GOOGLE CHANNEL
GOOGLE CHART API
GOOGLE CHECKOUT
GOOGLE CHROME
GOOGLE CO-OP
GOOGLE CODE
GOOGLE COMPUTE
GOOGLE CONTENT NETWORK
GOOGLE CUSTOM SEARCH
GOOGLE CUSTOM SEARCH ENGINE
GOOGLE DASHBOARD WIDGETS
GOOGLE DESKTOP
GOOGLE DIARY
GOOGLE DIRECTORY
GOOGLE DOCS
GOOGLE DOCS & SPREADSHEETS
GOOGLE EARTH
GOOGLE ENTERPRISE
GOOGLE EXTENSIONS
GOOGLE FINANCE
GOOGLE FOUNDATION
GOOGLE FRIEND
GOOGLE GADGET ADS
GOOGLE GADGET CENTER
GOOGLE GADGETS
GOOGLE GEARS
GOOGLE GLOSSARY
GOOGLE GRANTS
GOOGLE GROUPS
GOOGLE HEALTH
GOOGLE IMAGE SEARCH
GOOGLE IMAGES
GOOGLE LABS
GOOGLE LANGUAGE TOOLS
GOOGLE MAPS
GOOGLE MARS
GOOGLE MESSAGE DISCOVERY
GOOGLE MESSAGE ENCRYPTION
GOOGLE MESSAGE FILTERING
GOOGLE MESSAGE SECURITY
GOOGLE MINI
GOOGLE MOBILE
GOOGLE MOBILE ADS
GOOGLE MOBILE UPDATER
GOOGLE MUSIC SEARCH
GOOGLE MUSIC TRENDS
GOOGLE NEWS
GOOGLE NEWS ALERTS
GOOGLE NOTEBOOK
GOOGLE OCEAN
GOOGLE PACK
GOOGLE PAGE CREATOR
GOOGLE PATENT SEARCH
GOOGLE PERSONALIZED SEARCH
GOOGLE PODIUM
GOOGLE PRINT ADS
GOOGLE PRODUCT SEARCH
GOOGLE PROFILES
GOOGLE READER
GOOGLE RIDE FINDER
GOOGLE SAFE BROWSING
GOOGLE SCHOLAR
GOOGLE SEARCH
GOOGLE SEARCH APPLIANCE
GOOGLE SETS
GOOGLE SIDEBAR
GOOGLE SITE SEARCH
GOOGLE SITEMAPS
GOOGLE SKETCHUP
GOOGLE SKY
GOOGLE SMS
GOOGLE STORE
GOOGLE SUGGEST
GOOGLE TALK
GOOGLE TOOLBAR
GOOGLE TRANSIT
GOOGLE TRANSLATE
GOOGLE TRENDS
GOOGLE TV ADS
GOOGLE UPDATER
GOOGLE VIDEO
GOOGLE VOICE
GOOGLE WAVE
GOOGLE WEB ACCELERATOR
GOOGLE WEB ALERTS
GOOGLE WEB SEARCH
GOOGLE WEB SECURITY
GOOGLE WEB TOOLKIT
GOOGLE WEBMASTER CENTRAL
GOOGLE WEBSITE OPTIMIZER
GOOGLE ZEITGEIST
GRANDCENTRAL
IGOOGLE
I'M FEELING LUCKY
IT'S ALL ABOUT RESULTS
JAIKU
JOGA
KEYHOLE
KNOL
LISTEN IN
MAESTRO
MEASURE MAP
ONE NUMBER FOR LIFE
OPEN HANDSET ALLIANCE
OPENSOCIAL
ORKUT
PAGERANK
PANORAMIO
PICASA
PICASAWEB
PICTURE SIMPLICITY
POSTINI
RECHARGE IT
RINGSHARE
SEARCH APPLIANCE
SKETCHUP
SONGNOW
TRENDALYZER
UNIVERSAL SEARCH
URCHIN
WEB SEARCH
WEBMASTER TOOLS
YOUTUBE
YOUTUBE SCREENING ROOM
ZINGKU

Advertising Agencies:
BBH New York
32 Avenue of the Americas 19th Fl
New York, NY 10013
Tel.: (212) 812-6600
Fax: (212) 242-4110
Google Chrome
— Jessica Bigarel *(Acct Exec)*
— Rossa Hsieh *(Acct Exec)*

BGT Partners
2627 NE 203rd St Ste 202
Miami, FL 33180
Tel.: (305) 438-1800
Fax: (305) 438-1560

Chlopak, Leonard, Schechter & Associates
1850 M St NW Ste 800
Washington, DC 20036-5803
Tel.: (202) 289-5900
Fax: (202) 289-4141

Cutwater
55 Union St
San Francisco, CA 94111-1227

Key to Media (For complete agency information see *The Advertising Red Books-Agencies* edition):
1. Bus. Publs. 2. Cable T.V. 3. Catalogs & Directories. 4. Co-op Adv. 5. Consumer Mags. 6. D.M. to Bus. Estab.7. D.M. to Consumers 8. Daily Newsp. 9. Exhibits/Trade Shows 10. Foreign 11. Infomercial 12. Internet Adv.13. Multimedia 14. Network Radio 15. Network T.V. 16. Newsp. Distr. Mags. 17. Other 18. Outdoor (Posters, Transit) 19. Point of Purchase20. Premiums, Novelties 21. Product Samples 22. Special Events Mktg. 23. Spot Radio 24. Spot T.V. 25. Weekly Newsp. 26. Yellow Page Adv.

Google Inc. — (Continued)

Tel.: (415) 315-4100
Fax: (415) 315-4200

GoConvergence
4545 36th St
Orlando, FL 32811
Tel.: (407) 235-3210
Fax: (407) 299-9907

Johannes Leonardo
41 East 11th St 6th Fl
New York, NY 10003
Tel.: (212) 462-8111
Fax: (212) 645-0861
Demo Slam
Google Innovations
— Dean Rubinstein *(Acct Exec)*

The McRae Agency
6045 N Scottsdale Rd Ste 205
Scottsdale, AZ 85250
Tel.: (480) 990-0282
Fax: (480) 990-0048

Rokkan
176 Grand St 2nd Fl
New York, NY 10012-4003
Tel.: (212) 835-9300
Fax: (212) 251-9393

The Search Agency
3420 Ocean Park Blvd Ste 2020
Santa Monica, CA 90405
Tel.: (310) 582-5700
Fax: (310) 452-2422

Wieden + Kennedy Japan
7-5-6 Roppongi
Tokyo, 106-0032, Japan
Tel.: (81) 3 5771 2900
Fax: (81) 3 5771 2711

WorldWalk Media
417A E Washington Blvd
San Francisco, CA 94129-1145
Tel.: (415) 933-8450

GOPHERCENTRAL.COM

(Unit of NextEra Media, LLC)
7851 W 185th St Ste 106
Tinley Park, IL 60477
Tel.: (708) 478-4500
Fax: (708) 478-5470
Web Site: www.gophercentral.com
Approx. Number Employees: 25
Year Founded: 1998
Business Description:
Newlsetter Site
S.I.C.: 8742; 8721
N.A.I.C.S.: 541611; 541219
Media: 13
Personnel:
Jaffer Ali *(Pres)*

GOVDELIVERY, INC.

(Sub. of INTERNET CAPITAL GROUP, INC.)
408 Saint Peter St Ste 600
Saint Paul, MN 55102
Tel.: (651) 665-0930
Fax: (651) 665-0943
Toll Free: (866) 276-5583
E-mail: info@govdelivery.com
Web Site: www.govdelivery.com
Sales Range: $10-24.9 Million
Year Founded: 1999
Business Description:
Governmental & Regulatory Information & Data Processing Services
S.I.C.: 7389; 7374
N.A.I.C.S.: 519190; 518210
Media: 2-7-8-13
Personnel:
Scott Burns *(Co-Founder & CEO)*
Dave Sommerness *(COO)*
Mark Capaldini *(Exec VP)*
Bobbi Browning *(Sr VP)*
Brent Kastner *(VP-Technology)*
Sarah Heikkila *(Dir-Client Svcs)*
Jennie Olson *(Dir-Mktg)*
Brands & Products:
ENGAGE. CULTIVATE. CONNECT.
GOVDELIVERY

GRASSROOTS ENTERPRISE, INC.

1875 Eye St NW Ste 900
Washington, DC 20006
Tel.: (202) 371-0200
E-mail: info@corp.grassroots.com
Web Site: www.grassroots.com
Sales Range: $25-49.9 Million
Approx. Number Employees: 45
Year Founded: 1999
Business Description:
Nonpartisan Political Action Website & Online Community
S.I.C.: 2711; 7375
N.A.I.C.S.: 511110; 518111
Media: 13
Personnel:
Sherry Reilly *(Dir-Comm)*
Brands & Products:
GRASSROOTS
GRASSROOTS MULTIPLIER

GREENWICH VILLAGE GAZETTE

(Unit of Gilford Graphics International)
PO Box 1023
Island Heights, NJ 08732
Tel.: (732) 349-6854
Fax: (732) 736-9324
Toll Free: (800) 670-3898
E-mail: editor@nycny.com
Web Site: www.nycny.com
Sales Range: Less than $1 Million
Approx. Number Employees: 12
Year Founded: 1996
Business Description:
Online Provider of New York City News & Information
S.I.C.: 7375; 7373; 7379
N.A.I.C.S.: 518111; 541512; 541519
Media: 3-7-8-9-10-13-18-22-23-24-25-26
Personnel:
Dick Gilford *(Owner)*
Prescott Bush *(Pres)*
Howard Flysher *(Dir-Mktg & Adv)*
Brands & Products:
GREENWICH VILLAGE GAZETTE

GROMCO, INC.

Ste 73 501 Silverside Rd
Wilmington, DE 19809-1394
Tel.: (646) 304-2761
Fax: (646) 304-2761
E-mail: info@gromco.com
Web Site: www.gromco.com
E-Mail For Key Personnel:
Marketing Director: suzanne@gromco.com
Approx. Number Employees: 5
Year Founded: 1996
Business Description:
Consumer Websites
S.I.C.: 7336; 7375
N.A.I.C.S.: 541430; 518111
Media: 13-17
Personnel:
Michael Powell *(Chm)*
Evan Guillemin *(CFO, COO & Treas)*
Edward D. Taffet *(Sec & Sr VP)*
Chris Garvin *(Art Dir)*
Brands & Products:
CREDIT CARD MENU
ENERGY MENU
FREELANCE BBS
GROMCO
ISP MENU
LONG DISTANCE MENU
ROOMMATE BBS

GROUPON INC.

600 W Chicago Ave Ste 620
Chicago, IL 60654
Tel.: (480) 388-2527
E-mail: press@groupon.com
Web Site: www.groupon.com
Sales Range: $750-799.9 Million
Approx. Number Employees: 4,000
Business Description:
Online Coupon Website Operator
N.A.I.C.S.: 519130
Personnel:
Andrew Mason *(Founder & CEO)*
Jason Child *(CFO)*
Lee Brown *(Sr VP-Natl Sls)*
Brands & Products:
GROUPON
GROUPONLIVE
Advertising Agency:
Euro RSCG Worldwide PR
36 E Grand Ave 3rd Fl
Chicago, IL 60611
Tel.: (312) 640-6800
Fax: (312) 640-6801

GROUPSYSTEMS CORPORATION

520 Zang St Ste 211
Broomfield, CO 80021
Tel.: (303) 468-8680
Fax: (303) 468-8681
Toll Free: (800) 368-6338
E-mail: info@groupsystems.com
Web Site: www.groupsystems.com
Approx. Int. Income: $6,889,169
Approx. Number Employees: 20
Year Founded: 1989
Business Description:
Developer of Collaborative Knowledge Software & Systems
S.I.C.: 7372; 8742
N.A.I.C.S.: 511210; 541611
Advertising Expenditures: $500,000
Media: 2-6-10-13
Personnel:
Jay F. Nunamaker, Jr. *(Founder)*
Bob Schafer *(VP-Sls)*
Brands & Products:
COGNITO

GSI COMMERCE, INC.

(Sub. of eBay Inc.)
935 1st Ave
King of Prussia, PA 19406
Tel.: (610) 491-7000
Fax: (610) 491-7366
E-mail: ir@gsicommerce.com
Web Site: www.gsicommerce.com
E-Mail For Key Personnel:
Public Relations: ryang@gsicommerce.com
Approx. Rev.: $1,357,994,000
Approx. Number Employees: 5,304
Year Founded: 1986
Business Description:
E-Commerce & Interactive Marketing Services
S.I.C.: 8742; 5961; 7371
N.A.I.C.S.: 541613; 454111; 541511
Export
Advertising Expenditures: $19,998,000
Media: 4-10
Distr.: Natl.
Budget Set: Nov.
Personnel:
Michael G. Rubin *(Chm, Pres & CEO)*
Michael R. Conn *(CFO & Exec VP-Fin)*
Stephen Denton *(Pres-GSI Media)*
Reuben Hendell *(CEO-Global Agency Svcs)*
Chris Saridakis *(CEO-Mktg Svcs)*
Arthur H. Miller *(Gen Counsel & Exec VP)*
Fiona P. Dias *(Exec VP-Strategy & Mktg)*
James Flanagan *(Exec VP-HR)*
Scott Hardy *(Exec VP-Bus Mgmt)*
Robert W. Liewald *(Exec VP-Mdsg)*
Damon Mintzer *(Exec VP-Strategic Bus Dev)*
Robert Wuesthoff *(Exec VP-Global Ops)*
Jan Dobris *(Sr VP-Global Agency Svcs, Ops & Fin)*
Ronald C. Williamson *(Sr VP-Customer Care)*
Dorian Sweet *(VP & Exec Dir-Creative-GSI Interactive)*
Kelly Henry *(Dir-Corp Mktg)*
Brands & Products:
FOGDOG
GSI COMMERCE
Advertising Agency:
Active Integrated Marketing
1060 1st Ave Ste 400
King of Prussia, PA 19406
Tel.: (215) 885-3351
Fax: (215) 885-3352

THE GUILD INC.

(d/b/a Guild.com)
931 E Main St Ste 9
Madison, WI 53703
Tel.: (608) 257-2590
Fax: (608) 257-2690
Toll Free: (877) 344-8453
E-mail: artfulhome@guild.com
Web Site: www.guild.com
Sales Range: $10-24.9 Million
Approx. Number Employees: 58
Year Founded: 1985
Business Description:
Direct Retailer of Hand-Crafted Art & Home Furnishings
S.I.C.: 5719; 5961
N.A.I.C.S.: 442299; 454111; 454113
Advertising Expenditures: $200,000
Media: 2-13
Personnel:
Lisa Bayne *(CEO)*

Key to Media (For complete agency information see *The Advertising Red Books-Agencies* edition):
1. Bus. Publs. 2. Cable T.V. 3. Catalogs & Directories. 4. Co-op Adv. 5. Consumer Mags. 6. D.M. to Bus. Estab.7. D.M. to Consumers
8. Daily Newsp. 9. Exhibits/Trade Shows 10. Foreign 11. Infomercial 12. Internet Adv.13. Multimedia 14. Network Radio
15. Network T.V. 16. Newsp. Distr. Mags. 17. Other 18. Outdoor (Posters, Transit) 19. Point of Purchase20. Premiums, Novelties
21. Product Samples 22. Special Events Mktg. 23. Spot Radio 24. Spot T.V. 25. Weekly Newsp. 26. Yellow Page Adv.

GXS, INC.
(Holding of Francisco Partners Management, LLC)
100 Edison Park Dr
Gaithersburg, MD 20878-3204
Tel.: (301) 340-4000
Fax: (301) 340-5299
Toll Free: (800) 560-4347
Web Site: www.gxs.com
Approx. Number Employees: 1,300
Year Founded: 1965
Business Description:
Electrical Apparatus, Wire & Cable Products
S.I.C.: 7374
N.A.I.C.S.: 518210
Media: 10-13
Personnel:
David Stanton *(Chm)*
Bob Segert *(Pres & CEO)*
Gregg Clevenger *(CFO & Exec VP)*
Karl Salnoske *(CIO & Exec VP-Svc Delivery)*
Robert Patrick *(CMO & Sr VP)*
John Duvall *(Sr VP-Fin)*
Steven Scala *(Sr VP-Corp Dev)*
Doug Kern *(Dir-Corp Comm)*
Brands & Products:
EDI EXPRESS SM
QUIK-COMM

THE HACKETT GROUP, INC.
1001 Brickell Bay Dr Ste 3000
Miami, FL 33131
Tel.: (305) 375-8005
Fax: (305) 379-8810
E-mail: boardofdirectors@thehackettgroup.com
Web Site: www.thehacketgroup.com
Approx. Rev.: $201,348,000
Approx. Number Employees: 800
Year Founded: 2001
Business Description:
Management & Advisory Consulting Services
S.I.C.: 8742; 6282; 8748
N.A.I.C.S.: 541611; 523930; 541618
Media: 1-7-22
Personnel:
Ted A. Fernandez *(Chm & CEO)*
David N. Dungan *(Vice Chm & COO)*
Robert A. Ramirez *(CFO & Exec VP-Fin)*
Gary Baker *(Dir-Comm)*

HALF.COM, INC.
(Sub. of eBay Inc.)
500 S Gravers Rd
Plymouth Meeting, PA 19462-1719
Tel.: (610) 680-4000
Fax: (610) 680-4005
E-mail: info@half.com
Web Site: www.half.com
E-Mail For Key Personnel:
Marketing Director: mark@half.com
Sales Range: $75-99.9 Million
Approx. Number Employees: 115
Year Founded: 1999
Business Description:
Internet Based Retailer
S.I.C.: 5999
N.A.I.C.S.: 453998
Media: 13-22-24

HARMONIX MUSIC SYSTEMS, INC.
(Sub. of MTV Networks Company)
675 Massachusetts Ave 6th Fl
Cambridge, MA 02139
Tel.: (617) 491-6144
Fax: (617) 491-7411
E-mail: info@harmonixmusic.com
Web Site: www.harmonixmusic.com
Year Founded: 1995
Business Description:
Developer of Music Based Videogames
S.I.C.: 7389; 7999
N.A.I.C.S.: 541490; 713990
Personnel:
Alex Rigopulos *(Co-Founder & CEO)*
Eran Egozy *(Co-Founder & CTO)*
Greg LoPiccolo *(Sr VP-Product Dev)*
Advertising Agency:
The Barbarian Group
129 S St 2nd Fl
Boston, MA 02111
Tel.: (617) 424-8887
Fax: (617) 437-9499

HARRIS INTERACTIVE INC.
161 6th Ave
New York, NY 10013
Tel.: (212) 539-9600
Fax: (212) 539-9669
E-mail: info@harrisinteractive.com
Web Site: www.harrisinteractive.com
E-Mail For Key Personnel:
Marketing Director: DBakken@harrisinteractive.com
Public Relations: HZawaneh@harrisinteractive.com
Approx. Rev.: $165,264,000
Approx. Number Employees: 733
Year Founded: 1956
Business Description:
Internet & Traditional Market Research & Polling Services
S.I.C.: 8732; 2741; 7379; 8742
N.A.I.C.S.: 541910; 516110; 541519; 541611
Advertising Expenditures: $1,496,000
Media: 2-7-10-13-16-22
Personnel:
Al Angrisani *(Interim CEO)*
Eric W. Narowski *(Interim CFO, Principal Acctg Officer, Sr VP & Global Controller)*
Marc H. Levin *(Chief Admin Officer, Gen Counsel, Sec & Exec VP)*
Michael de Vere *(Pres-Bus Grp-US)*
Stefan Schmelcher *(Pres-Global Loyalty Solutions)*
Jeni Lee Chapman *(Exec VP-Global Brand & Comm Consulting)*
Todd Myers *(Sr VP & Interim Head-Tech, Ops & Panel)*
Brands & Products:
THE HARRIS POLL
HARRISINTERACTIVE
QUICKSCREENER
SHELF IMPACT
Advertising Agencies:
Butler/Till Media Services, Inc.
2349 Monroe Ave
Rochester, NY 14618
Tel.: (585) 473-3740
Fax: (585) 473-3862

Webworks Alliance
95 Caterson Ter
Hartsdale, NY 10530
Tel.: (914) 390-0060
Fax: (914) 390-0061

HARRIS MYCFO, INC.
(Sub. of Harris Bancorp, Inc.)
1080 Mars Rd Ste 100
Menlo Park, CA 94025
Tel.: (312) 461-3754
Fax: (312) 765-8375
Toll Free: (877) 692-3611
E-mail: clientinfo@harrismycfo.com
Web Site: www.mycfo.com
Approx. Number Employees: 100
Business Description:
Financial Management Services
S.I.C.: 6282; 7299
N.A.I.C.S.: 523930; 812990
Media: 13
Personnel:
Joe Calabrese *(Pres)*
Thomas Meilinger *(Mng Dir)*

HEALTH GRADES, INC.
(Holding of Vestar Capital Partners, Inc.)
999 18th St Ste 600
Denver, CO 80202
Tel.: (303) 716-0041
Fax: (303) 716-1298
E-mail: cs@healthgrades.com
Web Site: www.healthgrades.com
Approx. Rev.: $52,520,026
Approx. Number Employees: 209
Year Founded: 1999
Business Description:
Medical Practice Management Services
S.I.C.: 8011; 7374; 8742
N.A.I.C.S.: 621111; 518210; 541613
Advertising Expenditures: $2,600,000
Media: 7-10-13
Personnel:
David G. Hicks *(CEO)*
Allen Dodge *(CFO & Exec VP)*
Wes Crews *(COO & Exec VP)*
Tod Baker *(Sr VP-Consulting)*
Mark Bartling *(Sr VP-IT)*
Carolyn Inhoffer Montes *(Sr VP-Professional Svcs)*
John Neal *(Sr VP-Bus Dev)*
Michael Shanks *(Sr VP)*
Brian Vacanti *(VP-Mktg)*
Brands & Products:
CHECKMARK DESIGN
COMPAREYOURCARE
DISTINGUISHED HOSPITAL AWARD
GUIDING AMERICA TO BETTER HEALTHCARE
HEALTH GRADES
THE HEALTHCARE QUALITY EXPERTS
THE HEALTHCARE RATINGS EXPERTS
HEALTHGRADES
HEALTHGRADES.COM
HOME HEALTH QUALITY GUIDE
HOME HEALTH REPORT CARDS
HOSPICE REPORT CARDS
HOSPITAL QUALITY GUIDE
HOSPITAL REPORT CARDS
NURSING HOME QUALITY GUIDE
NURSING HOME REPORT CARDS
PHYSICIAN QUALITY GUIDE
PHYSICIAN REPORT CARDS
QUALITY RATINGS SUITE
SMARTCHOICE

HEALTHANSWERS EDUCATION
1140 Welsh Rd Ste 100
North Wales, PA 19454-2046
Tel.: (215) 412-3900
Fax: (215) 412-4100
E-mail: information@healthanswers.com
Web Site: www.healthanswers.com
Approx. Number Employees: 60
Year Founded: 1997
Business Description:
Producer of Interactive Training Healthcare Website for Consumers & Professionals
S.I.C.: 4899; 8742
N.A.I.C.S.: 517910; 541611
Media: 6-8-9-13-23
Personnel:
Mark Samuel *(Pres)*
Tom Docherty *(CFO)*
Brands & Products:
HEALTHANSWERS

THE HEALTHCENTRAL NETWORK, INC.
2300 Wilson Blvd Ste 600
Arlington, VA 22201
Tel.: (703) 302-1040
Fax: (703) 248-0830
Web Site: www.thehealthcentralnetwork.com
Approx. Sls.: $29,900,000
Approx. Number Employees: 8
Year Founded: 1999
Business Description:
Online Medical Information Provider
S.I.C.: 2741
N.A.I.C.S.: 516110
Media: 13
Personnel:
Jeremy Shane *(Pres & COO)*
Christopher M Schroeder *(CEO & Dir)*
Robert Cecere *(Exec VP-Strategic Sls & Product Dev)*
Peter A. Horn *(Chief Revenue Officer & Exec VP)*
Advertising Agency:
5W Public Relations
888 7th Ave 12th Fl
New York, NY 10106
Tel.: (212) 999-5585
Fax: (646) 328-1711
Public Relations

HEALTHCOMMUNITIES.COM, INC.
136 W St
Northampton, MA 01060-3709
Tel.: (413) 587-0244
Fax: (413) 587-0387
Toll Free: (800) 950-0808
E-mail: info@healthcommunities.com
Web Site: www.healthcommunities.com
E-Mail For Key Personnel:
Marketing Director: TomL@healthcommunities.com
Sales Range: $1-9.9 Million
Approx. Number Employees: 18
Year Founded: 1998
Business Description:
Online Health Information
S.I.C.: 7375
N.A.I.C.S.: 518111
Media: 13
Brands & Products:
HEALTHCOMMUNITIES.COM
PHYSICIAN DEVELOPED AND MONITORED.

Key to Media (For complete agency information see *The Advertising Red Books-Agencies* edition):
1. Bus. Publs. 2. Cable T.V. 3. Catalogs & Directories. 4. Co-op Adv. 5. Consumer Mags. 6. D.M. to Bus. Estab.7. D.M. to Consumers
8. Daily Newsp. 9. Exhibits/Trade Shows 10. Foreign 11. Infomercial 12. Internet Adv.13. Multimedia 14. Network Radio
15. Network T.V. 16. Newsp. Distr. Mags. 17. Other 18. Outdoor (Posters, Transit) 19. Point of Purchase20. Premiums, Novelties
21. Product Samples 22. Special Events Mktg. 23. Spot Radio 24. Spot T.V. 25. Weekly Newsp. 26. Yellow Page Adv.

HIGHBEAM RESEARCH, INC.
65 E Wacker Pl Ste 400
Chicago, IL 60601-7203
Tel.: (312) 782-3900
Fax: (312) 782-3901
Web Site: www.highbeam.com
Approx. Number Employees: 34
Year Founded: 2002
Business Description:
Online Research Services
S.I.C.: 2741
N.A.I.C.S.: 516110
Media: 13
Personnel:
Thomas M. Ballard *(Sr VP-Ops & Web Tech)*
Brands & Products:
HIGHBEAM

HIGHER POWER INC.
(Sub. of Liberty Media LLC)
(d/b/a Bodybuilding.com)
2026 Silverstone Way
Meridian, ID 83642
Tel.: (208) 377-9002
Fax: (208) 377-9993
Toll Free: (877) 991-3411
E-mail: webmaster@bodybuilding.com
Web Site: www.bodybuilding.com
Sales Range: $100-124.9 Million
Approx. Number Employees: 65
Year Founded: 1999
Business Description:
Bodybuilding Information Website
S.I.C.: 2741
N.A.I.C.S.: 516110
Media: 6-13
Personnel:
Ryan DeLuca *(CEO)*
Michael McClane *(CFO)*
Kelly Householder *(CIO)*
Theresa Schwarz *(Dir-Customer Svcs)*
Bill Baldry *(Receiving Mgr)*

HIRERIGHT, INC.
(Sub. of Altegrity, Inc.)
5151 California Ave
Irvine, CA 92617
Tel.: (949) 428-5800
Fax: (949) 224-6020
Toll Free: (800) 400-2761
E-mail: media@hireright.com
Web Site: www.hireright.com
Sales Range: $50-74.9 Million
Approx. Number Employees: 407
Year Founded: 1995
Business Description:
Internet-Based Pre-Employment Screening & Assessment Services
S.I.C.: 7361; 7379; 7381
N.A.I.C.S.: 541612; 541519; 561611
Advertising Expenditures: $300,000
Media: 1-5-7-10-13-17
Personnel:
Mike Petrullo *(Pres & CEO)*
Mark Mayo *(CFO & VP)*
Stefano Malnati *(Sr VP-Engrg)*
Robert J. Pickell *(Sr VP-Customer Solutions)*
Marc Maloy *(VP-Sls-Worldwide)*
Janet Randolph *(VP-HR)*
Advertising Agency:
Strategies, a Marketing Communications Corporation
13681 Newport Ave Ste 8 Ste 616
Tustin, CA 92780
Tel.: (714) 957-8880
Fax: (714) 957-8880

HOLLYWOOD MEDIA CORP.
2255 Glades Rd Ste 221 A
Boca Raton, FL 33431-7382
Tel.: (561) 998-8000
Fax: (561) 998-2974
Toll Free: (800) 722-7573
E-mail: ir@hollywoodmedia.com
Web Site: www.hollywoodmedia.com
Approx. Rev.: $3,995,177
Approx. Number Employees: 36
Year Founded: 1994
Business Description:
Online Ticketing of Entertainment News, Information & Services
S.I.C.: 7299; 2741; 7389; 7999
N.A.I.C.S.: 519190; 516110; 711410; 713990; 812990
Advertising Expenditures: $14,496
Media: 1-2-3-4-5-6-7-8-9-10-11-12-13-14-15-16-17-19-20-21-22-23-24-25-26
Distr.: Direct to Consumer; Intl.; Natl.; Reg.
Budget Set: Nov.
Personnel:
Mitchell Rubenstein *(Chm & CEO)*
Scott A. Gomez *(Chief Acctg Officer)*
Brands & Products:
HOLLYWOOD

HOME SCHOOL HOLDINGS, INC.
2700 S River Rd Ste 106
Des Plaines, IL 60018
Tel.: (847) 391-5079
Fax: (800) 760-7015
E-mail: info@home-school-inc.com
Web Site: www.home-school-inc.com
Approx. Rev.: $63,378
Approx. Number Employees: 4
Year Founded: 2008
Business Description:
Instructional Materials, Curricula, Books, Teachers' Guides & Worksheets Internet Retailer & Information
S.I.C.: 8299; 2741
N.A.I.C.S.: 611710; 516110
Advertising Expenditures: $42,506
Media: 17
Personnel:
David Nicholson *(Interim Chm)*
Denise Kowalski *(Mgr-Adv Sls & Mktg)*

HOMEGAIN.COM, INC.
(Joint Venture of Gannett Co., Inc., The Washington Post Company, The McClatchy Company, Tribune Employee Stock Ownership Plan & A.H. Belo Corporation)
1250 45th St Ste 200
Emeryville, CA 94608-2924
Tel.: (510) 655-0800
Fax: (510) 655-0848
Toll Free: (888) 542-0800
E-mail: info@homegain.com
Web Site: www.homegain.com
Sales Range: $25-49.9 Million
Approx. Number Employees: 65
Year Founded: 1999
Business Description:
Online Real Estate Marketing & Advertising Services
S.I.C.: 6531; 7319
N.A.I.C.S.: 519130; 531390; 541890
Media: 2-7-8-10-13-26
Personnel:
Louis Cammarosano *(Gen Mgr)*
Jim Ridley *(Dir-Website Ops)*
Brands & Products:
AGENTEVALUATOR
AGENTVIEW
AIMS
BUYERLINK
HOME SALE MAXIMIZER

HOMEPORTFOLIO, INC.
288 Walnut St
Newton, MA 02460-1948
Tel.: (617) 965-0565
Fax: (617) 965-4082
E-mail: info@homeportfolio.com
Web Site: www.homeportfolio.com
Approx. Number Employees: 25
Year Founded: 1996
Business Description:
Online Marketplace For Home Design
S.I.C.: 5023; 7374
N.A.I.C.S.: 423220; 518210
Media: 2-6-7-8-10-13
Personnel:
Rolly Rouse *(Co-Founder & CEO)*
Shawn Becker *(Co-Founder)*
Brands & Products:
HOME DESIGN PORTFOLIO
HOMEPORTFOLIO

HOMES.COM, INC.
(Sub. of Dominion Enterprises)
5510 Morehouse Dr Ste 100
San Diego, CA 92121
Tel.: (858) 535-9332
Fax: (866) 600-5857
Toll Free: (866) 500-5857
E-mail: bizdev@homes.com
Web Site: www.homes.com
Approx. Number Employees: 120
Year Founded: 1992
Business Description:
Online Real Estate & Home Services
S.I.C.: 2741; 6531
N.A.I.C.S.: 516110; 531210; 531390
Media: 13
Personnel:
Patty McNease *(Gen Mgr)*
George Salvador *(Gen Mgr)*
Brands & Products:
AGENTADVANTAGE
BROKERADVANTAGE
ESTRATEGY SOLUTIONS
POWERSEARCH ADVANTAGE
Advertising Agency:
Homes.com
5440 Morehouse Dr Ste 3500
San Diego, CA 92121
Tel.: (858) 362-6127
Fax: (858) 535-9343

HOMESTEAD TECHNOLOGIES, INC.
(Sub. of Intuit Inc.)
3375 Edison Way
Menlo Park, CA 94025-1811
Tel.: (650) 549-3100
Fax: (650) 364-7329
E-mail: info@homestead-inc.com
Web Site: www.homestead.com
E-Mail For Key Personnel:
Marketing Director: marketing@homestead-inc.com
Approx. Sls.: $10,000,000
Approx. Number Employees: 150
Year Founded: 1997
Business Description:
Internet Content, Services & Technologies Integrator & Distr
S.I.C.: 7373; 7375
N.A.I.C.S.: 541512; 518111
Media: 2-8-13
Personnel:
Mona Bergevin Wu *(VP-Admin & HR)*
Nathaniel Chorale *(Dir)*
Alfred Newman *(Dir)*
Sol C. Siegel *(Dir)*
D. C. Coston *(Assoc Dir)*
Brands & Products:
HOMESTEAD
PHOTOSITE

HOOKED MEDIA GROUP
995 Market St 8th Fl
San Francisco, CA 94103
Tel.: (415) 369-9003
Fax: (415) 358-4897
E-mail: inquiries@hookedmediagroup.com
Web Site: www.hookedmediagroup.com
Business Description:
Online Gaming
S.I.C.: 2741
N.A.I.C.S.: 516110
Media: 13
Personnel:
Prita Uppal *(CEO)*

HOSTWAY CORPORATION
1 N State St Ste 1200
Chicago, IL 60602
Tel.: (312) 238-0125
Fax: (312) 236-1958
Toll Free: (866) 467-8929
E-mail: sales@hostway.com
Web Site: www.hostway.com
E-Mail For Key Personnel:
Marketing Director: marketing@hostway.com
Sales Director: sales@hostway.com
Public Relations: pr@hostway.com
Sales Range: $75-99.9 Million
Approx. Number Employees: 460
Year Founded: 1998
Business Description:
Internet Hosting Services
S.I.C.: 7375
N.A.I.C.S.: 518111
Media: 6-13
Personnel:
John Lee *(Co-Founder & VP-Mktg-Global)*
Lucas Roh *(Pres & CEO)*
Mark D. Adolph *(CFO & Exec VP)*
Catherine Sigmar *(Pres-RegistryPro)*

HOTELS.COM, L.P.
(Sub. of Expedia, Inc.)
10440 N Central Expy Ste 400
Dallas, TX 75231-4350
Tel.: (214) 361-7311
Fax: (214) 361-7299
Toll Free: (800) 964-6835
E-mail: info@hotels.com
Web Site: www.hotels.com
Sales Range: $900-999.9 Million
Approx. Number Employees: 1,150
Year Founded: 1991
Business Description:
Discount Travel Arrangement
S.I.C.: 4729
N.A.I.C.S.: 561599
Advertising Expenditures: $68,400,000

Key to Media (For complete agency information see *The Advertising Red Books-Agencies* edition):
1. Bus. Publs. 2. Cable T.V. 3. Catalogs & Directories. 4. Co-op Adv. 5. Consumer Mags. 6. D.M. to Bus. Estab.7. D.M. to Consumers
8. Daily Newsp. 9. Exhibits/Trade Shows 10. Foreign 11. Infomercial 12. Internet Adv.13. Multimedia 14. Network Radio
15. Network T.V. 16. Newsp. Distr. Mags. 17. Other 18. Outdoor (Posters, Transit) 19. Point of Purchase20. Premiums, Novelties
21. Product Samples 22. Special Events Mktg. 23. Spot Radio 24. Spot T.V. 25. Weekly Newsp. 26. Yellow Page Adv.

Media: 2-3-4-6-7-10-13-14-17-19-23-24
Personnel:
Victor Owens *(VP-Mktg-North America)*
Vic Walia *(Sr Dir-Brand Mktg-North America)*
Taylor L. Cole *(Dir-PR)*
Advertising Agencies:
GWP Brand Engineering
46 Spadina Ave Ste 200
Toronto, ON M5V 2H8, Canada
Tel.: (416) 593-4000
Fax: (416) 593-4001
Hotels.ca

The Ruder Finn Group
301 E 57th St
New York, NY 10022-2900
Tel.: (212) 593-6400
Fax: (212) 593-6397

TargetCast tcm
909 3rd Ave 31st Fl
New York, NY 10022
Tel.: (212) 500-6900
Fax: (212) 500-6880
Media

Young & Rubicam Chicago
233 N Michigan Ave 16th Fl
Chicago, IL 60601-5519
Tel.: (312) 596-3000
Fax: (312) 596-3130
Creative

HOWSTUFFWORKS, INC.
(Sub. of Discovery Communications, Inc.)
1 Capital City Plz 3350 Peachtree Rd Ste 1500
Atlanta, GA 30326
Tel.: (404) 760-4729
Fax: (404) 760-3459
E-mail: info@howstuffworks.com
Web Site: www.howstuffworks.com
E-Mail For Key Personnel:
Marketing Director: Doeseski@howstuffworks.com
Sales Range: $50-74.9 Million
Approx. Number Employees: 160
Year Founded: 2000
Business Description:
Online Publishing Company
S.I.C.: 2741
N.A.I.C.S.: 516110
Media: 1-2-5-6-10-13-21-24
Personnel:
Jeff Arnold *(Chm & CEO)*
Michael J. Cascone *(COO-Discovery Digital Media & Gen Mgr-HowStuffWorkscom)*

HYDRALIGN
(Div. of Butler Automatic, Inc.)
41 Leona Dr
Middleboro, MA 02346-1404
Tel.: (508) 923-0544
Fax: (508) 823-0886
Toll Free: (800) 544-0070
E-mail: info@butlerautomatic.com
Web Site: www.butlerautomatic.com
Year Founded: 1976
Business Description:
Electronic Web Guide Systems, Mechanical Core Chucks, Winding & Unwinding Machines Mfr
S.I.C.: 3999
N.A.I.C.S.: 339999
Import Export
Media: 2-4-10-11-22
Distr.: Natl.
Budget Set: Nov.
Personnel:
Andrew P. Butler *(Pres & CEO)*
Brands & Products:
BELTRAC
COR-TROL
HYDRALIGN
MONARCH-TACH
STATIC CONSUMER
STATIC MIZER
STATIC SENSOR
WEBMINDER

I2SMS
PO Box 421194
Atlanta, GA 30342
Tel.: (404) 944-1351
Web Site: www.i2sms.net
Business Description:
Mobile Advertising, Communications & Marketing
S.I.C.: 7319
N.A.I.C.S.: 541890
Media: 17-27
Personnel:
Giff Gfroerer *(Reg Dir)*

I365
(Sub. of i365)
6121 Hollis St Ste 2
Emeryville, CA 94608
Tel.: (510) 903-7100
Fax: (510) 903-7200
Toll Free: (877) 382-8581
E-mail: concierge@i365.com
Web Site: www.i365.com
E-Mail For Key Personnel:
Sales Director: sales@evault.com
Sales Range: $10-24.9 Million
Approx. Number Employees: 160
Year Founded: 1997
Business Description:
Data Protection, Retention Management & Recovery Solutions
S.I.C.: 7379
N.A.I.C.S.: 541519
Media: 10-13
Brands & Products:
EVAULT ARCWARE
EVAULT DESKTOP
EVAULT INFOSTAGE
EVAULT PROMAIL
EVAULT PROTECT
OUREVAULT

IA GLOBAL, INC.
101 California St Ste 2450
San Francisco, CA 94111
Tel.: (415) 946-8828
Fax: (415) 946-8801
E-mail: ir@iaglobalinc.com
Web Site: www.iaglobalinc.com
Approx. Rev.: $20,918
Approx. Number Employees: 12
Year Founded: 1998
Business Description:
Investment Services
S.I.C.: 6289
N.A.I.C.S.: 523999
Media: 13
Personnel:
Ranaga C. Krishna *(Pres)*
Brian L. Hoekstra *(CEO & Dir-Mgmt)*
Mark Scott *(CFO)*
Ryuhei Senda *(Dir-Mgmt & Mgr-Japan)*

IAC SEARCH & MEDIA, INC.
(Sub. of IAC/InterActiveCorp)
(d/b/a Ask.com)
555 12th St Ste 500
Oakland, CA 94607
Tel.: (510) 985-7400
Fax: (510) 985-7412
E-mail: information@ask.com
Web Site: www.ask.com
Sales Range: $250-299.9 Million
Approx. Number Employees: 505
Year Founded: 1996
Business Description:
Online Search Engine Services
S.I.C.: 8999
N.A.I.C.S.: 518112
Advertising Expenditures: $1,522,000
Media: 13
Personnel:
Doug Leeds *(CEO)*
Dominic Butera *(CFO)*
Mark Stockford *(CIO-Askcom)*
Andrew Moers *(Pres-Askcom Partner Network)*
Tao Yang *(Sr VP & Chief Scientist)*
Tomasz Imielinski *(Exec VP-Global Search & Answers)*
Mary Osako *(Sr VP-Worldwide Comm)*
Nicholas Graham *(VP-Comm)*
Scott Grieder *(Dir-Product Mgmt)*
Nadia Kelly *(Dir-PR)*
Jennifer Hallett *(Asst Mgr-Comm-Askcom)*
Amanda Conti *(Mgr-Consumer Comm)*
Brands & Products:
ASK
ASK JEEVES
ASK JEEVES FOR KIDS
ASK JEEVES UK
ASKERASER
EXCITE
IWON
MAXONLINE
MYSEARCH
MYWAY
MYWEBSEARCH
TEOMA
Advertising Agencies:
Dotted Line Communications
227 N Bowling Green
Los Angeles, CA 90049
Tel.: (310) 472-8600

Hanft Raboy & Partners
205 Hudson St 7th Fl
New York, NY 10013
Tel.: (212) 674-3100
Fax: (212) 228-7679
(Ask.com)

Mullen
40 Broad St
Boston, MA 02109
Tel.: (617) 226-9000
Fax: (617) 226-9100
(Ask.com, Media Buying)

ICE.COM, INC.
(Sub. of 94216 Canada Inc.)
4058 Jean Talon W Ste 200
Montreal, QC H4P 1V5, Canada
Tel.: (514) 393-9788
Fax: (514) 393-1295
Toll Free: (800) 539-3580
E-mail: info@ice.com
Web Site: www.ice.com
Sales Range: $1-9.9 Million
Approx. Number Employees: 30
Year Founded: 1999
Business Description:
Online Jewelry Retailer
S.I.C.: 5944
N.A.I.C.S.: 448310
Import
Advertising Expenditures: $7,000,000
Media: 8-13
Personnel:
Pinny Gniwisch *(Founder & Exec VP-Bus Dev & Comm)*
Mayer Gniwisch *(Founder)*
Sam Gniwisch *(CEO)*
Pardo Vincelli *(VP-Customer Care)*
Alan Woolff *(VP-Mdsg)*
Julie Schwartz *(Dir-Design)*
Brands & Products:
JULIE LEAH
MICHICO
RENATA CELINI

ICOLLECTOR.COM TECHNOLOGIES, INC.
(Sub. of SINOCOKING COAL & COKE CHEMICAL INDUSTRIES, INC.)
1963 Lougheed Hwy
Coquitlam, BC V3K 3T8, Canada
Tel.: (604) 777-3800
Fax: (604) 521-4911
Toll Free: (866) 313-0123
E-mail: customerservices@icollector.com
Web Site: www.icollectorlive.com
Approx. Number Employees: 120
Year Founded: 1994
Business Description:
Online Auction
S.I.C.: 5961
N.A.I.C.S.: 454112
Media: 13

ICRUISE.COM CORP.
220 Congress Park Dr Ste 140
Delray Beach, FL 33445
Tel.: (561) 243-0707
Toll Free: (800) 630-4406
E-mail: admin@icruise.com
Web Site: www.icruise.com
Approx. Number Employees: 20
Year Founded: 1999
Business Description:
Online Provider of Cruise & Travel Information & Sales
S.I.C.: 4724
N.A.I.C.S.: 561510
Media: 3-13-15-18-23-24
Personnel:
Uf Turkel *(Pres)*

IDEALAB, INC.
(Sub. of Idealab Holdings, LLC)
130 W Union St
Pasadena, CA 91103
Tel.: (626) 585-6900
Fax: (626) 535-2701
E-mail: info@idealab.com
Web Site: www.idealab.com
Approx. Number Employees: 100
Year Founded: 1996
Business Description:
Investments, Capital, Development Strategies, Financial Support, Network Infrastructure, Consulting, Marketing Advice & Branding for New Businesses
S.I.C.: 6289; 2741; 7389

Key to Media (For complete agency information see *The Advertising Red Books-Agencies* edition):
1. Bus. Publs. 2. Cable T.V. 3. Catalogs & Directories. 4. Co-op Adv. 5. Consumer Mags. 6. D.M. to Bus. Estab.7. D.M. to Consumers 8. Daily Newsp. 9. Exhibits/Trade Shows 10. Foreign 11. Infomercial 12. Internet Adv.13. Multimedia 14. Network Radio 15. Network T.V. 16. Newsp. Distr. Mags. 17. Other 18. Outdoor (Posters, Transit) 19. Point of Purchase20. Premiums, Novelties 21. Product Samples 22. Special Events Mktg. 23. Spot Radio 24. Spot T.V. 25. Weekly Newsp. 26. Yellow Page Adv.

Idealab, Inc. — (Continued)

N.A.I.C.S.: 523999; 516110; 561499
Media: 13
Personnel:
Marcia Goodstein *(Pres & COO)*
William Gross *(CEO)*
Craig Chrisney *(CFO)*
Tom Hughes *(Chief Design Officer)*
Douglas McPherson *(Gen Counsel & Mng Dir-New Ventures Grp)*
Teresa Bridwell *(VP-Corp Comm)*
Wes Ferrari *(VP-IT)*
Brands & Products:
AIRWAVE
COOKING
ENERGY INNOVATIONS
EVOLUTION ROBOTICS
IDEALAB
INSIDER PAGES
INTERNET BRANDS
NEWBURY NETWORKS
OMNILUX
ORAXION
PARTSEARCH TECHNOLOGIES
SNAP
VENDARE MEDIA
X1 TECHNOLOGIES

IENTERTAINMENT NETWORK, INC.
124-126 Quade Dr
Cary, NC 27513-7400
Tel.: (919) 678-8301
Fax: (919) 678-8302
E-mail: accounts@iencentral.com
Web Site: www.iencentral.com
E-Mail For Key Personnel:
Sales Director: adsales@ient.com
Approx. Number Employees: 18
Year Founded: 1994
Business Description:
Provider of Online Gaming & Entertainment Products
S.I.C.: 7372
N.A.I.C.S.: 511210
Media: 17
Brands & Products:
DAWN OF ACES
WARBIRDS
WARBIRDS AIR COMBAT

IFILM CORP.
(Sub. of MTV Networks Company)
1024 N Orange Dr
Hollywood, CA 90038-2318
Tel.: (323) 308-3400
Fax: (323) 308-3492
E-mail: info@ifilm.com
Web Site: www.ifilm.com
Approx. Number Employees: 60
Year Founded: 1998
Business Description:
Streaming Video Content Provider
S.I.C.: 7375
N.A.I.C.S.: 518111
Media: 13
Personnel:
Jason Jordan *(Sr VP-Ops & Fin)*
Brands & Products:
IFILM

IGA WORLDWIDE
111 Broadway Ste 602
New York, NY 10006
Tel.: (212) 381-0950
Fax: (212) 240-9055
Web Site: www.igaworldwide.com
Business Description:
In Game Advertising Services
S.I.C.: 7319
N.A.I.C.S.: 541890
Media: 17-27
Personnel:
Christian Vry *(Co-Founder & CEO)*
Peter Sispoidis *(Co-Founder & CTO)*
Justin Townsend *(Co-Founder & Chief Volunteer Officer)*

IGN ENTERTAINMENT, INC.
(Sub. of Fox Interactive Media, Inc.)
625 2nd St, 3rd Fl
San Francisco, CA 94107
Tel.: (415) 896-3700
E-mail: ir@ign.com
Web Site: www.ign.com
Sales Range: $50-74.9 Million
Approx. Number Employees: 291
Year Founded: 1999
Business Description:
Online Entertainment & Media Products & Services
S.I.C.: 7374; 2741
N.A.I.C.S.: 518210; 516110
Advertising Expenditures: $1,117,000
Media: 13
Personnel:
Roy Bahat *(Pres)*
Allen Maximillian *(CFO)*
Peer Schneider *(Publr & Sr VP)*
Charlie Barrett *(Sr VP-Sls)*
Scott Bender *(VP-Sls Brand)*
Kym Nelson *(VP-Sls Game)*
Kris Sharbaugh *(Sr. Comm Mgr)*
Brands & Products:
IGN GAMESTORE
IGN INSIDER
IGN.COM

IMAGINOVA CORP.
470 Park Ave S 9th Fl
New York, NY 10016
Tel.: (212) 703-5800
Fax: (212) 703-5801
E-mail: info@hq.space.com
Web Site: www.imaginova.com
Approx. Number Employees: 50
Year Founded: 1999
Business Description:
Space Related News, Information, Education & Entertainment Online Services
S.I.C.: 2741; 5734; 7383
N.A.I.C.S.: 516110; 443120; 519110
Media: 2-4-7-8-10-13-23-24
Personnel:
Thomas Dehn *(CFO)*
Bill Klanke *(VP & Publr)*
Peter Moreo *(VP & Gen Mgr)*
Liliana Cavazos *(Media Coord)*
Brands & Products:
IMAGINOVA
LIVESCIENCE
ORION
SPACE NEWS
SPACE.COM
STARRY NIGHT

IMDIVERSITY, INC.
140 Carondelet St
New Orleans, LA 70130
Tel.: (504) 523-0154
Fax: (504) 523-0271
E-mail: support@imdiversity.com
Web Site: www.imdiversity.com
E-Mail For Key Personnel:
Sales Director: sales@iminorities.com
Approx. Number Employees: 14
Year Founded: 1970
Business Description:
Online Career & Self-Development Information for Minorities
S.I.C.: 2741; 7361
N.A.I.C.S.: 516110; 561310
Media: 6-13-25
Personnel:
Preston J. Edwards, Sr. *(CEO & Publr)*
Lisa Edwards *(CFO)*
Richard Gonzales *(COO)*
Paul S. Williams *(Chief Legal Officer, Sec & Exec VP)*
Frank Griffith *(Brand Dir)*
Brands & Products:
THE BLACK COLLEGIAN MAGAZINE
IMDIVERSITY

IMEX EXCHANGE, INC.
(d/b/a Internet International Business Exchange)
120 E 36th St Ste 7H
New York, NY 10016
Tel.: (212) 745-9494
Fax: (212) 447-6595
Toll Free: (888) 491-8833
E-mail: info@imex.com
Web Site: www.imex.com
Approx. Number Employees: 25
Year Founded: 1994
Business Description:
International Trade on the Internet Promoter; Business Consulting Services
S.I.C.: 7373; 8748
N.A.I.C.S.: 541512; 541618
Media: 13
Personnel:
Dennis Stillwell *(Chm)*
Michael Oliu *(Mng Dir)*
Barney Lehrer *(Exec VP)*
Renee Toriumi *(Exec VP)*
Richard Ogawa *(VP-Intl Sls)*

IMODULES SOFTWARE, INC.
7400 W 132th St Ste 300
Overland Park, KS 66213-2628
Tel.: (913) 888-0772
Fax: (913) 341-2986
Toll Free: (800) 734-3853
E-mail: info@imodules.com
Web Site: www.imodules.com
Approx. Number Employees: 70
Year Founded: 1998
Business Description:
Online Hosting Solutions for Educational & Non-Profit Institutions
S.I.C.: 7373; 7375
N.A.I.C.S.: 541512; 518111
Media: 2-7-10
Personnel:
Thomas R. Palmer *(Chm)*
Thomas A. DeBacco *(CEO)*
Brands & Products:
BUILDING CONNECTIONS
CUSTOM COMMUNITY
IMODULES

IMPACT MOBILE INC.
400 Richmond Street West Ste 700
Toronto, ON M5V 1Y1, Canada
Tel.: (416) 368-8400
Fax: (416) 368-2157
Web Site: www.impactmobile.com
Business Description:
Mobile Advertising Services
S.I.C.: 2741
N.A.I.C.S.: 516110
Media: 8-13-27

INCENTIVE LOGIC, INC.
7835 E McClain Dr
Scottsdale, AZ 85260
Tel.: (480) 776-0800
Fax: (480) 776-0899
E-mail: info@incentivelogic.com
Web Site: www.incentivelogic.com
Sales Range: $75-99.9 Million
Approx. Number Employees: 45
Year Founded: 1998
Business Description:
Online Relationship Marketing Services
S.I.C.: 7371
N.A.I.C.S.: 541511
Media: 6-10-13
Personnel:
Craig King *(Pres & CEO)*
Debra Spamer *(VP-Sls, Mktg & Svc)*

INC.COM LLC
(Sub. of Inc. Magazine)
7 World Trade Ctr
New York, NY 10007-2195
Tel.: (212) 389-5300
Fax: (212) 389-5393
E-mail: contact@inc.com
Web Site: www.inc.com
Sales Range: $1-9.9 Million
Approx. Number Employees: 170
Year Founded: 1999
Business Description:
Online Business Magazine Publisher
S.I.C.: 5734; 7378
N.A.I.C.S.: 519130
Media: 13
Personnel:
David Grossman *(Dir-Bus Dev)*
Blake Taylor *(Dir-Creative)*

INFOACCESS.NET LLC
8801 E Pleasant Vly Rd
Cleveland, OH 44131-5510
Tel.: (216) 328-0100
Fax: (216) 328-0913
Toll Free: (800) 255-0253
E-mail: info@infoaccess.net
Web Site: www.infoaccess.net
Approx. Number Employees: 28
Year Founded: 1996
Business Description:
Electronic Business-to-Business Supply Chain & Order Management Services to the Food & Consumer Packaged Goods Industries
S.I.C.: 7372
N.A.I.C.S.: 511210
Advertising Expenditures: $500,000
Media: 13
Personnel:
Edward J. Schnell *(Owner)*
Daniel L. Andrew *(Pres)*
Michael T. Minch *(CFO)*
Brands & Products:
EDI CONVERSATION SERVICES
EPAYABLES
FOOD BROKERAGE SYSTEM
INFOACCESS.NET
MAKE OUR NUMBERS

INFOKALL, INC.
2850 Redhill Ave Ste 140
Santa Ana, CA 92705

Key to Media (For complete agency information see *The Advertising Red Books-Agencies* edition):
1. Bus. Publs. 2. Cable T.V. 3. Catalogs & Directories. 4. Co-op Adv. 5. Consumer Mags. 6. D.M. to Bus. Estab.7. D.M. to Consumers
8. Daily Newsp. 9. Exhibits/Trade Shows 10. Foreign 11. Infomercial 12. Internet Adv.13. Multimedia 14. Network Radio
15. Network T.V. 16. Newsp. Distr. Mags. 17. Other 18. Outdoor (Posters, Transit) 19. Point of Purchase20. Premiums, Novelties
21. Product Samples 22. Special Events Mktg. 23. Spot Radio 24. Spot T.V. 25. Weekly Newsp. 26. Yellow Page Adv.

Tel.: (949) 260-9697
Fax: (949) 253-9698
Toll Free: (888) 955-3503
E-mail: us_sales@infokall.com
Web Site: www.infokall.com
Approx. Number Employees: 45
Business Description:
E-Business & Wireless Integration Solutions
S.I.C.: 7373; 7371
N.A.I.C.S.: 541512; 541511
Media: 10-13

INFORMATION BUILDERS (CANADA) INC.
(Sub. of Information Builders Inc.)
150 York St Ste 1000
Toronto, ON M5H 3S5, Canada
Tel.: (416) 364-2760
Fax: (416) 364-6552
Web Site:
www.informationbuilders.com/about_us/images/iWay_worldMap.swf
Approx. Number Employees: 60
Business Description:
Computer Services
S.I.C.: 7373
N.A.I.C.S.: 541512
Media: 10
Personnel:
Brian Joynt *(VP & Gen Mgr-Info Builders Canada)*
Daniela Romendi *(Fin Controller)*
David Kerner *(Branch Mgr-Industry Mktg)*
Joe Walsh *(Technical Branch Mgr-Gen Bus Mktg)*

INFORMATIVE, INC.
(Sub. of Satmetrix Systems, Inc.)
701 Gateway Blvd Ste 270
South San Francisco, CA 94080-7041
Tel.: (650) 534-1010
Fax: (650) 534-1020
E-mail: info@informative.com
Web Site: www.informative.com
Sales Range: $1-9.9 Million
Approx. Number Employees: 40
Year Founded: 1998
Business Description:
Proactively Collect Critical Customer Input
S.I.C.: 7375
N.A.I.C.S.: 518111
Media: 13
Personnel:
Ed Sarraille *(Pres)*
Arthur Rock *(Gen Partner)*
Dana Smith *(Dir)*
Brands & Products:
DIALOGUE
INFORMATIVE
RESPOND

INFOSPACE, INC.
601 108th Ave NE
Bellevue, WA 98004-4383
Tel.: (425) 201-6100
Fax: (425) 201-6150
Toll Free: (866) GETINSP
E-mail: information@infospace.com
Web Site: www.infospaceinc.com
Approx. Rev.: $246,835,000
Approx. Number Employees: 174
Year Founded: 1996
Business Description:
Internet Infrastructure & Services
S.I.C.: 7374; 7375; 8231; 8999
N.A.I.C.S.: 518210; 518111; 518112; 519120
Advertising Expenditures: $22,800,000
Media: 2-7-8-9-10-13-18-20-22-23-25
Personnel:
John E. Cunningham, IV *(Chm)*
William J. Ruckelshaus *(Pres & CEO)*
David Bradley Binder *(CFO)*
Alesia Pinney *(Gen Counsel & Sec)*
Nathan Rohm *(Sr Product Mgr)*
Brands & Products:
100HOT
ACTIVESHOPPER
ADFOCUS
APRILFOOLS.COM
AQUASTAX
ARFIE
AUDIOTONES
CLASSIFIEDS2000
COOLNOTIFY
DELIVERING EXPERIENCE
DOGPILE
DOGPILE.COM
E-CASH
E-VOTE
ELKWARE
FXTONES
GIANTBEAR
GIANTBEAR.COM
GO2NET
GOLF CLUB
GOOD DOG. GREAT RESULTS.
HAGGLE ONLINE
HITTONES
INFOSPACE
INFOSPACE MOBILE
INFOSPACE MOBILE ZONE
INFOSPACE TOOLBAR BUILDER
INFOSPACE.COM
INTELLIFIND
JANGO
METACRAWLER
METASPY
MOBILEZONE
MODALYST
MOVISO
MUSICTONES
NUTONES
OPEN HOUSE
PAGEGREETINGS
PICSTER
POWERED BY INFOSPACE
PUB
PUB FIGHT
PUB FRUITY
RINGSTER
RUBBERCHICKEN.COM
SEARCH THE SEARCH ENGINES!
SEARCHSPY
SEXY SOCCER
SONG CENTRAL
SONGTONES
STARTONES
SYNCNOW
TOOLBAR BUILDER
TRUTONES
VALENTINE.COM
VIRTUAL OUTLET
WATCHDOG
WEB21
WEBCRAWLER
WEBFETCH
WEBMARKET
YOURMOBILE
ZOO
Advertising Agency:
Peppercom
470 Park Ave S 5th Fl
New York, NY 10016
Tel.: (212) 931-6100
Fax: (212) 931-6159

INGENIO, INC.
(Div. of AT&T Yellow Pages)
100 First St Ste 100
San Francisco, CA 94105
Tel.: (877) 529-1193
Fax: (415) 248-4100
Toll Free: (888) INGENIO
E-mail: info@ingenio.com
Web Site: www.ingenio.com
Sales Range: $10-24.9 Million
Approx. Number Employees: 85
Year Founded: 1999
Business Description:
Pay Per Use Telephone Services
S.I.C.: 7375; 4813; 4899
N.A.I.C.S.: 518111; 517110; 517310; 517910
Media: 8-13-26
Brands & Products:
INGENIO
KEEN
LIVE! ADVICE CENTERS
PAY PER CALL
YOUR PERSONAL ADVISOR

INNODATA ISOGEN, INC.
3 University Plz
Hackensack, NJ 07601
Tel.: (201) 371-2828
Fax: (201) 488-9099
E-mail: info@innodata-isogen.com
Web Site: www.innodata-isogen.com
Approx. Rev.: $61,513,000
Approx. Number Employees: 5,060
Year Founded: 1988
Business Description:
On-Line Data Conversion & Content Management
S.I.C.: 7374; 7375
N.A.I.C.S.: 518210; 518111
Media: 7-10-13-22
Personnel:
Jack S. Abuhoff *(Chm, Pres & CEO)*
O'Neil Nalavadi *(CFO & Sr VP)*
Ashok Kumar Mishra *(COO & Exec VP)*
Amy R. Agress *(Gen Counsel & VP)*
Jim Lewis *(Sr VP)*
Jan Palmen *(Sr VP-Publ Svcs)*
Klaas Brouwer *(VP-Tech)*
Al Girardi *(VP-Mktg)*
Brands & Products:
CONTENT SUPPLY CHAIN
INNODATA
INNODATA ISOGEN
THINK INNODATA ISOGEN
TRUTH VALUE SERVICE

INO.COM
Discovery Vlg 4800 Atwell Rd
Shady Side, MD 20764
Tel.: (410) 867-2100
Fax: (410) 867-4203
Toll Free: (800) 538-7424
E-mail: info@ino.com
Web Site: www.ino.com
E-Mail For Key Personnel:
President: adam@ino.com
Approx. Number Employees: 100
Year Founded: 1995
Business Description:
Market Trade Internet Information
S.I.C.: 8742; 6282
N.A.I.C.S.: 541611; 523930
Advertising Expenditures: $200,000
Media: 7-8-13
Personnel:
David Maher *(Founder & Tech Dir)*
J. Adam Hewison *(Pres)*
Bob Fladung *(Dir-Adv & Licensing)*
Brands & Products:
EXTREME SIGNALS
INO.COM
MARKET CLUB

INOVIS, INC.
(Sub. of GXS, Inc.)
11720 Amber Park Dr Ste 400
Alpharetta, GA 30009
Tel.: (404) 467-3000
Fax: (404) 467-3998
Toll Free: (800) 607-4334
Toll Free: (877) 4INOVIS
E-mail: info@inovis.com
Web Site: www.inovis.com
Sales Range: $1-4.9 Billion
Year Founded: 1985
Business Description:
E-Commerce Software, Services & Solutions for Supply Chain Management
S.I.C.: 5045
N.A.I.C.S.: 423430
Media: 2-7-10-13-22
Distr.: Natl.
Personnel:
Kenneth Williams *(CFO)*
James Eberle *(COO)*
Brands & Products:
BIZCONNECT
BIZLINK
BIZMANAGER
BIZWEB
INOVIS
MAILLINK
SECURELINK
TRUSTEDLINK
Advertising Agencies:
Arketi Group
2801 Buford Hwy Druid Chase Ste 375
Atlanta, GA 30329
Tel.: (404) 929-0091
Fax: (404) 321-3397

Fleishman-Hillard Inc.
229 Peachtree St NE International Twr Ste 1600
Atlanta, GA 30303
Tel.: (404) 659-4446
Fax: (404) 659-4452
Pub Rels

INTELIMAX MEDIA INC.
555 W Hastings St Ste 2320
Vancouver, BC V6B 4N4, Canada
Tel.: (604) 742-1111
Fax: (604) 909-5169
Toll Free: (866) 742-1759
E-mail: galln@intelimax.com
Web Site: www.intelimax.com
Approx. Rev.: $2,363
Approx. Number Employees: 1
Business Description:
Website & Internet Portal Operator
S.I.C.: 2741
N.A.I.C.S.: 516110
Advertising Expenditures: $54,246

Key to Media (For complete agency information see *The Advertising Red Books-Agencies* edition):
1. Bus. Publs. 2. Cable T.V. 3. Catalogs & Directories. 4. Co-op Adv. 5. Consumer Mags. 6. D.M. to Bus. Estab.7. D.M. to Consumers
8. Daily Newsp. 9. Exhibits/Trade Shows 10. Foreign 11. Infomercial 12. Internet Adv.13. Multimedia 14. Network Radio
15. Network T.V. 16. Newsp. Distr. Mags. 17. Other 18. Outdoor (Posters, Transit) 19. Point of Purchase20. Premiums, Novelties
21. Product Samples 22. Special Events Mktg. 23. Spot Radio 24. Spot T.V. 25. Weekly Newsp. 26. Yellow Page Adv.

Intelimax Media Inc. — (Continued)

Media: 17
Personnel:
Glenn Little *(Pres, CEO, CFO & Sec)*
Brands & Products:
CLIMATESEEK.COM
GAMBOOZLE.COM

INTELLIGENT MOBILE SOLUTIONS, INC.

(d/b/a CycleLogic Mobile Solutions)
1801 SW 3rd Ave 3rd Fl
Miami, FL 33129
Tel.: (786) 866-8050
Fax: (305) 854-4358
Web Site: www.cyclelogic.com
Approx. Number Employees: 390
Business Description:
Integrated Internet Media & Solutions Company for Spanish & Portuguese-Speaking Audiences
S.I.C.: 7375
N.A.I.C.S.: 518111
Media: 2-6-10-13-16-18-23-24
Personnel:
Eduardo Kawas *(Owner)*
Amaury Bonatto *(CFO)*
Jose Maria Carosella *(Sr VP-Product Dev)*
Brands & Products:
ADNET.COM.MX
BATEPAPO.COM.BR
CADAMUJER.COM
GUIARJ.COM.BR
GUIASP.COM.BR
LATINRED.NET
NACIDADE.COM.BR
OPENCHILE.CL
PANORAMAS.CL
PERISCOPIO.COM
PIASAS.COM
PIDEMAS.COM
STARMEDIA.COM
VIAMULHER.COM.BR
YOINVITO.COM
ZEEK.COM.BR

INTERCLICK, INC.

11 W 19th St 10th Fl
New York, NY 10011
Tel.: (646) 722-6260
Web Site: www.interclick.com
Approx. Rev.: $101,201,720
Approx. Number Employees: 117
Year Founded: 2002
Business Description:
Integrated Multi-Channel Internet Advertising Solutions
S.I.C.: 7319
N.A.I.C.S.: 541890; 519130
Advertising Expenditures: $600,000
Media: 13
Personnel:
Michael Brauser *(Co-Chm)*
Barry Honig *(Co-Chm)*
Michael Stephen Katz *(CEO)*
Roger Clark *(CFO)*
Jason Lynn *(Chief Strategy Officer)*
Dave Myers *(Exec VP-Ops)*
Jay Freedman *(Sr VP-Sls)*
Michael Marvul *(Sr VP-Sls)*
Kurt Munzinger *(Sr VP-Sls-West Coast)*
Heather Oxer *(VP-Sls-Midwest Reg)*
Rick Dalton *(Dir-Data Ops)*
Jeffrey W. Davis *(Dir-Acctg & Fin Reporting)*

INTERCOSMOS MEDIA GROUP, INC.

650 Poydras St Ste 1150
New Orleans, LA 70130
Tel.: (504) 679-5170
Fax: (504) 566-0484
E-mail: support@intercosmos.com
Web Site: www.directnic.com
E-Mail For Key Personnel:
Sales Director: sales@intercosmos.com
Approx. Number Employees: 40
Year Founded: 1999
Business Description:
Internet Hosting & Domain Name Registration Services
S.I.C.: 7373; 7375
N.A.I.C.S.: 541512; 518111
Media: 13
Personnel:
Sigmund Solares *(CEO)*
Butch Decossas *(CFO)*
Brands & Products:
DIRECTNIC.COM
INTERCOSMOS
INTERNIC.COM
SITECREATOR
SITERACER

INTERNET AMERICA, INC.

10930 W.Sam Houston Pkwy Ste 200
Houston, TX 77064-0753
Tel.: (713) 968-2500
Toll Free: (800) 232-4335
E-mail: info@airmail.net
Web Site: www.internetamerica.com
Approx. Rev.: $6,978,860
Approx. Number Employees: 35
Year Founded: 1995
Business Description:
Internet Services
S.I.C.: 7372; 7373; 7375
N.A.I.C.S.: 334611; 518111; 541512
Advertising Expenditures: $71,000
Media: 8-9-13-18-19-22-25-26
Personnel:
William E. Ladin, Jr. *(Chm, CEO, Acting CFO & Acting Chief Acctg Officer)*
Brands & Products:
1-800 BE A GEEK
AIRMAIL.NET
AIRNEWS.NET
AIRSTREAM
AIRWEB.NET
EXPRESSLANE DSL
INTERNET AMERICA
NEOSOFT
NETFAX
NETFAX PLUS
NETVOICE
PDQ.NET

INTERNET CALL WAITING CORPORATION

(Sub. of RingCentral, Inc.)
5875 Arnold Rd Ste 200
Dublin, CA 94568-7580
Tel.: (925) 479-1400
Toll Free: (888) 849-4222
Web Site: www.ringcentral.com
Approx. Number Employees: 100
Year Founded: 1997
Business Description:
Full Service Internet Phone Company
S.I.C.: 4899
N.A.I.C.S.: 517910
Media: 13
Brands & Products:
PAGOO

THE INTERNET LANGUAGE COMPANY

(d/b/a Multilingual Books)
11515 NE 26th Ave Ste 201
Seattle, WA 98125
Tel.: (253) 353-2761
Fax: (206) 400-1156
Toll Free: (800) 218-2737
E-mail: sales@multilingualbooks.com
Web Site: www.multilingualbooks.com
E-Mail For Key Personnel:
Sales Director: sales@multilingualbooks.com
Sales Range: Less than $1 Million
Approx. Number Employees: 7
Year Founded: 1995
Business Description:
Language & Translation Products Via The Internet
S.I.C.: 5192; 5942
N.A.I.C.S.: 424920; 451211
Media: 2-6-10-13-26
Personnel:
Kenneth Tomkins *(Pres & Partner)*
Brands & Products:
MULTILINGUAL BOOKS

INTERNET MEDIA SERVICES, INC.

1434 6th St Ste 9
Santa Monica, CA 90401
Tel.: (310) 295-1922
E-mail: info@internetmediaservices.com
Web Site:
www.internetmediaservices.com
Approx. Rev.: $570,732
Approx. Number Employees: 4
Year Founded: 2007
Business Description:
Internet Website Services
S.I.C.: 2741
N.A.I.C.S.: 516110
Advertising Expenditures: $41,700
Media: 17
Personnel:
Raymond J. Meyers *(Pres, CEO & Treas)*
Gaston Taratuta *(CEO)*
Christopher Gonzalez *(Gen Counsel-Special)*
Michael Buechler *(Sec & Exec VP)*

INTERNETFITNESS.COM, INC.

780 5th Ave Ste 200
King of Prussia, PA 19406
Tel.: (484) 751-0794
Fax: (484) 636-0364
Toll Free: (888) 800-1167
E-mail: info@internetfitness.com
Web Site: www.internetfitness.com
Approx. Number Employees: 52
Business Description:
Fitness Equipment Whslr & Online Retailer
S.I.C.: 5091; 5941; 5961
N.A.I.C.S.: 423910; 451110; 454111
Media: 6-13
Personnel:
William Olson *(Pres & CEO)*
Brands & Products:
SMOOTH FITNESS

INTRUSION INC.

1101 E Arapaho Rd Ste 200
Richardson, TX 75081
Tel.: (972) 234-6400
Fax: (972) 301-3685
Toll Free: (888) 637-7770
E-mail: sales@intrusion.com
Web Site: www.intrusion.com
E-Mail For Key Personnel:
Sales Director: sales@intrusion.com
Approx. Rev.: $5,588,000
Approx. Number Employees: 27
Year Founded: 1983
Business Description:
Security Networking Products
S.I.C.: 3669; 3571; 3577; 7373; 7382
N.A.I.C.S.: 334290; 334111; 334119; 541512; 561621
Media: 2-7-10
Distr.: Natl.
Personnel:
G. Ward Paxton *(Chm, Pres & CEO)*
T. Joe Head *(Vice Chm & VP)*
Michael L. Paxton *(CFO, VP)*
Garry Hemphill *(VP-Sls & Ops)*

INVENDA CORPORATION

6901 Rockledge Dr
Bethesda, MD 20817
Tel.: (240) 333-6100
Fax: (240) 333-6250
Toll Free: (877) 323-6848
E-mail: press@invenda.com
Web Site: www.invenda.com
Sales Range: $10-24.9 Million
Approx. Number Employees: 42
Year Founded: 1996
Business Description:
Digital Marketing & Promotional Services
S.I.C.: 7319
N.A.I.C.S.: 541890
Media: 7-10-13
Personnel:
Kamran Amjadi *(Co-Founder, Chm & CEO)*
Dadi Akhavan *(Co-Founder)*
Tracy Slavin *(CFO)*
Brands & Products:
E-CENTIVES
E-MAIL MARKETING SYSTEM
IDBM
INTERNET COUPON SYSTEM
ONLINE SWEEPSTAKES/INSTANT WIN SYSTEMS

IPARTY CORP.

270 Bridge St
Dedham, MA 02026
Tel.: (781) 329-3952
Fax: (781) 326-7143
E-mail: corporate@iparty.com
Web Site: www.iparty.com
Approx. Rev.: $81,291,429
Approx. Number Employees: 263
Year Founded: 1998
Business Description:
Party Related Supplies, Information & Services
S.I.C.: 5947; 5961; 5999
N.A.I.C.S.: 453220; 453998; 454113
Advertising Expenditures: $2,471,391
Media: 4-8-13-19-22-23-24-25
Personnel:
Sal V. Perisano *(Chm & CEO)*
David E. Robertson *(CFO)*
Dorice Dionne *(Sr VP-Mds)*

Brands & Products:
IPARTY

Advertising Agencies:
Aigner Associates PR/Events
214 Lincoln St Ste 300
Allston, MA 02134
Tel.: (617) 254-9500
Fax: (617) 254-3700

RCI
550 Heritage Dr Ste 200
Jupiter, FL 33458
Tel.: (561) 686-6800
Fax: (561) 686-8043

IPASS, INC.

3800 Bridge Pkwy
Redwood City, CA 94065
Tel.: (650) 232-4100
Fax: (650) 232-4111
E-mail: infoir@ipass.com
Web Site: www.ipass.com
E-Mail For Key Personnel:
Public Relations: pr@ipass.com
Approx. Rev.: $156,080,000
Approx. Number Employees: 363
Year Founded: 1996
Business Description:
Software-Enabled Enterprise Connectivity & Endpoint Management Services
S.I.C.: 7374; 7375
N.A.I.C.S.: 518210; 518111
Advertising Expenditures: $100,000
Media: 17
Personnel:
John D. Beletic *(Chm)*
Evan L. Kaplan *(Pres & CEO)*
Steven Gatoff *(CFO & Sr VP)*
William Garvey *(VP, Gen Counsel & Corp Sec)*
Christophe Culine *(Sr VP-Worldwide Sls)*
Steve Livingston *(Sr VP-Carrier Bus Dev)*
Steven Wastie *(Sr VP-Mktg & Product Mgmt)*
Brands & Products:
AIRPORT ACCESS
IOQ
IPASS
IPASS CONNECT
IPASS CORPORATE ACCESS
IPASS MANAGED ACCESS
NETSERVER
ROAMSERVER

IPOWERWEB INC.

2800 28th St Ste 205
Santa Monica, CA 90405
Tel.: (602) 716-5353
Toll Free: (888) 511-HOST
E-mail: sales@ipowerweb.com
Web Site: www.ipowerweb.com
Approx. Number Employees: 50
Business Description:
Web Hosting Services
S.I.C.: 7375
N.A.I.C.S.: 518111
Media: 13
Personnel:
Thomas Gorny *(Pres & CEO)*
Justin Reynolds *(Dir-Mktg)*
Brands & Products:
IPOWERWEB
THE POWER BEHIND EBUSINESS

IRONPLANET, INC.

4695 Chabot Dr Ste 102
Pleasanton, CA 94588
Tel.: (925) 225-8600
Fax: (925) 225-8610
Fax: (888) 433-3467
Toll Free: (888) 433-5426
E-mail: customercare@ironplanet.com
Web Site: www.ironplanet.com
Approx. Rev.: $54,674,396
Approx. Number Employees: 242
Year Founded: 1999
Business Description:
Online Heavy Construction Equipment Retailer
S.I.C.: 5961; 5045; 5082
N.A.I.C.S.: 454112; 423810; 425110
Advertising Expenditures: $2,429,970
Media: 2-7-9-10-13-18-22-25
Personnel:
Gregory J. Owens *(Chm & CEO)*
Michael J. O'Donnell *(CFO)*
Jeffrey L. Barca-Hall *(CTO & Sr VP-Engrg)*
Carol J. Parrella *(Chief Admin Officer & Sr VP)*
James J. Jeter *(Exec VP)*
Randall E. Berry *(Sr VP-Ops & Svcs)*
Michael D. Groves *(Sr VP-Sls)*
Andy Pyron *(VP-Natl Acct Sls)*
Regina Market *(Dir-Mktg)*

ITRADE NETWORK

4155 Hopeyard Rd Ste 100
Pleasanton, CA 94588
Tel.: (925) 660-1100
Fax: (925) 660-1101
E-mail: accounting@itradenetwork.com
Web Site: www.itradenetwork.com
E-Mail For Key Personnel:
Marketing Director: awalker@itradenetwork.com
Sales Range: $25-49.9 Million
Approx. Number Employees: 55
Year Founded: 1998
Business Description:
Products, Services & Information for the Perishable Foods Industry
S.I.C.: 8748
N.A.I.C.S.: 541618
Media: 13
Personnel:
Rob Bonavito *(Pres)*
Chuck Gregg *(VP-Sls)*
Pete Reuling *(Dir)*
Brands & Products:
ITRADENETWORK

IUNIVERSE, INC.

(Sub. of Author Solutions, Inc.)
1663 Liberty Dr Ste 200
Bloomington, IN 47403
Tel.: (402) 323-7800
Fax: (812) 359-0745
Toll Free: (800) AUTHORS
E-mail: press@iuniverse.com
Web Site: www.iuniverse.com
Approx. Number Employees: 390
Year Founded: 1999
Business Description:
Printed & Online Self Publishing Services
S.I.C.: 2741; 2731
N.A.I.C.S.: 511199; 511130
Advertising Expenditures: $1,000,000
Media: 2-8-10-13
Personnel:
Keith Ogorek *(Sr VP-Mktg)*
Brands & Products:
IUNIVERSE

IVILLAGE INC.

(Joint Venture of Comcast Corporation & General Electric Company)
500 7th Ave 14th Fl
New York, NY 10018-4502
Tel.: (212) 664-4444
Fax: (212) 664-4444
Web Site: www.ivillage.com
Sales Range: $75-99.9 Million
Approx. Number Employees: 278
Year Founded: 1995
Business Description:
Online Media Marketing & Interactive Services
S.I.C.: 2741; 7375
N.A.I.C.S.: 516110; 518111
Advertising Expenditures: $9,000,000
Media: 6-13
Personnel:
Jodi Kahn *(Pres)*
Linda Boff *(CMO-iVillage)*
Angela Matusik *(Chief Content Officer)*
Mike Skagerlind *(Sr VP & Gen Mgr)*
Catherine Balsam-Schwaber *(Sr VP-Mktg)*
John Curbishley *(Sr VP-Bus Dev)*
Adam Wiener *(Sr VP-Content, Community & Ops)*
Miriam Arias *(VP-Comm)*
Wanda Weber *(VP-Sls & Mktg)*
Advertising Agency:
Alison Brod Public Relations
373 Park Ave S 4th Fl
New York, NY 10016
Tel.: (212) 230-1800
Fax: (212) 230-1161

J2 GLOBAL COMMUNICATIONS, INC.

6922 Hollywood Blvd Ste 500
Los Angeles, CA 90028
Tel.: (323) 860-9200
Fax: (323) 464-1446
E-mail: investorinfo@j2.com
Web Site: www.j2global.com
E-Mail For Key Personnel:
Marketing Director: hemi.zucker@j2.com
Sales Director: Dolan@j2.com
Public Relations: jeff.adelman@j2.com
Approx. Rev.: $255,394,000
Approx. Number Employees: 600
Year Founded: 1995
Business Description:
Internet-Fax & Unified Messaging Services
S.I.C.: 4813; 4899; 7375
N.A.I.C.S.: 517110; 517910; 518111
Advertising Expenditures: $28,300,000
Media: 2-7-8-10-13
Personnel:
Richard S. Ressler *(Chm)*
Scott Turicchi *(Pres)*
Hemi Zucker *(CEO)*
Kathleen M. Griggs *(CFO)*
Jeff Adelman *(Gen Counsel, Sec & VP)*
Zohar Loshitzer *(Exec VP-Corp Strategy)*
Patty Brunton *(VP-HR)*
Vince Niedzielski *(VP-Engrg)*
Mike Pugh *(VP-Mktg)*
Rick Stevens *(Dir-Corp Mktg)*
Brands & Products:
CALL SCIENCES
CONSENSUS
DOCUMAGIX
EASY FAXING ANYWHERE
EFAX
EFAX BROADCAST
EFAX CORPORATE
EFAX FREE
EFAX MESSANGER
ELECTRIC MAIL
EVOICE
J2
J2 GLOBAL
JBLAST
JCONNECT
JCONNECT FREE
JCONNECT PREMIER
JFAX
M4
MESSENGER PLUS
ONEBOX
PAPERMASTER
PAPERMASTER PRO
TIMESHIFT
UNIFAX

JAJ ENTERPRISES, INC.

(d/b/a Alight.com)
300 Woodbury Rd 2nd Fl
Woodbury, NY 11797
Tel.: (516) 367-1095
Fax: (516) 367-1184
E-mail: marketing@alight.com
Web Site: www.alight.com
E-Mail For Key Personnel:
President: norman@alight.com
Marketing Director: marketing@alight.com
Approx. Number Employees: 10
Year Founded: 1999
Business Description:
Online Retailer of Plus-Size Apparel for Women
S.I.C.: 5621
N.A.I.C.S.: 448120
Media: 13
Personnel:
Norman Weiss *(Pres, CEO & COO)*
Brands & Products:
FUBU

JIGSAW DATA CORP.

(Sub. of Salesforce.com, Inc.)
777 Mariners Island Blvd
San Mateo, CA 94404
Tel.: (650) 235-8400
Fax: (650) 325-8425
Web Site: www.jigsaw.com
Sales Range: $1-9.9 Million
Approx. Number Employees: 100
Year Founded: 2004
Business Description:
Online Business Information & Data
S.I.C.: 2741; 7389
N.A.I.C.S.: 516110; 511140; 519190
Personnel:
Jim Fowler *(Co-Founder & CEO)*
Garth Moulton *(Co-Founder & VP-Community)*
Steven Klei *(CFO)*
Kevin Akeroyd *(COO)*
Deepa Krisnan *(Gen Counsel & Dir-Privacy)*

Key to Media (For complete agency information see *The Advertising Red Books-Agencies* edition):
1. Bus. Publs. 2. Cable T.V. 3. Catalogs & Directories. 4. Co-op Adv. 5. Consumer Mags. 6. D.M. to Bus. Estab.7. D.M. to Consumers
8. Daily Newsp. 9. Exhibits/Trade Shows 10. Foreign 11. Infomercial 12. Internet Adv.13. Multimedia 14. Network Radio
15. Network T.V. 16. Newsp. Distr. Mags. 17. Other 18. Outdoor (Posters, Transit) 19. Point of Purchase20. Premiums, Novelties
21. Product Samples 22. Special Events Mktg. 23. Spot Radio 24. Spot T.V. 25. Weekly Newsp. 26. Yellow Page Adv.

Jigsaw Data Corp. — (Continued)

Raymond Lim *(VP-Fin)*
Virendra Vase *(VP-Engrg)*
Susan Spaight *(Dir-Strategy)*

Advertising Agency:
Antenna Group, Inc.
135 Main St Ste 800
San Francisco, CA 94105-8110
Tel.: (415) 896-1800
Fax: (415) 896-1094

JOBREQ.COM, INC.

Research Park 244 Wall St
Princeton, NJ 08540-1512
Tel.: (609) 921-8142
Fax: (609) 924-2314
Toll Free: (800) 849-9359
E-mail: info@jobreq.com
Web Site: www.jobreq.com
Sales Range: $10-24.9 Million
Approx. Number Employees: 12
Year Founded: 1999
Business Description:
Staffing Services
S.I.C.: 7361
N.A.I.C.S.: 561310
Advertising Expenditures: $325,000
Media: 10-13

JPMORGAN CHASE VASTERA

(Sub. of JPMorgan Chase & Co.)
45025 Aviation Dr Ste 150
Dulles, VA 20166-7514
Tel.: (703) 661-9006
Fax: (703) 742-4580
Toll Free: (800) 275-1374
E-mail: investor.relations@jpmchase.com
Web Site: www.jpmchase.com
Sales Range: $75-99.9 Million
Approx. Number Employees: 90
Year Founded: 1992
Business Description:
Global Trade Management Services
S.I.C.: 8742
N.A.I.C.S.: 541611
Media: 2-10-17-22
Personnel:
John Murray *(VP-Corp Comm)*
Brands & Products:
GLOBAL TRADE CONTENT
TRADESPHERE

JUNIPER NETWORKS, INC.

1194 N Mathilda Ave
Sunnyvale, CA 94089-1206
Mailing Address:
PO Box 3786
Sunnyvale, CA 94088-3786
Tel.: (408) 745-2000
Fax: (408) 745-2100
Toll Free: (888) JUNIPER
E-mail: mlevine@juniper.net
Web Site: www.juniper.net
Approx. Rev.: $4,093,266,000
Approx. Number Employees: 8,772
Year Founded: 1996
Business Description:
Developer of Internet Infrastructure Management & Network Security Services & Products
S.I.C.: 3577; 3661
N.A.I.C.S.: 334119; 334210
Export
Advertising Expenditures: $11,400,000
Media: 8-11-13
Personnel:
Pradeep Sindhu *(Founder, Vice Chm & Chief Technical Officer)*
Scott G. Kriens *(Chm)*
Kevin R. Johnson *(CEO)*
Bask Iyer *(CIO & Sr VP)*
Lauren Flaherty *(CMO & Exec VP)*
Mitchell L. Gaynor *(Gen Counsel, Sec & Exec VP)*
Mark Bauhaus *(Exec VP & Gen Mgr-Device & Network Svcs Bus Grp)*
David W. Yen *(Exec VP & Gen Mgr-Fabric & Switching Bus Grp)*
Luis Avila-Marco *(Exec VP-Strategy & Corp Dev)*
Gerri Elliott *(Exec VP-Strategic Alliances)*
John Morris *(Exec VP-Worldwide Field Ops)*
Robert Muglia *(Exec VP-Software Solutions Div)*
Kim Perdikou *(Exec VP)*
Steven Rice *(Exec VP-HR)*
Michael J. Rose *(Exec VP-Svcs, Support & Ops)*
Nawaf Bitar *(Sr VP & Gen Mgr-Emerging Technolgies)*
Alexander J. Gray *(Sr VP & Gen Mgr-Ethernet Switching)*
Sean J. Dolan *(Sr VP-EMEA)*
Martin J. Garvin *(Sr VP-Mfg Ops)*
Brad Kashani *(Sr VP)*
Frank Vitagliano *(Sr VP-Worldwide Channels)*
Nicholas Barley *(VP-Mktg-EMEA)*
Brad Brooks *(VP-Worldwide Enterprise Mktg Solutions)*
David Shane *(VP-Global Corp Comm)*
Luanne Tierney *(VP-Global Partner Mktg)*
Adam Christensen *(Dir-Social Media & Digital Comm)*
Richard W. Palmer, Jr. *(Mgr-Sys Engrg (Northwest Enterprise))*
Brands & Products:
CTPVIEW
J-WEB
JUNIOSCOPE
JUNIPER NETWORKS
JUNOS
JUNOSE
NETSCREEN
NSM
NSMXPRESS
ODYSSEY ACCESS CLIENT
SDX-300
Advertising Agencies:
Daniel J. Edelman, Inc.
(d/b/a Edelman)
200 E Randolph St Fl 63
Chicago, IL 60601-6705
Tel.: (312) 240-3000
Fax: (312) 240-2900
Global Public Relations

Group 365 (Chicago) LLC
1111 E Warrenville Rd
Naperville, IL 60653
Tel.: (630) 671-0365
Fax: (630) 671-0366

K12, INC.

2300 Corporate Park Dr
Herndon, VA 20171
Tel.: (703) 483-7000
Toll Free: (866) 283-0300
E-mail: khaas@k12.com
Web Site: www.k12.com
Approx. Rev.: $384,470,000
Approx. Number Employees: 1,065
Year Founded: 1999
Business Description:
Online Curriculum, Software & Educational Services
S.I.C.: 8299; 2741
N.A.I.C.S.: 611710; 516110
Advertising Expenditures: $16,200,000
Media: 16
Personnel:
Ronald J. Packard *(Founder & CEO)*
Andrew H. Tisch *(Chm)*
Harry T. Hawks *(CFO & Exec VP)*
Robert L. Moon *(CIO & Sr VP)*
Celia Stokes *(CMO & Exec VP)*
Howard D. Polsky *(Gen Counsel & Sec)*
Bruce J. Davis *(Exec VP-Bus Dev-Worldwide)*
Chip Hughes *(Exec VP-School Svcs)*
John P. Olsen *(Exec VP-Ops)*
Howard Allentoff *(Sr VP-HR)*
Bryan W. Flood *(Sr VP-Pub Affairs)*
John Holdren *(Sr VP-Content & Curriculum)*
Peter G. Stewart *(Sr VP-School Dev)*
Maria A. Szalay *(Sr VP-Product Dev)*
Ray Williams *(Sr VP-Sys & Tech)*
Jeff Kwitowski *(VP-PR)*
Advertising Agency:
Zeta Interactive
716 Main St
Boonton, NJ 07005
Tel.: (973) 316-9696
Fax: (973) 316-8006
— Christopher Colella *(Acct Exec)*

KAYAK SOFTWARE CORPORATION

(Formerly Kayak.com)
55 N Water St Ste 1
Norwalk, CT 06854
Tel.: (203) 899-3100
Fax: (203) 899-3125
E-mail: prcontact@kayak.com
Web Site: www.kayak.com
Approx. Rev.: $112,698,000
Approx. Number Employees: 140
Year Founded: 2004
Business Description:
Online Travel Services
S.I.C.: 4729; 2741; 7372
N.A.I.C.S.: 561599; 511210; 516110
Media: 13-15
Personnel:
Daniel Stephen Hafner *(Co-Founder & CEO)*
Paul M. English *(Co-Founder & CTO)*
Terrell B. Jones *(Chm)*
Robert M. Birge *(CMO)*
Karen Ruzic Klein *(Gen Counsel)*
Paul D. Schwenk *(Sr VP-Engrg)*
Melissa H. Reiter *(VP-Fin)*
William T. O'Donnell, Jr. *(Chief Architect & Gen Mgr-KAYAK Mobile)*
Brands & Products:
KAYAK.COM
Advertising Agency:
Goodby, Silverstein & Partners, Inc.
(Part of Omnicom Group, Inc.)
720 California St
San Francisco, CA 94108-2404
Tel.: (415) 392-0669
Fax: (415) 788-4303

KAYAK.COM

(Name Changed to Kayak Software Corporation)

KENEXA

(Branch of Kenexa Technology, Inc.)
343 Winter St
Waltham, MA 02451
Tel.: (781) 530-5000
Fax: (781) 530-5500
Toll Free: (888) 747-HIRE
Web Site: www.kenexa.com/about-us/locations/north-america
Sales Range: $75-99.9 Million
Approx. Number Employees: 300
Business Description:
Online & Offline Recruitment Tools & Services; Joint Venture of The Washington Post Company (49.4%), Tribune Company (26.9%), Gannett Company, Inc. (12.4%) & Accel Partners (10.5%)
S.I.C.: 7372; 7373
N.A.I.C.S.: 511210; 541512
Media: 2-8-10-13-20-22-26

KEYNOTE NETMECHANIC

(Div. of Keynote Systems Incorporated)
2100 10th St Ste 500
Plano, TX 75074
Tel.: (972) 578-7431
Fax: (972) 422-6366
Toll Free: (877) 638-6324
E-mail: sales@netmechanic.com
Web Site: www.netmechanic.com
E-Mail For Key Personnel:
Sales Director: sales@netmechanic.com
Public Relations: pr@netmechanic.com
Sales Range: $10-24.9 Million
Approx. Number Employees: 25
Year Founded: 1996
Business Description:
Online Tools for Web Site Maintenance, Monitoring & Promotion
S.I.C.: 2741; 7371
N.A.I.C.S.: 516110; 541511
Media: 13
Personnel:
Umang Gupta *(Chm & CEO)*
Brands & Products:
ENGINE STARTER
GIFBOT
HTML TOOLBOX
NETMECHANIC
SEARCH ENGINE POWER PACK
SERVER CHECK PRO

KEYON COMMUNICATIONS HOLDINGS INC.

11742 Stonegate Cir
Omaha, NE 68164
Tel.: (402) 998-4000
Tel.: (402) 998-4098
Fax: (402) 998-4111
Toll Free: (866) 276-3300
E-mail: sales@keyon.com
Web Site: www.keyon.com
Approx. Rev.: $7,523,678
Approx. Number Employees: 86
Business Description:
Wireless Broadband Services
S.I.C.: 4899; 4812
N.A.I.C.S.: 517910; 517212
Advertising Expenditures: $86,209
Media: 5-13

Personnel:
Jonathan Snyder *(Pres & CEO)*
A. Robert Handell *(COO)*
Jason Lazar *(Gen Counsel & VP-Corp Dev)*
Rory Erchul *(VP-Mktg)*
Jon Fagan *(VP-Engrg)*

KFORCE INC.

1001 E Palm Ave
Tampa, FL 33605-3551
Tel.: (813) 552-5000
Fax: (813) 552-2493
E-mail: kforce@kforce.com
Web Site: www.kforce.com
Approx. Rev.: $990,807,000
Approx. Number Employees: 2,000
Year Founded: 1994
Business Description:
Temporary Staffing & Permanent Placement of Professional & Technical Personnel in the Information Technology, Accounting, Finance, Human Resources, Manufacturing, Health Care & Life Insurance Areas
S.I.C.: 7363; 7361
N.A.I.C.S.: 561320; 561310
Media: 13
Personnel:
David L. Dunkel *(Chm & CEO)*
Howard W. Sutter *(Vice Chm, VP-Mergers & Acq)*
Richard M. Cocchiaro *(Vice Chm)*
William L. Sanders *(Pres)*
Joseph J. Liberatore *(CFO & Exec VP)*
Jeffrey B. Hackman *(Chief Acctg Officer & VP)*
Peter M. Alonso *(Chief Talent Officer)*
Michael R. Blackman *(Chief Corp Dev Officer)*
Mike L. Ettore *(Chief Svcs Officer)*
Randy Marmon *(Chief Customer Dev Officer)*
Jeffrey Neal *(Pres-West)*
William S. Josey *(Gen Counsel)*
David Kelly *(Sr VP-Fin & Acctg)*
Andy Thomas *(Sr VP-Natl Champions & Product Mgmt)*
Sara R. Nichols *(VP-Fin)*
Brands & Products:
KFORCE
KFORCE KNOWLEDGE STAFFING MODEL
KFORCE ONSTAFF GROUP
THE KNOWLEDGEFORCE
PROFESSIONAL STAFFING

KIT DIGITAL, INC.

168 5th Ave Ste 302
New York, NY 10010
Tel.: (212) 661-4111
E-mail: info@kit-digital.com
Web Site: www.kit-digital.com
Approx. Rev.: $106,597,000
Approx. Number Employees: 720
Year Founded: 2003
Business Description:
Digital Media Services
S.I.C.: 2741
N.A.I.C.S.: 516110
Advertising Expenditures: $7,530,000
Personnel:
Kaleil Isaza Tuzman *(Chm & CEO)*
Gavin Campion *(Pres)*
Robin Smyth *(CFO)*
John E. Warren, III *(Chief Admin Officer)*
Steve W. Chung *(Exec VP-Strategic Initiatives)*
Thomas Wittig *(Exec VP-Global Client Ops)*
Daniel Goodfellow *(Sr VP-Corp Comm)*
Derek McKellar *(Sr VP-Client Ops)*
Christopher Williams *(Head-Product Dev)*

KLOUT, INC.

77 Stillman St
San Francisco, CA 94107
E-mail: press@klout.com
Web Site: www.klout.com
Business Description:
Social Media Influence Measurer
N.A.I.C.S.: 516110
Media: 29
Personnel:
Joe Fernandez *(Co-Founder & CEO)*
Binh Tran *(Co-Founder & CTO)*
Tim Mahlman *(Chief Revenue Officer)*
Dave Mariani *(VP-Engrg)*
Chris Makarsky *(Dir-Product)*

THE KNOT INC.

462 Broadway 6th Fl
New York, NY 10013
Tel.: (212) 219-8555
Fax: (212) 219-1929
Toll Free: (888) WEDKNOT
E-mail: feedback@theknot.com
Web Site: www.theknot.com
Approx. Rev.: $112,881,000
Approx. Number Employees: 605
Year Founded: 1996
Business Description:
Online Wedding Resource
S.I.C.: 7389; 2741; 5961; 7375
N.A.I.C.S.: 519190; 454111; 516110; 518111
Advertising Expenditures: $836,000
Media: 6-13-22-24
Personnel:
David Liu *(Co-Founder, Chm & CEO)*
Carley Roney *(Co-Founder & Editor-in-Chief)*
John P. Mueller *(CFO)*
Carol Koh Evans *(COO)*
Nic Di Iorio *(Mng Dir-Tech Grp & Exec VP)*
Stephanie Fitzgerald *(Mgr-Mktg)*

KODAK IMAGING NETWORK, INC.

(Sub. of Eastman Kodak Company)
(d/b/a Kodak Gallery)
1480 64th St Ste 300
Emeryville, CA 94608
Tel.: (510) 229-1200
Fax: (510) 229-2700
Toll Free: (800) 360-9098
E-mail: info@kodakgallery.com
Web Site: www.kodakgallery.com
Sales Range: $75-99.9 Million
Approx. Number Employees: 300
Year Founded: 1999
Business Description:
Online Photography Merchandise & Services
S.I.C.: 3861
N.A.I.C.S.: 333315; 325992
Media: 13
Personnel:
Victor Cho *(VP & Gen Mgr-Consumer Internet & Software Svcs Div)*
Wendy Kano *(VP-Site Mktg, Kodak Gallery)*
Robin Carr *(Dir-PR)*

THE LADDERS.COM, INC.

137 Varick St 8th Fl
New York, NY 10013
Tel.: (646) 453-1800
Fax: (646) 453-1932
Web Site: www.theladders.com
Approx. Rev.: $4,000,000
Approx. Number Employees: 70
Year Founded: 2003
Business Description:
Publisher Of Online Job Newsletters
S.I.C.: 7361
N.A.I.C.S.: 561310
Personnel:
Alexandre Douzet *(Co-Founder & Pres)*
Marc Cenedella *(Chm)*
Advertising Agency:
Stein Rogan + Partners
432 Park Ave S
New York, NY 10016-8013
Tel.: (212) 213-1112
Fax: (212) 779-7305

LAUNCH MEDIA, INC.

(Sub. of Yahoo! Inc.)
2700 Pennsylvania Ave
Santa Monica, CA 90404-4066
Tel.: (310) 526-4300
Fax: (310) 526-4400
Web Site: www.launch.com
Sales Range: $75-99.9 Million
Approx. Number Employees: 280
Year Founded: 1992
Business Description:
Online Music Supplier
S.I.C.: 7375
N.A.I.C.S.: 518111
Media: 13

LAUNCHFAX.COM INC.

623 River Rd
Fair Haven, NJ 07704
Tel.: (732) 450-3688
Fax: (732) 219-7799
E-mail: info@launchfax.com
Web Site: www.launchfax.com
E-Mail For Key Personnel:
President: afendrick@launchfax.com
Sales Director: sales@launchfax.com
Sales Range: $25-49.9 Million
Approx. Number Employees: 50
Year Founded: 1996
Business Description:
Fax Campaign Services
S.I.C.: 4813
N.A.I.C.S.: 517110
Advertising Expenditures: $200,000
Media: 8-13
Personnel:
Alan Fendrick *(Pres)*
Brands & Products:
LAUNCHFAX.COM

LAVALIFE INC.

(Sub. of Vertrue Inc.)
Toronto, ON M4S2C6, Canada
Tel.: (416) 640-6300
Fax: (416) 263-6301
E-mail: bizdevelopment@lavalife.com
Web Site: www.lavalife.com
Approx. Number Employees: 400
Business Description:
Online & IVR-Based Interactive Personal Services
S.I.C.: 7299
N.A.I.C.S.: 812990
Media: 6-13
Brands & Products:
LAVALIFE
Advertising Agency:
E&M Advertising
462 7th Ave 8th Fl
New York, NY 10018-7606
Tel.: (212) 981-5900
Fax: (212) 981-2121

LAW.COM

(Sub. of American Lawyer Media, Inc.)
10 United Nations Plz 3rd Fl
San Francisco, CA 94102
Tel.: (415) 633-2500
Toll Free: (800) 903-9872
Web Site: www.law.com
Approx. Number Employees: 42
Year Founded: 1999
Business Description:
Online Legal News, Information, Related Products & Services
S.I.C.: 7375
N.A.I.C.S.: 518111
Media: 13
Personnel:
Larry W. Sonsini *(Chm)*
Bill Pollak *(Pres)*

LCG TECHNOLOGIES CORPORATION

1818 Pot Spring Rd Ste 116
Timonium, MD 21286
Tel.: (410) 560-0307
Fax: (410) 560-0590
Toll Free: (877) 560-0307
E-mail: info@lcgtech.com
Web Site: www.lcgtech.com
Approx. Number Employees: 60
Year Founded: 1994
Business Description:
Information & Communications Technology Solutions
S.I.C.: 7373
N.A.I.C.S.: 541512
Advertising Expenditures: $200,000
Media: 5-13-22
Personnel:
Tom Lang *(Founder & CEO)*
Nigel Knowles *(Pres)*
Brands & Products:
IONEDIT 2001
LCG

LEGALZOOM.COM, INC.

7083 Hollywood Blvd Ste 180
Los Angeles, CA 90028
Tel.: (323) 962-8600
Fax: (323) 962-8300
Toll Free: (800) 773-0888
Web Site: www.legalzoom.com
Sales Range: $1-9.9 Million
Approx. Number Employees: 60
Business Description:
Online Legal Document Services
S.I.C.: 7389; 2741
N.A.I.C.S.: 541199; 516110
Media: 13
Personnel:
Brian S. Lee *(Co-Founder)*
Robert L. Shapiro *(Co-Founder)*
Brian P. Y. Liu *(Chm)*
Frank Monestere *(Pres & COO)*

Key to Media (For complete agency information see *The Advertising Red Books-Agencies* edition):
1. Bus. Publs. 2. Cable T.V. 3. Catalogs & Directories. 4. Co-op Adv. 5. Consumer Mags. 6. D.M. to Bus. Estab.7. D.M. to Consumers
8. Daily Newsp. 9. Exhibits/Trade Shows 10. Foreign 11. Infomercial 12. Internet Adv.13. Multimedia 14. Network Radio
15. Network T.V. 16. Newsp. Distr. Mags. 17. Other 18. Outdoor (Posters, Transit) 19. Point of Purchase20. Premiums, Novelties
21. Product Samples 22. Special Events Mktg. 23. Spot Radio 24. Spot T.V. 25. Weekly Newsp. 26. Yellow Page Adv.

LegalZoom.com, Inc. — (Continued)

John Suh *(CEO)*
Fred Kupica *(CFO)*
Tracy Terrill *(CIO)*
Michael Turner *(CMO)*
Eddie Hartman *(Pres-Attorney Svcs & Chief Strategy Officer)*
Chas Rampenthal *(Gen Counsel & VP-Product Dev)*
Scott MacDonell *(VP-Mktg)*

Advertising Agencies:
DonatWald+Haque
1316 Third St Ste 301
Santa Monica, CA 90401
Tel.: (310) 394-1717
Fax: (310) 394-1716

Rogers Ruder Finn
1875 Century Park E Ste 200
Los Angeles, CA 90067-2504
Tel.: (310) 552-6922
Fax: (310) 552-9052

LENDINGTREE, LLC

(Sub. of Tree.com, Inc.)
11115 Rushmore Dr
Charlotte, NC 28277
Tel.: (704) 541-5351
Web Site: www.lendingtree.com
Sales Range: $125-149.9 Million
Year Founded: 1996
Business Description:
Online Lending & Financial Services
S.I.C.: 6163
N.A.I.C.S.: 522310
Advertising Expenditures: $172,600,000
Media: 1-6-8-13-14-15-18-22
Personnel:
Gabriel Dalporto *(CMO)*
David Norris *(Sr VP-Ops)*

Advertising Agency:
Euro RSCG Worldwide HQ
350 Hudson St
New York, NY 10014-4504
Tel.: (212) 886-2000
Fax: (212) 886-2016

LEVEL 3 COMMUNICATIONS, INC.

1025 Eldorado Blvd
Broomfield, CO 80021-8869
Tel.: (720) 888-1000
Fax: (720) 888-5085
Toll Free: (877) 585-8266
E-mail: WebMaster@level3.com
Web Site: www.level3.com
Approx. Rev.: $3,651,000,000
Approx. Number Employees: 5,500
Year Founded: 1985
Business Description:
Internet Protocol & Communications Services
S.I.C.: 7373; 4813
N.A.I.C.S.: 541512; 517110; 517310
Advertising Expenditures: $7,000,000
Personnel:
Walter Scott, Jr. *(Chm)*
Charles C. Miller, III *(Vice Chm)*
Jeff K. Storey *(Pres & COO)*
Sunit S. Patel *(CFO & Exec VP)*
Mark Martinet *(CIO)*
Jack Waters *(CTO & Pres-Global Network Svcs)*
Thomas C. Stortz *(Chief Legal Officer, Sec & Exec VP)*
Andrew Crouch *(Pres-Sls)*
James Heard *(Pres-European Markets)*
Robin Grey *(Treas & Sr VP)*
John Neil Hobbs *(Exec VP-Ops)*
Eric J. Mortensen *(Sr VP & Controller)*
Daniel Sjoberg *(VP-Strategy, Bus Dev & Mktg)*
Jennifer Daumler *(Sr Dir-Indus Analyst Relations)*

Brands & Products:
(3)CENTER
(3)CONNECT
(3)CROSSROADS
(3)FLEX
(3)HUB
(3)LINK
(3)PACKET
(3)VOICE
(3)VOIP
LEVEL 3
ONTAP

Advertising Agency:
Sterling Rice Group
1801 13th St Ste 400
Boulder, CO 80302
Tel.: (303) 381-6400
Fax: (303) 444-6637

LEVEL 3 COMMUNICATIONS, INC.

(Sub. of Level 3 Communications, Inc.)
1122 Capital of Texas Hwy S
Austin, TX 78746-6426
Tel.: (512) 742-3700
Fax: (512) 742-5250
Toll Free: (800) 847-5705
E-mail: investor.relations@level3.com
Web Site: www.level3.com
Sales Range: $300-349.9 Million
Approx. Number Employees: 1,636
Year Founded: 1997
Business Description:
Optical Networking Products Mfr
S.I.C.: 3661
N.A.I.C.S.: 334210
Media: 10-17

LEXAR MEDIA, INC.

(Sub. of Micron Technology, Inc.)
47300 Bayside Pkwy
Fremont, CA 94538
Tel.: (510) 413-1200
Fax: (510) 440-3499
Toll Free: (800) 789-9418
E-mail: sales@lexar.com
Web Site: www.lexar.com
E-Mail For Key Personnel:
Sales Director: sales@lexar.com
Sales Range: $800-899.9 Million
Approx. Number Employees: 160
Year Founded: 1998
Business Description:
Designer, Marketer & Licensor of Removable Flash-Based Digital Storage Media & Card Readers for the Digital Photography, Consumer Electronics, Industrial & Communications Markets
S.I.C.: 3861
N.A.I.C.S.: 325992; 333315
Advertising Expenditures: $38,900,000
Media: 2-4-5-7-8-10-13-20-21-22
Personnel:
Mark Adams *(Pres)*
Leslie Adams *(VP-Mktg)*
Aaron Lee *(Sr Mgr-Product)*

Brands & Products:
COMPACTFLASH
FIREWIRE COMPACTFLASH
IMAGE RESCUE
JUMPDRIVE
JUMPDRIVE LIGHTNING
JUMPDRIVE SECURE 2.0
JUMPDRIVE TRIO
JUMPGEAR
JUMPSHOT READER
LEXAR
LEXAR MEDIA
MEMORY STICK
MINISD
MULTI-CARD
PHOTO MECHANIC
SLOT MULTI-CARD
SMARTMEDIA
TOUCHGUARD
USB MEMORY STICK
XD-PICTURE CARD

Advertising Agency:
Matter Communications
50 Water St, Mill #3, The Tannery
Newburyport, MA 01950
Tel.: (978) 499-9250
Fax: (978) 499-9253

LIGHTSPACE CORPORATION

383 Dorchester Ave Ste 220
Boston, MA 02127
Tel.: (617) 868-1700
Fax: (617) 222-1485
Toll Free: (877) 404-1700
E-mail: info@lightspacecorp.com
Web Site: www.lightspacecorp.com
Sales Range: $1-9.9 Million
Approx. Number Employees: 10
Year Founded: 2001
Business Description:
Interactive Systems
S.I.C.: 3641; 7373
N.A.I.C.S.: 335110; 541512
Advertising Expenditures: $35,264
Media: 6-10-13-17-22
Personnel:
Gary Florindo *(Chm, Pres & CEO)*
Brian Batease *(COO & VP)*

LIMELIGHT NETWORKS, INC.

2220 W 14th St
Tempe, AZ 85281
Tel.: (602) 850-5000
Fax: (602) 850-5001
Toll Free: (866) 200-LIME
E-mail: media@llnw.com
Web Site: www.limelightnetworks.com
Approx. Rev.: $183,327,000
Approx. Number Employees: 689
Year Founded: 2001
Business Description:
Internet Services
S.I.C.: 7371; 2741
N.A.I.C.S.: 541511; 516110
Advertising Expenditures: $2,100,000
Media: 1-8-10-13-17
Personnel:
Nathan F. Raciborski *(Co-Founder & CTO-Limelight Networks)*
Michael M. Gordon *(Co-Founder)*
Jeffrey W. Lunsford *(Chm & CEO-Limelight Networks)*
Douglas S. Lindroth *(CFO)*
Philip C. Maynard *(Chief Legal Officer, Sec & Sr VP)*
David Hatfield *(Sr VP-Worldwide Sls, Svcs & Mktg)*
Lonhyn Jasinskyj *(Sr VP-Software Engrg)*
David Frigeri *(Grp VP-Svcs-Global)*
Paul Alfieri *(Sr Dir-Corp Comm)*
John Gaffney *(Sr Dir-Quality & Release Mgmt)*

Brands & Products:
LIMELIGHT NETWORKS
LIMELIGHTDELIVER
LIMELIGHTHD
LIMELIGHTPS
LIMELIGHTSITE
LIMELIGHTSTREAM
LIMELIGHTSUPPORT
LIMIELIGHTEXCHANGE

Advertising Agencies:
PJA Advertising + Marketing
214 Grant Ave Ste 450
San Francisco, CA 94108
Tel.: (415) 200-0800
Fax: (415) 200-0801

Waggener Edstrom
185 Berry St Ste 5400
San Francisco, CA 94107-1759
Tel.: (415) 547-7000
Fax: (415) 547-7001
— Kristen Leon *(Acct Exec)*

Wirestone
920 20th St
Sacramento, CA 95811
Tel.: (916) 446-6550
Fax: (916) 446-6551

LINKEDIN CORPORATION

2029 Stierlin Ct
Mountain View, CA 94043
Tel.: (650) 687-3600
Fax: (650) 687-0505
E-mail: press@linkedin.com
Web Site: www.linkedin.com
Approx. Rev.: $120,127,000
Approx. Number Employees: 990
Year Founded: 2003
Business Description:
Online Social Networking Publisher
S.I.C.: 2741
N.A.I.C.S.: 519130
Media: 13
Personnel:
Jean-Luc Vaillant *(Co-Founder & CTO)*
Allen Blue *(Co-Founder & VP-Product Mgmt)*
Reid Hoffman *(Exec Chm & Co-Founder)*
Jeff Weiner *(CEO)*
Arvind Rajan *(Mng Dir)*
Steven Sordello *(CFO)*
Erika Rottenberg *(Gen Counsel, VP & Sec)*
Michael Gamson *(Sr VP-Global Sls)*
David Henke *(Sr VP-Ops & Engrg)*
Dipchand Nishar *(Sr VP-Products & User Experience)*
Clive Punter *(Mng Dir-Mktg Solutions-EMEA)*
Sharon McCooey *(Dir-Fin-Intl)*
Hari V. Krishnan *(Country Mgr)*
Jonathan Seitel *(Product Mgr)*
Matt Sonefeldt *(Mgr-IR)*

LIQUIDITY SERVICES, INC.

1920 L St NW 6th Fl
Washington, DC 20036
Tel.: (202) 467-6868
Fax: (202) 467-5475
Toll Free: (800) 310-4604

Key to Media (For complete agency information see *The Advertising Red Books-Agencies* edition):
1. Bus. Publs. 2. Cable T.V. 3. Catalogs & Directories. 4. Co-op Adv. 5. Consumer Mags. 6. D.M. to Bus. Estab.7. D.M. to Consumers
8. Daily Newsp. 9. Exhibits/Trade Shows 10. Foreign 11. Infomercial 12. Internet Adv.13. Multimedia 14. Network Radio
15. Network T.V. 16. Newsp. Distr. Mags. 17. Other 18. Outdoor (Posters, Transit) 19. Point of Purchase20. Premiums, Novelties
21. Product Samples 22. Special Events Mktg. 23. Spot Radio 24. Spot T.V. 25. Weekly Newsp. 26. Yellow Page Adv.

E-mail: sales@liquidityservicesinc.com
Web Site: www.liquidityservicesinc.com
Approx. Rev.: $286,791,000
Approx. Number Employees: 704
Year Founded: 1999
Business Description:
Online Auctions for Wholesale, Salvage & Surplus Assets
S.I.C.: 5961; 8742
N.A.I.C.S.: 454112; 541611
Advertising Expenditures: $4,012,000
Personnel:
William P. Angrick, III *(Chm & CEO)*
Jaime Mateus-Tique *(Pres & COO)*
Thomas B. Burton *(COO-Govt Liquidation, LLC & Exec VP-Pres)*
James M. Rallo *(CFO & Treas)*
Eric C. Dean *(CIO)*
Cayce Roy *(Pres-Asset Recovery Div & Exec VP)*
James E. Williams *(Gen Counsel, Sec & VP)*
Holger Schwarz *(Exec VP-Europe)*
Ben Hanna *(VP-Mktg Strategy & Comm)*
Richard P. Nespola *(Dir-Sls-Global)*

LIVE CURRENT MEDIA INC.
375 Water Street Suite 645
Vancouver, BC V6B 5C6, Canada
Tel.: (604) 453-4870
Tel.: (604) 453-4875 (Media & IR)
Fax: (604) 453-4871
Toll Free: (866) 898-4354
E-mail: information@livecurrent.com
Web Site: www.livecurrent.com
Approx. Sls.: $7,606,891
Approx. Number Employees: 18
Year Founded: 1994
Business Description:
Internet & Website Services
S.I.C.: 8999; 2741; 7373; 7374; 7379
N.A.I.C.S.: 518112; 516110; 518210; 541512; 541519
Advertising Expenditures: $594,367
Media: 13
Personnel:
David M. Jeffs *(CEO)*
Brands & Products:
BODY.COM
BRAZIL.COM
CANADIAN.COM
COLOGNE.COM
COMMUNICATE.COM
CRICKET.COM
DESTINATIONHUB
ELECTRONIC.COM
FREQUENTTRAVELER.COM
GREATBRITAIN.COM
IMPORTERS.COM
INDONESIA.COM
KARATE.COM
LEISURE.COM
LIVE CURRENT
MALAYSIA.COM
MOUSE.COM
NUMBER.COM
OVERSEAS.COM
PERFUME.COM
RODEO.COM
STEREOS.COM
VANCOUVER.COM
VEGGIE.COM
VIETNAM.COM
WRESTLING.COM
YEN.COM

LIVE365, INC.
950 Tower Ln Ste 400
Foster City, CA 94404
Tel.: (650) 345-7400
Fax: (650) 345-7497
E-mail: advertising@live365.com
Web Site: www.live365.com
Approx. Number Employees: 40
Year Founded: 1999
Business Description:
Internet Radio Broadcasting Services
S.I.C.: 7371; 4832; 7375
N.A.I.C.S.: 541511; 515111; 518111
Media: 13
Personnel:
N. Mark Lam *(Chm & CEO)*
Raghav Gupta *(COO & CEO)*
Raymond Barrett *(Dir-Product Mgmt)*
Brands & Products:
EASY LIVING RADIO
LIVE365.COM

LIVEPERSON, INC.
462 7th Ave 3rd Fl
New York, NY 10018-7445
Tel.: (212) 609-4200
Fax: (212) 609-4201
E-mail: info@liveperson.com
Web Site: www.liveperson.com
Approx. Rev.: $109,862,000
Approx. Number Employees: 481
Year Founded: 1995
Business Description:
Online Internet Sales & Customer Service Solutions
S.I.C.: 7372; 2741
N.A.I.C.S.: 511210; 516110
Advertising Expenditures: $6,132,000
Media: 2-7-8-10-13
Personnel:
Robert P. Locascio *(Chm & CEO)*
Daniel Murphy *(CFO)*
Eli Campo *(Exec VP & Gen Mgr-Tech Ops)*
Brands & Products:
A WORLD OF EXPERTS
LIVEPERSON
TIMPANI

LIVEWORLD, INC.
4340 Stevens Creek Blvd Ste 101
San Jose, CA 95129
Tel.: (408) 871-5200
Fax: (408) 871-5300
E-mail: sales@liveworld.com
Web Site: www.liveworld.com
E-Mail For Key Personnel:
Public Relations: pr@liveworld.com
Approx. Rev.: $9,774,000
Approx. Number Employees: 73
Year Founded: 1996
Business Description:
Internet Marketing & Support Services
S.I.C.: 4311; 2141; 7375
N.A.I.C.S.: 491110; 312229; 518111
Media: 7-10-13-22
Personnel:
Peter H. Friedman *(Chm & CEO)*
David Houston *(CFO)*
Jenna Woodul *(Chief Community Officer & Exec VP)*
Jay S. Bryant *(VP-Sls, US East Coast & Pharmaceuticals)*
Bruce Dembecki *(VP-Moderation Svcs)*
Trevor Griffiths *(VP-Engrg & Ops)*
Debbie Dembecki *(Dir-Client Svcs)*
Andrew Oliver *(Dir-Ops)*
Cheryl Paul *(Dir-Sls-Natl)*
Brands & Products:
LIVEBAR
LIVEWORLD
Advertising Agency:
The Blueshirt Group
456 Montgomery St 11th Fl
San Francisco, CA 94104
Tel.: (415) 217-7722
Fax: (415) 217-7721

LIVINGSOCIAL, INC.
829 7th St Ste 301
Washington, DC 20001
Tel.: (888) 808-6676
E-mail: affiliates@livingsocial.com
Web Site: www.livingsocial.com
Sales Range: $1-4.9 Billion
Approx. Number Employees: 1,300
Year Founded: 2007
Business Description:
Online Coupon Website Operator
N.A.I.C.S.: 519130
Media: 13-15-29
Personnel:
Eddie Frederick *(Co-Founder & Pres)*
Tim O'Shaughnessy *(Co-Founder & CEO)*
Val Aleksenko *(Co-Founder & CIO)*
Aaron Batalion *(Co-Founder & CTO)*
John Bax *(CFO)*
Eric Eichmann *(COO)*
James Bramson *(Gen Counsel)*
Mandy Cole *(Sr VP-Sls)*
Jake Maas *(Sr VP-Corp & Bus Dev)*
Mitch Spolan *(Sr VP-Natl Sls)*
Camille Watson *(VP-Mktg)*
Andrew Weinstein *(Head-Comm)*
Brands & Products:
LIVINGSOCIAL
Advertising Agencies:
ID Media
(Part of the Interpublic Group of Companies)
100 W 33rd St
New York, NY 10001
Tel.: (212) 907-7011
Fax: (212) 907-7290

The Martin Agency
One Shockoe Plz
Richmond, VA 23219-4132
Tel.: (804) 698-8000
Fax: (804) 698-8001

YellowHammer Media Group, LLC
111 W 28th St Ste 2B
New York, NY 10001
Tel.: (646) 490-9841

LOCAL.COM CORPORATION
7555 Irvine Ctr Dr
Irvine, CA 92618
Tel.: (949) 784-0800
Fax: (949) 784-0880
Toll Free: (877) 784-0805
E-mail: ctriebwasser@local.com
Web Site: www.local.com
E-Mail For Key Personnel:
President: BCrair@eliberation.com
Approx. Rev.: $84,137,000
Approx. Number Employees: 116
Year Founded: 1999
Business Description:
Local Search Engine; Advertising Network Services
S.I.C.: 7375; 5045; 7319; 8999
N.A.I.C.S.: 518111; 425110; 518112; 541890
Advertising Expenditures: $30,800,000
Media: 2-7-10-13
Personnel:
Heath B. Clarke *(Chm & CEO)*
Stanley Bruce Crair *(Pres & COO)*
Kenneth S. Cragun *(CFO & Sec)*
Scott Reinke *(Gen Counsel)*
Richard Szatkowski *(Sr VP & Gen Mgr-Network Properties)*
Peter Hutto *(Sr VP-Corp Dev)*
Tullio Siragusa *(Sr VP-Sls)*
Lori Chavez *(VP-Mktg)*
Heather Dilley *(VP-HR & Admin)*
Peter Mathews *(VP-Tech)*
Mark Wallin *(VP-Product Dev)*
Cameron Triebwasser *(Sr Dir-Corp Comm)*
Brands & Products:
ASSURED RESPONSE
KEYWORD DNA
LOCAL DIRECT
LOCAL.COM
NETWORK ADVANTAGE
PAID SEARCH PLUS
SMS LOCAL
Advertising Agency:
Madison Alexander PR
19 Wedgwood
Irvine, CA 92620
Tel.: (714) 832-8716
Fax: (714) 832-8916

LODGENET INTERACTIVE CORPORATION
3900 W Innovation St
Sioux Falls, SD 57107-7002
Tel.: (605) 988-1000
Fax: (605) 988-1511
Toll Free: (888) LODGENET
E-mail: communications@lodgenet.com
Web Site: www.lodgenet.com
E-Mail For Key Personnel:
Sales Director: sales@lodgenet.com
Approx. Rev.: $452,172,000
Approx. Number Employees: 1,049
Year Founded: 1980
Business Description:
Wired & Wireless High-Speed Internet Access & Networking Solutions
S.I.C.: 4841; 3663
N.A.I.C.S.: 517510; 334220; 515210
Advertising Expenditures: $1,173,808
Media: 2-7-10
Personnel:
Scott C. Petersen *(Chm & CEO)*
David M. Bankers *(CTO, Sr VP-Product & Tech Dev)*
Derek S. White *(Pres-Interactive & Media Networks)*
James G. Naro *(Gen Counsel & Sr VP-Legal & HR)*
Steven R. Pofahl *(Sr VP & Gen Mgr-Hospitality Ops)*
Gary L. Kolbeck *(Gen Mgr-LodgeNet Healthcare)*
Ann Parker *(Dir-IR & Corp Comm)*
Brands & Products:
CONNECT INFORM ENTERTAIN
EASYHD

Key to Media (For complete agency information see *The Advertising Red Books-Agencies* edition):
1. Bus. Publs. 2. Cable T.V. 3. Catalogs & Directories. 4. Co-op Adv. 5. Consumer Mags. 6. D.M. to Bus. Estab.7. D.M. to Consumers
8. Daily Newsp. 9. Exhbits/Trade Shows 10. Foreign 11. Infomercial 12. Internet Adv.13. Multimedia 14. Network Radio
15. Network T.V. 16. Newsp. Distr. Mags. 17. Other 18. Outdoor (Posters, Transit) 19. Point of Purchase20. Premiums, Novelties
21. Product Samples 22. Special Events Mktg. 23. Spot Radio 24. Spot T.V. 25. Weekly Newsp. 26. Yellow Page Adv.

LodgeNet Interactive Corporation — (Continued)

HOTEL SPORTSNET
LAUNCHPAD
LODGENET
LODGENETRX
ON COMMAND
POWERPLAY
POWERSTATION
ROOMDOCK
SIGNETURE PC
SIGNETURE TV

LOGIKA CORPORATION
3717 N Ravenswood Ste 244
Chicago, IL 60613
Tel.: (773) 529-3482
Fax: (773) 529-3483
E-mail: info@logika.net
Web Site: www.logika.net
Approx. Number Employees: 15
Business Description:
Internet Search Solutions
S.I.C.: 7371; 7373
N.A.I.C.S.: 541511; 541512
Media: 13
Personnel:
Matthew A. Fordham *(Pres, CEO & Chief Technologist)*
John Sortino *(VP-Sls, Mktg & Plng)*
Brands & Products:
FUSIONBOT
GALAXY
LOGIKA
NAMEDROPPERS.COM

LOGITECH INC.
(Sub. of Logitech International S.A.)
6505 Kaiser Dr
Fremont, CA 94555
Tel.: (510) 795-8500
Fax: (510) 792-8901
E-mail: info@logitech.com
Web Site: www.logitech.com
Approx. Number Employees: 8,000
Business Description:
Computer Peripheral Developer, Servicer & Marketer
S.I.C.: 3577
N.A.I.C.S.: 334119
Media: 13
Personnel:
Gerald P. Quindlen *(Pres & CEO)*
Junien Labrousse *(Exec VP-Products)*
L. Joseph Sullivan *(Sr VP-Worldwide Ops)*
Robert Wick *(Sr VP-Strategy)*
Ashish Arora *(VP & Gen Mgr-Logitech's Harmony Bus Unit)*
Nancy Morrison *(VP-Corp Comm)*
Denis Pavillard *(VP-Product Mktg)*
Greg S. Rhine *(VP-Sls & Mktg AMR)*
Jonathan Johnson *(Dir-Retail Mktg)*
Spencer Johnson *(Dir-Product Mktg)*
Ruben Mookerjee *(Dir-Product Mktg)*
Merrill Yeo *(Sr Mgr-Product Quality)*
Advertising Agency:
Goodby, Silverstein & Partners, Inc.
(Part of Omnicom Group, Inc.)
720 California St
San Francisco, CA 94108-2404
Tel.: (415) 392-0669
Fax: (415) 788-4303
Logitech Revue
— Erin Fromherz *(Acct Mgr)*

LOISLAW.COM, INC.
(Div. of Aspen Publishers, Inc.)
105 N 28th St
Van Buren, AR 72956
Tel.: (479) 471-5581
Fax: (479) 471-5635
Toll Free: (800) 364-2512
E-mail: info@loislaw.com
Web Site: www.loislaw.com
Approx. Number Employees: 310
Year Founded: 1987
Business Description:
Online Legal Research Products & Services
S.I.C.: 2741
N.A.I.C.S.: 511199
Advertising Expenditures: $450,000
Media: 2-7-10
Personnel:
John De Feo *(Exec Dir-Bus Dev)*
Deborah Sauer *(Dir-Mktg)*
Brands & Products:
LOIS BANKRUPTCY COURT COLLECTION
LOIS PROFESSIONAL LIBRARY
LOISLAW FEDERAL DISTRICT COURT OPINIONS
LOISLAW GLOBALCITE
LOISLAW LAWWATCH
LOISLAW PUBLIC RECORDS

LOOKSMART, LTD.
55 2nd St
San Francisco, CA 94105
Tel.: (415) 348-7000
Fax: (415) 348-7050
E-mail: carm@Lymanpr.com
Web Site: www.looksmart.com
Approx. Rev.: $47,479,000
Approx. Number Employees: 32
Year Founded: 1996
Business Description:
Web Directory & Search Engine Services
S.I.C.: 7374; 7375; 8999
N.A.I.C.S.: 518210; 518111; 518112
Export
Advertising Expenditures: $200,000
Media: 2-4-7-10-13
Personnel:
Jean-Yves Dexmier *(Exec Chm & CEO)*
William O'Kelly *(CFO & Sr VP-Ops)*
Brian R. Gibson *(VP-Fin & Principal Acctg Officer)*
Bert Knorr *(VP-Tech)*
Brands & Products:
FURL
LOOKSMART
SMART CHOICES.MADE EASY.
TRUELEAD
WISENUT

LOOPNET, INC.
185 Berry St Ste 4000
San Francisco, CA 94107
Tel.: (415) 243-4200
Fax: (415) 764-1622
E-mail: pr@loopnet.com
Web Site: www.loopnet.com
Approx. Rev.: $78,002,000
Approx. Number Employees: 300
Year Founded: 1997
Business Description:
Commercial Real Estate Online Information Services
S.I.C.: 6531; 2741
N.A.I.C.S.: 531390; 516110
Advertising Expenditures: $2,600,000
Media: 10-13-22
Personnel:
Richard J. Boyle, Jr. *(Chm & CEO)*
Thomas Byrne *(Pres & COO)*
Brent Stumme *(CFO)*
Jason Greenman *(Chief Strategy Officer & Sr VP-Corp Dev)*
Wayne Warthen *(CTO & Sr VP)*

LOWERMYBILLS.COM, INC.
(Sub. of Experian Information Solutions, Inc.)
2401 Colorado Ave Ste 200
Santa Monica, CA 90404
Tel.: (310) 234-0800
Fax: (310) 998-6999
E-mail: pr@lowermybills.com
Web Site: www.lowermybills.com
E-Mail For Key Personnel:
President: mcoffin@lowermybills.com
Marketing Director: marketing@lowermybills.com
Public Relations: pr@lowermybills.com
Approx. Number Employees: 125
Year Founded: 1999
Business Description:
Free Online Financial Services
S.I.C.: 7375
N.A.I.C.S.: 518111
Media: 3-8-13-15-24
Personnel:
Matthew R. Coffin *(Founder, Pres & CEO)*
Stephen Semprevivo *(Pres)*
Eva Boker *(Sr VP-Mktg)*

LUCID MEDIA NETWORKS INC.
11490 Commerce Pkwy Dr Ste 220
Reston, VA 20191
Tel.: (703) 207-0040
Fax: (703) 207-9050
E-mail: info@lucidmedia.com
Web Site: www.lucidmedia.com
Approx. Number Employees: 15
Year Founded: 1999
Business Description:
Information Categorization & On-Line Advertising Services
S.I.C.: 7319; 7372; 7379
N.A.I.C.S.: 541890; 511210; 541519
Media: 13
Personnel:
Ajay Sravanapudi *(Founder, Pres & CEO)*
Thomas V. Ervin *(CFO & VP-Bus Ops)*
Paul Rostkowski *(Chief Revenue Officer)*
Christopher Weiss *(Dir-Mktg & Pub Rel)*
Brands & Products:
CLICKSENSE
LUCIDMEDIA
SEE CLEARLY
SEMIO TAGGER
SEMIOSKYLINE

LUNAR PAGES INTERNET SOLUTIONS
1360 N Hancock St
Anaheim, CA 92807
Tel.: (714) 521-8150
Fax: (714) 521-8195
Web Site: www.lunarpages.com
Approx. Number Employees: 30
Business Description:
Web Hosting Services
S.I.C.: 7375
N.A.I.C.S.: 518111
Media: 7-13
Personnel:
Ronald Riddle *(CEO)*
Brands & Products:
FLASH-TEMPLATE-DESIGN
KICKME.TO
LPDEDICATED
LPQUICKSITE
LUNARFORUMS
LUNARPAGES
LUNARTICS BLOG
PAGEMASON
TEMPLATEHEAVEN
WEB-HOSTING-NEWSLETTER

LYCOS, INC.
(Sub. of Ybrant Networks Ltd.)
100 5th Ave
Waltham, MA 02451
Tel.: (781) 370-2700
Fax: (781) 370-2600
E-mail: webmaster@lycos.com
Web Site: www.lycos.com
Approx. Number Employees: 200
Year Founded: 1995
Business Description:
Internet Portal & Search Services
S.I.C.: 7379
N.A.I.C.S.: 541519
Media: 2-6-8-9-13-15-18-23-24-25
Distr.: Natl.
Personnel:
Jungwook Lim *(CEO)*
Edward Noel *(Chief Strategy Officer & VP)*
Christopher Cummings *(Dir-Product Mgmt)*
Joe Pranevich *(Dir-Tech & Ops)*
Brands & Products:
LYCOS
Advertising Agency:
Schwartz Communications, Inc.
230 3rd Ave
Waltham, MA 02451
Tel.: (781) 684-0770
Fax: (781) 684-6500

LYFE COMMUNICATIONS, INC.
912 W Baxter Dr Ste 200
South Jordan, UT 84095
Tel.: (801) 478-2470
Fax: (801) 214-1927
Web Site: www.connectedlyfe.com
Approx. Rev.: $204,516
Approx. Number Employees: 18
Business Description:
Internet Protocol Television, Internet & Voice Over Internet Protocol Telephone Application Services
S.I.C.: 7379; 3669
N.A.I.C.S.: 541519; 334290
Advertising Expenditures: $44,839
Media: 17
Personnel:
Gregory C. Smith *(Co-Founder & CEO)*
Robert A. Bryson *(Co-Founder & Exec VP-Bus Dev)*
Garrett R. Daw *(Sec & Sr VP-Mktg)*

MAGAZINES.COM INC.
Ste 150 325 Seaboard Ln
Franklin, TN 37067-6431
Tel.: (615) 778-2100
Fax: (615) 778-2139

Key to Media (For complete agency information see *The Advertising Red Books-Agencies* edition):
1. Bus. Publs. 2. Cable T.V. 3. Catalogs & Directories. 4. Co-op Adv. 5. Consumer Mags. 6. D.M. to Bus. Estab.7. D.M. to Consumers
8. Daily Newsp. 9. Exhibits/Trade Shows 10. Foreign 11. Infomercial 12. Internet Adv.13. Multimedia 14. Network Radio
15. Network T.V. 16. Newsp. Distr. Mags. 17. Other 18. Outdoor (Posters, Transit) 19. Point of Purchase20. Premiums, Novelties
21. Product Samples 22. Special Events Mktg. 23. Spot Radio 24. Spot T.V. 25. Weekly Newsp. 26. Yellow Page Adv.

Toll Free: (800) 929-2691
E-mail: feedback@magazines.com
Web Site: www.magazines.com
E-Mail For Key Personnel:
President: jclarke@magazines.com
Approx. Number Employees: 45
Year Founded: 1991
Business Description:
Online Magazine Subscription Agency
S.I.C.: 5961
N.A.I.C.S.: 454113
Media: 13
Personnel:
Jay Clarke *(Pres & CEO)*
Jeff Ballard *(CFO)*
Amy Fisher *(Exec Dir-Publr Rels)*
Lauren Pignataro *(Mgr-Publr Rels)*
Brands & Products:
MAGAZINES.COM

MAILNET SERVICES, INC.
830 Crecent Ctr Dr Ste 510
Franklin, TN 37067
Tel.: (615) 261-7600
Fax: (615) 843-7244
Toll Free: (800) 346-0073
E-mail: info@conclusivemarketing.com
Web Site: www.mailnetservices.com
E-Mail For Key Personnel:
Sales Director: sales@mailnetexpress.com
Public Relations: pr@mailnetservices.com
Approx. Rev.: $1,347,957
Approx. Number Employees: 35
Business Description:
Direct Marketing Services
S.I.C.: 7331
N.A.I.C.S.: 541860
Media: 2
Personnel:
Philip M. Pfeffer *(Chm)*
Don Leyrer *(Pres & CEO)*
Brands & Products:
LISTCLEANUP.COM

MAJORPOWER CORPORATION
7011 Indus Blvd
Mebane, NC 27302
Tel.: (919) 563-6610
Fax: (514) 369-4817
E-mail: sales@majorpower.com
Web Site: www.majorpower.com
Approx. Number Employees: 25
Year Founded: 1990
Business Description:
Power Supply Components & Parts Mfr, Distr & Supplier
S.I.C.: 3699; 5065
N.A.I.C.S.: 335999; 423690
Media: 2-4-7-10-13
Personnel:
Oren Nutik *(Dir)*
Brands & Products:
ASTRON
FERRUP
MAJORPOWER
NEWMAR
STATPOWER
WIREMOLD
XANTREX

MANAGING AUTOMATION
(Div. of Thomas Publishing Company LLC)
5 Penn Plz 9th Fl
New York, NY 10001
Tel.: (212) 695-0500
Fax: (212) 290-7362
E-mail: info@managingautomation.com
Web Site:
www.managingautomation.com
E-Mail For Key Personnel:
Marketing Director: kvennard@thomaspublishing.com
Approx. Number Employees: 400
Business Description:
Online & Print Publisher
S.I.C.: 2741
N.A.I.C.S.: 511199
Media: 10-13-22
Personnel:
Heather L. Mikisch *(Publr)*
David R. Brousell *(Editor-in-Chief)*

MAPQUEST, INC.
(Sub. of AOL Inc.)
555 17th St Ste 1600
Denver, CO 80202
Tel.: (303) 486-4000
E-mail: info@mapquest.com
Web Site: www.mapquest.com
E-Mail For Key Personnel:
Marketing Director: jgreiner@mapquest.com
Sales Range: $100-124.9 Million
Year Founded: 1996
Business Description:
Online Mapping, Directions & Local Searches
S.I.C.: 7389
N.A.I.C.S.: 519190
Media: 2-4-6-7-8-10-13-18
Personnel:
Christian Dwyer *(Sr VP & Gen Mgr)*
Anke Corbin *(VP-Mktg)*
Patrick McDevitt *(VP-Engrg)*

MARITIME BROADBAND
680 East 18th St
Brooklyn, NY 11230
Tel.: (212) 430-6369
Fax: (212) 898-1221
Web Site:
www.maritimebroadband.com/
Sales Range: $1-9.9 Million
Approx. Number Employees: 25
Year Founded: 1999
Business Description:
Turn-Key Solutions for Internet & Telephony Access on Merchant Ships
S.I.C.: 4899; 7375
N.A.I.C.S.: 517910; 518111
Media: 2-7-10
Personnel:
Mary Ellen Kramer *(Owner)*
Ira Greenstein *(Chm)*
Chris Citrone *(Mgr-Acctg)*
Brands & Products:
BROADBAND MARITIME

MARKET AMERICA WORLDWIDE, INC.
1302 Pleasant Ridge Rd
Greensboro, NC 27409
Tel.: (336) 605-0040
Web Site: www.marketamerica.com
Sales Range: $150-199.9 Million
Approx. Number Employees: 200
Year Founded: 1992
Business Description:
Product Brokerage & Internet Marketing Sales & Distr
S.I.C.: 5963; 5961; 7379
N.A.I.C.S.: 454390; 454111; 541519
Media: 4-8-13-22
Personnel:
James R. Ridinger *(Pres & CEO)*
Marc Ashley *(COO)*
Joe Bolyard *(Exec VP)*
Brands & Products:
BUILT ON PRODUCT. POWERED BY PEOPLE.
MALL WITHOUT WALLS
MARKETAMERICA
MATRAVEL
NUTRI-PHYSICAL
UNFRANCHISE

MARKET VELOCITY, INC.
(Sub. of Mediagrif Interactive Technologies, Inc.)
1305 Mall of georgia Blvd Ste 190
Buford, GA 30519
Tel.: (770) 325-6300
Fax: (770) 925-9064
Toll Free: (877) 519-2899
E-mail: customerservice@marketvelocity.com
Web Site: www.marketvelocity.com
Approx. Number Employees: 25
Year Founded: 2002
Business Description:
E-Commerce Software
S.I.C.: 7372
N.A.I.C.S.: 511210
Media: 2-13
Personnel:
Mark Eigenbauer *(Pres)*
Brands & Products:
MARKET VELOCITY
TRADEUPS

MARKETSMART INTERACTIVE, INC.
(Sub. of Inuvo, Inc.)
300 Perimeter Park Dr Ste D
Morrisville, NC 27560-6849
Tel.: (919) 433-3000
Fax: (919) 433-3030
E-mail: info@websourced.com
Web Site: www.websourced.com
Approx. Sls.: $1,400,000
Approx. Number Employees: 110
Year Founded: 1994
Business Description:
Online Marketing Services
S.I.C.: 7373
N.A.I.C.S.: 541512
Media: 13
Personnel:
Jeff Martin *(VP-Engrng)*
Brands & Products:
KEYWORD RANKING
Advertising Agency:
MSA: The Think Agency
2530 Meridian Pkwy Ste 200
Durham, NC 27713
Tel.: (919) 463-9680
Fax: (919) 463-9722
Toll Free: (800) 849-2118

MARKETTOOLS, INC.
1 Belvedere Pl
Mill Valley, CA 94941
Tel.: (415) 462-2200
Fax: (415) 462-2180
E-mail: info@markettools.com
Web Site: www.markettools.com
E-Mail For Key Personnel:
Sales Director: sales@markettools.com
Sales Range: $25-49.9 Million
Approx. Number Employees: 150
Year Founded: 1997
Business Description:
Internet-Based, Full-Service Market Research Software & Services
S.I.C.: 8732; 7371
N.A.I.C.S.: 541910; 541511
Media: 10
Personnel:
Amal M. Johnson *(Chm)*
Scott Arnold *(Pres & CEO)*
Mike Pope *(CFO & COO)*
Alex Terry *(Exec VP & Gen Mgr-Zoomerang Online Survey Bus Unit)*
Cynthia McCloud *(Exec VP & Gen Mgr-Res Solutions)*
John Ouren *(Exec VP & Gen Mgr)*
Beth Rounds *(Sr VP)*
Brands & Products:
CUSTOMERSAT
IDEA NETWORKS
INSIGHT NETWORKS
MARKETTOOLS
PANEL MANAGER
TRUESAMPLE
ZOOMERANG
ZOOMPANEL
ZTELLIGENCE

MARKETWATCH, INC.
(Sub. of Dow Jones Consumer Media)
201 California St 13th Fl
San Francisco, CA 94111-5002
Tel.: (415) 439-6400
Fax: (415) 680-1635
Web Site: www.marketwatch.com
Sales Range: $25-49.9 Million
Approx. Number Employees: 206
Year Founded: 1997
Business Description:
Online Financial News & Information Services
S.I.C.: 2741
N.A.I.C.S.: 516110
Media: 13
Personnel:
Jim Bernard *(Gen Mgr)*
David Callaway *(Editor-in-Chief)*

MASTERBEAT CORPORATION
30 Broad St
New York, NY 10004
Tel.: (212) 532-1813
E-mail: feedback@masterbeat.com
Web Site: www.masterbeat.com
Approx. Rev.: $1,104,897
Approx. Number Employees: 3
Year Founded: 2007
Business Description:
Music Downloading & E-Commerce Services
S.I.C.: 2741; 5961
N.A.I.C.S.: 516110; 454111
Advertising Expenditures: $171,058
Media: 13
Personnel:
Brett Henrichsen *(Pres)*

MATCH.COM, L.P.
(Sub. of IAC/InterActiveCorp)
Ste 800 8300 Douglas Ave
Dallas, TX 75225-5826
Mailing Address:
PO Box 940689
Plano, TX 75094-0689

Key to Media (For complete agency information see *The Advertising Red Books-Agencies* edition):
1. Bus. Publs. 2. Cable T.V. 3. Catalogs & Directories. 4. Co-op Adv. 5. Consumer Mags. 6. D.M. to Bus. Estab.7. D.M. to Consumers
8. Daily Newsp. 9. Exhibits/Trade Shows 10. Foreign 11. Infomercial 12. Internet Adv.13. Multimedia 14. Network Radio
15. Network T.V. 16. Newsp. Distr. Mags. 17. Other 18. Outdoor (Posters, Transit) 19. Point of Purchase20. Premiums, Novelties
21. Product Samples 22. Special Events Mktg. 23. Spot Radio 24. Spot T.V. 25. Weekly Newsp. 26. Yellow Page Adv.

Match.Com, L.P. — (Continued)

Tel.: (214) 576-9352
E-mail: customercare@match.com
Web Site: www.match.com
Sales Range: $10-24.9 Million
Approx. Number Employees: 175
Year Founded: 1995
Business Description:
Online Dating Services
S.I.C.: 7299
N.A.I.C.S.: 812990
Media: 3-6-8-9-12-13-14-15-22-23-24
Personnel:
Gayle Anderson *(CFO)*
Ayesha Gilarde *(VP-Mktg)*
Jerilyn Huddleston *(Dir-Product)*
Alexis Ferraro *(Sr Mgr-Mktg)*
Karl Gregory *(Mgr-MD Country)*
Brands & Products:
MATCH.COM
Advertising Agency:
Initiative Worldwide
(Part of The Interpublic Group of Companies, Inc.)
1 Dag Hammerskjold Plz 5th Fl
New York, NY 10017
Tel.: (212) 605-7000
Fax: (212) 605-7200
Media Buying & Planning

MBLOX INC.
455 W Maude Ave Ste 100
Sunnyvale, CA 94085
Tel.: (408) 617-3700
Fax: (408) 617-3799
E-mail: enquires@mblox.com
Web Site: www.mblox.com
Approx. Number Employees: 105
Business Description:
Mobile Messaging Infrastructure Services
S.I.C.: 4813
N.A.I.C.S.: 517110
Advertising Expenditures: $100,000
Media: 7-10-13-27
Personnel:
Andrew Bud *(Founder & Chief Strategy Officer)*
Andrew Dark *(CEO)*
Michele Turner *(CMO)*
Brian Johnson *(Sr VP-Sls & Mktg-Americas)*
Paul Cegielski *(Dir-Mktg Comm)*
Erin Young *(Mgr-Pub Rel)*
Advertising Agency:
Hotwire PR
33/41 Dallington Street
London, EC1V 0BB, United Kingdom
Tel.: (44) 20 7608 2500

MEDIASPAN NETWORKS
8687 Research Dr Ste 100
Irvine, CA 92618
Tel.: (949) 892-2929
Fax: (949) 892-2930
Toll Free: (800) 913-1299
Web Site:
www.mediaspannetwork.com
E-Mail For Key Personnel:
Sales Director: sales@mediaspanonline.com
Approx. Number Employees: 200
Business Description:
Online Advertising Sales
S.I.C.: 7319
N.A.I.C.S.: 541890
Media: 2-7-10-13

Personnel:
Tane Robert *(CEO)*

MEDIO SYSTEMS INC.
One Convention Place 701 Pike St 15th Fl
Seattle, WA 98101
Tel.: (206) 262-3700
Fax: (206) 262-3799
E-mail: jobs@medio.com
Web Site: www.medio.com
Business Description:
Mobile Search Services
N.A.I.C.S.: 519130
Media: 27
Personnel:
Brian Lent *(Chm & CTO)*
Robert P. Lilleness *(Pres & CEO)*
Advertising Agency:
Brew Media Relations
3015 Main St Ste 350
Santa Monica, CA 90405
Tel.: (310) 526-8576

MEDSITE, INC.
(Sub. of WebMD Health Corporation)
370 7th Ave Fl 11 Ste 1101
New York, NY 10001-5010
Tel.: (212) 417-9500
Tel.: (646) 674-1244
Fax: (212) 797-9295
Fax: (646) 674-1632
Toll Free: (877) 633-7483
E-mail: info@medsite.com
Web Site: www.medsite.com
Sales Range: $25-49.9 Million
Approx. Number Employees: 150
Year Founded: 1995
Business Description:
Online Medical Business-to-Business Services & Products
S.I.C.: 7375
N.A.I.C.S.: 518111
Media: 13
Personnel:
Sundeep Bhan *(Pres & CEO)*
Brands & Products:
MEDBOOKSTORE.COM
MEDSITE
MEDSITE REWARDS

MEMORY 4 LESS
2622 W Lincoln Ave Ste 104
Anaheim, CA 92801-6314
Tel.: (714) 821-3354
Fax: (714) 821-3361
Toll Free: (800) 821-3354
E-mail: support@memory4less.com
Web Site: www.memory4less.com
Sales Range: $25-49.9 Million
Approx. Number Employees: 17
Year Founded: 1985
Business Description:
Computer Memory Upgrade Services
S.I.C.: 5045; 5734
N.A.I.C.S.: 423430; 443120
Media: 13
Personnel:
Faisal Ismael *(Co-Owner)*

MERGE ECLINICAL INC.
(Sub. of Merge Healthcare, Inc.)
4000 Aerial Center Pkwy
Morrisville, NC 27560
Tel.: (919) 653-3400
Fax: (919) 653-3620
E-mail: info@etrials.com
Web Site: www.merge.com/eclinical/index.aspx
Approx. Rev.: $16,242,320
Approx. Number Employees: 100
Year Founded: 1999
Business Description:
Computer Software Design & Services for Clinical Trial Management
S.I.C.: 7372; 7371
N.A.I.C.S.: 511210; 334611; 541511
Advertising Expenditures: $667,000
Personnel:
Charles J. Piccirillo *(VP-Tech)*
John T. DeVries *(Gen Mgr)*

MESSAGEBROADCAST INC.
4685 MacArthur Court Ste 250
Newport Beach, CA 92660-6476
Tel.: (949) 428-3111
Fax: (949) 253-9055
Toll Free: (888) 749-8000
E-mail: Marketing@messagebroadcast.com
Web Site:
www.messagebroadcast.com
E-Mail For Key Personnel:
Marketing Director: marketing@messagebroadcast.com
Approx. Number Employees: 20
Year Founded: 1997
Business Description:
Voice Messaging Services
S.I.C.: 4899
N.A.I.C.S.: 517910
Advertising Expenditures: $200,000
Media: 13
Personnel:
David Baker *(Pres)*
William H. Potter *(CEO)*

MFG.COM, INC.
2700 Cumberland Pkwy Ste 500
Atlanta, GA 30339
Tel.: (770) 444-9686
Fax: (770) 444-9819
Toll Free: (888) 404-9686
Web Site: www.mfg.com
E-Mail For Key Personnel:
Sales Director: sales@mfg.com
Approx. Rev.: $4,000,000
Approx. Number Employees: 26
Year Founded: 1999
Business Description:
Web-Based Marketplace for the Buying & Selling of Custom Manufacturing Services
S.I.C.: 7389
N.A.I.C.S.: 561499
Advertising Expenditures: $200,000
Media: 2-10-13
Personnel:
Mitch Free *(Founder & CEO)*
Brands & Products:
MFG.COM
MFGJOBS.COM
MFGQUOTE.COM

MICROSOFT OFFICE LIVE MEETING
(Sub. of Microsoft Business Division)
295 N Bernardo Ave
Mountain View, CA 94043-5205
Tel.: (425) 703-5869
Toll Free: (866) 463-3866
Toll Free: (866) 493-2825
Toll Free: (888) 526-6170
Web Site: www.livemeeting.com
Sales Range: $75-99.9 Million
Approx. Number Employees: 240
Year Founded: 1996
Business Description:
Internet Conferencing Services
S.I.C.: 7379; 2741
N.A.I.C.S.: 541519; 516110
Media: 13-20

MICROSTRATEGY, INC.
1850 Towers Crescent Plz
Vienna, VA 22182
Tel.: (703) 848-8600
Fax: (703) 848-8610
Toll Free: (866) 966-MSTR
E-mail: info@microstrategy.com
Web Site: www.microstrategy.com
Approx. Rev.: $454,577,000
Approx. Number Employees: 2,597
Year Founded: 1989
Business Description:
E-Business Software & Services
S.I.C.: 7372; 7371
N.A.I.C.S.: 334611; 511210; 541511
Advertising Expenditures: $900,000
Media: 2-6-7-9-13-16-18-19
Personnel:
Michael J. Saylor *(Chm, Pres & CEO)*
Douglas K. Thede *(CFO & Exec VP-Fin)*
Jeffrey A. Bedell *(CTO & Exec VP-Tech)*
Jonathan F. Klein *(Gen Counsel & Exec VP-Law)*
Peter Isaacson *(Sr VP-WW Mktg)*
Chris Broyles *(Dir-PS)*
Claudia Cahill *(Mgr-Customer Mktg)*
Sanju K. Bansal *(Vice Chm, COO & Exec VP)*
Brands & Products:
ADMINISTRATOR
ALARM
ALERT.COM
ANGEL
ARCHITECT
BEST IN BUSINESS INTELLIGENCE
CHANGING THE WAY GOVERNMENT LOOKS AT INFORMATION
DESKTOP
DSS BROADCASTER
DSS BROADCASTER SERVER
DSS OFFICE
DSS SUBSCRIBER
DSS TELECASTER
DSSARCHITECT
DSSSERVER
DSSWEB
EBROADCASTER
ECASTER
ESTRATEGY
ETELECASTER
THE FOUNDATION FOR INTELLIGENT E-BUSINESS
INDUSTRIAL-STRENGTH BUSINESS INTELLIGENCE
INFORMATION LIKE WATER
INSIGHT IS EVERYTHING
THE INTELLIGENCE COMPANY
INTELLIGENCE SERVER
INTELLIGENT CUBES
INTELLIGENT E-BUSINESS
IWAPU
MICROSTRATEGY
MICROSTRATEGY 6
MICROSTRATEGY 7
MICROSTRATEGY 7I
MICROSTRATEGY 7I EVALUATION EDITION
MICROSTRATEGY 7I OLAP SERVICES

Key to Media (For complete agency information see *The Advertising Red Books-Agencies* edition):
1. Bus. Publs. 2. Cable T.V. 3. Catalogs & Directories. 4. Co-op Adv. 5. Consumer Mags. 6. D.M. to Bus. Estab.7. D.M. to Consumers 8. Daily Newsp. 9. Exhibits/Trade Shows 10. Foreign 11. Infomercial 12. Internet Adv.13. Multimedia 14. Network Radio 15. Network T.V. 16. Newsp. Distr. Mags. 17. Other 18. Outdoor (Posters, Transit) 19. Point of Purchase20. Premiums, Novelties 21. Product Samples 22. Special Events Mktg. 23. Spot Radio 24. Spot T.V. 25. Weekly Newsp. 26. Yellow Page Adv.

MICROSTRATEGY 8
MICROSTRATEGY 9
MICROSTRATEGY AGENT
MICROSTRATEGY ANALYST
MICROSTRATEGY BI AUTHOR
MICROSTRATEGY BI DEVELOPER KIT
MICROSTRATEGY BI MODELER
MICROSTRATEGY BROADCAST SERVER
MICROSTRATEGY BROADCASTER
MICROSTRATEGY BROADCASTER SERVER
MICROSTRATEGY BUSINESS INTELLIGENCE PLATFORM
MICROSTRATEGY COMMAND MANAGER
MICROSTRATEGY CONSULTING
MICROSTRATEGY CONSUMER
MICROSTRATEGY CUSTOMER ANALYZER
MICROSTRATEGY DESKTOP ANALYST
MICROSTRATEGY DISTRIBUTION SERVICES
MICROSTRATEGY ECRM 7
MICROSTRATEGY EDUCATION
MICROSTRATEGY ETRAINER
MICROSTRATEGY EVALUATION EDITION
MICROSTRATEGY INFOCENTER
MICROSTRATEGY MDX ADAPTER
MICROSTRATEGY MULTISOURCE OPTION
MICROSTRATEGY OBJECT MANAGER
MICROSTRATEGY OBJECTS
MICROSTRATEGY OFFICE
MICROSTRATEGY OLAP PROVIDER
MICROSTRATEGY SDK
MICROSTRATEGY SUPPORT
MICROSTRATEGY TELECASTER
MICROSTRATEGY TRANSACTOR
MICROSTRATEGY WEB
MICROSTRATEGY WEB MMT
MICROSTRATEGY WEB SERVICES
MICROSTRATEGY WORLD
NARROWCAST SERVER
OFFICE INTELLIGENCE
OLAP SERVICES
THE PLATFORM FOR INTELLIGENT E-BUSINESS
THE POWER OF INTELLIGENT E-BUSINESS
THE POWER OF INTELLIGENT EBUSINESS
REPORT SERVICES
STRATEGY.COM
YOUR TELEPHONE JUST GOT SMARTER

MICROWAY, INC.

Plymouth Indus Pk 12 Richards Rd
Plymouth, MA 02360
Tel.: (508) 746-7341
Fax: (508) 746-4678
E-mail: info@microway.com
Web Site: www.microway.com
E-Mail For Key Personnel:
Marketing Director: annf@microway.com
Approx. Number Employees: 40
Year Founded: 1982
Business Description:
Computer Related Services
S.I.C.: 3571; 3577
N.A.I.C.S.: 334111; 334119
Media: 13
Personnel:
Ann Fried *(Chm)*
Stephen Fried *(Pres)*
Brands & Products:
ALPHA
ATHLON
FASTREE
GIGACUBE
INTEL
ITANIUM
MCMS
MICROWAY
MPI LINK-CHECKER
NAVION
NODEWATCH
NUMBERSMASHER
QUADPUTER
RUGGED-RACK
WHISPERSTATION

MIDPHASE SERVICES, INC.

164 N Spring Creek Pkwy
Providence, UT 84332
Tel.: (435) 755-3433
Fax: (888) 846-8730
Toll Free: (866) MIDPHASE
E-mail: support@midphase.com
Web Site: www.midphase.com
E-Mail For Key Personnel:
Sales Director: sales@midphase.com
Business Description:
Web Hosting Services
S.I.C.: 2741
N.A.I.C.S.: 516110
Media: 13
Personnel:
Ditlev Bredahl *(CEO)*

MIDWEST MICROSYSTEMS, LLC

Ste 7 3100 O St
Lincoln, NE 68510-1532
Tel.: (402) 323-6969
Fax: (402) 323-6968
E-mail: info@midwestmicro.com
Web Site: www.midwestmicro.com
Approx. Number Employees: 3
Year Founded: 1993
Business Description:
Information Management Solution Services for the Cattle Industry
S.I.C.: 0212; 7373
N.A.I.C.S.: 112111; 541512
Media: 6-13
Personnel:
Jim Lowe *(Pres)*
Brands & Products:
ACCU-TRAC
COW COMM
COW SENSE
EID PRODUCTS

MILITARY ADVANTAGE, INC.

(Sub. of Monster Worldwide, Inc.)
799 Market St Ste 700
San Francisco, CA 94103-2045
Tel.: (415) 820-3434
Fax: (415) 820-0552
E-mail: press@military-inc.com
Web Site: www.military.com
E-Mail For Key Personnel:
Marketing Director: ashleigh.emerick@military-inc.com
Sales Range: $1-9.9 Million
Approx. Number Employees: 20
Year Founded: 1999
Business Description:
Online Services, Products & Resources for Active & Retired Military & Their Families
S.I.C.: 7375
N.A.I.C.S.: 519130
Media: 8-13
Personnel:
T. L. McCreary *(Pres)*
Ward Carroll *(Editor)*
Josh Brody *(Dir-Sls)*
Jeff Kimble *(Dir-Network Ops & IT)*
Brian McGlothlen *(Dir-Software Engrg)*
Vince Patton *(Dir-Govt Partnerships & Alliances)*
Heather Rader *(Dir-Acct Mgmt)*
Tony Baker *(Mgr-Mktg)*
Brands & Products:
MILITARY.COM

MILLENNIUM INFORMATION GROUP, INC.

422 49th St Ste 4F
Brooklyn, NY 11220-1964
Tel.: (718) 492-4313
Fax: (212) 430-3843
E-mail: mgr@miginc.com
Web Site: www.miginc.com
E-Mail For Key Personnel:
Sales Director: sales@miginc.com
Approx. Number Employees: 15
Year Founded: 1998
Business Description:
Internet Technology Services
S.I.C.: 7371; 7373
N.A.I.C.S.: 541511; 541512
Media: 7-13
Brands & Products:
KNOWEX
MIG

MINDBLAZER, INC.

6120 Harish Technology Blvd
Charlotte, NC 28269-2325
Tel.: (704) 554-9555
Fax: (704) 644-0742
Toll Free: (800) 223-9877
E-mail: royan@mindblazer.com
Web Site: www.mindblazer.com
E-Mail For Key Personnel:
Marketing Director: marketing@mindblazer.com
Approx. Sls.: $4,500,000
Approx. Number Employees: 11
Year Founded: 1999
Business Description:
Education Based Marketing Firm
S.I.C.: 7373
N.A.I.C.S.: 541512
Media: 7-13
Brands & Products:
MINDBLAZER
POWERING NEW MEDIA

MINDLEADERS.COM, INC.

(Sub. of ThirdForce Ltd.)
5500 Glendon Ct Ste 200
Dublin, OH 43016
Tel.: (614) 781-7300
Fax: (614) 781-6510
Toll Free: (800) 223-3732
E-mail: internationalsales@mindleaders.com
Web Site: www.mindleaders.com
Sales Range: $75-99.9 Million
Approx. Number Employees: 120
Year Founded: 1981
Business Description:
Web-Based Training & Enterprise-Quality Courses to Businesses, Government Agencies, Non-Profit Organizations & Home Office Users
S.I.C.: 8299; 8243
N.A.I.C.S.: 611710; 611420
Advertising Expenditures: $200,000
Media: 7-8-10-13
Personnel:
Paul MacCartney *(Pres)*
Jeff Croson *(VP-Sls)*
Brands & Products:
ELEARNING THAT WORKS
MINDLEADERS

MINDSPARK INTERACTIVE NETWORK, INC.

(Sub. of IAC/InterActiveCorp)
One North Lexington 9th Fl
White Plains, NY 10601
Tel.: (914) 826-2000
Web Site: www.mindspark.com
Sales Range: $50-74.9 Million
Business Description:
Social & Entertainment Internet Services
S.I.C.: 2741; 7375
N.A.I.C.S.: 516110; 518111
Media: 13
Personnel:
Joey Levin *(CEO)*
Mark Stein *(Chief Strategy Officer)*
Gui Karyo *(Pres-iWon.com)*

MIQ LOGISTICS, LLC

(Formerly YRC Logistics, Inc.)
(Holding of Austin Ventures, LP)
5200 W 110th St
Overland Park, KS 66211
Tel.: (877) 246-4909
Fax: (913) 906-6996
Toll Free: (877) 246-4909
E-mail: contact_us@miq.com
Web Site: www2.miq.com
Sales Range: $1-4.9 Billion
Approx. Number Employees: 1,500
Year Founded: 2002
Business Description:
Global Transportation Logistics Services
S.I.C.: 4731; 2741; 8742
N.A.I.C.S.: 488510; 516110; 541614
Media: 13
Personnel:
Joseph L. Carnes *(Chm & CEO)*
John E. Carr *(Pres & COO)*
Brenda Stasiulis *(CFO)*
Dan Bentzinger *(CIO)*
Reid Schultz *(Chief Admin Officer & Gen Counsel)*
Michael Collins *(Sr VP-Global Ops)*
David N. Griffith *(Sr VP-Logistics)*

MIRROR IMAGE INTERNET, INC.

(Sub. of Xcelera Inc.)
Ste 101 2 Highwood Dr
Tewksbury, MA 01876-1100
Tel.: (781) 376-1100
Fax: (781) 376-1110
Toll Free: (800) 353-2923
Web Site: www.mirrorimage.net
Approx. Number Employees: 77
Year Founded: 1996
Business Description:
Developer & Operator of Internet Technology Companies

Key to Media (For complete agency information see *The Advertising Red Books-Agencies* edition):
1. Bus. Publs. 2. Cable T.V. 3. Catalogs & Directories. 4. Co-op Adv. 5. Consumer Mags. 6. D.M. to Bus. Estab.7. D.M. to Consumers 8. Daily Newsp. 9. Exhibits/Trade Shows 10. Foreign 11. Infomercial 12. Internet Adv.13. Multimedia 14. Network Radio 15. Network T.V. 16. Newsp. Distr. Mags. 17. Other 18. Outdoor (Posters, Transit) 19. Point of Purchase20. Premiums, Novelties 21. Product Samples 22. Special Events Mktg. 23. Spot Radio 24. Spot T.V. 25. Weekly Newsp. 26. Yellow Page Adv.

Mirror Image Internet, Inc. — (Continued)

S.I.C.: 7375
N.A.I.C.S.: 518111
Personnel:
Alexander M. Vik *(Chm)*
Gustav Vik *(Pres & CEO)*
Chad Dyer *(Mng Dir)*
James G. Hart *(VP-Sls & Mktg)*
Brands & Products:
CONTENT ACCESS POINT
INSTA DELIVERY
Advertising Agencies:
PAN Communications
300 Brickstone Sq 7th Fl
Andover, MA 01810
Tel.: (978) 474-1900
Fax: (978) 474-1903

Springbox, Ltd.
706 Congress Ave Ste A
Austin, TX 78701
Tel.: (512) 391-0065
Fax: (512) 391-0064
— Brian Hjelm *(Acct Dir)*

MOBIFORM SOFTWARE, INC.

1255 N Vantage Point Dr Ste A
Crystal River, FL 34429
Tel.: (352) 564-9610
Fax: (352) 564-9611
E-mail: info@mobiform.com
Web Site: www.mobiform.com
E-Mail For Key Personnel:
President: rdeserranno@mobiform.com
Sales Director: pbarker@mobiform.com
Approx. Rev.: $824,508
Approx. Number Employees: 10
Year Founded: 2003
Business Description:
Online Graphics & Visualization Software Products Developer
S.I.C.: 7372; 2741
N.A.I.C.S.: 511210; 516110
Advertising Expenditures: $265,625
Personnel:
Allen Ronald DeSerranno *(CEO)*

MOBILE CONTENT NETWORKS INC.

204 E 2nd Ave #340
San Mateo, CA 94401-3963
Tel.: (650) 206-2297
Fax: (650) 618-1988
Web Site: www.mcn-inc.com
Business Description:
Supplies Mobile Telephone Operators or Mobile Internet Portals with Mobile Internet Search Technology & Monetizations Programs
N.A.I.C.S.: 519130
Media: 2-10-17-27
Personnel:
Marc Bookman *(CEO)*
Subhash Bhatia *(Exec VP-Engrg & Ops)*
Richard Reed *(Exec VP-Bus Ops)*
Stephen Burke *(Sr VP-Sls & Mktg)*

MONDERA.COM

45 W 45th St
New York, NY 10036-4602
Tel.: (800) 666-3372
Fax: (212) 997-9691
Toll Free: (800) 666-3372
E-mail: proposals@mondera.com
Web Site: www.mondera.com
Approx. Number Employees: 100
Year Founded: 1998
Business Description:
Online Retailer of Jewelry & Luxury Items
S.I.C.: 5944
N.A.I.C.S.: 448310
Media: 13
Personnel:
Fred Mouawad *(Chm & CEO)*
Marla Nitke *(Dir-Mktg Comm)*

MONDO MEDIA CORPORATION

444 De Haro St Ste 201
San Francisco, CA 94107
Tel.: (415) 865-2700
Fax: (415) 865-2645
E-mail: feedback@mondomedia.com
Web Site: www.mondomedia.com
Approx. Number Employees: 20
Year Founded: 1989
Business Description:
Animated Entertainment Services
S.I.C.: 7336; 7375
N.A.I.C.S.: 541430; 518111
Media: 8-13-18-19-22
Personnel:
John W. Evershed *(Co-Founder & CEO)*
Deirdre O'Malley *(Co-Founder & Dir-Bus Affairs)*
Douglas S. Kay *(CFO)*
Dean MacDonald *(Dir-Creative)*
Brands & Products:
ABSOLUTE ZERO
BEHIND THE MUSIC THAT SUCKS
THE GOD & DEVIL SHOW
HAPPY TREE FRIENDS
HARD DRINKIN' LINCOLN
HEAVY METAL GUY
JULIUS & FRIENDS
KEVIN SPENCER
LIKE, NEWS
THE MODERN WORLD
PIKI & POKO
POKER NIGHT
THUGS ON FILM
ZOMBIE COLLEGE

MONEXA TECHNOLOGIES CORPORATION

Ste 1100 555 W Hastings St
PO Box 12026
Vancouver, BC V6B 4N4, Canada
Tel.: (604) 630-5660
Fax: (604) 630-5652
Toll Free: (877) 604-7277
E-mail: info@ipapplications.com
Web Site: www.ipapplications.com
Approx. Rev.: $4,113,864
Approx. Number Employees: 20
Year Founded: 1989
Business Description:
Internet Business Processes & Services Facilitator
S.I.C.: 7379; 4812
N.A.I.C.S.: 541519; 517212
Advertising Expenditures: $841,031
Media: 10
Personnel:
John Jacobson *(Pres, CEO & Dir)*
Garth Albright *(CFO)*
Kevin Lennox *(VP-Sls)*

MONEY.NET, INC.

9 Desbrosses St Ste 303
New York, NY 10013
Tel.: (212) 334-2000
Fax: (212) 334-4464
E-mail: abe@money.net
Web Site: www.money.net
E-Mail For Key Personnel:
Sales Director: sales@money.net
Sales Range: $1-9.9 Million
Approx. Number Employees: 30
Year Founded: 1997
Business Description:
Real-Time Market Data Direct to Individual Investors & Customized Software Systems
S.I.C.: 7375; 6289
N.A.I.C.S.: 518111; 523999
Media: 7-13
Personnel:
Brian King *(Pres)*
Harold L. Van Arnem *(CEO)*
Janet Christofano *(CFO)*
Nancy Joyce *(Dir-Ops)*
Brands & Products:
LEVEL II VIEWER
MARKET MOSAIC
MARKET MOSAIC PRO
MARKETHEAT
MARKETMETER
MARKETSCREEN
MONEY.NET
NEWSSTREAM
PCQUOTE.COM
SCREAMER
SECTORTRACKER
SMARTCHARTS
SNAPQUOTES
TOTALVIEW
WIRELESS & EMAIL ALERTS

MONSTER WORLDWIDE, INC.

622 3rd Ave 39th Fl
New York, NY 10017
Tel.: (212) 351-7000
Fax: (646) 658-0540
Web Site: www.about-monster.com
Approx. Rev.: $914,133,000
Approx. Number Employees: 5,850
Business Description:
Recruitment Advertising Services
S.I.C.: 7361; 8742
N.A.I.C.S.: 561310; 519130; 541611; 541612; 541613
Advertising Expenditures: $120,000,000
Media: 2-3-9-10-13-14-15-16
Personnel:
Salvatore Iannuzzi *(Chm, Pres & CEO)*
James M. Langrock *(CFO & Exec VP)*
Mark Conway *(CIO)*
Lise Poulos *(Chief Admin Officer & Exec VP)*
Michael C. Miller *(Gen Counsel, Sec & Exec VP)*
Ted Gilvar *(Global CMO & Exec VP)*
Edward Lo *(Exec VP-Greater China)*
Arthur O'Donnell *(Exec VP-Global Customer Svcs)*
Mark Stoever *(Exec VP-Corp Dev & Strategic Alliances)*
Timothy T. Yates *(Exec VP)*
Rick Cotton *(Sr VP & Gen Mgr)*
Steve Cooker *(Sr VP-US)*
Patrick Manzo *(Chief Privacy Officer & Sr VP-Customer Svc-Global)*
Kathy Paladino *(Sr VP-Sls-North America)*
Matthew Henson *(VP-PR)*
Mark Nelson *(Dir-Product Mgmt)*
Colleen McGrath *(Sr Mgr-Workplace Comm)*
Valerie Roush *(Mgr-Bus Dev-Sls Partnership)*
Jonathan Luther *(Engr)*
Brands & Products:
MONSTER
YOUR CALLING IS CALLING
Advertising Agencies:
Atmosphere Proximity
1285 Ave of the Americas 5th Fl
New York, NY 10019
Tel.: (212) 827-2500
Fax: (212) 827-2525

BBDO New York
1285 Ave of the Americas 7th Fl
New York, NY 10019-6028
Tel.: (212) 459-5000

BBDO Worldwide Inc.
(Sub. of Omnicom Group, Inc.)
1285 Ave of the Americas
New York, NY 10019-6028
Tel.: (212) 459-5000
Fax: (212) 459-6645

OMD Worldwide
195 Broadway
New York, NY 10007
Tel.: (212) 590-7100

The VIA Group LLC
34 Danforth St Ste 309
Portland, ME 04101
Tel.: (207) 221-3000
Fax: (207) 761-9422
Monster.com

Weber Shandwick
(Sub. of The Interpublic Group of Companies)
919 3rd Ave
New York, NY 10022
Tel.: (212) 445-8000
Fax: (212) 445-8001
Pub Rels
— Christian Harper *(Sr VP)*

MOTHERNATURE.COM, INC.

322 7th Ave Fl 3
New York, NY 10001
Tel.: (212) 279-4350
Fax: (212) 279-4290
Toll Free: (800) 439-5506
E-mail: info@mothernature.com
Web Site: www.mothernature.com
Approx. Number Employees: 40
Business Description:
Online Health Supplement Store
S.I.C.: 5499
N.A.I.C.S.: 446191
Media: 8-13
Personnel:
Cathy Ross *(Pres)*
Whitney Anderson *(CEO)*
Dan Krebs *(COO)*
Brands & Products:
JASON
MOTHERNATURE.COM
NATURAL PRODUCTS. HEALTHY ADVICE.

MOVE, INC.

910 E Hamilton Ave
Campbell, CA 95008
Tel.: (805) 557-2300
Fax: (805) 557-2680

Key to Media (For complete agency information see *The Advertising Red Books-Agencies* edition):
1. Bus. Publs. 2. Cable T.V. 3. Catalogs & Directories. 4. Co-op Adv. 5. Consumer Mags. 6. D.M. to Bus. Estab.7. D.M. to Consumers
8. Daily Newsp. 9. Exhibits/Trade Shows 10. Foreign 11. Infomercial 12. Internet Adv.13. Multimedia 14. Network Radio
15. Network T.V. 16. Newsp. Distr. Mags. 17. Other 18. Outdoor (Posters, Transit) 19. Point of Purchase20. Premiums, Novelties
21. Product Samples 22. Special Events Mktg. 23. Spot Radio 24. Spot T.V. 25. Weekly Newsp. 26. Yellow Page Adv.

Web Site: www.move.com
Approx. Rev.: $197,503,000
Approx. Number Employees: 966
Year Founded: 1996
Business Description:
Real Estate, Internet Media & Technology Services
S.I.C.: 6531; 2741
N.A.I.C.S.: 531210; 516110; 531390
Advertising Expenditures: $13,700,000
Media: 2-13
Personnel:
Joe F. Hanauer *(Chm)*
Steven H. Berkowitz *(CEO)*
Scott Boecker *(Chief Product Officer)*
Errol G. Samuelson *(Chief Revenue Officer)*
James S. Caulfield *(Gen Counsel, Sec & Exec VP)*
Brands & Products:
FEATURED AGENT
FEATURED COMPANY
FEATURED HOMES
THE FIRST CHOICE FOR NEW HOMES
HOMEBUILDER.COM
MOVE
MOVE.COM
THE POWER OF THE INTERNET
REALTOR.COM
RENTNET.COM
TOP PRODUCER
TOP PRODUCER FLAGSHIP 8I
WELCOME WAGON
WYLDFRYE
Advertising Agency:
MOST Brand Development + Advertising
25 Enterprise Ste 250
Aliso Viejo, CA 92656
Tel.: (949) 475-4050
Fax: (949) 475-4051

MUSICMATCH, INC.
(Sub. of Yahoo! Inc.)
16935 W Bernardo Dr Ste 270
San Diego, CA 92127
Tel.: (858) 485-4300
Fax: (858) 485-4208
E-mail: web@musicmatch.com
Web Site: www.musicmatch.com
Sales Range: $50-74.9 Million
Approx. Number Employees: 140
Year Founded: 1997
Business Description:
Digital Audio Software Developer
S.I.C.: 5734; 7373; 7379
N.A.I.C.S.: 443120; 541512; 541519
Media: 13
Personnel:
Dennis Mudd *(Chm & CEO)*
Gary Acord *(CFO)*
William Caid *(CTO & CIO)*
Doug Leigh *(Gen Counsel & Sr VP)*
Christopher Allen *(Sr VP-Mktg & Strategic Plng)*
Brands & Products:
FREEDOM FOR MUSIC LOVERS
MUSICMATCH

MUSICNET
(Sub. of Baker Capital Partners, LLC)
220 W 42nd St 16th Fl
New York, NY 10036
Tel.: (212) 704-0280
E-mail: marketing@musicnet.com
Web Site: www.musicnet.com
Year Founded: 1999
Business Description:
Customized Music Download & Subscription Services
S.I.C.: 7379
N.A.I.C.S.: 541519
Media: 13
Personnel:
Robert Glaser *(Chm)*
Cindy Charles *(Gen Counsel, Sr VP-Law & Bus Affairs)*

MUSICNOTES, INC.
8020 Excelsior Dr Ste 201
Madison, WI 53717
Tel.: (608) 662-1680
Fax: (608) 662-1688
Toll Free: (800) 944-4667
E-mail: press@musicnotes.com
Web Site: www.musicnotes.com
Approx. Number Employees: 35
Business Description:
Online Digital Sheet Music Retailer & Downloading Services
S.I.C.: 5736; 5961
N.A.I.C.S.: 451140; 454111
Media: 13
Personnel:
Kathleen Marsh *(Co-Founder & CEO)*
Walter Burt *(Co-Founder & Sr Analyst-Sys)*
Tom Hall *(Co-Founder)*
Tim Reiland *(Chm & CFO)*
Bill Aicher *(Dir-Web & Mktg)*
Matt Reif *(Mgr-Mktg & Mdsg)*
Brands & Products:
GUITAR GURU
MUSIC BOOKS & MORE
MUSICNOTES
MUSICNOTES.COM

MYERS INTERNET, INC.
250 E Kilbourn Ave
Milwaukee, WI 53202
Tel.: (414) 347-6480
Fax: (414) 347-6485
Toll Free: (800) 693-7770
E-mail: info@myersnet.com
Web Site: www.myersinternet.com
E-Mail For Key Personnel:
Sales Director: sales@myersinternet.com
Approx. Number Employees: 80
Year Founded: 1995
Business Description:
Internet Website Designing, Hosting & Marketing Company for the Mortgage Industry
S.I.C.: 7371; 2741; 7375
N.A.I.C.S.: 541511; 516110; 518111
Advertising Expenditures: $200,000
Media: 2-10-13
Personnel:
Paula Stretz *(Dir-Servicing Rel)*
Brands & Products:
AGENTCENTER.COM
BESTRATE.COM
MORTGAGE-NET
MYERS.COM
ORIGINATORNETWORK.COM
WEBSUITE.COM

MYPOINTS.COM, INC.
(Sub. of ClassMates Media Corporation)
525 Markert St Ste 3400
San Francisco, CA 94105
Tel.: (415) 615-1100
Fax: (415) 829-6122
Toll Free: (800) 890-9351
E-mail: publicrelations@mypoints.com
Web Site: www.mypoints.com
Sales Range: $25-49.9 Million
Approx. Number Employees: 100
Business Description:
Online Direct Marketing Membership Services
S.I.C.: 7311
N.A.I.C.S.: 541810
Media: 8-13
Personnel:
John Fullmer *(Pres)*
Stefan DeCota *(Sr VP-Media & Partner Sls)*
Brands & Products:
MYPOINTS
MYPOINTS.COM

MYSPACE, INC.
(Sub. of Fox Interactive Media, Inc.)
407 N Maple Dr
Beverly Hills, CA 90210
Tel.: (310) 969-7400
E-mail: msmedia@myspace.com
Web Site: www.myspace.com
Sales Range: $50-74.9 Million
Approx. Number Employees: 200
Year Founded: 2004
Business Description:
Online Social Networking Services
Website Developer & Hosting Services
S.I.C.: 7374
N.A.I.C.S.: 518210; 519130
Export
Media: 8-11-13
Personnel:
Michael Jones *(CEO)*
Nada Stirratt *(Chief Revenue Officer)*
Mark Rosenbaum *(CFO & Exec VP)*
Bryce Emo *(Sr VP & Head-Sls)*
David Donegan *(Sr VP-Mktg)*
Shari Friedman *(Sr VP-Sls)*
Rosabel Tao *(Sr VP-Corp Comm)*
Valeh Vakili *(Sr VP-Sls Ops)*
Nicolle Anderson *(VP-Sls East)*
Tom Bosco *(VP-Sls-TV)*
Manny Miravete *(VP-Sls & Strategy-Hispanic)*
Tony Sicanolfi *(VP-Sls)*
Sandeep Suvarna *(Head-Mktg)*
Hari V. Krishnan *(Country Mgr-India)*
Chip Kanne *(Sr Reg Mgr-Sls)*
Jose Casanova *(Mgr-Mktg-Mexico)*
Advertising Agency:
Pereira & O'Dell
215 2nd St
San Francisco, CA 94105
Tel.: (415) 284-9916
Fax: (415) 284-9926
Web Site Relaunch

MYWEBGROCER.COM CORP.
354 Mountain View Dr Ste 350
Colchester, VT 05446
Tel.: (802) 857-1200
Fax: (802) 764-1844
Toll Free: (888) 662-2284
E-mail: info@mywebgrocer.com
Web Site: www.mywebgrocer.com
Business Description:
Online Groceries Whslr
S.I.C.: 7375
N.A.I.C.S.: 518111
Media: 13
Personnel:
Richard Tarrant *(Founder & CEO)*
Dan Vanchieri *(Sr VP-Adv Sls-Eastern Reg)*
Ed Page *(Sr Dir-CPG)*
Gerry Howatt *(Dir-Digital Shopper Mktg)*

MZINGA, INC.
230 3rd Ave 2nd Fl
Waltham, MA 02451
Tel.: (781) 328-2800
Tel.: (781) 577-8905
Fax: (781) 930-5430
Toll Free: (888) 694-6428
E-mail: learnmore@mzinga.com
Web Site: www.mzinga.com
Approx. Number Employees: 100
Business Description:
Online Training Program Software Publisher
S.I.C.: 7372
N.A.I.C.S.: 511210
Media: 1-7-10-13-22
Personnel:
Chip Matthes *(Co-Founder)*
Barry Libert *(Chm)*
Alan Nugent *(CEO)*
Diana McKearney *(Gen Counsel & VP)*
Dan Bruns *(Sr VP-Advanced Tech)*
Randy J. Saari *(Sr VP-Customer Experience)*

NAMEMEDIA, INC.
230 3rd Ave
Waltham, MA 02451
Tel.: (781) 839-2800
Fax: (781) 839-2801
E-mail: inquiries@namemedia.com
Web Site: www.namemedia.com
Sales Range: $50-74.9 Million
Approx. Number Employees: 150
Business Description:
Domain Name Registration Services
S.I.C.: 2741; 5045
N.A.I.C.S.: 516110; 425110
Advertising Expenditures: $125,000
Media: 2-7-13
Personnel:
Kelly P. Conlin *(Chm & CEO)*
Jeffrey S. Bennett *(CEO)*
Brian D. Lucy *(CFO)*
Keith Davis *(VP-Engrg)*

NATIONAL BUSINESS FURNITURE INC
(Div. of National Business Furniture Inc.)
735 N Water St
Milwaukee, WI 53202
Tel.: (414) 276-8511
Fax: (414) 276-8371
Toll Free: (800) 343-4222
E-mail: info@officefurniture.com
Web Site: www.furnitureonline.com
Approx. Number Employees: 120
Year Founded: 1998
Business Description:
Online Retailer of Office Furniture
S.I.C.: 5712
N.A.I.C.S.: 442110
Media: 4-13
Personnel:
Steve Twining *(Brand Mgr)*
Brands & Products:
FURNITUREONLINE.COM

Key to Media (For complete agency information see *The Advertising Red Books-Agencies* edition):
1. Bus. Publs. 2. Cable T.V. 3. Catalogs & Directories. 4. Co-op Adv. 5. Consumer Mags. 6. D.M. to Bus. Estab.7. D.M. to Consumers
8. Daily Newsp. 9. Exhibits/Trade Shows 10. Foreign 11. Infomercial 12. Internet Adv.13. Multimedia 14. Network Radio
15. Network T.V. 16. Newsp. Distr. Mags. 17. Other 18. Outdoor (Posters, Transit) 19. Point of Purchase20. Premiums, Novelties
21. Product Samples 22. Special Events Mktg. 23. Spot Radio 24. Spot T.V. 25. Weekly Newsp. 26. Yellow Page Adv.

NAVISITE, INC.
(Sub. of Time Warner Cable Inc.)
400 Minute Man Rd
Andover, MA 01810
Tel.: (978) 682-8300
Fax: (978) 688-8100
E-mail: webinfo@navisite.com
Web Site: www.navisite.com
Approx. Rev.: $126,147,000
Approx. Number Employees: 579
Year Founded: 1996
Business Description:
Computer Applications & Internet Support & Management Services
S.I.C.: 7376; 7379
N.A.I.C.S.: 541513; 541519
Advertising Expenditures: $700,000
Media: 1-2-7-8-10-13
Personnel:
Andrew Ruhan *(Chm)*
R. Brooks Borcherding *(Pres & CEO)*
Jim Pluntze *(CFO)*
Denis Martin *(CTO & Exec VP)*
Mark Clayman *(Sr VP-Enterprise Sls)*
Sumeet Sabharwal *(Sr VP-Global Delivery)*
Roger Schwanhausser *(Sr VP-Svc Delivery)*
Dennis Sherwood *(Gen Mgr-Western Reg)*
Daniel J. Van Dixhorn *(Gen Mgr-Central Reg)*
Brands & Products:
ALABANZA
NAVISITE
RUN WITH US
Advertising Agencies:
Greenough Communications
9 Harcourt St
Boston, MA 02116
Tel.: (617) 275-6500
Fax: (617) 275-6501

Rain
4 Greenleaf Woods Ste 301
Portsmouth, NH 03801
Tel.: (603) 498-5864
Fax: (603) 430-0142

NERVE.COM, INC.
520 Broadway
New York, NY 10012-4436
Tel.: (212) 625-9914
Fax: (212) 625-8929
E-mail: info@nerve.com
Web Site: www.nerve.com
Approx. Number Employees: 20
Year Founded: 1997
Business Description:
Online Magazine
S.I.C.: 2721
N.A.I.C.S.: 511120
Media: 13
Personnel:
Sean Mills *(CEO)*
Brands & Products:
LOVE. SEX. CULTURE
NERVE

NET ACCESS CORPORATION
1719 Rte 10 E
Parsippany, NJ 07054
Tel.: (973) 590-5000
Fax: (973) 590-5080
E-mail: sales@nac.net
Web Site: www.nac.net
E-Mail For Key Personnel:
Sales Director: sales@nac.net
Approx. Sls.: $7,000,000
Approx. Number Employees: 40
Year Founded: 1995
Business Description:
Internet Services
S.I.C.: 7375
N.A.I.C.S.: 518111
Media: 2-8
Personnel:
Blake Ellman *(Co-Founder & Pres)*
Alex Rubenstein *(Owner)*
Kathy Lopez *(Coord-Mktg & Coord-Sls)*

NET-TEMPS, INC.
55 Middlesex St Unit 220
North Chelmsford, MA 01863-1570
Tel.: (978) 251-7272
Fax: (978) 251-7250
Toll Free: (800) 307-0062
E-mail: pr@net-temps.com
Web Site: www.net-temps.com
Approx. Number Employees: 40
Year Founded: 1995
Business Description:
Online Employment Service
S.I.C.: 7361
N.A.I.C.S.: 561310
Advertising Expenditures: $5,000,000
Media: 2-7-8-10-13
Personnel:
Gregory A. Booth *(Pres)*
Dorothy Gianotti *(Dir-HR)*
Brands & Products:
NET-TEMPS
WE WORK

NET2PHONE, INC.
(Sub. of IDT Corporation)
520 Broad St
Newark, NJ 07102
Tel.: (973) 438-3111
Fax: (973) 438-1829
Toll Free: (877) N2PHONE
E-mail: pr@net2phone.com
Web Site: web.net2phone.com
Sales Range: $75-99.9 Million
Approx. Number Employees: 273
Year Founded: 1995
Business Description:
Internet-Based Telecommunications Services
S.I.C.: 4813; 4812
N.A.I.C.S.: 517110; 517212; 517310
Advertising Expenditures: $1,800,000
Media: 6-10-13-25
Personnel:
Howard S. Jonas *(Chm)*
Liore Alroy *(CEO)*
David Lando *(COO)*
Brands & Products:
COMMUNICATION WITHOUT BORDERS
NET2PHONE
NET2PHONE COMMCENTER
NET2PHONE DIRECT
PENNYTALK

NET32, INC.
250 Towne Village Dr
Cary, NC 27513
Tel.: (919) 468-1177
Fax: (919) 468-1178
Toll Free: (800) 517-1997
E-mail: staff@net32.com
Web Site: www.net32.com
Approx. Number Employees: 6
Year Founded: 2001
Business Description:
Products & Services for the Dental Care Industry
S.I.C.: 5047
N.A.I.C.S.: 423450
Media: 7-10-13-22
Personnel:
Donna Cassidy *(Pres)*
Patrick Cassidy *(CEO)*

NETFIRMS, INC.
5160 Yonge St Ste 1800
Toronto, ON Canada
Tel.: (416) 661-2100
Fax: (416) 661-0700
Toll Free: (866) 317-4678
E-mail: info@netfirms.com
Web Site: www.netfirms.com
Approx. Number Employees: 30
Year Founded: 1998
Business Description:
Web Hosting for Small Businesses
S.I.C.: 7373; 7379
N.A.I.C.S.: 541512; 541519
Media: 13
Personnel:
Thomas Savundra *(Pres)*
Gary Przykelnk *(Mgr-Mktg)*
Brands & Products:
COMMERCE PRO
NETFIRMS
NETFIRMS ADVANTAGE
NETFIRMS BUSINESS
NETFIRMS PLUS
PICTURE PRO
YOUR WEBSITE BUILD IT TODAY

NETFLIX, INC.
100 Winchester Circle
Los Gatos, CA 95032
Tel.: (408) 540-3700
Fax: (408) 540-3737
Toll Free: (888) 638-3549
E-mail: publicrelations@netflix.com
Web Site: www.netflix.com
Approx. Rev.: $2,162,625,000
Approx. Number Employees: 2,180
Year Founded: 1997
Business Description:
Online DVD Rental Services
S.I.C.: 7841
N.A.I.C.S.: 532230
Advertising Expenditures: $212,400,000
Media: 3-6-8-10-13-15-16-21-23-24
Personnel:
Reed Hastings *(Founder, Chm & CEO)*
David Wells *(CFO)*
Leslie Kilgore *(CMO)*
Neil Hunt *(Chief Product Officer)*
Patty McCord *(Chief Talent Officer)*
Ted Sarandos *(Chief Content Officer)*
Andy Rendich *(CEO-Qwikster)*
Robert W. Dean, II *(Dir-Acctg)*
Jennifer Olesh *(Mgr-Content Mktg)*
Brands & Products:
FRIENDS
NETFLIX
Advertising Agency:
Goodby, Silverstein & Partners, Inc.
(Part of Omnicom Group, Inc.)
720 California St
San Francisco, CA 94108-2404
Tel.: (415) 392-0669
Fax: (415) 788-4303

NETLIBRARY, INC.
(Div. of Online Computer Library Center, Inc.)
4888 Pearl E Cir
Boulder, CO 80301
Tel.: (303) 544-0076
E-mail: info@netlibrary.com
Web Site: www.netlibrary.com
Approx. Number Employees: 50
Year Founded: 1998
Business Description:
Electronic Book Service
S.I.C.: 8231
N.A.I.C.S.: 519120
Media: 10-18

NETRATINGS, INC.
(Div. of VNU Media Measurement & Information Group)
770 Broadway
New York, NY 10003
Tel.: (212) 703-5900
Fax: (646) 654-7763
Web Site: www.nielsen-netratings.com
Approx. Rev.: $81,769,000
Approx. Number Employees: 397
Year Founded: 1997
Business Description:
Internet Media & Market Research Services
S.I.C.: 8732
N.A.I.C.S.: 541910
Advertising Expenditures: $400,000
Media: 1-2-13-22
Personnel:
Alan Shapiro *(Gen Counsel & Sr VP)*
Manish Bhatia *(Exec VP)*
Kenneth Cassar *(Chief Analyst & Sr Dir-Indus Solutions)*
Stephan Achstetter *(Dir-Client Svc)*
Guido Mazzoccola *(Dir-Client Svc)*
Cristina Papini *(Project Mgr-Sls)*
Brands & Products:
ADRELEVANCE
@PLAN
NETVIEW
WEBRF

NETSCAPE COMMUNICATIONS CORPORATION
(Sub. of AOL Inc.)
22000 AOL Way
Dulles, VA 20166
Tel.: (703) 265-1000
E-mail: info@netscape.com
Web Site: netscape.aol.com
Sales Range: $100-124.9 Million
Business Description:
Open Client & Server Software, Commercial Applications & Development Tools that Link People & Information over the Internet & Provide Transmission Control Protocol
S.I.C.: 7372
N.A.I.C.S.: 511210
Media: 2-5-6-8-9-13-15-19
Distr.: Natl.

NETSCOUT SYSTEMS, INC.
310 Littleton Rd
Westford, MA 01886-4105
Tel.: (978) 614-4000
Fax: (978) 614-4004
Toll Free: (800) 357-7666
E-mail: info@netscout.com
Web Site: www.netscout.com

Key to Media (For complete agency information see *The Advertising Red Books-Agencies* edition):
1. Bus. Publs. 2. Cable T.V. 3. Catalogs & Directories. 4. Co-op Adv. 5. Consumer Mags. 6. D.M. to Bus. Estab.7. D.M. to Consumers 8. Daily Newsp. 9. Exhibits/Trade Shows 10. Foreign 11. Infomercial 12. Internet Adv.13. Multimedia 14. Network Radio 15. Network T.V. 16. Newsp. Distr. Mags. 17. Other 18. Outdoor (Posters, Transit) 19. Point of Purchase20. Premiums, Novelties 21. Product Samples 22. Special Events Mktg. 23. Spot Radio 24. Spot T.V. 25. Weekly Newsp. 26. Yellow Page Adv.

Approx. Rev.: $290,540,000
Approx. Number Employees: 845
Year Founded: 1984
Business Description:
Integrated Network Performance Management Solutions for Enterprises & Service Providers
S.I.C.: 7373; 3577; 3669
N.A.I.C.S.: 541512; 334119; 334290
Advertising Expenditures: $175,000
Media: 1-2-7-10-11-13
Personnel:
Anil K. Singhal *(Founder, Chm, Pres & CEO)*
David P. Sommers *(CFO & Sr VP-Gen Ops)*
Michael Szabados *(COO)*
Ken Boyd *(CIO & Sr VP-Svcs)*
Jean Bua *(Chief Acctg Officer & VP-Fin)*
Jeff Levinson *(Gen Counsel & VP)*
John Downing *(Sr VP-Worldwide Sls Ops)*
Ashwani Singhal *(Sr VP-R&D)*
Victor Becker *(VP-HR)*
Steven ShalitaV *(VP-Mktg)*
June Nugent *(Dir-Corp Knowledge Resources)*
Catherine Taylor *(Dir-IR)*
Brands & Products:
NETSCOUT
NGENIUS
NGENIUS INFINISTREAM
NGENIUS PERFORMANCE MANAGER
NGENIUS PROBE
SNIFFER
Advertising Agency:
Davies Murphy Group
200 Wheeler Rd N Tower
Burlington, MA 01803
Tel.: (781) 418-2400
Fax: (781) 418-2480

NETSOL TECHNOLOGIES, INC.
23901 Calabasas Rd Ste 2072
Calabasas, CA 91302
Tel.: (818) 222-9195
E-mail: info@netsoltek.com
Web Site: www.netsoltek.com
Approx. Rev.: $36,779,897
Approx. Number Employees: 732
Business Description:
Software Solutions
S.I.C.: 7372; 7371
N.A.I.C.S.: 334611; 511210; 541511
Advertising Expenditures: $227,045
Media: 1-2-10
Personnel:
Salim Ullah Ghauri *(Chm, Pres & CEO)*
Naeem Ullah Ghauri *(Chm & CEO)*
Najeeb Ullah Ghauri *(Chm & CEO)*
Boo-Ali Siddiqui *(CFO)*
Patti L.W. McGlasson *(Gen Counsel & Sec)*
Malea Farsai *(Corp Counsel)*
Sajjad Kirmani *(Exec VP-IT & Ops)*
Brands & Products:
BESTSHORING DELIVERS BESTSOLUTION
HEALTHSTREAM
LEASEPAK
LEASESOFT
LEASESOFT ASSET
LEASESOFT EVOLVE
LEASESOFT INSURANCE PREMIUM
LEASESOFT.CAP
LEASESOFT.CMS
LEASESOFT.WFS
NETSOL
NETSOL FINANCIAL SUITE
SMARTOCI
Advertising Agency:
PondelWilkinson Inc.
1880 Century Park E Ste 350
Los Angeles, CA 90067
Tel.: (310) 279-5980
Fax: (310) 279-5988
Investor Relations

NETSUITE, INC.
2955 Campus Dr Ste 100
San Mateo, CA 94403-2511
Tel.: (650) 627-1000
Fax: (650) 627-1001
Toll Free: (800) 638-5334
E-mail: info@netsuite.com
Web Site: www.netsuite.com
Approx. Rev.: $193,149,000
Approx. Number Employees: 1,084
Year Founded: 1998
Business Description:
Enterprise Resource Planning & Customer Relationship Management Software & Services
S.I.C.: 7372; 7379; 7389
N.A.I.C.S.: 511210; 541519; 561499
Advertising Expenditures: $1,900,000
Media: 2-6-13-25
Personnel:
Evan M. Goldberg *(Founder, Chm & CTO)*
Dave Lipscomb *(Co-Founder & Sr VP-Vertical Markets)*
Zachary Nelson *(Pres & CEO)*
Ronald Gill *(CFO)*
James McGeever *(COO)*
Timothy Dilley *(Chief Customer Officer, Exec VP-Worldwide Svcs)*
Douglas P. Solomon *(Gen Counsel, Corp Dev Exec & Sec)*
Stephen C. Wolfe *(Sr VP-Worldwide Support)*
David Downing *(Sr VP-Mktg)*
Mei Li *(Sr VP-Corp Comm)*
Ed Marshall *(Sr VP-Product Strategy)*
James Ramsey *(Sr VP-Worldwide Sls & Distr)*
Andy Lloyd *(Gen Mgr-ECommerce Products)*
Brands & Products:
NETCOMMERCE
NETCRM
NETERP
NETFLEX
NETSUITE
NETSUITE CENTRAL
NETSUITE CRM+
NETSUITE ONEWORLD
NETSUITE SMALL BUSINESS
NS-BOS
ONE SYSTEM. NO LIMITS.
PREMIER PAYROLL SERVICE
SUITECONSULTING
SUITEFLEX
SUITESCRIPT
SUITESUCCESS
SUITESUPPORT
SUITETRAINING

NETWOLVES CORPORATION
4710 Eisenhower Blvd Ste E8
Tampa, FL 33634-7527
Tel.: (813) 579-3200
Fax: (813) 286-8744
E-mail: corp@netwolves.com
Web Site: www.netwolves.com
E-Mail For Key Personnel:
Sales Director: sales@netwolves.com
Sales Range: $10-24.9 Million
Approx. Number Employees: 54
Year Founded: 1998
Business Description:
Turnkey, Multifunctional, Internet Access Security Platforms, Applications & Services
S.I.C.: 7373; 4899; 7389
N.A.I.C.S.: 541512; 517910; 561499
Media: 2-4-10-13
Personnel:
Peter C. Castle *(Pres, COO, Sec & Treas)*
Scott Foote *(CEO)*
Ryan Kelly *(Pres-Channel Program)*
Leonard M. Luttinger *(Sr VP-Strategic Sls)*
Brands & Products:
ASURECALL
ASURENET
ASUREROUTE
FOXBOX
NETWOLVES
SHADOWNET
SRM2
WOLFPAC

NETWORK COMMUNICATIONS INC.
(Holding of Court Square Capital Partners, L.P.)
2305 Newpoint Pkwy
Lawrenceville, GA 30043
Tel.: (770) 962-7220
Web Site: www.nci.com
Approx. Sls.: $181,215,667
Approx. Number Employees: 821
Year Founded: 1978
Business Description:
Online Real Estate Magazine Publisher
S.I.C.: 2721; 2741; 6531
N.A.I.C.S.: 511120; 516110; 531390
Import Export
Advertising Expenditures: $1,700,000
Personnel:
Gerard Parker *(Pres & CFO)*
Fulton Collins *(Interim CEO)*
Scott Dixon *(Pres-Real Estate Area & Sr VP)*
Adam Japko *(Pres-Home Design Area & Sr VP)*
Susan Deese *(Gen Counsel & Sr VP)*
Ed Barnes *(Sr VP-Home design)*
Marcia Bollinger *(Sr VP-Multi-Family Area)*
Stuart Christian *(Sr VP-Production & Ops)*
Rebecca Chandler *(VP-Mktg)*
Stuart Richens *(VP-Interactive Media)*
Brands & Products:
APARTMENT BLUE BOOK
APARTMENT FINDER
AT HOME IN ARKANSAS
ATLANTA HOME IMPROVEMENT
ATLANTA HOMES & LIFESTYLES
BLACK'S GUIDE
COLORADO HOMES & LIFESTYLES
COMMERCIAL AND INVESTMENT PROPERTIES
CORPORATE CHOICES
ENCLAVE
KANSAS CITY HOMES & GARDENS
LIVINGCHOICES.COM
LOFTS, CONDOMINIUMS AND TOWNHOMES
THE LUXURY REAL ESTATE BOOK
MATURE LIVING CHOICES
MOUNTAIN LIVING
NEW HOME FINDER
THE REAL ESTATE BOOK
RELOCATING IN LAS VEGAS
RELOCATING IN ST. LOUIS
SEATTLE HOMES & LIFESTYLES
ST. LOUIS HOMES & LIFESTYLES
UNIQUE HOMES

NETWORK ENGINES INC.
25 Dan Rd
Canton, MA 02021-2817
Tel.: (781) 332-1000
Fax: (781) 770-2000
E-mail: ir@nei.com
Web Site: www.nei.com
Approx. Rev.: $221,620,000
Approx. Number Employees: 226
Year Founded: 1997
Business Description:
Engineering, Manufacturing, Logistics & Technical Services for Software Applications
S.I.C.: 3577; 7372; 7373
N.A.I.C.S.: 334119; 334611; 541512
Advertising Expenditures: $101,000
Media: 17
Personnel:
Gregory A. Shortell *(Pres & CEO)*
Douglas G. Bryant *(CFO)*
Charles N. Cone, III *(Sr VP-Sls & Mktg)*
Rusty Cone *(Sr VP-Sls & Mktg)*
Richard P. Graber *(Sr VP-Engrg & Ops)*
Lois Farkas *(VP-HR)*
Jim Herlihy *(VP-Fin & Admin)*
Tommy Morris *(Mgr-IAG Channel Sls-Western Reg)*
Brands & Products:
NEI

NEWEGG INC.
(d/b/a Newegg.com)
16839 E Gale Ave
City of Industry, CA 91745
Tel.: (626) 271-9700
Fax: (626) 271-9466
Toll Free: (800) 390-1119
E-mail: public_relations@newegg.com
Web Site: www.newegg.com
Sales Range: $10-24.9 Million
Approx. Number Employees: 1,000
Year Founded: 2001
Business Description:
On-Line Only Computer Electronics & Computing Products Distr
S.I.C.: 5961; 5734
N.A.I.C.S.: 454111; 443120; 454113
Advertising Expenditures: $21,700,000
Media: 2-5-6-8-10-13
Personnel:
Fred Chang *(Founder & Chm & Global CEO)*
Robert Bellack *(CFO)*
Shi-Chi Lee *(Pres-North America)*
Lee C. Cheng *(Gen Counsel , Corp Sec, VP-HR & Head-Office of the CEO)*
Bernard Luthi *(VP-Mktg, Mdsg, Web Mgmt & Customer Svc)*
Richard Quiroga *(VP-Fin)*

Key to Media (For complete agency information see *The Advertising Red Books-Agencies* edition):
1. Bus. Publs. 2. Cable T.V. 3. Catalogs & Directories. 4. Co-op Adv. 5. Consumer Mags. 6. D.M. to Bus. Estab.7. D.M. to Consumers
8. Daily Newsp. 9. Exhibits/Trade Shows 10. Foreign 11. Infomercial 12. Internet Adv.13. Multimedia 14. Network Radio
15. Network T.V. 16. Newsp. Distr. Mags. 17. Other 18. Outdoor (Posters, Transit) 19. Point of Purchase20. Premiums, Novelties
21. Product Samples 22. Special Events Mktg. 23. Spot Radio 24. Spot T.V. 25. Weekly Newsp. 26. Yellow Page Adv.

Newegg Inc. — (Continued)

Brands & Products:
EGGXPERT
NEWEGG
NEWEGG MALL
ONCE YOU KNOW, YOU NEWEGG

Advertising Agencies:
Goodness Mfg.
6922 Hollywood Blvd 12th Fl
Los Angeles, CA 90028
Tel.: (310) 845-3035
Fax: (310) 845-3470

KSL Media, Inc.
367 Park Ave S 4th Fl
New York, NY 10016
Tel.: (212) 352-5800
Fax: (212) 352-5935

NEWSMAX MEDIA, INC.

560 Vlg Blvd Ste 120
West Palm Beach, FL 33409
Tel.: (561) 686-1165
Fax: (561) 686-3350
Toll Free: (888) 766-7542
E-mail: comments@newsmax.com
Web Site: www.newsmax.com
E-Mail For Key Personnel:
Marketing Director: darlas@newsmax.com
Sales Director: nancyh@newsmax.com
Approx. Sls.: $11,000,000
Approx. Number Employees: 100
Year Founded: 1998
Business Description:
Online News & Information; Financial & Health Newsletters, Nationally Distributed Magazine
S.I.C.: 2741; 2721
N.A.I.C.S.: 511199; 511120
Advertising Expenditures: $4,000,000
Media: 2-4-7-8-13
Personnel:
Christopher Ruddy *(CEO)*
Darryle Burnham *(CFO)*
Brian Todd *(COO)*
Nancy Harrington *(VP-Sls & Mktg)*
Elizabeth Dole *(Dir-Production & Graphics)*
Brands & Products:
MONEYNEWS.COM
NEWSMAX MAGAZINE
NEWSMAX.COM

NEXAGE, INC.

400 Fifth Ave Ste 505
Waltham, MA 02451
Tel.: (781) 890-0071
Fax: (781) 890-0031
E-mail: marketing@nexage.com
Web Site: www.nexage.com
Approx. Number Employees: 9
Year Founded: 1999
Business Description:
Software Development
S.I.C.: 8748
N.A.I.C.S.: 541618
Advertising Expenditures: $200,000
Media: 13-27
Personnel:
Mike Baker *(Chm)*
Ernie Cormier *(Pres & CEO)*
Brands & Products:
ADMAX
ENVIVIO
NEXAGE
PHONECAST TV
WYSDOM INFOTECH

NEXCURA, INC.

(Sub. of US Oncology, Inc.)
10101 Woodloch Forest
The Woodlands, TX 77380
Tel.: (206) 270-0225
Fax: (206) 270-0229
Toll Free: (877) 422-3228
E-mail: sales@nexcura.com
Web Site: www.nexcura.com
Approx. Sls.: $1,000,000
Approx. Number Employees: 20
Year Founded: 1998
Business Description:
Clinical Data Collection Services
S.I.C.: 7372
N.A.I.C.S.: 511210
Media: 2-7-9-10-13-18-22
Personnel:
Peter A. Hoover *(CEO)*
Angela Belland *(Mgr-Client Svcs)*
Brands & Products:
HEART PROFILER
NEXCURA
NEXPROFILER

NEXTMONET, INC.

(Sub. of Mill Pond Holdings LLC)
250 Center Ct
Venice, FL 34285
Mailing Address:
PO Box 1723
Venice, FL 34284
Tel.: (941) 497-6020
Fax: (941) 497-6026
Toll Free: (888) 914-5050
E-mail: service@nextmonet.com
Web Site: www.nextmonet.com
Approx. Number Employees: 45
Year Founded: 1998
Business Description:
Limited Edition Fine Art Retailer
S.I.C.: 2741; 5999
N.A.I.C.S.: 511199; 453920
Advertising Expenditures: $500,000
Media: 4-8-10
Brands & Products:
NEXTMONET
NEXTMONET EDITIONS
NEXTMONET.COM

NHN USA, INC.

(Sub. of NHN Corporation)
3353 Michelson Dr Ste 250
Irvine, CA 92612
Mailing Address:
PO Box 57040
Irvine, CA 92619-7040
Tel.: (949) 863-1292
E-mail: help@nhnusainc.com
Web Site: www.nhnusainc.com
Year Founded: 2005
Business Description:
Interactive Online Entertainment Publisher
S.I.C.: 2741
N.A.I.C.S.: 516110
Advertising Agency:
Wonacott Communications, LLC
11835 W Olympic Blvd Ste 435
Los Angeles, CA 90064
Tel.: (310) 477-2871
— Jason Wonacott *(Acct Supvr)*

NOBLESTAR SYSTEMS CORP.

585 Grove St Ste 202
Herndon, VA 20170
Tel.: (571) 323-7800
Fax: (571) 323-7809
E-mail: info@noblestar.com
Web Site: www.noblestar.com
Approx. Number Employees: 300
Year Founded: 1987
Business Description:
E-Business Consulting & Wireless Solutions Services
S.I.C.: 7373
N.A.I.C.S.: 541512
Media: 2-4-7-8-10-13-18-26
Personnel:
Paul Opalack *(Chm)*
Brands & Products:
EXCEPTIONAL BY DESIGN
GEARS OF PROCESS
NOBLESTAR

NOVICA UNITED, INC.

11835 W Olympic Blvd Ste 750
Los Angeles, CA 90064-5001
Tel.: (310) 479-6685
Fax: (310) 479-7246
E-mail: service@novica.com
Web Site: www.novica.com
Approx. Number Employees: 50
Year Founded: 1998
Business Description:
Online Retailer of Art Merchandise
S.I.C.: 5999
N.A.I.C.S.: 453920
Media: 4-7-8-9-10-13-16-23-25
Personnel:
Robert Milk *(CEO)*
Brands & Products:
KEEPERS OF THE ARTS
NOVICA
TREASURES OF THE WORLD

NSTEIN TECHNOLOGIES INC.

(Sub. of Open Text Corporation)
75 Queen Street Suite 4400
Montreal, QC H3C 2N6, Canada
Tel.: (514) 908-5406
Fax: (514) 908-5407
Toll Free: (877) 678-3461
E-mail: info@nstein.com
Web Site: www.nstein.com
Approx. Rev.: $20,518,444
Approx. Number Employees: 145
Year Founded: 2000
Business Description:
Web Content Management, Digital Asset Management, Text Mining Engine & Picture Management Desk Products
S.I.C.: 7371; 2759; 7389; 8748
N.A.I.C.S.: 541511; 323115; 541618; 561439; 561499
Media: 10
Personnel:
Frederic Brabant *(VP-Engrg)*

NUANCE DOCUMENT IMAGING SOLUTIONS

(Unit of Nuance Communications, Inc.)
1 Oracle Dr
Nashua, NH 03062
Tel.: (603) 324-8500
Web Site: www.ecopy.com
E-Mail For Key Personnel:
Marketing Director: marketing@ecopy.com
Sales Director: sales@ecopy.com
Sales Range: $10-24.9 Million
Approx. Number Employees: 250
Year Founded: 1992
Business Description:
Online Document Copying & Transfer Services
S.I.C.: 7371; 7372
N.A.I.C.S.: 541511; 511210
Export
Media: 2-7-11-13
Personnel:
Tim James *(VP & Gen Mgr)*
Michael Conley *(VP-Engrg)*
Vickie Malis *(VP-Mktg)*
Mark Roy *(VP-Customer Support Svcs)*
Peter Charnock *(Gen Mgr-Opers-Asia Pacific)*
Ellen Bzomowski *(Dir-Intl Channel Ops)*
Brands & Products:
ECOPY
MAKING PAPER WORK
PAPERWORKS
SHARESCAN

NUTRIO.COM, INC.

2225 N Commerce Pkwy Ste 7
Weston, FL 33326
Tel.: (954) 385-4700
Fax: (954) 385-4701
E-mail: contact@nutrio.com
Web Site: www.nutrio.com
Approx. Number Employees: 8
Year Founded: 1999
Business Description:
Healthy Living, Nutrition & Fitness Websites Licenser & Services
S.I.C.: 8049
N.A.I.C.S.: 621399
Media: 13
Personnel:
Kim Evenson *(Sr VP-Mktg)*
Brands & Products:
THE HEALTHY WAY TO LIVE
NUTRIO.COM

OASYS MOBILE, INC.

8000 Regency Pkwy
Cary, NC 27518
Tel.: (919) 807-5600
Fax: (919) 807-5601
E-mail: info@oasysmobile.com
Web Site: www.oasysmobile.com
Approx. Rev.: $8,687,867
Approx. Number Employees: 38
Business Description:
Mobile Media Services
S.I.C.: 7371; 4812
N.A.I.C.S.: 541511; 517212
Advertising Expenditures: $2,230,944
Media: 6-13
Personnel:
Doug Dyer *(CEO)*
Tracy Livers *(VP-Publ)*
Advertising Agency:
Schwartz Communications, Inc.
230 3rd Ave
Waltham, MA 02451
Tel.: (781) 684-0770
Fax: (781) 684-6500

OLM, LLC

4 Trefoil Dr
Trumbull, CT 06611-1330
Tel.: (203) 445-7700
Fax: (203) 445-8154
Toll Free: (877) 741-6813

Key to Media (For complete agency information see *The Advertising Red Books-Agencies* edition):
1. Bus. Publs. 2. Cable T.V. 3. Catalogs & Directories. 4. Co-op Adv. 5. Consumer Mags. 6. D.M. to Bus. Estab.7. D.M. to Consumers
8. Daily Newsp. 9. Exhibits/Trade Shows 10. Foreign 11. Infomercial 12. Internet Adv.13. Multimedia 14. Network Radio
15. Network T.V. 16. Newsp. Distr. Mags. 17. Other 18. Outdoor (Posters, Transit) 19. Point of Purchase20. Premiums, Novelties
21. Product Samples 22. Special Events Mktg. 23. Spot Radio 24. Spot T.V. 25. Weekly Newsp. 26. Yellow Page Adv.

Web Site: www.olm.net
Approx. Number Employees: 100
Year Founded: 1996
Business Description:
Web Hosting & Custom Internet Software Services
S.I.C.: 7375
N.A.I.C.S.: 518111
Media: 6-13
Personnel:
George D. DeVack *(Founder & Pres)*

OMNICOMM SYSTEMS, INC.
2101 W Commercial Blvd Ste 4000
Fort Lauderdale, FL 33309
Tel.: (954) 473-1254
Fax: (954) 473-1256
Toll Free: (877) 468-6332
E-mail: info@omnicomm.com
Web Site: www.omnicomm.com
Approx. Rev.: $12,427,511
Approx. Number Employees: 84
Year Founded: 1996
Business Description:
Web-Based Electronic Data Capture & eClinical Software & Services
S.I.C.: 7372; 2741
N.A.I.C.S.: 511210; 516110
Advertising Expenditures: $242,168
Personnel:
Randall G. Smith *(Chm & CTO)*
Cornelis F. Wit *(Pres & CEO)*
Stephen E. Johnson *(Pres & COO)*
Ronald T. Linares *(CFO)*
Kenneth A. Light *(Exec VP-Ops)*
Beverly Hudson *(Sr VP-Bus Dev)*
Brands & Products:
ECLINICAL
TRIALMASTER
TRIALONE

OMNIS NETWORK, LLC
3655 Torrance Blvd Ste 230
Torrance, CA 90503
Tel.: (310) 316-9600
Fax: (310) 347-4075
Toll Free: (877) 393-HOST
E-mail: info@omnis.com
Web Site: www.omnis.com
Approx. Number Employees: 15
Year Founded: 1999
Business Description:
Internet Hosting & Domain Name Registration Services
S.I.C.: 7375
N.A.I.C.S.: 518111
Media: 13

OMNITURE INC.
(Sub. of Adobe Systems Incorporated)
550 E Timpanogos Cir
Orem, UT 84097-6212
Tel.: (801) 722-7000
Fax: (801) 722-7001
Toll Free: (877) 722-7088
E-mail: ir@omniture.com
Web Site: www.omniture.com
Approx. Rev.: $295,613,000
Approx. Number Employees: 1,189
Year Founded: 1996
Business Description:
Online Business Optimization Software
S.I.C.: 7371; 7372; 7374
N.A.I.C.S.: 541511; 511210; 518210
Advertising Expenditures: $510,000
Media: 2-7-13-18-22
Personnel:
Gail M. Ennis *(CMO)*
Lina C. George *(Sr VP-HR)*
Christopher Harrington *(VP & Gen Mgr-Sls & Svcs)*
Ron Belanger *(VP-Worldwide Agency Sls)*
Melanie Branon *(VP-Corp Mktg)*
Michael S. Herring *(VP-Fin)*
Patrick Kelliher *(VP-Fin)*
Jeff McCall *(VP-Customer Relationship Mgmt)*
Neil Morgan *(VP-Mktg & Channels)*
Chris Duskin *(Sr Dir-Product Mktg)*
Stefan Berger *(Country Mgr-Germany, Austria & Switzerland)*
Brands & Products:
DATAWAREHOUSE
DISCOVER
GENESIS
METRICS-DRIVEN MERCHANDISING
OFFERMATICA
OMNITURE
OMNITURE CLOSED LOOP MARKETING
OMNITURE DISCOVER ONPREMISE
OMNITURE MERCHANDISING
OMNITURE ONLINE MARKETING SUITE
OMNITURE PUBLISH
OMNITURE RECOMMENDATIONS
OMNITURE SURVEY
SALESFORCE
SEARCHCENTER
SITECATALYST
SITESEARCH
TEST&TARGET

OMNITURE INC.
(Branch of Omniture Inc.)
10182 Telesis Ct 4th Fl
San Diego, CA 92121
Tel.: (858) 546-0040
Fax: (858) 754-2609
Web Site: www.omniture.com
Sales Range: $75-99.9 Million
Approx. Number Employees: 278
Year Founded: 1996
Business Description:
Web Analytics Services
S.I.C.: 7372
N.A.I.C.S.: 511210
Advertising Expenditures: $627,000
Media: 13-17
Personnel:
Avonlie Wylson *(Sr Dir-Acct Mgmt)*
Brands & Products:
ACTIVE MARKETING SUITE
HITBOX
THE PULSE OF THE INTERNET
STATMARKET
TRAFFIC
WEBSIDESTORY
YEP

ON2 TECHNOLOGIES, INC.
(Sub. of Google Inc.)
(d/b/a Google On2)
3 Corporate Dr Ste 100
Clifton Park, NY 12065
Tel.: (518) 348-0099
Fax: (518) 348-2098
E-mail: sales@on2.com
Web Site: www.on2.com
E-Mail For Key Personnel:
Sales Director: sales@on2.com
Approx. Rev.: $16,268,000
Approx. Number Employees: 106
Year Founded: 1992
Business Description:
Video Compression Software & Solutions
S.I.C.: 7371; 7372
N.A.I.C.S.: 511210; 334611; 541511
Advertising Expenditures: $119,000
Media: 10-13

ON24, INC.
201 3rd St 3rd Fl
San Francisco, CA 94103-2046
Tel.: (415) 369-8000
Fax: (415) 369-8388
E-mail: info@on24.com
Web Site: www.on24.com
Approx. Number Employees: 20
Year Founded: 1998
Business Description:
Online Financial News & Investment Services
S.I.C.: 2741
N.A.I.C.S.: 516110
Media: 2-10-13
Personnel:
Sharat Sharan *(Pres & CEO)*
Andrew Hamer *(CFO)*
Ed van Petten *(CIO)*
Denise Persson *(CMO & VP-Mktg & Bus Dev)*
Jayesh Sahasi *(CTO & VP-Engrg)*
Michael Nelson *(VP-Sls)*
Brands & Products:
ENGAGING COMMUNICATION
ON24

ON4 COMMUNICATIONS, INC.
16413 91st Street C 100
Scottsdale, AZ 85260
Tel.: (480) 619-5510
Web Site:
www.on4communications.com
Approx. Sls.: $204,120
Business Description:
Digital Music & Other Content Services
S.I.C.: 2741
N.A.I.C.S.: 516110
Advertising Expenditures: $10,648
Media: 13
Personnel:
Cameron Robb *(Pres & CEO)*
Gordon C. Jessop *(Pres & COO)*

ONE WORLD NETWORKS INTEGRATED TECHNOLOGIES, INC.
(d/b/a OneWorldLive)
12424 Wilshire Blvd Ste 1400
Los Angeles, CA 90025-1057
Tel.: (310) 447-6300
Fax: (310) 447-6333
E-mail: info@oneworldlive.com
Web Site: www.oneworldlive.com
Approx. Number Employees: 25
Year Founded: 1999
Business Description:
Online Products & Services
S.I.C.: 5961; 8742
N.A.I.C.S.: 454111; 541611
Media: 5-13-19-22
Personnel:
Liz Edlich *(Co-Founder, Chm & CEO)*
Rachel Edlich *(Co-Founder & Pres)*
Agnes Yang *(CFO)*
Jacqueline Ochsner *(VP-CRM Mktg)*

ONESOURCE INFORMATION SERVICES, INC.
(Sub. of Infogroup Inc.)
300 Baker Ave
Concord, MA 01742-2131
Tel.: (978) 318-4300
Fax: (978) 318-4690
Toll Free: (800) 554-5501
E-mail: sales@onesource.com
Web Site: www.onesource.com
E-Mail For Key Personnel:
Sales Director: sales@onesource.com
Sales Range: $50-74.9 Million
Approx. Number Employees: 100
Year Founded: 1993
Business Description:
Online Business Database Publisher & Information Services
S.I.C.: 2741; 7389
N.A.I.C.S.: 511140; 519130; 519190
Advertising Expenditures: $48,000
Media: 2-7-13-26
Personnel:
Philip J. Garlick *(Pres)*
Colleen Honan *(Sr VP-Sls & Svcs-Global)*
Brands & Products:
BUSINESS BROWSER
CATALYST
ONESOURCE EXPRESS
SYNERGY SOLUTIONS

ONVIA, INC.
509 Olive Way Ste 400
Seattle, WA 98101
Tel.: (206) 282-5170
Fax: (206) 373-8961
E-mail: corporateinfo@onvia.com
Web Site: www.onvia.com
Approx. Rev.: $26,991,881
Approx. Number Employees: 139
Year Founded: 1996
Business Description:
Online Research & Business Intelligence About Government & Industry Transactions
S.I.C.: 4311; 7371; 7373; 9199
N.A.I.C.S.: 491110; 541511; 541512; 921190
Media: 13
Personnel:
David Van Skilling *(Chm)*
Henry G. Riner *(Pres & CEO)*
Cameron Way *(CFO)*
Soyoung Kwon *(Gen Counsel, Corp Sec & VP-HR)*
Irvine Alpert *(Exec VP)*
Brands & Products:
DOMINION
ONVIA
ONVIA.COM
QUOTEWIRE

OPENAIR, INC.
(Sub. of NetSuite, Inc.)
211 Congress St 8th Fl
Boston, MA 02110
Tel.: (617) 351-0230
Fax: (617) 904-1617
Toll Free: (888) 367-1715
E-mail: sales@openair.com
Web Site: www.openair.com
Sales Range: $10-24.9 Million
Approx. Number Employees: 50
Year Founded: 1997
Business Description:
Professional Web Based Services
S.I.C.: 8732; 7372
N.A.I.C.S.: 541910; 511210
Internet Adv.: 100%

Key to Media (For complete agency information see *The Advertising Red Books-Agencies* edition):
1. Bus. Publs. 2. Cable T.V. 3. Catalogs & Directories. 4. Co-op Adv. 5. Consumer Mags. 6. D.M. to Bus. Estab.7. D.M. to Consumers
8. Daily Newsp. 9. Exhibits/Trade Shows 10. Foreign 11. Infomercial 12. Internet Adv.13. Multimedia 14. Network Radio
15. Network T.V. 16. Newsp. Distr. Mags. 17. Other 18. Outdoor (Posters, Transit) 19. Point of Purchase20. Premiums, Novelties
21. Product Samples 22. Special Events Mktg. 23. Spot Radio 24. Spot T.V. 25. Weekly Newsp. 26. Yellow Page Adv.

OpenAir, Inc. — (Continued)

Personnel:
Jeff Honeycomb *(Sr VP-Worldwide Distr)*
Kelly Paszamant *(Dir-Mktg)*
Michael Monahan *(Dir-Art)*

Brands & Products:
EZ INVOICE
OPENAIR.COM

OPENX TECHNOLOGIES, INC.

(Owned by OpenX Limited)
20 E Del Mar Blvd
Pasadena, CA 91105
Tel.: (626) 466-1142
E-mail: media@openx.org
Web Site: www.openx.com
Business Description:
Digital Advertising Technology Services
N.A.I.C.S.: 541890
Media: 27
Personnel:
Tim Cadogan *(CEO)*
Rick Gombos *(CFO)*
Jason Fairchild *(Chief Revenue Officer)*
Al Duncan *(Head-Comm)*
Paul Martecchini *(Head-Mktg)*

OPTUMHEALTH ALLIES

PO Box 10340
Glendale, CA 91209
Fax: (818) 484-9826
Toll Free: (800) 377-0263
E-mail: info@optumhealthallies.com
Web Site: www.optumhealthallies.com
Approx. Number Employees: 100
Year Founded: 1999
Business Description:
Online Marketplace for Medical Services
S.I.C.: 8748; 6411
N.A.I.C.S.: 541618; 524210
Media: 2-10-13
Personnel:
Andy Slavitt *(CEO)*

ORANGE BUSINESS SERVICES

(Sub. of Orange Business Services)
13775 Mclearen Rd
Herndon, VA 20171
Tel.: (703) 471-2300
Fax: (703) 471-2515
Toll Free: (800) 568-7808
Web Site: www.mnc.orange-business.com
Approx. Number Employees: 820
Year Founded: 1996
Business Description:
Global Data, Voice & Video Business Services & Carrier Services
S.I.C.: 4899
N.A.I.C.S.: 517910
Media: 2-7
Personnel:
Barbara Dalibard *(Pres)*
Carlos Sartorius *(COO)*
Vincent Kelly *(CIO)*
Howard Ford *(Pres-Sls & Mktg)*
Bala Mahadevan *(CEO-India Ops)*
Michael Berg *(Gen Counsel)*
Stephane Rougeot *(Exec VP-Sls-Mktg)*
Diana Einterz Leonard *(Sr VP-America)*
Yee-May Leong *(Sr VP-Asia Pacific)*
Michael Burrell *(Sr Mgr-Solutions)*
Elizabeth Mayeri *(Mgr-Media Rels & Corp Comm)*

OVERSTOCK.COM, INC.

6350 S 3000 E
Salt Lake City, UT 84121-6937
Tel.: (801) 947-3100
Fax: (801) 453-7798
Toll Free: (800) 989-0135
E-mail: info@overstock.com
Web Site: www.overstock.com
Approx. Rev.: $1,089,873,000
Approx. Number Employees: 1,500
Business Description:
Surplus & Close-Out Merchandise Wholesaler
S.I.C.: 5961
N.A.I.C.S.: 454111; 454113
Advertising Expenditures: $48,900,000
Media: 3-13-14-15
Personnel:
Patrick M. Byrne *(Chm & CEO)*
Jonathan E. Johnson III.*(Pres)*
Geoffrey R. Atkinson *(Sr VP-CRM, Buying & Demand Mgmt)*
Steve Chesnut *(Sr VP-Fin)*
Samuel J. Peterson *(Sr VP-Tech)*
Stormy D. Simon *(Sr VP)*
Stephen P. Tryon *(Sr VP-Logistics)*
Ralph Mondeaux *(VP-Website Mktg)*
Roger Johnson *(Coord-Pub Rels)*

Brands & Products:
CLOVE LOVE
HANAUMA SURF CO
LAURA CREEK
MASHIDA
OVERSTOCK
OVERSTOCK.COM
YOUR ONLINE OUTLET

Advertising Agency:
Ocean Media Inc.
2100 Main St
Huntington Beach, CA 92648
Tel.: (714) 969-5244
Fax: (714) 969-6589

OVID TECHNOLOGIES, INC.

(Sub. of Wolters Kluwer Health & Pharma Solutions)
333 7th Ave 20th Fl
New York, NY 10001-5004
Tel.: (646) 674-6300
Fax: (646) 674-6301
Toll Free: (800) 343-0064
E-mail: sales@ovid.com
Web Site: www.ovid.com
E-Mail For Key Personnel:
Sales Director: sales@ovid.com
Approx. Number Employees: 75
Year Founded: 1988
Business Description:
Information Retrieval Services & Knowledge Management Solutions
S.I.C.: 7375
N.A.I.C.S.: 518111
Import Export
Media: 2-4-7-10-11-13-16-18-22-26
Personnel:
Karen Abramsom *(Pres & CEO)*
Carl Gustafson *(COO)*

Brands & Products:
MEDLINE
OVID
SILVERPLATTER

OWENS ONLINE, INC.

6501 N Himes Ave Ste 104
Tampa, FL 33614-4045
Tel.: (813) 877-2008
Fax: (813) 877-1826
Toll Free: (800) 745-4656
E-mail: email@owens.com
Web Site: www.owens.com
Approx. Number Employees: 50
Year Founded: 1986
Business Description:
Online Credit Reporting
S.I.C.: 7323
N.A.I.C.S.: 561450
Media: 7-13-17
Personnel:
Mark Owens *(Pres)*

Brands & Products:
OWENS ONLINE
TRUS BUT VERIFY

PANDORA MEDIA INC.

2101 Webster St Ste 1650
Oakland, CA 94612
Tel.: (510) 451-4100
Fax: (510) 451-4286
E-mail: pandora-info@pandora.com
Web Site: www.pandora.com
Approx. Rev.: $55,189,000
Approx. Number Employees: 295
Year Founded: 2000
Business Description:
Internet Radio
S.I.C.: 2741; 4832
N.A.I.C.S.: 516110; 515112
Advertising Expenditures: $6,300,000
Personnel:
Joseph Kennedy *(Pres & CEO)*
Steve Cakebread *(CFO)*
Etienne Handman *(COO)*
Simon Fleming-Wood *(CMO)*
Thomas Conrad *(CTO & Exec VP-Product)*
Tim Westergren *(Chief Strategy Officer)*
John Trimble *(Chief Revenue Officer)*
Delida Costin *(Gen Counsel & Sec)*
Jessica Steel *(Exec VP-Corp & Bus Dev)*
Steven Kritzman *(Sr VP-Adv Sls)*
Peter Ekman *(VP-HR)*
Kim Luegers *(Dir-Mobile)*

PANTHEON SOFTWARE, INC.

2020 N 14th St 7th Fl
Arlington, VA 22201-1706
Tel.: (703) 387-4000
Fax: (703) 387-4001
Toll Free: (888) 387-8652
E-mail: info@pantheonsoftware.com
Web Site: www.pantheonsoftware.com
Approx. Sls.: $1,200,000
Approx. Number Employees: 15
Year Founded: 1994
Business Description:
Internet & Computer Services Including Website Development & Design, Database Development, Site Hosting, Marketing Consulting Services & ASP Application Development
S.I.C.: 7371; 8748
N.A.I.C.S.: 541511; 541690
Media: 7-10-13
Personnel:
Oron Strauss *(Chm)*
Mark Tobias *(Pres)*

PARAGO, INC.

700 St Hwy 121 Bypass Ste 200
Lewisville, TX 75067
Tel.: (972) 538-3900
Fax: (972) 745-2407
Web Site: www.parago.com
E-Mail For Key Personnel:
Marketing Director: mktg@parago.com
Sales Director: sales@parago.com
Approx. Number Employees: 200
Year Founded: 1999
Business Description:
Promotional Marketing Technology
S.I.C.: 7375
N.A.I.C.S.: 518111
Media: 2-7-8-13
Personnel:
Juli C. Spottiswood *(Pres & CEO)*
Glen Holbert *(Exec VP-Sls)*
Michael Larson *(Exec VP-Ops)*
Michael Reynolds *(Exec VP-Mktg Dev & Strategy)*

Brands & Products:
PARAGO

PARTMINER, INC.

10 Dubont Court
Farmingdale, NY 11735
Tel.: (631) 501-2800
Fax: (631) 501-2830
Toll Free: (800) 969-2000
E-mail: nyc@partminer.com
Web Site: www.partminer.com
Approx. Number Employees: 250
Year Founded: 1993
Business Description:
Full Service Online Automated Spot & Excess Market-Maker for Electronic Components
S.I.C.: 5065; 5063
N.A.I.C.S.: 423690; 423610
Media: 4-7-13
Personnel:
L. Christopher Meyer *(Chm)*
Greg Nash *(CFO)*
Jeff Greenblatt *(Gen Counsel, Sec & VP)*

Brands & Products:
IMPART
INTERACTIVE INTELLIGENCE FOR ELECTRONIC COMPONENTS
MARKETPULSE
PARTMINER
PARTMINER DIRECT
PARTMINER INFORMATION SERVICES
POWERBUYER

PASSKEY INTERNATIONAL, INC.

221 Crescent St
Waltham, MA 02453
Tel.: (781) 373-4100
Fax: (781) 547-5413
Toll Free: (866) 649-1539 (Sales & Marketing)
E-mail: info@passkey.com
Web Site: www.passkey.com
Approx. Number Employees: 50
Year Founded: 1996
Business Description:
Web-based Solutions & Services for Hotel Reservations Management & Distribution
S.I.C.: 4729; 2741
N.A.I.C.S.: 561599; 516110
Media: 10-13

Key to Media (For complete agency information see *The Advertising Red Books-Agencies* edition):
1. Bus. Publs. 2. Cable T.V. 3. Catalogs & Directories. 4. Co-op Adv. 5. Consumer Mags. 6. D.M. to Bus. Estab.7. D.M. to Consumers
8. Daily Newsp. 9. Exhibits/Trade Shows 10. Foreign 11. Infomercial 12. Internet Adv.13. Multimedia 14. Network Radio
15. Network T.V. 16. Newsp. Distr. Mags. 17. Other 18. Outdoor (Posters, Transit) 19. Point of Purchase20. Premiums, Novelties
21. Product Samples 22. Special Events Mktg. 23. Spot Radio 24. Spot T.V. 25. Weekly Newsp. 26. Yellow Page Adv.

Personnel:
Greg Pesik *(Pres & CEO)*
Steven L. Shapiro *(CFO & Sr VP-Ops)*
Sam Fahmy *(Sr VP-Products & Mktg)*
Paul Rantilla *(Sr VP-Global Sls)*

Brands & Products:
CITYWIDE
GROUPLINK
HOTELDIRECT
PASSKEY
PASSKEY-ENABLED
REGLINK

PAYPAL INC.

(Sub. of eBay Inc.)
2211 N First St
San Jose, CA 95131
Tel.: (408) 376-7400
E-mail: info@paypal.com
Web Site: www.paypal.com
Sales Range: $150-199.9 Million
Approx. Number Employees: 618
Business Description:
Internet Payment Services
S.I.C.: 7374; 6099
N.A.I.C.S.: 518210; 522320
Personnel:
Scott Thompson *(Pres)*
Patrick Dupuis *(CFO)*
Robert E. Garrison *(CIO)*
Barry Herstein *(CMO & Gen Mgr-North America)*
John C. Muller *(Gen Counsel & VP-Legal)*
Rupert Keeley *(Sr VP-Asia Pacific Reg)*

Advertising Agencies:
Access Communications, LLC
101 Howard St 2nd Fl
San Francisco, CA 94105
Tel.: (415) 904-7070
Fax: (415) 904-7055

Carat International
Parker Tower 43-49 Parker St
London, WC2B 5PS, United Kingdom
Tel.: (44) 207 430 6000
Fax: (44) 207 430 6299
Media Planning & Buying

Krow Communications
65 Clerkenwell Rd
London, EC1R 5BL, United Kingdom
Tel.: (44) 20 7025 0000
Fax: (44) 20 7025 0001
Creative

PCQUOTE.COM, INC.

(Sub. of Money.net, Inc.)
155 Spring St 3rd Fl
New York, NY 10012
Tel.: (888) 860-4800
Fax: (212) 334-4464
Toll Free: (888) PCQUOTE
E-mail: support@pcquote.com
Web Site: www.pcquote.com
E-Mail For Key Personnel:
Sales Director: MKronenberger@pcquote.com
Approx. Number Employees: 10
Business Description:
Real-Time Securities Quotations, News & Investment Tools Via the Internet
S.I.C.: 7389
N.A.I.C.S.: 561499
Media: 13

Brands & Products:
LEVEL II VIEWER
MARKETSCREEN
MARKETSMART
NEWSSTREAM
OPENBOOK
ORBIT
PC QUOTE SCREAMER
SMARTCHARTS
SNAPQUOTES
TOTALVIEW

PEOPLEPC, INC.

(Sub. of EarthLink, Inc.)
1375 Peachtree St
Atlanta, GA 30309
Tel.: (404) 815-0770
Toll Free: (866) PPCMBRS
E-mail: info@peoplepc.com
Web Site: www.peoplepc.com
Approx. Rev.: $173,978,000
Approx. Number Employees: 98
Year Founded: 1999
Business Description:
Internet Services
S.I.C.: 7375
N.A.I.C.S.: 518111
Advertising Expenditures: $1,000,000
Media: 8-13

Brands & Products:
A BETTER WAY TO INTERNET

Advertising Agency:
Direct Partners
4755 Alla Rd
Marina Del Rey, CA 90292-6311
Tel.: (310) 482-4200
Fax: (310) 482-4201

PERFICIENT, INC.

520 Maryville Ctr Dr
Saint Louis, MO 63141
Tel.: (314) 529-3600
E-mail: pr@perficient.com
Web Site: www.perficient.com
Approx. Rev.: $214,952,000
Approx. Number Employees: 1,088
Year Founded: 1997
Business Description:
Information Technology Consulting Services
S.I.C.: 7373; 7371; 7379; 8748
N.A.I.C.S.: 541512; 541511; 541519; 541690
Media: 2-13
Personnel:
Jeffrey S. Davis *(Pres & CEO)*
Paul E. Martin *(CFO)*
Kathy Henely *(COO)*
Richard T. Kalbfleish *(VP-Fin/Admin & Controller)*
John Griffin *(Gen Mgr-Great Lakes)*
David Hastoglis *(Gen Mgr-Healthcare)*
Hari Madamalla *(Gen Mgr-IBM BPMS)*
Jeff Martini *(Gen Mgr)*
Thomas Pash *(Reg Gen Mgr)*
Tim Robinson *(Gen Mgr-Oracle)*
Jackie Thorn *(Gen Mgr-Client Assurance)*
Bill Davis *(Dir-Mktg & IR)*

Brands & Products:
PERFICIENT

PERSONAL CREATIONS INC.

(Sub. of Creative Catalogs Corporation)
19 W 661 101st St
Lemont, IL 60439
Tel.: (630) 783-2400
Fax: (630) 783-6400
Web Site: www.personalcreations.com
Sales Range: $10-24.9 Million
Approx. Number Employees: 150
Business Description:
Mail Order Catalog & E-Commerce Services
S.I.C.: 5961
N.A.I.C.S.: 454111; 454113
Media: 4-8-13
Personnel:
John Semmelhack *(Pres)*

PFSWEB, INC.

500 N Central Expy 5th Flr
Plano, TX 75074-6772
Tel.: (972) 881-2900
Fax: (972) 423-8616
Toll Free: (888) 330-5504
E-mail: investor@pfsweb.com
Web Site: www.pfsweb.com
Approx. Rev.: $274,516,000
Approx. Number Employees: 1,100
Business Description:
E-Commerce & Logistics Solutions Company
S.I.C.: 4311; 7373; 7374; 7379; 7389
N.A.I.C.S.: 491110; 518210; 541512; 541519; 541990; 561422
Advertising Expenditures: $900,000
Media: 7-13
Personnel:
Mark C. Layton *(Chm & CEO)*
Michael C. Willoughby *(Pres & Sr Partner)*
Cynthia Almond *(Partner & Exec VP-Client Svcs)*
Dave Reese *(Partner, Sr VP-Solutions & Intl Dev)*
Gib Dawson *(Partner, VP & Controller)*
Mark Fuentes *(Partner & VP-IT)*
Lawrence Lubrano *(Partner & VP-Client Svcs)*
Bruce Mcclung *(Partner & VP-Sls)*
Scott Talley *(Partner & VP-Worldwide Distr)*
Thomas J. Madden *(CFO, Chief Acctg Officer & Sr Partner)*
Steven S. Graham *(Chief Solutions Officer & Sr Partner)*

Brands & Products:
ENTENTE SUITE
PFS WEB
PFSWEB'S END2END ECOMMERCE

Advertising Agency:
KCSA Strategic Communications (Kanan, Corbin, Schupak & Aronow, Inc.)
880 3rd Ave 6th Fl
New York, NY 10022
Tel.: (212) 682-6300
Fax: (212) 697-0910

PLANETOUT, INC.

(Sub. of Here Media Inc.)
Folsom St 1069
San Francisco, CA 94107-4226
Mailing Address:
PO Box 500
San Francisco, CA 94104-0500
Tel.: (415) 834-6500
Fax: (415) 834-6502
Web Site: www.planetout.com
Approx. Rev.: $19,820,000
Approx. Number Employees: 95
Year Founded: 1995
Business Description:
Online Information & Publications for Lesbian, Gay, Bisexual & Transgender Individuals
S.I.C.: 7389
N.A.I.C.S.: 519190
Advertising Expenditures: $2,363,000
Media: 8-13

Brands & Products:
BUYGAY.COM
GAY.COM
HIVPLUSMAG.COM
KLEPTOMANIAC.COM
OUTTRAVELER.COM
PLANETOUT
PLANETOUT.COM

PLANPRESCRIBER, INC.

(Sub. of eHealth, Inc.)
8 Clock Tower Pl Ste 400
Maynard, MA 01754
Tel.: (978) 450-4200
Fax: (978) 450-0212
E-mail: info@experionsystems.com
Web Site: www.planprescriber.com
Sales Range: $1-9.9 Million
Approx. Number Employees: 20
Year Founded: 1999
Business Description:
Financial & Insurance Product Software
S.I.C.: 7371
N.A.I.C.S.: 541511
Media: 2-10-13
Personnel:
Ross Blair *(Pres & CEO)*
Kev Coleman *(VP-Product Dev)*

PLASTICS.COM, INC.

Montachusett Pk Bldg 225
Fitchburg, MA 01420
Tel.: (978) 342-9000
E-mail: info@plastics.com
Web Site: www.plastics.com
Approx. Number Employees: 10
Year Founded: 2000
Business Description:
Provider of Information to the Plastics Industry
S.I.C.: 3089
N.A.I.C.S.: 326199
Media: 2-7-13
Personnel:
Greg Koski *(Founder)*

PLUCK CORPORATION

(Sub. of Demand Media, Inc.)
200 Academy Dr Ste 120
Austin, TX 78704
Tel.: (512) 457-5220
Fax: (512) 457-5221
Web Site: www.pluck.com
Approx. Number Employees: 120
Year Founded: 2003
Business Description:
Integrated Social Media Solutions
S.I.C.: 7371
N.A.I.C.S.: 541511
Media: 7-10-13
Personnel:
Rachel Brush *(Sr VP-Sls Ops-Demand Media)*
Brett Andrew *(VP-Bus Dev & Sls-Demand Media)*
Stephanie Himoff *(VP-Sls & Bus Dev-Demand Media)*
Jason Jaynes *(VP-Mktg & Products-Demand Media)*

Key to Media (For complete agency information see *The Advertising Red Books-Agencies* edition):
1. Bus. Publs. 2. Cable T.V. 3. Catalogs & Directories. 4. Co-op Adv. 5. Consumer Mags. 6. D.M. to Bus. Estab.7. D.M. to Consumers 8. Daily Newsp. 9. Exhibits/Trade Shows 10. Foreign 11. Infomercial 12. Internet Adv.13. Multimedia 14. Network Radio 15. Network T.V. 16. Newsp. Distr. Mags. 17. Other 18. Outdoor (Posters, Transit) 19. Point of Purchase20. Premiums, Novelties 21. Product Samples 22. Special Events Mktg. 23. Spot Radio 24. Spot T.V. 25. Weekly Newsp. 26. Yellow Page Adv.

Pluck Corporation — (Continued)
Jeff Branc *(Sr Dir-Global Acct Svcs & Support)*
Don Roedner *(Dir-Mktg-Demand Media)*
Brands & Products:
PLUCK

PLUS VISION CORP. OF AMERICA
(Sub. of PLUS Vision Corp. of Japan)
9610 SW Sunshine Ct Ste 500
Beaverton, OR 97005-4686
Tel.: (503) 748-8700
Fax: (503) 643-9756
Toll Free: (800) 211-9001
Toll Free: (866) 427-8855
E-mail: sales@plus-america.com
Web Site: www.plus-america.com
E-Mail For Key Personnel:
Sales Director: sales@plus-america.com
Approx. Number Employees: 30
Year Founded: 1995
Business Description:
Internet Retailer of Portable Projectors & Electonic Copy Boards
S.I.C.: 3861; 5045
N.A.I.C.S.: 333315; 423430
Media: 10-13
Personnel:
Tsutomu Oishi *(Pres)*

POGO.COM
(Div. of EA.com)
209 Redwood Shores Pkwy
Redwood City, CA 94065
Tel.: (650) 628-1500
Web Site: www.pogo.com
Sales Range: $25-49.9 Million
Approx. Number Employees: 95
Year Founded: 1995
Business Description:
Online Games & Entertainment
S.I.C.: 7372; 7375
N.A.I.C.S.: 511210; 518111
Media: 13
Personnel:
John Riccitiello *(CEO)*
Jana Friedman *(Sr Dir-Interactive Adv Sls)*
Brands & Products:
ALCHEMY
ALI BABA SLOTS
ANIMAL ARK
BIG SHOT ROULETTE
BUCKAROO BLACKJACK
CLUB POGO
COLLAPSE
FREEKSTYLE
PEBBLE BEACH
PILEUP
POPPIT
ROCKET MANIA
SWEET TOOTH
TANK HUNTER
TIPTOP
TRIVIATRON
TURBO 21
WORD WHOMP

POINTS INTERNATIONAL LTD.
179 John St 8th Fl
Toronto, ON M5P 1X4, Canada
Tel.: (416) 596-6370
Tel.: (416) 595-0000
Fax: (416) 595-6444
Toll Free: (866) 340-3717
E-mail: info@points.com
Web Site: www.points.com
Approx. Rev.: $95,678,000
Approx. Number Employees: 93
Business Description:
Reward-Program Management
S.I.C.: 4311; 7371
N.A.I.C.S.: 491110; 541511
Advertising Expenditures: $2,217,032
Media: 1-8-13
Personnel:
Stephen K. Bannon *(Chm)*
Christopher J.D. Barnard *(Pres)*
T. Robert MacLean *(CEO)*
Anthony Lam *(CFO)*
Peter Lockhard *(COO)*
Erika Boyd *(VP-HR)*
Graeme Clark *(Dir-IT Ops)*
Brands & Products:
POINTS INTERNATIONAL LTD.
POINTS.COM

POLAR COVE, INC.
150 Chestnut St
Providence, RI 02903-4645
Tel.: (401) 454-3949
Fax: (401) 490-7574
E-mail: info@polarcove.com
Web Site: www.polarcove.com
E-Mail For Key Personnel:
Marketing Director: marketing@orbidex.com
Approx. Number Employees: 100
Year Founded: 1999
Business Description:
Information Security Services
S.I.C.: 7389; 7371
N.A.I.C.S.: 561499; 541511
Advertising Expenditures: $250,000
Media: 7-13
Personnel:
Bruce Eissner *(CEO)*

PREMIERE GLOBAL SERVICES, INC.
3280 Peachtree Rd NW Ste 1000
Atlanta, GA 30305
Tel.: (404) 262-8400
Fax: (404) 504-2134
Toll Free: (866) 619-2113
Web Site: www.pgi.com/us/en/
Approx. Rev.: $441,753,000
Approx. Number Employees: 1,700
Year Founded: 1991
Business Description:
Holding Company; Conferencing & Collaboration Servicesses
S.I.C.: 6719; 4899; 7372
N.A.I.C.S.: 551112; 511210; 517910
Advertising Expenditures: $10,200,000
Personnel:
Boland T. Jones *(Chm & CEO)*
Theodore P. Schrafft *(Pres)*
David E. Trine *(CFO, Principal Acctg Officer & Exec VP-Fin)*
Jacqueline E. Yeaney *(CMO)*
Erik Petrik *(Chief People Officer)*
Scott Askins Leonard *(Gen Counsel, Sec & Sr VP-Legal)*
Mark Alexander *(Exec VP-Sls & Mktg)*
John D. Stone *(Exec VP-European Ops)*
Michael E. Havener *(Sr VP-Corp Fin)*
Sean O'Brien *(Sr VP-Strategic Plng & IR)*
Bryan Stibbard *(Channel Sls Dir-Southeast Asia)*
Sara Pilling *(Media Coord)*
Brands & Products:
AUDITORIUM
CAMPAIGN ACCELERATOR ADVANCED
CAMPAIGN ACCELERATOR PROFESSIONAL
FAX2MAIL (STYLIZED)
FAXREACH
GLOBALMEET
IMEET
INTELLISEND
IRGENT
MESSAGEREACH
MOBILE MARKETING
NETSPOKE
NETSPOKE & DESIGN
PGI & DESIGN
PGICONNECT
PGIMARKET
PGIMEET
PGINOTIFY
PGINOTIFY MEDS
PGISEND
PGITV
POWERED BY PREMIERE & DESIGN
PREMIERE GLOBAL SERVICES & DESIGN
PREMIERECALL AUDITORIUM
PREMIERECALL CONNECT
PREMIERECALL EVENT
READYCAST
READYCONFERENCE
READYCONFERENCE PLUS
SALES GENERATOR
SAVEONCONFERENCES.COM
SMSREACH
SOUNDPATH
TRANSACTIONAL MESSAGING
VISIONCAST
VOICEREACH

PRICELINE.COM INCORPORATED
800 Connecticut Ave
Norwalk, CT 06854-1631
Tel.: (203) 299-8000
Fax: (203) 299-8948
E-mail: affiliates@priceline.com
Web Site: www.priceline.com
Approx. Rev.: $3,084,905,000
Approx. Number Employees: 3,400
Year Founded: 1997
Business Description:
Travel Arrangement & Reservation Services
S.I.C.: 4729
N.A.I.C.S.: 561599
Advertising Expenditures: $172,700,000
Media: 13-14-15
Personnel:
Ralph M. Bahna *(Chm)*
Robert J. Mylod Jr. *(Vice Chm & Head-Worldwide Strategy & Plng)*
Jeffery H. Boyd *(Pres & CEO)*
Daniel J. Finnegan *(CFO)*
Michael Diliberto *(CIO)*
Brett Keller *(CMO)*
Christopher L. Soder *(Pres-Travel-North America)*
Peter J. Millones *(Gen Counsel & Exec VP)*
Glenn D. Fogel *(Exec VP-Corp Dev)*
Patricia D'Angelo *(Sr VP)*
Lisa Gillingham *(Sr VP-Customer Svc & Ops)*
Tim Gordon *(Sr VP-Hotels)*
Paul J. Hennessy *(Chief Distr Officer & Sr VP-Online Mktg)*
Mark Koehler *(Sr VP-Airlines)*
Thomas L. Trotta *(Sr VP-Vacation Packages & Cruises)*
Matthew N. Tynan *(Sr VP-Fin & IR)*
Brands & Products:
NAME YOUR OWN PRICE
NO ONE DEALS LIKE WE DO
PRICELINE.COM
Advertising Agency:
Butler, Shine, Stern & Partners
20 Liberty Ship Way
Sausalito, CA 94965-3312
Tel.: (415) 331-6049
Fax: (415) 331-3524

PROMOTIONS.COM, INC.
(Joint Venture of Comcast Corporation & General Electric Company)
8420 Bryn Mawr Ave Ste 950
Chicago, IL 60631
Tel.: (773) 444-4040
Fax: (773) 444-0639
Web Site: www.promotions.com
Sales Range: $1-9.9 Million
Business Description:
Online & Offline Promotions & Direct Marketing
S.I.C.: 8742; 2741
N.A.I.C.S.: 541613; 516110
Media: 13

PROVIDE COMMERCE, INC.
(Sub. of Liberty Media LLC)
4840 Eastgate Mall
San Diego, CA 92121
Tel.: (858) 729-2800
Fax: (858) 638-4724
Toll Free: (888) 373-7437
E-mail: info@providecommerce.com
Web Site: www.prvd.com
Sales Range: $800-899.9 Million
Year Founded: 1998
Business Description:
Flowers, Gift Baskets, Meats & Fruits Online Retailer
S.I.C.: 5961; 5947; 5992
N.A.I.C.S.: 454111; 453110; 453220
Advertising Expenditures: $25,143,000
Media: 3-7-8-10-13-14-21-23-24-26
Personnel:
William Strauss *(Pres & COO)*
Kevin Hall *(CIO)*
Blake Bilstad *(Gen Counsel, Sec & Sr VP)*
Rex Bosen *(Treas & VP-Fin & Acctg)*
Steven Goldstein *(Sr VP-Gourmet Food & Retention Mktg)*
John Kuehn *(Sr VP-Supply Chain Ops)*
Jonathan Sills *(Sr VP-Strategy & Corp Dev)*
Penny Handscomb *(VP-HR & Trng)*
Greg Smith *(VP-Mdsg)*
Brands & Products:
CHERRY MOON FARMS
PROFLOWERS
UPTOWN PRIME
Advertising Agency:
BBDO North America
1285 Ave of the Americas

Key to Media (For complete agency information see *The Advertising Red Books-Agencies* edition):
1. Bus. Publs. 2. Cable T.V. 3. Catalogs & Directories. 4. Co-op Adv. 5. Consumer Mags. 6. D.M. to Bus. Estab.7. D.M. to Consumers
8. Daily Newsp. 9. Exhibits/Trade Shows 10. Foreign 11. Infomercial 12. Internet Adv.13. Multimedia 14. Network Radio
15. Network T.V. 16. Newsp. Distr. Mags. 17. Other 18. Outdoor (Posters, Transit) 19. Point of Purchase20. Premiums, Novelties
21. Product Samples 22. Special Events Mktg. 23. Spot Radio 24. Spot T.V. 25. Weekly Newsp. 26. Yellow Page Adv.

New York, NY 10019-6028
Tel.: (212) 459-5000
Fax: (212) 459-6814

PUBLITEK, INC.
(d/b/a Fotosearch)
2155 Watertown Rd
Waukesha, WI 53186-1898
Tel.: (262) 717-0600
Fax: (262) 717-0745
Toll Free: (800) 827-3920
E-mail: comments@fotosearch.com
Web Site: www.fotosearch.com
Approx. Number Employees: 27
Business Description:
Online Stock Photography, Stock Illustration, Stock Video, Stock Audio & Maps; Royalty Free & Rights Managed
S.I.C.: 2741
N.A.I.C.S.: 516110
Media: 2-4-7-8-13
Personnel:
Rick Wintersberger *(Owner & Pres)*
Jeff Montgomery *(Product Mgr-Mktg)*

Q INTERACTIVE INC.
(Sub. of Selling Source, LLC)
1 N Dearborn St 12th Fl
Chicago, IL 60602
Tel.: (312) 224-5000
Fax: (312) 224-5001
Toll Free: (888) 729-6465
Web Site: www.qinteractive.com
Sales Range: $25-49.9 Million
Approx. Number Employees: 133
Year Founded: 1995
Business Description:
E-Marketing Services
S.I.C.: 7319; 7331
N.A.I.C.S.: 541870; 541860; 541890
Advertising Expenditures: $9,944,000
Media: 8-13
Brands & Products:
COOLSAVINGS

QUALI-PRO
4515 Falls of Neuse Rd Ste 300
Raleigh, NC 27609
Tel.: (206) 812-8600
Fax: (206) 812-8640
Toll Free: (800) 979-8994
E-mail: russm@quali-pro.com
Web Site: www.farmsaver.com
E-Mail For Key Personnel:
Marketing Director: allanl@farmsaver.com
Approx. Number Employees: 20
Year Founded: 2000
Business Description:
Farming Products Mfr & Online Marketer
S.I.C.: 5191; 8111
N.A.I.C.S.: 424910; 541110
Media: 2-8-10-13-16-18-23
Personnel:
Allan Las *(Chief Product Dev Officer)*
Brands & Products:
ABBA
AGRI-MEK
BIFENTHRIN
CHLORPYRIFOS
DROPP
ETHEPHON
FOSETYL
GLYPHOSATE
LAMBDA
MEFENOXAM
ORYZALIN
PRODIAMINE
PROPICONAZOLE
QUALI-PHITE
QUALI-PRO
QUINCLORAC
REDI-PIK
SETUP
T-NEX

QUEPASA CORPORATION
(Branch of Quepasa Corporation)
220E 23 St Ste 407
New York, NY 10017
Tel.: (561) 650-8075
Web Site: www.quepasacorp.com
Sales Range: $100-124.9 Million
Business Description:
Online Marketing, Advertising & Sales
S.I.C.: 7319
N.A.I.C.S.: 541870
Export
Advertising Expenditures: $267,000
Media: 1-2-6-8-11-22

QUESTIA MEDIA INC.
24 E Greenway Plz Ste 1050
Houston, TX 77046
Tel.: (713) 358-2500
Tel.: (713) 358-2600
Fax: (713) 358-2601
E-mail: info@questia.com
Web Site: www.questia.com
Sales Range: $25-49.9 Million
Approx. Number Employees: 55
Business Description:
Online Library Services
S.I.C.: 7375; 8231
N.A.I.C.S.: 518111; 519120
Media: 13
Personnel:
Timothy Harris *(Pres & CEO)*
Michael Miller *(CFO)*

QUIDSI, INC.
(Sub. of Amazon.com, Inc.)
10 Exchange Place 25th Fl
Jersey City, NJ 07302
Mailing Address:
PO Box 483
Jersey City, NJ 07303
Tel.: (973) 509-5444
Fax: (888) 466-1158
Toll Free: (800) 342-7377
E-mail: customercare@diapers.com
Web Site: www.diapers.com
Approx. Number Employees: 200
Business Description:
E-Commerce for Baby, Personal Care & Household Products
N.A.I.C.S.: 516110
Personnel:
Marc Lore *(Co-Founder, Chm & CEO)*
Vinit Bhara *(Co-Founder & COO)*
Eugene Hertz *(CIO)*
Scott Hilton *(Exec VP-Ops)*
John K. Anderson *(Sr VP-HR)*
Christina Carbonell *(Sr VP-Retail)*
David Licata *(VP-Fin & Acctg)*
Brands & Products:
BEAUTYBAR.COM
DIAPERS.COM
SOAP.COM
WAG.COM
Advertising Agency:
LaunchSquad
116 New Montgomery St Ste 620
San Francisco, CA 94105
Tel.: (415) 625-8555
Fax: (415) 625-8559

QUINSTREET, INC.
1051 E Hillsdale Blvd Ste 800
Foster City, CA 94404
Tel.: (650) 578-7700
Fax: (650) 578-7604
Web Site: www.quinstreet.com
Approx. Rev.: $334,835,000
Approx. Number Employees: 637
Year Founded: 1999
Business Description:
Online Vertical Marketing & Media Services
S.I.C.: 8742; 7319
N.A.I.C.S.: 541613; 519130; 541890
Advertising Expenditures: $139,000
Media: 17
Personnel:
Bronwyn Syiek *(Pres & COO)*
Douglas Valenti *(CEO)*
Kenneth R. Hahn *(CFO)*
Daniel Caul *(Gen Counsel & Sr VP)*
Christopher Mancini *(Exec VP & Gen Mgr)*
Tom Cheli *(Exec VP)*
Scott Mackley *(Exec VP)*
Timothy J. Stevens *(Sr VP-Corp Dev)*
Shane Tripcony *(Sr Mgr-PPC & Fin Svcs)*

RACKSPACE HOSTING, INC.
5000 Walzem Rd
San Antonio, TX 78218
Tel.: (210) 312-4700
Fax: (210) 312-4300
Toll Free: (800) 961-2888
E-mail: ir@rackspace.com
Web Site: www.rackspace.com
Approx. Rev.: $780,555,000
Approx. Number Employees: 3,262
Year Founded: 1998
Business Description:
Website Hosting & Other IT Services
S.I.C.: 7374; 7379
N.A.I.C.S.: 518210; 541519
Advertising Expenditures: $30,700,000
Media: 13-17
Personnel:
Graham M. Weston *(Chm)*
A. Lanham Napier *(Pres, CEO & Dir)*
Karl Pichler *(Acting CFO & Treas)*
Mark Roenigk *(COO)*
Steve Mills *(CIO)*
Lew Moorman *(Chief Strategy Officer & Pres-Cloud)*
Alan Schoenbaum *(Gen Counsel, Sec & Sr VP)*
David Kelly *(Sr VP-Intl)*
Klee Kleber *(Sr VP-Mktg & Product Dev)*
Jim Lewandowski *(Sr VP-Worldwide Sls)*
Wayne Roberts *(Sr VP-HR)*
Taylor Rhodes *(VP & Gen Mgr, Enterprise Markets, EMEA)*
Pat Cathey *(VP-Sls)*
Amanda Nevins *(VP-Fin)*
Troy Toman *(Dir-Cloud Compute Engrg)*
Brands & Products:
FANATICAL SUPPORT

RADIANCE TECHNOLOGIES, INC.
350 Wynn Dr
Huntsville, AL 35805
Tel.: (256) 704-3400
Fax: (256) 704-3412
Web Site: www.radiancetech.com
Sales Range: $25-49.9 Million
Approx. Number Employees: 271
Year Founded: 1999
Business Description:
Telecommunications Services & Solutions for Government & Military
S.I.C.: 4899
N.A.I.C.S.: 517910
Media: 7-10-13-18-20-22
Personnel:
Ashfaq A. Munshi *(Chm & CEO)*
George Clark *(Pres)*
Brands & Products:
CAMERA LINK
HOTLINK II
HYPERPACS
RADIANCE TECHNOLOGIES
TRIAGE SENSOR
WEAPONWATCH

RAM DISTRIBUTION, LLC
(d/b/a AtomicPark.com, LLC)
757 N Broadway Ste 400
Milwaukee, WI 53202
Tel.: (414) 431-0172
Fax: (414) 270-9507
Toll Free: (888) 322-4250
E-mail: customerservice@atomicpark.com
Web Site: www.atomicpark.com
Approx. Number Employees: 32
Year Founded: 1998
Business Description:
Retailer of Computer Software via Internet
S.I.C.: 5734
N.A.I.C.S.: 443120
Media: 6

RCN METRO OPTICAL NETWORKS
(Sub. of RCN Telecom Services, LLC.)
(d/b/a Sidera Networks)
2200 W Park Dr
Westborough, MA 01581
Tel.: (508) 616-7800
Fax: (508) 616-7895
Web Site: www.sidera.net
Sales Range: $50-74.9 Million
Approx. Number Employees: 330
Year Founded: 1989
Business Description:
High-Speed Internet Connections & Related Services
S.I.C.: 7375
N.A.I.C.S.: 518111
Media: 10-13
Personnel:
Maura Mahoney *(VP-Mktg & Bus Dev)*
Advertising Agencies:
FastLane
55 Mountain Ave
Caldwell, NJ 07006
Tel.: (973) 226-4379
Fax: (973) 364-0122

Lotus Public Relations Inc.
305 Madison Ave Ste 1050
New York, NY 10165
Tel.: (212) 922-5885

Key to Media (For complete agency information see *The Advertising Red Books-Agencies* edition):
1. Bus. Publs. 2. Cable T.V. 3. Catalogs & Directories. 4. Co-op Adv. 5. Consumer Mags. 6. D.M. to Bus. Estab.7. D.M. to Consumers 8. Daily Newsp. 9. Exhibits/Trade Shows 10. Foreign 11. Infomercial 12. Internet Adv.13. Multimedia 14. Network Radio 15. Network T.V. 16. Newsp. Distr. Mags. 17. Other 18. Outdoor (Posters, Transit) 19. Point of Purchase20. Premiums, Novelties 21. Product Samples 22. Special Events Mktg. 23. Spot Radio 24. Spot T.V. 25. Weekly Newsp. 26. Yellow Page Adv.

RCN Metro Optical Networks — (Continued)

Fax: (212) 656-1206
Public Relations

REACHLOCAL, INC.
21700 Oxnard St Ste 1600
Woodland Hills, CA 91367
Tel.: (818) 274-0260
Web Site: www.reachlocal.com
Approx. Rev.: $291,689,000
Approx. Number Employees: 1,381
Year Founded: 2004
Business Description:
Internet Advertising Solutions & Marketing Services
S.I.C.: 7319; 8742
N.A.I.C.S.: 541890; 519130; 541613
Advertising Expenditures: $1,633,000
Personnel:
Alan E. Salzman *(Chm)*
Zorik Gordon *(Pres, CEO & Dir)*
Ross G. Landsbaum *(CFO)*
Michael Kline *(COO & Chief Product Officer)*
Chris Powell *(Chief Acctg Officer, Sr VP & Corp Controller)*
Nathan Hanks *(Chief Distr Officer)*
Adam F. Wergeles *(Gen Counsel)*
Robert Wright *(Exec VP & Gen Mgr-Xchange)*
Steven Power *(Exec VP-Global Sls Ops)*
Gadi Shamia *(Sr VP-Advanced Product Dev)*
Jason Whitt *(Sr VP-Corp Dev)*
Shane Garoutte *(VP-IT)*
Kamran Izadpanah *(VP-Engrg)*
Alex Hawkinson *(Gen Mgr-Digital Presence)*
Robert Florian *(Sr Dir-Engrg-Digital Presence)*
Ed Merrick *(Mgr-Sls)*
Brands & Products:
REACHLOCAL
Advertising Agency:
The Blueshirt Group
456 Montgomery St 11th Fl
San Francisco, CA 94104
Tel.: (415) 217-7722
Fax: (415) 217-7721
Investor Relations

REALHOME.COM INC.
3001 Summer St
Stamford, CT 06905
Mailing Address:
PO Box 16817
Stamford, CT 06905
Tel.: (203) 323-7715
Fax: (203) 323-4558
Toll Free: (800) 549-8282
E-mail: memberservices@ahahome.com
Web Site: www.ahahome.com
E-Mail For Key Personnel:
President: rroll@realhome.com
Approx. Number Employees: 37
Year Founded: 1994
Business Description:
Online Provider of Information & Services for Homeowners & Homebuyers
S.I.C.: 7299
N.A.I.C.S.: 812990
Media: 13
Personnel:
Richard J. Roll *(Founder, Pres & CEO)*
Peggy Vincento *(Dir-Mktg)*
Brands & Products:
AMERICAN HOMEOWNERS ASSN
HOMEBASE FOR YOUR HOME

REALPAGE, INC.
4000 International Pkwy Ste 1000
Carrollton, TX 75007
Tel.: (972) 820-3000
Fax: (972) 820-3036
Toll Free: (877) 325-7243
E-mail: sales@realpage.com
Web Site: www.realpage.com
E-Mail For Key Personnel:
Sales Director: sales@realpage.com
Approx. Rev.: $188,274,000
Approx. Number Employees: 1,759
Business Description:
Property Management Software Developer
S.I.C.: 7372; 6531; 7371
N.A.I.C.S.: 511210; 531390; 541511
Advertising Expenditures: $7,700,000
Media: 10-13-17-22
Personnel:
Stephen T. Winn *(Founder, Chm & CEO)*
Dirk D. Wakeham *(Pres)*
Timothy J. Barker *(CFO)*
Jason D. Lindwall *(COO)*
Dean Schmidt *(Chief Product Officer)*
David Carner *(Pres-LeasingDesk)*
William Chaney *(Pres-Velocity)*
Tony Pusateri *(Pres-CrtossFire COntact Center & Education)*
Sina Shekou *(Pres-Propertyware)*
Sukhi Singh *(Pres-OpsTech)*
Janine Steiner Jovanovic *(Pres-YieldStar)*
Leslie Turner *(Pres-OneSite)*
Ashley Chaffin Glover *(Exec VP-Multifamily Solutions)*
Michael Britti *(Sr VP-Mergers & Acq)*
Andrea Massey *(Sr VP-Mktg)*
John Yager *(Sr VP-Sls)*
Randy Hargrove *(VP-Corp Comm)*

RED BOOKS
475 Springfield Ave
Suite 401
Summit, NJ 07901
Fax: (908) 665-3572
Toll Free: (800) 908-5395
E-mail: info@redbooks.com
Web Site: www.redbooks.com
Sales Range: $1-9.9 Million
Approx. Number Employees: 10
Year Founded: 1922
Business Description:
Database Publisher
S.I.C.: 2741
N.A.I.C.S.: 511140
Media: 1-2-7-10-11-13-22
Personnel:
Sameer Jagetia *(Chm & Pres)*
Paul Amar Sethi *(CEO)*
Peter Valli *(Gen Mgr)*
Brands & Products:
THE ADVERTISING RED BOOKS

RED HERRING, INC.
1900 Alameda de Las Pulgas Ste112
San Mateo, CA 94403-1295
Tel.: (650) 215-1520
Fax: (619) 923-2792
E-mail: info@redherring.com
Web Site: www.redherring.com
Approx. Number Employees: 130
Year Founded: 1993
Business Description:
Online Magazine Publisher
S.I.C.: 2721
N.A.I.C.S.: 519130
Media: 10-11-13-22
Personnel:
Alex Vieux *(Founder, Chm & CEO)*
Joel Dreyfus *(Editor-in-Chief)*

REDENVELOPE, INC.
(Sub. of Provide Commerce, Inc.)
4840 Eastgate Mall
San Diego, CA 92121
Mailing Address:
PO Box 600040
San Diego, CA 92160-0040
Tel.: (619) 528-4888
Toll Free: (877) 733-3683
E-mail: pr@redenvelope.com
Web Site: www.redenvelope.com
E-Mail For Key Personnel:
Sales Director: corporategifts@redenvelope.com
Approx. Rev.: $121,772,000
Approx. Number Employees: 180
Year Founded: 1999
Business Description:
Online Retailer
S.I.C.: 5961
N.A.I.C.S.: 454113
Advertising Expenditures: $8,800,000
Media: 4-13
Personnel:
William Strauss *(CEO)*
Rick Sliter *(Sr VP-Mktg)*

REGISTER.COM, INC.
(Sub. of Web.com Group, Inc.)
575 8th Ave 11th Fl
New York, NY 10018-3011
Tel.: (212) 798-9100
Fax: (212) 594-9876
E-mail: hrjobs@register.com
Web Site: www.register.com
Approx. Number Employees: 489
Year Founded: 1994
Business Description:
Domain Name Registration Service
S.I.C.: 7389; 7375
N.A.I.C.S.: 541990; 518111
Advertising Expenditures: $10,000,000
Media: 7-8-10-13
Personnel:
David L. Brown *(Pres)*
Gary Michel *(COO)*
Brands & Products:
REGISTER.COM
Advertising Agency:
Horn Group
55 Broad St Fl 29
New York, NY 10004
Tel.: (646) 202-9750
Fax: (646) 826-0022

RELIAQUOTE, INC.
(Sub. of Fiserv, Inc.)
1312 Vincent Pl
McLean, VA 22101
Tel.: (703) 289-0200
Fax: (703) 289-1234
Toll Free: (800) 940-3002
E-mail: info@reliaquote.com
Web Site: www.reliaquote.com
Sales Range: $10-24.9 Million
Approx. Number Employees: 80
Year Founded: 1997
Business Description:
Online Insurance Service
S.I.C.: 6411
N.A.I.C.S.: 524210
Media: 13
Brands & Products:
RELIAQUOTE

REPLY! INC.
12667 Alcosta Blvd Ste 200
San Ramon, CA 94583
Tel.: (925) 983-3400
Fax: (925) 983-3410
E-mail: info@reply.com
Web Site: www.reply.com
Approx. Rev.: $34,295,000
Approx. Number Employees: 127
Year Founded: 2001
Business Description:
Online Auction Marketplace & Marketing Services
S.I.C.: 5961; 5045; 7319
N.A.I.C.S.: 454112; 425110; 541890
Advertising Expenditures: $416,000
Personnel:
W. Samuel Veazey *(CFO)*
Sean Fox *(COO)*
Brian Bowman *(CMO)*
William Perrault *(VP-IT)*

RESPOND NETWORKS, INC.
(Sub. of TEOCO Corporation)
12150 Monument Dr Ste 400
Fairfax, VA 22033
Tel.: (703) 259-4457
Fax: (703) 259-4487
Toll Free: (866) 638-5323
E-mail: info@respond.com
Web Site: www.respond.com
Approx. Number Employees: 10
Year Founded: 1999
Business Description:
Local Leads to Small & Medium Size Businesses in the Service Industries
S.I.C.: 7389
N.A.I.C.S.: 519190; 519130
Media: 13-17
Brands & Products:
RESPOND.COM

RICK'S CABARET INTERNATIONAL, INC.
10959 Cutten Rd
Houston, TX 77066-5003
Tel.: (281) 397-6730
Fax: (281) 820-1445
Web Site: www.ricks.com
E-Mail For Key Personnel:
President: eric@ricks.com
Approx. Rev.: $82,987,000
Approx. Number Employees: 1,000
Year Founded: 1994
Business Description:
Owner & Operator of Night Clubs; Owner of Adult Websites
S.I.C.: 5813; 2741
N.A.I.C.S.: 722410; 516110
Advertising Expenditures: $8,091,745
Media: 2-8-13-18-22-23
Personnel:
Eric Scott Langan *(Chm, Pres & CEO)*
Phillip K. Marshall *(CFO)*
Travis Reese *(VP & Dir-Tech)*
Brands & Products:
RICK'S CABARET

Key to Media (For complete agency information see *The Advertising Red Books-Agencies* edition):
1. Bus. Publs. 2. Cable T.V. 3. Catalogs & Directories. 4. Co-op Adv. 5. Consumer Mags. 6. D.M. to Bus. Estab.7. D.M. to Consumers
8. Daily Newsp. 9. Exhibits/Trade Shows 10. Foreign 11. Infomercial 12. Internet Adv.13. Multimedia 14. Network Radio
15. Network T.V. 16. Newsp. Distr. Mags. 17. Other 18. Outdoor (Posters, Transit) 19. Point of Purchase20. Premiums, Novelties
21. Product Samples 22. Special Events Mktg. 23. Spot Radio 24. Spot T.V. 25. Weekly Newsp. 26. Yellow Page Adv.

XTC CABARETS

RITZ INTERACTIVE, INC.
2010 Main St Ste 400
Irvine, CA 92614
Tel.: (949) 442-0202
Fax: (949) 442-0210
E-mail: info@ritzinteractive.com
Web Site: www.ritzinteractive.com
Approx. Number Employees: 44
Year Founded: 1999
Business Description:
Online Photographic, Sporting Goods & Boating Products Retailer
S.I.C.: 5961; 5941; 5946
N.A.I.C.S.: 454111; 443130; 451110
Advertising Expenditures: $4,060,000
Media: 4-5-6-9-13-25
Personnel:
David M. Ritz *(Chm)*
Fred H. Lerner *(Pres & CEO)*
Scott F. Neamand *(CFO & Exec VP)*
Andre Brysha *(CMO & Sr VP)*
Brands & Products:
WWW.BOATERWORLD.COM
WWW.BOATINGONLY.COM
WWW.CAMERAWORLD.COM
WWW.FISHINGONLY.COM
WWW.OUTERBANKSOUTFITTERS.COM
WWW.PHOTOALLEY.COM
WWW.PHOTOGRAPHY.COM
WWW.RITZCAMERA.COM
WWW.RITZELECTRONICS.COM
WWW.RITZPIX.COM
WWW.WOLFCAMERA.COM
Advertising Agency:
Wolfbone Marketing
3455 Peachtree Rd NE Ste 600
Atlanta, GA 30326
Tel.: (404) 995-4620
Fax: (404) 995-4625

RIVERBED TECHNOLOGY, INC.
199 Fremont St
San Francisco, CA 94105
Tel.: (415) 247-8800
Fax: (415) 247-8801
E-mail: info@riverbed.com
Web Site: www.riverbed.com
Approx. Rev.: $551,889,000
Approx. Number Employees: 1,244
Year Founded: 2002
Business Description:
Wide-Area Data Services (WDS) Solutions
S.I.C.: 7372; 7375
N.A.I.C.S.: 511210; 518111
Advertising Expenditures: $1,700,000
Personnel:
Jerry M. Kennelly *(Chm & CEO)*
Randy S. Gottfried *(CFO)*
Thomas Bakewell *(CIO & VP)*
Brett A. Nissenberg *(Gen Counsel & VP-Corp & Legal Affairs)*
David M. Peranich *(Sr VP-Worldwide Sls)*
Eric Wolford *(Sr VP-Mktg & Bus Dev)*
Rob Booth *(VP-Worldwide Sls Ops)*
Gordon Chaffee *(VP-Engrg)*
Carolyn Crandall *(VP-Mktg-Worldwide)*
Randy Schirman *(VP-WW Channels)*
Andres Hurtado *(Dir-Latin America)*
Sue Stokes *(Reg Mgr-Sls)*
Advertising Agency:
Heat
Pier 33 S 3rd Fl
San Francisco, CA 94111
Tel.: (415) 477-1999
Fax: (415) 477-1990
— Nei Caetano *(Dir-Creative)*

ROXIO CINEMANOW, INC.
(Sub. of Sonic Solutions)
4553 Glencoe Ave Ste 200
Marina Del Rey, CA 90292
Tel.: (310) 314-3000
Fax: (310) 314-3050
Web Site: www.cinemanow.com
E-Mail For Key Personnel:
Sales Director: sales@cinemanow.com
Sales Range: $10-24.9 Million
Approx. Number Employees: 50
Year Founded: 1999
Business Description:
Online Film Distr
S.I.C.: 7822
N.A.I.C.S.: 512120
Media: 4-10-13-16-21-22

RUE LA LA
(Owned by NRG Commerce LLC)
20 Channel Center St
Boston, MA 02210-3402
Tel.: (617) 830-3330
E-mail: atyourservice@ruelala.com
Web Site: www.ruelala.com
Business Description:
Online Retailer
N.A.I.C.S.: 453998
Media: 27-29
Personnel:
Michael Rubin *(Owner)*

S1 CORPORATION
705 Westech Dr
Norcross, GA 30092
Tel.: (404) 923-3500
Fax: (404) 923-6727
Toll Free: (888) 457-2237
E-mail: moreinfo@s1.com
Web Site: www.s1.com
Approx. Rev.: $209,086,000
Approx. Number Employees: 1,670
Year Founded: 1995
Business Description:
Enterprise E-Finance Solutions
S.I.C.: 5045; 6719; 7371; 7372
N.A.I.C.S.: 425110; 511210; 541511; 551112
Advertising Expenditures: $31,500,000
Media: 2-4-7-10-13
Personnel:
Johann J. Dreyer *(CEO)*
Paul M. Parrish *(CFO)*

SAJAN, INC.
625 Whitetail Blvd
River Falls, WI 54022
Tel.: (715) 426-9505
Fax: (715) 426-0105
E-mail: investors@sajan.com
Web Site: www.sajan.com
Approx. Rev.: $15,990,596
Approx. Number Employees: 112
Business Description:
On-Demand Language Translation Solutions
S.I.C.: 7372
N.A.I.C.S.: 511210
Advertising Expenditures: $36,453
Media: 17
Personnel:
Shannon Zimmerman *(Chm & CEO)*
Timothy C. Clayton *(CFO)*
Angela Zimmerman *(COO & Dir)*
Harold Fagley *(Gen Mgr-Sajan Software)*
Brands & Products:
ARRIX
FPOA
MATHSTAR
THE NEXT GENERATION OF PROGRAMMABLE LOGIC

SALESFORCE.COM, INC.
The Landmark 1 Market St Ste 300
San Francisco, CA 94105-1420
Tel.: (415) 901-7000
Fax: (415) 901-7040
Toll Free: (800) NO-SOFTWARE
E-mail: info@salesforce.com
Web Site: www.salesforce.com
E-Mail For Key Personnel:
Marketing Director: marketing@salesforce.com
Sales Director: info@salesforce.com
Approx. Rev.: $1,657,139,000
Approx. Number Employees: 5,306
Year Founded: 1999
Business Description:
Customer Relationship Management (CRM) Services
S.I.C.: 7372; 2741
N.A.I.C.S.: 334611; 511210; 516110
Advertising Expenditures: $61,400,000
Media: 2-5-7-8-10-13-22
Personnel:
Marc Benioff *(Chm & CEO)*
Graham V. Smith *(CFO & Exec VP)*
Jim Steele *(Chief Customer Officer)*
Polly A. Sumner *(Chief Adoption Officer)*
Frank van Veenendaal *(Pres-Worldwide Sls & Svcs)*
Parker Harris *(Exec VP-Tech)*
George Hu *(Exec VP-Mktg & Platform)*
Hilarie Koplow-McAdams *(Exec VP-Sls)*
Maria Martinez *(Exec VP-Customers For Life)*
David R. Schellhase *(Exec VP-Legal)*
Sarah Friar *(Sr VP-Fin & Strategy)*
John Somorjai *(Sr VP-Corp Dev & Strategy)*
Francisco Suarez *(Dir-Exploitation)*
Carolina Grimm *(Sr Mgr-Analyst Rels)*
Brands & Products:
APEX
APPEXCHANGE
EXPERIENCE SUCCESS
SALESFORCE.COM
SUCCESS ON DEMAND
SUCCESS.NOT SOFTWARE
Advertising Agency:
OutCast Communications
123 Townsend St Ste 500
San Francisco, CA 94107
Tel.: (415) 392-8282
Fax: (415) 392-8281

SALON MEDIA GROUP, INC.
101 Spear St Ste 203
San Francisco, CA 94105
Tel.: (415) 645-9200
Fax: (415) 645-9204
E-mail: investor@salon.com
Web Site: www.salon.com
E-Mail For Key Personnel:
Sales Director: harvey@salon.com
Public Relations: pr@salon.com
Approx. Rev.: $4,573,000
Approx. Number Employees: 41
Year Founded: 1995
Business Description:
Web Site Providing News, Features, Interviews & Regular Columnists
S.I.C.: 7375; 7371
N.A.I.C.S.: 518111; 541511
Advertising Expenditures: $1,200,000
Media: 13
Personnel:
David Talbot *(Founder)*
John E. Warnock *(Chm)*
Richard Gingras *(CEO)*
Norman Blashka *(CFO & Exec VP)*
Benjamin Zagorski *(VP-Sls)*
Kerry Lauerman *(Editor-in-Chief)*
David Daley *(Editor-Culture)*
Joan Walsh *(Editor-at-Large)*
Dragana Kalezic *(Dir-Adv Ops)*
Karen Templer *(Dir-Product & Engrg)*
Gail Ann Williams *(Dir-Communities)*
Alan Choi *(Mgr-Acctg)*
Eric Lieb *(Mgr-Sls-West)*
Ricardo Neto *(Mgr-Sls)*
Page Rockwell *(Mgr-Project & Content)*
Paul Lesniak *(Coord-Accounts Payable)*
Sergeja Plahhutta *(Coord-Ad Traffic)*
Brands & Products:
SALON

SANDBOX.COM, INC.
(Sub. of Gamebase, Inc.)
247 Route 100 Ste 2004
Somers, NY 10589
Tel.: (914) 232-1239
Fax: (914) 232-0984
Toll Free: (800) 267-1780
E-mail: advertising@sandbox-inc.com
Web Site: www.sandbox.com
E-Mail For Key Personnel:
Marketing Director: advertising@sandbox-inc.com
Approx. Number Employees: 15
Year Founded: 1997
Business Description:
Online Gaming Services
S.I.C.: 7375
N.A.I.C.S.: 518111
Media: 13

SCRIPPS NETWORKS INTERACTIVE, INC.
9271 Sherrill Blvd
Knoxville, TN 37932
Tel.: (865) 694-2700
Fax: (865) 985-7778
E-mail: corpcomm@scrippsnetworks.com
Web Site: www.scrippsnetworksinteractive.com
Approx. Rev.: $2,067,162,000
Approx. Number Employees: 2,000
Business Description:
Internet Publishing & Retailing
S.I.C.: 2741
N.A.I.C.S.: 516110
Advertising Expenditures: $19,172,000
Personnel:
Kenneth W. Lowe *(Chm, Pres & CEO)*
Joseph G. Necastro *(CFO & Chief Admin Officer)*
Susie Fogelson *(Sr VP-Mktg & Brand Strategy)*

Key to Media (For complete agency information see *The Advertising Red Books-Agencies* edition):
1. Bus. Publs. 2. Cable T.V. 3. Catalogs & Directories. 4. Co-op Adv. 5. Consumer Mags. 6. D.M. to Bus. Estab.7. D.M. to Consumers
8. Daily Newsp. 9. Exhibits/Trade Shows 10. Foreign 11. Infomercial 12. Internet Adv.13. Multimedia 14. Network Radio
15. Network T.V. 16. Newsp. Distr. Mags. 17. Other 18. Outdoor (Posters, Transit) 19. Point of Purchase20. Premiums, Novelties
21. Product Samples 22. Special Events Mktg. 23. Spot Radio 24. Spot T.V. 25. Weekly Newsp. 26. Yellow Page Adv.

Scripps Networks Interactive, Inc. — (Continued)

Anatolio B. Cruz, III *(Chief Legal Officer & Corp Sec)*
Mark S. Hale *(CTO & Exec VP)*
John F. Lansing *(Pres-Scripps Networks & Exec VP)*
Steve Gigliotti *(Pres-Natl Adv Sls & Mktg)*
Mark F. Schuermann *(Treas & Sr VP)*
Henry Ahn *(Exec VP-Content Distr & Mktg)*
James B. Clayton *(Exec VP-Plng & Strategy-Lifestyle Media)*
Cynthia L. Gibson *(Exec VP-Legal)*
Lori A. Hickok *(Exec VP-Fin)*
Christopher R. Powell *(Exec VP-HR)*
Chad M. Boydston *(Controller & Sr VP)*
Lisa Owens *(Sr VP & Gen Mgr-Scripps Networks Digital)*
Mary E. Ray *(Sr VP, Deputy Gen Counsel & Asst Corp Sec)*
Sameer Deen *(Sr VP-Corp Dev)*
Mark W. Kroeger *(Sr VP-Comm & IR)*
Elaine McCall *(Sr VP-Affiliate Fin)*
Terry L. Smithers *(Sr VP-Audit & Compliance)*
John E. Viterisi *(Sr VP-Tax)*
Michael Smith *(Gen Mgr-Cooking Channel)*

Brands & Products:
COOKING CHANNEL

Advertising Agency:
Rogers & Cowan
8687 Melrose Ave 7th Fl
Los Angeles, CA 90069
Tel.: (310) 854-8100
Fax: (310) 854-8106
Chinese Food Made Easy
Chuck's Day Off
David Rocco's Dolce Vita
Everyday Exotic
Media Relations
Promotional Marketing
The Cooking Channel (Agency of Record)
— Tara Walls *(Exec VP)*
— Maggie Gallant *(Sr VP)*

SEACHANGE INTERNATIONAL, INC.

50 Nagog Park
Acton, MA 01720-3409
Tel.: (978) 897-0100
Fax: (978) 897-0132
E-mail: jongeb@schange.com
Web Site: www.schange.com
Approx. Rev.: $216,727,000
Approx. Number Employees: 1,202
Year Founded: 1993

Business Description:
Digital Server Systems & Software Supplier
S.I.C.: 3663
N.A.I.C.S.: 334220
Advertising Expenditures: $319,000
Media: 8-13-23-24

Personnel:
William C. Styslinger, III *(Chm & CEO)*
Yvette Kanouff *(Pres)*
Kevin M. Bisson *(CFO, Treas, Sec, Sr VP-Fin & Admin)*
Erwin van Dommelen *(Pres-Software)*
Steven M. Davi *(Sr VP-Advanced Tech)*
Ira Goldfarb *(Sr VP-Worldwide Sls)*
Maria Duquette *(VP-Customer Svc)*
Michael Hunsicker *(VP-Sls)*
Yefim Nivoro *(VP-Sls-Latin America)*
Jim Sheehan *(Dir-PR)*
Laura Watson *(Dir-HR)*

Brands & Products:
ADPLUS
AFFINITY
AXIOM
DVD ON DEMAND
GAME NOW
MEDIACLIENT
MEDIACLUSTER
MEDIALIBRARY
MEDIAPUBLISHER
QUICKSILVER
SEACHANGE
VODCAST

Advertising Agency:
IN MOTION PROMOTION Mobile Event Marketing
2100 Cloverleaf St E
Columbus, OH 43232
Tel.: (614) 866-9111
Fax: (614) 866-6182
Toll Free: (888) 801-0078

SECONDSPIN, INC.

(Div. of Trans World Entertainment Corporation)
2230 E Carson St
Carson, CA 90812
Tel.: (310) 830-4930
Fax: (310) 835-8304
Toll Free: (800) 962-6445
E-mail: orders@secondspin.com
Web Site: www.secondspin.com
Sales Range: $125-149.9 Million
Year Founded: 1996

Business Description:
Used CDs, Video Tapes & DVDs
S.I.C.: 5735; 5734
N.A.I.C.S.: 451220; 443120
Media: 13

SECUREEYE SYSTEMS, INC.

19504 24th Ave W Ste 5
Lynnwood, WA 98036-4868
Tel.: (425) 640-2871
Fax: (425) 640-2872
E-mail: info@sesysInc.com
Web Site: www.secureeyesystems.com
Sales Range: $1-9.9 Million
Approx. Number Employees: 5
Year Founded: 1998

Business Description:
Remotely Accessable Compressed Digital Data & Real-Time Video Systems
S.I.C.: 5065
N.A.I.C.S.: 423690
Advertising Expenditures: $200,000
Media: 13

Personnel:
Jim Masten *(Pres)*
Dawn Myers *(Mgr-Software)*

Brands & Products:
ALWAYS LOOKING OUT FOR YOU.

SENDMAIL, INC.

6475 Christie Ave Ste 400
Emeryville, CA 94608
Tel.: (510) 594-5400
Fax: (510) 594-5429
Toll Free: (888) 594-3150
E-mail: info@sendmail.com
Web Site: www.sendmail.com
E-Mail For Key Personnel:
Sales Director: sales@sendmail.com
Sales Range: $25-49.9 Million
Approx. Number Employees: 120
Year Founded: 1997

Business Description:
Internet Mail Solutions
S.I.C.: 7372; 7371
N.A.I.C.S.: 511210; 541511
Media: 13

Personnel:
Merritt M. Lutz *(Chm)*
Glen D. Vondrick *(Pres & COO)*
Donald J. Massaro *(CEO)*
Mark W. Davis *(CFO, VP-Fin & Admin)*
Gregory Shapiro *(CTO & VP-Engrg)*
Eric Allman *(Chief Science Officer)*
Stephanie Nevin *(VP-Mktg & Bus Dev)*

Brands & Products:
ADVANCED MESSAGE SERVER
CONTENT MANAGER
INTELLIGENT BOX
MAILCENTER
MAILCENTER QUARANTINE
MAILCENTER STORE
MAILSTREAM FLOW CONTROL
MAILSTREAM MANAGER
MAILSTREAM SWITCH
MOBILE MESSAGE SERVER
SENDMAIL DIRECTORY SERVICES
SENDMAIL SWITCH
SENTRION

SENDONLINE.COM, INC.

(Sub. of The Impex Group of Companies)
100 Canal Pointe Blvd Ste 204
Princeton, NJ 08540-7063
Tel.: (609) 720-0300
Fax: (609) 720-0505
Toll Free: (800) 420-7636
E-mail: info@send.com
Web Site: www.send.com
Approx. Number Employees: 13

Business Description:
E-Commerce Network Operator
S.I.C.: 5947
N.A.I.C.S.: 453220
Media: 5-13

Personnel:
Ranjan Wijesinghe *(Founder & CEO)*
James Imperato *(Co-Founder & VP)*

Brands & Products:
SEND.COM
SENDFLORAL.COM
SENDFOODS.COM
SENDGIFTS.COM
SENDLIQUOR.COM

SENDTRAFFIC.COM, INC.

(Sub. of Atrinsic, Inc.)
450 7th Ave
New York, NY 10123
Tel.: (212) 273-1141
Fax: (845) 215-0101
Toll Free: (866) 487-2334
E-mail: sales@sendtraffic.com
Web Site: www.sendtraffic.com
Sales Range: $1-9.9 Million
Approx. Number Employees: 25
Year Founded: 1999

Business Description:
Internet Marketing Services
S.I.C.: 7311
N.A.I.C.S.: 541810
Media: 7-13

SHOPLOCAL, LLC

(Sub. of Gannett Co., Inc.)
225 N Michigan Ave Ste 1600
Chicago, IL 60601
Tel.: (312) 616-5800
Fax: (312) 616-6620
Web Site: www.shoplocal.com
Sales Range: $75-99.9 Million
Approx. Number Employees: 110
Year Founded: 1999

Business Description:
Online Shopping & Advertising Services
S.I.C.: 5961; 7319
N.A.I.C.S.: 454111; 541890
Media: 8-10-13

Personnel:
Vikram Sharma *(CEO)*
Loch Rose *(Sr VP-Analytics)*
Jamie Ray *(VP-Retail)*

SHOPPING.COM, LTD.

(Sub. of eBay Inc.)
8000 Marina Blvd 5th Fl
Brisbane, CA 94005
Tel.: (650) 616-6500
Fax: (650) 616-6510
Toll Free: (800) 597-5808
E-mail: info@shopping.com
Web Site: www.shopping.com
Sales Range: $75-99.9 Million
Approx. Number Employees: 200
Year Founded: 1997

Business Description:
Online Comparison Shopping Services
S.I.C.: 7319; 8999
N.A.I.C.S.: 541890; 518112
Media: 10-13

Personnel:
Andre Haddad *(CEO)*

Brands & Products:
DEALTIME
EPINIONS
EPINIONS.COM
SHOPPING.COM

SHOWBUYER, INC.

501 5th Ave Ste 805
New York, NY 10017
Tel.: (212) 730-5375
Fax: (212) 730-8316
E-mail: info@showbuyer.com
Web Site: www.showbuyer.com
Approx. Number Employees: 26

Business Description:
Online Professional Networking Tool for the Performing Arts Community
S.I.C.: 2741; 7375
N.A.I.C.S.: 516110; 518111
Media: 13

Personnel:
Marvin Reiss *(Pres)*
Chaim Roberts *(Mgr-Opers)*

SHUTTERFLY, INC.

2800 Bridge Pkwy
Redwood City, CA 94065-1162
Tel.: (650) 610-5200
Fax: (650) 654-1299
E-mail: info@shutterfly.com
Web Site: www.shutterfly.com
E-Mail For Key Personnel:
Marketing Director: ads@shutterfly.com
Public Relations: pr@shutterfly.com
Approx. Rev.: $307,707,000
Approx. Number Employees: 611
Year Founded: 1999

Key to Media (For complete agency information see *The Advertising Red Books-Agencies* edition):
1. Bus. Publs. 2. Cable T.V. 3. Catalogs & Directories. 4. Co-op Adv. 5. Consumer Mags. 6. D.M. to Bus. Estab.7. D.M. to Consumers 8. Daily Newsp. 9. Exhibits/Trade Shows 10. Foreign 11. Infomercial 12. Internet Adv.13. Multimedia 14. Network Radio 15. Network T.V. 16. Newsp. Distr. Mags. 17. Other 18. Outdoor (Posters, Transit) 19. Point of Purchase20. Premiums, Novelties 21. Product Samples 22. Special Events Mktg. 23. Spot Radio 24. Spot T.V. 25. Weekly Newsp. 26. Yellow Page Adv.

Business Description:
Online Digital Photo Printing Services
S.I.C.: 7384
N.A.I.C.S.: 812921
Advertising Expenditures:
$14,576,000
Media: 13
Personnel:
Philip A. Marineau *(Chm)*
Jeffrey T. Housenbold *(CEO)*
Mark J. Rubash *(CFO & Sr VP)*
Peter Elarde *(CMO & Sr VP)*
Neil Day *(CTO & Sr VP)*
Charlotte Falla *(Gen Counsel & VP-Legal)*
Dwayne A. Black *(Sr VP-Ops)*
Douglas J. Galen *(Sr VP-Bus & Corp Dev)*
Dan McCormick *(Sr VP-Products & Svcs)*
Peter Navin *(Sr VP-HR)*
Sean Foley *(VP-Mktg Strategy)*
Brian Osborn *(VP-Brand Mktg)*
Brands & Products:
SHUTTERFLY
SHUTTERFLY EXPRESS
SHUTTERFLY STUDIO
TELL YOUR STORY

SHUTTERSTOCK, INC.

1133 Broadway Ste 1427
New York, NY 10010
Tel.: (646) 419-4452
Fax: (347) 402-0710
Toll Free: (866) 663-3954, ext. 102
Web Site: www.shutterstock.com
Business Description:
Online Royalty Free Subscription Based Stock Photography Agency
S.I.C.: 7335
N.A.I.C.S.: 541922
Media: 2-6-13
Personnel:
Jon Oringer *(Founder & CEO)*
Tyler Cole *(Product Mgr-Revenue)*

SILENTAUTOAUCTION.COM, LLC

PO Box 15333
Brooksville, FL 34604
Tel.: (707) 722-2277
Web Site: www.silentautoauction.com
Business Description:
Online Auto Auction
S.I.C.: 5961
N.A.I.C.S.: 454112
Media: 8-13
Personnel:
Doug Silvester *(Founder & Pres)*

SIMONDELIVERS, INC.

3440 Winpark Dr
New Hope, MN 55427
Tel.: (763) 656-5600
Tel.: (763) 971-4900 (Cust Svc)
Toll Free: (866) 586-2530
E-mail: feedback@CobornsDelivers.com
Web Site: www.cobornsdelivers.com
Sales Range: $50-74.9 Million
Approx. Number Employees: 450
Year Founded: 1999
Business Description:
Direct Seller & Delivery of Farm-Fresh Produce, Cut-To-Order Meats, Fresh Baked Goods, Grocery & Household Products & Wine, Beer & Spirits
S.I.C.: 5963
N.A.I.C.S.: 454390
Media: 8-13
Brands & Products:
SIMON DIRECT CHECK
SIMONDELIVERS

SINA CORP.

(Sub. of Sina Corporation)
883 N Shoreline Blvd Ste C 200
Mountain View, CA 94043
Tel.: (650) 210-9888
Fax: (650) 691-9898
E-mail: info@staff.sina.com
Web Site: www.sina.com
Approx. Number Employees: 45
Business Description:
Internet Media for the Chinese in North America & Abroad
S.I.C.: 7375
N.A.I.C.S.: 518111
Export
Advertising Expenditures:
$28,600,000
Media: 8-11-13-22

SITESTAR CORPORATION

7109 Timberlake Rd
Lynchburg, VA 24502
Tel.: (434) 239-4272
Toll Free: (888) 271-9672
Web Site: www.sitestar.com
Approx. Rev.: $5,051,916
Approx. Number Employees: 15
Business Description:
Internet Services
S.I.C.: 7375
N.A.I.C.S.: 518111
Advertising Expenditures: $36,000
Media: 17
Personnel:
Frank R. Erhartic, Jr. *(Pres & CEO)*
Daniel Judd *(CFO & Controller)*
Michael Collado *(VP-Mktg & Bus Dev)*

SKINNYCORP L.L.C.

4043 N Ravenswood Ave Ste 106
Chicago, IL 60613-1174
Tel.: (773) 878-3557
Fax: (888) 595-3258
E-mail: info@skinnycorp.com
Web Site: www.skinnycorp.com
Sales Range: $25-49.9 Million
Approx. Number Employees: 60
Business Description:
E-Commerce & Internet Website Owner & Operator; Apparel Mfr & Sls
S.I.C.: 5961; 2389; 2741; 5651
N.A.I.C.S.: 454111; 315999; 448140; 516110
Media: 13
Personnel:
Tom Ryan *(CEO)*

SKYAUCTION.COM, INC.

501 Madison Ave
New York, NY 10022-5602
Tel.: (212) 486-1250
Fax: (212) 486-7566
E-mail: bizdev@skyauction.com
Web Site: www.skyauction.com
Approx. Number Employees: 65
Year Founded: 1999
Business Description:
Online Auction for Airline Flights
S.I.C.: 4724
N.A.I.C.S.: 561510
Media: 13-22
Personnel:
Michael Hering *(Co-Founder, Pres & CEO)*
Salvatore Esposito *(Co-Founder & COO)*
Tilly M. Bachmann *(Dir-Sls & Svcs)*
DeeDee Flagg *(Dir-Creative)*
Maxine Fried *(Dir-Customer Svc)*
Brands & Products:
NOW YOU'RE GOING SOMEWHERE
SKYAUCTION.COM
SKYCASH

SKYSCAPE.COM INC.

(Sub. of Physicians Interactive Inc.)
100 Locke Dr Ste 2
Marlborough, MA 01752
Tel.: (508) 460-6500
Fax: (508) 460-6510
E-mail: info@skyscape.com
Web Site: www.skyscape.com
Approx. Sls.: $4,000,000
Approx. Number Employees: 41
Year Founded: 2000
Business Description:
Mobile & Desktop References for the Medical Community
S.I.C.: 7371
N.A.I.C.S.: 541511
Media: 2-13
Personnel:
Kartik Shah *(Founder & Chief Content Officer & Chief Innovation Officer)*
Sandeep Shah *(Founder & Chief Content Officer & Chief Innovation Officer)*
Jaap Vermeulen *(VP-Tech)*
Brands & Products:
DRDRUGS
SKYSCAPE
SMARTLINK

SMAATO INC.

3 Lagoon Dr Ste 170
Redwood Shores, CA 94065
Tel.: (650) 286-1198
Fax: (650) 240-0708
Web Site: www.smaato.com
Business Description:
Mobiel Advertising Provider for Mobile Applications & Mobile Websites; Aggregator of Ad Networks
S.I.C.: 7319
N.A.I.C.S.: 541890
Media: 2-5-10-13-27
Personnel:
Ragnar Kruse *(Founder & CEO)*
Harald Neidhardt *(Co-Founder & CMO)*
Petra Vorsteher *(Co-Founder & Exec VP-Strategic Alliances)*
Oliver Reiss *(CFO)*
Marc Junker *(CIO & CTO)*
Joerg Anhalt *(Sr VP-Mobile Publr Dev & Monetization)*

SMARTPROS LTD.

12 Skyline Dr
Hawthorne, NY 10532-2133
Tel.: (914) 345-2620
Tel.: (253) 863-8280 (Advertising)
Fax: (914) 345-2603
E-mail: info@smartpros.com
Web Site: corporate.smartpros.com
E-Mail For Key Personnel:
Marketing Director:
marketingservices@smartpros.com
Approx. Rev.: $17,623,417
Approx. Number Employees: 80
Year Founded: 1981
Business Description:
Continuing Education Products & Services
S.I.C.: 8732; 8299
N.A.I.C.S.: 541910; 611691; 611699; 611710
Advertising Expenditures: $115,000
Media: 1-2-5-7-9-13-22
Personnel:
Allen S. Greene *(Chm & CEO)*
Jack Fingerhut *(Pres)*
Stanley P. Wirtheim *(CFO)*
Joseph Fish *(CTO & Exec VP)*
Steve Henn *(Pres-Legal & Ethics)*
Jeffrey Jacobs *(Publr & VP)*
Mike Fowler *(Sr VP-Bus Dev)*
Shane Gillispie *(VP-Mktg & ECommerce)*
Jay D. Gregory *(VP-Ops & Fin Svcs)*
Mark R. Luciano *(VP-Engrg & Channel Partners)*
Brands & Products:
CPA REPORT
CPA REPORT ONLINE
CPA REPORT VIDEO
CVE
FMN ONLINE
KEEPSMART ENGINEERING
KNOWLEDGE FOR PROFESSIONALS
PE PREP COURSE
SMARTPROS
SMARTPROS ADVANTAGE
SMARTPROS CONSULTING
SMARTPROS ENGINEERING
SMARTPROS FINANCIAL SERVICES
SMARTPROS LEGAL
WILEY VIRTUAL

SMITH MICRO SOFTWARE, INC.

(Sub. of Smith Micro Software, Inc.)
185 Westridge Dr
Watsonville, CA 95076-4168
Tel.: (831) 761-6200
Fax: (831) 761-6206
Toll Free: (800) 732-8881
E-mail: cs@smithmicro.com
Web Site: www.smithmicro.com
Sales Range: $10-24.9 Million
Approx. Number Employees: 65
Year Founded: 1988
Business Description:
Software Products Designer & Developer
S.I.C.: 7372
N.A.I.C.S.: 511210
Media: 4-10
Brands & Products:
THE BIG MIX
CREATIVE ESSENTIALS
DRAGSTRIP
EVERYDAY SOLUTIONS
FLASHBACK
GOBAR
HOTTIME
ICLEAN
ICSPYWARE SUITE
INTERNET CLEANUP
SECURE DELETE
SHRINKWRAP
SPAMCATCHER
SPRING CLEANING
STUFFIT

Key to Media (For complete agency information see *The Advertising Red Books-Agencies* edition):
1. Bus. Publs. 2. Cable T.V. 3. Catalogs & Directories. 4. Co-op Adv. 5. Consumer Mags. 6. D.M. to Bus. Estab.7. D.M. to Consumers 8. Daily Newsp. 9. Exhibits/Trade Shows 10. Foreign 11. Infomercial 12. Internet Adv.13. Multimedia 14. Network Radio 15. Network T.V. 16. Newsp. Distr. Mags. 17. Other 18. Outdoor (Posters, Transit) 19. Point of Purchase20. Premiums, Novelties 21. Product Samples 22. Special Events Mktg. 23. Spot Radio 24. Spot T.V. 25. Weekly Newsp. 26. Yellow Page Adv.

Smith Micro Software, Inc. — (Continued)

STUFFIT ENGINE
STUFFIT EXPRESS
STUFFIT INSTALLERMAKER
ZIPMAGIC

SNAP INTERACTIVE, INC.

363 7th Ave 13th Fl
New York, NY 10001
Tel.: (516) 942-2030
Fax: (516) 626-6691
E-mail: contact@snap-interactive.com
Web Site: www.snap-interactive.com
Approx. Rev.: $6,668,627
Approx. Number Employees: 21
Year Founded: 2005
Business Description:
Online Dating Services & Applications
S.I.C.: 7299; 7379
N.A.I.C.S.: 812990; 541519
Advertising Expenditures: $306,140
Media: 13-17
Personnel:
Clifford Lerner *(Founder & CEO)*

SNAPFISH

(Unit of HP Imaging & Printing Group)
303 Second St S Tower Ste 500
San Francisco, CA 94107
Tel.: (301) 595-5308
Fax: (415) 979-3708
Toll Free: (800) 634-4500
E-mail: service@snapfish.com
Web Site: www.snapfish.com
E-Mail For Key Personnel:
Sales Director: sales@snapfish.com
Sales Range: $10-24.9 Million
Approx. Number Employees: 30
Year Founded: 1999
Business Description:
Online Film & Digital Photography Services
S.I.C.: 7384; 2741
N.A.I.C.S.: 812921; 516110
Media: 6-8-13
Personnel:
Paul Schumer *(VP-Mktg & Sls)*
Ben Nelson *(Gen Mgr)*
Brands & Products:
SNAPFISH

SO ACT NETWORK, INC.

10685-B Hazelhurst Dr #6572
Houston, TX 77043
Tel.: (210) 401-7667
Web Site: www.soact.net
Approx. Rev.: $6,643
Business Description:
Search Engine & Internet Services
S.I.C.: 2741
N.A.I.C.S.: 516110
Advertising Expenditures: $22,146
Media: 17
Personnel:
Greg Halpern *(Pres & CFO)*
John Blaisure *(CEO)*

SOFTMAN PRODUCTS COMPANY, LLC

(d/b/a BuyCheapSoftware)
13470 Washington Blvd
Marina Del Rey, CA 90292
Tel.: (310) 305-3644
Fax: (310) 305-3645
Toll Free: (888) 999-2611
E-mail: sales@buycheapsoftware.com
Web Site: www.buycheapsoftware.com
E-Mail For Key Personnel:
Sales Director: sales@buycheapsoftware.com
Approx. Number Employees: 15
Year Founded: 1997
Business Description:
Computer Products Online Retailer
S.I.C.: 5961
N.A.I.C.S.: 454113
Media: 2-3-4-6-7-8-10-13-18-20-22-23-24-26
Personnel:
Jonathan Dracup *(CEO)*
Brent Robinson *(CFO)*

SONUS NETWORKS INC.

7 Technology Park Dr
Westford, MA 01886
Tel.: (978) 614-8100
Fax: (978) 614-8101
E-mail: ir@sonusnet.com
Web Site: www.sonusnet.com
E-Mail For Key Personnel:
Sales Director: sales@sonusnet.com
Approx. Rev.: $249,307,000
Approx. Number Employees: 968
Year Founded: 1997
Business Description:
IP Communications Infrastructure Products
S.I.C.: 4812; 3661; 3663
N.A.I.C.S.: 517212; 334210; 334220
Advertising Expenditures: $100,000
Personnel:
Raymond P. Dolan *(Pres & CEO)*
Maurice Castonguay *(CFO & Sr VP)*
Bill Scudder *(CIO & VP)*
Rajiv Laroia *(CTO & Sr VP)*
Elmer Lai *(Chief Acctg Officer, VP-Fin & Controller)*
Howard E. Janzen *(CEO-One Communications Corp)*
Jeffrey M. Snider *(Gen Counsel, Sec & Sr VP)*
Wayne M. Pastore *(Treas & Sr VP)*
Todd Abbott *(Sr VP-Worldwide Sls)*
Gale England *(VP-Product Ops)*
Mehdi Ghasem *(VP-Strategy & Bus Dev)*
Kathy Harris *(VP-HR)*
David Tipping *(VP-Product Mktg & Product Mgmt)*
Brands & Products:
3GPP MULTIMEDIA TELEPHONY
ACCESS & LD TANDEM
ACCESS GATEWAY CONTROL FUNCTION
API INTEGRATION WORKSHOP
ASX FEATURE SERVER
BILLING MEDIATION
CDMA (CONSUMER)
CDMA (ENTERPRISE)
CENTRALIZED ROUTE SERVER
CENTRALIZED ROUTE SERVER (MNP)
CLASS 4 OFFLOAD
CLASS 4 TANDEM
CLASS 5 REPLACEMENT (BUSINESS)
CLASS 5 REPLACEMENT (RESIDENTIAL)
CUSTOM SOFTWARE DEVELOPMENT
DSI ADAPTOR DEVELOPMENT
ENGINEERING, FURNISHING & INSTALLATION
GATEWAY MSC
GSM (CONSUMER)
GSM (ENTERPRISE)
GSX4000
GSX9000
IMS/PC 2.0
IMS/SIP CORE (CONSUMER)
IMS/SIP CORE (ENTERPRISE)
IMS/TISPAN
IMX 2.1
IN SERVICES
INSIGHT
INTERNATIONAL GATEWAY
IP BUSINESS TRUNKS
IP CENTREX/VOBB
IPTV
LTE
MANAGED SERVICES
MEDIA GATEWAY
MEDIA TRANSCODING
MIGRATION SERVICES
MOBILEDGE 4000
MOBILEDGE 9000
MULTIMEDIA APPLICATION DEVELOPMENT PLATFORM
NETWORK AUDIT SERVICES
NETWORK BORDER SWITCH
NETWORK COMMISSIONING
NETWORK DEPLOYMENT DESIGN
NETWORK MANAGEMENT
NETWORK VERIFICATION
NUMBER PORTABILITY
OSS INTEGRATION CONSULTING
PACKETCABLE 1.5
PACKETCABLE MIGRATION
PACKETCABLE MULTIMEDIA (PCMM)
PICO/FEMTOCELL CONVERGENCE
PROGRAM MANAGEMENT
PSX CENTRALIZED ROUTE SERVER
REGULATORY SOLUTIONS
RESIDENT ENGINEER FOR NOC
SERVICE DELIVERY PLATFORM
SERVICE MANAGEMENT SOLUTIONS
SERVICE PROVISIONING
SESSION BORDER CONTROL (ACCESS)
SESSION BORDER CONTROL/IP PEERING
SESSION BORDER CONTROL (PEERING)
SOLUTION INTEGRATION
SONUS NETWORKS
SONUS NETWORKS HSX
SONUS NETWORKS PSX
SONUS NETWORKS SRX
SRX CALL SESSION SERVER
SS7/SIGTRAN MIGRATION
UMTS (CONSUMER)
UMTS (ENTERPRISE)
UPGRADE SERVICES
VIDEO TRANSPORT
VOICE OVER BROADBAND
VOICE VPN
WIFI CONVERGENCE (VCC)
WIMAX
WIMAX CONVERGENCE
Advertising Agency:
Racepoint Group, Inc.
404 Wyman St Ste 375
Waltham, MA 02451
Tel.: (781) 487-4600
Fax: (781) 890-5822

SONY ONLINE ENTERTAINMENT, INC.

(Sub. of Sony Pictures Digital)
8928 Terman Ct
San Diego, CA 92121
Tel.: (858) 577-3100
Fax: (858) 577-3200
E-mail: info@sonyonline.com
Web Site: www.sonyonline.com
Approx. Number Employees: 600
Business Description:
Online Gaming Products
S.I.C.: 7999
N.A.I.C.S.: 713990
Personnel:
John Smedley *(Pres)*
Russell Shanks *(COO & Exec VP)*
Michelle Hall *(Dir-Online Mktg)*
Advertising Agencies:
Ayzenberg Group, Inc.
49 E Walnut St
Pasadena, CA 91103
Tel.: (626) 584-4070
Fax: (626) 584-3954

SHIFT Communications LLC
20 Guest St Ste 200
Brighton, MA 02135
Tel.: (617) 779-1800
Fax: (617) 779-1899
Corporate Communications Agency of Record

SPECTORSOFT CORPORATION

1555 Indian River Blvd Bldg B210
Vero Beach, FL 32960
Tel.: (772) 770-5670
Fax: (772) 770-3442
Toll Free: (888) 598-2788
E-mail: info@spectorsoft.com
Web Site: www.spectorsoft.com
E-Mail For Key Personnel:
Sales Director: sales@spectorsoft.com
Approx. Sls.: $42,000,000
Approx. Number Employees: 90
Year Founded: 1999
Business Description:
Internet Monitoring & Surveillance Tools
S.I.C.: 7371
N.A.I.C.S.: 541511
Media: 13
Personnel:
Jason Judge *(Pres)*
Sharon Woolley *(Dir-Mktg Comm)*
Brands & Products:
EBLASTER
EBLASTER MAC
SPECTOR 2.2
SPECTOR 3.0
SPECTOR 360
SPECTOR CNE
SPECTOR FOR WINDOWS
SPECTOR PRO 5.0
SPECTOR PRO MAC
SPECTORSOFT
Advertising Agency:
Crossroads Public Relations
136 E Morgan St Ste 100
Raleigh, NC 27601
Tel.: (919) 821-2822
Fax: (919) 834-0448

Key to Media (For complete agency information see *The Advertising Red Books-Agencies* edition):
1. Bus. Publs. 2. Cable T.V. 3. Catalogs & Directories. 4. Co-op Adv. 5. Consumer Mags. 6. D.M. to Bus. Estab.7. D.M. to Consumers 8. Daily Newsp. 9. Exhibits/Trade Shows 10. Foreign 11. Infomercial 12. Internet Adv.13. Multimedia 14. Network Radio 15. Network T.V. 16. Newsp. Distr. Mags. 17. Other 18. Outdoor (Posters, Transit) 19. Point of Purchase20. Premiums, Novelties 21. Product Samples 22. Special Events Mktg. 23. Spot Radio 24. Spot T.V. 25. Weekly Newsp. 26. Yellow Page Adv.

SPORTSDIRECT INC.
211 Horseshoe Lake Dr
Halifax, NS B3S 0B9, Canada
Tel.: (902) 835-3320
Fax: (902) 835-3622
E-mail: info@sportsdirectinc.com
Web Site: www.sportsdirectinc.com
Sales Range: $10-24.9 Million
Approx. Number Employees: 120
Year Founded: 1995
Business Description:
On-Line Sports Information
S.I.C.: 2741
N.A.I.C.S.: 516110
Media: 13
Personnel:
Paul Lavers *(Founder & CEO)*
Dan MacDonald *(VP-Tech)*
Kelly Moss *(VP-Fin)*
Bill Organ *(VP-Sls)*
Christal Godfrey *(Mgr-Pub Rels)*

SPORTVISION, INC.
4619 N Ravenswood
Chicago, IL 60640
Tel.: (773) 293-4350
Fax: (773) 293-2155
E-mail: info@sportvision.com
Web Site: www.sportvision.com
Sales Range: $10-24.9 Million
Year Founded: 1998
Business Description:
Online Sports Information & Broadcasts
S.I.C.: 4833
N.A.I.C.S.: 515120
Media: 2-10-13
Personnel:
Mike Jakob *(Pres, COO & CFO)*
Hank Adams *(CEO)*
Jeff Jonas *(Exec VP & Gen Mgr-Football & Emerging Sports)*
Brands & Products:
FIRST AND TEN
K-ZONE
RACE F/X
VIRTUAL PLAYBOOK

SPREE.COM CORP.
1155 Phoenixville Pike Park Valley Ste 103
West Chester, PA 19380
Tel.: (610) 719-0412
Fax: (610) 516-1001
Toll Free: (888) 887-7733
E-mail: info@spree.com
Web Site: www.spree.com
Approx. Number Employees: 50
Year Founded: 1996
Business Description:
Online Shopping Rewards Program
S.I.C.: 7375
N.A.I.C.S.: 518111
Media: 13

SRT COMMUNICATIONS INC.
3615 N Broadway
Minot, ND 58703
Tel.: (701) 858-1200
Fax: (701) 858-5449
Web Site: www.srt.com
Approx. Sls.: $36,447,494
Approx. Number Employees: 200
Business Description:
Local Telephone Communications
S.I.C.: 4813; 4841
N.A.I.C.S.: 517310; 515210
Personnel:
Steven Lysne *(CEO & Gen Mgr)*
Perry Erdmann *(CFO)*
John A Reiser *(COO & Asst Gen Mgr)*
Advertising Agency:
Odney
1400 W Century Ave
Bismarck, ND 58503
Tel.: (701) 222-8721
Fax: (701) 222-8172
Toll Free: (888) 500-8721

STAMPS.COM INC.
12959 Coral Tree Pl
Los Angeles, CA 90066-7020
Tel.: (310) 482-5800
Fax: (310) 482-5900
E-mail: affiliates@stamps.com
Web Site: www.stamps.com
Approx. Rev.: $85,544,000
Approx. Number Employees: 220
Year Founded: 1996
Business Description:
Online Postage & Mailing Services
S.I.C.: 4311; 5943; 5961
N.A.I.C.S.: 491110; 453210; 454111
Advertising Expenditures: $5,500,000
Media: 7-8-10-13
Personnel:
Kenneth Mcbride *(Pres & CEO)*
Kyle Huebner *(CFO)*
Seth Weisberg *(Chief Legal Officer)*
James M. Bortnak *(Sr VP-Corp & Bus Dev)*
J.P. Leon *(VP-Postal Affairs & Tech)*
Eric Nash *(Dir-Online Mktg)*
Brands & Products:
HIDDEN POSTAGE
INTERNET POSTAGE
NETSTAMPS
PHOTOSTAMPS
POSTAGE FROM YOUR PRINTER
POSTAGE ON DEMAND
STAMPS.COM

STARBAND COMMUNICATIONS INC.
1750 Old Meadow Rd - 7th Fl
McLean, VA 22102-4302
Tel.: (703) 287-3000
Fax: (703) 245-6302
Toll Free: (800) 4STARBAND
Web Site: www.starband.com
Approx. Sls.: $12,000,000
Approx. Number Employees: 150
Business Description:
Internet Service Provider
S.I.C.: 5999; 4899
N.A.I.C.S.: 453998; 517910
Media: 13-23
Personnel:
Andreas M. Georghiou *(CEO)*
Jill Robins *(Dir-Mkg)*
Brands & Products:
STARBAND
STARBAND 480 PRO
STARBAND MODEL 360

STARTSAMPLING, INC.
130 E Saint Charles Rd Ste C
Carol Stream, IL 60188-2059
Tel.: (630) 868-2000
Fax: (630) 260-0800
E-mail: sales@startsampling.com
Web Site: www.startsampling.com
E-Mail For Key Personnel:
President: lburns@startsampling.com
Sales Director: sales@startsampling.com
Approx. Number Employees: 30
Year Founded: 1998
Business Description:
Online Provider of Product Sampling
S.I.C.: 8743
N.A.I.C.S.: 541820
Media: 2-4-7-8-10-13-20
Personnel:
Larry Burns *(CEO)*
Michael Weiss *(Exec VP)*
Brands & Products:
FREQUENT TRYER MILES
STARTSAMPLING
TRY SOMETHING NEW

STRANGE'S FLORIST & GREENHOUSES
3313 Mechanicsville Pike
Richmond, VA 23223-1726
Tel.: (804) 321-2200
Fax: (804) 329-2421
Toll Free: (800) 421-4070
E-mail: service@stranges.com
Web Site: www.stranges.com
Approx. Number Employees: 100
Business Description:
Online Flowers & Floral Arrangements Retailer
S.I.C.: 5992; 5261
N.A.I.C.S.: 453110; 444220
Media: 13-26
Personnel:
William J. Gouldin, Jr. *(Pres & CEO)*

STRATEGIC FOCUS
2275 French St
Livermore, CA 94550
Tel.: (408) 568-3993
E-mail: jay@strategicfocus.com
Web Site: www.strategicfocus.com
E-Mail For Key Personnel:
President: jay@strategicfocus.com
Sales Range: Less than $1 Million
Approx. Number Employees: 14
Year Founded: 1986
Business Description:
Business Strategy Consulting & Software Evaluation
S.I.C.: 7373
N.A.I.C.S.: 541512
Media: 13
Personnel:
Jay Prakash *(Pres)*
Brands & Products:
ITENOL
SOLUTION ACQUISITION MANGAGER

STRATIFY, INC.
(Div. of Iron Mountain Incorporated)
501 Ellis St
Mountain View, CA 94043
Tel.: (650) 988-2000
Fax: (650) 988-2159
E-mail: sales@stratify.com
Web Site: www.stratify.com
E-Mail For Key Personnel:
Sales Director: sales@stratify.com
Approx. Sls.: $2,500,000
Approx. Number Employees: 55
Year Founded: 1999
Business Description:
Legal Document Organization & Management Software Developer
S.I.C.: 7372; 7371
N.A.I.C.S.: 511210; 541511
Media: 2-7-10-13-22-26
Personnel:
Meena Srinivasan *(VP-HR & Fin)*
Brands & Products:
STRATIFY
STRATIFY LEGAL DISCOVERY
Advertising Agency:
Levick Strategic Communications, LLC
1900 M St NW Ste 400
Washington, DC 20036
Tel.: (202) 973-1300
Fax: (202) 973-1301

STREAMING MEDIA HOSTING, INC.
2280 University Dr Ste 104
Newport Beach, CA 92660
Tel.: (949) 722-8600
Fax: (949) 266-9470
Toll Free: (800) 963-4347
E-mail: info@streamingmediahosting.com
Web Site:
www.streamingmediahosting.com
Approx. Number Employees: 21
Business Description:
Internet Broadcasting of Video & Audio; Content Distribution Network (CDN)
S.I.C.: 2741
N.A.I.C.S.: 516110
Media: 1-2-4-7-8-10-13-22-23-24
Personnel:
Ben Byassee *(Founder & COO)*
Robert Klug *(CEO)*
David Sanchez *(VP-Sls)*

STS JEWELS
42 West 48th St Ste 1600
New York, NY 10036
Tel.: (646) 688-5559
Fax: (646) 688-4826
Web Site: www.stsjewels.com
E-Mail For Key Personnel:
President: sunila@stsjewels.com
Sales Range: $25-49.9 Million
Approx. Number Employees: 1,600
Year Founded: 1996
Business Description:
Online Jewelry Store
S.I.C.: 5094
N.A.I.C.S.: 423940
Advertising Expenditures: $200,000
Media: 2-10-13
Personnel:
Sunil Agrawal *(Chm)*

STUDENTCITY.COM INC.
8 Essex Ctr Dr
Peabody, MA 01960
Tel.: (978) 531-3301
Fax: (978) 563-1852
Toll Free: (888) 777-4642
Web Site: www.studentcity.com
E-Mail For Key Personnel:
Sales Director: sales@studentcity.com
Approx. Number Employees: 40
Year Founded: 1996
Business Description:
Internet Based Travel Agency Specializing in Student Travel
S.I.C.: 4724
N.A.I.C.S.: 561510
Advertising Expenditures: $300,000
Media: 9-13-17-25

Key to Media (For complete agency information see *The Advertising Red Books-Agencies* edition):
1. Bus. Publs. 2. Cable T.V. 3. Catalogs & Directories. 4. Co-op Adv. 5. Consumer Mags. 6. D.M. to Bus. Estab.7. D.M. to Consumers
8. Daily Newsp. 9. Exhibits/Trade Shows 10. Foreign 11. Infomercial 12. Internet Adv.13. Multimedia 14. Network Radio
15. Network T.V. 16. Newsp. Distr. Mags. 17. Other 18. Outdoor (Posters, Transit) 19. Point of Purchase20. Premiums, Novelties
21. Product Samples 22. Special Events Mktg. 23. Spot Radio 24. Spot T.V. 25. Weekly Newsp. 26. Yellow Page Adv.

STUDENTMARKET.COM, INC.
8 Faneuil Hall Marketplace 3rd Fl
Boston, MA 02109-6114
Tel.: (781) 398-1841
Fax: (425) 671-3496
Toll Free: (888) 788-3348
E-mail: service@studentmarket.com
Web Site: www.studentmarket.com
Approx. Number Employees: 10
Year Founded: 1995
Business Description:
Online College Product Retailer
S.I.C.: 5961
N.A.I.C.S.: 454113
Media: 2-4-6-8-20-21-22-23-24
Personnel:
Oren Milgram *(Pres & CEO)*
Brands & Products:
STUDENTMARKET
STUDENTMARKET.COM

SUBMIT EXPRESS, INC.
315 W Verdugo Ave Ste 101
Burbank, CA 91502-2341
Tel.: (818) 567-3030
Fax: (818) 567-0202
Toll Free: (877) 737-3083
E-mail: feedbacks@submitexpress.com
Web Site: www.submitexpress.com
Approx. Number Employees: 30
Year Founded: 1998
Business Description:
Search Engine
S.I.C.: 8999; 2741
N.A.I.C.S.: 518112; 516110
Media: 4-7-10-13
Personnel:
Pierre Zarokian *(Pres & CEO)*
Brands & Products:
SUBMIT EXPRESS

SUNGARD FINANCIAL SYSTEMS-NEW YORK
(Branch of SunGard Financial Systems, Inc.)
340 Madison Ave Fl 8
New York, NY 10173
Tel.: (212) 506-0300
Fax: (212) 977-7144
Toll Free: (800) 825-2518
E-mail: getinfo@sungard.com
Web Site: www.sungard.com
Approx. Number Employees: 300
Year Founded: 1982
Business Description:
Customized Financial Software Solutions
S.I.C.: 7371
N.A.I.C.S.: 541511
Media: 10-13

SUPPORT.COM, INC.
1900 Seaport Blvd 3rd Fl
Redwood City, CA 94063
Tel.: (650) 556-9440
Fax: (650) 556-1195
Toll Free: (877) 493-2778
E-mail: info@support.com
Web Site: www.support.com
Approx. Rev.: $44,177,000
Approx. Number Employees: 761
Year Founded: 1997
Business Description:
Technical Support Automation Software
S.I.C.: 7372; 7371
N.A.I.C.S.: 519130; 511210; 541511
Advertising Expenditures: $10,600,000
Media: 2-7-10-13
Personnel:
Jimmie E. Stephens *(Chm)*
Joshua W.R. Pickus *(Pres & CEO)*
Shelly Schaffer *(CFO & Exec VP)*
Anthony Rodio *(COO & Exec VP)*
Rich Matta *(VP-Engrg)*
Brands & Products:
INTELLIGENT ASSISTANCE SUITE
KNOWLEDGE CENTER
LIVEASSIST
REAL TIME SERVICE MANAGEMENT
REINVENTING TECHNOLOGY SUPPORT
SELF-SERVICE SUITE
SERVICE AUTOMATION SUITE
SERVICEGATEWAY
SERVICEVERIFY
SMARTACCESS
SUPPORTSOFT

SURETY, INC.
12020 Sunrise Valley Dr
Reston, VA 20191
Tel.: (703) 707-9901
Fax: (703) 707-9910
Toll Free: (800) 298-3115
E-mail: sales@surety.com
Web Site: www.surety.com
E-Mail For Key Personnel:
Sales Director: sales@surety.com
Approx. Number Employees: 10
Year Founded: 1993
Business Description:
Tamperproof Data Solutions Services
S.I.C.: 7389; 7375
N.A.I.C.S.: 541199; 518111
Media: 13
Personnel:
Addison Fischer *(Chm)*
Tom Klaff *(CEO)*
Jim O'Connor *(Exec VP-Engrg)*
Michael Castle *(VP-Sls & Bus Dev)*
Robert P. Flinton *(VP-Mktg & Product Mgmt)*
Brands & Products:
ABSOLUTEPROOF
THE POWER OF PROOF
SURETY

SURFCONTROL USA
(Sub. of Websense)
10240 Sorrento Valley Rd
San Diego, CA 92121
Tel.: (858) 320-8000
Fax: (858) 458-2850
E-mail: info@websense.com
Web Site: www.surfcontrol.com
Sales Range: $75-99.9 Million
Approx. Number Employees: 200
Business Description:
Content Security Software
S.I.C.: 5045; 7372
N.A.I.C.S.: 423430; 511210
Media: 10-13

SWAPDRIVE, INC.
(Sub. of Symantec Corporation)
1313 F St NW 4th Fl
Washington, DC 20004-1102
Tel.: (202) 393-9900
Fax: (202) 393-9232
E-mail: info@swapdrive.com
Web Site: www.swapdrive.com
E-Mail For Key Personnel:
Sales Director: sales@swapdrive.com
Sales Range: $10-24.9 Million
Approx. Number Employees: 15
Year Founded: 1999
Business Description:
Online Computer Storage Solutions
S.I.C.: 3572
N.A.I.C.S.: 334112
Media: 13
Brands & Products:
FILESHARE
WHALEMAIL

SWS GROUP, INC.
1201 Elm St Ste 3500
Dallas, TX 75270
Tel.: (214) 859-1800
Fax: (214) 859-9312
E-mail: info@swst.com
Web Site: www.swst.com
Approx. Rev.: $389,819,000
Approx. Number Employees: 1,073
Year Founded: 1972
Business Description:
Securities Transaction Processing, Investment Banking & Asset Management Services
S.I.C.: 6211; 6282
N.A.I.C.S.: 523120; 523110; 523930
Advertising Expenditures: $4,547,000
Personnel:
Donald A. Buchholz *(Chm)*
James H. Ross *(Pres & CEO)*
Stacy M. Hodges *(CFO, Treas & Exec VP)*
W. Norman Thompson *(CIO & Exec VP)*
Allen R. Tubb *(Gen Counsel, Sec & VP)*
Daniel R. Leland *(Exec VP)*
Richard H. Litton *(Exec VP)*
Jeffrey J. Singer *(Exec VP)*
Paul D. Vinton *(Exec VP)*

SYNACOR, INC.
40 La Riviere Dr Ste 300
Buffalo, NY 14202
Tel.: (716) 362-3311
Fax: (716) 332-0081
Web Site: www.synacor.com
Sales Range: $25-49.9 Million
Approx. Number Employees: 163
Year Founded: 1998
Business Description:
Internet Platform for Digital Content & Services
S.I.C.: 2741; 7373
N.A.I.C.S.: 516110; 541512
Media: 13
Personnel:
George Chamoun *(Sr VP-Client Svcs & Co-Founder)*
Ronald Frankel *(Pres & CEO)*
William J. Stuart *(CFO)*
Scott Bailey *(COO)*
Theodore May *(Sr VP-Strategy & Bus Affairs)*
Greg Riker *(Sr VP-Worldwide Sls)*
CJ Singh *(Sr VP-Product & Engrg)*
Ron Bernstein *(VP-Online Adv)*
Julia Culkin *(VP-HR)*
Bill Lindquist *(VP-Mktg)*
Ralph Wasner *(VP-IT & Technical Ops)*
Mike Major *(Sr Dir-Bus Ops)*
Laura Casillo *(Mgr-Fin Plng & Analysis)*
Rachel McCabe *(Mgr-HR)*
Brands & Products:
SYNACOR

SYNAPSE GROUP, INC.
(Sub. of Time Inc.)
225 High Ridge Pk
Stamford, CT 06905-1325
Tel.: (203) 595-8255
Toll Free: (800) 884-3350
E-mail: webmaster@synapsemail.com
Web Site: www.synapsegroupinc.com
Sales Range: $75-99.9 Million
Approx. Number Employees: 300
Year Founded: 1991
Business Description:
Management Services for Publishers of Consumer Magazines; Online Magazine Retailer
S.I.C.: 8748
N.A.I.C.S.: 541618
Media: 8-13
Personnel:
Jeff Blatt *(CEO)*

SYNCSORT INCORPORATED
50 Tice Blvd Ste 250
Woodcliff Lake, NJ 07677
Tel.: (201) 930-9700
Fax: (201) 930-8282
E-mail: info@syncsort.com
Web Site: www.syncsort.com
Approx. Number Employees: 200
Business Description:
Computer Software Development
S.I.C.: 7371
N.A.I.C.S.: 541511
Personnel:
Flavio Santoni *(CEO)*
W. Sean Ford *(CMO)*
Mike Kuehn *(Mgr-Natl Sls)*
Brands & Products:
BEX
BEX INSTANT VIRTUALIZATION
DMEXPRESS
EXPRESSDR
FILEPORT
PARASORT
PIPESORT
PROC SYNCSORT
SYNCSORT
SYNCSORT VSE
VISUAL SYNCSORT
XRSERVER
Advertising Agency:
Stein Rogan + Partners
432 Park Ave S
New York, NY 10016-8013
Tel.: (212) 213-1112
Fax: (212) 779-7305

TECHHEALTH, INC.
14025 Riveredge Dr Ste 400
Tampa, FL 33637-2003
Tel.: (813) 490-1900
Fax: (813) 490-1945
Toll Free: (877) 611-3145
E-mail: customerservice@techhealth.com
Web Site: www.techhealth.com
Approx. Number Employees: 200
Year Founded: 1998
Business Description:
Web-Based Solutions for the Delivery & Payment of Ancillary Healthcare Services
S.I.C.: 7371
N.A.I.C.S.: 541511

Key to Media (For complete agency information see *The Advertising Red Books-Agencies* edition):
1. Bus. Publs. 2. Cable T.V. 3. Catalogs & Directories. 4. Co-op Adv. 5. Consumer Mags. 6. D.M. to Bus. Estab.7. D.M. to Consumers
8. Daily Newsp. 9. Exhibits/Trade Shows 10. Foreign 11. Infomercial 12. Internet Adv.13. Multimedia 14. Network Radio
15. Network T.V. 16. Newsp. Distr. Mags. 17. Other 18. Outdoor (Posters, Transit) 19. Point of Purchase20. Premiums, Novelties
21. Product Samples 22. Special Events Mktg. 23. Spot Radio 24. Spot T.V. 25. Weekly Newsp. 26. Yellow Page Adv.

Advertising Expenditures: $250,000
Media: 13
Personnel:
Thomas R. Sweet *(CEO)*
Mickel Schopke *(CFO & Exec VP)*
Michael L. Apple *(Exec VP-Network & Provider Rels)*
Tim Rametta *(Exec VP-IT)*
Bridgette Summers *(Exec VP-HR & Bus Admin)*
Tamra Keener *(Mgr-Events & Sls)*
Brands & Products:
TECHHEALTH
TECHHEALTH CONNECTIONS

TECHNICAL COMMUNITIES, INC.
(d/b/a TesMart)
1000 Cherry Ave Ste 100
San Bruno, CA 94066-3022
Tel.: (650) 624-0525
Fax: (650) 624-0535
Toll Free: (888) 665-2765
Web Site:
www.technicalcommunities.com
Approx. Number Employees: 20
Year Founded: 1998
Business Description:
Test & Measurement Equipment Products, Information & Services
S.I.C.: 7375
N.A.I.C.S.: 518111
Import Export
Advertising Expenditures: $150,000
Media: 2-7-8-10-13-25
Personnel:
Peter Ostrow *(Pres & CEO)*
Jeffrey Wheeler *(CFO)*
Sudip Barman *(VP-Engrg)*
James Ferraro *(VP-Mktg)*
Nitin Shroff *(Sr Product Mgr)*
Brands & Products:
NAVICPMART
TECHNICAL COMMUNITIES
TESTMART

TECHSKILLS, LLC
110 Wild Basin Rd Ste 310
Austin, TX 78746
Tel.: (512) 328-4235
E-mail: info@techskills.com
Web Site: www.techskills.com
Approx. Number Employees: 430
Year Founded: 1996
Business Description:
Computer Classes & Educational Services
S.I.C.: 8243
N.A.I.C.S.: 611420
Media: 13
Brands & Products:
CAREERFORGE
GET THE SKILLS. GET AHEAD.
TECHSKILLS
Advertising Agency:
Gragg Advertising
450 E 4th St Ste 100
Kansas City, MO 64106
Tel.: (816) 931-0050
Fax: (816) 931-0051
Toll Free: (800) 649-4225

TEKSELL, INC.
1835 Moriah Woods Blvd Ste 1
Memphis, TN 38117
Tel.: (901) 758-8179
Fax: (901) 758-1667
E-mail: employment@teksell.com
Approx. Number Employees: 25
Year Founded: 1999
Business Description:
Online Marketplace for IT Professionals to Buy & Sell New, Remanufactured & Previously Owned Data, Video & Voice Equipment
S.I.C.: 7375
N.A.I.C.S.: 518111
Media: 2-7-19-20-21-22
Personnel:
Ray Lewallen *(Pres)*
Tara Williams *(Dir-Mktg)*
Brands & Products:
TEKSELL

TELCOIQ, INC.
4300 Forbes Blvd Ste 110
Lanham, MD 20706
Tel.: (202) 595-1500
Fax: (202) 403-3684
E-mail: contact@telcoiq.com
Web Site: www.telcoiq.com
Sales Range: $75-99.9 Million
Approx. Number Employees: 20
Business Description:
Telecom Resellers
S.I.C.: 4813
N.A.I.C.S.: 517310
Media: 10-13
Personnel:
Joel Sam *(Pres)*

TERAGO INC.
(d/b/a TeraGo Networks)
55 Commerce Valley Dr W Suite 710
Thornhill, ON L3T 7V9, Canada
Tel.: (905) 707-0788
Fax: (905) 707-6212
E-mail: scean.mecinnf@terago.ca
Web Site: www.terago.ca
Approx. Rev.: $34,030,661
Approx. Number Employees: 173
Business Description:
Wireless Broadband Data Communications Services
S.I.C.: 4812
N.A.I.C.S.: 517212
Media: 7-13-17
Personnel:
Bryan Boyd *(Pres & CEO)*
Scott Browne *(CFO)*
Jim Nikopoulos *(Gen Counsel & VP-Corp Dev)*
Kevin Hickey *(VP-Engrg & Ops)*
Michael Testa *(VP-Mktg)*

TERRESTAR CORPORATION
(Filed Ch 11 Bankruptcy #11-10612 on 2/23/11 in U.S. Bankruptcy Court, Southern Dist of NY, Manhattan)
12010 Sunset Hills Rd
Reston, VA 21090
Tel.: (703) 483-7800
E-mail: webmaster@terrestar.com
Web Site: www.terrestarcorp.com
Approx. Rev.: $2,384,000
Approx. Number Employees: 104
Year Founded: 1988
Business Description:
Satellite Wireless Communication Services
S.I.C.: 4899; 4812
N.A.I.C.S.: 517410; 517212
Advertising Expenditures: $1,500,000
Media: 6-13
Personnel:
William M. Freeman *(Chm)*
Jeffrey W. Epstein *(Pres & CEO)*
Vincent Loiacono *(CFO)*
Douglas Brandon *(Gen Counsel, Sec & Sr VP)*
Brands & Products:
ELINK
ELINKMAIL
MSAT
PERPETUAL MOTIENT
SKYCELL
TERRESTAR

TFC.NET CORPORATION
15211 Lk Maurine Dr
Odessa, FL 33556
Tel.: (813) 880-0909
Fax: (866) 692-0366
E-mail: emartin@tfc.net
Web Site: www.tfc.net
Approx. Number Employees: 30
Year Founded: 1991
Business Description:
Forensic & Data Retrieval Services
S.I.C.: 7373
N.A.I.C.S.: 541512
Media: 13
Personnel:
Earl Martin *(Pres)*

THELADDERS.COM
Mailing Address:
137 Varick St
New York, NY 10013
Tel.: (646) 453-1800
Web Site: www.theladders.com
Business Description:
Employment Search Engine
N.A.I.C.S.: 561311
Advertising Agency:
Stein Rogan + Partners
432 Park Ave S
New York, NY 10016-8013
Tel.: (212) 213-1112
Fax: (212) 779-7305

THESTREET.COM, INC.
14 Wall St 15th Fl
New York, NY 10005-2140
Tel.: (212) 321-5000
Fax: (212) 321-5038
Toll Free: (800) 572-9571
E-mail: ir@thestreet.com
Web Site: www.thestreet.com
E-Mail For Key Personnel:
President: thomas.clarke@thestreet.com
Approx. Rev.: $57,186,379
Approx. Number Employees: 291
Year Founded: 1996
Business Description:
Financial News, Commentary & Investment Information Internet-Related Sources, Mobile Devices & Online TV Channels Publisher
S.I.C.: 2741; 4833; 7389
N.A.I.C.S.: 516110; 511199; 515120; 519190
Advertising Expenditures: $4,100,000
Media: 3-6-7-8-9-13-14-15-18-21-22-23-24
Personnel:
Christopher P. Marshall *(Chm)*
Daryl R. Otte *(CEO)*
Thomas J. Etergino *(CFO & Exec VP)*
Daniel Flax *(CIO)*
Richard Broitman *(Chief Acctg Officer)*
Gregory E. Barton *(Gen Counsel, Sec, Exec VP-Bus & Legal Affairs)*
Erika Faust *(Sr VP-Mktg)*
Brian Hecht *(Sr VP-Premium Svcs)*
Tom O'Regan *(Sr VP-Adv Sls)*
Kurt Tietjen *(Sr VP-Ops)*
Ronni Diamant *(VP-HR)*
Glenn Hall *(Editor-in-Chief)*
Carol Steel *(Dir-Creative)*
Brands & Products:
ACTIONALERTS PLUS
REALMONEY.COM
THESTREET.COM

THINKRONIZE, INC.
3630 Park 42 Dr Ste 170F
Cincinnati, OH 45241
Tel.: (513) 731-4090
Fax: (513) 731-1710
Toll Free: (877) 517-1125
E-mail: customersupport@nettrekker.com
Web Site: www.nettrekker.com
Sales Range: $10-24.9 Million
Approx. Number Employees: 80
Year Founded: 2000
Business Description:
Search Engine to Limit Web Content for Schools
S.I.C.: 7373
N.A.I.C.S.: 541512
Personnel:
Randy L. Wilhelm *(CEO)*
Joe Vallo *(COO)*
Steve Nordmark *(Dir-Product Dev)*
Brands & Products:
DIGITALBACKPACK
NETTREKKER
NETTREKKER CLASSIC
NETTREKKER D.I.
Advertising Agency:
Middleberg Communications, LLC
317 Madison Ave Ste 1500
New York, NY 10017
Tel.: (212) 812-5663
Tel.: (212) 812-5665
Fax: (212) 202-4118

THIRDAGE, INC.
210 Lincoln St Ste 302
Boston, MA 02111
Tel.: (617) 350-9962
E-mail: karen@thirdage.com
Web Site: www.thirdage.com
Approx. Number Employees: 25
Year Founded: 1996
Business Description:
Online Publisher of Lifestyle & Health Related Content for Older Adults
S.I.C.: 2741
N.A.I.C.S.: 516110; 511199
Media: 6-8-13-17
Personnel:
Sharon P. Whiteley *(CEO)*
Seana Baruth *(Sr VP-Product Devel)*
Brands & Products:
MENOPAUSE ONLINE
THIRDAGE
THIRDAGE CAFE
THIRDAGE CONNECTIONS
THIRDAGE INC.
THIRDAGE.COM
THE WEB...FOR GROWNUPS

THOMAS TECHNOLOGY SOLUTIONS INC.
(Sub. of Thomas Publishing Company LLC)

Key to Media (For complete agency information see *The Advertising Red Books-Agencies* edition):
1. Bus. Publs. 2. Cable T.V. 3. Catalogs & Directories. 4. Co-op Adv. 5. Consumer Mags. 6. D.M. to Bus. Estab.7. D.M. to Consumers
8. Daily Newsp. 9. Exhibits/Trade Shows 10. Foreign 11. Infomercial 12. Internet Adv.13. Multimedia 14. Network Radio
15. Network T.V. 16. Newsp. Distr. Mags. 17. Other 18. Outdoor (Posters, Transit) 19. Point of Purchase20. Premiums, Novelties
21. Product Samples 22. Special Events Mktg. 23. Spot Radio 24. Spot T.V. 25. Weekly Newsp. 26. Yellow Page Adv.

Thomas Technology Solutions Inc. — (Continued)

1 Progress Dr
Horsham, PA 19044-3502
Tel.: (215) 682-5000
Fax: (215) 682-5381
Toll Free: (800) 872-2828
E-mail: info@thomastechsolutions.com
Web Site: www.thomastechsolutionsmaster.com
Business Description:
Online Database Services
S.I.C.: 2791; 7373; 7375
N.A.I.C.S.: 323122; 518111; 541512
Media: 4-10-13
Personnel:
Christine DeCia *(Mgr-Mktg)*

TICKETMASTER ENTERTAINMENT LLC

(Sub. of Live Nation Entertainment, Inc.)
9348 Civic Center Dr
Beverly Hills, CA 90210
Tel.: (310) 867-7000
Tel.: (310) 360-2354 (IR)
Fax: (310) 360-2492
E-mail: ir@ticketmaster.com
Web Site: www.ticketmaster.com
Approx. Rev.: $1,486,167,000
Approx. Number Employees: 3,900
Year Founded: 1976
Business Description:
Live Entertainment Ticketing & Marketing Services
S.I.C.: 7999; 7319
N.A.I.C.S.: 713990; 541890
Advertising Expenditures: $21,600,000
Media: 5-16-23-24
Personnel:
Popi Mavros *(Dir-Client Dev)*
Tony Cortez *(Sr Mgr-Partner Adv)*
Advertising Agencies:
Mechanica
75 Water St Level 2
Newburyport, MA 01950
Tel.: (978) 499-7871
Fax: (978) 499-7876

Ooyala, Inc.
800 W El Camino Real Ste 350
Mountain View, CA 94040
Tel.: (650) 961-3400

TOWERSTREAM CORP.

55 Hammarlund Way
Middletown, RI 02842
Tel.: (401) 848-5848
E-mail: info@towerstream.com
Web Site: www.towerstream.com
Approx. Rev.: $19,645,893
Approx. Number Employees: 129
Business Description:
Wireless Broadband Services
S.I.C.: 7299
N.A.I.C.S.: 812990
Advertising Expenditures: $962,000
Personnel:
Philip Urso *(Founder & Chm)*
Jeffrey M. Thompson *(Pres, CEO & Dir)*
Joseph Hernon *(CFO)*
Mel Yarbrough *(COO)*
Arthur G. Giftakis *(VP-Engrg & Network Ops)*

TRACK DATA CORPORATION

95 Rockwell Pl
Brooklyn, NY 11217-1515
Tel.: (718) 522-7373
Tel.: (212) 943-4555
Fax: (718) 260-4375
E-mail: info@trackecn.com
Web Site: www.trackdata.com
Approx. Rev.: $30,659,000
Approx. Number Employees: 115
Year Founded: 1981
Business Description:
Real-Time Online Trading & Market Data to Institutional & Individual Investors
S.I.C.: 6289; 2741; 6211; 6282
N.A.I.C.S.: 523999; 516110; 523120; 523930
Advertising Expenditures: $274,000
Media: 7-10
Personnel:
Barry Hertz *(Founder & CTO)*
E. Bruce Fredrikson *(Chm)*
Martin Kaye *(CEO & CFO)*
Stanley Stern *(Sr VP & Chief Compliance Officer)*
William Olsen *(VP-Sls)*
Barbara Karol *(Dir-HR)*
Brands & Products:
AIQ SYSTEMS
DIAL-DATA
MARKETRACK
MARKETRACK MX-NT
MYTRACK
MYTRACK PRO
NEWSWATCH
NEWSWATCH API
OPTRACK
PROTRACK
TRACK ECN
TRACKDATA
TRACKTRADE

TRADECARD INC.

75 Maiden Ln Fl 12
New York, NY 10038
Tel.: (212) 405-1800
Fax: (212) 405-1801
Web Site: www.tradecard.com
Approx. Number Employees: 100
Business Description:
Online Service Providers
S.I.C.: 7375
N.A.I.C.S.: 518111
Personnel:
Kurt Cavano *(Chm & CEO)*
Guy Rey-Herme *(Pres & COO)*
Lois Bruu *(Sr VP-Strategic Initiatives)*
Chris Clinton *(Sr VP-Global Channel Mgmt)*
Bob Copeland *(Sr VP-Product Strategy & Bus Dev)*
Frank Bakker *(VP-Sls-France)*
Natalie Lindsey *(VP-HR)*
Bryan Nella *(Dir-Corp Comm)*
Veeresh Singh *(Product Mgr)*
Brands & Products:
CONNECT. TRANSACT. PROFIT.
SOURCEVIEW
TRADECARD
Advertising Agency:
Impressions-A.B.A. Industries, Inc.
393 Jericho Tpk
Mineola, NY 11501
Tel.: (516) 739-3210
Fax: (516) 739-9246

TRADEPAQ CORPORATION

33 Maiden Ln 9th Fl
New York, NY 10038-3202
Tel.: (212) 482-8080
Fax: (212) 482-8081
E-mail: info@tradepaq.com
Web Site: www.tradepaq.com
Approx. Number Employees: 50
Year Founded: 1996
Business Description:
Developer & Marketer of Graphical User Interface Connectivity Products for Mainframes & AS/400 Systems
S.I.C.: 7371
N.A.I.C.S.: 541511
Export
Media: 7-8-11-13
Personnel:
David Janay *(Exec VP)*
Brands & Products:
BOLEROPAQ
MEDPAQ
SECURITYPAQ
TRADEPAQ

TRAFFIC MARKETPLACE, INC.

(Name Changed to Epic Marketplace, Inc.)

TRAFFIC.COM, INC.

(Sub. of NAVTEQ Corp.)
851 Duportail Rd
Wayne, PA 19087
Tel.: (610) 725-9700
E-mail: info@traffic.com
Web Site: www.traffic.com
Sales Range: $25-49.9 Million
Approx. Number Employees: 600
Business Description:
Accurate, Real-Time Traffic Information Services
S.I.C.: 4789; 2741; 8713
N.A.I.C.S.: 488999; 516110; 541360
Advertising Expenditures: $2,200,000
Media: 2-10-13-14-15-18-23-24
Personnel:
Peter Doyle *(Sr VP-Media & Affiliations)*
Peter Menninger *(Sr VP-Opers-Sys Architecture)*
Brian Smyth *(Sr VP-Software Dev)*

TRAVELOCITY.COM LP

(Sub. of Sabre Holdings Corporation)
3150 Sabre Dr
Southlake, TX 76092
Tel.: (682) 605-1000
E-mail: travelocity@travelocity.com
Web Site: www.travelocity.com
Sales Range: $500-549.9 Million
Approx. Number Employees: 1,554
Year Founded: 2000
Business Description:
Online Travel Reservations
S.I.C.: 4729
N.A.I.C.S.: 561599
Media: 3-8-11-13-14-15-23-24
Personnel:
Hugh Jones *(Pres & CEO)*
Ross Mantione *(VP & Partner-Mktg)*
Nejib Ben-Khedher *(COO)*
Andy Donkin *(Sr VP-Global Mktg & Media)*
Noreen Henry *(Sr VP-Global Partner Mktg)*
Mamie Millard *(Sr VP-Product Dev & Delivery)*
Richard Harris *(VP)*
Carl Sparks *(VP-Media)*
Lisa Zeng *(Asst Product Mgr)*
Brands & Products:
TRAVELOCITY
TRAVELOCITY.COM
Advertising Agencies:
hawkeye
2828 Routh St Ste 300
Dallas, TX 75201
Tel.: (214) 659-5615
Fax: (214) 747-1897

iCrossing, Inc.
15169 N Scottsdale Rd Ste C400
Scottsdale, AZ 85254
Tel.: (480) 505-5800
Fax: (480) 505-5801
Toll Free: (866) 620-3780
Paid Search

Leo Burnett Worldwide, Inc.
35 W Wacker Dr
Chicago, IL 60601-1723
Tel.: (312) 220-5959
Fax: (312) 220-3299
Agency of Record
Brand Strategy
Creative

RAPP
437 Madison Ave 3rd Fl
New York, NY 10022
Tel.: (212) 817-6800
Fax: (212) 590-8400

Razorfish
821 2nd Ave Ste 1800
Seattle, WA 98104-2343
Tel.: (206) 816-8800
Fax: (206) 816-8808
Agency of Record
Interactive Channel Strategy

Zenith Media Services
(Regional Headquarters for ZenithOptimedia, the Americas)
299 W Houston St 10th Fl
New York, NY 10014-4806
Tel.: (212) 859-5100
Fax: (212) 727-9495
Agency of Record
Media

TRUE.COM

5215 N O'Connor Ste 1600
Irving, TX 75039
Tel.: (972) 402-4802
Fax: (972) 402-4838
Toll Free: (866) 583-8783
Web Site: www.true.com
Approx. Number Employees: 100
Business Description:
Online Dating Service
S.I.C.: 7299
N.A.I.C.S.: 812990
Advertising Expenditures: $30,000,000
Media: 13
Personnel:
Ruben Buell *(Pres)*
Ted Sinclair *(CFO)*
Cornell McGee *(CMO & Exec VP)*
David Reid *(Chief Legal Officer)*
John Aldredge *(Project Mngmt Officer)*

TRULIA, INC.

208 Utah St Ste 310
San Francisco, CA 94103

Key to Media (For complete agency information see *The Advertising Red Books-Agencies* edition):
1. Bus. Publs. 2. Cable T.V. 3. Catalogs & Directories. 4. Co-op Adv. 5. Consumer Mags. 6. D.M. to Bus. Estab.7. D.M. to Consumers 8. Daily Newsp. 9. Exhibits/Trade Shows 10. Foreign 11. Infomercial 12. Internet Adv.13. Multimedia 14. Network Radio 15. Network T.V. 16. Newsp. Distr. Mags. 17. Other 18. Outdoor (Posters, Transit) 19. Point of Purchase20. Premiums, Novelties 21. Product Samples 22. Special Events Mktg. 23. Spot Radio 24. Spot T.V. 25. Weekly Newsp. 26. Yellow Page Adv.

Tel.: (415) 648-4358
Fax: (866) 298-1231
E-mail: sales@trulia.com
Web Site: www.trulia.com
E-Mail For Key Personnel:
Sales Director: sales@trulia.com
Approx. Number Employees: 60
Year Founded: 2005
Business Description:
Residential Real Estate Search Portal
S.I.C.: 2741
N.A.I.C.S.: 516110
Personnel:
Sam Inkinen *(Co-Founder & Pres)*
Pete Flint *(CEO)*
Paul Levine *(COO)*
Daniele Farnedi *(VP-Engrg)*
Heather Mirjahangir Fernandez *(VP-Mktg)*
Eric Oldfield *(VP-Adv Sls & Ops)*
Louis Bennett *(Head-Engrg)*
Matt Holder *(Product Mgr-Social Search)*
Isaac Reyes *(Mgr-Strategic Partnerships)*
Advertising Agency:
SutherlandGold Group
550 15th St Ste 27
San Francisco, CA 94103
Tel.: (415) 934-9600
Fax: (800) 886-7452

TRUSTWAVE HOLDINGS, INC.
70 W Madison Ste 1050
Chicago, IL 60602
Tel.: (312) 873-7500
Fax: (312) 443-8028
Toll Free: (888) 878-7817
E-mail: info@trustwave.com
Web Site: www.trustwave.com
Approx. Rev.: $111,503,000
Approx. Number Employees: 550
Business Description:
On-Demand Data Security & Payment Card Industry Compliance Management Products & Services
S.I.C.: 7372; 7374; 7382
N.A.I.C.S.: 511210; 518210; 561621
Advertising Expenditures: $579,000
Personnel:
Robert J. McCullen *(Chm, Pres & CEO)*
Mark Iserloth *(CFO)*
Leo J. Cole *(CMO)*
Justin C. Choi *(Gen Counsel, Exec VP & Sec)*
Douglas Klotnia *(Exec VP-Payment Svcs & Channel Sls)*
James Kunkel *(Exec VP-Corp Dev & Emerging Tech)*
David Parkinson *(Exec VP-Field Ops-Americas)*
Andrew Bokor *(Exec Dir-EMEA & APAC)*
Brands & Products:
MAILMAX
MOSECURITY
SMART TAG
SPIDERLABS
TRUSTED COMMERCE
TRUSTEDAPP
TRUSTEDSENTRY
TRUSTKEEPER
TRUSTMINDER
TRUSTWAVE
TRUSTWAVE SECURITY DATA WAREHOUSE
WEBDEFEND

TUCOWS, INC.
96 Mowat Avenue
Toronto, ON M6K 3M1, Canada
Tel.: (416) 535-0123
Fax: (416) 531-5584
Toll Free: (800) 371-6992
E-mail: info@tucows.com
Web Site: www.tucowsinc.com
Approx. Rev.: $84,578,505
Approx. Number Employees: 150
Year Founded: 1993
Business Description:
Internet Services to ISP's & Web Hosting Companies; Software Downloads
S.I.C.: 7374; 7375
N.A.I.C.S.: 518210; 518111
Advertising Expenditures: $3,200,000
Media: 2-7-8-10-13-18
Personnel:
Stanley Stern *(Chm)*
Elliot Noss *(Pres & CEO)*
Michael Cooperman *(CFO)*
David Woroch *(Exec VP-Sls)*
Carla Goertz *(VP-HR)*
Ken Shafer *(VP-Mktg Mgmt)*
Ross Rader *(Gen Mgr-Hover)*
Brands & Products:
HOVER
TUCOWS

TURBOLINUX, INC.
(Sub. of Turbolinux, Japan K.K.)
600 Townsend St Ste 120E
San Francisco, CA 94103
Tel.: (415) 503-4330
Fax: (415) 437-2892
E-mail: info@turbolinux.com
Web Site: www.turbolinux.com
Approx. Number Employees: 60
Year Founded: 1992
Business Description:
Computer Software & Services
S.I.C.: 5045; 5734
N.A.I.C.S.: 423430; 443120
Media: 13
Personnel:
Claude Zhou *(Gen Mgr)*

TWITTER INC.
795 Folsom St Ste 600
San Francisco, CA 94107
Tel.: (415) 896-2008
Web Site: www.twitter.com
Year Founded: 2006
Business Description:
Social Networking Site
N.A.I.C.S.: 516110
Media: 8-13
Personnel:
Dick Costolo *(CEO)*
Adam Bain *(Pres-Revenue-Global)*
Alexander Macgillivray *(Gen Counsel)*
Matt Graves *(Dir-Comm)*
Advertising Agency:
Daniel J. Edelman, Inc.
(d/b/a Edelman)
200 E Randolph St Fl 63
Chicago, IL 60601-6705
Tel.: (312) 240-3000
Fax: (312) 240-2900
PR

TWO RIVERS WATER COMPANY
2000 S Colorado Blvd Ste 200
Denver, CO 80222
Tel.: (303) 222-1000
Fax: (303) 222-1012
Toll Free: (800) 797-7565
E-mail: info@2riverswater.com
Web Site: www.2riverswater.com
E-Mail For Key Personnel:
Sales Director: sales@navidec.com
Approx. Rev.: $196,000
Approx. Number Employees: 7
Year Founded: 2002
Business Description:
Water Storage & Distribution Services
S.I.C.: 4941
N.A.I.C.S.: 221310
Advertising Expenditures: $186,000
Media: 2-10
Personnel:
John R. McKowen *(Chm & CEO)*
Wayne E. Harding, III *(CFO & Sec)*

TYBIT UNIFIED SEARCH
421 Maiden Ln
Fayetteville, NC 28301
Toll Free: (877) 404-7250
E-mail: info@tybit.com
Web Site: www.tybit.com
Internet Adv.: 100%
Personnel:
Clarence E. Briggs, III *(Chm, Pres & CEO)*
Steven P. Young *(CFO)*
Michael J. Roberts *(CIO)*
Sean A. McCoy *(CMO)*
Kitty Jo Finch *(Gen Mgr)*

UBID.COM
(Sub. of Enable Holdings, Inc.)
8725 W Higins Rd Ste 900
Chicago, IL 60631
Tel.: (773) 272-5000
Toll Free: (866) WIN-UBID
Web Site: www.ubid.com
E-Mail For Key Personnel:
Public Relations: pr@ubid.com
Sales Range: $75-99.9 Million
Year Founded: 1997
Business Description:
Online Auction Services
S.I.C.: 5961
N.A.I.C.S.: 454112; 454111; 454113
Media: 13

UGO ENTERTAINMENT, INC.
(Sub. of IGN Entertainment, Inc.)
670 Broadway 2nd Fl
New York, NY 10012
Tel.: (917) 934-6767
Fax: (212) 624-3310
E-mail: sales@ugo.com
Web Site: www.ugo.com
E-Mail For Key Personnel:
Sales Director: sales@ugo.com
Approx. Number Employees: 65
Year Founded: 1997
Business Description:
Online Gaming & Entertainment Information Publisher
S.I.C.: 2741; 2721
N.A.I.C.S.: 519130
Media: 6-13-22
Personnel:
Nick Flynn *(Sr VP-Sls-Natl)*
Richard Kennedy *(Sr VP-Bus Dev)*
Lisa Mark *(VP-HR)*
Brands & Products:
UGO.COM
UNDERGROUNDONLINE

UNITED ONLINE, INC.
21301 Burbank Blvd
Woodland Hills, CA 91367
Tel.: (818) 287-3000
E-mail: investor@untd.com
Web Site: www.untd.com
Approx. Rev.: $920,553,000
Approx. Number Employees: 1,606
Business Description:
Online Services
S.I.C.: 2741; 7389
N.A.I.C.S.: 516110; 519190
Personnel:
Mark R. Goldston *(Chm, Pres & CEO)*
Scott H. Ray *(CFO & Exec VP)*
Jeremy Helfand *(Chief Sls Officer & Exec VP)*
Frederic A. Randall, Jr. *(Exec VP & Chief Strategy Officer)*
Robert Taragan *(Pres-Comm Segment)*
Charles B. Ammann *(Gen Counsel, Sec & Exec VP)*
Neil P. Edwards *(Sr VP-Fin)*
Brett Thompson *(Sr VP-HR)*
Brands & Products:
CLASSMATES
FTD
HIGHSCHOOLPEOPLESEARCH.COM
JUNO
MYPOINTS
MYSITE
NETZERO
UNITED ONLINE
Advertising Agency:
GENERAL LEVITATION
1635 Tower Grove Dr
Beverly Hills, CA 90210
Tel.: (310) 454-1188

UNITED SYSTEMS ACCESS TELECOM, INC.
(d/b/a USA Telephone)
5 Bragdon Ln Ste 200
Kennebunk, ME 04043
Tel.: (207) 467-8000
Fax: (207) 467-8008
Toll Free: (877) USA-2800
E-mail: info@savewithusa.com
Web Site: www.savewithusa.com
E-Mail For Key Personnel:
Sales Director: sales@savewithusa.com
Approx. Number Employees: 30
Business Description:
Local, Long Distance & Wireless Telecommunications Services
S.I.C.: 4899; 4812
N.A.I.C.S.: 517910; 517212
Media: 13-15-23
Personnel:
L. William Fogg *(Pres & CEO)*
Alan Silver *(CFO)*
Brands & Products:
USA TELEPHONE

UNIVERSUM USA
1518 Walnut St 18th Fl
Philadelphia, PA 19102
Tel.: (215) 546-4900
Fax: (215) 546-9921
Web Site: www.universumglobal.com
Business Description:
Employee Branding Services
S.I.C.: 7375
N.A.I.C.S.: 519130; 518111
Media: 6-13

Key to Media (For complete agency information see *The Advertising Red Books-Agencies* edition):
1. Bus. Publs. 2. Cable T.V. 3. Catalogs & Directories. 4. Co-op Adv. 5. Consumer Mags. 6. D.M. to Bus. Estab.7. D.M. to Consumers 8. Daily Newsp. 9. Exhibits/Trade Shows 10. Foreign 11. Infomercial 12. Internet Adv.13. Multimedia 14. Network Radio 15. Network T.V. 16. Newsp. Distr. Mags. 17. Other 18. Outdoor (Posters, Transit) 19. Point of Purchase20. Premiums, Novelties 21. Product Samples 22. Special Events Mktg. 23. Spot Radio 24. Spot T.V. 25. Weekly Newsp. 26. Yellow Page Adv.

Universum USA — (Continued)

Personnel:
Catharina Mannerfelt *(Pres)*
Tracy Lynn Drye *(Global Acct Dir)*

Brands & Products:
WETFEET

US DATAWORKS, INC.

One Sugar Creek Center Blvd 5th Fl
Sugar Land, TX 77478
Tel.: (281) 504-8000
Toll Free: (866) 337-5477
E-mail: sales@usdataworks.com
Web Site: www.usdataworks.com
Approx. Rev.: $8,531,698
Approx. Number Employees: 36
Year Founded: 1998
Business Description:
Application Software for Financial Services
S.I.C.: 7371; 7372
N.A.I.C.S.: 334611; 511210; 541511
Advertising Expenditures: $63,093
Media: 10-13
Personnel:
Charles E. Ramey *(Chm & CEO)*
Mario Villarreal *(Pres & COO)*
Randall J. Frapart *(CFO)*
Brands & Products:
MICRWORKS
REMITWORKS
RETURNWORKS

US INTERNET CORPORATION

12450 Wayzata Blvd Ste 121
Minnetonka, MN 55305
Tel.: (952) 253-3200
Fax: (952) 545-0302
Toll Free: (800) 874-6837
E-mail: info@usinternet.com
Web Site: www.usinternet.com
Approx. Number Employees: 45
Year Founded: 1995
Business Description:
Internet & Hosting Services
S.I.C.: 7375
N.A.I.C.S.: 518111
Media: 13
Personnel:
Travis Carter *(Founder & VP-Tech)*
Joe Caldwell *(Co-Founder)*

US ONLINE.COM, INC.

430 Olds Stations Rd
Wenatchee, WA 98801-1468
Tel.: (509) 663-6031
Fax: (888) 468-2720
E-mail: info@corp.usonline.com
Web Site: www.usonline.com
Sales Range: Less than $1 Million
Approx. Number Employees: 5
Year Founded: 1998
Business Description:
Internet Service
S.I.C.: 7375; 5045
N.A.I.C.S.: 518111; 423430
Advertising Expenditures: $100,000
Media: 7-13
Personnel:
Steve Klock *(CEO)*
Brands & Products:
SUDDENVALUES.COM

USADATA, INC.

292 Madison Ave Fl 3
New York, NY 10017-6322
Tel.: (212) 679-1411
Fax: (212) 679-8507
Toll Free: (800) 599-5030
E-mail: info@usadata.com
Web Site: www.usadata.com
Approx. Sls.: $1,800,000
Approx. Number Employees: 50
Year Founded: 1995
Business Description:
Market Research & Information
S.I.C.: 8732; 7375
N.A.I.C.S.: 541910; 518111
Advertising Expenditures: $300,000
Media: 2-6-7-13
Personnel:
Ric Murphy *(CEO)*
Jon Rapkin *(Sr VP-Data & Leads Grp)*
Brands & Products:
DIRECT MARKETING PORTAL
NCOALINK
SALES LEADS. ON DEMAND
USADATA

USA.NET, INC.

1155 Kelly Johnson Blvd Ste 300
Colorado Springs, CO 80920-3932
Tel.: (719) 265-2930
Fax: (719) 265-2922
Toll Free: (800) 653-0179
E-mail: enterprisesales@corpx.usa.net
Web Site: www.usa.net
Sales Range: $25-49.9 Million
Approx. Number Employees: 65
Year Founded: 1998
Business Description:
Electronic Messaging Services
S.I.C.: 7375
N.A.I.C.S.: 518111
Advertising Expenditures: $50,000
Media: 6-10-13
Personnel:
Jason Maston *(VP-Sls)*
Brands & Products:
NET@DDRESS
USA.NET
YOU RUN YOUR BUSINESS WE'LL RUN YOUR EMAIL

VACATION.COM, INC.

(Sub. of Travel Leaders Group, LLC)
1650 King St Ste 450
Alexandria, VA 22314-2747
Tel.: (703) 535-5505
Fax: (703) 548-6815
Toll Free: (800) 843-0733
E-mail: feedback@vacation-corp.com
Web Site: www.vacation.com
Approx. Number Employees: 75
Year Founded: 1998
Business Description:
Online Travel Agent Network
S.I.C.: 4724; 2741
N.A.I.C.S.: 561510
Advertising Expenditures: $600,000
Media: 8-10-13
Personnel:
John Lovell *(Pres)*
Stephen McGillivray *(VP-Mktg)*
Brands & Products:
VACATION.COM
Advertising Agency:
Kahn Travel Communications
77 N Centre Ave Ste 215
Rockville Centre, NY 11570
Tel.: (516) 594-4100
Fax: (516) 594-4104

VALASSIS COMMUNICATIONS, INC.

19975 Victor Pkwy
Livonia, MI 48152-7001
Tel.: (734) 591-3000
Fax: (734) 591-4503
Fax: (734) 591-4994
Toll Free: (800) 437-0479
E-mail: ir@valassis.com
Web Site: www.valassis.com
Approx. Rev.: $2,333,512,000
Approx. Number Employees: 6,735
Year Founded: 1971
Business Description:
Global Marketing Services
S.I.C.: 2752; 7319; 8742
N.A.I.C.S.: 323110; 541613; 541870
Media: 2-5-7-8-9-10-13-16-25
Personnel:
Alan F. Schultz *(Chm, Pres & CEO)*
Robert L. Recchia *(CFO, Treas & Exec VP)*
Brian J. Husselbee *(Pres/CEO-NCH Mktg Svcs, Inc.)*
John A Lieblang *(Pres-Digital Media)*
Barry P. Hoffman *(Gen Counsel, Sec & Exec VP)*
Richard P. Herpich *(Exec VP-Strategic Initiatives)*
Linda J. Schalek *(Sr VP & Controller)*
Michael F. Kowalczyk *(Sr VP & Gen Mgr)*
Brian Costello *(Gen Mgr & VP-RedPlum.com, RedPlum Network & Digital Strategy)*
Thomas Murray *(VP-Mktg)*
Rex Boatright *(Dir-Creative Svcs)*
David D. McNulty *(Asst Treas)*
Brands & Products:
BRAND BAG
BRAND BAG+
CO-OP INSERT
DIRECT MAIL
DIRECT-TO-DOOR
EXPRESS INSERT
EXTENDED REACH BLOW-IN
EXTENDED REACH INSERT
HISPANIC CO-OP INSERT
MARKETEXPERT XR
NEWSPAC
NEWSPOUCH
ONLINE DIRECT MARKETING MANAGER
ONLINE PROMOTION LINK
PREPRINTED INSERT
PROMOTION WATCH
REDPLUM.COM
RETAIL CONNECTION
RUN-OF-PRESS
TARGETEXPERT XR
THEMED EVENTS
VALASSIS
Advertising Agency:
PAN Communications
300 Brickstone Sq 7th Fl
Andover, MA 01810
Tel.: (978) 474-1900
Fax: (978) 474-1903

VALU.NET CORPORATION

11710 Plz America Dr Ste 2000
Reston, VA 20190
Tel.: (703) 689-0780
Fax: (703) 689-0781
Web Site: www.valu.net
Approx. Number Employees: 15
Year Founded: 1996
Business Description:
Business-to-Business Internet E-Commerce Solutions Including Software & Portal Products, Web & Catalog Hosting Facilities & Custom Systems Integration Services
S.I.C.: 5734; 5045
N.A.I.C.S.: 443120; 423430
Media: 13
Brands & Products:
ORDERHOUSE
VALU.NET

VARSTREET, INC.

2620 Augustine Dr Ste 120
Santa Clara, CA 95054
Tel.: (408) 562-5600
Fax: (408) 986-1196
E-mail: info@varstreet.com
Web Site: www.varstreet.com
Approx. Sls.: $2,000,000
Approx. Number Employees: 20
Year Founded: 1999
Business Description:
eBusiness Services & Information Network
S.I.C.: 7379
N.A.I.C.S.: 541519
Advertising Expenditures: $200,000
Media: 2-13
Personnel:
Bob Godgart *(CEO)*
Brands & Products:
VARSTREET
THE XC E-COMMERCE PLATFORM

VAULT.COM, INC.

(Holding of Veronis Suhler Stevenson Partners LLC)
79 Varick St
New York, NY 10013
Tel.: (212) 366-4212
Fax: (212) 366-6712
E-mail: questions@staff.vault.com
Web Site: www.vault.com
Approx. Sls.: $9,600,000
Approx. Number Employees: 75
Year Founded: 1996
Business Description:
Human Resources & Employment Information Directory Publisher
S.I.C.: 2731; 2741; 7361; 7389
N.A.I.C.S.: 511130; 511140; 516110; 519190; 561310
Advertising Expenditures: $420,000
Media: 13
Personnel:
Hussam Hamadeh *(Co-Founder & Co-Pres)*
Claude P. Sheer *(CEO)*
Elizabeth Rose *(Chief Digital Officer)*
Lisa Hahnel *(Product Mgr)*
Brands & Products:
ELECTRONIC WATERCOOLER
THE HR GUY
THE MOST TRUSTED NAME IN CAREER INFORMATION
VAULT
VAULT.COM
VAULTMATCH

VENDIO, INC.

2800 Campus Dr
San Mateo, CA 94403
Tel.: (650) 293-3500
Tel.: (650) 808-5800
E-mail: kwray@corp.vendio.com
Web Site: www.vendio.com

Key to Media (For complete agency information see *The Advertising Red Books-Agencies* edition):
1. Bus. Publs. 2. Cable T.V. 3. Catalogs & Directories. 4. Co-op Adv. 5. Consumer Mags. 6. D.M. to Bus. Estab.7. D.M. to Consumers
8. Daily Newsp. 9. Exhibits/Trade Shows 10. Foreign 11. Infomercial 12. Internet Adv.13. Multimedia 14. Network Radio
15. Network T.V. 16. Newsp. Distr. Mags. 17. Other 18. Outdoor (Posters, Transit) 19. Point of Purchase20. Premiums, Novelties
21. Product Samples 22. Special Events Mktg. 23. Spot Radio 24. Spot T.V. 25. Weekly Newsp. 26. Yellow Page Adv.

Approx. Number Employees: 50
Year Founded: 1999
Business Description:
Online Auctions
S.I.C.: 7375
N.A.I.C.S.: 518111
Media: 10-13
Personnel:
Mike Effle *(CEO)*
Brands & Products:
CUSTOMER MANAGER
SALES MANAGER
ZOOMSTREAM IMAGES

VERIO INC.
(Sub. of NTT Communications Corporation)
8005 S Chester St Ste 200
Centennial, CO 80112-3523
Tel.: (303) 645-1900
Fax: (303) 792-3869
E-mail: info@verio.com
Web Site: www.verio.com
E-Mail For Key Personnel:
Sales Director: sales@verio.com
Approx. Number Employees: 2,900
Year Founded: 1996
Business Description:
Global Web Hosting & Internet Services
S.I.C.: 7375
N.A.I.C.S.: 518111
Advertising Expenditures: $3,430,966
Media: 2-6-13
Personnel:
Hideyuki Yamasawa *(Pres & CEO)*
Steve Renda *(Sr VP-Global Sls & Mktg)*
Gus Salamoun *(Sr VP-Svc Delivery)*
Toshi Yamasaki *(Sr VP-Global Dev & Products)*
Wendy St. Clair Pearson *(Sr Dir-Mktg & Comm)*
Kenneth Giffin *(Sr Dir-Mktg & Comm)*
Cody Christman *(Dir-Product Engineering)*
Anne Stone *(Dir-Mktg & Channel Programs)*

VERSANT CORPORATION
255 Shoreline Dr Ste 450
Redwood City, CA 94065
Tel.: (650) 232-2400
Fax: (650) 232-2401
Toll Free: (800) VERSANT
E-mail: info@versant.com
Web Site: www.versant.com
Approx. Rev.: $15,766,000
Approx. Number Employees: 61
Year Founded: 1988
Business Description:
Designs, Develops, Markets & Supports Database Management Systems
S.I.C.: 7371; 7372
N.A.I.C.S.: 511210; 334611; 541511
Advertising Expenditures: $3,400,000
Media: 7-10-13
Personnel:
William Henry Delevati *(Chm, Pres & Interim CEO)*
Jochen Witte *(CEO)*
Jerry Wong *(CFO, VP-Fin, Sec & Dir)*
Dirk Bartels *(VP-Mktg & Strategic Product Mgmt-Worldwide)*
Robert Greene *(VP-Open Source Ops)*
Brands & Products:
FASTOBJECTS
REVIND
VAREHOUSE
VDS
VEDDING
VERSANT
VERSANT ENJIN
VERSANT JDO
VHISPER
VHISTLE
VILDCARD
VITNESS
VORKOUT

VERTRO, INC.
143 Varick St
New York, NY 10013
Tel.: (212) 231-2000
Fax: (212) 809-0926
E-mail: info@vertro.com
Web Site: www.vertro.com
Approx. Rev.: $35,894,000
Approx. Number Employees: 49
Year Founded: 1998
Business Description:
Online Advertising Network; Software Publisher
S.I.C.: 7372; 8742
N.A.I.C.S.: 519130; 511210; 541613
Advertising Expenditures: $21,000,000
Media: 2-10-13
Personnel:
Lawrence Weber *(Chm)*
Peter A. Corrao *(Pres & CEO)*
James G. Gallagher *(CFO)*
David Rae *(Chief Strategy Officer)*
John B. Pisaris *(Gen Counsel)*
Brenda Agius *(Sr VP-Admin)*
Brands & Products:
ADANALYZER
ADREVENUE
ADREVENUE EXTRESS
AUTO BID
AUTOREPLENISH
BIDPOTIMIZER
BUSINESSBUILDER
COMET
ESPOTTING
FINDWHAT.COM NETWORK
INTELLIMAP
MIVA
MIVA CENTRAL
MIVA MEANS BUSINESS
MIVA MERCHANT
PPC2
SCREENSAVERS.COM

VETJOBS, INC.
PO Box 71445
Marietta, GA 30007-1445
Tel.: (770) 993-5117
Fax: (770) 993-2875
Toll Free: (877) VETJOBS
E-mail: info@vetjobs.com
Web Site: www.vetjobs.com
E-Mail For Key Personnel:
President: tdaywalt@vetjobs.com
Approx. Number Employees: 10
Year Founded: 1999
Business Description:
Online Employment Services for Veterans
S.I.C.: 7361
N.A.I.C.S.: 561310
Media: 2-6-8-9-10-13-25
Personnel:
Ted Daywalt *(Pres & CEO)*
Gene Rascle *(CIO)*
Buddy Inlow *(VP-Sls)*
Brands & Products:
EXPERIENCE ONBOARD
VETERANS MAKE THE BEST EMPLOYEES
VETJOBS

VIEWCAST CORPORATION
3701 W Plano Pkwy Ste 300
Plano, TX 75075-7840
Tel.: (972) 488-7200
Fax: (972) 488-7299
Toll Free: (800) 540-4119
E-mail: info@viewcast.com
Web Site: www.viewcast.com
Approx. Rev.: $17,335,953
Approx. Number Employees: 84
Year Founded: 1958
Business Description:
Digital Video & Audio Communications Hardware & Software
S.I.C.: 3663; 3651; 7371
N.A.I.C.S.: 334220; 334310; 541511
Advertising Expenditures: $675,861
Media: 10-11-13
Personnel:
George C. Platt *(Chm)*
John Hammock *(Pres & COO)*
David T. Stoner *(CEO)*
Laurie L. Latham *(CFO, Sr VP-Fin & Admin)*
Adrian Giuhat *(CTO & Sr VP-Product Dev)*
Howard Barouxis *(VP-Sls)*
Mark Hershey *(VP-Engrg)*
Jeffrey A. Kopang *(VP-Mktg)*
Brands & Products:
GOSTREAM
NIAGARA
NIAGARA 2100
NIAGRA SCX
OSPREY
SIMULSTREAM
VIEWCAST
VIEWCAST IVN
VIEWCAST ONLINE
VIEWPOINT VBX
WORKFONE
Advertising Agency:
Michael A. Burns & Associates, Inc.
3333 Lee Pkwy Ste 450
Dallas, TX 75219-5139
Tel.: (214) 521-8596
Fax: (214) 521-8599
Public Relations

VIPDESK, INC.
324 N Fairfax St
Alexandria, VA 22314-2625
Tel.: (703) 299-4422
Fax: (703) 299-9769
E-mail: info@vipdesk.com
Web Site: www.vipdesk.com
Approx. Number Employees: 125
Year Founded: 1997
Business Description:
Online Concierge Services
S.I.C.: 7373
N.A.I.C.S.: 541512
Media: 13
Personnel:
Paul J. Schmitt *(Chm)*
Sally Hurley *(Pres)*
Mary Naylor *(CEO)*
Dan Fontaine *(Sr VP-Tech)*
Tim Gordon *(Sr VP-Svc Delivery)*
Brands & Products:
VIPDESK
VIPDESK CONNECT

VIRTUMUNDO, INC.
8400 W 110 St Ste 330
Overland Park, KS 66210
Tel.: (913) 660-1300
Fax: (913) 660-1301
Toll Free: (866) 356-8636
E-mail: press@virtumundo.com
Web Site: www.virtumundo.com
Approx. Number Employees: 18
Year Founded: 1997
Business Description:
Internet Entertainment
S.I.C.: 7319
N.A.I.C.S.: 541850
Media: 13

VITANET HEALTH FOODS
235 Market Ave SW
Hartville, OH 44632-9050
Tel.: (330) 877-8786
Fax: (330) 877-8787
Toll Free: (800) 877-8702
E-mail: support@vitanet.net
Web Site: www.vitanetonline.com
Approx. Number Employees: 7
Year Founded: 1995
Business Description:
Health Foods & Supplements Online Retailer
S.I.C.: 5912; 5499; 5961
N.A.I.C.S.: 446110; 446191; 454111; 454113
Media: 13-25
Personnel:
Darryl Miller *(Owner)*
Brands & Products:
VITANET

VIZERGY
4237 Salisbury Rd N Ste 200
Jacksonville, FL 32216
Tel.: (904) 389-1130
Fax: (904) 899-5809
Web Site: www.vizergy.com
Approx. Number Employees: 50
Business Description:
Internet Marketing Services for the Hospitality Industry
S.I.C.: 2741
N.A.I.C.S.: 516110
Personnel:
Joseph R. Hyman *(Founder & CEO)*
Susan Hart *(VP-Ops & Fin)*
Stacy Kimbrough *(Dir-Client Mktg Svcs)*
Advertising Agency:
AXIA
200 E Forsyth St
Jacksonville, FL 32202
Tel.: (904) 425-6652
Fax: (904) 425-6653
Toll Free: (866) 999-AXIA

VOXA, INC.
1020 Corporation Way Ste 205
Palo Alto, CA 94303
Tel.: (650) 964-1733
E-mail: info@voxa.com
Sales Range: $1-9.9 Million
Approx. Number Employees: 25
Year Founded: 1999

Key to Media (For complete agency information see *The Advertising Red Books-Agencies* edition):
1. Bus. Publs. 2. Cable T.V. 3. Catalogs & Directories. 4. Co-op Adv. 5. Consumer Mags. 6. D.M. to Bus. Estab.7. D.M. to Consumers
8. Daily Newsp. 9. Exhibits/Trade Shows 10. Foreign 11. Infomercial 12. Internet Adv.13. Multimedia 14. Network Radio
15. Network T.V. 16. Newsp. Distr. Mags. 17. Other 18. Outdoor (Posters, Transit) 19. Point of Purchase20. Premiums, Novelties
21. Product Samples 22. Special Events Mktg. 23. Spot Radio 24. Spot T.V. 25. Weekly Newsp. 26. Yellow Page Adv.

Voxa, Inc. — (Continued)

Business Description:
Business-to-Business E-Commerce Software Solutions
S.I.C.: 7375
N.A.I.C.S.: 518111
Media: 13
Personnel:
Beatrice Hom *(Co-Founder & Pres)*
Brands & Products:
TOTALACCESS
TOTALTEST
VCONNECTOR
VDEVELOPER
VOXA
VSERVER

WAL-MART.COM
(Div. of Wal-Mart Stores, Inc.)
7000 Marina Blvd
Brisbane, CA 94005
Tel.: (650) 837-5000
Web Site: www.walmart.com
Sales Range: $250-299.9 Million
Approx. Number Employees: 600
Year Founded: 2000
Business Description:
Online Retail Services
S.I.C.: 5311; 5961
N.A.I.C.S.: 452112; 454111
Media: 3-8-13-15-19-25-31
Personnel:
Duncan McNaughton *(Exec VP-Consumables, Health & Wellness)*
Karenann K. Terrell *(Exec VP)*
Raul Vazquez *(Exec VP-Global eCommerce & Developed Market)*
Sharon Orlopp *(Chief Diversity Officer-Global & Sr VP-Corp People)*
Jeff Gruener *(VP-Fin & Strategy-Entertainment)*
Fergal Burke *(Sr Mgr-Bus-Online Media Program)*
Advertising Agency:
Daniel J. Edelman, Inc.
(d/b/a Edelman)
200 E Randolph St Fl 63
Chicago, IL 60601-6705
Tel.: (312) 240-3000
Fax: (312) 240-2900

WALT DISNEY INTERNET GROUP
(Name Changed to Disney Interactive Media Group)

WAND, INC.
820 16th St Ste 605
Denver, CO 80202
Tel.: (303) 623-1200
Fax: (303) 573-0337
E-mail: info@wandinc.com
Web Site: www.wandinc.com
Sales Range: $25-49.9 Million
Approx. Number Employees: 50
Business Description:
Structured Multi Lingual Vocabularies Developer to Power Search & Classification Internet Applications; Internet Taxonomy Structures Developer
S.I.C.: 2741
N.A.I.C.S.: 516110
Media: 10-13
Personnel:
Ross Leher *(Founder, Chm & CEO)*
Richard Avery *(Sr VP-Corp Dev)*
Marc A. Brombert *(Sr VP-Corp Dev)*

WARMLYYOURS.COM INC.
2 Corporate Dr Ste 100
Lake Zurich, IL 60047
Tel.: (847) 540-7775
Fax: (800) 408-1100
Toll Free: (800) 875-5285
E-mail: info@warmlyyours.com
Web Site: www.warmlyyours.com
Sales Range: $25-49.9 Million
Approx. Number Employees: 20
Year Founded: 1998
Business Description:
Online Retailer of Home Heating Products & Services
S.I.C.: 5075; 5999
N.A.I.C.S.: 423730; 453998
Advertising Expenditures: $200,000
Media: 6-13
Personnel:
Julia Stalfort *(Founder & COO)*
Brands & Products:
ENVIRON II
TEMPZONE

WEB RESULTS, INC.
440 E Sample Rd Ste 206
Pompano Beach, FL 33064
Tel.: (954) 360-0636
Fax: (954) 360-0377
Toll Free: (877) 974-9327
E-mail: info@webresultsinc.com
Web Site: www.webresultsinc.com
Sales Range: $1-9.9 Million
Approx. Number Employees: 40
Year Founded: 1998
Business Description:
Website Hosting, Design & Development Services
S.I.C.: 7374
N.A.I.C.S.: 518210
Media: 13
Personnel:
Michael A. Caputa *(Pres)*

WEBAIR INTERNET DEVELOPMENT, INC.
501 Franklin Ave
Garden City, NY 11530
Tel.: (516) 938-4100
Web Site: www.webair.com
Approx. Rev.: $1,500,000
Approx. Number Employees: 25
Year Founded: 1996
Business Description:
Web Hosting & Internet Development Services
S.I.C.: 7375
N.A.I.C.S.: 518111
Media: 10-13-15-17-29
Personnel:
Michael Orza *(Pres)*

WEBAXXS.COM
(Div. of OLM, LLC)
4 Trefoil Dr
Trumbull, CT 06611-1330
Tel.: (203) 445-7700
Fax: (203) 445-8135
Toll Free: (800) 741-6813
E-mail: office@olm.net
Web Site: www.webaxxs.net
Year Founded: 1996
Business Description:
Solutions for Web-Hosting, E-Commerce & Portal Services
S.I.C.: 7375
N.A.I.C.S.: 518111
Media: 13
Brands & Products:
WEBAXXS

WEB.COM GROUP, INC.
12808 Gran Bay Pkwy W
Jacksonville, FL 32258
Tel.: (904) 680-6600
Fax: (904) 880-0350
Toll Free: (800) 438-7483
E-mail: info@web.com
Web Site: www.web.com
Approx. Rev.: $120,289,000
Approx. Number Employees: 1,148
Year Founded: 1999
Business Description:
Website Development, Marketing & Consulting Services
S.I.C.: 7379; 7319; 8742; 8748
N.A.I.C.S.: 541519; 519130; 541613; 541690; 541890
Advertising Expenditures: $8,000,000
Media: 5-7-13
Personnel:
David L. Brown *(Chm, Pres & CEO)*
Kevin M. Carney *(CFO)*
Jason Teichman *(CMO)*
Matthew P. McClure *(Chief Legal Officer & Sec)*
William H. Borzage *(Sr VP-Mktg & Lead Generation)*
Vikas Rijsinghani *(Sr VP-Online Mktg)*
Alexander Ross *(Sr VP-Sls)*
Robert C. Wiegand *(Sr VP-Bus Dev)*
Joel Williamson *(Sr VP-Ops)*
Gregory Wong *(Sr VP-Corp Dev)*

WEB.COM, INC.
(Sub. of Web.com Group, Inc.)
303 Peachtree Ctr Ave 5th Flr
Atlanta, GA 30303-1238
Tel.: (404) 260-2477
Fax: (404) 260-2760
Toll Free: (800) 589-5060
E-mail: investor@corp.web.com
Web Site: www.web.com
Approx. Rev.: $49,140,000
Approx. Number Employees: 290
Year Founded: 1998
Business Description:
Web & Application Hosting Services
S.I.C.: 7374; 7375
N.A.I.C.S.: 518210; 518111
Advertising Expenditures: $8,900,000
Media: 2-5-7-8-10-13
Personnel:
David L. Brown *(Chm, Pres & CEO)*
Kevin Carney *(CFO)*
Matthew McClure *(Chief Legal Officer & Sec)*
Vikas Rijsinghani *(Sr VP-Online Mktg)*
Susan Datz Edelman *(Dir-IR)*
Brands & Products:
INTERLAND

WEBMD HEALTH CORPORATION
111 8th Ave
New York, NY 10011
Tel.: (212) 624-3700
Fax: (212) 624-3800
E-mail: businessdevelopment@webmd.net
Web Site: www.wbmd.com
Approx. Rev.: $534,519,000
Approx. Number Employees: 1,630
Business Description:
Health Information Online Services
S.I.C.: 2741
N.A.I.C.S.: 511140; 516110
Advertising Expenditures: $5,264,000
Media: 5-13
Personnel:
Martin J. Wygod *(Chm)*
Wayne T. Gattinella *(Pres & CEO)*
Craig Froude *(Pres)*
Anthony Vuolo *(CFO & COO)*
William Pence *(CTO & Exec VP)*
Douglas W. Wamsley *(Gen Counsel, Sec & Exec VP)*
Nan-Kirsten Forte *(Exec VP-Consumer Svcs)*
Steven Zatz *(Exec VP-Prof Svcs)*
Tara Wacks *(Dir-Consumer Product Mktg)*
Brands & Products:
EMEDICINE.COM
EMEDICINEHEALTH.COM
MEDGENMED.COM
MEDICINENET.COM
MEDSCAPE.COM
RXLIST.COM
THEHEART.ORG
WEBMD.COM

WEBMEDIABRANDS INC.
50 Washington St Ste 912
Norwalk, CT 06854
Tel.: (203) 662-2800
Fax: (203) 655-4686
E-mail: press@webmediabrands.com
Web Site: www.webmediabrands.com
E-Mail For Key Personnel:
Marketing Director: mdemilt@internet.com
Public Relations: mboland@internet.com
Approx. Rev.: $8,987,000
Approx. Number Employees: 66
Year Founded: 1998
Business Description:
Website Owner & Operator
S.I.C.: 2741; 7374; 7389
N.A.I.C.S.: 516110; 518210; 519190
Advertising Expenditures: $1,800,000
Media: 2-5-8-10-13
Personnel:
Alan M. Meckler *(Chm, Pres, CEO & COO)*
Donald J. O'Neill *(CFO & VP)*
Mitchell S. Eisenberg *(Gen Counsel & Exec VP)*
Michael DeMilt *(VP-Mktg)*
Amanda Barrett *(Dir-Mktg)*
Brands & Products:
GRAPHICS.COM
INTERNET.COM
JUSTTECHJOBS.COM
MEDIABISTRO.COM
Advertising Agency:
Schwartz Communications, Inc.
230 3rd Ave
Waltham, MA 02451
Tel.: (781) 684-0770
Fax: (781) 684-6500

WEBROOT SOFTWARE, INC.
2560 55th St
Boulder, CO 80301
Tel.: (303) 442-3813
Fax: (303) 442-3846

Key to Media (For complete agency information see *The Advertising Red Books-Agencies* edition):
1. Bus. Publs. 2. Cable T.V. 3. Catalogs & Directories. 4. Co-op Adv. 5. Consumer Mags. 6. D.M. to Bus. Estab.7. D.M. to Consumers
8. Daily Newsp. 9. Exhibits/Trade Shows 10. Foreign 11. Infomercial 12. Internet Adv.13. Multimedia 14. Network Radio
15. Network T.V. 16. Newsp. Distr. Mags. 17. Other 18. Outdoor (Posters, Transit) 19. Point of Purchase20. Premiums, Novelties
21. Product Samples 22. Special Events Mktg. 23. Spot Radio 24. Spot T.V. 25. Weekly Newsp. 26. Yellow Page Adv.

Toll Free: (800) 772-9383
E-mail: marketing@webroot.com
Web Site: www.webroot.com
E-Mail For Key Personnel:
President: talleyk@webroot.com
Approx. Number Employees: 250
Year Founded: 1997
Business Description:
Developer of Internet Utilities & Privacy Software & Tools
S.I.C.: 7371
N.A.I.C.S.: 541511
Export
Advertising Expenditures: $264,000
Media: 4-5-13-23
Personnel:
Dick Williams *(CEO)*
Frederick A. Ball *(CFO)*
Gerry Coady *(CIO)*
Chris Benham *(CMO)*
Paul Lipman *(Chief Strategy Officer)*
Michael Malloy *(Exec VP-Products & Strategy)*
Don Beck *(Sr VP-Worldwide Field Ops)*
Steve Holton *(Sr VP-Sls & Field Ops-North America)*
Michelle Marian *(Sr VP-Global Online Bus)*
Lee Allen *(VP-Retail Sls-North America)*
Elizabeth Andora *(VP-HR)*
Rene Cirulli *(VP-Worldwide Recruiting)*
Takashi Sawai *(Dir-Rep & Mgr-Country)*
David Bennett *(Dir-Consumer Bus Dev-EMEA)*
Brands & Products:
THE BEST SECURITY IN AN UNSECURED WORLD
DESKTOP FIREWALL
E-MAIL SECURITY SAAS
POP-UP WASHER
SECURE BACKUP
SPAM SHREDDER
SPY SWEEPER
WEB SECURITY SAAS
WEBROOT
WEBROOT INTERNET SECURITY ESSENTIALS
WEBROOT PARENTAL CONTROLS
WINDOW WASHER
Advertising Agency:
104 degrees West Partners
1925 Blake St Ste 200
Denver, CO 80202
Tel.: (720) 407-6060
Fax: (720) 407-6061
Pub Rels

WEDDINGCHANNEL.COM
Ste 600 700 S Flower St
Los Angeles, CA 90017-4108
Tel.: (213) 599-4410
Fax: (213) 599-4180
Toll Free: (888) 750-1550
E-mail: information@weddingchannel.com
Web Site: www.weddingchannel.com
Approx. Number Employees: 70
Year Founded: 1997
Business Description:
Online Wedding Planning Services
S.I.C.: 2741; 5621
N.A.I.C.S.: 511199; 448120
Media: 6-13
Advertising Agency:
The MWW Group
1 Meadowlands Plz 6th Fl
East Rutherford, NJ 07073
Tel.: (201) 507-9500
Fax: (201) 507-0092

WELOCALIZE, INC.
241 E 4th St Ste 207
Frederick, MD 21701-3612
Tel.: (301) 668-0330
Fax: (301) 668-0335
Toll Free: (800) 370-9515
E-mail: info@welocalize.com
Web Site: www.welocalize.com
Sales Range: $10-24.9 Million
Approx. Number Employees: 102
Year Founded: 1997
Business Description:
Multilingual Software, Product Localization & Translation Services
S.I.C.: 7389; 7379
N.A.I.C.S.: 541930; 541519
Media: 2-7-10-13
Personnel:
Smith E. Yewell *(Founder & CEO)*
Julia Yewell *(VP-Fin)*
Brands & Products:
WELOCALIZE
XCI
XTEND
XTK

WF ACQUISITION SUB, INC.
(Sub. of PC Mall, Inc.)
(d/b/a Wareforce)
19 Morgan
Irvine, CA 92618
Tel.: (949) 472-9000
Fax: (949) 452-1413
E-mail: info@wareforce.com
Web Site: www.wareforce.com
E-Mail For Key Personnel:
Marketing Director: marketing@wareforce.com
Sales Range: $75-99.9 Million
Approx. Number Employees: 200
Year Founded: 1985
Business Description:
Provider of IT Hardware, Software & Software Site Licenses; Designer of Information Systems; Provider of Technical & Asset Management & Technical Staffing Services; Distributor of Optical Storage Devices & Provider of Online Purchasing Services
S.I.C.: 5045
N.A.I.C.S.: 423430
Media: 13
Personnel:
Bill Neary *(Chm)*
Don Hughes *(CFO & COO)*
Harry Martin *(Sec & VP)*
Leroy Wyman *(Dir-Client Svcs)*

WHITEPAGES.COM INC.
1301 5th Ave Ste 1600
Seattle, WA 98101
Tel.: (206) 973-5100
Fax: (206) 621-1375
Web Site: www.whitepagesinc.com
Sales Range: $10-24.9 Million
Approx. Number Employees: 100
Business Description:
Online Directory Services
S.I.C.: 2741
N.A.I.C.S.: 516110
Media: 13
Personnel:
Alex Algard *(Founder & CEO)*
Kevin Nakao *(COO)*
Suki Hayre *(VP-Fin & Admin)*
Craig Paris *(VP-Online Adv Sls)*
Maxwell Bardon *(Dir)*

WHOLECELLULAR.COM, INC.
12701 Country Brook Ln
Tampa, FL 33625
Tel.: (813) 969-4300
Fax: (813) 354-3341
Toll Free: (877) 727-6300
Web Site: www.wholecellular.com
Sales Range: $50-74.9 Million
Approx. Number Employees: 2
Year Founded: 1995
Business Description:
Distributor of Cellular Communications Accessories
S.I.C.: 5065
N.A.I.C.S.: 423690
Advertising Expenditures: $200,000
Media: 13-17

WILD BRAIN, INC.
15000 Ventura Blvd
Sherman Oaks, CA 91403
Tel.: (818) 290-7080
E-mail: info@wildbrain.com
Web Site: www.wildbrain.com
Approx. Number Employees: 85
Year Founded: 1994
Business Description:
Animation Studio
S.I.C.: 7812
N.A.I.C.S.: 512110
Media: 13
Personnel:
David Graber *(Gen Counsel & Head-Bus Affairs)*

WINDOWBOX.COM INC.
6088 Corte del Cedro
Carlsbad, CA 92011
Fax: (323) 277-1130
Toll Free: (888) GARDEN-BOX
E-mail: service@windowbox.com
Web Site: www.windowbox.com
Approx. Sls.: $1,500,000
Approx. Number Employees: 20
Year Founded: 1997
Business Description:
Retailer of Plants & Flowers Specializing in Terrace & Balcony Gardening
S.I.C.: 5193; 3524
N.A.I.C.S.: 424930; 333112
Media: 8-13
Personnel:
Mark Thompson *(Mgr-Sls)*
Brands & Products:
FLORASERV
GIFTS THAT GROW
WINDOWBOX.COM

WINTEGRA INC.
6850 Austin Ctr Blvd Ste 215
Austin, TX 78731
Tel.: (512) 345-3808
Fax: (512) 345-3828
E-mail: treyo@wintegra.com
Web Site: www.wintegra.com
Sales Range: $10-24.9 Million
Approx. Number Employees: 100
Year Founded: 2000
Business Description:
Access Processing Semiconductors
S.I.C.: 3669; 3674
N.A.I.C.S.: 334290; 334413
Advertising Expenditures: $4,294,000
Personnel:
Jacob Ben-Zvi *(Co-Founder, Pres & CEO)*
Michael Phillip *(Sr VP & Gen Mgr-Wireless Sys)*
Sigal Hazak *(Dir-HR & Admin)*

WOODLIST, INC.
277 Linden St Ste 204
Wellesley, MA 02482
Tel.: (781) 283-5757
Fax: (781) 283-5707
E-mail: info@woodlist.com
Web Site: www.woodlist.com
Approx. Sls.: $2,500,000
Approx. Number Employees: 8
Year Founded: 1999
Business Description:
Wood Product Buying & Selling Services
S.I.C.: 5961; 5031
N.A.I.C.S.: 454113; 423310
Advertising Expenditures: $50,000
Media: 2-6-10-13
Personnel:
Arnold A. Kraft *(Owner)*

WORKBRAIN CORPORATION
(Joint Venture of Summit Partners L.P. & Golden Gate Capital)
250 Ferrand Dr Ste 1200
Toronto, ON M3C 3G8, Canada
Tel.: (416) 421-6700
Fax: (416) 421-8440
Toll Free: (888) 219-9993
Web Site: www.workbrain.com
Approx. Rev.: $92,605,426
Approx. Number Employees: 450
Year Founded: 1998
Business Description:
Workforce Management Software Solutions
S.I.C.: 7371
N.A.I.C.S.: 541511
Media: 7-10-11-13
Brands & Products:
ENTERPRISE SCHEDULING
ENTERPRISE TIME & ATTENDANCE
WORKBRAIN FOR HEALTHCARE
WORKBRAIN FOR MANUFACTURING
WORKBRAIN FOR RETAIL
WORKBRAIN INTELLIGENCE

WORKS, INC.
Shepherd Mountain Plz 6034 W Courtyard Dr Ste 210
Austin, TX 78730-5032
Tel.: (512) 685-8600
Fax: (888) 930-9238
Toll Free: (888) 967-5726
E-mail: press@works.com
Web Site: www.works.com
Approx. Sls.: $5,700,000
Approx. Number Employees: 180
Year Founded: 1997
Business Description:
Online Provider of Business Purchasing Services
S.I.C.: 7389
N.A.I.C.S.: 561499
Media: 7-13
Brands & Products:
ACTIVE CARD CONTROL
ACTIVE CARD INTEGRATION

Key to Media (For complete agency information see *The Advertising Red Books-Agencies* edition):
1. Bus. Publs. 2. Cable T.V. 3. Catalogs & Directories. 4. Co-op Adv. 5. Consumer Mags. 6. D.M. to Bus. Estab.7. D.M. to Consumers 8. Daily Newsp. 9. Exhibits/Trade Shows 10. Foreign 11. Infomercial 12. Internet Adv.13. Multimedia 14. Network Radio 15. Network T.V. 16. Newsp. Distr. Mags. 17. Other 18. Outdoor (Posters, Transit) 19. Point of Purchase20. Premiums, Novelties 21. Product Samples 22. Special Events Mktg. 23. Spot Radio 24. Spot T.V. 25. Weekly Newsp. 26. Yellow Page Adv.

Works, Inc. — (Continued)

AP FASTTRACK
WORKMATCH
WORKS

WORLDWIDE BIGGIES
545 W 45th St
New York, NY 10036
Tel.: (646) 442-1700
Fax: (646) 557-0019
E-mail: veranica@wwbiggies.com
Web Site: wwbiggies.com
Approx. Number Employees: 14
Year Founded: 2005
Business Description:
Digital Entertainment Studio
S.I.C.: 7389
N.A.I.C.S.: 541490
Personnel:
Albie Hecht *(CEO)*
Kari Kim *(VP-Production & Dev)*
Advertising Agency:
Dan Klores Communications
(d/b/a dkc)
386 Park Ave S 10th Fl
New York, NY 10016
Tel.: (212) 685-4300
Fax: (212) 685-9024

WSA CORPORATION
6333 Long
Shawnee Mission, KS 66216-1903
Tel.: (913) 631-3800
Fax: (913) 268-0468
Fax: (913) 631-9898
Toll Free: (800) WSACORP
E-mail: info@wsacorp.com
Web Site: www.wsacorp.com/
Approx. Number Employees: 80
Year Founded: 1976
Business Description:
Online Executive Recruitment & Replacement Services
S.I.C.: 7338; 7361
N.A.I.C.S.: 561410; 561310
Media: 9-13
Brands & Products:
PARTNERS IN YOUR CAREER SUCCESS
WSA CORP

X10 WIRELESS TECHNOLOGY, INC.
19823 58th Pl S
Kent, WA 98032
Tel.: (253) 437-3800
Fax: (253) 437-3810
Toll Free: (800) 675-3044
E-mail: info@x10.com
Web Site: www.x10.com
Approx. Sls.: $7,000,000
Approx. Number Employees: 50
Year Founded: 1999
Business Description:
Online Retailer of Cameras & Electronics
S.I.C.: 3669; 7372
N.A.I.C.S.: 334290; 511210
Advertising Expenditures: $300,000
Media: 4-13
Personnel:
George Stevenson *(Founder & CEO)*
Alex Peder *(Pres)*

XAP CORPORATION
3534 Hayden Ave
Culver City, CA 90232-2413
Tel.: (310) 842-9800
Fax: (310) 842-9898
E-mail: info@xap.com
Web Site: www.xap.com
Approx. Sls.: $7,000,000
Approx. Number Employees: 60
Year Founded: 1996
Business Description:
Online College Admission Preparation Services
S.I.C.: 7371; 7375
N.A.I.C.S.: 541511; 518111
Media: 10-13
Personnel:
J. Michael Thompson *(Pres & CEO)*
Brands & Products:
MENTOR

XEBRA, INC
(d/b/a GoCollect.com)
65 Broadway 7th Fl
New York, NY 10006
Tel.: (212) 731-8357
Fax: (212) 405-1039
E-mail: shanna@gocollect.com
Web Site: www.gocollect.com
E-Mail For Key Personnel:
President: rrafaloff@gocollect.com
Approx. Number Employees: 25
Year Founded: 1999
Business Description:
Online Source for Collectors, Manufacturers & Retailers Serving the Contemporary Collectibles & Gift Industry
S.I.C.: 5961
N.A.I.C.S.: 454113
Media: 4-8-13-19
Personnel:
Mike Baker *(Chm & CEO)*
Ron Rafaloff *(Pres & COO)*

XENOS GROUP INC.
(Sub. of Actuate Corporation)
95 Mural St Ste 201
Richmond Hill, ON L4B 3G2, Canada
Tel.: (905) 709-1020
Fax: (905) 709-1023
Toll Free: (888) 242-0692 (Canada)
Toll Free: (888) 436-8398 (United States)
E-mail: info@xenos.com
Web Site: www.xenos.com
E-Mail For Key Personnel:
Sales Director: sales@xenos.com
Approx. Sls.: $17,246,526
Approx. Number Employees: 87
Business Description:
Data & Document Management Solutions
S.I.C.: 8748; 7338; 7374; 7379
N.A.I.C.S.: 541690; 518210; 541519; 561410
Export
Media: 2-7-10-11-13
Personnel:
Pete Cittadini *(Chm, Pres, CEO)*
Paul Walker *(COO & Exec VP)*
Craig Smith *(VP-Sls & Global Mktg)*
Calvin Galatiuk *(Product Mgr)*
Brands & Products:
D2E VISION
INFOWEB
JESMASTER-PLUS
STREAMLINING ENTERPRISE INFORMATION SUPPLY CHAINS
XENOS
XENOS ENTERPRISE SERVER
XML2PDF MERGE

XOOM CORPORATION
301 Brannan St 5th Fl
San Francisco, CA 94107
Tel.: (415) 777-4800
Fax: (415) 777-8690
Web Site: www.xoom.com
Business Description:
Online-to-Offline International Money Transfer Service
S.I.C.: 6371
N.A.I.C.S.: 525990
Media: 13
Personnel:
John Kunze *(CEO)*
Ryno Blignaut *(CFO)*
Julian King *(Sr VP-Mktg & Corp Dev)*
Christopher Ferro *(VP-Legal & Compliance)*
Fausto Gortaire *(Mgr-Online Mktg)*
Brands & Products:
THE SMARTER WAY TO SEND MONEY
XOOM
Advertising Agency:
Ameredia, Inc.
101 Howard St Ste 380
San Francisco, CA 94105
Tel.: (415) 788-5100
Fax: (415) 449-3411

YAHOO! CANADA CO.
(Sub. of Yahoo! Inc.)
207 Queens Quay
Toronto, ON M5J 1A7, Canada
Tel.: (416) 341-8605
Fax: (416) 341-8800
E-mail: kmunro@yahoo-inc.com
Web Site: www.yahoo.ca
Sales Range: $25-49.9 Million
Approx. Number Employees: 100
Business Description:
Provider of Comprehensive Online Products & Services to Consumers & Businesses
S.I.C.: 7389
N.A.I.C.S.: 561499
Personnel:
Emma Harrington *(Dir-Bus Dev & Direct Response Adv)*
Brands & Products:
YAHOO
Advertising Agencies:
Environics Communications
33 Bloor Street E Suite 900
Toronto, ON M4W 3H1, Canada
Tel.: (416) 920-9000
Fax: (416) 920-1822

Launchfire Interactive
200 Isabella St 5th Fl
Ottawa, ON K1S 1V7, Canada
Tel.: (613) 728-5865
Fax: (613) 728-1527
Toll Free: (800) 896-4115
Yahoo! Music Canada

YAHOO! INC.
701 1st Ave
Sunnyvale, CA 94089
Tel.: (408) 349-3300
Fax: (408) 349-3301
E-mail: corporateinfo@yahoo-inc.com
Web Site: www.yahoo.com
Approx. Rev.: $7,208,502,000
Approx. Number Employees: 13,600
Year Founded: 1994
Business Description:
Online Products & Services to Consumers & Businesses
S.I.C.: 7373; 8999
N.A.I.C.S.: 541512; 518112
Advertising Expenditures: $220,000,000
Media: 2-6-13-14-15-16-18-20-22-23-24
Distr.: Intl.
Budget Set: Nov.
Personnel:
David Filo *(Co-Founder & Chief)*
Jerry Yang *(Co-Founder & Chief Yahoo)*
Roy J. Bostock *(Chm)*
Timothy R. Morse *(Interim CEO)*
Elisa Steele *(CMO & Exec VP)*
Raymie Stata *(CTO & Sr VP)*
David Windley *(Chief HR Officer & Exec VP)*
Aman S. Kothari *(Chief Acctg Officer & Sr VP & Global Controller)*
Michael J. Callahan *(Gen Counsel, Sec & Exec VP)*
Blake Irving *(Chief Products Officer & Exec VP)*
Ross Levinsohn *(Exec VP-Americas Reg)*
Jeff Russakow *(Exec VP-Customer Advocacy)*
Hilary A. Schneider *(Exec VP-Americas)*
Penny Baldwin *(Sr VP-Global Integrated Mktg & Brand Mgmt)*
Mark Morrissey *(Sr VP-Product Mgmt)*
Wayne Powers *(Sr VP-Sls-North America)*
Shashi Seth *(Sr VP-Search & Marketplaces)*
Bill Shaughnessy *(Sr VP-Product Mgmt & Product Mktg)*
Mollie Spilman *(Sr VP-Global B2B Mktg)*
Raymond Stern *(Sr VP-Bus Dev & Partnerships-North America)*
Lem Lloyd *(VP-Channel Sls & Small Bus)*
Seth Dellaire *(Head-Sls-Mid-Market & Audience Channels)*
Andrew Snyder *(Exec Dir-Content Solutions)*
Todd A. Porch *(Sr Dir-Display Adv Ops)*
Andrew Strickman *(Sr Dir-Experiential Mktg)*
Kelly Burke *(Dir-Strategic Sls Dev)*
Kerry Lange *(Dir-Social Mktg)*
Alex Linde *(Dir-Mobile & Tablet Adv)*
Edwin Wong *(Dir-B2B Strategic Insights)*
Kerry Trainor *(Product Mgr)*
Brands & Products:
1-800-MY-YAHOO
12 DAYS OF GIVING
ADDRESSGUARD
APT FROM YAHOO!
BIG IDEA CHAIR
BLOG FOR HOPE
CAMP YAHOO!
CHUNGDESIGN
CONNECT FROM YAHOO!
DO YOU YAHOO

THE EXPERIENCED PROFESSIONAL'S JOB BOARD
FLICKR
LIFE ENGINE
MY YAHOO!
MYLAUNCH
PEARL HUNTER
SMARTVIEW
SOFTSHOE
STATTRACKER
TOKI TOKI BOOM
TRAFFIC SERVER
VALUELAB
THE WEB'S HOTTEST JOBS
WORKWORLD
Y!
Y! BUZZ
Y! ONESEARCH
YA-HOO!
YAHOO!
YAHOO! 360?
YAHOO! BUZZ
YAHOO! GEOPLANET
YAHOO! GO
YAHOO! GROUPS
YAHOO! ONECONNECT
YAHOO! ONESEARCH
YAHOO! SEARCH BOSS
YAHOOLIGANS!
YAHOOPHONE
Y.COM
Y!MUSIC
YOU WITNESS NEWS

Advertising Agencies:
Fleishman-Hillard Inc.
200 N Broadway
Saint Louis, MO 63102-2730
Tel.: (314) 982-1700
Fax: (314) 982-0586

Goodby, Silverstein & Partners, Inc.
(Part of Omnicom Group, Inc.)
720 California St
San Francisco, CA 94108-2404
Tel.: (415) 392-0669
Fax: (415) 788-4303
Yahoo Bus Stop Derby

MediaVest USA
1675 Broadway
New York, NY 10019
Tel.: (212) 468-4000
Fax: (212) 468-4110
Traditional & Digital Media Assignment

YAHOO! MOBILE
(Unit of Yahoo! Connected Life)
701 1st Ave
Sunnyvale, CA 94089
Tel.: (408) 349-3300
Fax: (408) 349-3301
Sales Range: $100-124.9 Million
Approx. Number Employees: 500
Business Description:
Mobile Network Services
S.I.C.: 7375
N.A.I.C.S.: 518111
Media: 13-27
Personnel:
Lee Ott *(Sr Dir-Local)*

YAHOO! SEARCH MARKETING
(Sub. of Yahoo! Inc.)
701 1st Ave
Sunnyvale, CA 94089
Tel.: (408) 349-3300
Toll Free: (866) 924-6676
Web Site: searchmarketing.yahoo.com
Sales Range: $650-699.9 Million
Approx. Number Employees: 876
Year Founded: 1997
Business Description:
Internet Search Engine & Online Advertising Services
S.I.C.: 8999; 7389
N.A.I.C.S.: 518112; 541930
Media: 13
Personnel:
Eric Thomas *(Mgr)*
Brands & Products:
ALTAVISTA
CONTENT MATCH
SITE MATCH

YELLOWBRIX, INC.
500 Montgomery St Ste 700
Alexandria, VA 22314-1591
Tel.: (703) 548-3300
Fax: (705) 548-9151
Toll Free: (888) 325-9366
E-mail: info@yellowbrix.com
Web Site: www.yellowbrix.com
Approx. Number Employees: 158
Year Founded: 1997
Business Description:
Content Infrastructure & Software Provider
S.I.C.: 8748
N.A.I.C.S.: 541618
Media: 2-7-9-10-25
Personnel:
Jeffrey P. Massa *(Pres & CEO)*
Kevin Lapidus *(Gen Counsel & Sr VP)*
Thomas Hargis *(VP-Sls & Mktg)*
Brands & Products:
ARCHITEXT
INDUSTRYWATCH
INTELLICLIX
ISYNDICATE

YELLOWPAGES.COM LLC
(Sub. of AT&T Inc.)
7 N Fair Oaks Ave Ste 200
Pasadena, CA 91103-3608
Tel.: (626) 585-2800
Fax: (626) 303-3342
Toll Free: (800) 343-7390
E-mail: ypcsupport@yellowpages.com
Web Site: www.yellowpages.com
Sales Range: $25-49.9 Million
Approx. Number Employees: 75
Year Founded: 2004
Business Description:
Internet Directory Services; Joint Venture Owned by AT&T Inc. & Bell South Advertising & Publishing Corp.
S.I.C.: 2741
N.A.I.C.S.: 511140; 516110
Personnel:
David Krantz *(Pres & CEO)*
Matt Crowley *(CMO)*
Advertising Agency:
GSD&M
828 W 6th St
Austin, TX 78703-5420
Tel.: (512) 242-4736
Fax: (512) 242-4700

YET2.COM, INC.
10 Kearney Rd
Needham, MA 02494
Tel.: (781) 972-0600
Fax: (781) 972-0601
E-mail: info@yet2.com
Web Site: www.yet2.com
Approx. Number Employees: 20
Year Founded: 1999
Business Description:
Online Technology Purchasing, Selling, Licensing & Information Services
S.I.C.: 7375
N.A.I.C.S.: 518111
Media: 6-10-13
Personnel:
Ben du Pont *(Co-Founder & Pres)*
Phillip B. Stern *(Founder & CEO)*
Tim Bernstein *(Exec VP)*

YOUTUBE, LLC
(Sub. of Google Inc.)
901 Cherry Ave
San Bruno, CA 94066
Tel.: (650) 253-0000
Fax: (650) 253-0001
E-mail: press@youtube.com
Web Site: www.youtube.com
Sales Range: $1-9.9 Million
Approx. Number Employees: 67
Year Founded: 2005
Business Description:
Consumer-Oriented Online Video Broadcasting Services
S.I.C.: 2741; 7374
N.A.I.C.S.: 516110; 518210
Media: 13
Personnel:
Steve Chen *(Co-Founder & CTO)*
Anna Bateson *(Head-Mktg-Europe)*
Chris Di Cesare *(Head-Mktg & Programming)*
Andy Tress *(Dir-Sls-NW Reg)*
Mike Yapp *(Dir-Creative Content Dev)*
Gustavo Marcus *(Reg Mgr-Sls-Google Media Sls)*
Nikhil Chadhock *(Product Mgr-Video Syndication)*
Hunter Walk *(Product Mgr)*
Phil Farhi *(Sr Product Mgr)*
Brian Glick *(Product Mgr)*
Megan Jordan *(Mgr-Mktg Programs Team)*
Suzanne Szostak *(Mgr-Strategic Initiatives)*
Brands & Products:
YOUTUBE
Advertising Agency:
Allison & Partners
505 Sansome St 7th Fl
San Francisco, CA 94111-3310
Tel.: (415) 217-7500
Fax: (415) 217-7503

ZAPPOS.COM, INC.
(Sub. of Amazon.com, Inc.)
2280 Corporate Cir Ste 100
Henderson, NV 89074
Tel.: (702) 943-7677
Toll Free: (888) 492-7767
Toll Free: (800) 927-7671
E-mail: cs@zappos.com
Web Site: www.zappos.com
Sales Range: $1-4.9 Billion
Approx. Number Employees: 1,300
Year Founded: 1999
Business Description:
Online Shoe, Apparel & Accessories Retailer
S.I.C.: 5661
N.A.I.C.S.: 448210
Media: 6-13-18-29
Personnel:
Tony C. Hsieh *(CEO)*
Fred Mossler *(Sr VP-Mdsg)*
Matt Burchard *(Sr Dir-Content, Direct Mktg & User Experience)*
Lynn Dizon *(Brand Mgr-Mktg)*
Michelle Thomas *(Brand Mgr-Mktg)*
Ned Farra *(Mgr-Mktg-Online Partnerships)*
Advertising Agency:
Mullen
40 Broad St
Boston, MA 02109
Tel.: (617) 226-9000
Fax: (617) 226-9100
Agency of Record

ZILLOW, INC.
999 3rd Ave Ste 4600
Seattle, WA 98104
Tel.: (206) 470-7000
Fax: (206) 470-7001
Toll Free: (866) 324-4005
E-mail: press@zillow.com
Web Site: www.zillow.com
Approx. Rev.: $30,467,000
Approx. Number Employees: 252
Year Founded: 2004
Business Description:
Real Estate Services Website
S.I.C.: 2741; 6531
N.A.I.C.S.: 516110; 531390
Media: 1-13
Personnel:
Lloyd Frink *(Co-Founder & Vice Chm)*
Richard N. Barton *(Co-Founder & Exec Chm)*
Spencer Rascoff *(CEO)*
Chad Cohen *(CFO)*
Amy Bohutinsky *(CMO)*
Greg Schwartz *(Chief Revenue Officer)*
Kathleen Philips *(Gen Counsel)*
Kristin Acker *(VP-Product Teams)*
Chloe Harford *(VP-Product Mgmt & Strategy)*
Garrett McAuliffe *(VP-Product Teams)*
Christopher Roberts *(VP-Product Teams)*
Doug Slotkin *(VP-Local Adv Sls)*
Tony Small *(VP-Sls Strategy & Ops)*
Chris Staats *(VP-IT & Ops)*
Stan Humphries *(Chief Economist)*
Brands & Products:
ZESTIMATE
ZILLOW.COM
ZINDEX
Advertising Agency:
Deutsch LA
5454 Beethoven St
Los Angeles, CA 90066-7017
Tel.: (310) 862-3000
Fax: (310) 862-3100

ZONES, INC.
1102 15th St SW Ste 102
Auburn, WA 98001-6509
Tel.: (253) 205-3000
Fax: (253) 205-2558
Toll Free: (800) 258-2088
E-mail: ir@zones.com
Web Site: www.zones.com
Sales Range: $600-649.9 Million
Approx. Number Employees: 710
Year Founded: 1986

Zones, Inc. — (Continued)

Business Description:
Information Technology Products & Services
S.I.C.: 8742; 5961; 7389
N.A.I.C.S.: 541613; 454113; 519190
Advertising Expenditures: $6,618,000
Media: 4-5-7-13

Personnel:
Firoz H. Lalji *(Chm & CEO)*
Ronald P. McFadden *(CFO & Sr VP)*
Anwar Jiwani *(CIO & Sr VP)*
Tom J. Ducatelli *(Exec VP-Sls & Bus Dev)*
P. Sean Hobday *(Exec VP-Sls)*

Brands & Products:
COMPANY
CONNECTING BUSINESSES & TECHNOLOGY
MAC ZONE
ZONES
ZONESCONNECT

ZOOSK INC
130 Battery St
San Francisco, CA 94111
Tel.: (301) 641-4319
Web Site: www.zoosk.com

Business Description:
Online Dating Services
S.I.C.: 7299
N.A.I.C.S.: 812990

Personnel:
Alex F. Mehr *(Co-Founder & Co-CEO)*
Kelly Steckelberg *(CFO)*
Jeff Titterton *(VP-Mktg)*

Advertising Agency:
The Kluger Agency
1200 Brickell Ave 14th Fl
Miami, FL 33131
Tel.: (305) 639-8750
Fax: (305) 639-8751

Key to Media (For complete agency information see *The Advertising Red Books-Agencies* edition):
1. Bus. Publs. 2. Cable T.V. 3. Catalogs & Directories. 4. Co-op Adv. 5. Consumer Mags. 6. D.M. to Bus. Estab.7. D.M. to Consumers 8. Daily Newsp. 9. Exhibits/Trade Shows 10. Foreign 11. Infomercial 12. Internet Adv.13. Multimedia 14. Network Radio 15. Network T.V. 16. Newsp. Distr. Mags. 17. Other 18. Outdoor (Posters, Transit) 19. Point of Purchase20. Premiums, Novelties 21. Product Samples 22. Special Events Mktg. 23. Spot Radio 24. Spot T.V. 25. Weekly Newsp. 26. Yellow Page Adv.

Lighting

Electrical Equipment — Electrical Supplies — Lighting Fixtures

A. SCHONBEK & CO.
61 Industrial Blvd
Plattsburgh, NY 12901-1908
Tel.: (518) 563-7500
Fax: (518) 563-4228
Toll Free: (800) 836-1892
E-mail: sales@schonbek.com
Web Site: www.schonbek.com
E-Mail For Key Personnel:
Sales Director: sales@schonbek.com
Sales Range: $50-74.9 Million
Approx. Number Employees: 480
Year Founded: 1870
Business Description:
Mfr. of Crystal Chandelier & Lighting Fixtures
S.I.C.: 3645; 3646
N.A.I.C.S.: 335121; 335122
Import Export
Media: 4-5-6-10-11-17-19
Distr.: Intl.; Natl.
Personnel:
Mike Dupuis *(Dir-Fin)*
Brands & Products:
ADAGIO
ALLEGRO
ARIA
ARTEMIS
ARTIFACT
ATHENA
BAGATELLE
BEYOND LIGHTING
BOCINA
BORDEAUX
BUCKINGHAM
CAMELOT
CELLINI
CENTURY
CHAMPLAIN CRYSTAL
COLONADE
DIADEM
DIAMANTE
DYNASTY
EARLY AMERICAN
EQUINOXE
ESPLANADE
ETOILE
EXCELSIOR
FLORENTINE
GEMCUT
GENESIS
GEOMETRIX
HAMILTON
HARLEQUIN
HERITAGE HANDCUT
JASMINE
JUBILEE
KIROV
LA SCALA
LAUREL
LUXOR
MARDI GRAS
MARIA THERESA
MINUET
MIRAGE
MUSEE
NEW ORLEANS
OLDE WORLD
PETIT CRYSTAL DELUXE
PIROUETTE
PRINCESSA
RENAISSANCE
RHIANNON
RIVENDELL
ROCCA
ROMA
ROMANOFF
RONDELLE
SCHEHERAZADE
SCHONBEK
STRASS
STRELING
SWAROVSKI SPECTRA
TAHITIAN
TESORO
TRILLIANE
VENDOME
VENEZIA
VICTORIAN
VINTAGE
VINTAGE CRYSTAL
VIVALDI
ZOE

ACUITY BRANDS, INC.
1170 Peachtree St NE Ste 2400
Atlanta, GA 30309
Tel.: (404) 853-1400
Fax: (404) 853-1411
E-mail: webmaster@AcuityBrands.com
Web Site: www.acuitybrands.com
Approx. Sls.: $1,626,900,000
Approx. Number Employees: 6,000
Year Founded: 2002
Business Description:
Specialty Cleaning, Sanitation Preparations & Commercial & Industrial Lighting Fixtures Mfr
S.I.C.: 3645; 3646; 3648; 5169
N.A.I.C.S.: 335121; 335122; 335129; 424690
Advertising Expenditures: $12,000,000
Media: 2-8-10
Personnel:
Vernon J. Nagel *(Chm, Pres & CEO)*
Richard K. Reece *(CFO & Exec VP)*
Jim Young *(Gen Mgr-Specialty Indoor Lighting)*
Brands & Products:
ACUITY BRANDS
AMERICAN ELECTRIC LIGHTING
ENFORCER
GOTHAM
HOLOPHANE
HYDREL
LITHONIA LIGHTING
METALOPTICS
PEERLESS
SELIG
ZEP
Advertising Agency:
Mitchell, Lindberg & Taylor, Inc.
4020 E Ponce De Leon Ave
Clarkston, GA 30021
Tel.: (404) 292-4502
Fax: (404) 292-4480
Toll Free: (800) 265-1244

AFC CABLE SYSTEMS, INC.
(Sub. of Tyco Engineered Products & Services)
272 Duchaine Blvd
New Bedford, MA 02745-1222
Tel.: (508) 998-1131
Fax: (508) 998-1447
Toll Free: (800) 757-6996
E-mail: info@afcweb.com
Web Site: www.afcweb.com
Approx. Number Employees: 1,300
Year Founded: 1926
Business Description:
Electrical Distribution Products Designer, Mfr & Supplier
S.I.C.: 3496; 3317; 3355; 3356; 3357; 3469; 3537
N.A.I.C.S.: 332618; 331210; 331319; 331422; 331491; 332214; 333924; 335921; 335929
Export
Media: 2-4-5-7-10-20-21-22
Distr.: Natl.
Budget Set: Oct.
Personnel:
Edward D. Breen *(Chm & CEO)*
Martina Mejean *(Treas & Sr VP)*
Edward Arditte *(Sr VP-Investor Rels)*
Laurie Siegel *(Sr VP-HR)*
Charles Young *(Sr VP-Corp Mktg)*
Joe Colangelo *(VP-Sls)*
Brands & Products:
AC-90
AC-90 LITE
COLORSPEC
FIRE ALARM/CONTROL CABLE
HCF
HCF-90
HCF-LITE
HOME RUN CABLE
MC-LITE
MC/OF
MC TUFF
MOF
PARKING DECK/LOT CABLE
SUPER NEUTRAL CABLE
TEMP-LITES

AMERICAN LOUVER COMPANY
7700 Austin Ave
Skokie, IL 60077-2603
Tel.: (847) 470-3300
Fax: (847) 470-0420
Toll Free: (800) 323-4250
Telex: 3124700420
E-mail: mlinville@americanlouver.com
Web Site: www.americanlouver.com
Approx. Number Employees: 130
Year Founded: 1946
Business Description:
Louvers & Lenses, Security Mirrors, Shopping Baskets, Plastic Barricades & Traffic Devices & Plastic Sign Stands Mfr
S.I.C.: 3646; 3231
N.A.I.C.S.: 335122; 327215
Media: 4-10-13-21
Distr.: Intl.; Natl.
Budget Set: June -July
Personnel:
Walter Glass *(Founder)*

Key to Media (For complete agency information see *The Advertising Red Books-Agencies* edition):
1. Bus. Publs. 2. Cable T.V. 3. Catalogs & Directories. 4. Co-op Adv. 5. Consumer Mags. 6. D.M. to Bus. Estab.7. D.M. to Consumers
8. Daily Newsp. 9. Exhibits/Trade Shows 10. Foreign 11. Infomercial 12. Internet Adv.13. Multimedia 14. Network Radio
15. Network T.V. 16. Newsp. Distr. Mags. 17. Other 18. Outdoor (Posters, Transit) 19. Point of Purchase20. Premiums, Novelties
21. Product Samples 22. Special Events Mktg. 23. Spot Radio 24. Spot T.V. 25. Weekly Newsp. 26. Yellow Page Adv.

American Louver Company — (Continued)

Geoffrey Glass, Jr. *(Pres)*
Lucy Polk *(CFO)*
Donner Kelner *(Dir-Mktg)*
Brands & Products:
ALUMICUBE
AMERICAN BASKET
AMERICAN LOUVER
AMERICAN LOUVER COMPANY
AMERICAN MIRROR
PARACUBE
PARAWEDGE

AMERICAN PERIOD LIGHTING, INC.

3004 Columbia Ave
Lancaster, PA 17603
Tel.: (717) 392-5649
Fax: (717) 509-3127
Web Site: www.americanperiod.com
Approx. Number Employees: 3
Year Founded: 1970
Business Description:
Traditional Brass Lighting Fixture Mfr
S.I.C.: 3645; 3646
N.A.I.C.S.: 335121; 335122
Media: 4-6
Personnel:
Jack R. Cunningham *(Owner)*
Brands & Products:
AMERICAN PERIOD
PERIOD COLLECTION

BIG BEAM EMERGENCY SYSTEMS, INC.

290 E Prairie St
Crystal Lake, IL 60039-4415
Mailing Address:
PO Box 518
Crystal Lake, IL 60039-4415
Tel.: (815) 459-6100
Tel.: (815) 459-6143 (Sales)
Fax: (815) 459-6126
E-mail: info@bigbeam.com
Web Site: www.bigbeam.com
Approx. Number Employees: 80
Year Founded: 1938
Business Description:
Portable & Emergency Lighting Equipment
S.I.C.: 3648; 5063
N.A.I.C.S.: 335129; 423610
Export
Media: 2-4-6-7-8-10-11-13-19-20
Distr.: Intl.; Natl.
Budget Set: Oct.
Personnel:
Nick Shah *(Pres)*

BUZTRONICS, INC.

4343 W 62nd St
Indianapolis, IN 46268
Tel.: (317) 876-3413
Fax: (317) 876-3450
Toll Free: (800) 878-3413
Web Site: www.buzline.com
E-Mail For Key Personnel:
Sales Director: sales@buzline.com
Approx. Number Employees: 145
Year Founded: 1989
Business Description:
Electronic Blinking Buttons, Lights & Flashing Point of Purchase Signs in Celluloid, Metal & Custom Plastic for Promotional Efforts; Light Harnesses, Circuits Mfr
S.I.C.: 3999; 3961; 3993
N.A.I.C.S.: 339999; 339914; 339950
Import Export
Media: 4-7-8-10-13-21
Distr.: Intl.; Natl.
Personnel:
Edward Lewis *(Founder & CEO)*
Brands & Products:
BIKE PIPE
BUZLINE
BUZTRONICS
ELECTROPODS
TIREFLYS

CAPITOL LIGHTING

365 Rte 10
East Hanover, NJ 07936
Tel.: (973) 887-8600
Fax: (973) 887-8605
Toll Free: (800) -LIGHTING
E-mail: info@1800lighting.com
Web Site: www.1800lighting.com
Sales Range: $10-24.9 Million
Approx. Number Employees: 150
Business Description:
Lamps & Lamp Shades
S.I.C.: 5719; 5712
N.A.I.C.S.: 442299; 442110
Media: 4-6-25
Personnel:
Herman Lebersfeld *(Co-Chm)*
Max Lebersfeld *(Co-Chm)*
Eric Lebersfeld *(Pres & Chief Mktg Officer)*
Ken Lebersfeld *(CEO & COO)*
Brian Lebersfeld *(VP & Mgr-eCommerce Ops)*

CIRCA LIGHTING, INC.

405 Whitaker St
Savannah, GA 31401
Tel.: (912) 447-1008
Fax: (912) 447-1009
E-mail: info@circalighting.com
Web Site: www.circalighting.com
Business Description:
Lighting Retailer
S.I.C.: 3646
N.A.I.C.S.: 335122
Media: 13
Personnel:
Gale Singer *(Principal)*
Brands & Products:
CIRCA LIGHTING
SIMPLYBRILLIANT

CLEAR-LITE HOLDINGS, INC.

102 NE 2nd Street Ste 400
Boca Raton, FL 33432-3908
Tel.: (561) 544-6966
E-mail: investors@clear-lite.net
Web Site: www.clear-lite.net
Approx. Sls.: $457,934
Approx. Number Employees: 5
Year Founded: 2005
Business Description:
Lighting Products
S.I.C.: 3646
N.A.I.C.S.: 335122
Advertising Expenditures: $50,864
Media: 17
Personnel:
Milton C. Ault, III *(Chm & Interim CEO)*
Advertising Agency:
Beckerman Public Relations
One University Plz Ste 507
Hackensack, NJ 07601
Tel.: (908) 781-6420
Fax: (201) 465-8040

COLORSTARS GROUP

300 Center Ave Ste 202
Bay City, MI 48708
Tel.: (989) 509-5924
Web Site: www.colorstars.com
Sales Range: $1-9.9 Million
Approx. Number Employees: 12
Year Founded: 2002
Business Description:
LED Lighting Products Developer & Mfr
S.I.C.: 3648; 3646; 3827
N.A.I.C.S.: 335129; 333314; 335122
Advertising Expenditures: $77,144
Media: 2-10
Personnel:
Wei Rur Chen *(Chm, Pres, CEO & CFO)*
Brands & Products:
COLORSTARS
EZSTAR
GEMSTAR
LUXMAN
STARSTRIP
TRISTAR

CONDUCTIX INC.

(Sub. of Delachaux SA)
(d/b/a Conductix-Wampfler)
10102 F St
Omaha, NE 68127-1104
Tel.: (402) 339-9300
Fax: (402) 339-9627
Toll Free: (800) 521-4888
E-mail: info.us@conductix.com
Web Site: www.conductix.us
Approx. Number Employees: 150
Year Founded: 1948
Business Description:
Safety Electrification Products Mfr for Cranes, Monorails, Conveyors, Tools & Transport
S.I.C.: 3699
N.A.I.C.S.: 335999
Import Export
Advertising Expenditures: $100,000
Media: 4-8-10
Distr.: Natl.
Budget Set: Oct.
Personnel:
Lon Miller *(CEO)*
Stuart Zastrow *(CFO)*
Chris Michl *(CIO)*
Rod Griffith *(Dir-Mktg)*
Christian Nunez *(Mgr-Bus Dev-SMO Americas & Latin America)*
David Vazquez *(Mgr-Mexico Office)*
Brands & Products:
CLUSTER BAR
HEVI-BAR
HEVI-BAR II
PROTEAN
SAFE-LEC

COOPER CROUSE-HINDS, LLC

(Sub. of Cooper Industries plc)
Wolf 7th N St
Syracuse, NY 13221
Mailing Address:
PO Box 4999
Syracuse, NY 13221-4999
Tel.: (315) 477-5531
Fax: (315) 477-5179
Toll Free: (866) 764-5454
E-mail: crouse.customerctr@cooperindustries.com
Web Site: www.crouse-hinds.com
Sales Range: $250-299.9 Million
Approx. Number Employees: 600
Year Founded: 1897
Business Description:
Explosion-Proof & Non-Explosion-Proof Fittings, Enclosures, Industrial Lighting Plugs & Receptacles, Molded Electrical Products & Conduit & Cable Fittings Mfr
S.I.C.: 5084; 3648
N.A.I.C.S.: 423830; 335129
Export
Advertising Expenditures: $1,500,000
Media: 2-4-7-8-10
Distr.: Intl.; Natl.
Budget Set: Nov.
Personnel:
Tom McCarron *(VP-Sls & Market Dev)*

COOPER WIRING DEVICES

(Sub. of Cooper Industries plc)
203 Cooper Cir
Peachtree City, GA 30269
Tel.: (770) 631-2100
Fax: (770) 631-2106
Toll Free: (866) 853-4293
E-mail: custserv@cooperwiringdevices.com
Web Site: www.cooperwiringdevices.com
Sales Range: $100-124.9 Million
Year Founded: 1920
Business Description:
Wiring Device Mfr
S.I.C.: 3643; 3613
N.A.I.C.S.: 335931; 335313
Import Export
Advertising Expenditures: $1,000,000
Media: 2-3-4-7-10-13-20-21
Distr.: Natl.
Budget Set: Oct.
Personnel:
David A. Barta *(CFO & Sr VP)*
Rick L. Johnson *(Chief Acctg Officer, VP & Controller)*
Bruce M. Taten *(Chief Complience Officer, Gen Counsel & Sr VP)*
C. Thomas O'Grady *(Sr VP-Bus Dev)*
Tom Benton *(VP-Mktg)*
Rodney Long *(VP-Sls-ED/OEM Div)*
Rick McDonnell *(VP-Consumer Sls Div)*
Heath B. Monesmith *(VP-HR)*
Art Hansen *(Prod Mgr-New Venture Products)*
Michele Salimbeni *(Mgr-Comml Product)*

COPPERWELD BIMETALLICS, LLC

(Sub. of Fushi Copperweld, Inc.)
254 Cotton Mill Rd
Fayetteville, TN 37334-7249
Tel.: (931) 433-7177
Fax: (931) 433-0419
Toll Free: (888) 284-9473
Toll Free: (888) 350-CLAD
Toll Free: (888) 350-2523
E-mail: bimetallic@copperweld.com
Web Site: www.copperweld.com
Sales Range: $50-74.9 Million
Approx. Number Employees: 130
Year Founded: 1915
Business Description:
Bimetallic Wire & Strand Products Mfr
S.I.C.: 3496; 3357
N.A.I.C.S.: 332618; 331422
Export

Key to Media (For complete agency information see *The Advertising Red Books-Agencies* edition):
1. Bus. Publs. 2. Cable T.V. 3. Catalogs & Directories. 4. Co-op Adv. 5. Consumer Mags. 6. D.M. to Bus. Estab.7. D.M. to Consumers 8. Daily Newsp. 9. Exhibits/Trade Shows 10. Foreign 11. Infomercial 12. Internet Adv.13. Multimedia 14. Network Radio 15. Network T.V. 16. Newsp. Distr. Mags. 17. Other 18. Outdoor (Posters, Transit) 19. Point of Purchase20. Premiums, Novelties 21. Product Samples 22. Special Events Mktg. 23. Spot Radio 24. Spot T.V. 25. Weekly Newsp. 26. Yellow Page Adv.

Exhibits/Trade Shows: 75%; Other: 25%
Distr.: Direct to Consumer; Natl.
Budget Set: Nov.

CRAFTMADE INTERNATIONAL, INC.
650 S Royal Ln Ste 100
Coppell, TX 75019-3836
Mailing Address:
PO Box 1037
Coppell, TX 75019-1037
Tel.: (972) 393-3800
Fax: (972) 304-3753
Fax: (877) 304-1728
Toll Free: (800) 486-4892
E-mail: investorrelations@craftmade.com
Web Site: www.craftmade.com
Approx. Sls.: $153,920,000
Approx. Number Employees: 288
Year Founded: 1985
Business Description:
Ceiling Fans, Light Kits & Related Accessories Designer & Distr
S.I.C.: 3646; 5063; 5064
N.A.I.C.S.: 335122; 423610; 423620
Advertising Expenditures: $3,484,000
Media: 2-4-5-6-10-16-26
Personnel:
James R. Ridings *(Chm)*
Brad D. Heimann *(Pres & COO)*
J. Marcus Scrudder *(CEO)*
C. Brett Burford *(CFO)*
J. Carl Loreto *(CMO)*
Todd Teiber *(Sr VP-Specialty Sls)*
Clifford F. Crimmings *(VP-Sls)*
Brands & Products:
5TH AVENUE
ACCOLADE
AMERICAN TRADITION
AMERICANA
AMPHORA
ARTISTRY
ATHENA
AZTEC
BARCELONA
BEAUMONT
BLOOM
BROWNSTONE
BUILDERS
CANOE
CATHRYN
CD UNIPACK 201
CD UNIPACK 202
CD UNIPACK 203
CD UNIPACK 204
CENTURION
CEYLON
CHALICE
CHAMBERLAIN
CHAPARRAL
CIVIC
CIVIC UNIPACK
CONSTANTINA
CONTEMPORARY
CONTRACTOR'S DESIGN
CONTRACTOR'S SELECT
CORDOVA
COSMOS UNIPACK
CRAFTMADE
CRESCENT
CS UNIPACK
CXL RANGER
DC EPIC
DESIGNER SURFACE
FIORI
FLAME
FLAT
FRESCO
FRESH AIR
FRESNO
FRONTIER
GRANT
HALSTEAD
HEAT VENT
HERITAGE
IMPULSE
ISABELLA
KIRA
KONA BAY
LA TOUR
LA VELA
LEGION
LEONA
LITE RAIL
LOG CABIN
LYON SHAW
MADISON
MARQUIS
MATTHEW
MEDINA
METRO
MIA
MIDORO
MOONGLOW
OL' MADRID 2
OLIVIER
OMNI
OPHELIA
OUTDOOR MIA
OUTDOOR PATIO FAN
PALOMA
PANACHE
PARAGON
PAVILION
PHALANX
PHOENIX
PICCOLO
PORCH FAN
PRESIDENTIAL LL
PROSTAR BASKETBALL
QUEST
RACETRACK
RIATA
RYAN
SALERNO
SAN LORENZ
SAN MIGUEL
SAVANNAH
SCROLL
SENTRY
SILO
SOLID
SOLO
SOMERSET
SPLIT
SUTTON
TERRAZZO
TORDERA
TOSCANA
TOWNSEND
TRADITIONAL
TRELLIS
TRIUMPH
TSI PRIME
UNIVERSAL HUGGER
VALENCIA
VELOCITY
WARBIRDS
WARPLANES
WELLINGTON
WOODARD

CRESCENT/STONCO SUPPLY DIVISION
(Sub. of Philips Lighting)
2345 Vauxhall Rd
Union, NJ 07083
Tel.: (908) 964-7000
Fax: (908) 964-1404
Web Site: www.crescentlighting.com
E-Mail For Key Personnel:
President: chavers@genlyte.com
Marketing Director: PHenry@genlyte.com
Approx. Number Employees: 125
Business Description:
Outdoor Commercial & Industrial Lighting; Incandescent, High Intensity Discharge & Fluorescent Lighting Mfr
S.I.C.: 3646
N.A.I.C.S.: 335122
Advertising Expenditures: $360,000
Media: 1-2-4-10-18-19
Distr.: Natl.
Budget Set: Dec.
Personnel:
Chuck Havers *(Pres)*
Phil Henry *(VP-Mktg)*
Jim Lewis *(VP-Sls)*
Tom Russello *(VP-Engrg)*
Helen Ferraro *(Dir-Fin)*
Marie Vener *(Dir-Sls)*
Susan Woodruff *(Dir-Pur)*
Laurie Boss *(Mgr-HR)*
Harry Wingerter *(Mgr-Quality Control)*
Brands & Products:
GLO BAY
LYTEPRO
PARAFLOOD
ROUGHLYTE
STONCO
SVL
TWILIGHTER

CYALUME TECHNOLOGIES HOLDINGS, INC.
96 Windsor St
West Springfield, MA 01089
Tel.: (413) 858-2500
Fax: (413) 734-4290
Toll Free: (888) 858-7881
E-mail: info@cyalume.com
Web Site: www.cyalume.com
Approx. Rev.: $38,024,000
Approx. Number Employees: 164
Business Description:
Holding Company; Chemical & Electronic Light Systems Designer, Developer & Mfr
S.I.C.: 6719; 3646; 3648
N.A.I.C.S.: 551112; 335122; 335129
Advertising Expenditures: $81,000
Media: 17
Personnel:
Winston J. Churchill, Jr. *(Chm)*
Yaron I. Eitan *(Vice Chm)*
Derek Dunaway *(Pres & CEO)*
Michael Bielonko *(CFO)*
Monte L. Pickens *(Exec VP)*
Edgar Cranor *(VP-Tech)*
Thomas McCarthy *(VP-Sls & Mktg)*
Tomas Ogas *(VP-Ops & IT)*
Brands & Products:
CHEMLIGHTS
CYALUME
CYFLECT
LIGHTSHAPES
LIGHTSTATION
PML
S.E.E.
SNAPLIGHT
S.O.S

CYMER, INC.
17075 Thornmint Ct
San Diego, CA 92127-1712
Tel.: (858) 385-7300
Fax: (858) 385-7100
E-mail: custservice@cymer.com
Web Site: www.cymer.com
Approx. Rev.: $534,209,000
Approx. Number Employees: 953
Year Founded: 1986
Business Description:
Excimer Lasers Mfr for Semiconductor Fabrication
S.I.C.: 3559
N.A.I.C.S.: 333295
Advertising Expenditures: $572,000
Personnel:
Robert P. Akins *(Chm & CEO)*
Edward J. Brown, Jr. *(Pres & COO)*
Paul B. Bowman *(CFO, Sec & Sr VP)*
William Partlo *(CTO & Sr VP)*
Karen K. McGinnis *(Chief Acctg Officer, VP & Controller)*
Richard L. Sandstrom *(Sr VP)*
Brands & Products:
CYMER
CYMERONLINE
GLX
INSIST ON CYMER
NANOLITH
ONPULSE
XLR
Advertising Agency:
Formula PR
810 Parkview Dr N
El Segundo, CA 90245
Tel.: (310) 578-7050
Fax: (310) 578-7077

DAZOR MANUFACTURING CORP.
2079 Congressional Dr
Saint Louis, MO 63146
Tel.: (314) 652-2400
Fax: (314) 652-2069
Toll Free: (800) 345-9103
E-mail: info@dazor.com
Web Site: www.dazor.com
Approx. Number Employees: 18
Year Founded: 1938
Business Description:
Mfr. of Portable & Adjustable Lighting Fixtures & Video Microscopes
S.I.C.: 3646
N.A.I.C.S.: 335122
Import Export
Media: 7-10-19
Distr.: Natl.
Personnel:
Stan Hogrebe *(Pres & CEO)*
Brands & Products:
ASYMMETRIA
DAZOR
HALOGEN FLEX
HANGTIGHT
MAGNIFIER-FLEX
SPECK FINDER
STRETCH VIEW
WORLD-LITE

DOLAN NORTHWEST LLC
(d/b/a Seattle Lighting Fixture Co.)
(d/b/a Globe Lighting)
1919 Northwest 19th Ave

Key to Media (For complete agency information see *The Advertising Red Books-Agencies* edition):
1. Bus. Publs. 2. Cable T.V. 3. Catalogs & Directories. 4. Co-op Adv. 5. Consumer Mags. 6. D.M. to Bus. Estab.7. D.M. to Consumers 8. Daily Newsp. 9. Exhibits/Trade Shows 10. Foreign 11. Infomercial 12. Internet Adv.13. Multimedia 14. Network Radio 15. Network T.V. 16. Newsp. Distr. Mags. 17. Other 18. Outdoor (Posters, Transit) 19. Point of Purchase20. Premiums, Novelties 21. Product Samples 22. Special Events Mktg. 23. Spot Radio 24. Spot T.V. 25. Weekly Newsp. 26. Yellow Page Adv.

Dolan Northwest LLC — (Continued)

Portland, OR 97209
Tel.: (503) 225-9009
Fax: (503) 221-1962
Toll Free: (800) 691-7895
E-mail: frontdesk@seattlelighting.com
Web Site: www.seattlelighting.com
Approx. Number Employees: 300
Year Founded: 1917
Business Description:
Lighting Fixtures & Related Products Mfr & Distr
S.I.C.: 5063; 5719
N.A.I.C.S.: 423610; 442299
Advertising Expenditures: $1,500,000
Media: 9-10-19-23
Personnel:
Dan Dolan *(Pres)*
Dave McKee *(COO)*
Pat Dolan *(Exec VP)*
Brands & Products:
DOLAN DESIGNS
SEATTLE LIGHTING

DUALITE SALES & SERVICE, INC.

1 Dualite Ln
Williamsburg, OH 45176-1121
Tel.: (513) 724-7100
Fax: (513) 724-9029
E-mail: dualite@dualite.com
Web Site: www.dualite.com
E-Mail For Key Personnel:
Sales Director: bstephany@dualite.com
Sales Range: $25-49.9 Million
Approx. Number Employees: 295
Year Founded: 1947
Business Description:
Mfr. & Sales of Illuminated Indoor & Outdoor Signs, Clocks & Menu Signs
S.I.C.: 5099; 1799
N.A.I.C.S.: 423990; 238990
Import Export
Advertising Expenditures: $82,000
Catalogs & Directories: $12,000; D.M. to Bus. Estab.: $5,000; Exhibits/Trade Shows: $50,000; Product Samples: $15,000
Distr.: Intl.; Natl.
Budget Set: Sept.
Personnel:
Greg Schube *(Pres & CEO)*
Dennis Emery *(VP-Sls)*
Kenneth E. Syberg *(VP-Sls)*
Betty Jewell *(Dir-HR)*
Patrick Seggerson *(Dir-Design)*
Robert Stephany *(Natl Sls Mgr)*
Taryn Wainscott *(Coord-Mktg & Sls)*
Brands & Products:
DUALITE

EATON CORPORATION - INDUSTRIAL CONTROLS

(Unit of Eaton Corporation)
4201 N 27th St
Milwaukee, WI 53216-1807
Tel.: (414) 449-6207
Fax: (414) 449-7368
Toll Free: (800) 962-0820
Telex: 26-716 EATON CH MIL
Web Site: www.eaton.com
Sales Range: $25-49.9 Million
Approx. Number Employees: 50
Business Description:
Switches Mfr
S.I.C.: 3621; 5211
N.A.I.C.S.: 335312; 444190
Export
Advertising Expenditures: $600,000
Media: 1-2-4-7-10-11-13-19-20-21
Distr.: Intl.; Natl.
Budget Set: Sept.
Personnel:
Steven M. Boccadoro *(Sr VP-Sls & Mktg)*
Darrick Finan *(VP-Sls-America)*
Prakash Megchiani *(Reg Dir-Mktg-Middle East)*
Donald Alles *(Dir-Branding & Comm-Global)*
Bill Carter *(Dir-Sls & Mktg)*
Mike Dixon *(Dir-Sls-Electric Transportation Infrastructure-Natl)*
Graciano Beyhaut *(Reg Mgr-Sls)*
Ciaran Bolton *(Product Mgr-Data Centre Solutions)*
Joe Dzierwa *(Product Mgr-Aeroquip Braided & Spiral Hose Products-Global)*
Bill Genaw *(Product Mgr-HVAC Drives)*
Harry Broussard *(Mgr-Mktg-Medium Voltage Drives-Global)*
Margaret DeAngelis *(Mgr-Mktg-Americas)*
Rob Jarrell *(Mgr-Govt Sls)*
Arthur R. Mulligan *(Mgr-Mktg)*
Brands & Products:
CUTLER-HAMMER
HEINEMANN CIRCUIT BREAKERS

EGS ELECTRICAL GROUP

(Joint Venture of Emerson Electric Co. & SPX Corporation)
9377 W Higgins Rd
Rosemont, IL 60018
Tel.: (847) 268-6000
Fax: (847) 268-6011
Web Site: www.egseg.com
Sales Range: $350-399.9 Million
Approx. Number Employees: 1,000
Year Founded: 1847
Business Description:
Conduit Fittings, Electrical Connectors, Bushings & Cast Boxes for Utility & Secondary Power Distribution, Hazardous Location Fittings, Enclosures, Motor Control & Industrial Lighting Services
S.I.C.: 3679
N.A.I.C.S.: 334419
Export
Media: 2-4-5-19-20-21
Distr.: Natl.
Budget Set: Oct.
Brands & Products:
COPPER-PLUS
FIRE-SEAL
GROUND-TITE
LAY-IN-LUG
SPLIT-COUPLING

EGS ELECTRICAL GROUP LLC

(Joint Venture of Emerson Electric Co. & SPX Corporation)
9377 W Higgins Rd
Rosemont, IL 60018-4938
Tel.: (847) 679-7800
Fax: (847) 268-6020
Web Site: www.egseg.com
E-Mail For Key Personnel:
Sales Director: sales@sola-hevi-duty.com
Sales Range: $50-74.9 Million
Approx. Number Employees: 150
Year Founded: 1997
Business Description:
Industrial Electrical Products Mfr; Joint Venture of Emerson Electric Company (52.5%) & SPX Corporation (47.5%)
S.I.C.: 3644; 3643
N.A.I.C.S.: 335932; 335931
Export
Media: 2-4-5-10-11-19-20-21-26
Distr.: Intl.; Natl.
Budget Set: May
Personnel:
Eric Meyer *(Pres)*
Michael Bryant *(CFO)*
George Mulligan *(Pres-Industrial Products)*
Miriam Blazowski *(Dir-Sls)*
Tom Mueller *(Dir-Natl Accts)*
Jim Tehan *(Dir-Technical)*
Steve Henry *(Mgr-Mktg-Lighting)*
Loretta Chazen *(Mgr-Credit)*
Mary Krauss *(Mgr-Pricing)*
Brands & Products:
APPLETON
ATX
CURLEE
EASY HEAT
MCGILL
NELSON E & C
NELSON FIRESTOP
NELSON HEAT TRACE
O-Z/GEDNEY
SOLA/HEVI-DUTY
SOLATRON

ELECTRONIC THEATRE CONTROLS, INC.

3031 Pleasant View Rd
Middleton, WI 53562-1754
Tel.: (608) 831-4116
Fax: (608) 836-1736
Toll Free: (800) 688-4116
E-mail: mail@etcconnect.com
Web Site: www.etcconnect.com
Approx. Sls.: $47,500,000
Approx. Number Employees: 550
Year Founded: 1975
Business Description:
Lighting Control Systems Mfr
S.I.C.: 3648; 3646
N.A.I.C.S.: 335129; 335122
Media: 10
Personnel:
Richard Titus *(Pres)*
Fred Foster *(CEO)*
Julie Cymbalak *(VP-HR & IT)*
Bill Gallinghouse *(VP-Bus Dev & Mktg)*
Mark Veldey *(VP-Fin)*
Tom Littrell *(Product Mgr-Fixtures)*
Brands & Products:
CONGO
EOS
EXPRESSION
ION
IPAQ
OBSESSION
QUIETDRIVE
REVOLUTION
SENSOR
SMART SOLUTIONS
SMARTFADE
SMARTPACK
SMARTSOFT
SMARTSWITCH
SOURCE FOUR
SOURCE FOUR REVOLUTION
UNISON

ELITE COLLECTIONS, INC.

1139 Hwy 77 N
Marion, AR 72364-0936
Mailing Address:
PO Box 688
Marion, AR 72364-9027
Tel.: (870) 735-1826
Fax: (870) 732-3017
Toll Free: (800) 249-3357
E-mail: customerservice@vintagev.com
Web Site: www.vintagev.com
Sales Range: $50-74.9 Million
Approx. Number Employees: 170
Year Founded: 1963
Business Description:
Furniture Whslr
S.I.C.: 5023
N.A.I.C.S.: 423220
Media: 2-4
Personnel:
James O. Pike *(Pres & CEO)*
Dan Macintyre *(CFO)*
Todd Sawvelle *(Dir-Mktg)*

EMERSON ELECTRIC CO.

8000 W Florissant Ave
Saint Louis, MO 63136-1494
Mailing Address:
PO Box 4100
Saint Louis, MO 63136-8506
Tel.: (314) 553-2000
Fax: (314) 553-3527
Telex: 643743
E-mail: info@emerson.com
Web Site: www.emerson.com
Approx. Sls.: $21,039,000,000
Approx. Number Employees: 127,700
Year Founded: 1890
Business Description:
Process Control Systems, Climate Control Systems, Power Technologies, Electric Motors & Other Electrical Appliances Mfr
S.I.C.: 3621; 3625; 3699; 3822
N.A.I.C.S.: 335312; 334512; 335314; 335999
Personnel:
David N. Farr *(Chm & CEO)*
Walter J. Galvin *(Vice Chm)*
Edward L. Monser *(Pres & COO)*
Frank J. Dellaquila *(CFO & Sr VP)*
Kathleen McElligott *(CIO)*
Katherine Button Bell *(CMO & VP)*
Randall D. Ledford *(CTO & Sr VP)*
R. J. Schlueter *(Chief Acctg Officer & VP-Acctg)*
Dale A. Kubly *(VP & Assoc Gen Counsel)*
B. J. Walsh *(VP & Gen Counsel-Emerson Network Power)*
F. L. Steeves *(Gen Counsel)*
C. L. Tucker *(Dir-IR & Asst Treas)*
Craig W. Ashmore *(Exec VP)*
D. K. Feeney *(Exec VP)*
Ed Feeney *(Exec VP-Emerson Network Power)*
Jay L. Geldmacher *(Exec VP)*
Jean-Paul L. Montupet *(Exec VP)*
Steven A. Sonnenberg *(Exec VP)*
W. W. Withers *(Exec VP-Special Legal Advisor)*
Robert M. Cox, Jr. *(Sr VP-Admin)*
P. A. Hutchison *(Sr VP-HR)*
Paul E. McKnight *(Sr VP-Org Plng)*

Key to Media (For complete agency information see *The Advertising Red Books-Agencies* edition):
1. Bus. Publs. 2. Cable T.V. 3. Catalogs & Directories. 4. Co-op Adv. 5. Consumer Mags. 6. D.M. to Bus. Estab.7. D.M. to Consumers 8. Daily Newsp. 9. Exhibits/Trade Shows 10. Foreign 11. Infomercial 12. Internet Adv.13. Multimedia 14. Network Radio 15. Network T.V. 16. Newsp. Distr. Mags. 17. Other 18. Outdoor (Posters, Transit) 19. Point of Purchase20. Premiums, Novelties 21. Product Samples 22. Special Events Mktg. 23. Spot Radio 24. Spot T.V. 25. Weekly Newsp. 26. Yellow Page Adv.

M. G. Rohret *(Sr VP-HR)*
R. P. Kerstetter *(Grp VP-Storage Solutions)*
P. K. Murphy *(Grp VP)*
E. M. Shanahan *(Grp VP)*
T. G. Westman *(VP & Assoc Gen Counsel)*
C. A. Doiron *(VP-Product Dev)*
K. D. Hahn *(VP-IT)*
S. C. Roemer *(VP-Fin Plng)*
D. D. Sollberger *(VP-Procurement)*
Lynne Maxeiner *(Dir-IR)*
John Payton *(Dir-IT)*
R. E. Keefe *(Mgr-IT Project)*

Brands & Products:
AIR COMFORT
ASCO
ASTEC
BRANSON
BROWNING
COMMERCIAL CAM
COPELAND
CPS
DOERR
EMERSON
EMERSON APPLIANCE SOLUTIONS
EMERSON CLIMATE TECHNOLOGIES
EMERSON INDUSTRIAL AUTOMATION
EMERSON MOTOR TECHNOLOGIES
EMERSON NETWORK POWER
EMERSON PROCESS MANAGEMENT
EMERSON PROFESSIONAL TOOLS
EMERSON STORAGE SOLUTIONS
FUSITE
HURST MANUFACTURING
IN-SINK-ERATOR
INDUSTRIAL AUTOMATION
JOUCOMATIC
LIEBERT
LOW CONTROL
METRO
MICRO MOTION
MOTOR TECHNOLOGIES
NETWORK POWER
RIDGE
RIDGID
ROSEMOUNT
STORAGE SOLUTIONS
U.S. ELECTRICAL MOTORS
VAREC
WESTERN FORGE

Advertising Agencies:
CO-OP PROMOTIONS
2301 S Ocean Dr Ste 2504
Hollywood, FL 33019
Tel.: (954) 922-2323

DDB Chicago
200 E Randolph St
Chicago, IL 60601
Tel.: (312) 552-6000
Fax: (312) 552-2370

Landau Public Relations
700 W Saint Clair Ave Ste 414
Cleveland, OH 44113
Tel.: (216) 696-1686
Fax: (216) 771-5206
Emerson Ceiling Fans

ENVIRONMENTAL LIGHTING CONCEPTS, INC.

1214 W Cass St
Tampa, FL 33606
Tel.: (813) 621-0058
Fax: (813) 626-8790
Toll Free: (800) 842-8848
E-mail: prdept@ott-lite.com
Web Site: www.ott-lite.com
Approx. Sls.: $7,000,000
Approx. Number Employees: 60
Year Founded: 1989
Business Description:
Natural Lighting Products Mfr
S.I.C.: 3646; 5719
N.A.I.C.S.: 335122; 442299
Media: 2-6-9-13-19
Personnel:
Don Barry *(Pres & CEO)*
Karen Garnes *(Dir-Adv-Creative Svcs)*
Brands & Products:
ENJOY LIFE IN HD
HIGH DEFINITION NATURAL LIGHTING
THE LEARNING LIGHT
NATURAL LIGHT SUPPLEMENT
OTT-LITE
TRUE COLOR

ETL SEMKO - INTERTEK TESTING SERVICES N.A. INC.

(Div. of Intertek Group plc)
3933 US Rte 11
Cortland, NY 13045
Tel.: (607) 753-6711
Fax: (607) 756-9891
Toll Free: (800) 345-3851
Approx. Number Employees: 300
Year Founded: 1896
Business Description:
Independent Testing Laboratory
S.I.C.: 8733
N.A.I.C.S.: 541710
Media: 4-8-10-11-13
Distr.: Natl.
Budget Set: Aug.
Personnel:
Gregg Tieman *(Pres)*

FERRAZ SHAWMUT
(Name Changed to Mersen)

GE CANADA COMPANY

(Sub. of GE Industrial)
2300 Meadowvale Blvd
Mississauga, ON L5N 5P9, Canada
Tel.: (905) 858-5100
Fax: (905) 858-5106
Telex: 6-22023
E-mail: info@ge.com
Web Site: www.ge.com/ca
Sales Range: $250-299.9 Million
Approx. Number Employees: 600
Business Description:
Appliances, Lighting Products, Plastics & Engineered Materials Mfr
S.I.C.: 3639; 3089; 3648
N.A.I.C.S.: 335228; 326199; 335129
Media: 2-4-6-26
Distr.: Intl.; Natl.
Personnel:
Elyse Allan *(Pres & CEO)*
Bruce Futterer *(Gen Counsel & VP)*
Anna Cvecich *(VP-HR)*
Manjit Sharma *(VP-Fin)*
Kim Warburton *(VP-Comm & Pub Rel)*
Advertising Agencies:
Fuel Industries
7 Hinton Ave N Ste 100
Ottawa, ON K1Y 4P1, Canada
Tel.: (613) 224-6738
Fax: (613) 224-6802

OMD Canada
67 Richmond St W 2nd Fl
Toronto, ON M5H 1Z5, Canada
Tel.: (416) 681-5600
Fax: (416) 681-5620

GE INFRASTRUCTURE SECURITY

(Div. of GE Technology Infrastructure)
90 Fieldstone Ct
Cheshire, CT 06410-1212
Tel.: (203) 699-3000
Fax: (203) 699-3216
Sales Range: $25-49.9 Million
Approx. Number Employees: 90
Year Founded: 1963
Business Description:
Fire Detection & Life Safety Solutions
S.I.C.: 3812
N.A.I.C.S.: 334511
Media: 1-2-4-10-17-19-20-21-26
Distr.: Natl.
Budget Set: Dec.
Brands & Products:
ENABLED
FIRESHIELD
FIREWORKS
QUICKSTART
SYNERGY ENABLED INTEGRATION
Advertising Agency:
Adkins Design Visual Communications LLC
35 Corporate Drive Suite 1090
Trumbull, CT 06614
Tel.: (203) 375-2887
Fax: (203) 386-1203
(Emergency Lighting)

GENERAL ELECTRIC COMPANY

3135 Easton Tpke
Fairfield, CT 06828-0001
Tel.: (203) 373-2211
Fax: (203) 373-3131
E-mail: ir.contacts@corporate.ge.com
Web Site: www.ge.com
Approx. Rev.: $150,211,000,000
Approx. Number Employees: 287,000
Year Founded: 1892
Business Description:
Holding Company; Appliances, Lighting Products, Plastics, Engineered Materials, Power Systems, Medical Systems, Aircraft Engines & Locomotives, Electric Motors & Electrical Controls Mfr; Commercial & Consumer Lending Services
S.I.C.: 6719; 3511; 3519; 3621; 3639; 3641; 3724; 3822; 3841; 3845; 6099; 6141; 6159
N.A.I.C.S.: 551112; 333611; 333618; 334510; 334512; 335110; 335228; 335312; 336412; 339112; 522291; 522298; 522390
Import Export
Advertising Expenditures: $1,916,800,000
Media: 3-6-9-13-14-15-16-17-18-23-24
Distr.: Intl.; Natl.
Budget Set: Oct.
Personnel:
Michael A. Neal *(Co-Vice Chm & Chm & CEO-GE Capital)*
Jeffrey R. Immelt *(Chm & CEO)*
John Krenicki, Jr. *(Co-Vice Chm & Pres & CEO-GE Energy)*
Keith S. Sherin *(Co-Vice Chm & CFO)*
John G. Rice *(Co-Vice Chm & Pres/ CEO GE Global Growth/Ops)*
Charlene Begley *(CIO & Sr VP)*
Elizabeth J. Comstock *(CMO & Sr VP)*
Ferdinando Beccalli-Falco *(Pres/CEO-GE Europe & North Asia)*
John L. Flannery *(Pres/CEO-GE India)*
Omar S. Ishrak *(Pres/CEO-GE Healthcare Sys)*
David L. Joyce *(Pres/CEO-Aviation)*
Dennis C. Cooke *(Pres-Homeland Protection & Security)*
Brackett B. Denniston III *(Gen Counsel & Sr VP)*
Kathryn A. Cassidy *(Treas & Sr VP)*
Mark M. Little *(Sr VP & Dir-Global Res)*
Steve Bolze *(Sr VP)*
Jeffrey S. Bornstein *(Sr VP)*
William H. Cary *(Sr VP)*
Pamela Daley *(Sr VP-Bus Dev)*
John J. Falconi *(Sr VP)*
Yoshiaki Fujimori *(Sr VP)*
John F. Lynch *(Sr VP-Corp HR)*
Andrew Markowitz *(Dir-Digital Svcs)*
Joanna H. Morris *(Dir-Corp Investor Comm)*
Chris Jobling *(Product Mgr-GE Intelligent Platforms)*
Michael Stern *(Product Mgr-GE Intelligent Platforms)*
Brands & Products:
ADVANTIUM
CALROD
E-Z LUX
ENERGY SMART
ENTELLISYS
EVOLUTION
FASTLAB
GE
GE CAFE
GE EDISON
GE ENTRYSCAN
GE INNOVA
GE PROFILE
HOTPOINT
IMAGINATION AT WORK
LEXAN
MONOGRAM
NORYL
NORYL GTX
ONPOINT
PROFILE ARCTICA
REVEAL
SMARTWATER
TRIVECTION
ULTEM
VALOX IQ
XENOY IQ
Advertising Agencies:
Atmosphere Proximity
1285 Ave of the Americas 5th Fl
New York, NY 10019
Tel.: (212) 827-2500
Fax: (212) 827-2525
Online

The Barbarian Group
129 S St 2nd Fl
Boston, MA 02111

Key to Media (For complete agency information see *The Advertising Red Books-Agencies* edition):
1. Bus. Publs. 2. Cable T.V. 3. Catalogs & Directories. 4. Co-op Adv. 5. Consumer Mags. 6. D.M. to Bus. Estab.7. D.M. to Consumers
8. Daily Newsp. 9. Exhibits/Trade Shows 10. Foreign 11. Infomercial 12. Internet Adv.13. Multimedia 14. Network Radio
15. Network T.V. 16. Newsp. Distr. Mags. 17. Other 18. Outdoor (Posters, Transit) 19. Point of Purchase20. Premiums, Novelties
21. Product Samples 22. Special Events Mktg. 23. Spot Radio 24. Spot T.V. 25. Weekly Newsp. 26. Yellow Page Adv.

General Electric Company — (Continued)

Tel.: (617) 424-8887
Fax: (617) 437-9499

BBDO New York
1285 Ave of the Americas 7th Fl
New York, NY 10019-6028
Tel.: (212) 459-5000
(Corporate Image, Appliances, Lighting, Financial Services)

BBDO Worldwide Inc.
(Sub. of Omnicom Group, Inc.)
1285 Ave of the Americas
New York, NY 10019-6028
Tel.: (212) 459-5000
Fax: (212) 459-6645
— Elizabeth Daggett *(Worldwide Acct Dir)*

BLITZ
1453 3rd St Promenade Ste 420
Santa Monica, CA 90401
Tel.: (310) 551-0200
Fax: (310) 551-0022

Brandtrust
John Hancock Bldg 875 N Michigan Ave Ste 2945
Chicago, IL 60611
Tel.: (312) 440-1833
Fax: (312) 440-9987
(Trade Adv.)

OMD-USA
195 Broadway
New York, NY 10007
Tel.: (212) 590-7100

SS+K Agency
88 Pine St 30th Fl
New York, NY 10005
Tel.: (212) 274-9500
— Alvaro Rivera *(Dir-Art)*
— Nathan Phillips *(Copywriter)*

TDA Advertising & Design
1500 Pearl St Ste 300
Boulder, CO 80302
Tel.: (303) 247-1180
Fax: (303) 247-1214
eVent

GEORGE RISK INDUSTRIES, INC.

GRI Plz 802 S Elm St
Kimball, NE 69145
Tel.: (308) 235-4645
Fax: (308) 235-2609
Fax: (308) 235-3561
Toll Free: (800) 523-1227
Toll Free: (800) 445-5218
E-mail: gri@megavision.com
Web Site: www.grisk.com
Approx. Sls.: $8,858,000
Approx. Number Employees: 160
Year Founded: 1968
Business Description:
Military & Commercial Reed Switches, Keyboards & Burglar Alarm Switches
S.I.C.: 3669; 3575
N.A.I.C.S.: 334290; 334113
Export
Advertising Expenditures: $320,000
Media: 2-4-10-13-21-22
Distr.: Direct to Consumer; Intl.; Natl.
Budget Set: Jan.
Personnel:
Ken R. Risk *(Chm, Pres & CEO)*
Stephanie M. Risk *(CFO & Controller)*
Brands & Products:
GRI
GRI SECURITY PRODUCTS

GRAYBAR ELECTRIC COMPANY, INC.

34 N Meramec Ave
Saint Louis, MO 63105-3844
Mailing Address:
PO Box 7231
Saint Louis, MO 63177-1231
Tel.: (314) 573-9200
Fax: (314) 573-9267
Toll Free: (800) 472-9227
Toll Free: (800) GRAYBAR
E-mail: media@gbe.com
Web Site: www.graybar.com
Approx. Sls.: $4,616,377,000
Approx. Number Employees: 7,000
Year Founded: 1925
Business Description:
Electrical, Telecommunications & Networking Products Distr
S.I.C.: 5063; 5045; 5065
N.A.I.C.S.: 423610; 423430; 423690
Export
Media: 2-4-7-10-22-25
Distr.: Natl.
Budget Set: Nov.
Personnel:
Robert A. Reynolds, Jr. *(Chm, Pres & CEO)*
D. Beatty D'Alessandro *(CFO & Sr VP)*
Kathleen M. Mazzarella *(COO & Exec VP)*
Matthew W. Geekie *(Gen Counsel, Sr VP & Sec)*
Lawrence R. Giglio *(Sr VP-Ops)*
Karen Gough *(Dir-Bus Dev-Energy Mgmt)*
Brett Felton *(Mgr-Indus Market)*
Tony Frantal *(Natl Mgr-Comml Market)*
Brands & Products:
GRAYBAR
WORKS TO YOUR ADVANTAGE

HAHL INC.

(Sub. of Hahl Filaments GmbH)
126 Glassmaster Rd
Lexington, SC 29072-3710
Mailing Address:
PO Box 788
Lexington, SC 29071-0788
Tel.: (803) 359-9740
Fax: (803) 359-0074
Approx. Sls.: $20,412,802
Approx. Number Employees: 175
Year Founded: 1946
Business Description:
Plastics Mfr
S.I.C.: 2821
N.A.I.C.S.: 325211
Import Export
Media: 17
Brands & Products:
COMPCORE
COMPOSITES MODULAR BUILDING SYSTEM
GLASSMASTER
NYBRAD

HD ELECTRIC COMPANY

1475 Lakeside Dr
Waukegan, IL 60085-8314
Tel.: (847) 473-4980
Fax: (847) 473-4981
Web Site:
www.hdelectriccompany.com
E-Mail For Key Personnel:
Marketing Director: khuggins@hdelec.com
Approx. Number Employees: 25
Year Founded: 1933
Business Description:
Testing Instruments, Current Transformers, Ammeters, Transformers, Emergency Lights, Voltage Detectors, Voltmeters & Phasers, Control Instrumentation Devices & System Measurement Devices Mfr
S.I.C.: 3825
N.A.I.C.S.: 334515
Import Export
Media: 2-4-7-10-13
Distr.: Intl.; Natl.
Budget Set: Nov.
Personnel:
Mark R. Hoffman *(Pres & CEO)*
Bill McNulty *(Dir-Technical)*
Kimberly Huggins *(Mgr-Mktg)*
Brands & Products:
ARCPRO V.2
AT-100
CAP CHECK
CAP CHECK I
CAP CHECK II
CAP CHECK III
CDM-75
CHM-600
CYCLOPS
DIGITAL VOLTAGE INDICATOR
DIGIVOLT
ELECTRIC TILT II
HALO
HD ELECTRIC
HISAT
IT-4
MARK
NOMAX
NOMAX 2000
PHASE IDENTIFIER
PRM-100
QUICK-CHECK
RAMCORDER
RAMCORDER OH1600
RAMCORDER RCMB
RITE LITE
RITE-LITE
RT-200
SANGAMO
TAG-200
TAG-200MR
TAG-330
TAG-5000
TAG SERIES
TEST-M-LITE
TILT II
V-WATCH
VERSA-LITE

H.E. WILLIAMS, INC.

831 W Fairview Ave
Carthage, MO 64836-3736
Tel.: (417) 358-4065
Fax: (417) 358-6015
E-mail: info@hew.com
Web Site: www.hew.com
Approx. Number Employees: 275
Year Founded: 1921
Business Description:
Mfr. of Electrical Lighting Fixtures
S.I.C.: 3646; 5063
N.A.I.C.S.: 335122; 423610
Export
Advertising Expenditures: $175,000
Media: 4-5-6-10-13-18-19-22
Personnel:
Ron Snyder *(Pres)*
Mark Williams *(CEO)*
Paul Eckels *(CFO)*
Brands & Products:
A VISIBLE DIFFERENCE
THE BLADE
DIFFERENCE
EXECUTIVE
INFINITY
WILFLEX
WILLIAMS

HIGH END SYSTEMS, INC.

(Sub. of Barco N.V.)
2105 Gracy Farms Ln
Austin, TX 78758-4031
Tel.: (512) 836-2242
Fax: (512) 837-5290
Toll Free: (800) 890-8989
E-mail: info@highend.com
Web Site: www.highend.com
E-Mail For Key Personnel:
Marketing Director: Bill_Morris@highend.com
Approx. Sls.: $44,000,000
Approx. Number Employees: 156
Year Founded: 1986
Business Description:
Stage Lighting & Control Systems Mfr
S.I.C.: 3648; 5063
N.A.I.C.S.: 335129; 423610
Media: 2-4-7-8-10-13-18-20-22
Personnel:
Richard Belliveau *(Co-Founder & CTO)*
Lowell Fowler *(Founder)*
Merritt Belisle *(Chm)*
Bill Morris *(CEO)*
Jeff Pelzl *(VP-Sls & Svc)*
David Hansen *(Dir-Ops)*
Becky Koester *(Dir-HR)*
Mike Bell *(Sr Mgr-Product)*
Craig Burross *(Mgr-US Reg Sls Rentals & Staging)*
Brands & Products:
ART GLASS
ATMOSPHERES C-16
CATALYST
COLOR COMMAND
COLOR POWER
COLOR PRO
COLORCOMMAND
COLORMERGE
CYBERLIGHT
CYBERLIGHT TURBO
D-TEX D-MIX PRO
DATAFLASH
DL.1
EC-2
ENVIRONMENTAL COLOR-2
F-100
HOG
HOG IPC
INTELLABEAM
LITHOPATTERNS
SPECIAL EFFECTS
STUDIO BEAM
STUDIO COLOR
STUDIO COMMAND
STUDIO SPOT
TECHNOBEAM

Key to Media (For complete agency information see *The Advertising Red Books-Agencies* edition):
1. Bus. Publs. 2. Cable T.V. 3. Catalogs & Directories. 4. Co-op Adv. 5. Consumer Mags. 6. D.M. to Bus. Estab.7. D.M. to Consumers 8. Daily Newsp. 9. Exhibits/Trade Shows 10. Foreign 11. Infomercial 12. Internet Adv.13. Multimedia 14. Network Radio 15. Network T.V. 16. Newsp. Distr. Mags. 17. Other 18. Outdoor (Posters, Transit) 19. Point of Purchase20. Premiums, Novelties 21. Product Samples 22. Special Events Mktg. 23. Spot Radio 24. Spot T.V. 25. Weekly Newsp. 26. Yellow Page Adv.

TRACKSPOT
WHOLEHOG
X.SPOT

HINKLEY LIGHTING INC.

12600 Berea Rd
Cleveland, OH 44111
Tel.: (216) 671-3300
Fax: (216) 671-4537
Toll Free: (800) 446-5539
E-mail: info@hinkleylighting.com
Web Site: www.hinkleylighting.com
Approx. Number Employees: 60
Year Founded: 1922
Business Description:
Lighting & Accessories for Commercial & Residential
S.I.C.: 3646; 3648
N.A.I.C.S.: 335122; 335129
Import Export
Media: 2-4-7-8-10-16
Distr.: Natl.
Personnel:
Richard A. Wiedemer *(Pres)*
Kim Mager *(Dir-Mktg)*
Brands & Products:
DESIGN. ILLUMINATE. ENJOY
HINKLEY LIGHTING

HUBBELL INCORPORATED

40 Waterview Dr
Shelton, CT 06484
Tel.: (475) 882-4000
E-mail: info@hubbell.com
Web Site: www.hubbell.com
Approx. Sls.: $2,541,200,000
Approx. Number Employees: 13,000
Year Founded: 1888
Business Description:
Lighting, Wiring & Power System & Electrical Component Mfr
S.I.C.: 3699; 3643; 3644
N.A.I.C.S.: 335999; 335931; 335932
Export
Media: 2-4-5-10-17-20
Distr.: Natl.
Budget Set: Oct.
Personnel:
Timothy H. Powers *(Chm, Pres & CEO)*
David G. Nord *(CFO & Sr VP)*
Richard W. Davies *(Gen Counsel, Sec & VP)*
W. Robert Murphy *(Exec VP-Sls & Mktg)*
Gary N. Amato *(Grp VP)*
Scott H. Muse *(Grp VP-Lighting Products)*
William T. Tolley *(Grp VP)*
Stephen M. Mais *(VP-HR)*
William R. Sperry *(VP-Corp Strategy & Dev)*
Charles M. Tencza *(VP-IT)*
Brands & Products:
ALERA
BELL
BELL OUTDOOR
BRYANT
CHALMIT
CHANCE
CIRCUIT GUARD
COLUMBIA LIGHTING
CONTROLUX
THE DETECTOR
DEVINE
DISCONEX
DUA-PULL
DUAL-LITE
ENTRALUX
EUCLID
FARGO
GAI-TRONICS
GLEASON REEL
GOTCHA
HAEFELY TEST
HAWKE
HELICAL PIER
HERCULES
HIPOTRONICS
HUBBELL
KELLEMS
KILLARK
KIM
LIGHTSCAPER
LIGHTWATT
MAGNULITER
MAGNUSQUARE
MICROLITER
MINILITER
MOLDCAST
NITETORCH
OHIO BRASS
PERIMALUX
PRESCOLITE
PROGRESS LIGHTING
PULSECOM
RACO
SECURITY
SPAULDING
SPIKESHIELD
SPORTSLITER
STERNER
SUPERBAY
TETTEX
WHITEWAY
WIEGMANN
Advertising Agency:
Maier Advertising, Inc.
1789 New Britain Ave
Farmington, CT 06032-3317
Tel.: (860) 677-4581
Fax: (860) 677-5854
Fax: (860) 677-4898

HUBBELL LIGHTING - PROGRESS LIGHTING DIVISION

(Sub. of Hubbell Incorporated)
701 Millenium Blvd
Greenville, SC 29607
Mailing Address:
PO Box 5704
Spartanburg, SC 29304-5704
Tel.: (864) 599-6000
Fax: (864) 678-1065
Web Site: www.HubbellLighting.com
Sales Range: $250-299.9 Million
Approx. Number Employees: 500
Year Founded: 1906
Business Description:
Residential & Commercial Lighting Fixtures
S.I.C.: 3634
N.A.I.C.S.: 335211
Import Export
Media: 2-4-5-6-7-8-10-13-19-20-21-26
Distr.: Intl.; Natl.
Budget Set: Oct.
Personnel:
Bob Sale *(VP-Sls)*
Paige Malouche *(Mgr-Mktg Svcs)*
Brands & Products:
FIREBOX
PROGRESS

HUMPHREY PRODUCTS CORPORATION

5070 E N Ave
Kalamazoo, MI 49048
Tel.: (269) 381-5500
Fax: (269) 381-4113
Toll Free: (800) 477-8707
E-mail: info@humphrey-products.com
Web Site: www.humphrey-products.com
Approx. Number Employees: 200
Year Founded: 1901
Business Description:
Pneumatic Valves & Actuators Mfr
S.I.C.: 3492; 3677
N.A.I.C.S.: 332912; 334416
Import Export
Advertising Expenditures: $200,000
Media: 1-2-4-5-7-9-10-11-13-16-19-20-21
Distr.: Intl.; Natl.
Budget Set: Jan.
Personnel:
Randall M. Webber *(Chm & CEO)*
Tom Gambon *(CFO)*
Linda Rynd *(Mgr-HR)*
Brands & Products:
HUMPHREY
MINI-MIZER
MINI-MYTE
TAC
TAC 2
TAC 3
TYNA-MYTE

INTERMATIC, INC.

7777 Winn Rd
Spring Grove, IL 60081-7801
Tel.: (815) 675-2321
Fax: (815) 675-7105
E-mail: webmaster@intermatic.com
Web Site: www.intermatic.com
Approx. Number Employees: 1,800
Year Founded: 1891
Business Description:
Mfr of Low-Voltage Outdoor Lighting; Consumer & Industrial Timers; Pool & Spa Controls; Surge Suppressors
S.I.C.: 3645; 3648; 3873
N.A.I.C.S.: 335121; 334518; 335129
Export
Personnel:
Michael Werner *(Chm)*
Brands & Products:
ARRESTERGUARD
I-WAVE
IGFLUSH
INTERMATIC
MALIBU
PANELGUARD
POLY-STAR
PROVIDING A BRIGHTER SOLUTION
TIME-ALL
Advertising Agency:
Finn Partners
211 E Ontario St Ste 1600
Chicago, IL 60611-3297
Tel.: (312) 644-8600
Fax: (312) 932-0367
— Nissy Atassi *(Sr Acct Exec)*

JUNO LIGHTING, INC.

(Sub. of Schneider Electric USA, Inc.)
(d/b/a Juno Lighting Group)
1300 S Wolf Rd
Des Plaines, IL 60017-5065
Mailing Address:
PO Box 5065
Des Plaines, IL 60017-5065
Tel.: (847) 827-9880
Fax: (847) 827-3666
Toll Free: (800) 323-5068
Web Site: www.junolighting.com
Approx. Number Employees: 1,000
Year Founded: 1976
Business Description:
Designer & Mfr of Recessed & Track Lighting Fixtures
S.I.C.: 3645
N.A.I.C.S.: 335121
Export
Media: 1-2-4-5-7-10-17-19-20-21-22
Distr.: Natl.
Budget Set: Oct. -Nov.
Personnel:
John Mabbott *(Pres & CEO)*
Maureen Calvo *(Dir-HR)*
Brands & Products:
ABERDEEN
ACCUFLOOD
ACCUGLASS
ACCUGLO
ACCULUME
ACCUPAK
ACCUPARK
ACCUSQUARE
ARIES
CARIBE
CARLETON
DANALITE
DARK-SKY
DURALUME
DURALYTE
ECONOBAY
EXETER
FLOOD-LUX
GEMINI
HI-LUX
MAIN STREET
MERCHANDISER
NITELYTE
ORION
PARALUME
PARKLUME
PRISMA-LUX
QUARTZ-LUX
QUASAR
SECUR-LUX
SIGNLUME
SIMCOE
TITAN
VAPOURLUME
WALL-LUX
Advertising Agency:
Advertising & Promotional Services, Inc. (Adpro, Inc.)
(d/b/a ADPRO, INC)
6 S 503 Wildwood Dr
Aurora, IL 60506
Tel.: (630) 801-9900
Fax: (630) 801-9663
Toll Free: (866) 895-2535

KILLARK ELECTRIC

(Sub. of Hubbell Incorporated)
3940 Martin Luther King Dr
Saint Louis, MO 63113
Mailing Address:
3940 Dr Martin Luther King Dr
Saint Louis, MO 63113-3316
Tel.: (314) 531-0460
Fax: (314) 531-7164

Key to Media (For complete agency information see *The Advertising Red Books-Agencies* edition):
1. Bus. Publs. 2. Cable T.V. 3. Catalogs & Directories. 4. Co-op Adv. 5. Consumer Mags. 6. D.M. to Bus. Estab.7. D.M. to Consumers 8. Daily Newsp. 9. Exhibits/Trade Shows 10. Foreign 11. Infomercial 12. Internet Adv.13. Multimedia 14. Network Radio 15. Network T.V. 16. Newsp. Distr. Mags. 17. Other 18. Outdoor (Posters, Transit) 19. Point of Purchase20. Premiums, Novelties 21. Product Samples 22. Special Events Mktg. 23. Spot Radio 24. Spot T.V. 25. Weekly Newsp. 26. Yellow Page Adv.

Killark Electric — (Continued)

E-mail: killark@hep.hubbell.com
Web Site: www.hubbell-killark.com
Sales Range: $25-49.9 Million
Approx. Number Employees: 150
Year Founded: 1913
Business Description:
Weatherproof & Hazardous Location Products Mfr
S.I.C.: 3644
N.A.I.C.S.: 335932
Export
Media: 2-4-5-7-10-11-19-20-21
Distr.: Intl.; Natl.
Budget Set: Oct.
Personnel:
Mac Criswell *(VP & Gen Mgr)*
Jim Geisler *(Dir-Tech Mktg)*
Wayne Ormson *(Product Mgr-Fittings)*
Howard Clayton *(Prod Mgr-Lighting)*
Tom Hinkson *(Mgr-Sls-Porter)*
Brands & Products:
ACCEPTOR
CERTI-LITE
CLENCHER
DURATECH
HOSTILE-LITE
PRISM
QUANTUM
SEAL-X
SNAPPY FITTINGS

KOCH & LOWY, INC.

481 W Main St
Avon, MA 02322
Tel.: (508) 588-4700
Fax: (508) 587-7592
E-mail: info@kochlowy.com
Web Site: www.chapmanco.com
Approx. Number Employees: 25
Year Founded: 1945
Business Description:
Lamps, Fixtures, Furniture & Accessories Mfr
S.I.C.: 3645; 5021
N.A.I.C.S.: 335121; 423210
Advertising Expenditures: $500,000
Media: 4-5-6-9-10-11-14-16-19-21-23-25-26
Distr.: Intl.; Natl.
Budget Set: Dec. -Jan.
Personnel:
Tom Ruskin *(Pres)*
Rosanne Regent *(Dir-Mktg)*
Brands & Products:
KOCH & LOWY

KOEHLER-BRIGHT STAR, INC.

(Sub. of Marmon Industrial Companies LLC)
380 Stewart Rd
Wilkes Barre, PA 18706
Tel.: (570) 825-1900
Fax: (570) 825-1984
Toll Free: (800) 788-1696
E-mail: sales@kbs-inc.net
Web Site: www.koehlerlighting.com
E-Mail For Key Personnel:
Sales Director: sales@kbs-inc.net
Sales Range: $10-24.9 Million
Approx. Number Employees: 30
Year Founded: 1909
Business Description:
Portable Industrial Lighting Mfr
S.I.C.: 3648
N.A.I.C.S.: 335129
Import Export
Media: 2-4-7-10
Personnel:
Mark Dirsa *(Pres)*
Lori Cywinski *(CFO)*
Brands & Products:
THE FIRST NAME IN FLASH LIGHTS.

LA MARCHE MANUFACTURING COMPANY

106 Bradrock Dr
Des Plaines, IL 60018
Tel.: (847) 299-1188
Fax: (847) 299-3061
Web Site: www.lamarchemfg.com
E-Mail For Key Personnel:
President: tsteinke@lamarchemfg.com
Sales Director: sburg@lamarchemfg.com
Sales Range: $10-24.9 Million
Approx. Number Employees: 110
Year Founded: 1945
Business Description:
Mfr. of Industrial & Utility Battery Chargers, DC Power Systems, Power Supplies, DC to AC Inverters; Consta-Volt Chargers, Uninterruptible Power Systems
S.I.C.: 3699; 3625
N.A.I.C.S.: 335999; 335314
Import Export
Media: 2-4-10-13-20-26
Distr.: Intl.; Natl.
Budget Set: Nov.
Personnel:
Rick Rutkowski *(Pres)*
Raj Dhiman *(Exec VP-DP)*
Brands & Products:
A31
A40R
A45M
A85MD
AVIA
CONSTA-VOLT
INVERTA-VOLT
LA MARCHE
TPSD

LAMPS PLUS INC.

20250 Plummer St
Chatsworth, CA 91311
Tel.: (818) 886-5267
Fax: (818) 886-1011
Toll Free: (800) 782-1967
Web Site: www.lampsplus.com
Sales Range: $125-149.9 Million
Approx. Number Employees: 800
Business Description:
Lighting; Lamps & Accessories
S.I.C.: 5719; 5063
N.A.I.C.S.: 442299; 423610
Media: 4-7-8-10-13-15-18-19-22-24-26
Personnel:
Dennis Swanson *(Chm & Pres)*
Jerry Bass *(CEO)*
Clark Linstone *(CFO)*

LEVITON MANUFACTURING COMPANY, INC.

201 N Service Rd
Melville, NY 11747
Tel.: (631) 812-6000
Fax: (800) 832-9538
Web Site: www.leviton.com
Approx. Number Employees: 4,500
Year Founded: 1906
Business Description:
Electrical Wiring Devices & Related Products
S.I.C.: 3496; 3613
N.A.I.C.S.: 332618; 335313
Export
Advertising Expenditures: $3,000,000
Media: 1-2-4-6-7-10-11-19-20-22
Distr.: Intl.; Natl.
Budget Set: Jan.
Personnel:
Donald J. Hendler *(Pres)*
William Marshall *(Sr VP-Mktg & Sls)*
Mike Mattei *(VP & Gen Mgr)*
Chris Doveala *(VP-OEM Mktg)*
Bruno Filio *(VP-Intl Bus Dev)*
Carol Lynch *(VP-Retail Mktg & Sls)*
Chris Carrella *(Dir-Tech-Distr Mktg & Sls)*
William Fodor *(Dir-Distr Channel Mktg)*
Brands & Products:
ACENTI
DECORA
DIMENSIONS
ILLUMATECH
LEVITON
LEVITON INTEGRATED NETWORKS
POWERJACK
POWERSWITCH
SURE-SLIDE
TOGGLETOUCH
VIZIA
WETGUARD
Z-MAX
Advertising Agency:
Marquardt & Roche and Partners
5 High Ridge Pk
Stamford, CT 06905
Tel.: (203) 327-0890
Fax: (203) 353-8487

LIGHTING SCIENCE GROUP CORPORATION

1227 S Patrick Dr Bldg 2A
Satellite Beach, FL 32937
Tel.: (321) 779-5520
Fax: (321) 779-5521
Toll Free: (877) 999-5742
E-mail: info@lsgc.com
Web Site: www.lsgc.com
Approx. Rev.: $53,169,013
Approx. Number Employees: 243
Business Description:
LED Lighting Devices & Systems Designer, Mfr & Marketer
S.I.C.: 3648; 3674; 5065
N.A.I.C.S.: 335129; 334413; 423690
Advertising Expenditures: $548,000
Personnel:
Richard A. Weinberg *(Chm)*
James Haworth *(CEO)*
Gregory T. Kaiser *(CFO)*
John T. Stanley *(COO)*
Frederic Maxik *(Chief Scientific Officer)*
Greg Horn *(Chief Global Trade Officer)*
Zvi Raskin *(Gen Counsel)*
Harry V. Ericson *(VP-Fin)*
Edward Russ *(Gen Mgr-Illumination Bus-North America)*

LIGHTOLIER

(Sub. of Philips Lighting)
631 Airport Rd
Fall River, MA 02720-4722
Tel.: (508) 679-8131
Fax: (508) 674-4710
Toll Free: (800) 215-1068
Web Site: www.lightolier.com
Approx. Number Employees: 200
Year Founded: 1904
Business Description:
Mfr. of Residential & Commercial Lighting Fixtures Including Track Lighting, Recessed Fixtures & Decorative
S.I.C.: 3645; 3648
N.A.I.C.S.: 335121; 335129
Export
Advertising Expenditures: $300,000
Media: 5-6-8-10-11-13-19-21
Distr.: Intl.; Natl.
Budget Set: Oct.
Personnel:
William Schoettler *(Pres)*
Jeff Ridgell *(VP-Sls)*
Brands & Products:
CALCULITE
LYTECASTER
LYTESPAN
PROSPEC

LITECONTROL CORPORATION

100 Hawks Ave
Hanson, MA 02341-1960
Tel.: (781) 294-0164
Fax: (781) 293-2849
E-mail: info@litecontrol.com
Web Site: www.litecontrol.com
E-Mail For Key Personnel:
President: vfc@litecontrol.com
Sales Director: bmg@litecontrol.com
Sales Range: $200-249.9 Million
Approx. Number Employees: 220
Year Founded: 1936
Business Description:
Architectural Fluorescent Lighting Mfr
S.I.C.: 3646
N.A.I.C.S.: 335122
Import
Media: 2-4-7-9-10-21-22
Distr.: Natl.
Budget Set: Oct.
Personnel:
Brian Golden *(Pres & CEO)*
Adrian Grundy *(CFO)*
Bob Davis *(Dir-Product Innovation & Mktg)*
Julie Burke *(Mgr-HR)*
Jim Feringa *(Mgr-Sls-Central Reg)*
Jeffrey Niedermaier *(Mgr-Sls-Southeast Reg & Intl)*
Paula Surette *(Mgr-Customer Svc)*
Stephanie Seal *(Coord-Mktg)*
Brands & Products:
ARCOS
AVIVA
BEDLITE
CIROS
CLASSICA
ECHELON
EMPLOYEE OWNED [C]USTOMER DRIVEN
HACEL-NETWORK
INDE-PENDANTS
LATITUDE
LC-EURO
LITECONTROL
LITESPEED
MANTRA
MOD-22XA
MOD-66
MOD2
NETWORK
NEXUS

Key to Media (For complete agency information see *The Advertising Red Books-Agencies* edition):
1. Bus. Publs. 2. Cable T.V. 3. Catalogs & Directories. 4. Co-op Adv. 5. Consumer Mags. 6. D.M. to Bus. Estab.7. D.M. to Consumers 8. Daily Newsp. 9. Exhibits/Trade Shows 10. Foreign 11. Infomercial 12. Internet Adv.13. Multimedia 14. Network Radio 15. Network T.V. 16. Newsp. Distr. Mags. 17. Other 18. Outdoor (Posters, Transit) 19. Point of Purchase20. Premiums, Novelties 21. Product Samples 22. Special Events Mktg. 23. Spot Radio 24. Spot T.V. 25. Weekly Newsp. 26. Yellow Page Adv.

RADI-X
RECESSED WALL
SAE SYSTEM
SCION
SDX
SLOT SYSTEM
STAKLITE 500
V3
VC1
VCOPTIC
WALL
WALL/SLOT
WALL/WASH

Advertising Agency:
Larson O'Brien Marketing Group
3591 Ridgeway Dr Ste 200
Bethel Park, PA 15102
Tel.: (412) 831-1959
Fax: (412) 833-2838

LITTELFUSE, INC.

8755 West Higgins Rd Ste 500
Chicago, IL 60631
Tel.: (773) 628-1000
Web Site: www.littelfuse.com
E-Mail For Key Personnel:
Public Relations: thovey@littelfuse.com
Approx. Sls.: $608,021,000
Approx. Number Employees: 6,000
Year Founded: 1927
Business Description:
Electronic, Automotive & Power Fuses & Other Circuit Protection Devices Mfr & Distr
S.I.C.: 3613; 3612; 3625
N.A.I.C.S.: 335313; 335311; 335314
Export
Advertising Expenditures: $1,200,000
Media: 2-4-5-7-10-11-13-19-20-21
Distr.: Natl.
Budget Set: Nov.
Personnel:
Gordon B. Hunter *(Chm, Pres & CEO)*
Philip G. Franklin *(CFO & VP-Ops Support)*
Ryan Stafford *(Gen Counsel & VP-HR)*
Paul Dickinson *(VP & Gen Mgr-Semiconductor Bus Unit)*
Dal Ferbert *(VP & Gen Mgr-Electrical Div)*
Dieter Roeder *(VP & Gen Mgr-Automotive Bus Unit)*
Chen-Ming Wang *(VP & Gen Mgr-Electronics Bus Unit)*
Deepak Nayar *(VP-Global Sls)*
Tony Locker *(Product Mgr-Littelfuse Protection Relays)*
Tom Hovey *(Mgr-E-Mktg)*
Brands & Products:
ATO
AUTOFUSE
BATTRAX
CABLEPRO
EXPERTISE APPLIED ANSWERS DELIVERED
FOLDBAK
IDSR INDICATOR
INLINK
ISIS
ITMOV
JCASE
LFFB
LITTELFUSE
MAXI FUSE
MEGA
MICROFUSE
MIDI
MINI
NANO2 SMF
NANOFUSE
OMNI-BLOK
PICO
PICO FUSE
POWER-GARD
POWERCELL
PULSEGUARD
SIBOD
SIDACTOR
SLO-BLO
TMOV

Advertising Agency:
Moveo
1 Parkview Plz Ste 150
Oakbrook Terrace, IL 60181
Tel.: (630) 570-4800
Fax: (630) 571-3031

MAGNETEK, INC.

N49 W13650 Campbell Drive
Menomonee Falls, WI 53051
Tel.: (262) 783-3500
Fax: (262) 790-4147
Fax: (800) 298-3503
Toll Free: (800) 288-8178
E-mail: information@magnetek.com
Web Site: www.magnetek.com
Approx. Sls.: $109,832,000
Approx. Number Employees: 311
Year Founded: 1984
Business Description:
Digital Electronic Power & Motion Control Products Mfr
S.I.C.: 3829; 4931
N.A.I.C.S.: 334519; 221119
Import Export
Advertising Expenditures: $114,000
Media: 1-2-4-7-10-19-20-21
Distr.: Intl.; Natl.
Personnel:
Mitchell I. Quain *(Chm)*
Peter M. Mccormick *(Pres & CEO)*
Marty J. Schwenner *(CFO & VP)*
Scott S. Cramer *(Gen Counsel, Sec & VP)*
Brad Taylor *(VP & Gen Mgr-Energy Sys)*
Lynn Bostrom *(Dir-Comm)*
Ed Butte *(Dir-Renewable Energy Bus)*
Mark Haug *(Dir-Alternative Energy)*
Brands & Products:
DSD
ENERGY ENGINEERED
ENGINEERED ENERGY
GPD
MAGNETEK
MICROTRAC
SD 1000
SD 500
VCD

MECHANICAL PRODUCTS INC.

1824 River St
Jackson, MI 49202
Tel.: (517) 782-0391
Fax: (517) 788-6773
E-mail: mechanicalproducts@mechprod.com
Web Site: www.mechprod.com
E-Mail For Key Personnel:
Sales Director: mpsales@mechprod.com
Sales Range: $10-24.9 Million
Approx. Number Employees: 25
Year Founded: 1940
Business Description:
Circuit Breaker Mfr
S.I.C.: 3613
N.A.I.C.S.: 335313
Export
Media: 4-5-6-13-21
Distr.: Natl.
Budget Set: Nov.
Personnel:
Larry Bajorek *(Owner)*
Rich Regole *(Pres & CEO)*
Mark Baker *(CFO)*
Jim Allison *(VP-Engrng)*
Jan Bailey *(Mgr-Sls-Worldwide)*
Brands & Products:
MP

MERSEN

(Formerly Ferraz Shawmut)
(Sub. of Le Carbone Lorraine)
374 Merrimac St
Newburyport, MA 01950-1930
Tel.: (978) 462-6662
Fax: (978) 465-6795
Fax: (978) 465-6419
Web Site: www.mersen.com
Approx. Number Employees: 200
Year Founded: 1885
Business Description:
Mfr. of Low & Medium Voltage Fuses, Fuse Blocks, Power Distribution Blocks & Taylor Wiring Duct for Commercial & Industrial Applications
S.I.C.: 5063; 3613
N.A.I.C.S.: 423610; 335313
Export
Advertising Expenditures: $616,500
Distr.: Intl.; Natl.
Budget Set: Sept.
Personnel:
Marc Renart *(CEO)*
Dean Cousins *(Sr VP-Mktg & Bus Dev)*
Doyle Anderson *(Reg VP-Sls)*
Stephen Colvin *(VP-Mktg)*
Jim Kosciolek *(VP-Sls)*
John Phillips *(VP-Fin)*
Mark Taylor *(VP-OEM Sls)*
Mike Quinlan *(Sr Product Mgr)*
Brands & Products:
AMP-TRAP
AMP-TRAP 2000
AMP-TRAP E RATED
AMP-TRAP FORM 101
AMP-TRAP FORM 480
AMP-TRAP II
AMP-TRAP R RATED
TRI-ONIC

MOLE-RICHARDSON CO.

937 N Sycamore Ave
Hollywood, CA 90038-2384
Tel.: (323) 851-0111
Fax: (323) 851-5593
E-mail: info@mole.com
Web Site: www.mole.com
Approx. Number Employees: 150
Year Founded: 1927
Business Description:
Lighting & Power Equipment Mfr
S.I.C.: 3648; 3621
N.A.I.C.S.: 335129; 335312
Media: 4-6-13
Personnel:
Anna Mole Parker *(Co-Chm)*
Warren K. Parker *(Co-Chm)*
Mike Parker *(Pres)*
Larry Parker *(Exec VP)*
Don Phillips *(VP-Sls)*
Arleen Gemigniani *(Dir-Cust Svc)*
Brands & Products:
LIGHTING FROM HOLLYWOOD
MOLE
MOLE-RICHARDSON
MOLETOWN
STUDIO DEPOT
STUDIODEOT.COM
THEATRE DEPOT

MULBERRY METAL PRODUCTS, INC.

2199 Stanley Ter PO Box 443
Union, NJ 07083-4300
Tel.: (908) 688-8850
Fax: (908) 688-7294
E-mail: richard.mueller@mulberrymetal.com
Web Site: www.mulberrymetal.com
Approx. Rev.: $35,000,000
Approx. Number Employees: 150
Year Founded: 1926
Business Description:
Mfr. of Metal Wall Plates, Wiring Devices, Outlet Boxes & Covers, & Installation Accessories
S.I.C.: 3644; 5065
N.A.I.C.S.: 335932; 423690
Media: 2-4-6-7-10-17
Distr.: Natl.
Personnel:
Richard Horn *(Pres & Treas)*
Richard E. Mueller *(Exec VP)*
Kristina Horn *(VP)*
Bob Walker *(National Sls Mgr)*
Brands & Products:
ENDURA
MULBERRY

NEXXUS LIGHTING, INC.

124 Floyd Smith Dr Ste 300
Charlotte, NC 28262
Tel.: (704) 405-0416
Fax: (704) 405-0422
Web Site: www.nexxuslighting.com
Approx. Rev.: $5,422,443
Approx. Number Employees: 33
Year Founded: 1993
Business Description:
Light Emitting Diode (L.E.D.) Lighting Mfr & Distr
S.I.C.: 3357; 3229; 3355; 3646; 3648
N.A.I.C.S.: 335921; 327212; 331319; 335122; 335129
Advertising Expenditures: $298,000
Media: 2-4-10
Personnel:
Michael A. Bauer *(Pres & CEO)*
Gary Langford *(CFO)*
Kevin Carpenter *(Dir-Engrg & R&D)*
Dennis Bonet *(Mgr-Intl Sls & Svc)*
Brands & Products:
6S-HC
8S-SB
ARRAY LED G4
ARRAY LED MR16
ARRAY LED PAR16
ARRAY LED PAR30
COMLIGHT
DLS-2
EB900
EB901
EB902

Key to Media (For complete agency information see *The Advertising Red Books-Agencies* edition):
1. Bus. Publs. 2. Cable T.V. 3. Catalogs & Directories. 4. Co-op Adv. 5. Consumer Mags. 6. D.M. to Bus. Estab.7. D.M. to Consumers
8. Daily Newsp. 9. Exhibits/Trade Shows 10. Foreign 11. Infomercial 12. Internet Adv.13. Multimedia 14. Network Radio
15. Network T.V. 16. Newsp. Distr. Mags. 17. Other 18. Outdoor (Posters, Transit) 19. Point of Purchase20. Premiums, Novelties
21. Product Samples 22. Special Events Mktg. 23. Spot Radio 24. Spot T.V. 25. Weekly Newsp. 26. Yellow Page Adv.

NEXXUS LIGHTING, INC. — (Continued)

EB903
EC
ECLIPSE II
ECWMS
ELUM
ELUM COVE RGB
ENDGLOW
ESG
ESTDC
ESTDS
EWS
EYEBALL FIXTURE
FD700SC
FD700SP
FD701SC
FD701SP
FD702SC
FD702SP
FD703SC
FD703SP
FIBER OPTIC STEP LIGHT
FIBERPRO
FIXED DOWNLIGHTS
FLEXLED
FLOOD STRIP II
GALAXY POOL LIGHTS
HYPERION R-LITE
LIFE'S BRIGHTER
LIGHT STICKS
LIVELED
LIVELED 100
LIVELED 12
LIVELED 35
LIVELED BEAM BLASTER
LUMEON360
LUMIFICIENT
LYTELAUNCH 150
LYTETRAK
M4
MINI SCONCE
NEXXUS
PAVERLYTE FIXTURE
SAVI
SAVI 512
SAVI COVE RGB
SAVI FLARE
SAVI FLOOD
SAVI FLOOD STRIP
SAVI KEY PAD
SAVI LINEAR
SAVI MELODY
SAVI MINI SCONCE
SAVI NOTE
SAVI POOL & SPA
SAVI SHO WHITE
SAVI SOURCE
SHO RGB
SIDEGLOW
SL500
SL502
SL503
SS400
STAINLESS STEEL FIXTURE
STARPRO
SUPER NITELYTE
SUPER VISION
SV100EG
SV126
SV12EG
SV1500
SV150EG
SV150EGW
SV150T
SV225EG
SV225EGW
SV25EG
SV300C
SV300EG
SV300EGW
SV32
SV42
SV42ULTRA
SV4EG
SV50EG
SV600C
SV750
SV75EG
SV84
SV84ULTRA
SV8EG
SVA200
SVA205
SVC30
SVE30
SVF100
SVL300
SVPAF60
SVPAVER4X4
ULTRA SIDE-GLOW

Advertising Agency:
Fleishman-Hillard Inc.
200 N Broadway
Saint Louis, MO 63102-2730
Tel.: (314) 982-1700
Fax: (314) 982-0586

NIAGARA TRANSFORMER CORP.

1747 Dale Rd
Buffalo, NY 14225
Mailing Address:
PO Box 233
Buffalo, NY 14225-0233
Tel.: (716) 896-6500
Fax: (716) 896-8871
Toll Free: (800) 817-5652
E-mail: mail@niagaratransformer.com
Web Site:
www.niagaratransformer.com
Approx. Number Employees: 100
Year Founded: 1938
Business Description:
Power, Lighting & Distribution Transformers Mfr
S.I.C.: 3612; 5063
N.A.I.C.S.: 335311; 423610
Media: 2-4-10-16
Distr.: Natl.
Personnel:
John Darby *(Pres)*
William Hanavan *(Mgr-Industrial Sls)*
William Mangum *(Mgr-Sls-Utility)*
Brands & Products:
ENVIROTEMP
FR3
NIAGARA
Advertising Agency:
Harold Warner Advertising, Inc.
232 Delaware Ave
Buffalo, NY 14202-2000
Tel.: (716) 852-4410
Fax: (716) 852-4725

NKK SWITCHES

(Affil. of Nihon Kaiheiki Ind. Co. Ltd.)
7850 E Gelding Dr
Scottsdale, AZ 85260-2950
Mailing Address:
PO Box 13570
Scottsdale, AZ 85267-3570
Tel.: (480) 991-0942
Fax: (480) 998-1435
E-mail: nkkwebdomain@nkkswitches.com
Web Site: www.nkkswitches.com
E-Mail For Key Personnel:
Sales Director: sales@nkkswitches.com
Approx. Number Employees: 60
Business Description:
Electrical Switches Mfr
S.I.C.: 5063; 5065
N.A.I.C.S.: 423610; 423690
Media: 2-4-10-20-21
Distr.: Natl.
Budget Set: Sept.
Personnel:
Kiyoko Toyama *(Pres)*
Frances Amoss *(VP-Sls)*
Brands & Products:
NKK

THE OKONITE COMPANY

102 Hilltop Rd
Ramsey, NJ 07446
Tel.: (201) 825-0300
Fax: (201) 825-3524
E-mail: info@okonite.com
Web Site: www.okonite.com
Approx. Number Employees: 1,100
Year Founded: 1878
Business Description:
Mfr. of Insulated Wires & Cables
S.I.C.: 3496
N.A.I.C.S.: 332618
Advertising Expenditures: $1,000,000
Media: 4-7-10-16-20-21-26
Distr.: Natl.
Budget Set: Sept.
Personnel:
Alfred C. Coppola *(Pres & COO)*
David J. Sokira *(CFO & VP)*
Eric Loyka *(Dir-Mktg)*
Brands & Products:
C-L-X
LOXARMOR
OKOBON
OKOBUS
OKOCLAD
OKOCLEAR TP
OKOCLEAR TS
OKOCORD
OKOGUARD
OKOLENE
OKOLENE-OKOSEAL
OKOLON
OKONITE
THE OKONITE COMPANY
OKONITE FMR
OKONITE-OKOCLEAR
OKONITE-OKOLON
OKOPACT
OKOPRENE
OKOSEAL
OKOSHEATH
OKOSHEATH-CP
OKOTHERM
OKOZEL
UR-X
URO-J
X-OLENE

OSRAM SYLVANIA, INC.

(Sub. of Osram GmbH)
100 Endicott St
Danvers, MA 01923-3623
Tel.: (978) 777-1900
Toll Free: (800) 544-4828
Web Site: www.sylvania.com
Approx. Number Employees: 11,200
Year Founded: 1901
Business Description:
Lighting Products & Precision Materials Mfr & Distr
S.I.C.: 3641; 3647
N.A.I.C.S.: 335110; 336321
Import Export
Media: 2-4
Distr.: Natl.
Personnel:
Rick Leaman *(CEO)*
Denise Champagne *(Dir-Brand Strategy)*
Jennifer Dolin *(Mgr-Environmental Mktg)*
Brands & Products:
SEE THE WORLD IN A NEW LIGHT
Advertising Agency:
Chletcos/Gallagher Inc.
63 Greene St Ste 602
New York, NY 10012
Tel.: (212) 334-2455
Fax: (212) 334-2463

PASS & SEYMOUR/LEGRAND

(Sub. of Legrand S.A.)
50 Boyd Ave
Syracuse, NY 13209
Mailing Address:
PO Box 4822
Syracuse, NY 13221-4822
Tel.: (315) 468-6211
Fax: (800) 223-4196
Fax: (315) 468-6296
Toll Free: (800) 223-4162
Toll Free: (800) 611-7277
Telex: 93-7232
Web Site: www.passandseymour.com
Approx. Sls.: $160,000,000
Approx. Number Employees: 1,200
Year Founded: 1890
Business Description:
Mfr. of Electrical Wiring Devices
S.I.C.: 3643; 5063
N.A.I.C.S.: 335931; 423610
Import Export
Media: 2-4-6-8-10-11-13-19-20-21
Distr.: Natl.
Budget Set: Jan.
Personnel:
Pat Davin *(VP & Gen Mgr)*
Sue Bird *(VP-HR)*
Jim Osterbrock *(VP-Engrg)*
Brands & Products:
AUTO-GROUND
CAB 3
COLRING
COLSON
DECORATOR SERIES
DESPARD
DIPLOMAT
DURASHEILD
ELECTECH
FLEXCOR
FLIP LID
HITCH-HIKER
IMPRESSIONS
LIFETIME
LUMA VI
LUMASPEC
MEDALIST SST
P&S PLUGTAIL
P&S SIGNATURE
QUICK/CLICK
QUICK/ENTRY
SAF-T-GAP
SAFELOCK

Key to Media (For complete agency information see *The Advertising Red Books-Agencies* edition):
1. Bus. Publs. 2. Cable T.V. 3. Catalogs & Directories. 4. Co-op Adv. 5. Consumer Mags. 6. D.M. to Bus. Estab.7. D.M. to Consumers 8. Daily Newsp. 9. Exhibits/Trade Shows 10. Foreign 11. Infomercial 12. Internet Adv.13. Multimedia 14. Network Radio 15. Network T.V. 16. Newsp. Distr. Mags. 17. Other 18. Outdoor (Posters, Transit) 19. Point of Purchase20. Premiums, Novelties 21. Product Samples 22. Special Events Mktg. 23. Spot Radio 24. Spot T.V. 25. Weekly Newsp. 26. Yellow Page Adv.

SIERRA
SIERRAPLEX
SIR
SLATER
STA-KLEEN
SURFEX
SWITCHPLAN
TOMIC
TURNLOK
ULTRA-DUCT
WIREUP

PEERLESS LIGHTING CORP.

(Sub. of Acuity Brands, Inc.)
2246 5th St
Berkeley, CA 94710-2217
Mailing Address:
PO Box 2556
Berkeley, CA 94702-0556
Tel.: (510) 845-2760
Fax: (510) 845-2776
E-mail: info@peerless-lighting.com
Web Site: www.peerless-lighting.com
Sales Range: $25-49.9 Million
Approx. Number Employees: 100
Year Founded: 1932
Business Description:
Lighting Equipment Mfr
S.I.C.: 3646
N.A.I.C.S.: 335122
Import Export
Advertising Expenditures: $600,000
Consumer Mags.: $300,000; D.M. to Consumers: $150,000; Exhibits/Trade Shows: $60,000; Premiums, Novelties: $90,000
Distr.: Intl.; Natl.
Brands & Products:
ENVISION
LIGHTEDGE
LIGHTFOIL
LIGHTING FOR THE PEOPLE
LIGHTLINE
LIGHTSCREEN INDIRECT
MIRAGE
PEERLESS
PEERLITE

PHILIPS EMERGENCY LIGHTING

(Formerly Bodine Group Holding Company Inc.)
(Unit of Philips Lighting)
236 Mount Pleasant Rd PO Box 460
Collierville, TN 38017-2752
Tel.: (901) 853-7211
Fax: (901) 853-5009
Toll Free: (800) 223-5728
E-mail: bodineinfo@philips.com
Web Site: www.bodine.com
Sales Range: $10-24.9 Million
Approx. Number Employees: 190
Year Founded: 1962
Business Description:
Emergency Lighting Equipment/ Holding Company
S.I.C.: 3648
N.A.I.C.S.: 335129
Import Export
Advertising Expenditures: $500,000
Media: 2-4-6-7-8-10-13-16-18-19-20-21
Personnel:
John Levesque *(Gen Mgr)*
Rob Sumner *(Sls Mgr-Natl & Reg Sls Mgr-West)*
Porter Wafler *(Mgr-Reg Sls-Eastern Div)*
Lorrie Gillespie *(Supvr-Inside Sls & Customer Svcs)*
David Crenshaw *(Engr-Res & Devel)*
Brands & Products:
PHILIPS BODINE

PHILIPS LIGHTING

(Div. of Philips Lighting)
3 Burlingtonwoods Woods
Burlington, MA 01803
Tel.: (781) 418-7900
Web Site: www.philipsna.com
Approx. Rev.: $1,484,833,000
Approx. Number Employees: 3,891
Year Founded: 1985
Business Description:
Lighting Fixtures & Electronic Lighting Controls Mfr
S.I.C.: 3646; 3634; 3641; 3645; 3648; 5063
N.A.I.C.S.: 335122; 335110; 335121; 335129; 335211; 423610
Export
Advertising Expenditures: $12,459,000
Media: 5-7-10-17-20
Distr.: Natl.
Budget Set: Oct.
Personnel:
Daniel R. Fuller *(Gen Counsel, VP & Asst Sec)*
John Angelo, Sr. *(Sr Dir-Supply Chain)*
Dawn Zhao *(Sr Mgr-Mktg Comm)*
Claire Lipnicki *(Mgr-Internet Mktg)*
Brands & Products:
ALKCO
ALLSCAPE
ARDEE
BRONZELITE
CANLYTE
CAPRI
CHLORIDE SYSTEMS
CRESCENT
D'AC LIGHTING
DAY-BRITE
EMCO
ENTERTAINMENT TECHNOLOGY
EXCELINE
FORECAST
GARDCO
GUTH
HADCO
HIGHLITES
HOFFMEISTER
HORIZON
LAM LIGHTING SYSTEMS
LEDALITE
LIGHTGUARD
LIGHTOLIER
LIGHTOLIER CONTROLS
LITE-ENERGY
LUMEC
LUMEC-SCHREDER
MCPHILBEN
MCPHILBEN OUTDOOR
METROLUX
MORLITE
NESSEN
NIGHT LIFE
OMEGA
QUALITY LIGHTING
SHAKESPEARE COMPOSITE STRUCTURES
STONCO
STRAND LIGHTING
STRUCTURES
THOMAS CANADA
THOMAS LIGHTING RESIDENTIAL
TRANSLITE
VARI-LITE
WIDE-LITE
Advertising Agencies:
Firelight Group
PO Box 2407
Madison, WI 53701
Tel.: (608) 441-3473
Fax: (914) 397-0815

IMC
960 Holmdel Rd
Holmdel, NJ 07733-2138
Tel.: (732) 332-0515
Fax: (732) 332-0520

Kingdon-Nichols
5272 W Sunrise Canyon Pl
Marana, AZ 85658
Tel.: (520) 820-3498

READY366
33 E 17th St Union Sq
New York, NY 10003
Tel.: (212) 488-5366
Fax: (212) 228-2474

PHILIPS SOLID-STATE LIGHTING SOLUTIONS

(Div. of Philips Lighting)
3 Burlington Woods Dr, 4th Fl
Burlington, MA 01803
Tel.: (617) 423-9999
Fax: (617) 423-9998
Toll Free: (888) 385-5742
Web Site: www.colorkinetics.com
Approx. Rev.: $65,424,000
Approx. Number Employees: 137
Year Founded: 1997
Business Description:
Digital Lighting Products Mfr
S.I.C.: 3646; 1731; 3648
N.A.I.C.S.: 335122; 238210; 335129
Advertising Expenditures: $300,000
Personnel:
Jeffrey A. Cassis *(CEO)*
Philip O'Daudnell *(VP-Sls)*
Daniel Gaudet *(Deputy Gen Counsel-Licensing)*
Brands & Products:
CHROMACORE
CHROMASIC
COLOR COVE
COLOR KINETICS
COLORBLAST
COLORBLAZE
COLORBURST
COLORCAST
COLORDIAL
COLORPLAY
COLORSCAPE
DIRECT LIGHT
DIRECT LIGHT PLAYER
ICOLOR
ICOLOR COVE
INTELLIWHITE
IPLAYER
JOOLZ
LIGHT WITHOUT LIMITS
LIGHTORB
LIGHTSAUCER
LIGHTSPRITE
LIGHTTRO
LIGHTWAND
LIGHTWASHER
MICROLIGHTWAND
MINILIGHTWAND
OPTIBLIN
QUICKPLAY
SAUCE
SMARTJUICE
SYNCHRONIZER
ZAPI

PHOENIX PRODUCTS COMPANY

8711 W Port Ave
Milwaukee, WI 53224-3429
Tel.: (414) 973-3300
Fax: (414) 973-3210
E-mail: marketing@phoenixproducts.com
Web Site: www.phoenixproducts.com
Approx. Number Employees: 90
Year Founded: 1892
Business Description:
Mfr. of Industrial Lighting Fixtures
S.I.C.: 3646
N.A.I.C.S.: 335122
Export
Media: 2-4-7-10-20
Distr.: Natl.
Personnel:
George J. Wordingham *(Pres)*
Scott Fredrick *(CEO)*
Yazi Fletcher *(VP-Engrg)*
Bob Gueldenzopf *(Dir-Sls, Comml & Indus)*
Tom Feldhusen *(Mgr-Natl Acct)*
Brands & Products:
CHARISMA
CITATION
DOCKLITE
DRYROD
DRYWIRE
ELEGANT
EPIC
EUROTECH
HLS SERIES
INTRIGUE
KL SERIES
LARGE CONCORD
MARVEL
MYSTIQUE
ODYSSEY
PHOENIX
SAFETUBE

PHOTOWATT TECHNOLOGIES INC.

(Sub. of ATS Automation Tooling Systems Inc.)
25 Reuter Drive
Cambridge, ON N3E 1A9, Canada
Tel.: (519) 650-6505
Approx. Sls.: $121,916,000
Approx. Number Employees: 711
Business Description:
Solar Energy Products Mfr
S.I.C.: 3612
N.A.I.C.S.: 335311
Media: 10-11
Personnel:
Nelson M. Sims *(Chm)*
Gary J. Seiter *(COO)*

PRESCOLITE INC.

(Sub. of Hubbell Incorporated)
101 Corporate Dr
Spartanburg, SC 29303
Tel.: (864) 599-6000
Fax: (864) 699-1337
E-mail: webtechnical@prescolite.com
Web Site: www.prescolite.com

Key to Media (For complete agency information see *The Advertising Red Books-Agencies* edition):
1. Bus. Publs. 2. Cable T.V. 3. Catalogs & Directories. 4. Co-op Adv. 5. Consumer Mags. 6. D.M. to Bus. Estab.7. D.M. to Consumers 8. Daily Newsp. 9. Exhibits/Trade Shows 10. Foreign 11. Infomercial 12. Internet Adv.13. Multimedia 14. Network Radio 15. Network T.V. 16. Newsp. Distr. Mags. 17. Other 18. Outdoor (Posters, Transit) 19. Point of Purchase20. Premiums, Novelties 21. Product Samples 22. Special Events Mktg. 23. Spot Radio 24. Spot T.V. 25. Weekly Newsp. 26. Yellow Page Adv.

Prescolite Inc. — (Continued)
Sales Range: $10-24.9 Million
Approx. Number Employees: 70
Year Founded: 1944
Business Description:
Residential Electric Lighting Fixtures Mfr
S.I.C.: 3645
N.A.I.C.S.: 335121
Import Export
Advertising Expenditures: $500,000
Catalogs & Directories: $500,000
Distr.: Natl.
Budget Set: Nov.
Brands & Products:
PRESCOLITE

PURESPECTRUM, INC.

118 Pipemakers Cir Ste 105
Pooler, GA 31322
Tel.: (912) 351-4523
E-mail: info@purespectrumlighting.com
Web Site: www.purespectrumlighting.com
Approx. Rev.: $79,634
Approx. Number Employees: 18
Business Description:
Ballast-Driven Lighting Technology
S.I.C.: 3648
N.A.I.C.S.: 335129
Personnel:
Gregory K. Clements *(Pres & CEO)*
Advertising Agency:
The Hauser Group
530 Means St Ste G1
Atlanta, GA 30318
Tel.: (404) 222-0600
Fax: (404) 222-0580

QUOIZEL INC.

6 Corp Pkwy
Goose Creek, SC 29445-7144
Tel.: (631) 273-2700
Fax: (631) 231-7102
E-mail: customerservice@quoizel.com
Web Site: www.quoizel.com
Approx. Number Employees: 300
Year Founded: 1930
Business Description:
Mfr. of Lamps & Lighting Fixtures
S.I.C.: 3645
N.A.I.C.S.: 335121
Import Export
Advertising Expenditures: $5,000,000
Media: 1-2-3-4-5-8-9-10-13-14-19-20-23-24-25
Distr.: Intl.; Natl.
Budget Set: Dec.
Personnel:
Ira H. Phillips *(Chm)*
Rick Seidman *(Pres & CEO)*
Toni Phillips *(Exec VP)*
Ed Clark *(Sr VP)*
Jo Douglas *(Controller, Dir-Intl Trade)*
Bobbie Pearsall *(Dir-Adv)*
Brands & Products:
ABIGAIL ADAMS
ADANO
AGATE PORTABLE
ALABASTER
AMALFI
AMHERST
ASTORIA
BARRINGTON
BELLE
BISTRO
BRAXTON
BRISTOL MANOR
CABALLERO
CARLETON
CHALMERS
CHAMONIX
CHAPARRAL
COZY COTTAGE
DELRAY
DELUXE
DEMITRI
DEVEREAUX
DEVON
DOMINIQUE
DORADO
DUCHESS
ELECTRA
ELITE
ELLERBEE
ELLIS
EMERY
EMILY
EMPIRE
ENGLEWOOD
ENGLISH LIBRARY
EVELYN
FAIRMONT
FELICE
GENOVA
GENTRY
GRANADA
GUTHRIE
HANNAH
HARMONY
HARRINGTON
HILLCREST
HOLLISTER
HYACINTH
IBSEN
ISABELLA
JACKSON
KEANE
KEATING
KENDALL
KENDRA
LA CRYSTA
LA PARRA
LAKEWOOD
LOGAN
LOMBARD
MADELINE
NAUTICAL
NORTHRIDGE
PALAZZIO
PETALO
QUEENSGATE
QUOIZEL
RESTORATION
RHAPSODY
RIVERBEND
ROXY
SALAMANDER
SONATA
TIFFANY
TRIBECA
TUSCANY
URBANA
VALERIA
VALLEY FORGE
WILMINGTON
WINSLET
WOODLAND
YUMA
ZEPHYR

RADIX WIRE COMPANY

26000 Lakeland Blvd
Cleveland, OH 44132-2638
Tel.: (216) 731-9191
Fax: (216) 731-7082
E-mail: info@radix-wire.com
Web Site: www.radix-wire.com
Approx. Number Employees: 90
Year Founded: 1944
Business Description:
High Temperature Insulated Wire & Cable Mfr
S.I.C.: 3496
N.A.I.C.S.: 332618
Export
Media: 2-4-7-10-13-20
Distr.: Direct to Consumer; Natl.
Budget Set: Nov.
Personnel:
Chuck VerMerris *(Pres)*
Brian Bukovec *(COO & VP)*
Dan Polasky *(Gen Mgr-Res)*
George Doll *(Mgr-IT)*
Dave Leonard *(Mgr-Sls)*
Anna Nero *(Matls Mgr)*
Brands & Products:
DURAFLEX
FIL-A-BLEND
RADIX
Advertising Agency:
Richard Desberg & Associates
15321 Russell Rd
Chagrin Falls, OH 44022
Tel.: (440) 247-9500
Fax: (440) 247-9505

REJUVENATION INC.

(d/b/a Rejuvenation Lamp & Fixture)
2550 NW Nicolai St
Portland, OR 97210
Tel.: (503) 231-1900
Fax: (800) 526-7329
Toll Free: (888) 401-1900
E-mail: info@rejuvenation.com
Web Site: www.rejuvenation.com
Sales Range: $25-49.9 Million
Approx. Number Employees: 230
Year Founded: 1977
Business Description:
Period-Authentic Lighting & House Parts Mfr & Direct Marketer
S.I.C.: 3648; 5961
N.A.I.C.S.: 335129; 454113
Media: 4-6
Personnel:
Alysa Rose *(Pres & CEO)*
Kimberly Howard *(Dir-Fin & Acctg)*
Tony Penca *(Mgr-Product)*
Tina King *(Mgr-Product)*

REULAND ELECTRIC COMPANY

17969 E Railroad St
City of Industry, CA 91748
Tel.: (626) 964-6411
Fax: (626) 956-0840
E-mail: sales@reuland.com
Web Site: www.reuland.com
E-Mail For Key Personnel:
Sales Director: sales@reuland.com
Sales Range: $25-49.9 Million
Approx. Number Employees: 250
Year Founded: 1930
Business Description:
Mfr. of Motors; Fluid-Shaft & Electric
S.I.C.: 3621; 3566
N.A.I.C.S.: 335312; 333612
Media: 2-10
Distr.: Natl.
Budget Set: Oct.
Personnel:
Noel Reuland *(Pres)*
Todd Reuland *(VP-Mktg)*
Bob Clise *(Mgr)*
Wayne Foreman *(Engr)*
Steven Parez *(Sls Engr)*
Brands & Products:
CUSHION DRIVE
DYNA STOP
FLUID-SHAFT
RE
REULAND
RTC SOFT START

THE RIPLEY COMPANY

(Sub. of Capewell Components Company, L.P.)
46 Nooks Hill Rd
Cromwell, CT 06416
Tel.: (860) 635-2200
Fax: (860) 635-3631
Toll Free: (800) 528-8665
E-mail: webinfo@ripley-tools.com
Web Site: www.ripley-tools.com
E-Mail For Key Personnel:
Sales Director: rick@ripley-tools.com
Public Relations: edd@ripley-tools.com
Sales Range: $1-9.9 Million
Approx. Number Employees: 75
Year Founded: 1936
Business Description:
Mfr of Cable Preparation Tools
S.I.C.: 3357
N.A.I.C.S.: 335921
Export
Media: 2-4-5-7-10-11
Distr.: Direct to Consumer; Intl.; Natl.
Budget Set: Jan.
Personnel:
Keith D'Amato *(Dir-Sls & Ops-Intl)*
Sean Powell *(Dir-Sls)*
Ed Pulaski *(Mgr-Natl Sls)*
Hugh Quinones *(Mgr-Sls)*
Brands & Products:
ABECO
CABLEMATIC
CLAUSS
MILLER
MILLER HOT STRIPPER
MILLER MICROSTRIP
RIPLEY
RIPLEY MILLER
UTILITY TOOL

ROGERS CORPORATION

One Technology Dr
Rogers, CT 06263-0217
Mailing Address:
PO Box 188
Rogers, CT 06263-0188
Tel.: (860) 774-9605
Fax: (860) 779-5509
Toll Free: (800) 227-6437
Web Site: www.rogerscorp.com
Approx. Sls.: $379,188,000
Approx. Number Employees: 2,440
Year Founded: 1832
Business Description:
Mfr of Polymer & Electronic Materials
S.I.C.: 3672; 2821; 3083
N.A.I.C.S.: 334412; 325211; 326130
Export
Advertising Expenditures: $1,400,000
Media: 1-2-4-5-7-10-17

Key to Media (For complete agency information see *The Advertising Red Books-Agencies* edition):
1. Bus. Publs. 2. Cable T.V. 3. Catalogs & Directories. 4. Co-op Adv. 5. Consumer Mags. 6. D.M. to Bus. Estab.7. D.M. to Consumers 8. Daily Newsp. 9. Exhibits/Trade Shows 10. Foreign 11. Infomercial 12. Internet Adv.13. Multimedia 14. Network Radio 15. Network T.V. 16. Newsp. Distr. Mags. 17. Other 18. Outdoor (Posters, Transit) 19. Point of Purchase20. Premiums, Novelties 21. Product Samples 22. Special Events Mktg. 23. Spot Radio 24. Spot T.V. 25. Weekly Newsp. 26. Yellow Page Adv.

Distr.: Intl.; Natl.
Budget Set: Nov.
Personnel:
Robert D. Wachob *(Chm)*
Bruce D. Hoechner *(Pres & CEO)*
Dennis M. Loughran *(CFO & VP-Fin)*
Robert C. Daigle *(CTO & Sr VP-R&D)*
Terrence W. Mahoney *(Gen Counsel & VP)*
Peter G. Kaczmarek *(Sr VP)*
Jeffrey M. Grudzien *(VP-Sls & Mktg)*
Brands & Products:
BISCO SILICONES
COOLSPAN
DUREL
ENDUR
HEATWAVE
INDUFLEX
NITROPHYL
PORON
R/BAK
R/FLEX
RO-LINX
ROGERS
THE WORLD RUNS BETTER WITH ROGERS

ROYAL HAEGER LAMP COMPANY
1300 W Piper St
Macomb, IL 61455
Mailing Address:
PO Box 218
Macomb, IL 61455-0218
Tel.: (309) 837-9966
Fax: (309) 837-5267
E-mail: info@royalhaegerlamp.com
Web Site: www.royalhaegerlamp.com
Approx. Number Employees: 20
Year Founded: 1969
Business Description:
Ceramic Lamps & Shades Mfr
S.I.C.: 3645; 3641
N.A.I.C.S.: 335121; 335110
Import Export
Media: 4-10-17
Distr.: Intl.; Natl.
Personnel:
Nicholas Estes *(Pres & Gen Mgr)*

RUUD LIGHTING, INC.
9201 Washington Ave
Racine, WI 53406
Tel.: (262) 886-1900
Fax: (262) 884-3309
Web Site: www.ruudlighting.com
E-Mail For Key Personnel:
Sales Director: sales@ruudlighting.com
Approx. Sls.: $46,100,000
Approx. Number Employees: 460
Business Description:
Commercial Industrial & Institutional Electric Lighting Fixture Mfr
S.I.C.: 3646
N.A.I.C.S.: 335122
Personnel:
Alan J. Ruud *(Founder)*
Christopher Ruud *(Pres)*
Theodore O. Sokoly *(Exec VP)*
Kevin Orth *(VP-Sls)*
Steve Waters *(Dir-Fin & Acctg)*
Grege Muller *(Mgr-Mktg Staff)*
Advertising Agency:
Design North, Inc.
8007 Douglas Ave
Racine, WI 53402
Tel.: (262) 639-2080
Tel.: (262) 898-1090
Fax: (262) 639-5230
Toll Free: (800) 247-8494

S&C ELECTRIC COMPANY
6601 N Ridge Blvd
Chicago, IL 60626-3904
Tel.: (773) 338-1000
Fax: (773) 338-3657
Fax: (773) 338-8081
Toll Free: (800) 621-5546
Web Site: www.sandc.com
E-Mail For Key Personnel:
Sales Director: insidesales@sandc.com
Sales Range: $350-399.9 Million
Approx. Number Employees: 2,000
Year Founded: 1911
Business Description:
Developer of High Voltage Transmission, Distribution & Protection Equipment, Fuses, Switchgear & Switches & Power Quality & Reliability Systems; Molded Epoxy Insulation Components; Power Systems Services
S.I.C.: 3613; 3643
N.A.I.C.S.: 335313; 335931
Export
Media: 1-2-4-5-7-10-13-20-21
Distr.: Intl.; Natl.
Budget Set: Nov.
Personnel:
John W. Estey *(Pres & CEO)*
Stanley F. Slabas *(CFO & Sr VP)*
Steven L. Thunander *(VP)*
Vilma M. Bell *(VP-HR)*
Steven A. Strand *(Supvr-Adv Program)*
Brands & Products:
ALDUTI-RUPTER
AVC
BANKGUARD PLUS
CIRCUIT-ISOLATOR II
CIRCUITSWITCHER
CYPOXY
CYPOXYLATED
DURABAKE
ENERGYLINE
ENERGYLINE 5800
EPOXY
EXCELLENCE THROUGH INNOVATION
FAULT TAMER
FUSISTOR
FVR
GRAPPLER
INTELLI-TEAM
INTELLICAP
INTELLICAP PLUS
INTELLILINK
INTELLIMANAGER
INTELLIRUPTER
INTELLITEAM II
LINE-RUPTER
LOADBUSTER
LOADBUSTER DISCONNECT
LOADBUSTER DISCONNECTS
M SERIES
MANUAL PME
MANUAL PMH
MICRO-AT
MNI-RUPTER
NL
OMNI-MATE
OMNI-PLUS
OMNI-RUPTER
PENTA-LATCH
PMX
POSITECT
POSITROL
PUREWAVE
PUREWAVE AVC
PUREWAVE DSTATCOM
PUREWAVE DVR
PUREWAVE UPS
S&C ELECTRIC COMPANY
SCADA-MATE
SCADA-MATE CX
SM
SM-4
SMD
SMD-20
SMD-40
SML-20
SMU-20
SMU-40
SPEEDNET
SUPER DURABRAKE II
SYSTEM II MODULAR
SYSTEM VI
TALON
TRANS-RUPTER
TRANS-RUPTER II
TRIPSAVER
ULTRADUR
UNDERCOVER
UNI-RUPTER
VISTA
WINMON
XL
XS

SAG HARBOR INDUSTRIES
1668 Sag Harbor Tpke
Sag Harbor, NY 11963
Tel.: (631) 725-0440
Fax: (631) 725-4234
Toll Free: (800) 724-5952
E-mail: info@sagharborind.com
Web Site: www.sagharborind.com
Approx. Sls.: $4,700,000
Approx. Number Employees: 100
Year Founded: 1940
Business Description:
Electrical Coils, Assemblies & Surface Mount PC Assemblies; Transformers
S.I.C.: 3621; 5065
N.A.I.C.S.: 335312; 423690
Export
Media: 2-4-10
Distr.: Natl.
Budget Set: Jan.
Personnel:
Mary Scheerer *(Pres)*
Bernard Cecire *(VP-Engrg & Gen Mgr)*

SANDWICH LANTERN WORKS
17 Jan Sebastian Way Unit #1
Sandwich, MA 02563-2362
Tel.: (508) 833-0547
Fax: (508) 833-0547
Toll Free: (888) 741-0714
Web Site: www.sandwichlantern.com
Approx. Number Employees: 4
Year Founded: 1987
Business Description:
Reproduction Lighting Fixture Mfr
S.I.C.: 3645
N.A.I.C.S.: 335121
Media: 4-6
Personnel:
Dick Putnam *(Owner)*

SCHNEIDER ELECTRIC USA, INC.
(Div. of Schneider Electric S.A.)
(d/b/a Schneider Electric North America Operating Division (Square D))
1415 Roselle Rd
Palatine, IL 60067
Tel.: (847) 397-2600
Fax: (847) 925-7500
Web Site: www.squared.com
Sales Range: $1-4.9 Billion
Year Founded: 1903
Business Description:
Electrical Distribution Equipment, Industrial Control Products, Power Surge Protectors & Lighting Fixtures Mfr
S.I.C.: 3613; 3643; 3645; 3646
N.A.I.C.S.: 335313; 335121; 335122; 335931
Import Export
Media: 2-10-11-13-22
Personnel:
Chris Curtis *(Pres & CEO-North America)*
Aaron Davis *(CMO)*
Jeff Drees *(Pres-US)*
Robert P. Fiorani *(VP-Corp Comm)*
Nicole Brabender *(Sr Specialist-Mktg)*
Brands & Products:
FIRE-GARD
HVL
HVL/CC
MASTERCLAD
MASTERPACT
MICROLOGIC
MINIBREAK
MOTORPACT
POWER-ZONE 4
POWERLOGIC
POWERSUB
REACTIVAR
SPEED-D
SQUARE-DUCT
SUBWAY
VISI/VAC
Advertising Agency:
Impressions-A.B.A. Industries, Inc.
393 Jericho Tpk
Mineola, NY 11501
Tel.: (516) 739-3210
Fax: (516) 739-9246

SIEMENS POWER GENERATION INC
(Sub. of Siemens Energy)
30 Milton Ave
Hamilton, ON LSL 6E6, Canada
Mailing Address:
PO Box 2510, Station LCD 1
Hamilton, ON L8N 3K2, Canada
Tel.: (905) 528-8811
Fax: (905) 577-0275
Telex: 618826
Web Site: www.siemens.ca
Sales Range: $400-449.9 Million
Approx. Number Employees: 600
Year Founded: 1903
Business Description:
Manufacturing & Servicing Facility of Gas Turbines & Industrial Steam Turbines
S.I.C.: 3511
N.A.I.C.S.: 333611
Export
Advertising Expenditures: $600,000
Media: 2-4-26
Distr.: Intl.

Key to Media (For complete agency information see *The Advertising Red Books-Agencies* edition):
1. Bus. Publs. 2. Cable T.V. 3. Catalogs & Directories. 4. Co-op Adv. 5. Consumer Mags. 6. D.M. to Bus. Estab.7. D.M. to Consumers
8. Daily Newsp. 9. Exhibits/Trade Shows 10. Foreign 11. Infomercial 12. Internet Adv.13. Multimedia 14. Network Radio
15. Network T.V. 16. Newsp. Distr. Mags. 17. Other 18. Outdoor (Posters, Transit) 19. Point of Purchase20. Premiums, Novelties
21. Product Samples 22. Special Events Mktg. 23. Spot Radio 24. Spot T.V. 25. Weekly Newsp. 26. Yellow Page Adv.

Siemens Power Generation Inc — (Continued)

Personnel:
Craig Laviouette *(CFO)*
Brian Maragno *(Gen Mgr)*
Dan Hosfeld *(Dir-HR)*
Peter Strinich *(Mktg Mgr)*

SOR, INC.
14685 W 105th St
Lenexa, KS 66215-2003
Tel.: (913) 888-2630
Fax: (913) 894-1538
E-mail: info@sorinc.com
Web Site: www.sorinc.com
Approx. Number Employees: 175
Year Founded: 1956
Business Description:
Pressure & Temperature Switches; Level & Flow Switches Mfr
S.I.C.: 3625; 3822
N.A.I.C.S.: 335314; 334512
Import Export
Media: 2-4-10-20-21
Distr.: Intl.; Natl.
Budget Set: June
Personnel:
Burke Benton *(Pres & CEO)*
Charisse Konrady *(Sr VP-Fin & Admin)*
John Fortino *(VP-Engrg)*
Kamal Khan *(Reg Mgr-Sls)*
Steve Highberger *(Mgr-Sls)*
Brands & Products:
ECHOSONIX
SGT
SOR
SOR LEVEL CONTROLS
STATIC O RING

STANDARD WIRE & CABLE CO.
2050 E Vista Bella Way
Rancho Dominguez, CA 90220
Tel.: (310) 609-1811
Fax: (310) 609-1862
Toll Free: (800) 326-0006
E-mail: sales@std-wire.com
Web Site: www.std-wire.com
E-Mail For Key Personnel:
President: rskrable@std-wire.com
Sales Director: sales@std-wire.com
Sales Range: $10-24.9 Million
Approx. Number Employees: 40
Year Founded: 1945
Business Description:
Electrical & Electronic Wires, Fiber Optic Cables, Cables & Cords Mfr & Distr
S.I.C.: 3357; 5063
N.A.I.C.S.: 335929; 335921; 423610
Import Export
Media: 2-4-7-10
Distr.: Intl.; Natl.
Personnel:
Dick Hampikian *(Chm)*
Russ Skrable *(Pres)*
Bud Gardner *(VP-Sls & Mktg)*
Bruce Haft *(Mgr-Information Svcs)*
Brands & Products:
DETECTA-DUCT
FLEXOPRENE
MICROMINUM
STANCOTE
STANDARD WIRE & CABLE
STANFLEX

STREAMLIGHT INC.
30 Eagleville Rd
Eagleville, PA 19403
Tel.: (610) 631-0600
Fax: (610) 631-0712
Fax: (800) 220-7007
Toll Free: (800) 523-7488
E-mail: cs@streamlight.com
Web Site: www.streamlight.com
Sales Range: $75-99.9 Million
Approx. Number Employees: 110
Year Founded: 1973
Business Description:
Mfr of Portable Lighting Equipment
S.I.C.: 3648
N.A.I.C.S.: 335129
Export
Media: 2-4-5-10-13-19
Distr.: Intl.; Natl.
Personnel:
Harry French *(Chm)*
George Collier *(CFO & Exec VP)*
Raymond Sharrah *(COO)*
Michael Dineen *(VP-Sls & Mktg)*
Loring Grove *(Dir-Mktg)*
Charles Craft *(Mgr-Engrg)*
Brands & Products:
3C-XP
ARGO
ARGO HP
C4
CAMO-LIGHT
CLIPMATE
CUFFMATE
E-FLOOD
ENDURO
EXTREME LIGHT
FIBERWRAP
FIRE VULCAN
FIREBOX
GREEN TRIDENT
HAZ-LO
HEROES TRUST STREAMLIGHT
ILLUMINATE. NAVIGATE. DOMINATE.
KEY-MATE
KNUCKLEHEAD
LITEBOX
MEGA STINGER
MICROSTREAM
MULTI OPS
NANO LIGHT
NF-2
NIGHT COM
NIGHTFIGHTER
NIGHTFIGHTER-2
NOVA
PACKMATE
PIGGYBACK
POLYSTINGER
POLYSTINGER DS
POLYSTYLUS
POLYTAC
PROPOLYMER
SCORPION
SEPTOR
SIDEWINDER
SIDEWINDER HP
SL-20X
SL-20XP
SL-35X
SMOKE CUTTER
STINGER
STINGER DS
STINGER HP
STINGER XT
STINGER XT HP
STREAMLIGHT
STREAMLIGHT JR.
STRION
STYLUS
STYLUS PRO
STYLUS REACH
SUPER TAC
SURVIVOR
SYCLONE
TACTCAP
TACTICAL LIGHT
TASK-LIGHT
TASK-LIGHTS
TIGER RING
TL-2
TL-3
TLR-1
TLR-2
TLR-3
TLR-VIR
TOOLS NOT TOYS
TOPSPOT
TRIDENT
TRIDENT HP
TWIN-TASK
ULTRASTINGER
VANTAGE
VULCAN
WOW
XTREME LIGHT

SUREFIRE, LLC
18300 Mount Baldy Cir
Fountain Valley, CA 92708
Tel.: (714) 545-9444
Fax: (714) 545-9537
Toll Free: (800) 828-8809
E-mail: surefire@surefire.com
Web Site: www.surefire.com
Approx. Number Employees: 700
Business Description:
Mfr. & Supplier of Flashlights & Weapon-Mounted Tactical Lights
S.I.C.: 3648; 3699
N.A.I.C.S.: 335129; 335999
Media: 6
Personnel:
John Matthews *(Founder & Pres)*
Sean Zo *(CFO)*
Barry Dueck *(Dir-SureFire Suppressors)*
Kalon Pilmanis *(Mgr-Product Mktg)*
Jeremy Rosenberg *(Mgr-Sls-Reg)*
Brands & Products:
AVIATOR
CENTURION
COMBATLIGHT
COMMANDER
DEVASTATOR
GUARDIAN
LASER SIGHTS
LUMAMAX
NITROLON
SUREFIRE
ULTRA
WEAPONLIGHTS

SWIVELIER CO., INC.
600 Bradley Hill Rd
Blauvelt, NY 10913-1187
Tel.: (845) 353-1455
Fax: (845) 353-1512
E-mail: info@swivelier.com
Web Site: www.swivelier.com
Approx. Number Employees: 150
Year Founded: 1947
Business Description:
Mfr. of Adjustable Lighting Fixtures, Track Lighting & Recessed Lighting Fixtures for Commercial, Institutional & Residential Use
S.I.C.: 3646; 3645
N.A.I.C.S.: 335122; 335121
Import Export
Advertising Expenditures: $100,000
Media: 2-4-7-10-19
Distr.: Natl.
Personnel:
Michael I. Schwartz *(Pres)*
Brands & Products:
ADAPT-A-LITE
ADD-A-PIPES
BALI
BERMUDA
BRIGHT EYES
BULLET SHADE
CAPRI
CATALINA
CHANNELITES
CINEMA
CIRCA 200
CIRCA 250
CIRCA 325
CLAMP-ON
CLASSIC TORPEDO
COMBO-LITE
COMPACT 38
CONE SHADE
CONVERT-A-LITE
CONVERT-A-TRACK
COOL-GLO
COOLITE
COUNTER-POINT
COZY-LITE
CROWN SPOT
CYLINDER BEAM
DECORATOR WALL LIGHT
DEXTRA-LITE
DISKOS
DO-IT-ALL
DOME-LITES
DUO-LIGHT
EXTENDER
FLAIR
FLASH-FAR
FLAT BACK
GIRAFEE LIGHT
GRIPPER
GYRO-LITE
GYRO-LUX
HANDYMATE
HANG-UP LIGHT
HNK
JAVA
LAMPHUGGER
LAZY SUSAN
LEM
LIDO
LIGHTING FIXTURES
LINEAR
LITE-FLEX
LITE-SAVER
LITESTRIP
LOOPER
MARINER
MASTER CYLINDER
MICRO-CROWN
MICRO-MINI
MICRO-SPOT
MICRO-STEP
MIDGET SHADE
MINI CONE
MINI HALOGEN
MINI-LITE
MULTIMATIC

Key to Media (For complete agency information see *The Advertising Red Books-Agencies* edition):
1. Bus. Publs. 2. Cable T.V. 3. Catalogs & Directories. 4. Co-op Adv. 5. Consumer Mags. 6. D.M. to Bus. Estab.7. D.M. to Consumers
8. Daily Newsp. 9. Exhibits/Trade Shows 10. Foreign 11. Infomercial 12. Internet Adv.13. Multimedia 14. Network Radio
15. Network T.V. 16. Newsp. Distr. Mags. 17. Other 18. Outdoor (Posters, Transit) 19. Point of Purchase20. Premiums, Novelties
21. Product Samples 22. Special Events Mktg. 23. Spot Radio 24. Spot T.V. 25. Weekly Newsp. 26. Yellow Page Adv.

NEW ANGLES
NIGHT EYES
NIMBLE-LITE
ORBITER
PAR-BEAM-LITE
PEGMATE
PINMATE
PLAYMATE
PLUG-A-LITE
PLUG MOUNTS
PLUG-RACK
PLUGMATE
POINT ELECTRIC
PROBE
QUICK-MOUNT
RAYLUX
ROCKET
ROOM MATE
ROUND BACK
ROYAL
ROYAL BELL
SAHARA
SAMOA
SCOPE
SCREW-IN
SEVILLE
SHELFMATE
SHUR-MOUNT
SKYHOOK
SMOOTHEE
SPACE-MATE
SPARTAN
SPIDER LIGHT
SQUARE SHOOTER
SQUEEZEMATE
STAR TRACK
STARSPOT
STARTRON
STEP CYLINDER
STUDIO 38
SUNSPOT
SUPER SPOT
SUTTON
SWIV-O-FLEX
SWIVELIER
SWIVOMATIC
TAHITI
TEE-BALL
TOPLITE
TORPEDO
TRAPEZE
TRIPOLI
TRUSS-TECH
UFO
VANESSA
VOGUE-LITE
VOYAGER
WALLITE SWIVEL
WIDE EYES
WIRE GEM
ZEROMATIC

TENSOLITE, LLC

(Sub. of Carlisle Applied Technologies Group)
(d/b/a Carlisle Interconnect Technologies)
100 Tensolite Dr
Saint Augustine, FL 32092-0590
Tel.: (904) 829-5600
Fax: (904) 824-6706
Toll Free: (800) 458-9960
Web Site: www.carlisleit.com
E-Mail For Key Personnel:
Sales Director: sales@tensolite.com
Sales Range: $125-149.9 Million
Approx. Number Employees: 300
Year Founded: 1941
Business Description:
Specialty Insulated Wire & Cable Mfr
S.I.C.: 3496; 3643
N.A.I.C.S.: 332618; 335931
Import Export
Media: 2-4-7-8-10-20-21
Distr.: Direct to Consumer; Natl.
Budget Set: Dec.
Personnel:
John E. Berlin *(Pres)*
Corrie Hartline *(Mgr-Mktg Comm)*
Brands & Products:
ACCULITE
EPTFE
NET FLITE
TUFFLITE

TOPBULB.COM LLC

5204 Indianapolis Blvd
East Chicago, IN 46312-3838
Tel.: (219) 398-2362
Fax: (219) 329-2852
Toll Free: (866) TOP-BULB
E-mail: sales@topbulb.com
Web Site: www.topbulb.com
E-Mail For Key Personnel:
President: phil@topbulb.com
Sales Director: sales@topbulb.com
Approx. Number Employees: 25
Year Founded: 1989
Business Description:
Online Retailer of Specialty, Consumer, Photographic, Medical & Other Light Bulbs
S.I.C.: 5063; 5064
N.A.I.C.S.: 423610; 423620
Media: 4-7-8-13-23
Personnel:
Philip Bonello *(CEO)*
Steven M. Dombar *(Dir-Sls, Mktg & Ops)*
Brian Brown *(Internet Mktg Specialist)*
Brands & Products:
ANY LIGHT BULB ANYTIME
TOPBULB
WE LIGHT UP OUR CUSTOMERS' LIVES!

UNIVERSAL LIGHTING TECHNOLOGIES

(Sub. of Panasonic Corporation)
26 Century Blvd Ste 500
Nashville, TN 37214-3683
Tel.: (615) 316-5100
Fax: (615) 316-5184
Toll Free: (800) BALLAST
Web Site: www.unvlt.com
Approx. Number Employees: 4,000
Year Founded: 1947
Business Description:
Electronic, Magnetic, Compact & Fluorescent Lightning Ballasts, High Intensity Discharges, Capacitors, Wire & Neon Transformers Mfr
S.I.C.: 3612; 3648
N.A.I.C.S.: 335311; 335129
Import Export
Advertising Expenditures: $225,000
Media: 4-7
Distr.: Intl.; Natl.
Personnel:
Pat Sullivan *(Chm & CEO)*
Dave Riesmeyer *(CFO & Sr VP)*
Luis L. Buentello *(Sr VP-HR & Safety)*
Joseph Damiani *(Sr VP-Sls)*
Christopher A. Dimino *(Sr VP-Mktg & Product Dev)*
Dan Cheetham *(VP-OEM Sls)*
Brands & Products:
ACCUSTART
BALLASTAR
OCTEK
TRIAD
UNIVERSAL
Advertising Agency:
Gish, Sherwood & Friends, Inc.
(d/b/a GS&F)
4235 Hillsboro Pike
Nashville, TN 37215-3344
Tel.: (615) 385-1100
Fax: (615) 783-0500
(Fluorescents, Signs, Neons, HID, and Dimming Ballasts)

WENGER CORPORATION

555 Pk Dr
Owatonna, MN 55060-0448
Tel.: (507) 455-4100
Fax: (507) 455-4258
Toll Free: (800) 733-0393
Toll Free: (800) 887-7145
Web Site: www.wengercorp.com
Approx. Number Employees: 550
Year Founded: 1946
Business Description:
Mfr of Music Chairs, Music Stands, Lighting & Sound Systems, Standard & Custom Stages, Risers & Acoustical Shells
S.I.C.: 2542; 2519
N.A.I.C.S.: 337215; 337125
Import Export
Advertising Expenditures: $1,500,000
Bus. Publs.: $300,000; Catalogs & Directories: $150,000; Consumer Mags.: $150,000; D.M. to Bus. Estab.: $150,000; D.M. to Consumers: $150,000; Daily Newsp.: $150,000; Exhibits/Trade Shows: $150,000; Other: $150,000; Premiums, Novelties: $150,000
Distr.: Natl.
Budget Set: Nov.
Personnel:
Ken Pizel *(VP-Fin)*
Gregg Nelson *(Sr Mgr-Mktg)*
Brands & Products:
BRAVO
CLASIC 50
DIVA
FLIPFORMS
FOOTNOTES
FORTE
GIG STAND
HANDIHOLDER
LEGACY
LESSONWORKS
ORFFGARAGE
ORFFMOBILE
PREFACE
ROLL-A-DECK
ROUGHNECK
SHOWMOBILE
SIGNATURE
STAGEHAND
STAGEMOBILE
TOURMASTER
TRAVELMASTER
TROUPER
UPPER DECK AUDIENCE SEATING SYSTEM
V-READY
V-ROOM
VERSALITE
WENGER

WESTERN PHOTOMETRIC LABORATORIES

(Div. of Dupree, Inc.)
14395 Ramona Ave
Chino, CA 91710-5740
Tel.: (909) 597-4889
Fax: (909) 597-3043
E-mail: wplsales@dupreeinc.com
Web Site: www.dupreeinc.com/wpl
Approx. Number Employees: 70
Business Description:
Mfr. of Lamp Testing Products & Lamp Adaptors
S.I.C.: 3641; 5722
N.A.I.C.S.: 335110; 443111
Media: 7-13
Personnel:
J. D. Pon *(Pres)*

WHITNEY BLAKE CO., INC.

20 Indus Dr
Bellows Falls, VT 05101-3122
Tel.: (802) 463-9558
Fax: (802) 463-1138
Toll Free: (800) 323-0479
E-mail: sales@wblake.com
Web Site: www.whitneyblake.com
E-Mail For Key Personnel:
Sales Director: sales@wblake.com
Approx. Number Employees: 75
Year Founded: 1985
Business Description:
Mfr. of Rubber & Plastic Insulated Retractile Cords & Communications Cables
S.I.C.: 3643
N.A.I.C.S.: 335931
Import Export
Media: 2-4-5-7-9-10-13-16-19-21
Distr.: Natl.; Reg.
Budget Set: Jan.
Personnel:
Sheldon Scott *(Pres)*
Hardy Merrill *(VP-Fin & Admin)*
Brands & Products:
KOILED KORDS
TUFF-SEAL
WHITNEY BLAKE

XENONICS HOLDINGS, INC.

3186 Lionshead Ave
Carlsbad, CA 92010-4701
Tel.: (760) 477-8900
Fax: (760) 438-1184
E-mail: webmaster@xenonics.com
Web Site: www.xenonics.com
Approx. Rev.: $4,397,000
Approx. Number Employees: 17
Year Founded: 1996
Business Description:
Holding Company; Lightweight, Rugged, Ultra-High Intensity Illumination & Digital Low-Light Viewing Products Developer & Mfr
S.I.C.: 3641; 3648; 6719
N.A.I.C.S.: 335110; 335129; 551112
Advertising Expenditures: $48,000
Media: 17
Personnel:
Alan P. Magerman *(Chm)*
Jeffrey P. Kennedy *(Pres & COO)*
Richard S. Kay *(CFO)*
Lupita Anderson *(Coord-IR)*
Shannon Deeley *(Coord-Govt Sls)*
Brands & Products:
HIGH DEFINITION NIGHT VISION
HIGH POWER ILLUMINATION
NIGHTHUNTER

Key to Media (For complete agency information see *The Advertising Red Books-Agencies* edition):
1. Bus. Publs. 2. Cable T.V. 3. Catalogs & Directories. 4. Co-op Adv. 5. Consumer Mags. 6. D.M. to Bus. Estab.7. D.M. to Consumers 8. Daily Newsp. 9. Exhibits/Trade Shows 10. Foreign 11. Infomercial 12. Internet Adv.13. Multimedia 14. Network Radio 15. Network T.V. 16. Newsp. Distr. Mags. 17. Other 18. Outdoor (Posters, Transit) 19. Point of Purchase20. Premiums, Novelties 21. Product Samples 22. Special Events Mktg. 23. Spot Radio 24. Spot T.V. 25. Weekly Newsp. 26. Yellow Page Adv.

Xenonics Holdings, Inc. — (Continued)

SUPERVISION
XENONICS
XENONICS HOLDINGS

YOUNG ELECTRIC SIGN COMPANY

(d/b/a YESCO)
2401 Foothill Dr
Salt Lake City, UT 84109
Tel.: (801) 487-8481
Fax: (801) 483-0998
E-mail: info@yesco.com
Web Site: www.yesco.com
Approx. Number Employees: 1,250
Year Founded: 1920
Business Description:
Mfr of Neon & Electric Signs; Sign Rental, Installation & Maintenance & Sales
S.I.C.: 3993; 7359
N.A.I.C.S.: 339950; 532299
Media: 2-4-7-10-13-26
Distr.: Reg.
Personnel:
Thomas Young, Jr. *(Chm)*
Michael T. Young *(Pres)*
Duane Wardle *(CFO & Sr VP)*
Jeffrey S. Young *(Sec & Div Mgr)*
Paul Young *(Exec VP)*
Ben F. Jones *(Sr VP-Engrg)*
Ryan Young *(Mgr-Sls-Outdoor Media)*

ZEVOTEK, INC.

900 SE Ocean Blvd
Stuart, FL 34994
Tel.: (772) 600-2676
E-mail: info@zevotek.com
Web Site: www.zevo-tek.com
Approx. Sls.: $184,919
Approx. Number Employees: 2
Year Founded: 2005
Business Description:
Consumer Product Direct Marketer & Distr; Energy Saving Light Bulb Mfr, Marketer & Distr
S.I.C.: 5963; 3641
N.A.I.C.S.: 454390; 335110
Advertising Expenditures: $287,696
Personnel:
Robert Babkie *(CEO, CFO & Member)*

Key to Media (For complete agency information see *The Advertising Red Books-Agencies* edition):
1. Bus. Publs. 2. Cable T.V. 3. Catalogs & Directories. 4. Co-op Adv. 5. Consumer Mags. 6. D.M. to Bus. Estab.7. D.M. to Consumers 8. Daily Newsp. 9. Exhibits/Trade Shows 10. Foreign 11. Infomercial 12. Internet Adv.13. Multimedia 14. Network Radio 15. Network T.V. 16. Newsp. Distr. Mags. 17. Other 18. Outdoor (Posters, Transit) 19. Point of Purchase20. Premiums, Novelties 21. Product Samples 22. Special Events Mktg. 23. Spot Radio 24. Spot T.V. 25. Weekly Newsp. 26. Yellow Page Adv.

Machinery & Supplies

Compressors — Construction Machinery & Equipment — Control Apparatus — Conveyors — Drilling Equipment — Electrical Instruments — Engines — Machine Tools — Material Handling Equipment — Motors — Pollution Controls — Pumps — Railway Equipment — Welding Apparatus

A&A MANUFACTURING COMPANY, INC.
(Holding of Audax Management Company, LLC)
2300 S Calhoun Rd
New Berlin, WI 53151-2708
Tel.: (262) 786-1500
Fax: (262) 786-3280
Toll Free: (800) 298-2066
E-mail: sales@gortite.com
Web Site: www.gortite.com
E-Mail For Key Personnel:
Sales Director: sales@gortite.com
Approx. Number Employees: 300
Year Founded: 1945
Business Description:
Bellows, Machinery Protectors, Cable Carriers Mfr
S.I.C.: 3545
N.A.I.C.S.: 333515
Advertising Expenditures: $200,000
Media: 2-4-7-10-13-26
Distr.: Intl.; Natl.
Budget Set: Oct. -Dec.
Personnel:
James O'Rourke *(Pres)*
Lawrence M. Kean *(CFO)*
Tony Cavalo *(VP-Sls)*
Ken Czyzewski *(Mgr-Sls & Mktg)*
Brands & Products:
ALUMAFLEX
ARMORCOIL
ATD ACTUATOR
DURATITE
GORFRAME
GORTIFLEX
GORTITE
GORTRAC
GORTUBE
HYPALON
LASERTUBES
NYLATRAC
NYLATUBE
STEELCLAD
STEELFLEX
TELAFLEX
TELATUBES
THERMIC WELD
VERTIFLEX

A. FINKL & SONS CO.
(Sub. of Schmolz + Bickenbach AG)
2011 N Southport Ave
Chicago, IL 60614-4015
Tel.: (773) 975-2510
Fax: (773) 348-5347
Toll Free: (800) DIE-BLOCK
Web Site: www.finkl.com
E-Mail For Key Personnel:
Sales Director: sales@finkl.com
Approx. Sls.: $100,000,000
Approx. Number Employees: 340
Year Founded: 1879
Business Description:
Steel Ingots, Forgings, Die Blocks & Hot Works, Forged Rolls & Open Die Forgings Mfr
S.I.C.: 3312; 3462
N.A.I.C.S.: 331111; 332111
Export
Advertising Expenditures: $150,000
Media: 2-7-10
Distr.: Intl.; Natl.
Personnel:
Joseph E. Curci *(Pres)*
Dave Laurenson *(CIO & VP-Ops)*
Tim Mealt *(VP-Sls & Mktg)*
Brands & Products:
420M
ALU
ALU-C
ALU-X
CUPRODIE
CUPRODIE 2
CX
DC
DC (VAD)
DC-XTRA
DCF
DRX
DURODI
FINKL
HB
HI-HARD
HI-HARD P-20
LR
MAR-X
MOLD-DIE
NITRODE
PRESS DIE
RA40
SHELLDIE
SHELLEX
WF-XTRA
Advertising Agency:
Jasculca/Terman and Associates
730 N Franklin St Ste 510
Chicago, IL 60654
Tel.: (312) 337-7400
Fax: (312) 337-8189

A123 SYSTEMS INC.
Arsenal on the Charles 321 Arsenal St
Watertown, MA 02472
Tel.: (617) 778-5700
Fax: (617) 778-5749
Fax: (617) 924-8910
E-mail: contact_us@a123systems.com
Web Site: www.a123systems.com
Approx. Rev.: $97,312,000
Approx. Number Employees: 2,032
Year Founded: 2001
Business Description:
Rechargeable Lithium-Ion Battery & Battery Systems Designer, Developer, Mfr & Sales
S.I.C.: 3692
N.A.I.C.S.: 335912
Media: 10-17
Personnel:
Ric Fulop *(Co-Founder & VP-Mktg & Bus Dev)*
Gururaj Deshpande *(Chm)*
David P. Vieau *(Pres & CEO)*
David J. Prystash *(CFO & Chief Acctg Officer)*
Eric J. Pyenson *(Gen Counsel & VP)*
John Granara *(Controller & VP-Fin)*
Andrew Cole *(VP-HR & Org Dev)*

ABATIX CORP.
2400 Skyline Dr
Dallas, TX 75149
Tel.: (214) 381-0322
Fax: (214) 381-9513
Fax: (214) 388-0443
Toll Free: (888) 222-8499
Telex: 888-ABATIX-X
E-mail: investorrelations@abatix.com
Web Site: www.abatix.com
Approx. Sls.: $55,018,031
Year Founded: 1983
Business Description:
Supplier of Safety, Construction & Industrial Products
S.I.C.: 5084; 5085
N.A.I.C.S.: 423830; 423840
Advertising Expenditures: $287,000
Personnel:
Terry W. Shaver *(Pres & CEO)*
Frank J. Cinatl, IV *(CFO & VP)*
Gary L. Cox *(COO & Exec VP)*
Brands & Products:
ABATIX

ABB INC.
(Sub. of ABB Ltd.)
501 Merrit 7
Norwalk, CT 06851-5308
Mailing Address:
P.O. Box 5308
Norwalk, CT 06851-7000
Tel.: (203) 750-2226
Fax: (203) 750-2283
Telex: 965950 COMBENG STD
Web Site: www.abb.us
Approx. Number Employees: 11,250
Year Founded: 1988
Business Description:
Power & Automation Products, Systems, Solutions & Services
S.I.C.: 3612; 3613
N.A.I.C.S.: 335311; 335313
Import Export
Media: 2-3-9-10-13-15
Distr.: Intl.; Natl.
Budget Set: Aug.
Personnel:
Enrique O. Santacana *(Pres & CEO)*
Ismo Haka *(CFO & Sr VP)*
Eugene E. Madara *(Gen Counsel, Sec & Sr VP)*
Martin W. Gross *(Sr VP & Head-Power Sys Div)*
Deidre E. Cusack *(Sr VP & Gen Mgr)*
Don Allen *(Sr VP-Operational Excellence)*
Roger Bailey *(Reg Mgr-Power Products Div)*
Kirk Goins *(Reg Mgr-Low Voltage Products Div)*
Phil Lloyd *(Reg Mgr-HR)*
Greg Scheu *(Reg Mgr-Div Discrete Automation & Motion)*
Bruce Talley *(Reg Mgr-Function Govt Affairs & Intl Trade-North America)*
Brands & Products:
COR-PAK
HAZEN
LJUNGSTROM
Q-PIPE
RAY-JET
RAYMOND
Advertising Agency:
Richards Communications
3201 Enterprise Pkwy Ste 400
Beachwood, OH 44122

Key to Media (For complete agency information see *The Advertising Red Books-Agencies* edition):
1. Bus. Publs. 2. Cable T.V. 3. Catalogs & Directories. 4. Co-op Adv. 5. Consumer Mags. 6. D.M. to Bus. Estab.7. D.M. to Consumers 8. Daily Newsp. 9. Exhibits/Trade Shows 10. Foreign 11. Infomercial 12. Internet Adv.13. Multimedia 14. Network Radio 15. Network T.V. 16. Newsp. Distr. Mags. 17. Other 18. Outdoor (Posters, Transit) 19. Point of Purchase20. Premiums, Novelties 21. Product Samples 22. Special Events Mktg. 23. Spot Radio 24. Spot T.V. 25. Weekly Newsp. 26. Yellow Page Adv.

ABB Inc. — (Continued)

Tel.: (216) 514-7800
Fax: (216) 514-7801
Power Generation
Products & Power Systems

ABBEY ETNA MACHINE CO.
11140 Ave Rd
Perrysburg, OH 43552-0408
Tel.: (419) 874-4301
Fax: (419) 874-8200
E-mail: sales@abbeyetna.com
Web Site:
www.abbeyinternational.com
E-Mail For Key Personnel:
Sales Director: sales@abbeyetna.com
Approx. Number Employees: 5
Year Founded: 1901
Business Description:
Pipe & Tube Mills, Draw Benches, Tube Cut-Off Machines, Stationary Die & Rotary Swaging Machines, Slitters, Shear End Welders & Allied Equipment Mfr
S.I.C.: 3549; 3541
N.A.I.C.S.: 333518; 333512
Export
Media: 2-4-10
Distr.: Intl.; Natl.
Budget Set: July
Personnel:
Nelson D. Abbey *(Pres & CEO)*
Brands & Products:
ABBEY ETNA
ABBEY INTERNATIONAL

ABC PACKAGING MACHINE CORPORATION
811 Live Oak St
Tarpon Springs, FL 34689-4137
Tel.: (727) 937-5144
Fax: (727) 938-1239
Toll Free: (800) 237-5975
Web Site: www.abcpackaging.com
E-Mail For Key Personnel:
Sales Director: sales@abcpackaging.com
Approx. Number Employees: 80
Year Founded: 1940
Business Description:
Mfr of Case Sealing, Packing, Traymaker & Unscrambler/Unloading Equipment & Erectors
S.I.C.: 3565
N.A.I.C.S.: 333993
Export
Media: 2-4-6-7-11
Distr.: Direct to Consumer; Intl.; Natl.
Budget Set: Nov.
Personnel:
Mark Reichert *(Pres)*
Bryan Sinicrope *(VP-Sls & Mktg)*
Brands & Products:
ABC

ACCO MATERIAL HANDLING SOLUTIONS
(Sub. of Melrose PLC)
76 Acco Drive
York, PA 17402-0792
Tel.: (717) 741-4863
Fax: (717) 741-8568
Toll Free: (800) 967-7333
E-mail: info@accomhs.com
Web Site: www.accomhs.com
Approx. Number Employees: 150
Year Founded: 1904
Business Description:
Chain & Lifting Equipment Mfr
S.I.C.: 3536; 3537
N.A.I.C.S.: 333923; 333924
Export
Advertising Expenditures: $900,000
Media: 1-2-4-10-19
Distr.: Natl.
Budget Set: Oct.
Brands & Products:
ACCO
ACCOLIFT
ACCOLOY
BINDEX
LOUDEN
MANSAVER
VAC-U-LIFT
WEED
WRIGHT

ACCURATE FASTENERS INC.
550 E 1st St
Boston, MA 02127-1403
Tel.: (617) 268-8300
Fax: (617) 269-8783
Toll Free: (888) ACTFAST
E-mail: sales@actfast.com
Web Site: www.actfast.com
E-Mail For Key Personnel:
Sales Director: sales@actfast.com
Approx. Number Employees: 30
Business Description:
Industrial Fasteners Distr
S.I.C.: 5085
N.A.I.C.S.: 423840
Media: 2-4-6-7-8-9-21
Distr.: Direct to Consumer; Natl.
Budget Set: Aug.
Personnel:
Peter Sullivan *(Exec VP)*

ACCURATE PERFORATING COMPANY, INC.
3636 S Kedzie Ave
Chicago, IL 60632-2727
Tel.: (773) 254-3232
Fax: (773) 254-9453
Toll Free: (800) 621-0273
E-mail: sales@accurateperforating.com
Web Site:
www.accurateperforating.com
E-Mail For Key Personnel:
Sales Director: sales@accurateperforating.com
Approx. Number Employees: 80
Business Description:
Perforated Metal Stampings Mfr
S.I.C.: 3469
N.A.I.C.S.: 332116
Media: 2-4-7-10-26
Distr.: Natl.
Personnel:
Alan J. Cohen *(Chm)*
Larry H. Cohen *(Pres)*
Phillip B. Penner *(COO)*

ACF INDUSTRIES LLC
101 Clark St
Saint Charles, MO 63301
Tel.: (636) 949-2399
Fax: (636) 949-2825
Web Site: www.acfindustries.com
Approx. Sls.: $600,000,000
Approx. Number Employees: 20
Year Founded: 1899
Business Description:
Railroad Replacement Parts Mfr
S.I.C.: 3743; 4013
N.A.I.C.S.: 336510; 488210
Import Export
Advertising Expenditures: $500,000
Media: 2-4-7-10
Distr.: Intl.; Natl.
Personnel:
James E. Bowles *(Pres & CEO)*
Brands & Products:
ACF

ACME METAL CAP CO., INC.
3353 62nd St
Woodside, NY 11377-2235
Tel.: (718) 335-3000
Fax: (718) 335-3037
Toll Free: (800) 338-3581
E-mail: acmemetal@aol.com
Web Site: www.acmepans.com
Sales Range: Less than $1 Million
Approx. Number Employees: 50
Year Founded: 1935
Business Description:
Metal & Non-Metallic Stamping Services
S.I.C.: 3469
N.A.I.C.S.: 332116
Import Export
Media: 2-4-7-10
Distr.: Intl.
Budget Set: Dec.
Personnel:
Thomas Petrosino *(Pres)*
Michael Bruno *(Dir-Mktg)*

ACRISON, INC.
20 Empire Blvd
Moonachie, NJ 07074-1303
Tel.: (201) 440-8300
Fax: (201) 440-4939
Toll Free: (800) 4-ACRISON
E-mail: infomail@acrison.com
Web Site: www.acrison.com
E-Mail For Key Personnel:
Marketing Director: terryshaw@acrison.com
Approx. Number Employees: 225
Year Founded: 1963
Business Description:
Metering, Mixing & Blending Equipment Mfr
S.I.C.: 3823
N.A.I.C.S.: 334513
Export
Media: 2-4-7-10
Distr.: Intl.; Natl.
Personnel:
Terry Shaw *(Mng Dir)*
Ronald Ricciardi *(VP & Gen Mgr)*
Roger Frost *(Head-Engrg)*
John Stinson *(Mgr-Maintenance & Engrg)*
Brands & Products:
ACRI-DATA
ACRISON
DELRIN
ETHERLINK
POLYMAIR
PROFILINK
RATIOMETRIC

ADAMATION
(Sub. of Superior Equipment Solutions)
950 Boylston St
Newton Highlands, MA 02461
Tel.: (888) 383-8800
Fax: (617) 244-4609
Toll Free: (888) 383-8800
E-mail: info@adamationinc.com
Web Site: www.adamationinc.com
Approx. Number Employees: 25
Year Founded: 1957
Business Description:
Food Conveyors, Commercial Dishwashers & Silver Burnishers Mfr
S.I.C.: 5722
N.A.I.C.S.: 443111
Export
Media: 2-4-7-10-11
Distr.: Intl.; Natl.
Brands & Products:
ADAMATION

ADEPT TECHNOLOGY, INC.
5960 Inglewood Dr
Pleasanton, CA 94588
Tel.: (925) 245-3400
Fax: (925) 960-0452
E-mail: info@adept.com
Web Site: www.adept.com
Approx. Rev.: $57,505,000
Approx. Number Employees: 183
Year Founded: 1983
Business Description:
Mfr. of Robotics, Motion Controllers & Machine Vision
S.I.C.: 3823; 3559; 7373
N.A.I.C.S.: 334513; 332410; 333298; 541512
Import Export
Advertising Expenditures: $50,000
Media: 7-10-13
Personnel:
Michael P. Kelly *(Chm)*
John D. Dulchinos *(Pres & CEO)*
Lisa M. Cummins *(CFO & VP-Fin)*
Jeff Baird *(VP-Engrg)*
Rush LaSelle *(Dir-Sls & Mktg-Worldwide)*
Brands & Products:
ADEPT
ADEPT ACE
ADEPT ANYFEEDER
ADEPT APPROFLEX
ADEPT COBRA
ADEPT COBRA SMART600
ADEPT MOTIONBLOX
ADEPT PYTHON
ADEPT QUATTRO
ADEPT SIGHT
ADEPT SMARTCONTROLLER
ADEPT SMARTMOTION
ADEPT SMARTSERVO
ADEPT V+
ADEPT VIPER
ADEPT VISION
ADEPT-XL
ADEPTONE-XL
ADEPTSIX
ADEPTVICRON 300S
AIM
FIREBLOX
HEXSIGHT
MOTIVITY BY MOBILEROBOTS
PATROLBOT
SMARTAMP
SMARTAXIS
SMARTCONTROLLER CS
SMARTCONTROLLER CX
SMARTMODULES
YOUR INTELLIGENT ROBOTICS PARTNER

Key to Media (For complete agency information see *The Advertising Red Books-Agencies* edition):
1. Bus. Publs. 2. Cable T.V. 3. Catalogs & Directories. 4. Co-op Adv. 5. Consumer Mags. 6. D.M. to Bus. Estab.7. D.M. to Consumers
8. Daily Newsp. 9. Exhibits/Trade Shows 10. Foreign 11. Infomercial 12. Internet Adv.13. Multimedia 14. Network Radio
15. Network T.V. 16. Newsp. Distr. Mags. 17. Other 18. Outdoor (Posters, Transit) 19. Point of Purchase20. Premiums, Novelties
21. Product Samples 22. Special Events Mktg. 23. Spot Radio 24. Spot T.V. 25. Weekly Newsp. 26. Yellow Page Adv.

ADMIRAL TOOL & MANUFACTURING COMPANY INC.
38010 Amrhein Rd
Livonia, MI 48150
Tel.: (734) 462-0222
Fax: (734) 462-4242
E-mail: webmaster@admiraltool.com
Web Site: www.admiraltool.com
Approx. Number Employees: 180
Year Founded: 1945
Business Description:
Metal Stampings
S.I.C.: 3469; 3544
N.A.I.C.S.: 332116; 333514
Import Export
Advertising Expenditures: $250,000
Media: 4-13
Personnel:
Ernest S. Levine *(Owner)*
Steve Waldre *(Dir-Engrng)*

ADVANCED ENVIRONMENTAL RECYCLING TECHNOLOGIES, INC.
914 N Jefferson St
Springdale, AR 72764
Mailing Address:
PO Box 1237
Springdale, AR 72765
Tel.: (479) 756-7400
Fax: (479) 756-7410
Toll Free: (800) 951-5117
E-mail: info@aertinc.com
Web Site: www.aertinc.com
Approx. Sls.: $69,819,000
Approx. Number Employees: 402
Year Founded: 1988
Business Description:
Converts Recycled Plastics & Wood Filler into Building Materials
S.I.C.: 2431; 2435; 2493
N.A.I.C.S.: 321911; 321211; 321219
Advertising Expenditures: $700,000
Media: 6-7-10
Personnel:
Joseph G. Brooks *(Chm & CEO)*
Tim Morrison *(Pres)*
J. R. Brian Hanna *(CFO)*
Stephen W. Brooks *(COO)*
J. Douglas Brooks *(Sr VP)*
Alford Drinkwater *(Sr VP-Dev & Governmental Affairs)*
Jim Precht *(Sr VP-Sls & Mktg)*
Brands & Products:
AERT
ENVIRONMENTALLY FRIENDLY COMPOSITE DECKING
LIFECYCLE
MOISTURESHIELD

AEC, INC.
(Sub. of The ACS Group)
1100 E Woodfield Rd
Schaumburg, IL 60173
Tel.: (630) 595-1060
Fax: (847) 273-7804
Web Site: www.aecinternet.com
Approx. Number Employees: 100
Year Founded: 1949
Business Description:
Mfr. of Water Cooling, Water Recovery & Energy Recapture Products & Systems; Automated Parts, Material Reclaim Systems; Automated Material Handling Systems, Conveyance Systems; Robots
S.I.C.: 3585; 3823
N.A.I.C.S.: 333415; 334513
Import Export
Media: 1-2-4-8-10-11-13-20-22
Distr.: Intl.; Natl.
Budget Set: Oct.
Personnel:
Thomas Breslin *(Pres & CEO)*
Keith Larson *(VP-Sls & Mktg)*
Bob Shingledecker *(Technical Sls Mgr-Midwest)*
Advertising Agency:
Scott, Inc. of Milwaukee
(dba Scott Advertising)
1031 N Astor St
Milwaukee, WI 53202-3324
Tel.: (414) 276-1080
Fax: (414) 276-3327
— Mike Taylor *(Acct. Exec.)*

A.G. DAVIS/AA GAGE
6533 Sims Dr
Sterling Heights, MI 48313
Tel.: (586) 977-9000
Fax: (586) 977-9190
E-mail: inquire@agdavis.com
Web Site: www.agdavis-aagage.com
Sales Range: $10-24.9 Million
Approx. Number Employees: 70
Business Description:
Gage Components, Custom Gaging Equipment & Automatic Gaging Systems Mfr
S.I.C.: 3545; 5084
N.A.I.C.S.: 333515; 423830
Media: 4-10
Distr.: Natl.
Personnel:
Edwin G. Chapman *(Pres)*
Greg Chapman *(Mgr-Sls)*
Brands & Products:
CHECKMATE
CON-AX
ULTRADEX
ULTRARON

AIR DRAULICS ENGINEERING CO.
(Sub. of Applied Industrial Technologies, Inc.)
4250 Pilot Dr
Memphis, TN 38118-6932
Tel.: (901) 794-4300
Fax: (901) 795-5841
E-mail: info@airdraulic.com
Web Site: www.airdraulic.com
Sales Range: $25-49.9 Million
Approx. Number Employees: 20
Year Founded: 2000
Business Description:
Hydraulic Systems Equipment & Supplies Distr
S.I.C.: 5084
N.A.I.C.S.: 423830
Media: 26
Personnel:
Renee Topham *(Dir-Mktg)*
Russ Jacobs *(Mgr-IT)*
Brands & Products:
TECHNOLOGIES FOR INDUSTRIAL AUTOMATION

AIR-SERV GROUP, LLC
1370 Mendota Heights Rd
Mendota Heights, MN 55120-1190
Tel.: (651) 454-0465
Fax: (651) 454-9542
Toll Free: (800) 247-8363
E-mail: customer.service@air-serv.com
Web Site: www.air-serv.com
E-Mail For Key Personnel:
Marketing Director: jconfer@air-serv.com
Sales Director: dfabry@air-serv.com
Approx. Sls.: $4,000,000
Approx. Number Employees: 100
Year Founded: 1981
Business Description:
Tire Inflators, Auto Vacuum Cleaners & Vending Machine Mfr
S.I.C.: 3563; 3581
N.A.I.C.S.: 333912; 333311
Export
Advertising Expenditures: $400,000
Media: 2-6-7-8
Distr.: Intl.; Natl.
Budget Set: Monthly
Personnel:
John Confer *(Sr Mgr-Ntl Accts)*
Brands & Products:
ABS-OIL
AIR-SERVE
ALGLEEM
ATTACK SANITIZER
BUY TIME
CITRI-CLENZ
CONCLEN
CRYSTAL CLEAR
DIS-GO
DISCON
DUO-SERV
FLEET CLEAN
GLEEM
GOLD
HANX GEL
HANZ BAC
HANZ SOAP
HY-SEC
IMAGE PLUS
MAGIC WITH SHINE
MILLENNIUM
MIRACLE WORKER WITH SHINE
RESHINE
SAECO
SANI-FORM FOAM SANITIZER
SANITOL
SPARKLE
SPEED CLEAN
ULTIMATE HANZ
WONDER WASH

AIXTRON INC.
(Sub. of AIXTRON Aktiengesellschaft)
1139 Karlstad Dr
Sunnyvale, CA 94089-2117
Tel.: (408) 747-7120
Fax: (408) 747-7199
E-mail: usinfo@aixtron.com
Web Site: www.aixtron.com/index.php?id=420
E-Mail For Key Personnel:
Public Relations: pr@genus.com
Approx. Number Employees: 100
Year Founded: 1981
Business Description:
Capital Equipment & Processes Designer, Mfr & Marketer For Advanced Semiconductor Manufacturing
S.I.C.: 3559; 3674
N.A.I.C.S.: 332410; 334413
Export
Media: 10
Personnel:
Randy Singh *(VP-Fin)*
Brands & Products:
AN ENABLING THIN FILM EQUIPMENT COMPANY
LYNX
LYNX2
LYNX3
STRATAGEM

A.J. JERSEY INC.
125 St Nicholas Ave
South Plainfield, NJ 07080
Tel.: (908) 754-7333
Fax: (908) 754-6188
E-mail: parts@ajjersey.net
Web Site: www.ajjersey.net
Approx. Sls.: $18,000,000
Approx. Number Employees: 125
Year Founded: 1970
Business Description:
Material Handling Equipment Mfr
S.I.C.: 5084
N.A.I.C.S.: 423830
Media: 2-7-8-10-13-18-22-26
Personnel:
David Rizzo *(Pres)*
Susan Janisch *(Supvr-Sls & Mktg)*
Brands & Products:
AJ JERSEY
GOOD EQUIPMENT, PROPERLY SOLD & SERVICED

AK STEEL HOLDING CORPORATION
9227 Centre Point Dr
West Chester, OH 45069
Tel.: (513) 425-5000
Fax: (513) 425-2676
Toll Free: (866) 571-6351
Web Site: www.aksteel.com
Approx. Sls.: $5,968,300,000
Approx. Number Employees: 6,600
Year Founded: 1993
Business Description:
Flat-Rolled Carbon, Stainless & Electrical Steel Products & Carbon & Stainless Tubular Steel Products Mfr
S.I.C.: 3312; 3316; 3317
N.A.I.C.S.: 331111; 331210; 331221
Export
Media: 7-11
Personnel:
James L. Wainscott *(Chm, Pres & CEO)*
Albert E. Ferrara Jr. *(CFO & Sr VP-Fin)*
John F. Kaloski *(COO & Exec VP)*
Richard S. Williams *(Chief Acctg Officer & Controller)*
Gary T. Barlow *(VP-Sls & Customer Svc)*
Alan H. McCoy *(VP-Govt & PR)*
Lawrence F. Zizzo, Jr. *(VP-HR)*
Lisa A. Vensel *(Gen Mgr-Electric Steel Sls)*
Doug O. Mitterholzer *(Asst Treas)*
Brands & Products:
1 SR
11 CR-CB
12 SR
15-5 PH
17-14 CU MO
17-4 PH
17-7 PH
18-9 LW
18 CR-CB
18 SR
19-9DL
2 SR

Key to Media (For complete agency information see *The Advertising Red Books-Agencies* edition):
1. Bus. Publs. 2. Cable T.V. 3. Catalogs & Directories. 4. Co-op Adv. 5. Consumer Mags. 6. D.M. to Bus. Estab.7. D.M. to Consumers 8. Daily Newsp. 9. Exhibits/Trade Shows 10. Foreign 11. Infomercial 12. Internet Adv.13. Multimedia 14. Network Radio 15. Network T.V. 16. Newsp. Distr. Mags. 17. Other 18. Outdoor (Posters, Transit) 19. Point of Purchase20. Premiums, Novelties 21. Product Samples 22. Special Events Mktg. 23. Spot Radio 24. Spot T.V. 25. Weekly Newsp. 26. Yellow Page Adv.

AK Steel Holding Corporation —
(Continued)

303MA
311 DQ
6 SR
AK FORMTUBE
AK-SPECTRA
AK STEEL
ALUMI-THERM
ANTI STICK
AQUAMET
ARMCO
BLACK COAT
BORON STEEL
CARLITE
CEM
COLOR LOCK
COSHOCTON STAINLESS
DI-MAX
ELECTRASMOOTH
EXTRASMOOTH
FORMABLE
GREYSTONE
GREYSTONE BRIGHT
GREYSTONE DULL
HCR
HIGH PERFORMANCE-10
I-F
NI TERNE XL
NITRONIC
ORIENTED LS
PAINTGRIP
PH 13-8 MO
PH 15-7 MO
TRAN-COR
TRIBONIC 20
ULTRA FORM
ULTRACHEM
ULTRASMOOTH
UNIBRITE
UNIGRAIN
UNIVIT
VIT-PLUS
ZINCGRIP

AKERUE INDUSTRIES, INC.

(Sub. of Akerue Industries, LLC)
(d/b/a Kay Home Products, Inc.)
26210 Emery Rd Unit 101
Warrensville Heights, OH 44128
Tel.: (440) 975-0503
Fax: (216) 896-6903
Toll Free: (800) 600-7009
E-mail: info@kayhomeproducts.com
Web Site:
www.kayhomeproducts.com
Approx. Number Employees: 5
Year Founded: 1989
Business Description:
Mfr & Marketer of Housewares, Lawn, Garden Equipment, & Hardware Goods
S.I.C.: 3524; 5211
N.A.I.C.S.: 333112; 444110
Import Export
Advertising Expenditures: $25,000
Media: 1-2-3-4-5-6-7-8-9-13-14-16-19-21-22-23-24-25
Brands & Products:
CASITA
MARSHALLAN
PATIO-MATE
TWIST-N-GRILL
VORTEX

AKRION, INC.

(Holding of Bayside Capital, Inc.)
(d/b/a Akrion Systems)
6330 Hedgewood Dr Ste 150
Allentown, PA 18106
Tel.: (610) 391-9200
Fax: (610) 391-1982
E-mail: info@akrion.com
Web Site: www.akrion.com
Approx. Rev.: $80,158,000
Approx. Number Employees: 344
Year Founded: 1999
Business Description:
Batch-Immersion & Single-Wafer Wet Cleaning Systems for the Semiconductor Industry Mfr
S.I.C.: 3674
N.A.I.C.S.: 334413
Media: 2-10
Personnel:
Michael Ioannou *(Pres & CEO)*
W. James Whittle *(CFO)*
Mehran Asdigha *(VP-Engrg)*
Ismail Kashkoush *(VP-Applications & Tech)*
Brands & Products:
CLEAN
GAMA SOLAR
GOLDFINGER
V3 SOLAR
VELOCITY

AKRON BRASS COMPANY

(Sub. of Premier Farnell plc)
343 Venture Blvd
Wooster, OH 44691
Mailing Address:
PO Box 86
Wooster, OH 44691
Tel.: (330) 264-5678
Fax: (330) 264-2944
Toll Free: (800) 228-1161
E-mail: custserv@akronbrass.com
Web Site: www.akronbrass.com
Approx. Number Employees: 277
Year Founded: 1918
Business Description:
Fire Fighting Equipment Mfr
S.I.C.: 3561
N.A.I.C.S.: 333911
Media: 1-2-4-7-10-11-21
Distr.: Intl.; Natl.
Budget Set: Apr.
Personnel:
Thomas H. Hudak *(Pres)*
David Durstine *(VP-Mktg)*
Dennis Jones *(VP-Sls-Intl)*
Steve Robertson *(Dir-Bus Dev)*
Brands & Products:
3000 SERIES
APOLLO
ASSAULT
DECKMASTER
FIREFOX
GEMINI
MERCURY
NAVIGATOR
OZZIE
RENEGADE
SABERJET
SABERMASTER
STORM
STREAMMASTER
SWING-OUT
TUCKAWAY
TURBOJET

ALAMO GROUP INC.

1627 East Walnut
Seguin, TX 78155-5202
Tel.: (830) 379-1480
Fax: (830) 372-9683
E-mail: info@alamo-group.com
Web Site: www.alamo-group.com
Approx. Sls.: $524,540,000
Approx. Number Employees: 2,300
Year Founded: 1955
Business Description:
Industrial & Agricultural Mowing Equipment & Accessories Mfr
S.I.C.: 3523; 3423; 3531; 3537
N.A.I.C.S.: 333111; 332212; 333120; 333924
Advertising Expenditures: $5,135,000
Media: 2-10-20
Personnel:
Ronald A. Robinson *(Pres & CEO)*
Dan E. Malone *(CFO & Exec VP)*
Donald C. Duncan *(Gen Counsel & VP)*
Jeffery A. Leonard *(Exec VP-Indus-North America)*
Brands & Products:
ALAMCO SMC
ALAMO INDUSTRIAL
ALAMO INDUSTRIAL MAVERICK
BOMFORD
BUZZBAR
FAUCHEUX
FORGES GORCE
GRADALL
HENKE
HERSCHEL
INTERSTATER
M&W
MCCONNELL
NITE-HAWK
RHINO
RHINO FLEX FLAIL
RIVARD
ROUSSEAU
SCHULTE
SCHULTE 5026
SCHWARZE
SCHWARZE M6000
S.M.A
SPEARHEAD
TIGER
TIGER TRUCKAT
TWOSE
VACALL
VALU-BILT

ALAMO IRON WORKS

943 AT&T Ctr Pkwy
San Antonio, TX 78219
Tel.: (210) 223-6161
Fax: (210) 704-8351
Web Site: www.aiwnet.com
Approx. Number Employees: 500
Year Founded: 1875
Business Description:
Industrial Supplies
S.I.C.: 5084; 5051
N.A.I.C.S.: 423830; 423510
Media: 4
Personnel:
Francis Shea *(Pres)*
Mark Sobotik *(CFO)*

ALFA LAVAL, INC.

(Sub. of Alfa Laval Inc.)
9560 58th Pl Ste 300
Kenosha, WI 53144
Tel.: (262) 605-2600
Toll Free: (866) ALFALAVAL
E-mail: customerservice.usa@alfalaval.com
Web Site: www.alfalaval.us
Approx. Number Employees: 100
Year Founded: 1919
Business Description:
Flow Equipment Mfr & Retailer
S.I.C.: 5084; 3561
N.A.I.C.S.: 423830; 333911
Import Export
Advertising Expenditures: $500,000
Media: 1-4-10-21
Distr.: Intl.
Budget Set: Sept. -Oct.
Brands & Products:
ALDEC G2
ALFA-PURE
MAIN STREAM
STREAMLINE
THINKTOP
TRI-BLENDER
TRI-CLAMP
TRI-CLOVER
TRI-FLO
TRI-WELD
Advertising Agency:
Core Creative, Inc.
126 N Jefferson St Ste 250
Milwaukee, WI 53202
Tel.: (414) 291-0912
Fax: (414) 291-0932

ALGAS-SDI

(Sub. of Eclipse Inc.)
151 S Michigan
Seattle, WA 98108
Tel.: (206) 789-5410
Fax: (206) 789-5414
E-mail: contact@algas-sdi.com
Web Site: www.algas-sdi.com
Approx. Number Employees: 27
Year Founded: 1943
Business Description:
Mfr. of Liquified Petroleum Gas Processing, Vaporizing & Mixing Equipment
S.I.C.: 3569
N.A.I.C.S.: 333999
Import Export
Media: 2-4-10-11-20
Distr.: Intl.; Natl.
Budget Set: May
Personnel:
Randy Ervin *(Pres)*
Flemming Ethelfeld *(Reg Mgr-Sls-Europe & Middle East)*
Michael Hojel *(Reg Mgr-Sls-Mexico, Central & South America)*
Sean Guichon *(Sls Mgr-Engrg Sys)*
John Hartfield *(Sls Mgr-LP-Gas Distributed Products-Intl)*
Michael Hu *(Sls Mgr-China)*
Ana Torres *(Engr-Apllications)*
Brands & Products:
ALGAS-SDI
AQUAVAIRE
AZEOVAIRE
BLENDAIRE
CONSTA-MIX
FILTAIRE
GA500
POWER
POWER XP
QM
STABILAIRE
TORREXX

Key to Media (For complete agency information see *The Advertising Red Books-Agencies* edition):
1. Bus. Publs. 2. Cable T.V. 3. Catalogs & Directories. 4. Co-op Adv. 5. Consumer Mags. 6. D.M. to Bus. Estab.7. D.M. to Consumers 8. Daily Newsp. 9. Exhibits/Trade Shows 10. Foreign 11. Infomercial 12. Internet Adv.13. Multimedia 14. Network Radio 15. Network T.V. 16. Newsp. Distr. Mags. 17. Other 18. Outdoor (Posters, Transit) 19. Point of Purchase20. Premiums, Novelties 21. Product Samples 22. Special Events Mktg. 23. Spot Radio 24. Spot T.V. 25. Weekly Newsp. 26. Yellow Page Adv.

VAPORAIRE
ZIMMER

ALL AMERICAN SEMICONDUCTOR LLC

(Holding of Rock River Capital LLC)
16115 NW 52nd Ave
Miami, FL 33014-6205
Tel.: (305) 621-8282
Fax: (305) 620-7831
Toll Free: (800) 573-2727
Toll Free: (800) 573-ASAP
E-mail: info@allamerican.com
Web Site: www.allamerican.com
Approx. Number Employees: 600
Year Founded: 1964
Business Description:
Electronic Components Distr
S.I.C.: 5065
N.A.I.C.S.: 423690
Media: 2-4-7-19
Personnel:
Jamil Nizan *(Pres & CEO)*
Jacqueline Chapman *(Product Mgr-Pur)*
Brands & Products:
ALL AMERICAN

ALLIED CONSTRUCTION PRODUCTS, LLC

(Sub. of Pubco Corporation)
3900 Kelley Ave
Cleveland, OH 44114-4536
Tel.: (216) 431-2600
Fax: (216) 431-2601
E-mail: sales@alliedcp.com
Web Site: www.alliedcp.com
E-Mail For Key Personnel:
Sales Director: sales@alliedcp.com
Approx. Number Employees: 50
Year Founded: 1942
Business Description:
Construction Machinery & Equipment Mfr
S.I.C.: 3531
N.A.I.C.S.: 333120
Advertising Expenditures: $800,000
Media: 2-4-10-19-20
Distr.: Intl.; Natl.
Budget Set: Oct.
Personnel:
Greg Smith *(Mgr-Mktg & Comm)*
Brands & Products:
ALLIED
AR SERIES
CARRIER MOUNTED LUBRICATING SYSTEM
GRIP-LUG
HO-PAC
HOLE-HOG
HY-RAM
PEDESTAL BREAKER
POWERBOOM
POWERMAX
POWERPLUS
RAMMER
ROTO-CUT
SANDVIK
TREN-SHORE
VMS MOUNTING SYSTEM

THE ALLIED POWER GROUP

10131 Mills Rd
Houston, TX 77070
Tel.: (281) 444-3535
Fax: (281) 444-3529
E-mail: info@alliedpg.com
Web Site: www.alliedpg.com
Sales Range: $50-74.9 Million
Approx. Number Employees: 70
Year Founded: 2000
Business Description:
Machine Part Refurbishing Services
S.I.C.: 8711
N.A.I.C.S.: 541330
Media: 10
Personnel:
Bruce Agardy *(CEO)*
Louis Green *(COO)*
Keith Marler *(Pres)*

THE ALPINE GROUP, INC.

1 Meadowlands Plz Ste 801
East Rutherford, NJ 07073
Tel.: (201) 549-4400
Fax: (201) 549-4428
Web Site: www.alpine-group.net
Approx. Sls.: $36,677,000
Approx. Number Employees: 410
Year Founded: 1957
Business Description:
Holding Company; Industrial Mfr
S.I.C.: 3355; 3351; 3661; 6719
N.A.I.C.S.: 331319; 331421; 334210; 551112
Import Export
Advertising Expenditures: $200,000
Personnel:
Steven S. Elbaum *(Chm & CEO)*
Stewart H. Wahrsager *(Gen Counsel, Sec & Sr VP)*
K. Mitchell Posner *(Exec VP)*
Michael E. Smith *(VP-Fin)*

ALSTOM SIGNALING, INC.

(Sub. of Alstom Inc)
1025 John St
West Henrietta, NY 14586
Mailing Address:
PO Box 20600
Rochester, NY 14602-0600
Tel.: (585) 783-2000
Fax: (585) 274-8777
Toll Free: (800) 717-4477
E-mail: info@alstomsignalingsolutions.com
Web Site:
www.alstomsignalingsolutions.com
Approx. Number Employees: 657
Year Founded: 1904
Business Description:
Mfr. & Whslr of Transportation Control Equipment for Railroad & Rail Mass Transit Systems
S.I.C.: 3669
N.A.I.C.S.: 334290
Import Export
Media: 1-2-4-7-9-10-11-17-20
Distr.: Direct to Consumer; Intl.; Natl.
Personnel:
Jim Heinlein *(Mgr-Mktg)*
Brands & Products:
AURORA
CABMATIC
CENTRACODE II
GENVAKODE II
LEX-C
MICRO CABMATIC
MICROCHRON II
PERSONAL TRAFFIC MASTER
SPECTROM
TRANSPORTATION MANAGEMENT SYSTEM
VPI

ALTAIR CORPORATION

350 Barclay Blvd
Lincolnshire, IL 60069-3606
Tel.: (847) 634-9540
Fax: (847) 634-2627
Sales Range: $100-124.9 Million
Approx. Number Employees: 300
Year Founded: 1957
Business Description:
Holding Company; Industrial Electronic Equipment & Control Systems Mfr
S.I.C.: 6719; 3559; 3625; 5084
N.A.I.C.S.: 551112; 333298; 335314; 423830
Media: 1-2-4-5-6-7-10-19-21-22-23
Distr.: Natl.
Personnel:
Garry Brainin *(Pres)*
Brands & Products:
HURLETRON
STOCKADE
VACUDYNE
W-P FEEDS

ALTEC INDUSTRIES INC.

210 Inverness Ctr Dr
Birmingham, AL 35242-4834
Tel.: (205) 991-7733
Fax: (205) 991-9993
Web Site: www.altec.com
Approx. Number Employees: 200
Year Founded: 1929
Business Description:
Mobile Utility Equipment, Hydraulic Digger Derricks & Aerial Devices Mfr
S.I.C.: 3531; 3536
N.A.I.C.S.: 333120; 333923
Export
Advertising Expenditures: $200,000
Media: 2-10-20
Distr.: Intl.; Natl.
Budget Set: Dec.
Personnel:
Lee J. Styslinger, III *(Pres & CEO)*
Jon C. Styslinger *(Sr VP)*
Brands & Products:
ACCU-LEVEL
ALTEC
ALTEC DIRECT
ALTEC SENTRY
ISO-GRIP
OPTI-VIEW
SAFER & SMARTER

ALTRA INDUSTRIAL MOTION, INC.

(Sub. of Altra Holdings, Inc.)
300 Granite St Ste 201
Braintree, MA 02184
Tel.: (781) 917-0600
Fax: (781) 843-0709
E-mail: ir@altraindustrialmotion.com
Web Site:
www.altraindustrialmotion.com
Sales Range: $25-49.9 Million
Approx. Number Employees: 30
Business Description:
Power Transmission & Motion Control Products Designer, Mfr & Marketer
S.I.C.: 3568; 3625
N.A.I.C.S.: 333613; 335314
Advertising Expenditures: $2,300,000
Personnel:
Michael L. Hurt *(Chm)*
Carl R. Christenson *(Pres & CEO)*
Christian Storch *(CFO & VP)*
Glenn Deegan *(Gen Counsel, Sec, VP-Legal & HR)*
Todd B. Patriacca *(Controller, Asst Treas & VP-Fin)*
Craig Schuele *(VP-Mktg & Bus Dev)*
Advertising Agency:
Heinzeroth Marketing Group
415 Y Blvd
Rockford, IL 61107-3059
Tel.: (815) 967-0929
Fax: (815) 967-0983

AMERICAN CASTING & MANUFACTURING CORPORATION

51 Comml St
Plainview, NY 11803-2401
Tel.: (516) 349-7010
Fax: (516) 349-8389
Toll Free: (800) 342-0333
E-mail: info@americancasting.com
Web Site: www.americancasting.com
Approx. Number Employees: 50
Year Founded: 1910
Business Description:
Mfr., Designer & Producer of Seals
S.I.C.: 3089; 3364
N.A.I.C.S.: 326199; 331522
Advertising Expenditures: $200,000
Media: 2-4-7-10-13-26
Distr.: Direct to Consumer; Natl.
Personnel:
Norman Wenk, III *(Pres)*
James Wenk *(VP-Sls & Mktg)*
Brands & Products:
AC&M
CRATE SECURE
KEYED STEEL PADLOCK
LABELZON
SECURE PERF
STRETCH WRAP
Advertising Agency:
Industrial Advertising, Inc.
14 S Main St 2nd Fl
Sayville, NY 11782-3104
Tel.: (631) 563-1945
Fax: (631) 567-6576

AMERICAN CRANE & EQUIPMENT CORPORATION

531 Old Swede Rd
Douglassville, PA 19518-1205
Tel.: (610) 385-6061
Fax: (610) 385-4876
Toll Free: (877) 877-6778
E-mail: info@americancrane.com
Web Site: www.americancrane.com
E-Mail For Key Personnel:
President: onorheim@americancrane.com
Sales Range: $100-124.9 Million
Approx. Number Employees: 100
Year Founded: 1972
Business Description:
Overhead Electrical Cranes & Hoists Mfr
S.I.C.: 3536; 7389
N.A.I.C.S.: 333923; 561990
Import Export
Advertising Expenditures: $60,000
Bus. Publs.: $10,000; Catalogs & Directories: $20,000; D.M. to Bus. Estab.: $10,000; Foreign: $10,000; Yellow Page Adv.: $10,000
Distr.: Intl.; Natl.
Budget Set: Apr.
Personnel:
Oddvar Norheim *(Pres)*

Key to Media (For complete agency information see *The Advertising Red Books-Agencies* edition):
1. Bus. Publs. 2. Cable T.V. 3. Catalogs & Directories. 4. Co-op Adv. 5. Consumer Mags. 6. D.M. to Bus. Estab.7. D.M. to Consumers 8. Daily Newsp. 9. Exhibits/Trade Shows 10. Foreign 11. Infomercial 12. Internet Adv.13. Multimedia 14. Network Radio 15. Network T.V. 16. Newsp. Distr. Mags. 17. Other 18. Outdoor (Posters, Transit) 19. Point of Purchase20. Premiums, Novelties 21. Product Samples 22. Special Events Mktg. 23. Spot Radio 24. Spot T.V. 25. Weekly Newsp. 26. Yellow Page Adv.

American Crane & Equipment Corporation — (Continued)

Dave Hope *(CFO, Gen Counsel & VP)*
Scott Harner *(Reg Mgr-Svc)*
Bonnie Marquette *(Mgr-HR)*
Paul Smyk *(Engr-Sls)*

Brands & Products:
ACECO
DUOBOX
MONOBOX
MUNCK
SAFLIFT
SAFWATCH
YOUR CRITICAL LIFT EXPERTS

AMERICAN DRILL BUSHING CO.
5740 Hunt Rd
Valdosta, GA 31606
Tel.: (229) 253-8928
Fax: (229) 253-8929
Toll Free: (800) 423-4425
E-mail: info@adbhoistrings.com
Web Site: www.americandrillbushing.com
Approx. Number Employees: 50
Year Founded: 1943
Business Description:
Bushings, Tooling Components & Toggle Clamps Mfr
S.I.C.: 3545; 3544
N.A.I.C.S.: 333515; 333514
Media: 2-4-10-19
Distr.: Natl.
Budget Set: Nov.
Personnel:
Phil Stranahan *(VP & Gen Mgr)*
Brands & Products:
ADB
LUG LOK

AMERICAN FELT & FILTER COMPANY
(d/b/a AFFCO)
361 Walsh Ave
New Windsor, NY 12553-6727
Tel.: (845) 561-3560
Fax: (845) 561-0967
E-mail: affco@affco.com
Web Site: www.affco.com
Approx. Number Employees: 250
Year Founded: 1899
Business Description:
Mfr. & Fabricator of Natural & Synthetic Felts
S.I.C.: 3569
N.A.I.C.S.: 333999
Media: 1-2-4-5-7-10-11-13-20-21-22
Distr.: Intl.; Natl.
Budget Set: Oct. -Nov.
Personnel:
Wilson H. Pryne *(Pres & CEO)*
Phyllis Pryne *(Asst Controller)*
Brands & Products:
AFFCO
AIRSTAR
CALSTAR
DECOR WALL
FELTAN
FELTASTIC
FEUTRON
FIBERSTRUCT
FLEXIFLO
FLO-CLEAN
HEAT SHIELD
HUSHALON
IMPERIAL
MEDSTAR
MONK'S
MONKS FOOT QUALITY
MYSTO-GRIP
PROSTAR
SOLEIL
STARLINE
SUNLINE SLIPPER
WEATHERPAD

AMERICAN GILSONITE CO.
(Holding of Palladium Equity Partners, LLC)
350 Cambridge Ave Ste 350
Palo Alto, CA 94306
Tel.: (650) 233-7166
E-mail: info@americangilsonite.com
Web Site: www.americangilsonite.com
Approx. Number Employees: 70
Year Founded: 1888
Business Description:
Mining, Processing & Marketing of Gilsonite Hydrocarbon-Based Resin
S.I.C.: 1499; 2821
N.A.I.C.S.: 212399; 325211
Export
Media: 2-6-7-8-10-11-21
Distr.: Intl.; Natl.
Budget Set: Dec.
Personnel:
Sebastiano Scarampi *(Pres)*
Richard Long *(CFO)*
Bill Britton *(VP-Sls & Mktg)*
Ted Stevens *(VP-Sls & Mktg)*

AMERICAN LAUBSCHER CORPORATION
80 Finn Ct
Farmingdale, NY 11735-1107
Tel.: (631) 694-5900
Fax: (631) 293-0935
E-mail: sales@alcprecision.com
Web Site: www.alcprecision.com
E-Mail For Key Personnel:
Sales Director: sales@alcprecision.com
Approx. Number Employees: 50
Year Founded: 1950
Business Description:
Mfr. of Precision Components; Screw Machine Products; Jewel Bearings; Wire Guides; Ground Shafts
S.I.C.: 5084
N.A.I.C.S.: 423830
Import Export
Media: 2-4-7-10-11
Distr.: Intl.; Natl.
Budget Set: Mar.
Personnel:
Lloyd Miller *(Pres)*
Richard Fox *(CFO)*
Brands & Products:
ALC
Advertising Agency:
Smith & Dress Ltd.
432 W Main St
Huntington, NY 11743
Tel.: (631) 427-9333
Fax: (631) 427-9334

AMERICAN TANK & FABRICATING COMPANY
12314 Elmwood Ave
Cleveland, OH 44111-5906
Tel.: (216) 252-1500
Fax: (216) 252-4871
Toll Free: (800) 544-5316
E-mail: info@amtank.com
Web Site: www.amtank.com
Approx. Number Employees: 100
Year Founded: 1940
Business Description:
Mfr. & Retailer of Steel Plates
S.I.C.: 3443; 5051
N.A.I.C.S.: 332313; 423510
Media: 2-4-10-20-21-26
Distr.: Natl.
Personnel:
Terry Ripich *(CEO)*

AMETEK U.S. GAUGE
(Unit of AMETEK Electronic Instruments Group)
820 Pennsylvania Blvd
Feasterville Trevose, PA 19053
Tel.: (215) 257-6531
Fax: (215) 354-1802
E-mail: usg@ametekusg.com
Web Site: www.ametekusg.com
Sales Range: $25-49.9 Million
Approx. Number Employees: 60
Year Founded: 1904
Business Description:
Industrial Gauges Mfr
S.I.C.: 3621; 3823
N.A.I.C.S.: 335312; 334513
Export
Media: 2-4-7-10-11-20-26
Distr.: Natl.
Budget Set: Sept.
Personnel:
Bob Diloreto *(Mng Dir)*
Brands & Products:
HYDRA-LITE
SOLFRUNT
SUPERTHERM
Advertising Agency:
Lefton Company
100 Independence Mall W
Philadelphia, PA 19106-2399
Tel.: (215) 923-9600
Fax: (215) 351-4298

AMF BAKERY SYSTEMS
2115 W Laburnum Ave
Richmond, VA 23227-4315
Tel.: (804) 355-7961
Fax: (804) 355-1074
Toll Free: (800) 225-3771
E-mail: sales@amfbakery.com
Web Site: www.amfbakery.com
E-Mail For Key Personnel:
Sales Director: sales@amfbakery.com
Approx. Number Employees: 145
Year Founded: 1997
Business Description:
Industrial Bakery Equipment Mfr & Marketer
S.I.C.: 3556
N.A.I.C.S.: 333294
Export
Advertising Expenditures: $100,000
Media: 2-4-10-22
Distr.: Intl.; Natl.
Budget Set: Jan. -Feb.
Personnel:
Ken Newsome *(Pres)*
Edward Meise *(Exec VP)*
Tim Cook *(VP-Sls-Mktg)*
Margaret Shaia *(VP-Fin)*
Larry Gore *(Dir-Mktg & Sls)*
Daniel Gullerian *(Mgr-Sls)*

AMPCO-PITTSBURGH CORPORATION
600 Grant St Ste 4600
Pittsburgh, PA 15219-2700
Tel.: (412) 456-4400
Fax: (412) 456-4404
Web Site: www.ampcopgh.com
Approx. Sls.: $326,886,000
Approx. Number Employees: 1,264
Year Founded: 1929
Business Description:
Forged Hardened Steel Rolls & Centrifugal Pumps Mfr
S.I.C.: 3462; 5084; 7699
N.A.I.C.S.: 332111; 423830; 562991
Import Export
Advertising Expenditures: $250,000
Media: 1-2-4-7-8-10-18-19-26
Distr.: Intl.; Natl.
Budget Set: Oct.
Personnel:
Robert A. Paul *(Chm & CEO)*
Terrence W. Kenny *(Grp VP)*
Linda Sismondo *(Dir-Pension & Risk Mgmt)*

AMSCOMATIC, INC.
(Sub. of M&R Printing Equipment Inc.)
6200 Howard St
Niles, IL 60714
Tel.: (847) 967-4400
Fax: (847) 967-9664
Toll Free: (800) 962-8883
Approx. Sls.: $3,000,000
Approx. Number Employees: 50
Year Founded: 1989
Business Description:
Packaging Machinery Mfr
S.I.C.: 3861; 3555
N.A.I.C.S.: 333315; 333293
Export
Media: 2-10-17
Distr.: Natl.
Budget Set: Apr.
Personnel:
Rich Hoffmann *(Pres)*
Brands & Products:
AIRWELD-PE
AMSCOMATIC
OMNIBAGGER

ANDERSON INTERNATIONAL CORP.
6200 Harvard Ave
Cleveland, OH 44105-4861
Tel.: (216) 641-1112
Fax: (216) 641-0709
Fax: (216) 641-1571
Web Site: www.andersonintl.net
Approx. Number Employees: 85
Year Founded: 1888
Business Description:
Food Processing Equipment Mfr
S.I.C.: 3556; 3559
N.A.I.C.S.: 333294; 333220
Export
Media: 2-4-7-10-13
Distr.: Intl.; Natl.
Budget Set: Oct.
Personnel:
Len Trocono *(Pres)*
Rob Williams *(VP-Engrng)*
Vincent J. Vavpot *(Mgr-Worldwide Bus)*
Brands & Products:
ANDERSON
ANDERSON INTERNATIONAL

Key to Media (For complete agency information see *The Advertising Red Books-Agencies* edition):
1. Bus. Publs. 2. Cable T.V. 3. Catalogs & Directories. 4. Co-op Adv. 5. Consumer Mags. 6. D.M. to Bus. Estab.7. D.M. to Consumers 8. Daily Newsp. 9. Exhibits/Trade Shows 10. Foreign 11. Infomercial 12. Internet Adv.13. Multimedia 14. Network Radio 15. Network T.V. 16. Newsp. Distr. Mags. 17. Other 18. Outdoor (Posters, Transit) 19. Point of Purchase20. Premiums, Novelties 21. Product Samples 22. Special Events Mktg. 23. Spot Radio 24. Spot T.V. 25. Weekly Newsp. 26. Yellow Page Adv.

COPRA
EXPANDER
EXPANDER-DRYER
EXPANDER-EXTRUDER-COOKER
EXPELLER
HIVEX
SOLVEX

ANDERSON MACHINE SALES INC.
(Filed Ch 7 Bankruptcy #930582 on 08/06/09 in U.S. Bankruptcy Ct, Dist of NJ, Newark)
15 Spielman Rd
Fairfield, NJ 07004
Tel.: (201) 818-2797
Fax: (201) 818-0340
E-mail: amscapper@aol.com
Web Site: www.andersonmachinesales.com
Approx. Sls.: $6,200,000
Approx. Number Employees: 20
Business Description:
Packaging Machinery Mfr
S.I.C.: 5084
N.A.I.C.S.: 423830
Media: 2-4-7-10
Distr.: Natl.
Budget Set: Sept.

ANDERSON PRODUCTS
(Sub. of Weiler Corporation)
1 Weiler Dr
Cresco, PA 18326
Tel.: (508) 755-6100
Fax: (80) 072-94694
Toll Free: (800) 755-6101
E-mail: info@andersonproducts.com
Web Site: www.andersonproducts.com
Approx. Number Employees: 50
Year Founded: 1928
Business Description:
Industrial Power Brushes, Maintenance & Paint Brushes, Non-Woven Abrasives, Anderlex Non-Woven Abrasives, Maintenance Brushes
S.I.C.: 3991
N.A.I.C.S.: 339994
Import Export
Media: 2-4-7-10-21
Distr.: Natl.
Budget Set: Nov.
Brands & Products:
ANDERBOND
ANDERLEX
ANDERLITZ
ANDERSON
CYCLONE
CYCLONE XTREME

ANIXTER INTERNATIONAL INC.
2301 Patriot Blvd
Glenview, IL 60026-8020
Tel.: (224) 521-8000
Fax: (224) 521-8100
Toll Free: (800) 323-8166
E-mail: info@anixter.com
Web Site: www.anixter.com
Approx. Sls.: $5,472,100,000
Approx. Number Employees: 7,989
Year Founded: 1957
Business Description:
Global Distr of Communication & Security Products, Electrical & Electronic Wire & Cable & Fasteners
S.I.C.: 5063; 7382
N.A.I.C.S.: 423610; 561621
Export
Advertising Expenditures: $10,000,000
Media: 2-4-7-10-20
Distr.: Intl.; Natl.
Budget Set: Oct.
Personnel:
Samuel Zell *(Chm)*
Robert J. Eck *(Pres & CEO)*
Dennis J. Letham *(CFO & Exec VP-Fin)*
John A. Dul *(Gen Counsel, Sec & VP)*
Theodore A. Dosch *(Sr VP-Global Fin)*
Rodney A. Smith *(VP-HR)*
Tom Bubulka *(Mgr-Mktg)*
Brands & Products:
ANIXTER
ANIXTER INTERNATIONAL

ANIXTER PENTACON, INC.
(Sub. of Anixter International Inc.)
21123 Nordhoff St
Chatsworth, CA 91311
Tel.: (818) 727-7800
Fax: (713) 727-8037
Toll Free: (800) 554-4449
E-mail: information@pentacon-inc.com
Web Site: www.pentacon.com
Sales Range: $200-249.9 Million
Approx. Number Employees: 650
Year Founded: 1998
Business Description:
Fasteners & Small Parts Distr to Original Equipment Manufacturers
S.I.C.: 5085; 5063
N.A.I.C.S.: 423840; 423610
Import Export
Media: 2-4-7
Personnel:
Gary Conrad *(Exec VP)*
Theodore A. Dosch *(Sr VP-Global Fin)*
Melissa McKay *(Sr VP)*
Dennis Catallo *(Reg VP-Sls-Intl)*
Ron Webber *(VP-Mktg)*
Marty Martin *(Dir-Bus Processes)*

ANVIL ATTACHMENTS, LLC
261 Hwy 19
Slaughter, LA 70777-0216
Tel.: (225) 654-8222
Fax: (225) 654-7520
E-mail: sales@hawcomfg.com
Web Site: www.hawcomfg.com
E-Mail For Key Personnel:
Sales Director: sales@hawcomfg.com
Sales Range: $500-549.9 Million
Approx. Number Employees: 80
Year Founded: 1968
Business Description:
Mfr. of Bulk Material Clamshell Buckets, Grabs & Grapples
S.I.C.: 3531
N.A.I.C.S.: 333120
Advertising Expenditures: $350,000
Media: 1-2-4-7-9-10-13-20
Distr.: Natl.
Personnel:
John Craft *(Pres)*
Brands & Products:
ANVIL
DROTT
HAWCO
OWEN
PRO-LINE
WILLIAMS
YAUN

A.O. SMITH CORPORATION
11270 W Park Pl
Milwaukee, WI 53224-9508
Mailing Address:
PO Box 245008
Milwaukee, WI 53224
Tel.: (414) 359-4000
Fax: (414) 359-4115
E-mail: info@aosmith.com
Web Site: www.aosmith.com
Approx. Sls.: $1,489,300,000
Approx. Number Employees: 10,400
Year Founded: 1874
Business Description:
Residential & Commercial Water Heating Equipment & Protective Coatings Mfr
S.I.C.: 3559; 3433
N.A.I.C.S.: 332410; 333414
Advertising Expenditures: $42,000,000
Media: 2-4-5-6-7-8-9-10-18-19-20
Personnel:
Paul W. Jones *(Chm & CEO)*
Ajita G. Rajendra *(Pres & COO)*
John J. Kita *(CFO & Exec VP)*
Randall S. Bednar *(CIO & Sr VP)*
James F. Stern *(Gen Counsel, Sec & Exec VP)*
Christopher L. Mapes *(Exec VP)*
Wilfried Brouwer *(Sr VP-Asia)*
Robert J. Heideman *(Sr VP-Corp Tech)*
Mark A. Petrarca *(Sr VP-HR & Pub Affairs)*
Steve W. Rettler *(Sr VP-Corp Dev)*
Brands & Products:
BURKAY GENESIS
CENTURY
CONSERVATIONIST
CYCLONE XHE
DIA-SCAN
DURA MAX
DURA-POWER
DYNACLEAN
GLASCOTE
LEGEND 2000
MASTER-FIT
PERMAGLAS ULTRA COAT
POWER SHOT
PROMAX
R-16 PERMAFOAM
SEALED SHOT
SURE SHOT
TAKAGI
THERMOTRAP
UNIVERSAL
Advertising Agency:
AOS Ads
531 N 4th St
Tipp City, OH 45371
Tel.: (937) 667-2431
(Corp. & Indus. Adv.)

A.O. SMITH WATER PRODUCTS COMPANY
(Sub. of A.O. Smith Corporation)
500 Tennessee Waltz Pkwy
Ashland City, TN 37207
Tel.: (615) 792-4371
Fax: (800) 365-3292
Toll Free: (800) 365-0024
E-mail: webmaster@stateind.com
Web Site: www.stateind.com
E-Mail For Key Personnel:
Marketing Director: richg@stateind.com
Sales Range: $550-599.9 Million
Approx. Number Employees: 2,000
Year Founded: 1946
Business Description:
Mfr. of Water Heaters & Pump Tanks
S.I.C.: 3639; 3443
N.A.I.C.S.: 335228; 332313
Export
Personnel:
David Chisholm *(Brand Mgr-Effex)*
Advertising Agency:
Gish, Sherwood & Friends, Inc. (d/b/a GS&F)
4235 Hillsboro Pike
Nashville, TN 37215-3344
Tel.: (615) 385-1100
Fax: (615) 783-0500

APEX BROACHING SYSTEMS INC.
22862 Hoover Rd
Warren, MI 48089
Tel.: (586) 758-2626
Fax: (586) 758-2627
E-mail: apexbroach@apbsi.com
Web Site: www.apexbroach.com
Approx. Number Employees: 30
Year Founded: 1931
Business Description:
Broach Tools Mfr
S.I.C.: 3541; 3545
N.A.I.C.S.: 333512; 333515
Export
Media: 4-26
Distr.: Direct to Consumer; Intl.; Natl.
Budget Set: Oct.
Personnel:
Leonard Buntleon *(Pres)*

APEX WELDING INC.
(d/b/a Apex Bulk Handlers)
30 W Interstate St
Cleveland, OH 44146-4249
Tel.: (440) 232-6770
Fax: (440) 232-6747
Toll Free: (888) 822-2739
E-mail: apexwelding@att.net
Web Site: www.thomasregister.com
Approx. Number Employees: 15
Year Founded: 1946
Business Description:
Self Dumping Hoppers, Crane Dumping Buckets & Multidump Buckets Mfr
S.I.C.: 3444; 3443
N.A.I.C.S.: 332322; 332313
Media: 4-7-9-10-18-26
Distr.: Direct to Consumer; Natl.
Personnel:
D.J. Warner *(Pres)*
Brands & Products:
APEX BULK HANDLERS
TOW-N-DUMP

APPLIED WASTEWATER SYSTEMS
(Formerly F.E. Myers)
(Div. of Pentair, Inc.)
1101 Myers Pkwy
Ashland, OH 44805-1969
Tel.: (419) 289-1144
Fax: (419) 289-6658
E-mail: info@femyers.com
Web Site: www.femyers.com

Key to Media (For complete agency information see *The Advertising Red Books-Agencies* edition):
1. Bus. Publs. 2. Cable T.V. 3. Catalogs & Directories. 4. Co-op Adv. 5. Consumer Mags. 6. D.M. to Bus. Estab.7. D.M. to Consumers
8. Daily Newsp. 9. Exhibits/Trade Shows 10. Foreign 11. Infomercial 12. Internet Adv.13. Multimedia 14. Network Radio
15. Network T.V. 16. Newsp. Distr. Mags. 17. Other 18. Outdoor (Posters, Transit) 19. Point of Purchase20. Premiums, Novelties
21. Product Samples 22. Special Events Mktg. 23. Spot Radio 24. Spot T.V. 25. Weekly Newsp. 26. Yellow Page Adv.

Applied Wastewater Systems — (Continued)
Sales Range: $200-249.9 Million
Approx. Number Employees: 600
Year Founded: 1870
Business Description:
Water System, Industrial Pump, Waste Handling Product & Grey Iron Casting Mfr
S.I.C.: 3561; 3321
N.A.I.C.S.: 333911; 331511
Import Export
Media: 2-4-10
Distr.: Intl.; Natl.
Budget Set: Sept.
Personnel:
Bill Walsh *(Pres)*
Brands & Products:
MYERS

APTAR OF STRATFORD
(Formerly EMSAR Inc.)
(Sub. of AptarGroup, Inc.)
125 Access Rd
Stratford, CT 06615-7414
Tel.: (203) 377-8100
Fax: (203) 377-0500
Web Site: www.aptar.com
Sales Range: $100-124.9 Million
Approx. Number Employees: 240
Year Founded: 1950
Business Description:
Holding Company; Mfr of Aerosol Valves & Pump Sprayers
S.I.C.: 3494; 3089
N.A.I.C.S.: 332919; 326199
Export
Advertising Expenditures: $100,000
Media: 2-4-7-10-21-22
Distr.: Natl.
Budget Set: Nov.
Personnel:
Francesco Mascitelli *(Pres)*
Keith Kleps *(VP & Gen Mgr)*
Brian Connolly *(VP-Sls & Mktg)*
Des McEttrich *(Dir-Mktg)*
Mark Katz *(Dir-Matl)*

APW WYOTT FOOD SERVICE EQUIPMENT, INC.
(Sub. of Standex Cooking Solutions Group)
729 3rd Ave
Dallas, TX 75226
Tel.: (214) 421-7366
Fax: (214) 565-0976
Toll Free: (800) 527-2100
E-mail: info@apwwyott.com
Web Site: www.apwwyott.com
Sales Range: $50-74.9 Million
Approx. Number Employees: 180
Year Founded: 1967
Business Description:
Foodservice Equipment Mfr
S.I.C.: 3556; 3469
N.A.I.C.S.: 333294; 332214
Import Export
Media: 1-4-10-13
Distr.: Intl.; Natl.
Budget Set: Nov.
Personnel:
David Sebastianelli *(VP-Sls & Mktg)*
Brands & Products:
C RADIANT
CHAMPION COOK SERIES
CLASSIC
LOWERATOR
RACER
X-TREME
X-WAV

ARBURG, INC.
(Sub. of Arburg GmbH & Co.)
125 Rockwell Rd
Newington, CT 06111
Tel.: (860) 667-6500
Fax: (860) 667-6522
E-mail: usa@arburg.com
Web Site: www.arburg.com/com/US
Approx. Number Employees: 57
Year Founded: 1990
Business Description:
Plastic Processing Equipment; Injection Molding Machines Mfr
S.I.C.: 5084
N.A.I.C.S.: 423830
Import Export
Media: 2-10
Distr.: Natl.
Budget Set: Apr.
Personnel:
Friedrich Kanz *(Pres)*
Robert Arace *(CFO & VP)*
John Ward *(VP-Sls & Mktg)*
Marko Koellmer *(Mgr-Parts & Inside Sls)*
Brands & Products:
ARBURG

ARGO INTERNATIONAL CORPORATION
(Holding of Delcal Enterprises, Inc.)
140 Franklin St
New York, NY 10013
Tel.: (212) 431-1700
Fax: (212) 226-0694
Toll Free: (877) ARGOINT
E-mail: info@argointl.com
Web Site: www.argointl.com
Approx. Number Employees: 56
Year Founded: 1952
Business Description:
Distr. of Mechanical & Electrical Components, Renewal Parts & General Supplies for Marine & Industrial Use
S.I.C.: 5084; 5088
N.A.I.C.S.: 423830; 423860
Media: 2-10
Distr.: Natl.
Personnel:
John Calicchio *(Chm)*
Victor G. Ventura *(Pres)*

ARNOLD MACHINERY COMPANY
2975 West 2100 South PO Box 30020
Salt Lake City, UT 84119-1207
Tel.: (801) 972-4000
Fax: (801) 975-9749
Web Site: www.arnoldmachinery.com
E-Mail For Key Personnel:
Sales Director: slmhsales@arrnoldmachinery.com
Sales Range: $200-249.9 Million
Approx. Number Employees: 497
Year Founded: 1929
Business Description:
Industrial Equipment, Construction & Material Handling Equipment & Implements, Concrete Aggregate Equipment & Large Buckets, Shovels & Loaders Distr
S.I.C.: 5082; 5084
N.A.I.C.S.: 423810; 423830
Import
Media: 1-2-5-7-9-10-13-20-26
Distr.: Direct to Consumer; Reg.
Budget Set: Oct.
Personnel:
Alvin Richer *(Chm)*
Russ Fleming *(Pres & CEO)*
Kayden Bell *(CFO)*
Tom O'Byrne *(Corp VP, Pres-CE Div)*
Gary Bryden *(Div VP & Dir-Fin Svcs)*
Ken Kaylor *(Dir-Adv)*
Brands & Products:
ARNOLD
CUSTOMER SATISFACTION IS OUR ONLY POLICY
POWER STEMMER
SILVER SERVICE
UNDERGRADER

ARROW PNEUMATICS INC.
2111 W 21st St
Broadview, IL 60155-4627
Tel.: (708) 343-9595
Fax: (708) 343-1907
Web Site: www.arrowpneumatics.com
Approx. Number Employees: 100
Year Founded: 1914
Business Description:
Compressed Industrial Air Dryers Mfr
S.I.C.: 3585
N.A.I.C.S.: 333415
Import Export
Advertising Expenditures: $250,000
Media: 2-4-5-10
Distr.: Natl.
Budget Set: Jan.
Personnel:
Jerry Brown *(CEO)*
Brands & Products:
ARROW

ARROWHEAD CONVEYOR CORPORATION, INC.
3255 Medalist Dr
Oshkosh, WI 54902-7123
Mailing Address:
PO Box 2408
Oshkosh, WI 54903-2408
Tel.: (920) 235-5562
Fax: (920) 235-3638
E-mail: inquiry@arrowheadconveyor.com
Web Site: www.arrowheadconveyor.com
Approx. Number Employees: 310
Year Founded: 1998
Business Description:
Tabletop, Belt & Case-Handling Conveyors; Custom Steel & Stainless Steel Mfr
S.I.C.: 3535
N.A.I.C.S.: 333922
Export
Media: 1-4-6-8-10-20-26
Distr.: Natl.
Budget Set: May
Brands & Products:
ADVANTAGE
ARROWHEAD
ECLIPSE
HAWK
LYNX
'R' SERIES
TURBO
VIPER
'W' SERIES

ARTUS CORPORATION
201 S Dean St
Englewood, NJ 07631-4107
Mailing Address:
PO Box 511
Englewood, NJ 07631-0511
Tel.: (201) 568-1000
Fax: (201) 568-8865
E-mail: shims@artusworld.com
Web Site: www.artuscorp.com
Approx. Sls.: $6,435,000
Approx. Number Employees: 100
Year Founded: 1941
Business Description:
Plastic, Aluminum & Metal Shims Mfr
S.I.C.: 3089; 3444
N.A.I.C.S.: 326199; 332322
Media: 2-4-7-10-11-13
Distr.: Intl.; Natl.
Personnel:
Edwin Katzenstein *(Pres)*
Pinchas Katzenstein *(Comptroller)*
Brands & Products:
ARTUS
THE COLOR TELLS THE THICKNESS
SLITTER TOOLING

ASCO POWER TECHNOLOGIES, L.P.
(Sub. of Emerson Electric Co.)
50 Hanover Rd
Florham Park, NJ 07932-1503
Tel.: (973) 966-2000
Fax: (973) 966-5709
Toll Free: (800) 800-ASCO
E-mail: info-valve@asco.com
Web Site: www.ascovalves.com
Sales Range: $450-499.9 Million
Approx. Number Employees: 1,400
Year Founded: 1888
Business Description:
Fluid & Electric Power Control Mfr
S.I.C.: 3679
N.A.I.C.S.: 334419
Export
Media: 2-4-7-10-13-20
Distr.: Direct; Intl.; Natl.
Personnel:
Armand Visioli, Jr. *(Pres)*
Stan Pukash *(Dir-Intl Sls)*
Brian J. Phelan *(Dir-Mktg Svc)*
Brands & Products:
FIRETROL
POWERQUEST
SITEWEB
SYNCHROPOWER

ASHWORTH BROS., INC.
Ste 3 222 Milliken Blvd
Fall River, MA 02721-1623
Mailing Address:
222 Milliken Blvd Ste 7
Fall River, MA 02721-1623
Tel.: (508) 674-4693
Fax: (508) 675-9622
Toll Free: (800) 682-4594
E-mail: ashworth@ashworth.com
Web Site: www.ashworth.com
Approx. Number Employees: 450
Year Founded: 1894
Business Description:
Mfr. of Metal & Plastic Conveyor Belting & Conveyor Systems
S.I.C.: 3535; 3552
N.A.I.C.S.: 333922; 333292
Export
Media: 2-4-7-10-11

Key to Media (For complete agency information see *The Advertising Red Books-Agencies* edition):
1. Bus. Publs. 2. Cable T.V. 3. Catalogs & Directories. 4. Co-op Adv. 5. Consumer Mags. 6. D.M. to Bus. Estab.7. D.M. to Consumers 8. Daily Newsp. 9. Exhibits/Trade Shows 10. Foreign 11. Infomercial 12. Internet Adv.13. Multimedia 14. Network Radio 15. Network T.V. 16. Newsp. Distr. Mags. 17. Other 18. Outdoor (Posters, Transit) 19. Point of Purchase20. Premiums, Novelties 21. Product Samples 22. Special Events Mktg. 23. Spot Radio 24. Spot T.V. 25. Weekly Newsp. 26. Yellow Page Adv.

Distr.: Intl.; Natl.
Personnel:
Vincent Moretti *(Pres)*
Brands & Products:
ADVANTAGE
THE ADVANTAGE
ASHWORTH
BAKING BAND
CB5 BAKING BAND
CHEMGUARD
CHEMGUARD PRESTOFLEX
CLEARTRAC
EZ CLEAN
FATIGUE RESISTANT OMNIFLEX
FUSION GRID
HD TOTE-CHAIN
HEAVY DUTY TOTE-CHAIN
HYBRI-FLEX
HYBRI-GRID
KPAD
MEGA-FLEX
OMNI-FLEX
OMNI-GRID
OMNI-LITE
OMNI-PRO
OMNI-TOUGH
PRESTOFLEX
REDUCED RADIUS FUSION GRID
REDUCED RADIUS HYBRI-GRID
REDUCED RADIUS OMNI-GRID
SMALL RADIUS OMNI-FLEX
SMALL RADIUS OMNI-GRID
SPACE SAVER OMNI-GRID
SUPER SMALL RADIUS OMNI-GRID
TRUSEAT
WE KEEP YOU RUNNING

ATI CASTING SERVICE
(Unit of Allegheny Technologies Incorporated)
300 Philadelphia St
La Porte, IN 46350-3927
Mailing Address:
PO Box 488
La Porte, IN 46352-0488
Tel.: (219) 362-1000
Fax: (219) 362-4413
Web Site: www.castingservice.com
Sales Range: $50-74.9 Million
Approx. Number Employees: 200
Business Description:
Machines & Metals Designer & Mfr
S.I.C.: 3321
N.A.I.C.S.: 331511
Media: 4
Distr.: Natl.
Budget Set: Dec.
Personnel:
David R. Neil *(Pres)*

ATLAS COPCO COMPTEC LLC
(Sub. of Atlas Copco Energas Gmbh)
46 School Rd
Voorheesville, NY 12186-9608
Tel.: (518) 765-3344
Fax: (518) 765-3357
Toll Free: (800) 334-1237
Web Site: www.atlascopco.com
Approx. Number Employees: 200
Business Description:
Mfr. of Custom-Built Turbomachinery
S.I.C.: 3563
N.A.I.C.S.: 333912
Import Export
Media: 2-7-10-20
Distr.: Direct to Consumer; Natl.
Budget Set: Jan.
Personnel:
Robert Radimecky *(Gen Mgr)*
Alan Keybart *(Mgr-Mktg)*

ATMI, INC.
7 Commerce Dr
Danbury, CT 06810-4131
Tel.: (203) 794-1100
Fax: (203) 792-8040
Toll Free: (800) 766-2681
E-mail: info@atmi.com
Web Site: www.atmi.com
E-Mail For Key Personnel:
Public Relations: pr@atmi.com
Approx. Rev.: $367,256,000
Approx. Number Employees: 773
Year Founded: 1986
Business Description:
Semiconductor Materials & Packaging Products Mfr
S.I.C.: 3674; 2671; 2899
N.A.I.C.S.: 334413; 322221; 325998
Export
Media: 4-10-11-22
Personnel:
Douglas A. Neugold *(Chm, Pres & CEO)*
Eugene Gene Banucci *(Chm)*
Timothy C. Carlson *(CFO, Treas & Exec VP)*
Ellen Harmon *(Chief Legal Officer, Chief Compliance Officer, Exec VP & Sec)*
Lawrence H. Dubois *(CTO & Sr VP)*
Tod A. Higinbotham *(Exec VP & Gen Mgr-Microelectronics)*
Mario Philips *(Gen Mgr-Life Sciences & Sr VP)*
Paul Hohlstein *(Sr VP-Supply Chain & Ops)*
Brands & Products:
3CHEM
ATMI
AUTOCLEAN
BAG-IN-A-BOTTLE
BAG-IN-A-CAN
BAG-IN-A-DRUM
BULKFILL
CDO
CLUSTERBORON
CLUSTERCARBON
CMPLICITY
GUARDIAN
HIGH PRODUCTIVITY DEVELOPMENT
MINIBULK
NEWFORM
NOVAPURE
NOVASAFE
NOWPAK
NOWTRAK
PDMPAK
PLANARCHEM
PLANARCLEAN
REGENSI
RPM
SAGE
SDS
SMARTPROBE
THESEUS
ULTRAPUR
UNICHEM
VAC
VECTOR
VIAFORM

THE AUBURN MANUFACTURING COMPANY
29 Stack St
Middletown, CT 06457-2265
Tel.: (860) 346-6677
Fax: (860) 346-1334
Toll Free: (800) GASKETS
E-mail: info@auburn-mfg.com
Web Site: www.auburn-mfg.com
Sales Range: $10-24.9 Million
Approx. Number Employees: 27
Year Founded: 1925
Business Description:
Sealing Components, Bushings, Gaskets, Packings, O-Rings, Rod Wipers, Shims & Spacers
S.I.C.: 3053; 3069
N.A.I.C.S.: 339991; 326299
Media: 2-4-13-19-21-26
Distr.: Intl.; Natl.
Budget Set: Oct. -Nov.
Personnel:
Gary Mittelman *(VP-Adv)*
Brands & Products:
AUBURN
PLASTI-FLEX
PORON
STRIP-N-STICK

AUSTIN SEMICONDUCTOR, INC.
(Sub. of PMC Global)
8701 Cross Park Dr
Austin, TX 78754-4580
Tel.: (512) 339-1188
Fax: (512) 339-6641
Web Site:
www.austinsemiconductor.com
Approx. Number Employees: 68
Year Founded: 1988
Business Description:
Semiconductor Mfr
S.I.C.: 3674
N.A.I.C.S.: 334413
Import Export
Personnel:
Bobby Aleman *(Reg Mgr-Sls)*
Karen Looney *(Sls Mgr)*
Advertising Agency:
Door Number 3
1050 E 11th St Ste 250
Austin, TX 78702
Tel.: (512) 391-1773
Fax: (512) 391-1926

AUTO CRANE COMPANY
(Sub. of Ramsey Industries Inc.)
4707 N Mingo Rd
Tulsa, OK 74117-5904
Mailing Address:
PO Box 580697
Tulsa, OK 74158-0697
Tel.: (918) 836-0463
Fax: (918) 834-5979
Telex: 158108
E-mail: info@autocrane.com
Web Site: www.autocrane.com
Year Founded: 1958
Business Description:
Truck Mounted Field Service Electric & Hydraulic Telescopic Cranes, Hydraulic Articulating Cranes, Crane Service Bodies, & Hydraulic Air Compressors
S.I.C.: 3537; 3711
N.A.I.C.S.: 333924; 336211
Export
Media: 2-4-5-10
Distr.: Natl.
Personnel:
Michael Gelsthorpe *(Reg Sls Mgr)*
Bryan Keller *(Reg Sls Mgr)*
Brands & Products:
SMART CRANE
TITAN

AUTOMATIC EQUIPMENT CORPORATION
(d/b/a AEC Magnetics)
4699 Inter State Dr
Cincinnati, OH 45246
Tel.: (513) 771-3833
Fax: (513) 326-3614
Fax: (800) 635-3955
Toll Free: (800) 635-3954
E-mail: aec@aecmagnetics.com
Web Site: www.aecmagnetics.com
Sales Range: $25-49.9 Million
Approx. Number Employees: 19
Year Founded: 1961
Business Description:
Electro Magnets, Lifting Equipment, Permanent Magnetic Sweepers, Magnetic Assemblies Mfr
S.I.C.: 3499; 3537
N.A.I.C.S.: 332999; 333924
Import Export
Advertising Expenditures: $360,000
Bus. Publs.: 15%; Catalogs & Directories: 20%; D.M. to Bus. Estab.: 50%; Internet Adv.: 15%
Distr.: Direct to Consumer; Intl.; Natl.; Reg.
Budget Set: Sept.
Personnel:
William Klaus *(Pres)*
Michael Sprague *(Exec VP & Mgr-Traffic)*

AUTOMATION DEVICES, INC.
7050 W Ridge Rd
Fairview, PA 16415-2099
Tel.: (814) 474-5561
Fax: (814) 474-2131
Web Site: www.autodev.com
E-Mail For Key Personnel:
Sales Director: sales@autodev.com
Approx. Number Employees: 40
Year Founded: 1947
Business Description:
Automation Equipment Mfr
S.I.C.: 3569; 3625
N.A.I.C.S.: 333999; 335314
Export
Media: 2-7-9-13
Distr.: Direct to Consumer; Intl.; Natl.
Budget Set: Oct.
Personnel:
Kevin Smith *(Pres)*
Larry V. Smith *(CEO)*
Brands & Products:
AUTOMATION DEVICES
CENTRIFEED
FORK RHINO
JET-TRON
MUFFLE MODULE
SENSI-TRON

AUTORAD, INC.
(Sub. of Alfa Laval AB)
(d/b/a/ Standard Refrigeration Co.)
2050 N Ruby St
Melrose Park, IL 60160
Tel.: (708) 345-5400
Fax: (708) 345-3513

Key to Media (For complete agency information see *The Advertising Red Books-Agencies* edition):
1. Bus. Publs. 2. Cable T.V. 3. Catalogs & Directories. 4. Co-op Adv. 5. Consumer Mags. 6. D.M. to Bus. Estab.7. D.M. to Consumers 8. Daily Newsp. 9. Exhibits/Trade Shows 10. Foreign 11. Infomercial 12. Internet Adv.13. Multimedia 14. Network Radio 15. Network T.V. 16. Newsp. Distr. Mags. 17. Other 18. Outdoor (Posters, Transit) 19. Point of Purchase20. Premiums, Novelties 21. Product Samples 22. Special Events Mktg. 23. Spot Radio 24. Spot T.V. 25. Weekly Newsp. 26. Yellow Page Adv.

Autorad, Inc. — (Continued)

E-mail: customerservice@alfalaval.com
Web Site: www.stanref.com
Approx. Rev.: $36,500,000
Approx. Number Employees: 185
Year Founded: 1922
Business Description:
Refrigerants
S.I.C.: 3585; 3559
N.A.I.C.S.: 333415; 332410
Media: 4

AVERY WEIGH-TRONIX CANADA

(Sub. of Avery Weigh-Tronix, Inc.)
217 Brunswick Blvd
Pointe-Claire, QC H9R 4R7, Canada
Tel.: (514) 695-0380
Fax: (514) 695-0385
Toll Free: (800) 561-9461
Telex: 5 822620
E-mail: canadainfo@awtxglobal.com
Web Site: www.weigh-tronix.ca
E-Mail For Key Personnel:
President: tcassidy@weigh.tronix-ca.com
Sales Range: $25-49.9 Million
Approx. Number Employees: 100
Year Founded: 1998
Business Description:
Sales of Scales & Weighing Systems
S.I.C.: 3823
N.A.I.C.S.: 334513
Import
Media: 2-4-7-10-19-26
Distr.: Intl.; Natl.
Budget Set: Mar.

AVERY WEIGH-TRONIX, INC.

(Sub. of Illinois Tool Works Inc.)
1000 Armstrong Dr
Fairmont, MN 56031
Tel.: (507) 238-4461
Fax: (507) 238-8258
Toll Free: (800) 368-2039
E-mail: jfenrich@awtxglobal.com
Web Site: www.wtxweb.com
Sales Range: $200-249.9 Million
Approx. Number Employees: 400
Year Founded: 1971
Business Description:
Industrial & Retail Weighing Systems Mfr
S.I.C.: 3596; 5083
N.A.I.C.S.: 333997; 423820
Import Export
Advertising Expenditures: $900,000
Media: 1-2-4-7-10-17-20
Distr.: Intl.; Natl.
Budget Set: Feb. -Mar.
Personnel:
Ross Hunwardsen *(CEO)*
Peggi Trimble *(Mktg Dir)*
Jean Ann Fenrich *(Mgr-Mktg)*
Don Halbert *(Mgr-Indus Products)*
Brands & Products:
B806
BM-75
BRIDGEMONT
HARMONIZER
LP 2844
PC-220
PC-802
PC-805
PC-820
PC-821
PROBENCH
QC3265 L CAPACITY
QC3265 M CAPACITY
QC3275 L CAPACITY
QUARTZELL
RCU WI-125
RD-125
RD-4100/6100
SP-100
STEEL BRIDGE
TM-234 IMPACT
TM-U590
VERI TEST
WEIGH BAR
WI-105
WI-125 GROUP
WI-125 LED
WI-127
WI-130
WI-150 LOW POWER
WI-152 BATTERY
WP-233 IMPACT
WP-234 IMPACT
Advertising Agency:
Next Communications
10249 Yellow Circle Dr
Minnetonka, MN 55343
Tel.: (952) 934-8220
Fax: (952) 934-2375

A.W. CHESTERTON COMPANY

500 Unicorn Pk
Woburn, MA 01801
Tel.: (781) 438-7000
Fax: (781) 481-2500
E-mail: info@chesterton.com
Web Site: www.chesterton.com
Approx. Number Employees: 500
Year Founded: 1884
Business Description:
Mechanical Packing Seals, Pumps & Special Technical Products
S.I.C.: 3053; 2851
N.A.I.C.S.: 339991; 325510
Media: 2-4-10-17-18-20
Personnel:
Brian O'Donnell *(Pres & CEO)*
Ronald Maxwell *(CFO & VP)*
Tom Meier *(VP-IT)*
Ralph Merullo *(Mgr-Mktg Svcs)*
Brands & Products:
10K
1400
155
156
1724
180 SEAL
221
225
255
280
380
380 MACHINERY COOLANT
442
5K
6K
723
772
785
800
860
891
8K
BELT-FLO
CHESCO
CHESTERTON
DUOSEAL
GLOBAL SOLUTIONS, LOCAL SERVICE.
GOLDEND
INNERLUBE
MACHINERY COOLANT
MILL PACK
MILL PACK 1730
MONOSEAL
MULTI-LON
ONE
PARACHUTE
PEEL&SEAL
RUST TRANSFORMER
RUSTSOLVO
SELF-ALIGNING STATIONARY
SELF-CENTERING LOCK RING
SPIRALTRAC
SPRAFLEX
SPRAGRIP
SPRASOLVO
STEEL TRAP
SUPER GRAPHITE PACKING
SUPER-LON
SUPER MONOSEAL
SUPER WIPER
SUPERCUP
UNIFIED SEAL ALIGNMENT

AWISCO NY CORPORATION

55-15 43rd St
Maspeth, NY 11378
Tel.: (718) 786-7788
Fax: (718) 361-1855
Toll Free: (800) 834-1925
E-mail: info@awisco.net
Web Site: www.awisco.com
Approx. Number Employees: 60
Business Description:
Whslr of Welding Machinery & Equipment
S.I.C.: 5084; 5169
N.A.I.C.S.: 423830; 424690
Media: 10
Personnel:
Lloyd Robinson *(Pres)*
Victor Fuhrman *(CIO & VP-Mktg)*
Dennis Dicocchi *(VP-Sls)*

A.Y. MCDONALD MANUFACTURING CO.

4800 Chavenelle Rd
Dubuque, IA 52002-2631
Mailing Address:
PO Box 508
Dubuque, IA 52004-0508
Tel.: (563) 583-7311
Fax: (563) 588-0720
Telex: 43-9020 AYMCD DUQU
E-mail: sales@aymcdonald.com
Web Site: www.aymcdonald.com
E-Mail For Key Personnel:
Sales Director: sales@aymcdonald.com
Sales Range: $150-199.9 Million
Approx. Number Employees: 320
Year Founded: 1856
Business Description:
Plumbing Fixture & Valve Mfr
S.I.C.: 3432; 3491; 3561
N.A.I.C.S.: 332913; 332911; 333911
Import Export
Advertising Expenditures: $300,000
Media: 2-4-5-7-9-10-20-21-23-24-25-26
Distr.: Intl.; Natl.
Budget Set: Dec.
Personnel:
Mike McDonald *(Pres & CEO)*
L.J. Sherman *(Sr VP)*
Brands & Products:
GREENTOP
MAC-PAK
MCDONALD
SCOT-PAK

AZO, INC.

(Sub. of AZO GmbH & Co. KG)
4445 Malone Rd
Memphis, TN 38118-1070
Tel.: (901) 794-9480
Fax: (901) 794-9934
E-mail: info@azo.com
Web Site: www.azo.com
E-Mail For Key Personnel:
President: bmoore@azo.com
Marketing Director: rmalone@azo.com
Sales Director: bnesti@azo.com
Approx. Number Employees: 65
Business Description:
Materials Handling Machinery Mfr
S.I.C.: 5084; 5045
N.A.I.C.S.: 423830; 425110
Media: 2-10
Brands & Products:
AZO BIG BAG FILLING SYSTEM
AZO BULK BAG UNLOADING SYSTEM
AZO COMPONENTER
AZO PROCESS CONTROLS
AZO SCREENERS
COMPONENTER
DOSIBOX
PRODUCTIVITY THROUGH TECHNOLOGY

B&H MANUFACTURING COMPANY

(d/b/a B&H Labeling Systems)
3461 Roeding Rd
Ceres, CA 95307
Tel.: (209) 537-5785
Fax: (209) 537-6854
E-mail: marketing@bhlabeling.com
Web Site: www.bhlabeling.com
Approx. Number Employees: 150
Year Founded: 1969
Business Description:
Labeling Machines Mfr
S.I.C.: 3565
N.A.I.C.S.: 333993
Media: 4-10
Personnel:
Bob Adamson *(VP-Sls)*
Lee Smith *(Mgr-Sls)*
Brands & Products:
COMPUTERIZED REGISTRATION SYSTEM
CRS
ENDURA
MARATHON
PRO-WATCH
RCO
SMARTDRIVE

BADGER DAYLIGHTING LTD.

715 5th Ave SW Ste 2820
Calgary, AB T2P 2X6, Canada
Tel.: (403) 264-8500
Fax: (403) 228-9773
Toll Free: (800) 465-4273
E-mail: corporate@badgerinc.com
Web Site: www.badgerinc.com

Key to Media (For complete agency information see *The Advertising Red Books-Agencies* edition):
1. Bus. Publs. 2. Cable T.V. 3. Catalogs & Directories. 4. Co-op Adv. 5. Consumer Mags. 6. D.M. to Bus. Estab.7. D.M. to Consumers
8. Daily Newsp. 9. Exhibits/Trade Shows 10. Foreign 11. Infomercial 12. Internet Adv.13. Multimedia 14. Network Radio
15. Network T.V. 16. Newsp. Distr. Mags. 17. Other 18. Outdoor (Posters, Transit) 19. Point of Purchase20. Premiums, Novelties
21. Product Samples 22. Special Events Mktg. 23. Spot Radio 24. Spot T.V. 25. Weekly Newsp. 26. Yellow Page Adv.

Approx. Rev.: $132,092,903
Approx. Number Employees: 112
Year Founded: 1992
Business Description:
Excavating Services
S.I.C.: 1381; 1389
N.A.I.C.S.: 213111; 213112
Media: 10-17
Personnel:
George Watson *(Exec Chm)*
George Watson *(Trustees:)*
Tor Wilson *(Pres & CEO)*
David Calnan *(Partner)*
Greg Kelly *(CFO & VP)*
Brands & Products:
BADGER DAYLIGHTING

BADGER EQUIPMENT COMPANY
(Sub. of Manitex International, Inc.)
217 Patenaude Dr
Winona, MN 55987-1463
Tel.: (507) 454-1563
Fax: (507) 453-6441
Toll Free: (800) 533-8013
E-mail: tlg@badgerequipment.com
Web Site: www.badgerequipment.com
Sales Range: $25-49.9 Million
Approx. Number Employees: 50
Year Founded: 1945
Business Description:
Excavating Equipment, Hydraulic RT Cranes, Burro R.R. Locomotive Cranes & C-F Under Hook Lifters Mfr
S.I.C.: 3531
N.A.I.C.S.: 333120
Export
Media: 2-7-10
Distr.: Natl.
Budget Set: Aug.
Personnel:
Lael E. Boren *(Pres)*
Rick Laehn *(Dir-Pur)*
Paul Isakson *(Mgr-Parts & Waranty)*
Brands & Products:
BADGER
BURRO
C-F
WRIST-O-TWIST

BADGER TRANSFORMER COMPANY, INC.
7939 W Tower Ave
Milwaukee, WI 53223
Tel.: (414) 362-4441
Fax: (414) 362-4440
E-mail: info@badgertransformer.com
Web Site:
www.badgertransformer.com
Sales Range: $25-49.9 Million
Approx. Number Employees: 20
Business Description:
Electromagnetic Products Mfr
S.I.C.: 3677
N.A.I.C.S.: 334416
Personnel:
Richard K. Noel *(Pres)*
Advertising Agency:
Celtic, Inc.
330 S Executive Dr Ste 206
Brookfield, WI 53005-4215
Tel.: (262) 789-7630
Fax: (262) 789-9454

BAKER ATLAS
(Sub. of Baker Hughes Incorporated)
2001 Rankin Rd
Houston, TX 77073-5100
Mailing Address:
PO Box 1407
Houston, TX 77251-1407
Tel.: (713) 625-4200
Fax: (713) 625-4525
Telex: 6717084 WAIAWS
E-mail: info@bakeratlas.com
Sales Range: $450-499.9 Million
Approx. Number Employees: 3,000
Business Description:
Wireline Logging & Completion Services
S.I.C.: 7353
N.A.I.C.S.: 532412
Export
Advertising Expenditures: $1,000,000
Media: 2-10-22
Distr.: Intl.
Personnel:
Stephen K. Ellison *(Pres & VP)*
Shraga Wolf *(VP-Tech & Mfg)*
Brands & Products:
ACOUSTILOG
ALPHA JET
ARRAY ACOUSTILOG
ATLAS
ATLAS WIRELINE SERVICES
AZIMUTH DIPFRAC
BAL
BCN
CBIL
CHESS II
CHLORINLOG
CLASS
CLS II
COREGUN
DATREX
DENSILOG
DIKONE
DIPLOG
DPIL
DRB
ECLIPS
ELECTROLOG
EMO
EPILOG
FRACLOG
GAMMA-GUN
GOLDEN JET
HORIZON
HYDROLOG
INDUCTION ELECTROLOG
JUMBO JET
LOGSTAR
MAGNA-TECTOR
MCCULLOUGH
MFP
MICRO ACOUSTILOG
MINILOG
NDT
NGP
OMNIKONE
OPTIMA
PDK-100
PETRO-TECH
PRISM
PVT-EXPERT
PROLOG
SCINTILLOMETER
SELECTFIRE
SILVER JET
SPECTRALOG
SPRING TECTOR
STL
STRATA DIP
STRATAGON
STRATALOGIK
TBRT
TCP
TRI-DET
TRI MAG
TTRM
ULTRASONIC DIPLOG
VERTILOC
VISION
WDS
WELL DATA SYSTEM
Z-DENSILOG

BAKER HUGHES INCORPORATED
2929 Allen Pkwy Ste 2100
Houston, TX 77019
Mailing Address:
PO Box 4740
Houston, TX 77210-4740
Tel.: (713) 439-8600
Fax: (713) 439-8699
Toll Free: (888) 408-4244
E-mail: info@bakerhughes.com
Web Site: www.bakerhughes.com
Approx. Rev.: $14,414,000,000
Approx. Number Employees: 53,100
Year Founded: 1986
Business Description:
Products & Services for the Oil, Gas, Mining & Processing Industries
S.I.C.: 3533; 2869
N.A.I.C.S.: 333132; 325110
Import Export
Advertising Expenditures: $2,000,000
Media: 1-2-4-7-10-13-24
Distr.: Natl.
Budget Set: Oct.
Personnel:
Chadwick C. Deaton *(Chm & CEO)*
Martin S. Craighead *(Pres & COO)*
Peter A. Ragauss *(CFO & Sr VP)*
Clifton Triplett *(CIO)*
Christopher P. Beaver *(Pres-Oil Tools & VP)*
John A. O'Donnell *(Pres-Western Hemisphere Ops & VP)*
Paul S. Butero *(Pres-US Land)*
Belgacem Chariag *(Pres-Eastern Hemisphere)*
F. Mike Davis *(Pres-Canada)*
Darrell C. Howard *(Pres-Integrated Ops Org)*
Derek Mathieson *(Pres-Product Lines & Tech)*
Nelson Ney *(Pres-Latin America)*
Gary G. Rich *(Pres-Europe)*
Richard L. Williams *(Pres-Mexico)*
Alan R. Crain Jr. *(Gen Counsel & Sr VP)*
Didier Charreton *(VP-HR)*
Jim Lockwood *(Head-Functional Process-Sls & Mktg IT)*
John Thompson *(Sr Mgr-Mktg)*
Scott A. Bieber *(Mgr-Mktg-Downstream Chemicals)*
Brands & Products:
BAKER HUGHES
Advertising Agency:
GyroHSR
60 Madison Ave Ste 1101
New York, NY 10010
Tel.: (212) 915-2490
Fax: (212) 915-2491

BAKER HUGHES INTEQ
(Sub. of Baker Hughes Incorporated)
2001 Rankin Rd
Houston, TX 77073-5114
Mailing Address:
PO Box 670968
Houston, TX 77267-0968
Tel.: (713) 625-4200
Fax: (713) 625-5800
E-mail: info@bakerhughes.com
Web Site: www.bakerhughes.com
Sales Range: $450-499.9 Million
Approx. Number Employees: 1,800
Year Founded: 1934
Business Description:
Oil Field Machinery & Equipment Mfr
S.I.C.: 3533
N.A.I.C.S.: 333132
Import Export
Advertising Expenditures: $250,000
Media: 4-6-10
Distr.: Intl.; Natl.
Budget Set: Sept.
Personnel:
Paul S. Butero *(Pres-US Land)*
Ron Bitto *(Dir-Employee Comm)*
Brands & Products:
ACCU-TRAK
ACOUSTIC PROPERTIES EXPLORER
AUTOTRAK
BALLASET
COPILOT
COREGARD
COREMASTER
DAAB
DMWD
DOT
DRILLING DYNAMICS
EGGBEATER
HEVI-HITTER
HYDRO-LIFT
INTEGRAL BLADE
JAR KING
KING CUTTER
MOSAIC
NAVI-DRILL
NAVI-TRAK
NORTRAK
PIGGYBACK
POWER-TORQUE
PRESSTEQ
PRESSURE CORING
RIGS
RUBBER SLEEVE
SEEKER
SHOCK-EZE
SPEED-MILL
TESTRAK
VERTITRAK
VSS
WHIRLBUSTER

BAKERS PRIDE OVEN COMPANY
(Sub. of Standex Cooking Solutions Group)
145 Huguenot St
New Rochelle, NY 10801-6906
Tel.: (914) 576-0200
Fax: (914) 576-0605
E-mail: sales@bakerspride.com
Web Site: www.bakerspride.com
E-Mail For Key Personnel:
Sales Director: sales@bakerspride.com
Sales Range: $50-74.9 Million
Approx. Number Employees: 10

Key to Media (For complete agency information see *The Advertising Red Books-Agencies* edition):
1. Bus. Publs. 2. Cable T.V. 3. Catalogs & Directories. 4. Co-op Adv. 5. Consumer Mags. 6. D.M. to Bus. Estab.7. D.M. to Consumers 8. Daily Newsp. 9. Exhibits/Trade Shows 10. Foreign 11. Infomercial 12. Internet Adv.13. Multimedia 14. Network Radio 15. Network T.V. 16. Newsp. Distr. Mags. 17. Other 18. Outdoor (Posters, Transit) 19. Point of Purchase20. Premiums, Novelties 21. Product Samples 22. Special Events Mktg. 23. Spot Radio 24. Spot T.V. 25. Weekly Newsp. 26. Yellow Page Adv.

Bakers Pride Oven Company — (Continued)

Business Description:
Commercial Baking, Cooking & Pizza Equipment
S.I.C.: 3589; 3556
N.A.I.C.S.: 333319; 333294
Media: 4
Personnel:
Dennis Molloy *(Mgr-Matls)*
Brands & Products:
COOKLINE
CYCLONE
DANTE
DUALAIR
HEARTHBAKE
IL FORNO CLASSICO
SUPERDECK
ULTIMATE OUTDOOR

BALDOR ELECTRIC COMPANY

(Sub. of ABB Inc.)
5711 RS Boreham Jr St
Fort Smith, AR 72901-8301
Mailing Address:
PO Box 2400
Fort Smith, AR 72902-2400
Tel.: (479) 646-4711
Fax: (479) 648-5792
E-mail: cdtechsupp@baldor.com
Web Site: www.baldor.com
Approx. Sls.: $1,524,072,000
Approx. Number Employees: 7,181
Year Founded: 1920
Business Description:
Energy-Efficient Electric Motors & Electronic Drives Designer, Mfr & Marketer
S.I.C.: 3621; 3549; 3559; 3568; 3589; 3625
N.A.I.C.S.: 335312; 333298; 333319; 333518; 333613; 335314
Export
Advertising Expenditures: $1,000,000
Media: 1-2-5-10-11-26
Distr.: Intl.; Natl.
Budget Set: Nov.
Personnel:
Ronald E. Tucker *(Pres & COO)*
George E. Moschner *(CFO)*
Randy L. Colip *(Exec VP-Sls)*
Gene J. Hagedorn *(Exec VP-Matls)*
Edward L. Ralston *(Exec VP-Bus Integration)*
Ronald Wayne Thurman *(Exec VP-Engrg)*
Randy G. Waltman *(Exec VP-Mfg)*
Jason W. Green *(VP-HR)*
Tracy L. Long *(VP-Mktg)*
John A. McFarland *(Exec Chm & Mgr-Integration)*
Brands & Products:
BALDOR
BALDOR SMARTMOTOR
DIRTY DUTY
EUROFLEX
FLEX DRIVE II
HYCORE
INVERTER DRIVE MOTOR
INVERTER SPIKE RESISTANT
MATCHED PERFORMANCE
MICROFLEX
MINT
MINTDRIVE
MOD EXPRESS
MOTIFLEX
NEXTMOVE
OPTIGEN
OUR JOB IS MAKING YOURS EASIER
POW'R GARD
PROSPEC
STANDARD-E
SUPER-E
VECTOR DRIVE
WASHDOWN DUTY
Advertising Agency:
The Communications Group
400 W Capitol Ste 1391
Little Rock, AR 72201
Tel.: (501) 376-8722
Fax: (501) 376-9405
(Business-to-Business Advertising)

BALDWIN FILTERS

(Div. of CLARCOR, Inc.)
4400 E Hwy 30
Kearney, NE 68847
Tel.: (308) 234-1951
Fax: (308) 233-9424
Toll Free: (800) 828-4453
E-mail: info@baldwinfilter.com
Web Site: www.clarcor.com
Sales Range: $250-299.9 Million
Approx. Number Employees: 800
Year Founded: 1936
Business Description:
Mfr. of Filters for Internal Combustion Engines
S.I.C.: 3714; 3564
N.A.I.C.S.: 336399; 333412
Export
Advertising Expenditures: $1,500,000
Media: 2-4-7-8-10-13-19-20
Distr.: Intl.; Natl.
Budget Set: June
Personnel:
Sam Ferrise *(Pres)*
Kevin Connolly *(VP-Mktg)*
Brands & Products:
BALDWIN
CASITE
DAHL
HASTINGS

BALDWIN TECHNOLOGY COMPANY, INC.

2 Trap Falls Rd Ste 402
Shelton, CT 06484-4616
Tel.: (203) 402-1000
Fax: (203) 402-5500
E-mail: info@globaltec.co.uk
Web Site: www.baldwintech.com
Approx. Sls.: $151,818,000
Approx. Number Employees: 592
Year Founded: 1918
Business Description:
Printing Press Equipment Mfr
S.I.C.: 3555
N.A.I.C.S.: 333293
Export
Advertising Expenditures: $147,000
Media: 2-4-10-22
Distr.: Natl.
Personnel:
Gerald A. Nathe *(Chm)*
Mark T. Becker *(Pres & CEO)*
Ivan R. Habibe *(CFO, Treas & VP)*
Leon Richards *(Chief Acctg Officer & Controller)*
Peter Hultberg *(VP-Global Sls & Mktg)*
Brands & Products:
BALDWIN
WERE THERE'S PRINTING THERE'S BALDWIN

BALTIMORE DREDGES, LLC

1425 Wicomomico St
Baltimore, MD 21230-2020
Tel.: (410) 837-7900
Fax: (410) 752-3294
E-mail: rmanning@dredge.com
Web Site: www.dredge.com
Approx. Sls.: $16,000,000
Approx. Number Employees: 150
Year Founded: 1885
Business Description:
Mfr. & Distr of Dredges & Dredging Machinery; Contract Machining, Fabrication & Assembly Services
S.I.C.: 3731
N.A.I.C.S.: 336611
Export
Media: 1-2-4-11-13
Distr.: Intl.; Natl.
Budget Set: Jan. -Dec.
Personnel:
Joe Wentel *(CFO)*
Robert Troom *(Mgr-Pur)*
Brands & Products:
DRAGON
DUAL WHEEL EXCAVATOR
ELLICOTT
MUD CAT
SANDMINER
SUPER DRAGON
WHEEL DRAGON

BARBOUR STOCKWELL INCORPORATED

55 6th Rd
Woburn, MA 01801-1746
Tel.: (781) 933-5200
Fax: (781) 939-5778
E-mail: admin@barbourstockwell.com
Web Site: www.barbourstockwell.com
E-Mail For Key Personnel:
President: kmaillar@barbourstockwell.com
Sales Range: $25-49.9 Million
Approx. Number Employees: 17
Business Description:
High Speed Vertical & Horizontal Air & Steam Turbines Mfr
S.I.C.: 3511; 8733
N.A.I.C.S.: 333611; 541710
Import Export
Media: 2-4-7-10
Distr.: Intl.; Natl.
Budget Set: Jan.
Personnel:
Kenneth Maillar *(Pres)*
Tony Enos *(VP)*

THE BARDEN CORP.

(Sub. of FAG Holding Corp.)
200 Park Ave
Danbury, CT 06813-2449
Mailing Address:
PO Box 2449
Danbury, CT 06813-2449
Tel.: (203) 744-2211
Fax: (203) 744-3756
Toll Free: (800) 243-1060
E-mail: bashley@bardenbearings.com
Web Site: www.bardenbearings.com
Sales Range: $50-74.9 Million
Approx. Number Employees: 480
Business Description:
Mfr. of High Precision Bearings & Components
S.I.C.: 3562; 3312
N.A.I.C.S.: 332991; 331111
Import Export
Media: 2-4-8-11-13
Distr.: Natl.
Budget Set: Nov.
Personnel:
John A. McCloskey *(Pres)*
Brands & Products:
BARTEMP
EX-CELL-O
FLEXEAL
X-LIFE ULTRA BEARINGS

BARDONS & OLIVER, INC.

5800 Harper Rd
Solon, OH 44139-1833
Tel.: (440) 498-5800
Fax: (440) 498-2001
E-mail: info@bardonsoliver.com
Web Site: www.bardonsoliver.com
Approx. Number Employees: 100
Year Founded: 1892
Business Description:
Mfr. of Turret Lathes, Cutting Lathes & Special Machinery
S.I.C.: 3541; 3549
N.A.I.C.S.: 333512; 333518
Advertising Expenditures: $200,000
Media: 2-4-10-26
Distr.: Natl.
Personnel:
Bill Beattie *(Pres)*
Jim Daffinee *(Reg Mgr-Sls)*

BARKSDALE, INC.

(Sub. of Crane Controls)
3211 Fruitland Ave
Los Angeles, CA 90058-3717
Mailing Address:
PO Box 58843
Los Angeles, CA 90058-0843
Tel.: (323) 589-6181
Fax: (323) 589-3463
Toll Free: (800) 835-1060
E-mail: sales@barksdale.com
Web Site: www.barksdale.com
E-Mail For Key Personnel:
Sales Director: sales@barksdale.com
Sales Range: $50-74.9 Million
Approx. Number Employees: 150
Year Founded: 1949
Business Description:
Valves, Transducers, Temperature & Pressure Switches & Electronics Mfr
S.I.C.: 3829; 3491
N.A.I.C.S.: 334519; 332911
Import Export
Advertising Expenditures: $300,000
Media: 2-4-7-8-10-13-18-21
Distr.: Natl.
Budget Set: Dec.
Personnel:
Ian C. Dodd *(Pres)*
Irasema Rodriguez *(Mgr-Mktg & Comm)*
Brands & Products:
MINI-LEVELSITE
SHEAR-SEAL

BARNES GROUP INC.

123 Main St
Bristol, CT 06010-6307
Mailing Address:
PO Box 489
Bristol, CT 06011-0489
Tel.: (860) 583-7070
Fax: (860) 589-3507

Key to Media (For complete agency information see *The Advertising Red Books-Agencies* edition):
1. Bus. Publs. 2. Cable T.V. 3. Catalogs & Directories. 4. Co-op Adv. 5. Consumer Mags. 6. D.M. to Bus. Estab.7. D.M. to Consumers
8. Daily Newsp. 9. Exhibits/Trade Shows 10. Foreign 11. Infomercial 12. Internet Adv.13. Multimedia 14. Network Radio
15. Network T.V. 16. Newsp. Distr. Mags. 17. Other 18. Outdoor (Posters, Transit) 19. Point of Purchase20. Premiums, Novelties
21. Product Samples 22. Special Events Mktg. 23. Spot Radio 24. Spot T.V. 25. Weekly Newsp. 26. Yellow Page Adv.

E-mail: info@bginc.com
Web Site: www.barnesgroupinc.com
Approx. Sls.: $1,133,199,000
Approx. Number Employees: 4,906
Year Founded: 1857
Business Description:
Custom Metal Parts, Components, Assemblies & Distr of Industrial Maintenance Parts & Supplies Mfr
S.I.C.: 8711; 3469; 3495; 3499
N.A.I.C.S.: 541330; 332116; 332612; 332999
Import Export
Media: 2-4-7-10-18-19-20-21-22
Distr.: Natl.
Budget Set: Sept. -Oct.
Personnel:
Thomas O. Barnes, Jr. *(Chm)*
Gregory F. Milzcik *(Pres & CEO)*
Christopher J. Stephens, Jr. *(CFO & Sr VP-Fin)*
Claudia S. Toussaint *(Gen Counsel, Sec & Sr VP)*
Dawn N. Edwards *(Sr VP-HR)*
William Pitts *(Dir-Plng & IR)*
Brands & Products:
BARNES
HYSON
KALLER
Advertising Agency:
Goodman Media International, Inc.
750 7th Ave 28th Fl
New York, NY 10016
Tel.: (212) 576-2700
Fax: (212) 576-2701

BARNES INTERNATIONAL INC.

814 Chestnut St
Rockford, IL 61105
Tel.: (815) 964-8661
Fax: (815) 964-5074
Toll Free: (800) 435-4877
E-mail: sales@barnesintl.com
Web Site: www.barnesintl.com
E-Mail For Key Personnel:
Sales Director: sales@barnesintl.com
Approx. Number Employees: 50
Year Founded: 1907
Business Description:
Machine Tools, Super Abrasive Honing Systems, Honing Machines, Honing Tools, Coolant Filtration Equipment & Gantry Robotics Mfr
S.I.C.: 3541; 3291
N.A.I.C.S.: 333512; 327910
Export
Media: 2-4-6-7-10-26
Distr.: Intl.; Natl.
Budget Set: Nov.
Personnel:
Marvin E. Gollob *(Pres & COO)*
Terry Connell *(VP-Sls & Mgr-Adv)*
Carl Springer *(VP-Engrg)*
Brands & Products:
BARNES
KLEENALL

BARRY CONTROLS

(Sub. of Hutchinson S.A.)
82 South St
Hopkinton, MA 01748-2205
Tel.: (508) 417-7000
Fax: (508) 417-7224
Toll Free: (800) BARRYMA
Toll Free: (800) 227-7962
Web Site: www.barrycontrols.com/company/locations.cfm
Approx. Number Employees: 350
Year Founded: 1943
Business Description:
Designs, Manufactures & Markets Shock, Vibration, Noise & Motion Solutions for Defense, Industrial & Commercial Aerospace Markets
S.I.C.: 3545
N.A.I.C.S.: 333515
Media: 4-7-10
Distr.: Intl.; Natl.
Budget Set: Sept.
Personnel:
James Collins *(Mgr-Indus Market)*
Joanne Cook *(Mgr-HR)*
Brands & Products:
BARRY
BARRYMOUNT

BAYLOFF STAMPED PRODUCTS

(Formerly Target Stamped Products Corporation)
(Sub. of Bayloff Die & Machine Co.)
8091 State Route 5
Kinsman, OH 44428-9628
Mailing Address:
PO Box 289
Kinsman, OH 44428-0289
Tel.: (330) 876-4511
Fax: (330) 876-4632
Web Site: www.bayloff.com
Approx. Number Employees: 160
Year Founded: 1948
Business Description:
Steel Stampings & Dies Mfr
S.I.C.: 3469; 7699
N.A.I.C.S.: 332116; 811490
Advertising Expenditures: $600,000
Bus. Publs.: $90,000; Catalogs & Directories: $150,000; D.M. to Bus. Estab.: $210,000; Point of Purchase: $150,000
Distr.: Intl.; Natl.
Personnel:
Dan Moore *(VP-Sls & Mktg)*

BELCO INDUSTRIES, INC. - FAMCO MACHINE DIVISION

(Div. of Belco Industries, Inc.)
1001 31st St
Kenosha, WI 53140-1926
Tel.: (262) 654-3516
Fax: (262) 654-0803
Toll Free: (800) 465-2233
E-mail: info@famcomachine.com
Web Site: www.famcomachine.com
Sales Range: $1-9.9 Million
Approx. Number Employees: 28
Year Founded: 1927
Business Description:
Air, Arbor, Foot Presses; Power Squaring Shears; Foot Shears; Engraving Machines
S.I.C.: 3542; 3552
N.A.I.C.S.: 333513; 333292
Export
Media: 2-4-7-10-13-22-26
Distr.: Intl.; Natl.
Personnel:
William Blasi *(Pres)*

BELMONT METALS, INC.

330 Belmont Ave
Brooklyn, NY 11207
Tel.: (718) 342-4900
Fax: (718) 342-0175
E-mail: mail@belmontmetals.com
Web Site: www.belmontmetals.com
Sales Range: $25-49.9 Million
Approx. Number Employees: 75
Year Founded: 1896
Business Description:
Non-Ferrous Metals
S.I.C.: 3339; 3341
N.A.I.C.S.: 331419; 331492
Import Export
Media: 2-4-7
Personnel:
Richard G. Henning *(Pres)*
Herbert Doyl *(Dir-Sls & Mktg)*

BELSHAW BROTHERS, INC.

(Sub. of The AFE Group Ltd.)
(d/b/a Belshaw Adamatic Bakery Group)
814 44th St NW Ste 103
Auburn, WA 98001
Tel.: (206) 322-5474
Fax: (206) 322-5425
Toll Free: (800) 578-2547
E-mail: info@belshaw.com
Web Site: www.belshaw.com
Approx. Number Employees: 200
Year Founded: 1923
Business Description:
Commercial & Industrial Bakery & Donut Production Equipment Mfr
S.I.C.: 3556; 3586; 3589
N.A.I.C.S.: 333294; 333319; 333913
Export
Media: 4-6-7-10-11
Distr.: Intl.; Natl.
Budget Set: Dec.
Personnel:
Roger A. Faw *(Pres)*
John DeMarre *(VP-Sls)*
Brands & Products:
BELSHAW
CUT-N-FRY
DOMIX
DONUT ROBOT
THERMOGLAZE

BERKEL COMPANY

(Sub. of Illinois Tool Works Inc.)
701 S Ridge Ave
Troy, OH 45374
Tel.: (937) 332-3000
Toll Free: (800) 348-0251
Web Site: www.berkelequipment.com
Sales Range: $25-49.9 Million
Approx. Number Employees: 30
Year Founded: 1916
Business Description:
Slicers & Other Food Retail Equipment Mfr
S.I.C.: 3556
N.A.I.C.S.: 333294
Import
Media: 5-13
Distr.: Intl.; Natl.
Budget Set: Oct.
Brands & Products:
BERKEL

BESSER COMPANY

801 Johnson St
Alpena, MI 49707-1870
Tel.: (989) 354-4111
Fax: (989) 354-3120
Toll Free: (800) 968-0444
E-mail: sales@besser.com
Web Site: www.besser.com
E-Mail For Key Personnel:
Sales Director: sales@besser.com
Public Relations: trondeau@besser.com
Sales Range: $75-99.9 Million
Approx. Number Employees: 1,000
Year Founded: 1904
Business Description:
Concrete Block Machinery & Product Handling Equipment
S.I.C.: 3559; 3531
N.A.I.C.S.: 333298; 333120
Import Export
Media: 1-2-4-8-10-11-20
Distr.: Direct to Consumer; Intl.; Natl.
Budget Set: Apr.
Personnel:
Kevin L. Curtis *(Pres)*
Julie Musch *(CFO)*
Gary Ericson *(Dir-Sls-Concrete Pipe & Precast-N America)*
John Reedy *(Dir-Sls)*
Richard Dolly *(Reg Mgr-Sls-Southeast US-Masonry/Landscape)*
Eloy Gonzalez *(Reg Mgr-Sls-Latin America & Caribbean-Masonry/Landscape)*
Richard Matzke *(Reg Mgr-Sls-Eastern US-Masonry/Landscape)*
Ralph Schlereth *(Reg Mgr-Sls-Midwest US & Ontario-Masonry/Landscape)*
Dan Winger *(Reg Mgr-Sls-Western US & Canada-Masonry/Landscape)*
Terry McNamee *(Reg Mgr-Sls)*
Bradley Gardner *(Sls Mgr-Molds)*
Ron Schriever *(Sls Mgr)*
Bob Akerberg *(Mgr-Customer Svc)*
Don Andor *(Mgr-Engrg)*
Arthur C. Kendziorski *(Mgr-Acctg)*
Dan Leman *(Mgr-Sls)*
Bruce Muenchow *(Mgr-Capital Equipment Installation)*
Brands & Products:
AUTOPAC 1000
BESCO
BESCOPAC
BESSER
BIDI
BRIK BLOK
DYNAPAC
EZ BASE
EZ BOX
FLARE
FLEXLOCK
HYDROPAK
NOVABRIK
QUIKSPLIT
SPECMASTER
SPECMASTER II
STRAPACKER
SUPERPAC
TEX TRU
ULTRAPAC
ULTRAPAC II
UNISTACK
V-200 NOVABRIK
V3-12 VIBRAPAC
VIBRAPAC
VIBRO-MAC
Advertising Agencies:
Industrial Image
111 S 2nd Ave
Alpena, MI 49707
Tel.: (989) 358-7100

Rhea + Kaiser
Naperville Financial Ctr 400 E Diehl Rd Ste 500

Key to Media (For complete agency information see *The Advertising Red Books-Agencies* edition):
1. Bus. Publs. 2. Cable T.V. 3. Catalogs & Directories. 4. Co-op Adv. 5. Consumer Mags. 6. D.M. to Bus. Estab.7. D.M. to Consumers 8. Daily Newsp. 9. Exhibits/Trade Shows 10. Foreign 11. Infomercial 12. Internet Adv.13. Multimedia 14. Network Radio 15. Network T.V. 16. Newsp. Distr. Mags. 17. Other 18. Outdoor (Posters, Transit) 19. Point of Purchase20. Premiums, Novelties 21. Product Samples 22. Special Events Mktg. 23. Spot Radio 24. Spot T.V. 25. Weekly Newsp. 26. Yellow Page Adv.

Besser Company — (Continued)

Naperville, IL 60563-1342
Tel.: (630) 505-1100
Fax: (630) 505-1109

BETTER WIRE PRODUCTS, INC.

1255 Niagara St
Buffalo, NY 14213-1501
Tel.: (716) 883-3377
Fax: (716) 883-5075
Toll Free: (800) YES-WIRE
E-mail: feedback@betterwire.com
Web Site: www.betterwire.com
Approx. Sls.: $2,000,000
Approx. Number Employees: 25
Year Founded: 1952
Business Description:
Wire Forms Fabricator, Designer & Mfr
S.I.C.: 3496
N.A.I.C.S.: 332618
Media: 2-4-7-26
Distr.: Natl.
Budget Set: Apr.-Dec.
Personnel:
William Breeser *(Owner)*
Brands & Products:
BETTER WIRE PRODUCTS
FRUIT BRUTE
JIFFY WIRE
STA-PUT
ZIP-CLIPS

BIG JOE MANUFACTURING CO.

1060 N Garfield St
Lombard, IL 60148
Tel.: (630) 629-2700
Fax: (630) 629-3410
E-mail: sales@bigjoemfg.com
Web Site: www.bigjoemfg.com
Approx. Sls.: $18,000,000
Approx. Number Employees: 20
Year Founded: 1949
Business Description:
Hydraulic Lift Trucks
S.I.C.: 3537
N.A.I.C.S.: 333924
Media: 2-4-7-10
Distr.: Natl.
Budget Set: Sept.
Personnel:
Andy Cameron *(Pres & CEO)*
Brands & Products:
BIG JOE
POWER-DRIVE
WALKIE

BIMBA MANUFACTURING COMPANY

Rte 50 N
Monee, IL 60449
Tel.: (708) 534-8544
Fax: (708) 534-9521
Toll Free: (800) 442-4622
E-mail: support@bimba.com
Web Site: www.bimba.com
Approx. Number Employees: 200
Year Founded: 1957
Business Description:
Hydraulic & Pneumatic Fluid Power Cylinders
S.I.C.: 3593
N.A.I.C.S.: 333995
Export
Media: 2-4-7-10-11-13-26
Distr.: Intl.; Natl.
Budget Set: Sept.-Oct.
Personnel:
Charles W. Bimba, Jr. *(Chm)*
Patrick Ormsby *(Pres)*
Brands & Products:
BIMBA
DOUBLE-WALL
FLAT-I
MAGNALUBE
PNEU-MOMENT
PNEU-TURN
PNEUMOMENT
QUIK-FLO
SPACE-SAVING FLAT-1
SQUARE FLAT-1
ULTRAN

BLACK LAB CORP.

PO Box 236
Wedron, IL 60557
Tel.: (815) 792-8055
Toll Free: (800) 258-3878
Web Site: www.wedronflux.com
Approx. Number Employees: 25
Year Founded: 1987
Business Description:
Toll Blender & Molten Aluminum Service
S.I.C.: 3241; 2899
N.A.I.C.S.: 327310; 325998
Import Export
Personnel:
Douglas L. Gerner *(Pres)*
Peter Hoyt *(CEO)*
Charles R. Nelson *(Head-Sls & VP)*
Dave Caskey *(Plant Mgr, Dir-Safety & Quality)*
John Reynolds *(Dir-Sls)*
Daryl Deckard *(Sls Mgr-All Kleer & Acct Mgr-Black Lab Custom Products)*
Melissa Noel *(Agent-Pur & Coord-Bus Solutions)*
Advertising Agency:
Richards Communications
3201 Enterprise Pkwy Ste 400
Beachwood, OH 44122
Tel.: (216) 514-7800
Fax: (216) 514-7801

BLACKSMITHS DEPOT

(Sub. of Kayne & Son Custom Hardware Inc.)
100 Daniel Ridge Rd
Candler, NC 28715
Tel.: (828) 667-8868
Fax: (828) 665-8303
Web Site: www.blacksmithsdepot.com
Sales Range: Less than $1 Million
Approx. Number Employees: 10
Business Description:
Mfr & Distr of Quality Blacksmithing Tools
S.I.C.: 3429
N.A.I.C.S.: 332510
Import Export
Media: 4-8-11-13

BLUE RHINO CORPORATION

(Sub. of Ferrellgas Partners, L.P.)
470 W Hanes Mill Rd Ste 200
Winston Salem, NC 27105
Tel.: (336) 659-6900
Fax: (336) 659-6750
E-mail: investorrelations@bluerhino.com
Web Site: www.bluerhino.com
Sales Range: $250-299.9 Million
Approx. Number Employees: 100
Year Founded: 1994
Business Description:
Exchanges Empty Propane Cylinders For Prefilled Ones
S.I.C.: 5984
N.A.I.C.S.: 454312
Media: 5-7-10-19
Personnel:
Bob S. Travatello *(CIO & VP)*
Todd Brown *(Pres-Blue Rhino & Sr VP-Ferrellgas)*
William Dull *(VP-Fin)*
Chris Hartley *(VP-Mktg)*
Brands & Products:
AMERICA'S CHOICE FOR GRILL GAS
BISON
DURACLAY
ENDLESS SUMMER COMFORT
GARDENART
GRILL GAS
RHINOTUFF
TRI-SAFE
UNIFLAME
UNIGRILL
Advertising Agency:
SBC Advertising
333 W Nationwide Blvd
Columbus, OH 43215
Tel.: (614) 891-7070
Fax: (614) 255-2600
Toll Free: (866) 891-7001

BODINE ASSEMBLY & TEST SYSTEMS

317 Mtn Grove St
Bridgeport, CT 06605-2139
Tel.: (203) 334-3100
Fax: (203) 330-8716
E-mail: sales@bodine-assembly.com
Web Site: www.bodine-assembly.com
E-Mail For Key Personnel:
Sales Director: sales@bodine-assembly.com
Approx. Number Employees: 150
Year Founded: 1933
Business Description:
Synchronous & Asynchronous Assembly & Test Systems
S.I.C.: 3569; 3829
N.A.I.C.S.: 333999; 334519
Export
Media: 1-2-4-7-8-10-11-13-18
Distr.: Intl.
Budget Set: May
Personnel:
Richard P. Bodine *(Chm)*
William E. Bodine *(Pres)*
Robert Carlson *(COO)*
Brands & Products:
GANG TEST MODULE
INDEXING CAROUSEL
WALKING BEAM

BODINE ELECTRIC COMPANY

2500 W Bradley Pl
Chicago, IL 60618
Tel.: (773) 478-3515
Fax: (773) 478-3232
Toll Free: (800) 7BODINE
Web Site: www.bodine-electric.com
Approx. Number Employees: 200
Year Founded: 1905
Business Description:
Electric FHP Motors, Gearmotors & Motion Control Systems
S.I.C.: 3621; 3625
N.A.I.C.S.: 335312; 335314
Import Export
Media: 2-4-7-10-13-18-21
Distr.: Intl.; Natl.
Budget Set: Dec.
Personnel:
John R. Bodine *(Owner)*
Jeffrey Stahl *(CFO)*
Jeffrey P. Bodine *(Exec VP)*
Michael Gschwind *(VP-Sls & Mktg)*
James E. Marth *(VP-Engrg)*
Terry Auchstetter *(Mgr-Bus Dev-Custom Products)*
Edmund Glueck *(Mgr-Mktg & Product Dev)*
Mike Marhoefer *(Mgr-Engrg)*
Brands & Products:
BODINE
E-TORQ
INTEGRA MOTOR
PACESETTER
QUALITY IN MOTION
QUINTSULATION

BOHLER-UDDEHOLM CORPORATION

(Sub. of Bohler-Uddeholm AG)
2505 Millennium Dr
Elgin, IL 60124
Tel.: (847) 577-2220
Fax: (630) 883-3117
Toll Free: (800) 638-2520
E-mail: info@bucorp.com
Web Site: www.bucorp.com
Sales Range: $50-74.9 Million
Approx. Number Employees: 175
Year Founded: 1923
Business Description:
Tool Die, Cold Rolled Precision Strip Steel
S.I.C.: 5051
N.A.I.C.S.: 423510
Import
Advertising Expenditures: $250,000
Media: 2-4-7-10-13
Distr.: Intl.; Natl.
Personnel:
Eric Henn *(Pres)*

BOILER TUBE COMPANY OF AMERICA

(Sub. of Babcock Power, Inc.)
506 Charlotte Hwy
Lyman, SC 29365
Tel.: (864) 439-4489
Fax: (864) 439-8292
Toll Free: (800) 845-3052
E-mail: sales@boilertubes.com
Web Site: www.boilertubes.com
E-Mail For Key Personnel:
Sales Director: sales@boilertubes.com
Approx. Number Employees: 150
Year Founded: 1918
Business Description:
Waste Heat Recovery Plants, Fired Boilers, Shell & Tube Heat Exchangers, Economisers, Feedwater Heaters, Condensers, Moisture Separator Reheaters & Boiler Spares
S.I.C.: 3443
N.A.I.C.S.: 332313
Import Export
Media: 1-2-4-6-7-8-10-17-20-22

Key to Media (For complete agency information see *The Advertising Red Books-Agencies* edition):
1. Bus. Publs. 2. Cable T.V. 3. Catalogs & Directories. 4. Co-op Adv. 5. Consumer Mags. 6. D.M. to Bus. Estab.7. D.M. to Consumers
8. Daily Newsp. 9. Exhibits/Trade Shows 10. Foreign 11. Infomercial 12. Internet Adv.13. Multimedia 14. Network Radio
15. Network T.V. 16. Newsp. Distr. Mags. 17. Other 18. Outdoor (Posters, Transit) 19. Point of Purchase20. Premiums, Novelties
21. Product Samples 22. Special Events Mktg. 23. Spot Radio 24. Spot T.V. 25. Weekly Newsp. 26. Yellow Page Adv.

Distr.: Natl.
Personnel:
Donald Laing *(Pres)*

BOLT TECHNOLOGY CORPORATION
4 Duke Pl
Norwalk, CT 06854
Tel.: (203) 853-0700
Fax: (203) 854-9601
E-mail: info@bolt-technology.com
Web Site: www.bolt-technology.com
Approx. Sls.: $38,858,000
Approx. Number Employees: 165
Year Founded: 1960
Business Description:
Designer, Developer & Marketer for Seismic Exploration Products for Oil, Gas & Minerals
S.I.C.: 8713; 3533; 3824; 3829
N.A.I.C.S.: 541360; 333132; 334514; 334519
Advertising Expenditures: $74,000
Media: 7-10
Personnel:
Raymond M. Soto *(Chm, Pres & CEO)*
Joseph Espeso *(CFO, Treas, Sr VP-Fin & Asst Sec)*
Michael C. Hedger *(Exec VP)*
Joseph Mayerick, Jr. *(Sr VP-Mktg & Asst Sec)*
Charles Christiano *(Mgr-Pur)*
Brands & Products:
ANNULAR
DOWN-HOLE
LONG-LIFE
OMNIPULSE
PAR
WELLSEIS

BOLTON-EMERSON AMERICAS, INC.
9 Osgood St
Lawrence, MA 01843-1859
Tel.: (978) 686-3961
Fax: (978) 688-8225
E-mail: boltonemersonamericas@mail.com
Approx. Sls.: $2,500,000
Approx. Number Employees: 14
Year Founded: 1905
Business Description:
Industrial & Coating Equipment
S.I.C.: 3554; 5084
N.A.I.C.S.: 333291; 423830
Import Export
Media: 2-4-6-8-10-21
Distr.: Intl.; Natl.
Budget Set: Dec.
Personnel:
Sandra Krug *(Pres)*
Brands & Products:
BOLTOBAR
CLAFLIN
DEVELOMAX
ELECTRO-4 DISC REFINER
EMERSON
HYDROTRUSS
MICROLYZED
PARK
TORNADO
TRIPLE ATTACK

BOMAG AMERICAS, INC.
(Sub. of BOMAG GmbH)
2000 Kentville Rd
Kewanee, IL 61443-1714
Tel.: (309) 853-3571
Fax: (309) 853-1319
Toll Free: (800) 782-6624
E-mail: usa@bomag.com
Web Site: www.bomag.com
Approx. Number Employees: 125
Year Founded: 1875
Business Description:
Construction Machinery Mfr
S.I.C.: 3531
N.A.I.C.S.: 333120
Import Export
Advertising Expenditures: $350,000
Media: 2-4-5-7-10-20
Distr.: Intl.; Natl.
Budget Set: Nov.
Personnel:
Walter Link *(Pres)*
Rob Mueckler *(VP-Sls & Mktg)*
Dave Dennison *(Product Mgr)*
Brands & Products:
BOMAG
HYPAC

BOMAR INTERCONNECT PRODUCTS, INC.
1850 US Hwy 46
Ledgewood, NJ 07852
Tel.: (973) 347-4040
Fax: (973) 347-2111
E-mail: mailstop@bomarinterconnect.com
Web Site: www.bomarinterconnect.com
Approx. Number Employees: 12
Business Description:
RF & Modular Connector Mfr
S.I.C.: 3678; 3643
N.A.I.C.S.: 334417; 335931
Media: 4-10
Personnel:
Bob Behrent *(Pres)*
Brands & Products:
E-SNAPS
ELIMINATOR
EZ-RJ
PRESS FIT'S
PUSH-EZ
SHADOW
V-BITE

BOMBARDIER INC.
800 Rene Levesque Boulevard West
Montreal, QC H3B 1Y8, Canada
Tel.: (514) 861-9481
Fax: (514) 861-7053
E-mail: info@bombardier.com
Web Site: www.bombardier.com
Approx. Rev.: $17,712,000,000
Approx. Number Employees: 65,400
Year Founded: 1902
Business Description:
Business Aircraft, Regional Aircraft, Amphibious Aircraft, Pilot Training, Mass Transit Vehicles, Snowgrooming Vehicles, Tracked Vehicles for Utility Work, All-Terrain Vehicles & Electric Neighborhood Vehicles
S.I.C.: 3721; 4111
N.A.I.C.S.: 336411; 485113
Export
Media: 4-6-9-10-11-14-15-18-20-21-22-24
Distr.: Intl.; Natl.
Budget Set: Mar. -June
Personnel:
Laurent Beaudoin *(Chm)*
J. R. Andre Bombardier *(Co-Vice Chm)*
Jean-Louis Fontaine *(Co-Vice Chm)*
Pierre Beaudoin *(Pres & CEO)*
Pierre Alary *(CFO & Sr VP)*
Ginette Cousineeu *(Coord-Media)*
Frederick W. Reid *(Pres-Flexjet & Skyjet-US)*
Daniel Desjardins *(Gen Counsel, Sr VP & Asst Sec)*
Richard C. Bradeen *(Sr VP-Strategy, Corp Audit Svcs & Risk Assessment)*
John Paul Macdonald *(Sr VP-HR & Pub Affairs)*
Mike Fahey *(VP-Worldwide Learjet & Preowned Aircraft Sls)*
Shirley Chenier *(Sr Dir-IR)*
Isabelle Rondeau *(Dir-Comm)*
Chiko Kundi *(Mgr-Intl Preowned Aircraft Sls-Bus Aircraft)*
Brands & Products:
BOMBARDIER
CHALLENGER
EBI TOOL
FLEXJET
LEARJET
SUPERSCOOPER
Advertising Agencies:
Cramer-Krasselt
225 N Michigan Ave
Chicago, IL 60601-7601
Tel.: (312) 616-9600
Fax: (312) 616-3839

Greteman Group
1425 E Douglas 2nd Fl
Wichita, KS 67211
Tel.: (316) 263-1004
Fax: (316) 263-1060

Media Experts
495 Wellington St W Ste 250
Toronto, ON M5V 1E9, Canada
Tel.: (416) 597-0707
Fax: (416) 597-9927

Team One
(Sub. of Saatchi & Saatchi Advertising Worldwide)
1960 E Grand Ave
El Segundo, CA 90245-5059
Tel.: (310) 615-2000
Fax: (310) 322-7565

BOSCH REXROTH CORPORATION
(Branch of Bosch Rexroth Corporation)
2315 City Line Rd
Bethlehem, PA 18017
Mailing Address:
PO Box 25407
Bethlehem, PA 18017
Tel.: (610) 694-8300
Fax: (610) 694-8467
Toll Free: (877) ATBOSCH
E-mail: webmaster.atus@us.bosch.com
Web Site: www.boschrexroth.com
Approx. Sls.: $70,000,000
Approx. Number Employees: 500
Year Founded: 1906
Business Description:
Hydraulic Pumps, Valves & Systems Mfr
S.I.C.: 3492; 3594
N.A.I.C.S.: 332912; 333996
Import Export
Media: 2-4-5-10-20
Distr.: Intl.; Natl.
Budget Set: May
Brands & Products:
ACCU-TRIM
BOSCH PNEUMATICS & HYDRAULICS
PSO
RACINE SECO
SILENTVANE
SMARTVANE
TWINVANE
WHISPER PUMP
WORLDVANE
Advertising Agency:
Brewer Associates Marketing Communications
39555 Orchard Hill Pl Ste 600
Novi, MI 48375
Tel.: (734) 458-7180

BOURN & KOCH MACHINE TOOL COMPANY
2500 Kishwaukee St
Rockford, IL 61104
Tel.: (815) 965-4013
Fax: (815) 965-0019
Web Site: www.bourn-koch.com
Approx. Sls.: $5,000,000
Approx. Number Employees: 60
Year Founded: 1975
Business Description:
Machine Tools Mfr
S.I.C.: 3542; 3545
N.A.I.C.S.: 333513; 333515
Media: 2-7-10-13
Personnel:
Tim Helle *(Pres)*
Brands & Products:
AMERICAN TOOL
BARBER COLMAN
BLANCHARD
BROWN & SHARPE
BULLARD
CONOMATIC
DEVLIEG
FELLOWS
FUTUREMILL
JONES & LAMSON
MATTISON GRINDERS
MATTISON WOODWORKING
MOTCH
NATIONAL ACME
NEW BRITAIN
ROCKFORD MACHINE TOOLS
ROCKFORD PUNCH PRESS
ROTO-TECH
SPRINGFIELD
WHITE-SUNDSTRAND

BRAD FOOTE GEAR WORKS, INC.
(Sub. of BROADWIND ENERGY, INC.)
1309 S Cicero Ave
Cicero, IL 60804-1404
Tel.: (708) 298-1100
Fax: (708) 652-4140
Toll Free: (800) 242-1163
Web Site: www.bradfoote.com
Sales Range: $75-99.9 Million
Approx. Number Employees: 200
Year Founded: 1924
Business Description:
Custom Gear & Gearbox Mfr
S.I.C.: 3566
N.A.I.C.S.: 333612
Export
Media: 7-8
Distr.: Natl.
Budget Set: Sept.

Key to Media (For complete agency information see *The Advertising Red Books-Agencies* edition):
1. Bus. Publs. 2. Cable T.V. 3. Catalogs & Directories. 4. Co-op Adv. 5. Consumer Mags. 6. D.M. to Bus. Estab.7. D.M. to Consumers
8. Daily Newsp. 9. Exhibits/Trade Shows 10. Foreign 11. Infomercial 12. Internet Adv.13. Multimedia 14. Network Radio
15. Network T.V. 16. Newsp. Distr. Mags. 17. Other 18. Outdoor (Posters, Transit) 19. Point of Purchase20. Premiums, Novelties
21. Product Samples 22. Special Events Mktg. 23. Spot Radio 24. Spot T.V. 25. Weekly Newsp. 26. Yellow Page Adv.

Brad Foote Gear Works, Inc. — (Continued)

Personnel:
Daniel E. Schueller *(Pres)*

BRANSON ULTRASONICS CORPORATION
(Sub. of Emerson Industrial Automation)
41 Eagle Rd
Danbury, CT 06810
Mailing Address:
PO Box 1961
Danbury, CT 06813-1961
Tel.: (203) 796-0400
Fax: (203) 796-9838
Toll Free: (888) 282-5646
E-mail: info@emerson.com
Web Site:
www.bransonultrasonics.com
Sales Range: $150-199.9 Million
Approx. Number Employees: 250
Year Founded: 1946
Business Description:
Industrial Ultrasonic Equipment
S.I.C.: 3699; 3548
N.A.I.C.S.: 335999; 333992
Export
Advertising Expenditures: $500,000
Media: 2-4-9-10-19
Personnel:
Robert M. Brown *(VP-Sls & Mktg)*
Byron D. Peterson *(VP-HR)*
Jon C. Piasecki *(VP-Engrg & Automotive)*
Robert G. Tibbets *(VP-Fin)*

BRANSON ULTRASONICS CORPORATION-PRECISION CLEANING DIV
(Div. of Branson Ultrasonics Corporation)
41 Eagle Rd
Danbury, CT 06813-1961
Tel.: (203) 796-0400
Fax: (203) 796-0320
E-mail: info@bransoncleaning.com
Web Site: www.bransoncleaning.com
E-Mail For Key Personnel:
President: apajk@bransonultrasonics.com
Marketing Director: jhilgea@bransonultrasonics.com
Sales Director: jharman@bransonultrasonics.com
Sales Range: $450-499.9 Million
Approx. Number Employees: 1,300
Year Founded: 1984
Business Description:
Precision Cleaning Equipment
S.I.C.: 3699; 3548
N.A.I.C.S.: 335999; 333992
Import Export
Advertising Expenditures: $200,000
Media: 2-4-7-10-11-19
Distr.: Natl.
Budget Set: Sept.
Personnel:
Anthony Pajk *(Pres & CEO)*
Bob Brown *(VP-Sls & Mktg)*
Brands & Products:
BENCHMARK

BREEZE-EASTERN CORPORATION
35 Melanie Ln
Whippany, NJ 07981
Tel.: (973) 602-1001
Fax: (908) 686-9292
E-mail: marketing@breeze-eastern.com
Web Site: www.breeze-eastern.com
Approx. Sls.: $78,200,000
Approx. Number Employees: 164
Year Founded: 1962
Business Description:
Aerospace & Defense Equipment Mfr
S.I.C.: 3728; 3566
N.A.I.C.S.: 336413; 333612
Export
Media: 2-4-7-9-20-21
Distr.: Intl.
Personnel:
Charles W. Grigg *(Chm)*
Donald Michael Harlan, Jr. *(Pres & CEO)*
Mark D. Mishler *(CFO, Treas, Sec & Sr VP)*
Brands & Products:
BREEZE EASTERN
BREEZE-EASTERN CORPORATION
ENGINEERED PRODUCTS FOR GLOBAL PARTNERS

BRENCO, INC.
(Div. of AMSTED Industries Incorporated)
2580 Frontage Rd
Petersburg, VA 23805
Mailing Address:
PO Box 389
Petersburg, VA 23804
Tel.: (804) 732-0202
Fax: (804) 732-4722
E-mail: info@amspetrail.com
Web Site: www.brencoqbs.com
Approx. Number Employees: 550
Year Founded: 1949
Business Description:
Railroad Bearings & Components Mfr
S.I.C.: 3743; 3561; 4013
N.A.I.C.S.: 336510; 333911; 482112
Import Export
Advertising Expenditures: $300,000
Media: 1-2-4-7-10-13-17-20-22
Distr.: Intl.; Natl.
Budget Set: Oct. -Nov.
Personnel:
J. Craig Rice *(Co-Pres & COO)*
Dave Liming *(Co-Pres)*
Jacob Feichtner *(Sec & Exec VP)*
Jim Drum *(VP-Pur)*
Donald E. Fitzsimmons *(VP-Railroad)*
Robert V. Lawrence *(VP-Engrng)*
Brian A. Hawkins *(Dir-Sls-Ponte Vedra-Fl)*
Kevin C. Kasperbauer *(Dir-Sls-Vancouver-WA)*
Thomas S. Lubinsky *(Dir-Sls-McKees Rocks-PA)*
Larry Myers *(Dir-Sls-Montgomery)*
Ellen M. Owen *(Dir-Sls-Hammond-IN)*
Brands & Products:
GENERATION 2000
QBS GOLD
Advertising Agency:
RPMiller Advertising
690 Bluff St
Glencoe, IL 60622
Tel.: (847) 835-2600
— Richard P. Miller *(Pres.)*

BRENNAN INDUSTRIES INC.
6701 Cochran Rd
Cleveland, OH 44139
Tel.: (440) 248-1880
Fax: (440) 248-7282
Toll Free: (888) 331-1523
Web Site: www.brennaninc.com
Sales Range: $25-49.9 Million
Approx. Number Employees: 300
Business Description:
Supplier of Hydraulic Fittings & Adapters
S.I.C.: 5084
N.A.I.C.S.: 423830
Personnel:
David D. Carr *(CEO)*
John Dewey *(Dir-IT)*
Faye Stropki *(Office Mgr)*
Brands & Products:
BI
CR3
THE LOGICAL CHOICE
Advertising Agency:
Sonnhalter
633 W Bagley Rd
Berea, OH 44017-1356
Tel.: (440) 234-1812
Fax: (440) 234-1890

BRIDON AMERICAN CORP.
(Sub. of Bridon International Limited)
280 New Commerce Blvd
Wilkes Barre, PA 18706-1448
Mailing Address:
PO Box 6000
Wilkes Barre, PA 18773-6000
Tel.: (570) 822-3349
Fax: (570) 822-9180
Toll Free: (800) 521-5555
Web Site: www.bridonamerican.com
Approx. Number Employees: 400
Year Founded: 1972
Business Description:
Wire & Wire Rope Assemblies Mfr
S.I.C.: 3496; 2515
N.A.I.C.S.: 332618; 337910
Import Export
Media: 2-4-7-10
Distr.: Intl.; Natl.
Budget Set: Nov. -Dec.
Personnel:
Robert Madden *(Dir-Mktg & Sls)*
Brands & Products:
CONSTRUCTEX
DYFORM
TIGER BLUE
TIGER BRAND
Advertising Agency:
Independent Graphics Inc.
1679 River Rd
Pittston, PA 18640
Tel.: (570) 654-4040

BRION TECHNOLOGIES INC.
(Formerly ASML MaskTools, Inc.)
(Sub. of ASML HOLDING N.V.)
4211Burton Dr
Santa Clara, CA 95054-1228
Tel.: (408) 653-1500
Fax: (408) 653-1501
E-mail: info@brion.com
Web Site: www.brion.com
Approx. Number Employees: 3,389
Year Founded: 1977
Business Description:
Optical Lithography Extension Solutions
S.I.C.: 7371
N.A.I.C.S.: 541511
Export
Media: 1-2-4-8-10-20-22-26
Distr.: Natl.
Personnel:
Fung Chen *(VP-Tech)*
Stephen Hsu *(Sr Mgr-RET)*
Keith Gronlund *(Mgr-Mktg)*
Brands & Products:
CPL
EXTENDING THE LIMITS
LITHOCRUISER
SCATTERING BAR

BROADWIND ENERGY, INC.
47 E Chicago Ave Ste 332
Naperville, IL 60540
Tel.: (630) 637-0315
Fax: (630) 637-8472
E-mail: hr@broadwindenergy.com
Web Site: www.broadwindenergy.com
Approx. Rev.: $136,896,000
Approx. Number Employees: 850
Business Description:
Wind Towers, Oil, Gas, Mining & Other Industrial Products & Equipment Mfr
S.I.C.: 3448; 3441
N.A.I.C.S.: 332311; 332312
Advertising Expenditures: $274,000
Personnel:
David P. Reiland *(Chm)*
Peter C. Duprey *(Pres & CEO)*
Stephanie K. Kushner *(CFO & Exec VP)*
Paul Smith *(COO-Towers Platform & VP)*
Jesse E. Collins, Jr. *(COO & Exec VP)*
Donald C. Nabb *(Pres-Gearing Platform)*
Paul Seppanen *(Pres-Energy Maintenance Svc)*
J. D. Rubin *(Gen Counsel & VP)*
Mike Ford *(VP-Sls)*
John Segvich *(Dir-Investor & Mktg Comm)*

BROOKS AUTOMATION, INC.
15 Elizabeth Dr
Chelmsford, MA 01824
Tel.: (978) 262-2400
Fax: (978) 262-2500
E-mail: info@brooks.com
Web Site: www.brooks.com
Approx. Rev.: $592,972,000
Approx. Number Employees: 1,410
Year Founded: 1948
Business Description:
Automation Products Developer, Mfr & Distr & Solutions for the Semiconductor Market
S.I.C.: 3559; 3535
N.A.I.C.S.: 332410; 333295; 333922
Media: 2-7-10
Personnel:
Joseph R. Martin *(Chm)*
Stephen S. Schwartz *(Pres & CEO)*
Martin S. Headley *(CFO & Exec VP)*
Gregory A. Marvell *(Sr VP & Gen Mgr)*
Steven A. Michaud *(Sr VP & Grp Gen Mgr)*
William T. Montone *(Sr VP-HR)*
Ralf Wuellner *(Sr VP)*
Jeff Spurrier *(Dir-Mobile Banking Application Svcs)*
Barbara Culhane *(Mgr-Corp Mktg)*
Brands & Products:
ACCELERATING YOUR PROFIT
ACUTRAN
ACUTRAY
AQUATRAP

Key to Media (For complete agency information see *The Advertising Red Books-Agencies* edition):
1. Bus. Publs. 2. Cable T.V. 3. Catalogs & Directories. 4. Co-op Adv. 5. Consumer Mags. 6. D.M. to Bus. Estab.7. D.M. to Consumers
8. Daily Newsp. 9. Exhibits/Trade Shows 10. Foreign 11. Infomercial 12. Internet Adv.13. Multimedia 14. Network Radio
15. Network T.V. 16. Newsp. Distr. Mags. 17. Other 18. Outdoor (Posters, Transit) 19. Point of Purchase20. Premiums, Novelties
21. Product Samples 22. Special Events Mktg. 23. Spot Radio 24. Spot T.V. 25. Weekly Newsp. 26. Yellow Page Adv.

AXM
B
BISYMMETRIK
COOL SOLUTIONS
CRYO-TORR
CTI-CRYOGENICS
ERGOSPEED
EXPRESSLOCKS
FABEXPRESS
FIXLOAD
FROGLEG
FUSION
GEMINI EXPRESS
GRANVILLE-PHILLIPS
HERCULES EXPRESS
INLIGNER
INLINE EXPRESS
JET
LEAPFROG
MAGNATRAN
MAPTRAK EXPRESS
MARATHON 2
MARATHON EXPRESS
MULTITRAN
ON-BOARD
ONEFAB
ONEFAB AMHS
POLYCOLD
PROMIS
RAZOR
RELIANCE
RELIANCE ATR
RETROEASE
RETROFAST
STABIL-ION
TIME OPTIMAL PATH
TRAJECTORY
TRUEBLUE
TURBOPLUS
ULTRASORT 408
VAC-407
VISION
WIP
ZARIS

BROOKTRONICS ENGINEERING CORPORATION

28231 Ave Crocker Bldg 60 & 70
Valencia, CA 91355-1276
Tel.: (661) 294-1195
Fax: (661) 294-9032
Toll Free: (800) 394-0922
E-mail: sales@brooktronics.com
Web Site: www.brooktronics.com
E-Mail For Key Personnel:
Sales Director: sales@brooktronics.com
Approx. Rev.: $750,000
Approx. Number Employees: 5
Year Founded: 1960
Business Description:
Brush Electroplating Equipment Supplies & Services
S.I.C.: 3471; 2899
N.A.I.C.S.: 332813; 325998
Export
Media: 2-4-7-10-26
Distr.: Intl.; Natl.
Personnel:
Eloise Helwig *(Chm & CEO)*
Chris Helwig *(Pres & COO)*
Brands & Products:
THE BROOKTRON PROCESS
BROOKTRONICS ENGINEERING

BRUNNER & LAY, INC.

1510 N Old Missouri Rd
Springdale, AR 72764
Tel.: (479) 756-0880
Fax: (479) 756-5366
Toll Free: (800) 872-6899
E-mail: info@brunnerlay.com
Web Site: www.brunnerlay.com
E-Mail For Key Personnel:
Sales Director: tbeaman@brunnerlay.com
Sales Range: $25-49.9 Million
Approx. Number Employees: 200
Year Founded: 1882
Business Description:
Mfr. of Rock Drilling & Pneumatic Tool Accessories
S.I.C.: 3532; 3546
N.A.I.C.S.: 333131; 333991
Export
Media: 10-20
Distr.: Intl.; Natl.
Budget Set: Jan.
Personnel:
M. F. Brunner *(Pres)*
Walter Shook *(Mgr-Adv)*
Brands & Products:
BRUNNER & LAY

BRUSH ENGINEERED MATERIALS INC.

6070 Parkland Blvd
Mayfield Heights, OH 44124
Tel.: (216) 486-4200
Fax: (216) 383-4091
Toll Free: (800) 321-2076
E-mail: contact_corporate_hdq@BEMinc.com
Web Site: www.beminc.com
Approx. Sls.: $715,186,000
Approx. Number Employees: 2,196
Year Founded: 2000
Business Description:
Holding Company; Advanced Engineered Materials Mfr
S.I.C.: 6719; 3313; 3341; 3444; 3463; 3469; 3479; 3499
N.A.I.C.S.: 551112; 331112; 331492; 332112; 332116; 332322; 332812; 332999
Advertising Expenditures: $400,000
Personnel:
Richard J. Hipple *(Chm, Pres & CEO)*
John D. Grampa *(CFO & Sr VP-Fin)*
Gregory R. Chemnitz *(Gen Counsel & VP)*
Daniel A. Skoch *(Sr VP-Admin)*
Mark Jasany *(VP-IT)*
Gary W. Schiavoni *(Asst Treas & Asst Sec)*
Brands & Products:
ADVANCING THE WORLD'S TECHNOLOGIES
BRUSH ENGINEERED MATERIALS
MOLDMAX XL
TOUGHMET
Advertising Agency:
Fahlgren Mortine
4030 Easton Station Ste 300
Columbus, OH 43219
Tel.: (614) 383-1500
Fax: (614) 383-1501

BRYANT GRINDER

(Div. of Vermont Machine Tool Corp.)
65 Pearl St
Springfield, VT 05156
Tel.: (802) 885-5161
Fax: (802) 885-9444
Web Site: www.bryantgrinder.com
Approx. Number Employees: 35
Year Founded: 1909
Business Description:
Mfr. of Machine Tools
S.I.C.: 3542; 5084
N.A.I.C.S.: 333513; 423830
Import Export
Media: 1-2-4-10-11-13-20
Distr.: Direct to Consumer; Natl.
Budget Set: June
Personnel:
Craig Barrett *(Founder, Pres & CEO)*
Karin Lewis *(Mgr-Part Sls)*
Brands & Products:
BRYANT
CENTA-FORM
CENTALIGN
HI-SPEEDPOWER
LECTRAFORM
LECTRALINE
ULTRA FORM
ULTRALINE

BTM CORPORATION

300 Davis Rd
Marysville, MI 48040
Tel.: (810) 364-4567
Fax: (810) 364-3355
E-mail: info@btmcorp.com
Web Site: www.btmcorp.com
Approx. Number Employees: 115
Year Founded: 1966
Business Description:
Mfr. of Machine Tools
S.I.C.: 3542; 3429
N.A.I.C.S.: 333513; 332510
Media: 2-4-10
Personnel:
Faisal Hoque *(CEO)*
Stephen Sawdon *(Mgr-Sls & Mktg)*
Brands & Products:
BTM
LANCE-N-LOC
TOG-L-LOC

BTU INTERNATIONAL, INC.

23 Esquire Rd
North Billerica, MA 01862
Tel.: (978) 667-4111
Fax: (978) 667-9068
Toll Free: (800) 998-0666
E-mail: info@btu.com
Web Site: www.btu.com
Approx. Sls.: $81,607,000
Approx. Number Employees: 383
Year Founded: 1950
Business Description:
Thermal Processing Equipment Mfr & Supplier
S.I.C.: 3567; 3559; 5084
N.A.I.C.S.: 332410; 333295; 333994; 423830
Export
Media: 2-7-10
Personnel:
Paul J. van der Wansem *(Chm & CEO)*
Peter J. Tallian *(CFO)*
James Michael Griffin *(VP-Sls & Svcs, Officer)*
John J. McCaffrey, Jr. *(VP-Ops & Engrg)*
Jan-Paul van Maaren *(VP-Mktg)*
Stephen J. Parrott *(Dir-Engrg)*
Donald A. Seccombe *(Dir-R & D)*
Bruce Quigley *(Mgr-Global Svc)*
Brands & Products:
BTU
PYRAMAX
WINCON

BUCYRUS INTERNATIONAL, INC.

1100 Milwaukee Ave
South Milwaukee, WI 53172-0500
Mailing Address:
PO Box 500
South Milwaukee, WI 53172-0500
Tel.: (414) 768-4000
Fax: (414) 768-4474
E-mail: ir@bucyrus.com
Web Site: www.bucyrus.com
Approx. Sls.: $3,650,563,000
Approx. Number Employees: 9,800
Year Founded: 1880
Business Description:
Mining Equipment Designer, Mfr & Marketer
S.I.C.: 1311; 3531; 3532
N.A.I.C.S.: 211111; 333120; 333131
Import Export
Media: 1-2-4-7-10-11-20
Distr.: Intl.; Natl.
Personnel:
Theodore C. Rogers *(Chm)*
Timothy W. Sullivan *(Pres & CEO)*
Craig R. Mackus *(CFO & Sec)*
Mark J. Knapp *(Chief Acctg Officer & Corp Controller)*
William S. Tate *(Exec VP)*
Barbara H. Stephens *(Sr VP-HR)*
Brands & Products:
BUCYRUS
HOISTBOSS
LATCHFREE
MARC
PEAK
RELIABILITY AT WORK
SWINGBOSS

BUNTING MAGNETICS CO.

500 S Spencer Rd
Newton, KS 67114-4109
Mailing Address:
PO Box 468
Newton, KS 67114-0468
Tel.: (316) 284-2020
Fax: (316) 283-4975
Toll Free: (800) 835-2526
E-mail: bmc@buntingmagnetics.com
Web Site: www.buntingmagnetics.com
Sales Range: $10-24.9 Million
Approx. Number Employees: 140
Year Founded: 1959
Business Description:
Magnetic Conveyors, Magnetic Separators & Filters, Cast Magnets, Ceramic Holding Magnets, Printing Cylinders Mfr
S.I.C.: 3264
N.A.I.C.S.: 327113
Import Export
Media: 2-7-10
Distr.: Intl.; Natl.
Budget Set: Sept. -Oct.
Personnel:
Robert J. Bunting *(Pres)*
Charles W. Whitt *(Dir-Mktg)*
Simon Ayling *(Mgr-Production-Berkhamsted)*
Rick Bigham *(Mgr-Product-Magnetic Separation)*
Vanessa Pereira *(Mgr-HR)*
Brands & Products:
BUNTING
CENTER FLOW MAGNET

Bunting Magnetics Co. — (Continued)

CERFACE
IMPRESSION
MAGLIFT
MAGSLIDE
MOVE-IT
NO-SPILL
POWERTRAC
RAGSDALE
RUTHERFORD
SLIDETRACK
VALUEMAG
X-TREME
XTRACTOR

Advertising Agency:
MarketAide Services, Inc.
PO Box 500
Salina, KS 67402-0500
Tel.: (785) 825-7161
Fax: (785) 825-4697
Toll Free: (800) 204-2433

BURGESS MANNING, INC.

(Sub. of Nitram Energy Inc.)
227 Thorn Ave
Orchard Park, NY 14127-2600
Tel.: (716) 662-6540
Fax: (716) 662-6548
E-mail: info@nitram.com
Web Site: www.burgessmanning.com
Sales Range: $10-24.9 Million
Approx. Number Employees: 50
Year Founded: 1920
Business Description:
Liquid, Gas & Air Separation, Filtration, Cleaning, Pulsation & Noise Pollution Control Products
S.I.C.: 3625
N.A.I.C.S.: 335314
Advertising Expenditures: $25,000
Media: 4-10
Distr.: Intl.; Natl.
Budget Set: Oct.

BUTECH BLISS

550 S Ellsworth Ave
Salem, OH 44460-3067
Tel.: (330) 332-9913
Fax: (330) 337-0800
E-mail: sales@butech.com
Web Site: www.butechbliss.com
E-Mail For Key Personnel:
Sales Director: sales@butech.com
Approx. Number Employees: 200
Year Founded: 1985
Business Description:
Industrial Machinery Mfr
S.I.C.: 3541; 3549
N.A.I.C.S.: 333512; 333518
Export
Media: 2-4-10
Distr.: Natl.

Brands & Products:
BUTECH BLISS

BUTLER AUTOMATIC, INC.

41 Leona Dr
Middleboro, MA 02346-1404
Tel.: (508) 923-0544
Fax: (508) 923-0885
Toll Free: (800) 544-0070
E-mail: butler@butlerautomatic.com
Web Site: www.butlerautomatic.com
Sales Range: $25-49.9 Million
Approx. Number Employees: 100
Year Founded: 1956
Business Description:
Machinery for the Printing & Packaging Industries Mfr
S.I.C.: 3555; 3565
N.A.I.C.S.: 333293; 333993
Import Export
Media: 2-4-7-10-11
Distr.: Intl.; Natl.
Personnel:
Andrew P. Butler *(Pres & CEO)*
Dave Ewan *(Engr-Sls)*

Brands & Products:
BUTLER
HYDRALIGN
NON-STOP PRODUCTION

BUTLER MACHINERY COMPANY

3401 33rd St SW
Fargo, ND 58104
Tel.: (701) 232-0033
Fax: (701) 298-1717
Web Site: www.butler-machinery.com
Approx. Sls.: $167,042,539
Approx. Number Employees: 80
Business Description:
Construction & Mining Machinery
S.I.C.: 5082; 7353
N.A.I.C.S.: 423810; 532412
Media: 5-7-8-10-13-22-26
Personnel:
Dan Butler *(Pres)*
Kelly Humble *(Mgr-Mktg)*
David Scott *(Mgr-IT)*
Stacey Bangert *(Coord-HR)*

BW TECHNOLOGIES LTD.

(Sub. of Honeywell Life Safety)
2840 2nd Ave SE
Calgary, AB T2A 7X9, Canada
Tel.: (403) 248-9226
Fax: (403) 273-3708
Toll Free: (800) 663-4164 (Canada)
Toll Free: (888) 749-8878 (USA)
E-mail: info@bwtnet.com
Web Site: www.gasmonitors.com
Sales Range: $25-49.9 Million
Approx. Number Employees: 302
Year Founded: 1961
Business Description:
Gas Detection Equipment Mfr
S.I.C.: 3533
N.A.I.C.S.: 333132
Advertising Expenditures: $200,000
Media: 10

Brands & Products:
GASALERTCLIP
GASALERTMAX
GASALERTMICRO
GASPOINT
RIG RAT
SHACK RAT
TOXYCLIP
TOXYPOINT

CAMERON DRILLING & PRODUCTION SYSTEMS

(Div. of Cameron International Corporation)
4646 W Sam Houston Pkwy N
Houston, TX 77041
Mailing Address:
PO Box 1212
Houston, TX 77251-1212
Tel.: (713) 939-2211
Fax: (713) 939-2019
Telex: 775422
E-mail: info@c-a-m.com
Sales Range: $150-199.9 Million
Approx. Number Employees: 700
Year Founded: 1920
Business Description:
Pressure Control Equipment Mfr
S.I.C.: 3494; 3533
N.A.I.C.S.: 332919; 333132
Advertising Expenditures: $600,000
Bus. Publs.: $180,000; Catalogs & Directories: $90,000; Exhibits/Trade Shows: $180,000; Premiums, Novelties: $150,000
Distr.: Intl.; Natl.
Budget Set: June
Personnel:
John D. Carne *(COO & Exec VP)*
Harold Conway *(Pres-Drilling Sys)*
Gary M. Halverson *(Pres-Surface Systems)*
John Bartoes *(VP-Tech)*
Steven Beatty *(VP-Fin)*
Edward E. Will *(VP-Mktg)*
Mike Mikulenka *(Mgr-Mktg Comm)*

Brands & Products:
CAMERONDC

Advertising Agency:
Cameron Adworks
4646 W Sam Houston Pkwy N
Houston, TX 77041
Tel.: (713) 939-2211
Fax: (713) 939-2753
(Oil Fill Prods.)

CAMERON VALVES & MEASUREMENT

(Div. of Cameron International Corporation)
3250 Briarpark Dr Ste 300
Houston, TX 77042-4239
Mailing Address:
PO Box 2117
Missouri City, TX 77252
Tel.: (281) 499-8511
Fax: (281) 499-5211
Web Site: www.c-a-m.com/content/vm
Sales Range: $150-199.9 Million
Business Description:
Valves & Related Equipment
S.I.C.: 5085; 3494
N.A.I.C.S.: 423840; 332919
Media: 10
Personnel:
Willy B. Findlay *(Pres)*
James E. Wright *(Pres-Valves & Measurement & Sr VP)*
Mark T. Cordell *(Pres-Distr & Process Valve Div)*
Rick Steans *(VP-Fin)*

CAMPBELL HAUSFELD

(Div. of The Scott Fetzer Company)
100 Production Dr
Harrison, OH 45030-1477
Tel.: (513) 367-4811
Fax: (513) 367-3176
Toll Free: (866) 88CHPOWER
Web Site: www.chpower.com
Sales Range: $300-349.9 Million
Approx. Number Employees: 913
Year Founded: 1836
Business Description:
Portable Air Compressor, Painting Systems, Air Tools, Generators, Pressure Washers & Welders
S.I.C.: 3563; 3546
N.A.I.C.S.: 333912; 333991
Import Export
Media: 2-4-6-8-10-13
Distr.: Natl.
Budget Set: Jan.

Brands & Products:
CAMPBELL HAUSFELD
MAXUS
POWEREX
WORKHORSE
ZERO BREAKDOWNS

CANADA FORGINGS INC.

130 Hagar St
PO Box 308
Welland, ON Canada
Tel.: (905) 735-1220
Fax: (905) 735-6992
E-mail: canforge@iaw.on.ca
Web Site: www.canforge.com
Approx. Number Employees: 115
Year Founded: 1912
Business Description:
Mfr of Open & Closed Die Forgings & Seamless Rolled Rings
S.I.C.: 2999; 3312; 3316
N.A.I.C.S.: 324199; 331111; 331221
Export
Media: 4-7-26
Distr.: Intl.; Natl.
Budget Set: Sept.
Personnel:
G. Guilbeault *(Pres)*
M. Ackroyd *(Mgr-Quality Control)*
W. Buchanan *(Mgr-Sls)*

CANNON EQUIPMENT COMPANY

(Sub. of Cannon Solutions)
15100 Business Pkwy
Rosemount, MN 55068
Tel.: (651) 322-6300
Fax: (651) 322-1583
Toll Free: (800) 825-8501
E-mail: info@cannonequipment.com
Web Site: www.cannonequipment.com
Approx. Number Employees: 150
Year Founded: 1980
Business Description:
Design, Engineering & Manufacturing of POP Displays & Material Handling Systems
S.I.C.: 2519; 3496
N.A.I.C.S.: 337125; 332618
Export
Advertising Expenditures: $400,000
Media: 2-4-7-10-13
Distr.: Natl.
Personnel:
Kenny Ramsey *(VP-Mktg)*

Brands & Products:
CART
COMET
CONNECT-A-BENCH
MAGNA-BAR
SHIP 'N SHOP
SLIP

CANTRELL INTERNATIONAL

(Div. of A.C. Horn & Company)
1269 Majesty Dr
Dallas, TX 75247
Tel.: (214) 630-3311
Fax: (214) 630-0130
Toll Free: (800) 657-6155
Web Site: www.cantrellinternational.com
Approx. Number Employees: 30

Key to Media (For complete agency information see *The Advertising Red Books-Agencies* edition):
1. Bus. Publs. 2. Cable T.V. 3. Catalogs & Directories. 4. Co-op Adv. 5. Consumer Mags. 6. D.M. to Bus. Estab.7. D.M. to Consumers 8. Daily Newsp. 9. Exhibits/Trade Shows 10. Foreign 11. Infomercial 12. Internet Adv.13. Multimedia 14. Network Radio 15. Network T.V. 16. Newsp. Distr. Mags. 17. Other 18. Outdoor (Posters, Transit) 19. Point of Purchase20. Premiums, Novelties 21. Product Samples 22. Special Events Mktg. 23. Spot Radio 24. Spot T.V. 25. Weekly Newsp. 26. Yellow Page Adv.

Business Description:
Popcorn Machines & Supplies; Systems for Corn Curls, Corn Chips, Caramel Corn & Peanut Brittle; Continuous Fryers, Extruders & Oil Seed Equipment Mills; Nut Processing Equipment, Roasters, Granulators & Blanchers Mfr
S.I.C.: 3444; 3441
N.A.I.C.S.: 332322; 332312
Export
Media: 2-26
Distr.: Direct to Consumer; Intl.; Natl.
Personnel:
Doug Horn *(Pres & CEO)*
Mark Ritter *(Exec VP & Mgr-Sls)*
Brands & Products:
MANLEY

CARBON SCIENCES, INC.

5511C Ekwill St
Santa Barbara, CA 93111
Tel.: (805) 456-7000
Fax: (805) 879-9892
E-mail: info@carbonsciences.com
Web Site: www.carbonsciences.com
Approx. Number Employees: 3
Year Founded: 2006
Business Description:
Non-Harmful Greenhouse Gas, Carbon Dioxide (CO2) Conversion Technology
S.I.C.: 1389; 8733
N.A.I.C.S.: 213112; 541710
Advertising Expenditures: $88,600
Personnel:
Byron H. Elton *(Pres & CEO)*
Advertising Agency:
RedChip Companies, Inc.
500 Winderely Pl Ste 100
Maitland, FL 32751
Tel.: (407) 644-4256
Fax: (407) 644-0758
Toll Free: (800) 733-2447

CARISTRAP INTERNATIONAL INC.

1760 Fortin Blvd
Laval, QC Canada
Tel.: (450) 667-4700
Fax: (450) 663-1520
E-mail: info@caristrap.com
Web Site: www.caristrap.com
E-Mail For Key Personnel:
President: akarass@caristrap.com
Sales Director: sales@caristrap.com
Approx. Sls.: $5,886,720
Approx. Number Employees: 250
Year Founded: 1954
Business Description:
Polyester Cord Strapping Systems Mfr
S.I.C.: 2298
N.A.I.C.S.: 314991
Export
Advertising Expenditures: $350,000
Media: 2-4-6-10-21
Distr.: Intl.
Personnel:
Audrey Karass *(Pres)*
Brands & Products:
CARISTRAP
CARISTRAP WEATHERGUARD

THE CARLYLE JOHNSON MACHINE COMPANY, L.L.C.

291 Boston Tpke PO Box 9546
Bolton, CT 06043-7252
Tel.: (860) 643-1531
Fax: (860) 646-2645
Toll Free: (888) 629-4867
Web Site: www.cjmco.com
Sales Range: $1-9.9 Million
Approx. Number Employees: 50
Year Founded: 1903
Business Description:
Industrial Clutches Mfr
S.I.C.: 3568; 3625
N.A.I.C.S.: 333613; 335314
Media: 2-4-10
Distr.: Natl.
Budget Set: Nov.
Personnel:
Michael E. Gamache *(Pres)*
Ron Gamache *(Mgr-Sls-US Comml)*
Thomas Thiffault *(Mgr-Mktg-Aerospace, Military & Intl)*
Brands & Products:
CJ
GROUNDED IN THE PAST, FOCUSED ON THE FUTURE
MAXITORQ

CARRIER COMMERCIAL REFRIGERATION

(Div. of Carrier Corporation)
9300 Harris Corners Pkwy Ste 200
Charlotte, NC 28269
Tel.: (704) 494-2600
Fax: (704) 494-2558
Sales Range: $50-74.9 Million
Approx. Number Employees: 5
Year Founded: 1984
Business Description:
Mfr. of Restaurant Equipment & Supplies; Maker of Dryers for Hands & Hair
S.I.C.: 5122
N.A.I.C.S.: 446120
Export
Advertising Expenditures: $1,004,000
Media: 2-4-7-10-26
Distr.: Intl.; Natl.
Brands & Products:
BEVERAGE-AIR
BLOOMFIELD
DRYBABY
EZA84
HORIZON
ICE CRAFT
RAZZLE
TAYLOR
WELLS
WORLD

CARRIER RENTAL SYSTEMS

(Sub. of Carrier Corporation)
40 Southbelt Industrial Dr
Houston, TX 77047-7010
Tel.: (713) 413-4200
Fax: (713) 434-3751
Toll Free: (800) 586-8336
E-mail: info@carrierrentals.com
Web Site: www.carrierrentals.com
Sales Range: $25-49.9 Million
Approx. Number Employees: 75
Year Founded: 1993
Business Description:
Heavy Construction Equipment including Air Conditioners, Air Handlers, Boilers, Chillers, Cooling Towers, Spot Coolers, Dehumidifiers, Heaters, Heat Exchangers, Generators, Pumps, Transformers, Fuel Tanks & Accesories Rental
S.I.C.: 7353; 7359
N.A.I.C.S.: 532412; 532490
Media: 2-7-10-13
Personnel:
Chris Opie *(VP & Gen Mgr-Carrier Rental Sys)*

CARTER DAY INTERNATIONAL, INC.

500 73rd Ave NE
Minneapolis, MN 55432-3270
Tel.: (763) 571-1000
Fax: (763) 571-3012
E-mail: bulldog@carterday.com
Web Site: www.carterday.com
Approx. Number Employees: 100
Year Founded: 1920
Business Description:
Mfr. of Processing Equipment
S.I.C.: 3556; 3569
N.A.I.C.S.: 333294; 333999
Import Export
Media: 2-7-8-10-11
Distr.: Intl.; Natl.
Budget Set: Apr.
Brands & Products:
BULLDOG
CARTER DAY
JACOBSON

CARTER MOTOR COMPANY

400 S Railroad St
Warren, IL 61087
Tel.: (815) 745-2100
Fax: (815) 745-2135
Toll Free: (866) 745-2100
E-mail: sales@cartermotor.com
Web Site: www.cartermotor.com
E-Mail For Key Personnel:
Sales Director: sales@cartermotor.com
Sales Range: $25-49.9 Million
Approx. Number Employees: 35
Year Founded: 1932
Business Description:
DC to AC Rotary Converters, Dynamotors & Rotary Power Supplies, Motors, Gearmotors & Tach Generators
S.I.C.: 3621; 3825
N.A.I.C.S.: 335312; 334515
Import Export
Media: 2-4-7
Distr.: Natl.
Personnel:
Keith Geisler *(Owner)*
Brands & Products:
CARTER
CLASSIC
MAGNUM
REGENT
TITAN

CASCADE CORPORATION

2201 NE 201st Ave
Fairview, OR 97024-9718
Mailing Address:
PO Box 20187
Portland, OR 97294-0187
Tel.: (503) 669-6300
Fax: (503) 669-6716
Toll Free: (800) 227-2233
E-mail: investorrelations@cascorp.com
Web Site: www.cascorp.com/americas
E-Mail For Key Personnel:
Marketing Director: MKern@cascorp.com
Approx. Sls.: $409,858,000
Approx. Number Employees: 1,800
Year Founded: 1943
Business Description:
Designer, Mfr & Marketer of Materials Handling Equipment & Related Technologies
S.I.C.: 3537; 3499; 3593
N.A.I.C.S.: 333924; 332439; 333995
Import Export
Media: 1-2-7-10-13-18
Distr.: Intl.; Natl.
Budget Set: May
Personnel:
Robert C. Warren, Jr. *(Pres & CEO)*
Joseph G. Pointer *(CFO)*
Richard S. Anderson *(COO & Sr VP)*
Gregory S. Anderson *(Sr VP-HR)*
Kevin B. Kreiter *(VP-Engrg & Mktg)*
Susan Wright *(VP-HR)*
Todd Finney *(Mgr-Strategic Acct)*
Clive Perry *(Mgr-Sls Office)*
Madalyn Piar-Katter *(Mgr-Corp Comm)*
Jonas Rofors *(Mgr-Sls)*
Jean Pierre Trucas *(Mgr-Sls-MHP)*
Brands & Products:
CASCADE
LOAD CUSHION
Advertising Agency:
Kennedy Communications
1701 Broadway St Ste 266
Vancouver, WA 98663
Tel.: (360) 213-5001
Fax: (360) 213-0246
Toll Free: (800) 877-0485

CATERPILLAR, INC.

100 NE Adams St
Peoria, IL 61629-0001
Tel.: (309) 675-1000
Fax: (309) 675-1182
E-mail: CATir@CAT.com
Web Site: www.cat.com
Approx. Rev.: $42,588,000,000
Approx. Number Employees: 104,490
Year Founded: 1925
Business Description:
Mfr of Construction & Mining Equipment, Diesel & Natural Gas Engines, Industrial Gas Turbines & Diesel-Electric Locomotives
S.I.C.: 3531; 3519; 3532; 3714
N.A.I.C.S.: 333120; 333131; 333618; 336312
Import Export
Media: 2-4-6-7-10-11-19
Distr.: Intl.; Natl.
Budget Set: Aug.
Personnel:
Douglas R. Oberhelman *(Chm & CEO)*
Edward J. Rapp *(Grp Pres & CFO)*
Stephen P. Larson *(Pres-CAT Logistics & VP)*
Stuart L. Levenick *(Grp Pres)*
John S. Heller *(CIO & VP)*
James B. Buda *(Chief Legal Officer & VP-Legal Svcs Div)*
Tana L. Utley *(CTO & VP-Tech & Solutions Div)*
Jananne A. Copeland *(Chief Acctg Officer)*
Frank Crespo *(Chief Procurement Officer-Global Purchasing Div & VP)*
Steven H. Wunning *(Grp Pres-Resource Indus)*
Steven A. Gosselin *(VP-Mktg & Product Support Center)*

Key to Media (For complete agency information see *The Advertising Red Books-Agencies* edition):
1. Bus. Publs. 2. Cable T.V. 3. Catalogs & Directories. 4. Co-op Adv. 5. Consumer Mags. 6. D.M. to Bus. Estab.7. D.M. to Consumers 8. Daily Newsp. 9. Exhibits/Trade Shows 10. Foreign 11. Infomercial 12. Internet Adv.13. Multimedia 14. Network Radio 15. Network T.V. 16. Newsp. Distr. Mags. 17. Other 18. Outdoor (Posters, Transit) 19. Point of Purchase20. Premiums, Novelties 21. Product Samples 22. Special Events Mktg. 23. Spot Radio 24. Spot T.V. 25. Weekly Newsp. 26. Yellow Page Adv.

Caterpillar, Inc. — (Continued)

Bradley M. Halverson *(VP-Fin & Acctg)*
Kimberly S. Hauer *(Dir-HR-EAME Reg)*
Ken Erdman *(Product Mgr)*
Robin D. Beran *(Asst Treas)*
Laurie J. Huxtable *(Asst Sec)*
Brands & Products:
CAT
CATERPILLAR
CATERPILLAR YELLOW
POWER EDGE
Advertising Agencies:
BKV Inc.
10561 Barkley St Ste 200
Overland Park, KS 66212
Tel.: (913) 648-8333
Fax: (913) 648-5024

Rhea + Kaiser
Naperville Financial Ctr 400 E Diehl Rd Ste 500
Naperville, IL 60563-1342
Tel.: (630) 505-1100
Fax: (630) 505-1109

CATERPILLAR WORK TOOLS, INC.
(Sub. of Caterpillar, Inc.)
600 Balderson Blvd
Wamego, KS 66547-1836
Tel.: (785) 456-2224
Fax: (785) 456-6302
Toll Free: (800) 255-2372
Sales Range: $150-199.9 Million
Approx. Number Employees: 356
Year Founded: 1915
Business Description:
Snow Plows, U-Blades, Buckets & Quick Couplers, Forestry & Landclearing Attachments Mfr
S.I.C.: 3531; 3536; 3546; 3743
N.A.I.C.S.: 333120; 333923; 333991; 336510
Media: 5-7-10-20
Distr.: Intl.; Natl.
Budget Set: June
Brands & Products:
BALDERSON
BALDERSON OVERSEA & S.A.
FLECO

CEMTREX, INC.
19 Engineers Ln
Farmingdale, NY 11735
Tel.: (631) 756-9116
Fax: (631) 420-4985
Web Site: www.cemtrex.com
Approx. Rev.: $3,304,055
Approx. Number Employees: 12
Business Description:
Emission Monitoring Equipment & Instruments Designer, Mfr & Sales
S.I.C.: 3559
N.A.I.C.S.: 333298
Advertising Expenditures: $25,450
Media: 17
Personnel:
Arun Govil *(Chm, Pres, CEO & Treas)*
Renato Dela Rama *(VP-Fin)*

CENTRIFUGAL & MECHANICAL INDUSTRIES, INC.
(Sub. of Roberts & Schaefer Company)
201 President St
Saint Louis, MO 63118-4111
Tel.: (314) 776-2848
Fax: (314) 776-2918
Telex: 477256 CMI STL
E-mail: info@cmi-centrifuges.com
Web Site: www.cmi-centrifuges.com
E-Mail For Key Personnel:
Sales Director: sales@cmi-centrifuges.com
Approx. Number Employees: 50
Year Founded: 1938
Business Description:
Centrifuges & Process Equipment
S.I.C.: 3532
N.A.I.C.S.: 333131
Export
Advertising Expenditures: $300,000
Media: 2-4-7-10-11-20
Distr.: Intl.; Natl.
Budget Set: Dec.
Personnel:
Alan Lattina *(Reg Mgr-Sls & Svcs)*
Brands & Products:
CMI

CENTRILIFT
(Sub. of Baker Hughes Incorporated)
200 W Stuart Roosa Dr
Claremore, OK 74017-3028
Tel.: (918) 341-9600
Fax: (918) 342-0260
Toll Free: (800) 533-5088
E-mail: sales@centrilift.com
Web Site: www.centrilift.com
E-Mail For Key Personnel:
Sales Director: sales@centrilift.com
Approx. Sls.: $150,000,000
Approx. Number Employees: 800
Year Founded: 1958
Business Description:
Mfr. of Pumps & Cables
S.I.C.: 3533; 1389
N.A.I.C.S.: 333132; 213112
Import Export
Media: 1-2-4-8-10-17-26
Distr.: Intl.; Natl.
Budget Set: Sept.
Brands & Products:
CENTRILINE
ELECTROSPEED

CENTURYVALLEN SAFETY SUPPLY COMPANY LTD
(Sub. of Hagemeyer Canada)
650 Jamieson Pkwy
Cambridge, ON N3C 0A5, Canada
Tel.: (519) 658-4182
Fax: (519) 658-2150
E-mail: peter.hitchen@sonepardis.ca
Web Site: www.centuryvallen.com
Approx. Number Employees: 5
Business Description:
Industrial Supply Distribution
S.I.C.: 5084; 5063
N.A.I.C.S.: 423830; 423610
Media: 4
Personnel:
David Key *(Pres)*
Brands & Products:
CENTURYVALLEN

CERRO FABRICATED PRODUCTS, INC.
(Sub. of Marmon Industrial Companies LLC)
300 Triangle Dr
Weyers Cave, VA 24486
Tel.: (540) 234-9252
Fax: (540) 234-8416
Web Site: www.cerrofabricated.com
Sales Range: $75-99.9 Million
Approx. Number Employees: 165
Business Description:
Aluminum, Brass, Copper, Bronze & Other Specialized Non-Ferrous Alloys Custom Mfr
S.I.C.: 3463
N.A.I.C.S.: 332112
Media: 4-7
Personnel:
John Tayloe *(Pres)*
Brands & Products:
ADVANCED COMPONENT SERIES
CHARDEN
LOMAG
PROTEK
TALLON
TITAN

C.H. HANSON COMPANY
2000 N Aurora Rd
Naperville, IL 60563-8793
Tel.: (630) 848-2000
Fax: (630) 848-2515
E-mail: sales@chhanson.com
Web Site: www.chhanson.com
E-Mail For Key Personnel:
Sales Director: sales@chhanson.com
Approx. Number Employees: 75
Year Founded: 1866
Business Description:
Marking Devices Mfr
S.I.C.: 3953; 5085
N.A.I.C.S.: 339943; 423840
Media: 4-6
Personnel:
Craig F. Hanson *(CEO)*
Phil Hanson *(Exec VP)*
Brands & Products:
ARMOR
ASQUARE
C.H. HANSON
CRAYON ARMOR
END-MATE
HANSON
PRECISION BALL LEVEL
PRO-SHARP
QUICKFIL
REESE
RHINO
STRINGLINGER
Advertising Agencies:
Freedman, Gibson & White Inc.
100 E Business Way Ste 300
Cincinnati, OH 45241
Tel.: (513) 241-3900
Fax: (513) 241-2220

Strata-G Communications
830 Main St 10th Fl
Cincinnati, OH 45202
Tel.: (513) 381-8855
Fax: (513) 381-0385
Toll Free: (800) 540-6986
Construction Tools

THE CHALLENGE MACHINERY COMPANY
6125 Norton Ctr Dr
Norton Shores, MI 49441
Tel.: (231) 799-8484
Fax: (231) 798-1275
E-mail: info@challengemachinery.com
Web Site: www.challengemachinery.com
Approx. Number Employees: 50
Year Founded: 1870
Business Description:
Mfr of Graphic Arts Bindery Equipment
S.I.C.: 3554; 3423
N.A.I.C.S.: 333291; 332212
Import Export
Media: 1-2-4-7-10
Distr.: Intl.; Natl.
Budget Set: Dec.
Personnel:
Larry Ritsema *(Pres & CEO)*
Britt Cary *(Dir-Sls & Mktg)*
Brands & Products:
CHALLENGE POWER LIFT
CHALLENGER
CHAMPION
EH 3C
JF
JO
MEDALIST
MORGANA
MORGANA EZ FOLDER
MS-10A
MS-5
PADDY WAGON
PAK-RAK
SPARTAN
TITAN

CHANDLER PRODUCTS
(Sub. of Elgin Fastener Group)
1491 Chardon Rd
Cleveland, OH 44117-1510
Tel.: (216) 481-4400
Fax: (216) 481-4427
E-mail: info@chandlerproducts.com
Web Site: www.chandlerproducts.com
Approx. Number Employees: 100
Business Description:
Cold Headed Fasteners Mfr
S.I.C.: 3452; 3451
N.A.I.C.S.: 332722; 332721
Media: 4-10

CHARLES MACHINE WORKS, INC.
(d/b/a Ditch Witch)
1959 W Fir Ave
Perry, OK 73077-5803
Mailing Address:
PO Box 66
Perry, OK 73077-0066
Tel.: (580) 336-4402
Fax: (580) 572-3523
Fax: (580) 336-3458
Toll Free: (800) 654-6481
E-mail: info@ditchwitch.com
Web Site: www.ditchwitch.com
Sales Range: $300-349.9 Million
Approx. Number Employees: 1,300
Year Founded: 1949
Business Description:
Trenching & Underground Machinery Mfr
S.I.C.: 3531; 3541; 3545; 3546; 3829
N.A.I.C.S.: 333120; 333512; 333515; 333991; 334519
Export
Media: 2-4-7-10-11
Distr.: Intl.; Natl.
Personnel:
Mary Malzahn *(Vice Chm)*
Tiffany Sewell-Howard *(CEO)*

Richard Levings *(Product Mgr-Trenchless Applications)*
Jeri Lamerton *(Mgr-PR & Adv)*
Brands & Products:
AUTOCROWD
CMW
DITCH WITCH
FLUID MISER
HAMMERHEAD
JET TRAC
MODULARMATIC
PERMASOIL
PIERCE AIRROW
ROTO WITCH
SIDEKICK
SUBSITE
SUPER WITCH
SUPER WITCH II

CHARMILLES MIKRON
(Sub. of Agie Charmilles Holding Limited)
560 Bond St
Lincolnshire, IL 60069-4224
Tel.: (847) 913-5300
Fax: (847) 913-5340
Toll Free: (800) CTC-1EDM
E-mail: info@charmillesus.com
Web Site: www.charmillesus.com
E-Mail For Key Personnel:
President: harry.moser@charmillesus.com
Marketing Director: gisbert.ledvon@charmillesus.com
Sales Director: martin.gorski@charmillesus.com
Approx. Number Employees: 100
Year Founded: 1956
Business Description:
Mfr. of Electro Discharge Machines (EDM) & Machine Tools
S.I.C.: 5084
N.A.I.C.S.: 423830
Import Export
Advertising Expenditures: $1,000,000
Media: 2-4-7-10-11-13-16-17-18-20
Distr.: Intl.; Natl.
Budget Set: Oct.
Personnel:
Gisbert Ledvon *(Mgr-Bus Dev)*

CHESHER EQUIPMENT LTD.
6599 Kitimat Rd Unit 2
Mississauga, ON L5N4J4, Canada
Tel.: (905) 363-0309
Fax: (905) 890-5618
Toll Free: (800) 668-8765
E-mail: sales@chesher.com
Web Site: www.chesher.com
E-Mail For Key Personnel:
Sales Director: sales@chesher.com
Sales Range: Less than $1 Million
Approx. Number Employees: 6
Year Founded: 1967
Business Description:
Food Machinery & Equipment Distr
S.I.C.: 5087; 5064
N.A.I.C.S.: 423850; 423620
Import
Media: 2-4-10-17
Distr.: Natl.
Personnel:
Michaela Chesher *(Mgr-Opers)*
Darlene Hann *(Mgr-Sls)*
Brands & Products:
CHESHER
COOKTEK
CRES COR
DITO
ELECTROLUX
NILMA
RHENINGHAUS
ROTOR
ROUNDUP
SANAMAT
SUPERHOT
VIKAN HYGIENE SYSTEM
VITA-MIX
VITA-PREP
VITA-PRO
VITAMAT
WOOD STONE

CHICAGO METAL FABRICATORS, INC.
3724 S Rockwell St
Chicago, IL 60632-1051
Tel.: (773) 523-5755
Fax: (773) 523-8680
E-mail: info@chicagometal.com
Web Site: www.chicagometal.com
Approx. Sls.: $6,200,000
Approx. Number Employees: 80
Year Founded: 1908
Business Description:
Distr. of Metal Fabricating Products
S.I.C.: 3469; 5084
N.A.I.C.S.: 332116; 423830
Media: 2-4-7
Distr.: Natl.
Budget Set: Nov.
Personnel:
Randy Hauser *(Pres)*

CHICAGO PNEUMATIC TOOL COMPANY LLC
(Sub. of Atlas Copco North America LLC)
13325 Carowinds Blvd
Charlotte, NC 28273
Tel.: (704) 936-4000
Fax: (800) 228-9096
Toll Free: (800) 624-4735
Web Site: www.chicagopneumatic.com
Approx. Number Employees: 100
Business Description:
Vehicle Service Tools, Vehicle Assembly Tools, Pneumatic Tools
S.I.C.: 3546; 3563
N.A.I.C.S.: 333991; 333912
Import Export
Media: 2-4-7-10-11-13-19-26
Distr.: Natl.
Budget Set: Jan.
Personnel:
Martin Paulsen *(Gen Mgr)*
Brands & Products:
REDIPOWER GRINDERS
SUITOR

CHICAGO RIVET & MACHINE COMPANY
901 Frontenac Rd
Naperville, IL 60563
Mailing Address:
PO Box 3061
Naperville, IL 60566
Tel.: (630) 357-8500
Fax: (630) 983-9314
E-mail: info@chicagorivet.com
Web Site: www.chicagorivet.com
E-Mail For Key Personnel:
Sales Director: sales@chicagorivet.com
Approx. Sls.: $28,520,510
Approx. Number Employees: 219
Year Founded: 1920
Business Description:
Rivets, Rivet Setting Machines & Cold Headed Parts Mfr
S.I.C.: 3452; 3542
N.A.I.C.S.: 332722; 333513
Export
Advertising Expenditures: $1,000,000
Media: 4-26
Distr.: Direct to Consumer; Intl.; Natl.
Budget Set: Jan.
Personnel:
Michael J. Bourg *(Pres, COO & Treas)*
John A. Morrissey *(CEO)*

CHICAGO TUBE & IRON CO.
1 Chicago Tube Dr
Romeoville, IL 60446
Tel.: (815) 834-2500
Fax: (815) 588-3958
Toll Free: (800) 972-0217
E-mail: ctichgo@chicagotube.com
Web Site: www.chicagotube.com
Approx. Sls.: $137,000,000
Approx. Number Employees: 400
Year Founded: 1914
Business Description:
Steel Service Center Warehouse
S.I.C.: 5051; 3498
N.A.I.C.S.: 423510; 332996
Import Export
Media: 2-4-5-10-20-22-26
Distr.: Natl.
Budget Set: Oct.
Personnel:
Robert B. Haigh *(Chm & CEO)*
Donald R. McNeeley *(Pres & COO)*
Michael S. DiNanno *(CFO & VP-Fin)*
Thomas M. Moran *(VP-IT)*
William J. Zielinski *(VP-Mktg)*
Walter J. Kobiernicki *(Comptroller)*
Dan Deffenbaugh *(Dir-Mktg-Stainless Steel & Aluminum)*
Paul Doering *(Dir-Mktg-Pipe, Valves & Fittings)*
Wally Wahlstrom *(Dir-Mktg Pipe, Valves & Fittings)*
Dan Cartiea *(Mgr-Payroll)*
James Kent *(Mgr-Transportation)*
Lee Thompson *(Mgr-Quality)*
Robert Wojtalewicz *(Mgr-Corp Credit)*

CHIEF INDUSTRIES, INC.
3942 W Old Hwy 30
Grand Island, NE 68802
Tel.: (308) 389-7200
Fax: (308) 389-7221
Toll Free: (800) 765-7245
E-mail: corporate@chiefind.com
Web Site: www.chiefind.com
Approx. Sls.: $103,000,000
Approx. Number Employees: 1,800
Year Founded: 1954
Business Description:
Grain Bins, Metal Building Systems; Factory Built Homes; Recreational Vehicles; Cabinets & Components; Electronic Display Systems; Wastewater Treatment Systems; Concrete Breaking Machines, Aeration Systems, Pole Buildings & Correctional Products; Ethanol
S.I.C.: 3448; 2451
N.A.I.C.S.: 332311; 321991
Export
Advertising Expenditures: $1,000,000
Media: 2-5-6-7-8-10-11-20-26
Distr.: Intl.; Natl.
Budget Set: June
Personnel:
Robert Eihusen *(Chm)*
Mark Moravic *(Dir-HR)*
Corey Tompkins *(Plant Mgr)*
Chad Micek *(Sls Mgr)*
Wayne Garrett *(Mgr-Sls & Mktg)*
Jim Krajicek *(Mgr-Corp Environmental, Health & Safety)*
Gary Werner *(Coord-Adv)*
Brands & Products:
BONNAVILLA
CHIEF
CHIEF AGRI INDUSTRIES
CHIEF BUILDING
CHIEF CONSTRUCTION
CHIEF CUSTOM PRODUCTS
CHIEF ETHANOL FUELS
CHIEF FABRICATION
CHIEF INTERMODAL
CHIEF TRANSPORTATION PRODUCTS
EDS
GROUND ISLAND CONTRACT CARRIER
KING OF THE ROAD

CHRISTIANSON SYSTEMS, INC.
20421 15th St SE
Blomkest, MN 56216
Tel.: (320) 995-6141
Fax: (320) 995-6145
Toll Free: (800) 328-8896
Telex: 6791028 CSI UW
E-mail: info@christianson.com
Web Site: www.christianson.com
Approx. Sls.: $4,000,000
Approx. Number Employees: 37
Year Founded: 1942
Business Description:
Pneumatic Conveying Systems Mfr
S.I.C.: 3535
N.A.I.C.S.: 333922
Export
Advertising Expenditures: $400,000
Media: 1-2-4-5-9-10-11-13-17-22-25
Distr.: Intl.; Natl.
Personnel:
Jim Gerhart *(Pres)*
Frank Christianson *(Sr VP)*
Barb Gilberts *(Mgr-Mktg-Sls)*
Brands & Products:
AUGERVAC
BLOWERGARD
CHEM-VAC
CHRISTIANSON
HANDLAIR
PUSH-PAC
ROCKVAC
SEEDVAC
SUPER PORTABLE
SUPER TOWER
VAC-U-VATOR
VACBOSS
Advertising Agency:
CES Advertising
20421 15th St SE
Blomkest, MN 56216
Tel.: (320) 995-6141
Fax: (320) 995-6145
Toll Free: (800) 328-8896
(Mfr. Ship Unloaders)

THE CINCINNATI GILBERT MACHINE TOOL COMPANY, L.L.C.
3366 Beekman St
Cincinnati, OH 45223-2424
Tel.: (513) 541-4815
Fax: (513) 541-4885
E-mail: information@cincinnatigilbert.com
Web Site: www.cincinnatigilbert.com
Sales Range: $10-24.9 Million
Approx. Number Employees: 10
Year Founded: 1893
Business Description:
Horizontal Drilling, Boring & Milling Machines & Rotary Tables Mfr; Horizontals, Machining Centers
S.I.C.: 3541; 3545
N.A.I.C.S.: 333512; 333515
Export
Media: 2-4-10
Distr.: Intl.; Natl.
Budget Set: Oct.
Personnel:
Reinhold Petry *(Co-Owner & Pres)*
Eva Petry *(Co-Owner)*
John Vollmer *(Asst Mgr-Sls)*
Brands & Products:
AIRMIST
CINCINNATI GILBERT

CLARK MATERIAL HANDLING COMPANY
(Sub. of Young An Hat Co., Ltd.)
700 Enterprise Dr
Lexington, KY 40510
Tel.: (859) 422-6400
Fax: (859) 422-6508
Toll Free: (866) -252-5275
Web Site: www.clarkmhc.com
Sales Range: $350-399.9 Million
Approx. Number Employees: 80
Year Founded: 1917
Business Description:
Material Handling Equipment Mfr
S.I.C.: 5084
N.A.I.C.S.: 423830
Media: 13
Personnel:
Dennis Lawrence *(Pres & CEO)*
Chuck Moratz *(COO & VP)*
Michael Grossman *(Gen Counsel & Exec VP)*
Farrukh Ghani *(VP-Fin & Tech)*
Bo Maslanyk *(VP-Sls & Mktg)*
Mark Dyster *(Dir-Engrg & Product Support)*
Brian Woodford *(Dir-Creative, Adv & Mktg)*
Brands & Products:
CLARK
CLARK LIFT
GENESIS
GENII
POWRWORKER

CLAYTON & LAMBERT MANUFACTURING CO.
3813 W Hwy 146
Buckner, KY 40010-0009
Mailing Address:
PO Box 9
Buckner, KY 40010-0009
Tel.: (502) 222-1411
Fax: (502) 222-1415
Toll Free: (800) 626-5819
E-mail: info@claytonlambert.com
Web Site: www.claytonlambert.com
Approx. Number Employees: 13
Year Founded: 1888
Business Description:
Swimming Pools & Industrial Storage Structures Mfr
S.I.C.: 3448
N.A.I.C.S.: 332311
Media: 17-21
Distr.: Natl.
Budget Set: Jan.
Personnel:
John W. Lambert *(Pres)*
Brands & Products:
CLAYTON & LAMBERT

CLAYTON INDUSTRIES CO.
17477 Hurley St
City of Industry, CA 91744-5106
Tel.: (626) 443-9381
Tel.: (626) 435-1200
Fax: (626) 442-1701
Fax: (626) 435-0180
Toll Free: (800) 423-4585
E-mail: sales@claytonindustries.com
Web Site: www.claytonindustries.com
E-Mail For Key Personnel:
Sales Director: sales@claytonindustries.com
Approx. Number Employees: 600
Year Founded: 1930
Business Description:
Steam Generators Mfr
S.I.C.: 3569; 3829
N.A.I.C.S.: 333999; 334519
Export
Advertising Expenditures: $250,000
Media: 1-2-4-7-10-11-20-26
Distr.: Intl.; Natl.
Budget Set: Oct.
Personnel:
Allen Cluer *(Exec VP-Mfg & Engrg)*
Brands & Products:
CD/410
CLAYTON
CLEAN-MASTER
CSS/1200
HP-80
INSTEEMATIC
KARBONOFF
KAYSTRIP
KERFUL
KERLITE
KERMEED
KERRICK KLEANERS
KLEEN-KOIL
LIQUIDEMON
STEAM-SAFE 20
STEAMIN DEMON
SUMMERAIRE
WONDERWASH

CLEVELAND MOTION CONTROLS
(Sub. of International Motion Control, Inc.)
7550 Hub Pkwy
Cleveland, OH 44125-5705
Tel.: (216) 524-8800
Fax: (216) 642-2199
Toll Free: (800) 321-8072
Web Site: www.cmccontrols.com
Approx. Sls.: $12,400,000
Approx. Number Employees: 50
Year Founded: 1958
Business Description:
Controls for Adjustable Speed Drives & Web Tension Control Equipment; Numerical Controls; Measuring Tools & Machines
S.I.C.: 3625; 3823
N.A.I.C.S.: 335314; 334513
Export
Advertising Expenditures: $500,000
Media: 1-2-4-5-7-10-11-20-21-22-26
Distr.: Natl.
Personnel:
Greg Clark *(Pres-Sls & Mktg)*
Brands & Products:
AXIMASTER
BURNY
CLEVELAND KIDDER
DATATORQUE
DIGIMASTER
DIGIVEC
TORQUEMASTER

CLINTON INDUSTRIES, INC.
207 Redneck Ave
Little Ferry, NJ 07643-1320
Tel.: (201) 440-0400
Fax: (201) 440-5040
Toll Free: (800) 899-2546
E-mail: general@clintonind.com
Web Site: www.clintonind.com
Sales Range: $10-24.9 Million
Approx. Number Employees: 18
Year Founded: 1954
Business Description:
Mfr. of Peripherals for Industrial Sewing Machines
S.I.C.: 3559
N.A.I.C.S.: 333298
Export
Media: 2-4-7-10-11
Distr.: Intl.; Natl.
Personnel:
Larry Paricio *(COO)*
Dara Silver *(VP-HR)*
Bob Pulliam *(Mgr-Sls & Mktg)*

CMI-SCHNEIBLE COMPANY
714 N Saginaw St
Holly, MI 48442-1345
Tel.: (248) 634-8211
Fax: (248) 634-2240
Toll Free: (800) 627-6508
E-mail: info@cmischneible.com
Web Site: www.cmischneible.com
Sales Range: $10-24.9 Million
Approx. Number Employees: 40
Year Founded: 1935
Business Description:
Precision Machining, Maintenance Programs & Light Assembly
S.I.C.: 3443; 3564
N.A.I.C.S.: 332313; 333412
Media: 8
Distr.: Natl.
Budget Set: Apr.
Personnel:
Hank Harvey *(Pres & CEO)*
Jason Popour *(Mgr-Plng)*

COFFMAN MANUFACTURING CORPORATION
305 Cary Point Dr
Cary, IL 60013
Tel.: (847) 639-5721
Fax: (847) 639-5755
E-mail: coffman@ameritech.net
Web Site: www.normancontrol.com
Approx. Number Employees: 2
Year Founded: 1948
Business Description:
General Machining Mfr; Welding, Fabricating & Specialty Work
S.I.C.: 3599
N.A.I.C.S.: 332710
Advertising Expenditures: $225,000
Media: 2-4-7
Distr.: Natl.
Budget Set: Oct.
Personnel:
Richard J. Coffman *(Pres)*
Brands & Products:
NORMAN CONTROL

COILCRAFT, INC.
1102 Silver Lake Rd
Cary, IL 60013-1658
Tel.: (847) 639-2361
Fax: (847) 639-1469
Toll Free: (800) 322-2645
E-mail: info@coilcraft.com
Web Site: www.coilcraft.com
Approx. Number Employees: 250
Year Founded: 1946
Business Description:
Intermediate Frequency Coils, Power Transformers, Industrial Coils, Transformers & Chip Inductors Mfr
S.I.C.: 3677; 5065
N.A.I.C.S.: 334416; 423690
Export
Media: 2-4-7-10-11-13
Distr.: Intl.; Natl.
Personnel:
Tom Liebman *(Pres)*
John Stellberg *(Dir-Mktg Comm)*
Paul Liebman *(Mgr-Mktg)*
Brands & Products:
ADS
AGILENT
AIR CORE SPRING
COILCRAFT
GENESYS
GLOBEL MODEL LIBRARY
MICRO SPRING
MODELITHICS
POWER WAFER
ROHS COMPLIANT
SIMPLE SWITCHER
TRUST
WAFERS
THE WORLD'S MOST POWERFUL MAGNETIC FIELD

COIN ACCEPTORS, INC.
300 Hunter Ave
Saint Louis, MO 63124-2081
Tel.: (314) 725-0100
Fax: (314) 725-7198
Toll Free: (800) 325-2646
E-mail: info@coinco.com
Web Site: www.coinco.com
Approx. Number Employees: 1,100
Year Founded: 1958
Business Description:
Coin Handling Devices Mfr & Distr for Vending Machines
S.I.C.: 3581
N.A.I.C.S.: 333311
Export
Media: 2-4-7-10
Distr.: Intl.; Natl.
Budget Set: Nov.

Key to Media (For complete agency information see *The Advertising Red Books-Agencies* edition):
1. Bus. Publs. 2. Cable T.V. 3. Catalogs & Directories. 4. Co-op Adv. 5. Consumer Mags. 6. D.M. to Bus. Estab.7. D.M. to Consumers
8. Daily Newsp. 9. Exhibits/Trade Shows 10. Foreign 11. Infomercial 12. Internet Adv.13. Multimedia 14. Network Radio
15. Network T.V. 16. Newsp. Distr. Mags. 17. Other 18. Outdoor (Posters, Transit) 19. Point of Purchase20. Premiums, Novelties
21. Product Samples 22. Special Events Mktg. 23. Spot Radio 24. Spot T.V. 25. Weekly Newsp. 26. Yellow Page Adv.

Personnel:
Parker B. Condie *(Pres)*
Kevin Ward *(COO & Exec VP-Royal Vendors)*

Brands & Products:
BILLPRO
COINCO
COINCO GLOBAL
COMPACTVENDOR
ECONO-COOL
MAG-PRO
MAGPRO
QUANTUMPRO
VORTEX

COINSTAR, INC.
1800 114th Ave SE
Bellevue, WA 98004-6946
Tel.: (425) 943-8000
Fax: (425) 943-8000
Toll Free: (800) 928-2274
E-mail: info@coinstar.com
Web Site: www.coinstar.com
Approx. Rev.: $1,436,421,000
Approx. Number Employees: 2,585
Year Founded: 1991
Business Description:
Coin Counting & Processing Machines Mfr, Owner & Operator
S.I.C.: 5962; 3581; 7299
N.A.I.C.S.: 454210; 333311; 812990
Advertising Expenditures: $15,400,000
Media: 2-3-10-17-22-23-24
Personnel:
Deborah L. Bevier, Sr. *(Chm)*
Gregg A. Kaplan *(Pres & COO)*
Paul D. Davis *(CEO)*
J. Scott Di Valerio *(CFO)*
Saul M. Gates *(Chief Acctg Officer & VP)*
James C. Blakely *(Chief Customer Officer)*
Michael J. Skinner *(Pres-Coin)*
Donald R. Rench *(Gen Counsel)*
Stephen J. Verleye *(Sr VP & Gen Mgr-Electronic Payment Solutions)*
Alex Doumani *(VP-Tech-New Ventures)*
Christi Liebe *(Corp VP-IT)*
Sarah Jones *(Mgr-Cause Marketing & PR)*

Brands & Products:
COINS THAT COUNT
COINSTAR
COINSTAR 4TH WALL

Advertising Agencies:
The MWW Group
1 Meadowlands Plz 6th Fl
East Rutherford, NJ 07073
Tel.: (201) 507-9500
Fax: (201) 507-0092
Corporate Communications Agency of Record
Crisis
CSR
Financial Media Outreach

Swirl Advertising
1620 Montgomery St Ste 140
San Francisco, CA 94111
Tel.: (415) 276-8300
Fax: (415) 276-8301

COLEMAN CABLE, INC.
1530 Shields Dr
Waukegan, IL 60085-8309
Tel.: (847) 672-2300
Fax: (847) 689-1192
Toll Free: (800) 323-9355
E-mail: info@coleman-cable.com
Web Site: www.colemancable.com
Approx. Sls.: $703,763,000
Approx. Number Employees: 1,052
Year Founded: 1970
Business Description:
Electronic Wire & Cable Products Developer, Mfr & Distr
S.I.C.: 3496; 3357
N.A.I.C.S.: 335921; 332618; 335929
Import Export
Advertising Expenditures: $2,325,000
Media: 2-4-10-13
Personnel:
David Bistricer *(Co-Chm)*
Nachum John Stein *(Co-Chm)*
G. Gary Yetman *(Pres & CEO)*
Richard N. Burger *(CFO, Treas, Sec & Exec VP)*
Mark Andrews *(CIO)*
Michael A. Frigo *(Exec VP-OEM Grp)*
J. Kurt Hennelly *(Exec VP-Ops)*
Kenneth A. McAllister *(Exec VP-Distr Grp)*
Kathy Jo Van *(Exec VP-Retail Grp)*
Howard Caccia *(Sr VP-Engrng)*
John P. Pappas *(Sr VP-Sls & Mktg-US Retail Grp)*
Rick Brambley *(VP-Hardware-Retail & Automotive Grp Sls)*
Dan Hastings *(VP-Security & Home Tech Div)*
Kurt Markshausen *(VP-Retail)*
Tony Gabriel *(Dir-Engrg)*
Dale Plautz *(Dir-Corp Pur)*
Mark Rogers *(Dir-Quality)*
Cliff Sanderson *(Dir-HR)*
Bob Bennish *(Mgr-Natl Accts)*
Rod Davis *(Mgr-Credit)*
Todd Hermon *(Mgr-Natl Accts)*
Frank Scortino *(Mgr-Inside Sls)*
Jim Smole *(Mgr-Customer Svc)*
Gene Wethington *(Mgr-Mdsg)*

Brands & Products:
AIM RITE
AMERICAN CONTRACTOR
BARO-PAK
BARO-SPLIT
BAROGATION
BARON
BAROPLEN
BAROSTAT
BOOSTER-IN-A-BAG
CCI
CLEAR SIGNALTM
CLEARSIGNAL
COILEX
COMPACT 600
COOL COLORS
COPPERFIELD
CORD-O-LITE
CORRACLAD
INDOOR TRINECTOR
LITE STREAMER
LUMA-SITE
MAXIMUM ENERGY
OSWEGO
PLENCOTE
POLAR-FLEX
POLAR-GLO
POLAR-RIG 125
POLAR SOLAR
POWERSTATION
POWERWATCH
PUSH-LOCK
QUADNECTOR
ROAD POWER
ROYAL
SEOPRENE
SIGLAN 350
SIGNA-WAVE
SIGNAL
SIGNALPLUS
SIGNET
SLENDER PLUG
SOLAR PLUS
SOUNDSATIONAL
SOVEREIGN
STRIPES
T-PRENE
TRI-SOURCE
TRIANGLE
X-TREME BOX
YOUR COMPLETE CABLE SOLUTION

COLFAX CORPORATION
8170 Maple Lawn Blvd Ste 180
Fulton, MD 20759
Tel.: (301) 323-9000
Fax: (301) 323-9001
E-mail: info@colfaxcorp.com
Web Site: www.colfaxcorp.com
Approx. Sls.: $541,987,000
Approx. Number Employees: 1,524
Year Founded: 1995
Business Description:
Pump & Power Transmission Products Mfr & Marketer
S.I.C.: 3561; 3492; 3594
N.A.I.C.S.: 333911; 332912; 333996
Advertising Expenditures: $500,000
Personnel:
Mitchell P. Rales *(Chm)*
Clay H. Kiefaber *(Pres & CEO)*
C. Scott Brannan *(CFO & Sr VP-Fin)*
A. Lynne Puckett *(Gen Counsel, Sec & Sr VP)*
Mario E. Didomenico *(Sr VP & Gen Counsel-Colfax ESBU)*
William E. Roller *(Exec VP-Colfax Fluid Handling)*
Arne Forslund *(Sr VP-Europe, Middle East, Africa & Asia)*
Joseph B. Niemann *(Sr VP-Mktg & Strategic Plng)*
Daniel A. Pryor *(Sr VP-Strategy & Bus Dev)*
Bill Rothenbach *(Sr VP-HR)*
Steve Wittig *(Sr VP-Bus Sys & Supply Chain Strategy)*

COLUMBIAN TECTANK
(Div. of CST Industries, Inc.)
5400 Kansas Ave
Kansas City, KS 66116
Mailing Address:
PO Box 2907
Kansas City, KS 66110-2907
Tel.: (913) 621-3700
Fax: (913) 621-2145
E-mail: info@columbiantectank.com
Web Site: www.columbiantectank.com
Approx. Number Employees: 160
Year Founded: 1893
Business Description:
Bolted Storage Tanks
S.I.C.: 3443
N.A.I.C.S.: 332420
Import Export
Media: 2-4-7-10-26
Distr.: Intl.
Budget Set: Jan.

COLUMBUS MCKINNON CORPORATION
140 John James Audubon Pkwy
Amherst, NY 14228-1112
Tel.: (716) 689-5400
Fax: (716) 689-5644
Toll Free: (800) 888-0985 (Sales)
Telex: 6854301
E-mail: hr@cmworks.com
Web Site: www.cmworks.com
Approx. Sls.: $524,065,000
Approx. Number Employees: 2,531
Year Founded: 1875
Business Description:
Hoists, Cranes, Chains, Conveyors, Material Handling Systems, Lift Tables & Component Parts Designer, Mfr & Marketer
S.I.C.: 3531; 3496; 3536
N.A.I.C.S.: 333120; 332618; 333923
Import Export
Advertising Expenditures: $3,700,000
Media: 2-4-10
Distr.: Intl.; Natl.
Budget Set: Apr.
Personnel:
Ernest R. Verebelyi *(Chm)*
Timothy T. Tevens *(Pres & CEO)*
Gregory P. Rustowicz *(CFO)*
Alan Korman *(Gen Counsel, Sec & VP)*
Karen L. Howard *(VP-Strategic Initiatives)*
Richard A. Steinberg *(VP-HR)*
Rob Beightol *(Dir-Market Res & Comm)*
John Ficara *(Dir-Tax)*
Otto Gretzinger *(Dir-Fin Plng & Analysis)*

Brands & Products:
AMERICAN LIFTS
BIG ORANGE
BUDGIT
CADY
CAMLOK
CHESTER
CM
COFFING
COLUMBUS MCKINNON
CRANEMART
DI
DUFF-NORTON
HAMMERLOK
HERC ALLOY
HOISTALOY
LITTLE MULE
LODELOK
LODESTAR
PFAFF
SHAW-BOX
TIGRIP
TUGIT
YALE

Advertising Agency:
Travers Collins & Company
726 Exchange St Ste 500
Buffalo, NY 14210-1495
Tel.: (716) 842-2222
Fax: (716) 842-6424

COMMERCIAL SOLUTIONS INC.
4203 95th Street
Edmonton, AB T6E 5R6, Canada
Tel.: (780) 432-1611
Fax: (780) 433-5176
E-mail: international@csinet.ca

Key to Media (For complete agency information see *The Advertising Red Books-Agencies* edition):
1. Bus. Publs. 2. Cable T.V. 3. Catalogs & Directories. 4. Co-op Adv. 5. Consumer Mags. 6. D.M. to Bus. Estab.7. D.M. to Consumers 8. Daily Newsp. 9. Exhibits/Trade Shows 10. Foreign 11. Infomercial 12. Internet Adv.13. Multimedia 14. Network Radio 15. Network T.V. 16. Newsp. Distr. Mags. 17. Other 18. Outdoor (Posters, Transit) 19. Point of Purchase20. Premiums, Novelties 21. Product Samples 22. Special Events Mktg. 23. Spot Radio 24. Spot T.V. 25. Weekly Newsp. 26. Yellow Page Adv.

Commercial Solutions Inc. — (Continued)

Web Site:
www.commercialsolutions.ca
Approx. Rev.: $91,138,875
Approx. Number Employees: 240
Business Description:
Bearing, Power, Transmission, Industrial, Safety, Forestry, Mining & Resource Management Equipment Products Sales & Distr
S.I.C.: 5099
N.A.I.C.S.: 423990
Advertising Expenditures: $723,480
Personnel:
James Barker *(Pres & CEO)*
Rozina Kassam *(CFO)*
William Rosser *(Dir)*

COMPAIR USA
(Sub. of CompAir UK Ltd.)
130 Fox Dr
Piqua, OH 45356
Tel.: (937) 778-2500
Fax: (937) 778-4123
E-mail: compair@bright.net
Web Site: www.compairusa.com
Sales Range: $75-99.9 Million
Approx. Number Employees: 150
Year Founded: 1916
Business Description:
Air & Gas Compressors, Air Dryers & Parts Mfr
S.I.C.: 3563; 3559
N.A.I.C.S.: 333912; 333298
Import Export
Media: 1-2-4-7-16-21
Distr.: Intl.; Natl.
Brands & Products:
BROOMWADE
COMPAIR
HYDROVANE
QUANTIMA

COMVERGE, INC.
5390 Triangle Pkwy Ste 300
Norcross, GA 30092
Tel.: (678) 392-4954
Toll Free: (888) 565-5525
E-mail: invest@comverge.com
Web Site: www.comverge.com
E-Mail For Key Personnel:
Sales Director: sales@comverge.com
Approx. Rev.: $119,389,000
Approx. Number Employees: 562
Business Description:
Electric Utility Measuring & Control Device Mfr
S.I.C.: 3822; 3825
N.A.I.C.S.: 334512; 334515
Advertising Expenditures: $3,503,000
Personnel:
Alec G. Dreyer *(Chm)*
R. Blake Young *(Pres & CEO)*
David Mathieson *(CFO)*
Steve Moffitt *(COO)*
Chris Camino *(CMO & Exec VP-Sls)*
Arthur Vos, IV *(CTO & Sr VP-Product Strategy & Alliances)*
Michael D. Picchi *(Pres-Comverge Intl)*
Edward J. Myszka *(Exec VP-Program Delivery)*
David D. Ellis *(Sr VP-Bus Dev & Gen Mgr-Intl)*
George Hunt *(Sr VP-Sls)*
Chris Quire *(VP-Engrg)*
Padraic McFreen *(Sr Mgr-Mktg)*
Kristin Mastrandrea *(Mgr-Comm)*
Brands & Products:
APOLLO
APOLLO PLATFORM
APOLLO SMARTGRID
COMVERGE
COOLIBRIUM
DATAPULT
END-TO-END ENERGY INTELLIGENCE
KILL-A-WATT
MAINGATE
POWERPORTAL
SIXTH DIMENSION
SUPERSTAT
VIRTUAL PEAKING CAPACITY
Advertising Agency:
Mass Transmit
453 W17th St
New York, NY 10011
Tel.: (704) 706-2670
Fax: (704) 447-7262

CONAX TECHNOLOGIES LLC
2300 Walden Ave
Buffalo, NY 14225-4740
Tel.: (716) 684-4500
Fax: (716) 684-7433
Toll Free: (800) 223-2389
E-mail: conax@conaxtechnologies.com
Web Site:
www.conaxtechnologies.com
Approx. Number Employees: 100
Year Founded: 1955
Business Description:
Mfr. of Thermocouples & Temperature Sensors
S.I.C.: 3823
N.A.I.C.S.: 334513
Media: 4-10
Personnel:
Robert Fox *(Pres)*
Daniel Mitchell *(Dir-Sls-Pan Pacific)*
Brands & Products:
CONAX
GRAFOIL & LAVA
NEOPRENE
PDT-440
VITON

CONBRACO INDUSTRIES INC.
701 Matthews Mint Hill Rd
Matthews, NC 28105-1706
Tel.: (704) 841-6000
Fax: (704) 841-6020
E-mail: customer.services@conbraco.com
Web Site: www.apollovalves.com
Approx. Number Employees: 1,550
Year Founded: 1935
Business Description:
Mfr. of Ball Valves & Cylinders
S.I.C.: 3494; 3625
N.A.I.C.S.: 332919; 335314
Import Export
Advertising Expenditures: $200,000
Media: 2-4-7-10-11-13-20-26
Distr.: Intl
Budget Set: Feb.
Personnel:
Glen Mosack *(Pres)*
Eric Miller *(CFO)*
Carole Mosack Lee *(VP-Mktg)*
Donna Bult *(Dir-Sls & Mktg-Intl)*
Brands & Products:
ACUTORQUE
APOLLO
CONBRACO

CONERGY, INC.
(Sub. of Conergy AG)
1730 Camino Carlos Rey Ste 103
Santa Fe, NM 87507
Tel.: (505) 473-3800
Fax: (505) 473-3830
Toll Free: (888) 396-6611
Web Site: www.conergy.us
Sales Range: $10-24.9 Million
Approx. Number Employees: 18
Year Founded: 1983
Business Description:
Mfr of Solar-Powered Water Pumps
S.I.C.: 3561
N.A.I.C.S.: 333911
Media: 2-4-6-7-10-13-18-20-22
Personnel:
Jyl Safier *(Dir-Mktg)*
Brands & Products:
LORENTZ
SOLARAM
SOLARFORCE
SUNCENTRIC

CONNELL LIMITED PARTNERSHIP
1 Intl Pl 31 Fl
Boston, MA 02110-2635
Tel.: (617) 737-2700
Fax: (617) 737-1617
Web Site: www.connell-lp.com
Approx. Number Employees: 1,700
Year Founded: 1987
Business Description:
Holding Company; Industrial Equipment Mfr
S.I.C.: 3334; 3544; 3559
N.A.I.C.S.: 331312; 333298; 333514
Export
Advertising Expenditures: $250,000
Media: 2-4-10
Distr.: Intl.; Natl.
Budget Set: Sept.
Personnel:
Margot C. Connell *(Chm)*
Frank Doyle *(Pres & CEO)*
Kurt J. Keady *(CFO & VP)*
John V. Curtin *(VP-Legal & Environmental)*

CONNEY SAFETY PRODUCTS
(Holding of CI Capital Partners LLC)
3202 Latham Dr
Madison, WI 53744-4190
Tel.: (608) 271-3300
Toll Free: (888) 356-9100
E-mail: safety@conney.com
Web Site: www.conney.com
E-Mail For Key Personnel:
Sales Director: salesservice@conney.com
Sales Range: $25-49.9 Million
Approx. Number Employees: 150
Year Founded: 1946
Business Description:
Safety & First-Aid Products Mfr
S.I.C.: 5085; 5199
N.A.I.C.S.: 423840; 424990
Media: 4-13
Personnel:
Mourad Flood Elyasi *(Warehouse Mgr)*
Micahel Glenn *(Mgr-Bus Dev)*
Brands & Products:
CONNEY SAFETY PRODUCTS
YOUR SAFETY PROBLEM SOLVER

CONSOLIDATED METAL PRODUCTS, INC.
1028 Depot St
Cincinnati, OH 45204-2012
Tel.: (513) 251-2624
Fax: (513) 251-2488
E-mail: kcastellini@cmpubolt.com
Web Site: www.cmpubolt.com
Approx. Number Employees: 130
Year Founded: 1942
Business Description:
Mfr. of Threaded Steel Bar Products & U-bolts
S.I.C.: 3452; 3316
N.A.I.C.S.: 332722; 331221
Import Export
Advertising Expenditures: $300,000
Media: 2-4-7-10-17
Distr.: Natl.
Personnel:
Larry Talbott *(Exec VP)*
Kathy Castellini *(VP-Sls)*

CONSOLIDATED METCO INC.
(Div. of AMSTED Industries Incorporated)
5701 SE Columbia Way
Vancouver, WA 98661
Tel.: (360) 828-2599
Toll Free: (800) 547-9473
Web Site: www.conmet.com
Sales Range: $25-49.9 Million
Approx. Number Employees: 50
Year Founded: 1964
Business Description:
Lightweight Aluminum Components Mfr
S.I.C.: 3365; 3363
N.A.I.C.S.: 331524; 331521
Media: 2-4-10
Personnel:
Ed Oeltjem *(Pres & CEO)*
Rob Edstrom *(VP-Sls & Mktg)*
Larry Sanford *(Dir-Bus Dev)*
Mark Jorgensen *(Mktg Comm Mgr)*
Brands & Products:
CONMET
Advertising Agency:
Rains Marketing
5440 SW Westgate Dr
Portland, OR 97221
Tel.: (503) 297-1791
Fax: (503) 297-2282

CONTINENTAL EAGLE CORPORATION
201 Gin Shop Hill Rd
Prattville, AL 36067-1000
Mailing Address:
PO Box 1000
Prattville, AL 36067-1000
Tel.: (334) 365-8811
Fax: (334) 361-7627
E-mail: cec@coneagle.com
Web Site: www.coneagle.com
Sales Range: $50-74.9 Million
Approx. Number Employees: 45
Year Founded: 1832
Business Description:
Mfr. of Cotton Gins & Related Products
S.I.C.: 3559; 5085
N.A.I.C.S.: 333298; 423840
Export

Key to Media (For complete agency information see *The Advertising Red Books-Agencies* edition):
1. Bus. Publs. 2. Cable T.V. 3. Catalogs & Directories. 4. Co-op Adv. 5. Consumer Mags. 6. D.M. to Bus. Estab.7. D.M. to Consumers 8. Daily Newsp. 9. Exhibits/Trade Shows 10. Foreign 11. Infomercial 12. Internet Adv.13. Multimedia 14. Network Radio 15. Network T.V. 16. Newsp. Distr. Mags. 17. Other 18. Outdoor (Posters, Transit) 19. Point of Purchase20. Premiums, Novelties 21. Product Samples 22. Special Events Mktg. 23. Spot Radio 24. Spot T.V. 25. Weekly Newsp. 26. Yellow Page Adv.

Media: 1-2-4-5-6-7-8-9-10-11-13-16-18-20-22-23-25-26
Distr.: Direct to Consumer; Intl.; Natl.
Budget Set: Dec.
Personnel:
Bill Goodwin *(VP-Fin & Acctg)*
Brands & Products:
800 UNIDEN PRESS
8400 UNIDEN PRESS
CENTRIFUGAL ELBOW CLEANER
CONTINENTAL/BESPRESS
DOUBLE EAGLE 141
EAGLE II DELINTER
FISH20
GOLDEN EAGLE EXTRACTOR 9000
GOLDEN EAGLE SERIES 161
GOLDEN EAGLE SERIES 24-D
MURRAY PHX
SIXTEEN-D
SUCTION COMMAND
VERTICAL FLOW DRIER

COOPER BUSSMANN, INC.
(Sub. of Cooper Industries plc)
114 Old State Rd
Ellisville, MO 63021-5942
Mailing Address:
PO Box 14460
Saint Louis, MO 63178-4460
Tel.: (636) 394-2877
Fax: (636) 527-1405
E-mail: fusebox@cooperindustries.com
Web Site: www.cooperbussmann.com
Sales Range: $150-199.9 Million
Approx. Number Employees: 520
Year Founded: 1914
Business Description:
Circuit Protection Management Products Mfr
S.I.C.: 3613; 3679
N.A.I.C.S.: 335313; 334419
Export
Advertising Expenditures: $3,000,000
Media: 1-2-4-5-7-10-19-20-21-22
Distr.: Intl.; Natl.
Budget Set: Aug.
Personnel:
Ivo Jurek *(Pres)*

COOPER INDUSTRIES PLC
600 Travis Ste 5600
Houston, TX 77002-3008
Mailing Address:
PO Box 4446
Houston, TX 77210-4446
Tel.: (713) 209-8400
Fax: (713) 209-8995
Telex: 775525 COOPER IND HOU
E-mail: info@cooperindustries.com
Web Site: www.cooperindustries.com
Approx. Rev.: $5,065,900,000
Approx. Number Employees: 24,795
Year Founded: 1833
Business Description:
Electrical Products, Tools, Hardware & Metal Support Products Mfr
S.I.C.: 5063; 3612; 3641; 3646; 3823
N.A.I.C.S.: 423610; 334513; 335110; 335122; 335311
Import Export
Media: 2-10
Distr.: Intl.; Natl.
Budget Set: Nov.
Personnel:
Kirk S. Hachigian *(Chm, Pres & CEO)*
David A. Barta *(CFO & Sr VP)*
Robert L. Taylor *(CMO)*
Bruce M. Taten *(Gen Counsel, Sr VP & Chief Compliance Officer)*
Rick L. Johnson *(Chief Acctg Officer, VP & Controller)*
Grant L. Gawronski *(Pres-Cooper Crouse-Hinds)*
C. Thomas O'Grady *(Sr VP-Bus Dev)*
James P. Williams *(Sr VP-HR)*
Heath B. Monesmith *(VP-HR)*
Brands & Products:
ACCESS CABINETS
AMETRIX
ASPIRE
B&S
BUSS
CAPRI
CENT-R-RAIL
CHAMP
CHICO
COLLINS
CONDULET
COOPER
DGD/GARDNER-DENVER
DIAMOND
DIGITAL LIGHTING SYSTEM
DLS
DOMEX
DOTCO
DURA-GREEN
E2 CABINETS
EDISON
ENVIROTEMP
FULLEON
FUSETRON
GLOCOIL
HAZARD-GARD
H.K. PORTER
INVUE
LIMITRON
MENVIER BLESSING
MENVIER CSA
MINI-LINE
NICHOLSON
NORTEM
OPTIMA
POSI-BREAK
POSI-LOK
POWERPLUS
R-TEMP
REDI-RAIL
REGALSAFE
ROTOR TOOL
SHAPER
STREETWORKS
SURGBLOC
TRANSX
ULTRASIL
VARIGAP
VARISTAR

COOPER SPLIT ROLLER BEARING CORP.
(Sub. of Cooper Roller Bearing Company Limited)
5365 Robin Hood Rd Ste B
Norfolk, VA 23513
Tel.: (757) 460-0925
Fax: (757) 464-3067
E-mail: info@cooperbearings.com
Web Site: www.cooperbearings.com
Sales Range: $10-24.9 Million
Approx. Number Employees: 12
Business Description:
Mfr. of Bearings
S.I.C.: 3562
N.A.I.C.S.: 332991
Advertising Agency:
Grant Marketing
2020 Commonwealth Ave
Newton, MA 02466
Tel.: (617) 796-0186
Fax: (617) 796-0188
Toll Free: (888) 809-2317

CORKEN, INC.
(Sub. of Liquid Controls, Inc.)
3805 Northwest 36th
Oklahoma City, OK 73112
Mailing Address:
PO Box 12338
Oklahoma City, OK 73157
Tel.: (405) 946-5576
Fax: (405) 948-7343
E-mail: info.corken@idexcorp.com
Web Site: www.corken.com
Sales Range: $75-99.9 Million
Approx. Number Employees: 150
Year Founded: 1924
Business Description:
Mfr. of Small Horsepower Compressors, Pumps & Valves
S.I.C.: 3563; 3561
N.A.I.C.S.: 333912; 333911
Export
Media: 2-7-10-13-20-21
Distr.: Natl.
Budget Set: Oct.
Personnel:
Richard Jones *(Mgr-Adv)*
Brands & Products:
CORKEN
CORO-FLO
CORO-VAC
CORO-VANE
SABRE

CORLEY MANUFACTURING CO.
2900 Crescent Cir
Chattanooga, TN 37407
Mailing Address:
PO Box 471
Chattanooga, TN 37401
Tel.: (423) 698-0284
Fax: (423) 622-3258
E-mail: sales@corleymfg.com
Web Site: www.corleymfg.com
E-Mail For Key Personnel:
Sales Director: sales@corleymfg.com
Approx. Number Employees: 15
Year Founded: 1905
Business Description:
Saw Mill Machinery & Related Supplies
S.I.C.: 3553; 3625
N.A.I.C.S.: 333210; 335314
Advertising Expenditures: $200,000
Consumer Mags.: $180,000; D.M. to Bus. Estab.: $6,000; D.M. to Consumers: $4,000; Exhibits/Trade Shows: $10,000
Distr.: Intl.; Natl.
Budget Set: Apr.
Personnel:
A. J. Corley *(Pres)*

CRANE CHEMPHARMA FLOW SOLUTIONS
(Sub. of Crane Fluid Handling)
4444 Cooper Rd
Cincinnati, OH 45242-5615
Tel.: (513) 745-6000
Fax: (513) 745-6086
Web Site: www.cranechempharma.com
Sales Range: $75-99.9 Million
Approx. Number Employees: 175
Year Founded: 1956
Business Description:
Industrial Valves & Actuators Mfr
S.I.C.: 3491; 3593
N.A.I.C.S.: 332911; 333995
Media: 2-10
Personnel:
Bill Hayes *(Pres)*
Brands & Products:
S2
TUFLINE

CRANE ENVIRONMENTAL INC.
(Sub. of Crane Controls)
Ste 100A 2650 Eisenhower Ave
Norristown, PA 19403-2337
Tel.: (610) 631-7700
Fax: (610) 631-6800
Toll Free: (800) 633-7435
E-mail: ebusiness@cranenv.com
Web Site: www.cranenv.com
Sales Range: $25-49.9 Million
Approx. Number Employees: 50
Year Founded: 1863
Business Description:
Specialized Water Purification Solutions Distr
S.I.C.: 3589
N.A.I.C.S.: 333319
Export
Media: 2-4-7-10-11-13
Distr.: Natl.
Budget Set: Nov. -Dec.
Personnel:
Michael Boyer *(CFO & Controller)*
Russ Burke *(Dir-Ops & Site Leader)*
Don Paolicelli *(Dir-Sls & Svc)*
Brands & Products:
COCHRANE
DELTA
EPRO

CRANE MANUFACTURING & SERVICE CORPORATION
5318 S Emmer Dr
New Berlin, WI 53151
Tel.: (262) 785-4444
Fax: (262) 785-4441
Toll Free: (800) 272-6363
E-mail: info@cranemfg.com
Web Site: www.cranemfg.com
Approx. Number Employees: 20
Year Founded: 1961
Business Description:
Mfr. of Overhead Cranes
S.I.C.: 3536
N.A.I.C.S.: 333923
Advertising Expenditures: $300,000
Media: 2-3-7-8
Brands & Products:
CLEVELAND CRANE
CRANE MANUFACTURING & SERVICE
NORTHERN ENGINEERING
RELI-A-BILT

CRES-COR
5925 Heisley Rd
Mentor, OH 44060-1833
Tel.: (440) 350-1100
Fax: (440) 350-7267
Toll Free: (800) 321-7174
Toll Free: (877) CRESCOR
Toll Free: (800) 822-0393

Key to Media (For complete agency information see *The Advertising Red Books-Agencies* edition):
1. Bus. Publs. 2. Cable T.V. 3. Catalogs & Directories. 4. Co-op Adv. 5. Consumer Mags. 6. D.M. to Bus. Estab.7. D.M. to Consumers 8. Daily Newsp. 9. Exhibits/Trade Shows 10. Foreign 11. Infomercial 12. Internet Adv.13. Multimedia 14. Network Radio 15. Network T.V. 16. Newsp. Distr. Mags. 17. Other 18. Outdoor (Posters, Transit) 19. Point of Purchase20. Premiums, Novelties 21. Product Samples 22. Special Events Mktg. 23. Spot Radio 24. Spot T.V. 25. Weekly Newsp. 26. Yellow Page Adv.

Cres-Cor — (Continued)

E-mail: email@crescor.com
Web Site: www.crescor.com
Approx. Number Employees: 200
Year Founded: 1936
Business Description:
Mfr & Distr of Mobile Food Service Related Equipment
S.I.C.: 3556; 5812
N.A.I.C.S.: 333294; 722310
Export
Bus. Publs.: 25%; D.M. to Bus. Estab.: 50%; Exhibits/Trade Shows: 25%
Distr.: Intl.; Natl.
Budget Set: Dec.
Personnel:
Cliff Baggott *(Pres & CEO)*
Brands & Products:
AQUA TEMP HOLDING CABINETS
CRES COR
KOLD KEEPER
RACK-N-ROLL
ROAST-N-HOLD
ROLL-IN REFRIGERATOR RACKS

CROLL-REYNOLDS COMPANY, INC.

6 Campus Dr
Parsippany, NJ 07054
Tel.: (908) 232-4200
Fax: (908) 232-2146
E-mail: info@croll.com
Web Site: www.croll.com
E-Mail For Key Personnel:
President: scroll@croll.com
Sales Director: hhage@croll.com
Public Relations: breynolds@croll.com
Approx. Number Employees: 50
Year Founded: 1917
Business Description:
Mfr. of Custom Designed Vacuum Pumps & Air Pollution Control Equipment
S.I.C.: 3569
N.A.I.C.S.: 333999
Import Export
Media: 2-4-7-10
Distr.: Natl.
Personnel:
Samuel W. Croll *(CEO)*
Phillip Reynolds *(VP-Engrg)*
Henry Hage *(Mgr-Sls)*
Brands & Products:
AQUA-DUCTOR
AQUA-VACTOR
CHILL-VACTOR
CROLL REYNOLDS
EVACTOR
PICCOLO
ROTAJECTOR
SCRUB-VACTOR

CUMBERLAND ENGINEERING

(Holding of Harbour Group Ltd.)
100 Roddy Ave
South Attleboro, MA 02703-7900
Tel.: (508) 399-6400
Fax: (508) 399-6653
Telex: 6814044 JBBROWN UW
E-mail: sales@cumberland-plastics.com
Web Site: www.cumberland-plastics.com
E-Mail For Key Personnel:
Sales Director: sales@cumberland-plastics.com
Approx. Number Employees: 35
Year Founded: 1939
Business Description:
Plastics & Textile Machinery Mfr
S.I.C.: 8711
N.A.I.C.S.: 541330
Media: 9-10
Distr.: Intl.; Natl.
Budget Set: Oct.

CUMMINS INC.

500 Jackson St
Columbus, IN 47201-6258
Mailing Address:
PO Box 3005
Columbus, IN 47202-3005
Tel.: (812) 377-5000
Fax: (812) 377-3334
E-mail: powermaster@cummins.com
Web Site: www.cummins.com
Approx. Sls.: $13,226,000,000
Approx. Number Employees: 39,200
Year Founded: 1919
Business Description:
Diesel & Natural Gas Engine Designer, Mfr & Distributor
S.I.C.: 3519; 3621; 3714
N.A.I.C.S.: 333618; 335312; 336312; 336399
Import Export
Advertising Expenditures: $1,000,000
Media: 2-4-5-7-8-10-19-20-23-26
Distr.: Intl.; Natl.
Budget Set: Aug.
Personnel:
Theodore M. Solso *(Chm & CEO)*
N. Thomas Linebarger *(Pres & COO)*
Patrick J. Ward *(CFO & VP)*
Richard Harris *(Chief Investment Officer & VP)*
Livingston L. Satterthwaite *(Pres-Power Generation Bus & VP)*
Pamela L. Carter *(Pres-Cummins Distr Svcs)*
Richard J. Freeland *(Pres-Engine Bus)*
Anant J. Talaulicar *(Pres-Components Bus)*
Marya M. Rose *(Gen Counsel, Sec & VP)*
Steven M. Chapman *(Grp VP-China & Russia Ops)*
Ed Pence *(VP & Gen Mgr-Heavy Duty Engine Bus)*
Jill Cook *(VP-HR)*
Thad Ewald *(VP-Corp Strategy & Bus Dev)*
Christine M. Vujovich *(VP-Mktg & Environ Policy)*
Mark Land *(Exec Dir-Corp Comm)*
Ricardo Patron *(Exec Dir-Intl Distr)*
Dean Cantrell *(Dir-IR)*
Carol Lavengood *(Dir-Mktg Comm-Cummins Engine)*
Flavio A. C. Mello *(Mgr-Global Mktg Comm-Power Generation)*
Brands & Products:
CELECT
COMFORTGUARD
CUMMINS
CUMMINS ENGINE
FLEETGUARD/NELSON
HOLSET
KUSS
NELSON
ONAN
Advertising Agency:
PriceWeber Marketing Communications, Inc.
10701 Shelbyville Rd
Louisville, KY 40243
Tel.: (502) 499-9220
Fax: (502) 491-5593
(Natural Gas Engines, Diesel Engines)

CUMMINS POWER GENERATION

(Sub. of Cummins Inc.)
1400 73rd Ave NE
Minneapolis, MN 55432-3702
Tel.: (763) 574-5000
Fax: (763) 574-5298
Telex: 275477
Web Site: www.cumminspower.com
Sales Range: $125-149.9 Million
Approx. Number Employees: 1,800
Year Founded: 1920
Business Description:
Portable & Stand-By Electric Generators & Gasoline Engines Mfr
S.I.C.: 3621; 3519
N.A.I.C.S.: 335312; 333618
Import Export
Distr.: Intl.; Natl.
Personnel:
Tony Satterthwaite *(Pres)*
Steve Iverson *(Dir-Mktg & Sls)*
Carl Westenfield *(Dir-Transfer Switch Bus)*
Lee Ann Duval *(Product Mgr-Global Rentals)*
Rich Scroggins *(Product Mgr)*
Henry Zeng *(Product Mgr-Comml Genset Bus)*
Devesh Dahale *(Mgr-Reliability Engrg)*
Brands & Products:
INPOWER
POWERCARE ADVANTAGE
POWERCOMMAND
Advertising Agency:
Creative Communications Inc.
111 S 3rd
Minneapolis, MN 55401
Tel.: (612) 338-5098

CURTIS-TOLEDO, INC.

(Sub. of FS Precision Tech Co. LLC)
1905 Kienlen Ave
Saint Louis, MO 63133-2517
Tel.: (314) 383-1300
Fax: (314) 381-1439
Toll Free: (800) 925-5431
E-mail: info@curtistoledo.com
Web Site: www.curtistoledo.com
Approx. Number Employees: 107
Year Founded: 1854
Business Description:
Air Compressors Mfr
S.I.C.: 3563; 3541
N.A.I.C.S.: 333912; 333512
Import Export
Advertising Expenditures: $40,000
Media: 5-10-16-18-26
Distr.: Intl.; Natl.
Personnel:
Jerome Elsen *(Mgr-Sls)*
Brands & Products:
CURTIS
CURTIS-TOLEDO
THREADEZY
TOLEDO TOOL
VACU-PLUS

CWC TEXTRON

(Sub. of Kautex Textron GmbH & Co. KG)
1085 W Sherman Blvd
Muskegon, MI 49441
Tel.: (231) 733-1331
Fax: (231) 739-2649
Sales Range: $125-149.9 Million
Approx. Number Employees: 323
Year Founded: 1908
Business Description:
Gray Iron, Alloyed Iron, Ductile Iron, Steel, Chilled Iron
S.I.C.: 3714
N.A.I.C.S.: 336312
Export
Media: 2
Distr.: Natl.
Personnel:
J.M. Heethuis *(CEO)*
Mike Baldwin *(Mgr-IT Site-Kautex-Muskegon)*
Brands & Products:
CWC

CXM INC.

(d/b/a Chicago Extruded Metals Co)
1601 S 54 Ave
Cicero, IL 60804-1898
Tel.: (708) 656-7900
Fax: (708) 780-3479
Toll Free: (800) 323-8102
Web Site: www.cxm.com
Sales Range: $75-99.9 Million
Approx. Number Employees: 100
Year Founded: 1923
Business Description:
Brass Smelting & Refining (Secondary)
S.I.C.: 3351
N.A.I.C.S.: 331421
Media: 10-13-25
Personnel:
Patrick Balson *(Pres & CEO)*

CYPRESS SEMICONDUCTOR CORPORATION

198 Champion Ct
San Jose, CA 95134
Tel.: (408) 943-2600
Fax: (408) 943-4730
E-mail: usbsales@cypress.com
Web Site: www.cypress.com
Approx. Rev.: $877,532,000
Approx. Number Employees: 3,500
Year Founded: 1982
Business Description:
Integrated Circuits, Static RAMs, Programmable Logic, Data Communications Chips, Universal Serial Business Microcontrollers & Timing Chips Mfr
S.I.C.: 3674
N.A.I.C.S.: 334413
Advertising Expenditures: $4,000,000
Media: 2-10-13
Personnel:
Eric A. Benhamou *(Chm)*
T. J. Rodgers *(Pres & CEO)*
Brad W. Buss *(CFO, Exec VP-Fin & Admin)*
Cathal Phelan *(CTO & Exec VP)*
Shahin Sharifzadeh *(Pres-China Ops & Exec VP-WW Wafer Fabs & Tech)*
Sabbas A. Daniel *(Exec VP-Quality)*
Dana Nazarian *(Exec VP-Memory & Imaging Div)*

Key to Media (For complete agency information see *The Advertising Red Books-Agencies* edition):
1. Bus. Publs. 2. Cable T.V. 3. Catalogs & Directories. 4. Co-op Adv. 5. Consumer Mags. 6. D.M. to Bus. Estab.7. D.M. to Consumers 8. Daily Newsp. 9. Exhibits/Trade Shows 10. Foreign 11. Infomercial 12. Internet Adv.13. Multimedia 14. Network Radio 15. Network T.V. 16. Newsp. Distr. Mags. 17. Other 18. Outdoor (Posters, Transit) 19. Point of Purchase20. Premiums, Novelties 21. Product Samples 22. Special Events Mktg. 23. Spot Radio 24. Spot T.V. 25. Weekly Newsp. 26. Yellow Page Adv.

Dinesh Ramanathan *(Exec VP-Data Comm)*
Christopher A. Seams *(Exec VP-Mktg & Sls)*
Norman P. Taffe *(Exec VP-Consumer & Computation Div)*
Rajeev Mehtani *(Sr VP-Ops-India)*
Brands & Products:
ANTIOCH
AUTOMOBL
BY ENGINEERS. FOR ENGINEERS.
C8
C9
CAPSENSE
CAPSENSE EXPRESS
CONNECTIONCENTER
CONSUMOBL
CUT THE CORD WITH CYPRESS WIRELESS
CYBERCLOCKS
CYCLOCKS
CYDESIGNER
CYFI
CYNAPSE
CYPRESS
CYPRESS.BIZ
CYPRESS.COM
CYPROS
DEEP SYNC
DEEP SYNC 36
DEEP SYNC II
DELTA39K
DIRECT RAMBUS
ENCORE
EZ-COLOR
EZ-LINK
EZ-OTG
EZ-USB AT2LPTM L8
EZ-USB AT2S
EZ-USB FX
EZ-USB FX2
EZ-USB FX2LP
EZ-USB HX2
EZ-USB HX2LP
EZ-USB MX2
EZ-USB SX2
EZ-USB SX2LP
EZ-USB SX2LPTM L8
EZ-USB TX2
FAILSAFE
FAST ACCESS
FASTEDGE
FIRSTTOUCH
FLASH370
FLASH370I
FLASHISR
FLEX36
FLEX72
FLEX72-E
FLEXO
HOTLINK
HOTLINK DX
HOTLINK II
HOTLINK III
HOTLINKDX
HYPERCACHE
HYPERCACHE PLUS
IN-SYSTEM REPROGRAMMABLE
INSRKIT
IP OASIS
KISSBIND
KNOWLEDGEBASE
LONTALK
M8
MEDIACLOCK
METROLINK
METROLINK2T-2
MICROPOWER
MINI-KEY
MOBL
MOBL-USB
MOBL2
MOBL3
MOBL4
MORE BATTERY LIFE
N-WELL PIXEL
NEURON
NO BUS LATENCY
NOBL
OVATIONONS
OVATIONSLIM
PACKETCLOCK
PACKETRAM
PASIC380
PCI-DP
PCI-DPPSI
PERFORM
PIONEER NODE
POSIC
POSIC10G
POSIC2G
POSIC2GVC
POSIC2GVCA
POWERPSOC
PREMIS
PROC
PROGRAMMABLE SERIAL INTERFACE
PSOC
PSOC DESIGNER
PSOC EXPRESS
PSOC ONS
PSOC PROS
QDR
QUAD DATA RATE
QUADPORT
QUANTUM38K
R1
R2
R3
R4
R5
R6
R7
R8
R9
RAM1
RAM2
RAM3
RAM4
RAM5
RAM6
RAM7
RAM8
RAM9
ROBOCLOCK
ROBOCLOCK II
ROBOCLOCK JR.
ROBOCONFIG
SAHASRA
SLIM
SPECKLEMOUSE
SPREAD AWARE
SUPER BUFFER
TETRAHUB
TOUCHWAKE
TRUETOUCH
TTB
UBL
ULTRA
UNIVERSAL BUS LOGIC
VSE
WARP
WARP ENTERPRISE
WARP PROFESSIONAL
WARP2
WARP2ISR
WARP2SIM
WARP3
WARPISR
WEST BRIDGE
WIRELESSHID
WIRELESSLON
WIRELESSUSB
WIRELESSUSB LR
WIRELESSUSB LS
WISPI
ZBL
ZEPTOCLOCK
ZERO BUS LATENCY
Advertising Agencies:
Catapult Direct
1700 Winchester Blvd
Campbell, CA 95008
Tel.: (408) 369-8111
— Lisa Mistry *(Acct Exec)*

PRx, Inc.
991 W Hedding St Ste 201
San Jose, CA 95126
Tel.: (408) 287-1700
Fax: (408) 556-1487

D&S CAR WASH EQUIPMENT CO.

4200 Brandi Ln
High Ridge, MO 63049
Tel.: (636) 677-3442
Fax: (636) 677-4105
E-mail: sales@dscarwash.com
Web Site: www.dscarwash.com
E-Mail For Key Personnel:
Sales Director: sales@dscarwash.com
Approx. Number Employees: 100
Year Founded: 1972
Business Description:
Car Washing Equipment Mfr
S.I.C.: 3589; 3625; 5084
N.A.I.C.S.: 333319; 335314; 423830
Media: 10
Personnel:
Jon Jansky *(Pres)*
Tim Sater *(Dir-Mktg & Reg Sls)*
Brands & Products:
BUG OFF
D & S 5000
DUAL OVAL
MINI-STACK
ODYSSEY
POWER GLOSS
SUPER
SUPER 5000
SWEET MIST
TRI-COLOR
TRIGLOSS

DAIKIN U.S. CORPORATION

(Sub. of Daikin Industries, Ltd.)
Fl 18 475 5th Ave
New York, NY 10017-6220
Tel.: (212) 935-4890
Fax: (212) 935-4895
E-mail: tyagi@daikin.ny.com
Web Site: www.daikin.com
Approx. Number Employees: 24
Business Description:
Mfr. of Air Conditioning Equipment
S.I.C.: 5075
N.A.I.C.S.: 423730
Advertising Expenditures: $2,000,000
Advertising Agency:
Messer & Susslin & Others, Inc.
274 N Middletown Rd
Pearl River, NY 10965-1216
Tel.: (845) 735-3030
Fax: (845) 735-2270

DANAHER MOTION

(Div. of Danaher Motion Company)
110 Westtown Rd
West Chester, PA 19382-4978
Tel.: (610) 692-2700
Fax: (610) 696-4598
Telex: 835486
Web Site: www.danahermotion.com
Approx. Sls.: $16,000,000
Approx. Number Employees: 100
Year Founded: 1956
Business Description:
Mechanical & Electronic Motors & Components Mfr
S.I.C.: 5084; 3569
N.A.I.C.S.: 423830; 333999
Export
Advertising Expenditures: $300,000
Media: 2-10-17
Distr.: Natl.
Budget Set: Nov.
Personnel:
D. K. Begedali *(Pres)*
Lorin Cassidy *(Mgr-Ops)*
Brands & Products:
DOVER
KOLLMORGEN
PORTESCAP
THOMSON
Advertising Agency:
Backe Digital Brand Marketing
35 Cricket Ter Ctr
Ardmore, PA 19003-2203
Tel.: (610) 896-9260
Fax: (610) 896-9242
Portescap

DANAHER MOTION

(Div. of Danaher Motion Company)
43-45 Channel Dr
Port Washington, NY 11050-2214
Tel.: (516) 883-8000
Fax: (516) 883-9039
E-mail: contactus@danahermotion.com
Web Site: www.danahermotion.com
Sales Range: $550-599.9 Million
Approx. Number Employees: 2,500
Year Founded: 1944
Business Description:
Ball Bushing, Linear Motion Ball Bearings, Nyliner Bearings, Nylon Bearings for Rotation & Reciprocating, 60 Case Hardened & Ground Shafts & Bars, Roundway Bearings, Linear Motion Roller Bearings & Ball Screw Drives
S.I.C.: 3562
N.A.I.C.S.: 332991
Media: 1-2-4-5-7-10-11-20-21-22
Distr.: Intl.; Natl.
Budget Set: Aug.
Brands & Products:
60 CASE LINEAR RACE
NYLINER
PROFILERAIL
ROUNDWAY
SUPER BALL
XR BEARINGS

Key to Media (For complete agency information see *The Advertising Red Books-Agencies* edition):
1. Bus. Publs. 2. Cable T.V. 3. Catalogs & Directories. 4. Co-op Adv. 5. Consumer Mags. 6. D.M. to Bus. Estab.7. D.M. to Consumers 8. Daily Newsp. 9. Exhibits/Trade Shows 10. Foreign 11. Infomercial 12. Internet Adv.13. Multimedia 14. Network Radio 15. Network T.V. 16. Newsp. Distr. Mags. 17. Other 18. Outdoor (Posters, Transit) 19. Point of Purchase20. Premiums, Novelties 21. Product Samples 22. Special Events Mktg. 23. Spot Radio 24. Spot T.V. 25. Weekly Newsp. 26. Yellow Page Adv.

DANFOSS FLOMATIC CORPORATION
(Sub. of Danfoss A/S)
15 Pruyn's Island Dr
Glens Falls, NY 12801-4424
Tel.: (518) 761-9797
Fax: (518) 761-9798
Fax: (800) 314-3155
Toll Free: (800) 333-2040
E-mail: flomatic@flomatic.com
Web Site: www.flomatic.com
Approx. Number Employees: 50
Year Founded: 1933
Business Description:
Valves Mfr
S.I.C.: 3491; 3494
N.A.I.C.S.: 332911; 332919
Media: 2-4-6-7-10-19-20-21
Personnel:
Nick Farrara *(VP-Mktg & Sls)*
Brands & Products:
COMBOAIR
CYCLEGARD
E-Z VALVE
ENVIRO-CHECK
FLO-DRAIN
FLO-LARM
MAXIAIR
MINIAIR
MS II
SEWAIR
SPLIT-DISC
SUBGARD
VALVACTIVE.FAX
WELDAPTOR
WELDRAIN
WELLAIR

DAVIS-STANDARD LLC
(Joint Venture of Chemtura Corporation & Hamilton Robinson LLC)
1 Extrusion Dr
Pawcatuck, CT 06379-2313
Tel.: (860) 599-1010
Fax: (860) 599-6169
Telex: 966455
Web Site: www.davis-standard.com
Sales Range: $100-124.9 Million
Approx. Number Employees: 370
Year Founded: 1948
Business Description:
Extrusion Systems & Process Controls Mfr
S.I.C.: 3559; 3549
N.A.I.C.S.: 333220; 333518
Export
Media: 2-4-7-10-11
Distr.: Intl.; Natl.
Budget Set: Oct.
Personnel:
Charles E. Buckley *(CEO)*
Mike Perrigo *(Dir-Tech)*
Steve Kriger *(Bus Mgr)*
Simon Dominey *(Mgr-Bus)*
Luann Kupka *(Mgr-Mktg & Sls Admin)*
Gary Peacock *(Mgr-Product Integration)*
Brands & Products:
DSB
DSBM-T
DUAL-THERM
EPIC III
GP94
MARK V
MARK VI
MESA PACK
MESA PACK PRO
PROPAK
SCRAPPER
THERMATIC
VERSA
WESJET
WOODTRUDER

DAYTON ROGERS MFG. CO.
8401 W 35 W Service Dr
Minneapolis, MN 55449-7260
Tel.: (763) 717-6450
Fax: (763) 784-8209
Toll Free: (800) 677-8881
Web Site: www.daytonrogers.com
Approx. Sls.: $40,000,000
Approx. Number Employees: 600
Year Founded: 1929
Business Description:
Small & Medium Lot Stampings Mfr; Precision Sheet Metal; Metal Fabrication
S.I.C.: 3469
N.A.I.C.S.: 332116
Export
Advertising Expenditures: $500,000
Media: 2-4-10-26
Distr.: Direct to Consumer; Natl.
Budget Set: June
Personnel:
Mark Erickson *(Gen Mgr)*

DAYTON SUPERIOR CORPORATION
7777 Washington Village Dr Ste 130
Dayton, OH 45459
Tel.: (937) 428-6360
Fax: (937) 428-9115
E-mail: info@daytonsuperior.com
Web Site: www.daytonsuperior.com
Approx. Sls.: $475,871,000
Approx. Number Employees: 600
Year Founded: 1924
Business Description:
Concrete Accessories, Masonry Products, Welded Dowel Assemblies, Paving Products, & Corrosive-preventing Epoxy Coatings Mfr
S.I.C.: 3317; 3272; 3441; 3452; 3496
N.A.I.C.S.: 331210; 327390; 332312; 332618; 332722
Import Export
Media: 10
Personnel:
Stephen Berger *(Chm)*
Eric R. Zimmerman *(Pres & CEO)*
Lutz Richter *(CFO)*
Thomas W. Roehrig *(VP-Fin & Sec)*
Peter J. Astrauskas *(VP-Engrng & Product Mgmt)*
Keith M. Sholos *(VP-Sls)*
Bob Roeller *(Mgr-Sls)*
Brands & Products:
P-24 DELTA TIE
POLYTITE

DCX-CHOL, INC.
(Sub. of DCX-CHOL Enterprises, Inc.)
12831 S Figueroa St
Los Angeles, CA 90061-1157
Mailing Address:
PO Box 569
Franktown, CO 80116-0569
Tel.: (310) 516-1692
Web Site: www.dcxchol.com
E-Mail For Key Personnel:
Sales Director: sales@dcxchol.com
Approx. Number Employees: 50
Year Founded: 1984
Business Description:
Cable Assemblies, Wire Harnesses, Electromechanical Devices, Special Application Fluid, Pneumatic Signal & Control Mechanisms Mfr, Designer, Developer & Tester
S.I.C.: 3365; 8733
N.A.I.C.S.: 331524; 541710
Export
Media: 1-2-4-5-10
Distr.: Natl.
Brands & Products:
GEONOVA

DEL-TRON PRECISION, INC.
5 Trowbridge Dr
Bethel, CT 06801
Mailing Address:
PO Box 505
Bethel, CT 06801-0505
Tel.: (203) 778-2727
Fax: (203) 778-2721
Toll Free: (800) 245-5013
E-mail: deltron@deltron.com
Web Site: www.deltron.com
Approx. Sls.: $5,000,000
Approx. Number Employees: 50
Year Founded: 1974
Business Description:
Linear Motion Position Equipment Mfr
S.I.C.: 3562; 5084
N.A.I.C.S.: 332991; 423830
Import Export
Media: 2-4-7-10
Distr.: Natl.
Personnel:
Ralph McIntosh *(Pres)*
Emil Melvin *(Dir-Sls & Mktg)*
Brands & Products:
AIRPOT
ANTI-CREEP
DEL-TRON
POSI-DRIVE
POSI-LOCK
PRECISION

DELCAL ENTERPRISES, INC.
140 Franklin St
New York, NY 10013
Tel.: (212) 431-2233
Approx. Number Employees: 225
Business Description:
Holding Company; Industrial, Electrical & Mechanical Equipment Distr
S.I.C.: 6719; 5063; 5084
N.A.I.C.S.: 551112; 423610; 423830
Import Export
Media: 2-10
Personnel:
John Calicchio *(Chm)*
John SantaCroce *(Pres & CEO)*
Paul Persaud *(CFO)*

DEUTZ CORPORATION
(Sub. of DEUTZ AG)
3883 Steve Reynolds Blvd
Norcross, GA 30093-3051
Tel.: (770) 564-7100
Fax: (770) 564-7272
E-mail: engines@deutzusa.com
Web Site: www.deutzusa.com
E-Mail For Key Personnel:
Marketing Director: marketing@deutzusa.com
Sales Range: $125-149.9 Million
Approx. Number Employees: 100
Business Description:
Air Cooled Diesel Engines & Spare Parts Distr
S.I.C.: 5084
N.A.I.C.S.: 423830
Advertising Expenditures: $200,000
Media: 2-10-13-17-26
Distr.: Intl.; Natl.
Budget Set: Jan.
Personnel:
Christian Krupp *(Pres)*

DEWALT INDUSTRIAL TOOL COMPANY
(Sub. of Stanley Black & Decker, Inc.)
701 E Joppa Rd
Baltimore, MD 21286
Tel.: (410) 716-3900
Web Site: www.dewalt.com
Sales Range: $10-24.9 Million
Approx. Number Employees: 10
Year Founded: 2000
Business Description:
Industrial Power Tools Mfr
S.I.C.: 3563
N.A.I.C.S.: 333912
Media: 4
Personnel:
John Schiech *(Pres-Ops)*
Susan Wiercinski *(Brand Mgr)*
Jim Benton *(Associate Product Mgr)*
Chris Lavigna *(Mgr-Interactive Mktg)*
Advertising Agency:
Fitzgerald+CO
3060 Peachtree Rd NW
Atlanta, GA 30305
Tel.: (404) 504-6900
Fax: (404) 239-0548

THE DEWEY ELECTRONICS CORPORATION
27 Muller Rd
Oakland, NJ 07436
Tel.: (201) 337-4700
Fax: (201) 337-3976
Toll Free: (800) 526-5174
E-mail: dewey@deweyelectronics.com
Web Site: www.deweyelectronics.com
Approx. Rev.: $7,494,099
Approx. Number Employees: 31
Year Founded: 1955
Business Description:
Mfr., Researcher, Developer & Designer of Diesel Generators; Torpedo & Mine Casings; Electronic Sonar, Communications & Other Anti-Submarine Warfare Special Purpose Equipment
S.I.C.: 3489; 3483; 3812
N.A.I.C.S.: 332995; 332993; 334511
Export
Media: 2-4-10
Distr.: Natl.
Budget Set: Aug.
Personnel:
John H. D. Dewey *(Pres & CEO)*
Edward L. Proskey *(Sr VP-Ops)*
Brands & Products:
HEDCO
PITOMETER
Advertising Agency:
KCSA Strategic Communications
(Kanan, Corbin, Schupak & Aronow, Inc.)
880 3rd Ave 6th Fl
New York, NY 10022

Key to Media (For complete agency information see *The Advertising Red Books-Agencies* edition):
1. Bus. Publs. 2. Cable T.V. 3. Catalogs & Directories. 4. Co-op Adv. 5. Consumer Mags. 6. D.M. to Bus. Estab.7. D.M. to Consumers
8. Daily Newsp. 9. Exhibits/Trade Shows 10. Foreign 11. Infomercial 12. Internet Adv.13. Multimedia 14. Network Radio
15. Network T.V. 16. Newsp. Distr. Mags. 17. Other 18. Outdoor (Posters, Transit) 19. Point of Purchase20. Premiums, Novelties
21. Product Samples 22. Special Events Mktg. 23. Spot Radio 24. Spot T.V. 25. Weekly Newsp. 26. Yellow Page Adv.

Tel.: (212) 682-6300
Fax: (212) 697-0910

DFCI SOLUTIONS INC.
425 Union Blvd
West Islip, NY 11795-3116
Tel.: (631) 669-0494
Fax: (631) 669-0785
E-mail: quotes@dfcis.com
Web Site: www.dfcis.com
Sales Range: $1-9.9 Million
Approx. Number Employees: 100
Year Founded: 1936
Business Description:
Fasteners Mfr
S.I.C.: 3965; 3452
N.A.I.C.S.: 339993; 332722
Export
Media: 2-4-10-13
Distr.: Intl.; Natl.
Budget Set: Aug.
Personnel:
Stephen Meshover *(Pres)*

DIAMOND CHAIN COMPANY
(Div. of AMSTED Industries Incorporated)
402 Kentucky Ave
Indianapolis, IN 46225-1175
Mailing Address:
PO Box 7045
Indianapolis, IN 46207-7045
Tel.: (317) 638-6431
Fax: (317) 613-2243
E-mail: webmaster@diamondchain.com
Web Site: www.diamondchain.com
Approx. Number Employees: 800
Year Founded: 1890
Business Description:
Mfr. of Roller & Conveyor Chains
S.I.C.: 3568; 3562
N.A.I.C.S.: 333613; 332991
Import Export
Media: 2-4-6-16-21
Distr.: Natl.
Budget Set: Oct.
Personnel:
Brice Barker *(Pres)*
Brands & Products:
ACE
DIAMOND
DURALUBE
FLAT TOP
RING LEADER
SAPPHIRE

DIAMOND INNOVATIONS, INC.
(Sub. of Sandvik Tooling AB)
6325 Huntley Rd
Columbus, OH 43229-1007
Mailing Address:
PO Box 568
Worthington, OH 43085-0568
Tel.: (614) 438-2000
Fax: (614) 438-2888
Fax: (800) 472-7329 (Sales)
Toll Free: (800) 443-1955
Web Site: www.abrasivesnet.com
Approx. Number Employees: 650
Year Founded: 1957
Business Description:
Industrial Diamond, Cubic Boron Nitride & Polycrystalline Abrasive Products Mfr & Distr
S.I.C.: 3291; 3544; 5085
N.A.I.C.S.: 327910; 333514; 423840
Import Export
Media: 2-5-10-11-13
Distr.: Intl.; Natl.
Personnel:
Tanya D. Fratto *(Pres & CEO)*
Brands & Products:
BORAZON CUBIC BORON NITRIDE
BZN COMPACTS
COMPAX BLANKS
MBG DIAMOND
MBS DIAMOND
RVG DIAMOND
STRATAPAX

DIEHL WOODWORKING MACHINERY, INC.
981 S Wabash St
Wabash, IN 46992-4125
Tel.: (260) 563-2102
Fax: (260) 563-0206
E-mail: sales@diehlmachines.com
Web Site: www.diehlmachines.com
E-Mail For Key Personnel:
Sales Director: sales@diehlmachines.com
Approx. Sls.: $6,500,000
Approx. Number Employees: 60
Year Founded: 1909
Business Description:
Woodworking Machinery Mfr
S.I.C.: 3553; 5084
N.A.I.C.S.: 333210; 423830
Export
Media: 2-7-10
Distr.: Natl.
Personnel:
Robert Rozman *(Pres)*
Gary Fredrickson *(Mgr-Sls)*
Brands & Products:
CHALLONER
DIEHL MACHINES
Advertising Agency:
Sesler Agency
17607 Wesley Chapel Rd.
Churubusco, IN 46723
Tel.: (219) 693-9801
Woodworking Machines

THE DOALL COMPANY
1480 S Wolf Rd
Wheeling, IL 66090
Tel.: (847) 824-1122
Fax: (847) 803-7343
Toll Free: (800) 923-0255
E-mail: info@doall.com
Web Site: www.doall.com
Approx. Number Employees: 80
Year Founded: 1940
Business Description:
Machine Tools, Cutting Tools, Industrial Supplies, Precision Gauges, Measuring Equipment & Cutting Fluids Distr & Mfr
S.I.C.: 5085; 5084
N.A.I.C.S.: 423840; 423830
Import Export
Advertising Expenditures: $2,095,000
Multimedia: $25,000; Bus. Publs.: $300,000; Catalogs & Directories: $500,000; Co-op Adv.: $25,000; D.M. to Bus. Estab.: $530,000; Exhibits/Trade Shows: $250,000; Foreign: $35,000; Other: $300,000; Product Samples: $30,000; Yellow Page Adv.: $100,000
Distr.: Intl.; Natl.
Budget Set: June
Personnel:
Michale L. Wilkie *(Chm & Pres)*
Jon Henricks *(Vice Chm)*
Jim Hobbs *(Pres-DoALL Canada)*
William Henricks *(COO)*
Timothy Moran *(Gen Counsel)*
Chuck Davis *(Sr VP-Contour Saws)*
David Crawford *(Sr VP)*
Brands & Products:
BRIGHT-EDGE
DOALL
INVADER-X
INVADER-XP
KLEEN-KOOL
KOOL-ALL
POWER-CUT
SILENCER
STRUCTURALL
TRIPLE-CHIP
TUFF KUT
VALU-PAC
Advertising Agency:
Industrial Marketing Services, Inc.
2375 Touhy Ave
Elk Grove Village, IL 60007
Tel.: (847) 258-8850
Fax: (847) 593-0462

DONALDSON COMPANY, INC.
1400 W 94th St
Bloomington, MN 55431-2370
Mailing Address:
PO Box 1299
Minneapolis, MN 55440-1299
Tel.: (952) 887-3131
Tel.: (952) 887-3344
Fax: (952) 887-3155
Telex: 290434
E-mail: aircraftfilters@mail.donaldson.com
Web Site: www.donaldson.com
Approx. Sls.: $2,294,029,000
Approx. Number Employees: 13,000
Year Founded: 1915
Business Description:
Filtration Systems & Replacement Parts Mfr
S.I.C.: 3564; 3569; 3714
N.A.I.C.S.: 333411; 333999; 336399
Import Export
Media: 1-2-4-7-10-13-19-20-22-26
Distr.: Intl.; Natl.
Budget Set: May -June
Personnel:
William M. Cook *(Chm, Pres & CEO)*
Thomas R. Verhage *(CFO & VP)*
Mary Lynne Perushek *(CIO & VP)*
Charles J. McMurray *(Chief Admin Officer & Sr VP)*
Norman C. Linnell *(Gen Counsel, Sec & VP)*
Tod E. Carpenter *(Sr VP-Engine Products)*
Jay L. Ward *(Sr VP-Indus Products)*
Dennis D. Jandik *(VP-Global Engine OEM Sls)*
Sandra N. Joppa *(VP-HR)*
Brands & Products:
AUTOCLEAN
BLUE COLOR FILTER
BONDURA
BURAN
CELLULEX
CYCLOPAC
D LOGO
DONACLONE
DONALDSON
DONALDSON INDURANCE
DONASONIC
DOWNFLO
DRYFLO
DURA-LIFE
DURAFAXX
DURALITE
DURAMAX
DURATEK
ENDURA-TEK
ENDURANCE
ETO-ABATOR
FIBER-WEB
FLEX-TRUNK
FORMIX
THE INFORMER
KONEPAC
LITHOGUARD
PORTA-TRUNK
POWERCORE
RADIALSEAL
SEALCLAMP
SERVISIGNAL
SILENT PARTNER
SPIRACLE
STRATA
SYNTEQ
TETRATEX
THERMO-TEK
TORIT
TORIT-BUILT
TORIT-TEX
TRIBOGUARD
TRUNK 2000
ULTRA AIRE
ULTRA-TEK
ULTRA-WEB
ULTRAAQUA
ULTRABEV
ULTRAC
ULTRACOOL
ULTRADRI
ULTRAIR
ULTRAMESH
ULTRAPAC
ULTRASORP
ULTRASULFOMEM
ULTREX
ULTRFILTER
UTRAMAT
VEE PAC
VOC ABATOR
Advertising Agencies:
Padilla Speer Beardsley
1101 W River Pkwy Ste 400
Minneapolis, MN 55415-1241
Tel.: (612) 455-1700
Fax: (612) 455-1060
Public Relations

Strother Communications
222 S 9th St Fl 41
Minneapolis, MN 55402
Tel.: (612) 288-2400
Fax: (612) 288-0504

DORNER MANUFACTURING CORP.
975 Cottonwood Ave
Hartland, WI 53029
Mailing Address:
PO Box 20
Hartland, WI 53029-0020
Tel.: (262) 367-7600
Fax: (262) 367-5827
Toll Free: (800) 369-2440
E-mail: info@dorner.com

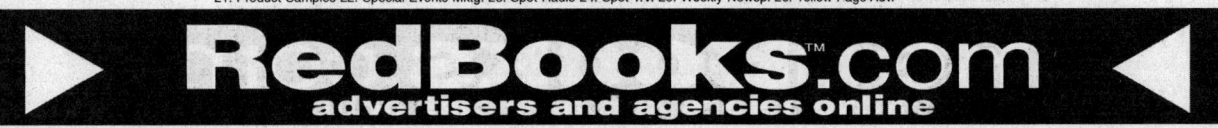

Key to Media (For complete agency information see *The Advertising Red Books-Agencies* edition):
1. Bus. Publs. 2. Cable T.V. 3. Catalogs & Directories. 4. Co-op Adv. 5. Consumer Mags. 6. D.M. to Bus. Estab.7. D.M. to Consumers
8. Daily Newsp. 9. Exhibits/Trade Shows 10. Foreign 11. Infomercial 12. Internet Adv.13. Multimedia 14. Network Radio
15. Network T.V. 16. Newsp. Distr. Mags. 17. Other 18. Outdoor (Posters, Transit) 19. Point of Purchase20. Premiums, Novelties
21. Product Samples 22. Special Events Mktg. 23. Spot Radio 24. Spot T.V. 25. Weekly Newsp. 26. Yellow Page Adv.

Dorner Manufacturing Corp. — (Continued)

Web Site: www.dorner.com
Approx. Number Employees: 150
Year Founded: 1965
Business Description:
Belt Conveyors Mfr
S.I.C.: 3535
N.A.I.C.S.: 333922
Export
Media: 2-4-7-10-11-13-16-20-26
Distr.: Intl.; Natl.
Budget Set: Aug.
Personnel:
Werner Dorner *(Pres)*
Dale Visgar *(CFO)*
Matt Jones *(Dir-Channel Sls)*
Steven Stuff *(Dir-Sls Support)*
Tom Daly *(Reg Mgr)*
Ken Detmer *(Reg Mgr)*
Scott Oechsner *(Reg Mgr)*
Bob Southard *(Reg Mgr)*
Will Keast *(Mgr-Svc-USA)*
John Kuhnz *(Mgr-Food Mktg)*
Brands & Products:
2200 SERIES
4100 SERIES
AQUA PRUF
DORNER
IMPAC
LPZ
MPB SERIES
NEWS THAT MOVES

DOVER CORPORATION
3005 Highland Pkwy Ste 200
Downers Grove, IL 60515
Tel.: (630) 541-1540
Fax: (630) 743-2671
E-mail: webmaster@dovercorp.com
Web Site: www.dovercorporation.com
Approx. Rev.: $7,132,648,000
Approx. Number Employees: 32,000
Year Founded: 1941
Business Description:
Diversified Industrial, Production & Servicing Equipment Mfr
S.I.C.: 3559; 3537; 3561; 3565; 3585; 3589; 3679; 3823; 3825
N.A.I.C.S.: 333298; 333319; 333415; 333911; 333924; 333993; 334418; 334419; 334513; 334515
Export
Advertising Expenditures: $45,500,000
Personnel:
Robert W. Cremin *(Chm)*
Robert A. Livingston *(Pres & CEO)*
Brad M. Cerepak *(CFO & VP)*
Thomas W. Giacomini *(Pres/CEO-Indus Products & VP)*
Raymond Hoglund *(Pres/CEO-Engineered Sys & VP)*
William W. Spurgeon *(Pres/CEO-Fluid Mgmt & VP)*
David Van Loan *(Pres/CEO-Dover Electronic Tech & VP)*
Sivasankaran Somasundaram *(Pres-Fluid Solutions Platform & Exec VP)*
Joseph W. Schmidt *(Gen Counsel, Sec & VP)*
Paul E. Goldberg *(Treas & Dir-IR)*
Ivonne M. Cabrera *(VP & Deputy Gen Counsel)*
Jay L. Kloosterboer *(VP-HR)*
Rob Guertin *(Mgr-Mktg)*
Scott Howard *(Mgr-Fin Plng & Analysis)*

DOWNS CRANE & HOIST CO, INC.
8827 S Juniper St
Los Angeles, CA 90002-1827
Tel.: (323) 589-6061
Fax: (323) 589-6066
Toll Free: (800) 748-5994
E-mail: Support@DownsCrane.com
Web Site: www.downscrane.com
E-Mail For Key Personnel:
Sales Director: sales@downscrane.com
Sales Range: $10-24.9 Million
Approx. Number Employees: 25
Year Founded: 1922
Business Description:
Below the Hook Lifting Devices Mfr
S.I.C.: 3536; 5082
N.A.I.C.S.: 333923; 423810
Export
Media: 2-4-7
Distr.: Intl.; Natl.
Budget Set: July
Personnel:
J.W. Downs, Jr. *(Pres)*
J.W. Downs III *(VP-Fin)*
Brands & Products:
DOWNS
GRABMASTER

DOYLE SYSTEMS
5186 New Haven Cir
Barberton, OH 44203
Tel.: (330) 564-4000
Fax: (330) 564-4005
Toll Free: (800) 445-3856
E-mail: sales@doylesystems.com
Web Site: www.doylesystems.com
E-Mail For Key Personnel:
Sales Director: sales@doylesystems.com
Sales Range: $10-24.9 Million
Approx. Number Employees: 20
Year Founded: 1922
Business Description:
Cleaning & Inspection Systems for the Prining Industry
S.I.C.: 3555
N.A.I.C.S.: 333293
Advertising Expenditures: $200,000
Media: 2-4-7-10-11
Distr.: Intl.; Natl.
Budget Set: Nov.
Personnel:
Joseph M. Lynch *(Pres)*
Jean Reash *(Gen Mgr)*
Brands & Products:
DOYLE SYSTEMS
LANDSCO LIGHT
STATIBRUSH
STATIKIL
STATITINSEL

DRAEGER SAFETY, INC.
(Sub. of Draegerwerk AG & Co. KGaA)
101 Technology Dr
Pittsburgh, PA 15275-1005
Tel.: (412) 787-8383
Fax: (412) 787-2207
Toll Free: (800) 922-5518
Telex: 86-6704
E-mail: shelly.cosmides@draeger.com
Web Site: www.draeger.com
Approx. Number Employees: 175
Year Founded: 1977
Business Description:
Toxic Gas Monitoring Instrumentation & Respiratory Protection Equipment Mfr
S.I.C.: 3829; 5084
N.A.I.C.S.: 334519; 423830
Import Export
Advertising Expenditures: $200,000
Media: 1-2-4-7-8-10-11-13-17-19-22
Distr.: Natl.
Budget Set: Dec.
Personnel:
Shelli Cosmides *(Mgr-Mktg Comm)*
Brands & Products:
ACCURO
AIR BOSS
DRAEGER-CMS
DRAEGER-TUBES
PRO AIR

DREIS & KRUMP MANUFACTURING COMPANY
481 S Governors Hwy
Peotone, IL 60468-9116
Tel.: (708) 258-1200
Fax: (708) 258-9682
E-mail: chicago@dreis-krump.com
Web Site: www.dreis-krump.com
Approx. Number Employees: 23
Year Founded: 1899
Business Description:
Machine Tools Mfr
S.I.C.: 3542; 3568
N.A.I.C.S.: 333513; 333613
Import Export
Media: 2-4-10-16-26
Distr.: Intl.; Natl.
Budget Set: Sept. -Oct.
Personnel:
Rudy Wolfer *(Pres)*
Al Anderson *(VP-Fin)*
Brands & Products:
CHICAGO
DREIS & KRUMP

DRESSER, INC.
(Sub. of GE Energy)
15455 Dallas Pkwy Ste 1100
Addison, TX 75001-6771
Tel.: (972) 361-9800
Fax: (972) 361-9903
Web Site: www.dresser.com
Approx. Number Employees: 6,500
Year Founded: 2001
Business Description:
Flow Control Products, Measurement Systems & Power Systems Mfr
S.I.C.: 3491; 3825
N.A.I.C.S.: 332911; 334515
Advertising Expenditures: $1,580,000
Personnel:
John P. Ryan *(Pres & CEO)*
N. John Lancaster *(Mng Dir)*
Marty R. Kittrell *(Exec VP & CFO)*
Darrin F. Whitney *(CIO & VP-IT)*
Martha Bixby *(Chief Sustainability Officer & VP-EHS Affairs)*
Barry Glickman *(Pres-Flow Technologies)*
Neil H. Thomas *(Pres-Measurement & Distr)*
Brian White *(Pres-Power & Compression)*
Linda Rutherford *(Gen Counsel & Sr VP)*
Robbir Marshall *(Interim VP-HR)*
Sandro Esposito *(Mgr-Mktg-Global)*
Brands & Products:
ASHCROFT
BECKER
DRESSER
EBRO
GROVE
HEISE
LEDEEN
MASONEILAN
MOOEY
RING-O
ROOTS
SPOOLCAL
TEXSTEAM
URAI-G
WAUKESHA
WEKSLER
WHEATLEY
WHISPAIR
WILLY

DRESSER ROOTS
(Sub. of Dresser, Inc.)
16240 Port NW Dr
Houston, TX 77041-2045
Mailing Address:
PO Box 42176
Houston, TX 77242-2176
Tel.: (832) 590-2305
Fax: (281) 590-2326
Web Site: www.rootsblower.com
Approx. Number Employees: 275
Year Founded: 1854
Business Description:
Rotary Positive Blowers, Vacuum Pumps & Centrifugal Units Mfr
S.I.C.: 3621
N.A.I.C.S.: 335312
Export
Advertising Expenditures: $350,000
Media: 2-4-10-13-18-19-20
Distr.: Intl
Budget Set: Oct.
Personnel:
John Parrish *(Sr VP-Global Sls, Infrastructure Solutions Segment)*
Jenny Haynes *(VP-Comm)*
Glenn Heinrich *(Dir-Product Tech)*
Dean Adams *(Mgr-Svcs)*
John Stout *(Mgr-Sls)*
Jim Wolford *(Supvr-Mktg Comm)*
Advertising Agency:
Bob Fowler & Associates
1710 Mossbach Cir
Fresno, TX 77545
Tel.: (281) 431-9166
Fax: (281) 431-9247

DRESSER WAYNE DIVISION
(Div. of Dresser, Inc.)
3814 Jarrett Way
Austin, TX 78728-1212
Tel.: (512) 388-8311
Fax: (512) 388-8429
E-mail: webmaster@wayne.com
Web Site: www.wayne.com
Approx. Number Employees: 1,500
Year Founded: 1891
Business Description:
Fuel Dispensing Systems Mfr
S.I.C.: 3491; 3825
N.A.I.C.S.: 332911; 334515
Export
Advertising Expenditures: $600,000

Key to Media (For complete agency information see *The Advertising Red Books-Agencies* edition):
1. Bus. Publs. 2. Cable T.V. 3. Catalogs & Directories. 4. Co-op Adv. 5. Consumer Mags. 6. D.M. to Bus. Estab.7. D.M. to Consumers 8. Daily Newsp. 9. Exhibits/Trade Shows 10. Foreign 11. Infomercial 12. Internet Adv.13. Multimedia 14. Network Radio 15. Network T.V. 16. Newsp. Distr. Mags. 17. Other 18. Outdoor (Posters, Transit) 19. Point of Purchase20. Premiums, Novelties 21. Product Samples 22. Special Events Mktg. 23. Spot Radio 24. Spot T.V. 25. Weekly Newsp. 26. Yellow Page Adv.

Media: 2-4-7-10-11-26
Distr.: Intl.; Natl.
Budget Set: June
Personnel:
Scott Campbell *(VP-Procurement)*
Jorge Mendez-Penate *(VP-Intl Sls)*
Bill Reichhold *(VP-Sls)*
Brian Sullivan *(VP-HR)*
Peter Parmentier *(Gen Mgr)*
Keith Moynihan *(Sr Dir-Ops)*
Brands & Products:
QUADRO

DRIL-QUIP, INC.
13550 Hempstead Hwy
Houston, TX 77040-5851
Tel.: (713) 939-7711
Fax: (713) 939-8063
E-mail: information@dril-quip.com
Web Site: www.dril-quip.com
Approx. Rev.: $566,251,000
Approx. Number Employees: 2,127
Year Founded: 1981
Business Description:
Offshore Drilling & Production Equipment Mfr
S.I.C.: 1311; 3533
N.A.I.C.S.: 211111; 333132
Media: 2
Personnel:
J. Mike Walker *(Co-Chm)*
Jerry M. Brooks *(CFO & VP-Fin)*
Brands & Products:
ACTUATED GATE VALVES
ADJUSTMENT SUB
BIGBORE
CS-10 CASING SUPPORT SYSTEMS
DH, DHS & DL SERIES GATE VALVES
DHF SERIES FIRE-RESISTANT GATE VALVES
DIVERTER SYSTEMS
DL SERIES GATE VALVES & DLH ACTUATORS
DRIL-QUIP
DRIL-THRU
DRIL-THRU COMPLETION SYSTEMS
DUAL BORE PRODUCTION SYSTEM
DX WELLHEAD CONNECTORS
EMERGENCY BACKOUT SUB
GUIDELINELESS SUBSEA PRODUCTION SYSTEMS
LOWER RISER & EMERGENCY DISCONNECT PACKAGES
LS-15 LINER HANGER SYSTEM
MARINE DRILLING RISER CONNECTORS
MARINE DRILLING RISER SYSTEMS
MS-10 MUDLINE SUSPENSION SYSTEMS
MS-15 MUDLINE SUSPENSION SYSTEMS
MUDLINE CONVERSION SYSTEMS
MULTI-THREAD
PR-80
QMF
QMFC
QUIK-CLAMP CONNECTOR
QUIK-JAY CONNECTORS
QUIK-LOK CONNECTORS
QUIK-STAB
QUIK-STAB CONNECTORS
QUIK-THREAD
QUIK-THREAD/MULTI THREAD CONNECTORS
RADIAL BOLT CONNECTOR
SB-PLUGS
SC-90 CONVENTIONAL WELLHEAD SYSTEMS
SETTING A GLOBAL STANDARD
SINGLEBORE
SINGLEBORE PRODUCTION SYSTEM
SPAR PRODUCTION & DRILLING RISER SYSTEMS
SPAR PRODUCTION RISER CONNECTORS
SPECIAL APPLICATIONS CUTTINGS INJECTION SYSTEMS
SS-10/SS-10C SUBSEA WELLHEAD SYSTEMS
SS-15 BIGBORE SUBSEA WELLHEAD SYSTEMS
SS-15 DEEPWATER SUBSEA WELLHEAD SYSTEMS
SS-15 SUBSEA WELLHEAD SYSTEMS
SS-15ES DEEPWATER SUBSEA WELLHEAD SYSTEMS
SU-90
SU-902 UNITIZED WELLHEAD SYSTEMS
SUBSEA TEMPLATE SYSTEMS
SUBSEA TIE-BACK SYSTEM TO FIXED PLATFORM
SUBSEA TIE-BACK SYSTEM TO TLP/SPAR
SUPPLEMENTAL CASING HANGER SYSTEM
SURFACE PRODUCTION SYSTEMS
TEFLON

DRYCLEAN USA, INC.
290 NE 68th St
Miami, FL 33138
Tel.: (305) 754-4551
Fax: (305) 754-8010
Toll Free: (800) 746-4583
E-mail: ir@drycleanusa.com
Web Site: www.drycleanusa.com
Approx. Rev.: $231,555,417
Approx. Number Employees: 29
Business Description:
Drycleaning & Laundry Services; Coin-Operated Laundry Machines Whslr
S.I.C.: 7212; 3582
N.A.I.C.S.: 812320; 333312
Advertising Expenditures: $93,000
Media: 2-10-20
Personnel:
William K. Steiner *(Chm)*
Michael S. Steiner *(Pres & CEO)*
Venerando J. Indelicato *(CFO & Treas)*
Brands & Products:
CLEAN AROUND THE WORLD
DRYCLEAN USA

DUMORE CORPORATION
1030 Veterans St
Mauston, WI 53948-9314
Tel.: (608) 847-6420
Fax: (608) 847-7418
Toll Free: (800) 338-6673
E-mail: chanson@dumorecorp.com
Web Site: www.dumorecorp.com
Approx. Number Employees: 70
Year Founded: 1913
Business Description:
Automatic Drills, Portable Machinery, Custom Designed OEM Motors & Industrial Tools Mfr
S.I.C.: 3621; 3541
N.A.I.C.S.: 335312; 333512
Export
Advertising Expenditures: $341,000
Multimedia: $10,000; Bus. Publs.: $36,000; Catalogs & Directories: $50,000; Co-op Adv.: $100,000; Exhibits/Trade Shows: $15,000; Point of Purchase: $50,000; Premiums, Novelties: $20,000; Product Samples: $50,000; Yellow Page Adv.: $10,000
Distr.: Intl.; Natl.
Personnel:
Dave Messer *(Pres)*
Brenda Belk *(VP-Fin)*
Brands & Products:
DUMORE
QUALITY IS OUR LEGACY

DUPLEX MILL & MANUFACTURING CO.
415 Sigler St
Springfield, OH 45506-1144
Mailing Address:
PO Box 1266
Springfield, OH 45501-1266
Tel.: (937) 325-5555
Fax: (937) 325-0859
E-mail: sales@dmmc.com
Web Site: www.dmmc.com
E-Mail For Key Personnel:
President: eww@dmmc.com
Sales Director: sales@dmmc.com
Approx. Sls.: $4,500,000
Approx. Number Employees: 11
Year Founded: 1884
Business Description:
Machinery Mfr
S.I.C.: 3535; 3531
N.A.I.C.S.: 333922; 333120
Export
Media: 2-7-8
Distr.: Intl.; Natl.
Budget Set: Dec.
Personnel:
E. W. Wise *(Pres & Treas)*

DUPREE, INC.
14395 Ramona Ave
Chino, CA 91710-5740
Tel.: (909) 597-4889
Fax: (909) 597-3043
E-mail: sales@dupreeinc.com
Web Site: www.dupreeinc.com
E-Mail For Key Personnel:
Sales Director: sales@dupreeinc.com
Approx. Rev.: $3,000,000
Approx. Number Employees: 40
Year Founded: 1958
Business Description:
Designer, Mfr., & Developer of Stake Fasteners & Western Photometric Systems
S.I.C.: 3499; 2821
N.A.I.C.S.: 332999; 325211
Media: 2-4-8-10-13-16
Distr.: Intl.; Natl.
Brands & Products:
CALIBRATION LAMP SETS
DUPREE

DUSENBERY WORLDWIDE
220 Franklin Rd
Randolph, NJ 07869
Tel.: (973) 366-7500
Fax: (973) 366-7453
Toll Free: (800) 845-1073
E-mail: sales@dusenbery.com
Web Site: www.dusenbery.com
E-Mail For Key Personnel:
President: tonycirillo@dusenbury.com
Sales Director: sales@dusenbery.com
Approx. Number Employees: 125
Year Founded: 1948
Business Description:
Paper Film & Foil Machinery Accessories & Parts Mfr
S.I.C.: 3569
N.A.I.C.S.: 333999
Import Export
Advertising Expenditures: $300,000
Media: 2-4-7-10
Distr.: Natl.
Budget Set: Apr.
Personnel:
Tony Cirillo *(Pres)*
Roger Young *(Exec VP)*
Manny Mayo *(Sls Mgr)*
Mike Pakonis *(Sls Mgr)*
John Marold *(Mgr-Sls)*
Brands & Products:
DUSENBERY
REVOLUTION

DWYER INSTRUMENTS INC.
102 Indiana Hwy 212
Michigan City, IN 46360-1956
Tel.: (219) 879-8000
Fax: (219) 872-9057
E-mail: info@dwyermail.com
Web Site: www.dwyer-inst.com
Approx. Number Employees: 700
Year Founded: 1931
Business Description:
Mfr. of Industrial Instruments & Controls
S.I.C.: 3823; 3824
N.A.I.C.S.: 334513; 334514
Import Export
Advertising Expenditures: $600,000
Media: 2-4-7-10-11-13-26
Distr.: Intl.; Natl.
Personnel:
Stephen S. Clark *(Pres)*
Mark Fisher *(VP-Sls, Engrg & Mktg)*
Brands & Products:
ANDERSON-MIDWEST
CAPSU-PHOTOHELIC
CAPSUHELIC
DIGIHELIC
DUAL-RANGE
DUOTECT
DURABLOCK
DWYER
FLEX-TUBE
FLOTECT
LOVE
LOVELINK
MARK II
MERCOID
MICROTECTOR
MIDWEST
MINI-MASTER
MINIGRAPH
MINIMASTER
PRECISOR
PROXIMITY
PROXIMITY DETECTOR
PROXIMITY MARK
QUICK SCAN
QUICK-VIEW
RATE-MASTER
SAFE-T-OHM
SLACK TUBE
SLIQUID

Key to Media (For complete agency information see *The Advertising Red Books-Agencies* edition):
1. Bus. Publs. 2. Cable T.V. 3. Catalogs & Directories. 4. Co-op Adv. 5. Consumer Mags. 6. D.M. to Bus. Estab.7. D.M. to Consumers
8. Daily Newsp. 9. Exhibits/Trade Shows 10. Foreign 11. Infomercial 12. Internet Adv.13. Multimedia 14. Network Radio
15. Network T.V. 16. Newsp. Distr. Mags. 17. Other 18. Outdoor (Posters, Transit) 19. Point of Purchase20. Premiums, Novelties
21. Product Samples 22. Special Events Mktg. 23. Spot Radio 24. Spot T.V. 25. Weekly Newsp. 26. Yellow Page Adv.

Dwyer Instruments Inc. — (Continued)

SPIRAHELIC
TEFLON
TOTAL INSTRUMENT SOLUTION
ULTRA-MAG
VANEOMETER
VISI-FLOAT
W.E. ANDERSON
WEA

DYNACAST LTD.

(Formerly FisherCast Ltd.)
(Sub. of Dynacast Inc.)
710 Neal Drive
Peterborough, ON K9J 6X7, Canada
Tel.: (705) 748-9522
Web Site: www.dynacast.com
Approx. Number Employees: 250
Year Founded: 1942
Business Description:
Small Precise Zinc Die Castings; Designers & Injected Metal Assembly & Injected Metal Machines Mfr
S.I.C.: 3369
N.A.I.C.S.: 331528
Export
Media: 1-2-4-7-10-11-13-21-26
Distr.: Intl.
Budget Set: Nov.
Personnel:
Bill Davie *(Mgr-Fin)*
Brands & Products:
ACUZINC
FISHER
FISHERCAST
FISHERCAST GLOBAL CORPORATION
FISHERCAST IMA
FISHERCOTEIII
FISHERTECH
FIXTURBLOK
IMA
INJECTED METAL ASSEMBLY
ZAMAK

DYNAPOWER CORPORATION

85 Meadowland Dr
South Burlington, VT 05403
Tel.: (802) 860-7200
Fax: (802) 864-3782
E-mail: drogers@dynapower.com
Web Site: www.dynapower.com
Approx. Number Employees: 140
Business Description:
Power Conversion Products & Transformers Mfr
S.I.C.: 3612
N.A.I.C.S.: 335311
Media: 10
Personnel:
Peter Pollak *(Pres)*
Adam Knudsen *(COO)*
Jeff Nazarko *(Mgr-Sls & Mktg-iTHERM Technologies)*
Mary Duncan *(Supvr-Customer Svc Team)*
Pete Abele *(Engr-Sls)*
Jason McGahey *(Engr-Sls)*
Stan Popp *(Engr-Sls)*
George Viola *(Engr-Sls)*
Brands & Products:
DYNAPOWER RAPID POWER
ULTRACAST

EAGLE TECHNOLOGIES GROUP

9850 Red Arrow Hwy
Bridgman, MI 49106
Tel.: (269) 465-6986
Fax: (269) 465-6952
Web Site:
www.eagletechnologies.com
Approx. Number Employees: 90
Year Founded: 1953
Business Description:
Provider of Systems Integration Products
S.I.C.: 3569; 3829
N.A.I.C.S.: 333999; 334519
Import Export
Advertising Expenditures: $400,000
Media: 7-9-13
Distr.: Direct to Consumer; Intl.; Natl.
Budget Set: Aug.
Personnel:
Mike Koziel *(Gen Mgr)*
Brands & Products:
PARTNERS IN PRODUCTIVITY
PRECISION
WELDUN

EAGLE TEST SYSTEMS, INC.

(Sub. of Teradyne Inc.)
2200 Millbrook Dr
Buffalo Grove, IL 60089
Tel.: (847) 367-8282
Fax: (847) 367-8640
E-mail: support@eagletest.com
Web Site: www.eagletest.com
Approx. Rev.: $85,982,000
Approx. Number Employees: 351
Year Founded: 1976
Business Description:
Automated Test Equipment Mfr
S.I.C.: 3559; 3825
N.A.I.C.S.: 333295; 334515
Media: 10
Personnel:
Jack E. Weimer *(CTO & Mgr-Technical Solutions)*
Craig B. Smith *(Mgr-Product Dev)*
Brands & Products:
EAGLE VISION

EAST CHICAGO MACHINE TOOL CORPORATION

(d/b/a Balemaster USA)
980 Crown Ct
Crown Point, IN 46307-2732
Tel.: (219) 663-4525
Fax: (219) 663-4591
E-mail: sales@balemaster.com
Web Site: www.balemaster.com
E-Mail For Key Personnel:
Sales Director: sales@balemaster.com
Approx. Sls.: $5,000,000
Approx. Number Employees: 60
Year Founded: 1946
Business Description:
Scrap Paper Handling & Baling Equipment Mfr
S.I.C.: 3569; 3589
N.A.I.C.S.: 333999; 333319
Export
Media: 2-4-7-10
Distr.: Direct to Consumer; Natl.
Budget Set: Nov.
Personnel:
Cornel Raab *(Pres)*
Brands & Products:
BALEMASTER
BALEWEL
CYCLOMATIC

EASTERN AIR DEVICES INC.

(Sub. of Delany Capital Management Corp.)
(d/b/a EADmotors)
1 Progress Dr
Dover, NH 03820-5450
Tel.: (603) 742-3330
Fax: (603) 742-9080
E-mail: info@eadmotors.com
Web Site: www.eadmotors.com
E-Mail For Key Personnel:
Sales Director: info@eadmotors.com
Sales Range: $10-24.9 Million
Approx. Number Employees: 170
Year Founded: 1942
Business Description:
Precision Motors, Rotating Components, Blowers & Fans Designer & Mfr
S.I.C.: 3621; 3825
N.A.I.C.S.: 335312; 334515
Import Export
Media: 2-4-7-10-13
Distr.: Natl.
Personnel:
Logan D. Delany *(Chm)*
Jim Elsner *(Pres & CEO)*
John Arico *(VP-Fin & Admin)*
Tom Ouellette *(VP-Sls & Mktg)*
Brands & Products:
EAD
Advertising Agency:
Think Nocturnal LLC
8 Continental Dr Unit E
Exeter, NH 03833
Tel.: (603) 929-2131
Fax: (603) 686-5477

THE EASTERN COMPANY

112 Bridge St PO Box 460
Naugatuck, CT 06770-0460
Tel.: (203) 729-2255
Fax: (203) 723-8653
E-mail: ir@easterncompany.com
Web Site: www.easterncompany.com
Approx. Sls.: $130,130,360
Approx. Number Employees: 633
Year Founded: 1858
Business Description:
Locks & Industrial Hardware Mfr for Safety & Security
S.I.C.: 7382; 2439; 3429; 3444; 3451; 3452; 3499
N.A.I.C.S.: 561621; 321214; 332322; 332510; 332721; 332722; 332999
Import Export
Advertising Expenditures: $446,899
Media: 17
Distr.: Intl.; Natl.
Personnel:
Leonard F. Leganza *(Chm, Pres & CEO)*
John L. Sullivan III *(CFO & VP)*
Kenneth R. Sapack *(Chief Acctg Officer & Corp Controller)*
Brands & Products:
DUO
EBERHARD
ECLIPSE
GUNBLOK
ILLINOIS
PRESTOLOCK
SEARCH ALERT
SESAMEE

EASTMAN INDUSTRIES

70 Ingersoll Dr
Portland, ME 04103
Tel.: (207) 878-5353
Fax: (207) 878-9109
Toll Free: (800) 760-1680
E-mail: info@eastmanind.com
Web Site:
www.eastmanindustries.com
Approx. Number Employees: 15
Business Description:
Mfr & Distr of Hover Mowers & Eastman Mowers
S.I.C.: 3524
N.A.I.C.S.: 333112
Media: 4-7-13
Personnel:
Nicholas Nikazmerad *(Owner)*
Brands & Products:
EASTMAN MOWERS
HOVERMOWER

EASTMAN MACHINE COMPANY

779 Washington St
Buffalo, NY 14203-1308
Tel.: (716) 856-2200
Fax: (716) 856-1140
Toll Free: (800) 872-5571
E-mail: contact@eastmancuts.com
Web Site: www.eastmancuts.com
E-Mail For Key Personnel:
President: rlstevenson@eastmancuts.com
Sales Director: sales@eastmancuts.com
Sales Range: $10-24.9 Million
Approx. Number Employees: 120
Year Founded: 1889
Business Description:
Manual & Automated Cutting Machines, Spreading Equipment & Material Handling Systems Mfr
S.I.C.: 3552; 3541
N.A.I.C.S.: 333292; 333512
Import Export
Advertising Expenditures: $577,900
Multimedia: $19,000; Bus. Publs.: $238,000; Catalogs & Directories: $10,000; Exhibits/Trade Shows: $150,000; Foreign: $45,900; Internet Adv.: $25,000; Other: $60,000; Premiums, Novelties: $10,000; Special Events Mktg.: $20,000
Personnel:
Wade Stevenson *(Pres-Eastman Export)*
J. Resetar *(VP-Fin & Admin-Manual Cutting Machine Inquiries)*
Trevor Stevenson *(VP-Technical Svc & Product Dev)*
Elizabeth Hagen *(Mgr-Mktg)*
Carl Leinweber *(Mgr-Sls-Northeast Reg)*
Brands & Products:
AIR BRUTE
BLUE JAY
BLUE STREAK
BRUTE
BUZZAIRD
CARDINAL
CHICKADEE
EAGLE
EASICUT
EASIDNA
EASIHOLD

Key to Media (For complete agency information see *The Advertising Red Books-Agencies* edition):
1. Bus. Publs. 2. Cable T.V. 3. Catalogs & Directories. 4. Co-op Adv. 5. Consumer Mags. 6. D.M. to Bus. Estab.7. D.M. to Consumers 8. Daily Newsp. 9. Exhibits/Trade Shows 10. Foreign 11. Infomercial 12. Internet Adv.13. Multimedia 14. Network Radio 15. Network T.V. 16. Newsp. Distr. Mags. 17. Other 18. Outdoor (Posters, Transit) 19. Point of Purchase20. Premiums, Novelties 21. Product Samples 22. Special Events Mktg. 23. Spot Radio 24. Spot T.V. 25. Weekly Newsp. 26. Yellow Page Adv.

EASILABEL
EASIMARK
EASIPULL
EASISELECT
EASTMAN
EC3
EPDS
ETADS
EXPANDABLE
FALCON
GENTLE GIANT
HEAVYDUTY CARDINAL
HOT NOTCHER
LIGHTWEIGHT CARDINAL
LITTLE GIANT
M9000
MICRO FOG
MPC-5000
OVER A CENTURY OF CUTTING EXPERTISE
PACEMAKER
PLASTIC MASTER
ROLL CARRIER
ROLL STAND
SABER SELECT
STANDARD CARDINAL
SUPER DUTY CARDINAL
TURNTABLE
WORKERBEE

Advertising Agency:
Fusion Design & Marketing
19 Limestone Dr Ste 7
Williamsville, NY 14221
Tel.: (716) 631-9400

EATON CORPORATION

Eaton Ctr 1111 Superior Ave
Cleveland, OH 44114-2584
Tel.: (216) 523-5000
Fax: (216) 523-4787
Toll Free: (800) 386-1911
E-mail: customer@eaton.com
Web Site: www.eaton.com
Approx. Sls.: $13,715,000,000
Approx. Number Employees: 70,000
Year Founded: 1911
Business Description:
Electrical Power Systems, Aerospace Fuel & Hydraulic System & Automotive Drivetrain Mfr
S.I.C.: 3699; 3625; 3714
N.A.I.C.S.: 335999; 335314; 336322; 336399
Import Export
Advertising Expenditures: $68,534,183
Multimedia: $77,945; Bus. Publs.: $6,819,627; Catalogs & Directories: $9,925,219; Co-op Adv.: $1,252,978; D.M. to Bus. Estab.: $614,666; Exhibits/Trade Shows: $5,396,077; Foreign: $4,803,853; Other: $2,662; Outdoor (Posters, Transit): $14,500; Point of Purchase: $688,844; Premiums, Novelties: $3,106,309; Product Samples: $35,831,503
Distr.: Intl.; Natl.
Budget Set: Nov.
Personnel:
Alexander M. Cutler *(Chm, Pres & CEO)*
Richard H. Fearon *(Vice Chm, CFO & Chief Plng Officer)*
Craig Arnold *(Vice Chm & COO-Indus Sector)*
Thomas S. Gross *(Vice Chm & COO-Electrical Sector)*
William W. Blausey, Jr. *(CIO & Sr VP)*
Lennart Jonsson *(CTO & Exec VP)*
James W. McGill *(Chief HR Officer & Exec VP)*
Frank C. Campbell *(Pres-Electrical-EMEA)*
Kenneth F. Davis *(Pres-Vehicle Grp)*
Richard D. Holder *(Pres-Electrical Components)*
Jake Hooks *(Pres-Engine Air Mgmt Bus)*
Curtis J. Hutchins *(Pres-Asia Pacific Region)*
Richard B. Jacobs *(Pres-Filtration)*
Nanda Kumar *(Pres-Vehicle Grp-EMEA)*
J. Kevin McLean *(Pres-APAC)*
Bradley J. Morton *(Pres-Aerospace Bus)*
Patrick Randrianarison *(Pres-Corp America & South Group Vhicles)*
Yannis P. Tsavalas *(Pres-EMEA)*
William R. VanArsdale *(Pres-Hydraulics Grp)*
Jerry R. Whitaker *(Pres-Electrical Americas Region)*
Mark M. McGuire *(Gen Counsel & Exec VP)*
Ken D. Semelsberger *(Treas & Sr VP-Corp Dev)*
Thomas E. Moran *(Sec & Sr VP)*
Uday Yadav *(Exec VP-Eaton Bus Sys)*
Billie K. Rawot *(Sr VP & Controller)*
Steve Boccadoro *(Sr VP-Sls & Mktg)*
William B. Doggett *(Sr VP-Pub & Community Affairs)*
Scott A. Gray *(Sr VP-Corp Quality)*
William C. Hartman *(Sr VP-IR)*
Harold Jones *(Sr VP-Environment, Health & Safety)*
Jack Matejka *(Sr VP-Internal Audit)*
Donald J. Mcgrath *(Sr VP-Comm)*
Kurt B. McMaken *(Sr VP-Corp Dev & Treasury)*
John S. Mitchell *(Sr VP-Taxes)*
Ramanath Ramakrishnan *(Sr VP-Tech)*
Craig Reed *(Sr VP-Supply Chain Mgmt)*
Kirk Thomsen *(Sr VP-HR)*
Jeff Finch *(VP & Gen Mgr)*
Dimitri Kazarinoff *(VP & Gen Mgr-Hybrid Power Sys)*
Dave Bennett *(VP-Sls & Estimating)*
James Even *(VP-Fin-The Americas)*
Gregory A. Gumbs *(VP-Sls-Americas)*
Paolo Baretta *(Dir & Controller-VG EMEA)*
Anita Miller *(Dir-Corp Dev)*
Monica Alston *(Dir-Corp Environ, Health & Safety)*
Kile Bell *(Dir-Internal Control Program Office)*
Dan DeRoma *(Dir-Corp Acq & Divestiture Acctg)*
Gerard DeVito *(Dir-Engrg)*
Shelley McGrail *(Dir-Organizational Dev)*
Kenneth D. Narod *(Dir-Govt Sales & Solutions)*
Jim Sahli *(Dir-Global Field Sls & Mktg-Vehicle Grp)*
Dwayne McGrody *(Product Mgr)*
Skip Brabelton *(Mgr-Mktg Comm)*
John Sczesny *(Mgr-Bus Unit)*
Brands & Products:
ADVANTAGE
AEROQUIP
AIRFLEX
AMPGARD
ARGO-TECH
BILL
BOSTON
CENTURION
CHAR-LYNN
CUTLER-HAMMER
DANA
DANA SPICER
DUAL DUROMETER
DURANT
EATON
EATONCARE
ELEK
FAWICK
FIREGUARD
FREEDOM
FULLER
GOLF PRIDE
HEINEMANN
HOLEC
HYDRO-LINE
INSIGHT
IPROX
MAGNUM
MARINA POWER
MEM
NEW DECADE
PANELMATE
POWERCHAIN MANAGEMENT
POWERING BUSINESS WORLDWIDE
POWERWARE
ROADRANGER
RYNGLOK
SMART BREAKER
SOLO
STERER
SYNFLEX
TABULA
TEDECO
TOUR VELVET
U-PLEX
VICKERS
VORAD
VORAD EVT-300
WEATHERHEAD
Advertising Agency:
Brunner
11 Stanwix St 5th Fl
Pittsburgh, PA 15222-1312
Tel.: (412) 995-9500
Fax: (412) 995-9501
Agency of Record - Vehicles Group

EATON CORPORATION - AIRFLEX

(Unit of Eaton Corporation)
9919 Clinton Rd
Cleveland, OH 44144-1035
Tel.: (216) 281-2211
Fax: (216) 281-3890
Toll Free: (800) AIRFLEX
Telex: 212-559 aflx ur
E-mail: airflexcustomerservice@eaton.com
Web Site: www.airflex.com
E-Mail For Key Personnel:
President: SandyCutler@eaton.com
Sales Director: SubhasisChatterjee@eaton.com
Sales Range: $75-99.9 Million
Approx. Number Employees: 200
Year Founded: 1938
Business Description:
Industrial Clutches, Brakes & Assemblies Mfr
S.I.C.: 3714; 3568
N.A.I.C.S.: 336340; 333613
Import Export
Advertising Expenditures: $300,000
Media: 2-4-7-10-11
Distr.: Intl.; Natl.
Budget Set: Oct.
Personnel:
Sandy Cutler *(Chm & CEO)*
Subhasis Chatterjee *(Mgr-Sls)*
Donald Keck *(Sls Acct Exec)*
Brands & Products:
AIRFLEX

EATON CYLINDER

(Div. of Eaton Hydraulics Inc.)
2425 W Michigan Ave
Jackson, MI 49202-3964
Tel.: (517) 787-7220
Fax: (517) 787-3450
Sales Range: $75-99.9 Million
Approx. Number Employees: 200
Year Founded: 1917
Business Description:
Hydraulic & Pneumatic Cylinder Mfr
S.I.C.: 3593
N.A.I.C.S.: 333995
Import Export
Media: 2-4-7-10-20
Distr.: Natl.
Budget Set: Nov.
Brands & Products:
T-J

EATON HYDRAULICS INC.

(Div. of Eaton Corporation)
14615 Lone Oak Rd
Eden Prairie, MN 55344-2079
Tel.: (952) 937-9800
Fax: (952) 937-7394
Toll Free: (888) 258-0222
Web Site: www.eaton.com/hydraulics
Sales Range: $75-99.9 Million
Approx. Number Employees: 250
Business Description:
Hydraulic Motors, Pumps & Hydrostatic Transmissions Mfr
S.I.C.: 3625; 3714
N.A.I.C.S.: 335314; 336399
Export
Media: 2-4-7-10-11-19-20-21
Distr.: Intl.; Natl.
Budget Set: July
Personnel:
Bill VanArsdale *(Pres)*

ECLIPSE INC.

1665 Elmwood Rd
Rockford, IL 61103-1211
Tel.: (815) 877-3031
Fax: (815) 877-3336
Fax: (815) 877-2656
E-mail: eclipse@eclipsenet.com
Web Site: www.eclipsenet.com
Approx. Number Employees: 200
Year Founded: 1908
Business Description:
Heating Solutions
S.I.C.: 3433; 3564
N.A.I.C.S.: 333414; 333412
Import Export
Advertising Expenditures: $350,000
Media: 2-4-7-10-13-21-26
Distr.: Direct to Consumer; Intl.; Natl.
Budget Set: Jan.

Key to Media (For complete agency information see *The Advertising Red Books-Agencies* edition):
1. Bus. Publs. 2. Cable T.V. 3. Catalogs & Directories. 4. Co-op Adv. 5. Consumer Mags. 6. D.M. to Bus. Estab.7. D.M. to Consumers 8. Daily Newsp. 9. Exhibits/Trade Shows 10. Foreign 11. Infomercial 12. Internet Adv.13. Multimedia 14. Network Radio 15. Network T.V. 16. Newsp. Distr. Mags. 17. Other 18. Outdoor (Posters, Transit) 19. Point of Purchase20. Premiums, Novelties 21. Product Samples 22. Special Events Mktg. 23. Spot Radio 24. Spot T.V. 25. Weekly Newsp. 26. Yellow Page Adv.

Eclipse Inc. — (Continued)

Personnel:
Lachlan L. Perks *(Pres & COO)*
Greg Bubp *(CFO & VP)*
David Collier *(VP-Engrg)*
Al Benz *(Dir-Technical Solutions)*

Brands & Products:
AH
ALGAS-SDI
BLAST GATE
BOOSTPAK
BRIGHTFIRE
COMAX
COMBUSTION TEC
CROSS FLOW
ECLIPSE
ECLIPSE BAYONET
ECLIPSE BI-FLAME
ECLIPSE EXTENSOJET
ECLIPSE RATIOMATIC
ECLIPSE SPIRAL FLAME
ECLIPSE THERMJET
ECLIPSE THERMTHIEF
ECLIPSE VERI-FLAME
ECLIPSE VORTOMETRIC
EXO
EXO ALUMINUM AIR
EXO HEATPAK
EXO RED-RAY
EXO RIELLO
EXOTHERMICS
EXTERN-A-THERM
FUME INCINERATION
HERMATIC GAS
HERMETIC BOOSTER
IMMERSOJET
IMMERSOPAK
INCINI-CONE
INNOVATIVE THERMAL SOLUTIONS WORLDWIDE
LOCK TITE
MINNOX
MULTI-FLAME
PRIMEFIRE
RATIOMATIC
RHT
ROTARY
SIMAFLAME
SMJ BLOWER
SP-VT
SUPER OX SENSOR
THERMAIR
THERMJET
THERMTHIEF
WINNOX

E.D. BULLARD COMPANY

1898 Safety Way
Cynthiana, KY 41031-9303
Tel.: (859) 234-6611
Fax: (859) 234-8987
Toll Free: (800) 227-0423
E-mail: info@bullard.com
Web Site: www.bullard.com
E-Mail For Key Personnel:
President: rick_miller@bullard.com
Approx. Sls.: $69,000,000
Approx. Number Employees: 325
Year Founded: 1898
Business Description:
Industrial Head Protection, Respiratory Protection & Thermal Imaging Equipment Mfr & Distr
S.I.C.: 3842; 3564; 9224
N.A.I.C.S.: 339113; 333411; 922160
Import Export
Advertising Expenditures: $200,000
Media: 2-4-5-7-10-11-13-16-19-20-21
Distr.: Natl.
Budget Set: Jan.
Personnel:
Edward D. Bullard *(Chm)*
Richard Miller *(Pres)*
Eric Pasch *(CFO & Exec VP)*
Deb Purcchio *(Head-Protection & Product Mgr)*
Paul Guglielmi *(Dir-Sls)*
Manfred Kihn *(Reg Mgr-Sls & TI Trainer)*
Bruno Bonnaire *(Mgr-Sls)*
John Hays *(Product Mgr-Thermal Imaging)*
Grant Rowe *(Product Mgr)*
Greg Steller *(Mgr-Natl Accts-Life Sciences-North America)*
Brands & Products:
ADVENT
BULLARD
CLASSIC
DUAL-COOL
ECLIPSE
FAMB
FIREDOME
FLEX-GEAR
FREE AIR
FREE-AIR
FRIGITRON
GOLD LINE
HARD BOILED
THE HUMAN SIDE OF SAFETY
INDICATOR
ISOTHERM
IT'S YOUR LIFE AND YOU'RE WORTH IT
LANCER
QUICK-ATTACH
RED HOT
SENTINEL
SURE-LOCK
T3LT
T3MAX
TACPOLE
TACPORT
TACSCOPE
TACSIGHT
THERMOGLAS
TOUGH
TRAKLITE
TURTLE CLUB
TYCHEM
VECTOR
WILDFIRE

EDAC TECHNOLOGIES CORPORATION

1806 New Britain Ave
Farmington, CT 06032-3114
Tel.: (860) 677-2603
Fax: (860) 674-2718
E-mail: info@edactechnologies.com
Web Site: www.edactechnologies.com
Approx. Sls.: $73,058,000
Approx. Number Employees: 384
Year Founded: 1946
Business Description:
Tools, Fixtures, Jet Engine Components, Injection Molds, Gages & Spindles Designer & Mfr
S.I.C.: 3545; 3541; 3724
N.A.I.C.S.: 333515; 333512; 336412
Media: 2-10
Personnel:
Daniel C. Tracy *(Chm)*
Dominick A. Pagano *(Pres & CEO)*
Glenn L. Purple *(CFO, Sec & VP-Fin)*
Dave Derynoski *(Mgr-Sls & Mktg-Apex Machines Div)*
Ken Scibelli *(Mgr-New Bus Dev)*

EDWARDS VACUUM, INC.

(Sub. of Edwards Limited)
1 Highwood Dr Ste 101
Tewksbury, MA 01876
Tel.: (978) 658-5410
Fax: (978) 658-7969
Toll Free: (800) 848-9800
E-mail: info@edwardsvacuum.com
Web Site: www.edwardsvacuum.com
Approx. Number Employees: 100
Year Founded: 1902
Business Description:
Mfr & Marketing of Vacuum Dry Pumps, Turbo Pumps, Instrumentation
S.I.C.: 3825; 3563
N.A.I.C.S.: 334515; 333912
Media: 2-4-7-10
Distr.: Intl.; Natl.
Budget Set: Nov.
Personnel:
Phil Blakey *(Pres)*

EISAI MACHINERY U.S.A. INC.

(Sub. of Eisai Corporation of North America)
90 Boroline
Allendale, NJ 07401
Tel.: (201) 746-2111
Fax: (201) 692-1972
E-mail: emu@eisai.com
Web Site: www.eisaiusa.com
Approx. Number Employees: 20
Business Description:
Pharmaceutical Machinery Sales
S.I.C.: 5084; 5047
N.A.I.C.S.: 423830; 423450
Media: 10
Personnel:
Michael de la Montaigne *(Pres)*

ELECTRO-MOTIVE DIESEL, INC.

(Sub. of Progress Rail Services Corporation)
9301 W 55th St
La Grange, IL 60525-3211
Tel.: (708) 387-6000
Fax: (708) 387-6626
Toll Free: (800) 255-5355
E-mail: emd.careers@emdiesels.com
Web Site: www.emdiesels.com
Sales Range: $1-4.9 Billion
Year Founded: 1922
Business Description:
Diesel-Electric Locomotives & Diesel Engines Mfr
S.I.C.: 3519
N.A.I.C.S.: 333618
Export
Media: 2-4-10-20
Distr.: Intl.; Natl.
Budget Set: Aug.
Personnel:
John Hamilton *(Pres & CEO)*
Glen Lehmann *(CMO-Intl)*
Frank Ward *(Reg VP-Sls)*
Albert Enste *(VP & Gen Mgr-Intl Bus)*

ELECTRO-SENSORS, INC.

6111 Blue Circle Dr
Minnetonka, MN 55343
Tel.: (952) 930-0100
Fax: (952) 930-0130
Toll Free: (800) 328-6170
E-mail: sales@electro-sensors.com
Web Site: www.electro-sensors.com
E-Mail For Key Personnel:
Sales Director: sales@electro-sensors.co
Approx. Sls.: $6,201,000
Approx. Number Employees: 30
Year Founded: 1968
Business Description:
Motion Monitoring & Speed Control Systems Mfr
S.I.C.: 3823; 3829
N.A.I.C.S.: 334513; 334519
Export
Advertising Expenditures: $166,000
Media: 2-7-10-11-13-16-21-26
Personnel:
Bradley D. Slye *(Pres)*
Carol Preston *(Mgr-Pur)*
Brands & Products:
ELECTRO SENSORS
ELECTRO-SENTRY
EZ-SCP
HE950
SUPERIOR SYSTEMS SOLUTIONS
VS1

ELECTROFILM MFG. CO.

25395 Rye Cyn Rd
Valencia, CA 91385-1205
Tel.: (661) 257-2242
Fax: (661) 257-7738
E-mail: sales@ef-heaters.com
Web Site: www.ef-heaters.com
E-Mail For Key Personnel:
Sales Director: sales@ef-heaters.com
Approx. Sls.: $5,000,000
Approx. Number Employees: 85
Year Founded: 1948
Business Description:
Industrial Electrical Heaters, Silinex, Kapinex & Flex Circuits
S.I.C.: 3699; 3672
N.A.I.C.S.: 335999; 334412
Advertising Expenditures: $200,000
Media: 2-4-21
Distr.: Intl.; Natl.
Budget Set: Dec.
Personnel:
Rohl Jacob *(VP-Sls)*
Brands & Products:
EF
ELECTROBOND
ELECTROFILM
KAPINEX
SILINEX

ELECTROID CO

(Sub. of Valcor Engineering Corporation)
45 Fadem Rd
Springfield, NJ 07081-3115
Tel.: (973) 467-8100
Fax: (973) 467-2606
Toll Free: (800) 242-7184
Telex: 139241
E-mail: sales@electroid.com
Web Site: www.electroid.com
E-Mail For Key Personnel:
Sales Director: sales@electroid.com
Approx. Number Employees: 80
Year Founded: 1949
Business Description:
Mfr of Electromagnetic & Pneumatic Devices for Rotary Motion Control
S.I.C.: 3621; 3714

Key to Media (For complete agency information see *The Advertising Red Books-Agencies* edition):
1. Bus. Publs. 2. Cable T.V. 3. Catalogs & Directories. 4. Co-op Adv. 5. Consumer Mags. 6. D.M. to Bus. Estab.7. D.M. to Consumers 8. Daily Newsp. 9. Exhibits/Trade Shows 10. Foreign 11. Infomercial 12. Internet Adv.13. Multimedia 14. Network Radio 15. Network T.V. 16. Newsp. Distr. Mags. 17. Other 18. Outdoor (Posters, Transit) 19. Point of Purchase20. Premiums, Novelties 21. Product Samples 22. Special Events Mktg. 23. Spot Radio 24. Spot T.V. 25. Weekly Newsp. 26. Yellow Page Adv.

N.A.I.C.S.: 335312; 336399
Import Export
Media: 2-4-7-10
Distr.: Intl.; Natl.
Budget Set: Mar.
Personnel:
Steve Etter *(Pres)*
Steve DiGerolamo *(Mgr-Clutches)*
Brands & Products:
ACFB
BI-STABLE BRAKE
BMGR
FAILSAFE
SSB
TENSIONERS

ELGIN NATIONAL INDUSTRIES, INC.
(Holding of GFI Energy Ventures LLC)
2001 Butterfield Rd Ste 1020
Downers Grove, IL 60515-1084
Tel.: (630) 434-7243
Fax: (630) 434-7272
E-mail: info@eni.com
Web Site: www.eni.com
Approx. Number Employees: 50
Year Founded: 1993
Business Description:
Holding Company
S.I.C.: 3559
N.A.I.C.S.: 333298
Export
Media: 4
Distr.: Direct to Consumer; Natl.
Personnel:
Peter Walier *(CEO)*
Graham Sayers *(CFO)*
David Hall *(Pres-Elgin Equipment Grp)*

ELKHART BRASS MANUFACTURING CO.
1302 W Beardsley Ave
Elkhart, IN 46514
Tel.: (574) 295-8330
Fax: (574) 293-9914
E-mail: info@elkhartbrass.com
Web Site: www.elkhartbrass.com
Approx. Sls.: $17,100,000
Approx. Number Employees: 151
Business Description:
Firefighting Apparatus
S.I.C.: 3569; 3494
N.A.I.C.S.: 333999; 332919
Brands & Products:
CHIEF
ELK-O-LITE
ELKHART BRASS
ELKHART PRESSURE-MATIC
GIANT DECK GUN
HYDRO-FOAM
HYDRO-LOC
THE PIPE
PYTHON
SCORPION
SELECT-O-FLOW
SELECT-O-MATIC
SELECT-O-STREAM
SIDEWINDER
SPIT-FIRE
STINGRAY
Advertising Agency:
Villing & Company, Inc.
5909 Nimtz Pkwy
South Bend, IN 46628
Tel.: (574) 277-0215
Fax: (574) 277-5513

ELLIOTT COMPANY
(Sub. of Ebara Corporation)
901 N 4th St
Jeannette, PA 15644-1473
Tel.: (724) 527-2811
Fax: (724) 600-8442
E-mail: info@elliott-turbo.com
Web Site: www.elliott-turbo.com
Sales Range: $125-149.9 Million
Approx. Number Employees: 800
Year Founded: 1910
Business Description:
Plant Air & Gas Compressors, Steam Turbines & Other Related Power Generating Equipment Mfr
S.I.C.: 3511; 3563
N.A.I.C.S.: 333611; 333912
Media: 2-4-7-10-11
Distr.: Intl.; Natl.
Budget Set: Dec.
Personnel:
Antonio Casillo *(Pres)*
Yasuyuki Uruma *(CEO)*
William E. Cox *(VP-Legal)*
Brands & Products:
PAP
PAP PLUS

ELLWOOD CITY FORGE
(Sub. of Ellwood Group, Inc.)
800 Commercial Ave PO Box 31
Ellwood City, PA 16117-2354
Mailing Address:
PO Box 31
Ellwood City, PA 16117-0031
Tel.: (724) 752-0055
Fax: (724) 752-2424
Toll Free: (800) 843-0166
E-mail: sales@ecf.elwd.com
Web Site: www.ellwoodgroup.com
E-Mail For Key Personnel:
Sales Director: sales@ecf.elwd.com
Sales Range: $75-99.9 Million
Approx. Number Employees: 300
Year Founded: 1910
Business Description:
Mfr. of Open Die Steel Forgings
S.I.C.: 3462; 3312
N.A.I.C.S.: 332111; 331111
Import Export
Media: 2-4-7-9-20-26
Distr.: Natl.
Personnel:
Larry L. Symons *(CFO & Exec VP)*
Daniel P. Hamilton *(Pres-ECF)*

ELLWOOD NATIONAL FORGE COMPANY, LLC
(Sub. of Ellwood Group, Inc.)
1 Front St
Irvine, PA 16329
Tel.: (814) 563-7522
Fax: (814) 563-7529
E-mail: enfsales@elwd.com
Web Site: www.ellwoodgroup.com
E-Mail For Key Personnel:
Marketing Director: marketing@nationalforge.com
Approx. Number Employees: 600
Year Founded: 2003
Business Description:
Alloy Steel Ingots & Billets, Rough & Finish Machined Forgings & Assemblies Mfr
S.I.C.: 3599; 3462
N.A.I.C.S.: 332710; 332111
Export
Advertising Expenditures: $600,000
Media: 1-2-4-7-13-20
Distr.: Intl.; Natl.
Budget Set: Apr.
Personnel:
David E. Barensfeld *(Pres & CEO)*
Glenn C. Fegely *(Pres)*
Bentraum D. Huffman *(CFO & Treas)*
Dana Beyeler *(VP-Sls & Mktg)*

EMERSON CLIMATE TECHNOLOGIES, INC.
(Sub. of Emerson Electric Co.)
1675 W Campbell Rd
Sidney, OH 45365-2479
Mailing Address:
PO Box 669
Sidney, OH 45365
Tel.: (937) 498-3011
Fax: (937) 498-3334
Web Site: www.copeland-corp.com
Sales Range: $700-749.9 Million
Approx. Number Employees: 3,000
Year Founded: 1921
Business Description:
Condensing Units & Motor-Compressors for Air Conditioning & Refrigeration Sales & Mfr
S.I.C.: 3585
N.A.I.C.S.: 333415
Import Export
Media: 2-4-10
Distr.: Intl.; Natl.
Budget Set: Aug.
Personnel:
Tom Bettcher *(CEO)*
Richard A. DeNuzzo *(CFO & Head-IT Ops)*
Edgar Purvis *(Exec VP-Emerson Climate Technologies)*
Warren Beeton *(VP-Engrg)*
Don Newlon *(VP-Mktg-Asia)*
Bill Shockley *(VP-Sls & Mktg)*
Karl Zellmer *(VP-Sls)*
Rajan Rajendran *(Dir-Engrg Svcs)*
Brands & Products:
COPELAND SCROLL
COPELAND SCROLL ULTRATECH
Advertising Agency:
Fahlgren Mortine (Dayton)
9049 Springboro Pike
Miamisburg, OH 45342-4418
Tel.: (937) 560-2840
Fax: (937) 560-2841

EMERSON MACHINERY HEALTH MANAGEMENT COMPANY
(Div. of Emerson Process Management)
835 Innovation Dr
Knoxville, TN 37932-2563
Tel.: (865) 675-2400
Fax: (865) 218-1401
E-mail: mhm.info@emersonprocess.com
Web Site: www.compsys.com
Sales Range: $75-99.9 Million
Approx. Number Employees: 500
Year Founded: 1984
Business Description:
Reliability Based Maintenance Products & Services for Industrial Rotating & Reciprocating Machinery
S.I.C.: 3829
N.A.I.C.S.: 334519
Export
Media: 2-7-10-11-22
Distr.: Intl.
Personnel:
Todd Parker *(CFO)*
Bob Walker *(VP-Sls)*
Robert Skeirik *(Sr Product Mgr)*
Brands & Products:
RBMWARE

EMERSON PROCESS MANAGEMENT ROSEMOUNT INC.
(Div. of Emerson Process Management)
8200 Market Blvd
Chanhassen, MN 55317-9685
Tel.: (952) 941-5560
Tel.: (952) 906-8888 (Sls & Mktg)
Fax: (952) 949-7949
Toll Free: (800) 999-9307
E-mail: info@emersonprocess.com
Web Site: www.rosemount.com
Sales Range: $700-749.9 Million
Approx. Number Employees: 3,500
Year Founded: 1956
Business Description:
Industrial Instrumentation Mfr
S.I.C.: 3823; 3829
N.A.I.C.S.: 334513; 334519
Advertising Expenditures: $400,000
Media: 2-4-7-8-10-17
Distr.: Intl.; Natl.
Personnel:
Tracy Thompson *(CFO & VP-Ops)*
Jim Cobb *(Mgr-Mktg Resources)*
Brands & Products:
APEX
APEX SENTRY
DELTAV
MASS PROBAR
MODBUS
MULTIVARIABLE
PROBAR
PROFIBUS
REDUCER

EMSAR INC.
(Name Changed to Aptar of Stratford)

ENCON SAFETY PRODUCTS
(Sub. of Hagemeyer North America)
6825 W Sam Houston Pkwy N
Houston, TX 77041-4026
Tel.: (843) 745-2400
Fax: (713) 466-1703
E-mail: customerservice@enconsafety.com
Web Site: www.enconsafety.com
Approx. Sls.: $19,925,000
Approx. Number Employees: 160
Year Founded: 1983
Business Description:
Safety & Protective Equipment
S.I.C.: 5085; 3842
N.A.I.C.S.: 423840; 339113
Media: 4
Personnel:
Jim Johnson *(Gen Mgr)*
Brands & Products:
AQUARION
AWARENESS
BREEZE
ENCOMPASS
ENCON
ENCOTE
ENFOG
FIRSTEP

Key to Media (For complete agency information see *The Advertising Red Books-Agencies* edition):
1. Bus. Publs. 2. Cable T.V. 3. Catalogs & Directories. 4. Co-op Adv. 5. Consumer Mags. 6. D.M. to Bus. Estab.7. D.M. to Consumers
8. Daily Newsp. 9. Exhibits/Trade Shows 10. Foreign 11. Infomercial 12. Internet Adv.13. Multimedia 14. Network Radio
15. Network T.V. 16. Newsp. Distr. Mags. 17. Other 18. Outdoor (Posters, Transit) 19. Point of Purchase20. Premiums, Novelties
21. Product Samples 22. Special Events Mktg. 23. Spot Radio 24. Spot T.V. 25. Weekly Newsp. 26. Yellow Page Adv.

Encon Safety Products — (Continued)

FIRSTFLUSH
HYDROSEP
LITES
QD2
SPORT
VERATTI
YELLO-BOWL

ENERGY RECOVERY, INC.

1717 Doolittle Dr
San Leandro, CA 94577
Tel.: (510) 483-7370
Fax: (510) 483-7371
Web Site: www.energy-recovery.com
E-Mail For Key Personnel:
Sales Director: sales@energy-recovery.com
Approx. Rev.: $45,853,000
Approx. Number Employees: 129
Year Founded: 1992
Business Description:
Energy Recovery Devices & Pumps Utilized in Water Desalination Designer & Mfr
S.I.C.: 3559; 3594; 4941
N.A.I.C.S.: 333298; 221310; 333996
Advertising Expenditures: $112,000
Media: 2-13
Personnel:
Hans Peter Michelet *(Chm)*
Thomas S. Rooney, Jr. *(Pres & CEO)*
Alexander J. Buehler *(CFO)*
Deno G. Bokas *(Chief Acctg Officer & VP-Fin)*
Carolyn F. Bostick *(Gen Counsel & VP)*
Borja Sanchez-Blanco *(Sr VP)*
Imad Al Sharif *(VP-Sls-OEM Grp)*

ENERSYS INC.

2366 Bernville Rd
Reading, PA 19605
Tel.: (610) 208-1991
Fax: (610) 372-8457
E-mail: investorrelations@enersysinc.com
Web Site: www.enersysinc.com
Approx. Sls.: $1,964,462,000
Approx. Number Employees: 8,400
Year Founded: 1888
Business Description:
Industrial Battery Mfr, Marketer & Distr
S.I.C.: 3691; 3692
N.A.I.C.S.: 335911; 335912
Import Export
Advertising Expenditures: $3,000,000
Media: 2-4-5-6-9-10-13-19-20
Distr.: Natl.
Personnel:
John D. Craig *(Chm, Pres & CEO)*
Michael J. Schmidtlein *(CFO & Sr VP-Fin)*
Raymond R. Kubis *(Pres-Europe, Middle East & Africa)*
David M. Shaffer *(Pres-Asia)*
Richard W. Zuidema *(Exec VP)*
Sanjay L. Deshpande *(Sr VP-Advanced Sys)*
Todd M. Sechrist *(Sr VP-Americas)*
Brands & Products:
ABSL
ABSL POWER
ABSL SPACE
ARMASAFE PLUS
CYCLON
DATASAFE
DESERTHOG
DOUGLAS
ECOSAFE
ENERGIA
ENERGY PLUS
ENERSYS
ENERSYS IRONCLAD
ENVIROLINK
EON TECHNOLOGY
EXIDE
EXPRESS
FIAMM MOTIVE POWER
GENERAL BATTERY
GENESIS
HAWKER
HUP
IRONCLAD
LIFE SPEED
LIFEGUARD
LIFEPLUS
LOADHOG
ODYSSEY
OERLIKON
OLDHAM
POWER/FULL SOLUTIONS
POWERGUARD
POWERLEASE
POWERLINE
POWERPLUS
POWERSAFE
REDION
RENEGADE
SMARTHOG
SUPERHOG
SUPERSAFE
VARTA
WATERLESS
WORKHOG
Advertising Agency:
Reese
955 Berkshire Blvd
Wyomissing, PA 19610-1229
Tel.: (610) 378-1835
Fax: (610) 378-1676

ENGINEERED CONTROLS INTERNATIONAL LLC

(Holding of Sentinel Capital Partners LLC)
100 Rego Dr
Elon, NC 27244-9159
Tel.: (336) 449-7707
Fax: (336) 449-6594
E-mail: ecii@regoproducts.com
Web Site: www.regoproducts.com
Approx. Number Employees: 330
Year Founded: 1908
Business Description:
Mfr. of Valves & Controls for LP Gas & Fluids; Cryogenic Valves & Regulators
S.I.C.: 3491; 3494
N.A.I.C.S.: 332911; 332919
Advertising Expenditures: $250,000
Media: 2-4-5-10-20-21
Distr.: Intl.; Natl.
Budget Set: Sept.
Personnel:
Gary Boone *(Pres)*
Brands & Products:
CHEK-LOK
DUOPORT
ECII
FLOMATIC
MULTIBONNET
MULTIPORT
MULTIVALVE
REGO
REGO PRODUCTS

ENPRO INDUSTRIES, INC.

5605 Carnegie Blvd Ste 500
Charlotte, NC 28209-4674
Tel.: (704) 731-1500
Fax: (704) 731-1511
E-mail: info@enproindustries.com
Web Site: www.enproindustries.com
Approx. Rev.: $865,000,000
Approx. Number Employees: 3,600
Year Founded: 1990
Business Description:
Engineered Industrial Products Marketer & Mfr
S.I.C.: 3053; 3021; 3519
N.A.I.C.S.: 339991; 316211; 333618
Media: 10
Distr.: Natl.
Personnel:
Stephen E. MacAdam *(Pres & CEO)*
Alexander W. Pease *(CFO & Sr VP)*
Richard L. Magee *(Gen Counsel, Sec & Sr VP)*
William Dries *(Sr VP)*
Robert P. McKinney *(VP-HR)*
Don Washington *(Dir-IR)*
Brands & Products:
ENPRO INDUSTRIES
QUINCY COMPRESSOR
STEMCO

ENTECH SOLAR, INC.

13301 Park Vista Blvd Ste 100
Fort Worth, TX 76177
Tel.: (817) 379-0100
Tel.: (817) 224-3600
Fax: (817) 224-3601
E-mail: ir@entechsolar.com
Web Site: www.entechsolar.com
E-Mail For Key Personnel:
Sales Director: sales@worldwater.com
Approx. Rev.: $246,000
Approx. Number Employees: 18
Year Founded: 1984
Business Description:
Solar & Water Power Equipment Mfr
S.I.C.: 3612; 3823; 4939; 4941; 9511
N.A.I.C.S.: 335311; 221111; 221310; 334513; 924110
Advertising Expenditures: $51,000
Media: 10
Personnel:
David Gelbaum *(CEO)*
Shelley Hollingsworth *(CFO)*
A. J. McDanal *(COO)*
Brands & Products:
AQUADRIVE
AQUAMAX
AQUAMETER
MOBILE MAXPURE

EQUIPMENT DEPOT LTD.

(Sub. of Pon North America, Inc.)
4100 S Interstate 35
Waco, TX 76706
Tel.: (254) 662-4322
Fax: (254) 662-0344
Toll Free: (800) 627-5438
E-mail: waco@eqdepot.com
Web Site: www.eqdepot.com
Approx. Sls.: $44,218,137
Approx. Number Employees: 75
Year Founded: 1968
Business Description:
Industrial, Construction & Agricultural Equipment Supplier
S.I.C.: 5084
N.A.I.C.S.: 423830
Media: 2-4-7-9-10-13-18-22-23-24-26
Personnel:
Donald Moes *(Founder & Chm)*
E. G. White-Swift *(Dir-Mktg & Adv)*
Brands & Products:
EQUIPMENT DEPOT
Advertising Agency:
The Ousset Agency, Inc.
20475 Hwy 46 W Ste 180-602
Spring Branch, TX 78070
Tel.: (830) 885-5130
Fax: (830) 885-5140
Toll Free: (866) 268-7738

ERICO INTERNATIONAL CORPORATION

3100 Solon Rd
Solon, OH 44139-2221
Tel.: (440) 349-2630
Fax: (440) 349-2996
E-mail: info@erico.com
Web Site: www.erico.com
Sales Range: $350-399.9 Million
Approx. Number Employees: 1,350
Year Founded: 1903
Business Description:
Specialty Metal Products Designer, Mfr & Marketer
S.I.C.: 3499; 3494; 3496
N.A.I.C.S.: 332999; 332618; 332919
Media: 4-7-10-11-19-20-21-26
Distr.: Natl.
Budget Set: Dec.
Personnel:
William H. Roj *(Pres)*
Jeffrey R. Steinhilber *(CFO)*
Daniel S. Mominee *(Exec VP)*
Peter B. Korte *(Dir-Acquisition Mktg)*
Brands & Products:
CADDY
CADWELD
CRITEC
ERICO
ERIFLEX
ERISTRUT
ERITECH
FLEXIBAR
LENTON

ERIEZ MANUFACTURING CO. INC.

2200 Asbury Rd
Erie, PA 16506-1402
Tel.: (814) 835-6000
Fax: (814) 838-4960
Toll Free: (800) 345-4946
E-mail: eriez@eriez.com
Web Site: www.eriez.com
Approx. Number Employees: 600
Year Founded: 1942
Business Description:
Magnetic, Vibratory & Metal Detection Equipment Designer, Developer, Mfr & Marketer
S.I.C.: 3559
N.A.I.C.S.: 333298
Import Export
Media: 1-2-4-7-10-11
Distr.: Intl.; Natl.
Budget Set: Nov.
Personnel:
R. A. Merwin *(Chm)*

Key to Media (For complete agency information see *The Advertising Red Books-Agencies* edition):
1. Bus. Publs. 2. Cable T.V. 3. Catalogs & Directories. 4. Co-op Adv. 5. Consumer Mags. 6. D.M. to Bus. Estab.7. D.M. to Consumers 8. Daily Newsp. 9. Exhibits/Trade Shows 10. Foreign 11. Infomercial 12. Internet Adv.13. Multimedia 14. Network Radio 15. Network T.V. 16. Newsp. Distr. Mags. 17. Other 18. Outdoor (Posters, Transit) 19. Point of Purchase20. Premiums, Novelties 21. Product Samples 22. Special Events Mktg. 23. Spot Radio 24. Spot T.V. 25. Weekly Newsp. 26. Yellow Page Adv.

Tim Shuttleworth *(Pres & CEO)*
Charlie Ingram *(VP-Sls & Mktg)*
Keith W. Jones *(Dir-Corp Comm)*

Brands & Products:
ERIEZ
ERIUM
SAFEHOLD
SELECTO
SUPER B
ULTRA FORCE

Advertising Agencies:
Altman-Hall Associates
235 W 7th St
Erie, PA 16501-1601
Tel.: (814) 454-0158
Fax: (814) 454-3266

Stevens Strategic Communications, Inc.
Gemini Towers, Ste 500, 1991 Crocker Rd
Westlake, OH 44115-1900
Tel.: (440) 617-0100
Fax: (440) 614-0529
Public Relations

ESAB WELDING & CUTTING PRODUCTS
(Sub. of ESAB AB)
411 S Ebenezer Rd
Florence, SC 29501-7916
Tel.: (843) 669-4411
Fax: (843) 664-4459
Fax: (843) 664-4258
Toll Free: (800) ESAB123
E-mail: email@esab.com
Web Site: www.esab.com
Approx. Number Employees: 700
Year Founded: 1906
Business Description:
Welding Equipment Mfr & Distr
S.I.C.: 3548; 3541
N.A.I.C.S.: 333992; 333512
Export
Media: 1-2-4-5-6-7-8-10-21
Distr.: Intl.
Budget Set: July

ESCO BUCYRUS
(Sub. of ESCO Engineered Products)
260 E Beal Ave
Bucyrus, OH 44820
Mailing Address:
PO Box 628
Bucyrus, OH 44820-0628
Tel.: (419) 562-6015
Fax: (419) 562-8360
Toll Free: (800) 532-5233
E-mail: bucyruscs@bucyrusblades.com
Web Site: www.bucyrusblades.com
Approx. Number Employees: 230
Year Founded: 1951
Business Description:
Mfr of Cutting Edges & Related Wearing Parts for Dozers, Scrapers, Front-End Loaders & Graders
S.I.C.: 3531; 3524
N.A.I.C.S.: 333120; 333112
Import Export
Media: 2-4-7-10-16-18-19-20-21
Distr.: Intl.; Natl.
Budget Set: Oct.
Personnel:
Tim Myers *(Pres & COO)*

Brands & Products:
BUCYRUS BLADES
CARBIDE PLUS
DOUBLEDUTY
FORGETEMP
MAGNUM
MAXTEMP

ESCO CORPORATION
2141 NW 25th Ave
Portland, OR 97210
Tel.: (503) 228-2141
Fax: (503) 778-6467
E-mail: corpinfo@escocorp.com
Web Site: www.escocorp.com
Approx. Rev.: $849,481,000
Approx. Number Employees: 4,679
Year Founded: 1913
Business Description:
Engineered Metal Parts & Components Mfr
S.I.C.: 3441; 3499; 3532
N.A.I.C.S.: 332312; 332999; 333131
Import Export
Advertising Expenditures: $250,000
Media: 1-2-4-5-7-10-11-13-19-20-22
Distr.: Intl.
Budget Set: Sept. -Nov.
Personnel:
Steven D. Pratt *(Chm & CEO)*
Calvin W. Collins *(Pres & COO)*
Ray Verlinich *(CFO & VP-Fin)*
Francois Baril *(Pres-Turbine Tech Grp)*
Kevin S. Thomas *(Gen Counsel, VP & Sec)*
Jeff Kershaw *(Grp VP & Mng Dir-Asia Pacific Reg)*
F. Patrick Fonner *(Grp VP-Engineered Products)*
Eric Blackburn *(VP-Strategy & Bus Dev)*
Nicholas L. Blauwiekel *(VP-HR)*
Brands & Products:
ALL-CAST
BARDON
BUCYRUS BLADE
CARBIDE PLUS
CAT
CONICAL
DELTA
DRP
E3
ECO-BAK
ESCO
ESCO POSILOK
ESCO SUPER V
ESCO ZIPPER LIP
ESCOALLOY
ESCOBAK
EVERSHARP
FORGE TEMP
FORGETEMP
GEOVOR
HELILOK
HI-LIFE
INFINITY
KWIK-EDGE
KWIK-LOK
KWIK-LOK II
KWIK-TIP
LOADMASTER
MAXBAK
MAXDRP
MAXTEMP
POSILOK
POSILOK PLUS
PRODUCTION MASTER
QUADRILOK
RIP-A-PAK
RPM
S-SERIES POSILOK
SCREWY
SIDEWINDER
SPHERILOK
SUPER V
SV2
SYSTEM 2000
TOPLOK
ULTRALOK
UNI-LOK
VORTEX
WHISLER PLUS
X-TRA-EDGE
ZIPPER-LIP

ESTAD STAMPING & MANUFACTURING COMPANY
1005 Griggs St
Danville, IL 61832
Tel.: (217) 442-4600
Fax: (217) 442-4632
E-mail: bmestad@comcast.net
Web Site: www.estadstamping.com
Approx. Sls.: $3,000,000
Approx. Number Employees: 17
Year Founded: 1996
Business Description:
Metal Stamping Mfr
S.I.C.: 3496; 3469
N.A.I.C.S.: 332618; 332116
Export
Media: 2-4
Personnel:
Robert Rew *(Pres)*

EUBANKS ENGINEERING CO.
3022 Inland Empire Blvd
Ontario, CA 91764
Tel.: (909) 483-2456
Fax: (909) 483-2498
E-mail: stripper@eubanks.com
Web Site: www.eubanks.com
Approx. Number Employees: 38
Year Founded: 1956
Business Description:
Automatic Wire Processing Equipment Mfr
S.I.C.: 3549; 3825
N.A.I.C.S.: 333518; 334515
Media: 2-4-8-10
Distr.: Intl.; Natl.
Budget Set: June
Personnel:
David Eubanks *(Pres)*

EXACT EQUIPMENT CORPORATION
(Sub. of Mettler-Toledo Inc.)
920 Town Ctr Dr Ste I 80
Langhorne, PA 19047
Tel.: (215) 295-2000
Fax: (215) 295-2080
Web Site: www.exactequipment.com
Approx. Number Employees: 15
Year Founded: 1986
Business Description:
Manufactures & Markets Packaging Machinery & Weighing Equipment
S.I.C.: 3596; 3565
N.A.I.C.S.: 333997; 333993
Import Export
Media: 4-7-10
Distr.: Natl.
Budget Set: Aug.

Brands & Products:
CASE READY FRESH RETAIL PACKAGES MADE SIMPLE
SPEEDMASTER
UPC PRE-PAC
WORK HORSE

FABCO-AIR, INC.
3716 NE 49th Ave
Gainesville, FL 32609-1699
Tel.: (352) 373-3578
Fax: (352) 375-8024
E-mail: fabco@fabco-air.com
Web Site: www.fabco-air.com
Approx. Number Employees: 120
Year Founded: 1958
Business Description:
Pneumatic Cylinders & Valves Mfr
S.I.C.: 3491; 3542
N.A.I.C.S.: 332911; 333513
Import Export
Advertising Expenditures: $200,000
Media: 2-4-6-13
Distr.: Natl.
Budget Set: Oct.
Personnel:
William R. Schmidt *(Pres)*
Brands & Products:
GLOBAL SERIES
HI-POWER
LONGSTROKE
MULTI-POWER
NFPA
ORIGINAL PANCAKE
PANCAKE
PANCAKE II
SQUARE
SQUARE 1
STOPPER CYLINDER

FALLBROOK TECHNOLOGIES INC.
9444 Waples St Ste 410
San Diego, CA 92121
Tel.: (858) 623-9557
Fax: (858) 623-9563
E-mail: info@fallbrooktech.com
Web Site: www.fallbrooktech.com
Sales Range: $1-9.9 Million
Approx. Number Employees: 47
Year Founded: 2000
Business Description:
Transmission Mfr
S.I.C.: 3568
N.A.I.C.S.: 333613
Advertising Expenditures: $281,000
Media: 5-10-13
Personnel:
William G. Klehm, III *(Chm & CEO)*
Allan R. Kammerer *(Pres)*
Nicole T. Nicks *(CFO, Treas & Asst Sec)*
Paul A. DeHart *(COO)*
Alan M. Nordin *(Pres-Bicycle Products Div)*
Jeffrey A. Birchak *(Sec & VP-Intellectual Property)*
David W. Markley *(VP-Product Dev)*
Chris Vasiliotis *(Product Mgr-NuVinci)*
Brands & Products:
NUVINCI

FANCORT INDUSTRIES, INC.
31 Fairfield Pl
West Caldwell, NJ 07006-6206
Tel.: (973) 575-0610
Fax: (973) 575-9234
Toll Free: (888) 326-2678

Key to Media (For complete agency information see *The Advertising Red Books-Agencies* edition):
1. Bus. Publs. 2. Cable T.V. 3. Catalogs & Directories. 4. Co-op Adv. 5. Consumer Mags. 6. D.M. to Bus. Estab.7. D.M. to Consumers 8. Daily Newsp. 9. Exhibits/Trade Shows 10. Foreign 11. Infomercial 12. Internet Adv.13. Multimedia 14. Network Radio 15. Network T.V. 16. Newsp. Distr. Mags. 17. Other 18. Outdoor (Posters, Transit) 19. Point of Purchase20. Premiums, Novelties 21. Product Samples 22. Special Events Mktg. 23. Spot Radio 24. Spot T.V. 25. Weekly Newsp. 26. Yellow Page Adv.

Fancort Industries, Inc. — (Continued)
E-mail: avitale@fancort.com
Web Site: www.fancort.com
Approx. Sls.: $5,000,000
Approx. Number Employees: 18
Year Founded: 1970
Business Description:
Assembly & Handling Equipment Mfr
S.I.C.: 3544
N.A.I.C.S.: 333514
Import Export
Media: 1-2-4-7-10-11
Distr.: Intl.; Natl.
Personnel:
Ronald J. Corey *(CEO)*
Robert Antonelli *(VP-Sls)*
Brands & Products:
FANCORT
KARRY-ALL
RACK-ALL
SOLDER RECOVERY SYSTEM

FANUC ROBOTICS NORTH AMERICA, INC.
(Sub. of FANUC Ltd.)
3900 W Hamlin Rd
Rochester Hills, MI 48309
Tel.: (248) 377-7000
Fax: (248) 377-7362
Toll Free: (800) 47ROBOT
E-mail: privacy@fanucrobotics.com
Web Site: www.fanucrobotics.com
E-Mail For Key Personnel:
Marketing Director: marketing@fanucrobotics.com
Approx. Number Employees: 1,100
Year Founded: 1982
Business Description:
Robotic Automation Supplier
S.I.C.: 3559; 3548
N.A.I.C.S.: 333298; 333992
Import Export
Media: 2-4-7-10
Personnel:
Rick Schneider *(Pres)*
Brands & Products:
ARC MATE
LASER MATE SYSTEM 1
LR MATE 200iB/5WP
M-410IB SERIES
PAINTPRO
PALLETPRO

FARRAND CONTROLS
(Div. of Ruhle Companies, Inc.)
99 Wall St
Valhalla, NY 10595
Tel.: (914) 761-2600
Fax: (914) 761-0405
E-mail: sales@ruhle.com
Web Site: www.ruhle.com
E-Mail For Key Personnel:
Sales Director: sales@ruhle.com
Approx. Number Employees: 40
Year Founded: 1955
Business Description:
Mfr. of Transducers for Machine Industry/Military Aerospace Industry & Numerical Control Systems
S.I.C.: 3679; 3625
N.A.I.C.S.: 334419; 335314
Import Export
Media: 2-10-17
Brands & Products:
INDUCTOSYN

FARREL CORPORATION
25 Main St
Ansonia, CT 06401-1605
Tel.: (203) 736-5500
Fax: (203) 736-5580
E-mail: support@farrel.com
Web Site: www.farrel.com
Sales Range: $50-74.9 Million
Approx. Number Employees: 308
Year Founded: 1986
Business Description:
Machinery Mfr for Rubber & Plastics Industries
S.I.C.: 3559
N.A.I.C.S.: 333220
Import Export
Media: 2-4-7-10-11-22
Distr.: Intl.; Natl.
Budget Set: Jan.
Personnel:
Paul Zepp *(CFO, VP-Fin & Owner-Mgmt)*
Alberto Shaio *(Pres & CEO)*
James Burns *(Gen Counsel)*
Brands & Products:
BANBURY
CARD
CP SERIES II
FARREL
FCM
FTX
GPX
INNOVATING PROCESSING SOLUTIONS
INTERMIX
MVX
NST
ST
TECHNOLAB

FEINTOOL EQUIPMENT CORP.
(Sub. of Feintool International Holding)
6833 Creek Rd
Cincinnati, OH 45242
Tel.: (513) 791-0066
Fax: (513) 791-1589
E-mail: fec@feintool-usa.com
Web Site: www.feintool-usa.com
Approx. Number Employees: 11
Year Founded: 1980
Business Description:
Sales & Consulting Services for Peripheral Systems & Presses
S.I.C.: 8711; 7629
N.A.I.C.S.: 541330; 811219
Import Export
Media: 2-4-7-10-21
Distr.: Natl.
Budget Set: May
Personnel:
Beat Andres *(Dir-Mktg & Sls)*

FENNER DRIVES
(Unit of Fenner PLC)
311 W Stiegel St
Manheim, PA 17545-1747
Tel.: (717) 665-2421
Fax: (717) 664-8214
Toll Free: (800) 243-3374
Web Site: www.fennerdrives.com
E-Mail For Key Personnel:
Marketing Director: robinpalmer@fennerdrives.com
Approx. Number Employees: 300
Year Founded: 1911
Business Description:
Mfr. of Industrial Belting, Power Transmission & Motion Control Components
S.I.C.: 2299; 3568
N.A.I.C.S.: 314999; 333613
Export
Media: 2-8-26
Distr.: Intl.; Natl.
Personnel:
Mike Turek *(Pres & Mng Dir)*
Nicholas Hobson *(Mng Dir)*
Ian L. Smith *(Exec Dir)*
Robin Palmer *(Mgr-Mktg)*
Brands & Products:
CLEAR GO
FENATRAK
FENNER DRIVES
FHT
GREEN-GO
MVS
ORANGE-GO
POWERTWIST-V
QUIK-GO
RED-GO 85 CXF
TWISTFLEX
VEELOS-V

FERROTEC (USA) CORPORATION
(Sub. of Ferrotec Corporation)
33 Constitution Dr
Bedford, NH 03110
Tel.: (603) 472-6800
Fax: (603) 472-2511
E-mail: info@ferrotec.com
Web Site: www.ferrotec.com
Year Founded: 1968
Business Description:
Thermal Modules, Vacuum Feedthroughs, E-Beam Guns & Ferrofluids Mfr & Sales
S.I.C.: 3053; 3568
N.A.I.C.S.: 339991; 333613
Import Export
Media: 4-6-11-13
Distr.: Natl.
Personnel:
Eiji Miyanaga *(Pres)*

FIRE KING SECURITY GROUP
101 Security Pkwy
New Albany, IN 47150-9366
Tel.: (812) 948-8400
Fax: (812) 948-0437
Toll Free: (800) 457-2424
E-mail: fireking@fireking.com
Web Site: www.fireking.com
Approx. Number Employees: 500
Year Founded: 1951
Business Description:
Fire Resistant Insulated Filing Cabinet & Safe & Digital Video Recorders Mfr
S.I.C.: 2522; 5044; 7382
N.A.I.C.S.: 337214; 423420; 561621
Export
Advertising Expenditures: $1,000,000
Media: 1-2-4-5-7-10-19-22
Distr.: Intl
Personnel:
Van G. Carlisle *(Pres & CEO)*
Joe Smith *(Dir-Mktg)*
Brands & Products:
ADESCO
FIREKING
FKI SECURITY GROUP
GARY
IMAGE VAULT
MCGUNN
MEDECO
MEDIAVAULT
MEILINK
NKL
PERFECTCASH

FISHER CONTROLS INTERNATIONAL, LLC
(Sub. of Emerson Process Management)
205 S Ctr St
Marshalltown, IA 50158-2823
Tel.: (641) 754-3011
Fax: (641) 754-2626
Web Site: www.emersonprocess.com
Sales Range: $750-799.9 Million
Approx. Number Employees: 5,500
Year Founded: 1880
Business Description:
Final Control Systems, Regulators & Field Automation Systems Mfr
S.I.C.: 3491; 3823
N.A.I.C.S.: 332911; 334513
Import Export
Media: 1-2-8-10
Distr.: Intl
Budget Set: Oct.
Personnel:
John Wells *(Mgr-Mktg Comm)*
Brands & Products:
BAUMANN
ENVIRO SEAL
EPLUG
FIELDVUE
FLOVUE
LEVEL-TROL
POSI-SEAL
VEE-BALL

FLAMBEAU, INC.
(Holding of Nordic Group of Companies, Ltd.)
801 Lynn Ave
Baraboo, WI 53913
Tel.: (608) 355-6500
Tel.: (608) 356-5551
Fax: (608) 356-8044
Toll Free: (800) 457-5252
E-mail: jtrudell@flambeau.com
Web Site: www.flambeau.com
Year Founded: 1947
Business Description:
Injection & Blow Molded Components Mfr
S.I.C.: 3089; 3949
N.A.I.C.S.: 326199; 339920
Import Export
Media: 2-3-4-6-7-10-13-19-20-22-24
Distr.: Natl.
Personnel:
Jeff Bush *(Sr VP-Retail Markets Grp)*
Bob Terlep *(VP-Automotive Grp & Mgr-Mktg)*
Randy Thomas *(Mgr-Indus Markets & Pkg Grp)*
Brands & Products:
ARTBIN
DUNCAN
FLAMBEAU

FLANDERS CORPORATION
531 Flanders Filters Rd
Washington, NC 27889
Tel.: (252) 946-8081
Fax: (252) 946-3425
Toll Free: (800) 637-2803

Key to Media (For complete agency information see *The Advertising Red Books-Agencies* edition):
1. Bus. Publs. 2. Cable T.V. 3. Catalogs & Directories. 4. Co-op Adv. 5. Consumer Mags. 6. D.M. to Bus. Estab.7. D.M. to Consumers
8. Daily Newsp. 9. Exhibits/Trade Shows 10. Foreign 11. Infomercial 12. Internet Adv.13. Multimedia 14. Network Radio
15. Network T.V. 16. Newsp. Distr. Mags. 17. Other 18. Outdoor (Posters, Transit) 19. Point of Purchase20. Premiums, Novelties
21. Product Samples 22. Special Events Mktg. 23. Spot Radio 24. Spot T.V. 25. Weekly Newsp. 26. Yellow Page Adv.

E-mail: customerservice@corp.precisionaire.com
Web Site: www.flanderscorp.com
Approx. Sls.: $222,380,000
Approx. Number Employees: 2,139
Year Founded: 1950
Business Description:
Precision Air Filters & Filtration Equipment Mfr
S.I.C.: 3564
N.A.I.C.S.: 333412; 333411
Advertising Expenditures: $3,880,000
Media: 1-4-6
Personnel:
Harry L. Smith, Jr. *(Chm & CEO)*
John Oakley *(Pres & CFO)*
Tom Justice *(COO)*
Kevin Boyd *(Sr VP-High Purity Ops)*
Brenda Davis *(VP-HR)*
Brands & Products:
ALPHA
ARM AND HAMMER
ASTR
FLANDERS
FOREMOST IN AIR FILTRATION
LYSOL
MAGNAHELIC
NATURALAIRE
PERMA FRAME
PRE PLEAT
PRECISION PAK
PRECISIONCELL
PRECISIONCELL GT
PRECISIONCELL HT
PRECISIONCELL II
PRECISIONCELL M16
PRECISIONCELL MSH
PREPLEAT
PUREFLO
PUREFORM
RIGID-AIR
SUPER FLOW
SUPER FLOW-V
SUREAIRE
SUREFLO
SURELOCK
SUREPLEAT
SURESEAL
SWISSAIRE

FLEETWOODGOLDCOWYARD
(Div. of Barry-Wehmiller Companies, Inc.)
1305 Lakeview Dr
Romeoville, IL 60446-3950
Tel.: (630) 759-6800
Fax: (630) 759-2299
E-mail: donna.wolfe@fgwa.com
Web Site: www.fgwa.com
E-Mail For Key Personnel:
Sales Director: sales@fleetinc.com
Sales Range: $25-49.9 Million
Approx. Number Employees: 150
Year Founded: 1956
Business Description:
Conveying, Palletizing & Material Handling Equipment Mfr
S.I.C.: 3535
N.A.I.C.S.: 333922
Media: 2-4-7-10-17
Distr.: Natl.
Personnel:
Phil Ostapowicz *(Pres & CEO)*
Neal McConnellogue *(Exec VP)*

FLEETWOODGOLDCOWYARD AMBEC, INC.
(Group of FleetwoodGoldcoWyard)
10615 Beaver Dam Rd
Hunt Valley, MD 21030
Tel.: (410) 785-1934
Fax: (410) 785-2909
Toll Free: (800) 899-4406
Web Site: www.fgwa.com
Approx. Number Employees: 125
Year Founded: 1960
Business Description:
Mfr of Stainless Steel Conveyor Products
S.I.C.: 3535
N.A.I.C.S.: 333922
Media: 2-13
Brands & Products:
AUTOBLEND
CAN JET
LITE TOUCH

FLETCHER INDUSTRIES, INC.
1485 Central Dr
Southern Pines, NC 28387-2105
Tel.: (910) 692-7133
Fax: (910) 692-3345
Toll Free: (800) 992-4075
E-mail: info@fletcherindustries.com
Web Site: www.fletcherindustries.com
Approx. Number Employees: 25
Year Founded: 1960
Business Description:
Yarn Processing, Winding/Weaving Machinery & Accessories Worldwide Mfr & Distr
S.I.C.: 3552
N.A.I.C.S.: 333292
Import Export
Media: 6-7-8-9-10-25
Distr.: Natl.
Personnel:
John Taws *(Pres)*
Brands & Products:
FLETCHER
FLETCHER INDUSTRIES INTERNATIONAL
METAG

FLEXBAR MACHINE CORP.
250 Gibbs Rd
Islandia, NY 11749-2612
Tel.: (631) 582-8440
Fax: (631) 582-8487
Toll Free: (800) 879-7575
E-mail: sales@flexbar.com
Web Site: www.flexbar.com
E-Mail For Key Personnel:
Sales Director: sales@flexbar.com
Approx. Number Employees: 25
Year Founded: 1965
Business Description:
Mfr of Machine Tools & Gauging Specialties
S.I.C.: 3545; 3841
N.A.I.C.S.: 333515; 339112
Import Export
Advertising Expenditures: $250,000
Media: 2-4-5-7-10-21
Distr.: Intl.; Natl.
Personnel:
Jonathan Adler *(Pres)*
Steve Culver *(VP-Sls & Mktg)*
Larry Derrig *(Gen Mgr)*
Lou Valenti *(Dir-Sls)*
Maria Blando *(Mgr-Pur)*
Margie Cruz *(Mgr-Ops)*
Brands & Products:
ADHAESIUM
AUTOSTIC
FACSIMILE
FLEXBAR
LATHERGUARD
MAGNAFLUX SPOTCHECK
OPTIFLEX
REPRORUBBER

FLEXIBLE STEEL LACING COMPANY
(d/b/a Flexco)
2525 Wisconsin Ave
Downers Grove, IL 60515-4241
Tel.: (630) 971-0150
Fax: (630) 971-1180
E-mail: info@flexco.com
Web Site: www.flexco.com
Approx. Number Employees: 350
Year Founded: 1907
Business Description:
Fastener Mfr
S.I.C.: 3429
N.A.I.C.S.: 332510
Export
Media: 1-2-4-7-8-10-11-19
Distr.: Intl.; Natl.
Budget Set: Oct.
Personnel:
Krista Howland *(Head-HR)*
Brands & Products:
ALLIGATOR
CLIPPER
DURALINK
ELIMINATOR
FAR-PUL
FLEX-LAG
FLEXCO
MICRO
MINELINE
ROCKLINE
TATCH-A-CLEAT

FLEXIBLE TECHNOLOGIES INC.
(Sub. of Smiths Specialty Engineering)
528 Carwellyn Rd
Abbeville, SC 29620
Mailing Address:
PO Box 888
Abbeville, SC 29620-0888
Tel.: (864) 366-8775
Fax: (864) 459-8771
Toll Free: (800) 459-4882
E-mail: info@wereflexible.com
Web Site:
www.flexibletechnologies.com/
Approx. Number Employees: 600
Business Description:
Non Metallic Flexible Ducting & Hose Mfr
S.I.C.: 3089; 3052
N.A.I.C.S.: 326199; 326220
Import
Advertising Expenditures: $450,000
Media: 2-10-19-21
Distr.: Natl.
Budget Set: Oct.
Personnel:
William T. Smith *(Pres & CEO)*
Robert M Speer *(CFO)*
James Lollis *(Mgr-Natl Sls)*
Brands & Products:
CONDUCTAFLEX
FLEXFLYTE
PRO SERIES
SUPER VAC-U-FLEX
THERMAFLEX

FLEXITALLIC LP
(Sub. of The Flexitallic Group, Inc.)
6915 Hwy 225
Deer Park, TX 77536-2414
Tel.: (281) 604-2400
Fax: (281) 604-2415
Toll Free: (800) 527-1935
Web Site: www.flexitallic.com/contactus.html
Approx. Number Employees: 205
Year Founded: 1995
Business Description:
Mfr. of Spiral Wound Gaskets, Sheet Materials & Heat Exchangers
S.I.C.: 3053
N.A.I.C.S.: 339991
Import Export
Media: 2-10
Distr.: Natl.
Personnel:
Jim Lenahan *(Dir-Mktg)*
Greg English *(Mgr-Fin)*
Advertising Agency:
4 Guys Interactive
8203 S Willow Pl Ste 230
Houston, TX 77070
Tel.: (281) 807-4344
Fax: (281) 807-4384

FLIGHT SYSTEMS, INC.
505 Fishing Creek Rd
Lewisberry, PA 17339-9517
Tel.: (717) 932-9900
Fax: (717) 932-9925
Fax: (800) 333-9912
Toll Free: (800) 403-3728
E-mail: rds@flightsystems.com
Web Site: www.flightsystems.com
Approx. Number Employees: 25
Year Founded: 1968
Business Description:
Mfr. & Rebuilder of Electronic Controls for Generator & Diesel Engines
S.I.C.: 3625
N.A.I.C.S.: 335314
Import Export
Media: 1-2-5-7-10-11-20
Distr.: Intl.; Natl.
Personnel:
Robert Shaffner *(Chm & CEO)*
Robert A. York *(VP-Engrg)*
John D. Weaver *(Mgr-Generator Controls Sls)*
Josh Leeds *(Specialist-Customer Svc)*
Brands & Products:
ASCO
BASLER
COLEMAN
DELCO
ENGINE SAVER
FLIGHTS SYSTEM
GENERAC
KOHLER
NEW ONAN
REPLACEMENT NEWAGE
WESTERBEKE
WESTINGHOUSE

FLOW INTERNATIONAL CORPORATION
23500 64th Ave S
Kent, WA 98032
Tel.: (253) 850-3500
Fax: (253) 813-3285
Toll Free: (800) 446-3569
E-mail: info@flowcorp.com

Key to Media (For complete agency information see *The Advertising Red Books-Agencies* edition):
1. Bus. Publs. 2. Cable T.V. 3. Catalogs & Directories. 4. Co-op Adv. 5. Consumer Mags. 6. D.M. to Bus. Estab.7. D.M. to Consumers
8. Daily Newsp. 9. Exhibits/Trade Shows 10. Foreign 11. Infomercial 12. Internet Adv.13. Multimedia 14. Network Radio
15. Network T.V. 16. Newsp. Distr. Mags. 17. Other 18. Outdoor (Posters, Transit) 19. Point of Purchase20. Premiums, Novelties
21. Product Samples 22. Special Events Mktg. 23. Spot Radio 24. Spot T.V. 25. Weekly Newsp. 26. Yellow Page Adv.

Flow International Corporation — (Continued)

Web Site: www.flowcorp.com
E-Mail For Key Personnel:
Public Relations: LBrandli@flowcorp.com
Approx. Sls.: $216,524,000
Approx. Number Employees: 616
Year Founded: 1974
Business Description:
Developer & Mfr of Ultrahigh-Pressure (UHP) Waterjet & Abrasive Waterjet Cutting & Machining Technologies for Advanced Industrial & Manufacturing Applications
S.I.C.: 3291; 3561; 3589
N.A.I.C.S.: 327910; 333319; 333911
Import Export
Advertising Expenditures: $800,000
Media: 1-2-7-13
Personnel:
Jerry L. Calhoun *(Chm)*
Charles M. Brown *(Pres & CEO)*
Allen M. Hsieh *(CFO & VP)*
Daric Schweikart *(CIO & VP)*
John S. Leness *(Gen Counsel & Sec)*
Richard A. LeBlanc *(Exec VP-Global Sls)*
Mohamed Hashish *(Sr VP-Tech)*
Craig Sunada *(VP-Engrg & Ops)*
Theresa Signorini Treat *(VP-HR)*
Brands & Products:
DECKHOG
DIESEL EAGLE
DYNAMIC WATERJET
ELIMINATOR
FLOW
FLOWMASTER
FRESHER UNDER PRESSURE
HUSKY
HYDROCAT
HYPLEX
PASER
WATERVEYOR

FOLEY-BELSAW COMPANY
1760 Universal Ave
Kansas City, MO 64120
Tel.: (816) 483-2700
Fax: (816) 483-5010
Toll Free: (800) 821-3452
Web Site: www.foleycompanies.com
Approx. Number Employees: 180
Year Founded: 1926
Business Description:
Holding Company
S.I.C.: 8249; 2511
N.A.I.C.S.: 611519; 337122
Import Export
Advertising Expenditures: $2,500,000
Media: 2-4-5-6-7-8-16-25
Distr.: Natl.
Budget Set: July
Personnel:
Walter M. Ringer, Jr. *(Chm)*
Walter M. Ringer, III *(Vice Chm & CEO)*
Brands & Products:
FOLEY-BELSAW
Advertising Agency:
Field Advertising
6301 Equitable Rd
Kansas City, MO 64120-1332
Tel.: (816) 483-6400
Fax: (816) 483-5010
Toll Free: (800) 821-3452
(Correspondence Courses, Equipment-Sharpening, Locksmith Outdoor Power Equipment Parts, Electronic Supplies, Vinyl Supplies)

FORMTEK, INC.
(Sub. of Mestek, Inc.)
4899 Commerce Pkwy
Warrensville Heights, OH 44128
Tel.: (216) 292-4460
Fax: (216) 292-2898
Toll Free: (800) 631-0520
E-mail: info@formtekinc.com
Web Site: www.formtekinc.com/index.asp
Sales Range: $125-149.9 Million
Business Description:
Metal Forming Solutions & Services
S.I.C.: 3542
N.A.I.C.S.: 333513
Media: 10

FOX CONTRACTORS CORP.
5430 W Ferguson Rd
Fort Wayne, IN 46809-9612
Tel.: (260) 747-7461
Fax: (260) 747-7717
E-mail: foxcontrac@aol.com
Web Site: www.foxcontractors.com
Approx. Number Employees: 50
Year Founded: 1974
Business Description:
Highway & Street Excavation
S.I.C.: 1622
N.A.I.C.S.: 237310
Media: 17
Personnel:
Dallas Day *(Pres)*
Matt Michaels *(Controller & CFO)*
Adam Day *(Gen Mgr)*

FRANKLIN ELECTRIC CO., INC.
400 E Spring St
Bluffton, IN 46714-3737
Tel.: (260) 824-2900
Fax: (260) 824-2909
E-mail: webmaster@fele.com
Web Site: www.franklinelect.com
Approx. Sls.: $713,792,000
Approx. Number Employees: 3,470
Year Founded: 1944
Business Description:
Electric Motors, Drives, Controls, Submersible Water & Fueling Systems Mfr
S.I.C.: 3714; 3621; 3829
N.A.I.C.S.: 336322; 334519; 335312; 336312
Import Export
Media: 2-4-10-19-21
Distr.: Intl.; Natl.
Personnel:
R. Scott Trumbull *(Chm & CEO)*
John J. Haines *(CFO, Sec & VP)*
Robert J. Stone *(Pres-Americas Water Systems Grp & Sr VP)*
DeLancey W. Davis *(Pres-US/Canada Comml Bus Unit & VP)*
Gregg C. Sengstack *(Sr VP-Intl Water Sys & Fueling Grp)*
Steve Aikman *(VP-Water Sys Engrg)*
Brands & Products:
FRANKLIN ELECTRIC
FRANKLIN FUELING SYSTEMS

FREEWAY CORPORATION
9301 Allen Dr
Cleveland, OH 44125-4632
Tel.: (216) 524-9700
Fax: (216) 524-6954
E-mail: infi@freewaycorp.com
Web Site: www.freewaycorp.com
Approx. Number Employees: 150
Year Founded: 1946
Business Description:
Metal Stampings, Assemblies & Screw Machine Products
S.I.C.: 3452; 3469
N.A.I.C.S.: 332722; 332116
Export
Advertising Expenditures: $200,000
Media: 2-4-10
Distr.: Natl.
Budget Set: Oct. -Nov.
Personnel:
Robb Scherler *(Pres)*
Randy Scherler *(VP-Mktg & Sls)*
Brands & Products:
FREEWAY

THE FROG, SWITCH & MANUFACTURING COMPANY
600 E High St
Carlisle, PA 17013-2651
Tel.: (717) 243-2454
Fax: (717) 243-1385
E-mail: inquiries@frogswitch.com
Web Site: www.frogswitch.com
Approx. Number Employees: 167
Year Founded: 1881
Business Description:
Mfr. of Manganese Steel Castings; High Chrome Iron Castings; Pulvomatic Impact Crushers
S.I.C.: 3325; 3531
N.A.I.C.S.: 331513; 333120
Media: 4-10
Personnel:
Bill Walters *(VP-Sls & Mktg)*
Alf Basson *(Asst Dir-Sls & Mktg)*
Kim Hurley *(Mgr-Sls)*
Brands & Products:
DURADIG
FROGSWITCH
WEARWOLF

FSI INTERNATIONAL, INC.
3455 Lyman Blvd
Chaska, MN 55318-3052
Tel.: (952) 448-5440
Fax: (952) 448-2825
Toll Free: (800) 274-5440
E-mail: fsi@fsi-intl.com
Web Site: www.fsi-intl.com
E-Mail For Key Personnel:
President: don.mitchell@fsi-intl.com
Marketing Director: laurie.walker@fsi-intl.com
Public Relations: laurie.walker@fsi-intl.com
Approx. Sls.: $90,985,000
Approx. Number Employees: 293
Year Founded: 1973
Business Description:
Special Industry Machinery Mfr
S.I.C.: 3553; 3559; 3821
N.A.I.C.S.: 333210; 332410; 333295; 339111
Import Export
Advertising Expenditures: $160,000
Media: 2-4-7-10-13
Personnel:
Donald S. Mitchell *(Chm & CEO)*
Patricia Hollister *(CFO & Asst Sec)*
Benno G. Sand *(Sec & Exec VP-Bus Dev/IR)*
Scott Becker *(VP-Engrg)*
John C. Ely *(VP-Sls & Mktg Svcs)*
Brands & Products:
ALWAYS THINKING.BETTER.
ANTARES
ECOBLEND
EXCALIBUR
FSI
MAGELLAN
MERCURY
ORION
POLARIS
REFRESH PROGRAM
SATURN
SYMFLOW
YIELDUP
ZETA
Advertising Agency:
Loomis Group
345 Spear St Ste 110
San Francisco, CA 94105
Tel.: (415) 882-9494
Fax: (415) 882-7209

G&W ELECTRIC COMPANY
3500 W 127th St
Blue Island, IL 60406
Tel.: (708) 388-5010
Fax: (708) 388-0755
E-mail: webmail@gwelec.com
Web Site: www.gwelec.com
Approx. Number Employees: 300
Year Founded: 1905
Business Description:
Medium & High Voltage Electrical Equipment
S.I.C.: 3613; 3643
N.A.I.C.S.: 335313; 335931
Import Export
Media: 2-4-7-10
Distr.: Intl.; Natl.
Budget Set: Oct.
Personnel:
John Mueller *(Chm & Pres)*
Flavio L. Corsi *(Reg VP-Latin America)*
K. L. Ng *(Reg VP)*
Manish Patel *(Reg VP)*
Anthony Woon *(Reg VP)*
Tim Foley *(VP-Sls & Mktg)*
Marcelo Jaramillo *(Gen Mgr)*
Mohammed Madkhoom *(Exec Dir)*
Larry Arends *(Mgr-Mktg)*
Dan Dykas *(Mgr-Sls)*
Oscar Retana *(Mgr-Sls)*
Pichate Yarnsukol *(Mgr-Sls)*
Brands & Products:
CLIP
EPOX
G&W
PAF
SLIP-ON
TRIDENT
VIPER-G
VIPER-S
VIPER-ST
X-LIMINATOR

GAINES MOTOR LINES INCORPORATED
2349 13th Ave SW
Hickory, NC 28602
Tel.: (828) 322-2000
Fax: (828) 324-7026
E-mail: info@gainesml.com
Web Site: www.gainesml.com
Approx. Number Employees: 100

Key to Media (For complete agency information see *The Advertising Red Books-Agencies* edition):
1. Bus. Publs. 2. Cable T.V. 3. Catalogs & Directories. 4. Co-op Adv. 5. Consumer Mags. 6. D.M. to Bus. Estab.7. D.M. to Consumers
8. Daily Newsp. 9. Exhibits/Trade Shows 10. Foreign 11. Infomercial 12. Internet Adv.13. Multimedia 14. Network Radio
15. Network T.V. 16. Newsp. Distr. Mags. 17. Other 18. Outdoor (Posters, Transit) 19. Point of Purchase20. Premiums, Novelties
21. Product Samples 22. Special Events Mktg. 23. Spot Radio 24. Spot T.V. 25. Weekly Newsp. 26. Yellow Page Adv.

Business Description:
Contract Haulers
S.I.C.: 4213; 4731
N.A.I.C.S.: 484121; 488510
Advertising Agency:
Koroberi
1506 E Franklin St Ste 300
Chapel Hill, NC 27514
Tel.: (919) 960-9794
Fax: (919) 960-8570

GARDNER DENVER, INC.

1500 Liberty Ridge Dr Ste 300
Wayne, PA 19087
Tel.: (610) 249-2000
Web Site: www.gardnerdenver.com
E-Mail For Key Personnel:
Marketing Director: mktg@gardnerdenver.com
Approx. Rev.: $1,895,104,000
Approx. Number Employees: 6,100
Year Founded: 1859
Business Description:
Blowers, Stationary Air Compressors, Petroleum Drilling & Production Pumps & Water Jetting Equipment
S.I.C.: 3533; 3561; 3563; 3564
N.A.I.C.S.: 333132; 333412; 333911; 333912
Import Export
Advertising Expenditures: $1,000,000
Media: 2-4-5-7-10-13-17-26
Distr.: Intl.; Natl.
Budget Set: Jan.
Personnel:
Frank J. Hansen *(Chm)*
Barry L. Pennypacker *(Pres & CEO)*
Michael M. Larsen *(CFO & VP)*
Bob D. Elkins *(CIO & VP)*
Brent A. Walters *(Chief Compliance Officer, Gen Counsel, Sec & VP)*
Christopher R. Celtruda *(Pres-Indus Products Grp & VP)*
T. Duane Morgan *(Pres-Engineered Products Grp & VP)*
Armando L. Castorena *(VP-HR)*
Brands & Products:
AEON
AIR RELIEF
BELLIS & MORCOM
CYCLOBLOWER
DRUM
DUROFLOW
ELMO RIETSCHLE
EMCO WHEATON
GARDNER DENVER
HELIFLOW
HOFFMAN
LAMSON
OBERDORFER
SUTORBILT
TAMROTOR
THOMAS
TODO-GAS
TODO-MATIC
TRIFLOW
TURBOTRON
WEBSTER
WELCH
WITTIG

GARDNER DENVER NASH

(Sub. of Gardner Denver Ltd.)
9 Trefoil Dr
Trumbull, CT 06611-1330
Tel.: (203) 459-3900
Fax: (203) 459-3988
Toll Free: (800) 553NASH
E-mail: nash@gardnerdenver.com
Web Site: www.gardnerdenvernash.com
Sales Range: $25-49.9 Million
Approx. Number Employees: 45
Year Founded: 1905
Business Description:
Vacuum Pumps & Compressors
S.I.C.: 3563; 5084
N.A.I.C.S.: 333912; 423830
Import Export
Media: 2-4-7-10-11-13-20-26
Distr.: Natl.
Personnel:
Peter W. Klipfel *(Dir-Global Mktg)*
Brands & Products:
904
DRY-PRO
HYTOR
KINEMA
NASH
NASH-ELMO
NASH ENGINEERING
SEAM SAVER

GAS-FIRED PRODUCTS, INC.

305 Doggett St
Charlotte, NC 28203-4923
Mailing Address:
PO Box 36485
Charlotte, NC 28236-6485
Tel.: (704) 372-3485
Fax: (704) 332-5843
Toll Free: (800) 830-3983
E-mail: info@gasfiredproducts.com
Web Site: www.gasfiredproducts.com
Approx. Number Employees: 100
Year Founded: 1949
Business Description:
Gas-Fired Heating Equipment Mfr
S.I.C.: 3433; 3523
N.A.I.C.S.: 333414; 333111
Import Export
Media: 2-5-7-9-18-25
Distr.: Intl.; Natl.
Budget Set: June
Personnel:
Frank L. Horne, Jr. *(Pres)*
Brands & Products:
BULKTOBAC
COMPUHEAT
CORCHO
GASTOBAC
GFC
GFP
SPACE-RAY
SUNSTAR
UNIRACK

GAST MANUFACTURING, INC.

(Sub. of IDEX Corporation)
2300 S M 139
Benton Harbor, MI 49022-6114
Mailing Address:
PO Box 97
Benton Harbor, MI 49023-0097
Tel.: (269) 926-6171
Fax: (269) 925-8288
E-mail: sales.gast@idexcorp.com
Web Site: www.gastmfg.com
E-Mail For Key Personnel:
Sales Director: sales.gast@idexcorp.com
Sales Range: $100-124.9 Million
Approx. Number Employees: 250
Year Founded: 1921
Business Description:
Air Pumps & Pneumatic Motors Mfr & Distr
S.I.C.: 3563; 3594
N.A.I.C.S.: 333912; 333996
Export
Advertising Expenditures: $500,000
Media: 6-10
Distr.: Natl.
Budget Set: Apr.
Personnel:
Eric Ashlemn *(Pres)*
Brands & Products:
DDL
GAST
PERFORMACE LE
REGENAIR
ROC-R
SERVICE PLAN PLUS
SMART-AIR

GE ENERGY

(Div. of GE Technology Infrastructure)
4200 Wildwood Pkwy
Atlanta, GA 30339
Tel.: (678) 844-6000
Fax: (678) 844-6690
Toll Free: (800) 626-2004
Web Site: www.gepower.com
Approx. Number Employees: 35,000
Business Description:
Gas, Steam, Hydro, Nuclear & Wind Turbines & Electrical Transmission Equipment Mfr
S.I.C.: 3533
N.A.I.C.S.: 333132
Media: 17
Personnel:
John Krenicki, Jr. *(Pres & CEO)*
Dan Janki *(CFO & VP)*
Happy Perkins *(Gen Counsel & VP)*
Mark M. Little *(Sr VP)*
Sharon R. Daley *(VP-HR)*
James N. Suciu *(VP-Global Sls)*
Sherrell Collins *(Specialist-Comm)*
Brands & Products:
AC TENSIONING TOOL
AQUADRAN
AQUAOIL
BHA TEX
CABA WIN
CB-MAP
CENTERFIRE
CESIC
COALOGIC
DESIGN MANAGER
EFFICIENCYMAPE
EGIL
ENIMAC
FARADAY
FILTERSKILLS
FLAMEMASTEER
FLOWMASTEER
FRANCIS
FREJA
GATECYCLE
GENGAUGE
H SYSTEM
HYDRAN
IMPAK
IN-DUCT HUMIDIFICATION
INPOINT
INSUL-DRYER
INTELLI-CLEAN
IPLAS
JUICECAN
KAPLAN
KWIK-SKRENE
LTC-MAP
MAGNEHELIC
MAGNUS
NEUTRALITE
ODEN AT
PHOTOHELIC
POWERON
POWERWAVE
PULSE-ON-DEMAND
Advertising Agencies:
Maier Advertising, Inc.
1789 New Britain Ave
Farmington, CT 06032-3317
Tel.: (860) 677-4581
Fax: (860) 677-5854
Fax: (860) 677-4898

Masto Public Relations
1811 Western Ave
Albany, NY 12203
Tel.: (518) 786-6488
Fax: (518) 786-6497

Peppercom
470 Park Ave S 5th Fl
New York, NY 10016
Tel.: (212) 931-6100
Fax: (212) 931-6159

Pratt & Buehl
3390 Peachtree Rd Ste 500
Atlanta, GA 30326
Tel.: (404) 231-2311
Fax: (404) 231-0543

GE ENERGY

(Sub. of GE Energy)
795 George V Ave
Lachine, QC H8S 4K8, Canada
Tel.: (514) 485-4037
Fax: (514) 485-4231
Telex: 5-821673
Web Site: www.gepower.com
Sales Range: $200-249.9 Million
Approx. Number Employees: 700
Year Founded: 1920
Business Description:
Hydro Turbines & Generators Mfr
S.I.C.: 3511
N.A.I.C.S.: 333611
Export
Advertising Expenditures: $350,000
Media: 2-10
Distr.: Intl.
Personnel:
Tracy Moore *(Gen Mgr)*

GE FANUC AUTOMATION, INC.

(Joint Venture of General Electric Company & FANUC Ltd.)
2500 Austin Dr
Charlottesville, VA 22911
Mailing Address:
PO Box 8106
Charlottesville, VA 22906
Tel.: (434) 978-5000
Fax: (434) 978-5035
Toll Free: (800) 433-2682
E-mail: gefanuc@gefanuc.com
Web Site: www.gefanuc.com
Sales Range: $400-449.9 Million
Approx. Number Employees: 1,000
Business Description:
Automation Hardware & Software Mfr; Owned 50% by General Electric Company & 50% by Fanuc Ltd.
S.I.C.: 3571; 3829; 7372; 7373

Key to Media (For complete agency information see *The Advertising Red Books-Agencies* edition):
1. Bus. Publs. 2. Cable T.V. 3. Catalogs & Directories. 4. Co-op Adv. 5. Consumer Mags. 6. D.M. to Bus. Estab.7. D.M. to Consumers
8. Daily Newsp. 9. Exhibits/Trade Shows 10. Foreign 11. Infomercial 12. Internet Adv.13. Multimedia 14. Network Radio
15. Network T.V. 16. Newsp. Distr. Mags. 17. Other 18. Outdoor (Posters, Transit) 19. Point of Purchase20. Premiums, Novelties
21. Product Samples 22. Special Events Mktg. 23. Spot Radio 24. Spot T.V. 25. Weekly Newsp. 26. Yellow Page Adv.

GE Fanuc Automation, Inc. — (Continued)

N.A.I.C.S.: 334111; 334519; 511210; 541512
Media: 2-10-25
Personnel:
Maryrose Sylvester *(Pres & CEO)*
Bill Black *(Controllers Product Mgr-GE Fanuc Intelligent Platforms)*
Brands & Products:
PROFICY

GE WATER & PROCESS TECHNOLOGIES

(Div. of GE Technology Infrastructure)
4636 Somerton Rd
Trevose, PA 19053-6742
Tel.: (215) 355-3300
Fax: (215) 953-5524
Web Site: www.gewater.com
Sales Range: $350-399.9 Million
Year Founded: 1925
Business Description:
Water Treatment, Wastewater Treatment & Water Processing Systems & Services
S.I.C.: 4941; 1623
N.A.I.C.S.: 221310; 237110
Import Export
Media: 1-2-4-7-10-20-26
Distr.: Intl.; Natl.
Budget Set: Dec.
Brands & Products:
ACCUTRAK
ACTION
ACUFEED
ALERT
ALKAT-XL
APPLICATIONS ATLAS
AQUA-SHED
AQUAMATIC
AUTOTROL
BES
BETZDEARBORN KLEEN
BIO-TROL
CAMEO
CHEMSURE
CLAM-TROL
CONTINUUM AEC
COPPER-TROL
CORRSHIELD
CORTROL
CREPEPLUS
DARAMAX
DARASPRAY
DEARTEK
DESAL
DETAC
DIANODIC
DIMETALLIC
E-CELL
E-SERIES OZONE
E-SERIES RO
FLOTREX
FLOWPRO
FOAM-TROL
FUEL-SOLV
GCP SERIES
HTP-2
HYPURE
HYTREX
HYZEEN
KLARAID
LOGIX CONTROLLERS
LOSALT
MAX-AMINE
MEMTREX
MILLENIUM RO SYSTEMS
NEUTRAFILM
NEUTRAMEEN
NOVUS
OCTAFILM
OPTIFLEX
OPTISPERSE
OSMO BEV
OSMO MUNI
OSMO PHARMA
OSMO PRO SERIES
OSMONICS HOUSEHOLD FILTER
PACESETTER PLUS
PERMATREAT
PETROFLO
PETROMEEN
PHOSGARD
POLY-FLOC
POLYCERAGUARD
POLYNODIC
PROSHIELD
PUTREX
REC OIL
RES-Q
ROSAVE.Z
SELEX
SIDTEC
SLIME-TROL
SPEC AID
STEAMATE
STERISAFE
STYREX
TONKAFLO
ULTRASPERSE
WASTEWIZARD
WELLPRO.Z
XPLEAT
Z.PLEX
Advertising Agency:
OMD Worldwide
195 Broadway
New York, NY 10007
Tel.: (212) 590-7100
Adv Placement

GEERPRES INC.

1780 Harvey St
Muskegon, MI 49442-5378
Mailing Address:
PO Box 658
Muskegon, MI 49443-0658
Tel.: (231) 773-3211
Fax: (231) 773-8263
Toll Free: (800) 253-0373
E-mail: sales@geerpres.com
Web Site: www.geerpres.com
E-Mail For Key Personnel:
Sales Director: sales@geerpres.com
Approx. Number Employees: 28
Year Founded: 1935
Business Description:
Cleaning Equipment Mfr
S.I.C.: 3589
N.A.I.C.S.: 333319
Import Export
Advertising Expenditures: $200,000
Media: 1-2-4-5-7-8-10-11-16-20-21
Distr.: Intl.; Natl.
Personnel:
Michael Gluhanich *(Pres)*
Bryan Depree *(CFO)*
Sam Waites *(Dir-Sls)*
Brands & Products:
BIOSHIELD
CARRY MATE
CEASE
CHAMP
DELUXE RX
DYNAMATE
ECONOLINE
ECONOMATE
EPOXY II
ESCORT
ESCORT RX
FEATHERWEIGHT
GEERPRES
GPS
GRIPIT
MAXI-GRIP
QUICK MATE
RALLY
SEAWAY
SIDE KICK
SPEED-GRIP
ULTRA
WAGON MASTER
WALL MATE
WASTE-WAGON

GEHL COMPANY

(Sub. of Manitou BF S.A.)
1 Gehl Way
West Bend, WI 53095-3415
Tel.: (262) 334-9461
Fax: (262) 338-7517
Telex: 26701 GEHLCO
E-mail: parts@gehl.com
Web Site: www.gehl.com
Approx. Sls.: $457,612,000
Approx. Number Employees: 375
Year Founded: 1859
Business Description:
Designer, Mfr & Retailer of Equipment Used in the Light -Construction & Agricultural Equipment Industries
S.I.C.: 3423; 3523; 3531; 3537
N.A.I.C.S.: 332212; 333111; 333120; 333924
Import Export
Advertising Expenditures: $1,000,000
Media: 1-2-5-8-9-10-20-25
Distr.: Intl.; Natl.
Budget Set: Oct.
Personnel:
Daniel L. Miller *(Pres & CEO)*
James Green *(Gen Counsel & Corp Sec, VP)*
Serge Bosche *(VP-Sls-Mktg)*
Shannon K. Van Dyke *(VP-Fin)*
Brands & Products:
AGRI-LOADER
ALL-TACH
AUTO-MAX
AVANTAGE
CROP PROCESSOR
DYNALIFT
EDGE
FORAGE MAX
GEHL
GEHL FINANCE
HYDALOC
HYDRAGLIDE
HYDRALOC
METAL-STOP
MIX-ALL
MUSTANG
POWER-A-TACH
POWER BOX
POWERVIEW
PROTECTADRIVE
SCAVENGER
SELECT-A-BOOM
VORTEX
Advertising Agency:
The McFarland Group, Inc.
15255 Watertown Plank Rd
Elm Grove, WI 53122
Tel.: (262) 786-5891
Fax: (262) 786-3913

GEMINI GROUP

175 Thompson Rd
Bad Axe, MI 48413
Tel.: (989) 269-6272
Fax: (989) 269-8622
Web Site: www.geminigroup.net
Approx. Number Employees: 480
Year Founded: 1977
Business Description:
Mfr. of Plastics Products
S.I.C.: 8742; 3089
N.A.I.C.S.: 541611; 326199
Import Export
Advertising Agency:
MRW Communications LLC
2 Fairfield St
Hingham, MA 02043
Tel.: (781) 740-4525
Fax: (781) 926-0371

GENCOR INDUSTRIES, INC.

5201 N Orange Blossom Trl
Orlando, FL 32810-1008
Tel.: (407) 290-6000
Fax: (407) 297-6238
Web Site: www.gencor.com
Approx. Rev.: $55,587,000
Approx. Number Employees: 214
Year Founded: 1968
Business Description:
Mfr., Designer & Marketer of Process Machinery Equipment For the Production of Highway Construction Materials, Related Equipment & Machinery Used In the Production of Pelletized Animal Feeds, Edible Oil, Sugar & Citrus Juice; Asphalt Plant Builder
S.I.C.: 3531; 3559; 3567
N.A.I.C.S.: 333120; 333298; 333994
Import Export
Media: 5-11
Personnel:
E. J. Elliott *(Chm & CEO)*
Marc G. Elliott *(Pres)*
John E. Elliott *(Exec VP)*
Dennis Hunt *(Sr VP)*
Ralph Vock *(Dir-Procurement)*

GENERAC HOLDINGS INC.

(Holding of CCMP Capital Advisors, LLC)
S45 W29290 Hwy 59
Waukesha, WI 53187
Tel.: (262) 544-4811
Fax: (262) 968-3791
Web Site: www.generac.com
Approx. Sls.: $592,880,000
Approx. Number Employees: 1,282
Year Founded: 2006
Business Description:
Holding Company; Generator Mfr
S.I.C.: 3621; 3612; 6719
N.A.I.C.S.: 335312; 335311; 551112
Advertising Expenditures: $11,985,000
Personnel:
Aaron Jagdfeld *(CEO)*
York A. Ragen *(CFO)*
Dawn Tabat *(COO)*

Key to Media (For complete agency information see *The Advertising Red Books-Agencies* edition):
1. Bus. Publs. 2. Cable T.V. 3. Catalogs & Directories. 4. Co-op Adv. 5. Consumer Mags. 6. D.M. to Bus. Estab.7. D.M. to Consumers
8. Daily Newsp. 9. Exhibits/Trade Shows 10. Foreign 11. Infomercial 12. Internet Adv.13. Multimedia 14. Network Radio
15. Network T.V. 16. Newsp. Distr. Mags. 17. Other 18. Outdoor (Posters, Transit) 19. Point of Purchase20. Premiums, Novelties
21. Product Samples 22. Special Events Mktg. 23. Spot Radio 24. Spot T.V. 25. Weekly Newsp. 26. Yellow Page Adv.

Alan Gillette *(Sr VP-Engrg)*
Roger Pascavis *(Sr VP-Ops)*
Roger Schaus, Jr. *(Sr VP-Svc Ops)*

GENERAC POWER SYSTEMS INC.

(Sub. of GENERAC HOLDINGS INC.)
Hillside Rd & Hwy 59
Waukesha, WI 53187
Tel.: (262) 544-4811
Fax: (262) 968-3791
Toll Free: (888) 436-3722
E-mail: info@generac.com
Web Site: www.generac.com
Approx. Number Employees: 1,000
Year Founded: 1959
Business Description:
Commercial & Residential Motor & Generator Mfr
S.I.C.: 3621; 3511
N.A.I.C.S.: 335312; 333611
Import Export
Personnel:
Aaron Jagdfeld *(CEO)*
Terry Dolan *(Sr VP-Sls)*
Brands & Products:
BI-FUEL
GENERAC
GENLINK
POWERMANAGER
Advertising Agencies:
Cramer-Krasselt
246 E Chicago St
Milwaukee, WI 53202
Tel.: (414) 227-3500
Fax: (414) 276-8710
Marketing
Public Relations Agency of Record

Phoenix Marketing Group, Inc.
6750 Maple Terr
Milwaukee, WI 53213
Tel.: (414) 771-1044
Fax: (414) 771-1084

GENERAL PROCESSING SYSTEMS, INC.

40A Stonehill Rd
Oswego, IL 60543-9400
Tel.: (630) 554-7804
Fax: (630) 554-7805
Toll Free: (800) 547-9370
Web Site: www.productsaver.com
Sales Range: $10-24.9 Million
Approx. Number Employees: 12
Year Founded: 1965
Business Description:
Mfr. of Customized Product Reclaiming Equipment; Screen Separators; Rotary Sifters; Belt Conveying Equipment; Ductless Air Distribution Systems
S.I.C.: 3565; 3496
N.A.I.C.S.: 333993; 332618
Export
Media: 2-7-10
Distr.: Intl.; Natl.
Budget Set: Nov.
Personnel:
Edwin C. Swiatlo *(Pres)*
Jeff Swiatlo *(Gen Mgr)*
Brands & Products:
PRODUCT SAVER

GENMARK AUTOMATION INC.

1201 Cadillac Ct
Milpitas, CA 95035-3000
Tel.: (408) 678-8500
Fax: (408) 942-7560
E-mail: marketing@genmarkautomation.com
Web Site: www.genmarkautomation.com
Sales Range: $25-49.9 Million
Approx. Number Employees: 135
Year Founded: 1986
Business Description:
Mfr of Industrial & Commercial Products for Factory Automation
S.I.C.: 3599; 7371; 7372
N.A.I.C.S.: 332710; 334611; 541511
Media: 4-10
Personnel:
Mila Genov *(Chm)*
Brands & Products:
BIOBOT
EZTEACH
GENCOBOT TOOL BOX
GIFT
MINI-MAX
PORTA
SORT-MAX

THE GEORGE E. FAILING COMPANY

(Sub. of Blue Tee Corporation)
(d/b/a GEFCO)
2215 S Van Buren St
Enid, OK 73701
Mailing Address:
PO Box 872
Enid, OK 73702-0872
Tel.: (580) 234-4141
Fax: (580) 233-6807
E-mail: domsales@gefco.com
Web Site: www.gefco.com
Approx. Number Employees: 200
Year Founded: 1932
Business Description:
Mfr. of Mobile Rotary Drill Rigs & Seismic Vibrators for Oil & Mineral Exploration
S.I.C.: 3612; 3533
N.A.I.C.S.: 335311; 333132
Advertising Expenditures: $200,000
Media: 2-10
Distr.: Intl.; Natl.
Budget Set: Apr.
Personnel:
Aaron Harmon *(Pres)*
Art Kleiwer *(VP-Intl Sls)*
Brands & Products:
FAILING
KING OIL TOOL
SD 300 E
SPEED STAR
STRATA STAR 15
STRATA STAR 25
STRATA STAR 5

GEORGE T. SCHMIDT, INC.

6151 W Howard St
Niles, IL 60714-3401
Mailing Address:
PO Box 480390
Niles, IL 60714-3401
Tel.: (847) 647-7117
Fax: (847) 647-7593
Toll Free: (800) 323-1332
E-mail: info@gtschmidt.com
Web Site: www.gtschmidt.com
Approx. Number Employees: 70
Year Founded: 1895
Business Description:
Permanent Marking Identification Systems Mfr
S.I.C.: 3542; 3544
N.A.I.C.S.: 333513; 333514
Advertising Expenditures: $300,000
Media: 1-2-4-7-10-17
Distr.: Natl.
Personnel:
Neal O'Connor *(Pres)*
Kate Giacometti *(Mgr-Mktg)*
Brands & Products:
MICROLASE
SCHMIDT MICROLASE
SCRIBELINER
STINGER
STYLINER
STYLINER MARK

GESSNER INDUSTRIES INC.

384 Faggart Ave
Concord, NC 28027-6069
Tel.: (704) 782-3100
Fax: (704) 782-3177
E-mail: gessnerwj@aol.com
Sales Range: Less than $1 Million
Approx. Number Employees: 7
Year Founded: 1984
Business Description:
Textile Machinery
S.I.C.: 7629; 3552
N.A.I.C.S.: 811219; 333292
Import
Media: 4-10-26
Distr.: Natl.
Personnel:
Frances Phillips *(Gen Mgr)*
Linda Shaver *(Mgr-Accts)*
Brands & Products:
WINSOR & JERAULD

GESSNER/MILLER CORPORATION

(Div. of GHM Industries, Inc.)
100 A Sturbage Rd
Charlton, MA 01507
Tel.: (508) 248-3941
Fax: (508) 248-0639
E-mail: info@millerproduct.net
Web Site: www.gessner.net
Approx. Sls.: $5,000,000
Approx. Number Employees: 20
Business Description:
Mfr. of Textile Finishing; Packaging & Carpet Shearing Machinery
S.I.C.: 3552; 3531
N.A.I.C.S.: 333292; 333120
Advertising Expenditures: $200,000
Media: 2-10-17
Distr.: Natl.
Personnel:
Paul Jankovic *(Pres)*
Brands & Products:
PACKTECH

GIANT INDUSTRIES, INC.

900 N Westwood Ave
Toledo, OH 43607-3261
Tel.: (419) 531-4600
Fax: (419) 531-6836
Toll Free: (800) 633-4565
E-mail: sales@giantpumps.com
Web Site: www.giantpumps.com
E-Mail For Key Personnel:
Sales Director: sales@giantpumps.com
Approx. Number Employees: 35
Year Founded: 1934
Business Description:
Triplex Pumps & Accessories Mfr
S.I.C.: 5084; 3589
N.A.I.C.S.: 423830; 333319
Import Export
Media: 2-4-7-10-13-26
Distr.: Natl.
Budget Set: Nov.
Personnel:
Edward Simon *(Pres)*
Brands & Products:
AQUA
GIANT
MOISTWIPE
PERFORMANCE UNDER PRESSURE
SUPER
TURBO-LASER

GIBRALTAR INDUSTRIES, INC.

3556 Lake Shore Rd
Buffalo, NY 14219-1445
Mailing Address:
PO Box 2028
Buffalo, NY 14219-0228
Tel.: (716) 826-6500
E-mail: Khouseknecht@Gibraltar1.com
Web Site: www.gibraltar1.com
Approx. Sls.: $685,068,000
Approx. Number Employees: 2,054
Year Founded: 1972
Business Description:
Thermal Processing & Heat Treating Services; Custom Processed Metal Products & Building Materials Mfr
S.I.C.: 1522; 3312; 3316; 3398; 3446; 3499
N.A.I.C.S.: 236220; 331111; 331221; 332323; 332811; 332999
Import Export
Media: 4-10
Distr.: Natl.
Personnel:
Brian J. Lipke *(Chm & CEO)*
Henning N Kornbrekke *(Pres & COO)*
Brent Liston *(Pres-Appleton Supply)*
Kenneth W. Smith *(CFO & Sr VP)*
Andrew Blanchard *(Pres-Processed Metals Grp)*
Robert C. Brunson *(Grp Pres-Building Products)*
Gary K. Henry *(Pres-Noll & Norwesco)*
Timothy J. Heasley *(Sec, Sr VP & Controller)*
Paul M. Murray *(Sr VP-HR & Org Dev)*
Tim OMara *(VP-Sls)*
Peter Ciotta *(Dir-Corp Comm)*
Shelly Doubet *(Mgr-Customer Svc)*
Advertising Agency:
Travers Collins & Company
726 Exchange St Ste 500
Buffalo, NY 14210-1495
Tel.: (716) 842-2222
Fax: (716) 842-6424

GIDDINGS & LEWIS, LLC

(Sub. of ThyssenKrupp Technologies AG)
142 Doty St
Fond Du Lac, WI 54935-3331
Mailing Address:
PO Box 590
Fond Du Lac, WI 54936-0590
Tel.: (920) 921-9400
Fax: (920) 906-2522
E-mail: glmt@giddings.com
Web Site: www.giddings.com

Key to Media (For complete agency information see *The Advertising Red Books-Agencies* edition):
1. Bus. Publs. 2. Cable T.V. 3. Catalogs & Directories. 4. Co-op Adv. 5. Consumer Mags. 6. D.M. to Bus. Estab.7. D.M. to Consumers 8. Daily Newsp. 9. Exhibits/Trade Shows 10. Foreign 11. Infomercial 12. Internet Adv.13. Multimedia 14. Network Radio 15. Network T.V. 16. Newsp. Distr. Mags. 17. Other 18. Outdoor (Posters, Transit) 19. Point of Purchase20. Premiums, Novelties 21. Product Samples 22. Special Events Mktg. 23. Spot Radio 24. Spot T.V. 25. Weekly Newsp. 26. Yellow Page Adv.

Giddings & Lewis, LLC — (Continued)

E-Mail For Key Personnel:
Marketing Director: lkieckha@giddings.com
Approx. Number Employees: 2,700
Year Founded: 1859
Business Description:
Machine Tools & Factory Automation Equipment Mfr & Services
S.I.C.: 3541; 3549
N.A.I.C.S.: 333512; 333518
Import Export
Advertising Expenditures: $2,385,000
Multimedia: $100,000; Bus. Publs.: $800,000; Catalogs & Directories: $400,000; D.M. to Bus. Estab.: $50,000; Exhibits/Trade Shows: $800,000; Foreign: $200,000; Premiums, Novelties: $25,000; Yellow Page Adv.: $10,000
Distr.: Intl.; Natl.
Budget Set: Aug.
Personnel:
Linda Kieckhafer *(Mktg Mgr)*
Brands & Products:
AVERY MACHINE TOOL
BICKFORD
BUHR MACHINE TOOL
CORDAX
CROSS AUTOMATION
THE CROSS COMPANY
CROSS EUROPA WERK
CROSS INTERNATIONAL
DAVIS
DRILLUNIT
G.A. GRAY
GIDDINGS & LEWIS FOUNDRY
GIDDINGS & LEWIS FRASER
GILMAN
GISHOLT
KEARNEY & TRECKER
KT-M
KT-SWASEY
LASALLE MACHINE TOOL
MICHIGAN SPECIAL MACHINING
NEXES AUTOMATION
PLACE MACHINE TOOL
SHEFFIELD MEASUREMENT
WARNER & SWASEY

GIESECKE & DEVRIENT AMERICA-PRINT INSPECTION DIVISION
(Div. of Giesecke & Devrient America, Inc.)
14 Craig Rd
Acton, MA 01720-5405
Tel.: (978) 206-2600
Fax: (978) 206-2626
E-mail: info@gdai.com
Web Site: www.gdai.com
Approx. Number Employees: 15
Year Founded: 1968
Business Description:
Credit Cards, Security Cards, Bank Notes & Money Sorting Machines Mfr
S.I.C.: 7389
N.A.I.C.S.: 561499
Media: 10-18

GIW INDUSTRIES, INC.
(Sub. of KSB Aktiengesellschaft)
5000 Wrightsboro Rd
Grovetown, GA 30813-2842
Tel.: (706) 863-1011
Fax: (706) 860-5897
Web Site: www.giwindustries.com
Sales Range: $50-74.9 Million
Approx. Number Employees: 400
Year Founded: 1890
Business Description:
Solids Handling Pumps, Pump Parts Mfr
S.I.C.: 3561; 3559
N.A.I.C.S.: 333911; 333298
Advertising Expenditures: $250,000
Bus. Publs.: $100,000; Catalogs & Directories: $25,000; Exhibits/Trade Shows: $75,000; Premiums, Novelties: $50,000
Distr.: Intl.; Natl.
Budget Set: Sept.
Personnel:
Dennis Ziegler *(Pres)*
Charlie Stone *(VP-Sls & Mktg)*
Brands & Products:
LCC PUMPS
LSA PUMPS

GKN SINTER METALS
(Sub. of GKN Sinter Metals Ltd.)
112 Harding St
Worcester, MA 01604-5020
Tel.: (508) 792-6400
Fax: (508) 792-6407
Web Site: www.gknsintermetals.com/
Approx. Number Employees: 350
Year Founded: 1943
Business Description:
Powder Metallurgy Mfr, Structurals & Bearings Including Secondary Machining
S.I.C.: 3499; 3398
N.A.I.C.S.: 332117; 332811
Export
Media: 1-2-4-10
Distr.: Natl.
Personnel:
Dan Donovan *(Controller-Div)*

GLEASON CORPORATION
1000 University Ave
Rochester, NY 14607-1239
Tel.: (585) 473-1000
Fax: (585) 461-4348
E-mail: careers@gleason.com
Web Site: www.gleason.com
E-Mail For Key Personnel:
Marketing Director: afinegan@gleason.com
Sales Director: sales@gleason.com
Sales Range: $350-399.9 Million
Approx. Number Employees: 2,600
Year Founded: 1865
Business Description:
Holding Company
S.I.C.: 5084
N.A.I.C.S.: 423830
Media: 10
Personnel:
James S. Gleason *(Chm)*
John J. Perrotti *(Pres & CEO)*
Edward J. Pelta *(Gen Counsel, Sec & VP)*
John W. Pysnack *(Treas & VP-Fin)*
Gerald R. Adamski *(Dir-Global Customer Svc)*
Thomas P. Courtney *(Dir-New Product Dev)*
Randall P. Terho *(Dir-Corp IT)*
Brands & Products:
ACRUF
BALAC
CAGE
CONIFLEX
CROWN CUT
CURVIC
CYCLEX
CYCLOCUT
ENDREM
EQUICURV
FORMATE
G-AGE
G-LAB
G-MAXX
G-PLETE
G-TECH
G-TRAC
GLEASON
GLEASON BPG
GLEASON-HURTH
HARDAC
HELIXFORM
HI-SPAND
HURTH
HURTH SPHERIC
ISO-SPAND
ISOFORM
K-KUT
KEEPING THE WORLD IN MOTION
MICRO-TOP
PENTAC
PFAUTER
PFAUTER-MAAG
PHOENIX
PHOENIX CB
PHOENIXII
POWER CUTTING
POWER DRY CUTTING
POWER LUBE
POWER SHAVING
POWERCUTTING
POWERDRYCUTTING
QUICKEDGE
RESCH
REVACYCLE
REVEX
RIDG-AC
ROUGHAC
RSR
SERCOS
SHOBBER
SIGMA 3
SIGMA 7
SINGLE CYCLE
SPHERIC
SPIROFORM
TAN-TRU
TANLINE
TANRUF
TINITE
TOPREM
TRI-AC
TURBO TESTER
UMC
UMC ULTIMA
UNI-SPAND
VERS-GRIP
THE WAFER CUTTER
THE WAFER HOB
WEDG-AC
WICH
X-PANDISK

GLEASON INDUSTRIAL PRODUCTS INC.
(Sub. of Gleason Corporation)
8575 W Forest Home Ave #100
Milwaukee, WI 53228-3417
Mailing Address:
100 8575 W Forest Home Ave
Milwaukee, WI 53228-3417
Tel.: (414) 529-8357
Fax: (414) 529-3491
E-mail: info@gleason.com
Web Site: www.gleason.com
Approx. Number Employees: 8
Year Founded: 1946
Business Description:
Tubular Steel Products; Hand Trucks; Dollies; Specialty Material Handling Manual Equipment Mfr
S.I.C.: 5013
N.A.I.C.S.: 423120
Export
Advertising Expenditures: $500,000
Media: 2-4-7-10-19-20-21
Distr.: Natl.
Budget Set: Mar. -Apr.
Personnel:
Jay Kvasnicka *(Corp VP-Sls & Mktg)*
Brands & Products:
MILWAUKEE HAND TRUCK
Advertising Agency:
Gleason Advertising
(House Agency)
316 N. Milwaukee St., Ste. 200
Milwaukee, WI 53202
Tel.: (414) 271-8357
Fax: (414) 271-4345

GLEASON - M&M PRECISION SYSTEMS CORPORATION
(Sub. of Gleason Corporation)
300 Progress Rd
West Carrollton, OH 45449
Tel.: (937) 859-8273
Fax: (937) 859-4452
Web Site: www.precision.com
Approx. Number Employees: 50
Year Founded: 1953
Business Description:
Mfr Precision Motion Systems, Rotary Tables & Metrology Systems
S.I.C.: 3829; 3823
N.A.I.C.S.: 334519; 334513
Import Export
Media: 2-4-6-7-10-11-26
Distr.: Intl.; Natl.
Budget Set: July
Personnel:
Douglas C. Beerck *(VP & Gen Mgr)*
Dennis Traynor *(Mgr-Sls)*
Brands & Products:
CIGMA 3
CIGMA 7
MICR-TOP
MV-52
Advertising Agency:
Weber, Geiger & Kalat, Inc.
11 W Monument Ave Ste 612
Dayton, OH 45402
Tel.: (937) 222-4683
Fax: (937) 222-9149
(Machine Tool)

THE GLEASON WORKS
(Sub. of Gleason Corporation)
1000 University Ave
Rochester, NY 14607-1239
Mailing Address:
PO Box 22970
Rochester, NY 14692-2970
Tel.: (585) 473-1000
Fax: (585) 461-4348
E-mail: careers@gleason.com
Web Site: www.gleason.com
E-Mail For Key Personnel:
Sales Director: sales@gleason.com

Key to Media (For complete agency information see *The Advertising Red Books-Agencies* edition):
1. Bus. Publs. 2. Cable T.V. 3. Catalogs & Directories. 4. Co-op Adv. 5. Consumer Mags. 6. D.M. to Bus. Estab.7. D.M. to Consumers 8. Daily Newsp. 9. Exhibits/Trade Shows 10. Foreign 11. Infomercial 12. Internet Adv.13. Multimedia 14. Network Radio 15. Network T.V. 16. Newsp. Distr. Mags. 17. Other 18. Outdoor (Posters, Transit) 19. Point of Purchase20. Premiums, Novelties 21. Product Samples 22. Special Events Mktg. 23. Spot Radio 24. Spot T.V. 25. Weekly Newsp. 26. Yellow Page Adv.

Sales Range: $200-249.9 Million
Approx. Number Employees: 2,000
Year Founded: 1865
Business Description:
Bevel Gear, Curvic Coupling, Spur & Helical Machinery Mfr
S.I.C.: 3714; 3728
N.A.I.C.S.: 336350; 336413
Export
Advertising Expenditures: $1,927,000
Media: 1-2-7-10-11-17-20
Distr.: Natl.
Budget Set: Jan.
Personnel:
James S. Gleason *(Chm)*
John J. Perrotti *(Pres & CEO)*
Wilhelm Pfauter *(Mng Dir)*
Edward J. Pelta *(Gen Counsel, Sec & VP)*
Robert P. Phillips *(Sr VP-Tooling Products Grp)*
Stuart D. Piper *(VP & Gen Mgr)*
Douglas C. Beerck *(VP & Gen Mgr)*
Gerald R. Adamski *(Dir-Global Customer Svc)*
Thomas P. Courtney *(Dir-New Product Dev)*
Randall P. Terho *(Dir-Corp IT)*
John M. Lange *(Product Mgr)*
Brands & Products:
GLEASON

GLOUCESTER ENGINEERING, CO.
(Holding of Mousam Ventures LLC)
Blackburn Industrial Park 11 Dory Rd
Gloucester, MA 01931-0900
Mailing Address:
PO Box 900
Gloucester, MA 01931-0900
Tel.: (978) 281-1800
Fax: (978) 282-9111
Web Site: www.gloucesterengineering.com
Sales Range: $25-49.9 Million
Approx. Number Employees: 410
Year Founded: 1961
Business Description:
Plastics Processing & Converting Machinery Mfr
S.I.C.: 3559
N.A.I.C.S.: 333220
Advertising Expenditures: $400,000
Media: 2-3-4-10-11
Distr.: Natl.
Budget Set: July
Personnel:
John Sarood *(Chm)*
Dick Murphy *(Vice Chm)*
Carl Johnson *(Pres & CEO)*
Advertising Agency:
Gloucester Engineering-Marketing Department
11 Dory Rd
Gloucester, MA 01931-0900
Tel.: (978) 281-1800
Fax: (978) 282-9111
(Plastics Processing Machinery)

GMT CORPORATION
2116 E Braemer Ave PO Box 358
Waverly, IA 50677-0358
Tel.: (319) 352-1509
Fax: (319) 352-3354
E-mail: info@gmtcorporation.com
Web Site: www.gmtcorporation.com
Approx. Sls.: $26,000,000
Approx. Number Employees: 400
Year Founded: 1973
Business Description:
Provider of Industrial Machinery
S.I.C.: 3599; 3544
N.A.I.C.S.: 332710; 333514
Personnel:
Larry H. Graening *(CEO)*
Jared Graening *(Mgr-Sls & Mktg)*
Brands & Products:
GMT CORPORATION
METAL CASTING
Advertising Agency:
Arketi Group
2801 Buford Hwy Druid Chase Ste 375
Atlanta, GA 30329
Tel.: (404) 929-0091
Fax: (404) 321-3397

GOODWAY TECHNOLOGIES CORPORATION
420 W Ave
Stamford, CT 06902-6329
Tel.: (203) 359-4708
Fax: (203) 359-9601
Fax: (800) 359-9625
Toll Free: (800) 243-7932
Toll Free: (800) 333-7467
E-mail: goodway@goodway.com
Web Site: www.goodway.com
Approx. Sls.: $10,000,000
Approx. Number Employees: 65
Year Founded: 1966
Business Description:
Tube Cleaning Systems, Pressure Washers, Drain Cleaners, Vacuums, Floor Machines & Duct Cleaning Systems Mfr
S.I.C.: 3589
N.A.I.C.S.: 333319
Import Export
Media: 6-7-10-22
Distr.: Intl.; Natl.
Budget Set: Oct.
Personnel:
Tim Kane *(Pres)*
David L. Walsh *(Sr VP-Sls & Mktg)*
Paul R. Bozek *(VP-Engrg)*
Frank Intrieri, Jr. *(VP-Sls)*
David Lobelson *(VP-Fin & Acctg)*
Christopher K. VanName *(Dir-Mktg & Adv)*
Charles McNamara *(Mgr-Export)*
Steve Spielmann *(Mgr-Tech & Customer Svc)*
Brands & Products:
CHIP-MASTER
COILPRO
DRAINRAM
JETCLEANER
JETLOAD
PULSE JETTER
QUICK SHOT
REAM-A-MATIC
SOOT-A-MATIC
SOOT-VAC

THE GORMAN-RUPP COMPANY
600 S Airport Rd
Mansfield, OH 44903
Tel.: (419) 755-1011
Fax: (419) 755-1233
E-mail: gradmin@gormanrupp.com
Web Site: www.gormanrupp.com
Approx. Sls.: $296,808,000
Approx. Number Employees: 1,082
Year Founded: 1933
Business Description:
Pump & Pumping Equipment Mfr
S.I.C.: 3561; 3491; 3586; 3594
N.A.I.C.S.: 333911; 332911; 333913; 333996
Import Export
Advertising Expenditures: $2,700,000
Media: 1-2-4-5-10-11-13-20-26
Distr.: Intl.; Natl.
Budget Set: Oct.
Personnel:
James C. Gorman *(Chm)*
Jeffrey S. Gorman *(Pres & CEO)*
Wayne L. Knabel *(CFO)*
David P. Emmens *(Gen Counsel & Sec)*
Ronald D. Pittenger *(VP, Asst Sec & Asst Treas)*
Lee A. Wilkins *(VP-HR)*
Vince Baldasare *(Mgr-Engineered Sys Sls)*
Brands & Products:
GORMAN-RUPP INDUSTRIES
GORMAN-RUPP INTERNATIONAL
GORMAN-RUPP PUMPS
GR
GRI
JW SERIES
THE PUMP PEOPLE
ST SERIES
T SERIES
U SERIES
ULTRA V SERIES
ULTRAMATE
Advertising Agency:
D&S Creative Communications Inc.
140 Park Ave E
Mansfield, OH 44902-1830
Tel.: (419) 524-4312
Fax: (419) 524-6494

GORMAN-RUPP OF CANADA LTD.
(Sub. of The Gorman-Rupp Company)
70 Burwell Rd
Saint Thomas, ON N5P 3R7, Canada
Tel.: (519) 631-2870
Fax: (519) 631-4624
E-mail: grcanada@grcanada.com
Web Site: www.grcanada.com
Sales Range: $25-49.9 Million
Approx. Number Employees: 30
Year Founded: 1960
Business Description:
Pumps Mfr
S.I.C.: 3561
N.A.I.C.S.: 333911
Import Export
Media: 1-2-4-5-6-9-10
Distr.: Natl.
Personnel:
Gary W. Creeden *(VP & Gen Mgr)*
Mike Cosgrove *(Sls Mgr-Natl & Mgr-Western District)*
Mark Neal *(Mktg Mgr)*
MIchel Boyer *(Mgr-Eastern District)*
Chris Chapman *(Mgr-Mfg)*
Stefan Fediw *(Mgr-Engineered Sys)*

GOULDS PUMPS, INCORPORATED
(Div. of ITT Fluid Technology Corporation)
240 Fall St
Seneca Falls, NY 13148-1590
Tel.: (315) 568-2811
Fax: (315) 568-2418
Toll Free: (800) 446-8537
E-mail: info@gouldspumps.com
Web Site: www.gouldspumps.com
E-Mail For Key Personnel:
Public Relations: jbeca@fluids.ittind.com
Sales Range: $800-899.9 Million
Approx. Number Employees: 3,300
Year Founded: 1848
Business Description:
Mfr. of Centrifugal Pumps For Industrial Markets
S.I.C.: 3561; 5084
N.A.I.C.S.: 333911; 423830
Import Export
Advertising Expenditures: $1,600,000
Media: 2-5-7-10-13-19-20
Distr.: Intl.; Natl.
Budget Set: Sept.
Personnel:
John Beca *(Dir-Commun)*
Anthony E. Stavale *(Mgr-R&D)*
Brands & Products:
A-C PUMP
GOULDS PUMPS
PRO SERVICES
PUMPSMART

GRACO, INC.
Russell J Gray Center 88 11th Ave NE
Minneapolis, MN 55413
Mailing Address:
PO Box 1441
Minneapolis, MN 55440-1441
Tel.: (612) 623-6000
Fax: (612) 378-3505
Toll Free: (800) 328-0211
E-mail: customerservice@graco.com
Web Site: www.graco.com
Approx. Sls.: $744,065,000
Approx. Number Employees: 2,200
Year Founded: 1926
Business Description:
Lubricating & Fluid Material Handling Equipment, Paint Circulating & Application Equipment, Atomizing Devices, Control Hardware & Software & Specialized Pumps, Regulators & Dispensing Valves Mfr
S.I.C.: 3561; 3563; 3594
N.A.I.C.S.: 333911; 333912; 333996
Import Export
Media: 5-13-22
Personnel:
Lee R. Mitau *(Chm, Exec VP & Gen Counsel-US Bancorp)*
Patrick J. McHale *(Pres & CEO)*
James A. Graner *(CFO)*
Karen Park Gallivan *(Gen Counsel, Sec & VP)*
Dale D. Johnson *(VP & Gen Mgr-Contractor Equipment Div)*
Jeffery P. Johnson *(VP & Gen Mgr-Asia Pacific)*
David M. Lowe *(VP & Gen Mgr)*
Simon J.W. Paulis *(VP & Gen Mgr-Europe)*
Mark W. Sheahan *(VP & Gen Mgr-Applied Fluid Tech Div)*
Brian J. Zumbolo *(VP & Gen Mgr-Lubrication Equipment Div)*
David M. Ahlers *(VP-HR & Corp Comm)*
Jodi Ehlers Swanson *(Coord-Corp Comm)*

Key to Media (For complete agency information see *The Advertising Red Books-Agencies* edition):
1. Bus. Publs. 2. Cable T.V. 3. Catalogs & Directories. 4. Co-op Adv. 5. Consumer Mags. 6. D.M. to Bus. Estab.7. D.M. to Consumers 8. Daily Newsp. 9. Exhibits/Trade Shows 10. Foreign 11. Infomercial 12. Internet Adv.13. Multimedia 14. Network Radio 15. Network T.V. 16. Newsp. Distr. Mags. 17. Other 18. Outdoor (Posters, Transit) 19. Point of Purchase20. Premiums, Novelties 21. Product Samples 22. Special Events Mktg. 23. Spot Radio 24. Spot T.V. 25. Weekly Newsp. 26. Yellow Page Adv.

Graco, Inc. — (Continued)

Brands & Products:
150 RPX
190ES
230ES
270ES
290 EASY
330GS
390
495ST
960
AA PLUS
AA SERIES
ACCU-CAT
ADJUST-A-STROKE
ADVANTAGE
ADVANTAGE DRIVE
AIR FLEX
AIR GUARD
AIR KING
AIR-SHOT
AIRLESS
AIRLESS SPRAY CENTER
AL PLUS
ALPHA
ALPHA PLUS
AMPLOCK
AMV
AP2
APEX
AQUARIUS 421
ASM
ASM COMPANY INC.
AUDIO TRACKMASTER
AUTO-LAYOUT
AUTO PLUS
AUTO TUNE
AUTOCLEAN
BATCH DISPENSE SYSTEM
BES 300
BI-FLO
BIG HAULER
BIG RIG
BIN EVACUATION SYSTEM
BLACK MAX
BLACK STEEL
BLUE COLOR
BLUE DEVIL
BLUE MAX
BULLDOG
CERAMTIP
CHAINMASTER
CHAMPION
CHECK-MATE
CHROMEX
CLEANLINE FILTER
CLEANSHOT
COLOR CHANGE SYSTEM
COMFORT GRIPS
COMMANDER
CONCORDE
CONTRACTOR
CONTRACTOR FTX
CONTRACTOR II
CONTROL IS EVERYTHING
CX-7
CYCLEFLO
CYCLONE
CYCLONE-MIX
DDV
DECKER
DECKER INDUSTRIES
DELTA SPRAY
DELTA SPRAY II
DELTA SPRAY XT
DEMAND DELIVERY
DIGI-TEL
DIGITAL TRACKING SYSTEM
DIRT-TERGENT
DISPENSIT
DISPENTECH
DOCTOR GUN
DOWNTIME ELIMINATOR
DRIPLESS
DROPLETS ON CIRCLE
DT
DTX
DUKE
DUO-FLO
DUO-MIX
DUOBOND
DURA DC
DURA-FLO
DURAFLEX
DURAMATIC
DURAPRO
DX
DYNA-STAR
DYNAMELT
DYNAMINI
DYNAMITE
DYNAPPLY
DYNAPRO
E-FLO
EAGLE
EAGLE-CAT
EASY OUT
EASYACCESS
EASYGLIDE
EASYKEY
EASYTURN
ECOMIX
ECONOSHOT
EDGE
EMXXX
ENDURANCE
ENDURANCE ADVANTAGE
ENDURANCE E
ENDURANCE PISTON PUMP
ENDURE
ENGARDE
EUROPRO
EVENFLO
EVENFLOW
EXPERIENCE THE DIFFERENCE
EZ BEAD
EZ GREASER
EZ SHOT
EZVIEW
FALCON
FAST-BALL
FAST-FLO
FAST TRACK
FF
FIELDLAZER
FILMSTAR
FINEX
FINISHING TOUCH
FINISHPRO
FIRE-BALL
FIRST CHOICE WHEN QUALITY COUNTS
FIRST NAME FIRST CHOICE
FLEX PLUS
FLEXBEAM
FLEXHEAD
FLEXI-MONITOR
FLEXPRO
FLOCONTROL
FLUID COMMANDER
FOAM CAT
FTX
FUSION
G
G-15
G-40
G DESIGN
G FORCE
G HYDRA-MIX
GEAR METERS
GEDI
GEOSPERSE
GH
GLASCRAFT
GMAX
GMXXX
GRACO
GREASE JOCKEY
GTS-980
GUN FLUSH BOX
GUSMER
H2700
H3700
HANDTITE
HIGH-FLO
HORIZON
HOT SHOT
HP
HP CAM DRIVE
HURRICANE
HUSKY
HVLP 2500
HVLP 3800
HVLP 4900
HYBRID COMMANDER
HYDRA-CAT
HYDRA-CLEAN
HYDRA-MATE
HYDRA-SPRAY
HYDRAMAX
HYDRAPORT
ICEBLASTER
IMPERIAL
INFINITE RADIUS LOCK-IN
INFORMER
INJECTO-FLO
INSTACLEAN
KING-SHROUD
KWIK-TIP
L1900
LCC/DISPENSIT
LEGEND
LINEDRIVER
LINELAZER
LIQUID CONTROL
LIQUID CONTROL & DESIGN
LIQUID CONTROL CORPORATION
LITTLE MAN & GUN
LITTLE PURGE
LOC DOT
LSA
LSR
LTI
LUBE MASTER
LUBEMASTER
THE LUBRICATION PROFESSIONALS (SM) - SERVICE MARK
LUBRIQUIP
LUBRIQUIP LUBRICATING & DISPENSING SOLUTIONS
LUBRISYSTEM
M2300
MAGNUM
MAGNUM DX
MAGNUM RS PRO
MAGNUM TEXFINISH
MAN & GUN
MANAGED EQUIPMENT PROGRAM
MANZEL
MARK V
MATRIX
MAX FLO
MAXI-FLO
MAXI-MONITOR
MAXIM
MAXLIFE
MEGA
MEGA-FLO
MEP
MERKUR
METER MIST
METERFLO
MICROPOINT
MILL-GARD
MINI MIX
MISCELLANEOUS DESIGN
MISCELLANEOUS DROP DESIGN
MMV
MOD-PLUS
MODU-FLO
MONARK
MONARK-SHROUD
MONOPLANE
MULTI FLO
MULTIFLOW
NGM ROADWARRIOR
NOVA
NOVAPLUS
NOVAPRO
NOVASP
NOVASPX
NXT
NYLINER
OIL KING
OILACE
OM 5
OM 5000
ONESEAL
OPCO
OPCONET
OPTIMISER
ORANGE (TIP COLOR)
ORION
P2390
PACKING SEAL
PAINT SAVER
PAINTER'S TEAM
PARADYNE
PERFORMANCE 390
PERFORMANCE MAX 395
PERFORMANCE MAX 495
PERFORMANCE SERIES
PISTON PUMP
PLASMACOAT
PMXXX
POCKET HEAD
POLYCARBALLOY
POSI-RATIO
POSIDOT
POSILOAD
POSIMETER
POSIMIXER
POSIPOWER
POWER FLUSH
POWER-LOCK
THE POWER-PISTON
POWER POINTS
POWER-SHOT
POWER STAR
POWERFLO
POWERSTROKE
PPM 100
PRECISION VIEW
PRECISIONDOSE
PRECISIONFLO
PRECISIONFLO LT
PRECISIONFLO PLUS

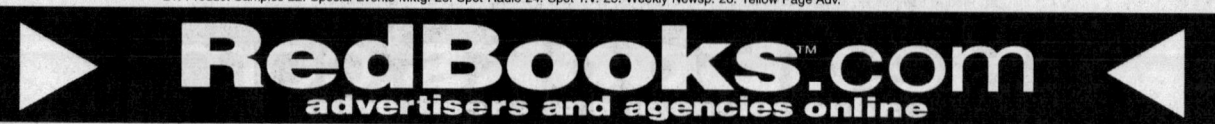

Key to Media (For complete agency information see *The Advertising Red Books-Agencies* edition):
1. Bus. Publs. 2. Cable T.V. 3. Catalogs & Directories. 4. Co-op Adv. 5. Consumer Mags. 6. D.M. to Bus. Estab.7. D.M. to Consumers
8. Daily Newsp. 9. Exhibits/Trade Shows 10. Foreign 11. Infomercial 12. Internet Adv.13. Multimedia 14. Network Radio
15. Network T.V. 16. Newsp. Distr. Mags. 17. Other 18. Outdoor (Posters, Transit) 19. Point of Purchase20. Premiums, Novelties
21. Product Samples 22. Special Events Mktg. 23. Spot Radio 24. Spot T.V. 25. Weekly Newsp. 26. Yellow Page Adv.

PRECISIONMIX
PRECISIONSWIRL
PREMIER
PRESIDENT
PRESIDENT-SHROUD
PRESTO-PAK
PRINCE
PRO BATCH
PRO DISPENSE
PRO WASH
PRO XS
PROBATCH
PROCART
PROCOMP
PRODISPENSE
PROFILL CORP.
PROMIX
PROMIX AUTO
PROSTART
PROTOTE
PROVEN QUALITY LEADING TECHNOLOGY
PROXXXX
PTXXXX
PUMP ARMOR
PUMP DEFENDER
PUMP LIFE
PUMP WORKS
PUMPORTATION
PYLES
QUICK-CLOSE
QUICK-FIX
QUICK-LOCK CYLINDER PIN
QUICK-SHOT
QUICKFLO
QUIK-OUT
QUIK PARTS PLUS PROGRAM (SM) - SERVICE MARK
QUIKACCESS
QUIKCHANGE
QUIKPIN
QUIKSELECT
RAC
RAC X
RACPAK
RAZOR
REACTOR
REDI-SPRAY
REGULUS
RENTAL-ZIP
RENTALPRO
REVERSE-A-CLEAN
REVOLUTIONIZING ROBOTICS
RIM CELL PRIME MIX
RIM EXCEL
RIM FUSION
RIM POLYMER
RIM SUPRAMIX
RIMCELL
RIMCELL ACE
RIMCELL SELECT
RIMPAK
RIMSPRAY
ROADLAZER
ROOF RIGS
ROTOBLAST
ROTOFLEX
RPX
RS-7
RTX
SELECT COMFORT GRIP
SENATOR
SERIES FLO
SG1
SG1-EF
SG2
SG3
SHARPE
SHARPE S
SHOT
SHOT FOAM
SILVER PLUS
SMART DISPLAY
SMARTCONTROL
SMARTMIX
SMOOTH GLIDE
SNAPACTION
SNAPBACK
SOFT-SURROUND
SP
SPACKMAX
SPOTWHEEL
SPRAY CENTER
SPRAY GUN (DESIGN)
SPX
SR
ST
STRATAMIX
STX
SUPER-FLEX
SUPER NOVA 700
SUPER-ZIP
SUPERCAT
SUPERMIX
SUPERNOVAPRO
SUPERSHOT
SWITCH TIP
SWIVELHOSE
SYSTEM 2500
SYSTEM 3800
SYSTEM 4900
SYSTEM-PROCART
SYSTEM-PROCOMP
TEX FINISH
TEXSPRAY
TEXSPRAY RTX 1000
TEXSPRAY RTX 750
TF
THERM-O-FLOW
THRIF-T-LUBER
TILTBACK
TIP SEAL
TOOL TOTE
TOTAL FLUID MANAGEMENT SYSTEM
TRABON
TRITON
TRIUMPH
TSL
TSU
TUFF-STACK
TURBOFORCE
TURFLINER
TWINCOOL
TWINFLOW
TWINMIXER
TWISTORK
TX
ULTIMATE
ULTIMATE MX
ULTIMATE NOVA
ULTIMATE PLUS
ULTRA
ULTRA-FLEX
ULTRA-FLO
ULTRA-LITE
ULTRA-MIX
UNDERLOCK
UNI-TIP
UNIDRUM
V-COMP
V-MAX BLUE
VALUEMIX
VISCON
VISCOUNT
VXXXX
WATCHDOG PUMP PROTECTION SYSTEM
WB100
WIDERAC
X-PACK
X-PLUS
XL POWER-PISTON
XTREME
XTREME POWER-PISTON
XTREMEMIX
XTREMESEALS
ZINC-RIG
ZIP-CLEAN
ZIP-CLIP
ZIP-ROLL
ZIP-SPRAY
ZIP SPRAY-N-ROLL
ZIP-TEX
ZIP-TIP

GRADCO HOLDINGS, LLC

371 Coronado Center Dr Ste 200
Henderson, NV 89052
Tel.: (702) 940-2266
E-mail: sales@gradco.com
Web Site: www.gradco.com
Sales Range: $10-24.9 Million
Approx. Number Employees: 35
Year Founded: 1973
Business Description:
Supplier of Paper Handling Equipment to the Office Automation Market
S.I.C.: 3555; 3577; 3579; 3861
N.A.I.C.S.: 333293; 333313; 333315; 334119
Import
Media: 10

GRAPHITE METALLIZING CORPORATION

1050 Nepperhan Ave
Yonkers, NY 10703
Tel.: (914) 968-8400
Fax: (914) 968-8468
E-mail: sales@graphalloy.com
Web Site: www.graphalloy.com
E-Mail For Key Personnel:
Sales Director: sales@graphalloy.com
Sales Range: $25-49.9 Million
Approx. Number Employees: 60
Year Founded: 1913
Business Description:
Graphalloy Mechanical & Electro-Mechanical Products Mfr
S.I.C.: 3624
N.A.I.C.S.: 335991
Media: 2-4-7-10
Distr.: Natl.
Personnel:
Eben Walker *(Pres)*
Eric Ford *(Dir-Sls & Mktg)*
Brands & Products:
GRAPHALLOY

GRAVER TECHNOLOGIES LLC

(Sub. of Marmon Water Treatment)
200 Lake Dr
Glasgow, DE 19702-3319
Tel.: (302) 731-1700
Fax: (302) 731-1707
E-mail: info@gravertech.com
Web Site: www.gravertech.com
Sales Range: $75-99.9 Million
Approx. Number Employees: 165
Year Founded: 1993
Business Description:
Industrial Filtration, Separation & Purification Products
S.I.C.: 3559; 3564
N.A.I.C.S.: 333298; 333411
Media: 10
Personnel:
John Schroeder *(Pres)*
Bill Cummings *(VP & Gen Mgr-Liquid Filters)*
John McPeak *(VP & Gen Mgr-Utilities)*
Mike Butz *(VP-Fin & Admin)*
John Weaver *(VP-Sls & Mktg)*

GRAVOGRAPH-NEW HERMES

(Sub. of Gravograph Industrie International S.A.)
2200 Northmont Pkwy
Duluth, GA 30096-5895
Tel.: (770) 623-9697
Fax: (770) 533-7637
Toll Free: (800) 843-7637
E-mail: sales@newhermes.com
Web Site: www.gravograph.com
E-Mail For Key Personnel:
Sales Director: sales@gravograph_newhermes.com
Approx. Number Employees: 70
Year Founded: 1938
Business Description:
Engraving Technology Services
S.I.C.: 3555; 5162
N.A.I.C.S.: 333293; 424610
Advertising Expenditures: $300,000
Media: 2-4-8-10-26
Distr.: Intl.; Natl.
Budget Set: Jan.
Personnel:
Gerard Guyard *(Chm)*
Joe Crydle *(CFO & VP-Fin)*
Brands & Products:
2 PLEX
ENGRAVOGRAPH
GRAVOFLEX
GRAVOPLY
METALLEX
NHI 1219
NHI 810

GRC ENTERPRISES, INC.

(d/b/a Taylor Chain)
3477 Watling St
East Chicago, IN 46312-1708
Mailing Address:
PO Box 481
East Chicago, IN 46312-0481
Tel.: (219) 932-2220
Fax: (219) 397-8884
Toll Free: (800) 352-4246
E-mail: taylorchain@taylorchain.com
Sales Range: Less than $1 Million
Approx. Number Employees: 15
Business Description:
Industrial Link-Type Chains Mfr
S.I.C.: 3496; 7629
N.A.I.C.S.: 332618; 811219
Export
Media: 2-4-6-26
Distr.: Natl.
Budget Set: Nov.-Dec.
Personnel:
Gerhard Volkmann *(Pres)*
Robert Volkmann *(VP-Sls)*
Fred Craute *(Dir-Sls)*
Brands & Products:
MAGNET-MASTER

Key to Media (For complete agency information see *The Advertising Red Books-Agencies* edition):
1. Bus. Publs. 2. Cable T.V. 3. Catalogs & Directories. 4. Co-op Adv. 5. Consumer Mags. 6. D.M. to Bus. Estab.7. D.M. to Consumers 8. Daily Newsp. 9. Exhibits/Trade Shows 10. Foreign 11. Infomercial 12. Internet Adv.13. Multimedia 14. Network Radio 15. Network T.V. 16. Newsp. Distr. Mags. 17. Other 18. Outdoor (Posters, Transit) 19. Point of Purchase20. Premiums, Novelties 21. Product Samples 22. Special Events Mktg. 23. Spot Radio 24. Spot T.V. 25. Weekly Newsp. 26. Yellow Page Adv.

GREENE, TWEED & CO.
2075 Detwiler Rd
Kulpsville, PA 19443
Mailing Address:
PO Box 207
Kulpsville, PA 19443-0305
Tel.: (215) 256-9521
Fax: (215) 256-0189
E-mail: webmaster@gtweed.com
Web Site: www.gtweed.com
Sales Range: $150-199.9 Million
Approx. Number Employees: 1,200
Year Founded: 1863
Business Description:
Gaskets, Packing & Sealing Devices
S.I.C.: 3053
N.A.I.C.S.: 339991
Import Export
Media: 2-4-10-13
Personnel:
Kevin J. Lukiewski *(CFO)*
Brands & Products:
ACGT
ACGTL
ACT
ADVANCAP
AGT
AGTL
AR
ARLON
AVALON
BARREL SEAL
CELE-CONNECT
CGT
CHEM-F
CHEMRAZ
CHEMTYTE
D-W ROD SEAL
DOVETAIL
ENER-CAP
ENERLIP
ENVIROCAM
ENVIROTIGHT
EXTENSIS
FIBER-PROTEC
FLUORAZ
FLUOROMER
G-T
GLIDETEC
GREENE TWEED
GTB
GTL
GTU
HERMACRIMP
THE INSIDE ADVANTAGE
MSE
NYSILON
ORTHTEK
ROTALIP
ROTOLON
RSA SEAL
RSR
RSS
SEAL-CONNECT
SELE-CONNECT
ST-DRY
STATIC FACE
SUPERFLEX
VORAZ
WR
XACTACPAK
XYCOMP
XYFLUOR

GROSCHOPP, INC.
(Sub. of Groschopp AG)
420 15th St NE
Sioux Center, IA 51250-2115
Tel.: (712) 722-4135
Fax: (712) 722-1445
Toll Free: (800) 829-4135
E-mail: info@groschopp.com
Web Site: www.groschopp.com
Sales Range: $10-24.9 Million
Year Founded: 1941
Business Description:
Mfr. of Custom FHP Motors, Gearmotors & Reducers
S.I.C.: 3621; 5063
N.A.I.C.S.: 335312; 423610
Import Export
Advertising Expenditures: $200,000
Media: 2-4
Distr.: Intl.; Natl.
Budget Set: Oct.
Personnel:
John S. Maatman *(Mgr-Sls)*
Brands & Products:
GROSCHOPP
MOTORTEC
STP PLUS

GROSSENBURG IMPLEMENT, INC.
31341 US Hwy 18
Winner, SD 57580-6484
Tel.: (605) 842-2040
Fax: (605) 842-3485
Toll Free: (800) 658-3440
E-mail: grossenburgs@gwtc.net
Web Site: www.grossenburg.com
Approx. Number Employees: 65
Year Founded: 1937
Business Description:
Own & Operate Wholesale & Retail Stores; Sales of Farm Machinery, Tires & Appliances
S.I.C.: 5083; 7699
N.A.I.C.S.: 423820; 811310
Advertising Expenditures: $75,000
Media: 8-22-23-24-25
Personnel:
Gene C. Grossenburg *(Co-Owner)*
Marilyn Grossenburg *(Co-Owner)*
Barry Grossenburg *(Pres)*
Doug Percy *(Office Mgr & Controller)*
Charlie Grossenburg *(Mgr-Winner Store & Mgr-Corp Sls)*
Ray Hannett *(Mgr-Sls)*

GROVE U.S. LLC
(Sub. of Manitowoc Crane Companies, Inc.)
1565 Buchanan Trail E
Shady Grove, PA 17256
Mailing Address:
PO Box 21
Shady Grove, PA 17256
Tel.: (717) 597-8121
Fax: (717) 597-4062
Web Site:
www.manitowoccranes.com/MCG_GRO/Home/EN/BrandHome.asp
Sales Range: $150-199.9 Million
Approx. Number Employees: 2,400
Year Founded: 1947
Business Description:
Mfr of Mobile Hydraulic Cranes & Self Propelled Aerial Work Platforms
S.I.C.: 3499
N.A.I.C.S.: 332999
Export
Advertising Expenditures: $3,000,000
Media: 1-2-5-10
Distr.: Intl.; Natl.
Budget Set: Aug. -Sept.
Personnel:
Jeff Brundell *(Mng Dir)*
Ingo Schiller *(Sr VP-Sls-Grove Crane)*
Dave Hull *(Dir-Sls)*
Chris Bratthauar *(Mgr-Adv)*
Brands & Products:
GROVE
NATIONAL CRANE
POTAIN

GRUNDFOS PUMPS CORPORATION
(Sub. of Grundfos Management A/S)
17100 W 118th Ter
Olathe, KS 66061
Tel.: (913) 227-3400
Fax: (913) 227-3500
E-mail: partnerservices@us.grundfos.com
Web Site: www.us.grundfos.com
Approx. Number Employees: 115
Business Description:
Pump Sales & Distr
S.I.C.: 5084
N.A.I.C.S.: 423830
Personnel:
Bill May *(Pres)*
Advertising Agency:
Callahan Creek, Inc.
805 New Hampshire St
Lawrence, KS 66044-2739
Tel.: (785) 838-4774
Fax: (785) 838-4033

GUSHER PUMPS, INC.
(Sub. of Ruthman Pump & Engineering Inc.)
22 Ruthman Dr
Dry Ridge, KY 41035-9784
Tel.: (859) 824-5001
Fax: (859) 824-3011
E-mail: info@gusher.com
Web Site: www.gusher.com
Approx. Number Employees: 100
Year Founded: 1912
Business Description:
Mfr. of Industrial Pumps & Valves
S.I.C.: 3561
N.A.I.C.S.: 333911
Export
Media: 2-7
Distr.: Natl.
Personnel:
Thomas R. Ruthman *(Owner & Pres)*
Larry Conrad *(Gen Mgr-Sls)*
Becky Bowen *(Mgr-Expediting)*
Tim Bowen *(Mgr-Assembly)*
Buford Doane *(Mgr-Production)*
Sherry Kelley *(Mgr-Pur)*
Brands & Products:
FULFLO SPECIALTIES
GUSHER
PIONEER
RUTHMAN PUMPS

HACO-ATLANTIC, INC.
(Sub. of Haco N.V.)
11629 N Houston Rosslyn Rd
Houston, TX 77086
Tel.: (281) 445-3985
Fax: (281) 445-3989
E-mail: sales.tx@hacoatlantic.com
Web Site: www.hacoatlantic.com
E-Mail For Key Personnel:
Sales Director: sales.tx@hacoatlantic.com
Approx. Number Employees: 12
Business Description:
Metal Forming Machinery Importer, Retailer & Servicer
S.I.C.: 5084
N.A.I.C.S.: 423830
Media: 10
Personnel:
Daniel Kint *(Gen Mgr)*

HAMMOND MACHINERY, INC.
1600 Douglas Ave
Kalamazoo, MI 49007-1630
Tel.: (269) 345-7151
Fax: (269) 345-1710
E-mail: sales@hammondmach.com
Web Site: www.hammondmach.com
E-Mail For Key Personnel:
Sales Director: sales@hammondmach.com
Approx. Sls.: $9,000,000
Approx. Number Employees: 40
Year Founded: 1881
Business Description:
Mfr. of Abrasive Belt Grinders, Polishing & Buffing Machines, Dust Collectors
S.I.C.: 3541; 5085
N.A.I.C.S.: 333512; 423840
Media: 2-4-7-10-17
Distr.: Natl.
Personnel:
Robert Hammond *(Pres)*
Chuck J. Aldrich *(Mgr-Svc)*
Brands & Products:
DUSKOLECTORS
MULTI-PASS
ROTO-MAX
SPIRABLAST
SPIRATRON
VIBRATRON

HANNAY REELS INC.
553 State Rte 143
Westerlo, NY 12193-0159
Tel.: (518) 797-3791
Fax: (518) 797-3259
Fax: (800) 733-5464
Toll Free: (877) GOREELS
E-mail: reels@hannay.com
Web Site: www.hannay.com
E-Mail For Key Personnel:
Marketing Director: advertising@hannay.com
Sales Director: dave@hannay.com
Approx. Number Employees: 150
Year Founded: 1933
Business Description:
Mfr. of Reels to Handle Hose & Electric Cable
S.I.C.: 3499
N.A.I.C.S.: 332999
Export
Advertising Expenditures: $1,100,000
Media: 1-2-4-5-7-8-10-11-17-19-20
Distr.: Intl.; Natl.
Budget Set: Oct. -Nov.
Personnel:
Roger A. Hannay *(Pres)*
Elaine A. Gruener *(VP-Mktg & HR)*
Edward Rash *(Dir-Adv & PR)*
Mike Ferguson *(Mgr-Production)*
Brands & Products:
CORE
GUIDEMASTER
HANNAY REELS
THE REEL LEADER.
SUPER BOOSTER

Key to Media (For complete agency information see *The Advertising Red Books-Agencies* edition):
1. Bus. Publs. 2. Cable T.V. 3. Catalogs & Directories. 4. Co-op Adv. 5. Consumer Mags. 6. D.M. to Bus. Estab.7. D.M. to Consumers
8. Daily Newsp. 9. Exhibits/Trade Shows 10. Foreign 11. Infomercial 12. Internet Adv.13. Multimedia 14. Network Radio
15. Network T.V. 16. Newsp. Distr. Mags. 17. Other 18. Outdoor (Posters, Transit) 19. Point of Purchase20. Premiums, Novelties
21. Product Samples 22. Special Events Mktg. 23. Spot Radio 24. Spot T.V. 25. Weekly Newsp. 26. Yellow Page Adv.

Advertising Agency:
Gelia-Media, Inc.
390 S Youngs Rd
Williamsville, NY 14221
Tel.: (716) 629-3200
Fax: (716) 629-3299
(Hose & Cable Reels)

HARDINGE INC.

1 Hardinge Dr
Elmira, NY 14903
Mailing Address:
PO Box 1507
Elmira, NY 14902-1507
Tel.: (607) 734-2281
Fax: (607) 732-4925
Toll Free: (800) 843-8801
E-mail: info@hardinge.com
Web Site: www.hardinge.com
Approx. Sls.: $257,007,000
Approx. Number Employees: 1,189
Year Founded: 1890
Business Description:
Machine Tools Mfr & Distr
S.I.C.: 3541; 3545
N.A.I.C.S.: 333512; 333515
Import Export
Advertising Expenditures: $2,000,000
Media: 1-2-4-7-10-11-13-16-18-20
Distr.: Intl.; Natl.
Budget Set: Oct.
Personnel:
Richard L. Simons *(Pres & CEO)*
James P. Langa *(Sr VP-Ops-Asia)*
Douglas C. Tifft *(Sr VP-Admin)*
Brands & Products:
AHC
AUTOLOAD
BRIDGEPORT
CHNC
COBRA
CONQUEST
DEAD-LENGTH
ELITE
HANSVEDT
HAR-MATIC
HARCRETE
HARDINGE
HARDINGE CHNC II SUPER-PRECISION
HAUSER
HLV
HYDROGLIDE
KEL-VARIA
KEL-VISION
KELLENBERGER
LEADER BY DESIGN
QUEST
SUPER-PRECISION
SURE-GRIP
TALENT
TFB
TRIPET
TSCHUDIN
TWIN-TURN
VARI-GRIP
Advertising Agency:
Riger Advertising Agency, Inc.
53 Chenango St
Binghamton, NY 13902
Tel.: (607) 723-7441
Fax: (607) 723-7623

HARIG MANUFACTURING CORPORATION

5757 W Howard St
Niles, IL 60714-4012
Tel.: (847) 647-9500
Fax: (847) 647-8351
E-mail: sales@harigmfg.com
Web Site: www.harigmfg.com
E-Mail For Key Personnel:
Sales Director: sales@harigmfg.com
Approx. Number Employees: 25
Business Description:
Grindall Fixture, Metal Stampings & Dies Mfr
S.I.C.: 3545; 3544
N.A.I.C.S.: 333515; 333514
Advertising Expenditures: $200,000
Media: 2-4-7-10-20-26
Distr.: Natl.
Budget Set: Sept.

HARRINGTON HOISTS, INC.

401 W End Ave
Manheim, PA 17545-1754
Tel.: (717) 665-2000
Fax: (717) 665-2861
Toll Free: (800) 233-3010
E-mail: hessdc@harringtonhoists.com
Web Site: www.harringtonhoists.com
Sales Range: $50-74.9 Million
Approx. Number Employees: 85
Year Founded: 1876
Business Description:
Mfr. of Manual & Electric Chain Hoists & Overhead Traveling Bridge Cranes
S.I.C.: 3536
N.A.I.C.S.: 333923
Import
Advertising Expenditures: $250,000
Media: 2-4-5-7-10-13-20-26
Distr.: Natl.
Budget Set: Jan.
Personnel:
Med Hunter *(Pres & CEO)*
Carlo Lonardi *(VP-Sls & Mktg)*
Hope Arment *(Mgr-Customer Svc)*
Chris Hess *(Mgr-Engrg & Quality)*
Brands & Products:
HARRINGTON
JOIN THE REVOLUTION
MINI-CAT
Advertising Agency:
Godfrey Advertising
40 N Christian St
Lancaster, PA 17602
Tel.: (717) 393-3831
Fax: (717) 393-1403
(Hoists & Cranes)

HARRIS HOLDINGS INC.

(d/b/a Insect-O-Cutor)
1641 Lewis Way
Stone Mountain, GA 30083
Tel.: (770) 939-2835
Fax: (770) 621-0100
E-mail: info@insect-o-cutor.com
Web Site: www.insect-o-cutor.com
E-Mail For Key Personnel:
Sales Director: sales@insect-o-cutor.com
Approx. Number Employees: 19
Year Founded: 1938
Business Description:
Mfr. of Electrical Flying Insect Control Equipment
S.I.C.: 3648; 3643
N.A.I.C.S.: 335129; 335931
Export
Media: 2-4-7-8-10-11-13-20
Distr.: Intl.; Natl.
Budget Set: Nov.
Brands & Products:
GERM-O-RAY
GOLD LABEL
GUARDIAN
INSECT-O-CUTOR
IOC
Advertising Agency:
J&J Promotions
1641 Lewis Way
Stone Mountain, GA 30083-1107
Tel.: (770) 939-2835
Fax: (770) 621-0100
(Insect Light Traps)

THE HARRIS PRODUCTS GROUP

(Div. of Lincoln Electric Holdings, Inc.)
2345 Murphy Blvd
Gainesville, GA 30504-6001
Tel.: (770) 536-8801
Fax: (770) 535-0544
Toll Free: (800) 241-0804
Web Site:
www.harrisproductsgroup.com/
Sales Range: $50-74.9 Million
Approx. Number Employees: 160
Year Founded: 1905
Business Description:
Gas Welding Equipment Mfr
S.I.C.: 3548; 3612
N.A.I.C.S.: 333992; 335311
Import Export
Media: 2-4-5-7-10-19
Distr.: Natl.
Personnel:
Dave Nangle *(Pres & CEO)*
Greg Lingstone *(VP-Sls)*
Ira Bennett *(Dir-Mktg)*
Jeff Crawford *(Dir-IT)*
Marco Giannelli *(Dir-Engrg, Quality, Global Production Mgmt, R & D)*
Barbara Buganza *(Mktg Mgr-Intl)*
Jean Graham *(Mgr-Bus-Intl)*
Betty Peltier *(Mgr-Sls-Intl)*
Bartosz Zynkin *(Mgr-Quality Assurance & Quality Control-Harris Calorific Intl Ltd)*
Brands & Products:
CUTWELD
CUTWELDER
FLASH GUARD
HARRIS
MULTI-STAGE
PRO SERIES
SURGE GUARD
V-SERIES

HARRIS WASTE MANAGEMENT GROUP, INC.

(Sub. of Melrose PLC)
200 Clover Reach
Peachtree City, GA 30269-1657
Tel.: (770) 631-7290
Fax: (770) 631-7299
Toll Free: (800) 373-9131
E-mail: info@harrisequip.com
Web Site: www.harrisequip.com
Approx. Sls.: $60,000,000
Approx. Number Employees: 500
Year Founded: 1889
Business Description:
Presses, Shears & Balers Mfr
S.I.C.: 3569; 3523
N.A.I.C.S.: 333999; 333111
Export
Media: 2-4-7-10-11
Budget Set: Apr.
Personnel:
Kenneth Galason *(Pres)*
Douglas Sebastian *(Sr VP)*
Chris Bryan *(VP-Fin)*
Javier Herrera *(VP-Bus Dev & Tech)*
Mike Lee *(Gen Mgr)*
Lonnie Leeman *(Dir-Quality)*
Bob Pfeffer *(Dir-Sls-US, Canada, Australia & New Zealand)*
Mark Sibley *(Dir-Customer Svc & Support)*
Randy Hengst *(Mgr-Sls-Northeast Reg)*
Jamie Johnson *(Mgr-Svcs)*
Page McDaniel *(Mgr-Sls-Mid-Atlantic Reg)*
Coleen Helland *(Supvr-Mktg)*
Brands & Products:
HARRIS
HRB
MOSLEY
SELCO
TRANS-PAK

HARSCO RAIL

(Div. of Harsco Corporation)
2401 Edmund Hwy Box 20
West Columbia, SC 29171-0020
Tel.: (803) 822-9160
Fax: (803) 822-8107
E-mail: info@harscorail.com
Web Site: www.harscotrack.com
Sales Range: $500-549.9 Million
Approx. Number Employees: 1,100
Year Founded: 1909
Business Description:
Mfr. of Railway Maintenance Equipment
S.I.C.: 3743; 3443; 3559; 3561
N.A.I.C.S.: 336510; 332313; 332410; 332420; 333911
Import Export
Media: 1-2-4-7-10-20
Distr.: Intl.; Natl.
Personnel:
Jonathan Reilly *(Mng Dir)*
Joseph Dougherty *(VP-Intl Sls & Mktg)*
Jay Gowan *(VP-Sls & Mktg)*
Tim Brake *(Sls Dir-Western Reg)*
Suzie Sine *(Sls Dir)*
Charles Stith *(Sls Dir-Asia)*
Danny Thomas *(Sls Dir-Eastern Reg)*
Nick Tosto *(Sls Dir)*
Buster Johnson *(Dir-Sls-North America)*
Glenn Newby *(Dir-Sls-North America)*
Ladislav Novotny *(Dir-Sls)*
Garner Regenovich *(Dir-Sls-North America)*
Peter Watson *(Sr Mgr-Bus Dev)*
Dereck Bartz *(Product Mgr-Rail Grinding)*
Allen Branham *(Product Mgr-Surfacing Equipment)*
Steve Byers *(Product Mgr-Track Renewal)*
Chris Larsen *(Product Mgr-Tie Equipment)*
Craig Sandsted *(Product Mgr-HY RAIL)*
Joerg Althoefer *(Mgr-Bus Dev-Europe)*
Ordell Koch *(Mgr-Sls-Intl)*
Roger Sanders *(Mgr-Hy Rail Ops)*
Susan Sheldon *(Mgr-Equipment Sls)*
M. Rick Teeter *(Mgr-Adv)*
Brands & Products:
TIE MASTERS

Key to Media (For complete agency information see *The Advertising Red Books-Agencies* edition):
1. Bus. Publs. 2. Cable T.V. 3. Catalogs & Directories. 4. Co-op Adv. 5. Consumer Mags. 6. D.M. to Bus. Estab.7. D.M. to Consumers
8. Daily Newsp. 9. Exhibits/Trade Shows 10. Foreign 11. Infomercial 12. Internet Adv.13. Multimedia 14. Network Radio
15. Network T.V. 16. Newsp. Distr. Mags. 17. Other 18. Outdoor (Posters, Transit) 19. Point of Purchase20. Premiums, Novelties
21. Product Samples 22. Special Events Mktg. 23. Spot Radio 24. Spot T.V. 25. Weekly Newsp. 26. Yellow Page Adv.

Harsco Rail — (Continued)

TOTAL QUALITY KEEPS US ON TRACK!

HARSH INTERNATIONAL, INC.
600 Oak Ave
Eaton, CO 80615-3404
Tel.: (970) 454-2291
Fax: (970) 454-3491
Toll Free: (800) 227-1702
E-mail: harsh@harshenviro.com
Web Site: www.harshenviro.com
Approx. Sls.: $20,000,000
Approx. Number Employees: 88
Year Founded: 1948
Business Description:
Mfr. of Hydraulic Cylinder Hoists, Mobile Feed Mixers & Body Combination
S.I.C.: 3523; 3536
N.A.I.C.S.: 333111; 333923
Media: 2-4-5-7-8-10-19-25
Distr.: Natl.
Budget Set: Dec.
Personnel:
Andrew Brown *(Chm)*
Bob Brown *(Pres)*
Brands & Products:
HARSH

HASKEL INTERNATIONAL, INC.
(Sub. of Hamilton Sundstrand Corporation)
100 E Graham Pl
Burbank, CA 91502-2027
Tel.: (818) 843-4000
Fax: (818) 841-4291
E-mail: sales@haskel.com
Web Site: www.haskel.com
E-Mail For Key Personnel:
Sales Director: sales@haskel.com
Sales Range: $50-74.9 Million
Approx. Number Employees: 330
Year Founded: 1946
Business Description:
Mfr. of Air Driven Liquid Pumps, Air Amplifiers & Gas Boosters For the Production, Control & Storage of Extreme Hydraulic & Gas Pressures & Electric Metering Pumps
S.I.C.: 3561; 3594
N.A.I.C.S.: 333911; 333996
Import Export
Advertising Expenditures: $100,000
Media: 1-2-4-10-11-13-18-20-26
Distr.: Intl.; Natl.
Budget Set: May
Brands & Products:
BUTECH
DURAMETER
HASKEL
HYDROSWAGE
JETFLOW
NANOJET
SAFETY ARMS
TEST PAC
TUBE-LOCK

HAUCK MANUFACTURING COMPANY, INC.
(Sub. of Elster Group GmbH)
100 N Harris St
Cleona, PA 17042
Mailing Address:
PO Box 90
Lebanon, PA 17042-0090
Tel.: (717) 272-3051
Fax: (717) 273-9882
E-mail: hauck@hauckburner.com
Web Site: www.hauckburner.com
Approx. Sls.: $15,000,000
Approx. Number Employees: 125
Year Founded: 1888
Business Description:
Industrial Oil & Gas Burners & Equipment Mfr
S.I.C.: 3433; 3564
N.A.I.C.S.: 333414; 333412
Export
Advertising Expenditures: $220,000
Bus. Publs.: $90,000; Catalogs & Directories: $40,000; Co-op Adv.: $30,000; Exhibits/Trade Shows: $60,000
Distr.: Intl.; Natl.
Budget Set: Dec.
Personnel:
Michael Shay *(Pres)*
Brian Kelly *(Gen Mgr-Sls)*
Richard A. Carpenter *(Mgr-Sls & Adv)*
Ben Gatto *(Mgr-Sys Engrg)*
Pat Horn *(Mgr-Svc)*
Brands & Products:
BBG
ECO-STAR
HAUCK PULSE FIRING SYSTEM
HMC
MBG
SSVG
SVG
TRIOX

HAYDOCK CASTER COMPANY
331 Riverview Dr
Hustisford, WI 53034
Tel.: (920) 349-4350
Fax: (920) 349-3487
Toll Free: (877) 282-1295
E-mail: info@haydockcasters.com
Web Site: www.haydockcasters.com
Sales Range: $10-24.9 Million
Approx. Number Employees: 1,000
Year Founded: 1955
Business Description:
Mfr. of Casters & Rivets, Wheels, Plastic Plugs & Tips
S.I.C.: 3089
N.A.I.C.S.: 326199
Import Export
Media: 2-4-10
Distr.: Natl.
Personnel:
Jerry Boll *(Pres)*

HEAT SEAL LLC
(d/b/a Ampak)
4580 E 71 St
Cleveland, OH 44125
Tel.: (216) 341-2022
Fax: (216) 341-2163
E-mail: custserv@heatsealco.com
Web Site: www.heatsealco.com
Approx. Sls.: $12,600,000
Approx. Number Employees: 110
Year Founded: 1950
Business Description:
Mfr for Packaging Machinery
S.I.C.: 3565; 2519
N.A.I.C.S.: 333993; 337125
Media: 2-4-7-13
Brands & Products:
AMPAK
HEAT SEAL

HELMICK CORPORATION
998 Minor Ave
Fairmont, WV 26554-3682
Tel.: (304) 366-3520
Fax: (304) 366-8923
E-mail: custserv@helmickcorp.com
Web Site: www.helmickcorp.com
Approx. Number Employees: 35
Year Founded: 1868
Business Description:
Mfr. of Boiler Tube Shields & Replacement Parts for Pulverized Coal & Ash Handling Systems for Electric Generating Stations
S.I.C.: 3369; 3599
N.A.I.C.S.: 331528; 332710
Import Export
Media: 2-4-7-11
Distr.: Intl.; Natl.
Personnel:
David G. Helmick *(Owner-Real Estate, Consultant-Investor & Wholesaler)*
Louis G. Helmick, III *(Chm & CEO)*
Bruce Gezon *(VP-Mktg)*

HELWIG CARBON PRODUCTS, INC.
8900 W Tower Ave
Milwaukee, WI 53224-2849
Tel.: (414) 354-2411
Fax: (414) 354-2421
Fax: (800) 365-3113
Toll Free: (800) 962-4851
E-mail: info@helwigcarbon.com
Web Site: www.helwigcp.com
E-Mail For Key Personnel:
Sales Director: jay.koenitzer@helwigcp.com
Approx. Number Employees: 300
Year Founded: 1928
Business Description:
Mfr. of Carbon Brushes, Mechanical Carbon Parts, Constant Pressure Brush Holders & Quick Disconnect Terminals
S.I.C.: 3624; 8733
N.A.I.C.S.: 335991; 541710
Import Export
Media: 7-10-20
Distr.: Natl.
Budget Set: Oct.
Personnel:
Jeff D. Koenitzer *(Pres)*
Mark Umhoefer *(CFO)*
Jay G. Koenitzer *(VP-Mktg)*
Paul Casper *(Gen Mgr)*
Douglas Koethny *(Mgr-Pur)*
Gale Knight *(Supvr-Acctg)*
Brands & Products:
HCP
HELWIG CARBON

HENSCHEL AMERICA INC.
(Sub. of ThyssenKrupp Materials NA)
941 Ashwaubenon St Ste G
Green Bay, WI 54304-5629
Tel.: (920) 336-4000
Fax: (920) 336-3131
Web Site: www.henschelusa.com
Sales Range: Less than $1 Million
Approx. Number Employees: 6
Year Founded: 1996
Business Description:
Foundry Machinery & Equipment
S.I.C.: 3559
N.A.I.C.S.: 333298
Media: 2-7-10-16
Brands & Products:
ANDROMAT

HERR-VOSS STAMCO, INC.
(Holding of Grey Mountain Partners, LLC)
130 Main St
Callery, PA 16024
Tel.: (724) 538-3180
Fax: (724) 538-3056
E-mail: sales@herr-voss.com
Web Site: www.herr-voss.com
E-Mail For Key Personnel:
Sales Director: sales@herr-voss.com
Approx. Sls.: $32,000,000
Approx. Number Employees: 350
Year Founded: 1909
Business Description:
Metal Working Machinery & Strip Metal Processing Machinery Mfr
S.I.C.: 3541
N.A.I.C.S.: 333512
Import Export
Advertising Expenditures: $200,000
Media: 1-2-7-8-9-10-11-17
Distr.: Intl.; Natl.
Budget Set: Nov.
Personnel:
Gary Hart *(Pres)*
Kip Mostowy *(CEO)*
Vince Meneice *(Product Mgr)*
Brands & Products:
GENCOAT
HERR-VOSS
STAMCO

HF GROUP INC.
(d/b/a Houston Fearless 76)
203 W Artesia Blvd
Compton, CA 90220-5517
Tel.: (310) 605-0755
Fax: (310) 608-1556
Toll Free: (800) 421-5000
E-mail: information@myhfi.com
Web Site: www.myhfi.com
E-Mail For Key Personnel:
President: M.S.L@houstonfearless.com
Approx. Number Employees: 125
Year Founded: 1976
Business Description:
Remedial Environmental & Industrial Water Purification Equipment Mfr
S.I.C.: 3564
N.A.I.C.S.: 333412
Export
Media: 2-7-8-10-11
Distr.: Intl.; Natl.
Budget Set: Dec.
Personnel:
James Lee *(Pres)*
Virginia Clarke *(CFO)*
Brands & Products:
EXTEK
HF
ONE COMPANY, ONE MISSION

HIGHFIELD MANUFACTURING CO.
(Sub. of Rexnord LLC)
380 Mountain Grove St
Bridgeport, CT 06605-2137
Mailing Address:
PO Box 549
Bridgeport, CT 06601-0549
Tel.: (203) 384-2281
Fax: (203) 368-3906

Key to Media (For complete agency information see *The Advertising Red Books-Agencies* edition):
1. Bus. Publs. 2. Cable T.V. 3. Catalogs & Directories. 4. Co-op Adv. 5. Consumer Mags. 6. D.M. to Bus. Estab.7. D.M. to Consumers 8. Daily Newsp. 9. Exhibits/Trade Shows 10. Foreign 11. Infomercial 12. Internet Adv.13. Multimedia 14. Network Radio 15. Network T.V. 16. Newsp. Distr. Mags. 17. Other 18. Outdoor (Posters, Transit) 19. Point of Purchase20. Premiums, Novelties 21. Product Samples 22. Special Events Mktg. 23. Spot Radio 24. Spot T.V. 25. Weekly Newsp. 26. Yellow Page Adv.

E-mail: sales@highfield-mfg.com
Web Site: www.highfield-mfg.com
Approx. Number Employees: 60
Year Founded: 1930
Business Description:
Security Systems Mfr
S.I.C.: 3699
N.A.I.C.S.: 335999
Import Export
Advertising Expenditures: $250,000
Media: 4-6-7-8-20
Distr.: Natl.
Budget Set: Sept.
Brands & Products:
ELON-O-LOCK
FIROMATIC
HIGHFIELD
REVPRO

HILL ENGINEERING, INC.

(Sub. of Formtek, Inc.)
373 Randy Rd
Carol Stream, IL 60188
Tel.: (630) 834-4430
Fax: (834) 834-4755
E-mail: info@hillengr.com
Web Site: www.hillengr.com
Sales Range: $25-49.9 Million
Approx. Number Employees: 18
Business Description:
Tooling & Special Machinery Builder
S.I.C.: 3544; 3546
N.A.I.C.S.: 333514; 333991
Export
Media: 7-10

HILMAN, INC.

12 Timber Ln
Marlboro, NJ 07746
Tel.: (732) 462-6277
Fax: (732) 462-6355
Toll Free: (888) 2ROLLIT
Telex: 283782 Hilm UR
E-mail: sales@hilmanrollers.com
Web Site: www.hilmanrollers.com
E-Mail For Key Personnel:
Sales Director: sales@hilmanrollers.com
Approx. Number Employees: 60
Year Founded: 1953
Business Description:
Mfr. of Rollers & Rolling Systems for Moving Heavy Weights
S.I.C.: 3537; 5084
N.A.I.C.S.: 333924; 423830
Export
Media: 2-4-5-7-8-10-11-18
Distr.: Intl.; Natl.
Budget Set: Dec.
Personnel:
Susan Montgomery *(VP-Fin)*
Brands & Products:
ACCU-ROLL
HILMAN
HILMAN ERF SERIES
HILMAN ERS SERIES
HILMAN FLYING FORMS SERIES
HILMAN FT SERIES
HILMAN LIGHT DUTY SERIES
HILMAN NT/NTB SERIES
HILMAN NYTON SERIES
HILMAN OT/OTB SERIES
HILMAN PIPE ROLLER SERIES
HILMAN SHD/SHD-B SERIES
HILMAN SPACESAVER ROLLERS
HILMAN TRACKMATE SERIES
HILMAN TRI-GLIDE
HILMAN TTB SERIES
HILMAN WB SERIES
HILMAN XYS SERIES
SPACESAVER

HILTI, INC.

(Sub. of Hilti AG)
5400 S 122nd Et Ave
Tulsa, OK 74146-6007
Mailing Address:
PO Box 21148
Tulsa, OK 74121
Tel.: (918) 252-6000
Fax: (918) 252-6742
Fax: (800) 879-7000
Toll Free: (800) 879-8000
E-mail: custserv@us.hilti.com
Web Site: www.us.hilti.com
E-Mail For Key Personnel:
Marketing Director: kelslea@us.hilti.com
Approx. Number Employees: 750
Year Founded: 1941
Business Description:
Mfr of Anchors, Direct Fastening Systems & Drilling Systems
S.I.C.: 3496; 3545
N.A.I.C.S.: 332618; 333515
Import Export
Media: 1-2-4-7-8-9-10-18-19-20-21-23-26
Distr.: Natl.
Budget Set: Aug.
Personnel:
Leah T. Kelso *(Dir-Mar Comm & Brand Dev)*
Brands & Products:
HILTI
KWIK-BOLT
KWIK-TOG

HOBART BROTHERS COMPANY

(Div. of Hobart Corporation)
400 Trade Sq E
Troy, OH 45373-2463
Tel.: (937) 332-4000
Fax: (937) 332-5178
Toll Free: (800) 424-1543
Telex: 28-2865
E-mail: resume@hobartbrothers.com
Web Site: www.hobartbrothers.com
Sales Range: $200-249.9 Million
Approx. Number Employees: 700
Year Founded: 1917
Business Description:
Welding Systems & Equipment, Industrial Battery Chargers, Aircraft Ground Power & Support Equipment Mfr
S.I.C.: 3548; 3559
N.A.I.C.S.: 333992; 333298
Import Export
Advertising Expenditures: $750,000
Media: 2-4-10-18-20
Distr.: Natl.
Budget Set: Jan.
Personnel:
Grant Harvey *(VP & Gen Mgr-Tubular Wire Div)*
Mark Thibeault *(Gen Mgr-Distr)*
Debra Doench *(Mgr-Adv & Comm)*
Tim Hensley *(Mgr-Tubular Wire Div-Distr Support)*
Dean Phillips *(Mgr-Welding Engrng)*
Steve Barhorst *(Engr-Welding)*
Brands & Products:
COREX
HOBART
MCKAY
PERFORMANCE WELDING
TRI-MARK

HOBART CORPORATION

(Sub. of Illinois Tool Works Inc.)
701 S Rdg Ave
Troy, OH 45374
Tel.: (937) 332-3000
Fax: (937) 332-2852
Toll Free: (888) 446-2278
Web Site: www.hobartcorp.com
Sales Range: $300-349.9 Million
Approx. Number Employees: 900
Year Founded: 1897
Business Description:
Commercial Food Equipment Mfr
S.I.C.: 3589; 3556
N.A.I.C.S.: 333319; 333294
Import Export
Media: 2-4-5-7-10-13-17-19-20-26
Distr.: Intl.; Natl.
Budget Set: Monthly
Personnel:
Ken Lee *(Pres-Hobart Svc)*
Tom Szafranski *(Pres-ITW Food Equipment Grp)*
Sarah Pauls *(Dir-Sls & Mktg)*

HOLCIM (U.S.) INC.

(Sub. of Holcim Ltd.)
6211 N Ann Arbor Rd
Dundee, MI 48131-0122
Tel.: (734) 529-2411
Fax: (734) 529-5512
Web Site: www.holcim.com/us
Approx. Rev.: $1,000,000,000
Approx. Number Employees: 300
Business Description:
Holding Company
S.I.C.: 3241; 3272
N.A.I.C.S.: 327310; 327390
Brands & Products:
CEMENT
Advertising Agency:
Ricochet Partners, Inc.
521 SW 11th Ave Ste 400
Portland, OR 97205
Tel.: (503) 220-0212
Fax: (503) 220-0213

HOLLYMATIC CORPORATION

600 E Plainfield Rd
Countryside, IL 60525-6914
Tel.: (708) 579-3700
Fax: (708) 579-1057
E-mail: hollyinfo@hollymati.com
Web Site: www.hollymatic.com
Approx. Number Employees: 55
Year Founded: 1938
Business Description:
Meat Portioning Machines, Automatic Meat Mixer/Grinders, Patty Paper, Lubricants & Supplies, Sausage Stuffers, Vacuum Packaging Machines, Vacuum Tumbling, Mixers & Juice Machines Mfr
S.I.C.: 3556; 5113
N.A.I.C.S.: 333294; 424130
Import Export
Media: 2-4-7-10-20-26
Distr.: Intl.; Natl.
Budget Set: July -Sept.
Personnel:
James D. Azzar *(Chm)*
Marilyn Krische *(Gen Mgr)*
Brands & Products:
GOURMET
HI-YIELD
HOLLY MINI-MATIC
HOLLYMATIC
THE POWER OF THE DEALER NETWORK

HOLMATRO, INC.

(Sub. of Holmatro Industrial & Rescue Equipment B.V.)
505 McCormick Dr
Glen Burnie, MD 21061-3254
Tel.: (410) 768-9662
Fax: (410) 768-4878
E-mail: info@holmatro-usa.com
Web Site: www.holmatro-usa.com
Approx. Number Employees: 50
Year Founded: 1984
Business Description:
Mfr. & Sales of Rescue Equipment
S.I.C.: 3569; 5084
N.A.I.C.S.: 333999; 423830
Import Export
Media: 1-2-4-10
Distr.: Intl.; Natl.
Personnel:
William G. Swayne *(Pres)*
Fran Dunigan *(Mgr-Mktg)*
Brands & Products:
CORE TECHNOLOGY
HOLMATRO

HORIX MANUFACTURING COMPANY

1384 Is Ave
Pittsburgh, PA 15136-2518
Tel.: (412) 771-1111
Fax: (412) 331-8599
E-mail: info@horix.net
Web Site: www.horix.net
Approx. Number Employees: 25
Year Founded: 1903
Business Description:
Liquid & Semi-liquid Filling Equipment, Capping & Closing Machines, Belt Warmers, Coolers, Bottle Rinsers & Complete Bottle Lines
S.I.C.: 3565; 5084
N.A.I.C.S.: 333993; 423830
Import Export
Media: 4-8-10
Distr.: Intl.; Natl.
Budget Set: Nov.
Personnel:
Linda Szramawski *(Pres & Exec-Fin)*
Brands & Products:
DURA-SHIELD
HORIX
HYTAMATIC
VAR-I-VOL
WALK A BEAM
WEIGHMASTER

HOSOKAWA MICRON INTERNATIONAL INC.

(Sub. of Hosokawa Micron Corporation)
10 Chatham Rd
Summit, NJ 07901-1310
Tel.: (908) 273-6360
Fax: (908) 273-7432
E-mail: info@hmps.hosokawa.com
Web Site: www.hmicronpowder.com
Approx. Number Employees: 60
Year Founded: 1985

Key to Media (For complete agency information see *The Advertising Red Books-Agencies* edition):
1. Bus. Publs. 2. Cable T.V. 3. Catalogs & Directories. 4. Co-op Adv. 5. Consumer Mags. 6. D.M. to Bus. Estab.7. D.M. to Consumers
8. Daily Newsp. 9. Exhibits/Trade Shows 10. Foreign 11. Infomercial 12. Internet Adv.13. Multimedia 14. Network Radio
15. Network T.V. 16. Newsp. Distr. Mags. 17. Other 18. Outdoor (Posters, Transit) 19. Point of Purchase20. Premiums, Novelties
21. Product Samples 22. Special Events Mktg. 23. Spot Radio 24. Spot T.V. 25. Weekly Newsp. 26. Yellow Page Adv.

Hosokawa Micron International Inc. — (Continued)

Business Description:
Mfr. of Specialized Industrial Machinery for Process Applications
S.I.C.: 3559; 2393
N.A.I.C.S.: 333298; 314911
Import Export
Advertising Expenditures: $1,000,000
Media: 2-4-7-10-17-20-26
Distr.: Intl.; Natl.
Budget Set: June
Personnel:
Rob Vorhees *(Gen Mgr)*
Brands & Products:
HOSOKAWA MICRON
MAJAC

HOSOKAWA MICRON POWDER SYSTEMS
(Div. of Hosokawa Micron International Inc.)
10 Chatham Rd
Summit, NJ 07901
Tel.: (908) 273-6360
Fax: (908) 273-7432
Fax: (908) 277-9329
Toll Free: (800) 526-4491
E-mail: info@hmps.hosokawa.com
Web Site: www.hmicronpowder.com
Sales Range: $125-149.9 Million
Approx. Number Employees: 72
Year Founded: 1923
Business Description:
Powder Process, Equipment & Systems Mfr & Engineer
S.I.C.: 3559; 2393
N.A.I.C.S.: 333298; 314911
Export
Media: 2-7-10
Distr.: Intl.; Natl.
Budget Set: July
Personnel:
Greg Boyer *(Mgr-Mktg)*
Brands & Products:
ACUCUT
MICRON AIR JET SIEVE
MIKRO
MIKRO-ACM
MIKRO-ACM CX
MIKRO-AIRLOCK
MIKRO-ATOMIZER
MIKRO-BANTAM
MIKRO-PULVERIZER
MIKRO-SAMPLMILL
NAUTA
X-PRESS MILL

HOUGEN MANUFACTURING INC.
3001 Hougen Dr
Swartz Creek, MI 48473-7935
Tel.: (810) 635-7111
Fax: (810) 635-8277
Toll Free: (800) 426-7818
E-mail: info@hougen.com
Web Site: www.hougen.com
Approx. Number Employees: 125
Year Founded: 1959
Business Description:
Mfr. of Cutting Tools, Drill Bits & Portable Holemaking Equipment
S.I.C.: 3545; 5084
N.A.I.C.S.: 333515; 423830
Import Export
Media: 1-2-4-7-10-13-17-19-20
Distr.: Natl.
Personnel:
Randall Hougen *(Pres & CEO)*
Jim Kaiser *(Mgr-Sls)*
Jeff Miller *(Mgr-Engrg)*
Brands & Products:
COOPERHEAD
EDGE
HOLCUTTERS
HOUGEN
JACOBS
OGURA
PUNCH-PRO
RATALOC
ROTABROACH
ROTACUT
ROTALOC
ROTALOC PLUS
SOLVING HOLEMAKING PROBLEMS THROUGH INNOVATION
TORNADO
Advertising Agency:
Kracoe Szykula & Townsend Inc.
2950 W Square Lake Rd Ste 207
Troy, MI 48098-5725
Tel.: (248) 641-7500
Fax: (248) 641-4779
(Rotabroach)
(Trak-Star Portable Rail)
(Drills)
(Punch-Pro Electro-Hydraulic Hole Punchers)
(Drillmate Portable Drill Presses)
(Vac-Pad)

HPM AMERICA DIVISION
(Div. of Taylor's Industrial Services, L.L.C.)
820 W Marion Rd
Mount Gilead, OH 43338-1087
Tel.: (419) 946-0222
Fax: (419) 946-2473
Approx. Number Employees: 165
Year Founded: 1877
Business Description:
Plastics Molding Machinery, Die Casting Machines & Extrusion Systems Mfr
S.I.C.: 3542
N.A.I.C.S.: 333513
Import Export
Media: 2-4-7-10
Distr.: Intl
Budget Set: Mar.
Personnel:
Christopher Filos *(Pres & CEO)*
Gerard J. Sposato *(VP-Sls & Mktg)*
Charles Clark *(Dir-Mfg)*
Ken Eichhorn *(Dir-Engrg)*
Rick Eichler *(Dir-Opers)*
William T. Purcell *(Dir-Sls & Svc)*
John Rexford *(Dir-Prod Devel)*
Dave Johnson *(Parts Mgr)*
Brands & Products:
CAST MASTER
FREEDOM LINE MACHINES
PH
PRODEX
TCO3 CONTROLS
TRUEBLOOD

HUSSMANN INTERNATIONAL, INC.
(Div. of Ingersoll-Rand Company)
(d/b/a Ingersoll-Rand Climate Control Technologies)
12999 Saint Charles Rock Rd
Bridgeton, MO 63044-2419
Tel.: (314) 291-2000
Fax: (314) 298-4756
E-mail: hussmann-marketing@irco.com
Web Site: www.hussmann.com
Approx. Number Employees: 9,100
Year Founded: 1997
Business Description:
Holding Company; Commercial Refrigeration Equipment Mfr
S.I.C.: 6719; 3585
N.A.I.C.S.: 551112; 333415
Media: 2-4-7-10-26
Distr.: Natl.
Brands & Products:
HUSSMANN
IMPACT
PROTOCOL

HYCO INTERNATIONAL INC
(Holding of Centre Partners Management LLC)
100 Galleria Pkwy Ste 1000
Atlanta, GA 30339
Tel.: (770) 980-1935
Fax: (770) 980-1936
E-mail: info@hycoweb.com
Web Site: www.hycoweb.com
Approx. Rev.: $189,058,000
Approx. Number Employees: 1,200
Business Description:
Producer of Mobile Hydraulic Cylinders
S.I.C.: 3593
N.A.I.C.S.: 333995
Media: 7-8
Personnel:
Ronald C. Whitaker *(CEO)*
Craig Wolf *(CFO)*
Kurt Wittich *(COO)*

HYDRIL PRESSURE CONTROL
(Sub. of GE Oil & Gas)
3300 N Sam Houston Pkwy E
Houston, TX 77032-3411
Tel.: (281) 449-2000
Fax: (281) 985-3480
Web Site: www.geoilandgas.com/hydril
Sales Range: $400-449.9 Million
Approx. Number Employees: 750
Year Founded: 1933
Business Description:
Petroleum Drilling Connection & Pressure Control Products Mfr
S.I.C.: 3533
N.A.I.C.S.: 333132
Export
Advertising Expenditures: $21,516,000
Media: 2-4-10
Distr.: Intl.; Natl.
Budget Set: Nov.
Brands & Products:
REDEFINING RELIABILITY

HYDRO CARBIDE INC.
(Sub. of HBD Industries, Inc.)
4439 Rt 982 S
Latrobe, PA 15650
Tel.: (724) 539-9701
Fax: (724) 539-8140
E-mail: info@hydrocarbide.com
Web Site: www.hydrocarbide.com
Approx. Number Employees: 80
Business Description:
Wear Parts
S.I.C.: 3321; 2819
N.A.I.C.S.: 331511; 325188
Media: 7
Personnel:
Paul Kuhns *(Dir-Pur)*
Advertising Agency:
GWA Communications, Inc.
5200 Upper Metro Pl Ste 110
Dublin, OH 43017-5378
Tel.: (614) 526-7015
Fax: (614) 526-7020

HYSTER-YALE MATERIALS HANDLING
(Sub. of NACCO Industries, Inc.)
650 NE Holladay St Ste 1600
Portland, OR 97232-2045
Tel.: (503) 721-6000
Fax: (503) 721-6002
E-mail: info@nmhg.com
Web Site: www.nmhg.com
Sales Range: $25-49.9 Million
Approx. Number Employees: 70
Year Founded: 1989
Business Description:
Mfr. of Trucks, Industrial Forklifts & Platforms
S.I.C.: 3537
N.A.I.C.S.: 333924
Personnel:
Michael Brogan *(Pres & CEO)*
Mike Smith *(CFO)*
Brands & Products:
HYSTER-YALE
Advertising Agency:
Jackson Marketing Group
2 Task Ct
Greenville, SC 29607
Tel.: (864) 272-3000
Fax: (864) 272-3040

IDEX CORPORATION
1925 W Field Ct Ste 200
Lake Forest, IL 60045-4824
Tel.: (847) 498-7070
Fax: (847) 498-3940
E-mail: communications@idexcorp.com
Web Site: www.idexcorp.com
Approx. Sls.: $1,513,073,000
Approx. Number Employees: 5,966
Year Founded: 1987
Business Description:
Fluid Handling & Industrial Products Mfr, Designer & Marketer
S.I.C.: 3593; 3559; 3561; 3586; 3594; 9224
N.A.I.C.S.: 333995; 333298; 333911; 333913; 333996; 922160
Export
Advertising Expenditures: $11,000,000
Media: 2-4-5-7-8-10-17-25
Distr.: Direct to Consumer; Intl.; Natl.
Budget Set: May -June
Personnel:
Lawrence D. Kingsley *(Chm, Pres & CEO)*
Heath A. Mitts *(CFO)*
Divakar Kamath *(CIO)*
Michael J. Yates *(Chief Acctg Officer & VP)*
Frank J. Notaro *(Gen Counsel, Sec & VP)*
John L. Mcmurray *(Exec VP-Process Tech)*
Kevin G. Hostetler *(VP-Fluid & Metering Tech)*
Harold Morgan *(VP-HR)*

Key to Media (For complete agency information see *The Advertising Red Books-Agencies* edition):
1. Bus. Publs. 2. Cable T.V. 3. Catalogs & Directories. 4. Co-op Adv. 5. Consumer Mags. 6. D.M. to Bus. Estab.7. D.M. to Consumers
8. Daily Newsp. 9. Exhibits/Trade Shows 10. Foreign 11. Infomercial 12. Internet Adv.13. Multimedia 14. Network Radio
15. Network T.V. 16. Newsp. Distr. Mags. 17. Other 18. Outdoor (Posters, Transit) 19. Point of Purchase20. Premiums, Novelties
21. Product Samples 22. Special Events Mktg. 23. Spot Radio 24. Spot T.V. 25. Weekly Newsp. 26. Yellow Page Adv.

Daniel J. Salliotte *(VP-Strategy & Bus Dev)*
Andrew K. Silvernail *(VP-Health, Science Tech & Global Dispensing)*

Brands & Products:
ACCULOBE
ACCUTINTER
AQUARIUS
ASA AROMA
BAND-IT
BAND-IT JR.
BAND-LOK
BLAGDON
BLENDORAMA
BOTTOM-OF-THE-BOTTLE
CAFSPRO
CELLMASTER
CENTAUR
CHEM-TECH
CHROMTRAC
CLASS 1
CLASSIC
CLASSIC ENGINEERING
COLOR-IT
COLORPRO
CORKEN
CORO-FLO
CORO-VAC
CORO-VANE
CRUISE CONTROL
DDL
DDS
DELIVERING PERFORMANCE
DINGLEE
DISCIPLINED BY OUR OPERATING MODEL
DRIVEN BY INNOVATION
DURALIFE
DURALOBE
EAR-LOKT
EASTERN
ECO
ECOLINE
ELIMA-MATIC
ES-KEY
EUROCOMBI
EUROTINTER
EZ-BANNER
FAST FLUID MANAGEMENT
FLOWMASTER
FLUSHNUT
FOAMLOGIX
FOSTER
FRIT-IN-A-FERRULE
GALILEO
GAST
GIOTTO
GODIVA
HALE
HARBIL
HERCULES
HURST
HYDRA-STOP
HYDRA-STOPPER
HYDRA-TAPPER
HYDRA-TURN
HYPOPUMP
IDEX
IP SERIES
IQ
ISMATEC
ISOCHEM
JAWS OF LIFE
JONATHAN
JR.
JUNIOR
KLE DISHMACHINES
KNIGHT
KP PUMPS
KP1H
LABPRO
LC
LCMAG
LCMASS
LCR
LCRII
LECTROCOUNT
LEOLUX
LEONARDO
LID EASE
LIFETOUCH
LUBRIQUIP
LUERTIGHT
LUKAS
MAGNUM
MAGNUS
MANZEL
MARATHON
MAXIM
MAXSTREAM
MBB
MCP SERIES
MEC-O-MATIC
MICHELANGELO
MICROPRO
MICROPUMP
MICROTIGHT
MICROTRAC
MICROVISION
MIGHTYVALVE
MINI-MATIC
MPC
MRA
MS-CA
MULTIFLOW
MULTILOAD II
MULTIPLEXING
MULTIPUMP
MX
NANOFILTER
NANOFOLD
NANOMIXER
NANOPEAK
NANOPORT
NANOTIGHT
NEWTON
NO-OX
OMNI
ON-LINE
ONE SHOT
PITOMETER
PORTA-MATIC
PORTAPUMP
PRISMAPRO
PRO SERIES
PULSA SERIES
PULSAR
PULSATROL
PULSATRON
PULSATRON PLUS
PUMPERPARTS
PUREBLEND
PURUS
QFLO
QMAX
QPAK
QTWO
QUADRO
QUADRO COMIL
QUADRO VAC
QUADRO YTRON
QUANTUM
QUICK DISCONNECT
QUICK RELEASE
RAINALERT II
RCU II
REFUELERS
REGENAIR
REGLO
REPORTER
RHEBUILD
RHEFLEX
RHEODYNE
ROC-R
RTP
SAMPI
SANDPIPER
SCRU-LOKT
SEALTIGHT
SELF-LOK
SHADOW
SKANDEX
SLUDGEMASTER
SPIRAL-LINK
SPONSLER
SPRAY GUARD
STAINLESS MAX
STERILOBE
SUPER FLANGELESS
SYSTEC
TDS
TELEFLO
THRIFTOOL
TIE-DEX
TIE-LOK
TINTIA
TINTMASTER
TINYTIGHT
TITANCL
TITANEX
TITANHP
TITANHT
TIZIANO
TORRENT
TRA SERIES
TRABON
TRANQUILIZER
TREBOR
TRI-LOKT
TYPHOON
ULTR-LOK
ULTRA-MATIC
ULTRALIFE
UNICOVER
UNITECH
UPCHURCH SCIENTIFIC
VACUTIGHT
VALUBAND
VALUCLIPS
VALUSTRAP
VEPRO
VERSA-DOME
VERSA-MATIC
VERSA-RUGGED
VERSA-SENSE
VERSA-TUFF
VETTER
VI-CORR
VICAN
VIKING
VIKING MAG DRIVE
VIKING PUMP
VINCENT
WARREN RUPP
ZFR
ZHCR

Advertising Agency:
MarketSense
7020 High Grove Blvd
Burr Ridge, IL 60527-7599
Tel.: (630) 654-0170
Fax: (630) 654-0302
Toll Free: (800) 827-0170

ILLINOIS TOOL WORKS INC.

3600 W Lake Ave
Glenview, IL 60026-1215
Tel.: (847) 724-7500
Fax: (847) 657-4261
Toll Free: (800) 544-3354
E-mail: info@itw.com
Web Site: www.itw.com
Approx. Rev.: $15,870,376,000
Approx. Number Employees: 61,000
Year Founded: 1912

Business Description:
Fasteners, Components, Equipment, Consumable Systems, Specialty Products & Equipment Mfr
S.I.C.: 3569; 3089; 3559; 3965
N.A.I.C.S.: 333999; 326199; 333298; 339993
Export
Advertising Expenditures: $79,259,000
Media: 2-4-5-7-10-14-20-21-23-26
Distr.: Intl.; Natl.

Personnel:
David B. Speer *(Chm & CEO)*
Thomas J. Hansen *(Vice Chm)*
David C. Parry *(Vice Chm)*
E. Scott Santi *(Vice Chm)*
Ronald D. Kropp *(CFO & Sr VP)*
James H. Wooten, Jr. *(Gen Counsel, Sec & Sr VP)*
Robert E. Brunner *(Exec VP)*
Timothy J. Gardner *(Exec VP)*
Philip M. Gresh, Jr. *(Exec VP)*
Craig A. Hindman *(Exec VP)*
Roland M. Martel *(Exec VP)*
Sundaram Nagarajan *(Exec VP-Global Welding Bus)*
Juan Valls *(Exec VP)*
Jane L. Warner *(Exec VP)*
Sharon M. Brady *(Sr VP-HR)*
Allan C. Sutherland *(Sr VP-Taxes & Investments)*
Mark W. Croll *(VP-Patents & Tech)*

Advertising Agency:
Rose Communications, Inc.
720 Monroe St Ste E314B
Hoboken, NJ 07030
Tel.: (201) 656-7178
Fax: (201) 221-8734

ILPEA INDUSTRIES, INC.

(Sub. of Ilpea Inc.)
745 S Gardner St
Scottsburg, IN 47170
Tel.: (812) 752-2526
Fax: (812) 752-3563
Web Site: www.ilpeaindustries.com
Sales Range: $75-99.9 Million
Approx. Number Employees: 1,200
Year Founded: 1978

Business Description:
Mfr of Vinyl & Magnetic Profile Extrusions
S.I.C.: 3053; 3089
N.A.I.C.S.: 339991; 326199
Advertising Expenditures: $300,000
Media: 4-10-17
Distr.: Natl.
Budget Set: Dec.

Personnel:
Wayne Heverly *(Pres)*
Katrina King *(Mgr-Sls)*

Key to Media (For complete agency information see *The Advertising Red Books-Agencies* edition):
1. Bus. Publs. 2. Cable T.V. 3. Catalogs & Directories. 4. Co-op Adv. 5. Consumer Mags. 6. D.M. to Bus. Estab.7. D.M. to Consumers
8. Daily Newsp. 9. Exhibits/Trade Shows 10. Foreign 11. Infomercial 12. Internet Adv.13. Multimedia 14. Network Radio
15. Network T.V. 16. Newsp. Distr. Mags. 17. Other 18. Outdoor (Posters, Transit) 19. Point of Purchase20. Premiums, Novelties
21. Product Samples 22. Special Events Mktg. 23. Spot Radio 24. Spot T.V. 25. Weekly Newsp. 26. Yellow Page Adv.

IMI CORNELIUS INC.
(Sub. of IMI plc)
101 Broadway St W Ste 100
Osseo, MN 55369-1542
Tel.: (763) 488-8200
Fax: (763) 488-4870
Toll Free: (800) 238-3600
E-mail: publications@cornelius.com
Web Site: www.imi.plc.uk
Approx. Number Employees: 45
Year Founded: 1942
Business Description:
Beverage & Food Dispensing Equipment Mfr
S.I.C.: 3585; 3586
N.A.I.C.S.: 333415; 333913
Import Export
Advertising Expenditures: $250,000
Bus. Publs.: $37,500; Catalogs & Directories: $12,500; Consumer Mags.: $37,500; D.M. to Bus. Estab.: $25,000; Exhibits/Trade Shows: $125,000; Premiums, Novelties: $12,500
Distr.: Intl.; Natl.
Budget Set: Sept.
Personnel:
Tim Hubbard *(Pres)*
Charles Fleming *(Exec VP)*
Bob Lindell *(Exec VP)*
Brands & Products:
CORNELIUS
JET SPRAY
WILSHIRE

IMI CORNELIUS, INC.
(Sub. of IMI Cornelius Inc.)
2421 15th St SW
Mason City, IA 50401-5631
Tel.: (641) 424-6150
Fax: (641) 424-3601
Toll Free: (800) 535-4240
E-mail: publications@cornelius.com
Web Site: www.cornelius.com
Approx. Number Employees: 300
Year Founded: 1935
Business Description:
Commercial Ice & Beverage Systems, Flakers, Cubers, Dispensers, Ice Storage Bins & Carbonation Cabinets Mfr
S.I.C.: 3585
N.A.I.C.S.: 333415
Import Export
Advertising Expenditures: $250,000
Media: 2-4-7-10
Distr.: Intl.; Natl.
Budget Set: Oct.
Brands & Products:
JET SPRAY
REMCOR
WILSHIRE

IMPLANT SCIENCES CORPORATION
600 Research Dr
Wilmington, MA 01887
Tel.: (781) 246-0700
Fax: (978) 752-1711
E-mail: info@implantsciences.com
Web Site: www.implantsciences.com
Approx. Rev.: $3,474,000
Approx. Number Employees: 29
Year Founded: 1984
Business Description:
Security, Safety & Defense Industry Sensors & Detection Equipment Developer & Mfr
S.I.C.: 3812; 3829
N.A.I.C.S.: 334511; 334519
Media: 2-7-10-13
Personnel:
Glenn D. Bolduc *(Pres & CEO)*
Bruce Bower *(Sr VP)*
Roger P. Deschenes *(VP-Fin)*
Brands & Products:
ADVANCED TECHNOLOGY. EXACTING STANDARDS.
CHRONOFLEX
I-PLANT
IMPLANT SCIENCES
MICROFUSION
QUANTUM SNIFFER
VARIAN

INDEL, INC.
10 Indel Ave
Rancocas, NJ 08073-0157
Mailing Address:
PO Box 157
Rancocas, NJ 08073-0157
Tel.: (609) 267-9000
Fax: (609) 267-3537
Toll Free: (800) 257-9527
Telex: 685-1048
Web Site: www.indelinc.com
E-Mail For Key Personnel:
Sales Director: sales@inductotherm.com
Sales Range: $700-749.9 Million
Approx. Number Employees: 5,000
Year Founded: 1954
Business Description:
Holding Company; Induction Melting & Heating Products
S.I.C.: 6719
N.A.I.C.S.: 551112
Media: 2-7-10
Distr.: Natl.
Budget Set: Nov.
Personnel:
Henry M. Rowan *(Founder, Chm & Pres)*
Larry A. Krupnick *(Gen Counsel & Sec)*
Manning J. Smith, III *(Treas & Grp VP-Diversified Products & Corp Devel)*
Frank D. Manley *(VP-Fin)*
Advertising Agency:
Diccicco Battista Communications
1200 River Rd Ste 300 E
Conshohocken, PA 19428
Tel.: (215) 957-0300
Fax: (484) 342-3602

INDUCTOTHERM CORP.
(Sub. of Indel, Inc.)
10 Indel Ave
Rancocas, NJ 08073-0157
Tel.: (609) 267-9000
Fax: (609) 267-3537
Toll Free: (888) INDUCTO
Web Site: www.inductotherm.com
Approx. Number Employees: 150
Year Founded: 1954
Business Description:
Mfr. of Induction Melting Systems; Electric Resistance Melting Furnaces, Automatic Metal Pouring Systems
S.I.C.: 3567
N.A.I.C.S.: 333994
Import Export
Advertising Expenditures: $300,000
Media: 2-4-6-7-10
Distr.: Intl.; Natl.
Personnel:
Henry M. Rowan *(Chm & Pres)*
Virginia R. Smith *(Chm)*
Brands & Products:
ACUTRAK
BATCHPAC
DURA-LINE
INDUCTO-POUR
LINEMELT
MELTMINDER
MINI-HEEL
MULTI-TRAK
UNIPAC
VIP
VIP POWER TRAK

INDUSTRIAL RUBBER PRODUCTS, INC.
(Joint Venture of Thompson Street Capital Partners LLC & Lime Rock Partners)
3516 E 13th Ave
Hibbing, MN 55746
Tel.: (218) 262-5211
Fax: (218) 262-4103
E-mail: info@irproducts.com
Web Site: www.irproducts.com
Approx. Number Employees: 94
Year Founded: 1986
Business Description:
Protective Materials; Abrasion Resistant Products & Equipment; Protective Linings Designer & Producer; Owned by Thompson Street Capital & Lime Rock Partners
S.I.C.: 3069
N.A.I.C.S.: 326299
Media: 2-7-10
Personnel:
Daniel O. Burkes *(Pres & CEO)*
James Skalski *(CFO & Comptroller)*
Christopher Liesmaki *(COO & VP)*
Brands & Products:
IRACORE
IRATHANE
IRP

INGERSOLL MACHINES TOOLS, INC. (IMTA)
(Holding of Camozzi Group)
707 Fulton Ave
Rockford, IL 61103-4069
Mailing Address:
PO Box 246
Ford City, PA 16226-0246
Tel.: (815) 987-6000
Fax: (815) 987-6725
E-mail: info@ingersoll.com
Web Site: www.ingersoll.com
Approx. Number Employees: 200
Year Founded: 1978
Business Description:
Special Machine Tools Mfr
S.I.C.: 3541; 3545
N.A.I.C.S.: 333512; 333515
Advertising Expenditures: $200,000
Media: 1-2-4-7-8-10-11-20-26
Distr.: Intl.; Natl.
Budget Set: Nov.
Personnel:
Tino Oldani *(Pres & CEO)*
John Osborn *(Dir-Mktg)*
Brands & Products:
HIGH VELOCITY
MASTERCENTER
MULTI TEC

INGERSOLL-RAND COMPANY
(Sub. of Ingersoll-Rand Company Limited)
155 Chestnut Ridge Rd
Montvale, NJ 07645
Tel.: (201) 57-3 0123
E-mail: seekinfo@ingersollrand.com
Web Site: www.irco.com
Year Founded: 1871
Business Description:
Pneumatic, Hydraulic & General Machinery & Tools, Pumps, Compressors, Drilling Equipment, Locks, Bearings, Hoists, Winches, Off-Road Forklifts Mfr
S.I.C.: 3559; 3553; 3563; 3569
N.A.I.C.S.: 333298; 333210; 333912; 333999
Import Export
Media: 1-2-3-4-7-8-10-11-13-21
Distr.: Direct to Consumer; Intl.; Natl.
Budget Set: Nov.
Personnel:
Steven R. Shawley *(CFO & Sr VP)*
John W. Conover, IV *(Pres-Security Tech Sector & Sr VP)*
Steven B. Hochhauser *(Pres-Residential Solutions & Sr VP)*
Didier Teirlinck *(Pres-Climate Control Technologies Sector & Sr VP)*
Edward Schlesinger *(CFO-Indus Technologies Sector & VP-Fin)*
Marcia J. Avedon *(Sr VP-HR & Comm)*
William B. Gauld *(Sr VP-Enterprise Svcs)*
Richard W. Randall *(VP-Fin)*
Allison Aiken *(Specialist-Comm)*
Scott Lieberman *(Coord-Mktg & Bus Dev)*
Brands & Products:
ALL SEASON SELECT
BLAW-KNOX
BOBCAT
CISA
CLUB CAR
DEXTER
DOR-O-MATIC
DRESSER-RAND
FALCON
GHH-RAND
GLYNN-JOHNSON
HANDKEY
HANDPUNCH
HUSSMANN
INGERSOLL-RAND
INSPIRING PROGRESS
INTERFLEX
IVES
JOHNSTONE
KENT
KOXKA
KRACK
KRYPTONITE
LCN
LEGGE
LOCKNETICS
MARTIN ROBERTS
MONARCH
MONTABERT
NIRVANA
NORMBAU
PRECEDENT
PREMAIR
PROVENAIR
RANDI
SCHLAGE
SIERRA

Key to Media (For complete agency information see *The Advertising Red Books-Agencies* edition):
1. Bus. Publs. 2. Cable T.V. 3. Catalogs & Directories. 4. Co-op Adv. 5. Consumer Mags. 6. D.M. to Bus. Estab.7. D.M. to Consumers 8. Daily Newsp. 9. Exhibits/Trade Shows 10. Foreign 11. Infomercial 12. Internet Adv.13. Multimedia 14. Network Radio 15. Network T.V. 16. Newsp. Distr. Mags. 17. Other 18. Outdoor (Posters, Transit) 19. Point of Purchase20. Premiums, Novelties 21. Product Samples 22. Special Events Mktg. 23. Spot Radio 24. Spot T.V. 25. Weekly Newsp. 26. Yellow Page Adv.

SIMPLAIR
STEELCRAFT
THERMO KING
UNIGY
UNSTALLABLE
VON DUPRIN
ZIMMERMAN

Advertising Agency:
Noble
33 W Monroe St Ste 300
Chicago, IL 60603
Tel.: (312) 670-2900
Fax: (312) 670-7420
Toll Free: (800) 986-6253

INSTRON CORPORATION

(Sub. of Illinois Tool Works Inc.)
825 University Ave
Norwood, MA 02062-2643
Tel.: (781) 828-2500
Fax: (781) 575-5751
E-mail: webmaster@instron.com
Web Site: www.instron.com
Sales Range: $200-249.9 Million
Approx. Number Employees: 1,200
Year Founded: 1946
Business Description:
Markets & Services Materials; Structural Testing Systems, Software & Accessories Mfr.
S.I.C.: 3829; 7629
N.A.I.C.S.: 334519; 811219
Import Export
Advertising Expenditures: $200,000
Media: 2-4-7-10-11-13-17
Distr.: Intl.; Natl.
Budget Set: Nov.
Personnel:
Steve Martindale *(Pres & CEO)*
Yahya Gharagozlou *(Exec VP & Gen Mgr)*
Lorenzo Majno *(VP-Mktg)*
Darci Hunter *(Gen Mgr)*
Patty Hartsell *(Dir-Mktg Commun)*
Jim Ritchey *(Dir-Medical Devices & Biomaterials Markets)*
Stephanie Williams *(Brand Mgr-Dynatup & Dynatup Impulse)*
Bill Oneill *(Brand Mgr-Rockwell & Tukon)*
Theresa Smith *(Sls Mgr-District)*
Diana Hamblin *(Mgr-Marketing Comm)*
Frank Lio *(Mgr-Bus Team Support)*
Devang Patel *(Mgr-Quality)*
Brands & Products:
DYNAMIGHT
DYNATUP
DYNATUP IMPULSE
EXTEND
FASTTRACK
IN-SPEC
INSTRON
MERLIN
PARTNER
PRODYN
SATEC
SERIES IX
SHORE
TESTMASTER
TUKON
WILSON

INTEGRATED PAVING CONCEPTS INC.

(d/b/a StreetPrint)
55th Ave Ste 102 17957
Surrey, BC V3S 6C4, Canada
Tel.: (604) 574-7510
Fax: (604) 574-7520
E-mail: info@streetprint.com
Web Site: www.streetprint.com
E-Mail For Key Personnel:
Public Relations: pr@streetprint.com
Approx. Number Employees: 45
Year Founded: 1992
Business Description:
Paving Industry Decorative Asphalt Solutions
S.I.C.: 2951
N.A.I.C.S.: 324121
Personnel:
John C. Simmons *(Founder & Chm)*
Clark G. Quintin *(Pres & CEO)*
Janice C. Stasiuk *(CFO & Corp Sec)*
Brands & Products:
IMPRINT
IPC
RIDE-A-WAY
STONEGRIP
STREETPRINT DURATHERM
STREETPRINT LOGOTHERM
STREETPRINT PAVEMENT TEXTURING
STRETPRINT
TYREGRIP
Advertising Agency:
Margo Bates Publicity, Inc.
Ocean Park
RPO Box 45019
Surrey, BC BC V4A 9L1, Canada
Tel.: (604) 536-9501
Toll Free: (888) 581-2299

INTELITEK, INC.

(Sub. of RoboGroup T.E.K. Ltd.)
444 E Industrial Pk Dr
Manchester, NH 03109
Tel.: (603) 625-8600
Fax: (603) 625-2137
Toll Free: (800) 777-6268
E-mail: info@intelitek.com
Web Site: www.intelitek.com
Approx. Number Employees: 145
Business Description:
Developer, Producer & Supplier of Technology Training Products
S.I.C.: 5099
N.A.I.C.S.: 423990
Media: 10-13
Personnel:
Brenda K. Quinn *(CEO)*
Uri Sela *(VP-Mktg & Sls)*
Brands & Products:
PERFORMER-SV3
SCORA-ER 14
SCORBASE
SCORBOT-ER 4U
SCORBOT-ER 5PLUS
SCORBOT-ER 9

INTELLIGRATED, INC.

(Holding of Gryphon Investors, LLC)
7901 Innovation Way
Mason, OH 45040
Tel.: (513) 701-7300
Fax: (513) 701-7320
Toll Free: (866) 936-7300
E-mail: info@intelligrated.com
Web Site: www.intelligrated.com
Approx. Number Employees: 1,679
Year Founded: 2001
Business Description:
Supplier of Integrated Material Handling Systems, Services & Products
S.I.C.: 3535; 5084
N.A.I.C.S.: 333922; 423830
Media: 4-10-13
Personnel:
Jim McCarthy *(Pres & COO)*
Christopher C. Cole *(CEO)*
Edward Puisis *(CFO & Exec VP)*
Steve Crone *(CIO)*
Mark Tefend *(Gen Counsel & VP-HR-Legal)*
Greg Cronin *(Exec VP)*
Jim Sharp *(Exec VP)*
Jim McDonald *(Sr VP & Gen Mgr-Loop Sorters)*
Mike Blough *(Sr VP-Engrg)*
Dennis Gates *(Sr VP-Customer Svc & Support)*
Jim McKnight *(Sr VP-Sys Sls & Mktg)*
Royal Smith *(Sr VP-Reg Ops)*
Bryan Jones *(VP-Fin & Strategic Sourcing-Fin)*
Stephanie Chapman *(Controller)*
Michael Hession *(Gen Mgr-Order Fulfillment)*
Alfred Rebello *(Dir-Project Mgmt)*
Steve Hunt *(Mgr-Engrg)*
Patrick McLaughlin *(Mgr-Sys Sls)*
Larry Townsley *(Mgr-Sys Sls)*
Brands & Products:
I-WATCH
INCONTROLWARE
INTELLIGRATED
INTELLIPRICING
INTELLIQ

INTELLIGRATED SYSTEMS INC.

(Plant of Intelligrated, Inc.)
10045 International Blvd
Cincinnati, OH 45246-4845
Tel.: (513) 874-0788
Fax: (513) 881-5205
Approx. Number Employees: 400
Year Founded: 1932
Business Description:
Conveyor Systems Mfr
S.I.C.: 3535
N.A.I.C.S.: 333922
Export
Advertising Expenditures: $415,000
Multimedia: $40,000; Bus. Publs.: $250,000; Catalogs & Directories: $50,000; Exhibits/Trade Shows: $50,000; Yellow Page Adv.: $25,000
Distr.: Natl.
Budget Set: Nov.
Personnel:
David Leen *(Mgr-Accts)*
Emily Smith *(Mgr-Mktg)*

INTELLIGRATED SYSTEMS LLC

(Plant of Intelligrated, Inc.)
9301 Olive Blvd
Saint Louis, MO 63132-3207
Tel.: (314) 993-4700
Fax: (314) 995-2400
Toll Free: (800) 325-1596
Approx. Sls.: $150,000,000
Approx. Number Employees: 700
Year Founded: 1911
Business Description:
Mfr of Automatic Palletizers, Package Handling Conveyors & Pallet Handling Conveyors
S.I.C.: 5084; 3537
N.A.I.C.S.: 423830; 333924
Export
Advertising Expenditures: $900,000
Distr.: Intl.; Natl.
Budget Set: Oct.
Personnel:
David Baker *(CFO)*
Steve Ackermann *(Exec VP-Mfg Sys)*
Ken Thouvenot *(VP-Project Mgmt & Installation)*
Matt Wicks *(VP-Sys Engrg)*
Jerry Koch *(Dir-Product Mgmt & Corp Mktg)*
Brands & Products:
ACCUGLIDE
ACCUGLIDE PLUS
EZ SET
ZIP SORTER
ZIP SWITCH
Advertising Agency:
Koroberi
1506 E Franklin St Ste 300
Chapel Hill, NC 27514
Tel.: (919) 960-9794
Fax: (919) 960-8570

INTERNATIONAL BALER CORP.

5400 Rio Grande Ave
Jacksonville, FL 32254
Tel.: (904) 358-3812
Fax: (904) 358-7013
Toll Free: (800) 231-9286
Web Site: www.intl-baler.com
E-Mail For Key Personnel:
Sales Director: sales@intl-baler.com
Approx. Sls.: $7,646,901
Approx. Number Employees: 41
Year Founded: 1975
Business Description:
Balers (Machines Used to Compress & Compact Various Waste Materials) Mfr
S.I.C.: 4953; 3559
N.A.I.C.S.: 562213; 333298
Media: 10
Personnel:
D. Roger Griffin *(Pres & CEO)*
William E. Nielsen *(CFO)*
David B. Wilhelmy *(VP-Mktg & Sls)*

INTERNATIONAL CONTROLS & MEASUREMENTS CORP.

(d/b/a ICM Controls)
7313 William Barry Blvd
North Syracuse, NY 13212
Tel.: (315) 233-5266
Fax: (315) 233-5276
E-mail: info@icmcontrols.com
Web Site: www.icmcontrols.com
Sales Range: $10-24.9 Million
Approx. Number Employees: 350
Year Founded: 1984
Business Description:
Mfr. of Industrial Timers, Controls, Motor Starters Designed for the Heating, Ventilating, Air Conditioning and Refrigeration (HVACR) Market
S.I.C.: 3625; 3822
N.A.I.C.S.: 335314; 334512
Media: 2-4-7-10-21
Distr.: Intl.; Natl.
Budget Set: Jan. -July
Personnel:
Ronald B. Kadah *(Pres)*
Brands & Products:
ICM CONTROLS
OMNEPHASE
OMNETIME

Key to Media (For complete agency information see *The Advertising Red Books-Agencies* edition):
1. Bus. Publs. 2. Cable T.V. 3. Catalogs & Directories. 4. Co-op Adv. 5. Consumer Mags. 6. D.M. to Bus. Estab.7. D.M. to Consumers 8. Daily Newsp. 9. Exhibits/Trade Shows 10. Foreign 11. Infomercial 12. Internet Adv.13. Multimedia 14. Network Radio 15. Network T.V. 16. Newsp. Distr. Mags. 17. Other 18. Outdoor (Posters, Transit) 19. Point of Purchase20. Premiums, Novelties 21. Product Samples 22. Special Events Mktg. 23. Spot Radio 24. Spot T.V. 25. Weekly Newsp. 26. Yellow Page Adv.

International Controls & Measurements Corp. — (Continued)

RAPIDSTART
SIMPLECOMFORT

INTERSYSTEMS
(Sub. of Enduro Systems, Inc.)
9575 N 109th Ave
Omaha, NE 68142-1111
Tel.: (402) 330-1500
Fax: (402) 330-3350
E-mail: intersys@intersystems.net
Web Site: www.intersystems.net
Approx. Number Employees: 185
Year Founded: 1959
Business Description:
Material Handling Equipment Mfr & Sales
S.I.C.: 3535
N.A.I.C.S.: 333922
Export
Advertising Expenditures: $250,000
Media: 2-7-10-13
Personnel:
Walter Craig *(Chm, Pres & CEO)*
Joe Gallant *(Product Mgr)*
Gary Maggiolino *(Program Mgr-Mktg)*
Joe Zitek *(Mgr-Inside Sls)*
Brands & Products:
MATERIAL HANDLING PRODUCTS

THE INTERTECH GROUP, INC.
4838 Jenkins Ave
Charleston, SC 29405-4816
Tel.: (843) 744-5174
Fax: (843) 747-4092
E-mail: pr@intertechsc.com
Web Site: www.theintertechgroup.com
Sales Range: $1-4.9 Billion
Year Founded: 1978
Business Description:
Holding Company
S.I.C.: 6719
N.A.I.C.S.: 551112
Import Export
Media: 1-4-10
Distr.: Intl.; Natl.
Budget Set: Oct.
Personnel:
J. Tiedemann *(COO & Exec VP)*
Joseph L. Myers *(Dir-Fin)*

INTRALOX LLC
(Sub. of The Laitram LLC)
201 Laitram Ln
Harahan, LA 70123
Tel.: (504) 733-0463
Fax: (504) 733-2420
Toll Free: (800) 535-8848
Telex: 6821268
Web Site: www.intralox.com
Approx. Number Employees: 500
Year Founded: 1971
Business Description:
Mfr. of Conveyor Belting & Accessories
S.I.C.: 3535
N.A.I.C.S.: 333922
Import Export
Advertising Expenditures: $200,000
Media: 2-4-5-7-8-10-11-13-20-21
Distr.: Intl.; Natl.
Budget Set: Mar.
Personnel:
James M. Lapeyre, Jr. *(Chm & Pres)*
Lawrence P. Oertling *(CFO)*
Barry LaCour *(Gen Counsel)*
Frank Profumo *(Dir-Adv)*
Tre Lapeyre *(Mgr-Product Mktg)*
Brands & Products:
EZ ROLLER
INTRALOX
SERIES 1600
SERIES 1700
SERIES 2400
SERIES 900
Advertising Agency:
LIDGroup Inc.
200 Laitram Ln.
Harahan, LA 70123
Tel.: (504) 733-1050
Fax: (504) 733-2420

INVENSYS PROCESS SYSTEMS
(Sub. of Invensys plc)
33 Commercial St
Foxboro, MA 02035
Tel.: (508) 543-8750
Fax: (508) 549-2735
Web Site: www.invensys.com
Business Description:
Supplier of Plant Operation Automation & Optimization Products & Services
S.I.C.: 3823
N.A.I.C.S.: 334513
Media: 2-10-13
Personnel:
Mark Balcunas *(Pres-Controls Americas & APAC)*

ION GEOPHYSICAL CORPORATION
2105 CityWest Blvd Ste 400
Houston, TX 77042-2839
Tel.: (281) 933-3339
Fax: (281) 879-3626
E-mail: info@iongeo.com
Web Site: www.i-o.com
Approx. Rev.: $444,322,000
Approx. Number Employees: 915
Year Founded: 1968
Business Description:
Seismic Imaging Technology & Equipment
S.I.C.: 3829; 3824; 8713
N.A.I.C.S.: 334519; 334514; 541360
Export
Media: 5-10
Personnel:
James M. Lapeyre, Jr. *(Chm)*
Robert P. Peebler *(CEO)*
R. Brian Hanson *(CFO & Exec VP)*
David Roland *(Gen Counsel, Corp Sec & Sr VP)*
Doug Allinson *(Sr VP-Next Gen Land)*
Nick Bernitsas *(Sr VP-GXT Imaging Solutions)*
David Moffat *(Sr VP-Marine Imaging Sys)*
Tim Rigsby *(Sr VP-Strategic Initiatives)*
Ken Williamson *(Sr VP-Integrated Seismic Solutions)*
Brands & Products:
AFRICASPAN
AIRLOCK
APPLIED MEMS
ASMA
CARIBESPAN
CHARGED WITH INNOVATION
DESIGN FOR SIGNAL
DIGIBIRD
DIGICOURSE
DIGIFIN
DIGISTREAMER
DYNACON
DYNACON GEO
FASTRING
FIREFLY
GATOR
GULFSPAN
ILLUMINATOR
INDIASPAN
MESA
ORCA
PRESEIS
REFLEX
SCORPION
SPAN
SPECTRA
SPRINT
SYSTEM FOUR
SYSTEM ONE
SYSTEM TWO
TESCORP
TRUE DIGITAL
VECTOR BROADBAND
VECTORSEIS
VIB NET
VIB PRO
XVIB
XVIB-LOGO
Advertising Agency:
Axiom
1210 W Clay Ste 9
Houston, TX 77019
Tel.: (713) 523-5711
Fax: (713) 523-6083

IOWA PRECISION INDUSTRIES
(Sub. of Formtek, Inc.)
5480 6th St SW
Cedar Rapids, IA 52404-4814
Tel.: (319) 364-9181
Fax: (319) 364-3436
E-mail: sales@iowaprecision.com
Web Site: www.iowaprecision.com
E-Mail For Key Personnel:
Sales Director: sales@iowaprecision.com
Sales Range: $50-74.9 Million
Approx. Number Employees: 130
Year Founded: 1958
Business Description:
Automated Coil Processing Systems Mfr
S.I.C.: 3542; 3549
N.A.I.C.S.: 333513; 333518
Export
Media: 2-7-10-13
Brands & Products:
FMI DAHLSTROM
MULTI-PRO
SLEAR

IRVINE SENSORS CORPORATION
3001 Red Hill Ave Bldg 3 Ste 108
Costa Mesa, CA 92626-4532
Tel.: (714) 549-8211
Fax: (714) 444-8773
E-mail: investorrelations@irvine-sensors.com
Web Site: www.irvine-sensors.com
E-Mail For Key Personnel:
Sales Director: mpdsales@irvine-sensors.com
Approx. Rev.: $11,716,800
Approx. Number Employees: 67
Year Founded: 1980
Business Description:
Solid-State Microcircuitry Technology Research & Development Services
S.I.C.: 3674
N.A.I.C.S.: 334413
Media: 2-7-8-10-13
Personnel:
Seth W. Hamot *(Chm)*
John C. Carson *(Vice Chm)*
Bill Joll *(Pres & CEO)*
John J. Stuart, Jr. *(CFO, Sec & Sr VP)*
Peter Kenefick *(Gen Mgr-Thermal Imaging Div)*
Brands & Products:
3DANN
CAM-NOIR
IRVINE SENSORS CORPORATION
NEO-STACK
PMTV
TOWHAWK
UNIVERSAL CAPACITIVE READOUT
VIP/BALBOA

ITOCHU INTERNATIONAL INC.
(Sub. of ITOCHU Corporation)
335 Madison Ave
New York, NY 10017-4611
Tel.: (212) 818-8000
Tel.: (212) 818-8542 (Corp Commun)
Fax: (212) 818-8554
Web Site: www.itochu.com
Approx. Sls.: $2,147,500,032
Approx. Number Employees: 4,671
Year Founded: 1880
Business Description:
Holding Company; Textiles; Machinery; Motor Vehicles; Steel & Raw Materials; Non-Ferrous & Light Metals; Grains; Provisions; General Merchandise; Chemicals & Energy
S.I.C.: 5131; 5084
N.A.I.C.S.: 424310; 423830
Import Export
Media: 2-4-6-7-8-9-10-18-19-20-26
Personnel:
Yoshihisa Suzuki *(Pres & CEO)*
Yasuhiro Baba *(CFO & Sr VP)*
Toshio Obayashi *(Chief Admin Officer & Sr VP)*
Mitsugu Kuno *(Exec VP & Gen Mgr-Food Div)*
Naohiro Jokei *(Sr VP & Gen Mgr-Energy, Metals & Minerals)*
Eric Laptook *(Sr VP & Gen Mgr-Legal Div)*
Harutoshi Okita *(Sr VP & Gen Mgr-Machinery Div)*
Kazunobu Sakai *(Sr VP & Gen Mgr-IT & Aerospace Div)*
Hiroaki Tamamaki *(Sr VP & Gen Mgr-Textile Div)*
Ichiro Tsuge *(Sr VP & Gen Mgr-Chemical, Forest Products & Gen Merchandise Div)*
Advertising Agency:
The Gunter Agency
N9191 Cardinal Crest Ln
New Glarus, WI 53574
Tel.: (608) 527-4800

ITT CORPORATION
1133 Westchester Ave
White Plains, NY 10604
Tel.: (914) 641-2000
Fax: (914) 696-2950
Web Site: www.itt.com
Approx. Rev.: $10,995,000,000
Approx. Number Employees: 40,000
Year Founded: 1995
Business Description:
Advanced Engineering Services, Design & Mfr

Key to Media (For complete agency information see *The Advertising Red Books-Agencies* edition):
1. Bus. Publs. 2. Cable T.V. 3. Catalogs & Directories. 4. Co-op Adv. 5. Consumer Mags. 6. D.M. to Bus. Estab.7. D.M. to Consumers
8. Daily Newsp. 9. Exhibits/Trade Shows 10. Foreign 11. Infomercial 12. Internet Adv.13. Multimedia 14. Network Radio
15. Network T.V. 16. Newsp. Distr. Mags. 17. Other 18. Outdoor (Posters, Transit) 19. Point of Purchase20. Premiums, Novelties
21. Product Samples 22. Special Events Mktg. 23. Spot Radio 24. Spot T.V. 25. Weekly Newsp. 26. Yellow Page Adv.

S.I.C.: 5084; 3561; 3625; 3823; 3826
N.A.I.C.S.: 423830; 333911; 334513; 334516; 335314
Media: 2-6-10-17-19
Personnel:
Steven R. Loranger *(Chm, Pres & CEO)*
Denise L. Ramos *(Sr VP)*
Peter Milligan *(CFO)*
Carol Zierhoffer *(CIO & VP)*
Angela A. Buonocore *(Chief Comm Officer & Sr VP)*
Janice Marolda Klettner *(Chief Acctg Officer & VP)*
Robert L. Ellis *(Chief Inclusion Officer & Chief Diversity Officer)*
Gretchen W. McClain *(Pres-ITT Fluid & Motion Control & Sr VP)*
David F. Melcher *(Pres-Defense & Info Solutions & Sr VP)*
Robert J. Pagano *(Pres-Indus Process)*
Ken A. Peterman *(Pres-Comm Sys)*
William E. Taylor *(Pres-Interconnect Solutions Bus)*
Ann D. Davidson *(Gen Counsel & Sec)*
Aris C. Chicles *(Sr VP & Dir-Corp Strategy & Dev)*
Alan Gilden *(Dir-Global Strategic Sourcing Ops)*
Jon Herkins *(Dir-Americas, European & Middle East Sourcing)*
Andy Hilton *(Dir-Comm)*
Linda Mahran *(Dir-Indirect Sourcing)*
Thomas Scalera *(Dir-IR)*
Charles Dougherty *(Mgr-Stock Admin & Cash Mgmt)*
Paul Stellato *(Mgr-IR)*
Amy Taney *(Mgr-HR)*
Mary Dudley *(Specialist-Mktg)*
Kathleen S. Stolar *(Deputy Gen Counsel)*
Brands & Products:
A-C PUMP
ABJ
BELL & GOSSETT
ENGINEERED FOR LIFE
FLYGT
GOULD PUMPS
HOFFMAN SPECIALTY
HYDROVAR
ITT
ITT STANDARD
KONI
LOWARA
MCDONNELL & MILLER
N-PUMP
NIGHT ENFORCER
POSI-LOCK
PROSMART
PUMPSMART
PURE-FLOW
RED JACKET
RICHTER
SANITAIRE
VOGEL
Advertising Agency:
Doremus
(Sub. of Omnicom Group, Inc.)
200 Varick St 11Fl
New York, NY 10014-4810
Tel.: (212) 366-3000
Fax: (212) 366-3060

ITT INDUSTRIES - JABSCO
(Div. of ITT Fluid Technology Corporation)
666 E Dyer Rd
Santa Ana, CA 92705
Tel.: (714) 557-4700
Fax: (714) 628-8478
Web Site: www.jabsco.com
Sales Range: $100-124.9 Million
Approx. Number Employees: 270
Year Founded: 1941
Business Description:
Mfr. of Self Priming Flexible Impeller Pumps & Centrifugal Pumps For Industry, Marine & Recreational Vehicles
S.I.C.: 3561; 3621
N.A.I.C.S.: 333911; 335312
Export
Media: 1-2-4-5-6-7-10-11-20
Distr.: Intl.; Natl.
Budget Set: Dec. -Jan.
Brands & Products:
HOSECOIL
SENSOR-MAX

ITW DYNATEC
(Sub. of Illinois Tool Works Inc.)
31 Volunteer Dr
Hendersonville, TN 37075-3156
Tel.: (615) 824-3634
Fax: (615) 264-5248
Toll Free: (800) 860-6150
E-mail: dynatec@itwdynatec.com
Web Site: www.itwdynatec.com
Sales Range: $50-74.9 Million
Approx. Number Employees: 112
Business Description:
Industrial Adhesive Application Equipment Mfr
S.I.C.: 3559; 2891
N.A.I.C.S.: 333298; 325520
Media: 10
Personnel:
Dan Bourget *(Gen Mgr)*
Jud Broom *(Gen Mgr)*
George Hoff *(Mgr-Bus Unit)*
David Shumaker *(Mgr-Intl Sls & Market)*

ITW GEMA
(Sub. of Illinois Tool Works Inc.)
4141 W 54th St
Indianapolis, IN 46254
Mailing Address:
PO Box 88220
Indianapolis, IN 46208-0220
Tel.: (317) 298-5000
Fax: (317) 298-5010
Toll Free: (800) 628-0601
E-mail: powdersales@itwgema.com
Web Site: www.itwgema.us
Sales Range: $25-49.9 Million
Approx. Number Employees: 50
Business Description:
Powder Paint Application Equipment Mfr
S.I.C.: 5084
N.A.I.C.S.: 423830
Media: 10
Personnel:
Christopher R. Merritt *(Gen Mgr)*
Jeffrey W. Hale *(Dir-Mktg & Sls)*
Brands & Products:
AUTOTRACKER
CHAMELEON
MAGICCYLINDER
XTREME

ITW IMTRAN
(Sub. of Illinois Tool Works Inc.)
39 Shelley Rd
Haverhill, MA 01835
Tel.: (978) 372-3443
Fax: (978) 372-9817
E-mail: tbeaupre@itwimtran.com
Web Site: www.itwimtran.com
Sales Range: $10-24.9 Million
Business Description:
Pad Printing Supplies & Machine Accessories
S.I.C.: 2679; 2675
N.A.I.C.S.: 322231; 322226; 322299
Media: 10
Personnel:
Ted Beaupre *(Mgr-Bus Unit)*

IVANHOE MINES LTD.
World Trade Center Suite 654-999 Canada Place
Vancouver, BC V6C 3E1, Canada
Tel.: (604) 688-5755
Fax: (604) 682-2060
Toll Free: (888) 273-9999
E-mail: info@ivanhoemines.com
Web Site: www.ivanhoemines.com
Approx. Rev.: $79,777,000
Approx. Number Employees: 1,347
Year Founded: 1994
Business Description:
Copper & Gold Mining
S.I.C.: 1011; 1021; 1041
N.A.I.C.S.: 212210; 212221; 212234
Export
Media: 10
Personnel:
Robert Martin Friedland *(Chm & CEO)*
Peter M. Meredith, Jr. *(Deputy Chm)*
John Anthony Macken *(Pres)*
Tony Giardini *(CFO)*
David Woodall *(Pres-Gold Ops)*
Jay Gow *(VP-Mktg)*
Pierre Masse *(VP-Fin)*

JACOBS VEHICLE SYSTEMS
(Sub. of Danaher Corporation)
22 E Dudley Town Rd
Bloomfield, CT 06002
Tel.: (860) 243-1441
Fax: (860) 243-7632
E-mail: jsupport@jakebrake.com
Web Site: www.jakebrake.com
Sales Range: $100-124.9 Million
Approx. Number Employees: 100
Year Founded: 1961
Business Description:
Engine Retarders
S.I.C.: 3519; 3714
N.A.I.C.S.: 333618; 336399
Export
Media: 2-4-7-10-19-20-21-23
Distr.: Intl.; Natl.
Budget Set: Nov.
Personnel:
Robert Perkins *(VP-Mktg & Bus Dev)*
Brands & Products:
JACOBS BLEEDER BRAKE
JACOBS EXHAUST BRAKE
JAKE BRAKE
JAKE ENGINE BRAKE

JAGUAR FINANCIAL INC.
145 King Street West Suite 2020
Toronto, ON M5H 1J8, Canada
Tel.: (416) 363-1124
Fax: (416) 360-0728
E-mail: info@jaguarnickel.com
Web Site: www.jaguarfinancial.ca
Approx. Rev.: $7,984,986
Year Founded: 1956
Business Description:
Merchant Banking Services
S.I.C.: 6211; 6289
N.A.I.C.S.: 523110; 523999
Media: 2
Personnel:
Vic Alboini *(Pres & CEO)*
Doug Chornoboy *(CFO & Sr VP)*
Kyler Wells *(Gen Counsel & Sec)*
Robert Bruggeman *(Sr VP-Investments)*

JAMES L. TAYLOR MANUFACTURING CO.
108 Parker Ave
Poughkeepsie, NY 12601
Tel.: (845) 452-0691
Tel.: (845) 452-3780
Fax: (845) 452-0764
Toll Free: (800) 952-1320
E-mail: info@jamesltaylor.com
Web Site: www.jamesltaylor.com
Year Founded: 1911
Business Description:
Woodworking Machinery Mfr
S.I.C.: 3553
N.A.I.C.S.: 333210
Media: 2-10
Distr.: Natl.
Budget Set: Jan.
Personnel:
Michael Burdis *(Chm & Pres)*
Brands & Products:
CLAMP CARRIER
DP2
MIX-MIZER
OPTI-SIZER
SMART CLAMP
SUPER AUTOMATED CLAMP CARRIER

JAZZ SEMICONDUCTOR, INC.
(Sub. of Tower Semiconductor Ltd.)
4321 Jamboree Rd
Newport Beach, CA 92660-3007
Tel.: (949) 435-8000
Fax: (949) 435-8200
Web Site: www.jazzsemi.com
Approx. Number Employees: 780
Year Founded: 2002
Business Description:
Semiconductor Wafer Foundry
S.I.C.: 3674
N.A.I.C.S.: 334413
Advertising Expenditures: $200,000
Personnel:
Russell C. Ellwanger *(CEO)*
Allen R. Grogan *(Chief Legal Officer, Sr VP & Sec)*
Susanna Bennett *(Asst CFO & Exec VP)*
Marco Racanelli *(VP-Tech, Engr & Gen Mgr-Areospace & Defense)*
Andy Chan *(VP-Corp Dev & Pur)*
Daniel T. Lynch *(VP-HR)*

JBT FOODTECH MADERA
(Div. of John Bean Technologies Corporation)
2300 W Industrial Ave PO Box A
Madera, CA 93637-5210
Tel.: (559) 661-3200
Fax: (559) 661-3222
Web Site: www.fmctechnologies.com

Key to Media (For complete agency information see *The Advertising Red Books-Agencies* edition):
1. Bus. Publs. 2. Cable T.V. 3. Catalogs & Directories. 4. Co-op Adv. 5. Consumer Mags. 6. D.M. to Bus. Estab.7. D.M. to Consumers 8. Daily Newsp. 9. Exhibits/Trade Shows 10. Foreign 11. Infomercial 12. Internet Adv.13. Multimedia 14. Network Radio 15. Network T.V. 16. Newsp. Distr. Mags. 17. Other 18. Outdoor (Posters, Transit) 19. Point of Purchase20. Premiums, Novelties 21. Product Samples 22. Special Events Mktg. 23. Spot Radio 24. Spot T.V. 25. Weekly Newsp. 26. Yellow Page Adv.

JBT FoodTech Madera — (Continued)

Approx. Sls.: $20,000,000
Approx. Number Employees: 180
Year Founded: 1966
Business Description:
In-Container & In-Flow Processing Systems Mfr
S.I.C.: 3556
N.A.I.C.S.: 333294
Media: 2-4-7-10-26
Distr.: Intl.; Natl.
Budget Set: Dec.
Personnel:
Prian Perkins *(Gen Mgr)*

JERVIS B. WEBB COMPANY

(Sub. of Daifuku Co., Ltd.)
34375 W 12 Mi Rd
Farmington Hills, MI 48331
Tel.: (248) 553-1000
Fax: (248) 553-1228
Toll Free: (800) 526-9322
Telex: 211892 jwebb ur
E-mail: info@jervisbwebb.com
Web Site: www.jervisbwebb.com
Sales Range: $300-349.9 Million
Approx. Number Employees: 2,000
Year Founded: 1919
Business Description:
Material Handling Systems
S.I.C.: 3559; 3536
N.A.I.C.S.: 333298; 333923
Import Export
Advertising Expenditures: $700,000
Media: 1-2-4-7-9-10-11-13-16-20-21-26
Distr.: Intl.
Budget Set: Nov.
Personnel:
Ryuichi Kitaguchi *(Pres & Co-CEO)*
Brian G. Stewart *(Pres & Co-CEO)*
John S. Doychich *(CFO & Sr VP)*
Kenneth Hamel *(Sr VP-Airport Sys)*
Bruce Buscher *(VP-Distr, Mktg & Sls)*
Gerard Gonos *(Dir-Mfg)*
Brands & Products:
ALUMITRAK
AUTO-TRANS
D-TR DOOR
DOG MAGIC
JERVISBWEBB
LIFT-PAK
MICROLOY
MINI-CART
OVER-N-UNDER
PC/AIM
PRONTOW
RED SEAL
RED SEAL GUARD
RETRIEVER
SHALLO-TOW
SMART T CAR
STOP-N-FLOW
TOWVEYOR
TRIAX
UNIBEAM
UNIBILT
V-SORT
VSM
WEBB
WEBB ALLOY II
WEBB-KEY
WEBB-X
WEBBALLOY
WEBBVIEW
WF
Advertising Agency:
Campbell, Henry & Calvin, Inc.
34375 W 12 Mile Rd
Farmington Hills, MI 48331-3375
Tel.: (248) 553-1203
Fax: (248) 553-1228
(Conveyors)

JH INDUSTRIES, INC.

1981 E Aurora Rd
Twinsburg, OH 44087
Tel.: (330) 963-4105
Fax: (330) 963-4111
Toll Free: (800) 321-4968
Web Site: www.copperloy.com
Approx. Sls.: $3,000,000
Approx. Number Employees: 50
Year Founded: 1986
Business Description:
Material Handling Equipment; Special Contract Work; Aluminum & Steel Fabrications
S.I.C.: 3448; 3599
N.A.I.C.S.: 332311; 332710
Media: 7
Distr.: Natl.
Personnel:
John Hallack *(Pres)*
Brands & Products:
COPPERLOY

JLG INDUSTRIES, INC.

(Sub. of Oshkosh Corporation)
1 JLG Dr
McConnellsburg, PA 17233-9533
Tel.: (717) 485-5161
Fax: (717) 485-6417
Toll Free: (877) 534-5438
E-mail: comments@jlg.com
Web Site: www.jlg.com
Approx. Rev.: $2,289,400,064
Approx. Number Employees: 4,088
Year Founded: 1969
Business Description:
Specialized Hydraulic Machinery Mfr
S.I.C.: 3536; 3531; 3535; 7353
N.A.I.C.S.: 333923; 333120; 333922; 532412
Export
Advertising Expenditures: $10,000,000
Media: 2-4-5-10-18-20
Distr.: Intl.; Natl.
Budget Set: Sept.
Personnel:
Wilson R. Jones *(Pres-Access Equipment & Exec VP)*
Timothy M. Morris *(Sr VP-Sls & Mktg & Customer Support)*
Frank Cholewicki *(VP-Fin)*
Tim Hatch *(VP-Engrg)*
Chris Mellott *(VP-Sls & Market Dev-Americas)*
Bob Nelson *(VP-Sls & Svc-North America)*
Brad Nelson *(Global VP-Mktg)*
Andrew Satterley *(VP-Customer Support, Mktg & Sls-Asia Pacific Reg)*
Todd Truax *(Dir-Market Dev & Sls Ops)*
Maye Houck *(Sr Mgr-Mktg-Global)*
Brands & Products:
EASI-CLADDER
GRADALL
JLG
JLGLIFT
LULL
POWER DECK
QUIKSTICK
QUIKWELDER
SKYAIR
SKYCLEANER
SKYCUTTER
SKYGLAZIER
SKYPOWER
SKYSAW
SKYTRAK
SKYWELDER
TOW-PRO
TOWPRO
TRANSFORMER
TRIPLE-L
Advertising Agencies:
Godfrey Advertising
40 N Christian St
Lancaster, PA 17602
Tel.: (717) 393-3831
Fax: (717) 393-1403
(Aerial Work Platforms, Personnel Lifts)

Industrial Marketing Services, Inc.
2375 Touhy Ave
Elk Grove Village, IL 60007
Tel.: (847) 258-8850
Fax: (847) 593-0462

JOHN DEERE COFFEYVILLE WORKS INC

(Sub. of Deere & Company)
Hwy 169 N Industrial Pk
Coffeyville, KS 67337
Mailing Address:
PO Box 577
Coffeyville, KS 67337-0588
Tel.: (620) 251-3400
Fax: (620) 251-3250
Toll Free: (800) 844-1337
Web Site: www.deere.com/en_US/deerecom/johndeere_worldwide/index.html
Sales Range: $150-199.9 Million
Approx. Number Employees: 400
Business Description:
Specialty Hydraulic & Mechanical Power Transmissions Pump Drives
S.I.C.: 3714
N.A.I.C.S.: 336350
Import Export
Media: 2-7-9-10-16-25
Budget Set: Oct. -Nov.
Personnel:
Robert Chopp *(VP & Gen Mgr)*
Brands & Products:
FUNK

JOY GLOBAL, INC.

100 E Wisconsin Ave Ste 2780
Milwaukee, WI 53202-4127
Mailing Address:
PO Box 554
Milwaukee, WI 53201-0554
Tel.: (414) 319-8500
Tel.: (414) 486-6400
Fax: (414) 319-8510
E-mail: info@amstock.com
Web Site: www.joyglobal.com
Approx. Sls.: $3,524,334,000
Approx. Number Employees: 11,900
Year Founded: 1884
Business Description:
Mining Equipment Mfr
S.I.C.: 3532; 5082
N.A.I.C.S.: 333131; 423810
Import Export
Advertising Expenditures: $500,000
Media: 2-4-7-10-11
Distr.: Natl.
Budget Set: Nov.
Personnel:
Michael W. Sutherlin *(Pres & CEO)*
Michael S. Olsen *(CFO, Treas & Exec VP)*
Ricky T. Dillon *(Chief Acctg Officer, VP & Controller)*
Randal W. Baker *(Pres/COO-P&H Mining Equipment & Exec VP)*
Edward L. Doheny, II *(Pres/COO-Joy Mining Machinery & Exec VP)*
Eric Nielsen *(Exec VP-Bus Dev)*
Dennis R. Winkleman *(Exec VP-Admin)*
Brands & Products:
EVERYTHING IS EITHER GROWN OR MINED
JOY
P&H

JOY MINING MACHINERY

(Sub. of Joy Global, Inc.)
177 Thorn Hill Rd
Warrendale, PA 15086
Tel.: (724) 779-4500
Fax: (724) 779-4554
E-mail: contactjoy@joy.com
Web Site: www.joy.com
Sales Range: $25-49.9 Million
Approx. Number Employees: 45
Year Founded: 1920
Business Description:
Heavy Machinery Mfr
S.I.C.: 3532; 3535
N.A.I.C.S.: 333131; 333922
Import Export
Advertising Expenditures: $300,000
Media: 1-2-4-10-11-20
Distr.: Intl.; Natl.
Budget Set: Aug.
Personnel:
Louis Boltik *(Dir-Mktg Comm)*

KABA ILCO INC.

(Holding of Kaba Holding AG)
7301 Decarie Boulevard
Montreal, QC H4P 2G7, Canada
Tel.: (514) 735-5410
Fax: (514) 735-8707
Web Site: www.kaba-ilco.com
Sales Range: $300-349.9 Million
Approx. Number Employees: 250
Year Founded: 1964
Business Description:
Hotel Locks Mfr
S.I.C.: 3429
N.A.I.C.S.: 332510
Import Export
Media: 2-7-10
Personnel:
Jim Topolniski *(Mgr-Mktg)*
Brands & Products:
ACCU-BORE
GENERATION E-760
ILCO
KEIL
MILLENIUM
ORACODE
POWERLEVER
SIMPLEX
SOLITAIRE

KADANT BLACK CLAWSON INC.

(Sub. of KADANT INC.)
7312 Central Parke Blvd

Key to Media (For complete agency information see *The Advertising Red Books-Agencies* edition):
1. Bus. Publs. 2. Cable T.V. 3. Catalogs & Directories. 4. Co-op Adv. 5. Consumer Mags. 6. D.M. to Bus. Estab.7. D.M. to Consumers
8. Daily Newsp. 9. Exhibits/Trade Shows 10. Foreign 11. Infomercial 12. Internet Adv.13. Multimedia 14. Network Radio
15. Network T.V. 16. Newsp. Distr. Mags. 17. Other 18. Outdoor (Posters, Transit) 19. Point of Purchase20. Premiums, Novelties
21. Product Samples 22. Special Events Mktg. 23. Spot Radio 24. Spot T.V. 25. Weekly Newsp. 26. Yellow Page Adv.

Mason, OH 45040
Tel.: (513) 229-8100
Fax: (513) 229-8194
E-mail: info@kadantbc.com
Web Site: www.kadant.com
Sales Range: $25-49.9 Million
Approx. Number Employees: 80
Year Founded: 1873
Business Description:
Fiberline Process Equipment Mfr & Supplier
S.I.C.: 3554
N.A.I.C.S.: 333291
Import Export
Advertising Expenditures: $250,000
Media: 2-4-7-10-11-13-20-22
Distr.: Intl.; Natl.
Budget Set: Oct.
Personnel:
Peter Flynn *(Pres)*
Woody Tyler *(VP-Sls & Mktg)*
Brands & Products:
CHEMI-WASHER
DNT
FIBER-NET
MAC
SPH
SPM
ULTRA-V
XTREME
XX-CLONE

KADANT INC.
1 Technology Park Dr
Westford, MA 01886
Tel.: (978) 776-2000
Fax: (978) 635-1593
E-mail: info@kadant.com
Web Site: www.kadant.com
Approx. Rev.: $270,029,000
Approx. Number Employees: 1,600
Year Founded: 1991
Business Description:
Papermaking & Paper Recycling Equipment Developer, Mfr & Marketer
S.I.C.: 3554
N.A.I.C.S.: 333291
Import Export
Media: 2-4
Distr.: Natl.
Budget Set: Dec.
Personnel:
William A. Rainville *(Chm)*
Jonathan W. Painter *(CEO)*
Thomas M. O'Brien *(CFO & Exec VP)*
Eric T. Langevin *(COO)*
Michael J. McKenney *(Chief Acctg Officer & VP-Fin)*
Sandra L. Lambert *(Gen Counsel, Sec & VP)*
Jeffrey L. Powell *(Sr VP-Fiberline)*
Wesley A. Martz *(VP-Mktg)*

KAUFMAN MFG. COMPANY
547 S 29th St
Manitowoc, WI 54220
Mailing Address:
PO Box 1056
Manitowoc, WI 54221-1056
Tel.: (920) 684-6641
Fax: (920) 686-4103
E-mail: sales@kaufmanmfg.com
Web Site: www.kaufmanmfg.com
E-Mail For Key Personnel:
Sales Director: sales@kaufmanmfg.com
Approx. Number Employees: 100
Year Founded: 1927
Business Description:
Machining Centers for Metal-Cutting Industries Mfr
S.I.C.: 3541
N.A.I.C.S.: 333512
Import Export
Advertising Expenditures: $200,000
Media: 1-2-4-7-10-26
Distr.: Natl.
Budget Set: Oct.
Personnel:
Robert E. Kaufman *(Owner)*
Mike Kurtem *(VP-Engrg)*
Brands & Products:
KAUFMAN
KAUFMANFLEX

KAWASAKI HEAVY INDUSTRIES (U.S.A.), INC.
(Sub. of Kawasaki Heavy Industries, Ltd.)
60 E 42nd St Ste 2501
New York, NY 10165
Tel.: (212) 759-4950
Fax: (212) 759-6421
Telex: 237004 KHINY UR
Web Site: www.khi.co.jp.com
Sales Range: $10-24.9 Million
Approx. Number Employees: 3
Business Description:
Sales Promotion & Liaison for Aircraft, Industrial Plants & Shipbuilding
S.I.C.: 8742
N.A.I.C.S.: 541613
Personnel:
Kazushi Hattori *(Pres)*
Advertising Agency:
SiiTE Interactive
419 Park Ave S Ste 907
New York, NY 10016
Tel.: (212) 481-9070
Fax: (212) 481-9074

KAYDON CORPORATION
315 E Eisenhower Pkwy Ste 300
Ann Arbor, MI 48108-3330
Tel.: (734) 747-7025
Fax: (734) 747-6565
Web Site: www.kaydon.com
Approx. Sls.: $463,988,000
Approx. Number Employees: 2,172
Year Founded: 1941
Business Description:
Bearing Systems & Components, Filters & Filter Housings, Custom Rings, Shaft Seals, Linear Deceleration Products, Specialty Retaining Rings, Specialty Balls, Fuel Cleansing Systems, Gas-Phase Air Filtration Systems & Replacement Media, Industrial Presses & Metal Alloy Products Designer & Mfr
S.I.C.: 3562; 3569
N.A.I.C.S.: 332991; 333999
Export
Advertising Expenditures: $2,800,000
Media: 1-2-4-7-10-11
Distr.: Intl.; Natl.
Budget Set: Jan. -Feb.
Personnel:
James O'Leary *(Chm, Pres & CEO)*
Peter C. DeChants *(CFO, Treas, Sr VP-Corp Dev & Strategy)*
John R. Emling *(COO & Sr VP)*
Laura Kowalchik *(Chief Acctg Officer, VP & Controller)*
Debra K. Crane *(Gen Counsel, Sec & VP)*
Anthony T. Behrman *(VP-HR)*
John A. Madison *(VP-IT & Ops Plng)*
David V. Raguckas *(VP-Internal Audit)*
Tim Mills *(Product Mgr)*
M. Richard Mosteller *(Asst Controller)*
Brands & Products:
ACE
CANFIELD
COOPER
ITI
KAYDON
PURAFIL
TRIDAN
Advertising Agency:
Brewer Associates Marketing Communications
39555 Orchard Hill Pl Ste 600
Novi, MI 48375
Tel.: (734) 458-7180
Kaydon Custom Bearings

KDINDUSTRIES
1525 E Lake Rd
Erie, PA 16511
Tel.: (814) 453-6761
Fax: (800) 548-9392
Toll Free: (800) 840-9577
E-mail: info@kold-draft.com
Web Site: www.kold-draft.com
Approx. Number Employees: 27
Year Founded: 2004
Business Description:
Mfr. of Automatic Ice Cube Machines, Ice Storage Bins, Ice Crushers & Ice Dispensers
S.I.C.: 3585; 3586
N.A.I.C.S.: 333415; 333913
Export
Advertising Expenditures: $300,000
Media: 2-4-7-10-20-26
Distr.: Intl.; Natl.
Brands & Products:
KOLD-DRAFT
Advertising Agencies:
Benghiat Marketing & Communications
23240 Chagrin Blvd Ste 445
Beachwood, OH 44122
Tel.: (216) 831-8580
Fax: (216) 831-4240

Tillman Group
5415 Westlake Rd
Erie, PA 16505
Tel.: (814) 833-8204

KEMPSMITH MACHINE COMPANY
1819 S 71st St
Milwaukee, WI 53214
Tel.: (414) 256-8160
Fax: (414) 476-0564
E-mail: sales@kempsmith-dl.com
Web Site: www.kempsmith-dl.com
E-Mail For Key Personnel:
Sales Director: sales@kempsmith-dl.com
Approx. Number Employees: 50
Year Founded: 1888
Business Description:
Designer & Mfr Paper Folding, Converting, Cutting & Creasing Machinery & Flexographic Printers
S.I.C.: 3554; 3599
N.A.I.C.S.: 333291; 332710
Import Export
Media: 1-2-4-10-26
Distr.: Intl.; Natl.
Personnel:
Robert Burris *(Owner & CEO)*
Brett Burris *(Pres)*
Brands & Products:
KEMPSMITH

KENNAMETAL EXTRUDE HONE
(Unit of Kennametal Advanced Materials Solutions Group)
235 Industry Blvd
Irwin, PA 15642-2794
Mailing Address:
PO Box 1000
Irwin, PA 15642
Tel.: (724) 863-5900
Fax: (724) 863-8759
Toll Free: (800) 367-1109
E-mail: extrudehone.sales@kennametal.com
Web Site: www.extrudehone.com
E-Mail For Key Personnel:
Sales Director: sales@Kennameta.com
Sales Range: $25-49.9 Million
Approx. Number Employees: 60
Year Founded: 1969
Business Description:
Metal Cutting Tool Finishing
S.I.C.: 3541
N.A.I.C.S.: 333512
Media: 10
Personnel:
Ralf Krieger *(Sls Mgr)*
Peter DeJongh *(Mgr-Tech Svcs)*
Brands & Products:
DYNETICS
ECM GROUP
EXTRUDE HONE
MICROFLOW
MINIBURR
ORBITEX
PROMETAL
SPECTRUM
STORM
SUPERPULSE
SURFTRAN
THERMOBURR
VECTOR

KENNAMETAL IPG
(Sub. of Kennametal Metalworking Solutions & Services Group)
1662 MacMillan Park Dr
Fort Mill, SC 29707
Mailing Address:
PO Box 2587
Augusta, GA 30903-2587
Tel.: (800) 892-9919
Fax: (888) 434-4313
Toll Free: (888) 434-4311
E-mail: ftmill.service@kennametal.com
Web Site: www.kennametalipg.com
Sales Range: $150-199.9 Million
Approx. Number Employees: 100
Year Founded: 1880
Business Description:
Expendable Cutting Tools & Accessories Mfr
S.I.C.: 3423; 3544; 3545
N.A.I.C.S.: 332212; 333511; 333514; 333515
Import Export

Kennametal IPG — (Continued)

Advertising Expenditures: $2,400,000
Media: 2-4-7-10-19-20
Distr.: Intl.
Budget Set: Oct.
Personnel:
Frank P. Simpkins *(CFO & VP)*
Steven R. Hanna *(CIO & VP)*
John H. Jacko, Jr. *(CMO & VP)*
John R. Tucker *(Pres-Bus Grps & VP)*
Kevin G. Nowe *(Sec, VP & Gen Counsel)*
Martha A. Bailey *(Controller & VP-Fin)*
John Deluca *(Mgr)*
Brands & Products:
AGGRESSOR
ATRAX
BASSETT
BLU-MOL
CAPEWELL
CHICAGO-LATROBE
CLE-LINE
ECLIPSE
FIT-AL
GREENFIELD
GREENFIELD GAGE
GUN
HANITA
METAL REMOVAL
METCUT
PUTNAM
REMGRIT
RTW
SIZE CONTROL
SPEED-BAND
THREADS
TRU-LEDE
VAN KEUREN
VTD

KENNEDY MANUFACTURING COMPANY

1260 Industrial Dr
Van Wert, OH 45891
Tel.: (419) 238-2442
Fax: (419) 238-5644
Toll Free: (800) 413-8665
E-mail: kmcinfo@kennedymfg.com
Web Site: www.kennedymfg.com
Approx. Number Employees: 70
Year Founded: 1911
Business Description:
Tool Boxes, Chests, Roller Cabinets & Work Benches Mfr
S.I.C.: 3469
N.A.I.C.S.: 332116
Import Export
Advertising Expenditures: $750,000
Media: 2-4-7-10-11
Distr.: Natl.
Budget Set: Oct.
Personnel:
George Garifalis *(Pres & CEO)*
Ed Barnhirt *(Dir-Engrg)*
Brands & Products:
BENCHMARK
CUTTERKART
KENCRAFT
KENNEDY
VERSA-BENCH
VERSA-CARTS

KENNEDY VALVE

(Div. of McWane, Inc.)
1021 E Water St
Elmira, NY 14902
Mailing Address:
PO Box 931
Elmira, NY 14902-0931
Tel.: (607) 734-2211
Fax: (607) 734-3288
E-mail: sales@kennedyvalve.com
Web Site: www.kennedyvalve.com
E-Mail For Key Personnel:
Sales Director: sales@kennedyvalve.com
Approx. Number Employees: 400
Year Founded: 1875
Business Description:
Mfr of Valves & Fire Hydrants
S.I.C.: 3491; 3561
N.A.I.C.S.: 332911; 333911
Export
Media: 2-4-7-10-21
Distr.: Intl.; Natl.
Budget Set: June
Personnel:
Arne Feyling *(Asst Gen Mgr)*
Brands & Products:
GUARDIAN
KENSEAL II

KEYSTONE POWDERED METAL COMPANY

251 State St
Saint Marys, PA 15857
Tel.: (814) 781-1591
Fax: (814) 781-4306
E-mail: kpmsales@keystonepm.com
Web Site: www.keystonepm.com
Approx. Rev.: $86,000,000
Approx. Number Employees: 750
Year Founded: 1927
Business Description:
Powder Metal Parts Mfr
S.I.C.: 3316; 3568
N.A.I.C.S.: 331221; 333613
Export
Media: 2-4-10-21
Distr.: Intl.; Natl.
Budget Set: Dec.
Personnel:
William B. Hirsch *(Pres)*
Conrad J. Kogovsek *(CFO)*
Brands & Products:
KEYSTONE

KINGSBURY CORPORATION

(Sub. of Donson Group, Ltd.)
80 Laurel St
Keene, NH 03431-4207
Tel.: (603) 352-5212
Fax: (603) 352-8789
E-mail: sales@kingsburycorp.com
Web Site: www.kingsburycorp.com
E-Mail For Key Personnel:
Sales Director: sales@kingsburycorp.com
Sales Range: $25-49.9 Million
Approx. Number Employees: 150
Year Founded: 1928
Business Description:
Metalcutting Designer & Mfr & Assembly Equipment & Turning & Machining Centers
S.I.C.: 3541; 3559
N.A.I.C.S.: 333512; 333298
Export
Media: 2
Distr.: Intl.; Natl.
Budget Set: Sept.
Personnel:
Iris A. Mitropoulis *(Pres)*
Charles Goodale *(VP-Engrg)*
Brands & Products:
CYBERCELL II
VMC 600
VTC-3
VTC-4
VTC-400
VTC-5

KINGSLEY MACHINE

(Sub. of Illinois Tool Works Inc.)
2538 Wisconsin Ave
Downers Grove, IL 60515-4230
Tel.: (630) 968-0647
Fax: (630) 968-7672
Fax: (800) 830-4983
Toll Free: (800) 421-0995
E-mail: info@kingsleymachine.com
Web Site: www.kingsleymachine.com
Sales Range: $25-49.9 Million
Approx. Number Employees: 45
Year Founded: 1930
Business Description:
High Performance Precision Printing Equipment & Supplies Mfr
S.I.C.: 3555
N.A.I.C.S.: 333293
Export
Advertising Expenditures: $400,000
Media: 2-4-7-10-21
Distr.: Intl.; Natl.
Budget Set: Aug. -Nov.
Personnel:
Larry Kulik *(Gen Mgr)*

KIRK & BLUM MANUFACTURING COMPANY INC.

(Div. of CECO Environmental Corp.)
3120 Forrer St
Cincinnati, OH 45209
Tel.: (513) 458-2600
Fax: (513) 458-2647
Toll Free: (800) 333-5475
E-mail: contracting@kirkblum.com
Web Site: www.kirkblum.com
Sales Range: $100-124.9 Million
Approx. Number Employees: 400
Year Founded: 1907
Business Description:
Industrial Sheet Metal Contractor; Custom Sheet & Plate Fabricator; Industrial Air System Component Mfr
S.I.C.: 1799; 3444
N.A.I.C.S.: 238390; 332322
Advertising Expenditures: $50,000
Media: 2-4-7-10-13-20-26
Distr.: Natl.
Budget Set: Jan.
Personnel:
Richard J. Blum *(Pres & COO)*
Brands & Products:
KB DUCT
KIRK & BLUM

KLA-TENCOR CORPORATION

1 Technology Dr
Milpitas, CA 95035
Tel.: (408) 875-3000
Fax: (408) 875-4144
E-mail: info@kla-tencor.com
Web Site: www.kla-tencor.com
Approx. Rev.: $3,175,167,000
Approx. Number Employees: 5,500
Year Founded: 1975
Business Description:
Semiconductor Testing Equipment Mfr
S.I.C.: 3825; 3559; 3674
N.A.I.C.S.: 334515; 333295; 334413
Import Export
Advertising Expenditures: $1,600,000
Media: 2-4-7-10
Distr.: Intl.; Natl.
Personnel:
Edward W. Barnholt *(Chm)*
Richard P. Wallace *(Pres & CEO)*
Mark P. Dentinger *(CFO & Exec VP)*
Ben Tsai *(CTO & Exec VP-Corp Alliances)*
Brian M. Martin *(Gen Counsel)*
Virendra Kirloskar *(Controller & VP-Fin)*
Meggan Powers *(Sr Dir-Corp Comm)*
Brands & Products:
ACUSHAPE
AIT
AIT UV
AIT XUV
ALERIS
ALPHA-STEP IQ
AMDD
ARCHER
ARCHER 10
ARCHER 10XT
ARCHER AIM
ASET-FSX
CANDELA
CUSEAL
FABVISION
IDO
INM
INS
IPARTNER
ISUPPORT
K-T ANALYZER
KERRMAPPER
KLA-TENCOR
KLARITY
KLARITY ACE XP
KLARITY BITMAP
KLARITY DEFECT
LDS
LITHOWARE
LMS IPRO4
LWM9045
METRIX 100
MICROLOOP
MPX
NANOPICS
OMNIMAP
OPTI-PROBE
PLASMATEMP
PLASMAVOLT
POLAR KERR
PROBEAM
PRODATA
PROLITH
PROMETRIX
PUMA
PWQ
QUANTOX
QUANTOX XP
RS-100
SPECTRA
SPECTRACD
SPECTRAFX 100
STARLIGHT
SURFMONITOR
SURFSCAN
TERAFAB
TERASCAN

Key to Media (For complete agency information see *The Advertising Red Books-Agencies* edition):
1. Bus. Publs. 2. Cable T.V. 3. Catalogs & Directories. 4. Co-op Adv. 5. Consumer Mags. 6. D.M. to Bus. Estab.7. D.M. to Consumers
8. Daily Newsp. 9. Exhibits/Trade Shows 10. Foreign 11. Infomercial 12. Internet Adv.13. Multimedia 14. Network Radio
15. Network T.V. 16. Newsp. Distr. Mags. 17. Other 18. Outdoor (Posters, Transit) 19. Point of Purchase20. Premiums, Novelties
21. Product Samples 22. Special Events Mktg. 23. Spot Radio 24. Spot T.V. 25. Weekly Newsp. 26. Yellow Page Adv.

TERASCANHR
TERASCANXR
TERASTAR
THERMA-PROBE
VIPER
VISEDGE
WAFERSIGHT

KNUDSON MANUFACTURING, INC.

10401 W 120th Ave
Broomfield, CO 80021
Tel.: (303) 469-2101
Fax: (303) 469-7994
Toll Free: (800) 548-2622
E-mail: sales@knudsonmfg.com
Web Site: www.knudsonmfg.com
E-Mail For Key Personnel:
Sales Director: sales@knudsonmfg.com
Approx. Number Employees: 12
Year Founded: 1966
Business Description:
Metal Roll Machines Mfr
S.I.C.: 3542; 3559
N.A.I.C.S.: 333513; 333298
Export
Advertising Expenditures: $200,000
Media: 1-2-10
Distr.: Intl.; Natl.
Budget Set: June -July
Personnel:
Gary A. Knudson *(Founder & Pres)*
Pat Flood *(Gen Mgr)*
Brands & Products:
FRAMEMAKER
KNUDSON
KNUDSON MODEL 1700
KNUDSON MODEL 1700-C5
KNUDSON MODEL 1770
KNUDSON MODEL KR-16
KNUDSON MODEL KR-18
KNUDSON MODEL KR-20
KNUDSON MODEL KR-24
KNUDSON MODEL KR-56
KNUDSON MODEL KR-612H
KNUDSON MODEL KR-8/10
KNUDSON MODEL KS-246
LET ROLL'S
ULTRALOK

KOBELCO STEWART BOLLING, INC.

(Sub. of Kobe Steel, Ltd.)
1600 Terex Rd
Hudson, OH 44236
Tel.: (330) 655-3111
Fax: (330) 656-9724
Web Site: www.ksbiusa.com
E-Mail For Key Personnel:
Sales Director: d.norman@ksbi.com
Approx. Number Employees: 100
Year Founded: 1989
Business Description:
Rubber & Plastic Processing Machinery Mfr & Distr
S.I.C.: 3569; 3542
N.A.I.C.S.: 333999; 333513
Import Export
Media: 6-9-25
Distr.: Intl.; Natl.
Brands & Products:
ECONOMIX

KODAK GRAPHIC COMMUNICATIONS GROUP

(Sub. of Eastman Kodak Company)
343 State St
Rochester, NY 14650
Tel.: (585) 724-4000
Toll Free: (800) 698-3324
Web Site: www.graphics.kodak.com
Sales Range: $550-599.9 Million
Approx. Number Employees: 2,500
Year Founded: 1998
Business Description:
Printing Software & Supplies
S.I.C.: 3555
N.A.I.C.S.: 333293
Export
Advertising Expenditures: $1,500,000
Media: 1-2-4-7-10-20-26
Distr.: Direct to Customers; Intl.; Natl.
Budget Set: Oct. -Nov.
Personnel:
Anthonio Perez *(Chm & CEO)*
Doug Edwards *(VP & Gen Mgr-Prepress Solutions)*
Stephen Green *(VP & Reg Mng Dir-Sls, Customer Ops, Asia Pacific Reg)*
Judi Hess *(Gen Mgr-Enterprise Solutions)*
Beth Hogan Scott *(Dir-Mktg Comm)*
Advertising Agency:
Butler/Till Media Services, Inc.
2349 Monroe Ave
Rochester, NY 14618
Tel.: (585) 473-3740
Fax: (585) 473-3862

KOLBERG-PIONEER, INC.

(Sub. of Astec Industries, Inc.)
700 W 21st St
Yankton, SD 57078
Tel.: (605) 665-8771
Fax: (605) 665-8858
Toll Free: (800) 542-9311
E-mail: mail@kpijci.com
Web Site: KPIJCI.COM
Sales Range: $100-124.9 Million
Approx. Number Employees: 370
Year Founded: 1928
Business Description:
Aggregate & Recycling Processing Equipment Mfr
S.I.C.: 3531; 3535
N.A.I.C.S.: 333120; 333922
Export
Advertising Expenditures: $250,000
Media: 1-2-4-5-7-10-13-22
Distr.: Intl.; Natl.
Budget Set: Jan.
Personnel:
Joseph P. Vig *(Pres)*
Mike Johnson *(VP-Sls & Mktg)*
Lisa Carson *(Mgr-Mktg)*
Rhonda Kocer *(Mgr-HR)*
Brands & Products:
COMBO
FAST PACK
MESABI
SERIES 2

KOMATSU AMERICA CORPORATION

(Sub. of Komatsu Ltd.)
1701 W Golf Rd 1 Centennial Towers
Rolling Meadows, IL 60008-4227
Tel.: (847) 437-5800
Fax: (847) 437-1016
Toll Free: (866) 513-5778
E-mail: info@komatsuamerica.com
Web Site: www.komatsuamerica.com
Approx. Number Employees: 350
Year Founded: 1970
Business Description:
Construction & Mining Equipment Mfr, Retailer & Servicer
S.I.C.: 3531; 3532
N.A.I.C.S.: 333120; 333131
Export
Media: 7-10-11
Personnel:
David W. Grzelak *(Chm & CEO)*
Hisashi Shinozuka *(Pres & COO)*
Steve Cihock *(Mgr-Adv, Promotions & Events)*

KOMATSU AMERICA INDUSTRIES, LLC

(Sub. of Komatsu Ltd.)
(d/b/a Komatsu Press Division)
One Continental Twr 1701 W Golf Rd Ste 300
Rolling Meadows, IL 60008
Tel.: (847) 437-3888
Fax: (847) 437-1811
Telex: 27-0260
Web Site: www.komatsupress.com
Approx. Number Employees: 25
Year Founded: 1985
Business Description:
Industrial Machinery Retailer & Servicer
S.I.C.: 5084; 7629
N.A.I.C.S.: 423830; 811219
Import Export
Media: 10
Distr.: Natl.
Personnel:
Hideo Suzuki *(Pres)*

KOMATSU CANADA LIMITED

(Sub. of Sumitomo Corporation)
1725 B Sismet Rd
Mississauga, ON L4W 1P9, Canada
Tel.: (905) 625-6292
Fax: (905) 625-3036
E-mail: webmaster@komatsu.ca
Web Site: www.komatsuamerica.com
Sales Range: Less than $1 Million
Approx. Number Employees: 70
Year Founded: 1972
Business Description:
Construction & Mining Machinery Distr
S.I.C.: 7353
N.A.I.C.S.: 532412
Media: 2-6-9
Personnel:
Kenny Sato *(Product Mgr)*
Advertising Agency:
Marketing Strategies & Solutions
433 William St
London, ON N6B 3E1, Canada
Tel.: (519) 432-8327
Fax: (519) 642-3372

KOMLINE-SANDERSON ENGINEERING CORPORATION

12 Holland Ave
Peapack, NJ 07977
Tel.: (908) 234-1000
Fax: (908) 234-9487
Toll Free: (800) 225-5457
E-mail: info@komline.com
Web Site: www.komline.com
Approx. Number Employees: 130
Year Founded: 1946
Business Description:
Liquid-Solids Separation Equipment, Pumps & Drying Equipment Mfr
S.I.C.: 3569
N.A.I.C.S.: 333999
Import Export
Advertising Expenditures: $275,000
Media: 2-4-7-10-11-13-20
Distr.: Natl.
Budget Set: Nov.
Personnel:
Annette Oswald *(Mgr-Adv)*

KOMORI AMERICA CORPORATION

(Sub. of Komori Corporation)
5520 Meadowbrook Industrial Ct
Rolling Meadows, IL 60008
Tel.: (847) 806-9000
Fax: (847) 806-0987
Fax: (847) 806-9038
E-mail: komori.america@attglobal.net
Web Site: www.komori-america.us
Approx. Int. Income: $14,240,000
Approx. Number Employees: 60
Year Founded: 1983
Business Description:
Printing Equipment Mfr, Retailer, Servicer & Distr
S.I.C.: 5084; 5044
N.A.I.C.S.: 423830; 423420
Advertising Expenditures: $2,000,000
Media: 2-7-10
Distr.: Natl.
Personnel:
Sue Baines *(Dir-Mktg)*

KONE INC.

(Sub. of KONE Corporation)
1 Kone Ct
Moline, IL 61265
Tel.: (309) 764-6771
Fax: (309) 743-5474
Telex: 468436
E-mail: us.communications@kone.com
Web Site: www.us.kone.com
Approx. Number Employees: 325
Year Founded: 1892
Business Description:
Elevator, Escalator & Autowalks Mfr, Servicer & Installer
S.I.C.: 7699; 3534
N.A.I.C.S.: 811490; 333921
Export
Media: 2-4-7-10
Distr.: Natl.
Budget Set: Aug.
Personnel:
Dennis Gerard *(Sr VP-Central Reg)*
Charles D. Moore *(Sr VP-HR)*
John Bril *(Dir-Engrg)*

KSB INC.

(Sub. of KSB Aktiengesellschaft)
4415 Sarellen Rd
Richmond, VA 23231-4428
Tel.: (804) 222-1818
Fax: (804) 226-6961
Telex: 82710
E-mail: info@ksbusa.com
Web Site: www.ksbusa.com
Sales Range: $10-24.9 Million
Approx. Number Employees: 60
Year Founded: 1969
Business Description:
Mfr. of Submersible Motor Sewage & Wastewater Pumps & High Pressure Boiler Feed-Pumps
S.I.C.: 5084; 7629
N.A.I.C.S.: 423830; 811219
Media: 2-11-26
Distr.: Intl.; Natl.

Key to Media (For complete agency information see *The Advertising Red Books-Agencies* edition):
1. Bus. Publs. 2. Cable T.V. 3. Catalogs & Directories. 4. Co-op Adv. 5. Consumer Mags. 6. D.M. to Bus. Estab.7. D.M. to Consumers 8. Daily Newsp. 9. Exhibits/Trade Shows 10. Foreign 11. Infomercial 12. Internet Adv.13. Multimedia 14. Network Radio 15. Network T.V. 16. Newsp. Distr. Mags. 17. Other 18. Outdoor (Posters, Transit) 19. Point of Purchase20. Premiums, Novelties 21. Product Samples 22. Special Events Mktg. 23. Spot Radio 24. Spot T.V. 25. Weekly Newsp. 26. Yellow Page Adv.

KSB Inc. — (Continued)

Budget Set: Sept.

KURZ TRANSFER PRODUCTS, L.P.

(Sub. of Leonhard Kurz GmbH & Co. KG)
3200 Woodpark Blvd
Charlotte, NC 28206
Tel.: (704) 927-3700
Fax: (704) 927-3701
E-mail: sales@kurzusa.com
Web Site: www.kurzusa.com
E-Mail For Key Personnel:
Sales Director: sales@kurzusa.com
Approx. Sls.: $28,000,000
Approx. Number Employees: 180
Year Founded: 1992
Business Description:
Metal Foil & Leaf Manufacturing
S.I.C.: 3499; 2789
N.A.I.C.S.: 332999; 323121
Import Export
Media: 10
Personnel:
Drew Barringer *(COO)*

L-3 COMMUNICATIONS WESTWOOD CORPORATION

(Div. of L-3 Power & Control Systems Group)
12402 E 60th St
Tulsa, OK 74146-6920
Tel.: (918) 252-0481
Fax: (918) 252-0486
Web Site: www.l-3com.com/divisions/overview.aspx?id=80
Approx. Sls.: $52,100,000
Approx. Number Employees: 211
Year Founded: 1986
Business Description:
Electrical Distribution & Control Equipment Mfr
S.I.C.: 3568
N.A.I.C.S.: 333613
Media: 7

L&J TECHNOLOGIES

5911 Butterfield Rd
Hillside, IL 60162
Tel.: (708) 236-6000
Fax: (708) 236-6006
E-mail: market@ljtechnologies.com
Web Site: www.ljtechnologies.com
E-Mail For Key Personnel:
Sales Director: sales@ljtechnologies.com
Approx. Number Employees: 130
Year Founded: 1976
Business Description:
Level Controls, Liquid Level Controls, Tank Fittings, Valves, Gauges, Hydraulic Controls & Related Systems Mfr; Level Gauging Solutions
S.I.C.: 3829; 3491
N.A.I.C.S.: 334519; 332911
Export
Media: 4-8-10-13
Distr.: Intl.
Budget Set: Dec.
Personnel:
Lou Jannotta *(Pres & CEO)*
Bob Schwaan *(CFO)*
Michael Landato *(Mgr-Mktg & Product)*
Brands & Products:
GPE CONTROLS
MCG-1095
MCG 1500 SFI
MCG 1600 SFI
MCG 2000 SFI
MCG-2151
MCG-5101
MCG-5102
MCG-5150
SMART FLASH

THE LAITRAM LLC

220 Laitram Ln
Harahan, LA 70123
Tel.: (504) 733-6000
Fax: (504) 733-2143
Web Site: www.laitram.com
Approx. Number Employees: 1,100
Year Founded: 1949
Business Description:
Shrimp Processing Machinery, Plastic Modular Conveyor Belting, Alternating Metal Stairtreads
S.I.C.: 3535; 3556
N.A.I.C.S.: 333922; 333294
Export
Media: 2
Distr.: Intl.; Natl.
Budget Set: Apr.
Personnel:
James M. Lapeyre, Jr. *(Pres)*
Lawrence P. Oertling *(CFO)*
Frank Profumo *(Creative Dir)*
Brands & Products:
CONE TOP
CYLINDRICAL HEATING
EZ ROLLER RETROFIT
EZ TRACK
INTRALON
INTRALOX
LAITRAM MACHINERY
LAPEYRE STAIR
ONEPIECE
PLANAR DRYING
SEAMFREE
SPIRALOX
Advertising Agency:
LIDGroup Inc.
200 Laitram Ln.
Harahan, LA 70123
Tel.: (504) 733-1050
Fax: (504) 733-2420
(Laitram Corp.)
(Digicourse)
(Intralox)

LAKELAND INDUSTRIES, INC.

701 Koehler Ave Ste 7
Ronkonkoma, NY 11779-7403
Tel.: (631) 981-9700
Fax: (631) 981-9751
Toll Free: (800) 772-8353
Toll Free: (800) 645-9291
E-mail: info@lakeland.com
Web Site: www.lakeland.com
Approx. Sls.: $101,236,325
Approx. Number Employees: 2,000
Year Founded: 1982
Business Description:
Industrial Safety Garments & Accessories Mfr & Seller
S.I.C.: 3999; 2389; 2676; 3842
N.A.I.C.S.: 339999; 315299; 322291; 339113
Import Export
Advertising Expenditures: $233,000
Media: 2-4-10-17
Personnel:
Raymond J. Smith *(Co-Founder)*
Stephen M. Bachelder *(Chm)*
Christopher J. Ryan *(CEO)*
Gary Pokrassa *(CFO)*
Gregory D. Willis *(Exec VP)*
Harvey Pride, Jr. *(Sr VP-Mfg)*
Teri Hunt *(VP-Fin)*
Scott Conover *(Dir-Art & Designer-Graphic)*
Donna Brown *(Dir-Pur)*
Brands & Products:
ATAC
BE SAFE, BE SURE, WEAR LAKELAND
BLENDED KEVLAR
CHEMESOL
CHEMMAX
CLEANSCREEN
CODE ONE
CROCSKIN
CROCSKINS
DESPRO
DEXTRAGARD
DINOHYDE
DYNEEMA
EXTRA WIDE KEVLAR
FRONTIER
FYREPEL
FYRETRED
GLEAMCLEAN
GOLDLEAF
GRAPOLATOR
GRIPPLUS
KUTBUSTER
LAKELAND
MICROGARD
MICROMAX
MOCKTWISTAFE
NATRASOL
NEOSOL
NITROSOL
NOMEX
PYROLON
PYROLON PLUS 2
PYROLON XT
RYTEX
SAFEGARD
SHURRITE
SILVERLEAF
SPIDERGRIP
STATICSORB
THERMBAR
TOMTEX
TYCHEM
TYPAR
TYVEK

LAM RESEARCH CORPORATION

(d/b/a LAM RESEARCH)
4650 Cushing Pkwy
Fremont, CA 94538
Mailing Address:
PO Box 5010
Fremont, CA 94536
Tel.: (510) 572-0200
Fax: (510) 572-2935
Toll Free: (800) 526-7678
E-mail: investor.relations@lamresearch.com
Web Site: www.lamresearch.com
Approx. Rev.: $3,237,693,000
Approx. Number Employees: 3,700
Year Founded: 1980
Business Description:
Semiconductor Processing Equipment Used in the Fabrication of Integrated Circuits Designer, Mfr, Marketer & Servicer
S.I.C.: 3523; 3559
N.A.I.C.S.: 333111; 333295
Export
Media: 2-10
Distr.: Intl.
Personnel:
James W. Bagley *(Chm)*
Stephen G. Newberry *(Vice Chm & CEO)*
Martin B. Anstice *(Pres & COO)*
Lisa Garber *(Mng Dir)*
Ernest E. Maddock *(CFO & Sr VP)*
Sarah A. O'Dowd *(Chief Legal Officer & Grp VP)*
George M. Schisler, Jr. *(Gen Counsel)*
Abdi Hariri *(Grp VP-Ops-Global)*
Thomas J. Bondur *(VP-Sls & Field Ops-Global)*
Brands & Products:
2300 VERSYS
9400DSIE
ALLIANCE
AUTOETCH
AUTOPM
C3
CHANGING THE VALUE EQUATION
CONFINED CHEMICAL CLEANING
CORONUS
DA VINCI
DUAL FREQUENCY CONFINED
DV-PRIME
EXELAN
FLEX
FLEX45
KIYO
KIYO45
LAM RESEARCH
METAL45
MYLAM
RAINBOW
STAR
SYNDION
SYNERGY INTEGRA
TCP
TRANSFORMER COUPLED PLASMA
VALUEPOINT
VERSYS
WAC
WAFERLESS AUTOCLEAN

LATSHAW ENTERPRISES, INC.

800 W 47th St Ste 716
Kansas City, MO 64112
Tel.: (816) 361-6161
Fax: (816) 361-6891
Toll Free: (888) 452-8742
Web Site: www.latshawenterprises.com
Approx. Number Employees: 450
Year Founded: 1947
Business Description:
Mfr of Mechanical Controls, Cable Assemblies, Screw Machine Parts & Hand Tools; Custom Injection Molding Services
S.I.C.: 8742
N.A.I.C.S.: 541611
Import Export
Media: 2-4-5-7-10-19-21
Distr.: Natl.
Budget Set: Oct.
Brands & Products:
ANDERSON & FORRESTER
MC ELECTRONICS

Key to Media (For complete agency information see *The Advertising Red Books-Agencies* edition):
1. Bus. Publs. 2. Cable T.V. 3. Catalogs & Directories. 4. Co-op Adv. 5. Consumer Mags. 6. D.M. to Bus. Estab.7. D.M. to Consumers
8. Daily Newsp. 9. Exhibits/Trade Shows 10. Foreign 11. Infomercial 12. Internet Adv.13. Multimedia 14. Network Radio
15. Network T.V. 16. Newsp. Distr. Mags. 17. Other 18. Outdoor (Posters, Transit) 19. Point of Purchase20. Premiums, Novelties
21. Product Samples 22. Special Events Mktg. 23. Spot Radio 24. Spot T.V. 25. Weekly Newsp. 26. Yellow Page Adv.

Advertising Agency:
Nye & Associates
PO Box 11402
Wichita, KS 67202
Tel.: (316) 263-5878

LAWRENCE PUMPS, INC.

371 Market St
Lawrence, MA 01843
Tel.: (978) 682-5248
Fax: (978) 975-4291
E-mail: info@lawrencepumps.com
Web Site: www.lawrencepumps.com
Sales Range: $75-99.9 Million
Approx. Number Employees: 300
Year Founded: 1934
Business Description:
Mfr. of Centrifugal Pumps for Industrial Applications
S.I.C.: 3561
N.A.I.C.S.: 333911
Export
Media: 2-4-10-13
Budget Set: Oct. -Nov.
Personnel:
Paul Reddick *(CEO)*
S.H. Kwek *(VP & Gen Mgr)*
Mike McHale *(Reg Mgr-Sls)*
Paul Griggs *(Reg Sls Mgr-Southern USA)*
Brian Smith *(Mgr)*
Robert Walsh *(Mgr-Tech Svc & Support-Asia)*
Ralph Atchison *(Engr-Field Svc)*
Lillian Hey *(Coord-Customer Accts)*
Mary Hosterman *(Coord-Customer Accts)*
Nick Sirois *(Applications Sls Engr)*

LAWSON PRODUCTS, INC.

1666 E Touhy Ave
Des Plaines, IL 60018-3607
Tel.: (847) 827-9666
Fax: (847) 297-0063
Toll Free: (866) 529-7664
E-mail: info@lawsonproducts.com
Web Site: www.lawsonproducts.com
Approx. Sls.: $316,780,000
Approx. Number Employees: 930
Year Founded: 1952
Business Description:
Screws, Rivets & Related Fastener Distr
S.I.C.: 5085; 1796; 5072
N.A.I.C.S.: 423840; 238290; 423710
Import Export
Media: 2-4-7-8-9-10-11-13-20-21-26
Distr.: Natl.
Personnel:
Ronald B. Port *(Chm)*
Thomas J. Neri *(Pres & CEO)*
Ron Knutson *(CFO & Sr VP)*
Frank Ziegler *(Chief Compliance Officer, VP & Asst Sec)*
Neil E. Jenkins *(Gen Counsel, Sec & Exec VP)*
Harry Dochelli *(Exec VP)*
Stewart A. Howley *(Sr VP-Strategic Bus Dev)*
Lawrence J. Krema *(Sr VP-HR)*
Michelle Russell *(Sr VP & Exec Sponsor-ERP)*
Mike Tuvell *(VP-Fin)*

LAYSTROM MANUFACTURING CO.

3900 W Palmer St
Chicago, IL 60647-2208
Tel.: (773) 342-4800
Fax: (773) 342-9762
E-mail: sales@laystrom.com
Web Site: www.laystrom.com
E-Mail For Key Personnel:
Sales Director: sales@laystrom.com
Approx. Number Employees: 45
Year Founded: 1951
Business Description:
Metal Fabrications & Stampings, Prototypes & Assemblies Mfr
S.I.C.: 3469; 3441
N.A.I.C.S.: 332116; 332312
Export
Media: 2-4-7-10
Distr.: Natl.
Personnel:
Robert A. Laystrom *(Pres)*

L.B. FOSTER COMPANY

415 Holiday Dr
Pittsburgh, PA 15220
Mailing Address:
PO Box 2806
Pittsburgh, PA 15230-2806
Tel.: (412) 928-3417
Fax: (412) 928-7891
Toll Free: (800) 255-4500
E-mail: investors@lbfosterco.com
Web Site: www.lbfoster.com
E-Mail For Key Personnel:
President: shasselbusch@lbfosterco.com
Approx. Sls.: $475,050,000
Approx. Number Employees: 866
Year Founded: 1902
Business Description:
Mfr, Fabricator & Distr of Products & Services for Rail, Construction, Energy & Utility Markets
S.I.C.: 3462; 3272; 3317; 4013; 5051; 5088
N.A.I.C.S.: 332111; 327390; 331210; 423510; 423860; 488210
Export
Advertising Expenditures: $250,000
Media: 1-2-4-7-10-13-20
Distr.: Intl.; Natl.
Budget Set: Oct.
Personnel:
Lee B. Foster, II *(Chm)*
Stan L. Hasselbusch *(Pres & CEO)*
David J. Russo *(CFO, Treas & Sr VP)*
David L. Voltz *(Gen Counsel, Sec & VP)*
Donald L. Foster *(Sr VP-Construction Products)*
John F. Kasel *(Sr VP-Ops & Mfg)*
Brian H. Kelly *(VP-HR)*

LECO CORPORATION

3000 Lakeview Ave
Saint Joseph, MI 49085-2396
Tel.: (269) 983-5531
Fax: (269) 982-8977
Toll Free: (800) 292-6141
E-mail: info@leco.com
Web Site: www.leco.com
Approx. Number Employees: 900
Year Founded: 1936
Business Description:
Laboratory Apparatus Mfr
S.I.C.: 3821; 4493
N.A.I.C.S.: 339111; 713930
Import Export
Advertising Expenditures: $300,000
Media: 2-6-10-13-22
Personnel:
Joel Debruyne *(CFO)*
Robert J. Warren *(Dir-Media)*
Veronica Jackson *(Mgr-Technical Comm)*
Brands & Products:
CAMEO
CHROMATOF
LECO
OLYMPUS
PEGASUS
SPECTRUM
TRUSPEC
UNIQUE

LECTRODRYER LLC

135 Quality Dr
Richmond, KY 40475
Tel.: (859) 624-2091
Fax: (859) 623-2436
E-mail: info@lectrodryer.com
Web Site: www.lectrodryer.com
Sales Range: Less than $1 Million
Approx. Number Employees: 25
Year Founded: 1932
Business Description:
Equipment for Drying Air, Gases & Liquids
S.I.C.: 3569
N.A.I.C.S.: 333999
Export
Media: 2-4-10-11
Distr.: Intl.
Budget Set: Dec.
Personnel:
John McPherson *(Pres)*
Brands & Products:
LECTRODRYER

LETOURNEAU, INC.

(Sub. of Rowan Companies, Inc.)
2401 S High St
Longview, TX 75602
Mailing Address:
PO Box 2307
Longview, TX 75606-2307
Tel.: (903) 237-7000
Fax: (903) 237-7020
Fax: (903) 237-7036
E-mail: gcupstid@letourneau-inc.com
Web Site: www.letourneau-inc.com
Sales Range: $650-699.9 Million
Approx. Number Employees: 2,285
Year Founded: 1948
Business Description:
Earthmoving Equipment Mfr
S.I.C.: 3799
N.A.I.C.S.: 336999
Export
Media: 2-7-10-11-13-20
Distr.: Intl.; Natl.
Budget Set: Dec.
Personnel:
Dan C. Eckermann *(Pres & CEO)*
David Farrar *(Sr VP & Gen Mgr-Dealer Ops)*
John Clutter *(Sr VP-Mktg & Sls)*
Dave Blazek *(VP & Gen Mgr)*
George Cupstid *(VP & Gen Mgr-Offshore Products)*
Brad Rogers *(VP & Gen Mgr)*
Lowry Wood *(VP & Gen Mgr)*
Julian Bowes *(VP-Mktg, Sls & Design Engrg)*
Butch Brooks *(VP-HR)*
Sean Hopkins *(Dir-IT)*
Collin Cox *(Reg Mgr-US)*
Dennis Duffy *(Reg Mgr-Latin America & Mexico)*
Michael Fleet *(Reg Mgr-Intl)*
Bill Miller *(Branch Mgr)*
Barry Morgan *(Product Mgr)*
Robbie Brengle *(Mgr)*
Teresa Davis *(Mgr-Customer Service)*
Nancy Dewey *(Mgr-Parts Sls)*
Gary Palmer *(Mgr-Product Support Sls)*
Robert Parker *(Mgr-Plng)*
Michael P. Thomas *(Mgr-Sls & Mktg)*
Jeff Townlin *(Mgr-Marine Products-Parts Sls)*
Bo Sheridan *(Engr)*
Goran Badzic *(Trng Coord)*
Robert Jackson *(Logistics Coord)*
Brands & Products:
GORILLA
JC-40
JC52KP
KLENZ
L-2350
LINCS
SST-100
SUPER 300 XL
SUPER GORILLA
SUPER GORILLA XL
TARZAN
WORKHORSE
Advertising Agency:
Triad Business Marketing
10670 N Central Expy Ste 300
Dallas, TX 75231
Tel.: (214) 953-6223
Fax: (214) 953-3101

LEVER MANUFACTURING CORP.

(Sub. of Thermwell Products Co., Inc.)
420 Rte 17 S
Mahwah, NJ 07430
Tel.: (201) 684-4400
Fax: (201) 529-0188
Toll Free: (800) 526-5265
E-mail: info@levercorp.com
Web Site: www.levercorp.com
Approx. Number Employees: 25
Year Founded: 1910
Business Description:
Roll Slitter & Bias Binding Machinery Designer & Mfr
S.I.C.: 3552; 3549
N.A.I.C.S.: 333292; 333518
Export
Advertising Expenditures: $90,000
Media: 2-7-10
Distr.: Natl.
Budget Set: Jan. -June
Personnel:
William M. Corbett *(VP & Gen Mgr)*
Don Bower *(Mgr-Parts)*
Brands & Products:
LEVER 1500
LEVER 300
LEVER 6200

LEWMAR INC.

(Div. of Lewmar Ltd.)
351 New Whitfield St
Guilford, CT 06437-0388
Tel.: (203) 458-6200
Fax: (203) 453-5669
E-mail: info@lewmarusa.com
Web Site: www.lewmar.com
Business Description:
Marine Equipment Mfr

Key to Media (For complete agency information see *The Advertising Red Books-Agencies* edition):
1. Bus. Publs. 2. Cable T.V. 3. Catalogs & Directories. 4. Co-op Adv. 5. Consumer Mags. 6. D.M. to Bus. Estab.7. D.M. to Consumers
8. Daily Newsp. 9. Exhibits/Trade Shows 10. Foreign 11. Infomercial 12. Internet Adv.13. Multimedia 14. Network Radio
15. Network T.V. 16. Newsp. Distr. Mags. 17. Other 18. Outdoor (Posters, Transit) 19. Point of Purchase20. Premiums, Novelties
21. Product Samples 22. Special Events Mktg. 23. Spot Radio 24. Spot T.V. 25. Weekly Newsp. 26. Yellow Page Adv.

Lewmar Inc. — (Continued)

S.I.C.: 5088
N.A.I.C.S.: 423860
Personnel:
Peter Tierney *(Chm & CEO)*
Advertising Agency:
Blumenfeld and Associates, Inc.
28 Ctr St
Darien, CT 06820
Tel.: (203) 655-1600
Fax: (203) 655-1622

LINCOLN ELECTRIC HOLDINGS, INC.

22801 Saint Clair Ave
Cleveland, OH 44117-2524
Tel.: (216) 481-8100
Fax: (216) 486-1751
Telex: 98-5471
E-mail: newsletter@lincolnelectric.com
Web Site: www.lincolnelectric.com
Approx. Sls.: $2,070,172,000
Approx. Number Employees: 9,472
Year Founded: 1895
Business Description:
Electrodes & Welding Supplies Mfr; Flux Cored Wire & Solid Core Wire for Mig & Submerged Arc Welding
S.I.C.: 8611; 2813; 3548; 3549
N.A.I.C.S.: 813910; 325120; 333518; 333992
Import Export
Advertising Expenditures: $7,982,000
Media: 2-4-10-19-26
Distr.: Direct to Consumer; Intl.; Natl.
Personnel:
John M. Stropki, Jr. *(Chm, Pres & CEO)*
Vincent K. Petrella *(CFO, Treas & Sr VP)*
Joseph G. Doria *(Pres/CEO-Lincoln Electric Canada & Indalco Alloys)*
George D. Blankenship *(Pres-Lincoln Electric North America & Sr VP)*
David M. LeBlanc *(Pres-Lincoln Electric Intl & Sr VP)*
Thomas A. Flohn *(Pres-Lincoln Electric Europe, Middle East & Africa)*
Frederick G. Stueber *(Gen Counsel, Sec & Sr VP)*
Gretchen A. Farrell *(Sr VP-HR & Compliance)*
Richard J. Seif *(Sr VP-Mktg & Product Dev-Global)*
Steven B. Hedlund *(VP-Strategy & Bus)*
Michael S. Mintun *(VP-Sls-North America)*
Ferry Naber *(Dir-Global Machine Dev)*
Ronald A. Nelson *(Dir-Counseling & Career Svcs)*
Peter Pletcher *(Dir-Global Consumable Dev)*
Patrick S. Wahlen *(Dir-Global Bus-Power Generation)*
Eric Snyder *(Sr Product Mgr)*
Brands & Products:
ALUMINWELD
BLUE MAX
FERROWELD
FLEETWELD
INVERTEC
JET-LH
JETWELD
LINCOLN ELECTRIC
LINCOLNWELD
LINCORE
MAGNUM
OUTERSHIELD
PRO-CUT
SHIELD-ARC
WEARSHIELD
WELDANPOWER
Advertising Agency:
Falls Communications
50 Public Sq 25th Fl
Cleveland, OH 44113
Tel.: (216) 696-0229
Fax: (216) 696-0269

LINCOLN INDUSTRIAL CORP.

(Holding of Harbour Group Ltd.)
1 Lincoln Way
Saint Louis, MO 63120-1508
Tel.: (314) 679-4200
Fax: (800) 424-5359
Fax: (314) 679-4359
E-mail: info@lincolnindustrial.com
Web Site: www.lincolnindustrial.com
Approx. Number Employees: 415
Year Founded: 1910
Business Description:
Lubricating Equipment Mfr
S.I.C.: 3586; 3561
N.A.I.C.S.: 333913; 333911
Media: 2-4-5-7-10-19-26
Distr.: Intl.; Natl.
Budget Set: Nov.
Personnel:
Peter Laucis *(Mgr-Rail Sys Product)*
Kenneth Walsh *(Mgr-Mktg Comm & Res)*
Brands & Products:
CENTRO-MATIC
DUO-MATIC
HELIOS
KLEENSEAL
LINCOLN
MODULAR LUBE
ORSCO
PILEDRIVER
POWERLUBER
POWERMASTER
QUICKLUB

LIND ELECTRONICS, INC.

6414 Cambridge St
Minneapolis, MN 55426
Tel.: (952) 927-6303
Fax: (952) 927-7740
Toll Free: (800) 697-3702
E-mail: llind@lindelectronics.com
Web Site: www.lindelectronics.com
Approx. Number Employees: 50
Year Founded: 1975
Business Description:
Portable Power Supplies, Adapters & Accessories Mfr for Laptop Computers
S.I.C.: 3699; 3691
N.A.I.C.S.: 335999; 335911
Media: 2-6-10
Personnel:
Leroy R. Lind *(Pres)*
David Murphy *(VP-Sls & Mktg)*

LINDE GAS LLC

(Sub. of The BOC Group plc)
575 Mountain Ave
New Providence, NJ 07974-2097
Tel.: (908) 464-8100
Fax: (908) 771-1460
Toll Free: (800) 932-0803
E-mail: info@lindegas.com
Web Site: www.us.lindegas.com
Approx. Number Employees: 1,200
Year Founded: 1886
Business Description:
Industrial Gases
S.I.C.: 2813; 3569
N.A.I.C.S.: 325120; 333999
Advertising Expenditures: $1,000,000
Media: 2-4-5-7-8-10-20-26
Distr.: Natl.
Budget Set: Oct.
Personnel:
Patrick Murphy *(Pres)*
Peter Thomas *(VP-Mktg & Electronics)*
Brands & Products:
ARGOSHIELD
BOC
MAPP GAS
Advertising Agency:
The Maitland Consultancy
Orion House 5 Upper St Martins Ln
London, WC2H 9EA, United Kingdom
Tel.: (44) 20 7379 5151
Fax: (44) 20 7379 6161

LINDE HYDRAULICS CORPORATION

(Joint Venture of The Goldman Sachs Group, Inc. & KKR & CO. L.P.)
5089 Western Reserve Rd PO Box 82
Canfield, OH 44406
Tel.: (330) 533-6801
Fax: (330) 533-2091
Telex: 98 2445
E-mail: info@lindeamerica.com
Web Site: www.lindeamerica.com
Sales Range: $25-49.9 Million
Approx. Number Employees: 55
Year Founded: 1970
Business Description:
High Pressure Hydraulic Piston Pumps, Motors & Power Units Distr
S.I.C.: 3594
N.A.I.C.S.: 333996
Media: 2-4-7
Distr.: Intl.; Natl.
Personnel:
Frank Cobb *(Pres & CEO)*
Thomas Pryor *(CFO, Controller & Dir-HR)*
Louie Woods *(Mgr-Quality Control)*
Brands & Products:
HMF-02
HMF/VR-02
HMR-02
HMV-02
HPV-02
LINDE LSC VALVE

LINDSAY CORPORATION

2222 N 111th St
Omaha, NE 68164
Tel.: (402) 829-6800
Fax: (402) 829-6834
Web Site:
www.lindsaymanufacturing.com.
Approx. Rev.: $358,440,000
Approx. Number Employees: 891
Year Founded: 1955
Business Description:
Irrigation Equipment Mfr
S.I.C.: 2813; 3523; 4941
N.A.I.C.S.: 325120; 221310; 333111
Import Export
Advertising Expenditures: $1,300,000
Media: 2-5-7-10-13-18-20-22-23
Distr.: Intl.; Natl.
Budget Set: Aug.
Personnel:
Michael N. Christodolou *(Chm)*
Richard W. Parod *(Pres & CEO)*
James Raabe *(CFO & VP)*
Douglas A. Taylor *(CIO & VP)*
Timothy J. Paymal *(Chief Acctg Officer & VP)*
Chris Sanders *(Pres/CEO-Barrier Sys Inc)*
Steven Cotariu *(Pres-Infrastructure Bus)*
David B. Downing *(Pres-Intl Ops)*
Barry A. Ruffalo *(Pres-Irrigation Bus)*
Eric Arneson *(Gen Counsel, Sec & VP)*
Dan G. Keller *(VP-HR)*
Dirk A. Lenie *(VP-Export Sls & Mktg)*
Ernie Giordano *(Bus Mgr-Mfg)*
Brands & Products:
FIELDNET
FIELDPLUS
FIELDSENTRY
GREENFIELD
GROWSMART
HYDRA-CELL
HYDRA INJECT
HYDRA INJECT I
HYDRA INJECT II
HYDRA INJECT III
INTELLIGENT DESIGN & INNOVATION
LINDSAY CORPORATION
MAXFIELD
SOILMAX
ZIMMATIC

LIQUID CONTROLS, INC.

(Sub. of IDEX Corporation)
105 Albrecht Dr
Lake Bluff, IL 60044
Tel.: (847) 295-1050
Fax: (847) 295-1057
Toll Free: (800) 458-5262
E-mail: lc-info.lcmeter@idexcorp.com
Web Site: www.lcmeter.com
Sales Range: $25-49.9 Million
Approx. Number Employees: 150
Year Founded: 1954
Business Description:
Mfr. of Positive Displacement Flow Meters & Accessories
S.I.C.: 3824
N.A.I.C.S.: 334514
Export
Media: 2-4-7-10-11-13
Distr.: Intl.
Budget Set: Jan. -Feb.
Personnel:
Royal Wollberg *(VP-Sls)*
Pedro Jimenez *(Dir-Bus Dev-Latin America)*
Les Bottoms *(Reg Mgr-Gulf Coast)*
Rick Hallowell *(Reg Mgr-Eastern)*
Rick Hembree *(Reg Mgr-Southeast)*
Don Crowder *(Product Mgr)*
Ken Fleming *(Product Mgr)*
Dan Campion *(Mgr-Midwest Reg)*
Kevin Nugent *(Mgr-Western Reg)*
Ruben Treto *(Engr-Sls)*
Mary Kay Diedrich *(Coord-Mktg)*
Brands & Products:
LECTROCOUNT LCR-II

LIQUIDMETAL TECHNOLOGIES, INC.

30452 Esperanza
Rancho Santa Margarita, CA 92688

Key to Media (For complete agency information see *The Advertising Red Books-Agencies* edition):
1. Bus. Publs. 2. Cable T.V. 3. Catalogs & Directories. 4. Co-op Adv. 5. Consumer Mags. 6. D.M. to Bus. Estab.7. D.M. to Consumers
8. Daily Newsp. 9. Exhibits/Trade Shows 10. Foreign 11. Infomercial 12. Internet Adv.13. Multimedia 14. Network Radio
15. Network T.V. 16. Newsp. Distr. Mags. 17. Other 18. Outdoor (Posters, Transit) 19. Point of Purchase20. Premiums, Novelties
21. Product Samples 22. Special Events Mktg. 23. Spot Radio 24. Spot T.V. 25. Weekly Newsp. 26. Yellow Page Adv.

Tel.: (949) 635-2100
Fax: (949) 635-2188
E-mail: information@liquidmetal.com
Web Site: www.liquidmetal.com
Approx. Rev.: $33,292,000
Approx. Number Employees: 29
Year Founded: 1987
Business Description:
Research, Development & Commercialization of Amorphous Metals
S.I.C.: 2893; 2911; 3331; 3479
N.A.I.C.S.: 325910; 324110; 331411; 332812
Advertising Expenditures: $500
Media: 10
Personnel:
Abdi Mahamedi *(Chm)*
Thomas W. Steipp *(Pres & CEO)*
Tony Chung *(CFO)*
Brands & Products:
ARMACOR
DUOCOR
LIQUIDMETAL

LISLE CORPORATION
807 E Main St PO Box 89
Clarinda, IA 51632
Tel.: (712) 542-5101
Fax: (712) 542-6591
E-mail: info@lislecorp.com
Web Site: www.lislecorp.com
Approx. Number Employees: 300
Year Founded: 1903
Business Description:
Mfr. of Garage Tools, Creepers, Drill Grinders, Magnetic Plugs & Chip Detectors
S.I.C.: 3423; 3714
N.A.I.C.S.: 332212; 336399
Import Export
Media: 2-4-5-7-10-13-19-20-21
Distr.: Intl.; Natl.
Budget Set: Nov.
Personnel:
Bill Lisle *(Pres)*
John Lisle *(Pres)*
Jon Bielfeldt *(VP-Sls & Mktg)*
Brands & Products:
HANDY PACKER
JEEPERS CREEPER
LISLE
SPILL-FREE

LITTLE GIANT PUMP COMPANY
(Sub. of Franklin Electric Co., Inc.)
3810 N Tulsa St
Oklahoma City, OK 73112-2935
Mailing Address:
PO Box 12010
Oklahoma City, OK 73157-2010
Tel.: (405) 947-2511
Fax: (405) 947-8720
Toll Free: (888) 956-0000
E-mail: customerservice@littlegiant.com
Web Site: www.lgpc.com
Sales Range: $150-199.9 Million
Approx. Number Employees: 550
Year Founded: 1941
Business Description:
Pumps & Accessories Mfr
S.I.C.: 3561; 5084
N.A.I.C.S.: 333911; 423830
Export
Media: 2-4-10-19-20-26
Distr.: Intl.; Natl.
Budget Set: Nov.
Personnel:
Robert J. Stone *(Pres & Sr VP)*
John J. Haines *(CFO, Sec & VP)*
Delancey W. Davis *(Pres-US/Canada & VP)*
Michelle Sherrill *(Mktg Mgr-Comml Plumbing & HVAC Pump Products)*
Ted Foti *(Mgr-Sls-Mktg)*
Brands & Products:
BIG JOHN
EC-400
ELIMINATOR
LITTLE GIANT
MD-HC
MD SERIES
POWERSEWER
QTI
SAHARA SERIES
SIMPLEX PACKAGES
VC SERIES
VCMA SERIES
WHIRLWIND

LITTLEFORD DAY INC.
7451 Empire Dr
Florence, KY 41042
Tel.: (859) 525-7600
Fax: (859) 525-1446
Toll Free: (800) 365-8555
E-mail: sales@littleford.com
Web Site: www.littleford.com
E-Mail For Key Personnel:
Marketing Director: bbarker@littleford.com
Sales Director: sales@littleford.com
Approx. Number Employees: 65
Year Founded: 1882
Business Description:
Mixers & Mixing Systems Mfr
S.I.C.: 3556; 3559
N.A.I.C.S.: 333294; 333298
Export
Advertising Expenditures: $200,000
Media: 1-2-10-16-20-26
Distr.: Intl.
Personnel:
Donald Bowers *(Pres)*
Rick Kesig *(VP-Engrg)*
Charles R. Kroeger *(VP-Sls)*
Bill Barker *(Mgr-Mktg)*
Brands & Products:
CB
DAY NAUTA
DAYMAX
DOUBLE ARM
DVT
EK
FKM
FM
KM
LITTLEFORD
MIXTRUDER

LOCKFORMER COMPANY
(Div. of Mestek, Inc.)
5480 6th St SW
Cedar Rapids, IA 52404
Tel.: (319) 364-9181
Fax: (319) 364-3436
Web Site: www.lockformer.com
Sales Range: $25-49.9 Million
Approx. Number Employees: 22
Year Founded: 1937
Business Description:
Roll-Forming Machinery Mfr
S.I.C.: 3542; 3541
N.A.I.C.S.: 333513; 333512
Export
Media: 2-4-7-10-11
Distr.: Intl.; Natl.; Reg.
Budget Set: Apr.
Brands & Products:
AUTO-GUIDE
CLEATFORMER
CORNER CADET
EASY EDGER
GALV-OFF
PIPEFAB
QUICLOK
SPEEDNOTCH
TRIPLEX CLEATFORMER
VULCAN

LOOS & COMPANY, INC.
1 Cable Rd
Pomfret, CT 06258
Mailing Address:
PO Box 98
Pomfret, CT 06258-0098
Tel.: (860) 928-7981
Fax: (860) 928-6167
Toll Free: (800) 533-5667
E-mail: sales@loosco.com
Web Site: www.loosco.com
E-Mail For Key Personnel:
President: richard@loosco.com
Marketing Director: mike@loosco.com
Sales Director: sales@loosco.com
Public Relations: mike@loosco.com
Approx. Number Employees: 300
Year Founded: 1964
Business Description:
Mfr. of Mechanical Steel Cable, Cable Assemblies, Tools & Hardware, Plastic Jacketed Cable & Stainless Steel Wire
S.I.C.: 3229
N.A.I.C.S.: 327212
Import Export
Media: 2-4-10-13
Distr.: Intl.; Natl.
Budget Set: Sept.
Personnel:
Richard Griswold *(Pres)*
Michael Wallace *(VP-Sls & Mktg)*
Mike Fredrickson *(Product Mgr)*
Brands & Products:
BRITE-STAY
CABLEWARE
CANVEYOR
CASTLOK
GOLDEN BEAR
GOLDILOCKS
K-FLEX
LOCOLOC
LOLON
LOOS & CO
LOOS ENDS
LOOSLAY
MONOKORE
REFLEXITE

LORD CORPORATION
111 Lord Dr
Cary, NC 27511
Tel.: (919) 468-5979
Fax: (919) 469-5598
Telex: 291935
Web Site: www.lord.com
Sales Range: $700-749.9 Million
Approx. Number Employees: 2,600
Year Founded: 1924
Business Description:
Mfr. & Retailer of Adhesives, Polyurethane Coatings, Electronics Adhesives & Coatings, Devices & Systems to Manage Mechanical Motion & Control Noise & Products & Systems Utilizing Magnetically-Responsive (MR) Technology
S.I.C.: 2891; 3724
N.A.I.C.S.: 325520; 336412
Import Export
Media: 2-10-26
Distr.: Intl.; Natl.
Budget Set: Oct.
Personnel:
Richard L. McNeel *(Chm, Pres & CEO)*
Tesa L. Oechsle *(CFO & Treas)*
Jack De Leon *(COO)*
Joseph W. Marotta *(Pres-Americas)*
David Siporin *(Pres-Asia Pacific)*
Jonathan D. Oechsle *(Sec & VP-Legal)*
Rebecca Williams *(VP-Global Mktg & Bus Dev)*
Brands & Products:
AEROGLAZE
ASK US HOW
AUTOSEAL
BALANCE CHECK
CA GEL
CHEMGLAZE
CHEMLOK
CIRCALOK
CIRCUITSAF
DBQDO
DYNAFLEX
DYNAFOCAL
FLEX-BOLT
FLOCKLOK
FLUIDLASTIC
FUSOR
GELEASE
LASTOFLEX
LASTOSPHERE
LC-PAD
LOASTOFLEX
LORD
LORD ACCELERATOR
LORD-PAK
MAGNERIDE
METALJACKET
MICRO-MOUNTS
MOTION MASTER
MOTORGUARD
NVX
PHOTOGLAZE
POLY DNB
PRISMATIC
QDO
REALTIME
RHEONETIC
SPE
TFD
THERMOSET
TY PLY
TYRITE
VELVET-RIDE
VERSILOK
WONDER BOX
WONDERBOX
Advertising Agency:
Gibbs & Soell, Inc.
60 E 42nd St
New York, NY 10165
Tel.: (212) 697-2600
Fax: (212) 697-2646
Communications
Strategic Counsel

Key to Media (For complete agency information see *The Advertising Red Books-Agencies* edition):
1. Bus. Publs. 2. Cable T.V. 3. Catalogs & Directories. 4. Co-op Adv. 5. Consumer Mags. 6. D.M. to Bus. Estab.7. D.M. to Consumers 8. Daily Newsp. 9. Exhibits/Trade Shows 10. Foreign 11. Infomercial 12. Internet Adv.13. Multimedia 14. Network Radio 15. Network T.V. 16. Newsp. Distr. Mags. 17. Other 18. Outdoor (Posters, Transit) 19. Point of Purchase20. Premiums, Novelties 21. Product Samples 22. Special Events Mktg. 23. Spot Radio 24. Spot T.V. 25. Weekly Newsp. 26. Yellow Page Adv.

LOUIS BERKMAN CO.
330 N 7th St
Steubenville, OH 43952
Mailing Address:
PO Box 820
Steubenville, OH 43952-5820
Tel.: (740) 283-3722
Fax: (740) 283-1224
Web Site: www.louisberkman.com
Approx. Number Employees: 50
Year Founded: 1931
Business Description:
Wholesale of Industrial Supplies & Equipment
S.I.C.: 3444; 3711
N.A.I.C.S.: 332322; 336120
Media: 2-4-10-17-26
Distr.: Natl.
Personnel:
Louis Berkman *(Pres)*

LUFKIN INDUSTRIES, INC.
601 S Raguet St
Lufkin, TX 75904-3951
Mailing Address:
PO Box 849
Lufkin, TX 75902-0849
Tel.: (936) 634-2211
Fax: (936) 637-5272
E-mail: bob-leslie@lufkin.com
Web Site: www.lufkin.com
Approx. Sls.: $645,643,000
Approx. Number Employees: 3,000
Year Founded: 1902
Business Description:
Oilfield Pumping Equipment, Industrial & Marine Propulsion Gears, Truck Trailers & Industrial Hardware Mfr
S.I.C.: 4939; 3533; 3715; 4911; 4924; 4931; 5045; 5084; 7389
N.A.I.C.S.: 221122; 221119; 221121; 221210; 333132; 336212; 423830; 425110; 425120
Export
Media: 2-7-9-10-11-15-23-24-25-26
Distr.: Intl.; Natl.
Budget Set: Oct.
Personnel:
John F. Glick *(Pres & CEO)*
Christopher L. Boone *(CFO, Treas & VP)*
Alejandro Cestero *(Gen Counsel & VP)*
C. D. Hay *(VP & Gen Mgr-Power Transmission)*
Brian J. Gifford *(VP-HR)*
Steve Reynolds *(Gen Mgr)*
Kelvin Cole *(Mgr-Repair Acct)*
Scott Franks *(Mgr-Engrg)*
Ben Jordan *(Mgr-Ops)*
Mike May *(Mgr-Repair Acct)*
Bruce Mott *(Mgr-Repair Acct)*
Art Nelson *(Mgr-Inside Sls-Quality)*
Bill Reneau *(Mgr-Field Svc)*
Brands & Products:
LUFKIN
SROD

LYDALL, INC.
1 Colonial Rd
Manchester, CT 06040
Mailing Address:
PO Box 151
Manchester, CT 06045-0151
Tel.: (860) 646-1233
Fax: (860) 646-4917
Toll Free: (800) 365-9325
E-mail: info@lydall.com
Web Site: www.lydall.com
Approx. Sls.: $338,007,000
Approx. Number Employees: 1,600
Year Founded: 1969
Business Description:
Thermal & Acoustical Barriers, Automotive Heat Shields & Insulation Products Mfr
S.I.C.: 5033; 2258; 3053; 3499
N.A.I.C.S.: 423330; 313249; 332999; 339991
Export
Media: 2-4-7-8-9-10-20-25
Distr.: Intl.; Natl.
Budget Set: Oct.
Personnel:
W. Leslie Duffy *(Chm)*
Dale G. Barnhart *(Pres & CEO)*
Erika K. Turner *(CFO, Treas & VP)*
Paul G. Igoe *(Gen Counsel, Sec & VP)*
Mona G. Estey *(VP-HR)*
Joe Petrosky *(VP-Global Sls & Mktg)*
Brands & Products:
ACTIPURE
AFFINITY
ARIOSO
CAPRATON
CRS-WRAP
CRYO-LITE
CRYOTHERM
DBCORE
DBLYTE
LYDAIR
LYDALL
LYFLEX
LYPORE
LYTHERM
MANNIGLAS
MANNING
SPECIALTY ENGINEERED PRODUCTS
ZEROCLEARANCE
Advertising Agency:
The Donaldson Group
88 Hopmeadow St
Weatogue, CT 06089-9602
Tel.: (860) 658-9777
Fax: (860) 658-0533

LYNCH TECHNOLOGIES, INC.
(Sub. of Olivotto Glass Technologies S.p.A.)
207 Airport Rd
Bainbridge, GA 39817
Tel.: (229) 248-2345
Fax: (229) 243-0987
E-mail: info@lynchsystems.com
Web Site: www.olivotto.it
Approx. Sls.: $7,750,000
Approx. Number Employees: 75
Year Founded: 1914
Business Description:
Hollow Glass Forming Machinery Mfr
S.I.C.: 3559; 3823; 7389
N.A.I.C.S.: 333298; 334513; 541420
Export
Media: 4-6-17
Distr.: Intl.; Natl.
Budget Set: Oct.
Personnel:
Randy Brouillet *(Dir-Tech)*
Dick Robinson *(Mgr-Sls)*
Jeff Shirah *(Mgr-Ops)*

M-B COMPANIES, INC.
1615 Wisconsin Ave
New Holstein, WI 53061
Mailing Address:
PO Box 200
New Holstein, WI 53061
Tel.: (920) 898-1560
Fax: (920) 898-4588
Toll Free: (800) 558-5800
E-mail: info@m-bco.com
Web Site: www.m-bco.com
E-Mail For Key Personnel:
Sales Director: sales@m-bco.com
Approx. Number Employees: 90
Year Founded: 1907
Business Description:
Pavement Sweeping & Marking Equipment Mfr
S.I.C.: 8741
N.A.I.C.S.: 561110
Import Export
Media: 2-4-7-8-10
Distr.: Intl.; Natl.
Budget Set: Dec.
Personnel:
Terrence J. Cosgrove *(Chm & CEO)*
Sue Torrison *(Mgr-Admin)*
Brands & Products:
APOLLO
APOLLO II
ECON LINER
GL-3000-P
HOLOVISION
MB
MERCURY
NAVIGATOR-20
PAINTMASTER PRO
PM ERASER
POWERLINER
PRO-CHIP
PRO CHIP 625
THERMOKIT
TITAN 1000D
VULCAN

MAC EQUIPMENT, INC.
(Holding of George K. Baum Merchant Banc)
7901 NW 107th Ter
Kansas City, MO 64153-1910
Tel.: (816) 891-9300
Fax: (816) 891-8978
Toll Free: (888) 821-2476
E-mail: macequipment@macequipment.com
Web Site: www.macequipment.com
Approx. Number Employees: 300
Year Founded: 1955
Business Description:
Air Filtration & Material Management Equipment Mfr
S.I.C.: 3535; 3564
N.A.I.C.S.: 333922; 333411
Media: 4-7-10
Personnel:
Jay Brown *(CEO)*

MACLEAN-FOGG COMPANY INC.
1000 Allanson Rd
Mundelein, IL 60060
Tel.: (847) 566-0010
Fax: (847) 566-0026
Toll Free: (800) 323-4536
E-mail: info@maclean-fogg.com
Web Site: www.maclean-fogg.com
Approx. Sls.: $800,000,000
Approx. Number Employees: 4,500
Year Founded: 1925
Business Description:
Electronic Connectors Mfr
S.I.C.: 3679
N.A.I.C.S.: 334419
Import Export
Media: 1-2-3-4-7-8-10-12-13-19-20-21-26
Personnel:
Barry L. MacLean *(Pres)*
George H. Cook *(CFO & VP-Fin)*
Brands & Products:
AXILOK
CLINCH-LOK
DECOREX
MACLEAN-FOGG
MACLOCK
POGOSTIK
SECURELOK
STA-TITE
STRANDLINK
STRANDVISE
TWO-WAY
WHIZLOCK
WIRELINK
WIREVISE

MADISON-KIPP CORPORATION
201 Waubesa St
Madison, WI 53704
Mailing Address:
PO Box 8043
Madison, WI 53708-8043
Tel.: (608) 244-3511
Fax: (608) 242-5284
Toll Free: (800) 356-6148
E-mail: info@madison-kipp.com
Web Site: www.madison-kipp.com
E-Mail For Key Personnel:
Sales Director: marketing@madison-kipp.com
Approx. Number Employees: 600
Year Founded: 1898
Business Description:
Mfr of Aluminum & Zinc Castings
S.I.C.: 3363; 3364
N.A.I.C.S.: 331521; 331522
Import Export
Media: 1
Distr.: Intl.; Natl.
Budget Set: Oct.
Personnel:
J. Reed Coleman *(CEO)*
Mark Daniel *(CFO)*

MAGBEE CONTRACTORS SUPPLY
1065 Bankhead Hwy
Winder, GA 30680-8415
Tel.: (678) 425-2600
Fax: (678) 425-2602
E-mail: help@magbee.com
Web Site: www.magbee.com
Sales Range: $25-49.9 Million
Approx. Number Employees: 50
Year Founded: 1954
Business Description:
Millwork
S.I.C.: 2431; 5031
N.A.I.C.S.: 321918; 423310
Import Export
Media: 4-13-26

MAGLINE, INC.
503 S Mercer St
Pinconning, MI 48650
Tel.: (989) 879-2411
Fax: (989) 879-5399
Toll Free: (800) MAGLINE
E-mail: info@magliner.com
Web Site: www.magliner.com

Key to Media (For complete agency information see *The Advertising Red Books-Agencies* edition):
1. Bus. Publs. 2. Cable T.V. 3. Catalogs & Directories. 4. Co-op Adv. 5. Consumer Mags. 6. D.M. to Bus. Estab.7. D.M. to Consumers
8. Daily Newsp. 9. Exhibits/Trade Shows 10. Foreign 11. Infomercial 12. Internet Adv.13. Multimedia 14. Network Radio
15. Network T.V. 16. Newsp. Distr. Mags. 17. Other 18. Outdoor (Posters, Transit) 19. Point of Purchase20. Premiums, Novelties
21. Product Samples 22. Special Events Mktg. 23. Spot Radio 24. Spot T.V. 25. Weekly Newsp. 26. Yellow Page Adv.

E-Mail For Key Personnel:
Marketing Director: marketing@magliner.com
Approx. Number Employees: 130
Year Founded: 1947
Business Description:
Hand Trucks & Accessories Mfr
S.I.C.: 3537; 8742
N.A.I.C.S.: 333924; 541611
Import Export
Media: 2-4-5-6-7-10
Distr.: Intl.; Natl.
Budget Set: Jan.
Brands & Products:
AXIOM 360
COOLIFT
CRDS
EQUALIZER
GEMINI
KEG MOVER
MAGLINER
POSI-STEP
ROUTEMASTER
SERIES 2000
SLIDER

MAGNETIC METALS CORP.
(Sub. of Indel, Inc.)
1900 Hayes Ave
Camden, NJ 08105
Tel.: (856) 964-7842
Fax: (856) 963-8569
Toll Free: (800) 257-8174
E-mail: info@magmet.com
Web Site: www.magmet.com
E-Mail For Key Personnel:
Marketing Director: marketing@magmet.com
Approx. Number Employees: 400
Year Founded: 1942
Business Description:
Mfr of Magnetic Components
S.I.C.: 3691
N.A.I.C.S.: 335911
Export
Media: 1-2-4-10-11-13-20-26
Distr.: Intl.; Natl.
Budget Set: Nov. -Dec.
Personnel:
Henry M. Rowan *(Chm)*
Frank A. Raneiro *(Pres)*
Chris Clee *(Reg Mgr-Sls)*
Kurt Haley *(Mgr-Sls & Mktg)*

MAGNETROL INTERNATIONAL INC.
5300 Belmont Rd
Downers Grove, IL 60515-4499
Tel.: (630) 969-4000
Fax: (630) 969-9489
Toll Free: (800) 624-8765
E-mail: info@magnetrol.com
Web Site: www.magnetrol.com
Approx. Number Employees: 400
Year Founded: 1932
Business Description:
Liquid Level & Flow Instrumentation Mfr
S.I.C.: 3823; 3812
N.A.I.C.S.: 334513; 334511
Export
Media: 2-10
Distr.: Intl.; Natl.
Budget Set: Jan.
Personnel:
Judy G. Stevenson *(Pres & CEO)*
Dave Miller *(Dir-Mktg WW & Exec Dir. European Sls & Mktg)*
Ann Kulesza *(Mgr-Mktg Commun)*
Brands & Products:
APM
ATLAS
AURORA
DIGITAL ES II MODULEVEL
ECHOTEL
ECLIPSE
ES II
EZ
EZ MODULEVEL
GEMINI
HORIZON
JUPITER
KOTRON
MAGNETROL
MODULEVEL
PROOF-ER
PULSAR
SOLITEL
THERMATEL
TUFFY
TUFFY I
TUFFY II

MAHR FEDERAL, INC.
(Sub. of Carl Mahr Holding GmbH)
1144 Eddy St
Providence, RI 02905-4511
Tel.: (401) 784-3100
Fax: (401) 784-3246
Toll Free: (800) 343-2050
E-mail: information@mahr.com
Web Site: www.mahr.com
Approx. Number Employees: 300
Business Description:
Dimensional Measuring Instruments Mfr
S.I.C.: 3823
N.A.I.C.S.: 334513
Media: 2-10-13
Personnel:
Tony Picone *(Pres)*
Gary Robison *(Dir-Mktg)*
Brands & Products:
MAHR

MAKINO INC.
(Sub. of Makino USA Inc.)
7680 A Innovation Way
Mason, OH 45040
Tel.: (513) 573-7200
Fax: (513) 573-7360
Toll Free: (800) 552-3288
Web Site: www.makino.com
Approx. Number Employees: 250
Year Founded: 1887
Business Description:
Manufacturing System Designer, Mfr & Retailer
S.I.C.: 3541; 5084
N.A.I.C.S.: 333512; 423830
Import
Media: 1-2-4-5-7-10-13
Distr.: Natl.
Budget Set: Nov.
Personnel:
Donald Lane *(Pres & CEO)*
Jeff Kiszonas *(Product Mgr-EDM)*
Bark Larson *(Mgr-Titanium Process Dev)*
Mark Rentschler *(Mgr-Mktg)*
Brands & Products:
A55
H-SERIES
MC1213
MC1513
MC1813
MC2210
SNC

MAKITA U.S.A., INC.
(Sub. of Makita Corporation)
14930 Northam St
La Mirada, CA 90638
Tel.: (714) 522-8088
Fax: (714) 522-8133
Web Site: www.makitatools.com
Approx. Number Employees: 140
Year Founded: 1970
Business Description:
Portable Electric Power Tools Mfr & Sales
S.I.C.: 5072
N.A.I.C.S.: 423710
Import
Media: 2-10-13-19-22-26
Distr.: Intl.; Natl.
Budget Set: Dec.
Personnel:
Hiroshi Okamoto *(Pres)*
Richard Chapman *(Sr VP-Natl Sls)*
Ken Hefley *(Sr VP-Mktg)*
Brent Withey *(Dir-Mktg)*
Anthony Corwin *(Product Mgr)*
Bill Austin *(Mgr-Adv)*

MAKO
(Sub. of CompAir USA)
1634 SW 17th St
Ocala, FL 34471
Tel.: (877) 272-1675
Fax: (352) 351-5211
E-mail: email@compairmako.com
Web Site: www.compairmako.com
Sales Range: $25-49.9 Million
Approx. Number Employees: 50
Year Founded: 1952
Business Description:
Air, Breathing Air & Gas Compressors Mfr
S.I.C.: 3563; 3564
N.A.I.C.S.: 333912; 333411
Import Export
Media: 1-2-4-10-13
Advertising Agency:
Tomes Rabold Advertising & Design
226 N E Sanchez Ave
Ocala, FL 34470
Tel.: (352) 622-7115
Fax: (352) 622-5605
(Breathing Air Compressors)

MANITEX INTERNATIONAL, INC.
9725 Industrial Dr
Bridgeview, IL 60455-2406
Tel.: (708) 430-7500
E-mail: djlangevin@manitexinternational.com
Web Site: www.manitexinternational.com
Approx. Rev.: $95,875,000
Approx. Number Employees: 229
Business Description:
Engineered Lifting Equipment Mfr & Distr
S.I.C.: 3536; 3537; 3559; 5084
N.A.I.C.S.: 333923; 333298; 333924; 423830
Advertising Expenditures: $155,000
Media: 17
Personnel:
David J. Langevin *(Chm & CEO)*
Andrew M. Rooke *(Pres & COO)*
Scott Rolston *(Pres)*
David H. Gransee *(CFO & VP)*

THE MANITOWOC COMPANY, INC.
2400 S 44th St
Manitowoc, WI 54220
Mailing Address:
PO Box 66
Manitowoc, WI 54221-0066
Tel.: (920) 684-4410
Fax: (920) 652-9778
Web Site: www.manitowoc.com
Approx. Sls.: $3,141,700,000
Approx. Number Employees: 13,300
Year Founded: 1902
Business Description:
Holding Company; Crane & Foodservice Equipment Mfr & Distr
S.I.C.: 6719; 3536; 3556; 3585; 5046; 5082
N.A.I.C.S.: 551112; 333294; 333415; 333923; 423440; 423810
Export
Media: 2-4-7-10-17-20-26
Distr.: Intl.
Budget Set: Oct.
Personnel:
Glen E. Tellock *(Chm, Pres & CEO)*
Eric Etchart *(Pres, Sr VP & Gen Mgr)*
Carl J. Laurino *(CFO & Sr VP)*
Michael J. Kachmer *(Sr VP & Pres/Gen Mgr-Manitowoc Foodservice)*
Maurice D. Jones *(Gen Counsel, Sec & Sr VP)*
Dean J. Nolden *(VP-Fin & Treas)*
Donald M. Condon, Jr. *(Sr VP-Olefins & Corp Bus Dev)*
Thomas G. Musial *(Sr VP-HR & Admin)*
Brands & Products:
MANITOWOC
MANITOWOC CRANE CARE

MARCH MANUFACTURING INC.
1819 Pickwick Ave
Glenview, IL 60025
Tel.: (847) 729-5300
Fax: (847) 729-7062
E-mail: sales@marchpump.com
Web Site: www.marchpump.com
E-Mail For Key Personnel:
Sales Director: sales@marchpump.com
Approx. Number Employees: 65
Year Founded: 1954
Business Description:
Centrifugal Pumps Mfr
S.I.C.: 3561; 3586
N.A.I.C.S.: 333911; 333913
Import Export
Advertising Expenditures: $200,000
Media: 2-4-10-13
Distr.: Intl.; Natl.
Budget Set: Monthly
Personnel:
Rick Dickinson *(Reg Mgr)*
Mark Longobardi *(Reg Mgr)*
Fred N. Zimmermann *(Mgr-Mktg)*
Brands & Products:
MARCH

MARINE & OFFSHORE CANADA
113 Cushman Rd Unit 29
Saint Catharines, ON Canada
Tel.: (905) 688-4922

Marine & Offshore Canada — (Continued)

Fax: (905) 688-9028
E-mail: sales@marineandoffshore.com
Web Site: www.marineandoffshore.com
E-Mail For Key Personnel:
Sales Director: sales@marineandoffshore.com
Approx. Sls.: $1,232,898
Approx. Number Employees: 4
Business Description:
Pump Parts & Compressors Distr
S.I.C.: 3563
N.A.I.C.S.: 333912
Media: 4-7-10-13
Personnel:
Roger McNeill *(Mng Dir)*
Brands & Products:
HAMWORTHY

MARINE TRAVELIFT, INC.

49 E Yew St
Sturgeon Bay, WI 54235
Tel.: (920) 743-6202
Fax: (920) 743-1522
E-mail: lifts@marinetravelift.com
Web Site: www.marinetravelift.com
Sales Range: $25-49.9 Million
Approx. Number Employees: 140
Year Founded: 1975
Business Description:
Marine Hoists, Boat Lifts & Marine ForkLifts
S.I.C.: 3531; 3536
N.A.I.C.S.: 333120; 333923
Import Export
Media: 2-4-6-7-10
Distr.: Intl.; Natl.
Budget Set: Oct.
Personnel:
Jim Ashton *(Chm)*
Erich Pfeifer *(Pres & COO)*
Stephan Pfeifer *(CEO)*
Jason Johnson *(Mgr-Sls-North America)*
Brands & Products:
CARRYDECK
MARINE
MARINE TRAVELIFT
MARINER
PITMAN
SHUTTLELIFT

MARK ANDY, INC.

(Holding of American Industrial Partners)
18081 Chesterfield Airport Rd
Chesterfield, MO 63005
Tel.: (636) 532-4433
Fax: (636) 532-1510
Toll Free: (800) 700-6275
E-mail: info@markandy.com
Web Site: www.markandy.com
Sales Range: $100-124.9 Million
Approx. Number Employees: 400
Year Founded: 1946
Business Description:
Narrow Web Printing Equipment Mfr
S.I.C.: 3555; 3565
N.A.I.C.S.: 333293; 333993
Import Export
Media: 2-4-10-11
Distr.: Intl.; Natl.
Budget Set: Oct.
Personnel:
Paul Brauss *(Pres & CEO)*
Mike Howard *(CFO)*
John Howard *(VP-Engrng)*
Greg Palm *(VP-Sls & Mktg)*
Steve Schulte *(Dir-Sls-Natl)*
Mary Sullivan *(Dir-Global Mktg)*
Michael Schneider *(Reg Mgr-Sls-South & Southwest)*
Jerry Henson *(Mgr-Print Svcs)*
Brands & Products:
LP3000
XP5000

MARLIN MFG. CO.

12800 Corporate Dr
Cleveland, OH 44130
Tel.: (216) 676-1340
Fax: (216) 676-1344
Toll Free: (800) 321-6648
E-mail: marlincle@marlinmfg.com
Web Site: www.marlinmfg.com
Approx. Number Employees: 70
Year Founded: 1952
Business Description:
Temperature Instrumentation Mfr, Servicer & Distr for Research & Industry
S.I.C.: 3823; 3829
N.A.I.C.S.: 334513; 334519
Media: 4-10-13
Distr.: Natl.
Budget Set: Aug.
Personnel:
Allen Tymkewicz *(Pres)*
Brands & Products:
THE FOOD THERMICATOR
JAB-IN CONNECTORS
MARLIN
MARLOX
STRIPANEL
THERMO-DIP

MARMON/KEYSTONE CORPORATION

(Sub. of Marmon Distribution Services)
225 E Cunningham St
Butler, PA 16001-6018
Mailing Address:
PO Box 992
Butler, PA 16003-0992
Tel.: (724) 283-3000
Fax: (724) 283-0558
Toll Free: (800) 544-1748
Web Site: www.marmonkeystone.com
Sales Range: $700-749.9 Million
Approx. Number Employees: 1,317
Year Founded: 1970
Business Description:
Pipe & Tubing Steel Whslr
S.I.C.: 5051
N.A.I.C.S.: 423510
Media: 4
Personnel:
Norman E. Gottschalk, Jr. *(Pres & CEO)*
Andrew Seka *(Exec VP & Controller)*
Jim Spatafore *(Exec VP)*
Alan L. Wilkinson *(Reg VP)*
Linda Mccue *(VP-HR)*
Marc Brandt *(Mgr-White Metals Product)*
Bart Gardina *(Mgr-Pur)*
James J. McElhaney *(Mgr-Corp Pur)*

MASTER MECHANIC MFG. CO.

(Div. of Certified Power Inc.)
970 Campus Dr
Mundelein, IL 60060
Tel.: (847) 573-3812
Fax: (847) 573-3836
Toll Free: (800) 877-8350
Web Site: www.certifiedpower.com/cpi_master.aspx
Approx. Number Employees: 7
Year Founded: 1953
Business Description:
Distr Hydraulic & Fluid Power Products & Accessories for Marine & Heavy Equipment Applications
S.I.C.: 2621; 5084
N.A.I.C.S.: 322121; 423830
Import Export
Media: 6-8-13
Distr.: Natl.
Budget Set: Monthly

MATHEWSON CORPORATION

86 Finnell Dr Unit 6
Weymouth, MA 02188
Tel.: (781) 331-8440
Fax: (781) 331-8870
Toll Free: (800) 245-7250
E-mail: info@unitedmattressmachy.com
Web Site: www.unitedmattressmachy.com
Sales Range: $75-99.9 Million
Approx. Number Employees: 16
Year Founded: 1885
Business Description:
Mattress Machinery & Sewing Machine Mfr
S.I.C.: 3552; 3542
N.A.I.C.S.: 333292; 333513
Export
Media: 2-10
Distr.: Intl.; Natl.
Budget Set: Dec.
Personnel:
Tom Brewer *(Pres)*
Brands & Products:
FALES
MATHEWSON CORPORATION
UNITED

MAXON CORPORATION

(Sub. of Honeywell Environmental & Combustion Controls)
201 E 18th St
Muncie, IN 47302
Mailing Address:
PO Box 2068
Muncie, IN 47307-0068
Tel.: (765) 284-3304
Fax: (765) 286-8394
E-mail: info@maxoncorp.com
Web Site: www.maxoncorp.com
Sales Range: $75-99.9 Million
Approx. Number Employees: 500
Year Founded: 1916
Business Description:
Industrial Combustion Equipment & Valves Mfr
S.I.C.: 3433
N.A.I.C.S.: 333414
Export
Media: 1-2-4-7-10-11
Distr.: Direct to Consumer; Intl.; Natl.
Budget Set: Nov.
Personnel:
Richard Clasby *(COO)*
Terry VanPelt *(Coord-Pur)*
Brands & Products:
ACTIONAIR
AIRFLO
APX
CIRCULAR INCINO-PAK
COMBUSTIFUME
CROSSFIRE
CYCLOMAX
DELTA-TE
EBMRV CYCLOMAX LOW NOX
HC AIRFLO
KINEDIZER
KINEMAX
LINOFLAME
LO-NOX
M-PAKT ULTRA LOW NOX
MAXON
MEGAFIRE
MICRO-RATIO
MULTI-RATIO
MULTIFIRE
NP-LE AIRFLO
OVENPAK
OVENPAK-II
OXY-PILOT
OXY-THERM
P/S RADIANT II
PAKT
PILOTPAK
PREMIX
RADMAX
RAMFIRE
RG AIRFLO
SERIES 300 OXY-THERM
SERIES 66 AIRFLO
SERIES LV AIRFLO
SERIES NP
SLS
SMARTFIRE
SMARTLINK
STICKTITE
SYNCHRO
TUBE-O-FLAME
TUBE-O-THERM
UNI-RAD
VALUPAK
VENTITE
VORTIFLARE
WIDE-RANGE

MAYFRAN INTERNATIONAL, INC.

6650 Beta Dr
Cleveland, OH 44143-2321
Mailing Address:
PO Box 43038
Cleveland, OH 44143-0045
Tel.: (440) 461-4100
Fax: (440) 461-5565
Toll Free: (800) 321-6988
Telex: 241585
E-mail: info@mayfran.com
Web Site: www.mayfran.com
Sales Range: $75-99.9 Million
Approx. Number Employees: 290
Year Founded: 1933
Business Description:
Conveyor & Scrap Handling Systems Mfr
S.I.C.: 3535; 5084
N.A.I.C.S.: 333922; 423830
Advertising Expenditures: $250,000
Media: 1-2-4-10-13-16-26
Distr.: Intl.; Natl.
Budget Set: Feb.
Personnel:
J. D. Sullivan *(Chm & CEO)*
William Centa *(Pres)*
Andy Tiltins *(VP & Gen Mgr)*
Advertising Agency:
Beta Advertising Services
(A Unit of Mayfran International)

Key to Media (For complete agency information see *The Advertising Red Books-Agencies* edition):
1. Bus. Publs. 2. Cable T.V. 3. Catalogs & Directories. 4. Co-op Adv. 5. Consumer Mags. 6. D.M. to Bus. Estab.7. D.M. to Consumers
8. Daily Newsp. 9. Exhibits/Trade Shows 10. Foreign 11. Infomercial 12. Internet Adv.13. Multimedia 14. Network Radio
15. Network T.V. 16. Newsp. Distr. Mags. 17. Other 18. Outdoor (Posters, Transit) 19. Point of Purchase20. Premiums, Novelties
21. Product Samples 22. Special Events Mktg. 23. Spot Radio 24. Spot T.V. 25. Weekly Newsp. 26. Yellow Page Adv.

6650 Beta Dr
Cleveland, OH 44143-2321
Tel.: (440) 461-4100
Tel.: (440) 461-5565
Fax: (440) 461-0147
Toll Free: (800) 321-6988

MCDONOUGH MANUFACTURING COMPANY
2320 Melby St
Eau Claire, WI 54702
Tel.: (715) 834-7755
Fax: (715) 834-3968
E-mail: mcdonough@mcdonough-mfg.com
Web Site: www.mcdonough-mfg.com
Sales Range: $10-24.9 Million
Approx. Number Employees: 63
Year Founded: 1888
Business Description:
Sawmill Products Mfr
S.I.C.: 3559; 3541
N.A.I.C.S.: 333298; 333512
Export
Media: 2-4-6-10-13
Distr.: Natl.
Personnel:
Susan K. Tietz *(Pres & CEO)*
Brands & Products:
MCDONOUGH
STERLING

MCLAUGHLIN MANUFACTURING COMPANY
2006 Perimeter Rd
Greenville, SC 29605
Tel.: (864) 277-5870
Fax: (864) 235-9661
Toll Free: (800) 435-9340
E-mail: mmole@mightymole.com
Web Site: www.mightymole.com
Approx. Number Employees: 61
Year Founded: 1921
Business Description:
Horizontal Mining & Earth Drilling Equipment Mfr
S.I.C.: 3545; 3546
N.A.I.C.S.: 333515; 333991
Import Export
Advertising Expenditures: $224,000
Bus. Publs.: $120,000; Catalogs & Directories: $36,000; Co-op Adv.: $26,000; Other: $36,000; Premiums, Novelties: $6,000
Distr.: Intl.; Natl.
Budget Set: Nov.
Personnel:
David J. Gasmovic *(Pres & CEO)*
Mike Moore *(VP-Sls)*
Brands & Products:
HOLE HAMMER
MCLAUGHLIN
MIGHTYMOLE
VAXCAVATOR
VERIFIER
VERIFIER VISION
VERSA-MOLE

MCNEIL & NRM INC.
96 E Crosier St
Akron, OH 44311
Tel.: (330) 253-2525
Fax: (330) 253-7022
Toll Free: (800) 669-2525
Sales Range: $50-74.9 Million
Approx. Number Employees: 100
Year Founded: 1904
Business Description:
Tire Cutting Presses & Equipment Mfr
S.I.C.: 3559; 3569
N.A.I.C.S.: 333220; 333999
Export
Media: 1-2-4-7-10-16-26
Distr.: Intl.; Natl.
Personnel:
Robert Nelson *(CFO & VP-Fin)*
John McCormick *(Exec VP-Sls)*
A.M. Melek *(Exec VP)*
A. P. Singh *(Exec VP)*
B.F. Lesneski *(Chief Engr)*
Brands & Products:
BAG-O-MATIC
ROTOCAST
RUBBER MATE

MEAD FLUID DYNAMICS, INC.
4114 N Knox Ave
Chicago, IL 60641
Tel.: (773) 685-6800
Fax: (773) 685-7002
E-mail: sales@mead-usa.com
Web Site: www.mead-usa.com
E-Mail For Key Personnel:
President: burnett@meadfluiddynamics.com
Sales Director: sales@mead-usa.com
Approx. Number Employees: 55
Year Founded: 1939
Business Description:
Pneumatic Components Designer & Mfr for the Industrial Automation Market
S.I.C.: 3492; 3593
N.A.I.C.S.: 332912; 333995
Import Export
Media: 2-4-7-10-13-20-21
Distr.: Natl.
Personnel:
Tom Kane *(VP-Sls)*
Brands & Products:
CAPSULA
CENTAUR
CSV
DURA-MATIC
DYLA-TROL
DYNA-MATION
DYNA-MATION II
ISONIC
ISONIC MOD 3
LIGHT TOUCH
MEAD
NOVA
SMALL BORE
SPACE SAVER
Advertising Agency:
Arcturus Group
2610 Lake Cook Rd Ste 210
Riverwoods, IL 60015
Tel.: (847) 282-3540
Fax: (847) 282-3541

MEADVILLE FORGING COMPANY INC.
(Sub. of Keller Group Inc.)
15309 Baldwin St Ext
Meadville, PA 16335
Mailing Address:
PO Box 459
Meadville, PA 16335
Tel.: (814) 332-8200
Fax: (814) 333-4657
E-mail: info@meadforge.com
Web Site: www.meadforge.com
Approx. Number Employees: 330
Year Founded: 1955
Business Description:
Designer & Producer of Custom Forged Iron & Steel Parts
S.I.C.: 3462
N.A.I.C.S.: 332111
Media: 2-4-7-20
Distr.: Natl.
Personnel:
Gasper Buffa *(Pres)*
Tom McGinnis *(VP-Sls)*

MEASUREMENT SPECIALTIES INC.
1000 Lucas Way
Hampton, VA 23666-1573
Tel.: (757) 766-1500
Fax: (757) 766-4297
Toll Free: (800) 745-8008
E-mail: info@msiusa.com
Web Site: www.meas-spec.com
Approx. Sls.: $274,789,000
Approx. Number Employees: 2,923
Year Founded: 1981
Business Description:
Sensors & Pressure Transmitters Mfr
S.I.C.: 3824; 3596; 3829
N.A.I.C.S.: 334514; 333997; 334519
Import Export
Advertising Expenditures: $110,000
Media: 17
Personnel:
Morton L. Topfer *(Chm)*
Frank D. Guidone, Jr. *(Pres & CEO)*
Mark Thomson *(CFO & Sec)*
Steven Smith *(COO)*
Jeffrey Kostelni *(Treas & VP-Fin)*
Glen MacGibbon *(Exec VP)*
Brands & Products:
ACCUSTAR
ACCUTAPE
ACCUTIRE
ANGLESTAR
BRASS LINGUINI
ENTRAN
MEAS
MEASUREMENT SPECIALTIES
MICROFUSED
PARK-ZONE
ROADTRAX
SCHAEVITZ
SENSOR LINE
SENSORSELECT
THINNER

MECO CORPORATION
1500 Industrial Rd
Greeneville, TN 37745
Tel.: (423) 639-1171
Fax: (423) 639-2570
E-mail: csr@meco.net
Web Site: www.meco.net
Approx. Number Employees: 263
Year Founded: 1959
Business Description:
Mfr & Marketer Residential Folding Furniture & Outdoor Barbecue Grills & Accessories
S.I.C.: 3469; 3631
N.A.I.C.S.: 332116; 335221
Import Export
Media: 2-10-13-19-20
Distr.: Natl.
Budget Set: Mar.
Personnel:
Robert Austin *(Owner)*
Harrell Ward *(Pres)*
Brands & Products:
LOCK & GO
MECO
OUTDOOR ESSENTIALS
SAMSONITE

MEGGITT AIRDYNAMICS, INC.
(Sub. of Meggitt PLC)
2616 Research Dr
Corona, CA 92882-6917
Tel.: (951) 734-0070
Fax: (951) 734-2594
Telex: 963425
Web Site: www.meggair.com
Approx. Number Employees: 75
Business Description:
Mfr. of Mechanical & Electrical Fans, Compressors & Hydraulic Pumps
S.I.C.: 3564; 3563
N.A.I.C.S.: 333412; 333912
Import Export
Advertising Expenditures: $300,000
Media: 4-17
Distr.: Intl.; Natl.
Personnel:
Lloyd Oshiro *(Pres)*

MET-PRO CORPORATION
160 Cassell Rd
Harleysville, PA 19438-2013
Mailing Address:
PO Box 144
Harleysville, PA 19438-0144
Tel.: (215) 723-6751
Fax: (215) 723-6758
E-mail: mpr@met-pro.com
Web Site: www.met-pro.com
Approx. Sls.: $88,865,426
Approx. Number Employees: 349
Year Founded: 1966
Business Description:
Mfr & Retailer of Product Recovery & Pollution Control Equipment
S.I.C.: 3564; 3561; 3567
N.A.I.C.S.: 333411; 333911; 333994
Export
Advertising Expenditures: $988,217
Media: 2-7-10-11-19-21
Distr.: Intl.; Natl.
Budget Set: Nov.
Personnel:
Raymond J. de Hont *(Chm, Pres & CEO)*
Gary J. Morgan *(CFO, Treas, Sec & VP-Fin)*
Paul A. Tetley *(Exec VP-Product Recovery & Pollution Control Tech)*
Gennaro A. D'Alterio *(VP & Gen Mgr)*
Gregory C. Kimmer *(VP & Gen Mgr-Met Pro Environmental Air Solutions)*
Lewis E. Osterhoudt *(VP & Gen Mgr-Keystone Filter Div)*
Vincent J. Verdone *(VP & Gen Mgr-Pristine Water Solutions Inc)*
Brands & Products:
AQUADENE
DEAN
DUALL
FLEX-KLEEN
FYBROC
KEYSTONE
MEFIAG
MET-PRO CORPORATION
OXYCAT
TRISTACK

Key to Media (For complete agency information see *The Advertising Red Books-Agencies* edition):
1. Bus. Publs. 2. Cable T.V. 3. Catalogs & Directories. 4. Co-op Adv. 5. Consumer Mags. 6. D.M. to Bus. Estab.7. D.M. to Consumers 8. Daily Newsp. 9. Exhibits/Trade Shows 10. Foreign 11. Infomercial 12. Internet Adv.13. Multimedia 14. Network Radio 15. Network T.V. 16. Newsp. Distr. Mags. 17. Other 18. Outdoor (Posters, Transit) 19. Point of Purchase20. Premiums, Novelties 21. Product Samples 22. Special Events Mktg. 23. Spot Radio 24. Spot T.V. 25. Weekly Newsp. 26. Yellow Page Adv.

MET-PRO CORPORATION, SYSTEMS DIVISION
(Div. of Met-Pro Corporation)
1555 Bustard Rd
Kulpsville, PA 19443
Mailing Address:
PO Box 144
Harleysville, PA 19438
Tel.: (215) 631-9500
Fax: (215) 631-1801
Web Site: www.met-pro.com
Sales Range: $50-74.9 Million
Approx. Number Employees: 12
Business Description:
Mfr of Thermal & Catalytic Oxidizer systems
S.I.C.: 3561; 3567
N.A.I.C.S.: 333911; 333994
Export
Media: 2-4-7-10
Distr.: Intl.; Natl.
Budget Set: Aug.
Brands & Products:
OXYCAT

METALCENTER, INC.
(Sub. of Reliance Steel & Aluminum Co.)
12034 Greenstone Ave
Santa Fe Springs, CA 90670-0101
Tel.: (562) 944-3322
Fax: (562) 944-1346
E-mail: info@rsac.com
Web Site: www.rsac.com
Sales Range: $25-49.9 Million
Approx. Number Employees: 85
Year Founded: 1986
Business Description:
Metals Processing & Distribution
S.I.C.: 5051
N.A.I.C.S.: 423510
Media: 2-26
Distr.: Natl.
Personnel:
Bob Thommen *(Gen Mgr)*

METALFAB, INC.
Prices Switch Rd PO Box 9
Vernon, NJ 07462
Tel.: (973) 764-2000
Fax: (973) 764-0272
Toll Free: (800) 764-2999
E-mail: metalfab@metalfabinc.com
Web Site: www.metalfabinc.com
E-Mail For Key Personnel:
Sales Director: sales@metalfabinc.com
Sales Range: $10-24.9 Million
Approx. Number Employees: 30
Year Founded: 1977
Business Description:
Dry Solids Processing Equipment Mfr
S.I.C.: 3444; 3535
N.A.I.C.S.: 332322; 333922
Export
Advertising Expenditures: $150,000
Bus. Publs.: 100%
Distr.: Natl.
Personnel:
Mike Randazzo *(COO)*
Dan Higgins *(VP-Sls & Mktg)*
Brands & Products:
BETTER-WEIGH
CONVEY-ALL
M.A.P
METATECH
POSIBIN
POSIBINS

METRO MACHINE & ENGINEERING CORP.
8001 Wallace Rd
Eden Prairie, MN 55344-2224
Tel.: (952) 937-2800
Fax: (952) 937-2374
E-mail: info@metromachine.com
Web Site: www.metromachine.com
Approx. Sls.: $8,000,000
Approx. Number Employees: 65
Year Founded: 1951
Business Description:
Designer & Builder of Hydraulic Couplers, Lock Valves, Selector Valves, Restrictors, Check Valves, Hydraulic Components & Directional Control Valves
S.I.C.: 3549; 3565
N.A.I.C.S.: 333518; 333993
Media: 2-4-7-10-21
Distr.: Natl.
Budget Set: Mar.
Personnel:
Robert Midness *(Pres & CEO)*
Paul Sivula *(VP-Engrg & Sls)*
Joray Dunlavy *(Project Mgr-Sls)*
Dave Brahee *(Mgr-Sls)*
Russ Butchart *(Mgr-Controls)*
Brands & Products:
METRO

METSO MINERALS
(Div. of Metso Minerals Oy)
314 8th St NW
Cedar Rapids, IA 52405
Tel.: (319) 558-0160
Fax: (319) 247-0822
Toll Free: (800) 366-2051
Web Site: www.metsominerals.com
Approx. Sls.: $25,000,000
Approx. Number Employees: 130
Year Founded: 1906
Business Description:
Sales of Portable & Stationary Crushing, Screening, Washing & Loading Equipment
S.I.C.: 1429
N.A.I.C.S.: 212319
Import Export
Advertising Expenditures: $440,000
Multimedia: $5,000; Bus. Publs.: $200,000; Catalogs & Directories: $35,000; Co-op Adv.: $75,000; D.M. to Bus. Estab.: $5,000; D.M. to Consumers: $20,000; Exhibits/Trade Shows: $50,000; Foreign: $25,000; Other: $20,000; Premiums, Novelties: $5,000
Distr.: Direct to Consumer; Natl.
Budget Set: Apr.
Personnel:
Bryce Sandell *(Mgr-Pur)*
Brands & Products:
4 MOST
CRAWLMASTER
GRAVELMASTER
HAMMERMASTER
IMPACTMASTER
IMPACTMASTER II
SCORPION

METZGAR CONVEYOR COMPANY
901 Metzgar Dr
Comstock Park, MI 49321-9758
Tel.: (616) 784-0930
Fax: (616) 784-4100
Toll Free: (888) 266-8390
E-mail: info@metzgarconveyors.com
Web Site: www.metzgarconveyors.com
E-Mail For Key Personnel:
Sales Director: sales@metzgarconveyors.com
Sales Range: $50-74.9 Million
Approx. Number Employees: 75
Year Founded: 1933
Business Description:
Line-Shaft Driven Conveyors
S.I.C.: 3535; 5084
N.A.I.C.S.: 333922; 423830
Export
Media: 2-4-7-10
Distr.: Natl.
Personnel:
Rob Metzgar *(Owner & Pres)*
Brands & Products:
FLEXA-SWITCH
METZGAR CONVEYOR
NYLO-BEARING
NYLO-WHEEL
THE RIGHT CHOICE FOR YOUR MATERIAL HANDLING NEEDS

MICRO-OHM CORPORATION
1088 Hamilton Rd
Duarte, CA 91010
Tel.: (626) 357-5377
Fax: (626) 358-6478
Toll Free: (800) 845-5167
E-mail: microohm@vividnet.com
Web Site: www.micro-ohm.com
Approx. Number Employees: 25
Year Founded: 1960
Business Description:
Precision Wire Wound & Power Resistors Mfr
S.I.C.: 3676
N.A.I.C.S.: 334415
Import Export
Media: 4
Personnel:
Charles Schwab *(Pres)*
Byron Ritchey *(CEO)*

MICRO PRODUCTS COMPANY
1296 Mark St
Bensenville, IL 60106-1022
Tel.: (630) 787-9350
Fax: (630) 787-9360
Toll Free: (800) 872-1068
Web Site: www.micro-weld.com
Sales Range: $1-9.9 Million
Approx. Number Employees: 75
Year Founded: 1928
Business Description:
Electric Welding Equipment Whslr
S.I.C.: 5084
N.A.I.C.S.: 423830
Personnel:
Jody Oltman *(CFO)*
Bill Keiler *(VP-Mktg)*
Brands & Products:
MICRO
MICRO-WELD
STRYCO
Advertising Agency:
Dayal & Associates
150 E. Anton Dr.
Romeoville, IL 60441
Tel.: (815) 886-3245

MIDDLE ATLANTIC PRODUCTS INC.
300 Fairfield Rd
Fairfield, NJ 07004
Tel.: (973) 839-1011
Fax: (973) 839-1976
Toll Free: (800) 266-7226
Web Site: www.middleatlantic.com
E-Mail For Key Personnel:
Sales Director: sales@middleatlantic.com
Approx. Number Employees: 345
Year Founded: 1978
Business Description:
Sheet Metalwork
S.I.C.: 3444
N.A.I.C.S.: 332322
Import Export
Media: 2-7-10
Personnel:
Robert Schluter *(CEO & Chief Engr)*
Craig Decker *(Dir-Customer & Sls Resources)*
Mark Tracy *(Dir-Mktg)*
Lisa Zorn *(Product Mgr)*
Brands & Products:
DECORA
ISOCENTER
MIDDLE ATLANTIC PRODUCTS
RACK TOOLS
SPEC CLIPS
SPIKE
Advertising Agency:
Griffin Public Relations & Marketing
260 Fifth Ave Ste 600
New York, NY 10001
Tel.: (212) 481-3456
Fax: (212) 684-0606

THE MIDDLEBY CORPORATION
1400 Toastmaster Dr
Elgin, IL 60120-9274
Tel.: (847) 741-3300
Fax: (847) 741-0015
E-mail: sales@middleby.com
Web Site: www.middleby.com
Approx. Sls.: $719,121,000
Approx. Number Employees: 2,060
Year Founded: 1888
Business Description:
Commercial Foodservice Equipment Mfr & Retailer
S.I.C.: 3556; 3589
N.A.I.C.S.: 333294; 333319
Import Export
Media: 2
Distr.: Intl.; Natl.; Reg.
Personnel:
Selim A. Bassoul *(Chm, Pres & CEO)*
Timothy J. FitzGerald *(CFO & VP)*
Darcy Bretz *(Dir-Comm)*
Brands & Products:
BLODGETT
BLODGETT COMBI
BLODGETT RANGE
BLOOMFIELD
CARTER HOFFMAN
COOKTEK
CTX
FRIFRI
GIGA
HOLMAN
HUONO
JADE
LANG
MAGIKITCH'N

Key to Media (For complete agency information see *The Advertising Red Books-Agencies* edition):
1. Bus. Publs. 2. Cable T.V. 3. Catalogs & Directories. 4. Co-op Adv. 5. Consumer Mags. 6. D.M. to Bus. Estab.7. D.M. to Consumers
8. Daily Newsp. 9. Exhibits/Trade Shows 10. Foreign 11. Infomercial 12. Internet Adv.13. Multimedia 14. Network Radio
15. Network T.V. 16. Newsp. Distr. Mags. 17. Other 18. Outdoor (Posters, Transit) 19. Point of Purchase20. Premiums, Novelties
21. Product Samples 22. Special Events Mktg. 23. Spot Radio 24. Spot T.V. 25. Weekly Newsp. 26. Yellow Page Adv.

THE MIDDLEBY CORPORATION
MIDDLEBY MARSHALL
NU-VU
PITCO FRIALATOR
SOUTHBEND
STAR
TOASTMASTER
TURBOCHEF
WELLS

MIDWEST INTERNATIONAL STANDARD PRODUCTS, INC.
105 Stover Rd
Charlevoix, MI 49720-1756
Tel.: (231) 547-4000
Fax: (231) 547-9453
Telex: 23-1166
Web Site: www.midwestmagic.com
Approx. Number Employees: 18
Year Founded: 1968
Business Description:
Air Pollution Equipment, Truck & Railcar Loading Equipment & Ship Loading Equipment Mfr
S.I.C.: 3564
N.A.I.C.S.: 333411
Export
Media: 1-2-10-11
Distr.: Intl.; Natl.
Personnel:
Edith Pair *(Dir-Adv & Mktg)*
Brands & Products:
AGRILOADER
AIRFLO
ARTICULOADER
BULLDOG
CAMLOC
CHOKEFEEDER
COMPACTULOADER
FAILSAFE
FLATTOP
HEAVY DUTY MINING SERIES
HYDRATILT
LADDERLOADER
MULTIFLO
PAL
PARAGON
PAT
RHINOFLEX
ROCKLOADER
ROUNDABOUT
RUNAWAY
SEALMASTER
SEALTITE
SPINFILTER
SPINTRIM
TILTAWAY
TITELIP
TIVAR
TORQUEMASTER
VACULOADER
VACUPAC
XTRATHIN

MIETHER BEARING PRODUCTS, INC.
(Sub. of Alco Industries, Inc.)
8720 N County Rd W
Odessa, TX 79764-1926
Tel.: (432) 366-3838
Fax: (432) 363-8211
Toll Free: (800) 643-8437
E-mail: meither@meither.com
Web Site: www.miether.com
Sales Range: $50-74.9 Million
Approx. Number Employees: 50
Business Description:
Spherical Bearing Housings, Inserts, Adapters, Parts & Accessories Mfr
S.I.C.: 3599; 3568
N.A.I.C.S.: 332710; 333613
Export
Media: 2-4-7-22
Distr.: Natl.
Budget Set: Aug.
Personnel:
Mike Smith *(Pres)*
Brands & Products:
MIETHER

MILACRON LLC
(Holding of Avenue Capital Group)
4165 Half Acre Rd
Batavia, OH 45103
Tel.: (513) 536-2000
Fax: (513) 536-3515
Fax: (800) 205-3293
Toll Free: (888) 246-2665
E-mail: info@milacron.com
Web Site: www.milacron.com
Sales Range: $800-899.9 Million
Approx. Number Employees: 2,500
Year Founded: 1884
Business Description:
Plastics Processing Technologies & Industrial Fluids for Metalworking Mfr
S.I.C.: 3544; 3559
N.A.I.C.S.: 333298; 333220; 333511
Export
Advertising Expenditures: $5,600,000
Media: 1-2-4-7-10-20
Distr.: Intl.; Natl.
Budget Set: Oct.
Personnel:
Dennis Smith *(Pres & CEO)*
John C. Francy *(CFO, Chief Admin Officer, Treas & VP-Fin)*
Robert C. McKee *(Pres-Global Indus Fluids & Head-Global Mold Tech Segment)*
David E. Lawrence *(Pres-Plastics Machinery)*
Dean Roberts *(Pres-Aftermarket Svcs-Americas)*
Hugh C. O'Donnell *(Gen Counsel, Sec & Sr VP)*
Advertising Agency:
Milacron Inc. Marketing
3000 Disney St.
Cincinnati, OH 45209
Tel.: (513) 458-8121
Metals

MILL-ROSE COMPANY
7995 Tyler Blvd
Mentor, OH 44060-4896
Tel.: (440) 255-9171
Fax: (440) 255-5039
Toll Free: (800) 321-3533
E-mail: info@millrose.com
Web Site: www.millrose.com
Approx. Sls.: $20,000,000
Approx. Number Employees: 200
Year Founded: 1920
Business Description:
Mfr of Industrial Brushes
S.I.C.: 3991; 3841
N.A.I.C.S.: 339994; 339112
Import Export
Media: 2-4-7-10-13
Distr.: Natl.
Personnel:
Vince Pona *(CFO)*
Brands & Products:
4 IN 1
ABRALON
CLEAN FIT
COLDSHIELD
DEBURRING TOOL
DUPONT
INSURANCE PAD
NYBRAD
QUICK-TWIST
RINGBUSTER
TARGET
TEFLON
TYNEX
WATER-GATE
Advertising Agency:
Knudsen, Gardner & Howe, Inc.
2103 Saint Clair Ave NE
Cleveland, OH 44114-4018
Tel.: (216) 781-5000
Fax: (216) 781-5004

MILLER ELECTRIC MANUFACTURING CO.
(Sub. of Illinois Tool Works Inc.)
1635 W Spencer St
Appleton, WI 54914-4911
Tel.: (920) 734-9821
Fax: (877) 327-8132
Toll Free: (800) 426-4553
E-mail: info@millerwelds.com
Web Site: www.millerwelds.com
Sales Range: $400-449.9 Million
Approx. Number Employees: 1,300
Year Founded: 1929
Business Description:
Welding & Cutting Equipment Mfr
S.I.C.: 3548
N.A.I.C.S.: 333992
Advertising Expenditures: $350,000
Media: 4-6-7-8-10-18-23-24
Distr.: Intl.
Personnel:
Mike Weller *(Pres)*
Ricky Rhiner *(Dir-Mktg)*
John Leisner *(Product Mgr)*
Jim Brook *(Product Mgr-TIG Solutions)*
Jim Rappl *(Product Mgr-Advanced Tech Products)*
Chris Roehl *(Product Mgr)*
Mike Roth *(Mgr-Mktg)*
Brands & Products:
AEROWAVE
AXCESS
BIG 40
BIG BLUE
BLUE STAR
BOBCAT
DELTA-FAB
DELTAWELD
DIALARC
DIMENSION
DYNASTY
ECONOTIG
GOLD STAR
INVISION
MAXSTAR
MILLER
MILLER DU-OP
MILLER LEGEND
MILLERMATIC
PIPEPRO 304
RACKS
SPECTRUM
SPOOLMATE
SRH
SUITCASE
SYNCROWAVE
THUNDERBOLT
TRAILBLAZER
XR

MILTON ROY COMPANY
(Div. of Hamilton Sundstrand Corporation)
201 Ivyland Rd
Ivyland, PA 18974-1706
Tel.: (215) 441-0800
Fax: (215) 441-8620
Toll Free: (888) 603-3950
Telex: 47-61138
E-mail: info@miltonroy.com
Web Site: www.miltonroy.com
Sales Range: $75-99.9 Million
Approx. Number Employees: 150
Year Founded: 1936
Business Description:
Controlled Volume (Metering) Pumps & Related Equipment Mfr
S.I.C.: 3561; 3826
N.A.I.C.S.: 333911; 334516
Import Export
Advertising Expenditures: $250,000
Media: 2-4-10-13-20-21-22
Distr.: Natl.
Budget Set: Dec.
Personnel:
Jean Claude Pharamond *(Pres)*
Pete Brownell *(Gen Mgr-Sls)*
Hubert Gartner *(Area Mgr-Canada)*
Tom Humphreys *(Area Mgr-Western)*
Jeff Ives *(Area Mgr-Eastern)*
Kenny Louque *(Area Mgr-Southern)*
David Urena *(Area Mgr-Latin America)*
Coogan Cameron *(Product Mgr)*
Jim Carling *(Product Mgr)*
Kris Kimmel *(Product Mgr)*
Laurel Bloch *(Mgr-Mktg Comm)*
James Casey *(Mgr-Corp Mktg)*
Taseen Karim *(Mgr-Municipal Sls)*
Rita Dougherty *(Coord-Mktg)*
Brands & Products:
HARTELL
HASKEL
LINC PUMPS
MILTON ROY
WILLIAMS
YZ SYSTEMS

MILWAUKEE VALVE COMPANY, INC.
16550 W Stratton Dr
New Berlin, WI 53151-7301
Tel.: (262) 432-2800
Fax: (262) 432-2801
Web Site: www.milwaukeevalve.com
E-Mail For Key Personnel:
President: rick@milwaukeevalve.com
Marketing Director: tlaguard@mikwaukeevalve.com
Approx. Number Employees: 640
Year Founded: 1901
Business Description:
Mfr of Specialty Valves
S.I.C.: 3494; 3492
N.A.I.C.S.: 332919; 332912
Import Export
Advertising Expenditures: $300,000
Media: 2-4-5-6-7-10-13-20-22-26
Distr.: Intl.; Natl.
Budget Set: Aug.
Personnel:
Tom LaGuardia *(VP-Mktg)*
Ricky Seward *(VP-Sls)*

Key to Media (For complete agency information see *The Advertising Red Books-Agencies* edition):
1. Bus. Publs. 2. Cable T.V. 3. Catalogs & Directories. 4. Co-op Adv. 5. Consumer Mags. 6. D.M. to Bus. Estab.7. D.M. to Consumers
8. Daily Newsp. 9. Exhibits/Trade Shows 10. Foreign 11. Infomercial 12. Internet Adv.13. Multimedia 14. Network Radio
15. Network T.V. 16. Newsp. Distr. Mags. 17. Other 18. Outdoor (Posters, Transit) 19. Point of Purchase20. Premiums, Novelties
21. Product Samples 22. Special Events Mktg. 23. Spot Radio 24. Spot T.V. 25. Weekly Newsp. 26. Yellow Page Adv.

Milwaukee Valve Company, Inc. — (Continued)

Tammy Wallch *(Head-HR)*
Joe Myers *(Reg Mgr)*
Elias Rizk *(Reg Mgr)*
Chris Tarantello *(Reg Mgr)*
Brands & Products:
BUTTERBALL BUTTERFLY
INNOVATION IN EVERY VALVE
MILWAUKEE VALVE
ULTRA PURE
Advertising Agency:
KW Advertising
333 Bishops Way Ste 148
Brookfield, WI 53005-6209
Tel.: (262) 786-4402
Fax: (262) 786-7236
(Valves)

MINE SAFETY APPLIANCES COMPANY

(d/b/a MSA)
MSA Corp Center 1000 Cranberry Woods Dr
Cranberry, PA 16066
Tel.: (724) 776-8600
E-mail: info@msanet.com
Web Site: www.msanet.com
E-Mail For Key Personnel:
Public Relations: bendemaria@msanet.com
Approx. Sls.: $982,668,000
Approx. Number Employees: 5,200
Year Founded: 1914
Business Description:
Safety & Health Equipment Mfr
S.I.C.: 3999; 3532
N.A.I.C.S.: 339999; 333131
Export
Advertising Expenditures: $300,000
Media: 2-4-7-8-10
Distr.: Natl.
Budget Set: Nov.
Personnel:
John T. Ryan, III *(Chm)*
William M. Lambert *(Pres & CEO)*
Dennis L. Zeitler *(CFO, Treas & Sr VP)*
Markus H. Weber *(CIO & VP)*
Joseph A. Bigler *(Pres-MSA North America & VP)*
Douglas K. McClaine *(Gen Counsel, Sec & VP)*
Roberto M. Canizares *(Exec VP)*
Ronald N. Herring Jr. *(VP-Global Product Leadership)*
Paul R. Uhler *(VP-Global HR)*
Ken Krause *(Dir-Decision Support)*
Brands & Products:
1-TOUCH
880 TRADITION
ABRASI-BLAST
ADVANTAGE
ADVANTAGE 1000
AIRHAWK
AIROX
ALPINE
ALTAIR
APTURA
ARCSAFE
ARCTIC
AURORA
BACKPACKER
BEAMGLIDE
BEAMGRIP
BIOSENSOR
BLACKHAWK
CAIRNS
CANADIAN SUPER V
CHEMGARD
CHILLGARD
CLEAR COMMAND
CLEARVIEW
CLEARVUE
COMFO
COMFO-CAP
COMFO CLASSIC
COMFO ELITE
COMFORT BAND
COMMAND
CONFIDENCE PLUS
CUSTOM AIR V
DEFENDER
DIGICAL
DUO-TWIN
DYNA-BRAKE
DYNA-GLIDE
DYNA-LINE
DYNA-LOCK
DYNA-MIGHT
DYNESCAPE
DYNEVAC
EASY-FLEX
ECONO-CAL
ECONOMUFF
ESCORT
EVOLUTION
EVOLUTION 5000
EXPANYARD
EXPLOSIMETER
FIREHAWK
FIVESTAR
FLAMEGARD
FLEXI-FILTER
FORCEFIELD
FORMFIT
FP DIAMOND
FP PRO
FP STRYDER
FPSK
FREEDOM SERIES
GALAXY
GAS MISER
GAS-TESTER
GASCOPE
GRAVITY
HANDS-OFF
HAZMATCAD
HERITAGE
HIP-AIR
HORIZON
HOUSTON
IMPRESSION
INTRUDER
INVADER
KWIK-DRAW
LOGO EXPRESS
LUXOR
LYNX
MAG
MANSAFE
MAVERICK
METRO
MICH
MILLENNIUM
MINE
MINIOX
MK II
MMR XTREME
MSA
MULTIGARD
NEW YORKER
ONYX
OPTIFILTER
OPTIMAIR
ORION
PAGER
PHALANX
POINTGUARD
POWERBUILDER
PREMAIRE
PULLOVER
PULSAR
PYRENEES
QUAD GAS
QUIKCHEK
RAILRIDER
RCD
RESPONDER
RESPONSE
RIGHT
S-CAP
SAFE & SOPHISTICATED
SAFE ESCAPE
SAFECONNECT
SAFESITE
SAFETOX
SAFETY AT HEIGHTS
THE SAFETY COMPANY
SAFEVOC
SAFEYE
SEDONA
SENTRY
SHORT-STOP
SIERRA
SIRIUS
SKULLGARD
SKYLINK
SOLARIS
SQUIRT
SUPREMA
SUPREME PRO
SURE-CLIMB
SURE-GRAB
SURE-LOCK
SURE-STOP
SURE-STRONG
SYNERGY
TACTICAL
TANKSCOPE
TECHNACURV
THERMALGARD
THERMATEK
TOPGARD
TOXGARD
TOXIMETER
TRADESMAN
TRADEWIND
TRADITION
TRANSAIR
TRIGARD
ULTIMA
ULTRA ELITE
ULTRA FILTER
ULTRA-TWIN
ULTRALIGHT
ULTRAVUE
V-GARD
VANGUARD
VANGUARD II
VERSA-HOOD
VESTYPE
VULCAN
WATCHMAN
WILDLAND
WORKMAN
Z GARD

MINER ENTERPRISES, INC.

1200 E State St
Geneva, IL 60134-2440
Tel.: (630) 232-3000
Fax: (630) 232-3123
Web Site: www.minerent.com
Approx. Number Employees: 120
Year Founded: 1894
Business Description:
Transportation & Material Handling Equipments Mfr
S.I.C.: 3743; 3537
N.A.I.C.S.: 336510; 333924
Export
Advertising Expenditures: $225,000
Media: 2-4
Distr.: Natl.
Personnel:
David W. Withall *(Chm, Pres & CEO)*
Brands & Products:
AUTOLOK
AUTOMEC
BACKLOK
CROWN
DRAWGUARD
ENTERPRISE VERSA FLOW
GRAVAC
MINER
MINI-BUFFGEAR
SANILOK
SELFLOK
TECSPAK
Advertising Agency:
ARENDS
515 N River St Ste 101
Batavia, IL 60510
Tel.: (630) 482-9800
Fax: (630) 482-9833
(Railroad Equipment)

MISTRAS GROUP, INC.

195 Clarksville Rd
Princeton Junction, NJ 08550
Tel.: (609) 716-4000
Fax: (609) 716-4145
Web Site: www.mistrasgroup.com
E-Mail For Key Personnel:
Sales Director: sales@pacndt.com
Approx. Rev.: $272,128,000
Approx. Number Employees: 600
Year Founded: 1978
Business Description:
Mechanical Integrity & Non-Destructive Testing Technology & Services
S.I.C.: 3829; 8734
N.A.I.C.S.: 334519; 541380
Advertising Expenditures: $800,000
Media: 2-13
Personnel:
Sotirios J. Vahaviolos *(Chm, Pres & CEO)*
Francis T. Joyce *(CFO, Treas & Exec VP)*
Michael C. Keefe *(Gen Counsel, Exec VP & Sec)*
Mark F. Carlos *(Exec VP-Products & Sys)*
Ralph L. Genesi *(Exec VP-Mktg & Sls)*
Michael J. Lange *(Exec VP-Svcs)*
Brands & Products:
AEWIN
AEWINPOST
CORPAC
MICRO-SAMOS
MICRODISP
MOMENT TENSOR
MONPAC
MONPAC-PLUS
NOESIS

Key to Media (For complete agency information see *The Advertising Red Books-Agencies* edition):
1. Bus. Publs. 2. Cable T.V. 3. Catalogs & Directories. 4. Co-op Adv. 5. Consumer Mags. 6. D.M. to Bus. Estab.7. D.M. to Consumers
8. Daily Newsp. 9. Exhibits/Trade Shows 10. Foreign 11. Infomercial 12. Internet Adv.13. Multimedia 14. Network Radio
15. Network T.V. 16. Newsp. Distr. Mags. 17. Other 18. Outdoor (Posters, Transit) 19. Point of Purchase20. Premiums, Novelties
21. Product Samples 22. Special Events Mktg. 23. Spot Radio 24. Spot T.V. 25. Weekly Newsp. 26. Yellow Page Adv.

PACSHARE
POLYMODAL
POWERPAC
TANKPAC
VPAC
WAVELETS

MIYANO MACHINERY USA, INC.
(Sub. of Miyano Machinery, Inc.)
940 N Central Ave
Wood Dale, IL 60191-1216
Tel.: (630) 766-4141
Fax: (630) 860-7266
E-mail: sales@miyano-usa.com
Web Site: www.miyano-usa.com
E-Mail For Key Personnel:
Sales Director: sales@miyano-usa.com
Approx. Number Employees: 30
Year Founded: 1975
Business Description:
Machine Tools Mfr
S.I.C.: 5084; 3541
N.A.I.C.S.: 423830; 333512
Import Export
Media: 2-4-7-10-18
Distr.: Natl.
Budget Set: June -Aug.
Personnel:
Henry Marchionne *(Chm)*
Norm Klein *(Asst Mgr-Parts)*

MKS INSTRUMENTS, INC.
2 Tech Dr Ste 201
Andover, MA 01810
Tel.: (978) 645-5500
Fax: (978) 557-5100
Toll Free: (800) 227-8766
E-mail: mks@mksinst.com
Web Site: www.mksinst.com
Approx. Rev.: $853,114,000
Approx. Number Employees: 2,673
Year Founded: 1961
Business Description:
Instruments, Subsystems & Process Control Solutions Mfr
S.I.C.: 3823; 3491; 3612
N.A.I.C.S.: 334513; 332911; 335311
Media: 10
Personnel:
John R. Bertucci *(Chm)*
Leo Berlinghieri *(Pres & CEO)*
Seth H. Bagshaw *(CFO, Treas & VP)*
Gerald G. Colella *(COO & VP)*
Kathleen F. Burke *(Gen Counsel, VP & Asst Sec)*
John T.C. Lee *(Grp VP-Controls & PFMC Products)*
Brands & Products:
AEROBAR
AIRGARD
ALTA
ASTEX
ASTRON
AUTO-SOFT
BARATRON
BLUE BOX
CALIFLOW
CALSTAND
CIRRUS
CLUSTER GAUGE
COMMUNICATORR
CONTROLWEB
DELTA
DEVICENET
DUAL-ZONE
DUALTRANS
E-BARATRON
E-VISION
EASYVIEW
ELECTROMAGNETIC CV
ENI
ENI DEVELOPMENT SYSTEM
ENTUNE
ETCH MANOMETER
FLEXIGNAL
FLEXTRACT
GBROR
GENESIS
HPS
I-BARATRON
I-MAG
INDUCT
JALAPENO LOPRO
KALREZ
LIQUOZON
LOPRO
MASS-FLO
MATCHWORK
MICRONODE
MICROPIRANI
MICROVISION PLUS
MINI-LAB
MKS
MKS INSTRUMENTS
MULTIGAS
NOVA
O3MEGA
OPTIMA
PICO
PR INDEX
PROCESS EYE
PROCESS SENSE
PROFIBUS
QUATTRO
RESIST-TORR
REVOLUTION
SECSTRACE
SEMOZON
SENSELINK
SMARTMATCH
SMARTPOWER
SPECTRUM
TECHNOLOGY FOR PRODUCTIVITY
TOOLLINK
TOOLWEB
TRU-FLO
V/I PROBE
VAC-CHECK
VACUUM SENTRY
VIRTUAL AC
VIRTUAL WALL
VISTA
YIELD BASE
YIELD DYNAMICS
YIELD MINE

MOBILE MINI, INC.
7420 S Kyrene Rd Ste 101
Tempe, AZ 85283
Tel.: (480) 894-6311
Fax: (480) 894-6433
Toll Free: (800) 950-6464
E-mail: sales@mobilemini.com
Web Site: www.mobilemini.com
Approx. Rev.: $330,757,000
Approx. Number Employees: 1,458
Year Founded: 1983
Business Description:
Portable Storage Containers & Modular Steel Buildings Lessor & Mfr
S.I.C.: 4226; 3441; 3448; 4225
N.A.I.C.S.: 493190; 332311; 332312; 531130
Advertising Expenditures: $11,400,000
Media: 8-26
Personnel:
Steven G. Bunger *(Pres & CEO)*
Mark Funk *(CFO & Exec VP)*
Deborah K. Keeley *(Chief Acctg Officer & Sr VP)*
Chris Miner *(Gen Counsel & Sr VP)*
William E. Armstead *(Sr VP-Western Div)*
Kyle G. Blackwell *(Sr VP-Eastern Div)*
Jon D. Keating *(Sr VP-Ops)*
Ronald J. Marshall *(Sr VP-Western Div)*
Brands & Products:
MOBILE MINI
THE STORAGE AND OFFICE SOLUTIONS SPECIALISTS
Advertising Agency:
Ketchum Directory Advertising/Kansas City
7015 College Blvd Ste 700
Overland Park, KS 66211-1524
Tel.: (913) 344-1900
Fax: (913) 344-1960
Toll Free: (800) 922-6977

MOCON, INC.
7500 Mendelssohn Ave N
Minneapolis, MN 55428
Tel.: (763) 493-6370
Fax: (763) 493-6358
E-mail: info@mocon.com
Web Site: www.mocon.com
Approx. Sls.: $31,548,629
Approx. Number Employees: 135
Year Founded: 1966
Business Description:
Instrumentation, Consulting & Laboratory Services to Medical, Pharmaceutical, Food & Other Industries Worldwide
S.I.C.: 3829; 3824; 3826; 8733; 8748
N.A.I.C.S.: 334519; 334514; 334516; 541690; 541710
Export
Advertising Expenditures: $450,000
Media: 2-4-7-10-11-13
Distr.: Intl.; Natl.
Budget Set: Dec.
Personnel:
Robert L. Demorest *(Chm, Pres & CEO)*
Darrell B. Lee *(CFO & VP)*
Daniel W. Mayer *(CTO & Exec VP)*
Douglas J. Lindemann *(VP & Gen Mgr)*
Alan Traylor *(Mgr-Food Safety Products Bus)*
Guy Wray *(Mgr-Mktg)*
Brands & Products:
AQUATRACE
AQUATRAN
AROMATRAN
CAL-SMART
COULOX
FLO SMART
HERSCH
LIPPKE
MOCON
MOCON AB PLUS
OPTI-PERM
OX-TRAN
PAC CHECK
PAC GUARD
PERM-NET
PERMATRAN-C
PERMATRAN-W
PETRO-ALERT
PID-TECH
PROFILER
QUICK START
VERICAP

MODERN EQUIPMENT COMPANY
(Sub. of Alco Industries, Inc.)
369 W Western Ave
Port Washington, WI 53074-0993
Mailing Address:
PO Box 993
Port Washington, WI 53074-0993
Tel.: (262) 284-9431
Fax: (262) 284-9433
Toll Free: (800) 558-8526
Telex: 910-260-3642
E-mail: sales@moderneq.com
Web Site: www.moderneq.com
E-Mail For Key Personnel:
President: vsocks@moderneq.com
Sales Director: sales@moderneq.com
Approx. Number Employees: 55
Year Founded: 1919
Business Description:
Foundry Melting & Hot Metal Handling Equipment Mfr
S.I.C.: 3559; 3491
N.A.I.C.S.: 333298; 332911
Import Export
Advertising Expenditures: $50,000
Media: 2-4-6-7-10
Distr.: Intl.; Natl.
Budget Set: Sept.
Personnel:
Jim Winistorfer *(Pres & Head Coach)*
Larry Market *(Exec VP)*
Advertising Agency:
Top Floor Technologies
2425 S 162 St
New Berlin, WI 53151
Tel.: (262) 364-0010
Fax: (262) 364-0015

MODERN WELDING COMPANY, INC.
2880 New Hartford Rd
Owensboro, KY 42303-1321
Tel.: (270) 685-4400
Fax: (270) 684-6972
Toll Free: (800) 922-1932
E-mail: webmaster@modweldco.com
Web Site: www.modweldco.com
Approx. Number Employees: 775
Year Founded: 1932
Business Description:
Custom Metal Mfr
S.I.C.: 3443; 5051
N.A.I.C.S.: 332420; 423510
Export
Media: 2-4-7-9-10-20-23-26
Distr.: Natl.
Personnel:
John W. Jones *(Pres & CEO)*
James E. Jones *(CFO)*
Ronald Ecleberry *(VP-Sls & Mktg)*
Brands & Products:
FIREGUARD
FLAMESHIELD
GLASTEEL
GLASTEEL II
IOC
KLEERWATER
MODERN
POURSTER
SUPERVAULT

Key to Media (For complete agency information see *The Advertising Red Books-Agencies* edition):
1. Bus. Publs. 2. Cable T.V. 3. Catalogs & Directories. 4. Co-op Adv. 5. Consumer Mags. 6. D.M. to Bus. Estab.7. D.M. to Consumers
8. Daily Newsp. 9. Exhibits/Trade Shows 10. Foreign 11. Infomercial 12. Internet Adv.13. Multimedia 14. Network Radio
15. Network T.V. 16. Newsp. Distr. Mags. 17. Other 18. Outdoor (Posters, Transit) 19. Point of Purchase20. Premiums, Novelties
21. Product Samples 22. Special Events Mktg. 23. Spot Radio 24. Spot T.V. 25. Weekly Newsp. 26. Yellow Page Adv.

Modern Welding Company, Inc. — (Continued)

Advertising Agency:
Kron & Associates Advertising Inc.
1849 Broad Ripple Ave
Indianapolis, IN 46220-2339
Tel.: (317) 253-9050
Fax: (317) 253-9010

MOOG FLO-TORK

(Sub. of Moog Inc.)
1701 N Main St
Orrville, OH 44667-9172
Tel.: (330) 682-0010
Fax: (330) 683-6857
E-mail: executive@flo-tork.com
Web Site: www.flo-tork.com
E-Mail For Key Personnel:
Sales Director: tmleaver@flo-tork.com
Sales Range: $10-24.9 Million
Approx. Number Employees: 60
Year Founded: 1957
Business Description:
Mfr of Hydraulic & Pneumatic Rack & Pinion Rotary Actuators
S.I.C.: 3625
N.A.I.C.S.: 335314
Export
Media: 2-4-10-11-17-26
Distr.: Intl.; Natl.
Personnel:
James I. Jelinek *(Gen Mgr)*
R.E. Bergman *(Mgr-Sls-Power Generation)*
Jim King *(Mgr-Acctg)*
T. M. Leaver *(Mgr-Bus Dev)*
Michael Smith *(Mgr-Pur)*

MOORE FANS LLC

800 S Missouri Ave
Marceline, MO 64658-1602
Tel.: (660) 376-3575
Fax: (660) 376-2909
E-mail: info@moorefans.com
Web Site: www.moorefans.com
Approx. Number Employees: 60
Year Founded: 1939
Business Description:
Industrial Air Moving Equipment, Louvers, Dampers, Storm Louvers, Solar Shades, Lighting Control Electronics Mfr
S.I.C.: 3564
N.A.I.C.S.: 333412
Media: 2-4-6-7-8-26
Distr.: Intl.; Natl.
Budget Set: Jan.-July
Personnel:
John D. Moore *(Pres)*
Carol Schreckhise *(CFO)*
Randy Ward *(VP-Sls)*
Brands & Products:
MOORE

MOORE TOOL COMPANY, INC.

(Sub. of PMT Group Inc)
800 Union Ave
Bridgeport, CT 06607-0088
Mailing Address:
PO Box 4088
Bridgeport, CT 06607-0906
Tel.: (203) 366-3224
Fax: (203) 367-0418
E-mail: custserv@producto.com
Web Site: www.mooretool.com
E-Mail For Key Personnel:
President: nmarsilius@pmt-group.com
Sales Range: $50-74.9 Million
Approx. Number Employees: 184
Year Founded: 1924
Business Description:
Jig Boring, Jig Grinding & Measuring Machines, Diamond Turning Machines & Accessories, Flexible Machining Systems
S.I.C.: 3541; 3544
N.A.I.C.S.: 333512; 333514
Export
Media: 1-2-4-10-20-23
Distr.: Intl.; Natl.
Budget Set: Nov.
Personnel:
Newman M. Marsilius *(Pres)*
Henry Kuo *(Gen Mgr)*
Brands & Products:
MOORE AUTOSIZE
MOORE TOOL

MOREHOUSE-COWLES

(Div. of Microfluidics International Corporation)
13930 Magnolia Ave
Chino, CA 91710-7029
Tel.: (909) 627-7222
Toll Free: (800) 625-4819
Web Site: www.morehousecowles.com
Sales Range: $100-124.9 Million
Business Description:
Technology & Equipment Mfr for Material Production, Purification & Processing
S.I.C.: 3559; 3556
N.A.I.C.S.: 333298; 333294
Media: 10
Personnel:
Rocky Courtain *(Sls Mgr)*
Brands & Products:
COWLES
MOREHOUSE-COWLES
VISCO/MAX
ZINGER

MORGAN ADVANCED CERAMICS

(Plant of Morgan Technical Ceramics)
225 Theodore Rice Blvd
New Bedford, MA 02745
Tel.: (508) 995-1725
Fax: (508) 995-6954
E-mail: adx@alberox.com
Web Site: www.alberox.com
Approx. Number Employees: 184
Year Founded: 1961
Business Description:
Mfr of High Temperature Ceramics, Carbons, Graphites, Refractory & Specialty Metals
S.I.C.: 2899; 3251
N.A.I.C.S.: 325998; 327121
Export
Media: 2-4-7-10
Distr.: Natl.
Budget Set: Dec.
Personnel:
Brian Roznoy *(Gen Mgr)*
Brands & Products:
ALBEROX

MULTI-METALS

715 E Gray St
Louisville, KY 40202
Tel.: (502) 589-3781
Fax: (502) 587-5656
Web Site: www.multi-metals.com
Approx. Number Employees: 100
Year Founded: 1955
Business Description:
Mfr. of Tungsten Carbide Tool Bits, Blanks & Wear Parts
S.I.C.: 3545; 2819
N.A.I.C.S.: 333515; 325188
Advertising Expenditures: $250,000
Media: 4-7
Personnel:
Franc Koljaka *(VP-Ops & Engrg)*
Shawn Teague *(VP-Sls & Mktg)*
Lenny Wiseman *(VP-Fin & Admin)*
Brands & Products:
DYANITE

MULTIVEND LLC

(d/b/a Vendstar)
880 Grad Blvd
Deer Park, NY 11729-5708
Tel.: (631) 243-4995
Fax: (631) 243-1073
Web Site: www.vendstar.com
Sales Range: $1-9.9 Million
Approx. Number Employees: 100
Business Description:
Candy Vending Machines Mfr & Operator
S.I.C.: 5962; 3581
N.A.I.C.S.: 454210; 333311
Media: 6
Personnel:
Ned Weaver *(Pres & CEO)*
Brands & Products:
VENDSTAR

MUSTANG MANUFACTURING COMPANY, INC.

(Sub. of Gehl Company)
1880 Austin Rd 1 Gehl Way
West Bend, WI 53095
Mailing Address:
PO Box 547
Owatonna, MN 55060-0547
Tel.: (262) 334-9461
Fax: (262) 338-7517
Telex: 933001
E-mail: sales@mustangmfg.com
Web Site: www.mustangmfg.com
E-Mail For Key Personnel:
Sales Director: sales@mustangmfg.com
Approx. Number Employees: 1,000
Year Founded: 1865
Business Description:
Skid Steer Loaders, Mini Excavators & Telehandlers Mfr
S.I.C.: 3531
N.A.I.C.S.: 333120
Export
Media: 1-2-4-5-8-10-11-19-20-23-24
Distr.: Intl.; Natl.
Budget Set: Sept.
Personnel:
Kelly Moore *(Product Mgr)*
Brands & Products:
MUSTANG

MUSTANG TRACTOR & EQUIPMENT COMPANY

12800 NW Fwy
Houston, TX 77040-6302
Mailing Address:
PO Box 1373
Houston, TX 77251-1373
Tel.: (713) 460-2000
Fax: (713) 690-2287
Toll Free: (800) 256-1001
E-mail: contact@mustangcat.com
Web Site: www.mustangcat.com
Sales Range: $10-24.9 Million
Approx. Number Employees: 750
Year Founded: 1952
Business Description:
Distr of Diesel & Natural Gas Engines; Material Handling & Heavy Equipment
S.I.C.: 5082; 5084
N.A.I.C.S.: 423810; 423830
Media: 1-5-6-8-10-18-19-20-22-26
Distr.: Reg.
Budget Set: Oct.-Nov.
Personnel:
Brad Tucker *(Pres)*
Brands & Products:
MUSTANG CAT
SOS

NACHI AMERICA INC.

(Sub. of Nachi-Fujikoshi Corp.)
17500 23 Mile Rd
Macomb, MI 48044
Tel.: (586) 226-5151
Fax: (586) 263-0445
E-mail: general@nachiamerica.com
Web Site: www.nachiamerica.com
Business Description:
Industrial Machinery & Equipment Whslr
S.I.C.: 5084
N.A.I.C.S.: 423830
Advertising Agency:
Goda Advertising
1603 Colonial Pkwy
Inverness, IL 60067
Tel.: (847) 776-9900
Fax: (847) 776-9901

NACHI MACHINING TECHNOLOGY CO.

17500 23 Mi Rd
Macomb, MI 48044-1103
Tel.: (586) 263-0100
Fax: (586) 263-4571
E-mail: sales@nachimtc.com
Web Site: www.nachimtc.com
E-Mail For Key Personnel:
Sales Director: sales@nachimtc.com
Sales Range: $25-49.9 Million
Approx. Number Employees: 100
Year Founded: 1929
Business Description:
Machine & Tools: Shaving, Honing, Grinding, Gaging, Sound Testing, Hobbing, Shaping, Deburring, Tooth Pointing, Chamfering, Precision Ball Screws, Contract Heat Treatment
S.I.C.: 3541; 3462
N.A.I.C.S.: 333512; 332111
Import Export
Media: 1-2-7-17-20-21-22
Distr.: Intl.; Natl.
Budget Set: May
Personnel:
Francis Wisner *(VP-Engrg)*
Rodney Soenen *(Product Mgr)*
Dave Petrimoulx *(Sls Mgr)*
Brands & Products:
DURAHONE
GEAR ROLL
GLOBAL EXPERTISE FOR ALL APPLICATIONS
NACHI

Key to Media (For complete agency information see *The Advertising Red Books-Agencies* edition):
1. Bus. Publs. 2. Cable T.V. 3. Catalogs & Directories. 4. Co-op Adv. 5. Consumer Mags. 6. D.M. to Bus. Estab.7. D.M. to Consumers
8. Daily Newsp. 9. Exhibits/Trade Shows 10. Foreign 11. Infomercial 12. Internet Adv.13. Multimedia 14. Network Radio
15. Network T.V. 16. Newsp. Distr. Mags. 17. Other 18. Outdoor (Posters, Transit) 19. Point of Purchase20. Premiums, Novelties
21. Product Samples 22. Special Events Mktg. 23. Spot Radio 24. Spot T.V. 25. Weekly Newsp. 26. Yellow Page Adv.

NACOM
NALOY
PERIFORM
RED RING
RING ROUNDER
ROLLSHAVE
UNI ROLL
Advertising Agency:
Leo J. Brennan, Inc.
2359 Livernois Rd
Troy, MI 48083-1692
Tel.: (248) 362-3131
Fax: (248) 362-2355

NAMCO CONTROLS CORPORATION

(Sub. of Danaher Corporation)
6095 Parkland Blvd Ste 310 2100 W Broad St
Elizabethtown, NC 28337
Tel.: (440) 460-1360
Fax: (910) 879-5486
Toll Free: (800) NAMTECH
E-mail: contact@namcocontrols.com
Web Site: www.namcocontrols.com
Sales Range: $75-99.9 Million
Approx. Number Employees: 300
Year Founded: 1936
Business Description:
Limit Switches; Proximity Switches; Solenoids; Coils; Logic Drivers, Electrical & Electronic Controls: Fiber Optic Switches & Photoelectric Switches: Lasernet Sensors
S.I.C.: 3679
N.A.I.C.S.: 334419
Import Export
Media: 1-4-7-16-17-20
Distr.: Natl.
Budget Set: Sept. -Oct.
Personnel:
Ken Verhulst *(Mgr)*
Brands & Products:
C2
CYLINDICATOR
DURAPROX
FLEX-LOCK
HOTSPOT
MILLPAK
NAMCO
PROXCOUPLER
SNAP-LOCK

NANOINK, INC.

8025 Lamon Ave
Skokie, IL 60077
Tel.: (847) 679-6266
Fax: (847) 679-8767
E-mail: info@nanoink.net
Web Site: www.nanoink.net
Approx. Number Employees: 70
Year Founded: 2001
Business Description:
Molecular Scale Products Fabrication Tools Mfr
S.I.C.: 5065
N.A.I.C.S.: 423690
Media: 2-7-10-13
Personnel:
Mark Slezak *(Chm)*
Robert J. Janosky *(Pres & COO)*
James M. Hussey *(CEO)*
Ben Pothast *(CFO)*
Robert Marchmont *(Gen Mgr-EMEA Reg)*
Tom Warwick *(Gen Mgr-NanoFabrication Sys Div)*
Oliver Yeh *(Gen Mgr-Asia Pacific Reg)*
Brands & Products:
ACTIVE
CHIP CRACKER
DIP PEN NANOLITHOGRAPHY
DPNWRITER
GET SMALL
INKCAD
INKWELL
NSCRIPTOR
Advertising Agency:
Rhea + Kaiser
Naperville Financial Ctr 400 E Diehl Rd Ste 500
Naperville, IL 60563-1342
Tel.: (630) 505-1100
Fax: (630) 505-1109

NAP TOOLS LLC

(Holding of Cameron Holdings Corporation)
(d/b/a NAP GLADU)
1180 Wernsing Rd
Jasper, IN 47546-8171
Tel.: (812) 482-2000
Fax: (800) 457-7458
Toll Free: (800) 634TOOL
E-mail: napsales@naptools.com
Web Site: www.naptools.com
Approx. Number Employees: 500
Year Founded: 1941
Business Description:
Carbide & Diamond Cutting Tools Designer, Mfr, Whslr & Services
S.I.C.: 3545; 3541; 5049
N.A.I.C.S.: 333515; 333512; 423490
Import Export
Media: 2-4-6-7-10-13-21-26
Distr.: Natl.
Budget Set: Mar.
Personnel:
Don Metzger *(Pres)*
Brands & Products:
NEXT G SERIES
SIDEWINDER
SPIRAMAX

NATIONAL MACHINERY LLC

(Sub. of NM Group Global LLC)
161 Greenfield St
Tiffin, OH 44883-2422
Tel.: (419) 447-5211
Fax: (4) 1 4-475299
Web Site: www.nationalmachinery.com
Sales Range: $25-49.9 Million
Approx. Number Employees: 350
Year Founded: 1874
Business Description:
Cold Forging Machinery Mfr
S.I.C.: 3542
N.A.I.C.S.: 333513
Import Export
Media: 2-7-10-11
Distr.: Intl.; Natl.
Budget Set: May
Personnel:
Andrew Kalnow *(Owner & CEO)*
Robert J. Foster *(VP-Fin)*
Brands & Products:
BOLTMAKER
FORMAX
FORMAX PLUS
MAXIPRES
NATIONAL

NATIONAL METAL FINISHING CORP.

897 S Ave
Middlesex, NJ 08846-2534
Mailing Address:
PO Box 486
Middlesex, NJ 08846-0486
Tel.: (732) 752-7770
Fax: (732) 752-6579
Toll Free: (800) 543-6285
E-mail: natmetfin@att.net
Approx. Number Employees: 27
Year Founded: 1971
Business Description:
Chromium Plated Machine Rolls & Cylinders Mfr for Plastic & Paper
S.I.C.: 3569; 3471
N.A.I.C.S.: 333999; 332813
Export
Media: 2-4-7-10
Distr.: Natl.
Personnel:
Lou Fahsbender *(Owner)*

NATIONAL OILWELL VARCO, INC.

7909 Parkwood Cir Dr
Houston, TX 77036
Tel.: (713) 375-3700
Fax: (713) 435-2195
Toll Free: (888) 262-8645
Telex: 422397
Telex: 762128
E-mail: customer.service@natoil.com
Web Site: www.nov.com
Approx. Rev.: $12,156,000,000
Approx. Number Employees: 35,584
Year Founded: 1995
Business Description:
Oilwell Drilling Equipment, Pump & Machinery Mfr
S.I.C.: 3533; 5084
N.A.I.C.S.: 333132; 423830
Import Export
Media: 4-11-20
Personnel:
Clay C. Williams *(CFO & Exec VP)*
Robert W. Blanchard *(Chief Acctg Officer, VP & Controller)*
Burk Ellison *(Pres-Distr Svcs)*
Mark Reese *(Pres-Rig Solutions)*
Haynes B. Smith, III *(Pres-Svcs)*
Robert R. Workman *(Pres-Distr & Transmission)*
Dwight W. Rettig *(Gen Counsel & VP)*
Santosh Mathilakath *(Sr VP-Mono Grp)*
Toby Zyroll *(Sr VP-Ameron Infrastructure Products)*

NATIONAL RIVET & MANUFACTURING COMPANY

21 E Jefferson St
Waupun, WI 53963-1942
Mailing Address:
PO Box 471
Waupun, WI 53963-0471
Tel.: (920) 324-5511
Fax: (920) 324-3388
Toll Free: (888) 324-5511
E-mail: mail@nationalrivet.com
Web Site: www.nationalrivet.com
Approx. Number Employees: 135
Year Founded: 1928
Business Description:
Rivets & Automatic Rivet Setting Machines Mfr
S.I.C.: 3452; 3542
N.A.I.C.S.: 332722; 333513
Advertising Expenditures: $2,000,000
Media: 2
Distr.: Natl.
Budget Set: Oct.
Personnel:
J. Gibbons Zeratsky *(Pres & CEO)*
J. Bur Zeratsky *(CEO)*
A. A. Zeratsky *(Exec VP)*
Brands & Products:
NATIONAL RIVET

NAYLOR PIPE COMPANY

1230 E 92nd St
Chicago, IL 60619-7991
Tel.: (773) 721-9400
Fax: (773) 721-9494
E-mail: sales@naylorpipe.com
Web Site: www.naylorpipe.com
E-Mail For Key Personnel:
Sales Director: sales@naylorpipe.com
Approx. Sls.: $16,000,000
Approx. Number Employees: 100
Year Founded: 1925
Business Description:
Steel Pipe Mfr
S.I.C.: 3317
N.A.I.C.S.: 331210
Export
Advertising Expenditures: $27,000
Media: 2-4-7-10-11
Distr.: Intl.; Natl.
Personnel:
John J. Czulno *(Pres)*
James Martin *(VP-Sls)*
Michael O'Rourke *(Dir-Pur)*
Advertising Agency:
Fred H. Ebersold, Inc.
6040 Main St
Downers Grove, IL 60516
Tel.: (630) 512-9922
Fax: (630) 512-0033

NCI BUILDING SYSTEMS, INC.

(Holding of Clayton, Dubilier & Rice, LLC)
10943 N Sam Houston Pkwy W
Houston, TX 77064
Mailing Address:
PO Box 692055
Houston, TX 77269-2055
Tel.: (281) 897-7788
Fax: (281) 477-9647
Toll Free: (888) 624-8678
E-mail: info@ncilp.com
Web Site: www.ncilp.com
Approx. Sls.: $870,526,000
Approx. Number Employees: 3,606
Year Founded: 1984
Business Description:
Holding Company; Metal Building Components & Engineered Building Systems Mfr & Metal Coil Coating Services
S.I.C.: 6719; 3448; 3479
N.A.I.C.S.: 551112; 332311; 332812
Import Export
Advertising Expenditures: $4,600,000
Personnel:
Norman C. Chambers *(Chm, Pres & CEO)*
Mark E. Johnson *(CFO, Treas & Exec VP)*
Mark W. Dobbins *(COO & Exec VP)*
Eric J. Brown *(CIO & Exec VP)*

Key to Media (For complete agency information see *The Advertising Red Books-Agencies* edition):
1. Bus. Publs. 2. Cable T.V. 3. Catalogs & Directories. 4. Co-op Adv. 5. Consumer Mags. 6. D.M. to Bus. Estab.7. D.M. to Consumers
8. Daily Newsp. 9. Exhibits/Trade Shows 10. Foreign 11. Infomercial 12. Internet Adv.13. Multimedia 14. Network Radio
15. Network T.V. 16. Newsp. Distr. Mags. 17. Other 18. Outdoor (Posters, Transit) 19. Point of Purchase20. Premiums, Novelties
21. Product Samples 22. Special Events Mktg. 23. Spot Radio 24. Spot T.V. 25. Weekly Newsp. 26. Yellow Page Adv.

NCI BUILDING SYSTEMS, INC. — (Continued)

Richard W. Allen *(Chief Acctg Officer & VP-Fin)*
Charles Wayne Dickinson *(Pres-Metal Components Div)*
John L. Kuzdal *(Pres-Metal Coil Coating Div)*
Bradley D. Robeson *(Pres-NCI Buildings & Robertson-Ceco Buildings)*
Todd R. Moore *(Gen Counsel, Sec & Exec VP)*
Rick Morrow *(VP-HR)*

NEOMAGIC CORPORATION

2372-A Qume Dr
San Jose, CA 95131
Tel.: (408) 428-9725
Fax: (408) 428-9712
E-mail: ir@neomagic.com
Web Site: www.neomagic.com
Approx. Rev.: $1,547,000
Approx. Number Employees: 4
Year Founded: 1993
Business Description:
High-Performance Semiconductor Solutions Designer, Developer & Marketer for Sale to Original Equipment Manufacturers of Mobile Computing Products Including Notebook PCs, Digital Cameras & DVD Drives
S.I.C.: 3674
N.A.I.C.S.: 334413
Advertising Expenditures: $3,000
Media: 2-7-10
Personnel:
David Tomasello *(Chm)*
Syed Zaidi *(Pres & CEO)*
Charlotte A. Wilson *(Chief Acctg Officer, VP-Fin & Admin)*
Brands & Products:
MIMAGIC
NEOMAGIC

NEOPOST CANADA LIMITED

(Sub. of Neopost S.A.)
150 Steelcase Road West
Markham, ON L3R 3J9, Canada
Tel.: (905) 475-3722
Fax: (905) 475-7699
Toll Free: (800) NEOPOST
E-mail: info@neopost.ca
Web Site: www.neopost.ca
Approx. Sls.: $10,000,000
Approx. Number Employees: 50
Year Founded: 1925
Business Description:
Shipping Room Products, Gummed Tape Dispensing Machinery, Case Tape Machinery, Scales & Postal Meter Bases, Mailroom Furniture, Inserters, Mailroom Equipment Mfr; Parking Systems, Carpark Management
S.I.C.: 3952
N.A.I.C.S.: 339942
Import
Advertising Expenditures: $500,000
Media: 2-4-5-7-8-10-13-20-26
Distr.: Natl.
Personnel:
Lou Gizzarelli *(Pres)*
Grant Gillham *(VP-Fin)*
Monique Moreau-Gray *(Dir-HR)*
Terry Stroup *(Dir-Dealers Sls)*
Larry Crook *(Mgr-Natl Sls-IPS Solutions Grp)*
Brands & Products:
IJ SERIES
SI SERIES
Advertising Agency:
Barefoot Creative
236 Victoria Street N, Unit 3A
Kitchener, ON N2H 5C8, Canada
Tel.: (519) 571-5058
Fax: (519) 571-5059

NETZSCH PUMPS NORTH AMERICA, LLC

(Sub. of Erich Netzsch GmbH & Co. Holding KG)
119 Pickering Way
Exton, PA 19431-1393
Tel.: (610) 363-8010
Fax: (610) 363-0971
E-mail: netzsch@netzschusa.com
Web Site: www.netzschusa.com
Sales Range: $25-49.9 Million
Approx. Number Employees: 120
Year Founded: 1969
Business Description:
Mfr of Special Industrial Machinery, Pumps, Grinding & Filtration System Equipments
S.I.C.: 3561; 3541
N.A.I.C.S.: 333911; 333512
Import Export
Media: 2-4-7-10-13
Distr.: Intl.; Natl.
Budget Set: May -June
Personnel:
John Maguire *(VP-Sls)*
David Miller *(Mgr-Sls-Central Reg)*
Barbara White *(Mgr-HR)*
Brands & Products:
NEMO PUMPS

NEW ENGLAND MACHINERY, INC.

6204 29th St E
Bradenton, FL 34203-5304
Tel.: (941) 755-5550
Fax: (941) 751-6281
E-mail: webmaster@neminc.com
Web Site: www.neminc.com
E-Mail For Key Personnel:
Marketing Director: mbonura@neminc.com
Approx. Number Employees: 46
Year Founded: 1974
Business Description:
Mfr of Packaging Machinery & Equipment
S.I.C.: 3565; 5084
N.A.I.C.S.: 333993; 423830
Export
Media: 1-2-4-7-10-11-13
Distr.: Intl.; Natl.
Budget Set: Dec.
Personnel:
Judith Nickse *(Pres)*
Marge Bonura *(Dir-Sls & Mktg)*
Andy Hodgson *(Mgr-Sls)*
Eta Kozak *(Mgr-Parts Sls)*
John Nieves *(Mgr-Sls)*
Brands & Products:
NEDHC
NEDP
NEHA
NEHCP
NEHHBT
NEHHLP
NELC
NEM
NEPMT
NERBU
NERCA
NERCC
NERO
NERPA
NERSC
NERSI
NESHC
NESHC-S
NESOL
NESSTC
NEUP
NOL
ORIENTER
RETORQUER

NEW JERSEY TOOL & DIE CO.

800 Colfax Ave
Kenilworth, NJ 07033-2006
Tel.: (908) 931-0026
Fax: (908) 245-8822
E-mail: tpkemps@njtool.com
Sales Range: $10-24.9 Million
Approx. Number Employees: 25
Year Founded: 1945
Business Description:
Molds Mfr
S.I.C.: 3544
N.A.I.C.S.: 333511
Media: 2-4-7-10
Distr.: Natl.
Budget Set: Nov.
Personnel:
Ted Kemps *(Owner)*
Anton Kemps *(Pres)*

THE NEW JERSEY WIRE STITCHING MACHINE CO.

(Sub. of Precision Automation Co., Inc.)
1841 Old Cuthbert Rd
Cherry Hill, NJ 08034-1478
Tel.: (856) 365-0196
Fax: (856) 365-0197
E-mail: nj@precisionautomationinc.com
Web Site: www.newjerseywire.com
Sales Range: $10-24.9 Million
Approx. Number Employees: 25
Year Founded: 1890
Business Description:
Mfr. Wire Stitching Machines
S.I.C.: 3545
N.A.I.C.S.: 333515
Import
Media: 2-4-7-10-11-17-26
Distr.: Natl.
Budget Set: Nov.
Personnel:
Fred Rexon *(Pres)*
Michael Menaquale *(Gen Mgr)*
Brands & Products:
NEW JERSEY WIRE STITCHER

NICHOLSON STEAM TRAP

(Div. of Spence Engineering Co., Inc.)
150 Coldenham Rd
Walden, NY 12586-2000
Tel.: (845) 778-5566
Fax: (845) 778-0417
Toll Free: (800) 210-1300
E-mail: sales@nicholsonsteamtrap.com
Web Site: www.spenceengineering.com
E-Mail For Key Personnel:
Sales Director: sales@nicholsonsteamtrap.com
Sales Range: $75-99.9 Million
Approx. Number Employees: 150
Year Founded: 1883
Business Description:
Mfr. of Steam Traps, Floats, Strainers, Pipe Unions, Valves and Pipe Fittings, Compressed Air Mufflers, Pipe Couplings, Air Traps & Pumps
S.I.C.: 3491; 3444
N.A.I.C.S.: 332911; 332322
Import Export
Media: 1-2-4-5-6-7-8-10-11-13-16-21-22-26
Distr.: Intl.; Natl.
Budget Set: Nov.
Personnel:
Bill Higgins *(Pres)*

NITRAM ENERGY INC.

(Div. of PMFG, INC.)
50 Cobham Dr
Orchard Park, NY 14127-2600
Tel.: (716) 662-6540
Fax: (716) 662-6548
E-mail: info@nitram.com
Web Site: www.nitram.com
Sales Range: $75-99.9 Million
Approx. Number Employees: 220
Year Founded: 1973
Business Description:
Heat Exchangers, Industrial Silencers & Gas Separators Mfr
S.I.C.: 3625; 3559
N.A.I.C.S.: 335314; 332410
Media: 2-4-10
Distr.: Intl.; Natl.
Personnel:
Peter Burlage *(Pres)*
Tony R. Walton *(Dir-Natl Sls)*
Brands & Products:
ALCO
BOS-HATTEN
BURGESS-MANNING

NLB CORP.

(Sub. of Interpump Group S.p.A.)
29830 Beck Rd
Wixom, MI 48393-2824
Tel.: (248) 624-5555
Fax: (248) 624-0908
E-mail: nlbmktg@nlbusa.com
Web Site: www.nlbcorp.com
Approx. Number Employees: 165
Year Founded: 1971
Business Description:
High Pressure Water Pump Mfr & Distr
S.I.C.: 3594; 7359
N.A.I.C.S.: 333996; 532490
Import Export
Personnel:
Forrest A. Shook *(Pres)*
Advertising Agency:
Brewer Associates Marketing Communications
39555 Orchard Hill Pl Ste 600
Novi, MI 48375
Tel.: (734) 458-7180

NN, INC.

2000 Waters Edge Dr Ste 12
Johnson City, TN 37604-8318
Tel.: (423) 743-9151
Fax: (423) 743-2670
E-mail: willk@nnbr.com
Web Site: www.nnbr.com

Key to Media (For complete agency information see *The Advertising Red Books-Agencies* edition):
1. Bus. Publs. 2. Cable T.V. 3. Catalogs & Directories. 4. Co-op Adv. 5. Consumer Mags. 6. D.M. to Bus. Estab.7. D.M. to Consumers 8. Daily Newsp. 9. Exhibits/Trade Shows 10. Foreign 11. Infomercial 12. Internet Adv.13. Multimedia 14. Network Radio 15. Network T.V. 16. Newsp. Distr. Mags. 17. Other 18. Outdoor (Posters, Transit) 19. Point of Purchase20. Premiums, Novelties 21. Product Samples 22. Special Events Mktg. 23. Spot Radio 24. Spot T.V. 25. Weekly Newsp. 26. Yellow Page Adv.

Approx. Sls.: $365,369,000
Approx. Number Employees: 1,829
Year Founded: 1980
Business Description:
Precision Steel Balls & Rollers Mfr
S.I.C.: 3562
N.A.I.C.S.: 332991
Media: 1-10
Personnel:
Roderick R. Baty *(CEO)*
James H. Dorton *(CFO & Sr VP)*
William C. Kelly, Jr. *(VP & Chief Admin Officer)*
Nicola Trombetti *(CEO-NN Europe & NN Inc. & Corp VP)*
Frank T. Gentry, III *(Sr VP & Global Mng Dir-Precision Metal Bearing Components)*
Robert R. Sams *(VP-Sls)*
Jeffrey W. Fenn *(Gen Mgr)*
Rajesh J. Bhadarka *(Mgr-Bus-India)*
Jeffrey H. Hodge *(Mgr)*

THE NOLAN COMPANY
1016 9th St SW
Canton, OH 44707-4108
Tel.: (330) 453-7922
Fax: (330) 453-7449
Fax: (800) 225-0984
Toll Free: (800) 297-1383
E-mail: sales@nolancompany.com
Web Site: www.nolancompany.com
E-Mail For Key Personnel:
Sales Director: sales@nolancompany.com
Approx. Sls.: $1,400,000
Approx. Number Employees: 15
Year Founded: 1909
Business Description:
Railroad Maintenance Products Mfr
S.I.C.: 3743; 3532
N.A.I.C.S.: 336510; 333131
Export
Media: 2-4-6-8-10-26
Distr.: Intl.; Natl.
Budget Set: Dec.
Personnel:
G.R. Lucas *(Chm)*
J.L. Anderson *(Pres)*
Rob Lucas *(Dir-Mktg)*

NORDCO, INC.
(Sub. of OMERS Private Equity Inc.)
245 W Forest Hill Ave
Oak Creek, WI 53154
Tel.: (414) 766-2180
Fax: (414) 766-2379
Toll Free: (800) 445-9258
E-mail: info@nordco.com
Web Site: www.nordco.com
Approx. Number Employees: 75
Year Founded: 1926
Business Description:
Track Maintenance Machinery Mfr
S.I.C.: 3743; 7353
N.A.I.C.S.: 336510; 532412
Export
Media: 4-10-20
Distr.: Intl.; Natl.
Budget Set: Nov.
Personnel:
Bruce Boczkiewicz *(Pres & CEO)*
Bill Straub *(VP-Engrng)*
Steve Wiedenfeld *(Mgr-Nordco Reg Sls)*

NORDSON CORPORATION
28601 Clemens Rd
Westlake, OH 44145-1148
Tel.: (440) 892-1580
Fax: (440) 892-9507
Telex: 156-1271
E-mail: bfields@nordson.com
Web Site: www.nordson.com
Approx. Sls.: $1,041,551,000
Approx. Number Employees: 3,680
Year Founded: 1954
Business Description:
Liquid & Powder Coatings, Sealants & Adhesives Application Systems Mfr
S.I.C.: 3581; 3479; 3559; 3569; 3812
N.A.I.C.S.: 333311; 332812; 333298; 333999; 334511
Export
Advertising Expenditures: $8,267,000
Media: 1-2-4-7-10-26
Distr.: Intl.; Natl.
Budget Set: Oct.
Personnel:
Joseph P. Keithley *(Chm, Pres & CEO-Keithley Instruments, Inc.)*
Michael F. Hilton *(Pres & CEO)*
John P. Byers *(Pres)*
Gregory Thaxton *(CFO & VP)*
Shelly M. Peet *(CIO & VP-HR)*
Beverly J. Coen *(Chief Tax & Risk Officer)*
Robert Veillette *(Gen Counsel, Sec & VP)*
John J. Keane *(Sr VP-Advanced Tech Sys)*
Peter Lambert *(Sr VP-Adhesive Dispensing Sys)*
George Porter *(VP-Sls, Svc & Mktg-North America)*
John Dillon *(Dir-Supply Chain Mgmt)*
James R. Jaye *(Dir-Comm & IR)*
Anne M. Pombier *(Dir-Corp Dev)*
John Schnarr *(Dir-Strategic Mktg)*
David Titone *(Dir-Bus Dev & Sls Ops)*
Ray McHenry *(Mgr-HR)*
Alan Ramspeck *(Mgr-Product Line)*
J. Bradford Leaheey *(Asst Gen Counsel)*
Brands & Products:
ACCUBAR
AERODECK
AEROWASH
AIRGUARD
AQUACURE
AQUAGUARD
ASYMTEK
ATS
AUTO-FLO
BETTERBOOK
BICOFIL
CANNECK
CANWORKS
CF
CHAMELEON
CLASSICBLUE
CLEANSPRAY
COLOR-ON-DEMAND
COLORMAX
CONTROL COAT
COOLARC
COOLWAVE
CROSS-CUT
DOME
DROPCURE
DRUM HEAD
DURA-SCREEN
DURABLUE
DURADRUM
DURAPAIL
EASYON
ECLIPSE
ECODRY
ECOLINER
E.DOT
EMERALD
EUV
EXCEL
FIBERIZATION
FILL SENTRY
FILLEASY
FILLMASTER
FLEX-O-COAT
FLEXICOAT
FOAMMELT
G-NET
GALLON RHINO
HORIZON
ICONTROL
IFLOW
ISO-FLO
ITRACK
ITRAX
ITREND
KINETIX
LEAN CELL
LOGICOMM
MEG
METALCURE
MICROFIL
MINI SQUIRT
MINIBLUE
MINICURE
MONOCURE
MULTISCAN
NORDSON
OPTISTROKE
PATTERNPRO
PERMAFLO
POROUS COAT
POWERGRID
PREVENTIVE
PRIMARC
PRISM
PRO-FLO
PRO-METER
PROBLUE
PROCESS SENTRY
PRODIGY
PROLINK
QUADCURE
QUANIX
RHINO
SATURN
SCOREGUARD
SEAL SENTRY
SELECT CURE
SELECT SERIES
SERVO DRIVEN SHOT
SIGNATURE
SLAUTTERBACK
SOLIDBLUE
SPECTRONIC
SPECTRUM
SPEED-COAT
SPEEDKING
SUMMIT
SURE CLEAN
SUREBEAD
SUREMIX
SURESEAL
SUREWRAP
TRAK
TRIBOMATIC
TRUEBLUE
UNIVERSAL
VANTAGE
VERSA-SPRAY
VERSABLUE
VERSADRUM
VERSAPAIL
VISTA
WHITEUV
WHITEUV+
Advertising Agencies:
Burson-Marsteller
(Part of Young & Rubicam Brands, a Sub. of WPP Group plc)
230 Park Ave S
New York, NY 10003-1566
Tel.: (212) 614-4000
Fax: (212) 598-5407

Dix & Eaton Incorporated
200 Public Sq Ste 1400
Cleveland, OH 44114
Tel.: (216) 241-0405
Fax: (216) 241-3070

Stevens Strategic Communications, Inc.
Gemini Towers, Ste 500, 1991 Crocker Rd
Westlake, OH 44115-1900
Tel.: (440) 617-0100
Fax: (440) 614-0529

NORSHIELD SECURITY PRODUCTS
(Div. of Norment Security Group, Inc.)
3232 Mobile Hwy
Montgomery, AL 36108-4454
Tel.: (334) 281-8440
Fax: (334) 286-4399
Toll Free: (800) 633-1968
E-mail: info@norshield.net
E-Mail For Key Personnel:
Sales Director: sales@norshieldsecurity.com
Approx. Number Employees: 300
Year Founded: 1981
Business Description:
Mfr & Supplier of Ballistic, Attack & Blast Resistant Products
S.I.C.: 3669; 1799
N.A.I.C.S.: 334290; 238990
Export
Media: 2-4-10-11-13
Personnel:
Gary Hart *(Pres & CEO)*
John Wood *(Mgr-Sls & Mktg)*
Brands & Products:
AIRTEQ
BRG-1
BRG-2
BRG-3
BRG-4
FIBER SENSYS
FIBRESHIELD FS 1
FIBRESHIELD FS 2
FIBRESHIELD FS 3
FIBRESHIELD FS 4
GUARDVUE
NORGLAS
NORSHIELD

NORTH STAR ICE EQUIPMENT CORPORATION
8151 Occidental Ave S
Seattle, WA 98108
Mailing Address:
PO Box 80227
Seattle, WA 98108
Tel.: (206) 763-7300
Fax: (206) 763-7323

Key to Media (For complete agency information see *The Advertising Red Books-Agencies* edition):
1. Bus. Publs. 2. Cable T.V. 3. Catalogs & Directories. 4. Co-op Adv. 5. Consumer Mags. 6. D.M. to Bus. Estab.7. D.M. to Consumers
8. Daily Newsp. 9. Exhibits/Trade Shows 10. Foreign 11. Infomercial 12. Internet Adv.13. Multimedia 14. Network Radio
15. Network T.V. 16. Newsp. Distr. Mags. 17. Other 18. Outdoor (Posters, Transit) 19. Point of Purchase20. Premiums, Novelties
21. Product Samples 22. Special Events Mktg. 23. Spot Radio 24. Spot T.V. 25. Weekly Newsp. 26. Yellow Page Adv.

North Star Ice Equipment Corporation — (Continued)

Toll Free: (800) 321-1381
E-mail: info@northstarice.com
Web Site: www.northstarice.com
Approx. Sls.: $10,000,000
Approx. Number Employees: 40
Year Founded: 1950
Business Description:
Mfr of Continuous Flake Ice Makers & Mechanical Ice Dispensing Systems
S.I.C.: 3585; 3535
N.A.I.C.S.: 333415; 333922
Export
Advertising Expenditures: $200,000
Media: 1-2-4-7-10-25-26
Distr.: Intl.; Natl.
Budget Set: Nov. -Dec.
Personnel:
Lee Shepardson *(Chm)*
John Deex *(Pres & CEO)*
Tom Crawford *(VP-Sls & Mktg)*
Chuck Pfeiffer *(Reg Mgr-Sls)*
Cecil Ugarte *(Reg Mgr-Sls)*
Jeff Wittenberger *(Reg Mgr-Sls)*
Brands & Products:
COLDISC
NORTH STAR
WORLDWIDE SOLUTIONS IN FLAKE ICE TECHNOLOGY

NORTHLAND MOTOR TECHNOLOGIES

(Div. of The Scott Fetzer Company)
968 Bradley St
Watertown, NY 13601-1209
Tel.: (315) 782-2350
Fax: (315) 788-1180
E-mail: info@northlandmotor.com
Web Site: www.northlandmotor.com
Sales Range: $125-149.9 Million
Year Founded: 1959
Business Description:
Fractional Horsepower Motors Mfr
S.I.C.: 3594
N.A.I.C.S.: 333996
Advertising Expenditures: $25,000
Media: 2-4-10-13
Brands & Products:
NORTHLAND

NORTON COMPANY

(Sub. of Saint-Gobain Abrasives, Inc)
PO Box 15008
Worcester, MA 01615-0008
Tel.: (508) 795-5000
Fax: (508) 795-2599
Toll Free: (800) 446-1119
Telex: 920428
Web Site: www.nortonabrasives.com
Approx. Number Employees: 1,000
Year Founded: 1885
Business Description:
Abrasives, Grinding Wheels, Pulpstones, Diamond & CBN Diamond Dressing Tools & Wheels, Coated Abrasives, Floor Maintenance Products, Sharpening Stones, Masonry & Concrete Saws & Blades, Tower Packings, Polyvinyl Tubing, Safety Products, Plastic Components, Diamond Drilling & Coring Bits for Gas & Oil Exploration, Sealants & Fluoropolymers, Industrial Ceramics, Refractories, Igniters & Kiln Furniture Mfr
S.I.C.: 6719
N.A.I.C.S.: 551112
Import Export
Media: 1-2-4-7-8-10-13-19-20-21-22
Distr.: Intl.; Natl.
Budget Set: Annually
Personnel:
Dean Arvidson *(Technical Mktg Dir)*
Abby Marschke *(Mgr-Mktg Comm)*
Brands & Products:
ADALOX
ALUNDUM
BEAR
BEAR-TEX
CERAFLO
CHRISTENSEN
CLIPPER
CRYSTAR
CRYSTOLON
CRYSTON
DURITE
ECONOMAX
INDIA
INTALOX
METALITE
MICROLITE
NORALIDE
NORAX
NORMAX
NOROC
NORTON
NORTON CONSTRUCTION PRODUCTS
NORTON SG
NORTRAK
NORZON
NU-BLOCK
QUEER CREEK
SCREEN-BAK
SELEXOL
TUFBAK
TYGON
YANKEECLIPPER

NORWALK COMPRESSOR COMPANY, INC.

1650 Stratford Ave
Stratford, CT 06615-6419
Tel.: (203) 386-1234
Fax: (203) 386-1300
Toll Free: (800) 556-5001
E-mail: info@norwalkcompressor.com
Web Site: www.norwalkcompressor.com
Sales Range: $50-74.9 Million
Approx. Number Employees: 70
Year Founded: 1864
Business Description:
Mfr of High & Low Pressure Air & Gas Compressors
S.I.C.: 3563; 3586
N.A.I.C.S.: 333912; 333913
Export
Media: 2-4-8-10-13-26
Distr.: Intl.; Natl.
Budget Set: July -Aug.
Personnel:
Arthur McCauley *(Chm, Pres & CEO)*
Mario Perrotta *(Mgr-Mktg)*
Brands & Products:
CENTURY
CHARGER
NORWALK
NORWALK NATURAL GAS FUELING SYSTEMS
SLIMLINE

NOSHOK INC.

1010 W Bagley Rd
Berea, OH 44017
Tel.: (440) 243-0888
Fax: (440) 243-3472
E-mail: noshok@noshok.com
Web Site: www.noshok.com
Sales Range: $10-24.9 Million
Approx. Number Employees: 45
Year Founded: 1967
Business Description:
Process Control Instruments Mfr & Distr
S.I.C.: 3823; 5084
N.A.I.C.S.: 334513; 423830
Media: 4-10-13
Personnel:
James B. Cole *(Owner)*
Jeff N. Scott *(Pres)*
Robert V. Liddle *(Reg Mgr-Sls)*
Frederick H. Vaughan *(Reg Mgr-Sls)*
Michael D. Walker *(Reg Mgr-Sls)*
Jeffery C. Dillen *(Reg Sls Mgr-Great Lakes)*
Stephen A. Dalziel *(Mgr-Pur)*
Emily J. Dillen *(Mgr-Fiscal Affairs)*
Michael F. Lancaster *(Mgr-Engrg)*
Robert K. Manjura *(Mgr-Quality Assurance)*
Corbin Schmitt *(Mgr-Customer Svc)*
Stanley A. Wright *(Mgr-Natl Sls)*
Brands & Products:
NOSHOK
TRI-CLAMP

NOVELLUS SYSTEMS, INC.

4000 N First St
San Jose, CA 95134
Tel.: (408) 943-9700
Fax: (408) 943-3422
E-mail: info@novellus.com
Web Site: www.novellus.com
Approx. Sls.: $1,349,158,000
Approx. Number Employees: 2,700
Year Founded: 1984
Business Description:
Microchip Mfr
S.I.C.: 3199; 3674; 7379
N.A.I.C.S.: 316999; 334413; 541519
Import Export
Advertising Expenditures: $2,200,000
Media: 2-4-10
Distr.: Intl.; Natl.
Personnel:
Richard S. Hill *(Chm & CEO)*
John D. Hertz *(CFO & VP)*
Timothy M. Archer *(COO)*
Fusen E. Chen *(Exec VP-Semiconductor Sys Products)*
Patrick J. Lord *(Sr VP)*
Wilbert Hoek *(VP-Integration-Advanced Dev)*
Brands & Products:
ALTUS
ATHENA
ATHENA KNOWLEDGE BASE
ATHENA REMOTE
CONCEPT ONE
CONCEPT THREE
CONCEPT TWO
DIRECTFILL
G400
GAMMA
GXT
INNOVATIVE TECHNOLOGY. TRUSTED PRODUCTIVITY.
INOVA
MAX
NEXT
PEP IRIDIA
PNL
SABRE
SABRE EXTREME
SABRE NEXT
SEQUEL
SEQUEL EXPRESS
SOLA
SPEED
VECTOR
XCEDA
Advertising Agency:
The Hoffman Agency
70 N 2nd St
San Jose, CA 95113-1204
Tel.: (408) 286-2611
Fax: (408) 286-0133
— Jen Bernier *(Acct Exec)*

NRG ENERGY, INC.

211 Carnegie Ctr
Princeton, NJ 08540-6213
Tel.: (609) 524-4500
Fax: (609) 524-4501
Web Site: www.nrgenergy.com
Approx. Rev.: $8,849,000,000
Approx. Number Employees: 4,964
Year Founded: 1989
Business Description:
Power Generation, Power Plant Engineering & Consulting Services
S.I.C.: 4939; 4911; 4931
N.A.I.C.S.: 221111; 221119; 221122
Media: 22
Personnel:
Howard E. Cosgrove *(Chm)*
David W. Crane *(Pres & CEO)*
Jan C. Paulin *(Pres & CEO-Padoma Wind Power)*
Kirkland B. Andrews *(CFO & Exec VP)*
Mauricio Gutierrez *(COO & Exec VP)*
Denise Wilson *(Chief Admin Officer & Exec VP)*
James J. Ingoldsby *(Chief Acctg Officer & VP)*
Jeff Baudier *(Reg Pres-South Central Reg & Sr VP)*
John W. Ragan *(Reg Pres-Texas & Exec VP)*
Steve Hoffmann *(Reg Pres-West & Sr VP)*
Michael Bramnick *(Gen Counsel & Exec VP)*
Steven C. Winn *(Exec VP-Mergers & Acquisitions)*
Nahla Azmy *(Sr VP)*
Meredith Moore *(Sr VP-Comm)*
Lori Neuman *(Dir-Comm)*
Dave Klein *(Mgr-Fin Plng & Analysis)*
Advertising Agency:
Aurora Coast Productions
802 W Park Ave Ste 222
Ocean, NJ 07712
Tel.: (212) 375-0700 (New York City)
Tel.: (732) 905-5200 (New Jersey)
Tel.: (215) 995-2424 (Philadelphia)

NUMATICS, INC.

(Sub. of Emerson Industrial Automation)
1185 Equity Dr
Highland, MI 48357-4560
Mailing Address:
PO Box 1155
Highland, MI 48084

Key to Media (For complete agency information see *The Advertising Red Books-Agencies* edition):
1. Bus. Publs. 2. Cable T.V. 3. Catalogs & Directories. 4. Co-op Adv. 5. Consumer Mags. 6. D.M. to Bus. Estab.7. D.M. to Consumers
8. Daily Newsp. 9. Exhibits/Trade Shows 10. Foreign 11. Infomercial 12. Internet Adv.13. Multimedia 14. Network Radio
15. Network T.V. 16. Newsp. Distr. Mags. 17. Other 18. Outdoor (Posters, Transit) 19. Point of Purchase20. Premiums, Novelties
21. Product Samples 22. Special Events Mktg. 23. Spot Radio 24. Spot T.V. 25. Weekly Newsp. 26. Yellow Page Adv.

Tel.: (248) 887-4111
Fax: (248) 887-1930
Fax: (248) 887-9190
Web Site: www.numatics.com
Sales Range: $150-199.9 Million
Approx. Number Employees: 925
Year Founded: 1945
Business Description:
Developer & Manufacturer of Pneumatic Components for Machinery
S.I.C.: 3491; 3612
N.A.I.C.S.: 332911; 335311
Media: 4-10
Brands & Products:
CIRCLEVISION
COMBIGROOVE
DELTA SERIES
FLEXIBLOK
GEOMETRIC SERIES
MICRO-FILTRATION
MICROPATH
MODUBLOK
NUMATICS
STOCKBLOK
ULTRADRY

NUTTING
(Div. of Acco Material Handling Solutions)
450 Pheasant Ridge Dr
Watertown, SD 57201-5610
Tel.: (605) 882-3000
Fax: (605) 882-4226
Toll Free: (800) 533-0337
Web Site: www.acconutting.com
Approx. Sls.: $6,000,000
Approx. Number Employees: 100
Year Founded: 1891
Business Description:
Floor Trucks, Wheels & Casters: Cargo Carts, Pallet Trucks, Two Wheel Hand Trucks, Custom Engineered Material Handling Equipment & Contract Mfr
S.I.C.: 3537; 5084
N.A.I.C.S.: 333924; 423830
Export
Media: 2-4-10-26
Distr.: Intl.; Natl.
Personnel:
Darla Becking *(Coord-Sls)*

O.A. NEWTON & SON CO
16356 Sussex Hwy
Bridgeville, DE 19933
Mailing Address:
PO Box 397
Bridgeville, DE 19933-0397
Tel.: (302) 337-8211
Fax: (302) 337-3780
Toll Free: (800) 726-5745
E-mail: info@oanewton.com
Web Site: www.oanewton.com
E-Mail For Key Personnel:
President: rob.riderjr@oanewton.com
Approx. Number Employees: 81
Year Founded: 1916
Business Description:
Materials Handling Systems; Agricultural Irrigation & Millwright Work Services
S.I.C.: 5084; 5083
N.A.I.C.S.: 423830; 423820
Export
Media: 2-4-7-10
Distr.: Intl.; Natl.
Personnel:
Robert F. Rider, Jr. *(CEO)*
Orville E. Hammond *(Sr VP-Material Control)*

OIL PURIFICATION SYSTEMS, INC.
4 Research Dr Ste 403
Shelton, CT 06484
Tel.: (203) 926-6855
Fax: (203) 926-6914
Toll Free: (866) OIL-PURE
Web Site: www.oilpursys.com
Business Description:
Oil Refiner System for Internal Combustion Engines
S.I.C.: 3519
N.A.I.C.S.: 333618
Personnel:
Greg Slawson *(CEO)*
Mark Smith *(CFO)*
Bill Priest *(VP-Engrg)*
Advertising Agency:
DPR Group, Inc.
12850 Middlebrook Rd Ste 107
Germantown, MD 20874
Tel.: (240) 686-1000
Fax: (240) 686-0600

THE OILGEAR COMPANY
(Holding of Mason Wells, Inc.)
2300 S 51st St
Milwaukee, WI 53219-2340
Mailing Address:
PO Box 343924
Milwaukee, WI 53234-3924
Tel.: (414) 327-1700
Fax: (414) 327-0532
Toll Free: (800) 558-6636
E-mail: usa@oilgear.com
Web Site: www.oilgear.com
Sales Range: $1-4.9 Billion
Approx. Number Employees: 748
Year Founded: 1921
Business Description:
Hydraulic Systems & Components, Flow Measurement Equipment, Petrochemical & Oilfield Equipment Mfr
S.I.C.: 3492; 3594
N.A.I.C.S.: 332912; 333996
Import Export
Advertising Expenditures: $344,000
Multimedia: $20,000; Bus. Publs.: $200,000; Catalogs & Directories: $50,000; Exhibits/Trade Shows: $30,000; Other: $40,000; Yellow Page Adv.: $4,000
Distr.: Natl.
Budget Set: Oct.
Personnel:
Chuck Germane *(CFO)*
Brands & Products:
BALL PRODUCTS
HYDRO-STACK PRODUCTS
HYDURA PRODUCTS
OILGEAR
PETRODYNE PRODUCTS
SALEM PRODUCTS
SERVOCONTROL PRODUCTS
TOWLER PRODUCTS

OKUMA AMERICA CORPORATION
(Sub. of Okuma Corporation)
11900 Westhall Dr
Charlotte, NC 28278-7127
Mailing Address:
PO Box 7866
Charlotte, NC 28241-7866
Tel.: (704) 588-7000
Fax: (704) 588-6503
E-mail: info@okumaamerica.com
Web Site: www.okuma.com
Approx. Number Employees: 116
Year Founded: 1987
Business Description:
CNC Machining Centers, Lathes & Grinders Mfr
S.I.C.: 5084; 3541
N.A.I.C.S.: 423830; 333512
Import Export
Advertising Expenditures: $1,500,000
Media: 1-2-4-7-10-13-16-20-22
Distr.: Natl.
Budget Set: Feb. -Sept.
Personnel:
Jim King *(Pres & COO)*
Lisa Rummel *(CFO)*
Larry Schwartz *(Chief Strategy Officer)*
Mindy Mikami *(Coord-Mktg)*
Brands & Products:
CNC MACHINE TOOLS

OLIVER PRODUCTS COMPANY INC.
(Holding of Mason Wells, Inc.)
445 6th St NW
Grand Rapids, MI 49504-5253
Tel.: (616) 456-7711
Fax: (616) 456-5820
Toll Free: (800) 253-3893
Web Site: www.oliverproducts.com
Approx. Number Employees: 220
Year Founded: 1981
Business Description:
Food & Medical Products Packaging Materials Mfr
S.I.C.: 2672; 3556
N.A.I.C.S.: 322222; 333294
Media: 2-7-10-11-21
Distr.: Intl.
Budget Set: Sept.
Personnel:
Jerry Bennish *(Pres & CEO)*
Jon Andreasen *(Dir-Creative)*
Paul Dege *(Dir-Sls & Mktg)*
Jeff Murak *(Dir-Sls & Mktg)*
Brands & Products:
ARTISAN
CLUSTERSLICER
DOTCOAT
MYLAR
OLIVER
OSURANCE
OVANTEX
TYVEK
VARISLICER
X-HALE
XHALE
Advertising Agency:
Scott, Inc. of Milwaukee (dba Scott Advertising)
1031 N Astor St
Milwaukee, WI 53202-3324
Tel.: (414) 276-1080
Fax: (414) 276-3327

OMG, INC.
(Sub. of Handy & Harman Ltd.)
153 Bowles Rd
Agawam, MA 01001-2900
Tel.: (413) 789-0252
Fax: (413) 789-1069
Toll Free: (800) 633-3800
E-mail: info@olyfast.com
Web Site: www.olyfast.com
Sales Range: $50-74.9 Million
Approx. Number Employees: 350
Year Founded: 1981
Business Description:
Fastener Mfr & Supplier for the Construction Industry
S.I.C.: 3499; 3544
N.A.I.C.S.: 332999; 333514
Media: 2-10
Personnel:
Hubert McGovern *(Pres)*
Brands & Products:
FASTENMASTER

OMNI ENERGY SERVICES CORP.
(Holding of Wellspring Capital Management LLC)
4500 NE Evangeline Thruway
Carencro, LA 70520-5253
Mailing Address:
PO Box 3761
Lafayette, LA 70502-3761
Tel.: (337) 896-6664
Fax: (337) 896-6655
Toll Free: (800) 319-5347
E-mail: infot@omnienergy.com
Web Site: www.omnienergy.com
Approx. Rev.: $122,426,000
Approx. Number Employees: 625
Year Founded: 1987
Business Description:
Seismic Drilling Services & Dock-Side & Offshore Hazardous & Non-Hazardous Oilfield Waste Management & Environmental Cleaning Services
S.I.C.: 1389
N.A.I.C.S.: 213112
Advertising Expenditures: $800,000
Media: 2-4-7-13
Personnel:
Brian J. Recatto *(Pres & CEO)*
Gregory B. Milton *(Chief Acctg Officer & VP)*
Mark Stipe *(Gen Counsel & VP)*

ORBOTECH INC.
(Sub. of Orbotech Ltd.)
44 Manning Rd
Billerica, MA 01821-3931
Tel.: (800) 800-3208
Fax: (978) 667-9969
E-mail: infousa@orbotech.com
Web Site: www.orbotech.com
Approx. Number Employees: 70
Year Founded: 1983
Business Description:
Instruments & Control Equipment Distr
S.I.C.: 5065; 7629
N.A.I.C.S.: 423690; 811219
Media: 2-4-7-10
Distr.: Intl.; Natl.
Budget Set: Aug.
Personnel:
Amichai Steinberg *(COO)*
Margaret Duncan *(Exec VP-Ops)*
Ken Maylor *(VP-Sls)*
Lars Pettersson *(Product Mgr)*

ORION ENERGY SYSTEMS, INC.
2210 Woodland Dr
Manitowoc, WI 54220
Tel.: (920) 892-9340
Fax: (920) 892-4274
Web Site: www.oriones.com

Orion Energy Systems, Inc. — (Continued)

Approx. Rev.: $80,687,000
Approx. Number Employees: 223
Business Description:
Energy Management Systems Utilizing Energy Efficient Lighting Systems, Controls & Related Services
S.I.C.: 3646; 3823
N.A.I.C.S.: 335122; 334513
Advertising Expenditures: $384,000
Personnel:
Michael J. Potts *(Pres & COO)*
Neal R. Verfuerth *(CEO)*
Michael Harris *(CFO)*
Scott R. Jensen *(Chief Acctg Officer)*
John H. Scribante *(Pres-Orion Engineered Sys)*
Daniel J. Waibel *(Pres-Orion Asset Mgmt)*
Richard Gaumer *(Exec VP-Ops)*
James Jackson *(Sr VP-Sls)*
Stuart Ralsky *(Sr VP-HR)*
Steve Heins *(VP-Comm & Govt Affairs)*
Brands & Products:
APOLLO
COMPACT MODULAR
INTERLITE
LIGHT YEARS AHEAD
ORION
PARTNERS FOR PROFIT

O.S. WALKER CO. INC.

(Div. of Walker Magnetics Group, Inc.)
20 Rockdale St
Worcester, MA 01606-1922
Tel.: (508) 853-3232
Fax: (508) 852-8649
E-mail: info@walkermagnet.com
Web Site: www.walkermagnet.com
E-Mail For Key Personnel:
Sales Director: sales@walkermagnet.com
Approx. Number Employees: 80
Year Founded: 1896
Business Description:
Magnetic Chucks, Lift Magnets & Instruments; Ceramax; Separation Equipment
S.I.C.: 3545; 3826
N.A.I.C.S.: 333515; 334516
Import Export
Advertising Expenditures: $250,000
Media: 2-4-7-8-10-13-20-25
Distr.: Intl.; Natl.
Budget Set: Sept.
Personnel:
Kristian Knights *(Mgr-Mktg)*
Brands & Products:
O.S. WALKER

OSBORN INTERNATIONAL

(Div. of Jason Incorporated)
5401 Hamilton Ave
Cleveland, OH 44114-3911
Tel.: (216) 361-1900
Fax: (216) 361-1913
Telex: 985321
E-mail: brushes@osborn.com
Web Site: www.osborn.com
Sales Range: $25-49.9 Million
Approx. Number Employees: 150
Year Founded: 1887
Business Description:
Industrial Power Brushes, Paint Brushes, Idler Rollers, Industrial Aerosols, Grinding Wheels, Load Runners, Cut-off Wheels, Abrasive Specialties, Maintenance Brushes, Buffs & Compounds Mfr
S.I.C.: 3999
N.A.I.C.S.: 339999
Export
Advertising Expenditures: $200,000
Bus. Publs.: $140,000; Exhibits/Trade Shows: $60,000
Distr.: Intl.; Natl.
Budget Set: Nov.
Personnel:
Helen Rich *(Pres)*
Mark Johnson *(VP-Sls)*
Brands & Products:
LOAD RUNNERS
ORBIT
OSBORN

P/A INDUSTRIES, INC.

522 Cottage Grove Rd
Bloomfield, CT 06002-3111
Tel.: (860) 243-8306
Fax: (860) 242-4870
Toll Free: (800) 243-8306
E-mail: service@pa.com
Web Site: www.pa.com
E-Mail For Key Personnel:
Sales Director: sales@pa.com
Approx. Number Employees: 50
Year Founded: 1954
Business Description:
Mfr. of Coil-Handling Equipment
S.I.C.: 3549; 3625
N.A.I.C.S.: 333518; 335314
Import Export
Advertising Expenditures: $250,000
Media: 1-2-4-10-11-13-20
Distr.: Intl.; Natl.
Personnel:
Edward Morris *(Pres)*
Paul Werkheiher *(Mgr-IT)*
Brands & Products:
THE ADVANTAGE
CHALLENGER
THE EDGE
MARK III SERIES AIR FEED
PA
PRECISION AIR FEED
SOFT-AIRE
SONATORQ
YOU SUPPLY THE PRESS. WE'LL SUPPLY THE REST

PACCAR WINCH DIVISION

(Div. of PACCAR Inc.)
800 E Dallas St PO Box 547 74013
Broken Arrow, OK 74012-4300
Mailing Address:
PO Box 547
Broken Arrow, OK 74013-0547
Tel.: (918) 251-8511
Fax: (918) 259-1575
Fax: (800) 678-9462
Telex: 492340
E-mail: winchsales@paccar.com
Web Site: www.paccarwinch.com
E-Mail For Key Personnel:
Marketing Director: mark.saunders@paccar.com
Sales Director: mike.lawson@paccar.com
Approx. Sls.: $60,000,000
Approx. Number Employees: 200
Year Founded: 1924
Business Description:
Mfr. of Electric, Mechanical & Hydraulic Worm Gear Winches, Planetary Winches & Construction Hoists, Gear Boxes, Turning Mechanisms, Tractor & Skid-Mounted Winches
S.I.C.: 3536; 3462
N.A.I.C.S.: 333923; 332111
Export
Advertising Expenditures: $300,000
Media: 2-4-5-10-11-20-26
Distr.: Intl.; Natl.
Budget Set: Nov. -Dec.
Personnel:
Mark C. Pigott *(Chm & CEO)*
Michelle Wilson *(Sr Mgr-Mktg & Inside Sls)*
Brands & Products:
30B PS
50B PS
70A PS
AHGU5-12FEB
AHGUS5
AHLU2-10F
AHS10-12
AHS10-18A
AHS10-18AEB
AHS10-18B
AHS10-23AEB
AHS20-18B
AHS3-10
AHS3-7
AHS7-12
AHS7-15A
AHS7-15AEB
AHS7-15B
AHSU10-12FEB
AHSU12P-12F
AHSU3-10F
AHSU3-10FEB
ALGU2-10F
ALU2-10F
AMGU5-12FEB
AMS10-12
AMS10-18A
AMS10-18AEB
AMS10-18B
AMS10-23AEB
AMS20-18B
AMS3-10
AMS3-7
AMS7-12
AMS7-15A
AMS7-15AEB
AMS7-15B
AMSU10-12FEB
AMSU3-10F
AMSU3-10FEB
BG4A
BG6A
BG8A
BP200B
BR30B
CH150A
CH175A
CH210A
CH230A
CH240A
CH330A
CH400A
CH640A
GH15
GH30
GH50
H110
H20R
HP125
HP160
HP50
HP70
HS30P-20B
HU8A
HUP12
HUP30B
MR-S3
MS30-20B
MS50-20B
MS50P-20B
MU8A
PCD24B
PD12C
PD15C
PD17C
PD18B
SD1200
SD180
SD40
SD80
SD900
W150A
WR30

PACIFIC SCIENTIFIC, ELECTRO KINETICS DIVISION

(Div. of Danaher Motion Company)
4607 SE International Way
Milwaukee, OR 97222
Tel.: (503) 659-5999
E-mail: mkraus@ekd.pacsci.com
Web Site: www.psekd.com
Sales Range: $50-74.9 Million
Approx. Number Employees: 150
Year Founded: 1963
Business Description:
Alternators & Generators Systems Mfr for Aerospace Applications
S.I.C.: 3621; 3714
N.A.I.C.S.: 335312; 336322
Export
Advertising Expenditures: $300,000
Media: 4-17
Distr.: Direct to Consumer; Natl.
Personnel:
Jeremy Davis *(Pres-Electro Kinetics & OECO Div)*
Chris McKlevicz *(VP-Mktg)*

PACKAGE MACHINERY COMPANY, INC.

380 Union St Ste 58
West Springfield, MA 01089-4123
Tel.: (413) 732-4000
Fax: (413) 732-1163
E-mail: customerservice@packagemachinery.com
Web Site:
www.packagemachinery.com
E-Mail For Key Personnel:
President: kputnam@packagemachinery.com
Approx. Sls.: $7,000,000
Approx. Number Employees: 21
Year Founded: 1913
Business Description:
Mfr of Automatic Wrapping & Packaging Machines & Injection Molding Machinery
S.I.C.: 3565; 3559
N.A.I.C.S.: 333993; 333220
Export
Media: 2-4-8-10-11
Distr.: Intl
Budget Set: Oct.
Personnel:
Katherine E. Putnam *(Pres)*
Brands & Products:
DUPLIMATIC
FA-ST
PACKAGE

Key to Media (For complete agency information see *The Advertising Red Books-Agencies* edition):
1. Bus. Publs. 2. Cable T.V. 3. Catalogs & Directories. 4. Co-op Adv. 5. Consumer Mags. 6. D.M. to Bus. Estab.7. D.M. to Consumers 8. Daily Newsp. 9. Exhibits/Trade Shows 10. Foreign 11. Infomercial 12. Internet Adv.13. Multimedia 14. Network Radio 15. Network T.V. 16. Newsp. Distr. Mags. 17. Other 18. Outdoor (Posters, Transit) 19. Point of Purchase20. Premiums, Novelties 21. Product Samples 22. Special Events Mktg. 23. Spot Radio 24. Spot T.V. 25. Weekly Newsp. 26. Yellow Page Adv.

REED
TRANSWRAP
WRAPSTER

PACKAGING TECHNOLOGIES, INC.

(Sub. of OYSTAR Holding GmbH)
807 W Kimberly Rd
Davenport, IA 52806-5706
Tel.: (563) 391-1100
Fax: (563) 391-0017
Toll Free: (800) 257-5622
E-mail: sales@packt.com
Web Site: www.packt.com
E-Mail For Key Personnel:
Sales Director: sales@packt.com
Approx. Number Employees: 250
Business Description:
Packaging Machinery Mfr
S.I.C.: 3565
N.A.I.C.S.: 333993
Import Export
Media: 1-2-4-6-7-8-10-11
Distr.: Intl.; Natl.
Personnel:
Barry W. Shoulders *(Pres & CEO)*
Tom Riggins *(VP-Sls & Mktg)*
Suzanne Zeitler *(VP-Fin)*
Mark Austin *(Mgr-Sls)*
Brands & Products:
CHUBMAKER
PT

PANGBORN CORPORATION

4630 Coates Dr
Fairburn, GA 30213
Tel.: (301) 739-3500
Fax: (404) 665-5701
Toll Free: (800) 638-3000
E-mail: info@pangborn.com
Web Site: www.pangborn.com
E-Mail For Key Personnel:
President: rstewart@pangborn.com
Marketing Director: twojcik@pangborn.com
Approx. Number Employees: 50
Year Founded: 1904
Business Description:
Blast Cleaning, Shot Peening, Abrasives & Supplies, Sand Systems Services
S.I.C.: 3569; 3564
N.A.I.C.S.: 333999; 333411
Export
Media: 1-2-4-7-10-11-21-26
Distr.: Intl.
Budget Set: Aug.
Brands & Products:
THE CURVANE
GENESIS
PANGBORN
RIM-LOC
ROTOBLAST

PARAGON TECHNOLOGIES, INC.

600 Kuebler Rd
Easton, PA 18040-9201
Tel.: (610) 252-3205
Fax: (610) 252-3102
Toll Free: (800) 523-9464
E-mail: info@ptgamex.com
Web Site: www.ptgamex.com
Sales Range: $10-24.9 Million
Approx. Number Employees: 49
Year Founded: 1958
Business Description:
Automated Material Handling & Order Selection Equipment
S.I.C.: 1796; 1442; 3535; 5082; 7699
N.A.I.C.S.: 811490; 212321; 238290; 333922; 423810; 811310
Import Export
Advertising Expenditures: $200,000
Media: 1-2-4-7-10
Distr.: Intl.; Natl.
Budget Set: Nov. -Dec.
Personnel:
Theodore W. Myers *(Chm)*
Ronald J. Semanick *(CFO, Treas, Sec & VP-Fin)*
William J. Casey *(Exec VP)*
Brands & Products:
ACCUPIC
ACCUROL
CARTRAC
CRUZCONTROL
CSS
DC XCELLERATOR
DISPEN-SI-MATIC
DISTRIBUTION SYSTEM OPTIMIZER
ERS
ESA60
ETV
EWX100
INTELLIROL
LIGHTWORX
LO-TOW
MCN2000
MINI-CARTRAC
MTN 2000
NBA
NBS
NBS 30
NBS 90
NBS 90-SP
NBT
P4
PARAGON TECHNOLOGIES
ROBODRIVE
ROBOLITE
ROBORAIL
SI
SI ORDERMATIC
SINTHESIS
SWITCH-CART
WE BUILD PRODUCTIVITY
XCELSORT
XENOPRESSURE
XENOROL
XENOSORT
XENOTRACTION

PARKER AEROSPACE

(Group of Parker Hannifin Corporation)
14300 Alton Pkwy
Irvine, CA 92618-1814
Tel.: (949) 833-3000
Fax: (949) 851-3799
Sales Range: $400-449.9 Million
Approx. Number Employees: 2,500
Business Description:
Specialty Sealing Devices, O-Rings, Gaskets, Fastener Seals & Packing Products Mfr
S.I.C.: 3053
N.A.I.C.S.: 339991
Distr.: Intl.; Natl.
Personnel:
Robert P. Barker *(Pres-Aerospace Grp, Exec VP & Operating Officer)*
Mark Czaja *(VP-Tech & Innovation)*
Brands & Products:
CHROMASSURE
GASK-O-SEAL
LOCK-O-SEAL
PARBAK
PARKUT
POLYPAK
STAT-O-SEAL
THRED SEAL
Advertising Agency:
Brokaw Inc.
425 W Lakeside Ave
Cleveland, OH 44113-1029
Tel.: (216) 241-8003
Fax: (216) 241-8033

PARKER HANNIFIN CORPORATION

6035 Parkland Blvd
Cleveland, OH 44124-4141
Tel.: (216) 896-3000
Fax: (216) 896-4000
Toll Free: (800) CPARKER
Telex: 980636
Web Site: www.parker.com
Approx. Sls.: $12,345,870,000
Approx. Number Employees: 58,409
Year Founded: 1918
Business Description:
Commercial, Mobile, Industrial & Aerospace Market Motion & Control Technologies Mfr
S.I.C.: 3829; 3563; 3564; 3585; 3589; 3593; 3594
N.A.I.C.S.: 334519; 333319; 333411; 333415; 333912; 333995; 333996
Export
Advertising Expenditures: $1,080,000
Media: 2-4-7-9-10-20-21-25-26
Distr.: Intl.
Personnel:
Donald E. Washkewicz *(Chm, Pres & CEO)*
Jon P. Marten *(CFO & Exec VP-Fin & Admin)*
William G. Eline *(CIO & VP)*
Robert P. Barker *(Pres-Aerospace Grp & Exec VP)*
Robert W. Bond *(Pres-Fluid Connectors Grp & VP)*
Michael Yoon Chung *(Pres-Asia Pacific Grp & VP)*
Jeffery A. Cullman *(Pres-Hydraulics Grp & VP)*
John R. Greco *(Pres-Instrumentation Grp & VP)*
Thomas F. Healy *(Pres-Climate & Indus Controls Grp & VP)*
Kurt A. Keller *(Pres-Seal Grp & VP)*
Antonio Ricardo Machado *(Pres-Latin America Grp & VP)*
Peter Popoff *(Pres-Filtration Grp & VP)*
Charly Saulnier *(Pres-Europe, Middle East & Africa Grp & VP)*
Roger S. Sherrard *(Pres-Automation Grp & VP)*
Thomas A. Piraino, Jr. *(Gen Counsel, Sec & VP)*
Lee C. Banks *(Exec VP)*
Daniel S. Serbin *(Exec VP-HR)*
Thomas L. Williams *(Exec VP)*
Cathy Suezer *(Sr VP-Fin)*
John G. Dedinsky *(VP-Global Supply Chain & Procurement)*
Christopher M. Farage *(VP-Comm & External Affairs)*
M. Craig Maxwell *(VP-Tech & Innovation)*
Aidan Gormley *(Dir-Corp Comm)*
Ron Paduchak *(Mgr-Strategic Pricing)*
Brands & Products:
ANYTHING POSSIBLE
PARKER
Advertising Agencies:
Brokaw Inc.
425 W Lakeside Ave
Cleveland, OH 44113-1029
Tel.: (216) 241-8003
Fax: (216) 241-8033

Catalyst Marketing Communications Inc. –
2777 Summer St Ste 301
Stamford, CT 06905
Tel.: (203) 348-7541
Fax: (203) 348-5688
Fluid Control Division

Innis Maggiore
4715 Whipple Ave NW
Canton, OH 44718-2651
Tel.: (330) 492-5500
Fax: (330) 492-5568
Toll Free: (800) 460-4111

PARKER HANNIFIN WATTS FLUID AIR

(Div. of Parker Aerospace)
9 Cutts Rd
Kittery, ME 03904-5567
Tel.: (207) 439-9511
Fax: (207) 475-4010
Web Site: www.wattsfluidair.com
Sales Range: $50-74.9 Million
Approx. Number Employees: 100
Year Founded: 1970
Business Description:
Mfr. of Compressed Air Line Filters, Regulators, Lubricators & Valves
S.I.C.: 3714
N.A.I.C.S.: 336399
Media: 17
Distr.: Intl.; Natl.
Budget Set: Mar.
Personnel:
Lee Scott *(Mgr-Product Sls)*
Brands & Products:
QIX
QUBE

PEACE INDUSTRIES INC.

(d/b/a Spotnails)
1100 Hicks Rd
Rolling Meadows, IL 60008-1016
Tel.: (847) 259-1620
Fax: (888) 369-2588
E-mail: wwaterman@spotnails.com
Web Site: www.spotnails.com
Approx. Number Employees: 50
Year Founded: 1940
Business Description:
Mfr. of Pneumatic Tools & Fasteners of Office Supplies
S.I.C.: 3496; 3952
N.A.I.C.S.: 332618; 339942
Import Export
Media: 10
Personnel:
Mark Wilson *(Pres)*
Rex A. Jandernoa *(CFO & VP)*
Win Waterman *(VP-Sls & Mktg)*

Key to Media (For complete agency information see *The Advertising Red Books-Agencies* edition):
1. Bus. Publs. 2. Cable T.V. 3. Catalogs & Directories. 4. Co-op Adv. 5. Consumer Mags. 6. D.M. to Bus. Estab.7. D.M. to Consumers
8. Daily Newsp. 9. Exhibits/Trade Shows 10. Foreign 11. Infomercial 12. Internet Adv.13. Multimedia 14. Network Radio
15. Network T.V. 16. Newsp. Distr. Mags. 17. Other 18. Outdoor (Posters, Transit) 19. Point of Purchase20. Premiums, Novelties
21. Product Samples 22. Special Events Mktg. 23. Spot Radio 24. Spot T.V. 25. Weekly Newsp. 26. Yellow Page Adv.

Peace Industries Inc. — (Continued)

Brands & Products:
ACE FASTNER
SPOTNAILS
T-JAK
TEBO DECKER
TEBO FASTENER

PECO, INC.

(d/b/a PECO Manufacturing)
4707 SE 17th Ave
Portland, OR 97202-4714
Mailing Address:
PO Box 82189
Portland, OR 97282-0189
Tel.: (503) 233-6401
Fax: (503) 233-6407
E-mail: sales@pecomanufacturing.com
Web Site: www.pecomanufacturing.com
E-Mail For Key Personnel:
Sales Director: sales@pecomanufacturing.com
Approx. Rev.: $50,000,000
Approx. Number Employees: 350
Year Founded: 1938
Business Description:
Zinc & Aluminum Die Castings & Temperature Controls Equipment Mfr
S.I.C.: 3363; 3364; 3822
N.A.I.C.S.: 331521; 331522; 334512
Import Export
Advertising Expenditures: $350,000
Media: 4
Distr.: Intl.; Natl.
Budget Set: June
Personnel:
Steven Michaelis *(CEO)*
Merrick Smith *(CFO & VP)*
Michael Loescher *(Dir-Engrg)*
Cathy Engel *(Mgr-Comm)*
Brands & Products:
CARTALL
HANDI-STAND
LYONS
NEMA 4X
PECO
PECO PAK
SUNNE

PELLERIN MILNOR CORPORATION

700 Jackson St
Kenner, LA 70062-7774
Tel.: (504) 467-9591
Fax: (504) 471-2377
Toll Free: (800) 469-8780
E-mail: mktg@milnor.com
Web Site: www.milnor.com
Approx. Sls.: $70,000,000
Approx. Number Employees: 650
Year Founded: 1947
Business Description:
Commercial Laundry Washer-Extractors; Large Automatic Dryers, Laundry Materials Handling Systems & Continuous Batch Washing Systems Mfr
S.I.C.: 3582; 3552
N.A.I.C.S.: 333312; 333292
Export
Media: 2-4-7-10
Distr.: Intl.; Natl.
Budget Set: Sept. -Nov.
Personnel:
James W. Pellerin *(Pres)*
Rick Kelly *(Pres-Sls & Mktg)*
Peter Youngblood *(VP-Fin)*
Stephanie Russell *(Mgr-Adv)*
Brands & Products:
CBW
E-P PLUS
HANDS-OFF
HYDRO-CUSHION
MILNOR
RAPID LOAD
STAPH-GUARD
SYSTEM 4
SYSTEM 7
Advertising Agency:
Trumpet LLC
2803 St Philip St
New Orleans, LA 70119
Tel.: (504) 525-4600
Fax: (504) 525-4620

PENTAIR WATER

(Sub. of Pentair, Inc.)
800 Airport Rd
North Aurora, IL 60542-1403
Tel.: (630) 859-7000
Fax: (630) 859-1226
E-mail: aurora_info@pentair.com
Web Site: www.aurorapump.com
Sales Range: $75-99.9 Million
Approx. Number Employees: 205
Year Founded: 1919
Business Description:
Pumps for Sewage & Waste Handling & Chemical, Commercial HVAC, Petrochemical, Water & Wastewater Treatment Markets
S.I.C.: 5084
N.A.I.C.S.: 423830
Export
Advertising Expenditures: $850,000
Media: 1-2-4-5-7-10-11-20-26
Distr.: Natl.
Budget Set: Dec.
Personnel:
David Goddard *(VP-Sls & Mktg)*
Mike Shabel *(Mgr-Mktg)*
Brands & Products:
AURORA
Advertising Agency:
Alexander Marketing
801 Broadway Ave Ste 300
Grand Rapids, MI 49504
Tel.: (616) 957-2000
Fax: (616) 957-3514

PERRY PRODUCTS CORPORATION

(Affil. of Perry Videx LLC)
25 Mount Laurel Rd
Hainesport, NJ 08036
Tel.: (609) 267-1600
Fax: (609) 267-4499
E-mail: info@perryproducts.com
Web Site: www.perryproducts.com
Approx. Number Employees: 30
Year Founded: 1950
Business Description:
Heat Exchangers Mfr
S.I.C.: 3559
N.A.I.C.S.: 332410
Export
Advertising Expenditures: $250,000
Media: 2-4-10
Distr.: Intl.; Natl.
Budget Set: Sept.
Personnel:
Gregg P. Epstein *(Pres)*
John L. Coia *(VP, Sls)*
Suren Shah *(Mgr-Engrg)*

PERRY VIDEX LLC

25 Mt Laurel Rd
Hainesport, NJ 08036
Tel.: (609) 267-1600
Fax: (609) 267-4499
E-mail: info@perryvidex.com
Web Site: www.perryvidex.com
E-Mail For Key Personnel:
President: gepstein@perryvidex.com
Sales Director: ljacobs@perryvidex.com
Approx. Number Employees: 45
Year Founded: 1932
Business Description:
Mfr of Heat Exchangers & Process Vessels; Dealers of Used Process Equipment
S.I.C.: 5084; 3443
N.A.I.C.S.: 423830; 332313
Import Export
Advertising Expenditures: $200,000
Media: 2-4-10-11-13
Distr.: Intl.; Natl.
Personnel:
Jerome P. Epstein *(Chm)*
Gregg Epstein *(Pres-Chemicals, Foods, & Pharmaceuticals)*
Kenneth Miller *(Exec VP)*
Suren Shah *(Engr)*

PETTIBONE, LLC

(Sub. of Heico Companies, LLC)
2626 Warrenville Rd
Downers Grove, IL 60515-1775
Tel.: (630) 353-5000
Fax: (630) 353-5026
E-mail: webmail@pettibone.com
Web Site: www.pettibone.com
Sales Range: $750-799.9 Million
Approx. Number Employees: 2,000
Year Founded: 1880
Business Description:
Construction Equipment Mfr
S.I.C.: 3531; 3537
N.A.I.C.S.: 333120; 333924
Export
Advertising Expenditures: $1,500,000
Distr.: Intl.; Natl.
Budget Set: Apr.
Personnel:
Michael Heisley, Sr. *(Chm & Pres)*
Larry Wolski *(CFO)*
Ron Schuster *(Pres-Construction Grp)*
Douglas Johnson *(Gen Counsel & Sec)*
Brands & Products:
BARKO HYDRAULIC
CARRYLIFT
MATCH-BLOMATIC
PETTIBONE
PETTIBONE KRANE
PETTIBONE MERCURY
PETTIBONE MICHIGAN
ROL-A-DRAW
SANDSLINGER
SPEED-COMPOUNDER
SPEEDFLOW
SPEEDMULLOR

PHILADELPHIA GEAR CORPORATION

(Sub. of Wind River Holdings, L.P.)
901 E 8th Ave Ste 100
King of Prussia, PA 19406-1354
Tel.: (610) 265-3000
Fax: (610) 337-5637
Web Site: www.philagear.com
Approx. Sls.: $45,000,000
Approx. Number Employees: 50
Year Founded: 1892
Business Description:
Mfr. of Gears, Speed Reducing Units, Sphereflex Coupling, Fluid Agitators, Industrial Clutches
S.I.C.: 3566; 7629
N.A.I.C.S.: 333612; 811219
Import Export
Media: 1-2-4-10-20
Distr.: Intl.; Natl.
Budget Set: Dec.
Personnel:
Carl D. Rapp *(Pres & CEO)*
Stephen Verget *(CFO)*
Jules DeBaecke *(VP-Engrg)*
Kirk Keserick *(VP-HR)*
Gerry Natteson *(VP-Mktg)*
Boyd Swearingen *(Gen Mgr-Gulf Coast & Latin American Regs)*
Nels Mitchel *(Gen Mgr-Midwest Reg)*
Tony Tartaglio *(Gen Mgr)*
Bill Clifton *(Mgr-OTS Asst)*
Brands & Products:
GEARLOGIC

PIERCE EQUIPMENT

(Sub. of Ram Consolidated Industries, Inc.)
642 W Iris Dr
Nashville, TN 37204
Tel.: (615) 269-7272
Fax: (615) 292-4418
Toll Free: (800) 828-3120
E-mail: tomr@pierceusa.com
Web Site: www.pierceusa.com
Approx. Number Employees: 14
Year Founded: 1955
Business Description:
Printing & Office Equipment Mfr & Distr
S.I.C.: 3555; 3579
N.A.I.C.S.: 333293; 333313
Import Export
Media: 4-7-10
Distr.: Natl.
Personnel:
Tom J. Ritter *(Pres)*

PLANET PRODUCTS CORPORATION

4200 Malsbary Rd
Cincinnati, OH 45242-5510
Tel.: (513) 984-5544
Fax: (513) 984-5580
E-mail: sales@planet-products.com
Web Site: www.planet-products.com
E-Mail For Key Personnel:
Sales Director: sales@planet-products.com
Approx. Number Employees: 75
Year Founded: 1947
Business Description:
Machinery & Equipment Mfr for the Food & Meat Packing Industries
S.I.C.: 3556; 3599
N.A.I.C.S.: 333294; 332710
Export
Media: 2-4-7-10-26
Distr.: Intl.; Natl.
Personnel:
Carter Randolph *(Owner)*
Kathy Randolph *(Owner)*

Key to Media (For complete agency information see *The Advertising Red Books-Agencies* edition):
1. Bus. Publs. 2. Cable T.V. 3. Catalogs & Directories. 4. Co-op Adv. 5. Consumer Mags. 6. D.M. to Bus. Estab.7. D.M. to Consumers 8. Daily Newsp. 9. Exhibits/Trade Shows 10. Foreign 11. Infomercial 12. Internet Adv.13. Multimedia 14. Network Radio 15. Network T.V. 16. Newsp. Distr. Mags. 17. Other 18. Outdoor (Posters, Transit) 19. Point of Purchase20. Premiums, Novelties 21. Product Samples 22. Special Events Mktg. 23. Spot Radio 24. Spot T.V. 25. Weekly Newsp. 26. Yellow Page Adv.

Brands & Products:
ATLAS VAC
PLANET
PLANET PRODUCTS

PMC INDUSTRIES INC.
(Sub. of Park-Ohio Industries, Inc.)
29100 Lakeland Blvd
Wickliffe, OH 44092-2323
Tel.: (440) 943-3300
Fax: (440) 944-1974
E-mail: pmc@pmcindustries.com
Web Site: www.pmcindustries.com
Sales Range: $50-74.9 Million
Approx. Number Employees: 92
Business Description:
Gages, Instruments, Machinery, Tools & Sub-Contract Graphic Instrumentation; High Speed Machinery Threading & Tapping
S.I.C.: 3541; 3545
N.A.I.C.S.: 333512; 333515
Media: 2-4-13-20-26
Distr.: Intl.; Natl.
Budget Set: Dec.
Brands & Products:
PMC INDUSTRIES

PMC WIRE & CABLE
(Name Changed to RSCC Aerospace & Defense)

PMFG, INC.
14651 N Dallas Pkwy Ste 500
Dallas, TX 75254
Tel.: (214) 357-6181
Fax: (214) 351-0194
Web Site: www.peerlessmfg.com
Approx. Rev.: $121,794,000
Approx. Number Employees: 400
Business Description:
Moisture Removal Systems, Gas Filtration & Separation Systems, & Selective Catalytic Reduction Systems
S.I.C.: 3559; 3569; 3823
N.A.I.C.S.: 333298; 333999; 334513
Export
Advertising Expenditures: $127,000
Media: 17
Personnel:
Sherrill Stone *(Chm)*
Peter J. Burlage *(Pres & CEO)*
Ronald L. McCrummen *(CFO & VP)*
Warren R. Hayslip *(COO & VP)*
Melissa G. Beare *(Gen Counsel, Sec & VP)*
John H. Conroy *(VP-Engrg & Product Dev)*
Jon P. Segelhorst *(VP-Sls & Market Bus Units)*

PNEUMATIC PRODUCTS CORP.
(Sub. of SPX Air Treatment Corporation)
4647 SW 40th Ave
Ocala, FL 34474-5788
Tel.: (352) 873-5793
Fax: (352) 873-5770
E-mail: pneumatic.products.sales@spx.com
Web Site: www.pneumaticproducts.com
Sales Range: $125-149.9 Million
Approx. Number Employees: 300
Year Founded: 1946
Business Description:
Filters for Air, Gases & Liquids Mfr
S.I.C.: 3564; 3594
N.A.I.C.S.: 333412; 333996
Import Export
Advertising Expenditures: $250,000
Media: 2-4-7-10
Distr.: Natl.
Budget Set: Jan.
Personnel:
James Doherty *(Sr VP-Sls & Mktg)*

PNEUMATIC SCALE CORPORATION
(Div. of Barry-Wehmiller Companies, Inc.)
10 Ascot Pkwy
Cuyahoga Falls, OH 44223-3325
Tel.: (330) 923-0491
Fax: (330) 923-5570
Telex: 940169
E-mail: sales@pneumaticscale.com
Web Site: www.pneumaticscale.com
E-Mail For Key Personnel:
Sales Director: sales@pneumaticscale.com
Approx. Sls.: $41,896,000
Approx. Number Employees: 250
Year Founded: 1895
Business Description:
Packaging, Bottling Machinery & Parts Mfr
S.I.C.: 3565; 3535
N.A.I.C.S.: 333993; 333922
Import Export
Media: 1-2-4-8-10-11-20
Distr.: Intl.; Natl.
Budget Set: Oct.
Personnel:
Robert H. Chapman *(Chm & CEO)*
Jim Foley *(VP-Sls)*
Paul Kearney *(VP-Sls)*
Brands & Products:
ACCUFLOW
CLOSETECH SEAMERS
CONSOLIDATED CAP FEEDERS
PNEUMACAPPER
PNEUMACLEANER
PNEUMAFLOW
PNEUMAPLUGGERS
ULTRACLEANER
VACUFLOW

POLYFLON COMPANY
(Sub. of Crane Engineered Materials)
1 Willard Rd
Norwalk, CT 06851
Tel.: (203) 840-7555
Fax: (203) 840-7565
E-mail: info@polyflon.com
Web Site: www.polyflon.com
Sales Range: $25-49.9 Million
Approx. Number Employees: 20
Year Founded: 1953
Business Description:
Electroplates & Teflon Mfr
S.I.C.: 3492; 3494
N.A.I.C.S.: 332912; 332919
Export
Media: 2-7-10-21
Personnel:
William Larusso *(Pres)*

POND FILTRATION, INC.
2717 3rd Ave N
Fargo, ND 58102
Tel.: (701) 365-4240
Fax: (701) 365-4245
Toll Free: (800) 882-5327
E-mail: janderson@pondfiltration.com
Web Site: www.pondfiltration.com
Approx. Number Employees: 3
Year Founded: 1992
Business Description:
Filtration Systems Mfr
S.I.C.: 3677; 5961
N.A.I.C.S.: 334416; 454113
Media: 4-6
Personnel:
James Anderson *(Pres)*
Brands & Products:
KOI QUAD-MATIC
NO MORE GREEN WATER
POND FILTRATION
TRU-VAC

PORTEC GROUP INTERNATIONAL
(Holding of PNC Equity Partners, L.P.)
1 Forge Rd
Canon City, CO 81212
Mailing Address:
PO Box 589
Canon City, CO 81215
Tel.: (719) 275-7471
Fax: (719) 269-3750
E-mail: portec@portec-mhg.com
Web Site: www.portec.com
Sales Range: $50-74.9 Million
Approx. Number Employees: 125
Year Founded: 1906
Business Description:
Mfr of Material Handling Equipment & Components
S.I.C.: 3535
N.A.I.C.S.: 333922
Export
Advertising Expenditures: $1,500,000
Media: 1-2-4-7-9-10-11-16-20-25
Distr.: Intl.; Natl.
Budget Set: Sept.
Personnel:
Kirk Martin *(Pres & CEO)*
Richard Alter *(Dir-QA & HR)*
Joe Forte *(Dir-Sls & Applications)*

PORTEC RAIL PRODUCTS, INC.
(Sub. of L.B. Foster Company)
900 Old Freeport Rd
Pittsburgh, PA 15238-3132
Mailing Address:
PO Box 38250
Pittsburgh, PA 15238-8250
Tel.: (412) 782-6000
Fax: (412) 782-1037
E-mail: corporate@portecrail.com
Web Site: www.portecrail.com
Sales Range: $75-99.9 Million
Year Founded: 1906
Business Description:
Mfr of Railroad Track & Maintenance Products for Railcars & Locomotives
S.I.C.: 3499; 4011; 4013
N.A.I.C.S.: 332999; 482111; 488210
Import Export
Advertising Expenditures: $316,000
Media: 2-10-21-26
Distr.: Natl.
Budget Set: Dec.
Personnel:
John S. Cooper *(Vice Chm)*
John N. Pesarsick *(CFO)*
David Hartman *(Mgr-Mktg)*
Brands & Products:
761 HYDRAULUBE
CATCH-ALL
COMPLY
CURVE
DISPOSABULK
E-Z FILL
ELIMINATOR PLUS
ENVIRO-FORCETM
EXI RAIL ANCHOR
FAIR
FRICTION FORCE
GREASE BARTENDER
GTPLUS ABSORBENT TRACK MAT
HL-1
IMPROVED FAIR
KELTRACK
LEXAN
LUBE CREW
MAC JACK
MACK
MATMATE
MC
MC-3
MC-4
MC-4TR
MC-4XL
MC-4XL WITH GREASEGUIDE
MOTORPUMP
OIL BUSTERS
OUR ROOTS RUN DEEP
POLY-INSULATED
POLY PLATE
PORTEC-BOND
PORTEC RAIL
PORTEC RAIL PRODUCTS, INC.
PORTEC RAIL WELD-MATE
PORTEC RAIL XL-1
POWERBLOCK
PROTECTOR
RAIL CAP
ROAD-RUNNER
SOYTRAK
SURVEYOR
SWITCH POINT PROTECTORS-MACK
THERMABOND
TOR-XL
TOTAL FRICTION MANAGEMENT
TRACKSIDE
Advertising Agency:
Studio 2 Advertising
1641 Broad St
Greensburg, PA 15601
Tel.: (724) 836-2220
Fax: (724) 836-2060

PORTLAND FORGE
(Unit of Allegheny Technologies Incorporated)
250 E Lafayette St
Portland, IN 47371-0905
Tel.: (260) 726-8121
Fax: (260) 726-8021
E-mail: info@portlandforge.com
Web Site: www.portlandforge.com
Sales Range: $125-149.9 Million
Approx. Number Employees: 270
Business Description:
Mfr. of Forgings
S.I.C.: 3463; 3462
N.A.I.C.S.: 332112; 332111
Export
Media: 2-17
Distr.: Natl.
Budget Set: Sept.
Personnel:
Patrick W. Bennett *(Pres)*

Key to Media (For complete agency information see *The Advertising Red Books-Agencies* edition):
1. Bus. Publs. 2. Cable T.V. 3. Catalogs & Directories. 4. Co-op Adv. 5. Consumer Mags. 6. D.M. to Bus. Estab.7. D.M. to Consumers
8. Daily Newsp. 9. Exhibits/Trade Shows 10. Foreign 11. Infomercial 12. Internet Adv.13. Multimedia 14. Network Radio
15. Network T.V. 16. Newsp. Distr. Mags. 17. Other 18. Outdoor (Posters, Transit) 19. Point of Purchase20. Premiums, Novelties
21. Product Samples 22. Special Events Mktg. 23. Spot Radio 24. Spot T.V. 25. Weekly Newsp. 26. Yellow Page Adv.

POTDEVIN MACHINE COMPANY
26 Fairfield Pl
West Caldwell, NJ 07006-6207
Mailing Address:
PO Box 1409
Caldwell, NJ 70071-1409
Tel.: (201) 288-1941
Fax: (201) 288-3770
Web Site: www.potdevin.com
Approx. Number Employees: 15
Year Founded: 1893
Business Description:
Gluing, Pasting & Coating Machinery Mfr
S.I.C.: 3565
N.A.I.C.S.: 333993
Export
Media: 2-4-7-10
Distr.: Natl.
Personnel:
Robert A. Potdevin *(Chm & CEO)*
Robert S. Potdevin *(Pres)*

POWER EQUIPMENT COMPANY INC
3300 Alcoa Hwy
Knoxville, TN 37920-5558
Tel.: (865) 577-5563
Fax: (865) 579-7365
Web Site: www.powerequipco.com
Sales Range: $75-99.9 Million
Approx. Number Employees: 125
Year Founded: 1946
Business Description:
Construction & Mining Machinery
S.I.C.: 5082; 7353
N.A.I.C.S.: 423810; 532412
Import Export
Personnel:
Chris Gaylor *(Pres)*
Shawn Robins *(Sr VP-Products)*
Jim McNeillie *(VP-Fin)*
Andy Moon *(VP-Sls)*
Advertising Agency:
Ackermann PR
1111 Northshore Dr Ste N-400
Knoxville, TN 37919
Tel.: (865) 584-0550
Fax: (865) 588-3009
Toll Free: (866) 896-4069
Toll Free: (888) 414-7787

POWER INTEGRATIONS, INC.
5245 Hellyer Ave
San Jose, CA 95138-1002
Tel.: (408) 414-9200
Fax: (408) 414-9201
Web Site: www.powerint.com/
Approx. Rev.: $299,803,000
Approx. Number Employees: 444
Year Founded: 1988
Business Description:
High-Voltage Analog Integrated Circuit Mfr
S.I.C.: 3674
N.A.I.C.S.: 334413
Advertising Expenditures: $400,000
Personnel:
Steven J. Sharp *(Chm)*
Balu Balakrishnan *(Pres & CEO)*
Sandeep Nayyar *(CFO & VP-Fin)*
Douglas G. Bailey *(VP-Mktg)*
Derek Bell *(VP-Engrg)*
Ben Sutherland *(Acting VP-Sls)*
Clifford Walker *(VP-Corp Dev & IT)*
Joe Shiffler *(Dir-IR & Corp Comm)*
Brands & Products:
APPSTV
C-BALANCE
CLAMPLESS
DIODE-CC
DPA-SWITCH
E-SHIELD
ECOSMART
ESIP
FILTERFUSE
FLYFORWARD
HIPER
HIPERPLC
HISIDE
LINKSWITCH
LOWDROP-CC
PEAKSWITCH
PI EXPERT
PI FACTS
POWER INTEGRATIONS
PS-SERIES
SLIMCORE
STACKFET
TINYSWITCH
TOPSWITCH

POWIN CORPORATION
6975 SW Sandburg Rd Ste 326
Tigard, OR 97223
Tel.: (503) 598-6659
Fax: (503) 598-3941
E-mail: powin@powin.com
Web Site: www.powin.biz
Approx. Sls.: $48,441,459
Approx. Number Employees: 33
Year Founded: 1989
Business Description:
Original Equipment Manufacturer (OEM) Products Distr
S.I.C.: 5084
N.A.I.C.S.: 423830
Advertising Expenditures: $64,952
Media: 17
Personnel:
Joseph Lu *(Pres)*
David W. Chambers *(CFO)*
Jingshuang Liu *(Gen Mgr & Mgr-Ops)*

PRAB, INC.
5944 E Kilgore Rd
Kalamazoo, MI 49048
Tel.: (269) 382-8200
Fax: (269) 349-2477
Toll Free: (800) 968-7722
E-mail: info@prab.com
Web Site: www.prab.com
Sales Range: $10-24.9 Million
Approx. Number Employees: 81
Year Founded: 1950
Business Description:
Conveyors, Metal Scrap Reclamation Systems & Related Equipment Mfr
S.I.C.: 3535; 5084
N.A.I.C.S.: 333922; 423830
Export
Advertising Expenditures: $370,000
Media: 2-7-11
Personnel:
Ned Thompson *(Pres & CEO)*
Robert W. Klinge *(CFO)*
Greg Patterson *(VP-Sls & Mktg)*
Brands & Products:
BRIQUETTER
HAPMAN
HARPOON
HELIX
MINISYSTEM
PACESSETTER
PIVOT BELT
SCRAPVEYOR

PRATT & WHITNEY CANADA CORP.
(Sub. of Pratt & Whitney)
1000 Marie Victorin Blvd
Longueuil, QC J4G 1A1, Canada
Tel.: (450) 677-9411
Fax: (450) 647-3620
Toll Free: (800) 268-8000
Web Site: www.pwc.ca
Sales Range: $1-4.9 Billion
Approx. Number Employees: 8,650
Year Founded: 1928
Business Description:
Small Gas Turbine Engines for Air, Land, & Marine-Based Applications
S.I.C.: 3724
N.A.I.C.S.: 336412
Export
Media: 2-4-7-9-10-11-22-25
Distr.: Intl.; Natl.
Personnel:
John Saabas *(Pres)*
Akhil Bhandari *(CIO)*
Alain Rondeau *(Gen Counsel, Sec & VP)*
Benoit Brossoit *(Sr VP-Ops-Global)*
Maria Della Posta *(Sr VP-Mktg)*
Walter Di Bartolomeo *(VP-Engrg)*
John Di Bert *(VP-Fin)*
Richard Dussault *(VP-Mktg)*
Nancy German *(VP-Comm)*
Kevin P. Smith *(VP-HR)*
Raffaele Virgili *(VP-Customer Svc)*
Henri Hudon *(Dir-Mktg)*
Claude Lachapelle *(Dir-Strategic & Customer After Markets)*
Brands & Products:
JT15D
PT6
PW100
PW200
PW300
PW500
PW901A
TWIN-PAC

PRAXAIR-TAFA
(Sub. of Praxair Surface Technologies, Inc.)
146 Pembroke Rd
Concord, NH 03301-5706
Tel.: (603) 224-9585
Fax: (603) 225-4342
E-mail: info@tafa.com
Web Site: www.praxair.com/thermalspray
Sales Range: $25-49.9 Million
Approx. Number Employees: 75
Year Founded: 1976
Business Description:
Mfr. of Arc Spray Systems for Thermal Coatings
S.I.C.: 3563
N.A.I.C.S.: 333912
Advertising Expenditures: $200,000
Media: 7-8-10-25
Personnel:
Charlie Muzzey *(Mgr-Plant Quality & Field Svc)*
Joan Rich *(Coord-Mktg Svcs)*
Brands & Products:
JP 8000

PRECISION DORMER
(Unit of Dormer Tools Ltd.)
301 Industrial Ave
Crystal Lake, IL 60012
Tel.: (815) 459-2040
Fax: (815) 459-2804
Toll Free: (800) 877-3745
E-mail: cs@precisiondormer.com
Web Site: www.precisiondormer.com
E-Mail For Key Personnel:
Sales Director: sales.ptd@sandvik.com
Sales Range: $25-49.9 Million
Approx. Number Employees: 300
Year Founded: 1952
Business Description:
Solid Carbide & High-Speed Steel Drill Bits & Other Metal-Cutting Tools Mfr & Distr
S.I.C.: 3545; 5072
N.A.I.C.S.: 333515; 423710
Export
Media: 4-13
Distr.: Intl.; Natl.
Budget Set: Mar.
Personnel:
Mark Wilcox *(Pres)*
Gary Kirchoff *(Product Mgr)*
Brands & Products:
PRECISION

PRECISION RINGS, INC.
5611 Progress Rd
Indianapolis, IN 46241
Mailing Address:
PO Box 421189
Indianapolis, IN 46241
Tel.: (317) 247-4786
Fax: (317) 248-9781
E-mail: prisales@precisionrings.com
Web Site: www.precisionrings.com
E-Mail For Key Personnel:
Sales Director: prisales@precisionrings.com
Approx. Sls.: $8,000,000
Approx. Number Employees: 45
Year Founded: 1950
Business Description:
Ring & Gap Mfr
S.I.C.: 3592; 3492
N.A.I.C.S.: 336311; 332912
Export
Media: 2-4-7-10-11-17
Distr.: Intl.; Natl.
Personnel:
Lee Crannell *(Pres)*
J.S. Crannell *(CEO)*

PRECISION ROLL GRINDERS, INC.
6356 Chapmans Rd
Allentown, PA 18106-9364
Tel.: (610) 395-6966
Fax: (610) 481-9130
Fax: (610) 395-8906
E-mail: pasales@precisionrollgrinders.com
Web Site: www.precisionrollgrinders.com
Approx. Number Employees: 100
Year Founded: 1970
Business Description:
Roll Grinding Mfr & Polisher
S.I.C.: 7389; 3471
N.A.I.C.S.: 561990; 332813
Export
Advertising Expenditures: $200,000
Media: 2-4-7-10-11-17-20

Key to Media (For complete agency information see *The Advertising Red Books-Agencies* edition):
1. Bus. Publs. 2. Cable T.V. 3. Catalogs & Directories. 4. Co-op Adv. 5. Consumer Mags. 6. D.M. to Bus. Estab.7. D.M. to Consumers
8. Daily Newsp. 9. Exhibits/Trade Shows 10. Foreign 11. Infomercial 12. Internet Adv.13. Multimedia 14. Network Radio
15. Network T.V. 16. Newsp. Distr. Mags. 17. Other 18. Outdoor (Posters, Transit) 19. Point of Purchase20. Premiums, Novelties
21. Product Samples 22. Special Events Mktg. 23. Spot Radio 24. Spot T.V. 25. Weekly Newsp. 26. Yellow Page Adv.

Distr.: Intl.; Natl.
Personnel:
James Manley *(Pres & CEO)*
Ernest LaBranche *(Mgr-Sls Dev)*
Bob Rourke *(Mgr-Natl Sls & Mktg)*
Brands & Products:
NO ONE ELSE EVEN COMES CLOSE
PRAXAIR
PRECISION ROLL GRINDERS
ROLL ARMOR
TOKUDEN
Advertising Agency:
Keenan-Nagle Advertising
1301 S 12th St
Allentown, PA 18103-3814
Tel.: (610) 797-7100
Fax: (610) 797-8212

PREFORMED LINE PRODUCTS COMPANY
660 Beta Dr
Cleveland, OH 44143-2355
Mailing Address:
PO Box 91129
Cleveland, OH 44101-3129
Tel.: (440) 461-5200
Fax: (440) 442-8816
Telex: 980407
E-mail: inquiries@preformed.com
Web Site: www.preformed.com
Approx. Sls.: $338,305,000
Approx. Number Employees: 2,617
Year Founded: 1947
Business Description:
Mfr. of Products for Constructing Electrical Power Lines & Telecommunications Systems
S.I.C.: 1623; 3644; 3661
N.A.I.C.S.: 237130; 237110; 334210; 335932
Export
Advertising Expenditures: $1,600,000
Media: 1-2-4-7-10-21
Distr.: Intl.; Natl.
Budget Set: Nov.
Personnel:
Robert G. Ruhlman *(CEO)*
Eric R. Graef *(CFO)*
Caroline A. Saylor *(Gen Counsel & Sec)*
J. Cecil Curlee *(VP-HR)*
Dennis F. Mckenna *(VP-Mktg & Bus Dev)*
David C. Sunkle *(VP-Res & Engrg)*
Wade Cutting *(Product Mgr)*
Jean Reilly *(Supvr-Mktg Comm)*
Advertising Agency:
Liggett Stashower
LS Brand Bldg 1240 Huron Rd
Cleveland, OH 44115
Tel.: (216) 348-8500
Fax: (914) 407-1475

PREMIER MILL CORP.
(Sub. of SPX Corporation)
1 Birchmont Dr
Reading, PA 19606-3298
Tel.: (610) 779-9500
Fax: (610) 779-9666
Telex: 423628 Premill
Web Site: www.netzsch-grinding.com
E-Mail For Key Personnel:
Sales Director: sales@premiermill.com
Sales Range: $25-49.9 Million
Approx. Number Employees: 9
Year Founded: 1925
Business Description:
Dispersing & Milling Equipment for the Paint, Ink & Coatings Industries
S.I.C.: 3559; 3531
N.A.I.C.S.: 333298; 333120
Export
Media: 2-4-10
Distr.: Intl.; Natl.
Budget Set: Aug.-Sept.
Personnel:
Don L. Canterna *(Pres)*
Jeff Ropers *(CFO)*
Bruce Freeland *(VP-Engrg)*
Gordon Hurst *(VP-Sls)*
Dan Shane *(VP-HR)*
Greg Penn *(Gen Mgr)*
Chris Eckert *(Dir Tech)*
Brands & Products:
COLLOID MILL
CSD/ESD
HIDROBAT
MAXSHEAR
MSM
PLM
PSM
SUPERMILL
SUPERMILL 2
Advertising Agency:
In-House-Premier Mill
One Birchmont Dr.
Reading, PA 19606-3298
Tel.: (610) 779-9500
Fax: (610) 779-9666

PRESSCO TECHNOLOGY INC.
29200 Aurora Rd
Cleveland, OH 44139
Tel.: (440) 498-2600
Fax: (440) 498-2600
E-mail: sales@pressco.com
Web Site: www.pressco.com
E-Mail For Key Personnel:
Sales Director: sales@pressco.com
Sales Range: $10-24.9 Million
Approx. Number Employees: 120
Year Founded: 1966
Business Description:
Physical Property Testing Equipment
S.I.C.: 3829; 3825
N.A.I.C.S.: 334519; 334515
Personnel:
Don W. Cochran *(Chm & CEO)*
Fritz Awig *(VP-Engrg & Ops)*
Brands & Products:
CHROMAPULSE
EDGE ALERT II
INTELLIMASS
INTELLISENSE
INTELLISPEC
PRESSCO
RETRO-SPEC
Advertising Agency:
Richards Communications
3201 Enterprise Pkwy Ste 400
Beachwood, OH 44122
Tel.: (216) 514-7800
Fax: (216) 514-7801

PRESSURE SYSTEMS, INC.
(Sub. of Measurement Specialties Inc.)
34 Research Dr
Hampton, VA 23666-1325
Tel.: (757) 865-1243
Fax: (757) 766-2644
Toll Free: (800) 678-7226
Telex: 901-406
E-mail: sales@pressuresystems.com
Web Site: www.psih.com
E-Mail For Key Personnel:
Sales Director: sales@pressuresystems.com
Sales Range: $25-49.9 Million
Approx. Number Employees: 95
Year Founded: 1977
Business Description:
Electronic Pressure Transducers & Measurement Systems Mfr
S.I.C.: 3823; 3829
N.A.I.C.S.: 334513; 334519
Media: 10-11
Personnel:
Dave Marsell *(VP-Engrg)*

PROCESS CONTROL CORPORATION
6875 Mimms Dr
Atlanta, GA 30340
Tel.: (770) 449-8810
Fax: (770) 449-5445
E-mail: sales@process-control.com
Web Site: www.process-control.com
E-Mail For Key Personnel:
Sales Director: sales@process-control.com
Approx. Number Employees: 75
Year Founded: 1967
Business Description:
Auxiliary Machinery to the Plastic Processing Industry Designer, Mfr & Marketer
S.I.C.: 3559
N.A.I.C.S.: 333220
Media: 10
Personnel:
Joseph D. Robertson *(Chm & CEO)*
David Metzloff *(Mgr-Ops & IT)*
Brands & Products:
ASR
AST
GRAVIFUFF
GRAVITROL
GUARDIAN
PCC WEB
PCCWEB

THE PROTECTOSEAL COMPANY
225 Foster Ave
Bensenville, IL 60106-1631
Tel.: (630) 595-0800
Fax: (630) 595-8059
E-mail: info@protectoseal.com
Web Site: www.protectoseal.com
Sales Range: $10-24.9 Million
Approx. Number Employees: 100
Business Description:
Mfr of Safety Equipment For Handling, Storing & Dispensing Flammable Liquids
S.I.C.: 9224; 5999
N.A.I.C.S.: 922160; 453998
Advertising Expenditures: $200,000
Media: 2-4-7-10-21-26
Distr.: Intl.; Natl.
Budget Set: Apr.
Personnel:
Ken Nosek *(Reg Mgr-Midwest)*
Carol Beem *(Mgr-Mktg Comm)*
John McDonough *(Mgr-Mktg Support)*
Brands & Products:
FIRE CHECK
LIFT MATES
PIN-TECH
PRO-FLOW
PROTECTOSEAL
PROTECTOSEAL PLUS
SAFETY WITHOUT COMPROMISE
SMOKERS' OUTPOST
ZIACOTE

PTC ALLIANCE CORP.
(Holding of Black Diamond Capital Management LLC)
6051 Wallace Rd Ext Ste 200
Wexford, PA 15090
Tel.: (412) 299-7900
Fax: (412) 299-2619
E-mail: sales@ptcalliance.com
Web Site: www.ptcalliance.com
E-Mail For Key Personnel:
Sales Director: sales@ptcalliance.com
Approx. Number Employees: 1,400
Year Founded: 1924
Business Description:
Cold Drawn Buttweld & Electric Weld Mechanical Steel Tubing Marketer & Mfr
S.I.C.: 3317
N.A.I.C.S.: 331210
Media: 2-4
Distr.: Natl.
Budget Set: Aug.
Personnel:
Peter Whiting *(Chm, Pres & CEO)*
Warren MacKenzie *(VP-Mktg & Sls)*
Brands & Products:
PITTSBURGH TUBE
PTCALLIANCE

PUNCH GRAPHIX AMERICAS INC.
(Sub. of Punch Graphics International PLC)
1375 E Irving Park Rd
Itasca, IL 60143
Tel.: (630) 438-7900
Fax: (630) 438-7915
Toll Free: (877) XEIKON1
Web Site: www.xeikon.com
Sales Range: $10-24.9 Million
Approx. Number Employees: 65
Business Description:
Developer, Mfr & Distr of High Quality Digital Printing Systems
S.I.C.: 3555
N.A.I.C.S.: 333293
Export
Media: 4-7-8-10-11-13

PURVIS BEARING SERVICE LTD.
10500 N Stemmons Fwy PO Box 540757
Dallas, TX 75220
Tel.: (214) 358-5588
Fax: (214) 350-2419
E-mail: info@purvisbearing.com
Web Site: www.purvisbearing.com
Approx. Sls.: $50,000,000
Approx. Number Employees: 60
Year Founded: 1945
Business Description:
Power Transmission Products, Bearings & Linear Components Distr
S.I.C.: 5085; 5013
N.A.I.C.S.: 423840; 423120
Media: 2
Personnel:
Robert W. Purvis *(Pres)*
George W. Purvis, Jr. *(CEO)*
Stacy Mikkelsen *(VP-Mktg & Bus)*

Key to Media (For complete agency information see *The Advertising Red Books-Agencies* edition):
1. Bus. Publs. 2. Cable T.V. 3. Catalogs & Directories. 4. Co-op Adv. 5. Consumer Mags. 6. D.M. to Bus. Estab.7. D.M. to Consumers
8. Daily Newsp. 9. Exhibits/Trade Shows 10. Foreign 11. Infomercial 12. Internet Adv.13. Multimedia 14. Network Radio
15. Network T.V. 16. Newsp. Distr. Mags. 17. Other 18. Outdoor (Posters, Transit) 19. Point of Purchase20. Premiums, Novelties
21. Product Samples 22. Special Events Mktg. 23. Spot Radio 24. Spot T.V. 25. Weekly Newsp. 26. Yellow Page Adv.

PUTZMEISTER AMERICA
(Sub. of Putzmeister AG)
1733 90th St
Sturtevant, WI 53177-1805
Tel.: (262) 886-3200
Fax: (262) 884-6338
Toll Free: (800) 884-7210
E-mail: pmr@putzam.com
Web Site: www.putzmeister.com
Sales Range: $125-149.9 Million
Approx. Number Employees: 200
Business Description:
Mfr. of Pumps & Equipment.
S.I.C.: 3561; 3535
N.A.I.C.S.: 333911; 333922
Import Export
Media: 2-4-5-7-10-20-22
Distr.: Natl.
Budget Set: Oct.
Personnel:
Marc Aguilar *(VP-Sls)*
Bill Dwyer *(VP-Sls & Mktg)*
Eric Zimmermann *(Gen Mgr-Esser Pipe Tech Div & Putzmeister Americas Water Tech Di)*
Doug Brunet *(Dir-Customer Support)*
Bill Carbeau *(Dir-Special Applications Bus)*
Stefan Fritz *(Dir-Supply Chain)*
Craig Olson *(Mgr-Sls Admin)*
Brands & Products:
BIG BLUE
TELEBELT
THOM-KATT
TOMMY GUN

Q.E.P. CO., INC.
1001 Broken Sound Pkwy NW Ste A
Boca Raton, FL 33487
Tel.: (561) 994-5550
Fax: (561) 241-2830
Toll Free: (800) 777-8665 (Sales)
E-mail: info@qep.com
Web Site: www.qep.com
Approx. Sls.: $205,853,000
Approx. Number Employees: 381
Year Founded: 1979
Business Description:
Tools & Related Products Used In the Tile, Masonry, Dry Wall & Carpeting Trades Mfr, Marketer & Distr
S.I.C.: 3423; 3545; 5072
N.A.I.C.S.: 332212; 333515; 423710
Advertising Expenditures: $100,000
Media: 4-5-18-19
Personnel:
Lewis Gould *(Chm, Pres & CEO)*
Richard A. Brooke *(CFO, Treas & Sr VP)*
Lawrence P. Levine *(Gen Counsel & Sr VP)*
Jamie L. Clingan *(Sr VP-Intl Mktg)*
Ken Fordik *(VP-HR)*
Brian Johnson *(VP-Mktg)*
Brands & Products:
FRESH
Q-SET
QEP
Q.E.P CO., INC.
VITREX

QUALITY PRODUCTS INC.
2222 S 3rd St
Columbus, OH 43207
Tel.: (614) 228-0185
Fax: (614) 228-2358
E-mail: multipress@multipress.com
Web Site: www.multipress.com
Sales Range: $10-24.9 Million
Approx. Number Employees: 80
Year Founded: 1998
Business Description:
Holding Company; Industrial Hydraulic Bench Presses, Floor Presses & Hydraulic Jacks Mfr; Custom Packaging & Crating Services
S.I.C.: 3542; 3569; 6719
N.A.I.C.S.: 333513; 333999; 551112
Media: 2-10
Personnel:
Richard Drexler *(Chm & CEO)*
Tac Kensler *(CFO & Sec)*

QUANTUM FUEL SYSTEMS TECHNOLOGIES WORLDWIDE, INC.
17872 Cartwright Rd
Irvine, CA 92614-6217
Tel.: (949) 399-4500
Fax: (949) 399-4600
E-mail: info@qtww.com
Web Site: www.qtww.com
Approx. Rev.: $20,274,248
Approx. Number Employees: 102
Year Founded: 2002
Business Description:
Fuel Control Systems, Pressure Regulators, & Storage Cylinders Mfr
S.I.C.: 3711; 3593; 3823
N.A.I.C.S.: 336211; 333995; 334513
Media: 10-13
Personnel:
Dale L. Rasmussen *(Chm)*
Alan P. Niedzwiecki *(Pres & CEO)*
William B. Olson *(CFO & Treas)*
David Mazaika *(COO)*
Bradley J. Timon *(Chief Acctg Officer & Controller)*
Kenneth R. Lombardo *(Gen Counsel & Sec)*

QUEST ENVIRONMENTAL & SAFETY PRODUCTS, INC.
9892 E 121st St
Fishers, IN 46037
Tel.: (317) 594-4500
Fax: (317) 594-4501
Toll Free: (800) 878-4872
E-mail: catalog@questsafety.com
Web Site: www.questsafety.com
Approx. Number Employees: 26
Year Founded: 1991
Business Description:
Asbestos & Lead Abatement Products Distr
S.I.C.: 5085
N.A.I.C.S.: 423840
Media: 4-7
Personnel:
Sam Yadav *(Pres)*
Vanita K Yadav *(CFO)*
Andy Bowman *(Sr Mgr-Territory & Sls)*
Mark Dieterle *(Div Mgr-Environ Sls)*
Kelli Marti *(Mgr-Opers)*
Keith Skeel *(Mgr-Pur)*

QUINCY COMPRESSOR INC.
(Sub. of Atlas Copco North America LLC)
3501 Wisman Ln
Quincy, IL 62301-1257
Tel.: (217) 222-7700
Fax: (217) 222-5109
E-mail: trueblue@quincycompressor.com
Web Site: www.quincycompressor.com
Sales Range: $125-149.9 Million
Approx. Number Employees: 420
Year Founded: 1920
Business Description:
Rotary & Reciprocating Air Compressors Mfr
S.I.C.: 3519; 3563
N.A.I.C.S.: 333618; 333912
Export
Advertising Expenditures: $300,000
Media: 2-7-10
Distr.: Natl.
Budget Set: Nov.
Personnel:
John Thompson *(Pres)*
Jacqueline Gay *(Mgr-Mktg Svcs)*
Brands & Products:
QT
QUINCY
QUINCY AIR MASTER
QUINCY COMPRESSOR
QUINCY PLT

QUIPP SYSTEMS
(Sub. of Illinois Tool Works Inc.)
4800 NW 157th St
Miami, FL 33014-6434
Tel.: (305) 623-8700
Fax: (305) 623-0980
Toll Free: (800) 345-9680
E-mail: info@quipp.com
Web Site: www.quipp.com
Approx. Sls.: $24,616,602
Approx. Number Employees: 91
Year Founded: 1980
Business Description:
Material Handling Eqiupment Designer & Mfr; Newspaper Printing Services
S.I.C.: 3523; 3554; 3555
N.A.I.C.S.: 333111; 333291; 333293
Export
Advertising Expenditures: $34,812
Media: 2-7-10
Brands & Products:
QUIPP
QUIPP-GRIP III
QUIPP OFF PRESS
QUIPP PACKMAN II
QUIPP SERIES 500
SERIES 4152
TWIN-TRAK
VIPER

R.A. JONES & CO. INC.
(Sub. of OYSTAR Holding GmbH)
2701 Crescent Springs Rd
Covington, KY 41017-1504
Tel.: (859) 341-0400
Fax: (859) 341-0519
Web Site: www.oystar.rajones.com
Approx. Number Employees: 350
Year Founded: 1905
Business Description:
Packaging Machinery Mfr
S.I.C.: 3565
N.A.I.C.S.: 333993
Import Export
Media: 1-2-4-7-10-11-13-20-22
Distr.: Intl.; Natl.
Personnel:
Gordon B. Bonfield *(Pres)*
Susan Awadalla *(CFO)*

R.A. MUELLER, INC.
(Sub. of DXP Enterprises, Inc.)
11270 Cornell Pk Dr
Cincinnati, OH 45242
Tel.: (513) 489-5200
Fax: (513) 247-5330
Toll Free: (800) 793-7867
E-mail: jhook@dxpe.com
Web Site: www.ramueller.com
E-Mail For Key Personnel:
Sales Director: sales@ramueller.com
Sales Range: $25-49.9 Million
Approx. Number Employees: 40
Year Founded: 1952
Business Description:
Fluid Processing Equipment
S.I.C.: 5084
N.A.I.C.S.: 423830
Media: 2-4-7-10-17
Distr.: Natl.
Personnel:
David Little *(Pres)*
Jim Hook *(VP-Mktg & Sls)*

RATHBONE PRECISION METALS, INC.
(Sub. of Calvi Holding S.r.l.)
1241 Park St
Palmer, MA 01069-1606
Tel.: (413) 283-8961
Fax: (413) 283-9722
Toll Free: (888) 283-8961
E-mail: info@rathboneprofiles.com
Web Site: www.rathboneprofiles.com
Approx. Number Employees: 50
Business Description:
Custom, Cold-Drawn Metal Shapes Mfr
S.I.C.: 3316; 3351
N.A.I.C.S.: 331221; 331421
Personnel:
Dick Leger *(Pres)*
Advertising Agency:
tomsheehan worldwide
645 Penn St
Reading, PA 19601-3408
Tel.: (610) 478-8448
Fax: (610) 478-8449

THE RAYMOND CORPORATION
(Sub. of Toyota Industries North America, Inc.)
8 S Canal St #20
Greene, NY 13778-1202
Tel.: (607) 656-2311
Fax: (607) 656-9005
Toll Free: (800) 235-7200
E-mail: webmaster@raymondcorp.com
Web Site: www.raymondcorp.com
Approx. Number Employees: 947
Year Founded: 1922
Business Description:
Warehouse Equipment Mfr & Sales
S.I.C.: 3537; 3535
N.A.I.C.S.: 333924; 333922
Import Export
Media: 1-2-4-7-10-13-20-26
Distr.: Intl.; Natl.
Budget Set: Dec.
Personnel:
Edward J. Rompala *(CFO)*
Timothy Koval *(Chief Legal Officer & VP-Aftermarket Ops)*
Kurt Schoepfle *(Chief Procurement Officer)*
Michael G. Field *(Exec VP-Ops & Engrg)*

Key to Media (For complete agency information see *The Advertising Red Books-Agencies* edition):
1. Bus. Publs. 2. Cable T.V. 3. Catalogs & Directories. 4. Co-op Adv. 5. Consumer Mags. 6. D.M. to Bus. Estab.7. D.M. to Consumers
8. Daily Newsp. 9. Exhibits/Trade Shows 10. Foreign 11. Infomercial 12. Internet Adv.13. Multimedia 14. Network Radio
15. Network T.V. 16. Newsp. Distr. Mags. 17. Other 18. Outdoor (Posters, Transit) 19. Point of Purchase20. Premiums, Novelties
21. Product Samples 22. Special Events Mktg. 23. Spot Radio 24. Spot T.V. 25. Weekly Newsp. 26. Yellow Page Adv.

Chuck Pascarelli *(Exec VP-Mktg & Sls)*
John F. Everts *(VP-Fin)*
David M. Furman *(VP-Mktg)*
Joseph Ginnetti *(VP-Sls)*
Stephen E. VanNostrand *(VP-HR)*
Frank Devlin *(Mktg Mgr-Advanced Technologies)*
Brands & Products:
4-D
DEEP-REACH
DOCKSTOCKER
EASI
FIDDLER
GOFER
HANDYLIFT
INTELLIDRIVE
INTELLIDRIVE 2
INTELLIGUIDE
INTELLISPEED
LIFT PARTNERS
PACER
RAY-DATA
RAYBUILT
RAYPARTS
REACH-FORK
SAFETY ON THE MOVE
SWING-REACH
WALKIE
Advertising Agency:
Pear Creative Group
201 N McKinley Ave
Endicott, NY 13760
Tel.: (607) 748-8748
Fax: (607) 748-1098
Toll Free: (800) 494-PEAR
(Lift Partners Program for Ray Built Parts)

RBS GLOBAL, INC.
(Sub. of Rexnord Holdings, Inc.)
4701 W Greenfield Ave
Milwaukee, WI 53214
Tel.: (414) 643-3000
Fax: (414) 643-2430
Fax: (414) 643-3078
Telex: 26-727
Web Site: www.rexnord.com
Approx. Sls.: $1,510,000,000
Approx. Number Employees: 5,700
Year Founded: 1966
Business Description:
Holding Company; Power Transmission Components Mfr
S.I.C.: 6719; 3568
N.A.I.C.S.: 551112; 333613
Export
Advertising Expenditures: $8,200,000
Distr.: Natl.
Budget Set: Feb. -Mar.
Personnel:
George M. Sherman *(Chm)*
Todd A. Adams *(Pres & CEO)*
Michael H. Shapiro *(CFO & VP)*
Patricia Whaley *(Gen Counsel & VP)*
Praveen R. Jeyarajah *(Exec VP-Corp & Bus Dev)*
George C. Moore *(Exec VP)*

REEL-O-MATIC, INC.
6408 S Eastern Ave
Oklahoma City, OK 73149-5134
Tel.: (405) 672-0000
Fax: (405) 672-7200
Toll Free: (888) 873-4000
E-mail: info@reelomatic.com
Web Site: www.reelomatic.com
Sales Range: $10-24.9 Million
Approx. Number Employees: 50
Year Founded: 1936
Business Description:
Mfr. of Material Handling Equipment for Wire, Cable, Steel Wire Rope, Tubing, Hose & other Flexible or Coilable Products
S.I.C.: 3569
N.A.I.C.S.: 333999
Export
Advertising Expenditures: $250,000
Media: 1-2-4-10-11-13
Distr.: Natl.
Budget Set: Oct. -Sept.
Personnel:
Terry T. Simmons *(Pres)*
Brands & Products:
AUTO REEL
AUTOSPOOL
LENGTH-TRAC
LONG-RUN
NK SERIES
QUALITY, SERVICE AND RELIABILITY AROUND THE WORLD
THE REAL DEAL
THE REEL-MAGIC
REEL-O-MATIC
SPOOL-TOOLS

REID SUPPLY COMPANY
(Div. of Reid Entities)
2265 Black Creek Rd
Muskegon, MI 49444
Tel.: (231) 777-3951
Fax: (231) 773-4485
Fax: (800) 438-1145
Toll Free: (800) 253-0421
E-mail: mail@reidsupply.com
Web Site: www.reidsupply.com
Approx. Number Employees: 200
Business Description:
Industrial Components Whslr
S.I.C.: 5085
N.A.I.C.S.: 423840
Media: 2-4-5-6-7-8-10-11-13
Distr.: Intl.
Personnel:
Greg Palmer *(Dir-Mktg & Interim Dir-Sls)*
Joan Sherburn *(Mgr-Mktg Svcs)*
Brands & Products:
REID

RELIANCE STEEL & ALUMINUM CO.
350 S Grand Ave Ste 5100
Los Angeles, CA 90071
Tel.: (213) 687-7700
Fax: (213) 687-8792
Web Site: www.rsac.com
Approx. Sls.: $6,312,795,000
Approx. Number Employees: 9,610
Year Founded: 1939
Business Description:
Metal Processing & Distribution
S.I.C.: 5051
N.A.I.C.S.: 423510
Import Export
Personnel:
David H. Hannah *(Chm & CEO)*
Gregg J. Mollins *(Pres & COO)*
Karla R. Lewis *(CFO & Exec VP)*
Colleen A. Wolf *(CIO)*
Kay Rustand *(Gen Counsel & VP)*
William K. Sales, Jr. *(Sr VP-Nonferrous Ops)*
Donna Newton *(VP-HR)*
Kim Feazle *(Dir-IR)*
Advertising Agency:
ANEW Marketing Group
811 W Jericho Tpke Ste 109E
Smithtown, NY 11787
Tel.: (631) 982-4000
Fax: (631) 434-1129

REMMELE ENGINEERING, INC.
(Holding of Goldner Hawn Johnson & Morrison Inc.)
10 Old Hwy 8 SW
New Brighton, MN 55112
Tel.: (651) 635-4100
Fax: (651) 635-4168
Toll Free: (800) 222-7737
E-mail: info@remmele.com
Web Site: www.remmele.com
Approx. Rev.: $88,000,000
Approx. Number Employees: 450
Year Founded: 1949
Business Description:
Tools, Dies, Special Machines & Precision Parts Mfr
S.I.C.: 3544; 3569
N.A.I.C.S.: 333514; 333999
Import Export
Media: 2-10
Distr.: Intl.; Natl.
Budget Set: Nov.
Personnel:
Mike Hackner *(CFO)*

RENOLD, INC.
(Sub. of Renold plc)
(d/b/a Renold Ajax Inc.)
100 Bourne St
Westfield, NY 14787-9706
Tel.: (716) 326-3121
Fax: (716) 326-6121
Toll Free: (800) 879-2529
E-mail: ainfo@renoldajax.com
Web Site: www.renold.com/nmsruntime/saveasdialog.asp?lID=467&sID=750
Sales Range: $10-24.9 Million
Approx. Number Employees: 100
Year Founded: 1920
Business Description:
Mfr. of Flexible Coupling for Director Connected Machines; Vibratory Conveyors & Shaker Drives; Custom Made Gears & Gearboxes; Power Transmission & Mechanical Handling Products
S.I.C.: 3568; 3535
N.A.I.C.S.: 333613; 333922
Import Export
Media: 2-4-7-10-26
Distr.: Intl.; Natl.
Budget Set: Dec.
Personnel:
Thomas Murrer *(Pres)*
Winston Woodard *(Controller & VP-Fin)*
Brands & Products:
AJAX FLEXIBLE COUPLINGS
AJAX SHAKER
RENOLD GEARBOXES

REPUBLIC POWDERED METALS, INC.
(Sub. of RPM Industrial Holding Co.)
2628 Pearl Rd
Medina, OH 44256
Tel.: (330) 273-8712
Fax: (330) 273-5061
Toll Free: (800) 551-7081
E-mail: info@rpmrepublic.com
Web Site: www.rpmrepublic.com
Sales Range: $25-49.9 Million
Approx. Number Employees: 35
Business Description:
Roof & Wall Restoration Products Mfr
S.I.C.: 2851; 2951; 2952
N.A.I.C.S.: 325510; 324121; 324122
Personnel:
Ray Leake *(Reg Mgr)*
Brands & Products:
ALUMANATION 301
GEOFLEX
GEOGARD
RAMUC
SOLARGARD
Advertising Agency:
The Lauerer Markin Group, Inc.
1700 Woodlands Dr
Maumee, OH 43537-4043
Tel.: (419) 893-2500
Fax: (419) 893-1050
Toll Free: (800) 535-3212

RIDGE TOOL COMPANY
(Div. of Emerson Tool Company)
400 Clark St
Elyria, OH 44035-6108
Tel.: (440) 323-5581
Fax: (440) 323-5204
Toll Free: (888) 743-4333
Telex: 24-3420
Web Site: www.ridgid.com
Sales Range: $350-399.9 Million
Approx. Number Employees: 1,000
Business Description:
Specialty Plumbing, Piping, Power & Miscellaneous Tools & Hardware Mfr
S.I.C.: 3541; 3423
N.A.I.C.S.: 333512; 332212
Media: 1-4-10-20
Distr.: Intl.; Natl.
Budget Set: June
Personnel:
Fred Pond *(Pres)*
Scott Garfield *(CFO & VP-Fin)*
Edward McKiernan *(VP-Mktg)*
Steven D Dyer *(Dir-Mktg Commu)*
Brands & Products:
RIDGID/KOLLMAN
SEASNAKE
Advertising Agency:
Media II, Inc.
2778 SOM Center Rd Ste 200
Willoughby, OH 44094
Tel.: (440) 943-3600
Fax: (440) 943-3660

RING PRECISON COMPONENTS
(Div. of The Producto Machine Co.)
2980 Turner Rd
Jamestown, NY 14701
Tel.: (716) 484-7131
Fax: (716) 484-2235
Toll Free: (800) 828-2216
E-mail: administrator@ringprecision.com
Web Site: www.ringprecision.com
E-Mail For Key Personnel:
President: administrator@ringprecision.com
Approx. Number Employees: 115
Year Founded: 1945
Business Description:
Tooling Components for Metal

Key to Media (For complete agency information see *The Advertising Red Books-Agencies* edition):
1. Bus. Publs. 2. Cable T.V. 3. Catalogs & Directories. 4. Co-op Adv. 5. Consumer Mags. 6. D.M. to Bus. Estab.7. D.M. to Consumers
8. Daily Newsp. 9. Exhibits/Trade Shows 10. Foreign 11. Infomercial 12. Internet Adv.13. Multimedia 14. Network Radio
15. Network T.V. 16. Newsp. Distr. Mags. 17. Other 18. Outdoor (Posters, Transit) 19. Point of Purchase20. Premiums, Novelties
21. Product Samples 22. Special Events Mktg. 23. Spot Radio 24. Spot T.V. 25. Weekly Newsp. 26. Yellow Page Adv.

Ring Precison Components — (Continued)

Forming, Rubber & Plastics Molding, Injection & Mold Components Tooling, & Metal Stamping Mfr
S.I.C.: 3544; 3542
N.A.I.C.S.: 333514; 333513
Export
Media: 2-4-8-10-26
Distr.: Intl.; Natl.
Budget Set: Apr.-Mar.
Personnel:
Newman M. Marsilius *(Pres & CEO)*
Dale R. Gier *(Gen Mgr & VP)*

RITCHIE BROS. AUCTIONEERS INCORPORATED
9500 Glenlyon Pkwy
Burnaby, BC V5J 0C6, Canada
Tel.: (778) 331-5500
Toll Free: (800) 663-8457 (USA)
Toll Free: (800) 663-1739 (Canada)
E-mail: info@rbauction.com
Web Site: www.rbauction.com
Approx. Rev.: $357,369,000
Approx. Number Employees: 1,162
Year Founded: 1963
Business Description:
Industrial Equipment Auctioneer
S.I.C.: 1541; 5083; 5961
N.A.I.C.S.: 236210; 423820; 454112
Media: 4-26
Personnel:
Robert W. Murdoch *(Chm)*
Robert K. Mackay *(Pres)*
Peter James Blake *(CEO)*
Robert A. McLeod *(CFO)*
Robert S. Armstrong *(COO)*
Guylain Turgeon *(Sr VP & Mng Dir-Europe, Middle East & Asia)*
Curtis C. Hinkelman *(Sr VP-Eastern United States)*
David D. Nicholson *(Sr VP-Central US, Mexico & South America)*
Victor E. Pospiech *(Sr VP-Admin & HR)*
Steven C. Simpson *(Sr VP-Western US)*
Kevin R. Tink *(Sr VP-Canada & Agriculture)*
Robert K. Whitsit *(Sr VP)*
Michael Zhou *(Bus Dev Mgr)*
Vicki Cunningham *(Supvr-Corp Comm)*

RITE-HITE HOLDING CORPORATION
8900 N Arbon Dr
Milwaukee, WI 53223-2451
Tel.: (414) 355-2600
Fax: (414) 355-9248
Toll Free: (800) 456-0600
E-mail: info@ritehite.com
Web Site: www.ritehite.com
Approx. Number Employees: 1,400
Year Founded: 1967
Business Description:
Holding Company
S.I.C.: 5084; 3537
N.A.I.C.S.: 423830; 333924
Export
Advertising Expenditures: $900,000
Multimedia: $75,000; Bus. Publs.: $400,000; Catalogs & Directories: $100,000; D.M. to Bus. Estab.: $50,000; Exhibits/Trade Shows: $200,000; Premiums, Novelties: $50,000; Yellow Page Adv.: $25,000
Distr.: Intl.; Natl.
Budget Set: Jan.
Personnel:
Michael White *(Owner & Chm)*
Mark Petri *(Pres & CEO)*
Mark Kirkish *(CFO)*
Mary Blaser *(Mgr-Mktg)*
Brands & Products:
AUTO-STRIP
BARRIER GLIDER
BUGSHIELD
CORNER-VU
DOK-COMMANDER
DOK-DOR
DOK-LOK
DOK-LOKS
DUAL-DOKLIFT/LEVELER
DURATHON
FASTRAX
GUARD-RITE
HD-3000 STL HYDRAULIC LEVELER
HEATSHIELD
INSUL-RITE
INSULATOR
ISO-TEK
JUMBO
LEVELER-VU
PEDESTRIAN-VU
POWR-FOLD
POWR-SLIDE
PROTECDOR
PROTECDOR XL
RAIN GUARD
RAM-RITE
RITE-VU
SAFE-T-LIP
SAFE-T-SPRINT
SMOOTH TRANSITION DOK SYSTEM
SOFT-EDGE
SOFT-STOP
SPEED-FEED
STEEL-RITE II
THINMAN
TRAKLINE
TRAKLINE PLUS
V-FLEX
WHEEL-LOK
WORKHORSE
WORKHORSE 1000
Z-DECK

ROBBINS & MYERS, INC.
51 Plum St Ste 260
Dayton, OH 45440-1397
Tel.: (937) 458-6600
Fax: (937) 458-6614
E-mail: christopher.hix@robn.com
Web Site: www.robbinsmyers.com
Approx. Sls.: $584,694,000
Approx. Number Employees: 2,965
Year Founded: 1878
Business Description:
Fluid Management Products & Systems Mfr
S.I.C.: 5084; 3559; 3561
N.A.I.C.S.: 423830; 333298; 333911
Export
Media: 2-4-7-8-10-21
Distr.: Intl.; Natl.
Budget Set: Sept.
Personnel:
Thomas P. Loftis *(Chm)*
Peter C. Wallace *(Pres & CEO)*
Christopher M. Hix *(CFO & VP)*
Saeid Rahimian *(Pres-Fluid Mgmt Grp & VP)*
Linn Harson *(Gen Counsel & Sec)*
Jeffrey L. Halsey *(VP-HR)*

ROBERTSHAW INDUSTRIAL PRODUCTS
(Div. of Invensys Control Systems)
1602 Mustang Dr
Maryville, TN 37801-3766
Tel.: (865) 981-3094
Fax: (865) 981-3168
Toll Free: (800) 228-7429
Web Site:
www.robertshawindustrial.com
Approx. Number Employees: 50
Year Founded: 1927
Business Description:
Industrial Valves, Vibration Detection & Monitoring Systems Mfr.
S.I.C.: 3491
N.A.I.C.S.: 332911
Import Export
Media: 4-5-6-10-16-19-20
Distr.: Intl.; Natl.; Reg.
Budget Set: Jan. -Mar.
Brands & Products:
EXTRA PERFORMANCE
INVEN-TEL
SYLPHON

ROBERTSON INC.
(Sub. of Marmon Food Service Equipment)
97 Bronte St North
Milton, ON L9T 2N8, Canada
Tel.: (905) 878-2861
Fax: (905) 878-2867
Toll Free: (800) 268-5090
E-mail: info@robertsonscrew.com
Web Site: www.robertsonscrew.com
Sales Range: $25-49.9 Million
Approx. Number Employees: 20
Year Founded: 1908
Business Description:
Standard & Specialty Fasteners
S.I.C.: 3452
N.A.I.C.S.: 332722
Media: 4
Personnel:
Jeff Bent *(Gen Mgr)*
Brands & Products:
CAMTAP
CANDRIL
DRILLCRETE
FRAMELOK
KWIXIN
LO-ROOT
ORIGINAL ROBERTSON
ROBERTSON

ROCKBESTOS-SURPRENANT CABLE CORP.
(Sub. of RSCC Wire & Cable Group)
20 Bradley Park Rd
East Granby, CT 06026-9789
Tel.: (860) 653-8300
Fax: (860) 653-8301
Toll Free: (800) 444-3792
E-mail: info@r-scc.com
Web Site: www.r-scc.com
Sales Range: $75-99.9 Million
Approx. Number Employees: 500
Year Founded: 1918
Business Description:
Wire & Cable Product Mfr
S.I.C.: 3496
N.A.I.C.S.: 332618
Import Export
Advertising Expenditures: $60,000
Media: 1-2-4-7-10-13
Distr.: Natl.
Budget Set: Nov.
Personnel:
Dennis Chalk *(Pres)*
James Belanger *(Mgr-Mktg & Comm)*
Brands & Products:
EXANE
FIREWALL
FIREZONE
GARDEX
IRRAFLEX
MICATEMP
ROCKTHERM
VITALINK
X LINK

ROCKFORD ACROMATIC PRODUCT CO.
(Div. of Aircraft Gear Corporation)
611 Beacon St
Loves Park, IL 61111
Tel.: (815) 877-7473
Fax: (815) 877-1218
E-mail: technical@rockfordacromatic.com
Web Site:
www.rockfordacromatic.com
Approx. Number Employees: 100
Year Founded: 1949
Business Description:
Automotive & Driveline Components Mfr
S.I.C.: 3714
N.A.I.C.S.: 336330
Export
Media: 1-2-4-5-7-8-10-13-19-20-23-26
Distr.: Intl.; Natl.
Budget Set: Sept.
Brands & Products:
AXLEMASTER
DURABOOT
ROCKFORD ACROMATIC
ROCKFORD CONSTANT VELOCITY

ROCKFORD PRODUCTS CORP.
(Holding of BlackEagle Capital Partners, LLC)
707 Harrison Ave
Rockford, IL 61104-7162
Tel.: (815) 397-6000
Fax: (815) 381-6500
E-mail: info@rockfordproducts.com
Web Site: www.rockfordproducts.com
Approx. Number Employees: 600
Year Founded: 1929
Business Description:
Specialty Fasteners & Cold-Formed Components Mfr
S.I.C.: 3452; 5072
N.A.I.C.S.: 332722; 423710
Import Export
Media: 2-4-6-7-10-13-21-26
Distr.: Natl.
Budget Set: Nov.
Personnel:
Dick Mowris *(Pres)*
Jim Wood *(VP-Sls & Mktg)*
Brands & Products:
FASTNERS
ROCKFORD

RODNEY HUNT COMPANY
(Sub. of GA Industries, Inc.)
46 Mill St
Orange, MA 01364-1251

Key to Media (For complete agency information see *The Advertising Red Books-Agencies* edition):
1. Bus. Publs. 2. Cable T.V. 3. Catalogs & Directories. 4. Co-op Adv. 5. Consumer Mags. 6. D.M. to Bus. Estab.7. D.M. to Consumers 8. Daily Newsp. 9. Exhibits/Trade Shows 10. Foreign 11. Infomercial 12. Internet Adv.13. Multimedia 14. Network Radio 15. Network T.V. 16. Newsp. Distr. Mags. 17. Other 18. Outdoor (Posters, Transit) 19. Point of Purchase20. Premiums, Novelties 21. Product Samples 22. Special Events Mktg. 23. Spot Radio 24. Spot T.V. 25. Weekly Newsp. 26. Yellow Page Adv.

Tel.: (978) 544-2511
Fax: (978) 544-7204
Toll Free: (800) 448-8860
E-mail: rh@rodneyhunt.com
Web Site: www.rodneyhunt.com
Approx. Number Employees: 207
Year Founded: 1840
Business Description:
Water & Sewage Control Flow Control Equipment Gates & Valves
S.I.C.: 3441; 3491
N.A.I.C.S.: 332312; 332911
Export
Media: 2-4-7-10
Distr.: Intl.; Natl.
Personnel:
John Kemp *(Pres)*
Tom McAndrews *(VP-Mktg)*
Brands & Products:
GLYDASEAL
HOWELL BUNGER VALVE
HY-Q
ROTOVALVE
SCUBA
STREAMSEAL

ROLLEM CORPORATION OF AMERICA
1650 S Lewis St
Anaheim, CA 92805
Tel.: (714) 935-9130
Fax: (714) 935-9131
Web Site: www.rollemusa.com
Approx. Number Employees: 30
Business Description:
Printing Trades Machinery, Equipment, & Supplies
S.I.C.: 5084
N.A.I.C.S.: 423830
Media: 10
Personnel:
Larry Corwin *(Pres)*

ROLLS-ROYCE ENERGY SYSTEMS INC.
(Sub. of Rolls-Royce North America Inc.)
105 N Sandusky St
Mount Vernon, OH 43050-2495
Tel.: (740) 393-8888
Fax: (740) 393-8336
Web Site: www.rolls-royce.com
Approx. Sls.: $20,000,000
Approx. Number Employees: 50
Year Founded: 1974
Business Description:
Gas Turbine Generator & Compressor Sets Mfr
S.I.C.: 3511; 5084
N.A.I.C.S.: 333611; 423830
Export
Media: 1-2-4-7-10-11-26
Distr.: Intl.; Natl.
Budget Set: Sept.
Personnel:
Simon M. Robertson *(Chm)*
Tom Curley *(Pres)*
Andrew Heath *(Pres)*
John Cheffins *(COO)*
Thomas P. Dale *(Gen Counsel & Exec VP)*
David J. Whetton *(Exec VP)*
Martin Johnson *(VP-Commun)*
Jonathan Ashersonx *(Reg Dir)*
Andrew Shilston *(Dir-Fin)*
Colin P. Smith *(Dir-Engrg & Tech)*

ROPER INDUSTRIES, INC.
6901 Professional Pkwy E Ste 200
Sarasota, FL 34240
Tel.: (941) 556-2601
Fax: (941) 556-2670
E-mail: investor_relations@roperind.com
Web Site: www.roperind.com
Approx. Sls.: $2,386,112,000
Approx. Number Employees: 8,050
Year Founded: 1894
Business Description:
Energy, Analytical Instrumentation, Fluid Handling, Medical & Industrial Control Equipment Mfr
S.I.C.: 3823; 3491; 3824; 7382
N.A.I.C.S.: 334513; 332911; 334514; 561621
Media: 2-7-10-17
Distr.: Intl.; Natl.
Budget Set: Sept.
Personnel:
Brian D. Jellison *(Chm, Pres & CEO)*
John Humphrey *(CFO & VP)*
David B. Liner *(Gen Counsel, Sec & VP)*

ROSEMOUNT ANALYTICAL INC.
(Div. of Emerson Process Management Rosemount Inc.)
2400 Barranca Pkwy
Irvine, CA 92606-5018
Tel.: (949) 757-8500
Fax: (949) 863-9159
Toll Free: (800) 854-8257
E-mail: liquid.csc@emersonprocess.com
Web Site: www.rauniloc.com
Sales Range: $100-124.9 Million
Approx. Number Employees: 350
Year Founded: 1978
Business Description:
Instruments, Analyzers, Transmitters & Sensors
S.I.C.: 3699
N.A.I.C.S.: 335999
Import Export
Advertising Expenditures: $500,000
Media: 1-2-4-10
Distr.: Intl.; Natl.
Budget Set: Nov. -Dec.
Personnel:
Ken Biele *(Pres)*
Mike Pinchot *(CFO & VP-Fin)*
Advertising Agency:
Strategies, a Marketing Communications Corporation
13681 Newport Ave Ste 8 Ste 616
Tustin, CA 92780
Tel.: (714) 957-8880
Fax: (714) 957-8880

ROURA IRON WORKS, INC.
35355 Forton Ct
Clinton Township, MI 48035-3133
Tel.: (586) 790-6100
Fax: (586) 790-6102
Toll Free: (800) 968-9070
E-mail: hoppers@rourairon.com
Approx. Number Employees: 10
Year Founded: 1915
Business Description:
Materials Handling Equipment & Self Dumping Hoppers Mfr
S.I.C.: 3444
N.A.I.C.S.: 332322
Export
Media: 2-4-7-26
Distr.: Direct To Businesses; Intl.; Natl.
Budget Set: Dec.
Brands & Products:
BUILT TO LAST
GORILLA ROTATOR BOXES
ROURA HOOPERS
ROURA IRON WORKS

ROYLE SYSTEMS GROUP
111 Bauer Dr
Oakland, NJ 07436
Tel.: (201) 644-0345
Fax: (201) 644-0346
Web Site: www.roylesystems.com
E-Mail For Key Personnel:
President: gramsey@johnroyle.com
Sales Director: sales@roylesystems.com
Sales Range: $10-24.9 Million
Approx. Number Employees: 50
Year Founded: 1855
Business Description:
Rubber & Plastics Extruders; Complete Insulating Systems for the Wire & Cable Industry
S.I.C.: 3549; 3542
N.A.I.C.S.: 333518; 333513
Import Export
Media: 2-4-7-9-10
Distr.: Intl.; Natl.
Personnel:
Gregory J. Ramsey *(Chm & CEO)*
John C. Ramsey *(Chm & CEO)*
Vinod Sareen *(VP-Fin)*
Brands & Products:
AUTOLINE
COLOR-O-METER
FREEFOAM
ROYLE SYSTEMS GROUP

R.P. ADAMS COMPANY, INC.
(Sub. of SERFILCO, Ltd.)
225 E Park Dr
Tonawanda, NY 14150-7813
Mailing Address:
PO Box 963
Buffalo, NY 14240-0963
Tel.: (716) 877-2608
Fax: (716) 877-9385
Toll Free: (800) 896-8869
E-mail: info@rpadams.com
Web Site: www.rpadams.com
Approx. Sls.: $11,000,000
Approx. Number Employees: 50
Year Founded: 1937
Business Description:
Air, Water & Chemical Filters, Automatic Water Strainers, Aftercoolers, Cyclone Separators, Heat Exchangers Mfr; Shell & Tube Design
S.I.C.: 3563; 3569
N.A.I.C.S.: 333912; 333999
Import Export
Media: 1-2-4-7-10
Distr.: Intl.; Natl.
Budget Set: Oct.
Brands & Products:
AKU
ECONOMAT
PORO CARBON
PORO EDGE
PORO STONE

RSC HOLDINGS INC.
(d/b/a RSC Equipment Rental)
6929 E Greenway Pkwy Ste 200
Scottsdale, AZ 85254
Tel.: (480) 905-3300
Fax: (480) 905-3400
Toll Free: (800) 222-7777
Web Site: www.rscrental.com
Approx. Rev.: $1,234,424,000
Approx. Number Employees: 4,427
Business Description:
Equipment Rental Services
S.I.C.: 7359; 7519
N.A.I.C.S.: 532490; 532120
Advertising Expenditures: $15,500,000
Media: 2-5-26
Personnel:
Denis J. Nayden *(Chm)*
Erik Olsson *(Pres & CEO)*
Patricia Chiodo *(CFO & Sr VP)*
Kevin Groman *(Gen Counsel, Sec & Sr VP)*
Juan Corsillo *(Sr VP-Sls, Mktg & Corp Ops)*
Mark W. Krivoruchka *(Sr VP-HR)*
David Ledlow *(Sr VP-Ops)*
Michael Abbey *(Specialist-Mktg)*
Advertising Agency:
Gibbs & Soell, Inc. - San Francisco
111 Pine St Ste 1530
San Francisco, CA 94111
Tel.: (415) 362-9930
Fax: (415) 362-9935

RSCC AEROSPACE & DEFENSE
(Formerly PMC Wire & Cable)
(Sub. of Rockbestos-Surprenant Cable Corp.)
680 Hayward St
Manchester, NH 03103
Tel.: (603) 622-3500
Fax: (603) 622-8149
E-mail: info@rsccaerodefense.com
Web Site: www.rsccaerodefense.com
Sales Range: $50-74.9 Million
Approx. Number Employees: 100
Business Description:
Engineered Wire & Cable Products
S.I.C.: 3496
N.A.I.C.S.: 332618
Media: 4
Personnel:
Timothy Grass *(Pres)*
Fran Shannis *(VP-Sls & Mktg-Thermocouple Products)*
Ernie Charon *(Mgr-Inside Sls-Military & Aerospace Products)*
Chris Weiner *(Coord-Sls-Aerospace & Defense Products)*
Janice Welch *(Coord-Inside Sls)*

RUG DOCTOR, LP
(Holding of AMERICAN CAPITAL, LTD.)
4701 Old Shepard Pl
Plano, TX 75093-5218
Tel.: (972) 673-1400
Fax: (972) 673-1401
E-mail: consumer.support@rugdoctor.com
Web Site: www.rugdoctor.com
Sales Range: $25-49.9 Million
Year Founded: 1972
Business Description:
Water Extraction Carpet Cleaning Machines & Related Products
S.I.C.: 3589; 5087
N.A.I.C.S.: 333319; 423850

Rug Doctor, LP — (Continued)

Advertising Expenditures: $10,000,000
Media: 3-5-13-18-19-24
Personnel:
Tim Wall *(Pres & CEO)*
Ken Johnson *(Sr VP-Sls)*
Walter Haug *(VP-Mktg)*
Brands & Products:
EVER FRESH
MIGHTYPRO
RUG DOCTOR
STREAMING MAD AT DIRT
WIDE TRACK

RYERSON INC.
(Sub. of RYERSON HOLDING CORPORATION)
2621 W 15th Pl
Chicago, IL 60608-1712
Tel.: (847) 426-9966
Fax: (773) 788-4212
E-mail: questions@ryerson.com
Web Site: www.ryerson.com
Approx. Sls.: $3,895,500,000
Approx. Number Employees: 4,200
Year Founded: 1842
Business Description:
Metal Processing, Fabrication & Distr
S.I.C.: 5051; 3499
N.A.I.C.S.: 423510; 332999
Import
Media: 2
Personnel:
Michael C. Arnold *(CEO)*
Terence R. Rogers *(CFO & Exec VP)*
Brands & Products:
RYTEC
Advertising Agency:
Romani Bros.
1327 W Washington Blvd Ste 3C
Chicago, IL 60607
Tel.: (312) 829-0099
Fax: (312) 829-3364

S. HOWES, INC.
25 Howard St
Silver Creek, NY 14136-1007
Tel.: (716) 934-2611
Fax: (716) 934-2081
Toll Free: (888) 255-2611
E-mail: sales@showes.com
Web Site: www.showes.com
E-Mail For Key Personnel:
Sales Director: sales@showes.com
Sales Range: Less than $1 Million
Approx. Number Employees: 24
Year Founded: 1856
Business Description:
Mfr. & Designer of Processing Equipment
S.I.C.: 3559; 3565
N.A.I.C.S.: 333298; 333993
Export
Media: 2-10-17
Distr.: Intl.; Natl.
Budget Set: Nov.
Personnel:
Wayne Mertz *(Pres & CEO)*
Frederick Mertz *(VP & Gen Mgr)*
Brands & Products:
GRANULATOR
POWER GRATER
S. HOWES

S.A. ARMSTRONG LIMITED
23 Bertrand Ave
Scarborough, ON M1L 2P3, Canada
Tel.: (416) 755-2291
Fax: (416) 759-9101
E-mail: info@armlink.com
Web Site: www.armstrongpumps.com
Sales Range: $50-74.9 Million
Approx. Number Employees: 350
Year Founded: 1934
Business Description:
Pumps, Valves, Heat Exchangers Mfr for Industrial & Commercial Building Applications
S.I.C.: 3561; 3491; 3559
N.A.I.C.S.: 333911; 332410; 332911
Advertising Expenditures: $3,000,000
Media: 2-4-7-8-10
Distr.: Intl
Budget Set: Dec.
Personnel:
Charles A. Armstrong *(Pres)*
James C. Armstrong *(Exec VP)*
Tony Meo *(Gen Mgr)*
Brent Ross *(Dir-Mktg)*

SAMMONS ENTERPRISES, INC.
5949 Sherry Ln Ste 1900
Dallas, TX 75225-8015
Tel.: (214) 210-5000
Fax: (214) 210-5099
E-mail: questions@sammonscorp.com
Web Site:
www.sammonsenterprises.com
Sales Range: $75-99.9 Million
Approx. Number Employees: 4,500
Year Founded: 1938
Business Description:
Holding Company; Industrial Equipment & Machinery; Insurance Carriers; Bottled Water; Hotel
S.I.C.: 6311; 5084
N.A.I.C.S.: 524113; 423830
Import Export
Media: 2-3-8-9-10-19-20-21-23-25
Distr.: Natl.
Personnel:
Robert W. Korba *(Chm)*
Heather Kreager *(Pres)*
Darron Ash *(CFO & Sr VP)*
Paul E. Rowsey *(Pres/CEO-Compatriot Capital, Inc)*
Michael Costello *(Sr VP)*
Mark D. Van Kirk *(Sr VP-Compatriot Capital, Inc)*
Carol Cochran *(Dir-Benefits)*

SANDUSKY INTERNATIONAL INC.
615 W Market St
Sandusky, OH 44870-2413
Tel.: (419) 626-5340
Fax: (419) 626-8674
E-mail: info@sanduskyintl.com
Web Site: www.sanduskyintl.com
Approx. Sls.: $50,000,000
Approx. Number Employees: 120
Year Founded: 1904
Business Description:
Machinery Equipment, Rolls & Spare Parts For Pulp & Paper Industry Mfr, Mill & Engineering Services
S.I.C.: 3325; 3369
N.A.I.C.S.: 331513; 331528
Export
Advertising Expenditures: $353,000
Bus. Publs.: $230,000; Catalogs & Directories: $40,000; D.M. to Bus. Estab.: $5,000; Other: $75,000; Premiums, Novelties: $3,000
Distr.: Intl.; Natl.
Budget Set: Oct.
Personnel:
Edward R. Ryan *(Pres & CEO)*
Brands & Products:
ALLOY 86
ALLOY EPV
POLYCAST
SANDUSKY

SANISERV
(Sub. of The Affinis Group)
451 E County Line Rd
Mooresville, IN 46158
Mailing Address:
PO Box 1089
Mooresville, IN 46158
Tel.: (317) 831-7030
Fax: (317) 831-7036
Web Site: www.saniserv.com
E-Mail For Key Personnel:
Sales Director: sales@saniserv.com
Approx. Number Employees: 60
Year Founded: 1929
Business Description:
Food Service Equipment Mfr
S.I.C.: 3556; 3589
N.A.I.C.S.: 333294; 333319
Import Export
Advertising Expenditures: $200,000
Media: 2-4
Distr.: Intl.; Natl.
Budget Set: Apr.
Personnel:
Robert Mcafee *(Pres)*
Greg Wertz *(CFO)*
Brands & Products:
CYCLONE
SANISERV

SATCON TECHNOLOGY CORPORATION
Ste 8 27 Drydock Ave
Boston, MA 02210-2383
Tel.: (617) 661-0540
Tel.: (617) 897-2400
Fax: (617) 661-3373
E-mail: investor.relations@satcon.com
Web Site: www.satcon.com
Approx. Rev.: $173,301,973
Approx. Number Employees: 340
Year Founded: 1986
Business Description:
Power Electronics & Control Systems Designer, Developer & Mfr
S.I.C.: 3674; 3679
N.A.I.C.S.: 334413; 334419
Media: 2-4-10
Personnel:
John M. Carroll *(Chm)*
Charles Steve Rhoades *(CEO)*
Clemens van Zeyl *(Pres-SatCon Power Sys & Canada)*
Dave O'Neil *(Treas & VP-Fin)*
Pete Degraff *(Exec VP-Worldwide Sls & Mktg)*
Michael Levi *(Sr Dir-Worldwide Mktg)*
Brands & Products:
MAGMOTOR
POWERGATE
SATCON
SOLSTICE

SAUER-DANFOSS INC.
(Sub. of Danfoss A/S)
2800 E 13th St
Ames, IA 50010
Tel.: (515) 239-6000
E-mail: info@sauer-danfoss.com
Web Site: www.sauer-danfoss.com
Approx. Sls.: $1,640,583,000
Approx. Number Employees: 6,000
Year Founded: 1987
Business Description:
Hydraulic, Electronic, Electrical & Mechanical Components & Systems for Mobile Equipment Designer, Mfr & Whslr
S.I.C.: 3594; 3491; 3492; 3561; 3568; 3589; 3592; 3714
N.A.I.C.S.: 333996; 332911; 332912; 333319; 333613; 333911; 336311; 336322; 336350
Advertising Expenditures: $150,000
Media: 17
Personnel:
Jorgen M. Clausen *(Chm)*
Sven Ruder *(Pres & CEO)*
Jesper V. Christensen *(CFO & Exec VP)*
C. Kells Hall *(Pres-Propel Div & Exec VP)*
Wolfgang Schramm *(Pres-Controls Div & Exec VP)*
Anne Wilkinson *(Exec VP-HR)*
Timothy P. Hanson *(VP-Sls)*
Randy Rodgers *(Mgr-Product Porfolio)*
Brands & Products:
PLUS 1
WEBGPI

SCHAEFER MARINE INC.
158 Duchaine Blvd
New Bedford, MA 02745
Tel.: (508) 995-9511
Fax: (508) 995-4882
E-mail: sales@schaefermarine.com
Web Site: www.schaefermarine.com
E-Mail For Key Personnel:
Sales Director: sales@schaefermarine.com
Approx. Sls.: $7,000,000
Approx. Number Employees: 65
Year Founded: 1965
Business Description:
Mfr. of Stamped Forgings & Marine Hardware Castings, Stainless Steel Fabrications
S.I.C.: 3429; 3949
N.A.I.C.S.: 332510; 339920
Advertising Expenditures: $200,000
Media: 10-13-26
Distr.: Intl.; Natl.
Budget Set: Jan.
Personnel:
Dave Anderson *(Owner)*
Fred Cook *(Pres)*
Antone Correia *(Treas & VP-Fin)*
Brands & Products:
BATTSLIDE
LEGENDARY STRENGTH
SCHAEFER
SCHAEFER MARINE
TUFF LUFF

SCHAFER GEAR WORKS, INC.
4701 Nimitz Pkwy
South Bend, IN 46628-6151
Tel.: (574) 234-4116
Fax: (574) 234-4115
Web Site: www.schafergear.com

Key to Media (For complete agency information see *The Advertising Red Books-Agencies* edition):
1. Bus. Publs. 2. Cable T.V. 3. Catalogs & Directories. 4. Co-op Adv. 5. Consumer Mags. 6. D.M. to Bus. Estab.7. D.M. to Consumers 8. Daily Newsp. 9. Exhibits/Trade Shows 10. Foreign 11. Infomercial 12. Internet Adv.13. Multimedia 14. Network Radio 15. Network T.V. 16. Newsp. Distr. Mags. 17. Other 18. Outdoor (Posters, Transit) 19. Point of Purchase20. Premiums, Novelties 21. Product Samples 22. Special Events Mktg. 23. Spot Radio 24. Spot T.V. 25. Weekly Newsp. 26. Yellow Page Adv.

Approx. Number Employees: 100
Business Description:
Produces Gears & Mechanized Parts
S.I.C.: 3566; 3599
N.A.I.C.S.: 333612; 332710
Personnel:
Bipin Doshi *(Pres)*
Robert Doshi *(Mgr-Ops)*
Ruth Cheek *(Asst Controller)*
Advertising Agency:
Villing & Company, Inc.
5909 Nimtz Pkwy
South Bend, IN 46628
Tel.: (574) 277-0215
Fax: (574) 277-5513

SCHLUMBERGER WELL COMPLETIONS
(Sub. of Services Petroliers Schlumberger)
7030 Ardmore St
Houston, TX 77054-2302
Tel.: (713) 747-4000
Fax: (713) 747-6751
E-mail: info@slb.com
Web Site: www.slb.com
Approx. Number Employees: 85,000
Year Founded: 1945
Business Description:
Oilfield Equipment, Tools & Pumps Mfr
S.I.C.: 1389
N.A.I.C.S.: 213112
Export
Media: 2-4-7-8-10
Distr.: Intl.; Natl.
Personnel:
Simon Ayat *(CFO)*
Chakib Sbiti *(Exec VP)*
Mark Danton *(VP & Dir-Taxes)*
Dave Mason *(Product Dir)*
Brands & Products:
HYCALOG
LAWRENCE TECHNOLOGY
NOWCAM
REDA
REED

THE SCHMIDT GROUP, INC.
I 385 At Roper Mtn Rd
Greenville, SC 29615
Mailing Address:
PO Box 25189
Greenville, SC 29616-0189
Tel.: (864) 288-9460
Fax: (864) 288-2944
Approx. Number Employees: 10
Year Founded: 1908
Business Description:
Mfr. of Textile Machinery & Parts; Laminated Wood Parts
S.I.C.: 5084; 8742
N.A.I.C.S.: 423830; 541611
Import Export
Media: 4-6-9-11-25-26
Distr.: Intl.; Natl.
Budget Set: Aug.
Personnel:
Carl V. Schmidt *(Pres)*
Ralph F. Schmidt *(CEO)*
Brands & Products:
POLYDUR

SCHMITT INDUSTRIES, INC.
2765 NW Nicolai St
Portland, OR 97210
Tel.: (503) 227-7908
Fax: (503) 223-1258
E-mail: info@schmitt-ind.com
Web Site: www.schmitt-ind.com
Approx. Sls.: $11,492,859
Approx. Number Employees: 47
Business Description:
Mfr of Computerized Balancing Equipment for Rotating Devices
S.I.C.: 3823; 3451
N.A.I.C.S.: 334513; 332721
Advertising Expenditures: $56,463
Media: 2-10-13
Personnel:
Wayne A. Case *(Chm & CEO)*
James A. Fitzhenry *(Pres)*
Jeffrey T. Siegal *(CFO & Treas)*
Brands & Products:
ACUITY
ACUITY RESEARCH
SBS
SCHMITT INDUSTRIES INC.
SMS CASI

SCHNEIDER AUTOMATION, INC.
(Sub. of Schneider Electric USA, Inc.)
1 High St
North Andover, MA 01845-2601
Tel.: (978) 794-0800
Fax: (978) 975-9400
Web Site: www.modicon.com
Approx. Number Employees: 2,000
Year Founded: 1969
Business Description:
Mfr. of Programmable Control Systems & Industrial Automation Equipment; Direct/Connect Communication Interface
S.I.C.: 3822; 3823
N.A.I.C.S.: 334512; 334513
Import Export
Media: 1-2-4-7-9-10-13-17
Distr.: Intl.; Natl.
Brands & Products:
MERLIN GERIN
MODICON
TELEMECANIUE

SCHNEIDER CANADA, INC.
(Sub. of Schneider Electric USA, Inc.)
19 Waterman Avenue
Toronto, ON M4B 1Y2, Canada
Tel.: (416) 752-8020
Fax: (416) 752-6230
Fax: (416) 752-8944
Web Site: www.schneiderelectric.ca
Approx. Number Employees: 20
Business Description:
Electrical Distr, Industrial Control & Automation Products, Systems & Services
S.I.C.: 3699
N.A.I.C.S.: 335999
Media: 2-4-10
Distr.: Natl.
Budget Set: Dec.
Personnel:
Gary Abrams *(Pres-Schneider Electric Canada)*
Kent Haugh *(Mgr-Mktg)*

SCIAKY, INC.
(Sub. of Phillips Service Industries, Inc.)
4915 W 67th St
Chicago, IL 60638-6408
Tel.: (708) 594-3800
Fax: (708) 594-9213
Toll Free: (800) 827WELD
E-mail: info@sciaky.com
Web Site: www.sciaky.com
Approx. Number Employees: 100
Year Founded: 1940
Business Description:
Mfr. of Electron Beam, Advanced Arc, Resistance, & Laser Welding Systems
S.I.C.: 3699; 3625
N.A.I.C.S.: 335999; 335314
Export
Media: 1-2-4-7-10-11-20-26
Distr.: Natl.
Budget Set: Apr.
Personnel:
Bob Phillips *(VP-Mktg)*
Brands & Products:
ACUWELD
SIGMA SIX
TOUCH WELD

SCIENTIFIC-ATLANTA, INC.
(Sub. of Cisco Systems, Inc.)
5030 Sugarloaf Pkwy
Lawrenceville, GA 30044-2869
Tel.: (770) 236-5000
Fax: (770) 236-6777
Toll Free: (800) 433-6222
Web Site: www.scientificatlanta.com
E-Mail For Key Personnel:
Sales Director: sales@sciatl.com
Sales Range: $1-4.9 Billion
Approx. Number Employees: 7,860
Year Founded: 1951
Business Description:
End-To-End Video Distribution Networks & Video Systems Integration Equipment Mfr
S.I.C.: 3663; 3699
N.A.I.C.S.: 334220; 335999
Media: 2-4-7-9-10-11-18-20-22
Distr.: Intl.; Natl.
Personnel:
Julian W. Eidson *(CFO, Treas & Sr VP)*
H. Allen Ecker *(Exec VP)*
J. Lawrence Bradner *(Sr VP)*
Wallace G. Haislip *(Sr VP-Fin & Ops)*
Brian C. Koenig *(Sr VP-HR)*
David B. Davies *(VP-Product Mktg)*
Brands & Products:
EXPLORER
POWERVU
PRISMA
ROSA
SCICARE
SCIENTIFIC-ATLANTA
WEBSTAR

SCINTREX LTD.
222 Snidercroft Rd
Concord, ON L4K 2K1, Canada
Tel.: (905) 669-2280
Fax: (905) 669-6403
E-mail: scintrex@scintrexltd.com
Web Site: www.scintrexltd.com
Approx. Number Employees: 130
Year Founded: 1967
Business Description:
Research, Design & Manufacture Earth Science Exploration Instrumentation, Bomb Sniffers, Air Pollution Monitors, Nuclear Reactor Monitoring Devices, Defense-Related Equipment and Other Scientific Products
S.I.C.: 3829
N.A.I.C.S.: 334519
Export
Media: 4-6-10-20-25
Distr.: Intl.; Natl.
Budget Set: Jan.
Personnel:
Chris Nind *(Pres & CEO)*
Anna Balcy *(Dir-Production)*
Richard Lachapelle *(Mgr-Intl Sls)*
Bill Male *(Mgr-Intl Sls)*
Radka Tamchyna *(Mgr-Intl Sls)*
Gail Dawson *(Coord-Sls)*
Brands & Products:
AUTOGRAV
ENVI MAG
ENVI PRO
GPHONE
GRAVILOG
HELIGRAV
NAVMAG
SARIS
SCINTREX
SEAGRAV
SETTING THE STANDARDS

SCOTCHMAN INDUSTRIES, INC.
(Sub. of Krofam Inc.)
180 E Hwy 14
Philip, SD 57567
Mailing Address:
PO Box 850
Philip, SD 57567-0850
Tel.: (605) 859-2542
Fax: (605) 859-2499
Toll Free: (800) 843-8844
E-mail: info@scotchman.com
Web Site: www.scotchman.com
Approx. Sls.: $18,000,000
Year Founded: 1967
Business Description:
Mfr. of Machine Tools
S.I.C.: 3547; 3542
N.A.I.C.S.: 333516; 333513
Import Export
Advertising Expenditures: $250,000
Media: 1-4-6-7-8-10-11-13-19-20
Distr.: Intl.; Natl.
Budget Set: Jan.
Personnel:
Jerry Kroetch *(Pres)*
Brands & Products:
SCOTCHMAN
Advertising Agency:
Linn Productions
1222 Oregon St
Rapid City, SD 57701
Tel.: (605) 348-8675
Fax: (605) 355-0664
Toll Free: (877) 248-8675

SCOTSMAN GROUP LLC
(Group of Scotsman Industries, Inc.)
(d/b/a Scotsman Ice Systems)
775 Corporate Woods Pkwy
Vernon Hills, IL 60061-3112
Tel.: (847) 215-4500
Fax: (847) 913-9844
Toll Free: (800) 726-8762
E-mail: technical.service@scotsman-ice.com
Web Site: www.scotsman-ice.com
E-Mail For Key Personnel:
Marketing Director: marketing@scotsman-ice.com
Approx. Number Employees: 100
Year Founded: 1950

Key to Media (For complete agency information see *The Advertising Red Books-Agencies* edition):
1. Bus. Publs. 2. Cable T.V. 3. Catalogs & Directories. 4. Co-op Adv. 5. Consumer Mags. 6. D.M. to Bus. Estab.7. D.M. to Consumers
8. Daily Newsp. 9. Exhibits/Trade Shows 10. Foreign 11. Infomercial 12. Internet Adv.13. Multimedia 14. Network Radio
15. Network T.V. 16. Newsp. Distr. Mags. 17. Other 18. Outdoor (Posters, Transit) 19. Point of Purchase20. Premiums, Novelties
21. Product Samples 22. Special Events Mktg. 23. Spot Radio 24. Spot T.V. 25. Weekly Newsp. 26. Yellow Page Adv.

Scotsman Group LLC — (Continued)

Business Description:
Commercial Ice-Making Equipment Mfr
S.I.C.: 3585
N.A.I.C.S.: 333415
Import Export
Media: 1-2-4-5-6-7-10-19-20-26
Distr.: Natl.
Budget Set: Jan.
Personnel:
David S. McCulloch *(Chm & CEO)*
Jeff Biel *(Product Mgr)*
Terry Toth *(Mgr-Mktg Comm)*
Brands & Products:
OREF
PRODIGY
SCOTSMAN
SIMAG

SCREW CONVEYOR INDUSTRIES

700 Hoffman St
Hammond, IN 46327-1827
Tel.: (219) 931-1450
Fax: (219) 931-0209
Web Site: www.screwconveyor.com
E-Mail For Key Personnel:
Sales Director: sales@screwconveyor.com
Approx. Sls.: $20,000,000
Approx. Number Employees: 300
Year Founded: 1932
Business Description:
Mfr. of Screw Conveyors
S.I.C.: 3535
N.A.I.C.S.: 333922
Export
Media: 2-4-7-8-10-11-20-26
Distr.: Intl.; Natl.
Budget Set: Oct.
Personnel:
Gary M. Abraham *(CEO & Gen Mgr)*
Randolph Block *(VP-Sls & Promo)*
Brands & Products:
ENDURO-FLO
THE EXPERIENCE TO HANDLE IT RIGHT
HAMMOND
KEWANEE
NORWAY
NU-WELD
SCC
SCREW CONVEYOR
SCREW-LIFT
SUPER-FLO
SUPER-V
TEM-U-LAC
TEM-U-LOC
Advertising Agency:
Liberty Graphics
18626 W. Creek Dr.
Tinley Park, IL 60477
Tel.: (708) 633-7860
Fax: (708) 633-7449
(Bulk Material Handling Equipment)

SECURITY ENGINEERED MACHINERY CO., INC.

5 Walkup Dr
Westborough, MA 01581-1018
Tel.: (508) 366-1488
Fax: (508) 366-6814
E-mail: info@semshred.com
Web Site: www.semshred.com
Approx. Number Employees: 40
Year Founded: 1967
Business Description:
Paper Shredders & Disintegrator Systems Mfr
S.I.C.: 3589
N.A.I.C.S.: 333319
Media: 2-4-7-10
Distr.: Intl.; Natl.
Budget Set: Dec.
Personnel:
Leonard Rosen *(Chm, CEO & Treas)*
Advertising Agency:
Norris & Company
437 Tpke St
Canton, MA 02021-2824
Tel.: (781) 821-8300
Fax: (781) 821-8301

SENCO PRODUCTS, INC.

(Sub. of Senco Brands, Inc.)
4270 Ivy Point Blvd
Cincinnati, OH 45242
Tel.: (513) 388-2000
Fax: (513) 388-2883
Toll Free: (800) 543-4596
Web Site: www.senco.com
Approx. Number Employees: 1,600
Year Founded: 1951
Business Description:
Industrial Fasteners Mfr
S.I.C.: 3546; 3496
N.A.I.C.S.: 333991; 332618
Import Export
Advertising Expenditures: $500,000
Bus. Publs.: $400,000; D.M. to Consumers: $50,000; Daily Newsp.: $50,000
Personnel:
Ben Johansen *(Pres)*

SENECA FALLS MACHINES

314 Fall St
Seneca Falls, NY 13148-1543
Tel.: (315) 568-5804
Fax: (315) 568-5800
E-mail: info@senecafallsmachine.com
Web Site:
www.senecafallsmachine.com
Approx. Number Employees: 20
Year Founded: 1864
Business Description:
Custom Built, Precision Metal Working Machines Designer & Mfr
S.I.C.: 3541; 3545
N.A.I.C.S.: 333512; 333515
Import Export
Advertising Expenditures: $100,000
Media: 1-2-4-7-10
Distr.: Intl.; Natl.
Budget Set: Nov.
Personnel:
E. David Matteson *(Sr VP)*
Brands & Products:
ENERGY EFFICIENT
ROYAL OAK
ROYAL OAK (R-O)
SENECA
SENECA FALLS
WATERBURY
WATERBURY HEADERS

SENIOR FLEXONICS INC.

(Sub. of Senior plc)
300 E Devon Ave
Bartlett, IL 60103-4608
Tel.: (630) 837-1811
Fax: (630) 837-2672
Web Site: www.seniorflexonics.com
Approx. Number Employees: 700
Year Founded: 1902
Business Description:
Flexible Metal Hose, Expansion Joints, Compensators, Flexible Ducting & Connectors, Fabricated Metal Components Mfr
S.I.C.: 3499
N.A.I.C.S.: 332999
Export
Media: 2-4-5-7-10-13-20-26
Distr.: Natl.
Budget Set: Oct.
Personnel:
Joe Mockus *(Pres)*
Brands & Products:
FLEXONICS

SENSCIENT INC.

2951 Marina Bay Dr
League City, TX 77573
Tel.: (281) 639-9168
Fax: (877) 374-1919
E-mail: senscient@senscient.com
Web Site: www.senscient.com
Sales Range: Less than $1 Million
Approx. Number Employees: 16
Business Description:
Gas Detection Products Mfr
S.I.C.: 3822
N.A.I.C.S.: 334512
Personnel:
Jean Berthold *(CMO & VP)*
Advertising Agency:
EJW Associates, Inc.
Crabapple Village Office Park 1602 Abbey Ct
Alpharetta, GA 30004
Tel.: (770) 664-9322
Fax: (770) 664-9324

SERFILCO, LTD.

(d/b/a Service Filtration Corporation)
2900 MacArthur Blvd
Northbrook, IL 60062-2005
Tel.: (847) 559-1777
Fax: (847) 559-1995
Toll Free: (800) 323-5431
E-mail: sales@serfilco.com
Web Site: www.serfilco.com
E-Mail For Key Personnel:
Sales Director: sales@serfilco.com
Approx. Sls.: $40,000,000
Approx. Number Employees: 175
Year Founded: 1961
Business Description:
Mfr. of Pumps, Filtration Systems & Waste Treatment & Recover Systems
S.I.C.: 3569; 3561
N.A.I.C.S.: 333999; 333911
Import Export
Advertising Expenditures: $400,000
Media: 2-4-7-10-13
Distr.: Intl.; Natl.
Personnel:
Jack H. Berg *(CEO)*
Charles A. Remied *(Mgr-Sls-Central Reg)*
Brands & Products:
CAMELOT
FILTERSPUN ACCUWOUND
GUARDIAN
LABMASTER
PACER
POLYMAR
SENTRY
SERDUCTOR
SERFILCO
SPACE-SAVER
TITAN 90
TITAN FILTER
Advertising Agency:
Knight Adv. Co.
2900 MacArthur Blvd
Northbrook, IL 60062-2005
Tel.: (847) 559-1777
Tel.: (847) 509-2900
Fax: (847) 559-1995

SERVOTRONICS, INC.

1110 Maple Rd
Elma, NY 14059-9573
Mailing Address:
PO Box 300
Elma, NY 14059-0300
Tel.: (716) 655-5990
Fax: (716) 655-6012
E-mail: info@servotronics.com
Web Site: www.servotronics.com
Approx. Rev.: $31,659,000
Approx. Number Employees: 275
Year Founded: 1959
Business Description:
Mfr. & Marketer of Precision Control Components
S.I.C.: 3593; 3492; 3594
N.A.I.C.S.: 333995; 332912; 333996
Media: 13
Personnel:
Nicholas D. Trbovich, Jr. *(Founder, Pres & Chm)*
Nicholas D. Trbovich *(Chm & CEO)*
Cari L. Jaroslawsky *(CFO)*
Salvatore SanFilippo *(VP-Mktg & Sls)*
Bernadine E. Kucinski *(Asst Sec)*

SHEFFIELD LABORATORIES

(Div. of Faria Corporation)
170 Broad St
New London, CT 06320-5313
Mailing Address:
PO Box 351
New London, CT 06320
Tel.: (860) 442-4451
Fax: (860) 442-0356
Toll Free: (800) 222-1087
E-mail: general@sheffield-labs.com
Web Site: www.sheffield-labs.com
Approx. Number Employees: 125
Year Founded: 1850
Business Description:
Toilet & Pharmaceutical Preparation Mfr
S.I.C.: 2844; 2834
N.A.I.C.S.: 325620; 325412
Export
Media: 2-4-10-26
Distr.: Natl.
Budget Set: Oct. -Nov.
Personnel:
Thomas G. Faria *(Pres)*
Brands & Products:
SHEFFIELD
TOOTHWHITE

SHILOH INDUSTRIES, INC.

880 Steel Dr
Valley City, OH 44280
Tel.: (330) 558-2600
Tel.: (734) 354-3116 (Sls/Mktg)
Fax: (330) 558-2666
E-mail: sales@shiloh.com
Web Site: www.shiloh.com
Approx. Rev.: $457,272,000
Approx. Number Employees: 1,250
Year Founded: 1950

Key to Media (For complete agency information see *The Advertising Red Books-Agencies* edition):
1. Bus. Publs. 2. Cable T.V. 3. Catalogs & Directories. 4. Co-op Adv. 5. Consumer Mags. 6. D.M. to Bus. Estab.7. D.M. to Consumers 8. Daily Newsp. 9. Exhibits/Trade Shows 10. Foreign 11. Infomercial 12. Internet Adv.13. Multimedia 14. Network Radio 15. Network T.V. 16. Newsp. Distr. Mags. 17. Other 18. Outdoor (Posters, Transit) 19. Point of Purchase20. Premiums, Novelties 21. Product Samples 22. Special Events Mktg. 23. Spot Radio 24. Spot T.V. 25. Weekly Newsp. 26. Yellow Page Adv.

Business Description:
Engineered Metal Products Mfr
S.I.C.: 3469; 3499
N.A.I.C.S.: 332116; 332999
Advertising Expenditures: $250,000
Media: 7
Personnel:
Curtis E. Moll *(Chm)*
Theodore K. Zampetis *(Pres & CEO)*
Thomas M. Dugan *(Treas & VP-Fin)*

SHINGLE BELTING COMPANY
420 Drew Ct
King of Prussia, PA 19406
Tel.: (610) 239-6667
Fax: (610) 239-6668
Toll Free: (800) 345-6294
E-mail: belting@shinglebelting.com
Web Site: www.shinglebelting.com
Approx. Number Employees: 32
Year Founded: 1918
Business Description:
Industrial Beltings, Leather Packings, Flat Conveyer Beting & Extruded Profiles, PVC, Urethane & Polyester
S.I.C.: 3535; 3052
N.A.I.C.S.: 333922; 326220
Import Export
Advertising Expenditures: $200,000
Media: 2-4-7-8-10-21
Distr.: Natl.
Personnel:
Renwick E. Keating *(Owner & Pres)*
Bob Frasetto *(VP-Sls)*
Brands & Products:
MONOFILAMENT
NYCOR
POLYFLEX
ROUNTHANE
SHINGLE BELTING
VEETHANE

SHOP-VAC CORPORATION
2323 Reach Rd
Williamsport, PA 17701-5579
Tel.: (570) 326-0502
Fax: (570) 326-7185
E-mail: service@shopvac.com
Web Site: www.shopvac.com
E-Mail For Key Personnel:
Sales Director: ltempesco@shopvac.com
Approx. Sls.: $48,000,000
Approx. Number Employees: 275
Year Founded: 1965
Business Description:
Mfr. of Wet/Dry Utility Vacuum Cleaners & Portable Vacuum Cleaners
S.I.C.: 3589
N.A.I.C.S.: 333319
Export
Advertising Expenditures: $5,000,000
Catalogs & Directories: $750,000; D.M. to Bus. Estab.: $500,000; Daily Newsp.: $2,500,000; Other: $750,000; Point of Purchase: $500,000
Distr.: Intl.; Natl.
Budget Set: Oct.
Personnel:
Jonathan Miller *(Pres)*
Larry Tempesco *(Sr VP-Sls & Mktg)*
Robert Ball *(VP-Pur)*
Rick Shadle *(Dir-Creative Svcs)*
Brands & Products:
ALLAROUND
BLOWER VAC
BRUTE
BULL DOG
DRYWALL VAC
FLOORMASTER
HANG UP MINI
HEAVY DUTY PORTABLE
HIPPO-VAC
INDUSTRIAL
IXI
MIGHTY MINI
QPV
QSP
SHOP-SWEEP
SHOP-VAC

SHOPSMITH, INC.
6530 Poe Ave
Dayton, OH 45414
Tel.: (937) 898-6070
Fax: (937) 890-5197
Toll Free: (800) 543-7586
E-mail: webmaster@shopsmith.com
Web Site: www.shopsmith.com
Sales Range: $10-24.9 Million
Approx. Number Employees: 95
Year Founded: 1972
Business Description:
Power Woodworking Equipment Mfr & Marketer
S.I.C.: 3553
N.A.I.C.S.: 333210
Import Export
Advertising Expenditures: $1,300,000
Media: 4-10-13
Distr.: Direct to Consumer; Intl.; Natl.
Budget Set: Mar.
Personnel:
John R. Folkerth *(Founder, Chm & CEO)*
Brands & Products:
SHOPSMITH
Advertising Agency:
Shopsmith Advertising
6530 Poe Ave
Dayton, OH 45414-2527
Tel.: (937) 898-6070
Fax: (937) 898-9762

SHUR-LOK COMPANY
(Sub. of SPS Aerospace Fasteners Group)
2541 White Rd
Irvine, CA 92614-6235
Tel.: (949) 474-6000
Fax: (949) 660-8601
E-mail: Sales@Shur-Lok.com
Web Site: www.shur-lok.com
E-Mail For Key Personnel:
Sales Director: sales@shur-lok.com
Sales Range: $75-99.9 Million
Approx. Number Employees: 180
Year Founded: 1951
Business Description:
Fasteners, Nuts, Mounts, Hooks, Clamps & Hydraulic Fittings for Aerospace Industry Mfr
S.I.C.: 3452
N.A.I.C.S.: 332722
Media: 2-4-10
Distr.: Intl.; Natl.
Personnel:
John Markert *(VP & Gen Mgr)*
Robert Skidmore *(Dir-Bus Dev)*
Bill Jackson *(Mgr-Quality)*
Barbel Moscoe *(Mgr-Purchasing)*
Cynthia Slocum *(Mgr-HR)*

SHUTTLEWORTH, INC.
(Sub. of Pro Mach, Inc.)
10 Commercial Rd
Huntington, IN 46750-8805
Tel.: (260) 356-8500
Fax: (260) 359-7810
Toll Free: (800) 444-7412
E-mail: sna.sales@shuttleworth.com
Web Site: www.shuttleworth.com
Approx. Number Employees: 100
Year Founded: 1962
Business Description:
Custom Conveyor Systems Mfr
S.I.C.: 3535
N.A.I.C.S.: 333922
Import Export
Media: 2-4-7-10-11-13-26
Distr.: Intl.
Personnel:
Carol Shuttleworth *(Owner)*
Bret Ranc *(Gen Mgr)*
Bill Toth *(Gen Mgr)*
John Naunas *(Dir-Sls & Reg Sls Mgr)*
Linda Grush *(Dir-Mktg)*
Kim Hildebrand *(Reg Sls Mgr-Indiana)*
Mike Parks *(Mgr-Info Sys)*
Brands & Products:
CLEAN PASSAGE
CLEANGLIDE1
EASY CLEAN
LOW PROFILE
SHUTTLEWORTH
SLIP-TORQUE
SLIP-TRAK
SMARTFEED
SWINGERS
ZONE CONTROL

SIEBURG INTERNATIONAL, INC.
1901 Clydesdale St
Maryville, TN 37801-3728
Tel.: (865) 982-6300
Fax: (865) 982-6347
E-mail: sales@tensilkut.com
Web Site: www.tensilkut.com
E-Mail For Key Personnel:
Sales Director: sales@tensilkut.com
Sales Range: $10-24.9 Million
Approx. Number Employees: 25
Year Founded: 1955
Business Description:
Mfr. of Tensile Testing Equipment
S.I.C.: 3541; 3542
N.A.I.C.S.: 333512; 333513
Export
Advertising Expenditures: $480,000
Media: 2-4-7-8-10-13
Distr.: Intl.; Natl.
Personnel:
Michael B. McDonald *(Pres)*
Brands & Products:
CNC TENSILATHE
CNC TENSILKUT III
IMPACTKUT
IMPACTMILL
TENSILATHE/505
TENSILGRIND
TENSILKUT
TENSILSAW
TENSILSHEAR

SIEMENS BUILDING TECHNOLOGIES, INC.
(Sub. of Siemens Building Technologies AG, Landis & Staefa Division)
1000 Deerfield Pkwy
Buffalo Grove, IL 60089-4547
Tel.: (847) 215-1000
Fax: (847) 215-1093
E-mail: webmaster@sbt.siemens.com
Web Site: www.sbt.siemens.com
E-Mail For Key Personnel:
Marketing Director: randy.drolen@sbt.siemens.com
Approx. Number Employees: 7,400
Year Founded: 1925
Business Description:
Building Controls, Fire Alarms & Safety Systems Mfr
S.I.C.: 3822; 5063
N.A.I.C.S.: 334512; 423610
Advertising Expenditures: $2,000,000
Media: 1-2-4-7-10-17
Distr.: Intl.; Natl.
Budget Set: Oct.
Personnel:
Jennifer Olmstead *(VP-HR)*
Tom Rule *(Product Mgr)*
Brands & Products:
CP820
DATAGYR 1000
DUNCAN
PHONOCARD
POLYGYR
TELEGYR 8500
Advertising Agency:
Alexander Marketing Services
801 Broadway NW Ste 300
Grand Rapids, MI 49504
Tel.: (616) 957-2000

SIEMENS BUILDING TECHNOLOGIES LTD.
(Sub. of Siemens Canada Limited)
2 Kenview Blvd
Brampton, ON L6T 5E4, Canada
Tel.: (905) 799-9937
Fax: (905) 799-9858
E-mail: info@siemens.com
Web Site: www.siemens.com
Approx. Number Employees: 150
Year Founded: 1988
Business Description:
Distributor of Fire Alarm Equipment
S.I.C.: 3669
N.A.I.C.S.: 334290
Media: 2-6-10-15-18-23-26
Personnel:
Len Collins *(Mgr-Mktg & Sls Support)*

SIEMENS ENERGY & AUTOMATION, INC.
(Unit of Siemens Industry)
1201 Sumneytown Pike
Spring House, PA 19477-1019
Mailing Address:
PO Box 900
Spring House, PA 19477
Tel.: (215) 646-7400
Fax: (215) 283-6358
E-mail: info@sea.siemens.com
Web Site: www.sea.siemens.com
Approx. Number Employees: 500
Year Founded: 1940
Business Description:
Mfr. of Industrial Automated Systems & Dimensional Measuring Gages
S.I.C.: 3823
N.A.I.C.S.: 334513
Export
Media: 2-4-5-7-9-10-11-13-20-22-26
Distr.: Intl.; Natl.

Key to Media (For complete agency information see *The Advertising Red Books-Agencies* edition):
1. Bus. Publs. 2. Cable T.V. 3. Catalogs & Directories. 4. Co-op Adv. 5. Consumer Mags. 6. D.M. to Bus. Estab.7. D.M. to Consumers
8. Daily Newsp. 9. Exhibits/Trade Shows 10. Foreign 11. Infomercial 12. Internet Adv.13. Multimedia 14. Network Radio
15. Network T.V. 16. Newsp. Distr. Mags. 17. Other 18. Outdoor (Posters, Transit) 19. Point of Purchase20. Premiums, Novelties
21. Product Samples 22. Special Events Mktg. 23. Spot Radio 24. Spot T.V. 25. Weekly Newsp. 26. Yellow Page Adv.

Siemens Energy & Automation, Inc. — (Continued)

Budget Set: Aug.
Brands & Products:
APACS
THE MEASURABLE DIFFERENCE
MYCRO
MYCRO ADVANTAGE
NULLMATIC
PROCIDIA
QUADLOG
SYNCRO
VERTIGAGE
VIEWPAC
XTC TRANSMITTER

SIEMENS INTELLIGENT TRANSPORTATION SYSTEMS
(Unit of Siemens Industry)
8004 Cameron Rd
Austin, TX 78754-3808
Tel.: (512) 837-8310
Fax: (512) 837-0196
E-mail: info@itssiemens.com
Web Site: www.itssiemens.com
Approx. Number Employees: 250
Year Founded: 1929
Business Description:
Traffic Systems Mfr
S.I.C.: 3799
N.A.I.C.S.: 336999
Import Export
Media: 2-4-7-10-11
Distr.: Intl.; Natl.
Budget Set: Dec.
Personnel:
Christy Peebles *(Gen Mgr)*

SIEMENS WATER TECHNOLOGIES
(Sub. of Siemens Industrial Solutions & Services Group)
181 Thorn Hill Rd
Warrendale, PA 15086
Tel.: (724) 772-0044
Fax: (724) 772-1300
E-mail: information.water@siemens.com
Web Site: www.usa.siemens.com
Approx. Number Employees: 5,700
Year Founded: 1990
Business Description:
Water & Waste Water Treatment Systems, Products & Services
S.I.C.: 4959
N.A.I.C.S.: 562998
Media: 2-10-11-17
Distr.: Intl.
Budget Set: Apr.
Personnel:
Lori Conen *(Exec VP-HR)*
Richard Smith *(Exec VP-Sls & Mktg)*
Greg Gross *(Sr VP)*
Robert Bosgraaf *(Dir-Product Mgmt)*
Rick Eustace *(Mgr)*
Advertising Agency:
Ad Club
1304 W Roseburg Ave
Modesto, CA 95350-4855
Tel.: (209) 529-9067
Fax: (209) 529-5265
Toll Free: (800) 333-1228

THE SIMCO CO
(Sub. of Illinois Tool Works Inc.)
2257 N Penn Rd
Hatfield, PA 19440-1906
Tel.: (215) 822-2171
Tel.: (215) 822-6401
Fax: (215) 822-3795
Toll Free: (800) 538-0750
E-mail: sales@simco.biz
Web Site: www.simco-static.com
E-Mail For Key Personnel:
Sales Director: sales@simco.biz
Sales Range: $25-49.9 Million
Approx. Number Employees: 100
Year Founded: 1936
Business Description:
Static Control Products Mfr
S.I.C.: 3699; 5084
N.A.I.C.S.: 335999; 423830
Export
Media: 2-4-7-10-11-13
Distr.: Direct to Consumer; Intl.; Natl.
Budget Set: Dec.
Personnel:
Mike Oldt *(Gen Mgr)*
Brands & Products:
AEROSTAT
BLUE BAR HL
CADET
CHARGEMASTER
COBRA
FLEXTAC
HE NOZZLE
HEXCLAM
HS NOZZLE
MAGNUM FORCE
PERFORMAX
PHOENIX
PINNER
PINNER SUPERBAR
QUADCLAM
SENTRY
SIMCO
TETRA
TOP GUN
VAC-N-TAC
Advertising Agency:
Gaul Advertising, Inc.
485 Devon Park Dr Ste 106
Wayne, PA 19087-1807
Tel.: (610) 225-0761
Fax: (610) 225-0766

SIMONDS INTERNATIONAL CORPORATION
135 Intervale Rd
Fitchburg, MA 01420-6519
Tel.: (978) 343-3731
Fax: (978) 424-2212
Fax: (800) 541-6224
Toll Free: (800) 343-1616
Web Site:
www.simondsinternational.com
Approx. Number Employees: 350
Year Founded: 1832
Business Description:
Mfr. of Industrial Cutting Tools
S.I.C.: 3545
N.A.I.C.S.: 333515
Export
Advertising Expenditures: $330,000
Multimedia: $15,000; Bus. Publs.: $75,000; Catalogs & Directories: $75,000; D.M. to Consumers: $10,000; Exhibits/Trade Shows: $50,000; Foreign: $20,000; Premiums, Novelties: $20,000; Product Samples: $60,000; Yellow Page Adv.: $5,000
Distr.: Natl.
Personnel:
Raymond Martino *(Pres & CEO)*
Henry Botticello *(CFO)*
David Miles *(VP-Sls & Mktg)*
Brands & Products:
BLACK MAXI-SHARP
BLUE TIP
CENTAUR
DIEBAND
DOMINATOR
EPIC
EPIC SI-CLONE
FRICTION
FURN-WOOD
HARD EDGE
MULTI-KUT
THE PROFESSIONALS' EDGE
RED STREAK
SCROO-ZON
SI-CHROME
SIMET
SIMOGRIT
SIMONDS
SKROO-ZON
STAND-ALL
SYSTIMATIC
TRIPLE CHIP
TUNGSWELD
VIXEN
Advertising Agency:
Core Advertising, Marketing & Public Relations
523 Baldwin Ave
Meriden, CT 06450
Tel.: (203) 639-8343
Fax: (203) 235-0011

SIMPSON MANUFACTURING COMPANY, INC.
5956 Las Positas Blvd
Pleasanton, CA 94588
Tel.: (925) 560-9000
Fax: (925) 847-1608
Toll Free: (800) 999-5099
E-mail: web@strongtie.com
Web Site: www.simpsonmfg.com
E-Mail For Key Personnel:
Sales Director: sales@strongtie.com
Approx. Sls.: $555,487,000
Approx. Number Employees: 1,851
Year Founded: 1914
Business Description:
Holding Company; Construction Connectors & Venting Systems
S.I.C.: 3429; 3441; 3444; 3452
N.A.I.C.S.: 332510; 332312; 332322; 332722
Advertising Expenditures: $6,000,000
Media: 4-6-7-19
Personnel:
Barclay Simpson *(Chm)*
Thomas J. Fitzmyers *(Pres & CEO)*
Karen Colonias *(CFO, Treas & Sec)*
Brands & Products:
COMMITMENT AT ALL LEVELS
SIMPSON

SLY, INC.
8300 Dow Cir
Strongsville, OH 44136-1760
Tel.: (440) 891-3200
Fax: (440) 891-3210
Toll Free: (800) 200-9524
E-mail: info@slyinc.com
Web Site: www.slyinc.com
Sales Range: $10-24.9 Million
Approx. Number Employees: 75
Year Founded: 1874
Business Description:
Mfr of Dust Collectors, Wet Scrubbers & Bulk Loadout Equipment
S.I.C.: 3564
N.A.I.C.S.: 333411
Export
Media: 2-4-10-11
Distr.: Natl.
Budget Set: Sept. -Oct.
Personnel:
Steve Ragan *(Pres)*
Mike Maxwell *(Mgr-Engrg)*
Rob Cook *(Coord-Project)*
Brands & Products:
DYNACLONE
E-Z VIEW
IMPINJET
PACTECON
PLEATJET
PLEATJET II
SBR
STJ
TUBEJET
Advertising Agency:
R.H. Blake, Inc.
26600 Renaissance Pkwy
Cleveland, OH 44128-5773
Tel.: (216) 595-2400
Fax: (216) 595-2410

SMC CORPORATION OF AMERICA
(Sub. of SMC Corporation)
10100 SMC Blvd
Noblesville, IN 46060
Tel.: (317) 899-4440
Fax: (317) 899-3102
E-mail: info@smcusa.com
Web Site: www.smcusa.com
Approx. Number Employees: 500
Business Description:
Industrial Valve Mfr
S.I.C.: 3491
N.A.I.C.S.: 332911
Personnel:
Yoshiki Takada *(Gen Mgr)*
Advertising Agency:
E&M Advertising
462 7th Ave 8th Fl
New York, NY 10018-7606
Tel.: (212) 981-5900
Fax: (212) 981-2121

SMITH INTERNATIONAL, INC.
(Sub. of Services Petroliers Schlumberger)
1301 Rankin Rd
Houston, TX 77073
Tel.: (281) 443-3370
Toll Free: (800) US-SMITH
Web Site: www.slb.com/services/smith_bits_smith_services.aspx
E-Mail For Key Personnel:
President: drock@smith.com
Approx. Rev.: $8,218,559,000
Approx. Number Employees: 21,931
Year Founded: 1902
Business Description:
Supplier of Premium Products & Services to the Worldwide Oil & Gas Drilling & Production & Mining Industries
S.I.C.: 3533; 5162
N.A.I.C.S.: 333132; 424610

Key to Media (For complete agency information see *The Advertising Red Books-Agencies* edition):
1. Bus. Publs. 2. Cable T.V. 3. Catalogs & Directories. 4. Co-op Adv. 5. Consumer Mags. 6. D.M. to Bus. Estab.7. D.M. to Consumers 8. Daily Newsp. 9. Exhibits/Trade Shows 10. Foreign 11. Infomercial 12. Internet Adv.13. Multimedia 14. Network Radio 15. Network T.V. 16. Newsp. Distr. Mags. 17. Other 18. Outdoor (Posters, Transit) 19. Point of Purchase20. Premiums, Novelties 21. Product Samples 22. Special Events Mktg. 23. Spot Radio 24. Spot T.V. 25. Weekly Newsp. 26. Yellow Page Adv.

Export
Advertising Expenditures: $445,000
Catalogs & Directories: $400,000;
D.M. to Bus. Estab.: $20,000;
Premiums, Novelties: $25,000
Distr.: Intl.; Natl.
Personnel:
William Restrepo *(CFO, Treas & Sr VP)*
Geraldine D. Wilde *(VP-Tax & Asst Treas)*
Shawn Housley *(Dir-IR)*
Brands & Products:
ANCHOR-STOCK
CELLULAR
DOG
DOUBLE DIAMOND
DUAL TORQUE
E TRUDE
EBUSINESS IT'S WORKING
ECONO-STOCK
GEMINI
GEODIAMOND
HDS
HYDRA-DRIVE
HYDRA-TORAX
JAR-PACT
MEGASTIR
MUD CHEK
MX CONNECT
MX DIRECT
MX LOCATE
MX SELECT
REAMASTER
RHINO
SHAMAL
SMITH
SPHINX
TRACKMASTER
TRU-TORQUE
VELOCITY

SMITHCO, INC.
34 West Ave
Wayne, PA 19087
Tel.: (610) 688-4009
Fax: (610) 688-6069
Toll Free: (800) 891-9435
E-mail: smithco@smithco.com
Web Site: www.smithco.com
Approx. Sls.: $11,000,000
Approx. Number Employees: 8
Year Founded: 1967
Business Description:
Mfr. of Turf Maintenance Machinery
S.I.C.: 5083
N.A.I.C.S.: 423820
Media: 10
Personnel:
Ted Smith *(Founder & CEO)*
Donald H. Smith *(Pres)*
Bill Kenney *(VP-Sls & Mktg)*
Brands & Products:
BIG VAC
BUNKER RAKE IMPLEMENTS
E-STAR
G-STAR
GOOD PEOPLE MAKE BETTER PRODUCTS
GREEN STAR
INFIELDER
LINE STAR
LINE STAR JR.
MOW-N-GO
RED RIDER
SMITHCO
SPRAY STAR
STAR SHIELD BOOM
SUPER RAKE
SUPER STAR
SUPREME
SWEEP STAR
TOP LINER
TOURNAMENT X-PRESS ROLLER
WIND STAR

SNAP-TITE INC.
8325 Hessinger Dr
Erie, PA 16509-8003
Tel.: (814) 860-5700
Fax: (814) 833-0145
E-mail: snaptite@snap-tite.com
Web Site: www.snap-tite.com
Approx. Number Employees: 700
Year Founded: 1935
Business Description:
Quick Disconnect Couplings, Hydraulic & Pneumatic Valves, Hoses & Hose Hardware
S.I.C.: 3494; 3052
N.A.I.C.S.: 332919; 326220
Import Export
Advertising Expenditures: $489,000
Multimedia: $10,000; Bus. Publs.: $250,000; D.M. to Bus. Estab.: $25,000; Daily Newsp.: $30,000; Exhibits/Trade Shows: $50,000; Foreign: $20,000; Outdoor (Posters, Transit): $50,000; Spot Radio: $29,000; Spot T.V.: $15,000; Weekly Newsp.: $5,000; Yellow Page Adv.: $5,000
Distr.: Intl.; Natl.
Budget Set: Oct.
Personnel:
John S. Clark *(Pres & CEO)*
Gary L. Clark *(Chief Admin Officer & VP)*
Michael O'Keane *(Dir-Mktg)*
Brands & Products:
DIREC-TROL
EDUCATOR
NATIONAL
OPTI-PULSE
PACTECON
PLEATJET II
PONN
PROTECTOR
SLY
TUBEJET
VENTURI
WATTMIZER
Advertising Agency:
STI Creative, A Div. of Snap-Tite Inc.
6424 Westridge Rd.
Erie, PA 16505
Tel.: (814) 833-5296
(Hydraulic & Pneumatic Componentry; High Pressure Valves & Tubing)

SNOW-NABSTEDT POWER TRANSMISSIONS
(Sub. of Granite State Manufacturing)
1011 Joliette St
Manchester, NH 03102
Tel.: (603) 314-0017
Fax: (603) 668-1438
E-mail: sales@snpt.biz
Web Site: www.snpt.biz
E-Mail For Key Personnel:
Sales Director: sales@snpt.biz
Approx. Number Employees: 15
Year Founded: 1938
Business Description:
Transmissions Mfr
S.I.C.: 7537
N.A.I.C.S.: 811113
Import Export
Media: 2-4-7-10
Distr.: Intl.; Natl.
Budget Set: May
Personnel:
Glen Lawton *(CEO)*
Lee A. Tack *(Product Mgr)*
Brands & Products:
HOT SHIFT
SNOW-NABSTEDT

SNYDER INDUSTRIES, INC.
(Holding of Olympus Partners)
4700 Fremont St
Lincoln, NE 68504-1646
Tel.: (402) 467-5221
Fax: (402) 465-1220
E-mail: info@snydernet.com
Web Site: www.snydernet.com
Sales Range: $75-99.9 Million
Approx. Number Employees: 225
Year Founded: 1957
Business Description:
Mfr.& Designer of Plastic Bulk Storage, Processing & Transportation Tank Systems
S.I.C.: 3089
N.A.I.C.S.: 326199
Advertising Expenditures: $200,000
Media: 2-4-6-7-8-10-13-20-21-23-25-26
Distr.: Canada; Natl.
Budget Set: June
Personnel:
Thomas O'Connell *(Pres & CEO)*
Michael Spurrier *(VP-Sls & Mktg)*
Dale Ohlrich *(Product Mgr)*
Steve Hansen *(Mgr-HR)*
Jason Harrington *(Mgr-Sls)*
Dana Janssen *(Mgr-Customer Svc)*
Connie Lintz *(Mgr-Mktg Svcs)*
Rick Wagner *(Mgr-Sls-Agriculture)*
Brands & Products:
SII

SOLAR TURBINES INCORPORATED
(Sub. of Caterpillar, Inc.)
2200 Pacific Hwy
San Diego, CA 92101-1745
Mailing Address:
PO Box 85376
San Diego, CA 92186-5376
Tel.: (619) 544-5000
Fax: (619) 595-7511
Web Site: www.solarturbines.com
Sales Range: $1-4.9 Billion
Approx. Number Employees: 5,500
Year Founded: 1927
Business Description:
Turbine Engines, Turbine Powered Natural-Gas Compressor Sets, Generator Sets & Mechanical-Drive Packages Mfr
S.I.C.: 3511
N.A.I.C.S.: 333611
Export
Media: 2-4-5-7-10-11-20
Distr.: Intl.; Natl.
Budget Set: Aug.
Personnel:
D. W. Esbeck *(VP-Customer Svcs)*
Claudette Carmine Harris *(Mgr-Mktg & Commun)*
W. C. Swanson *(Mgr-Corp Comm)*
Brands & Products:
CENTAUR
MARS
MERCURY
SATURN
SOLAR
SOLONOX
TAURUS
TITAN
TURBOTRONIC

SOLARSA, INC.
4015 S Dale Mabry Hwy
Tampa, FL 33611
Tel.: (813) 258-4488
Fax: (813) 258-5488
E-mail: info@solarsa.com
Web Site: www.solarsa.com
Sales Range: Less than $1 Million
Approx. Number Employees: 8
Year Founded: 2005
Business Description:
Renewable Energy & Energy Efficiency Systems Control, Optimization & Monitoring Services
S.I.C.: 3559; 3823
N.A.I.C.S.: 333298; 334513
Advertising Expenditures: $10,640
Media: 17-22
Personnel:
Greg Hilty *(Exec VP)*
Bala Nemani *(Exec VP)*
Brands & Products:
ENERGY COMMUNICATOR

SOUTH CAROLINA MANUFACTURING EXTENSION PARTNERSHIP
817 Calhoun St
Columbia, SC 29201-2305
Tel.: (803) 252-6976
Fax: (803) 254-8512
Toll Free: (800) MEP4MFG
E-mail: info@scmep.org
Web Site: www.scmep.org
Approx. Number Employees: 20
Business Description:
Manufacturing Consultants
S.I.C.: 8742
N.A.I.C.S.: 541611
Media: 13
Personnel:
John Irion *(Pres)*
Martha Baker *(Mgr-Fin)*
Patrick Loveland *(Mgr-IT)*

SOUTHWEST PLASTIC BINDING COMPANY
109 Millwell Ct
Maryland Heights, MO 63043
Tel.: (314) 739-4400
Fax: (314) 739-7606
Toll Free: (800) 325-3268
Web Site: www.swplastic.com
E-Mail For Key Personnel:
Sales Director: sales@swplastic.com
Approx. Number Employees: 120
Year Founded: 1966
Business Description:
Bookbinding Machinery & Supplies Mfr & Sales
S.I.C.: 2789; 2631
N.A.I.C.S.: 323121; 322130
Media: 2-4-7-10-20

Key to Media (For complete agency information see *The Advertising Red Books-Agencies* edition):
1. Bus. Publs. 2. Cable T.V. 3. Catalogs & Directories. 4. Co-op Adv. 5. Consumer Mags. 6. D.M. to Bus. Estab.7. D.M. to Consumers
8. Daily Newsp. 9. Exhibits/Trade Shows 10. Foreign 11. Infomercial 12. Internet Adv.13. Multimedia 14. Network Radio
15. Network T.V. 16. Newsp. Distr. Mags. 17. Other 18. Outdoor (Posters, Transit) 19. Point of Purchase20. Premiums, Novelties
21. Product Samples 22. Special Events Mktg. 23. Spot Radio 24. Spot T.V. 25. Weekly Newsp. 26. Yellow Page Adv.

Southwest Plastic Binding Company — (Continued)

Personnel:
Mark J. Mercer *(Sr VP)*
Michael Mercer *(Sr VP)*
Patrick Rhodes *(VP-Fin)*

Brands & Products:
EZ COIL
MOUNT-A-SIGN
SOUTHWEST
STANDARD SUPER-SEALER

SOUTHWEST WIRE ROPE, L.P.

(Sub. of Teleflex Commercial Group)
1902 Federal Rd
Houston, TX 77015
Tel.: (713) 453-8518
Fax: (713) 453-7209
Toll Free: (800) 256-7997
E-mail: info@swwrinc.com
Web Site:
www.southwestwirerope.com
Approx. Sls.: $50,000,000
Approx. Number Employees: 45
Year Founded: 1966
Business Description:
Wire Rope & Rigging Product Mfr
S.I.C.: 3496; 2298
N.A.I.C.S.: 332618; 314991
Media: 4

Brands & Products:
GOLD STRAND
SW

SPADONE-HYPEX INC.

(Sub. of HyPex Inc.)
45 Banner Dr
Milford, CT 06460
Tel.: (203) 877-1041
Fax: (203) 877-1173
E-mail: info@spadone.com
Web Site: www.spadone.com
Approx. Number Employees: 4
Year Founded: 1917
Business Description:
Mfr of Machinery for the Tire Industry
S.I.C.: 7389; 3559
N.A.I.C.S.: 541420; 333220
Export
Media: 1-2-4-6-7-10-16-17
Distr.: Intl.; Natl.
Personnel:
George Pihonak *(Gen Mgr)*

SPARTAN TOOL

(Div. of Pettibone, LLC)
1506 W Division St
Mendota, IL 61342-2426
Mailing Address:
PO Box 950
Mendota, IL 61342-0950
Tel.: (815) 539-7411
Fax: (815) 539-9786
Fax: (888) 876-2371
Toll Free: (800) 435-3866
E-mail: info@spartantool.com
Web Site: www.spartantool.com
Approx. Sls.: $17,000,000
Approx. Number Employees: 300
Year Founded: 1926
Business Description:
Commercial & Industrial Sewer Cleaner & Barometric Draft Controls Mfr; Material Handling Equipment
S.I.C.: 3589; 1541; 1623
N.A.I.C.S.: 333319; 236210; 237110
Advertising Expenditures: $200,000
Media: 4
Distr.: Intl.; Natl.
Budget Set: Apr.
Personnel:
Tom Pranka *(Pres)*

Brands & Products:
FIELD
SPARTAN

SPARTON CORPORATION

425 N Martingale Ste 2050
Schaumburg, IL 60173-2213
Tel.: (847) 762-5800
E-mail: corporatecommunications@sparton.com
Web Site: www.sparton.com
Approx. Sls.: $203,352,000
Approx. Number Employees: 873
Year Founded: 1900
Business Description:
Technical Products Mfr for Worldwide Commercial Electronics, Telecommunications & Governmental Customers
S.I.C.: 3679; 3672; 3674; 3711; 3812
N.A.I.C.S.: 334418; 334412; 334413; 334511; 336211
Export
Media: 1-2-4-7-10-20
Distr.: Intl.; Natl.
Budget Set: July
Personnel:
David P. Molfenter *(Chm)*
Cary B. Wood *(Pres & CEO)*
Gregory A. Slome *(CFO 7 Sr VP)*
Steven M. Korwin *(Sr VP-Quality, Engrg & Info Sys)*
Gordon B. Madlock *(Sr VP-Ops)*
Michael W. Osborne *(Sr VP-Bus Dev)*
Robert L. Grimm, II *(VP/Gen Mgr-Complex Sys)*
James M. Lackemacher *(VP/Gen Mgr-Defense & Security Sys)*
Jake Rost *(VP/Gen Mgr-Medical Bus Unit)*
Duane K. Stierhoff *(VP/Gen Mgr-Medical Device Ops)*
Lawrence R. Brand *(VP-Corp HR)*

Brands & Products:
POWERCOM
SPARTON
SPARTON MEDICAL SYSTEMS

SPECIAL METALS CORPORATION

(Sub. of Precision Castparts Corp.)
3200 Riverside Dr
Huntington, WV 25705
Tel.: (304) 526-5100
Fax: (304) 526-5643
Toll Free: (800) 334-4626
E-mail: info@specialmetals.com
Web Site: www.specialmetals.com
Sales Range: $700-749.9 Million
Approx. Number Employees: 1,495
Year Founded: 1998
Business Description:
Mfr of Super Alloys & Special Alloys
S.I.C.: 3356
N.A.I.C.S.: 331491
Media: 10
Personnel:
Joseph I. Snowden *(Pres)*
Robert Hennessey *(Sr VP-Mfg)*
Brett McBrayer *(VP & Gen Mgr)*
Stanton D. Kirk *(VP-Sls & Mktg)*
Tracy D. Hutson *(Mgr-Corp Commun)*

Brands & Products:
BRIGHTRAY
DEPOLARIZED
DURANICKEL
FERRY
INCOBAR
INCOLOY
INCONEL
INCOTHERM
MONEL
NI-SPAN-C
NILO
NILOMAG
NIMONIC
RESISTOHM
UDIMAR
UDIMET

SPEEDGRIP CHUCK, INC.

2000 Indus Pkwy
Elkhart, IN 46516
Tel.: (574) 294-1506
Fax: (574) 294-2465
E-mail: salesweb@speedgrip.com
Web Site: www.speedgrip.com
E-Mail For Key Personnel:
Sales Director: salesweb@speedgrip.com
Approx. Sls.: $25,000,000
Approx. Number Employees: 65
Year Founded: 1943
Business Description:
Precision Workholding Equipment Mfr
S.I.C.: 3545
N.A.I.C.S.: 333515
Import Export
Media: 2-4-6
Distr.: Natl.
Budget Set: Feb.
Personnel:
Gary Renaud *(Pres & CEO)*
James Runyon *(Mgr-Sls)*

Brands & Products:
CAMERON
MADISON
SPEEDGRIP CHUCK

SPEEDLINE TECHNOLOGIES, INC.

(Sub. of Illinois Tool Works Inc.)
16 Forge Park
Franklin, MA 02038
Tel.: (508) 520-0083
Fax: (508) 520-2288
E-mail: info@speedlinetech.com
Web Site: www.speedlinetech.com
Sales Range: $100-124.9 Million
Year Founded: 1953
Business Description:
Electronics Assembly & Semiconductor Packaging Machinery Mfr
S.I.C.: 3559; 3555
N.A.I.C.S.: 333298; 333293
Export
Media: 2-4-8-10
Distr.: Intl
Budget Set: Sept.
Personnel:
Wayne Platz *(VP-Fin & Admin)*
John Ufford *(VP-Engrg)*

Brands & Products:
ACCEL
AQUASTORM
CAMALOT
ELECTROVERT
MPM
OMNIEXCEL
OMNIFLEX
SMARTSTREAM
XYFLEXPRO

Advertising Agency:
Tiziani & Whitmyre, Inc.
Sharon Commerce Ctr 2 Commercial St
Sharon, MA 02067
Tel.: (781) 793-9380
Fax: (781) 793-9395

SPENCE ENGINEERING CO., INC.

(Sub. of CIRCOR International, Inc.)
150 Coldenham Rd
Walden, NY 12586-2035
Tel.: (845) 778-5566
Fax: (845) 778-1072
Toll Free: (800) 398-2493
E-mail: sales@spenceengineering.com
Web Site:
www.spenceengineering.com
E-Mail For Key Personnel:
Sales Director: sales@spenceengineering.com
Sales Range: $75-99.9 Million
Approx. Number Employees: 130
Year Founded: 1926
Business Description:
Mfr of Temperature Regulator
S.I.C.: 3491; 3444
N.A.I.C.S.: 332911; 332322
Import Export
Media: 1-2-4-5-6-7-10-13-16-21-22-26
Distr.: Intl.; Natl.
Budget Set: Nov.

SPENCER INDUSTRIES, INC.

1508 N Mascher St
Philadelphia, PA 19122-3908
Tel.: (215) 634-2700
Fax: (215) 634-2790
Approx. Sls.: $2,000,000
Approx. Number Employees: 65
Business Description:
Signs, Metal Letters & Bronze Plaques Mfr
S.I.C.: 3993; 2759
N.A.I.C.S.: 339950; 323119
Media: 2-4-6-7-8-9-18-26
Distr.: Natl.
Budget Set: Jan.
Personnel:
Steven Y. Glickman *(Pres)*

Brands & Products:
SPENCER

THE SPENCER TURBINE CO.

(Holding of Alliance Holdings, Inc.)
600 Day Hill Rd
Windsor, CT 06095-1703
Tel.: (860) 688-8361
Fax: (860) 688-0098
Toll Free: (800) 232-4321
E-mail: marketing@spencer-air.com
Web Site: www.spencerturbine.com
E-Mail For Key Personnel:
Sales Director: sales@spencer-air.com
Approx. Number Employees: 140
Year Founded: 1892
Business Description:
Air & Gas Moving Equipment, Centrifugal Blowers & Exhausters, PD Blowers, Hose, Tools, Electrical

Key to Media (For complete agency information see *The Advertising Red Books-Agencies* edition):
1. Bus. Publs. 2. Cable T.V. 3. Catalogs & Directories. 4. Co-op Adv. 5. Consumer Mags. 6. D.M. to Bus. Estab.7. D.M. to Consumers 8. Daily Newsp. 9. Exhibits/Trade Shows 10. Foreign 11. Infomercial 12. Internet Adv.13. Multimedia 14. Network Radio 15. Network T.V. 16. Newsp. Distr. Mags. 17. Other 18. Outdoor (Posters, Transit) 19. Point of Purchase20. Premiums, Novelties 21. Product Samples 22. Special Events Mktg. 23. Spot Radio 24. Spot T.V. 25. Weekly Newsp. 26. Yellow Page Adv.

Control Panels, Regenerative Blowers, Vacuum Cleaning Systems, Tubing, Fittings, Separators & Dust Collectors Mfr
S.I.C.: 3564; 3589
N.A.I.C.S.: 333412; 333319
Import Export
Media: 2-4-5-7-10-13-26
Distr.: Intl.; Natl.
Budget Set: Jan.
Personnel:
Richard Hart *(Pres)*
John Dulak *(Gen Mgr-Engrng)*
Janis Cayne *(Mgr-Mktg)*
Brands & Products:
DIRT ERASER
FUME ERASER
INDUSTRAVAC
JET-CLEAN
LOBE-AIRE
POWER MIZER
SPENCER
SUMP-VAC
TOP DRUM
VORTEX

SPIRE CORPORATION
1 Patriots Park
Bedford, MA 01730-2343
Mailing Address:
PO Box 3939
Bedford, MA 01731
Tel.: (781) 275-6000
Fax: (781) 275-7470
Toll Free: (800) 510-4815
E-mail: info@spirecorp.com
Web Site: www.spirecorp.com
Approx. Rev.: $79,842,000
Approx. Number Employees: 188
Year Founded: 1969
Business Description:
Solar Energy Manufacturing Equipment & Solar Systems, Biomedical Devices & Optoelectronic Components Developer, Mfr & Marketer
S.I.C.: 3674; 3841; 8733
N.A.I.C.S.: 334413; 339112; 541710
Export
Media: 2-7-10
Distr.: Intl.
Budget Set: Dec.
Personnel:
Roger G. Little *(Chm, Pres & CEO)*
Robert S. Lieberman *(CFO & Treas)*
Rodger W. LaFavre *(COO)*
Mark C. Little *(CEO-Spire Biomedical & Dir-Spire Corp)*
Stephen J. Hogan *(Exec VP & Gen Mgr-Spire Solar)*
Edward Hurley *(Mgr-Sls & Mktg)*
Brands & Products:
ALTA
CARBOTHANE
DECATHLON
HIBICLENS
ION-JOIN
ION-SIGHT
IONGUARD
IONGUARD 3000
POURCHEZ RETRO
POURCHEZ XPRESSO
RETRO
SAFETRAC
SPI-ARGENT
SPI-ARRAY TESTER
SPI-ASSEMBLER
SPI-CELL TEST
SPI-CERAMIC
SPI-CONNECT 1000
SPI-FRET
SPI-ION 3Q00ME
SPI-LAMINATOR
SPI-LASE50-50
SPI-LINE
SPI-MET
SPI-POLYMER
SPI-PULSE
SPI-SIGHT
SPI-SPECTRUM
SPI-STRINGER
SPI-SUN SIMULATOR
SPI-TAB 1000
SPI-TAB 500
SPI-TEXT
SPI-TRIBOTESTER
SPI-VAC PIK
SPIRE

SPIROL INTERNATIONAL CORPORATION
30 Rock Ave
Danielson, CT 06239-1425
Tel.: (860) 774-8571
Fax: (860) 774-2048
E-mail: information@spirol.com
Web Site: www.spirol.com
Approx. Number Employees: 500
Year Founded: 1948
Business Description:
Mfr. of Engineered Fasteners, Including Coiled, Slotted, Spring & Solid Pins; Inserts, Spacers & Other Tubular Products; Shims; Metal Stampings; Pin & Insert Assembly Equipment; Parts Feeding Systems; Milled Brass Nuts
S.I.C.: 3452; 3499
N.A.I.C.S.: 332722; 332999
Import Export
Media: 2-4-7-10-11-17-21
Distr.: Intl.; Natl.
Budget Set: June
Personnel:
Jeffrey F. Koehl *(Pres)*
John Ferdinandi *(CFO & Treas)*
William Hunt *(Pres/COO-North America)*
Christie Jones *(Mgr-Market Dev)*
Brands & Products:
SPIROL
Advertising Agency:
Spirol Advertising
(House Agency)
30 Rock Ave.
Danielson, CT 06239-1434
Tel.: (860) 774-8571
Fax: (860) 744-0487
(Spirol Coiled Pins, Slotted Pins, Solid Pins, Tubular Products Including Spacers, Connectors, Rivets, Dowel Bushings, Tension Sleeves & Spring Dowels, Threaded Inserts, Shims, Pin & Insert Installation Equipment, Vibratory Parts Feeding Equipment)

SPX COOLING TECHNOLOGIES
(Unit of SPX Corporation)
7401 W 129th St
Overland Park, KS 66213-2634
Tel.: (913) 664-7400
Fax: (913) 664-7753
Fax: (913) 664-7897
Toll Free: (800) 462-7539
E-mail: spxcooling@ct.spx.com
Web Site: spxcooling.com/en/contact/
Sales Range: $400-449.9 Million
Approx. Number Employees: 1,500
Year Founded: 1922
Business Description:
Cooling Technologies & Services
S.I.C.: 3585
N.A.I.C.S.: 333415
Import Export
Media: 1-2-4-8-10-21
Distr.: Natl.
Budget Set: Nov.
Personnel:
Drews Ladau *(Pres)*
Don Lillig *(Mgr-Mktg & Comm)*
Brands & Products:
MARLEY COOLING TOWER
MODULUS
PRIMUS

SPX PRECISION COMPONENTS - FENN DIVISION
(Unit of SPX Corporation)
300 Fenn Rd
Newington, CT 06111-2244
Tel.: (860) 594-4300
Fax: (860) 667-4667
Telex: 99314
Web Site: www.spxprecision.com/phpwcms/index.php?aid=189
Sales Range: $75-99.9 Million
Approx. Number Employees: 200
Year Founded: 1900
Business Description:
Precision Machining Services
S.I.C.: 3541
N.A.I.C.S.: 333512
Import Export
Media: 2-4-10
Distr.: Intl.; Natl.
Personnel:
Steven Bedard *(Gen Mgr)*
Colin Welsh *(Product Mgr)*
Brands & Products:
FENN

SPX PROCESS EQUIPMENT
(Unit of SPX Corporation)
135 Mt Read Blvd
Rochester, NY 14611
Mailing Address:
PO Box 31370
Rochester, NY 14603
Tel.: (585) 436-5550
Fax: (585) 436-5589
Telex: 97-8244
Web Site: www.lightninmixers.com
Sales Range: $200-249.9 Million
Approx. Number Employees: 300
Year Founded: 1923
Business Description:
Mfr of Industrial Mixers & Aerators
S.I.C.: 5045; 3082; 3084; 3089; 5046
N.A.I.C.S.: 425110; 326121; 326122; 326199; 423440
Import Export
Media: 1-2-4-7-10-26
Distr.: Intl.; Natl.
Budget Set: Oct.
Personnel:
Jim Myers *(Gen Mgr)*
Neil Meadows *(Product Mgr-Lightnin Mixers)*
Brands & Products:
LIGHTNIN

SPX PROCESS EQUIPMENT
(Unit of SPX Corporation)
5620 W Rd
McKean, PA 16426
Tel.: (814) 476-5800
Fax: (814) 476-5854
Web Site: www.spxfc.com
Sales Range: $50-74.9 Million
Approx. Number Employees: 62
Year Founded: 1903
Business Description:
Control Valves
S.I.C.: 3491
N.A.I.C.S.: 332911
Import Export
Media: 2-4-10
Distr.: Intl.; Natl.
Budget Set: Sept.
Personnel:
Jerry Skolnik *(Dir-Site)*
Richards Kuntz *(Mgr-Engrg)*
Brands & Products:
GAD
GS-700
HUSH
MNSD
RAVEN
SD-1000
TANDEM
VAD
VO 11
VO 76

STANDARD SAFETY EQUIPMENT CO.
1407 Ridgeview Dr
McHenry, IL 60050
Tel.: (815) 363-8565
Fax: (815) 363-8633
Toll Free: (888) 345-4773
E-mail: info@standardsafety.com
Web Site: www.standardsafety.com
Approx. Number Employees: 50
Year Founded: 1921
Business Description:
Mfr. of Personal Safety Equipment & Protective Clothing
S.I.C.: 2389
N.A.I.C.S.: 315299
Import Export
Media: 2-10
Distr.: Direct to Consumer; Natl.
Budget Set: Nov.
Personnel:
Scott R. Olson *(Chm, Pres & CEO)*
Steve Medves *(Exec VP)*
Brands & Products:
ACIDMASTER
ARMORED
CHEMMASTER
CPE
EBONY
FLASHMASTER
GRALITE
GRALITE-20
HAIRGUARDS
HI-GLO
KOOLPADS
MANHOLE COVER/SAFETY POOL
MITIGATOR
PERKS SAFETY WASHERS
POLYETTE
SEALTITE
SKIDMASTER
STANDARD GRALITE
THERMO BAN
TOE CLIPS

Key to Media (For complete agency information see *The Advertising Red Books-Agencies* edition):
1. Bus. Publs. 2. Cable T.V. 3. Catalogs & Directories. 4. Co-op Adv. 5. Consumer Mags. 6. D.M. to Bus. Estab.7. D.M. to Consumers
8. Daily Newsp. 9. Exhibits/Trade Shows 10. Foreign 11. Infomercial 12. Internet Adv.13. Multimedia 14. Network Radio
15. Network T.V. 16. Newsp. Distr. Mags. 17. Other 18. Outdoor (Posters, Transit) 19. Point of Purchase20. Premiums, Novelties
21. Product Samples 22. Special Events Mktg. 23. Spot Radio 24. Spot T.V. 25. Weekly Newsp. 26. Yellow Page Adv.

Standard Safety Equipment Co. — (Continued)

WHITESIDE
WINTER-GLO
WINTER-GLO-20
WORKMASTER

STANLEY FASTENING SYSTEMS, L.P.

(Sub. of Stanley Black & Decker, Inc.)
1 Briggs Dr
East Greenwich, RI 02818
Tel.: (401) 884-2500
Fax: (401) 885-3122
Toll Free: (800) 556-6696
E-mail: info@bostitch.com
Web Site: www.bostitch.com
Sales Range: $25-49.9 Million
Approx. Number Employees: 100
Year Founded: 1947
Business Description:
Stapling Equipment & Wire Stitching Machines Mfr
S.I.C.: 3559; 3496
N.A.I.C.S.: 333298; 332618
Export
Advertising Expenditures: $500,000
Media: 2-4-5-7-8-10-19-20-21-26
Distr.: Direct to Consumer; Natl.
Budget Set: Jan.
Personnel:
Michael Albright *(Pres)*
Brands & Products:
ATRO
HARTCO
PALLET PLUS
SPENAX
STANLEY
Advertising Agency:
Keiler & Company
304 Main St
Farmington, CT 06032-2985
Tel.: (860) 677-8821
Fax: (860) 676-8164

STEDMAN MACHINE COMPANY

129 Franklin St
Aurora, IN 47001
Mailing Address:
PO Box 299
Aurora, IN 47001-0299
Tel.: (812) 926-0038
Fax: (812) 926-3482
Toll Free: (800) 262-5401
E-mail: sales@stedman-machine.com
Web Site: www.stedman-machine.com
E-Mail For Key Personnel:
Sales Director: sales@stedman-machine.com
Approx. Number Employees: 50
Year Founded: 1834
Business Description:
Mfr. of Crushing Machinery
S.I.C.: 3532; 8711
N.A.I.C.S.: 333131; 541330
Import Export
Media: 2-4-5-7-10-17-21
Distr.: Natl.
Personnel:
Dennis Gilmour *(Pres)*
Chuck Hagedorn *(Mgr-Midwest-Aggregate Sls)*
Ginny Lane *(Coord-Sls)*
Brands & Products:
A-SERIES
AURORA
F-SERIES
G-SERIES
GRAND SLAM
H-SERIES
MEGA SLAM
MICRO-MAX
STEDMAN
V-SLAM
Y-SERIES
YOUR SOLUTION TO PARTICLE SIZE REDUCTION

STERLING CRANE

(Sub. of Marmon Construction Services)
2440 - 76 Avenue
PO Box 8610 Station South
Edmonton, AB Canada
Tel.: (780) 440-4434
Fax: (780) 440-2560
E-mail: bservices@sterlingcrane.com
Web Site: www.sterlingcrane.ca
Sales Range: $25-49.9 Million
Approx. Number Employees: 175
Year Founded: 1954
Business Description:
Crane Rentals
S.I.C.: 7353
N.A.I.C.S.: 532412
Media: 4
Personnel:
Dave Snyder *(Pres)*

STERLING, INC.

(Sub. of The ACS Group)
2900 S 160th St
New Berlin, WI 53151
Tel.: (262) 641-8600
Fax: (262) 641-8653
Web Site: www.sterlco.com
Approx. Number Employees: 140
Year Founded: 1916
Business Description:
Mfr. of Packaged Temperature Control Systems, Condensation Pumps, Control Valves, Hydraulic Presses, Granulators, Automatic Parts Removal Equipment, Automatic Handling & Processing Equipment
S.I.C.: 3823; 3542
N.A.I.C.S.: 334513; 333513
Media: 4-10-13
Personnel:
Thomas Breslin *(Pres & CEO)*

STEVENS TECHNOLOGY, LLC

(Filed Ch 11 Bankruptcy #10-45112 on 08/02/2010 in U.S. Bankruptcy Ct, Northern Dist of TX, Ft Worth)
5700 E Belknap St
Fort Worth, TX 76117
Tel.: (817) 831-3500
Fax: (817) 759-4044
E-mail: info@stevens-technology.com
Web Site: www.stevenstechnologies.com
E-Mail For Key Personnel:
Sales Director: sales@stevens-technology.com
Sales Range: $1-9.9 Million
Approx. Number Employees: 17
Year Founded: 1950
Business Description:
High Quality Packaging & Printing Equipment Systems & High-Speed Automatic Currency Examination Equipment
S.I.C.: 3555
N.A.I.C.S.: 333293
Export
Advertising Expenditures: $595,000
Multimedia: $25,000; Bus. Publs.: $25,000; Catalogs & Directories: $5,000; D.M. to Bus. Estab.: $40,000; Exhibits/Trade Shows: $500,000
Distr.: Intl.; Natl.
Personnel:
Paul I. Stevens *(Chm & CEO)*
Richard E. Moreman *(Dir-Engrng)*
Duncan S. Wood *(Dir-Customer Svc)*
Richard I. Stevens *(Gen Mgr)*
Claudia Teague *(Office Mgr)*
Brands & Products:
MORESTORE
MULTI-SIZE
STEVENS TECHNOLOGY

STEWART & STEVENSON SERVICES, INC.

(Sub. of BAE Systems Mobility & Protection Systems)
1000 Louisiana Ste 5900
Houston, TX 77002-1051
Mailing Address:
PO Box 1637
Houston, TX 77251-1637
Tel.: (713) 751-2600
Telex: 794221
Web Site: www.ssss.com
Approx. Sls.: $942,148,000
Approx. Number Employees: 1,200
Year Founded: 1902
Business Description:
Diesel Engines, Diesel Generators, Irrigation Equipment, Pumps, Aircraft Ground Support Equipment & Oil Field Equipment Mfr
S.I.C.: 3519; 3511; 3711; 3795
N.A.I.C.S.: 333618; 333611; 336211; 336992
Media: 1-2-4-6-7-8-10-22
Personnel:
Hushang Ansary *(Chm)*
Frank C. Carlucci *(Vice Chm)*
Gary W. Stratulate *(Pres & COO)*
Robert L. Hargrave *(CEO)*
Jeff Merecka *(CFO, Sec & VP)*
Brands & Products:
ALLISON
OCTA
RAIL KING
TRI-MET
WAUKESHA
Advertising Agency:
Axiom
1210 W Clay Ste 9
Houston, TX 77019
Tel.: (713) 523-5711
Fax: (713) 523-6083

STOCKHAM VALVES & FITTINGS, INC.

(Sub. of Crane Fluid Handling)
2129 3rd Ave SE
Cullman, AL 35055-5477
Tel.: (256) 775-3800
Fax: (256) 775-3860
Web Site: www.stockham.com
Sales Range: $50-74.9 Million
Approx. Number Employees: 50
Year Founded: 1903
Business Description:
Flow Control Devices & Valves Mfr
S.I.C.: 3494; 3321
N.A.I.C.S.: 332919; 331511
Export
Media: 2-4-5-10-13-19-20-21
Brands & Products:
STOCKHAM

STORK TOWNSEND INC.

(Sub. of Stork Food & Dairy Systems B.V.)
2425 Hubbell Ave
Des Moines, IA 50317-6415
Tel.: (515) 265-8181
Fax: (515) 263-3333
Fax: (515) 263-3355
Toll Free: (800) 247-8609
E-mail: info.townsendusa@stork.com
Web Site: www.townsendeng.com
Sales Range: $75-99.9 Million
Approx. Number Employees: 150
Year Founded: 1946
Business Description:
Meat Processing Equipment Mfr
S.I.C.: 3556
N.A.I.C.S.: 333294
Import Export
Media: 2-6-7-10-13
Distr.: Natl.
Budget Set: Sept.
Personnel:
Theo Bruinsmas *(Pres)*
Brands & Products:
NL FLEXLINKER
NL SMARTLINKER
QX
SMOKE-A-MATIC
TURBOTWIST

STORM VULCAN MATTONI

2225 Burbank St
Dallas, TX 75235-3124
Mailing Address:
PO Box 35667
Dallas, TX 75235
Tel.: (214) 637-1430
Fax: (214) 634-8201
Toll Free: (800) 527-2442
Web Site: www.stormvulcan.com
Approx. Number Employees: 16
Business Description:
Automotive Engine Rebuilding Equipment Mfr
S.I.C.: 3589; 5013
N.A.I.C.S.: 333319; 423120
Media: 2-4-10
Distr.: Intl.; Natl.
Budget Set: Nov.
Personnel:
Richie Mattoni *(CEO)*
Terry Davis *(CFO)*
George Fuentes *(Plant Mgr)*
Jimmy Laferney *(Plant Mgr)*
Brands & Products:
MARK II
MARK III
MARK IV
MARK V
MARK VI
STORM VULCAN
SVM

Key to Media (For complete agency information see *The Advertising Red Books-Agencies* edition):
1. Bus. Publs. 2. Cable T.V. 3. Catalogs & Directories. 4. Co-op Adv. 5. Consumer Mags. 6. D.M. to Bus. Estab.7. D.M. to Consumers 8. Daily Newsp. 9. Exhibits/Trade Shows 10. Foreign 11. Infomercial 12. Internet Adv.13. Multimedia 14. Network Radio 15. Network T.V. 16. Newsp. Distr. Mags. 17. Other 18. Outdoor (Posters, Transit) 19. Point of Purchase20. Premiums, Novelties 21. Product Samples 22. Special Events Mktg. 23. Spot Radio 24. Spot T.V. 25. Weekly Newsp. 26. Yellow Page Adv.

STRAHMAN VALVES, INC.
2801 Baglyos Cir Lehigh Vly Indus Pk VI
Bethlehem, PA 18020
Tel.: (973) 377-4900
Tel.: (484) 893-5080
Fax: (973) 377-8288
Fax: (484) 893-5099
Toll Free: (877) STRAHMAN
Toll Free: (877) 787-2462
E-mail: strahman@strahman.com
Web Site: www.strahmanvalves.com
E-Mail For Key Personnel:
Sales Director: kcarroll@strahman.com
Approx. Number Employees: 90
Year Founded: 1921
Business Description:
Wash Down Equipment & Industrial Valve Products Mfr
S.I.C.: 3494
N.A.I.C.S.: 332919
Export
Media: 2-4-10-11-21-26
Distr.: Intl.; Natl.
Budget Set: Dec.
Personnel:
August Percoco *(Pres & CEO)*
Arthur Pultz *(Dir-Ops)*
Jon Hill *(Mgr-Sls)*
Brands & Products:
BIORAM
ERGONOMIC HOSE PACKAGE
HYDRO-PRO
HYDRO-PRO 150
KWIK-CLEAN
MINI M-70
QUIK
QUIK SAMPLING VALVE
SANITARY RAM
STRAHMAN
SWIVEL-PRO
THERMO-PRO
THERMO-PRO 2000

STURTEVANT INC.
348 Circuit St
Hanover, MA 02339-2129
Tel.: (781) 829-6501
Fax: (781) 829-6515
Toll Free: (800) 992-0209
E-mail: sales@sturtevantinc.com
Web Site: www.sturtevantinc.com
E-Mail For Key Personnel:
Sales Director: sales@sturtevantinc.com
Approx. Number Employees: 30
Year Founded: 1883
Business Description:
Materials Processing Equipment Mfr
S.I.C.: 3559
N.A.I.C.S.: 333298
Import Export
Media: 2-4-7-10-17
Distr.: Intl.; Natl.
Budget Set: Aug.
Personnel:
William S. English, Jr. *(Chm)*
Steven Olson *(VP-Engrg)*
Rick Fortini *(Mgr-Parts)*
Kathleen Leary *(Pur Mgr)*
Charlotte Stevens *(Mgr-Mktg)*
Steven Coulombe *(Engr-Sls)*
Brands & Products:
MICRONIZER
POWDERIZER
PULVERMILL
SDM
SIDE DRAFT
SIMPACTOR
STURTEVANT
SUPERFINE
SUPERFINE AIR SEPARATOR
WHIRLWIND
WHIRLWIND AIR SEPARATOR
Advertising Agency:
Read, Tatulli & Purdy, Inc.
334 Broadway
Providence, RI 02909
Tel.: (401) 351-0787
Fax: (401) 351-0788

SULLAIR CORPORATION
(Sub. of Hamilton Sundstrand Corporation)
3700 E Michigan Blvd
Michigan City, IN 46360-6527
Tel.: (219) 879-5451
Fax: (219) 874-1273
Toll Free: (800) 785-5247
Web Site: www.sullair.com
Sales Range: $150-199.9 Million
Approx. Number Employees: 520
Year Founded: 1965
Business Description:
Air & Gas Compressors
S.I.C.: 3563; 3569
N.A.I.C.S.: 333912; 333999
Advertising Expenditures: $1,740,000
Media: 2-4-5-7-10-11-20-26
Distr.: Intl.; Natl.
Budget Set: Jan.
Personnel:
Henry Brooks *(Pres)*
Cathy Hamilton *(Dir-Fin)*
Brands & Products:
SULLAIR
Advertising Agency:
Riallus Advertising, Inc.
351 Valley Brook Rd
McMurray, PA 15317
Tel.: (724) 941-8075
Fax: (724) 941-3950

SULZER PUMPS INC.
(Sub. of Sulzer Pumpen AG)
2800 NW Frnt Ave
Portland, OR 97210-1502
Tel.: (503) 226-5200
Fax: (503) 205-3740
E-mail: newsales@sulzerpumps.com
Web Site: www.sulzerpumps.com
Approx. Number Employees: 200
Year Founded: 1921
Business Description:
Sales of Custom Pumps; Repair & Maintenance of Pumps & Pump Components
S.I.C.: 3594
N.A.I.C.S.: 333996
Import Export
Advertising Expenditures: $550,000
Media: 2-7-10-11-13
Distr.: Direct to Consumer; Natl.
Budget Set: Sept. -Nov.

SUNNEN PRODUCTS COMPANY
7910 Manchester Ave
Saint Louis, MO 63143-2712
Tel.: (314) 781-2100
Fax: (314) 781-2268
Toll Free: (800) 325-3670
E-mail: sunnen@sunnen.com
Web Site: www.sunnen.com
Approx. Number Employees: 500
Year Founded: 1924
Business Description:
Industrial Honing Machines & Auto Engine Rebuilding Equipment; Precision Gages
S.I.C.: 3549; 3541
N.A.I.C.S.: 333518; 333512
Import Export
Advertising Expenditures: $1,000,000
Media: 1-2-4-7-10-11-20-26
Distr.: Intl.; Natl.
Budget Set: Nov.
Personnel:
Matt Kreider *(Pres)*
Rob Ludwig *(CFO)*
Tom Dustman *(Dir-Intl Sls)*
Barry Rogers *(Dir-Global Sls & Mktg)*
Gerry Schnitzler *(Sr Mgr-Product)*
Bob Davis *(Mgr-Corp Comm)*
Brian Krausz *(Mgr-Tech Svcs)*
Richard Moellenberg *(Mgr-Sys Sls)*
Dennis Westhoff *(Mgr-New Bus Dev)*
Brands & Products:
ABOVE AND BEYOND HONING
GENERAL HONE
GRIT GUARD
HONALL
KROSSGRINDING
SINGLE STROKE
SINGLE STROKE HONING
SUNNEN
TURBOHONE

SUNTEC INDUSTRIES INC.
60 Aberdeen Dr
Glasgow, KY 42141
Mailing Address:
PO Box 5000
Glasgow, KY 42142
Tel.: (270) 651-7116
Fax: (270) 651-9276
E-mail: info@suntecpumps.com
Web Site: www.suntecpumps.com
Sales Range: $10-24.9 Million
Approx. Number Employees: 25
Year Founded: 1984
Business Description:
Fuel Oil Pumps Mfr
S.I.C.: 3586; 3561
N.A.I.C.S.: 333913; 333911
Import Export
Advertising Expenditures: $500,000
Media: 2-4-7-10-19
Distr.: Intl.; Natl.
Budget Set: May
Personnel:
Dominique Emaille *(Chm & CEO)*
Brands & Products:
SUNTEC

SUPERIOR DIE SET CORP.
900 W Drexel Ave
Oak Creek, WI 53154
Tel.: (414) 764-4900
Fax: (414) 764-2811
E-mail: info@supdie.com
Web Site: www.supdie.com
Approx. Number Employees: 225
Business Description:
Special Dies, Tools, Jigs, & Fixtures
S.I.C.: 3544; 3443
N.A.I.C.S.: 333514; 332313
Media: 10
Personnel:
Casey Janiszewski *(Pres & CEO)*
Lynette Ellman *(CFO)*
Joe Kucharski *(Mgr-Engrg, CAD & CAM Svcs)*
Mark Ullstrup *(Mgr-Customer Svc)*
Ed Wosilait *(Mgr-HR)*
Brands & Products:
AJAX PRESS
BANNING
BE-FAST
BECHE
BRONZE-RITE
CECO
CHAMBERSBURG ENGINEERING
CLOZ-IT
EIRE
ERIE PRESS
FORGE-RITE
FORTAL
GLIDE PINS
GLIDE RITE
GLIDE SLEEVE
GLIDE SLEEVES
GORTITE
IOSSO
JERGEN
KALLER
LASCO
NATIONAL PRESS
POZ-E-LOCK
RAYMOND
RETURN-RITE
SLIDE LOCKS
SUPERIOR
THREADFORMER

SURPLUS CENTER
(Div. of Burden Sales Company)
1015 W O St
Lincoln, NE 68528-1322
Mailing Address:
PO Box 82209
Lincoln, NE 68501-2209
Tel.: (402) 474-4055
Fax: (877) 474-5198
Toll Free: (800) 488-3407
E-mail: customerservice@surpluscenter.com
Web Site: www.surpluscenter.com
Approx. Number Employees: 100
Year Founded: 1933
Business Description:
Wholesale Compressors, Power Plants, Hydraulics & Electronic Components
S.I.C.: 5049
N.A.I.C.S.: 423490
Export
Advertising Expenditures: $400,000
Catalogs & Directories: $400,000
Distr.: Direct to Consumer; Natl.
Personnel:
David P. Burden *(Pres)*
Chris Cole *(VP-Sls)*
Mike Burden *(Mgr-Sls)*

SWECO
(Unit of M-I L.L.C.)
8029 Dixie Hwy 25
Florence, KY 41042-2903
Mailing Address:
PO Box 1509
Florence, KY 41022-1509
Tel.: (859) 371-4360
Fax: (859) 283-8469
Toll Free: (800) 807-9326
E-mail: info@sweco.com
Web Site: www.sweco.com

Key to Media (For complete agency information see *The Advertising Red Books-Agencies* edition):
1. Bus. Publs. 2. Cable T.V. 3. Catalogs & Directories. 4. Co-op Adv. 5. Consumer Mags. 6. D.M. to Bus. Estab.7. D.M. to Consumers
8. Daily Newsp. 9. Exhibits/Trade Shows 10. Foreign 11. Infomercial 12. Internet Adv.13. Multimedia 14. Network Radio
15. Network T.V. 16. Newsp. Distr. Mags. 17. Other 18. Outdoor (Posters, Transit) 19. Point of Purchase20. Premiums, Novelties
21. Product Samples 22. Special Events Mktg. 23. Spot Radio 24. Spot T.V. 25. Weekly Newsp. 26. Yellow Page Adv.

Sweco — (Continued)

Sales Range: $125-149.9 Million
Approx. Number Employees: 310
Year Founded: 1942
Business Description:
Vibrating Screen Separators, Grinding Mills, Finishing Mills, Water Filters, Turbo Screen Air Classifiers, Stationary Screens, Hydrocyclones, Replacement Screens, Centrifugal Sifters Mfr
S.I.C.: 3559
N.A.I.C.S.: 333298
Import Export
Advertising Expenditures: $4,000,000
Media: 2-4-7-10-11-20
Distr.: Intl.; Natl.
Budget Set: July
Personnel:
Tom Radank *(Dir-Sls)*
Jeff Dierig *(Mgr-Mktg)*

SWISSLOG LOGISTICS
(Sub. of Swisslog North America)
161 Enterprise Dr
Newport News, VA 23603-1369
Mailing Address:
PO Box 3135
Newport News, VA 23603-0135
Tel.: (757) 820-3400
Fax: (757) 887-5588
E-mail: info@swisslognorthamerica.com
Web Site: www.swisslog.com
Approx. Number Employees: 80
Year Founded: 1985
Business Description:
Automated Material Handling Systems
S.I.C.: 3535; 7371
N.A.I.C.S.: 333922; 541511
Import Export
Advertising Expenditures: $300,000
Media: 2-4-6-7-8-10-13
Distr.: Intl.
Budget Set: Dec.
Personnel:
Charlie Kegley *(Pres)*
Remo Brunschwiler *(CEO)*
Bradley Moore *(VP-Sls & Mktg & Exec Mgr-Acct-WalMart)*

TAIYO YUDEN (U.S.A.), INC.
(Sub. of Taiyo Yuden Company Ltd.)
440 Stevens Ave Ste 300
Solana Beach, CA 92075
Tel.: (760) 510-3200
Fax: (858) 350-6846
Toll Free: (800) 493-6835
Web Site: www.t-yuden.com
Approx. Number Employees: 80
Year Founded: 1973
Business Description:
Power Supply Equipment Sales
S.I.C.: 5065
N.A.I.C.S.: 423690
Export
Media: 2-4
Personnel:
Shinya Miyazawa *(Pres)*
Jun Nakajima *(Sls Mgr)*
Brands & Products:
LIFE GUARD
POWER GUARD
Advertising Agency:
WelComm, Inc.
7975 Raytheon Rd Ste 340
San Diego, CA 92111-1622
Tel.: (858) 279-2100
Fax: (858) 279-5400
Toll Free: (888) WELCOMM
(Power Supplies, Power Conditioners)

TAMURA CORPORATION OF AMERICA
(Sub. of Tamura Corporation)
43352 Bus Pk Dr
Temecula, CA 92590-3665
Tel.: (951) 699-1270
Fax: (951) 676-9482
Web Site: www.tamuracorp.com
E-Mail For Key Personnel:
Marketing Director: sales@tamuracorp.com
Sales Director: sales@tamuracorp.com
Approx. Number Employees: 35
Year Founded: 1986
Business Description:
Mfr. of Power Supplies & Transformers
S.I.C.: 5065; 5063
N.A.I.C.S.: 423690; 423610
Advertising Expenditures: $300,000
Media: 2-4-10
Distr.: Natl.
Personnel:
Tony Shinonuma *(CEO & CFO)*
Ted Nakakariya *(COO-Sls & Mktg)*
Brands & Products:
QOLLE

TANNEWITZ, INC.
794 Chicago Dr
Jenison, MI 49428-9354
Tel.: (616) 457-5999
Fax: (616) 457-3620
Toll Free: (800) 458-0590
E-mail: saws@tannewitz.com
Web Site: www.tannewitz.com
Approx. Sls.: $4,000,000
Approx. Number Employees: 50
Year Founded: 1892
Business Description:
Bandsaws for Wood & Metalworking; Sanders, Routers & Conveying Equip.
S.I.C.: 3549; 3553
N.A.I.C.S.: 333518; 333210
Media: 2-7
Distr.: Natl.
Budget Set: Oct.
Personnel:
Morry Pysarchik *(Pres & Mgr-Adv)*
Brands & Products:
MAX
RAMCO
TANNEWITZ

TB WOOD'S INCORPORATED
(Group of ALTRA INDUSTRIAL MOTION, INC.)
440 N 5th Ave
Chambersburg, PA 17201
Tel.: (717) 264-7161
Fax: (717) 264-6420
Toll Free: (888) 829-6637
E-mail: info@tbwoods.com
Web Site: www.tbwoods.com
E-Mail For Key Personnel:
Marketing Director: AChien@tbwoods.com
Approx. Sls.: $118,935,000
Approx. Number Employees: 830
Year Founded: 1857
Business Description:
Electronic & Mechanical Industrial Power Transmission Equipment
S.I.C.: 3568
N.A.I.C.S.: 333613
Advertising Expenditures: $2,200,000
Media: 2-4-5-8-10-13
Personnel:
Harold L. Coder III *(VP-Sls)*
Eric Schuchart *(Product Mgr)*
Brands & Products:
AMBI-TECH
BRAKE-PAK
BRAKETRON
CHIPPER STOPPER
DISC-O-TORQUE
DURA-FLEX
E-TRAC
E-TROL
FAN-STOP
FORM-FLEX
MODBUS
PEC
QT POWER CHAIN
ROTO-CAM
SHORT-STOP
STAR-BRAKE
SURE-FLEX
SURE-GRIP
SURE GRIP
TB WOOD'S
ULTRA-HELIX
ULTRACON
VOLKMANN

TCI PRECISION METALS, INC.
240 E Rosecrans Ave
Gardena, CA 90248
Mailing Address:
PO Box 2069
Gardena, CA 90247-0069
Tel.: (310) 323-5613
Fax: (310) 323-1255
Toll Free: (800) 234-5613
E-mail: tci@tciprecision.com
Web Site: www.tciprecision.com
E-Mail For Key Personnel:
President: jbelzer@tciprecision.com
Approx. Number Employees: 80
Year Founded: 1956
Business Description:
Metal Distr with Job Shop Services
S.I.C.: 5051; 3429
N.A.I.C.S.: 423510; 332510
Import Export
Media: 2-7-10-20-21
Distr.: Natl.
Personnel:
John D. Belzer *(Pres)*
John Martinez *(Mgr-Sls)*

TCR CORPORATION
1600 67th Ave N
Minneapolis, MN 55430-1742
Tel.: (763) 560-2200
Fax: (763) 561-0949
Toll Free: (800) 328-8961
E-mail: info@tcr-corp.com
Web Site: www.tcr-corp.com
Approx. Number Employees: 160
Year Founded: 1953
Business Description:
Specialty Threaded Fasteners
S.I.C.: 6512
N.A.I.C.S.: 531120
Media: 10
Personnel:
Michael Rott *(CEO-TCR Engineered Components LLC)*

T.D. WILLIAMSON, INC.
5727 S Lewis Ave Ste 300
Tulsa, OK 74105-7144
Tel.: (918) 447-5001
Fax: (918) 447-5050
Toll Free: (888) 839-6766
E-mail: contact@tdwilliamson.com
Web Site: www.tdwilliamson.com
E-Mail For Key Personnel:
Marketing Director: marketing@tdwilliamson.com
Approx. Number Employees: 730
Year Founded: 1920
Business Description:
Engineered Pipeline Equipment & Plant Piping Systems Mfr & Maintenance
S.I.C.: 3533; 7629
N.A.I.C.S.: 333132; 811219
Export
Media: 1-2-4-7-13-20-26
Distr.: Direct to Consumer; Intl.
Budget Set: Oct.
Personnel:
Richard B. Williamson *(Chm)*
D. Bruce Binkley *(Pres & CEO)*
Robert D. McGrew *(CFO, Treas & VP)*
Judy Seymour Eliot *(Gen Counsel & Corp Sec)*
Joe Antonacci *(Supvr-Mktg Comm Grp)*
Brands & Products:
BIDIRECTIONALL
CLOCK-KALIPER
D2000
FINALSTOPP
FORMULA SI
GAZOCAL
GAZOMAT
GEO 2000
KALIPER
LINEMASTER
LOCK-O-RING
M-STOPP
MAGPIE
OPTIONALL
PIG-SIG
PIG-SIG IV
PITBOSS
REALSEAL
ROUGHRIDER
SANDWICH
SHORTCUTT
SHORTPLUG
SHORTSLEEVE
SHORTSTOPP
SHORTSTOPP II
SPHERICAL 3-WAY
STOPPLE
T203
TDW
THINSULATOR
THREAD-O-RING
TRACMASTER
U SEAL
ULTRA
UNISPHERE
V-JET
VANTAGE
VANTAGE V
WEDGE-LOCK
WHITESKIN
XPIG

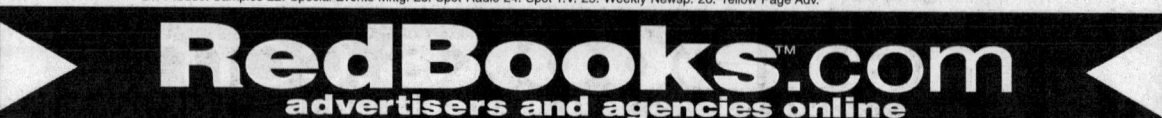

Key to Media (For complete agency information see *The Advertising Red Books-Agencies* edition):
1. Bus. Publs. 2. Cable T.V. 3. Catalogs & Directories. 4. Co-op Adv. 5. Consumer Mags. 6. D.M. to Bus. Estab.7. D.M. to Consumers 8. Daily Newsp. 9. Exhibits/Trade Shows 10. Foreign 11. Infomercial 12. Internet Adv.13. Multimedia 14. Network Radio 15. Network T.V. 16. Newsp. Distr. Mags. 17. Other 18. Outdoor (Posters, Transit) 19. Point of Purchase20. Premiums, Novelties 21. Product Samples 22. Special Events Mktg. 23. Spot Radio 24. Spot T.V. 25. Weekly Newsp. 26. Yellow Page Adv.

Z SEAL

TDK-LAMBDA HIGH POWER DIVISION

(Div. of TDK-Lambda Americas Inc.)
405 Essex Rd
Neptune, NJ 07753-7701
Tel.: (732) 922-9300
Fax: (732) 922-9334
E-mail: sales@lambda-emi.com
Web Site: www.lambda.com
E-Mail For Key Personnel:
Sales Director: sales@lambda-emi.com
Sales Range: $10-24.9 Million
Approx. Number Employees: 250
Year Founded: 1948
Business Description:
Mfr & Designers of Standard & Custom High Power Switchmode DC & Capacitor Changing Power Supplies
S.I.C.: 3699; 3679
N.A.I.C.S.: 335999; 334419
Export
Advertising Expenditures: $500,000
Media: 2-4-21
Distr.: Intl.; Natl.
Budget Set: Sept.
Personnel:
Pascal Chausson *(Pres)*
Ray Owen *(VP-Sls & Mktg)*
John Asilo *(Reg Mgr)*
Brad Canfield *(Reg Mgr)*

TECHNIBUS LLC

(Holding of Pfingsten Partners, LLC)
1501 Raff Rd SW
Canton, OH 44710
Tel.: (330) 478-6395
Fax: (330) 478-8377
Toll Free: (800) 422-4299
Web Site: www.technibus.com
E-Mail For Key Personnel:
President: dchojnowski@technibus.com
Approx. Number Employees: 100
Year Founded: 1966
Business Description:
Metal Enclosed Bus Duct Mfr
S.I.C.: 5063; 3699
N.A.I.C.S.: 423610; 335999
Media: 1-2-4-7-10-11-13-20
Distr.: Intl.; Natl.
Budget Set: Nov. -Dec.
Personnel:
Dan Pomerleau *(Pres)*
Dean Chojnowski *(Gen Mgr)*
James Polgar *(Mgr-Sls)*

TECHPRECISION CORPORATION

1 Bella Dr
Westminster, MA 01473
Tel.: (978) 874-0591
Fax: (978) 874-2748
E-mail: info@ranor.com
Web Site: www.ranor.com
Approx. Sls.: $28,346,751
Approx. Number Employees: 134
Business Description:
Large Metal Fabrications Mfr & Precision Machining Services
S.I.C.: 3441; 3599
N.A.I.C.S.: 332312; 332710
Advertising Expenditures: $31,162
Media: 17
Personnel:
James S. Molinaro *(CEO)*
Richard F. Fitzgerald *(CFO)*
Christopher L. Poplaski *(Pres-Wuxi Critical Mechanical Components Co., Ltd.)*
Stanley A. Youtt *(CEO-Ranor, Inc.)*
William N. Hogenauer *(Dir-Bus Dev)*

TECUMSEH PRODUCTS COMPANY

1136 Oak Valley Dr
Ann Arbor, MI 48108
Tel.: (734) 585-9500
Web Site: www.tecumseh.com
Approx. Sls.: $933,800,000
Approx. Number Employees: 8,600
Year Founded: 1930
Business Description:
Compressors, Small Engines, Power-Train Products & Pump Mfr
S.I.C.: 3563; 3519; 3561; 3594
N.A.I.C.S.: 333912; 333618; 333911; 333996
Import Export
Advertising Expenditures: $300,000
Media: 2-4-10-11
Distr.: Natl.
Budget Set: June
Personnel:
Kent B. Herrick *(Chm)*
James J. Connor *(Pres & CEO)*
Lynn Dennison *(Gen Counsel, Sec & VP-Law & Risk Mgmt)*
Michael A. Noelke *(Exec VP-Sls, Engrg & Mktg)*
Keith Gifford *(Dir-Global Mktg)*
Tim Wright *(Dir-Corp)*
David Hoffman *(Mgr-Global Pricing)*
Michael Smith *(Mgr-Global Mktg Comm & Branding)*
Brands & Products:
SILENT TRAC
TECUMSEH
Advertising Agencies:
J.R. Thompson Co.
26970 Haggerty Rd Ste 100
Farmington Hills, MI 48331
Tel.: (248) 553-4566
Fax: (248) 553-2138
North American Marketing Agency of Record
PR Communications

Kekst & Co.
437 Madison Ave
New York, NY 10022
Tel.: (212) 593-2655
Fax: (212) 521-4900

TEGAL CORPORATION

2201 S McDowell Blvd
Petaluma, CA 94954-6903
Tel.: (707) 763-5600
Fax: (707) 765-9311
Toll Free: (800) 82TEGAL
E-mail: info@tegal.com
Web Site: www.tegal.com
Approx. Rev.: $16,000
Approx. Number Employees: 3
Year Founded: 1972
Business Description:
Designs, Manufactures, Markets & Services Plasma Etch Systems Used In the Fabrication of Integrated Circuits
S.I.C.: 3679; 3674
N.A.I.C.S.: 334419; 334413
Import Export
Advertising Expenditures: $2,444,000
Media: 2-10-11-13
Personnel:
Thomas R. Mika *(Chm, Pres & CEO)*
Christine T. Hergenrother *(CFO, Treas, Sec & VP)*
Brands & Products:
110 SE
200 SE
3200 SE
4200 SE
COMPACT
COMPACT 360 NLD
ONCORE
TEGAL

TEI STRUTHERS WELLS

(Sub. of Babcock Power, Inc.)
36 Clark St
Warren, PA 16365
Mailing Address:
PO Box 8
Warren, PA 16365
Tel.: (814) 726-1000
Fax: (814) 726-1025
Web Site: www.strutherswells.com
Approx. Number Employees: 15
Year Founded: 1851
Business Description:
Engineering & Sales Office
S.I.C.: 3585
N.A.I.C.S.: 333415
Import Export
Media: 4-7-9-11-20
Distr.: Intl.; Natl.
Budget Set: Dec.
Personnel:
Richard Mancuso *(VP & Gen Mgr)*
Brands & Products:
MULTIWALL
Advertising Agency:
J.G. Ashby Advertising
1722 W 8th St
Erie, PA 16505
Tel.: (814) 455-2757

TELEFLEX MARINE INDUSTRIAL

(Sub. of Sierra International Inc.)
640 N Lewis Rd
Limerick, PA 19468-1228
Tel.: (610) 495-7011
Fax: (610) 495-7470
Web Site: www.teleflexmarine.com
Sales Range: $125-149.9 Million
Approx. Number Employees: 200
Business Description:
Marine Pleasure Craft Mechanical Steering & Engine Control Systems Mfr
S.I.C.: 3714; 3519; 3829
N.A.I.C.S.: 336330; 333618; 334519
Media: 4-10
Personnel:
Tom Douglass *(VP-Sls)*

TELESIS TECHNOLOGIES INC.

(Sub. of Tyden Group Inc.)
(d/b/a Telesis Marking Systems)
28181 River Dr
Circleville, OH 43113
Tel.: (740) 477-5000
Fax: (740) 477-5001
E-mail: inquiries@telesis.com
Web Site: www.telesis.com
Approx. Rev.: $30,000,000
Approx. Number Employees: 135
Business Description:
Laser Marking System Mfr
S.I.C.: 3679
N.A.I.C.S.: 334419
Personnel:
Steven Shang *(Pres)*
Advertising Agency:
Richards Communications
3201 Enterprise Pkwy Ste 400
Beachwood, OH 44122
Tel.: (216) 514-7800
Fax: (216) 514-7801

TELSCO INDUSTRIES, INC.

(d/b/a Weathermatic)
3301 W Kingsley Rd
Garland, TX 75041-2207
Tel.: (972) 278-6131
Fax: (972) 271-5710
Toll Free: (888) 4THEPRO
Web Site: www.weathermatic.com
Approx. Number Employees: 53
Year Founded: 1945
Business Description:
Mfr. of Underground Sprinkler Systems
S.I.C.: 3432; 3431
N.A.I.C.S.: 332913; 332998
Export
Media: 1-2-4-5-7-10-11-13-19-20-22
Distr.: Intl.; Natl.
Budget Set: July -Sept.
Personnel:
Max Snoddy *(Founder)*
L. Mike Mason *(Pres)*
Andy Plagens *(CFO)*
Brodie Bruner *(VP-Sls & Mktg)*
Hayley Messing *(Dir-Mktg)*
Brands & Products:
WEATHERMATIC

TELSMITH, INC.

(Sub. of Astec Industries, Inc.)
10910 N Industrial Dr
Mequon, WI 53092-4331
Tel.: (262) 242-6600
Fax: (262) 242-5812
Fax: (262) 242-7861
Fax: (262) 242-7390
Fax: (262) 238-8761
Toll Free: (800) 765-6601
E-mail: e-mail@telsmith.com
Web Site: www.telsmith.com
Sales Range: $50-74.9 Million
Approx. Number Employees: 300
Year Founded: 1906
Business Description:
Crushers, Screens, Quarry Plants, Gravel Plants & Other Products
S.I.C.: 3532; 3531
N.A.I.C.S.: 333131; 333120
Export
Media: 2-4-5-7-8-10-11-13-18-20-22
Distr.: Intl.; Natl.
Budget Set: Oct.
Personnel:
Richard A. Patek *(Pres-Telsmith & Grp VP)*
Dennis Maurer *(Dir-HR)*
Robert J. Meyers *(Dir-Sls & Mktg)*
Steve Miscikowski *(Dir-Admin & Fin)*
Bernie Radobicky *(Dir-Quality Assurance)*
David Ansay *(Mgr-Svc & Warranty)*
Rodd Rosenthal *(Mgr-Parts)*
Jim Schreiner *(Mgr-Product Application & Mktg)*
Brands & Products:
DYNA-DECK
GYRASPHERE
QUIKLOK

Telsmith, Inc. — (Continued)
ROAD-KING
SPECMAKER
STRATACRAWLER SERIES
SUPER-SCRUBBER
TELSMITH
VALU-KING
VFC
VIBRO-KING

TEMPLETON, KENLY & CO., INC.

(Sub. of Actuant Corporation)
(d/b/a Simplex)
2525 Gardner Rd
Broadview, IL 60155-3719
Tel.: (708) 865-1500
Fax: (708) 865-0894
Toll Free: (800) 275-5225
Web Site: www.tksimplex.com
Approx. Rev.: $33,000,000
Approx. Number Employees: 120
Year Founded: 1899
Business Description:
Mechanical & Hydraulic Jacks, Hydraulic Cylinders & Accessories & Worm Gear Linear Actuators Mfr
S.I.C.: 3423; 3569
N.A.I.C.S.: 332212; 333999
Import Export
Advertising Expenditures: $250,000
Media: 2
Distr.: Intl.; Natl.
Budget Set: Dec.
Personnel:
Thomas Danza *(Pres)*
Brands & Products:
SIMPLEX
UNI-LIFT

TENNANT COMPANY

701 N Lilac Dr
Minneapolis, MN 55440
Mailing Address:
PO Box 1452
Minneapolis, MN 55440-1452
Tel.: (763) 540-1200
Fax: (763) 513-2142
Toll Free: (800) 553-8033
E-mail: info@tennantco.com
Web Site: www.tennantco.com
Approx. Sls.: $667,667,000
Approx. Number Employees: 2,793
Year Founded: 1870
Business Description:
Non-Residential Floor Maintenance Equipment & Related Products Mfr., Designer & Retailer
S.I.C.: 3569; 3589
N.A.I.C.S.: 333999; 333319
Import Export
Advertising Expenditures: $5,516,000
Media: 1-2-4-5-7-10-22-26
Distr.: Intl.; Natl.
Budget Set: Oct.
Personnel:
H. Chris Killingstad *(Pres & CEO)*
Thomas J. Paulson *(CFO & VP)*
Heidi M. Hoard *(Gen Counsel & VP)*
Andrew J. Eckert *(VP-Americas)*
Steven K. Weeks *(VP-North America Strategic Plng)*
Kathryn Lovik *(Dir-Corp HR)*
Mark Morrison *(Dir-Ops)*
Brands & Products:
ATLV
CENTURION
CREATING A CLEANER, SAFER WORLD
CYVLONE
EC-H2O
ECO-ADVANTAGE
ECO-DFS
ECO-DQS
ECO-ECT
ECO-HARD-N-SEAL
ECO-HPS
ECO-PJS
ECO-PROTEKT
ECO-SHOPFLOOR
ES
EZ RIDER
FAST
FAST-PAK
FLEXCLEAN
FLOORSMART
HYGENIC
INSTACURE
INTELLI-POWER
LITTER HAWK
LOWER THE COST OF OWNERSHIP
MARKSMAN
MAXPRO
MORE THAN CLEAN IT'S READYSPACE
NOBLES
NOBLES CAPITAL
PORTAPAC
POWER EAGLE
QA CONTROLS
QUICK CLEAN
QUICKMOP
READY SPACE
THE SAFE SCRUBBING ALTERNATIVE
SENTINEL
SERVICELINK
SPEED SCRUB
SPEEDSHINE
SRS
STREET SMART
STRIVE RIDER
TENNANT CAPITAL
TENNANT FINANCIAL
TIDY- VAC
TRAILBLAZER
TRAILBLAZER LITE
TYPHOON
ULTRAGLIDE
ULTRASHINE
VCS

TENSILKUT ENGINEERING

(Div. of Sieburg International, Inc.)
1901 Clydesdale St
Maryville, TN 37801-3728
Tel.: (865) 982-6300
Fax: (865) 982-6347
E-mail: sales@tensilkut.com
Web Site: www.tensilkut.com
E-Mail For Key Personnel:
Sales Director: sales@tensilkut.com
Approx. Number Employees: 5
Business Description:
Engineering of Machine Tools
S.I.C.: 3829; 3559
N.A.I.C.S.: 334519; 333298
Advertising Expenditures: $48,000
Media: 2-4-8-10
Distr.: Intl.; Natl.
Personnel:
M.B. McDonald *(Pres)*
Brands & Products:
CNC TENSILATHE
CNC TENSILKUT III
IMPACTMILL
TENSILATHE/505
TENSILBITS
TENSILGRIND
TENSILKUT I
TENSILKUT II
TENSILSAW
TENSILSHEAR

TEREX CEDARAPIDS

(Sub. of Terex Materials Processing & Mining)
909 17th St NE
Cedar Rapids, IA 52402
Tel.: (319) 363-3511
Fax: (319) 399-4871
Toll Free: (800) 821-5600
E-mail: info@cedarapids.com
Web Site: www.cedarapids.com
Sales Range: $25-49.9 Million
Approx. Number Employees: 100
Business Description:
Crushing & Screening Pavers & Hot Mix Asphalt Mfr
S.I.C.: 3531
N.A.I.C.S.: 333120
Export
Media: 10-13
Personnel:
David Schuchmann *(Dir-Applications)*
Brands & Products:
COBRATRACK

TEREX CORPORATION

200 Nyala Farm Rd
Westport, CT 06880
Tel.: (203) 222-7170
Fax: (203) 222-7976
E-mail: info@terex.com
Web Site: www.terex.com
Approx. Sls.: $4,418,200,000
Approx. Number Employees: 16,300
Year Founded: 1986
Business Description:
Heavy-Duty Earthmoving & Lifting Equipment for the Infrastructure, Construction & Mining Industries
S.I.C.: 5084; 3531; 3537
N.A.I.C.S.: 423830; 333120; 333924
Import Export
Media: 7-10
Distr.: Intl.
Budget Set: Sept.
Personnel:
Ronald M. DeFeo *(Chm & CEO)*
Phillip C. Widman *(CFO & Sr VP)*
Mark I. Clair *(Chief Acctg Officer, VP & Controller)*
Steve Filipov *(Pres-Developing Markets & Strategic Accts)*
Ramon Oliu *(Pres-Fin Svcs)*
Eric I. Cohen *(Gen Counsel, Sec & Sr VP)*
Kevin A. Barr *(Sr VP-HR)*
Doug Friesen *(Sr VP-Terex Bus Sys)*
Brian J. Henry *(Sr VP-Fin & Bus Dev)*
Jacob Thomas *(Sr VP-Product Dev & Mktg)*
Jeffrey A. Gershowitz *(Asst Sec, Deputy Gen Counsel & VP)*
Roger Brown *(VP-Compensation & Benefits)*
Mike Bazinet *(Dir-Corp Comm & Pub Affairs)*
Tony Galuardi *(Dir-Global Parts Bus)*
Brands & Products:
ADVANCE
AMIDA
ATLAS
BARTELL
BENDINI
BENFORD
BID-WELL
CANICA
CEDARAPIDS
CIFALI
CMI
COMEDIL
CPV
DEMAG
FERMEC
FINLAY
FRANNA
FUCHS
GENIE
GRAYHOUND
HI-RANGER
ITALMACCHINE
JAQUES
JOHNSON-ROSS
KOEHRING
LECTRA HAUL
LOAD KING
LORAIN
MARKLIFT
MORRISON
MULLER
O&K
PAYHAULER
PEGSON
PEINER
POWERSCREEN
PPM
RE-TECH
REEDRILL
ROYER
SCHAEFF
SIMPLICITY
SQUARE SHOOTER
TATRA
TELELECT
TEREX
TEREX AMERICAN
TEREXLIFT
UNIT RIG
Advertising Agency:
Media Concepts Corporation
25 N Main St
Assonet, MA 02702-1136
Tel.: (508) 644-3131
Fax: (508) 644-5201

TESSERA TECHNOLOGIES INC.

3025 Orchard Pkwy
San Jose, CA 95134
Tel.: (408) 321-6000
Fax: (408) 894-0768
E-mail: info@tessera.com
Web Site: www.tessera.com
Approx. Rev.: $301,393,000
Approx. Number Employees: 480
Year Founded: 1990
Business Description:
Semiconductor Packaging Technologies
S.I.C.: 3674
N.A.I.C.S.: 334413
Advertising Expenditures: $82,000,000
Personnel:
Henry R. Nothhaft *(Chm, Pres & CEO)*
Michael Anthofer *(CFO & Exec VP)*
Robert Yung *(CTO & Exec VP)*

Key to Media (For complete agency information see *The Advertising Red Books-Agencies* edition):
1. Bus. Publs. 2. Cable T.V. 3. Catalogs & Directories. 4. Co-op Adv. 5. Consumer Mags. 6. D.M. to Bus. Estab.7. D.M. to Consumers 8. Daily Newsp. 9. Exhibits/Trade Shows 10. Foreign 11. Infomercial 12. Internet Adv.13. Multimedia 14. Network Radio 15. Network T.V. 16. Newsp. Distr. Mags. 17. Other 18. Outdoor (Posters, Transit) 19. Point of Purchase20. Premiums, Novelties 21. Product Samples 22. Special Events Mktg. 23. Spot Radio 24. Spot T.V. 25. Weekly Newsp. 26. Yellow Page Adv.

H. Thomas Blanco *(Chief Admin Officer & Sr VP)*
Bob Roohparvar *(Pres-Imaging & Optics)*
Bernard J. Cassidy *(Gen Counsel & Exec VP)*
Liam Goudge *(Sr VP & Gen Mgr-Silent Air Cooling Tech)*
Steven T. Chen *(Sr VP-Sls & Bus Dev)*
John Keating *(Sr VP-Corp Dev)*
Brands & Products:
TESSERA
Advertising Agency:
JAM Associates LLC
(d/b/a JHG)
9707 Waples St Ste 102
San Diego, CA 92121
Tel.: (858) 457-4888
Fax: (858) 952-7841
Agency of Record

THERMAL CERAMICS INC.
(Sub. of Morgan Thermal Ceramics)
2102 Old Savannah Rd
Augusta, GA 30906-2133
Mailing Address:
PO Box 923
Augusta, GA 30903-0923
Tel.: (706) 796-4200
Fax: (706) 796-4398
E-mail: tceramics@thermalceramics.com
Web Site: www.thermalceramics.com
E-Mail For Key Personnel:
Marketing Director: DHadden@thermalceramics.com
Sales Director: DHadden@thermalceramics.com
Approx. Number Employees: 430
Year Founded: 1923
Business Description:
Ceramics Products Mfr
S.I.C.: 3299; 3255
N.A.I.C.S.: 327999; 327124
Import Export
Media: 2-4-10-20
Distr.: Intl.
Personnel:
Curtis South *(VP-Fin)*
Lance Caspersen *(Dir-Mktg)*
Tom Rebernack *(Dir-Mktg)*

THERMAL PRODUCT SOLUTIONS
(Unit of SPX Corporation)
2821 Old Rt 15
New Columbia, PA 17856
Mailing Address:
PO Box 150
Williamsport, PA 17887
Tel.: (570) 538-7200
Fax: (570) 538-7380
E-mail: tpxinfo@spx.com
Web Site:
www.thermalproductsolutions.com
Sales Range: $75-99.9 Million
Approx. Number Employees: 175
Year Founded: 1932
Business Description:
Thermal Solution Products
S.I.C.: 3567; 3821
N.A.I.C.S.: 333994; 339111
Export
Advertising Expenditures: $200,000
Media: 2-7-8-10-20
Distr.: Intl.; Natl.
Budget Set: Oct.
Personnel:
Bruce Williamson *(Pres)*
Brands & Products:
BENCHMASTER
COMPROTENN
DIGITENN
HERMETICOOL
HUMITENN
KOLD PAK
LINKTENN
LOGITENN
MICROTENN
MULTI-RANGE
RELIALAB
TEMPGARD
TENNEY JR.
TENNEYMITE
TENNTROL
TH JR.
TSA
VAPORFLO
VERSATENN
VIDEOTENN

THERMATRIX, INC.
(Sub. of Selas Fluid Processing Corp.)
5 Sentry Pkwy E Ste 204
Blue Bell, PA 19422
Tel.: (610) 834-0300
Fax: (610) 834-0473
E-mail: info@thermatrix.com
Web Site: www.selasfluid.com
Approx. Number Employees: 125
Year Founded: 1992
Business Description:
Pollution Treatment Products Mfr
S.I.C.: 1521
N.A.I.C.S.: 236115
Media: 2-4-10
Personnel:
Jason Faulkner *(VP-Sls)*
Brands & Products:
THERMATRIX

THERMWOOD CORPORATION
904 Dale Buffaloville Rd
Dale, IN 47523-9057
Tel.: (812) 937-4476
Fax: (812) 937-2956
Toll Free: (800) 533-6901
E-mail: internet@thermwood.com
Web Site: www.thermwood.com
E-Mail For Key Personnel:
Sales Director: sales@thermwood.com
Approx. Number Employees: 150
Year Founded: 1969
Business Description:
Machine Tools & Routers Mfr & Distr for Woodworking, Plastics, Aerospace, Boating & Auto Industries
S.I.C.: 3541
N.A.I.C.S.: 333512
Media: 5-10-13
Personnel:
Kenneth J. Susnjara *(Chm & CEO)*
David J. Hildenbrand *(Pres)*

THOMAS CONVEYOR COMPANY
555 N Burleson Blvd
Burleson, TX 76028-2907
Tel.: (817) 295-7151
Fax: (817) 447-3840
Toll Free: (800) 433-2217
E-mail: sales@thomasconveyor.com
Web Site: www.thomasconveyor.com
E-Mail For Key Personnel:
Sales Director: sales@thomasconveyor.com
Approx. Sls.: $22,000,000
Approx. Number Employees: 180
Year Founded: 1953
Business Description:
Mfr. of Bulk Material Conveyors, Screw Conveyors, Bucket Elevators & Drag Conveyors
S.I.C.: 3535; 2655
N.A.I.C.S.: 333922; 322214
Export
Media: 2-4-10
Distr.: Natl.
Personnel:
Mark Ellis *(Mgr-Sls & Mktg)*
Brands & Products:
HI-TEMP
THOMAS CONVEYOR COMPANY

THOMAS ENGINEERING INC.
575 W Central Rd
Hoffman Estates, IL 60192-1937
Tel.: (847) 358-5800
Fax: (847) 358-5817
Toll Free: (800) 634-9910
E-mail: teimktg@tomaseng.com
Web Site: www.thomaseng.com
Approx. Number Employees: 100
Year Founded: 1959
Business Description:
Mfr. & Designer of Pharmaceutical Tablet Presses & Coaters, Packaging Machinery, Punches & Dies
S.I.C.: 3559; 5084
N.A.I.C.S.: 333298; 423830
Export
Advertising Expenditures: $245,000
Media: 2-7-10-13
Distr.: Natl.
Budget Set: Nov. -Dec.
Personnel:
Rich Karbowiak *(Mgr-Mktg)*
Brands & Products:
ACCELA-COTA
COMPU-COAT
COMPU-LAB
SPECTRUM
SPECTRUM SPRAY BAR
THOMAS ENGINEERING
THOMAS TABLET SENTINEL 5 (TTS 5)

THOMPSON INTERNATIONAL INC.
5840 Airline Rd
Henderson, KY 42420-9561
Tel.: (270) 826-3751
Fax: (270) 826-3881
Toll Free: (800) 626-7054
Telex: 20-4297
E-mail: cthompson@thompsoninternational.com
Web Site:
www.thompsoninternational.com
Approx. Number Employees: 75
Year Founded: 1951
Business Description:
Rotary Drilling Tool Mfr
S.I.C.: 5084; 3546
N.A.I.C.S.: 423830; 333991
Export
Media: 2-4-10-11
Distr.: Intl. Natl.
Personnel:
Clifford H. Thompson *(Pres & CEO)*
Don Thompson, Jr. *(Exec VP)*
Elizabeth Thompson *(Exec VP)*
Doug Black *(Product Mgr-Drilco)*
Brands & Products:
THOMPSON INTERNATIONAL

TIDEL ENGINEERING, L.P.
(Sub. of Sentinel Technologies Inc.)
Ste 114 2025 W Belt Line Rd
Carrollton, TX 75006-6453
Tel.: (972) 484-3358
Fax: (972) 484-1014
Toll Free: (800) 678-7577
E-mail: sales@tidel.com
Web Site: www.tidel.com
E-Mail For Key Personnel:
President: pres@tidel.com
Sales Director: sales@tidel.com
Approx. Number Employees: 100
Year Founded: 1991
Business Description:
Cash Handling Equipment; Automated Teller Machines Mfr
S.I.C.: 3577; 3499
N.A.I.C.S.: 334119; 332439
Import Export
Media: 2-7-10
Distr.: Intl.; Natl.
Personnel:
Jeff Galgano *(Owner)*
Mark Levenick *(Pres & CEO)*
Ed Grondahl *(Exec VP-Sls & Mktg)*
Flynt Moreland *(Exec VP-Engrg)*
Troy Richard *(Exec VP)*
Brands & Products:
ANYCARD ATM
CHAMELEON
IGNITION SERIES ATM
TACC

TIMESAVERS INC.
(Sub. of Holden Industries, Inc.)
11123 89th Ave N
Maple Grove, MN 55369
Tel.: (763) 488-6600
Fax: (763) 488-6601
Toll Free: (800) 537-3611
E-mail: info@timesaversinc.com
Web Site: www.timesaversinc.com
Sales Range: $10-24.9 Million
Approx. Number Employees: 55
Year Founded: 1949
Business Description:
Wide Abrasive Sanding & Grinding Machines Mfr
S.I.C.: 3541
N.A.I.C.S.: 333512
Advertising Expenditures: $250,000
Media: 2-4-7-10
Distr.: Intl.; Natl.
Budget Set: Sept. -Oct.
Personnel:
Gregory K. Larson *(Pres)*
Gary Besonen *(Mgr-Natl Woodworking Equipment Sls)*
Brands & Products:
TIMESAVERS

TIPPER TIE, INC.
(Sub. of Dover Engineered Systems, Inc.)
2000 Lufkin Rd
Apex, NC 27502
Tel.: (919) 362-8811
Fax: (919) 303-3272
Toll Free: (800) 331-2905
E-mail: sales@tippertie.com
Web Site: www.tippertie.com

Key to Media (For complete agency information see *The Advertising Red Books-Agencies* edition):
1. Bus. Publs. 2. Cable T.V. 3. Catalogs & Directories. 4. Co-op Adv. 5. Consumer Mags. 6. D.M. to Bus. Estab.7. D.M. to Consumers 8. Daily Newsp. 9. Exhibits/Trade Shows 10. Foreign 11. Infomercial 12. Internet Adv.13. Multimedia 14. Network Radio 15. Network T.V. 16. Newsp. Distr. Mags. 17. Other 18. Outdoor (Posters, Transit) 19. Point of Purchase20. Premiums, Novelties 21. Product Samples 22. Special Events Mktg. 23. Spot Radio 24. Spot T.V. 25. Weekly Newsp. 26. Yellow Page Adv.

Tipper Tie, Inc. — (Continued)

E-Mail For Key Personnel:
Marketing Director: marketing@tippertie.com
Sales Director: sales@tippertie.com
Sales Range: $125-149.9 Million
Approx. Number Employees: 400
Year Founded: 1952
Business Description:
Packaging Machinery & Clip Closures Mfr
S.I.C.: 3556; 3565
N.A.I.C.S.: 333294; 333993
Import Export
Media: 1-2-4-7-10-11-22
Distr.: Intl.; Natl.
Personnel:
Gurnot Forester *(Pres)*
Sandra Engel *(Dir-Mktg)*
Brands & Products:
NET-ALL
RS4203
SIGNATURE
SWOPPERV
TECHNOCLIPPER
TIPPER CLIPPER
TIPPER TAG
TIPPER TAGGER SYSTEM
TIPPER TIE
TIPPER TIE-NET
TIPPER TIE TECHNOPACK

TITAN MACHINERY INC.
644 E Beaton Dr
Fargo, ND 58078-2648
Tel.: (701) 356-0130
Fax: (701) 356-0139
E-mail: us@titanmachinery.com
Web Site: www.titanmachinery.com
Approx. Rev.: $1,094,489,000
Approx. Number Employees: 1,596
Year Founded: 1980
Business Description:
New & Used Agricultural & Construction Equipment Rental & Sales
S.I.C.: 5999; 5082; 5083; 7353
N.A.I.C.S.: 453998; 423810; 423820; 532412
Import Export
Advertising Expenditures: $3,000,000
Media: 2-7-10
Personnel:
David J. Meyer *(Chm & CEO)*
Peter J. Christianson *(Pres & COO)*
Mark P. Kalvoda *(CFO)*
Ted Christianson *(Treas & VP-Fin)*
Advertising Agency:
ICR
20 Custom House St Ste 930
Boston, MA 02110
Tel.: (617) 956-6725
Fax: (617) 956-6726

TITAN TOOL, INC.
(Sub. of Wagner Spray Tech Corporation)
107 Bauer Dr
Oakland, NJ 07436
Tel.: (201) 337-1240
Fax: (201) 337-8350
Toll Free: (800) 526-5362
E-mail: titan@titantool.com
Web Site: www.titantool.com
Approx. Number Employees: 300
Year Founded: 1968
Business Description:
Mfr. of Paint Spraying Systems for Contractors
S.I.C.: 3563
N.A.I.C.S.: 333912
Import Export
Media: 2-4-5-7-10-11-17-19-20-22
Distr.: Intl.
Personnel:
Tony F. Sulilapsi *(Product Mgr)*
Patrick Macalalag *(Sls Mgr)*
Gary Bailey *(Mgr-Tech & Sls-Intl)*
Brands & Products:
EPIC 330
HYDRA
HYDRA PRO
HYDRA PRO SUPER
POWRLINER
POWRTWIN
PRO-FINISH
SEVERE SERVICE 500
TITAN

TOLEDO COMMUTATOR CO.
(Sub. of Kirkwood Holding, Inc.)
1101 S Chestnut St
Owosso, MI 48867-4096
Tel.: (989) 725-8192
Fax: (989) 725-5930
E-mail: toledosales@kirkwood-ind.com
Web Site: www.kirkwood-ind.com
Approx. Number Employees: 250
Year Founded: 1895
Business Description:
Commutators Mfr for Electrical Machinery, Slip Rings & Brush Springs
S.I.C.: 3621
N.A.I.C.S.: 335312
Import Export
Media: 2-4-10
Distr.: Natl.
Budget Set: Oct.
Personnel:
Paul Hansen *(Pres)*
Tom Koechley *(CEO)*
Tim Kildea *(VP-Sls)*
Brands & Products:
CORTEM

TORNADO INDUSTRIES, INC.
7401 W Lawrence Ave
Chicago, IL 60706
Tel.: (708) 867-5100
Fax: (708) 867-6968
Toll Free: (800) 822-8867
E-mail: sales@tornadovac.com
Web Site: www.tornadovac.com
E-Mail For Key Personnel:
Sales Director: sales@tornadovac.com
Approx. Number Employees: 120
Year Founded: 1927
Business Description:
Carpet Care Machines & Industrial Vacuum Cleaners, Portable Blowers, Floor Machines & Combination Scrub-Vacuum-Dry Machines Mfr
S.I.C.: 3589
N.A.I.C.S.: 333319
Import Export
Advertising Expenditures: $250,000
Media: 2-4-7-10-16-26
Distr.: Intl.; Natl.
Budget Set: Jan.
Personnel:
Michael Schaffer *(Pres & CEO)*
Jolynn Kennedy *(Dir-Mktg)*
Brands & Products:
BISPEED
BRUTE FORCE
CARPETKEEPERS
FLOORKEEPERS
FLOORMACHINES
GLAZER
HEADMASTER
HEADMASTERS/TASKFORCE
JUMBO VACS
MARATHON
TASKFORCE
TORNADO
WINDSHEAR

TORRMETAL CORPORATION
12125 Bennington Ave
Cleveland, OH 44135
Tel.: (216) 671-1616
Fax: (216) 671-3705
E-mail: torr@torrmetal.com
Web Site: www.torrmetal.com
Approx. Sls.: $4,000,000
Approx. Number Employees: 20
Year Founded: 1972
Business Description:
High Production Metal, Precision Stampings & Dies Mfr
S.I.C.: 3469; 3544
N.A.I.C.S.: 332116; 333514
Media: 2-4-7-10-17
Distr.: Natl.
Personnel:
Patrick Sheehan *(Pres)*

TRANTER PHE, INC.
(Sub. of Alfa Laval AB)
1900 Old Burk Hwy
Wichita Falls, TX 76307
Mailing Address:
PO Box 2289
Wichita Falls, TX 76307
Tel.: (940) 723-7125
Fax: (940) 723-5131
Web Site: www.tranter.com
Sales Range: $125-149.9 Million
Approx. Number Employees: 227
Year Founded: 1932
Business Description:
Welded & Gasketed Plate Heat Exchangers Mfr
S.I.C.: 3559
N.A.I.C.S.: 332410
Import Export
Advertising Expenditures: $1,000,000
Media: 1-2-4-5-7-11-21-22-26
Distr.: Intl.; Natl.
Budget Set: Oct.
Personnel:
Feroze Patel *(Exec VP)*
Jody Stonecipher *(Mgr-Sls & Mktg-WP)*
Brands & Products:
MAXCHANGER
PLATECOIL
SUPERCHANGER
SUPERMAX
ULTRAMAX
Advertising Agency:
Shorey & Associates Inc.
450-B E Park Ave
Greenville, SC 29601-2242
Tel.: (864) 242-5407
Fax: (864) 242-5456
(Industrial Heat Exchangers)

TRC COMPANIES, INC.
21 Griffin Rd N
Windsor, CT 06095
Tel.: (978) 970-5600
Fax: (978) 453-1995
E-mail: trr@investorrelations.com
Web Site: www.trcsolutions.com
Approx. Rev.: $333,209,000
Approx. Number Employees: 2,300
Year Founded: 1971
Business Description:
Environmental Engineering & Consulting
S.I.C.: 8999; 8711; 8748
N.A.I.C.S.: 541620; 541330; 541690
Export
Media: 2-7-10-20
Distr.: Natl.
Budget Set: June
Personnel:
Christopher P. Vincze *(Chm & CEO)*
Thomas W. Bennet, Jr. *(CFO & Sr VP)*
Robert P. Jurasin *(Principal, VP & Mgr-Trasportation Design Practice)*
Martin H. Dodd *(Gen Counsel, Sec & Sr VP)*
Robert C. Petersen *(Exec VP & Dir-Bus)*
Glenn Harkness *(Sr VP)*
Brands & Products:
EXIT STRATEGIES
SECURITY MASTER PLAN
TRC

TREIBACHER SCHLEIFMITTEL NORTH AMERICA, INC.
(Sub. of Treibacher Schleifmittel AG)
2000 College Ave M
Niagara Falls, NY 14305-1734
Mailing Address:
PO Box 1438
Niagara Falls, NY 14302
Tel.: (716) 286-1250
Tel.: (716) 286-1234
Fax: (716) 286-1224
Toll Free: (800) 394-8872
E-mail: marketing@treibacher-us.com
Web Site: www.treibacher-schleifm.com
Approx. Number Employees: 35
Year Founded: 1914
Business Description:
Mfr. of Fused Aluminum Oxides & Silicon Carbide Abrasive Grits
S.I.C.: 3291
N.A.I.C.S.: 327910
Import Export
Advertising Expenditures: $2,300,000
Media: 1-2-4-5-7-11-13-16-21-26
Distr.: Natl.
Budget Set: Nov.
Brands & Products:
CARBONITE
HECCOLON
LIONITE/LIONBLAST

TRIANGLE PACKAGE MACHINERY CO.
6655 W Diversey Ave
Chicago, IL 60707-2239
Tel.: (773) 889-0200
Fax: (773) 889-4221
Toll Free: (800) 621-4170
Telex: 910-221-4064
E-mail: info@trianglepackage.com
Web Site: www.trianglepackage.com

Key to Media (For complete agency information see *The Advertising Red Books-Agencies* edition):
1. Bus. Publs. 2. Cable T.V. 3. Catalogs & Directories. 4. Co-op Adv. 5. Consumer Mags. 6. D.M. to Bus. Estab.7. D.M. to Consumers
8. Daily Newsp. 9. Exhibits/Trade Shows 10. Foreign 11. Infomercial 12. Internet Adv.13. Multimedia 14. Network Radio
15. Network T.V. 16. Newsp. Distr. Mags. 17. Other 18. Outdoor (Posters, Transit) 19. Point of Purchase20. Premiums, Novelties
21. Product Samples 22. Special Events Mktg. 23. Spot Radio 24. Spot T.V. 25. Weekly Newsp. 26. Yellow Page Adv.

Approx. Number Employees: 250
Year Founded: 1923
Business Description:
Packaging Machinery Mfr
S.I.C.: 3565
N.A.I.C.S.: 333993
Export
Media: 2-4-7-10-26
Distr.: Natl.
Budget Set: Nov.
Personnel:
Bryan Muskat *(Pres)*
Bob Williams *(VP-Sls-Mktg)*
Will C. Cray *(Dir-Mktg)*
Mike Summers *(Dir-Fin)*
John Cooke *(Sls Mgr-Triangle Eastern)*
Ray Kondracki *(Mgr-Mktg)*
John McCall *(Mgr-Natl Accts)*
Charles Muskat *(Mgr-Sls-Western Region & Intl)*
Brands & Products:
ACCELERON
ADVANTAGE
BAG-IN-BOX
FLEX-CELL
PROLINE
SELECTACOM
TRIANGLE

TRICON INDUSTRIES, INC.

(Filed Ch 11 Bankruptcy #923100 on 06/25/09 in U.S. Bankruptcy Ct, Northern Dist of IL, Chicago)
2325 Wisconsin Ave
Downers Grove, IL 60515
Tel.: (630) 964-2330
Fax: (630) 964-5179
E-mail: sales@triconinc.com
Web Site: www.triconinc.com
E-Mail For Key Personnel:
Sales Director: sales@triconinc.com
Approx. Number Employees: 500
Year Founded: 1944
Business Description:
Custom Switches & Connectors, Insert Molding Products, Electrical Contact Assemblies, Preforms, Bulkwire & Copper, Silver & Nickel Paste & Fluxes Mfr
S.I.C.: 3089; 3613
N.A.I.C.S.: 326199; 335313
Import Export
Media: 1-4-10-11-13-17-21
Distr.: Intl.
Budget Set: Oct.
Personnel:
Jeffery S. Terrell *(Pres)*
Patricia L. Grandle *(VP-Sls & Mktg)*
J. P. Bonny *(Dir-Bus Dev)*
Bill McDannel *(Mgr-Product Engrg)*
Brands & Products:
TRICON

TRIMAS CORPORATION

39400 Woodward Ave Ste 130
Bloomfield Hills, MI 48304
Tel.: (248) 631-5450
Fax: (248) 631-5455
E-mail: email@trimascorp.com
Web Site: www.trimascorp.com
Approx. Sls.: $942,650,000
Approx. Number Employees: 3,900
Business Description:
Commercial, Industrial & Consumer Engineered Product Mfr
S.I.C.: 5013; 3452; 3463; 3799
N.A.I.C.S.: 441310; 332112; 332722; 336999
Advertising Expenditures: $4,800,000
Media: 16
Personnel:
Samuel Valenti, III *(Chm)*
David M. Wathen *(Pres & CEO)*
A. Mark Zeffiro *(CFO)*
Kurt Allen *(Pres-Lamons Gasket Company)*
Lynn A. Brooks *(Pres-Pkg Sys)*
Brian McGuire *(Pres-Monogram Aerospace Fasteners)*
Jerad Van Auken *(Pres-Norris Cylinder)*
Joshua A. Sherbin *(Gen Counsel & VP)*
Robert J. Zalupski *(VP-Corp Dev & Treasury)*
Brands & Products:
ARROW
ENGLASS
HIDDEN HITCH
HIGHLAND
KEO
LAMONS
REESE
RIEKE
STOLZ
WESBAR
Advertising Agency:
Bianchi Public Relations Inc.
888 W Big Beaver Rd Ste 777
Troy, MI 48084
Tel.: (248) 269-1122
Fax: (248) 269-8202

TRIMBLE NAVIGATION LIMITED

935 Stewart Dr
Sunnyvale, CA 94085-3913
Tel.: (408) 481-8000
Fax: (408) 481-7781
E-mail: pr@trimble.com
Web Site: www.trimble.com
E-Mail For Key Personnel:
Public Relations: pr@trimble.com
Approx. Rev.: $1,293,937,000
Approx. Number Employees: 4,166
Year Founded: 1978
Business Description:
Advanced Positioning & Navigation Technologies & Software Mfr
S.I.C.: 3824; 3812; 4812; 4899; 7372; 7374; 7379; 8711; 8748
N.A.I.C.S.: 334514; 334511; 511210; 517212; 517410; 517910; 518210; 541330; 541519; 541690
Export
Advertising Expenditures: $20,400,000
Media: 1-2-4-5-10-11-13-20-22
Distr.: Intl.
Personnel:
Ulf J. Johansson *(Chm)*
Nickolas W. Vande Steeg *(Vice Chm)*
Steven W. Berglund *(Pres & CEO)*
Rajat Bahri *(CFO)*
Julie A. Shepard *(Chief Acctg Officer & VP-Fin)*
Richard A. Beyer *(Officer)*
James A. Kirkland *(Gen Counsel & VP)*
Jurgen Kliem *(VP-Strategy & Bus Dev)*
Mary Kay Strangis *(VP-HR)*
Greg Brott *(Sr Dir-Product Plng & Alliances)*
Lea Ann McNabb *(Mgr-PR)*
Brands & Products:
4000DSI
4000IM MSK
4000MSK DGPS
4000RSI
4000SSI
4600 LS
ACE III GPS
ACE UTC
ACUTIME
ADVENTURE PLANNER
AGGPS
ASSET SURVEYOR
ASSETPAD
AUTOLOCK
AUTOPILOT
AUTOSEED
AVL MANAGER
BCS
BD112
BD122
BD750
BOB
BUCKETPRO
BULLET
CENTURION
COLOSSUS
CONNECTED SITE
CROSSCHECK
CUGR
DIALGRADE
DRGPS
DRIVESAFE
DSM
ECHOLDX
ECHORTX
ECHOVST
ELTA
ERTK
EVEREST
EZ-GUIDE
EZ-STEER
FIRSTGPS
FLEETVISION
FLIGHTBAR
FORCE
FORCE GPS
GALAXY
GALAXY COURIER
GALAXY INMARSAT-C/GPS
GALAXY SENTINEL
GEOBEACON
GEODETIC SYSTEM SURVEYOR
GEODIMETER
GEOEXPLORER
GEOGENIUS
GEOSTAR
GEOTRACER
GEOXM
GEOXT
GP400
GPLOAD
GPS ANALYST
GPS PATHFINDER
GPS TOTAL STATION
GPSCORRECT
GPSNET
GPSURVEY
GRADEEYE
GRADEPRO
GRADIO
HYDROBMS
HYDROCONTOUR
HYDRODREDGE
HYDROEDIT
HYDROEXAMINE
HYDROPRO
HYDROPROCESSING
HYDROPROFILE
HYDRORIG
HYDROSEISMIC
HYDROTIDE
HYDROTRANSFER
HYDROTUG
HYDROVSP
INTEGRATED SURVEYING
IQEVENT ENGINE
IS
LASERLEVEL
LASERPLANE
LASERSTATION
LASSEN
LINE LEVEL
LOADDXF
M-LOC
MAXWELL
METSMANAGER
MS750
MS860
MULTIPLANE
NETRS
NT300D
PALISADE
PAYDIRT
PLACER
PLUMB POINTER
PROBEACON
PSC-200
QUADRIGA
QUICKPLAN
RANGER
RECON
RESOLUTION
ROADLINK
RTKNET
SCHEDULE TRACK
SCREEDPRO
SIERRA
SITE SURVEYOR
SITENET
SITEVISION
SPECTRA PRECISION
SURVEY MANAGER
SVEE EIGHT PLUS GPS
TANS III
TANS VECTOR
TARGET:PILE
TARGET:STRUCTURES
TASMAN
TDC1
TDC2
TEK
TELVISANT
TERRAMODAL
TERRASAT
TERRASYNC
TERRAVISTA
TERRESTRIAL TOTAL STATION
THUNDERBOLT
TRACKLIGHT
TRANS PAK
TRENCHWORK
TRIMBLE
TRIMBLE GEOMATICS OFFICE
TRIMBLE SURVEY CONTROLLER
TRIMBLE SURVEY PRO
TRIMBLE TOTAL CONTROL
TRIMCOMM
TRIMFLIGHT
TRIMMARK
TRIMPACK
TRIMTRAC
TRS
TSC1

Trimble Navigation Limited — (Continued)

TSCE
TSIP TALKER
TSM
TTS
URS
VRS
VRS NOW
WAVE
ZEPHYR
ZEPHYR GEODETIC

Advertising Agency:
Barnhart
1732 Champa St
Denver, CO 80202-1233
Tel.: (303) 626-7200
Fax: (303) 626-7252

TRIO-TECH INTERNATIONAL
16139 Wyandotte St
Van Nuys, CA 91406
Tel.: (818) 787-7000
Fax: (818) 787-9130
E-mail: sales@triotech.com
Web Site: www.triotech.com
Approx. Rev.: $35,535,000
Approx. Number Employees: 501
Year Founded: 1958
Business Description:
Semiconductor & Test Equipment Mfr
S.I.C.: 3559; 3589; 3674
N.A.I.C.S.: 333295; 333319; 334413
Advertising Expenditures: $19,000
Media: 2-10-13
Personnel:
A. Charles Wilson *(Chm)*
S. W. Yong *(Pres & CEO)*
Victor H. M. Ting *(CFO & VP)*

TRIQUINT SEMICONDUCTOR, INC.
2300 NE Brookwood Pkwy
Hillsboro, OR 97124
Tel.: (503) 615-9000
Fax: (503) 615-8900
E-mail: info-general@tqs.com
Web Site: www.tqs.com
Approx. Rev.: $878,703,000
Approx. Number Employees: 2,777
Year Founded: 1985
Business Description:
Supplier of Modules & Components for Communications Industry; Radio Frequency, Analog & Mixed Signal Intergrated Circuits Mfr
S.I.C.: 3674
N.A.I.C.S.: 334413
Import Export
Personnel:
Steven J. Sharp *(Chm)*
Ralph G. Quinsey *(Pres & CEO)*
Steve Buhaly *(CFO)*
Debbie Burke *(VP-HR)*
Todd Debonis *(VP-Sls & Strategic Dev-Global)*
Shane Smith *(Sr Dir-Global Mktg)*
Gailon Brehm *(Dir-Mktg-Military Products)*
Brandi Frye *(Dir-Corp Mktg & Comm)*
Mike Peters *(Dir-Mktg-Comml Foundry)*
Shannon Rudd *(Mgr-Mktg Comm)*
Mark Andrews *(Mgr-Strategic Mktg Comm)*

Advertising Agency:
McClenahan Bruer Communications
5331 SW Macadam Ave Ste 220
Portland, OR 97239
Tel.: (503) 546-1000
Fax: (503) 546-1001
Customer Engagement, Online Advertising, Web Site Development & Lead Generation

TRITON INDUSTRIES, INC.
1020 N Kolmar Ave
Chicago, IL 60651-3343
Tel.: (773) 384-3700
Fax: (773) 384-8748
Web Site: www.tritonindustries.com
Approx. Number Employees: 150
Year Founded: 1961
Business Description:
Metal Stampings & Fabrications; Electronic Enclosures
S.I.C.: 3469; 3441
N.A.I.C.S.: 332116; 332312
Export
Media: 2-4-7-10-13
Distr.: Intl.; Natl.
Personnel:
Brent Wortell *(Pres & CEO)*
Tom Fuss *(Controller)*
Brands & Products:
METAL STAMPING
TRITON INDUSTRIES

TROJAN TECHNOLOGIES, INC.
(Sub. of Danaher Corporation)
3020 Gore Rd
London, ON N5V 4T7, Canada
Tel.: (519) 457-3400
Fax: (519) 457-3030
E-mail: info@trojanuv.com
Web Site: www.trojanuv.com
Sales Range: $75-99.9 Million
Approx. Number Employees: 400
Business Description:
Ultraviolet Disinfection Systems Mfr
S.I.C.: 3648
N.A.I.C.S.: 335129
Media: 2-7-10
Personnel:
Marvin R. DeVries *(Pres)*
Ric Clark *(Mng Dir & VP)*
Jeffrey S. Kafka *(Gen Counsel & Sec)*
Wesley D. From *(VP-Engrng)*
Tanya Testa Fleming *(Mgr-Domestic Sls & Mktg)*
Brands & Products:
TROJAN
TROJANOPTIVIEW
TROJANUV3000
TROJANUV3000PLUS
TROJANUV3000PTP
TROJANUV4000PLUS
TROJANUVLOGIC
TROJANUVMAX
TROJANUVPHOX
TROJANUVSWIFT
TROJANUVSWIFTECT

TRUMPF INC.
(Sub. of TRUMPF GmbH + Co. KG)
111 Hyde Rd
Farmington, CT 06032
Tel.: (860) 255-6000
Fax: (860) 255-6424
E-mail: info@us.trumpf.com
Web Site: www.us.trumpf.com
E-Mail For Key Personnel:
Public Relations: press@us.trumpf.com
Approx. Number Employees: 500
Year Founded: 1969
Business Description:
Metal Fabrication Machinery Mfr & Laser Technology
S.I.C.: 3542; 3546
N.A.I.C.S.: 333513; 333991
Export
Media: 2-4-7-10-11-13-17-20-22
Distr.: Intl.; Natl.
Personnel:
Rolf Biekert *(Pres & CEO)*
Doug Devnew *(VP-Fin & Admin)*
Burke Doar *(VP-Sls & Mktg)*
Sheila LaMothe *(Mgr-Mktg)*
Brands & Products:
TRUMPF

TUFFALOY PRODUCTS, INC.
1400 S Batesville Rd
Greer, SC 29650-4809
Tel.: (864) 879-0763
Fax: (864) 879-2212
E-mail: tuffaloy@tuffaloy.com
Web Site: www.tuffaloy.com
Approx. Sls.: $3,800,000
Approx. Number Employees: 45
Year Founded: 1937
Business Description:
Resistance Welding Electrodes
S.I.C.: 3625
N.A.I.C.S.: 335314
Import Export
Advertising Expenditures: $250,000
Media: 2-4-7-10-11
Distr.: Intl.; Natl.
Personnel:
Michael S. Simmons *(Pres)*
Preash Dodhia *(Dir-Engrg)*
Brands & Products:
TUFFALOY

TUTHILL CORPORATION
8500 S Madison St
Burr Ridge, IL 60527-6284
Tel.: (630) 382-4900
Fax: (630) 382-4999
E-mail: webmaster@tuthill.com
Web Site: www.tuthill.com
Sales Range: $300-349.9 Million
Year Founded: 1892
Business Description:
Industrial Pumps, Blowers, Quick Connective Couplings, Control Linkage Components & Push-Pull Cables Mfr
S.I.C.: 3511; 3492
N.A.I.C.S.: 333611; 332912
Import Export
Media: 1-2-4-5-7-10-11-17-19-20-21-26
Distr.: Natl.
Personnel:
James G. Tuthill, Jr. *(Pres)*
Thomas M. Carmazzi *(CEO)*
Mark Hampshire *(Pres-Tuthill Drive Sys)*
Brands & Products:
ACOUSTICAIR
AIRGLIDE
ATLANTIC FLUIDICS
BLOWERXPERT
BRISTOW
CABLECRAFT
CHEMTRAVELLER
COMPETITOR
EQUALIZER
GLOBALGEAR
HUCK
KINNEY
MAX
MUD HOG
PD PLUS
REYCO
TUTHILL
VIBRALINK

TUTHILL CORPORATION PUMP GROUP
(Div. of Tuthill Corporation)
12500 S Pulaski Rd
Alsip, IL 60803-1911
Tel.: (630) 382-4900
Fax: (708) 388-0869
E-mail: webmaster@tuthill.com
Web Site: www.tuthill.com
Approx. Number Employees: 130
Year Founded: 1897
Business Description:
Rotary Pumps & Plugs Mfr
S.I.C.: 3561
N.A.I.C.S.: 333911
Import Export
Advertising Expenditures: $500,000
Media: 2-4-7-11-16-26
Distr.: Intl.; Natl.
Budget Set: Nov.
Personnel:
Drad Boyd *(Pres)*
Jeff Lillig *(Comptroller)*
Brands & Products:
BUMP PUMP
CHEMCON
QUICK-SEAL

TUTHILL VACUUM & BLOWER SYSTEMS
(Div. of Tuthill Corporation)
4840 W Kearney St
Springfield, MO 65803-8702
Mailing Address:
PO Box 2877
Springfield, MO 65801-2877
Tel.: (417) 865-8715
Fax: (417) 865-2950
Toll Free: (800) 825-6937
E-mail: vacuum@tuthill.com
Web Site: www.tuthill.com
Approx. Number Employees: 260
Year Founded: 1958
Business Description:
Mfr. of Positive Displacement Blowers & Vacuum Pumps
S.I.C.: 3561
N.A.I.C.S.: 333911
Import Export
Media: 1-2-4-5-10-11-13-20-26
Distr.: Natl.
Budget Set: Oct.
Personnel:
John D. Ermold *(Pres)*
James Ashcraft *(Controller)*
Advertising Agency:
Schilling Sellmeyer
1031 E Battlefield St Ste 121B
Springfield, MO 65807
Tel.: (417) 889-3030
Fax: (417) 889-0210

TYCO THERMAL CONTROLS (CANADA) LTD
(Sub. of Tyco Thermal Controls LLC)
250 W St
Trenton, ON K8V 5S2, Canada

Key to Media (For complete agency information see *The Advertising Red Books-Agencies* edition):
1. Bus. Publs. 2. Cable T.V. 3. Catalogs & Directories. 4. Co-op Adv. 5. Consumer Mags. 6. D.M. to Bus. Estab.7. D.M. to Consumers 8. Daily Newsp. 9. Exhibits/Trade Shows 10. Foreign 11. Infomercial 12. Internet Adv.13. Multimedia 14. Network Radio 15. Network T.V. 16. Newsp. Distr. Mags. 17. Other 18. Outdoor (Posters, Transit) 19. Point of Purchase20. Premiums, Novelties 21. Product Samples 22. Special Events Mktg. 23. Spot Radio 24. Spot T.V. 25. Weekly Newsp. 26. Yellow Page Adv.

Tel.: (613) 392-6571
Fax: (613) 392-6401
Toll Free: (800) 234-6501
E-mail: info@tycothermal.com
Web Site: www.tycothermal.com
Approx. Number Employees: 185
Year Founded: 1949
Business Description:
Mineral Insulated Power, Heating & Thermoelectric Cables Mfr
S.I.C.: 3699
N.A.I.C.S.: 335999
Import Export
Media: 2-6-10-25
Distr.: Natl.
Budget Set: Dec.
Personnel:
Barry O'Connell *(Mgr-Mktg & Commun)*

TYROLIT WICKMAN INC.
(Sub. of Tyrolit Schleifmittelwerke Swarovski KG)
10325 Capital Ave
Oak Park, MI 48237-3139
Tel.: (248) 548-3822
Fax: (248) 548-3831
E-mail: info@tyrolit.com
Web Site: www.tyrolit.com
Approx. Number Employees: 50
Year Founded: 1941
Business Description:
Diamond CBN Wheels & Homes
S.I.C.: 3291
N.A.I.C.S.: 327910
Import
Media: 2-6-10
Distr.: Direct to Consumer; Natl.
Budget Set: Nov.
Personnel:
Jeffrey Kelchner *(CFO)*
John Guenther *(VP-Sls)*
Christopher Golfer *(Mgr-Mktg)*
Brands & Products:
TYROLIT
WICKMAN

ULINE SHIPPING SUPPLIES
2200 S Lakeside Dr
Waukegan, IL 60085
Tel.: (847) 473-3000
Fax: (847) 473-2348
E-mail: customerservice@uline.com
Web Site: www.uline.com
Sales Range: $25-49.9 Million
Approx. Number Employees: 2,000
Business Description:
Shipping, Industrial, & Packing Materials Distr
S.I.C.: 5113
N.A.I.C.S.: 424130
Media: 4-13-26
Personnel:
Elisabeth Uihlein *(Pres)*
Richard E. Uihlein *(CEO)*
Carl Fedders *(Sr Analyst-Mktg)*
Brands & Products:
ULINE

ULLMAN DEVICES CORPORATION
664 Danbury Rd
Ridgefield, CT 06877-2720
Tel.: (203) 438-6577
Fax: (203) 431-9064
E-mail: ullman@ntplx.net
Web Site: www.ntplx.net
Approx. Number Employees: 40
Year Founded: 1935
Business Description:
Work Inspection Mirrors, Magnetic Tools, Piston Ring Compressors, Screw Starters
S.I.C.: 3423
N.A.I.C.S.: 332212
Media: 2-4
Distr.: Natl.
Personnel:
Edward Coleman *(Pres)*

ULTRALIFE CORPORATION
2000 Technology Pkwy
Newark, NY 14513-2175
Tel.: (315) 332-7100
Fax: (315) 331-7800
Toll Free: (800) 332-5000
E-mail: bfishback@ulbi.com
Web Site: www.ulbi.com
Approx. Rev.: $178,577,000
Approx. Number Employees: 1,169
Year Founded: 1991
Business Description:
Primary Lithium Batteries, Lithium Ion Batteries & Lithium Polymer Rechargeable Batteries Mfr
S.I.C.: 3691; 3692; 8733
N.A.I.C.S.: 335911; 335912; 541710
Advertising Expenditures: $1,200,000
Media: 2-4-7-10
Personnel:
Bradford Todd Whitmore *(Chm)*
Michael D. Popielec *(Pres & CEO)*
Philip A. Fain *(CFO & Treas)*
Philip M. Meek *(COO)*
Peter F. Comerford *(Gen Counsel & VP-Admin)*
Julius M. Cirin *(VP-Corp Mktg & Tech)*
Brands & Products:
HIRATE
LITHIUM ION
LITHIUM POWER
MILITARY
THE NEW POWER GENERATION
POLYMER
THIN CELL
ULTRALIFE
ULTRALIFE HIRATE
ULTRALIFE POLYMER
THE ULTRALIFE POWER SOURCE
ULTRALIFE THIN CELL
Advertising Agency:
Lippert/Heilshorn & Associates, Inc.
800 Third Ave 17th Fl
New York, NY 10022
Tel.: (212) 838-3777
Fax: (212) 838-4568

UNEX MANUFACTURING, INC.
50 Progress Pl
Jackson, NJ 08527-3002
Tel.: (732) 928-2800
Fax: (732) 928-2828
Toll Free: (800) 695-SPAN
E-mail: span@unex.com
Web Site: www.unex.com
Approx. Number Employees: 90
Year Founded: 1964
Business Description:
Industrial Carton Flow Track Mfr
S.I.C.: 3535
N.A.I.C.S.: 333922
Media: 1-2-4-7-10-20-21
Distr.: Natl.
Budget Set: Jan.
Personnel:
Brian Neuwirth *(Pres)*
Chuck Doty *(Mgr-Reg Sls)*
Brands & Products:
THE CARTON FLOW AUTHORITY
FLOW BED
FLOW CELL
GRAVITY CONVEYOR
ROLLERRACK
SHELFTRACK
SKUBE
SPAN-TRACK
UNEX

UNIFIED BRANDS INC.
(Sub. of Dover Engineered Systems, Inc.)
1055 Mendell Davis Dr
Jackson, MS 39272-9788
Tel.: (601) 372-3903
Fax: (601) 373-9587
Toll Free: (800) 676-9040
Web Site: www.unifiedbrands.net
E-Mail For Key Personnel:
Sales Director: sales@unifiedbrands.net
Approx. Sls.: $2,300,000,000
Approx. Number Employees: 300
Year Founded: 1907
Business Description:
Steam Jacketed Kettles, Braising Pans, Steamers, Cooker Mixers, Continuous Process Equipment, Combination Steamer-Ovens & Cook-Chill Systems Mfr
S.I.C.: 3556
N.A.I.C.S.: 333294
Export
Media: 2-4-5-6-7-10-11-13-19-20
Distr.: Intl.; Natl.
Budget Set: Oct.
Personnel:
Blair Alford *(VP-Sls & Mktg)*
Mike Curry *(Product Mgr)*
Joe White *(Mgr-Field Svc Trng & Admin-Groen)*
Brands & Products:
AVTEC
CAPKOLD
CHINOOK
CONVECTION COMBO
GROEN
HYPER STEAM
PURESTEEM
RANDELL
SMARTSTEAM
TAKU
VORTEX
Advertising Agencies:
The Ramey Agency
3100 N State St Ste 300
Jackson, MS 39216
Tel.: (404) 962-4412
Fax: (601) 898-8999

The Ramey Agency
1322 Hardwood Trail
Cordova, TN 38016
Tel.: (901) 761-3685
Fax: (901) 761-3688

UNION SPECIAL CORPORATION
1 Union Special Plz
Huntley, IL 60142-7007
Tel.: (847) 669-5101
Fax: (847) 669-4425
E-mail: sales@unionspecial.com
Web Site: www.unionspecial.com
E-Mail For Key Personnel:
Sales Director: sales@unionspecial.com
Sales Range: $25-49.9 Million
Approx. Number Employees: 115
Business Description:
Mfr. of Industrial Sewing Machines & Automated Sewing Systems for Apparel Manufacturers
S.I.C.: 3559; 3589; 5084
N.A.I.C.S.: 333298; 333319; 423830
Import Export
Advertising Expenditures: $50,000
Media: 2-4-10-13
Distr.: Intl.; Natl.
Personnel:
Terence A. Hitpas *(Pres & COO)*
Doug Kanies *(Dir-Trng)*
Brands & Products:
HEMMER SEAMER
MARK IV
THE NEEDLE'S EYE
UNICON
UNION SPECIAL

UNITED RENTALS, INC.
5 Greenwich Office Pk
Greenwich, CT 06830
Tel.: (203) 622-3131
Fax: (203) 622-6080
Toll Free: (800) UR-RENTS
Web Site: www.unitedrentals.com
Approx. Rev.: $2,237,000,000
Approx. Number Employees: 7,300
Year Founded: 1997
Business Description:
Equipment Rental & Leasing Services
S.I.C.: 5084; 7353; 7359
N.A.I.C.S.: 423830; 532210; 532310; 532412; 532490
Advertising Expenditures: $2,000,000
Media: 2-4-6-7-8-10-13-17-22-23-26
Personnel:
Jenne K. Britell *(Chm)*
Michael J. Kneeland *(Pres & CEO)*
William B. Plummer *(CFO & Exec VP)*
Kenneth E. Dewitt *(CIO & VP)*
Jonathan M. Gottsegen *(Gen Counsel, Sec & Sr VP)*
Irene Moshouris *(Treas & Sr VP)*
Matthew J. Flannery *(Exec VP-Ops & Sls)*
Dale A. Asplund *(Sr VP-Bus Svcs)*
Paul I. Mcdonnell *(Sr VP-Trench Safety, Power & HVAC)*
Christopher M. Brown *(VP & Asst Controller)*
Fred Bratman *(VP-Corp Comm & IR)*
Joseph A. Dixon *(VP-Sls)*
Kenneth B. Mettel *(VP-Strategy & Plng)*
Craig A. Pintoff *(VP-HR)*
Kurtis T. Barker *(Mgr-Special Projects)*
Jeffrey M. Johnson *(Mgr-Acct-Natl)*
Brands & Products:
E-RENTAL STORE
INFOMANAGER
RENTALMAN
THE RIGHT EQUIPMENT RIGHT NOW!
SAFETYCADE
SAFETYCOR
TOUGHLITE
UNITED RENTALS
URDATA

Key to Media (For complete agency information see *The Advertising Red Books-Agencies* edition):
1. Bus. Publs. 2. Cable T.V. 3. Catalogs & Directories. 4. Co-op Adv. 5. Consumer Mags. 6. D.M. to Bus. Estab.7. D.M. to Consumers 8. Daily Newsp. 9. Exhibits/Trade Shows 10. Foreign 11. Infomercial 12. Internet Adv.13. Multimedia 14. Network Radio 15. Network T.V. 16. Newsp. Distr. Mags. 17. Other 18. Outdoor (Posters, Transit) 19. Point of Purchase20. Premiums, Novelties 21. Product Samples 22. Special Events Mktg. 23. Spot Radio 24. Spot T.V. 25. Weekly Newsp. 26. Yellow Page Adv.

United Rentals, Inc. — (Continued)

VERTICADE

Advertising Agency:
Sillery and Partners
10 Signal Rd
Stamford, CT 06902
Tel.: (203) 961-9993
Fax: (203) 961-9133

UNITED STATES MACHINE TOOLS CORP.

70 Horizon Dr
Bristol, CT 06010-7473
Tel.: (860) 953-8306
Fax: (860) 953-0364
Toll Free: (800) 664-0013
E-mail: info@usmt.com
Approx. Sls.: $2,800,000
Approx. Number Employees: 25
Year Founded: 1967
Business Description:
Machine Tool Remanufacturer & Retrofitter of CNC Controls to Metal Cutting Machine Tools
S.I.C.: 3541
N.A.I.C.S.: 333512
Export
Media: 2-7-10
Distr.: Natl.
Budget Set: Jan.

UNIVERSAL-AUTOMATIC CORPORATION

2064 S Mannheim Rd
Des Plaines, IL 60018-2909
Tel.: (847) 296-6181
Fax: (847) 296-2642
E-mail: sales@universalautomatic.com
Web Site: www.universalautomatic.com
E-Mail For Key Personnel:
Sales Director: sales@universalautomatic.com
Approx. Number Employees: 35
Year Founded: 1957
Business Description:
Drilling & Tapping Machine Systems, Special Automation Packages, Integrated Machining Cells
S.I.C.: 3541; 5084
N.A.I.C.S.: 333512; 423830
Import Export
Media: 2-4-5-6-7-10-13
Distr.: Direct to Consumer; Natl.
Personnel:
Kenneth Klancnik *(Pres)*
Ken Major *(CFO)*
Brands & Products:
AD-B
UNIVERSAL-AUTOMATIC CORPORATION

UNIVERSAL VOLTRONICS CORPORATION

57 Commerce Dr
Brookfield, CT 06804-3405
Tel.: (203) 740-8555
Fax: (203) 740-9555
E-mail: sales@voltronics.com
Web Site: www.voltronics.com
E-Mail For Key Personnel:
Sales Director: sales@voltronics.com
Approx. Number Employees: 65
Year Founded: 1960
Business Description:
High-Voltage Power Supplies Mfr
S.I.C.: 3612
N.A.I.C.S.: 335311
Media: 2-10
Personnel:
Leonard Braverman *(Pres & CEO)*
Bill Carney *(Pres)*

UNIVEX CORPORATION

3 Old Rockingham Rd
Salem, NH 03079-2133
Tel.: (603) 893-6191
Fax: (603) 893-1249
Toll Free: (800) 258-6358
E-mail: info@univexcorp.com
Web Site: www.univexcorp.com
Approx. Number Employees: 75
Year Founded: 1948
Business Description:
Food Preparing Machines Mfr
S.I.C.: 3556
N.A.I.C.S.: 333294
Import Export
Advertising Expenditures: $315,000
Media: 2-4-7-10-11-18
Distr.: Intl.; Natl.
Budget Set: Jan.
Brands & Products:
BIZERBA
DURO
GENIE
MAX
PREPSAVER
UNIVEX

UOP LLC

(Sub. of Honeywell Specialty Materials)
25 E Algonquin Rd Bldg A
Des Plaines, IL 60016-6101
Tel.: (847) 391-2000
Fax: (847) 391-2253
Toll Free: (800) 877-6184
Web Site: www.uop.com
Sales Range: $1-4.9 Billion
Approx. Number Employees: 2,500
Year Founded: 1914
Business Description:
Supplier of Process Technology, Catalysts, Process Plants & Consulting Services
S.I.C.: 2819; 8711
N.A.I.C.S.: 325188; 541330
Export
Media: 2-4-10-11
Distr.: Intl.; Natl.
Budget Set: Oct.
Personnel:
Rajeev Gautam *(Pres & CEO)*
Jim Rekoske *(VP, Gen Mgr-Renewable Energy & Chemicals Bus)*
Zak Alzein *(VP-Strategy & Mktg)*
Mark Houdek *(Mgr-Mktg)*
Brands & Products:
HYCYCLE UNICRACKING
ISOMAR
KLP
MOLEX
OLEFLEX

URS CORPORATION

(Branch of URS Corporation)
Amber Oaks 9400 Amberglen Blvd
Austin, TX 78729
Mailing Address:
PO Box 201088
Austin, TX 78720
Tel.: (512) 454-4797
Fax: (512) 454-8807
Web Site: www.urs.com
Sales Range: $300-349.9 Million
Approx. Number Employees: 2,000
Year Founded: 1969
Business Description:
Engineering & Environmental Technology
S.I.C.: 8711; 8733
N.A.I.C.S.: 541330; 541720
Media: 2
Distr.: Natl.
Budget Set: Nov.

URSCHEL LABORATORIES INCORPORATED

2503 Calumet Ave
Valparaiso, IN 46383-2715
Mailing Address:
PO Box 2200
Valparaiso, IN 46384-2200
Tel.: (219) 464-4811
Fax: (219) 462-3879
E-mail: info@urschel.com
Web Site: www.urschel.com
E-Mail For Key Personnel:
Public Relations: mktg@urschel.com
Approx. Number Employees: 260
Year Founded: 1910
Business Description:
Machinery for Cutting, Chopping, Grinding & Mixing; Chemical Milling Machines
S.I.C.: 3556; 7374
N.A.I.C.S.: 333294; 518210
Import Export
Media: 2-4-5-7-10-11
Distr.: Intl.; Natl.
Personnel:
Debra Novello *(Mgr-Adv)*
Brands & Products:
COMITROL
DIVERSACUT
DIVERSACUT 2110
FLO-CUT
MICROSLICE
QUANTICUT
TRANSLICER
TRANSLICER 2000
TRANSLICER 2500
URSCHEL
VELOCICUT
Advertising Agency:
Vale Communications
(House Agency)
2503 Calumet Ave.
Valparaiso, IN 46383
(Comitrol Processor, TranSlicer Cutter, Velocicut)

THE U.S. BAIRD CORPORATION

1700 Stratford Ave
Stratford, CT 06615
Tel.: (203) 375-3361
Fax: (203) 378-5197
E-mail: info@usbaird.com
Web Site: www.usbaird.com
Approx. Number Employees: 300
Year Founded: 1846
Business Description:
Mfr. of Production Machine Tools
S.I.C.: 3542; 3541
N.A.I.C.S.: 333513; 333512
Import Export
Advertising Expenditures: $100,000
Media: 17
Distr.: Natl.
Brands & Products:
FOUR SLIDE
GLOBE
JM SYSTEMS CNC
MULTI-SLIDE
MULTIPLE TRANSFER
MULTIPLE TRANSFER PRESS
NILSON
SPRINGENERATOR
US BAIRD

U.S. BOTTLERS MACHINERY COMPANY

11911 Steele Creek Rd
Charlotte, NC 28273-3773
Tel.: (704) 588-4750
Fax: (704) 588-3808
E-mail: sales@usbottlers.com
Web Site: www.usbottlers.com
E-Mail For Key Personnel:
Sales Director: sales@usbottlers.com
Approx. Number Employees: 85
Year Founded: 1912
Business Description:
Bottling & Packaging Equipment Mfr
S.I.C.: 3565
N.A.I.C.S.: 333993
Export
Media: 2-10-26
Distr.: Intl.; Natl.
Budget Set: Dec.
Personnel:
Tom Risser *(Owner & Pres)*
John Owen *(Head-Engrng)*
Emil Popa *(Dir-Sls)*
Brands & Products:
CHUCK STYLE CAPPER
PISTON FILLER
PRESSURE GRAVITY FILLER
RINSER
SANITAIR
WEIGH SCALE FILLER

VACUUM TECHNOLOGY ASSOCIATES, INC.

(d/b/a DynaVac)
110 Indus Pk Rd
Hingham, MA 02043-4369
Tel.: (781) 740-8600
Fax: (781) 740-9996
E-mail: sales@dynavac.com
Web Site: www.dynavac.com
E-Mail For Key Personnel:
Sales Director: sales@dynavac.com
Sales Range: $50-74.9 Million
Approx. Number Employees: 60
Business Description:
Mfr. of Vacuum Deposition Coating Equipment & Other Vacuum Items
S.I.C.: 3821
N.A.I.C.S.: 339111
Media: 2-7-10
Budget Set: Feb.
Personnel:
Thomas P. Foley *(Pres)*

VALCOR ENGINEERING CORPORATION

2 Lawrence Rd
Springfield, NJ 07081-3121
Tel.: (973) 467-8400
Fax: (973) 467-8382
E-mail: advertising@valcor.com
Web Site: www.valcor.com
Approx. Number Employees: 300

Key to Media (For complete agency information see *The Advertising Red Books-Agencies* edition):
1. Bus. Publs. 2. Cable T.V. 3. Catalogs & Directories. 4. Co-op Adv. 5. Consumer Mags. 6. D.M. to Bus. Estab.7. D.M. to Consumers
8. Daily Newsp. 9. Exhibits/Trade Shows 10. Foreign 11. Infomercial 12. Internet Adv.13. Multimedia 14. Network Radio
15. Network T.V. 16. Newsp. Distr. Mags. 17. Other 18. Outdoor (Posters, Transit) 19. Point of Purchase20. Premiums, Novelties
21. Product Samples 22. Special Events Mktg. 23. Spot Radio 24. Spot T.V. 25. Weekly Newsp. 26. Yellow Page Adv.

Year Founded: 1941
Business Description:
Solenoid & Manual Valves, Metering Pumps, Fluid Control Components, Pressure Regulators, Accumulators, Electromagnetic & Electronic Devices
S.I.C.: 3625
N.A.I.C.S.: 335314
Export
Media: 1-2-4-7-10-20
Distr.: Intl.; Natl.
Budget Set: Feb.
Personnel:
A.J. Lamastra *(Gen Mgr-Scientific)*
Steven Gatcomb *(Dir-Sls & Mktg-Nuclear)*
Leo Loiacono *(Dir-Program Mgmt)*
Paul Meyers *(Dir-Mktg & Sls-Aerospace)*
Paul Russ *(Dir-Intl Licensing)*
Jimmy Shieh *(Dir-QA)*
Jeffrey D. Kelly *(Mgr-Aircraft/QA & Aerospace)*
Thien Nguyen *(Mgr-Nuclear Applications)*
Tom Stang *(Mgr-Sls & Mktg)*
Brands & Products:
DRI-CONTROL
DRI-SOLONOID
FLOATING SEAL
VALCOR

VALK MANUFACTURING COMPANY
66 E Main St PO Box 428
New Kingstown, PA 17072-0428
Tel.: (717) 766-0711
Fax: (717) 697-6297
E-mail: valk@valkmfg.com
Web Site: www.valkmfg.com
E-Mail For Key Personnel:
President: tvalk@valkmfg.com
Approx. Number Employees: 90
Year Founded: 1952
Business Description:
Mfr. of Snow Plows & Replacement Cutting Edges
S.I.C.: 3531; 3545
N.A.I.C.S.: 333120; 333515
Import Export
Media: 2-4-7-10-26
Distr.: Intl.; Natl.
Personnel:
Ted P. Valk *(Pres & CEO)*
Brands & Products:
VALK
VIPER

VALMONT INDUSTRIES, INC.
1 Valmont Plaza
Omaha, NE 68154-5214
Tel.: (402) 963-1000
Fax: (402) 963-1199
E-mail: investor_relations@valmont.com
Web Site: www.valmont.com
Approx. Sls.: $1,975,505,000
Approx. Number Employees: 9,188
Year Founded: 1946
Business Description:
Steel & Aluminum Street & Area Lighting Poles; Electrical Transmission & Distribution Structures; Steel Tubing; Wireless Communication Poles, Towers & Components; Center Pivot & Linear Move Irrigation Systems Mfr
S.I.C.: 5084; 3316; 3441
N.A.I.C.S.: 423830; 331221; 332312
Import Export
Media: 2-9-26
Distr.: Intl.; Natl.
Budget Set: Oct.
Personnel:
Mogens C. Bay *(Chm & CEO)*
Richard S. Cornish *(Pres & Gen Mgr)*
Terry J. Mcclain *(CFO & Sr VP)*
Leonard M. Adams *(Pres-Irrigation-North America-Tubing Div)*
Earl R. Foust *(Pres-Utility Support Structures Div)*
Huang Xiao Yong *(Pres-China)*
E. Robert Meaney *(Corp Sec & Sr VP)*
Michael Banat *(VP-Sls & Mktg-Intl Structures)*
John G. Graboski *(VP-HR)*
Wally Pasko *(VP-Procurement)*
Douglas C. Sherman *(VP-Mktg)*
Jeffrey Laudin *(Mgr-IR)*
Brands & Products:
PRECISION IRRIGATION MADE EASY
VALLEY

VAN AIR, INC.
2950 Mechanic St
Lake City, PA 16423-2023
Tel.: (814) 774-2631
Fax: (814) 774-0778
Toll Free: (800) 840-9906
E-mail: info@vanairsystems.com
Web Site: www.vanairsystems.com
E-Mail For Key Personnel:
Marketing Director: jmace@vanairsystems.com
Approx. Number Employees: 50
Year Founded: 1944
Business Description:
Compressed Air Drying & Treating Equipment Mfr
S.I.C.: 3563; 3669
N.A.I.C.S.: 333912; 334290
Import Export
Advertising Expenditures: $140,000
Media: 4-6-7-8-10
Distr.: Intl.; Natl.
Budget Set: Mar.
Personnel:
Jeff J. Mace *(VP-Mktg & Sls)*
Brands & Products:
BLAST PAK
CLIMATE-COOL
CYCLE SAVER
DRY-O-LITE
DRY PAK
EMCON
ENVIROSAVER
FREEDOM
HYDRO-COOL
QUIK-PURE
SENTINEL
TERMINATOR
TURBO-COOL
VAN AIR SYSTEMS

VAN GORP CORPORATION
1410 Washington St
Pella, IA 50219-1502
Tel.: (641) 628-9212
Fax: (641) 621-4229
Toll Free: (800) VAN-GORP
E-mail: vangorp@vangorp.biz
Web Site: www.vangorp.biz
Approx. Number Employees: 65
Business Description:
Pulleys Mfr
S.I.C.: 3535
N.A.I.C.S.: 333922
Media: 4-7
Personnel:
Joseph Canfield *(Owner & Pres)*
Brands & Products:
DOUBLE DRUM
H.D.R
SEALMASTER
SLIDE-LAG
SNAP-BACK
STEEL PULLY
TURN CLEAN
VAN GORP
XT
XT-REME

VARIAN, INC.
(Sub. of Agilent Technologies, Inc.)
5301 Stevens Creek Blvd
Santa Clara, CA 95051
Tel.: (925) 939-2400
Fax: (925) 945-2360
E-mail: ir@varianinc.com
Web Site: www.varianinc.com
Approx. Sls.: $806,744,000
Approx. Number Employees: 3,500
Year Founded: 1949
Business Description:
Scientific Instruments & Equipment Mfr
S.I.C.: 3826; 3672
N.A.I.C.S.: 334516; 334412
Export
Advertising Expenditures: $4,000,000
Personnel:
Garry W. Rogerson *(CEO)*
Phillip Binns *(Mng Dir & Gen Mgr-Pacific Rim)*
G. Edward McClammy *(CFO & Sr VP)*
Michael W. Fitzgerald *(Sr VP-HR)*
Martin O'Donoghue *(Sr VP-Scientific Instruments)*
Sergio Piras *(Sr VP-Vacuum Tech)*
Beverly Williamson *(Mgr)*
Brands & Products:
BENCHSAVER
BIOMELT
BOND ELUT
CAPTIVA
CHEM ELUT
CHROMSPHER
CONFLAT
CONTRA-FLOW
CUPKIT
ENHANCER CELL
EXCALIBUR
EYESYS
EYESYS CONVECTORR
EZ-GRIP
EZ-GUARD
FACTORFOUR
FOCUS
FTS 7000
FULL FLOW FILTERS
HELITEST
HELIX
HYDROMATRIX
INSPIRING EXCELLENCE
IONOSPHER
KLAMP-FLANGE
MACROTORR
METAFLASH
MICROSORB
MICROSPHER
MINI-TASK
MULTI-GAUGE
OMIX
OMNISPHER
ON-SITE
ONTRAK TESTCARD
ONTRAK TESTCUP
ONTRAK TESTSTIK
ORALAB
ORALYZER
ORATUBE
PEAK VESSEL
PLEXA
POLARIS
POWER RINSE
PURSUIT
RAPID-MS
SCIMITAR
SELECT
SENTORR
SMARTRAK
SPEC
STAR
STARCELL
STRATOSPHERE
SYNERGY
TASK
TESTRAK
TESTRAK ID
THERMASEP
TOP
TOXI-LAB
TOXILAB
TRISCROLL
TRUCENTER
TURBO
TURBO-V
ULTIMETAL
VACION PLUS
VANKEL
VARIAN
VARIPEP
VARIPURE
VARITIDE
VERSAPLATE
VK
Advertising Agency:
Remedy
121 W Wacker Dr Ste 2250
Chicago, IL 60601
Tel.: (312) 377-3410
Fax: (312) 377-3420

VIBCO INC.
75 Stilson Rd
Wyoming, RI 02898
Mailing Address:
PO Box 8
Wyoming, RI 02898
Tel.: (401) 539-2392
Fax: (401) 539-2584
Toll Free: (800) 633-0032
E-mail: vibrators@vibco.com
Web Site: www.vibco.com
Approx. Number Employees: 55
Year Founded: 1962
Business Description:
Industrial, Construction, Electric, Pneumatic & Hydraulic Vibrators, Vibratory Plate Compactors & Vibratory Single Drum Rollers Mfr
S.I.C.: 3531; 3829
N.A.I.C.S.: 333120; 334519
Export
Media: 2-4-5-10-11-13-20-21-26
Distr.: Intl.; Natl.
Budget Set: Jan.

Key to Media (For complete agency information see *The Advertising Red Books-Agencies* edition):
1. Bus. Publs. 2. Cable T.V. 3. Catalogs & Directories. 4. Co-op Adv. 5. Consumer Mags. 6. D.M. to Bus. Estab.7. D.M. to Consumers 8. Daily Newsp. 9. Exhibits/Trade Shows 10. Foreign 11. Infomercial 12. Internet Adv.13. Multimedia 14. Network Radio 15. Network T.V. 16. Newsp. Distr. Mags. 17. Other 18. Outdoor (Posters, Transit) 19. Point of Purchase20. Premiums, Novelties 21. Product Samples 22. Special Events Mktg. 23. Spot Radio 24. Spot T.V. 25. Weekly Newsp. 26. Yellow Page Adv.

Vibco Inc. — (Continued)

Personnel:
Karl Wadensten *(Pres)*
Ted S. Wadensten *(CEO & COO)*
Brands & Products:
BIG BERTHA
THE SILENT TURBINE
VIBCO
WE'RE THE SILENT VIBRATOR GUYS

VIBRA SCREW INC.
755 Union Blvd
Totowa, NJ 07512-2207
Tel.: (973) 256-7410
Fax: (973) 256-7567
E-mail: info@vibrascrew.com
Web Site: www.vibrascrew.com
Approx. Number Employees: 100
Year Founded: 1955
Business Description:
Dry Materials Feeders, Bin Activators & Continuous Blenders Mfr
S.I.C.: 5084
N.A.I.C.S.: 423830
Advertising Expenditures: $50,000
Media: 2-4-7-8-13
Distr.: Intl.; Natl.
Budget Set: Nov.
Personnel:
Eugene Wahl *(Pres)*
Rich Wahl *(Reg Mgr-Sls)*
Brands & Products:
BINACTIVATOR
MASSWEIGH
VERSIFEEDER
VIBRA
VIBRA-BLENDER
THE VIBRA-BLENDER
VIBRA-METRIC

VIKING PUMP, INC.
(Sub. of IDEX Corporation)
406 State St
Cedar Falls, IA 50613-3343
Mailing Address:
PO Box 8
Cedar Falls, IA 50613-0008
Tel.: (319) 266-1741
Fax: (319) 273-8157
E-mail: info.viking@idexcorp.com
Web Site: www.vikingpump.com
Sales Range: $200-249.9 Million
Approx. Number Employees: 750
Year Founded: 1911
Business Description:
Positive Displacement Rotary Internal Gear, Spur Gear & Metering Pumps Mfr
S.I.C.: 3561
N.A.I.C.S.: 333911
Import Export
Advertising Expenditures: $600,000
Media: 2-4-7-10-11-20-21-22
Distr.: Intl.; Natl.
Budget Set: Sept.
Personnel:
Jeff Erhardt *(CFO)*

VISHAY TRANSDUCERS LTD.
(Sub. of Vishay Intertechnology, Inc.)
801 Sentous Ave
City of Industry, CA 91748
Tel.: (714) 731-1234
Fax: (714) 731-2019
Toll Free: (800) 872-4784
E-mail: info@sitechnologies.com
Web Site: www.vishaymg.com
Sales Range: $25-49.9 Million
Approx. Number Employees: 225
Year Founded: 1979
Business Description:
Electronic Weighing Systems & Sales
S.I.C.: 3596
N.A.I.C.S.: 333997
Media: 4-7-10-13
Personnel:
Ralph E. Crump *(Chm)*
Carrie Hynes *(Dir-Sls & Mktg)*

VOITH HYDRO INC.
(Sub. of Voith Hydro GmbH & Co. KG)
760 E Berlin Rd
York, PA 17408
Mailing Address:
PO Box 712
York, PA 17405-0712
Tel.: (717) 792-7000
Fax: (717) 792-7263
E-mail: marketing@voith.com
Web Site: www.york.voithhydro.com/e_york.htm
Sales Range: $100-124.9 Million
Approx. Number Employees: 400
Year Founded: 1867
Business Description:
Water Turbines & Digital Governors Mfr
S.I.C.: 3511; 7629
N.A.I.C.S.: 333611; 811219
Import Export
Media: 2-7
Distr.: Intl.
Personnel:
Kevin Frank *(Pres & CEO)*
John McCambridge *(Dir-HR)*

VOSSLOH TRACK MATERIAL, INC.
(Sub. of Vossloh AG)
5662 Leesport Ave
Reading, PA 19605-9802
Mailing Address:
PO Box 13613
Reading, PA 19612-3613
Tel.: (610) 926-5400
Web Site: www.vossloh-track-material.com
Sales Range: $50-74.9 Million
Year Founded: 1970
Business Description:
New & Used Railroad Supplies
S.I.C.: 3743
N.A.I.C.S.: 336510
Import Export
Personnel:
Michael Joffered *(CFO)*
Advertising Agency:
Reese
955 Berkshire Blvd
Wyomissing, PA 19610-1229
Tel.: (610) 378-1835
Fax: (610) 378-1676

W.A. WHITNEY CO.
(Div. of Whitney/Piranha/Bertsch)
650 Race St
Rockford, IL 61101-1434
Mailing Address:
PO Box 1206
Rockford, IL 61105
Tel.: (815) 964-6771
Fax: (815) 964-3175
E-mail: sales@wawhitney.com
Web Site: www.wawhitney.com
E-Mail For Key Personnel:
Sales Director: sales@wawhitney.com
Approx. Number Employees: 40
Year Founded: 1922
Business Description:
Machine Builder & Punches & Dies Mfr
S.I.C.: 3542; 3544
N.A.I.C.S.: 333513; 333514
Media: 7-10
Brands & Products:
28XX
36TC
44TC
HYPERTHERM
THE LEADER IN PLATE TECHNOLOGY
PARTHANDLER
PLATELASER
PLATEPARTNER
RAMPAGE
TRUECUT
TUFFSKIN

WAH CHANG
(Unit of Allegheny Technologies Incorporated)
1600 Old Salem Rd NE
Albany, OR 97321-4548
Mailing Address:
PO Box 460
Albany, OR 97321-0460
Tel.: (541) 926-4211
Tel.: (541) 967-6977
Fax: (541) 967-6990
Toll Free: (888) 926-4211
E-mail: custserv@wahchang.com
Web Site: www.wahchang.com
Sales Range: $700-749.9 Million
Approx. Number Employees: 1,000
Year Founded: 1958
Business Description:
Machines & Metals Designer & Mfr
S.I.C.: 3339
N.A.I.C.S.: 331419
Import Export
Media: 2-10-17-22
Distr.: Natl.
Budget Set: Dec.
Personnel:
Jim Denham *(Gen Counsel)*
Joe Frazier *(VP-Fin)*
Ron Graham *(VP-Tech & Quality)*
Bill Stamps *(VP-HR)*
Gary Kneisel *(Dir-Sls & Bus Dev)*
Wally Vernitsky *(Plant Mgr)*
Gary Arbelbide *(Mgr-Quality Assurance)*
Doug Brenizer *(Mgr-Comml Zirconium)*
David Gatlin *(Mgr-Export)*
Dennis Hamm *(Mgr-Aerospace, Medical Rod & Wire)*
Susan Huse *(Mgr-Titanium Sls)*
Carrie Jackson *(Mgr-Nuclear Sls)*
Larry Martin *(Bus Dev Mgr-ATI Armors)*
Kirk Richardson *(Mgr-Mktg Comm)*
Jack Schra *(Mgr-Conversion Production)*
Carl Shawber *(Mgr-Bus Dev)*
Rick Sutherlin *(Mgr-Tech Mktg)*
Ron Williams *(Bus Dev Project Mgr)*
Brands & Products:
ZIRCADYNE

WALL LENK CORPORATION
81950 Dr MLK Jr Blvd
Kinston, NC 28501-1802
Mailing Address:
PO Box 3349
Kinston, NC 28502-3349
Tel.: (252) 527-4186
Fax: (252) 527-4189
Toll Free: (888) 527-4186
Web Site: www.wlenk.com
Approx. Sls.: $5,000,000
Approx. Number Employees: 40
Year Founded: 1864
Business Description:
Electric Soldering Irons, Pencils & Guns, Butane Torches, Solder, Decorative Stencils Mfr
S.I.C.: 3423; 3821
N.A.I.C.S.: 332212; 339111
Export
Media: 2-4-6-8
Distr.: Natl.
Budget Set: Sept.
Personnel:
Paul A. Ricciarelli *(Pres & VP-Sls & Mktg)*
Brands & Products:
CRAFTMARK
CUTLASS
MICRO-JET
PRO-TORCH
SOLDERPRO
TRIG-R HEAT
WALLBRAND
WL LENK

WALSH PARTS & SERVICE
1222 Hannah Ave
Forest Park, IL 60130-2448
Tel.: (708) 771-2480
Fax: (708) 771-2539
Sales Range: Less than $1 Million
Approx. Number Employees: 9
Year Founded: 1907
Business Description:
Mfr of Punch Presses
S.I.C.: 3541; 3544
N.A.I.C.S.: 333512; 333514
Media: 17
Distr.: Natl.
Budget Set: Jan.
Personnel:
David Paulinski *(Pres)*
Brands & Products:
WALSH

WASHINGTON PRODUCTS INC.
1875 Harsh Ave SE
Massillon, OH 44646
Tel.: (330) 837-5101
Fax: (330) 837-5401
Web Site: www.wpimass.com
E-Mail For Key Personnel:
Sales Director: sales@wpimass.com
Sales Range: Less than $1 Million
Approx. Number Employees: 8
Year Founded: 1972
Business Description:
Point of Purchase Displays Mfr & Designer; Lightshields Painter for the Automotive Industry; Built-in Kitchen Hardware
S.I.C.: 3469; 3443
N.A.I.C.S.: 332116; 332313
Media: 8
Distr.: Intl.; Natl.
Budget Set: Dec.

Key to Media (For complete agency information see *The Advertising Red Books-Agencies* edition):
1. Bus. Publs. 2. Cable T.V. 3. Catalogs & Directories. 4. Co-op Adv. 5. Consumer Mags. 6. D.M. to Bus. Estab.7. D.M. to Consumers
8. Daily Newsp. 9. Exhibits/Trade Shows 10. Foreign 11. Infomercial 12. Internet Adv.13. Multimedia 14. Network Radio
15. Network T.V. 16. Newsp. Distr. Mags. 17. Other 18. Outdoor (Posters, Transit) 19. Point of Purchase20. Premiums, Novelties
21. Product Samples 22. Special Events Mktg. 23. Spot Radio 24. Spot T.V. 25. Weekly Newsp. 26. Yellow Page Adv.

Personnel:
John Boring *(Pres)*

WATER SERVICES OF AMERICA, INC.
(Name Changed to WSA Engineered Systems Inc.)

WATERBURY FARREL TECHNOLOGIES
(Div. of Magnum Integrated Technologies, Inc.)
200 First Gulf Blvd
Brampton, ON L6W 4T5, Canada
Tel.: (905) 595-1998
Fax: (905) 455-0422
Toll Free: (800) 206-8822
Web Site: www.waterburyfarrel.com
E-Mail For Key Personnel:
Sales Director: sales@waterbury-farrel.com
Approx. Number Employees: 30
Year Founded: 1851
Business Description:
Mfr. of Machine Tools
S.I.C.: 3542
N.A.I.C.S.: 333513
Media: 2-4-11
Distr.: Intl.; Natl.
Budget Set: Sept.
Personnel:
Andre Nazarian *(Pres)*
Brands & Products:
AS-U-ROLL
CLEVELAND HOBBERS
MICRON AGC
SENDZIMIR
THOMPSON GRINDERS
WATERBURY FARREL
Z MILL

WATEROUS COMPANY
(Sub. of American Cast Iron Pipe Company)
125 Hardman Ave S
South Saint Paul, MN 55075-1129
Tel.: (651) 450-5000
Fax: (651) 450-5090
E-mail: djhaugen@waterousco.com
Web Site: www.waterousco.com
E-Mail For Key Personnel:
President: dhaugen@waterous.com
Sales Range: $100-124.9 Million
Approx. Number Employees: 300
Year Founded: 1886
Business Description:
Fire Hydrants, Fire Pumps & Valves Mfr
S.I.C.: 3491; 3561
N.A.I.C.S.: 332911; 333911
Advertising Expenditures: $250,000
Media: 2-4-7-10-13
Distr.: Intl.; Natl.
Budget Set: Jan.
Personnel:
William Smith *(Pres & CEO)*
Steve Toren *(Dir-Sls & Mktg)*
Dejan Marinkovic *(Sls Mgr-Central & Eastern Europe)*
Gregg Geske *(Mgr-CAFS & Foam Sys Sls)*
Peter A. Ledgar *(Mgr-Sls-Western Europe & Africa)*
Steve Morelan *(Mgr-Svcs)*
Robert Peterson *(Mgr-Sls-Asia Pacific)*
Mike Sterbentz *(Mgr-Applications)*
Brands & Products:
FLOGO

Advertising Agency:
Linnihan Foy Advertising
615 1st Ave. NE, Ste 320
Minneapolis, MN 55413
Tel.: (612) 331-3586
Fax: (612) 238-3000

WAUKESHA ENGINE DRESSER, INC.
(Sub. of Dresser, Inc.)
1101 Saint Paul Ave
Waukesha, WI 53188-4958
Tel.: (262) 547-3311
Fax: (262) 549-2795
Telex: 26769
E-mail: webmaster@waukeshaengine.com
Web Site:
www.waukeshaengine.dresser.com
Sales Range: $250-299.9 Million
Approx. Number Employees: 700
Year Founded: 1906
Business Description:
Mfr of Gaseous Fueled Internal Combustion Engines for Gas & Air Compression, Prime & Standby Power Generation, Pump, Chiller, Blower & Other Industrial Applications
S.I.C.: 3511; 3621
N.A.I.C.S.: 333611; 335312
Import Export
Media: 2-4-7-8-10-13-16-26
Distr.: Intl.; Natl.
Budget Set: Mar.
Personnel:
Brian White *(Pres)*
Lloyd Beauchamp *(VP-Sls)*
Tomasz Staszek *(Reg Mgr-Power Generation)*
Bernd Haasken *(Product Mgr-Parts)*
Brands & Products:
ENGINATOR
ENGOMATIC
MODULATOR

WAUKESHA FOUNDRY INC.
1300 Lincoln Ave
Waukesha, WI 53186
Tel.: (262) 542-0741
Fax: (262) 549-8440
Toll Free: (800) 727-0741
Web Site: www.waukeshafoundry.com
Approx. Number Employees: 250
Year Founded: 1912
Business Description:
Stainless Steel, High Alloy Steel, Brass & Aluminum Castings Mfr
S.I.C.: 3325; 3369
N.A.I.C.S.: 331513; 331528
Media: 2-4
Distr.: Intl
Budget Set: Jan.
Personnel:
Tom Feltz *(VP-Sls & Mktg)*
Todd Kurtz *(Mgr-Sls)*
Brands & Products:
FOAM CAST
FORGING
GALL-TOUGH
INVAR
WAUKESHA 88
WAUKESHA 88 METAL
WF REPCO

WEBSTER INDUSTRIES INC.
325 Hall St
Tiffin, OH 44883-1419
Tel.: (419) 447-8232
Fax: (419) 448-1618
Toll Free: (800) 243-9327
E-mail: sales@websterchain.com
Web Site: www.websterchain.com
E-Mail For Key Personnel:
Marketing Director: market@websterchain.com
Sales Director: sales@websterchain.com
Sales Range: $25-49.9 Million
Approx. Number Employees: 225
Year Founded: 1876
Business Description:
Mfr. of Conveying & Engineering Chains & Malleable Iron Castings
S.I.C.: 3535; 3496
N.A.I.C.S.: 333922; 332618
Import Export
Media: 1-4-10-11-20-21
Distr.: Natl.
Budget Set: Oct.
Personnel:
Fredric C. Spurck *(Pres & CEO)*
Dean Bogner *(VP-Sls)*
Brands & Products:
BAKOS IRON
COILWEB
DURAMAL
ENDURO-FLITE
FIBRENE
PORTALLOY
QUALITY, OUR MOST IMPORTANT PRODUCT
WEBLOY
WEBSTER

WEIR CANADA INC.
(Sub. of Weir Engineering Services)
2360 Millrace Ct
Mississauga, ON L5N 1W2, Canada
Tel.: (905) 812-7100
Fax: (905) 812-0069
Web Site:
www.weirpowerindustrial.com
Sales Range: $100-124.9 Million
Approx. Number Employees: 110
Year Founded: 1897
Business Description:
Pumps & Control Systems Distr
S.I.C.: 3594
N.A.I.C.S.: 333996
Import Export
Advertising Expenditures: $200,000
Media: 1-2-4-5-7-10-13-19-20
Distr.: Natl.
Personnel:
Bill Dube *(Pres-North America)*
Brands & Products:
MARSH
PEACOCK

WEIR VALVES & CONTROLS USA INC.
(Sub. of Weir Valves & Controls UK Ltd.)
29 Old Right Rd
Ipswich, MA 01938-4544
Tel.: (978) 744-5690
Fax: (978) 741-3626
E-mail: sales@weirvalvesusa.com
Web Site: www.weigroup.com
E-Mail For Key Personnel:
Sales Director: sales@weigroup.com
Approx. Number Employees: 110
Year Founded: 1900
Business Description:
Mfr. of Valves for Power, Atomic Energy, Process Industries & Marine
S.I.C.: 3491
N.A.I.C.S.: 332911
Export
Media: 2-7-10-11-13
Distr.: Natl.
Personnel:
Steve Smallburn *(Dir-HR)*
Chris Gilbert *(Mgr-Nuclear Product)*
Brands & Products:
ATWOOD & MORRILL
TRICENTRIC

WELDON SOLUTIONS
(d/b/a Weldon Solutions)
425 E Berlin Rd
York, PA 17408
Tel.: (717) 846-4000
Fax: (717) 846-3624
E-mail: info@weldonsolutions.com
Web Site: www.weldonsolutions.com
E-Mail For Key Personnel:
President: gsipe@weldonsolutions.com
Marketing Director: drowe@weldonsolutions.com
Sales Range: $10-24.9 Million
Approx. Number Employees: 33
Year Founded: 1971
Business Description:
Mfr. of CNC Cylindrical Grinders
S.I.C.: 3541
N.A.I.C.S.: 333512
Import Export
Media: 2-4-7-10-13
Distr.: Natl.
Budget Set: Oct. -Nov.
Personnel:
George C. Sipe *(Pres)*
Travis Gentzler *(CFO)*
Denny L. Rowe *(Dir-Sls & Mktg)*
John Bennett *(Mgr-Engrg)*
Charles C. Gales *(Mgr-Automation Sls)*
Brands & Products:
AGN4
FANUC
FANUC ROBOTICS
GOLD
LIDTENDER
MIDAS
P175
P175 PUNCH GRINDER
PANTENDER
PANVERTER
PHOENIX
PHOENIX ID GRINDER

WELLMASTER CARTS
1494 Bell Mill Rd
Tillsonburg, ON N4G 4J1, Canada
Tel.: (519) 688-0500
Fax: (519) 688-0563
Toll Free: (800) 387-9355
E-mail: carts@wellmaster.ca
Web Site: www.wellmaster.ca
E-Mail For Key Personnel:
President: dwhite@wellmaster.ca
Sales Range: $10-24.9 Million
Approx. Number Employees: 75
Year Founded: 1987
Business Description:
Mfr. & Distributor of Material Handling Carts
S.I.C.: 3533
N.A.I.C.S.: 333132

Key to Media (For complete agency information see *The Advertising Red Books-Agencies* edition):
1. Bus. Publs. 2. Cable T.V. 3. Catalogs & Directories. 4. Co-op Adv. 5. Consumer Mags. 6. D.M. to Bus. Estab.7. D.M. to Consumers 8. Daily Newsp. 9. Exhibits/Trade Shows 10. Foreign 11. Infomercial 12. Internet Adv.13. Multimedia 14. Network Radio 15. Network T.V. 16. Newsp. Distr. Mags. 17. Other 18. Outdoor (Posters, Transit) 19. Point of Purchase20. Premiums, Novelties 21. Product Samples 22. Special Events Mktg. 23. Spot Radio 24. Spot T.V. 25. Weekly Newsp. 26. Yellow Page Adv.

Wellmaster Carts — (Continued)

Import Export
Media: 1-2-4-5-6-7-9-10-11-18-19-20-21-23-25-26
Distr.: Intl.; Natl.
Budget Set: Oct.
Personnel:
Douglas White *(Pres)*
Cam Campbell *(Mgr-Environ Products Div)*
Jeff Hanson *(Mgr-Matl Handling System Sls)*
Don Lane *(Mgr-Pump Div)*
Brands & Products:
QUIET CART
WELLMASTER

WES-TECH AUTOMATION SOLUTIONS

(d/b/a Wes-Tech Automation)
720 Dartmouth Ln
Buffalo Grove, IL 60089
Tel.: (847) 541-5070
Fax: (847) 541-0096
E-mail: info@wes-tech.com
Web Site: www.wes-tech.com
Approx. Number Employees: 100
Year Founded: 1976
Business Description:
Assembly Machines
S.I.C.: 3549; 3535
N.A.I.C.S.: 333518; 333922
Export
Media: 7-10-11-13
Personnel:
Jason Arends *(VP & Gen Mgr)*
Brands & Products:
CELLMASTER
TECH-TRAK
WES-TECH AUTOMATION SOLUTIONS

WESTERBEKE CORPORATION

Myles Standish Indus Pk 150 John Hancock Rd
Taunton, MA 02780
Tel.: (508) 823-7677
Fax: (508) 884-9688
Web Site: www.westerbeke.com
Sales Range: $10-24.9 Million
Approx. Number Employees: 70
Year Founded: 1937
Business Description:
Mfr. of Marine Diesel Engines, Diesel & Gasoline Generators, Marine Air Conditioning with Land Based Generator
S.I.C.: 3621; 3519; 3585
N.A.I.C.S.: 335312; 333415; 333618
Import Export
Advertising Expenditures: $637,100
Media: 2-4-5-6-7-8-10-11-13-20-26
Distr.: Intl.; Natl.
Budget Set: Oct.
Personnel:
John H. Westerbeke, Jr. *(Pres & CEO)*
Gregory Haidemenos *(CFO & COO)*
Thomas Sutherland *(Dir-Sls & Mktg)*
Brands & Products:
CENTURY
D-NET
ROTARY-AIRE
SAFE-CO
SOUND GUARD SST
UNIVERSAL
WESTERBEKE
Advertising Agency:
Brewster Strategies
21 Eliot St
Natick, MA 01760-6085
Tel.: (508) 647-6282
Fax: (508) 647-0651
(Marine & Industrial Engines)

WESTERN STATES MACHINE COMPANY

PO Box 327
Hamilton, OH 45012-0327
Tel.: (513) 863-4758
Fax: (513) 863-3846
E-mail: sales@westernstates.com
Web Site: www.westernstates.com
E-Mail For Key Personnel:
Sales Director: sales@westernstates.com
Approx. Number Employees: 50
Year Founded: 1917
Business Description:
Mfr. of Centrifugals for the Sugar, Chemical & Pharmaceutical Industries
S.I.C.: 3569
N.A.I.C.S.: 333999
Import Export
Media: 2-4-7-10
Distr.: Natl.
Budget Set: Dec.
Personnel:
Richard Nichting *(VP-HR)*
Jeffrey Hoffmann *(Mgr-Sls)*
Scott Kunke *(Mgr-Materials)*
Brands & Products:
CONCENT
QUADRAMATIC
ROBERTS
STEVENS
TITAN
TORK MASTER
WHISPERDYNE

WESTINGHOUSE AIR BRAKE TECHNOLOGIES CORPORATION

(d/b/a Wabtec Corporation)
1001 Air Brake Ave
Wilmerding, PA 15148-1036
Tel.: (412) 825-1000
Fax: (412) 825-1019
Web Site: www.wabtec.com
Approx. Rev.: $1,507,012,000
Approx. Number Employees: 6,654
Year Founded: 1999
Business Description:
Components, Parts & Electronic Systems Designer & Mfr for Locomotives, Railway Freight Cars, Subways & Buses
S.I.C.: 3743; 3561; 3799; 4013; 4111
N.A.I.C.S.: 336510; 333911; 336999; 485112; 488210
Export
Media: 2-7-10
Distr.: Natl.
Budget Set: Sept.
Personnel:
William E. Kassling *(Chm)*
Emilio A. Fernandez *(Vice Chm)*
Albert J. Neupaver *(Pres & CEO)*
Alvaro Garcia-Tunon *(CFO, Sec & Exec VP)*
Raymond T. Betler *(COO)*
Gerald M. Rowe *(Pres-Transit-Europe)*
Charles F. Kovac *(Sr VP-Freight Products)*
Patrick D. Dugan *(VP-Fin & Controller)*
Robert S. Andress, Jr. *(VP & Gen Mgr-Global Transit Braking)*
Ronald L. Witt *(VP & Gen Mgr-Intl)*
Scott E. Wahlstrom *(VP-HR)*
Timothy R. Wesley *(VP-IR & Corp Comm)*
David M. Seitz *(Asst Sec)*
Brands & Products:
SWIGER
WABTEC
Advertising Agency:
Newton Associates Marketing Communications, Inc.
527 Plymouth Rd Ste 411 Plymouth Woods
Plymouth Meeting, PA 19462
Tel.: (610) 964-9300
Fax: (610) 964-9306

W.H. MAZE COMPANY

(d/b/a Maze Nails)
100 Church St
Peru, IL 61354
Tel.: (815) 223-8290
Fax: (815) 223-7585
Toll Free: (800) 435-5949
E-mail: info@mazenails.com
Web Site: www.mazenails.com
Approx. Number Employees: 150
Year Founded: 1848
Business Description:
Mfr. of Specialty Nails
S.I.C.: 3496
N.A.I.C.S.: 332618
Export
Media: 2-4-7
Distr.: Natl.
Personnel:
Roelif Loveland *(Pres)*
Kim Pohl *(Dir-Mktg)*
Tom Koch *(Mgr-Sls)*
Brands & Products:
ANCHOR-DOWN
CALK-SCREW
GRIPSTAY
HARDITRIM
LEAD-GASKET
MAZE
MAZEMADE
SCREW-DOWN
SCREWS-ZINCLAD
SKINNY SPIKES
SPLIT-LESS
STORMGUARD

WHITING CORPORATION

(Sub. of GK Enterprises, Inc.)
26000 Whiting Way
Monee, IL 60449-8060
Tel.: (708) 587-2000
Fax: (708) 587-2001
Toll Free: (888) 861-5744
E-mail: info@whitingcorp.com
Web Site: www.whitingcorp.com
E-Mail For Key Personnel:
Sales Director: sales@whitingcorp.com
Approx. Number Employees: 145
Year Founded: 1884
Business Description:
Overhead Cranes, Foundry Equipment & Rail Transportation Maintenance Equipment Mfr
S.I.C.: 3559
N.A.I.C.S.: 333298
Export
Advertising Expenditures: $450,000
Media: 1-2-4-7-10-13-18-20-22-26
Distr.: Intl.; Natl.
Budget Set: Nov.
Personnel:
Jeffrey L. Kahn *(Pres)*
Brian Shapiro *(VP-Sls)*
Ed Slota *(Product Mgr)*
Brands & Products:
ULTRA DRIVE
W-CRANE
WHITING

WHITMAN CASTINGS, INC.

40 Raynor Ave
Whitman, MA 02382
Tel.: (781) 447-4417
Fax: (781) 447-0720
E-mail: whitmancasting@aol.com
Web Site: www.whitmancastings.com
Sales Range: $25-49.9 Million
Approx. Number Employees: 25
Business Description:
Ductile & Gray Iron Castings Mfr
S.I.C.: 3321; 3542
N.A.I.C.S.: 331511; 333513
Media: 26

WHITMAN CONTROLS CORP.

201 Dolphin Rd
Bristol, CT 06010-8000
Tel.: (860) 583-1847
Fax: (860) 583-5293
E-mail: info@whitmancontrols.com
Web Site: www.whitmancontrols.com
Approx. Sls.: $2,000,000
Approx. Number Employees: 13
Year Founded: 1972
Business Description:
Miniature Pressure & Vacuum Switches & Liquid Level Switches & Temperature & Differential Switches Mfr
S.I.C.: 3822
N.A.I.C.S.: 334512
Export
Media: 2-4-7-10
Distr.: Natl.
Personnel:
J. Yancey Brame *(VP-Sls)*
Brands & Products:
WHITMAN

WILLIAMS PATENT CRUSHER & PULVERIZER CO., INC.

2701 N Broadway
Saint Louis, MO 63102-1509
Mailing Address:
813 Montgomery St
Saint Louis, MO 63102-1513
Tel.: (314) 621-3348
Fax: (314) 436-2639
E-mail: info@williamscrusher.com
Web Site: www.williamscrusher.com
E-Mail For Key Personnel:
President: rob@williamscrusher.com
Sales Director: sales@williamscrusher.com
Approx. Number Employees: 100
Year Founded: 1886
Business Description:
Crushing & Grinding Machinery Mfr
S.I.C.: 3532; 3569
N.A.I.C.S.: 333131; 333999
Export
Media: 2-4-7-10-11-13-20
Distr.: Intl.; Natl.

Key to Media (For complete agency information see *The Advertising Red Books-Agencies* edition):
1. Bus. Publs. 2. Cable T.V. 3. Catalogs & Directories. 4. Co-op Adv. 5. Consumer Mags. 6. D.M. to Bus. Estab.7. D.M. to Consumers
8. Daily Newsp. 9. Exhibits/Trade Shows 10. Foreign 11. Infomercial 12. Internet Adv.13. Multimedia 14. Network Radio
15. Network T.V. 16. Newsp. Distr. Mags. 17. Other 18. Outdoor (Posters, Transit) 19. Point of Purchase20. Premiums, Novelties
21. Product Samples 22. Special Events Mktg. 23. Spot Radio 24. Spot T.V. 25. Weekly Newsp. 26. Yellow Page Adv.

Personnel:
Robert M. Williams, Jr. *(Pres)*
Dijana Taylor *(Mgr-Pur)*
Becky Schmidt *(Coord-Mktg)*
Brands & Products:
METEOR
ROCKET
SLUGGER CRUSHERS
WILLIAMS
WILLPACTOR

WILLIAMS WHITE & COMPANY

(Sub. of Doerfer Engineering Corp.)
600 River Dr
Moline, IL 61265-1122
Tel.: (309) 797-7650
Fax: (309) 797-7655
Fax: (309) 797-7677
Web Site: www.williamswhite.com
E-Mail For Key Personnel:
Sales Director: sales@williamswhite.com
Year Founded: 1854
Business Description:
Heavy Machinery, Custom Hydraulic Presses & Machinery Mfr
S.I.C.: 3542
N.A.I.C.S.: 333513
Export
Media: 1-4-10
Distr.: Intl.; Natl.
Budget Set: Oct.-Nov.
Personnel:
Sunder Subbaroyan *(Chm & Pres)*

WIRECO WORLDGROUP

(Holding of Paine & Partners, LLC)
12200 NW Ambassador Dr
Kansas City, MO 64163
Tel.: (816) 270-4700
Fax: (816) 270-4707
E-mail: wirerope@worldgroup.com
Web Site:
www.wirecoworldgroup.com
E-Mail For Key Personnel:
President: iraglazer@wrca.com
Sales Range: $350-399.9 Million
Approx. Number Employees: 100
Year Founded: 1931
Business Description:
Steel Wire Rope, Wire Slings & Assemblies Mfr
S.I.C.: 3496; 3315
N.A.I.C.S.: 332618; 331222
Import Export
Media: 2-7-10-13
Budget Set: Nov.
Personnel:
Ira Glazer *(Pres & CEO)*
Keith McKinnish *(CFO & Sr VP)*
Eric V. Bruder *(COO & Exec VP)*
Miguel Gomez *(Sr VP-Sls)*
David T. Hornaday *(Sr VP-Corp Admin)*
John D. Josendale *(Sr VP-Sls)*
Don Bell *(VP-IT)*
Dennis Fetter *(VP-Product Engrg/R & D)*
Blake Chandler *(Dir-Sls-Mining)*
Richard Humiston *(Sls Dir-Structures)*
Heather Bennett *(Dir-Treasury & Acctg Svcs)*
John Embray *(Dir-Sls-Gen Purpose Rope & Galvanized Strand)*
Michael Clinard *(Mgr-Fabricated Products)*
Ed Gower *(Mgr-Intl Engrg & Tech Svcs)*
Brands & Products:
7-FLEX
BRODERICK & BASCOM
FLEX-X
LOADSTAR
MACWHYTE
POWERMAX
POWERSTEEL TECHNOLOGY
ROCHESTER ROPES
TUF-GRIP
TUF-KOTE/PFV
TUF-MAX
TUF-STRAND
UNION
WIRECO

WIRECO WORLDGROUP

(Plant of WireCo WorldGroup)
24150 Oak Grove Ln
Sedalia, MO 65301-9540
Mailing Address:
PO Box 844
Sedalia, MO 65302
Tel.: (660) 827-3131
Fax: (660) 827-5717
Web Site:
www.wirecoworldgroup.com
Sales Range: $25-49.9 Million
Approx. Number Employees: 225
Year Founded: 1876
Business Description:
Steel Wire Rope & Wire Rope Slings Mfr
S.I.C.: 3496; 3315
N.A.I.C.S.: 332618; 331222
Export
Media: 2-10-18-21
Distr.: Intl.; Natl.
Budget Set: Nov.
Personnel:
Sam Jones *(Mgr-HR-Sedalia)*
Randy Ritter *(Mgr-Ops)*

WIRTZ MANUFACTURING COMPANY INC.

1105 24th St
Port Huron, MI 48060
Mailing Address:
PO Box 5006
Port Huron, MI 48061-5006
Tel.: (810) 987-4700
Fax: (810) 987-8135
E-mail: wolsales@wirtzusa.com
Web Site: www.wirtzusa.com
Approx. Number Employees: 126
Year Founded: 1932
Business Description:
Industrial Equipment Mfr
S.I.C.: 3559; 3544
N.A.I.C.S.: 333298; 333511
Media: 13
Brands & Products:
WIRTZ

WISCO PRODUCTS, INC.

109 Commercial St
Dayton, OH 45402-2211
Tel.: (937) 228-2101
Fax: (937) 228-2407
Toll Free: (800) 367-6570
E-mail: sales@wiscoproducts.com
Web Site: www.wiscoproducts.com
E-Mail For Key Personnel:
Sales Director: sales@wiscoproducts.com
Approx. Number Employees: 25
Year Founded: 1936
Business Description:
Mfr. of Fuel Caps, Adapters, Strainers, Stampings & Metal Assemblies
S.I.C.: 3469; 3089
N.A.I.C.S.: 332116; 326199
Export
Media: 2-4-7
Distr.: Natl.
Personnel:
Mark Paxson *(Pres)*
D. J. Maier *(Mgr-Sls)*
Advertising Agency:
Communications Strategies
416 West Place
Trenton, OH 45067
Tel.: (513) 988-6800
Fax: (513) 988-6808

WISCONSIN MACHINE TOOL CORPORATION

3225 Gateway Rd Ste 100
Brookfield, WI 53045-5139
Tel.: (262) 317-3048
Fax: (262) 317-3049
Toll Free: (800) 243-3078
E-mail: sales@wmtc.com
Web Site: www.machine-tool.com
E-Mail For Key Personnel:
Sales Director: sales@wmtc.com
Approx. Number Employees: 30
Year Founded: 1993
Business Description:
Metal Working Machinery Mfr
S.I.C.: 3545; 3541
N.A.I.C.S.: 333515; 333512
Import Export
Advertising Expenditures: $500,000
Media: 2-7-10
Distr.: Natl.
Personnel:
Patrick F. Cherone *(Pres & CEO)*
Jim Imrie *(Dir-Mktg)*
Brands & Products:
BREAKING THE RULES
WISCONSIN
WISMATIC

THE WM. POWELL COMPANY

2503 Spring Grove Ave
Cincinnati, OH 45214-1729
Tel.: (513) 852-2000
Fax: (513) 852-2997
E-mail: wmpowell@powellvalves.com
Web Site: www.powellvalves.com
Approx. Number Employees: 50
Year Founded: 1846
Business Description:
Valves & Engineering Specialties Mfr
S.I.C.: 3491; 3494
N.A.I.C.S.: 332911; 332919
Import Export
Advertising Expenditures: $250,000
Media: 1-2-4-7-8-10-20
Distr.: Natl.
Budget Set: Oct.-Nov.
Personnel:
Randy Cowart *(Pres & CEO)*
Brandy Cowart *(Exec VP)*
Jim Hengehold *(VP-Engrg & Quality Control)*
Lamar Ivey *(VP-Sls-SW Region)*
Jeff Thompson *(VP-Fin)*
Ryan Rasch *(Mgr-Inside Sls)*
Brands & Products:
CRESCENT
MODEL STAR
POWELL
STARFLO
UNION
WHITE STAR
W.S.

WMH TOOL GROUP, INC.

(Sub. of Walter Meier Holding AG)
2420 Vantage Rd
Elgin, IL 60123
Tel.: (847) 851-1000
Fax: (847) 851-1045
Toll Free: (800) 274-6848
E-mail: webmaster@wmhtoolgroup.com
Web Site: www.wmhtoolgroup.com
Approx. Number Employees: 433
Business Description:
Woodworking & Metalworking Equipment Distr
S.I.C.: 5084; 5085
N.A.I.C.S.: 423830; 423840
Media: 4-10
Personnel:
Robert Romano *(Gen Counsel, Sec & VP)*
Hardy Hamann *(Sr VP-Org & Strategy)*
Bob Varzino *(VP-Mktg)*
Brands & Products:
BRINK & COTTON
COLUMBIAN
HARGRAVE
JET
PERFORMAX
POLISHMASTER
POWERMATIC
W6 DRIVER
WAXMASTER
WILTON

THE WOLF MACHINE CO.

5570 Creek Rd
Cincinnati, OH 45242-4004
Tel.: (513) 791-5194
Fax: (513) 791-0925
Toll Free: (800) 543WOLF
Telex: 275189
E-mail: info@wolfmachine.com
Web Site: www.wolfmachine.com
Approx. Number Employees: 40
Year Founded: 1888
Business Description:
Cloth & Meat Cutting Machines & Equipment Mfr
S.I.C.: 3552; 5084
N.A.I.C.S.: 333292; 423830
Export
Media: 2-4-5-7-8-10-11-19-20-26
Distr.: Intl.; Natl.
Budget Set: Oct.
Personnel:
Scott E. Andre *(Pres)*
Brands & Products:
AIRHAWK
BIG O
BLAZER
CLIPPER
DUAL SPEED
JEANS MACHINE
MINI-CLIP
PACER
PACER JR.
PUP
PUP & AIR PUP
SELVAGE CUTTER
SLIM JIM
SPEEDI-NOTCH
SUPER TALL
TOMAHAWK

The Wolf Machine Co. — (Continued)

WARRIOR
WOLF-BOSCH
WOLF MACHINE COMPANY

WOLF ROBOTICS, LLC
(Div. of Rimrock Corporation)
4600 Innovation Dr
Fort Collins, CO 80525-3437
Tel.: (970) 225-7600
Fax: (970) 225-7700
E-mail: sales@wolfrobotics.com
Web Site: www.wolfrobotics.com
E-Mail For Key Personnel:
Sales Director: sales@wolfrobotics.com
Approx. Number Employees: 55
Year Founded: 1976
Business Description:
Robotic Welding & Cutting Systems
S.I.C.: 3569
N.A.I.C.S.: 333999
Media: 10
Personnel:
Chuck Boyer *(Mgr-Mktg)*
Brands & Products:
ABB ROBOTS

WOODCRAFT SUPPLY CORP.
(Sub. of Simonton Windows, Inc.)
1177 Rosemar Rd
Parkersburg, WV 26105-8272
Mailing Address:
PO Box 1686
Parkersburg, WV 26102-1686
Tel.: (304) 422-5412
Fax: (304) 428-8271
Toll Free: (800) 535-4482
E-mail: custserv@woodcraft.com
Web Site: www.woodcraft.com
Sales Range: $150-199.9 Million
Approx. Number Employees: 1,000
Year Founded: 1928
Business Description:
Woodworking Tools & Accessories Supplier
S.I.C.: 3553; 3545
N.A.I.C.S.: 333210; 333515
Media: 3-4-6-8-9-10-12-13-15-18-19-20-22-24-25-26
Distr.: Natl.
Personnel:
Jeff Forbes *(Pres)*
Dawn Knost *(CFO)*
Joseph Garrett *(VP-Sls & Mktg)*
Gary Lombard *(VP-Franchise & Retail Dev)*
Liz Matheny *(Mgr-Mktg)*
Peter Parker *(Mgr-Retail Adv)*

WOODSAGE INDUSTRIES
(Sub. of Woodsage Holdings, LLC)
7400 Airport Hwy
Holland, OH 43528
Tel.: (419) 866-8000
Fax: (419) 868-3533
E-mail: woodsage@woodsage.com
Web Site: www.woodsage.com
Approx. Number Employees: 100
Year Founded: 1948
Business Description:
Metal Tube & Bar Cutting & Fabricating Services
S.I.C.: 3317
N.A.I.C.S.: 331210
Import Export
Advertising Expenditures: $500,000
Media: 1-2-4-7-9-10-11-16-20-25
Personnel:
Jim Cannaley *(Gen Mgr)*
Brands & Products:
READYROLL

WRAP-ADE PACKAGING SYSTEMS LLC
27 Law Dr Ste B C
Fairfield, NJ 07004
Tel.: (973) 773-6150
Fax: (973) 773-6010
Web Site: www.wrapade.com
E-Mail For Key Personnel:
Sales Director: sales@wrapade.com
Approx. Number Employees: 15
Year Founded: 1989
Business Description:
Packaging Machinery Mfr
S.I.C.: 3565; 5084
N.A.I.C.S.: 333993; 423830
Media: 2-4-10-13
Distr.: Intl.; Natl.
Budget Set: Dec.
Personnel:
Bill Beattie *(Pres)*
Brands & Products:
WRAP-ADE

WSA ENGINEERED SYSTEMS INC.
(Formerly Water Services of America, Inc.)
2018 S 1st St
Milwaukee, WI 53207-6408
Tel.: (414) 481-4120
Fax: (414) 481-4121
Web Site: www.wsaes.com
Approx. Number Employees: 200
Year Founded: 1971
Business Description:
Mfr of Automatic Tube Cleaning Systems For Condensers, Heat Exchangers & Backflush Valves
S.I.C.: 3589; 3564
N.A.I.C.S.: 333319; 333412
Export
Media: 2-4-7
Distr.: Intl.; Natl.
Budget Set: Oct.
Personnel:
Kaveh Someah *(Pres & CEO)*
Brands & Products:
ADFS
ATCS
BRACKETT BRIEDEN
DURO

WSF INDUSTRIES, INC.
7 Hackett Dr
Tonawanda, NY 14150-3711
Mailing Address:
PO Box 400
Buffalo, NY 14217-0400
Tel.: (716) 692-4930
Fax: (716) 692-4135
Toll Free: (800) 874-8265
E-mail: sales@wsfindustries.com
Web Site: www.wsf-inc.com
E-Mail For Key Personnel:
Sales Director: sales@wsfindustries.com
Sales Range: $10-24.9 Million
Approx. Number Employees: 25
Year Founded: 1941
Business Description:
Fabricator of Processing Equipment, Autoclaves, Bonders, Cappers, Canners, Curers, Couplers, Vacuums, Cookers & Loaders
S.I.C.: 3443
N.A.I.C.S.: 332313
Import Export
Media: 6-8-10
Distr.: Direct to Consumer; Intl.; Natl.
Budget Set: Monthly
Personnel:
John L. Hettrick, Jr. *(Chm & CEO)*
Gary R. Fornasiero *(Pres)*
Brands & Products:
RAPID/BONDER
RAPID/CANNER
RAPID/CAPPER
RAPID/COOKER
RAPID/COUPLER
RAPID/CURE
RAPID/LOADER
RAPID/VAC
RAPIDOOR
Advertising Agency:
Harold Warner Advertising, Inc.
232 Delaware Ave
Buffalo, NY 14202-2000
Tel.: (716) 852-4410
Fax: (716) 852-4725

W.W. GRAINGER, INC.
(d/b/a Grainger Group of Companies)
100 Grainger Pkwy
Lake Forest, IL 60045-5201
Tel.: (847) 535-1000
Fax: (847) 535-0878
Toll Free: (888) 361-8649
Web Site: www.grainger.com
Approx. Sls.: $7,182,158,000
Approx. Number Employees: 18,500
Year Founded: 1927
Business Description:
Facilities Maintenance Product Mfr & Distr
S.I.C.: 5085
N.A.I.C.S.: 423840
Import Export
Advertising Expenditures: $114,600,000
Media: 2-3-4-5-7-10-11-13-18-20-23
Distr.: Natl.
Budget Set: Dec.
Personnel:
James T. Ryan *(Chm, Pres & CEO)*
Ronald L. Jadin *(CFO & Sr VP)*
Court D. Carruthers *(Pres-Grainger Intl & Sr VP)*
Michael A. Pulick *(Pres-Grainger US & Sr VP)*
John L. Howard *(Gen Counsel & Sr VP)*
Laura D. Brown *(Sr VP-Comm & IR)*
Nancy A. Hobor *(Sr VP-Commun & IR)*
Will Lomax *(VP-Fin, Grainger Intl)*
William Chapman *(Dir-IR)*
Ernest Duplessis *(Dir-External Comm)*
Robb Kristopher *(Mgr-External Comm)*
Yesid Mendez *(Mgr-Territory Sls)*
Brands & Products:
ACKLANDS-GRAINGER
AIR HANDLER
CONDOR
DAYTON
DEM-KOTE
FINDMRO
FOR THE ONES WHO GET IT DONE
GRAINGER
GRAINGER INTEGRATED SUPPLY
GRAINGER.COM
LUMAPRO
SPEEDAIRE
WESTWARD
Advertising Agency:
Johnson Direct
250 N Sunnyslope Rd Ste 203
Brookfield, WI 53005
Tel.: (262) 782-2750
Fax: (262) 782-2751
Toll Free: (800) 710-2750

THE W.W. WILLIAMS COMPANY
835 W Goodale Blvd
Columbus, OH 43212
Tel.: (614) 228-5000
Fax: (614) 228-4490
E-mail: info@wwwilliams.com
Web Site: www.wwwilliams.com
Approx. Number Employees: 700
Year Founded: 1912
Business Description:
Industrial Parts Distribution & Repair Services
S.I.C.: 5084; 5013; 7699
N.A.I.C.S.: 423830; 423120; 811310
Media: 2-4-6-7-8-10-14-18-20-21-23-25-26
Distr.: Intl.; Natl.
Budget Set: Nov.
Personnel:
Mark French *(Pres)*
Bill Bates *(VP-Mktg)*
Advertising Agency:
Conrad, Phillips & Vutech, Inc.
1398 Goodale Blvd
Columbus, OH 43212
Tel.: (614) 224-3887
Fax: (614) 222-0737

THE WYCO TOOL COMPANY
(Div. of Racine Federated, Inc.)
8635 Washington Ave
Racine, WI 53406
Tel.: (262) 639-6770
Fax: (262) 639-2267
Toll Free: (800) 233-9926
E-mail: wycosales@wycotool.com
Web Site: www.wycotool.com
Sales Range: $1-9.9 Million
Approx. Number Employees: 130
Year Founded: 1930
Business Description:
Mfr. Concrete Vibrators
S.I.C.: 3531; 3823
N.A.I.C.S.: 333120; 334513
Import Export
Media: 2-4-7-10-19
Distr.: Intl.; Natl.
Budget Set: Jan.
Personnel:
David Perkinf *(Pres)*
Dominic Cariello *(Gen Mgr)*
Paul Jaworski *(Gen Mgr)*
Brands & Products:
WYCO

WYSSMONT CO., INC.
1470 Bergen Blvd
Fort Lee, NJ 07024-2116
Tel.: (201) 947-4600
Fax: (201) 947-0324
E-mail: sales@wyssmont.com
Web Site: www.wyssmont.com
E-Mail For Key Personnel:
Sales Director: sales@wyssmont.com

Key to Media (For complete agency information see *The Advertising Red Books-Agencies* edition):
1. Bus. Publs. 2. Cable T.V. 3. Catalogs & Directories. 4. Co-op Adv. 5. Consumer Mags. 6. D.M. to Bus. Estab.7. D.M. to Consumers 8. Daily Newsp. 9. Exhibits/Trade Shows 10. Foreign 11. Infomercial 12. Internet Adv.13. Multimedia 14. Network Radio 15. Network T.V. 16. Newsp. Distr. Mags. 17. Other 18. Outdoor (Posters, Transit) 19. Point of Purchase20. Premiums, Novelties 21. Product Samples 22. Special Events Mktg. 23. Spot Radio 24. Spot T.V. 25. Weekly Newsp. 26. Yellow Page Adv.

Approx. Number Employees: 25
Business Description:
Industrial Equipment Systems Mfr & Related Services & Sales
S.I.C.: 3567; 3559
N.A.I.C.S.: 333994; 333298
Export
Media: 2-4-5-7-10-11-26
Distr.: Intl.; Natl.
Budget Set: Oct.
Personnel:
Ed Wiesselberg *(Pres)*
Joseph Bevaqua *(VP, Gen Mgr-Sls, Adv & Mktg)*
Jim Ulrich *(VP-Engrng)*
Brands & Products:
CLEAN-SIGHT
ROTOCAGE
ROTOSCOOP
TRISKELION
TURBO-DRYER
WYSSMONT

XTEK, INC.
11451 Reading Rd
Cincinnati, OH 45241-2246
Tel.: (513) 733-7800
Fax: (513) 733-7939
Toll Free: (888) 332XTEK
E-mail: unsubscribe@xtek.com
Web Site: www.xtek.com
E-Mail For Key Personnel:
Marketing Director: jim.raible@xtek.com
Approx. Number Employees: 200
Year Founded: 1909
Business Description:
Mfr. of Hardened Steel Machine Components
S.I.C.: 3568; 3312
N.A.I.C.S.: 333613; 331111
Export
Media: 2-4-7-10-20-26
Distr.: Intl.; Natl.
Budget Set: Jan.
Personnel:
Kyle H. Seymour *(Chm, Pres & CEO)*
Edward R. Plavko *(CFO & VP)*
James J. Raible *(VP-Sls)*
John W. Mayhan *(Gen Mgr-Power Transmission Grp)*
Thomas J. Ryan *(Gen Mgr-Indus Components Grp)*
Jennifer G. King *(Dir-HR)*
Kris Tegeder *(Product Mgr)*
Brands & Products:
SOLUTIONS IN MOTION
TSP
XTEK

XYONICZ CORPORATION
6754 Martin St
Rome, NY 13440-7119
Tel.: (315) 334-4214
Fax: (315) 336-3177
Web Site: www.xyonicz.com
Sales Range: Less than $1 Million
Approx. Number Employees: 10
Year Founded: 1994
Business Description:
Mfr. of Material Handling Equipment for the Newspaper Industry & Softmetal Melting Industry
S.I.C.: 3398; 3599
N.A.I.C.S.: 332811; 332710
Export
Media: 2-4-7-10-17
Distr.: Natl.
Budget Set: July
Personnel:
Edward Zionc *(Pres & CEO)*

YARDLEY PRODUCTS CORPORATION
(Sub. of Dixon Valve & Coupling Company)
10 W College Ave
Yardley, PA 19067-1517
Mailing Address:
PO Box 357
Yardley, PA 19067-8357
Tel.: (215) 493-2723
Fax: (215) 493-6796
Toll Free: (800) 457-0154
E-mail: info@yardleyproducts.com
Web Site: www.yardleyproducts.com
Approx. Number Employees: 15
Year Founded: 1946
Business Description:
Threaded Inserts for Fastening Applications Mfr
S.I.C.: 3429; 3541
N.A.I.C.S.: 332510; 333512
Import Export
Advertising Expenditures: $150,000
Media: 2-4-8-10-13
Distr.: Intl.; Natl.
Personnel:
Tim E. Bailey *(Pres)*
Ken Grady *(VP)*
Brands & Products:
BI-SERT
FIBER-SERT
INTRO-SERT
QUICK-SERT
SHARP-SERT
TRISERT
YARDLEY PRODUCTS
ZAMAK FIBER-SERT

YATES-AMERICAN MACHINE COMPANY
2880 Kennedy Dr
Beloit, WI 53511-3933
Mailing Address:
PO Box 958
Beloit, WI 53512-0958
Tel.: (608) 364-0333
Fax: (608) 364-0481
Toll Free: (800) 752-6377
E-mail: vrullo@yatesam.com
Web Site: www.yatesamerican.com
Approx. Sls.: $7,000,000
Approx. Number Employees: 20
Year Founded: 1883
Business Description:
Woodworking Machinery Cutterheads & Knives
S.I.C.: 3553
N.A.I.C.S.: 333210
Media: 2-6
Distr.: Direct to Consumer; Natl.
Budget Set: May-June
Personnel:
Darrell Borghi *(Pres)*
Brands & Products:
YATES-AMERICAN

YOUNG & FRANKLIN, INC.
942 Old Liverpool Rd
Liverpool, NY 13088-5552
Tel.: (315) 457-3110
Fax: (315) 451-3589
E-mail: info@yf.com
Web Site: www.yf.com
Sales Range: $25-49.9 Million
Approx. Number Employees: 300
Year Founded: 1918
Business Description:
Mfr. of Specialty Fluid Control Valves For Land-based Gas Turbines; Aircraft & Marine Applications
S.I.C.: 3492; 3594
N.A.I.C.S.: 332912; 333996
Import Export
Media: 2-4-7-10-11
Distr.: Intl.; Natl.
Personnel:
Dudley Disosway Johnson *(CEO)*
Daniel Corwin *(VP-Bus Dev & Mktg)*
Lawrence Mitter *(VP-Sls)*
Advertising Agency:
Cowley Associates, Inc.
235 Walton St
Syracuse, NY 13202
Tel.: (315) 475-8453
Fax: (315) 475-8408

ZEPHYR MANUFACTURING CO., INC.
(Sub. of SHG Holdings Corp.)
201 Hindry Ave
Inglewood, CA 90301-1519
Tel.: (310) 410-4907
Fax: (310) 410-2913
E-mail: zephyr@zephyrtool.com
Web Site: www.zephyrtool.com
Approx. Number Employees: 87
Year Founded: 1939
Business Description:
Mfr. of Cutting Tools
S.I.C.: 3546; 3545
N.A.I.C.S.: 333991; 333515
Export
Advertising Expenditures: $1,500,000
Media: 2-7-10
Personnel:
Bernard J. Kersulis *(Pres)*

ZIMMERMAN-MCDONALD MACHINERY, INC.
2272 Weldon Pkwy
Saint Louis, MO 63146-3206
Tel.: (314) 291-9360
Fax: (314) 291-2981
E-mail: zimsales@zimmermanmcdonald.com
Web Site: www.zimmermanmcdonald.com
Approx. Number Employees: 8
Year Founded: 1886
Business Description:
Machine Tools Sales
S.I.C.: 5084
N.A.I.C.S.: 423830
Import Export
Media: 2-4-8-9
Distr.: Natl.
Personnel:
Brad Zimmerman *(Pres)*
Brands & Products:
JET
ZIMMERMAN MACDONALD MACHINERY

Key to Media (For complete agency information see *The Advertising Red Books-Agencies* edition):
1. Bus. Publs. 2. Cable T.V. 3. Catalogs & Directories. 4. Co-op Adv. 5. Consumer Mags. 6. D.M. to Bus. Estab.7. D.M. to Consumers 8. Daily Newsp. 9. Exhibits/Trade Shows 10. Foreign 11. Infomercial 12. Internet Adv.13. Multimedia 14. Network Radio 15. Network T.V. 16. Newsp. Distr. Mags. 17. Other 18. Outdoor (Posters, Transit) 19. Point of Purchase20. Premiums, Novelties 21. Product Samples 22. Special Events Mktg. 23. Spot Radio 24. Spot T.V. 25. Weekly Newsp. 26. Yellow Page Adv.

Miscellaneous

To provide the user of the Miscellaneous Classification with a guide for quick selection of Companies in the same or similar industries, the following chart outlining the Standard Industrial Classification Major Group codes is provided. The Standard Industrial Classification (S.I.C.) system was developed by the Technical Committee on Standard Industrial Classifications under the sponsorship and supervision of the Office of Statistical Standards of the Bureau of the Budget, Executive Office of the President.

KEY TO THE STANDARD INDUSTRIAL CLASSIFICATION (S.I.C.) MAJOR GROUPS

S.I.C.	MAJOR GROUP
01	Agricultural Production - Crops
02	Agricultural Production - Livestock
07	Agricultural Services
08	Forestry
09	Fishing, Hunting and Trapping
10	Metal Mining
12	Coal Mining
13	Oil and Gas Extraction
14	Mining and Quarrying of Nonmetallic Minerals, Except Fuels
15	Building Construction - General Contractors and Operative Builders
16	Heavy Construction Other Than Building Construction - Contractors
17	Construction - Special Trade Contractors
20	Food and Kinder Products
21	Tobacco Products
22	Textile Mill Products
23	Apparel and Other Finished Products Made from Fabrics and Similar Materials
24	Lumber and Wood Products, Except Furniture
25	Furniture and Fixtures
26	Paper and Allied Products
27	Printing, Publishing and Allied Industries
28	Chemicals and Allied Products
29	Petroleum Refining and Related Industries
30	Rubber and Miscellaneous Plastics Products
31	Leather and Leather Products
32	Stone, Clay, Glass and Concrete Products
33	Primary Metal Industries
34	Fabricated Metal Products, Except Machinery and Transportation Equipment
35	Industrial and Commercial Machinery and Computer Equipment
36	Electronic and Other Electrical Equipment and Components, Except Computer Equipment
37	Transportation Equipment
38	Measuring, Analyzing and Controlling Instruments; Photographic, Medical and Optical Goods; Watches and Clocks
39	Miscellaneous Manufacturing Industries
40	Railroad Transportation
41	Local and Suburban Transit and Interurban Highway Passenger Transportation
42	Motor Freight Transportation
43	Postal Service
44	Water Transportation
45	Transportation by Air
46	Pipelines, Except Natural Gas
47	Transportation Services

S.I.C.	MAJOR GROUP
48	Communications
49	Electric, Gas and Sanitary Services
50	Wholesale Trade - Durable Goods
51	Wholesale Trade - Nondurable Goods
52	Building Materials, Hardware Garden Supplies and Mobile Home Dealers
53	General Merchandise Stores
54	Food Stores
55	Automotive Dealers and Gasoline Service Stations
56	Apparel and Accessory Stores
57	Home Furniture, Furnishings and Equipment Stores
58	Eating and Drinking Places
59	Miscellaneous Retail
60	Depository Institutions
61	Nondepository Credit Institutions
62	Security and Commodity Brokers, Dealers, Exchanges and Services
63	Insurance Carriers
64	Insurance Agents, Brokers and Services
65	Real Estate
67	Holding and Other Investment Offices
70	Hotels, Rooming Houses, Camps and Other Lodging Places
72	Personal Services
73	Business Services
75	Auto Repair, Services and Parking
76	Miscellaneous Repair Services
78	Motion Pictures
79	Amusement and Recreations Services
80	Health Services
81	Legal Services
82	Educational Services
83	Social Services
84	Museums, Art Galleries and Botanical and Zoological Gardens
86	Membership Organizations
87	Engineering, Accounting, Research, Management and Related Services
88	Private Households
89	Miscellaneous Services
91	Executive, Legislative and General Government, Except Finance
92	Justice, Public Order and Safety
93	Public Finance, Taxation and Monetary Policy
94	Administration of Human Resource Programs
95	Administration of Environmental Quality and Housing Programs
96	Administration of Economic Programs
97	National Security and International Affairs
99	Nonclassifiable Establishments

Key to Media (For complete agency information see *The Advertising Red Books-Agencies* edition):
1. Bus. Publs. 2. Cable T.V. 3. Catalogs & Directories. 4. Co-op Adv. 5. Consumer Mags. 6. D.M. to Bus. Estab.7. D.M. to Consumers
8. Daily Newsp. 9. Exhibits/Trade Shows 10. Foreign 11. Infomercial 12. Internet Adv.13. Multimedia 14. Network Radio
15. Network T.V. 16. Newsp. Distr. Mags. 17. Other 18. Outdoor (Posters, Transit) 19. Point of Purchase20. Premiums, Novelties
21. Product Samples 22. Special Events Mktg. 23. Spot Radio 24. Spot T.V. 25. Weekly Newsp. 26. Yellow Page Adv.

ABERDEEN GROUP, INC.
(Sub. of HARTE-HANKS, INC.)
451D St 7th Fl Ste 710
Boston, MA 02210
Tel.: (617) 723-7890
Fax: (617) 723-7897
Toll Free: (800) 577-7891
E-mail: member.services@aberdeen.com
Web Site: www.aberdeen.com
Approx. Number Employees: 100
Year Founded: 1998
Business Description:
Fact-Based Research Services
S.I.C.: 8732
N.A.I.C.S.: 541910
Media: 2-10-13
Personnel:
Andrew Boyd *(Pres)*
Kevin Martin *(Sr VP-Res Ops)*
Derek Brink *(VP & Dir-Res-IT Security)*
Peter Ostrow *(VP-Research & Dir-Sls Effectiveness)*
Deborah Casey *(VP-Sls)*
John Pearson *(VP-Product-Tech)*
Julie Zadow *(VP-Mktg)*
Christopher J. Dwyer *(Editor-Global Supply Mgmt)*
Kevin Prouty *(Dir-Res-Enterprise Applications Res Practice)*
Advertising Agency:
Linden Alschuler & Kaplan, Inc.
1251 Ave of the Americas Ste 940
New York, NY 10020
Tel.: (212) 575-4545
Fax: (212) 575-0519

ACCENTURE, INC.
1345 Ave of the Americas
New York, NY 10105
Tel.: (917) 452-4400
Fax: (917) 527-9915
Web Site: www.accenture.com
Business Description:
Business Management, Outsourcing & Technology Consulting Services
S.I.C.: 8742
N.A.I.C.S.: 541611
Media: 2-6-15-23-24
Personnel:
Michael D. Lyman *(Mng Partner)*
Soren Kristensen *(Partner-North America Lead for Innovation)*
Mark Sullivan *(Partner & Sr Exec)*
Tim Thompson *(Partner & Sr Exec)*
Roxanne Taylor *(CMO & Chief Comm Officer)*
Kerry L. Bianchi *(Sr Dir-Accenture Media Mgmt-North America)*
Molly Spatara *(Sr Dir-Internet Mktg-Global)*
Advertising Agency:
Young & Rubicam Inc.
285 Madison Ave
New York, NY 10017-6401
Tel.: (212) 210-3000
Fax: (212) 490-9073

AEROGROW INTERNATIONAL, INC.
6075 Longbow Dr Ste 200
Boulder, CO 80301
Tel.: (303) 444-7755
Fax: (303) 444-0406
Toll Free: (800) 476-9669
Web Site: www.aerogrow.com
Approx. Rev.: $17,251,347
Approx. Number Employees: 40
Year Founded: 2002
Business Description:
Indoor Garden Systems Mfr & Distr
S.I.C.: 7699
N.A.I.C.S.: 811411
Advertising Expenditures: $2,299,431
Personnel:
Jack J. Walker *(Chm)*
J. Michael Wolfe *(CEO)*
H. MacGregor Clarke *(CFO)*
Grey H. Gibbs *(Chief Acctg Officer & Controller)*
John K. Thompson *(Sr VP-Sls & Mktg)*
Brands & Products:
ADVANCED GROWING SYSTEM
AEROFLOWER
AEROGARDEN
AEROGROW
BIO-DOME
CHEF IN A BOX
ENGLISH COTTAGE
FARMER'S MARKET FRESH
FLORIST IN A BOX
GET THE GARDEN
GROW ANYTHING, ANYTIME, ANYWHERE
GROWNOW
HERB APPEAL
HERB IT UP
HERB 'N SERVE
LEAVES
MASTER CHEF IN A BOX
MOUNTAIN MEADOW
PLUG & GROW
SNIP IT CHOP IT HERB IT UP
SPLASH OF COLOR
SWEET RUBIES
ULTIMATE KITCHEN GARDENER
VEG-E-GARDEN
WALL FARM
WALL GARDEN

AMERICAN MOLD REMOVAL, INC.
1630 N US Hwy 1
Jupiter, FL 33469
Tel.: (561) 667-0150
Toll Free: (888) 561-6653
Web Site:
www.americanmoldremoval.net
Business Description:
Chemically Free Removal of Mold, Bacteria, Viruses & Odor; Inspections & Testing, Cleaning & Sanitizing
S.I.C.: 7389
N.A.I.C.S.: 561499
Media: 7-8-13-26
Personnel:
Don Dillon *(Partner)*
Randy Peterson *(Partner)*

AMPAL-AMERICAN ISRAEL CORPORATION
555 Madison Ave
New York, NY 10022
Toll Free: (866) 447-8636
E-mail: main@ampal.com
Web Site: www.ampal.com
Approx. Rev.: $504,962,000
Approx. Number Employees: 2,666
Year Founded: 1942
Business Description:
Investment Services
S.I.C.: 6289
N.A.I.C.S.: 523999
Advertising Expenditures: $1,112,000
Personnel:
Yosef A. Maiman *(Chm, Pres & CEO)*
Irit Eluz *(CFO, Treas & Sr VP-Fin)*
Advertising Agency:
KCSA Strategic Communications (Kanan, Corbin, Schupak & Aronow, Inc.)
880 3rd Ave 6th Fl
New York, NY 10022
Tel.: (212) 682-6300
Fax: (212) 697-0910

APPLIED DNA SCIENCES, INC.
25 Health Sciences Dr Ste 113
Stony Brook, NY 11790
Tel.: (631) 444-6862
Tel.: (631) 444-6370
Fax: (631) 444-8848
E-mail: info@adnas.com
Web Site: www.adnas.com
Approx. Sls.: $519,844
Approx. Number Employees: 14
Business Description:
Anti-Counterfeiting & Product Authentication Solutions
S.I.C.: 7382; 2836
N.A.I.C.S.: 561621; 325414
Advertising Expenditures: $50,195
Media: 17
Personnel:
James A. Hayward *(Chm, Pres & CEO)*
Kurt Jensen *(CFO)*

ASK THE SEAL, LLC
3001 N Rocky Point Dr E Ste 223
Tampa, FL 33607
Fax: (727) 474-0197
Toll Free: (800) 410-7325
E-mail: info@asktheseal.com
Web Site: www.asktheseal.com
Business Description:
Company & Employee Credential Inspection Services
S.I.C.: 9651
N.A.I.C.S.: 926150
Media: 13-23-24
Personnel:
Ed Marchiselli *(Pres)*

ASSISTED LIVING CONCEPTS, INC.
W140 N8981 Lilly Rd
Menomonee Falls, WI 53051-2325
Tel.: (262) 257-8888
Fax: (262) 251-7627
Toll Free: (888) 252-5001
E-mail: info@alcco.com
Web Site: www.alcco.com
Approx. Rev.: $233,128,000
Approx. Number Employees: 4,200
Year Founded: 1994
Business Description:
Owner, Operator & Developer of Assisted Living Residences
S.I.C.: 6311; 6513; 8361
N.A.I.C.S.: 524113; 531110; 623990
Advertising Expenditures: $800,000
Personnel:
David J. Hennigar *(Chm)*
Melvin A Rhinelander *(Vice Chm)*
Laurie A. Bebo *(Pres & CEO)*
John Buono *(CFO, Treas & Sr VP)*

AURORA CASKET COMPANY, INC.
10944 Marsh Rd
Aurora, IN 47001
Mailing Address:
PO Box 29
Aurora, IN 47001-0029
Tel.: (812) 926-1111
Fax: (812) 926-0208
Toll Free: (800) 457-1111
Web Site: www.auroracasket.com
Approx. Number Employees: 700
Year Founded: 1890
Business Description:
Mfr. of Metal Burial Caskets
S.I.C.: 3995
N.A.I.C.S.: 339995
Export
Advertising Expenditures: $250,000
Media: 2-4-7-10-17
Distr.: Natl.
Budget Set: Oct.
Personnel:
William D. Backman, III *(Pres)*
William Barrott *(CEO)*
Tom Heintz *(CFO)*
Chris Barrott *(Exec VP)*
Tim Dugan *(Sr VP-Sls & Mktg)*
Jason Barrott *(Dir-Mktg Dev)*
Calvin Toler *(Mgr-Strategic Acct-Orlando)*
Brands & Products:
AURORA
BECAUSE YOU CARE
EXPRESSIONS OF LIFE
FUNERALPLAN.COM
PERSONAL EXPRESSIONS
POSITIVE CHOICES

BATESVILLE CASKET COMPANY, INC.
(Sub. of Hillenbrand, Inc.)
1 Batesville Blvd
Batesville, IN 47006
Tel.: (812) 934-7500
Fax: (812) 934-7613
Toll Free: (800) 622-8373
E-mail: post.master@batesville.com
Web Site: www.batesville.com
Sales Range: $650-699.9 Million
Year Founded: 1884
Business Description:
Retailer of Funeral Services Products
S.I.C.: 7261
N.A.I.C.S.: 812210
Export
Media: 1-2-4-7-10-19-20
Distr.: Natl.
Personnel:
Joe A. Raver *(Pres & COO)*
Michael L. DiBease *(VP-Mktg)*
Chris Foster *(Reg Dir)*
Brands & Products:
KEEPSAKE
LIVING MEMORIAL
MEMENTO

BEACON SOLAR ENERGY INC.
6340 Techster Blvd Ste 1
Fort Myers, FL 33966-4798
Tel.: (239) 425-2627
E-mail: info@beaconsolarenergy.com
Web Site:
www.beaconsolarenergy.com
Business Description:
Solar Energy Services
N.A.I.C.S.: 221119
Media: 8-10
Personnel:
James E. McMurray *(Pres & CEO)*
Edward J. Cassidy, IV *(COO & Treas)*

Key to Media (For complete agency information see *The Advertising Red Books-Agencies* edition):
1. Bus. Publs. 2. Cable T.V. 3. Catalogs & Directories. 4. Co-op Adv. 5. Consumer Mags. 6. D.M. to Bus. Estab.7. D.M. to Consumers 8. Daily Newsp. 9. Exhibits/Trade Shows 10. Foreign 11. Infomercial 12. Internet Adv.13. Multimedia 14. Network Radio 15. Network T.V. 16. Newsp. Distr. Mags. 17. Other 18. Outdoor (Posters, Transit) 19. Point of Purchase20. Premiums, Novelties 21. Product Samples 22. Special Events Mktg. 23. Spot Radio 24. Spot T.V. 25. Weekly Newsp. 26. Yellow Page Adv.

BERNARD HODES GROUP
(U.S. Office of Bernard Hodes Group)
1230 Peachtree St NE Ste 2200
Atlanta, GA 30309
Tel.: (404) 602-1050
Fax: (404) 602-1051
E-mail: khensley@hodes.com
Web Site: www.hodes.com
Approx. Number Employees: 25
Business Description:
Communications, Recruitment
S.I.C.: 7311
N.A.I.C.S.: 541810
Personnel:
Kevin Hensley *(Sr VP & Branch Mgr)*
Advertising Agency:
EXCELER8
325 Clematis St Ste 138
West Palm Beach, FL 33401
Tel.: (561) 584-9088
Fax: (561) 659-1370

BOUNCE LOGISTICS, INC.
(Sub. of Express-1 Expedited Solutions, Inc.)
5838 W Brick Rd
South Bend, IN 46628
Tel.: (574) 243-1550
Fax: (574) 243-1584
Toll Free: (877) 677-5623
E-mail: info@bouncelogistics.com
Web Site: www.bouncelogistics.com
Sales Range: $1-9.9 Million
Approx. Number Employees: 5
Year Founded: 2008
Business Description:
Full-Truckload Freight Brokerage Services
S.I.C.: 4731
N.A.I.C.S.: 488510
Personnel:
Tim Hindes *(Pres)*
Advertising Agency:
Killian Branding
322 S Green St Ste 510
Chicago, IL 60607
Tel.: (312) 836-0050
Fax: (312) 836-0233

BREWER ASSOCIATES MARKETING COMMUNICATIONS
39555 Orchard Hill Pl Ste 600
Novi, MI 48375
Tel.: (734) 458-7180
E-mail: klangham@brewer-associates.com
Web Site: www.brewer-associates.com
E-Mail For Key Personnel:
President: klangham@brewer-associates.com
Approx. Number Employees: 5
Year Founded: 1956
S.I.C.: 7311
N.A.I.C.S.: 541810
Personnel:
John Ojala *(Chm)*
Keith Langham *(Pres & CEO)*
David Jankowski *(Exec Dir-Art)*
Dawn Hathaway *(Media Dir)*
Gale Halbert *(Office Mgr)*
Advertising Agency:
Brewer Associates Marketing Communications
39555 Orchard Hill Pl Ste 600
Novi, MI 48375
Tel.: (734) 458-7180

BRIABE MEDIA INC.
634 A Venice Blvd
Venice, CA 90291
Tel.: (310) 710-2380
Fax: (310) 694-3284
E-mail: info@briabemedia.com
Web Site: www.briabemedia.com
Sales Range: Less than $1 Million
Approx. Number Employees: 8
Business Description:
Mobile Marketing
S.I.C.: 7311
N.A.I.C.S.: 541810
Personnel:
James Briggs *(CEO & Mng Dir)*
Advertising Agency:
Harvest One Media
406 Main St Ste 501
Boonton, NJ 07005
Tel.: (973) 588-3335

CADILLAC VENTURES INC.
181 Bay Street Suite 2840
Toronto, ON M5J 2T3, Canada
Tel.: (416) 203-7722
Fax: (416) 203-7782
E-mail: info@cadillacventures.com
Web Site: www.cadillacventures.com
Approx. Int. Income: $24,353
Approx. Number Employees: 1
Year Founded: 1995
Business Description:
Gold Mining Services
S.I.C.: 1041
N.A.I.C.S.: 212221
Advertising Expenditures: $80,999
Media: 17
Personnel:
William McCullough *(Chm)*
Norman Brewster *(Pres, CEO & Dir)*
Leo O'Shaughnessy *(CFO)*

CANADIAN SOLAR INC.
(Corporate Headquarters of Canadian Solar Inc.)
675 Cochrane Drive East Tower 6th Floor
Markham, ON L3R 0B8, Canada
Tel.: (905) 530-2334
Fax: (905) 530-2001
E-mail: inquire@csisolar.com
Web Site: www.csisolar.com
Approx. Number Employees: 150
Business Description:
Executive Office
S.I.C.: 9111
N.A.I.C.S.: 921110
Advertising Expenditures: $5,148,215
Personnel:
Robert Patterson *(VP-Corp & Product Dev)*

CARTER, LEDYARD & MILBURN
2 Wall St
New York, NY 10005
Tel.: (212) 732-3200
Fax: (212) 732-3232
Web Site: www.clm.com
Personnel:
Jeffrey S. Boxer *(Partner)*
Clifford P. Case, III *(Partner)*
Jerome J. Caulfield *(Partner)*
Tom Davis *(Partner)*
Steven J. Glusband *(Partner)*
Guy P. Lander *(Partner)*
Judith A. Lockhart *(Partner)*
Advertising Agency:
Gibbs & Soell, Inc.
60 E 42nd St
New York, NY 10165
Tel.: (212) 697-2600
Fax: (212) 697-2646

CK DESIGN INTERNATIONAL
1201 N Pinellas Ave
Tarpon Springs, FL 34689
Tel.: (727) 937-4811
Business Description:
Hair Salon
S.I.C.: 7231
N.A.I.C.S.: 812112
Media: 9-13-22-25
Personnel:
Cathy Koursiotis *(Owner)*

CORONET DRY CLEANER
2211 Westheimer Rd
Houston, TX 77098
Tel.: (713) 526-4623
Fax: (713) 526-0830
E-mail: mknudsen@coronetcleaners.com
Web Site: www.coronetcleaners.com
Approx. Number Employees: 15
Business Description:
Upscale Dry Cleaning Services
S.I.C.: 7212
N.A.I.C.S.: 812320
Media: 22-26
Personnel:
Mary Helen Knudsen *(Gen Mgr)*
Brands & Products:
CORONET
Advertising Agency:
Paul Orseck
5800 Woodway, Ste. 1223
Houston, TX 77057
Tel.: (713) 781-8008

DCI GROUP
1828 L St NW Ste 400
Washington, DC 20036
Tel.: (202) 546-4242
Fax: (202) 546-4243
Web Site: www.dcigroup.com
Business Description:
Government/Political/Public Affairs, Public Relations
S.I.C.: 8743
N.A.I.C.S.: 541820
Personnel:
Thomas J. Synhorst *(Chm)*
Douglas M. Goodyear *(CEO)*
Justin Peterson *(Mng Partner)*
Dan Combs *(Partner)*
Advertising Agency:
Bergman Group
4880 Sadler Rd Ste 220
Glen Allen, VA 23060
Tel.: (804) 225-0600
Fax: (804) 225-0900

DISPLAY BOYS
17032 Murphy Ave
Irvine, CA 92614
Tel.: (949) 833-0100
Fax: (949) 838-0110
E-mail: info@displayboys.com
Web Site: www.displayboys.com
Approx. Billings: $5,000,000
Approx. Number Employees: 40
Year Founded: 1989
Business Description:
Collateral, Corporate Identity, Exhibit/Trade Shows, Logo & Package Design, Merchandising, Point of Purchase, Point of Sale, Production
S.I.C.: 7311; 7319
N.A.I.C.S.: 541810; 541850; 541890
Personnel:
John Riley *(Co-Founder & VP)*
Advertising Agency:
The Pollack PR Marketing Group
1901 Ave of the Stars Ste 1040
Los Angeles, CA 90067
Tel.: (310) 556-4443
Fax: (310) 286-2350

EDUCATIONAL TESTING SERVICE INC.
Rosedale Rd
Princeton, NJ 08541-0001
Tel.: (609) 921-9000
Fax: (609) 734-5410
E-mail: research@ets.org
Web Site: www.ets.org
Approx. Rev.: $803,500,000
Approx. Number Employees: 2,433
Year Founded: 1948
Business Description:
Educational Testing & Consulting Services
S.I.C.: 8299; 8733
N.A.I.C.S.: 611710; 541720
Import Export
Personnel:
Kurt M. Landgraf *(Pres & CEO)*
Frank R. Gatti *(CFO)*
Walt MacDonald *(Exec VP-Programs & Svcs)*
Yvette Donado *(Sr VP-People, Process & Comm)*
Brands & Products:
AP
CRITERION
ETS
GRE
ISKILLS
LISTENING. LEARNING. LEADING
PRAXIS SERIES
PROOFWRITER
PSAT/NMSQT
SAT
SCOREITNOW
SIR II
TOEFL
TOEIC
TSE
Advertising Agencies:
Outside the Box Interactive LLC
150 Bay St Ste 706
Jersey City, NJ 07302
Tel.: (201) 610-0625
Fax: (201) 610-0627

Tierney Communications
(A Div. of the Interpublic Group of Companies)
The Bellevue 200 S Broad St
Philadelphia, PA 19102-3803
Tel.: (215) 790-4100
Fax: (215) 790-4363

ENER1, INC.
1540 Broadway Ste 25C
New York, NY 10036
Tel.: (212) 920-3500
E-mail: info@ener1group.com
Web Site: www.ener1group.com

Key to Media (For complete agency information see *The Advertising Red Books-Agencies* edition):
1. Bus. Publs. 2. Cable T.V. 3. Catalogs & Directories. 4. Co-op Adv. 5. Consumer Mags. 6. D.M. to Bus. Estab.7. D.M. to Consumers 8. Daily Newsp. 9. Exhibits/Trade Shows 10. Foreign 11. Infomercial 12. Internet Adv.13. Multimedia 14. Network Radio 15. Network T.V. 16. Newsp. Distr. Mags. 17. Other 18. Outdoor (Posters, Transit) 19. Point of Purchase20. Premiums, Novelties 21. Product Samples 22. Special Events Mktg. 23. Spot Radio 24. Spot T.V. 25. Weekly Newsp. 26. Yellow Page Adv.

Approx. Sls.: $77,406,000
Approx. Number Employees: 769
Year Founded: 1985
Business Description:
Lithium Ion Batteries & Fuel Cells Mfr
S.I.C.: 3692; 3699
N.A.I.C.S.: 335912; 335999
Personnel:
Thomas J. Snyder *(Chm)*
Christopher L. Cowger *(CEO)*
Jeffrey Seidel *(CFO)*
Robert R. Kamischke *(Chief Acctg Officer & VP-Fin)*
Bruce Curtis *(Pres-Grid Energy Storage)*
Ulrik Grape *(Pres-Ener1 Europe)*
Nicholas Brunero *(Gen Counsel & VP)*
Grace Paglen *(Brand Mgr)*
Brands & Products:
ENER1
Advertising Agency:
Waggener Edstrom
225 108th Ave NE Ste 700
Bellevue, WA 98004-5737
Tel.: (425) 638-7000
Fax: (425) 638-7001
(Lithium-Ion Batteries)

ETERNAL IMAGE, INC.
28800 Orchard Lake Rd Ste 130
Farmington Hills, MI 48334
Tel.: (248) 932-3333
Fax: (248) 932-3006
Toll Free: (888) 662-7538
E-mail: info@eternalimage.net
Web Site: www.eternalimage.net
Approx. Rev.: $330,399
Approx. Number Employees: 3
Year Founded: 2006
Business Description:
Caskets & Other Burial Products Mfr
S.I.C.: 3995
N.A.I.C.S.: 339995
Advertising Expenditures: $66,646
Media: 2-6-7
Personnel:
Clint Mytych *(Pres & CEO)*
Frank P. Colapinto *(Pres-Gift Div)*
Wallace N. Popravsky *(VP-Sls & Mktg)*

EURO RSCG EDGE
(United States of Euro RSCG Worldwide HQ)
915 SW Stark St 2nd Fl
Portland, OR 97205-3017
Tel.: (503) 228-5555
Fax: (503) 228-0560
E-mail: info@eurorscg-drtv.com
Web Site: www.eurorscgedge.com
Approx. Number Employees: 60
Year Founded: 1988
S.I.C.: 7311
N.A.I.C.S.: 541810
Personnel:
Greg Johnson *(Pres & COO)*
Steve Netzley *(CEO)*
Jack Kirby *(Pres-Electronic Commerce)*
Shannon Ellis *(Exec VP-Bus Dev)*
Graham Turner *(Exec Dir-Creative)*
Robert Orr *(Supvr-Online Media)*
Advertising Agency:
Lane PR
905 SW 16th Ave
Portland, OR 97205
Tel.: (503) 221-0480
Fax: (503) 221-9765

FAMILY FITNESS CENTERS, INC.
4028 Little Rd
New Port Richey, FL 34655
Tel.: (727) 375-1116
Web Site:
www.familyfitnesscenters.net
Approx. Number Employees: 60
Business Description:
Fitness Centers & Wellness Programs
S.I.C.: 7991
N.A.I.C.S.: 713940
Media: 22
Personnel:
John Chelene *(Gen Mgr)*

FREEDOM RINGS DOCUMENT PREPARATION SERVICES
3003 S Tamiami Trl
Sarasota, FL 34239
Tel.: (941) 894-3733
Fax: (941) 894-3735
E-mail: info@freedomrings.biz
Web Site: www.freedomrings.biz
Business Description:
Document Preparation Services
S.I.C.: 7338
N.A.I.C.S.: 561410
Media: 24
Personnel:
Julie Jefferson *(Owner)*

GLOBALOPTIONS GROUP, INC.
75 Rockefeller Plz 27th Fl
New York, NY 10019
Tel.: (212) 445-6262
Fax: (212) 445-0053
Web Site:
www.globaloptionsgroup.com
Approx. Int. Income: $2,000
Approx. Number Employees: 4
Business Description:
High-End Risk Assessment & Mitigation Services
S.I.C.: 9711; 8742
N.A.I.C.S.: 928110; 541611
Advertising Expenditures: $32,000
Media: 17
Personnel:
Harvey W. Schiller *(Chm & CEO)*
Per-Olof Loof *(Vice Chm)*
Jeffery O. Nyweide *(CFO & Exec VP-Dev)*
Samuel V. King *(Exec VP)*

GOODBY, SILVERSTEIN & PARTNERS, INC.
(Parent Company of of Omnicom Group Inc.)
(Part of Omnicom Group, Inc.)
720 California St
San Francisco, CA 94108-2404
Tel.: (415) 392-0669
Fax: (415) 788-4303
E-mail: contact@gspsf.com
Web Site: www.gspsf.com
Approx. Number Employees: 525
Year Founded: 1983
S.I.C.: 7311
N.A.I.C.S.: 541810
Personnel:
Jeffrey Goodby *(Co-Chm & Partner)*
Richard Silverstein *(Co-Chm & Dir-Creative)*
Robert Riccardi *(Mng Partner)*
Derek Robson *(Mng Partner)*
Jerry Barnhart *(Partner & COO)*
Christian Haas *(Exec Dir-Creative)*
Margaret Johnson *(Assoc Partner & Exec Dir-Creative)*
Will McGinness *(Assoc Partner & Exec Dir-Creative)*
Todd Grantham *(Assoc Partner & Acct Dir)*
Gareth Kay *(Chief Strategy Officer)*
Mike Geiger *(Chief Digital Officer)*
Adam Deringer *(Sr VP & Chief Digital Officer)*
Erin Allsman *(VP & Dir-PR)*
Christine Chen *(Head-Comm Strategy)*
Rick Condos *(Exec Dir-Creative & Assoc Partner)*
Hunter Hindman *(Exec Dir-Creative)*
Jamie Barrett *(Exec Dir-Creative)*
Dan Glass *(Sr Dir-Creative)*
Gabriel Mattar *(Sr Dir-Art)*
Nancy Reyes *(Grp Acct Dir)*
Joe Burrascano *(Dir-Creative)*
Bryan Houlette *(Dir-Art)*
Emily Ianacone *(Art Dir)*
Kevin Koller *(Art Dir)*
Wyeth Koppenhaver *(Art Dir)*
Devin Sharkey *(Art Dir)*
Johan Arlig *(Dir-Art)*
Jon Barco *(Dir-Art)*
Suzee Barrabee *(Dir-Print Production & Art Buying)*
Adrien Bindi *(Dir-Art)*
Joakim Borgstrom *(Dir-Creative)*
Stuart Brown *(Dir-Art)*
Lucas Buick *(Dir-Creative)*
Aladino Debert *(Dir-Creative)*
Aaron Dietz *(Dir-Art)*
Cindy Fluitt *(Dir-Brdcst Production)*
Croix Gagnon *(Dir-Art)*
Kristin Graham *(Dir-Art)*
Anders Gustafsson *(Dir-Creative)*
Linda Harless *(Dir-Creative Resources)*
Hunter Hindeman *(Dir-Creative)*
Patrick Kelly *(Dir-Brand Publicity)*
David Kolbusz *(Dir-Creative)*
Caio Lazzuri *(Dir-Art)*
Chris Logan *(Dir-Art)*
Ronny Northrop *(Dir-Creative)*
Christine O'Donnell *(Dir-Agency Rels)*
Mark Sikes *(Dir-Art)*
Steve Simpson *(Dir-Creative)*
Danielle Thornton *(Dir-Art)*
Jack Woodworth *(Dir-Art)*
Brian Gunderson *(Assoc Dir-Creative & Designer)*
Rus Chao *(Assoc Dir-Creative)*
Paul Charney *(Assoc Dir-Creative)*
Stefan Copiz *(Assoc Dir-Creative)*
Toria Emery *(Assoc Dir-Creative)*
Brian McPherson *(Assoc Dir-Acct Mgmt)*
Karin Onsager-Birch *(Assoc Dir-Creative)*
Chris Roe *(Assoc Dir-Creative)*
Marty Senn *(Assoc Dir-Creative)*
Jean Weisman *(Assoc Dir-Creative)*
Nicole Strada *(Sr Brand Strategist)*
Molly Conklin *(Mgr-Ops)*
Renee Fisher *(Mgr-Ops)*
Deborah McCauley-Ellis *(Mgr-Bus Affairs)*
Todd Porter *(Supvr-Music)*
Ricardo Lopez *(Coord-Facilities)*
Advertising Agency:
Harvest One Media
406 Main St Ste 501
Boonton, NJ 07005
Tel.: (973) 588-3335

GREAT AMERICAN GROUP, INC.
21860 Burbank Blvd Ste 300 S
Woodland Hills, CA 91367
Tel.: (818) 884-3737
E-mail: info@greatamerican.com
Web Site: www.greatamerican.com
Approx. Rev.: $42,145,000
Approx. Number Employees: 136
Year Founded: 2009
Business Description:
Holding Company; Corporate Liquidation, Asset Disposition, Auction & Appraisal Services
S.I.C.: 6719; 7389
N.A.I.C.S.: 551112; 541990; 561499; 561990
Advertising Expenditures: $498,000
Personnel:
Andrew Gumaer *(Chm & CEO)*
Harvey M. Yellen *(Vice Chm & Pres)*
Michael A. Petruski *(Exec VP & Gen Mgr-Machinery & Equipment Valuation Practice)*

GREATER THAN ONE
395 Hudson St 5th Fl
New York, NY 10014
Tel.: (212) 252-1999
Fax: (212) 252-7364
Web Site: www.greaterthanone.com
Approx. Billings: $30,000,000
Approx. Number Employees: 62
Year Founded: 2000
S.I.C.: 7311
N.A.I.C.S.: 541810
Personnel:
Richard Newman *(Pres)*
Elizabeth Izard Apelles *(CEO)*
Pilar Belhumeur *(Partner-Experience Design)*
Steve Longbons *(Partner-Tech)*
John Mahler *(Partner-Strategy & Insights)*
Christa Toole *(Partner-Search & Analytics)*
Advertising Agency:
G.S. Schwartz & Co. Inc.
470 Park Ave S 10th Fl S
New York, NY 10016-6819
Tel.: (212) 725-4500
Fax: (212) 725-9188

HARTE-HANKS, INC.
9601 McAllister Freeway Ste 610
San Antonio, TX 78216
Tel.: (210) 829-9000
Fax: (210) 829-9403
Toll Free: (800) 456-9748
E-mail: contactus@harte-hanks.com
Web Site: www.harte-hanks.com
Approx. Rev.: $860,526,000
Approx. Number Employees: 4,850
Year Founded: 1920
Business Description:
Business Publications, Direct Response Marketing, Direct-to-Consumer
S.I.C.: 7331; 2741; 8732
N.A.I.C.S.: 541860; 511140; 511199; 541910

Key to Media (For complete agency information see *The Advertising Red Books-Agencies* edition):
1. Bus. Publs. 2. Cable T.V. 3. Catalogs & Directories. 4. Co-op Adv. 5. Consumer Mags. 6. D.M. to Bus. Estab.7. D.M. to Consumers
8. Daily Newsp. 9. Exhibits/Trade Shows 10. Foreign 11. Infomercial 12. Internet Adv.13. Multimedia 14. Network Radio
15. Network T.V. 16. Newsp. Distr. Mags. 17. Other 18. Outdoor (Posters, Transit) 19. Point of Purchase20. Premiums, Novelties
21. Product Samples 22. Special Events Mktg. 23. Spot Radio 24. Spot T.V. 25. Weekly Newsp. 26. Yellow Page Adv.

HARTE-HANKS, INC. — (Continued)

Advertising Expenditures: $66,792,000
Media: 2-4-7-10-11-13-22
Distr.: Intl.; Natl.
Budget Set: Oct.

Personnel:
Larry D. Franklin *(Chm, Pres & CEO)*
Houston H. Harte *(Vice Chm)*
Douglas C. Shepard *(CFO & Exec VP)*
Dave LaGreca *(CIO & Corp VP)*
Jessica M. Huff *(Chief Acctg Officer & VP-Fin)*
Robert J. Colucci *(Corp Officer)*
Peter E. Gorman *(Pres-Shoppers & Exec VP)*
Gary J. Skidmore *(Pres-Direct Mktg & Exec VP)*
Robert L. R. Munden *(Gen Counsel, Sec & Sr VP)*
David Hatch *(Sr VP)*
Jeff Simpson *(Sr VP-Mktg)*
Jeannine Falcone *(VP-Direct Mktg)*
Matthew Coddaire *(Dir-Digital Media)*

Brands & Products:
ADQ DIRECT
ADVANCED DATA QUALITY
ALLINK
CI TECHNOLOGY DATABASE
CUSTOMER OPTIMIZATION
THE FLYER.COM
HARTE-HANKS
HARTE-HANKS POSTFUTURE
MARKETING ENABLER
NEXTOUCH
PENNYSAVERUSA.COM
POSTFUTURE
TRILLIUM
TRILLIUM SOFTWARE SYSTEM
WE MAKE IT HAPPEN.

HILLENBRAND, INC.

1 Batesville Blvd
Batesville, IN 47006
Tel.: (812) 934-7000
Fax: (812) 934-7613
E-mail: investors@hillenbrand.com
Web Site: www.hillenbrand.com
Approx. Rev.: $749,200,000
Approx. Number Employees: 3,200

Business Description:
Funeral Services
S.I.C.: 7261
N.A.I.C.S.: 812210
Advertising Expenditures: $3,000,000

Personnel:
Ray J. Hillenbrand *(Chm)*
James A. Henderson *(Vice Chm)*
Kenneth A. Camp *(Pres & CEO)*
Cynthia L. Lucchese *(CFO & Sr VP)*
Paul Douglas Wilson *(Chief Admin Officer & Sr VP)*
Elizabeth E. Dreyer *(Chief Acctg Officer, VP & Controller)*
John R. Zerkle *(Gen Counsel, Sec & Sr VP)*

Advertising Agency:
Northlich Public Relations
720 E Pete Rose Way Ste 120
Cincinnati, OH 45202-3579
Tel.: (513) 421-8840
Fax: (513) 287-1858

JUSTRITE MANUFACTURING COMPANY, LLC

(Holding of The Riverside Company)
2454 E Dempster St
Des Plaines, IL 60016
Tel.: (847) 298-9250
Fax: (847) 298-9261
Toll Free: (800) 798-9250
Web Site: www.justritemfg.com
Approx. Number Employees: 200
Year Founded: 1907

Business Description:
Safety Containment Systems Mfr
S.I.C.: 3443; 1791
N.A.I.C.S.: 332313; 238120
Export
Media: 1-2-4-7-8-10
Distr.: Natl.
Budget Set: June

Personnel:
Pat Malone *(CEO)*
Patricia Maruszak *(Mgr-Mktg Comm)*

Brands & Products:
CEASE-FIRE
CENTURA
CHEMCOR
GUARD MASTER
SAFESITE

KIMCO CORPORATION

(Sub. of Eurest Services, Inc.)
4700 N Oketo Ave
Harwood Heights, IL 60706
Tel.: (708) 583-9800
Fax: (708) 583-9888
E-mail: sglowinski@usservices.com
Web Site: www.kimcocorp.com
Approx. Number Employees: 2,300
Year Founded: 1972

Business Description:
Building Maintenance Services
S.I.C.: 7349
N.A.I.C.S.: 561720
Import Export
Media: 4

Personnel:
Elliott Tarson *(Founder)*
John H. Barrett *(Pres)*
Nathaniel B. Shaw *(Exec VP)*
Richard Wender *(Exec VP)*
Stacey S. Glowinski *(Sr VP & Controller)*
Rick Dassow *(Sr VP)*
Sean Letwat *(Sr VP)*
Robert McGrath *(Sr VP-CBSE)*
Sandra Melton *(Sr VP)*
Tom Konor *(VP-Bus Ops)*
Dana Bertogli *(Comptroller)*

LAMAR ADVERTISING COMPANY

5321 Corporate Blvd
Baton Rouge, LA 70808
Tel.: (225) 926-1000
Fax: (225) 926-1005
Toll Free: (800) 235-2627
E-mail: infotdoran@lamarhq.com
Web Site: www.lamar.com
E-Mail For Key Personnel:
President: kreilly@lamarhq.com
Approx. Rev.: $1,092,291,000
Approx. Number Employees: 3,000
Year Founded: 1902

Business Description:
Outdoor Advertising Services
S.I.C.: 7319; 7311
N.A.I.C.S.: 541850; 541810
Advertising Expenditures: $397,725,000
Media: 18

Personnel:
Kevin P. Reilly, Jr. *(Chm & Pres)*
Sean Reilly *(CEO)*
Keith A. Istre *(CFO & Treas)*
Thomas F. Teepell *(CMO)*
Floyd Williams *(Pres-Interstate Logos)*
James R. McIlwain *(Gen Counsel & Sec)*
Brent McCoy *(Exec VP)*
Charles Brent McCoy *(Exec VP)*
John M. Miller *(VP & Dir-Natl Sls)*
Tammy Duncan *(VP-HR)*
Al Ferrara *(Dir-Creative)*

LENCO MOBILE INC.

345 Chapala St
Santa Barbara, CA 93101
Tel.: (310) 308-9199
Toll Free: (888) LENCOUS
E-mail: info@lencomobile.com
Web Site: www.lencomobile.com
Approx. Rev.: $8,357,331
Approx. Number Employees: 102

Business Description:
Mobile Phone & Internet Advertising Platforms Owner & Operator
S.I.C.: 4812; 7319
N.A.I.C.S.: 517212; 541890
Advertising Expenditures: $287,000

Personnel:
Michael Levinsohn *(Pres & CEO)*
Thomas Banks *(CFO)*

LIVEWIRE LLC

8 Taylor St
Salem, NH 03079
Tel.: (603) 458-5200
Fax: (603) 458-5205
E-mail: sales@livewirellc.com
Web Site: www.livewirellc.com
Approx. Sls.: $60,000,000
Approx. Number Employees: 700
Year Founded: 2002

Business Description:
Fibre Optic Cable & Electrical Services
S.I.C.: 3357; 1731
N.A.I.C.S.: 335921; 238210

Advertising Agency:
Cypress Consulting
100 S King St Ste 300
Seattle, WA 98104
Tel.: (206) 281-8240
Fax: (206) 281-8266

MARCHEX, INC.

520 Pike St Ste 2000
Seattle, WA 98101
Tel.: (206) 331-3300
Fax: (206) 331-3695
E-mail: info@marchex.com
Web Site: www.marchex.com
Approx. Rev.: $97,565,607
Approx. Number Employees: 390
Year Founded: 2003

Business Description:
Internet/Web Design
S.I.C.: 7389; 7311; 7375; 8742
N.A.I.C.S.: 541490; 518111; 541613; 541810
Advertising Expenditures: $3,800,000
Media: 10-13-22

Personnel:
Russell C. Horowitz *(Chm & CEO)*
John Keister *(Vice Chm)*
Michael A. Arends *(CFO)*
Peter Christothoulou *(COO)*
Ethan Caldwell *(Chief Admin Officer, Gen Counsel & Sec)*
Matthew Berk *(Exec VP-Product Engrg)*
Brent Turner *(Exec VP-Call Products)*
Brooks McMahon *(Sr VP & Gen Mgr-Small Bus Mktg Products)*
Leigh McMillan *(Sr VP & Gen Mgr-Call Analytics)*
Tom Leung *(Sr VP-Product)*
Tamara Colagross *(Dir-Corp Mktg)*

Brands & Products:
ADVANCING LOCAL SEARCH & PERFORMANCE ADVERTISING
MARCHEX
MARCHEX ADHERE
MARCHEX CONNECT
OPEN VIEW

MASSEY ENERGY COMPANY

4 N 4th St
Richmond, VA 23219-2230
Tel.: (804) 788-1800
Fax: (804) 788-1870
E-mail: katharine.kenny@masseyenergyco.com
Web Site: www.masseyenergyco.com
Approx. Rev.: $3,038,974,000
Approx. Number Employees: 7,359

Business Description:
Produces, Processes, Sells & Transships Butuminous Coal of Metallurgical & Steam Grades
S.I.C.: 1221; 1241
N.A.I.C.S.: 212111; 213113

Personnel:
Baxter F. Phillips, Jr. *(Pres & CEO)*
Eric B. Tolbert *(CFO & VP)*
J. Christopher Adkins *(COO & Sr VP)*
Jeffrey M. Jarosinski *(VP-Fin & Chief Compliance Officer)*
John M. Poma *(Chief Admin Officer & VP)*
M. Shane Harvey *(Gen Counsel & VP)*
Mark A. Clemens *(Sr VP-Grp Ops)*
Jeffrey M. Gillenwater *(VP-HR)*
Steve E. Sears *(VP-Sls)*

Brands & Products:
MASSEY ENERGY

Advertising Agency:
Public Strategies, Inc.
98 San Jacinto Blvd Ste 1200
Austin, TX 78701
Tel.: (512) 474-8848
Fax: (512) 474-0120

MEDICAL CONNECTIONS HOLDINGS, INC.

4800 T-Rex Ave Ste 310
Boca Raton, FL 33431
Tel.: (561) 353-1110
Fax: (866) 689-6058
Web Site: www.medicalconnections.com
Approx. Rev.: $7,805,523
Approx. Number Employees: 33
Year Founded: 1999

Business Description:
Medical Recruitment & Staffing Services
S.I.C.: 7361
N.A.I.C.S.: 541612; 561310
Advertising Expenditures: $294,373

Key to Media (For complete agency information see *The Advertising Red Books-Agencies* edition):
1. Bus. Publs. 2. Cable T.V. 3. Catalogs & Directories. 4. Co-op Adv. 5. Consumer Mags. 6. D.M. to Bus. Estab.7. D.M. to Consumers
8. Daily Newsp. 9. Exhibits/Trade Shows 10. Foreign 11. Infomercial 12. Internet Adv.13. Multimedia 14. Network Radio
15. Network T.V. 16. Newsp. Distr. Mags. 17. Other 18. Outdoor (Posters, Transit) 19. Point of Purchase20. Premiums, Novelties
21. Product Samples 22. Special Events Mktg. 23. Spot Radio 24. Spot T.V. 25. Weekly Newsp. 26. Yellow Page Adv.

Personnel:
Anthony J. Nicolosi *(Owner)*
Jeffrey Rosenfeld *(CEO)*
Brian R. Neill *(CFO)*

MERCER INC.
(Sub. of Marsh & McLennan Companies Inc.)
1166 Ave of the Americas
New York, NY 10036-2708
Tel.: (212) 345-7000
Fax: (212) 345-7414
Web Site: www.mercer.com
Sales Range: $1-4.9 Billion
Approx. Number Employees: 15,000
Business Description:
Human Resource Consulting Services
S.I.C.: 7361; 8742
N.A.I.C.S.: 541612; 541611
Personnel:
M. Michele Burns *(Chm & CEO)*
Bob Van Pelt *(CFO)*
Terry Thompson *(COO)*
Phil de Cristo *(Pres-Investments & Grp Exec)*
Tom Elliot *(Pres-Health & Benefits)*
Jeff Miller *(Pres-Outsourcing & Grp Exec)*
Matricia Milligan *(Pres-Human Capital)*
Simon O'Regan *(Pres-Retirement, Risk & Fin Consulting)*
Bruce Lee *(Principal-PR)*
Caroline Cheng *(Gen Counsel-Mercer)*
Larry Woerner *(Global Head-Reg)*
Advertising Agency:
Impressions-A.B.A. Industries, Inc.
393 Jericho Tpk
Mineola, NY 11501
Tel.: (516) 739-3210
Fax: (516) 739-9246

MIA'S THERAPEUTIC MASSAGE
5217 Trouble Creek Rd
New Port Richey, FL 34652
Tel.: (727) 845-1257
Web Site: www.relaxatmias.com
Business Description:
Massage Therapy
S.I.C.: 7032
N.A.I.C.S.: 721214
Media: 13

MORPHEUS MEDIA
127 W 26th St 7th Fl
New York, NY 10003
Tel.: (212) 253-1588
Fax: (212) 353-8793
E-mail: contact@morpheusmedia.com
Web Site: www.morpheusmedia.com
S.I.C.: 7311
N.A.I.C.S.: 541810
Personnel:
Jamie Driver *(Co-Founder & Mng Dir)*
Alex Golimbu *(Co-Founder & Mng Dir)*
Shenan Reed *(Co-Founder & Mng Dir)*
Advertising Agency:
Squeakywheel Promotions
75 S Broadway Ste 400
White Plains, NY 10601
Tel.: (914) 304-4277

MYRIAD MARKETING
(Branch of Ypartnership)
1334 Parkview Ave Ste 300
Manhattan Beach, CA 90266
Tel.: (310) 545-4200
Web Site: www.myriadmarketing.com/
S.I.C.: 7311
N.A.I.C.S.: 541810
Personnel:
Al Merschen *(Mng Partner)*
Michael Price *(VP & Dir-Mktg)*
Advertising Agency:
Myriad Marketing
1334 Parkview Ave Ste 300
Manhattan Beach, CA 90266
Tel.: (310) 545-4200

NATUREWORKS LLC
(Joint Venture of Cargill, Inc.)
(d/b/a NatureWorks)
15305 Minnetonka Blvd
Minnetonka, MN 55343
Tel.: (952) 742-0400
Toll Free: (877) 423-7659
Web Site: www.natureworksllc.com
Approx. Number Employees: 25
Business Description:
Vegetable Oil Mills; 50% Owned by Cargill Incorporated & 50% Owned by The Dow Chemical Company
S.I.C.: 2062
N.A.I.C.S.: 311312
Personnel:
Marc Verbruggen *(Pres & CEO)*
Steve Davies *(Dir-Mktg)*
Advertising Agency:
Waggener Edstrom
225 108th Ave NE Ste 700
Bellevue, WA 98004-5737
Tel.: (425) 638-7000
Fax: (425) 638-7001
(Ingeo Bioplastics)

OPTIONS MEDIA GROUP HOLDINGS, INC.
123 NW 13th St Ste 300
Boca Raton, FL 33432
Tel.: (561) 368-5067
Fax: (561) 892-2618
Web Site: www.optionsmedia.com
Approx. Rev.: $7,430,760
Approx. Number Employees: 33
Year Founded: 1998
Business Description:
Bilingual Marketing, Business-To-Business, Consumer Marketing, Corporate Communications, Direct Marketing, E-Commerce, Electronic Media, Fashion/Apparel, Graphic Design, Internet/Web Design, Investor Relations, Over-50 Market, Sales Promotion, Technical Advertising, Teen Market, Travel & Tourism
S.I.C.: 7311
N.A.I.C.S.: 541810
Advertising Expenditures: $258,100
Personnel:
Keith Robert St. Clair *(Chm)*
Russell Strunk *(Pres)*
Scott Frohman *(CEO)*
Steven Stowell *(CFO & Treas)*

PULSAR ADVERTISING, INC.
8383 Wilshire Blvd Ste 334
Beverly Hills, CA 90211
Tel.: (323) 302-5110
Fax: (323) 966-4907
E-mail: agonzalez@pulsaradvertising.com
Web Site: www.pulsaradvertising.com
E-Mail For Key Personnel:
President: agonzalez@pulsaradvertising.com
Approx. Billings: $17,000,000
Approx. Number Employees: 35
Year Founded: 1992
Business Description:
Advertising Agencies, Bilingual Marketing, Brand Development, Consumer Marketing, Corporate Identity, E-Commerce, Event Marketing, Interactive Agencies, Internet/Web Design, Logo & Package Design, Planning & Consultation, Public Relations
S.I.C.: 7311
N.A.I.C.S.: 541810
Personnel:
Alberto Gonzalez *(Pres, Exec Dir-Creative)*
David Uratsu *(CFO)*
James Wright *(Reg Dir-East Coast)*
Morgan Daniels *(Assoc Dir-Creative)*
Advertising Agency:
Publicity Matters
14644 McKnew Rd
Burtonsville, MD 20866
Tel.: (301) 385-2090
(Media Relations)

RESIDENT HOME CORPORATION
3030 W Fork Rd
Cincinnati, OH 45211-1944
Tel.: (513) 389-7500
Web Site: www.rhcorp.org
Business Description:
Services Rendered for People with Developmental Disabilities
S.I.C.: 8322
N.A.I.C.S.: 624120
Media: 10-13-17
Personnel:
Patrick Maynard *(Pres & CEO)*
Chris Bohn *(CFO)*
Larry Mullins *(Dir-HR)*
Mary Beth Poulimenos *(Mgr-Mktg Comm)*

ROSE HILLS COMPANY
(Sub. of Service Corporation International)
3888 Workman Mill Rd
Whittier, CA 90601
Tel.: (562) 699-0921
Fax: (562) 576-1535
E-mail: rosehillsinformation@rosehills.com
Web Site: www.rosehills.com
Sales Range: $50-74.9 Million
Approx. Number Employees: 600
Year Founded: 1914
Business Description:
Funeral Services
S.I.C.: 6553; 5992
N.A.I.C.S.: 812220; 453110
Import Export
Media: 22
Personnel:
Kenton C. Woods *(Pres & CEO)*
Mary C. Guzman *(VP-Fin)*
Michelle Lin *(Exec Dir)*
Nick Clark *(Dir-Mktg & Comm)*
Advertising Agency:
Sense Advertising Consultant Agency
3731 Wilshire Blvd Ste 508
Los Angeles, CA 90010-2823
Tel.: (213) 385-3303
Fax: (213) 385-2755

SANTINELLI INTERNATIONAL INC.
325 Oser Ave
Hauppauge, NY 11788
Tel.: (631) 435-3343
Fax: (631) 435-9200
Toll Free: (800) 644-3343
E-mail: sales@santinelli.com
Web Site: www.santinelli.com
E-Mail For Key Personnel:
Sales Director: sales@santinelli.com
Approx. Number Employees: 65
Year Founded: 1970
Business Description:
Optical Goods
S.I.C.: 5049; 3541
N.A.I.C.S.: 423490; 333512
Personnel:
Joseph Santinelli *(Chm)*
Gerard Santinelli *(Pres & CEO)*
Rick Clemente *(Exec VP-Sls & Svc)*
Franco Aluigi *(Product Mgr)*
Brands & Products:
LE-9000SX
LEX 1000
ME-1000
SANTINELLI INTERNATIONAL
Advertising Agency:
FSC Marketing Communications
Gulf Tower 707 Grant St, Ste 2900
Pittsburgh, PA 15222
Tel.: (412) 471-3700
Fax: (412) 471-9323

SCA PROMOTIONS, INC.
3030 LBJ Freeway Ste 300
Dallas, TX 75234
Tel.: (214) 860-3700
Fax: (214) 860-3723
Toll Free: (888) 860-3700
E-mail: info@scapromo.com
Web Site: www.scapromotions.com
Sales Range: $75-99.9 Million
Approx. Number Employees: 75
Year Founded: 1986
Business Description:
Sales Promotion, Sweepstakes
S.I.C.: 7311
N.A.I.C.S.: 541810
Personnel:
Robert D. Hamman *(CEO)*
Hemant Lall *(COO)*
Tanya Mathis *(Dir-Mktg)*
Advertising Agency:
Triad Business Marketing
10670 N Central Expy Ste 300
Dallas, TX 75231
Tel.: (214) 953-6223
Fax: (214) 953-3101

SERVICE CORPORATION INTERNATIONAL
1929 Allen Pkwy
Houston, TX 77019
Tel.: (713) 522-5141
Fax: (713) 525-5586
E-mail: GeneralInquiries@sci-us.com
Web Site: www.sci-corp.com
Approx. Rev.: $2,190,552,000
Approx. Number Employees: 13,063
Year Founded: 1962
Business Description:
Funeral Homes & Cemeteries Operator, Products & Services
S.I.C.: 6553; 7261
N.A.I.C.S.: 812220; 812210
Media: 13-18-23-24-26

Key to Media (For complete agency information see *The Advertising Red Books-Agencies* edition):
1. Bus. Publs. 2. Cable T.V. 3. Catalogs & Directories. 4. Co-op Adv. 5. Consumer Mags. 6. D.M. to Bus. Estab.7. D.M. to Consumers
8. Daily Newsp. 9. Exhibits/Trade Shows 10. Foreign 11. Infomercial 12. Internet Adv.13. Multimedia 14. Network Radio
15. Network T.V. 16. Newsp. Distr. Mags. 17. Other 18. Outdoor (Posters, Transit) 19. Point of Purchase20. Premiums, Novelties
21. Product Samples 22. Special Events Mktg. 23. Spot Radio 24. Spot T.V. 25. Weekly Newsp. 26. Yellow Page Adv.

Service Corporation International — (Continued)

Personnel:
Robert L. Waltrip *(Chm)*
Thomas L. Ryan *(Pres & CEO)*
Eric D. Tanzberger *(CFO, Treas & Sr VP)*
Michael R. Webb *(COO & Exec VP)*
Philip C. Jacobs *(CMO & Sr VP)*
Gregory T. Sangalis *(Gen Counsel, Sec & Sr VP)*
Stephen M. Mack *(Sr VP-Middle Market Ops)*
Elisabeth G. Nash *(Sr VP-Ops Svcs)*
Sumner J. Waring III *(Sr VP-Major Market Ops)*
George J. Owens *(Mng Dir-Mktg)*
Joseph A. Hayes *(Asst Gen Counsel, VP-Ethics & Bus Conduct)*
John Del Mixon, II *(VP-IT)*
Jane D. Jones *(VP-HR)*
Debbie Young *(Dir-IR)*
Advertising Agency:
The Leslie Corporation
15110 Mintz Ln
Houston, TX 77014
Tel.: (281) 591-0915
Fax: (281) 591-0921

SIMS METAL MANAGEMENT

(Div. of Sims Metal Management Limited - Australia Head Office)
(d/b/a Sims Metal Management - Finance & Administration Office)
325 N LaSalle St Ste 550
Chicago, IL 60610
Tel.: (312) 645-0700
Fax: (312) 645-0570
Web Site: www.simsmm.com
Sales Range: $1-4.9 Billion
Business Description:
Holding Company; Metal Recycling Service Centers Operator
S.I.C.: 6719; 4953; 5051; 5093; 9131
N.A.I.C.S.: 551112; 423510; 423930; 562920; 921140
Media: 2-7-8-26
Personnel:
Amit N. Patel *(Chief Acctg Officer & Sr VP)*
Joseph P. Reinmann *(Exec VP-Non-Ferrous Metals)*

SPENCER REED GROUP INC.

6900 College Blvd Ste 1
Shawnee Mission, KS 66211
Tel.: (913) 663-4400
Fax: (913) 663-4410
Web Site: www.spencerreed.com
Approx. Sls.: $66,922,653
Approx. Number Employees: 105
Business Description:
Placement Agencies
S.I.C.: 7361; 7363
N.A.I.C.S.: 561310; 561320
Personnel:
William T. Solon *(Pres & CEO)*
Advertising Agency:
Morris Advertising Inc.
16229 W 65th Pl
Arvada, CO 80007
Tel.: (303) 431-5087
Fax: (303) 380-9630

ST. MARY'S MEDICAL CENTER

(Sub. of Catholic Healthcare West Southern California)
450 Stanyan St
San Francisco, CA 94117-1079
Tel.: (415) 668-1000
Fax: (415) 668-4531
E-mail: info@stmarysmedicalcenter.org
Web Site: www.stmarysmedicalcenter.org
Approx. Number Employees: 150
S.I.C.: 8093; 7335; 8099
N.A.I.C.S.: 621410; 541922; 621999
Advertising Agency:
Motivo
205 E Third Ave Ste 303
San Mateo, CA 94401
Tel.: (650) 996-1108
Fax: (650) 532-0519

STONEMOR PARTNERS L.P.

311 Veterans Hwy Ste B
Levittown, PA 19056
Tel.: (215) 826-2800
Fax: (215) 826-2851
E-mail: WebMaster@StoneMor.com
Web Site: www.stonemor.com/
Approx. Rev.: $197,292,000
Approx. Number Employees: 2,156
Year Founded: 1999
Business Description:
Cemetery Subdividers & Developers
S.I.C.: 6553
N.A.I.C.S.: 812220
Import Export
Media: 8-13-17
Personnel:
Lawrence Miller *(Chm, Pres & CEO)*
William R. Shane *(CFO & Exec VP)*
Michael L. Stache *(COO & Sr VP)*
Paul Waimberg *(VP-Fin)*

TARGUSINFO

8010 Towers Crescent Dr
Vienna, VA 22182
Tel.: (703) 272-6200
Fax: (703) 272-6201
Toll Free: (800) 682-7487
E-mail: pr@targusinfo.com
Web Site: www.targusinfo.com
Approx. Rev.: $100,000,000
Approx. Number Employees: 150
Year Founded: 1993
Business Description:
Business Information Services
S.I.C.: 7389; 2741
N.A.I.C.S.: 519190; 511140
Personnel:
George Moore *(Chm & CEO)*
Mike Sullivan *(CFO & Exec VP)*
Dennis G. Ainge *(Exec VP-Corp Dev)*
Jim Schaffer *(Exec VP)*
Craig Schmackpfeffer *(VP-Engrg)*
Advertising Agency:
Datamark Inc.
2305 Presidents Dr
Salt Lake City, UT 84120-7230
Tel.: (801) 886-2002
Fax: (801) 886-0102
Toll Free: (800) 279-9335

TARP WORLDWIDE

2425 Wilson Blvd Ste 400
Arlington, VA 22201
Tel.: (703) 524-1456
Fax: (703) 524-6374
E-mail: info@tarp.com
Web Site: www.tarp.com
Approx. Number Employees: 100
Year Founded: 1971
Business Description:
Customer Experience Research Consultancy
S.I.C.: 8732
N.A.I.C.S.: 541910
Personnel:
John Goodman *(Vice Chm)*
Dennis Gonier *(CEO)*
Crystal D. Collier *(COO & Sr VP-Practices)*
Brands & Products:
BEACON
BELLWETHER
FANFARE
HARMONY
LANDMARK
PERFECT PITCH
Advertising Agency:
Strategic Communications Group
1400 Spring St Ste 330
Silver Spring, MD 20910
Tel.: (301) 408-4500
Fax: (301) 408-4506
(Social Media Campaign)

TELEBRANDS, INC.

79 Two Bridges Rd
Fairfield, NJ 07004
Tel.: (973) 244-0300
Web Site: www.telebrands.com
Approx. Rev.: $6,900,000
Approx. Number Employees: 34
Year Founded: 1987
Business Description:
Designs, Manufactures & Promotes Personal Care, Pet Care & Home Products
S.I.C.: 5023
N.A.I.C.S.: 423220
Media: 6-15
Personnel:
Ajit Khubani *(Pres)*
Lois Sischeach *(Office Mgr)*
Shail Prasad *(Mgr-Mktg)*
Brands & Products:
BARKOFF
Advertising Agency:
Steinreich Communications
411 Hackensack Ave
Hackensack, NJ 07601
Tel.: (201) 498-1600
Fax: (201) 498-1590

TITAN

850 Third Ave
New York, NY 10022
Tel.: (212) 644-6200
Fax: (212) 644-2010
Web Site: www.titan360.com
Sales Range: $450-499.9 Million
Approx. Number Employees: 700
Year Founded: 2001
Business Description:
Full Service Advertising
S.I.C.: 7311
N.A.I.C.S.: 541810
Personnel:
William M. Apfelbaum *(Chm)*
Donald R. Allman *(CEO)*
Craig Abolt *(CFO, Chief Admin Officer & Exec VP)*
Scott E. Goldsmith *(Pres-Transit)*
Reid S. Schuster *(Pres-Sls & Mktg)*
Jamie Lowe *(Exec VP & Mgr-Sls-Natl)*
Dave Etherington *(Sr VP & Dir-Mktg)*
Stephen Hillwig *(Sr VP & Dir-Ops-North America)*
Mike Collins *(VP & Gen Mgr)*
Natalie Tomasella *(Dir-Mktg)*
Chris Pezzello *(Mgr-Sls)*
Advertising Agency:
KCSA Strategic Communications (Kanan, Corbin, Schupak & Aronow, Inc.)
880 3rd Ave 6th Fl
New York, NY 10022
Tel.: (212) 682-6300
Fax: (212) 697-0910

TRINITYCARE SENIOR LIVING, INC.

227 E Edgewood Ave
Friendswood, TX 77546
Tel.: (281) 482-9700
Fax: (281) 482-9705
Web Site: www.trinitycare.com
Approx. Rev.: $6,484,598
Approx. Number Employees: 100
Business Description:
Senior Housing
S.I.C.: 8361
N.A.I.C.S.: 623312
Advertising Expenditures: $321,743
Personnel:
Donald W. Sapaugh *(Chm & CEO)*
Joe M. Wiley *(CFO)*

UNDERWRITERS LABORATORIES INC.

333 Pfingsten Rd
Northbrook, IL 60062-2096
Tel.: (847) 272-8800
Fax: (847) 272-8129
Toll Free: (877) ULHELPS
E-mail: cec@us.ul.com
Web Site: www.ul.com
Approx. Sls.: $607,400,000
Approx. Number Employees: 2,000
Year Founded: 1894
Business Description:
Product Safety Testing Services
S.I.C.: 8734
N.A.I.C.S.: 541380
Media: 10-11-13
Personnel:
Keith E. Williams *(Pres & CEO)*
Christian Anschuetz *(CIO)*
Sara Greenstein *(Sr VP, CMO & Chief Strategy Officer)*
Don Mader *(CTO & Exec VP)*
Randy Haseman *(Principal Engr)*
Jim Beyreis *(VP-Tech)*
Jane Coen *(Mgr-Corp Citizenship-Global)*
Brands & Products:
UNDERWRITERS LABORATORIES

VISANT HOLDING CORP.

(Joint Venture of KKR & CO. L.P. & Credit Suisse Group AG)
357 Main St
Armonk, NY 10504
Tel.: (914) 595-8200
Fax: (914) 595-8239
E-mail: paul.carousso@visant.net
Web Site: www.visant.net
Approx. Sls.: $1,255,325,000
Approx. Number Employees: 5,250
Year Founded: 2004
Business Description:
Holding Company; Owned by KKR & Co. L.P. & by DLJ Merchant Banking Partners

Key to Media (For complete agency information see *The Advertising Red Books-Agencies* edition):
1. Bus. Publs. 2. Cable T.V. 3. Catalogs & Directories. 4. Co-op Adv. 5. Consumer Mags. 6. D.M. to Bus. Estab.7. D.M. to Consumers 8. Daily Newsp. 9. Exhibits/Trade Shows 10. Foreign 11. Infomercial 12. Internet Adv.13. Multimedia 14. Network Radio 15. Network T.V. 16. Newsp. Distr. Mags. 17. Other 18. Outdoor (Posters, Transit) 19. Point of Purchase20. Premiums, Novelties 21. Product Samples 22. Special Events Mktg. 23. Spot Radio 24. Spot T.V. 25. Weekly Newsp. 26. Yellow Page Adv.

S.I.C.: 6719
N.A.I.C.S.: 551112
Advertising Expenditures: $5,500,000
Personnel:
Marc L. Reisch *(Chm, Pres & CEO)*
Paul B. Carousso *(CFO & Sr VP)*
Marie D. Hlavaty *(Gen Counsel & VP)*

WES CONSULTING, INC.
2745 Bankers Industrial Dr
Atlanta, GA 30360
Tel.: (770) 246-6400
E-mail: ron.scott@liberator.com
Web Site: www.liberator.com
Approx. Sls.: $11,079,760
Approx. Number Employees: 108
Year Founded: 1999
Business Description:
Sexual Wellness Retailer
S.I.C.: 5999; 5961
N.A.I.C.S.: 453998; 454111; 454113
Advertising Expenditures: $682,332
Personnel:
Louis S. Friedman *(Chm, Pres & CEO)*
Ronald P. Scott *(CFO & Sec)*
Fyodor Petrenko *(Exec VP)*

WINSTON ADVERTISING
122 E 42nd St
New York, NY 10168
Tel.: (212) 682-1063
Fax: (212) 983-2594
Toll Free: (800) 562-2371
E-mail: winston@winston.net
Web Site: www.winston.net
E-Mail For Key Personnel:
President: bpapkin@winston.net
Sales Range: Less than $1 Million
Approx. Number Employees: 10
Year Founded: 1984
Business Description:
Magazines, Print, Radio, Real Estate, Recruitment
S.I.C.: 7311
N.A.I.C.S.: 541810
Personnel:
Sy Kaye *(Chm)*
Bruce Papkin *(Pres)*
Jesse Ulezalka *(CFO)*
Advertising Agency:
Forward Media Inc.
245 8th Ave Ste 129
New York, NY 10011
Tel.: (646) 290-7535

XZERES WIND CORP.
9025 SW Hillman Ct Ste 3126
Wilsonville, OR 97070
Tel.: (503) 388-7350
Fax: (503) 212-0109
E-mail: info@xzeres.com
Web Site: www.xzeres.com
Approx. Rev.: $1,489,061
Approx. Number Employees: 38
Business Description:
Wind Turbine Systems & Equipment Mfr
S.I.C.: 3511
N.A.I.C.S.: 333611
Advertising Expenditures: $70,849
Media: 17
Personnel:
David N. Baker *(Chm)*
Frank Greco *(Pres & CEO)*
Steven Shum *(CFO & Sec)*
S. Clayton Wood *(Exec VP-Ops)*
Brands & Products:
XZERES 110
XZERES 442SR

YAMANA GOLD INC.
150 York Street Suite 1102
Toronto, ON M5H 3S5, Canada
Tel.: (416) 815-0220
Fax: (416) 815-0021
E-mail: investor@yamana.com
Web Site: www.yamana.com
Approx. Rev.: $1,686,811,000
Approx. Number Employees: 4,513
Year Founded: 2003
Business Description:
Gold Mining Properties Acquirer, Explorer & Developer
S.I.C.: 1041; 1021; 1081; 1099
N.A.I.C.S.: 212221; 212234; 212299; 213114
Personnel:
Peter J. Marrone *(Chm & CEO)*
Ludovico Costa *(Pres & COO)*
Charles B. Main *(CFO & Exec VP-Fin)*
Betty Soares *(Chief Acctg Officer, VP & Corp Controller)*
Sofia Tsakos *(Gen Counsel, Corp Sec & VP)*
Jason LeBlanc *(Treas & VP-Fin)*
Evandro Cintra *(Sr VP-Tech Svcs)*
Darcy E. Marud *(Sr VP-Exploration)*
Greg Mcknight *(Sr VP-Bus Dev)*
Lisa Doddridge *(VP-Corp Comm & IR)*
Letitia Wong *(Dir-IR)*
Advertising Agency:
Mansfield Communications, Inc.
225 Richmond Street West Suite 302
Toronto, ON M5V 1W2, Canada
Tel.: (416) 599-0024
Fax: (416) 599-7484

ZENTRIC, INC.
Unit C2 802 Southdown Road
Mississauga, ON L5J 2Y4, Canada
Tel.: (416) 245-8000
Year Founded: 2008
Business Description:
Battery Technology Services
S.I.C.: 3692; 8733
N.A.I.C.S.: 335912; 541710
Advertising Expenditures: $50,000
Media: 17
Personnel:
Jeff Mak *(Pres, CEO, CFO, Treas & Sec)*

Key to Media (For complete agency information see *The Advertising Red Books-Agencies* edition):
1. Bus. Publs. 2. Cable T.V. 3. Catalogs & Directories. 4. Co-op Adv. 5. Consumer Mags. 6. D.M. to Bus. Estab.7. D.M. to Consumers 8. Daily Newsp. 9. Exhibits/Trade Shows 10. Foreign 11. Infomercial 12. Internet Adv.13. Multimedia 14. Network Radio 15. Network T.V. 16. Newsp. Distr. Mags. 17. Other 18. Outdoor (Posters, Transit) 19. Point of Purchase20. Premiums, Novelties 21. Product Samples 22. Special Events Mktg. 23. Spot Radio 24. Spot T.V. 25. Weekly Newsp. 26. Yellow Page Adv.

Optical, Photo & Scientific Instruments

Cameras — Clocks — Contact Lenses — Controlling Instruments — Eyeglasses — Lenses — Optical Goods — Photo Finishing Services — Photo Supplies

1-800 CONTACTS, INC.
(Holding of Fenway Partners, Inc.)
66 E Wadsworth Park Dr 3rd Fl
Draper, UT 84020-7942
Tel.: (801) 924-9800
Fax: (801) 924-9905
Toll Free: (800) CONTACTS
E-mail: info@1800contacts.com
Web Site: www.1800contacts.com
Approx. Sls.: $248,676,000
Approx. Number Employees: 1,101
Year Founded: 1995
Business Description:
Contact Lens Retailer
S.I.C.: 5995; 5961
N.A.I.C.S.: 446130; 454111; 454113
Advertising Expenditures: $13,600,000
Media: 1-3-4-6-8-13-15-16-18-20-22-23-24
Personnel:
Jonathan C. Coon *(Owner)*
Brian W. Bethers *(Pres)*
Robert G. Hunter *(CFO)*
John R. Murray *(CIO & VP)*
Joan Blackwood *(CMO)*
R. Joe Zeidner *(Chief Legal Officer, Gen Counsel & Sec)*
Max Neves *(VP-HR)*
Joel Sodano *(VP-Mdsg-Glasses.com)*
Brands & Products:
1-800 CONTACTS
LENS 1ST
LENS EXPRESS
WE DELIVER, YOU SAVE.
Advertising Agencies:
Duncan Channon
114 Sansome St 14th Fl
San Francisco, CA 94104
Tel.: (415) 306-9200
Fax: (415) 306-9201
Agency of Record
Creative
Strategic Branding

Ingenuity Media Group at The Martin Agency
1 Shockoe Plz
Richmond, VA 23219-4132
Tel.: (804) 698-8600
Fax: (804) 698-8401
Media Buying
Media Planning

AAI.FOSTERGRANT, INC.
George Washington Hwy
Smithfield, RI 02917-1926
Tel.: (401) 231-3800
Fax: (401) 232-7235
E-mail: info@fgx.com
Web Site: www.fgx.com
Approx. Sls.: $87,000,000
Approx. Number Employees: 400
Year Founded: 1971
Business Description:
Mfr. & Marketer of Sunglasses & Other Accessories
S.I.C.: 5199
N.A.I.C.S.: 424990
Media: 2-8-10-19-23
Personnel:
John H. Flynn, Jr. *(Exec VP)*
Brands & Products:
ANARCHY
ANGEL
FOSTERGRANT
G-FORCE
GARGOYLES
GXP
IDOLEYEZ
Advertising Agency:
Phillips Design Group
25 Drydock Ave
Boston, MA 02210
Tel.: (617) 423-7676

ABB INC. - AUTOMATION TECHNOLOGIES INSTRUMENTATION PRODUCTS
(Div. of ABB Inc.)
125 E County Line Rd
Warminster, PA 18974-4995
Tel.: (215) 674-6000
Fax: (215) 674-7183
Toll Free: (800) 829-6001
Web Site: www.abb.us
Approx. Number Employees: 500
Year Founded: 1937
Business Description:
Process Control Instruments & Systems Mfr
S.I.C.: 3823
N.A.I.C.S.: 334513
Import Export
Media: 6-10
Distr.: Dir. To Consumer; Intl.; Natl.; Reg.
Budget Set: Oct.
Personnel:
Robert Mapleston *(Mgr-Mktg)*

ACACIA RESEARCH CORPORATION
500 Newport Ctr Dr 7th Fl
Newport Beach, CA 92660-7007
Tel.: (949) 480-8300
Fax: (949) 480-8301
E-mail: info@acaciares.com
Web Site: www.acaciaresearch.com
Approx. Rev.: $131,829,000
Approx. Number Employees: 48
Year Founded: 1999
Business Description:
Engineering, Production & Research Services
S.I.C.: 3679; 6289; 7371
N.A.I.C.S.: 334419; 523999; 541511
Advertising Expenditures: $253,000
Personnel:
Paul R. Ryan *(Chm & CEO)*
Robert L. Harris, II *(Pres)*
Clayton J Haynes *(CFO)*
Edward J. Treska *(Gen Counsel, Sec & Sr VP)*
Dooyong Lee *(Exec VP)*
Robert Stewart *(Sr VP-Corp Fin)*
Jeffrey Anderson *(VP-Engrg)*
Debbie Stephen *(Dir-Ops)*
Brands & Products:
DIGITAL MEDIA TRANSMISSION

ADORAMA CAMERA INC.
42 W 18th St
New York, NY 10011
Tel.: (212) 741-0052
Fax: (212) 645-4533
Fax: (212) 741-9087
Toll Free: (800) 223-2500
E-mail: sales@adorama.com
Web Site: www.adorama.com
E-Mail For Key Personnel:
Sales Director: sales@adorama.com
Approx. Sls.: $20,900,000
Approx. Number Employees: 45
Business Description:
Mail Order of Cameras & Photography Supplies
S.I.C.: 5961; 5946
N.A.I.C.S.: 454113; 443130
Media: 4-5-13
Personnel:
Mendel Mendelowits *(Pres)*
Brian Green *(VP-Mktg)*

ADVANCED DIGITAL PHOTO SOLUTIONS, INC.
(d/b/a PrintRoom.com)
2520 Mission College Blvd Ste 102
Santa Clara, CA 95054
Tel.: (408) 855-0771
Toll Free: (888) 868-4157
E-mail: support@printroom.com
Web Site: www.printroom.com
Approx. Number Employees: 30
Year Founded: 2001
Business Description:
Digital Services
S.I.C.: 7384
N.A.I.C.S.: 812921
Advertising Expenditures: $300,000
Media: 2-10-20-22
Personnel:
Mike Kapul *(Pres)*
Carlton Osborne *(CEO)*
Brands & Products:
DVD PHOTOSHOW
PRINTROOM DIRECT
PRO STUDIO MANAGER

ADVANCED PHOTONIX, INC.
2925 Boardwalk
Ann Arbor, MI 48104
Tel.: (734) 864-5600
Fax: (734) 998-3474
E-mail: ir@advancedphotonix.com
Web Site: www.advancedphotonix.com
E-Mail For Key Personnel:
Sales Director: sales@advancedphotonix.com
Approx. Sls.: $28,838,000
Approx. Number Employees: 185
Year Founded: 1988
Business Description:
Optoelectronic Devices, Systems & Sub-Systems Developer & Mfr
S.I.C.: 3674
N.A.I.C.S.: 334413
Advertising Expenditures: $76,000
Media: 2-4
Personnel:
Richard D. Kurtz *(Chm & CEO)*
Jeffrey Anderson *(CFO)*
Robin F. Risser *(COO)*

Key to Media (For complete agency information see *The Advertising Red Books-Agencies* edition):
1. Bus. Publs. 2. Cable T.V. 3. Catalogs & Directories. 4. Co-op Adv. 5. Consumer Mags. 6. D.M. to Bus. Estab.7. D.M. to Consumers 8. Daily Newsp. 9. Exhibits/Trade Shows 10. Foreign 11. Infomercial 12. Internet Adv.13. Multimedia 14. Network Radio 15. Network T.V. 16. Newsp. Distr. Mags. 17. Other 18. Outdoor (Posters, Transit) 19. Point of Purchase20. Premiums, Novelties 21. Product Samples 22. Special Events Mktg. 23. Spot Radio 24. Spot T.V. 25. Weekly Newsp. 26. Yellow Page Adv.

Brands & Products:
ADVANCED PHOTONIX
API
FILTRODE
T-RAY

AGFA CORPORATION
(Sub. of Agfa-Gevaert N.V.)
100 Challenger Rd
Ridgefield Park, NJ 07660
Tel.: (201) 440-2500
Fax: (201) 342-4742
Web Site: www.agfa.com
Approx. Number Employees: 100
Year Founded: 1989
Business Description:
Mfr & Marketer Electronic Imaging Systems for Medical Pre-Press & Photography Processes; Mfr of Films, Laser Imaging Systems & Digital Radiography Systems
S.I.C.: 3861; 7379
N.A.I.C.S.: 333315; 541519
Import Export
Media: 2-7-8-9-10-11-13-20-22
Distr.: Natl.
Personnel:
Gunther Mertens *(CFO & VP)*
Deborah Hutcheson *(Dir-Mktg-Graphics-North America)*
Peter Wilkens *(Dir-Newspaper Segment)*
Brands & Products:
MAMORAY

AGILTRON, INC.
15 Cabot Rd
Woburn, MA 01801
Tel.: (781) 935-1200
Fax: (781) 935-2040
E-mail: info@agiltron.com
Web Site: www.agiltron.com
Sales Range: $25-49.9 Million
Approx. Number Employees: 85
Year Founded: 2001
Business Description:
Optic Components & Systems Developer & Producer
S.I.C.: 4899; 3357
N.A.I.C.S.: 517910; 335921
Media: 10
Personnel:
Jack Salerno *(Pres)*
Jing Zhao *(CEO)*

THE A.H. EMERY COMPANY
73 Cogwheel Ln
Seymour, CT 06483
Tel.: (203) 881-9333
Fax: (203) 881-9477
Toll Free: (800) 891-3952
E-mail: homeoffice@emerywinslow.com
Web Site: www.emerywinslow.com
Approx. Number Employees: 100
Business Description:
Mfr & Distr of Scales
S.I.C.: 3596
N.A.I.C.S.: 333997
Export
Media: 2-7-10-11-13
Personnel:
William Fischer *(Pres)*

ALAN GORDON ENTERPRISES, INC.
5625 Melrose Ave
Los Angeles, CA 90038-3909
Tel.: (323) 466-3561
Fax: (323) 871-2193
E-mail: contactus@alangordon.com
Web Site: www.alangordon.com
Approx. Sls.: $5,000,000
Approx. Number Employees: 25
Year Founded: 1945
Business Description:
Mfr. & Retailer of Professional Motion Picture Equipment, Aerial Reconnaissance Equipment, Photo Instrumentation Equipment & Photogrammetric Equipment
S.I.C.: 3861; 7359
N.A.I.C.S.: 532210; 325992; 333315; 532299; 532310; 532420; 532490
Import Export
Media: 2-4-7-8-10-11-13-26
Distr.: Direct to Consumer; Natl.
Budget Set: Oct.
Personnel:
Grant Loucks *(Owner)*
Brands & Products:
A-G-E
APPLE BOXES
DV CAMCORDERS
GSAP
HI-HAT
IMAGE 300
LO-HAT
MARK VB
MC-1
MINICAM
NCE
POCKET MINI
SLAM CAM
SONIC PLUS
SUNDOG
SUPER GRIP
TRINITAR
ZEPPELIN
Advertising Agency:
Alan Gordon Advertising
5625 Melrose Ave
Los Angeles, CA 90038-3909
Tel.: (323) 466-3561
Fax: (323) 871-2193
(Products & Services for T.V. & Film Industry)

ALLIANCE FIBER OPTIC PRODUCTS, INC.
(d/b/a AFOP)
275 Gibraltar Dr
Sunnyvale, CA 94089-2918
Tel.: (408) 736-6900
Fax: (408) 736-4882
E-mail: sales@afop.com
Web Site: www.afop.com/
E-Mail For Key Personnel:
Sales Director: sales@afop.com
Approx. Rev.: $45,406,000
Approx. Number Employees: 1,137
Year Founded: 1995
Business Description:
Mfr. of Fiber Optic Components & Integrated Modules
S.I.C.: 3674; 3661
N.A.I.C.S.: 334413; 334210
Media: 2-7-10
Personnel:
Helen Chan *(Pres & CEO)*
Peter C. Chang *(CEO)*
Wei-Shin Tsay *(Sr VP-Product Dev)*
David A. Hubbard *(VP-Sls & Mktg)*
Brands & Products:
AFOP
THE ART & SCIENCE OF FIBER OPTICS
FUSED-LOCK
MICS
OPIS
QUICKPATH
SCOUT
SPECTRAMAX
TRIWAVE
Advertising Agency:
Robert Goldberg & Associates
315 Central Ave
Alameda, CA 94501
Tel.: (510) 238-0800
Fax: (510) 238-8554

AMERICAN MEDICAL SYSTEMS, INC.
(Branch of American Medical Systems, Inc.)
3052 Orchard Dr
San Jose, CA 95134-2011
Tel.: (408) 943-0636
Fax: (408) 943-9630
Fax: (408) 943-4162
Sales Range: $75-99.9 Million
Approx. Number Employees: 296
Year Founded: 1984
Business Description:
Designer, Mfr, Sales & Servicer of Medical Laser Equipment & Systems
S.I.C.: 3845
N.A.I.C.S.: 334510
Export
Media: 2-7-10-22
Brands & Products:
800 SERIES KTP/YAG
ACCUSTAT
ADD/STAT
ANGLED MICROSTATS
AURA
AURA-I
BARE ENDOSTATS
BAYONET MICROSTATS
COOLSPOT
CURVED MICROSTATS
DEMASTATS
DERMASTAT
DISCKIT
ENDO-SUCTION SINUS MICROSTATS
ENDOSTAT
GEMINI
GREENLIGHT PV SYSTEM
HEALING WITH LIGHT
KTP/532
KTP/YAG
LAPROSTAT
LASERSCOPE
LYRA
LYRA-I
MICROBEAM
MICRONSPOT
MICROSTAT
ORION
SCULPTURED ENDOSTATS
SMARTSCAN
SOLIS
SPINESTAT
STARPULSE
STRAIGHT MICROSTATS
VENUS
VENUS-I
VERSASTAT
VERSASTAT I

AMERICAN SCIENCE AND ENGINEERING, INC.
829 Middlesex Tpke
Billerica, MA 01821-3907
Tel.: (978) 262-8700
Fax: (978) 262-8804
Toll Free: (800) 225-1608
E-mail: ir@as-e.com
Web Site: www.as-e.com
E-Mail For Key Personnel:
President: AFabiano@as-e.com
Public Relations: lberman@as-e.com
Approx. Rev.: $278,576,000
Approx. Number Employees: 420
Year Founded: 1958
Business Description:
Mfr, Developer & Marketer of X-Ray Inspection Systems, Instrumentation Used in Scientific Applications & Industry Control Systems
S.I.C.: 3844; 3826
N.A.I.C.S.: 334517; 334516
Import Export
Media: 2-4-7-10-13
Personnel:
Denis R. Brown *(Chm)*
Anthony R. Fabiano *(Pres & CEO)*
Kenneth J. Galaznik *(CFO, Treas & Sr VP)*
Patricia A. Gray *(Gen Counsel & Sr VP)*
Kenneth A. Breur *(Sr VP-Advanced Dev & Logistics)*
Joseph Callerame *(Sr VP-Science & Tech)*
Robert Cline *(Sr VP-Ops)*
Paul H. Grazewski *(Sr VP-Strategic Plng)*
George M. Peterman *(Sr VP-HR)*
Robert G. Postle *(Sr VP-Worldwide Sls & Mktg)*
Michael N. Tropeano *(Sr VP-Product Mgmt)*
Michael Williams *(Sr VP-Engrg & Dev)*
Laura Berman *(Dir-Corp Comm)*
Brands & Products:
101 GT
101 Z
101 ZZ
101GT
101VAN
101Z
66Z
AS AND E
AS&E-EDS
BODYSEARCH
CARGOSEARCH
CUSTOMS & BORDER PROTECTION
FLYING SPOT
GEMINI
INSPECTION
ISO SEARCH
ISOSEARCH
MICRO-DOSE
MOBILESEARCH
MODEL 101ZZ
OMNIVIEW
PALLETSEARCH
PARCELSEARCH
RADIOACTIVE THREAT DETECTION
SENTRY
SHAPED ENERGY
SMART CHECK
WHERE YOU CAN'T AFFORD TO COMPROMISE

Key to Media (For complete agency information see *The Advertising Red Books-Agencies* edition):
1. Bus. Publs. 2. Cable T.V. 3. Catalogs & Directories. 4. Co-op Adv. 5. Consumer Mags. 6. D.M. to Bus. Estab.7. D.M. to Consumers
8. Daily Newsp. 9. Exhibits/Trade Shows 10. Foreign 11. Infomercial 12. Internet Adv.13. Multimedia 14. Network Radio
15. Network T.V. 16. Newsp. Distr. Mags. 17. Other 18. Outdoor (Posters, Transit) 19. Point of Purchase20. Premiums, Novelties
21. Product Samples 22. Special Events Mktg. 23. Spot Radio 24. Spot T.V. 25. Weekly Newsp. 26. Yellow Page Adv.

American Science and Engineering, Inc. — (Continued)

Z BACKSCATTER
Z BACKSCATTER VAN
Z PORTAL

ANALOGIC CORPORATION
8 Centennial Dr
Peabody, MA 01960-7902
Tel.: (978) 326-4000
Fax: (978) 977-6809
E-mail: csd@analogic.com
Web Site: www.analogic.com
Approx. Rev.: $423,597,000
Approx. Number Employees: 1,400
Year Founded: 1967
Business Description:
Medical & Security Imaging Systems & Subsystems Developer, Designer & Mfr
S.I.C.: 3825; 3577; 3827
N.A.I.C.S.: 334515; 333314; 334119
Import Export
Media: 2-10-20-26
Distr.: Intl.; Natl.
Budget Set: June
Personnel:
Edward F. Voboril *(Chm)*
Gerald L. Wilson *(Vice Chm)*
James W. Green *(Pres & CEO)*
John J. Fry *(Gen Counsel, Corp Sec & VP)*
Peter Cempellin *(Corp VP & Gen Mgr)*
John P. O'Connor *(VP-Engineering & Tech)*
Douglas B. Rosenfeld *(VP-HR)*
Lonnie Weaver *(Gen Mgr-LifeCare)*
Brands & Products:
ANALOGIC
COBRA
EXACT
FETALGARD
FETALGARDLITE
LIFEGARD
POWERLINK

ANGIODYNAMICS
(Formerly RITA Medical Systems, Inc.)
(Sub. of AngioDynamics, Inc.)
46421 Landing Pkwy
Fremont, CA 94538-6496
Tel.: (510) 771-0400
Fax: (510) 771-0460
Fax: (877) 467-9501
Toll Free: (800) 472-5221
Web Site: www.angiodynamics.com
Sales Range: $25-49.9 Million
Approx. Number Employees: 221
Year Founded: 1994
Business Description:
Medical Devices Mfr
S.I.C.: 3845; 3841
N.A.I.C.S.: 334510; 339112
Advertising Expenditures: $198,000
Media: 2-7-10
Personnel:
Sean Morris *(VP-Mktg)*
Stephen Pedroff *(VP-Mktg Comm)*
Brands & Products:
HABIB
RITA
STARBURST
XLI
XLI ENHANCED

APPLIED BIOSYSTEMS INC.
(Sub. of Life Technologies Corporation)
850 Lincoln Centre Drive
Foster City, CA 94404
Tel.: (650) 638-5800
Toll Free: (800) 327-3002
Telex: 96-5954
Web Site:
www3.appliedbiosystems.com/AB_Home/index.htm
Sales Range: $1-4.9 Billion
Approx. Number Employees: 5,000
Year Founded: 1939
Business Description:
Instrument-Based Systems, Reagents, Software Developer & Contract-Related Services to Life Science Industries; Genomic & Related Medical Information
S.I.C.: 8733; 3826
N.A.I.C.S.: 541710; 334516
Media: 2-4-7-10-22
Distr.: Intl.; Natl.
Budget Set: May
Personnel:
William B. Sawch *(Gen Counsel & Sr VP)*
Barbara J. Kerr *(Sr VP-HR)*
Brands & Products:
ABI
ABI PRISM
ABI PRISM 310
AMPF/STR
AMPF/STR COFILER
CELERA
CHEMPUTER
COFILER
FMAT
LIMS 2000
MARINER
MASTERLAB SYSTEM
NORTHSTAR
QSTAR
TROPIX

APPLIED IMAGE GROUP INC.
1653 E Main St
Rochester, NY 14609
Tel.: (585) 482-0300
Fax: (585) 224-0402
E-mail: corporate@appliedimage.com
Web Site: www.appliedimage.com
Approx. Number Employees: 22
Business Description:
Optical Elements & Assemblies; Except Ophthalmic
S.I.C.: 3827
N.A.I.C.S.: 333314
Media: 2-4-10-13
Personnel:
David Doubletee *(Pres)*
Brands & Products:
ACCU-PLACE
APPLIED IMAGE INC

ARIZONA INSTRUMENT LLC
3375 N Delaware St
Chandler, AZ 85225
Tel.: (602) 470-1414
Fax: (602) 804-0656
Toll Free: (800) 528-7411
E-mail: azic@azic.com
Web Site: www.azic.com
E-Mail For Key Personnel:
Marketing Director: marketing@azic.com
Sales Director: sales@azic.com
Sales Range: $75-99.9 Million
Approx. Number Employees: 60
Year Founded: 1981
Business Description:
Quality Control Instruments & Environmental Monitoring Instruments Mfr, Designer & Marketer
S.I.C.: 3823; 3829
N.A.I.C.S.: 334513; 334519
Export
Media: 2-4-5-7-8-10-11-13
Distr.: Intl.; Natl.
Budget Set: Dec.
Personnel:
George G. Hays *(Pres & CEO)*
Rick Ervin *(Dir-Sls)*
Brands & Products:
431-X MERCURY VAPOR ANALYZER
631-X HYDROGEN SULFIDE ANALYZER
ARIZONA INSTRUMENT
BAPOR PRO RX
COMPUTRAC
C.T. 3000
HYDRO PRO
JEROME
MAX
MAX 1000-MOISTURE ANALYZER
MAX 2000-MOISTURE ANALYZER
MAX 2000XL
MAX-50
VAPOR PRO

ARKWRIGHT, INC.
(Sub. of Oce-USA Holding, Inc.)
538 Main St
Fiskeville, RI 02823
Tel.: (401) 821-1000
Fax: (401) 826-3926
Web Site: www.arkwright.com
Approx. Number Employees: 500
Year Founded: 1810
Business Description:
Mfr. of Overhead Transparency Films & other Specialized Reprographics Films
S.I.C.: 3861; 2671
N.A.I.C.S.: 325992; 322221
Advertising Expenditures: $1,000,000
Media: 4-8-10-11-21
Distr.: Intl.; Natl.
Budget Set: Oct.
Brands & Products:
COPY VIEW
DATA VIEW
DURESTER
LASERKEY
THERMAVIEW
ULTRA DURABLE

ART ADVANCED RESEARCH TECHNOLOGIES INC.
2300 Alfred Nobel Boulevard
Saint Laurent, QC H4S 2A4, Canada
Tel.: (514) 832-0777
Fax: (514) 832-0778
E-mail: info@art.ca
Web Site: www.art.ca
E-Mail For Key Personnel:
Public Relations: PCouture@art.ca
Sales Range: $1-9.9 Million
Approx. Number Employees: 58
Year Founded: 1993
Business Description:
Optical Imaging Products Developer, Mfr & Marketer
S.I.C.: 3827; 3841
N.A.I.C.S.: 333314; 339112
Advertising Expenditures: $350,000
Media: 10-13
Personnel:
Sebastien Gignac *(Chm, Pres & CEO)*
Jacques Bedard *(CFO)*
Marie-France Nantel *(Gen Counsel & Corp Sec)*
Brands & Products:
ART
EXPLORE OPTIX
FENESTRA
OPTISCAN
OPTIVIEW
OPTIX
OPTIX MX2
OPTIX MX3
OPTIXCARE
SEE THE CURE
SOFTSCAN

ASCENT HEALTHCARE SOLUTIONS, INC.
(Sub. of Stryker Corporation)
10232 S 51st St
Phoenix, AZ 85044
Tel.: (480) 763-5300
Fax: (480) 763-5310
Toll Free: (888) 888-3433
Web Site: www.ascenths.com
Sales Range: $100-124.9 Million
Approx. Number Employees: 900
Business Description:
Medical Device Reprocessing & Remanufacturing
S.I.C.: 3841
N.A.I.C.S.: 339112
Media: 4
Personnel:
Rick Michael Ferreira *(COO)*

ASPEN SURGICAL PRODUCTS, INC.
(Sub. of Aspen Surgical Products Holdings, Inc.)
6945 Southbelt Dr SE
Caledonia, MI 49316
Tel.: (616) 698-7100
Fax: (616) 698-9281
Toll Free: (888) 364-7004
E-mail: customerservice@aspensurgical.com
Web Site: www.aspensurgical.com
Approx. Number Employees: 250
Business Description:
Surgical Products
S.I.C.: 3841
N.A.I.C.S.: 339112
Media: 4-10-21
Personnel:
Terry O'Rourke *(Pres)*
Terry Meredith *(Sr VP-Sls & Mktg)*

ASSOCIATED RESEARCH INC.
(Sub. of Ikonix Group, Inc.)
13860 W Laurel Dr
Lake Forest, IL 60045-4531
Tel.: (847) 367-4077
Fax: (847) 367-4080
Toll Free: (800) 858-8378
E-mail: info@asresearch.com
Web Site: www.asresearch.com
Approx. Number Employees: 60
Year Founded: 1936
Business Description:
Mfr. & Designer of Electrical Testing Instruments
S.I.C.: 3825; 3829
N.A.I.C.S.: 334515; 334519
Import Export
Advertising Expenditures: $300,000

Key to Media (For complete agency information see *The Advertising Red Books-Agencies* edition):
1. Bus. Publs. 2. Cable T.V. 3. Catalogs & Directories. 4. Co-op Adv. 5. Consumer Mags. 6. D.M. to Bus. Estab.7. D.M. to Consumers
8. Daily Newsp. 9. Exhibits/Trade Shows 10. Foreign 11. Infomercial 12. Internet Adv.13. Multimedia 14. Network Radio
15. Network T.V. 16. Newsp. Distr. Mags. 17. Other 18. Outdoor (Posters, Transit) 19. Point of Purchase20. Premiums, Novelties
21. Product Samples 22. Special Events Mktg. 23. Spot Radio 24. Spot T.V. 25. Weekly Newsp. 26. Yellow Page Adv.

Media: 2-4-5-10-26
Distr.: Intl.; Natl.
Budget Set: Nov.
Personnel:
Michael R. Braverman *(Pres)*
Joe Guerriero *(VP & Gen Mgr)*
Brands & Products:
AUTOWARE
CAL-ALERT
HYAMP
HYPOT
HYPOTPLUS
HYPOTULTRA
LINECHEK
OMNIA
QUADCHEK
RUNCHEK
SMARTGFI
VERI-CHEX

ASTROTECH CORPORATION
401 Congress Ave Ste 1650
Austin, TX 78701
Tel.: (512) 485-9530
Web Site: www.spacehab.com
Approx. Rev.: $20,149,000
Approx. Number Employees: 66
Year Founded: 1984
Business Description:
Space Habitat Modules to Operate In the Cargo Bay of Space Shuttles
S.I.C.: 3761; 3769
N.A.I.C.S.: 336414; 336419
Media: 2
Personnel:
Thomas B. Pickens, III *(Chm & CEO)*
James D. Royston *(Pres)*
John M. Porter *(CFO & Sr VP)*
Don M. White *(VP & Gen Mgr-Space Ops)*
Brands & Products:
ASTROTECH SPACE OPERATIONS
SPACEHAB
WE MEAN BUSINESS IN SPACE

ATRION CORPORATION
1 Allentown Pkwy
Allen, TX 75002-4206
Tel.: (972) 390-9800
Fax: (972) 396-7581
E-mail: ir-info@atrioncorp.com
Web Site: www.atrioncorp.com
Approx. Rev.: $108,569,000
Approx. Number Employees: 437
Year Founded: 1944
Business Description:
Ophthalmic, Diagnostic & Cardiovascular Equipment Mfr
S.I.C.: 3845; 3841
N.A.I.C.S.: 334510; 339112
Import Export
Advertising Expenditures: $117,000
Media: 17
Personnel:
Emile A. Battat *(Chm & CEO)*
David A. Battat *(Pres & CEO)*
Jeffery Strickland *(CFO & VP)*
Brands & Products:
ATRION

AVALIGN TECHNOLOGIES
(Holding of RoundTable Healthcare Partners, LP)
272 E Deerpath Rd Ste 208
Lake Forest, IL 60045
Tel.: (847) 739-3239
Web Site: www.avaligntech.com/locations.cfm
Business Description:
Medical Instrument Delivery Systems & Precision Machining
S.I.C.: 3841
N.A.I.C.S.: 339112
Media: 10
Personnel:
Forrest Whittaker *(CEO)*
Brands & Products:
AVALIGN TECHNOLOGIES

AXCELIS TECHNOLOGIES, INC.
108 Cherry Hill Dr
Beverly, MA 01915-1053
Tel.: (978) 787-4000
Fax: (978) 787-3000
E-mail: info@axcelis.com
Web Site: www.axcelis.com
Approx. Rev.: $275,212,000
Approx. Number Employees: 1,018
Year Founded: 1995
Business Description:
Ion Implantation, Dry Strip, Thermal Processing & Curing Equipment Used in the Production of Semiconductor Chips Mfr
S.I.C.: 3559; 3829
N.A.I.C.S.: 333295; 334519
Media: 2-7-10
Personnel:
Mary G. Puma *(Chm, Pres & CEO)*
Stephen G. Bassett *(CFO & Exec VP)*
Jay Zager *(CFO & Exec VP)*
Lynnette C. Fallon *(Gen Counsel & Exec VP)*
Bill Bintz *(Exec VP-Engrg & Mktg)*
Kevin J. Brewer *(Exec VP-Mfg Ops)*
Matthew P. Flynn *(Exec VP-Global Customer Ops)*
Brands & Products:
AXCELIS
ETERNA
INTEGRA RS
OPTIMA HD
OPTIMA MD
OPTIMA XE
PARADIGM
POWERED BY INSIGHT
RADIANTSTRIP
RAPIDCURE
RAPIDSTRIP
SUMMIT
ULTRA

AXT, INC.
4281 Technology Dr
Fremont, CA 94538-6339
Tel.: (510) 683-5900
Fax: (510) 353-0668
E-mail: sales@axt.com
Web Site: www.axt.com
Approx. Rev.: $95,493,000
Approx. Number Employees: 1,302
Year Founded: 1986
Business Description:
Semiconductor Substrates & Opto-Electronic Semiconductor Devices Mfr, Designer & Distr
S.I.C.: 3674; 3559
N.A.I.C.S.: 334413; 333295
Advertising Expenditures: $83,000
Media: 2-10-22
Personnel:
Jesse Chen *(Chm)*
Morris S. Young *(CEO)*
Raymond A. Low *(CFO)*
Davis Zhang *(Pres-China Ops)*
Robert G. Ochrym *(VP-Bus Dev, Strategic Sls & Mktg)*
Brands & Products:
AXT
VGF STRENGTH. PERFORMANCE. INNOVATION

AZONIX CORPORATION
(Sub. of Crane Controls)
900 Middlesex Tpke Bldg 6
Billerica, MA 01821-3929
Tel.: (978) 670-6300
Fax: (978) 670-8855
Toll Free: (800) 967-5558
E-mail: webmaster@azonix.com
Web Site: www.azonix.com
Sales Range: $10-24.9 Million
Approx. Number Employees: 47
Year Founded: 1981
Business Description:
Control & Measurement Devices Mfr
S.I.C.: 3823; 3829
N.A.I.C.S.: 334513; 334519
Media: 10
Personnel:
Greg Baletsa *(Pres)*
Parag Shah *(VP-Tech)*
Dani Alkalay *(Dir-Mktg)*

BACHARACH INC.
(Holding of PNC Equity Partners, L.P.)
621 Hunt Vly Cir
New Kensington, PA 15068-7074
Tel.: (724) 334-5000
Fax: (724) 334-5001
Toll Free: (800) 736-4666
E-mail: help@bacharach-inc.com
Web Site: www.bacharach-inc.com
Sales Range: $50-74.9 Million
Approx. Number Employees: 125
Year Founded: 1909
Business Description:
Mechanical, Chemical & Electrical Measuring Instruments Mfr
S.I.C.: 3829; 3826
N.A.I.C.S.: 334519; 334516
Export
Media: 2-4-10-11-13-16-19-20-22-26
Distr.: Intl.; Natl.
Budget Set: Oct. -Dec.
Personnel:
Stapy Brovitz *(Pres)*
Jim Mowery *(Sls Dir)*
John Anuskiewicz *(Mgr-Diesel Products)*
Brands & Products:
BACHARACH
COMFORT CHECK
DIOXOR
DRAFTRITE
FLORET
FLORITE
FLORITE 500
FLORITE 600
FLORITE 700
FLORITE 800
FRYITE PRO
FYRITE
FYRITE TECH
FYRIZER
GA500 PLUS
GAS HUNTER
GAS-POINTER
GAS POINTER II
GAS PUP
HI FLOW
HI-FLOW
HI FLOW SAMPLER
HUNTER
INFORMANT
INFORMANT 2
LEAKATOR
LEAKATOR 10
MAC
MAC2000
MONOXOR
MONOXOR II
MONOXOR III
NONOXOR
OXOR
PUP
SMARTEC
SNIFIT
SNIFIT 40
SNIFIT 50
STINGER MODEL 2000
TEMPSCRIBE
TOP GUN H10XPRO
TRU POINTE
TRUE SPOT

BADGER METER, INC.
4545 W Brown Deer Rd
Milwaukee, WI 53223
Mailing Address:
PO Box 245036
Milwaukee, WI 53224-9536
Tel.: (414) 355-0400
Fax: (414) 371-5956
Web Site: www.badgermeter.com
Approx. Sls.: $276,634,000
Approx. Number Employees: 1,293
Year Founded: 1905
Business Description:
Flow Measurement Devices & Precision Valves Mfr
S.I.C.: 3824; 3491; 3494
N.A.I.C.S.: 334514; 332911; 332919
Export
Advertising Expenditures: $220,000
Media: 1-2-4-7-10-20
Distr.: Intl.; Natl.
Budget Set: Oct. -Nov.
Personnel:
Richard A. Meeusen *(Chm, Pres & CEO)*
Richard E. Johnson *(CFO, Treas, Sr VP & Fin)*
William R.A. Bergum *(Gen Counsel, Sec & VP)*
Gregory M. Gomez *(VP-Engrg)*
Dennis J. Webb *(VP-Sls)*
Brands & Products:
ACCESSPLUS
ADE
BADGER
BADGER METER
BADGERTOUCH
CONNECT
CYBERSENSOR
DATAMATIC
DIALOG
EASYPROBE
FLO-TRAC
GALAXY
HEXAGRAM
ITRON
M-SERIES
MAGNETOFLOW
MC-V
MEASURE RITE
ORION
PRIMO
RAMAR
READ-O-MATIC
READALL

Key to Media (For complete agency information see *The Advertising Red Books-Agencies* edition):
1. Bus. Publs. 2. Cable T.V. 3. Catalogs & Directories. 4. Co-op Adv. 5. Consumer Mags. 6. D.M. to Bus. Estab.7. D.M. to Consumers 8. Daily Newsp. 9. Exhibits/Trade Shows 10. Foreign 11. Infomercial 12. Internet Adv.13. Multimedia 14. Network Radio 15. Network T.V. 16. Newsp. Distr. Mags. 17. Other 18. Outdoor (Posters, Transit) 19. Point of Purchase20. Premiums, Novelties 21. Product Samples 22. Special Events Mktg. 23. Spot Radio 24. Spot T.V. 25. Weekly Newsp. 26. Yellow Page Adv.

Badger Meter, Inc. — (Continued)

READCENTER
RECORDALL
RESEARCH
RESEARCH CONTROL
RET
RTR
SOLAR-FLO
SPEEDREAD
SYMBOL
TRACE
VERSAPROBE

BARR ASSOCIATES, INC.

(Sub. of Materion Microelectronics & Services)
2 Lyberty Way
Westford, MA 01886-3616
Tel.: (978) 692-7513
Fax: (978) 692-7443
E-mail: barr@barrassociates.com
Web Site: www.barrassociates.com
Sales Range: $25-49.9 Million
Approx. Number Employees: 300
Year Founded: 1971
Business Description:
Precision Thin Film Coatings & Optical Filters Mfr
S.I.C.: 3827
N.A.I.C.S.: 333314
Import Export
Media: 2-4-10-13

BATTELLE MEMORIAL INSTITUTE

505 King Ave
Columbus, OH 43201-2696
Tel.: (614) 424-6424
Fax: (614) 424-5263
Toll Free: (800) 201-2011
E-mail: solutions@battelle.org
Web Site: www.battelle.org
Approx. Rev.: $5,547,200,000
Approx. Number Employees: 20,000
Year Founded: 1925
Business Description:
Laboratory Management, Scientific Research & Technological Products Development & Commercialization Services
S.I.C.: 8733
N.A.I.C.S.: 541710
Media: 2-4-10
Personnel:
John B. McCoy *(Chm)*
Jeffrey Wadsworth *(CEO)*
Richard C. Adams *(Sr VP-Intl Partnerships)*
I. Martin Inglis *(CFO & Exec VP)*
Gwendolyn Von Holten *(Treas)*
Donald P. McConnell *(Pres-Energy Tech)*
Steven D. McLaughlin *(Pres-Health & Life Sciences Global Bus)*
Russell P. Austin *(Gen Counsel & Sec)*
Stephen H. Valentine *(Controller & Asst Treas)*
Daniel W. O'Bryan *(Asst Sec & Asst Treas)*
Judith L. Mobley *(Asst Treas)*
Stephen E. Kelly *(Sr VP & Gen Mgr)*
Barbara L. Kunz *(Sr VP & Gen Mgr)*
Anthony T. Hebron *(Sr VP-Corp Rels)*
Robert W. Smith, Jr. *(Sr VP-Org Dev)*
John J. Grossenbacher *(Dir-Lab)*
Brands & Products:
HEAT SEAT
HI-SPACE
HUMAPEN
ODYSSEY ATLASPHERE
PATROL
REX
SOYL

BAUSCH & LOMB INCORPORATED

(Holding of Warburg Pincus LLC)
1 Bausch & Lomb Pl
Rochester, NY 14604
Tel.: (585) 338-6000
Fax: (585) 338-6007
Toll Free: (800) 344-8815
Web Site: www.bausch.com
Approx. Sls.: $2,292,400,000
Approx. Number Employees: 13,000
Year Founded: 1853
Business Description:
Ophthalmic Care Products, Pharmaceuticals & Ophthalmic Equipment Developer & Mfr
S.I.C.: 3851; 2834; 3841; 5048
N.A.I.C.S.: 339115; 325412; 339112; 423460
Import Export
Advertising Expenditures: $229,100,000
Media: 2-4-5-6-7-8-10-11-13-15-16-19-20-21-23-24
Distr.: Intl.; Natl.
Budget Set: Dec. -Jan.
Personnel:
Fred Hassan *(Chm)*
Brent Saunders *(CEO)*
Brian J. Harris *(CFO & Corp VP)*
Alan H. Farnsworth *(CIO, Corp VP & Sr VP-Customer Svc & IT)*
David N. Edwards *(Pres-Asia Pacific & Corp VP)*
Peter Valenti, III *(Global Pres-Vision Care & Corp VP)*
John H. Brown *(Pres-EMEA)*
Steven F. Robins *(Pres-Vision Care Div-North America)*
A. Robert D. Bailey *(Corp VP & Gen Counsel)*
John Loughlin *(Sr VP)*
Jane G. Mazur *(VP-PR)*
Michael McDougall *(VP-Corp Comm & Pub Affairs-Global)*
Lisa VanDeMark *(VP-Mktg)*
Daniel L. Ritz *(Dir-IR)*
John Stewart *(Dir-Mktg Nutritionals)*
Dawn Sevene *(Mgr-Web Svcs-Global)*
Brands & Products:
ADATO
AKREOS
ALL-CLEAR
ALREX
BOSTON
BOSTON ADVANCE
BOSTON SIMPLUS
CARTEOL
CATALYST
CONCENTRIX
EQUALENS
HANSATOME
INDOCOLLYRE
LIPOSIC
LOTEMAX
MEDALIST
MERIDIAN
MILLENNIUM
MINIMS
MOISTURE EYES
MPORT
MURO-128
OCCUCOAT
OCUVITE
OPCON-A
ORBSCAN
PC MAGNI-VIEWER
PREMIERE
PRESERVISION
PUREVISION
RENU
RENUCARES.COM
RETISERT
SENSITIVE EYES
SIGHT SAVERS
SILSOFT
SOFLENS
SOFLEX SE
SOFPORT
STORZ
TECHNOLAS 217
VIDISIC
VISION SHAPING TREATMENT
ZYLET
ZYOPTIX
ZYWAVE
Advertising Agencies:
Butler/Till Media Services, Inc.
2349 Monroe Ave
Rochester, NY 14618
Tel.: (585) 473-3740
Fax: (585) 473-3862

Digital Pulp
220 E 23rd St Ste 900
New York, NY 10010
Tel.: (212) 679-0676
Fax: (212) 679-6217

Gotham Incorporated
150 E 42nd St 12th Fl
New York, NY 10017
Tel.: (212) 414-7000
Fax: (212) 414-7095

Grey Group
200 5th Ave
New York, NY 10010
Tel.: (212) 546-2020
Fax: (212) 546-2001
Eye Drops
Global Advertising Duties
Prescription Medicine
Vitamins

Partners+Napier
192 Mill St Ste 600
Rochester, NY 14614-1022
Tel.: (585) 454-1010
Fax: (585) 454-1575
Toll Free: (800) 274-4954

tag idea revolution
275 Renfrew Dr Ste 200
Markham, ON L3R 0C8, Canada
Tel.: (905) 940-2806
Fax: (905) 940-4489

BAUSCH & LOMB SURGICAL, INC.

(Sub. of Bausch & Lomb Incorporated)
30 Enterprise Blvd Ste 450
Aliso Viejo, CA 92656
Tel.: (949) 916-9352
Fax: (949) 716-8362
Toll Free: (866) 393-6642
E-mail: contact@crystalens.com
Web Site: www.crystalens.com
Approx. Rev.: $17,068,000
Approx. Number Employees: 105
Year Founded: 1998
Business Description:
Intraocular Lense Medical Device Designer, Developer & Mfr
S.I.C.: 3841; 3827
N.A.I.C.S.: 339112; 333314
Media: 7-10-11-22
Personnel:
James A. Lightman *(Gen Counsel & VP)*
Anne Davies *(Sr Mgr-Product & Pharmaceuticals)*
Brands & Products:
CRYSTALENS
EYONICS

BD DIAGNOSTICS - TRIPATH

(Div. of BD Diagnostic Systems)
780 Plantation Dr
Burlington, NC 27215
Tel.: (336) 222-9707
Fax: (336) 222-8819
Toll Free: (800) 426-2176
Web Site: www.tripathimaging.com
Sales Range: $75-99.9 Million
Approx. Number Employees: 300
Year Founded: 1999
Business Description:
Cervical Cancer Screening Products Mfr
S.I.C.: 2835; 5045
N.A.I.C.S.: 325413; 423430
Advertising Expenditures: $1,645,000
Media: 10
Brands & Products:
CYTORICH
FOCALPOINT
PREPSTAIN
SUREPATH
TRIPATH IMAGING

BECKMAN COULTER, INC.

250 S Kramer Blvd
Brea, CA 92821
Tel.: (714) 993-5321
Fax: (714) 773-8283
Toll Free: (800) 233-4685
E-mail: cgskoglund@beckman.com
Web Site: www.beckmancoulter.com
Approx. Rev.: $3,663,400,000
Approx. Number Employees: 11,900
Year Founded: 1935
Business Description:
Biomedical Testing Equipment Designer, Mfr & Marketer
S.I.C.: 3826; 3821
N.A.I.C.S.: 334516; 339111
Import Export
Media: 4-7-10-11-13
Distr.: Intl.; Natl.
Personnel:
J. Robert Hurley *(Pres, CEO & Chm-Beckman Coulter-Japan)*
Charles P. Slacik *(CFO & Sr VP)*
Carolyn D. Beaver *(Chief Acctg Officer, Corp VP & Controller)*
Cynthia Skoglund *(Officer-IR)*
Arnold A. Pinkston, Jr. *(Gen Counsel, Sec & Sr VP)*
Scott C. Atkin *(Exec VP-Chemistry, Discovery & ISDC)*
Robert W. Kleinert *(Exec VP-Worldwide Comml Ops)*

Key to Media (For complete agency information see *The Advertising Red Books-Agencies* edition):
1. Bus. Publs. 2. Cable T.V. 3. Catalogs & Directories. 4. Co-op Adv. 5. Consumer Mags. 6. D.M. to Bus. Estab.7. D.M. to Consumers 8. Daily Newsp. 9. Exhibits/Trade Shows 10. Foreign 11. Infomercial 12. Internet Adv.13. Multimedia 14. Network Radio 15. Network T.V. 16. Newsp. Distr. Mags. 17. Other 18. Outdoor (Posters, Transit) 19. Point of Purchase20. Premiums, Novelties 21. Product Samples 22. Special Events Mktg. 23. Spot Radio 24. Spot T.V. 25. Weekly Newsp. 26. Yellow Page Adv.

Paul Glyer *(Sr VP-Strategy, Bus Dev & Comm)*
Pamela A. Miller *(Sr VP-Supply Chain Mgmt)*
Clair K. O'Donovan *(Sr VP-Quality & Regulatory Affairs)*
Cynthia Collins *(Grp VP-Cellular Bus Grp)*
Richard S. Creager *(Grp VP-Immunoassay & Molecular Diagnostics)*
Peter Heseltine *(VP & Dir-Medical)*
Allan D Harris *(Dir-Global Mktg)*
Robert Raynor *(Dir-Corp Bus Dev)*
Brands & Products:
A2
ACCESS
ACCUTNI
ACL
AC*T
AC*T DIFF
AC*T DIFF 2
ADMETOX
AIRFUGE
ALLEGRA
ALTRA
APPRAISE
ARRAY
AUTOMATE
AVANTI
BIOMEK
BIORAPTR FRD
CELL LAB QUANTA
CELLOMICS
CELLPROBE
CELLQUANT
CEQ
CHEMLIB
COULTER
COULTER CLENZ
COULTER CLONE
COULTER COUNTER
CX
CYAN
CYTO-STAT
CYTOMICS FC 500
CYTOMICS FC 500 MPL
DELSA
DNA PREP
DU
DXI
EL-ISE
ELABNOTEBOOK
ELECTRA
ELECTROPHORESISTUTOR
EPICS
EXPO 32
FLEXSURE
GALLIOS
GASTROCCULT
GENOMELAB
GEN*S
GLUCOSE
HEMOCCULT
HEMOCCULT II
HYBRITECH
ICON
IL
IMMAGE
IMMUNO-BRITE
IMMUNO-TROL
IMMUNOPREP
IMMUNOTECH
INTRAPREP
IOPATH
IOTEST
ITAG
ITOPIA
J6-MI
KARAT
LH
LS
LX
MAGNESIL
MAXM
MICROALBUMIN
MICROBORE
MICROFUGE
MOFLO
MULTIMEK
MULTISIZER
N5
NANOVETTE
OPTICLONE
OPTILYSE
OPTIMA
ORCA
OSTASE
P/ACE
PARADIGM
PARAGON
PARAGON CZE
PICORAPTR
PREALBUMIN
PREPPLUS
PROTEOMELAB
Q-PREP
QUANTA
RAPIDVUE
REMISOL
RETICONE
SA 3100
SAGIAN
SAMI
SENSA
SILAS
SITEMAX
SNPSTREAM
SPINCHRON
STEM-KIT
STEM-TROL
SYNCHRON
SYNCHRON CX
SYNCHRON LX
SYSTEM GOLD
TETRAONE
TQ-PREP
UNICEL DXL
VGAMMA9
VI-CELL
VIDIERA
WIZARD
XL-MCL
Z1
Z2
Advertising Agencies:
Andersen Jones Medical Advertising
31473 Rancho Viejo Rd Ste 206
San Juan Capistrano, CA 92675
Tel.: (949) 240-6802
Fax: (949) 240-8437

Level Brand
724 N 1st St
Minneapolis, MN 55401-1143
Tel.: (612) 338-8000
Fax: (612) 338-9824

BETA CALIBRATORS CORPORATION
(Div. of Martel Electronics, Corp.)
1F Commons Dr Ste 39
Londonderry, NH 03053
Tel.: (603) 434-1433
Fax: (603) 434-1653
Toll Free: (800) 821-0023
E-mail: sales@martelcorp.com
Web Site: www.martelcalibrators.com
Approx. Sls.: $10,000,000
Approx. Number Employees: 8
Year Founded: 1939
Business Description:
Mfr of Instrument Calibrators & Calibration Systems
S.I.C.: 3829
N.A.I.C.S.: 334519
Export
Media: 7-11
Brands & Products:
BETA CALIBRATORS
BETAFLEX
CALTOOL

BG PICTURES LLC
5318 Bob White Dr
Holiday, FL 34690
Tel.: (727) 946-1000
E-mail: bryan@bgpictures.com
Web Site: www.bgpictures.com
Sales Range: Less than $1 Million
Approx. Number Employees: 1
Business Description:
Photography Shop
S.I.C.: 7335
N.A.I.C.S.: 541922
Media: 6-13
Personnel:
Bryan Gynn *(Owner)*

BIO-REFERENCE LABORATORIES, INC.
481 Edward H Ross Dr
Elmwood Park, NJ 07407-3118
Tel.: (201) 791-2600
Fax: (201) 791-1941
Toll Free: (800) 229-5227
E-mail: showlett@bioreference.com
Web Site: www.bioreference.com
Approx. Rev.: $458,024,000
Approx. Number Employees: 1,787
Year Founded: 1981
Business Description:
Diagnostic Testing Services
S.I.C.: 8071; 8734
N.A.I.C.S.: 621511; 541380
Advertising Expenditures: $2,065,000
Media: 5-10-19
Personnel:
Marc D. Grodman *(Chm, Pres & CEO)*
Sam Singer *(CFO & Sr VP)*
Howard Dubinett *(COO & Exec VP)*
Richard L. Faherty *(CIO & Pres-PsiMedica)*
James Weisberger *(Chief Medical Officer & Sr VP, Dir-Laboratory)*
Cory Fishkin *(Pres-CareEvolve)*
Warren Erdmann *(Sr VP & Dir-Ops)*
Azmy Awad *(Sr VP)*
Scott Fein *(Sr VP)*
Nicholas Papazicos *(Sr VP-Fin Ops)*
Charles T. Todd *(Sr VP-Sls & Mktg)*
Nick Cetani *(VP-Technical Ops & Dir-Laboratory)*
Tara Mackay *(Coord-IR)*

BIOANALYTICAL SYSTEMS, INC.
(d/b/a BASi)
2701 Kent Ave
West Lafayette, IN 47906-1350
Tel.: (765) 463-4527
Fax: (765) 497-1102
Toll Free: (800) 845-4246
E-mail: basi@basinc.com
Web Site: www.basinc.com
Approx. Rev.: $28,781,000
Approx. Number Employees: 233
Year Founded: 1974
Business Description:
Life Science Research & Development Services; Analytical Instruments Mfr
S.I.C.: 8733; 3826; 8734
N.A.I.C.S.: 541710; 334516; 541380; 541711
Advertising Expenditures: $180,000
Media: 10
Personnel:
John B. Landis *(Chm)*
Michael R. Cox *(CFO, VP-Fin & Admin)*
Craig S. Bruntlett *(Sr VP-Instruments Div)*
Lina L. Reeves-Kerner *(Sr VP-HR)*
Alberto Hidalgo *(VP-Bus Dev & Mktg)*
James Plassard *(Gen Mgr-Ops-West Lafayette)*
Ed Burrow *(Dir-Mfg)*
James F. Gitzen *(Dir-Sls)*
Josef Ludwig *(Dir-Pharmaceutical Analysis)*
Brands & Products:
BASI
BEE HIVE
C-3
CHADS FOR VIALS
CHROMGRAPH
CULEX
DIGISIM
ECG ANALYZER
HONEYCOMB
KINFITSIM
LCEC
PETIT AMPERE
POLLEN
POWER MODULE
RDE-2
RODENT WORKSTATION
UNIJET
UNISWITCH
WORKER BEE
YOUR SCIENTIFIC CONNECTION

BOLLE INC.
(Sub. of Bushnell Outdoor Products, Inc.)
9200 Cody
Overland Park, KS 66214
Tel.: (913) 752-3400
Fax: (913) 752-6112
Toll Free: (800) 222-6553
E-mail: info@bolle.com
Web Site: www.bolle.com
Approx. Rev.: $52,550,000
Approx. Number Employees: 215
Year Founded: 1888
Business Description:
Mfr. of Nylon Frames, Shatterproof Polycarbonate Lenses & Prescription Sunglass Lenses
S.I.C.: 5099; 3827; 5091
N.A.I.C.S.: 423990; 333314; 423910
Media: 6-8-13-24
Personnel:
Blake Lipham *(Pres & CEO)*
Chuck Gessler *(CFO & Exec VP)*
Phil Gyori *(VP-Mktg)*
Mark Welch *(VP-Sls)*
Brands & Products:
HYDRALON
SNAKES

Key to Media (For complete agency information see *The Advertising Red Books-Agencies* edition):
1. Bus. Publs. 2. Cable T.V. 3. Catalogs & Directories. 4. Co-op Adv. 5. Consumer Mags. 6. D.M. to Bus. Estab.7. D.M. to Consumers
8. Daily Newsp. 9. Exhibits/Trade Shows 10. Foreign 11. Infomercial 12. Internet Adv.13. Multimedia 14. Network Radio
15. Network T.V. 16. Newsp. Distr. Mags. 17. Other 18. Outdoor (Posters, Transit) 19. Point of Purchase20. Premiums, Novelties
21. Product Samples 22. Special Events Mktg. 23. Spot Radio 24. Spot T.V. 25. Weekly Newsp. 26. Yellow Page Adv.

Bolle Inc. — (Continued)

SPORTS METAL
STREET METAL

BOVIE MEDICAL CORPORATION
734 Walt Whitman Rd
Melville, NY 11747
Tel.: (631) 421-5452
Fax: (631) 421-5821
Fax: (800) 323-1640
Toll Free: (800) 537-2790
Web Site: www.boviemedical.com
Approx. Sls.: $24,230,000
Approx. Number Employees: 143
Business Description:
Surgical & Medical Instruments Mfr & Marketer
S.I.C.: 3841
N.A.I.C.S.: 339112
Advertising Expenditures: $276,000
Media: 2-8-10
Personnel:
Andrew Makrides *(Chm & CEO)*
J. Robert Saron *(Pres)*
Gary D. Pickett *(CFO)*
Moshe Citronowicz *(COO & VP)*
Rick Pfahl *(COO & VP-Bus Dev)*
Janis Dezso *(VP-Sls & Mktg)*
Jeff Rencher *(VP-Sls & Mktg-Surgical Products)*
Nieves Rivas *(Dir-Creative)*
Johan Segers *(Dir-Sls & Mktg-Europe/ Middle East)*
Genard Mccauley *(Product Mgr-ESU)*
Vera Macelroy *(Mgr-HR)*
Brands & Products:
AARON
AARON 1250
AARON 2250
AARON 3250
AARON 900
AARON 950
BOVIE
BOVIE FCFS
BOVIEDED
BOVIEFDFS
BOVIENEM
CHANGE-A-TIP
THE FIRST NAME IN ELECTROSURGERY.
FSDS
NEM
NEURO-PULSE
SMOKE SHARK

BRANSON ULTRASONICS CORPORATION - PLASTICS JOINING DIVISION
(Div. of Branson Ultrasonics Corporation)
41 Eagle Rd
Danbury, CT 06810-4127
Tel.: (203) 796-0400
Fax: (203) 796-9838
Toll Free: (888) 282-5646
Telex: 643743
E-mail: info@bransonultrasonics.com
Web Site:
www.bransonultrasonics.com
E-Mail For Key Personnel:
Marketing Director: smainolfi@bransonultrasonics.com
Public Relations: bstephens@bransonultrasonics.com
Sales Range: $100-124.9 Million
Approx. Number Employees: 250
Year Founded: 1946
Business Description:
Ultrasonic Cleaners & Generators & Plastic Joining & Metal Welding Equipment
S.I.C.: 3589; 3548
N.A.I.C.S.: 333319; 333992
Export
Advertising Expenditures: $500,000
Media: 2-4-5-7-10-11-19-26
Distr.: Natl.
Budget Set: Sept.
Personnel:
Robert M. Brown *(VP-Sls & Mktg)*
Rodger F. Martin *(VP-Sls)*
Byron D. Peterson *(VP-HR)*
Jon C. Piasecki *(VP-Engrg & Automotive)*
Robert G. Tibbetts *(VP-Fin)*
Crystal Rumph *(Mgr-Mktg Comm)*

BRIMROSE CORPORATION
19 Loveton Cir
Baltimore, MD 21152-9201
Tel.: (410) 472-7070
Fax: (410) 472-7960
E-mail: office@brimrose.com
Web Site: www.brimrose.com
Approx. Sls.: $20,000,000
Approx. Number Employees: 50
Year Founded: 1989
Business Description:
Search & Navigation Equipment
S.I.C.: 3812; 8733
N.A.I.C.S.: 334511; 541710
Media: 10
Personnel:
Ronald G. Rosemeier *(Pres)*
Jolanta Soos *(Mgr-Mktg)*

BRINKMANN INSTRUMENTS, INC.
(Sub. of Eppendorf AG)
1 Cantiague Rd
Westbury, NY 11590
Mailing Address:
PO Box 1019
Westbury, NY 11590-0207
Tel.: (516) 334-7500
Fax: (516) 334-7506
Toll Free: (800) 645-3050
E-mail: info@brinkmann.com
Web Site: www.brinkmann.com
Sales Range: $75-99.9 Million
Approx. Number Employees: 260
Year Founded: 1941
Business Description:
Importer & Distributor of Scientific Instruments Used in Laboratories, for Quality Control of Manufacturing Processes & for Environmental Monitoring
S.I.C.: 5049; 5047
N.A.I.C.S.: 423490; 423450
Import Export
Media: 2-4-7-10-13-20-21
Distr.: Natl.
Budget Set: Sept.
Personnel:
Martin N. Farb *(Pres & CEO)*
Lothar Hartmann *(Treas, Sec & VP-Fin)*
Hans Ulrich *(Production Dir)*
Susan Garfinkel *(Mgr)*
Brands & Products:
BRINKMANN
COLLEGIATE
EASYCARE
ENVIROTIPS
PIPET HELPER
REPEATER
SAFETYVAP
VACUFUGE

BROOKFIELD ENGINEERING LABORATORIES, INC.
11 Commerce Blvd
Middleboro, MA 02346
Tel.: (508) 946-6200
Fax: (508) 946-6262
Toll Free: (800) 628-8139
E-mail: sales@brookfieldengineering.com
Web Site:
www.brookfieldengineering.com
E-Mail For Key Personnel:
Sales Director: sales@brookfieldengineering.com
Approx. Number Employees: 165
Year Founded: 1934
Business Description:
Mfr. of Viscosity Measuring Instruments
S.I.C.: 3826; 3823
N.A.I.C.S.: 334516; 334513
Export
Media: 2-4-7-10-13
Distr.: Intl.; Natl.
Personnel:
David A. Brookfield *(Pres)*
Donald W. Brookfield, Jr. *(Pres)*
Jim Kaufmann *(CFO & Treas)*
Robert G. McGregor *(Mgr-Natl Sls-Mktg)*
Brands & Products:
AST-100
BROOKFIELD
CAP-1000+
CAP-2000+
CAPCALC
DV-E
DV-I+
DV-II+ PRO
DV-III ULTRA
DV-III+
DV-LOADER
EZ-YIELD
HELIPATH
KU-1+
R/S
RHEO-LOADER
RHEO2000
RHEO3000
RHEOCALC
RHEOVISION
STT-100
THERMOSEL
TRAPPER
TT-100
ULTRA LOW ADAPTER
VISCAL
VISCOSEL
VTE
WINGATHER
YR-1
Advertising Agency:
Stebbings Partners
427 John L Dietsch Blvd
Attleboro Falls, MA 02763-1000
Tel.: (508) 699-7899
Fax: (508) 699-7897
— David A. Stebbings *(V.P.)*

BROOKS INSTRUMENT, LLC
(Holding of American Industrial Partners)
407 W Vine St
Hatfield, PA 19440-0903
Tel.: (215) 362-3500
Fax: (215) 362-3745
Fax: (215) 362-3595
Toll Free: (888) 554-FLOW
Web Site: www.brooksinstrument.com
Approx. Number Employees: 500
Year Founded: 1946
Business Description:
Flow & Level Measurement Control Equipment Mfr
S.I.C.: 3822; 3823
N.A.I.C.S.: 334512; 334513
Import Export
Advertising Expenditures: $750,000
Media: 2-10-13-20
Distr.: Intl.; Natl.
Budget Set: July
Personnel:
Jim Dillon *(Product Mgr-Foundation Fieldbus Flow Meter)*
Brands & Products:
AR-MET
BROOKSMITE
FULL VIEW
QUANTIM
SHO-RATE
VOL-U-METER
Advertising Agency:
Praxis Communications, Inc.
2600 Philmont Ave Ste 111
Huntingdon Valley, PA 19006-5307
Tel.: (215) 947-2080
Fax: (215) 947-2256

BUEHLER, LTD.
(Sub. of Illinois Tool Works Inc.)
41 Waukegan Rd
Lake Bluff, IL 60044
Mailing Address:
PO Box 1
Lake Bluff, IL 60044-1699
Tel.: (847) 295-6500
Tel.: (847) 295-4662 (Export Sls)
Fax: (847) 295-7979
Toll Free: (800) 283-4537
Telex: 72-4404
E-mail: info@buehler.com
Web Site: www.buehler.com
Approx. Sls.: $70,000,000
Approx. Number Employees: 150
Year Founded: 1936
Business Description:
Scientific Instruments & Supplies Mfr
S.I.C.: 3821; 5049
N.A.I.C.S.: 339111; 423490
Import Export
Advertising Expenditures: $1,000,000
Media: 2-4-8-10
Distr.: Intl.; Natl.
Budget Set: Oct.
Personnel:
Tracy Putnam *(Pres)*
Brands & Products:
ABRASIMATIC
ABRASIMET
APEX
AUTOMET
BUEHLER
BUEHLERVANGUARD
DELTA

Key to Media (For complete agency information see *The Advertising Red Books-Agencies* edition):
1. Bus. Publs. 2. Cable T.V. 3. Catalogs & Directories. 4. Co-op Adv. 5. Consumer Mags. 6. D.M. to Bus. Estab.7. D.M. to Consumers 8. Daily Newsp. 9. Exhibits/Trade Shows 10. Foreign 11. Infomercial 12. Internet Adv.13. Multimedia 14. Network Radio 15. Network T.V. 16. Newsp. Distr. Mags. 17. Other 18. Outdoor (Posters, Transit) 19. Point of Purchase20. Premiums, Novelties 21. Product Samples 22. Special Events Mktg. 23. Spot Radio 24. Spot T.V. 25. Weekly Newsp. 26. Yellow Page Adv.

DUOMET
ECOMET
ELECTROMET
ENVIRONMET
EPO-EASE
FIBRMET
FIBRSKOPE
HANDIMET
ISOMET
MACROMET
MACROVICKERS
METASERV
MINIMET
MIROMET
MPC
NELSON-ZIMMER
OMNIMET
OSCILLAMET
PETRO-THIN
PETROCUT
PETROPOL
POWERPRO
PRIMET
SAMPLMET 2
SIMPLIMET
SUPERMET
TECH-MET
ULTRAMET
VIBROMET

BUFFALO OPTICAL COMPANY INC.
280 Delaware Ave
Buffalo, NY 14202
Tel.: (716) 854-1620
Fax: (716) 854-1623
E-mail: info@buffaloptical.com
Web Site: www.buffalooptical.com
Sales Range: Less than $1 Million
Approx. Number Employees: 15
Year Founded: 1895
Business Description:
Opticians & Optical Retail
S.I.C.: 5995
N.A.I.C.S.: 446130
Advertising Expenditures: $25,000
Media: 9-18-23-25-26
Distr.: Reg.
Budget Set: Jan.
Personnel:
Joseph Gugliuzza *(Pres)*
Brands & Products:
BUFFALO

BUSHNELL OUTDOOR PRODUCTS, INC.
(Holding of MidOcean Partners, LLP)
9200 Cody St
Overland Park, KS 66214-1734
Tel.: (913) 752-3400
Fax: (913) 752-6112
Web Site: www.bushnell.com
Sales Range: $350-399.9 Million
Approx. Number Employees: 350
Year Founded: 1990
Business Description:
Optical Lense & Binocular Mfr
S.I.C.: 3827; 3851
N.A.I.C.S.: 333314; 339115
Media: 4-8-10-13
Personnel:
Blake Lipham *(CFO)*
Paul Arnhold *(Mgr-Mktg)*
Brands & Products:
BANNER
BOLLE
BUSHNELL
CUSTOM
DISCOVERER
DUSK AND DAWN
ELITE
EXCURSION
FALCON
FIREFLY
H2O
HARBORMASTER
HOLOSIGHT
IMAGE VIEW
INSTANT REPLAY
LEGACY
LEGEND
MARINE
MULTI-X
NATUREVIEW
NORTHSTAR
PERMAFOCUS
PINSEEKER
POWERVIEW
QUEST
RAINGUARD
SCOUT
SENTRY
SERENGETI
SPACEMASTER
SPEEDSTER
SPORT
SPORTSMAN
SPORTVIEW
STABLEVIEW
TASCO
TRAIL SCOUT
TRIPODS
TROPHY
VELOCITY
VOYAGER
WRIST-TOP
XTRA-WIDE
YARDAGE PRO
Advertising Agency:
VITRO
(An MDC Partners Company)
625 Broadway Fl 4
San Diego, CA 92101-5403
Tel.: (619) 234-0408
Fax: (619) 234-4015

CALIFORNIA INSTRUMENTS CORPORATION
(Sub. of AMETEK Electronic Instruments Group)
9689 Towne Ctr Dr
San Diego, CA 92121
Tel.: (858) 677-9040
Fax: (858) 677-0940
E-mail: sales@calinst.com
Web Site: www.calinst.com
E-Mail For Key Personnel:
President: brian_hull@calinst.com
Sales Director: sales@calinst.com
Sales Range: $10-24.9 Million
Approx. Number Employees: 85
Year Founded: 1961
Business Description:
AC & DC Power Sources Mfr & Supplier
S.I.C.: 3825; 3829
N.A.I.C.S.: 334515; 334519
Export
Media: 10-11
Distr.: Intl.; Natl.
Budget Set: Oct.
Personnel:
John P. Hernandez *(Engr-QA)*
Brands & Products:
ARGANTIX
BTS

CALUMET PHOTOGRAPHIC, INC.
(Sub. of Vector Industries, Ltd.)
900 W Bliss St
Chicago, IL 60642
Tel.: (630) 860-7447
Fax: (630) 860-7105
Toll Free: (800) CALUMET
Web Site: www.calumetphoto.com
Approx. Number Employees: 650
Year Founded: 1939
Business Description:
Photographic Equipment & Supplies; Video & Electronics Retailer
S.I.C.: 5043; 5946; 5961
N.A.I.C.S.: 423410; 443130; 454113
Import Export
Media: 4-5-6-8-9-10-13-16-19-26
Distr.: Direct to Consumer; Natl.
Budget Set: Monthly
Personnel:
Chris Ergo *(CFO & Exec VP)*
Brands & Products:
BOWENS
BRILLIANT PAPER
CALTAR LENSES
CALUMET CAMERAS
CALUMET LIGHT STANDS
CAMBO CAMERAS
CAMBO STUDIO STANDS

CANDELA CORPORATION
(Sub. of Syneron Medical Ltd.)
530 Boston Post Rd
Wayland, MA 01778-1833
Tel.: (508) 358-7400
Fax: (508) 358-5602
Toll Free: (800) 733-8550
E-mail: info@candelalaser.com
Web Site: www.candelalaser.com
Sales Range: $100-124.9 Million
Approx. Number Employees: 350
Year Founded: 1970
Business Description:
Aesthetic Laser Therapy Technologies Developer, Mfr & Distr
S.I.C.: 3845; 5047
N.A.I.C.S.: 334510; 423450
Export
Personnel:
Lewis Levine *(VP-Engrg)*
L. Bryant Helton *(Mgr)*
Brands & Products:
ALEXTRIVANTAGE
CANDELA
GENTLELASE
GENTLEMAX
GENTLEYAG
SEE THE DIFFERENCE
SMOOTHBEAM
SMOOTHPEEL
VBEAM
Advertising Agency:
The Ruth Group
141 5th Ave 5th Fl
New York, NY 10010
Tel.: (646) 536-7000

CANDID COLOR SYSTEMS, INC.
1300 Metropolitan Ave
Oklahoma City, OK 73108-2042
Tel.: (405) 947-8747
Fax: (405) 951-7353
Toll Free: (800) 336-4550
E-mail: christy@candid.com
Web Site: www.candid.com
Approx. Number Employees: 300
Business Description:
Photography Studio & Photofinishing Lab
S.I.C.: 7384
N.A.I.C.S.: 812921
Media: 8-9-10-13-18-23-24-26
Distr.: Natl.
Personnel:
Jack Counts *(Pres)*
Holly McCoy *(Mgr-Adv)*
Brands & Products:
CANDID COLOR SYSTEMS
CANDIDNET
CCSFTP
CORE
GLAMOUR SHOTS
GRAD PHOTO NETWORK
JUMP STUDIO
KLINGONS
LEVEL TWO
MAESTRO
PARTY PICS
PAYFIRST
PEARLIZED
THE PHOTO NETWORK
QEMS
QUICPICS
QUICPOST
RACE PHOTO NETWORK
VIEWFIRST
Advertising Agency:
Jordan Associates
3201 Quail Springs Pkwy Ste 100
Oklahoma City, OK 73134-2611
Tel.: (405) 840-3201
Fax: (405) 840-4149
— Amy Hindman *(Acct. Exec.)*

CANON U.S.A., INC.
(Sub. of Canon Inc.)
1 Canon Plz
Lake Success, NY 11042
Tel.: (516) 328-5000
Fax: (516) 328-5069
Toll Free: (800) 652-2666
E-mail: pr@cusa.canon.com
Web Site: www.usa.canon.com
Approx. Sls.: $9,722,099,712
Approx. Number Employees: 900
Year Founded: 1966
Business Description:
Photographic & Office Products Importer, Marketer & Distr
S.I.C.: 5044; 3861; 5065
N.A.I.C.S.: 423420; 333315; 423690
Import
Advertising Expenditures: $120,000,000
Media: 2-3-6-9-13-14-15-18-24
Distr.: Natl.
Budget Set: Dec.
Personnel:
Kunihiko Tedo *(CFO, Sr VP & Treas-Fin & Acctg)*
Seymour E. Liebman *(Chief Admin Officer, Gen Counsel & Exec VP)*
Masahiro Haga *(Exec Officer & Adviser-Canon Finetech Inc)*
Tod D. Pike *(Pres-Canon Bus Solutions)*
Yuichi Ishizuka *(Exec VP-Imaging Technologies & Comm Grp)*
Tamotsu Nakamura *(Exec VP-Imaging Sys Grp)*

Canon U.S.A., Inc. — (Continued)

Jim Rosetta *(VP & GM)*
Michelle Fernandez *(Dir)*
Rob Altman *(Mgr-Camera Mktg)*
Tamara Hohnberg *(Product Mgr-Digital Video)*

Advertising Agencies:
BDS Marketing
10 Holland
Irvine, CA 92618
Tel.: (949) 472-6700
Fax: (949) 597-2220

Dentsu America, Inc.
32 Ave of the Americas 16th Fl
New York, NY 10013
Tel.: (212) 397-3333
Fax: (212) 397-3322
Powershot Camera
— Jerry Von Verichten *(Dir-Media)*

Grey New York
777 3rd Ave
New York, NY 10017-1401
Tel.: (212) 546-2000
Fax: (212) 546-1495
Beyond The Still

NFM Group Inc.
320 Fort Duquesne Blvd 26 H
Pittsburgh, PA 15222
Tel.: (412) 394-6400
Fax: (412) 394-6411
Cameras
Sports Marketing

CANTEL MEDICAL CORP.
150 Clove Rd
Little Falls, NJ 07424
Tel.: (973) 890-7220
Fax: (973) 890-7270
E-mail: webmaster@minntech.com
Web Site: www.cantelmedical.com
Approx. Sls.: $273,952,000
Approx. Number Employees: 883
Year Founded: 1963
Business Description:
Endoscopy & Scientific Instrumentation Products
S.I.C.: 3841; 3845
N.A.I.C.S.: 339112; 334510
Import Export
Advertising Expenditures: $1,853,000
Distr.: Natl.
Personnel:
Charles M. Diker *(Chm)*
George L. Fotiades *(Vice Chm)*
Andrew A. Krakauer *(Pres & CEO)*
Craig A. Sheldon *(CFO, Treas & Sr VP)*
Eric Nodiff *(Gen Counsel, Sec & Sr VP)*
Seth R. Segel *(Exec VP)*
Christopher Fournier *(VP-Mktg)*
Joanna Zisa Albrecht *(Asst Sec)*

CAPINTEC INC.
6 Arrow Rd
Ramsey, NJ 07446-1236
Tel.: (201) 825-9500
Fax: (201) 825-4829
Toll Free: (800) 631-3826
E-mail: getinfo@capintec.com
Web Site: www.capintec.com
E-Mail For Key Personnel:
Marketing Director: jviscovic@capintec.com
Sales Range: $10-24.9 Million
Approx. Number Employees: 80
Year Founded: 1964
Business Description:
Mfr, Developer & Marketer of Radiation Measuring & Monitoring Instrumentation
S.I.C.: 3829; 3823
N.A.I.C.S.: 334519; 334513
Import Export
Advertising Expenditures: $200,000
Media: 2-4-7-10-11-16
Distr.: Intl.; Natl.
Budget Set: June
Personnel:
Arthur M. Weis *(Chm)*
Jessica Bede *(Pres & CEO)*
John Viscovic *(VP-Domestic Sls & Mktg)*
Brands & Products:
BETA CT
C-TEC
CAP-CELL
CAPCELL
CAPIMAGE
CAPMAC
CAPRAC
CAPTUS
CII
CRC
DIARAD
GAMMED II B
GAMMED VI
GENERATION II VEST
PIN-TEC
THERARAD

CARDIACASSIST, INC.
240 Alpha Dr
Pittsburgh, PA 15238
Tel.: (412) 963-7770
Fax: (412) 963-0800
Toll Free: (800) 373-7421
E-mail: info@cardiacassist.com
Web Site: www.cardiacassist.com
Approx. Number Employees: 30
Business Description:
Medical Device Mfr
S.I.C.: 3841
N.A.I.C.S.: 339112
Media: 10
Personnel:
John C. Marous, Jr. *(Chm)*
Kraig J. McEwen *(Pres & CEO)*

CARL ZEISS CANADA LTD.
(Sub. of Carl Zeiss AG)
45 Valleybrook D
Toronto, ON M3B 2S6, Canada
Tel.: (416) 449-4660
Fax: (416) 449-3524
E-mail: fsomogy@zeiss.com
Web Site: www.zeiss.ca
E-Mail For Key Personnel:
Sales Director: sales@zeiss.com
Sales Range: $25-49.9 Million
Approx. Number Employees: 150
Business Description:
Production of Scientific, Medical & Optical Instruments
S.I.C.: 3841
N.A.I.C.S.: 339112
Import
Media: 2-10
Brands & Products:
CARL ZEISS

CARL ZEISS, INC.
(Sub. of Carl Zeiss AG)
1 Zeiss Dr
Thornwood, NY 10594-1939
Tel.: (914) 747-1800
Fax: (914) 681-7482
Web Site: www.zeiss.com
Sales Range: $300-349.9 Million
Approx. Number Employees: 700
Year Founded: 1925
Business Description:
Distr of Scientific Instruments: Laboratory Microscopes, Surgical Microscopes & Ophthalmic Diagnostic Equipment
S.I.C.: 5047; 3827
N.A.I.C.S.: 423450; 333314
Import Export
Media: 2-4-10-11
Distr.: Natl.
Budget Set: Oct.
Personnel:
Jim Sharp *(Pres)*

CARL ZEISS OPTICAL, INC.
(Sub. of Carl Zeiss AG)
13017 N Kingston Ave
Chester, VA 23836-2743
Tel.: (804) 530-8300
Fax: (804) 530-8311
Toll Free: (800) 338-2984
E-mail: lenses@zeiss.com
Web Site: www.zeiss.com/optical
E-Mail For Key Personnel:
President: jsharp@zeiss.com
Approx. Number Employees: 96
Business Description:
Binoculars, Riflescopes, Ophthalmic Lenses & Coatings Mfr
S.I.C.: 3851
N.A.I.C.S.: 339115
Media: 2-8-10-11-13
Distr.: Natl.; Retailers
Budget Set: Sept.
Personnel:
James Sharp *(Pres & CEO)*
Roland Citzler *(VP-Sls)*
Brands & Products:
CLARLET
GOLDET
GRADAL
SUPER ET
Advertising Agency:
Neathawk Dubuque & Packett
1 E Cary St
Richmond, VA 23219-3732
Tel.: (804) 783-8140
Fax: (804) 783-0098
Toll Free: (800) 847-2674

CASCADE MICROTECH, INC.
2430 NW 206th Ave
Beaverton, OR 97006
Tel.: (503) 601-1000
Fax: (503) 601-1002
E-mail: steven_sipowicz@cmicrotech.com
Web Site: www.cascademicrotech.com
Approx. Rev.: $95,799,000
Approx. Number Employees: 401
Business Description:
Integrated Circuit, Microchip & Semiconductor Industry Electrical Measurement & Testing Equipment Developer, Mfr & Marketer
S.I.C.: 3825; 3829; 5063
N.A.I.C.S.: 334515; 334519; 423610
Advertising Expenditures: $64,000
Media: 2-4-7-10
Personnel:
F. Paul Carlson *(Chm)*
Michael D. Burger *(Pres & CEO)*
Jeff A. Killian *(CFO & VP-Fin)*
Steven L. Harris *(Exec VP)*
Michael Kondrat *(VP-Mktg)*
Paul O'Mara *(VP-Sls & Support)*
Ellen Raim *(VP-HR)*
Art Smith *(Dir-HR)*
Brands & Products:
AIRCOPLANAR
ATTOGUARD
CASCADE MICROTECH, INC.
CRYOGENIC
EDGE
ELITE
EVUE
FEMTOGUARD
INFINITY PROBE
INNOVATING TEST TECHNOLOGIES
INNOVATIVE PYRAMID
LABVIEW
MICROCHAMBER
NUCLEUS
PYRAMID
SUMMIT
WINCAL

CECO ENVIRONMENTAL CORP.
4625 Red Bank Rd
Cincinnati, OH 45227
Tel.: (513) 458-2600
Fax: (513) 458-2647
Toll Free: (800) 333-5475
E-mail: sales@cecoenviro.com
Web Site: www.cecoenviro.com
Approx. Sls.: $140,602,000
Approx. Number Employees: 552
Year Founded: 1966
Business Description:
Air Filters Mfr
S.I.C.: 3564
N.A.I.C.S.: 333412; 333411
Advertising Expenditures: $324,000
Personnel:
Phillip DeZwirek *(Chm)*
Jeffrey Lang *(CEO)*
Dennis W. Blazer *(CFO)*
Brands & Products:
CECO

CELESTRON, LLC
2835 Columbia St
Torrance, CA 90503-3804
Tel.: (310) 328-9560
Fax: (310) 212-5835
Telex: 182471
E-mail: info@celestron.com
Web Site: www.celestron.com
Approx. Number Employees: 100
Business Description:
Mfr. of Telescopes, Telephoto Lenses, Binoculars & Spotting Scopes
S.I.C.: 3827; 5049
N.A.I.C.S.: 333314; 423490
Export
Media: 2-4-5-6-7-8-10
Distr.: Intl.; Natl.
Budget Set: Apr.
Personnel:
Joseph A. Lupica, Jr. *(Pres & CEO)*
Victor Aniceto *(Sr VP-Sls & Mktg)*

Key to Media (For complete agency information see *The Advertising Red Books-Agencies* edition):
1. Bus. Publs. 2. Cable T.V. 3. Catalogs & Directories. 4. Co-op Adv. 5. Consumer Mags. 6. D.M. to Bus. Estab.7. D.M. to Consumers
8. Daily Newsp. 9. Exhibits/Trade Shows 10. Foreign 11. Infomercial 12. Internet Adv.13. Multimedia 14. Network Radio
15. Network T.V. 16. Newsp. Distr. Mags. 17. Other 18. Outdoor (Posters, Transit) 19. Point of Purchase20. Premiums, Novelties
21. Product Samples 22. Special Events Mktg. 23. Spot Radio 24. Spot T.V. 25. Weekly Newsp. 26. Yellow Page Adv.

Brands & Products:
CELESTRON
NEXSTAR
NOBLE
OCEANA
OPTIVIEW
OUTLAND
REGAL LS
SKYMASTER
STARBRIGHT
TRAVELER
ULTIMA
UPCLOSE
VISTAPIX
Advertising Agency:
The MWW Group
1 Meadowlands Plz 6th Fl
East Rutherford, NJ 07073
Tel.: (201) 507-9500
Fax: (201) 507-0092

CEM CORPORATION
3100 Smith Farm Rd
Matthews, NC 28104-5044
Tel.: (704) 821-7015
Fax: (704) 821-8794
Toll Free: (800) 726-3331
Telex: 802118
E-mail: info@cem.com
Web Site: www.cemsynthesis.com
Approx. Number Employees: 180
Year Founded: 1972
Business Description:
Mfr. of Analytical Instruments
S.I.C.: 3826; 3829
N.A.I.C.S.: 334516; 334519
Export
Advertising Expenditures: $375,000
Media: 1-2-4-7-10-11-13-17
Distr.: Intl.
Personnel:
Michael Collins *(Pres & CEO)*
Richard Decker *(CFO, Treas, Sec & VP-Fin)*
Ken Corliss *(Sr VP)*
Will Grooms *(Dir-Mktg)*
Brands & Products:
DISCOVER
EXPLORER
FOCUSED SYNTHESIS
MARS XPRESS
ODYSSEY
SMART TRAC
VOYAGER

CHARLES BESELER CO.
PO Box 431
Stroudsburg, PA 18360
Tel.: (570) 517-0400
Fax: (800) 966-4515
Toll Free: (800) 237-3537
Telex: 219485
E-mail: tech@beseler-photo.com
Web Site: www.beseler.com
Approx. Number Employees: 100
Year Founded: 1869
Business Description:
Mfr. of Packaging & Photographic Equipment
S.I.C.: 3861; 5043
N.A.I.C.S.: 333315; 423410
Import Export
Media: 5-6-7-13
Distr.: Intl.; Natl.
Budget Set: Sept. -Oct.
Personnel:
Hank Gasikowski *(Pres)*
Brands & Products:
2-STEP
23CIII
45 MXT
45 V-XL
45 VXL
BESELER
BESELER H D
BESLAR
BESTFILE
CADET
CADET II
CHARLES BESELER COMPANY
DIAMOND
NEGAFLAT
NEGATRANS
SHRINK-PAK
STANDARD
UNISTAND
UNIVERSAL 45 SYSTEM
UNIVERSAL TANK & REEL

CHART INDUSTRIES, INC.
(d/b/a Chart Inc.)
1 Infinity Corporate Centre Dr Ste 300
Garfield Heights, OH 44125-5370
Tel.: (440) 753-1490
Fax: (440) 753-1491
Web Site: www.chart-ind.com
Approx. Sls.: $555,455,000
Approx. Number Employees: 3,013
Year Founded: 1992
Business Description:
Industrial Process Equipment Mfr
S.I.C.: 3559; 1321; 3563
N.A.I.C.S.: 332410; 211112; 333912
Import Export
Advertising Expenditures: $3,268,000
Personnel:
Samuel F. Thomas *(Chm & CEO)*
Steven T. Shaw *(Pres)*
Michael F. Biehl *(CFO, Treas & Exec VP)*
Kenneth J. Webster *(VP, Chief Acctg Officer & Controller)*
Matthew J. Klaben *(Gen Counsel, Sec & VP)*
Mark H. Ludwig *(VP-HR)*
Rita S. Carroll *(Dir-Corp Dev)*
Timothy A. Neeser *(Dir-Mktg & New Product Devel)*
Brands & Products:
CAIRE
CARBO-CHARGER
CARBO-DRAUGHT
CARBO-MAX
CARBO-MITE
CARBO-MIZER
CHART
CORE-IN-KETTLE
COVAC
CRYO-CYL
DURA-CYL
INNOVATION. EXPERIENCE. PERFORMANCE.
LASER-CYL
LASER-TEC
MEDLEY
MEGA-CYL
ORCA
PERMA-CYL
PORTA VAC
PVAC
SURE-FILL
THERMAX SUPERGAP
TRIFECTA
TVAC

CIBA VISION CORPORATION
(Sub. of Novartis AG)
11460 Johns Creek Pkwy
Duluth, GA 30097-1518
Tel.: (678) 415-3937
Fax: (678) 415-3001
E-mail: corporate.communications@cibavision.com
Web Site: www.cibavision.com
Sales Range: $1-4.9 Billion
Approx. Number Employees: 2,300
Year Founded: 1980
Business Description:
Contact Lenses & Vision Care Products Mfr
S.I.C.: 3851
N.A.I.C.S.: 339115
Media: 14-15
Personnel:
Andrea Saia *(Pres)*
John McKenna *(CFO)*
Ed Vlacich *(CMO)*
Francesco Balestrieri *(Pres-Americas Reg)*
Hon Keong Choo *(Pres-Asia Pacific-Emerging Growth Markets Reg)*
Hidekazu Hayakawa *(Pres-Japan)*
Susanne Kohout *(Pres-Europe, Russia & Africa)*
Bettina Maunz *(VP-Global Comm)*
Atul Khosla *(Head-HR-Global)*
Brands & Products:
FOCUS DAILIES
FOCUS PROGRESSIVES
FRESH LOOK RADIANCE
FRESHLOOK COLOR STUDIO
NIGHT & DAY
SOLO-CARE
Advertising Agency:
G2 Branding and Design
200 5th Ave
New York, NY 10010
Tel.: (212) 537-3700
Fax: (212) 537-3737

CIBA VISION WESLEY JESSEN
(Sub. of CIBA Vision Corporation)
333 E Howard Ave
Des Plaines, IL 60018-1907
Tel.: (847) 294-3000
Web Site: www.cibasoft.com/about_worldwide/worldwide_locations.shtml#americas
Approx. Number Employees: 2,602
Business Description:
Contact Lenses, Supplies & Services
S.I.C.: 3851
N.A.I.C.S.: 339115
Advertising Expenditures: $8,000,000
Media: 2-4-6-7-8-10
Distr.: Intl.; Natl.
Personnel:
Tom Steiner *(VP-Mktg)*
Brands & Products:
AOSEPT
AQUIFY
CLEAR CARE
DURASOFT
DURASOFT COLORS
FRESH LOOK
SOLO-CARE

CINEMATOGRAPHY ELECTRONICS INC.
5321 Derry Ave Ste G
Agoura Hills, CA 91301
Tel.: (818) 706-3334
Fax: (818) 706-3335
E-mail: info@cinemaelec.com
Web Site: www.cinematographyelectronics.com
Approx. Number Employees: 9
Year Founded: 1976
Business Description:
Supplier of Photographic Equipment
S.I.C.: 3861
N.A.I.C.S.: 333315
Media: 6
Personnel:
Larry Barton *(Pres)*

CLEARFIELD, INC.
5480 Nathan Lane
Plymouth, MN 55442
Tel.: (763) 784-4995
Fax: (763) 784-2038
E-mail: sales@clfd.net
Web Site: www.clearfieldconnection.com/
Approx. Rev.: $24,366,755
Approx. Number Employees: 136
Year Founded: 1979
Business Description:
Fiber Optic Cable, Optical Networking Equipment, Gallium Nitride Based Transistors, Components & Devices & Ultraviolet Measurement Instruments Mfr
S.I.C.: 3827; 3826; 8733
N.A.I.C.S.: 333314; 334516; 541710
Export
Media: 4-10-13
Distr.: Intl.; Natl.
Budget Set: Dec.
Personnel:
Ronald G. Roth *(Chm)*
Cheryl Podzimek Beranek *(Pres & CEO)*
Daniel Herzog *(Interim CFO)*
Johnny Hill *(COO)*
Brands & Products:
CHANGING THE WAY YOU THINK ABOUT FIBER MANAGEMENT
CLEARFIELD
CLEARVIEW
CLEARVIEW MULTIPLIED
Advertising Agency:
Calysto Communications
861 Sapphire Ln Sugar Hill
Atlanta, GA 30518
Tel.: (404) 266-2060
Fax: (404) 266-2041
Content Development
Media & Analyst Relations
Public Relations
Social Media
Strategic Planning

COASTAL OPTICAL SYSTEMS, INC.
(Sub. of Jenoptik Laser, Optik, Systeme GmbH)
164 Innovation Dr
West Palm Beach, FL 33407
Tel.: (561) 881-7400
Fax: (561) 881-1947
E-mail: sales@coastalopt.com
Web Site: www.coastalopt.com
E-Mail For Key Personnel:
Sales Director: sales@coastalopt.com
Approx. Number Employees: 40
Year Founded: 1991

Key to Media (For complete agency information see *The Advertising Red Books-Agencies* edition):
1. Bus. Publs. 2. Cable T.V. 3. Catalogs & Directories. 4. Co-op Adv. 5. Consumer Mags. 6. D.M. to Bus. Estab.7. D.M. to Consumers 8. Daily Newsp. 9. Exhibits/Trade Shows 10. Foreign 11. Infomercial 12. Internet Adv.13. Multimedia 14. Network Radio 15. Network T.V. 16. Newsp. Distr. Mags. 17. Other 18. Outdoor (Posters, Transit) 19. Point of Purchase20. Premiums, Novelties 21. Product Samples 22. Special Events Mktg. 23. Spot Radio 24. Spot T.V. 25. Weekly Newsp. 26. Yellow Page Adv.

Coastal Optical Systems, Inc. — (Continued)

Business Description:
Custom Optical Assemblies Mfr & Designer
S.I.C.: 3827
N.A.I.C.S.: 333314
Media: 2-10-13
Personnel:
Marc Neer *(Principal, Member & Technical Staff)*
Susan Wilder *(VP-Fin)*

CODA INC.
30 Indus Ave
Mahwah, NJ 07430
Tel.: (201) 825-7400
Fax: (201) 825-8133
E-mail: sales@codamount.com
Web Site: www.codamount.com
E-Mail For Key Personnel:
Sales Director: sales@codamount.com
Approx. Sls.: $4,000,000
Approx. Number Employees: 25
Business Description:
Photographic Equipment & Supplies Mfr
S.I.C.: 3861
N.A.I.C.S.: 333315
Media: 10
Personnel:
Lee Coda *(Owner)*
Greg White *(Reg Mgr)*
Brands & Products:
CODA
COLD-MOUNT
FINISHING PRODUCTS FOR THE IMAGING INDUSTRY

COGNEX CORPORATION
1 Vision Dr
Natick, MA 01760-2059
Tel.: (508) 650-3000
Fax: (508) 650-3333
Fax: (508) 650-3324 (Public Relations)
Fax: (508) 650-3344 (Sales & Marketing)
E-mail: pr@cognex.com
Web Site: www.cognex.com
E-Mail For Key Personnel:
Marketing Director: mktg@cognex.com
Public Relations: pr@cognex.com
Approx. Rev.: $290,691,000
Approx. Number Employees: 824
Year Founded: 1981
Business Description:
Machine Vision Systems Used to Replace Human Vision in Manufacturing Processes
S.I.C.: 3823; 3812; 3827; 3829
N.A.I.C.S.: 334513; 333314; 334511; 334519
Advertising Expenditures: $1,402,000
Media: 1-2-7-10-13
Personnel:
Robert J. Shillman *(Chm & Chief Culture Officer)*
Robert Willett *(Pres & CEO)*
Richard A. Morin *(CFO, Treas, Exec VP-Fin & Admin)*
Thomas F. Nash *(Pres-Surface Inspection Sys Div)*
Kris Nelson *(Principal & Programmer Analyst)*
Markku Jaaskelainen *(Exec VP)*
Patrick A. Alias *(Sr VP)*
Edward J. Dineen *(Sr VP)*
Kerry A. Galvin *(Sr VP)*
Stanley Luboda *(Sr VP-Sls & Bus Dev)*
E. John McGarry *(Sr VP-R&D)*
Susan M. Conway *(Dir-IR)*
Brands & Products:
CAMERA LINK
CHECKER
CHECKPOINT
COGNEX
DATAMAN
DISPLAYINSPECT
DVT
EASYBUILDER
FIBERINSPECT
FIREWIRE
IN-SIGHT
MVS-8000
OMI FIDUCIAL FINDER
PATFLEX
PATINSPECT
PATMAX
PEOPLESENSOR
PROOFREAD
SMARTVIEW
VISIONPRO
VISIONVIEW
Advertising Agency:
Media Concepts Corporation
25 N Main St
Assonet, MA 02702-1136
Tel.: (508) 644-3131
Fax: (508) 644-5201

COHEN'S FASHION OPTICAL INC.
(Sub. of Houchens Industries Inc.)
100 Quentin Roosevelt Blvd Ste 400
Garden City, NY 11530-1558
Tel.: (516) 599-5500
Fax: (515) 465-6960
Toll Free: (888) 777-5273
Web Site: www.cohensfashionoptical.com
Approx. Number Employees: 100
Year Founded: 1924
Business Description:
Eyeglass Retailer
S.I.C.: 5995; 8011
N.A.I.C.S.: 446130; 621111
Advertising Expenditures: $1,000,000
Media: 3-5-6-8-9-18-19-22-23-24-25-26
Distr.: Natl.
Budget Set: Jan.
Personnel:
Robert Cohen *(Pres & CEO)*
Rich Winter *(CFO)*
Alan Cohen *(Exec VP)*
Marni Adler *(Dir-New Bus Dev)*
Karen Miller *(Dir-Franchise Ops)*
Brands & Products:
COHEN'S FASHION OPTICAL
Advertising Agencies:
Flying Point Media
494 8th Ave 20th Fl
New York, NY 10001
Tel.: (212) 629-4960
Fax: (212) 629-4967

freshbrick, inc.
761 Koehler Ave
Ronkonkoma, NY 11779
Tel.: (631) 285-7825
Fax: (631) 285-7826

COHERENT, INC.
5100 Patrick Henry Dr
Santa Clara, CA 95054
Tel.: (408) 764-4000
Fax: (408) 764-4800
Web Site: www.coherent.com
Approx. Sls.: $605,067,000
Approx. Number Employees: 2,006
Year Founded: 1966
Business Description:
Photonics Solutions to Commercial & Scientific Research
S.I.C.: 3679; 3589; 3826; 3845
N.A.I.C.S.: 334419; 333319; 334510; 334516
Export
Advertising Expenditures: $2,600,000
Media: 2-4-10-13
Distr.: Intl.; Natl.
Budget Set: Sept.
Personnel:
Garry W. Rogerson *(Chm)*
John R. Ambroseo *(Pres & CEO)*
Helene Simonet *(CFO & Exec VP)*
Luis Spinelli *(CTO & Exec VP)*
Brands & Products:
3SIGMA
AAA
ALMETA XS
AVIA
AZURE
BEAMMASTER
BEAMVIEW
CHAMELEON
COHERENT
COMPASS
COMPEXPRO
CRYSTALAS
CUBE
DBCHECK
DIAMOND
ENTERPRISE
EVOLUTION
EXCISTAR
FIBER ARRAY PACKAGE
FIELDMASTER
FIELDMATE
FIELDMAX
FRED
GEM
GEOLASPRO
HIDRA
HIGHLIGHT
INDIGO
INDYSTAR
INNOVA
LABMAX
LAMBDA
LASERCAM
LASERCHECK
LASERGAGE
LASERMATE
LASERPAD
LEGEND
LIBRA
LITHOTEX
LPXPRO
MANTIS
MATRIX
MICRA
MICROLAS
MIRA
MODEMASTER
NOVALINE
NOVATEX
ONYX
OPERA
PALADIN
POWERMAX
PRISMA
PRODUCTIVITY PLUS
PULSELIFE
PURELIGHT
REGA
SABRE
SAPPHIRE
SCANMATEPRO
SIFIR
SILHOUETTE
SKYLIGHT
SUPERIOR RELIABILITY & PERFORMANCE
TALISKAR
TOPAS
TRACER
ULTIMA
ULTRAFAST
VARIOLAS
VECTOR
VERDI
VIPER
VITESSE
WAVEMASTER
XANTOS XS

COLE-PARMER INSTRUMENT COMPANY
(Sub. of Thermo Fisher Scientific Inc.)
625 E Bunker Ct
Vernon Hills, IL 60061-1844
Tel.: (847) 549-7600
Fax: (847) 247-2929
Toll Free: (800) 323-4340
E-mail: info@coleparmer.com
Web Site: www.coleparmer.com
Sales Range: $150-199.9 Million
Approx. Number Employees: 315
Year Founded: 1955
Business Description:
Scientific Instruments
S.I.C.: 5943
N.A.I.C.S.: 453210
Import Export
Media: 4-10
Personnel:
Michael Sesterhenn *(Dir-Warehouse)*
Brands & Products:
COLE-PARMER
DELIVERING SOLUTIONS YOU TRUST

COLOR IMAGING INC.
4350 Peachtree Industrial Blvd Ste 100
Norcross, GA 30071
Tel.: (770) 840-1090
Fax: (770) 840-6846
Fax: (800) 783-9010
Toll Free: (800) 783-1090
E-mail: sales@colorimaging.com
Web Site: www.colorimaging.com
E-Mail For Key Personnel:
Sales Director: sales@colorimaging.com
Sales Range: $10-24.9 Million
Approx. Number Employees: 100
Year Founded: 1989
Business Description:
Develops, Manufactures & Markets Products Used in Electronic Printing
S.I.C.: 3555; 2893; 3861; 3955
N.A.I.C.S.: 333293; 325910; 325992; 333315; 339944
Advertising Expenditures: $171,510
Media: 7-10-13

Key to Media (For complete agency information see *The Advertising Red Books-Agencies* edition):
1. Bus. Publs. 2. Cable T.V. 3. Catalogs & Directories. 4. Co-op Adv. 5. Consumer Mags. 6. D.M. to Bus. Estab.7. D.M. to Consumers 8. Daily Newsp. 9. Exhibits/Trade Shows 10. Foreign 11. Infomercial 12. Internet Adv.13. Multimedia 14. Network Radio 15. Network T.V. 16. Newsp. Distr. Mags. 17. Other 18. Outdoor (Posters, Transit) 19. Point of Purchase20. Premiums, Novelties 21. Product Samples 22. Special Events Mktg. 23. Spot Radio 24. Spot T.V. 25. Weekly Newsp. 26. Yellow Page Adv.

Personnel:
Sueling Wang *(Pres)*
Morris E. Van Asperen *(Exec VP)*

COMBIMATRIX CORPORATION
(Sub. of Acacia Research Corporation)
310 Goddard Ste 150
Irvine, CA 92618
Tel.: (949) 753-0624
Toll Free: (800) 985CMBX
E-mail: info@combimatrix.com
Web Site: www.combimatrix.com
Approx. Rev.: $3,554,000
Approx. Number Employees: 40
Business Description:
Customizable Biological Arrays
S.I.C.: 3826; 7371
N.A.I.C.S.: 334516; 541511
Advertising Expenditures: $337,000
Media: 2-10
Personnel:
Mark P. McGowan *(Chm)*
R. Judd Jessup *(Pres & CEO)*
Scott Burell *(CFO, Treas & Sec)*
Mansoor Mohammed *(CEO-CombiMatrix Molecular Diagnostics)*
Daniel R. Forche *(Sr VP-Sls & Mktg)*
H. Sho Fuji *(VP-Engrg & Production)*
Dindyal Ramkissoon *(VP-Sls & Mktg)*
Chris Emery *(Dir-Bus Dev)*
Tim Flores *(Dir-Sls)*
Jeff Hayes *(Dir-Sls-Oncology Market)*
Brands & Products:
CUSTOM ARRAY
EXPRESS TRACK
Advertising Agencies:
Allen & Caron
18200 Von Karman Ave Ste 780
Irvine, CA 92612-0192
Tel.: (949) 474-4300
Fax: (949) 474-4330

INK, Inc.
511 Delaware St Ste 200
Kansas City, MO 64105
Tel.: (816) 753-6222
Fax: (816) 753-8188
Toll Free: (866) 753-6222

CONTINENTAL SALES COMPANY OF AMERICA, LTD.
180 Westgate Dr
Watsonville, CA 95076
Tel.: (831) 763-6931
Fax: (831) 763-6938
Toll Free: (800) 288-2721
E-mail: csc_info@csclabs.com
Web Site: www.csclabs.com
Approx. Sls.: $22,000,000
Approx. Number Employees: 225
Business Description:
Eyeglasses Mfr
S.I.C.: 3851
N.A.I.C.S.: 339115
Media: 4-19
Personnel:
Doug K. Kim *(Pres & CEO)*
Brands & Products:
CSC
GARRISON
GATTINONI
MARTINI
RENATO BALESTRA
WEST

CONTROL PRODUCTS, INC.
(Div. of Calculagraph Co.)
280 Ridgedale Ave
East Hanover, NJ 07936
Tel.: (973) 887-9400
Fax: (973) 887-5083
E-mail: sales@cpi-nj.com
Web Site: www.cpi-nj.com
E-Mail For Key Personnel:
Marketing Director: john@cpi-nj.com
Sales Director: sales@cpi-nj.com
Approx. Number Employees: 65
Year Founded: 1946
Business Description:
Thermal Device & Waterproof Snap-Action Switches Mfr
S.I.C.: 3643; 3822
N.A.I.C.S.: 335931; 334512
Export
Media: 2-4-17
Distr.: Natl.
Budget Set: July -Aug.
Personnel:
Clifford Moodie *(Pres)*
John Crozier *(Reg Mgr)*
Brands & Products:
CPI

COOPER-ATKINS CORPORATION
33 Reeds Gap Rd
Middlefield, CT 06455
Tel.: (860) 349-3473
Fax: (860) 349-8994
Toll Free: (800) 835-5011
E-mail: info@cooper-atkins.com
Web Site: www.cooper-atkins.com
E-Mail For Key Personnel:
President: carolyn@cooperinstrument.com
Sales Range: $25-49.9 Million
Approx. Number Employees: 125
Year Founded: 1885
Business Description:
Mfr. of Time, Temperature & Humidity Instruments
S.I.C.: 3841
N.A.I.C.S.: 339112
Import Export
Advertising Expenditures: $235,000
Bus. Publs.: $40,000; Catalogs & Directories: $100,000; Exhibits/Trade Shows: $75,000; Product Samples: $20,000
Distr.: Intl.; Natl.
Budget Set: Sept.
Personnel:
Carol P. Wallace *(Pres & CEO)*
Carol Duplessis *(Corp Sec & VP-HR)*
Jon Esping *(VP-Sls-Intl)*
Barry Potter *(VP-Fin)*
Brands & Products:
ACCUTUFF
COOPER
COOPER ATKINS
MICROTHERM
VERSATUFF

COOPERVISION, INC.
(Sub. of The Cooper Companies, Inc.)
370 Woodcliff Dr Ste 200
Fairport, NY 14450
Tel.: (585) 385-6810
Fax: (888) 385-3217
Toll Free: (800) 538-7850
E-mail: info@coopervision.com
Web Site: www.coopervision.com
Sales Range: $200-249.9 Million
Approx. Number Employees: 150
Business Description:
Contact Lenses Mfr & Sales
S.I.C.: 3851
N.A.I.C.S.: 339115
Media: 2-7-8-11-13
Personnel:
Jeffrey A. McLean *(Exec VP-Global Comml Strategy)*
Paul Soik *(Sr VP-Corp Accts)*
Mary Angrisani *(VP-Sls)*
Richard Clompus *(VP-Pro Affairs-Global)*
Brands & Products:
COOPERVISION
Advertising Agency:
Martino Flynn LLC
175 Sully's Trl Ste 100
Pittsford, NY 14534
Tel.: (585) 421-0100
Fax: (585) 421-0121

CORNING CABLE SYSTEMS LLC
(Sub. of Corning Incorporated)
800 17th St NW
Hickory, NC 28601
Mailing Address:
PO Box 489
Hickory, NC 28603-0489
Tel.: (828) 901-5000
Fax: (828) 325-5060
Toll Free: (800) 743-2671
E-mail: info@corning.com
Web Site: www.corningcablesystems.com
Sales Range: $250-299.9 Million
Approx. Number Employees: 500
Year Founded: 1977
Business Description:
Supplier of Fiber Optic Cables, Connectors, Splices, Hardware, Test Equipment & Network Interfaces
S.I.C.: 3357; 3661
N.A.I.C.S.: 335921; 334210
Export
Media: 2
Distr.: Natl.
Personnel:
Clark Kinlin *(Pres & CEO)*
Tony Tripeny *(Sr VP & Corp Controller)*
Brands & Products:
EVOLANT
FDC
FIBERGAIN
GUIDELINES
INFINICOR
LANSCAPE
LEAF
MAXI-BUNDLE
PLATINUM
SMF-28E

COSTA DEL MAR SUNGLASSES, INC.
(Div. of A. T. CROSS COMPANY)
2361 Mason Ave Ste 100
Daytona Beach, FL 32117
Tel.: (386) 274-4000
Fax: (386) 274-4001
Toll Free: (800) 447-3700
E-mail: info@costadelmarsunglasses.com
Web Site: www.costadelmar.com
Approx. Sls.: $6,000,000
Approx. Number Employees: 100
Year Founded: 1983
Business Description:
Sunglasses Mfr
S.I.C.: 5311
N.A.I.C.S.: 452111
Import Export
Media: 1-2-4-5-6-7-8-10-11-16-19-20-21-22-25-26
Distr.: Intl.; Natl.
Personnel:
Charles R. MacDonald *(Pres)*
Terri Ossi *(VP-Mktg)*
Brands & Products:
COSTA DEL MAR SUNGLASSES
FLUID METAL SUNGLASSES
LIGHT WAVE SUNGLASSES
WAVE 400
WAVE 580
WAVE TECHNOLOGY
Advertising Agency:
McGarrah Jessee
205 Brazos
Austin, TX 78701
Tel.: (512) 225-2000
Fax: (512) 225-2020
Sunglasses

CPI CORPORATION
1706 Washington Ave
Saint Louis, MO 63103-1717
Tel.: (314) 231-1575
Fax: (314) 621-9286
Toll Free: (800) 669-9699
E-mail: internet@cpicorp.com
Web Site: www.cpicorp.com
Approx. Sls.: $407,035,000
Approx. Number Employees: 4,900
Year Founded: 1942
Business Description:
Studio Portrait Photography Services
S.I.C.: 7221
N.A.I.C.S.: 541921
Advertising Expenditures: $28,100,000
Media: 2-3-4-5-6-7-8-13-15-16-19-20-22-24
Distr.: Natl.
Budget Set: June -Dec.
Personnel:
David M. Meyer *(Chm)*
Renato Cataldo *(Pres & CEO)*
Dale E. Heins *(CFO & Sr VP-Fin)*
Keith W. Laakko *(CMO & Exec VP)*
Jane E. Nelson *(Gen Counsel)*
Richard L. Tarpley *(Exec VP)*
Rose O'Brien *(Controller & VP-Fin)*
Brands & Products:
CENTRICS TECHNOLOGY
PORTRAIT STUDIOS
SEARS PORTRAIT STUDIOS
SEARSPHOTO.COM

CUNO INC.
(Sub. of 3M Company)
400 Research Pkwy
Meriden, CT 06450-7172
Tel.: (203) 237-5541
Fax: (203) 238-8977
Toll Free: (800) 243-6894
E-mail: cuno@cuno.com
Web Site: www.cuno.com
Sales Range: $350-399.9 Million
Approx. Number Employees: 2,200
Business Description:
Filtration Products Mfr
S.I.C.: 2679; 3569; 3589
N.A.I.C.S.: 322299; 333319; 333999
Advertising Expenditures: $4,000,000
Media: 10

Key to Media (For complete agency information see *The Advertising Red Books-Agencies* edition):
1. Bus. Publs. 2. Cable T.V. 3. Catalogs & Directories. 4. Co-op Adv. 5. Consumer Mags. 6. D.M. to Bus. Estab.7. D.M. to Consumers
8. Daily Newsp. 9. Exhibits/Trade Shows 10. Foreign 11. Infomercial 12. Internet Adv.13. Multimedia 14. Network Radio
15. Network T.V. 16. Newsp. Distr. Mags. 17. Other 18. Outdoor (Posters, Transit) 19. Point of Purchase20. Premiums, Novelties
21. Product Samples 22. Special Events Mktg. 23. Spot Radio 24. Spot T.V. 25. Weekly Newsp. 26. Yellow Page Adv.

CUNO Inc. — (Continued)

Personnel:
Timothy B. Carney *(Sr VP)*
Thomas Hamlin *(Sr VP-R&D)*
Colin McLaren *(VP-Sls)*
Witold J. Witwicki *(VP-IT)*
Bob Marcotte *(Dir-Sls-Mktg)*
Brands & Products:
AQUA-PURE
BETA-KLEAN
BETAFINE
BETAPURE
BEVASSURE
CTG-KLEAN
DUOFLO
LIFEASSURE
MACCLEAN
MAXIMIZER
MICRO-KLEAN
MICRO-WYND
MICROFLUOR
POLYNET
POLYPRO
WATER FACTORY SYSTEMS
ZETA PLUS
ZETAPOR

CUSTOM SENSORS & TECHNOLOGIES

(Sub. of Schneider Electric USA, Inc.)
14401 Princeton Ave
Moorpark, CA 93201
Tel.: (805) 552-3599
Fax: (805) 523-8475
E-mail: sales@cstsensors.com
Web Site: www.cstsensors.com
E-Mail For Key Personnel:
Sales Director: sales@cstsensors.com
Sales Range: $250-299.9 Million
Approx. Number Employees: 1,024
Year Founded: 1974
Business Description:
Sensors & Engineered Subsystems Mfr
S.I.C.: 3679; 3577
N.A.I.C.S.: 334419; 334119
Media: 1-2-4-7-10-11
Personnel:
Lori Appel *(Mgr-Mktg Comm)*
Rosie Franco *(Mgr-Mktg)*
Brands & Products:
BEI
BEI ENCODER
DIGISINE
DUNCAN SENSOR
GYROCHIP
KIMCO ACTUATOR
MICROSYN
NCAPS
SERVOREADY
SERVOSMART
SPHEROSYN

CVI MELLES GRIOT

(Sub. of CVI Melles Griot)
2051 Palomar Airport Rd 200
Carlsbad, CA 92011
Tel.: (760) 438-2131
Fax: (760) 438-5208
Toll Free: (800) 645-2737
E-mail: lasers@cvimellesgriot.com
Web Site: www.mellesgriot.com
E-Mail For Key Personnel:
Sales Director: sales@rochester.mellesgriot.com
Sales Range: $50-74.9 Million
Approx. Number Employees: 170
Year Founded: 1981
Business Description:
High Performance Lenses & Imaging Systems for Industry & Science; Nano-Positioning Sub Systems
S.I.C.: 3827; 3699
N.A.I.C.S.: 333314; 335999
Import Export
Media: 2-4-7-10-13
Distr.: Natl.
Budget Set: Oct.
Personnel:
Blake Fennell *(Pres)*
Brands & Products:
APT
CLEANBEAM
INVARIGON
MELLES GRIOT

CYBEROPTICS CORPORATION

5900 Golden Hills Dr
Golden Valley, MN 55416-1040
Tel.: (763) 542-5000
Fax: (763) 542-5100
Toll Free: (800) 746-6315
E-mail: info@cyberoptics.com
Web Site: www.cyberoptics.com
Approx. Rev.: $56,951,000
Approx. Number Employees: 181
Year Founded: 1984
Business Description:
Sensors & Sensor Systems Mfr
S.I.C.: 3829; 3826; 3827
N.A.I.C.S.: 334519; 333314; 334516
Media: 2-10
Personnel:
Kathleen P. Iverson *(Chm)*
Jeffrey A. Bertelsen *(VP-Fin & Admin)*
Timothy A. Skunes *(VP-Tech & Bus Dev)*
Brands & Products:
CYBEROPTICS
CYBERSCAN
EMBEDDED PROCESS VERIFICATION
EPV
FLEX HR
IMAGENATION
LASER ALIGN
PROCESS INSIGHT
SE 300 ULTRA
SE500
WAFERSENSE

DANAHER INDUSTRIAL CONTROLS

(Sub. of Danaher Corporation)
1675 N Delany Rd
Gurnee, IL 60031-1237
Tel.: (847) 662-2666
Fax: (847) 662-4150
Toll Free: (800) 873-8731
Web Site: www.dynapar.com
Sales Range: $25-49.9 Million
Approx. Number Employees: 110
Year Founded: 1969
Business Description:
Factory Automatic & Process Controls Mfr
S.I.C.: 3824
N.A.I.C.S.: 334514
Import Export
Media: 2-4-7-8-10-13-26
Distr.: Intl.; Natl.
Budget Set: July
Personnel:
Alex Joseph *(Pres)*
Brands & Products:
DYNAOPAR
DYNAPAR
EAGLE SIGNAL
HENGSTLER
LSE
NORTH STAR
PARTLOW
RUST RAK
WEST
Advertising Agency:
The Media Center
735 McArdle Dr Ste F
Crystal Lake, IL 60014
Tel.: (815) 455-3882
Fax: (815) 455-3904

DANIEL MEASUREMENT & CONTROL INC.

(Div. of Emerson Process Management)
11100 Brittmore Park Dr
Houston, TX 77041
Mailing Address:
PO Box 19097
Houston, TX 77224
Tel.: (713) 467-6000
Fax: (713) 827-3880
Telex: 775421
E-mail: webmaster@danielind.com
Web Site: www.danielind.com
E-Mail For Key Personnel:
Sales Director: sales@daniel.com
Sales Range: $75-99.9 Million
Approx. Number Employees: 500
Year Founded: 1930
Business Description:
Custody Transfer & Flow Measurement Products
S.I.C.: 3823
N.A.I.C.S.: 334513
Import Export
Advertising Expenditures: $1,000,000
Media: 4-7-10-20-21
Distr.: Direct to Consumer; Intl.; Natl.
Budget Set: Sept.
Personnel:
Girard Wang *(Mgr-Adv)*
Brands & Products:
FISHER
SENIOR ORIFICE FITTING
SENIOR SONIC ULTRASONIC FLOW MOTOR

DANKER LABORATORIES INC.

6805 33rd St E
Sarasota, FL 34243-4144
Tel.: (941) 758-7711
Fax: (941) 758-5965
Toll Free: (800) 237-9641
E-mail: sales@dankerlabs.com
Web Site: www.dankerlabs.com
E-Mail For Key Personnel:
Sales Director: sales@dankerlabs.com
Approx. Number Employees: 20
Year Founded: 1958
Business Description:
Contact Lenses & Ophthalmic Cleaning Solutions Mfr
S.I.C.: 3851; 5048
N.A.I.C.S.: 339115; 423460
Export
Advertising Expenditures: $250,000
Media: 2-7
Distr.: Natl.
Personnel:
Jeri Struve *(Pres)*
Frederick J. Danker *(CEO)*
Gwen Norris *(VP-Mktg)*
Brands & Products:
AQUAPERM
ASPHERO-B
ASPHERO-F
ASPHERO-FB
AUSTIL-FOCAL
CENTRAVUE
CLEARSIGHT
CLEARSIGHT THIN
CRESCENT 1 PIECE
CRESCENT FUSED
DANKERSITE
DCL TRANSLATING
FRONT SURFACE
GUILDCRAFT
INVERTED CRESCENT
LATITUDE GP
LATITUDE SOFT
PANO-SITE
PERMA-BRITE
PERMACOTE
PERMATEARS
THE RGP MULTIFOCAL SPECIALISTS
ST-90
ST-BIFOCAL
STRAIGHTOP
VISIONALL
VISIONALL MULTI

DARBY GROUP COMPANIES, INC.

300 Jericho Quadrangle Ste 200
Jericho, NY 11753
Tel.: (516) 683-1800
Fax: (516) 688-2820
Toll Free: (888) 683-5001
E-mail: info@darbygroup.com
Web Site: www.darbygroup.com
Sales Range: $650-699.9 Million
Approx. Number Employees: 1,400
Year Founded: 1948
Business Description:
Medical, Dental, Veterinary Supplies, Dental Laboratory Equipment, & Pharmaceutical Products Distr
S.I.C.: 5047
N.A.I.C.S.: 423450
Advertising Expenditures: $200,000
Media: 9-17
Distr.: Direct to Consumer; Intl.; Natl.; Reg.
Budget Set: Oct.
Personnel:
Michael Ashkin *(Chm)*
Carl Ashkin *(CEO)*
Justina Sorraci *(CFO)*
Michael Bochen *(VP)*
Laura Kahn *(VP-Corp Mktg)*
Advertising Agency:
The Lanmark Group Inc.
527 Industrial Way W
Eatontown, NJ 07724-2211
Tel.: (732) 389-4500
Fax: (732) 389-4998

DATA BASE ACCESS SYSTEMS, INC.

60 Midvale Rd
Mountain Lakes, NJ 07046-1354
Tel.: (973) 335-0800
Fax: (973) 335-1956
E-mail: info@dbasinc.com

Key to Media (For complete agency information see *The Advertising Red Books-Agencies* edition):
1. Bus. Publs. 2. Cable T.V. 3. Catalogs & Directories. 4. Co-op Adv. 5. Consumer Mags. 6. D.M. to Bus. Estab.7. D.M. to Consumers
8. Daily Newsp. 9. Exhibits/Trade Shows 10. Foreign 11. Infomercial 12. Internet Adv.13. Multimedia 14. Network Radio
15. Network T.V. 16. Newsp. Distr. Mags. 17. Other 18. Outdoor (Posters, Transit) 19. Point of Purchase20. Premiums, Novelties
21. Product Samples 22. Special Events Mktg. 23. Spot Radio 24. Spot T.V. 25. Weekly Newsp. 26. Yellow Page Adv.

Web Site: www.dbasinc.com
Sales Range: $1-9.9 Million
Approx. Number Employees: 12
Year Founded: 1997
Business Description:
Fiber Optic Networking Solutions
S.I.C.: 1731; 3577
N.A.I.C.S.: 238210; 334119
Media: 2-4-7-10-13
Personnel:
Michael Palazzi *(Pres)*
Joe Ferraro *(Gen Mgr)*
John Bazin *(Mgr-Mktg)*
Brands & Products:
CODELINK
CODENET
CODESTAR
DBASCODENOLL

DAVID WHITE, LLC
(Div. of Robert Bosch Tool Corp)
255 W Fleming
Watseka, IL 60970
Mailing Address:
PO Box 359
Watseka, IL 60970
Tel.: (815) 432-5237
Fax: (815) 432-5390
Toll Free: (800) 435-1859
E-mail: custserv@davidwhite.com
Web Site: www.davidwhite.com
E-Mail For Key Personnel:
Marketing Director: marketing@davidwhite.com
Sales Range: $75-99.9 Million
Approx. Number Employees: 300
Year Founded: 1895
Business Description:
Optical Instruments Mfr
S.I.C.: 3827
N.A.I.C.S.: 333314
Advertising Expenditures: $400,000
Media: 2-7-8-10-11-19-20
Distr.: Intl.; Natl.
Budget Set: Nov.
Personnel:
Bill Christy *(Gen Mgr)*
Brands & Products:
AUTO LASER 1550
AUTO LASER 200
AUTO LASER 300
AUTO LASER 350
AUTO LASER 500
AUTO LASER 700
DAVID WHITE
MERIDIAN
UNIVERSAL

DEDERT CORPORATION
(Formerly Anhydro Inc.)
20000 Governors Dr
Olympia Fields, IL 60461-1034
Tel.: (708) 747-7000
Fax: (708) 755-8815
E-mail: dedert@dedert.com
Web Site: www.dedert.com
Sales Range: $10-24.9 Million
Approx. Number Employees: 35
Year Founded: 1968
Business Description:
Supplier of Evaporators, Liquid Solid Separation Equipment & Solvent Recovery Systems
S.I.C.: 3559; 3556; 5084
N.A.I.C.S.: 333298; 333294; 423830
Import Export
Advertising Expenditures: $50,000
Media: 2-4-7-10
Distr.: Natl.
Personnel:
Guy Lonergan *(Pres)*
Tim Pasbrig *(Gen Mgr)*

DIGITALGLOBE, INC.
1601 Dry Creek Dr Ste 260
Longmont, CO 80503
Tel.: (303) 684-4000
Fax: (303) 684-4048
Toll Free: (800) 655-7929
E-mail: info@digitalglobe.com
Web Site: www.digitalglobe.com
Approx. Rev.: $275,200,000
Approx. Number Employees: 629
Year Founded: 1994
Business Description:
Commercial High Resolution Earth Imagery Solutions
S.I.C.: 7335; 4899; 7379
N.A.I.C.S.: 541922; 517410; 541519
Media: 7-8-10-13-17-22
Personnel:
Howell M. Estes, III *(Chm)*
Jeffrey R. Tarr *(Pres & CEO)*
Yancey L. Spruill *(CFO, Treas & Exec VP)*
Scott M. Hicar *(CIO & Sr VP)*
Walter S. Scott *(CTO & Exec VP)*
Carl Long *(Chief Acctg Officer)*
J. Alison Alfers *(Gen Counsel, Sec & Sr VP)*
H. John Oechsle *(Exec VP-Strategy & Product)*
Jeffrey S. Kerridge *(Sr VP & Gen Mgr-Defense & Intelligence)*
A. Rafay Khan *(Sr VP-Comml Sls)*
David Banks *(Head-IR & PR)*
Brett Thomassie *(Dir-Civil Govt Sls)*
Chuck Herring *(Dir-Mktg Comm)*
Robert Keosheyan *(Dir-Corp Comm)*
Brands & Products:
CITYSPHERE
DIGITALGLOBE
IMAGEATLAS
IMAGEBUILDER
IMAGECONNECT
IMAGESCAPE
PHOTOMAPPER
Advertising Agency:
Allen & Gerritsen
The Arsenal on the Charles 311
Arsenal St 4th Fl
Watertown, MA 02472
Tel.: (617) 926-4005
Fax: (617) 926-0133

DIONEX CORPORATION
1228 Titan Way
Sunnyvale, CA 94085-4015
Mailing Address:
PO Box 3606
Sunnyvale, CA 94088-3603
Tel.: (408) 737-0700
Fax: (408) 730-9403
Toll Free: (800) 346-6390
E-mail: info@dionex.co.uk
Web Site: www.dionex.com
Approx. Sls.: $419,607,000
Approx. Number Employees: 1,550
Year Founded: 1975
Business Description:
Analytical Medical Instrumentation Mfr
S.I.C.: 3823; 2819; 3826
N.A.I.C.S.: 334513; 325188; 334516
Export
Advertising Expenditures: $5,600,000
Media: 2-4-7-10-13-20
Distr.: Intl.; Natl.
Budget Set: Monthly
Personnel:
Franklin R. Witney *(Pres & CEO)*
Craig A. McCollam *(CFO & Exec VP-Fin & Admin)*
Bruce Barton *(Chief Comml Officer & Exec VP)*
Peter Jochum *(Sr VP-Life Sciences)*
David Fairbanks *(VP-IT)*
Brands & Products:
AAA-DIRECT
ACCLAIM
ACURATE
AES
AMINOPAC
AMINOTRAP
AMMS
ANION ATLAS
ASE
ASI-100
ASI-100P
ASI-100PT
ASI-100T
ASRN
ASRS
ATLAS
AUTOASE
AUTOION
AUTONEUTRALIZATION
AUTOQ
AUTOREGEN
AUTOSELECT
AUTOSUPPRESSION
AUTOTRACE
BIOLC
BORATETRAP
CARBOPAC
CATION ATLAS
CHROMELEON
CMD
CMMS
CSRN
CSRS
DIONEX
DIONIUM
DNAPAC
DNAPHOR
DX-LAN
ELUGEN
FASTLOC
FLAREFIT
HPICE
ION BRIGHT
IONPAC
IONSEP
METPAC
MICROBEAD
MICROMEMBRANE
MONODISC
MONOSTANDARD
MPIC
OLIGOSTANDARDS
OMNIPAC
ONGUARD
OPERATIONAL SIMPLICITY
PASSION.POWER.PRODUCTIVITY.
PEAKNET
PEPMAP
PICO-BUFFER
POLYVIAL
PROBOT
PROPAC
PROSWIFT
PURIFICATION WORKFLOW AUTOMATION
REAGENT-FREE
RFIC
RFIC-ER
SC-CSRS
SELF-REGENERATING SUPPRESSION
SELF-REGENERATING SUPPRESSOR
SMARTFLOW
SMARTPEAKS
SUMMIT
SWITCHOS
TCC-1
TCC-100
THERMOFLARE
TRINITY
U-Z VIEW
UCI-50
ULTICHROM
ULTIFLOW
ULTIMATE
UVD 170S/170U HPLC UV/VIS
UVD 340S/340U HPLC
VIRTUAL COLUMN

DISTRICT PHOTO INC.
10501 Rhode Is Ave
Beltsville, MD 20705-2317
Tel.: (301) 937-5300
Fax: (301) 937-5627
E-mail: info@districtphoto.com
Web Site: www.districtphoto.com
Approx. Number Employees: 700
Year Founded: 1949
Business Description:
Photo Finisher
S.I.C.: 7384; 5043
N.A.I.C.S.: 812921; 423410
Media: 6-8-25
Distr.: Natl.
Budget Set: Sept. -Oct.
Personnel:
Melvin S. Cohen *(Founder & Chm)*
Neil Cohen *(Pres)*
Bob Friend *(Exec VP & Gen Mgr)*
Brands & Products:
CLARK
DISTRICT PHOTO
MYSTIC COLOR LAB
SNAPFISH

DYNAMICS RESEARCH CORPORATION
2 Tech Dr
Andover, MA 01810-2434
Tel.: (978) 289-1500
Fax: (978) 475-8205
Toll Free: (800) 522-4321
E-mail: webmaster@drc.com
Web Site: www.drc.com
Approx. Rev.: $272,065,000
Approx. Number Employees: 1,300
Year Founded: 1955
Business Description:
Technical Services, Integrated Systems Solutions & Precision Products Services
S.I.C.: 7373
N.A.I.C.S.: 541512
Import Export
Advertising Expenditures: $230,000
Media: 2-4-7-10-11-21
Distr.: Intl.; Natl.
Budget Set: Sept.
Personnel:
James P. Regan *(Chm, Pres & CEO)*
David Keleher *(CFO, Sr VP & Treas)*
Richard A. Covel *(Gen Counsel & VP)*

Key to Media (For complete agency information see *The Advertising Red Books-Agencies* edition):
1. Bus. Publs. 2. Cable T.V. 3. Catalogs & Directories. 4. Co-op Adv. 5. Consumer Mags. 6. D.M. to Bus. Estab.7. D.M. to Consumers
8. Daily Newsp. 9. Exhibits/Trade Shows 10. Foreign 11. Infomercial 12. Internet Adv.13. Multimedia 14. Network Radio
15. Network T.V. 16. Newsp. Distr. Mags. 17. Other 18. Outdoor (Posters, Transit) 19. Point of Purchase20. Premiums, Novelties
21. Product Samples 22. Special Events Mktg. 23. Spot Radio 24. Spot T.V. 25. Weekly Newsp. 26. Yellow Page Adv.

Dynamics Research Corporation — (Continued)

Jeanne D. Lefevre *(Sr VP & Gen Mgr-Strategic Bus Dev)*
Lawrence H. O'Brien, Jr. *(Sr VP & Gen Mgr-Bus Dev)*
Robert L. Smith *(Sr VP & Gen Mgr-Defense Group)*
Steven P. Wentzell *(Sr VP & Gen Mgr-HR)*
Frank Grosso *(VP & Gen Mgr-Defense Sys Div)*
Bruce Harris *(VP & Gen Mgr-Readiness & Trng Div)*
Jerry R. Picard *(VP, Gen Mgr-Defense Svcs & Solutions Div)*
Irv Zaks *(VP-Strategy & Dev, Defense Grp)*

Brands & Products:
DRC
ETAPS
METRIFILM
METRIFORM
METRIGRAPHICS
RESOURCES. RESPONSIVENESS. RELIABILITY.
SERTAC

Advertising Agency:
Sage Communications
8229 Boone Blvd Ste 410
Vienna, VA 22182
Tel.: (703) 748-0300
Fax: (703) 564-0101

DYNASIL CORPORATION OF AMERICA

44 Hunt St
Watertown, MA 02472
Tel.: (607) 272-3320
E-mail: info@dynasil.com
Web Site: www.dynasilcorp.com
Approx. Rev.: $42,969,762
Approx. Number Employees: 212
Year Founded: 1960
Business Description:
Optical Materials, Components, Coatings & Specialized Instruments Mfr
S.I.C.: 3299; 3674; 3826; 3827
N.A.I.C.S.: 327999; 333314; 334413; 334516
Advertising Expenditures: $219,275
Personnel:
Peter Sulick *(Chm)*
James Saltzman *(Vice Chm)*
Steven K. Ruggieri *(Pres)*
Richard Johnson *(CFO)*
Bruce Leonetti *(VP-Sls & Mktg)*
Mark Caldwell *(Gen Mgr-RMD Instruments)*
Kevin Osborn *(Dir-Res & Comml Dev)*

DYNEX TECHNOLOGIES, INC.

(Sub. of Magellan Biosciences, Inc.)
14340 Sullyfield Cir
Chantilly, VA 20151-1621
Tel.: (703) 631-7800
Fax: (703) 803-1441
Toll Free: (800) 288-2354
E-mail: customerservice@dynextechnologies.com
Web Site: www.dynextechnologies.com
Approx. Number Employees: 40
Year Founded: 1952
Business Description:
Clinical Laboratory Instruments, Automated Workstations & Associated Consumables Developer, Mfr & Whslr
S.I.C.: 3826; 5047
N.A.I.C.S.: 334516; 423450
Advertising Expenditures: $400,000
Media: 7-10
Personnel:
Adrian Bunce *(Pres)*
Doug Kaspar *(VP-Fin & Admin)*
Dean Sequera *(Dir-Tech)*
John Enescu *(Mgr-Ops)*
Tanveer Wahid *(Mgr-Quality)*

EASTMAN KODAK COMPANY

343 State St
Rochester, NY 14650-0001
Tel.: (585) 724-4000
Fax: (585) 724-1089
Toll Free: (800) 698-3324
Telex: 978481
E-mail: support@kodak.com
Web Site: www.kodak.com
Approx. Sls.: $7,187,000,000
Approx. Number Employees: 18,800
Year Founded: 1880
Business Description:
Photographic & Digital Imaging Products Developer, Marketer & Mfr
S.I.C.: 3861; 3577
N.A.I.C.S.: 333315; 325992; 334119
Advertising Expenditures: $271,000,000
Media: 1-2-3-4-5-6-7-8-9-10-11-12-13-14-15-16-17-18-19-20-22-23-24
Distr.: Intl.; Natl.
Budget Set: Sept. -Oct.
Personnel:
Antonio M. Perez *(Chm & CEO)*
Philip J. Faraci *(Pres & COO)*
Antoinette P. McCorvey *(CFO & Sr VP)*
Kim VanGelder *(CIO & VP)*
Pradeep Jotwani *(CMO, Pres-Consumer Digital Imaging Grp & Sr VP)*
Terry R. Taber *(CTO & Sr VP)*
Robert L. Berman *(Chief HR Officer & Sr VP)*
Eric H. Samuels *(Chief Acctg Officer & Controller)*
Essie L. Calhoun *(Chief Diversity Officer)*
Brad W. Kruchten *(Sr VP & Pres-Film & Entertainment Grp)*
Laura G. Quatela *(Sr VP, Gen Counsel & Chief Intellectual Property Officer)*
John E. Blake, Jr. *(VP & Gen Mgr-Digital Capture & Imaging Devices)*
Steven B. Decker *(VP & Gen Mgr-Film Capture, Paper & Output Sys-Entertainment Grp)*
Douglas J. Edwards *(VP & Gen Mgr-Prepress Solutions)*
Dolores K. Kruchten *(VP & Gen Mgr-Bus Solutions & Svcs)*
Michael L. Marsh *(VP & Gen Mgr-Digital Capture Solutions)*
Diane McCue *(VP & Gen Mgr-Paper & Output Sys)*
Gustavo Oviedo *(Chief Customer Officer, Gen Mgr-Worldwide Reg Ops & VP)*
Susan H. Tousi *(VP & Gen Mgr-Consumer Inkjet Sys)*
Mary L. Burkhardt *(Corp VP & Dir-Global Shared Svcs)*
Gerard K. Meuchner *(Dir-Comm, Pub Affairs & VP)*
Bob Ohlweiler *(Dir & VP-Consumer InkJet Europe, Africa and Middle East)*
Stephen Green *(Reg Mng Dir-Sls & Customer Ops-Asia Pacific Reg & VP)*
Eric Owen *(VP-Sls & Bus Dev)*
Barry Quart *(Gen Mgr-Bus Solutions & Svc-Kodak Americas)*
Lauren Coberly *(Dir-Worldwide Mktg-Kodak Direct)*
Thierry Perronnet *(Mktg Dir-Europe, Middle East & Africa)*
Stacey Stern Albert *(Dir-Tech Policy)*
Erin Foster *(Dir-Worldwide Mktg & Branded Entertainment)*
Donna Preston *(Dir-Branding & Adv)*
Sandra E. Rowland *(Dir-IR)*
Jennifer Cisney *(Sr Mgr-Blogger & Social Media)*
Mary-Irene Marek *(Sr Mgr-Mktg)*
Michel Golitzinsky *(Sls Mgr-Post Production-Canada)*
Jennifer Blauvelt *(Mgr-Branding & Adv-Worldwide)*
Sherrie Fawle *(Dev Mgr-Scanners)*
Trevor Garratt *(Mgr-Micrographic Consumables)*
Lisa Hackett *(Mgr-Global Adv-Consumer Digital Grp)*
Christopher Veronda *(Mgr-Corp Comm)*
John Witzel *(Mgr-Market Dev)*
Francis Yanga *(Mgr-Channel)*
Barbara J. Standish *(Coord-Shareholder Svcs)*

Brands & Products:
A BETTER VIEW OF LIFE
AATON-A MINIMA
ACADEMY
ACCUMAX
ACTIMETER
AD-TYPE
ADVANCED PHOTO SYSTEM
ADVANTIX
AERECON
AERO
AERO-NEG
AEROCHROME
AEROCOLOR
AEROGRAPHIC
AMERICA'S STORYTELLER
AQUA-IMAGE
AUTOCLASS
AUTOPOSITIVE
AUTOTOUCH
AZO
BIOMAX
CAMEO
CAPTURE
CAROUSEL
CHALLENGER
CHIQUITA
CINEFLURE
CLINICSELECT
COLORAMA
COLORBRITE
COLORBURST
COLOREDGE
COLORS
COLORWATCH
COOK-WAITE
CORNER CURL DESIGN
CREATE-A-PRINT
CREO
DACOMATIC
DATA-FRAME
DATAGUIDE
DATAPAK
DC-210 PLUS
DC-240
DC-3200
DEKTOL
DEKTOMATIC
DELAWARE
DENVER
DICOM
DIGIMASTER
DIGITAL GEM
DIGITAL ROC
DIGITAL SHO
DIMEZONE
DIRECTVIEW
DK-50
DK-50R
DOUBLE-X
DP-2000
DRYVIEW
DUEX
DURACLEAR
DURAFLEX
DURAFLO
DURATRANS
DX DESIGN
E-6 ECK
EASTMAN
EASYSHARE
ECDEL
EKTACHROME
EKTACHROME-X
EKTACOLOR
EKTAFICHE
EKTAFLO
EKTAGRAPHIC
EKTALITH
EKTALURE
EKTALUX
EKTAMARK
EKTAMAT
EKTAMATE
EKTAMATIC
EKTAMITE
EKTANAR
EKTANON
EKTAPAN
EKTAPRESS
EKTAPRINT
EKTAPRO
EKTAR
EKTASCAN
EKTASPEED
EKTATHERM
EKTAVISION
EKTAVOLT
EKTAWRITE
EKTON
EKTONOL
EKTRA
EKTRALITE
ELECTROSILVER
ELITE
ELITYS
ELON
ELYSEES
ENCOMPASS
ENVIROWATCH
ESTAR
ESTAR-AH
EURO-35
EXPERTEAM
EXPLORER
EXR
FACIL
FIESTA
FILM/FLASH

Key to Media (For complete agency information see *The Advertising Red Books-Agencies* edition):
1. Bus. Publs. 2. Cable T.V. 3. Catalogs & Directories. 4. Co-op Adv. 5. Consumer Mags. 6. D.M. to Bus. Estab.7. D.M. to Consumers 8. Daily Newsp. 9. Exhibits/Trade Shows 10. Foreign 11. Infomercial 12. Internet Adv.13. Multimedia 14. Network Radio 15. Network T.V. 16. Newsp. Distr. Mags. 17. Other 18. Outdoor (Posters, Transit) 19. Point of Purchase20. Premiums, Novelties 21. Product Samples 22. Special Events Mktg. 23. Spot Radio 24. Spot T.V. 25. Weekly Newsp. 26. Yellow Page Adv.

THE FILM IN THE FAMILIAR YELLOW BOX
THE FILM THAT'S A CAMERA
FLASHMITE
FLEXCEL
FLEXICOLOR
FLEXO
FLING
FLOMATIC
FOR A GOOD LOOK
FOR THE TIMES OF YOUR LIFE
FUN SAVER
FUNSAVER
FUNTIME
GALACTIC
GALLERY
THE GENIUS IS IN THE DETAILS
GIMINI
GOLD
GOLD K BILD
GOOD LOOK
GRAFFITI
HAWKEYE
HOBBY
HOBBY-PAC
HRP
IMAGE GUARD
IMAGELINK
IMAGELITE
IMAGEMASTER
IMAGEMATE
IMAGESOURCE
IMAGESTAR
IMAGEWATCH
IMPACT PLUS
IMT
INDUSTREX
INFO-LINK
INFO-TEL
INSIGHT
INSTAFAX
INSTAGRAPHIC
INSTATECH
INSTRACRYL
IQSMART
IRTRAN
JUBILEE
K-CHROME
K-COLOR
K-II
KEYKODE
KICNET
KIDS
KODABROME
KODABROMIDE
KODACEL
KODACHROME
KODACHROME-X
KODACOLOR
KODACOLOR VR
KODACOLOR-X
KODACRAFT
KODAFIX
KODAFLEX
KODAGRAPH
KODAK
KODAK APPROVAL
KODAK BEACON
KODAK BISNET
KODAK DIAPORAMA
KODAK EXPRESS
KODAK PREVIEW
KODAK PROFESSIONAL
KODAK SIGNATURE
KODAK VISION
KODAKERY
KODALINE
KODALITH
KODALK
KODALUX
KODAMATIC
KODARAMA
KODASCAN
KODASE
KODASLIDE
KODASTAR
KODESTAR
KOLORKINS
KOMSTAR
KPL
LANEX
LAREDO
LEAD PACK
LEGACY
LEGEND
LINAGRAPH
LINE-O-GRAPH
LIONHEART
LOG 911
LOTEM
LVT
MAGNUS
MAILSCAPE
MARKETMOVER
MATCHPRINT
MEDALIST
MEGAPLUS
MEGASOURCE
MEMORY BANK
MESA
METHELON
MICRO-FILE
MICRODOL-X
MICROEDGE
MIN-R
MINICARD
MY FIRST CAMERA
NEW YORK
NEWSWORTHY
NUVUE
OPEN ME FIRST
OPTIGUARD
OPTISTAR
OPTIWRITER
ORACLE
ORDER-MATIC
ORTHOTRAC
ORTHOWARE
PAGEANT
PAGI-SET
PANALURE
PANATOMIC-X
PANDORA
PAZZAZZ
PHOTO-FLO
PHOTOLIFE
PLUS-X
PMT
POLY-PAC
POLY-SOFT
POLYCONTRAST
POLYDOL
POLYFIBER
POLYMATIC
POLYMAX
POLYPRINT
PORTRA
POWERFILM
PRECISION LINE
PRECISION-LITE
PREMIER
PRESSTAPE
PRESTIGE
PRIMETIME
PRINERGY
PRINTCOM
PRINTIQUES
PRISM
PRO PASSPORT
PRO-TALK
PRO-TEK
PROACT
PROFESSIONAL COLLECTION
PROFIT STRIP
PROPHECY
PROSHOTS
PROSTAR
Q-LAB
QCF
QCF7
QCP
QDF
QDF7
QUICK-FINISH
RADIANCE
RAR
RAYOSCOPE
RAYTREX
READING
READY-MOUNT
READY-PACK II
READYLOAD
READYMATIC
READYPRO
REEL PEOPLE
REFLECTIONS
REGENT
RELIANT
RETINA
RETINAR
RETINETTE
RID-X
ROYAL-X
ROYALPRINT
RUSHES
SAYETT
SCANNER-PACK
SELECTOL-SOFT
SELECTOMAT
SENSALITE
SHARE MOMENTS. SHARE LIFE.
SHELLBURST
SHOOTSAVER
SHOW YOUR TRUE COLORS
SIGNATURE
SIGNET
SII
SNAP-CAP
SNAPSWAB
SOFTDENT
SONOTRACK
SPINALLOY
SQUARESPOT
STACCATO
STAR
STARFICHE
STARFILE
STARFLASH
STARMATE
STARTECH
STARVUE
STICKNEY
STYLELITE
SUPER POLY-SOFT
SUPPORTLINK
SUPRA
SUPRALIFE
SWORD
SWORD EXCEL
T-GRAIN
T-MAT
T-MAX
TACOMA
TCF
TCP
TDF
TECH BITS
TECH PACK 2
TECHNIDOL
TELASSISTANCE
TELE-CUSTOMER
TELE-EKTRALITE
TELE-STYLELITE
THERMACOLOR
THERMAL GOLD
THERMAL PLATINUM
THERMALNEWS
THERMOFLEX
THERMOSPEED
THREAD-EASY
TRAC12
TRACELESS
TRANSLITE
TRANSTAR
TRANSVUE
TRENDSETTER
TRI-X
TRIMLITE
TRIMMATE
TRIMPRINT
ULTIMA
ULTRA
ULTRA-SPEED
ULTRALINE
ULTRATEC
UNIFIX
UPFRONT
VARIO-RETINAR
VERIBROM
VERICHROME
VERICOLOR
VERIFAX
VERSAFLO
VERSAFORM
VERSALITE
VERSAMAT
VERSAMOUNT
VERSATOL
VERSATONE
VICTOR
VIDEOFILM NOTES
VISAGE
VISCOMAT
VOYAGER
VR
VR-G
WEBSTER
WEEKEND
WINNER
WINNER GOLD
WINOMS CS
WRATTEN
X-OMAT
X-OMATIC
XTOL
XTRALIFE
ZORCAINE

Advertising Agencies:

Butler/Till Media Services, Inc.
2349 Monroe Ave
Rochester, NY 14618
Tel.: (585) 473-3740
Fax: (585) 473-3862

Cahan & Associates
171 2nd St #5
San Francisco, CA 94105
Tel.: (415) 621-0915

Key to Media (For complete agency information see *The Advertising Red Books-Agencies* edition):
1. Bus. Publs. 2. Cable T.V. 3. Catalogs & Directories. 4. Co-op Adv. 5. Consumer Mags. 6. D.M. to Bus. Estab.7. D.M. to Consumers
8. Daily Newsp. 9. Exhibits/Trade Shows 10. Foreign 11. Infomercial 12. Internet Adv.13. Multimedia 14. Network Radio
15. Network T.V. 16. Newsp. Distr. Mags. 17. Other 18. Outdoor (Posters, Transit) 19. Point of Purchase20. Premiums, Novelties
21. Product Samples 22. Special Events Mktg. 23. Spot Radio 24. Spot T.V. 25. Weekly Newsp. 26. Yellow Page Adv.

Eastman Kodak Company — (Continued)

Fax: (415) 621-7642

Catalyst
110 Marina Dr
Rochester, NY 14626
Tel.: (585) 453-8300
Toll Free: (800) 836-7720
Camera Accessories Mfr

Catalyst, Science + Soul
110 Marina Dr
Rochester, NY 14626
Tel.: (585) 453-8300
Toll Free: (877) AURAGEN

Deutsch, Inc.
(A Lowe & Partners Company)
111 8th Ave 14th Fl
New York, NY 10011-5201
Tel.: (212) 981-7600
Fax: (212) 981-7525
(Inkjet Printers, Creative & Media)

Eric Mower and Associates
211 West Jefferson St.
Syracuse, NY 13202
Tel.: (315) 466-1000
Fax: (315) 466-2000
(Full Product-Line Brochure)

Partners & Napier
192 Mill St Ste 600
Rochester, NY 14614
Tel.: (585) 454-1010
Fax: (585) 454-1575
Toll Free: (800) 274-4954

EATON ELECTRICAL, INC.
(Unit of Eaton Corporation)
1000 Cherrington Pkwy
Moon Township, PA 15108-4312
Tel.: (412) 893-3300
Fax: (412) 893-2113
Toll Free: (800) 356-1243
Web Site: www.eaton.com
Sales Range: $200-249.9 Million
Approx. Number Employees: 500
Year Founded: 1983
Business Description:
Suppliers of Electrical Power Distribution Equipment & Control Products
S.I.C.: 5063; 3812
N.A.I.C.S.: 423610; 334511
Export
Advertising Expenditures: $1,500,000
Media: 2-4-7-10-11-13-19-26
Distr.: Intl.; Natl.
Brands & Products:
PERFORMANCE POWER

ECOLOGY AND ENVIRONMENT, INC.
368 Pleasant View Dr
Lancaster, NY 14086
Tel.: (716) 684-8060
Fax: (716) 684-0844
E-mail: jmye@ene.com
Web Site: www.ene.com
Approx. Rev.: $144,874,534
Approx. Number Employees: 1,100
Year Founded: 1970
Business Description:
Environmental, Scientific & Engineering Services
S.I.C.: 8711; 8734; 8748
N.A.I.C.S.: 541330; 541380; 541690
Export
Advertising Expenditures: $8,563,688
Distr.: Intl.; Natl.
Personnel:
Gerhard J. Neumaier *(Chm)*
Kevin S. Neumaier *(Pres & CEO)*
H. John Mye *(CFO, Treas & VP)*
Ronald L. Frank *(Exec VP)*
Frank B. Silvestro *(Exec VP)*
Gerald A. Strobel *(Exec VP-Tech Svcs)*
Gerard A. Gallagher, III *(Sr VP-Environ Sustainability)*
Cheryl A. Karpowicz *(Sr VP)*
Craig Hathaway *(VP-Fin)*
Coleen C. Mullaney-Westfall *(Asst Sec)*
Brands & Products:
GREENRIDE
HAZCAT
HAZWOPER
METHCAT

ECRM IMAGING SYSTEMS, INC.
554 Clark Rd
Tewksbury, MA 01876-1631
Tel.: (978) 851-0207
Fax: (978) 851-7016
E-mail: sales@ecrm.com
Web Site: www.ecrm.com
E-Mail For Key Personnel:
Sales Director: sales@ecrm.com
Sales Range: $50-74.9 Million
Approx. Number Employees: 100
Year Founded: 1969
Business Description:
Mfr & Supplier of Quality Imaging Technologies for Commercial Graphic Arts & Publishing Businesses
S.I.C.: 3555; 3577
N.A.I.C.S.: 333293; 334119
Media: 2-7-10-11-13-21
Distr.: Direct to Consumer; Intl.; Natl.
Budget Set: Apr.
Personnel:
Richard B. Black *(Pres & CEO)*
Michael Hurton *(CFO)*
Quana Choi *(Office Mgr)*
Brands & Products:
BLUEFIN
DESERTCAT 8 PLATESETTER
DESERTCAT 88
ECRM
MAKO
MAKO 2 CTP
MAKO IMAGESETTER
MARLIN
MARLIN IMAGESETTER
MAXWORKFLOW
NEWSMATIC
STINGRAY
STINGRAY IMAGESETTER
TIGERCAT PLATESETTER
WILDCAT PLATESETTER

EDMUND INDUSTRIAL OPTICS INC.
101 E Gloucester Pike
Barrington, NJ 08007-1380
Mailing Address:
PO Box 3030
Portland, OR 97208-3030
Tel.: (856) 573-6250
Fax: (856) 573-6295
Toll Free: (800) 363-1992
E-mail: industrialoptics@edmundoptics.com
Web Site: www.edmundoptics.com
Approx. Number Employees: 60
Year Founded: 1942
Business Description:
Mfr & Distr of Industrial Optics & Lens Related Products
S.I.C.: 5961; 3827
N.A.I.C.S.: 454113; 333314
Import Export
Advertising Expenditures: $4,800,000
Media: 2-4-6-7-13
Distr.: Intl.
Budget Set: Aug.
Personnel:
Robert Edmund *(CEO)*
John Cleather *(Mng Dir)*
Marisa Edmund Ay *(Exec VP-Mktg)*
Jeff Harvey *(Dir-IS)*
Gretchen Morris *(Dir-Catalogue Production)*
Susan Tunney *(Dir-HR)*
Brands & Products:
ANCHOR OPTICAL
EDMUND
EO
HAWKEYE
INFINITY ACHROVID
MANTIS
MMS
MVO
NIKON COOLPIX
PROTO-KUT
RKE
TECH SPEC
TML
VZM

EDMUND OPTICS
(Sub. of Edmund Industrial Optics Inc.)
601 Montgomery Ave
Pennsburg, PA 18073-1515
Tel.: (215) 679-6272
Fax: (215) 679-2277
Toll Free: (800) 445-0776
Web Site: www.edmundoptics.com/about-us/directions/
Approx. Number Employees: 100
Year Founded: 1942
Business Description:
Mfr of Precision Optical Components
S.I.C.: 3827; 3851
N.A.I.C.S.: 333314; 339115
Import Export
Advertising Expenditures: $4,000,000
Media: 2-4-7-8-10-11
Distr.: Intl.; Natl.
Budget Set: Dec.
Personnel:
David Schantz *(Dir-Info Svcs)*

EDROY PRODUCTS CO., INC.
245 N Midland Ave
Nyack, NY 10960-1907
Tel.: (845) 358-6600
Fax: (845) 358-4098
Toll Free: (800) 233-8803
E-mail: info@edroyproducts.com
Web Site: www.edroyproducts.com
Approx. Number Employees: 7
Year Founded: 1937
Business Description:
Optical Products Mfr
S.I.C.: 3851
N.A.I.C.S.: 339115
Export
Media: 2-4-5-6
Distr.: Natl.
Budget Set: Oct.
Personnel:
Steven Stoltze *(Owner)*
Brands & Products:
EDROY PRODUCTS
FLIP FOCALS
MAGNI-FOCUSER
MAGNI-FOCUSER BIFOCAL
MAGNI-FOCUSER WITH LIGHT
MAGNI-SPECS
MULTI-DISTANCE HEADBAND LOUPE
OPTICAID CLIP-ON
OPTICAID SPRING-TOP
PRO-LOUPE
STEREOPTIC

ELECTRO-OPTICAL SCIENCES, INC.
(Name Changed to MELA Sciences, Inc.)

ELSTER AMCO WATER, INC.
(Sub. of Elster Group GmbH)
1100 SW 38th Ave
Ocala, FL 34474
Mailing Address:
PO Box 1852
Ocala, FL 34478-4670
Tel.: (352) 732-4670
Fax: (352) 368-1950
Toll Free: (800) 874-0890
E-mail: watermeters@amcowater.com
Web Site: www.amcowater.com
Approx. Number Employees: 200
Year Founded: 1968
Business Description:
Water Metering Systems Developer
S.I.C.: 3824
N.A.I.C.S.: 334514
Media: 2-7-10
Personnel:
Roman Thomassin *(Pres & Reg Dir)*
John Sutherland *(CFO & VP-Fin/IT)*
Alistair Vaughan-Edwards *(VP-Engrg & Quality)*
Brands & Products:
ENERGYAXIS

ELSTER AMERICAN METER COMPANY
(Sub. of Elster Group GmbH)
208 S Rogers Ln
Raleigh, NC 27610
Tel.: (919) 250-5413
Fax: (919) 212-4801
Toll Free: (800) 338-5251
E-mail: webmaster@americanmeter.com
Web Site: www.americanmeter.com
Approx. Sls.: $200,000,000
Approx. Number Employees: 1,250
Year Founded: 1836
Business Description:
Natural Gas Measurement & Controlling Devices Mfr
S.I.C.: 3824; 3829
N.A.I.C.S.: 334514; 334519
Export
Advertising Expenditures: $200,000
Media: 1-2-4-7-10-17
Distr.: Intl.; Natl.
Budget Set: Oct.
Personnel:
Roy Sutterfield *(Pres)*
Tod Bradley *(Product Mgr)*

Key to Media (For complete agency information see *The Advertising Red Books-Agencies* edition):
1. Bus. Publs. 2. Cable T.V. 3. Catalogs & Directories. 4. Co-op Adv. 5. Consumer Mags. 6. D.M. to Bus. Estab.7. D.M. to Consumers
8. Daily Newsp. 9. Exhibits/Trade Shows 10. Foreign 11. Infomercial 12. Internet Adv.13. Multimedia 14. Network Radio
15. Network T.V. 16. Newsp. Distr. Mags. 17. Other 18. Outdoor (Posters, Transit) 19. Point of Purchase20. Premiums, Novelties
21. Product Samples 22. Special Events Mktg. 23. Spot Radio 24. Spot T.V. 25. Weekly Newsp. 26. Yellow Page Adv.

Brands & Products:
AMERICAN
AXIAL FLOW VALVE
DURAMIC
LO-FLO
PANTHEON
RPM
TRACE

EMERGING VISION, INC.
(d/b/a Sterling Optical)
520 8th Ave 23 Fl
New York, NY 10018
Tel.: (646) 737-1500
E-mail: investor.relations@emergingvision.com
Web Site: www.emergingvision.com
Approx. Rev.: $67,587,000
Approx. Number Employees: 150
Year Founded: 1992
Business Description:
Optical Retail Stores, Franchisor, Owner & Operator
S.I.C.: 5995; 5999
N.A.I.C.S.: 446130; 453998
Advertising Expenditures: $146,000
Media: 3-5-7-8-9-10-15-18-19-20-22-23-24-25
Personnel:
Alan Cohen *(Chm)*
Glenn Spina *(Pres & CEO)*
Brian P. Alessi *(CFO & Treas)*
Brands & Products:
ARMORGARD
EASYWEAR
GRADUATES
OPTITINT
SAFESITE
SITE FOR SORE EYES
SPECTA CLEAR
STERLING OPTICAL
STERLING VISIONCARE
UVEE STOPPERS
WISPATHINS
Advertising Agency:
The EGC Group
1175 Walt Whitman Rd Ste 200
Melville, NY 11747-3030
Tel.: (516) 935-4944
Fax: (516) 942-3915

ENERGY CONVERSION DEVICES, INC.
(d/b/a ECD Ovonics)
3800 Lapeer Rd
Auburn Hills, MI 48326
Tel.: (248) 293-0440
Fax: (248) 844-1214
Toll Free: (800) 528-0617
E-mail: informationbusiness@ovonic.com
Web Site: www.ovonic.com
Approx. Rev.: $232,546,000
Approx. Number Employees: 1,300
Year Founded: 1960
Business Description:
Thin-Film Solar Cell, Nickel Metal Hydride Batteries & New Materials Mfr
S.I.C.: 4931; 3612; 3692
N.A.I.C.S.: 221119; 335311; 335912
Import Export
Media: 4-7-10
Distr.: Natl.
Personnel:
Stephen Rabinowitz *(Chm)*
Jay B. Knoll *(Interim Pres)*
William Christopher Andrews *(CFO & Exec VP)*
Kevin Fok *(CMO)*
Ted F. Amyuni *(Exec VP-Global Sls)*
Joseph P. Conroy *(Exec VP-Ops)*
Subhendu Guha *(Exec VP-PV Tech)*
Brands & Products:
ECD
ONE STEP AHEAD OF TOMORROW
OVONIC
UNI-SOLAR

ENERGY FOCUS, INC.
32000 Aurora Rd
Solon, OH 44139
Tel.: (440) 715-1300
Fax: (440) 715-1329
Toll Free: (800) 327-7877
Web Site: www.energyfocusinc.com
Approx. Sls.: $35,129,000
Approx. Number Employees: 68
Year Founded: 1935
Business Description:
Lighting Products Developer Using Fiber Optic Technology for Commercial Lighting & Swimming Pool & Spa Lighting Applications
S.I.C.: 3645; 3229; 3641; 3648
N.A.I.C.S.: 335121; 327212; 335110; 335129
Advertising Expenditures: $206,000
Media: 2-7-8-10
Personnel:
John M. Davenport *(Pres)*
Joseph Kaveski *(CEO)*
Eric Hilliard *(VP-Ops & COO)*
Roger Buelow *(CTO, VP & Gen Mgr)*
Frank Lamanna *(Interim Chief Acctg Officer)*
Brands & Products:
BRITECORE TT
BRITEPAK
DIALUX
EFFICIENT FIBER OPTICS
EFO-ICE
ENERGY FOCUS
FIBERJACKS
FIBERSPOTS
FIBERSTARS EFO
FX LIGHT
FX SPA LIGHT
JAZZ LIGHT
JELLY LIGHTS
LIGHTLY EXPRESSED
LOW PROFILE SIDE ENTRY
MAXCORE
OPTICORE
SIDE ENTRY
TECHNOLOGY IN FIBER OPTIC LIGHTING

ENVIRONMENTAL TECTONICS CORPORATION
(d/b/a ETC)
125 James Way
Southampton, PA 18966-3877
Tel.: (215) 355-9100
Fax: (215) 357-4000
E-mail: info@etcusa.com
Web Site: www.etcusa.com
E-Mail For Key Personnel:
President: WMitchell@etcusa.com
Approx. Sls.: $55,451,000
Approx. Number Employees: 321
Year Founded: 1969
Business Description:
Simulation Systems & Chamber-Based Products Mfr & Designer
S.I.C.: 3559
N.A.I.C.S.: 333298
Import Export
Advertising Expenditures: $569,000
Media: 1-2-4-7-10-11-17-19-20
Distr.: Intl.; Natl.; Reg.
Budget Set: Feb.
Personnel:
William F. Mitchell *(Chm, Pres & CEO)*
Robert Laurent, Jr. *(CFO)*
Thomas G. Loughlin *(COO)*
Richard A. Leland *(Pres-NASTAR)*
Steve Wood *(Pres-Biomedical Div)*
Husnu Onus *(VP-Sls & Mktg-Intl)*
David Kong *(Gen Mgr-China)*
Paul Comtois *(Dir-Aircraft Upset Prevention & Recovery Training & Res)*
Donna M. Averell *(Mgr-Mktg)*
Brands & Products:
ADMS
ATFS
ATFS-400
AUTHENTIC TACTICAL FIGHTING SYSTEM
BARA-LAB
BARA-MED
BARA-PRESS
BIG MAC
DMI
EAGLE-VISION
EPC
G-POINTING
MRC MONSTER ROLL CAGE
NASTAR
QUALITY THROUGH INTEGRITY & TECHNOLOGY
THE RIDE WORKS
SMOOTH-RIDE

EPILOG CORPORATION
(d/b/a Epilog Laser)
16371 Table Mountain Pkwy
Golden, CO 80403
Tel.: (303) 277-1188
Fax: (303) 277-9669
Toll Free: (888) 437-4564
E-mail: sales@epiloglaser.com
Web Site: www.epiloglaser.com
E-Mail For Key Personnel:
Sales Director: sales@epiloglaser.com
Sales Range: $1-9.9 Million
Approx. Number Employees: 50
Year Founded: 1988
Business Description:
Laser Systems Designer & Mfr
S.I.C.: 3827; 3559
N.A.I.C.S.: 333314; 333298
Media: 6
Personnel:
Steve Garnier *(Pres)*

EPSILON SYSTEMS SOLUTIONS
9242 Lightwave Ave
San Diego, CA 92123
Tel.: (619) 702-1700
Fax: (619) 702-1711
E-mail: info@epsilonsystems.com
Web Site: www.epsilonsystems.com
Approx. Number Employees: 200
Year Founded: 1998
Business Description:
Marine, Industrial, Energy, Environmental & Applied Technology Services
S.I.C.: 8711
N.A.I.C.S.: 541330
Media: 2-10
Personnel:
Bryan B. Min *(Founder, Pres & CEO)*
Alan Stewart *(CFO & Exec VP)*
Stuart Teshima *(Sr VP & Controller)*
Grady Petty *(Sr VP & Gen Mgr-Nuclear Ops & Environ Mgmt)*
Brands & Products:
AMBER
EPSILON SYSTEMS SOLUTIONS
GARNET
RUBY
SAPPHIRE
TOPAZ

ERM GROUP, INC.
350 Eagleview Blvd
Exton, PA 19341-2843
Tel.: (610) 524-3500
Fax: (610) 524-7335
E-mail: mkt-info@erm.com
Web Site: www.erm.com
Sales Range: $200-249.9 Million
Approx. Number Employees: 102
Year Founded: 1977
Business Description:
Environmental Engineering & Consulting Services
S.I.C.: 8711; 8748
N.A.I.C.S.: 541330; 541690
Media: 2-4-7-20
Distr.: Natl.

ESCALON MEDICAL CORP.
435 Devon Park Dr Bldg 100
Wayne, PA 19087
Tel.: (610) 688-6830
Fax: (610) 688-3641
E-mail: info@escalonmed.com
Web Site: www.escalonmed.com
E-Mail For Key Personnel:
Sales Director: sales@escalonmed.com
Approx. Rev.: $29,944,212
Approx. Number Employees: 158
Year Founded: 1987
Business Description:
Ophthalmic Medical Devices Mfr & Distr
S.I.C.: 3845
N.A.I.C.S.: 334510
Advertising Expenditures: $67,959
Media: 2-7-10
Personnel:
Richard J. DePiano *(Chm & CEO)*
Richard J. DePiano, Jr. *(Pres & Gen Counsel)*
Robert M. O'Connor *(CFO)*
Mark G. Wallace *(COO)*
Brands & Products:
ECD
ESCALON
SONOMED-ESCALON
VUMAX

ESCORT, INC.
(Holding of AMERICAN CAPITAL, LTD.)
5440 W Chester Rd
West Chester, OH 45069-2950
Tel.: (513) 870-8500
Fax: (513) 870-8509
Toll Free: (800) 433-3487
E-mail: sales@escortradar.com
Web Site: www.escortradar.com
E-Mail For Key Personnel:
Sales Director: sales@escortradar.com

Key to Media (For complete agency information see *The Advertising Red Books-Agencies* edition):
1. Bus. Publs. 2. Cable T.V. 3. Catalogs & Directories. 4. Co-op Adv. 5. Consumer Mags. 6. D.M. to Bus. Estab.7. D.M. to Consumers 8. Daily Newsp. 9. Exhibits/Trade Shows 10. Foreign 11. Infomercial 12. Internet Adv.13. Multimedia 14. Network Radio 15. Network T.V. 16. Newsp. Distr. Mags. 17. Other 18. Outdoor (Posters, Transit) 19. Point of Purchase20. Premiums, Novelties 21. Product Samples 22. Special Events Mktg. 23. Spot Radio 24. Spot T.V. 25. Weekly Newsp. 26. Yellow Page Adv.

Escort, Inc. — (Continued)

Sales Range: $50-74.9 Million
Approx. Number Employees: 230
Year Founded: 1997
Business Description:
Mfr. & Distr of Radar & Laser Detectors
S.I.C.: 3812
N.A.I.C.S.: 334511
Advertising Expenditures: $4,500,000
Media: 6-13-19
Personnel:
Mark Carr *(CFO)*
Dave Smidebush *(VP-Mktg & Cust Svc)*
Brands & Products:
ESCORT
PASSPORT
SOLO

ESSILOR OF AMERICA, INC.
(Sub. of Essilor International, S.A.)
13555 N Stemmons Fwy
Dallas, TX 75234
Tel.: (214) 496-4000
Fax: (972) 241-1162
Toll Free: (800) THE-EYES
Web Site: www.essilorusa.com
Business Description:
Eyeglass Lenses & Other Ophthalmic Products Mfr & Whslr
S.I.C.: 3827; 3851; 5048
N.A.I.C.S.: 333314; 339115; 423460
Import Export
Media: 22-23-24
Personnel:
Jean Carrier-Guillomet *(Pres)*
Kevin A. Rupp *(CFO & Sr VP-Fin & Admin)*
Konstantinos Voyiatzis *(CIO & VP)*
Bob Colucci *(Pres-Independent Distr Div)*
Carl Bracy *(Sr VP-Mktg & New Bus)*
Leslie Wilemon *(VP-HR)*
John McMahan *(Dir-Mktg-Independent Labs)*
Brands & Products:
ACCOLADE

ESTERLINE TECHNOLOGIES CORPORATION
City Ctr Bellevue 500 108th Ave NE Ste 1500
Bellevue, WA 98004
Tel.: (425) 453-9400
Fax: (425) 453-2916
Toll Free: (800) 522-6645
E-mail: info@esterline.com
Web Site: www.esterline.com
Approx. Sls.: $1,526,601,000
Approx. Number Employees: 8,976
Year Founded: 1967
Business Description:
Technology Interface Systems, High-Precision Temperature Sensors & Elastomer Products Mfr
S.I.C.: 3823; 3541
N.A.I.C.S.: 334513; 333512
Import Export
Media: 1-2-4-7-10-11
Distr.: Intl.; Natl.
Budget Set: Nov.
Personnel:
Robert W. Cremin *(Chm)*
R. Bradley Lawrence *(Pres & CEO)*
Robert D. George *(CFO, Treas, Sec & VP)*
Gary J. Posner *(Chief Acctg Officer & Controller)*
Kevin Moschetti *(Pres-Comm Sys)*
Marcia J.M. Greenberg *(VP-HR)*
Stephen R. Larson *(VP-Strategy & Tech)*
Marcia J. Mason *(VP-HR)*
Peter Bobkowski *(Dir-Internal Audit)*
Brian Keogh *(Dir-Corp Comm)*
Teresa Sebert *(Dir-Benefits)*
Brands & Products:
ESTERLINE
FASTBLOCK
LEACH

EV3 INC.
(Formerly Micro Therapeutics, Inc.)
(Div. of ev3 Inc.)
9775 Toledo Way
Irvine, CA 92618
Tel.: (949) 837-3700
Fax: (949) 837-2044
Toll Free: (800) 684-6733
E-mail: inquiry@1mti.com
Web Site: www.ev3.net
Year Founded: 1993
Business Description:
Medical Device Mfr
S.I.C.: 3841
N.A.I.C.S.: 339112
Advertising Expenditures: $54,000
Media: 1-10
Personnel:
Brett Wall *(Pres)*

EVAPORATED METAL FILMS CORP.
(Sub. of Dynasil Corporation of America)
239 Cherry St
Ithaca, NY 14850
Tel.: (607) 272-3320
Fax: (800) 456-3227
E-mail: info@emf-corp.com
Web Site: www.emf-corp.com
Sales Range: $25-49.9 Million
Approx. Number Employees: 25
Year Founded: 1936
Business Description:
Thin Film Coatings Mfr
S.I.C.: 3479
N.A.I.C.S.: 332812
Media: 2-13
Personnel:
Paul Schulz *(Pres)*
Craig T. Dunham *(CEO)*
Joseph Howe *(Mgr-Sls)*
Bobbi Thoman *(Mgr-Production & Pur)*
Dan Thoman *(Mgr-XLS Bus)*

EXCEL TECHNOLOGY, INC.
(Sub. of GSI Group Inc.)
41 Research Way
East Setauket, NY 11733-3454
Tel.: (631) 784-6175
Fax: (631) 784-6195
Telex: 6852167 QUANTRNX UW
E-mail: info@exceltechinc.com
Web Site: www.exceltechinc.com
Approx. Sls.: $160,023,000
Approx. Number Employees: 719
Year Founded: 1985
Business Description:
Laser Systems & Electro-Optical Components Designer, Developer & Mfr
S.I.C.: 3559; 3827; 3845
N.A.I.C.S.: 333298; 333314; 334510
Export
Media: 2-4-10
Distr.: Natl.
Personnel:
J. Donald Hill *(Chm)*
Antoine Dominic *(Pres, CEO & COO)*
Shelly Wojtkiewicz *(Mgr-Mktg)*

EXERGEN CORPORATION
400 Pleasant St
Watertown, MA 02172
Tel.: (617) 923-9900
Fax: (617) 923-9911
Toll Free: (800) 422-3006
E-mail: marketing@exergen.com
Web Site: www.exergen.com
Approx. Number Employees: 50
Business Description:
Non-Invasive Thermometry Systems: Infrared Scanners, Thermometers, Sensors & Controls Mfr
S.I.C.: 3826
N.A.I.C.S.: 334516
Media: 5-6-10-14-22
Personnel:
Frank Pompei *(Founder & Pres)*
Marybeth Pompei *(Chief Clinical Scientist & Sr VP)*
Brands & Products:
ADJUSTABLE IRT/C
DERMATEMP
EXERGEN D-SERIES
EXERGEN DX-SERIES
EXERGEN E-SERIES
EXERTHERM
IRT/C
MICRO IRT/C
OTOTEMP
SMART IRT/C
SNAKEEYE
TEMPORALSCANNER

EYE CARE CENTERS OF AMERICA, INC.
(Sub. of Highmark Inc.)
11103 West Ave
San Antonio, TX 78213-1370
Tel.: (210) 340-3531
Fax: (210) 524-6996
Toll Free: (800) 669-1183
E-mail: customerservice@ecca.com
Web Site: www.ecca.com
Approx. Rev.: $537,570,000
Approx. Number Employees: 5,543
Year Founded: 1984
Business Description:
Optical Goods Retailer
S.I.C.: 5995
N.A.I.C.S.: 446130
Advertising Expenditures: $41,879,000
Media: 8-9-16-24
Personnel:
James N. Eisen *(Pres)*
David L. Holmberg *(CEO)*
Jennifer L. Kelley *(CFO, Treas, Sec & Exec VP)*
George E. Gebhardt *(Chief Mdsg Officer & Exec VP)*
Omero Montec *(Exec VP-Store Ops)*
John D. Jordan *(Sr VP-Store Ops)*
Linda L. Lubecki *(Sr VP-Store Ops)*
James E. Carroll *(Reg VP)*
Charles M. Kellstadt *(Reg VP)*
Robert T. Cox *(VP-HR)*
David Rhodes *(Dir-Territory)*
Brands & Products:
BINYON'S
DOCTOR'S VALUVISION
DOCTOR'S VISIONWORKS
DR. BIZER'S VALUVISION
DR. BIZER'S VISIONWORLD
EYE DRX
EYEMASTERS
HOUR EYES
STEIN OPTICAL
VISION WORLD
VISIONWORKS

FEI COMPANY
5350 NE Dawson Creek Dr
Hillsboro, OR 97124
Tel.: (503) 726-7500
Fax: (503) 726-2570
E-mail: cust-info@feico.com
Web Site: www.fei.com
Approx. Sls.: $634,222,000
Approx. Number Employees: 1,788
Year Founded: 1971
Business Description:
Structural Process Management Solutions of Semiconductor Data Storage Materials Science & Life Science Businesses
S.I.C.: 3674; 3826
N.A.I.C.S.: 334413; 334516
Advertising Expenditures: $2,400,000
Personnel:
Gerhard H. Parker *(Chm)*
Don R. Kania *(Pres & CEO)*
Raymond A. Link *(CFO & Exec VP)*
Michael R. Scheinfein *(CTO & Exec VP-Bus Dev)*
Bradley J. Thies *(Gen Counsel & VP)*
Rob H.J. Fastenau *(Exec VP)*
Benjamin Loh *(Exec VP-Global Sls & Svcs)*
Tony Edwards *(Sr VP-Market Div)*
Brian E. Pierson *(Sr VP)*
Dominique Hubert *(VP & Gen Mgr-Life Sciences)*
Paul Scagnetti *(VP & Gen Mgr-Natural Resources)*
Timothy Ashcroft *(VP-HR)*
Dirk Lanens *(VP-Sls & Svcs-Europe)*
Brands & Products:
ACCURA
ALTURA
CERTUS-3D
CLM-3D
DEFECT ANALYZER
DUALBEAM
EXPIDA
FEI
HELIOS NANOLAB
INSPECT
MAGELLAN
MORGAGNI
NANOLIFT
NOVA
PHENOM
QUANTA
STRATA
TECNAI
TITAN
TRUEIMAGE
ULTRAVIEW
V600
VECTRAVISION
VITROBOT
XPLORE3D

Key to Media (For complete agency information see *The Advertising Red Books-Agencies* edition):
1. Bus. Publs. 2. Cable T.V. 3. Catalogs & Directories. 4. Co-op Adv. 5. Consumer Mags. 6. D.M. to Bus. Estab.7. D.M. to Consumers
8. Daily Newsp. 9. Exhibits/Trade Shows 10. Foreign 11. Infomercial 12. Internet Adv.13. Multimedia 14. Network Radio
15. Network T.V. 16. Newsp. Distr. Mags. 17. Other 18. Outdoor (Posters, Transit) 19. Point of Purchase20. Premiums, Novelties
21. Product Samples 22. Special Events Mktg. 23. Spot Radio 24. Spot T.V. 25. Weekly Newsp. 26. Yellow Page Adv.

Advertising Agency:
MindWrite Communications, Inc.
117 Bernal Rd Ste 70-126
San Jose, CA 95119
Tel.: (408) 224-4024
Helios
Magellan
Titan

FLETCHER CHICAGO INC.
1000 N Northbranch St
Chicago, IL 60642
Tel.: (312) 932-2700
Fax: (312) 932-2799
Toll Free: (800) 6FLETCH
E-mail: frontdesk@fletch.com
Web Site: www.fletch.com
Approx. Sls.: $2,400,000
Approx. Number Employees: 28
Year Founded: 1987
Business Description:
Film & Video Camera Equipment Retailer
S.I.C.: 5999; 7359
N.A.I.C.S.: 453998; 532299
Media: 6
Personnel:
Archie Fletcher *(Pres & CEO)*
Thomas Fletcher *(VP-Mktg)*
Zoe Iltsopoulos Borys *(Gen Mgr)*

FLIR SYSTEMS, INC.
27700 SW Parkway Ave
Wilsonville, OR 97070
Tel.: (503) 498-3547
Fax: (503) 498-3904
Toll Free: (800) 727-3547 (Sales)
Toll Free: (800) 322-3731 (General)
E-mail: Investor@flir.com
Web Site: www.flir.com
Approx. Rev.: $1,385,301,000
Approx. Number Employees: 3,215
Year Founded: 1978
Business Description:
Thermal Imaging & Camera Systems Mfr
S.I.C.: 3812; 3861; 7372
N.A.I.C.S.: 334511; 333315; 511210
Advertising Expenditures: $8,200,000
Media: 2-7-10-13
Distr.: Intl.
Budget Set: Oct.
Personnel:
Earl R. Lewis *(Chm, Pres & CEO)*
Andrew C. Teich *(Pres-Comml Sys)*
Anthony L. Trunzo *(CFO & Sr VP)*
Arne Almerfors *(Pres-Thermography Div & Exec VP)*
William A. Sundermeier *(Pres-Govt Sys)*
William W. Davis *(Gen Counsel, Sec & Sr VP)*
Angel Bennett *(Dir-Mktg)*
Darren Haley *(Mgr-Product Line-Transportation Products)*
Brands & Products:
ALPHA NIR
ALTAIR
ANALYZIR
BRITE STAR
CENTURION
FIREFLIR
FIREWIRE
FLASHSIGHT
FLIR QUICKPLOT & FLIR RESEARCHIR
FLIR QUICKREPORT
FLIR REPORTER BUILDING
FLIR REPORTER STANDARD / PRO
FLIR RTOOLS
FLIR SYSTEM
IMAGING SOLUTIONS FOR EVERY MISSION
IRVISTA
MERLIN
MICROCOOLER
MILCAM
MILCAM RECON
MIRV
PHOENIX
QWIP
RANGER
RCAL
RDAC
REDIT
RPRO
SEA STARSAFIRE
SEAFLIR
SENTRY
STAR SAFIRE
TALON
THERMACAM
THERMACAM RESEARCHER
THERMOSIGHT
THERMOVISION
THERMOVISION LABVIEW TOOLKIT
THERMOVISION SDK
THESA
ULTRA
ULTRA 7000
ULTRA 8000
ULTRA 8500
ULTRAMEDIA
Advertising Agency:
Transcendigital Ltd.
520 Burlington Rd
Harwinton, CT 06791
Tel.: (860) 748-4891
Fax: (860) 689-0088

FLUIDIGM CORPORATION
7000 Shoreline Ct Ste 100
South San Francisco, CA 94080
Tel.: (650) 266-6000
Fax: (650) 871-7152
Toll Free: (866) 358-4354
Web Site: www.fluidigm.com
Approx. Rev.: $33,560,000
Approx. Number Employees: 206
Year Founded: 1999
Business Description:
Integrated Fluidic Circuit Systems Developer, Mfr & Marketer
S.I.C.: 3593; 3826; 8733
N.A.I.C.S.: 333995; 334516; 541710
Advertising Expenditures: $514,000
Media: 19
Personnel:
Gajus V. Worthington *(Co-Founder, Pres & CEO)*
Samuel D. Colella *(Chm)*
Vikram Jog *(CFO)*
William M. Smith *(Gen Counsel, Sec & VP-Legal Affairs)*
Robert C. Jones *(Exec VP-R & D)*

FLUKE CORPORATION
(Sub. of Danaher Corporation)
6920 Seaway Blvd
Everett, WA 98203-5829
Mailing Address:
PO Box 9090
Everett, WA 98206-9090
Tel.: (425) 347-6100
Fax: (425) 446-5998
Toll Free: (800) 44FLUKE
Telex: 185102 FLUKE EVT
E-mail: fluke-info@fluke.com
Web Site: www.fluke.com
Sales Range: $400-449.9 Million
Approx. Number Employees: 2,525
Year Founded: 1948
Business Description:
Electronic Test Tools Mfr
S.I.C.: 3825; 3823
N.A.I.C.S.: 334515; 334513
Export
Media: 2-4-5-6-7-8-10-11-13-19-20-21
Distr.: Intl.; Natl.
Budget Set: Dec.-Jan.
Personnel:
Barbara Hulit *(Pres)*
Rob Blaskowsky *(CIO)*
Jim Cavoretto *(CTO & Sr VP)*
Ken Konopa *(Pres-Fluke Indus)*
Daren Couture *(Sr VP-Ops)*
Peter Vandenbroek *(Sr VP-Fluke Europe)*
Monti Ackerman *(VP-Fin)*
Clement Feng *(VP-Mktg)*
Rick Laporte *(VP-Sls-Americas)*
Kurt Loring *(VP-HR)*
Martin Girard *(Gen Mgr-Fluke Calibration)*
Harvey Trager *(Dir-Special Projects)*
Gavin Kirk *(Sr Product Mgr-Electrical Products)*
Rick Koske *(Product Mgr)*
Jerry Zion *(Mgr-Training)*

FONAR CORPORATION
110 Marcus Dr
Melville, NY 11747-4228
Tel.: (631) 694-2929
Fax: (631) 753-5150
E-mail: info@fonar.com
Web Site: www.fonar.com
E-Mail For Key Personnel:
Sales Director: sales@fonar.com
Approx. Rev.: $31,815,555
Approx. Number Employees: 238
Year Founded: 1978
Business Description:
Upright MRI Scanners & Diagnostic Imaging Mfr
S.I.C.: 3845; 7629
N.A.I.C.S.: 334510; 811219
Export
Advertising Expenditures: $415,000
Media: 2-4-7-10-15-17-18-22-23-26
Distr.: Natl.
Budget Set: Sept.
Personnel:
Raymond V. Damadian *(Chm, Pres & Treas)*
Sol Ginzburg *(VP-Sls)*
Daniel Culver *(Dir-Comm)*
Brands & Products:
FONAR 360
THE INVENTOR OF MR SCANNING
IRON-FRAME
MPEXTREMITY MRI
OPEN SKY MRI
OR-360
THE PATIENT FRIENDLY MRI
POSITION IMAGING
QUAD
SIGNAL PLUS
THE UPRIGHT MRI
VERSAREST

FOSS NIRSYSTEMS, INC.
(Sub. of Foss A/S)
7703 Montpelier Rd Ste 1
Laurel, MD 20723
Tel.: (301) 680-9600
Fax: (301) 236-0134
Toll Free: (800) 343-2036
E-mail: info@foss-nirsystems.com
Web Site: www.foss-nirsystems.com
E-Mail For Key Personnel:
Sales Director: pirring@foss-nirsystems.com
Approx. Number Employees: 18
Year Founded: 1968
Business Description:
Analytical Instruments Mfr & Supplier
S.I.C.: 3826; 5049
N.A.I.C.S.: 334516; 423490
Import Export
Media: 4-6-8-10-20
Distr.: Intl.; Natl.
Budget Set: Nov.
Personnel:
Phil Irving *(Pres)*

FRYE ELECTRONICS, INC.
9826 SW Tigard St
Tigard, OR 97223
Tel.: (503) 620-2722
Fax: (503) 639-0128
Toll Free: (800) 547-8209
E-mail: sales@frye.com
Web Site: www.frye.com
E-Mail For Key Personnel:
Sales Director: sales@frye.com
Approx. Number Employees: 35
Year Founded: 1973
Business Description:
Hearing Aid Test Systems Mfr
S.I.C.: 3825
N.A.I.C.S.: 334515
Media: 2-7-10
Distr.: Intl.; Natl.
Personnel:
George Frye *(Pres)*
Anson Feng *(Sls Mgr)*
Sallie Frye *(Mgr-Mktg-Intl)*
Brands & Products:
FONIX
FRYE
WINCHAP

FUJIFILM CANADA INC.
(Sub. of FUJIFILM Corporation)
600 Suffolk Ct
Mississauga, ON L5R 4G4, Canada
Tel.: (905) 890-6611
Fax: (905) 890-6446
Toll Free: (800) 263-5018
E-mail: info@fujifilm.ca
Web Site: www.fujifilm.ca
Approx. Number Employees: 150
Business Description:
Photographic Supplies Distr
S.I.C.: 5043
N.A.I.C.S.: 423410
Media: 22
Personnel:
Nobuhiko Koshimizu *(Pres)*
John Stevenson *(Sr Mgr-Strategy & Comm)*
Advertising Agencies:
The Henderson Robb Group
401 Bay St Ste 1600
Toronto, ON M5H 2Y4, Canada
Tel.: (416) 362-8262

John St.
172 John Street
Toronto, ON M5T 1X5, Canada
Tel.: (416) 348-0048

Key to Media (For complete agency information see *The Advertising Red Books-Agencies* edition):
1. Bus. Publs. 2. Cable T.V. 3. Catalogs & Directories. 4. Co-op Adv. 5. Consumer Mags. 6. D.M. to Bus. Estab.7. D.M. to Consumers
8. Daily Newsp. 9. Exhibits/Trade Shows 10. Foreign 11. Infomercial 12. Internet Adv.13. Multimedia 14. Network Radio
15. Network T.V. 16. Newsp. Distr. Mags. 17. Other 18. Outdoor (Posters, Transit) 19. Point of Purchase20. Premiums, Novelties
21. Product Samples 22. Special Events Mktg. 23. Spot Radio 24. Spot T.V. 25. Weekly Newsp. 26. Yellow Page Adv.

FUJIFILM Canada Inc. — (Continued)

Fax: (416) 348-0050

FUJIFILM HUNT CHEMICALS USA, INC.
(Sub. of FUJIFILM Corporation)
40 Boroline Rd
Allendale, NJ 07401-1613
Tel.: (201) 995-2200
Fax: (201) 995-2299
Toll Free: (877) 385-4486
E-mail: info@fujihuntusa.com
Web Site: www.fujihunt.com
Approx. Number Employees: 150
Business Description:
Photographic Chemicals Mfr & Distr
S.I.C.: 3861; 5043
N.A.I.C.S.: 325992; 423410
Media: 2-7-11

FUJIFILM U.S.A., INC.
(Sub. of FUJIFILM Corporation)
200 Summit Lake Dr
Valhalla, NY 10595
Tel.: (914) 789-8100
Fax: (914) 789-8295
Toll Free: (800) 755-3854
Web Site: www.fujifilmusa.com
Approx. Number Employees: 10,000
Year Founded: 1965
Business Description:
Digital & Analog Photographic Imaging Systems & Services
S.I.C.: 5043; 6719
N.A.I.C.S.: 423410; 551114
Import Export
Media: 2-3-5-6-7-10-13-14-15-18-19-20-22-23-24
Distr.: Natl.
Budget Set: Apr.
Personnel:
Ryutaro Hosoda *(Pres & CEO)*
Masato Yamamoto *(Pres-Imaging Div)*
Rafi Haqqani *(Dir-Mktg)*

FUJINON INC.
(Sub. of Fujinon Corporation)
10 Highpoint Dr
Wayne, NJ 07470-7431
Tel.: (973) 633-5600
Fax: (973) 633-5216
E-mail: info@fujinon.com
Web Site: www.fujinon.com
Approx. Number Employees: 70
Year Founded: 1973
Business Description:
Optics & Lenses Marketer
S.I.C.: 5048; 5049
N.A.I.C.S.: 423460; 423490
Media: 6

GAERTNER SCIENTIFIC CORPORATION
3650 Jarvis Ave
Skokie, IL 60076
Tel.: (847) 673-5006
Fax: (847) 673-5009
E-mail: email@gaertnerscientific.com
Web Site: www.gaertnerscientific.com
Approx. Number Employees: 22
Year Founded: 1896
Business Description:
Electro-Optical Instruments Mfr
S.I.C.: 3827; 3826
N.A.I.C.S.: 333314; 334516
Export
Media: 2-8-10
Distr.: Direct to Consumer; Intl.; Natl.
Budget Set: Aug.
Personnel:
Rusty Kutko *(Pres)*
Brands & Products:
GAERTNER
STOKES WAFERSKAN

GARMIN INTERNATIONAL, INC.
(Corporate Headquarters of Garmin Ltd.)
1200 E 151st St
Olathe, KS 66062-3426
Tel.: (913) 397-8200
Fax: (913) 397-8282
Web Site: www.garmin.com
Approx. Number Employees: 1,100
Business Description:
Navigation Communications & Information Devices
S.I.C.: 3812
N.A.I.C.S.: 334511
Media: 6-9-10-13-15-25
Personnel:
Min H. Kao *(Chm & CEO)*
Kevin Rauckman *(CFO & Treas)*
Carl Wolf *(Sls & Sr Dir-Aviation Mktg)*
Roger Jollis *(Dir-Mobility & OEM Mktg)*
Ted Gartner *(Sr Mgr-Corp Comm)*
Brands & Products:
GARMIN
GMX 200
WAAS

GENDEX DENTAL SYSTEMS
(Sub. of Danaher Corporation)
901 W Oakton St
Des Plaines, IL 60018-1843
Tel.: (847) 364-2420
Fax: (847) 640-6165
Toll Free: (800) 586-9190
Web Site: www.gendexxray.com
Sales Range: $75-99.9 Million
Approx. Number Employees: 300
Year Founded: 1983
Business Description:
Mfr., Designer, Developer & Marketer of X-Ray Systems & Various Support Equipment for the Dental Market
S.I.C.: 3844
N.A.I.C.S.: 334517
Media: 10
Brands & Products:
ACUCAM CONCEPT IV
DENOPTIX
GENDEX 765DC
ORTHORALIX 9200

GERBER SCIENTIFIC, INC.
83 Gerber Rd W
South Windsor, CT 06074-3230
Tel.: (860) 644-1551
Fax: (860) 643-7039
E-mail: investor@gerberscientific.com
Web Site: www.gerberscientific.com
Approx. Rev.: $458,355,000
Approx. Number Employees: 1,950
Year Founded: 1948
Business Description:
Designs, Develops, Manufactures, Markets & Services CAD/CAM Mass Customization Systems, Software & Related Aftermarket Supplies
S.I.C.: 3559; 3823; 5085
N.A.I.C.S.: 333298; 334513; 423840
Import Export
Media: 1-2-6-7-8-10-22
Distr.: Intl.; Natl.
Budget Set: Dec. -Jan.
Personnel:
Donald P. Aiken *(Chm)*
Marc T. Giles *(Pres & CEO)*
Michael R. Elia *(CFO & Exec VP)*
Thomas Patrick Finn *(Pres-Asia Pacific & Sr VP-Global Ops)*
William V. Grickis, Jr. *(Gen Counsel & Sr VP)*
Patricia L. Burmahl *(Sr VP-HR-Global)*
Rodney W. Larson *(Sr VP)*
Stephen P. Lovass *(Sr VP)*
Joseph R. Mele *(Sr VP-Ops)*
Mark Goebel *(Exec Dir-Product Dev)*
Mark Hessinger *(Exec Dir-Global Customer Svc)*
Bud McCann *(Exec Dir-Global Sls)*
Jay Dorman *(Dir-Sls-Americas)*
Brands & Products:
ACCUMARK
ACUBLOCK
ACUITY
CUTWORKS
ECLIPSE SURFACE BLOCKER
EDGE FX
ENVISION
EURO AQUASAVE
EURO KLEENCHILL POLISH SYSTEM
GERBER CAT
GERBER EDGE
GERBER NORTHSTAR
GERBER SOLARA ION
GERBERCOLOR
GERBERCUTTER
GERBERGAUGE
GERBERLABELER
GERBERNET
GERBERPLANNER
GERBERSAVER
GERBERSERVICE
GERBERSPREADER
INFINITY
INFOJET
INFOMARK
INNOVATIONS
INVISION
IQ SL2 EXPRESS
LENSCOATER EX
LENSMAKER XRT
MATCHED TECHNOLOGY SYSTEM
MICRO-BRISTLE
OMEGA
SABRE
SOLARA ION
SPARTAN
STEP TWO
STRATUM
STRIKEGUARD
SYNCHRON
TAURUS
TITAN
TORIC SURFACER
WEBPDM

GILSON COMPANY, INC.
7975 N Central Dr
Lewis Center, OH 43035
Mailing Address:
PO Box 200
Lewis Center, OH 43035-0200
Tel.: (740) 548-7298
Fax: (740) 548-5314
E-mail: sales@gilsonco.com
Web Site: www.globalgilson.com
E-Mail For Key Personnel:
Sales Director: sales@gilsonco.com
Approx. Sls.: $13,000,000
Approx. Number Employees: 50
Year Founded: 1939
Business Description:
Testing Equipment Mfr & Distr
S.I.C.: 5049; 3829
N.A.I.C.S.: 423490; 334519
Media: 4-7-10-11-13
Personnel:
Trent R. Smith *(Pres & CEO)*

GLASS FAB INC.
257 Ormond St
Rochester, NY 14605
Tel.: (585) 262-4000
Fax: (585) 454-4305
E-mail: info@glassfab.com
Web Site: www.glassfab.com
Sales Range: $1-9.9 Million
Approx. Number Employees: 45
Year Founded: 1974
Business Description:
Mfr. of Optical Lenses
S.I.C.: 3827; 3231
N.A.I.C.S.: 333314; 327215
Media: 2-10-13
Personnel:
Robert Saltzman *(Founder & CEO)*
Daniel Saltzman *(Pres)*
Wayne Leon *(Gen Mgr)*

GLOBAL GEOPHYSICAL SERVICES, INC.
13927 S Gessner Rd
Missouri City, TX 77489
Tel.: (713) 972-9200
Fax: (713) 972-1008
E-mail: contact@globalgeophysical.com
Web Site:
www.globalgeophysical.com
Approx. Rev.: $254,704,813
Approx. Number Employees: 1,667
Business Description:
Seismic Data Solutions
S.I.C.: 7374; 8713
N.A.I.C.S.: 518210; 541360
Advertising Expenditures: $596,000
Personnel:
Richard A. Degner *(Chm, Pres & CEO)*
P. Mathew Verghese *(CFO & Sr VP)*
Chris T. Usher *(CTO & Sr VP)*
Christopher P. Graham *(Gen Counsel, Sec & Sr VP)*
William Anthony Clark *(Sr VP-Multi Client Svcs)*
Thomas J. Fleure *(Sr VP-Geophysical Tech)*
Craig A. Lindberg *(Sr VP-Strategic Initiatives)*
Russell Roundtree *(VP-Tech-Global Microseismic ServicesSM, Inc.)*
John Asma *(Dir-Sls)*
Alba Willis *(Mgr-Mktg)*
John Barrett *(Mgr-Health, Safety, Environ & Quality)*
Jack Litchenberg *(Mgr-Bus Dev-US)*
Brands & Products:
EXCITING THE PLANET
GLOBAL GEOPHYSICAL SERVICES

GOODRICH ISR BARRINGTON
(Formerly Recon/Optical, Inc.)
(Sub. of Goodrich Corporation-ISR Systems)
550 W NW Hwy
Barrington, IL 60010-3094

Key to Media (For complete agency information see *The Advertising Red Books-Agencies* edition):
1. Bus. Publs. 2. Cable T.V. 3. Catalogs & Directories. 4. Co-op Adv. 5. Consumer Mags. 6. D.M. to Bus. Estab.7. D.M. to Consumers 8. Daily Newsp. 9. Exhibits/Trade Shows 10. Foreign 11. Infomercial 12. Internet Adv.13. Multimedia 14. Network Radio 15. Network T.V. 16. Newsp. Distr. Mags. 17. Other 18. Outdoor (Posters, Transit) 19. Point of Purchase20. Premiums, Novelties 21. Product Samples 22. Special Events Mktg. 23. Spot Radio 24. Spot T.V. 25. Weekly Newsp. 26. Yellow Page Adv.

Tel.: (847) 381-2400
Fax: (847) 381-1390
Web Site: www.goodrich.com/Goodrich/Businesses/ISR-Systems
Sales Range: $125-149.9 Million
Approx. Number Employees: 250
Year Founded: 1922
Business Description:
Mfr of Aerospace & Defense Products; Aerial Reconnaissance Cameras, Sighting Systems, Precision Optical Lenses, Stabilized Weapons Mounts
S.I.C.: 9661; 3728; 3827
N.A.I.C.S.: 927110; 333314; 336413
Export
Media: 2-7-10
Personnel:
Scott E. Kuechle *(CFO & Exec VP)*
Terrence G. Linnert *(Gen Counsel & Exec VP-Admin)*
Jerry Witowski *(Exec VP-Operational Excellence & Tech)*
Jennifer Pollino *(Sr VP-HR)*
Sally L. Geib *(VP, Asst Sec & Assoc Gen Counsel)*
John Stachura *(Dir-Quality Assurance)*
Donn Zawis *(Dir-Material Ops)*
Tom Jacobs *(Mgr-Mktg Comm & Publications)*

GOODRICH ISR SYSTEMS

(Sub. of Goodrich Corporation-ISR Systems)
100 Wooster Hts
Danbury, CT 06810-7509
Tel.: (203) 797-5000
Fax: (203) 797-6539
Telex: 6819115
Sales Range: $200-249.9 Million
Approx. Number Employees: 500
Year Founded: 1952
Business Description:
Infrared & Electro-Optical Instruments & Systems Mfr
S.I.C.: 3721
N.A.I.C.S.: 336411
Export
Advertising Expenditures: $200,000
Media: 2-7-10
Distr.: Direct to Consumer; Intl.; Natl.
Budget Set: June
Personnel:
Andreas Nonnenmacher *(VP & Gen Mgr)*
Phillip J. Zeller *(Dir-Programs-Land & Airborne)*
Nance Romans *(Dir-Bus Unit & Mgr-Capture)*
Glenn Benecke *(Dir-Bus Dev)*
Charles D. Cox *(Dir-Special Programs)*
Tom Danckwerth *(Dir-Engrg)*
Dave Imbrogno *(Dir-Precision Engagement Sys)*
Roy England *(Mgr-Bus Dev)*
Randy Farwell *(Mgr-Program)*

GRAPHIC LAMINATING, INC.

6185 Cochran Rd
Solon, OH 44139-3305
Tel.: (440) 498-3400
Fax: (440) 498-3410
Toll Free: (800) 345-5300
E-mail: info@graphiclaminating.com
Web Site:
www.graphiclaminating.com
Approx. Number Employees: 50
Business Description:
Mfr. of Laminating Film & Equipment; Lamination Service
S.I.C.: 5162; 7389
N.A.I.C.S.: 424610; 561990
Export
Advertising Expenditures: $200,000
Media: 2-4-5-7-8-10-13-17-19-20-21-26
Distr.: Intl.; Natl.
Personnel:
Michael Hannon *(Pres)*
Brands & Products:
DURAFILM
GRAPHIC LAMINATING
KEEPING YOUR BEST WORK IN THE CLEAR
LEDCO

GRAPHLINE INC.

1100 International Pkwy Ste 100
Sunrise, FL 33323
Tel.: (954) 722-3000
Fax: (954) 724-2255
Toll Free: (800) 998-3200
E-mail: marketing@graphline.com
Web Site: www.graphline.com
Sales Range: $75-99.9 Million
Approx. Number Employees: 100
Year Founded: 1984
Business Description:
Photo Electronic Imaging, Graphic Arts Cameras & Computer Equipment Distr
S.I.C.: 5199; 5084
N.A.I.C.S.: 424990; 423830
Import Export
Media: 2-4-5-7-8-10-19-20-22
Distr.: Natl.
Budget Set: Dec.
Personnel:
Michael I. Ostroff *(Pres & CEO)*
Reggie Hughes *(Mgr-Sls-Southern Reg)*
Joe Murray *(Mgr-Sls-Northern Reg)*
Bill Paolisso *(Mgr-Sls-Western Reg)*
Melanie Rault *(Mgr-Customer Svc)*
Tim Palleschi *(Coord-Mktg)*
Brands & Products:
GRAPHLINE
PANTONE
YOUR NATIONAL GRAPHIC ARTS SOURCE

GSI GROUP INC.

125 Middlesex Tpke
Bedford, MA 01730
Tel.: (781) 266-5700
Fax: (781) 266-5114
Toll Free: (800) 342-3757
Web Site: www.gsig.com
Approx. Sls.: $383,516,000
Approx. Number Employees: 1,593
Year Founded: 1970
Business Description:
Laser-Based Automated Advanced Manufacturing Systems, Components & Service to the Semiconductor, Electronics, Medical, Automotive & Aerospace Markets
S.I.C.: 3559; 3423; 3555; 3699
N.A.I.C.S.: 333298; 332212; 333293; 335999
Advertising Expenditures: $600,000
Media: 7-10-13-26
Distr.: Intl.; Natl.
Personnel:
Stephen W. Bershad *(Chm)*
John A. Roush *(CEO)*
Robert Buckley *(CFO)*
Philippe Brak *(VP & Gen Mgr)*
Brands & Products:
BEAMDIRECTOR
CIRCUITTRIM
DRILLSTAR
ECO2
ENABLING TECHNOLOGY
GENERAL OPTICS
GENERAL SCANNING
GMAX
GSI
IMPACT
INDEX
INTELLIGENT SERVO DRIVER
IPEX
JK
LASERDYNE
LASERMARK
LIGHTWRITER
LUMINATOR
LUMONICS
M430
MICROE SYSTEMS
MINISAX
OHMEGA-PLY
OMNI-100
PULSEMASTER
SCRIBESMART
SIGMA
SPECTRON
SUPERSOFTMARK
SVS
TRIMPULSE
TRIMSMART
WAFERMARK
WAFERREPAIR
WAFERTRIM
WAVEPRECISION
WESTWIND
XYMARK

H. WILSON COMPANY

(Div. of EBSCO Industries, Inc.)
2245 Delany Rd
Waukegan, IL 60087
Mailing Address:
PO Box 365
South Holland, IL 60473-0365
Tel.: (708) 339-5111
Fax: (708) 210-2069
Fax: (800) 245-8224
Toll Free: (800) 245-7224
E-mail: sales@hwilson.com
Web Site: www.hwilson.com
E-Mail For Key Personnel:
Sales Director: sales@hwilson.com
Approx. Number Employees: 25
Business Description:
Audio Visual Equipment & Library Furniture Mfr
S.I.C.: 2517
N.A.I.C.S.: 337129
Export
Media: 2-4-6-7-10-21
Distr.: Intl.; Natl.
Budget Set: Nov.
Personnel:
Paula McManamam *(Coord-Customer Svc)*
Andy Tess *(VP & Gen Mgr)*
Michael Glab *(Dir-Sls & Mktg)*
Leah Del Nagro *(Mgr-Mktg)*
Brands & Products:
CHAIRMAN SERIES
TUFFY
TUFFYLAND PRODUCTS

HACH COMPANY

(Sub. of Danaher Corporation)
5600 Lindbergh Dr
Loveland, CO 80538-8842
Mailing Address:
PO Box 389
Loveland, CO 80539-0389
Tel.: (970) 669-3050
Fax: (970) 669-2932
Toll Free: (800) 227-4224
Telex: 410-930-9038
Telex: 910-930-9038
E-mail: info@hach.com
Web Site: www.hach.com
Approx. Sls.: $95,000,000
Approx. Number Employees: 1,000
Year Founded: 1947
Business Description:
Chemical & Laboratory Testing Equipment, Process Analyzers & Water Test Kits Mfr
S.I.C.: 3826; 3823
N.A.I.C.S.: 334516; 334513
Import Export
Advertising Expenditures: $1,500,000
Media: 1-2-4-7-10-11
Distr.: Intl.; Natl.
Budget Set: May
Personnel:
Gary R. Dreher *(CFO)*
Jeff Throckmorton *(Pres-Homeland Security)*
Katy Craig *(Dir)*
LeAnn Zuellig *(Dir-Global Mktg)*
Brands & Products:
ALLUVER
BARIVER
BIVER
BOROVER
CALVER
CHLORIVER
CHROMAVER
CYANIVER
DIGESDAHL
FERROVER
FERROZINE
FLUORIVER
FORMULA 2533
FORMULA 2589
GELEX
HACH
HACH ONE
HEXAVER
HYDRAVER
INCUTROL
LEADTRAK
MANVER
MERCUVER
METALTRACE
MOLYVER
MONOVER
NITRAVER
NITRIVER
NTRAK
PHOSVER
PORTALAB
PUMP-COLORIMETER
RATIO
REGENEVER
ROVER
STANNAVER
STILLVER
SULFAVER
SURFACE SCATTER
TANNIVER
TENSETTE

Key to Media (For complete agency information see *The Advertising Red Books-Agencies* edition):
1. Bus. Publs. 2. Cable T.V. 3. Catalogs & Directories. 4. Co-op Adv. 5. Consumer Mags. 6. D.M. to Bus. Estab.7. D.M. to Consumers 8. Daily Newsp. 9. Exhibits/Trade Shows 10. Foreign 11. Infomercial 12. Internet Adv.13. Multimedia 14. Network Radio 15. Network T.V. 16. Newsp. Distr. Mags. 17. Other 18. Outdoor (Posters, Transit) 19. Point of Purchase20. Premiums, Novelties 21. Product Samples 22. Special Events Mktg. 23. Spot Radio 24. Spot T.V. 25. Weekly Newsp. 26. Yellow Page Adv.

Hach Company — (Continued)

TITRASTIR
TITRIVER
UNIVER
VOLUETTE
ZINCOVER

HACKER INSTRUMENTS & INDUSTRIES INC.
1132 Kincaid Bridge Rd
Winnsboro, SC 29180
Tel.: (803) 712-6100
Fax: (803) 712-6116
Toll Free: (800) 4HACKER
E-mail: hackerlab@aol.com
Web Site: www.hackerinstruments.com
Approx. Number Employees: 6
Year Founded: 1942
Business Description:
Mfr. of Microtomes, Cryostats, Microtome Knives, Fiber Optic Illuminators, Histology/Cytology Instruments, Mortuary/Autopsy Instruments, Slide Stainers, Tissue Processors, Robot Cover Slippers
S.I.C.: 5049
N.A.I.C.S.: 423490
Import Export
Advertising Expenditures: $345,000
Media: 2-4-7-10-13-16-18-20-21
Distr.: Intl.; Natl.
Personnel:
Elfi L. Hacker *(Pres)*
James Mullen, Jr. *(VP & Gen Mgr)*
Brands & Products:
AUTOSLIPPER
CLINI-RF
CRYO-HISTOMAT
EDGE
HACKER
HACKER-MILESTONE
MARS
MICROSLIP
SUPERSLIP

HAMAMATSU CORPORATION
(Sub. of Hamamatsu Photonics K.K.)
360 Foothill Rd
Bridgewater, NJ 08807
Mailing Address:
PO Box 6910
Bridgewater, NJ 08807-0910
Tel.: (908) 231-0960
Fax: (908) 231-1218
Toll Free: (800) 524-0504
E-mail: usa@hamamatsu.com
Web Site: www.usa.hamamatsu.com
Sales Range: $600-649.9 Million
Approx. Number Employees: 180
Year Founded: 1969
Business Description:
Photosensitive Devices & Special Lamps Mfr
S.I.C.: 5065; 3671
N.A.I.C.S.: 423690; 334411
Import Export
Advertising Expenditures: $500,000
Media: 2-4-10-13-22
Distr.: Intl.; Natl.
Budget Set: Oct.
Personnel:
Darren Martindill *(VP-Sls)*
Leo Kohyama *(Mgr-Mktg Comm)*
Advertising Agency:
K2 Communications
PO Box 1641
Doylestown, PA 18901-9838
Tel.: (215) 230-7671
Fax: (215) 230-8385

HAMILTON CO., INC.
4970 Energy Way
Reno, NV 89502-4123
Tel.: (775) 858-3000
Fax: (775) 856-7259
Toll Free: (800) 648-5950
E-mail: sales@hamiltoncompany.com
Web Site: www.hamiltoncompany.com
E-Mail For Key Personnel:
Sales Director: sales@hamiltoncompany.com
Approx. Number Employees: 400
Year Founded: 1953
Business Description:
Laboratory Instruments & Supplies Mfr & Designer
S.I.C.: 3826
N.A.I.C.S.: 334516
Import Export
Media: 2-4-7-10-11
Distr.: Intl.; Natl.
Personnel:
Steven Hamilton *(Pres)*
Terri Bradfield *(Dir-HR)*
Jaison March *(Dir-Mktg)*
Louis Rachal *(Mgr-IT)*
Brands & Products:
ACCUDIL
ADVAN TIP
CALPACK
CHEESETRODE
CHEMOTRODE
DIGITAL SYRINGE
DOUBLE FLUSH
DOUBLE PORE
DURACAL
EASYCONTROL
EASYFERM
EVEREF
FERMOTRODE
FLANGE-ADAPTER
FLEXIFIT
FLEXIFLANGE
FLUSHTRODE
FREEZETRODE
GASTIGHT
GEL CADDY
GEL-PLAST
IONOTRODE
LAB CLIPBOARD
LIQ-GLASS
LIQ-PLAST
MASTERFIT
THE MEASURE OF EXCELLENCE
MECOREF
MECOTRODE
MICROLAB
MICROLITER
MINITRODE
MODIFIED MICROFILTER
MODIFIED MICROLITER
MULTI-PAK
OLIGOPURE
OXYFERM
OXYLITE
OXYTRODE
POLILYTE
POLYCLAVE
POLYFERM
POLYRESIST
PROFIREF
PROFITRODE
PROTEGEL
PROTELYTE
QUICK-ACCESS
RETRACTOFIT
RETRACTOMASTER
RETRACTOMATIC
SAMPLELOCK
SINGLE PORE
SKYLITE
SLIMTRODE
SOFTAIDE
SOFTGRIP
SOFTOP
SOFTSTART
SOFTTOUCH
SPINTRODE
TIPTRODE
UPDATE
WATERS
WISP

HASSELBLAD USA, INC.
(Sub. of Victor Hasselblad AB)
10 Madison Rd
Fairfield, NJ 07004-2330
Tel.: (973) 227-7320
Fax: (973) 227-3249
E-mail: info@hasselbladusa.com
Web Site: www.hasselbladusa.com
Approx. Number Employees: 35
Year Founded: 1980
Business Description:
Importer & Distributor of Cameras
S.I.C.: 5043
N.A.I.C.S.: 423410
Import Export
Media: 2-4-6-10-19
Distr.: Natl.
Budget Set: Sept.-Oct.
Personnel:
Tom Olesen *(Pres)*
Advertising Agencies:
Hasselblad USA
333 New Rd Ste 5
Parsippany, NJ 07054
Tel.: (973) 227-7320
Fax: (973) 227-1063

Kalmar Advertising
2083 Center Ave.
Fort Lee, NJ 07024
Tel.: (201) 947-7770

HEMCO CORPORATION
111 Powell Rd
Independence, MO 64056
Tel.: (816) 796-2900
Fax: (816) 796-3333
Toll Free: (800) 779-4362
Telex: 286771 HELD Assocksc
E-mail: info@hemcocorp.com
Web Site: www.hemcocorp.com
Approx. Number Employees: 40
Year Founded: 1958
Business Description:
Laboratory Fume Hoods, Laboratory Designated Work Area Enclosures, Clean Rooms & Robotic Chambers Mfr
S.I.C.: 3821; 3842
N.A.I.C.S.: 339111; 339113
Export
Media: 2-4-7-8-10
Distr.: Intl.; Natl.
Budget Set: Nov.
Personnel:
David Campbell *(VP-Sls)*
Brands & Products:
CLEANLAB
ENVIROMAX
HAZMAX
HEMCO
UNIFLOW
UNILAB
UNILINE
UNIMAX

HERLEY INDUSTRIES, INC.
(Sub. of Kratos Defense & Security Solutions, Inc.)
101 N Pointe Blvd
Lancaster, PA 17601
Tel.: (717) 735-8117
Fax: (717) 397-9503
E-mail: ir@herley.com
Web Site: www.herley.com
E-Mail For Key Personnel:
President: levy@herley.com
Sales Director: sales@generalmicrowave.com
Approx. Sls.: $160,089,000
Approx. Number Employees: 1,022
Year Founded: 1965
Business Description:
Flight Instrumentation Products, Range Safety Transponders & Microwave Components Mfr & Designer for the Defense, Aerospace, Medical & Communications Industries
S.I.C.: 3812; 3679
N.A.I.C.S.: 334511; 334419
Advertising Expenditures: $72,000
Media: 2-7-10-11
Personnel:
John A. Thonet *(Chm)*
Richard Poirier *(Pres & CEO)*
Anello C. Garefino *(CFO & VP-Fin)*
Yohah Adelman *(Sr VP)*
Howard M. Eckstein *(Sr VP)*
Rozalie Schachter *(VP-Strategic Initiatives & Gen Mgr-Herley New York)*
John A. Carroll *(VP-HR)*
Brands & Products:
HERLEY
RAHAM
SATCOM
ULTRA WIDEBAND
Advertising Agency:
Godfrey Advertising
40 N Christian St
Lancaster, PA 17602
Tel.: (717) 393-3831
Fax: (717) 393-1403

HID GLOBAL CORPORATION
(Sub. of Assa Abloy AB)
15370 Barranca Pkwy
Irvine, CA 92618-1905
Tel.: (949) 732-2000
Fax: (949) 732-2120
Toll Free: (800) 237-7769
E-mail: info@hidcorp.com
Web Site: www.hidcorp.com
Sales Range: $10-24.9 Million
Approx. Number Employees: 160
Year Founded: 1991
Business Description:
Access Control Cards & Readers Mfr
S.I.C.: 3825
N.A.I.C.S.: 334515
Import Export
Media: 10
Personnel:
Denis Hebert *(Pres & CEO)*
Will West *(CFO & Sr VP)*
Selva Selvaratnam *(CTO & Sr VP)*
Tam Hulusi *(Sr VP-Strategic Innovation & Intellectual Property)*

Key to Media (For complete agency information see *The Advertising Red Books-Agencies* edition):
1. Bus. Publs. 2. Cable T.V. 3. Catalogs & Directories. 4. Co-op Adv. 5. Consumer Mags. 6. D.M. to Bus. Estab.7. D.M. to Consumers
8. Daily Newsp. 9. Exhibits/Trade Shows 10. Foreign 11. Infomercial 12. Internet Adv.13. Multimedia 14. Network Radio
15. Network T.V. 16. Newsp. Distr. Mags. 17. Other 18. Outdoor (Posters, Transit) 19. Point of Purchase20. Premiums, Novelties
21. Product Samples 22. Special Events Mktg. 23. Spot Radio 24. Spot T.V. 25. Weekly Newsp. 26. Yellow Page Adv.

Anthony Ball *(Sr VP-Identity & Access Mgmt-EMEA)*
Jason Bohrer *(Sr VP-Global Ops)*
Mark Scaparro *(Sr VP-Sls & Mktg Identification Solutions)*
Michele DeWitt *(VP-HR)*
Mary Procyk *(VP-Fin)*
Mark Rivoli *(VP-Customer Svc & Tech Support)*
Holly Sacks *(VP-Mktg & Corp Comm)*
Kathleen Carroll *(Dir-Govt Rels)*
Richard Coombs *(Dir-Sls)*
Jim Pelk *(Dir-OEMs-East)*
Stacey Rooks *(Mgr-Accounts Payable)*
Tom Brown *(Mgr-Southern Reg)*
David Chose *(Mgr-Sls-North America)*
Jim Rawlinson *(Mgr-Eastern Reg)*
Eric Widlitz *(Mgr-Tech)*

THE HILSINGER CO.

(d/b/a Hilco, Inc.)
33 W Bacon St
Plainville, MA 02762-2418
Tel.: (508) 699-4406
Fax: (508) 699-4579
Toll Free: (800) 955-6544
Web Site: www.hilco.com
Approx. Number Employees: 180
Year Founded: 1956
Business Description:
Optical Accessories, Small Parts & Tools Mfr & Distr
S.I.C.: 3851; 3827
N.A.I.C.S.: 339115; 333314
Import Export
Advertising Expenditures: $221,000
Media: 2-4-10-11-19-22
Distr.: Intl.; Natl.
Budget Set: Oct.
Personnel:
Robert Nahmias *(Pres & CEO)*
Paul Janell *(CFO)*
Brands & Products:
CONTOUR FIT LOGIC
DURA-TEC
ERGOPRO
HILCO
LOGIC
SAFE-LOK
SMART SYSTEM PRO
SURE-LOK
TAP'N LOK
TEMPMASTER
THREAD-SEEKER

HINDS INSTRUMENTS, INC.

3175 NW Aloclek Dr 7245 NW Evergreen Pkwy
Hillsboro, OR 97124-7124
Tel.: (503) 690-2000
Fax: (503) 690-3000
Toll Free: (800) 688-4463
E-mail: info@hindsinstruments.com
Web Site: www.hindsinstruments.com
Sales Range: $25-49.9 Million
Approx. Number Employees: 42
Year Founded: 1971
Business Description:
Mfr. & Sales of Measuring Instruments
S.I.C.: 3827; 3829
N.A.I.C.S.: 333314; 334519
Export
Media: 2-4-7-8-10-11
Distr.: Direct to Consumer; Intl.; Natl.
Budget Set: June
Personnel:
Paul W. Hinds *(Pres)*
Tom Hinds *(VP-Fin & Admin)*
Brands & Products:
CAPRICORN
EXICOR
HINDS
HINDS I
HINDS II
PEM
PEM-90

HOLO-SOURCE CORPORATION

12060 Hubbard St
Livonia, MI 48150
Tel.: (734) 427-1530
Fax: (734) 525-8520
E-mail: cpomish@holo-source.com
Web Site: www.holo-source.com
Approx. Sls.: $3,000,000
Approx. Number Employees: 15
Year Founded: 1986
Business Description:
Holograms, Holographic Imaging & Printing Mfr
S.I.C.: 2671
N.A.I.C.S.: 322221
Import Export
Media: 2-4-8-10-21-26
Distr.: Natl.
Budget Set: June
Personnel:
Lee Lacey *(CEO)*
Brands & Products:
HOLO-SOURCE
HYPER-BOX
HYPER-CARD
HYPER-FLEX
HYPER-LABEL

HOLOGIC, INC.

35 Crosby Dr
Bedford, MA 01730
Tel.: (781) 999-7300
Fax: (781) 280-0669
E-mail: investor@hologic.com
Web Site: www.hologic.com
Approx. Rev.: $1,679,552,000
Approx. Number Employees: 4,220
Year Founded: 1985
Business Description:
Medical Diagnostic Products Mfr
S.I.C.: 3841
N.A.I.C.S.: 339112
Export
Advertising Expenditures: $12,100,000
Media: 2-4-7-10-11-22
Distr.: Natl.
Personnel:
John W. Cumming *(Chm & Exec Officer)*
Robert A. Cascella *(Pres & CEO)*
Glenn P. Muir *(CFO, Exec VP-Fin & Admin)*
Mark D. Myslinski *(Sr VP & Gen Mgr-Diagnostics)*
Peter Soltani *(Sr VP & Gen Mgr-Breast Health)*
John Pekarsky *(Sr VP-Sls)*
David Uffer *(Sr Dir-Bus Dev)*
Pam Cumming *(Dir-Mktg)*
Frances Crecco *(Dir-IR)*
Jerry Baur *(Mgr-Indus Imaging)*
Brands & Products:
ACCLAIM
ADIANA
AFFINITY
AFFINITY PLATINUM
ALEXA
APEX
ATEC
AUTO FILM ID
BACKTRACK
CADFX
CELERO
CELEROMARK
CELLIENT
CENOVA
CERVISTA
CHECKMATE
CITRA
CONTOUR
DATAPORT
DEFINING THE STANDARD OF CARE IN WOMEN'S HEALTH
DELPHI
DIGISPOT
DIGITALNOW
DIMENSIONS
DIRECT RADIOGRAPHY
DIRECTRAY
DISCOVERY
DUAL HIP
DXA
E-TEGRITY
EARLIER. SIMPLER. BETTER
EMPHASIZE
ENDOCHECK
ENHANCYT
EPEX
EPEX ER
EPEX SYMPHONY
EVIVA
EXAM COACH
EXPLORER
EXPRESS BMD
EXPRESS EXAM
FAST PADDLE
FIRSTCYTYC
FLUOROSCAN
FULLTERM
GILASITE
HIBRITE
HOLOGIC
HTC
IMAGE PRO
INPLEX
INSTANT VERTEBRAL ASSESSMENT
IRIS
IVA
IVA WORKS
LORAD
LORAD DSM
LORAD ELITE
LOTREX
M-IV
M-IV PLATINUM
MALC
MAMMOPAD
MAMMOSITE
MEDCYT
MIMS
MIRVADER
MULTICARE
NOVASURE
OFFICEMATE
OMNIFLEX
ONE TIME
ONEPAGE DX
ONEPAGE FX
PE
PEERVIEW
PERMAGRID
PERNESTA
PHYSICIANS REPORT WRITER
PHYSICIANS VIEWER
PICTURING LIFE
PREMIER
PREMIER ENCORE
PRESERVCYT
PTDCHECK
QCETTE
QDR
QDR-1000
QDR-4500
QINVADER
QUANTRA
R2
R2 IMAGE CHECKER
RADEX
RIGHTON
RIGHTSIZE
ROMCHECK
SAHARA
SALEST
SCOUTMARC
SECURMARK
SECURVIEW
SECURVIEW DX
SELENIA
SMART PADDLE
SMARTWINDOW
STEREOLOC
SURELOCK
TECH TIPS
TECHMATE
THINPREP
TLI
TLI IQ
TRANSCYT
TRIMARK
UBA
XRE
Advertising Agency:
Media Concepts Corporation
25 N Main St
Assonet, MA 02702-1136
Tel.: (508) 644-3131
Fax: (508) 644-5201

HORNER RAUSCH OPTICAL COMPANY EAST, INC.

968 Main St
Nashville, TN 37206-3614
Tel.: (615) 226-0251
Fax: (615) 226-8527
Web Site:
www.hornerrauschoptical.com/
Sales Range: Less than $1 Million
Approx. Number Employees: 4
Year Founded: 1960
Business Description:
Retailer of Optical Products
S.I.C.: 5995
N.A.I.C.S.: 446130
Advertising Expenditures: $600,000
Media: 8-14-25
Distr.: Natl.
Budget Set: Jan.
Personnel:
Glenna Fenn *(Owner)*
Mark Severence *(Dir-Mktg)*
Brands & Products:
HORNER RAUSCH

HOWELL INSTRUMENTS INC.

8945 South Freeway
Fort Worth, TX 76140-5722
Tel.: (817) 336-7411
Fax: (817) 336-7874
E-mail: info@howellinst.com
Web Site: www.howellinst.com
E-Mail For Key Personnel:

Key to Media (For complete agency information see *The Advertising Red Books-Agencies* edition):
1. Bus. Publs. 2. Cable T.V. 3. Catalogs & Directories. 4. Co-op Adv. 5. Consumer Mags. 6. D.M. to Bus. Estab.7. D.M. to Consumers
8. Daily Newsp. 9. Exhibits/Trade Shows 10. Foreign 11. Infomercial 12. Internet Adv.13. Multimedia 14. Network Radio
15. Network T.V. 16. Newsp. Distr. Mags. 17. Other 18. Outdoor (Posters, Transit) 19. Point of Purchase20. Premiums, Novelties
21. Product Samples 22. Special Events Mktg. 23. Spot Radio 24. Spot T.V. 25. Weekly Newsp. 26. Yellow Page Adv.

Howell Instruments Inc. — (Continued)

Public Relations: cbasham@howellinst.com
Sales Range: $25-49.9 Million
Approx. Number Employees: 80
Year Founded: 1951
Business Description:
Aircraft Engine Test Systems, Airborne Monitors & Indicators, Test Cell Instrumentation Systems, Aircraft Industrial & Laboratory Test Equipment Mfr & Distr
S.I.C.: 3823
N.A.I.C.S.: 334513
Export
Media: 2-4-7-10-13-21
Distr.: Direct to Consumer; Intl.; Natl.
Budget Set: Aug.
Personnel:
William Howell *(Chm & CEO)*
Scott Worrel *(Pres)*
Wes Ragle *(VP-Engrg)*
Lonnie J. Thompson *(VP-Fin)*
Brands & Products:
AEDATS III/IV
ALUMEL
AUTOTAK
AUTOTEMP
CHROMEL
HOWELL
JETCAL
JETCAL2000
JETCAL2000 ANALYZER
TA'POT
TCIP
TEMPCAL
TEMPCAL TESTER

HP MARKETING CORP.

(Holding of Gepe Holding AG)
16 Chapin Rd
Pine Brook, NJ 07058-9718
Mailing Address:
PO Box 715
Pine Brook, NJ 07058
Tel.: (973) 808-9010
Tel.: (973) 808-9626
Fax: (973) 808-9004
Fax: (800) 282-9010
Toll Free: (800) 735-4373
E-mail: info@hpmarketingcorp.com
Web Site: www.hpmarketingcorp.com
Approx. Number Employees: 10
Year Founded: 1971
Business Description:
Photography Equipment Importer & Distr
S.I.C.: 5043
N.A.I.C.S.: 423410
Import
Media: 2-4-6-8-10
Distr.: Natl.
Budget Set: Sept.
Personnel:
Roger Bartzke *(Pres)*

ICARE INDUSTRIES, INC.

4399 35th St N
Saint Petersburg, FL 33714-3717
Tel.: (727) 526-0501
Fax: (727) 522-1408
Toll Free: (800) 648-7463
E-mail: contact@icare.com
Web Site: www.icare.com
E-Mail For Key Personnel:
President: jspayne@icare.com
Approx. Number Employees: 100
Year Founded: 1968
Business Description:
Prescription Lenses & Diving Lenses Mfr
S.I.C.: 3851; 5995
N.A.I.C.S.: 339115; 446130
Advertising Expenditures: $500,000
Media: 4-9-10-13-19-25
Personnel:
J.T. Payne *(Pres)*
J. Scott Payne *(CEO)*
Greg Gerhig *(CFO)*
Kassandra Bidot *(Dir-Mktg)*
Brands & Products:
CRIZAL
FEATHERLITE
ICARELABS
OPTI-MART
REFLECTION FREE
SEAVISION
SEAVISION DIVE
SKIVISION
SWIMVISION

ID SHOP, INC.

1219 Montague Ave
Greenwood, SC 29649
Tel.: (864) 223-9600
Fax: (864) 223-4992
Toll Free: (800) 228-6522
E-mail: info@idshop.com
Web Site: www.idshop.com
Approx. Number Employees: 10
Year Founded: 1983
Business Description:
ID Products Mfr & Supplier
S.I.C.: 5043
N.A.I.C.S.: 423410
Media: 4-7-10-13-22
Personnel:
Earl Brewington, Jr. *(Pres)*

II-VI INCORPORATED

(d/b/a Two-Six Incorporated)
375 Saxonburg Blvd
Saxonburg, PA 16056
Tel.: (724) 352-4455
Tel.: (724) 352-5211
Fax: (724) 352-5284
E-mail: info@ii-vi.com
Web Site: www.ii-vi.com
Approx. Rev.: $502,801,000
Approx. Number Employees: 6,195
Year Founded: 1971
Business Description:
Optical Components, Thermo-Electric Systems & Engineered Materials Developer, Mfr & Marketer
S.I.C.: 3827; 3541; 3674; 3679; 3812; 3826; 3845
N.A.I.C.S.: 333314; 333512; 334413; 334419; 334510; 334511; 334516
Media: 7-10-17
Personnel:
Francis J. Kramer *(Pres & CEO)*
Craig A. Creaturo *(CFO & Treas)*
Vincent D. Mattera, Jr. *(Exec VP)*
Robert R. Keefer *(Dir-Internal Audit)*
Marlene L. Acre *(Mgr-HR)*
Richard P. Figel *(Mgr-Fin Reporting)*
Brian R. Fisher *(Mgr-Taxation)*
Carrie J. Manzer *(Mgr-Corp Acctg)*
Brands & Products:
EEO
EPIREADY
EV PRODUCTS
HIGHYAG
INFRAREADY OPTICS
MLA
MP-5
PHOTOP
PRM
VLOC
THE WORLDWIDE LEADER IN CRYSTAL GROWTH TECHNOLOGY

ILX LIGHTWAVE CORPORATION

31950 E Frontage Rd
Bozeman, MT 59715
Tel.: (406) 586-1244
Fax: (406) 586-9405
Toll Free: (800) 459-9459
E-mail: sales@ilxlightwave.com
Web Site: www.ilxlightwave.com
E-Mail For Key Personnel:
Sales Director: sales@ilxlightwave.com
Approx. Number Employees: 35
Year Founded: 1986
Business Description:
Laser Scientific & Engineering Instruments
S.I.C.: 3826; 3827
N.A.I.C.S.: 334516; 333314
Export
Media: 10-13
Personnel:
Steve Gwinner *(VP-Sls & Mktg)*
Brands & Products:
ELECTRICO OPTICAL

IMAX CORPORATION

2525 Speakman Dr
Mississauga, ON L5K 1B1, Canada
Tel.: (905) 403-6500
Fax: (905) 403-6450
E-mail: info@imax.com
Web Site: www.imax.com
Approx. Rev.: $248,614,000
Approx. Number Employees: 361
Year Founded: 1967
Business Description:
Designer, Mfr, Retailer & Lessor of Large Format Motion Picture Projection Systems, Film & Equipment
S.I.C.: 3861
N.A.I.C.S.: 333315; 325992
Import Export
Advertising Expenditures: $7,800,000
Personnel:
Bradley J. Wechsler *(Chm)*
Richard L. Gelfond *(CEO)*
Joseph Sparacio *(CFO & Exec VP)*
Gary Moss *(COO)*
Marc de Grandpre *(CMO)*
Greg Foster *(Chm/Pres-Filmed Entertainment)*
David B. Keighley *(Pres-David Keighley Productions 7MM Inc.& Exec VP)*
Robert D. Lister *(Gen Counsel & Sr Exec VP)*
G. Mary Ruby *(Exec VP-Corp Svcs & Corp Sec)*
Brian Bonnick *(Exec VP-Tech)*
Larry O'Reilly *(Exec VP-Theatre Dev)*
Mark Welton *(Exec VP-Corp Digital Dev & Theater Ops)*
Philip E. Groves *(Sr VP-Worldwide Distr & Studio Exhibitor Rels)*
Carrie Lindzon-Jacobs *(Sr VP-HR)*
Ann Sommerlath *(VP-Corp Comm)*
Brands & Products:
IMAX
IMAX 3D
IMAX DMR
IMAX DOME
THE IMAX EXPERIENCE
OMNIMAX
PROPORTIONAL POINT SOURCE
THINK BIG
Advertising Agencies:
Hauser Advertising Inc.
309 Bellino Dr
Pacific Palisades, CA 90272
Tel.: (310) 459-5911
Fax: (310) 459-5919

Nemer Fieger
6250 Excelsior Blvd Ste 203
Minneapolis, MN 55416-2735
Tel.: (952) 925-4848
Fax: (952) 925-1907

Rogers & Cowan
919 3rd Ave 18th Fl
New York, NY 10022
Tel.: (310) 854-8100
Fax: (212) 445-8477

SID LEE
75 Queen Street Ofc 1400
Montreal, QC H3C 2N6, Canada
Tel.: (514) 282-2200
Fax: (514) 282-0499
Creative Agency of Record
Marketing Strategy

INSIGHT HEALTH SERVICES HOLDINGS CORP.

(d/b/a Insight Imaging)
(Filed Ch 11 Bankruptcy #10-16564 on 12/2/10 in U.S. Bankruptcy Ct, Southern Dist of NY, NY)
26250 Enterprise Ct Ste 100
Lake Forest, CA 92630
Tel.: (949) 282-6000
Fax: (949) 455-9816
Web Site: www.insighthealth.com
Approx. Rev.: $190,938,000
Approx. Number Employees: 1,094
Year Founded: 1982
Business Description:
Holding Company; Diagnostic Medical Imaging Services
S.I.C.: 6719; 8071
N.A.I.C.S.: 551112; 621512
Media: 7
Personnel:
Wayne B. Lowell *(Chm)*
Louis E. Hallman, III *(Pres & CEO)*
Keith S. Kelson *(CFO & Exec VP)*
Bernard O'Rourke *(COO)*
Donald F. Hankus *(CIO & Exec VP)*
Mike Jones *(Gen Counsel, Sec & Exec VP)*
Patricia R. Blank *(Exec VP-Bus Process Mgmt)*

INVENSYS CONTROL SYSTEMS

(Sub. of Invensys Process Systems)
191 E North Ave
Carol Stream, IL 60187
Tel.: (630) 260-3400
Fax: (630) 260-7325
Web Site: www.invensys.com
Approx. Number Employees: 40
Year Founded: 1998

Key to Media (For complete agency information see *The Advertising Red Books-Agencies* edition):
1. Bus. Publs. 2. Cable T.V. 3. Catalogs & Directories. 4. Co-op Adv. 5. Consumer Mags. 6. D.M. to Bus. Estab.7. D.M. to Consumers
8. Daily Newsp. 9. Exhibits/Trade Shows 10. Foreign 11. Infomercial 12. Internet Adv.13. Multimedia 14. Network Radio
15. Network T.V. 16. Newsp. Distr. Mags. 17. Other 18. Outdoor (Posters, Transit) 19. Point of Purchase20. Premiums, Novelties
21. Product Samples 22. Special Events Mktg. 23. Spot Radio 24. Spot T.V. 25. Weekly Newsp. 26. Yellow Page Adv.

Business Description:
Temperature & Pressure Controls, Oven & Water Heater Thermostats, Building Control Systems, Industrial Controls Mfr
S.I.C.: 3822; 3823
N.A.I.C.S.: 334512; 334513
Export
Advertising Expenditures: $2,100,000
Bus. Publs.: $225,000; Cable T.V.: $50,000; Catalogs & Directories: $50,000; Co-op Adv.: $400,000; Consumer Mags.: $500,000; Daily Newsp.: $50,000; Exhibits/Trade Shows: $100,000; Point of Purchase: $200,000; Product Samples: $200,000; Spot Radio: $50,000; Spot T.V.: $150,000; Yellow Page Adv.: $125,000
Distr.: Intl.
Budget Set: Oct.
Personnel:
Mark Balcunas *(Pres)*
Brands & Products:
COM-TROL
FASCO
FLAME MASTER
FLAME SET
HOBBS
MAPLE CHASE
RANCO
ROBERTSHAW

IRCAMERAS NORTHEAST, INC.
425 3rd St SW
Walpole, MA 20024
Tel.: (508) 668-5650
Fax: (508) 668-5054
Toll Free: (877) 472-2637
E-mail: info@ircameras.com
Web Site: www.ircameras.com
E-Mail For Key Personnel:
President: northeast@ircameras.com
Approx. Number Employees: 40
Business Description:
Infared Imaging Systems & Services Retailer
S.I.C.: 5946
N.A.I.C.S.: 443130
Media: 4-7-13
Personnel:
Elliot Rittenberg *(Pres)*

IROBOT CORP.
8 Crosby Dr
Bedford, MA 01730
Tel.: (781) 430-3000
Fax: (781) 430-3001
E-mail: info@irobot.com
Web Site: www.irobot.com
Approx. Rev.: $400,952,000
Approx. Number Employees: 657
Year Founded: 1990
Business Description:
Household & Military Robot Mfr
S.I.C.: 3589; 3635
N.A.I.C.S.: 333319; 335212
Export
Advertising Expenditures: $13,800,000
Media: 5-7-8-10-13-17
Personnel:
Colin M. Angle *(Chm & CEO)*
John J. Leahy *(CFO)*
Joseph W. Dyer *(COO)*
Jay Leader *(CIO & Sr VP-IT)*
Alison Dean *(Sr VP-Corp Fin & Principal Acctg Officer)*
Jeffrey A. Beck *(Pres/Gen Mgr-Home Robots Div)*
Glen D. Weinstein *(Gen Counsel & Sr VP)*
Russell J. Campanello *(Sr VP-HR)*
Howard Leyda *(VP-Mktg)*
Brands & Products:
IROBOT
IROBOT CONNECTR
IROBOT CREATE
IROBOT DIRT DOG
IROBOT LOOJ
IROBOT NEGOTIATOR
IROBOT RANGER
IROBOT SEAGLIDER
IROBOT TRANSPHIBIAN
IROBOT WARRIOR
PACKBOT
ROBOTS THAT MAKE A DIFFERENCE
ROOMBA
ROOMBA 500 SERIES
SCOOBA
VERRO
Advertising Agency:
Brand Content
580 Harrison Ave
Boston, MA 02116
Tel.: (617) 338-9111
Fax: (617) 338-9121

ISOMET CORPORATION
5263 Port Royal Rd
Springfield, VA 22151-2103
Tel.: (703) 321-8301
Fax: (703) 321-8546
E-mail: isomet@isomet.com
Web Site: www.isomet.com
Sales Range: $10-24.9 Million
Approx. Number Employees: 23
Year Founded: 1956
Business Description:
Lasers, Scanners & Other Components Mfr
S.I.C.: 3699; 3826; 3827
N.A.I.C.S.: 335999; 333314; 334516
Media: 10
Personnel:
Michael Hillier *(Pres)*
Sidney Neely *(Treas, Sec & Exec VP-Fin)*
Everett Taylor *(VP-Sls & Mktg)*

ITW BGK FINISHING SYSTEMS
(Sub. of Illinois Tool Works Inc.)
4131 Pheasant Ridge Dr NE
Minneapolis, MN 55449-7104
Tel.: (763) 784-0466
Fax: (763) 784-1362
Toll Free: (800) 663-5498
E-mail: info@itwbgk.com
Web Site: www.itwbgk.com
E-Mail For Key Personnel:
Sales Director: sales@itwbgk.com
Sales Range: $10-24.9 Million
Approx. Number Employees: 50
Year Founded: 1980
Business Description:
Electric Infrared Equipment Mfr
S.I.C.: 3823
N.A.I.C.S.: 334513
Media: 10

ITW MAGNAFLUX
(Sub. of Illinois Tool Works Inc.)
3624 W Lk Ave
Glenview, IL 60026
Tel.: (847) 657-5300
Fax: (847) 657-4720
Fax: (800) 421-1569
Fax: (847) 657-5388
E-mail: info@magnaflux.com
Web Site: www.magnaflux.com
Sales Range: $10-24.9 Million
Approx. Number Employees: 25
Year Founded: 1934
Business Description:
Magnetic Particle & Dye Penetrant Inspection Equipment Mfr & Supplier
S.I.C.: 3823
N.A.I.C.S.: 334513
Advertising Expenditures: $250,000
Media: 2-4-7-10-22-26
Distr.: Natl.
Budget Set: July
Personnel:
Steve Groeninger *(Gen Mgr)*
John Beasey *(Reg Mgr-Sls-Intl)*
Bernardo Ordonez *(Reg Mgr-Sls)*
Dean Ritchey *(Reg Mgr-Sls)*
David Geis *(Product Mgr-Quasar)*
Suzanne Oliver *(Sls Mgr)*
Susan Rogers *(Sls Mgr)*
Kevin Walker *(Product Mgr-Matls)*
Ken Boden *(Mgr-MPI Equipment)*
Phyllis Doyle *(Mgr-Sls-Natl)*
Paul Dunnwald *(Mgr-Tech Svcs)*
Noemi Gonzalez *(Mgr-Sls--Intl)*
Tim Harz *(Mgr-Bus Dev)*
Kim Hayes *(Mgr-Sls-Reg)*
Mathew Plamoottil *(Quality Assurance Mgr)*
Brands & Products:
DARACLEAN
MAGNAFLUX
MAGNAGLO
MAGNAPURE
SPOTCHECK
ZYGLO

JDS UNIPHASE CORPORATION
430 N McCarthy Blvd
Milpitas, CA 95035
Tel.: (408) 546-5000
Fax: (408) 546-4300
Fax: (800) 898-8537
Toll Free: (800) 498-JDSU
E-mail: sales@jdsu.com
Web Site: www.jdsu.com
E-Mail For Key Personnel:
Sales Director: sales@jdsu.com
Approx. Rev.: $1,804,500,000
Approx. Number Employees: 5,000
Year Founded: 1999
Business Description:
Fiber Optic Components, Modules & Subsystems Designer, Developer, Mfr & Distr
S.I.C.: 3674; 3679
N.A.I.C.S.: 334413; 334419
Advertising Expenditures: $2,400,000
Personnel:
Martin A. Kaplan *(Chm)*
Kevin J. Kennedy *(Vice Chm)*
Thomas Waechter *(Pres & CEO)*
David W. Vellequette *(CFO)*
Chris Bedi *(CIO)*
Andrew Pollack *(Gen Counsel & Sec)*
Roy W. Bie *(Sr VP-Advanced Optical Tech Bus Segment)*
David Holly *(Sr VP-Emerging Markets & Strategic Projects)*
Rex Jackson *(Sr VP-Bus Svcs)*
Debora C. Shoquist *(Sr VP-Ops)*
Judith Kay *(Head-Exec Ops & Corp Strategy)*
Alan Lowe *(Head-Comm & Comml Optical Products Bus Segment)*
Michelle Levine *(Dir-IR)*
Brands & Products:
APE
BRIGHTAMP
BRIGHTJACK
BRIGHTSWITCH
CHROMAFLAIR
COLORSHIFT
DEFINITV
FIBERSHELF
GBX
JDSU
LGX
LOWOHM
SECURESHIFT
SPECTRAFLAIR
ULTREX
WAVEREADY

JEWELL INSTRUMENTS, LLC
850 Perimeter Rd
Manchester, NH 03103
Tel.: (603) 669-6400
Fax: (603) 669-5962
Toll Free: (800) 638-3771
E-mail: sales@jewellinstruments.com
Web Site: www.jewellinstruments.com
E-Mail For Key Personnel:
Sales Director: sales@jewellinstruments.com
Approx. Number Employees: 200
Year Founded: 1936
Business Description:
Panel Meters, Avionics Components, Inertial Sensors & Precision Solenoids Mfr & Distributor
S.I.C.: 3613; 3829
N.A.I.C.S.: 335313; 334519
Import Export
Media: 2-7-20
Distr.: Intl.; Natl.
Budget Set: Nov.
Personnel:
Carlo Carluccio *(Pres & CEO)*
Steve Morin *(CFO)*
Jim Burgess *(COO)*
Don Descoteaux *(VP-Sls & Mktg)*
Mike Harbour *(Prod Mgr)*
Gary Dudman *(Mgr-Sls)*
Brands & Products:
AIR-1000
JEWELL
LCF-2310
LCM-100
LSM
MAGNETEC
Advertising Agency:
SMS
Weymouth Rd.
Landisville, NJ 08326
Tel.: (856) 697-1257

JMAR, LLC
10905 Technology Pl
San Diego, CA 92127
Tel.: (858) 946-6800
Fax: (858) 946-6899
E-mail: info@jmar.com
Web Site: www.jmar.com
Sales Range: Less than $1 Million
Approx. Number Employees: 16
Business Description:
Laser & X-Ray Technologies Developer & Mfr

JMAR, LLC — (Continued)

S.I.C.: 3841; 3679
N.A.I.C.S.: 339112; 334419
Export
Media: 4-7-10-11
Personnel:
Charles A. Dickinson *(Chm)*
Robert A. Selzer *(Sr VP-Tech)*
Brands & Products:
BIOSENTRY
BRITELIGHT
CPL
JMAR
NANOPULSAR

JONAS SUPPLY CO.

1850 Dogwood St
Louisville, CO 80027
Tel.: (303) 466-1112
Fax: (303) 466-1111
Toll Free: (800) 525-6379
E-mail: bill@jonastaxidermy.com
Web Site: www.jonastaxidermy.com
Approx. Number Employees: 14
Year Founded: 1908
Business Description:
Taxidermy Services
S.I.C.: 7389; 5087
N.A.I.C.S.: 541990; 423850
Import Export
Advertising Expenditures: $200,000
Media: 2-4-7-10-20-26
Distr.: Intl.
Budget Set: May
Personnel:
R. J. Losasso *(Pres)*
Brands & Products:
JONAS

KEITHLEY INSTRUMENTS, INC.

(Sub. of Tektronix, Inc.)
28775 Aurora Rd
Solon, OH 44139-1837
Tel.: (440) 248-0400
Fax: (440) 248-6168
Toll Free: (800) 552-1115
E-mail: info@keithley.com
Web Site: www.keithley.com
Approx. Sls.: $126,870,000
Approx. Number Employees: 490
Year Founded: 1946
Business Description:
High-Precision Electrical Measuring Instruments Mfr
S.I.C.: 3823; 3824; 3825; 5065
N.A.I.C.S.: 334513; 334514; 334515; 423690
Import Export
Advertising Expenditures: $4,956,000
Media: 2-4-6-7-8-10-11-16
Distr.: Direct to Consumer; Intl.; Natl.
Budget Set: Aug.
Personnel:
Linda C. Rae *(COO & Exec VP)*
Daniel A. Faia *(VP-Sls & Support)*
Mark A. Hoersten *(VP-Mktg)*
Thomas J. Mego *(Dir-Quality Sys/ Continuous Improvement & Info Sys)*
Gloria L. Smith *(Dir-HR)*
Brands & Products:
A GREATER MEASURE OF CONFIDENCE
ADAPTEST
BSIMPRO
DASCARD
DRIVERLINX
EASYEST AG
EXCELINX
IC-CAP
KEITHLEY
PROBECARDMANAGER
QUANTOX
SOURCEMETER
SPECDIRECT
TCLIBRARY
TESTPOINT
TPDOC
TRIAD ACCREDIT
VISUAL TEST EXTENSIONS
VISUALSCOPE
WORKHORSE
Advertising Agency:
Goldstein Group Communications
6000 Freedom Square Dr., Ste. 165
Cleveland, OH 44131
Tel.: (216) 573-2300
Fax: (216) 573-9964
(Public Rels.)

KOFAX IMAGE PRODUCTS, INC.

(Sub. of Kofax plc)
15211 Laguna Canyon Rd
Irvine, CA 92618-3603
Tel.: (949) 727-1733
Fax: (949) 727-3144
E-mail: info@kofax.com
Web Site: www.kofax.com
Approx. Number Employees: 300
Year Founded: 1985
Business Description:
Custom Computer Programming Services
S.I.C.: 7371; 3577
N.A.I.C.S.: 541511; 334119
Import Export
Personnel:
James Arnold, Jr. *(CFO)*
Steve Johnson *(Sr VP-Americas)*
Rob Jensen *(Sr Dir-Corp Comm)*
Bruce Orcutt *(Dir-Product Mktg)*
Mark Broome *(Mgr-Solutions)*
Advertising Agency:
Westbound Communications, Inc.
625 The City Dr Ste 360
Orange, CA 92868
Tel.: (714) 663-8188
Fax: (714) 663-8181

KOLLMORGEN ELECTRO-OPTICAL

(Div. of Danaher Motion Company)
347 King St
Northampton, MA 01060
Tel.: (413) 586-2330
Fax: (413) 586-1324
E-mail: info@eo.kollmorgen.com
Web Site: www.eo.kollmorgen.com
Sales Range: $125-149.9 Million
Approx. Number Employees: 350
Business Description:
Electro-Optical Defense Technology Mfr
S.I.C.: 3844; 3625; 3845
N.A.I.C.S.: 334517; 334510; 335314
Media: 2-4-7-10
Personnel:
Micahel J. Wall *(Pres)*
Brands & Products:
CLAWS
MK 38 MOD
MK 46
SEA CLAWS

KONICA MINOLTA BUSINESS SOLUTIONS USA, INC.

(Sub. of Konica Minolta Holdings, Inc.)
100 Williams Dr
Ramsey, NJ 07446
Tel.: (201) 825-4000
Fax: (201) 825-7567
Web Site: www.kmbs.konicaminolta.us
Approx. Number Employees: 300
Business Description:
Photographic Cameras, Office Copiers, Microfilm & Office Equipment Whslr
S.I.C.: 5065; 5044
N.A.I.C.S.: 423690; 423420
Media: 2-4-10-22
Personnel:
Richard K. Taylor *(Pres & COO)*
Michael Leonczyk *(CFO & Exec VP-Fin)*
Nelson Lin *(CIO & VP-IT Svcs)*
Alan Nielsen *(Exec VP-Dealer Sls)*
Kevin P. Kern *(Sr VP-Mktg)*
Bill Corry *(VP-Strategic Acq & Bus Dev)*
Todd Fooe Foote *(VP-Govt Sls & Mktg)*
Mark Pollack *(VP-Mktg Comm, Pricing & Program Dev)*
Brands & Products:
COPIERS
CS PRO
EP SERIES COPIERS
FAXES
PRINTERS
VECTIS
WEATHERMATICA
Advertising Agency:
Lois Paul & Partners
150 Presidential Way
Woburn, MA 01801
Tel.: (781) 782-5000
Fax: (781) 782-5999

L-3 WESCAM INC.

(Sub. of L-3 Communications Corporation)
649 North Service Rd West
Burlington, ON L7P 5B9, Canada
Tel.: (905) 633-4000
Fax: (905) 633-4100
Web Site: www.wescam.com
Sales Range: $100-124.9 Million
Approx. Number Employees: 500
Business Description:
Visual Information Systems Mfr & Designer
S.I.C.: 3827
N.A.I.C.S.: 333314
Media: 10
Personnel:
John Dehne *(Pres)*
Lou Park *(CFO)*
Allan Bignell *(VP & Gen Mgr)*
Roman M. Turchyn *(Corp VP-HR)*
Peter Larsson *(Gen Mgr-Brdcst Sports)*
Rod Till *(Dir-Customer Svc)*

L&R MANUFACTURING COMPANY

577 Elm St
Kearny, NJ 07032
Tel.: (201) 991-5330
Fax: (201) 991-5870
E-mail: info@lrultrasonics.com
Web Site: www.lrultrasonics.com
E-Mail For Key Personnel:
Public Relations: BLetch@ lrultrasonics.com
Approx. Number Employees: 200
Year Founded: 1930
Business Description:
Ultrasonic Cleaning Systems, Solutions & Accessories Mfr
S.I.C.: 2842; 3841
N.A.I.C.S.: 325612; 339112
Import Export
Media: 2-4-7-10-21
Distr.: Intl.; Natl.
Budget Set: Nov.
Personnel:
James J. Lazarus *(Chm & CEO)*
Robert Lazarus *(Pres)*
Bruce Letch *(Sr VP-Sls & Mktg)*
Brands & Products:
AGLON
AQUA TORCH
DIP
ELLANAR
HYDRO SONIC
L & R
PREPCLEAN
PREPCLEAN PLUS
QUANTREX
QUANTREX PC3
SCBA
SWEEPZONE
SWEEPZONE AG
ULTRADOSE
ULTRASONIC
Advertising Agency:
St. Jacques Marketing
60 Washington St Ste 203
Morristown, NJ 07960
Tel.: (973) 829-0858
Fax: (973) 624-3836
Toll Free: (800) 708-9467

LAB PRODUCTS, INC.

(Sub. of Bio Medic Corporation)
742 Sussex Ave
Seaford, DE 19973-2057
Tel.: (302) 628-4300
Fax: (302) 628-4309
E-mail: lpi@labproductsinc.com
Web Site: www.labproductsinc.com
Approx. Number Employees: 50
Business Description:
Laboratory Animal Housing Care Equipment Mfr
S.I.C.: 7389
N.A.I.C.S.: 541990
Media: 10
Personnel:
Neil Campbell *(Pres)*

LANDEC CORPORATION

3603 Haven Ave
Menlo Park, CA 94025
Tel.: (650) 306-1650
Fax: (650) 368-9818
E-mail: info@landec.com
Web Site: www.landec.com
E-Mail For Key Personnel:
Sales Director: sales@landec.com
Approx. Rev.: $276,729,000
Approx. Number Employees: 255
Year Founded: 1986
Business Description:
Temperature-Activated & Other Specialty Polymer Product Designer, Developer, Mfr & Retailer
S.I.C.: 2821; 2819; 2833
N.A.I.C.S.: 325211; 325188; 325411

Key to Media (For complete agency information see *The Advertising Red Books-Agencies* edition):
1. Bus. Publs. 2. Cable T.V. 3. Catalogs & Directories. 4. Co-op Adv. 5. Consumer Mags. 6. D.M. to Bus. Estab.7. D.M. to Consumers
8. Daily Newsp. 9. Exhibits/Trade Shows 10. Foreign 11. Infomercial 12. Internet Adv.13. Multimedia 14. Network Radio
15. Network T.V. 16. Newsp. Distr. Mags. 17. Other 18. Outdoor (Posters, Transit) 19. Point of Purchase20. Premiums, Novelties
21. Product Samples 22. Special Events Mktg. 23. Spot Radio 24. Spot T.V. 25. Weekly Newsp. 26. Yellow Page Adv.

Export
Advertising Expenditures: $557,000
Media: 4-7-8-10-16
Personnel:
Gary T. Steele *(Chm, Pres & CEO)*
Gregory S. Skinner *(CFO & VP-Fin & Admin)*
David D. Taft *(COO)*
Brands & Products:
BREATHEWAY
CHIQUITA TO GO
EARLY PLANT
EAT SMART
INTELIMER
INTELLICOAT
LANDEC INTELLIGENT MATERIALS
POLLINATOR PLUS
PORT
RELAY

LASER TECHNOLOGY, INC.

7070 S Tucson Way
Centennial, CO 80112
Tel.: (303) 649-1000
Fax: (303) 649-9710
Toll Free: (800) 790-7364
E-mail: info@lasertech.com
Web Site: www.lasertech.com
E-Mail For Key Personnel:
Public Relations: mphillips@lasertech.com
Approx. Number Employees: 81
Year Founded: 1985
Business Description:
Laser-Based Speed & Distance Measuring Instruments Mfr
S.I.C.: 3699; 3829
N.A.I.C.S.: 335999; 334519
Export
Advertising Expenditures: $248,000
Media: 2-5-7-10-13-16-26
Personnel:
Eric A. Miller *(Pres & CEO)*
Pamela Sezy *(CFO, Treas, Sec & VP)*
Roosevelt Rogers *(VP-Sls & Mktg)*
Brands & Products:
CRITERION
ENCAMPO
FACE PROFILER
FOREST PRO
IMPULSE
MAPSTAR
MAPSTAR ANGLE ENCODER
MAPSTAR II
MARKSMAN
QUICK MAP 3D
SPEEDSTAT
TRUPULSE
ULTRALYTE
ULTRALYTE COMPACT
ULTRALYTE LRB
YARDAGE PRO

LCA-VISION INC.

7840 Montgomery Rd
Cincinnati, OH 45236
Tel.: (513) 792-9292
Fax: (513) 792-5620
Toll Free: (800) 688-4550
E-mail: pforsythe@lca.com
Web Site: www.lasikplus.com
Approx. Rev.: $99,825,000
Approx. Number Employees: 318
Year Founded: 1986
Business Description:
Laser Vision Correction Centers
S.I.C.: 8011; 8042; 8049; 8093
N.A.I.C.S.: 621491; 621320; 621399; 621498
Advertising Expenditures: $33,784,000
Media: 8-23-24-25
Personnel:
Michael J. Celebrezze *(CFO, Treas & Sr VP-Fin)*
David L. Thomas *(COO)*
Bharat Kakar *(VP-Mktg)*
Brands & Products:
LASIKPLUS
TRUST THE PLUS
Advertising Agency:
Empower MediaMarketing (MEDIA THAT WORKS)
1111 Saint Gregory St
Cincinnati, OH 45202
Tel.: (513) 871-9454
Fax: (513) 871-1804
Digital Creative
Digital Media Buying & Planning
Traditional Media Buying & Planning

LEADER INSTRUMENTS CORPORATION

(Sub. of Leader Electronics Corporation)
6484 Commerce Dr
Cypress, CA 90630-5224
Tel.: (714) 527-9300
Fax: (714) 527-7490
Toll Free: (800) 645-5104
E-mail: sales@leaderusa.com
Web Site: www.leaderusa.com
E-Mail For Key Personnel:
Sales Director: sales@leaderusa.com
Approx. Number Employees: 25
Year Founded: 1953
Business Description:
Distr & Marketer of Electronic Test & Measuring Equipment
S.I.C.: 5063
N.A.I.C.S.: 423610
Import Export
Media: 2-4-7-10
Distr.: Intl.; Natl.
Budget Set: Aug.
Personnel:
Hiro Sawa *(Pres)*
George Gonos *(VP-Sls & Mktg)*
Brands & Products:
LEADER

LECROY CORPORATION

700 Chestnut Ridge Rd
Chestnut Ridge, NY 10977
Tel.: (845) 425-2000
Fax: (845) 425-8967
Toll Free: (800) 553-2769
E-mail: contact.corp@lecroy.com
Web Site: www.lecroy.com
Approx. Rev.: $178,100,000
Approx. Number Employees: 494
Year Founded: 1964
Business Description:
Test & Measurement Equipment Mfr & Retailer
S.I.C.: 3825; 3824; 3829
N.A.I.C.S.: 334515; 334514; 334519
Advertising Expenditures: $2,000,000
Media: 2-10
Personnel:
Allyn C. Woodward, Jr. *(Chm)*
Thomas H. Reslewic *(Pres & CEO)*
Sean B. O'Connor *(CFO, Treas, Sec & VP-Fin)*
Corey L. Hirsch *(CIO)*
Conrad J. Fernandes *(VP-Sls-Asia Pacific)*
Roberto Petrillo *(VP-Sls-Worldwide)*
Brands & Products:
AUDITOR
BUSENGINE
CATC TRACE
CHIEF
EXPRESSCARD
FCTRACER
FIREINSPECTOR
IBTRACER
INFUSION
LECROY
MERLIN
MERLIN II
PETRACER
PETRAINER
POWERMEASURE
SAS INFUSION
SASTRACER
SMAP
TRACER
TRAINER
UWBTRACER
WAVEACE
WAVEEXPERT
WAVEJET 300A
WAVEMASTER
WAVEPRO
WAVERUNNER
WAVESURFER
WIMEDIA
X-STREAM
XDEV
XMAP
XMATH

THE LEE COMPANY

2 Pettipaug Rd
Westbrook, CT 06498
Mailing Address:
PO Box 424
Westbrook, CT 06498-0424
Tel.: (860) 399-6281
Fax: (860) 399-2270
Toll Free: (800) 533-7584
Web Site: www.theleeco.com
Approx. Number Employees: 800
Year Founded: 1949
Business Description:
Miniature Hydraulic Inserts & Electro-Fluidic Systems Mfr
S.I.C.: 3823; 3841
N.A.I.C.S.: 334513; 339112
Export
Media: 2-4-7-10
Distr.: Intl.; Natl.
Budget Set: Jan. -Oct.
Personnel:
Lee Leighton, III *(Pres)*
J. A. Stamos *(VP-Sls)*
John Kingsbury *(Mgr-Adv)*
Brands & Products:
HI-BAR
INNOVATION IN MINIATURE
LEE
LEE CHEK
LEE FLOSERT
LEE FLOW CONTROL
LEE HYDAMP
LEE JELA
LEE JET
LEE KIPSTER
LEE MICRO DAMP
LEE MINSTAC
LEE PLUG
LEE RESTRICTOR CHEK
LEE SPIN JET
LEE TRI
LEEPRI
VISCO JET

LEICA CAMERA, INC.

(Sub. of Leica Camera AG)
1 Pearl Ct Unit A
Allendale, NJ 07401-1610
Tel.: (201) 995-0051
Fax: (201) 995-1686
Toll Free: (800) 222-0118
E-mail: literature@leicacamerausa.com
Web Site: www.leica-camera.com
Sales Range: $25-49.9 Million
Approx. Number Employees: 30
Business Description:
Distr of Cameras, Binoculars & Accessories
S.I.C.: 3827; 3861
N.A.I.C.S.: 333314; 333315
Media: 2
Personnel:
Roger Horn *(Pres)*
Christian Erhardt *(Dir-Mktg & Photo)*
Brands & Products:
LEICA M7
LICA
Advertising Agency:
Evins Communications, Ltd.
635 Madison Ave
New York, NY 10022-1009
Tel.: (212) 688-8200
Fax: (212) 935-6730
Pub Rels
— Karen Anslinger *(Acct Exec)*

LEICA GEOSYSTEMS GEOSPATIAL IMAGING, LLC

(Div. of Leica Geosystems AG)
5051 Peachtree Corner Cir Ste 250
Norcross, GA 30092
Tel.: (770) 447-6361
Fax: (770) 776-3500
E-mail: info@gi.leica-geosystems.com
Web Site: www.gi.leica-geosystems.com
Approx. Number Employees: 65
Business Description:
Developer of Image Processing & Digital Mapping Technologies
S.I.C.: 3829; 3827; 8713
N.A.I.C.S.: 334519; 333314; 541360
Advertising Agency:
Arketi Group
2801 Buford Hwy Druid Chase Ste 375
Atlanta, GA 30329
Tel.: (404) 929-0091
Fax: (404) 321-3397

LEICA MICROSYSTEMS, INC.

(Sub. of Leica Microsystems GmbH)
2345 Waukegan Rd
Bannockburn, IL 60015-1515
Tel.: (847) 405-0123
Fax: (847) 405-0147
Fax: (847) 405-0164
Toll Free: (800) 248-0123
E-mail: info@leica-microsystems.us
Web Site: www.leica-microsystems.us

Key to Media (For complete agency information see *The Advertising Red Books-Agencies* edition):
1. Bus. Publs. 2. Cable T.V. 3. Catalogs & Directories. 4. Co-op Adv. 5. Consumer Mags. 6. D.M. to Bus. Estab.7. D.M. to Consumers
8. Daily Newsp. 9. Exhibits/Trade Shows 10. Foreign 11. Infomercial 12. Internet Adv.13. Multimedia 14. Network Radio
15. Network T.V. 16. Newsp. Distr. Mags. 17. Other 18. Outdoor (Posters, Transit) 19. Point of Purchase20. Premiums, Novelties
21. Product Samples 22. Special Events Mktg. 23. Spot Radio 24. Spot T.V. 25. Weekly Newsp. 26. Yellow Page Adv.

Leica Microsystems, Inc. — (Continued)

Sales Range: $25-49.9 Million
Approx. Number Employees: 90
Year Founded: 1908
Business Description:
Microscopes & Scientific Instruments Mfr
S.I.C.: 3826; 3827
N.A.I.C.S.: 334516; 333314
Media: 1-2-4-7-10-13-20-22
Distr.: Natl.
Budget Set: Mar.
Personnel:
Sandre Prandmeier *(Pres)*
Art Giecek *(VP-HR)*
Donna Horowitz *(VP-HR)*

LENSCRAFTERS, INC.

(Sub. of Luxottica Retail)
4000 Luxottica Pl
Mason, OH 45040
Tel.: (513) 765-6000
Fax: (513) 765-6249
Web Site: www.lenscrafters.com
Sales Range: $800-899.9 Million
Approx. Number Employees: 14,000
Year Founded: 1983
Business Description:
Eyewear Retailer
S.I.C.: 5995; 3851
N.A.I.C.S.: 446130; 339115
Media: 3-4-6-8-9-13-15-24-25-26
Distr.: Direct to Consumer; Intl.; Natl.
Personnel:
Mark Weikel *(Pres & Gen Mgr)*
Kerry Bradley *(COO)*
Aubyn Elaine Thomas *(CMO-LensCrafters Retail North America & Sr VP)*
Tom Coleman *(Exec VP-Devel)*
Mildred Curtis *(Sr VP-HR)*
Brands & Products:
LENSCRAFTERS
OPEN YOUR EYES
Advertising Agencies:
Cutwater
55 Union St
San Francisco, CA 94111-1227
Tel.: (415) 315-4100
Fax: (415) 315-4200

Starcom MediaVest Group
35 W Wacker Dr
Chicago, IL 60601-1723
Tel.: (312) 220-3535
Fax: (312) 220-6530

LEUPOLD & STEVENS, INC.

14400 NW Greenbrier Pkwy
Beaverton, OR 97006-5790
Tel.: (503) 526-1400
Fax: (503) 526-1402
E-mail: info@leupold.com
Web Site: www.leupold.com
E-Mail For Key Personnel:
Marketing Director: mslack@leupold.com
Approx. Number Employees: 550
Year Founded: 1907
Business Description:
Scopes, Binoculars & Mounts Mfr
S.I.C.: 3827
N.A.I.C.S.: 333314
Import Export
Media: 2-4-6-7-8-10-20
Distr.: Intl.; Natl.
Budget Set: July
Personnel:
Calvin S. Johnston *(Pres & CEO)*
Howard D. Werth *(CFO)*
Mary Manning *(VP-HR & OD)*
Andrew York *(VP-Sls Mktg)*
Linda Haas *(Controller-Fin)*
Tim O'Connor *(Mgr-Law Enforcement Sls)*
Michael Slack *(Mktg Mgr)*
Tom Dubay *(Mgr-IT)*
LeRoy Nelson *(Mgr-Supply Chain Stategy & Svc Ops)*
Dave Sonsteng *(Mgr-Supply Chain)*
Carol Schmidlin *(Coord-Tactical Sls Ops & Tradeshow)*
Brands & Products:
AMERICA'S OPTICS AUTHORITY
CASCADE
CQ/T
DUAL DOVETAIL
GOLDEN RING
KATMAI
LEUPOLD
LPS
MARK
MARK 4
MESA
OLYMPIC
PINNACLE
QRW
RIFLEMAN
SCOPESMITH
SEQUOIA
STD
TIMBER HD
VARI-X
VX
WIDE DUPLEX
WIND RIVER
Advertising Agency:
Swanson Russell Associates
1222 P St
Lincoln, NE 68508-1425
Tel.: (402) 437-6400
Fax: (402) 437-6401
(Golden Ring Binoculars & Rifle Scopes)

LIFE TECHNOLOGIES

(Sub. of Life Technologies Corporation)
29851 Willow Creek Rd
Eugene, OR 97402
Tel.: (541) 465-8300
Fax: (541) 344-6504
Web Site: www.lifetechnologies.com
Sales Range: $25-49.9 Million
Approx. Number Employees: 300
Business Description:
Biological Detection Products
S.I.C.: 2836
N.A.I.C.S.: 325414
Media: 4-10
Personnel:
Murali Prahalad *(Gen Mgr-Cell Analysis Bus Unit)*

LIFETOUCH, INC.

11000 Viking Dr Ste 400 W
Eden Prairie, MN 55344-7294
Tel.: (952) 826-4000
Fax: (952) 826-4563
Toll Free: (800) 588-9151
Web Site: www.lifetouch.com
Sales Range: $200-249.9 Million
Approx. Number Employees: 500
Year Founded: 1936
Business Description:
Photographic Studios
S.I.C.: 7221
N.A.I.C.S.: 541921
Media: 3-5-6-8-9-10-11-13-18-19-20-22-23-24-25
Distr.: Direct to Consumer; Intl.; Natl.; Reg.
Budget Set: Jan.
Personnel:
Paul Harmel *(CEO)*
John McCormick *(CFO & Sr VP)*
Chad Zimmerman *(Sr Dir-Mktg)*
Brands & Products:
LIFETOUCH
PHOTOGRAPHY FOR A LIFETIME

LIGHTPATH TECHNOLOGIES INC

2603 Challenger Tech Ct Ste 100
Orlando, FL 32826
Tel.: (407) 382-4003
Fax: (407) 382-4007
Toll Free: (800) 472-3486
E-mail: info@lightpath.com
Web Site: www.lightpath.com
Approx. Sls.: $10,000,602
Approx. Number Employees: 200
Year Founded: 1992
Business Description:
Mfr of Optoelectronics
S.I.C.: 3674; 3357; 3661; 3679; 3827
N.A.I.C.S.: 334413; 333314; 334210; 334418; 334419; 335921
Advertising Expenditures: $2,000,000
Media: 2-4-7-10-13
Personnel:
Robert Ripp *(Chm)*
Joseph Gaynor *(Pres & CEO)*
Dorothy Cipolla *(CFO, Treas, Sec & Corp VP)*
Brian Soller *(VP-Bus Dev & Sls)*
Alan Symmons *(VP-Corp Engrg)*
Michael Lancaster *(Dir-Ops & Interim Gen Mgr-Ops-Shanghai)*
Brands & Products:
BLACK DIAMOND
CIRCULIGHT
DURAYAG
FUSION
GENS COLLIMATER
GRADIUM
LIGHTPATH TECHNOLOGIES
OASIS
TX

LOGETRONICS CORPORATION

(Div. of Amergraph Corporation)
6521 Arlington Blvd Ste 20
Falls Church, VA 22042
Tel.: (973) 383-8700
Fax: (703) 912-7610
E-mail: loge@erols.com
Web Site: www.logetronics.com
Sales Estimate: $20-39 Million
Approx. Number Employees: 20
Year Founded: 1955
Business Description:
Mfr. & Distributor of Graphic Arts Equipment
S.I.C.: 3861
N.A.I.C.S.: 333315
Import Export
Advertising Expenditures: $250,000
Media: 2-4-7-8-10-11-20
Distr.: Intl.; Natl.
Budget Set: Feb. -Mar.
Brands & Products:
CHEMAIRE
LOGE
LOGE-ON-LINE
LOGELINE
LOGETEK
MAXIM
SR-1000
SR-2000
SR-500
WATERMATE

LOWEL-LIGHT MANUFACTURING, INC.

(Div. of Tiffen Manufacturing Corp.)
(d/b/a The Tiffen Co.)
90 Oser Ave
Hauppauge, NY 11788
Tel.: (631) 273-2500
Fax: (631) 273-2557
Toll Free: (800) 645-2522
E-mail: info@lowel.com
Web Site: www.lowel.com
Year Founded: 1959
Business Description:
Photographic & Video Lighting Equipment Mfr
S.I.C.: 3648; 3861
N.A.I.C.S.: 335129; 333315
Media: 4-6-10
Personnel:
Marvin Seligman *(Pres)*
Brands & Products:
BIG-FOOT
BLIP-CLIP
BLIP-SET
BLIPS
CASELITE
CORE KITS
DP BRELLA
DP LIGHT
EGO
FIN-S
FLAG-LINK
FLEXI-SHAFT
FRAME-UP
GEL-JAWZ
GO KITS
HOLLYWOOD-STRIP
IR DMX CONTROLLER
IR DMX TRANSLATOR
L-LIGHT
LIGHT ARRAY
LIGHTFLECTOR
LITEBAGS
LOBO
LOWEL EGO
LOWEL GEL FILE
LOWEL I-LIGHT
LOWEL OMNI-SYSTEM
LOWEL RIFA EXCHANGE
LOWEL SOFTLIGHT 2
LOWEL TOTA-SYSTEM
LOWEL V-LIGHT
LOWELDIMMER
LOWELSCANDLES
MAXA-MOUNT
MISSING-LINK
OMNI-LIGHT
OMNI-SYSTEM
PRO-LIGHT
RIFA EXCHANGE
RIFA-LITE
TOTA-BRELLA
TOTA-DAPTOR
TOTA-FLAG
TOTA-FLECTOR

Key to Media (For complete agency information see *The Advertising Red Books-Agencies* edition):
1. Bus. Publs. 2. Cable T.V. 3. Catalogs & Directories. 4. Co-op Adv. 5. Consumer Mags. 6. D.M. to Bus. Estab.7. D.M. to Consumers 8. Daily Newsp. 9. Exhibits/Trade Shows 10. Foreign 11. Infomercial 12. Internet Adv.13. Multimedia 14. Network Radio 15. Network T.V. 16. Newsp. Distr. Mags. 17. Other 18. Outdoor (Posters, Transit) 19. Point of Purchase20. Premiums, Novelties 21. Product Samples 22. Special Events Mktg. 23. Spot Radio 24. Spot T.V. 25. Weekly Newsp. 26. Yellow Page Adv.

TOTA-LIGHT
TOTA-SHADE
TOTA-SYSTEM
TOTA-TATCH
V-LIGHT
VARIFLECTOR
VIP ID LIGHT
VIP SYSTEM

THE L.S. STARRETT COMPANY

121 Crescent St
Athol, MA 01331-1913
Tel.: (978) 249-3551
Fax: (978) 249-8495
E-mail: webmaster@starrett.com
Web Site: www.starrett.com
Approx. Sls.: $244,841,000
Approx. Number Employees: 1,951
Year Founded: 1880
Business Description:
Precision Measuring Tools, Steel Tapes, Electronic Gages, Dial Indicators, Gage Blocks & Digital Measuring Tools, Granite Surface Plates, Vises, Hacksaws, Hole Saws, Band Saws, Precision Ground Flat Stock
S.I.C.: 3545; 3423; 3829
N.A.I.C.S.: 333515; 332212; 334519
Export
Advertising Expenditures: $5,000,000
Media: 2-4-10
Distr.: Intl.; Natl.
Budget Set: July
Personnel:
Douglas A. Starrett *(Pres & CEO)*
Stephen F. Walsh *(Sr VP-Ops)*
Joel Shaughnessy *(Dir-Personnel)*
Roy Lake *(Asst Treas)*
Brands & Products:
ADVANZ
BI-METAL UNIQUE
CODE TAPE
CONTROLOK
DATASURE
DURATEC
GALILEO
HIDDEN EDGE
INTENSS
KING CUT
MASTER PRO
MEATKUTTER
PRESSURE POINT
PROSITE
QUADRA-CHECK
QUALITY PRECISION INNOVATION ... SINCE 1880
RADID-EIGHTHS
STA-TRUE
STARRETT
THIS IS THE SPLIT-CHIP ADVANTAGE
TOUGH TAPES
TRU-LOK
VERSATIX
WOODPECKER
WOODPECKER XF

LUMINEX CORPORATION

12212 Technology Blvd
Austin, TX 78727
Tel.: (512) 219-8020
Fax: (512) 219-5195
Toll Free: (888) 219-8020
E-mail: info@luminexcorp.com
Web Site: www.luminexcorp.com
Approx. Rev.: $141,557,000
Approx. Number Employees: 525
Business Description:
Mfr & Marketer Proprietary Biological Testing Technologies
S.I.C.: 8733; 3821; 3826; 3829
N.A.I.C.S.: 541710; 334516; 334519; 339111
Advertising Expenditures: $2,800,000
Personnel:
G. Walter Loewenbaum, II *(Chm)*
Patrick J. Balthrop, Sr. *(Pres & CEO)*
Harriss T. Currie *(CFO, Treas & VP-Fin)*
David S. Reiter *(Gen Counsel, Sec & VP)*
Jeremy Bridge Cook *(Sr VP)*
Michael F. Pintek *(Sr VP-Ops)*
Russell W. Bradley *(VP-Bus Dev & Strategic Plng)*
Darin Leigh *(VP-Sls & Mktg)*
Matthew D. Scalo *(Sr Dir-IR)*
Brands & Products:
FLEXMAP
FLEXMAP 3D
FLEXMIR
FLEXMIR MICRORNA
FLEXMIR SELECT
FLOWMETRIX
LUMAVIDIN
LUMINEX
LUMINEX 100
LUMINEX 100 IS
LUMINEX 200
LUMINEX HTS
LUMINEX IS
LUMINEX SD
LUMINEX XYP
MAGPLEX
MAGPLEX C
MICROPLEX
SEROMAP
XMAP
XPONENT
XTAG

LUNA IMAGING LTD.

2702 Media Center Dr
Los Angeles, CA 90065-1733
Tel.: (323) 908-1400
Fax: (323) 908-1441
Toll Free: (800) 452-LUNA
E-mail: contact@luna-img.com
Web Site: www.lunaimaging.com
Business Description:
Digital Imaging
S.I.C.: 2759
N.A.I.C.S.: 323115
Media: 10
Personnel:
David Rumsey *(Chm)*
Marlo Lee *(CEO)*
Nancy Harm *(Dir-Bus Dev)*

MAGELLAN NAVIGATION, INC.

(Holding of Shah Capital Partners, LP)
960 Overland Ct
San Dimas, CA 91773
Tel.: (909) 394-5000
Fax: (909) 394-7050
Web Site: www.magellangps.com
Approx. Number Employees: 635
Business Description:
Global Satellite Positioning, Navigation & Guidance Equipment
S.I.C.: 3812; 3829
N.A.I.C.S.: 334511; 334519
Media: 10
Personnel:
Christian Bubenheim *(VP-Consumer Product Mktg)*
Raphel Finelli *(Sr Mgr-Pub Rel)*
Brands & Products:
MAGELLAN
MAGELLAN EXPLORIST
MAGELLAN PROMARK
MAGELLAN ROADMATE
MAGELLAN SAYWHERE
MAGELLAN SMARTDETOUR
MAGELLAN TRAFFICKIT

MAGNETIC ANALYSIS CORPORATION

103 Fairview Pk Dr
Elmsford, NY 10523
Tel.: (914) 699-9450
Fax: (914) 699-9837
Toll Free: (800) 4ND-TMAC
E-mail: info@mac-ndt.com
Web Site: www.mac-ndt.com
Sales Range: $25-49.9 Million
Approx. Number Employees: 130
Year Founded: 1928
Business Description:
Mfr of Electro-Magnetic Testing Equipment & Ultrasonic Instrumentation
S.I.C.: 3829; 3825
N.A.I.C.S.: 334519; 334515
Export
Media: 2-4-7-10-11-13
Distr.: Intl.; Natl.
Budget Set: Nov.
Personnel:
William S. Gould, III *(Chm & Pres)*
Donald Bugden *(VP-Mktg)*
Goran Malmberg *(Mgr-Plant)*
Brands & Products:
AUTOSORT
ECHOMAC
ERIC
MAC SERIES
MINIMAC
PROMAC
ROTOFLUX
ROTOMAC
VARIMAC
Advertising Agency:
Catalyst Marketing Communications Inc.
2777 Summer St Ste 301
Stamford, CT 06905
Tel.: (203) 348-7541
Fax: (203) 348-5688
(Non-Destructive Testing Equipment)
— Charles Wintrub *(Pres.)*

MAGNETICS

(Div. of Spang & Company)
110 Delta Dr
Pittsburgh, PA 15238
Mailing Address:
PO Box 11422
Pittsburgh, PA 15238-0422
Tel.: (412) 696-1333
Fax: (412) 696-0333
Toll Free: (800) 245-3984
E-mail: magnetics@spang.com
Web Site: www.mag-inc.com
Approx. Number Employees: 60
Year Founded: 1949
Business Description:
Mfr. of a Broad Range of Magnetic Cores
S.I.C.: 3544; 5065
N.A.I.C.S.: 333511; 423690
Import Export
Media: 4-10-13
Personnel:
Thomas Watson *(Pres)*
Bruce W. Mitchell *(VP-Engrng)*
Brands & Products:
KOOLMU E CORES
MAGNETICS
MPP THINZ

MAGNIVISION INC.

(Sub. of AAi.FosterGrant, Inc.)
500 Washington Hwy
Smithfield, RI 02917-1926
Mailing Address:
PO Box 835588
Hollywood, FL 33083
Tel.: (954) 450-3242
Fax: (954) 986-3814
Toll Free: (800) 237-4231
Web Site: www.magnivision.com
Approx. Number Employees: 200
Year Founded: 1993
Business Description:
Sales of Ophthalmic Goods & Reading Glasses
S.I.C.: 5048; 3851
N.A.I.C.S.: 423460; 339115
Personnel:
Jack Flynn *(Pres)*
Advertising Agency:
Duffy & Shanley, Inc.
10 Charles St
Providence, RI 02904
Tel.: (401) 274-0001
Fax: (401) 274-3535

MARCHON EYEWEAR, INC.

(Sub. of Vision Service Plan)
35 Hub Dr
Melville, NY 11747
Tel.: (631) 755-2020
Fax: (631) 755-2491
Toll Free: (800) 645-1300
E-mail: CS@marchon.com
Web Site: www.marchon.com
Approx. Rev.: $525,000,000
Approx. Number Employees: 1,500
Year Founded: 1983
Business Description:
Eyewear & Sunwear Designer & Distr
S.I.C.: 5048
N.A.I.C.S.: 423460
Export
Advertising Expenditures: $17,000,000
Media: 2-3-4-5-6-7-8-10-13-18-19-20-22-24
Distr.: Intl.; Natl.
Personnel:
Al Berg *(Vice Chm)*
Claudio Gottardi *(Pres & CEO-Intl)*
Larry Roth *(Co-Pres)*
Len LaSalandra *(CFO & Sr VP)*
Marty Fox *(COO)*
Jelena Halliburton *(Brand Mgr-Americas & Asia)*
Brands & Products:
AIRLOCK
CHECK YEARLY SEE CLEARLY
FLEXON
MARCHON
OFFICEMATE

MARCOLIN USA INC.

(Sub. of Marcolin S.p.A.)
7543 E Tierra Buena Ln

Key to Media (For complete agency information see *The Advertising Red Books-Agencies* edition):
1. Bus. Publs. 2. Cable T.V. 3. Catalogs & Directories. 4. Co-op Adv. 5. Consumer Mags. 6. D.M. to Bus. Estab.7. D.M. to Consumers 8. Daily Newsp. 9. Exhibits/Trade Shows 10. Foreign 11. Infomercial 12. Internet Adv.13. Multimedia 14. Network Radio 15. Network T.V. 16. Newsp. Distr. Mags. 17. Other 18. Outdoor (Posters, Transit) 19. Point of Purchase20. Premiums, Novelties 21. Product Samples 22. Special Events Mktg. 23. Spot Radio 24. Spot T.V. 25. Weekly Newsp. 26. Yellow Page Adv.

Marcolin USA Inc. — (Continued)

Scottsdale, AZ 85260
Tel.: (480) 951-7174
Fax: (480) 951-8052
E-mail: info@marcolin.com
Web Site: www.marcolinusa.com
Approx. Number Employees: 2
Business Description:
Frames, Ophthalmic
S.I.C.: 5048
N.A.I.C.S.: 423460
Media: 6
Personnel:
Joe Ivans *(CFO)*

MATEC INSTRUMENT COMPANIES, INC.

56 Hudson St
Northborough, MA 01532-1922
Tel.: (508) 393-0155
Fax: (508) 393-5476
E-mail: sales@matec.com
Web Site: www.matec.com
E-Mail For Key Personnel:
Sales Director: sales@matec.com
Sales Range: $10-24.9 Million
Approx. Number Employees: 30
Year Founded: 1968
Business Description:
Holding Company; Ultrasonic Quality Control Inspection & Production Testing Equipment Mfr
S.I.C.: 6719; 3699; 3823; 3825
N.A.I.C.S.: 551112; 334513; 334515; 335999
Import Export
Advertising Expenditures: $200,000
Media: 2-4-5-7-10-21
Distr.: Intl.; Natl.
Budget Set: Nov.
Personnel:
Kenneth C. Bishop *(Pres)*
Gene A. Murray *(CFO & Treas)*
Brands & Products:
MATEC

MCNAB, INC.

383-2 E 29th St
Buena Vista, VA 24416
Tel.: (914) 699-1616
Fax: (540) 261-1268
E-mail: info@themcnab.com
Web Site: www.themcnab.com
Sales Range: $10-24.9 Million
Approx. Number Employees: 25
Year Founded: 1909
Business Description:
Conductivity & Resistance Measuring Instruments Mfr
S.I.C.: 3823; 3812
N.A.I.C.S.: 334513; 334511
Media: 2-4-7-10-17
Distr.: Natl.
Personnel:
H.A. Teass, Jr. *(Pres)*
Garnette S. Teass *(Controller)*

MEADE INSTRUMENTS CORPORATION

27 Hubble
Irvine, CA 92618
Tel.: (949) 451-1450
Fax: (949) 451-1460
Web Site: www.meade.com
Approx. Sls.: $26,340,000
Approx. Number Employees: 155
Year Founded: 1972
Business Description:
Designer, Mfr, Importer & Distr of Telescopes, Telescope Accessories, Binoculars, Microscopes & Riflescopes
S.I.C.: 3827; 5049
N.A.I.C.S.: 333314; 423490
Advertising Expenditures: $300,000
Media: 4-5-6-10-13-19-23-24
Personnel:
Timothy C. McQuay *(Chm)*
Steven G. Murdock *(CEO)*
John A. Elwood *(CFO, Sr VP-Fin & Admin)*
Greg Bragg *(VP-Sls & Specialty Channel)*
Brands & Products:
ACF
ADVANCED COMA- FREE
ASTRO
AUTOALIGN
AUTOSTAR
AUTOSTAR SUITE
CAPTUREVIEW
CORONADO
DEEP SKY IMAGER
DEEP SKY IMAGER II
DEEP SKY IMAGER III
DEEP SKY IMAGER PRO
DS-2OOO
EASYVIEW
ETX
ETX-70AT
ETX PREMIER
ETX SPOTTING SCOPE
FLASHBACK
GLACIER
KESTREL
LIGHTBRIDGE
LUNAR PLANETARY IMAGER
LX200
LX90
LXD55
LXD75
MAGELLAN I
MAGELLAN II
MAX MOUNT
MEADE
MEADE DS-2114ATS-LNT
MONTANA
MYSKY PLUS
NIGHTVIEW
#497 AUTOSTAR
PICTOR-XT
RCX400
SERIES 4000
SERIES 5000
SMART DRIVE
STARFINDER
STARNAVIGATOR
TELESTAR
TRAVEL
TRAVELVIEW
UHTC

MECHANICAL TECHNOLOGY, INCORPORATED

431 New Karner Rd
Albany, NY 12205
Tel.: (518) 533-2200
Fax: (518) 533-2223
Toll Free: (800) 828-8210
E-mail: contact@mechtech.com
Web Site: www.mechtech.com
Approx. Rev.: $8,413,000
Approx. Number Employees: 51
Year Founded: 1961
Business Description:
Direct Methanol Micro Fuel Cell Power Systems Developer & Commercializer; Test & Measurement Instruments & Systems Designer, Mfr & Retailer
S.I.C.: 3829; 3824; 8733
N.A.I.C.S.: 334519; 334514; 541710
Export
Advertising Expenditures: $102,000
Media: 2-5-10-13
Distr.: Intl.
Budget Set: Aug.
Personnel:
Peng K. Lim *(Chm & CEO)*
Rick Jones *(CFO)*
Jim Prueitt *(VP-Engrg & Ops-MTI MicroFuel Cells)*
James Frawley *(Dir-Bus Dev)*
Brands & Products:
ACCUMEASURE
FOTONIC
MECHANICAL TECHNOLOGY
MICROTRAK
MTI
PROFORMA
Advertising Agency:
Eric Mower and Associates
41 State St Ste 500
Albany, NY 12207-2834
Tel.: (518) 462-0318
Fax: (518) 462-0688

MEDTOX SCIENTIFIC, INC.

402 W County Rd D
Saint Paul, MN 55112-3522
Tel.: (651) 636-7466
Fax: (651) 636-5351
Toll Free: (800) 832-3244
E-mail: webmaster@medtox.com
Web Site: www.medtox.com
Approx. Rev.: $97,101,000
Approx. Number Employees: 633
Year Founded: 1984
Business Description:
Laboratory Services & Onsite Point of Collection Devices
S.I.C.: 8071; 2834; 8734
N.A.I.C.S.: 621511; 325412; 541380
Media: 10
Personnel:
Richard J. Braun *(Chm, Pres & CEO)*
Kevin J. Wiersma *(CFO, Chief Admin Officer & VP)*
James A. Schoonover *(CMO & VP-Sls & Mktg)*
Brands & Products:
DARS
EZ-SCREEN
MEDTOX
PROFILE
SURE-SCREEN
VERDICT
WEBTOX

MEGGER INC.

(Div. of TBG Holdings NV)
Megger Vly Forge Corporate Ctr 2621 Van Buren Ave
Norristown, PA 19403
Tel.: (610) 676-8500
Fax: (610) 676-8625
Toll Free: (800) 723-2861
E-mail: vfcustomerservice@megger.com
Web Site: www.megger.com
Approx. Number Employees: 100
Year Founded: 1895
Business Description:
Mfr. of Electrical Testing & Precision Measuring Instruments & Systems
S.I.C.: 3825; 7629
N.A.I.C.S.: 334515; 811219
Advertising Expenditures: $250,000
Media: 1-2-4-5-7-10-20-26
Distr.: Intl.; Natl.
Budget Set: Mar.
Personnel:
Gary Guthrie *(Dir-Mktg)*
Peg Houck *(Mgr-Mktg)*
Brands & Products:
APIEZON
DLRO
MEGGER
TTR
VERSA-CAL
VERSAPOT

MELA SCIENCES, INC.

(Formerly Electro-Optical Sciences, Inc.)
50 S Buckhout St Ste 1
Irvington, NY 10533
Tel.: (914) 591-3783
Fax: (914) 591-3785
E-mail: info@melasciences.com
Web Site: www.melasciences.com
Approx. Number Employees: 42
Business Description:
Hand-Held Medical Devices Mfr
S.I.C.: 3841
N.A.I.C.S.: 339112
Advertising Expenditures: $57,000
Media: 7
Personnel:
Breaux B. Castleman *(Chm)*
Joseph V. Gulfo *(Pres & CEO)*
Richard I. Steinhart *(CFO, Treas & VP-Fin)*
Brands & Products:
MELAFIND

MERIDIAN BIOSCIENCE INC.

3471 River Hills Dr
Cincinnati, OH 45244-3023
Tel.: (513) 271-3700
Fax: (513) 271-3762
Toll Free: (800) 696-0739
E-mail: mbi@meridianbioscience.com
Web Site: www.meridianbioscience.com
Approx. Sls.: $143,000,000
Approx. Number Employees: 498
Year Founded: 1977
Business Description:
Diagnostic Test Kits, Purified Reagents & Related Products, Enabling Early Diagnosis & Treatment of Gastrointestinal, Viral, Urinary Tract & Respiratory Infections Mfr., Developer & Marketer
S.I.C.: 2834; 3841
N.A.I.C.S.: 325412; 339112
Import Export
Advertising Expenditures: $222,000
Media: 2-4-7-10-20
Personnel:
William J. Motto *(Chm)*
John A. Kraeutler *(CEO)*
Melissa A. Lueke *(CFO & Exec VP)*
Richard L. Eberly *(Pres-Meridian Life Science & Exec VP)*
Lawrence J. Baldini *(Exec VP-Ops & Info Sys)*

Key to Media (For complete agency information see *The Advertising Red Books-Agencies* edition):
1. Bus. Publs. 2. Cable T.V. 3. Catalogs & Directories. 4. Co-op Adv. 5. Consumer Mags. 6. D.M. to Bus. Estab.7. D.M. to Consumers 8. Daily Newsp. 9. Exhibits/Trade Shows 10. Foreign 11. Infomercial 12. Internet Adv.13. Multimedia 14. Network Radio 15. Network T.V. 16. Newsp. Distr. Mags. 17. Other 18. Outdoor (Posters, Transit) 19. Point of Purchase20. Premiums, Novelties 21. Product Samples 22. Special Events Mktg. 23. Spot Radio 24. Spot T.V. 25. Weekly Newsp. 26. Yellow Page Adv.

Susan D. Rolih *(Sr VP-Regulatory Affairs & Quality Assurance)*
Marviette Dale *(VP-HR)*
Slava A. Elagin *(VP-Res & Product Dev)*

Brands & Products:
ADENOCLONE
CALAS
HPSA
IMMUNOCARD
IMMUNOCARD STAT!
MACRO-CON
MERIDIAN
MERIFLUOR
MERISTAR
MERITEC
MONOLERT
MONOSPOT
PARAPAK
PREMIER
PREMIER PLATINUM
ROTACLONE

M.H. RHODES, INC.
(Sub. of Capewell Components Company, L.P.)
105 Nutmeg Rd S
South Windsor, CT 06074
Tel.: (860) 291-8402
Fax: (860) 610-0897
Toll Free: (800) 548-4637
E-mail: customer_service@mhrhodes.com
Web Site: www.mhrhodes.com
Year Founded: 1930
Business Description:
Mechanical Timers & Switches Mfr
S.I.C.: 3823; 3674
N.A.I.C.S.: 334513; 334413
Import Export
Advertising Expenditures: $300,000
Media: 2-7-10-26
Distr.: Natl.
Budget Set: Dec.
Personnel:
Deborah Sage *(Mgr-Mktg)*

Brands & Products:
MARK TIME

MICRO THERAPEUTICS, INC.
(Name Changed to ev3 Inc.)

MICROAIRE SURGICAL INSTRUMENTS INC.
(Sub. of Colson Associates, Inc.)
1641 Edlich Dr
Charlottesville, VA 22911
Tel.: (434) 975-8000
Fax: (800) 648-4309
Toll Free: (800) 722-0822
E-mail: info@microaire.com
Web Site: www.microaire.com
Approx. Number Employees: 125
Year Founded: 1976
Business Description:
Surgical & Medical Instruments Mfr
S.I.C.: 3841; 3842
N.A.I.C.S.: 339112; 339113
Media: 2-4-10
Personnel:
George Saiz *(Pres)*

Brands & Products:
EPICUT
FOR SURGERY. FOR LIFE.
MICROAIRE
PAL

MICROLAB
(Sub. of Wireless Telecom Group, Inc.)
25 Eastmans Rd
Parsippany, NJ 07054
Tel.: (973) 386-9696
Fax: (973) 386-9191
E-mail: sales@microlab.fxr.com
Web Site: www.microlab.fxr.com
E-Mail For Key Personnel:
Sales Director: sales@microlab.fxr.com
Sales Range: $1-9.9 Million
Approx. Number Employees: 50
Year Founded: 1950
Business Description:
Microwave Components & Instruments
S.I.C.: 7389
N.A.I.C.S.: 561499
Import Export
Media: 2-4-8-9-10-20
Distr.: Natl.
Budget Set: Dec.
Personnel:
Anthony Ramsden *(Pres)*

Brands & Products:
CA-14
CF-N
CK-10N
D2-51FN
D2-65FN
DK-N
DX-64FN
SUPERSCOUT
TA WIRELESS

MICROSCAN SYSTEMS INC.
(Formerly Siemens Energy & Automation)
(Sub. of Spectris Plc)
486 Amherst St
Nashua, NH 03063
Tel.: (603) 598-8400
Fax: (781) 828-8942
Web Site: microscan.com
Sales Range: $10-24.9 Million
Approx. Number Employees: 100
Year Founded: 1968
Business Description:
Mfr of Machine Vision Sensors & Equipment for Automated Identification of Bar Codes
S.I.C.: 3577; 3827
N.A.I.C.S.: 334119; 333314
Import Export
Media: 1-2-4-7-10
Distr.: Intl.; Natl.
Personnel:
John Adapakis *(VP-Sls & Mktg)*

Brands & Products:
DATA MATRIX
DMX AUTOID +
DMX AUTOID + EXPRESS
HAWKEYE
MX-700
MXI
VIAL READER 4000

MILLIPORE CORPORATION
(Sub. of Merck KGaA)
290 Concord Rd
Billerica, MA 01821
Tel.: (978) 715-4321
Fax: (781) 533-3110
Toll Free: (800) 225-3384
Toll Free: (800) 645-5476
E-mail: tech_service@millipore.com
Web Site: www.millipore.com
Approx. Rev.: $1,654,410,000
Approx. Number Employees: 6,100
Year Founded: 1954
Business Description:
Markets Products & Systems Incorporating Synthetic Membrane Filters & Chromatographic Media for the Purification & Analysis of Fluids & Gases
S.I.C.: 3826; 2836
N.A.I.C.S.: 334516; 325414
Import Export
Advertising Expenditures: $1,500,000
Media: 3-4-6-8-10-21
Distr.: Intl.; Natl.
Budget Set: Nov.
Personnel:
Anthony L. Mattacchione *(Chief Acctg Officer, VP & Corp Controller)*
Jean Paul Mangeolle *(Pres-Bioprocess Div & VP)*
David P. Hutchinson *(Gen Counsel)*
John Sweeney *(VP-Life Science Bus Unit)*
Roy Millender *(Dir-Tech Transfer)*
Joshua Young *(Dir-IR)*

Brands & Products:

Buyer Advertising, Inc.
189 Wells Ave 2nd Fl
Newton, MA 02459
Tel.: (617) 969-4646
Fax: (617) 969-6807

Captains of Industry
21 Union St
Boston, MA 02108
Tel.: (617) 725-1959
Fax: (617) 725-0089
Millipore Blot Race Viral

Warner Communications
41 Raymond St
Manchester, MA 01944
Tel.: (978) 526-1960
Fax: (978) 526-8206

MYSTIC COLOR LAB, INC.
(Sub. of District Photo Inc.)
10619 Baltimore Ave
Beltsville, MD 20705
Mailing Address:
PO Box 144
Mystic, CT 06355-0144
Tel.: (301) 937-5300
Fax: (301) 937-5627
Toll Free: (800) 367-6061
E-mail: cservice@mysticcolorlab.com
Web Site: www.districtphoto.com
Approx. Number Employees: 800
Year Founded: 1969
Business Description:
Online Photofinishing Services
S.I.C.: 7384; 5043; 5961
N.A.I.C.S.: 812921; 423410; 454113
Advertising Expenditures: $200,000
Media: 6-8-13-26
Distr.: Natl.

NANOMETRICS INCORPORATED
1550 Buckeye Dr
Milpitas, CA 95035-7418
Tel.: (408) 435-9600
Fax: (408) 232-5910
Toll Free: (800) 955-6266
E-mail: contact@nanometrics.com
Web Site: www.nanometrics.com
Approx. Rev.: $188,065,000
Approx. Number Employees: 456
Year Founded: 1975
Business Description:
High-Performance Process Control Metrology Systems Designer & Mfr
S.I.C.: 3824; 3559; 3823; 7629
N.A.I.C.S.: 334514; 333295; 334513; 811219
Import Export
Advertising Expenditures: $100,000
Media: 2-7-10-13-20
Personnel:
Timothy J. Stultz *(Pres & CEO)*
Ronald W. Kisling *(CFO)*
Bruce A. Crawford *(COO)*

Brands & Products:
CALIPER ELAN
CALIPER MOSAIC
HL 5500
IMPULSE
IVS 185
NANOCD
NANOMETRICS
NANOMETRICS ATLAS
NANOMETRICS ATLAS-M
NANOMETRICS ATLAS XP
NANOMETRICS FLX
NANOMETRICS LYNX
NANOOCD 9010M
NANOSPEC
NANOSPEC 3000
NANOSPEC 6100
NANOSPEC 9200
NANOUDI
NANOUDI 9300
PREDICTIVE METRICS FOR THE NANO WORLD
Q240AT
QS-FRS
QS1200
QS2200
QS3300
RPM2000
SIPHER
STRATUS
TRAJECTORY
VEKTOR
VERTEX

NATIONAL VISION, INC.
(Holding of Berkshire Partners LLC)
296 Grayson Hwy
Lawrenceville, GA 30045
Tel.: (770) 822-3600
Fax: (770) 822-2027
Fax: (770) 822-3601
Toll Free: (800) 571-5020
E-mail: nve@nationalvision.com
Web Site: www.nationalvision.com
Sales Range: $200-249.9 Million
Approx. Number Employees: 1,913
Year Founded: 1990
Business Description:
Retail Optical Company
S.I.C.: 5995; 5961
N.A.I.C.S.: 446130; 454111; 454113
Media: 23-24
Distr.: Natl.
Personnel:
J. Bruce Steffey *(COO & Exec VP)*
Paul Gross *(Sr VP-Mktg)*
Billie Ackerman *(Dir-Mktg)*
Stacey Abler *(Mgr-Digital Mktg)*

Advertising Agency:
Robin Shepherd Group
500 Bishopgate Ln

Key to Media (For complete agency information see *The Advertising Red Books-Agencies* edition):
1. Bus. Publs. 2. Cable T.V. 3. Catalogs & Directories. 4. Co-op Adv. 5. Consumer Mags. 6. D.M. to Bus. Estab.7. D.M. to Consumers
8. Daily Newsp. 9. Exhibits/Trade Shows 10. Foreign 11. Infomercial 12. Internet Adv.13. Multimedia 14. Network Radio
15. Network T.V. 16. Newsp. Distr. Mags. 17. Other 18. Outdoor (Posters, Transit) 19. Point of Purchase20. Premiums, Novelties
21. Product Samples 22. Special Events Mktg. 23. Spot Radio 24. Spot T.V. 25. Weekly Newsp. 26. Yellow Page Adv.

National Vision, Inc. — (Continued)

Jacksonville, FL 32204-4111
Tel.: (904) 359-0981
Fax: (904) 359-0808

NDC INFRARED ENGINEERING INC.

(Sub. of Spectris Plc)
5314 N Irwindale Ave
Irwindale, CA 91706-2089
Tel.: (626) 960-3300
Fax: (626) 939-3870
E-mail: info@ndcinfrared.com
Web Site: www.ndcinfrared.com
Approx. Number Employees: 85
Year Founded: 1998
Business Description:
Measurement, Control & Laboratory Analysis Devices Wholesaler
S.I.C.: 3823; 3829
N.A.I.C.S.: 334513; 334519
Media: 10
Personnel:
Bromley Beadle *(Pres)*
Hector Marchandt *(Dir-Mktg)*

NEW BRUNSWICK SCIENTIFIC CO., INC.

(Sub. of Eppendorf AG)
44 Talmadge Rd
Edison, NJ 08817-3319
Mailing Address:
PO Box 4005
Edison, NJ 08818-4005
Tel.: (732) 287-1200
Fax: (732) 287-4222
Toll Free: (800) 631-5417
E-mail: bioinfo@nbsc.com
Web Site: www.nbsc.com
Approx. Sls.: $75,460,000
Approx. Number Employees: 437
Year Founded: 1946
Business Description:
Designer, Mfr & Marketer of High-Technology Equipment & Instruments for Research & Development to Produce Therapeutic Drugs, Enzymes, Biochemicals, Antibiotics, Vaccines & Other Biological Products
S.I.C.: 3821
N.A.I.C.S.: 339111
Import Export
Media: 1-2-4-7-10-11-13-17-20
Distr.: Intl.; Natl.
Budget Set: Oct.
Personnel:
James T. Orcutt *(Pres & CEO)*
Thomas E. Bocchino *(CFO)*
Suzy Kedzierski *(Mgr-Mktg Comm)*
Brands & Products:
AFS BIOCOMMAND
AGAR MATIC
BIOCOMMAND
BIOFLO
CELLIGEN PLUS
DIOGENESIS
FIBRACEL
GYROTORY
INNOVA
NUCLEOCASSETTE
NUCLEOCOUNTER
POUR MATIC
SPINNER BASKET

NEW WAVE RESEARCH INCORPORATED

(Sub. of Electro Scientific Industries, Inc.)
48660 Kato Rd
Fremont, CA 94538
Tel.: (510) 249-1550
Fax: (510) 249-1551
Toll Free: (800) 566-1743
Sales Range: $25-49.9 Million
Approx. Number Employees: 150
Business Description:
Laser Systems & Equipment Mfr
S.I.C.: 3699
N.A.I.C.S.: 335999
Media: 10
Personnel:
Pei Hsien Fang *(CEO)*
Brands & Products:
LASERMILL
NEW WAVE

NEWPORT CORPORATION

1791 Deere Ave
Irvine, CA 92606
Mailing Address:
PO Box 19607
Irvine, CA 92623-9607
Tel.: (949) 863-3144
Fax: (949) 253-1680
Toll Free: (800) 222-6440
Telex: 685-535 NRC FNVY
E-mail: info@newport.com
Web Site: www.newport.com
Approx. Sls.: $479,787,000
Approx. Number Employees: 1,745
Year Founded: 1969
Business Description:
Vibration Control Products, Precision Instruments, Laser Optics & Mechanical Components Mfr
S.I.C.: 3821; 3699; 3827
N.A.I.C.S.: 339111; 333314; 335999
Import Export
Advertising Expenditures: $3,100,000
Media: 4-10-13
Personnel:
Kenneth F. Potashner *(Chm)*
Robert J. Phillippy *(Pres & CEO)*
Charles F. Cargile *(CFO, Treas & Sr VP)*
Gary R. Reischlein *(CIO & VP)*
Jeffrey B. Coyne *(Gen Counsel)*
David J. Allen *(VP & Gen Mgr-Lasers Div)*
Lawrence D. Parson *(VP & Gen Mgr-Integrated Solutions Div)*
Ellen M. McGuirk *(VP-Corp Mktg-Worldwide)*
Gary Spiegel *(VP-Sls, Mktg & Bus Dev)*
Dan Crowley *(Dir-Sls)*
James Fisher *(Dir-Vibration Control)*
Brands & Products:
760 Series
841-PE
AEGIS QUBE
AGILIS
AUTOALIGN
BALLDRIVER
BENCHTOP
CYAN
DATASTAR
DYNAMYX
DYNAMYX 300
ELITE
ELITE 3
EVIS
EXCELSIOR
FABFLOOR
HYBRYX
ILS SERIES
INSTASPEC
INTEGRA
KEVLAR
LABASIX
LABLEGS
LAMBDA COMMANDER
LASERWELD
LIGHT SHAPING DIFFUSERS
LINESPEC
LOA
MERCURY-SC
MOPO
MS257
NAVIGATOR
NEWDAMP
NEWPORT
NEWPORT AUTOALIGN
OPM
OPTICAL TABLES FEATURING IQ
ORIEL CORNERSTONE
ORIEL GOLDILUX
ORIEL LINESPEC
ORIEL MERLIN
ORIEL MIR8025
ORION
OSM SERIES
OSP-9500
OTS
PANTERA
PCS
PERFORMA
PERFORMIX
PINHOLEFREE
POLARIS
POLARIS ULTRA
PV ISOSTATION
QUANTA RAY
ROI
RPR RELIANCE
S-2000 STABILIZER
SLIMLINE
SMARTTABLE
STABILIFE
SUPER INVAR
SUPERCAVITY
SUPREMA
TOPAS
TSUNAMI
ULTIMA
ULTRALIGN
V-XTREME
VALUMAX
VANGUARD
VH ISOSTATION

NEWPORT ELECTRONICS, INC.

(Affil. of OMEGA Engineering, Inc.)
2229 S Yale St
Santa Ana, CA 92704-4401
Tel.: (714) 540-4914
Fax: (714) 546-3022
Toll Free: (800) NEWPORT
E-mail: info@newportus.com
Web Site: www.newportusa.com
Approx. Number Employees: 100
Year Founded: 1965
Business Description:
Mfr of High-Technology Digital Measurement Instrumentation
S.I.C.: 3823; 3829
N.A.I.C.S.: 334513; 334519
Import Export
Media: 2-3-4-7-8-10
Distr.: Intl.; Natl.
Budget Set: Nov. -Dec.

NIKON AMERICAS INC.

(Sub. of Nikon Corporation)
1300 Walt Whitman Rd
Melville, NY 11747-3064
Tel.: (631) 547-4200
Fax: (631) 547-0299
Web Site: www.nikonusa.com
Approx. Number Employees: 250
Business Description:
Cameras, Lenses, Accessories, Binoculars, Optical Equipment, Riflescopes, Spotting Scopes & Electronic Imaging Products Wholesale Distr
S.I.C.: 5043; 5049
N.A.I.C.S.: 423410; 423490
Import
Media: 3-4-5-6-13-18-19-20-23
Distr.: Natl.
Personnel:
N. Gokyo *(Pres & CEO)*
Bill Pekala *(Gen Mgr-Nikon Prof Svcs)*
Bill Giordano *(Dir-Mktg)*
Brands & Products:
COOLPIX
COOLSCAN 4000
COOLSCAN 8000
COOLSCAN IX
D40
DIH-PRO-SLR DIGITAL
DIX-PRO-SLR DIGITAL
ECLIPSE
ECLIPSE T 100
FM3A MANUAL
LITE-TOUCH ZOOM 140
MIKRON
N65 SLR
N80 SLR
NEXIV
NIKKOR
NIKON LITE EFFORT
NIKON V-20B
NIKONOS
NIKONOS RS
NUVIS S 2000
PRONEA 6 I
RETINOMAX
SOLTES CP I
SOLTES CP II
Advertising Agencies:
McCann Erickson/New York
622 3rd Ave
New York, NY 10017
Tel.: (646) 865-2000
Fax: (646) 487-9610
D40 Cameras

MRM Worldwide
622 3rd Ave
New York, NY 10017-6707
Tel.: (646) 865-6230
Fax: (646) 865-6264

NORTH ATLANTIC INDUSTRIES INC.

110 Wilbur Pl
Bohemia, NY 11716
Tel.: (631) 567-1100
Fax: (631) 567-1823
E-mail: sales@naii.com
Web Site: www.naii.com
E-Mail For Key Personnel:
Sales Director: sales@naii.com

Key to Media (For complete agency information see *The Advertising Red Books-Agencies* edition):
1. Bus. Publs. 2. Cable T.V. 3. Catalogs & Directories. 4. Co-op Adv. 5. Consumer Mags. 6. D.M. to Bus. Estab.7. D.M. to Consumers
8. Daily Newsp. 9. Exhibits/Trade Shows 10. Foreign 11. Infomercial 12. Internet Adv.13. Multimedia 14. Network Radio
15. Network T.V. 16. Newsp. Distr. Mags. 17. Other 18. Outdoor (Posters, Transit) 19. Point of Purchase20. Premiums, Novelties
21. Product Samples 22. Special Events Mktg. 23. Spot Radio 24. Spot T.V. 25. Weekly Newsp. 26. Yellow Page Adv.

Approx. Sls.: $10,000,000
Approx. Number Employees: 110
Business Description:
Instruments to Measure Electricity & Testing Equiment
S.I.C.: 3825; 3829
N.A.I.C.S.: 334515; 334519
Media: 10
Personnel:
William Forman *(Pres & CEO)*
Lino Massafra *(VP-Sls & Mktg)*

NORTHROP GRUMMAN INFORMATION TECHNOLOGY, INC.
(Div. of Northrop Grumman Corporation)
(d/b/a Northrop Grumman Information Systems)
7575 Colshire Dr
McLean, VA 22102
Tel.: (703) 556-1000
Tel.: (703) 556-1144 (Civil/Defense)
Web Site:
www.is.northropgrumman.com
Sales Range: $5-14.9 Billion
Approx. Number Employees: 18,500
Year Founded: 1939
Business Description:
Communications & Engineering Systems
S.I.C.: 7373; 8711
N.A.I.C.S.: 541512; 541330
Media: 10
Personnel:
Nigel Essenhigh *(CEO)*
Stephen C. Movius *(VP-Bus Mgmt & CFO)*
Dave Nastase *(VP & CIO)*
Linda A. Mills *(Pres-Northrop Grumman Info Sys & Corp VP)*
Roger U. Fujii *(Sr VP-Network Comm Div)*
James M. Myers *(VP & Gen Mgr-Civil Sys Div)*
Barry L. Rhine *(VP & Gen Mgr-Defense Sys Div)*
Kathy Warden *(VP & Gen Mgr-Cyber Intelligence Div)*
Karen A. Williams *(VP & Gen Mgr-Defense Tech Div)*
Samuel Abbate *(VP)*
Larry W. Edelman *(VP-Strategy & Ops)*
Cheryl L. Janey *(VP-Comm)*
Edward Sturms *(VP)*
Michele Toth *(VP-HR & Admin)*
Carl Williamson *(Exec Dir-Cyber Strategy)*
J. Michael Landrum *(Dir-Sector Comm)*

NORTHROP GRUMMAN SYNOPTICS
(Unit of Northrop Grumman Aerospace Systems)
1201 Continental Blvd
Charlotte, NC 28273-6320
Tel.: (704) 588-2340
Fax: (704) 588-2516
E-mail: stsynopticssales@ngc.com
Web Site:
www.as.northropgrumman.com
Sales Range: $50-74.9 Million
Approx. Number Employees: 200
Business Description:
Solid-State Laser Industry Synthetic Crystals & Optical Components Mfr
S.I.C.: 3827; 3999
N.A.I.C.S.: 333314; 339999
Media: 2-10
Personnel:
Joe Rutherford *(VP & Gen Mgr)*
Scott E. Griffin *(Dir-Sls & Mktg)*

NORWICH AERO PRODUCTS, INC.
(Sub. of Esterline Technologies Corporation)
50 O'Hara Dr
Norwich, NY 13815-2029
Tel.: (607) 336-7636
Fax: (607) 336-2610
E-mail: noraero@norwichaero.com
Web Site: www.norwichaero.com
Sales Range: $25-49.9 Million
Approx. Number Employees: 100
Year Founded: 1983
Business Description:
Temperature Sensors, Speed Sensors & Interconnect Products Mfr
S.I.C.: 3799
N.A.I.C.S.: 336999
Media: 13-16

NOVATEL INC.
(Div. of Hexagon Measurement Technologies)
1120 68th Avenue Northeast
Calgary, AB T2E 8S5, Canada
Tel.: (403) 295-4500
Tel.: (403) 295-4900
Fax: (403) 295-4501
Fax: (403) 295-4901
Toll Free: (800) NOVATEL
Telex: 3-821264
Web Site: www.novatel.com
E-Mail For Key Personnel:
Sales Director: sales@novatel.ca
Sales Range: $50-74.9 Million
Approx. Number Employees: 230
Year Founded: 1978
Business Description:
Global Positioning Systems & Components Mfr
S.I.C.: 3812; 3679; 3823
N.A.I.C.S.: 334511; 334419; 334513
Import Export
Advertising Expenditures: $500,000
Media: 2-4-5-6-7-8-10-13-20-26
Distr.: Intl.; Natl.
Personnel:
Michael Ritter *(Pres & CEO)*
Lori Winkler *(Mgr-Mktg Comm)*
Brands & Products:
ADVANCERTK
AG-20
BEELINE
EUROPAK
FLEXPAK
GPSDREDGER
GPSOLUTION
GPSTATION
HYDROGRAPHIC SURVEYOR
MAT
MEDLL
MET
MILLENNIUM
NARROW CORRELATOR
NOVATEL
PINWHEEL
POWERPAK
PROPAK
RT-2
RT-20
SOFTSURV
WAAS RECEIVER

NUCLETRON CORPORATION
(Sub. of Nucletron B.V.)
8671 Robert Fulton Dr
Columbia, MD 21046
Tel.: (410) 312-4100
Fax: (410) 872-4434
Toll Free: (800) 336-2249
E-mail: info@nucusa.com
Web Site: www.nucletron.com
Approx. Number Employees: 110
Business Description:
Cancer Treatment Device Mfr & Sales
S.I.C.: 3841
N.A.I.C.S.: 339112
Advertising Agency:
Rose Communications Inc.
100 N Charles St 15th Fl
Baltimore, MD 21201
Tel.: (410) 245-0094
Fax: (201) 221-8734

OCEAN OPTICS INC.
830 Douglas Ave
Dunedin, FL 34698
Mailing Address:
830 Douglas Ave
Dunedin, FL 34698
Tel.: (727) 733-2447
Fax: (727) 733-3962
E-mail: rob.randleman@oceanoptics.com
Web Site: www.oceanoptics.com
Approx. Number Employees: 33
Business Description:
Analytical Instruments
S.I.C.: 3826; 3827
N.A.I.C.S.: 334516; 333314
Media: 13
Personnel:
Rob Randleman *(Pres)*
Brands & Products:
DICHROIC FILTER ARRAY
INNOVATIONS IN EDUCATIONAL SPECTROSCOPY
JAZ
MAYA
NIRQUEST
OCEAN OPTICS
OOI SENSORS
SMART. INNOVATIVE. FLEXIBLE. SOLVERS.
SPECLINE

OCLARO, INC.
2584 Junction Ave
San Jose, CA 95134
Tel.: (408) 383-1400
Fax: (408) 919-6083
E-mail: ir@oclaro.com
Web Site: www.oclaro.com/
Approx. Rev.: $392,545,000
Approx. Number Employees: 2,865
Year Founded: 1988
Business Description:
Optical Components, Modules & Subsystems Designer, Mfr & Marketer
S.I.C.: 3695; 3669; 3827
N.A.I.C.S.: 334613; 333314; 334290
Advertising Expenditures: $212,000
Media: 8-10-11-13
Personnel:
Bernard J. Couillaud *(Chm)*
Alain A. Couder *(Pres & CEO)*
James D. Haynes *(Pres & Gen Mgr-Photonic Components Bus Unit)*
Jerry Turin *(CFO)*
Robert Quinn *(CIO)*
Terry Unter *(Pres/Gen Mgr-Optical Networks Solutions Bus Unit)*
Kate Rundle *(Gen Counsel, Sec & Exec VP)*
Adam Price *(Exec VP & Gen Mgr-Transmission Div)*
Kenneth G. Ibbs *(Exec VP)*
Yves LeMaitre *(Exec VP-Strategy & Corp Dev)*
Gray Williams *(Exec VP-Supply Chain Ops & Quality)*
Kathy Zwickert *(Exec VP-HR)*

OCLARO, INC.
(Sub. of Oclaro, Inc.)
40919 Encyclopedia Cir
Fremont, CA 94538-2436
Tel.: (510) 897-4188
Fax: (510) 897-4189
Web Site: www.avanex.com
Approx. Rev.: $208,094,000
Approx. Number Employees: 576
Year Founded: 1997
Business Description:
Optical Components, Modules & Subsystems Designer, Mfr & Marketer
S.I.C.: 3674; 3695; 3827
N.A.I.C.S.: 334413; 333314; 334613
Advertising Expenditures: $598,647,000
Media: 8-10-11-13-22
Personnel:
Scott Parker *(Exec VP-Sls & Mktg Comm)*
Myo Ohn *(Sr Dir-Strategic Mktg & Bus Dev)*
Brands & Products:
LEAF
POWERATTENUATOR
POWERBIT
POWERBLOCKER
POWERBRAGG
POWERDEEP
POWEREQUALIZER
POWEREXCHANGER
POWEREXPRESS
POWERFILTER
POWERFLEX
POWERFORM
POWERLIFE
POWERLOG
POWERMUX
POWERNODE
POWERPORT
POWERPURE
POWERREACH
POWERSHAPER
POWERSOURCE
POWERWATCHER
PUREGAIN

OFS
(Div. of OFS Brightwave)
50 Hall Rd
Sturbridge, MA 01566-1279
Tel.: (508) 347-2261
Fax: (508) 347-2747
Fax: (508) 347-1211
Web Site: www.ofsoptics.com/
Approx. Number Employees: 350
Year Founded: 1980
Business Description:
Multi Mode Optical Fibers Mfr
S.I.C.: 3229
N.A.I.C.S.: 327212
Media: 2-4-7-10-17
Distr.: Natl.

Key to Media (For complete agency information see *The Advertising Red Books-Agencies* edition):
1. Bus. Publs. 2. Cable T.V. 3. Catalogs & Directories. 4. Co-op Adv. 5. Consumer Mags. 6. D.M. to Bus. Estab.7. D.M. to Consumers
8. Daily Newsp. 9. Exhibits/Trade Shows 10. Foreign 11. Infomercial 12. Internet Adv.13. Multimedia 14. Network Radio
15. Network T.V. 16. Newsp. Distr. Mags. 17. Other 18. Outdoor (Posters, Transit) 19. Point of Purchase20. Premiums, Novelties
21. Product Samples 22. Special Events Mktg. 23. Spot Radio 24. Spot T.V. 25. Weekly Newsp. 26. Yellow Page Adv.

OFS — (Continued)

Personnel:
Michele Neifing *(Mgr-Cust Svcs)*

OHARA CORPORATION
(Sub. of Ohara Inc.)
23141 Arroyo Vista Ste 200
Rancho Santa Margarita, CA 92688-2609
Tel.: (949) 858-5700
Fax: (949) 858-5455
E-mail: sales@oharacorp.com
Web Site: www.oharacorp.com
E-Mail For Key Personnel:
Sales Director: sales@oharacorp.com
Approx. Number Employees: 3
Year Founded: 1981
Business Description:
Precision Optical Glasses Mfr
S.I.C.: 5048
N.A.I.C.S.: 423460
Media: 2-13
Personnel:
Brion Hoffman *(Pres)*

OLAN MILLS, INC.
4325 Amnicola Hwy
Chattanooga, TN 37422-3456
Mailing Address:
PO Box 23456
Chattanooga, TN 37422-3456
Tel.: (423) 622-5141
Fax: (423) 629-8128
E-mail: info@olanmills.com
Web Site: www.olanmills.com
Approx. Number Employees: 5,500
Year Founded: 1932
Business Description:
Family Portraits
S.I.C.: 7221; 2752
N.A.I.C.S.: 541921; 323110
Advertising Expenditures: $700,000
Media: 7-13
Personnel:
Robert L. McDowell *(Pres & CEO)*
Laura Carden *(CFO)*
A.V. Tery Blunt *(VP-HR)*
Brands & Products:
OLAN MILLS

OLYMPUS AMERICA INC.
(Sub. of Olympus Corporation)
3500 Corporate Pkwy
Center Valley, PA 18034-0610
Tel.: (484) 896-5000
Fax: (631) 844-5262
Toll Free: (800) 622-6372
Web Site: www.olympusamerica.com
Approx. Number Employees: 800
Business Description:
Cameras, Endoscopes, Microscopes, Clinical Analyzers & Other Products Sales
S.I.C.: 5043
N.A.I.C.S.: 423410
Import
Advertising Expenditures: $1,500,000
Media: 2-3-5-6-10-15-18
Distr.: Natl.
Budget Set: Apr. -Mar.
Personnel:
F. Mark Gumz *(Pres & CEO)*
Donna Miller *(Gen Counsel & Corp VP)*
Elizabeth Sullivan *(Exec Dir-Corp Comm)*
Louis Chatel *(Dir-Sls & Mktg)*
Jason Bortzfield *(Product Mgr)*
Tomoko Matsunaga *(Product Mgr)*
Glenn Schwartz *(Product Mgr)*
Susan M. Watanabe *(Sr Product Mgr)*
Kenneth Wolcott *(Sr Product Mgr)*
Marie Foyt *(Product Mgr)*
Jennifer Schmell *(Product Mgr-Olympus Imaging)*
Brands & Products:
OLYMPUS
OM SYSTEM
PEARLCORDER
Advertising Agencies:
deutschMedia
111 8th Ave 14th Fl
New York, NY 10011-5201
Tel.: (212) 981-7600
Fax: (212) 981-7525
Cameras
Media Buying

GolinHarris
919 3rd Ave 15th Fl
New York, NY 10022
Tel.: (212) 373-6000
Fax: (212) 373-6001

OMRON SCIENTIFIC TECHNOLOGIES INCORPORATED
(Sub. of OMRON Corporation)
6550 Dumbarton Cir
Fremont, CA 94555-3605
Tel.: (510) 608-3400
Fax: (510) 744-1442
Toll Free: (888) 510-4357
E-mail: sales@sti.com
Web Site: www.sti.com
E-Mail For Key Personnel:
Sales Director: sales@sti.com
Sales Range: $50-74.9 Million
Approx. Number Employees: 321
Year Founded: 1967
Business Description:
Safety & Protective Equipment Mfr
S.I.C.: 3827; 3823
N.A.I.C.S.: 333314; 334513
Advertising Expenditures: $548,000
Media: 2-4-10-13-20-21
Personnel:
James Ashford *(Pres & COO)*
Frank Webster *(VP-Engrng)*
Brands & Products:
BEAMSAFE
DUOSAFE
FASTSCAN
LASERSAFE
OPTOSHIELD
QUADSAFE
STI
TOUCHSTART
VALUSCAN
Advertising Agency:
Longren & Parks
14101 Brandbury Walk
Minnetonka, MN 55345
Tel.: (952) 945-0572
Fax: (952) 945-9970

OPHTHALMIC IMAGING SYSTEMS
221 Lathrop Way Ste I
Sacramento, CA 95831
Tel.: (916) 646-2020
Fax: (916) 646-0207
Toll Free: (800) 338-8436
E-mail: info@oisi.com
Web Site: www.oisi.com
Approx. Rev.: $18,631,912
Approx. Number Employees: 123
Business Description:
Ophthalmic Imaging Systems & Software Developer & Mfr
S.I.C.: 3851; 5048; 7372
N.A.I.C.S.: 339115; 423460; 511210
Advertising Expenditures: $292,946
Media: 17
Personnel:
Uri Ram *(Chm)*
Gil Allon *(CEO)*
Ariel Shenhar *(CFO & Sec)*

OPTOSIGMA CORP.
3210 S Croddy Way
Santa Ana, CA 92704
Tel.: (949) 851-5881
Fax: (949) 851-5058
E-mail: sales@optosigma.com
Web Site: www.optosigma.com
E-Mail For Key Personnel:
Sales Director: sales@optosigma.com
Approx. Number Employees: 15
Business Description:
Optics & Optomechanics Mfr & Distr
S.I.C.: 3827
N.A.I.C.S.: 333314
Media: 2-13
Personnel:
Michelle Young *(Mgr-Sls)*
Brands & Products:
HEATBUSTER
ONETOUCH
OPTOMIKE
OPTOSIGMA
TOPMIKE
ULTRA-STABLE

ORBITAL SCIENCES CORPORATION
21839 Atlantic Blvd
Sterling, VA 20166-6850
Tel.: (703) 406-5000
Fax: (703) 406-5572
E-mail: investor.relations@orbital.com
Web Site: www.orbital.com
Approx. Rev.: $1,294,577,000
Approx. Number Employees: 3,400
Year Founded: 1982
Business Description:
Satellite Space Systems & Launch Vehicles Designer, Developer & Mfr; Infrastructure Systems, Satellite Access Products & Satellite Services Including Launch Vehicles, Sensors & Electronics, Satellite Ground Systems & Software, Navigation & Communications Products & Earth Imaging Services
S.I.C.: 3663; 3761; 3812
N.A.I.C.S.: 334220; 334511; 336414
Advertising Expenditures: $250,000
Media: 1-2-10-18-19-20-21-22
Distr.: Natl.
Budget Set: Jan.
Personnel:
David W. Thompson *(Chm, Pres & CEO)*
Garrett E. Pierce *(Vice Chm & CFO)*
James R. Thompson, Jr. *(Vice Chm)*
Ken U. Bell *(CIO & Sr VP)*
Susan Herlick *(Gen Counsel, Sec & Sr VP)*
Antonio L. Elias *(Exec VP & Gen Mgr-Advanced Programs Grp)*
Ronald J. Grabe *(Exec VP & Gen Mgr-Launch Sys Grp)*
Michael E. Larkin *(Exec VP & Gen Mgr-Space Sys Grp)*
Hollis M. Thompson *(Sr VP & Controller)*
W. Jean Floyd *(Sr VP & Deputy Gen Mgr-APG)*
Ali Atia *(Sr VP)*
Emily S. Bender *(Sr VP-HR)*
Michael Hamel *(Sr VP-Corp Strategy & Dev)*
Kate Kronmiller *(Sr VP-Govt Rels)*
Christopher R. Richmond *(Sr VP-Comm Satellite Programs)*
Sally K. Richardson *(VP & Deputy Dir-Tech Ops)*
Barron S. Beneski *(VP-Corp Comm)*
Amer Khouri *(VP-Mktg & Bus Dev)*
David Anhalt *(Sr Dir-Advanced Programs Grp)*
Larry Slivinski *(Dir-Tech Svcs Engrg)*
Michael R. Williams *(Engr-Electrical)*
Brands & Products:
CYGNUS
FORMOSAT
GALEX
HYPER-X
INDOSTAR
INNOVATION YOU CAN COUNT ON
MINOTAUR
OPTUS
ORBITAL
ORBVIEW
PEGASUS
SORCE
STAR
TAURUS
TELKOM-2

ORTHOVITA, INC.
77 Great Valley Pkwy
Malvern, PA 19355-1302
Tel.: (610) 640-1775
Fax: (610) 640-2603
E-mail: customerservice@orthovita.com
Web Site: www.orthovita.com
Approx. Sls.: $94,663,000
Approx. Number Employees: 256
Year Founded: 1993
Business Description:
Mfr, Developer & Marketer of Bone Regeneration Products & Devices
S.I.C.: 3841
N.A.I.C.S.: 339112
Personnel:
William E. Tidmore, Jr. *(Chm)*
Antony Koblish *(Pres & CEO)*
Nancy C. Broadbent *(CFO & Sr VP)*
Erik M. Erbe *(Chief Science Officer)*
Chistopher H. Smith *(Sr VP-Sls & Mktg)*
Kevin B. Connolly *(VP-Mktg)*
Brands & Products:
ALIQUOT
ARCHITECTS OF THE NEW BIOMATERIALS AGE
CORTOSS
ENDOSKELETON
IMBIBE
ORTHOCOMP
ORTHOVITA
VITAGEL
VITASURE

Key to Media (For complete agency information see *The Advertising Red Books-Agencies* edition):
1. Bus. Publs. 2. Cable T.V. 3. Catalogs & Directories. 4. Co-op Adv. 5. Consumer Mags. 6. D.M. to Bus. Estab.7. D.M. to Consumers 8. Daily Newsp. 9. Exhibits/Trade Shows 10. Foreign 11. Infomercial 12. Internet Adv.13. Multimedia 14. Network Radio 15. Network T.V. 16. Newsp. Distr. Mags. 17. Other 18. Outdoor (Posters, Transit) 19. Point of Purchase20. Premiums, Novelties 21. Product Samples 22. Special Events Mktg. 23. Spot Radio 24. Spot T.V. 25. Weekly Newsp. 26. Yellow Page Adv.

VITOMATRIX
VITOSS

Advertising Agency:
Stiegler, Wells, Brunswick & Roth, Inc.
(d/b/a SWB&R)
3865 Adler Pl
Bethlehem, PA 18017-9000
Tel.: (610) 866-0611
Fax: (610) 866-8650

OSTEOMED CORPORATION

(Sub. of Colson Associates, Inc.)
3885 Arapaho Rd
Addison, TX 75001
Tel.: (972) 677-4600
Fax: (972) 677-4601
Toll Free: (800) 456-7779
E-mail: webinfo@osteomed.com
Web Site: www.osteomedcorp.com
Approx. Number Employees: 125
Year Founded: 1999
Business Description:
Surgical Instruments & Apparatus Mfr
S.I.C.: 3841; 3842
N.A.I.C.S.: 339112; 339113
Media: 10
Personnel:
Walt Humann *(Pres)*
Beth Kriske *(Asst Controller)*
Brands & Products:
AUTO-DRIVE
BIO-ACTION
CALFIX
ENVISION XD
EXTREMFIX
FAST-FLAP
HEMI
INION CPS
INTERPHLEX
KOBYGARD
LOGIC
LOGIC HR.
M3-X
M4 RIGID FIXATION SYSTEM
MANDIBULAR FRACTURE SYSTEM
MINCRO
OMI
ORTHOGNATHIC SYSTEM
OSA SYSTEM
OSTEOFARM MESH
OSTEOFLAP
OSTEOGRAFT
OSTEOHARVESTER
OSTEOMATCH
OSTEOMED
OSTEOVATION
OSTEOVATIONEX
QUICK-FIX
REFLEXION
RIDGE-FORM MESH
SPECTRUM
TALAR-FIT
TCA

OTTO NEMENZ INTERNATIONAL INC.

870 N Vine St
Los Angeles, CA 90038
Tel.: (323) 469-2774
Web Site: www.ottonemenz.com
Approx. Sls.: $3,500,000
Approx. Number Employees: 40
Business Description:
Motion Picture Cameras Rental
S.I.C.: 7359; 5946
N.A.I.C.S.: 532299; 443130
Media: 2-8
Personnel:
Otto Nemenz *(Pres & CEO)*

OZ OPTICS LIMTED

219 Westbrook Rd
Carp, ON Canada
Tel.: (613) 831-0981
Fax: (613) 836-5089
E-mail: sales@ozoptics.com
Web Site: www.ozoptics.com
E-Mail For Key Personnel:
Sales Director: sales@ozoptics.com
Approx. Number Employees: 125
Year Founded: 1985
Business Description:
Visual Fault Locators, Motor Driven Attenuators, Stable Light Sources, Extinction Ratio Meters, Optical Delay Lines, Variable Backreflectors, Splitters, Polarization Rotators, Controllers, Analyzers, Fixed or Tunable Filters, Collimators & Focusers, Power Meters, Metalized Fibres, & Optical Benches Mfr
S.I.C.: 3827
N.A.I.C.S.: 333314
Media: 2-10-11-13
Personnel:
Omur M. Sezerman *(Founder, Chm, Pres & CEO)*
Zahide Sezerman *(VP-HR)*
Martin Powell *(Mgr-Ops)*

PALOMAR MEDICAL TECHNOLOGIES, INC.

15 Network Dr
Burlington, MA 01803
Tel.: (781) 993-2300
Fax: (781) 993-2330
Toll Free: (800) 725-6627
E-mail: info@palomarmedical.com
Web Site: www.palmed.com
Approx. Number Employees: 70
Year Founded: 1991
Business Description:
Cosmetic Laser Products Mfr
S.I.C.: 3845
N.A.I.C.S.: 334510
Advertising Expenditures: $361,000
Media: 2-3-6-9-13-14-15-23-24-25
Personnel:
Louis P. Valente *(Chm)*
Joseph P. Caruso *(Pres & CEO)*
Paul S. Weiner *(CFO, Treas & Sr VP)*
Patricia A. Davis *(Gen Counsel, Sec & Sr VP)*
Gregory Altshuler *(Sr VP-Res)*
Steven Armstrong *(Sr VP-Ops)*
Jeffrey Knight *(VP-Sls & Mktg-North America)*
Brands & Products:
ACCUSPECTRUM
ADVANCED CONTACT COOLING
LUX1064
LUX1440
LUX1540
LUX2940
LUXB
LUXDEEPIR
LUXG
LUXIR
LUXR
LUXRS
LUXV
LUXY
LUXYS
MEDILUX
PALOMAR
PHOTON RECYCLING
Q-YAG 5
REJUVELUX
SLIMLIPO
SMOOTH PULSE
STARLUX

PARKERVISION, INC.

7915 Baymeadows Way Ste 400
Jacksonville, FL 32256-7517
Tel.: (904) 737-1367
Fax: (904) 731-0958
Toll Free: (800) 532-8034
E-mail: sales@parkervision.com
Web Site: www.parkervision.com
Approx. Rev.: $63,735
Approx. Number Employees: 46
Year Founded: 1989
Business Description:
Wireless Radio Frequency (RF) Designer, Developer & Mfr
S.I.C.: 3663; 3651; 3674
N.A.I.C.S.: 334220; 334310; 334413
Media: 1-5-7-8-13
Personnel:
Jeffrey L. Parker *(Chm & CEO)*
Cynthia Poehlman *(CFO & Sec)*
Envy Bowman *(HR Dir)*
Brands & Products:
CAMERAMAN
D2P
DIRECT2DATA
DIRECT2POWER
ENERGY SIGNAL PROCESSING
PARKERVISION
SIGNALMAX

PARMELEE INDUSTRIES, INC.

(d/b/a U.S. Safety)
8101 Lenexa Dr
Lenexa, KS 66214-1653
Tel.: (913) 599-5555
Fax: (913) 599-1703
Fax: (800) 252-5002
Toll Free: (800) 821-5218
E-mail: info@ussafety.com
Web Site: www.ussafety.com
Approx. Sls.: $20,000,000
Approx. Number Employees: 70
Year Founded: 1935
Business Description:
Industrial Personal Protective Equipment Including Safety Eyewear, Faceshields, Goggle Lenses, Welding Goggles, Helmets, Hearing Protectors & Respirators
S.I.C.: 3851; 3842
N.A.I.C.S.: 339115; 339113
Import Export
Media: 4-5-7-10-21-26
Distr.: Direct to Consumer; Intl.; Natl.
Budget Set: Dec.
Personnel:
J.P Sankpill *(Pres & CEO)*
Terry Meyers *(Treas & VP)*
Bob Shirvanian *(Dir-Corp Accts)*
Len Harrison *(Reg Mgr-AL, FL, GA, MS, NC, SC & TN)*
Tina Shabel *(Reg Mgr)*
Steve Fredricksen *(Mgr-Rx Bus)*
John Hilton, IV *(Mgr-Safety DP-US)*
Bab Lazzari *(Mgr-Sls-OH)*
Brands & Products:
ARRIVA
ASPEN
BLAZE
COM-FLEX
COMFORT-AIR
COMFORT-EASE
CUSHION/FLEX
DISKIT
LEGEND
MATRIX
MIRADA
OPTILITE
PHOENIX EDGE
PHOENIX I
PHOENIX II
RAZ
RENEGADE
SAF-EAR-SHIELD
SAF-I-CHEM
SAF-I-CHIPPER
SAF-I-FLEX
SAF-I-GARD
SAF-I-WELD
SAF-TWIST
SAFETY-MATE
SOFTSEAL-D
STYL-SAFE
WESTON
Advertising Agency:
P.I. Advertising
(House Agency)
8101 Lenexa Dr.
Lenexa, KS 66214
Tel.: (913) 599-5555

PEARLE VISION, INC.

(Sub. of Luxottica Retail)
4000 Luxottica Pl
Mason, OH 45040
Tel.: (513) 765-6000
Fax: (513) 765-6249
Web Site: www.pearlevision.com
Sales Range: $200-249.9 Million
Approx. Number Employees: 3,700
Business Description:
Eyewear Retailer
S.I.C.: 5995
N.A.I.C.S.: 446130
Personnel:
Kerry Bradley *(COO)*
Eric Anderson *(VP-Mktg)*
Advertising Agencies:
Arnold Worldwide
101 Huntington Ave
Boston, MA 02199-7603
Tel.: (617) 587-8000
Fax: (617) 587-8004

Critical Mass Inc.
225 N Michigan Ave Ste 2050
Chicago, IL 60601-7757
Tel.: (312) 288-2500
Fax: (312) 288-2501

PEGASUS IMAGING CORPORATION

(d/b/a Accusoft Pegasus)
4001 N Riverside Dr
Tampa, FL 33603
Tel.: (813) 875-7575
Fax: (813) 875-7705
Toll Free: (800) 875-7009
E-mail: jobs@accusoft.com
Web Site: www.accusoft.com
Sales Range: $10-24.9 Million
Approx. Number Employees: 100
Business Description:
Digital Imaging Software Technology
S.I.C.: 7372
N.A.I.C.S.: 511210
Media: 10

Key to Media (For complete agency information see *The Advertising Red Books-Agencies* edition):
1. Bus. Publs. 2. Cable T.V. 3. Catalogs & Directories. 4. Co-op Adv. 5. Consumer Mags. 6. D.M. to Bus. Estab.7. D.M. to Consumers
8. Daily Newsp. 9. Exhibits/Trade Shows 10. Foreign 11. Infomercial 12. Internet Adv.13. Multimedia 14. Network Radio
15. Network T.V. 16. Newsp. Distr. Mags. 17. Other 18. Outdoor (Posters, Transit) 19. Point of Purchase20. Premiums, Novelties
21. Product Samples 22. Special Events Mktg. 23. Spot Radio 24. Spot T.V. 25. Weekly Newsp. 26. Yellow Page Adv.

Pegasus Imaging Corporation — (Continued)

Personnel:
Jack Berlin *(Pres)*
Jaime Saeger *(Dir-Mktg)*

PENTAX CANADA, INC.
(Sub. of Pentax Corporation)
1770 Argentia Rd
Mississauga, ON L5N 3S7, Canada
Tel.: (905) 286-5585
Fax: (905) 286-5586
Web Site: www.pentax.ca
E-Mail For Key Personnel:
Sales Director: sales@pentaxcanada.ca
Approx. Number Employees: 50
Year Founded: 1978
Business Description:
Distr & Marketing of Cameras, Optical, CCTV Lenses, Surveying Instruments, Binoculars & GPS Equipment
S.I.C.: 3861; 3827
N.A.I.C.S.: 333315; 333314
Import
Advertising Expenditures: $330,000
Media: 4-5-6-9-10-20-22-26
Distr.: Natl.
Budget Set: Apr.
Personnel:
Greg Hall *(Pres)*
Peter Lodge *(Mgr-Territory)*

PENTAX IMAGING COMPANY
(Div. of Pentax of America, Inc.)
600 12th St Ste 300
Golden, CO 80401
Tel.: (303) 799-8000
Fax: (303) 728-0301
Toll Free: (800) 877-0155
Web Site: www.pentaximaging.com
Approx. Number Employees: 100
Business Description:
Optical Equipment & Camera Mfr
S.I.C.: 5043; 3827
N.A.I.C.S.: 423410; 333314
Media: 2-10
Personnel:
Ned Bunnell *(Pres)*
Advertising Agency:
RPA
(Rubin Postaer and Associates)
2525 Colorado Ave
Santa Monica, CA 90404
Tel.: (310) 394-4000
Fax: (310) 633-7099

PENTAX OF AMERICA, INC.
(Sub. of Pentax Corporation)
600 12th St Ste 300
Golden, CO 80401-6142
Tel.: (303) 799-8000
Fax: (303) 790-1131
Toll Free: (800) 877-0155
E-mail: pentaxinfo@pentax.com
Web Site: www.pentaxusa.com
Approx. Number Employees: 100
Year Founded: 1977
Business Description:
Mfr. & Sales of Security Lenses, Photographic Products, Cameras, Binoculars & Surveying Instruments
S.I.C.: 3861
N.A.I.C.S.: 325992
Advertising Expenditures: $200,000
Media: 2-3-5-6-10-14-15-19-20-21-22-23-24-26
Distr.: Intl.; Natl.
Budget Set: Feb.
Personnel:
Ned Nunnell *(Pres)*
John Hodnett *(VP-Fin-Admin)*
Lorri Avery *(Sr Mgr-Mktg Comm)*
Advertising Agency:
RPA
(Rubin Postaer and Associates)
2525 Colorado Ave
Santa Monica, CA 90404
Tel.: (310) 394-4000
Fax: (310) 633-7099

PERCEPTICS, LLC
9737 Cogdill Rd Ste 200N
Knoxville, TN 37932-3350
Tel.: (865) 966-9200
Fax: (865) 966-9330
Toll Free: (800) 448-8544
E-mail: sales@perceptics.com
Web Site: www.perceptics.com
E-Mail For Key Personnel:
Sales Director: sales@perceptics.com
Year Founded: 1980
Business Description:
Security, Traffic Management & Machine Vision Systems Equipment Mfr
S.I.C.: 3699; 3799; 5046; 7372
N.A.I.C.S.: 335999; 336999; 423440; 511210
Media: 2-10
Personnel:
John Dalton *(Pres)*
Tom Hayes *(VP-Sls & Mktg)*
Michelle Bethel *(Mgr-HR)*
Juan Herrera *(Mgr-Engrg)*

PERKINELMER, INC.
940 Winter St
Waltham, MA 02451
Tel.: (781) 663-6900
Fax: (781) 663-5985
E-mail: productinfo@perkinelmer.com
Web Site: www.perkinelmer.com
Approx. Sls.: $1,704,346,000
Approx. Number Employees: 6,200
Year Founded: 1947
Business Description:
Instruments, Optoelectronics, Life Sciences & Fluid Sciences Products
S.I.C.: 3826; 8734
N.A.I.C.S.: 334516; 541380
Export
Advertising Expenditures: $2,500,000
Media: 2-4-5-8-10-11-13-21
Distr.: Intl.; Natl.
Budget Set: Sept.
Personnel:
Robert F. Friel *(Chm, Pres & CEO)*
Frank Anders Wilson *(CFO & Sr VP)*
Lapo Paladini *(CMO & Sr VP)*
Daniel R. Marshak *(Pres-Emerging Diagnostics,Chief Scientific Officer & Sr VP)*
Andrew Okun *(Chief Acctg Officer & VP)*
Richard Begley *(Pres-Emerging Tech)*
John J. Engel *(Pres-Bio-Discovery)*
Reiner Quad *(Pres-Sensors Bus)*
Ann-Christine Sundell *(Pres-Genetic Screening Bus)*
Maurice H. Tenney, III *(Pres-Analytical Sciences & Laboratory Svcs Bus)*
Joel S. Goldberg *(Gen Counsel, Sec & Sr VP)*
Stephen P. Defalco *(Sr VP)*
John R. Letcher *(Sr VP-HR)*
Achim Leoprechting *(VP & Gen Mgr-Imaging & Detection Technologies)*
Stephanie Moore *(Mgr-Sls)*
Christine Mylo *(Mgr-Sls)*
Antoniette Violo *(Mgr-Bus Dev-Oceania)*
Brands & Products:
AANALYST
ABSOLVE
ACYCLOPRIME
AEQUASCREEN
AEQUOZEN
ALPHALISA
ALPHAPLATE
ALPHASCREEN
AMORPHOUS SILICON
ATPLITE
BRITELITE
CAMPZEN
CLARUS
COBRA
COLUMBUS
COUNT-OFF
CULTUR PLATE
CYCLONE PLUS
DELFIA
DRC
ECOANALYTIX
ELAN
ELAST
EN3HANCE
ENSPIRE
ENVISION
FLASHPLATE
FLEXAR
FLEXDROP
FLO-SCINT
FOR THE BETTER
GREENLIMS
HYPERDSC
HYPURE
ISOSCAN
JANUS
LABWORKS
LAMBDA
LANCE
LIFECYCLE
LUMIJET
MICROBETA
MICROSCINT
MINITRAK
MULTIPROBE
NEOGRAM
ONESOURCE
ONPOINT
OPERA
OPTIMA
OPTIPLATE
OPTIQUANT
PERKINELMER
PHOTOSCREEN
PLATESTAK
PLATETRAK
PLATEWASH
POLYSCREEN
PROSCANARRAY
PROXCISION
PROXIPLATE
PROXPRESS
PROXPRESSION
QUANTUM
RADIOMATIC
SCINTIPLATES
SIGNALSCREEN
SOFTLINK
SPOTARRAY
STEADYLITE
SURELIGHT
TOFPREP
TOPCOUNT
TOTALCHROM
TRUPOINT
TSA
TURBOMATRIX
ULTIMAGOLD
VALISCREEN
VICTOR
VIEWLUX
WIZARD
Advertising Agency:
Brodeur Partners
855 Boylston St 2nd Fl
Boston, MA 02116-2622
Tel.: (617) 587-2800
Fax: (617) 587-2828

PERKINELMER LIFE & ANALYTICAL SCIENCES, INC.
(Unit of PerkinElmer, Inc.)
940 Winter St
Waltham, MA 02451
Tel.: (781) 663-6900
Fax: (781) 663-6052
Toll Free: (800) 762-4000
E-mail: info@perkinelmer.com
Web Site: las.perkinelmer.com
Sales Range: $75-99.9 Million
Approx. Number Employees: 500
Year Founded: 1965
Business Description:
Scientific Instruments Mfr
S.I.C.: 3826
N.A.I.C.S.: 334516
Import Export
Advertising Expenditures: $300,000
Media: 2-4-7-10-13-22
Distr.: Natl.
Budget Set: Dec.
Advertising Agency:
Brodeur Partners
855 Boylston St 2nd Fl
Boston, MA 02116-2622
Tel.: (617) 587-2800
Fax: (617) 587-2828
Public Relations

PHILIPS MEDICAL SYSTEMS
(Div. of Philips Medical Systems)
22100 Bothell Everett Hwy
Bothell, WA 98021-8431
Mailing Address:
PO Box 3003
Bothell, WA 98041-3003
Tel.: (425) 487-7000
Fax: (425) 485-6080
Toll Free: (800) 722-7900
Web Site: www.medical.philips.com
Approx. Number Employees: 200
Business Description:
Medical Diagnostic Systems Mfr
S.I.C.: 5047; 7629
N.A.I.C.S.: 423450; 811219
Media: 4-7-10
Distr.: Natl.
Personnel:
Gerard J. Kleisterlee *(Chm, Pres & CEO)*
Barbara Franciose *(CEO-Clinical Care Sys)*
Richard Facian *(VP-Mktg)*

Key to Media (For complete agency information see *The Advertising Red Books-Agencies* edition):
1. Bus. Publs. 2. Cable T.V. 3. Catalogs & Directories. 4. Co-op Adv. 5. Consumer Mags. 6. D.M. to Bus. Estab.7. D.M. to Consumers
8. Daily Newsp. 9. Exhibits/Trade Shows 10. Foreign 11. Infomercial 12. Internet Adv.13. Multimedia 14. Network Radio
15. Network T.V. 16. Newsp. Distr. Mags. 17. Other 18. Outdoor (Posters, Transit) 19. Point of Purchase20. Premiums, Novelties
21. Product Samples 22. Special Events Mktg. 23. Spot Radio 24. Spot T.V. 25. Weekly Newsp. 26. Yellow Page Adv.

PHOTOGENIC PROFESSIONAL LIGHTING
1268 Humbracht Cir
Bartlett, IL 60103-1631
Tel.: (630) 830-2500
Fax: (630) 830-2525
Toll Free: (800) 682-7668
Web Site: www.photogenicpro.com
E-Mail For Key Personnel:
Sales Director: sales@photogenicpro.com
Approx. Number Employees: 60
Year Founded: 1921
Business Description:
Mfr. of Photographic Lighting Equipment
S.I.C.: 3861
N.A.I.C.S.: 333315
Import Export
Advertising Expenditures: $250,000
Media: 4-5-6-7-10-21
Distr.: Natl.
Budget Set: Dec.
Personnel:
Ken Orlando *(Pres)*
Bob Higging *(Mgr-Sls)*
Brands & Products:
FLASHMASTER
MASTER-RAIL
PERFORMAX
PHOTOGENIC
POWERLIGHT
QUICK-CHANGE
STUDIO MAX

PHOTOWORKS, INC.
(Sub. of AG Interactive)
71 Columbia St
Seattle, WA 98104-1444
Tel.: (206) 281-1390
Fax: (206) 284-5357
Toll Free: (800) 746-8696
E-mail: bizdev@photoworks.com
Web Site: www.photoworks.com
Approx. Rev.: $10,685,000
Approx. Number Employees: 55
Year Founded: 1976
Business Description:
Online Photography Services
S.I.C.: 7384
N.A.I.C.S.: 812921
Advertising Expenditures: $535,000
Brands & Products:
EMAIL-A-BOOK
PHOTO CLUTCH
PHOTOMAIL
PHOTOWORKS

PIC DESIGN
86 Benson Rd
Middlebury, CT 06762-3215
Mailing Address:
PO Box 1004
Middlebury, CT 06762-1004
Tel.: (203) 758-8272
Fax: (203) 758-8271
Toll Free: (800) 243-6125
E-mail: sales@pic-design.com
Web Site: www.pic-design.com
E-Mail For Key Personnel:
Sales Director: sales@pic-design.com
Approx. Sls.: $10,000,000
Approx. Number Employees: 50
Year Founded: 1954
Business Description:
Mfr. of Standard & Special Precision Mechanical Components
S.I.C.: 3549; 3568
N.A.I.C.S.: 333518; 333613
Import Export
Media: 2-4-5-7-10-11-13
Distr.: Intl.; Natl.
Budget Set: Jan.
Personnel:
Michael Hamburg *(Mgr-Sls)*
Brands & Products:
E-P-S
NO-MAR
NO-SLIDE
NO-SLIP
PIC
PIC STIX
SILVER-GRIP

POLAROID CORPORATION
(Joint Venture of Gordon Brothers Group, LLC & Hilco Trading, LLC)
(Filed for Chapter 11 Bankruptcy 12/18/2008)
300 Baker Ave
Concord, MA 01742-2131
Tel.: (781) 936-5000
Fax: (781) 386-8588
Toll Free: (800) 343-5000
Web Site: www.polaroid.com
Sales Range: $1-4.9 Billion
Approx. Number Employees: 300
Year Founded: 1937
Business Description:
Photographic Cameras, Films, Light Polarizing Filters, Lenses, & Diversified Chemical, Optical & Commercial Products Mfr
S.I.C.: 3861; 3827
N.A.I.C.S.: 333315; 325992; 333314
Import Export
Media: 2-3-4-5-6-7-8-10-13-15-17-19-22
Distr.: Direct to Consumer; Natl.
Personnel:
Scott W. Hardy *(Pres)*
Jon Pollock *(CMO & Sr VP)*
Stefani Joanne Angelina Germanotta *(Dir-Creative)*
Brands & Products:
600 SE
DIGITAL MINIPORTRAIT (DMP)
DIGITAL PALETTE HR 6000
I-ZONE 300 & 550
ID CARD MAKER SOFTWARE
JOYCAM & 500 FILM
MACRO 5 SLR
MICROCAM SLR
MIO
ONE600 CLASSIC
ONE600 JOBPRO
ONE600 PRO
ONE600 ULTRA
PDC
PEP
POLACOLOR
POLAROID
PP46D
SPECTRA SYSTEM
SPRINTSCAN
SUN 600
Advertising Agencies:
Connelly Partners
46 Waltham St Fl 4
Boston, MA 02118
Tel.: (617) 956-5050
Fax: (617) 956-5054

Weber Shandwick
(Sub. of The Interpublic Group of Companies)
919 3rd Ave
New York, NY 10022
Tel.: (212) 445-8000
Fax: (212) 445-8001

PORTRAIT INNOVATIONS HOLDING COMPANY
2016 Ayrsley Town Blvd Ste 200
Charlotte, NC 28273
Tel.: (704) 499-9300
Fax: (704) 499-9301
Web Site: www.portraitinnovations.com
Approx. Sls.: $111,009,000
Approx. Number Employees: 1,432
Business Description:
Commercial Photography
S.I.C.: 7221; 7335
N.A.I.C.S.: 541921; 541922
Advertising Expenditures: $10,925,000
Personnel:
John Grosso *(Pres & CEO)*
William K. Bailey, II *(CFO & VP-Fin & IR)*
John M. Davis *(Chief Dev Officer, Sec & Exec VP)*
Robert Venetucci *(CTO & Exec VP)*
Susan M. Tabler *(Treas & VP-Fin)*
Brands & Products:
PORTRATI INNOVATIONS

POWER TECHNOLOGY, INC.
PO Box 191117
Little Rock, AR 72119-1117
Tel.: (501) 407-0712
Fax: (501) 407-0036
E-mail: sales@powertechnology.com
Web Site: www.powertechnology.com
E-Mail For Key Personnel:
Sales Director: sales@powertechnology.com
Sales Range: $25-49.9 Million
Approx. Number Employees: 45
Year Founded: 1969
Business Description:
Laser Power Supplies & Laser Diode Modules Mfr
S.I.C.: 3679
N.A.I.C.S.: 334419
Media: 2-4-10
Personnel:
Thomas H. Burgess *(Pres)*
Kara Guire *(CEO)*

PPT VISION, INC.
6301 W Old Shakopee Rd Ste A
Bloomington, MN 55438
Tel.: (952) 996-9500
Fax: (952) 996-9501
E-mail: info@pptvision.com
Web Site: www.pptvision.com
Sales Range: $1-9.9 Million
Approx. Number Employees: 30
Year Founded: 1981
Business Description:
Machine Vision-Based Automated Inspection Systems for Manufacturing Applications Designer, Mfr, Marketer & Integrator
S.I.C.: 3823; 3827
N.A.I.C.S.: 334513; 333314
Advertising Expenditures: $41,000
Media: 2-10-13
Personnel:
Robert W. Heller *(Pres & CEO)*
Gary Kocken *(Mgr-Sls)*
Brands & Products:
IMPACT
INSPECTION BUILDER
PPT VISION

PRECITECH, INC.
(Sub. of Taylor Hobson Holdings Ltd.)
44 Black Brook Rd
Keene, NH 03431
Tel.: (603) 357-2511
Fax: (603) 358-6174
E-mail: sales@precitech.com
Web Site: www.precitech.com
E-Mail For Key Personnel:
Sales Director: sales@precitech.com
Sales Range: $10-24.9 Million
Approx. Number Employees: 100
Year Founded: 1986
Business Description:
Design & Manufacture Ultra Precision Machine & Metrology Systems For Global Markets; Mfr of Standard Customized Air Bearing Components & Modular Geometry & Metology Systems
S.I.C.: 3423; 3552
N.A.I.C.S.: 332212; 333292
Import Export
Media: 2-10
Distr.: Natl.
Budget Set: Apr.
Personnel:
Joe DePanfilis *(Fin Dir)*
Frank Vorwald *(VP-Div & Mgr-Bus)*
Jon Harman *(Dir-Sls & Mktg)*
Jeffrey W. Roblee *(Dir-R&D)*
Haresh Baxani *(Mgr-Sls & Mktg)*
Kirk Rogers *(Sls Mgr-North America)*
Christopher Stroshine *(Sls Mgr-North America)*
T. H. Tsai *(Sls Mgr)*
Walter Lewandowski *(Mgr-R&D)*
Brands & Products:
FREEFORM
NANOTURN
PLANOFORM
VERIFORM

PREISER SCIENTIFIC, INC.
94 Oliver St
Saint Albans, WV 25177
Tel.: (304) 727-2902
Fax: (304) 727-2932
Toll Free: (800) 624-8285
E-mail: preiser@preiser.com
Web Site: www.preiser.com
Approx. Number Employees: 40
Year Founded: 1924
Business Description:
Scientific Instruments, Laboratory Equipment & Related Supplies
S.I.C.: 5049; 5169
N.A.I.C.S.: 423490; 424690
Import Export
Media: 4-6-8-9-10
Distr.: Direct to Consumer; Intl.; Natl.
Budget Set: Jan.
Personnel:
Alvin E. Preiser *(Pres)*
Gayle S. Preiser *(CEO)*
Brands & Products:
ALL THE RIGHT STUFF FOR YOUR LABORATORY
FRICO

Key to Media (For complete agency information see *The Advertising Red Books-Agencies* edition):
1. Bus. Publs. 2. Cable T.V. 3. Catalogs & Directories. 4. Co-op Adv. 5. Consumer Mags. 6. D.M. to Bus. Estab.7. D.M. to Consumers 8. Daily Newsp. 9. Exhibits/Trade Shows 10. Foreign 11. Infomercial 12. Internet Adv.13. Multimedia 14. Network Radio 15. Network T.V. 16. Newsp. Distr. Mags. 17. Other 18. Outdoor (Posters, Transit) 19. Point of Purchase20. Premiums, Novelties 21. Product Samples 22. Special Events Mktg. 23. Spot Radio 24. Spot T.V. 25. Weekly Newsp. 26. Yellow Page Adv.

Preiser Scientific, Inc. — (Continued)

PREISER

PROPHOTONIX LIMITED

32 Hampshire Rd
Salem, NH 03079
Tel.: (603) 893-8778
Fax: (603) 893-5604
E-mail: salesusa@prophotonix.com
Web Site: www.prophotonix.com
Approx. Rev.: $15,194,000
Approx. Number Employees: 177
Year Founded: 1946
Business Description:
Optical Subcomponents for Telecommunications Industry & Advance Illumination Systems for the Machine Vision Industry
S.I.C.: 3827; 3699; 3812
N.A.I.C.S.: 333314; 334511; 335999
Export
Advertising Expenditures: $843,000
Media: 2-4-5-7-10-13-17-20-26
Distr.: Natl.
Budget Set: Oct.
Personnel:
Mark Wentworth Blodgett *(Chm & CEO)*
Timothy Paul Losik *(CFO & COO)*
Marianne Molleur *(VP-HR & IT)*
Howard Longin *(Dir-Sls-Americas)*
Brands & Products:
COBRA
INSPECTOR
JACKLITE
LASIRIS
LITE MITE
SATURN
SLIM-LINE
SPECBRIGHT
STEAD-LITE
STOCKERYALE
SUPERLITE
ULTRAVISION

PYROMETER INSTRUMENT CO., INC.

(Sub. of Makke LLC)
92 N Main St Bldg 18-D
Windsor, NJ 08561-0479
Tel.: (609) 443-5522
Fax: (609) 443-5590
Toll Free: (800) HOTPYRO
E-mail: sales@pyrometer.com
Web Site: www.pyrometer.com
E-Mail For Key Personnel:
Sales Director: sales@pyrometer.com
Approx. Sls.: $5,000,000
Approx. Number Employees: 25
Year Founded: 1928
Business Description:
Precision Temperature Measurement Instruments for Space, Defense, Science & Industry
S.I.C.: 3823; 3822
N.A.I.C.S.: 334513; 334512
Import Export
Media: 2-4-7-13-26
Distr.: Intl.; Natl.
Budget Set: Sept.
Personnel:
David Crozier *(Owner)*
Brands & Products:
MICROTHERM
OPTITHERM
PRT-5
PYRO
PYROFIBER
PYROLASER
THERMATRACE II

Q A GROUP LLC.

(D/B/A Quantum Analytics)
363 Vintage Pk Dr
Foster City, CA 94404-1185
Tel.: (650) 312-0900
Fax: (650) 312-0313
Toll Free: (800) 992-4199
E-mail: lqa@lqa.com
Web Site: www.lqa.com
Approx. Number Employees: 40
Year Founded: 1989
Business Description:
Rent, Lease & Sell Analytical Instruments
S.I.C.: 7359; 5085
N.A.I.C.S.: 532490; 423840
Advertising Expenditures: $250,000
Media: 4-5-7-10-13
Distr.: Natl.
Budget Set: Nov.
Personnel:
Gerard M. Farren *(Pres & CEO)*
Neil Kranz *(CFO)*
Bruce Harris *(Mgr-Mktg)*

QUALMARK CORPORATION

4580 Florence St
Denver, CO 80238
Tel.: (303) 254-8800
Fax: (303) 254-8343
Toll Free: (888) 425-8669
E-mail: info@qualmark.com
Web Site: www.qualmark.com
Sales Range: $10-24.9 Million
Approx. Number Employees: 45
Year Founded: 1991
Business Description:
Highly Accelerated Life Test & Stress Screen Equipment Mfr & Marketer
S.I.C.: 3821; 3823; 5047
N.A.I.C.S.: 339111; 334513; 423450
Media: 2-7-10-13-22
Personnel:
Christopher Roser *(Chm)*
Andrew Drenick *(Pres & CEO)*
Carol Drake *(VP-Engrg)*
Ross Atwood *(Dir-Svcs)*
Mark Feero *(Dir-Ops)*
Brands & Products:
ASK THE EXPERTS
OVS
QUALMARK
Advertising Agency:
Power PR
18103 Prairie Ave
Torrance, CA 90504
Tel.: (310) 787-1940
Fax: (310) 787-1970

QUEST TECHNOLOGIES, INC.

(Sub. of 3M Company)
1060 Corporate Ctr Dr
Oconomowoc, WI 53066-4828
Tel.: (262) 567-9157
Fax: (262) 567-4047
Toll Free: (800) 245-0779
E-mail: quest.mail@mmm.com
Web Site: www.quest-technologies.com
E-Mail For Key Personnel:
Sales Director: sales@quest-technologies.com
Sales Range: $25-49.9 Million
Approx. Number Employees: 90
Year Founded: 1946
Business Description:
Health, Safety & Environmental Noise, Heat Stress & Vibration Monitoring Equipment Mfr
S.I.C.: 3829
N.A.I.C.S.: 334519
Import Export
Advertising Expenditures: $300,000
Media: 2-4-7-10-11
Distr.: Intl.; Natl.; Reg.
Budget Set: Aug.
Personnel:
Nick Eleftheriou *(Pres & CEO)*
Dan Heerey *(CFO)*
James D. Banach *(COO & Exec VP)*
Wilson Rodriguez *(VP-Intl Sls)*
Mike Wurm *(VP-Engrg)*
Sheila Goodson *(Dir-Quality)*
Brands & Products:
HAVPRO
NOISEPRO
QUEST TECHNOLOGIES
QUESTEMP
QUESTSUITE
SOUNDPRO

QUESTAR CORPORATION

6204 Ingham Rd
New Hope, PA 18938-9663
Tel.: (215) 862-5277
Fax: (215) 862-0512
Toll Free: (800) 247-9607
E-mail: questar@questarcorporation.com
Web Site: www.questarcorporation.com
Approx. Number Employees: 5
Year Founded: 1950
Business Description:
Telescopes & Telephoto Lenses & other Optical Systems Including Long-Distance Microscopes & Computer Analytic Systems Mfr & Distr
S.I.C.: 3827; 7371
N.A.I.C.S.: 333314; 541511
Import Export
Media: 2-4-6-7
Distr.: Intl.; Natl.
Budget Set: Jan.
Personnel:
Donald J. Bandurick *(Pres)*
Brands & Products:
CORONADO SOLAR MAX 40
THE OPTICAL INNOVATORS
QMAX
QUESTAR

RAVEN INDUSTRIES, INC. - ENGINEERED FILMS DIV.

(Div. of Raven Industries, Inc.)
1813 E Ave PO Box 5107
Sioux Falls, SD 57104
Tel.: (605) 336-2750
Tel.: (605) 335-0174
Fax: (605) 331-0333
Toll Free: (800) 635-3456
E-mail: efdsales@ravenind.com
Web Site: www.rufco.com
Sales Range: $25-49.9 Million
Approx. Number Employees: 120
Year Founded: 1956
Business Description:
Balloons, Inflatables & Tarpaulins Mfr. & Researcher
S.I.C.: 3672; 3081
N.A.I.C.S.: 334412; 326113
Media: 2-10
Personnel:
James D. Groninger *(VP & Gen Mgr)*
Brands & Products:
CANVEX C94WB
CANVEX CB12WB
CANVEX I
CONKURE
DURA-SKRIM 10HUV
DURA-SKRIM 2
DURA-SKRIM 2FR
DURA-SKRIM 6BB
DURA-SKRIM 6WW
DURA-SKRIM 8BBR
DURA-SKRIM 8WB
DURASKRIM
RUFCO 300
RUFCO 400
RUFCO 4SSB
RUFCO 4WB
RUFCO 610B
RUFCO SUPER SAMPSON
RUFCO WRAP
VAPOR BLOCK
Advertising Agency:
Main Ideas
26485 482nd Ave
Brandon, SD 57005
Tel.: (605) 582-7800
Fax: (605) 582-8922

REALD INC.

100 N Crescent Dr Ste 120
Beverly Hills, CA 90210
Tel.: (310) 385-4000
Fax: (310) 385-4001
E-mail: rheineman@reald.com
Web Site: www.reald.com
Approx. Rev.: $246,136,000
Approx. Number Employees: 114
Year Founded: 2003
Business Description:
Stereoscopic 3D Technologies Mfr & Licensor
S.I.C.: 3827
N.A.I.C.S.: 333314
Advertising Expenditures: $4,300,000
Personnel:
Michael V. Lewis *(Chm & CEO)*
Andrew A. Skarupa *(CFO & COO)*
Gary Sharp *(CTO and Chief Innovation Officer)*
Robert Mason *(Pres-Consumer Electronics)*
Joseph Peixoto *(Pres-Worldwide Cinema)*
Craig Gatarz *(Gen Counsel & Exec VP)*
Steve Shannon *(Exec VP-Consumer Electronics)*
Brands & Products:
REALD

RECON/OPTICAL, INC.

(Name Changed to Goodrich ISR Barrington)

RESEARCH, INCORPORATED

7041 Boone Ave
Brooklyn Park, MN 55428
Tel.: (952) 941-3300
Fax: (952) 941-3628
Telex: 29-0502
E-mail: info@researchinc.com
Web Site: www.researchinc.com
E-Mail For Key Personnel:

Key to Media (For complete agency information see *The Advertising Red Books-Agencies* edition):
1. Bus. Publs. 2. Cable T.V. 3. Catalogs & Directories. 4. Co-op Adv. 5. Consumer Mags. 6. D.M. to Bus. Estab.7. D.M. to Consumers
8. Daily Newsp. 9. Exhibits/Trade Shows 10. Foreign 11. Infomercial 12. Internet Adv.13. Multimedia 14. Network Radio
15. Network T.V. 16. Newsp. Distr. Mags. 17. Other 18. Outdoor (Posters, Transit) 19. Point of Purchase20. Premiums, Novelties
21. Product Samples 22. Special Events Mktg. 23. Spot Radio 24. Spot T.V. 25. Weekly Newsp. 26. Yellow Page Adv.

Public Relations: investment@researchinc.com
Approx. Number Employees: 129
Year Founded: 1952
Business Description:
Process Control Instrument & Radiant Heating Devices Designer & Mfr
S.I.C.: 3567; 3823
N.A.I.C.S.: 333994; 334513
Export
Media: 4-5-10-16-20
Personnel:
Chad Carney *(Dir-Mktg)*
Brands & Products:
CHAMBIR
CONTROLIR
COOLIR
DRYIR
HI-TEMPIR
LINEIR
MODULEIR
SIMULATEIR
SPEED-DRI
SPOTIR
STRIPIR
TESTIR
Advertising Agency:
JAM Advertising Inc.
7270 Forestview Ln N Ste 200
Maple Grove, MN 55369
Tel.: (763) 898-3794
Fax: (763) 898-3804

RICHARD-ALLAN SCIENTIFIC COMPANY
(Sub. of Thermo Fisher Scientific Inc.)
4481 Campus Dr
Kalamazoo, MI 49008
Tel.: (269) 544-5600
Fax: (269) 272-2674
Toll Free: (800) 522-7270
Web Site: www.thermofisher.com/global/en/home.asp
Sales Range: $25-49.9 Million
Approx. Number Employees: 145
Business Description:
Anatomical Pathology Instruments Mfr
S.I.C.: 3821
N.A.I.C.S.: 339111
Media: 2-10-20-21
Personnel:
Leo Kulmazewski *(Gen Mgr)*
Brands & Products:
SIGNATURE SERIES
TECH-RITE

RITZ CAMERA CENTERS, INC.
(Filed Ch 11 Bankruptcy #910617 on 02/22/09 in U.S. Bankruptcy Ct, Dist of DE, Wilmington)
6711 Ritz Way
Beltsville, MD 20705-1318
Tel.: (301) 419-0000
Fax: (301) 419-2995
Toll Free: (800) 444-9615
E-mail: customerservice@ritzcamera.com
Web Site: www.ritzcamera.com
Approx. Number Employees: 11,000
Year Founded: 1918
Business Description:
Retailer of Photographic Equipment & Supplies; Video & Electronics
S.I.C.: 5946; 5941
N.A.I.C.S.: 443130; 451110
Media: 4-5-6-8-9-10-13-16-19-23-24-26
Personnel:
David M. Ritz *(Chm)*
Fred H. Lerner *(Pres & CEO)*
Scott F. Neamand *(CFO & Exec VP-Ritz Interactive)*
Andre Brysha *(CMO & Sr VP-Ritz Interactive)*
Richard Tranchida *(Exec VP)*

ROCKY MOUNTAIN INSTRUMENT, INC.
106 Laser Dr
Lafayette, CO 80026
Tel.: (303) 664-5000
Fax: (303) 664-5001
Web Site: www.rmico.com
Sales Range: $75-99.9 Million
Approx. Number Employees: 100
Business Description:
Provider of Optical & Laser Technology Solutions
S.I.C.: 3827; 3229
N.A.I.C.S.: 333314; 327212
Media: 2
Personnel:
Steven Hahn *(CEO)*
Zhiming Lu *(VP-Tech)*
Deborah Hunt *(Mgr)*
Yubong Hahn *(Chief Scientist & Strategist)*

ROHDE & SCHWARZ, INC.
(Sub. of Rohde & Schwarz GmbH & Co. KG)
8661A Robert Fulton Dr
Columbia, MD 21046-2265
Tel.: (410) 910-7800
Fax: (410) 910-7801
E-mail: info@rsa.rohde-schwarz.com
Web Site: www.rohde-schwarz.com/usa
Approx. Number Employees: 55
Year Founded: 1978
Business Description:
Electronic Test & Measurement, Communications & Direction Finding Equipment Sales & Services
S.I.C.: 5065
N.A.I.C.S.: 423690
Import
Advertising Expenditures: $264,000
Bus. Publs.: $48,000; D.M. to Bus. Estab.: $36,000; Exhibits/Trade Shows: $180,000
Distr.: Intl.; Natl.
Budget Set: Oct.
Personnel:
Scott Bausback *(Pres, CEO & Mng Dir)*

ROPER SCIENTIFIC, INC.
(Sub. of Roper Industries, Inc.)
3660 Quakerbridge Rd
Trenton, NJ 08619
Tel.: (609) 587-9797
Fax: (609) 587-1970
E-mail: moreinfo@princetoninstruments.com
Web Site:
www.princetoninstruments.com
Sales Range: $50-74.9 Million
Approx. Number Employees: 225
Year Founded: 1979
Business Description:
Mfr. of Instruments for Digital Imaging & Spectroscopy
S.I.C.: 3827; 3861
N.A.I.C.S.: 333314; 333315
Export
Media: 7-10-11-13

S-T INDUSTRIES, INC.
301 Armstrong Blvd N
Saint James, MN 56081-1206
Mailing Address:
PO Box 517
Saint James, MN 56081-0517
Tel.: (507) 375-3211
Fax: (507) 375-4503
Toll Free: (800) 326-2039
E-mail: sales@stindustries.com
Web Site: www.stindustries.com
E-Mail For Key Personnel:
Sales Director: sales@stindustries.com
Approx. Number Employees: 100
Year Founded: 1942
Business Description:
Optical Comparators & Precision Measuring Tools Mfr
S.I.C.: 3423; 3829
N.A.I.C.S.: 332212; 334519
Import Export
Media: 2-4-10
Distr.: Indus. Distrs.; Natl.
Budget Set: Nov.
Personnel:
Margaret A. Smith *(Pres & CFO)*
Robert Friesen *(VP-Mktg)*
Grant Lillevold *(VP-Engrg)*
Brands & Products:
S-T
SCHERR-TUMICO

SCHNEIDER OPTICS INC.
(Sub. of Jos. Schneider Optische Werke GmbH)
285 Oser Ave
Hauppauge, NY 11788
Tel.: (631) 761-5000
Fax: (631) 761-5090
E-mail: info@schneideroptics.com
Web Site: www.schneideroptics.com
Approx. Number Employees: 30
Business Description:
Photographic Cameras, Projectors, Equipment & Supplies Mfr
S.I.C.: 5043
N.A.I.C.S.: 423410
Media: 6-10
Personnel:
Dwight Lindsey *(CEO)*
Brands & Products:
APO-SYMMAR
CINE-DIGITAR
GAUSSOPT_IK
MACRO-SYMMAR
SUPER CINELUX
THEATRE DESIGN PRO

SCHUTTE & KOERTING INC.
2510 Metropolitan Dr
Trevose, PA 19053
Tel.: (215) 639-0900
Fax: (215) 639-1597
E-mail: sales@s-k.com
Web Site: www.s-k.com
E-Mail For Key Personnel:
Sales Director: sales@s-k.com
Approx. Number Employees: 50
Year Founded: 1876
Business Description:
Flow Measuring Instruments & Flow Indicators, Turbine Meters, Flow Calibration Stands, Jet Ejectors, Condensers, Power Valves, Desuperheaters, Ejector-Venturi Scrubbers, XO Technologies Airborne Management Systems Mfr
S.I.C.: 3823
N.A.I.C.S.: 334513
Export
Advertising Expenditures: $400,000
Media: 2-7
Distr.: Natl.
Budget Set: Sept.
Brands & Products:
S&K
SCHUTTE & KOERTING
TURBO DRAFT

SCIENTIFIC INSTRUMENTS, INC.
4400 W Tiffany Dr
West Palm Beach, FL 33407-3225
Tel.: (561) 881-8500
Fax: (561) 881-8556
E-mail: info@scientificinstruments.com
Web Site:
www.scientificinstruments.com
Approx. Sls.: $3,000,000
Approx. Number Employees: 50
Year Founded: 1967
Business Description:
Laboratory Instrumentation & Temperature Sensing Products
S.I.C.: 3679; 3829
N.A.I.C.S.: 334419; 334519
Export
Media: 2-4-7-10-11-13
Distr.: Intl.; Natl.
Budget Set: Dec.
Personnel:
Leigh Ann Capers *(Owner)*
Brands & Products:
SCIENTIFIC INSTRUMENTS

SELLSTROM MANUFACTURING CO.
1 Sellstrom Dr
Palatine, IL 60067-6260
Tel.: (847) 358-2000
Fax: (847) 358-8564
Toll Free: (800) 323-7402
E-mail: sellstrom@sellstrom.com
Web Site: www.sellstrom.com
Approx. Number Employees: 150
Year Founded: 1923
Business Description:
Protective Gear & Personal Safety Products Engineer, Mfr & Marketer
S.I.C.: 3851; 2389
N.A.I.C.S.: 339115; 315999
Export
Media: 2-4-5-7-8-10-11-17-19-20-22
Distr.: Intl.; Natl.
Personnel:
David Peters *(Pres & CEO)*
James R. Franklin *(VP-Sls & Mktg)*
Lawrence Schmidt *(VP-Fin)*
Brands & Products:
ADVANTAGE
ARCFLASH
ATLANTIS
AVALANCHE
B5
DE-TONE
DOLPHINS
DP4
DYNO-MITES

Key to Media (For complete agency information see *The Advertising Red Books-Agencies* edition):
1. Bus. Publs. 2. Cable T.V. 3. Catalogs & Directories. 4. Co-op Adv. 5. Consumer Mags. 6. D.M. to Bus. Estab.7. D.M. to Consumers 8. Daily Newsp. 9. Exhibits/Trade Shows 10. Foreign 11. Infomercial 12. Internet Adv.13. Multimedia 14. Network Radio 15. Network T.V. 16. Newsp. Distr. Mags. 17. Other 18. Outdoor (Posters, Transit) 19. Point of Purchase20. Premiums, Novelties 21. Product Samples 22. Special Events Mktg. 23. Spot Radio 24. Spot T.V. 25. Weekly Newsp. 26. Yellow Page Adv.

Sellstrom Manufacturing Co. — (Continued)

ECONOMY
FIREBIRDS
GRAFIT
GRAVIT-EYE
GUEST-GARD
HAND HELD IRON MASK
HOTSHOTS
IMPULSE
IRON MASK
KNEE-PRO ULTRA FLEX III
KNEEL-EZE
MATRIX
MAXVIEW
MONITOR
NEOPRENE
NUISANCE
ODYSSEY
PHANTOM
PHANTOM ELECTRO
PT9
QUICK SNAP
RAPID-CLEAR
SAF-STOR
SAFEGUARD
SAFEGUARDS
SEBRING
SEL-KLEEN
SELLSTROM
SENTRYWASH
SHOCK ABSORBING EXPANDER
SIGHTLINE
SILICONE
SONIX
SPATTER-GUARD FM
STA-CLEAR
STRIKER
SUPER TUFF
SUPERVISOR
TECHNOSPORTS II
TIEBACK
TITAN
TONEDOWN
VICTORY LANE
WELD-FLEX
WINGS
X100
X12
X200
X300
XX2
ZIP-KLIP

SERADYN, INC.

(Sub. of Richard-Allan Scientific Company)
7998 Georgetown Rd Ste 1000
Indianapolis, IN 46268
Tel.: (317) 610-3800
Fax: (317) 610-3888
Fax: (317) 610-0018
Toll Free: (800) 428-4072
E-mail: info@seradyn.com
Web Site: www.seradyn.com
Sales Range: $25-49.9 Million
Approx. Number Employees: 65
Year Founded: 1984
Business Description:
Diagnostic Reagents & Instruments & Latex Microparticles Mfr
S.I.C.: 2834
N.A.I.C.S.: 325412
Media: 2-4-7-10-11-20-21
Distr.: Natl.
Budget Set: Oct.
Personnel:
Lili Arabshahi *(VP-Product Devel)*
Rick Galloway *(VP-Mktg)*

SERVO CORPORATION OF AMERICA

123 Frost St
Westbury, NY 11590-5027
Tel.: (516) 938-9700
Fax: (516) 938-9644
E-mail: steveb@servo.com
Web Site: www.servo.com
Sales Range: $10-24.9 Million
Approx. Number Employees: 17
Year Founded: 1946
Business Description:
Provider of Transportation & Control Products: Hot Box Detection Systems; Data Equipment Displays; Malfunction Detection Systems; Electronic Crossing Control & Protection Systems; Microwave Signal Analyzers; Electro-Optical Systems & Components
S.I.C.: 3812; 3821; 3824; 3829; 3873
N.A.I.C.S.: 334511; 334514; 334518; 334519; 339111
Export
Media: 1-2-4-10-11-17
Distr.: Intl.; Natl.
Budget Set: Oct.
Personnel:
Stephen A. Barre *(Pres)*
George Rullman *(VP-Engrg)*
Brands & Products:
HORIZON CROSSING INDICATOR
MIDES
SERVO
SERVOFLIGHT
SERVOSEA

SETRA SYSTEMS, INC.

(Sub. of Gems Sensors Inc.)
159 Swanson Rd
Boxboro, MA 01719-1316
Tel.: (978) 263-1400
Fax: (978) 266-2105
Toll Free: (800) 257-3872
E-mail: transducer.sales@setra.com
Web Site: www.setra.com
Sales Range: $50-74.9 Million
Approx. Number Employees: 150
Year Founded: 1967
Business Description:
Pressure Transducers & Weighing Systems Mfr
S.I.C.: 3829; 3821
N.A.I.C.S.: 334519; 339111
Export
Advertising Expenditures: $300,000
Media: 2-7-10-25
Distr.: Natl.
Personnel:
Srinivas Bagatelli *(CEO)*
Mike Guerra *(Sls Mgr)*
Sameer Trikha *(Sls Mgr)*
Tiago Anes *(Mgr-Natl Sales)*
Diane Shaughnessy *(Mgr-Mktg Commun)*
Brands & Products:
SETRA CRAM
SUPER II

SGS NORTH AMERICA INC.

(Sub. of Societe Generale de Surveillance Holding SA)
201 Route 17 N
Rutherford, NJ 07070
Tel.: (201) 508-3000
Fax: (201) 508-3039
E-mail: sgsna.us@sgs.com
Web Site: www.us.sgs.com
Approx. Number Employees: 200
Year Founded: 1980
Business Description:
Holding Company; Regional Managing Office
S.I.C.: 6719
N.A.I.C.S.: 551112; 551114
Media: 2-4-7-9-10-17-25-26
Distr.: Natl.
Budget Set: Nov. -Dec.
Personnel:
Christian Jilch *(Owner)*
Michael Briganti *(CFO & Sr VP)*
Jeffrey McDonald *(COO)*

SHIMADZU SCIENTIFIC INSTRUMENTS, INC.

(Sub. of Shimadzu Corporation)
7102 Riverwood Dr
Columbia, MD 21046
Tel.: (410) 381-1227
Fax: (410) 381-1222
Toll Free: (800) 477-1227
E-mail: webmaster@shimadzu.com
Web Site: www.ssi.shimadzu.com
Approx. Number Employees: 220
Year Founded: 1975
Business Description:
Mfr of Analytical, Testing & Characterizations Instruments
S.I.C.: 5049
N.A.I.C.S.: 423490
Import Export
Advertising Expenditures: $735,000
Multimedia: $10,000; Bus. Publs.: $300,000; Catalogs & Directories: $5,000; D.M. to Bus. Estab.: $20,000; Exhibits/Trade Shows: $350,000; Foreign: $30,000; Premiums, Novelties: $20,000
Distr.: Natl.
Personnel:
Kevin McLaughlin *(Coord-Mktg Comm)*
Advertising Agencies:
Schubert Communications, Inc.
112 Schubert Dr
Downingtown, PA 19335-3382
Tel.: (610) 269-2100
Fax: (610) 269-2275

SMS
Weymouth Rd.
Landisville, NJ 08326
Tel.: (856) 697-1257

SIEMENS MOLECULAR IMAGING, INC.

(Sub. of Siemens Medical Solutions USA, Inc.)
810 Innovation Dr
Knoxville, TN 37932
Tel.: (865) 218-2000
Fax: (865) 218-3004
Toll Free: (800) 841-7226
Sales Range: $400-449.9 Million
Approx. Number Employees: 963
Year Founded: 1983
Business Description:
Medical Analytical Equipment Mfr
S.I.C.: 3845
N.A.I.C.S.: 334510
Media: 2-10
Personnel:
Mark S. Andreaco *(Sr VP)*
Brands & Products:
ECAT

SIGNATURE EYEWEAR, INC.

498 N Oak St
Inglewood, CA 90302-3315
Tel.: (310) 330-2700
Fax: (310) 330-2765
Toll Free: (888) 393-2891
Toll Free: (800) 765EYES
E-mail: customerservice@signatureeyewear.com
Web Site:
www.signatureeyewear.com
E-Mail For Key Personnel:
Sales Director: webmaster@signatureeyewear.com
Approx. Sls.: $20,831,013
Approx. Number Employees: 105
Year Founded: 1983
Business Description:
Prescription Eyeglass Frames Designer, Marketer & Distr
S.I.C.: 3851; 3827; 5048
N.A.I.C.S.: 339115; 333314; 423460
Import Export
Advertising Expenditures: $451,395
Personnel:
Richard M. Torre *(Chm)*
Michael Prince *(CEO)*
Jill Gardner *(Sr VP-Design)*
Raul Khantzis *(Sr VP)*
Kevin D. Seifert *(Sr VP)*
Brands & Products:
BRAVADO
INTUITION
LIFESCAPE
SIGNATURE
SIGNATURE EYEWEAR

SIGNET ARMORLITE, INC.

(Sub. of Essilor of America, Inc.)
1001 Armorlite Dr
San Marcos, CA 92069-1440
Tel.: (760) 744-4000
Fax: (760) 471-6255
Toll Free: (800) 759-4630
E-mail: info@signetarmorlite.com
Web Site: www.signetarmorlite.com
Sales Range: $125-149.9 Million
Approx. Number Employees: 200
Year Founded: 1947
Business Description:
Ophthalmic Lenses Mfr
S.I.C.: 3851
N.A.I.C.S.: 339115
Advertising Expenditures: $5,000,000
Media: 1-2-4-5-7-10-13-19-21
Distr.: Intl.; Natl.
Budget Set: Sept.
Personnel:
Bruno Salvadori *(Pres)*
M. Kathryn Bernard *(VP-Fin)*
Edward P. DeRosa *(VP-Sls & Mktg)*
Jim Misco *(VP-Sls)*
Jan Kubiak *(Mgr-Mktg)*
Brands & Products:
ARMORLITE
CLEAR
CONCISE
EVOCLEAR
INSTASHADES
MULTI-MATRIX TECHNOLOGY
NAVIGATOR
NAVIGATOR SHORT
POLARSHADES

Key to Media (For complete agency information see *The Advertising Red Books-Agencies* edition):
1. Bus. Publs. 2. Cable T.V. 3. Catalogs & Directories. 4. Co-op Adv. 5. Consumer Mags. 6. D.M. to Bus. Estab.7. D.M. to Consumers
8. Daily Newsp. 9. Exhibits/Trade Shows 10. Foreign 11. Infomercial 12. Internet Adv.13. Multimedia 14. Network Radio
15. Network T.V. 16. Newsp. Distr. Mags. 17. Other 18. Outdoor (Posters, Transit) 19. Point of Purchase20. Premiums, Novelties
21. Product Samples 22. Special Events Mktg. 23. Spot Radio 24. Spot T.V. 25. Weekly Newsp. 26. Yellow Page Adv.

POLYCLEAR
PRACTICEPLUS
PRECISE
RLX PLUS
RLXPLUS
SIGNET ARMORLITE
VISION FIRST DESIGN
ZONE OF MAXIMUM USE

SILHOUETTE OPTICAL LTD.
(Sub. of Silhouette International Schmied AG)
260 Cannon St
Green Island, NY 12183
Tel.: (518) 272-5500
Fax: (518) 272-5700
E-mail: customer.service@us.silhouette.com
Web Site: www.us.silhouette.com
Approx. Number Employees: 100
Business Description:
Eyewear
S.I.C.: 3842
N.A.I.C.S.: 339113
Personnel:
Chris Juergens *(Pres)*
Advertising Agency:
Lippe Taylor
215 Park Ave S 16th Fl
New York, NY 10003
Tel.: (212) 598-4400
Fax: (212) 598-0620

SIMPSON ELECTRIC COMPANY
520 Simpson Ave
Lac Du Flambeau, WI 54538
Tel.: (715) 588-3311
Tel.: (715) 788-3947 (Customer Svc)
Fax: (715) 588-3326
Fax: (715) 588-1248 (Customer Svc)
E-mail: dservice@simpsonelectric.com
Web Site: www.simpsonelectric.com
Approx. Sls.: $182,200,000
Approx. Number Employees: 350
Year Founded: 1936
Business Description:
Mfr. of Analog & Digital Test Instrumentation & Panel Meters
S.I.C.: 3663; 3829
N.A.I.C.S.: 334220; 334519
Import Export
Media: 2-4-5-7-10-11-13
Distr.: Intl.; Natl.
Budget Set: Oct.
Personnel:
William Conn *(Pres & CEO)*

SIRONA DENTAL SYSTEMS, INC.
30-30 47th Ave Ste 500
Long Island City, NY 11101-3492
Tel.: (718) 482-2011
Tel.: (718) 937-5765
Fax: (718) 937-5962
Toll Free: (888) 472-4425
E-mail: contact@sirona.com
Web Site: www.sirona.com
Approx. Rev.: $770,276,000
Approx. Number Employees: 2,345
Year Founded: 1992
Business Description:
Dental Digital Imaging Equipment Mfr
S.I.C.: 3843
N.A.I.C.S.: 339114
Advertising Expenditures: $22,769
Media: 2-10
Personnel:
Jost Fischer *(Chm & CEO)*
Jeffrey T. Slovin *(Pres)*
Simone Blank *(CFO & Exec VP)*
Jonathan I. Friedman *(Gen Counsel & Sec)*
Walter Petersohn *(Exec VP-Sls)*
Stan Mandelkern *(VP-Engrng)*
Michael Williamson *(VP-Sls & Mktg)*
John Smithson *(Mktg Dir-Sirona USA Imaging Sys)*
Kent Albrecht *(Mgr-Territory)*
Jose Balta *(Territory Mgr-Handpieces Northern California)*
Clark Colwell *(Mgr-Territory)*
Gary Fitzpatrick *(Mgr-Territory-Southern California)*
Art Geier *(Territory Mgr-Handpieces)*
Bob Gess *(Mgr-Territory)*
Mark Hahn *(Mgr-Territory-Metro New York)*
Mohamad Hamden *(Territory Mgr-Florida)*
Don Harvey *(Mgr-Territory)*
Craig Hennings *(Territory Mgr)*
Pat Hess *(Mgr-Territory-New York)*
Tim Knight *(Territory Mgr-Illinois & Wisconsin)*
Chris Lashley *(Territory Mgr)*
Lamar Lutz *(Mgr-Territory-North)*
Tracy MacDonald *(Territory Mgr-Handpieces)*
Rick McLane *(Mgr-Territory-Eastern Pennsylvania)*
Ashish Mittal *(Mgr-India)*
Steven Pryce *(Mgr-Natl Accts)*
David Ruesch *(Territory Sls Mgr-Eastern)*
Jay Schroeder *(Mgr-Territory)*
Tom Thuente *(Mgr-Territory)*
Alan Twible *(Territory Mgr-Florida)*
Ross Webb *(Mgr-Territory-Handpieces)*
Steve Winik *(Territory Mgr)*
Brands & Products:
CDR
DAC PROFESSIONAL
DAC UNIVERSAL
GALILEOS
HELIODENT
IMPLANT 20:1
INLAB
NITRASEAL
ORTHOPHOS
SIDEXIS XG
SIRODEM
SIROLASER
SIRONA
SIRONITI
SIROPURE
TENEO
Advertising Agency:
The Lanmark Group Inc.
527 Industrial Way W
Eatontown, NJ 07724-2211
Tel.: (732) 389-4500
Fax: (732) 389-4998

SMITH VICTOR CORPORATION
1268 Humbracht Cir
Bartlett, IL 60103
Tel.: (630) 830-2500
Fax: (630) 830-2525
E-mail: sales@smithvictor.com
Web Site: www.smithvictor.com
E-Mail For Key Personnel:
Sales Director: sales@smithvictor.com
Sales Range: $1-9.9 Million
Approx. Number Employees: 30
Year Founded: 1874
Business Description:
Mfr. & Wholesaler of Photographic Lighting Equipment & Home Video Accessories
S.I.C.: 3861; 3646
N.A.I.C.S.: 333315; 335122
Import Export
Media: 2-4-5-6-7-8-10-17
Distr.: Intl.; Natl.
Budget Set: Mar.
Personnel:
Ken Orlando *(Pres)*
Brands & Products:
MEDLIGHT
SMITH VICTOR
TORCHLAMP

SOLA INTERNATIONAL INC.
(Sub. of Carl Zeiss Meditec AG)
10590 W Ocean Air Dr Ste 300
San Diego, CA 92130-4682
Tel.: (858) 509-9899
Fax: (858) 509-9898
E-mail: info@sola.com
Web Site: www.sola.com
Sales Range: $650-699.9 Million
Approx. Number Employees: 6,634
Year Founded: 1960
Business Description:
Plastic & Glass Eyeglass Lenses Mfr & Sales
S.I.C.: 3851; 3544
N.A.I.C.S.: 339115; 333511
Import Export
Advertising Expenditures: $7,500,000
Brands & Products:
AO COMPACT
AO EASY
ASL
SOLAMAX
SOLAONE
UTMC

SOLSTICE MARKETING CONCEPTS, LLC
(Sub. of Safilo USA Inc.)
404 5th Ave 2nd Fl
New York, NY 10018
Tel.: (646) 348-6100
Fax: (646) 348-6110
E-mail: christinac@solsticestores.com
Web Site: www.solsticestores.com
Sales Range: $350-399.9 Million
Approx. Number Employees: 800
Business Description:
Sunglasses Retailer
S.I.C.: 5995
N.A.I.C.S.: 446130
Media: 19-22
Personnel:
Ross Brownlee *(CEO)*
Rick Talmage *(COO)*
Jan Michel *(VP-Retail)*

SONOSITE, INC.
21919 30th Dr SE
Bothell, WA 98021-3904
Tel.: (425) 951-1200
Fax: (425) 951-1201
Toll Free: (888) 482-9449
E-mail: admin@sonosite.com
Web Site: www.sonosite.com
Approx. Rev.: $275,362,000
Approx. Number Employees: 878
Business Description:
Hand-Carried Ultrasound & Other Medical Imaging Device Developer, Mfr & Distr
S.I.C.: 3845; 3841
N.A.I.C.S.: 334510; 339112
Advertising Expenditures: $10,000,000
Personnel:
Kevin M. Goodwin *(Pres & CEO)*
Marcus Y. Smith *(CFO & Sr VP)*
Jack Sparacio *(COO)*
Matthew C. Damron *(Global CMO)*
Marla R. Koreis *(Chief Admin Officer & VP-HR)*
Diku Mandavia *(Chief Medical Officer & Sr VP)*
John S. Bowers, Jr. *(Sr VP-Strategic Dev & Patient Safety Innovations)*
Graham D. Cox *(Sr VP-Worldwide Sls & Market Dev)*
James M. Gilmore *(Sr VP-Product Innovation & Delivery)*
Brands & Products:
180PLUS
ILOOK
M-TURBO
MICROMAXX
S SERIES
SONOCALC
SONOHEART
SONOSITE
TITAN
Advertising Agency:
Crowell Advertising, Marketing and PR
12 S 400 W 2nd Fl
Salt Lake City, UT 84101
Tel.: (801) 531-0533
Fax: (801) 531-0547

SOURCE PHOTONICS, INC.
(Holding of Francisco Partners Management, LLC)
20550 Nordhoff St
Chatsworth, CA 91311-6113
Tel.: (818) 773-9044
Fax: (818) 773-0261
E-mail: sales@sourcephotonics.com
Web Site: www.sourcephotonics.com
E-Mail For Key Personnel:
Sales Director: sales@sourcephotonics.com
Sales Range: $75-99.9 Million
Approx. Number Employees: 1,486
Year Founded: 1988
Business Description:
Fiber Optic Components & Subsystems Designer, Developer & Mfr
S.I.C.: 3357; 3679
N.A.I.C.S.: 335921; 334419
Advertising Expenditures: $225,746
Media: 10
Personnel:
Alexis Black Bjorlin *(Pres)*
Near Margalit *(CEO)*
Brett Chloupek *(CFO & Sec)*
Yu-Heng Jan *(COO & Gen Mgr-Taiwan)*
Thomas Liljeberg *(Sr VP-Product Dev & Product Line Mgmt)*
Alex Leibovitch *(VP-AMER Sls)*
Weiming Li *(Gen Mgr-China)*

Key to Media (For complete agency information see *The Advertising Red Books-Agencies* edition):
1. Bus. Publs. 2. Cable T.V. 3. Catalogs & Directories. 4. Co-op Adv. 5. Consumer Mags. 6. D.M. to Bus. Estab.7. D.M. to Consumers
8. Daily Newsp. 9. Exhibits/Trade Shows 10. Foreign 11. Infomercial 12. Internet Adv.13. Multimedia 14. Network Radio
15. Network T.V. 16. Newsp. Distr. Mags. 17. Other 18. Outdoor (Posters, Transit) 19. Point of Purchase20. Premiums, Novelties
21. Product Samples 22. Special Events Mktg. 23. Spot Radio 24. Spot T.V. 25. Weekly Newsp. 26. Yellow Page Adv.

SOUTHWESTERN INDUSTRIES, INC.
2615 Homestead Pl Rancho Dominguez
Compton, CA 90224-9066
Tel.: (310) 608-4422
Fax: (310) 764-2668
E-mail: info@southwesternindustries.com
Web Site: www.southwesternindustries.com
E-Mail For Key Personnel:
Sales Director: sales@southwesternindustries.com
Approx. Number Employees: 175
Year Founded: 1951
Business Description:
Mfr. of Machine Tool Measurement, Control Products & Machine Tools
S.I.C.: 3423; 3625
N.A.I.C.S.: 332212; 335314
Import Export
Advertising Expenditures: $2,500,000
Media: 2-5-7-10-13
Personnel:
R. W. Leonhard *(Pres)*
Stephen F. Pinto *(VP-Fin & Mktg)*
Brands & Products:
P-TRAK
PROTOTRAK
TRAK
TRAK AGE2
TRAK AGE3
TRAV-A-DIAL
Advertising Agency:
Southwestern Industries, Inc.
2615 Homestead Pl
Rancho Dominguez, CA 90220
Tel.: (310) 608-4422
Fax: (310) 764-2668
Toll Free: (800) 367-3165

SPECTRAL DIAGNOSTICS INC.
135 The West Mall
Toronto, ON M9C 1C2, Canada
Tel.: (416) 626-3233
Fax: (416) 626-7383
Toll Free: (888) 426-4264
Web Site: www.spectraldx.com
Approx. Sls.: $3,213,006
Approx. Number Employees: 15
Year Founded: 1991
Business Description:
Disease Management Medical Technology Developer; Reagents, Calibrators & Diagnostic Controls Supplier
S.I.C.: 8733; 3841; 5047
N.A.I.C.S.: 541710; 339112; 423450
Media: 10
Personnel:
Paul M. Walker *(Pres & CEO)*
Anthony Businskas *(CFO & Exec VP)*
Yesmil Pena de Nunez *(Sr VP-Corp Quality, Scientific Affairs)*
Brands & Products:
CARDIAC STATUS
DECISION POINT
EAA
I-LYNX
RAPIDWN
SPECTRAL

SPECTROGON US, INC.
(Sub. of Spectrogon AB)
24B Hill Rd
Parsippany, NJ 07054-1001
Tel.: (973) 331-1191
Fax: (973) 331-1373
E-mail: sales@spectrogon.parsippany.nj.us
Web Site: www.spectrogon.com
Approx. Number Employees: 3
Year Founded: 1970
Business Description:
Interference Filters Mfr
S.I.C.: 3827; 5049
N.A.I.C.S.: 333314; 423490
Media: 2-10
Personnel:
Sam Ponzo *(VP & Gen Mgr)*

SPERRY MARINE INC.
(Sub. of Northrop Grumman Electronic Systems)
1070 Seminole Trl
Charlottesville, VA 22901-2891
Tel.: (434) 974-2000
Fax: (434) 974-2259
E-mail: info@sperry-marine.com
Web Site: www.sperrymarine.northropgrumman.com
Sales Range: $450-499.9 Million
Approx. Number Employees: 1,300
Business Description:
Marine Electronics
S.I.C.: 3812
N.A.I.C.S.: 334511
Media: 4-10
Personnel:
J. Nolasco DaCunha *(VP & Gen Mgr)*
Guy Babineau *(Dir-Engrg)*
John Early *(Dir-Design, ME & Test)*
Andrew Fraser *(Dir-Customer Svc)*
Dhanvant Goradia *(Dir-Sys)*
Jeff Holloway *(Dir-US Defense Bus Dev)*
Jim Isbister *(Dir-Ops)*
John Pyron *(Dir-Military Logistics & Product Support)*
Frank Soccoli *(Dir-Adv & Mktg)*
Robert Tinsley *(Dir-Mission Assurance)*
Brands & Products:
C. PLATH
DECCA
SPERRY
Advertising Agency:
Rhodes Communications, Inc.
4509 Colley Ave
Norfolk, VA 23508
Tel.: (757) 451-0602
Fax: (757) 451-3141

SRI/SURGICAL EXPRESS, INC.
12425 Race Track Rd
Tampa, FL 33626-3118
Tel.: (813) 891-9550
Fax: (813) 818-9076
E-mail: info@srisurgical.com
Web Site: www.surgicalexpress.com
Approx. Rev.: $100,864,000
Approx. Number Employees: 839
Year Founded: 1994
Business Description:
Surgical Products & Services
S.I.C.: 4119; 0752; 3842; 7213
N.A.I.C.S.: 621910; 115210; 339113; 812331
Advertising Expenditures: $30,000
Media: 2-7-8-10
Personnel:
Charles W. Federico *(Chm)*
Gerald G. Woodard *(CEO)*
Mark R. Faris *(CFO)*
William J. Braun *(Sr VP-Ops)*
Jack A. Hamilton *(Sr VP-R&D)*
D. Jon McGuire *(Sr VP-Sls)*
Brands & Products:
EFFICIENCY DELIVERED DAILY
GORE
READYCASE
SRI/SURGICAL EXPRESS
SURGICAL EXPRESS

STEFAN SYDOR OPTICS, INC.
31 Jet Veiw Dr
Rochester, NY 14624
Tel.: (585) 271-7300
Fax: (585) 271-7309
E-mail: sales@sydor.com
Web Site: www.sydor.com
E-Mail For Key Personnel:
Sales Director: sales@sydor.com
Sales Range: $10-24.9 Million
Approx. Number Employees: 60
Year Founded: 1964
Business Description:
Precision Optical Components Mfr
S.I.C.: 3827; 3229
N.A.I.C.S.: 333314; 327212
Media: 2-4-13
Personnel:
James M. Sydor *(Owner & Pres)*
Jude Schnarr *(Office Mgr)*
Sam Ezzezew *(Production Mgr)*
Carol Corey *(Engr-Sls)*

STOELTING CO.
620 Wheat Ln
Wood Dale, IL 60191-1164
Tel.: (630) 860-9700
Fax: (630) 860-9775
E-mail: info@stoeltingco.com
Web Site: www.stoeltingco.com
Sales Range: $1-9.9 Million
Approx. Number Employees: 30
Year Founded: 1886
Business Description:
Developer of Psychological & Physiological Apparatus & Tests, Educational Tests, Lie Detectors, Bio-Feedback Instruments & Employee Screening Materials
S.I.C.: 3826; 3825
N.A.I.C.S.: 334516; 334515
Import Export
Advertising Expenditures: $530,000
Media: 2-4-7-8-10-11-13-22
Distr.: Intl.; Natl.
Personnel:
L. A. Miller *(Chm & CEO)*
Mark Cochran *(CEO)*
Brands & Products:
ANY-ANGLE
ANY-MAZE
APP-1
AUTOCLIPS
AUTOGENICS
BASILE
COMPULAB
CUNNINGHAM
DELTA T
DIGITAL LAB STANDARD
DREMEL
DREMEL MOTO-TOOL
DUMONT
EZ CLIP
FIBER LITE
FIBER-LITE
HAND SAVER
JUST FOR MICE
JVP DOMES
LAB STANDARD
MACLAB
MCILWAIN
MICROMETER
MICROMOTOR
MIDGARD
MIDGUARD
NU GAUZE
NU-GAUZE
PAINLESS
PARAFILM
PARAFILM M
PERFECTUM
PLANTAR
PLANTAR VON FREY
POWERLAB
QUICK STICK
QUIXELL
SAFE-R
STARTFEAR
STELLAR
STOELTING
SURGILUBE
TOUCH TEST
UGO BASILE THERMAL PLANTAR

STORK-HERRON TESTING LABORATORIES, INC.
(Sub. of Stork B.V.)
5405 E Schaaf Rd
Cleveland, OH 44131-1337
Tel.: (216) 524-1450
Fax: (216) 524-1459
E-mail: info.herron@stork.com
Web Site: www.storksmt.com/
Sales Range: $1-9.9 Million
Approx. Number Employees: 50
Year Founded: 1911
Business Description:
Specialized Metals Testing
S.I.C.: 8733
N.A.I.C.S.: 541710
Media: 2-7-10
Distr.: Natl.
Personnel:
Michael R. Gaydos *(CEO, COO & Gen Mgr)*
Mike Robinson *(Mgr-Bus Dev)*

SUNLINK HEALTH SYSTEMS, INC.
900 Circle 75 Pkwy Ste 1120
Atlanta, GA 30339-3095
Tel.: (770) 933-7000
Fax: (770) 933-7010
E-mail: sunlink@sunlinkhealth.com
Web Site: www.sunlinkhealth.com
E-Mail For Key Personnel:
President: rmthornton@krugint.com
Approx. Rev.: $181,161,000
Approx. Number Employees: 1,376
Year Founded: 1959
Business Description:
Hospital Management Services
S.I.C.: 8062
N.A.I.C.S.: 622110
Media: 2-4
Personnel:
Robert M. Thornton, Jr. *(Chm & CEO)*
Mark J. Stockslager *(CFO)*
A. Ronald Turner *(COO)*
Jesus F. Ruiz *(Chief Compliance Officer & Asst VP)*
Byron D. Finn *(Pres-SunLink ScriptsRx, LLC)*

Key to Media (For complete agency information see *The Advertising Red Books-Agencies* edition):
1. Bus. Publs. 2. Cable T.V. 3. Catalogs & Directories. 4. Co-op Adv. 5. Consumer Mags. 6. D.M. to Bus. Estab.7. D.M. to Consumers
8. Daily Newsp. 9. Exhibits/Trade Shows 10. Foreign 11. Infomercial 12. Internet Adv.13. Multimedia 14. Network Radio
15. Network T.V. 16. Newsp. Distr. Mags. 17. Other 18. Outdoor (Posters, Transit) 19. Point of Purchase20. Premiums, Novelties
21. Product Samples 22. Special Events Mktg. 23. Spot Radio 24. Spot T.V. 25. Weekly Newsp. 26. Yellow Page Adv.

Jack M. Spurr, Jr. *(VP-Hospital Fin Ops)*
Chris Roberts *(Asst VP-IT)*
Gene E. Burleson *(Dir-HealthMont)*

SWIFT OPTICAL INSTRUMENTS, INC.

11113 Landmark 35 Dr
San Antonio, TX 78233
Tel.: (210) 967-9438
Toll Free: (877) 967-9438
E-mail: info@swiftoptics.com
Web Site: www.swiftoptics.com
E-Mail For Key Personnel:
Sales Director: sales@swiftoptics.com
Approx. Number Employees: 20
Year Founded: 1926
Business Description:
Whslr & Distr of Binoculars, Field Glasses, Astronomical Telescopes, Barometers, Thermometers, Hydrometers Specialty Magnifiers, Spotting Scopes, Microscopes & Related Accessories
S.I.C.: 3827
N.A.I.C.S.: 333314
Import Export
Media: 2-4-5-6-7-8-9-10-11-19-21
Distr.: Intl.; Natl.
Budget Set: Dec.
Personnel:
Cynthia-Syverson Mercer *(Dir-Mktg & Catalog Sls)*
David Doty *(Mgr-Bus Dev-Digital Products)*
Brands & Products:
ALTIMETER
CONSTELLATION
CONSTITUTION
COUGAR
COUNTESS
DUCHESS
FIREFLY
LANSDOWNE
LARK
LEOPARD
LEXINGTON
LYNX
NIGHTHAWK
PANTHER
PREMIER
PRINCESS
SCIENTIST
SCOUT
SEA HAWK
SEA KING
SEA WOLF
SEARCHER
SWIFT
TELEMASTER
TRILYTE
WATCHMASTER
WATCHMATE
WEATHER STATION
WEATHERMASTER
WICKFORD COMBINATION

SWORDFISH FINANCIAL, INC.

142 Wembley Way
Rockwall, TX 75032
Tel.: (972) 310-1830
Toll Free: (800) 787-8078
Approx. Int. Income: $175,000
Year Founded: 1959
Business Description:
Financial Services
S.I.C.: 6289
N.A.I.C.S.: 523999
Import Export
Advertising Expenditures: $129,230
Media: 1-2-4-7-10-22
Distr.: Intl.; Natl.
Budget Set: Oct.
Personnel:
Michael D. Alexander *(Chm, Pres & CEO)*
Randy J. Moseley *(CFO)*
Christopher S. Lausen *(Pres-Photography Div)*
Brands & Products:
AQUA-VU
BUZZ STIX
CASS CREEK GAME CALLS
CRAZY CRANK
FISH HAWK
FISH TV
GENZ STIX
ICE FISHING
PAK SHACK
QUICK SIT
REINVENTING THE OUTDOOR EXPERIENCE
SHOWDOWN
VECTOR
WELL-VU
WOODLAND WHISPER

SYSTRON DONNER INERTIAL DIVISION

(Div. of Custom Sensors & Technologies)
2700 Systron Dr
Concord, CA 94518
Tel.: (925) 979-4400
Fax: (925) 979-9826
E-mail: sales@systron.com
Web Site: www.systron.com
E-Mail For Key Personnel:
Sales Director: sales@systron.com
Approx. Number Employees: 500
Year Founded: 1990
Business Description:
Inertial Sensors & Subsystems, Accelerometers, Quartz Rate Sensors & Inertial Measurement Units
S.I.C.: 3812
N.A.I.C.S.: 334511
Import Export
Advertising Expenditures: $1,000,000
Media: 2-4-7-10
Distr.: Natl.
Budget Set: Apr.
Personnel:
Dean A. Johnson *(Gen Mgr)*
Dave Hoyh *(Dir-Sls & Mktg)*

TASC, INC.

(Joint Venture of KKR & CO. L.P. & General Atlantic LLC)
4805 Stonecroft Blvd
Chantilly, VA 20151
Tel.: (703) 633-8300
E-mail: TASC-Info@tasc.com
Web Site: www.tasc.com
Approx. Rev.: $1,600,000,000
Approx. Number Employees: 5,000
Year Founded: 1966
Business Description:
Intelligence & Defense Systems Engineering & Advisory Services
S.I.C.: 7373; 7389
N.A.I.C.S.: 541512; 541990
Media: 4-10
Personnel:
Peter A. Marino *(Chm)*
Wood Parker *(Vice Chm)*
David H. Langstaff *(Pres & CEO)*
Wayne Rehberger *(CFO & Sr VP)*
Barbie Bigelow *(CIO & Sr VP)*
Jim Lawler *(Chief HR Officer & Sr VP)*
Dale E. Luddeke *(Chief Growth Officer)*
Jerry Howe *(Gen Counsel & Sr VP)*
Joseph K. Dodd *(Sr VP-Bus Dev)*
Pamela Drew *(Sr VP-Enterprise Systems)*
John P. Hynes, Jr. *(Sr VP-Defense & Civil Grp)*
Al Pisani *(Sr VP-Intelligence Ops)*
Kerry D. Rines *(Sr VP-Natl Sys)*
Pat Talty *(Sr VP-Mission Engrg)*
Jay McCaffrey *(VP-Comm)*
Bob Silsby *(VP-Bus & Tech)*
Richard Bowers *(Dir-Cryptologic Sys Operating Unit)*
Rosemary Budd *(Dir-Bus Dev)*
Rashid Chotani *(Dir-Chemical & Biological Defense Programs)*
David Manser *(Dir-Tech)*

TECHNICOLOR CANADA INC.

(Sub. of Technicolor, Inc.)
3195 Bedford
Montreal, QC H3S 1G3, Canada
Tel.: (514) 737-2777
Fax: (514) 737-1427
Web Site: www.technicolor.com
Sales Range: $100-124.9 Million
Approx. Number Employees: 400
Business Description:
Video Distribution Services
S.I.C.: 3695
N.A.I.C.S.: 334613
Media: 4-9-19-23
Distr.: Natl.
Budget Set: Jan.

TEKTRONIX, INC.

(Sub. of Danaher Corporation)
14150 SW Karl Braun Dr
Beaverton, OR 97077-0001
Mailing Address:
P.O. Box 500
Beaverton, OR 97077
Tel.: (503) 627-7111
Fax: (503) 627-2406
Toll Free: (800) 833-9200
Web Site: www.tektronix.com
Sales Range: $1-4.9 Billion
Approx. Number Employees: 4,541
Year Founded: 1946
Business Description:
Test, Measurement & Monitoring Equipment Mfr
S.I.C.: 3823; 3829
N.A.I.C.S.: 334513; 334519
Export
Advertising Expenditures: $13,800,000
Media: 1-2-4-5-8-9-10-13-19
Distr.: Natl.
Budget Set: Apr.
Personnel:
Gilles Carlotti *(VP-Sls & Network Mgmt-Worldwide)*
Larry L. Pendergrass *(Dir-Engrg)*
Brands & Products:
TEKTRONIX
Advertising Agencies:
CMD
1631 NW Thurman St
Portland, OR 97209-2558
Tel.: (503) 223-6794
Fax: (503) 223-2430

Doremus (San Francisco)
555 Market St 19th Fl
San Francisco, CA 94105
Tel.: (415) 273-7817
Tel.: (415) 273-7840
Fax: (415) 398-0854

Impressions-A.B.A. Industries, Inc.
393 Jericho Tpk
Mineola, NY 11501
Tel.: (516) 739-3210
Fax: (516) 739-9246

TELEDYNE BENTHOS, INC.

(Sub. of Teledyne Technologies Incorporated)
49 Edgerton Dr
North Falmouth, MA 02556-2821
Tel.: (508) 563-1000
Fax: (508) 563-6444
Toll Free: (800) 446-1222
E-mail: info@benthos.com
Web Site: www.benthos.com
Sales Range: $10-24.9 Million
Approx. Number Employees: 124
Year Founded: 1962
Business Description:
Underwater, Environmental & Oceanographic Products Mfr; Food & Beverage Container Inspection Systems
S.I.C.: 3812; 3829; 3999
N.A.I.C.S.: 334511; 334519; 339999
Export
Advertising Expenditures: $104,000
Media: 4-5-7-10
Distr.: Intl.
Budget Set: Aug.
Personnel:
Ronald L. Marsiglio *(Pres & CEO)*
Francis E. Dunne *(CFO, Treas & VP)*
James Kearbey *(VP & Gen Mgr-Package Inspection Sys Div)*
Justin Manley *(Sr Dir-Bus Dev)*
Debbie King *(Mgr-Product Line)*
Darren Moss *(Mgr-Product Sls-Survey & Inspection Sys)*
Brands & Products:
BENTHOS
DATASONICS
IMUX
RAFOS
TAPTONE
VACUSEALED

TELEDYNE ISCO

(Sub. of Teledyne Technologies Incorporated)
4700 Superior St
Lincoln, NE 68504-1398
Mailing Address:
PO Box 82531
Lincoln, NE 68501
Tel.: (402) 464-0231
Fax: (402) 465-3022
E-mail: info@isco.com
Web Site: www.isco.com
Sales Range: $50-74.9 Million
Approx. Number Employees: 430
Year Founded: 1959
Business Description:
Water Pollution Monitoring Equipment, Wastewater Samplers & Chemical Separation Instruments Mfr, Designer & Marketer
S.I.C.: 3823; 3826

Teledyne Isco — (Continued)

N.A.I.C.S.: 334513; 334516
Import Export
Advertising Expenditures: $1,500,000
Media: 7

Brands & Products:
CHEMMAG
COMBIFLASH
FLOWLINK
REDISEP
SWIFT
UNIMAG

TEMPIL, INC.
(Sub. of Illinois Tool Works Inc.)
2901 Hamilton Blvd
South Plainfield, NJ 07080-2517
Tel.: (908) 757-8300
Fax: (908) 757-9273
Toll Free: (800) 757-8301
E-mail: tempil@tempil.com
Web Site: www.tempil.com
Sales Range: $25-49.9 Million
Approx. Number Employees: 100
Business Description:
Temperature Indication Products Mfr
S.I.C.: 2813
N.A.I.C.S.: 325120
Export
Media: 2-4-6-7-10-21
Distr.: Intl.; Natl.
Budget Set: Oct.

Brands & Products:
ANTI-HEAT
BLOXIDE
PYROMARK
TEMP-ALARM
TEMPIL
TEMPILABEL
TEMPILAQ
TEMPILINK
TEMPILSTIK
THERMAX

TERWILLIGER PRODUCTIONS
21363 Lassen St
Chatsworth, CA 91311
Tel.: (818) 717-0711
Web Site:
www.terwilligerproductions.com
Approx. Number Employees: 5
Business Description:
Film Production
S.I.C.: 7819
N.A.I.C.S.: 512191
Export
Media: 8-11
Personnel:
Brian J. Terwilliger *(Dir-Prod)*

Advertising Agency:
KV Associates
870 Market St #758
San Francisco, CA 94102
Tel.: (415) 433-6421

THERAGENICS CORPORATION
5203 Bristol Industrial Way
Buford, GA 30518-1799
Tel.: (770) 271-0233
Fax: (770) 831-5294
Web Site: www.theragenics.com
Approx. Rev.: $82,184,000
Approx. Number Employees: 500
Year Founded: 1986
Business Description:
Radioactive Implants for Disease Treatment
S.I.C.: 3825; 2834; 3824; 3842
N.A.I.C.S.: 334515; 325412; 334514; 339113
Advertising Expenditures: $1,365,000
Personnel:
M. Christine Jacobs *(Chm & CEO)*
Francis J. Tarallo *(CFO & Treas)*
Bruce W. Smith *(Sec & Exec VP-Strategy & Bus Dev)*
Anne Lane *(Mgr-Mktg)*

Brands & Products:
I-SEED
THERAGENICS
THERAGENICS CORPORATION
THERASEED
THERASIGHT
THERASOURCE

THERMO FISCHER SCIENTIFIC
(Formerly Thermo Electron Corporation Process Instruments)
(Div. of Thermo Fisher Scientific Inc.)
1410 W Gillings Ln
Sugar Land, TX 77476
Tel.: (713) 272-0404
Fax: (713) 272-2273
Toll Free: (877) 290-7422
Web Site: www.thermoscientific.com
Sales Range: $75-99.9 Million
Approx. Number Employees: 250
Year Founded: 1945
Business Description:
Analytical Instruments Mfr
S.I.C.: 3824; 3825
N.A.I.C.S.: 334514; 334515
Import Export
Media: 2-4-5-6-10-17-20
Distr.: Intl.; Natl.
Personnel:
Angie Zhang *(Mgr-Mktg)*

Brands & Products:
POLYSONICS
SARASOTA
TEXAS NUCLEAR

THERMO FISHER SCIENTIFIC INC.
81 Wyman St
Waltham, MA 02454-9046
Mailing Address:
PO Box 9046
Waltham, MA 02454-9046
Tel.: (781) 622-1000
Fax: (781) 622-1207
Toll Free: (800) 678-5599
Web Site: www.thermofisher.com
Approx. Rev.: $10,788,700,000
Approx. Number Employees: 37,200
Year Founded: 1956
Business Description:
Electronic Measurement Equipment, Laboratory Gear & Scientific Instrument Mfr
S.I.C.: 3826; 3829; 3845
N.A.I.C.S.: 334516; 334510; 334519
Export
Advertising Expenditures: $3,700,000
Media: 2-4-7-9-10-25
Distr.: Natl.
Personnel:
Jim P. Manzi *(Chm)*
Marc N. Casper *(Pres & CEO)*
Peter M. Wilver *(CFO & Sr VP)*
Peter E. Hornstra *(Chief Acctg Officer & VP)*
Ken Berger *(Pres-Specialty Diagnostics & Sr VP)*
Alan J. Malus *(Pres-Lab Products & Sr VP)*
Seth H. Hoogasian *(Gen Counsel)*
Elizabeth Bolgiano *(Sr VP-HR)*
Alexander G. Stachtiaris *(Sr VP-Global Bus Svcs)*
Karen A. Kirkwood *(VP-Corp Comm)*
Anthony H. Smith *(VP-Tax & Treasury)*
Brandon Pence *(Global Dir-Mktg, Cell Culture & Bioproduction)*
Richard Somerville *(Dir-Risk Mgmt)*

Brands & Products:
FISHER SCIENTIFIC
THERMO FISHER
THERMO SCIENTIFIC
THE WORLD LEADER IN SERVING SCIENCE

Advertising Agencies:
Brand Content
580 Harrison Ave
Boston, MA 02116
Tel.: (617) 338-9111
Fax: (617) 338-9121

Greenough Communications
9 Harcourt St
Boston, MA 02116
Tel.: (617) 275-6500
Fax: (617) 275-6501

Maier Advertising, Inc.
1789 New Britain Ave
Farmington, CT 06032-3317
Tel.: (860) 677-4581
Fax: (860) 677-5854
Fax: (860) 677-4898

THERMOGRAPHICS, INC.
(Sub. of Liquid Crystal Resources)
1820 Pickwick Ln
Glenview, IL 60026
Tel.: (847) 998-8580
Fax: (847) 998-9500
Web Site: www.thermographics.com
Sales Range: $1-9.9 Million
Approx. Number Employees: 8
Business Description:
Temperature Measuring Devices Mfr
S.I.C.: 3829; 3821; 3824
N.A.I.C.S.: 334519; 334514; 339111
Media: 2-4-10-21
Distr.: Natl.
Personnel:
Rocco Sapienza *(CEO)*

Brands & Products:
TENSOMETER
WINEMETER

THORLABS INC.
435 Rte 206 N
Newton, NJ 07860
Tel.: (973) 579-7227
Fax: (973) 300-3600
E-mail: hr@thorlabs.com
Web Site: www.thorlabs.com
Sales Range: $10-24.9 Million
Approx. Number Employees: 600
Year Founded: 1989
Business Description:
Photonics Products Mfr
S.I.C.: 3826; 3827
N.A.I.C.S.: 334516; 333314
Media: 10
Personnel:
Alex Cable *(Pres & CEO)*

Brands & Products:
FIREWIRE
SCIENCE DESK
THORLABS

THWING-ALBERT INSTRUMENT COMPANY
14 W Collings Ave
West Berlin, NJ 08091
Tel.: (856) 767-1000
Fax: (856) 767-2615
Telex: 710 670 1763 TAINCO PHA
E-mail: info@thwingalbert.com
Web Site: www.thwingalbert.com
Approx. Number Employees: 45
Year Founded: 1899
Business Description:
Advanced Testing Instruments Mfr
S.I.C.: 3829
N.A.I.C.S.: 334519
Import Export
Advertising Expenditures: $50,000
Media: 2-4-7-10-13-18-26
Distr.: Intl.; Natl.
Budget Set: Dec.
Personnel:
Joseph Raab *(Pres)*
Steve Berg *(VP-Sls & Mktg)*
Brenda Robinson *(Mktg Mgr)*

Brands & Products:
4340 GURLEY AUTOMATIC DENSOMETER
ACCUTACK
ALFA
ATS-600
EJA
HANDLE-O-METER
INKOMETER
JDC
PCA
PROGAGE
PROTEAR
QC
QUICKPEEK
SL10
TEARTESTER

THE TIFFEN COMPANY LLC
(Holding of Topspin Partners, L.P.)
90 Oser Ave
Hauppauge, NY 11788-3886
Tel.: (631) 273-2500
Fax: (631) 273-2557
Web Site: www.tiffen.com
Sales Range: $10-24.9 Million
Approx. Number Employees: 210
Year Founded: 1999
Business Description:
Holding Company; Consumer & Professional Photographic Filters & Other Accessories Mfr & Distr
S.I.C.: 6719; 3861; 5043
N.A.I.C.S.: 551112; 333315; 423410
Media: 2-6-10
Personnel:
Steven Tiffen *(Pres & CEO)*
Mike Cannata *(COO)*
Hilary Araujo *(VP-Mktg)*

Brands & Products:
COLOR-GRAD
DAVIS & SANFORD
DECAMIRED
DFX
DIFFUSION-FX
DOMKE
ENHANCING
GLIMMERGLASS
GOLD DIFFUSION/FX

Key to Media (For complete agency information see *The Advertising Red Books-Agencies* edition):
1. Bus. Publs. 2. Cable T.V. 3. Catalogs & Directories. 4. Co-op Adv. 5. Consumer Mags. 6. D.M. to Bus. Estab.7. D.M. to Consumers 8. Daily Newsp. 9. Exhibits/Trade Shows 10. Foreign 11. Infomercial 12. Internet Adv.13. Multimedia 14. Network Radio 15. Network T.V. 16. Newsp. Distr. Mags. 17. Other 18. Outdoor (Posters, Transit) 19. Point of Purchase20. Premiums, Novelties 21. Product Samples 22. Special Events Mktg. 23. Spot Radio 24. Spot T.V. 25. Weekly Newsp. 26. Yellow Page Adv.

HELPING CREATE THE WORLD'S GREATEST IMAGES
HOLLYWOOD
HOLLYWOOD-FX
PRO-MIST
PRO-TECTIVE
SAUNDERS
SILVER PIXEL PRESS
SMOQUE
SOFT
SOFT/FX
STEADICAM
STROBOFRAME
TIFFEN
ULTRAPOL
ZING

TINIUS OLSEN, INC.

1065 Easton Rd
Horsham, PA 19044-8009
Tel.: (215) 675-7100
Fax: (215) 441-0899
E-mail: info@tiniusolsen.com
Web Site: www.tiniusolsen.com
E-Mail For Key Personnel:
Sales Director: sales@tiniusolsen.com
Approx. Sls.: $17,300,000
Approx. Number Employees: 115
Year Founded: 1880
Business Description:
Testing & Balancing Machines, Instruments & Equipment Mfr
S.I.C.: 3829
N.A.I.C.S.: 334519
Import Export
Advertising Expenditures: $500,000
Media: 2-4-10
Budget Set: Dec. -Jan.
Personnel:
Robert Tate, III *(Pres)*
Wayne Hayward *(Mgr-Corp Mktg)*
Geralyn Polsky *(Mgr-Quality)*
Cheryl Spinieo *(Mgr-Svc Ops)*
Brands & Products:
MODUL-R
QMAT
STANPAC
TEST LITE
TEST NAVIGATOR
TINIUS OLSEN
W-SERIES
Advertising Agency:
Newton Associates Marketing Communications, Inc.
527 Plymouth Rd Ste 411 Plymouth Woods
Plymouth Meeting, PA 19462
Tel.: (610) 964-9300
Fax: (610) 964-9306

TOPPAN PHOTOMASKS, INC.

(Sub. of Toppan Printing Co., Ltd.)
131 E Old Settlers Blvd
Round Rock, TX 78664-2211
Tel.: (512) 310-6500
Fax: (512) 255-9627
Web Site: www.photomask.com
Sales Range: $350-399.9 Million
Approx. Number Employees: 1,540
Business Description:
Semiconductor Equipment & Materials Mfr
S.I.C.: 3559; 3827
N.A.I.C.S.: 333295; 333314
Media: 10
Personnel:
Akihiro Nagata *(Chm)*
David S. Murray *(Pres & CEO)*
Franklin Kalk *(CTO & Exec VP)*
Brands & Products:
PERFECTLY FOCUSED

TRANSITIONS OPTICAL, INC.

(Joint Venture of PPG Industries, Inc. & Essilor International, S.A.)
9251 Belcher Rd
Pinellas Park, FL 33782-4200
Mailing Address:
PO Box 700
Pinellas Park, FL 33782
Tel.: (727) 545-0400
Fax: (727) 546-4732
Web Site: www.transitions.com
Approx. Sls.: $250,000,000
Approx. Number Employees: 1,200
Business Description:
Lightweight Sundarkening Lenses Mfr; Owned 51% by PPG Industries, Inc. & 49% by Essilor International S.A.
S.I.C.: 3229
N.A.I.C.S.: 327212
Export
Media: 2-3-5-6-7-8-9-10-11-14-15-23-24-25
Distr.: Intl.
Budget Set: Aug.
Personnel:
Dave Cole *(Pres)*
Richard Elias *(CEO)*
Dan McLean *(Coord-Mktg & Customer Comm)*
Brands & Products:
RIGHT IN ANY LIGHT
TRANSITIONS
Advertising Agencies:
DDB New York
437 Madison Ave
New York, NY 10022-7001
Tel.: (212) 415-2000
Fax: (212) 415-3506

Euro RSCG Worldwide PR
(Corporate Headquarters)
200 Madison Ave
New York, NY 10016
Tel.: (212) 367-6800
Fax: (212) 367-7154

TRIMEDYNE, INC.

25901 Commercentre Dr
Lake Forest, CA 92630-8805
Tel.: (949) 951-3800
Fax: (949) 855-8206
Toll Free: (800) 733-5273
E-mail: info@trimedyne.com
Web Site: www.trimedyne.com
Approx. Rev.: $6,401,000
Approx. Number Employees: 53
Year Founded: 1980
Business Description:
Surgical Laser Mfr
S.I.C.: 3845; 3841
N.A.I.C.S.: 334510; 339112
Media: 2-7-10-13
Personnel:
Marvin P. Loeb *(Chm & CEO)*
Glenn D. Yeik *(Pres & COO)*
Jeffrey S. Rudner *(Principal Fin Officer)*
Brian T. Kenney *(VP-Sls-Mktg)*
Brands & Products:
DOUBLEPULSE
OMNI
OMNIPULSE
OMNIPULSE JR.
OMNIPULSE MAX
OMNITIP
OMNIVIEW
OPTILASE
R-50
STRAIGHTFIRE
TAPERTIP
TRIMEDYNE

TSI INCORPORATED

500 Cardigan Rd
Shoreview, MN 55126-3903
Tel.: (651) 490-2811
Fax: (651) 490-3824
Toll Free: (800) 874-2811
E-mail: tsiinfo@tsi.com
Web Site: www.tsi.com
Sales Range: $75-99.9 Million
Approx. Number Employees: 800
Year Founded: 1961
Business Description:
Precision Instruments Mfr
S.I.C.: 3451; 3821; 3822; 3823; 3824; 3826; 3829; 3873
N.A.I.C.S.: 332721; 334512; 334513; 334514; 334516; 334518; 334519; 339111
Import Export
Media: 2-4-7-10-13
Personnel:
Tom Kennedy *(Pres)*
Brands & Products:
ACCUBALANCE
AERODYNAMIC
AEROSIZER
AEROTRAK
AIRGARD
AIRGARD LAB HOOD MONITOR
ALNOR
BALOMETER JR.
CA-CALC
CERTIFIER AIR VELOCITY CALIBRATOR
CERTIFIER FA
CERTIFIER FA PLUS
COMPUFLOW
DP-CALC
DUSTTRAK
EBT721 ELECTRONIC BALANCING TOOL
ENGINE EXHAUST PARTICLE SIZER
EVERWATCH
FAST MOBILITY PARTICLE SIZER
IAQ-CALC
INSIGHT 3G
P-TRAK
PIEZOBALANCE
PORTACOUNT
POWERVIEW
POWERVIEW PLUS
PRESSURA
PROTECTAIR
Q-TRAK
SCANNING MOBILITY PARTICLE SIZER
SIDEPAK
SUREFLOW
TRUST. SCIENCE. INNOVATION
TSI
VELOCICALC AIR VELOCITY METER
VELOCICALC MULTI FUNCTION VENTILATION METER
VELOCICALC ROTATING VANE ANEMOMETER
VELOMETER
VELOMETER JR.
Advertising Agency:
Maccabee Group, Inc.
211 N 1st St Ste 425
Minneapolis, MN 55401
Tel.: (612) 337-0087
Fax: (612) 337-0054
Online Marketing
Public Relations
Social Media

TURA L.P.

123 Girton Dr
Muncy, PA 17756-6375
Tel.: (570) 546-9583
Fax: (800) 865-8872
Toll Free: (800) 242-8872
Web Site: www.tura.com
Approx. Number Employees: 70
Business Description:
Eyeglass Frames
S.I.C.: 5048
N.A.I.C.S.: 423460
Media: 4-13-19
Personnel:
John Weir *(Pres & CEO)*
Mike Pasnello *(VP-Fin)*
Audrey Pavia *(VP-Mktg)*

UDT SENSORS, INC.

(Sub. of OSI Systems, Inc.)
12525 Chadron Ave
Hawthorne, CA 90250-4807
Tel.: (310) 978-0516
Fax: (310) 644-1727
E-mail: sales@udt.com
Web Site: www.udt.com
E-Mail For Key Personnel:
Sales Director: sales@udt.com
Sales Range: $100-124.9 Million
Approx. Number Employees: 300
Year Founded: 1967
Business Description:
High Performance Light Sensor Products Designer, Developer, Mfr & Marketer
S.I.C.: 3674; 3827
N.A.I.C.S.: 334413; 333314
Export
Media: 2-6-10
Distr.: Natl.
Budget Set: July
Personnel:
Alan Edrick *(CFO)*
Victor Sze *(Gen Counsel, Sec & VP-Corp Affairs)*
Steven Cuffel *(VP-Sls & Mktg)*

ULTRA ELECTRONICS OCEAN SYSTEMS INC.

(Sub. of Ultra Electronics Holdings plc)
115 Bay State Dr
Braintree, MA 02184-5203
Tel.: (781) 848-3400
Fax: (781) 843-2153
Web Site: www.ultra-os.com
Sales Range: $10-24.9 Million
Approx. Number Employees: 130
Year Founded: 2003
Business Description:
Aircraft, Submarine & Surface Ship Special Purpose Acoustic & Radio Frequency Device & System Mfr; Open Water Acoustic Research & Production Test Site Operator
S.I.C.: 3446
N.A.I.C.S.: 334511; 334290

Key to Media (For complete agency information see *The Advertising Red Books-Agencies* edition):
1. Bus. Publs. 2. Cable T.V. 3. Catalogs & Directories. 4. Co-op Adv. 5. Consumer Mags. 6. D.M. to Bus. Estab.7. D.M. to Consumers 8. Daily Newsp. 9. Exhibits/Trade Shows 10. Foreign 11. Infomercial 12. Internet Adv.13. Multimedia 14. Network Radio 15. Network T.V. 16. Newsp. Distr. Mags. 17. Other 18. Outdoor (Posters, Transit) 19. Point of Purchase20. Premiums, Novelties 21. Product Samples 22. Special Events Mktg. 23. Spot Radio 24. Spot T.V. 25. Weekly Newsp. 26. Yellow Page Adv.

Ultra Electronics Ocean Systems Inc. — (Continued)

Personnel:
Richard J. Kielmeyer *(Pres)*
Richard Speer *(VP-Fin & Contracts)*
Advertising Agency:
DB Advertising Associates
2200 E 170th St
Lansing, IL 60438-1002
Tel.: (708) 418-2813

ULTRAOPTIX, INC.

17 Commerce St
East Haven, CT 06512-4113
Tel.: (203) 468-6090
Fax: (203) 468-6098
Toll Free: (800) 448-2968
E-mail: ultraoptix@aol.com
Web Site: www.ultraoptix.com
E-Mail For Key Personnel:
Sales Director: sales@ultraoptix.com
Approx. Number Employees: 8
Year Founded: 1977
Business Description:
Visual Aid Mfr
S.I.C.: 3827
N.A.I.C.S.: 333314
Import Export
Media: 7
Distr.: Natl.
Personnel:
Joseph Zalman *(Pres)*
Brands & Products:
EZREADER
HAND-LENS
SUPRVISION
ULTRADOME
ULTRAOPTIX

ULTRATECH, INC.

3050 Zanker Rd
San Jose, CA 95134-2126
Tel.: (408) 321-8835
Fax: (408) 325-6444
Toll Free: (800) 222-1213
Web Site: www.ultratech.com
Approx. Sls.: $140,603,000
Approx. Number Employees: 295
Business Description:
Photolithography Equipment Mfr, Designer & Marketer
S.I.C.: 3826; 3559; 3827
N.A.I.C.S.: 334516; 333295; 333314
Export
Media: 10-16
Personnel:
Arthur W. Zafiropoulo *(Chm, Pres & CEO)*
Bruce R. Wright *(CFO, Treas, Sec & Sr VP-Fin)*
Dave Holmes *(Sr VP-Svc Ops-Worldwide)*
Dave Ghosh *(VP-Corp Svcs & HR)*
Brands & Products:
NANOTECH
PRISMA-GHI
SATURN WAFER STEPPER
TITAN WAFER STEPPER
ULTRAMET
ULTRATECH
UNITY PLATFORM

UNILENS VISION INC.

10431 72nd St N
Largo, FL 33777-1511
Tel.: (727) 544-1511
E-mail: information@unilens.com
Web Site: www.unilens.com
Approx. Rev.: $9,194,190
Approx. Number Employees: 47
Year Founded: 1989
Business Description:
Contact Lens Developer, Mfr, Distr & Licensor
S.I.C.: 3827
N.A.I.C.S.: 333314
Advertising Expenditures: $252,606
Personnel:
Alfred W. Vitale *(Chm)*
Michael J. Pecora *(Pres & CEO)*
Leonard F. Barker *(CFO)*
Kelly McKnight-Goelz *(VP-Sls & Mktg)*
Joseph Bruno *(Dir-Quality Control)*
Alan Frazer *(Dir-Quality Assurance)*
Denis Rehse *(Dir-R & D)*
David Boyd *(Mgr-Production)*

UNITRON INC.

73 Mall Dr
Commack, NY 11725
Tel.: (631) 589-6666
Fax: (631) 589-6975
Telex: 679-1055
E-mail: info@unitronusa.com
Web Site: www.unitronusa.com
E-Mail For Key Personnel:
Sales Director: Peterl@unitronusa.com
Sales Range: $10-24.9 Million
Approx. Number Employees: 20
Year Founded: 1952
Business Description:
Industrial & Scientific Instruments Distr
S.I.C.: 5049
N.A.I.C.S.: 423490
Import Export
Advertising Expenditures: $200,000
Media: 2-4-6-7-8-10
Distr.: Natl.
Personnel:
Jay Berliner *(Pres)*
Peter I. Indrigo *(Sr VP)*
Brands & Products:
ANYWHERESCOPE
DIAZOOM
ED-U-SCOPE
NEOMET
UNITRON
VERSAMET

UNIVERSAL PHOTONICS, INC.

495 W John St
Hicksville, NY 11801-1028
Tel.: (516) 935-4000
Fax: (516) 935-4039
Toll Free: (800) 645-7173
E-mail: info@universalphotonics.com
Web Site:
www.universalphotonics.com
Approx. Number Employees: 100
Year Founded: 1926
Business Description:
Abrasives, Polishing Compounds, Machinery & Supplies Mfr & Distr for the Optical Industry
S.I.C.: 5049; 3541
N.A.I.C.S.: 423490; 333512
Import Export
Media: 2-4-7-10-13
Distr.: Intl.; Natl.
Personnel:
Alan C. Ritter *(Owner)*
Neil Johnson *(CEO)*
Martin Lerner *(Gen Counsel)*
John Sheridan *(VP-Fin)*
Angelika Criscione *(Mgr-Mktg)*
Brands & Products:
ACCELERON
ALOX
CHILLMATE
DIAMOND KOOL
DRI-KOOL
EDGEMATE
EVERFLO
KONTAX
LIBERATOR
MICROGRIT
POLYCLEAR
RHODITE
RHODOL
TECH-POL
UNALON
UNASIL
UNI-CER
UNI-CLEAR
UNI-CLOTH
UNI-MESH
UNI-PAD
UNI-SEMI-LEAF
UNIVERSAL
UNIVERSAL PHOTONICS
X-PAL

U.S. VISION, INC.

(Sub. of Refac Optical Group)
1 Harmon Dr Glen Oaks Industrial Park
Glendora, NJ 08029
Mailing Address:
PO Box 124
Glendora, NJ 08029-0124
Tel.: (856) 228-1000
Fax: (856) 228-6220
Toll Free: (800) 524-0789
Web Site: www.usvision.com
Approx. Number Employees: 2,500
Year Founded: 1991
Business Description:
Optical Products & Services Retailer
S.I.C.: 5995
N.A.I.C.S.: 446130
Media: 2-5-6-9-10-13-17-18-19-25-26
Distr.: Natl.
Budget Set: Monthly
Personnel:
William A. Schwartz, Jr. *(Pres & CEO)*
Carmen J. Nepa, III *(CFO)*
John Fryers *(VP-Canada)*
Marge Scirrotto *(VP-Product)*
Kathy Weiman *(VP-Mktg)*

UVEX SAFETY

(Sub. of Sperian Protection Americas, Inc.)
900 Douglas Pike
Smithfield, RI 02917-1874
Tel.: (401) 232-1200
Fax: (401) 232-1830
Toll Free: (800) 343-3411
E-mail: resume@uvex.com
Web Site: www.uvex.com
E-Mail For Key Personnel:
Sales Director: sales@uvex.com
Approx. Number Employees: 250
Business Description:
Plastic Eye Protection & Ophthalmic Accessories Mfr
S.I.C.: 3851; 3842
N.A.I.C.S.: 339115; 339113
Import Export
Advertising Expenditures: $1,000,000
Media: 1-2-4-5-7-10-11-13-20-21-22
Distr.: Natl.
Budget Set: Jan.
Personnel:
Henri-Dominique Petit *(Pres)*
George Phillips *(Dir-National Accts)*
Mark McLear *(Mgr-Product)*
Brands & Products:
4C +
ASTROSPEC
BANDIDO
BANDIT
CRICKET
EXCELSIOR
FLASHBACK
FLEXSEAL
FUTURA
GENESIS
HIGH FLYER
INFRADURA
OPTIDURA
PROSPEC
PROVISION
SCT (SPECTRUM CONTROL TECHNOLOGY)
STEALTH
TOPSIDER
ULTRADURA
ULTRAGUARD
ULTRASPEC
UVEX CLASSIC
UVEX FITLOGIC
UVEX FURY
UVEX SKYPER
UVEX SPITFIRE
UVEXTREME AF
X UVEX
Advertising Agency:
The Boston Group
500 Harrison Ave 3F
Boston, MA 02118
Tel.: (617) 350-7020
Fax: (617) 350-7021

UVP, INC.

2066 W 11th St
Upland, CA 91786-3509
Mailing Address:
PO Box 5015
Upland, CA 91785-5015
Tel.: (909) 946-3197
Fax: (909) 946-3597
Toll Free: (800) 452-6788
E-mail: info@uvp.com
Web Site: www.uvp.com
Approx. Number Employees: 120
Year Founded: 1932
Business Description:
Long Wave & Short Wave Lamps, Calibration Lamps, Germicidal Lamps, Viewing Cabinets, Fixtures, Erasing Units & Leak Detection Systems Mfr
S.I.C.: 3821; 3826
N.A.I.C.S.: 339111; 334516
Export
Media: 2-4-7-10-11-13-20-21
Distr.: Intl.; Natl.
Budget Set: Nov.
Personnel:
Alex Waluszko *(VP-Mktg & Sls)*
Cecilia Bernal *(Mgr-Natl Sls)*
Kathleen Buckman *(Mgr-Mktg Svc)*
Brands & Products:
2UV
3UV
ANYTHING YOU CAN IMAGINE, UVP CAN IMAGE!
AUTOCHEMI

Key to Media (For complete agency information see *The Advertising Red Books-Agencies* edition):
1. Bus. Publs. 2. Cable T.V. 3. Catalogs & Directories. 4. Co-op Adv. 5. Consumer Mags. 6. D.M. to Bus. Estab.7. D.M. to Consumers
8. Daily Newsp. 9. Exhibits/Trade Shows 10. Foreign 11. Infomercial 12. Internet Adv.13. Multimedia 14. Network Radio
15. Network T.V. 16. Newsp. Distr. Mags. 17. Other 18. Outdoor (Posters, Transit) 19. Point of Purchase20. Premiums, Novelties
21. Product Samples 22. Special Events Mktg. 23. Spot Radio 24. Spot T.V. 25. Weekly Newsp. 26. Yellow Page Adv.

BENCHTOP UV INCUBATOR
BENCHTOP UV STERILIZATION PCR WORKSTATION
BIOCHEM
BIOCHEMI
BIODOC-IT
BIOSPECTRUM
BLAK-RAY
CHEMIDOC-IT
CHROMADOC-IT
CHROMATO-VUE
COLONYDOC-IT
DIGIDOC-IT
DOC-IT LS
DOC-IT LS 1D
DVP
EC3
FIRSTLIGHT
FIRSTLIGHT UNIFORM UV ILLUMINATOR
FLUORESCENCE
GELDOC-IT
GELWORKS
HYBRICYCLER
HYBRILINKER
IBOX
MEMORASE
MINERALIGHT
MULTI-SENSE
MULTICHEM
MULTIDOC-IT
OPTICHEM
PEN-RAY
PHOTODOC-IT
REVEAL
SURE-CURE
TLC IMAGING WITH DOC-IT IMAGING
UPV
VISI-BLUE
VISIDOC-IT

VARIAN MEDICAL SYSTEMS, INC.

3100 Hansen Way
Palo Alto, CA 94304-1030
Tel.: (650) 493-4000
Fax: (650) 842-5196
Toll Free: (800) 544-4636
E-mail: investors@varian.com
Web Site: www.varian.com
Approx. Rev.: $2,356,585,000
Approx. Number Employees: 5,300
Year Founded: 1948
Business Description:
Integrated Cancer Therapy Systems, X-Ray Tubes & Flat Panel Digital Subsystems
S.I.C.: 3845; 3841; 3844
N.A.I.C.S.: 334510; 334517; 339112
Import Export
Media: 2-4-7-8-9-10-11-13-18-22-23-25-26
Distr.: Intl.; Natl.
Budget Set: Aug.
Personnel:
Richard M. Levy *(Chm)*
Timothy E. Guertin *(Pres & CEO)*
Elisha W. Finney *(CFO & Corp Sr VP-Fin)*
Jessica L. Denecour *(CIO & VP)*
Dow R. Wilson *(Pres-Oncology Sys & Corp Exec)*
Robert H. Kluge *(Pres-X-Ray Products & Corp VP)*
John W. Kuo *(Gen Counsel, Sec & Corp VP)*
John A. Thorson, II *(Corp VP-Fin & Treas)*
Tai-Yun Chen *(Controller & Corp VP-Fin)*
Franco N. Palomba *(Corp VP-Fin & Bus Dev)*
Wendy S. Reitherman *(Corp VP-HR)*
Spencer R. Sias *(VP-Corp Comm & IR)*
C. Clifton Ling *(Dir-Advanced Clinical Res-Oncology Sys)*
Maureen Zilly *(Dir-Fedral Affairs)*
Meryl Ginsberg *(Mgr-PR)*
Purvi Naik *(Mgr-Mktg Comm)*
Brands & Products:
A PARTNER FOR LIFE
ABACUS
ACUITY
ACUITY BT
ARGUS
BODYARRAY
BRACHYVISION
CADPLAN PLUS
CLINAC
CLINIC IX
DART
ECLIPSE
EMERALD
FASTPLAN
GAMMAMED
GAMMAMEDPLUS
HELIOS
IMMERGE
LASERGUARD
LINATRON-M
MEDONCOLOGY
PAXSCAN
POLARIS
PORTALVISION
SMARTBEAM
SOMAVISION
TRILOGY
VARIAN
VARIS
VARISEED
VARISOURCE
VISION
XIMAVISION

VARIAN MEDICAL SYSTEMS X-RAY PRODUCTS

(Div. of Varian Medical Systems, Inc.)
1678 Pioneer Rd
Salt Lake City, UT 84104-4205
Tel.: (801) 972-5000
Fax: (801) 973-5050
Toll Free: (800) 432-4422
E-mail: industrial@xtp.varian.com
Web Site: www.varian.com
Sales Range: $150-199.9 Million
Approx. Number Employees: 500
Year Founded: 1934
Business Description:
X-Ray Tubes, Cavity Amplifiers & Amorphous Silicon Based Imaging Systems
S.I.C.: 3671; 3844
N.A.I.C.S.: 334411; 334517
Import Export
Media: 4-8-10-16
Distr.: Natl.
Budget Set: Sept.
Personnel:
Robert H. Kluge *(Pres & Sr VP)*
Elaine Fairless *(Mgr-Comm)*

VASCULAR SOLUTIONS, INC.

6464 Sycamore Ct
Minneapolis, MN 55369
Tel.: (763) 656-4300
Fax: (763) 656-4250
E-mail: info@vascularsolutions.com
Web Site: www.vascularsolutions.com
Approx. Rev.: $78,443,000
Approx. Number Employees: 296
Business Description:
Mfr. of Medical Devices
S.I.C.: 3841; 3845
N.A.I.C.S.: 339112; 334510
Advertising Expenditures: $71,000
Media: 17
Personnel:
Howard Root *(CEO)*
James Hennen *(Sr VP-Fin, CFO & Sec)*
William Rutstein *(Sr VP-Worldwide Sls)*
Charmaine Sutton *(Sr VP-Ops)*
Susan Christian *(VP-Sls & Ops)*
Brands & Products:
ACOLYSIS
BRINGING SOLUTIONS TO VASCULAR MEDICINE
D-STAT
DUETT
EXPRO ELITE SNARE
GANDRAS
GOPHER
GUARDIAN
INNERCHANGE
LANGSTON
MAX-SUPPORT
MICRO-INTRODUCERS
MINNIE
PRONTO
PRONTO LP
PRONTO-SHORT
SKYWAY OTW
SKYWAY RX
TWIN-PASS
TWIN-PASS .023
VARI-LASE
VASCULAR SOLUTIONS

VEECO INSTRUMENTS INC.

Terminal Dr
Plainview, NY 11803
Tel.: (516) 677-0200
Fax: (516) 714-1200
E-mail: investorrelations@veeco.com
Web Site: www.veeco.com
Approx. Sls.: $933,231,000
Approx. Number Employees: 900
Year Founded: 1989
Business Description:
Metrology & Process Equipment Mfr
S.I.C.: 3674; 3679
N.A.I.C.S.: 334413; 334419
Export
Advertising Expenditures: $1,500,000
Media: 2-4-7-10-11
Distr.: Intl.; Natl.
Budget Set: Nov.
Personnel:
Edward H. Braun *(Chm)*
John R. Peeler *(CEO)*
David D. Glass *(CFO & Exec VP)*
Gregory A. Robbins *(Gen Counsel & Sr VP)*
Robert P. Oates *(Exec VP-Data Storage)*
John P. Kiernan *(Controller & Sr VP-Fin)*
Robert W. Bradshaw *(Sr VP-HR)*
Peter Collingwood *(Sr VP-Sls & Svc)*
Debra A. Wasser *(SVP-IR & CC)*
James Jenson *(VP-Mktg)*
Fran Brennen *(Sr Dir-Mktg Comm)*
Brands & Products:
AURORA-3
BIOSCOPE SPM
DEKTAK
DEKTAK 6M
DEKTAK 8
DIMENSION
DIMENSION 3100
DIMENSION 5000
DIMENSION VX 210
DIMENSION VX 330
DIMENSION X
EXPLORER
HARMONIX
MOLLY
MULTIMODE
NANODRIVE
NANOSCOPE 3D
NANOSCOPE V
NANOVATIONS
NEXUS
OASIS 1750
SATIS 2800
SOLUTIONS FOR A NANOSCALE WORLD
SUMO
TRMODE
TURBODISC
WYKO
WYKO HD8000
WYKO NT1100
WYKO NT3300

VERMILLION, INC.

12117 Bee Caves Rd Bldg II Ste 100
Austin, TX 78738
Tel.: (512) 519-0400
Fax: (512) 439-6980
Toll Free: (888) 864-3770
E-mail: info@vermillion.com
Web Site: www.vermillion.com
Approx. Rev.: $1,175,000
Approx. Number Employees: 26
Year Founded: 1993
Business Description:
Protein Research Products Mfr
S.I.C.: 3826
N.A.I.C.S.: 334516
Advertising Expenditures: $285,000
Media: 7-8-10-13
Personnel:
Gail S. Page *(Chm & CEO)*
Eric Schoen *(Chief Acctg Officer)*
Steve Lundy *(Sr VP-Sls & Mktg)*
William B. Creech *(VP-Sls & Mktg)*
Ashish Kohli *(VP-Corp Strategy)*
Sue Carruthers *(Dir-IR)*
Jeffrey M. Salzman *(Dir-Corp Reimbursement)*
Brands & Products:
BIOMARKER DISCOVERY CENTER
BIOMARKER PATTERNS
BIOSEPRA
CIPHERGENEXPRESS
VERMILLION
YOUR HEALTH, OUR PASSION.

VERSAR, INC.

6850 Versar Ctr
Springfield, VA 22151
Tel.: (703) 750-3000
Fax: (703) 642-6807
Toll Free: (800) 283-7727
E-mail: info@versar.com
Web Site: www.versar.com

Key to Media (For complete agency information see *The Advertising Red Books-Agencies* edition):
1. Bus. Publs. 2. Cable T.V. 3. Catalogs & Directories. 4. Co-op Adv. 5. Consumer Mags. 6. D.M. to Bus. Estab.7. D.M. to Consumers 8. Daily Newsp. 9. Exhibits/Trade Shows 10. Foreign 11. Infomercial 12. Internet Adv.13. Multimedia 14. Network Radio 15. Network T.V. 16. Newsp. Distr. Mags. 17. Other 18. Outdoor (Posters, Transit) 19. Point of Purchase20. Premiums, Novelties 21. Product Samples 22. Special Events Mktg. 23. Spot Radio 24. Spot T.V. 25. Weekly Newsp. 26. Yellow Page Adv.

Versar, Inc. — (Continued)

E-Mail For Key Personnel:
President: procithe@versar.com

Approx. Rev.: $137,599,000
Approx. Number Employees: 550
Year Founded: 1969

Business Description:
Engineering, Scientific & Technical Services; Identifier of Contaminants, Measurer of Environmental Impact & Assists in Compliance with Environmental Regulations; Pollution Control Solutions & Natural Resource Management
S.I.C.: 8711; 8748
N.A.I.C.S.: 541330; 541690

Media: 2-4-10-13-20-26
Distr.: Natl.

Personnel:
Paul J. Hoeper *(Chm)*
Jeffrey A. Wagonhurst *(Pres)*
Anthony L. Otten *(CEO)*
Cynthia A. Downes *(CFO, Treas & Exec VP)*
Michael J. Abram *(Chief Admin Officer & Sr VP-Corp Dev)*
May K. Tom *(Interim Chief Acctg Officer & VP)*
Lee A. Staab *(Pres-Intl & Sr VP)*
James C. Dobbs *(Gen Counsel, Sec & Sr VP)*
J. Joseph Tyler *(Sr VP & Dir-Corp Initiatives & Integration)*
Peter J. Cooper *(Sr VP-Natl Security Bus Segment)*
Daniel J. Cummings *(Sr VP)*
Gina Foringer *(Sr VP-Pro Svcs Bus Segment)*
Paul W. Kendall *(Sr VP)*
Jeffrey M. Moran *(Sr VP-Compliance & Environment Programs)*

VESTA INC.

(Holding of RoundTable Healthcare Partners, LP)
5400 W Franklin Dr
Franklin, WI 53132
Tel.: (414) 423-0550
Fax: (414) 423-0562
E-mail: sales@vestainc.com
Web Site: www.vestainc.com
E-Mail For Key Personnel:
Sales Director: sales@vestainc.com
Approx. Number Employees: 300
Year Founded: 1972

Business Description:
Silicone Medical Devices & Accessories Mfr
S.I.C.: 3069; 3841; 5047
N.A.I.C.S.: 326299; 339112; 423450

Media: 10

Personnel:
Phil Estes *(CEO)*

VICOR CORPORATION

25 Frontage Rd
Andover, MA 01810-5424
Tel.: (978) 470-2900
Fax: (978) 475-6715
E-mail: vicorexp@vicr.com
Web Site: www.vicr.com

Approx. Rev.: $250,733,000
Approx. Number Employees: 1,002
Year Founded: 1981

Business Description:
Mfr., Designer, Developer & Marketer of Modular Power System Components & Complete Power Systems
S.I.C.: 3663; 3677; 3679
N.A.I.C.S.: 334220; 334416; 334419
Import Export
Advertising Expenditures: $1,969,000
Media: 4-13

Personnel:
Patrizio Vinciarelli *(Chm, Pres & CEO)*
James A. Simms *(CFO & Sec)*
Douglas W. Richardson *(CIO & VP)*
Richard J. Nagel, Jr. *(Chief Acctg Officer & VP)*
H. Allen Henderson *(Pres-Westcor Div & VP)*
Barry Kelleher *(Pres-Vicors Brick Bus Unit)*
Richard E. Zengilowski *(VP-HR)*
Bob Lanoue *(Mgr-Applications)*

Brands & Products:
BADGER
BATMOD
COMPAC
FARM
FLATPAC
LOPAC
M-FIAM
MEGAMOD
MEGAPAC
MICRORAM
PICOR
RACKGUARD
VI-RAM
VICOR
VIPAC

VIDEOEYE! CORPORATION

9465 W Emerald St
Boise, ID 83704-9759
Tel.: (208) 323-9577
Fax: (208) 658-1762
Toll Free: (800) 416-0758
Web Site: www.videoeye.com
E-Mail For Key Personnel:
Sales Director: sales@videoeyecorp.com

Approx. Sls.: $3,400,000
Approx. Number Employees: 40

Business Description:
Optical Devices Mfr
S.I.C.: 3559
N.A.I.C.S.: 333298
Media: 6

Personnel:
Tim Waterman *(Pres)*

Brands & Products:
MILLENNIUM
MILLENNIUM II
POWERZOOM
SIDEKICK
STANDARD
TRIPP-LITE
VIDEOEYE!
VIDEOEYE WALLMOUNT
VIEWSONIC

VIRTEK VISION INTERNATIONAL, INC.

(Sub. of Gerber Technology, Inc.)
785 Bridge St
Waterloo, ON N2V 2K1, Canada
Tel.: (519) 746-7190
Fax: (519) 746-3383
E-mail: info@virtek.ca
Web Site: www.virtek.ca

Sales Range: $50-74.9 Million
Approx. Number Employees: 183
Year Founded: 1986

Business Description:
Laser-Based Templating, Inspection, Marking & Engraving Services
S.I.C.: 3479
N.A.I.C.S.: 332812
Media: 2-7-10-13

Brands & Products:
FOBA
GLASMARK
LASERCNC
LASERQC
PANELLINE
QUICKINSPEC
VIRTEK
VIRTEK LASERCNC
VIRTEK LASEREDGE
VIRTEK LASERMC
VIRTEK LPS7
VIRTEK LTG
VIRTEK TRUSSLINE
VIRTEK VIP
VIRTEK VISION

Advertising Agency:
Warne Marketing & Communications
65 Overlea Blvd Ste 112
Toronto, ON Canada
Tel.: (416) 927-0881
Fax: (416) 927-1676
Toll Free: (888) 279-7846

VISHAY INTERTECHNOLOGY, INC.

63 Lancaster Ave
Malvern, PA 19355-2143
Tel.: (610) 644-1300
Telex: 510-668-5812
E-mail: business-americas@vishay.com
Web Site: www.vishay.com
Approx. Rev.: $2,725,092,000
Approx. Number Employees: 22,600
Year Founded: 1962

Business Description:
Discrete Semiconductors & Passive Electronic Components Mfr & Supplier
S.I.C.: 3699; 3674; 3675; 3676; 3677
N.A.I.C.S.: 335999; 334413; 334414; 334415; 334416
Import Export
Media: 2-5-10
Distr.: Intl.; Natl.
Budget Set: Nov.

Personnel:
Marc Zandman *(Chm & Chief Bus Dev Officer)*
Gerald Paul *(Pres & CEO)*
Lori Lipcaman *(CFO)*
Dieter Wunderlich *(COO & Exec VP)*
Johan Vandoorn *(CTO & Exec VP)*
Peter G. Henrici *(Treas & Sr VP-Corp Comm)*
William M. Clancy *(Controller & Sr VP)*
Avner Lahat *(Sr Dir)*
Andrew Post *(Mgr-Global Comm)*
Brenda R. Tate *(Mgr-Corp IR)*

Brands & Products:
BULK METAL
HEXFRED
HOTS
MICRO FOOT
VISHAY
VISHAY ANGSTROHM
VISHAY AZTRONIC
VISHAY BCCOMPONENTS
VISHAY BEYSCHLAG
VISHAY BLH
VISHAY CELTRON
VISHAY CERA-MITE
VISHAY DALE
VISHAY DRALORIC
VISHAY ELECTRO-FILMS
VISHAY ESTA
VISHAY FOIL RESISTORS
VISHAY MICRO-MEASUREMENTS
VISHAY NOBEL
VISHAY PM ONBOARD
VISHAY REVERE
VISHAY ROEDERSTEIN
VISHAY SFERNICE
VISHAY SPECTROL
VISHAY SPRAGUE
VISHAY SYSTEMS
VISHAY TECHNO
VISHAY TEDEA-HUNTLEIGH
VISHAY THIN FILM
VISHAY TRANSDUCERS
VISHAY ULTRONIX
VISHAY VITRAMON

VISION-EASE LENS CORPORATION

(Holding of Insight Equity Holdings LLC)
7000 Sunwood Dr NW
Ramsey, MN 55303
Tel.: (763) 506-9000
Fax: (320) 251-4312
Toll Free: (800) 328-3449
E-mail: info@vision-ease.com
Web Site: www.vision-ease.com
Sales Range: $75-99.9 Million
Approx. Number Employees: 1,000
Year Founded: 1940

Business Description:
Hard Resin Plastic, Polycarbonate & Glass Eyewear Lenses Mfr
S.I.C.: 3827
N.A.I.C.S.: 333314
Export
Media: 4-7-10
Distr.: Intl.; Natl.

Personnel:
Douglas Hepper *(CEO)*
Richard Faber *(CFO & VP)*
Susan Linzmeier *(VP-HR)*
Scott Schaller *(VP-Sls & Mktg-Worldwide)*
Barry Resnick *(Dir-Mktg)*

WALLACH SURGICAL DEVICES, INC.

75 Corporate Dr
Trumbull, CT 06611
Tel.: (203) 799-2000
Fax: (203) 799-2002
Toll Free: (800) 243-2463
E-mail: wallach@wallachsurgical.com
Web Site: www.wallachsurgical.com
Sales Range: $25-49.9 Million
Approx. Number Employees: 50
Year Founded: 1980

Business Description:
Cryosurgical Instruments, Colposcopes, Operating Microscopes, Electrosurgical Instruments & Disposables Mfr for Gynecology
S.I.C.: 3841
N.A.I.C.S.: 339112
Export
Advertising Expenditures: $500,000

Key to Media (For complete agency information see *The Advertising Red Books-Agencies* edition):
1. Bus. Publs. 2. Cable T.V. 3. Catalogs & Directories. 4. Co-op Adv. 5. Consumer Mags. 6. D.M. to Bus. Estab.7. D.M. to Consumers
8. Daily Newsp. 9. Exhibits/Trade Shows 10. Foreign 11. Infomercial 12. Internet Adv.13. Multimedia 14. Network Radio
15. Network T.V. 16. Newsp. Distr. Mags. 17. Other 18. Outdoor (Posters, Transit) 19. Point of Purchase20. Premiums, Novelties
21. Product Samples 22. Special Events Mktg. 23. Spot Radio 24. Spot T.V. 25. Weekly Newsp. 26. Yellow Page Adv.

Bus. Publs.: $200,000; Catalogs & Directories: $25,000; D.M. to Consumers: $50,000; Exhibits/Trade Shows: $150,000; Other: $75,000
Distr.: Intl.
Budget Set: Sept.
Personnel:
Craig Citron *(VP-Sls & Mktg)*
Linda M. Cella *(Product Mgr)*
Brands & Products:
BIOVAC
COLPOSTAR
OMNIISENSE
PAINBLOCKER
PAPETTE
PENTASCOPE
PENTASTAR
QUANTUM
SONICAIDONE
TRISCOPE
TRISTAR
ULTRAFREEZE
ZOOM STAR
ZOOMSCOPE
ZOOMSTAR

WATERS CORPORATION

34 Maple St
Milford, MA 01757
Tel.: (508) 478-2000
Fax: (508) 872-1990
Toll Free: (800) 252-4752
Toll Free: (800) 252HPLC
E-mail: info@waters.com
Web Site: www.waters.com
Approx. Sls.: $1,643,371,000
Approx. Number Employees: 5,400
Year Founded: 1958
Business Description:
High Performance Liquid Chromatography (HPLC), Thermal Analysis & Mass Spectrometry (MS) Instruments, Columns Mfr & Distr & Related Services
S.I.C.: 3826; 3829
N.A.I.C.S.: 334516; 334519
Advertising Expenditures: $10,000,000
Media: 7-17
Personnel:
Douglas A. Berthiaume *(Chm, Pres & CEO)*
John A. Ornell *(CFO, VP-Fin & Admin)*
John R. Nelson *(Sr VP & Chief Scientific Officer)*
Arthur G. Caputo *(Pres-Waters Div & Exec VP)*
Terrence P. Kelly *(Pres-TA Instruments-Waters LLC)*
Aaron Wolkoff *(Pres-Waters Canada Ltd)*
Richard Blais *(VP & Mgr-Natl Sls)*
Elizabeth B. Rae *(VP-HR)*
Ken Eglinton *(Sr Mgr-Software)*
Nancy Mosteko *(Office Mgr & Mktg Admin)*
Keith Worrall *(Sr Product Mgr-SYNAPT)*
Brands & Products:
ACCELL
ACQUITY UPLC
ALPHA BAK
ATLANTIS
AUOTSPEC
AUTOSPEC-ULTIMA
BASELINE
BIOPHARMALYNX
BIOSUITE
BONDAPAK
BREEZE
CAPLC
CIA
CIA-PAK
CLEAR-100
CORASIL
DELTA
DELTA-PAK
DEXTRO-PAK
ECP
ELAB
EMPOWER
ENHANCER
FRACTIOLYNX
FRACTIONLYNX
GEN-PAK
GLYCO-PAK
GUARD-PAK
HDMS
HIGH DEFINITION MASS SPECTROMETRY
I-FIT
IC-PAK
INTELLIGENT SPEED
INTELLISTART
LCT
LECTRABOND
MALDI
MALDIMICRO
MASS FRAGMENT
MASSLYNX
MASSPREP
MASSSEQ
MICROMASS
MILLENNIUM
NANO FLOW
NANO LC
NANOEASE
NOVA-PAK
NUGENESIS
OASIS
OBD
OPENLYNX
PATROL
PEPSEQ
PICO TAG
PORAPAK
PREP
Q SERIES
Q-TOF
Q-TOF MICRO
QUANLYNX
QUATTRO
QUATTRO CONNECTIONS
QUATTRO MICRO
QUATTRO PREMIER
RADIAL-PAK
RAPIGEST
RESOLVE
RPS
SAMPLE CENTRIC
SCANWAVE
THE SCIENCE OF WHAT'S POSSIBLE.
SEP-PAK
SHODEX
SILICA-PAK
SIROCCO
SPHERISORB
SUNFIRE
SYMMETRY
T-WAVE
TA INSTRUMENTS
TAPERBEAM
TAPERSLIT
ULTRAHYDROGEL
ULTRASTYRAGEL
UPLC
V-OPTICS
W-OPTICS
WATERS
WATERS CRITICAL CLEAN
WAVS
XBRIDGE
XEVO
XPOSURE
XTERRA
ZQ
ZSPRAY
Advertising Agency:
Allen & Gerritsen
The Arsenal on the Charles 311 Arsenal St 4th Fl
Watertown, MA 02472
Tel.: (617) 926-4005
Fax: (617) 926-0133

WELCH ALLYN INC.

4341 State Street Rd
Skaneateles Falls, NY 13153-0220
Tel.: (315) 685-4100
Fax: (315) 685-3361
Web Site: www.welchallyn.com
Approx. Sls.: $350,000,000
Approx. Number Employees: 2,100
Year Founded: 1915
Business Description:
Surgical & Medical Instruments
S.I.C.: 3841; 2834
N.A.I.C.S.: 339112; 325412
Import Export
Media: 10-22
Personnel:
James Crook, Jr. *(Chm)*
Julie A. Shimer *(Pres & CEO)*
Karen Roscher *(CFO & Exec VP-Fin)*
Eric Hunt *(CIO & VP)*
Louise McDonald *(Exec VP & Pres-Intl)*
Steve Meyer *(Exec VP & Pres-US & Canada)*
Gregory Porter *(Gen Counsel & Sr VP)*
Doug Linquest *(Exec VP-Strategy & Bus Dev)*
Darrell A. Clapper *(Sr VP-Global Ops & Supply Chain Mgmt)*
Dan Fisher *(Sr VP-HR)*
Karen Hendricks *(Sr VP-Tech & Innovation)*
Tom Grant *(Grp Dir-Core Blood Pressure Prods)*
David Tufenkjian *(Sr Mgr-Product)*
Jamie Arnold *(Mgr-PR & Internal Comm)*
Evert Barneveld *(Mgr-Sls)*
Sean Karla *(Mgr-Category-Global)*
Douglas Rutan *(Mgr-Mktg)*
Wim Treurniet *(Mgr-Svc)*
Brands & Products:
ACUITY
AED 10
AED 20
ATLAS
AUTOSTEP
BRAUN THERMOSCAN
COMPACVIDEO
CONNEX
DIGITAL MACROVIEW
ELITE
EPISCOPE
EXAM LIGHT III
HALOGEN HPX
HARVEY
HARVEY ELITE
KLEENSPEC
LS135
LS150
LS200
MFI SOLARC
MICROPAQ
MOBILE ACUITY
PANOPTIC
PIC 30
PIC 40
PIC 50
POCKETSCOPE
PROPAQ
SPOT VITAL SIGNS
SURETEMP
TYCOS
VIDEOPATH
WELCH ALLYN
WELCH ALLYN ACUITYLINK
WELCH ALLYN CARDIOPERFECT
WELCH ALLYN CP 100
WELCH ALLYN CP 200
WELCH ALLYN FLEXNET
WELCH ALLYN MACROVIEW
WELCH ALLYN PC-BASED SPIROPERFECT
WELCH ALLYN PROXENON
Advertising Agency:
Pinckney Hugo Group
760 W Genesee St
Syracuse, NY 13204-2306
Tel.: (315) 478-6700
Fax: (315) 426-1392

WESTON SOLUTIONS HOLDINGS, INC.

1400 Weston Way
West Chester, PA 19380
Mailing Address:
PO Box 2653
West Chester, PA 19380
Tel.: (610) 701-3000
Fax: (610) 701-3186
E-mail: info@westonsolutions.com
Web Site: www.westonsolutions.com
Approx. Sls.: $113,300,000
Approx. Number Employees: 1,800
Year Founded: 1957
Business Description:
Holding Company; Environmental Engineering & Consulting Firm
S.I.C.: 8748; 8742
N.A.I.C.S.: 541618; 541611
Media: 2-5-7-9-10-20-26
Distr.: Intl.
Budget Set: Dec.
Personnel:
Patrick G. McCann *(Chm, Pres & CEO)*
Vincent A. Laino *(CFO, CIO & Sr VP)*
Peter A. Ceribelli *(COO & Sr VP)*
Arnold P. Borish *(Gen Counsel, Sec & Sr VP)*
Anthony Parisi *(Treas & Dir-Capital Markets)*
Lawrence J. Bove *(Sr VP & Mgr-Mid-Atlantic Div)*
Raymond J. Griffin *(Sr VP & Mgr-HR)*
Edmund B. Pettiss *(Sr VP & Mgr-Mktg & Comm)*
Kurt S. Stimpson *(Sr VP & Mgr-Central Div)*
Donald W. Grogan *(Sr VP)*

Key to Media (For complete agency information see *The Advertising Red Books-Agencies* edition):
1. Bus. Publs. 2. Cable T.V. 3. Catalogs & Directories. 4. Co-op Adv. 5. Consumer Mags. 6. D.M. to Bus. Estab.7. D.M. to Consumers
8. Daily Newsp. 9. Exhibits/Trade Shows 10. Foreign 11. Infomercial 12. Internet Adv.13. Multimedia 14. Network Radio
15. Network T.V. 16. Newsp. Distr. Mags. 17. Other 18. Outdoor (Posters, Transit) 19. Point of Purchase20. Premiums, Novelties
21. Product Samples 22. Special Events Mktg. 23. Spot Radio 24. Spot T.V. 25. Weekly Newsp. 26. Yellow Page Adv.

Weston Solutions Holdings, Inc. — (Continued)

Greg Janiec *(Dir-Tech)*
Cheryl Koshuta *(Dir-Seaports & Airports)*

WIKA INSTRUMENT CORPORATION
(Sub. of WIKA Alexander-Wiegand GmbH & Co. KG)
1000 Wiegand Blvd
Lawrenceville, GA 30043
Tel.: (770) 513-8200
Fax: (770) 338-5118
E-mail: info@wika.com
Web Site: www.wika.com
Sales Range: $50-74.9 Million
Approx. Number Employees: 600
Business Description:
Pressure & Temperature Controls Mfr
S.I.C.: 3823; 3053
N.A.I.C.S.: 334513; 339991
Media: 10
Personnel:
Alexander Wiegand *(Chm & CEO)*
Michael Gerster *(Pres)*
Jeff Carrier *(Reg Mgr)*
Rick Harpole *(Reg Mgr-Sls)*
Denise Oxley *(Reg Sls Mgr)*
Jack Clackley *(Mgr-Bus Dev)*
Joe Eskridge *(Mgr-Natl Sls)*

THE WILL-BURT CO., INC.
169 S Main St
Orrville, OH 44667-1801
Tel.: (330) 682-7015
Fax: (330) 684-1190
Web Site: www.willburt.com
Approx. Number Employees: 250
Year Founded: 1901
Business Description:
Pneumatic Telescoping Mast & Accessories Mfr
S.I.C.: 3599; 3443
N.A.I.C.S.: 332710; 332313
Export
Advertising Expenditures: $200,000
Media: 4-6-7-8-10-11-13-17-20
Distr.: Intl.; Natl.
Budget Set: Dec.
Personnel:
Jeff Evans *(Chm, Pres & CEO)*
Bruce Inzetta *(VP-Fin)*
Brands & Products:
D-TEC
DC VISTAR
ENSIGN DOCK BOX
ENSIGN DOCKSIDE UTILITY CENTER
ENSIGN MATE DOCKSIDE UTILITY CENTER
ENSIGN PLUS DOCKSIDE UTILITY CENTER
NIGHT SCAN
NIGHT SCAN CHIEF
NIGHT SCAN FEATHERLITE
NIGHT SCAN ILLUMINATOR
NIGHT SCAN METAL HALIDE
NIGHT SCAN PROFILER
NIGHT SCAN TAC STICK
NIGHT SCAN VERTICAL
WB
WILL-BURT

WILLOUGHBY'S KONICA MINOLTA IMAGING CENTER
298 5th Ave
New York, NY 10001
Tel.: (212) 564-1600
Fax: (212) 564-1608
E-mail: info@willoughbys.com
Web Site: www.willoughbys.com
E-Mail For Key Personnel:
Sales Director: sales@willoughbys.com
Approx. Number Employees: 20
Year Founded: 1898
Business Description:
Cameras, Binoculars, Camera Accessories, Audio Equipment & Home & Business Computers Retailer
S.I.C.: 7373
N.A.I.C.S.: 541512
Advertising Expenditures: $1,800,000
Media: 2-4-5-6-9-10-13-14-15-18-19-20-25-26
Distr.: Direct to Consumer
Budget Set: Sept.
Personnel:
Joseph Douek *(Pres)*
Brands & Products:
WILLOUGHBY'S

WILSON HARDNESS GROUP
(Sub. of Instron Corporation)
(d/b/a WILSON SHORE INSTRUMENTS)
825 University Ave
Norwood, MA 02062
Tel.: (781) 828-2500
Fax: (781) 575-5770
Toll Free: (800) 695-4273
E-mail: webmaster@instron.com
Web Site: www.wilsoninstruments.com
Approx. Number Employees: 300
Year Founded: 1923
Business Description:
Materials Testing Equipment, Hardness Testing Instruments & Systems; Laboratory & Metals Testing Instruments, Hardness Calibration Products, Access, Rockwell & Tukon Hardness Testers, Service, Repair, & Calibration of Laboratory Equipment
S.I.C.: 3829; 7629
N.A.I.C.S.: 334519; 811219
Import Export
Media: 6-9-17
Personnel:
Steve Martindale *(COO)*
Brands & Products:
BRALE
DYNATUP
SHORE DUROMETERS
SHORE INSTRUMENTS
TUKON
WILSON

X-RITE, INCORPORATED
4300 44th St SE
Grand Rapids, MI 49512
Tel.: (616) 803-2100
Fax: (616) 534-0723
Toll Free: (800) 248-9748
Web Site: www.x-rite.com
Approx. Sls.: $222,740,000
Approx. Number Employees: 746
Year Founded: 1958
Business Description:
Quality Control Instruments & Software Designer, Mfr & Marketer for Companies in the Paint, Plastic, Textile, Photographic, Graphic Arts & Medical Industries
S.I.C.: 3861; 3827
N.A.I.C.S.: 333315; 325992; 333314
Export
Advertising Expenditures: $500,000
Media: 1-2-7-10-11-13-19
Distr.: Intl.; Natl.; Reg.
Personnel:
John E. Utley *(Chm)*
Thomas J. Vacchiano, Jr. *(Pres & CEO)*
Rajesh K. Shah *(CFO & Exec VP)*
Iris Mangelschots *(Pres-Asia Pacific Reg)*
Robert Agnes *(Sr VP-Sls & Mktg-Worldwide)*
Bernard J. Berg *(Sr VP-Engrng)*
John Kowalski *(Dir-Strategic Mktg-Indus)*
Kenneth Phillips *(Product Mgr)*
Laura Pursley *(Mgr-Worldwide Product)*
Brands & Products:
COLOR IQC
COLORCHECKER
COLORDESIGNER
COLORMAIL EXPRESS
COLORMUNKI
COLORMUNKI CREATE
COLORMUNKI DESIGN
COLORPORT
COMPUTERIZED COLOR RESPONSE
DENSIEYE
ELECTRONIC FUNCTION SELECTION
EZCOLOR
ICPLATE2
INTELLITRAX
THE JUDGE
MATCHRITE IVUE
MATCHSTIK
MONACOEXCOLOR
MONACOOPTIX
MONACOPROFILER
MONACOQCCOLOR
NETPROFILER
PANTONE
PERSONALDESIGNER
PLATESCOPE
PROFILEMAKER5
QUICK CAL
RIGHT ON COLOR
SHADE-X
SHADEVISION
SPECTRALIGHT
TELEFLASH
VERICOLOR
VIPFLEX2
X-RITE
X-RITECOLOR
Advertising Agency:
Seyferth & Associates Inc.
40 Monroe Ctr NW Ste 202
Grand Rapids, MI 49503
Tel.: (616) 776-3511
Fax: (616) 776-3502
Toll Free: (800) 435-9539

YOUNGER MFG. CO.
(d/b/a Younger Optics)
2925 California St
Torrance, CA 90503-3914
Tel.: (310) 783-1533
Fax: (310) 783-6477
Web Site: www.youngeroptics.com
E-Mail For Key Personnel:
Marketing Director: rlee@youngeroptics.com
Approx. Number Employees: 700
Year Founded: 1955
Business Description:
Eyeglass Lenses & Optical Products Mfr
S.I.C.: 3851
N.A.I.C.S.: 339115
Export
Media: 1-2-5-7-10-11-13-19-21
Distr.: Intl.; Natl.
Personnel:
David Rips *(Pres)*
Tom Balch *(Mng Dir)*
Johann van Zyl *(Dir-Sls-Americas)*
Robert Lee *(Dir-Sls & Mktg)*
Brands & Products:
DRIVEWEAR
EASY LITE
IMAGE
NUPOLAR
POLYCARBONATE
TRILOGY

YSI INCORPORATED
1725 Brannum Ln
Yellow Springs, OH 45387-1107
Tel.: (937) 767-7241
Fax: (937) 767-9320
Telex: 205437
E-mail: support@ysi.com
Web Site: www.ysi.com
Approx. Number Employees: 130
Year Founded: 1948
Business Description:
Scientific & Industrial Instruments Mfr
S.I.C.: 3826; 3823
N.A.I.C.S.: 334516; 334513
Export
Advertising Expenditures: $750,000
Media: 2-4-10
Distr.: Intl.; Natl.
Budget Set: Dec.
Personnel:
Rick Omlor *(Pres & CEO)*
Lee Erdman *(CFO & VP)*
Mark W. Matson *(COO & VP-Ops)*
David Barclay *(Dir-Life Sciences)*
Tim Grooms *(Mgr-Bus Dev)*
Brands & Products:
ARGONAUT
ISOTHERM
PURE DATA FOR A HEALTHY PLANET
RAPID PULSE
SENSICHIP
TELE-THERMOMETER
THERMISTEMP
THERMIVOLT
VECO
YSI

ZANETT, INC.
635 Madison Ave
New York, NY 10022
Tel.: (646) 502-1800
Fax: (212) 753-5304
Web Site: www.zanett.com
Approx. Rev.: $48,040,515
Approx. Number Employees: 218
Business Description:
Business Process Outsourcing & Consulting Services
S.I.C.: 8742; 7374; 7389
N.A.I.C.S.: 541611; 518210; 541614; 541990
Personnel:
Claudio M. Guazzoni *(Founder)*
Dennis Harkins *(Pres & CFO)*

Key to Media (For complete agency information see *The Advertising Red Books-Agencies* edition):
1. Bus. Publs. 2. Cable T.V. 3. Catalogs & Directories. 4. Co-op Adv. 5. Consumer Mags. 6. D.M. to Bus. Estab.7. D.M. to Consumers 8. Daily Newsp. 9. Exhibits/Trade Shows 10. Foreign 11. Infomercial 12. Internet Adv.13. Multimedia 14. Network Radio 15. Network T.V. 16. Newsp. Distr. Mags. 17. Other 18. Outdoor (Posters, Transit) 19. Point of Purchase20. Premiums, Novelties 21. Product Samples 22. Special Events Mktg. 23. Spot Radio 24. Spot T.V. 25. Weekly Newsp. 26. Yellow Page Adv.

Brands & Products:
THE IT COMMONWEALTH

Advertising Agency:
RedChip Companies, Inc.
500 Winderely Pl Ste 100
Maitland, FL 32751
Tel.: (407) 644-4256
Fax: (407) 644-0758
Toll Free: (800) 733-2447

ZAREBA SYSTEMS INC.
(Sub. of The Woodstream Corporation)
13705 26th Ave N Ste 102
Minneapolis, MN 55441
Mailing Address:
PO Box 6117
Rochester, MN 55903
Tel.: (763) 551-1125
Fax: (763) 509-7450
Toll Free: (800) 272-9877
Web Site: www.zarebasystems.com
Approx. Sls.: $32,216,000
Approx. Number Employees: 111
Year Founded: 1960
Business Description:
Electric Fence Controllers Mfr to Contain Pets & Livestock & Deter Predators
S.I.C.: 3699; 3612; 3845
N.A.I.C.S.: 335999; 334510; 335311
Import Export
Advertising Expenditures: $791,000
Media: 7
Personnel:
Jeffrey S. Mathiesen *(CFO & COO)*
John Hossman *(Exec VP-Sls & Bus Dev)*
Donald G. Dalland *(VP-Engrg & Ops)*
Ron W. Oblizajek *(Dir-IT)*
Brands & Products:
AMERICAN FARMWORKS & DESIGN
BLITZER
BULLDOZER
CAPTIVATOR
ELECTRIC SHEPHERD
ELECTRO-LINE
EZEE CORRAL
GARDEN PROTECTOR
GUARD TOWER
HOLDEM
THE HORSE FENCE THAT MAKES SENSE
HORSE SENSE ELECTRIC FENCE SYSTEM
HOT SPARK
INTERNATIONAL
ONE STOP FENCING & DESIGN
PET CONTROLLER
RED SNAP'R
SUPER CHARGER
TARANTULA
ZAREBA
ZAREBA SECURITY

Key to Media (For complete agency information see *The Advertising Red Books-Agencies* edition):
1. Bus. Publs. 2. Cable T.V. 3. Catalogs & Directories. 4. Co-op Adv. 5. Consumer Mags. 6. D.M. to Bus. Estab.7. D.M. to Consumers
8. Daily Newsp. 9. Exhibits/Trade Shows 10. Foreign 11. Infomercial 12. Internet Adv.13. Multimedia 14. Network Radio
15. Network T.V. 16. Newsp. Distr. Mags. 17. Other 18. Outdoor (Posters, Transit) 19. Point of Purchase20. Premiums, Novelties
21. Product Samples 22. Special Events Mktg. 23. Spot Radio 24. Spot T.V. 25. Weekly Newsp. 26. Yellow Page Adv.

Paints, Varnishes & Enamels

Caulking & Spackling Compounds — Colors — Lacquers — Paint Applicators — Paint Brushes — Paint Removers — Pigments — Protective Coatings — Stains

AERVOE INDUSTRIES INCORPORATED
1198 Mark Cir
Gardnerville, NV 89410
Tel.: (775) 783-3100
Fax: (775) 782-5687
Toll Free: (800) 227-0196
E-mail: mailbox@wrtechpark.com
Web Site: www.aervoe.com
Approx. Number Employees: 125
Year Founded: 1979
Business Description:
Paints, Coatings, Cleaners & Lubricants Mfr
S.I.C.: 2851; 2841; 2992
N.A.I.C.S.: 325510; 324191; 325611
Media: 2-4-10
Personnel:
Mark Williams *(Pres)*
David A. Williams *(CEO)*
Brands & Products:
AERVOE
AERVOE SHIPPING ESSENTIALS
AERVOE TOOLMATES
ALL PURPOSE
APC
BRITE GALVANIZE
BUTTERCUTT
CAMOUFLAGE
CAN HAND'LER
CARTON
CHROME GALVANIZE
CLEAR ACRYLIC
CROWN
DUSTAIR
E-Z-EST COIN CLEANER
E-Z-EST SPEED DIP
ECONO
ESSENTIALS
FLO GLO
FOAM KLEAN
FUGITIVE
GALVA BRIGHT
HAND-Y
HAND-Y PRO
HI-HEAT
INDUSTRIAL
INVERT-A-CAP
KLEER KOTE
LUBE EZE
NU-SAFE
PERFORMANCE BLEND RUST-SOLV
POLYSHIELD
PRIMER
RUSTPROOF
SLIX-IT
SPRA-TOOL
SPRAY MATE
STEEL RENEW
STIR-N-POUR
SUPREME RUST SHIELD
SURVEY
TEF-LUBE
T.F.E.
THERE IS ALWAYS AN AERVOE SOLUTION...
VERS-A-STRIPER
ZINC RICH

AKZO NOBEL
(Sub. of Akzo Nobel Decorative Paints)
2505 De La Metropole St
Longueuil, QC J4G 1E5, Canada
Tel.: (514) 527-5111
Fax: (450) 646-7699
Telex: 5268858
Web Site: www.akzonobel.com
E-Mail For Key Personnel:
President: pierre.dufresne@sico.com
Marketing Director: yvon.savaria@sico.com
Approx. Number Employees: 1,000
Year Founded: 1941
Business Description:
Architectural Paint & Metal Coating Mfr
S.I.C.: 2851
N.A.I.C.S.: 325510
Export
Advertising Expenditures: $7,000,000
Media: 1-2-4-5-6-7-8-9-10-11-14-15-18-19-20-21-22-23-24-25-26
Distr.: Natl.
Budget Set: Apr.-Nov.
Personnel:
Pierre Dufresne *(Mng Dir)*
Martine Bazinet *(Sec & VP-Legal Affairs)*
Claude Brousseau *(VP-Sls & Mktg)*
Marc-Andre Chabot *(VP-Applied Tech & R & D)*
Yvon Savaria *(Dir-Mktg)*
Dominique Pepin *(marketing manager)*
Claude St. Pierre *(Mgr-HR)*
Brands & Products:
ACRYTHANE
AQUALUX
CACHEMIRE
CHAMOIS
CHATEAU
CHEMISOLID
CORRETEC
CORROSTOP
CROWN DIAMOND
FORMULA
LUXSICO
POLYPREP
POWDERFREE
PRILCO
SICO
SICOCERAM
SICOPOXY
SICORAD
THERMALKYD
ULTRASOLID
Advertising Agency:
Saint-Jacques Vallee Tactik
1600 boul Rene-Levesque W 10th Fl
Montreal, QC H3H 1P9, Canada
Tel.: (514) 935-6375
Fax: (514) 935-9479
(CrownDiamond)

AKZO NOBEL COATINGS INC.
(Branch of Akzo Nobel Coatings Inc.)
1313 Windsor Ave
Columbus, OH 43211-2851
Mailing Address:
PO Box 489
Columbus, OH 43216-0489
Tel.: (614) 294-3361
Fax: (614) 294-0436
Web Site: www.akzonobel.com/aboutus/locations/index.aspx
Approx. Sls.: $25,000,000
Approx. Number Employees: 180
Business Description:
Chemical Coatings Mfr
S.I.C.: 2851; 8733
N.A.I.C.S.: 325510; 541710
Advertising Expenditures: $750,000
Media: 2-4-6-9-10-11-14-18-20-23-26
Distr.: Intl.; Natl.
Budget Set: Sept.
Personnel:
Scott Hanna *(Mgr-IF Coil Americas)*
Ed Karper *(Mgr-Mktg)*

AKZO NOBEL DECORATIVE PAINTS, USA
(Sub. of AkzoNobel)
15885 Sprague Rd
Strongsville, OH 44136
Mailing Address:
PO Box 2535
Hudson, OH 44236-0035
Tel.: (330) 650-4070
Fax: (330) 650-1453
Toll Free: (800) 356-6346
Web Site: www.flood.com
Sales Range: $50-74.9 Million
Approx. Number Employees: 500
Year Founded: 1841
Business Description:
Interior & Exterior Wood Care Products Mfr
S.I.C.: 2851
N.A.I.C.S.: 325510
Export
Advertising Expenditures: $149,335,000
Consumer Mags.: $112,001,250;
Exhibits/Trade Shows: $22,400,250;
Point of Purchase: $14,933,500
Distr.: Intl.; Natl.
Budget Set: Sept.
Personnel:
Eric Bouts *(Gen Mgr)*
Brands & Products:
BRUSH STUFF
CWF
CWF-UV
DECKWORKS
DEKS OLJE
DEKSWOOD
DO SOMETHING AMAZING
EASY SURFACE PREP
EMULSA-BOND
ESP EASY SURFACE PREP
FLOETROL
FLOOD
FLOODPRO
GLASWORKS
HULLWORKS
NEW WOOD DEFENDER
PENEPREP
PENETROL
POWERLIFT
RESTORA
SEASONITE
SPA-N-DECK
STAINSTRIP
TEAKWORKS

Key to Media (For complete agency information see *The Advertising Red Books-Agencies* edition):
1. Bus. Publs. 2. Cable T.V. 3. Catalogs & Directories. 4. Co-op Adv. 5. Consumer Mags. 6. D.M. to Bus. Estab.7. D.M. to Consumers 8. Daily Newsp. 9. Exhibits/Trade Shows 10. Foreign 11. Infomercial 12. Internet Adv.13. Multimedia 14. Network Radio 15. Network T.V. 16. Newsp. Distr. Mags. 17. Other 18. Outdoor (Posters, Transit) 19. Point of Purchase20. Premiums, Novelties 21. Product Samples 22. Special Events Mktg. 23. Spot Radio 24. Spot T.V. 25. Weekly Newsp. 26. Yellow Page Adv.

AKZONOBEL DECORATIVE PAINTS U.S.
(Sub. of Akzo Nobel N.V.)
15885 W Sprague Rd
Strongsville, OH 44136-1772
Tel.: (216) 344-8000
Fax: (440) 297-8900
Toll Free: (800) 221-4100
Web Site: www.akzonobel.com
Approx. Number Employees: 500
Year Founded: 1986
Business Description:
Decorative Paints & Metal Coatings Mfr.
S.I.C.: 2851
N.A.I.C.S.: 325510
Import Export
Media: 2-3-4-5-6-7-8-9-10-14-15-18-19-23-25
Distr.: Natl.
Budget Set: Dec.
Personnel:
Cathie McKinley *(CFO & CIO)*
Cathy Fischer *(Chief Product Officer)*
Margurite Walz *(VP-HR)*
Linda Feldman *(Dir-Mktg)*
Derek Rance *(Dir-R&D)*
Brands & Products:
ALL-WEATHER
AMERITONE
AQUA CHEM
AQUABASE
AQUALURE
BAR OX
BAR RUST
BLENDZ ALL
BLOCKAID
BLOXFIL
CATHA COAT
CHEM-VY-KOTE
CHEMFAST
CLEAN AIR CHOICE
COLOR KEY COMPUTER
THE COLOR KEY PROGRAM
COLOR NATURALS
COVER PERFECT
DE-VO-KO
DE-VO-LAC
DE-VO-PRO
DE-VO-TEX
DECRASHIELD
DECRATREND
DEVCHEM
DEVCHLOR
DEVOE
DEVRAN
DRAMA TONE
DULUX
DULUX ENDURANCE
DULUX INSPIRATIONS
ENDURANCE
FLORENAMEL
FOR EVER
FULLER-O'BRIEN
GLID
GLID-GUARD
GLID-SHIELD
GLID-THANE
GLID-TILE
GLID-TONE
GLID-ZINC
GLIDDEN
GLIDE-ON
GRANITEX
HANDIMATCH
HARRIS
HYDRO-SHUR
HYDRODERM
HYDROFLEX
HYDROPATCH
HYDROPLASTIC
HYDROPRIME
HYDROSEALER
IMPERIAL GOLD
IMPERIAL TOUCH
INSUL-AID
INSUL-BLAZE
KILSTAIN
KILSTAIN WB
LIFEMASTER
LIFEMASTER 2000
LIFEMASTER-PRO
LIQUID NAILS
MACCO
MACHINECLAD
MASTER-GUARD
THE MASTER PALETTE
MILLITE
MIRROLAC
MIRROLAC WB
POLYCELL
PRIMECOAT
PRUFCOAT
RE-NEW-COAT
REGENCY
ROYALE
RUSTMASTER
RUSTMASTER METALLITE
SINCLAIR
SPEED DRY
SPEED-REX
SPEED-WALL
SPEEDCOTE
SPRA-MAX
SPRA-MAX 12
SPRA-MAX 40
SPRAY-DAY-LITE
SPRED
SPRED 2000
SPRED-DURA
SPRED ENAMEL
SPRED FLAT
SPRED GLOSS
SPRED HOUSE
SPRED KITCHEN AND BATH
SPRED LO-LUSTRE
SPRED LUSTRE
SPRED SATIN
SPRED SILK
SPRED SOLO
SPRED SUPREME
SUPER KLEAN
SUPER-POR-SEAL
T-40
TRAFFIC LINE
TRAFFIC LINE WB
TRIPLE COVER
TRU-GLAZE
TRU-GLAZE 2
TRU-GLAZE 4
ULTRA
ULTRA-HIDE
UNI-GRIP
VELOUR
WONDER BOND
WONDER GUARD
WONDER HIDE
WONDER-PRIME
WONDER-PRUF
WONDER SHIELD
WONDER-SPEED
WONDER-STICK
WONDER TINT
WONDER TONES
WONDER WOODTONES
WOODMASTER
XPERT
ZINCPRIME 100
Advertising Agencies:
Castells & Asociados
865 S Figueroa St Ste 1100
Los Angeles, CA 90017-2543
Tel.: (213) 688-7250
Fax: (213) 688-7067

Dix & Eaton Incorporated
200 Public Sq Ste 1400
Cleveland, OH 44114
Tel.: (216) 241-0405
Fax: (216) 241-3070

Euro RSCG Worldwide HQ
350 Hudson St
New York, NY 10014-4504
Tel.: (212) 886-2000
Fax: (212) 886-2016

AMERGRAPH CORPORATION
520 Lafayette Rd
Sparta, NJ 07871
Tel.: (973) 383-8700
Fax: (973) 383-9225
Toll Free: (800) 526-2852
E-mail: sales@amergraph.com
Web Site: www.amergraph.com
E-Mail For Key Personnel:
Sales Director: sales@amergraph.com
Business Description:
Graphic Arts Equipment Mfr & Distr
S.I.C.: 3861; 3555
N.A.I.C.S.: 333315; 333293
Media: 10
Personnel:
Robert Lesko *(Pres)*
Brands & Products:
ADVANTAGE
AMERGRAPH

AMERICAN INKS & COATINGS CORPORATION
(Sub. of Mosley Holdings Limited Partnership)
3400 N Hutchinson St
Pine Bluff, AR 71602
Tel.: (870) 247-2080
Fax: (870) 735-2411
Approx. Number Employees: 28
Year Founded: 1928
Business Description:
Coatings & Inks for the Printing Trade Mfr
S.I.C.: 2893; 2899
N.A.I.C.S.: 325910; 325998
Import Export
Media: 2
Distr.: Natl.
Budget Set: June
Personnel:
Jerry Mosley *(Pres)*
Brands & Products:
AMERGLOSS
AMERTECH
AMERTECH II

ANCHOR PAINT MANUFACTURING CO. INC.
6707 E 14th St
Tulsa, OK 74112-6615
Tel.: (918) 836-4626
Fax: (918) 836-6421
E-mail: info@anchorpaint.com
Web Site: www.anchorpaint.com
Approx. Number Employees: 175
Year Founded: 1962
Business Description:
Mfr. of Paints & Allied Products
S.I.C.: 2851; 2842
N.A.I.C.S.: 325510; 325612
Import Export
Media: 2-4-7-8-13-18-19-21-26
Personnel:
Chuck Taylor *(Pres)*
Charlotte David *(CFO)*
Brands & Products:
ANCHOR
ANCHORED FOR WEAR

ATHENA BRANDS INCORPORATED
(Sub. of Aervoe Industries Incorporated)
1100 Mark Cir
Gardnerville, NV 89410
Tel.: (775) 783-3100
Fax: (775) 782-5687
Toll Free: (888) 272-8603
E-mail: mailbox@zynolyte.com
Web Site: www.zynolyte.com
Approx. Sls.: $15,000,000
Approx. Number Employees: 80
Year Founded: 1928
Business Description:
Aerosol & Specialty Paint Products Distr
S.I.C.: 3089
N.A.I.C.S.: 326199
Media: 9-10-16-19-20
Distr.: Intl.; Natl.
Budget Set: Oct.
Personnel:
Mark Williams *(Pres)*
Brands & Products:
EPOXY RUST-MATE
FANTA-Z
FLEC-IT
KLENK'S AQUA TECH
KLENK'S EPOXY
SPEED E-NAMEL

THE ATLAS COMPANIES, INC.
(Sub. of Betco Corporation)
(d/b/a Basic Coatings)
1001 Brown Ave
Toledo, OH 43607
Tel.: (515) 288-0231
Fax: (515) 288-0615
Fax: (800) 942-2007
Toll Free: (800) 247-5471
E-mail: bcinfo@basiccoatings.com
Web Site: www.basiccoatings.com
Approx. Number Employees: 50
Year Founded: 1962
Business Description:
Hardwood Floor Coatings Mfr
S.I.C.: 2851; 2861
N.A.I.C.S.: 325510; 325191
Media: 2-4-7-10-13-20-21-22

BENJAMIN MOORE & CO.
(Holding of Berkshire Hathaway Inc.)
101 Paragon Dr
Montvale, NJ 07645
Tel.: (201) 573-9600
Fax: (201) 573-0046
Toll Free: (800) 344-0400
E-mail: info@benjaminmoore.com
Web Site: www.benjaminmoore.com
E-Mail For Key Personnel:

Key to Media (For complete agency information see *The Advertising Red Books-Agencies* edition):
1. Bus. Publs. 2. Cable T.V. 3. Catalogs & Directories. 4. Co-op Adv. 5. Consumer Mags. 6. D.M. to Bus. Estab.7. D.M. to Consumers 8. Daily Newsp. 9. Exhibits/Trade Shows 10. Foreign 11. Infomercial 12. Internet Adv.13. Multimedia 14. Network Radio 15. Network T.V. 16. Newsp. Distr. Mags. 17. Other 18. Outdoor (Posters, Transit) 19. Point of Purchase20. Premiums, Novelties 21. Product Samples 22. Special Events Mktg. 23. Spot Radio 24. Spot T.V. 25. Weekly Newsp. 26. Yellow Page Adv.

Benjamin Moore & Co. — (Continued)

Public Relations: eileen.mccomb@benjaminmoore.com
Approx. Sls.: $950,000,000
Approx. Number Employees: 2,951
Year Founded: 1883
Business Description:
Paints, Stains & Enamels Mfr
S.I.C.: 2851; 5231
N.A.I.C.S.: 325510; 444120
Export
Media: 2-5-6-7-8-10-13-18-19-20-24-26
Distr.: Natl.
Budget Set: Jan.
Personnel:
Yvan Dupuy *(Chm)*
Denis Abrams *(Pres & CEO)*
Bart Finnegan *(VP-HR)*
Ed Klein *(VP-Retail)*
Bruce Zeh *(VP-Corp Sls)*
Dan Claybaugh *(Gen Mgr-West Coast & Rocky Mountain Markets)*
Eileen McComb *(Dir-Corp Comm)*
Maureen Germinder *(Sr Mgr-Digital Media)*
Jeff Spillane *(Sr Mgr-Product)*
Daniela Guerriero *(Brand Mgr)*
Doreen Stellon *(Brand Mgr-Mktg)*
Peter Routsis *(Strategist-Consumer Mktg & Bus Dev)*
Brands & Products:
AQUAGLO
AQUAPEARL
AQUAVELVET
BENJAMIN MOORE
BENJAMIN MOORE CLASSIC COLOR COLLECTION
BENJAMIN MOORE CLASSIC COLORS
BENJAMIN MOORE FRESH START
BENJAMIN MOORE PAINTS
BENWOOD
BENWOOD FINISHES
BEST PAINT. BEST ADVICE.
BRILLIANT COATINGS
CHEX-WEAR
THE COLOR AUTHORITY
COLOR PREVIEW
COLOR PREVIEW STUDIO
COLOR PULSE
COLORSCAPES
CROWN DEVICE
DULAMEL
ECO SPEC
ENHANCE
FAUX FINESSE
IMPERVEX
IMPERVO
IMPERVO WITH DESIGN
IRONCLAD
K&B
MOORCRAFT
MOORCRAFT ROOF SPEC
MOORCRAFT SUPER CRAFT
MOORCRAFT SUPER HIDE
MOORCRAFT SUPER SPEC
MOORE'S
MOORE'S COATING COUNSELOR
MOORE'S COLORX AND DESIGN
MOORGARD
MOORGLO
MOORLASTIC
MOORLIFE
MOORSEAL
MOORWHITE
MOORWOOD
MURESCO
THE PAINT & COLOR EXPERTS
PAQUA
PENTAFLEX
PRISTINE
PRO SAVER
PRO-VYN-AL
PROFILES
QD 30 PLUS DESIGN
REGAL
REGAL AQUA PEARL
REGAL AQUA VELVET
REGAL AQUAGLO
REGAL FIRST COAT
REGAL WALL SATIN
RETARDO
RUST BLOK
SANI-FLAT AND DESIGN
SATIN IMPERVEX
SATIN IMPERVO
STAYS CLEAR
STUDIO FINISHES
TEMPGARD
TRIM CHIPS
UTILAC
VACO
VOL-PRO
WALL-GRIP
WALL-SATIN
WE MAKE IT SIMPLE, YOU MAKE IT BEAUTIFUL
Advertising Agency:
AKQA, Inc.
175 Varick St 10th Fl
New York, NY 10014
Tel.: (212) 989-2572
Fax: (212) 989-2363
Paint

THE BRON SHOE COMPANY
(d/b/a American Bronzing Company)
1313 Alum Creek Dr
Columbus, OH 43209
Tel.: (614) 252-0967
Tel.: (614) 252-7388
Fax: (614) 252-4602
Toll Free: (800) 423-5678
E-mail: bronzeinfo@bronshoe.com
Web Site: www.abcbronze.com
Approx. Number Employees: 50
Year Founded: 1934
Business Description:
Electroplating & Baby Shoe Bronzing Services
S.I.C.: 3471
N.A.I.C.S.: 332813
Export
Advertising Expenditures: $1,000,000
Media: 5-6-7-8-9-10-16-19-26
Distr.: Natl.
Personnel:
Robert J. Kaynes, Jr. *(Pres)*
Susan Lantz *(Controller)*
Brands & Products:
BRON-SHOE CO.

BRUNING PAINT COMPANY
4701 O'Donnell St
Baltimore, MD 21224-5303
Tel.: (410) 342-3636
Fax: (410) 675-5303
Toll Free: (800) 852-3636
E-mail: info@bruningpaints.com
Web Site: www.bruningpaints.com
Approx. Sls.: $50,000,000
Approx. Number Employees: 176
Year Founded: 1923
Business Description:
Architectural Coatings Mfr & Sales, Including Wall Coatings, Trim Enamels, House Paints, Clear Polyurethanes & Stains
S.I.C.: 2851
N.A.I.C.S.: 325510
Export
Advertising Expenditures: $1,000,000
Media: 1-2-3-5-6-7-8-10-16-18-19-21-23-25-26
Distr.: Intl.; Reg.
Budget Set: Dec.
Brands & Products:
BLOCK-OUT
BRUNING
BRUNING PAINT
CARRIAGE HOUSE
GRABBER PLUS
ONE PREP
SILATHANE
STORMPRUF
WALL COVER
WALL PLATE

CALIFORNIA PRODUCTS CORPORATION
(Holding of Apollo Management, L.P.)
150 Dascomb Rd
Andover, MA 01810-5873
Tel.: (978) 623-9980
Fax: (978) 623-9960
E-mail: info@plexipave.com
Web Site: www.calprocorp.com
Sales Range: $25-49.9 Million
Approx. Number Employees: 130
Year Founded: 1926
Business Description:
Paints, Tennis Court & Track Coating & Wood Stains
S.I.C.: 2851; 5231
N.A.I.C.S.: 325510; 444120
Export
Advertising Expenditures: $2,500,000
Media: 1-2-3-4-5-6-7-8-10-18-19-20-21-23-24-26
Distr.: Intl.; Natl.
Budget Set: Dec.-Nov.
Personnel:
Peter Longo *(Chm & Co-CEO)*
Steven McMenamin *(Co-CEO & CFO)*
Dave Lohr *(Pres-Trade Sls)*
Arthur F. Tucker *(VP)*
Dan Cohen *(VP-Sls & Mktg)*
Brands & Products:
A-B-C
ACRYLOTEX
CALIFORNIA
CALIFORNIA TI-COAT
CLEAR-GLO
CRACK FILLER
DECO TURF
HI-HIDE PLEXICOLOR
L-B-C
PLAY TIME
PLEXIBOND-FIBERGLASS SYSTEM
PLEXICHROME
PLEXICOURT
PLEXICUSHION
PLEXICUSHION PATCH
PLEXIFLOR
PLEXIPATCH
PLEXIPAVE
PLEXIPAVE GRAND PRIX
PLEXITRAC
STORMSTAIN

CARBOLINEUM WOOD PRESERVING CO.
6683 N 40th St
Milwaukee, WI 53209-3049
Tel.: (414) 353-5040
Fax: (414) 353-3325
Toll Free: (800) 671-0093
E-mail: carbolineum@execpc.com
Web Site: www.carbolineum.com
Sales Range: $10-24.9 Million
Approx. Number Employees: 15
Year Founded: 1876
Business Description:
Wood Coatings Mfr
S.I.C.: 2861; 2891
N.A.I.C.S.: 325191; 325520
Import Export
Media: 2-4-6-7-8-10-11-13-19-26
Distr.: Intl.; Natl.
Budget Set: Various
Personnel:
Frederick Leypoldt *(Pres)*
Brands & Products:
CARBOLINEUM
CARBOLINEUM IV COATING
CARBOLINEUM PINE TAR TREATMENT
HALT CRIBBING
HALT CRIBBING SPRAY CANS

CERAMIC COLOR & CHEMICAL MFG. CO.
PO Box 297
New Brighton, PA 15066
Tel.: (724) 846-4000
Fax: (724) 846-4123
E-mail: cccmfg@horizon.net
Web Site: www.ceramiccolor.com
Approx. Number Employees: 25
Year Founded: 1929
Business Description:
Ceramic Colors & Chemicals, Oxides & Industrial Chemicals Sales & Mfr
S.I.C.: 2816; 2819
N.A.I.C.S.: 325131; 325188
Import Export
Media: 2
Distr.: Intl.; Natl.
Budget Set: Nov.
Personnel:
Burges M. Hurd *(Chm)*
Bill Wenning *(Pres)*

CHROMA CORPORATION
3900 W Dayton St
McHenry, IL 60050
Tel.: (815) 385-8100
Fax: (815) 385-1518
Toll Free: (877) 385-8777
E-mail: chroma@chromacolors.com
Web Site: www.chromacolors.com
Approx. Number Employees: 100
Year Founded: 1967
Business Description:
Color & Additive Compounding for Thermoplastics
S.I.C.: 2851; 3083
N.A.I.C.S.: 325510; 326130
Import Export
Media: 2-7-10-20
Personnel:
Robert Swain *(Founder)*
Tom Bolger *(Pres & CEO)*
Stuart Swain *(Dir-Sls & Mktg)*
Brands & Products:
CHROMA-BLEND
CHROMA-CLEAN

Key to Media (For complete agency information see *The Advertising Red Books-Agencies* edition):
1. Bus. Publs. 2. Cable T.V. 3. Catalogs & Directories. 4. Co-op Adv. 5. Consumer Mags. 6. D.M. to Bus. Estab.7. D.M. to Consumers 8. Daily Newsp. 9. Exhibits/Trade Shows 10. Foreign 11. Infomercial 12. Internet Adv.13. Multimedia 14. Network Radio 15. Network T.V. 16. Newsp. Distr. Mags. 17. Other 18. Outdoor (Posters, Transit) 19. Point of Purchase20. Premiums, Novelties 21. Product Samples 22. Special Events Mktg. 23. Spot Radio 24. Spot T.V. 25. Weekly Newsp. 26. Yellow Page Adv.

CHROMA LAZER-TEC
CHROMA-PEARLS
CHROMA-SHERES
DRY-CHROMA COLOR
FOAMA-BAG
FOAMA-SPHERES
INJECTA COLOR
LAZER-TEC

CONSOLIDATED COATINGS CORPORATION

7651 Vantage Way
Delta, BC Canada
Tel.: (604) 946-7626
Fax: (604) 946-9609
Toll Free: (800) 663-5690
E-mail: info@consolidatedcoatings.com
Web Site: www.consolidatedcoatings.com
Sales Estimate: $500-999 Million
Approx. Number Employees: 25
Year Founded: 1904
Business Description:
Paints & Coatings Mfr & Marketer
S.I.C.: 2851; 5198
N.A.I.C.S.: 325510; 424950
Export
Media: 2-4-6-7-9-11-21-25
Distr.: Intl.; Natl.
Budget Set: Jan.
Personnel:
Dan Treleaven *(Founder)*
Jonathan Tong *(Controller)*
Brands & Products:
CEMENTPAL
CONSOLIDATED COATINGS
DECKSTONE
MAGNA PAINT
WOODPAL

COOK COMPOSITES & POLYMERS CO.

(Sub. of Total Chemical Division)
820 E 14th Ave
Kansas City, MO 64116
Mailing Address:
PO Box 419389
Kansas City, MO 64141
Tel.: (816) 391-6000
Fax: (816) 391-6276
Toll Free: (800) 821-3590
E-mail: mailroom@ccponline.com
Web Site: www.ccponline.com
Approx. Number Employees: 100
Year Founded: 1990
Business Description:
Industrial & Contracting Paint
Polyester Resin Polyurethane Foam
Variety of Industrial Coatings Market Coatings
S.I.C.: 3089; 2851
N.A.I.C.S.: 326199; 325510
Import Export
Advertising Expenditures: $500,000
Media: 1-2-4-7-8-10-13-20-22
Distr.: Natl.
Budget Set: Aug.
Personnel:
Paul Colonna *(CEO)*
Olivier Moulauert *(CFO)*
Brands & Products:
ARMORCOTE
CHEMPOL
CORO-FOAM
COROC
MIRASOL
POLYCOR

DAP PRODUCTS, INC.

(Sub. of RPM Consumer Holding Co.)
2400 Boston St Ste 200
Baltimore, MD 21224
Tel.: (410) 675-2100
Fax: (410) 558-0953
Toll Free: (800) 543-3840
E-mail: info@dap.com
Web Site: www.dap.com
Sales Range: $200-249.9 Million
Approx. Number Employees: 500
Year Founded: 1865
Business Description:
Caulks, Sealants, Adhesives, Spacklings & General Patch & Repair Products Mfr
S.I.C.: 2891; 2851
N.A.I.C.S.: 325520; 325510
Media: 1-2-3-4-5-6-7-9-10-14-15-16-19-20-21-23-24-25
Distr.: Intl.; Natl.
Budget Set: Aug.
Personnel:
John McLaughlin *(Pres & CEO)*
David Fuller *(VP-Mktg)*
Brands & Products:
ALEX
ALEX PLUS
BEATS THE NAIL
BLEND STICK
BLOCKADE
BONDEX
BUTYLFLEX
CAULK-BE-GONE
CONTACT
CRACKSHOT
DAP
DAP ALEX PLUS
DAP CAP
DAPTEX
DERUSTO
DRYDEX
DYNAFLEX 230
EASY SOLUTIONS
ELASTOPATCH
FAST'N FINAL
KWIK FOAM
KWIK SEAL
KWIK SEAL PLUS
PAINTER'S PUTTY '53'
PATCH STICK
PLASTIC WOOD
PRESTO PATCH
PROJECT SOLUTIONS
THE PUTTY-KNIFE LOGO
QUICK PLUG
RELY ON
SEAL'N PEEL
SIDE WINDER
SPRAY-N-GLUE
TI
TITANIUM
WOOD SWELL & LOCK
YOU'LL FIND US IN ALL THE RIGHT PLACES.

DAVIS PAINT COMPANY

1311 Iron St PO Box 7589
Kansas City, MO 64116-4010
Tel.: (816) 471-4447
Fax: (816) 471-1460
Toll Free: (800) 821-2029
Web Site: www.davispaint.com
Sales Range: $10-24.9 Million
Approx. Number Employees: 45
Year Founded: 1921
Business Description:
Paints Mfr
S.I.C.: 2851; 5231
N.A.I.C.S.: 325510; 444120
Advertising Expenditures: $200,000
Media: 5-7-8-9-18-23-26
Distr.: Reg.
Budget Set: Sept.
Personnel:
James L. Davis *(Chm)*
Kevin C. Ostby *(Pres)*
Brands & Products:
COOK
DAVIS
DAVIS INDUSTRIAL
DAVIS PAINT
ELI WEATHERBY
SAHARA
SAHARA OASIS

DAY-GLO COLOR CORP.

(Sub. of RPM, Inc.)
4515 Saint Clair Ave
Cleveland, OH 44103-1203
Tel.: (216) 391-7070
Fax: (216) 391-1408
E-mail: dayglo@dayglo.com
Web Site: www.dayglo.com
Sales Range: $100-124.9 Million
Approx. Number Employees: 300
Year Founded: 1946
Business Description:
Fluorescent Color Mfr
S.I.C.: 2816; 2851
N.A.I.C.S.: 325131; 325510
Import Export
Media: 1-2-4
Distr.: Intl.; Natl.
Budget Set: Oct.
Personnel:
Al Arida *(VP-Fin)*
John Aber *(Mgr-Mktg)*
Brands & Products:
DAY-GLO

DEFT, INC.

17451 Von Karman Ave
Irvine, CA 92614-6205
Tel.: (949) 474-0400
Fax: (949) 474-7269
Toll Free: (800) 544-3338
E-mail: proservice@deftfinishes.com
Web Site: www.deftfinishes.com
Approx. Number Employees: 100
Year Founded: 1938
Business Description:
Wood Finishing Products, Aerospace, Military Specification & Industrial Coatings Mfr
S.I.C.: 2851; 2891
N.A.I.C.S.: 325510; 325520
Media: 2-4-6-7-8-9-10-19-21-25
Distr.: Intl.; Natl.
Personnel:
William A. Desmond *(Pres)*
Tracy Garrett, Jr. *(VP-Sls)*
Randall Brady *(Mgr-Mktg)*
Brands & Products:
DEFT
DEFT CLEAR WOOD FINISH
DEFT INTERIOR POLYURETHANE
DEFT WOOD STAIN
DEFTHANE
DEFTOIL DANISH OIL FINISH
STEP SAVER WOOD STAIN & FINISH
Advertising Agency:
The King Group
20250 Acacia St., Ste. 220
Newport Beach, CA 92660
Tel.: (949) 253-0999

DIAMOND VOGEL PAINT, INC.

1110 Albany Pl SE
Orange City, IA 51041-1982
Tel.: (712) 737-8880
Fax: (712) 737-4998
Toll Free: (800) 728-6435
E-mail: marketing@vogelpaint.com
Web Site: www.vogelpaint.com
E-Mail For Key Personnel:
Marketing Director: marketing@vogelpaint.com
Approx. Sls.: $13,800,000
Approx. Number Employees: 500
Year Founded: 1926
Business Description:
Paint Mfr & Retailer
S.I.C.: 2851; 5231
N.A.I.C.S.: 325510; 444120
Media: 2-9-23-25
Personnel:
Drew Vogel *(Pres)*
Mark Vogel *(Dir-Sls Mktg)*
Brands & Products:
ALL SEASON
AQUA POX
COTE-ALL
DIA-PRO
DIAMOND VOGEL
EPEC
FIL-KOTE
FINIUM
FLEET DRY
FLOR-COTE
GLASS LOCK
HEALTH-KOTE
MINION
MIRACLE GLAZE
THE MIRACLE OF PAINT
MULT-E-POXY
MULTI-E-PROXY
NU-CLING
OLD MASTERS
PERIDIUM
PERMACRYL
PERMAFLEX
PINNACLE
POOL-COTE
PRIME-O-SEAL
PRO PLATE
PRO PLUS
QUANTUM
SATINAMEL
SUPER-BUILD
SUPER PRO
SUPER QUICK
SURE-BLOCK
SURE GRIP
V-COTE
V-TECH
WEATHER-PLATE

DUNN-EDWARDS CORPORATION

4885 E 52nd Pl
Los Angeles, CA 90058
Tel.: (323) 771-3330
Fax: (323) 826-2650
E-mail: sales@dunn-edwards.com
Web Site: www.dunnedwards.com
E-Mail For Key Personnel:
Sales Director: sales@dunn-edwards.com

Key to Media (For complete agency information see *The Advertising Red Books-Agencies* edition):
1. Bus. Publs. 2. Cable T.V. 3. Catalogs & Directories. 4. Co-op Adv. 5. Consumer Mags. 6. D.M. to Bus. Estab.7. D.M. to Consumers 8. Daily Newsp. 9. Exhibits/Trade Shows 10. Foreign 11. Infomercial 12. Internet Adv.13. Multimedia 14. Network Radio 15. Network T.V. 16. Newsp. Distr. Mags. 17. Other 18. Outdoor (Posters, Transit) 19. Point of Purchase20. Premiums, Novelties 21. Product Samples 22. Special Events Mktg. 23. Spot Radio 24. Spot T.V. 25. Weekly Newsp. 26. Yellow Page Adv.

Dunn-Edwards Corporation — (Continued)

Sales Range: $300-349.9 Million
Approx. Number Employees: 1,525
Year Founded: 1925
Business Description:
Full-Service Paint Retailer & Mfr
S.I.C.: 2851; 5231
N.A.I.C.S.: 325510; 444120
Import Export
Media: 2-4-10-19-20-21-22
Personnel:
Kenneth N. Edwards *(CEO)*
Robert W. Hill *(CFO)*
Darlene Mitchell *(CIO & VP)*
Nicholas J. Hess *(Sr VP-Ops)*
Tim Bosveld *(VP-Mktg)*
Joe Ingegneri *(Gen Mgr-Sls)*
Robert Wendoll *(Dir-Environ Affairs)*
Ed Edrosa *(Product Mgr-Specialty Coatings)*
Brands & Products:
ACOUSTIKOTE
ACRI-FLAT
ACRI-LOC
ACRY-BOND
ALKYFALL
ALKYLSEAL
AQUA PRIME
AQUAFALL
ARISTOSHEEN
ARISTOSHELL
BLOC-RUST
BLOCFIL
COMPO
CORROBAR
COVER KOTE
CRYSTACLEAR
DECOGLO
DECOLAC
DECOLAC II
DECOSHEEN
DECOVEL
DURA-TILT
DURAFLO
E-Z PRIME
EFF-STOP
ENDURA-COAT
ENDURACRYL
ENDURAGLOSS
ENDURAPATCH
ENDURASEAL
ENDURATEC
ENDURAWALL
EVERSHIELD
FLEX-PRIME
FLEX-TEX
GALV-ALUM
KWIK-TIP
MAX-WALL
ONYX
PERFECTA GOLD
PERMAGLOSS
PERMASHEEN
PERMASHELL
PROSEAL
QUIK-WALL
RANCHO
RECOVER
SILKY FLO
SPARTAGLO
SPARTAGLOSS
SPARTASHEEN
SPARTASHELL
STAINSEAL
SUMMERTIME PRO
SUPER-LOC
SUPER U-365
SUPREMA
SURFACO
SYN-LUSTRO
TILT-KOTE
TILT-PRIME
TITANIUM-PRO
ULTRA-GRIP
ULTRASHIELD
UNIKOTE
VERSA-GLO
VERSA-GLOSS
VERSAFLAT
VERSAPRIME
VERSASATIN
VERSAWALL
VIN-L-STRIPE
VINYLASTIC
WALLTONE
Advertising Agency:
The Phelps Group
901 Wilshire Blvd
Santa Monica, CA 90401-1854
Tel.: (310) 752-4400
Fax: (310) 752-4444

DUPONT POWDER COATINGS USA, INC.
(Sub. of DuPont Coatings & Color Technologies)
9800 Genard Rd
Houston, TX 77041-7624
Tel.: (713) 939-4000
Fax: (713) 939-4027
Toll Free: (800) 247-3886
E-mail: dupont@dupontpowder.com
Web Site: www.dupontpowder.com
Sales Range: $200-249.9 Million
Approx. Number Employees: 500
Year Founded: 1802
Business Description:
Thermoset Powder Coatings Mfr
S.I.C.: 2851
N.A.I.C.S.: 325510
Export
Media: 2-4-6-7-8-10-11-21-22
Distr.: Intl.; Natl.
Budget Set: Oct.
Personnel:
Thomas M. Connelly, Jr. *(CIO & Exec VP)*
Dave Lazzerri *(Mgr-Mktg & Bus)*
Trena Benson *(Mgr-Mktg)*
William Rising *(Mgr-Bus Svcs)*
Brands & Products:
ALESTA

DURON, INC.
(Sub. of The Sherwin-Williams Company)
10406 Tucker St
Beltsville, MD 20705
Tel.: (301) 937-4600
Fax: (301) 595-3919
Toll Free: (800) 723-8766
E-mail: paintinfo@duron.com
Web Site: www.duron.com
E-Mail For Key Personnel:
Marketing Director: marketing@duron.com
Sales Director: sales@duron.com
Sales Range: $300-349.9 Million
Approx. Number Employees: 1,800
Year Founded: 1949
Business Description:
Paints & Wallcoverings Mfr
S.I.C.: 5198; 5231
N.A.I.C.S.: 424950; 444120
Export
Advertising Expenditures: $500,000
Media: 2-7-9-10-19-20-22-26
Distr.: Reg.
Budget Set: Oct.
Brands & Products:
BUILDERS MASTERPIECE
DESIGN ACCENTS
DURA CLAD
EVERLAST
GENESIS ODOR-FREE
HARD KOTE
MAXWOOD STAINS
PLASTIC KOTE
SIDING IN A CAN
SIGNATURE SELECT
TERMINATOR
VARA-FLEC
WEATHERSHIELD

ECOLOGY COATINGS, INC.
24663 Mound Rd
Warren, MI 48091
Tel.: (586) 486-5308
Fax: (586) 486-5283
E-mail: dan.iannotti@ecologycoatings.com
Web Site: www.ecologycoatings.com
Approx. Rev.: $14,860
Approx. Number Employees: 4
Year Founded: 2002
Business Description:
Nano-Engineered, Ultra-Violet Curable Coatings Mfr
S.I.C.: 2851
N.A.I.C.S.: 325510
Media: 2-13-17
Personnel:
F. Thomas Krotine *(Pres & COO)*
Robert G. Crockett *(CEO)*
Kevin P. Stolz *(CFO, Chief Acctg Officer & Controller)*
Brands & Products:
ECOLOGY COATINGS
ECOQUIK
EZ RECOAT
LIQUID NANOTECHNOLOGY
Advertising Agency:
McCloud Communications, LLC
2973 Harbor Blvd Ste 322
Costa Mesa, CA 92626
Tel.: (949) 553-9748

ELMER'S PRODUCTS, INC.
(Sub. of Berwind Corporation)
1 Easton Oval
Columbus, OH 43219
Tel.: (614) 985-2600
Fax: (614) 985-2605
Toll Free: (888) 435-6377
Web Site: www.elmers.com
Approx. Rev.: $116,400,000
Approx. Number Employees: 740
Year Founded: 1947
Business Description:
Adhesives Caulks & Sealants Mfr
S.I.C.: 2891
N.A.I.C.S.: 325520
Import Export
Media: 6-8-9-19-21
Distr.: Intl.; Natl.
Personnel:
James Hamling *(Pres & CEO)*
Terri Brown *(Mgr-Mktg Svcs & Comm)*
Brands & Products:
CRAFTBOND
ELMER'S
KRAZY GLUE
PROBOND
ROSS
Advertising Agencies:
Child's Play Communications
135 W 29th St Ste 701
New York, NY 10001
Tel.: (212) 488-2060
Fax: (212) 488-2059
Children's Arts & Crafts

Fahlgren Mortine Public Relations
4030 Easton Sta Ste 300
Columbus, OH 43219
Tel.: (614) 383-1500
Fax: (614) 383-1501

ENGLISH COLOR & SUPPLY INC.
810 N Grove Rd
Richardson, TX 75081
Tel.: (972) 235-3104
Fax: (972) 231-7079
Toll Free: (800) 664-5272
Web Site: www.englishcolor.com
Approx. Sls.: $28,000,000
Approx. Number Employees: 20
Year Founded: 1946
Business Description:
Paints & Coatings Distr
S.I.C.: 5198; 5231
N.A.I.C.S.: 424950; 444120
Media: 4-13
Personnel:
Monique Flener *(Coord-Sls & Mktg)*

THE EUCLID CHEMICAL COMPANY
(Sub. of The Euclid Chemical Company)
3835 State Rte 72
Kirkland, IL 60146
Tel.: (815) 522-3394
Fax: (815) 522-2323
Toll Free: (800) 862-2667
E-mail: info@euclidchemical.com
Web Site: www.euclidchemical.com
E-Mail For Key Personnel:
Marketing Director: sscarp@tamms.com
Sales Range: $10-24.9 Million
Approx. Number Employees: 55
Year Founded: 1911
Business Description:
Concrete Restoration, Curing, Coating, Grouting, Waterproofing & Traffic Deck Products & Systems Mfr
S.I.C.: 2851; 2891; 3272
N.A.I.C.S.: 325510; 325520; 327390
Export
Media: 2-7-10
Distr.: Natl.
Budget Set: Dec.
Brands & Products:
AKKRO
AQUAFORM
AQUASEAL
AQUASTAIN
AQUATHANE
BARACADE
CHEMSTOP

Key to Media (For complete agency information see *The Advertising Red Books-Agencies* edition):
1. Bus. Publs. 2. Cable T.V. 3. Catalogs & Directories. 4. Co-op Adv. 5. Consumer Mags. 6. D.M. to Bus. Estab.7. D.M. to Consumers 8. Daily Newsp. 9. Exhibits/Trade Shows 10. Foreign 11. Infomercial 12. Internet Adv.13. Multimedia 14. Network Radio 15. Network T.V. 16. Newsp. Distr. Mags. 17. Other 18. Outdoor (Posters, Transit) 19. Point of Purchase20. Premiums, Novelties 21. Product Samples 22. Special Events Mktg. 23. Spot Radio 24. Spot T.V. 25. Weekly Newsp. 26. Yellow Page Adv.

CLEARSEAL
DEHYDRATINE
DURAL
DURALBOND
DURALCRETE
DURALFLEX
DURALITH
DURALKOTE
DURALTEX
DURALTOP
EXPRESS REPAIR
FLEX-LOK
FLEXOCRETE
FLEXOLITH
FORMSHIELD
HORNCURE
HORNFLEX
HORNOLITH
HORNWELD
LUSTER SEAL
LUSTERSEAL
POLYGROUT
RAPID ROCK
SPEED CRETE
SPEED PLUG
TAMMOLASTIC
TAMMOSHEEN
TAMMS THIN PATCH
TAMMSCOAT
TAMMSPATCH
TAMOSEAL
THIN PATCH
TRI-DAR

FIBRE GLASS-EVERCOAT
(Name Changed to ITW - Evercoat)

FLUID MANAGEMENT
(Sub. of IDEX Corporation)
1023 Wheeling Rd
Wheeling, IL 60090-5776
Tel.: (847) 537-0880
Fax: (847) 537-5530
Toll Free: (800) 462-2466
E-mail: info.fluid@idexcorp.com
Web Site: www.fluidman.com
Sales Range: $100-124.9 Million
Approx. Number Employees: 150
Business Description:
Paint Mixing & Dispensing Equipment
S.I.C.: 3559
N.A.I.C.S.: 333298
Media: 2-4-10-13-17
Personnel:
Dan Storto *(VP-Sls & Mktg)*

FOAMPRO MANUFACTURING, INC.
1791 Kaiser Ave Ste A
Irvine, CA 92614
Mailing Address:
PO Box 18888
Irvine, CA 92623-8888
Tel.: (949) 252-0112
Fax: (949) 252-0113
Toll Free: (800) 362-6776
E-mail: gisaac@foampromfg.com
Web Site: www.foampromfg.com
E-Mail For Key Personnel:
President: gisaac@foampromfg.com
Approx. Number Employees: 80
Year Founded: 1957
Business Description:
Foam Paint Applicators, Brooms & Waxers Mfr
S.I.C.: 3991
N.A.I.C.S.: 339994
Media: 4
Distr.: Natl.
Personnel:
Gregory Isaac *(Pres)*
Brands & Products:
FASTER START, FINER FINISH
FINISH COATER
FITS-ALL
FOAMPRO
HANDLE EEZ
QUICKCAPS

FOX VALLEY SYSTEMS, INC.
640 Indus Dr
Cary, IL 60013-1944
Tel.: (847) 639-5744
Fax: (847) 639-8190
E-mail: info@foxvalleysystems.com
Web Site: www.foxpaint.com
Approx. Number Employees: 20
Year Founded: 1988
Business Description:
Striping & Marking Equipment & Paints Mfr
S.I.C.: 2851; 3953
N.A.I.C.S.: 325510; 339943
Media: 2-4-7-8-24
Distr.: Intl.; Natl.
Budget Set: Dec.
Personnel:
Thomas J. Smart *(Pres)*
Brands & Products:
ATHLETIC SUPER STRIPER
DURACOTE
EASY MARKER
EASY STRIPER
HURR-A-CAN
MARKS ALL
SUPER STRIPER
TRIG-A-CAP

GEOCEL CORPORATION
2504 Marina Dr
Elkhart, IN 46514-8325
Mailing Address:
PO Box 398
Elkhart, IN 46515-0398
Tel.: (574) 264-0645
Fax: (800) 348-7009
Toll Free: (800) 348-7615
E-mail: customerservice@geocelworldwide.com
Web Site: www.geocelusa.com
Sales Range: $1-9.9 Million
Approx. Number Employees: 65
Year Founded: 1974
Business Description:
High Performance Sealants & Caulks Mfr
S.I.C.: 2891
N.A.I.C.S.: 325520
Export
Media: 9-10-17-20
Distr.: Natl.
Budget Set: Mar.
Personnel:
Don L. Krabill *(Chm & CEO)*
John Bencsics *(Dir-Mktg Svcs)*
Brands & Products:
ALL-IN-ONE
CORKY CAULKRIGHT
DURASEAL
GEOCEL
INSTANT GUTTER SEAL
INSTANT ROOF REPAIR
PAINTER'S CAULK
PRO FLEX
PROCOLOR
PROFESSIONAL
PROFESSIONAL 920
QUICK SHIELD
SHINGLE COAT
SPEED GRIP
STAIN MATCH
WATER SHIELD
WE SEPARATE THE ELEMENTS

GRAHAM PAINT COMPANY
(Sub. of The Muralo Company)
4100 W 76th St Unit G
Chicago, IL 60652
Tel.: (773) 585-9110
Fax: (773) 284-0989
Toll Free: (800) 255-2628
E-mail: grahampt@aol.com
Web Site: www.grahampaint.com
Sales Range: $1-9.9 Million
Approx. Number Employees: 20
Year Founded: 1946
Business Description:
Paint & Ceramic Products Mfr
S.I.C.: 2851; 3253
N.A.I.C.S.: 325510; 327122
Media: 2-3-5-7-9-10-19-21-25
Distr.: Natl.
Personnel:
Harry S. TRUE *(Pres)*
Brands & Products:
AQUA BORNE
AQUA BORNE CERAMIC ACRYLIC SOFT GLOSS
AQUA BORNE CERAMIC ACRYLIC SOLID HIDE
AQUA BORNE CERAMIC FLAT INTERIOR FINISH
AQUA BORNE CERAMIC FLOOR PAINT
AQUA BORNE CERAMIC PRIMERS
AQUA BORNE CERAMIC SATIN & GLOSS ENAMELS
AQUA BORNE CERAMITHANE
AQUA BORNE EPOXY TUFF

GRAPHIC VISION, INC.
272 Beaten Path Rd
Mooresville, NC 28117-8979
Tel.: (603) 352-2794
Fax: (603) 352-8356
Toll Free: (800) 242-2794
E-mail: info@graphicvisioninc.com
Web Site: www.graphicvisioninc.com
Approx. Number Employees: 3
Business Description:
Glue Products Mfr
S.I.C.: 2891
N.A.I.C.S.: 325520
Media: 2-4-6-10-21
Brands & Products:
AMBROID
CHAIR-LOK
GRAPHIC VISION

HAR ADHESIVE TECHNOLOGIES
60 S Park
Bedford, OH 44146
Tel.: (440) 786-7185
Fax: (440) 786-7186
Toll Free: (800) 732-5255
E-mail: info@haradhesive.com
Web Site: www.haradhesive.com
Approx. Number Employees: 14
Year Founded: 1970
Business Description:
Adhesive & Paint Mfr
S.I.C.: 2891; 2851
N.A.I.C.S.: 325520; 325510
Media: 2
Distr.: Natl.
Personnel:
Joseph A. Cerino *(Pres)*
Keith Nagy *(Gen Mgr-Sls & Svcs)*
Dennis Grosel *(Mgr-Product Delivery & Admin Sys)*
Gary Lepard *(Mgr-Plant Ops & Production Sys)*
Ken Schonauer *(Mgr-Natl Sls Sys & Support)*
Geri Horvath *(Coord-Pur)*

HENRY COMPANY-KIMBERTON
(Div. of Henry Company)
336 Coldstream Rd
Kimberton, PA 19442
Mailing Address:
PO Box 368
Kimberton, PA 19442-0368
Tel.: (610) 933-8888
Fax: (610) 933-4598
Toll Free: (800) 486-1278
E-mail: customerservice@henry.com
Web Site: www.henry.com
Sales Range: $25-49.9 Million
Approx. Number Employees: 350
Year Founded: 1939
Business Description:
Protective Roof Coatings & Sealers Mfr
S.I.C.: 2952; 2951
N.A.I.C.S.: 324122; 324121
Import Export
Advertising Expenditures: $100,000
Bus. Publs.: $5,000; Consumer Mags.: $50,000; Other: $25,000; Point of Purchase: $10,000; Premiums, Novelties: $10,000
Distr.: Intl.; Natl.
Budget Set: Jan.

HERESITE PROTECTIVE COATINGS, INC.
822 S 14th St
Manitowoc, WI 54220
Tel.: (920) 684-6646
Fax: (920) 684-0110
Toll Free: (800) 558-7747
E-mail: sales@heresite.com
Web Site: www.heresite.com
E-Mail For Key Personnel:
Sales Director: sales@heresite.com
Approx. Number Employees: 50
Year Founded: 1935
Business Description:
Corrosion Resistant Coatings & Paints Mfr
S.I.C.: 2821
N.A.I.C.S.: 325211
Import Export
Advertising Expenditures: $75,000
Media: 2-4-10-17-20
Distr.: Natl.
Personnel:
Geoffrey Liban *(Chm & CEO)*
Thomas L. Fritzke *(Pres)*
Brands & Products:
HERESITE PROTECTIVE COATING
WHERE QUALITY IS A TRADITION

HIRSHFIELD'S INC.
725 2nd Ave N
Minneapolis, MN 55405-1601
Tel.: (612) 377-3910
Fax: (612) 436-3384

Key to Media (For complete agency information see *The Advertising Red Books-Agencies* edition):
1. Bus. Publs. 2. Cable T.V. 3. Catalogs & Directories. 4. Co-op Adv. 5. Consumer Mags. 6. D.M. to Bus. Estab.7. D.M. to Consumers 8. Daily Newsp. 9. Exhibits/Trade Shows 10. Foreign 11. Infomercial 12. Internet Adv.13. Multimedia 14. Network Radio 15. Network T.V. 16. Newsp. Distr. Mags. 17. Other 18. Outdoor (Posters, Transit) 19. Point of Purchase20. Premiums, Novelties 21. Product Samples 22. Special Events Mktg. 23. Spot Radio 24. Spot T.V. 25. Weekly Newsp. 26. Yellow Page Adv.

Hirshfield's Inc. — (Continued)

E-mail: mrh@hirshfields.com
Web Site: www.hirshfields.com
Approx. Sls.: $63,596,750
Approx. Number Employees: 405
Year Founded: 1894
Business Description:
Paints, Wallcoverings & Industrial Coatings Retailer
S.I.C.: 5198; 5231
N.A.I.C.S.: 424950; 444120
Import Export
Media: 2-10
Personnel:
Hans Hirshfield *(CEO)*
Jeff Lein *(Dir-Mktg)*

IOWA PAINT MANUFACTURING COMPANY, INC.

(d/b/a IPM Group)
1625 Grand Ave PO Box 1417
Des Moines, IA 50309
Tel.: (515) 283-1501
Fax: (515) 283-1470
Toll Free: (800) 283-1933
Sales Range: $25-49.9 Million
Approx. Number Employees: 300
Year Founded: 1933
Business Description:
Paint & Coatings Mfr
S.I.C.: 2851; 5231
N.A.I.C.S.: 325510; 444120
Media: 2-4-7-8-9-10-19-20-23-26
Distr.: Reg.
Budget Set: Nov.
Brands & Products:
ARCTIC KOTE
EVERWEAR
IMPRESSIONS
INFINIUM SERIES
IOWA PAINT
MASTER SERIES
PRO-HOUSE
ROYAL HIDE
STERLING
ULTRA GOLD

ITW - EVERCOAT

(Formerly Fibre Glass-Evercoat)
(Sub. of Illinois Tool Works Inc.)
6600 Cornell Rd
Cincinnati, OH 45242-2033
Tel.: (513) 489-7600
Fax: (513) 489-9229
Web Site: www.evercoat.com
Sales Range: $50-74.9 Million
Approx. Number Employees: 130
Year Founded: 1953
Business Description:
Marine & Automotive Repair Products Mfr
S.I.C.: 2851; 2821
N.A.I.C.S.: 325510; 325211
Export
Media: 2-7-8-10-13
Personnel:
Tom Lehmkuhl *(Dir-Mktg)*
James Testa *(Product Mgr)*
Brands & Products:
BODY MAGIC
CHROME-A-LITE
DIRT PIC
EASY SAND
EURO-SOFT
EVERCLING
EVERCOAT
EVERGLASS
FEATHER FILL
FIBER TECH
GLASS-LITE
KITTY HAIR
LITE WEIGHT
LUBRI-SHINE
MAXIM
METAL-2-METAL
METAL GLAZE
METAL WORKS
POLY-FLEX
Q-PADS
RAGE
SPOT-LITE
TACKY COAT
TIGER HAIR
URO-FILL
VETTE PANEL ADHESIVE/FILLER
WHITE STAR
Z-GRIP

JONES-BLAIR COMPANY

2728 Empire Central
Dallas, TX 75235
Tel.: (214) 353-1600
Fax: (214) 350-7624
Toll Free: (800) 492-9400
E-mail: sales@jones-blair.com
Web Site: www.jones-blair.com
E-Mail For Key Personnel:
Sales Director: sales@jones-blair.com
Approx. Number Employees: 120
Year Founded: 1928
Business Description:
High Performance Coatings Developer, Mfr & Marketer
S.I.C.: 2851; 5198
N.A.I.C.S.: 325510; 424950
Import Export
Advertising Expenditures: $600,000
Media: 1-2-3-4-5-6-7-8-9-10-13-14-18-19-20-21-23-25-26
Distr.: Natl.
Budget Set: Various
Personnel:
Jeff Powell *(Pres & CEO)*
Mark Bossmann *(Gen Mgr-Indus)*
Bob Coleman *(Dir-Mktg)*
Will Dryden *(Mgr-Natl Mktg-Sls)*
Mike Flanigan *(Mgr-Ops)*
Bill Yeargan *(Mgr-Pur)*
Brands & Products:
ACRYLITHANE C
ALKYD ZONE
APEX
ASPHALTUM
CHEM-O-CONE
CHEM-O-LITE
CHEM-O-PON
CHEM-O-THIX
CHEM-O-Z
CHEM-O-Z II
DECOGLAZE
DECORATOR
EFFECTONE
GIL-CHEM
GLAMOR
HEATBAN
JB
JIFFY DRY
JIFFY PREP
LATEX ZONE
METALMATE
MIST COAT
MULTI-GRIP
MULTI-PURPOSE
NEOGARD
POLYFLEX
PORCH & FLOOR
QUICK DRY
RANCHERO
RANGER
RFD LATEX
RUST-NOT
RUST RID
SATIN-X
SPEED SEAL
STANTEST
SUNDIAL
SUPER-KOTE
SUPER SPAR
SUPER SPEED
SUPREME
SURE SEAL
TUFF-KOTE
UNI-FLEX
UREPRIME
VELV-IT
VELVA-GLO
VELVA-GRAIN
VERSA-TINT
WASH 'N WEAR
WATERSHED

JOTUN PAINTS, INC.

(Sub. of Jotun A/S)
9203 Hwy 23
Belle Chasse, LA 70037
Tel.: (504) 394-3538
Fax: (504) 394-3726
Toll Free: (800) 229-3538
E-mail: mailusa@jotun.com
Web Site: www.jotun.com
Approx. Number Employees: 50
Business Description:
Protective Coatings Mfr & Retailer
S.I.C.: 2851
N.A.I.C.S.: 325510
Media: 4-10
Personnel:
Emile Oustalet *(Pres)*

KELLY-MOORE PAINT COMPANY, INC.

987 Comml St
San Carlos, CA 94070
Tel.: (650) 592-8337
Fax: (650) 508-8563
E-mail: info@kellymoore.com
Web Site: www.kellymoore.com
Sales Range: $100-124.9 Million
Approx. Number Employees: 2,300
Year Founded: 1946
Business Description:
Paint & Paint Sundries Mfr & Retailer
S.I.C.: 2851; 3423
N.A.I.C.S.: 325510; 332212
Export
Advertising Expenditures: $1,300,000
Media: 2-4-5-7-9-10-13-19-21-23-25-26
Distr.: Natl.
Personnel:
Steve Devo *(Chm, Pres & CEO)*
Dan Stritmatter *(CFO)*
Jim Maul *(CIO)*
Keith Hussinger *(Sr VP-Mfg)*
Doug Merrill *(Sr VP-Mfg)*
Mary Lawlor *(Mgr-Color Mktg)*
Brands & Products:
ACRY-LUSTRE
ACRY-PLEX
ACRY-PRIME
ACRY-SHEILD
ACRY-TRED
ALKYDEX
AQUA-TRED
BULLS EYE
COLOR SHIELD
DIF
DRY FOG
DTM
DURA-POXY
ECOAT
ELASTAKOTE
ENVIRA-POXY
ENVIRO-COAT
EPOXYSHIELD
FLO-COTE
GARDZ
GRACO
KEL-AQUA
KEL-BOND
KEL-BOND II
KEL-COTE
KEL-GUARD
KEL-PRO
KEL-SEAL
KEL-SEAL 77
KEL-TEX
KEL-THANE
KEL-TONE
KELLY-MOORE PAINTS
KM PROFESSIONAL
LEAKGUARD
MARK RIGHT
MAXGUARD
MILL WHITE
MODERN WOOD FINISH
THE PAINTER'S PAINT STORE
PAPERTIGER
PEEL STOP
PLASTI-NAMEL
PROGRIP2
PROGUARD
Q-LAC
SANDBLASTER
SAT-N-SHEEN
STAIN LOCK
STUCCO SEAL
UNI-PRIME
VAPOR-SHIELD
WEATHER SHILED
WOODCRAFT

KING INDUSTRIES, INC.

Science Rd
Norwalk, CT 06852
Tel.: (203) 866-5551
Fax: (203) 866-1268
Toll Free: (800) 431-7900
E-mail: info@kingindustries.com
Web Site: www.kingindustries.com
Approx. Number Employees: 175
Year Founded: 1932
Business Description:
Coating & Lubricant Additives Mfr
S.I.C.: 2899; 2819
N.A.I.C.S.: 325998; 325188
Import Export
Media: 2-4-7-10-20
Personnel:
Richard S. King *(Pres)*
Robert Dipanni *(CFO)*
F. Abi Karam *(Exec VP)*
Bob Burk *(Mgr-Mktg & Commun)*
Bob Coughlin *(Mgr-Tech Svcs)*
Brands & Products:
CURENOX
DISPARLON
K-CORR
K-CURE
K-FLEX

Key to Media (For complete agency information see *The Advertising Red Books-Agencies* edition):
1. Bus. Publs. 2. Cable T.V. 3. Catalogs & Directories. 4. Co-op Adv. 5. Consumer Mags. 6. D.M. to Bus. Estab.7. D.M. to Consumers
8. Daily Newsp. 9. Exhibits/Trade Shows 10. Foreign 11. Infomercial 12. Internet Adv.13. Multimedia 14. Network Radio
15. Network T.V. 16. Newsp. Distr. Mags. 17. Other 18. Outdoor (Posters, Transit) 19. Point of Purchase20. Premiums, Novelties
21. Product Samples 22. Special Events Mktg. 23. Spot Radio 24. Spot T.V. 25. Weekly Newsp. 26. Yellow Page Adv.

K-KAT
K-SPERSE
K-STAY
K-STAY 501
KING
NA-LUBE
NA-SUL
NACON
NACORR
NACURE
SAMCURE

KOP-COAT, INC.

(Sub. of RPM, Inc.)
436 7th Ave 1850 Koppers Bldg
Pittsburgh, PA 15219
Tel.: (412) 227-2426
Fax: (412) 227-2618
E-mail: info@kop-coat.com
Web Site: www.kop-coat.com
Sales Range: $25-49.9 Million
Approx. Number Employees: 140
Year Founded: 1907
Business Description:
Marine Coatings, Wood Treatments & Fuel Compounds Mfr & Marketer
S.I.C.: 2851
N.A.I.C.S.: 325510
Media: 2-4-7-10-17
Distr.: Natl.
Budget Set: Oct.
Brands & Products:
KOP-COAT

KWAL-HOWELLS, INC.

(Sub. of Comex Group LLC)
(d/b/a Kwal Paint)
3900 Joliet St
Denver, CO 80239
Tel.: (303) 371-5600
Fax: (303) 373-5688
Toll Free: (800) 383-8406
E-mail: info@kwalhowells.com
Web Site: www.kwalhowells.com
Approx. Number Employees: 400
Year Founded: 1947
Business Description:
Paint & Coatongs Mfr
S.I.C.: 2851; 5198
N.A.I.C.S.: 325510; 424950
Export
Advertising Expenditures: $700,000
Bus. Publs.: $350,000; Exhibits/Trade Shows: $350,000
Distr.: Reg.
Budget Set: Dec.
Brands & Products:
ACCU-PRO
ACCU-TONE
AMBASSADOR
KWAL PAINT
POLY-VI
PRO-FINISH
WOODKRAFT

LAPOLLA INDUSTRIES, INC.

15402 Vantage Pkwy E Ste 322
Houston, TX 77032
Tel.: (281) 219-4700
Fax: (281) 219-4102
E-mail: info@lapollaindustries.com
Web Site: www.lapollaindustries.com
Approx. Sls.: $70,496,629
Approx. Number Employees: 79
Year Founded: 1989
Business Description:
Coatings, Foam, Paints, Sealants, Adhesives & Related Equipment Mfr & Distr
S.I.C.: 2851; 2891; 3053; 3086; 3559
N.A.I.C.S.: 325510; 325520; 326140; 333298; 339991
Advertising Expenditures: $156,838
Media: 7-10-13-17
Personnel:
Richard J. Kurtz *(Chm)*
Charles Zajaczkowski *(CFO & Treas)*
Michael T. Adams *(Dir)*
Douglas J. Kramer *(Dir)*
Brands & Products:
LAPOLLA
Advertising Agency:
Lippert/Heilshorn & Associates, Inc.
800 Third Ave 17th Fl
New York, NY 10022
Tel.: (212) 838-3777
Fax: (212) 838-4568

LECHLER, INC.

(Sub. of Lechler GmbH)
445 Kautz Rd
Saint Charles, IL 60174-5301
Tel.: (630) 377-6611
Fax: (630) 377-6657
Toll Free: (800) 777-2926
E-mail: generalmgr@lechlerusa.com
Web Site: www.lechler.com
Sales Range: $1-9.9 Million
Approx. Number Employees: 70
Year Founded: 1879
Business Description:
Industrial Spray Nozzles & Systems Mfr
S.I.C.: 3494
N.A.I.C.S.: 332919
Import Export
Advertising Expenditures: $350,000
Multimedia: $150,000; Catalogs & Directories: $15,000; Consumer Mags.: $30,000; D.M. to Bus. Estab.: $30,000; Exhibits/Trade Shows: $75,000; Other: $20,000; Premiums, Novelties: $10,000; Product Samples: $10,000; Yellow Page Adv.: $10,000
Distr.: Intl.; Natl.
Budget Set: Nov.
Personnel:
Adolf Pfeiffer *(Pres & CEO)*
Brands & Products:
SPRACO
VARIOCOOL

MASTERCHEM INDUSTRIES, LLC

(Sub. of Masco Corporation)
3135 Old Hwy M
Imperial, MO 63052
Tel.: (636) 942-2510
Fax: (636) 942-3663
Toll Free: (800) 325-3552
E-mail: techservice@masterchem.com
Web Site: www.masterchem.com
Sales Range: $50-74.9 Million
Approx. Number Employees: 125
Year Founded: 1954
Business Description:
Primers & Paints Mfr
S.I.C.: 2851; 2891
N.A.I.C.S.: 325510; 325520
Media: 2-6-10
Personnel:
Mike Walsh *(VP-Mktg & New Product Dev)*
Advertising Agency:
Cramer-Krasselt Public Relations
225 N Michigan Ave
Chicago, IL 60601-7601
Tel.: (312) 616-9600

THE MURALO COMPANY

148 E 5th St
Bayonne, NJ 07002
Tel.: (201) 437-0770
Fax: (800) 364-8969
Fax: (201) 437-2316
Toll Free: (800) 631-3440
E-mail: info@muralocompany.com
Web Site: www.murala.com
E-Mail For Key Personnel:
Marketing Director: dmartin@muralocompany.com
Sales Range: $50-74.9 Million
Approx. Number Employees: 300
Year Founded: 1894
Business Description:
Paints & Brushes Mfr & Whslr
S.I.C.: 5198
N.A.I.C.S.: 424950
Import Export
Media: 2-5-10-26
Personnel:
Edward Norton *(Chm)*
James S. Norton *(Pres)*
Chuck Lee, Jr. *(CFO)*
Peter Seaborg *(VP-Sls-Mid Atlantic)*
Daniele Martin *(Mgr-Mktg)*
Richard Norton *(Mgr-Production Scheduling)*
Brands & Products:
ADHESIUM
BREATHE SAFE
ELDER & JENKS
MURALO
NANOKOTE
SATIN FLOW
SPACKLE
ULTRA CERAMIC MATTE
ULTRA WATERBORNE

NATIONAL PAINT INDUSTRIES

1999 Elizabeth St
North Brunswick, NJ 08902
Tel.: (732) 821-3200
Fax: (732) 821-8180
Toll Free: (800) 332-6050
E-mail: info@nationalpaintsupply.us
Web Site: www.ipaint.us/
Approx. Sls.: $1,500,000
Approx. Number Employees: 10
Year Founded: 1908
Business Description:
Paint & Varnish Removers, Finishes, Paint Bonding Liquids, Cleaners, & Wallpaper Removal Systems Mfr
S.I.C.: 2851
N.A.I.C.S.: 325510
Export
Media: 4-5-6-10-19-21
Distr.: Natl.
Budget Set: Dec.
Personnel:
Mike Shinner *(Pres)*
Brands & Products:
CLEANWOODE
IMPERIAL
MISTER STRIPPER
PAINTLIFT
RAPID
SAF-TE-STRIP
WATER WASH BRUSH CLEANER
WIL-BOND
WIL-BOND 2
WIL-CLEAN
WONDER PASTE
WONDER WASH-OFF

NEW YORK CENTRAL ART SUPPLY

62 3rd Ave
New York, NY 10003-5534
Tel.: (212) 477-0400
Tel.: (212) 473-7705
Fax: (212) 475-2542
Fax: (212) 475-2513
Toll Free: (800) 950-6111
E-mail: sales@nycentralart.com
Web Site: www.nycentralart.com
E-Mail For Key Personnel:
Sales Director: sales@nycentralart.com
Sales Range: $10-24.9 Million
Approx. Number Employees: 40
Year Founded: 1907
Business Description:
Artist Materials Retailer
S.I.C.: 5999; 5961
N.A.I.C.S.: 453998; 454113
Import Export
Advertising Expenditures: $200,000
Media: 4-16-25-26
Personnel:
Steven Steinberg *(Pres & CEO)*
Brands & Products:
NEWYORK CENTRAL ART SUPPLY

OCEAN BIO CHEM, INC.

4041 SW 47th Ave
Fort Lauderdale, FL 33314-4023
Tel.: (954) 587-6280
Fax: (954) 587-2813
Toll Free: (800) 327-8583
Web Site: www.oceanbiochem.com
Approx. Sls.: $29,221,396
Approx. Number Employees: 103
Year Founded: 1973
Business Description:
Mfr. of Cleaning & Polishing Agents For Boats, Cars & Aircraft
S.I.C.: 2842
N.A.I.C.S.: 325612
Advertising Expenditures: $1,600,000
Personnel:
Jerry Pittman *(Sls Mgr)*
Brands & Products:
OBC
STAR BRITE
STARBRITE

OERLIKON BALZERS COATING USA, INC.

(Sub. of Oerlikon Balzers AG)
2511 Technology Dr Ste 114
Elgin, IL 60123
Tel.: (847) 844-1753
Fax: (847) 844-3306
Web Site: www.oerlikon.com/coatingservices/us/
E-Mail For Key Personnel:
President: Kent.Connell@balzers.com
Approx. Rev.: $43,000,000
Approx. Number Employees: 316
Year Founded: 1986
Business Description:
Coatings Supplier
S.I.C.: 5198

Key to Media (For complete agency information see *The Advertising Red Books-Agencies* edition):
1. Bus. Publs. 2. Cable T.V. 3. Catalogs & Directories. 4. Co-op Adv. 5. Consumer Mags. 6. D.M. to Bus. Estab.7. D.M. to Consumers 8. Daily Newsp. 9. Exhibits/Trade Shows 10. Foreign 11. Infomercial 12. Internet Adv.13. Multimedia 14. Network Radio 15. Network T.V. 16. Newsp. Distr. Mags. 17. Other 18. Outdoor (Posters, Transit) 19. Point of Purchase20. Premiums, Novelties 21. Product Samples 22. Special Events Mktg. 23. Spot Radio 24. Spot T.V. 25. Weekly Newsp. 26. Yellow Page Adv.

Oerlikon Balzers Coating USA, Inc. — (Continued)

N.A.I.C.S.: 424950
Advertising Expenditures: $100,000
Media: 2-10
Personnel:
Paul Olore *(Dir-Ops)*
Brands & Products:
BALINIT
Advertising Agency:
Travers Collins & Company
726 Exchange St Ste 500
Buffalo, NY 14210-1495
Tel.: (716) 842-2222
Fax: (716) 842-6424

OSI SEALANTS INC.
(Sub. of Sovereign Specialty Chemicals, Inc.)
7405 Production Dr
Mentor, OH 44060-4876
Tel.: (440) 255-8900
Fax: (440) 974-8774
Toll Free: (800) 321-3578
E-mail: info@osisealants.com
Web Site: www.osisealants.com
Approx. Number Employees: 200
Year Founded: 1997
Business Description:
Sealants, Caulks, Adhesives & Wood Patching Products Mfr
S.I.C.: 2891
N.A.I.C.S.: 325520
Advertising Expenditures: $200,000
Media: 4-7-10-11-13
Distr.: Natl.
Personnel:
Mark Longo *(Exec VP)*
Tom Rapps *(Dir-Mktg)*
Brands & Products:
FORMULA 36
FORMULA 38
POLYSEAMSEAL
PRO FOAM
QUICK BOND
S. B. R.
TRANS-SEAL
ULTRASIL-HM
ULTRASIL II
ULTRASIL-LM
WONDER FOAM
WOODMATE

PAASCHE AIRBRUSH COMPANY
4311 N Normandy
Chicago, IL 60634-1395
Tel.: (773) 867-9191
Fax: (773) 867-9198
E-mail: info@paascheairbrush.com
Web Site: www.paascheairbrush.com
Approx. Number Employees: 45
Year Founded: 1904
Business Description:
Airbrushes & Accessories, Compressors, Manual & Automatic Spray Guns, Automatic & Semi-Automatic Finishing Equipment Booths & Filter & Water Wash Booths
S.I.C.: 3952; 3563
N.A.I.C.S.: 339942; 333912
Export
Media: 4-6-10-16-21-26
Distr.: Intl.; Natl.
Budget Set: Aug.
Personnel:
J.P. Pettersen *(Pres)*
J. Lagerlof *(VP-Sls)*
Brian Pettersen *(VP-Mktg)*
Brands & Products:
FP
H AIRBRUSH
LEISURE TAN
PAASCHE
VL
VSR90

PECORA CORPORATION
(Holding of Navigation Capital Partners)
165 Wambold Rd
Harleysville, PA 19438-2014
Tel.: (215) 723-6051
Fax: (215) 721-0286
Toll Free: (800) 523-6688
E-mail: custserv@pecora.com
Web Site: www.pecora.com
Sales Range: $25-49.9 Million
Approx. Number Employees: 120
Year Founded: 1862
Business Description:
Sealants, Adhesives & Repellent Mfr & Sales
S.I.C.: 2891; 2821
N.A.I.C.S.: 325520; 325211
Export
Media: 2-4-7-10-13-20-22
Distr.: Intl.; Natl.
Budget Set: Jan.
Personnel:
Joe Virdone *(Pres & CEO)*
Robert Heim *(CFO)*
Roy Cannon *(Dir-Tech Svcs)*
Wendy Freed *(Mgr-Mktg)*
Brands & Products:
PECORA

PERRY & DERRICK CO.
2511 Highland Ave
Cincinnati, OH 45212-2319
Tel.: (513) 351-5800
Fax: (513) 342-1770
E-mail: med@pdpaints.com
Web Site: www.pdpaints.com
Approx. Sls.: $17,000,000
Approx. Number Employees: 140
Year Founded: 1913
Business Description:
Paints Mfr
S.I.C.: 2851; 5023
N.A.I.C.S.: 325510; 423220
Export
Advertising Expenditures: $200,000
Media: 1-2-3-4-5-6-8-9-14-15-16-18-19-20-21-22-23-24-25-26
Distr.: Reg.
Budget Set: Nov.
Personnel:
Sally H. Derrick *(Owner & Pres)*
Mark E. Derrick *(Dir-Sls)*
Brands & Products:
ACRYCOTE
CAMEO
DUTCH BRAND
HEAVY DUTY MAINTENANCE
MASTERPIECE
PERRY & DERRICK
STAY BRIGHT
WOOD PRO

THE PERVO PAINT COMPANY
6624 Stanford Ave
Los Angeles, CA 90001-1538
Mailing Address:
PO Box 01496
Los Angeles, CA 90001-0495
Tel.: (323) 758-1147
Fax: (323) 778-9719
Toll Free: (800) 892-3647
E-mail: sales@pervo.com
Web Site: www.pervo.com
E-Mail For Key Personnel:
Sales Director: sales@pervo.com
Approx. Number Employees: 50
Year Founded: 1929
Business Description:
Commercial, Industrial & Traffic Paints, Acrylic Emulsion-Alkyds Mfr
S.I.C.: 2851
N.A.I.C.S.: 325510
Advertising Expenditures: $200,000
Media: 2-4-22-26
Distr.: Intl.; Natl.
Personnel:
Brad DeRuiter *(Pres-Pervo Paint & Owner)*
Nick Perera *(CFO)*
Scott Shannon *(VP-Sls & Mktg)*
Brands & Products:
7000 PERVO+
ACROFLAT
COLORAMA
THE GOOD NEIGHBOR PAINT COMPANY
MARMET PRIMER 1800
MASTER PAINTER
PERVO
PERVO PAINT COMPANY
PERVO TRAFFIC CENTER
PERVOGLO
PERVOSTRIPE
PERVOTEX
SUPERMAX

PETTIT PAINT COMPANY
(Sub. of Kop-Coat, Inc.)
36 Pine St
Rockaway, NJ 07866
Tel.: (973) 625-3100
Fax: (973) 625-8303
Toll Free: (800) 221-4466
Web Site: www.pettitpaint.com
Sales Range: $25-49.9 Million
Approx. Number Employees: 50
Year Founded: 1853
Business Description:
Marine Paint Mfr
S.I.C.: 2851; 2891
N.A.I.C.S.: 325510; 325520
Media: 4-5-6-10-18-21-24
Distr.: Intl.; Natl.
Budget Set: July
Personnel:
John Ludgate *(Pres)*
Don Zabransky *(Dir-Sls & Mktg)*
Brands & Products:
340 GOLD
ALUMACOAT
BAK-V-SPAR
BITUMASTIC
CENTENNIAL
CUPROCURE
DURATHANE
EASYPOXY
GLAMORGLAZE
GLAMORTEX
HOBBYPOXY
HORIZONS 2
INERTOL
LIGHTNING SPAR
MEANER
PETTIT
PETTITROL
POLYPOXY
POWERCOAT
RAMUC
RESISTORUST
RUSTAMOR
RUSTLOK
SAILCOAT
SHIPENDEC
TEAK COTE
TRAILERCOAT
TRINIDAD
TROPICOP
UNEPOXY
VINYLCIDE
Z-SPAR
Advertising Agency:
Wolff Advertising, Inc.
896 Westport Rd
Easton, CT 06612-1533
Tel.: (203) 254-9070

PPG INDUSTRIES, INC.
1 PPG Place
Pittsburgh, PA 15272-0001
Tel.: (412) 434-3131
Fax: (412) 434-2011
Telex: 199107
E-mail: corporateinfo@ppg.com
Web Site: www.ppg.com
Approx. Sls.: $13,423,000,000
Approx. Number Employees: 38,300
Year Founded: 1883
Business Description:
Paints, Flat Glass, Auto & Aircraft Glass, Fiberglass & Chemicals Mfr & Supplier
S.I.C.: 2851; 2812; 3211; 3728
N.A.I.C.S.: 325510; 325181; 327211; 336413
Import Export
Advertising Expenditures: $288,000,000
Media: 7-11
Personnel:
Charles E. Bunch *(Chm & CEO)*
David B. Navikas *(CFO & Sr VP)*
Pierre-Marie De Leener *(Pres-PPG Europe & Exec VP-Architectural Coatings-EMEA)*
Glenn E. Bost, II *(Gen Counsel & Sr VP)*
Anne M. Foulkes *(Sec & Asst Gen Counsel)*
J. Rich Alexander *(Exec VP-Performance Coatings)*
Richard C. Elias *(Sr VP-Optical & Specialty Matls)*
Michael H. McGarry *(Sr VP-Commodity Chemicals)*
Cynthia A. Niekamp *(Sr VP-Automotive OEM Coatings)*
Viktor R. Sekmakas *(Sr VP)*
Werner Baer *(VP-IT)*
J. Craig Jordan *(VP-HR)*
Patrick J. Kenny *(VP-Corp Mktg)*
Steve T. Lampe *(VP-Pur & Distr)*
Mauro Eiras *(Gen Mgr-Architectural Coatings-Latin America)*
Michael Hartings *(Gen Mgr-PMC Coatings)*
Gregory C. Wagner *(Gen Mgr-Industrial Coatings-Americas)*
Howard Wright *(Gen Mgr-Global Coil & Extrusion Products)*
Bob Burgess *(Dir-Z1 Sls)*
Brett Candler *(Dir-Zone Sls & Automotive Refinish)*

Key to Media (For complete agency information see *The Advertising Red Books-Agencies* edition):
1. Bus. Publs. 2. Cable T.V. 3. Catalogs & Directories. 4. Co-op Adv. 5. Consumer Mags. 6. D.M. to Bus. Estab.7. D.M. to Consumers
8. Daily Newsp. 9. Exhibits/Trade Shows 10. Foreign 11. Infomercial 12. Internet Adv.13. Multimedia 14. Network Radio
15. Network T.V. 16. Newsp. Distr. Mags. 17. Other 18. Outdoor (Posters, Transit) 19. Point of Purchase20. Premiums, Novelties
21. Product Samples 22. Special Events Mktg. 23. Spot Radio 24. Spot T.V. 25. Weekly Newsp. 26. Yellow Page Adv.

Glenn Davis *(Dir-Sls East Region)*
Thomas P. Kerr *(Dir-Strategic Ops Fiber Glass)*
Wendy McAfoose *(Dir-Adv)*
John Parran *(Dir-Mktg, Automotive Refinish USCA)*
Mark Seeton *(Dir-Sls & Mktg)*
John Shaffer *(Dir-Bus-COEX Americas)*
Steve Zweig *(Dir-Zone)*
Pete Dishart *(Product Mgr)*
Pascal Colin *(Mgr-Mktg)*
Nicolas Girard *(Mgr-Acct Sls)*
Jane E. Harrington *(Mgr-Color Styling)*
Robert Rega *(Mgr-Bus Dev)*
Dee Schotter *(Mgr-Mktg Comm-Pittsburgh Paints)*
Michael Stucky *(Mgr-Product & Engrg)*
Denise R. Cade *(Asst Gen Counsel)*

Brands & Products:
ACCU-TAB
ACCUMATCH
ACRALANE
ACRI-PRO
ACRI-SHIELD
ACRYLI-CLEAN
ACRYNAR
ADVANTAGE 900
AIRCON
ALLYMER
ALUM-A-LEAD
ALUMIDE
ALUMIX
AQUACRON
AQUAPEL
AQUAPON
ARMAGRIP
ATLANTICA
AZDEL
AZLOY
AZMET
AZURIA
AZURLITE
BAIROCADE
BLANKIT
BPR
BUILDERS SPEC
CALSAN
CARHIDE
CARIBIA
CARRARA
CASTALUM
CEMENTHIDE
CHEMFIL
CHEMFOS
CHEMKLEEN
CHEMSEAL
CHEMSHEEN
CHROMAFLEX
CIPTANE
COAL CAT
COLOR DYNAMICS
COMBOMAT
CORABOND
CORAFLON
CR-39
CURESAN
DEL-SEAL
DELCLEAR
DELGLO
DELSTAR
DELTA
DELTHANE
DELTRON
DESIGNACOLOR
DESOBOND
DESOCLEAN
DESOFILL
DESOPRIME
DESOTHANE
DESOTO
DIAMOND-BACK
DIAMOND COAT
DIAMOND FLEX
DITZ-LAC
DITZ-O
DITZCO
DITZLER
DOUBLE COVER
DUPLATE
DURA-PRIME
DURABRITE
DURACARB
DURACOLOR
DURACRON
DURACRYL
DURAGRAPHIC
DURANAR
DURASTAR
DURASTAT
DURETHANE
EASY CARE
ECO-PRIME
ECOBRITE
ECS
EDGESEAL
EFG
ELECTRO IMAGE
ENDURA
ENVIRACRYL
ENVIRO-PRIME
ENVIROBASE
ENVIROCRON
ENVIRON
EVIROCRON
FENESHIELD
FILLERUP
FLEXACRON
FLEXANAR
FLEXATIVE
FLEXKLEER
FLEXSEAL
FLO-GARD
FLORHIDE
FLOW KOTE
FLUSHLOK
FRESH DECK
GILCOTE
GILLITE
GLASSROOT
GLASTRAC
GLYPTEX
GRATESTRIP
GRAYLITE
HERCUFLEX
HERCULITE
HERCUVIT
HESTRON
HI-HIDE
HI-SIL
HIGH-FIDELITY
HIRI
HTX
HYBON
IDEA SCAPES
INDUCLOR
INSULEDGE
THE INTELLIGENT WINDOW
INTERCEPT
IRCO
KONDAR
KOROFLEX
KOROPON
LAMIGLASS
LAROSTAT
LAVAX
LEPTYNE
L.E.X.
LHR
LO-VEL
LTA
LTA/SECURITECT
LUCITE
MACROBORE
MACROFLEX
MAESTRO COLORS
MAGNACOOL
MAGNU-SPRAY
MAGNUDRAW
MALUBE
MANOR HALL
MANOR HALL TIMELESS
MARATHON
MAX PRIME
MAXIMUM
MAXIMUM PERFORMANCE DISTINCTION
MAXIMUM PLUS
MEGAFLON
MEGASEAL
MEMBRELLE
METALEAF
METALHIDE
MICRO-PHASE
MICROFLO PROCESS
MILDEW CHECK
MIR-O-CRON
MONARCH MOPAKO
MULTIPLATE
MULTIPRIME
MULTISCRIPTOR
NCT
NESA
NESATRON
NOVACRON
NOVAPREP
NUPAL
OLYMPIC
OLYMPIC OVERCOAT
OLYMPIC WEATHERSCREEN
OPTIBRONZE
OPTICHEM 132
OPTIGRAY
ORGANOKROME
OVALITE
OVERCOAT
PATTERNCLAD
PATTERNLITE
PELS
PERKARE
PERMA-CRETE
PERMANIZER
PERMANIZER PLUS
PERMAPOL
PERMAWEAR
PERMION
PHOTOSOL
PILT
PITT BULL
PITT-CHAR
PITT-CRYL
PITT-FLEX
PITT-GLAZE
PITT-GUARD
PITT-THERM
PITTABS
PITTCHAR
PITTCHLOR
PITTEX
PITTGUARD
PITTHANE
PITTSBURGH
POLYCLUTCH
POLYCRON
POLYSTRIP
PORTER
PORTER DECK
PORTER GUARD
PORTER SEPT
POWER-PRIME
POWERCRON
PREET 33
PRIST
PRO COMM
PRO FLAT
PRO MASTER
PRO-SEAL
PRO SUPREME
PRO VANTAGE
PROSTARS
PURE PERFORMANCE
QUIKOTE
RAYCRON
REWARD
REZ
ROADGUARD
ROCC
SAFE AND SOUND
SAN-SIL
SATIN PRIME
SATINHIDE
SCUFF GUARD
SEAL-GRIP
SECURITECT
SEMCO
SEP TECH
SILENE
SILKEN TOUCH
SNOLITE
SOFT LOOK
SOLARBAN
SOLARBRONZE
SOLARCOOL
SOLARGRAY
SOLARGREEN
SOLEXIA
SOLEXTRA
SPANDRELITE
SPECTRACLAD
SPECTRACON
SPEED FINISH PLUS
SPEED LINE
SPEEDCRAFT
SPEEDHIDE
SPEEDLINE
SPEEDPRO
SPRAYCRON
STA-KIL
STARPHIRE
STARTHANE
STERLING FILL
STRIPPGARD
SUN-GLEAM
SUN-PROOF
SUNDURA
SUNGATE
SUNSASH
SUNSET
SUNSHADE
SUNTRON
SUPER ACRYLIC
SUSTAIN
SWIV-L-CUT
TANKHIDE
TECSTAR
TEPHRAM
TESLIN
TEXO

Key to Media (For complete agency information see *The Advertising Red Books-Agencies* edition):
1. Bus. Publs. 2. Cable T.V. 3. Catalogs & Directories. 4. Co-op Adv. 5. Consumer Mags. 6. D.M. to Bus. Estab.7. D.M. to Consumers
8. Daily Newsp. 9. Exhibits/Trade Shows 10. Foreign 11. Infomercial 12. Internet Adv.13. Multimedia 14. Network Radio
15. Network T.V. 16. Newsp. Distr. Mags. 17. Other 18. Outdoor (Posters, Transit) 19. Point of Purchase20. Premiums, Novelties
21. Product Samples 22. Special Events Mktg. 23. Spot Radio 24. Spot T.V. 25. Weekly Newsp. 26. Yellow Page Adv.

PPG Industries, Inc. — (Continued)

TOP GUN
TOTAL PRO
TRENDCAST
TRI-ETHANE
TRIM-CRAFT
TRIPLE PLUS PAK
TRIVEX
TRUEFINISH
TRUFORM
TURBOPREP
TVS
TWINDOW
UNI-PRIME
UROTEC
VERSATRANS
VINYL FLAT
VINYL SUEDE
VISENZA
VISTAGRAY
WALL HIDE
WALL SUPREME
WALLHIDE
WATCHGUARD
WEARGUARD
WEATHERPANE
WOOD GUARDIAN
XMC
XTRACTIVE

Advertising Agencies:
Bianchi Public Relations Inc.
888 W Big Beaver Rd Ste 777
Troy, MI 48084
Tel.: (248) 269-1122
Fax: (248) 269-8202

Dymun + Company
200 1st Ave
Pittsburgh, PA 15222-1512
Tel.: (412) 281-2345
Fax: (412) 281-3493

Euro RSCG Worldwide PR
(Corporate Headquarters)
200 Madison Ave
New York, NY 10016
Tel.: (212) 367-6800
Fax: (212) 367-7154

FSC Marketing Communications
Gulf Tower 707 Grant St, Ste 2900
Pittsburgh, PA 15222
Tel.: (412) 471-3700
Fax: (412) 471-9323

Garrett
2000 Smallman St Ste 205a
Pittsburgh, PA 15222
Tel.: (412) 904-1495

PRATT & LAMBERT PAINTS

(Sub. of The Sherwin-Williams Company)
101 Prospect Ave
Cleveland, OH 44115-1093
Tel.: (800) 289-7728
Fax: (216) 566-1655
Fax: (800) 573-2468
Web Site: www.prattandlambert.com
Sales Range: $100-124.9 Million
Approx. Number Employees: 150
Year Founded: 1849
Business Description:
Paint & Varnish Mfr
S.I.C.: 7389
N.A.I.C.S.: 561499
Import Export
Media: 1-2-3-4-5-6-7-8-9-10-13-18-19-20-23-24-25-26
Distr.: Natl.
Personnel:
Donna Schroeder *(Brand Mgr-Mktg)*
Andy Rzicznek *(Product Mgr)*
Bratt Palermo *(Mgr-Cust Svcs)*
Brands & Products:
38
61
ACCOLADE
ACGY-GLO
AMERICA'S PREMIUM WOOD FINISHES
AQUA GLOSS
AQUA ROYAL
AQUA-SATIN
CELLU-TONE SATIN
THE CROWN JEWEL
CRYSTAL
DESIGNER WHITE
DUOSOL
EFFECTO
ENDU-THANE
ENDURING ELEGANCE
FILTEX
FORECAST COLORS
HYDROGLOSS
LYT-ALL
MAGNALAC
MONO PAC
NEVER COMPROMISE
OKENE
OVATION
P & L
PALGARD
PERMALIZE
PERSONAL EXPRESSIONS
POOL SHIELD
POXY-GARD
POXY-GLO
PRATT & LAMBERT
PRIMAFIL
PRO-HIDE
PRO-HIDE PLUS
RED SEAL
SKYLIGHT
SOLID HIDE
STAINSHIELD
STYLE HIDE
SUN BOUNCE
SUPER ONE-COAT
SUPRIME
TECH-GUARD
TONETIC
TUSCAN VILLA
UNILUX
VAPEX
VARMOR
VITRA-SHIELD
VITRASIL
WITHSTAND
WOOD LORE
WOOD SONG
Advertising Agency:
Worldwide Directory Advertising
677A Alpha Park Dr.
Cleveland, OH 44143
Tel.: (440) 646-9932
Toll Free: (800) 646-9932
(Yellow Page Adv.)

PROGRESS PAINT MANUFACTURING CO., INC.

(Sub. of California Products Corporation)
201 E Market St
Louisville, KY 40202-1217
Mailing Address:
PO Box 33188
Louisville, KY 40232-3188
Tel.: (502) 587-8685
Fax: (502) 587-2440
Toll Free: (800) 626-6407
Web Site: www.progresspaint.com
E-Mail For Key Personnel:
Sales Director: jimheil@progresspaint.com
Approx. Number Employees: 101
Year Founded: 1912
Business Description:
Paint & Paint Sundries Mfr
S.I.C.: 2851
N.A.I.C.S.: 325510
Export
Advertising Expenditures: $500,000
Media: 4-5-7-8-9-10-18-19-20-21-23-24-26
Distr.: Direct to Independent Retailers
Budget Set: Dec.
Brands & Products:
BLATZ
COLOR CLASSICS II
DURALUX
FIXALL
FRESH AIR FORMULA
GRAY-SEAL
KURFEES
LUMI-SEAL
PROGRESSPAINT
SUREKOTE

THE REAL MILK PAINT CO.

11 W Pumping Sta Rd
Quakertown, PA 18951
Tel.: (215) 538-3886
Fax: (215) 538-5435
Toll Free: (800) 839-9748
E-mail: dosiever@realmilkpaint.com
Web Site: www.realmilkpaint.com
Approx. Number Employees: 3
Business Description:
Casein Paint for Antique Reproductions
S.I.C.: 2851
N.A.I.C.S.: 325510
Media: 4-6-10
Personnel:
Dwayne O. Siever *(Owner)*
Brands & Products:
REAL MILK PAINT
SOY GEL

RED SPOT PAINT & VARNISH CO., INC.

(Sub. of Fujikura Ltd.)
1107 E Louisiana St
Evansville, IN 47711
Tel.: (812) 428-9100
Fax: (812) 428-9167
Fax: (812) 435-1706
Toll Free: (800) 457-3544
E-mail: customerservice@redspot.com
Web Site: www.redspot.com
Approx. Rev.: $75,900,000
Approx. Number Employees: 390
Year Founded: 1903
Business Description:
Automotive & Industrial Coatings; Paints & Lacquers Mfr
S.I.C.: 2851; 2952
N.A.I.C.S.: 325510; 324122
Import Export
Media: 4-10-21
Personnel:
Daisuke Kato *(Pres & CEO)*
Steve Halling *(CFO)*
Brands & Products:
ADVANCED COATINGS FOR A WORLD OF PLASTICS
ARC
HYDROPLAS
PHOTOPLAS
POP-FREE
RED SPOT
SOFT FEEL
SRC

RPM INTERNATIONAL INC.

2628 Pearl Rd
Medina, OH 44258
Mailing Address:
PO Box 777
Medina, OH 44258
Tel.: (330) 273-5090
Fax: (330) 225-8743
Toll Free: (800) 776-4488
E-mail: info@rpminc.com
Web Site: www.rpminc.com
Approx. Sls.: $3,412,716,000
Approx. Number Employees: 9,862
Year Founded: 1947
Business Description:
Holding Company; Paint Mfr
S.I.C.: 6719; 2851; 2891
N.A.I.C.S.: 551112; 325510; 325520
Export
Advertising Expenditures: $33,300,000
Media: 1-2-20
Distr.: Natl.; Reg.
Budget Set: June
Personnel:
Frank C. Sullivan *(Chm & CEO)*
Ronald A. Rice *(Pres & COO)*
Robert L. Matejka *(CFO & Sr VP)*
Paul G.P. Hoogenboom *(CIO, Sr VP-Mfg & Ops)*
Edward W. Moore *(Chief Compliance Officer, Gen Counsel & VP)*
Keith R. Smiley *(Treas, VP & Asst Sec)*
Stephen J. Knoop *(Sr VP)*
Lonny R. DiRusso *(VP-IT)*
Kathie Rogers *(Mgr-IR)*
Tracy Crandall *(Assoc Gen Counsel & Asst Sec)*
Brands & Products:
DAP
THE EUCLID CHEMICAL COMPANY
RPM
TESTORS
VIVID
VULKEM
WATERTITE
ZINSSER
Advertising Agency:
Roop & Co.
925 Euclid Ave Ste 650
Cleveland, OH 44115-1408
Tel.: (216) 902-3800
Fax: (216) 902-3807

RUST-OLEUM CORPORATION

(Sub. of RPM Consumer Holding Co.)
11 Hawthorn Pkwy
Vernon Hills, IL 60061-1402
Tel.: (847) 367-7700
Fax: (847) 816-2272
E-mail: info@rust-oleum.com
Web Site: www.rust-oleum.com

Key to Media (For complete agency information see *The Advertising Red Books-Agencies* edition):
1. Bus. Publs. 2. Cable T.V. 3. Catalogs & Directories. 4. Co-op Adv. 5. Consumer Mags. 6. D.M. to Bus. Estab.7. D.M. to Consumers 8. Daily Newsp. 9. Exhibits/Trade Shows 10. Foreign 11. Infomercial 12. Internet Adv.13. Multimedia 14. Network Radio 15. Network T.V. 16. Newsp. Distr. Mags. 17. Other 18. Outdoor (Posters, Transit) 19. Point of Purchase20. Premiums, Novelties 21. Product Samples 22. Special Events Mktg. 23. Spot Radio 24. Spot T.V. 25. Weekly Newsp. 26. Yellow Page Adv.

Sales Range: $250-299.9 Million
Approx. Number Employees: 550
Year Founded: 1921
Business Description:
Rust-Preventive, General Purpose, Decorative, Specialty & Professional Paints Mfr
S.I.C.: 2851; 2899
N.A.I.C.S.: 325510; 325998
Media: 2-4-5-6-7-9-10-11-19-21-24-26
Distr.: Natl.
Budget Set: Sept. -Oct.
Personnel:
Kurt Hardy *(VP-Mktg & Res & Dev)*
Brendan Steidle *(Brand Mgr)*
Brands & Products:
SIERRA PERFORMANCE COATINGS
Advertising Agencies:
JAN Kelley Marketing
1005 Skyview Dr Ste 322
Burlington, ON L7P 5B1, Canada
Tel.: (905) 631-7934
Fax: (905) 631-8558
Toll Free: (800) 461-7304

McGarry Bowen, LLC
601 W 26th St Ste 1150
New York, NY 10001
Tel.: (212) 598-2900
Fax: (212) 598-2996
Creative

THE SAVOGRAN COMPANY

259 Lenox St
Norwood, MA 02062-3417
Mailing Address:
PO Box 130
Norwood, MA 02062-0130
Tel.: (781) 762-5400
Fax: (781) 762-1095
Toll Free: (800) 225-9872
E-mail: contactus@savogran.com
Web Site: www.savogran.com
Approx. Number Employees: 45
Year Founded: 1872
Business Description:
Paint & Varnish Remover, Cleaners, Compounders, Spackling Products, Liquid Paint Remover, Wallpaper Remover, Waterless Hand Cleaner, Tile Repairer, Crack Filler, Wood Putty & Brush Cleaner Mfr
S.I.C.: 2851; 5169
N.A.I.C.S.: 325510; 424690
Media: 5
Distr.: Natl.
Budget Set: Jan.
Personnel:
Mark Monique *(Pres)*
Steve McLean *(VP-Sls)*
Brands & Products:
BITREX
DIRTEX
FAST
GRAFFITI REMOVER
GROUT SEALER
H2 OFF
KUTZIT
KWIKEEZE
LEVEL-BEST
POWDERED DIRTEX
STRYPEEZE
SUPER STRIP
TILE GROUT
WOOD BLEACH

SEYMOUR OF SYCAMORE, INC.

917 Crosby Ave
Sycamore, IL 60178-1343
Tel.: (815) 895-9101
Fax: (815) 895-8475
Toll Free: (800) 435-4482
E-mail: seymour_syc@earthlink.net
Web Site: www.seymourpaint.com
Approx. Number Employees: 120
Year Founded: 1949
Business Description:
Aerosol Paint & Coatings Mfr
S.I.C.: 2851; 2899
N.A.I.C.S.: 325510; 325998
Export
Media: 2-5-6-7-8
Distr.: Reg.
Personnel:
Nancy Seymour Heatley *(CEO)*
Chris Heatley *(VP-Sls)*
Brands & Products:
ALUMI-BLAST
ALUMI-MATCH
FRESH-N-QUICK
HI-TECH
MRO
SEYMOUR
SPRUCE
SPRUCE SPRAY
STRIPE
SUN BURST
TOOL CRIB
WAVE MASTER

THE SHERWIN-WILLIAMS COMPANY

101 Prospect Ave NW
Cleveland, OH 44115-1075
Tel.: (216) 566-2000
Tel.: (216) 566-2140
Fax: (216) 566-2095
Telex: 858597 SHERWILCLEVE
Web Site: www.sherwin.com
Approx. Sls.: $7,776,424,000
Approx. Number Employees: 32,228
Year Founded: 1866
Business Description:
Paints, Varnishes, Lacquers, Enamels, Stains, Colors, Specialty Chemicals, Adhesives, Brushes, Rollers & Trays, Aerosol Sprays Mfr; Wallcoverings, Carpeting, Decorative Accessories, Painting Supplies & Window Treatment Distr
S.I.C.: 1721; 2851; 3089; 5231
N.A.I.C.S.: 238320; 325510; 326199; 444120
Import Export
Advertising Expenditures: $218,370,000
Media: 2-3-7-8-9-15-19-23-24-25-26
Distr.: Natl.
Budget Set: May -June
Personnel:
Christopher M. Connor *(Chm & CEO)*
John G. Morikis *(Pres & COO)*
Sean P. Hennessy *(CFO & Sr VP-Fin)*
Louis E. Stellato *(Gen Counsel, Sec & VP)*
Thomas E. Hopkins *(Sr VP-HR)*
Steven J. Oberfeld *(Sr VP-Plng & Dev)*
Thomas W. Seitz *(Sr VP-Strategic Excellence Initiatives)*
Robert J. Wells *(Sr VP-Corp Comm & Pub Affairs)*
Michael T. Cummins *(Asst Sec & VP-Taxes)*
Mike Conway *(Dir-Corp Comm & IR)*
Brands & Products:
A-100
ACRY GLO
ALL SURFACE
BACO
BESTT LIEBCO
BROD DUGAN
CASHMERE
CLASSIC
CLASSIC 99
COLOR PRIME
COLORACCENTS
COLORGIN
CONCO
CONTRACTOR SERIES
CUPRINOL
DECKSCAPES
DUPLI-COLOR
DURASEAL
DURATION
DURATION HOME
DUTCH BOY
E-BARRIER
EXCELO
FABULON
FILL BOND
FLEXBON
FORMBY'S
GLOBO
H&C PAINT & COATINGS
HARMONY
ILLUSIONS
JET GLO
JET GLO EXPRESS
JETFLEX
KRYLON
LAZZURIL
LOXON
MAB PAINTS
MARSON
MARTIN-SENOUR
MAUTZ
MINWAX
M.L. CAMPBELL
PORCH & FLOOR
PRATT & LAMBERT
PREMIUM XL
PREPRITE
PROBLOCK
PROCLASSIC
PROVAL
PULVERLAC
PURDY
PURDY ECO PRO
RED DEVIL
RESILIENCE
RONSEAL
RUBBERSET
SANDSCAPES
SCOTTWARREN
SHER-TIP
SHERWIN-WILLIAMS
SOFTSUEDE
SPRAYON
SUMARE
SUPERPAINT
SYMPHONY
THOMPSON'S
TRADEWORKS
TRI-FLOW
VISIBLE SOLUTIONS
WESTERN
WHITE LIGHTNING
WOOD CLASSICS
WOODSCAPES
Advertising Agencies:
Doner
25900 Northwestern Hwy
Southfield, MI 48075
Tel.: (248) 354-9700
Fax: (248) 827-8440
Krylon

Fahlgren Mortine
4030 Easton Station Ste 300
Columbus, OH 43219
Tel.: (614) 383-1500
Fax: (614) 383-1501
Protective & Marine Coatings

McKinney
(d/b/a McKinney Silver)
318 Blackwell St
Durham, NC 27701
Tel.: (919) 313-0802
Fax: (919) 313-0805
(Creative, Media Planning)

SHERWIN-WILLIAMS DIVERSIFIED BRANDS DIVISION

(Div. of The Sherwin-Williams Company)
101 Prospect Ave N W
Cleveland, OH 44115
Tel.: (216) 566-2000
Tel.: (216) 515-7697
Fax: (216) 566-2903
Web Site: www.sherwinwilliams.com
Sales Range: $200-249.9 Million
Approx. Number Employees: 400
Year Founded: 1949
Business Description:
Mfr., Distributor & Seller of Aerosol Custom Loaders & Industrial Aerosol Specialties, Paint Applicators
S.I.C.: 2851; 5231
N.A.I.C.S.: 325510; 444120
Media: 2-4-7-10-19-21
Distr.: Natl.
Budget Set: Oct.
Personnel:
Harvey Sass *(Pres & Gen Mgr-Diversified)*
Brands & Products:
711
727 QTL
AUTO PANEL
AUTO SPRAY
BRIGHT BEAUTY
BRITE TOUCH
CAST COAT
COLOR ALL
COLORWORKS
COUNTRY LOFT
CRYSTAL CLEAR
DANVERN
DUPLI-COLOR
FANSPRAY
ILLINOIS BRONZE
JET-PAK
KALIFORNIAKOLORS
KRYLINER
KRYLON
LET-GO
NOW
NU HUE
OMNI-FILL
OMNI-PAK

Key to Media (For complete agency information see *The Advertising Red Books-Agencies* edition):
1. Bus. Publs. 2. Cable T.V. 3. Catalogs & Directories. 4. Co-op Adv. 5. Consumer Mags. 6. D.M. to Bus. Estab.7. D.M. to Consumers
8. Daily Newsp. 9. Exhibits/Trade Shows 10. Foreign 11. Infomercial 12. Internet Adv.13. Multimedia 14. Network Radio
15. Network T.V. 16. Newsp. Distr. Mags. 17. Other 18. Outdoor (Posters, Transit) 19. Point of Purchase20. Premiums, Novelties
21. Product Samples 22. Special Events Mktg. 23. Spot Radio 24. Spot T.V. 25. Weekly Newsp. 26. Yellow Page Adv.

Sherwin-Williams Diversified Brands Division — (Continued)

P.D.R.P.
QUALITY CARE
REYNOLDS
RUST BREAKER
RUST FIX
RUST TOUGH
SCRATCH-FIX
SPARVAR
SPRAYON
UPSIDE DOWN
WEEKEND

SHERWIN-WILLIAMS WOOD CARE GROUP
(Div. of The Sherwin-Williams Company Wood Care Division)
10 Mountainview Rd
Upper Saddle River, NJ 07458-1933
Tel.: (201) 818-7500
Fax: (201) 818-7605
Toll Free: (800) 526-0495
Web Site: www.minwax.com
Sales Range: $50-74.9 Million
Approx. Number Employees: 80
Business Description:
Wood Care Products Mfr & Marketer
S.I.C.: 5231
N.A.I.C.S.: 444120
Media: 6-10-14-15
Distr.: Natl.
Budget Set: Dec.
Personnel:
Dominick Pisciotta *(Sr VP-Sls & Mktg)*
Janet Krakow *(VP-Mktg-Wood Care Grp)*
Brands & Products:
FORMSBY
MINWAX
THOMPSON'S
Advertising Agency:
BRUSHfire, Inc.
2 Wing Dr
Cedar Knolls, NJ 07927
Tel.: (973) 871-1700
Fax: (973) 871-1717
(Minwax)

SHERWIN WILLIAMS
(Div. of Sherwin-Williams Consumer Group)
101 Prospect Ave nw
Cleveland, OH 44115
Tel.: (216) 566-2000
Fax: (216) 566-1655
Toll Free: (800) MSP-5270
Web Site: www.sherwinwilliams.com
Sales Range: $300-349.9 Million
Approx. Number Employees: 2,000
Year Founded: 1878
Business Description:
Paint Mfr
S.I.C.: 8741
N.A.I.C.S.: 561110
Advertising Expenditures: $217,637,000
Media: 2-4-5-6-10-19-20-26
Distr.: Natl.
Budget Set: Jan.
Personnel:
Debbie Zietlow *(Mgr-Mktg-DIY Brands)*
Brands & Products:
BRIGHT LIFE
BRIGHT LIGHTS
GREAT LIFE
HOME STYLER
PRO LINE
PRO LINE PREMIUM
PRO LINE SUPREME
SUPER TOUGHCOAT
TOUGHCOAT
WILLIAMSBURG
Advertising Agency:
Doner
25900 Northwestern Hwy
Southfield, MI 48075
Tel.: (248) 354-9700
Fax: (248) 827-8440

SHUR-LINE
(Sub. of Newell Rubbermaid Inc.)
4051 S Iowa Ave
Saint Francis, WI 53235-4668
Tel.: (414) 481-4500
Fax: (414) 481-5158
Toll Free: (877) SHURLINE
Web Site: www.shurline.com
Sales Range: $100-124.9 Million
Approx. Number Employees: 400
Year Founded: 1945
Business Description:
Paint Brushes, Paint Rollers, Painting Pads, Paint Sundries Mfr
S.I.C.: 3991
N.A.I.C.S.: 339994
Import Export
Advertising Expenditures: $581,000
Media: 2-4-6-7-10-20-21-22
Distr.: Intl.; Natl.
Budget Set: Jan.
Personnel:
Dave Jarecki *(Mgr-Mktg)*

STANCHEM, INC.
401 Berlin St
East Berlin, CT 06023-1127
Tel.: (860) 828-0571
Fax: (860) 828-3297
E-mail: info@stanchem-inc.com
Web Site: www.stanchem-inc.com
Sales Range: $10-24.9 Million
Approx. Number Employees: 50
Year Founded: 1969
Business Description:
Fire Retardant Paints & Fire Proofing Coatings, Latex Polymers & Specialty Coatings Mfr
S.I.C.: 2899; 2851
N.A.I.C.S.: 325998; 325510
Import Export
Advertising Expenditures: $250,000
Media: 2-4-7-21
Distr.: Natl.
Budget Set: Sept. -Oct.
Personnel:
William Casey West *(Chm)*
Jack Waller *(Pres)*
Michael Evans *(Mgr-Sls-Central Reg)*
Daryl Orlich *(Mgr-Sls-Eastern Reg)*
Brands & Products:
ALBI CLAD
ALBI DRICLAD
INCRALAC
STANCHEM

STEELCOTE MANUFACTURING COMPANY
5147 Natural Bridge St
Saint Louis, MO 63115
Tel.: (314) 771-8053
Fax: (314) 771-7581
Toll Free: (800) 737-0282
Approx. Number Employees: 10
Year Founded: 1915
Business Description:
Industrial Coatings Mfr
S.I.C.: 2851
N.A.I.C.S.: 325510
Media: 2-4-5-7-10-19-21
Distr.: Direct to Consumer; Intl.; Natl.
Budget Set: Jan. -Feb.
Brands & Products:
CHEMTHANE 1800
COLORMASTIC 750
DAMP-TEX
EPO-LINE 164
EPO-LUX
EPO-LUX 595
EPO-MASTIC
FLOOR-NU
FLOOR-NU FINISH
MCU 2100
MONOMID
MONOMID CLEAR SEALER
MONOMID HI-BUILD
QUICK-X
SPEEDEPOXY
STEELCOTE MANUFACTURING
STEELMASTIC-168
THIOCAULK
TILE-X
WALL-NU

SURFACE PROTECTION INDUSTRIES, INTERNATIONAL
850 Ladd Rd
Walled Lake, MI 48390
Mailing Address:
PO Box 3360
Los Angeles, CA 90023
Tel.: (323) 269-9231
Fax: (248) 668-8134
Toll Free: (800) 810-2785
Web Site: www.zolatoneaim.com
Approx. Sls.: $50,000,000
Approx. Number Employees: 200
Year Founded: 1978
Business Description:
Paint Mfr
S.I.C.: 2851
N.A.I.C.S.: 325510
Export
Media: 2-4-5-7-10-16-20-21-26
Distr.: Reg.
Budget Set: Jan. -Feb.
Personnel:
Robert C. Davidson, Jr. *(Pres & CEO)*
Doug Omer *(CFO & Exec VP)*
Tim Archer *(Mgr-Western Territory)*
Brands & Products:
ZOLATONE

UES, INC.
4401 Dayton Xenia Rd
Dayton, OH 45432-1894
Tel.: (937) 426-6900
Fax: (937) 429-5413
E-mail: humanresources@ues.com
Web Site: www.ues.com
Sales Range: $10-24.9 Million
Approx. Number Employees: 200
Year Founded: 1973
Business Description:
Hi-Technology Research & Development
S.I.C.: 7371; 8733
N.A.I.C.S.: 541511; 541710
Media: 2-7-10-13-20
Personnel:
Nina Joshi *(Pres & CEO)*
John J. Gruenwald *(VP-Fin & Bus Ops)*
Deborah E. Yount *(Dir-HR)*
Brands & Products:
EXCELLENCE IN SCIENCE & TECHNOLOGY
ROBO-MET.3D
TITANCOAT
UES

UNITED GILSONITE LABORATORIES
(Filed Ch 11 Bankruptcy #1102032 on 03/23/11 in U.S. Bankruptcy Ct, Middle Dist of PA, Wilkes Barre)
1396 Jefferson Ave
Dunmore, PA 18509-2415
Mailing Address:
PO Box 70
Scranton, PA 18501-0070
Tel.: (570) 344-1202
Fax: (570) 969-7634
Toll Free: (800) 272-3235
E-mail: uglpr@ugl.com
Web Site: www.ugl.com
Approx. Number Employees: 210
Year Founded: 1932
Business Description:
Cement Paints, Glazing & Caulking Compounds, Wall Patching Materials, Paint Sundries, Clear Finishes, Drylok Masonry Waterproofing Products; Temproof Stove & Fireplace Maintenance Products
S.I.C.: 2851; 2891
N.A.I.C.S.: 325510; 325520
Export
Media: 1-2-3-4-5-6-7-10-19-20-22
Distr.: Natl.
Budget Set: Sept.
Personnel:
Thomas J. White *(Pres)*
Joseph M. McGraw *(Dir-Mktg & Adv)*
Brands & Products:
D-GLOSS
DRYLOK
FASTRIP
GLAZOL
LASTICAULK
TEMPROOF
UGL
ZAR

THE VALSPAR CORPORATION
901 Third Ave S
Minneapolis, MN 55402
Mailing Address:
PO Box 1461
Minneapolis, MN 55440-1461
Tel.: (612) 851-7000
Fax: (612) 851-7408
Toll Free: (800) 328-8044
Web Site: www.valsparglobal.com
Approx. Sls.: $3,226,687,000
Approx. Number Employees: 10,180
Year Founded: 1806
Business Description:
Paints, Coatings, Resins & Colorants Mfr
S.I.C.: 2851; 2816; 2821; 2865; 3991; 5198
N.A.I.C.S.: 325510; 325131; 325132; 325211; 339994; 424950
Advertising Expenditures: $84,807,000
Media: 2-4-5-7-8-9-10-16-18-19-20-21-23-24-25-26
Distr.: Reg.

Key to Media (For complete agency information see *The Advertising Red Books-Agencies* edition):
1. Bus. Publs. 2. Cable T.V. 3. Catalogs & Directories. 4. Co-op Adv. 5. Consumer Mags. 6. D.M. to Bus. Estab.7. D.M. to Consumers
8. Daily Newsp. 9. Exhibits/Trade Shows 10. Foreign 11. Infomercial 12. Internet Adv.13. Multimedia 14. Network Radio
15. Network T.V. 16. Newsp. Distr. Mags. 17. Other 18. Outdoor (Posters, Transit) 19. Point of Purchase20. Premiums, Novelties
21. Product Samples 22. Special Events Mktg. 23. Spot Radio 24. Spot T.V. 25. Weekly Newsp. 26. Yellow Page Adv.

Budget Set: Oct.
Personnel:
William L. Mansfield *(Chm)*
Gary E. Hendrickson *(CEO)*
Lori A. Walker *(CFO & Sr VP)*
Kathleen J. Bass *(CIO)*
J. R. Benites *(Corp Officer)*
Rolf Engh *(Gen Counsel, Sec & Exec VP)*
Steven L. Erdahl *(Exec VP)*
Anthony L. Blaine *(Sr VP-HR)*
Howard C. Heckes *(Sr VP-Global Architectural)*
Roeland H. Polet *(Sr VP)*
Thomas V. Kelliher *(VP-Pur)*
Steven D. Person *(VP-Sls Mktg)*
Bonnie Heinsohn *(Mgr-Mktg Svcs)*
Brands & Products:
THE BEAUTY GOES ON
CLIMATE ZONE
COLOR STYLE
CONTROLZ
DESCOGLAS
DESCOGLAZE
EPO-ROK
GLAZETITE
GOOF OFF
GYMSEAL
INTEGRITY
MERFLEX
MORRITEX
PERFECT SAMPLE
PREP-STEP
QUARTZITE
SPECIAL EFFECTS
STORM COAT
TONECRETE
TUNGSEAL
VERSACOLOR
Advertising Agencies:
MPG
(Div. of HAVAS)
195 Broadway 12th Fl
New York, NY 10007
Tel.: (646) 587-5000
Fax: (646) 587-5005
Media Buyer

Padilla Speer Beardsley
1101 W River Pkwy Ste 400
Minneapolis, MN 55415-1241
Tel.: (612) 455-1700
Fax: (612) 455-1060

WAGNER SPRAY TECH CORPORATION
(Sub. of J. Wagner AG)
1770 Fernbrook Ln
Plymouth, MN 55447-4661
Tel.: (763) 553-7000
Fax: (763) 519-3563
Toll Free: (800) 328-8251
E-mail: custserv@wagnerspraytech.com
Web Site: www.wagnerspraytech.com
Approx. Number Employees: 320
Year Founded: 1970
Business Description:
Paint Spraying Equipment Mfr & Marketer
S.I.C.: 3563
N.A.I.C.S.: 333912
Advertising Expenditures: $2,500,000
Media: 2-3-5-6-9-10-12-19-25
Distr.: Direct to Consumer; Intl.; Natl.
Budget Set: Jan.
Personnel:
Steve Liedtke *(Sr VP-Ops)*
Jackie McMartin *(Grp VP-HR)*
Tom Craig *(VP-Fin)*
Brands & Products:
PAINTMATE PLUS
PAINTNROLL PLUS
QUICKTOUCH
QUICKTOUCH PRO
SPRAY TECH
STAIN MATE
TITAN
TRIM-IT
WAGNER
WIDE SHOT MAX
WIDE SHOT PLUS
Advertising Agencies:
Barrie D'Rozario Murphy
400 1st Ave N Ste 220
Minneapolis, MN 55401
Tel.: (612) 279-1500
Fax: (612) 332-9995
Agency of Record

Risdall Marketing Group
550 Main St
New Brighton, MN 55112-3271
Tel.: (651) 286-6700
Fax: (651) 631-2561
Toll Free: (888) RISDALL

Rivet
555 Washington Ave
Saint Louis, MO 63101-1249
Tel.: (314) 231-2400
Fax: (314) 231-6622

WATSON-STANDARD COMPANY
(Sub. of Watson Industries, Inc.)
616 Hite Rd
Harwick, PA 15049-8945
Mailing Address:
PO Box 11250
Pittsburgh, PA 15238-0250
Tel.: (724) 275-1000
Fax: (724) 275-2000
Web Site: www.watsonstandard.com/contact.html
Approx. Number Employees: 200
Year Founded: 1902
Business Description:
Paints, Varnishes, Enamels, Industrial Finishes & Lithograph Coatings, Protective Coatings, Vinyl Plastic Coatings Mfr
S.I.C.: 2851
N.A.I.C.S.: 325510
Import Export
Media: 2-4-10
Distr.: Natl.
Budget Set: June

WILSONART INTERNATIONAL, INC.
(Sub. of Illinois Tool Works Inc.)
2400 Wilson Pl
Temple, TX 76504-5131
Tel.: (254) 207-7000
Fax: (254) 207-2384
Toll Free: (800) 433-3222
E-mail: info@wilsonart.com
Web Site: www.wilsonart.com
Sales Range: $700-749.9 Million
Approx. Number Employees: 3,400
Year Founded: 1956
Business Description:
Decorative Surfacing Products Mfr
S.I.C.: 2821; 2434
N.A.I.C.S.: 325211; 337110
Personnel:
Bill DiGaetano *(Pres)*
Rusty Booth *(Sr VP)*
Ron Gagnon *(VP-Mktg & Design)*
Allison DiMartino *(Mgr-Mktg)*
Brands & Products:
NATURALSTONE
WHERE GREAT IDEAS ARE SURFACING!
WILSONART
Advertising Agency:
JH&A Advertising Inc.
2312 Western Trl Ste 303C
Austin, TX 78745
Tel.: (512) 444-0716
Fax: (512) 444-0865

THE WOOSTER BRUSH COMPANY
604 Madison Ave
Wooster, OH 44691-4764
Tel.: (330) 264-4440
Fax: (330) 263-0495
Toll Free: (800) 392-7246
E-mail: customerservice@woosterbrush.com
Web Site: www.woosterbrush.com
Approx. Number Employees: 570
Year Founded: 1851
Business Description:
Mfr. of Paint Brushes, Roller Applicators & Accessory Items
S.I.C.: 3991
N.A.I.C.S.: 339994
Import Export
Media: 2-4-10-19-20-21-26
Distr.: Natl.
Budget Set: Apr.
Personnel:
Woodrow J. Zook *(Chm)*
Allan K. Rodd *(Pres & Treas)*
Keith Hancock *(VP-Production)*
Dennis D. Humphrey *(VP-Engrg)*
Scott Rutledge *(VP-Mktg)*
Sharon Dentz *(Dir-Mktg)*
Brands & Products:
ADVANTAGE
CANDY STRIPE
DOO-Z
EXPLODED-TIP
GOLDEN FLO
GOLDEN GLO
JOB RATED
JOURNEYMAN
JUMBO-KOTER
OHIO
PREP CREW
PRODUCTION PAINTER
PROO
SHASTA
SHERGRIP
SHERLOCK
SHORTCUT
SOFTIP
SUPER DOO-Z
SUPER/FAB
SUPER/PRO
ULTRA/PRO
WIDE BOY
WOOSTER
YACHTSMAN

YENKIN-MAJESTIC PAINT CORPORATION
1920 Leonard Ave
Columbus, OH 43219-2514
Tel.: (614) 253-8511
Fax: (614) 253-5315
E-mail: info@yenkin-majestic.com
Web Site: www.yenkin-majestic.com
Approx. Number Employees: 250
Year Founded: 1920
Business Description:
Paints, Resins, Varnishes & Enamels Mfr
S.I.C.: 2851; 2821
N.A.I.C.S.: 325510; 325211
Export
Media: 2-4-5-10-13-17-19-20-21-22
Distr.: Natl.
Personnel:
Bernard K. Yenkin *(Chm)*
Jonathan M. Petuchowski *(Pres)*
Merom Brachman *(CEO)*
John Gerhold *(VP-Matls)*
Brands & Products:
BARRICADE
EPOXOBOND
ISOBOND
MAJIC
POLYLIFE
YENKIN-MAJESTIC

ZINSSER CO., INC.
(Sub. of RPM Consumer Holding Co.)
173 Belmont Dr
Somerset, NJ 08875
Tel.: (732) 469-8100
Fax: (732) 652-2499
Toll Free: (800) 899-1211
Telex: 955439
E-mail: bullseye@zinsser.com
Web Site: www.zinsser.com
Sales Range: $50-74.9 Million
Approx. Number Employees: 450
Year Founded: 1849
Business Description:
Primers, Wallcovering Removal Products, Wallcovering Application Products, Clear Finishes & Mildew-Proofing Products Mfr
S.I.C.: 2851; 2821
N.A.I.C.S.: 325510; 325211
Media: 2-3-4-7-10-15-19-21-24
Distr.: Natl.
Personnel:
Thomas McNicholas *(Dir-Brand Mngmt)*
Brands & Products:
ADD2
B-I-N
BLEND & GLAZE
BULLS EYE
BULLS EYE 1-2-3
BULLSEYE ODORLESS PRIMER
COVER-STAIN
DIF
DIF GEL
GARDZ
H2OIL-BASE
JOMAX
OIL BASE SHIELDZ
PAPER SCRAPER
PAPERTIGER
PEEL STOP
PERMA-WHITE
SHIELDZ CLEAR ACRYLIC WALLCOVERING

Key to Media (For complete agency information see *The Advertising Red Books-Agencies* edition):
1. Bus. Publs. 2. Cable T.V. 3. Catalogs & Directories. 4. Co-op Adv. 5. Consumer Mags. 6. D.M. to Bus. Estab.7. D.M. to Consumers 8. Daily Newsp. 9. Exhibits/Trade Shows 10. Foreign 11. Infomercial 12. Internet Adv.13. Multimedia 14. Network Radio 15. Network T.V. 16. Newsp. Distr. Mags. 17. Other 18. Outdoor (Posters, Transit) 19. Point of Purchase20. Premiums, Novelties 21. Product Samples 22. Special Events Mktg. 23. Spot Radio 24. Spot T.V. 25. Weekly Newsp. 26. Yellow Page Adv.

Zinsser Co., Inc. — (Continued)

SHIELDZ WHITE UNIVERSAL WALLCOVERING
SURE-GRIP SUPER-CONCENTRATED
Z-54

Key to Media (For complete agency information see *The Advertising Red Books-Agencies* edition):
1. Bus. Publs. 2. Cable T.V. 3. Catalogs & Directories. 4. Co-op Adv. 5. Consumer Mags. 6. D.M. to Bus. Estab.7. D.M. to Consumers 8. Daily Newsp. 9. Exhibits/Trade Shows 10. Foreign 11. Infomercial 12. Internet Adv.13. Multimedia 14. Network Radio 15. Network T.V. 16. Newsp. Distr. Mags. 17. Other 18. Outdoor (Posters, Transit) 19. Point of Purchase20. Premiums, Novelties 21. Product Samples 22. Special Events Mktg. 23. Spot Radio 24. Spot T.V. 25. Weekly Newsp. 26. Yellow Page Adv.

Paper, Packaging & Containers

Adhesives — Bags — Boxboard — Buckets — Cans — Cardboard — Cordage — Corrugated Materials — Felts — Fibers — Glass — Metal — Plastic — Pressure Sensitive Tape — Printing Paper — Rope — Tissue — Waxed Paper

ABITIBIBOWATER
(Div. of AbitibiBowater Inc.)
1000 Papermill Rd
Grenada, MS 38901
Mailing Address:
PO Box 849
Grenada, MS 38902-0849
Tel.: (662) 227-7900
Fax: (662) 227-7901
E-mail: overstreepw@bowater.com
Web Site: www.abitibibowater.com
Approx. Number Employees: 195
Year Founded: 1989
Business Description:
Newsprint Mill
S.I.C.: 2621
N.A.I.C.S.: 322122
Import Export
Advertising Expenditures: $600,000
Media: 2-9-10-23-25
Distr.: Natl.
Budget Set: Nov.
Personnel:
Wade Taylor *(Mgr)*

ALPHA PACKAGING
(Sub. of Stonebridge Partners LP)
1555 Page Industrial Blvd
Saint Louis, MO 63132
Tel.: (314) 427-4300
Fax: (314) 427-5445
Web Site: www.alphap.com
Approx. Number Employees: 550
Year Founded: 1969
Business Description:
Pharmaceutical, Nutritional, Personal Care & Niche Food & Beverage Container Products
S.I.C.: 3089
N.A.I.C.S.: 326199
Media: 4-10
Personnel:
Dave Spence *(Pres & CEO)*

AMCOR PET PACKAGING INC.
(Sub. of Amcor Limited)
10521 South Hwy M 52
Manchester, MI 48158
Tel.: (734) 428-9741
Fax: (734) 428-4622
Web Site: www.amcor.com
Approx. Number Employees: 5,800
Business Description:
Plastic Packaging Products Mfr
S.I.C.: 2656
N.A.I.C.S.: 322215
Personnel:
William J. Long *(Pres)*
Larry Weber *(CFO & GLobal VP-Fin)*
Advertising Agency:
The Drucker Group
1440 N Dayton St Ste 202
Chicago, IL 60642
Tel.: (312) 867-4960
Fax: (312) 867-4967

AMERICAN DECORATIVE SURFACES, INC.
(Holding of AMERICAN CAPITAL, LTD.)
1188 Walters Way Ln
Saint Louis, MO 63132-2200
Tel.: (618) 286-6000
Fax: (618) 286-1610
Toll Free: (888) 417-8597
Web Site:
www.decorativesurfaces.com
E-Mail For Key Personnel:
President: mmarcum@decorativesurfaces.com
Sales Range: $50-74.9 Million
Approx. Number Employees: 180
Year Founded: 1998
Business Description:
Coated & Saturated Printed Decorative Papers; Printed Decorative Film, Furniture & Panel Papers Mfr
S.I.C.: 3081
N.A.I.C.S.: 326113
Import Export
Media: 4-21
Distr.: Direct to Consumer; Natl.

AMERICAN EXCELSIOR COMPANY
850 Ave H E
Arlington, TX 76011-7720
Tel.: (817) 385-3500
Fax: (817) 649-7816
Toll Free: (800) 777-SOIL
E-mail: info@americanexcelsior.com
Web Site:
www.americanexcelsior.com
Approx. Number Employees: 500
Year Founded: 1888
Business Description:
Urethane Foam, Polyethylene, Polystyrene, Carpet Underlay, Packaging & Erosion Control Products Mfr & Distr
S.I.C.: 3086; 2493
N.A.I.C.S.: 326150; 321219
Import Export
Media: 2-4-7-10-11-13-20-26
Distr.: Intl.; Natl.
Personnel:
Robert Gregerson *(Chm)*
Terry A. Sadowski *(Pres & CEO)*
Todd A. Eblen *(CFO & VP)*
Ken Starrett *(VP-Sls & Mktg)*
Marci Webb *(VP-HR)*
Brands & Products:
AEC PREMIER STRAW
AMCEL
AMERICAN MOSS
AMFLO
CURLEX
E-MAT
ECO-FLOW
ECO-LAM
ENFORCER
EROSIONLAB
EROSIONWORKS
EXCEL BUBBLE
FIBER-CEL
FIBEREX
FIBERMULCH
MOSS BLEND
POWER STOP
QUICKGRASS
RECYCLEX
ROADRUNNER
SEDIMENT LOG
SILT STOP
SILTTRAP
TRI-LOCK

AMERICAN PACKAGING CORPORATION
777 Driving Pk Ave
Rochester, NY 14613-1591
Tel.: (585) 254-9500
Fax: (585) 254-5801
Toll Free: (800) 551-8801
Web Site: www.ampkcorp.com
Approx. Number Employees: 700
Year Founded: 1902
Business Description:
Mfr. of Bags, Coated, Laminated Paper Films and Foils; Flexo & Roto Printing Up to Ten Colors
S.I.C.: 2671; 2674
N.A.I.C.S.: 322221; 322224
Import Export
Media: 2-6-7-10
Distr.: Natl.
Budget Set: Jan.
Personnel:
Peter B. Schottland *(Pres & CEO)*
Larry Walton *(VP-Sls & Mktg)*
Paul Fricano *(Dir-HR-Corp)*
Jeffrey T. Huber *(Dir-Pur)*
Sue Rotolo *(Mgr-Bus Dev)*
Debby Pruismann *(Coord-Sls & Mktg)*

AMERICANCHURCH, INC.
(Sub. of Our Sunday Visitor, Inc.)
8401 Southern Blvd
Youngstown, OH 44512
Mailing Address:
PO Box 3120
Youngstown, OH 44513-3120
Tel.: (330) 758-4545
Fax: (330) 758-9981
Toll Free: (800) 250-7112
E-mail: Sales@americanchurch.com
Web Site: www.americanchurch.com
E-Mail For Key Personnel:
Sales Director: Sales@americanchurch.com
Approx. Number Employees: 450
Year Founded: 1903
Business Description:
Mfr of Religious Products & Offering Envelopes
S.I.C.: 2677; 2759
N.A.I.C.S.: 322232; 323119
Media: 2-8-10-20
Distr.: Direct to Consumer; Natl.
Budget Set: Oct.

ANCHOR GLASS CONTAINER CORPORATION
401 E Jackson St Ste 2800
Tampa, FL 33602
Tel.: (813) 884-0000
Fax: (813) 882-7709
Web Site: www.anchorglass.com
E-Mail For Key Personnel:
Sales Director: sales@anchorglass.com
Approx. Number Employees: 2,840
Year Founded: 1997
Business Description:
Glass Container Products Mfr
S.I.C.: 3221
N.A.I.C.S.: 327213
Export
Media: 2-9-10
Distr.: Reg.
Budget Set: Sept.

Key to Media (For complete agency information see *The Advertising Red Books-Agencies* edition):
1. Bus. Publs. 2. Cable T.V. 3. Catalogs & Directories. 4. Co-op Adv. 5. Consumer Mags. 6. D.M. to Bus. Estab.7. D.M. to Consumers
8. Daily Newsp. 9. Exhibits/Trade Shows 10. Foreign 11. Infomercial 12. Internet Adv.13. Multimedia 14. Network Radio
15. Network T.V. 16. Newsp. Distr. Mags. 17. Other 18. Outdoor (Posters, Transit) 19. Point of Purchase20. Premiums, Novelties
21. Product Samples 22. Special Events Mktg. 23. Spot Radio 24. Spot T.V. 25. Weekly Newsp. 26. Yellow Page Adv.

Anchor Glass Container Corporation — (Continued)

Personnel:
Jim Fredlake *(CEO)*
Sam Wilson *(VP-Product Dev & Technical Sls)*
Brands & Products:
LASTING IMPRESSIONS

ANDRITZ INC.
(Sub. of Andritz AG)
1115 Northmeadow Pkwy
Roswell, GA 30076-3857
Tel.: (770) 640-2500
Fax: (770) 640-9454
Web Site: www.andritz.com
Approx. Number Employees: 250
Year Founded: 1989
Business Description:
Design & Engineering of Products for the Pulp Industry
S.I.C.: 8711; 7389
N.A.I.C.S.: 541330; 541420
Advertising Expenditures: $1,000,000
Media: 2-4-7-10
Distr.: Natl.
Budget Set: Nov.
Personnel:
Tim Ryan *(Pres)*
Jay Miele *(VP & Gen Mgr)*

APPLETON PAPERS INC.
(Sub. of Paperweight Development Corp.)
825 E Wisconsin Ave
Appleton, WI 54912
Mailing Address:
PO Box 359
Appleton, WI 54912-0359
Tel.: (920) 734-9841
Fax: (920) 991-8080
E-mail: bvandenbrandt@appletonideas.com
Web Site: www.appletonideas.com
Year Founded: 1907
Business Description:
Specialty Paper & Packaging Products Mfr
S.I.C.: 2671; 2621; 2679
N.A.I.C.S.: 322221; 322121; 322299
Export
Advertising Expenditures: $600,000
Media: 1-2-4-6-7-10-19-21
Distr.: Intl.; Natl.
Budget Set: Nov.
Personnel:
Mark R. Richards *(Chm, Pres & CEO)*
Thomas J. Ferree *(CFO, Treas & Sr VP-Fin)*
Jim C. Tyrone *(Sr VP)*
Sarah T. MacDonald *(VP & Gen Mgr-Carbonless Bus Unit)*
Kerry S. Arent *(VP-HR)*
Kent E. Willetts *(VP- Strategic Dev)*
Brands & Products:
ALPHA
DUAL
HEATSAFE
HIYIELD
LIGHTSAFE
NCR PAPER
POLYFILM
POS PLUS
PRESSPRO
RESISTE
ROYALE
THERMART
WAVEX
WHAT IDEAS CAN DO

APTARGROUP, INC.
475 W Terra Cotta Ave Ste E
Crystal Lake, IL 60014-9695
Tel.: (815) 477-0424
Fax: (815) 477-0481
E-mail: info@aptargroup.com
Web Site: www.aptar.com
Approx. Sls.: $2,076,719,000
Approx. Number Employees: 8,600
Year Founded: 1992
Business Description:
Convenience Dispensing Products & Systems for the Fragrance, Cosmetics, Personal Care, Pharmaceutical, Household Product & Food Industries
S.I.C.: 3089; 3082; 3466; 3499
N.A.I.C.S.: 326199; 326121; 332115; 332999
Import Export
Media: 2-7-10
Personnel:
King W. Harris *(Chm)*
Peter H. Pfeiffer *(Pres & CEO)*
Robert W. Kuhn *(CFO & Exec VP)*
Stephen J. Hagge *(COO, Sec & Exec VP)*
Olivier de Pous *(Pres-Beauty & Home)*
Olivier Fourment *(Pres-Pharma)*
Eric Ruskoski *(Pres-Aptar Food + Beverage)*
Ralph Poltermann *(Treas & Exec VP)*
Matthew DellaMaria *(VP-Corp Comm)*

ARVCO CONTAINER CORPORATION
845 Gibson St
Kalamazoo, MI 49001-2573
Tel.: (269) 381-0900
Fax: (269) 381-2919
Toll Free: (800) 968-2919
E-mail: customerservice@arvco.com
Web Site: www.arvco.com
Approx. Number Employees: 230
Year Founded: 1971
Business Description:
Corrugated & Solid Fiber Boxes Mfr
S.I.C.: 2653; 2631
N.A.I.C.S.: 322211; 322130
Export
Media: 2-4-7-10-13
Distr.: Intl.; Natl.
Personnel:
John Vrbensky *(Sr VP)*

ATLANTIC CORPORATION
806 N 23rd St
Wilmington, NC 28405
Tel.: (910) 343-0624
Fax: (910) 763-5421
Toll Free: (800) 722-5841
E-mail: rogert@atlanticpkg.com
Web Site: www.atlanticpkg.com
Approx. Number Employees: 500
Year Founded: 1946
Business Description:
Wholesale Distr of Paper, Packaging Materials & Paper Related Products
S.I.C.: 2679; 5113
N.A.I.C.S.: 322299; 424130
Import
Media: 2-4-7-10-13-21
Distr.: Direct to Consumer; Natl.
Personnel:
Russell Carter *(Pres-Wilmington)*
Bill Balkcum *(VP-Sls-Wilmington)*
Roger Teague *(VP-Fin)*

ATLAS HOLDINGS LLC
1 Sound Shore Dr Ste 203
Greenwich, CT 06830
Tel.: (203) 622-9138
Fax: (203) 622-0151
E-mail: info@atlasholdingsllc.com
Web Site: www.atlasholdingsllc.com
Business Description:
Private Equity Firm
S.I.C.: 6289
N.A.I.C.S.: 523999
Personnel:
Andrew M. Bursky *(Mng Partner)*
Timothy J. Fazio *(Mng Partner)*
Daniel E. Cromie *(Partner)*
Edward J. Fletcher *(Partner)*
Philip E. Schuch *(Partner)*
Jacob D. Hudson *(Principal)*
Zachary C. Sufrin *(Principal)*
Troy E. Schirk *(Dir-Info Sys)*
Margaret D. DeFonce *(Mgr-Admin)*
Advertising Agency:
Stoltz Marketing Group
615 W Main St 2nd Fl
Boise, ID 83702
Tel.: (208) 388-0766
Fax: (208) 388-0764

AUTOMATED PACKAGING SYSTEMS INC.
10175 Philipp Pkwy
Streetsboro, OH 44241-4706
Tel.: (330) 342-2000
Fax: (330) 342-2400
Toll Free: (800) 527-0733
E-mail: info@autobag.com
Web Site: www.autobag.com
Approx. Number Employees: 715
Year Founded: 1962
Business Description:
Mfr. of Packaging Equipment & Plastic Bags
S.I.C.: 2673; 3565
N.A.I.C.S.: 326111; 333993
Import Export
Media: 2-4-7-8-10-18-20-21-26
Personnel:
Hershey Lerner *(Chm)*
Cliff Brehm *(Pres & COO)*
Bernie Lerner *(CEO)*
Matt Lerner *(Exec VP)*
Brad Worman *(VP-Sls & Mktg)*
Lynne Greenfeather *(Mgr-Mktg Svcs)*
Colin Smith *(Mgr-Dispatch)*
Brands & Products:
ACCU-COUNT
ACCU-SCALE
AIRPOUCH
AUTOBAG
AUTOBAG AB 145
AUTOBAG AB 180
AUTOBAG AB 180 ONESTEP
AUTOBAG AB 255
AUTOBAG AB 255 ONESTEP
AUTOBAG CTS4000
AUTOBAG PACESETTER
AUTOBAG PACESETTER PS 125
AUTOLABEL
AUTOLABEL PI 412C
AUTOLABEL PI 412CW
AUTOMATED PACKAGING SYSTEMS
DURACLEAR
DURACLEAR 2000
EARTHAWARE
EXCEL
EZ-TEAR
FAS
KITVEYOR
LIFEX
MAXIMIZER
MILLENIA
ONESTEP
PACESETTER
POLYCLEAN
PRECISION
PRISM
SIDEPOUCH
SIMPLECOUNT
SPECGRADE
SPRINT
SYSTEMS ADVANTAGE
TAKEAWAY

AVERY DENNISON CORPORATION
150 N Orange Grove Blvd
Pasadena, CA 91103
Tel.: (626) 304-2000
Fax: (626) 304-2192
E-mail: communications@averydennison.com
Web Site: www.averydennison.com
E-Mail For Key Personnel:
Public Relations: communications@averydennison.com
Approx. Sls.: $6,512,700,000
Approx. Number Employees: 32,000
Year Founded: 1935
Business Description:
Pressure-Sensitive Adhesives & Materials, Office Products, Labels, Tags, Retail Systems & Specialty Chemicals Mfr
S.I.C.: 7389; 2671; 2672; 2891; 2899; 3565
N.A.I.C.S.: 561910; 322221; 322222; 325520; 325998; 333993
Import Export
Advertising Expenditures: $23,700,000
Media: 2-7-10-20-21
Distr.: Natl.
Personnel:
Dean A. Scarborough *(Chm, Pres & CEO)*
Mitchell R. Butier *(CFO & Sr VP)*
Daniel R. O'Bryant *(CFO)*
Richard W. Hoffman *(CIO & Sr VP)*
Anne Hill *(Chief HR Officer & Sr VP)*
Susan C. Miller *(Gen Counsel, Sec & Sr VP)*
Diane B. Dixon *(Sr VP-Corp Comm & Corp Affairs)*
Robert M. Malchione *(Sr VP-Corp Strategy & Tech)*
John M. Sallay *(Sr VP-New Growth Platforms)*
Timothy G. Bond *(Grp VP-Office Products)*
Timothy S. Clyde *(Grp VP-Specialty Matls & Converting)*
R. Shawn Neville *(Grp VP-Retail Info Svcs)*
Donald A. Nolan *(Grp VP-Roll Matls)*
Todd Thompson *(VP-Mktg,Res & Dev)*
Raj Srinivasan *(Gen Mgr)*
Peta Latibeaudiere *(Product Mgr)*
Brands & Products:
AVERY
AVERY DENNISON
AVERY GRAPHICS
COMFORT TAGS
COPYCODE

Key to Media (For complete agency information see *The Advertising Red Books-Agencies* edition):
1. Bus. Publs. 2. Cable T.V. 3. Catalogs & Directories. 4. Co-op Adv. 5. Consumer Mags. 6. D.M. to Bus. Estab.7. D.M. to Consumers
8. Daily Newsp. 9. Exhibits/Trade Shows 10. Foreign 11. Infomercial 12. Internet Adv.13. Multimedia 14. Network Radio
15. Network T.V. 16. Newsp. Distr. Mags. 17. Other 18. Outdoor (Posters, Transit) 19. Point of Purchase20. Premiums, Novelties
21. Product Samples 22. Special Events Mktg. 23. Spot Radio 24. Spot T.V. 25. Weekly Newsp. 26. Yellow Page Adv.

CRACK-BACK
DIRECT PRINT
DUALSHARP
DURAGRAPHIC
EASY APPLY RS
FASCAL
FASCLEAR
FASCOPY
FASSON
HI-LITER
MARKS-A-LOT
MINI-SHEETS
PIGGYBACK
PRIMAX
PRIMELINE
QUICK PEEL
SOABAR
STABLE-RITE
STAYSHARP
SUPERCLEAR
TABULABEL
THERMARK
TRANSCODE
U-PRINT
UNIVERSAL

Advertising Agencies:
Doner
4675 MacArthur Ct Ste 1000
Newport Beach, CA 92660
Tel.: (949) 623-4300
Fax: (949) 623-4342

Hill & Knowlton, Inc.
1601 Cloverfield Blvd Ste 3000N
Santa Monica, CA 90404
Tel.: (310) 633-9400
Fax: (310) 633-9401

MRM Worldwide
622 3rd Ave
New York, NY 10017-6707
Tel.: (646) 865-6230
Fax: (646) 865-6264

SWEENEY
20325 Center Rdg Rd Ph Ste
Cleveland, OH 44116
Tel.: (440) 333-0001
Fax: (440) 333-0005

BALL CORPORATION

10 Longs Peak Dr
Broomfield, CO 80021-2510
Mailing Address:
PO Box 5000
Broomfield, CO 80038-5000
Tel.: (303) 469-3131
Fax: (303) 460-2127
E-mail: corpinfo@ball.com
Web Site: www.ball.com
E-Mail For Key Personnel:
Public Relations: smccarty@ball.com
Approx. Sls.: $7,630,000,000
Approx. Number Employees: 14,000
Year Founded: 1880
Business Description:
Holding Company; Metal & Plastic Packaging Products Mfr ; Aerospace Products Mfr
S.I.C.: 6719; 3089; 3411; 3679; 3769; 3812
N.A.I.C.S.: 551112; 326199; 332431; 334419; 334511; 336419
Import Export
Media: 2-4-7-10-21
Distr.: Intl.
Personnel:
R. David Hoover *(Chm)*
John A. Hayes *(Pres & CEO)*
Scott C. Morrison *(CFO & Sr VP)*
Raymond J. Seabrook *(COO/Exec VP-Global Pkg Ops)*
Michael W. Feldser *(Pres-Div)*
Jennifer Hoover *(Pres-Div)*
Michael L. Hranicka *(Pres-Metal Beverage Pkg Div-Americas)*
David A. Westerlund *(Exec VP-Admin)*
Lisa A. Pauley *(Sr VP-HR & Admin)*
Harold L. Sohn *(Sr VP)*
James N. Peterson *(VP-Mktg & Corp Affairs)*
Leroy J. Williams *(VP-IT & Svc)*
Scott McCarty *(Dir-Corp Comm)*
Ann Scott *(Dir-IR)*
Brands & Products:
AIRLINK
BALL
SLEEK CANS

BARTON NELSON INC.

13700 Wyandotte St
Kansas City, MO 64145-1532
Tel.: (816) 942-3100
Fax: (816) 942-6995
Toll Free: (800) 821-6697
E-mail: info@bebco.com
Web Site: www.bebco.com
Approx. Number Employees: 200
Year Founded: 1962
Business Description:
Mfr. of Promotional Products
S.I.C.: 2678
N.A.I.C.S.: 322233
Export
Media: 2-4-20
Distr.: Intl.
Personnel:
Dwight Nelson *(Pres, CEO & COO)*
Chuck Nelson *(Pres-Sls Promo Div)*
Glen Riedesel *(VP-Sls)*
Jill Woltering *(Dir-HR)*
Brands & Products:
BEBCO

BEDFORD INDUSTRIES, INC.

1659 Rowe Ave
Worthington, MN 56187
Mailing Address:
PO Box 39
Worthington, MN 56187-0039
Tel.: (507) 376-4136
Fax: (507) 376-6742
Toll Free: (877) BEDFORD
E-mail: bedford@bedfordind.com
Web Site: www.bedfordind.com
Sales Range: $200-249.9 Million
Approx. Number Employees: 190
Year Founded: 1966
Business Description:
Mfr. of Twist-Ties & Tie Closure Machinery; Identification Ties & Tags
S.I.C.: 3089; 2297
N.A.I.C.S.: 326199; 313230
Import Export
Media: 2-10-11-19-21
Distr.: Intl.
Budget Set: Oct. -Dec.
Personnel:
Norma J. Cook *(Mgr-Mktg & Admin)*
Brands & Products:
BAG-TAG
BEDFORD INDUSTRIES
CINCH BAND
ELASTI TAG
ELASTITAG
MINI BEDFORD TIE-R
PEEL & STICK APPLY-R
PEEL & STICK
PEEL AND STICK
POLY-STRAP
POLY-TWIST
SNAP-A-TAG
SUPER BEDFORD TIE-R

BEMIS COMPANY, INC.

1 Neenah Ctr 4th Fl
Neenah, WI 54957
Mailing Address:
PO Box 669
Neenah, WI 54957
Tel.: (920) 727-4100
Fax: (920) 527-7600
E-mail: contactbemis@bemis.com
Web Site: www.bemis.com
Approx. Sls.: $4,835,042,000
Approx. Number Employees: 19,796
Year Founded: 1858
Business Description:
Flexible Packaging & Pressure Sensitive Products Mfr & Retailer
S.I.C.: 2675; 2671; 3081
N.A.I.C.S.: 322226; 322221; 326112; 326113
Import Export
Media: 2
Distr.: Intl.; Natl.
Personnel:
Jeffrey H. Curler *(Chm)*
Henry J. Theisen *(Pres & CEO)*
Scott Ullem *(CFO)*
Sheri H. Edison *(Gen Counsel, VP & Sec)*
Gene C. Wulf *(Exec VP)*
Gene H. Seashore *(Sr VP & VP-HR-Bemis Co Inc)*
Timothy S. Fliss *(VP-HR)*
Stanley A. Jaffy *(VP-Fin)*
Brands & Products:
BEMIS
BEMISTAPE
CLYSAR
MACTAC
SLIDERITE
Advertising Agencies:
Directions Marketing
600 S Commercial St
Neenah, WI 54956
Tel.: (920) 725-4848
Fax: (920) 725-9359
Toll Free: (800) 236-2189

DuFour Advertising
532 S 8th St
Sheboygan, WI 53081
Tel.: (920) 457-9191
Fax: (920) 457-1854
Toll Free: (800) 236-3848

BERRY PLASTICS LANCASTER

(Joint Venture of Apollo Advisors, L.P. & The Graham Group, Inc.)
1706 Hempstead Rd
Lancaster, PA 17601-6706
Tel.: (717) 299-6511
Fax: (717) 299-5844
Toll Free: (800) 367-1876
Sales Range: $25-49.9 Million
Approx. Number Employees: 50
Year Founded: 1903
Business Description:
Plastic Closure Mfr
S.I.C.: 3089
N.A.I.C.S.: 326199
Export
Advertising Expenditures: $200,000
Media: 2-7-10-21
Distr.: Natl.
Budget Set: Sept. -Oct.
Personnel:
John Rich *(CEO)*
Brands & Products:
KERR
PERFECTPAK
SURE-FIT
TAB II
Advertising Agency:
Schreiber & Roman, Inc.
106 N Market St
Elizabethtown, PA 17022
Tel.: (717) 361-6300
Fax: (717) 361-6349

B.H. BUNN COMPANY

2730 Drane Field Rd
Lakeland, FL 33811-1325
Tel.: (863) 647-1555
Fax: (863) 686-2866
Toll Free: (800) 222-BUNN
E-mail: sales@bunntyco.com
Web Site: www.bunntyco.com
E-Mail For Key Personnel:
Sales Director: sales@bunntyco.com
Approx. Number Employees: 15
Year Founded: 1907
Business Description:
Package Tying Machines, Strapping Equipment, Polypropylene Strapping, Strapping Hand Tools, Tying Twines & Poly Tape Mfr
S.I.C.: 3565
N.A.I.C.S.: 333993
Import Export
Media: 2-4-6-7-10-26
Distr.: Intl.; Natl.
Budget Set: Nov.
Personnel:
John R. Bunn *(Pres)*
Brands & Products:
BUNN

BLITZ USA, INC.

404 26th Ave NW
Miami, OK 74354-2206
Tel.: (918) 540-1515
Fax: (918) 542-1380
Toll Free: (800) 331-3795
E-mail: consumerservice@blitzusa.com
Web Site: www.blitzusa.com
Approx. Number Employees: 250
Year Founded: 1960
Business Description:
Fuel Containers & Pet Accessories Mfr
S.I.C.: 3085; 3999
N.A.I.C.S.: 326160; 339999
Media: 2-10-19
Distr.: Intl.; Natl.
Budget Set: Sept.
Personnel:
Rocky Flick *(Pres)*
Brands & Products:
A GENUINE BUILT PRODUCT
BLITZ
CRUDE CONTROL

Key to Media (For complete agency information see *The Advertising Red Books-Agencies* edition):
1. Bus. Publs. 2. Cable T.V. 3. Catalogs & Directories. 4. Co-op Adv. 5. Consumer Mags. 6. D.M. to Bus. Estab.7. D.M. to Consumers
8. Daily Newsp. 9. Exhibits/Trade Shows 10. Foreign 11. Infomercial 12. Internet Adv.13. Multimedia 14. Network Radio
15. Network T.V. 16. Newsp. Distr. Mags. 17. Other 18. Outdoor (Posters, Transit) 19. Point of Purchase20. Premiums, Novelties
21. Product Samples 22. Special Events Mktg. 23. Spot Radio 24. Spot T.V. 25. Weekly Newsp. 26. Yellow Page Adv.

Blitz USA, Inc. — (Continued)

DISPOS-KIT
ENVIRO-FLEX
ENVIRO-FLO
ENVIRO-FLO PLUS GAS CAN
EZ LIFT RIDER RAMP
FOOD-N-WATA
FUEL STATION
ICE BREAKER
ICE BUSTER
ICE GRIPPER
LOT-A-WATA
MESS BUSTER
RHINORAMP
ROLL CONTROL
SAFE-CYCLE
SPRAYGEE
SURE POUR
TIRE HUGGER
TRAILER SAFE
TRAVEL DINE

BOISE CASCADE
(Branch of Boise Building Materials Distribution)
32 Manning Rd
Billerica, MA 01862
Mailing Address:
PO Box 130
Nutting Lake, MA 01865-0130
Tel.: (978) 670-3800
Fax: (978) 670-3989
Toll Free: (800) 843-9663
E-mail: marketing@bc.com
Approx. Number Employees: 75
Year Founded: 1957
Business Description:
Lumber Distr
S.I.C.: 5031; 5033
N.A.I.C.S.: 423310; 423330
Media: 7-10-19-20-21
Distr.: Natl.
Budget Set: Feb.
Personnel:
Stan Bell *(Pres)*
Tina Fourier *(Mgr-Accts)*
Richard Viola *(Mgr-Sls)*

BOISE CASCADE HOLDINGS, L.L.C.
1111 W Jefferson St
Boise, ID 83702
Mailing Address:
PO Box 50
Boise, ID 83728-0050
Tel.: (208) 384-6161
Fax: (208) 384-7189
E-mail: bcweb@bc.com
Web Site: www.bc.com
Approx. Sls.: $2,240,591,000
Approx. Number Employees: 4,160
Year Founded: 1957
Business Description:
Holding Company; Plywood & Building Products Distr & Mfr
S.I.C.: 2421; 5031; 6719
N.A.I.C.S.: 321113; 423310; 551112
Export
Advertising Expenditures: $1,700,000
Media: 2-6-7-8-10-21-24
Distr.: Reg.
Personnel:
Duane Charles McDougall *(Chm)*
Thomas E. Carlile *(CEO)*
Wayne M. Rancourt *(CFO, Treas & Sr VP)*
John Sahlberg *(Corp Counsel, Sec & VP-HR)*
Dave Gadda *(VP-Legal)*
Brands & Products:
ADHESIVE MOCK-UP PAPER
AJS
ALLJOIST
ARRIVL
ASPEN
B-LINE
BC CALC
BC FRAMER
BC RIM BOARD
BC TRACKER
BCI
BCI JOIST
BCPAPER
BEWARE
BOISE
BOISE ALLBEAM
BOISE CLASSIC
BOISE GLULAM
BOISE GOLD
BOISE. IT COULDN'T BE EASIER
BOISE SELECT
BUILD-RITE
BUILDING PEACE OF MIND
BUILDING PROTECTION
CASCADE BOOK
CASCADE CREST
C.E.O
CHECKPROTECT
CUSTOMER INSIGHT REPORT
DAKOTA BOOK
DAKOTA DIGITAL BOOK
DATAGRIP
FLEXOCHOISE
FLEXOFOLD
FLEXOGLOSS
FLEXONEWS
GRIPSHIELD
HIGHMARK
HOMEPLATE
INTEGRIFORM
ISAP
JACK RABBIT
JOIST REWARDS & DESIGN
KAP
KNOCKOUT
LITE KOTE
MONTANA BOOK
MP BRITES
MP COLORS
MP COVER
MP GRANITES
OH!PAQUE
PENTAGON
PRO-88
PRO-92
RATTANWEAVE
RIM PLUS
SIMPLE FRAMING SYSTEM
SPLOX
STARLIGHTS
SUMMIT
SUPER SHELF
SUPER STEP
SWIFT RIVER
TAG-X
TIMBERLINE BOND
TONERGRIP
TRU-FORM
TRU-PLY
VALUESAFETY
VERITHERM
VERSA-DECK
VERSA-LAM
VERSA-LAM PLUS
VERSA-RIM
VERSA-RIM 98
VERSA-RIM PLUS
VERSA-STRAND
VERSA-STUD
VOYAGEUR ELITE
WORK. BUILD. CREATE.
WYOMING BOOK
XEROPAQUE
XMP

BONTEX, INC.
1 Bontex Dr
Buena Vista, VA 24416
Tel.: (540) 261-2181
Fax: (540) 261-3784
Toll Free: (800) 733-4234
E-mail: bontex@bontex.com
Web Site: www.bontex.com
Sales Range: $1-9.9 Million
Approx. Number Employees: 90
Year Founded: 1946
Business Description:
Specialty Papers & Vinyl Coated Fabrics Mfr for Luggage, Footwear, Gaskets & Automotive Applications
S.I.C.: 2824; 2631
N.A.I.C.S.: 325222; 322130
Import Export
Advertising Expenditures: $250,000
Media: 6-10-11-13-18-22-26
Distr.: Intl.; Natl.
Budget Set: Jan. -July
Personnel:
Larry E. Morris *(Gen Mgr)*
Victor Lan *(Dir-HR)*
Brands & Products:
BON-FOAM 400
BON-PEL
BON-STITCH
BONPEL
BONTEX
BONTEX 101
BONTEX 350
BONTEX 36
BONTEX 48
BONTEX-CONTOUR
BONTEX RECYCLED
CONTOUR
KORKTEX
MAXXON
MORI-FRESH
SIR-PEL
SUPERTEX
SUR-V-LON
Advertising Agency:
Hastings Design Co
PO Box 8813
Roanoke, VA 24014
Tel.: (540) 808-2233

BPM INC.
200 W Front St
Peshtigo, WI 54157
Tel.: (715) 582-4551
Fax: (715) 582-4853
E-mail: bpm@bpmpaper.com
Web Site: www.bpmpaper.com
Approx. Sls.: $27,000,000
Approx. Number Employees: 246
Year Founded: 1929
Business Description:
Specialty Papers & Flexible Packaging Products Mfr
S.I.C.: 2621; 2679; 3497
N.A.I.C.S.: 322121; 322225; 322299
Import Export
Media: 2-4-7-8-10-21
Distr.: Natl.
Personnel:
James S. Koronkiewicz *(Gen Mgr)*
Brands & Products:
ARTOPAQUE
BADGER PAPER
BADGER PAPER MILLS
COPYRITE
ENVIROGRAPHIC
FRESHRAP
NORTHERN BRIGHTS
SHARPRINT
TA-NON-KA

THE BRADEN SUTPHIN INK COMPANY
3650 E 93rd St
Cleveland, OH 44105-1620
Tel.: (216) 271-2300
Fax: (216) 271-0515
Web Site: www.bsink.com
Approx. Sls.: $38,700,000
Approx. Number Employees: 265
Year Founded: 1913
Business Description:
Printing Ink Products
S.I.C.: 2893; 2899
N.A.I.C.S.: 325910; 325998
Import Export
Personnel:
Cal Sutphin *(Pres)*
Jim Leitch *(CEO)*
Bob Nowak *(Gen Mgr-Flexo Mfg & Ops)*
Raymond Loomis *(Mgr-Sls-Natl)*
Luz Oyola-Webb *(Mgr-Mktg)*
Advertising Agency:
SWEENEY
20325 Center Rdg Rd Ph Ste
Cleveland, OH 44116
Tel.: (440) 333-0001
Fax: (440) 333-0005

BROWN PAPER GOODS COMPANY
3530 Birchwood Dr
Waukegan, IL 60085-8334
Tel.: (847) 688-1450
Fax: (847) 688-1458
Toll Free: (800) 323-9099
E-mail: sales@brownpapergoods.com
Web Site: www.brownpapergoods.com
E-Mail For Key Personnel:
Sales Director: sales@brownpapergoods.com
Approx. Number Employees: 125
Year Founded: 1918
Business Description:
Mfr. of Paper & Foil Bags
S.I.C.: 2674
N.A.I.C.S.: 322224
Advertising Expenditures: $200,000
Media: 2-10
Distr.: Natl.
Personnel:
Allen Mons *(Pres)*
Will Jefferson *(VP-Fin)*
P. Luthy *(VP-Sls)*
Brands & Products:
HAN-D-PAK

BUCKEYE CORRUGATED INC.
275 Springside Dr Ste 200
Akron, OH 44333-4551

Key to Media (For complete agency information see *The Advertising Red Books-Agencies* edition):
1. Bus. Publs. 2. Cable T.V. 3. Catalogs & Directories. 4. Co-op Adv. 5. Consumer Mags. 6. D.M. to Bus. Estab.7. D.M. to Consumers
8. Daily Newsp. 9. Exhibits/Trade Shows 10. Foreign 11. Infomercial 12. Internet Adv.13. Multimedia 14. Network Radio
15. Network T.V. 16. Newsp. Distr. Mags. 17. Other 18. Outdoor (Posters, Transit) 19. Point of Purchase20. Premiums, Novelties
21. Product Samples 22. Special Events Mktg. 23. Spot Radio 24. Spot T.V. 25. Weekly Newsp. 26. Yellow Page Adv.

Tel.: (330) 576-0590
Fax: (330) 576-0600
Web Site: www.buckeyecorrugated.com
Approx. Number Employees: 450
Year Founded: 1958
Business Description:
Packaging Material, Corrugated Boxes, Inner Packaging, Foam Packaging, In-Store Displays & High Quality Graphics Mfr
S.I.C.: 2653; 2671; 3053; 3499
N.A.I.C.S.: 322211; 322221; 332439; 339991
Media: 10
Personnel:
Douglas A. Bosnik *(Pres)*
Mark A. Husted *(CFO & Exec VP)*
Brands & Products:
ALL-SIZE
BUCKEYE
CONCORD
CRA-WAL
KOCH
TENNESSEE

BWAY HOLDING COMPANY
(Holding of Madison Dearborn Partners, LLC)
8607 Roberts Dr Ste 250
Atlanta, GA 30350-2230
Tel.: (770) 645-4800
Fax: (770) 645-4810
E-mail: sales@bwaycorp.com
Web Site: www.bwaycorp.com
E-Mail For Key Personnel:
Sales Director: sales@bwaycorp.com
Approx. Sls.: $904,400,000
Approx. Number Employees: 2,700
Year Founded: 1905
Business Description:
Holding Company; Metal & Plastic Container Mfr
S.I.C.: 3411; 3085; 3499; 6719
N.A.I.C.S.: 332431; 326160; 332439; 551112
Advertising Expenditures: $200,000
Media: 2
Personnel:
Michael B. Clauer *(CFO & Exec VP)*
Kevin C. Kern *(Chief Admin Officer & Sr VP)*
Dennis A. Bednar *(Exec VP-Ops)*
Joe Frabotta *(Dir-HR)*
Dennis Strobel *(Dir-IT)*

CALUMET CARTON COMPANY
16920 State St
South Holland, IL 60473-2841
Tel.: (708) 333-6521
Fax: (708) 333-8540
Toll Free: (888) 333-8540
E-mail: sales@calumetcarton.com
Web Site: www.calumetcarton.com
E-Mail For Key Personnel:
Sales Director: sales@calumetcarton.com
Approx. Number Employees: 100
Year Founded: 1930
Business Description:
Mfr. of Envelopes & Folding Cartons
S.I.C.: 2653; 2677
N.A.I.C.S.: 322211; 322232
Media: 2-4-7-8-10-17-21
Distr.: Direct to Consumer; Natl.
Budget Set: Jan.

Personnel:
John Inwood *(Pres)*
Albert Inwood *(CEO)*
Brands & Products:
CONFIRMAILER
EXPAND-A-MAILER
MICRO-CORR
MICROCORR
POSTAGE SAVER
STAYFLATS
STAYFLATS PLUS

CAMPBELL WRAPPER CORPORATION
1415 Fortune Ave
De Pere, WI 54115
Tel.: (920) 983-7100
Fax: (920) 983-7300
E-mail: info@campbellwrapper.com
Web Site: www.campbellwrapper.com
E-Mail For Key Personnel:
President: dykemaj@campbellwrapper.com
Marketing Director: stelzerd@campbellwrapper.com
Sales Range: $10-24.9 Million
Approx. Number Employees: 100
Business Description:
Design, Manufacturing, Sales & Servicing of Packaging System Lines
S.I.C.: 3565
N.A.I.C.S.: 333993
Export
Media: 10
Personnel:
John Dykema *(Pres)*
Todd Goodwin *(VP-Fin & Admin)*
Don Stelzer *(VP-Sls & Mktg)*
Steve Joosten *(Product Mgr)*
Gus Skapek *(Sls Mgr-Intl & Reg)*
Gary LeTourneau *(Engr)*
Rick Bramer *(Mgr-Svc)*
Jeff Ginzl *(Mgr-Engrg)*
Jeff Jende *(Mgr-Matls & Wrapper Assembly)*
Larry Leino *(Mgr-Customer Support Engrg)*
Chuck Matuszak *(Mgr-Sls-Reg)*
Jerry Tennison *(Mgr-Reg Sls)*
Brands & Products:
CAMPBELL WRAPPER
DUAL LANE
HERITAGE
LEGACY
PATRIOT
PIONEER
REVOLUTION
SANITARY SHRINK

CANFOR CORPORATION
1700 West 75th Avenue Suite 100
Vancouver, BC V6P 6G2, Canada
Tel.: (604) 661-5241
Fax: (604) 661-5226
E-mail: info@canfor.ca
Web Site: www.canfor.com
Approx. Rev.: $2,476,140,128
Approx. Number Employees: 7,300
Year Founded: 1938
Business Description:
Holding Company; Forest Products; Pulp, Paper, Lumber & Hardboard
S.I.C.: 6719; 2421; 2611; 2621; 2631
N.A.I.C.S.: 551112; 321113; 322110; 322121; 322130
Export
Media: 9-18-25

Personnel:
Ronald L. Cliff *(Chm)*
James F. Shepard *(Pres & CEO)*
Thomas Sitar *(CFO & VP-Fin)*
David M. Calabrigo *(Gen Counsel, Sec & VP-Corp Dev)*
Donald B. Kayne *(VP-Sls & Mktg-Wood Products)*
Joe Nemeth *(VP-Pulp & Paper Sls & Mktg)*
Rob Stewart *(VP-HR)*
Brands & Products:
CANFOR
ECOBRITE
KODIAK KRAFT
PANLGARD
POLAR KRAFT
SILVASTAR
WOODMAT
Advertising Agency:
Grey Vancouver
1600 - 1500 W Georgia St
Vancouver, BC V6G 2Z6, Canada
Tel.: (604) 687-1001
Fax: (604) 682-1827
Toll Free: (877) 250-2275

CARAUSTAR INDUSTRIES, INC.
5000 Austell-Powder Springs Rd Ste 300
Austell, GA 30106-3227
Mailing Address:
PO Box 115
Austell, GA 30168-0115
Tel.: (770) 948-3101
Fax: (770) 732-3401
Toll Free: (800) 223-1373
E-mail: info@caraustar.com
Web Site: www.caraustar.com
Approx. Sls.: $819,658,000
Approx. Number Employees: 3,200
Year Founded: 1938
Business Description:
Paper Products Recycling & Paper Board Mfr
S.I.C.: 2631; 2679
N.A.I.C.S.: 322130; 322299
Media: 1-2-4-6-10-20-21
Personnel:
Michael J. Keough *(Pres & CEO)*
Michael C. Patton *(CEO)*
William A. Nix III *(Chief Acctg Officer & VP-Fin)*
Wilma E. Beaty *(Chier HR Officer, General Counsel & Sec & VP)*
John Randall Foster *(VP-Sls & Mktg)*
Barry Alton Smedstad *(VP-HR & Pub Rel)*
Brands & Products:
BINDER TEX 45
CARAUSTAR
ECONOPOUR
KLIMATEPRO
KOLUMN FORM
KONVA-KORE
KRAFTEX
PROTECT-A-BOARD
PROTECT-A-COIL
PROTECT-A-FLEX
PROTECT-A-WRAP
SAFEFACE MR
STASQUARE 32

CARLISLE FOODSERVICE PRODUCTS INCORPORATED
(Sub. of Carlisle Applied Technologies Group)
4711 E Hefner Rd
Oklahoma City, OK 73131
Mailing Address:
PO Box 53006
Oklahoma City, OK 73152-3006
Tel.: (405) 475-5600
Fax: (800) 872-4701
Toll Free: (800) 654-8210
E-mail: customerservice@carlislefsp.com
Web Site: www.carlislefsp.com
E-Mail For Key Personnel:
President: davidhannone@carlislefsp.com
Sales Director: StuartSharp@carlislefsp.com
Sales Range: $100-124.9 Million
Approx. Number Employees: 500
Year Founded: 1955
Business Description:
Mfr. of Injection Molding, Food Service Equipment & Supply Items, Packaging Containers
S.I.C.: 3089; 3262
N.A.I.C.S.: 326199; 327112
Import Export
Advertising Expenditures: $2,000,000
Media: 1-2-4-5-7-8-10-11-12-13-19-20-21-22-26
Distr.: Intl.; Natl.
Budget Set: Sept. -Oct.
Personnel:
David M. Shannon *(Pres)*
Carolyn Ford *(CFO)*
Stuart Sharp *(VP-Sls)*
Brian Hutton *(Dir-Bus Dev)*
Brands & Products:
ANCHOR FLOOR SWEEPS
ARIA
BISTRO
BRAVO
CAFE
CARLISLE VERSAPOUR
CARLY
CATERAIDES
CHICAGO
COLDMASTER
CONTEMPORARY
CORINTHIAN
CRESCENDO
CRYSTALITE
CRYSTALON
DALLAS
DELIWARE
DURA-KOOL
DURATHERM
DURUS
ELAN
ELITE
ENCORE
ENVOY
FESTIVAL TRAYS
FIRESTAR
FLEX-ALL
FOLD 'N GO
THE GOTHAM COLLECTION
GRAINWARE
GRAND
GRIPTITE
ICE SCULPTURES
KINGLINE
LAFAYETTE
LEXINGTON

Key to Media (For complete agency information see *The Advertising Red Books-Agencies* edition):
1. Bus. Publs. 2. Cable T.V. 3. Catalogs & Directories. 4. Co-op Adv. 5. Consumer Mags. 6. D.M. to Bus. Estab.7. D.M. to Consumers 8. Daily Newsp. 9. Exhibits/Trade Shows 10. Foreign 11. Infomercial 12. Internet Adv.13. Multimedia 14. Network Radio 15. Network T.V. 16. Newsp. Distr. Mags. 17. Other 18. Outdoor (Posters, Transit) 19. Point of Purchase20. Premiums, Novelties 21. Product Samples 22. Special Events Mktg. 23. Spot Radio 24. Spot T.V. 25. Weekly Newsp. 26. Yellow Page Adv.

Carlisle FoodService Products Incorporated — (Continued)

LIONS HEAD
THE LIONS HEAD COLLECTION
MAESTRO
MAJESTIC
MANHATTAN
MAXIMIZER
MEASURE MISER
MIRACRYL
MONEY MAID
MOSAIC
MUNCHIE BASKETS
NAPKIN DELI
OMNI SWEEP
OPTIMIZER
PEBBLE OPTIC
PETAL MIST
POLLYPELLET
PORTION POUR
POUR FREE
POURA-CLEAN
QUEEN ANNE
RHAPSODY
SIX STAR
SKY RANCH
SMART LIDS
SPARTA
SPECTRUM
SQUIRE
SSAL2000
STACKABLE
STERI-PAIL
STORPLUS
SUPREME
THERMOINSULATOR
TOP NOTCH
TRIMLINE
TULIP DELI
UNIVERSAL
UNIVERSAL LID HOLDER
WEAVEWARE

CASE PAPER COMPANY INC.

500 Mamaroneck Ave 2nd Fl
Harrison, NY 10528-1633
Tel.: (914) 899-3500
Fax: (914) 777-1028
Toll Free: (800) 222-2922
E-mail: sales@casepaper.com
Web Site: www.casepaper.com
E-Mail For Key Personnel:
Sales Director: sales@casepaper.com
Approx. Number Employees: 325
Year Founded: 1943
Business Description:
Coated & Uncoated Paper & Paperboard Distr
S.I.C.: 5111; 5113
N.A.I.C.S.: 424110; 424130
Media: 1-2-4-10
Distr.: Natl.
Personnel:
Robin Schaffer *(Pres)*
Peter Schaffer *(CEO)*
Alan Hochstadt *(CFO)*
Charles Argianas *(Exec VP & Gen Mgr)*
Aaron Green *(VP & Gen Mgr)*
Louis Bernstein *(VP & Mgr-Sls)*
Todd Chesnut *(VP-Sls)*
Keith Goldberg *(VP-Mktg)*
Samantha Kossman *(Gen Mgr)*
Glen Braziel *(Gen Mgr)*
George Thornton *(Gen Mgr)*
Ken Weaver *(Sr Acct Mgr & Mgr-Mktg)*

CBS OUTDOOR INC.

(Sub. of CBS Corporation)
405 Lexington Ave
New York, NY 10174
Tel.: (212) 297-6400
Fax: (212) 370-1817
Web Site: www.cbsoutdoor.com
Approx. Number Employees: 1,600
Business Description:
Transit, Poster, Special Display & Bus Shelter Display Advertising Services
S.I.C.: 7319
N.A.I.C.S.: 541850
Media: 2-6-7-9-18
Distr.: Reg.
Budget Set: June
Personnel:
Wally C. Kelly *(Chm & CEO-North America)*
Mike Moran *(Mng Dir)*
Raymond Nowak *(CFO, Chief Acctg Officer & Exec VP)*
Dana Wells *(Pres-Billboard Div)*
Jodi Senese *(Exec VP-Mktg)*
Phil Stimpson *(Exec VP-Displays)*
Richard Ament *(Sr VP-Bus Dev)*
Colin Leahy *(Mng Dir-Ireland, Gen Mgr-Sls & Mktg)*
Christian Eidt *(VP-Info Sys & Tech)*
Lisa Rokny *(Head-Creative & Dev)*
Mark Chippendale *(Dir-Comml-UK)*
Christy Johnston *(Mgr-Strategy)*

CFC INTERNATIONAL, INC.

(Sub. of Illinois Tool Works Inc.)
500 State St
Chicago Heights, IL 60411-1206
Tel.: (708) 891-3456
Fax: (708) 758-5989
E-mail: cfcinfo@cfcintl.com
Web Site: www.cfcintl.com
Sales Range: $75-99.9 Million
Approx. Number Employees: 150
Year Founded: 1986
Business Description:
Specialty Coated Film Designer, Mfr & Marketer
S.I.C.: 2851; 3479; 3861
N.A.I.C.S.: 325510; 332812; 333315
Import Export
Advertising Expenditures: $196,000
Media: 10
Personnel:
William Herring *(Dir-Tech)*
Matthew Shields *(Mgr-Bus Unit)*
Brands & Products:
ACCUMAG STRIPE
CFC INTERNATIONAL
FLEXRITE
FLEXWRAP
HOLOLAM PLUS
INFRAPRINT

CHEM-TAINER INDUSTRIES, INC.

361 Neptune Ave
West Babylon, NY 11704-5818
Tel.: (631) 661-8300
Fax: (631) 661-8209
Toll Free: (800) 275-2436
E-mail: sales@chemtainer.com
Web Site: www.chemtainer.com
E-Mail For Key Personnel:
Sales Director: sales@chemtainer.com
Approx. Number Employees: 275
Year Founded: 1958
Business Description:
Rotationally Molded Plastic Containers Mfr
S.I.C.: 3089
N.A.I.C.S.: 326199
Export
Media: 2-4-10
Personnel:
Stuart Pivar *(Chm)*
James Glen *(Pres)*
Joe Destefano *(CFO)*
Brands & Products:
CHEM-TAINER
MAXI-MOVERS
OIL TAINER

CLARCOR, INC.

840 Crescent Ctr Dr Ste 600
Franklin, TN 37067
Tel.: (615) 771-3100
Fax: (615) 771-5603
E-mail: information@clarcor.com
Web Site: www.clarcor.com
Approx. Sls.: $1,011,429,000
Approx. Number Employees: 5,136
Year Founded: 1904
Business Description:
Air & Antimicrobial Filters for Commercial, Industrial, & Residential Buildings
S.I.C.: 3564; 2656; 3714
N.A.I.C.S.: 333411; 322215; 336399
Export
Media: 2-6
Distr.: Natl.
Budget Set: Oct.
Personnel:
Norman E. Johnson *(Chm & CEO)*
Christopher L. Conway *(Pres & COO)*
David J. Fallon *(CFO & VP-Fin)*
David J. Lindsay *(Chief Admin Officer & VP-Admin)*
Richard M. Wolfson *(Gen Counsel, Sec & VP)*

COLUMBIAN ROPE COMPANY

(Sub. of Unicord Corporation)
479 Export Cir
Newport News, VA 23601-3750
Mailing Address:
PO Box 270
Guntown, MS 38849-0270
Tel.: (757) 595-0364
Fax: (757) 595-3993
Toll Free: (800) 692-0151
E-mail: mail@plymkraft.com
Web Site: www.columbianrope.com
Approx. Number Employees: 250
Year Founded: 1903
Business Description:
Mfr & Distr of Rope, Twine & Industrial Fiber Products
S.I.C.: 2298; 2282
N.A.I.C.S.: 314991; 313112
Import Export
Media: 2-5-7-10-11-19-21
Distr.: Intl.
Budget Set: Nov.

COMAR INC.

1 Comar Pl
Buena, NJ 08310-1523
Tel.: (856) 692-6100
Fax: (856) 692-9251
E-mail: info@comar.com
Web Site: www.comar.com
Sales Range: $50-74.9 Million
Approx. Number Employees: 800
Year Founded: 1949
Business Description:
Mfr. of Custom Tubular Glass Vials, Media Tubes, Precision-Made Plastic Molded Containers & Components, Dropper Assemblies, Closures, Fitments, & Caluminum Seals for the Pharmaceutical, Medical Device, Diagnostic & Personal Care Markets
S.I.C.: 3089; 3231
N.A.I.C.S.: 326199; 327215
Import Export
Media: 2-4-10
Brands & Products:
ACCUCUP
COMAR
COMAR ORAL DISPENSER
NEUTRAPLEX
NO-CHOKE TIP CAP

COMPLEMAR PARTNERS

500 Lee Rd
Rochester, NY 14606
Tel.: (585) 647-5800
Fax: (585) 647-5803
Web Site: www.complemar.com
Approx. Sls.: $14,400,000
Approx. Number Employees: 60
Business Description:
Packaging & Labeling Services
S.I.C.: 5999; 7349
N.A.I.C.S.: 453998; 561790
Media: 7
Personnel:
Christine B. Whitman *(Chm, Pres & CEO)*
Lisa O'Brian *(VP-Mktg & Bus Dev)*
Brands & Products:
COMPLEMAR
WHERE TO GO FOR PACKAGING AND FULFILLMENT

C.R. DANIELS, INC.

3451 Ellicott Ctr Dr
Ellicott City, MD 21043
Tel.: (410) 461-2100
Fax: (410) 461-2987
E-mail: info@crdaniels.com
Web Site: www.crdaniels.com
Approx. Number Employees: 450
Year Founded: 1918
Business Description:
Truck Baskets & Hampers
S.I.C.: 2394; 3089
N.A.I.C.S.: 314912; 326199
Import Export
Media: 1-2-4-7-10-13-21
Distr.: Direct to Consumer; Natl.
Budget Set: Dec.
Personnel:
Gary V. Abel *(Pres)*
John E. Frangos *(Sr VP)*
Andy Szulinski *(VP-Sls & Mktg)*
Lee Smith *(Mgr-Adv)*
Brands & Products:
C.R.DANIELS
DANDUX
DRAKE WATERFOWL
LOADUMPER
WILD DUCK

CRANE & CO., INC.

30 South St
Dalton, MA 01226-1751

Key to Media (For complete agency information see *The Advertising Red Books-Agencies* edition):
1. Bus. Publs. 2. Cable T.V. 3. Catalogs & Directories. 4. Co-op Adv. 5. Consumer Mags. 6. D.M. to Bus. Estab.7. D.M. to Consumers 8. Daily Newsp. 9. Exhibits/Trade Shows 10. Foreign 11. Infomercial 12. Internet Adv.13. Multimedia 14. Network Radio 15. Network T.V. 16. Newsp. Distr. Mags. 17. Other 18. Outdoor (Posters, Transit) 19. Point of Purchase20. Premiums, Novelties 21. Product Samples 22. Special Events Mktg. 23. Spot Radio 24. Spot T.V. 25. Weekly Newsp. 26. Yellow Page Adv.

Tel.: (413) 684-2600
Fax: (413) 684-1820
Toll Free: (800) 268-2281
E-mail: customerservice@crane.com
Web Site: www.crane.com
Sales Range: $350-399.9 Million
Approx. Number Employees: 1,350
Year Founded: 1801
Business Description:
Specialty Cotton & Nonwoven Paper & Stationery Products Mfr; Personal & Commercial Print Services
S.I.C.: 2621; 2297; 2678; 2759
N.A.I.C.S.: 322121; 313230; 322233; 323119
Media: 4-6-7-8-10-13-16-19
Distr.: Natl.
Budget Set: Nov. -Dec.
Personnel:
Charles J. Kittredge, III *(Chm & CEO)*
Anil Jagtiani *(Pres)*
Megan Kuntze *(Dir-Mktg)*
Brands & Products:
CRANE & CO.
CRANEGLAS
CRANEMAT
CRANE'S BOND
CRANE'S CHOICE
CRANE'S CREST
CRANE'S PALETTE
LETTRA

CRESCENT CARDBOARD COMPANY, L.L.C.
(Sub. of Potomac Corporation)
100 W Willow Rd
Wheeling, IL 60090-6522
Tel.: (847) 537-3400
Fax: (847) 537-7153
Toll Free: (800) 323-1055
E-mail: custserv@crescentcardboard.com
Web Site: www.cresentcardboard.com
Approx. Sls.: $21,400,000
Approx. Number Employees: 200
Business Description:
Cardboard, Drafting & Drawing Boards, Mat Boards, Posterboard, Photograph & Showcard Mounts Mfr
S.I.C.: 2679
N.A.I.C.S.: 322299
Import Export
Media: 4-7-17-19
Distr.: Natl.
Personnel:
Kate McCarthy *(Pres)*

CROWN HOLDINGS, INC.
1 Crown Way
Philadelphia, PA 19154
Tel.: (215) 698-5100
Fax: (215) 676-7245
E-mail: ir@crowncork.com
Web Site: www.crowncork.com
Approx. Sls.: $7,941,000,000
Approx. Number Employees: 20,500
Business Description:
Holding Company; Consumer Packaging Products Mfr
S.I.C.: 3411; 6719
N.A.I.C.S.: 332431; 551112
Media: 2
Distr.: Intl.; Natl.
Personnel:
John W. Conway *(Chm, Pres & CEO)*
Timothy J. Donahue *(CFO & Exec VP)*
Christopher C. Homfray *(Pres-European Div)*
Raymond J. McGowan, Jr. *(Pres-America Div)*
William T. Gallagher *(Gen Counsel, Sec & Sr VP)*
Daniel A. Abramowicz *(Exec VP-Corp Tech & Regulatory Affairs)*
William H. Voss *(Exec VP)*
Thomas A. Kelly *(Sr VP-Fin)*
Michael F. Dunleavy *(VP-Affairs & PR)*
Michael J. Rowley *(Asst Sec & Asst Gen Counsel)*
Advertising Agency:
ABI Marketing Public Relations
29 Broadway Ste 1300
New York, NY 10006
Tel.: (212) 529-4500
Fax: (212) 529-4442

CROWN RISDON USA, INC.
(Sub. of Crown Holdings, Inc.)
1100 Buckingham St
Watertown, CT 06795
Tel.: (860) 417-1100
Tel.: (860) 417-1111
Fax: (860) 417-1101
Telex: 510-600-3694
E-mail: tcurrie@crowncork.com
Web Site: www.risdon.com
Sales Range: $150-199.9 Million
Approx. Number Employees: 800
Business Description:
Fragrance & Color Cosmetic Packaging Mfr
S.I.C.: 3089
N.A.I.C.S.: 326199
Import Export
Media: 2-10
Distr.: Intl.; Natl.
Budget Set: Oct.
Personnel:
Stephen T. Pearlman *(Pres)*
Faqueer Ahmad *(Exec VP-International)*
James Bigham *(Dir-Sls)*
Stephen J. Librandi *(Dir-HR)*
Brian Rayner *(Plant Mgr)*
Brands & Products:
COLORFIX
COLORSEAL
COLORTOUCH
DYMIST
MINI-MIST
MIXING MASCARA
STABRITE
TNT

CRYOVAC, INC.
(Sub. of Sealed Air Corporation)
100 Rogers Bridge Rd Bldg A
Duncan, SC 29334
Tel.: (864) 433-2000
Fax: (864) 433-2134
E-mail: info@sealedair.com
Web Site: www.sealedair.com
Sales Range: $250-299.9 Million
Approx. Number Employees: 930
Year Founded: 1940
Business Description:
Flexible Plastic Packaging Materials & Equipment Mfr & Sales
S.I.C.: 3086; 5085
N.A.I.C.S.: 326150; 423840
Media: 1-2-4-7-10-11-20
Distr.: Intl.; Natl.
Personnel:
Karl Deily *(Pres-Cryovac Food Packaging)*
Jeff Gardner *(VP-Mktg)*
Bill Armstrong *(Mgr-Tech Dev)*
Advertising Agencies:
Ames Scullin O'Haire
245 Peachtree Center Ave 23rd Fl
Atlanta, GA 30303
Tel.: (404) 659-2769
Fax: (404) 659-7664
Agency of Record

Fitzgerald+CO
3060 Peachtree Rd NW
Atlanta, GA 30305
Tel.: (404) 504-6900
Fax: (404) 239-0548

DIELECTRIC POLYMERS, INC.
(Sub. of Adhesive Applications, Inc.)
218 Race St
Holyoke, MA 01040
Mailing Address:
PO Box 110
Holyoke, MA 01041-0110
Tel.: (413) 532-3288
Fax: (413) 533-9316
Toll Free: (800) 628-9007
E-mail: info@dipoly.com
Web Site: www.dipoly.com
Year Founded: 1970
Business Description:
Adhesive Transfer Films & Pressure Sensitive Tapes Mfr
S.I.C.: 2891
N.A.I.C.S.: 325520
Export
Advertising Expenditures: $200,000
Media: 2-4-7-10-11-17-21
Distr.: Intl.; Natl.
Brands & Products:
NELTAPE

DOMTAR CORPORATION
395 de Maisonneuve Boulevard West
Montreal, QC H3A 1L6, Canada
Tel.: (514) 848-5400
Fax: (514) 848-6878
Toll Free: (800) 267-2040
Telex: 5560625
E-mail: ir@domtar.com
Web Site: www.domtar.com
Approx. Sls.: $5,850,000,000
Approx. Number Employees: 8,500
Year Founded: 1929
Business Description:
Pulp & Paper Products Mfr
S.I.C.: 2621; 2679
N.A.I.C.S.: 322121; 322299
Export
Advertising Expenditures: $20,000,000
Media: 2-4-6-21
Distr.: Natl.
Personnel:
Harold H. MacKay *(Chm)*
John D. Williams *(Pres & CEO)*
Daniel Buron *(CFO & Sr VP)*
Melissa Anderson *(Sr VP-HR)*
Steven A. Barker *(Sr VP-Mktg)*
Roger H. Brear *(Sr VP-Southern Reg Mills)*
Michel Dagenais *(Sr VP-HR)*
Ghislain Dinel *(Sr VP-Northern Region Mills)*
Michael Edwards *(Sr VP-Pulp & Paper Mfg Grp)*
Zygmunt Jablonski *(Sr VP-Law & Corp Affairs)*
James F. Lenhoff *(Sr VP-Distr)*
Patrick Loulou *(Sr VP-Corp Dev)*
Jean-Francois Merette *(Sr VP-Forest Products)*
Bart Nicholson *(Sr VP-Specialty Mills & Converting Ops)*
Gilles Pharand *(Sr VP-Law & Corp Affairs)*
Richard L. Thomas *(Sr VP-Sls & Mktg)*
Mark Ushpol *(Sr VP-Distr)*
Pascal Bosse *(VP-Comm & IR)*
Yves L. Parent *(VP-IT)*
John Mcateer *(Gen Mgr-Sls)*
Silvia Resera *(Gen Mgr-Sls)*
Bonny Skene *(Pub Affairs Mgr)*
Brands & Products:
CENTURY
COLORLOK
COUGAR
DIGITALCHOICE
DOMTAR
DOMTAR COLORS
DOMTAR CORNWALL
EARTHCHOICE
FIRST CHOICE
GUARDIAN
HOTS
HUSKY
IMAGEPRINT
IT ALL BEGINS WITH PAPER
LYNX
TITANIUM
TRADEBOOK
WHITEHALL

DOUGLAS MACHINE, INC.
3404 Iowa St
Alexandria, MN 56308-3345
Tel.: (320) 763-6587
Fax: (320) 763-5754
E-mail: info@douglas-machine.com
Web Site: www.douglas-machine.com
E-Mail For Key Personnel:
Sales Director: sales@douglas-machine.com
Approx. Number Employees: 550
Year Founded: 1964
Business Description:
Mfr. of Packaging Equipment
S.I.C.: 3565
N.A.I.C.S.: 333993
Export
Media: 10-11
Personnel:
Rick Paulsen *(Pres & COO)*
Vernon J. Anderson *(CEO)*
Tom Wosepka *(CFO)*
Steve Black *(VP & Gen Mgr)*
Jon Ballou *(Corp VP-Sls & Mktg)*
Brands & Products:
APEX
AXIOM
CONTOUR
DOUGLAS
MORE THAN A MACHINE
SPECTRUM

DUNMORE CORPORATION
145 Wharton Rd
Bristol, PA 19007-1621
Tel.: (215) 781-8895
Fax: (215) 781-9293
Toll Free: (800) 444-0242
Web Site: www.dunmore.com
Approx. Number Employees: 200
Year Founded: 1970

Key to Media (For complete agency information see *The Advertising Red Books-Agencies* edition):
1. Bus. Publs. 2. Cable T.V. 3. Catalogs & Directories. 4. Co-op Adv. 5. Consumer Mags. 6. D.M. to Bus. Estab.7. D.M. to Consumers
8. Daily Newsp. 9. Exhibits/Trade Shows 10. Foreign 11. Infomercial 12. Internet Adv.13. Multimedia 14. Network Radio
15. Network T.V. 16. Newsp. Distr. Mags. 17. Other 18. Outdoor (Posters, Transit) 19. Point of Purchase20. Premiums, Novelties
21. Product Samples 22. Special Events Mktg. 23. Spot Radio 24. Spot T.V. 25. Weekly Newsp. 26. Yellow Page Adv.

Dunmore Corporation — (Continued)

Business Description:
Coated, Laminated & Metallized Films Mfr
S.I.C.: 3081; 3083
N.A.I.C.S.: 326113; 326130
Import Export
Media: 2-4-7-10-13-17-21-26
Distr.: Natl.
Personnel:
Matthew Sullivan *(Pres & CEO)*
Mary Sullivan *(CFO)*
Daniel J. Sullivan *(Dir-Bus)*
Brands & Products:
DUN-AURA
DUN-BRITE
DUN-CHROME
DUN-DIGITAL
DUN-GUARD
DUN-KOTE
DUN-LAM
DUN-MET
DUN-NOVEL
DUN-ORO
DUN-PRINT
DUN-QUICK
DUN-SHIELD
DUN-SOLAR
DUN-STRIPE
DUN-TRAN
DUNMORE
MAKING FILMS FUNCTION AROUND THE GLOBE AND BEYOND
STARGLOSS

DUPONT LIQUID PACKAGING SYSTEMS

(Sub. of E.I. DuPont Canada Company)
6950 Worthington Galena Rd
Worthington, OH 43085
Tel.: (614) 888-9280
Fax: (614) 888-0982
Toll Free: (800) 260-4376
E-mail: liquibox@liquibox.com
Web Site: www.liquidpackaging.dupont.com/en/index.html
Sales Range: $150-199.9 Million
Approx. Number Employees: 700
Year Founded: 1961
Business Description:
Mfr of Flexible Packaging & Filling Equipment for the Beverage, Processed Foods, Dairy, Detergent, Wine & Specialty Industries
S.I.C.: 2673
N.A.I.C.S.: 326111
Export
Advertising Expenditures: $5,000,000
Media: 2-5-7-10
Distr.: Intl.; Natl.
Budget Set: Oct.
Personnel:
Kevin Derbyshire *(Gen Counsel)*
Brian D. Edwards *(Dir-Sls & Mktg)*
Al Forsyth *(Dir-Ops)*
Kendel Bradford *(Mktg Mgr)*
John Foster *(Mgr)*
Jason Peterson *(Engr-Control)*
Brands & Products:
LIQUI-BOX
ORBITER 6000
UNGLASS

DURO BAG MANUFACTURING COMPANY

7600 Empire Dr
Florence, KY 41042
Mailing Address:
PO Box 16250
Ludlow, KY 41016
Tel.: (859) 581-8200
Fax: (859) 581-8327
Toll Free: (800) 879-3876
E-mail: info@durobag.com
Web Site: www.durobag.com
Approx. Sls.: $300,000,000
Approx. Number Employees: 1,400
Year Founded: 1953
Business Description:
Paper & Plastic Bags Mfr
S.I.C.: 2674
N.A.I.C.S.: 322224
Media: 2-4-8
Distr.: Natl.
Personnel:
Charles Shor *(Owner, Pres & CEO)*
Jim Eaton *(Exec VP)*
Robert J. Lackman *(Exec VP-Supply Chain & Procurement)*
Scott Murchison *(Exec VP-Ops)*
Tim Young *(VP-HR)*
Chris Kline *(Dir-Customer Acq & Mktg)*
Don Rosing *(Dir-Sys nfrastructure)*
Paul Leonhard *(Mgr-Technical)*
Brands & Products:
DURO
DURO BAG MFG.CO.
HANDLE-BAG

ELECTROCAL/POLYMARK

(Sub. of Illinois Tool Works Inc.)
375 New State Rd
Manchester, CT 06042-1818
Tel.: (860) 647-5720
Fax: (860) 647-1712
Telex: 214136
E-mail: info@electrocal.com
Web Site: www.electrocal.com
Sales Range: $50-74.9 Million
Approx. Number Employees: 90
Year Founded: 1974
Business Description:
Heat Transfer Labels Mfr
S.I.C.: 7389; 2752; 2759; 2821
N.A.I.C.S.: 561910; 323110; 323113; 325211
Import Export
Media: 2-4-7-10-21
Distr.: Intl.; Natl.
Budget Set: Aug. -Sept.
Personnel:
Joe Tetreault *(Dir-Ops)*

ELOPAK, INC.

(Sub. of Elopak A/S)
30000 S Hill Rd
New Hudson, MI 48165
Tel.: (248) 486-4600
Fax: (248) 486-4601
Web Site: www.elopak.com
E-Mail For Key Personnel:
Sales Director: mwilcox@elopakus.com
Approx. Number Employees: 200
Year Founded: 1986
Business Description:
Sanitary Containers Mfr
S.I.C.: 2676
N.A.I.C.S.: 322291
Export
Media: 2-4-7-10-16-17-20
Distr.: Natl.
Budget Set: Aug.
Personnel:
Horst Bussien *(Mng Dir)*
Richard Taylor *(CMO)*
Martin N. Johnsen *(Dir-Mktg)*
Erik Akre *(Dir-Environmental)*
Jenny Francis *(Dir-HR)*
Sveinar Kildal *(Dir-Environment & Mktg Comm)*
Johannes I. Osmundsen *(Dir)*
Brands & Products:
UNIFILL
Advertising Agency:
Brewer Associates Marketing Communications
39555 Orchard Hill Pl Ste 600
Novi, MI 48375
Tel.: (734) 458-7180

FIBERMARK INC.

(Holding of American Securities LLC)
161 Wellington Rd
Brattleboro, VT 05301
Mailing Address:
PO Box 498
Brattleboro, VT 05302-0498
Tel.: (802) 257-0365
Fax: (802) 257-5973
Web Site: www.fibermark.com
Approx. Number Employees: 1,710
Year Founded: 1989
Business Description:
Specialty Fiber-Based Materials Mfr
S.I.C.: 2631; 2621
N.A.I.C.S.: 322130; 322121
Export
Advertising Expenditures: $679,000
Media: 1-2-4-5-9-10-13-20-21-26
Distr.: Intl.; Natl.
Budget Set: Sept.
Personnel:
Anthony MacLaurin *(Pres & CEO)*
Brian McAlary *(Sr VP-Sls & Mktg)*
Mike Wright *(Sr VP-Ops)*
Kevin Archbald *(VP-Sls-Decorative Coverings)*
Robert Archbald *(VP-Customer Svc)*
Joseph M. Benish *(VP-HR)*
Les Eustace *(VP-Sls-Office Products)*
Jeff Hopkins *(VP-Sls-Intl)*
A. Richard Taylor *(Dir-Quality & Process Improvement)*
Brands & Products:
ACADIA
ADIRONDACK
ALLOY
ARCOFLEX
ARCON
BALMORAL
BISCAYNE
CARE LABEL
CHESHIRE LINEN
CIMMARRON BONDED LEATHER
CLEAN ROOM
CORVON
COVER-CUT
DIMENSIONS
DOCU-COVER
DORSET
DURANGO
DURAPRESS
ECLISSE
ENDURA
EVIVA
EXPANLIN
FEORA
FORTESSE
GEN-GUARD
GENUINE PRESSBOARD
GRAFTON
GRANADA
GUIDEX
HILLCREST
HOLOTEX
HYFLEX
IRIDESCENTS
JERSEY
KAP
KIVAR
KIVARFLEX
LEXIDE
LEXOTONE
MONTANA COVER
MOTTLED
MULTICOLOR
MULTIKUT
NATURALLY CREATIVE
NORVAL
PAJCO
PANACHE SOFPRINT
PELLAQ
PERMACOLOR
PERMACOTE
PERMAFIBER
PERMALEX
PERMALIN
PREMIER
PREMOID
PRESS MATE
PRESSGUARD
RELIANCE
REPRISE
ROPACO
SARANAC
SAVANNAH
SEDONA
SENZO
SKIVERTEX
SOLERRA
SUEDETEX
SUPER ARCOFLEX
TEXT-GUARD
TOUCHE
TUFWITE
VALTEX
VERIGOOD

FINCH PAPER LLC

(Sub. of Finch Paper Holdings LLC)
1 Glen St
Glens Falls, NY 12801-4439
Tel.: (518) 793-2541
Fax: (518) 743-9656
Toll Free: (800) 833-9983
E-mail: webmaster@finchpaper.com
Web Site: www.finchpaper.com
Approx. Number Employees: 900
Year Founded: 1865
Business Description:
Specialty Paper Mfr & Converting Services
S.I.C.: 2621; 2679
N.A.I.C.S.: 322121; 322299
Import Export
Media: 2-7-10-21
Distr.: Natl.
Budget Set: Nov.
Personnel:
Richard J. Carota *(Chm)*
Kyle Brock *(VP-HR)*
Edward Klopfer *(VP-Sls & Mktg)*
Anthony T. McDowell *(VP-Sls & Mktg)*
Michael Bean *(Dir-Sls-East Reg)*

Key to Media (For complete agency information see *The Advertising Red Books-Agencies* edition):
1. Bus. Publs. 2. Cable T.V. 3. Catalogs & Directories. 4. Co-op Adv. 5. Consumer Mags. 6. D.M. to Bus. Estab.7. D.M. to Consumers
8. Daily Newsp. 9. Exhibits/Trade Shows 10. Foreign 11. Infomercial 12. Internet Adv.13. Multimedia 14. Network Radio
15. Network T.V. 16. Newsp. Distr. Mags. 17. Other 18. Outdoor (Posters, Transit) 19. Point of Purchase20. Premiums, Novelties
21. Product Samples 22. Special Events Mktg. 23. Spot Radio 24. Spot T.V. 25. Weekly Newsp. 26. Yellow Page Adv.

Michael W. Palmer *(Dir-Customer Satisfaction)*
Thomas D. Ruch *(Dir-Tech & Dev)*
Robert J. Huber *(Mktg Mgr-Digital Papers)*
Zoe A. Devoe *(Mgr-Midwest-Reg Sls)*
Michael A. Havens *(Mgr-Logistics)*
Madalyn B. Langdon *(Mgr-Customer Svc)*
Keith A. Londrigan *(Mgr-Credit)*
Judith A. O'Brien *(Mgr-Quality Assurance)*
Joe Ann Stockdale *(Coord-Sls)*

Brands & Products:
FINCH

FLEX-O-GLASS, INC.

1100 N Cicero Ave
Chicago, IL 60651
Tel.: (773) 261-5200
Fax: (773) 261-5422
Web Site: www.flexoglass.com
Approx. Number Employees: 180
Year Founded: 1924
Business Description:
Plastic Film & Plastic Products Mfr
S.I.C.: 3081; 3082
N.A.I.C.S.: 326113; 326121
Advertising Expenditures: $1,000,000
Media: 1-2-3-4-5-6-7-9-10-17-19-20-21-23-24-25
Distr.: Natl.
Budget Set: Nov.
Personnel:
Harold G. Warp *(Pres)*
David K. Roadruck *(Mgr-Adv)*
Brands & Products:
BANANA BAGS
EASY-EDGE
FLEX-O-BAG
FLEX-O-CRYLIC
FLEX-O-FILM
FLEX-O-GLASS
FLEX-O-GLAZE
JIFFY COVER
NO-HOE
NON-WET
POLY-COVER
POLY-RIB
POLY-WRAP
PROTECT-O-SHEET
REINFORCED COVERALL
STRETCH PACK
SUR-FLEX
WARPS

FLEXCON CORPORATION

1 Flexcon Indus Pk
Spencer, MA 01562-2642
Tel.: (508) 885-8200
Fax: (508) 885-8400
E-mail: info@flexcon.com
Web Site: www.flexcon.com
Approx. Number Employees: 1,200
Year Founded: 1955
Business Description:
Holding Company; Film & Adhesive Products Mfr
S.I.C.: 6719; 2891; 3081
N.A.I.C.S.: 551112; 325520; 326113
Media: 2-10
Personnel:
Neil McDonough *(Pres & CEO)*
Christine LaPalme *(VP-HR & Mktg)*
Gerrit-Jan Hulsenbeck *(Dir-Bus Dev)*
Jack Kisiel *(Dir-Intl Bus Dev)*
Brands & Products:
ADVANTACAL
ALPHAMAX
BRUSHCAL
BUSART
BUSMARK
CLASSICS PLUS
CLASSICS PLUS SELECT
COLORMARK
COLORTAPE
COMPUCAL
CRYOFLEX
DENSIL
DIGIPRO
DRUMCAL
DURABLE PRODUCT MARKING
EXCEL
FLEXCON
FLEXMARK
FLEXMOUNT
FLEXSTAT
FLEXTWIN
GARMENT SELECT
GENERATION
GENERATION 2000
GENERATION 3000
IMPCTFILM
JETBOND
LAZRFILM
LITECAL
MICROSAFE
OPTIFLEX
POLY 2000
POLY-2000
PRISMCAL
SEETHRU-SIGN
SELECT
SHIMMERCAL
SWITCHMARK
TAMPERMARK
THERMLFILM
THERMLFILM SELECT
TRACRITE
VALIDATE

FORT DEARBORN COMPANY

(Holding of KRG Capital Partners LLC)
1530 Morse Ave
Elk Grove Village, IL 60007-4027
Tel.: (847) 427-5405 (Marketing)
Tel.: (847) 357-9500
Fax: (847) 357-8726
E-mail: info@fortdearborn.com
Web Site: www.fortdearborn.com
E-Mail For Key Personnel:
President: MAnderson@fortdearborn.com
Approx. Number Employees: 150
Year Founded: 1923
Business Description:
Packaging & Labeling Services
S.I.C.: 7389
N.A.I.C.S.: 561910
Export
Media: 2-5-7-10-13
Personnel:
Mike Anderson *(Owner)*
Tim Trahey *(CFO)*

FRASER PAPERS INC.

181 Bay St Ste 200
Toronto, ON M5J 2T3, Canada
Tel.: (416) 359-8605
Fax: (416) 359-8606
Toll Free: (800) 920-9988
E-mail: investorrelations@toronto.fraserpapers.com
Web Site: www.fraserpapers.com
Sales Range: $300-349.9 Million
Approx. Number Employees: 250
Year Founded: 1929
Business Description:
Printing & Writing Papers Mfr
S.I.C.: 2621; 2672
N.A.I.C.S.: 322121; 322222
Import Export
Advertising Expenditures: $7,000,000
Media: 2-4-7-16-17-19-20-21-22-25-26
Distr.: Natl.
Budget Set: Sept. -Dec.
Personnel:
Dominic Gammiero *(Chm)*
Jeff Dutton *(Pres & CEO)*
Glen Mcmillan *(Chief Restructuring Officer)*
Jim Gehrman *(Pres-Sucampo Pharma Americas, Inc. & Sr VP-Sls & Mktg)*
Matthew Nightingale *(VP-Mktg)*
Willis Blevins *(Gen Mgr-Opers)*

GARAGETEK INC.

5 Aerial Way Ste 200
Syosset, NY 11791
Tel.: (516) 621-4300
Fax: (516) 992-8600
Toll Free: (800) 664-2724
Web Site: www.garagetek.com
Sales Range: $10-24.9 Million
Approx. Number Employees: 13
Year Founded: 2000
Business Description:
Garage Organization & Storage System
S.I.C.: 6794
N.A.I.C.S.: 533110
Media: 6
Personnel:
Marc Shuman *(Pres)*
Nick Paglino *(Gen Mgr)*
Barbara Butensky *(Dir-Mktg)*
John Maxworthy *(Dir-Engrg)*
Brands & Products:
GARAGETEK
TEKPANEL
WE DESIGN IT. WE INSTALL IT. YOU ENJOY IT.
THE WORLD'S CLEANEST GARAGE

GEORGIA-PACIFIC CORPORATION

(Div. of Koch Industries, Inc.)
133 Peachtree St NE
Atlanta, GA 30303
Mailing Address:
PO Box 105605
Atlanta, GA 30348-5605
Tel.: (404) 652-4000
Fax: (404) 749-2454
Web Site: www.gp.com
Sales Range: $1-4.9 Billion
Approx. Number Employees: 50,000
Year Founded: 1927
Business Description:
Pulp, Paper, Packaging, Building Products & Related Chemicals Mfr
S.I.C.: 5113; 2452; 2621; 2656; 2671; 2899
N.A.I.C.S.: 424130; 321992; 322121; 322215; 322221; 325998
Advertising Expenditures: $65,000,000
Media: 1-2-4-5-6-7-8-9-10-11-15-19-20-21-23-24
Distr.: Natl.
Personnel:
David L. Robertson *(Chm)*
James Hannan *(Pres & CEO)*
Tyler Woolson *(CFO & Sr VP)*
Randal Robison *(CIO & Sr VP)*
Douwe Bergsma *(CMO)*
William A. Frerking *(Chief Sustainability Officer & VP)*
Patrick Boushka *(Pres-Cellulose)*
Terry Cinotte *(Pres-Pkg)*
Curley M. Dossman, Jr. *(Pres-Foundation)*
Sean R. Fallmann *(Pres-North American Consumer Bus)*
Tarek Hallaba *(Pres-Consumer Bus-EMEA)*
Mark Luetters *(Pres-Wood Products)*
Rick Urschel *(Pres-Chemical)*
Tye Darland *(Gen Counsel & Sr VP)*
Christian Fischer *(Exec VP-Pkg)*
Kathleen A. Walters *(Exec VP-Global Consumer Products)*
Mike E. Adams *(Sr VP-Sourcing)*
Julie Brehm *(Sr VP-HR)*
Philip Ellender *(Sr VP-Govt & Pub Affairs)*
Paul Frederickson *(Sr VP-Consumer Products Mfg-North America)*
W. Wesley Jones *(Sr VP-Ops Excellence & Compliance)*
David Park *(Sr VP-Strategy & Bus Devel)*
Shiela M. Weidman *(Sr VP-Comm, Govt & Pub Affairs)*
Andrew Towle *(Gen Mgr & VP-Consumer Tissue)*
Erik Sjogren *(Dir-Mktg-Angel Soft)*
Jorge DeCastro *(Sr Brand Mgr-Quilted Northern Bath Tissue)*
Brands & Products:
ACCLAIM
ACCUDRY
ACCUWIPE
ACTRABASE
ACTRACOR
ACTRAFOS
ACTRALUBE
ACTRAMER
ACTRAMIDE
ACTRASOL
AMBOND
AMRES
ANGEL SOFT
ARYLZENE
BETTER ALTERNATIVE
BIGFOLD
BIGFOLD JR
BIGFOLD Z
BLUE RIBBON
BRAWNY
CAREX
CAREX 3000
CATAWBA
CECORR
CLASSIC IMPRESSIONS
CLOTHMASTER
COLHOGAR
COLORFUL IMPRESSIONS
COMPACT
COMPACT 3000
CORMATIC
CORMATIC/ULTIMA
DEMAK'UP
DENSARMOR
DENSDECK
DENSGLASS
DENSGLASS GOLD

Key to Media (For complete agency information see *The Advertising Red Books-Agencies* edition):
1. Bus. Publs. 2. Cable T.V. 3. Catalogs & Directories. 4. Co-op Adv. 5. Consumer Mags. 6. D.M. to Bus. Estab.7. D.M. to Consumers 8. Daily Newsp. 9. Exhibits/Trade Shows 10. Foreign 11. Infomercial 12. Internet Adv.13. Multimedia 14. Network Radio 15. Network T.V. 16. Newsp. Distr. Mags. 17. Other 18. Outdoor (Posters, Transit) 19. Point of Purchase20. Premiums, Novelties 21. Product Samples 22. Special Events Mktg. 23. Spot Radio 24. Spot T.V. 25. Weekly Newsp. 26. Yellow Page Adv.

Georgia-Pacific Corporation —
(Continued)

DENSGLASS SILVER
DENSGUARD
DENSSHIELD
DINE-A-FRESH
DINE-A-WIPE
DISPERSA
DIXIE
DIXIEWARE
DURAMINE
DUST-N-CLEAN
DYNACLOTH
DYNAMAX
EASYNAP
EMBO
ENMOTION
ENVISION
ESSENCE
ESSENCE IMPRESSIONS
EUREKA!
EXECUTIVE
EXECUTIVE 3000
FIBERSTRONG
FIREDEFENDER
FORTGUARD
FORTGUARD VISTA
G-P LAM
GEORGIA-PACIFIC
GORAG
GP ADVANTAGE
GP COLORS!
GP EUREKA!
GP GEOCYCLE
GP HOTS!
GP IMAGE PLUS
GP PASTELS!
GP PREMIUM LASER & COLOR COPIER COVER STOCK
GP PREMIUM LASER & COLOR COPIER PAPER
GPRI
GREEN FOREST
GUARDIAN
HANDI-FRESH
HANDI-SCRUBB
HUSHBOARD
HYNAP
INSOL-U-25
INTERSTATE
KITTENSOFT
KOWTOWL
KRAZY KRITTERS
LAMILUX
LETS STEAM OUT. KEEP SPLATTERS IN.
LYTOR
MARDI GRAS
MARQUIS
MAX 3000
MICRO-TWIN
MINI-MORNAP
MORNAP
MULTIPLATE
MULTISAVER
NEVEROUT
NEVEROUT 3000
NORTHERN
NOVABOND
NOVACOTE
NOVAFLO
NOVAPLUS
NUBRITE
NUROLL
OSB
PACIFIC GARDEN
PLY-BEAD
PLYTANIUM
POLYWEB
PREFERENCE
PRIMETRIM
QUIK CHANGE
QUILTED NORTHERN
READIROLL
RESI-BOND
RESI-MIX
RESI-STRAN
RESORSABOND
ROLLMASTR
SAFE-T-GARD
SEASONAL IMPRESSIONS
SHOPMASTER
SHUR-WIPE
SIGNATURE
SIGNATURE SOLUTIONS
SIZEXCEL
SO-DRI
SOFPULL
SOFT-N-FRESH
SOFT'N GENTLE
SPARKLE
SPECTRUM
SPECTRUM DP
STA-FORM 60
STURD-I-FLOOR
TASKMATE
TENDERLY
THERMOSTAT
TIDYNAP
TOUGHROCK
TOWLMASTR
TOWLSAVER
TUFFMATE
UDDERLICLEAN
UDDERLIDRY
ULTIMA
ULTRA SHAFTLINER
ULTRACORR
ULTRACYCLE
ULTRACYCLE PLUS
ULTRASTAK
ULTRASTAK PLUS
UNICREPE
VANITY FAIR
VISTA
VUALL CORMATIC
WOOD I BEAM
WOODWELD
XTOL
XTOLUBE
ZEE

Advertising Agencies:

Critical Mass Inc.
402 11th Ave SE
Calgary, AB T2G 0Y4, Canada
Tel.: (403) 262-3006
Fax: (403) 262-7185
Consumer Products

DDB New York
437 Madison Ave
New York, NY 10022-7001
Tel.: (212) 415-2000
Fax: (212) 415-3506
Brawny Paper Towels
Toilet Tissue
Sparkle Paper Towels
Angel Soft
Quilted Northern
GP Consumer Products

Edelman
101 Marietta St Ste 2900
Atlanta, GA 30303
Tel.: (404) 262-3000
Fax: (404) 264-1431

Eric Mower and Associates
7000 Central Pkwy NE Ste 1020
Atlanta, GA 30328-4586
Tel.: (678) 587-0301
Fax: (770) 481-1500
Dixie

IQ Interactive
280 Interstate N Cir SE Ste 300
Atlanta, GA 30339
Tel.: (404) 255-3550
Fax: (770) 956-8014

Ketchum
3500 Lenox Rd Ste 1250
Atlanta, GA 30326
Tel.: (404) 879-9000
Fax: (404) 879-9001

Loeffler Ketchum Mountjoy (LKM)
6115 Park S Dr Ste 350
Charlotte, NC 28210
Tel.: (704) 364-8969
Fax: (704) 364-8470
Toll Free: (800) 851-8436

Lopez Negrete Communications, Inc.
3336 Richmond Ave Ste 200
Houston, TX 77098
Tel.: (713) 877-8777
Fax: (713) 877-8796
Quilted Northern Bath Tissue

The Richards Group, Inc.
8750 N Central Expy Ste 100
Dallas, TX 75231-6430
Tel.: (214) 891-5700
Fax: (214) 265-2933

GIBRALTAR PACKAGING GROUP, INC.

(Sub. of Rosmar Litho, Inc.)
2000 Summit Ave
Hastings, NE 68901-6703
Mailing Address:
PO Box 2148
Hastings, NE 68902-2148
Tel.: (402) 463-1366
Fax: (402) 463-2467
E-mail: investorrelations@gibpack.com
Web Site: www.gibpack.com
Sales Range: $25-49.9 Million
Year Founded: 1956
Business Description:
Packaging Products Designer, Mfr & Marketer
S.I.C.: 2657; 2655; 2671; 7389
N.A.I.C.S.: 322212; 322214; 322221; 561910
Media: 2-7-10-20-21-22
Personnel:
James A. Downey *(VP & Gen Mgr-North Carolina Facility)*
Mark A. Lessor *(VP & Gen Mgr-Nebraska Facility)*
Brett E. Moller *(VP-Fin)*
Gregory B. Till *(VP-Sls)*
Teena Kucera *(Gen Mgr)*
Brands & Products:
GIBRALTAR PACKAGING GROUP

GLUEFAST COMPANY, INC.

3535 State Rte 66 Bldg 1
Neptune, NJ 07753
Tel.: (732) 918-4600
Fax: (732) 918-4646
Toll Free: (800) 242-7318
E-mail: info@gluefast.com
Web Site: www.gluefast.com
E-Mail For Key Personnel:
President: lmallet@gluefast.com
Approx. Sls.: $2,000,000
Approx. Number Employees: 12
Year Founded: 1939
Business Description:
Labeling Equipment, Glues & Adhesives Moisteners
S.I.C.: 2891
N.A.I.C.S.: 325520
Advertising Expenditures: $200,000
Media: 2-4-7-10
Distr.: Direct to Consumer; Natl.
Budget Set: Nov. -Dec.
Personnel:
Lester Mallet *(Pres)*
Joe Benenati *(Gen Mgr)*
Laura Hincapie *(Office Mgr)*
Brands & Products:
CAPTAIN B
COLONEL AG
GLUE DOTS
GLUEFAST
GLUEFAST DUOS
LABEL PRO
MELTCATOR
SENATOR
SKID-LOCK
SOLO GLUE RITER

GRAPHIC PACKAGING HOLDING COMPANY

814 Livingston Ct
Marietta, GA 30067
Tel.: (770) 644-3000
Fax: (770) 644-2962
E-mail: patti.gettinger@graphicpkg.com
Web Site: www.graphicpkg.com
Approx. Sls.: $4,095,000,000
Approx. Number Employees: 12,400
Year Founded: 1988
Business Description:
Holding Company; Packaging Mfr
S.I.C.: 6719; 2631; 2653; 2657
N.A.I.C.S.: 551112; 322130; 322211; 322212
Media: 2-7-10-19
Personnel:
John R. Miller, III *(Chm)*
David W. Scheible *(Pres & CEO)*
Daniel J. Blount *(CFO & Sr VP)*
Stephen A. Hellrung *(Gen Counsel, Sec & Sr VP)*
Brands & Products:
AQUA-KOTE
CAP-SAC
COMPOSIPAC
DI-NA-CAL
FRIDGE VENDOR
GRAPHIC PACKAGING
INTEGRAPAK
KITCHEN MASTER
LITHO-FLUTE
MICRORITE
MINNESOTA AUTOMATION
OMNI-KOTE
PACESETTER
PEARL-KOTE
PEEL PAK
QUILT WAVE
RADAR II

Key to Media (For complete agency information see *The Advertising Red Books-Agencies* edition):
1. Bus. Publs. 2. Cable T.V. 3. Catalogs & Directories. 4. Co-op Adv. 5. Consumer Mags. 6. D.M. to Bus. Estab.7. D.M. to Consumers
8. Daily Newsp. 9. Exhibits/Trade Shows 10. Foreign 11. Infomercial 12. Internet Adv.13. Multimedia 14. Network Radio
15. Network T.V. 16. Newsp. Distr. Mags. 17. Other 18. Outdoor (Posters, Transit) 19. Point of Purchase20. Premiums, Novelties
21. Product Samples 22. Special Events Mktg. 23. Spot Radio 24. Spot T.V. 25. Weekly Newsp. 26. Yellow Page Adv.

SONI-LOK
SONI-SEAL
SUS
THE YARD MASTER
Z-FLUTE

GREIF INC.
425 Winter Rd
Delaware, OH 43015-8903
Tel.: (740) 549-6000
Fax: (740) 549-6100
Web Site: www.greif.com
Approx. Sls.: $3,461,537,000
Approx. Number Employees: 12,250
Year Founded: 1877
Business Description:
Industrial Packaging Products Mfr
S.I.C.: 2655; 2631; 2652; 2653; 2657; 3429; 3499
N.A.I.C.S.: 322214; 322130; 322211; 322212; 322213; 332439; 332510; 332999
Media: 10-26
Personnel:
Michael J. Gasser *(Chm & CEO)*
David B. Fischer *(Pres & COO)*
Robert M. McNutt *(CFO & Sr VP)*
Scott R. Griffin *(Chief Sustainability Officer)*
Ivan Signorelli *(Pres-Industrial Pkg & Svcs-Europe, Middle East & Africa & Sr VP)*
Gary R. Martz *(Gen Counsel & Exec VP)*
Ronald L. Brown *(Sr VP)*
Karen P. Lane *(Sr VP-People Svcs & Talent Dev)*
William R. Mordecai *(VP-Containerboard Sls & Mktg)*
Debra Strohmaier *(VP-Comm)*
Rick Volker *(Product Manager-Water Bottles-North American)*
Sharon R. Maxwell *(Asst Sec)*
Brands & Products:
4S
A-DRUM
ALL-FI
COLD-FLO
CONCERTAINER
DOR-KOR
DRUM-KOR
DUAL RIDER
ECONOMY
GREIF
HARVESTPAK
HOT-FLO
LIQUIPAK
LOK-RIM
PAL-KOR
PAL PAK
PAYOFFPAK
QUADRATAINER
RDL
RO-CON
SPIRALON
SPIRALTAINER
TAB-SEAL
UNICUBE
VALEREX
VALETHENE
VERMATAINER
WEATHERPAK
WOOD-KOR

HAMMERMILL PAPER
(Div. of International Paper Company)
6400 Poplar Ave
Memphis, TN 38197-0100
Tel.: (901) 419-9000
Toll Free: (800) 242-2148
Web Site: www.internationalpaper.com
Sales Range: $900-999.9 Million
Approx. Number Employees: 3,000
Year Founded: 1898
Business Description:
Producer of a Wide Range of Printing & Office Papers
S.I.C.: 2621
N.A.I.C.S.: 322121
Export
Media: 1-2-3-4-6-7-8-9-10-12-13-14-19-20-21-22-23-24-26
Distr.: Natl.
Budget Set: Sept.
Personnel:
John V. Faraci *(CEO)*
Cindy Hamrick *(Mgr-Promos)*
Brands & Products:
FORE
HAMMERMILL
MAKES YOUR WORK LOOK BETTER
RELAY
TIDAL
Advertising Agency:
Euro RSCG Worldwide
350 Hudson St
New York, NY 10014-4504
Tel.: (212) 886-2000
Fax: (212) 886-2016
Toll Free: (800) 937-0233
— Dick Grinberg *(Acct. Exec.)*

HARDIGG INDUSTRIES, INC.
(Sub. of Pelican Products, Inc.)
147 N Main St
South Deerfield, MA 01373-1026
Mailing Address:
PO Box 201
South Deerfield, MA 01373-0201
Tel.: (413) 665-2163
Fax: (413) 665-4801
E-mail: info@hardigg.com
Web Site: www.hardigg.com
Approx. Number Employees: 600
Year Founded: 1954
Business Description:
Rotational & Injection Molded Plastic Storage Cases & Containers Designer, Mfr & Distr
S.I.C.: 3089; 5099
N.A.I.C.S.: 326199; 423990
Import Export
Media: 4-10
Personnel:
William Hamer *(COO & VP)*
Brands & Products:
DEFY THE ELEMENTS.
FLANGEMOUNT
FLASTCLIP
HARDIGG
HPX
RAPID RACK
SKID-MATE
STORM CASE
STORM TRAK
THE ULTIMATE PROTECTIVE SYSTEM.
VORTEX

HASLER, INC.
(Sub. of Neopost Inc.)
478 Wheelers Farms Rd
Milford, CT 06461
Mailing Address:
PO Box 959
Shelton, CT 06484-0903
Tel.: (203) 301-3400
Fax: (203) 929-6084
Toll Free: (800) 243-6275
E-mail: info@haslerinc.com
Web Site: www.haslerinc.com
Approx. Number Employees: 250
Year Founded: 1921
Business Description:
Precision Engineered Mailing Systems Including Mail Management and Postage Accounting Systems, Postage Meters, Electronic Scales, Manifest Shipping Systems, Mail Openers, Mailroom Furniture, Better Pack Tape Dispensing Machines & Labelers
S.I.C.: 5044; 3565
N.A.I.C.S.: 423420; 333993
Import Export
Advertising Expenditures: $1,250,000
Media: 1-2-4-5-8-10-20-26
Distr.: Intl.; Natl.
Budget Set: Oct. -Nov.
Personnel:
Dennis Lestrange *(CEO)*
Graham Fulghum *(Dir-Govt Rels)*
Robert Grant *(Dir-East)*
Larry Waters *(Dir-West)*
Brands & Products:
HASLER
INTELITOUCH
POSTLINK
POWERPOST
SMART SORT
SMART TRACK
WHISPER JET

HAZEN PAPER COMPANY
240 S Water St
Holyoke, MA 01040
Tel.: (413) 538-8204
Fax: (413) 533-1420
E-mail: customerservice@hazen.com
Web Site: www.hazen.com
E-Mail For Key Personnel:
President: jhh@hazen.com
Sales Director: sjs@hazen.com
Approx. Number Employees: 200
Year Founded: 1925
Business Description:
Converted Decorative Paper, Laminated Metallized Holographic Papers, & Decorative Packaging Materials; Speciality Papers Mfr
S.I.C.: 2672; 3497
N.A.I.C.S.: 322222; 322225
Import Export
Media: 7-10-21
Personnel:
John Hazen *(Pres)*
Robert E. Hazen *(Exec VP-Sls & Mktg)*
Stephen J. Smith *(VP-Sls)*
Gerald Buffan *(Engr-Plant)*
Brands & Products:
ECOBRIGHT
ECROMIUM
ENVIROFOIL
HAZEN
SHIMMER-E
ULTRACURE

HUHTAMAKI CONSUMER PACKAGING INC.
(Sub. of Huhtamaki, Inc.)
9201 Packaging Dr
De Soto, KS 66018
Tel.: (913) 583-3025
Fax: (913) 583-8756
Web Site: www.huhtamaki.com
Approx. Number Employees: 400
Year Founded: 1915
Business Description:
Paper Packaging Systems for Frozen Desserts & Foods Mfr
S.I.C.: 2656; 3565
N.A.I.C.S.: 322215; 333993
Export
Media: 7-10
Distr.: Natl.
Budget Set: Oct.
Personnel:
Penny Stats *(Prod Mgr)*
Brands & Products:
NESTYLE

HUHTAMAKI, INC.
(Sub. of Huhtamaki Oyj)
9201 Packaging Dr
De Soto, KS 66018-8600
Tel.: (913) 583-3025
Fax: (913) 583-8756
Web Site: www.us.huhtamaki.com
Approx. Number Employees: 50
Business Description:
Food Packaging
S.I.C.: 6719
N.A.I.C.S.: 551112
Personnel:
Julie Stoetzer *(Mgr-Mktg)*
Advertising Agencies:
The Buntin Group
1001 Hawkins St
Nashville, TN 37203-4758
Tel.: (615) 244-5720
Fax: (615) 244-6511

OLSON
1625 Hennepin Ave
Minneapolis, MN 55403
Tel.: (612) 215-9800
Fax: (612) 215-9801

HY-TEST PACKAGING CORP.
515 E 41st St
Paterson, NJ 07504-1209
Tel.: (973) 754-7000
Fax: (973) 754-7020
E-mail: hy-test@verizon.net
Web Site: www.hy-testpackaging.com
Approx. Sls.: $1,000,000
Approx. Number Employees: 20
Year Founded: 1956
Business Description:
Custom Chemical Packaging
S.I.C.: 7389; 2844
N.A.I.C.S.: 561910; 325620
Import Export
Media: 7-8
Distr.: Reg.
Budget Set: Jan.
Personnel:
John S. Smith *(Chm, Pres, CEO & COO)*
Ted Smith *(Vice Chm, CFO, Exec VP & Controller)*
Jack Smith *(VP-Mktg)*
Brands & Products:
HY-TEST

I/D/E/A/ INC.
1 Idea Way
Caldwell, ID 83605-6999
Tel.: (208) 459-6357
Fax: (208) 459-6484
Toll Free: (800) 635-9261

Key to Media (For complete agency information see *The Advertising Red Books-Agencies* edition):
1. Bus. Publs. 2. Cable T.V. 3. Catalogs & Directories. 4. Co-op Adv. 5. Consumer Mags. 6. D.M. to Bus. Estab.7. D.M. to Consumers 8. Daily Newsp. 9. Exhibits/Trade Shows 10. Foreign 11. Infomercial 12. Internet Adv.13. Multimedia 14. Network Radio 15. Network T.V. 16. Newsp. Distr. Mags. 17. Other 18. Outdoor (Posters, Transit) 19. Point of Purchase20. Premiums, Novelties 21. Product Samples 22. Special Events Mktg. 23. Spot Radio 24. Spot T.V. 25. Weekly Newsp. 26. Yellow Page Adv.

I/D/E/A/ Inc. — (Continued)
Web Site: www.ideaprinting.com
Approx. Number Employees: 75
Year Founded: 1955
Business Description:
Mfr. of Personalized Apparel & Mail-order Catalogs; Print Production
S.I.C.: 2752; 2791
N.A.I.C.S.: 323110; 323122
Import
Advertising Expenditures: $510,000
Distr.: Natl.
Budget Set: Nov. -Dec.
Personnel:
Stephen Fossler *(Pres & CEO)*
Jane McConnell *(Mgr-Mktg)*
Brands & Products:
AUTOFILE
I/D/E/A/

ICON DESIGN & DISPLAY, INC.
(d/b/a Napa Valley Box Co., Inc. & Vintage Wood Products)
1733 Sebastopol Rd
Santa Rosa, CA 95407-6816
Tel.: (707) 284-3400
Fax: (707) 284-3409
Toll Free: (800) 424-2269
E-mail: info@icondisplay.com
Web Site: www.icondisplay.com
Approx. Number Employees: 25
Year Founded: 1981
Business Description:
Mfr. of Wooden Point-of-Purchase Displays
S.I.C.: 2511; 2541
N.A.I.C.S.: 337122; 337212
Media: 10
Distr.: Intl.
Budget Set: Monthly
Personnel:
Mark Richard *(Pres & CEO)*

INDEPENDENT CAN COMPANY
1300 Brass Mill Rd
Belcamp, MD 21017-1211
Tel.: (410) 272-0090
Fax: (410) 273-7500
E-mail: salesdept@independentcan.com
Web Site: www.independentcan.com
E-Mail For Key Personnel:
Sales Director: salesdept@independentcan.com
Approx. Number Employees: 200
Year Founded: 1929
Business Description:
Mfr. of Decorative & Various Specialty Cans
S.I.C.: 3411; 2752
N.A.I.C.S.: 332431; 323110
Import Export
Media: 2-4-7-10-17
Distr.: Intl.
Personnel:
Douglas Huether *(Chm)*
Rick Huether *(Pres & CEO)*

INDUSTRIAL COATINGS GROUP, INC.
(Holding of ICG Holliston Holdings Corporation)
905 Holliston Mills Rd
Church Hill, TN 37642
Mailing Address:
PO Box 478
Kingsport, TN 37662
Tel.: (423) 357-6141
Fax: (423) 357-8840
Toll Free: (800) 251-0451
Web Site: www.icgholliston.com/
Year Founded: 1897
Business Description:
Industrial Fabrics & Polyethylene Films Mfr
S.I.C.: 2299; 2295
N.A.I.C.S.: 314999; 313320
Import Export
Media: 2-4-5-7-10-13-21
Distr.: Intl.; Natl.
Personnel:
Robert Dwyer *(Pres & CEO)*
Brands & Products:
ACRO-FLEX
ARRESTOX
BANNERLINE
ENVIRO-MATE
GALAXY
ICG
KENNETT
LINEN-SET
MERCURY
OMEGA
OPTIMA
PLASTUSA
POLYSEAL
SATURN
TECLAR

INLINE PLASTICS CORP.
42 Canal St
Shelton, CT 06484-3223
Tel.: (203) 924-5933
Fax: (203) 924-0370
Toll Free: (800) 826-5567
E-mail: sales@inlineplastics.com
Web Site: www.inlineplastics.com
E-Mail For Key Personnel:
Sales Director: sales@inlineplastics.com
Approx. Number Employees: 283
Year Founded: 1968
Business Description:
Plastic Food Containers Mfr
S.I.C.: 3089
N.A.I.C.S.: 326199
Import Export
Media: 4-7-10-13-21
Personnel:
Thomas Orkisz *(Pres)*
Kevin McGuane *(CFO)*
Dan Landan *(VP-Engrng)*
Augie Lanzetta *(VP-Sls)*
Pam Corba *(Mgr-Mktg)*
Brands & Products:
CRYSTAL VUE
EZ OPEN
GOOD THINGS COME IN OUR PACKAGES
INLINE PLASTICS
PARTY PLATTER
SAFE-T-FRESH
SAFE-T-GARD
SALAD BOWLS
SURELOCK
VALU PAK

INNOVATIVE PLASTICS CORPORATION
400 Rte 303
Orangeburg, NY 10962
Tel.: (845) 359-7500
Fax: (845) 359-0237
Toll Free: (800) 229-7501
E-mail: sales@innovative-plastics.com
Web Site: www.innovative-plastics.com
E-Mail For Key Personnel:
Sales Director: sales@innovative-plastics.com
Approx. Number Employees: 250
Year Founded: 1982
Business Description:
Plastic Packaging Mfr
S.I.C.: 2671; 3089
N.A.I.C.S.: 326112; 326199
Media: 2-10
Personnel:
Judith Hershaft *(Pres & CEO)*
Peter Streitman *(CFO)*
Brands & Products:
INNOVATIVE PLASTICS

INTERNATIONAL PAPER-BLEACHED BOARD DIV.
(Div. of International Paper Company)
6400 Poplar Ave
Memphis, TN 38197-0100
Tel.: (901) 419-9000
Web Site:
www.internationalpaper.com
Sales Range: $550-599.9 Million
Approx. Number Employees: 1,300
Business Description:
Marketer of Paperboard
S.I.C.: 2621
N.A.I.C.S.: 322121
Media: 7
Personnel:
Karen Bruder *(Mgr-Mktg & Sls)*
Advertising Agency:
Good Advertising, Inc.
5100 Poplar Ave Ste 1700
Memphis, TN 38137
Tel.: (901) 761-0741
Fax: (901) 682-2568
Toll Free: (800) 325-9857

INTERNATIONAL PAPER COMPANY
6400 Poplar Ave
Memphis, TN 38197
Tel.: (901) 419-9000
Toll Free: (800) 223-1268
Telex: 239403
Web Site: www.ipaper.com
Approx. Sls.: $25,179,000,000
Approx. Number Employees: 59,500
Year Founded: 1898
Business Description:
Pulp & Paper, Converted Paper Products, Paperboard, Wood & Specialty Products Mfr
S.I.C.: 2621
N.A.I.C.S.: 322121; 322122
Import Export
Media: 2-3-4-6-7-9-10-24
Distr.: Intl.; Natl.
Budget Set: Nov.
Personnel:
John V. Faraci *(Chm & CEO)*
Tim S. Nicholls *(CFO & Sr VP)*
John N. Balboni *(CIO & Sr VP)*
Maximo Pacheco *(Pres-IP Europe, Middle East, Africa & Russia & Sr VP)*
Paul Brown *(Pres-India)*
Sharon R. Ryan *(Gen Counsel, Sec & Sr VP)*
Jerome N. Carter *(Sr VP-HR)*
C. Cato Ealy *(Sr VP-Corp Dev)*
Thomas G. Kadien *(Sr VP-Consumer Pkg & IP-Asia)*
Carol L. Roberts *(Sr VP-Indus Pkg)*
Mark S. Sutton *(Sr VP-Printing & Comm Papers-Americas)*
Thomas A. Cleves *(VP & Gen Mgr-Containerboard & Recycling)*
Terri Herrington *(VP-Fin & Strategy-Consumer Pkg)*
Jim Berg *(Dir-Ethics & Business Practice)*
Brands & Products:
ACCENT
ACCENT OPAQUE
ACE PACKAGING
ADVOCATE
BALLET
BECKETT
BRITEHUE
CAROLINA
CHAMBRIL
CHAMEQUINHO
CHAMEX
CLASSICPAK
CLASSICPAK7WF
DATASPEED
DEFOR
DUO
ECOTAINER
ENVOY
EQUABIN
EVEREST
FIBRELIFT
GREAT WHITE
HAMMERMILL
IMPACEL
INFLUENCE
INTERNATIONAL PAPER
INVENT-IT
JET PRINT PHOTO
LIBERTY
ONE TOUCH SYSTEM
POL
POLSET
POSTMARK
PRECISION CONTAINER AERIAL DELIVERY SYSTEM
READYFILL
REY
RIDE RITE
SAVVY
SOUCHE
SPACE CRAFT
SPRINGHILL
STARCOLE
STRATHMORE
STRATHMORE ARTIST
SUPERSOFT
TRI-WALL
TRILOGY
UNISAT
VELOCITY
VIA
WILLIAMSBURG
XPEDX
Advertising Agencies:
Brandimage Desgrippes & Laga
990 Skokie Blvd
Northbrook, IL 60062
Tel.: (847) 291-0500
Fax: (847) 291-0516

Euro RSCG Worldwide
350 Hudson St
New York, NY 10014-4504
Tel.: (212) 886-2000
Fax: (212) 886-2016

Key to Media (For complete agency information see *The Advertising Red Books-Agencies* edition):
1. Bus. Publs. 2. Cable T.V. 3. Catalogs & Directories. 4. Co-op Adv. 5. Consumer Mags. 6. D.M. to Bus. Estab.7. D.M. to Consumers
8. Daily Newsp. 9. Exhibits/Trade Shows 10. Foreign 11. Infomercial 12. Internet Adv.13. Multimedia 14. Network Radio
15. Network T.V. 16. Newsp. Distr. Mags. 17. Other 18. Outdoor (Posters, Transit) 19. Point of Purchase20. Premiums, Novelties
21. Product Samples 22. Special Events Mktg. 23. Spot Radio 24. Spot T.V. 25. Weekly Newsp. 26. Yellow Page Adv.

Toll Free: (800) 937-0233
(Corporate)
— Catherine Payne *(Acct. Exec.)*

Rolling Wood Communications
47 Woodway Rd.
Stamford, CT 06907
Tel.: (203) 329-8287
(Directory Advertising)

ITW HI-CONE

(Sub. of Illinois Tool Works Inc.)
1140 W Bryn Mawr Ave
Itasca, IL 60143-1509
Tel.: (630) 438-5300
Fax: (630) 438-5315
Web Site: www.hi-cone.com
Sales Range: $50-74.9 Million
Approx. Number Employees: 100
Year Founded: 1950
Business Description:
Packaging Systems Mfr
S.I.C.: 3565; 7389
N.A.I.C.S.: 333993; 561910
Media: 10-22
Personnel:
Steve Henn *(VP & Gen Mgr)*
Sherri Pesch Lydon *(Mgr-Bus Unit)*
Gary J. Maus *(Mgr-Natl Acct-Breweries)*

ITW SPACE BAG

(Sub. of Illinois Tool Works Inc.)
7520 Airway Rd
San Diego, CA 92154
Tel.: (619) 671-9022
Fax: (619) 671-9036
Fax: (619) 671-9030
Toll Free: (800) 469-9044
E-mail: spacesaver@spacebag.com
Web Site: www.spacebag.com
Sales Range: $10-24.9 Million
Approx. Number Employees: 60
Business Description:
Plastics Storage Bags Mfr
S.I.C.: 3089; 2673
N.A.I.C.S.: 326199; 322223
Media: 12-13
Brands & Products:
SPACE BAG

J. JOSEPHSON, INC.

35 Horizon Blvd
South Hackensack, NJ 07606-1804
Tel.: (201) 440-7000
Fax: (201) 440-7140
Web Site: www.jjosephson.com
Approx. Number Employees: 150
Business Description:
Mfr. of Vinyl Wall Coverings
S.I.C.: 2672
N.A.I.C.S.: 322222
Personnel:
Mark Goodman *(Pres)*
Gilbert Goodman *(CEO)*
Brands & Products:
SYMPHONY
VYCON
Advertising Agency:
Richards Communications
3201 Enterprise Pkwy Ste 400
Beachwood, OH 44122
Tel.: (216) 514-7800
Fax: (216) 514-7801

JAMES ALEXANDER CORPORATION

845 State Rte 94
Blairstown, NJ 07825
Tel.: (908) 362-9266
Fax: (908) 362-5019
E-mail: info@james-alexander.com
Web Site: www.james-alexander.com
Sales Range: $1-9.9 Million
Approx. Number Employees: 70
Year Founded: 1976
Business Description:
Fill & Seal Glass & Plastic Ampoules
S.I.C.: 7389; 3842
N.A.I.C.S.: 561910; 339113
Import Export
Media: 2-7-10-11
Distr.: Intl.; Natl.
Personnel:
Alexander T. Davidson *(Owner)*
Francesca Fazzolari *(Pres)*
David Robinson *(VP & Gen Mgr)*
Brands & Products:
DISPENSING SOLUTIONS
JAC
JAMES ALEXANDER
MEDICAINE
Advertising Agency:
Turchette Advertising Agency LLC
9 Law Dr
Fairfield, NJ 07004
Tel.: (973) 227-8080
Fax: (973) 227-8342

KIMBERLY-CLARK CORPORATION

351 Phelps Dr
Irving, TX 75038-6540
Mailing Address:
PO Box 619100
Dallas, TX 75261-9100
Tel.: (972) 281-1200
Fax: (972) 281-1490
Web Site: www.kimberly-clark.com
Approx. Sls.: $19,746,000,000
Approx. Number Employees: 57,000
Year Founded: 1872
Business Description:
Consumer Products, Health Care Products, Newsprint & Specialty Paper Products Mfr
S.I.C.: 2621; 2676; 3842; 4512
N.A.I.C.S.: 322121; 322291; 339113; 481111
Import Export
Advertising Expenditures: $698,000,000
Media: 3-5-6-8-11-13-15-21-24
Distr.: Intl.; Natl.
Personnel:
Thomas J. Falk *(Chm & CEO)*
Mark A. Buthman *(CFO & Sr VP)*
Ramon F. Baez *(CIO & VP)*
Anthony J. Palmer *(CMO & Sr VP)*
Thomas J. Mielke *(Sr VP-Law & Govt Affairs & Chief Compliance Officer)*
Elane B. Stock *(Chief Strategy Officer & Sr VP)*
Robert E. Abernathy *(Pres-North Atlantic Consumer Products)*
Joanne B. Bauer *(Pres-Kimberly-Clark Health Care)*
Robert W. Black *(Pres-Intl)*
Christian A. Brickman *(Pres-Global Professional Products)*
R. Gordon Knapp *(Pres-Family Care)*
Lizanne C. Gottung *(Sr VP-HR)*
Jan B. Spencer *(Sr VP-Continuous Improvement, Sourcing & Sustainability)*
Michael T. Azbell *(VP & Controller)*
Andrew Meurer *(VP-Adult, Feminine & Sr Care)*
Mark Cammarota *(Brand Dir-Depend)*
Eric Seidel *(Brand Dir-Scott)*
Paul J. Alexander *(Dir-IR)*
Mark A. Kaline *(Dir-Global Media)*
Laura Keely *(Dir-Consumer Promo & IMP Ops)*
Christine Mau *(Dir-Brand Design)*
Marc Rosenstock *(Dir-Consumer Relationship Mktg)*
Ellen Wheeler *(Dir-Integrated Mktg Plng)*
James Richardson *(Assoc Dir-Advanced Capabilities & Analytics-Global)*
Don Klingseisen *(Sr Mgr-Shopper Mktg)*
Joey Mooring *(Sr Mgr-Global Mktg & Brand Comm)*
Blake Boulden *(Brand Mgr-Mktg)*
Amy Popp *(Brand Mgr)*
Steve Strubbe *(Brand Mgr-Huggies)*
Carolyn Eisele *(Mgr-Comml Program-KLEENEX Brand-Integrated Mktg Plng)*
Jeffrey Holecko *(Mgr-North American Media)*
Kate Johnson *(Mgr-Global Mktg Deployment)*
Kyle Mengwasser *(Mgr-Digital Mktg Strategy & Plng)*
Jim Schuh *(Mgr-Digital-Global)*
Melissa Sexton *(Mgr-Integrated Mktg)*
Brands & Products:
BLOCK-IT
CARLTON
CLEANTEAM
COTTONELLE
DENTABURST
DEPEND
DRY-TOUCH
FATHOM
GOODNITES
HUGGIES
INTREPID
KIMBERLY-CLARK
KIMGUARD
KIMTECH
KIMWIPES
KLEENEX
KLEENGUARD
KOTEX
LITTLE SWIMMERS
NEAT SHEET
NEW FREEDOM
POISE
PULL-UPS
SCOTT
SCOTT NATURALS
TAKE CONTROL WITH DEPEND
VIVA
WYPALL
Advertising Agencies:
Biggs Gilmore Communications
261 E Kalamazoo Ave Ste 300
Kalamazoo, MI 49007-3841
Tel.: (269) 349-7711
Fax: (269) 349-3051
Cottonelle

Directions Marketing
600 S Commercial St
Neenah, WI 54956
Tel.: (920) 725-4848
Fax: (920) 725-9359
Toll Free: (800) 236-2189

J. Walter Thompson Company
(d/b/a JWT)
466 Lexington Ave
New York, NY 10017-3140
Tel.: (212) 210-7000
Fax: (212) 210-7299
Cottonelle
Global Creative Agency - Family Care Brands
Kleenex

JWT
1 Knightsbridge Green
London, SW1X 7NW, United Kingdom
Tel.: (44) 20 7656 7000
Fax: (44) 20 7656 7010

JWT Action
388 S Main St Ste 410
Akron, OH 44311-4407
Tel.: (330) 376-6148, ext. 3243
Fax: (330) 253-1218
Feminine Care Products

Ketchum
(Part of Omnicom)
1285 Ave of the Americas
New York, NY 10019
Tel.: (646) 935-3900
Fax: (646) 935-4482

Marina Maher Communications
830 3rd Ave
New York, NY 10022
Tel.: (212) 485-6800
Fax: (212) 355-6318

Naked Communications New York
96 Greene St Ste 3
New York, NY 10012
Tel.: (212) 625-3082
Fax: (212) 625-3087

Ogilvy & Mather
(Sub. of WPP Group plc)
636 11th Ave
New York, NY 10036
Tel.: (212) 237-4000
Fax: (212) 237-5123
Depends
Huggies
Kotex
Lead Creative Agency for Baby, Child Care, Adult & Feminine Care
Poise Hourglass
— Alison Gragnano *(Exec Dir-Creative)*

Ogilvy Public Relations Worldwide
636 11th Ave
New York, NY 10036
Tel.: (212) 880-5200
Fax: (212) 370-4636

Organic, Inc.
1375 Broadway 8th Fl
New York, NY 10018
Tel.: (212) 827-2200
Fax: (212) 827-2201
Digital Agency of Record
Pull-Ups

Key to Media (For complete agency information see *The Advertising Red Books-Agencies* edition):
1. Bus. Publs. 2. Cable T.V. 3. Catalogs & Directories. 4. Co-op Adv. 5. Consumer Mags. 6. D.M. to Bus. Estab.7. D.M. to Consumers 8. Daily Newsp. 9. Exhibits/Trade Shows 10. Foreign 11. Infomercial 12. Internet Adv.13. Multimedia 14. Network Radio 15. Network T.V. 16. Newsp. Distr. Mags. 17. Other 18. Outdoor (Posters, Transit) 19. Point of Purchase20. Premiums, Novelties 21. Product Samples 22. Special Events Mktg. 23. Spot Radio 24. Spot T.V. 25. Weekly Newsp. 26. Yellow Page Adv.

Kimberly-Clark Corporation — (Continued)

Organic, Inc.
555 Market St 4th Fl
San Francisco, CA 94105
Tel.: (415) 581-5300
Fax: (415) 581-5400
Depends
Goodnites
Kotex
Poise
Pull-Ups
— Audrey Melofchik *(Sr VP-Engagement Mgmt)*

Taylor
350 Fifth Ave Ste 3800
New York, NY 10118
Tel.: (212) 714-1280
Fax: (212) 695-5685
Kleenex

TracyLocke
1999 Bryan St Ste 2800
Dallas, TX 75201
Tel.: (214) 259-3500
Fax: (214) 259-3550

Wunderman
(Worldwide Headquarters)
285 Madison Ave
New York, NY 10017
Tel.: (212) 941-3000
Fax: (212) 210-5454
Diapers

KIMBERLY-CLARK INC.
(Sub. of Kimberly-Clark Corporation - Personal Care Sector)
50 Burnhamthorpe Rd W
Mississauga, ON L5B 3Y5, Canada
Tel.: (905) 277-6500
Fax: (905) 277-6670
E-mail: info@kimberly-clark.com
Web Site: www.kimberly-clark.com/ask/kimberly-clark/canada.asp?country=Canada&Label=Cor[illegible]ue
Sales Range: $25-49.9 Million
Approx. Number Employees: 90
Business Description:
Personal Care Consumer Tissue & Travel Products Retailer & Marketer
S.I.C.: 2676
N.A.I.C.S.: 322291
Import Export
Media: 2-3-5-6-8-9-15-17-18-19-20-21-23-24-25
Distr.: Natl.
Budget Set: Nov.
Personnel:
Mark A. Buthman *(CFO & Sr VP)*
Anthony J. Palmer *(CMO & Sr VP)*
Thomas J. Mielke *(Chief Compliance Officer & Sr VP-Law, Govt Affairs)*
Elane B. Stock *(Chief Strategy Officer & Sr VP)*
Lizanne C. Gottung *(Chief HR OfficerSr VP)*
Jan B. Spencer *(Sr VP-Continuous Improvement Sourcing & Sustainability)*
Tony Ceci *(Dir-Mktg)*

KLW PLASTICS, INC.
(Sub. of KODA Specialty Products Group)
980 Deneen Ave
Monroe, OH 45050
Tel.: (513) 539-2673
Fax: (513) 539-4493
E-mail: info@klwplastics.com
Web Site: www.klwplastics.com
Approx. Rev.: $2,000,000
Approx. Number Employees: 14
Year Founded: 2004
Business Description:
Plastic Products Mfr
S.I.C.: 3089
N.A.I.C.S.: 326199
Media: 4
Personnel:
Mike Legeza *(Pres)*

KRUGER PAPER PRODUCTS LP
(Sub. of Kruger, Inc.)
1900 Minnesota Ct Ste 200
Mississauga, ON L5N 5R5, Canada
Tel.: (905) 812-6900
Fax: (905) 812-6910
Web Site: www.kruger.com
Sales Range: $400-449.9 Million
Approx. Number Employees: 1,700
Year Founded: 1922
Business Description:
Household & Commercial Paper Products Mfr & Marketer
S.I.C.: 2676
N.A.I.C.S.: 322291
Import Export
Media: 2-3-4-6-7-8-9-11-15-18-19-20-21-22-23-24
Distr.: Natl.
Budget Set: Sept.
Personnel:
Nancy Marcus *(Corp VP-Mktg)*
Advertising Agency:
John St.
172 John Street
Toronto, ON M5T 1X5, Canada
Tel.: (416) 348-0048
Fax: (416) 348-0050

LABELQUEST, INC.
578 N Michigan St
Elmhurst, IL 60126
Tel.: (630) 833-9400
Fax: (630) 833-9421
Toll Free: (800) 999-5301
E-mail: labelquest@sbcglobal.net
Approx. Sls.: $1,600,000
Approx. Number Employees: 15
Business Description:
Decals & Pressure Sensitive Labeling Items Mfr
S.I.C.: 2741
N.A.I.C.S.: 511199
Export
Media: 4-7-10-20-21-26
Distr.: Natl.
Budget Set: Jan.
Personnel:
Neil Vandenberg *(VP-Sls)*
Maurice Carter *(Mgr-Production)*

LANGSTON COMPANIES, INC.
1760 S 3rd St
Memphis, TN 38109
Tel.: (901) 774-4440
Fax: (901) 942-5402
Toll Free: (800) 238-5798
E-mail: info@langstonbag.com
Web Site: www.langstonbag.com
Approx. Number Employees: 425
Year Founded: 1946
Business Description:
Sacks, Bags, Wrappings, Containers & Covers Mfr & Distr
S.I.C.: 2674; 2671
N.A.I.C.S.: 322224; 322221
Import Export
Media: 2-4-7-10-17
Distr.: Natl.
Budget Set: Jan.
Personnel:
George Parkey *(VP-Fin)*
Brands & Products:
LANGSTON

LAWRENCE PAPER COMPANY
2801 Lakeview Rd PO Box 887
Lawrence, KS 66049
Tel.: (785) 843-8111
Fax: (785) 749-3904
Toll Free: (800) 535-4553
E-mail: info@lpco.net
Web Site: www.lpco.net
E-Mail For Key Personnel:
Sales Director: sales@lpco.net
Approx. Number Employees: 450
Year Founded: 1882
Business Description:
Corrugated Boxes & Thermoformed Packaging Mfr & Retailer
S.I.C.: 2653; 7373
N.A.I.C.S.: 322211; 541512
Media: 2
Distr.: Reg.
Personnel:
Justin Hill, Jr. *(Owner)*
Trudy Walker *(Asst Controller)*
Brands & Products:
JAYHAWK BOXES
LAWRENCE PAPER

LEPAGE'S, INC.
(Sub. of Jackson National Life Insurance Company)
12900 S Huron River Dr
Romulus, MI 48174
Tel.: (734) 942-9140
Fax: (734) 229-1130
E-mail: comments@lepages.com
Web Site: www.lepages.com
E-Mail For Key Personnel:
Sales Director: sales@lepages.com
Approx. Number Employees: 50
Year Founded: 1876
Business Description:
Adhesives Tapes & Glue Mfr
S.I.C.: 5085
N.A.I.C.S.: 423840
Import Export
Advertising Expenditures: $200,000
Media: 2-4-6-7-10-13-17-19
Distr.: Natl.
Budget Set: Sept.
Brands & Products:
HOLD-UP REMOVABLE
TAKE NOTE!

LINDENMEYR MUNROE
(Div. of Central National-Gottesman Inc.)
3 Manhattanville Rd
Purchase, NY 10577
Tel.: (914) 696-9000
Fax: (914) 696-9352
Web Site: www.lindenmeyr.com
Approx. Number Employees: 100
Year Founded: 1859
Business Description:
Business & Commercial Printing Paper Distr
S.I.C.: 5111
N.A.I.C.S.: 424110
Import Export
Media: 2-4-7-10-21
Distr.: Reg.
Personnel:
James W. Barrett *(Exec VP-Admin)*
Stephen J. Daly *(VP-Sls & Mktg)*
David Jones *(VP-Fin)*
Angela Pizzarello *(Asst Controller)*
Guy J. Barbieri *(Dir-Inventory Sys)*
Mark Walters *(Bus Mgr-Lindenmeyr Envelope)*
Brands & Products:
METEOR
METEOR COPY

LITTLE RAPIDS CORPORATION
PO Box 19031
Green Bay, WI 54307
Tel.: (920) 496-3040
Fax: (920) 494-5340
E-mail: hr@littlerapids.com
Web Site: www.littlerapids.com
Approx. Number Employees: 400
Year Founded: 1947
Business Description:
Paper Mill
S.I.C.: 2621
N.A.I.C.S.: 322121
Import Export
Personnel:
Kirk Ryan *(Pres & CEO)*
John Wirch *(VP-HR)*
Brands & Products:
GRAHAM
LITTLE RAPIDS
SHAWANO
Advertising Agency:
Weidert Group Inc.
210 W College Ave
Appleton, WI 54911
Tel.: (920) 731-2771
Fax: (920) 731-9142

LOVESHAW
(Sub. of Illinois Tool Works Inc.)
2206 Easton Tpk Box 83
South Canaan, PA 18459
Tel.: (570) 937-4921
Web Site: www.loveshaw.com
Sales Range: $25-49.9 Million
Approx. Number Employees: 70
Business Description:
Corrugated Box Sealing Machinery Mfr
S.I.C.: 3565
N.A.I.C.S.: 333993
Export
Advertising Expenditures: $100,000
Media: 10-13
Personnel:
Jim Fairchild *(Reg Mgr-Sls)*
Brands & Products:
LITTLE DAVID

THE LUCE CORPORATION
336 Putnam Ave
Hamden, CT 06517-2744
Tel.: (203) 787-0281
Fax: (203) 230-2753
Toll Free: (800) 344-6966
Approx. Number Employees: 7

Key to Media (For complete agency information see *The Advertising Red Books-Agencies* edition):
1. Bus. Publs. 2. Cable T.V. 3. Catalogs & Directories. 4. Co-op Adv. 5. Consumer Mags. 6. D.M. to Bus. Estab.7. D.M. to Consumers
8. Daily Newsp. 9. Exhibits/Trade Shows 10. Foreign 11. Infomercial 12. Internet Adv.13. Multimedia 14. Network Radio
15. Network T.V. 16. Newsp. Distr. Mags. 17. Other 18. Outdoor (Posters, Transit) 19. Point of Purchase20. Premiums, Novelties
21. Product Samples 22. Special Events Mktg. 23. Spot Radio 24. Spot T.V. 25. Weekly Newsp. 26. Yellow Page Adv.

Business Description:
Moisture-Absorbing Food Containers Mfr
S.I.C.: 2499; 3479
N.A.I.C.S.: 321999; 332812
Media: 2-4-7
Distr.: Natl.
Personnel:
Timothy F. Pagnam *(Pres)*
Brands & Products:
BLUE MAGIC
KRISPY KAN

MACTAC SCRANTON FACILITY

(Unit of Bemis Company, Inc.)
802 E Corey St
Scranton, PA 18505
Mailing Address:
PO Box 1106
Scranton, PA 18501-1106
Tel.: (570) 347-2035
Fax: (570) 941-5411
Web Site: www.mactac.com
Sales Range: $50-74.9 Million
Approx. Number Employees: 200
Year Founded: 1966
Business Description:
Mfr of Special & Technical Papers
S.I.C.: 2891
N.A.I.C.S.: 325520
Import Export
Media: 2-3-4-21
Distr.: Natl.
Personnel:
Gary Arvay *(Gen Mgr)*

MARCAL PAPER MILLS, INC.

1 Market St
Elmwood Park, NJ 07407
Tel.: (201) 796-4000
Fax: (201) 796-0470
E-mail: webmaster@marcalpaper.com
Web Site: www.marcalpaper.com
E-Mail For Key Personnel:
Public Relations: pmarcalus@marcalpaper.com
Approx. Number Employees: 1,000
Year Founded: 1932
Business Description:
Mfr & Marketer of Consumer & Institutional Tissue Products
S.I.C.: 2676; 2671
N.A.I.C.S.: 322291; 322221
Import Export
Media: 2-5-10-19-20-23
Distr.: Reg.
Personnel:
Fred Smagorinsky *(CEO)*
Robert Prongay *(Exec VP-Sls)*
James D'Agosta *(Sr VP-Sls & Mktg)*
Joseph Elvin *(Sr VP-Pur)*
Gordon Mayer *(Sr VP-Converting, Distr & HR)*
Brands & Products:
A SMALL, EASY STEP TO A GREENER EARTH
ASPEN
AT HOME & IN THE OFFICE
BELLA
EASY REACH
FLUFFY
KAOFIN
MARCAL
SANI-HANKS
SAVING TREES SINCE 1950
SMALLSTEPS
SOFPAC
SUNRISE
WORKFORCE

MARIETTA CORPORATION

(Holding of Ares Management LLC)
37 Huntington St
Cortland, NY 13045
Tel.: (607) 753-6746
Fax: (607) 756-0656
E-mail: dcardarelli@mariettacorp.com
Web Site: www.mariettacorp.com
Sales Range: $150-199.9 Million
Approx. Number Employees: 1,200
Year Founded: 1976
Business Description:
Personal Care Amenity Supplier
S.I.C.: 2841; 5122
N.A.I.C.S.: 325611; 424210
Import Export
Media: 10-21
Personnel:
Donald Sturdivant *(CEO)*
David P. Hempson *(Sr VP-Bus Dev)*
Brands & Products:
AROMAE
CAMBRIA & TAYLOR
EXECUSTAY
LORD & MAYFAIR
MARIETTA
PROTERRA
SERENE ELEMENTS
SUN AND SAND

MCCOURT LABEL COMPANY

20 Egbert Ln
Lewis Run, PA 16738
Tel.: (814) 362-3851
Fax: (814) 362-4156
Fax: (888) 735-0014
Toll Free: (800) 458-2390
E-mail: mccourt@mccourtlabel.com
Web Site: www.mccourtlabel.com
Approx. Number Employees: 60
Year Founded: 1896
Business Description:
Custom Pressure-Sensitive Labels Mfr
S.I.C.: 2679; 2752
N.A.I.C.S.: 322299; 323110
Import Export
Media: 2-4-7-8-10-21
Distr.: Natl.
Budget Set: Nov.
Personnel:
David Ferguson *(Pres)*

MEADWESTVACO CORPORATION

501 S 5th St
Richmond, VA 23219-0501
Tel.: (804) 444-1000
Web Site: www.meadwestvaco.com
Approx. Sls.: $5,693,000,000
Approx. Number Employees: 17,500
Year Founded: 2002
Business Description:
Coated & Specialty Papers, Office Products, Packaging & Specialty Chemicals Mfr
S.I.C.: 2621; 2631; 2653; 2671; 2675; 2679; 7389
N.A.I.C.S.: 322121; 322130; 322211; 322221; 322231; 322299; 561910
Media: 7-11
Personnel:
John A. Luke, Jr. *(Chm & CEO)*
James A. Buzzard *(Pres)*
E. Mark Rajkowski *(CFO & Sr VP)*
Peter Durette *(Chief Strategy Officer & VP)*
Jack C. Goldfrank *(Pres-Center for Package Innovation)*
Mark V. Gulling *(Pres-Global Bus Svcs)*
Neil A. McLachlan *(Pres-Consumer & Office Products Grp)*
Edward A. Rose *(Pres-Specialty Chemicals Div)*
John K. Sanfacon *(Pres-Food Svcs Pkg Bus)*
Stephen R. Scherger *(Pres-Beverage Media & Entertainment Folding Carton Ops)*
Diane Teer *(Pres-Food Pkg Bus)*
Wendell L. Willkie II *(Gen Counsel, Sec & Sr VP)*
Mark S. Cross *(Sr VP-Packaging)*
Linda V. Schreiner *(Sr VP-HR & Comm)*
Bruce V. Thomas *(Sr VP-Healthcare & Innovation)*
Mark T. Watkins, Sr. *(Sr VP-Forestry & Tech)*
Laurent Bourgoin *(VP-European Sls & Mktg-Fragrance Div)*
Guillaume de Demandolx *(VP-Sls & Mktg-Beauty, Personal Care, Home & Garden Bus)*
Kim Biechele *(Dir-Interactive Mktg)*
John J. Carrara *(Assoc Gen Counsel & Asst Sec)*
Brands & Products:
ACCUPUMP
AIR PLAS
AMCAL
ARIA
ARMOREZ
AROSURF
AT-A-GLANCE
BASKETWRAP
BOS
CAMBRIDGE
CARRIER KOTE
CEREPAK
CLUSTER-CLIP
CLUSTER-SIDE
CLUSTERPAK
COATED NATURAL KRAFT
COLUMBIAN
CONCERTO
CRESCENDO
CUSTOM KOTE
DAY RUNNER
DIACID
DIGIPAK
DIGISTAK
DIVA
DIWATEX
DOSEPAK
DOSEPAK EXPRESS
DUODOZEN
DUOFOLD
DUOPLY
DURALINE
DYNASPERSE
ELASTOREZ
EVOLUTION
FACER
FIREPLI
FIVE STAR
FLEXITECH
FRIDGEMASTER
FUSION
HARMONY
HAYES
HILROY
HVD
HYACT
INDULIN
INFINITY
INJECTAPAK
INSIGHT
INSIGHT SLIDER
JONREZ
KLAFOLD
KLEARFOLD
KRAFTPAK
KRAFTPLEX
KRAFTSPERSE
LIGNOSOL
LOKATOP
LUNA
LUSTRALITE
M300
MAESTRO
MARK LL
MARK VL
MARK VLL
MD150
MD3200
MEAD
MELODIE
MINI-TRIGGER
MIXOR
MK
MORTAR PLAS
NATRALOCK
NATURALSOURCE
NOC
NUCHAR
OCEAN
ORCHESTRA
P2000
PEARL
PERAL
PODLE
POLYFAC
POLYFON
PRELUDE
PRIMEBASE
PRINTKOTE
RADIANTLINE
READY SLEEVE
READY WRAP
REAX
RED TAG
RHAPSODY
RIGESA
SD 100
SD 200
SD 20C
SD 400T
SD 800T
SDS
SHELLPAK
SHOWERGUARD
SINFONIA
SONATA
SONNET
SPRAYETTE IV
STERLING
STYLE
SUREPAK
SYNPAQUE
SYSTEM 1
TANGO
TENAX
TOFAX
TRAPPER KEEPER
TS800
ULTRA PLAS

Key to Media (For complete agency information see *The Advertising Red Books-Agencies* edition):
1. Bus. Publs. 2. Cable T.V. 3. Catalogs & Directories. 4. Co-op Adv. 5. Consumer Mags. 6. D.M. to Bus. Estab.7. D.M. to Consumers
8. Daily Newsp. 9. Exhibits/Trade Shows 10. Foreign 11. Infomercial 12. Internet Adv.13. Multimedia 14. Network Radio
15. Network T.V. 16. Newsp. Distr. Mags. 17. Other 18. Outdoor (Posters, Transit) 19. Point of Purchase20. Premiums, Novelties
21. Product Samples 22. Special Events Mktg. 23. Spot Radio 24. Spot T.V. 25. Weekly Newsp. 26. Yellow Page Adv.

MeadWestvaco Corporation — (Continued)

UULTRAZINE
VANISPERSE
VORTEX
VORTEX BLUE-RAY
WECOTE
XPANZ
YOGOPAK

MEADWESTVACO PACKAGING SYSTEMS, LLC
(Sub. of MeadWestvaco Corporation)
1040 W Marietta St NW
Atlanta, GA 30318-5218
Tel.: (404) 875-2711
Fax: (404) 897-7970
Web Site: www.meadwestvaco.com
Sales Range: $1-9.9 Million
Approx. Number Employees: 80
Business Description:
Multiple Protective & Specialty Packaging Systems for Beverage, Food & Other Industries & Point-of-Purchase Display Merchandising Mfr
S.I.C.: 2621; 2677
N.A.I.C.S.: 322121; 322232
Export
Media: 2-4-10-19-20
Distr.: Intl.; Natl.
Budget Set: Aug.

MERCER INTERNATIONAL INC.
Suite 2840 650 West Georgia Street
Vancouver, BC V6B 4N8, Canada
Tel.: (604) 684-1099
Fax: (604) 684-1094
E-mail: info@mercerint.com
Web Site: www.mercerint.com
Approx. Rev.: $1,212,562,719
Approx. Number Employees: 1,491
Year Founded: 1968
Business Description:
Pulp & Paper Mill Owner & Operator
S.I.C.: 2611; 2621
N.A.I.C.S.: 322110; 322121; 322122
Personnel:
Jimmy S.H. Lee *(Pres & CEO)*
David M. Gandossi *(CFO, Sec & Exec VP)*
Claes-Inge Isacson *(COO)*
David M. Cooper *(VP-Sls & Mktg-Europe)*
Eric X. Heine *(VP-Sls & Mktg-North America & Asia)*
Michael Funk *(Mgr-Fiber Procurement)*
Advertising Agency:
FD U.S. Communications, Inc. (d/b/a Financial Dynamics)
Wall St Plz 88 Pine St 32nd Fl
New York, NY 10005
Tel.: (212) 850-5600
Fax: (212) 850-5790

MIDWESCO FILTER RESOURCES INC.
(Sub. of MFRI Inc.)
385 Battaile Dr
Winchester, VA 22604
Mailing Address:
PO Box 2075
Winchester, VA 22604-1275
Tel.: (540) 667-8500
Fax: (540) 722-9217
E-mail: sales@midwescofilter.com
Web Site: www.midwescofilter.com
E-Mail For Key Personnel:
Sales Director: sales@midwescofilter.com
Sales Range: $50-74.9 Million
Approx. Number Employees: 165
Year Founded: 1968
Business Description:
Protective Clothing, Filter Bags & Seamless Tube Filter Bags Mfr
S.I.C.: 3564
N.A.I.C.S.: 333411
Media: 2-4-7-10
Distr.: Natl.
Personnel:
Mark Foster *(Pres)*
Brands & Products:
LEAK SEEKER
PLEAT+PLUS
PREKOTE
SEAMLESS TUBE

MITCHEL-LINCOLN PACKAGING LTD
3737 Thimens Blvd
Ville Saint Laurent, QC H4R 1V1, Canada
Tel.: (514) 332-3480
Fax: (514) 332-2039
Toll Free: (800) 361-5727
E-mail: ml@ml-group.com
Web Site: www.ml-group.com
E-Mail For Key Personnel:
Sales Director: jiml@ml-group.com
Public Relations: davidg@ml-group.com
Approx. Number Employees: 346
Year Founded: 1965
Business Description:
Corrugated Boxes
S.I.C.: 2653
N.A.I.C.S.: 322211
Import Export
Media: 2-4-6-7-8-10-22
Distr.: Natl.
Budget Set: Oct.-Dec.
Personnel:
Jimmy Garfinkle *(Pres)*
David Garfinkle *(Sr VP)*
Normand Bonin *(VP-Fin)*
Jim Levia *(VP-Sls)*
Guy Desrochers *(Mgr-Quality Assurance)*
Stan Nikiel *(Mgr-Quality Sys)*

MOHAWK FINE PAPERS, INC.
465 Saratoga St
Cohoes, NY 12047-4626
Tel.: (518) 237-1740
Fax: (518) 237-7394
Toll Free: (800) THEMILL
E-mail: webmaster@mohawkpaper.com
Web Site: www.mohawkpaper.com
Approx. Number Employees: 800
Year Founded: 1931
Business Description:
Mfr of Coated Texts & Printing Papers
S.I.C.: 2672; 2621
N.A.I.C.S.: 322222; 322121
Import Export
Media: 2-4-7-10-11
Distr.: Intl.; Natl.
Budget Set: Nov.
Personnel:
Thomas D. O'Connor *(Chm & CEO)*
Walter A. Duignan *(Vice Chm & Exec VP)*
John F. Haren *(Pres & CFO)*
Kevin P. Richard *(COO & Exec VP-Ops)*
Paul Biesiadecki *(Sr VP-Sls & Mktg)*
George Milner *(Sr VP-Energy, Environmental & Govt Affairs)*
F. Joseph O'Connor *(Sr VP-Intl Sls)*
Laura J. Shore *(Sr VP-Comm & Innovation Strategies)*
Craig Slemp *(Sr VP-Strategic Plng & Direct Sls)*
Paul J. Stamas *(VP-IT)*
Maria Aggelonitis *(Reg Mgr-Sls)*
Robert Ferragina *(Reg Mgr-Sls)*
Christopher Morgan *(Mgr-District Sls-New England)*
Brands & Products:
BECKETT CONCEPT
BECKETT EXPRESSION
BRITEHUE
I-TONE
INXWELL
IRISH LINEN
MOHAWK
MOHAWK 50/10 PLUS
MOHAWK COLOR COPY
MOHAWK DIGITAL IMAGING SURFACE
MOHAWK IRISH LINEN
MOHAWK NAVAJO
MOHAWK OPAQUE
MOHAWK OPTIONS
MOHAWK SATIN
MOHAWK SUPERFINE
MOHAWK TOMOHAWK
MOHAWK ULTRAFELT
MOHAWK VELLUM
NAVAJO
OPAQUE
OPTIONS
SATIN
STRATHMORE
SUPERFINE
TOMOHAWK
ULTRAFELT
VELLUM
VIA COLORS

MOMENTIVE PERFORMANCE MATERIALS, INC.
(Sub. of Momentive Performance Materials Holdings LLC)
22 Corporate Woods Blvd 2nd Fl
Albany, NY 12211
Tel.: (607) 786-8131
Fax: (607) 786-8309
Toll Free: (800) 295-2392
E-mail: nancy.pitts@momentive.com
Web Site: www.momentive.com
Approx. Sls.: $2,588,423,000
Approx. Number Employees: 4,719
Business Description:
Thermoplastics, Silicon-Based Products & Fused Quartz & Ceramics Mfr
S.I.C.: 2821; 1459; 3089; 3299
N.A.I.C.S.: 325211; 212325; 326199; 327999
Advertising Expenditures: $6,406,000
Media: 2-13
Personnel:
Craig O. Morrison *(Pres & CEO)*
William Carter *(CFO & Exec VP)*
Shawn Williams *(Pres/CEO-Global Sealants)*
Steven P. Delarge *(Pres-Silicones & Quartz Div & Exec VP)*
Douglas A. Johns *(Gen Counsel & Exec VP)*
Eric Thaler *(VP-Tech)*
Gregory Strosaker *(Product Mgr-Semiconductor Tubing)*
Advertising Agency:
Chletcos/Gallagher Inc.
63 Greene St Ste 602
New York, NY 10012
Tel.: (212) 334-2455
Fax: (212) 334-2463

MONADNOCK PAPER MILLS, INC.
117 Antrim Rd
Bennington, NH 03442-4205
Tel.: (603) 588-3311
Fax: (603) 588-6289
E-mail: dlunati@mpm.com
Web Site: www.mpm.com
Approx. Sls.: $58,826,253
Approx. Number Employees: 230
Year Founded: 1948
Business Description:
Paper Mills
S.I.C.: 2621
N.A.I.C.S.: 322121
Import Export
Personnel:
Richard G. Verney *(Chm & CEO)*
Andrew Manns *(CFO & Treas)*
James M. Clemente *(VP-Sls & Mktg)*
David Lunati *(Dir-Mktg)*
Brands & Products:
ASTROLITE
ASTROLITE PC
CARESS
DULCET
PAPER
STAR-TEX
ULTRAFORM
ULTRAHIDE
Advertising Agency:
Signaltree Marketing & Advertising
160 Emerald St Ste 201
Keene, NH 03431
Tel.: (603) 358-5100
Fax: (603) 358-5109

NASHUA CORPORATION
(Sub. of Cenveo Inc.)
11 Trafalgar Sq 2nd Fl
Nashua, NH 03063
Tel.: (603) 880-2323
Fax: (603) 880-5671
Toll Free: (800) 258-1370
E-mail: info@nashua.com
Web Site: www.nashua.com
Approx. Sls.: $264,903,000
Approx. Number Employees: 659
Year Founded: 1849
Business Description:
Specialty Imaging Products & Services for Industrial & Commercial Customers; Products Include Thermal Papers, Pressure Sensitive Labels & Specialty Papers, Toners
S.I.C.: 3111; 2621; 2672; 2679; 3861
N.A.I.C.S.: 316110; 322121; 322222; 322299; 325992
Import Export
Advertising Expenditures: $33,500,000
Media: 2-5-7-8-10-11-13
Distr.: Intl.; Natl.
Budget Set: Oct.

Key to Media (For complete agency information see *The Advertising Red Books-Agencies* edition):
1. Bus. Publs. 2. Cable T.V. 3. Catalogs & Directories. 4. Co-op Adv. 5. Consumer Mags. 6. D.M. to Bus. Estab.7. D.M. to Consumers 8. Daily Newsp. 9. Exhibits/Trade Shows 10. Foreign 11. Infomercial 12. Internet Adv.13. Multimedia 14. Network Radio 15. Network T.V. 16. Newsp. Distr. Mags. 17. Other 18. Outdoor (Posters, Transit) 19. Point of Purchase20. Premiums, Novelties 21. Product Samples 22. Special Events Mktg. 23. Spot Radio 24. Spot T.V. 25. Weekly Newsp. 26. Yellow Page Adv.

Brands & Products:
DAVAC
ECHO
JET-PLOT
LOGIX
NASHUA
PERFECT PRINT
RITTENHOUSE
THERMO-SENSITIVE

NEENAH PAPER, INC.
3460 Preston Ridge Rd Ste 600
Alpharetta, GA 30005
Tel.: (678) 566-6500
E-mail: Investors@neenahpaper.com
Web Site: www.neenah.com
Approx. Sls.: $657,700,000
Approx. Number Employees: 1,660
Year Founded: 1873
Business Description:
Paper Mfr
S.I.C.: 2621; 2611
N.A.I.C.S.: 322121; 322110
Advertising Expenditures: $6,100,000
Personnel:
Sean T. Erwin *(Chm, Pres & CEO)*
Bonnie C. Lind *(CFO, Treas & Sr VP)*
John P. O'Donnell *(COO & Sr VP)*
Dennis P. Runsten *(Pres-Tech Products-US)*
Steven S. Heinrichs *(Gen Counsel, Sec & Sr VP)*
Thomas Wright *(Dir-Design)*
Kathy Kemps *(Brand Mgr)*
Brands & Products:
CLASSIC COLUMNS
CLASSIC COTTON
CLASSIC CREST
CLASSIC CREST DIGITAL
CLASSIC LAID
CLASSIC LINEN
CLASSIC LINEN DIGITAL
CORONADO SST
DURAFORM
EAMES
ENVIRONMENT
GESSNER
GILBERT
HEIRLOOM
HOWARD
IMAGE CLIP
IMAGECLIP
IRON MAN
JET-OPAQUE
JET-PRO
JET-TRANS
KIMDURA
KIMLON
LASER 1 OPAQUE
MUGS N MORE
MUNISING LP
NEENAH DIGITAL
OXFORD
PHOTO-TRANS
PREMASK
PREVAIL
SILVER
SOFSTRETCH
STARWHITE
SUNDANCE
TECHNI-PRINT
TEXOPRINT
UV/ULTRA
UV/ULTRA II
VARITESS

NETWORK 1 FINANCIAL GROUP, INC.
2 Bridge Ave Ste 241
Red Bank, NJ 07701
Tel.: (732) 758-9001
Toll Free: (800) 886-7007
Web Site: www.network1financial.com
E-Mail For Key Personnel:
Sales Director: sales@smart-sourcing.com
Approx. Rev.: $2,929,721
Approx. Number Employees: 19
Year Founded: 1970
Business Description:
Brokerage & Trading Services
S.I.C.: 6289
N.A.I.C.S.: 523999
Media: 10
Personnel:
Richard W. Hunt, Jr. *(Chm)*
Damon D. Testaverde *(Mng Dir)*

NETWORK SERVICES COMPANY
1100 E Woodfield Rd, Ste 200
Schaumburg, IL 60173
Tel.: (847) 803-4888
Fax: (847) 803-0482
Web Site: www.nsconline.com
Approx. Number Employees: 130
Business Description:
Branded Paper & Plastic Products & Cleaning Materials Mfr
S.I.C.: 5113
N.A.I.C.S.: 424130
Advertising Expenditures: $500,000
Multimedia: $125,000; Bus. Publs.: $125,000; D.M. to Bus. Estab.: $85,000; Exhibits/Trade Shows: $100,000; Internet Adv.: $30,000; Special Events Mktg.: $35,000
Distr.: Natl.
Budget Set: Nov.
Personnel:
Robert Mitchum *(CFO)*
Warren Noble *(Dir-Supplier Program)*
Janice F. Hoye *(Mgr-HR)*
Brands & Products:
NETCARE
NETWORK
VERSICOPY

NEW LEAF PAPER, LLC
116 New Montgomery Ste 830
San Francisco, CA 94105
Tel.: (415) 291-9210
Fax: (415) 291-9353
Toll Free: (888) 989-5323
E-mail: info@newleafpaper.com
Web Site: www.newleafpaper.com
Sales Range: $10-24.9 Million
Approx. Number Employees: 18
Business Description:
Recycled Paper Products Retailer
S.I.C.: 7389; 5111
N.A.I.C.S.: 541990; 424110
Media: 4-6-21
Personnel:
Jeff Mendelsohn *(Co-Founder & Pres)*

NEXUS PLASTICS, INC.
1 Loretto Ave
Hawthorne, NJ 07506-1303
Tel.: (973) 427-3311
Fax: (973) 427-4847
Toll Free: (800) 486-3987
E-mail: custserv@nexusplastics.com
Web Site: www.nexusplastics.com
Approx. Number Employees: 110
Year Founded: 1982
Business Description:
Specialty Extruded Films & Bags Mfr
S.I.C.: 3081; 2673
N.A.I.C.S.: 326113; 326111
Export
Advertising Expenditures: $500,000
Media: 2-4-7-10-11
Distr.: Intl.; Natl.
Personnel:
Marwan Sholakh *(Pres)*
Wayne Dzierzanowski *(Mgr-Quality Control)*
Kariman Sholakh *(Mgr-HR)*
Brands & Products:
NEXON
NEXU-PAK
NEXUS

NICE-PAK PRODUCTS, INC.
2 Nice Pak Pk
Orangeburg, NY 10962-1317
Tel.: (845) 365-1700
Fax: (845) 365-1729
Fax: (845) 365-1717
E-mail: info@nicepak.com
Web Site: www.nicepak.com
Approx. Number Employees: 1,000
Year Founded: 1957
Business Description:
Folded Moist Towelettes; Contract Packagers of Unit Packets to the Drug, Cosmetic & Pharmaceutical Industry
S.I.C.: 2621; 7389
N.A.I.C.S.: 322121; 561910
Export
Media: 1-2-5-6-10-13-19-21-22
Distr.: Intl.; Natl.
Budget Set: July
Personnel:
Shannon Shoptaw *(Dir-Healthy Hands Initiative)*
Brands & Products:
EZ ONES
GRIME BOSS
HYDRA SPUN
NICE 'N CLEAN
NICE-PAK
PDI
SANI-CLOTH
SANI-DEX
SANI-HANDS
WET-NAP

NIELSEN & BAINBRIDGE
(Holding of The Jordan Company, L.P.)
40 Eisenhower Dr
Paramus, NJ 07652-1404
Tel.: (201) 368-9191
Fax: (201) 845-7539
Toll Free: (800) 342-0124
E-mail: info@nielsen-bainbridge.com
Web Site: www.nielsen-bainbridge.com
Approx. Number Employees: 240
Year Founded: 1867
Business Description:
Picture Framing Products & Services
S.I.C.: 3999
N.A.I.C.S.: 339999
Advertising Expenditures: $500,000
Media: 2-7-10-13-21
Distr.: Natl.
Budget Set: Nov.
Personnel:
Barbara Sommer *(Exec VP-Mktg)*
Brands & Products:
ALPHAMAT
ALPHAMOUNT
ALPHARAG
ARTCARE
ARTMATE
BAINBRIDGE
BEVELACCENTS
BLACK BY BAINBRIDGE
FASCIA
FRAMEKIT

NORTON PACKAGING, INC.
20670 Corsair Blvd
Hayward, CA 94545
Tel.: (510) 786-3638
Fax: (510) 786-3082
Web Site: www.nortonpackaging.com
Business Description:
Plastic Pail Mfr
S.I.C.: 3089
N.A.I.C.S.: 326199
Advertising Expenditures: $70,950
Media: 17
Personnel:
Bernard W. Norton *(Founder)*

NVF COMPANY
(Filed Ch 11 Bankruptcy #911293 on 04/15/09 in U.S. Bankruptcy Ct, Dist of DE, Wilmington)
1166 Yorklyn Rd
Yorklyn, DE 19736
Tel.: (302) 239-5281
Fax: (302) 239-4406
E-mail: nvf@nvf.com
Web Site: www.nvf.com
Approx. Number Employees: 500
Year Founded: 1875
Business Description:
Mfr & Retailer of Vulcanized Fiber Sheets & Tubes; Mfr of Industrial Laminated Plastics
S.I.C.: 2822; 3555
N.A.I.C.S.: 325212; 333293
Advertising Expenditures: $100,000
Media: 2-7-10
Distr.: Intl.; Natl.
Budget Set: Oct. -Nov.
Brands & Products:
ABRASIVE 001
BONE 410
COMMERCIAL 585
FILAMITE
FORBON
HERMETIC 115
LAMICOR
PHENOLITE
POLYESTER FILM COMPOSITE 190
TAPE BACKER 200
TEXTILE 480
TRUNK & CASE 830
WHITE 220
WHITE TAG 202
YORKITE
YORKLITE

ORCHIDS PAPER PRODUCTS COMPANY
4826 Hunt St
Pryor, OK 74361
Tel.: (918) 825-0616
Fax: (918) 825-0060
E-mail: krschroeder@orchidspaper.com
Web Site: www.orchidspaper.com

Key to Media (For complete agency information see *The Advertising Red Books-Agencies* edition):
1. Bus. Publs. 2. Cable T.V. 3. Catalogs & Directories. 4. Co-op Adv. 5. Consumer Mags. 6. D.M. to Bus. Estab.7. D.M. to Consumers 8. Daily Newsp. 9. Exhibits/Trade Shows 10. Foreign 11. Infomercial 12. Internet Adv.13. Multimedia 14. Network Radio 15. Network T.V. 16. Newsp. Distr. Mags. 17. Other 18. Outdoor (Posters, Transit) 19. Point of Purchase20. Premiums, Novelties 21. Product Samples 22. Special Events Mktg. 23. Spot Radio 24. Spot T.V. 25. Weekly Newsp. 26. Yellow Page Adv.

Orchids Paper Products Company — (Continued)

Approx. Sls.: $92,504,000
Approx. Number Employees: 292
Year Founded: 1998
Business Description:
Paper Product Mfr
S.I.C.: 2621; 2676
N.A.I.C.S.: 322121; 322291
Advertising Expenditures: $408,000
Personnel:
Jay Shuster *(Chm)*
Robert A. Snyder *(Pres & CEO)*
Keith R. Schroeder *(CFO)*
Dan Daniels *(VP-Sls & Mktg)*
Brands & Products:
COLORTEX
DRI-MOP
MY SIZE
ORCHIDS PAPER PRODUCTS COMPANY
SOFT'N FLUFFY
VELVET

OWENS-ILLINOIS, INC.

1 Michael Owens Way
Perrysburg, OH 43551-2999
Tel.: (567) 336-5000
Tel.: (567) 336-1893 (Mktg)
Fax: (567) 336-2505
Web Site: www.o-i.com
Approx. Sls.: $6,633,000,000
Approx. Number Employees: 24,000
Year Founded: 1907
Business Description:
Glass Container Mfr
S.I.C.: 3221
N.A.I.C.S.: 327213
Advertising Expenditures: $5,000,000
Media: 4-10-11-21-26
Distr.: Natl.
Budget Set: Nov.
Personnel:
Albert P.L. Stroucken *(Chm & CEO)*
Edward C. White *(CFO & Sr VP)*
L. Richard Crawford *(CTO & COO & VP)*
Radhika Batra *(VP & Chief Procurement Officer)*
Jose Lorente *(Pres-O-I Europe)*
James W. Baehren *(Gen Counsel & Sr VP-Strategic Plng)*
Shaun McMackin *(VP & Mgr-Mfg)*
Paul Butts *(VP-Distributor Sls)*
John Haudrich *(VP-Fin)*
Michael Lonsway *(VP-Global Innovation)*
John Reynolds *(Controller-Fin Reporting)*
Joe Juarez *(Dir-Corp Dev)*
Brands & Products:
1-CLIC
BIDS
CLIC-LOC
CONTOUR
CONTOUR-PAK
DURAGLAS
EASY FLOW
EASYSEAL
FLEX-BAND
FLEX-LOC
FLIPTOP CONTOUR
FLODS
HILTON OVAL
OI
OPTICLEAR
PLASTI-SHIELD
PLASTOP
POL-E-LOC
QUALI-TOP
T-TOP

OZBURN-HESSEY LOGISTICS LLC

7101 Executive Ctr Dr Ste 333
Brentwood, TN 37027-3283
Tel.: (615) 401-6400
Fax: (615) 377-3977
Toll Free: (877) 401-6400
E-mail: ohlinfo@ohl.com
Web Site: www.ohl.com
Sales Range: $400-449.9 Million
Approx. Number Employees: 2,400
Year Founded: 1951
Business Description:
Supply Chain Management Services
S.I.C.: 4226; 4213; 4225; 4731; 8742
N.A.I.C.S.: 493190; 484121; 484230; 488510; 493110; 541611; 541614
Personnel:
Frank Eichler *(Chief Admin Officer & Gen Counsel)*
Bob Spieth *(Pres-Contract Logistics)*
Fred Loeffel *(Exec VP-Bus Dev)*
Charlie Pinto *(Exec VP-HR)*
Bob Stieth *(Exec VP-Logistics)*
Derek Fain *(Sr VP-Transportation Bus Dev)*
Joe Finney *(Sr VP-Transportation Svcs)*
John Peddie *(Sr VP-Warehouse Opers)*
Advertising Agency:
Gish, Sherwood & Friends, Inc. (d/b/a GS&F)
4235 Hillsboro Pike
Nashville, TN 37215-3344
Tel.: (615) 385-1100
Fax: (615) 783-0500

PACKAGING CORPORATION OF AMERICA

1900 W Field Ct
Lake Forest, IL 60045
Tel.: (847) 482-3000
Fax: (847) 482-4738
Toll Free: (800) 456-4725
Web Site: www.packagingcorp.com
Approx. Sls.: $2,435,606,000
Approx. Number Employees: 8,100
Year Founded: 1867
Business Description:
Containerboard & Corrugated Products Mfr
S.I.C.: 2653; 2652; 2657
N.A.I.C.S.: 322211; 322212; 322213
Export
Media: 2-4-7-10-13
Distr.: Natl.
Budget Set: July
Personnel:
Paul T. Stecko *(Chm)*
Mark W. Kowlzan *(CEO)*
Richard B. West *(CFO & Sr VP)*
Robert A. Schneider *(CIO)*
Thomas A. Hassfurther *(Exec VP-Corrugated Products)*
Stephen T. Calhoun *(VP-HR)*
Anil Sethy *(VP-Engrg)*

PACON CORPORATION

(Sub. of The Van Hoof Companies)
2525 N Casaloma Dr
Appleton, WI 54912-7068
Tel.: (920) 830-5050
Fax: (920) 830-5099
Toll Free: (800) 333-2545
Web Site: www.pacon.com
E-Mail For Key Personnel:
Sales Director: sales@pacon.com
Approx. Number Employees: 225
Year Founded: 1951
Business Description:
Mfr of Paper Products, Educational Aids, & Arts & Crafts Supplies
S.I.C.: 2679; 5111
N.A.I.C.S.: 322299; 424110
Import Export
Advertising Expenditures: $750,000
Media: 2-5-6-7-8-10-19-21-26
Distr.: Intl.; Natl.
Budget Set: Jan.
Personnel:
Jim Schmitz *(Pres & CEO)*
Tom Hurley *(CFO)*
Brands & Products:
ART KRAFT
ARTIST
BORDETTE
CLASSROOM KEEPERS
CONNOR
COROBUFF
CREATIVE LEARNER
DECOPUFFS
D'NEALIAN
FADELESS
FLAMELESS
KLONDIKERS
KOLOR FAST
LEARNING WALLS
PEACOCK
PLAST'R CRAFT
RAINBOW
SPECTRA
SPOTLIGHT
SUNWORKS
TANDEM TONES
TRAIT-TEX

PACTIV CORPORATION

(Holding of Reynolds Group Holdings Limited)
1900 W Field Ct
Lake Forest, IL 60045-4828
Tel.: (847) 482-2000
Fax: (847) 482-4738
Toll Free: (800) 828-2850
Web Site: www.pactiv.com
Approx. Sls.: $3,360,000,000
Approx. Number Employees: 12,000
Year Founded: 1960
Business Description:
Specialty Packaging Products Mfr
S.I.C.: 2673; 3499
N.A.I.C.S.: 322223; 326111; 332999
Export
Advertising Expenditures: $28,000,000
Media: 2-4-6-7-8-10-11-15-19-23-25-26
Distr.: Intl.; Natl.
Personnel:
Richard L. Wambold *(CEO)*
Michael O. Oliver *(Chief HR Officer & VP)*
John T. McGrath *(CEO-Pactiv Foodservice/Food Pkg)*
Joseph E. Doyle *(Gen Counsel)*
John N. Schwab *(Sr VP & Gen Mgr-Hefty Consumer Products)*
Tom Donohue *(VP-Mktg)*
Kevin Grogan *(Gen Mgr-APET Packaging)*
Greg Noethlich *(Dir-Mfg)*
Brands & Products:
ACCENT
ACTAZENE
ACTIVETECH
AIR
AIR-KRAFT
AIR-PAQ
ARMOR-LITE
ASTRO CELL
ASTRO-FOAM
ASTROBARRIER
BAG-ON-A-ROLL
BAGGIES
BARN
BASICS
BERIGARD
BLACKOUT
BUBBLE-OUT
CARRY-OUT
CARRY-SAFE
CATERBOWL
CATERMATE
CATERWARE
CHICKEN BARN
CINCH SAK
CLASSIC CARRY-OUT
CLASSIC IMPRESSIONS
CLEARVIEW
CORNERKEEPER
CRUISER MOVER
CRYSTAL CUT
CUSHION COMB
DIAMOND
EARTHCHOICE
EASY FLAPS
EASY GRIP
ECLIPSE
EDGE FOAM
ELEGANTWARE
ELLIPSO
EZ FOIL
EZ OZONEWARE
FAST-PAK
FIELDWARE
FOG-GARD
FRESH EXTEND
FRUITMASTER
FUNTENSILS
FURNITURE GUARD
FURNITURE GUARD LITE
GOLD CLASSIC CARRY-OUT
GREENGUARD
THE GRIPPER
GUESTWARE
HANDLESAK
HEARTY MEALS
HEFTY
HEFTY EXPRESS
HEFTY ONE ZIP
HEXABLOK
HEXACOMB
HEXQUISITE
HEXWARE
JIFFY
KEEP YOUR GARBAGE IN THE DARK
KITCHEN FRESH
KORDITE
MARKETOTE
MASTERCLEAR
MASTERDUO
MASTERVUE
MAX
MEADOWARE

Key to Media (For complete agency information see *The Advertising Red Books-Agencies* edition):
1. Bus. Publs. 2. Cable T.V. 3. Catalogs & Directories. 4. Co-op Adv. 5. Consumer Mags. 6. D.M. to Bus. Estab.7. D.M. to Consumers 8. Daily Newsp. 9. Exhibits/Trade Shows 10. Foreign 11. Infomercial 12. Internet Adv.13. Multimedia 14. Network Radio 15. Network T.V. 16. Newsp. Distr. Mags. 17. Other 18. Outdoor (Posters, Transit) 19. Point of Purchase20. Premiums, Novelties 21. Product Samples 22. Special Events Mktg. 23. Spot Radio 24. Spot T.V. 25. Weekly Newsp. 26. Yellow Page Adv.

MEALMASTER
MERRY PALS
MICROFOAM
ONECUP
ONEZIP
ORCA
OUTPAC
PACTIV
PACTIV AIR
PALS
PANTA-PAK
PARTY COLORS
PILLOPOST
PLACESETTER
POLYLITE
POLYPLANK
PRAIRIEHOLLOW
PRAIRIEWARE
PREFERRED
PREMIER
PROFLEX
PROPAFOAM
PROPYFLEX
PULPEX
QUIET CHOICE
RAINDROP
ROSE DOME
ROSEWARE
THE SELL OUT
SERVE 'N STORE
THE SHOW OFF
SHOWCAKE
SHOWCASE
SHOWPIE
SIGNATURE
SLEEVIT
SLIDE-RITE
SMARTLOCK
SMARTTOTE
SMARTVENT
SOFT-CELL
SPORTS PALS
STEELSAK
TOMATOGARD
TRAY-MATE
TUFF-KRAFT
TWIN-SIX
TWISTTIE
ULTRA FLEX
UNSCENTED ODOR BLOCK
X-CELL
ZOO PALS

Advertising Agency:
Campbell Mithun, Inc.
Campbell Mithun Tower 222 S 9th St
Minneapolis, MN 55402-3389
Tel.: (612) 347-1000
Fax: (612) 347-1515
(Hefty)

PERFECSEAL
(Unit of Bemis Company, Inc.)
3500 N Main St
Oshkosh, WI 54901-1233
Tel.: (920) 303-7000
Fax: (920) 303-7002
Toll Free: (800) 568-7626
Web Site: www.perfecseal.com
Sales Range: $100-124.9 Million
Approx. Number Employees: 800
Year Founded: 1905
Business Description:
Medical & Pharmaceutical Packaging Solutions
S.I.C.: 2671
N.A.I.C.S.: 322221
Import Export
Media: 2-4-7-8-10-11-13-20-21
Distr.: Natl.
Budget Set: Jan. -Dec.
Personnel:

PINNACLE COATING & CONVERTING, INC.
212 Natl Ave
Spartanburg, SC 29303-6316
Tel.: (864) 574-8400
Fax: (864) 574-8644
E-mail: info@pinnaclecoating.com
Web Site: www.pinnaclecoating.com
Approx. Number Employees: 35
Year Founded: 1955
Business Description:
Mfr. & Conversion of Sensitized Paper Used in Computers & Engineering & Design Applications; Supplier of Special Paper Machinery for Reproduction of Patterns & Other Products for the Apparel Industry
S.I.C.: 3554; 2672
N.A.I.C.S.: 333291; 322222
Import Export
Advertising Expenditures: $325,000
Media: 2-4-7-10-17
Distr.: Natl.
Budget Set: Dec.
Personnel:
Mike Greer *(Pres & CEO)*
Brands & Products:
PHOTO MARKER

PLASTIC PACKAGING, INC.
1246 Main Ave SE PO Box 2029
Hickory, NC 28602-1238
Tel.: (828) 328-2466
Fax: (828) 322-1830
E-mail: sales@ppi-hky.com
Web Site: www.ppi-hky.com
E-Mail For Key Personnel:
Sales Director: sales@ppi-hky.com
Approx. Number Employees: 200
Year Founded: 1957
Business Description:
Converter of Plastic Films Into Bags & Overwraps Both Printed & Plain
S.I.C.: 3089
N.A.I.C.S.: 326199
Export
Media: 2-4-6-7-10-17
Distr.: Natl.
Budget Set: Sept.-Oct.

POINT BLANK SOLUTIONS, INC.
(Filed Ch 11 Bankruptcy #10-11255 on 04/15/2010 in U.S. Bankruptcy Ct, Dist of DE, Wilmington)
2102 SW 2nd St
Pompano Beach, FL 33069
Tel.: (954) 630-0900
Fax: (954) 630-9225
Web Site: www.pointblanksolutionsinc.com
Sales Range: $150-199.9 Million
Approx. Number Employees: 1,200
Year Founded: 1992
Business Description:
Holding Company
S.I.C.: 2676; 2326; 2389; 3579
N.A.I.C.S.: 322291; 315225; 315999; 333313
Advertising Expenditures: $352,000
Personnel:
James R. Henderson *(Mng Dir & Operating Officer)*
William T. Nanovsky *(CFO)*
Dale Wise *(VP-Sls)*

POLY PAK AMERICA, INC.
2939 E Washington Blvd
Los Angeles, CA 90023-4277
Tel.: (323) 264-2400
Fax: (323) 264-2407
Toll Free: (800) 826-4000
E-mail: sales@polypakamerica.com
Web Site: www.polypakamerica.com
E-Mail For Key Personnel:
Sales Director: sales@polypakamerica.com
Sales Range: $50-74.9 Million
Approx. Number Employees: 125
Year Founded: 1972
Business Description:
Mfr. of Plastic Mailers, Bags & Packaging
S.I.C.: 3081; 2677
N.A.I.C.S.: 326113; 322232
Export
Advertising Expenditures: $1,400,000
D.M. to Consumers: $1,400,000
Distr.: Natl.
Personnel:
Richard Gurewitz *(Pres)*
Mark Freedman *(VP-Fin & Controller)*
Jezabel Weeks *(Office Mgr)*
Ian Young *(Mgr-Rigur Product)*
Brands & Products:
ALMOST FOREVER
DURA-SMOOTH
DURALITE
DURALITE ENVELOPES
DURALITE MAILERS
ENVIRO-TUFF
GURILLA
GURILLA-TUFF
POLY LOK
POLY MAIL
POLY PAK AMERICA
POLY-SHIELD
POLYLOK
POLYVAULT
PROLITE
PROLITE SHIPPER
RHINO
RIGUR
SHOWCASE
STOCK & CUSTOM PLASTIC AND POLY BAGS
SUPER-X
SURE-SAFE
SURE-SEAL
V ZUH

POLYAIR INTER PACK INC.
330 Humberline Drive
Toronto, ON M9W 1R5, Canada
Tel.: (416) 679-6600
Fax: (416) 679-6610
Toll Free: (888) POLYAIR
E-mail: marketing@polyair.com
Web Site: www.polyair.com
E-Mail For Key Personnel:
Marketing Director: marketing@polyair.com
Sales Range: $100-124.9 Million
Approx. Number Employees: 1,200
Year Founded: 1995
Business Description:
Protective Packaging Mfr & Developer
S.I.C.: 3086; 2671
N.A.I.C.S.: 326140; 326112
Media: 4-7-10-13
Personnel:
Gary Tessitore *(CEO)*
Michael Freel *(Dir-Fin)*
Trent Harkness *(Dir-Mktg)*
Brands & Products:
AIRSPACE
AQUA COVER
AQUA LINER
BOX-A-BUBBLE
DECOLITE
DURABOND
DURABUBBLE
DURAKRAFT
DURAMASK
ECOLITE
FASTPAK
FLEXFOIL
HANDI-PAK
LAMIBAG
LAMIFILM
LAMIFOAM
MOLLY BROWN
POLYAIR
PROTECT-A-POOL
ROLL STOCK
SECUR-A-MATIC
SECUR-A-POOL
STARBOND
STARFOAM
STARKRAFT
STARMASK
STARMOVER
STARNET
SUMMER FUN
TOTALFOAM
XPAK

POTLATCH CORPORATION
601 W First Ave Ste 1600
Spokane, WA 99201-0603
Tel.: (509) 835-1500
Fax: (509) 835-1555
Fax: (509) 835-1559
E-mail: info@potlatchcorp.com
Web Site: www.potlatchcorp.com
Approx. Rev.: $539,447,000
Approx. Number Employees: 870
Year Founded: 1903
Business Description:
Mfr & Distr of Paper, Pulp & Lumber Products
S.I.C.: 6798; 0811; 2621; 2631
N.A.I.C.S.: 525930; 113110; 322121; 322130
Export
Media: 1-2-4-6-7-9-10-19-21
Distr.: Intl.; Natl.
Budget Set: Dec.
Personnel:
Michael J. Covey *(Chm, Pres & CEO)*
Eric J. Cremers *(CFO & VP-Fin)*
Lorrie D. Scott *(Gen Counsel, Sec & VP)*
Jane Crane *(VP-HR)*
Steve Standridge *(VP-Sls-Consumer Products)*
Brands & Products:
ANCORA
CANDESCE
ENSTRON
MCCOY
OXBOARD
PINNACLE
POTLATCH
PRECISION CORE

Key to Media (For complete agency information see *The Advertising Red Books-Agencies* edition):
1. Bus. Publs. 2. Cable T.V. 3. Catalogs & Directories. 4. Co-op Adv. 5. Consumer Mags. 6. D.M. to Bus. Estab.7. D.M. to Consumers 8. Daily Newsp. 9. Exhibits/Trade Shows 10. Foreign 11. Infomercial 12. Internet Adv.13. Multimedia 14. Network Radio 15. Network T.V. 16. Newsp. Distr. Mags. 17. Other 18. Outdoor (Posters, Transit) 19. Point of Purchase20. Premiums, Novelties 21. Product Samples 22. Special Events Mktg. 23. Spot Radio 24. Spot T.V. 25. Weekly Newsp. 26. Yellow Page Adv.

Potlatch Corporation — (Continued)

RADEC
TERRAMICA

PRATT INDUSTRIES
(Formerly Love Box Company, Inc.)
(Sub. of Pratt Industries (USA) Inc.)
700 E 37th St N
Wichita, KS 67219-3510
Tel.: (316) 832-3275
Fax: (316) 832-3269
E-mail: pkgsyscs@prattindustries.com
Web Site: prattpkgsys.com/
Sales Range: $150-199.9 Million
Approx. Number Employees: 1,400
Year Founded: 1923
Business Description:
Corrugated Box Mfr & Retailer
S.I.C.: 2653; 2449
N.A.I.C.S.: 322211; 321920
Media: 10
Personnel:
Randy Love *(CEO)*
Brands & Products:
CUSTOMER SATISFACTION FROM DESIGN TO DELIVERY
DRYBOX
LOVE
STETA SYSTEMS

PROGRESSIVE DISTRIBUTION SERVICES, INC.
5505 36th St SE
Grand Rapids, MI 49512
Tel.: (616) 957-5900
Fax: (616) 957-2990
Toll Free: (800) 304-3699
E-mail: sales@prodist.com
Web Site: www.prodist.com
E-Mail For Key Personnel:
Sales Director: sales@prodist.com
Sales Range: $10-24.9 Million
Approx. Number Employees: 30
Year Founded: 1984
Business Description:
Warehousing & Distribution Services
S.I.C.: 4226
N.A.I.C.S.: 493190
Media: 2
Personnel:
John McGovern *(Pres)*
Brands & Products:
A BETTER WAY TO GROW
A COMPREHENSIVE FULLY INTERGRATED SOLUTION
@STORE
ORDERLINK
PROGRESSIVE COMMERCE

PUBLIC STORAGE
701 Western Ave
Glendale, CA 91201-2349
Mailing Address:
PO Box 25050
Glendale, CA 91221-5050
Tel.: (818) 244-8080
Fax: (818) 553-2388
E-mail: websales@PublicStorage.com
Web Site: www.publicstorage.com
Approx. Rev.: $1,646,722,000
Approx. Number Employees: 4,900
Year Founded: 1980
Business Description:
Real Estate Investment Trust; Self-Storage Facility Owner & Operator
S.I.C.: 6798; 4225; 6531; 6552
N.A.I.C.S.: 525930; 237210; 531130; 531390
Advertising Expenditures: $4,662,000
Media: 2-3-5-7-8-9-10-13-18-23-24-25-26
Distr.: Direct to Consumer; Natl.; Reg.
Personnel:
B. Wayne Hughes *(Chm)*
Ronald L. Havner, Jr. *(Vice Chm, Pres & CEO)*
John Reyes *(CFO & Sr VP)*
Shawn Weidmann *(COO & Sr VP)*
Brent C. Peterson *(CIO & Sr VP)*
Brian J. Fields *(Chief Legal Officer & Sr VP)*
David F. Doll *(Pres-Real Estate Grp & Sr VP)*
Stephanie G. Heim *(Corp Counsel, Sec & VP)*
Capri L. Haga *(Sr VP-Risk Mgmt)*
Candace N. Krol *(Sr VP-HR)*
Drew J. Adams *(VP & Dir-Taxes)*
Brands & Products:
PUBLIC STORAGE
Advertising Agencies:
MediaVest USA
6500 Wilshire Blvd Ste 1100
Los Angeles, CA 90046
Tel.: (323) 658-4500
Fax: (323) 658-4592
Media Buying

Webmetro
(d/b/a Multivest)
160 E Via Verde Ste 220
San Dimas, CA 91773
Tel.: (909) 599-8885

QUAD/GRAPHICS, INC.
N63 W23075 State Hwy 74
Sussex, WI 53089-2827
Tel.: (414) 566-6000
Fax: (414) 566-4650
Toll Free: (888) 782-3226
E-mail: qgraphics@qg.com
Web Site: www.qg.com
Approx. Sls.: $3,391,700,000
Approx. Number Employees: 25,000
Year Founded: 1971
Business Description:
Printing Services
S.I.C.: 2752; 2732; 2754; 2759; 2789; 7336
N.A.I.C.S.: 323110; 323111; 323115; 323117; 323119; 323121; 541430
Media: 2-8-10-11-13
Personnel:
J. Joel Quadracci *(Chm, Pres & CEO)*
John C. Fowler *(CFO & Exec VP)*
Dave Blais *(Pres-Magazines & Catalogs & Exec VP)*
Tom Frankowski *(Exec VP-Mfg & Ops & Pres-Europe)*
Dave Riebe *(Pres-Logistics & Distr)*
Andy Schiesl *(Gen Counsel & VP)*
Ron Nash *(VP-Customer Svc)*
Art Noe *(Dir-Corp Pur)*
Claire Ho *(Mgr-Corp Comm)*

QUALITY PERFORATING, INC.
166 Dundaff St
Carbondale, PA 18407-1565
Tel.: (570) 282-4344
Fax: (570) 282-4627
Fax: (800) 232-9737
Toll Free: (800) 872-7373
Toll Free: (800) USAPERF
E-mail: sales@qualityperf.com
Web Site: www.qualityperf.com
E-Mail For Key Personnel:
Sales Director: sales@qualityperf.com
Approx. Number Employees: 50
Year Founded: 1873
Business Description:
Perforated Sheets, Coils & Component Parts
S.I.C.: 3469; 3496
N.A.I.C.S.: 332116; 332618
Import Export
Media: 2-4-7-20-26
Distr.: Natl.
Budget Set: Dec.
Personnel:
Robert Farber *(Owner)*

REXAM BEVERAGE CAN NORTH AMERICA
(Sub. of Rexam PLC)
8770 W Bryn Mawr Ave
Chicago, IL 60631-3515
Tel.: (773) 399-3000
Fax: (773) 399-3354
Telex: 661279
Web Site: www.rexam.com/files/reports/results/inter08/index.asp?pageid=27
Approx. Number Employees: 250
Year Founded: 1899
Business Description:
Mfr of Metal & Plastic Packaging; Flexible & Tube Packaging
S.I.C.: 3411; 3221
N.A.I.C.S.: 332431; 327213
Export
Media: 2-6-7-9-10-11-13-25
Distr.: Intl.; Natl.
Budget Set: Nov.
Personnel:
Harry Barto *(Pres & CEO)*
Richard Grimley *(COO)*
Josephine Stephens *(Dir-Mktg)*
Brands & Products:
GAMMA
GLAMINATE
REDI-SERVE

SAMSON ROPE TECHNOLOGIES
(Sub. of Wind River Holdings, L.P.)
2090 Thornton St
Ferndale, WA 98248-9314
Tel.: (360) 384-4669
Fax: (360) 384-0572
Toll Free: (800) 227-7673
E-mail: custserv@samsonrope.com
Web Site: www.samsonrope.com
Approx. Number Employees: 250
Year Founded: 1884
Business Description:
Mfr. of Rope
S.I.C.: 2298
N.A.I.C.S.: 314991
Import Export
Media: 2-4-10-20-21-26
Distr.: Natl.
Personnel:
Charlotte Wells *(Mgr-Mktg)*
Brands & Products:
DYNEEMA
KEVLAR
SAMSON
SPECTRON
SSR-100
SSR-101
SSR-1200
SSR-301-R
TECHNORA
ULTRA ULTIMATE
ULTRALINE
ULTRASTRONG
Advertising Agency:
Smith Walker Design
19625 62nd Ave S Ste C 109
Kent, WA 98032
Tel.: (253) 872-2111
Fax: (253) 872-2140
Toll Free: (866) 542-4198
— Robin Walker *(Acct. Exec.)*

SAPPI FINE PAPER NORTH AMERICA
(Sub. of Sappi Limited)
225 Franklin St 28th Fl
Boston, MA 02110-2804
Tel.: (617) 423-7300
Fax: (617) 423-5494
E-mail: info@sappi.com
Web Site: www.na.sappi.com/contact
Approx. Number Employees: 3,300
Business Description:
Warrens Standard Printing Papers, Scott Printing Papers, Publishing Papers, Release Papers, Converting
S.I.C.: 2679; 2674
N.A.I.C.S.: 322299; 322224
Distr.: Intl.; Natl.
Budget Set: Oct.
Personnel:
Mark Gardner *(Pres & CEO)*
Anne Ayer *(CIO & VP-Corp Dev)*
Sarah Manchester *(Gen Counsel & VP-HR)*
Jennifer Miller *(Exec VP-Strategic Mktg & Comm)*
Kevin Clark *(VP-Sls & Bus Devel)*
Jim Mullen *(VP-HR)*
Harley Wood *(VP-Tech & Engrg)*
John Job *(Dir-Technical)*
Brands & Products:
PATINA
SOMERSET
SPECTRATECH
STROBE
WARREN
Advertising Agency:
Howard, Merrell & Partners, Inc.
8521 Six Forks Rd 4th Fl
Raleigh, NC 27615-5278
Tel.: (919) 848-2400
Fax: (919) 848-2420

SCA TISSUE NORTH AMERICA
(Sub. of Svenska Cellulosa Aktiebolaget)
PO Box 2400
Neenah, WI 54957-2400
Tel.: (920) 725-7031
Fax: (920) 727-8801
Toll Free: (800) 722-6659
E-mail: info.tissue-na@sca.com
Web Site: www.scatissue.com
Approx. Number Employees: 1,800
Year Founded: 1915
Business Description:
Tissue Products Mfr
S.I.C.: 2621
N.A.I.C.S.: 322121
Import Export
Media: 1-2-4-7-9-10-19
Budget Set: Nov.

Key to Media (For complete agency information see *The Advertising Red Books-Agencies* edition):
1. Bus. Publs. 2. Cable T.V. 3. Catalogs & Directories. 4. Co-op Adv. 5. Consumer Mags. 6. D.M. to Bus. Estab.7. D.M. to Consumers 8. Daily Newsp. 9. Exhibits/Trade Shows 10. Foreign 11. Infomercial 12. Internet Adv.13. Multimedia 14. Network Radio 15. Network T.V. 16. Newsp. Distr. Mags. 17. Other 18. Outdoor (Posters, Transit) 19. Point of Purchase20. Premiums, Novelties 21. Product Samples 22. Special Events Mktg. 23. Spot Radio 24. Spot T.V. 25. Weekly Newsp. 26. Yellow Page Adv.

Personnel:
Don Lewis *(Pres)*
Joe Fahley *(CFO & VP)*
John Drengler *(VP-Mktg & Product)*
Joe Russo *(VP-Sls)*
Brands & Products:
CORONET
MAINSTREET
PARK AVENUE
PARK AVENUE ULTRA
TORK
TORK INTUITION

SCHWARZ PAPER COMPANY
8338 Austin Ave
Morton Grove, IL 60053-3209
Tel.: (847) 966-2550
Fax: (847) 966-1271
Web Site: www.schwarz.com
Sales Range: $500-549.9 Million
Approx. Number Employees: 850
Year Founded: 1907
Business Description:
Paper & Packaging Products; Primary Printer
S.I.C.: 5113; 2752
N.A.I.C.S.: 424130; 323110
Media: 2-4-7-10-14-17
Distr.: Natl.
Personnel:
Andrew J. McKenna, Jr. *(Pres)*
Brands & Products:
SCHWARZ

SEALED AIR CORPORATION
200 Riverfront Blvd
Elmwood Park, NJ 07407
Tel.: (201) 791-7600
Fax: (201) 703-4205
Toll Free: (800) 845-7551
E-mail: investor.relations@sealedair.com
Web Site: www.sealedair.com
Approx. Sls.: $4,490,100,000
Approx. Number Employees: 16,100
Year Founded: 1960
Business Description:
Food & Protective Packaging Products & Systems Mfr & Sales
S.I.C.: 2673; 2671; 2674; 3161; 3565
N.A.I.C.S.: 326111; 316991; 322221; 322223; 322224; 333993
Export
Media: 1-4-6-7-10-11-21
Distr.: Direct to Consumer; Intl.; Natl.; Reg.
Budget Set: Oct.
Personnel:
William V. Hickey *(Pres & CEO)*
David H. Kelsey *(CFO & Sr VP)*
H. Katherine White *(Gen Counsel, Sec & VP)*
Charles Dunlap *(Dir-Mktg)*
Brands & Products:
ACCU-CUT
AIRCAP
BARRIER BAG
BARRIER BUBBLE
BDF
BUBBLE MASK
BUBBLE PAK
BUBBLE WRAP
BUBBLEBAGS
CELL-AIRE
CELLU-CUSHION
CELLU LINER
CELLU-MASK
CELLUPLANK
COINSAFE
COLD SEAL
COOK-N-SHIP
CORRO-FOAM
CORTUFF
CRISPAC
CRISPYWRAP
CRYOLITE
CRYOVAC
CRYOVAC BARRIER BAG
CRYOVAC BDF
CRYOVAC CASE READY
CRYOVAC MARKET-READY
CRYOVAC OSB
CRYOVAC PIZZAFRESH
CRYOVAC ROBOLOADER
CRYOVAC SLICEPAK
CUSHIONSHIELD
CUSTOM WRAP
DARFRESH
DLS
DOLPHIN
DOLPHIN PAD
DRI-LOC
DRY-PAK
FILL-AIR
FILL-AIR ELITE
FLOW RITE
GFLEX
IMPACT
INSTAFILL
INSTAFLEX
INSTAMATE
INSTAMOLDER
INSTAPACKER
INSTAPAD
INSTAPAK
INSTAPAK QUICK
INSTASHEETER
INSTASLITTER
INTACT
JIFFY
JIFFY EXPRESS
JIFFY MAILER
JIFFY PACKER
JIFFY PADWRAP
JIFFY PREMIUM PAD
JIFFY RIGI BAG
JIFFYLITE
JIFFYWRAP
KEEPSAFE
KORRVU
KUSHION KRAFT
LAB PAK
LABELLOK
LIDSYS
LITE-LOC
LOK-SUR
MAIL LITE
MAILTUFF
MICRO-LOC
MILFLEX
MILFORCE
MILTECH
NEWAIR I.B
NEWVAC
OPTI
OSB
OUR PRODUCTS PROTECT YOUR PRODUCTS
PACKFORUM
PAD-LOC
PLY-CEL
POLYCAP
PRIORITY PACK
PROTEC
QUICK POUCH
QUICKSILVER
RAPID FILL
READY-TO-ROLL
REFLECTIX
REFLEX
SEALED AIR
SHANKLIN
SHANKLIN EDGE
SHANKLIN HORIZON
SHRINKVAC
SHURTUFF
SIMPLE STEPS
SLICEPAK
SMARTPAK
SMARTWIRE
SPARKLEWRAP
SPEEDY PACKER INSIGHT
SPEEDYPACKER
STRATOCELL
SUPA-LOC
SUPERMICRO
TBG
TEMPSHIELD
TEMPSHIELD-MFL
THERMARITE
TM PLY
TRIFRESH
TRIGON
TUFFGARD
TUFFGARD EXTREME
ULTRALITE
ULTRASEAL
VANGUARD PREMIUM
VERSAPACKER
VOID KRAFT
XENITH
Advertising Agencies:
ANEW Marketing Group
811 W Jericho Tpke Ste 109E
Smithtown, NY 11787
Tel.: (631) 982-4000
Fax: (631) 434-1129

Leverage Marketing Group
(A GOODWICK/LIAZON Company)
117-119 S Main St
Newtown, CT 06470-2380
Tel.: (203) 270-6699
Fax: (203) 270-3491
(Engineered Packaging Products)

SETON NAME PLATE COMPANY
20 Thompson Rd
Branford, CT 06405-0819
Tel.: (203) 488-8059
Fax: (203) 488-0939
Toll Free: (800) 243-6624
E-mail: info@seton.com
Web Site: www.seton.com
Approx. Number Employees: 150
Business Description:
Name Plates, Labels & Identification Products Mfr; Pipe Identification Systems & Valve Marking Systems
S.I.C.: 7389
N.A.I.C.S.: 561910
Advertising Expenditures: $5,000,000
Media: 2-4-7-21
Distr.: Natl.
Budget Set: June
Personnel:
Janice Fowler *(Mgr-Adv)*
Brands & Products:
SETMARK
SETONCAL
SETONGUARD
VENTMARK

SHUFORD MILLS LLC
447 Main St
Hudson, NC 28638
Tel.: (828) 328-2141
Tel.: (828) 759-2100
Fax: (828) 759-2156
E-mail: info@shufordmills.com
Web Site: www.shufordmills.com
Approx. Number Employees: 500
Year Founded: 1880
Business Description:
Textile Yarns & Fabrics
S.I.C.: 2281
N.A.I.C.S.: 313111
Import Export
Media: 4-6-9-25
Distr.: Natl.
Personnel:
A. Pope Shuford *(Chm)*
C. P. Davis *(Pres)*
C. Hunt Shuford, Jr. *(CFO)*
Brands & Products:
ARCADIA
BIG SUR
CARLISLE
EDGEWOOD
LAUREL BAY
OAK GROVE
OUTDURA
OUTDURA TRIO
SOUTHPORT
SUMMERTON

SIGNODE PACKAGING SYSTEMS
(Sub. of Illinois Tool Works Inc.)
3600 W Lk Ave
Glenview, IL 60026
Tel.: (847) 398-0300
Fax: (847) 657-4261
Toll Free: (800) 323-2464
E-mail: info@signode.com
Web Site: www.signode.com
Sales Range: $150-199.9 Million
Approx. Number Employees: 450
Business Description:
Steel & Plastic Strapping, Stretch Film, Pressure Sensitive Carton Sealing Tape, Application Equipment & Accessories Mfr
S.I.C.: 7359; 3559; 3565
N.A.I.C.S.: 532490; 333220; 333993
Advertising Expenditures: $1,700,000
Media: 1-2-7-10
Distr.: Intl.; Natl.
Budget Set: Sept.
Personnel:
Philip Gresh *(Exec VP)*
Suvit Woravisitwongse *(Gen Mgr)*
James N. Fallon *(Dir-Mktg Comm)*
Brands & Products:
SIGNODE

SILGAN WHITE CAP AMERICAS LLC
(Sub. of Silgan Holdings, Inc.)
1140 31st St
Downers Grove, IL 60515-1212
Tel.: (630) 515-8383
Fax: (630) 515-5326
Toll Free: (800) 515-1565
Web Site: www.silganwhitecap.com
E-Mail For Key Personnel:
Marketing Director: marketing@silganclosures.com

Key to Media (For complete agency information see *The Advertising Red Books-Agencies* edition):
1. Bus. Publs. 2. Cable T.V. 3. Catalogs & Directories. 4. Co-op Adv. 5. Consumer Mags. 6. D.M. to Bus. Estab.7. D.M. to Consumers 8. Daily Newsp. 9. Exhibits/Trade Shows 10. Foreign 11. Infomercial 12. Internet Adv.13. Multimedia 14. Network Radio 15. Network T.V. 16. Newsp. Distr. Mags. 17. Other 18. Outdoor (Posters, Transit) 19. Point of Purchase20. Premiums, Novelties 21. Product Samples 22. Special Events Mktg. 23. Spot Radio 24. Spot T.V. 25. Weekly Newsp. 26. Yellow Page Adv.

Silgan White Cap Americas LLC — (Continued)

Sales Range: $150-199.9 Million
Approx. Number Employees: 1,800
Year Founded: 1926
Business Description:
Closures & Sealing Systems for Rigid Containers
S.I.C.: 5085; 3089
N.A.I.C.S.: 423840; 326199
Media: 2-6-7-8-10-21
Distr.: Intl.; Natl.
Budget Set: Nov.
Personnel:
Peter Konieczny *(Pres)*
Bob Anderson *(VP-Fin)*
Robert Rey *(VP-Sls)*
Brands & Products:
COMBI-TWIST
DUO PAK
GUARD-SEAL
PLASTI-TWIST
PRESS ON-TWIST OFF
PT
SNAP-RESEAL
TWIST-OFF
VAPOR-VACUUM
WHITE CAP

SMURFIT-MBI

(Sub. of Smurfit-Stone Container Canada Inc.)
7120 Hurontario Ste 200
Mississauga, ON L5W 0A9, Canada
Tel.: (905) 362-7474
Fax: (905) 362-7475
E-mail: info@smurfit-mbi.com
Web Site: www.smurfit-mbi.com
Sales Range: $10-24.9 Million
Approx. Number Employees: 50
Business Description:
Corrugated Containers
S.I.C.: 2653
N.A.I.C.S.: 322211
Media: 4
Personnel:
Noello Carvalho *(Dir-Fin)*

SMURFIT-STONE CONTAINER CORPORATION

222 N LaSalle St
Chicago, IL 60601
Tel.: (312) 346-6600
Toll Free: (877) 772-2999
E-mail: jhaudric@smurfit.com
Web Site: www.smurfit.com
Approx. Sls.: $3,262,000,000
Approx. Number Employees: 17,100
Business Description:
Packaging Products, Containerboard Kraft Paper & Paper Corrugated Containers
S.I.C.: 2653; 2621; 2631
N.A.I.C.S.: 322211; 322122; 322130
Export
Advertising Expenditures: $200,000
Media: 2-7-10-19-20-21
Distr.: Natl.
Budget Set: Dec.
Personnel:
Ralph F. Hake *(Chm)*
Patrick J. Moore *(CEO)*
Mark R. O'Bryan *(CIO & Sr VP-Strategic Initiatives)*
Craig A. Hunt *(Chief Admin Officer & Gen Counsel)*
Paul K. Kaufmann *(Sr VP & Controller)*
Mathew J. Blanchard *(Sr VP & Gen Mgr-Board Sls)*
Michael P. Exner *(Sr VP & Gen Mgr-Containerboard Mill Div)*
Michael R. Oswald *(Sr VP & Gen Mgr-RecyclingDiv)*
Steven C. Strickland *(Sr VP & Gen Mgr-Corrugated Container Div)*
Mathew T. Denton *(Sr VP-Bus Plng & Analysis)*
Ronald D. Hackney *(Sr VP-HR)*
John L. Knudsen *(Sr VP-Supply Chain & Board Sls)*
Susan M. Neumann *(Sr VP-Comm & Pub Affairs)*
Paul W. McCann *(VP & Gen Mgr)*
Ed Mirynowski *(VP & Gen Mgr-Smurfit Stone Image Pac)*
Jim Nolan *(VP-Corp Sls)*
Edmund L. Quatmann *(VP-Internal Audit)*
Tim Sullivan *(VP-Sls-Display & Graphics)*
Bruce Allred *(Dir-Corp Safety)*
Scott Dudley *(Dir-IR)*
Ronald J. Megna *(Asst Sec & Asst Gen Counsel)*
Brian Gardner *(Asst Treas)*
Brands & Products:
CLADWOOD
CORDECK
MIST-WITE II
PAYLOAD
PROTECH

SMURFIT-STONE CONTAINER CORPORATION

(Div. of Smurfit-Stone Container Corporation)
6 CityPlace Dr
Creve Coeur, MO 63141
Tel.: (314) 656-5300
Web Site: www.smurfit.com/asp/locateus.asp
Sales Range: $100-124.9 Million
Approx. Number Employees: 500
Year Founded: 1910
Business Description:
Corrugated Cases & Paperboard Mfr
S.I.C.: 2657; 2653; 2679
N.A.I.C.S.: 322212; 322211; 322299
Export
Advertising Expenditures: $250,000
Media: 7-8
Distr.: Natl.
Budget Set: Sept.
Personnel:
Matthew Blanchard *(Sr VP & Gen Mgr-Bd Sls)*

SOLO CUP COMPANY

150 S Saunders Rd Ste 150
Lake Forest, IL 60045
Tel.: (847) 444-5000
Fax: (847) 831-5849
E-mail: info@solocup.com
Web Site: www.solocup.com
Approx. Sls.: $1,582,861,000
Approx. Number Employees: 6,700
Year Founded: 1936
Business Description:
Paper & Plastic Cups Mfr & Distr
S.I.C.: 3089; 2676
N.A.I.C.S.: 326199; 322291
Export
Advertising Expenditures: $7,200,000
Media: 2-4-5-7-8-10-18-20-21
Distr.: Natl.
Personnel:
Kevin A. Mundt *(Chm)*
Robert M. Korzenski *(Pres & CEO)*
Robert D. Koney, Jr. *(CFO & Exec VP)*
George F. Chappelle, Jr. *(COO & Exec VP)*
Jan Stern Reed *(Exec VP-HR & Gen Counsel)*
Peter J. Mendola *(Sr VP-Ops)*
Chris Klem *(Dir-Mktg-Consumer)*
Brands & Products:
COZY
CREATIVE EXPRESSIONS
GALAXY
MERIDIAN
MISTIQUE
SIGNATURE COLORS
SOLO
STORABLE
TRAVELER PLUS LID
TRAVELERPLUS
ULTRA CLEAR
Advertising Agency:
Schafer Condon Carter
168 N Clinton
Chicago, IL 60661
Tel.: (312) 464-1666
Fax: (312) 464-0628
(Paper & Plastic Cups)

SONOCO PRODUCTS COMPANY

1 N 2nd St
Hartsville, SC 29550-3305
Mailing Address:
PO Box 160
Hartsville, SC 29551-0160
Tel.: (843) 383-7000
Fax: (843) 383-7008
Toll Free: (800) 377-2692
E-mail: corporate.communications@sonoco.com
Web Site: www.sonoco.com
Approx. Sls.: $4,124,121,000
Approx. Number Employees: 17,300
Year Founded: 1899
Business Description:
Industrial & Consumer Packaging Products & Services
S.I.C.: 2273; 2631; 2655; 2671
N.A.I.C.S.: 314110; 322130; 322214; 322221
Import Export
Media: 1-2-4-5-7-8-10-11-18-20-21-25-26
Distr.: Natl.
Budget Set: Aug.
Personnel:
Harris E. Deloach, Jr. *(Chm & CEO)*
M. Jack Sanders *(Pres & COO)*
Barry L. Saunders *(CFO & VP)*
Bernard W. Campbell *(CIO)*
Jim C. Bowen *(Sr VP)*
Cynthia A. Hartley *(Sr VP-HR)*
Ronald E. Holley *(Sr VP)*
R. Howard Coker *(VP & Gen Mgr-Rigid Paper & Closures)*
Marcy Thompson *(VP-Div & Gen Mgr-Sonoco Recycling)*
Allan McLeland *(VP-HR)*
Greg Powell *(Dir-Sls, Mktg-Reels & Transport Packaging)*
Joyce Beasley *(Mgr-Comm Svcs)*
Robin Montgomery *(Mgr-Corp Comm)*
Brands & Products:
AAPAK
ACB
ACCUSHAKE
APAK
AR-EL
AUTO-LOCK
AUTO-MATE
BAKER
BUILDER'S TUBE
CHILLWRAPPER
COREMATE
CPC
CPC-B
CUSTOMER CARE
CUSTOMER SATISFACTION THROUGH EXCELLENCE
DORPAK
DRICORE
DURABLOCK
DURO
DURO-CORES
DUROLENE
DURON
DUROX
ENVIRO-BAG
ENVIRO-MATE
ENVIROMULCH
FIBRE-U
FLOW-RITE
HELPMATE
HELPMATE 3000
HELPMATE JR.
HERMETEK
HQ
HQ ACB
INKPAK
JAWS
LID LASSO
LINEARPAK
LOADRIGHT
MILLENNIUM
MINIMATE
PERFORMANCE DESIGN
PLASTIC-DRUM
POLYPAK
QS
QUIK-START
QUIK-STIK
QUIKMATE
QUIKMATE EZ
QUIKSTAR
QUIKTAB
RAINGUARD
REEL TOUGH
REEL VALUE
RESPONSEPAK
RING PULL MIRASTRIP
RIXIE
RLM
ROLLMATE
ROLLMATE II
S SONOCO
SAFE-RIM
SAFE-TOP
SDS
SEALED-SAFE
SOFTUCK
SONOBASE
SONOCO
SONOCO PACKAGING SYSTEM
SONOCO XCHB
SONOGLO
SONOLOC
SONOPOP
SONOPOST
SONOSCORE
SONOTORT
SONOTUBE
SONOTUBE FINISH FREE

Key to Media (For complete agency information see *The Advertising Red Books-Agencies* edition):
1. Bus. Publs. 2. Cable T.V. 3. Catalogs & Directories. 4. Co-op Adv. 5. Consumer Mags. 6. D.M. to Bus. Estab.7. D.M. to Consumers 8. Daily Newsp. 9. Exhibits/Trade Shows 10. Foreign 11. Infomercial 12. Internet Adv.13. Multimedia 14. Network Radio 15. Network T.V. 16. Newsp. Distr. Mags. 17. Other 18. Outdoor (Posters, Transit) 19. Point of Purchase20. Premiums, Novelties 21. Product Samples 22. Special Events Mktg. 23. Spot Radio 24. Spot T.V. 25. Weekly Newsp. 26. Yellow Page Adv.

SONOTUBE PLUS
SONOVIEW
SONOVOID
SONOWARE
SONOWRAP
SPIRO-PAC
SRM
STANCADDY
STANCAPS
TWISTER-PAK
ULTRA-SEAL
ULTRAPEEL
ULTRASEAL
UPAK
VALVE-PAK
VALVED ULTRASEAL
WIDE/PLY

Advertising Agency:
Chernoff Newman
1411 Gervais St 5th Fl
Columbia, SC 29201-3125
Tel.: (803) 254-8158
Fax: (803) 252-2016

SOUTHWORTH COMPANY INC.

265 Main St
Agawam, MA 01001-1822
Tel.: (413) 789-1200
Fax: (413) 786-1529
Web Site: www.southworth.com
Approx. Number Employees: 150
Year Founded: 1839
Business Description:
Paper Mills
S.I.C.: 2621; 5961
N.A.I.C.S.: 322121; 454113
Import Export
Media: 2
Personnel:
David C. Southworth *(Pres)*
John Wahs *(VP-Fin)*
Brands & Products:
BECAUSE IT'S IMPORTANT
EATON
SOUTHWORTH
Advertising Agency:
Winstanley Partners
114 Main St
Lenox, MA 01240-2353
Tel.: (413) 637-9887
Fax: (413) 637-2045

SPINNAKER COATING, LLC

518 E Water St
Troy, OH 45373-3445
Tel.: (937) 332-6500
Fax: (937) 335-2843
E-mail: perry.schiller@spinps.com
Web Site: www.spinps.com
Approx. Number Employees: 200
Year Founded: 1928
Business Description:
Mfr of Dry Gummed Papers, Pressure Sensitive Sheet & Roll Products, Label Papers, Conventional Gummed Papers, Gummed Tapes & Acid Free Adhesive Coated Products
S.I.C.: 2672
N.A.I.C.S.: 322222
Media: 2-4-7-10-21
Distr.: Direct to Consumer; Natl.
Budget Set: Nov.
Personnel:
Louis A. Guzzetti, Jr. *(Chm & CEO)*
Perry J. Schiller *(CFO & VP)*
George E. Fuehrer *(Exec VP)*
Shauna Jackson *(Mgr-Comm)*
Brands & Products:
20-20
ATP
B-122
BC-20
BLACK SAPPHIRE
COVERGLOS
COVERMATTE
DIGIGLOSS
DIGIMATTE
DIVERSIPRINT
DURAFORM
FROSTBITE
GPR
IMIJ
INSIGHT
LABEL-LYTE
PRIMEGLOS
PRIMESCAN
PT. KROMEKOTE
REELPRINT
SAFETE
SATIN-L
SATIN MOTIQUE
SCANTHERM
SCANTHERM-POLY
SFA
SKWEEZE
SPINNAKER COATING, LLC
STRIP-RITE
STRIP-TAC
STRIP-TAC PLUS
TANDA-TAC
ULTRA MATTE
XTRAGLOS

SUMMIT PLASTIC CO.

1169 Brittain Rd PO Box 117
Akron, OH 44305
Tel.: (330) 633-3668
Fax: (330) 633-9738
Toll Free: (800) 814-3496
E-mail: info@summitplastic.com
Web Site: www.summitplastic.com
Approx. Sls.: $1,750,000
Approx. Number Employees: 100
Business Description:
Heat Sealed Vinyl Bags, Pouches, Cases, Covers, Rings Plastic Trays & Plant Starters
S.I.C.: 3081
N.A.I.C.S.: 326113
Media: 7
Personnel:
Norman Belliveau *(Pres)*
Deborah Belliveau *(Dir-MarCom)*
Connie Carper *(Mgr-Customer Svc)*
Rob Gumpf *(Mgr-Sls)*
Lou Mokodean *(Mgr-Matls)*
Brands & Products:
NU-POT
NU-TRAYS
ROOT TUTOR
SUMMIT PLASTIC

SURFACE COATINGS, INC.

2007 A Industrial Blvd
Rockwall, TX 75087
Tel.: (972) 722-7351
Fax: (972) 722-7321
E-mail: rick@surfacearmor.us
Web Site: www.surfacearmor.us
Approx. Rev.: $870,856
Approx. Number Employees: 3
Year Founded: 2007
Business Description:
Protection Films & Pressure Sensitive Tapes Mfr
S.I.C.: 2671; 3053
N.A.I.C.S.: 322221; 339991
Advertising Expenditures: $37,009
Media: 17
Personnel:
Richard Pietrykowski *(Pres-Surface Armor LLC)*

SOLO CUP OPERATING CORPORATION

(Sub. of Solo Cup Company)
10100 Reisterstown Rd
Owings Mills, MD 21117-3815
Tel.: (410) 363-1111
Fax: (800) 637-5800
Toll Free: (800) 800-0300
Web Site: www.solocup.com
E-Mail For Key Personnel:
Sales Director: sales@solocup.com
Sales Range: $900-999.9 Million
Approx. Number Employees: 5,100
Year Founded: 1911
Business Description:
Paper, Foam & Plastic Disposable Foodservice Products Mfr
S.I.C.: 3089; 2656
N.A.I.C.S.: 326199; 322215
Export
Advertising Expenditures: $1,000,000
Bus. Publs.: $100,000; D.M. to Bus. Estab.: $100,000; Exhibits/Trade Shows: $300,000; Point of Purchase: $500,000
Distr.: Intl.; Natl.
Budget Set: Aug.
Personnel:
Jennifer Davis *(Mgr-HR)*
Brands & Products:
BANANA BOAT
FLEX-E-FILL
FLEX-E-FORM
FLEXGUARD
GUILDWARE
JAZZ
MTRENE
MUNCHIE CUP
PERMA-FLEX STRAW
PREFERENCE DESIGN
SQUEEZEUP
TRAVELID
TROPHY

TECUMSEH PACKAGING SOLUTIONS

(Sub. of Akers Packaging Service Inc.)
707 S Evans St
Tecumseh, MI 49286-1919
Tel.: (517) 423-2126
Fax: (517) 423-7240
Sales Range: $25-49.9 Million
Approx. Number Employees: 320
Year Founded: 1963
Business Description:
Mfr of Corrugated Shipping Containers & Sheets
S.I.C.: 2653
N.A.I.C.S.: 322211
Export
Media: 2-4-7-10-11
Distr.: Intl.; Natl.
Personnel:
Jeffrey Robideau *(Gen Mgr)*

TEKNI-PLEX, INC.

201 Industrial Pkwy
Somerville, NJ 08876
Tel.: (908) 722-4800
Fax: (908) 722-4967
E-mail: info@tekni-plex.com
Web Site: www.tekni-plex.com
Approx. Sls.: $591,871,000
Approx. Number Employees: 3,200
Year Founded: 1967
Business Description:
Food, Cosmetics & Pharmaceutical Packaging Materials Mfr
S.I.C.: 2671; 3084; 3086; 3089
N.A.I.C.S.: 322221; 326122; 326150; 326199
Media: 2-10
Personnel:
Paul Young *(CEO)*
Brands & Products:
COLORITE
COLORITE WATERWORKS
CYBERTECH
DOLCO
DRYFLEX
NATVAR
PLASMED
PLASTRON PEARLS
PPLI
PS 22
PURE PLAST
PUREPLAST
PURETECH
PVC AND NATVAR
SOLVSEAL
SWAN
TEKNI-FILMS
TEKNI-PLEX
TEKNIFLEX
TEKNISEAL
TRI-SEAL
WATERCOLORS
WATERWORKS

TEMPLE-INLAND INC.

1300 S MoPac Expy 3rd Fl
Austin, TX 78746-6933
Mailing Address:
PO Box 40
Austin, TX 78767
Tel.: (512) 434-5800
Fax: (512) 434-3750 (Investor Relations)
Toll Free: (800) 500-4785
E-mail: information@templeinland.com
Web Site: www.templeinland.com
Approx. Rev.: $3,799,000,000
Approx. Number Employees: 10,500
Year Founded: 1983
Business Description:
Holding Company; Paper & Packaging Manufacturing, Building Products, Saw, Pulp & Paperboard Mills
S.I.C.: 2631; 2421; 6719
N.A.I.C.S.: 322130; 321113; 551112
Import Export
Advertising Expenditures: $15,000,000
Media: 10
Personnel:
Doyle R. Simons *(Chm & CEO)*
J. Patrick Maley, III *(Pres & COO)*
Randall D. Levy *(CFO)*
Scott Smith *(CIO)*
J. Bradley Johnston *(Chief Admin Officer)*
Grant F. Adamson *(Chief Governance Officer)*
Craig Knight *(Chief Real Estate Officer)*
C. Morris Davis *(Gen Counsel)*

Key to Media (For complete agency information see *The Advertising Red Books-Agencies* edition):
1. Bus. Publs. 2. Cable T.V. 3. Catalogs & Directories. 4. Co-op Adv. 5. Consumer Mags. 6. D.M. to Bus. Estab.7. D.M. to Consumers
8. Daily Newsp. 9. Exhibits/Trade Shows 10. Foreign 11. Infomercial 12. Internet Adv.13. Multimedia 14. Network Radio
15. Network T.V. 16. Newsp. Distr. Mags. 17. Other 18. Outdoor (Posters, Transit) 19. Point of Purchase20. Premiums, Novelties
21. Product Samples 22. Special Events Mktg. 23. Spot Radio 24. Spot T.V. 25. Weekly Newsp. 26. Yellow Page Adv.

Temple-Inland Inc. — (Continued)

Leslie K. O'Neal *(Sec & Sr VP)*
Kenneth R. Dubuque *(Grp VP-Fin Svcs)*
Larry C. Norton *(Grp VP-Corrugated Pkg)*
George D. Obernesser *(Grp VP-Paperboard)*
Jack C. Sweeny *(Grp VP-Building Products)*
Carolyn Sloan *(VP-Internal Audit)*
Brands & Products:
TEMFIBRE

TEXPAK INC.
130 New Hyde Pk Rd
Franklin Square, NY 11010
Tel.: (516) 326-7720
Fax: (516) 326-7970
Toll Free: (800) 645-3416
E-mail: info@textpak.com
Web Site: www.texpak.com
Approx. Number Employees: 25
Year Founded: 1934
Business Description:
Packaging Materials
S.I.C.: 7389
N.A.I.C.S.: 561910
Media: 4-13
Personnel:
Steven Kunreuther *(Pres)*
Brands & Products:
MATT MACHINE

TIMBERWEST FOREST CORP.
1055 W Georgia St Ste 2300
Vancouver, BC V6E 3P3, Canada
Tel.: (604) 654-4600
Fax: (604) 654-4662
Web Site: www.timberwest.com
Approx. Sls.: $147,095,604
Approx. Number Employees: 81
Business Description:
Logging & Lumbermill Services
S.I.C.: 2411
N.A.I.C.S.: 113310
Media: 2-7
Personnel:
Bev Park *(Interim Pres & Interim CEO)*
Robert Allen *(CFO & VP-Fin)*
John B. Mitchell *(Chief Forester Officer)*
John Kelvin *(VP-Legal Mktg & Sls)*
Brands & Products:
TIMBERWEST

TRANSILWRAP COMPANY, INC.
(Holding of Nicolet Capital Partners, LLC)
9201 W Belmont Ave
Franklin Park, IL 60131
Tel.: (847) 678-1800
Fax: (847) 233-0199
E-mail: webmaster@transilwrap.com
Web Site: www.transilwrap.com
Approx. Number Employees: 500
Year Founded: 1931
Business Description:
Plastics & Film Sheets Mfr
S.I.C.: 3081; 5162
N.A.I.C.S.: 326113; 424610
Import Export
Advertising Expenditures: $450,000
Media: 2-4-7-10-21
Distr.: Natl.
Budget Set: June
Personnel:
Mark Stevens *(Chm)*
Andy J. Brewer *(Pres & CEO)*
Claudio Colacino *(CFO)*
Thomas Carroll *(Product Mgr-Sheet Extrusion)*
Brands & Products:
AUTOMASK
AUTOMASK MX
CAPRAN
CLEAR FOCUS JETVUE
CLING-MATE
CLINGZ
DAKOTA
DIGI CORE
DIGIKOTE
IMPROVED MXM
JETVUE
LIGHTFAST
MXM
PRO-PRINT
PROBANNER
SIERRA
STAY-PAK
STICK-MATE
SUPER-TRANSTAY
TESLIN
TRAN-STAY
TRANS-BANNER I
TRANS-BANNER II
TRANS-BARRIER
TRANS-CLING
TRANS-CLING II
TRANS-CORE
TRANS-FLEX-CAST
TRANS-KOTE
TRANS-KOTE TRANSGUARD
TRANS-STICK
TRANS TEAR RESISTANT
TRANSALLOY
TRANSALLOY P-260EX
TRANSGRIP
TRANSGUARD
TRANSIL-MASK
TRANSIL-MATTE
TRANSILENE
TRANSILMASK
TRANSILMATTE
TRANSPAQUE
TRANSPET
TRANSPOLYCLEAR
TRANSPROP
TRANSSECURE
TRANSSTIFF
TRANSTAY
TRANSTAY II
TRANSTUFF
TRANSVY
TXP
TYVEK
TYVEK BRILLION
WALKERTALK
WALKERTALKER
X TRANS
XTRANS
YUKON BANNER

TRICORBRAUN
(Sub. of Kranson Industries, Inc.)
10330 Old Olive Street Rd
Saint Louis, MO 63141
Tel.: (314) 569-3633
Fax: (314) 569-5087
E-mail: design@tricorbraun.com
Web Site: www.tricorbraun.com
Year Founded: 1909
Business Description:
Designs & Supplies Decorative & Designer Glass, Plastic Bottles, Caps & Jars for the Cosmetic & Personal Care Industry
S.I.C.: 5085
N.A.I.C.S.: 423840
Import Export
Media: 2-4-7-21-26
Distr.: Intl.
Budget Set: Monthly
Personnel:
Keith Strope *(Pres & CEO)*
Douglas Bolen *(VP-Info Sys)*
Suzanne Fenton *(Dir-Mktg)*
Brands & Products:
BRAUNLOK
COMPONETICS
ECOSPRAY
EXPANDO SEAL
RAPIDFIND
TRICORBRAUN
Advertising Agency:
Drohlich Associates, Inc.
22 Balcony
Saint Louis, MO 63141
Tel.: (314) 567-4030
Fax: (314) 567-0703

UNCLE BOBS SELF-STORAGE
(Sub. of Sovran Self Storage, Inc.)
10640 Hempstead Rd
Houston, TX 77092-8432
Tel.: (713) 683-8992
Tel.: (713) 682-6559
Fax: (713) 682-6550
Toll Free: (800) 242-1715
Web Site: www.unclebobs.com
Sales Range: $25-49.9 Million
Approx. Number Employees: 3
Business Description:
Self Service Storage
S.I.C.: 4225
N.A.I.C.S.: 531130
Media: 26

UNIFLEX, INC.
(Holding of Brynwood Partners LP)
1600 Calebs Path Ext Ste 135
Hauppauge, NY 11788
Tel.: (516) 932-2000
Fax: (516) 932-3129
Toll Free: (800) 223-0564
Web Site: www.uniflexbags.com
E-Mail For Key Personnel:
Sales Director: sales@uniflexbags.com
Sales Range: $10-24.9 Million
Approx. Number Employees: 400
Year Founded: 1963
Business Description:
Polyethylene Products; Plastic Shopping Bags, Mailing Envelopes, Freight Courier Pouches, Disposable Specimen Bags, Disposable Cassette Covers, Medical Supply Items Mfr
S.I.C.: 2673; 2674
N.A.I.C.S.: 322223; 322224
Export
Media: 2-4-10
Distr.: Intl.; Natl.
Budget Set: Oct.
Personnel:
Rob Cunninghan *(Pres & CEO)*
Brands & Products:
THE BAGVERTISING COMPANY
CONFORMER
MILLENNIUM
PRESS AND CLOSE
SPECI-GARD
SPECIAL AIRTUFF
UFLINE
UNIFLEX

UNITED STATES BOX CORP.
1296 McCarter Hwy
Newark, NJ 07104-3714
Tel.: (973) 481-2000
Fax: (973) 481-2002
Toll Free: (800) 221-0999
E-mail: sales@usbox.com
Web Site: www.usbox.com
E-Mail For Key Personnel:
Sales Director: sales@usbox.com
Sales Range: $1-9.9 Million
Approx. Number Employees: 35
Business Description:
Mfr of Packing & Displays
S.I.C.: 2631; 2652
N.A.I.C.S.: 322130; 322213
Media: 2-4-7-10-20-21-26
Distr.: Natl.
Budget Set: Monthly
Personnel:
Alan S. Kossoff *(Owner)*
Tom Kossoff *(VP-Mktg)*
Brands & Products:
TUBE FLAT-PAC

VETERANS IN PACKAGING, INC.
48 Zephyr Ln
Springfield, MA 01128
Tel.: (413) 796-8396
Sales Range: Less than $1 Million
Approx. Number Employees: 1
Year Founded: 2005
Business Description:
Packaging Materials Sales
S.I.C.: 5112
N.A.I.C.S.: 424120
Advertising Expenditures: $76,982
Media: 17
Personnel:
Edward J. Peplinski *(Chm, Pres, CEO, CFO & Chief Acctg Officer)*

VISKASE COMPANIES, INC.
(Holding of Icahn Enterprises L.P.)
8205 S Cass Ave Ste 115
Darien, IL 60561-5319
Tel.: (630) 874-0700
Fax: (630) 874-0178
Toll Free: (800) 323-8562
E-mail: info@viskase.com
Web Site: www.viskase.com
Sales Range: $200-249.9 Million
Approx. Number Employees: 1,300
Year Founded: 1970
Business Description:
Cellulose, Fibrous & Plastic Packaging & Casings Mfr & Supplier
S.I.C.: 3089
N.A.I.C.S.: 326199
Export
Media: 2-4-7-10
Personnel:
Thomas D. Davis *(Pres & CEO)*
Michael Goldberg *(CFO & VP)*
Henry M. Palacci *(COO & VP)*
Maurice J. Ryan *(Sr VP-Worldwide Fibrous & Plastic Products)*
Myron D. Nicholson *(VP-New Products & Tech)*
Brands & Products:
E-Z PEEL
E-Z SMOKE
MEMBRA-CEL

Key to Media (For complete agency information see *The Advertising Red Books-Agencies* edition):
1. Bus. Publs. 2. Cable T.V. 3. Catalogs & Directories. 4. Co-op Adv. 5. Consumer Mags. 6. D.M. to Bus. Estab.7. D.M. to Consumers
8. Daily Newsp. 9. Exhibits/Trade Shows 10. Foreign 11. Infomercial 12. Internet Adv.13. Multimedia 14. Network Radio
15. Network T.V. 16. Newsp. Distr. Mags. 17. Other 18. Outdoor (Posters, Transit) 19. Point of Purchase20. Premiums, Novelties
21. Product Samples 22. Special Events Mktg. 23. Spot Radio 24. Spot T.V. 25. Weekly Newsp. 26. Yellow Page Adv.

NO-SOAK
NOJAX
REELKASE
SENTINEL
SHIRMATIC
SMOKE MASTER
VISFLEX
VISKASE
VISMAX

WARP BROTHERS

(Div. of Flex-O-Glass, Inc.)
4647 W Augusta Blvd
Chicago, IL 60651-3310
Tel.: (773) 261-5200
Fax: (773) 261-5204
Web Site: www.warps.com
Sales Range: $600-649.9 Million
Approx. Number Employees: 200
Year Founded: 1924
Business Description:
Plastic Window Materials; Plastic Film & Sheeting; Other Plastic Products Mfr
S.I.C.: 3081; 3082
N.A.I.C.S.: 326113; 326121
Media: 1-2-3-4-5-6-7-10-18-19-20-21-24-25-26
Distr.: Natl.
Budget Set: Aug.
Personnel:
Harold G. Warp *(Pres & COO)*
David K. Roadruck *(Mgr-Adv & Mktg)*
Brands & Products:
CARRY-HOME COVERALL
COVERALL
CRYSTAL-PANE
EASY-GROW
EASY-ON
FLEX-O-GLASS
FLEX-O-PANE
GLASS-O-NET
GRIP-MAT
JIFFY-COVER
LIFELINER
PLAST-O-MAT
PLASTI GLASS
PLASTI-PANE
POLY-PANE
SHRINK-IT
TAPE-ON
VINYL-PANE

WASAU PAPER CORP.

100 Paper Pl
Mosinee, WI 54455
Tel.: (715) 693-4470
Fax: (715) 692-2082
Web Site: www.wausaumosinee.com
Approx. Sls.: $1,055,688,000
Approx. Number Employees: 2,400
Year Founded: 1910
Business Description:
Mfr of Industrial Specialty Papers; Towel & Tissue Papers & Converter & Washroom Paper Distribution
S.I.C.: 2621; 2676
N.A.I.C.S.: 322122; 322121; 322291
Import Export
Media: 1-2-4-5-7-10-13-19-20-21-22-23-26
Distr.: Natl.
Budget Set: Oct.
Personnel:
San W. Orr, Jr. *(Chm)*
Thomas J. Howatt *(Pres & CEO)*
Henry C. Newell *(COO & Exec VP)*
Scott P. Doescher *(Treas, Sec & Exec VP-Fin)*
Pete R. Chiericozzi *(Sr VP-Towel & Tissue)*
Michael W. Nelson *(Sr VP-Paper)*
Michael R. Wildenberg *(Sr VP-Tissue)*
Sherri L. Lemmer *(VP, Controller, Asst Sec & Asst Treas)*
Patrick J. Medvecz *(VP-Mfg & Tech)*
Curtis R. Schmidt *(VP-HR)*
Brands & Products:
ASTROBRIGHTS
ASTROPAQUE
ASTROPARCHE
ECOSOFT
EXACT
ROYAL COMPLEMENT
ROYAL COTTON
ROYAL LAID
ROYAL LINEN
ROYAL MARBLE
ROYAL SILKPLUS
WAUSAU

WAUSAU PAPER

(Div. of Wasau Paper Corp.)
202 Second St
Brokaw, WI 54417-0305
Mailing Address:
PO Box 305
Brokaw, WI 54417-0305
Tel.: (715) 675-3361
Fax: (715) 675-5175
E-mail: info@wausaupaper.com
Web Site: www.wausaupaper.com
Sales Range: $25-49.9 Million
Approx. Number Employees: 50
Year Founded: 1899
Business Description:
Pulp & Paper Mill
S.I.C.: 2621; 2678
N.A.I.C.S.: 322121; 322233
Export
Advertising Expenditures: $3,000,000
Media: 1-2-4-5-10-19-20-21-26
Distr.: Direct to Consumer; Intl.; Natl.
Personnel:
Thomas J. Howatt *(Pres & CEO)*
Scott P. Doescher *(Treas, Sec & Exec VP)*
Charlie Peth *(VP-Mktg)*
Curtis R. Schmidt *(Corp VP-HR)*

WAUSAU PAPER BAY WEST

(Group of Wasau Paper Corp.)
700 Columbia Ave
Middletown, OH 45042-1931
Tel.: (513) 424-2999
Fax: (513) 420-8570
Web Site: www.wausaupaper.com
Sales Range: $75-99.9 Million
Approx. Number Employees: 190
Year Founded: 1990
Business Description:
Paper Products & Towel & Tissue Cabinets Mfr
S.I.C.: 2621; 2676
N.A.I.C.S.: 322121; 322291
Media: 2-7-10-19-21-26
Distr.: Natl.
Budget Set: Nov.
Personnel:
Michael Wildenberg *(Sr VP-Tissue)*
Jim McDonnell *(VP-HR)*
Melissa Cohee *(Mgr-Customer Svc)*
Brands & Products:
BAY WEST
COMPATIBLE
CUB-TOWLS
DUBL-SERV
DUBL-TOUGH
DUBLSOFT
GRIZZLY
SILHOUETTE
SINGLWIPES
SIRRUS
TWINWIPES
WAGON WHEEL
WAVE'N DRY

WEST PHARMACEUTICAL SERVICES, INC.

101 Gordon Dr
Lionville, PA 19341
Tel.: (610) 594-2900
Fax: (610) 594-3000
Toll Free: (800) 345-9800
E-mail: webmaster@westpharma.com
Web Site: www.westpharma.com
Approx. Sls.: $1,104,700,000
Approx. Number Employees: 6,600
Year Founded: 1923
Business Description:
Medical Packaging & Plastic Components Mfr
S.I.C.: 3842; 3069; 3466
N.A.I.C.S.: 339113; 326299; 332115
Import Export
Media: 2-4-10
Personnel:
Donald E. Morel, Jr. *(Chm & CEO)*
Steven A. Ellers *(Pres)*
William J. Federici *(CFO & VP)*
Jeffrey C. Hunt *(Pres-Pharmaceutical Packaging Systems)*
Robert J. Keating *(Pres-Pharmaceutical Sys Div-Europe & Asia Pacific)*
Donald A. Mcmillan *(Pres-Pharmaceutical Sys Div-North America)*
John R. Gailey III *(Gen Counsel, Sec, VP & Compliance Officer)*
Richard D. Luzzi *(VP-HR)*
Brands & Products:
CHISYS
CLIP 'N' JECT
D-I-D
ENVISION
FLIP-OFF
FLIP-TOP
FLUROTEC
INSOCAP
LYOTEC
MIX2VIAL
MIXJECT
THE READY PACK SYSTEM
TRUEDGE
VERISURE
VIAL2BAG
WEST
WEST ANALYTICAL SERVICES
WEST SPECTRA
WESTAR
WESTONESOURCE
Advertising Agency:
Schwartz Communications, Inc.
230 3rd Ave
Waltham, MA 02451
Tel.: (781) 684-0770
Fax: (781) 684-6500
Pub Rels
— Risa Goldman *(Acct Exec)*

WINTHROP-ATKINS CO., INC.

(Sub. of Chilcote Company)
35 E Main St
Middleboro, MA 02346
Tel.: (508) 947-4600
Fax: (888) 431-1890
Toll Free: (800) 331-3140
E-mail: ppart@winthropatkins.com
Web Site: www.winthropatkins.com
Approx. Number Employees: 100
Year Founded: 1919
Business Description:
Promotional Paper Products, Calendars, Presentation Folders, Frames, Certificates & Photo Packaging Mfr
S.I.C.: 2679; 2675; 2752
N.A.I.C.S.: 322231; 322226; 322299; 323114
Media: 2-4-7-10
Distr.: Intl.; Natl.
Budget Set: Oct.
Brands & Products:
ACE
AMBULANCE
BARGAINEER
BENTLEY
CITATION
COMMEMORATOR
COMPU
CONTEMPO
DAYTONA
DISCREET
EASYPROOF
ECONOMIZER
ELITE
FIRE RESCUE
FOLDERS MADE EASY
KNIGHT
LIMO
MAGNA
MANHATTAN
MARQUEE
MEDALLION
NORFOLK
NU-LETH-R
PACEMAKER
PIEDMONT
POCKET PLANNERS
POLICE CAR
POP-UP COURIER
PRUDENT
RECORDER
SPRITE
VAN
VIGILANT
WILLIAM PENN
WINTHROP

XPEDX

(Div. of International Paper Company)
6285 Tri Ridge Blvd
Loveland, OH 45140
Tel.: (513) 965-2900
Fax: (513) 965-2297
E-mail: stephanie.mangini@xpedx.com
Web Site: www.xpedx.com
Sales Range: $5-14.9 Billion
Approx. Number Employees: 8,000
Year Founded: 1992
Business Description:
Printing & Writing Paper Distr
S.I.C.: 2621
N.A.I.C.S.: 322121
Advertising Expenditures: $500,000

Key to Media (For complete agency information see *The Advertising Red Books-Agencies* edition):
1. Bus. Publs. 2. Cable T.V. 3. Catalogs & Directories. 4. Co-op Adv. 5. Consumer Mags. 6. D.M. to Bus. Estab.7. D.M. to Consumers 8. Daily Newsp. 9. Exhibits/Trade Shows 10. Foreign 11. Infomercial 12. Internet Adv.13. Multimedia 14. Network Radio 15. Network T.V. 16. Newsp. Distr. Mags. 17. Other 18. Outdoor (Posters, Transit) 19. Point of Purchase20. Premiums, Novelties 21. Product Samples 22. Special Events Mktg. 23. Spot Radio 24. Spot T.V. 25. Weekly Newsp. 26. Yellow Page Adv.

xpedx — (Continued)

Personnel:
Mary Laschinger *(Pres)*

XPEDX

(Branch of xpedx)
3900 Spring Garden St
Greensboro, NC 27407-1606
Mailing Address:
PO Box 21767
Greensboro, NC 27420-1767
Tel.: (336) 299-1211
Fax: (336) 852-8925
E-mail: rob.watson@xpedx.com
Web Site: www.xpedx.com
Sales Range: $50-74.9 Million
Approx. Number Employees: 150
Year Founded: 1926
Business Description:
Printing & Business Paper & Supplies Distr
S.I.C.: 2679; 5113
N.A.I.C.S.: 322299; 424130
Advertising Expenditures: $1,000,000
Media: 2-4-5-7-9-10-13-20-21-22-23-24-25-26
Distr.: Natl.
Personnel:
Rob Watson *(Dir-Mktg)*
Brands & Products:
COLORLOK
PARK AVENUE
REGENCY PROFESSIONAL
REPLICOPY
REPLIFAX
REPLIFORM
SEVILLE
SOFT BLOOM
TUFFLEX

XPEDX PAPER & GRAPHICS

(Unit of xpedx)
3351 W Addison St PO Box 18463
Chicago, IL 60618-4303
Tel.: (773) 442-6200
Fax: (773) 442-6415
Web Site: www.xpedxstores.com
Sales Range: $75-99.9 Million
Approx. Number Employees: 100
Year Founded: 1971
Business Description:
Mfr. of Films & Foils, Envelopes, Paper, Business Forms, Data Communications Supplies, Printing & Office Supplies; Laminating; Medical Packaging
S.I.C.: 5111; 8742
N.A.I.C.S.: 424110; 541611
Export
Advertising Expenditures: $500,000
Media: 1-2-4-10-16-20-23-25-26
Distr.: Intl.; Natl.
Budget Set: Oct.
Personnel:
Carol Butler *(VP & Gen Mgr)*

ZIMMER CUSTOM-MADE PACKAGING

1450 E 20th St
Indianapolis, IN 46218-3454
Tel.: (317) 636-3333
Fax: (317) 263-3427
Toll Free: (888) 692-4299
E-mail: info@zcmp.com
Web Site: www.zcmp.com
Approx. Number Employees: 100
Year Founded: 1930
Business Description:
Mfr of Coated Papers for Food Packaging & Industry Applications
S.I.C.: 2671
N.A.I.C.S.: 322221
Media: 2-10-13-20
Distr.: Natl.
Personnel:
Curt Lucas *(Pres & COO)*
Jeff Balogh *(CFO)*
David Brown *(Dir-Ops)*
David Haley *(Dir-Supply Chain & Ops)*
Herbert Henson *(Mgr-Quality Assurance)*
Mark Murphy *(Mgr-Sls & Mktg)*
Eric Rice *(Mgr-MIS)*
Brands & Products:
BEND & PEEL
PEEL & PEEK
TAMPALERT

ZIP-PAK

(Div. of Minigrip/Zip-Pak)
1800 Sycamore Rd
Manteno, IL 60950
Tel.: (815) 468-6500
Fax: (815) 468-6550
Toll Free: (800) 488-6973
E-mail: webmaster@zippak.com
Web Site: www.minigrip.com
Sales Range: $10-24.9 Million
Approx. Number Employees: 50
Year Founded: 1951
Business Description:
Reclosable Polyethylene Zipper Bags, Plastic Zippers, Reclosable Bagging Equipment Mfr
S.I.C.: 2671
N.A.I.C.S.: 322221
Advertising Expenditures: $200,000
Media: 2-5-7-10-11-13
Distr.: Natl.
Budget Set: July
Personnel:
Bob Hogan *(Dir-Sls & Dir-Mktg)*
Brands & Products:
ATL-140
EASY-STOMP
POWDER-PROOF
THERMOFORM
ULTRASEAL
ZIP-PAK
ZIP-PAK SLIDER
ZIPPER TAPE
Advertising Agency:
ABI Marketing Public Relations
29 Broadway Ste 1300
New York, NY 10006
Tel.: (212) 529-4500
Fax: (212) 529-4442

Pet Food, Livestock & Poultry Feed

Brooders — Incubators — Pet Foods — Poultry — Stock Feed — Veterinary Supplies

ADM ALLIANCE NUTRITION, INC.
(Div. of Archer-Daniels-Midland Company)
1000 N 30th St
Quincy, IL 62301-3400
Tel.: (217) 222-7100
E-mail: inquiries@admworld.com
Web Site: www.admani.com
Sales Range: $200-249.9 Million
Approx. Number Employees: 250
Year Founded: 1885
Business Description:
Feeds for Livestock; Livestock Equipment
S.I.C.: 0751
N.A.I.C.S.: 311611
Export
Advertising Expenditures: $1,250,000
Media: 1-2-10-20-21
Distr.: Reg.
Budget Set: Dec.-Jan.
Personnel:
Terry Myers *(Pres)*
Mike Mannink *(Mktg Mgr)*
Brands & Products:
ALLIANCE NUTRITION
CONSOLIDATED NUTRITION
MOORMAN
PROVEN PERFORMANCE FROM INNOVATIVE NUTRITION
SENIORGLO
TINDLE FEEDS

ALL AMERICAN PET COMPANY, INC.
9601 Wilshire Blvd Ste M200
Beverly Hills, CA 90210
Tel.: (310) 424-1600
Fax: (310) 424-1601
E-mail: info@aapbrands.com
Web Site: www.aapbrands.com
Approx. Number Employees: 6
Business Description:
Dog Food Mfr, Marketer & Retailer
S.I.C.: 2047
N.A.I.C.S.: 311111
Advertising Expenditures: $477,472
Media: 8-9-13-19-22-25
Personnel:
Lisa Bershan *(Pres)*
Barry Schwartz *(CEO)*
Victor A. Hollander *(CFO)*
Brands & Products:
BOWWOW BRANDS
BOWWOW BREAKFAST
BOWWOW BREAKFAST CEREAL

ANIMAL HEALTH INTERNATIONAL, INC.
7 Village Cir Ste 200
Westlake, TX 76262
Tel.: (817) 859-3000
Fax: (817) 859-3099
Toll Free: (877) 289-9252
E-mail: webmaster@ahii.com
Web Site: www.ahii.com
Approx. Sls.: $668,920,000
Approx. Number Employees: 939
Year Founded: 1954
Business Description:
Animal Health Products Distr
S.I.C.: 5122; 0752; 2834
N.A.I.C.S.: 424210; 325412; 812910
Media: 7-13
Personnel:
James C. Robison *(Chm, Pres & CEO)*
William F. Lacey *(CFO & Sr VP)*
Larry Delozier *(Grp Pres-Swine & Poultry)*
Doug Harris *(Pres-Production Animal-West)*
Jon A. Kuehl *(Grp Pres-Dealer)*
Mark Middleton *(Pres-Veterinary Grp)*
Damian Olthoff *(Gen Counsel & Sec)*
Brian N. Bagnall *(VP-Info Sys)*
Kathy C. Hassenpflug *(VP-HR)*
Robert Mart *(VP-Mktg)*
Jeff R. Williams *(VP-Sls)*

THE BLUE BUFFALO CO.
PO Box 770
Wilton, CT 06897
Tel.: (203) 762-9751
Fax: (203) 762-2526
Toll Free: (800) 919-2833
Web Site: www.bluebuff.com
Business Description:
Pet Food Distr
S.I.C.: 2047
N.A.I.C.S.: 311111
Media: 6-13
Personnel:
William Bishop *(Owner)*
Jay Davis *(VP-Ecommerce & Mktg)*

BLUE SEAL FEEDS, INC.
(Sub. of Muscatine Foods Corp.)
15 Buttrick Rd
Londonderry, NH 03053-3305
Mailing Address:
PO Box 8000
Londonderry, NH 03053-8000
Tel.: (603) 437-3400
Fax: (603) 437-3403
Toll Free: (800) 367-2730
Web Site: www.blueseal.com
Approx. Number Employees: 500
Year Founded: 1868
Business Description:
Mfr. & Distr. of Feeds for Livestock & Pets
S.I.C.: 2048; 5999
N.A.I.C.S.: 311119; 453998
Export
Media: 2-10-14-20
Distr.: Reg.
Budget Set: Nov.
Brands & Products:
BLUE SEAL CAPRINE CHALLENGER
BLUE SEAL FEEDS
CONCERTO
DAIRY-FLEX
NATURE'S CHOICE
SAFE 'N SIMPLE
SING ALONG
SONG MAKER
SONG MAKER SUPREME
Advertising Agency:
Eisenberg, Vital & Ryze Advertising
155 Dow St Ste 101
Manchester, NH 03101
Tel.: (603) 647-8606
Fax: (603) 647-8607

BOEHRINGER INGELHEIM VETMEDICA, INC.
(Sub. of Boehringer Ingelheim Corp.)
2621 N Belt Hwy
Saint Joseph, MO 64506
Tel.: (816) 233-2571
Fax: (816) 236-2735
Web Site: www.bi-vetmedica.com
Approx. Number Employees: 593
Year Founded: 1981
Business Description:
Veterinary Serums, Biologics, Pharmaceuticals, Insecticides & Efficiency Enhancers Mfr
S.I.C.: 2836; 2834
N.A.I.C.S.: 325414; 325412
Export
Advertising Expenditures: $785,000
Bus. Publs.: $500,000; D.M. to Bus. Estab.: $30,000; D.M. to Consumers: $60,000; Daily Newsp.: $15,000; Point of Purchase: $60,000; Premiums, Novelties: $30,000; Product Samples: $60,000; Spot Radio: $30,000
Distr.: Intl.; Natl.
Budget Set: Sept.
Personnel:
Dave Seales *(Assoc Dir-Learning & Dev)*
Brands & Products:
ALPHA-7
ANNIHILATOR
BUZZ OFF
CALIBER 3
CALIBER-7
COMMANDO
DISAL
ELITE
EXPRESS
HYVISC
NARAMUNE-2
PATRIOT
PERMECTRIN
PERMECTRIN II
PULMO-GUARD
PULMO-GUARD MPB
TYLOSIN
VAPONA
VETMEDIN
Advertising Agencies:
Carmichael Lynch Spong
110 N 5th St
Minneapolis, MN 55403
Tel.: (612) 375-8555
Fax: (612) 375-8501
Vetmedin

Grey New York
777 3rd Ave
New York, NY 10017-1401
Tel.: (212) 546-2000
Fax: (212) 546-1495

CAGLE'S INC.
1385 Collier Rd NW
Atlanta, GA 30318
Tel.: (404) 355-2820
Fax: (404) 355-9326
E-mail: cagles@caglesinc.com
Web Site: www.cagles.net

Key to Media (For complete agency information see *The Advertising Red Books-Agencies* edition):
1. Bus. Publs. 2. Cable T.V. 3. Catalogs & Directories. 4. Co-op Adv. 5. Consumer Mags. 6. D.M. to Bus. Estab.7. D.M. to Consumers 8. Daily Newsp. 9. Exhibits/Trade Shows 10. Foreign 11. Infomercial 12. Internet Adv.13. Multimedia 14. Network Radio 15. Network T.V. 16. Newsp. Distr. Mags. 17. Other 18. Outdoor (Posters, Transit) 19. Point of Purchase20. Premiums, Novelties 21. Product Samples 22. Special Events Mktg. 23. Spot Radio 24. Spot T.V. 25. Weekly Newsp. 26. Yellow Page Adv.

Cagle's Inc. — (Continued)

Approx. Sls.: $310,098,000
Approx. Number Employees: 1,911
Year Founded: 1945
Business Description:
Poultry Processing Services
S.I.C.: 2015; 0254
N.A.I.C.S.: 311615; 112340
Advertising Expenditures: $645,000
Personnel:
J. Douglas Cagle *(Chm, Pres & CEO)*
Mark M. Ham, IV *(CFO & Exec VP)*
Jared Mitchell *(Officer-Sls)*
Troy Dale Tolbert *(VP-Sls & Mktg)*
Laurice Coan *(Dir-Mktg)*
Lavon Waite *(Dir-HR)*
Raphael Zea *(Dir-IT)*
David Cagle, Jr. *(Mgr-Sls)*
Terry Edmondson *(Mgr-Sls)*
Thomas Mull *(Mgr-Sls)*
Nick Myers *(Mgr-Sls)*
Sally Thomas *(Mgr-Credit)*

CARGILL ANIMAL NUTRITION
(Div. of Cargill, Inc.)
PO Box 9300
Minnetonka, MN 55440-9300
Tel.: (952) 984-1871
Toll Free: (800) 367-4894
Web Site:
www.cargillanimalnutrition.com
Approx. Number Employees: 200
Business Description:
Livestock Fodder & Poultry Feeds Mfr
S.I.C.: 2048
N.A.I.C.S.: 311119
Personnel:
Jodi Dallman *(Specialist-Mktg)*
Advertising Agency:
Jackson Integrated
5804 Churchman Bypass
Indianapolis, IN 46203-6109
Tel.: (317) 791-9000
Fax: (317) 791-9800
Toll Free: (888) JACKSON

CARGILL LIMITED
(Sub. of Cargill, Inc.)
240 Graham Ave Ste 300
PO Box 5900
Winnipeg, MB R3C 0J7, Canada
Tel.: (204) 947-0141
Fax: (204) 947-6444
Telex: 7-57759 CARGILL WPG
Web Site: www.cargill.ca
E-Mail For Key Personnel:
Public Relations: robert_meijer@cargill.com
Sales Range: $1-4.9 Billion
Approx. Number Employees: 6,000
Business Description:
Agriculture & Agra Food
S.I.C.: 0139
N.A.I.C.S.: 111998
Import Export
Advertising Expenditures: $1,000,000
Bus. Publs.: $250,000; Daily Newsp.: $500,000; Other: $250,000
Distr.: Natl.
Budget Set: Dec.
Personnel:
Len Penner *(Pres)*
Robert Meijer *(Dir-Pub Affairs)*
Brands & Products:
ACCUBIND
ACCUFLO
ACCUGEL
ACCUMOULD
ACCURX
ACCUSET
ADVANTASOY
ALBERGER
ANGUS BEEF
ANGUS PRIDE
BRANDYWINE
BRONZE MEDAL
CALIFORNIA SEA SALT
CARGILL LECITHIN SBX
CASHMERE
CG90
CG90 SURFACE SAVER
CHAMPIONS CHOICE
CITRO PURE
CLEARBREW
CLEARDEX
CLEARLANE
CLEARSWEET
CMF
COLONIAL
CS/90
CUPID
DAIRY FOCUS
DRILLER'S CHOICE
DURA-CUBE
DYN-O MELT
ENCORE
ESL
FIGHTER
FLO-EVER
FRIESEN
GERKENS CACAO
GIBRALTAR
GLACIER MELT
GROUND BEEF
GUERNSEY
GULF SHORE BOAT AND BOIL
HALITE WINTER MELT
HARDI-CUBE
HARDY
HI-TEX
HONEYSUCKLE WHITE
HP
HUMMER
HYDRAGEL
HYDRO MELT
HYSOC
INSTANT ACCUGEL
ISOCLEAR
JEFFERSON ISLAND
JIFFY MELT
KILN
LA ESPANOLA
LESLIE
LI MING
LIBERTY
MARKET PROS
MEDO-GOLD
MICROSIZED
MIX-N-FINE
NATURE WORKS
NK MAGIC TOOL BOX
NORTH PACIFIC BOAT AND SHORE
NOVUS
NOXOUT
NUT-NOTS
OLIGGO-FIBER
OLINA
PALMIA
PLANTATION
PLATINUM 2000
PORK FOCUS
PORK WORKS
PREMIER
PROCROP
PROGRESSIVE BAKER
PROMOTE
PRO'S PICK
PURILEV
QUALITATE
QUINTA DOS OLIVAIS
RANCHERS STOCK
RED-OUT
REGAL
RENESSEN
RHEOGEL
RIVERSIDE
RUSTOP
SABLE
SALT SENSE
SCARLET
SEAFARER'S
SOCFAT
SOCOLATE
SOF-T
SOFTENER CARE
SPRING HEARTH
SPRING KING
STINE
SUN GEMS
SUNNYBROOK
SUPERSOCOLATE
TEXTRATEIN
VELEIRO
VELVET
VICTORIAN
VISCOGEL
WAHA
WARWICK
WILBUR BUDS
WINDSOR
ZEO TABS
ZERO TRANS

CENTRAL GARDEN & PET COMPANY
1340 Treat Blvd Ste 600
Walnut Creek, CA 94597
Tel.: (925) 948-4000
Fax: (925) 287-0601
Web Site: www.central.com
Approx. Sls.: $1,523,648,000
Approx. Number Employees: 3,900
Business Description:
Lawn, Garden & Pet Supply Products
S.I.C.: 5261; 5999
N.A.I.C.S.: 444220; 453910
Advertising Expenditures: $35,900,000
Media: 25
Personnel:
William E. Brown *(Chm & CEO)*
Lori Varlas *(CFO)*
John A. Casella *(CIO)*
Gus Halas *(Pres/CEO-Central Operating Companies)*
Glen Fleischer *(Pres-Pet Products Div)*
James V. Heim *(Pres-Bus Dev)*
George A. Yuhas *(Gen Counsel)*
Michael A. Reed *(Exec VP)*
Janet M. Brady *(Sr VP-HR)*
Sherry Perley *(VP-HR, Exec & Mgmt Dev)*
Howard Machek *(Controller & Asst Sec)*
Timothy J. Kane *(Dir-Tax & Asst Sec)*
Brooks M. Pennington, III *(Dir-Special Projects)*

CHARLES RIVER SPAFAS
(Sub. of Charles River Laboratories International, Inc.)
106 Rte 32
North Franklin, CT 06254-1811
Tel.: (860) 889-1389
Fax: (860) 889-1991
Toll Free: (800) SPAFAS1
E-mail: csdspf@crl.com
Web Site: www.criver.com
Sales Range: $10-24.9 Million
Approx. Number Employees: 141
Year Founded: 1961
Business Description:
Egg Research
S.I.C.: 5144
N.A.I.C.S.: 424440
Export
Media: 4-10-13-22
Distr.: Intl.

CONTINENTAL GRAIN COMPANY
277 Park Ave
New York, NY 10172
Tel.: (212) 207-5930
Fax: (212) 507-5499
Telex: 62-0398
E-mail: information@conti.com
Web Site: www.contigroup.com
Sales Range: $1-4.9 Billion
Approx. Number Employees: 14,500
Year Founded: 1813
Business Description:
Holding Company; Grains & Poultry Processing
S.I.C.: 2015; 2041
N.A.I.C.S.: 311615; 311211
Import Export
Media: 2-4-7-10-17-19
Personnel:
Paul J. Fribourg *(Chm, Pres & CEO)*
Michael J. Zimmerman *(CFO & Exec VP)*
Richard A. Anderson *(Treas & Sr VP)*
Teresa E. McCaslin *(Exec VP)*
David A. Tanner *(Exec VP-Investments)*
David Lee *(Sr VP-Fin)*
Joseph J. Bongiorno *(Asst VP-HR & Tech)*
Paul E. Gibson *(Asst VP-Investment Admin)*
Elvis A. Willie *(Asst VP-Acctg)*
Robin M. Derin *(Sr Mgr-HR & Comm)*
Joanne Hope *(Sr Mgr-Acctg)*
Brands & Products:
CONTINENTAL GRAIN COMPANY
WAYNE FARMS

DAD'S PRODUCTS COMPANY, INC.
18746 Mill St
Meadville, PA 16335-3644
Tel.: (814) 724-7710
Fax: (814) 337-2743
Toll Free: (800) 323-7738
E-mail: info@dadspetcare.com
Web Site: www.dadspetcare.com
Approx. Number Employees: 250
Year Founded: 1933
Business Description:
Mfr. & Marketer of Dry & Semi-Moist Canned Pet Foods
S.I.C.: 2047
N.A.I.C.S.: 311111
Advertising Expenditures: $1,000,000
Media: 13-14-19-21-23-24
Distr.: Reg.
Budget Set: Quarterly

Key to Media (For complete agency information see *The Advertising Red Books-Agencies* edition):
1. Bus. Publs. 2. Cable T.V. 3. Catalogs & Directories. 4. Co-op Adv. 5. Consumer Mags. 6. D.M. to Bus. Estab.7. D.M. to Consumers
8. Daily Newsp. 9. Exhibits/Trade Shows 10. Foreign 11. Infomercial 12. Internet Adv.13. Multimedia 14. Network Radio
15. Network T.V. 16. Newsp. Distr. Mags. 17. Other 18. Outdoor (Posters, Transit) 19. Point of Purchase20. Premiums, Novelties
21. Product Samples 22. Special Events Mktg. 23. Spot Radio 24. Spot T.V. 25. Weekly Newsp. 26. Yellow Page Adv.

Personnel:
Sean Lang *(CEO)*
Rick Moyer *(CFO & Treas)*
Faith Radcliffe *(Dir-Consumer Mktg)*
Brands & Products:
DAD'S
ECON-O-METS
HEARTY MEALS
KEBBLE SELECT
TRAIL MIX
Advertising Agency:
Engauge Communications
437 Grant St
Pittsburgh, PA 15219
Tel.: (412) 471-5300
Fax: (412) 471-3308
Toll Free: (800) 937-3657

DEL MONTE PET FOOD DIVISION
(Joint Venture of KKR & CO. L.P. , Vestar Capital Partners, Inc. & Centerview Partners LLC)
375 Northshore Dr
Pittsburgh, PA 15212
Tel.: (412) 222-2200
Web Site: www.pupperoni.com/
Sales Range: $250-299.9 Million
Business Description:
Mfr & Distr of Pet Foods
S.I.C.: 2048
N.A.I.C.S.: 311119
Import Export
Advertising Expenditures: $10,000,000
Media: 8-10-11-13
Brands & Products:
PUP-PERONI
Advertising Agency:
Smith Brothers Agency, LP
116 Federal St
Pittsburgh, PA 15212
Tel.: (412) 391-0555
Fax: (412) 391-3562

ELANCO ANIMAL HEALTH
(Div. of Eli Lilly and Company)
500 E 96th St Ste 125
Indiana, IN 46140
Mailing Address:
PO Box 708
Greenfield, IN 46140-0708
Tel.: (317) 277-3185
Fax: (317) 276-9434
Toll Free: (800) 428-4441
E-mail: elanco@elanco.com
Web Site: www.elanco.com
Sales Range: $1-4.9 Billion
Approx. Number Employees: 2,100
Year Founded: 1954
Business Description:
Animal Products & Agricultural Chemicals Mfr
S.I.C.: 0279
N.A.I.C.S.: 112990
Export
Advertising Expenditures: $2,000,000
Media: 1-2-7-19-20
Distr.: Intl.; Natl.
Budget Set: Sept.
Personnel:
Jeff Simmons *(Pres)*
Brands & Products:
COBAN
MAXIBAN
MAXUS
MONTEBAN
OPTAFLEXX
PAYLEAN
POSILAC
PULMOTIL
RUMESIN
SURMAX
TYLAN
TYLAN SULFA-G

EVERGREEN MILLS INC.
(Sub. of Kent Feeds Inc.)
314 S Broadway Ave Ste 202
Ada, OK 74820-5818
Mailing Address:
Ste 202 314 S Broadway Ave
Ada, OK 74820-5818
Tel.: (580) 332-6611
Fax: (580) 332-1956
Toll Free: (800) 654-3909
Web Site: www.evergreenmills.com
Approx. Number Employees: 2
Year Founded: 1920
Business Description:
Mfr. of Livestock & Poultry Feeds
S.I.C.: 2048
N.A.I.C.S.: 311119
Advertising Expenditures: $370,000
Media: 2-10
Distr.: Reg.
Budget Set: June
Personnel:
Jack Dougherty *(Chm)*
Brands & Products:
ANTLER KING
AUREOMYCIN
EVERGREEN
KENT MARAUDER
RAIN-COTE
TROPHY IMAGE

FROMM FAMILY PET FOODS, INC.
13145 N Green Bay Rd 56 W
Mequon, WI 53097
Mailing Address:
PO Box 365
Mequon, WI 53092-0365
Tel.: (262) 242-2200
Fax: (262) 242-3571
Toll Free: (800) 325-6331
E-mail: info@frommfamily.com
Web Site: www.frommfamily.com
Sales Range: $1-9.9 Million
Approx. Number Employees: 20
Year Founded: 1904
Business Description:
Premium Pet Foods Mfr
S.I.C.: 2047; 2048
N.A.I.C.S.: 311111; 311119
Export
Advertising Expenditures: $400,000
Media: 2-4-7-10
Distr.: Natl.
Personnel:
Tom Nieman *(Pres & Head Chef)*
Kathryn Nieman *(Controller)*
Sharon Ziebell *(Coord-Mktg & Sls)*
Brands & Products:
ADULT GOLD
CLASSIC NUTRITIONALS
FROMM
FROMM FOUR-STAR NUTRITIONALS
GOLD NUTRITIONALS
PUPPY GOLD

FURST-MCNESS COMPANY
120 E Clark St
Freeport, IL 61032
Tel.: (815) 235-6151
Fax: (815) 232-9705
Toll Free: (800) 435-5100
Web Site: www.mcness.com
E-Mail For Key Personnel:
President: martha.furst@mcness.com
Sales Range: $100-124.9 Million
Approx. Number Employees: 150
Year Founded: 1908
Business Description:
Feed Premix Products, Feed Commodities & Wet Brewers Grain for Swine, Dairy & Beef Mfr & Distr
S.I.C.: 2048; 5191
N.A.I.C.S.: 311119; 424910
Media: 1-2-4-8-10-13-20-21-23
Distr.: Direct to Consumer; Natl.
Budget Set: Oct.
Personnel:
Frank E. Furst *(Chm)*
Martha Furst *(Pres & CEO)*
Matt Hartman *(CFO)*
Matt Heinrich *(VP-Tech)*
Kevin Gyland *(Mgr-Mktg & Ops)*
Webb Howerton *(Mgr & Merchandiser)*
Shelley Martin *(Mgr-Mktg & Ops)*
Brad McDaniel *(Mgr & Merchandiser)*
Ralph Randall *(Mgr-Nutritional Svcs)*
Joel Reed *(Mgr & Merchandiser)*
Brands & Products:
MCNESS
TERRAPIN RIDGES GOURMET LINE

GOLDEN PRODUCTS CORPORATION
(Sub. of Nestle Purina PetCare Company)
Checkerboard Sq 6 T
Saint Louis, MO 63164-0001
Tel.: (314) 982-2400
Fax: (314) 982-2816
E-mail: robert.watt@purina.nestle.com
Web Site: www.purina.com/
Approx. Number Employees: 1,000
Year Founded: 1947
Business Description:
Mfr. of Cat Box Filler & Processors of Absorbent Clays
S.I.C.: 5999
N.A.I.C.S.: 453910
Export
Media: 2-6-13-14-15-19-20-24
Distr.: Natl.
Budget Set: Mar.
Personnel:
Robert Watt *(Pres)*
Chris Padgett *(VP-Mktg)*
Brands & Products:
COVER CAT
KITTY LITTER MAXX
KITTY LITTER MAXX SCOOP
SCAMP
SOPHISTACAT
TIDY CAT
TIDY CAT MC
TIDY SCOOP
TIDY SCOOP MULTIPLE CAT

HAPPY JACK INC.
2122 Hwy 258 S
Snow Hill, NC 28580
Tel.: (252) 747-2911
Fax: (252) 747-4111
Toll Free: (800) 326-5225
E-mail: mexum@happyjackinc.com
Web Site: www.happyjackinc.com
Sales Range: $10-24.9 Million
Approx. Number Employees: 10
Year Founded: 1946
Business Description:
Mfr. & Distributor of Pet Supplies
S.I.C.: 2834; 5699
N.A.I.C.S.: 325412; 448190
Export
Advertising Expenditures: $300,000
Media: 2-4-9-13-23-25
Distr.: Natl.
Budget Set: Dec.
Personnel:
Joe Exum *(CEO)*
Brands & Products:
ALOE BAN
FLEA BEACON
FLEA GARD
HAPPY JACK
MANGE MEDICINE
MILKADE
PAD KOTE
PARACIDE II SHAMPOO
SKIN BALM
SPOT BALM
STREAKER
TRIVERMICIDE

THE HARTZ MOUNTAIN CORP.
(Sub. of Sumitomo Corporation of America)
400 Plaza Dr
Secaucus, NJ 07094-3605
Tel.: (201) 271-4800
Fax: (201) 271-0164
Toll Free: (800) 275-1414
Telex: 138997
Web Site: www.hartz.com
Approx. Number Employees: 300
Year Founded: 1926
Business Description:
Pet Care Products & Accessories
S.I.C.: 2047; 3999
N.A.I.C.S.: 311111; 339999
Import
Media: 2-4-6-9-14-15-24
Distr.: Natl.
Budget Set: Oct.
Brands & Products:
2 IN 1
ADVANCED CARE BRAND
ALFA-CHEWS
AROUND THE BEND
AT PLAY
BANSHEE MOUSE
BATTABOUT
BETTA PREMIUM FOOD
BIZZY BALLS
BLINK BLINK
BLOWIN' BUBBLES
BONANZA
BREATH STRIPS
BRUSH 'N CLEAN
BUBBLE UP
BULLSEYE
BUMPABELL
CAT GYM
CATCH ME IF YOU CAN
CATNIP LEAVES 'N HERBS
CHEW 'N CLEAN
CICHLID PREMIUM FLAKES
DENTAL
FLEX FORM
FLEXA FOAM

Key to Media (For complete agency information see *The Advertising Red Books-Agencies* edition):
1. Bus. Publs. 2. Cable T.V. 3. Catalogs & Directories. 4. Co-op Adv. 5. Consumer Mags. 6. D.M. to Bus. Estab.7. D.M. to Consumers 8. Daily Newsp. 9. Exhibits/Trade Shows 10. Foreign 11. Infomercial 12. Internet Adv.13. Multimedia 14. Network Radio 15. Network T.V. 16. Newsp. Distr. Mags. 17. Other 18. Outdoor (Posters, Transit) 19. Point of Purchase20. Premiums, Novelties 21. Product Samples 22. Special Events Mktg. 23. Spot Radio 24. Spot T.V. 25. Weekly Newsp. 26. Yellow Page Adv.

The Hartz Mountain Corp. — (Continued)

GOLDFISH PREMIUM FLAKES
HARTZ
HARTZ AT PLAY
HARTZ DENTAL
HARTZ LIVING
HARTZ NUTRITION
HELP A HERO
L/M ANIMAL FARMS
LIVING
NATURE'S GOLD
NUTRITION
ONCE-A-MONTH
PACK MINI MICE
PET SHOPPE
PLIABLE PULLS
POND
POND ALLCLEAR II
PULLABLES
RID FLEA
SWAT 'N SWAY
TEETHING RING
TUG ALONG
UP IN THE AIR
WARDLEY

HILL'S PET NUTRITION, INC.

(Div. of Colgate-Palmolive Company)
400 SW 8th Ave
Topeka, KS 66603-3925
Mailing Address:
PO Box 148
Topeka, KS 66601-0148
Tel.: (785) 354-8523
Fax: (785) 368-5566
E-mail: info@hillspet.com
Web Site: www.colgate.com
Sales Range: $1-4.9 Billion
Approx. Number Employees: 2,500
Business Description:
Mfr. of Prescription Diet Therapeutic Pet Foods & Science Diet
S.I.C.: 5149; 2048
N.A.I.C.S.: 424490; 311119
Export
Media: 2-4-5-6-7-9-10-11-18-19-20-21-25
Distr.: Intl.; Natl.
Budget Set: Aug.
Personnel:
Neil Thomson *(Pres & CEO)*
Kostas Kontopanos *(Pres-Hill's U.S.)*
John Munchoff *(Dir-Mktg)*
Brands & Products:
HILL'S
PET FIT
PRESCRIPTION DIET
SCIENCE DIET
Advertising Agencies:
Callahan Creek, Inc.
805 New Hampshire St
Lawrence, KS 66044-2739
Tel.: (785) 838-4774
Fax: (785) 838-4033

Grey Healthcare Group
1656 Washington Ste 300
Kansas City, MO 64108
Tel.: (816) 842-8656
Fax: (816) 842-1522

Rhea + Kaiser
Naperville Financial Ctr 400 E Diehl Rd Ste 500
Naperville, IL 60563-1342
Tel.: (630) 505-1100
Fax: (630) 505-1109

Young & Rubicam Inc.
285 Madison Ave
New York, NY 10017-6401
Tel.: (212) 210-3000
Fax: (212) 490-9073
(Science Diet)

HOT-SHOT PRODUCTS

(Div. of Miller Manufacturing Company)
1450 W 13th St
Glencoe, MN 55336
Tel.: (651) 982-5180
Fax: (651) 982-5109
Web Site: www.hotshotproducts.com
Year Founded: 1939
Business Description:
Electric Prod Sticks for Livestock
S.I.C.: 3679
N.A.I.C.S.: 334419
Import Export
Media: 2-4-5-7-10
Distr.: Intl.
Brands & Products:
HOT-SHOT

HUBBARD FEEDS INC.

(Sub. of Ridley, Inc.)
424 N Riverfront Dr
Mankato, MN 56001
Mailing Address:
PO Box 8500
Mankato, MN 56002-8500
Tel.: (507) 388-9400
Fax: (507) 388-9453
E-mail: info@hubbardfeeds.com
Web Site: www.hubbardfeeds.com
Approx. Number Employees: 550
Year Founded: 1997
Business Description:
Feed Mfr & Pet Food Distr
S.I.C.: 2048
N.A.I.C.S.: 311119
Export
Advertising Expenditures: $500,000
Media: 2-4-5-7-8-9-10-13-19-20-23-25
Distr.: Reg.
Budget Set: May
Personnel:
Earl Witham *(Sls Mgr)*
Tom Koch *(Mgr-Mktg)*
Lori Stevermer *(Mgr-Swine Products)*
Brands & Products:
CALF COMPASS
COMPLEMIX
CRYSTALYX
CUD BUD
HILL CLIMBER
HUBBARD
HUBBARD MILLING
LACTA GAIN
LEAN VALUE
OPTICARE ANIMAL HEALTH PRODUCTS
PRAIRIE PRIDE
PRO-GOLD
PRODUCTS AND ANSWERS THAT WORK
SWEET BULKY KRUMS
Advertising Agency:
Paulsen Marketing Communications, Inc.
(d/b/a Paulsen AgriBranding)
3510 S 1st Ave Cir
Sioux Falls, SD 57105-5807
Tel.: (605) 336-1745
Fax: (605) 336-2305
Feed
— Greg Guse *(Acct Exec)*

H.W. NAYLOR COMPANY, INC.

121 Main St
Morris, NY 13808
Mailing Address:
PO Box 190
Morris, NY 13808-0190
Tel.: (607) 263-5145
Fax: (607) 263-2416
Web Site: www.drnaylor.com
Approx. Sls.: $1,300,000
Approx. Number Employees: 20
Year Founded: 1926
Business Description:
Veterinary Pharmaceuticals Mfr
S.I.C.: 0752
N.A.I.C.S.: 812910
Export
Media: 4-6-9-10
Distr.: Intl.; Natl.
Budget Set: June
Brands & Products:
DR. NAYLORS

IAMS COMPANY

(Sub. of The Procter & Gamble Company)
7250 Poe Ave
Dayton, OH 45414-2547
Tel.: (937) 898-7387
Fax: (937) 898-2408
Toll Free: (800) 675-3849
Web Site: www.iams.com
Sales Range: $1-4.9 Billion
Approx. Number Employees: 2,500
Year Founded: 1946
Business Description:
Pet Food Mfr
S.I.C.: 2047; 2048
N.A.I.C.S.: 311111; 311119
Export
Media: 2-3-6-7-8-9-10-13-14-15-19-20-21-22-23-24
Distr.: Intl.
Personnel:
Bruce Blue *(Dir-Global Internet Mktg)*
Jeffrey Metzner *(Brand Mgr-North America)*
Brands & Products:
ADULT PLUS
EUKANUBA
EUKANUBA HEALTHY EXTRAS
EUKANUBA NATURAL LAMB & RICE
EUKANUBA VETERINARY DIETS
GOOD FOR TODAY...GOOD FOR LIFE
IAMS ACTIVE MATURITY
IAMS CHUNKS
IAMS HAIRBALL CARE
IAMS INDOOR HAIRBALL CARE
IAMS INDOOR WEIGHT & HAIRBALL CARE
IAMS KITTEN
IAMS LARGE BREED
IAMS MINICHUNKS
IAMS PUPPY SAVORY SAUCE
IAMS SMART PUPPY
IAMS WEIGHT CONTROL
LOW PH/S
LOW-RESIDUE
MAXIMUM-CALORIE
MODERATE PH/O
RESPONSE
RESTRICTED-CALORIE
WHAT HEALTHY PETS ARE MADE OF.

Advertising Agencies:
Saatchi & Saatchi
(Sub. of Publicis Groupe S.A.)
(Worldwide Headquarters)
375 Hudson St
New York, NY 10014-3660
Tel.: (212) 463-2000
Fax: (212) 463-9856

Wieden + Kennedy, Inc.
224 NW 13th Ave
Portland, OR 97209-2953
Tel.: (503) 937-7000
Fax: (503) 937-8000

INTERVET/SCHERING-PLOUGH ANIMAL HEALTH

(Sub. of Intervet/Schering-Plough Animal Health)
556 Morris Ave
Summit, NJ 07901
Tel.: (800) 211-3573 (Technical Svcs)
Tel.: (800) 224-5318 (Technical Svcs)
Web Site: www.intervetusa.com
Sales Range: $300-349.9 Million
Approx. Number Employees: 664
Year Founded: 1936
Business Description:
Veterinary Pharmaceuticals Mfr
S.I.C.: 2834
N.A.I.C.S.: 325412
Export
Advertising Expenditures: $15,000,000
Media: 2-4-7-8-10-20-21-23-24-25
Distr.: Intl.; Natl.
Budget Set: Dec.
Personnel:
Raul E. Kohan *(Pres)*
Charles Broussard *(Dir-Tech Svcs-US Poultry)*

INTERVET/SCHERING-PLOUGH ANIMAL HEALTH

(Branch of Intervet/Schering-Plough Animal Health)
29160 Intervet Ln
Millsboro, DE 19966
Mailing Address:
PO Box 318
Millsboro, DE 19966
Tel.: (302) 934-8051
Fax: (302) 934-6087
E-mail: info.usa@intervet.com
Web Site: www.intervetusa.com
Sales Range: $250-299.9 Million
Approx. Number Employees: 300
Business Description:
Animal Vaccine Researcher, Mfr & Marketer
S.I.C.: 2834; 0752
N.A.I.C.S.: 325412; 812910
Import Export
Media: 2-4-7-10-22
Distr.: Natl.
Budget Set: Nov.
Personnel:
Brett Whitehead *(Dir-Equine & Retail Bus)*

J.D. HEISKELL & CO.

116 W Cedar St
Tulare, CA 93274-5348
Mailing Address:
PO Box 1379
Tulare, CA 93275-1379
Tel.: (559) 685-6100

Key to Media (For complete agency information see *The Advertising Red Books-Agencies* edition):
1. Bus. Publs. 2. Cable T.V. 3. Catalogs & Directories. 4. Co-op Adv. 5. Consumer Mags. 6. D.M. to Bus. Estab.7. D.M. to Consumers 8. Daily Newsp. 9. Exhibits/Trade Shows 10. Foreign 11. Infomercial 12. Internet Adv.13. Multimedia 14. Network Radio 15. Network T.V. 16. Newsp. Distr. Mags. 17. Other 18. Outdoor (Posters, Transit) 19. Point of Purchase20. Premiums, Novelties 21. Product Samples 22. Special Events Mktg. 23. Spot Radio 24. Spot T.V. 25. Weekly Newsp. 26. Yellow Page Adv.

Fax: (559) 686-8697
Toll Free: (800) 366-1886
Web Site: www.heiskell.com
Approx. Number Employees: 370
Year Founded: 1886
Business Description:
Grain & Commodity Trading Services
S.I.C.: 5191
N.A.I.C.S.: 424910
Media: 7-10
Personnel:
Scot Hillman *(Chm)*
Duane Fischer *(Pres & CEO)*
Timothy J Regan *(CFO & Exec VP)*
Ryan Pellett *(COO & Exec VP)*

JEFFERS, INC.
310 W Saunders Rd PO Box 100
Dothan, AL 36301
Tel.: (334) 793-6257
Fax: (334) 793-5179
Toll Free: (800) JEFFERS
E-mail: customerservice@jefferspet.com
Web Site: www.jefferspet.com
Sales Range: $125-149.9 Million
Approx. Number Employees: 300
Year Founded: 1975
Business Description:
Animal & Human Health Supplies
S.I.C.: 5122; 5999
N.A.I.C.S.: 424210; 453910
Media: 4-5-10-13-20-22-26
Personnel:
Dorothy Jeffers *(Pres & CEO)*
Shane Fundum *(CFO)*
Randy Britto *(Coord-Internet Adv & Circulation)*
Liz Morea *(Coord-Mktg, Print)*

KEENELAND ASSOCIATION INC.
4201 Versailles Rd
Lexington, KY 40510
Mailing Address:
PO Box 1690
Lexington, KY 40588-1690
Tel.: (859) 254-3412
Fax: (859) 288-4388
Toll Free: (800) 456-3412
E-mail: keeneland@keeneland.com
Web Site: www.keeneland.com
E-Mail For Key Personnel:
President: nnicholson@keeneland.com
Sales Director: grussell@keeneland.com
Sales Range: $750-799.9 Million
Approx. Number Employees: 160
Year Founded: 1936
Business Description:
Racer & Retailer of Thoroughbred Horses
S.I.C.: 5154; 7999
N.A.I.C.S.: 424520; 711219
Export
Advertising Expenditures: $1,000,000
Media: 2-3-4-7-8-9-15-18-22-23-24-26
Distr.: Intl.; Natl.
Personnel:
Nick Nicholson *(Pres & CEO)*
Walt Robertson *(VP-Sls)*
W.B. Rogers Beasley *(Dir-Racing)*
Geoffrey Russell *(Dir-Sls)*
Brands & Products:
ASHLAND STAKES
KEENELAND
THE KEENELAND LIBRARY
Advertising Agencies:
AGENCYSACKS
345 7th Ave 7th Fl
New York, NY 10001-5006
Tel.: (212) 826-4004
Fax: (212) 593-7824

Cornett Integrated Marketing Solutions
330 E Main St Ste 300
Lexington, KY 40507-1525
Tel.: (859) 281-5104
Fax: (859) 281-5107
(Thoroughbred Racing & Sales)

KENT FEEDS INC.
(Sub. of Muscatine Foods Corp.)
1600 Oregon St
Muscatine, IA 52761
Mailing Address:
PO Box 749
Muscatine, IA 52761-0076
Tel.: (563) 264-4211
Fax: (563) 264-4768
Toll Free: (800) 552-9620
E-mail: adv@kentfeeds.com
Web Site: www.kentfeeds.com
Approx. Number Employees: 1,000
Year Founded: 1927
Business Description:
Livestock & Poultry Feeds & Animal-Care & Pet-Food Products Mfr
S.I.C.: 2048
N.A.I.C.S.: 311119
Media: 1-2-4-5-6-7-8-10-13-14-18-19-23
Distr.: Reg.
Budget Set: May
Personnel:
Gage A. Kent *(Chm)*
Art Dean *(Reg Mgr-Sls)*
Brands & Products:
ACTIVE DOG
ADULT PRIME
ANTLER KING
AS700 PELLETS
BMD
BREEDER AIDE
CATTLE SAFE-GUARD
CHICK-GO
CTC CATTLE MINERAL AFC
CTC KRUMS
DAIRY FORTIFIER PLUS YEAST
DAIRY SEE
DYNASTY
ENERGILASS
EQUIGIZER
EQUINE
EQUINE BASE
EQUINE CHOICE
EQUINE FORTIFIER
FAMILY CARE
FEVERGUARD
FIRST RATE
GM PROTECTOR
HAVOC
HIGH FLYER
HORSEGO
KENT
KENTROL
KIT & CAT
MARAUDER
MIST 'R K
NET PROFIT
OIL-N-WICK
OMEGATIN
OR-E-O KRUMS 4
OXY-TET 8 PELLETS
PIG NURSERY FORMULA
PIG PROFILE
POINT-GUARD
PROTECTORS
PUPPY PRIME
REBOUND
RUB AND POUR-ON
RUMEN BUFF
SENIOR PRIDE
SILAGE SUPREME
SUCCESS
SUCCESSFOAL
SWEETGLO
SWINE SAFE-GUARD
TASTY NUGGETS
TOP SHOW
TROPHY IMAGE
WILD WING
WORLD'S BEST CAT LITTER

MANNA PRO CORPORATION
707 Spirit 40 Pk Dr Ste 150
Chesterfield, MO 63005-1137
Tel.: (636) 681-1700
Fax: (636) 681-1799
Toll Free: (800) 690-9908
E-mail: sales@mannapro.com
Web Site: www.mannapro.com
E-Mail For Key Personnel:
Sales Director: sales@mannapro.com
Approx. Number Employees: 175
Year Founded: 1985
Business Description:
Animal Feeds Mfr & Distr
S.I.C.: 2048
N.A.I.C.S.: 311119
Export
Media: 2-4-5-6-7-8-9-10-13-20-21-23-25-26
Distr.: Natl.
Budget Set: Jan.
Personnel:
John Howe *(Pres)*
Thomas Altwies *(Sr VP & Dir-Prod Supply)*
Sue Copeland *(VP-HR)*
Daniel T. Smith *(VP-Fin)*
Jennifer Hojnacki *(Dir-Mktg)*
Carolyn Brady *(Brand Mgr)*
Brands & Products:
AUREOMYCIN
BOUNCE BACK
CALF-MANNA
COLOSTRO-FIX
COUNTRY COUSIN
DECCOX
DIAMOND V
EQUI-PLETE
FLAXSNAX
HEARTY
HEARTY PERFORMANCE
HOOFSNAX
JUMP-STARTPLUS
LAMA
LEADING EDGE
MANNA E
MANNA MATE
MANNA PRO
MANNA SENIOR
MAX-E-GLO
MILK MATE
NURSEALL
OPTI-ZYME
OPTIMIL COMPLETE
PERFORMANCEXL
POSITIVE PELLET
POWERHOUSE
RAPID FLEX
ROUND-UP
SAFE PERFORMANCE
SCOUR-EASE
SCOUR-EASE PLUS
SHO-FLEX
SHO-GLO
SHO-HOOF
SHOW PRO
SMALL WORLD
STABLE GOURMET
SUCKLE
SUPER HORSE
SWEET 10
SWEET PDZ
SWEET RELY
TROPHY
ULTRA-SUCKLE
UNI-MILK
Advertising Agency:
Swanson Russell Associates
14301 FNB Pkwy Ste 312
Omaha, NE 68154-5299
Tel.: (402) 393-4940
Fax: (402) 393-6926

MARS CANADA INC.
(Holding of Mars, Incorporated)
37 Holland Dr
Bolton, ON L7E 5S4, Canada
Tel.: (905) 857-5780
Fax: (905) 857-5585
E-mail: info@marscanada.com
Web Site: www.mars.com/global/Who+We+Are/Locations/North+America/Canada/Canada.htm?filter=Regions
Sales Range: $700-749.9 Million
Approx. Number Employees: 600
Year Founded: 1974
Business Description:
Dog & Cat Food Mfr
S.I.C.: 2047
N.A.I.C.S.: 311111
Media: 2
Personnel:
Don Robinson *(Pres)*
Christine Parent-Inch *(Mgr-Global Mktg)*
Advertising Agencies:
BBDO Toronto
2 Bloor St W
Toronto, ON M4W 3R6, Canada
Tel.: (416) 972-1505
Fax: (416) 972-5656

Firstborn
630 9th Ave Ste 910
New York, NY 10036
Tel.: (212) 581-1100
Fax: (212) 765-7605

Fleishman-Hillard Canada Inc.
3575 Saint Laurent Blvd Ste 200
Montreal, QC H2X 2T7, Canada
Tel.: (514) 866-6776
Fax: (514) 86-6 8981
Pedigree

OMD Canada
67 Richmond St W 2nd Fl
Toronto, ON M5H 1Z5, Canada
Tel.: (416) 681-5600
Fax: (416) 681-5620

Proximity Canada

Key to Media (For complete agency information see *The Advertising Red Books-Agencies* edition):
1. Bus. Publs. 2. Cable T.V. 3. Catalogs & Directories. 4. Co-op Adv. 5. Consumer Mags. 6. D.M. to Bus. Estab.7. D.M. to Consumers 8. Daily Newsp. 9. Exhibits/Trade Shows 10. Foreign 11. Infomercial 12. Internet Adv.13. Multimedia 14. Network Radio 15. Network T.V. 16. Newsp. Distr. Mags. 17. Other 18. Outdoor (Posters, Transit) 19. Point of Purchase20. Premiums, Novelties 21. Product Samples 22. Special Events Mktg. 23. Spot Radio 24. Spot T.V. 25. Weekly Newsp. 26. Yellow Page Adv.

Mars Canada Inc. — (Continued)

2 Bloor W 29th Floor
Toronto, ON M4W 3R6, Canada
Tel.: (416) 323-9162
Fax: (416) 944-7886

MARS PETCARE

(Sub. of Mars North America)
315 Cool Springs Blvd
Franklin, TN 37067
Tel.: (615) 807-4626
Fax: (615) 309-1187
Web Site: www.marspetcare.com
Sales Range: $150-199.9 Million
Approx. Number Employees: 500
Business Description:
Pet Food Mfr
S.I.C.: 2047
N.A.I.C.S.: 311111
Media: 2-9-18-25
Distr.: Reg.
Personnel:
Olivier Goudet *(CFO & Exec VP)*
Paulette Kish *(Strategic Insights Officer)*
Alberto Mora *(Gen Counsel, Sec & VP)*
Ulf Hahnemann *(VP-HR)*
Aileen Richards *(VP-Personnel & Org)*
Fiona Hughes *(Mktg Dir-Global)*
Lisa Campbell *(Sr Brand Mgr-Pedigree)*
Scott Sutton *(Mgr-Comm)*
Eleanor Williams *(Mgr-Digital Mktg)*
Brands & Products:
BONKERS
G. WHISKERS
KOZY KITTEN
TRAIL BLAZER

THE MEOW MIX COMPANY

400 Plaza Dr 1st Fl
Secaucus, NJ 07094
Tel.: (201) 520-4000
Web Site: www.meowmix.com
Personnel:
Richard Thompson *(CEO)*
Brands & Products:
THE ACATEMY
CRUSTACEAN CRUNCH
KITTY CATCH
MEOW MIX
MEOW MIX MARKET SELECT
WHOLESOME GOODNESS
Advertising Agency:
Grand Central Marketing
111 E 12 St 2nd Fl
New York, NY 10003
Tel.: (212) 253-8777
Fax: (212) 253-6776
Meow Mix Treats
Meow Mix Market Select

MERCY GENERAL HEALTH PARTNERS

(Unit of Trinity Health)
1500 E Sherman Blvd
Muskegon, MI 49442-2407
Tel.: (231) 672-2000
Fax: (231) 672-3074
Web Site: www.mghp.com
Approx. Number Employees: 1,700
Business Description:
Acute Care Hospital
S.I.C.: 8399
N.A.I.C.S.: 813319
Media: 8-13-18-22-23-24-26

Personnel:
Roger W. Spoelman *(Pres & CEO)*

MFA INCORPORATED

201 Ray Young Dr
Columbia, MO 65201
Tel.: (573) 874-5111
Fax: (573) 876-5430
E-mail: info@mfa-inc.com
Web Site: www.mfa-inc.com
Sales Range: $600-649.9 Million
Approx. Number Employees: 1,400
Year Founded: 1914
Business Description:
Farm Cooperative; Mfr & Marketer of Animal Feeds, Plant Food, Hybrid Seeds; Marketer of Farm Supply Equipment & Grain
S.I.C.: 5999; 2875
N.A.I.C.S.: 453998; 325314
Export
Media: 2-10
Distr.: Natl.
Personnel:
Lester Evans *(Chm)*
Bill Streeter *(Pres & CEO)*
Allen Floyd *(Treas & Sr VP)*
Janice Schuerman *(Corp Sec & Sr VP-Corp, Member-Svcs)*
Mike John *(Dir-Livestock Ops Mktg)*
Chuck Lay *(Dir-Comm)*
Nikki Larimore *(Coord-Adv & Admin)*
Brands & Products:
MFA

MSC

260 S Washington St
Carpentersville, IL 60110-2627
Tel.: (847) 426-3411
Fax: (847) 426-4121
Toll Free: (800) 323-4274
E-mail: mail@msccompany.com
Web Site: www.msccompany.com
Approx. Number Employees: 350
Year Founded: 1944
Business Description:
Milk Products Mfr for Baby Animal Nutrition
S.I.C.: 2048
N.A.I.C.S.: 311119
Export
Media: 2-5-6-10-19-20-21-25
Distr.: Intl.; Natl.
Personnel:
Trevor Tomkins *(CEO)*
Michael Drennan *(CFO)*
Doug Schomberg *(VP-Sls & Mktg)*
Brands & Products:
ADVANCE
ARREST
CALF MEDIC CONCENTRATE
CALVITA
COLOSTRUM QUICK TEST
EACH ADVANCE
ENERGY BOOSTER 100
EXCELERATE
FAT PAK
KWIKMIX
LIQUI-WEAN
PERFORMANCE PAK
POWER FRESHEN
PRO-LYTE PLUS
PROVANCE
RITE START
RUMIN
SELECT FAT

NATIONAL BAND & TAG CO.

721 York St
Newport, KY 41071-1817
Tel.: (859) 261-2035
Fax: (859) 261-8247
E-mail: tags@nationalband.com
Web Site: www.nationalband.com
Sales Range: $25-49.9 Million
Approx. Number Employees: 38
Year Founded: 1902
Business Description:
Poultry & Turkey Leg Bands, Wing Bands, Cage & Nest Markers, Terminal Tags, Tool Checks, Dog License & Rabies Vaccination Tags, Swim Pool Tags & Advertising Specialty Tags Mfr
S.I.C.: 3469
N.A.I.C.S.: 332116
Import Export
Advertising Expenditures: $200,000
Media: 2-4
Distr.: Direct to Consumer; Natl.
Budget Set: Jan.
Personnel:
Eric A. Haas *(Pres)*
Faye Haas Wendel *(Treas, Sec & VP-Personnel)*
Brands & Products:
NB & T

NATIONAL BULK EQUIPMENT, INC.

12838 Stainless Dr
Holland, MI 49424-8218
Tel.: (616) 399-2220
Fax: (616) 399-7365
E-mail: sales@nbe-inc.com
Web Site: www.nbe-inc.com
E-Mail For Key Personnel:
Sales Director: sales@nbe-inc.com
Sales Range: $1-9.9 Million
Approx. Number Employees: 45
Year Founded: 1930
Business Description:
Mfr of Bulk Bag Handling, Mixing, Storage, Conveying, Dumping & Dry Bulk Material Equipment
S.I.C.: 3569; 5084
N.A.I.C.S.: 333999; 423830
Import Export
Advertising Expenditures: $350,000
Media: 1-2-4-5-7-10-13
Distr.: Intl.; Natl.
Personnel:
Joseph Reed *(Chm & CEO)*
C. Todd Reed *(Pres)*
Ellen Kaines *(VP-Fin)*
Dave Denhof *(Gen Mgr)*
Brands & Products:
FORWARD THINKING. REAL RESULTS.
NBE
Advertising Agency:
NATCO Associates
12838 Stainless Dr
Holland, MI 49424-8218
Tel.: (616) 399-2220
Fax: (616) 399-7365

NESTLE PURINA PETCARE CANADA

(Sub. of Nestle Purina PetCare Company)
2500 Royal Windsor Dr
Mississauga, ON L5J 1K8, Canada
Tel.: (905) 822-1611
Fax: (905) 855-5700
Fax: (905) 855-5719
E-mail: info@purina.ca
Web Site: www.purina.ca
Sales Range: $25-49.9 Million
Approx. Number Employees: 500
Business Description:
Animal Feeds & Pet Foods Mfr; Grocery Products
S.I.C.: 2048
N.A.I.C.S.: 311119
Media: 6-8-9-10-16-17-18-19-21-23-24-25
Distr.: Natl.
Personnel:
Karen Kuwahara *(Pres)*
David Katz *(VP-Fin)*
Brands & Products:
NESTLE
PURINA
Advertising Agencies:
Lowe Roche
260 Queen St W Ste 301
Toronto, ON M5V 1Z8, Canada
Tel.: (416) 927-9794
Fax: (416) 927-1188

Publicis Montreal
3530 Blvd St- Laurent St 400
Montreal, QC H2X 2V1, Canada
Tel.: (514) 285-1414
Fax: (514) 842-5907

NESTLE PURINA PETCARE COMPANY

(Div. of Nestle USA, Inc.)
Checkerboard Sq
Saint Louis, MO 63164-0001
Tel.: (314) 982-1000
Fax: (314) 982-2134
Telex: 447620
Web Site: www.purina.com
Approx. Number Employees: 6,749
Year Founded: 1894
Business Description:
Mfr of Pet Food
S.I.C.: 2047
N.A.I.C.S.: 311111
Media: 2-3-6-9-11-15-18-23
Distr.: Intl.; Natl.
Personnel:
Terence E. Block *(Pres-Purina Pet Foods North America)*
Steven L. Crimmins *(CMO-US Pet Foods & VP)*
Mark Stoddard *(Brand Dir-Purina One)*
Michael Moore *(Dir-Interactive Mktg)*
Carla Patterson *(Brand Mgr-Fancy Feast)*
Sheridan Budin *(Brand Mgr)*
Laura Lee *(Brand Mgr-Social Media & Mobile)*
Amy Good *(Mgr-Media, Mktg & Media Insights)*
Charla Finn *(Asst Mgr-Media)*
Brands & Products:
ALPO
BEGGIN' STRIPS
BENEFUL
CAT CHOW
CHEF MICHAEL'S
DELI CAT
DOG CHOW
FANCY FEAST
FIT 'N TRIM
HI-PRO
KIBBLES & CHUNKS
KIT 'N KABOODLE

Key to Media (For complete agency information see *The Advertising Red Books-Agencies* edition):
1. Bus. Publs. 2. Cable T.V. 3. Catalogs & Directories. 4. Co-op Adv. 5. Consumer Mags. 6. D.M. to Bus. Estab.7. D.M. to Consumers 8. Daily Newsp. 9. Exhibits/Trade Shows 10. Foreign 11. Infomercial 12. Internet Adv.13. Multimedia 14. Network Radio 15. Network T.V. 16. Newsp. Distr. Mags. 17. Other 18. Outdoor (Posters, Transit) 19. Point of Purchase20. Premiums, Novelties 21. Product Samples 22. Special Events Mktg. 23. Spot Radio 24. Spot T.V. 25. Weekly Newsp. 26. Yellow Page Adv.

KITTEN CHOW
PETS FOR PEOPLE
PRO PLAN
PUPPY CHOW
PURINA ONE
SECONDNATURE
T BONZ
TENDER VITTLES
TIDY CATS

Advertising Agencies:
Ansira
15851 Dallas Pkwy Ste 725
Addison, TX 75001
Tel.: (972) 663-1100
Fax: (972) 663-1300

Avrett Free Ginsberg
1 Dag Hammarskjold Plz 885 2nd Ave
New York, NY 10017-2205
Tel.: (212) 832-3800
Fax: (212) 418-7331
(Tidy Cats)

Barkley
304 N Broadway
Saint Louis, MO 63102
Tel.: (314) 727-9500
Fax: (314) 727-0561
Toll Free: (800) 886-0561

Fallon Worldwide
901 Marquette Ave Ste 2400
Minneapolis, MN 55402
Tel.: (612) 758-2345
Fax: (612) 758-2346

GolinHarris
(Part of the Interpublic Group of Companies)
111 E Wacker Dr 11th Fl
Chicago, IL 60601-4306
Tel.: (312) 729-4000
Fax: (312) 729-4010
— Josh Rangel *(Acct Exec)*

MRM Worldwide
622 3rd Ave
New York, NY 10017-6707
Tel.: (646) 865-6230
Fax: (646) 865-6264
Chef Michael's

NUTRISCIENCE TECHNOLOGIES

(Sub. of Mitsui & Co., Ltd.)
320 Springside Dr Ste 300
Fairlawn, OH 44333-4531
Tel.: (330) 665-1999
Fax: (330) 665-2195
Toll Free: (800) 722-7242
Web Site: www.bioproductsinc.com
Approx. Number Employees: 300
Year Founded: 1981
Business Description:
Feed Additives & Pet Food Palatability Enhancers
S.I.C.: 2048; 2869
N.A.I.C.S.: 311119; 325199
Import Export
Media: 2-10
Distr.: Natl.
Budget Set: Dec. -Jan.
Brands & Products:
BIOFLAVOR
BIOPRODUCTS
BUFFERIGHT
ENER GII
NUTRIUS
QC CHOLINE

NUTRITIONAL RESEARCH ASSOCIATES, INC.

407 E Broad St
South Whitley, IN 46787-1001
Mailing Address:
PO Box 354
South Whitley, IN 46787-0354
Tel.: (260) 723-4931
Fax: (260) 723-6297
Toll Free: (800) 456-4931
Approx. Number Employees: 15
Year Founded: 1934
Business Description:
Feeds & Supplements Whslr for Chinchillas, Cavys, Rabbits, Flamingos, Red Factor Canaries, Minks, Goats, Dogs, Pets & Other Farm Animals
S.I.C.: 5191
N.A.I.C.S.: 424910
Media: 2-4-6-7-8-9-10-20-21-25-26
Distr.: Natl.
Budget Set: Jan.
Brands & Products:
AQUA C
AQUA LYTE
AQUA VITE
BUNNETS
CAVY-LETS
CORNETS
KLINE'S SPECIAL
NUTRITIONAL RESEARCH ASSOCIATES
QUINTREX
RABBIT DE-WORMER
SHOW STOPPER
WHOLE GRAIN CONDITIONER
WOOLETS

OIL-DRI CORPORATION OF AMERICA

410 N Michigan Ave Ste 400
Chicago, IL 60611-4213
Tel.: (312) 321-1515
Fax: (312) 321-1271
Toll Free: (800) 233-9802
E-mail: info@oildri.com
Web Site: www.oildri.com
Approx. Sls.: $219,050,000
Approx. Number Employees: 812
Year Founded: 1941
Business Description:
Sorbent Products Mfr for Consumer, Industrial, Environmental, Agricultural & Fluids Purification Markets
S.I.C.: 2899; 1455; 1459; 3295; 3589; 3999; 5084
N.A.I.C.S.: 325998; 212324; 212325; 327992; 333319; 339999; 423830
Export
Advertising Expenditures: $2,102,000
Media: 17
Distr.: Natl.
Budget Set: May
Personnel:
Richard M. Jaffee *(Chm)*
Joseph C. Miller *(Vice Chm)*
Daniel S. Jaffee *(Pres & CEO)*
Jeffrey M. Libert *(CFO)*
Daniel T. Smith *(Chief Acctg Officer & VP)*
Douglas A. Graham *(Gen Counsel, Sec & VP)*
Brands & Products:
AGSORB
CAT'S PRIDE
CREATING VALUE FROM SORBENT MINERALS
JONNY CAT
KAT KIT
OIL-DRI
OIL.DRY
PRO MOUND
PURE-FLO
RAPID DRY
SELECT
SOILMASTER
Advertising Agencies:
Doner
25900 Northwestern Hwy
Southfield, MI 48075
Tel.: (248) 354-9700
Fax: (248) 827-8440
Agency of Record

Schafer Condon Carter
168 N Clinton
Chicago, IL 60661
Tel.: (312) 464-1666
Fax: (312) 464-0628
(Cats Pride)

PET VALU CANADA, INC.

(Sub. of Pet Valu Inc.)
121 McPherson St
Markham, ON L3R 3L3, Canada
Tel.: (905) 946-1200
Fax: (905) 946-0659
E-mail: pviirecruiter@petvalu.com
Web Site: www.petvalu.com
Approx. Sls.: $181,011,417
Approx. Number Employees: 100
Year Founded: 1993
Business Description:
Specialty Sale Services
S.I.C.: 5999
N.A.I.C.S.: 453910
Advertising Expenditures: $1,479,219
Personnel:
Kevin Brooks *(Owner-Franchise & Operator)*
Angelo Intorre *(Exec VP)*
John Turner *(Sr VP-Bus Dev)*
Christine A. Martin-Bevilacqua *(VP-HR)*
Denis McLaughlin *(VP-Mdsg Pet Nutrition)*
Alexandra Mouland *(Asst VP & Sr Assoc Counsel)*
Jim Young *(Asst VP-Store Ops)*
Brands & Products:
BETTER PET NUTRITION
CASEY'S CHOICE
PAULMAC'S PET FOOD
PET VALU

PETCO ANIMAL SUPPLIES, INC.

(Joint Venture of Leonard Green & Partners, L.P. & TPG Capital, L.P.)
9125 Rehco Rd
San Diego, CA 92121
Tel.: (858) 453-7845
Fax: (858) 784-3489
Toll Free: (877) 738-6742
Toll Free: (888) 824-PALS
Web Site: www.petco.com
Approx. Sls.: $1,996,089,000
Approx. Number Employees: 9,900
Year Founded: 1965
Business Description:
Pet Food, Supplies & Services Retailer; Owned by TPG & Leonard Green & Partners L.P.
S.I.C.: 5999; 0752
N.A.I.C.S.: 453910; 812910
Advertising Expenditures: $68,127,000
Media: 17-22
Distr.: Natl.
Personnel:
James M. Myers *(CEO)*
Michael Foss *(CFO & Exec VP)*
David Bolen *(CMO & Exec VP)*
Elisabeth Charles *(CMO & Sr VP)*
Tom Farello *(Sr VP-Ops)*
Frederick W. Major *(Sr VP-Strategy & Innovation)*
Razia Richter *(Sr VP-Ops)*
J. Scott Blanton *(VP-Brand Creative)*
Kevin Whalen *(VP-Corp Comm)*
Tina Nelson *(Brand Mgr-Private Brands)*
Brands & Products:
PETCO.COM
Advertising Agencies:
Carat
2450 Colorado Blvd Ste 300 E
Santa Monica, CA 90404
Tel.: (310) 255-1000
Fax: (310) 255-1021
Fax: (310) 255-1050

Draftfcb
17600 Gillette Ave
Irvine, CA 92614-5702
Tel.: (949) 851-3050
Fax: (949) 567-9465

Initiative
1 Dag Hammarskjold Plz
New York, NY 10017
Tel.: (212) 605-7000
Fax: (917) 305-4003
(Media Agency of Record)

M&C Saatchi
2032 Broadway
Santa Monica, CA 90404
Tel.: (310) 401-6070
Fax: (310) 264-1910

Red Door Interactive, Inc.
350 10th Ave Set 1100
San Diego, CA 92101
Tel.: (619) 398-2670
Fax: (619) 398-2671

PETEDGE

100 Cumming Centre Ste 307 B
Beverly, MA 01915
Tel.: (978) 998-8100
Fax: (978) 998-8600
Toll Free: (888) 637-3786
E-mail: support@petedge.com
Web Site: www.petedge.com
Sales Range: $10-24.9 Million
Approx. Number Employees: 110
Year Founded: 1956
Business Description:
Pet Supplies Mfr & Distr
S.I.C.: 5999; 5961
N.A.I.C.S.: 453910; 454113
Media: 4-13
Personnel:
Andy Katz *(Pres & CEO)*

Key to Media (For complete agency information see *The Advertising Red Books-Agencies* edition):
1. Bus. Publs. 2. Cable T.V. 3. Catalogs & Directories. 4. Co-op Adv. 5. Consumer Mags. 6. D.M. to Bus. Estab.7. D.M. to Consumers 8. Daily Newsp. 9. Exhibits/Trade Shows 10. Foreign 11. Infomercial 12. Internet Adv.13. Multimedia 14. Network Radio 15. Network T.V. 16. Newsp. Distr. Mags. 17. Other 18. Outdoor (Posters, Transit) 19. Point of Purchase20. Premiums, Novelties 21. Product Samples 22. Special Events Mktg. 23. Spot Radio 24. Spot T.V. 25. Weekly Newsp. 26. Yellow Page Adv.

PetEdge — (Continued)

Brands & Products:
BARKWORTH GOURMET
BRIGHT MAGIC
BUSINESS BUILDERS
CASUAL CANINE
CASUAL KITTY
CITRILUX
CLEAN GO PET
CLIPPERCOOL
DEDICATED TO BUILDING YOUR PET CARE BUSINESS
DERMED
EXTEND-A-LIFE
FRESH PET
GLOCOAT
GUARDIAN GEAR
HEALTHY BAKER
IKARIA
INTELLIPET
MASTER EQUIPMENT
MASTER GROOMING TOOLS
MEDISTYP
MEOW TOWN
PEACEFUL PET
PET EFFECTS
PET STUDIO
PETEDGE
PETRODEX ENZYMATIC
PRODENTAL
PROEAR
PROEYE
PROGLO
PROSELECT
SILKOTE
SLUMBER PET
TOP PERFORMANCE
TOTAL PET HEALTH
WAST SIDE COLLECTION
WINTERGREEN
ZANIES
ZOOM GROOM

PETFOODDIRECT.COM
189 Main St
Harleysville, PA 18936
Tel.: (215) 513-1999
Fax: (215) 513-7286
Toll Free: (800) 865-1333
Web Site: www.petfooddirect.com
Approx. Sls.: $5,000,000
Approx. Number Employees: 100
Year Founded: 1997
Business Description:
Online Pet Supply Store
S.I.C.: 5999
N.A.I.C.S.: 453910
Media: 5-13-22
Personnel:
Jon Roska, Jr. *(Founder, VP-Mdsg & Consumables)*
Brock Weltheruk *(CEO)*
Mathew Murray *(VP-Fin)*
Brands & Products:
AMERICA'S PET STORE ON THE WEB!
PETFOODDIRECT.COM

PETSMART, INC.
19601 N 27th Ave
Phoenix, AZ 85027
Tel.: (623) 580-6100
Fax: (623) 580-6183
Toll Free: (800) 738-1385
E-mail: cs@petsmart.com
Web Site: www.petsmart.com
Approx. Sls.: $5,693,797,000
Approx. Number Employees: 22,000
Year Founded: 1987
Business Description:
Pet Food, Supplies & Services
S.I.C.: 5999; 0752
N.A.I.C.S.: 453910; 115210
Import Export
Advertising Expenditures: $83,500,000
Media: 3-5-6-8-9-13-14-15-18-19-22-23-25
Distr.: Natl.
Personnel:
Philip L. Francis *(Chm)*
Robert F. Moran *(Pres & CEO)*
Lawrence P. Molloy *(CFO & Sr VP)*
Donald E. Beaver *(CIO & Sr VP)*
Emily Dickinson *(Gen Counsel & Sr VP)*
David K. Lenhardt *(Exec VP-Store Ops, Svcs, Info Sys & HR)*
Joseph O'Leary *(Exec VP-Mdsg, Supply Chain & Mktg)*
Kenneth T. Hall *(Sr VP-Strategic Planning & Bus Dev)*
Jaye D. Perricone *(Sr VP-Real Estate)*
Bruce Thorn *(Sr VP-Supply Chain)*
Cathy Hall *(VP-Customer Experience Mktg & Ecommerce)*
Mike Mullin *(Dir-Pub Affairs)*
Ross West *(Sr Mgr-Creative In-Home Comm)*
Brands & Products:
8 IN 1
ALL YOU NEED FOR THE LIFE OF YOUR PET
ANIMATE
AQUARIAN
AQUEON
AUTHORITY
BARGAIN HOUND
BEAK APPETIT
BEASLEY
BERGAN
BIRDOLA
BIRDOLA PLUS
BOUNCING BALL
C & S
CADDIS
CANINE ELEMENTS
CHAT RAVI
CHEWMOMETER
CHOOBLES
COMPANION ROAD
CONCEPTUAL CREATIONS
DENTLEY'S CHEWRITE
DENTLEY'S CHEWRITE ULTRA
DOGGIE DAY CAMP
DOSKOCIL
ECOTRITION
ENCORE
ENERGY SAVERS
EXACT
EXQUISICAT
FELIN MIGNON
FIESTA
FINFIDO
FIRST NATURE
FLEECY FRIENDS
FLUKER FARMS
FM BROWNS
FORTI-DIET
GRACEFUL FLIGHT
GROOMAX
HARTZ
HBH
HEATH
HIKARI
JUNGLE
JURASSIPET
JUST A BUCK, CHANGE THEIR LUCK
KAYTEE
KENT MARINE
LAFEBER
LIL' PAW
LIVING WORLD
LUV-A-PET
MARSHALL
MAZURI
METZ
MIDWEST
MONSTER
MORNING SONG
NATIONAL AUDUBON SOCIETY
NATURE ZONE
NATURES PROMISE
NUTRAFIN MAX
NUTRIPHASE
NUZZLE NEST
NYJER
OMEGA ONE
OPUS
OXBOW
PERKY PET
PET DREAMS
PET GOODS
PETMATE
PETPERKS
PETSAFE
PETSMART
PETSMART CHARITIES
PETSMART HOLIDAY VILLAGE
PETSMART PETSHOTEL
PETSMART.COM
PETZAZZ
PRETTY BIRD
PRICEDROP
PROQUATICS
QUICKO
RAISIN BLEND
RED RIVER
REP-CAL
ROUDYBUSH
SANTA CLAWS
SEACHEM
SHAREABLES FOR ME & MY PAL
SHEPPARD & GREENE
SMART PETS
STROKES SELECT
SUN SEED
SUPER PIF
SUPREME
T-REX
TETRA
TOP FIN
TOP PAW
TOTALLY FERRET
TROPICAL CARNIVAL
TROPICAN
VETSMART
VITAKRAFT
WHERE PETS ARE FAMILY
WHERE PETS FIND FAMILIES
WHISKER CITY
WILD DELIGHT
ZILLA
ZOO MED
ZUPREEM
Advertising Agency:
Bernstein-Rein Advertising, Inc.
4600 Madison Ave Ste 1500
Kansas City, MO 64112-3016
Tel.: (816) 756-0640
Fax: (816) 399-6000
Toll Free: (800) 571-6246
(Creative)

PFIZER ANIMAL HEALTH
(Div. of Pfizer Inc.)
235 E 42nd St
New York, NY 10017
Tel.: (212) 733-2323
Toll Free: (800) 366-5288
Web Site: www.pfizerah.com
Sales Range: $1-4.9 Billion
Approx. Number Employees: 4,000
Business Description:
Animal Health Products Development
S.I.C.: 2834; 2836
N.A.I.C.S.: 325412; 325414
Media: 6
Personnel:
Albert Bourla *(Pres & Gen Mgr-Established Products Bus Unit)*
Risa Wexler *(Sr Dir-Media, PR & Outreach)*
Amy Trettien *(Sr Mgr-Veterinary Ops)*
Advertising Agency:
Rhea + Kaiser
Naperville Financial Ctr 400 E Diehl Rd Ste 500
Naperville, IL 60563-1342
Tel.: (630) 505-1100
Fax: (630) 505-1109

PIC USA, INC.
(Sub. of Genus Plc)
100 Bluegrass Commons Blvd Ste 2200
Hendersonville, TN 37075
Tel.: (615) 265-2700
Fax: (615) 265-2844
Toll Free: (800) 325-3398
E-mail: usinfo@pic.com
Web Site: www.pic.com
Approx. Number Employees: 100
Business Description:
Supplier of Genetically Improved Swine Breeding Stock & Distr of Swine Semen
S.I.C.: 0213; 0752
N.A.I.C.S.: 112210; 115210
Advertising Expenditures: $300,000
Media: 5-9-10-20-26
Distr.: Natl.
Budget Set: June
Personnel:
Bill Christianson *(Gen Mgr)*

PURINA MILLS, LLC
(Sub. of Land O'Lakes, Inc.)
100 Danforth Dr
Gray Summit, MO 63039-5805
Mailing Address:
PO Box 66812
Saint Louis, MO 63166-6812
Tel.: (636) 742-6100
Fax: (314) 317-5278
Toll Free: (800) 227-8941
Web Site: www.purinamills.com
Approx. Sls.: $425,300,000
Approx. Number Employees: 2,600
Year Founded: 1894
Business Description:
Supplier of Animal Nutrition Products
S.I.C.: 2048; 2047
N.A.I.C.S.: 311119; 311111
Export
Media: 2-5-7-8-10-19-20-21-22
Distr.: Intl.; Natl.

Key to Media (For complete agency information see *The Advertising Red Books-Agencies* edition):
1. Bus. Publs. 2. Cable T.V. 3. Catalogs & Directories. 4. Co-op Adv. 5. Consumer Mags. 6. D.M. to Bus. Estab.7. D.M. to Consumers 8. Daily Newsp. 9. Exhibits/Trade Shows 10. Foreign 11. Infomercial 12. Internet Adv.13. Multimedia 14. Network Radio 15. Network T.V. 16. Newsp. Distr. Mags. 17. Other 18. Outdoor (Posters, Transit) 19. Point of Purchase20. Premiums, Novelties 21. Product Samples 22. Special Events Mktg. 23. Spot Radio 24. Spot T.V. 25. Weekly Newsp. 26. Yellow Page Adv.

Personnel:
Daniel Knutson *(CFO & Sr VP)*
Dave Hoogmoed *(Exec VP-Livestock Sys Grp)*
Fernando Palacios *(Exec VP-Ops & Supply Chain)*
Rod Nulik *(Mktg Mgr-Beef Cattle)*

RANCH-WAY FEED INC.
PO Box 2026
Fort Collins, CO 80522-2026
Tel.: (970) 482-1662
Fax: (970) 482-6963
E-mail: info@ranch-way.com
Web Site: www.ranch-way.com
Approx. Number Employees: 50
Year Founded: 1967
Business Description:
Livestock & Poultry Feeds Mfr
S.I.C.: 2048
N.A.I.C.S.: 311119
Media: 2-7-9-10-13-17-26
Distr.: Natl.
Budget Set: Dec.
Personnel:
Phyllis Bixler *(Pres)*
Joe Bixler *(CFO & VP)*
Brands & Products:
RANCH-WAY FEEDS

ROCCORP, INC.
(Div. of Boss Pet Products, Inc.)
1113 Industrial Pkwy N
Brunswick, OH 44212-2371
Mailing Address:
PO Box 785
Brunswick, OH 44212-0785
Tel.: (330) 273-8255
Fax: (330) 273-8224
E-mail: sales@roccorp.com
Web Site: www.rocpet.com
Sales Range: $1-9.9 Million
Approx. Number Employees: 10
Year Founded: 1936
Business Description:
Flea & Tick Killers, Pet Care Products, Pet Restraints
S.I.C.: 0752
N.A.I.C.S.: 115210
Media: 2-4-5-10-21
Distr.: Intl.; Natl.
Brands & Products:
ALOE CARE
CATONGA
HILO
PRESTIGE

THE SCOULAR COMPANY
2027 Dodge St
Omaha, NE 68102
Mailing Address:
PO Box 80269
Lincoln, NE 68501-0269
Tel.: (402) 342-3500
Fax: (402) 342-5568
Toll Free: (800) 488-3500
E-mail: resume@scoular.com
Web Site: www.scoular.com
E-Mail For Key Personnel:
Public Relations: kdaniels@scoular.com
Approx. Rev.: $4,300,000,000
Approx. Number Employees: 600
Year Founded: 1892
Business Description:
Buying, Selling, Storing, Handling & Transporting Agricultural Products
S.I.C.: 5153; 5159
N.A.I.C.S.: 424510; 424590
Export
Media: 2-4-7-10-13
Personnel:
Marshall E. Faith *(Chm)*
David M. Faith *(Pres)*
Robert Ludington *(COO)*
John Heck *(Sr VP-Asset Mgmt & Bus Dev)*
Todd Mcqueen *(Sr VP-Ops)*
Advertising Agency:
Ayres Kahler + Sacco
6800 Normal Blvd
Lincoln, NE 68506-2814
Tel.: (402) 450-7530
Fax: (402) 441-4739

SMARTPAK EQUINE, LLC
30 Worcester St
Natick, MA 01760
Tel.: (774) 773-1100
Fax: (774) 773-1444
Toll Free: (888) 752-5171
E-mail: CustomerCare@SmartPak.com
Web Site: www.smartpakequine.com
Sales Range: $25-49.9 Million
Approx. Number Employees: 105
Year Founded: 1999
Business Description:
Horse, Dog & Cat Nutritional Supplements Direct Sales
S.I.C.: 5122; 5961; 5963
N.A.I.C.S.: 424210; 454111; 454113; 454390
Media: 4-10-21
Personnel:
Becky Minard *(Founder & Pres)*
Paal Gisholt *(Founder & CEO)*
Colby Balazs *(VP-Mktg)*
Lydia Gray *(Dir-Medical)*
Brands & Products:
SMARTBLUE
SMARTPAK
SMARTPINK
SUPPLEMENTS SIMPLIFIED.

SOUTHERN STATES COOPERATIVE, INC.
6606 W Broad St
Richmond, VA 23230-1717
Tel.: (804) 281-1000
Fax: (804) 281-1119
E-mail: info@southernstates.com
Web Site: www.southernstates.com
Approx. Number Employees: 3,959
Year Founded: 1923
Business Description:
Wholesale & Retail Feed, Pet Food, Fertilizer, Seed, Petroleum, Farm, Home & Garden Supplies; Livestock, Grain, Cotton, & Peanut Marketing
S.I.C.: 2048
N.A.I.C.S.: 311119
Import Export
Media: 7-13
Distr.: Reg.
Budget Set: Apr.
Personnel:
Thomas R. Scribner *(Pres & CEO)*
G. L. Miller *(VP-Retail Div)*
Tracy Amburgey *(Dir)*
Jennifer R. Gwyn *(Mgr-Branding, Mktg & Rural Lifestyle)*
Ashley S. Brooks *(Asst Gen Counsel)*
Brands & Products:
BRANDS YOU TRUST. PEOPLE YOU KNOW.
EQUUSSOURCE
FARM PLUS
GREEN CHARGER
GROWMASTER
LEGENDS
RELIANCE
SOUTHERN STATES
STATESMAN
SUPERGOLD
TRIPLE CROWN
WEATHERSHED

SUNSHINE MILLS INC.
500 Sixth St SW
Red Bay, AL 35582
Tel.: (256) 356-9541
Fax: (256) 356-8287
Web Site: www.sunshinemills.com
Approx. Number Employees: 1,155
Year Founded: 1945
Business Description:
Animal Food Mfr
S.I.C.: 2047; 2048
N.A.I.C.S.: 311111; 311119
Personnel:
Alan O. Bostick *(Pres & CEO)*
Brands & Products:
SUNSHINE
SUNSHINE CAT FOOD
SUNSHINE DOG FOOD
Advertising Agency:
TotalCom Marketing, Inc.
922 20th Ave
Tuscaloosa, AL 35401-2307
Tel.: (205) 345-7363
Fax: (205) 345-7373

TRIUMPH PET INDUSTRIES, INC.
(Sub. of Sunshine Mills Inc.)
500 Sixth St SW
Red Bay, AL 35582
Tel.: (256) 356-9541
Toll Free: (800) 331-5144
E-mail: info@triumphpet.com
Web Site: www.triumphpet.com
Approx. Number Employees: 26
Business Description:
Dog & Cat Food Distr
S.I.C.: 2047; 5199
N.A.I.C.S.: 311111; 424990
Import Export
Advertising Expenditures: $200,000
Media: 5-6-8-9-10-13-19-24
Distr.: Direct to Consumer; Intl.; Natl.; Reg.
Brands & Products:
EVOLVE
HI-TOR
TRIUMPH

TROUW NUTRITION USA
(Sub. of Trouw Nutrition International B.V.)
115 Executive Dr
Highland, IL 62249-0219
Tel.: (618) 654-2070
Fax: (618) 654-6700
Toll Free: (800) 255-3582
Web Site: www.trouw-nutritionusa.com
Approx. Number Employees: 110
Business Description:
Custom Animal Feed Premixes
S.I.C.: 2048
N.A.I.C.S.: 311119
Export
Media: 2-10-21
Distr.: Intl.; Natl.
Personnel:
Bruce Crutcher *(Gen Mgr)*
Mike Hooper *(Dir-Mktg)*
Brands & Products:
ASPR-LITE
BIO-ADE
ELECTRA-VITA
GREENLINE
NOVASIL
NOVASILPLUS
OPTIMIN
PROGENIOS
PROTIMAX
PROTIONE
S.T.O.P.
SURVIVOR
TRANSITION PLUS
ULTRA LIFE

UNIVERSAL COOPERATIVES, INC.
1300 Corp Ctr Curve
Eagan, MN 55121-1233
Tel.: (651) 239-1000
Fax: (651) 239-1080
Telex: RCA 229-731
E-mail: info@ucoop.com
Web Site: www.ucoop.com
Approx. Number Employees: 390
Year Founded: 1972
Business Description:
International Farm Supply Cooperative; Agricultural Chemicals, Animal Health Products, Lubricating Oils, Baler Twine, Tractor, Truck & Passenger Tires, Automotive Accessories & Feed Additives Distr
S.I.C.: 5014; 5013
N.A.I.C.S.: 423130; 423120
Import Export
Media: 2-10
Distr.: Natl.
Budget Set: Apr.
Personnel:
Leon Westbrock *(Chm)*
Terrance Bohman *(Pres & CEO)*
Dennis Gyolai *(VP-Fin)*
L. Bryan Morrison *(VP-HR)*
Brands & Products:
ACTION 99
AIM
AMS COMPLETE
AQUQGENE 90
CLEANSE
CO-OP
CROP SURF
DOWN-RIGHT
DUO 638
FOAM BREAKER
GLY 4
GLY 4 PLUS
GUIDE-LINE
KEM LINK
LOGIC
METHYLATED SOYBEAN OIL PLUS
PRAMITOL
ROUNDUP READY
SUPERIOR MISCIBLE
TERMITE KILL III CONCENTRATE
THIODAN
UCPA
UNIVERSAL COOPERATIVE

Key to Media (For complete agency information see *The Advertising Red Books-Agencies* edition):
1. Bus. Publs. 2. Cable T.V. 3. Catalogs & Directories. 4. Co-op Adv. 5. Consumer Mags. 6. D.M. to Bus. Estab.7. D.M. to Consumers 8. Daily Newsp. 9. Exhibits/Trade Shows 10. Foreign 11. Infomercial 12. Internet Adv.13. Multimedia 14. Network Radio 15. Network T.V. 16. Newsp. Distr. Mags. 17. Other 18. Outdoor (Posters, Transit) 19. Point of Purchase20. Premiums, Novelties 21. Product Samples 22. Special Events Mktg. 23. Spot Radio 24. Spot T.V. 25. Weekly Newsp. 26. Yellow Page Adv.

VITUSA CORP.
110 Charlotte Pl
Englewood Cliffs, NJ 07632-2606
Tel.: (201) 569-0800
Fax: (201) 569-0849
E-mail: email@vitusa.com
Web Site: www.vitusa.com
Approx. Number Employees: 12
Year Founded: 1957
Business Description:
Mfr., Marketer & Distr of Feedstuffs, Foodstuffs, Dairy Products & Wastewater Treatment Solutions
S.I.C.: 2048; 5149
N.A.I.C.S.: 311119; 424490
Import Export
Media: 10
Personnel:
Denny J. Herzberg *(Pres)*
John Forbes *(CFO)*
Brands & Products:
ACID-V
AQUA CLEAN
BESTLAC
BIONOX
STARMILK
TOXIBOND
VITUGEN
VITUPROP

Key to Media (For complete agency information see *The Advertising Red Books-Agencies* edition):
1. Bus. Publs. 2. Cable T.V. 3. Catalogs & Directories. 4. Co-op Adv. 5. Consumer Mags. 6. D.M. to Bus. Estab.7. D.M. to Consumers
8. Daily Newsp. 9. Exhibits/Trade Shows 10. Foreign 11. Infomercial 12. Internet Adv.13. Multimedia 14. Network Radio
15. Network T.V. 16. Newsp. Distr. Mags. 17. Other 18. Outdoor (Posters, Transit) 19. Point of Purchase20. Premiums, Novelties
21. Product Samples 22. Special Events Mktg. 23. Spot Radio 24. Spot T.V. 25. Weekly Newsp. 26. Yellow Page Adv.

Pharmaceuticals & Health Care Products

Dental Equipment — Ethical Pharmaceuticals — Eye Care Products — Hospital & Medical Equipment & Supplies — Laboratory Equipment & Supplies — Medical Electronics — Orthopedic Appliances — Over-The-Counter Pharmaceuticals & Vitamins

3M INDIANAPOLIS
(Sub. of 3M Company)
5457 W 79th St
Indianapolis, IN 46268-1675
Tel.: (317) 692-6666
Fax: (317) 692-6772
E-mail: 3M_OHESD@mmm.com
Web Site: solutions.3m.com
Sales Range: $500-549.9 Million
Approx. Number Employees: 1,700
Year Founded: 1833
Business Description:
Hearing, Eye & Respiratory Protection & Energy Absorbing Products Mfr
S.I.C.: 3851
N.A.I.C.S.: 339115
Import Export
Advertising Expenditures: $7,300,000
Media: 5
Distr.: Natl.
Budget Set: Aug.
Personnel:
Jeffrey S. Kulka *(CFO, Sec & Sr VP)*
Frank Gavin *(Dir-Gov Sls)*
Clive Donovan *(Reg Mgr-Sls-Kensington)*
Doug Moses *(Sr Brand Mgr-Peltor)*
Gildas Henocq *(Sls Mgr)*
Wolfgang Kemper *(Sls Mgr)*
Marco Trazzi *(Sls Mgr)*
Michel Douar *(Mgr-Bus Dev-EMEA & TNA)*
Timothy Millar *(Mgr-Bus)*
Jose Montalvan *(Mgr-Bus Dev-Latin America)*
Brands & Products:
AO 5 STAR
AO SAFETY
AOSAFETY EX
CABOFLEX
E-A-R
E-A-R CLASSIC SOFT
E-A-RCAPS
E-A-RFLEX
E-A-RSOFT
EZ DROP
FECTOGGLES
FECTOIDS
FLYWEAR
GLAREX
GRIPPERS
MALIBU
MAXIM
METALIKS
NUVO
OMNI-STAR
PELTOR
PUSH-INS
QUICKLATCH
SAFEWAZE
TAPERFIT
UNISTAR
VIRTUA
WORKTUNES
ZORA
Advertising Agency:
Mitsch Communications
11844 Promontory Trl
Zionsville, IN 46077
Tel.: (317) 733-1316

3M UNITEK CORPORATION
(Sub. of 3M Health Care)
2724 S Peck Rd
Monrovia, CA 91016-5097
Tel.: (626) 574-4000
Fax: (626) 574-4892
Toll Free: (800) 634-5300
Web Site: www.3munitek.com
Sales Range: $75-99.9 Million
Approx. Number Employees: 500
Year Founded: 1948
Business Description:
Develops, Manufactures & Markets Products for Orthodontic Treatment for Dental Professionals
S.I.C.: 3843
N.A.I.C.S.: 339114
Export
Media: 2-4-8-10-19-20-21
Distr.: Intl.; Natl.
Budget Set: Nov.
Personnel:
Paul Keel *(Pres-3M Health Care)*
Mike Lane *(Mgr-Global Mktg)*
Brands & Products:
APC
ORTHOFORM
SMART CLIP
SONDHI
UNITEK
Advertising Agency:
Albarella Design
1990 Christiansen Ave.
Saint Paul, MN 55118
Tel.: (651) 552-8966

A-DEC, INC.
2601 Crestview Dr
Newberg, OR 97132-9529
Tel.: (503) 538-9471
Fax: (503) 538-0276
Toll Free: (800) 547-1883
E-mail: domestic@a-dec.com
Web Site: www.a-dec.com
Approx. Number Employees: 960
Year Founded: 1964
Business Description:
Mfr. of Dental Equipment
S.I.C.: 3843
N.A.I.C.S.: 339114
Export
Media: 2-4-5-10-11
Distr.: Intl.; Natl.
Budget Set: Oct.
Personnel:
G. Kenneth Austin *(Chm)*
Scott Parrish *(Pres)*
Marv Nelson *(CFO & CIO)*
Joan D. Austin *(Sr VP & Treas)*
Eileen Kunze *(VP-HR)*
Phil Westover *(Sr Mgr-Product)*
Paula Vogel *(Mgr-Corp Comm & PR)*
George K. Austin *(Coord-School Acct)*
Brands & Products:
A-DEC
ASSISTINA
CASCADE
CONTINENTAL
DECADE PLUS
EXCELLENCE
ICV
ICX
LISA
PERFORMER
PREFERENCE COLLECTION
RADIUS
Advertising Agencies:
HMH
1800 SW 1st Ave Ste 250
Portland, OR 97201
Tel.: (503) 295-1922
Fax: (503) 295-1938
Toll Free: (800) 350-9355

Karwoski & Courage
60 S 6th St Ste 2800
Minneapolis, MN 55402
Tel.: (612) 342-9898
Fax: (612) 342-4340
Media Relations

A-T SURGICAL MFG. CO., INC.
115 Clemente St
Holyoke, MA 01040-5644
Tel.: (413) 532-4551
Fax: (413) 532-0826
Toll Free: (800) 225-2023
E-mail: at@a-tsurgical.com
Web Site: www.a-tsurgical.com
Approx. Sls.: $3,000,000
Approx. Number Employees: 15
Year Founded: 1969
Business Description:
Elastic Surgical Supports Mfr
S.I.C.: 3842
N.A.I.C.S.: 339113
Import Export
Media: 13
Distr.: Intl.
Personnel:
Mark Shoham *(CEO)*
Brands & Products:
A-T
FIRST WITH AID, COMFORT AND QUALITY

ABAXIS, INC.
3240 Whipple Rd
Union City, CA 94587-1217
Tel.: (510) 675-6500
Fax: (510) 441-6150
Toll Free: (800) 822-2947
E-mail: abaxis@abaxis.com
Web Site: www.abaxis.com
E-Mail For Key Personnel:
President: clintseverson@abaxis.com
Approx. Rev.: $143,676,000
Approx. Number Employees: 388
Year Founded: 1989
Business Description:
Portable Blood Analysis Systems Mfr
S.I.C.: 3841; 3826
N.A.I.C.S.: 339112; 334516
Export
Advertising Expenditures: $1,700,000
Media: 2-10
Personnel:
Vladimir E. Ostoich *(Founder & VP-Mktg-Pacific Rim & Govt Affairs)*
Clinton H. Severson *(Chm, Pres & CEO)*
Alberto R. Santa Ines *(CFO)*
Donald P. Wood *(COO)*
Achim Henkel *(Mng Dir-Sls-Europe)*

Key to Media (For complete agency information see *The Advertising Red Books-Agencies* edition):
1. Bus. Publs. 2. Cable T.V. 3. Catalogs & Directories. 4. Co-op Adv. 5. Consumer Mags. 6. D.M. to Bus. Estab.7. D.M. to Consumers 8. Daily Newsp. 9. Exhibits/Trade Shows 10. Foreign 11. Infomercial 12. Internet Adv.13. Multimedia 14. Network Radio 15. Network T.V. 16. Newsp. Distr. Mags. 17. Other 18. Outdoor (Posters, Transit) 19. Point of Purchase20. Premiums, Novelties 21. Product Samples 22. Special Events Mktg. 23. Spot Radio 24. Spot T.V. 25. Weekly Newsp. 26. Yellow Page Adv.

Abaxis, Inc. — (Continued)

Brenton G. A. Hanlon *(VP-Medical Sls & Mktg-North America)*
Martin Mulroy *(VP-Mktg & Sls-Animal Health-North America)*
Bob Deans *(Dir-Sls-Medical Div-Central US)*
Mike Petrunich *(Dir-Sls-Medical Div-East US)*
Matthew Rapp *(Dir-Sls-Medical Div-West US)*
Lynn Snodgrass *(Dir-Sls-Animal Health Div-North Central)*
Rick Betts *(Dir-Mktg-Medical Diagnostics)*
Valerie Goodwin *(Dir-Mktg-Animal Health Div)*
Randy Knick *(Dir-Govt Affairs & Sls)*
Michael Solomon *(Dir-Bus Dev-Animal Health Div)*
Candice Cayson *(Area Mgr-Sls-Animal Health Div)*
Andy Koupas *(Mgr-Sls-West-Veterinary)*
Tom Beaver *(Mgr-Sls-Animal Health Div-Great Lakes)*
Gerard Cabrera *(Mgr-Sls-Animal Health Div-Northeast)*
Rick Heimendinger *(Mgr-Sls-Animal Health Div-South Central)*
Nick Malz *(Mgr-Sls-Animal Health Div-Southeast)*
Casey Rinehart *(Mgr-Sls-Animal Health Div-Mid-Atlantic)*
John Therrien *(Mgr-Sls-Animal Health Div-Northeast & Canada County)*
Kimjera Whittington *(Mgr-Sls-Animal Health Div-West)*
Chris Ballinger *(Mgr-Sls-Midwest-Veterinary)*
Jeff Sumpter *(Mgr-Distr-US & Sls-Animal Health Div-Central)*

Brands & Products:
ABAXIS
I-STAT
ORBOS
PICCOLO
PICCOLO XPRESS
VETSCAN

ABBOTT DIABETES CARE, INC.

(Sub. of Abbott Diagnostics)
1360 S Loop Rd
Alameda, CA 94502-7000
Tel.: (510) 749-5400
Fax: (510) 749-5401
Toll Free: (888) 522-5226
Web Site: www.diabetescare.com
Sales Range: $200-249.9 Million
Approx. Number Employees: 800
Business Description:
Medical Devices Mfr
S.I.C.: 2835; 3845
N.A.I.C.S.: 325413; 334510
Advertising Expenditures: $8,823,000
Media: 2-6
Personnel:
Stephanie Martins *(Mgr-Strategic Mktg-Global)*

Brands & Products:
FREESTYLE
FREESTYLE COPILOT
FREESTYLE TRACKER

Advertising Agency:
Stratagem Healthcare Communications, LLC
450 Sansome St 12th Fl
San Francisco, CA 94111
Tel.: (415) 397-3667
Fax: (415) 397-3668

ABBOTT LABORATORIES

100 Abbott Park Rd
Abbott Park, IL 60064-3500
Tel.: (847) 937-6100
Fax: (847) 937-1511
Web Site: www.abbott.com
Approx. Sls.: $35,166,721,000
Approx. Number Employees: 90,000
Year Founded: 1888
Business Description:
Pharmaceuticals, Hospital Equipment & Solutions, Nutritional Products, Industrial Chemicals, Diagnostic Products, Pediatric Products, Hygienic Products & Medical Electronics Equipment Mfr
S.I.C.: 2834; 2899; 3841; 3845
N.A.I.C.S.: 325412; 325998; 334510; 339112
Export
Media: 6-7-8-10-13-18-19-20-23-24-25
Distr.: Intl.; Natl.
Personnel:
Miles D. White *(Chm & CEO)*
Thomas C. Freyman *(CFO & Exec VP-Fin)*
Preston T. Simons *(CIO & VP-IT)*
Greg E. Arnsdorff *(Pres-Div & Corp VP)*
D. Stafford O'Kelly *(Pres-Molecular Diagnostics)*
Laura J. Schumacher *(Exec VP, Gen Counsel & Sec)*
Richard W. Ashley *(Exec VP-Corp Dev)*
John M. Capek *(Exec VP-Medical Devices)*
Richard A. Gonzalez *(Exec VP-Pharmaceutical Products Grp)*
John C. Landgraf *(Exec VP-Global Nutrition)*
Edward L. Michael *(Exec VP-Diagnostics Products)*
Carlos Alban *(Sr VP-Intl Pharmaceuticals)*
Brian J. Blaser *(Sr VP-Diagnostics Ops)*
Thomas F. Chen *(Sr VP-Intl Nutrition)*
David A. Forrest *(Sr VP-Intl Nutrition)*
Stephen R. Fussell *(Sr VP-HR)*
Robert B. Hance *(Sr VP-Vascular)*
John M. Leonard *(Sr VP-Pharmaceuticals R&D)*
Holger A. Liepmann *(Sr VP)*
Heather L. Mason *(Sr VP-Diabetes Care)*
James V. Mazzo *(Sr VP-Medical Optics)*
Donald V. Patton, Jr. *(Sr VP-US Pharmaceuticals)*
Mary T. Szela *(Sr VP-Global Strategic Mktg & Svcs)*
Michael J. Warmuth *(Sr VP-Established Products & Pharmaceutical Products Grp)*
J. Scott White *(Sr VP-US Nutrition)*
Thomas J. Dee *(VP-Fin & Controller-Abbott Intl)*
Melissa Brotz *(VP-External Comm)*
Jim Hynd *(VP-Sls & Mktg Div)*
John R. Schilling *(VP-Sls & Mktg)*
Susan M. Widner *(VP-Mktg)*
Don Braakman *(Sr Dir-Pub Affairs)*
Scott Davies *(Sr Dir-External Comm)*
Kurt Ebenhoch *(Sr Dir-External Comm)*
Jonathon Hamilton *(Sr Dir-Pub Affairs-Vascular)*
Kelly Morrison *(Sr Dir-External Comm)*
Tracey Noe *(Sr Dir-Global Citizenship & Policy)*
Simon C. Shorter *(Sr Dir-Clinical & Market Dev)*
Jennifer Smoter *(Sr Dir-Pub Affairs-Intl Nutrition)*
Steve Chesterman *(Dir-Pub Affairs-Vision Care)*
Robert B. Ford *(Dir-Comml-Latin America)*
Greg Miley *(Dir-Pub Affairs-Medical Products)*
Brad Santeler *(Dir-External Media)*
Scott Stoffel *(Dir-Fin & Legal Comm)*
Dirk van Eeden *(Dir-Pub Affairs-Intl Pharmaceutical)*
Karen Hardy *(Event Mgr-Intl Mktg)*

Brands & Products:
ABBOKINASE
ABBOTIC
ABBOTT PRISM
ABSOLUTE PRO
ACCELERATOR
ACCULINK
ACCUNET
ADVANCE
ADVANTEDGE
ADVICOR
AEROSET
AGILTRAC
ALIMENTUM
ALIMENTUM ADVANCE
ALITRA Q
ALPHATRAK
ALUVIA
ANCHOR
ANEUVYSION
ARCHITECT
ASAHI
ASAHI CONFIANZA
ASAHI GRAND SLAM
ASAHI MIRACLE BROS
ASAHI PROWATER
ASAHI TORNUS
AUSRIA
AUSZYME
AVONEX
AXSYM
AZMACORT
BIAXIN
BIAXIN XL
BICLAR
BLOPRESS
BRUFEN
CALCIJEX
CALCILO XD
CARDIZEM LA
CELEX
CELL-DYN
CHITO-SEAL
CLARITH
CLARITHROMYCIN
CLINCHER
CLINICARE
COMPANION
CONTROLIP
COPILOT
CYCLINEX-1
CYLLIND
CYSTIC FIBROSIS V 3.0
DAYAMINERAL
DEFLOX
DEPACON IV
DEPAKOTE
DOC
DUOSTAT
DYNALINK
ECTIVA
ELECARE
EMBOSHIELD
EMBOSHIELD BAREWIRE
EMBRACE
ENLIVE
ENRICH PLUS
ENSURE
ENSURE HIGH PROTEIN
ENSURE PLUS
EPIVAL
ERTHROCIN
ERY-PED
ERY-TAB
ERYTHROMYCIN, PCE
FACT PLUS
FLEX
FLEXIFLO
FLEXIFLO II
FLEXMASTER F1
FORMANCE
FOX PLUS
FREESTYLE
FREESTYLE FLASH
FREESTYLE FREEDOM
FREESTYLE FREEDOM LITE
FREESTYLE LITE
FREESTYLE MINI
FREESTYLE NAVIGATOR
GENGRAF
GLUCERNA
GLUTAREX-1
GOPTEN
GRAFTMASTER
HEITRIN
HELICLAR
HERCULINK
HI-TORQUE BALANCE
HI-TORQUE BALANCE MIDDLEWEIGHT UNIVERSAL
HI-TORQUE CROSS-IT XT
HI-TORQUE PILOT
HI-TORQUE SPARTACORE
HI-TORQUE WHISPER
HOMINEX-1
HUMIRA
HYTRIN
I-STAT
IBUFEN
IMX
INDEFLATOR
INDEFLATOR PLUS
ISOFLO
ISOMIL
ISOPTIN
ITRIN
JEVITY
JOCATH MAESTRO
JOCATH MAESTRO X
JOCATH MERCURY
JOCATH O.P.E.R.A.
JOGLIDE
JOGRAPHY
JOGUIDE
JOSTENT
JUVEN
K-LOR

Key to Media (For complete agency information see *The Advertising Red Books-Agencies* edition):
1. Bus. Publs. 2. Cable T.V. 3. Catalogs & Directories. 4. Co-op Adv. 5. Consumer Mags. 6. D.M. to Bus. Estab.7. D.M. to Consumers
8. Daily Newsp. 9. Exhibits/Trade Shows 10. Foreign 11. Infomercial 12. Internet Adv.13. Multimedia 14. Network Radio
15. Network T.V. 16. Newsp. Distr. Mags. 17. Other 18. Outdoor (Posters, Transit) 19. Point of Purchase20. Premiums, Novelties
21. Product Samples 22. Special Events Mktg. 23. Spot Radio 24. Spot T.V. 25. Weekly Newsp. 26. Yellow Page Adv.

K-TAB
KALETRA
KETONEX
KLACID
KLACIPED
KLARICID
KOFRON
LCX
LEPTOS
LEXAPRO
LUPRON
LUPRON DEPOT
MACLADIN
MACLAR
MALAFENE
MAVID
MAVIK
MERIDIA
MIVACRON
MONOZECLAR
MULTI-LINK FRONTIER
MULTI-LINK MINI VISION
MULTI-LINK PIXEL
MULTI-LINK ULTRA
MULTI-LINK VISION
MULTI-LINK ZETA
NAXY
NEOSURE
NEPRO
NIASPAN
NIMBEX
NORVIR
NUTRISURE
ODRIK
OGASTRO
OMNICEF
OMNILINK
OPENSAIL
OPTIMENTAL
OPTIUM XCEED
ORAQUICK
ORAQUICK ADVANCE
OSMOLITE
OXEPA
PAEDIASURE
PATHVYSION
PATROL
PCE
PEDIALYTE
PEDIASURE
PERATIVE
PERCLOSE
PHENEX
POLYCOSE
POWERSAIL
PRECISION
PRECISIONWEB
PREVACID
PRO-PHREE
PROMOD
PROMOTE
PROPIMEX-1
PROPOFLO
PROPOFOL
PROSOM
PROSTAR
PROSURE
PULMOCARE
QC MANAGER
RADUCTIL
REALTIME
REDUCTASE
REDUXADE
SELFX
SEVOFLO
SEVORANE
SIBUTRAL
SIMCOR
SIMILAC
SIMILAC ADVANCE
SIMILAC ALIMENTUM
SIMILAC GO & GROW
SIMILAC ISOMIL ADVANCE
SIMILAC NEOSURE
SIMILAC ORGANIC
SIMILAC SENSITIVE
SINALFA
STARCLOSE
STEELCORE
STRONGMOMS
SUPLENA
SUPRA CORE
SURVANTA
SYNAGIS
SYNTHROID
TARKA
TDX
TESTPACK
TESTPACK PLUS
TEVETEN
TRANSIVA
TRICOR
TRILIPIX
TWOCAL
ULTANE
URO-HYTRIN
URODIE
UROFLO
UROVYSION
VERIPATH
VIATRAC 14 PLUS
VICARD
VICODIN
VICOPROFEN
VIKING
VISION
VITAL
VOYAGER
XACT
XCEED
XIENCE V
XPERT
ZECLAR
ZEMPLAR
ZONEPERFECT

Advertising Agency:
Cresta Group
1050 N State St
Chicago, IL 60610
Tel.: (312) 944-4700
Fax: (312) 944-1582

ABBOTT MEDICAL OPTICS, INC.

(Sub. of Abbott Diagnostics)
(d/b/a AMO)
1700 E Saint Andrew Pl
Santa Ana, CA 92799-5162
Tel.: (714) 247-8200
Fax: (714) 247-8672
Web Site: www.amo-inc.com
Approx. Sls.: $1,185,035,000
Approx. Number Employees: 3,711
Business Description:
Ophthalmic Surgical & Medical Products Mfr & Distr
S.I.C.: 3841; 2834; 3827
N.A.I.C.S.: 339112; 325412; 333314
Media: 7
Personnel:
Holger Heidrich *(Pres-EAM & Intl Government Affairs & Corp VP)*
James V. Mazzo *(Sr VP)*
George Neal *(Sr VP-Global Refractive & Cataract Sls)*
Angelo Rago *(Sr VP-Global Customer Svcs & Equipment Ops)*
Diane W. Biagianti *(VP & Head-Legal)*
Brian Collins *(Div VP-Mktg)*
Chris Darragh *(Div VP-HR)*
Brian Durkin *(VP-Fin)*
Robert F. Gallagher *(VP-Fin)*
Paul Rockley *(Sr Dir-Comml Ops)*
Steve Chesterman *(Dir-Pub Affairs & Comm)*
Ward Lennon *(Dir-US Lens-Retail Sls & Mktg)*
Brands & Products:
BAERVELDT
BLINK
COMPLETE
COMPLETE BLINK N CLEAN
CUSTOMVUE
HEALON
OXYSEPT
REZOOM
SOVEREIGN
STABILEYES
STAR S4 IR
TECNIS
ULTRAZYME
WAVESCAN WAVEFRONT
WHITESTAR
Advertising Agencies:
Vertical Marketing Network LLC
15147 Woodlawn Ave
Tustin, CA 92780
Tel.: (714) 258-2400, ext. 420
Fax: (714) 258-2409
Promotions
— Danielle Conte *(Acct Dir)*

Williams-Labadie Advertising
57 W Grand Ave Ste 800
Chicago, IL 60650
Tel.: (312) 222-5800
Fax: (312) 222-2530
Contact Lens Solutions
Tear Solutions

ABBOTT NUTRITION

(Div. of Abbott Laboratories)
625 Cleveland Ave
Columbus, OH 43215-1724
Tel.: (614) 624-7677
Fax: (614) 624-6057
Web Site: www.abbottnutrition.com
Sales Range: $250-299.9 Million
Year Founded: 1903
Business Description:
Develops & Markets Infant Formulas, Medical Nutritionals, Nutrition & Energy Bars & Related Products
S.I.C.: 2099
N.A.I.C.S.: 311999
Media: 1-2-4-6-7-10-20-21
Distr.: Natl.
Budget Set: Nov.
Personnel:
Donald V. Patton, Jr. *(Sr VP)*
Randy Stodard *(Head-Mktg-Global)*
Jeff Boutelle *(Gen Mgr-Pediatric Products & Div VP)*
Tracey Noe *(Sr Dir-Global Citizenship & Policy)*
Ana Dan *(Brand Dir-Glucerna)*
Andrew Deister *(Dir-Mktg-Pediatric Nutrition)*
Rhonda Hoffman *(Sr Brand Mgr-Similac)*
Lindsy Delco *(Sr Mgr-Pub Affairs)*
Carolyn Valek *(Sr Mgr-Pub Affairs)*
Jeremy Barron *(Brand Mgr-CRM)*
Sharon Kornegay *(Mgr-Pub Affairs)*
Brands & Products:
ENSURE
GAIN
GLUCERNA
ISOMIL
ISOMIL ADVANCE
PEDIALYTE
PEDIASURE
SIMILAC
SIMILAC ADVANCE
Advertising Agencies:
Engauge Communications
437 Grant St
Pittsburgh, PA 15219
Tel.: (412) 471-5300
Fax: (412) 471-3308
Toll Free: (800) 937-3657

Engauge Communications
375 N Front St Ste 400
Columbus, OH 43215
Tel.: (614) 573-1010
Fax: (614) 573-1011

ABBOTT POINT OF CARE, INC.

(Sub. of Abbott Diagnostics)
400 College Road East
Princeton, NJ 08540
Tel.: (609) 454-9000
Fax: (609) 419-9370
Toll Free: (800) 827-7828
Web Site: www.abbottpointofcare.com
Sales Range: $150-199.9 Million
Approx. Number Employees: 400
Year Founded: 1983
Business Description:
Hand-Held Blood Test Products Mfr
S.I.C.: 3841
N.A.I.C.S.: 339112
Import Export
Brands & Products:
I-STAT
Advertising Agency:
Goodman Media International, Inc.
750 7th Ave 28th Fl
New York, NY 10016
Tel.: (212) 576-2700
Fax: (212) 576-2701
iSTAT Medical Diagnostic System

ACCELLENT INC.

(Holding of KKR & CO. L.P.)
100 Fordham Rd
Wilmington, MA 01887
Tel.: (978) 570-6900
Fax: (978) 657-0878
Toll Free: (866) 999-1392
E-mail: info@accellent.com
Web Site: www.accellent.com
Approx. Sls.: $506,954,000
Approx. Number Employees: 3,326
Business Description:
Medical Device Mfr
S.I.C.: 3841
N.A.I.C.S.: 339112
Media: 2-5
Personnel:
Kenneth W. Freeman *(Chm)*
Donald J. Spence *(Pres & CEO)*
Jeremy A. Friedman *(CFO & Exec VP)*

Key to Media (For complete agency information see *The Advertising Red Books-Agencies* edition):
1. Bus. Publs. 2. Cable T.V. 3. Catalogs & Directories. 4. Co-op Adv. 5. Consumer Mags. 6. D.M. to Bus. Estab.7. D.M. to Consumers
8. Daily Newsp. 9. Exhibits/Trade Shows 10. Foreign 11. Infomercial 12. Internet Adv.13. Multimedia 14. Network Radio
15. Network T.V. 16. Newsp. Distr. Mags. 17. Other 18. Outdoor (Posters, Transit) 19. Point of Purchase20. Premiums, Novelties
21. Product Samples 22. Special Events Mktg. 23. Spot Radio 24. Spot T.V. 25. Weekly Newsp. 26. Yellow Page Adv.

Accellent Inc. — (Continued)

William E. Howell *(CIO & Sr VP)*
Jeffrey M. Farina *(CTO & Exec VP)*
James McGorry *(Exec VP-Sls & Mktg)*
Dean D. Schauer *(Exec VP-Ops, Supply Chain & Engrg)*
Tricia M. McCall *(Sr VP-HR)*
Gerard Porreca *(Sr VP-Quality & Regulatory Affairs)*

ACCURAY INCORPORATED

1310 Chesapeake Terr
Sunnyvale, CA 94089
Tel.: (408) 716-4600
Fax: (408) 716-4601
Toll Free: (888) 522-3740
E-mail: investorrelations@accuray.com
Web Site: www.accuray.com
Approx. Rev.: $221,625,000
Approx. Number Employees: 451
Year Founded: 1990
Business Description:
Robotic Radiosurgery System Mfr
S.I.C.: 3841
N.A.I.C.S.: 339112
Advertising Expenditures: $1,800,000
Media: 10
Personnel:
Louis J. Lavigne, Jr. *(Chm)*
Elizabeth H. Davila *(Vice Chm)*
Euan S. Thomson *(Pres & CEO)*
Derek Bertocci *(CFO & Sr VP)*
Chris A. Raanes *(COO & Sr VP)*
Kelly Londy *(Chief Comml Officer & Sr VP)*
Vittorio Puppo *(Sr VP, Gen Mgr EMEA & India)*
Brands & Products:
4D
6D
ACCURAY
CYBERKNIFE
INTEMPO
INVIEW
IRIS
MONTE CARLO
MULTIPLAN
OUR BUSINESS BEGINS WITH PATIENTS
ROBOCOUCH
SYNCHRONY
XCHANGE
XSIGHT

ACORDA THERAPEUTICS, INC.

15 Skyline Drive
Hawthorne, NY 10532
Tel.: (914) 347-4300
Fax: (914) 347-4560
E-mail: info@acorda.com
Web Site: www.acorda.com
Approx. Rev.: $191,005,240
Approx. Number Employees: 305
Year Founded: 1995
Business Description:
Pharmaceutical Products Developer for Restoration of Neurological Function to People With Spinal Cord Injury (SCI), Multiple Sclerosis (MS) & Related Nervous System Conditions
S.I.C.: 2836; 2834
N.A.I.C.S.: 325414; 325412
Media: 21
Personnel:
Ron Cohen *(Pres & CEO)*
David Lawrence *(CFO)*
Jane Wasman *(Gen Counsel & Exec VP)*
Lauren Sabella *(Exec VP-Comml Dev)*
Denise Duca *(Sr VP-HR)*
Tierney Saccavino *(Sr VP-Corp Comm)*
Michelle Huie *(Asst Diir-Mktg)*
Kristen Graham *(Mgr-Payer Strategy)*
Brands & Products:
ACORDA THERAPEUTICS
ZANAFLEX

ADCARE HEALTH SYSTEMS, INC.

5057 Troy Rd
Springfield, OH 45502
Tel.: (937) 964-8974
Fax: (937) 964-8961
E-mail: info@adcarehealth.com
Web Site: www.adcarehealth.com
Approx. Rev.: $53,236,715
Approx. Number Employees: 1,652
Year Founded: 1988
Business Description:
Retirement Communities, Assisted Living Facilities, Nursing Homes, & Home Health Care Services Owner & Mgr
S.I.C.: 8059
N.A.I.C.S.: 623110; 623311
Advertising Expenditures: $425,700
Personnel:
David A. Tenwick *(Chm)*
Christopher F. Brogdon *(Vice Chm & Chief Acq Officer)*
Gary L. Wade *(Pres & CEO)*
Boyd P. Gentry *(Co-CEO)*
Scott Cunningham *(CFO & VP)*
Sharon Reynolds *(Sr VP-Nursing Home Ops)*
Carol Groeber *(VP-Mgmt Info Svcs & HR)*

ADDUS HOMECARE CORPORATION

2401 S Plum Grove Rd
Palatine, IL 60067
Tel.: (847) 303-5300
Fax: (847) 303-5376
E-mail: info1@addus.com
Web Site: www.addus.com
Approx. Rev.: $271,732,000
Approx. Number Employees: 2,435
Year Founded: 2006
Business Description:
Home Health Care Services
S.I.C.: 8082
N.A.I.C.S.: 621610
Media: 8
Personnel:
Mark S. Heaney *(Pres & CEO)*
Dennis B. Meulemans *(CFO)*
Daniel Schwartz *(COO)*

ADH HEALTH PRODUCTS, INC.

215 N Rte 303
Congers, NY 10920-1726
Tel.: (845) 268-0027
Fax: (845) 268-2988
E-mail: info@adhhealth.com
Web Site: www.adhhealth.com
E-Mail For Key Personnel:
Sales Director: sales@adhhealth.com
Approx. Number Employees: 65
Year Founded: 1976
Business Description:
Vitamin & Dietary Supplements Mfr
S.I.C.: 2834; 5122
N.A.I.C.S.: 325412; 424210
Import Export
Media: 7-10-13-19-21
Distr.: Natl.
Budget Set: Oct.
Personnel:
Balram Advani *(Chm & CEO)*
Ashwin Advani *(COO)*
Brands & Products:
ADH
ULTIMATE HEALTH

ADOLOR CORPORATION

700 Pennsylvania Dr
Exton, PA 19341-1129
Tel.: (484) 595-1500
Fax: (484) 595-1520
E-mail: questions@adolor.com
Web Site: www.adolor.com
Approx. Rev.: $43,302,518
Approx. Number Employees: 75
Year Founded: 1994
Business Description:
Developer of Pain Management Pharmaceuticals
S.I.C.: 2834
N.A.I.C.S.: 325412
Advertising Expenditures: $8,300,000
Personnel:
David M. Madden *(Chm)*
Stephen W. Webster *(CFO & Sr VP-Fin)*
John M. Limongelli *(Gen Counsel, Sec & Sr VP)*
George R. Maurer *(Sr VP-Technical Ops)*
Lee Techner *(VP-Medical Affairs & Dir-Medical)*
Michael D. Adelman *(VP-Mktg & Sls)*
Denise B. Kerton *(VP-HR)*
Brands & Products:
ADOLOR
DISCOVERY-DRIVEN. PAIN-FOCUSED. PATIENT-CENTERED
ENTEREG

ADVANCED NUTRITIONAL BIOSYSTEMS INC.

(d/b/a Scitec Nutrition)
8034 Sunport Dr Ste 401
Orlando, FL 32809
Tel.: (407) 447-1610
Fax: (407) 447-1622
Toll Free: (888) SCITEC-7
E-mail: info@scitecnutrition.com
Web Site: www.scitecnutrition.com
Sales Range: $10-24.9 Million
Approx. Number Employees: 35
Business Description:
Sports Supplements Mfr
S.I.C.: 2834; 2099
N.A.I.C.S.: 325412; 311999
Media: 6

ADVOCATE HEALTH CARE

2025 Windsor Dr
Oak Brook, IL 60523
Tel.: (630) 572-9393
Fax: (630) 572-9139
E-mail: info@advocatehealth.com
Web Site: www.advocatehealth.com
Approx. Number Employees: 28,000
Year Founded: 1995
Business Description:
Health Care Services
S.I.C.: 8062
N.A.I.C.S.: 622110
Media: 2-7-10-13-22
Personnel:
James H. Skogsbergh *(Pres & CEO)*
Dominic J. Nakis *(CFO, Sr VP & Treas)*
William P. Santulli *(COO)*
Bruce Smith *(CIO & Sr VP-IT)*
Lee B. Sacks *(Chief Medical Officer & Exec VP)*
Gail D. Hasbrouck *(Gen Counsel, Sec & Sr VP)*
Ben Grigaliunas *(Sr VP-HR)*
Jerry A. Wagenknecht *(Sr VP-Mission & Spiritual Care)*
Jim Doheny *(VP-Fin & Controller)*
Doug Diefenbach *(VP-Campaign Strategy & Comm)*
Brands & Products:
ADVOCATE HEALTH CARE
Advertising Agencies:
Hoffman York
142 E Ontario St Ste 13
Chicago, IL 60611-2818
Tel.: (312) 787-2330
Fax: (312) 787-2320

Huntsinger & Jeffer
809 Brook Hill Cir
Richmond, VA 23227-2503
Tel.: (804) 266-2499
Fax: (804) 266-8563
Toll Free: (800) 969-3342

AESCULAP, INC.

(Sub. of Aesculap AG & Co. KG)
3773 Corporate Pkwy
Center Valley, PA 18034-8217
Tel.: (610) 797-9300
Fax: (610) 791-6880
Toll Free: (800) 258-1946
E-mail: info@aesculap-usa.com
Web Site: www.aesculap-usa.com
Approx. Number Employees: 350
Year Founded: 1977
Business Description:
Surgical Instrumentation, Power Systems, Neurosurgical Instruments & Implants, Disposables, Cardiovascular Instruments & Sterile Processing Containers Whslr & Distr
S.I.C.: 5047; 7629
N.A.I.C.S.: 423450; 811219
Import Export
Media: 2-4-10-11
Distr.: Intl.; Natl.
Personnel:
Chuck Dinardo *(Pres)*
Brands & Products:
ABC CERVICAL PLATING SYSTEM
ACCU-DERMATOME
AXEL
CRANIOFIX
DAVID3
EQ TRAQ
HILAN
INSTACOUNT
LOAD TRAQ
NEEDLESCOPIC
ORTHOPILOT
PCMS
PRESTIGE
SOCON SYSTEM
SOVEREIGN
SPINE SYSTEM EVOLUTION
STERILCONTAINER
UNITRAC
YASARGIL TITANIUM ANEURYSM CLIP SYSTEM

Key to Media (For complete agency information see *The Advertising Red Books-Agencies* edition):
1. Bus. Publs. 2. Cable T.V. 3. Catalogs & Directories. 4. Co-op Adv. 5. Consumer Mags. 6. D.M. to Bus. Estab.7. D.M. to Consumers 8. Daily Newsp. 9. Exhibits/Trade Shows 10. Foreign 11. Infomercial 12. Internet Adv.13. Multimedia 14. Network Radio 15. Network T.V. 16. Newsp. Distr. Mags. 17. Other 18. Outdoor (Posters, Transit) 19. Point of Purchase20. Premiums, Novelties 21. Product Samples 22. Special Events Mktg. 23. Spot Radio 24. Spot T.V. 25. Weekly Newsp. 26. Yellow Page Adv.

AFEXA LIFE SCIENCES INC.
9604 20th Ave
Edmonton, AB T6N 1G1, Canada
Tel.: (780) 432-0022
Fax: (780) 432-7772
Toll Free: (888) 280-0022
E-mail: info@afexa.com
Web Site: www.afexa.com
Approx. Rev.: $35,020,919
Approx. Number Employees: 87
Year Founded: 1992
Business Description:
Diagnostic & Therapeutic Products
S.I.C.: 2834; 8733
N.A.I.C.S.: 325412; 541710
Advertising Expenditures: $442,890
Personnel:
William B. White *(Chm)*
Jack Moffatt *(Pres & CEO)*
Allan Cleiren *(CFO & Sr VP-Ops)*
Tracey Ramsay *(CMO & Sr VP-Sls)*
Michael Obert *(Chief Legal Officer & Sr VP-Corp Dev)*
Lei Ling *(VP-Product Dev)*
G. Warren Michaels *(VP-Comm)*
Frederick Pittman *(VP-Sls)*
Jason Vandenberg *(VP-Fin)*
Steve Wallace *(VP-Mktg)*
Jane Tulloch *(Sr Dir-Bd Affairs & IR)*
Brands & Products:
AD-FX
CELL-FX
CHEMBIOPRINT
COLD-FX
MENTA-FX
PRESSURE-FX
REMEMBER-FX

AFFINIA HOSPITALITY
551 5th Ave
New York, NY 10176
Tel.: (212) 465-3700
Fax: (212) 465-3511
E-mail: information@affinia.com
Web Site: www.affinia.com
Approx. Sls.: $20,600,000
Approx. Number Employees: 250
Business Description:
Real Estate Managers
S.I.C.: 6531
N.A.I.C.S.: 531210
Personnel:
Benjamin J. Denihan, Jr. *(CEO)*
Advertising Agency:
Manhattan Marketing Ensemble
443 Park Ave S 4th Fl
New York, NY 10016-7322
Tel.: (212) 779-2233
Fax: (212) 779-0825

AFFYMAX, INC.
4001 Miranda Ave
Palo Alto, CA 94304
Tel.: (650) 812-8700
Fax: (650) 424-0832
E-mail: info@affymax.com
Web Site: www.affymax.com
Approx. Rev.: $112,521,000
Approx. Number Employees: 140
Year Founded: 2001
Business Description:
Biopharmaceutical Mfr
S.I.C.: 2834
N.A.I.C.S.: 325412
Export
Media: 10-11
Personnel:
Hollings C. Renton, III *(Chm)*
John A. Orwin *(CEO)*
Herbert C. Cross *(CFO)*
Jeffrey H. Knapp *(Chief Comml Officer)*
Grace U. Shin *(Gen Counsel)*
Robert B. Naso *(Exec VP-R & D)*
Kay Slocum *(Sr VP-HR)*
Robert F. Venteicher *(Sr VP-Tech Ops)*
Tracy J. Dunn *(VP-Intellectual Property & Legal Affairs)*
Sylvia Wheeler *(VP-Corp Comm)*
Brands & Products:
HEMATIDE
INNOTIDE

Cahan & Associates
171 2nd St #5
San Francisco, CA 94105
Tel.: (415) 621-0915
Fax: (415) 621-7642

AGA MEDICAL HOLDINGS, INC.
(Sub. of St. Jude Medical, Inc.)
5050 Nathan Ln N
Plymouth, MN 55442
Tel.: (763) 513-9227
Fax: (763) 513-9226
Toll Free: (888) 546-4407
E-mail: info@amplatzer.com
Web Site: www.amplatzer.com
Approx. Sls.: $198,710,000
Approx. Number Employees: 500
Year Founded: 1995
Business Description:
Medical Device Mfr
S.I.C.: 3845; 3841
N.A.I.C.S.: 334510; 339112
Advertising Expenditures: $700,000
Personnel:
John R. Barr *(Pres)*
Brigid A. Makes *(CFO)*
Ronald E. Lund *(Chief Legal Officer, Gen Counsel & Sr VP)*
Frank J Callaghan *(Pres-Cardiovascular Div)*
Jack A. Darby *(Sr VP-WW Mktg & Distr Sls)*
Larry W. Found *(Sr VP-HR)*
Gianluca Iasci *(Sr VP-EMEA)*
Don O'Hearn *(VP-Sls-North America)*
Brands & Products:
AGA

AIR TECHNIQUES, INC.
1295 Walt Whitman Rd
Melville, NY 11747
Tel.: (516) 433-7676
Fax: (516) 433-7683
Toll Free: (800) AIR-TECH
E-mail: info@airtechniques.com
Web Site: www.airtechniques.com
Approx. Number Employees: 300
Year Founded: 1962
Business Description:
Equipment & Chemistry for the Medical & Dental Industry Mfr & Distr
S.I.C.: 3843
N.A.I.C.S.: 339114
Export
Media: 1-2-4-7-10-20-21
Distr.: Natl.
Budget Set: Aug.
Personnel:
Louis E. Brooks *(Founder & Chm)*
Richard Povak *(Pres)*
Michael Rubenstein *(CFO)*
Richard Campos *(Dir-Intl Sls)*
James Cascio *(Mgr-Digital Imaging Product)*
Jennifer Healey *(Asst Mgr-Mktg)*
Brands & Products:
A/T 2000
A/T SCANX
A/T SLC
ACCLAIM
AIR TECHNIQUE
AIRDENT II
AIRSTAR
ARC LIGHT
CLEANSTREAM
GUARDIAN
PERI-PRO
PROVECTA
STS
VACSTAR
VISTACAM

AJINOMOTO HEARTLAND LLC
(Sub. of Ajinomoto U.S.A., Inc.)
8430 W Bryn Mawr Ave Ste 650
Chicago, IL 60631-3421
Tel.: (773) 380-7000
Fax: (773) 380-7006
Telex: 350 467
Web Site: www.lysine.com
Approx. Number Employees: 20
Year Founded: 1984
Business Description:
Mfr. of Amino Acids for Feed Use
S.I.C.: 2048; 5159
N.A.I.C.S.: 311119; 424590
Advertising Expenditures: $500,000
Media: 2-4-6-17-26
Distr.: Natl.
Budget Set: Sept.
Personnel:
James Usry *(Dir-Tech Svcs)*

AKORN, INC.
1925 W Field Court Ste 300
Lake Forest, IL 60045
Tel.: (847) 279-6100
Fax: (800) 943-3694
Toll Free: (800) 535-7155
E-mail: investor.relations@akorn.com
Web Site: www.akorn.com
Approx. Rev.: $86,409,000
Approx. Number Employees: 410
Year Founded: 1971
Business Description:
Sterile Specialty Pharmaceutical Products Mfr, Marketer & Distr
S.I.C.: 2834
N.A.I.C.S.: 325412
Import Export
Media: 2-4-7-10-20-21-22
Distr.: Natl.
Personnel:
John N. Kapoor *(Chm)*
Rajat Rai *(CEO)*
Timothy A. Dick *(CFO)*
Joseph P. Bonaccorsi *(Gen Counsel, Sec & Sr VP)*
Mark M. Silverberg *(Exec VP-Global Quality Assurance & Technical Svcs)*
Sam Boddapati *(Sr VP-Regulatory Affairs)*
John R. Sabat *(Sr VP-Natl Accts, Mktg & Sls)*
Michael P. Stehn *(Sr VP-Ops)*
Brands & Products:
AFURIA
AK-CON
AK-DILATE
AK-FLUOR
AK-PENTOLATE
AK-POLYBOC
AK-TOB
AKORN
AKTEN
AKWA TEARS
ALFENTA
ATROPINE CARE
BAL-IN-OIL
FLURESS
FUL-GLO
GENTAK
GONAK
HYDASE
I-SENSE
IC-GREEN
INDIGO CARMINE
MYOCHRYSINE
OCUSHIELD
PAREMYD
SUBLIMAZE
SUFENTA
TEARS RENEWED

ALDA PHARMACEUTICALS CORP.
Unit 170 4320 Viking Way
Richmond, BC V6V 2l4, Canada
Tel.: (604) 521-8300
Fax: (604) 521-8322
Toll Free: (866) 521-ALDA
E-mail: general@aldacorp.com
Web Site: www.aldacorp.com
Approx. Sls.: $1,428,565
Approx. Number Employees: 3
Business Description:
Pharmaceutical Infection Control Products Developer & Marketer
S.I.C.: 2834
N.A.I.C.S.: 325412
Advertising Expenditures: $2,582,134
Media: 17
Personnel:
Terrance G. Owen *(Pres, CEO & Dir)*
Peter Chen *(CFO, Dir & Sec)*
Brian Conway *(Dir-Medical)*
Allan H. Shapiro *(Mgr-Bus Dev & Regulatory Affairs)*

ALERE HEALTH SYSTEMS, INC.
(Div. of Alere Medical, Inc.)
1850 Parkway Pl
Marietta, GA 30067
Tel.: (770) 767-4500
Fax: (770) 767-8849
Toll Free: (800) 456-4060
Web Site: www.alere.com
Year Founded: 1996
Business Description:
Medical Treatment Management Services
S.I.C.: 8082
N.A.I.C.S.: 621610
Import
Advertising Expenditures: $1,737,000
Media: 2-4-6-7-10-17
Distr.: Intl.; Natl.
Budget Set: Sept.
Personnel:
Joseph A. Blankenship *(CFO)*
Mark P. Ryan *(CIO & Sr VP)*
Ronald R. Loeppke *(Exec VP & Chief Strategic Officer)*
Thornton A. Kuntz Jr. *(Chief Admin Officer & Sr VP)*
Gregg E. Raybuck *(Pres-Womens & Childrens Health)*

Key to Media (For complete agency information see *The Advertising Red Books-Agencies* edition):
1. Bus. Publs. 2. Cable T.V. 3. Catalogs & Directories. 4. Co-op Adv. 5. Consumer Mags. 6. D.M. to Bus. Estab.7. D.M. to Consumers 8. Daily Newsp. 9. Exhibits/Trade Shows 10. Foreign 11. Infomercial 12. Internet Adv.13. Multimedia 14. Network Radio 15. Network T.V. 16. Newsp. Distr. Mags. 17. Other 18. Outdoor (Posters, Transit) 19. Point of Purchase20. Premiums, Novelties 21. Product Samples 22. Special Events Mktg. 23. Spot Radio 24. Spot T.V. 25. Weekly Newsp. 26. Yellow Page Adv.

Alere Health Systems, Inc. — (Continued)

Earl P. Rousseau *(Pres-Health Enhancement)*
Daniel J. Birach *(Exec VP-Sls & Client Svcs, Health Improvement)*
Patrick F. Cua *(Exec VP-Sls-Health Enhancement)*
Deborah L. Dean *(Exec VP-Tech)*
Garrett H. Hale *(Exec VP-Ops, Client Svcs, Womens & Childrens Health)*
Martin L. Olson *(Exec VP-Bus & Clinical Dev)*
Edward P. Stahel *(Exec VP-Ops-Health Enhancement)*
Gary J. Stanziano *(Exec VP-Medical Affairs, Womens & Childrens Health)*
Kenneth H. Wilson *(Exec VP-Sls, Managed Care, Womens & Childrens Health)*
Graham B. Cherrington *(Sr VP-Ops-Health Enhancement)*
Kathryn H. Creech *(Sr VP-Health Enhancement Prod Mgmt)*
Richard A. Dudley *(Sr VP-Product Mgmt)*
J. Scott McClintock *(Sr VP-Enterprise Mktg)*
Yvonne V. Scoggins *(Sr VP-Bus Analysis)*
Thomas J. Morrow *(VP & Dir-Medical)*

ALERE INC.
(Formerly INVERNESS MEDICAL INNOVATIONS, INC.)
51 Sawyer Rd Ste 200
Waltham, MA 02453
Tel.: (781) 647-3900
Fax: (781) 647-3939
Web Site: www.alere.com
Approx. Sls.: $2,155,347,000
Approx. Number Employees: 11,900
Year Founded: 2001
Business Description:
Consumer & Professional Medical Diagnostic Products, Vitamins & Nutritional Supplements Developer & Mfr
S.I.C.: 2835; 2834; 2836; 3841
N.A.I.C.S.: 325413; 325412; 325414; 339112
Advertising Expenditures: $14,400,000
Media: 11-13
Personnel:
Ron Zwanziger *(Chm, Pres & CEO)*
David Teitel *(CFO, Treas & VP)*
Gordon K. Norman *(Chief Innovation Officer)*
Daniel Delaney *(Pres-North America)*
Emanuel Hart *(Pres-LAmARCIS)*
David Toohey *(Pres-Europe & Middle East)*
David Walton *(Pres-Asia-Pacificq)*
Ellen Chiniara *(Gen Counsel, Sec & VP)*
Paul T. Hempel *(Sr VP-Leadership Dev, Asst Sec & Special Counsel)*
John Bridgen *(Sr VP-Bus Dev)*
Jerry F. McAleer *(Sr VP-R&D)*
Jon Russell *(VP-Fin)*
Doug Guarino *(Dir-Corp Rels)*
Brands & Products:
ACB
ACCEAVA
ADC ALERE
ALERE
ALLBEE
AN UNFAIR ADVANTAGE
ARRAYTUBE
ASCEND
ASCEND MULTIMMUNOASSAY
BABYLINE
BABYLINK
BACTURCULT
BACTURTEST
BALANCE ACTIV
THE BEST WAY TO TEST
BETTER RESULTS MEAN BETTER MEDICINE
BINAXNOW
BIOSITE
BIOSITE DISCOVERY AN UNFAIR ADVANTAGE
BIOSTAR
BLADDERCHEK
BLOCKAID
BNPCARE
BONEMAX
CAFE PTINR
CANCERPAGE.COM
CARBO CATCHER
CARDIO PROFILER
CARELINK
CAREPLAN
CCT
CER-COL
CERTISOY
CHOLESTECH
CHOLESTECH LDX
CLARITEST
CLEARBLUE
CLEARPLAN
CLEARVIEW
CLONDIAG
COMBOKKULT
COMBSCAN
CORADMINISTRATIVE CONNECTIONS
CORCHOICES
CORCONNECT
CORDIMENSIONS
CORSOLUTIONS
CRYPTO-LA
CRYSTAL CLEAR
CTX
CYSAVE
CYSPRAY
DAINE SCREEN
DAYLINK
DETERMINE
DOUBLECHECKGOLD
E-Z SPLIT KEY
EARLY RECOGNITION. EARLY DECISIONS.
ESTROHEALTH
ESTROSUPPORT
EXPRESS TEST
FACT PLUS
FERRO-SEQUELS
FIELDS OF NATURE
FIRST CHECK
FIRST SIGNAL
FOBCARE
FORMULA FORTE
GAB MED GMBH
GABCONTROL
GABCONTROL -AIRCHECK
GABOKKULT
GELUCAPS
GEVRABON
HAPTOKKULT
HEALTH ESSENTIALS
HEALTHDYNE
HEART SMART SOLUTIONS
HEMOSENSE
HERE TODAY...GONE TOMORROW
LATITUDES
LIFETRAX
MATERNALINK
MATRIA
MATRIA HEALTHCARE
MATRITECH
MEASURABLY IMPROVING LIVES
MED-STAPH
MED-STREP
MEGA SOURCE
MINIGEL
MONO-DIFF
MONO-LATEX
MONO-PLUS
MONO-TEST
MONOTEST
MULTI MARKER INDEX
MULTIPLETE
NATURE'S WONDER
NEOLINK
NEW DIMENSIONS IN DIAGNOSIS
NITE NITE
NMP179
NMP22
NMP22 BLADDERCHEK
NMP66
NO PLACE LIKE HOME
OBC
OIA
OIASYS
OMEGA HMJ
OMNICLONAL
ORALERT
ORANGE MEDICAL
OSTEOMARK
PANBIO
PANDA
PARADIGM
PARADIGMHEALTH
PARTISAN
PARTIZAN
PERIDATA
PERMAXIM
PERSONA
POSTURE-D
PRAISE
PREVUE
PROTEGRA
QAS
R2
RAPIDRELAY
RAPIDSIGNAL
REDITEST
REMIPAUSE
RHEUMATEX
RHEUMATON
ROTATEST
RUBELLA-PLUS
SIGNIFY
SILAS
SIMPLY CLEAR
SINGLE SOURCE
SMARTCARE
SMARTCHECK INR
SOYCARE
SPECTRAL
SPECTROVITE
STAT-CRIT
STREP A OIA MAX
STREP A TWIST
STREPTONASE-B
STREPTOZYME
STRESSTABS
SURESTEP
SURESTRIP
SYSTEM 37
THYROTEST
TMNS
TOTAL MATERNAL-NEWBORN SOLUTION
TOTALFLEX
TOUCHENGINE
TPM-TEST
TRIAGE
TRIAGE CENSUS
TRIMESTER
UAI
UCG-BETA SLIDE
UCG BETA-STAT
UCG-EARLY PROBE II
UCG-SLIDE TEST
UCG STICK
UCG-TEST
UCG-TITRATION SET
UCG TUBE TEST
UNMP
VADCARE
VADWATCH
VIROGEN
VITAL ANSWERS FOR BETTER HEALTH...NOW
VITAMIN K FOOD DIARY
VITRUVIUS
VOICE CONNECTIONS
WAMPOLE
WE DELIVER RESULTS
WEIGHT SENSE
WELL FOCUS
WINDOW OF CARE
Z-BEC
Advertising Agencies:
The Glenn Group
50 Washington St
Reno, NV 89503-5603
Tel.: (775) 686-7777
Fax: (775) 686-7750

Sky Advertising, Inc.
14 E 33 St 8th Fl
New York, NY 10016
Tel.: (212) 677-2500
Fax: (212) 677-2791
Toll Free: (888) 752-9664

ALEXIAN BROTHERS HEALTH SYSTEM FOUNDATION
3040 Salt Creek Ln
Arlington Heights, IL 60005
Tel.: (847) 385-7300
Fax: (847) 483-7045
Web Site: www.alexianfoundation.org
Approx. Number Employees: 5,000
Year Founded: 1965
Business Description:
Operates Hospitals & Health Care Programs
S.I.C.: 8062
N.A.I.C.S.: 622110
Advertising Expenditures: $6,000,000
Media: 2-4-10-13-18
Personnel:
James J. Sances *(CFO & VP)*
Sylvia Duchateau *(Dir-Mktg)*
Matt Wakely *(Dir-PR)*

ALEXION PHARMACEUTICALS, INC.
352 Knotter Dr
Cheshire, CT 06410-1138
Tel.: (203) 272-2596
Fax: (203) 271-8198
E-mail: investor.relations@alxn.com

Key to Media (For complete agency information see *The Advertising Red Books-Agencies* edition):
1. Bus. Publs. 2. Cable T.V. 3. Catalogs & Directories. 4. Co-op Adv. 5. Consumer Mags. 6. D.M. to Bus. Estab.7. D.M. to Consumers 8. Daily Newsp. 9. Exhibits/Trade Shows 10. Foreign 11. Infomercial 12. Internet Adv.13. Multimedia 14. Network Radio 15. Network T.V. 16. Newsp. Distr. Mags. 17. Other 18. Outdoor (Posters, Transit) 19. Point of Purchase20. Premiums, Novelties 21. Product Samples 22. Special Events Mktg. 23. Spot Radio 24. Spot T.V. 25. Weekly Newsp. 26. Yellow Page Adv.

Web Site: www.alexionpharmaceuticals.com
Approx. Rev.: $540,957,000
Approx. Number Employees: 792
Year Founded: 1992
Business Description:
Developer of Bio-Pharmaceutical Products for Treatment of Heart Disease & Inflammation, Immune System Diseases & Cancer
S.I.C.: 2834; 8733
N.A.I.C.S.: 325412; 541720
Personnel:
Max E. Link *(Chm)*
Leonard Bell *(Pres, CEO, Treas & Sec)*
Vikas Sinha *(CFO & Sr VP)*
Russell P. Rother *(Sr VP & Chief Scientific Officer)*
Scott Phillips *(Chief Acctg Officer & Controller)*
Thomas I.H. Dubin *(Gen Counsel & Sr VP)*
Stephen P. Squinto *(Exec VP & Head-R & D)*
David Hallal *(Sr VP-US Comml Ops)*
M. Stacy Hooks *(Sr VP-Tech Ops)*
Nancy C. Motola *(Sr VP-Quality & Regulatory Affairs)*
Scott A. Rollins *(Sr VP-Drug Dev & Project Mgmt)*
Barry P. Luke *(VP-Fin & Asst Sec)*
Daniel N. Caron *(VP-Site Ops & Engrg)*
Glenn Melrose *(VP-HR)*
Brands & Products:
ALEXION
EVERY DAY MATTERS
SOLIRIS
Advertising Agency:
Makovsky & Company, Inc.
16 E 34th St 15th Fl
New York, NY 10016
Tel.: (212) 508-9600
Fax: (212) 751-9710

ALIGN TECHNOLOGY, INC.

2560 Orchard Pkwy
San Jose, CA 95131
Tel.: (408) 470-1000
Fax: (408) 470-1010
Toll Free: (888) 822-5446
E-mail: align@ethoscommunication.com
Web Site: www.aligntech.com
Approx. Rev.: $387,126,000
Approx. Number Employees: 2,097
Year Founded: 1997
Business Description:
Orthodontic Appliances Designer, Mfr & Marketer
S.I.C.: 3843
N.A.I.C.S.: 339114
Advertising Expenditures: $20,200,000
Media: 3-6-7-10-13-15
Personnel:
C. Raymond Larkin, Jr. *(Chm)*
Thomas M. Prescott *(Pres & CEO)*
Kenneth B. Arola *(CFO & VP-Fin)*
Sheila Tan *(CMO & VP-Mktg)*
Roger E. George *(VP-Legal Affairs & Gen Counsel)*
Len M. Hedge *(Sr VP-Bus Ops)*
Dan S. Ellis *(VP-Sls-North America)*
Tim Parkyn *(Sr Mgr-Consumer Mktg)*
Brands & Products:
CLINCHECK
INVISALIGN
Advertising Agency:
Media Options, Inc.
10 Bank St Ste 540
White Plains, NY 10606
Tel.: (212) 612-1500
Fax: (914) 949-3260
Media Planning & Buying
— Philip Press *(Pres)*

ALIMED, INC.

297 High St
Dedham, MA 02026-2852
Tel.: (781) 329-2900
Fax: (781) 329-8392
Toll Free: (800) 225-2610
E-mail: info@alimed.com
Web Site: www.alimed.com
Approx. Number Employees: 150
Year Founded: 1970
Business Description:
Mfr. of Rehabilitation Products, Operating Room Products, X-Ray Accessories & Other Accessories; Ergonomics
S.I.C.: 5047; 3842
N.A.I.C.S.: 423450; 339113
Import Export
Advertising Expenditures: $1,100,000
Media: 2-4-5-7-10-13-17-21
Distr.: Intl.; Natl.
Budget Set: Dec.
Personnel:
Julian Cherubini *(Founder & Pres)*
Jonathan Bretz *(Sr VP-Mktg & Sls)*
Rich Clement *(Sr VP)*
Emily Holt *(Mgr-Mktg & Sls)*
Brands & Products:
ABLEWARE
ACTIVE LIFE
AGSILVER
AIREX
ALIEDGE
ALIMED
ALIMED BED STUFFER
ALISLIDE
ALLEN
ALLKARE
AMERIGEL
ANGELSTAT
AQUASONIC
BAND-AID
BASELINE
BEBAX
BIG HOOK
BIOCURVE
BROADWAY
CITRUS II
CLINSWOUND
CLINTON
COMFORTEASE
COMFORTTREAD
COMFY
COMFYPRENE
CONVAQUIP
COOL-WICK
COOLBAND
THE CRITICAL COMMUNICATOR
CUSTOMAIR
DERMAMITT
DERMASAVER
DERMASAVER RELEVATOR
DERMAWRAP
DETECTO
DIABETICARE
DISCIDE
DURABOOT
DURAHESIVE
DYCEM
E-Z BOOT
EHOB WAFFLE
ERGODYNE
EUROS RX
EZY
FREEDOM
GELFOM
HAUSMANN
HEALTH O METER
HEALTHLINE
THE HEARING AIDER
HEELBO
HEELIFT
HOLOFIBER
HYBRIDSELECT
IMPACTO
INVACARE
IRONCLAD
J & J BAND-AID
LOTCA
MEDI-STRIPS
MIDMARK
MOVEMASTER
MUELLER
MYOSSAGE
NATURA
NO-LIFT BOOSTER
NOVAGEL
PEDI COMFY
PEDIATRIC COMFY
PEDIATRIC SLIMLINE
PLASTAZOTE
POLYSONIC
POSEY
POWER WEB JR.
PRO PLUS
PROFLEX
PROFORE
PROSTRETCH
PROTECTA-COAT
PUCCI
Q-FACTOR
QUALCARE
QUALCRAFT
ROHO
ROHO BARISELECT
ROHO SELECTAIR
SANIGUARD
SELF WIPE
SEPTICARE
SHAMPOO-AIDE
SILIPOS
SILOPAD
SIMPLYTHICK
SKIL-CARE
SKILLBUILDERS
SMARTKNIT
SNAP-N-SAVE
SOMA
STOMAHESIVE
SUR-FIT
T-GEL
THERATOGS
THICK-IT
TOILEVATOR
TUMBLE FORMS2
TYCOS
UMP
UVEX BANDIT
VELCRO
VERSATECH
WELCH ALLYN
WHEATON
WONDERFLEX
X-CEL
Advertising Agency:
C&B Associates
297 High St
Dedham, MA 02026-2852
Tel.: (781) 329-2900
Fax: (800) 437-2966
Fax: (781) 326-9218
Toll Free: (800) 225-2610
(Orthopedic & Cognitive Rehabilitation Products, Diagnostic Imaging & Operating Room Products & Accessories, Dysphasia Management Products, Ergonomics, Physical Therapy, Speech Therapy & Alzheimer's Rehabilitation)

ALIMERA SCIENCES, INC.

6120 Winward Pkway Ste 290
Alpharetta, GA 30005
Tel.: (678) 990-5740
Fax: (678) 990-5744
Web Site: www.alimerasciences.com
Approx. Rev.: $73,000
Approx. Number Employees: 27
Year Founded: 2003
Business Description:
Prescription Ophthalmic Pharmaceuticals Researcher, Developer & Marketer
S.I.C.: 2834; 3851; 5048; 8733
N.A.I.C.S.: 325412; 339115; 423460; 541710
Advertising Expenditures: $52,000
Media: 8-13-17-22
Personnel:
Philip R. Tracy, Jr. *(Chm)*
C. Daniel Myers *(Pres & CEO)*
Richard S. Eiswirth, Jr. *(CFO & COO)*
Susan H. Caballa *(Sr VP-Regulatory & Medical Affairs)*
David R. Holland *(VP-Mktg)*
Brands & Products:
ALIMERA SCIENCES
DOING THE RIGHT THING FOR EYE CARE
FAME
ILUVIEN
Advertising Agency:
Fingerpaint Marketing
18 Division St Ste 414
Saratoga Springs, NY 12866
Tel.: (518) 693-6960
Fax: (518) 693-6962
Iluvien

ALL CHILDREN'S HOSPITAL INC.

501 6th Ave S
Saint Petersburg, FL 33701
Tel.: (727) 898-7451
Fax: (727) 767-4276
E-mail: humanresource@allkids.org
Web Site: www.allkids.org
Approx. Rev.: $190,000,000
Approx. Number Employees: 2,800
Year Founded: 1926
Business Description:
Children's Hospital
S.I.C.: 8062; 8069
N.A.I.C.S.: 622110; 622310
Media: 2-22
Personnel:
Gary A. Carnes *(Pres & CEO)*
Marc Jacobson *(Sr VP)*
Cindy Rose *(Dir-Admin Mktg)*

Key to Media (For complete agency information see *The Advertising Red Books-Agencies* edition):
1. Bus. Publs. 2. Cable T.V. 3. Catalogs & Directories. 4. Co-op Adv. 5. Consumer Mags. 6. D.M. to Bus. Estab.7. D.M. to Consumers
8. Daily Newsp. 9. Exhibits/Trade Shows 10. Foreign 11. Infomercial 12. Internet Adv.13. Multimedia 14. Network Radio
15. Network T.V. 16. Newsp. Distr. Mags. 17. Other 18. Outdoor (Posters, Transit) 19. Point of Purchase20. Premiums, Novelties
21. Product Samples 22. Special Events Mktg. 23. Spot Radio 24. Spot T.V. 25. Weekly Newsp. 26. Yellow Page Adv.

All Children's Hospital Inc. — (Continued)

Luci Weber *(Dir-Child Life Dept)*
Melodye Seals *(Mgr-Continuing Medical Education)*

ALLERGAN, INC.
2525 Dupont Dr
Irvine, CA 92612-1531
Mailing Address:
PO Box 19534
Irvine, CA 92623-9534
Tel.: (714) 246-4500
Fax: (714) 246-6987
E-mail: corpinfo@allergan.com
Web Site: www.allergan.com
Approx. Rev.: $4,919,400,000
Approx. Number Employees: 9,200
Year Founded: 1948
Business Description:
Ophthalmic & Dermatological Pharmaceuticals, Contact Lens Care, Ophthalmic Surgical & Neural Care Products Mfr
S.I.C.: 2834; 3841
N.A.I.C.S.: 325412; 339112
Export
Advertising Expenditures: $185,200,000
Media: 1-2-4-5-6-7-8-10-19-20-21-22
Distr.: Intl.; Natl.
Budget Set: Oct.
Personnel:
David E.I. Pyott *(Chm, Pres & CEO)*
Herbert W. Boyer *(Vice Chm)*
Douglas S. Ingram *(Pres)*
Jeffrey L. Edwards *(CFO & Exec VP-Fin & Bus Dev)*
Samuel J. Gesten *(Gen Counsel & Exec VP)*
Raymond H. Diradoorian *(Exec VP-Global Tech Ops)*
Scott M. Whitcup *(Exec VP-R & D)*
James F. Barlow *(Principal Acct Officer, Sr VP & Corp Controller)*
Greg Brooks *(VP-Global Strategic Mktg)*
Brands & Products:
ACULAR
ACULAR LS
ACZONE
ALLERGAN
ALOCRIL
ALPHAGAN
AVAGE
AZELEX
BOTOX
BOTOX COSMETIC
CELLUVISC
CLINIQUE MEDICAL
COMBIGAN
COSMODERM
COSMOPLAST
ELESTAT
FLUOROPLEX
INAMED
JUVEDERM
LAP-BAND
LATISSE
LUMIGAN
M.D. FORTE
NATRELLE COLLECTION
OCUFLOX
OPTIVE
OUR PURSUIT. LIFE'S POTENTIAL.
PRED FORTE
PREVAGE
PREVAGE MD
REFRESH
REFRESH CONTACTS
REFRESH DRY EYE THERAPY
REFRESH ENDURA
REFRESH LIQUIGEL
REFRESH PLUS
REFRESH P.M.
REFRESH TEARS
RELIEF
RESTASIS
TAZORAC
TRIVARIS
VISTABEL
VIVITE
ZYDERM
ZYMAR
ZYPLAST
Advertising Agencies:
Chandler Chicco Agency
450 W 15th St 7th Fl
New York, NY 10011
Tel.: (212) 229-8400
Fax: (212) 229-8496
Cervical Dystonia Awareness Campaign

Pacific Communications
575 Anton Blvd Ste 900
Costa Mesa, CA 92626-7665
Tel.: (714) 427-1900
Fax: (714) 796-3039
Sanctura XR (Agency of Record) — Karen Melanson *(Sr VP & Dir-Client Svcs)*

ALLIED HEALTHCARE INTERNATIONAL INC.
245 Park Ave 39th Fl
New York, NY 10167
Tel.: (212) 750-0064
Fax: (212) 750-7221
Web Site: www.alliedhealthcare.com
Approx. Rev.: $271,079,000
Approx. Number Employees: 1,160
Year Founded: 1972
Business Description:
Holding Company; Healthcare Staffing Services
S.I.C.: 7363; 6719; 8082; 8099
N.A.I.C.S.: 561320; 551112; 621610; 621999
Advertising Expenditures: $200,000
Personnel:
Alexander Young *(CEO)*
Paul D.J. Weston *(CFO)*
Marvet Abbassi *(Controller-Fin)*

ALLIED HEALTHCARE PRODUCTS, INC.
1720 Sublette Ave
Saint Louis, MO 63110-1927
Mailing Address:
PO Box 500547
Saint Louis, MO 63150-0547
Tel.: (314) 771-2400
Fax: (314) 771-0650
Toll Free: (800) 444-3954
E-mail: customerservice@alliedhpi.com
Web Site: www.alliedhpi.com
Approx. Sls.: $46,783,436
Approx. Number Employees: 313
Year Founded: 1979
Business Description:
Medical Gas System Equipment, Respiratory Therapy Equipment & Emergency Medical Products Mfr
S.I.C.: 3841; 3821; 3842; 3845
N.A.I.C.S.: 339112; 334510; 339111; 339113
Media: 2-4-10
Personnel:
John D. Weil *(Chm)*
Earl R. Refsland *(Pres & CEO)*
Daniel C. Dunn *(CFO, Sec & VP)*
Brands & Products:
ADVANTAGE
ALLIED
AUTOVENT
BARALYME
CHEMETRON
CONNECT2
GOMCO
IMPACT
LIBERTY
LIF-O-GEN
LIFE SUPPORT PRODUCTS ADVANTAGE
LSP ADVANTAGE
LSP HDX BACKBOARD
LSP XTRA
MEDSTAR
OHMEDA
OMNI-VENT
OPTIVAC
OXEQUIP
QUADRA-VAC
RESUSCITIMER
RHINO
SCHUCO
SURGEX
TIMETER
VACUTRON
XTRA

ALLINA HEALTH SYSTEM, INC.
(d/b/a Allina Hospitals & Clinics)
2925 Chicago Ave
Minneapolis, MN 55407
Tel.: (612) 775-5000
Fax: (612) 262-4087
E-mail: infodesk@allina.com
Web Site: www.allina.com
Approx. Number Employees: 21,500
Year Founded: 1994
Business Description:
Not-For-Profit Health Care System
S.I.C.: 8062; 8741
N.A.I.C.S.: 622110; 561110
Import Export
Media: 4-9-10-13-17-22-25
Personnel:
Kenneth Paulus *(Pres & CEO)*
Robert Plaszcz *(CIO)*
Brands & Products:
ALLINA.
EXERCARE
GETTING FIT JUST GOT EASIER
HEALTHY COMMUNITIES
LIVING SMARTER
MEDCREDIT
MEDFORMATION
MINNEAPOLIS NEUROSCIENCE INSTITUTE
PHYSICIAN-TO-PHYSICIAN
PIPER BREAST CENTER
PROVIDE-A-RIDE
SELECTCARE
SOUND HEALTH
WOMENCARE
Advertising Agency:
Bayard Advertising Agency, Inc.
9801 Dupont Ave S Ste 300
Minneapolis, MN 55431
Tel.: (952) 881-4411
Fax: (952) 881-2266

ALLION HEALTHCARE, INC.
(Holding of H.I.G. Capital, LLC)
1660 Walt Whitman Rd Ste 105
Melville, NY 11747
Tel.: (631) 547-6520
Fax: (631) 249-5863
Toll Free: (800) 218-5604
Web Site: www.allionhealthcare.com
Approx. Billings: $340,674,000
Approx. Number Employees: 249
Year Founded: 1984
Business Description:
Specialty Pharmacy & Disease Management Services for the Treatment of HIV & AIDS
S.I.C.: 5122; 5912
N.A.I.C.S.: 424210; 446110
Import Export
Advertising Expenditures: $108,000
Media: 10-17
Personnel:
Bill Jones *(Pres & CEO)*
Russell J. Fichera *(CFO & Sr VP)*
Anthony D. Luna *(Pres-MOMs Pharmacy)*

ALLIQUA, INC.
(Formerly HepaLife Technologies, Inc.)
850 Third Ave Ste 1801
New York, NY 10022
Tel.: (646) 218-1450
Web Site: www.alliqua.com
Approx. Rev.: $1,319,297
Approx. Number Employees: 8
Year Founded: 1997
Business Description:
Biomedical Products Researcher, Developer & Mfr
S.I.C.: 2835; 2834; 2836
N.A.I.C.S.: 541711; 325412; 325413; 325414
Advertising Expenditures: $218,864
Personnel:
David Stefansky *(Chm)*
Richard Rosenblum *(Pres)*
Steven Berger *(CFO, Treas & Sec)*
Matthew Harriton *(CEO-Alliqua BioMedical)*
Brands & Products:
HEPAMATE

ALLOS THERAPEUTICS, INC.
11080 CirclePoint Rd Ste 200
Westminster, CO 80020
Tel.: (303) 426-6262
Fax: (303) 426-4731
E-mail: investorrelations@allos.com
Web Site: www.allos.com
Approx. Sls.: $35,227,000
Approx. Number Employees: 156
Business Description:
Cancer Treatment Pharmaceuticals Developer
S.I.C.: 2834
N.A.I.C.S.: 325412
Advertising Expenditures: $4,700,000
Media: 2-7
Personnel:
Paul L. Berns *(Pres & CEO)*
Charles Morris *(Chief Medical Officer & Exec VP)*
Marc H. Graboyes *(Gen Counsel & Sr VP)*
David C. Clark *(Treas & VP-Fin)*
Bruce A. Goldsmith *(Sr VP-Corp Dev)*

Key to Media (For complete agency information see *The Advertising Red Books-Agencies* edition):
1. Bus. Publs. 2. Cable T.V. 3. Catalogs & Directories. 4. Co-op Adv. 5. Consumer Mags. 6. D.M. to Bus. Estab.7. D.M. to Consumers
8. Daily Newsp. 9. Exhibits/Trade Shows 10. Foreign 11. Infomercial 12. Internet Adv.13. Multimedia 14. Network Radio
15. Network T.V. 16. Newsp. Distr. Mags. 17. Other 18. Outdoor (Posters, Transit) 19. Point of Purchase20. Premiums, Novelties
21. Product Samples 22. Special Events Mktg. 23. Spot Radio 24. Spot T.V. 25. Weekly Newsp. 26. Yellow Page Adv.

Michael Schick *(VP-Sls & Mktg)*
Luke Seikkula *(Sr Dir-Materials & Logistics)*
Vicki Baca *(Sr Mgr-HR)*
Brands & Products:
ALLOS
AT THE FOREFRONT OF NEW CANCER THERAPIES
EFAPROXYN

ALLSCRIPTS HEALTHCARE SOLUTIONS, INC.
(Formerly Allscripts-Misys Healthcare Solutions, Inc.)
222 Merchandise Mart Plz Ste 2024
Chicago, IL 60654
Tel.: (312) 506-1213
Fax: (312) 555-1205
Toll Free: (800) 654-0889
E-mail: info@allscripts.com
Web Site: www.allscripts.com
Approx. Rev.: $704,502,000
Approx. Number Employees: 5,500
Year Founded: 1986
Business Description:
Clinical & Healthcare Software, Information, Connectivity & Support Services
S.I.C.: 7389; 7372; 7373; 7374; 7379
N.A.I.C.S.: 561499; 511210; 518210; 541512; 541519
Media: 2-7-10-22
Personnel:
Philip M. Pead *(Chm)*
Lee A. Shapiro *(Pres)*
Glen E. Tullman *(CEO)*
William J. Davis *(CFO)*
Dan Michelson *(CMO & Exec VP)*
John P. Gomez *(Pres-Product Strategy & Dev)*
Diane Adams *(Exec VP-Culture & Talent)*
Brands & Products:
AIC
ALLSCRIPTS
ALLSCRIPTS DIRECT
FORMS.MD
IMPACT.MD
PHYSICIANS INTERACTIVE
PI CONVENTION
PI E-DETAILING
PI SURVEY
PR OPINIONLEADER
TOUCHCHART
TOUCHSCRIPT
TOUCHWORKS

ALLSCRIPTS-MISYS HEALTHCARE SOLUTIONS, INC.
(Name Changed to Allscripts Healthcare Solutions, Inc.)

ALMOST FAMILY, INC.
9510 Ormsby Station Rd Ste 300
Louisville, KY 40223
Tel.: (502) 891-1000
Fax: (502) 891-8073
Toll Free: (800) 845-6987
E-mail: info@almost-family.com
Web Site: www.almost-family.com
Approx. Rev.: $336,924,000
Approx. Number Employees: 6,400
Year Founded: 1976
Business Description:
Home Nursing & Personal Care Services
S.I.C.: 8399; 7299; 8082; 8322
N.A.I.C.S.: 813319; 621610; 624120; 812990
Import Export
Advertising Expenditures: $364,000
Media: 4-7-26
Personnel:
William B. Yarmuth *(Chm, Pres & CEO)*
C. Steven Guenthner *(CFO & Sr VP)*
Jerry Perchik *(Gen Counsel & VP)*
Anne T. Liechty *(Sr VP-Ops)*
Todd P. Lyles *(Sr VP-Admin)*
Phyllis D. Montville *(Sr VP-Visiting Ops)*
Cathy Newhouse *(Sr VP-Sls & Clinical Programs)*
James Spriggs *(VP-Sls & Mktg)*
Mark Sutton *(VP-HR)*
Brands & Products:
EXCELLENCE THROUGH SENIOR ADVOCACY

ALPHA PRO TECH, LTD.
60 Centurian Drive Suite 112
Markham, ON L3R 9R2, Canada
Tel.: (905) 479-0654
Fax: (905) 479-9732
E-mail: sales@alphaprotech.com
Web Site: www.alphaprotech.com
E-Mail For Key Personnel:
Sales Director: infosales@alphaprotech.com
Approx. Sls.: $41,890,000
Approx. Number Employees: 128
Year Founded: 1989
Business Description:
Protective Apparel Mfr for Cleanroom, Industrial, Medical & Dental & Pharmaceutical Industries
S.I.C.: 5047; 2676; 3842; 3999
N.A.I.C.S.: 423450; 322291; 339113; 339999
Advertising Expenditures: $75,000
Media: 17
Personnel:
Alexander W. Millar *(Pres)*
Sheldon Hoffman *(CEO)*
Lloyd Hoffman *(CFO, Sr VP-Fin & Admin)*
Chris Louisos *(Sr VP-Sls & Mktg)*
Danny Montgomery *(Sr. VP-Mfg & Engineered Products)*
Brands & Products:
ALPHA AIRCON
ALPHAAIR
ALPHAGUARD
ALPHAPROTECH
AQUATRAK
BARRIERTECH
CERTIFIED
COMBO
COMFORT
COOLONE
GENPRO
MICROBREATHE
PFL
REX
SHIELDMATE
SMARTWEAR
SURE GRIP
ULTRAGRIP

ALTO PHARMACEUTICALS, INC.
PO Box 271150
Tampa, FL 33688-1150
Tel.: (813) 968-0522
Fax: (813) 968-0527
Toll Free: (800) 330-2891
E-mail: altopharm@aol.com
Web Site: www.altopharm.com
Sales Range: $10-24.9 Million
Approx. Number Employees: 5
Year Founded: 1968
Business Description:
Contract Mfr & Distr of Pharmaceuticals
S.I.C.: 5122
N.A.I.C.S.: 424210
Export
Media: 2-6-9
Distr.: Reg.
Budget Set: July -Nov.
Personnel:
John J. Cullaro *(Pres)*
Brands & Products:
ALTO
ZINC-220

ALVA/AMCO PHARMACAL COMPANIES, INC.
7711 N Merrimac Ave
Niles, IL 60714-3423
Tel.: (847) 663-0700
Fax: (847) 663-1400
E-mail: Customer_service@alva-amco.com
Web Site: www.alva-amco.com
Approx. Number Employees: 300
Year Founded: 1904
Business Description:
OTC Drugs, Dietary Supplements & Cosmetics Mfr & Distr
S.I.C.: 2834
N.A.I.C.S.: 325412
Export
Media: 2-3-4-5-6-7-9-10-11-13-14-15-18-19-20-21-23-24-25
Distr.: Intl.; Natl.
Budget Set: Jan. -Dec.
Personnel:
Jeffrey H. Gerchenson *(Pres & COO)*
Terry Riddel *(Sr VP)*
S. R. Gerchenson *(Dir-Mktg)*
Brands & Products:
ALVA
ARTHRITEN
BACKAID
CARBOFAST
CROM & CRUTHERS
DIUREX
FOOTICE
FUNGICURE
HERPETROL
KNEERELIEF
MYCOCURE
NAILCLEAR
NAUZENE
PEP-BACK
PHADE
PROSACEA
PSORIASIN
THERADENT
THINZ
THINZ CARBOFAST
TRANQUIL
ULTRA-FIBER
ULTRA PEP-BACK
URICALM

ALZA CORPORATION
(Sub. of Johnson & Johnson)
700 Eubanks Dr
Vacaville, CA 95688
Mailing Address:
PO Box 7210
Mountain View, CA 94039-7210
Tel.: (650) 564-5000
Fax: (650) 564-7070
Toll Free: (800) 564-5222
Web Site: www.alza.com
Sales Range: $300-349.9 Million
Approx. Number Employees: 1,845
Year Founded: 1968
Business Description:
Drug Delivery Technology Developer
S.I.C.: 8733; 2834
N.A.I.C.S.: 541710; 325412
Export
Media: 2-4-7-8-10-11-13-20-21
Distr.: Intl.; Natl.
Budget Set: Jan. -Dec.
Brands & Products:
ACTISITE
ALZAMER
ALZET
AUTOINJECTOR
CONCERTA
D-TRANS
DUROS
E-TRANS
IONSYS
MACOFLUX
OROS
PROGESTASERT
PUSH-PULL
STEALTH
TESTODERM
VIADUR

AMAG PHARMACEUTICALS, INC.
100 Hayden Ave
Lexington, MA 02421
Tel.: (617) 498-3300
Fax: (617) 499-3361
E-mail: contactus@agmapharma.com
Web Site: www.amagpharma.com
Approx. Rev.: $66,245,000
Approx. Number Employees: 226
Year Founded: 1981
Business Description:
Biopharmaceutical Mfr; Organ-Specific Contrast Agents & Therapeutic Iron Compounds for Treating Anemia, Developer, Mfr & Marketer
S.I.C.: 2834; 5122
N.A.I.C.S.: 325412; 424210
Import Export
Advertising Expenditures: $7,400,000
Media: 2-10-13
Personnel:
Michael A. Narachi *(Chm)*
Brian J.G. Pereira *(Pres & CEO)*
Frank E. Thomas *(CFO & Exec VP)*
Lee F. Allen *(Exec VP & Chief Medical Officer)*
Gary J. Zieziula *(Chief Comml Officer & Exec VP)*
David A. Arkowitz *(Chief Bus Officer & Exec VP)*
Joseph L. Farmer *(Gen Counsel & Sr VP-Legal Affairs)*
Chris White *(Sr VP-Bus Dev & Corp Plng)*
Stephen Andre *(VP-HR)*
Amy Sullivan *(VP-Corp Comm & IR)*
Carol Miceli *(Assoc Dir-IR)*
Brands & Products:
AMAG
COMBIDEX
FERAHEME

AMAG Pharmaceuticals, Inc. — (Continued)

FERIDEX I.V
FERUMOXYTOL
GASTROMARK

AMCOR FLEXIBLES INC.

(Sub. of Amcor Flexibles UK Ltd.)
1919 S Butterfield Rd
Mundelein, IL 60060-9735
Tel.: (847) 362-9000
Fax: (847) 362-1848
E-mail: info@amcor.com
Web Site: www.amcor.com
Sales Range: $125-149.9 Million
Approx. Number Employees: 300
Year Founded: 1970
Business Description:
Coating, Printing & Conversion of Paper & Plastic Films For Flexible Medical Packaging
S.I.C.: 7389
N.A.I.C.S.: 561910
Advertising Expenditures: $400,000
Media: 2-7-26
Distr.: Natl.
Budget Set: Oct.
Personnel:
Peter Brues *(Pres)*

AMEDISYS, INC.

5959 S Sherwood Forest Blvd
Baton Rouge, LA 70816
Tel.: (225) 292-2031
Fax: (225) 295-9624
Toll Free: (800) 467-2662
E-mail: info@amedisys.com
Web Site: www.amedisys.com
Approx. Rev.: $1,634,319,000
Approx. Number Employees: 16,300
Year Founded: 1982
Business Description:
Home Health Care & Hospice Services
S.I.C.: 8082
N.A.I.C.S.: 621610
Advertising Expenditures: $5,100,000
Personnel:
William F. Borne *(Chm & CEO)*
Dale E. Redman *(CFO)*
Michael D. Snow *(COO)*
G. Patrick Thompson, Jr. *(CIO & Exec VP)*
Jeffrey D. Jeter *(Chief Compliance Officer & Gen Counsel)*
Pete Hartley *(CTO & Sr VP-Bus Ops Sys)*
Bridget Montana *(Chief Nursing Officer-Hospice)*
James T. Robinson *(Exec VP-Hospice & Home Health Care)*
Patti Waller *(Exec VP)*
Scott Ginn *(Sr VP & Controller)*
Beth Boulet *(Sr VP-Audit)*
Janet Britt *(Sr VP-Billing & Collections)*
Tom Dolan *(Sr VP-Fin)*
Francis Mayer *(Sr VP)*
Jill Cannon *(Mgr-Therapy Recruitment-OH, IN, MI & AR)*
Advertising Agency:
The Ledlie Group
2970 Peachtree Rd Ste 805
Atlanta, GA 30305
Tel.: (404) 266-8833
Fax: (404) 266-9620

AMERICAN BIO MEDICA CORPORATION

122 Smith Rd
Kinderhook, NY 12106-2819
Tel.: (518) 758-8158
Fax: (518) 758-8171
Toll Free: (800) 227-1243
E-mail: info@abmc.com
Web Site: www.americanbiomedica.com
Approx. Sls.: $10,421,000
Approx. Number Employees: 86
Year Founded: 1986
Business Description:
Mfr, Developer & Marketer of Immunoassay Diagnostic Test Kits for Drug Abuse
S.I.C.: 3841
N.A.I.C.S.: 339112
Export
Advertising Expenditures: $3,184,000
Media: 2-5-7-10-19-21
Personnel:
Edmund Jaskiewicz *(Chm & Pres)*
Stan Cipkowski *(CEO & Interim CFO)*
Todd Bailey *(VP-Sls & Mktg)*
Jeanette Palella *(Mgr-Sls & Mktg)*
Brands & Products:
ABMC
ORALSTAT
RAPID DRUG SCREEN
RAPID ONE
RAPID READER
RAPID TEC
RAPID TOX
RDS
RDS INCUP

AMERICAN MEDICAL ALERT CORP.

3265 Lawson Blvd
Oceanside, NY 11572-3723
Tel.: (516) 536-5850
Fax: (516) 536-5276
Toll Free: (800) 286-2622
E-mail: info@amac.com
Web Site: www.amacalert.com
Approx. Rev.: $40,770,869
Approx. Number Employees: 516
Year Founded: 1981
Business Description:
Sells, Rents, & Monitors Healthcare Communication Appliances to Assist Seniors & Disabled People with Independent Living
S.I.C.: 5047
N.A.I.C.S.: 423450
Advertising Expenditures: $1,387,000
Media: 2-7-8-10-13-17-26
Personnel:
Howard M. Siegel *(Chm)*
Jack Rhian *(Pres & CEO)*
Richard Rallo *(CFO & COO-HSMS Div)*
Frederic S. Siegel *(Exec VP)*
Randi M. Baldwin *(Sr VP-Mktg & Program Dev)*
Kirk Amico *(Dir-MIS)*
Brands & Products:
AMAC
DESKTOP
HEALTH BUDDY
MED-TIME
MEDSMART
PERS BUDDY
VOICECARE

AMERICAN MEDICAL RESPONSE

(Sub. of Emergency Medical Services Corporation)
6200 S Syracuse Way Ste 200
Greenwood Village, CO 80111
Tel.: (303) 495-1200
Fax: (303) 495-1611
Toll Free: (877) 244-4890
Web Site: www.emsc.net
Approx. Number Employees: 17,000
Business Description:
Emergency & Non-Emergency Transportation
S.I.C.: 4119
N.A.I.C.S.: 621910
Personnel:
William A. Sanger *(Chm & CEO)*
Mark Bruning *(Pres)*
Randy Owen *(CFO & Exec VP)*
Don S. Harvey *(COO)*
Scott Wicke *(Sr Compliance Mgr & Privacy Officer-Dallas)*
Robert Zuckswert *(CEO-Central Reg)*
Todd G. Zimmerman *(Gen Counsel & Exec VP)*
Mark Hagan *(Sr VP-IT)*
Deborah Hileman *(VP-Pub Rels & Comm)*
Steve Murphy *(Coder)*
Advertising Agency:
ADWizz Inc.
2620 Carmichael Way
Turlock, CA 95382
Tel.: (209) 656-1323
Fax: (209) 633-2277
Recruitment

AMERICAN MEDICAL SYSTEMS HOLDINGS, INC.

10700 Bren Rd W
Minnetonka, MN 55343-9679
Tel.: (952) 930-6000
Fax: (952) 930-6157
Fax: (952) 930-6373
Toll Free: (800) 328-3881
E-mail: info@americanmedicalsystems.com
Web Site: www.americanmedicalsystems.com
Approx. Sls.: $542,316,000
Approx. Number Employees: 1,255
Year Founded: 1972
Business Description:
Medical Device Mfr
S.I.C.: 3841; 3842
N.A.I.C.S.: 339112; 339113
Advertising Expenditures: $7,700,000
Media: 2-7-10-13
Personnel:
Anthony P. Bihl, III *(Pres & CEO)*
Mark A. Heggestad *(CFO & Exec VP)*
Joe W. Martin *(Sr VP & Gen Mgr-BPH Therapy)*
John F. Nealon *(Sr VP & Gen Mgr-Womens Health)*
Randall Ross *(Sr VP-HR)*
Whitney D. Erickson *(VP & Gen Mgr-Mens Health)*
Francois Georgelin *(VP & Gen Mgr-EMEA Reg)*
Michael E. Ryan *(VP & Gen Mgr-Asia Pacific/Latin America Region)*
Brands & Products:
ACTICON
ADVANCE
AMS
AMS 650/600M
AMS 700
AMS 800
AMS AMBICOR
AMS DURA II
APOGEE
BIOARC
GREENLIGHT
GREENLIGHT HPS
HER OPTION
IN-FAST
INTEPRO
INVANCE
MINIARC
MONARC
PERIGEE
SOLUTIONS FOR LIFE
SPARC
STRAIGHT-IN
THERMATRX
UROLUME
Advertising Agency:
S&S Public Relations, Inc.
2700 Patriot Blvd
Glenview, IL 60026-8021
Tel.: (847) 955-0700
Fax: (847) 955-7720
Toll Free: (800) 287-2279

AMERICAN SHARED HOSPITAL SERVICES

4 Embarcadero Ctr Ste 3700
San Francisco, CA 94111-3823
Tel.: (415) 788-5300
Fax: (415) 788-5660
Toll Free: (800) 735-0641
E-mail: eabates@ashs.com
Web Site: www.ashs.com
Approx. Rev.: $16,675,000
Approx. Number Employees: 11
Year Founded: 1980
Business Description:
Gamma Knife Stereotactic Radiosurgery Services
S.I.C.: 8071
N.A.I.C.S.: 621511
Advertising Expenditures: $200,000
Media: 2-7-10
Distr.: Natl.
Personnel:
Craig K. Tagawa *(CFO & COO)*
Ernest A. Bates *(VP-Sls & Bus Dev)*
Brands & Products:
ASHS
THE OPERATING ROOM FOR THE 21ST CENTURY
OR21

AMERIFIT BRANDS, INC.

(Sub. of Martek Biosciences Corporation)
55 Sebethe Dr Ste 102
Cromwell, CT 06416
Tel.: (860) 894-1200
Fax: (860) 990-3476
E-mail: corporate@amerifit.com
Web Site: www.amerifit.com
Approx. Sls.: $50,000,000
Approx. Number Employees: 60
Business Description:
Vitamin Product Mfr
S.I.C.: 2833
N.A.I.C.S.: 325411
Personnel:
Wes Parris *(CEO)*
Victor H. Emerson *(CFO & Sr VP-Fin)*
Richard McIntosh *(Exec VP)*

Key to Media (For complete agency information see *The Advertising Red Books-Agencies* edition):
1. Bus. Publs. 2. Cable T.V. 3. Catalogs & Directories. 4. Co-op Adv. 5. Consumer Mags. 6. D.M. to Bus. Estab.7. D.M. to Consumers 8. Daily Newsp. 9. Exhibits/Trade Shows 10. Foreign 11. Infomercial 12. Internet Adv.13. Multimedia 14. Network Radio 15. Network T.V. 16. Newsp. Distr. Mags. 17. Other 18. Outdoor (Posters, Transit) 19. Point of Purchase20. Premiums, Novelties 21. Product Samples 22. Special Events Mktg. 23. Spot Radio 24. Spot T.V. 25. Weekly Newsp. 26. Yellow Page Adv.

Doug Meyer *(Exec VP)*
Craig Larsen *(VP-Legal Affairs)*
Steve Swenson *(Sr Dir-Mktg)*

Brands & Products:
AMERIFIT
AZO
CULTURELLE
ESTROVEN
FLEX ABLE
SOOTHERBS
VITABALL

Advertising Agency:
Horizon Media, Inc.
75 Varick St
New York, NY 10013
Tel.: (212) 220-5000
Toll Free: (800) 633-4201

AMERISOURCEBERGEN CORPORATION

1300 Morris Dr
Chesterbrook, PA 19087-5594
Mailing Address:
PO Box 959
Valley Forge, PA 19482-0959
Tel.: (610) 727-7000
Fax: (610) 727-3600
Toll Free: (800) 829-3132
E-mail: info@amerisourcebergen.com
Web Site:
www.amerisourcebergen.com
E-Mail For Key Personnel:
Public Relations: BBrungess@amerisourcebergen.com
Approx. Rev.: $77,953,979,000
Approx. Number Employees: 9,100
Year Founded: 2001
Business Description:
Pharmaceuticals & Medical Supplies Distr
S.I.C.: 5122; 5047
N.A.I.C.S.: 424210; 423450
Media: 2-5-7-10-14-16-20-23-25-26
Distr.: Natl.
Personnel:
Richard C. Gozon *(Chm)*
Steven H. Collis *(Pres & COO)*
R. David Yost *(CEO)*
Michael D. DiCandilo *(CFO & Exec VP)*
Thomas H. Murphy *(CIO & Sr VP)*
Ed Hancock *(Pres-Pkg Grp)*
John G. Chou *(Gen Counsel, Sec & Sr VP)*
Jerry Cline *(Sr VP-Retail Sls & Mktg)*
David M. Senior *(Sr VP-Strategy & Corp Dev)*

Brands & Products:
ACCULINE
AMERISOURCEBERGEN
AUTOMED FDS
FAMILY PHARMACY
GOOD NEIGHBOR PHARMACY
IECHO
INDICARE
INTERLINX
MEDPOINT
MEDSTORM
NEW PRODUCT PLACEMENT PROGRAM
PATIENTPLUS
PRO GENERIX
RXFOCUS
SCAN-A-DOSE PACKAGING
TODAY'S HEALTHCARE

Advertising Agency:
Reese, Tomases & Ellick, Inc. (RT&E)
1105 Market St Ste 100
Wilmington, DE 19801
Tel.: (302) 652-3211
Fax: (302) 428-3920
Toll Free: (888) 720-7561

AMGEN INC.

1 Amgen Center Dr
Thousand Oaks, CA 91320-1799
Tel.: (805) 447-1000
Fax: (805) 447-1010
Toll Free: (800) 282-6436
Telex: 499-4440
E-mail: investor.relations@amgen.com
Web Site: www.amgen.com
Approx. Rev.: $15,053,000,000
Approx. Number Employees: 17,400
Year Founded: 1980
Business Description:
Human Therapeutics Developer, Mfr & Marketer
S.I.C.: 2836; 8733
N.A.I.C.S.: 325414; 541710
Import Export
Advertising Expenditures: $98,000,000
Media: 6-7-8-10-11-13-15-21-24
Distr.: Intl.; Natl.
Personnel:
Kevin W. Sharer *(Chm)*
Robert A. Bradway *(Pres & COO)*
Jonathan Peacock *(CFO & Exec VP)*
Thomas Flanagan *(CIO & Sr VP)*
Anna S. Richo *(Chief Compliance Officer & Sr VP)*
Willard Dere *(Chief Medical Officer-Intl & Sr VP)*
Thomas Dittrich *(Chief Acctg Officer & VP-Fin)*
David J. Scott *(Gen Counsel, Sec & Sr VP)*
Fabrizio Bonanni *(Exec VP-Ops)*
Roger M. Perlmutter *(Exec VP-R & D)*
Madhu Balachandran *(Sr VP-Mfg)*
David W. Beier *(Sr VP-Global Govt Affairs & Corp Affairs)*
Rodger Currie *(Sr VP-Govt Affairs)*
Jim Daly *(Sr VP-North American Comml Ops)*
David L. Lacey *(Sr VP-Res)*
Brian McNamee *(Sr VP-HR)*
Joseph Miletich *(Sr VP-R&D)*
Ken Keller *(VP & Gen Mgr)*
Phyllis J. Piano *(VP-Corp Comm & Philanthropy)*
Jeanne Fitzgerald *(Exec Dir-Mktg Ops)*
Jonathan Landon *(Exec Dir-Global Strategic Sourcing)*
Paul J. Reider *(Exec Dir-Sls)*
J. Michael Sprafka *(Exec Dir-Center for Observational Res)*
Jay Appel *(Dir-Physician Relationship Mktg)*
Susanne Laningham *(Dir-Reimbursement)*
Suzy Yun *(Mgr-Mktg Strategic Sourcing)*

Brands & Products:
AMGEN
ARANESP
ENBREL
EPOGEN
INFERGEN
NEULASTA
NEUPOGEN
NPLATE
PIONEERING SCIENCE DELIVERS VITAL MEDICINES
REIMBURSEMENT CONNECTION
SENSIPAR
VECTIBIX

AMN HEALTHCARE SERVICES, INC.

12400 High Bluff Dr Ste 100
San Diego, CA 92130
Tel.: (858) 792-0711
Fax: (800) 282-1211
Fax: (888) 889-5247
Toll Free: (866) 871-8519
E-mail: info@amnhealthcare.com
Web Site: www.amnhealthcare.com
Approx. Rev.: $689,217,000
Approx. Number Employees: 1,833
Year Founded: 1981
Business Description:
Temporary & Permanent Healthcare Staffing Services
S.I.C.: 7363; 7361
N.A.I.C.S.: 561320; 561310
Advertising Expenditures: $3,109,000
Personnel:
Douglas D. Wheat *(Chm)*
Susan R. Nowakowski *(Pres & CEO)*
Brian M. Scott *(CFO & Chief Acctg Officer)*
Bruce R. Carothers *(CTO & Sr VP)*
Timothy Boes *(Pres-Locum Tenens)*
Ralph S. Henderson *(Pres-Nurse Staffing Div)*
Denise L. Jackson *(Gen Counsel, Sec & Sr VP)*
Marcia R. Faller *(Chief Clinical Officer & Exec VP-Ops)*
Julie Fletcher *(Sr VP-HR)*
Beth L. Machado *(Sr VP-Recruitment & Travel Nurse Staffing)*
Wendy Newman *(Sr VP-Mktg)*
Phil Miller *(VP-Comm)*
Carol Burke *(Sr Dir-Comm & Mktg)*
Don Cowan *(Sr Dir-Corp Comm)*

Brands & Products:
AMN HEALTHCARE
NURSINGJOBS.COM
RN.COM
STAFF CARE

Advertising Agency:
TMX Communications
1100 E Hector St Ste 242
Conshohocken, PA 19428
Tel.: (610) 897-2500
Fax: (610) 897-2501

AMO MILPITAS

(Sub. of Abbott Medical Optics, Inc.)
510 Cottonwood Dr
Milpitas, CA 95035
Tel.: (408) 273-4100
Fax: (408) 273-5950
Toll Free: (800) 733-9880
Web Site: www.amo-inc.com
Sales Range: $150-199.9 Million
Approx. Number Employees: 352
Year Founded: 1986
Business Description:
Ophthalmic Lasers Mfr
S.I.C.: 3845; 3841
N.A.I.C.S.: 334510; 339112
Media: 2-4-7-8-10-13-21

Brands & Products:
CUSTOMVUE
WAVEFRONT
WAVEPRINT
WAVESCAN

AMPLIFON USA

(Sub. of Amplifon S.p.A.)
5000 Cheshire Ln N
Minneapolis, MN 55446
Tel.: (763) 268-4000
Fax: (763) 268-4323
E-mail: mary@amplifon.com
Web Site: www.amplifonusa.com
Approx. Number Employees: 200
Business Description:
Hearing Aids Retailer & Distr
S.I.C.: 3999; 2676; 3842; 3845
N.A.I.C.S.: 339999; 322291; 334510; 339113
Personnel:
Heine Rouch *(Pres)*
Diana Beaufils *(Sr VP & Operating Officer)*
Advertising Agency:
YP Assistants
173 Chestnut Ridge Rd
Bethel, CT 06801
Tel.: (203) 748-8198

AMS HEALTH SCIENCES, INC.

711 NE 39th St
Oklahoma City, OK 73105
Tel.: (405) 842-0131
Fax: (405) 843-4935
Toll Free: (888) 267-6733
E-mail: info@amsmainline.com
Web Site: www.amsonline.com
Sales Range: $1-9.9 Million
Approx. Number Employees: 25
Year Founded: 1988
Business Description:
Weight Management, Dietary Supplement & Personal Care Products Developer & Distr
S.I.C.: 5122
N.A.I.C.S.: 424210
Media: 7-8-10-13
Personnel:
Randy Webb *(CFO)*
Brands & Products:
AM-300 WEIGHT LOSS
AMS
PRIME ONE
PRIME ONE CONCENTRATE
PRIME PLUS
SPARK OF LIFE

AMYLIN PHARMACEUTICALS, INC.

9360 Towne Centre Dr Ste 110
San Diego, CA 92121-3027
Tel.: (858) 552-2200
Fax: (858) 552-2212
E-mail: IR@amylin.com
Web Site: www.amylin.com
Approx. Rev.: $668,813,000
Approx. Number Employees: 1,400
Year Founded: 1987
Business Description:
Pharmaceutical Research & Development
S.I.C.: 2834; 8733
N.A.I.C.S.: 325412; 541720
Personnel:
Howard E. Greene, Jr. *(Co-Founder)*
Paulo F. Costa *(Chm)*
Daniel M. Bradbury *(Pres & CEO)*

Key to Media (For complete agency information see *The Advertising Red Books-Agencies* edition):
1. Bus. Publs. 2. Cable T.V. 3. Catalogs & Directories. 4. Co-op Adv. 5. Consumer Mags. 6. D.M. to Bus. Estab.7. D.M. to Consumers 8. Daily Newsp. 9. Exhibits/Trade Shows 10. Foreign 11. Infomercial 12. Internet Adv.13. Multimedia 14. Network Radio 15. Network T.V. 16. Newsp. Distr. Mags. 17. Other 18. Outdoor (Posters, Transit) 19. Point of Purchase20. Premiums, Novelties 21. Product Samples 22. Special Events Mktg. 23. Spot Radio 24. Spot T.V. 25. Weekly Newsp. 26. Yellow Page Adv.

Amylin Pharmaceuticals, Inc. — (Continued)

Mark G. Foletta *(CFO & Sr VP)*
Orville G. Kolterman *(Sr VP & Chief Medical Officer)*
Vincent P. Mihalik *(Chief Comml Officer & Sr VP-Sls/Mktg)*
Michael Hanley *(VP-Discovery Res & Chief Scientific Officer)*
Marcea Bland Lloyd *(Gen Counsel, Sr VP-Govt & Corp Affairs)*
Alain D. Baron *(Sr VP-Res)*
Mark J. Gergen *(Sr VP-Corp Dev)*
Roger Marchetti *(Sr VP-HR & Info Mgmt)*
Christian Weyer *(Sr VP-R & D)*
Joe A Young *(Sr VP-Comml)*
Mary Bauman *(VP-New Product Commercialization)*
Onaiza Cadoret-Manier *(VP-Mktg)*
Craig A. Eberhard *(VP-Sls)*
Sarah L. Hanssen *(VP-Comml Ops & Strategic Relationship Mgmt)*
Harry J. Leonhardt *(VP & Chief Intellectual Property Counsel)*
Phillip C. Ranker *(VP-Fin)*
Gregg Stetsko *(VP-Strategy & Tech Plng)*
David Kendall *(Exec Dir-Medical Affairs)*
Berthold Lensker *(Exec Dir-Ops-Europe)*

Brands & Products:
AMYLIN
BYETTA
SYMLIN

Advertising Agencies:
HealthEd
100 Walnut Ave Ste 407
Clark, NJ 07066
Tel.: (908) 654-4440
Fax: (732) 388-5203

Ignite Health
8955 Research Dr
Irvine, CA 92618-4237
Tel.: (949) 861-3200
Fax: (949) 861-3750

Manning Selvage & Lee
2001 The Embarcadero
San Francisco, CA 94133
Tel.: (415) 293-2800
Fax: (415) 293-2801

Perry Communications Group, Inc.
925 L St Ste 260
Sacramento, CA 95814
Tel.: (916) 658-0144
Fax: (916) 658-0155

ANCILLA SYSTEMS INCORPORATED

1419 S Lk Pk Ave
Hobart, IN 46342-5958
Tel.: (219) 947-8500
Fax: (219) 947-4037
E-mail: info@ancilla.org
Web Site: www.ancilla.org
Approx. Number Employees: 12
Year Founded: 1982
Business Description:
Operates Hospital & Health Care Services
S.I.C.: 8011
N.A.I.C.S.: 621491
Media: 9-22-25
Personnel:
Fred Arand *(VP-Fin)*

ANDROS INCORPORATED

3301 Leonard Ct
Santa Clara, CA 95054
Tel.: (408) 727-1600
Fax: (408) 727-1677
E-mail: info@andros.com
Web Site: www.andros.com
Approx. Number Employees: 110
Year Founded: 1968
Business Description:
Mfr., Designer & Sales of Environmental & Medical Monitoring Equipment
S.I.C.: 3826; 3845
N.A.I.C.S.: 334516; 334510
Export
Media: 4-10-17
Distr.: Intl.; Natl.
Personnel:
Joshi Vevek *(Founder & CEO)*

ANESIVA, INC.

400 Oyster Point Blvd Ste 502
South San Francisco, CA 94080
Tel.: (650) 624-9600
Fax: (650) 624-7540
E-mail: bd@corgentech.com
Web Site: www.anesiva.com
Approx. Rev.: $304,000
Approx. Number Employees: 78
Year Founded: 1999
Business Description:
Gene Therapy Drug Mfr & Developer
S.I.C.: 2834; 8733
N.A.I.C.S.: 325412; 541710
Personnel:
Joanna Byrnes *(Product Mgr)*
Brands & Products:
ADLEA
ANESIVA
CHANGING THE FACE OF PAIN
ZINGO
Advertising Agency:
WCG
60 Francisco St
San Francisco, CA 94133
Tel.: (415) 362-5018
Fax: (415) 362-5019

ANGIODYNAMICS, INC.

14 Plaza Dr
Latham, NY 12110
Tel.: (518) 795-1400
Fax: (518) 798-3625
Toll Free: (800) 772-6446
E-mail: info@angiodynamics.com
Web Site: www.angiodynamics.com
Approx. Sls.: $215,750,000
Approx. Number Employees: 681
Business Description:
Vascular Disease Treatment Devices Mfr
S.I.C.: 3841; 3845
N.A.I.C.S.: 339112; 334510
Advertising Expenditures: $1,281,000
Personnel:
Vincent A. Bucci *(Chm)*
Joseph M. DeVivo *(Pres & CEO)*
D. Joseph Gersuk *(CFO & Exec VP)*
Scott Solano *(CTO & Sr VP)*
Shawn P. McCarthy *(Sr VP & Gen Mgr-Peripheral Vascular Bus Unit)*
Stephen J. McGill *(Sr VP & Gen Mgr-Intl)*
Alan Panzer *(Sr VP & Gen Mgr-Vascular Div)*
Scott Etlinger *(Sr VP-Global Ops)*
Lynda Wallace *(Sr VP-Bus Dev)*
Brands & Products:
ABSCESSION
ACCU-VU
ANGIOFLOW
ANGIOFLUSH III
ANGIOPTIC
AQUALINER
CIRCLE-C
CRYSTALINE
DURA-FLOW
DYNAMIC FLOW
EMBOSAFE
ERGONOMIC INTRODUCER
EVENMORE
HABIB
INFUSE-A-PORT
LIFEJET F-16
LIFEPORT
LIFEVALVE
MAGNUM-Z-CATH
MARINER
MORPHEUS
NANOKNIFE
NEVERTOUCH
NIT-VU
OMNI
PEELPRO
PERCHIK BUTTON
PROFILER
PULSE SPRAY
PULSE-VU
QUICKSTIC
SCHON
SCHON XL
SMART PORT
SNAP-LOCK
SOFT-VU
SOTRADECOL
SPEEDLYSER
STARBURST
TITANPORT
TOTAL ABSCESSION
TRANSJUGULAR
TRIPLE LOCK
TRIUMPH-1
UNI FUSE
UNIBLATE
VENACURE EVLT
VORTEX
WORKHORSE

ANGIOTECH PHARMACEUTICALS, INC.-SURGICAL SPECIALTIES

(Sub. of Angiotech Pharmaceuticals, Inc.)
100 Dennis Dr
Reading, PA 19606
Tel.: (610) 404-1000
Fax: (610) 404-4010
Toll Free: (877) 991-1110
E-mail: AngioCSRDG@angio.com
Web Site: www.surgicalspecialties.com
Approx. Number Employees: 331
Year Founded: 1991
Business Description:
Surgical & Medical Instruments Mfr
S.I.C.: 3841; 3842
N.A.I.C.S.: 339112; 339113
Import Export
Advertising Expenditures: $400,000
Media: 4
Personnel:
Steven Briant *(Sr VP-Sls & Mktg-Medical Device Technologies)*
Brands & Products:
CLEARTRAP
DERMAGLIDE
IQ GEOMETRY
MSP
SHARPOINT
ULTRAFIT
ULTRAPLUG

ANIMAS CORPORATION

(Sub. of Johnson & Johnson)
200 Lawrence Dr
West Chester, PA 19380-3428
Tel.: (610) 644-8990
Fax: (610) 644-8717
Toll Free: (877) 767-7373
Web Site: www.animascorp.com
Sales Range: $50-74.9 Million
Approx. Number Employees: 348
Year Founded: 1996
Business Description:
Insulin Delivery Products Mfr
S.I.C.: 3841
N.A.I.C.S.: 339112
Media: 2-10-13
Personnel:
Audrey Finkelstein *(Exec VP-Clinical & Govt Affairs)*
Brands & Products:
ANIMAS
CARB SMART
CARB SMART PLUS
EXBG
EXFLEX PROGRAMMING
EXFLIP
EXWRAP
EZBOLUS
EZMANAGER
EZMANAGER PLUS
EZSET
EZSET INSERTER
EZVIEW
INSET
ONETOUCH
PRIMESMART

ANSELL

(Sub. of Ansell Limited)
200 Schultz Dr
Red Bank, NJ 07701-6745
Tel.: (732) 345-5400
Fax: (732) 219-5114
Web Site: www.ansellgloves.com
Business Description:
Mfr. of Healthcare Products
S.I.C.: 3069; 8742
N.A.I.C.S.: 326299; 541611
Personnel:
Peter L. Barnes *(Chm)*
Steve Genzer *(Sr VP-Global Ops)*
Carol Carrozza *(VP-Mktg)*
Advertising Agencies:
AMP Agency (Alloy Marketing & Promotion)
77 N Washington St
Boston, MA 02114
Tel.: (617) 723-8929
Fax: (617) 723-2188
LifeStyles

Test My Names
PO BOx 451
Madison, CT 06443
Toll Free: (877) 402-0649

Key to Media (For complete agency information see *The Advertising Red Books-Agencies* edition):
1. Bus. Publs. 2. Cable T.V. 3. Catalogs & Directories. 4. Co-op Adv. 5. Consumer Mags. 6. D.M. to Bus. Estab.7. D.M. to Consumers 8. Daily Newsp. 9. Exhibits/Trade Shows 10. Foreign 11. Infomercial 12. Internet Adv.13. Multimedia 14. Network Radio 15. Network T.V. 16. Newsp. Distr. Mags. 17. Other 18. Outdoor (Posters, Transit) 19. Point of Purchase20. Premiums, Novelties 21. Product Samples 22. Special Events Mktg. 23. Spot Radio 24. Spot T.V. 25. Weekly Newsp. 26. Yellow Page Adv.

ANX E-BUSINESS CORP.

(Formerly ProxyMed, Inc.)
(Sub. of Anx E-Business Corp.)
4106 Reas Ln Ste 3
New Albany, IN 47150
Tel.: (812) 944-3865
Fax: (812) 944-2711
Toll Free: (800) 773-4080
Year Founded: 1976
Business Description:
Remote Communication & Service Devices for the Clinical Laboratory Industry
S.I.C.: 5045; 7359
N.A.I.C.S.: 423430; 532420
Media: 2-4-7-10-13-24
Distr.: Natl.
Budget Set: Mar.

APOTHECARY PRODUCTS, INC.

11750 12th Ave S
Burnsville, MN 55337
Tel.: (952) 890-1940
Fax: (952) 814-8118
Toll Free: (800) 328-2742
E-mail: webmaster@apothecaryproducts.com
Web Site:
www.apothecaryproducts.com
Approx. Number Employees: 150
Year Founded: 1975
Business Description:
Pharmaceutical Supplies Mfr & Whslr
S.I.C.: 2834; 5122
N.A.I.C.S.: 325412; 424210
Media: 4-6-7-10-13-19-21
Personnel:
Terry Noble *(Founder & CEO)*
Brands & Products:
APOTHECARY
APOTHECARY PRODUCTS
DIABETIC WALLET
DRUG STORE
EZY-DOSE
EZY INFANT CARE
FAULTLESS
GOODHEALTH
KYLE CROCODILE
PINCH VALVE
PLAZA
QUIET! PLEASE
RECONSTITUBE
REMIND N' TIME
SAFETY GUARD
SLIM JIM
VITAPLAN RX

APP PHARMACEUTICALS, INC.

(Sub. of Fresenius Kabi AG)
1501 E Woodfield Rd Ste 300 E
Schaumburg, IL 60173-5837
Tel.: (847) 969-2700
Web Site: www.appharma.com
Approx. Rev.: $647,374,000
Approx. Number Employees: 1,375
Business Description:
Injectable Pharmaceutical Products Mfr
S.I.C.: 2834
N.A.I.C.S.: 325412
Media: 4-10
Personnel:
Bernhard Hampl *(Chm)*
John Ducker *(Pres & CEO)*
Richard J. Tajak *(CFO & Exec VP)*
Frank Harmon *(COO & Exec VP)*
Richard E. Maroun *(Gen Counsel & Sec)*
Brands & Products:
ADENCOCARD
ADRIAMYCIN
ADRUCIL
ANCEF
APRESOLINE
AREDIA
ASTRAMORPH
STERI-TAMP

APPLIED BIOSYSTEMS, INC.

(Div. of Applied Biosystems Group)
500 Old Connecticut Path
Framingham, MA 01701-4574
Tel.: (508) 383-7700
Fax: (508) 383-7885
E-mail: abcc@appliedbiosystems.com
Web Site:
www.appliedbiosystems.com
Approx. Rev.: $96,516,000
Approx. Number Employees: 400
Year Founded: 1987
Business Description:
Biomedical Research Products Mfr
S.I.C.: 8733
N.A.I.C.S.: 541710
Media: 2-4-7-10-11-20-22
Distr.: Intl.; Natl.
Budget Set: Mar.
Personnel:
Barbara Kerr *(VP-HR)*
Advertising Agency:
PJA
12 Arrow St
Cambridge, MA 02138-5105
Tel.: (617) 492-5899
Fax: (617) 661-1530
(Biocad, Poros, Integral, PNA, Mariner & Voyager-DE)

APRIA HEALTHCARE GROUP INC.

(Holding of The Blackstone Group L.P.)
26220 Enterprise Ct
Lake Forest, CA 92630-8405
Tel.: (949) 639-2000
Toll Free: (800) 277-4288
E-mail: contact_us@apria.com
Web Site: www.apria.com
Approx. Rev.: $2,080,718,000
Approx. Number Employees: 10,900
Year Founded: 1924
Business Description:
Home Healthcare Products & Services
S.I.C.: 8082; 5047; 5912
N.A.I.C.S.: 621610; 423450; 446110
Advertising Expenditures: $1,500,000
Media: 1-4-7-8-10-20
Distr.: Natl.
Budget Set: Oct.
Personnel:
Norman C. Payson *(Exec Chm & CEO)*
Chris A. Karkenny *(CFO & Exec VP)*
Lawrence A. Mastrovich *(COO)*
Peter Reynolds *(Chief Acctg Officer & Controller)*
Daniel E. Greenleaf *(Pres-Coram Specialty Infusion Svcs & COO-Apria Healthcare)*
Robert S. Holcombe *(Gen Counsel, Sec & Exec VP)*
Howard Derman *(Exec VP-HR)*
Lisa M. Getson *(Exec VP-Govt Rels & Corp Compliance)*
Cameron Thompson *(Exec VP-Logistics)*
Dena Parker *(Sr VP-Fin)*
Kimberlie Rogers-Bowers *(Sr VP-Regulatory Affairs & Acq Integration)*
Brands & Products:
APRIA HEALTHCARE

APRICUS BIOSCIENCES, INC.

(Formerly NEXMED, INC.)
6330 Nancy Ridge Dr Ste 103
San Diego, CA 92121
Tel.: (858) 222-8041
Fax: (858) 866-0482
E-mail: ecox@apricusbio.com
Web Site: www.apricusbio.com
Approx. Rev.: $4,972,737
Approx. Number Employees: 35
Year Founded: 1987
Business Description:
Pharmaceutical Mfr, Researcher & Developer
S.I.C.: 2834; 8733
N.A.I.C.S.: 325412; 541710
Personnel:
Bassam B. Damaj *(Chm, Pres & CEO)*
Mark Westgate *(CFO & VP)*
Brands & Products:
ALPROX-TD
DEVELOPING PATIENT FRIENDLY DRUGS
FEMPROX
NEXACT
VITAROS
Advertising Agency:
Rx Communications Group LLC
445 Park Ave 10th Fl
New York, NY 10022
Tel.: (917) 322-2568

APYRON TECHNOLOGIES, INC.

(Sub. of Streamline Capital, Inc.)
3342 International Pk Dr
Atlanta, GA 30316
Tel.: (678) 904-6591
Fax: (678) 904-6603
E-mail: products@apryon.com
Web Site: www.apyron.com
Sales Range: Less than $1 Million
Approx. Number Employees: 4
Year Founded: 1994
Business Description:
Developer & Mfr of Chemical Absorbents & Antimicrobial Products
S.I.C.: 2899
N.A.I.C.S.: 325998
Media: 10
Personnel:
Wei-Chih Chen *(Chm & CEO)*
Leslie J. Story *(Pres & COO)*
John A. Reade *(CFO)*
Eddie Kali *(Exec VP)*
Brands & Products:
AQUA-BIND
ICE WAND

AQUION PARTNERS L.P.

2080 Lunt Ave
Elk Grove Village, IL 60007-5606
Tel.: (847) 437-9400
Fax: (847) 758-5951
Web Site: www.aquionwater.com/
E-Mail For Key Personnel:
Public Relations: markserv@aquion.com
Approx. Number Employees: 130
Year Founded: 1989
Business Description:
Water Treatment
S.I.C.: 3589
N.A.I.C.S.: 333319
Media: 2-3-5-6-10-11-14-15-22

ARCADIA RESOURCES, INC.

9320 Priority Way West Dr
Indianapolis, IN 46240
Tel.: (317) 569-8234
E-mail: info@arcadiaservices.com
Web Site:
www.arcadiaresourcesinc.com
Approx. Rev.: $100,041,000
Approx. Number Employees: 4,229
Business Description:
Home Care Staffing Services
S.I.C.: 7361; 8082
N.A.I.C.S.: 561310; 621610
Advertising Expenditures: $675,000
Personnel:
Marvin R. Richardson *(Pres & CEO)*
Matthew R. Middendorf *(CFO, Treas & Sec)*
Steven L. Zeller *(COO & Gen Counsel)*
Charles L. Goodall *(Exec VP-Ops-Pharmacy)*
Cathy Sparling *(Exec VP)*
Brands & Products:
DAILYMED
Advertising Agency:
Caponigro Public Relations, Inc.
4000 Town Ctr Ste 1750
Southfield, MI 48034
Tel.: (248) 355-3200
Fax: (248) 353-6759

ARDEA BIOSCIENCES, INC.

4939 Directors Pl
San Diego, CA 92121
Tel.: (858) 652-6500
Fax: (858) 625-0760
E-mail: info@ardeabiosciences.com
Web Site: www.ardeabio.com
Approx. Rev.: $27,419,000
Approx. Number Employees: 77
Year Founded: 1994
Business Description:
Pharmaceutical Mfr
S.I.C.: 2834; 8733
N.A.I.C.S.: 325412; 541710
Personnel:
Barry D. Quart *(Pres, CEO & Dir)*
Steven R. Davis *(COO & Exec VP)*
Kimberly J. Manhard *(Sr VP-Regulatory Affairs & Ops)*
Colin E. Rowlings *(Sr VP-Pharmaceutical Sciences)*
Advertising Agency:
WCG
60 Francisco St
San Francisco, CA 94133
Tel.: (415) 362-5018
Fax: (415) 362-5019

ARENA PHARMACEUTICALS, INC.

6166 Nancy Ridge Dr
San Diego, CA 92121-3223
Tel.: (858) 453-7200
Fax: (858) 453-7210
E-mail: businessdevelopment@arenapharm.com
Web Site: www.arenapharm.com
Approx. Rev.: $16,613,000
Approx. Number Employees: 351

Key to Media (For complete agency information see *The Advertising Red Books-Agencies* edition):
1. Bus. Publs. 2. Cable T.V. 3. Catalogs & Directories. 4. Co-op Adv. 5. Consumer Mags. 6. D.M. to Bus. Estab.7. D.M. to Consumers 8. Daily Newsp. 9. Exhibits/Trade Shows 10. Foreign 11. Infomercial 12. Internet Adv.13. Multimedia 14. Network Radio 15. Network T.V. 16. Newsp. Distr. Mags. 17. Other 18. Outdoor (Posters, Transit) 19. Point of Purchase20. Premiums, Novelties 21. Product Samples 22. Special Events Mktg. 23. Spot Radio 24. Spot T.V. 25. Weekly Newsp. 26. Yellow Page Adv.

Arena Pharmaceuticals, Inc. — (Continued)

Business Description:
Drug Discovery Technology Developer
S.I.C.: 2834; 8733
N.A.I.C.S.: 325412; 541710
Personnel:
Jack Lief *(Chm, Pres & CEO)*
Dominic P. Behan *(Sr VP & Chief Scientific Officer)*
William R. Shanahan, Jr. *(VP & Chief Medical Officer)*
Steven W. Spector *(Gen Counsel, Sec & Sr VP)*
Louis J. Scotti *(VP-Mktg & Bus Dev)*
Brands & Products:
ARENA
ARENA PHARMACEUTICALS
CART
Advertising Agency:
Russo Partners LLC
75 9th Ave 2R
New York, NY 10011
Tel.: (212) 845-4200
Fax: (212) 845-4260

ARGONAUT TECHNOLOGIES, INC.

(Sub. of Biotage AB)
1725 Discovery Dr
Charlottesville, VA 22911
Tel.: (434) 979-2319
Fax: (434) 979-4743
Toll Free: (800) 446-4752
E-mail: 1-pointsupport@biotage.com
Web Site: www.biotage.com
Sales Range: $10-24.9 Million
Approx. Number Employees: 150
Business Description:
Drug Development Products Mfr
S.I.C.: 3841
N.A.I.C.S.: 339112
Advertising Expenditures: $450,000
Media: 2-4-10-11-22
Brands & Products:
ADVANTAGE SERIES
CAMILETG
ENDEAVOR
FIRSTMATE
FLASHMASTER
ISOLUTE
PYROGOLD
PYROMARK
PYROSEQUENCING
QUEST
SURVEYOR
TRIDENT
VACMASTER

ARIAD PHARMACEUTICALS, INC.

26 Landsdowne St
Cambridge, MA 02139-4234
Tel.: (617) 494-0400
Fax: (617) 494-8144
E-mail: investor@ariad.com
Web Site: www.ariad.com
Approx. Rev.: $178,980,000
Approx. Number Employees: 122
Year Founded: 1992
Business Description:
Pharmaceutical Developer
S.I.C.: 2836; 2834
N.A.I.C.S.: 325414; 325412
Media: 10
Personnel:
Harvey J. Berger *(Chm & CEO)*
Edward M. Fitzgerald *(CFO, Treas & Exec VP)*
Raymond T. Keane *(Chief Compliance Officer, Gen Counsel, Chief Legal, Sec & Sr VP)*
Timothy P. Clackson *(Chief Scientific Officer & Pres-R & D)*
David L. Berstein *(Chief Intellectual Property Officer & Sr VP)*
Daniel M. Bollag *(Sr VP-Regulatory Affairs & Quality)*
Pierre F. Dodion *(Sr VP-Corp Dev)*
John D. Iuliucci *(Sr VP-Dev)*
Joseph Bratica *(Controller & VP-Fin)*
Maria E. Cantor *(VP-Corp Comm & IR)*
Kelly M. Schmitz *(VP-IT & Ops)*
Kathy Lawton *(Sr Mgr-HR)*
Brands & Products:
ARIAD

THE ARISTOTLE CORPORATION

(Sub. of Geneve Corporation)
96 Cummings Point Rd
Stamford, CT 06902
Tel.: (203) 358-8000
Fax: (203) 358-0179
Web Site: www.aristotlecorp.net
Approx. Sls.: $212,817,000
Approx. Number Employees: 900
Year Founded: 1986
Business Description:
Mfr & Distr Educational, Health, Medical Technology & Agricultural Products
S.I.C.: 3841; 3589; 8299; 9411
N.A.I.C.S.: 339112; 333319; 611710; 923110
Advertising Expenditures: $10,420,000
Media: 4
Personnel:
Dean T. Johnson *(CFO & Sr VP)*
W. Phillip Niemeyer *(Pres-Nasco Div)*
H. William Smith *(Gen Counsel, Sec & VP)*

ARKRAY USA, INC.

(Sub. of ARKRAY, Inc.)
5198 W 76th St
Edina, MN 55439
Tel.: (952) 646-3200
Fax: (952) 646-3210
Toll Free: (800) 818-8877
E-mail: info@arkrayusa.com
Web Site: www.arkrayusa.com
Approx. Sls.: $22,000,000
Business Description:
Creates, Acquires, Markets, & Supports Diagnostic & Medical Testing Equipment
S.I.C.: 5047; 3841
N.A.I.C.S.: 423450; 339112
Media: 6
Personnel:
Jonathan Chapman *(Pres)*
Kerri O. Smith *(Mgr-Mktg)*

ARKSON NUTRACEUTICALS CORP.

(Name Changed to FIRST SURGICAL PARTNERS INC.)

ARRHYTHMIA RESEARCH TECHNOLOGY, INC.

25 Sawyer Passway
Fitchburg, MA 01420
Tel.: (978) 345-5000
Fax: (978) 342-0168
E-mail: service@arthrt.com
Web Site: www.arthrt.com
Approx. Sls.: $23,359,283
Approx. Number Employees: 107
Year Founded: 1982
Business Description:
Electrocardiographic Software for the Detection of Arrhythmias
S.I.C.: 3845; 7372
N.A.I.C.S.: 334510; 511210
Export
Media: 2-4
Personnel:
E. P. Marinos *(Chm)*
James E. Rouse *(Pres & CEO)*
David A. Garrison *(CFO & Exec VP-Fin)*
Brands & Products:
1200EPX
ART
PREDICTOR

ARROW INTERNATIONAL, INC.

(Sub. of Teleflex Medical Group)
2400 Bernville Rd
Reading, PA 19605-9607
Mailing Address:
PO Box 12888
Reading, PA 19612-2888
Tel.: (610) 378-0131
Fax: (610) 374-5360
Toll Free: (800) 233-3187
E-mail: webmaster@arrowintl.com
Web Site: www.arrowintl.com
Approx. Sls.: $511,848,000
Approx. Number Employees: 4,000
Year Founded: 1975
Business Description:
Disposable Catheters, Heart Assist Devices & Other Critical & Cardiac Care Related Products Developer, Mfr & Marketer
S.I.C.: 3841; 3845; 5047
N.A.I.C.S.: 339112; 334510; 423450
Brands & Products:
A.PORTS
ARROW-CLARK
ARROW-FLEX
ARROW-TREROTOLA
AUTOCAT
CANNON
CATH-GARD
FLEXTIP
GLOBAL HEALTHCARE EXCHANGE
HANDS OFF
HEMOSONIC
INTRODUCING ARROW SIMPLICITY
KARLAN
LIONHEART
MAC
NEO CARE
NEO PICC
PERCUTANEOUS THROMBOLYTIC DEVICES
PLEURA-SEAL
PTD
RAPID INFUSION CATHETER
RAULERSON
SITMUCATH
SNAPLOCK
STIMUCATH
THERACATH
TWINCATH
TWISTLOCK
Advertising Agency:
The VIA Group LLC
34 Danforth St Ste 309
Portland, ME 04101
Tel.: (207) 221-3000
Fax: (207) 761-9422

ARTHROCARE CORPORATION

7500 Rialto Blvd Bldg 2 Ste 100
Austin, TX 78735
Tel.: (512) 391-3900
Fax: (512) 391-3901
Toll Free: (800) 348-8929
E-mail: info@arthrocare.com
Web Site: www.arthrocare.com
Approx. Rev.: $355,379,000
Approx. Number Employees: 1,407
Year Founded: 1993
Business Description:
Soft Tissue Treatment Technology Mfr, Designer, Developer & Marketer
S.I.C.: 3845; 3841
N.A.I.C.S.: 334510; 339112
Advertising Expenditures: $1,100,000
Media: 2-7-10
Personnel:
David F. Fitzgerald *(Pres & CEO)*
Todd Newton *(CFO, Chief Acctg Officer & Sr VP)*
Jean Woloszko *(CTO & Sr VP-R&D)*
Richard W. Rew, II *(Gen Counsel & Sr VP)*
Andrew Miclot *(Sr VP & Gen Mgr-ENT Bus)*
Scott Schaffner *(Sr VP & Gen Mgr-Sports Medicine Bus)*
James Pacek *(Sr VP-Strategic Bus Units)*
Bruce C. Prothro *(Chief Regulatory Officer & Sr VP-Quality Sys & Assurance)*
Stu Gomm *(VP & Gen Mgr-Spine Bus)*
Brian T. Simmons *(VP-Fin-Americas)*
Brands & Products:
ANGIOCARE
ARTHROCARE
ATLANTECH
CAPS-LOCK
CAPSURE
COBLATION
MULTIVAC
PARAGON
PERC
TITAN
TRISTAR
TURBOVAC

ARYSTA LIFESCIENCE NORTH AMERICA LLC

(Sub. of Arysta LifeScience Corporation)
15401 Weston Pkwy Ste 150
Cary, NC 27513
Tel.: (919) 678-4900
Fax: (919) 678-2194
Fax: (901) 432-5021
Toll Free: (800) 642-7635
Web Site: www.arysta-na.com
Approx. Number Employees: 47
Year Founded: 1995
Business Description:
Agricultural Chemicals
S.I.C.: 5191; 2879
N.A.I.C.S.: 424910; 325320
Personnel:
William M. Lewis *(Pres & CEO-North America)*

Key to Media (For complete agency information see *The Advertising Red Books-Agencies* edition):
1. Bus. Publs. 2. Cable T.V. 3. Catalogs & Directories. 4. Co-op Adv. 5. Consumer Mags. 6. D.M. to Bus. Estab.7. D.M. to Consumers
8. Daily Newsp. 9. Exhibits/Trade Shows 10. Foreign 11. Infomercial 12. Internet Adv.13. Multimedia 14. Network Radio
15. Network T.V. 16. Newsp. Distr. Mags. 17. Other 18. Outdoor (Posters, Transit) 19. Point of Purchase20. Premiums, Novelties
21. Product Samples 22. Special Events Mktg. 23. Spot Radio 24. Spot T.V. 25. Weekly Newsp. 26. Yellow Page Adv.

Brands & Products:
ADIOS
ARENA
AUDIT
BATTALION
CAPTAN PRO
CAPTEVATE
CELERO
CENTURION
CLUTCH
ELEVATE
EVEREST
KANEMITE
MIDAS
SELECT

Advertising Agency:
True Media
29 S 9th St Ste 201
Columbia, MO 65201
Tel.: (573) 443-8783
Fax: (573) 443-8784

ASCENSION HEALTH, INC.
4600 Edmundson Rd
Saint Louis, MO 63134-3806
Tel.: (314) 733-8000
Fax: (314) 733-8012
Web Site: www.ascensionhealth.org
Approx. Rev.: $14,773,336,000
Approx. Number Employees: 106,000
Year Founded: 1999
Business Description:
Hospitals & Healthcare Service Organizations Network Operator
S.I.C.: 8062; 8011; 8049; 8063; 8069; 8093; 8099; 8361; 8399
N.A.I.C.S.: 622110; 621111; 621112; 621399; 621420; 621498; 621999; 622210; 622310; 623220; 813212
Advertising Expenditures: $1,000,000
Media: 2-4-10-13-22
Personnel:
Anthony R. Tersigni *(Pres & CEO)*
Anthony J. Speranzo *(CFO & Sr VP)*
Robert J. Henkel *(Pres-Healthcare Ops & COO)*
Mark D. Barner *(CIO & Sr VP)*
John D. Doyle *(Chief Strategy Officer & Gen Mgr-Transformational Dev)*
James K. Beckmann, Jr. *(Chief Risk Officer & Sr VP-Sys Support Svcs)*
Scott Caldwell *(Chief Supply Chain Officer & Sr VP)*
Susan Nestor Levy *(Chief Advocacy Officer)*
Joseph R. Impicciche *(Gen Counsel & Sr VP-Legal Svcs)*
Challis M. Lowe *(Sr VP-Organizational Dev & HR)*
Sister Maureen McGuire *(Sr VP-Mission Integration)*
Stephen D. LeResche *(VP-Comm)*

Advertising Agencies:
Ervin Marketing Creative Communications
5615 Pershing Ave Ste 27
Saint Louis, MO 63112
Tel.: (314) 454-1143
Fax: (314) 454-1160

Fister Lauberth, Inc.
275 Union Blvd 17th Fl
Saint Louis, MO 63108-1231
Tel.: (314) 367-5600
Fax: (314) 367-2288

ASD HEALTHCARE
(Sub. of AmerisourceBergen Specialty Group)
3101 Gaylord Pkwy 3rd Fl
Frisco, TX 75034
Tel.: (469) 365-8000
Fax: (800) 547-9413
Toll Free: (800) 746-6273
E-mail: marketing@asdhealthcare.com
Web Site: www.asdhealthcare.com
Sales Range: $75-99.9 Million
Approx. Number Employees: 100
Year Founded: 1994
Business Description:
Pharmaceuticals Distr
S.I.C.: 5122
N.A.I.C.S.: 424210
Media: 2-4-7
Personnel:
Neil Herson *(Pres)*
Jan Barnett *(Dir-Customer Svc)*
Colby Adams *(Mgr-Health Sys Sls)*

Brands & Products:
PLASMANET.COM

ASSOCIATED HYGIENIC PRODUCTS LLC
(Sub. of DSG International Limited)
3400 River Green Ct Ste 600
Duluth, GA 30096-8334
Tel.: (770) 497-9800
Fax: (770) 623-8679
Web Site: www.ahp-dsg.com
Approx. Number Employees: 55
Business Description:
Disposable Diapers Mfr
S.I.C.: 2676
N.A.I.C.S.: 322291
Export
Media: 6-8
Personnel:
George H. Jackson, III *(Pres & CEO)*
Steve H. Pankow *(Exec VP-Sls & Mktg)*
Paul K. Bois *(VP-HR & Admin)*
Owen G. Connelly *(VP-Fin & MIS)*
Robert A. Newman *(VP-Engrg & Mfg)*

Brands & Products:
CUDDLE UPS
DRYPERS
FITTI

ASTELLAS PHARMA US, INC.
(Sub. of Astellas Pharma Inc.)
3 Pkwy N
Deerfield, IL 60015-2548
Tel.: (847) 317-8800
Fax: (847) 317-7296
Toll Free: (800) 695-4321
E-mail: business.development@us.astellas.com
Web Site: www.us.astellas.com
Approx. Number Employees: 850
Year Founded: 1998
Business Description:
Pharmaceutical Product Developer & Mfr
S.I.C.: 2834
N.A.I.C.S.: 325412
Media: 2-6-7-10
Personnel:
Yoshihiko Hatanaka *(Pres & CEO)*
Masao Yoshida *(Pres & CEO)*
Patrick Shea *(Sr VP-Mktg & Sls)*
Walt Johnston *(VP-Mktg & Strategic New Product Plng)*

Advertising Agencies:
GolinHarris
(Part of the Interpublic Group of Companies)
111 E Wacker Dr 11th Fl
Chicago, IL 60601-4306
Tel.: (312) 729-4000
Fax: (312) 729-4010
(Immunology, Organ Donation)

Kane & Finkel Healthcare Communications
534 4th St
San Francisco, CA 94107
Tel.: (415) 777-4990
Fax: (415) 777-5019
Prograf (Agency of Record)

Williams-Labadie Advertising
57 W Grand Ave Ste 800
Chicago, IL 60650
Tel.: (312) 222-5800
Fax: (312) 222-2530

ASTRAZENECA PHARMACEUTICALS LP
(Sub. of AstraZeneca PLC)
1800 Concord Pike
Wilmington, DE 19850-5437
Tel.: (302) 886-3000
Fax: (302) 886-2972
Toll Free: (800) 456-3669
Web Site: www.astrazeneca-us.com
Approx. Sls.: $12,440,000,000
Approx. Number Employees: 12,500
Business Description:
Pharmaceuticals & Specialty Products Mfr & Distr
S.I.C.: 2834
N.A.I.C.S.: 325412
Media: 3-6-8-9-13-15-21-25
Personnel:
Rich Fante *(Pres-AstraZeneca US & CEO-North America)*
Glenn M. Engelmann *(Gen Counsel & VP)*
Kathy Monday *(Reg VP-Supply-Americas)*
Marta Illueca *(Exec Dir-Gastrointestinal Disorders)*
Steve Davis *(Brand Dir-Global)*
Vinay Deshmukh *(Brand Dir)*
Kaylor Kowash *(Brand Dir-Casodex & Zoladek)*
Greg Looney *(Brand Dir-Oncology)*
Emily Denney *(Dir-Brand Corp Affairs)*
Mike Kleha *(Dir-Strategic Sourcing-Sls & Mktg Procurement)*
Ed Seage *(Dir-Global IR)*
Jorgen Winroth *(Dir-IR)*
Abigail Baron *(Mgr-Media Rels)*

Advertising Agencies:
The Bravo Group HQ
285 Madison Ave 12th Fl
New York, NY 10017
Tel.: (212) 780-5800

CommonHealth
400 Interpace Pkwy
Parsippany, NJ 07054
Tel.: (973) 352-1000
Tel.: (973) 352-2000
Fax: (973) 352-1500
Fax: (973) 884-2487
Symbicort
Zactima
Recentin

Corporate Edge Inc.
1140 Broadway 22nd Fl
New York, NY 10018
Tel.: (212) 279-7200
Fax: (212) 683-1506

Digitas Health
100 Penn Square E 11th Fl
Philadelphia, PA 19107
Tel.: (215) 545-4444
Fax: (215) 545-4440

GHG
114 5th Ave
New York, NY 10011-5604
Tel.: (212) 886-3201
Tel.: (212) 886-3000
Fax: (212) 886-3297

HealthSTAR Communications, Inc.
1000 Wyckoff Ave
Mahwah, NJ 07430
Tel.: (201) 560-5370
Fax: (201) 891-2380

Publicis Healthcare Communications Group
1675 Broadway 8th Fl
New York, NY 10019
Tel.: (212) 468-4033
Fax: (212) 468-4021

Saatchi & Saatchi Advertising
375 Hudson St 9th Fl
New York, NY 10014-3658
Tel.: (212) 463-3400
Fax: (212) 463-4544

Wunderman
(Worldwide Headquarters)
285 Madison Ave
New York, NY 10017
Tel.: (212) 941-3000
Fax: (212) 210-5454
Faslodex
Arimidex
Casodex
Zoladex

Zenith Media Services
(Regional Headquarters for ZenithOptimedia, the Americas)
299 W Houston St 10th Fl
New York, NY 10014-4806
Tel.: (212) 859-5100
Fax: (212) 727-9495
(Nexium)

ATC HEALTHCARE, INC.
1983 Marcus Ave
New Hyde Park, NY 11042-1016
Tel.: (516) 750-1600
Fax: (516) 750-1683
E-mail: webmaster@atchealthcare.com
Web Site: www.atchealthcare.com
Sales Range: $75-99.9 Million
Approx. Number Employees: 74
Year Founded: 1982
Business Description:
Temporary Personnel Services
S.I.C.: 7361; 7363
N.A.I.C.S.: 561310; 561320
Advertising Expenditures: $206,000
Media: 8-17
Personnel:
Stephen Savitsky *(Chm & Pres)*
David Savitsky *(CEO)*

Key to Media (For complete agency information see *The Advertising Red Books-Agencies* edition):
1. Bus. Publs. 2. Cable T.V. 3. Catalogs & Directories. 4. Co-op Adv. 5. Consumer Mags. 6. D.M. to Bus. Estab.7. D.M. to Consumers
8. Daily Newsp. 9. Exhibits/Trade Shows 10. Foreign 11. Infomercial 12. Internet Adv.13. Multimedia 14. Network Radio
15. Network T.V. 16. Newsp. Distr. Mags. 17. Other 18. Outdoor (Posters, Transit) 19. Point of Purchase20. Premiums, Novelties
21. Product Samples 22. Special Events Mktg. 23. Spot Radio 24. Spot T.V. 25. Weekly Newsp. 26. Yellow Page Adv.

ATC Healthcare, Inc. — (Continued)
David Kimbell *(CFO & Sr VP)*
Joseph Travella *(VP-HR)*

Brands & Products:
A-TEAM
ATC
E-BILLING PLUS
QUALITY ASSURANCE ADVANTAGE
WHEREVER HEALTHCARE IS PROVIDED

ATC HEALTHCARE SERVICES, INC.

(Sub. of ATC Healthcare, Inc.)
1983 Marcus Ave
New Hyde Park, NY 11042-1029
Tel.: (516) 750-1600
Fax: (516) 750-1755
E-mail: webmaster@atchealthcare.com
Web Site: www.atchealthcare.com
Sales Range: $500-549.9 Million
Approx. Number Employees: 2,000
Year Founded: 1978
Business Description:
Healthcare Personnel Services
S.I.C.: 7361
N.A.I.C.S.: 561310
Media: 2-10
Personnel:
Stephen Savitsky *(Co-Founder, Chm & Pres)*
David Savitsky *(Co-Founder & CEO)*
David Kimbell *(CFO, Treas & Sr VP)*

ATHENAHEALTH, INC.

311 Arsenal St
Watertown, MA 02472
Tel.: (617) 402-1000
Fax: (617) 402-1099
Toll Free: (888) 652-8200
Web Site: www.athenahealth.com
Approx. Rev.: $245,538,000
Approx. Number Employees: 1,242
Year Founded: 1997
Business Description:
Internet-Based Healthcare Records Management Services
S.I.C.: 7389; 7379
N.A.I.C.S.: 561499; 541519
Media: 10-13
Personnel:
Jonathan S. Bush *(Chm & CEO)*
Timothy M. Adams *(CFO & Sr VP)*
Ed Park *(COO & Exec VP)*
Robert Cosinuke *(CMO & Sr VP)*
Stephen N. Kahane *(Pres-Enterprise Svcs Grp)*
Daniel H. Orenstein *(Gen Counsel, Sec & Sr VP)*
Derek Hedges *(Sr VP-Bus Dev)*
Robert M. Hueber *(Sr VP-Sls)*
Leslie Locke *(Sr VP-People & Process)*
John Hallock *(Dir-Global Corp Comm)*

Brands & Products:
ATHENACLINICALS
ATHENACOLLECTOR
ATHENACOMMUNICATOR
ATHENAHEALTH
ATHENANET
PAYERVIEW
RUN A PRACTICE, NOT AN OBSTACLE COURSE.

ATKINS NUTRITIONALS, INC.

(Holding of Roark Capital Group, Inc.)
1050 17th St Ste 1000
Denver, CO 80265
Tel.: (303) 633-2840
Toll Free: (800) 6ATKINS
Web Site: www.atkins.com
Approx. Number Employees: 100
Year Founded: 1989
Business Description:
Snack Food Mfr & Distr
S.I.C.: 2096; 2099; 5499
N.A.I.C.S.: 311919; 311999; 446191
Import Export
Advertising Expenditures: $14,600,000
Media: 6
Personnel:
Monty Sharma *(CEO)*
James J. Allwein *(CFO)*
Ronda Aurand *(Reg VP-Sls Ops & Natl Accts)*
Steve Ballard *(Reg VP-West)*
Jill Short *(Reg VP-East)*
John Fischbach *(VP-HR)*
Bob Gandert *(VP-Sls)*
Collette Heimowitz *(VP-Nutritional Comm & Education)*
Jennifer McGhee *(VP-Mktg)*
Allen Silkin *(Sr Dir-Mktg)*
Lisa Wells *(Brand Mgr)*

Brands & Products:
ATKINS

Advertising Agencies:
Abstract Edge
455 Broadway 4th Fl
New York, NY 10013
Tel.: (212) 352-9311
Fax: (212) 952-9498

Kohnstamm Communications
400 N Robert St Ste 1450 Securian Tower
Saint Paul, MN 55101
Tel.: (651) 228-9141
Fax: (651) 298-0628

Trailer Park
6922 Hollywood Blvd 12th Fl
Hollywood, CA 90028
Tel.: (310) 845-3000
Fax: (310) 845-3470
Agency of Record
Branding Campaign
Creative
Strategic

ATLANTIC HEALTH SYSTEM INC.

475 South St
Morristown, NJ 07960
Tel.: (973) 660-3100
E-mail: info@atlantichealth.org
Web Site: www.atlantichealth.org/atlantic/
Business Description:
General Hospitals
S.I.C.: 8062
N.A.I.C.S.: 622110
Media: 2-8-23
Personnel:
Joseph Trunfio *(Pres & CEO)*
Joanne M. Conroy *(COO & Exec VP)*
Linda Reed *(CIO & VP)*
Andrew L. Kovach *(Chief Admin Officer & VP-HR)*
Stephen Sepaniak *(VP-Legal)*

ATS MEDICAL, INC.

(Sub. of Medtronic, Inc.)
3905 Annapolis Ln N Ste 105
Minneapolis, MN 55447-5473
Tel.: (763) 553-7736
Fax: (763) 557-2244
Toll Free: (800) 399-1381
E-mail: info@atsmedical.com
Web Site: www.atsmedical.com
Approx. Sls.: $75,710,000
Approx. Number Employees: 321
Business Description:
Mechanical Heart Valves Mfr
S.I.C.: 3999; 2676; 3841; 3842
N.A.I.C.S.: 339999; 322291; 339112; 339113
Advertising Expenditures: $100,000
Media: 2-7
Personnel:
Michael D. Dale *(Chm, Pres & CEO)*
Xavier Bertrand *(VP & Gen Mgr-EMEA)*
Thad Coffindaffer *(VP-Sls)*
Jeremy A. Curtis *(VP-Mktg-Worldwide)*
James L. Cox *(Dir-Medical)*

Brands & Products:
ATS 3F
ATS 3F ENABLE
ATS CRYOMAZE
ATS CRYOMAZE CONSOLE
ATS FROSTBYTE
ATS MEDICAL
ATS OPEN PIVOT AP
ATS OPEN PIVOT AVG
ATS OPEN-PIVOT STANDARD
ATS SIMULUS ADJ
ATS SIMULUS FLX
ATS SIMULUS SRF
ENCLOSE II
FLEX-ZONE
SIMULUS

AUXILIUM PHARMACEUTICALS, INC.

40 Valley Stream Pkwy
Malvern, PA 19355
Tel.: (484) 321-5900
Fax: (484) 321-5999
Web Site: www.auxilium.com
Approx. Rev.: $211,429,000
Approx. Number Employees: 565
Business Description:
Pharmaceutical Mfr
S.I.C.: 2834
N.A.I.C.S.: 325412
Advertising Expenditures: $229,000
Personnel:
Rolf A. Classon *(Chm)*
Armando Anido *(Pres & CEO)*
James E. Fickenscher *(CFO)*
Jennifer Evans Stacey *(Gen Counsel, Sec & Exec VP-HR)*
Benjamin Del Tito, Jr. *(Exec VP-Regulatory Affairs & Project Mgmt)*
Roger D. Graham, Jr. *(Exec VP-Sls & Mktg)*
Mahesh Kolar *(Product Mgr-TestimR 1%)*

Brands & Products:
AUXILIUM
FEEL BETTER. AGE WELL
INNOVATION FOR LIFE
TESTIM
XIAFLEX

AVANIR PHARMACEUTICALS

101 Enterprise Ste 300
Aliso Viejo, CA 92656
Tel.: (949) 389-6700
Fax: (858) 658-7447
E-mail: ir@avanir.com
Web Site: www.avanir.com
Approx. Rev.: $2,895,474
Approx. Number Employees: 128
Year Founded: 1988
Business Description:
Pharmaceuticals Mfr
S.I.C.: 2834; 8733
N.A.I.C.S.: 325412; 541720
Advertising Expenditures: $1,200,000
Personnel:
Craig A. Wheeler *(Chm)*
Keith A. Katkin *(Pres & CEO)*
Gregory J. Flesher *(Chief Bus Officer & Sr VP-Corp Dev)*
Randall E. Kaye *(Sr VP-Clinical Res, Medical Affairs & Chief Medical Officer)*
William Sibold *(Chief Comml Officer & Sr VP)*
Joao Siffert *(Sr VP-R & D)*
Eric Benevich *(VP-Comm)*
Christine G. Ocampo *(VP-Fin)*
Patrice Saxon *(Mgr-IR & Coord)*

Brands & Products:
ABREVA
AVANIR
FAZACLO
NEURODEX
XENEREX
ZENVIA

AVENTIS PHARMACEUTICALS INC

(Sub. of Sanofi-Aventis US LLC)
10236 Marion Park Dr
Kansas City, MO 64137-1405
Mailing Address:
PO Box 6977
Bridgewater, NJ 08807-0977
Tel.: (816) 966-5100
Fax: (973) 394-7402
Toll Free: (800) 981-2491
Web Site: www.aventis-us.com
Year Founded: 1950
Business Description:
Pharmaceutical Products Mfr
S.I.C.: 2834
N.A.I.C.S.: 325412
Import
Advertising Expenditures: $13,495,000
Media: 2-3-5-6-10-13-14-15-21-23-24
Distr.: Intl.; Natl.
Budget Set: July

AVEO PHARMACEUTICALS, INC.

75 Sidney St
Cambridge, MA 02139
Tel.: (617) 299-5000
Fax: (617) 995-4995
Web Site: www.aveopharma.com
Approx. Rev.: $44,682,000
Approx. Number Employees: 147
Year Founded: 2001
Business Description:
Biopharmaceutical Developer & Mfr
S.I.C.: 2834
N.A.I.C.S.: 325412; 541711
Personnel:
Anthony B. Evnin *(Chm)*
Tuan Ha-Ngoc *(Pres & CEO)*
David B. Johnston *(CFO)*
Elan Z. Ezickson *(Chief Bus Officer & Exec VP)*
Jeno Gyuris *(Sr VP & Head-Res)*

Key to Media (For complete agency information see *The Advertising Red Books-Agencies* edition):
1. Bus. Publs. 2. Cable T.V. 3. Catalogs & Directories. 4. Co-op Adv. 5. Consumer Mags. 6. D.M. to Bus. Estab.7. D.M. to Consumers
8. Daily Newsp. 9. Exhibits/Trade Shows 10. Foreign 11. Infomercial 12. Internet Adv.13. Multimedia 14. Network Radio
15. Network T.V. 16. Newsp. Distr. Mags. 17. Other 18. Outdoor (Posters, Transit) 19. Point of Purchase20. Premiums, Novelties
21. Product Samples 22. Special Events Mktg. 23. Spot Radio 24. Spot T.V. 25. Weekly Newsp. 26. Yellow Page Adv.

Murray O. Robinson *(Sr VP-Translational Medicine)*
Gary Creason *(VP-Intellectual Property)*
Advertising Agency:
Pure Communications, Inc.
1015 Ashes Dr Ste 204
Wilmington, NC 28405
Tel.: (910) 509-3970

AVETA INC.
173 Bridge Plz N
Fort Lee, NJ 07024
Tel.: (201) 969-2300
Fax: (201) 969-2339
E-mail: info@aveta.com
Web Site: www.aveta.com
Sales Range: $700-749.9 Million
Approx. Number Employees: 1,115
Business Description:
Healthcare Management Services
S.I.C.: 9431
N.A.I.C.S.: 923120
Advertising Expenditures: $9,236,000
Media: 2-4-7-8-10
Personnel:
Daniel E. Straus *(CEO & Principal)*
Douglas Malton *(CFO)*
Claude Chevance *(Chief Acctg Officer)*

AXCAN PHARMA INC.
(Holding of TPG Capital, L.P.)
597 Laurier Blvd
Mont-Saint-Hilaire, QC J3H 6C4, Canada
Tel.: (450) 467-5138
Fax: (450) 464-9979
Toll Free: (800) 565-3255
E-mail: axcan@axcan.com
Web Site: www.axcan.com
Approx. Rev.: $348,947,000
Approx. Number Employees: 480
Year Founded: 1982
Business Description:
Pharmaceutical Mfr
S.I.C.: 2834; 2836
N.A.I.C.S.: 325412; 325414
Advertising Expenditures: $13,557,000
Media: 7-17-21
Personnel:
Frank A.G.M. Verwiel *(Pres & CEO)*
Steve Gannon *(CFO, Treas & Sr VP)*
David W. Mims *(Pres-US Specialty Pharmaceuticals)*
Richard Tarte *(Gen Counsel & VP-Corp Dev)*
Martha D. Donze *(VP-HR)*
Michael J. Pasternak *(VP-Sls Ops)*
Darcy Toms *(Sr Dir-Bus Dev Search & Evaluation)*
Maude Harpin *(Mgr-Customer Svc & Trade Rels)*
Brands & Products:
ADEKS
AQUADEKS
BENTYL
BENTYLOL
CANASA
CARAFATE
CORTENEMA
DELURSAN
FLUTTER
HELICIDE
LACTEOL
LANSOYL
MODULON
PHOTOFRIN
PROCTOSEDYL
PYLERA
SALOFALK
SCANDICAL
SCANDISHAKE
SULCRATE
TRANSULOSE
ULTRASE
URSO
URSO FORTE
VIATOL
VIOKASE

B&P COMPANY, INC.
PO Box 41184
Dayton, OH 45441
Tel.: (937) 298-0265
Fax: (937) 298-8064
Toll Free: (800) 648-6891
E-mail: info@frownies.com
Web Site: www.frownies.com
Approx. Number Employees: 10
Year Founded: 1889
Business Description:
Skincare Products Mfr
S.I.C.: 5122; 2841
N.A.I.C.S.: 446120; 325611
Media: 6-8-13
Personnel:
Kathy Wright *(CEO-Mktg-FROWNIES Anit-aging Skin Care)*
Brands & Products:
FACELIFT IN A BAG
FROWNIES
IMMUNE PERFECT
IMMUNE SHIELD

BACTOLAC PHARMACEUTICAL, INC.
7 Oser Ave Unit 14
Hauppauge, NY 11788
Tel.: (631) 951-4908
Fax: (631) 951-4749
E-mail: info@bactolac.com
Web Site: www.bactolac.com
Sales Range: $10-24.9 Million
Approx. Number Employees: 100
Business Description:
Pharmaceuticals Mfr
S.I.C.: 5122; 2833; 2834
N.A.I.C.S.: 424210; 325411; 325412
Media: 2-10
Personnel:
Pailla M. Reddy *(Pres & CEO)*
Renee Reynolds *(CFO & VP)*
Vanessa Jackson *(Mgr-Quality Assurance)*
Pylla Chandrasheker Reddy *(Mgr-Production)*
Jeffrey G. McGonegal *(Asst Sec)*
Brands & Products:
BACTOLAC

BANNER HEALTH SYSTEM
1441 N 12th St
Phoenix, AZ 85006-2837
Tel.: (602) 747-4000
Fax: (602) 495-4559
Web Site: www.bannerhealth.com
Approx. Rev.: $2,600,000,000
Approx. Number Employees: 25,000
Year Founded: 1999
Business Description:
Healthcare Services
S.I.C.: 8059; 8062
N.A.I.C.S.: 623110; 622110; 623311
Import Export
Advertising Expenditures: $350,000
Media: 4-8-10-13-22-23-26
Personnel:
Peter S. Fine *(Pres & CEO)*
Ron Bunnell *(Chief Admin Officer & Exec VP)*
Dan Green *(VP-Comm)*
Gerri Twomey *(VP-HR)*
Mary J. Vecchiarelli *(Dir-Mktg)*
Laverne Abe *(Coord-Digital Assets & Graphic Designer)*
Advertising Agency:
The Lavidge Company
2777 E Camelback Rd Ste 300
Phoenix, AZ 85016
Tel.: (480) 998-2600
Fax: (480) 998-5525

BAPTIST HOSPITAL INC.
(Sub. of Saint Thomas Health Services)
2000 Church St
Nashville, TN 37236-0002
Tel.: (615) 284-5555
Fax: (615) 284-4794
E-mail: info@baptisthospital.com
Web Site: www.baptisthospital.com
Sales Range: $250-299.9 Million
Approx. Number Employees: 3,500
Year Founded: 1919
Business Description:
Healthcare Services
S.I.C.: 8062; 8011
N.A.I.C.S.: 622110; 621111
Import Export
Advertising Expenditures: $600,000
Media: 2-4-6-7-8-9-10-13-18-20-21-22-23-24-25-26
Personnel:
Bernie Sherry *(Pres & CEO)*
Alan Strauss *(CFO)*
Renee Kessler *(COO)*

BARNHARDT MANUFACTURING COMPANY
1100 Hawthorne Ln
Charlotte, NC 28205-2918
Mailing Address:
PO Box 34276
Charlotte, NC 28234-4276
Tel.: (704) 376-0380
Fax: (704) 342-1892
Toll Free: (800) 277-0377
E-mail: custserv@barnhardt.net
Web Site: www.barnhardt.net
Approx. Number Employees: 340
Year Founded: 1900
Business Description:
Mfr of Polyurethane Foam & Absorbent Cotton Products
S.I.C.: 3086; 3842
N.A.I.C.S.: 326150; 339113
Export
Media: 2-4-5-6-7-10-21
Distr.: Intl.; Natl.
Budget Set: Aug.
Personnel:
Tom L. Barnhardt *(Chm)*
Lewis Barnhardt *(Pres & CEO)*
Ralph Falero *(VP-Fin & Admin)*
George Hargrove *(VP-Sls & Mktg)*
Brands & Products:
BARNHARDT
CAROLINA
FIBERSOFT
GET REAL GET COTTON
INTRINSICS
NEEDLEEZE
RICHMOND DENTAL
SCROOP
ULTRABLOCK
ULTRASCENT
ULTRASORB

THE BARTELL DRUG COMPANY
4727 Denver Ave S
Seattle, WA 98134
Tel.: (206) 763-2626
Fax: (206) 763-2062
Toll Free: (877) 227-8355
E-mail: comments@bartelldrugs.com
Web Site: www.bartelldrugs.com
Approx. Number Employees: 1,600
Year Founded: 1890
Business Description:
Drug Stores Chain
S.I.C.: 5912
N.A.I.C.S.: 446110
Import
Media: 9-10-22-23-24-25
Distr.: Natl.
Budget Set: Nov.
Personnel:
Jean L. Barber *(Vice Chm & Treas)*
George D. Bartell *(Pres)*
Ed Littleton *(COO)*
Ron Miller *(Sr VP-Mdsg)*
Rebecca Siegmund *(Asst VP-Mktg)*

BATTLE CREEK EQUIPMENT CO.
307 W Jackson St
Battle Creek, MI 49017-2306
Tel.: (269) 962-6181
Fax: (269) 962-8058
Toll Free: (800) 253-0854
E-mail: battlecreek@ctsmail.net
Web Site: www.battlecreekequipment.com
Approx. Number Employees: 45
Year Founded: 1931
Business Description:
Fitness Equipment, Portable Massage Tables, Automatic Moist Heat Pack, Air Purification Systems & Evaporative Humidifiers
S.I.C.: 5091; 3949
N.A.I.C.S.: 423910; 339920
Import Export
Media: 4-5-6-7-9-10-19-26
Distr.: Natl.
Budget Set: June -July
Personnel:
Mary Haywood Brown *(VP-Sls & Mktg)*
Brands & Products:
HEALTH BIKE
HEALTH WALKER
ICE-IT!
PEDLAR
POWER WALKER
PULSE STAR
THERMOPHORE
WALKABOUT

BAXTER INTERNATIONAL INC.
1 Baxter Pkwy
Deerfield, IL 60015-4625
Tel.: (847) 948-2000
Fax: (847) 948-3642
Toll Free: (800) 422-9837
E-mail: edi@baxter.com
Web Site: www.baxter.com
Approx. Sls.: $12,843,000,000
Approx. Number Employees: 48,000
Year Founded: 1931

Key to Media (For complete agency information see *The Advertising Red Books-Agencies* edition):
1. Bus. Publs. 2. Cable T.V. 3. Catalogs & Directories. 4. Co-op Adv. 5. Consumer Mags. 6. D.M. to Bus. Estab.7. D.M. to Consumers
8. Daily Newsp. 9. Exhibits/Trade Shows 10. Foreign 11. Infomercial 12. Internet Adv.13. Multimedia 14. Network Radio
15. Network T.V. 16. Newsp. Distr. Mags. 17. Other 18. Outdoor (Posters, Transit) 19. Point of Purchase20. Premiums, Novelties
21. Product Samples 22. Special Events Mktg. 23. Spot Radio 24. Spot T.V. 25. Weekly Newsp. 26. Yellow Page Adv.

Baxter International Inc. — (Continued)

Business Description:
Biopharmaceutical Fluid & Drug Delivery Products Mfr for Treatment of Hemophilia, Immune Deficiencies & Other Life-Threatening Disorders
S.I.C.: 2836; 2833; 2834; 3841; 3842
N.A.I.C.S.: 325414; 325411; 325412; 339112; 339113
Import Export
Advertising Expenditures: $2,030,000
Media: 2-7-10-13-21
Distr.: Intl.; Natl.
Personnel:
Robert L. Parkinson, Jr. *(Chm & CEO)*
Robert J. Hombach *(CFO & Corp VP)*
Robert M. Davis *(Pres-Medical Products & Corp VP)*
Ludwig N. Hantson *(Pres-BioScience & Corp VP)*
Gerald Lema *(Pres-Asia Pacific & Corp VP)*
Peter Nicklin *(Pres-Europe & Corp VP)*
David P. Scharf *(Gen Counsel & Corp VP)*
Ronald Lloyd *(VP & Gen Mgr-Regenerative Medicine)*
Jeanne K. Mason *(Corp VP-HR)*
Brands & Products:
6060
ACCURA
ACCUSOL
ADVATE
ALYX
AMICUS
ARENA
AURORA
AUTOMIX
AUTOPHERESIS-C
AVIVA
BAXJECT
BREVIBLOC
BUMINATE
CA
CAHP
CAPD
CEPROTIN
CLEARLINK
CLINIMIX
CLINIMIX E
CLINOLEIC
COLLEAGUE
CRYOCYTE
CS-3000
CT
CYTOMATE
DICEA
DUPLOCATH
DUPLOTIP
EXELTRA
EXTRANEAL
EXTRAPURE
FEIBA VH
FLEXBUMIN
FLO-GARD
FORANE
GAMMAGARD
HEMOFIL
HEMOFIL M
HOME CHOICE PRO
HOMECHOICE
HYLENEX
INFUSO.R
INTRAVIA
IPUMP
ISOLEX
ISOLEX 3001
IVEEGAM
KIOVIG
MERIDIAN
MESNEX
MICROMIX
MIDAZOLAM HCL
OLICLINOMEL
PD LINK
PEDIATRIC
PHYSIONEAL
PREMASOL
PRO CARD
PROPLEX T
PROPOFOL
QUANTUM PD
RECOMBINATE
RENALSOFT
RESTORE-X
REVERSE OSMOSIS
SEVOFLUORANE
SOLOMIX
SUPRANE
SYMPT-X
SYNDEO
SYSTEM 1000/TINA
TISEEL
TISSOMAT
TISSUCOL
TRAVASOL
ULTRA-FIT
ULTRA-SEAL
VIAFLEX
XENIUM
Advertising Agencies:
Cresta Group
1050 N State St
Chicago, IL 60610
Tel.: (312) 944-4700
Fax: (312) 944-1582

Porter Novelli
(Sub. of Omnicom Group, Inc.)
75 Varick St 6th Fl
New York, NY 10013
Tel.: (212) 601-8000
Fax: (212) 601-8101

Vox Medica Inc.
601 Walnut St Ste 250-S
Philadelphia, PA 19106-3514
Tel.: (215) 238-8500
Fax: (215) 238-0881

BAXTER PHARMACEUTICAL PRODUCTS, INC.
(Sub. of Baxter Healthcare Corporation)
95 Spring St
New Providence, NJ 07974-1143
Tel.: (908) 286-7000
Fax: (908) 286-7267
E-mail: edi@baxter.com
Web Site: www.baxter.com
Sales Range: $50-74.9 Million
Approx. Number Employees: 175
Year Founded: 1990
Business Description:
Health Care Products & Services
S.I.C.: 2834
N.A.I.C.S.: 325412
Export
Advertising Expenditures: $200,000
Media: 2-10-20
Distr.: Intl.; Natl.
Budget Set: Oct.
Personnel:
Laura Mastrosimone *(Sr Mgr-Mktg)*
Brands & Products:
WINRHO

BAYADA NURSES INC.
290 Chester Ave
Moorestown, NJ 08057
Tel.: (856) 231-1000
Fax: (856) 231-1955
E-mail: info@bayada.com
Web Site: www.bayada.com
Sales Range: $75-99.9 Million
Approx. Number Employees: 6,000
Business Description:
Home Health Care Services
S.I.C.: 8082
N.A.I.C.S.: 621610
Media: 2-22-23-24
Personnel:
J. Mark Baiada *(Pres)*
Susan Milstein *(Chief Trng Officer)*
Melissa Burnside *(Dir-Div)*
Nori Fey *(Dir-Legal Svcs)*
Steve Flannery *(Dir-Conferences)*
Susan Ingalls *(Dir-Div)*
Pat Mallee *(Dir-Conferences)*
Sherri Pillet *(Dir-Div)*
Eric Welsh *(Sr Mgr)*
Brands & Products:
BAYADA NURSES
Advertising Agency:
The In-House Agency, Inc.
55 Madison Ave Ste 400
Morristown, NJ 07960
Tel.: (973) 285-3259
Fax: (908) 996-3593

BAYER CORPORATION
(Div. of Bayer Aktiengesellschaft)
100 Bayer Rd
Pittsburgh, PA 15205-9707
Tel.: (412) 777-2000
Fax: (412) 777-2034
Toll Free: (800) 422-9374 (Sci Ed Prog)
Web Site: www.bayerus.com
Sales Range: $5-14.9 Billion
Approx. Number Employees: 22,300
Year Founded: 1884
Business Description:
Science & Technology Product Mfr
S.I.C.: 8733; 2879
N.A.I.C.S.: 541710; 325320
Import Export
Personnel:
Gregory S. Babe *(Pres & CEO)*
Jose Milan *(Dir-Green Bus Ops)*
Advertising Agencies:
BBDO New York
1285 Ave of the Americas 7th Fl
New York, NY 10019-6028
Tel.: (212) 459-5000
Alka-Seltzer

Energy BBDO
410 N Michigan Ave
Chicago, IL 60611-4213
Tel.: (312) 337-7860
Fax: (312) 337-6871

GroupM North America & Corporate HQ
498 Seventh Ave
New York, NY 10018
Tel.: (212) 297-8181
Fax: (212) 297-7001

BAYER HEALTHCARE BIOLOGICAL PRODUCTS DIVISION
(Div. of Bayer Corporation)
800 Dwight Way
Berkeley, CA 94710-2428
Mailing Address:
PO Box 1986
Berkeley, CA 94701-1986
Tel.: (510) 705-5000
Fax: (510) 705-5542
Web Site:
www.livingwithhemophilia.com
Approx. Number Employees: 1,500
Year Founded: 1987
Business Description:
Research Development & Products Facility for Pharmaceutical Drugs
S.I.C.: 2834
N.A.I.C.S.: 325412
Media: 2-4-6-7-10-14-19-20-21-23
Distr.: Intl.; Natl.
Budget Set: Aug.

BAYER HEALTHCARE CONSUMER CARE DIVISION
(Div. of Bayer Corporation)
36 Columbia Rd
Morristown, NJ 07962-1910
Mailing Address:
PO Box 1910
Morristown, NJ 07962
Tel.: (973) 254-5000
Fax: (973) 408-8126
Toll Free: (800) 348-2240
Web Site: www.bayercare.com
Approx. Number Employees: 500
Business Description:
Over-the-Counter Consumer Healthcare Products Research, Development, Mfr & Marketing
S.I.C.: 5122
N.A.I.C.S.: 424210
Personnel:
Frank Knapp *(Sr VP-Worldwide Fin & Controller)*
Timothy Hayes *(Sr VP & Reg Head-North America)*
Jay Kolpon *(VP-Strategic Bus Unit-Global)*
Karen May *(VP-Bus Grp Fin)*
Tricia McKernan *(VP-Comm-Global)*
Barton Warner *(VP-Mktg & New Bus)*
Erica Mann *(Gen Mgr)*
Margaret Waloschek *(Brand Mgr-Calcium Category)*
Janice Yearwood *(Brand Mgr)*
Brands & Products:
ALEVE
ALKA-MINTS
ALKA-SELTZER
BRONKAID
BUGS BUNNY VITAMINS
CAMPHO-PHENIQUE
DOMEBORO
FEMSTAT
FERGON
FLINTSTONES MULITVITAMINS
MIDOL
MYCELEX
NEO-SYNEPHRINE
ONE-A-DAY MULTIVITAMINS
ONE-A-DAY SPECIALIZED BLENDS
PHILLIPS' HALEY'S M-O
PHILLIPS' MILK OF MAGNESIA
RID
VANQUISH

Key to Media (For complete agency information see *The Advertising Red Books-Agencies* edition):
1. Bus. Publs. 2. Cable T.V. 3. Catalogs & Directories. 4. Co-op Adv. 5. Consumer Mags. 6. D.M. to Bus. Estab.7. D.M. to Consumers
8. Daily Newsp. 9. Exhibits/Trade Shows 10. Foreign 11. Infomercial 12. Internet Adv.13. Multimedia 14. Network Radio
15. Network T.V. 16. Newsp. Distr. Mags. 17. Other 18. Outdoor (Posters, Transit) 19. Point of Purchase20. Premiums, Novelties
21. Product Samples 22. Special Events Mktg. 23. Spot Radio 24. Spot T.V. 25. Weekly Newsp. 26. Yellow Page Adv.

Advertising Agencies:
Aragon Advertising
7036 Nansen St
Forest Hills, NY 11375
Tel.: (718) 575-1815
Fax: (718) 544-0757
(Hispanic)
— Michelle S. Aragon *(Acct. Exec.)*

Energy BBDO
410 N Michigan Ave
Chicago, IL 60611-4213
Tel.: (312) 337-7860
Fax: (312) 337-6871
(One-A-Day, Flintstones, Midol & Aleve)

BAYER HEALTHCARE PHARMACEUTICAL DIVISION
(Div. of Bayer Corporation)
6 West Belt
Wayne, Nj 07470
Tel.: (203) 812-2000
Fax: (973) 305-5399
Web Site: www.pharma.bayer.com
Approx. Number Employees: 1,400
Business Description:
Mfr. of Pharmaceuticals
S.I.C.: 2834
N.A.I.C.S.: 325412
Advertising Expenditures: $1,000,000
Media: 2-7-10-21
Distr.: Intl.; Natl.
Budget Set: Oct.
Personnel:
R. Christopher Seaton *(Sr VP-Global Transactions)*
Brands & Products:
ADALAT
AVELOX
BAYCOL
BILTRICIDE
CORT-DOME
DECHOLIN TABLETS
DOME PASTE
DOMOL
MEZLIN
MITHRACIN
MYCELEX-G
NIMOTOP
OTIC-DOME
PRECISE
STILPHOSTROL
TRASYLOL
TRIDESILON 0.05 PERCENT CREME
Advertising Agency:
Omnicom Group Inc.
437 Madison Ave 9th Fl
New York, NY 10022-7001
Tel.: (212) 415-3600
Fax: (212) 415-3530

BAYER HEALTHCARE PHARMACEUTICALS
(Sub. of Bayer HealthCare Pharmaceuticals Inc.)
6 W Belt Rd
Wayne, NJ 07470-6806
Tel.: (973) 694-4100
Fax: (973) 942-1610
Toll Free: (888) BERLEX4
Telex: 136 354
Web Site: www.bayerhealthcare.com
Sales Range: $1-4.9 Billion
Approx. Number Employees: 2,400
Business Description:
Diagnostic & Therapeutic Pharmaceuticals Distr & Mfr
S.I.C.: 2834; 8733
N.A.I.C.S.: 325412; 541710
Media: 6
Personnel:
Scott Meece *(Gen Counsel & Sr VP)*
Advertising Agency:
Omnicom Group Inc.
437 Madison Ave 9th Fl
New York, NY 10022-7001
Tel.: (212) 415-3600
Fax: (212) 415-3530

BAYFRONT HEALTH SYSTEM, INC.
701 6th St S
Saint Petersburg, FL 33701-4814
Tel.: (727) 893-6015
Tel.: (727) 893-6707 (Executive Office)
Tel.: (727) 893-6110 (Corp. Communications)
Fax: (727) 893-6085
Web Site: www.bayfront.org
Approx. Number Employees: 2,200
Year Founded: 1996
Business Description:
Operate Medical Centers
S.I.C.: 8741; 8062
N.A.I.C.S.: 561110; 622110
Media: 2-22
Personnel:
Sue G. Brody *(Pres & CEO)*
Bob Thornton *(CFO & Exec VP)*
Eric Feber *(COO)*
Kanika Tomalin *(Exec Dir-Strategic Plng & Pub Affairs)*
Marcey Stone *(Mgr-Strategic Plng & Pub Affairs)*
Vannetti Carter *(Coord-Admin)*

BAYLOR HEALTH CARE SYSTEM
3500 Gaston Ave
Dallas, TX 75246
Tel.: (214) 820-0111
Tel.: (214) 820-2116
Fax: (214) 820-7499
Toll Free: (800) 422-9567
Web Site: www.baylorhealth.com
Approx. Number Employees: 15,000
Year Founded: 1981
Business Description:
Not-For-Profit Regional Medical Network
S.I.C.: 8062
N.A.I.C.S.: 622110
Media: 2-4-7-8-9-11-13-18-19-20-22-25-26
Personnel:
Joel T. Allison *(Pres & CEO)*
Frederick Savelsbergh *(CFO)*
Gary Brock *(COO)*
Paul Convery *(Chief Medical Officer & Sr VP)*
Keith Holtz *(Chief HR Officer & Sr VP)*
James Pool *(Chief Acctg Officer & VP)*
David J. Ballard *(Chief Quality Officer & Sr VP)*
Donald Kennerly *(Chief Patient Safety Officer & VP-Patient Safety)*
Jim Walton *(Chief Equity Officer & VP-Health Equity)*
John B. McWhorter, III *(Pres-Baylor University Medical Ctr & Sr VP)*
Stephen Boyd *(Gen Counsel & Sr VP)*
Jennifer Coleman *(Sr VP-Consumer Affairs)*
Michael L. Taylor *(Sr VP-Ops)*
Janeen Browning *(Dir-Mktg)*

BAYSTATE HEALTH SYSTEM, INC.
280 Chestnut St
Springfield, MA 01199-1001
Tel.: (413) 794-0000
Fax: (413) 794-8274
Web Site: www.baystatehealth.com
E-Mail For Key Personnel:
Marketing Director: Suzanne. Hendery@bhs.org
Approx. Number Employees: 9,000
Year Founded: 1983
Business Description:
Health Management Services
S.I.C.: 8741; 8062
N.A.I.C.S.: 561110; 622110
Import Export
Media: 6-8-9-18-20-23-24-25-26
Personnel:
Mark R. Tolosky *(Pres & CEO)*
Dennis W. Chalke *(Sr VP, CFO & Treas)*
Mark B. Gorrell *(CIO & VP-Info Svcs)*
Donna J. Ross *(Chief Strategy Officer & Sr VP-Strategy & External Rels)*
Deborah Morsi *(Chief Nursing Officer & VP-Patient Care Svcs)*
Joan Sullivan *(Pres-Baystate Mary Lane Hospital & Baystate Health Eastern Reg)*
Evan M. Benjamin *(Sr VP-Healthcare Quality-Baystate Health)*
Paula S. Dennison *(Sr VP-HR)*
Suzanne B. Hendery *(VP-Mktg & Comm)*
Brands & Products:
BAYSTATE HEALTH SYSTEM

BAZI INTERNATIONAL, INC.
(Formerly XELR8 Holdings, Inc.)
1730 Blake St Ste 305
Denver, CO 80202
Tel.: (303) 316-8577
Fax: (303) 316-8078
Toll Free: (888) 935-7808
E-mail: info@drinkbazi.com
Web Site: www.drinkbazi.com
Approx. Sls.: $2,274,337
Approx. Number Employees: 9
Year Founded: 2001
Business Description:
Nutritional Supplement Product Developer, Marketer & Distr
S.I.C.: 2833; 2834; 5963
N.A.I.C.S.: 325411; 325412; 454390
Advertising Expenditures: $844,330
Media: 6-7-13
Personnel:
Daniel W. Rumsey *(Chm)*
Kevin C. Sherman *(Pres)*
Deborah K. Wildrick *(CEO)*
John D. Pougnet *(CFO)*
Scott Salik *(VP-Media)*
Aaron Lowe *(Dir-Nutritionals & Sports Mktg)*
Brands & Products:
BAZI

BD MEDICAL
(Formerly Becton Dickinson Medical)
(Div. of Becton, Dickinson & Company)
9450 S State St
Sandy, UT 84070-3213
Tel.: (801) 565-2300
Fax: (801) 565-2378
Web Site: www.bd.com
Sales Range: $1-4.9 Billion
Approx. Number Employees: 1,200
Business Description:
Catheters Mfr & Marketer
S.I.C.: 3821; 2676; 3842; 3845; 3999
N.A.I.C.S.: 339111; 322291; 334510; 339113; 339999
Personnel:
Gary M. Cohen *(Exec VP)*
Advertising Agency:
Richter7
280 S 400 W Ste 200
Salt Lake City, UT 84101
Tel.: (801) 521-2903
Fax: (801) 359-2420

BEACH PRODUCTS, INC.
5220 S Manhattan Ave
Tampa, FL 33611-3420
Tel.: (813) 839-6565
Fax: (813) 837-2511
Toll Free: (800) 322-8210
Web Site: www.pa-imc.net
Approx. Number Employees: 100
Year Founded: 1958
Business Description:
Pharmaceuticals Mfr
S.I.C.: 2834
N.A.I.C.S.: 325412
Import
Media: 2-7-21
Distr.: Natl.
Budget Set: Jan. -June
Personnel:
Richard B. Jenkins *(Chm, Pres & CEO)*
Richard S. Jenkins *(Exec VP)*
Carol Jenkins *(Mgr-Sls)*
Brands & Products:
BEELITH
CITROLITH
K-PHOS M.F.
K-PHOS NEUTRAL
K-PHOS NO. 2
K-PHOS ORIGINAL
UROQID-ACID
UROQID-ACID NO. 2

BEAMONE LLC
(Sub. of Synergy Healthcare plc)
9020 Activity Rd Ste D
San Diego, CA 92126
Tel.: (858) 586-1166
Fax: (858) 586-6641
Web Site: www.beam-one.com
Approx. Number Employees: 14
Business Description:
Medical Device & Pharmaceutical Mfg
S.I.C.: 2834
N.A.I.C.S.: 325412
Media: 10
Personnel:
Stephen P. Meyer *(Chm)*
Glenn Thibault *(Pres & CEO)*
Larry Gabele *(CFO)*

BECTON, DICKINSON & COMPANY
1 Becton Dr
Franklin Lakes, NJ 07417-1815
Tel.: (201) 847-6800
Fax: (201) 847-6475
Toll Free: (800) 284-6845
Web Site: www.bd.com

Key to Media (For complete agency information see *The Advertising Red Books-Agencies* edition):
1. Bus. Publs. 2. Cable T.V. 3. Catalogs & Directories. 4. Co-op Adv. 5. Consumer Mags. 6. D.M. to Bus. Estab.7. D.M. to Consumers
8. Daily Newsp. 9. Exhibits/Trade Shows 10. Foreign 11. Infomercial 12. Internet Adv.13. Multimedia 14. Network Radio
15. Network T.V. 16. Newsp. Distr. Mags. 17. Other 18. Outdoor (Posters, Transit) 19. Point of Purchase20. Premiums, Novelties
21. Product Samples 22. Special Events Mktg. 23. Spot Radio 24. Spot T.V. 25. Weekly Newsp. 26. Yellow Page Adv.

Becton, Dickinson & Company — (Continued)

E-Mail For Key Personnel:
Marketing Director:
Karen_Carolonza@bd.com
Approx. Rev.: $7,372,333,000
Approx. Number Employees: 28,803
Year Founded: 1897
Business Description:
Medical Supplies, Devices & Diagnostic Systems Mfr, Sales & Marketer
S.I.C.: 3841; 3842
N.A.I.C.S.: 339112; 339113
Import Export
Media: 2-4-6-7-8-10-13-21
Distr.: Intl.; Natl.
Personnel:
Edward J. Ludwig *(Chm & CEO)*
Vincent A. Forlenza *(Pres & COO)*
David V. Elkins *(CFO & Exec VP)*
Scott P. Bruder *(CTO & Sr VP)*
Jeffrey S. Sherman *(Gen Counsel & Sr VP)*
Gary M. Cohen *(Exec VP)*
William A. Kozy *(Exec VP)*
William A. Tozzi *(Sr VP & Controller)*
Donna M. Boles *(Sr VP-HR)*
David T. Durack *(Sr VP-Corp Medical Affairs)*
Patricia B. Shrader *(Sr VP-Corp Regulatory & External Affairs)*
David W. Highet *(VP-Chief Intellectual Property Counsel & Asst Sec)*
Robert J. Singley *(VP-Sls & Mktg)*
Patricia Spinella *(Dir-IR)*
Cassie Sullivan *(Dir-Mktg)*
John Tranfaglia *(Dir-Home Health Care Products)*
Colleen White *(Dir-Corp Comm)*
Kenneth Monkowski *(Asst Treas)*
Brands & Products:
ACCU-BEEP
ACE
ACE KIDZ
BAUER & BLACK
BD
BD A-CATH
BD A-LINE
BD ACCU-GLASS
BD ACCUCELL
BD ACCUSPRAY
BD ACIDCASE
BD ACTIV 8
BD ACTIVATION ASSIST
BD ACTONE
BD ADAMS
BD ADENO-X
BD ADSYTE
BD ADVANTAGE
BD AFFIRM
BD AMPHOPACK
BD AMPLATZ
BD ANGIO-SET
BD ANGIOCATH
BD ANGIOCATH AUTOGUARD
BD ANGIOCATH-N AUTOGUARD
BD ANGIOCATH PLUS/PRO
BD APEM
BD AQUEO PREMIUM
BD ARTHRO-LOK
BD ARTHRO-TRAC
BD ASEPTA-CELL
BD ASEPTO
BD ATOMIC EDGE
BD ATTO
BD ATTOFLUOR
BD ATTOVISION
BD ATTRACTORS
BD AUTOCRIT
BD AUTOGUARD
BD AUTOGUARD-N PRO
BD AUTOGUARD PRO
BD AUTOMAGIC
BD AUTONUTRIENT
BD AUTOSCEPTOR
BD AUTOSHIELD
BD AYRE CERVI-SCRAPER
BD BACT-PLATE
BD BACTEC
BD BACTEC MGIT
BD BACTO
BD BACTROL
BD BACULOGOLD
BD BARD-PARKER
BD BAUER & BLACK PRECISION
BD BBL
BD BBL CRYSTAL
BD BBLCRYSTAL
BD BEAVER
BD BEAVER-TAIL
BD BEAVERGUARD
BD BEAWARE
BD BIO-BAG
BD BIOCOAT
BD BIOSATE
BD BITEK
BD BONNANO
BD BUSHER
BD CALIBRITE
BD CALPHOS
BD CAMPYPAK
BD CAMPYPAK PLUS
BD CAMPYPOUCH
BD CAMPYSLIDE
BD CAREFLOW
BD CARV II
BD CDT
BD CEFINASE
BD CELL
BD CELL TAK
BD CELLFIT
BD CELLFIX
BD CELLMATICS
BD CELLQUEST PRO
BD CELLWASH
BD CHAMPION
BD CHEK
BD CHG
BD CLAY ADAMS
BD CLINIJECT
BD CLONECYT
BD CLONFECTIN
BD CLONTECH PCR-SELECT
BD CMVSCAN
BD COLORPAC
BD COMPRE-KNIT
BD CONNECTA
BD CORNWALL
BD CPT
BD CREATOR
BD CRITICATH
BD CRITIFLO
BD CRITIKIT
BD CRYSTAL
BD CRYSTALSPEC
BD CSI
BD CTA MEDIUM
BD CULTURESWAB
BD CULTURETTE
BD CUSTOMEYES
BD CYCLETEST
BD CYTOFIX
BD CYTOFIX/CYTOPERM
BD CYTOPERM
BD CYTOPRINT
BD CYTORICH
BD DECISIV
BD DELTACATH
BD DESCARTEX
BD DESTRUCLIP
BD DIFCO
BD DIRECTIGEN
BD DIRECTOR
BD DISCARDIT
BD DISCARDPLUS
BD DISCOVERY
BD DISPENSTIRS
BD DISPENSTUBE
BD DRIHEP
BD DRIHEP-PLUS
BD DRYSLIDE
BD DTX
BD DTXPLUS
BD DUOVIAL
BD DURASAFE
BD DYNAC
BD E-Z CARE
BD E-Z SCRUB
BD E-Z SET
BD EASY
BD EASY SAFE
BD EASYVENT
BD ECLIPSE
BD ECOPACK
BD EDGEAHEAD
BD ELECTRACODE
BD EMPIRE
BD ENSURE-IT
BD ENTEROCOCCOSEL
BD ENTEROTUBE
BD EPICENTER
BD EPILOR
BD EPLEX
BD EUGONAGAR
BD EUGONBROTH
BD EXACTA
BD EXPRESS
BD EXTRALIGHT
BD FACS
BD FACSANALYSIS
BD FACSARIA
BD FACSARRAY
BD FACSCALIBUR
BD FACSCAN
BD FACSCANTO
BD FACSCOMP
BD FACSCOUNT
BD FACSDIVA
BD FACSERVICE
BD FACSFLOW
BD FACSORT
BD FACSTAR
BD FACSTATION
BD FACSVANTAGE
BD FALCON
BD FASTIMMUNE
BD FC BLOCK
BD FIBROMETER
BD FIBROSYSTEM
BD FIBROTIP
BD FIBROTUBE
BD FILL
BD FINGER DAB
BD FIRELIGHT
BD FIRST MIDCATH
BD FIRST PICC
BD FLOPRO
BD FLOSWITCH
BD FLUOROSENSOR
BD FLUROBLOK
BD FOCALPOINT
BD FOS
BD FUSION-BLUE
BD G-FLEX
BD GABARITH
BD GASPAK
BD GC-LECT
BD GELYSATE
BD GENEOHM
BD GENIE
BD GENTEST
BD GETTING STARTED
BD GLASPAK
BD GLIDE
BD GOLGIPLUG
BD GOLGISTOP
BD HARDPAK
BD HEMOGARD
BD H.E.R.O.
BD HORIZON
BD HUBER
BD HYCHECK
BD HYDROCATH
BD HYDROCATH ASSURE
BD HYPAK
BD HYPAK PHYSIOLIS
BD HYPAK SCF
BD HYPOINT
BD I PLATE
BD I.C.E./HEAT
BD IMAGN
BD INFLUX
BD INSTAFLASH
BD INSYTE
BD INSYTE-A
BD INSYTE AUTOGUARD
BD INSYTE AUTOGUARD-P
BD INSYTE AUTOGUARD-W
BD INSYTE-N
BD INSYTE-N AUTOGUARD
BD INSYTE-W
BD INTEGRA
BD INTERACTIV
BD INTIMA
BD INTIMA II
BD INTRACATH
BD INTRAMEDIC
BD INTROSYTE
BD INTROSYTE-N
BD INTROSYTE-N AUTOGUARD
BD IPLAB
BD ISOVITALEX
BD IV START PAK
BD JAWZONE
BD JUSTRITE
BD L-CATH
BD LABO
BD LACTINEX
BD LEUCOCOUNT
BD LEUCOGATE
BD LINK2
BD LIQUI/DRY
BD LIQUIHEP
BD LITREPAK
BD LIVING COLORS
BD LO-DOSE
BD LOGIC
BD LOK-COLLET
BD LUER-LOK
BD LYOPLATE
BD MACRO-VUE
BD MACROSORT
BD MAGNETIX
BD MAGNI-GUIDE
BD MAKE IT SAFE
BD MAPAD

Key to Media (For complete agency information see *The Advertising Red Books-Agencies* edition):
1. Bus. Publs. 2. Cable T.V. 3. Catalogs & Directories. 4. Co-op Adv. 5. Consumer Mags. 6. D.M. to Bus. Estab.7. D.M. to Consumers 8. Daily Newsp. 9. Exhibits/Trade Shows 10. Foreign 11. Infomercial 12. Internet Adv.13. Multimedia 14. Network Radio 15. Network T.V. 16. Newsp. Distr. Mags. 17. Other 18. Outdoor (Posters, Transit) 19. Point of Purchase20. Premiums, Novelties 21. Product Samples 22. Special Events Mktg. 23. Spot Radio 24. Spot T.V. 25. Weekly Newsp. 26. Yellow Page Adv.

BD MARINER
BD MARSTERS INCUBATOR
BD MATRIGEL
BD MED-SAFE
BD MEDSAVER
BD MGIT
BD MICRO-BLADE
BD MICRO-FINE
BD MICRO-SHARP
BD MICRO-UNITOME
BD MICROGARD
BD MICROLANCE
BD MICROMGIT
BD MICROPROBE
BD MICROTAINER
BD MINICATH
BD MONOLIGHT
BD MONORINSE
BD MONOSLIDE
BD MONOVIAL
BD MP READACRIT
BD MULTI-DOSER
BD MULTIFIT
BD MULTIFLO
BD MULTISET
BD MULTITEST
BD MULTIVISC
BD MYCOBACTOSEL
BD MYCOFLASK
BD MYCOPHIL
BD MYCOPREP
BD MYCOSEL
BD MYOSATE
BD NA/LE
BD NANOPLEX
BD NATRIX
BD NEOFLON
BD NEURO-SHARP
BD NEXIVA
BD NOKOR
BD NU-SERUM
BD OCUSEAL
BD OMNICOMP
BD ONCOMARK
BD ONECATH
BD OPTEIA
BD OPTI-FINE
BD OPTILUX
BD OPTIMUM
BD OPTIMUS
BD ORALPAK
BD OXI/FERM
BD P10EZ
BD P23XL
BD PAINT-A-GATE
BD PANTA
BD PARASIGHT
BD PASCO
BD PATHWAY
BD PEDS PLUS
BD PEG
BD PENJECTOR
BD PERISAFE
BD PERM/WASH
BD PERSIST
BD PERTRACH
BD PHARM LYSE
BD PHARMINGEN
BD PHOENIX
BD PHOENIX PREFERRED
BD PHYSIOJECT
BD PHYTONE
BD PLASTICAT
BD PLASTIPAK
BD PLASTIPAK PROTECT
BD PLASTISET
BD PNEUMOSLIDE
BD POCKET
BD POLAR-PREENE
BD POLYPEPTONE
BD PORT-A-CUL
BD POSIFLOW
BD POSIFLUSH
BD POWERBLOT
BD PPT
BD PRECISION
BD PRECISIONCUT
BD PRECISIONGLIDE
BD PREPSTAIN
BD PRESET
BD PREVENTIS
BD PRIMAFILL
BD PRIMARIA
BD PROBETEC
BD PROCOUNT
BD PROEX
BD PRONTO
BD PSEUDOSEL
BD PST
BD PURECOAT
BD PUREFILL
BD Q-SYTE
BD QBC
BD QBC STAR
BD QTEST
BD QUALISWAB
BD QUANTIBRITE
BD QUIKHEEL
BD READACRIT
BD READYFILL
BD READYPAK
BD RECTIC-COUNT
BD RETRO-X
BD RETROPACK
BD RFSCAN
BD RIB-BACK
BD RIBOQUANT
BD RIGHTBORE
BD RODAC
BD R.O.S.E
BD RUBASCAN
BD RX
BD SAF-T-CATH
BD SAF-T E-Z SET
BD SAF-T-INTIMA
BD SAF-T PRN
BD SAFE-CLIP
BD SAFEDRAW
BD SAFEDWELL
BD SAFEGUARD
BD SAFELON
BD SAFESTART
BD SAFETY CRADLE
BD SAFETY FLOW
BD SAFETY-GARD
BD SAFETY-HEAD
BD SAFETY-LOK
BD SAFETY-MED
BD SAFETYGLIDE
BD SAFETYLOCK
BD SAFTI
BD SANA-LOK
BD SCEPTOR
BD SCF
BD SCLEROTOME
BD SEAL-EASE
BD SECALON
BD SECALON-T
BD SEDI-15
BD SEDI-CAL
BD SEDI-STAIN
BD SEDISCAN
BD SEDISYSTEM
BD SEDITAINER
BD SEDITUBE
BD SELECT APS
BD SENSABILITY
BD SENSI-DISC
BD SENTINEL
BD SEPTI-CHEK
BD SERO-FUGE
BD SERO-LINER
BD SIMULSET
BD SIMULTEST
BD SLIDEWIZARD
BD SOLOMED
BD SOLOSHOT
BD SOLUVIA
BD SPECTRAJECT
BD SPOTTEST
BD SPRAY-CYTE
BD SSA
BD SST
BD STACKER
BD STAPHYLOSLIDE
BD STERIFILL
BD STERIFILL SCF
BD STIMEX
BD STREPTOCARD
BD STREPTOSEL
BD SUPER-WARD
BD SUPERMIX
BD SUPERSOMES
BD SURE-MED
BD SUREPATH
BD SUREPREP
BD SURESAVE
BD SURESTART
BD SWUBE
BD SYPHILIGEN
BD SYSTEO
BD T-PLUS
BD TAMPER-TUF
BD TAXO
BD TEMPAWAY
BD THIOGEL
BD THIOTONE
BD TITANIUM
BD TOUCHGUARD
BD TRANSDUCTION LABORATORIES
BD TRANSFERETTES
BD TRIAC
BD TRICHOSEL
BD TRITEST
BD TRUCOUNT
BD TRYPTICASE
BD TUFFLINK
BD TUFROL
BD TURBOSORT
BD TWINPAK
BD ULTRA-FINE
BD ULTRADEX
BD ULTRAPOOL
BD UNI-LANCE
BD UNI-PAK
BD UNIJECT
BD UNITOME
BD UNOPETTE
BD VACUTAINER
BD VALU-SET
BD VASCULON
BD VAXINET
BD VECA-C
BD VECAFIX
BD VENAGUIDE
BD VENFLON
BD VIA-PROBE
BD VIACATH
BD VIALON
BD VIGGO
BD VIPER
BD VISC
BD VISCOFLOW
BD VISIDRAIN
BD VISIDRAPE
BD VISIFLEX
BD VISIMARK
BD VISISORB
BD VISISPEAR
BD VISISWAB
BD VISITEC
BD VISITREC
BD VISIWIPE
BD VITAFLON
BD VITAFLOW
BD VITALFLON
BD VZVSCAN
BD WALLMATE
BD XCALIBER
BD XSTAR
BD YALE
BD YANKEE
BDMODEM
CAS 200
ELASTO-PREENE
FACSPREP
FOX
HYPAK
IDI
INSYTE-A
INSYTE-W
INTEGRON
I.V. START PAK
LIQUI/DRY
MICROTEST
MINI-CATH
MULTI-FLO
NAP GUARD
PLASTIPAK
PRECISE HCG
RIATRAC
SAF-T-CATH
SAFESTART
SMARTSLIP
"T" PORT
TBL
TEKZONE
TENSOR
TRU-FIT
TUFFLINK
XTR

Advertising Agencies:
GWP, Inc.
32 Park Ave
Montclair, NJ 07042
Tel.: (973) 746-0500
Fax: (973) 746-5563

Purohit Navigation
111 S Wacker Dr Ste 4700
Chicago, IL 60606-4303
Tel.: (312) 341-8100
Fax: (312) 341-8119

BEE-ALIVE INC.

7 New Lake Rd
Valley Cottage, NY 10989
Tel.: (845) 268-0960
Fax: (845) 268-3247
Toll Free: (800) 692-5445
E-mail: info@beealive.com
Web Site: www.beealive.com
Approx. Sls.: $13,300,000
Approx. Number Employees: 50
Year Founded: 1984
Business Description:
Vitamins & Minerals
S.I.C.: 5122

Key to Media (For complete agency information see *The Advertising Red Books-Agencies* edition):
1. Bus. Publs. 2. Cable T.V. 3. Catalogs & Directories. 4. Co-op Adv. 5. Consumer Mags. 6. D.M. to Bus. Estab.7. D.M. to Consumers 8. Daily Newsp. 9. Exhibits/Trade Shows 10. Foreign 11. Infomercial 12. Internet Adv.13. Multimedia 14. Network Radio 15. Network T.V. 16. Newsp. Distr. Mags. 17. Other 18. Outdoor (Posters, Transit) 19. Point of Purchase20. Premiums, Novelties 21. Product Samples 22. Special Events Mktg. 23. Spot Radio 24. Spot T.V. 25. Weekly Newsp. 26. Yellow Page Adv.

Bee-Alive Inc. — (Continued)

N.A.I.C.S.: 424210
Media: 6-8-13
Personnel:
Madeline Balletta *(Founder)*
Jason Balletta *(Pres & CEO)*
Denise Boniface *(Sr VP)*
Rae Anne Gross *(Mgr-Adv & Mktg)*
Brands & Products:
BEE-ALIVE
BEE-ALIVE BUFFERED VITAMIN C
BEE-ALIVE DEFENSE FORMULA
BEE-ALIVE FEEL GOOD FORMULA
BEE-ALIVE PICK-ME-UP
BEE-ALIVE PURE & NATURAL
BEE-ALIVE QUEEN'S NECTAR
BEE-ALIVE QUEEN'S ROYALE
BEE-ALIVE SWEET ENERGY
BEE-HAPPY PLUS
BEE-MOISTURIZED
BEESATISFIED
COUNTERTOP PERFECT CHOICE
REMEMBER WHEN
SPECIAL DELIVERY B-12 PLUS
UNDER-THE-COUNTER PERFECT CHOICE

BEECH STREET CORPORATION

(Holding of Viant Holdings, Inc.)
25500 Commercentre Dr
Lake Forest, CA 92630-8855
Tel.: (949) 672-1000
Fax: (949) 672-1111
Toll Free: (800) 233-2478
E-mail: network.operations@viant.com
Web Site: www.beechstreet.com
Sales Range: $75-99.9 Million
Approx. Number Employees: 350
Year Founded: 1951
Business Description:
Health Care Industry Network Management & Payment Services
S.I.C.: 7389; 6411
N.A.I.C.S.: 561499; 524298
Media: 5-10
Personnel:
Daniel J. Thomas *(CEO-Viant Inc)*
Dana Cronin *(Coord-Mktg)*

BELLUS HEALTH INC.

275 Armand-Frappier Blvd
Laval, QC H7V 4A7, Canada
Tel.: (450) 680-4500
Fax: (450) 680-4501
E-mail: ir@bellushealth.com
Web Site: www.bellushealth.com
Approx. Rev.: $2,453,319
Approx. Number Employees: 10
Year Founded: 1993
Business Description:
Biopharmaceutical Drugs for Central Nervous System Disorders
S.I.C.: 2834; 2836
N.A.I.C.S.: 325412; 325414
Media: 2-10-11
Personnel:
Francesco Bellini *(Chm)*
Charles Cavell *(Deputy Chm)*
Roberto Bellini *(Pres & CEO)*
David Skinner *(Gen Counsel, Sec & VP)*
Denis Garceau *(Sr VP-Drug Dev)*
Francois Desjardins *(VP-Fin)*
Brands & Products:
ALZHEMED
BELLUS HEALTH
CEREBRIL
FIBRILLEX
VIVIMIND
Advertising Agency:
NATIONAL Public Relations
140 Grande Allee Est Ste 302
Quebec, QC G1R 5M8, Canada
Tel.: (418) 648-1233
Fax: (418) 648-0494

BELTONE ELECTRONICS LLC

(Sub. of GN ReSound A/S)
2601 Patriot Blvd
Glenview, IL 60026
Tel.: (773) 583-3600
Fax: (773) 583-3980
Toll Free: (800) BELTONE
Web Site: www.beltone.com
Approx. Number Employees: 500
Year Founded: 1940
Business Description:
Hearing Aids Mfr
S.I.C.: 3845; 5047
N.A.I.C.S.: 334510; 423450
Advertising Expenditures: $7,500,000
Media: 1-2-3-4-5-6-7-8-9-10-13-15-16-19-20-21-23-24-25-26
Distr.: Intl.; Natl.
Budget Set: Nov.
Personnel:
Todd Murray *(Pres)*
Barb Van Someren *(VP-Mktg)*
John Cariola *(Dir-Product Mgmt)*
Brands & Products:
ACCESS
ARCA
BELCARE
CLEAR VOICE
COMPOSER
COMPOSER 2000
CORUS
CSP 11
D61
D71
EDGE
INVISA
LINQ
MIRA
ODE
ONE!
OPERA
OPTIMA
OTOSONIC
PETITE
PETITE PLUS
PROFILE
SELECTAFIT
TRIO
ULTIMA 80
VOICE ENHANCER
Advertising Agencies:
Euro RSCG Worldwide
36 E Grand Ave
Chicago, IL 60611-3506
Tel.: (312) 337-4400
Fax: (312) 337-5930
Fax: (312) 337-2316

Topin & Associates, Inc.
205 N Michigan Ave Ste 2315
Chicago, IL 60601-5923
Tel.: (312) 645-0100
Fax: (312) 645-0120

BETH ABRAHAM HEALTH SERVICES INC.

612 Allerton Ave
Bronx, NY 10467-7404
Tel.: (718) 547-5609
Fax: (718) 519-4230
Toll Free: (888) BETH-ABE
E-mail: info@bethabe.org
Web Site: www.bethabe.org
Approx. Number Employees: 973
Year Founded: 1920
Business Description:
Healthcare Services
S.I.C.: 8059; 8351
N.A.I.C.S.: 623110; 624410
Import Export
Media: 2-7-8-10-18-20-21-22-25-26
Personnel:
Michael S. Fassler *(Pres & CEO)*
Stephen Mann *(CFO & Sr VP)*
Paul Rosenfeld *(Sr VP, COO-Long-Term Care)*
Connie Tejeda *(VP-Mktg & Pub Affairs)*
Concetta Tomaino *(Exec Dir)*
Benedikte Scheiby *(Adjunct Professor, Dir-Muic therapy Trng & Supervision)*
Sandra Selikson *(Dir-Medical)*

BEUTLICH PHARMACEUTICALS LP

1541 S Shields Dr
Waukegan, IL 60085-8304
Tel.: (847) 473-1100
Fax: (847) 473-1122
Toll Free: (800) 238-8542
E-mail: info@beutlich.com
Web Site: www.beutlich.com
E-Mail For Key Personnel:
President: fjbeutlich@beutlich.com
Marketing Director: rrosenberg@beutlich.com
Sales Director: aharmon@beutlich.com
Approx. Number Employees: 25
Year Founded: 1954
Business Description:
Pharmaceutical Products
S.I.C.: 2834
N.A.I.C.S.: 325412
Import Export
Media: 1-2-3-4-7-10-13-21
Distr.: Direct to Consumer; Intl.; Natl.
Budget Set: Aug.
Personnel:
Ron Rosenberg *(Office Mgr-Adv & Mktg)*
David Clinard *(Mgr-Sls)*
Catherine Gordon *(Direct Mktg & Direct Response Mgr)*
Brands & Products:
BEAUTLICH
CEO-TWO
DISCLOSE
HURRICANE
HURRISEAL
HURRIVIEW
PERIDIN-C

BIO-LOGIC SYSTEMS CORP.

(Sub. of Natus Medical Incorporated)
1 Bio Logic Plz
Mundelein, IL 60060-3708
Tel.: (847) 949-5200
Fax: (847) 949-8615
Toll Free: (800) 323-8326
Web Site: www.blsc.com
Sales Range: $25-49.9 Million
Approx. Number Employees: 124
Year Founded: 1979
Business Description:
Developer & Mfr of Hearing Screening & Diagnostic Products, Brain Activity Analysis Instruments & Sleep Diagnostic Products
S.I.C.: 3845; 3826; 3841
N.A.I.C.S.: 334510; 334516; 339112
Import Export
Media: 2-6-7-8-10
Brands & Products:
ABAER
AUDX
BIO-LOGIC
CEEGRAPH
CEEGRAPH NETLINK
M.A.S.T.E.R.
NAVIGATOR
NETLINK TRAVELER
SLEEPSCAN
SMARTPACK

BIO-PATH HOLDINGS, INC.

3293 Harrison Blvd Ste 220
Ogden, UT 84403
Tel.: (801) 399-5500
Web Site: www.biopathholdings.com
Approx. Rev.: $245,781
Approx. Number Employees: 2
Year Founded: 2007
Business Description:
Pharmaceutical Developer & Mfr
S.I.C.: 2834
N.A.I.C.S.: 325412
Advertising Expenditures: $983,000
Personnel:
Peter Nielsen *(Chm, Pres, CEO, CFO & Treas)*
Ana Maria Tari *(Dir-Preclinical Ops & Res)*

BIO-RAD LABORATORIES, INC.

1000 Alfred Nobel Dr
Hercules, CA 94547-1811
Tel.: (510) 724-7000
Fax: (510) 741-5815
Toll Free: (800) 424-6723
E-mail: investor_relations@bio-rad.com
Web Site: www.bio-rad.com
Approx. Sls.: $1,927,118,000
Approx. Number Employees: 6,880
Year Founded: 1952
Business Description:
Specialty Chemicals for Research & Related Instrumentation; Clinical Diagnostic Products, Test Kits, Complete Systems & Instrumentation; Analytical & Biomedical Instrumentation & Spectral Library Services
S.I.C.: 3826; 2899; 3841
N.A.I.C.S.: 334516; 325998; 339112
Import Export
Media: 2-4-7-10-13
Personnel:
David Schwartz *(Chm)*
Norman D. Schwartz *(Pres & CEO)*
Christine A. Tsingos *(CFO & VP)*
Sanford S. Wadler *(Gen Counsel, Sec & VP)*
Giovanni Magni *(VP & Mgr-Intl Sls)*
Tina Cuccia *(Mgr-Corp Comm)*
Brands & Products:
1-D ANALYST
2-D ANALYST

Key to Media (For complete agency information see *The Advertising Red Books-Agencies* edition):
1. Bus. Publs. 2. Cable T.V. 3. Catalogs & Directories. 4. Co-op Adv. 5. Consumer Mags. 6. D.M. to Bus. Estab.7. D.M. to Consumers 8. Daily Newsp. 9. Exhibits/Trade Shows 10. Foreign 11. Infomercial 12. Internet Adv.13. Multimedia 14. Network Radio 15. Network T.V. 16. Newsp. Distr. Mags. 17. Other 18. Outdoor (Posters, Transit) 19. Point of Purchase20. Premiums, Novelties 21. Product Samples 22. Special Events Mktg. 23. Spot Radio 24. Spot T.V. 25. Weekly Newsp. 26. Yellow Page Adv.

2-D DOCTOR
3D VIEWIT
ACCLAIM
AFFI-GEL
AFFI-PREP
AG
ALLERCOAT
ALPHA
ALPHA-PROBE
AMINEX
AMPLICHEK
AMPLICLEAR
AMPLIGHT
AMPLIPROBE
AMPLISIZE
AMPLITEK
AMPLITROL
ANALYZEIT
ANYGEL
AQUAPURE
ASSIGNIT
AURUM
AUTOIMMUNE ATLAS
AUTOPREP
AUXACOLOR
BACKTRACKER
BENCHMARK
BETHA GENE
BIO-BEADS
BIO-DIMENSION
BIO-DOT
BIO-GEL
BIO-ICE
BIO-LYTE
BIO-MARK
BIO-PLEX
BIO-PLEX MANAGER
BIO-PLEX PRECISION PRO
BIO-PLEX PRO
BIO-PLEX UNIVERSITY
BIO-PREP
BIO RAD
BIO-RAD & THE BIO-RAD LOGO
BIO-RAD EASYPACK
BIO-RAD GELTEC
BIO-RAD INPLACE
BIO-RAD MAINFRAME
BIO-RAD OCS
BIO-RAD PLUS
BIO-RAD UBZ
BIO-REX
BIO-SAFE
BIO-SCALE
BIO-SIL
BIO-SILECT
BIO-SPIN
BIOCAP
BIOFOCUS
BIOFRAC
BIOLOGIC
BIOLOGIC DUOFLOW
BIOLOGIC DUOFLOW MAXIMIZER
BIOLOGIC DUOFLOW PATHFINDER
BIOLOGIC DUOFLOW QUADTEC
BIOLOGIC LP DATA VIEW
BIOLOGIC MAXIMIZER
BIOLOGIC QUADTEC
BIOMARKER PATTERNS
BIOODYSSEY
BIOPLEX
BIOSUPPORT
BIOTECHNOLOGY EXPLORER
BIOTIN-BLOT
BROWSEIT
BST
C-MAX
C/P LIFT
C1000
C1000 MANAGER
CALLIGRAPHER
CANDISELECT
CAPCELLIA
CARTOGRAPHER
CDM
CERTIFIED
CFT
CFX MANAGER
CFX384
CFX96
CHECKMARK
CHEF-DR
CHEF MAPPER
CHELEX
CHEMIDOC
CHEMWINDOW
CHILL-OUT
CHLAMYDIAPROBE
CHROMO4
CHT
CLEANBOX
CLEANCUT
CLEARSPIN
CLEARVAC
CLONIS
CODA
CODA OP/DM
COMPAREIT
COMPLIANCE
CONCERTINO
CONCERTO
CONCORD
CONFIRM
COSFECTIN
COTUBE
CRIME SCENE INVESTIGATOR PCR BASICS
CRITERION
CRITERION STAIN FREE
CRYPTOTROL
CSN
CUBED SOLUTIONS
CYTOFECTENE
D-10
D GENE
DC
DCODE
DE-EXPOSE
DECILAB
DECISCAN
DEEP PROTEOME
DIAMAT
DIASTAT
DIGISHAKER
DIRECT CONNECT
DISCIPLE DESKTOP
THE DISCOVERY SERIES
DISK-VAC
DIVERSITY DATABASE
DNA ENGINE
DNA ENGINE DYAD
DNA ENGINE OPTICON
DNA ENGINE TETRAD
DNACODE
DODECA
DRAWIT
DUAL ALPHA
DYAD
DYAD DISCIPLE
DYNALOOP
E. COLI PULSER
EASY CAP
EASYPACK
EASYSHOCK
ECONO
ECONO-COLUMN
ECONO-PAC
EFLEX
ELAVIA
ELISA IMMUNO EXPLORER
ELITE
ENGINE DRIVER
ENVIROPAK
EP-MAX
EQAS
EQUALIZER
EVOLIS
EXPERION
EXQUEST
EZ LOAD
EZ MICRO
EZ RULES
EZ RUNS
EZLOGIC
FAST BLAST
FIGE MAPPER
FINGERPRINTING
FINGERPRINTING II INFORMATIX
FINGERPRINTING PLUS
FLAMINGO
FLAT BLOCK
FLEXI-SPOT
FLUOPLATE
FLUOR-S
FLUOR-S MAX
FLUOR-S MAX2
FLUORACE
FLUOROGUARD
FONGISCREEN
FPQUEST
FRAGPACK
FRAME-SEAL
FREEZE 'N SQUEEZE
FUNGISCREEN
FUNGITEST
GAP
GEL DOC
GELAIR
GELTEC
GENE CYCLER
GENE-LITE
GENE PULSER
GENE PULSER MXCELL
GENE PULSER XCELL
GENECOMB
GENEDIA
GENEDIA MIXT
GENEGAZER
GENELAVIA
GENEPATH
GENES IN A BOTTLE
GENESHOT
GENETIC SYSTEMS
GENIE
GENSCREEN
GLYCO DOC
GLYCOBLOT
GLYCOCHROM
GLYCOSAL
GMO INVESTIGATOR
GOLDCOAT
GONOPROBE
GOODLOOK
GOT PROTEIN?
GS-800
GS GENE LINKER
GS GENE PREP
HANDS FREE QC
HARD-SHELL
HAVEITALL
HB ADVISOR
HEKFECTIN
HELIOS
HELISAL
HEMAVISION
HEMOS
HEPTA
HI-PORE
HOT BONNET
HYB-SEAL
HYDROTECH
ICYCLER
ICYCLER IQ
IDQUEST
IMAGE LAB
IMARK
IMMUN-BLOT
IMMUN-LITE
IMMUN-STAR WESTERNC
IMMUNOWASH
IN2IT
INFOQUEST
INFRASCAN
INPLACE
INSTAGENE
INSTANT
INSTANT INCUBATION
INSTANTQC
INTEGRA
INTELLIBUCKET
IONIS
IPROOF
IPURE
IQ
IQ-CHECK
IQC
IR MENTOR PRO
ISCRIPT
ISPOT
ITAQ
KALEIDOSCOPE
KALLESTAD
KBB
KETOCHROME
KILOBASEPACK
KINESIS
KINETIC COLLECTOR
KNOWITALL
KNOWITALL ANYWARE
KNOWITALL QUICKSEARCH
LAB-IN-A-BOX
LABTOOLS
LINEARITY WEB
LIQUICHEK
LP DATA VIEW
LUMI
LUMIDOC
LUMIMARK
LUMIMARK PLUS
LYPHLINE
LYPHOCHEK
MACMELT
MACRO-PREP
MAINFRAME
MAPS
MASTER BLASTER
MCP
MDMS
MDX
METER TRAX
MICRO BIO-SPIN
MICRO-GUARD
MICROMAT
MICROPLATE MANAGER
MICROPULSER
MICROROTOFOR
MICROSEAL
MICROTECH
MINEIT

Key to Media (For complete agency information see *The Advertising Red Books-Agencies* edition):
1. Bus. Publs. 2. Cable T.V. 3. Catalogs & Directories. 4. Co-op Adv. 5. Consumer Mags. 6. D.M. to Bus. Estab.7. D.M. to Consumers
8. Daily Newsp. 9. Exhibits/Trade Shows 10. Foreign 11. Infomercial 12. Internet Adv.13. Multimedia 14. Network Radio
15. Network T.V. 16. Newsp. Distr. Mags. 17. Other 18. Outdoor (Posters, Transit) 19. Point of Purchase20. Premiums, Novelties
21. Product Samples 22. Special Events Mktg. 23. Spot Radio 24. Spot T.V. 25. Weekly Newsp. 26. Yellow Page Adv.

Bio-Rad Laboratories, Inc. — (Continued)

MINI-PROTEAN
MINI-SUB
MINI TRANS-BLOT
MINICYCLER
MINIOPTICON
MJ MINI
MJ MODULE
MJ RESEARCH & THE MJ RESEARCH LOGO
MOLECULAR ANALYST
MOLECULAR IMAGER
MOLECULAR IMAGER FX
MONO-POLY
MONOBRYTE
MONOFLUO
MONOFLUOSCREEN
MONOLISA
MOTO ALPHA
MOUSE TYPER
MRSASELECT
MULTI-ANALYST
MULTI-MIX
MULTIPLATE
MULTIQUAL
MULTISPOT
MUMZ
MUTA-GENE
MYCOPLASMA DUO
MYCYCLER
MYIQ
NAMEIT
NEOCHEK
NEOWASH 1575
NOVABLOT
NOVABLOT II
NOVABLOT VI
NOVAPATH
OCS
ONE-SHOT KINETICS
OPEN CHANNEL
OPTI-4CN
OPTICON
OPTICON MONITOR
OPTIMIZEIT
OSIRIS
OSIRIS EVOLUTION
OSK
OSTEOSAL
PASTOREX
PATHFINDER
PATTERN PLUS AUDITOR
PCR KLEEN
PDQUEST
PDS-1000/HE
THE PEOPLE BEHIND THE SCIENCE
PERSONAL MOLECULAR IMAGER
PERSONAL MOLECULAR IMAGER FX
PGLO
PHARMALYZIR
PHAROS
PHAROSFX
PHD
PHOSPHOR ANALYST
PLATE LIBRARIAN
PLATELIA
PLATELIA PASTEUR
PMI
PNEUMALL
PNEUMOTROL
POLY-PREP
POWER BONNET
POWERPAC
PRECESS 24
PRECESS 48
PRECISION MELT ANALYSIS
PRECISION PLUS PROTEIN WESTERNC
PRECISION PRO
PRECISION PROTEIN
PREDICTIT
PREP-A-GENE
PREP-DISC
PROBELIA
PROCEED
PROCESSION
PROCESSIT
PROFILEIT
PROFINIA
PROFINITY
PROFINITY EXACT
PROT/ELEC
PROTEAN
PROTEINCHIP
PROTEOMEWORKS
PROTEOMINER
PROTEOMWEAVER
PROTEON
PROTEON MANAGER
PTC-100
PULSETRAC
PULSEWAVE
PUREZOL
PYLORITROL
PYXIS 24
QC ONCALL
QC VALIDATOR
QCNET
QCS
QUANTAFLUOR
QUANTAPHASE
QUANTASE
QUANTIFY
QUANTIMUNE
QUANTITY ONE
QUANTUM PREP
QUICK START
RADIANT
RADIAS
RAISE
RAPID'E.COLI 2
RAPID'L.MONO
RC DC
READY GEL
READYAGAROSE
READYPREP
READYSTRIP
READYSUB-CELL
REAL TIME QA
REAL TIME QC
REFINEIT
REMEDI HS
REMOTE ALPHA DOCK
REPORTIT
RIBOLYSER
ROTOFOR
ROTOLYTE
RTQC DATA CONVERTER
RTQC DATA MANAGER
RTQC WEB
RTS 2000
S1000
SADTLER
SCANGEL
SCANPREP'S
SCIPION
SCREEN-GUARD
SEARCHIT
SEARCHMASTER
SECRETS OF THE RAINFOREST
SELF-SEAL
SEQUE/PRO
SEQUEAKY KLEEN
SEQUI-BLOT
SEQUI-GEN
SFD
SFD HIV 1/2 PA
SHOCKPOD
SILENTFECT
SILENTMER
SILVER STAIN PLUS
SIMPLICITY THROUGH INNOVATION
SLIDE CHAMBERS
SLIDE GRIDDLE
SMARTSPEC
SNP MANAGER
SOFT-START
SOFTCONNECT
SOLUTIONS
SONATA
SOURCESELECT
SP*ACE
SPECFINDER
SPECTRABASE
SPECTRAL SEARCHING MADE EASY
SPOTMAPPER
SSOFAST
STAPH-PLUS
STAT FAX
STAT ONE
SUB-CELL
SYMAPPS
SYPHILAM
SYPHILIA
TESEE
TESEE PRECESS 24
TESEE PRECESS 48
TETRAD
TITERTUBE
TOX/SEE
TRACER
TRANS-BLOT
TRANSCLONE
TRANSFECTIN
TRUVIEW
TURNKEY QC
UBZ
ULTRAMARK
ULTRAROCKER
UNITY
UNITY DESKTOP
UNITY PC
UNITY PLUS
UNITY PLUS/PRO
UNITY POST
UNITY PRO
UNITY REAL TIME
UNITY WEB
UNO
UNOSPHERE
UNOSPHERE SUPRA
URISELECT
UV GEL BED
VALIDATEIT
VALUECHROM
VARIANT
VARIANT EXPRESS
VARIANT II
VARIANT ONLINE LIBRARY
VDMS 2000
VERIFICATION PROBE
VERSADOC
VERSAFLUOR
VERSARRAY
VERSARRAY CHIPREADER
VIROCLEAR
VIROCLEAR MUMZ
VIRODETECT
VIROTROL
WEBCONNECT
WESTERNC
WESTGARD ADVISOR
WINBRYTE
WINMELT
WORKSBASE
X-PLEX
XCITABLUE
XCLUDA
XENOWORKS
XMARK
XPR
YOGURTNESS
ZETA-PROBE

BIOCLINICA, INC.

826 Newtown-Yardley Rd
Newtown, PA 18940-1721
Tel.: (267) 757-3000
Fax: (267) 757-3353
Toll Free: (800) 748-9032
E-mail: general@bioclinica.com
Web Site: www.bioclinica.com
Approx. Rev.: $75,188,000
Approx. Number Employees: 475
Business Description:
Contract Pharmaceutical Product Development Services
S.I.C.: 0742; 8071
N.A.I.C.S.: 541940; 621511
Export
Media: 2-7-10
Personnel:
David E. Nowicki *(Chm)*
Mark L. Weinstein *(Pres & CEO)*
Ted I. Kaminer *(CFO, Exec VP-Fin & Admin)*
Garry D. Johnson *(CTO & Sr VP)*
Peter S. Benton *(Pres-eClinical Div & Exec VP)*
David A. Pitler *(Pres-Bioimaging Svcs & Exec VP)*
Colin G. Miller *(Sr VP-Medical Affairs)*
James M. Dorsey *(VP-Mktg)*
Mark Endres *(VP-Sls)*
Robert S. Sammis *(VP-Fin-eClinical Div)*
Andrzej Dzik-Jurasz *(Sr Dir-Medical Affairs)*
Brands & Products:
BIO-IMAGING TECHNOLOGIES INC
BIOTRACK
CAMR

BIOFORM MEDICAL, INC.
(Name Changed to Merz Aesthetics)

BIOHORIZONS, INC.

2300 Riverchase Ctr
Birmingham, AL 35244
Tel.: (205) 967-7880
Fax: (205) 870-0304
E-mail: customercare@biohorizons.com
Web Site: www.biohorizons.com
Approx. Rev.: $69,038,000
Approx. Number Employees: 244
Business Description:
Dental Implant Device Mfr & Marketer
S.I.C.: 3843; 5047
N.A.I.C.S.: 339114; 423450
Advertising Expenditures: $882,000
Personnel:
Mortimer Berkowitz, III *(Chm)*
R. Steven Boggan *(Pres & CEO)*
David A. Wall *(CFO & Exec VP)*

Key to Media (For complete agency information see *The Advertising Red Books-Agencies* edition):
1. Bus. Publs. 2. Cable T.V. 3. Catalogs & Directories. 4. Co-op Adv. 5. Consumer Mags. 6. D.M. to Bus. Estab.7. D.M. to Consumers
8. Daily Newsp. 9. Exhibits/Trade Shows 10. Foreign 11. Infomercial 12. Internet Adv.13. Multimedia 14. Network Radio
15. Network T.V. 16. Newsp. Distr. Mags. 17. Other 18. Outdoor (Posters, Transit) 19. Point of Purchase20. Premiums, Novelties
21. Product Samples 22. Special Events Mktg. 23. Spot Radio 24. Spot T.V. 25. Weekly Newsp. 26. Yellow Page Adv.

J. Todd Strong *(COO)*
Kendyl D. Lowe *(Chief Acctg Officer & Sr VP)*
David P. Dutil *(Gen Counsel)*
Clark M. Barousse *(Sr VP-Global Sls & Mktg)*

BIOJECT MEDICAL TECHNOLOGIES INC.

20245 SW 95th Ave
Tualatin, OR 97062
Tel.: (503) 692-8001
Fax: (503) 692-6698
Toll Free: (800) 683-7221
E-mail: corporate@bioject.com
Web Site: www.bioject.com
Approx. Rev.: $5,577,441
Approx. Number Employees: 33
Year Founded: 1985
Business Description:
Needle-Free Injection Systems Developer
S.I.C.: 3841
N.A.I.C.S.: 339112
Media: 2-7-10
Personnel:
Albert Hansen *(Chm)*
Ralph Makar *(Pres & CEO)*
Richard Stout *(Chief Medical Officer & Exec VP)*
Christine Farrell *(VP-Fin & Admin)*
Brands & Products:
BIOJECT
BIOJECTOR
COOL.CLICK
CRYSTAL CHECK
SEROJET
VITAJET
ZETAJET
Advertising Agency:
MarketShare
136 Ridge Dr
Montville, NJ 07045
Tel.: (973) 299-8001
Fax: (973) 299-8033

BIOLASE TECHNOLOGY, INC.

4 Cromwell
Irvine, CA 92618
Tel.: (949) 361-1200
Fax: (949) 361-0204
Toll Free: (888) 4-BIOLASE
E-mail: dentists@biolase.com
Web Site: www.biolase.com
Approx. Rev.: $26,225,000
Approx. Number Employees: 145
Year Founded: 1994
Business Description:
Mfr. of Laser-Based Aesthetic, Dental & Surgical Products
S.I.C.: 3843; 5999
N.A.I.C.S.: 339114; 446199
Import Export
Advertising Expenditures: $610,000
Media: 1-2-4-5-7-8-10-13-18-19-20-21-22-23-24-26
Personnel:
Federico Pignatelli *(Chm & CEO)*
Frederick D. Furry *(CFO)*
Dmitri Boutoussov *(VP-Engrg)*
Richard Whipp *(Dir-Ops)*
Brands & Products:
BIOLASE
DIOLASEPLUS
EZLASE
HYDROKINETIC
HYDROPHOTONICS
LASERSMILE
WATERLASE
WATERLASE C100
WATERLASE DENTISTRY
WATERLASE MD
WATERLASE MD GOLD
WATERLASE MD TURBO

BIOLEX THERAPEUTICS, INC.

158 Cradle St
Pittsboro, NC 27312
Tel.: (919) 542-9901
Fax: (919) 542-9910
E-mail: info@biolex.com
Web Site: www.biolex.com
Sales Range: $1-9.9 Million
Approx. Number Employees: 105
Business Description:
Clinical-Stage Biopharmaceutical Developer, Researcher & Mfr
S.I.C.: 8733; 2834; 2836
N.A.I.C.S.: 541710; 325412; 325414
Media: 2-7-10
Personnel:
Kurt Graves *(Chm)*
Jan Turek *(Pres & CEO)*
Dale Sander *(CFO & Sr VP-Fin)*
David Spencer *(COO & Sr VP-R&D)*
Bipin Dalmia *(Sr VP-Bus Dev & Intellectual Property)*
Glen Williams *(Sr VP-Ops)*
Brands & Products:
LEX SYSTEM
LOCTERON

BIOMERICA, INC.

17571 Von Karman Ave
Irvine, CA 92614
Tel.: (949) 645-2111
Fax: (949) 553-1231
Toll Free: (800) 854-3002
E-mail: bmra@biomerica.com
Web Site: www.biomerica.com
Approx. Sls.: $4,899,375
Approx. Number Employees: 27
Year Founded: 1976
Business Description:
Medical Diagnostic Test Kits
S.I.C.: 2835; 2834; 3843
N.A.I.C.S.: 325413; 325412; 339114
Import Export
Advertising Expenditures: $57,000
Media: 3-4-5-6-7-10-11-13-23-24-25
Distr.: Direct to Consumer; Natl.
Personnel:
Zackary S. Irani *(CEO)*
Janet Moore *(CFO & Sec)*
Brands & Products:
ALLERQUANT
AWARE
BIOMERICA
CANDIGEN
CANDIQUANT
EZ DETECT
EZ-HCG
EZ-HP
EZ-LH
EZ-PSA
FORTEL
GAP
ISLETEST
NIMBUS

BIOMET, INC.

56 E Bell Dr
Warsaw, IN 46582
Mailing Address:
PO Box 587
Warsaw, IN 46581-0587
Tel.: (574) 267-6639
Fax: (574) 267-8137
Web Site: www.biomet.com
Approx. Sls.: $2,698,000,000
Approx. Number Employees: 3,453
Year Founded: 1977
Business Description:
Holding Company; Orthopedic & Musculoskeletal Medical Device Designer, Mfr & Distr; Owned 23.76% by KKR & Co. L.P., 23.2% by The Blackstone Group L.P., 23.2% by The Goldman Sachs Group, Inc. & 23.2% by TPG Capital
S.I.C.: 6719; 3841; 3842; 3845; 5047
N.A.I.C.S.: 551112; 334510; 339112; 339113; 423450
Export
Advertising Expenditures: $9,300,000
Media: 1-2-8-10-14-15-17-18-22
Distr.: Direct to Consumer; Natl.
Budget Set: June
Personnel:
Jeffrey R. Binder *(Pres & CEO)*
Daniel P. Florin *(CFO & Sr VP)*
Gregory W. Sasso *(Pres-Ops-Biomet SBU & Sr VP)*
Stuart G. Kleopfer *(Pres-Biomet Biologics)*
Bradley J. Tandy *(Gen Counsel, Sec & Sr VP)*
Margaret L. Anderson *(Sr VP)*
Robin T. Barney *(Sr VP-Ops-Worldwide)*
Robert E. Durgin *(Sr VP-Quality, Clinical & Regulatory Affairs)*
Glen A. Kashuba *(Sr VP)*
Jon C. Serbousek *(Sr VP)*
Peggy Taylor *(Sr VP-HR)*
Renaat Vermeulen *(Sr VP)*
William C. Kolter *(Corp VP-Pub Affairs, Govt Affairs & Corp Comm)*
Andrew Holst *(Dir-Mktg, Biomet Sports Medicine)*
Seth Nash *(Dir-Mktg of Hips, Extremeties, Bone Cement & Trauma)*
Brands & Products:
ADVANCED SCIENCE FOR REAL LIVING
AGC TOTAL KNEE SYSTEM
ANSWER HIP SYSTEM
ASCENT REVISION KNEE SYSTEM
BALANCE HIP SYSTEM
BI-METRIC HIP SYSTEM
BIO-MODULAR
BIOGROOVE
BIOMET
BIOMOORE
BIOMOORE HIP SYSTEM
CALCIGEN
DISCOVERY
ENDO
EXACT HIP INSTRUMENTATION
FINN REVISION KNEE SYSTEM
FREEDOM HIP SYSTEM
GENUS UNICONDYLAR KNEE SYSTEM
HEALEY
HIP FRACTURE HIP SYSTEM
IMPACT
INTEGRAL
INTEGRAL HIP SYSTEM
INTERLOK
INTRIGUE HIP SYSTEM
M2A-38 ACETABULAR
M2A ACETABULAR
M2A-TAPER ACETABULAR
MAGNUM
MALLORY-HEAD
MALLORY HEAD HIP SYSTEM
MAX-ROM HIP SYSTEM
MAXIM REVISION KNEE SYSTEM
MCLAUGHLIN
MICROPLASTY MINIMALLY INVASIVE PROGRAM
ORTHOPAEDIC AVENUE
OSTEOCAP
OSTEOCAP RS HIP SYSTEM
OXFORD
PAR 5
PLR HIP SYSTEM
PROGRESSIVE
PROGRESSIVE HIP SYSTEM
QSAC ACETABULAR
RADIAL ACETABULAR
RANAWAT-BURSTEIN HIP SYSTEM
REACH
REACH HIP SYSTEM
RECAP
RECOVERY PROTRUSIO CAGE
REPICCI
REPICCI II UNICONDYLAR KNEE SYSTEM
RINGLOC ACETABULAR
RX-90 HIP SYSTEM
STANMORE
STANMORE HIP SYSTEM
T1 REVISION KNEE SYSTEM
TAPER
TAPERLOC
TAPERLOC HIP SYSTEM
TRADITION
TRI-SPIKE ACETABULAR
UNIVERSAL ACETABULAR
VANGUARD
VISION HIP SYSTEM
Advertising Agency:
B.J. Thompson Associates, Inc.
1415 Lincoln Way W Ste H
Osceola, IN 46561
Tel.: (574) 674-6300
Fax: (574) 674-6802

BIOSCRIP, INC.

100 Clearbrook Rd
Elmsford, NY 10523
Tel.: (914) 460-1600
Fax: (914) 460-1660
Toll Free: (800) 677-4323
E-mail: corporate@bioscrip.com
Web Site: www.bioscrip.com
E-Mail For Key Personnel:
Marketing Director: marketing@bioscrip.com
Public Relations: pr@bioscrip.com
Approx. Rev.: $1,638,623,000
Approx. Number Employees: 2,281
Year Founded: 2004
Business Description:
Holding Company; Community Pharmacies, Pharmacy Benefit Management, Specialty Infusion Therapy & Mail-Order Fulfillment Services
S.I.C.: 6719; 5122; 5912; 5961; 7389; 8082
N.A.I.C.S.: 551112; 424210; 446110; 454113; 561499; 621610
Media: 10
Personnel:
Richard H. Friedman *(Chm)*
Richard M. Smith *(Pres & CEO)*
Mary Jane Graves *(Interim CFO & Treas)*

Key to Media (For complete agency information see *The Advertising Red Books-Agencies* edition):
1. Bus. Publs. 2. Cable T.V. 3. Catalogs & Directories. 4. Co-op Adv. 5. Consumer Mags. 6. D.M. to Bus. Estab.7. D.M. to Consumers
8. Daily Newsp. 9. Exhibits/Trade Shows 10. Foreign 11. Infomercial 12. Internet Adv.13. Multimedia 14. Network Radio
15. Network T.V. 16. Newsp. Distr. Mags. 17. Other 18. Outdoor (Posters, Transit) 19. Point of Purchase20. Premiums, Novelties
21. Product Samples 22. Special Events Mktg. 23. Spot Radio 24. Spot T.V. 25. Weekly Newsp. 26. Yellow Page Adv.

BioScrip, Inc. — (Continued)

Douglas A. Lee *(CIO)*
Patricia Bogusz *(Chief Acctg Officer & VP-Fin)*
Barbara Cormier *(Chief Complaince Officer)*
Barry A. Posner *(Gen Counsel & Exec VP)*
Alfred Carfora *(Exec VP-Mail & PBM Svcs)*
Stephen B. Cichy *(Exec VP)*
Robert F. Roose *(Chief Procurement Officer & Exec VP)*
David J. Evans *(Sr VP-Strateic ops)*
Scott W. Friedman *(Sr VP-Trade Rels & Bus Dev)*
Colleen M. Lederer *(Sr VP-Home Heatlh Svcs)*
Lisa Nadler *(Sr VP-HR)*
Nitin J. Patel *(Sr VP-Clinical Svcs)*
Vto Ponzio, Jr. *(Sr VP-Community Pharmacy Ops)*
Michael A Saracco *(Sr VP-Natl Sls)*
Joseph Smith *(Sr VP-Infusion & AIC Svcs)*
Randi Abramowitz *(VP-Oncology & Hospital Programs)*
Advertising Agency:
Joele Frank, Wilkinson Brimmer Katcher
140 E 45th St 37th Fl
New York, NY 10017
Tel.: (212) 355-4449
Fax: (212) 355-4554

BIOSITE INCORPORATED
(Sub. of ALERE INC.)
9975 Summers Ridge Rd
San Diego, CA 92121-1205
Tel.: (858) 805-4808
Tel.: (858) 805-2000
Fax: (858) 805-4815
Toll Free: (888) BIOSITE
Web Site: www.biosite.com
Approx. Rev.: $308,592,000
Approx. Number Employees: 883
Year Founded: 1988
Business Description:
Medical Diagnostic Products Designer & Mfr
S.I.C.: 3841
N.A.I.C.S.: 339112
Media: 2-10
Personnel:
Robert Anacone *(Sr VP-Mktg & Sls-Worldwide)*
Christopher R. Hibberd *(Sr VP-Corp Dev)*
Gunars E. Valkirs *(Sr VP-Biosite Discovery)*
Thomas G. Blassey *(VP-Sls-US)*
Brands & Products:
BECKMAN COULTER
ENCOMPASS
NEW DIMENSIONS IN DIAGNOSIS
TRIAGE
TRIAGE BNP TESTS
TRIAGE CARDIAC PANEL
TRIAGE CARDIAC SYSTEM
TRIAGE CARDIOPROFILER
TRIAGE CENSUS
TRIAGE METER
TRIAGE PROFILER SHORTNESS OF BREATH PANEL
TRIAGE TOX DRUG SCREEN

BIOTECH CORPORATION
107 Oakwood Dr
Glastonbury, CT 06033
Tel.: (860) 633-8111
Toll Free: (800) 774-3664
E-mail: info@biotechcorp.com
Web Site: www.biotechcorp.com
Approx. Sls.: $2,000,000
Year Founded: 1994
Business Description:
Vitamins & Vitamin Supplements
S.I.C.: 2833
N.A.I.C.S.: 325411
Media: 6-13
Personnel:
Gregory Kelly *(Pres)*
Lisa Livingston *(CFO)*

BIOVAIL CORPORATION
(Name Changed to Valeant Pharmaceuticals International, Inc.)

BIOVAIL PHARMACEUTICALS INC.
(Sub. of Valeant Pharmaceuticals International, Inc.)
700 Rte 202/206 N
Bridgewater, NJ 08807
Tel.: (908) 927-1400
Fax: (908) 927-1401
Web Site: www.biovail.com
Approx. Number Employees: 100
Business Description:
Pharmaceutical Products
S.I.C.: 2834
N.A.I.C.S.: 325412
Media: 4-17-22
Personnel:
Douglas J.P. Squires *(Chm)*

BIRNER DENTAL MANAGEMENT SERVICES, INC.
1777 S Harrison St Ste 1400
Denver, CO 80210
Tel.: (303) 691-0680
Fax: (303) 691-0889
Toll Free: (877) 898-1083
E-mail: bdms-investors@birnerdental.com
Web Site: www.bdms-perfectteeth.com
Approx. Rev.: $63,992,633
Approx. Number Employees: 509
Year Founded: 1995
Business Description:
Dental Practice Management Services
S.I.C.: 8021; 8742; 8748
N.A.I.C.S.: 621210; 541611; 541618
Advertising Expenditures: $463,000
Personnel:
Frederic W.J. Birner *(Chm & CEO)*
Mark A. Birner *(Pres)*
Dennis N. Genty *(CFO, Treas & Sec)*
Brands & Products:
PERFECT TEETH

BJC HEALTHCARE
4444 Forest Pk Ave Ste 500
Saint Louis, MO 63108
Tel.: (314) 286-2000
Fax: (314) 286-2060
Web Site: www.bjc.org
Sales Range: $1-4.9 Billion
Approx. Number Employees: 25,993
Year Founded: 1993
Business Description:
Hospitals & Healthcare Facilities Operator
S.I.C.: 8741
N.A.I.C.S.: 561110
Import Export
Media: 10-13-14-15-22-23-24
Personnel:
Steven H. Lipstein *(Pres & CEO)*
David A. Weiss *(CIO & VP)*
Joann M. Shaw *(Chief Learning Officer & VP)*
Robert W. Cannon *(Pres-Grp)*
Joan R. Magruder *(Pres-Missouri Baptist Medical Center)*
Michael A. Dehaven *(Gen Counsel & Sr VP)*
June Fowler *(VP-Corp & Pub Commu)*
Cathy Devries *(Dir-Mktg)*
Brands & Products:
BJC HEALTHCARE
IT'S TIME TO DISCOVER A HEALTHIER YOU

BLAIREX LABORATORIES, INC.
1600 Brian Dr
Columbus, IN 47201-4859
Mailing Address:
PO Box 2127
Columbus, IN 47202-2127
Tel.: (812) 378-1864
Fax: (812) 378-1033
Toll Free: (800) 252-4739
E-mail: info@blairex.com
Web Site: www.blairex.com
Sales Range: $75-99.9 Million
Approx. Number Employees: 130
Year Founded: 1976
Business Description:
Retailer of Medical Products: Respiratory, Eye, Cough & Cold & Wound Care Products
S.I.C.: 5122; 2834
N.A.I.C.S.: 424210; 325412
Personnel:
Anthony J. Moravec *(Pres)*
Brands & Products:
AQUA-BAN
BLAIREX
BRONCHO SALINE
CLEANSIGHT
ENCARE
GINKOGIN
NP-27
OPTICHAMBER
OPTIHALER
PARI DURA-NEB
PARI PRONEB
SIMPLY SALINE
SLEEPINAL
TEMPO
WOUND WASH SALINE
ZILACTIN
Advertising Agency:
Chestnut Communications, Inc.
15 E Putnam Ave
Greenwich, CT 06830-7242
Tel.: (203) 629-9098
Fax: (203) 869-0416

BLICKMAN HEALTH INDUSTRIES, INC.
500 Hwy 46 E
Clifton, NJ 07011-3808
Tel.: (201) 909-0807
Fax: (973) 330-0595
Toll Free: (800) 247-5070
E-mail: info@blickman.com
Web Site: www.blickman.com
Approx. Number Employees: 80
Year Founded: 1975
Business Description:
Stainless Steel Hospital Furniture & Food Equipment
S.I.C.: 3441
N.A.I.C.S.: 332312
Export
Media: 2-4-7-10-17
Distr.: Intl.; Natl.
Budget Set: June
Personnel:
Robert J. Freedman *(Pres)*
Paul D. Freedman *(CFO)*
Seth M. Flexo *(VP-Sls & Mktg)*
Brands & Products:
ALLEN
BLICKMAN BUILT
CLIFTON
CRESCENT
DONNELLY
EZ STACKING
HOWARD
KAY
KENNEDY
KENT
PASSAIC
PAUL
SAWYER
WALTER
WINDSOR

BLUE CROSS & BLUE SHIELD OF FLORIDA, INC.
PO Box 1798
Jacksonville, FL 32231-0014
Tel.: (904) 791-6111
Web Site: www.bcbsfl.com
Approx. Rev.: $7,475,000,000
Approx. Number Employees: 8,500
Year Founded: 1944
Business Description:
Health Care Services
S.I.C.: 6321
N.A.I.C.S.: 524114
Personnel:
Robert Lurna *(CEO)*
R. Chris Doerr *(CFO & Exec VP)*
Arnold Livermore *(COO & Exec VP)*
Tony Jenkins *(Pres-Market)*
David Pizzo *(Pres-Market)*
Cyrus M. Jollivette *(Sr VP-Pub Affairs)*
Bob Wall *(Sr VP-Human Svcs)*
Susan B. Towler *(VP)*
Sharon Wamble-King *(VP-Corp Comm)*
Brands & Products:
BCBSF
Advertising Agency:
Robin Shepherd Group
Gwinnett Commerce Ctr 3700
Crestwood Pkwy Ste 370
Duluth, GA 30096-7153
Tel.: (770) 295-2314
Fax: (770) 295-2321

BLUE CROSS & BLUE SHIELD OF KANSAS CITY, INC.
2301 Main St
Kansas City, MO 64108
Tel.: (816) 395-2222
Fax: (816) 395-2726
E-mail: webmaster@bcbskc.com
Web Site: www.bcbskc.com

Key to Media (For complete agency information see *The Advertising Red Books-Agencies* edition):
1. Bus. Publs. 2. Cable T.V. 3. Catalogs & Directories. 4. Co-op Adv. 5. Consumer Mags. 6. D.M. to Bus. Estab.7. D.M. to Consumers
8. Daily Newsp. 9. Exhibits/Trade Shows 10. Foreign 11. Infomercial 12. Internet Adv.13. Multimedia 14. Network Radio
15. Network T.V. 16. Newsp. Distr. Mags. 17. Other 18. Outdoor (Posters, Transit) 19. Point of Purchase20. Premiums, Novelties
21. Product Samples 22. Special Events Mktg. 23. Spot Radio 24. Spot T.V. 25. Weekly Newsp. 26. Yellow Page Adv.

Approx. Rev.: $714,000,000
Approx. Number Employees: 1,000
Year Founded: 1938
Business Description:
Hospital & Medical Service Plans
S.I.C.: 6321
N.A.I.C.S.: 524114
Import Export
Personnel:
John W. Kennedy *(Chm & CEO-Subsidiaries)*
Steven Marsh *(Vice Chm)*
Marilyn Tromans *(CFO)*
Julie Hinrichsen *(CIO & VP-Info Svcs)*
Roger L. Foreman *(CMO & Exec VP)*
Peter Yelorda *(Exec VP)*
Candice Westphal *(Dir-Producer Svcs)*
Advertising Agency:
Meers Advertising
1811 Walnut St
Kansas City, MO 64108
Tel.: (816) 474-2920
Fax: (816) 474-2925
Toll Free: (800) 259-7346

BLUEBONNET NUTRITION, CORP.
(Private-Parent-Single Location)
12915 Dairy Ashford Rd
Sugar Land, TX 77478
Tel.: (281) 240-3332
Fax: (281) 240-3535
Toll Free: (800) 580-8866
E-mail: info@bluebonnetnutrition.com
Web Site: www.bluebonnetnutrition.com
Approx. Rev.: $9,400,000
Approx. Number Employees: 75
Year Founded: 1991
Business Description:
Drugs, Proprietaries, And Sundries
S.I.C.: 2833
N.A.I.C.S.: 325411
Personnel:
Gary Barrows *(Pres, CEO & Dir)*
Advertising Agency:
Ellen Miller
75 Capwell Ave
Pawtucket, RI 02860
Tel.: (401) 724-3773

BMP SUNSTONE CORPORATION
(Sub. of Sanofi-Aventis)
600 W Germantown Pike Ste 400
Plymouth Meeting, PA 19462
Tel.: (610) 940-1675
Fax: (610) 940-1676
E-mail: info@beijingmedpharm.com
Web Site: www.beijingmedpharm.com
Approx. Rev.: $146,868,000
Approx. Number Employees: 1,198
Year Founded: 2003
Business Description:
Pharmaceutical Marketer & Distr
S.I.C.: 5122
N.A.I.C.S.: 424210
Advertising Expenditures: $12,124,000
Media: 2-22
Personnel:
Zhijun Tong *(Pres & Chm/Gen Mgr-Sunstone)*
Xiaoying Gao *(CEO & Dir)*
Fred M. Powell *(CFO)*
Yanping Zhao *(COO)*

BOEHRINGER INGELHEIM CORP.
(Sub. of Boehringer Ingelheim GmbH)
900 Ridgebury Rd
Ridgefield, CT 06877-1058
Mailing Address:
PO Box 368
Ridgefield, CT 06877-0368
Tel.: (203) 798-9988
E-mail: webmaster@rdg.boehringer-ingelheim.com
Web Site: us.boehringer-ingelheim.com
Approx. Sls.: $3,167,427,500
Approx. Number Employees: 6,493
Year Founded: 1971
Business Description:
Holding Company; Pharmaceutical Products & Chemical Drug Materials Developer & Mfr
S.I.C.: 6719; 2834; 2836; 2899
N.A.I.C.S.: 551112; 325412; 325414; 325998; 541711
Personnel:
Julie Edwards *(Mgr-Scientific Affairs-Canada)*
Kate O'Connor *(Mgr-PR)*
Advertising Agencies:
Chamberlain Healthcare Public Relations
111 Broadway 19th Fl
New York, NY 10006
Tel.: (212) 884-0650
Fax: (212) 884-0628
Pradaxa

Draftfcb HealthCare
100 W 33rd St
New York, NY 10001
Tel.: (212) 672-2300
Fax: (212) 672-2301

GHG
114 5th Ave
New York, NY 10011-5604
Tel.: (212) 886-3201
Tel.: (212) 886-3000
Fax: (212) 886-3297

Grey New York
777 3rd Ave
New York, NY 10017-1401
Tel.: (212) 546-2000
Fax: (212) 546-1495

HealthStar Public Relations
112 Madison Ave
New York, NY 10016
Tel.: (212) 532-0909
Fax: (212) 532-6907

Saatchi & Saatchi Healthcare Advertising
375 Hudson St
New York, NY 10014
Tel.: (212) 463-3400

BOIRON USA INC.
(Sub. of Boiron Group)
6 Campus Blvd
Newtown Square, PA 19073
Tel.: (610) 325-7464
Fax: (610) 325-7480
Web Site: www.boironusa.com
Sales Range: $25-49.9 Million
Approx. Number Employees: 90
Business Description:
Homeopathic Medical Products
S.I.C.: 2833
N.A.I.C.S.: 325411
Media: 6
Personnel:
Ludovic Rassat *(Pres & CEO)*
John Durkin *(VP-Sls & Mktg)*
Alissa Gould *(Mgr-Pub Rels)*
Advertising Agencies:
Medrageous
150 E 42nd St 16th Fl
New York, NY 10017
Tel.: (646) 742-2194
Fax: (646) 742-2206

Onit Marketing
1550 Larimer St, #767
Denver, CO 80202
Tel.: (202) 258-0657

Optimedia International U.S.
375 Hudson St 7th Fl
New York, NY 10014
Tel.: (212) 820-3200
Fax: (212) 820-3300
Media Planning & Buying

BON SECOURS HEALTH SYSTEM, INC.
1505 Marriottsville Rd
Marriottsville, MD 21104-1301
Tel.: (410) 442-5511
Fax: (410) 442-1082
E-mail: info@bshsi.com
Web Site: www.bshsi.com
Approx. Sls.: $2,305,000,000
Approx. Number Employees: 1,105
Year Founded: 1824
Business Description:
Hospitals & Nursing Homes
S.I.C.: 8062
N.A.I.C.S.: 622110
Import Export
Advertising Expenditures: $500,000
Media: 4-10-13-22
Personnel:
Patricia A. Eck *(Chm)*
Richard Statuto *(Pres & CEO)*
Katherine Arbuckle *(CFO & Exec VP)*
Timothy J. Davis *(Exec VP)*
Peter J. Bernard *(Sr VP)*
John Shea *(Sr VP-Bus Dev)*
Peggy Moseley *(VP-Corp Comm)*
Advertising Agency:
Bonnie Heneson Communications, Inc.
Valley Vlg Professional Ctr 9199 Reisterstown Rd Ste 212C
Owings Mills, MD 21117
Tel.: (410) 654-0000
Fax: (410) 654-0377

BOND LABORATORIES, INC.
11011 Q St Ste 106A
Omaha, NE 68137
Tel.: (402) 991-5618
Fax: (402) 884-1816
Web Site: www.bond-labs.com
Approx. Rev.: $8,148,053
Approx. Number Employees: 10
Year Founded: 2005
Business Description:
Nutraceutical Dietary Supplements
S.I.C.: 2833; 2834
N.A.I.C.S.: 325411; 325412
Advertising Expenditures: $1,994,111
Personnel:
Scott D. Landow *(Chm)*
John S. Wilson *(Pres & CEO)*
Michael S. Abrams *(Interim CFO)*

BOSLEY MEDICAL
(Sub. of Unihair Co., Ltd.)
9100 Wilshire Blvd East Tower Penthouse
Beverly Hills, CA 90212
Tel.: (310) 288-9999
Fax: (310) 887-0947
Toll Free: (800) 474-1254
Web Site: www.bosley.com
Year Founded: 1974
Business Description:
Hair Restoration
S.I.C.: 5047
N.A.I.C.S.: 423450
Personnel:
Armen Markarian *(Pres & CEO)*
Robert D. Spurrell *(VP-Sls & Mktg)*
Michael J. May *(Dir-HR)*
Advertising Agency:
KMR Communications
419 Park Ave S
New York, NY 10016
Tel.: (212) 213-6444
Fax: (212) 213-4699

BOSTON SCIENTIFIC CORPORATION
1 Boston Scientific Pl
Natick, MA 01760-1537
Tel.: (508) 650-8000
Fax: (508) 647-2393
E-mail: Investor_Relations@bsci.com
Web Site: www.bostonscientific.com
Approx. Sls.: $7,806,000,000
Approx. Number Employees: 25,000
Year Founded: 1960
Business Description:
Medical Devices Mfr
S.I.C.: 3841; 3842; 3845; 8733
N.A.I.C.S.: 339112; 334510; 339113; 541710
Import Export
Media: 2-7-10-11-13
Personnel:
John E. Abele *(Co-Founder & Dir)*
Michael Mahoney *(Pres)*
William H. Kucheman *(Interim CEO)*
Jeffrey D. Capello *(CFO & Exec VP)*
Samuel R. Leno *(COO & Exec VP)*
Timothy A. Pratt *(Chief Admin Officer, Gen Counsel & Exec VP)*
Jean Fitterer Lance *(Chief Compliance Officer & Sr VP)*
Keith D. Dawkins *(Chief Medical Officer-Cardiology, Rhythm & Vascular Grp & Sr VP)*
Joseph M. Fitzgerald *(Sr VP & Pres-Endovascular Unit)*
J. Michael Onuscheck *(Pres-Neuromodulation & Sr VP)*
John B. Pedersen *(Pres-Urology & Womens Health & Sr VP)*
Michael P. Phalen *(Sr VP & Pres-Endoscopy)*
Frederick D. Hrkac *(Pres-EMEA)*
Mark H. Paul *(Pres-Neurovascular)*
Brian R. Burns *(Exec VP-Quality & Regulatory Affairs)*
Fredericus A. Colen *(Exec VP)*
Kenneth J. Pucel *(Exec VP-Ops-Global)*
Denise Kaigler *(Sr VP-Corp Comm)*

Key to Media (For complete agency information see *The Advertising Red Books-Agencies* edition):
1. Bus. Publs. 2. Cable T.V. 3. Catalogs & Directories. 4. Co-op Adv. 5. Consumer Mags. 6. D.M. to Bus. Estab.7. D.M. to Consumers
8. Daily Newsp. 9. Exhibits/Trade Shows 10. Foreign 11. Infomercial 12. Internet Adv.13. Multimedia 14. Network Radio
15. Network T.V. 16. Newsp. Distr. Mags. 17. Other 18. Outdoor (Posters, Transit) 19. Point of Purchase20. Premiums, Novelties
21. Product Samples 22. Special Events Mktg. 23. Spot Radio 24. Spot T.V. 25. Weekly Newsp. 26. Yellow Page Adv.

Boston Scientific Corporation — (Continued)

Stephen F. Moreci *(Sr VP-Sls Ops-Global)*
Otha T. Spriggs, III *(Sr VP-HR)*
Rekha Ranganathan *(Dir-Mktg Strategy)*
David H. Cameron *(Mgr-Sls)*

Brands & Products:
A-FOCUS
ACCUSTICK
ACE
ACUITY
ADVANTAGE
ADVANTAGE FIT
AFOCUS
ALLIANCE II
ALTRUA
AMPLATZ SUPER STIFF
ATLANTIS
AUTOTOME RX
BLAZER
BLAZER DX-20
BLAZER II
BLAZER II XP
BLUE MAX 20
CAPIO
CAPTIVATOR
CHILLI
CHILLI II
CIRCUCOOL PUMP
COAPTITE
COBRA
COGNIS
CONFIENT
CONSTELLATION
CONTAK RENEWAL
CONTOUR
CONTOUR VL VARIABLE LENGTH PERCUFLEX
CONVOY
CRE
CUTTING BALLOON ULTRA2
DEXTRUS
DUOTOME SIDELITE
DYNAGLIDE
DYNAMIC
EASY CORE
EASYTRAK
ENDOTAK RELIANCE
ENDOVIVE
ENTERYX
EPT-1000
EQUALIZER
ESCAPE
EXCELON
EXCELSIOR
EXCELSIOR 1018
EXPLORER 360
EXPLORER 360 JR
EXPLORER ST
EXPRESS
EXPRESS2
EXTRACTOR
EXXCEL
FATHOM
FILTERWIRE EZ
FORTE
GALAXY
GEMINI
GLIDEWIRE
GOLD PROBE
GRASPIT
GUIDER SOFTIP
HEMASHIELD
HURRICANE
HYDRA JAGWIRE
HYDRATOME
HYDRO THERMABLATOR
ICROSS
ILAB
IMAGER
INQUIRY
INQUIRY H-CURVE
INTERJECT
KIESZ
LATITUDE
LEVEEN
LEVEEN COACCESS
LIBERTE
LIVIAN
LUBRIGUIDE
LUMA-CATH
LYNX
MACH 1
MAESTRO 3000
MAGIC TORQUE
MAVERICK
NAVIGATOR
NEPHROMAX
NEUROFORM
NEUROFORM3
OBTRYX
OPTIFLEX
OPTIFLO
PASSPORT
PERCUFLEX
PERIVAC
PINNACLE
PINPOINT
PIRANHA
POLARCATH
POLARIS
POLARIS DX
POLARIS X
POLYFLEX
POLYFORM
PRECISION PLUS
PRECISION SPEED TAC
PRECISION TWIST
PREFYX PPS
PROLIEVE
PROLIEVE THERMODILATATION
QUANTUM
RADIAL EDGE
RENEGADE
REPLIFORM
RESOLUTION
RF 3000
ROTABLATOR
ROTALINK
ROTAWIRE
RUNWAY
SCHNEIDER GUIDER
SEGURA HEMISPHERE
SENSATION
SENSOR
SENTINOL
SENTRY
SOLOIST
SOLYX
SONICATH
SPEEDBAND SUPERVIEW SUPER7
SPINNAKER
SPYGLASS
STEEROCATH-DX
STEEROCATH-T
STERLING
STERLING MONORAIL
STONE CONE
SUPER SHEATH
SWISS LITHOCLAST
SYMMETRY
SYNCHRO2
TAL MICRODRAINAGE
TAXUS
TAXUS EXPRESS2
TAXUS EXPRESS2 ATOM
TAXUS LIBERTE ATOM
TELIGEN
TEN-TEN
THRUWAY
TLC
TRACKER
TRACKER EXCEL
TRANSEND
TRICEP
ULTRA ICE
ULTRA-THIN
ULTRAFLEX
UPHOLD
UROMAX ULTRA
VAXCEL
VERSAPULSE POWERSUITE
VITALITY
VORTX
WALLFLEX
WALLGRAFT
WALLSTENT
WALLSTENT MONORAIL
WISEGUIDE
XENFORM
ZEBRA
ZEROTIP
ZIPWIRE

Advertising Agencies:
DaltonSherman
111 3rd Ave S Ste 130
Minneapolis, MN 55401
Tel.: (612) 341-2241
Fax: (612) 341-2281

JSML Media, LLC
11200 86th Ave N
Minneapolis, MN 55369
Tel.: (763) 657-2263
Fax: (763) 657-2261
Toll Free: (800) 657-3100

LehmanMillet
2 Atlantic Ave
Boston, MA 02110
Tel.: (617) 722-0019
Fax: (617) 722-6099
Toll Free: (800) 634-5315

OLSON
1625 Hennepin Ave
Minneapolis, MN 55403
Tel.: (612) 215-9800
Fax: (612) 215-9801
Cardiology, Rhythm & Vascular Group
Creative
Design
Interactive
Strategy

PJA
12 Arrow St
Cambridge, MA 02138-5105
Tel.: (617) 492-5899
Fax: (617) 661-1530

BOSTWICK LABORATORIES, INC.

4355 Innslake Dr
Glen Allen, VA 23060
Tel.: (804) 967-9225
Fax: (804) 288-6568
Toll Free: (800) 214-6628
Web Site: www.bostwicklaboratories.com
Sales Range: $100-124.9 Million
Approx. Number Employees: 753
Year Founded: 1999
Business Description:
Anatomic Pathology Laboratories
S.I.C.: 8071
N.A.I.C.S.: 621511
Advertising Expenditures: $700,000
Personnel:
David Bostwick *(Chm, Pres & CEO & Chief Dir-Medical)*
Richard Bostwick *(Gen Counsel & Sec)*
Jed Fulk *(Exec VP-Sls & Mktg)*

BRACCO DIAGNOSTICS, INC.

(Sub. of Bracco Imaging S.p.A.)
107 College Rd E
Princeton, NJ 08540-6612
Mailing Address:
PO Box 5225
Princeton, NJ 08543-5225
Tel.: (609) 514-2200
Fax: (609) 514-2424
Toll Free: (800) 631-5245
Approx. Number Employees: 250
Year Founded: 1994
Business Description:
Medical Imaging Equipment & Pharmaceutical Developer & Mfr
S.I.C.: 2834; 3841
N.A.I.C.S.: 325412; 339112
Advertising Expenditures: $200,000
Media: 2-7-8-18
Personnel:
Carlo Medici *(Pres & CEO)*
Ed Smith *(VP-Sls)*
Advertising Agency:
Stern + Associates
11 Commerce Dr
Cranford, NJ 07016
Tel.: (908) 276-4344
Fax: (908) 276-7007
(Media Relations)

BRADLEY PHARMACEUTICALS, INC.

(Sub. of Nycomed US, Inc.)
383 Rte 46 W
Fairfield, NJ 07004-2402
Tel.: (973) 882-1505
Fax: (973) 575-5366
Toll Free: (800) 929-9300
E-mail: info@bradpharm.com
Web Site: www.bradpharm.com
Approx. Sls.: $144,806,640
Approx. Number Employees: 300
Year Founded: 1985
Business Description:
Pharmaceuticals Mfr, Distr & Marketer
S.I.C.: 2834; 5122
N.A.I.C.S.: 325412; 424210
Import Export
Advertising Expenditures: $8,622,863
Media: 2-7-10-21
Distr.: Natl.
Personnel:
Gene L. Goldberg *(Sr VP-Mktg & Bus Plng)*
Stacey Glassman-Narotzky *(Dir-Pro Rels)*
Cecelia Heer *(Mgr-Investor Pub Rel)*
Brands & Products:
ACIDMANTLE
ADOXA
ANAMANTLE

Key to Media (For complete agency information see *The Advertising Red Books-Agencies* edition):
1. Bus. Publs. 2. Cable T.V. 3. Catalogs & Directories. 4. Co-op Adv. 5. Consumer Mags. 6. D.M. to Bus. Estab.7. D.M. to Consumers
8. Daily Newsp. 9. Exhibits/Trade Shows 10. Foreign 11. Infomercial 12. Internet Adv.13. Multimedia 14. Network Radio
15. Network T.V. 16. Newsp. Distr. Mags. 17. Other 18. Outdoor (Posters, Transit) 19. Point of Purchase20. Premiums, Novelties
21. Product Samples 22. Special Events Mktg. 23. Spot Radio 24. Spot T.V. 25. Weekly Newsp. 26. Yellow Page Adv.

BRONTEX
CARMOL
CARMOL-10
CARMOL-20
CARMOL 40
CARMOL HC
DECONAMINE
DOAK
DPM
ELESTRIN
ENTSOL
FLORA-Q
FORMULA 405
GLUTOFAC
KENWOOD THERAPEUTIC S
KERALAC
LE PONT
LIDAMANTLE
LUBRIN
PAMINE
ROSULA
SELSEB
SOLARAZE
TERSASEPTIC
TRANS-VER-SAL
TXSYSTEM
TYZINE
ZODERM
ZONALON

BRAINSTORM CELL THERAPEUTICS INC.

605 3rd Ave 34th Fl
New York, NY 10158
Tel.: (212) 557-7200
Fax: (212) 581-8958
E-mail: info@brainstorm-cell.com
Web Site: www.brainstorm-cell.com
Approx. Number Employees: 5
Business Description:
Stem Cell Research & Development Services
S.I.C.: 8733; 2836; 8071
N.A.I.C.S.: 541710; 325414; 621511
Personnel:
Abraham Israeli *(Chm)*
Adrian Harel *(CEO & COO)*
Liat Sossover *(CFO)*
Advertising Agency:
5W Public Relations
888 7th Ave 12th Fl
New York, NY 10106
Tel.: (212) 999-5585
Fax: (646) 328-1711

BRIOSCHI INC.

19-01 Pollitt Dr
Fair Lawn, NJ 07410-2827
Tel.: (201) 796-4226
Fax: (201) 796-0391
E-mail: corporate@brioschi.com
Web Site: www.brioschi-usa.com
Approx. Sls.: $2,000,000
Approx. Number Employees: 14
Year Founded: 1880
Business Description:
Mfr of Antacid Preparations
S.I.C.: 2834; 5122
N.A.I.C.S.: 325412; 424210
Import Export
Advertising Expenditures: $200,000
Media: 7-13-19-21-23-24
Distr.: Intl.; Natl.
Budget Set: July
Personnel:
Michael A. Brizzolara *(Pres)*
Brands & Products:
BRIOSCHI
THE FASTEST FIZZ THERE IS!

BRISTOL-MYERS SQUIBB U.S. PHARMACEUTICAL GROUP

(Sub. of Bristol-Myers Squibb Company)
777 Scudders Mill Rd
Plainsboro, NJ 08536-1615
Tel.: (609) 897-2000
Fax: (609) 897-6791
Sales Range: $150-199.9 Million
Business Description:
Nutritional & Pharmaceutical Products Mfr
S.I.C.: 2834
N.A.I.C.S.: 325412
Media: 2-6-10-19-21
Distr.: Natl.
Personnel:
Anthony C. Hooper *(Pres-Americas, Middle East & Africa)*
Brands & Products:
BUSPAR
MONOPRIL
MYCOSTATIN
PARAPLATIN
STADOL IM/IV
Advertising Agencies:
CAHG
211 E Chicago Ave
Chicago, IL 60611-2637
Tel.: (312) 664-5310
Fax: (312) 649-7232
(Pharmaceutical Products)

H4B Chelsea
75 9th Ave 2R
New York, NY 10011
Tel.: (212) 299-5000
Fax: (212) 299-5050
Toll Free: (800) 358-6420
(Pharmaceutical Products)

BROOKDALE SENIOR LIVING INC.

111 Westwood Pl Ste 200
Brentwood, TN 37027
Tel.: (615) 221-2250
Fax: (615) 221-2289
Toll Free: (866) 785-9025
E-mail: info@brookdaleliving.com
Web Site: www.brookdaleliving.com
Approx. Rev.: $2,213,264,000
Approx. Number Employees: 23,900
Year Founded: 1978
Business Description:
Senior Living Facilities Operator
S.I.C.: 8059; 8361
N.A.I.C.S.: 623311; 623110; 623312
Advertising Expenditures: $6,200,000
Media: 6-8-10-13-18-22-26
Personnel:
Wesley Robert Edens *(Chm)*
Mark W. Ohlendorf *(Co-Pres & CFO)*
John P. Rijos *(Co-Pres & COO)*
William E. Sheriff *(CEO)*
Bryan D. Richardson *(Chief Admin Officer & Exec VP)*
T. Andrew Smith *(Gen Counsel, Sec & Exec VP)*
Kristin A. Ferge *(Treas & Exec VP)*
George T. Hicks *(Exec VP-Fin)*
H. Todd Kaestner *(Exec VP-Corp Dev)*
Gregory B. Richard *(Exec VP-Field Ops)*
Ross Roadman *(Sr VP-IR)*
Holly Botsford *(Mgr-PR)*
Brands & Products:
BROOKDALE SENIOR LIVING
OPTIMUM LIFE
Advertising Agency:
POWERWORKS Studio
1023 N Winchester Ave
Chicago, IL 60622
Tel.: (773) 218-1266

BRUKER CORPORATION

40 Manning Rd
Billerica, MA 01821
Tel.: (978) 663-3660
Fax: (978) 667-5993
E-mail: info@bruker-biosciences.com
Web Site: www.bruker-biosciences.com
E-Mail For Key Personnel:
Public Relations: press@bruker-biosciences.com
Approx. Rev.: $1,304,900,000
Approx. Number Employees: 5,400
Business Description:
Life Science & Advanced Materials Research Tools Developer
S.I.C.: 3826; 3841; 5049; 8733
N.A.I.C.S.: 334516; 339112; 423490; 541710
Advertising Expenditures: $6,900,000
Media: 2-4-7-10-11-13-17-20-26
Personnel:
Frank H. Laukien *(Chm, Pres & CEO)*
William J. Knight *(CFO)*
Stacey Desrochers *(Treas & Dir-IR)*
Brian P. Monahan *(Exec VP-Fin)*
Brands & Products:
DRIFT
FLASHFORMULA
HYPERION
HYPERION 1000
HYPERION 2000
HYPERION 3000
MALDI MATRICES
METABOLIC PROFILER
MINISPEC PLUS
MINISPEC PROFILER
MONTEL 200
MULTI-RAM FT-RAMAN
NANOSTAR
PROTEINEER FC
PROTEUMPLUS
Q6 COLUMBUS
QUANTAX 400 STEEL
S2 RANGER
S4 EXPLERER
S4 PIONEER
SMART APEX
SMART APEX II
SMART BREEZE
SPECTRAPLUS
SUPER SPEED SOLUTIONS
TENSOR
THINK FORWARD
ULTRASCAN
VERTEX 80V
X8 PROSPECTOR
X8 PROTEUM
XFLASH QUAD

BSD MEDICAL CORPORATION

2188 W 2200 S
Salt Lake City, UT 84119-1326
Tel.: (801) 972-5555
Fax: (801) 972-5930
E-mail: info@bsdmc.com
Web Site: www.bsdmc.com
Approx. Rev.: $1,582,276
Approx. Number Employees: 29
Business Description:
Heat Therapy Systems Developer, Mfr & Marketer
S.I.C.: 3841
N.A.I.C.S.: 339112
Advertising Expenditures: $86,000
Media: 17
Personnel:
Timothy C. McQuay *(Chm)*
Harold R. Wolcott *(Pres)*
Dennis P. Gauger *(CFO)*
Brian L. Ferrand *(VP-Sls)*
Steven M. Smith *(VP-Mktg & Bus Dev)*
Todd H. Turnlund *(VP-Engrg)*
J. Richard Faux *(Dir-Ops)*
Jordan Wittmeier *(Dir-Intl MicroThermX Sls)*
Jim Fincher *(Mgr-Sls-Latin American)*
Mark Hagmann *(Engr)*

CALIFORNIA PACIFIC MEDICAL CENTER

(Affil. of Sutter Health)
2333 Buchanan St
San Francisco, CA 94115-1925
Tel.: (415) 600-6000
Fax: (415) 600-2995
E-mail: info@cpmc.org
Web Site: www.cpmc.org
Approx. Number Employees: 1,000
Business Description:
Operates Hospital & Health Care Services
S.I.C.: 8062
N.A.I.C.S.: 622110
Media: 2-4-8-10-18-20-22-26
Personnel:
Scott L. Minick *(Chm)*
Martin Brotman *(Pres)*
Jack Bailey *(Exec VP & Administrator)*

CALIPER LIFE SCIENCES, INC.

68 Elm St
Hopkinton, MA 01748
Tel.: (508) 435-9500
Fax: (508) 435-3439
Toll Free: (877) LABCHIP
E-mail: info@caliperls.com
Web Site: www.caliperls.com
Approx. Rev.: $123,696,000
Approx. Number Employees: 469
Year Founded: 1995
Business Description:
Research Tools for Drug Discovery & Development
S.I.C.: 3826; 8733
N.A.I.C.S.: 334516; 541710
Advertising Expenditures: $2,000,000
Media: 10
Personnel:
Robert C. Bishop *(Chm)*
E. Kevin Hrusovsky *(Pres & CEO)*
Peter F. Mcaree *(CFO & Sr VP)*
Stephen E. Creager *(Gen Counsel, Sec & Sr VP)*
Enrique Bernal *(Sr VP-In Vitro Bus Dev)*
David M. Manyak *(Exec VP-Drug Discovery Svcs)*
Bruce J. Bal *(Sr VP-Ops)*
Rick Bernal *(Sr VP-Bus Dev)*
Paula J. Cassidy *(Sr VP-HR)*
William C. Kruka *(Sr VP-Corp Dev)*
Bradley W. Rice *(Sr VP-Sys & R & D)*
Mark T. Roskey *(Sr VP-Applied Biology R & D)*

Key to Media (For complete agency information see *The Advertising Red Books-Agencies* edition):
1. Bus. Publs. 2. Cable T.V. 3. Catalogs & Directories. 4. Co-op Adv. 5. Consumer Mags. 6. D.M. to Bus. Estab.7. D.M. to Consumers
8. Daily Newsp. 9. Exhibits/Trade Shows 10. Foreign 11. Infomercial 12. Internet Adv.13. Multimedia 14. Network Radio
15. Network T.V. 16. Newsp. Distr. Mags. 17. Other 18. Outdoor (Posters, Transit) 19. Point of Purchase20. Premiums, Novelties
21. Product Samples 22. Special Events Mktg. 23. Spot Radio 24. Spot T.V. 25. Weekly Newsp. 26. Yellow Page Adv.

Caliper Life Sciences, Inc. — (Continued)

Brands & Products:
ALLEGRO
AUTOMATION CERTIFIED
AUTOTRACE
BIOWARE
CALIPER LIFESCIENCES
ILINK
IVIS
LABCHIP
LIGHTCYCLER
MULTIDOSE
PATHHUNTER
PRELUDE
PRESTO
RAPIDPLATE
RAPIDTRACE
SCICLONE
SEDSELECT
STACCATO
TPW3
TURBOVAP
TWISTER
XENOFLUOR 680
ZEPHYR
Advertising Agency:
Schwartz Communications, Inc.
230 3rd Ave
Waltham, MA 02451
Tel.: (781) 684-0770
Fax: (781) 684-6500
Pub Rels

CANADA DRUGS LTD.
24 Terracon Pl
Winnipeg, MB R2J 4G7, Canada
Tel.: (204) 949-1394
Tel.: (204) 654-7950
Fax: (204) 224-2376
Fax: (204) 258-7010
Fax: (800) 988-5440
Toll Free: (800) 226-3784
E-mail: info@canadadrugs.com
Web Site: www.canadadrugs.com
Sales Range: $25-49.9 Million
Approx. Number Employees: 250
Year Founded: 2001
Business Description:
Online & Mail Order Pharmacy
S.I.C.: 5912; 5961
N.A.I.C.S.: 446110; 454111; 454113
Media: 6-13
Personnel:
Kris Thorkelson *(Founder)*
Ron Sigurdson *(CFO)*
Eric Sigurdson *(Dir-Pharmacy)*
Brands & Products:
CANADADRUGS.COM

CANCER TREATMENT CENTERS OF AMERICA
1336 Basswood Rd
Schaumburg, IL 60173
Tel.: (847) 342-7400
Fax: (847) 872-6222
Toll Free: (800) 615-3055
Web Site: www.cancercenter.com
Approx. Rev.: $240,000,000
Approx. Number Employees: 1,100
Business Description:
Management of In-Patient Cancer Care Programs
S.I.C.: 8069; 8742
N.A.I.C.S.: 622310; 541611
Advertising Expenditures: $500,000
Media: 2-3-4-5-6-9-12-13-14-15-16-22-23-24-25-26
Distr.: Natl.
Personnel:
Robert W. Mayo *(Vice Chm)*
Stephen B. Bonner *(Pres & CEO)*
Adam Lefton *(VP-Mktg)*
Brands & Products:
CANCER TREATMENT CENTERS OF AMERICA
PATIENT EMPOWERMENT MEDICINE
WINNING THE FIGHT AGAINST CANCER, EVERYDAY
Advertising Agencies:
GSD&M
828 W 6th St
Austin, TX 78703-5420
Tel.: (512) 242-4736
Fax: (512) 242-4700

TargetCom, LLC
444 N Michigan Ave 33rd Fl
Chicago, IL 60611-3905
Tel.: (312) 822-1100
Fax: (312) 822-9628
Toll Free: (877) 423-7837

CANGENE CORPORATION
155 Innovation Dr
Winnipeg, MB R3T 5Y3, Canada
Tel.: (416) 675-8280
Fax: (204) 269-7003
Web Site: www.cangene.com
Approx. Rev.: $155,475,062
Approx. Number Employees: 800
Business Description:
Producer of Hyperimmune Biopharmaceuticals
S.I.C.: 2836
N.A.I.C.S.: 325414
Media: 10
Personnel:
R. Craig Baxter *(Chm)*
John Sedor *(Pres & CEO)*
Michael Graham *(CFO)*
Francis St. Hilaire *(Gen Counsel & Sec)*
William Labossiere Bees *(Sr VP-Ops)*
Andrew D. Storey *(Sr VP-Quality & Regulatory Affairs)*
D. Bruce Burlington *(Dir-HR)*
Jean Compton *(Mgr-Corp Comm)*
Brands & Products:
ACCRETROPIN
CANGENE
CANGENUS
HEPAGAM B
LEUCOTROPIN
VARIZIG

CAPITAL BLUECROSS INC.
2500 Elmerton Ave
Harrisburg, PA 17110-9764
Tel.: (717) 541-7000
Fax: (717) 541-6915
Toll Free: (800) 958-5558
E-mail: human.resources@capbluecross.com
Web Site: www.capbluecross.com
Approx. Rev.: $1,674,963,000
Approx. Number Employees: 2,000
Year Founded: 1938
Business Description:
Hospital & Medical Service Plans
S.I.C.: 6321; 6411
N.A.I.C.S.: 524114; 524210
Import Export
Personnel:
Gary St. Hilaire *(CFO, Treas & Exec VP)*
Michael Cleary *(VP-Fin)*
David Skerpon *(VP-Corp Comm & Adv)*
Robert E. Baker, Jr. *(Sr Dir-Govt Affairs)*
Sandy Senich *(Mgr-Pur)*
Brands & Products:
CAPITAL ADVANTAGE FOR HEALTH
CAPITAL BLUE CROSS
PRECIOUS BABY PRINTS
Advertising Agency:
MayoSeitz Media
532 E. Township Line Rd
Blue Bell, PA 19422
Tel.: (215) 641-8700
Fax: (215) 641-8712

CAPITAL HEALTH SYSTEMS INC.
446 Bellevue Ave
Trenton, NJ 08618
Tel.: (609) 394-4000
Tel.: (609) 394-6091 (Pub Rels)
Fax: (609) 394-4001
E-mail: info@capitalhealth.org
Web Site: www.capitalhealth.org
Sales Range: $400-449.9 Million
Approx. Number Employees: 3,000
Business Description:
Hospital Operator
S.I.C.: 8062
N.A.I.C.S.: 622110
Personnel:
Al Maghazehe *(Pres & CEO)*
Ronald J. Guy *(CFO)*
Larry DiSanto *(COO & Exec VP)*
Eugene Grochala *(CIO)*
Jan Gabin *(Gen Counsel)*
J. Scott Clemmensen *(VP-HR)*
Timothy Graham *(VP-Fin Svcs)*
James Simms *(Dir-Radiation)*
Advertising Agency:
Visions Advertising Media, LLC
426 Shore Rd Ste B
Atlantic City, NJ 08401
Tel.: (609) 926-6358
Fax: (609) 926-6358

CAPSTONE THERAPEUTICS CORP.
(Formerly OrthoLogic Corp.)
1275 W Washington St Ste 101
Tempe, AZ 85281-1210
Tel.: (602) 286-5520
Fax: (602) 286-5224
Toll Free: (800) 937-5520
E-mail: investorinquiries@capstonethx.com
Web Site: www.capstonethx.com
Approx. Int. Income: $356,000
Approx. Number Employees: 25
Year Founded: 1987
Business Description:
Biopharmaceutical Researcher, Developer & Mfr
S.I.C.: 2834; 2836; 8733
N.A.I.C.S.: 325412; 325414; 541710
Personnel:
John M. Holliman, III *(Chm & CEO)*
Randolph C. Steer *(Pres)*
Les M. Taeger *(CFO & Sr VP)*
Brands & Products:
CAPSTONE THERAPEUTICS
CHRYSALIN
Advertising Agency:
The Trout Group, Llc.
740 Broadway Ste 903
New York, NY 10003
Tel.: (212) 477-9007
Investor Relations

CARDIAC SCIENCE CORPORATION
(Sub. of Opto Circuits (India) Limited)
3303 Monte Villa Pkwy
Bothell, WA 98021
Tel.: (425) 402-2000
Fax: (425) 402-2001
Toll Free: (800) 426-0337
E-mail: info@cardiacscience.com
Web Site: www.cardiacscience.com
Approx. Rev.: $156,848,000
Approx. Number Employees: 556
Business Description:
Diagnostic & Therapeutic Cardiological Products Developer, Mfr & Marketer
S.I.C.: 3845; 3841
N.A.I.C.S.: 334510; 339112
Advertising Expenditures: $671,000
Media: 10-17
Personnel:
David L. Marver *(CEO)*
Robert W. Odell *(COO)*
Alfred J. Ford, Jr. *(Sr VP-Global Sls)*
Peter Kingma *(Sr VP-Sls & Mktg)*
Michael B. Adams *(VP-Info Sys)*
Barbara J. Thompson *(VP-HR)*
Brands & Products:
AT THE HEART OF SAVING LIVES
ATRIA
BLUEMAX
BURDICK
CARDIAC SCIENCE
CARDIOSENS
CARDIOVIVE
ECLIPSE
ECLIPSE PREMIER
EK-10
ELITE II
FIRSTSAVE
G3 PRO
HEARTCENTRIX
HEARTSTRIDE
HEARTWORKS
INTELLISENSE
MASTERTRAK
MDLINK
MEDTRACK
OFFICE MEDIC
POWERHEART
PYRAMIS
Q-STRESS
Q-TEL
QUEST
QUICK RESPONSE
QUIK-PREP
QUINTON
RESCUE LINK
RESCUE READY
SCHOOL SAFE
SENSAIRE
SERVICE LINK
SPIROCARD
SPIROXCARD
SURVIVALINK
TOTAL RESPONSE
ULTRADRIVE
UNIVERSAL
VISION

Key to Media (For complete agency information see *The Advertising Red Books-Agencies* edition):
1. Bus. Publs. 2. Cable T.V. 3. Catalogs & Directories. 4. Co-op Adv. 5. Consumer Mags. 6. D.M. to Bus. Estab.7. D.M. to Consumers 8. Daily Newsp. 9. Exhibits/Trade Shows 10. Foreign 11. Infomercial 12. Internet Adv.13. Multimedia 14. Network Radio 15. Network T.V. 16. Newsp. Distr. Mags. 17. Other 18. Outdoor (Posters, Transit) 19. Point of Purchase20. Premiums, Novelties 21. Product Samples 22. Special Events Mktg. 23. Spot Radio 24. Spot T.V. 25. Weekly Newsp. 26. Yellow Page Adv.

Advertising Agencies:
EVC Group, Inc.
60 East 42nd St Ste 936
New York, NY 10165
Tel.: (646) 443-6963
Fax: (212) 661-0035

GreenRubino
1938 Fairview Ave E Ste 200
Seattle, WA 98102
Tel.: (206) 447-4747
Fax: (206) 447-9494

CARDIMA, INC.
(Filed Ch 11 Bankruptcy #10-74445 on 12/17/10 in U.S. Bankruptcy Ct, Northern Dist of Oakland, CA)
47266 Benicia St
Fremont, CA 94538-7330
Tel.: (510) 354-0300
Fax: (510) 657-4476
Toll Free: (888) 354-0300
Toll Free: (800) 354-0102
E-mail: feedback@cardima.com
Web Site: www.cardima.com
Approx. Sls.: $2,247,000
Approx. Number Employees: 78
Year Founded: 1992
Business Description:
Cardiac Microcatheter Systems Mfr
S.I.C.: 3845; 2676
N.A.I.C.S.: 334510; 322291
Advertising Expenditures: $273,000
Media: 10
Personnel:
Phillip C. Radlick *(Interim Pres & Interim CEO)*
Brands & Products:
CARDIMA
INTELLITEMP
NAVIPORT
PATHFINDER
PATHFINDER MINI
REVELATION
REVELATION T-FLEX
REVELATION TX
TRACER
VENAPORT
VUEPORT

CARDINAL HEALTH, INC.
7000 Cardinal Pl
Dublin, OH 43017
Tel.: (614) 757-5000
Fax: (614) 757-8871
Toll Free: (800) 234-8701
Web Site: www.cardinal.com
Approx. Rev.: $102,644,200,000
Approx. Number Employees: 31,900
Year Founded: 1971
Business Description:
Medical & Pharmaceutical Products Manufacturing & Supply Chain Services
S.I.C.: 3842; 2834
N.A.I.C.S.: 339113; 325412
Media: 2-4-6-7-9-19-21
Distr.: Natl.
Budget Set: Jan.
Personnel:
George S. Barrett *(Chm & CEO)*
Jeffrey W. Henderson *(CFO)*
Patricia B. Morrison *(CIO)*
Craig S. Morford *(Chief Legal Officer & Chief Compliance Officer)*
Stuart G. Laws *(Chief Acctg Officer)*
Mark Rosenbaum *(Chief Customer Officer)*
Lisa Ashby *(Pres-Category Mgmt-Medical Segment)*
Meghan M. Fitzgerald *(Pres-Specialty Grp)*
Jon Giacomin *(Pres-Pharmaceutical Distr-United States)*
Steve Inacker *(Pres-Channel Mgmt-Medical Segment)*
John C. Rademacher *(Pres-Nuclear & Pharmacy Svcs)*
Michael C. Kaufmann *(CEO-Pharmaceutical Segment)*
Michael A. Lynch *(CEO-Medical Segment)*
Stephen T. Falk *(Gen Counsel, Sec & Exec VP)*
Shelley Bird *(Exec VP-Pub Affairs)*
Mark R. Blake *(Exec VP-Strategy & Corp Dev)*
Tony Caprio *(Exec VP-Sls)*
Mike Duffy *(Exec VP-Global Mfg & Supply Chain-Medical Segment)*
Jeffrey Scott *(Sr VP & Gen Mgr-P4 Healthcare)*
Sally J. Curley *(Sr VP-IR)*
Bill Owad *(Sr VP-Operational Excellence)*
Cynthia Rhomberg *(VP-Corp Mktg)*
Matt Blake *(Dir-IR)*
Carla Cantrell *(Mgr-Product Market)*
Brands & Products:
ALARIS
CAREFUSION
CHLORAPREP
CHLORAPREP FREPP
CHLORAPREP SEPP
CHLORAPREP SWABSTICK
GENESIS
LEADER DRUGSTORES
MEDICAP
MEDICINE SHOPPE
MEDMINED
ONESOURCE
ONSITE
PROXIMATE
PYXIS
SCRIPTLINE
SNOWDEN PENCER
V. MUELLER
VIASYS
ZYDIS
Advertising Agencies:
Northlich
Sawyer Point Bldg 720 Pete Rose Way
Cincinnati, OH 45202
Tel.: (513) 421-8840
Fax: (513) 455-4749

Red Brown Kle
840 N Old World Third St Ste 401
Milwaukee, WI 53203
Tel.: (414) 272-2600
Fax: (414) 272-2690
Toll Free: (888) 725-2041

CARDINAL HEALTH, INC.
(Sub. of Cardinal Health, Inc.)
1330 Enclave Pkwy
Houston, TX 77077-2025
Tel.: (281) 749-4000
Fax: (281) 749-2089
Toll Free: (800) 231-9807
Web Site: www.cardinalpps.com
Sales Range: $75-99.9 Million
Approx. Number Employees: 285
Year Founded: 1969
Business Description:
Health Care Management Services Provider
S.I.C.: 7363
N.A.I.C.S.: 561320
Media: 2-8-10
Distr.: Natl.
Budget Set: Oct.
Brands & Products:
OWEN HEALTHCARE

CARDINAL HEALTH, INC.
(Sub. of Cardinal Health, Inc.)
11400 Tomahawk Creek Pkwy
Leawood, KS 66211
Tel.: (913) 451-0880
Fax: (913) 451-8509
Sales Range: $125-149.9 Million
Approx. Number Employees: 600
Business Description:
Antiseptic Applicator Developer & Mfr
S.I.C.: 3841
N.A.I.C.S.: 339112
Media: 2-7-10

CARDIOGENESIS CORPORATION
11 Musick
Irvine, CA 92618
Tel.: (949) 420-1800
Fax: (949) 420-1875
Toll Free: (800) 238-2205
E-mail: info@cardiogenesis.com
Web Site: www.cardiogenesis.com
Approx. Rev.: $11,290,000
Approx. Number Employees: 32
Year Founded: 1989
Business Description:
Laser & Fiber-Optic Systems for Surgical Use on Cardiac Patients Designer, Developer, Mfr & Distr
S.I.C.: 2676; 3841
N.A.I.C.S.: 322291; 339112
Advertising Expenditures: $95,000
Media: 2-10
Personnel:
Paul J. McCormick *(Chm)*
William R. Abbott *(CFO & Sr VP)*
Richard P. Lanigan *(Exec VP-Mktg)*
Brands & Products:
CARDIOGENESIS
ECLIPSE ADVENT LASER SYSTEM
HEART OF NEW LIFE
PEARL
SOLOGRIP
SOLORGEN

CARDIOMEMS, INC.
75 Fifth St NW Ste 440
Atlanta, GA 30308
Tel.: (404) 920-6700
E-mail: info@cardiomems.com
Web Site: www.cardiomems.com
Sales Range: Less than $1 Million
Approx. Number Employees: 106
Business Description:
Human Body Wireless Sensing & Communication Technology Mfr
S.I.C.: 3841; 3845
N.A.I.C.S.: 339112; 334510
Advertising Expenditures: $117,525
Media: 7-10
Personnel:
Jay S. Yadav *(Founder, CEO & Dir)*
Mark G. Allen *(Co-Founder & CTO)*
Daniel H. Bauer *(CFO)*
Sandeep S. Yadav *(COO)*
David R. Stern *(Sr VP-Scientific Affairs)*
Matthew Borenzweig *(VP-Sls & Mktg)*

CARDIONET, INC.
227 Washington St
Conshohocken, PA 19428
Tel.: (610) 729-7000
Fax: (610) 828-8048
Toll Free: (888) 312BEAT
E-mail: investorrelations@cardionet.com
Web Site: www.cardionet.com
Approx. Rev.: $119,924,000
Approx. Number Employees: 754
Year Founded: 1999
Business Description:
Mobile Cardiac Outpatient Telemetry Enabling Heartbeat-By-Heartbeat, ECG Monitoring, Analysis & Response
S.I.C.: 3845; 5047; 8099
N.A.I.C.S.: 334510; 423450; 621999
Advertising Expenditures: $823,000
Personnel:
Randy H. Thurman *(Chm)*
Joseph H. Capper *(Pres & CEO)*
Heather C. Getz *(CFO)*
Peter Ferola *(Gen Counsel & Sr VP-Corp Dev)*
Charles Gropper *(Sr VP-R&D)*
George Hrenko *(Sr VP-HR & Organizational Excellence)*
Anna McNamara *(Sr VP-Clinical Ops)*
Daniel Wisniewski *(Sr VP-Bus Ops)*
Andy Broadway *(VP-Mktg)*
Derek Lucchese *(Dir-Trng)*

CARE ONE MANAGEMENT, LLC
173 Bridge Plz N
Fort Lee, NJ 07024
Tel.: (201) 242-4021
Web Site: www.care-one.com
Approx. Rev.: $1,000,000,000
Approx. Number Employees: 15,000
Business Description:
Nursing Care Facilities Owner & Operator
N.A.I.C.S.: 623110
Personnel:
Danette Manzi *(COO)*
Kevin Breslin *(Exec VP)*
Advertising Agency:
HealthStar Public Relations
112 Madison Ave
New York, NY 10016
Tel.: (212) 532-0909
Fax: (212) 532-6907

CAREFIRST, INC.
10455 Mill Run Cir
Owings Mills, MD 21117
Tel.: (410) 581-3000
Fax: (410) 998-5351
Web Site: www.carefirst.com
Sales Range: $1-4.9 Billion
Business Description:
Healthcare Services
S.I.C.: 9431
N.A.I.C.S.: 923120
Advertising Expenditures: $3,600,000
Personnel:
Michael R. Merson *(Chm)*
Edward J. Baran *(Vice Chm)*
G. Chaney *(CFO, Treas & Exec VP)*
Harry Fox *(CIO)*
Gregory Allen Devou *(CMO & Exec VP)*

Key to Media (For complete agency information see *The Advertising Red Books-Agencies* edition):
1. Bus. Publs. 2. Cable T.V. 3. Catalogs & Directories. 4. Co-op Adv. 5. Consumer Mags. 6. D.M. to Bus. Estab.7. D.M. to Consumers 8. Daily Newsp. 9. Exhibits/Trade Shows 10. Foreign 11. Infomercial 12. Internet Adv.13. Multimedia 14. Network Radio 15. Network T.V. 16. Newsp. Distr. Mags. 17. Other 18. Outdoor (Posters, Transit) 19. Point of Purchase20. Premiums, Novelties 21. Product Samples 22. Special Events Mktg. 23. Spot Radio 24. Spot T.V. 25. Weekly Newsp. 26. Yellow Page Adv.

CareFirst, Inc. — (Continued)

Eric R. Baugh *(Chief Medical Officer & Sr VP)*
John A. Picciotto *(Gen Counsel, Sec & Exec VP)*
Sharon J. Vecchioni *(Exec VP)*
Rita A. Costello *(Sr VP-Strategic Mktg)*
Livio Broccolino *(VP & Deputy Gen Counsel)*
Christine L. Alrich *(VP-Corp Mktg-Blue Cross Blue Shield-Delaware)*
Samuel L. Bennet *(VP-IT)*

Advertising Agency:
Cramer-Krasselt
7 W 22nd 8th Fl
New York, NY 10010
Tel.: (212) 889-6450
Fax: (212) 251-1265

CAREFIRST OF MARYLAND, INC.

(Sub. of CareFirst, Inc.)
(d/b/a CareFirst BlueCross BlueShield)
10455 Mill Run Cir
Owings Mills, MD 21117-4208
Tel.: (410) 581-3000
Fax: (410) 998-5351
Toll Free: (800) 321-3497
Web Site: www.carefirst.com
Approx. Number Employees: 500
Year Founded: 1937
Business Description:
Not-For-Profit Managed Health Company
S.I.C.: 6321
N.A.I.C.S.: 524114
Import Export
Media: 15-24
Personnel:
John M. Colmers *(Chm)*
Brands & Products:
CAREFIRST

CAREFUSION CORPORATION

3750 Torrey View Ct
San Diego, CA 92130-2622
Tel.: (858) 617-2000
Fax: (858) 617-2900
Toll Free: (888) 876-4287
E-mail: media@carefusion.com
Web Site: www.carefusion.com
Approx. Rev.: $3,528,000,000
Approx. Number Employees: 14,000
Business Description:
Medical Instrument Mfr
S.I.C.: 3841
N.A.I.C.S.: 339112
Personnel:
Kieran T. Gallahue *(Chm & CEO)*
James F. Hinrichs *(CFO)*
Joan Stafslien *(Chief Compliance Officer, Gen Counsel, Sec & Exec VP)*
Vivek Jain *(Pres-Procedural Solutions)*
Thomas Leonard *(Pres-Medical Sys)*
Don Abbey *(Exec VP-Quality, Regulatory & Medical Affair)*
Roger Marchetti *(Exec VP-HR)*
Neil Ryding *(Exec VP-Global Mfg & Supply)*
Scott Bostick *(Sr VP-Strategic Sls & Support-US)*
Marty Gluck *(Sr VP-IT)*
Jim Mazzola *(Sr VP-Global Mktg & Comm)*
Jason Strohm *(Sr VP-Portfolio & Channel Dev)*
Brands & Products:
ALARIS
AVEA
CHLORAPREP
JAEGER
MAXGUARD
MAXPLUS
PULMONETIC SYSTEMS
PYXIS
SENSORMEDICS
SMARTSITE
V. MUELLER
Advertising Agency:
Sullivan Higdon & Sink Incorporated
255 N Mead St
Wichita, KS 67202-2707
Tel.: (316) 263-0124
Fax: (316) 263-1084
Toll Free: (800) 577-5684

CAREGROUP, INC.

109 Brookline Dr Ste 300
Boston, MA 02215
Tel.: (617) 667-1715
Fax: (617) 667-1736
E-mail: info@caregroup.org
Web Site: www.caregroup.org
Sales Range: $1-4.9 Billion
Approx. Number Employees: 13,000
Business Description:
Hospital & Health Care Service Operator
S.I.C.: 8062
N.A.I.C.S.: 622110
Media: 17
Personnel:
Robert Melzer *(Chm)*
John Szum *(CFO & Exec VP)*
Brands & Products:
CAREGROUP

CAREMARK PHARMACY SERVICES

(Sub. of CVS Caremark Corporation)
445 Great Cir Rd
Nashville, TN 37228
Tel.: (615) 743-6600
Web Site: www.caremark.com
Sales Range: $5-14.9 Billion
Approx. Number Employees: 13,360
Year Founded: 1993
Business Description:
Prescription Benefits Management Services
S.I.C.: 5122; 5912; 5961
N.A.I.C.S.: 424210; 446110; 454113
Media: 8-10-13
Personnel:
Peter J. Clemens IV *(CFO & Exec VP)*
Douglas A. Sgarro *(Chief Legal Officer-CVS Caremark Corp & Exec VP)*
Sara J. Finley *(Sec, Sr VP & Asst Gen Counsel)*
Chris W. Bodine *(Exec VP)*
Jack E. Bruner *(Exec VP-Strategic Dev)*
Mark S. Weeks *(Sr VP & Controller)*
V. Michael Ferdinandi *(Sr VP-HR & Corp Comm)*
Bruce Lyons *(VP-Sls)*
Brands & Products:
CAREMARK
CAREPATTERNS
IT ALL STARTS WITH CARE
Advertising Agency:
WHITTMANHART
150 North Michigan Ave Ste 300
Chicago, IL 60601
Tel.: (312) 981-6000
Fax: (312) 981-6100

CARILION HEALTH SYSTEM

1906 Belleview Ave
Roanoke, VA 24014
Tel.: (540) 981-7000
Toll Free: (800) 422-8482
Web Site: www.carilionclinic.org
Sales Range: $750-799.9 Million
Approx. Number Employees: 9,600
Business Description:
Hospital & Health Care Services
S.I.C.: 8062
N.A.I.C.S.: 622110
Advertising Expenditures: $1,000,000
Media: 4-7-8-10-13-22
Personnel:
Edward G. Murphy *(Pres & CEO)*
Donald E. Lorton *(CFO)*
Briggs W. Andrews *(Gen Counsel)*

CARITAS CHRISTI INC.

736 Cambridge St
Brighton, MA 02135-2907
Mailing Address:
PO Box 17
Natchitoches, LA 71458
Tel.: (617) 789-5112
Fax: (617) 789-2337
E-mail: semcmail@cchcs.org
Web Site: www.caritas-semc.org
Approx. Number Employees: 5,300
Year Founded: 1985
Business Description:
Provider of Hospital Management Services
S.I.C.: 8082
N.A.I.C.S.: 621610
Import Export
Personnel:
Ralph de la Torre *(Pres & CEO)*
John Holiver *(Pres-St Elizabeths Medical Center)*
Steve Danehy *(Exec Dir)*
Advertising Agency:
Rasky Baerlein Strategic Communications
70 Franklin St 3rd Fl
Boston, MA 02110
Tel.: (617) 443-9933
Fax: (617) 443-9944
(Public Relations)

CAROLINA BIOLOGICAL SUPPLY COMPANY

2700 York Rd
Burlington, NC 27215
Tel.: (336) 584-0381
Fax: (800) 222-7112
Toll Free: (800) 334-5551
E-mail: carolina@carolina.com
Web Site: www.carolina.com
Sales Range: $25-49.9 Million
Approx. Number Employees: 530
Year Founded: 1927
Business Description:
Retailer of Living & Preserved Animals & Plants, Physics & Earth Sciences Materials, Space Science Materials, Biotechnology Materials, Mathematics Materials, Microscopes & Microscope Slides, Lab Supplies, Chemicals, Biological Models & Visual Aids
S.I.C.: 5049; 2836
N.A.I.C.S.: 423490; 325414
Import Export
Media: 2-4-5-7-10-21
Distr.: Intl.
Budget Set: Sept. -Oct.
Personnel:
Thomas E. Powell *(Chm)*
James Parrish *(Pres & CEO)*
Mark Meszaros *(VP-Production)*
George Ross *(VP-Sls & Mktg)*
Gray Amick *(Mgr-Adv)*
Mike Web *(Mgr-Adv Bus)*
Brands & Products:
ACTIVE SCIENCE
ALGA-GRO
BIO LAB
BIOKIT
BIOPHOTO
BIOREVIEW
BRAINLINK
CABISCO
CABISCO HEALTH & FITNESS
CAROLINA
CAROLINA BIOLOGICAL
CAROLINA MATHEMATICS
CAROLINA TIPS
CAROLINA'S PERFECT SOLUTION
CAROPAK
CAROSAFE
CAROSPRAY
CBR
ECO-SEEKER
FLYNAP
FORMULA 4-24
GEMS
JASON PROJECT
KLEERMOUNT
LAMOTTE
LIVING WONDERS
MICROKWIK CULTURE
MOLE-E-CLUES
THE MOLE PAD
MY HEALTH MY WORLD
OHAUS
PBLU
PLANASLO
PROTOSLO
PUFFNS
READI-STAIN
SCIENCE AND TECHNOLOGY FOR CHILDREN
STC
STC/MS
STERIGEL
TEAMED WITH TEACHERS
VITACHROME
WOLFE
WORLD CLASS SUPPORT FOR SCIENCE & MATH
X-JUMBO

CARSTENS INC.

7310 W Wilson Ave
Harwood Heights, IL 60706
Tel.: (708) 669-1500
Fax: (708) 669-1559
Toll Free: (800) 782-1524
E-mail: carstens@carstens.com
Web Site: www.carstens.com
Approx. Number Employees: 100
Year Founded: 1936
Business Description:
Mfr. of Hospital & Long Term Care Patient Charting Systems; Patient Chart Racks & Card-Indexers; Pressure Sensitive Labels
S.I.C.: 3841

Key to Media (For complete agency information see *The Advertising Red Books-Agencies* edition):
1. Bus. Publs. 2. Cable T.V. 3. Catalogs & Directories. 4. Co-op Adv. 5. Consumer Mags. 6. D.M. to Bus. Estab.7. D.M. to Consumers
8. Daily Newsp. 9. Exhibits/Trade Shows 10. Foreign 11. Infomercial 12. Internet Adv.13. Multimedia 14. Network Radio
15. Network T.V. 16. Newsp. Distr. Mags. 17. Other 18. Outdoor (Posters, Transit) 19. Point of Purchase20. Premiums, Novelties
21. Product Samples 22. Special Events Mktg. 23. Spot Radio 24. Spot T.V. 25. Weekly Newsp. 26. Yellow Page Adv.

N.A.I.C.S.: 339112
Export
Advertising Expenditures: $600,000
Media: 1-2-4-7-10-13-19-20-26
Distr.: Intl.; Natl.
Budget Set: Oct.
Personnel:
Peter Block *(Pres)*
Jaclyn Blend *(Mgr-Adv)*
Brands & Products:
CARSTENS
CUSTOMLINE
DESIGN-A-LINE
ECONOROO
HAL-A-ROO
HALF-A-ROO
MEDIX-VISITRAY
MOBILE CHARTING UNIT
PRIVACY COVERS
QUICKDESK
RECORD GUARD
STAT CHEK
WALKAROO III
WALLACART
WALLAROO
WALLAROO III
WALLAROO JR.
WIDE-TRAK

CAS MEDICAL SYSTEMS, INC.
(d/b/a CASMED)
44 E Industrial Rd
Branford, CT 06405
Tel.: (203) 488-6056
Fax: (203) 488-9438
Toll Free: (800) 227-4414
E-mail: custsrv@casmed.com
Web Site: www.casmed.com
Approx. Sls.: $24,086,011
Approx. Number Employees: 101
Business Description:
Mfr of Medical Equipment & Supplies
S.I.C.: 3821; 3841; 3842
N.A.I.C.S.: 339111; 339112; 339113
Advertising Expenditures: $666,000
Media: 4-7-8-10-11-21
Distr.: Intl.
Budget Set: Nov.
Personnel:
Louis P. Scheps *(Chm)*
Thomas M. Patton *(Pres & CEO)*
Jeffery A. Baird *(CFO)*
Matthew J. Herwig *(VP-Sls & Mktg)*
Frank P. Gregorio *(Dir-Sls-North America)*
Ignacio J. Silva *(Dir-Intl Bus Dev)*
Brands & Products:
AMI
BILIBOTTOMS
CAS EXPRESS
CAS MEDICAL
EDENTEC ASSURANCE
EDENTREND
EVENT-LINK
FOR EVERY LIFE & BREATH SITUATION
FOR WHAT'S VITAL
FORE-SIGHT
KLEAR-TRACE
LASER-SIGHT
LIMBOARD
MAXNIBP
NEOGUARD
OSCILLOMATE
PEDISPHYG
PREMIE NESTIE
SAFE-CUFF
SOFTCHECK
SWANK
TUFF-CUFF
ULTRACHECK
UNIFUSOR
WOODS PUMP

CATASYS, INC.
(Formerly HYTHIAM, INC.)
11150 Santa Monica Blvd Ste 1500
Los Angeles, CA 90025
Tel.: (310) 444-4300
Fax: (310) 444-5300
Web Site: www.catasyshealth.com
Approx. Rev.: $448,000
Approx. Number Employees: 33
Business Description:
Behavioral Health Management Services
S.I.C.: 8093; 8748
N.A.I.C.S.: 621420; 541618
Advertising Expenditures: $680,000
Personnel:
Terren S. Peizer *(Chm & CEO)*
Peter Donato *(CFO)*
Gary Ingenito *(Sr VP-Scientific Affairs)*
W. Greg McLane *(Sr VP-Sls & Mktg)*
Lawrence M. Weinstein *(Sr VP-Medical Affairs)*
Brands & Products:
CATASYS
ONTRAK
PROMETA
PROMETA CENTER
THE SCIENCE OF RECOVERY

CATHOLIC HEALTH EAST
3805 W Chester Pike Ste 100
Newtown Square, PA 19073
Tel.: (610) 355-2000
Fax: (610) 355-2050
E-mail: info@che.org
Web Site: www.che.org
Sales Range: $1-4.9 Billion
Approx. Number Employees: 44,000
Year Founded: 1998
Business Description:
Hospital & Health Care Services
S.I.C.: 8062
N.A.I.C.S.: 622110
Media: 4
Personnel:
Jacquelyn Kinder *(Chm)*
Robert Stanek *(Pres & CEO)*
Peter DeAngelis, Jr. *(CFO & Exec VP)*
Michael J. McCoy *(Chief Medical Info Officer)*
Michael Hemsley *(Gen Counsel & VP-Svcs)*
Mary Persico *(Exec VP-Mission Integration)*
Patricia Gathers *(VP-Fin)*

CATHOLIC HEALTHCARE SYSTEM
1339 York Ave
New York, NY 10021
Tel.: (212) 752-7300
Fax: (212) 752-7547
E-mail: info@chcsnet.org
Web Site:
www.catholichealthcaresystem.org
Year Founded: 1955
Business Description:
Operates Hospital & Health Care Services
S.I.C.: 8661
N.A.I.C.S.: 813110
Media: 4-10-13
Personnel:
Karl P. Adler *(Chm)*
Sara Strum *(Gen Counsel)*

C.B. FLEET COMPANY, INC.
4615 Murray Pl
Lynchburg, VA 24502-2235
Mailing Address:
PO Box 11349
Lynchburg, VA 24506-1349
Tel.: (434) 528-4000
Fax: (434) 522-8490
Toll Free: (800) 999-9711
Web Site: www.cbfleet.com
Approx. Number Employees: 450
Year Founded: 1869
Business Description:
Beauty & Healthcare Products Mfr
S.I.C.: 2844; 2834
N.A.I.C.S.: 325620; 325412
Export
Media: 2-3-5-6-7-9-10-15-19-20-21-24
Distr.: Natl.
Budget Set: Dec.
Personnel:
Douglas Bellaire *(Pres & CEO)*
Jeff Rowan *(Exec VP-Global Mktg & Intl Ops)*
Brands & Products:
CASEN-FLEET
CLINOMYN
DE WITT
FLEET
FLEET PHOSPHO-SODA
NORFORMS
SUERORAL
SUMMER'S EVE
WITCH

CCS MEDICAL HOLDINGS, INC.
(Holding of Warburg Pincus LLC)
14255 49th St N Ste 301
Clearwater, FL 33762
Tel.: (727) 531-9161
Fax: (727) 531-9160
Web Site: www.ccsmed.com
Approx. Rev.: $432,430,000
Approx. Number Employees: 1,434
Business Description:
Holding Company
S.I.C.: 6719
N.A.I.C.S.: 551112
Advertising Expenditures: $2,433,000
Personnel:
Dirk Allison *(Pres & CEO)*
Michael A. Sicuro *(CFO & Exec VP)*

CELERA CORPORATION
1401 Harbor Bay Pkwy
Alameda, CA 94502
Tel.: (510) 749-4200
Toll Free: (877) 235-3721
E-mail: mediainfo@celera.com
Web Site: www.celera.com
Approx. Rev.: $128,169,000
Approx. Number Employees: 490
Year Founded: 1998
Business Description:
Disease Testing, Treatment & Management Products & Services
S.I.C.: 8071; 8733
N.A.I.C.S.: 621511; 541710
Advertising Expenditures: $200,000
Personnel:
Kathy P. Ordonez *(CEO)*
Alfred G. Merriweather *(CFO & Sr VP)*
Thomas White *(Chief Scientific Officer & Sr VP)*
Paul Arata *(Sr VP-HR & Admin)*
Stacey Sias *(Sr VP-Bus Dev & Strategic Plng)*
Michael A. Zoccoli *(Sr VP-Products Grp)*
Raymond Cyrus *(Dir-Internet Strategies)*

CELGENE CORPORATION - ANTHROGENESIS DIVISION
(Sub. of Celgene Corporation)
45 Horsehill Rd
Cedar Knolls, NJ 07927-2009
Tel.: (973) 267-8200
Fax: (973) 267-8201
Web Site: www.celgene.com/about-celgene/celgene-locations-na.aspx
Sales Range: $75-99.9 Million
Approx. Number Employees: 50
Business Description:
Discovers, Develops & Commercializes Applications for Human Stem Cells or Biotherapeutics
S.I.C.: 8733
N.A.I.C.S.: 541720
Personnel:
Robert Feriri *(Chm)*
Craig C. Phillips *(VP-Sls & Oncology Div)*
Advertising Agency:
TeamNash, Inc.
4 Jonathan Dr
East Hampton, NY 11937
Tel.: (646) 497-0297

CELL THERAPEUTICS, INC.
501 Elliott Ave W Ste 400
Seattle, WA 98119-4230
Tel.: (206) 282-7100
Fax: (206) 284-6206
Toll Free: (800) 215-2355
E-mail: media@ctiseattle.com
Web Site: www.cticseattle.com
Approx. Rev.: $319,000
Approx. Number Employees: 87
Year Founded: 1992
Business Description:
Cancer Treatments Developer & Marketer
S.I.C.: 2834; 8733
N.A.I.C.S.: 325412; 541710
Advertising Expenditures: $900,000
Personnel:
James A. Bianco *(Founder, CEO & Principal)*
Craig W. Philips *(Pres)*
Jack W. Singer *(Chief Medical Officer & Exec VP)*
Louis A. Bianco *(Exec VP-Fin & Admin)*
Dan Eramian *(EVP-Corp Comm)*
Ed Bell *(Dir-IR)*
Brands & Products:
CTI
MY LIFE.MY CANCER.MY TREATMENT
OPAXIO
PG-TXL
PIXANTRONE
TAXOL

CENTOCOR, INC.
(Sub. of Johnson & Johnson)
800 Ridgeview Dr
Horsham, PA 19044
Tel.: (610) 651-6000
Fax: (610) 651-6100

Key to Media (For complete agency information see *The Advertising Red Books-Agencies* edition):
1. Bus. Publs. 2. Cable T.V. 3. Catalogs & Directories. 4. Co-op Adv. 5. Consumer Mags. 6. D.M. to Bus. Estab.7. D.M. to Consumers
8. Daily Newsp. 9. Exhibits/Trade Shows 10. Foreign 11. Infomercial 12. Internet Adv.13. Multimedia 14. Network Radio
15. Network T.V. 16. Newsp. Distr. Mags. 17. Other 18. Outdoor (Posters, Transit) 19. Point of Purchase20. Premiums, Novelties
21. Product Samples 22. Special Events Mktg. 23. Spot Radio 24. Spot T.V. 25. Weekly Newsp. 26. Yellow Page Adv.

Centocor, Inc. — (Continued)

Web Site: www.centocor.com
Sales Range: $1-4.9 Billion
Approx. Number Employees: 3,000
Year Founded: 1979
Business Description:
Injectable Monoclonal Antibody-Based Pharmaceuticals Mfr & Developer for Cardiovascular, Infectious & Autoimmune Diseases
S.I.C.: 2836; 2834; 2835
N.A.I.C.S.: 325414; 325412; 325413
Media: 7
Distr.: Intl.; Natl.

CENTRAL DUPAGE HEALTH, INC.
25 N Winfield Rd
Winfield, IL 60190
Tel.: (630) 871-6699
Fax: (630) 871-6696
E-mail: cdh_information@cdh.org
Web Site: www.cdh.org
Approx. Rev.: $391,889,000
Approx. Number Employees: 3,000
Year Founded: 1980
Business Description:
Hospital & Health Care Management Services; Hospital & Specialty Outpatient Clinic Operations
S.I.C.: 8062
N.A.I.C.S.: 622110
Personnel:
C. William Pollard *(Chm)*
Richard A. Mark *(Vice Chm)*
Luke McGuinness *(Pres & CEO)*
Jim Spear *(CFO & Exec VP)*
David Printz *(CIO & VP)*
Debra O'Donnell *(VP & Chief Nursing Officer)*
Michael Holzhueter *(Gen Counsel & VP-Legal Affairs)*
Michael Vivoda *(Exec VP)*
Maureen Taus *(VP-Fin & Controller)*
Jill Brown *(VP-Mktg & Comm)*
Rick Davis *(VP-HR)*
Liz Rosenberg *(VP-Strategic Plng)*
Advertising Agency:
Element 79
(Part of the Omincom Group)
200 E Randolph St 33rd Fl
Chicago, IL 60601
Tel.: (312) 233-8100
Fax: (312) 233-8298

CENTRASTATE HEALTHCARE SYSTEM INC.
901 W Main St
Freehold, NJ 07728
Tel.: (732) 431-2000
Tel.: (732) 294-4960 (Mktg & PR)
E-mail: info@centrastate.com
Web Site: www.centrastate.com
Approx. Number Employees: 1,900
Business Description:
Healthcare Services
S.I.C.: 8741; 8099
N.A.I.C.S.: 561110; 621999
Media: 2
Personnel:
John T. Gribbin *(Pres & CEO)*
John Dellocono *(CFO & Sr VP)*
Daniel J. Messina *(COO & Sr VP)*
Indranil Ganguly *(CIO & VP)*
Benjamin Weinstein *(Chief Medical Officer & Sr VP)*
Alice Guttler *(Sr VP & Corp Counsel)*
Frances Keane *(VP-HR)*
Debbie Connors *(Asst VP-Budget Reimbursement)*
Jane Girling *(Asst VP-Corp Matls Mgmt)*
Cathleen Janzekovich *(Asst VP-Nursing)*
Jim Karaman *(Asst VP-Ops)*
Jan McAvenia *(Asst VP-Patient Fin Svcs)*
Robert M. Nyman *(Asst VP-Fin)*
Brands & Products:
CENTRASTATE

CENTRIC GROUP LLC
1260 Andes Blvd
Saint Louis, MO 63132
Tel.: (314) 214-2700
Fax: (314) 214-2796
Toll Free: (800) 325-4500
E-mail: hr@centricgroup.com
Web Site: www.centricgroup.com
Approx. Sls.: $301,800,000
Approx. Number Employees: 70
Year Founded: 1999
Business Description:
Drugs, Proprietaries, & Sundries
S.I.C.: 5122; 5149
N.A.I.C.S.: 424210; 424490
Media: 4-10

CEPHALON, INC.
41 Moores Rd PO Box 4011
Frazer, PA 19355
Tel.: (610) 344-0200
Fax: (610) 738-6590
E-mail: USMedInfo@cephalon.com
Web Site: www.cephalon.com
Approx. Rev.: $2,811,057,000
Approx. Number Employees: 3,726
Year Founded: 1987
Business Description:
Biopharmaceutical Products for Treatment of Neurological Disorders, Sleep Disorders & Cancer
S.I.C.: 2834
N.A.I.C.S.: 325412
Personnel:
J. Kevin Buchi *(CEO)*
Wilco Groenhuysen *(CFO & Exec VP)*
Valli F. Baldassano *(Chief Compliance Officer & Exec VP)*
Carl A. Savini *(Chief Admin Officer & Exec VP)*
Lesley Russell *(Chief Medical Officer & Exec VP)*
Jeffry L. Vaught *(Chief Scientific Officer & Exec VP)*
Alain Aragues *(Pres-Cephalon Europe & Exec VP)*
Gerald Jerry Pappert *(Gen Counsel & Exec VP)*
Bob Repella *(Sr VP-Pharmaceutical Ops-US)*
Candace Steele Flippin *(Sr Dir-Product Comm)*
Jenifer Antonacci *(Assoc Dir)*
Stacey Beckhardt *(Assoc Dir-Alliance Dev)*
Karen McCollum *(Assoc Dir)*
Alexandria Cherry *(Sr Product Mgr-Oncology Mktg)*
Brands & Products:
ACTIQ
AMRIX
CEPHALON
CEPHALONCARES
FENTORA
GABITRIL
MYOCET
NUVIGIL
PROVIGIL
TREANDA
TRISENOX
VIVITROL
Advertising Agencies:
CHS
14350 Frank Lloyd Wright Blvd Ste A4
Scottsdale, AZ 85260
Tel.: (480) 305-5669
Fax: (480) 905-8394

Ignite Health
8955 Research Dr
Irvine, CA 92618-4237
Tel.: (949) 861-3200
Fax: (949) 861-3750

LLNS
220 E 42nd St
New York, NY 10017-5806
Tel.: (212) 771-3000
Fax: (212) 771-3010

nitrogen
One S Broad St Fl 11
Philadelphia, PA 19107
Tel.: (215) 625-0111
Fax: (215) 625-9037

Palio
260 Broadway
Saratoga Springs, NY 12866
Tel.: (518) 584-8924
Fax: (518) 583-1560

CEPHEID
904 Caribbean Dr
Sunnyvale, CA 94089-1189
Tel.: (408) 541-4191
Fax: (408) 541-4192
E-mail: marketing@cepheid.com
Web Site: www.cepheid.com
Approx. Rev.: $212,468,000
Approx. Number Employees: 576
Year Founded: 1996
Business Description:
Microfluidic Systems to Analyze Biological Samples
S.I.C.: 3826; 3841
N.A.I.C.S.: 334516; 339112
Media: 4
Personnel:
Thomas L. Gutshall *(Co-Founder)*
John L. Bishop *(CEO)*
Anita Herrstrom-Sjoberg *(Mng Dir)*
Andrew D. Miller *(CFO & Sr VP)*
Humberto V. Reyes *(COO & Exec VP)*
David H. Persing *(Exec VP, CTO & Chief Medical Officer)*
Nicolaas Arnold *(Exec VP-Worldwide Comml Ops)*
Peter J. Dailey *(Sr VP-R&D)*
Russel K. Enns *(Sr VP-Regulatory, Clinical, Govt Affairs & Quality Sys)*
Laurie King *(Sr VP-HR)*
Robert J. Koska *(Sr VP-Sls Ops-US)*
Joseph H. Smith *(Sr VP-Legal & Bus Dev)*
Sandra Finley *(VP-Mktg)*
Vincent M. Powers *(VP-Intellectual Property)*
Jan Steuperaert *(VP-IT)*
Jim Kennedy *(Exec Dir-Technical Support & Svcs)*
Jacquie Ross *(Sr Dir-IR)*
Jared Tipton *(Dir-Corp & Mktg Comm)*
Brands & Products:
CEPHEID
GENEXPERT
OMNIMIX
SMARTCYCLER

CERNER CORPORATION
2800 Rockcreek Pkwy
Kansas City, MO 64117
Tel.: (816) 221-1024
Fax: (816) 474-1742
E-mail: info@cerner.com
Web Site: www.cerner.com
Approx. Rev.: $1,850,222,000
Approx. Number Employees: 8,200
Year Founded: 1979
Business Description:
Information Technology Solutions for the Healthcare Industry
S.I.C.: 7373; 7372
N.A.I.C.S.: 541512; 511210
Export
Media: 2-4-7-8-10-22
Distr.: Natl.
Budget Set: Oct.
Personnel:
Neal L. Patterson *(Chm & CEO)*
Clifford W. Illig *(Vice Chm)*
Marc G. Naughton *(CFO & Sr VP)*
Michael R. Nill *(COO & Exec VP)*
Donald D. Trigg *(CMO & VP)*
Randy D. Sims *(Chief Legal Officer, Sec & VP)*
Julia M. Wilson *(Chief People Officer & Sr VP)*
Gay M. Johannes *(Chief Quality Officer & VP)*
Michael C. Neal *(VP-Cerner Corp & Pres-US West)*
Zane M. Burke *(Exec VP)*
Jeffrey A. Townsend *(Exec VP)*
Douglas M. Krebs *(Sr VP & Gen Mgr-Global)*
Jude G. Dieterman *(Sr VP-Client Dev)*
Alan Dietrich *(Sr VP)*
Richard J. Flanigan, Jr. *(Sr VP)*
Paul N. Gorup *(Sr VP & Chief-Innovation)*
John B. Landis *(Sr VP-Client Ops)*
John T. Peterzalek *(Sr VP)*
Paul J. Sinclair *(Sr VP-Svcs)*
Michael Battaglioli *(VP-Fin)*
Brands & Products:
ALL TOGETHER
APACHE
CAPSTONE
CAREAWARE
CARENET
CERNER
CERNER BRIDGE
CERNER LIFESCIENCES
CERNER MILLENNIUM
CVNET
DISCERN
DISCERN EXPERT
DISCERN EXPLORER
FIRSTNET
HEALTHSMART
INET
IQHEALTH
MILLENIUM
MULTUM
PATHNET

Key to Media (For complete agency information see *The Advertising Red Books-Agencies* edition):
1. Bus. Publs. 2. Cable T.V. 3. Catalogs & Directories. 4. Co-op Adv. 5. Consumer Mags. 6. D.M. to Bus. Estab.7. D.M. to Consumers
8. Daily Newsp. 9. Exhibits/Trade Shows 10. Foreign 11. Infomercial 12. Internet Adv.13. Multimedia 14. Network Radio
15. Network T.V. 16. Newsp. Distr. Mags. 17. Other 18. Outdoor (Posters, Transit) 19. Point of Purchase20. Premiums, Novelties
21. Product Samples 22. Special Events Mktg. 23. Spot Radio 24. Spot T.V. 25. Weekly Newsp. 26. Yellow Page Adv.

PHARMNET
POWERCHART
POWERCHART OFFICE
POWERVISION
POWERWORKS
PROCALL
PROCURE
PROFIT
PROVISION
RADNET
SURGINET

CHATTANOOGA GROUP
(Sub. of DJO Incorporated)
4717 Adams Rd
Hixson, TN 37343
Tel.: (423) 870-7200
Fax: (423) 870-7403
Toll Free: (800) 592-7329
E-mail: customerservice@chattgroup.com
Web Site: www.chattgroup.com
Sales Range: $75-99.9 Million
Approx. Number Employees: 280
Year Founded: 1947
Business Description:
Physical Therapy & Chiropractic Equipment & Supplies
S.I.C.: 3842
N.A.I.C.S.: 339113
Export
Media: 2-4-7-10-11-20
Distr.: Intl.; Natl.
Budget Set: Apr.
Personnel:
Judi Taylor *(Mgr-Event Plng)*
Brands & Products:
ADAPTA
COLPAC
DURA-STICK
DURA-STIM
FLUIDO
HOTPAC
HYDROCOLLATOR
NYLATEX
OPTIFLEX
PARA-CARE
SPINALATOR
VECTRA

CHATTEM, INC.
(Sub. of Sanofi-Aventis)
1715 W 38th St
Chattanooga, TN 37409-1248
Tel.: (423) 821-4571
Fax: (423) 821-0395
Toll Free: (800) 366-6077
Web Site: www.chattem.com
Approx. Rev.: $463,342,000
Approx. Number Employees: 547
Year Founded: 1879
Business Description:
Over-the-Counter Healthcare Products, Toiletries & Dietary Supplements Marketer & Mfr
S.I.C.: 2834; 2844
N.A.I.C.S.: 325412; 325620
Import Export
Advertising Expenditures: $105,684,000
Media: 2-3-6-7-8-9-10-15-18-22-24-25
Personnel:
Robert E. Bosworth *(Pres & COO)*
Zan Guerry *(CEO)*
Robert B. Long *(CFO)*
Theodore K. Whitfield, Jr. *(Gen Counsel, Sec & VP)*
J. Blair Ramey *(Sr VP)*
Charles M. Stafford *(Sr VP)*
John L. Stroud *(VP-Mktg)*
Brands & Products:
ACT
ACT RESTORING
ARTHRITIS HOT
ASPERCREME
BALMEX
BENZODENT
BULLFROG
CAPZASIN-HP
CAPZASIN-P
CHATTEM
CORTIZONE-10
DEXATRIM
FLEXALL
GARLIQUE
GOLD BOND
GOLD BOND ULTIMATE
HERPECIN-L
ICY HOT
ICY HOT PRO THERAPY
KAOPECTATE
LIVE BETTER
MELATONEX
MUDD
NEW PHASE
OMNIGEST
PAMPRIN
PHISODERM
PREMSYN
SELSUN BLUE
SPORTSCREME
SUN-IN
ULTRASWIM
UNISOM
Advertising Agency:
WF of R, Inc.
411 Branchway Rd
Richmond, VA 23236-3034
Tel.: (804) 794-2871
Fax: (804) 379-0961
(Media)

CHELSEA THERAPEUTICS INTERNATIONAL, LTD.
3530 Toringdon Way Ste 200
Charlotte, NC 28277
Tel.: (704) 341-1516
Fax: (704) 752-1479
E-mail: webemail06@chelseatherapeutics.com
Web Site:
www.chelseatherapeutics.com
Approx. Int. Income: $242,883
Approx. Number Employees: 30
Year Founded: 2002
Business Description:
Biopharmaceutical Mfr & Researcher
S.I.C.: 2834; 2836; 8733
N.A.I.C.S.: 325412; 325414; 541710
Advertising Expenditures: $524,000
Personnel:
Kevan Clemens *(Chm)*
Simon Pedder *(Pres & CEO)*
J. Nick Riehle *(CFO & VP-Admin)*
Keith Schmidt *(VP-Mktg & Sls)*
Cameron Szakacs *(Sr Dir-Drug Dev)*
Brands & Products:
CH-1504
CHELSEA THERAPEUTICS

CHG HEALTHCARE SERVICES, INC.
6440 S Newrock Dr
Salt Lake City, UT 84121
Tel.: (801) 930-3000
Fax: (801) 930-4517
Toll Free: (800) 453-3030
E-mail: info@chgcompanies.com
Web Site: www.chghealthcare.com
Sales Range: $400-449.9 Million
Approx. Number Employees: 1,000
Year Founded: 1979
Business Description:
Temporary & Permanent Healthcare Staffing Services
S.I.C.: 7361
N.A.I.C.S.: 561310
Advertising Expenditures: $4,954,000
Media: 2-4-7-8-10
Personnel:
Michael Weinholtz *(CEO)*
Sean Dailey *(CFO)*
Scott M. Beck *(COO)*
Michael Peterson *(CIO)*
Mark Law *(Grp Pres-Physician Staffing)*
Kevin S. Ricklefs *(Sr VP-Talent Mgmt)*
James M. Marshall *(VP-Fin)*

CHINA YCT INTERNATIONAL GROUP, INC.
c/o American Union Securities 100 Wall St 15th Fl
New York, NY 10005
Tel.: (212) 232-0120
Fax: (212) 785-5867
E-mail: mxia@ausbanking.com
Web Site: www.yongchuntang.net
Approx. Rev.: $32,012,404
Approx. Number Employees: 54
Business Description:
Pharmaceuticals
S.I.C.: 2834
N.A.I.C.S.: 325412
Advertising Expenditures: $501,729
Personnel:
Tinghe Yan *(Chm & CEO)*
Chuanmin Li *(CFO)*

CHOLESTECH CORPORATION
(Sub. of ALERE INC.)
3347 Investment Blvd
Hayward, CA 94545-3808
Tel.: (877) 696-2525
Fax: (510) 732-7227
Toll Free: (800) 733-0404
E-mail: ctec_hr@cholestech.com
Web Site: www.cholestech.com
Approx. Rev.: $69,526,000
Approx. Number Employees: 216
Year Founded: 1988
Business Description:
Medical Diagnostic Testing Systems Mfr
S.I.C.: 3845; 3826
N.A.I.C.S.: 334510; 334516
Import Export
Advertising Expenditures: $126,000
Media: 7-13
Brands & Products:
CHOLESTECH
CHOLESTECH GDX
CHOLESTECH LDX

CHRISTIANA CARE CORPORATION
501 W 14th St
Wilmington, DE 19801
Tel.: (302) 733-1000
E-mail: twalsh@christianacare.org
Web Site: www.christianacare.org
Sales Range: $1-9.9 Million
Approx. Number Employees: 1,000
Business Description:
Operates Hospital & Health Care Services
S.I.C.: 8062
N.A.I.C.S.: 622110
Media: 3-4-10-13-21-22-23-24-26
Personnel:
Robert J. Laskowski *(Pres & CEO)*
James Newman *(Chief Academic Officer, Sr VP & Exec Dir-Value Institute)*
Buddy Elmore *(Sr VP-Fin & Managed Care)*
Dana Hall *(Sr VP-HR)*
Michele A. Schiavoni *(Sr VP-External Affairs)*

CIGNA TEL-DRUG, INC.
(Unit of CIGNA Health Corporation)
4901 N 4th Ave
Sioux Falls, SD 57104-0444
Tel.: (605) 373-0100
Fax: (605) 373-4866
Toll Free: (800) 835-3784
Web Site: www.teldrug.com
Sales Range: $150-199.9 Million
Business Description:
Mail-Order Pharmaceutical Services
S.I.C.: 5912
N.A.I.C.S.: 446110
Media: 13
Personnel:
Jay Headley *(Dir-Mktg)*
Brands & Products:
DRUGSTORE.COM

CITY OF HOPE NATIONAL MEDICAL CENTER
1500 E Duarte Rd
Duarte, CA 91010
Tel.: (626) 256-4673
Fax: (626) 301-8448
E-mail: jobs@coh.org
Web Site: www.cityofhope.org
Sales Range: $300-349.9 Million
Approx. Number Employees: 200
Year Founded: 1913
Business Description:
Cancer Research Hospital
S.I.C.: 8062
N.A.I.C.S.: 622110
Media: 6-9-13-25
Personnel:
Michael A. Friedman *(Pres & CEO)*
Tennis Rusch *(CFO & Treas)*
Virginia Opipare *(COO & Exec VP)*
Gretory Schetina *(Gen Counsel)*
Kathleen L. Kane *(Exec VP-Devel & External Affairs)*
Theodore G. Krontiris *(Exec VP-Medical & Scientific Affairs)*
Debbie Land *(Mktg Dir)*
Brands & Products:
CANCER SCREENING & PREVENTION PROGRAM
CITY OF HOPE
WHERE THE POWER OF KNOWLEDGE SAVES LIVES

CLARIENT INC.
(Sub. of GE Healthcare)
31 Columbia
Aliso Viejo, CA 92656-1460
Tel.: (949) 425-5700
Fax: (949) 425-5701
Toll Free: (888) 443-3310
E-mail: info@clarientinc.com
Web Site: www.clarientinc.com

Key to Media (For complete agency information see *The Advertising Red Books-Agencies* edition):
1. Bus. Publs. 2. Cable T.V. 3. Catalogs & Directories. 4. Co-op Adv. 5. Consumer Mags. 6. D.M. to Bus. Estab.7. D.M. to Consumers 8. Daily Newsp. 9. Exhibits/Trade Shows 10. Foreign 11. Infomercial 12. Internet Adv.13. Multimedia 14. Network Radio 15. Network T.V. 16. Newsp. Distr. Mags. 17. Other 18. Outdoor (Posters, Transit) 19. Point of Purchase20. Premiums, Novelties 21. Product Samples 22. Special Events Mktg. 23. Spot Radio 24. Spot T.V. 25. Weekly Newsp. 26. Yellow Page Adv.

Clarient Inc. — (Continued)

Approx. Rev.: $91,599,000
Approx. Number Employees: 361
Year Founded: 1996
Business Description:
Medical Diagnostic Testing & Patient Treatment Consulting
S.I.C.: 3826
N.A.I.C.S.: 334516
Advertising Expenditures: $140,000
Media: 2-10-17
Personnel:
Michael J. Pellini *(Pres & COO)*
Ronald A. Andrews, Jr. *(CEO)*
Michael R. Rodriguez *(CFO & Sr VP)*
David J. Daly *(Chief Comml Officer & Sr VP)*
Michael Nall *(VP-Sales & Managed Care)*
Alan Wells *(Sr Dir-Ops)*
Sing-Tsung Chen *(Dir-Hematopathology)*
Neal S. Goldstein *(Dir-Surgical Pathology)*
Michele Hibbard *(Dir-Genetics)*
Ainura Kyshtoobayeva *(Dir-IHC)*
Richard Smooke *(Dir-Sls)*
James Wynne *(Dir-Sls)*
Anselm Hii *(Assoc Dir-Medical)*
Brands & Products:
CHROMAVISION ACIS
Advertising Agency:
Allen & Caron
18200 Von Karman Ave Ste 780
Irvine, CA 92612-0192
Tel.: (949) 474-4300
Fax: (949) 474-4330
(Investor & Media Relations)

CLEVELAND CLINIC

9500 Euclid Ave
Cleveland, OH 44195
Tel.: (800) 223-2273
Web Site: my.clevelandclinic.org
Year Founded: 1921
Business Description:
Academic Medical Center
S.I.C.: 8062
N.A.I.C.S.: 622110
Media: 17
Personnel:
Delos M. Cosgrove *(Pres & CEO)*
Steven C. Glass *(CFO)*
C. Martin Harris *(CIO)*
Paul Matsen *(CMO)*
David W. Rowan *(Chief Legal Officer, Chief Gov Officer & Sec)*
Cindy Hundorfean *(Chief Admin Officer-Clinical Svcs)*
Oliver Henkel *(Chief Govt Rels Officer)*
James Merlino *(Chief Experience Officer)*
Sarah Sinclair *(Exec Chief Nursing Officer)*
Anthony Stallion *(Chief Community Relations & Diversity Officer)*
Robert Wyllie *(Chief Medical Ops Officer)*
Brian Bolwell *(Dir-Bone Marrow Transplant Program)*
Advertising Agencies:
Consolidated Graphics Group Inc.
1614 E 40th St
Cleveland, OH 44103
Tel.: (216) 881-9191
Fax: (216) 881-3442

DigiKnow
3615 Superior Ave Bldg 44 4th Fl
Cleveland, OH 44114
Tel.: (216) 325-1800
Fax: (216) 325-1801

Hill Holliday
53 State St
Boston, MA 02109
Tel.: (617) 366-4000

Hill Holliday/New York
622 3rd Ave 14th Fl
New York, NY 10017
Tel.: (212) 905-7000
Fax: (212) 905-7100

Wyse
668 Euclid Ave
Cleveland, OH 44114
Tel.: (216) 696-2424
Fax: (216) 736-4425

COAST DENTAL SERVICES, INC.

4010 W Boy Scout Blvd Ste 1100
Tampa, FL 33607
Tel.: (813) 288-1999
Fax: (813) 289-4500
Web Site: www.coastdental.com
Approx. Rev.: $56,415,795
Approx. Number Employees: 750
Year Founded: 1992
Business Description:
Developer & Manager of General Dental Practices
S.I.C.: 8011; 8021; 8748
N.A.I.C.S.: 621111; 541618; 621210
Advertising Expenditures: $3,600,000
Media: 15
Personnel:
Adam Diasti *(Founder & Pres)*
Thomas J. Marler *(CEO)*
Michael Smith *(CIO)*
Patricia A. Huie *(Gen Counsel)*
Lauren K. Key *(VP-Mktg)*
Chris Duffy-Waldman *(Dir-Media)*
Brands & Products:
C3
CAPTEK
COAST COMPREHENSIVE CARE
COAST DENTAL
COAST DENTAL ADVANTAGE
ONE COMPANY. COUNTLESS OPPORTUNITIES.
OUR SMILES ARE EVERYWHERE
SMILE PLUS
VIZLITE PLUS
YOUR SMILE CAN BE A WORK OF ART
Advertising Agency:
ChappellRoberts
1600 E 8th Ave 3A133
Tampa, FL 33605
Tel.: (813) 281-0088
Fax: (813) 281-0271

COLGATE ORAL PHARMACEUTICAL

(Div. of Colgate-Palmolive Company)
300 Park Ave
New York, NY 10022
Tel.: (212) 310-2000
Toll Free: (800) 821-2880
Telex: 4992271 VPL UI
E-mail: info@colgateprofessional.com
Web Site: www.colgateprofessional.com
Sales Range: $25-49.9 Million
Approx. Number Employees: 100
Business Description:
Oral Hygiene Products Mfr & Distr
S.I.C.: 2834; 5122
N.A.I.C.S.: 325412; 424210
Advertising Expenditures: $15,000,000
Media: 1-5-6-10-19-21
Distr.: Natl.
Budget Set: Oct.
Personnel:
Ian Cook *(Chm, Pres & CEO)*
Dennis J. Hickey *(CFO)*
Nigel B. Burton *(Pres-Global Oral Care, Consumer Insights & Adv)*
Brands & Products:
ORABASE
PEROXYL
VIADENT

COLLAGENEX PHARMACEUTICALS, INC.

(Joint Venture of Nestle S.A. & L'Oreal S.A.)
41 University Dr
Newtown, PA 18940-1873
Tel.: (215) 579-7388
Fax: (215) 579-8577
Approx. Rev.: $63,586,000
Approx. Number Employees: 147
Business Description:
Dermatology Pharmaceutical Developer & Marketer
S.I.C.: 2834
N.A.I.C.S.: 325412
Advertising Expenditures: $1,245,000
Media: 21
Personnel:
Joseph Zakrzewski *(Chm)*
Brands & Products:
ALCORTIN
ATRIDOX
ATRISORB
FREEFLOW
IMPACS
METASTAT
NOVACORT
ORACEA
PANDEL
PERIOSTAT
RESTORADERM

COLORADO SERUM CO.

4950 York St
Denver, CO 80216-2246
Mailing Address:
PO Box 16428
Denver, CO 80216
Tel.: (303) 295-7527
Fax: (303) 295-1923
Toll Free: (800) 525-2065
E-mail: colorado-serum@colorado-serum.com
Web Site: www.colorado-serum.com
Approx. Number Employees: 100
Year Founded: 1923
Business Description:
Mfr. of Anti Serums, Vaccines, Laboratory Reagents, Animal Blood Products & Serums, Veterinary Serums, Biologicals; Producer of Veterinary, Dental & Surgical Instruments
S.I.C.: 2836; 3841
N.A.I.C.S.: 325414; 339112
Import Export
Media: 2-4-16
Distr.: Natl.
Budget Set: Jan.-July
Personnel:
J. N. Huff *(Pres)*
Ed Lehigh *(VP-Mktg)*
Brands & Products:
COLORADO SERUM

COLUMBIA LABORATORIES, INC.

354 Eisenhower Pkwy Plaza 1 2nd Fl
Livingston, NJ 07039
Tel.: (973) 994-3999
Fax: (866) 994-3001
Toll Free: (866) 566-5636
E-mail: general@columbialabs.com
Web Site: www.columbialabs.com
Approx. Rev.: $45,676,297
Approx. Number Employees: 22
Year Founded: 1986
Business Description:
Women's Healthcare Pharmaceutical Products Developer & Retailer
S.I.C.: 2834
N.A.I.C.S.: 325412
Import Export
Advertising Expenditures: $600,000
Media: 10-21-22
Personnel:
Stephen G. Kasnet *(Chm)*
Frank C. Condella, Jr. *(Pres & CEO)*
Lawrence A. Gyenes *(CFO, Treas & Sr VP)*
Michael Mcgrane *(Gen Counsel, Sec & Sr VP)*
Brands & Products:
CRINONE
PROCHIEVE
REPHRESH
STRIANT

COMBE INCORPORATED

1101 Westchester Ave
White Plains, NY 10604-3503
Tel.: (914) 694-5454
Fax: (914) 694-6233
Toll Free: (800) 873-7400
E-mail: info@combe.com
Web Site: www.combe.com
Approx. Number Employees: 600
Year Founded: 1949
Business Description:
Pharmaceutical Products Mfr
S.I.C.: 2844; 2841
N.A.I.C.S.: 325620; 325611
Export
Media: 2-3-4-5-6-7-8-9-11-15-16-18-21-23-24-25
Distr.: Natl.
Personnel:
Christopher B. Combe *(Chm)*
Douglas McGraime *(Pres)*
Joseph P. Gusmano *(CFO & Sr VP)*
John Lerch *(Chief Adv Officer Worldwide)*
Gail R. Perlow *(Pres-Media Insight)*
Rick Powers *(Pres-North America)*
John P. Alberto *(Sr VP-HR)*
Steven Berger *(Sr VP-Media Plng)*
Jerome S. Darby *(Sr VP-Ops)*
Dominic P. Demain *(Sr VP-New Bus Devel)*
Daniel R. Johnson *(Sr VP)*
Thomas Cunniff *(VP, Dir-Interactive & Assoc Dir-Creative)*
Michael Wendroff *(VP-Mktg)*

Mike Carroll *(VP-Mktg)*
Jim M. Healy *(Dir-Mktg)*
Brands & Products:
AQUA VELVA
BAN-A-STAIN
BRYLCREEM
CARRY-CLEAN
CEPACOL
DENTURITE
GRECIAN 5
GRECIAN FORMULA 16
GYNECORT
JOHNSON'S FOOT SOAP
JUST 5
JUST FOR MEN
JUST FOR MEN/MUSTACHE, BEARD & SIDEBURNS
LANABIOTIC
LANACANE
LANACORT
LECTRIC SHAVE
MAXIM HAIRCOLOR
NATURAL HARMONY
ODOR-EATERS
PLASTI-LINER
PODIACIN
POWERTHOLD
QUIK-FIX
SCALPICIN
SEA-BOND
VAGISIL
VIRACTIN
WILLIAMS MUG SHAVE SOAP
Advertising Agencies:
Media Insight
1101 Westchester Ave
White Plains, NY 10604
Tel.: (914) 694-5454
Fax: (914) 694-6809
(Just For Men/MBS, Grecian 5, Vagisil Cleansing Foam, Vagisil Creme, Odor Eaters Insoles, Odor Eaters Foot Powder, Johnson's Foot Soap, Sea Bond, Scalpicin, Lanacane)

Phids, Inc.
(D/B/A Acquirgy)
877 Executive Ctr Dr W Ste 300
Saint Petersburg, FL 33702-2474
Tel.: (727) 576-6630
Fax: (727) 576-4864

COMMUNITY HEALTH SYSTEMS, INC.
4000 Meridian Blvd
Franklin, TN 37067
Tel.: (615) 465-7000
Fax: (615) 371-1068
E-mail: corporate_communications@chs.net
Web Site: www.chs.net
Approx. Rev.: $12,986,500,000
Approx. Number Employees: 64,000
Year Founded: 1985
Business Description:
Holding Company; Hospital & Ambulatory Surgery Center Operator
S.I.C.: 8062; 6719; 8011
N.A.I.C.S.: 622110; 551112; 621493
Media: 3-4-9-14-15-18-23-24-25
Personnel:
Wayne T. Smith *(Chm, Pres & CEO)*
W. Larry Cash *(CFO & Exec VP)*
J. Gary Seay *(CIO & Sr VP)*
Debbie S. Landers *(CMO & VP)*
T. Mark Buford *(Chief Acctg Officer & Sr VP)*
Barbara R. Paul *(Chief Medical Officer & Sr VP)*
Kathie G. Thomas *(Pres-Home Care Div)*
Rachel A. Seifert *(Gen Counsel, Sec & Exec VP)*
Larry M. Carlton *(Sr VP-Revenue Mgmt)*
Kenneth D. Hawkins *(Sr VP-Acq & Dev)*
Carolyn S. Lipp *(Sr VP-Quality & Resource Mgmt)*
Martin G. Schweinhart *(Sr VP-Ops)*
Jan Hickman *(VP & Asst Controller)*
Shan Carpenter *(VP-Fin & Div I Ops)*
Brad Cash *(VP-Fin & Div IV Ops)*
Randy M. Cooper *(VP-Fin & Div III Ops)*
Eric Harrison *(VP-Tech & Data Center Ops)*
Mike Healey *(VP-Fin & Div II Ops)*
Robert A. Horrar *(VP-Admin & HR)*
Stephanie Moore *(VP-Fin & Div IV Ops)*
Eric Roach *(VP-Fin & Div I Ops)*
Tim P. Adams *(Mgr-Application Ops)*
Advertising Agency:
Creative Alliance
437 W Jefferson St
Louisville, KY 40202
Tel.: (502) 584-8787
Fax: (502) 589-9900
Toll Free: (800) 525-0294

COMPREHENSIVE CARE CORPORATION
3405 W Dr Martin Luther King Jr Blvd Ste 101
Tampa, FL 33607-3540
Tel.: (813) 288-4808
Fax: (813) 288-4844
E-mail: info@compcare.com
Web Site: www.compcare.com
Approx. Rev.: $35,214,000
Approx. Number Employees: 134
Year Founded: 1969
Business Description:
Health Care Management of Behavioral Hospital-Based Programs
S.I.C.: 6331; 8011; 8063
N.A.I.C.S.: 525190; 621112; 622210
Media: 2-10-13
Personnel:
Clark A. Marcus *(Chm & CEO)*
Joshua I. Smith *(Vice Chm)*
Robert J. Landis *(CFO)*
Robert Siegel *(Pres-Comprehensive Care Benefits Inc.)*
Susan Norris *(Sr VP-Ops)*
Richard L. Powers *(Sr VP-Corp Dev)*
Richard T. Wright *(Sr VP-Bus Dev)*
Brands & Products:
COMPCARE

CONCEPTUS, INC.
331 E Evelyn Ave
Mountain View, CA 94041-1530
Tel.: (650) 962-4000
Fax: (650) 962-5000
E-mail: webservices@conceptus.com
Web Site: www.conceptus.com
Approx. Sls.: $140,660,000
Approx. Number Employees: 304
Year Founded: 1992
Business Description:
Minimally Invasive Devices for Reproductive Medical Applications
S.I.C.: 3841; 3842
N.A.I.C.S.: 339112; 339113
Advertising Expenditures: $9,900,000
Personnel:
Kathryn A. Tunstall *(Chm)*
Mark M. Sieczkarek *(Pres & CEO)*
Gregory E. Lichtwardt *(CFO, Treas & Exec VP-Ops)*
Ulric Cote, III *(Exec VP-Sls & Bus Dev-Global)*
Feridun Ozdil *(Exec VP-R&D)*
Sam Trujillo *(Exec VP-Mktg)*
Todd Sloan *(VP-Mktg)*
Cindy T. Klimstra *(Sr Dir)*
Brands & Products:
CONCEPTUS
CPTS
ESSURE

CONMED CORPORATION
525 French Rd
Utica, NY 13502
Tel.: (315) 797-8375
Fax: (315) 797-0321
Toll Free: (800) 448-6506
E-mail: info@conmed.com
Web Site: www.conmed.com
Approx. Sls.: $713,723,000
Approx. Number Employees: 3,300
Year Founded: 1970
Business Description:
Electrosurgery & Other Medical Products
S.I.C.: 3812; 3841; 3845
N.A.I.C.S.: 334511; 334510; 339112
Export
Advertising Expenditures: $1,500,000
Media: 2-4-7-10
Distr.: Natl.
Budget Set: Oct. -Nov.
Personnel:
Eugene R. Corasanti *(Chm)*
Joseph J. Corasanti *(Pres & CEO)*
Robert D. Shallish *(CFO & VP-Fin)*
David R. Murray *(Pres-Electrosurgery)*
William W. Abraham *(Sr VP)*
Dennis M. Werger *(VP & Gen Mgr)*
Mark Donovan *(VP-Corp Mktg)*
Daniel S. Jonas *(VP-Legal Affairs)*
Mike Stannard *(Dir-Sls)*
Jeff Palmer *(Mgr-Corp Sls)*
David Toach *(Mgr-Mktg)*
Brands & Products:
A WORLD OF SOLUTIONS
ABC
ACCUTAC
AIRSOFT
APOLLO
APOLLO 3 AC
APOLLO3
ARTHRO-KNIFE
ARTICULATOR
ARTICULATOR 35
BANDITO
BEAMER
BEAMER MATE
BEAMER PLUS
BICAP
BICAP SUPERCONDUCTOR
BIG YANK
BIO-ANCHOR
BIOSCREW
BIOSTINGER
BIOTWIST
BLITZ
BLUE BULLET
BRONCHO
CHANNEL MASTER
CLEARSITE
CLEARTRACE
CLICK-TIP
CONCEPT
CONMED
COOLFLEX
CTS RELIEF KIT
DETACHATIP
DIRECTOR
DOLPHIN
DURAGLIDE
DYNA/TRACE
ELIMINATOR
ENTAKE
ESA
EXCALIBURPLUS PC
EXL
EXPOSE
EXTRACT
FASTRACE
FLEXITIP
FLEXXUS
FLOVAC
FXWIRE
GARG
HAWKEYE
HEATWAVE
HIGH-DEMAND
HORNET
HUGGABLES
HYDRODUCT
HYFRECATOR
INSTATRACE
INTEQ
INVISATRACE
MICROLAP
MICROMITE
MINI-REVO
MONOPTY
NAKAO SPIDER-NET
NEODERM
NEOTRODE
ONEPART
OPTIBITE
ORBIT-SNARE
PADPRO
PERMACLIP
PIVOTAL
PLIA-CELL
POLYTRAP
POSITRACE
POWERPRO
POWERPROMAX
PRECISOR
PRO2
PROFORMA
QUICKLATCH
RAPIDFIRE
REFLEX
REVO
RITEBITE
SABRE
SCOPE SAVER
SHUTT
SHUTTLE RELAY
SILVON
SINGULAR
SNAPTRACE
SOFTEE
SOFTTRACE
SPECTRUM
STAT
STAT 2
STIEGMANN-GOFF
SUPER REVO
SURE SHOT
SURECHARGE

Key to Media (For complete agency information see *The Advertising Red Books-Agencies* edition):
1. Bus. Publs. 2. Cable T.V. 3. Catalogs & Directories. 4. Co-op Adv. 5. Consumer Mags. 6. D.M. to Bus. Estab.7. D.M. to Consumers 8. Daily Newsp. 9. Exhibits/Trade Shows 10. Foreign 11. Infomercial 12. Internet Adv.13. Multimedia 14. Network Radio 15. Network T.V. 16. Newsp. Distr. Mags. 17. Other 18. Outdoor (Posters, Transit) 19. Point of Purchase20. Premiums, Novelties 21. Product Samples 22. Special Events Mktg. 23. Spot Radio 24. Spot T.V. 25. Weekly Newsp. 26. Yellow Page Adv.

Conmed Corporation — (Continued)

SURETRACE
SUTURE TRAM
THE SYSTEM
SYSTEM 2450
THE SYSTEM 2500
THE SYSTEM 5000
SYSTEM 7500
SYSTEM 7550
TRACTIONTOWER
TRIDENT
TROGARD FINESSE
ULTRABLATOR
ULTRAFIX
ULTRASORB
ULTRATRACE
UNIVERSAL PLUS
UNIVERSAL S/I
VCARE
VENI-GARD
VIABIL
VIZEON
WANG
WHISTLE
XTRALOK
XWIRE

Advertising Agencies:
FD U.S. Communications, Inc.
(d/b/a Financial Dynamics)
Wall St Plz 88 Pine St 32nd Fl
New York, NY 10005
Tel.: (212) 850-5600
Fax: (212) 850-5790

Romanelli Advertising
2 College St.
Clinton, NY 13323
Tel.: (315) 853-3941
Fax: (315) 853-3946

CONMED HEALTHCARE MANAGEMENT, INC.

7250 Parkway Dr Ste 400
Hanover, MD 21076
Tel.: (410) 567-5520
Fax: (410) 712-4760
Toll Free: (800) 609-8476
E-mail: info@conmed-inc.com
Web Site: www.conmed-inc.com
Approx. Rev.: $60,654,586
Approx. Number Employees: 528
Year Founded: 1984
Business Description:
Medical Services
S.I.C.: 6371; 5912; 8063; 8069; 8071; 8072
N.A.I.C.S.: 525120; 339116; 446110; 621511; 622210; 622310
Media: 2-7-10-13-17
Personnel:
Stephen B. Goldberg *(Founder & Pres)*
Ronald Grubman *(Founder)*
Richard W. Turner *(Chm)*
Thomas W. Fry *(CFO)*

CONTINENTAL ANALYTICAL SERVICES INC.

525 N 8th St
Salina, KS 67401
Tel.: (785) 827-1273
Fax: (785) 823-7830
Toll Free: (800) 535-3076
E-mail: caslab@midusa.com
Web Site: www.cas-lab.com
Approx. Sls.: $5,000,000
Approx. Number Employees: 30
Year Founded: 1985
Business Description:
Provider of Analytical Testing of Drinking Water, Waste Water, Solid & Hazardous Waste, Sludge & Soil for Government Agencies
S.I.C.: 8733; 8071
N.A.I.C.S.: 541710; 621511
Media: 2-7-10-16-25
Distr.: Natl.
Personnel:
Clifford Baker *(Mgr-Technical)*
Greg Groene *(Mgr-Project Mgmt)*

CONTINUCARE CORPORATION

7200 Corp Ctr Dr Ste 600
Miami, FL 33126
Tel.: (305) 350-7515
Fax: (305) 350-7749
Web Site: www.continucare.com
Approx. Rev.: $333,458,208
Approx. Number Employees: 870
Year Founded: 1996
Business Description:
Outpatient Services
S.I.C.: 8011; 8049; 8093
N.A.I.C.S.: 621111; 621399; 621420
Media: 9
Personnel:
Richard C. Pfenniger, Jr. *(Chm, Pres & CEO)*
Fernando Fernandez *(CFO)*
Alfredo Ginory *(Chief Medical Officer)*
Gemma Rosello *(Exec VP-Ops)*
Sadita Bustamante *(Sr VP-Center Ops)*
Luis H. Izquierdo *(Sr VP-Mktg & Bus Dev)*
Martha Irabien *(Reg Dir-Medical)*
Helena Martinez *(Dir-Mktg)*
Deborah Meck *(Dir-Compliance)*

CONVATEC LTD.

(Joint Venture of Nordic Capital AB & Avista Capital Partners, LP)
200 Headquarters Park Dr
Skillman, NJ 08558-2624
Mailing Address:
PO Box 5254
Princeton, NJ 08543-5254
Tel.: (908) 904-2500
Toll Free: (800) 422-8811
Web Site: www.convatec.com
Approx. Rev.: $1,155,000,000
Approx. Number Employees: 3,500
Year Founded: 1978
Business Description:
Medical Products Mfr
S.I.C.: 3841
N.A.I.C.S.: 339112
Export
Advertising Expenditures: $200,000
Media: 2-4-6-7-8-10
Distr.: Intl.
Personnel:
David Johnson *(CEO)*
Bradford Barton *(Pres-US Bus)*
Lucia Luce Quinn *(Sr VP-HR & Corp Affairs)*
Brands & Products:
ACTIVELIFE
ALOE VESTA
AQUACEL
CARBOFLEX
COMBIDERM
DUODERM
DURAHESIVE
ESTEEM SYNERGY
FLEXI-SEAL
KATOSTAT
OPTIPORE
SAF-GEL
SENSICARE
SEPTISOFT
SHUR-CLENS
SUR-FIT AUTOLOCK
SUR-FIT NATURA
SUREPRESS
TUBIGRIP
TUBIPAD
UNNA-FLEX
VERSIVA
Advertising Agencies:
ConvaTec Advertising
Rte. 206 & Province Line Rd.
Princeton, NJ 08540
Tel.: (609) 252-4000

Cramp & Associates, Inc.
1327 Grenox Rd
Wynnewood, PA 19096-2402
Tel.: (610) 649-6002
Fax: (610) 649-6005

Weber Shandwick
(Sub. of The Interpublic Group of Companies)
919 3rd Ave
New York, NY 10022
Tel.: (212) 445-8000
Fax: (212) 445-8001

COOK GROUP, INC.

PO Box 1608
Bloomington, IN 47402
Tel.: (812) 331-1025
Fax: (812) 331-8990
Toll Free: (800) 457-4500
E-mail: info@cook-inc.com
Web Site: www.cookgroup.com
Sales Range: $150-199.9 Million
Approx. Number Employees: 3,550
Year Founded: 1963
Business Description:
Medical Products Mfr
S.I.C.: 3841; 3821
N.A.I.C.S.: 339112; 339111
Import Export
Media: 10-13
Personnel:
Kem Hawkins *(Pres)*
Brands & Products:
ACCENT
ACUSNARE
ARNDT
AUROUS
BEACON
CENTRA-FLO
CHECK-FLO
CIAGLIA BLUE RHINO
COHEN
COOK
COOK-Z
COTTON CANNULATOME
COTTON-HUIBREGTSE
COTTON-LEUNG
CYTOMAX
ECHOTIP
ENVY
ESCORT BALLOONS
EZ-PASS
FIRM
FLEXOR
FLIPPER
GEENEN
GLOTIP ERCP
GRADUATE
GUNTHER TULIP
HYBRID TRACER
HYSTEROCATH
INTRO-TIP
LUMAX
MAC-LAC
MAXUM
METRO WIRE
MICROCOILS
MICROFERRET
MICRONESTER
MICROPUNCTURE
MINITOME
NAG BRACHYFLEX
NEST
NESTER
NIMBLE
NO TORQUE RIGHT
OASIS
OSTEO-FORCE
OSTEO-RX
OSTEO-SITE
OVER
PEEL-AWAY
PERFORMER
PURSUIT
QUANTUM
QUANTUM BILIARY DILATOR
QUICK-CORE
RECATH
RESNARE
ROADRUNNER
SAFE-T-J
SHILEY
SHORTY
SHUTTLE
SL FLEXOR
SLIP-CATH
SOEHENDRA DILATOR
SOEHENDRA LITHOTRIPTOR
SOEHENDRA ROTARY DILATOR
TANNENBAUM
TIGER TUBE
TIP TORCON
TIP TORCON NB
TORCON
TORNADO
TORQ-FLEX
TRIEX
TRITOME
ULTRATHANE
ZA STENT
ZENITH

THE COOPER COMPANIES, INC.

6140 Stoneridge Mall Rd Ste 590
Pleasanton, CA 94588
Tel.: (925) 460-3600
Fax: (925) 460-3649
Toll Free: (888) 822-2660
E-mail: ir@coopercompanies.com
Web Site: www.coopercos.com
Approx. Sls.: $1,158,517,000
Approx. Number Employees: 6,800
Year Founded: 1980
Business Description:
Proprietary Specialty Healthcare Products in Eyecare & Gynecology
S.I.C.: 3842; 3841
N.A.I.C.S.: 339113; 339112
Export
Media: 2-5-7-8-10-19-21
Distr.: Natl.
Budget Set: Oct.

Key to Media (For complete agency information see *The Advertising Red Books-Agencies* edition):
1. Bus. Publs. 2. Cable T.V. 3. Catalogs & Directories. 4. Co-op Adv. 5. Consumer Mags. 6. D.M. to Bus. Estab.7. D.M. to Consumers
8. Daily Newsp. 9. Exhibits/Trade Shows 10. Foreign 11. Infomercial 12. Internet Adv.13. Multimedia 14. Network Radio
15. Network T.V. 16. Newsp. Distr. Mags. 17. Other 18. Outdoor (Posters, Transit) 19. Point of Purchase20. Premiums, Novelties
21. Product Samples 22. Special Events Mktg. 23. Spot Radio 24. Spot T.V. 25. Weekly Newsp. 26. Yellow Page Adv.

Personnel:
A. Thomas Bender *(Chm)*
Allan E. Rubenstein *(Vice Chm)*
Robert S. Weiss *(Pres & CEO)*
Paul L. Remmell *(Pres & COO-CooperSurgical)*
Eugene J. Midlock *(CFO & Sr VP)*
Carol R. Kaufman *(Chief Admin Officer, Sec & Sr VP-Legal Affairs)*
Dennis J. Murphy *(Pres-Americas of CooperVision)*
Andrew Sedgwick *(Pres-EMEA-CooperVision)*
Nicholas J. Pichotta *(CEO-CooperSurgical)*
Daniel G. McBride *(Gen Counsel & VP)*
Kima Duncan *(Dir-IR)*
Brands & Products:
ASCEND
ASTRINGYN
COOPER HGP
COOPER VAC
COOPERCLEAR
COOPERSURGICAL SMOKE EVACUATION SYSTEM 6080
COOPERTHIN
CRYO-SURG
CS-76
DIAGNOSTIC HYSTEROSCOPY REDI-KIT
ENHANCEMENT COLORS
EYE DEVICE
EYE-SHAPED DESIGN
FLUOROFLEX
FLUOROFLEX UV
FREQUENCY COLORS
FREQUENCY EXPRESSIONS
FREQUENCY TORRIX XR
FRIGITRONICS
GYNE-ELECTRODE
GYNE-RESECTOSCOPE
HYSTEROSCOPY REDIKIT
LEEP
LEEP ELECTRODE
LEEP REDIKIT
LEEP SYSTEM 6000
LEEP VAC
LIPO-TEARS
NORLAND
PERMAFLEX
PERMAFLEX NATURALS
PERMAFLEX THIN
PERMAFLEX UV NATURALS
PERMALENS
PERMALENS APHAKIC
PERMALENS THERAPEUTIC
PERMALENS XL
PHYNYLTROPE
PORTA-FLOW
POTOCKY NEEDLE
PREFERENCE
SAGE BIOPHARMA
SANI-SPEC
THE SCIENCE OF BEAUTIFUL EYES
SPF
VANTAGE
VANTAGE ACCENTS
VANTAGE THIN
VANTAGE THIN ACCENTS

CORAM SPECIALTY INFUSION SERVICES

(Sub. of Apria Healthcare Group Inc.)
1675 Broadway Ste 900
Denver, CO 80202
Tel.: (303) 292-4973
Toll Free: (800) CORAMHC
Toll Free: (800) 267-2642
E-mail: info@coramhc.com
Web Site: www.coramhc.com
Sales Range: $500-549.9 Million
Approx. Number Employees: 2,100
Year Founded: 1994
Business Description:
Home Infusion Therapies & Ambulatory Suites Services
S.I.C.: 8082; 8093
N.A.I.C.S.: 621610; 621498
Advertising Expenditures: $500,000
Media: 4-7-8-10-26
Distr.: Natl.
Budget Set: Nov. -Dec.
Personnel:
Daniel E. Greenleaf *(Pres-Coram Specialty Infusion Svcs & COO-Apria Healthcare)*
Harriet Albery *(Exec VP-Sls)*
Robert Allen *(Exec VP-Ops)*
Marge Brown *(Sr VP-Quality & Compliance)*
Michael Dell *(VP, Asst Sec & Assoc Gen Counsel)*
Brands & Products:
CORAM

CORCELL COMPANIES, INC.

(Sub. of CORD BLOOD AMERICA, INC.)
221 S 12th St Ste 314S
Philadelphia, PA 19107
Tel.: (215) 864-0400
Fax: (215) 864-0936
Toll Free: (888) 326-7235
E-mail: info@corcell.com
Web Site: www.corcell.com
Approx. Sls.: $1,700,000
Year Founded: 1995
Business Description:
Collection & Cryogenic Storage of Umbilical Cord Blood
S.I.C.: 8099
N.A.I.C.S.: 621991
Media: 6-8
Personnel:
Matthew L. Schissler *(Founder, Chm & CEO)*
Shamoon Ahmad *(Dir-Medical)*
Brands & Products:
CORCELL

CORD BLOOD AMERICA, INC.

1857 Helm Dr
Las Vegas, NV 89119
Tel.: (702) 914-7250
E-mail: info@cordblood-america.com
Web Site: www.cordblood-america.com
Approx. Rev.: $4,128,439
Approx. Number Employees: 22
Year Founded: 2002
Business Description:
Umbilical Cord Blood Stem Cell Preservation Services
S.I.C.: 8099; 2835
N.A.I.C.S.: 621991; 325413
Advertising Expenditures: $193,527
Media: 17
Personnel:
Matthew L. Schissler *(Chm & CEO)*
Joseph R. Vicente *(COO)*

CORDIS CORPORATION

(Sub. of Johnson & Johnson)
14201 NW 60th Ave
Hialeah, FL 33014
Tel.: (908) 541-4040 (Corp Comm)
Tel.: (908) 541-4100
Toll Free: (800) 447-7585
Web Site: www.cordis.com
Sales Range: $600-649.9 Million
Approx. Number Employees: 2,070
Year Founded: 1959
Business Description:
Medical Devices, Anglographic & Neuroscience Products Mfr & Services
S.I.C.: 3841; 3842
N.A.I.C.S.: 339112; 339113
Media: 2-7-17
Budget Set: Dec.-Jan.
Personnel:
Ryan H. Saadi *(VP-Worldwide Health Economics & Strategic Pricing)*
Brands & Products:
CORDIS
CYPHER
S.M.A.R.T
Advertising Agency:
BBDO Worldwide Inc.
(Sub. of Omnicom Group, Inc.)
1285 Ave of the Americas
New York, NY 10019-6028
Tel.: (212) 459-5000
Fax: (212) 459-6645
Cypher

CORGENIX MEDICAL CORPORATION

11575 Main St Ste 400
Broomfield, CO 80020
Tel.: (303) 457-4345
Fax: (303) 457-4519
Toll Free: (800) 729-5661
E-mail: info@corgenix.com
Web Site: www.corgenix.com
Approx. Sls.: $7,941,576
Approx. Number Employees: 39
Year Founded: 1990
Business Description:
Specialized Diagnostic Test Kits Developer & Marketer for Vascular Diseases & Immunological Disorders
S.I.C.: 2835; 2834; 3841
N.A.I.C.S.: 325413; 325412; 339112
Advertising Expenditures: $46,274
Media: 2-7-10
Personnel:
Stephen P. Gouze *(Chm)*
Douglass T. Simpson *(Pres & CEO)*
William H. Critchfield *(CFO & Sr VP-Fin & Admin)*
Ann L. Steinbarger *(Sr VP-Ops)*
Taryn G. Reynolds *(VP-Facilities & IT)*
Brands & Products:
CORGENIX
Advertising Agency:
Avocet Communications
1501 S Sunset St Ste A
Longmont, CO 80501-6757
Tel.: (303) 678-7102
Fax: (303) 678-7109

CORNERSTONE THERAPEUTICS, INC.

1255 Crescent Green Dr Ste 250
Cary, NC 27518
Tel.: (919) 678-6611
Fax: (919) 678-6599
E-mail: investor.relations@crtx.com
Web Site: www.crtx.com
Approx. Rev.: $125,317,000
Approx. Number Employees: 147
Year Founded: 2000
Business Description:
Therapeutic Products for Asthma Prevention & Treatment Developer
S.I.C.: 2834; 8733
N.A.I.C.S.: 325412; 541710
Advertising Expenditures: $8,200,000
Media: 5-21
Personnel:
Craig A. Collard *(Chm & CEO)*
Kenneth McBean *(Pres)*
Vincent T. Morgus *(CFO & Exec VP-Fin)*
Ira Duarte *(Chief Acctg Officer & Dir-Acctg)*
Andrew K.W. Powell *(Gen Counsel, Sec & Exec VP)*
Steven M. Lutz *(Exec VP-Mfg & Trade)*
Joshua B. Franklin *(VP-Sls & Mktg)*
Linda S. Lennox *(VP-Media & IR)*
Brands & Products:
ALLENRX
ALLERX
ARISTOS PHARMACEUTICALS
BALACET
BALACET 325
CORNERSTONE
DECONSAL
HYOMAX
LIDOCORT
RESPIVENT
SPECTRACEF
ZYFLO
ZYFLO CR

COVENTRY HEALTH CARE, INC.

6705 Rockledge Dr Ste 900
Bethesda, MD 20817-7828
Tel.: (301) 581-0600
Fax: (301) 493-0731
Toll Free: (800) 843-7421
E-mail: investor-relations@cvty.com
Web Site: www.coventryhealthcare.com
Approx. Rev.: $11,587,916,000
Approx. Number Employees: 14,000
Year Founded: 1982
Business Description:
Health Care Benefit Options Supplier
S.I.C.: 6321; 8011
N.A.I.C.S.: 524114; 621111
Media: 2-7-8-9-10-23-24-25-26
Personnel:
Allen F. Wise *(Chm & CEO)*
Randy Giles *(CFO, Treas & Exec VP)*
Maria Fitzpatrick *(CIO & Sr VP)*
Patrisha L. Davis *(Chief HR Officer & Sr VP)*
Thomas C. Zielinski *(Gen Counsel & Exec VP)*
Kevin Conlin *(Exec VP)*
John J. Ruhlmann *(Sr VP & Controller)*
David A. Finkel *(Sr VP-Ops)*
John J. Stelben *(Interim CFO & Sr VP-Fin)*
James E. McGarry *(Mgr)*
Brands & Products:
ADVANTRA
CARE MANAGEMENT RESOURCE
COVENTRY HEALTH CARE
COVENTRYONE
Advertising Agencies:
DesignKitchen
1140 W Fulton Market

Key to Media (For complete agency information see *The Advertising Red Books-Agencies* edition):
1. Bus. Publs. 2. Cable T.V. 3. Catalogs & Directories. 4. Co-op Adv. 5. Consumer Mags. 6. D.M. to Bus. Estab.7. D.M. to Consumers 8. Daily Newsp. 9. Exhibits/Trade Shows 10. Foreign 11. Infomercial 12. Internet Adv.13. Multimedia 14. Network Radio 15. Network T.V. 16. Newsp. Distr. Mags. 17. Other 18. Outdoor (Posters, Transit) 19. Point of Purchase20. Premiums, Novelties 21. Product Samples 22. Special Events Mktg. 23. Spot Radio 24. Spot T.V. 25. Weekly Newsp. 26. Yellow Page Adv.

Coventry Health Care, Inc. — (Continued)

Chicago, IL 60607-1219
Tel.: (312) 455-0388
Fax: (312) 455-0285

gkv Communications
The Cascade Bldg 1030 Hull St Ste 400
Baltimore, MD 21230
Tel.: (410) 539-5400
Fax: (410) 234-2441

COVIDIEN
(Branch of Covidien Inc.)
675 McDonnell Blvd
Hazelwood, MO 63042-2301
Tel.: (314) 654-2000
Fax: (314) 654-5381
Web Site: www.mallinckrodt.com/index.aspx
Approx. Number Employees: 50
Year Founded: 1909
Business Description:
Medical Products Mfr
S.I.C.: 3841; 3829
N.A.I.C.S.: 339112; 334519
Import Export
Media: 1-2-4-7-10-18-19-20-21-23-25
Distr.: Intl.; Natl.
Budget Set: June
Personnel:
Steve Hanley *(Pres)*
Douglas A. McKinney *(CFO, VP-Shares Svcs & Fin)*
Eric A. Kraus *(Sr VP)*
Kathleen Schaefer *(VP-Fin & Controller)*
Lisa Britt *(VP-HR)*
Brands & Products:
ANAFRANIL
ARGYLE
BRONCHO-CATH
CAPNO-FLO
CAPNOPROBE
COMBITUBE
DAR
DEPADE
ENDOTROL
INDGO
LASER-FLEX
LO-CONTOUR
MAX-FAST
METHADOSE
MON-A-THERM
NASAL RAE
NEUTROSPEC
ORAL RAE
OXICLIQ
OXIFIRST
OXISENSOR
PAMELOR
PHONATE
RAINDROP
RESTORIL
SATIN-SLIP
SCORE
SHILEY
SOFTCARE
STERIVENT
STRONGHOLD
TOFRANIL
TRACHEOSOFT
WARMFLO
Advertising Agencies:
Fister Lauberth, Inc.
275 Union Blvd 17th Fl
Saint Louis, MO 63108-1231
Tel.: (314) 367-5600
Fax: (314) 367-2288

Liaison Marketing Communications, Ltd.
2354 Kemper Ln
Cincinnati, OH 45206
Tel.: (513) 281-2301
Fax: (513) 281-2363

COVIDIEN
(Branch of Covidien Inc.)
4280 Hacienda Dr
Pleasanton, CA 94588-2719
Tel.: (925) 463-4000
Toll Free: (800) NELLCOR
Toll Free: (800) 635-5267
Web Site: www.nellcor.com
Year Founded: 1981
Business Description:
Monitoring Instruments, Sensors, Airway Adapters & Detectors Mfr
S.I.C.: 3841; 3845
N.A.I.C.S.: 339112; 334510
Import Export
Media: 10
Personnel:
Ken Donlon *(VP-Corp Sls)*
Terri Wells *(VP-Mktg-Stapling Franchise-Global)*
Rhonda Soest *(Sr Dir-Mktg Imaging & Pharmaceuticals-US)*
Erich Faust *(Sr Mgr-Mktg-Global)*
Damian Aguirrechu *(Product Mgr-Mktg-Specialty Pharmaceuticals)*
Brands & Products:
700
ARGYLE
BRONCO-CATH
CAPNOPROBE
CAREDRAPE
CAREQUILT
COMBITUBE
DAR
EASY CAP
EMT
ENDOTROL
GENTLE-FLO
HI-LO
INCUTEMP
INDGO
INTERMEDIATE HI-LO
LANZ
LARYNGOSEAL
LASER-FLEX
LAVACUATOR
LO-CONTOUR
LO-PRO
MICROSTREAM
MLT
MON-A-THERM
NASAL RAE
NELLCOR
ORAL RAE
OXICLIQ
OXIFIRST
OXIMAX
OXINET
OXISENSOR
OXISENSOR II
RAINDROP
SATIN-SLIP
SCORE
SHILEY
SOFTCARE
STERIVENT
STRONGHOLD
VENTROL
WARMFLO
WARMTOUCH

COVIDIEN INC.
(Corporate Headquarters of Covidien plc)
15 Hampshire St
Mansfield, MA 02048
Tel.: (508) 261-8000
Fax: (508) 261-8424
Toll Free: (800) 346-7197
Web Site: www.covidien.com
Approx. Number Employees: 1,700
Year Founded: 1964
Business Description:
Disposable Medical Products, Wound-Care Products, Syringes & Needles, Sutures, Surgical Staplers, Incontinence Products, Electrosurgical Instruments & Laparoscopic Instruments Mfr, Developer & Marketer
S.I.C.: 3842; 3841
N.A.I.C.S.: 339113; 339112
Export
Advertising Expenditures: $84,000,000
Personnel:
Jose E. Almeida *(Pres)*
Charles J. Dockendorff *(CFO & Exec VP)*
Steven M. McManama *(CIO & VP)*
Richard G. Brown *(Chief Accounting Officer, VP & Controller)*
Eric C. Green *(Chief Tax Officer & VP)*
James C. Clemmer *(Pres-Medical Supplies)*
Timothy R. Wright *(Pres-Pharmaceutical Products & Imaging Solutions)*
John H. Masterson *(Gen Counsel & Sr VP)*
Michael P. Dunford *(Sr VP-HR)*
Eric A. Kraus *(Sr VP-Corp Comm)*
James M. Muse *(Sr VP-Global Supply Chain)*
Amy A. Wendell *(Sr VP-Strategy & Bus Dev)*
Bruce Farmer *(VP-PR)*
Brian Nameth *(Exec Dir-Audit)*
Paula Bissanti *(Dir-Mktg-Sharp Safety)*
Brands & Products:
BIS
Advertising Agency:
Hill Holliday
53 State St
Boston, MA 02109
Tel.: (617) 366-4000

C.R. BARD
(Formerly SenoRx, Inc.)
(Sub. of Bard Peripheral Vascular, Inc.)
3 Morgan
Irvine, CA 92618
Tel.: (949) 362-4800
Fax: (949) 362-3519
Fax: (949) 362-0300
Toll Free: (877) 210-1300
Web Site: www.bardbiopsy.com/home.php
Approx. Rev.: $55,577,299
Approx. Number Employees: 161
Year Founded: 1998
Business Description:
Cancer Treatment & Diagnostic Devices Developer & Mfr
S.I.C.: 3841
N.A.I.C.S.: 339112
Advertising Expenditures: $2,245,000
Media: 7-10
Personnel:
Kevin J. Cousins *(CFO & VP-Fin)*
Paul Lubock *(CTO & Sr VP)*
John E. Merritt *(Sr Dir-Advanced Engrg)*
Lila Churney *(Dir-IR)*
Karen Vallejo *(Mgr-Customer Svc)*
Brands & Products:
BIOPTY-CUT
DUALOK
FINESSE ULTRA
GHIATAS
MAGNUM
MAX-CORE
MONOPTY
OSTYCUT
TRUGUIDE
ULTRACLIP
ULTRAWIRE
VACORA
VACU-CUT

C.R. BARD, INC.
730 Central Ave
New Providence, NJ 07974-1139
Tel.: (908) 277-8000
Fax: (908) 277-8412
Toll Free: (877) 285-4158
E-mail: comments@crbard.com
Web Site: www.crbard.com
Approx. Sls.: $2,720,200,000
Approx. Number Employees: 11,700
Year Founded: 1907
Business Description:
Health Care Products Mfr
S.I.C.: 3841; 3845
N.A.I.C.S.: 339112; 334510
Import Export
Advertising Expenditures: $3,300,000
Media: 2-4-10-13
Distr.: Intl.; Natl.
Personnel:
Timothy M. Ring *(Chm & CEO)*
John H. Weiland *(Pres & COO)*
Todd C. Schermerhorn *(CFO & Sr VP)*
P. J. Byloos *(Pres-Europe)*
P. R. Curry *(Pres-Asia & Americas)*
D. W. LaFever *(Pres-Japan)*
Stephen J. Long *(Gen Counsel, Sec & VP)*
John A. DeFord *(Sr VP-Science, Tech & Clinical Affairs)*
Gary D. Dolch *(Sr VP-Quality, Regulatory & Medical Affairs)*
Sharon M. Alterio *(Grp VP)*
Jim C. Beasley *(Grp VP)*
Timothy P. Collins *(Grp VP-Ops & Electrophysiology Div)*
Brian P. Kelly *(Grp VP-Corp Sls & Mktg)*
J. D. Kondrosky *(VP & Gen Mgr-Canada)*
Richard C. Rosenzweig *(VP-Law & Asst Sec)*
Vincent J. Gurnari, Jr. *(VP-IT)*
Bronwen K. Kelly *(VP-HR)*
Robert L. Mellen *(VP-Strategic Plng & Bus Dev)*
Patrick D. Roche *(VP-IT)*
Eric J. Shick *(VP-Ops Strategic Programs)*
K. Delanghe *(Gen Mgr-France)*
Jean F. Miller *(Asst Sec)*

Brands & Products:
3DMAX
ADVANCING THE DELIVERY OF HEALTH CARE
ARTHRO-FLO
BIOPTY
DAVOL RELIA VAC
DAVOL SYSTEM 5000
DIRECT BITE
DULEX
DUPEN
ENDO-FLO
GYNE-PRO
HYDROFLEX
MAGNUM
MONOPTY
PERFIX
RECONIX
SIMPULSE
SMOKEVAC
STINGER
SURETRANS
SYRINGE AVITENE
VARICARE
VIGILON
VISILEX

Advertising Agency:
ImageSmith, Inc.
674 Rte 202-206 Bldg 4 N
Bridgewater, NJ 08807
Tel.: (908) 685-8686
Fax: (908) 685-8816

CRH MEDICAL CORPORATION

999 Canada Place Ste 522
Vancouver, BC V6C 3E1, Canada
Tel.: (604) 633-1440
Fax: (604) 633-1443
Web Site: www.crhcenter.com
Approx. Rev.: $7,064,858
Approx. Number Employees: 10
Year Founded: 1995
Business Description:
Medical Products Mfr
S.I.C.: 3841
N.A.I.C.S.: 339112
Advertising Expenditures: $200,000
Media: 2-9-10-13-23-25
Personnel:
Anthony F. Holler *(Chm)*
Edward Wright *(CEO)*
Richard Bear *(CFO)*
Iain Cleator *(Dir-Medical)*
Mitchel Guttenplan *(Dir-Medical)*

CRITICAL CARE SYSTEMS INTERNATIONAL, INC.

Executive Twr 61 Spit Brook Rd
Nashua, NH 03060
Tel.: (603) 888-1500
Fax: (603) 888-0990
Toll Free: (800) 966-5656
Web Site:
www.criticalcaresystems.com/home.html
Sales Range: $250-299.9 Million
Approx. Number Employees: 1,292
Year Founded: 1984
Business Description:
Chronic Wound Care & Disease Management Services
S.I.C.: 8049; 8011; 8093
N.A.I.C.S.: 621399; 621111; 621498
Advertising Expenditures: $2,600,000
Media: 10-23
Personnel:
Paul F. McConnell *(Pres & CEO)*
Roy McKinley *(Sr VP-Wound Care Mngmt)*
Andrew C. Walk *(Sr VP-Ops-Specialty Infusion)*

Brands & Products:
CURATIVE COURSEWARE
FOOTSENSE
MEDILINK
WOUND CARE CENTER
WOUND MANAGEMENT PROGRAM

CRITICARE SYSTEMS, INC.

(Sub. of Opto Circuits (India) Limited)
20925 Crossroads Cir Ste 100
Waukesha, WI 53186
Mailing Address:
PO Box 26556
Milwaukee, WI 53226
Tel.: (262) 798-8282
Fax: (262) 798-8290
E-mail: customerserv@csiusa.com
Web Site: www.csiusa.com
Approx. Sls.: $31,431,810
Approx. Number Employees: 95
Year Founded: 1984
Business Description:
Patient Monitoring Devices Developer, Marketer & Distr
S.I.C.: 3841; 3845
N.A.I.C.S.: 339112; 334510
Import Export
Advertising Expenditures: $97,460
Media: 2-4-7-10-11-17
Distr.: Natl.
Personnel:
Y. K. Gauba *(CEO)*
Mahesh Patel *(CFO, Sec & VP-Fin)*

Brands & Products:
506 DXN
COMFORTCUFF
DOX
IVAC
MINISPO2T
POET
POET PLUS 8100
PORT
RESCUEREADY
RHYTHMX
SCHOLAR
SMARTGAUGE
STAR
VITALVIEW

CROSS COUNTRY HEALTHCARE, INC.

6551 Park of Commerce Blvd Ste 200
Boca Raton, FL 33487-8244
Tel.: (561) 998-2232
Toll Free: (800) 347-2264
E-mail: corpinfo@crosscountry.com
Web Site:
www.crosscountryhealthcare.com
Approx. Rev.: $468,561,524
Approx. Number Employees: 2,579
Year Founded: 1975
Business Description:
Health Care Staffing Services
S.I.C.: 7363; 7361; 8748
N.A.I.C.S.: 561320; 541618; 561310
Advertising Expenditures: $2,506,000
Media: 2-8-9-13
Personnel:
Joseph A. Boshart *(Pres & CEO)*
Emil Hensel *(CFO)*
Elizabeth C. Gulacsy *(Chief Acctg Officer & Controller)*
Gregory F. Greene *(Pres-Cross Country Education)*
Lori Schutte *(Pres-Cejka Search)*
Franklin A. Shaffer *(Pres-Education & Trng)*
Tony Sims *(Pres-Clinical Trials Staffing)*
Jonathan W. Ward *(Pres-Cross Country Staffing)*
Susan E. Ball *(Gen Counsel & Sec)*
Vickie Anenberg *(Exec VP-Cross Country Staffing)*
Victor Kalafa *(VP-Corp Dev & Strategy)*

Brands & Products:
AKOS
ASSENT CONSULTING
ASSIGNMENT AMERICA
CEJKA SEARCH
CLINFORCE
CROSS COUNTRY HEALTHCARE
CROSSCOUNTRY EDUCATION
CROSSCOUNTRY LOCAL
CROSSCOUNTRY STAFFING
MEDICALDOCTOR
MEDSTAFF
MRA
MRA SEARCH
NOVAPRO
TRAVCORPS

CROSSTEX INTERNATIONAL INC.

(Sub. of Cantel Medical Corp.)
10 Ranick Rd
Hauppauge, NY 11788
Tel.: (631) 582-6777
Fax: (631) 582-1726
Toll Free: (888) CROSSTEX
E-mail: crosstex@crosstex.com
Web Site: www.crosstex.com
E-Mail For Key Personnel:
Marketing Director: andyw@crosstex.com
Sales Range: $10-24.9 Million
Approx. Number Employees: 50
Year Founded: 1953
Business Description:
Infection Control & Single-Use Disposable Products Mfr
S.I.C.: 3843
N.A.I.C.S.: 339114
Media: 4-10-13
Personnel:
Gary Steinberg *(CEO)*
Mitchell Steinberg *(Exec VP)*
Andrew Whitehead *(Sr VP-Sls & Mktg)*

Brands & Products:
ADVANTAGE PLUS
ALOECARE
CLASSIC PLUS
CROSSTEX
CROSSZYME
ECONOBACK
ECOTRU
EFFERZYME
FOG FREE
FORM-FIT
IC
IC PROTECTIVE
ISOFLUID
ISOLATOR
ISOLITE
LUER LOK
POLYBACK
POLYGARD
PROBACK
SAFETYLOCK
SANI-CLOTH
SANI-DEX
SANI-DEX PLUS
SANI-ROLL
SANI-TAB
SANI-TUBE
SANICARE
SANICLENZ
SANISEPT
SANITEX PLUS
SANITYZE
SEE-CLEAR
SUPER SANI-CLOTH
SURE CHECK
ULTRA GAUZE
ULTRA NO-FOG
ULTRA PLUS
ULTRAGARD
ULTRATEX

CROZER-KEYSTONE HEALTH SYSTEM INC.

100 W Sproul Rd 3rd Fl
Springfield, PA 19064
Tel.: (610) 338-8200
Fax: (610) 338-8230
E-mail: crozer@crozer.org
Web Site: www.crozer.org
Approx. Number Employees: 7,100
Year Founded: 1990
Business Description:
Health Care Services
S.I.C.: 8742
N.A.I.C.S.: 541611
Import Export
Media: 2-8-9-25-26
Personnel:
Bruce G. Fischer *(Chm)*
Philip Ryan *(CFO & Sr VP)*
Joan K. Richards *(COO)*
Kathy Scullin *(VP-Mktg-PR)*
Mary Wascavage *(Dir-PR & Mktg)*
Gwendolyn Smith *(Coord-IRB)*

Brands & Products:
CROZER KEYSTONE
HEALTHPLEX
SOMETHING TO FEEL GOOD ABOUT.

CRYO-CELL INTERNATIONAL, INC.

700 Brooker Creek Blvd Ste 1800
Oldsmar, FL 34677
Tel.: (813) 749-2100
Fax: (813) 855-4745
Toll Free: (800) 786-7235
E-mail: info@cryo-cell.com
Web Site: www.cryo-cell.com
Approx. Rev.: $17,639,576
Approx. Number Employees: 55
Year Founded: 1992
Business Description:
Medical Technologies Developer
S.I.C.: 8748; 8099
N.A.I.C.S.: 541690; 621991
Advertising Expenditures: $2,000,000
Media: 6
Personnel:
Mercedes A. Walton *(Chm & CEO)*
Jill M. Taymans *(CFO & VP-Fin)*
Buff Mair *(Dir-Medical)*

Brands & Products:
CRYOCELL
INNOVATIVE STEM CELL SOLUTIONS
#1 FAMILY CHOICE
U-CORD

Key to Media (For complete agency information see *The Advertising Red Books-Agencies* edition):
1. Bus. Publs. 2. Cable T.V. 3. Catalogs & Directories. 4. Co-op Adv. 5. Consumer Mags. 6. D.M. to Bus. Estab.7. D.M. to Consumers 8. Daily Newsp. 9. Exhibits/Trade Shows 10. Foreign 11. Infomercial 12. Internet Adv.13. Multimedia 14. Network Radio 15. Network T.V. 16. Newsp. Distr. Mags. 17. Other 18. Outdoor (Posters, Transit) 19. Point of Purchase20. Premiums, Novelties 21. Product Samples 22. Special Events Mktg. 23. Spot Radio 24. Spot T.V. 25. Weekly Newsp. 26. Yellow Page Adv.

CRYO-CELL International, Inc. — (Continued)

Advertising Agency:
Horizon Marketing Communications, Inc.
701 Palomar Airport Rd Ste 300
Carlsbad, CA 92011
Tel.: (760) 730-9232
Fax: (760) 730-9219
Toll Free: (888) 446-2237

CRYOLIFE, INC.

1655 Roberts Blvd NW
Kennesaw, GA 30144-3632
Tel.: (770) 419-3355
Fax: (770) 426-0031
Toll Free: (800) 438-8285
E-mail: info@cryolife.com
Web Site: www.cryolife.com
Approx. Rev.: $116,645,000
Approx. Number Employees: 393
Year Founded: 1984
Business Description:
Implantable Medical Devices Developer & Marketer; Human Tissues for Cardiovascular, Vascular & Orthopaedic Transplant Applications Preserver & Distr
S.I.C.: 3842; 3841; 8099
N.A.I.C.S.: 339113; 339112; 621991
Export
Advertising Expenditures: $531,000
Media: 2-13
Personnel:
Steven G. Anderson *(Chm, Pres & CEO)*
D. Ashley Lee *(CFO, COO, Treas & Exec VP)*
Amy D. Horton *(Chief Acctg Officer)*
Albert E. Heacox *(Sr VP-R & D)*
Gerald B. Seery *(Sr VP-Sls & Mktg)*
Bruce G. Anderson *(VP-Sls & Mktg US)*
Richard C. Gridley *(VP-Intl Sls & Mktg)*
Kenechi Munonyedi *(Mgr-Sls-UK)*
Brands & Products:
BIOGLUE
BIOLASTIC
BIOTECHNOLOGIES FOR MEDICINE
CARDIOWRAP
CRYOARTERY
CRYOGRAFT
CRYOKIDS
CRYOKIT
CRYOLIFE
CRYOLIFE-O'BRIEN
CRYOLIFE-ROSS
CRYOVALVE
CRYOVEIN
FIBRX
HEARTPAK
HEMOSTASE
PROPATCH
SYNERGRAFT

CSL BEHRING LLC

(Sub. of CSL Limited)
1020 1st Ave
King of Prussia, PA 19406
Mailing Address:
PO Box 61501
King of Prussia, PA 19406
Tel.: (610) 878-4000
Fax: (610) 878-4009
Toll Free: (800) 394-1290
Web Site: www.cslbehring.com
Approx. Number Employees: 4,300
Business Description:
Plasma-Derived & Recombinant Products Mfr
S.I.C.: 2836
N.A.I.C.S.: 325414
Export
Media: 2-4-7-10-11-21-22-26
Distr.: Intl.
Personnel:
Peter Turner *(Pres)*
Gordon Naylor *(CIO)*
Greg Boss *(Gen Counsel & Sr VP)*
Karen Etchberger *(Exec VP-Plasma, Supply Chain & Info Sys)*
Paul R. Perreault *(Exec VP-Comml Ops & Bus Dev-Worldwide)*
Wally Casey *(Sr VP & Gen Mgr)*
Randy L. Furby *(Sr VP & Gen Mgr)*
Uwe E. Jocham *(Sr VP & Gen Mgr)*
Roland Martin *(Sr VP & Gen Mgr)*
Dennis Jackman *(Sr VP-Pub Affairs)*
Kathy Quay *(Sr VP-HR)*
Val Romberg *(Sr VP-R & D)*
Chris Florentz *(Mgr-Corp Comm)*
Brands & Products:
ALBUMINAR
GAMMARP
GAMULIN RH
HELIXATE
HUMATE-P
MONOCLATE-P
MONONINE
STIMATE
STREPTASE
ZEMAIRA

CUBIST PHARMACEUTICALS, INC.

65 Hayden Ave
Lexington, MA 02421-7994
Tel.: (781) 860-8660
Fax: (781) 861-0556
E-mail: ir@cubist.com
Web Site: www.cubist.com
Approx. Rev.: $636,458,000
Approx. Number Employees: 638
Year Founded: 1992
Business Description:
New Antimicrobial Drugs Researcher, Developer & Commercializer
S.I.C.: 2834
N.A.I.C.S.: 325412
Advertising Expenditures: $4,800,000
Media: 10
Personnel:
Michael W. Bonney *(Pres & CEO)*
David W.J. Mcgirr *(CFO & Sr VP)*
Robert J. Perez *(COO)*
Anthony S. Murabito *(CIO)*
Tamara L. Joseph *(Gen Counsel, Sec & Sr VP)*
Barry I. Eisenstein *(Sr VP-Scientific Affairs)*
Charles Laranjeira *(Sr VP-Technical Ops)*
Gregory Stea *(Sr VP-Comml Ops)*
Santosh Vetticaden *(Chief Medical & Dev Officer, Sr VP)*
Eileen McIntyre *(Sr Dir-Corp Commun)*
Mary T. Thistle *(Sr Dir-Bus Dev)*
Brands & Products:
AUGMENTIN
BIAXIN
CONSERV
CUBICIN
CUBIST
ECALLANTIDE
HEPEX-B
ROCEPHIN
ZITHROMAX

CUMBERLAND PHARMACEUTICALS, INC.

2525 West End Ave Ste 950
Nashville, TN 37203
Tel.: (615) 255-0068
Fax: (615) 255-0094
Toll Free: (877) 484-2700
E-mail: info@cumberlandpharma.com
Web Site: www.cumberlandpharma.com
Approx. Rev.: $45,876,371
Approx. Number Employees: 131
Year Founded: 1999
Business Description:
Pharmaceutical Mfr
S.I.C.: 2834
N.A.I.C.S.: 325412
Advertising Expenditures: $800,000
Media: 2-6-7-8-10-21
Personnel:
A. J. Kazimi *(Chm & CEO)*
Rick S. Greene *(CFO)*
Martin E. Cearnal *(Chief Comml Officer & Sr VP)*
Jean W. Marstiller *(Sec & Sr VP)*
Leo Pavliv *(Sr VP-Ops)*
James Lowrance Herman *(Sr Dir-Natl Accounts & Corp Compliance Officer)*
Amy D. Rock *(Sr Dir-Regulatory & Scientific Affairs)*
Todd Anthony *(Dir-Sls Trng & Dev)*
Tan Cheow Choon *(Dir-Intl Bus)*
Barry L. Lee *(Dir-Product)*
Cindy Patton *(Dir-Sls & Mktg)*
Arthur P. Wheeler *(Dir-Medical Affairs)*
Doug Jack *(Sr Mgr-SEC Reporting)*

CURATIVE PHARMACY SERVICES

(Sub. of Critical Care Systems International, Inc.)
31332 via Colinas Ste 107
Westlake Village, CA 91362
Tel.: (408) 562-9222
Toll Free: (888) 805-8344
E-mail: info@ebiocare.com
Web Site: www.ebiocare.com
Approx. Number Employees: 45
Year Founded: 1997
Business Description:
Online Specialty Pharmacy Services
S.I.C.: 5912
N.A.I.C.S.: 446110
Media: 2-4-8-13
Personnel:
Michael McDonald *(Chm)*
Michael Weber *(Mng Dir)*
Laura Lewis *(Gen Mgr)*

CUTERA, INC.

3240 Bayshore Blvd
Brisbane, CA 94005
Tel.: (415) 657-5500
Fax: (415) 330-2444
Toll Free: (888) 4CUTERA
E-mail: info@cutera.com
Web Site: www.cutera.com
Approx. Rev.: $53,274,000
Approx. Number Employees: 187
Year Founded: 1998
Business Description:
Laser & Other Light Based Product Mfr
S.I.C.: 3845; 3841
N.A.I.C.S.: 334510; 339112
Advertising Expenditures: $947,000
Personnel:
Kevin P. Connors *(Pres & CEO)*
Ronald J. Santilli *(CFO & Exec VP)*
Maureen Brunner *(VP-Mktg)*
Michael Poole *(Reg Mgr-Sls)*
Brands & Products:
ACUTIP 500
COOLGLIDE
COOLGLIDE EXCEL
COOLGLIDE VANTAGE
COOLGLIDE XEO
COOLGUIDE CV
CUTERA
LASER GENESIS
LASERS & LIGHT
LIMELIGHT
PEARL
PEARL FRACTIONAL
PROWAVE 770
SOLERA OPUS
SOLERA TITAN
TITAN
TITAN V
TITAN XL
XEO

CVS PHARMACY

(Sub. of CVS Caremark Corporation)
15325 Michigan Ave
Dearborn, MI 48126-2954
Tel.: (313) 582-9422
Fax: (313) 846-1261
E-mail: info@cvs.com
Web Site: www.cvs.com
Sales Range: $50-74.9 Million
Approx. Number Employees: 50
Year Founded: 1963
Business Description:
Drug Stores
S.I.C.: 5912
N.A.I.C.S.: 446110
Personnel:
Mark S. Cosby *(Pres)*
Douglas A. Sgarro *(Chief Legal Officer & Exec VP)*
Chris W. Bodine *(Exec VP & Pres-CVS Health Svcs)*
V. Michael Ferdinandi *(Sr VP-HR & Corp Commun)*
Bari Harlam *(Sr VP-Mktg)*
Advertising Agencies:
(Add) Ventures
117 Chapman St
Providence, RI 02905
Tel.: (401) 453-4748
Fax: (401) 453-0095

Arnold Worldwide
101 Huntington Ave
Boston, MA 02199-7603
Tel.: (617) 587-8000
Fax: (617) 587-8004
Creative

Mindshare
498 7th Ave
New York, NY 10018
Tel.: (212) 297-7000
Fax: (212) 297-7001
Media Buying & Planning

CYBERONICS, INC.

100 Cyberonics Blvd
Houston, TX 77058
Tel.: (281) 228-7200

Key to Media (For complete agency information see *The Advertising Red Books-Agencies* edition):
1. Bus. Publs. 2. Cable T.V. 3. Catalogs & Directories. 4. Co-op Adv. 5. Consumer Mags. 6. D.M. to Bus. Estab.7. D.M. to Consumers 8. Daily Newsp. 9. Exhibits/Trade Shows 10. Foreign 11. Infomercial 12. Internet Adv.13. Multimedia 14. Network Radio 15. Network T.V, 16. Newsp. Distr. Mags. 17. Other 18. Outdoor (Posters, Transit) 19. Point of Purchase20. Premiums, Novelties 21. Product Samples 22. Special Events Mktg. 23. Spot Radio 24. Spot T.V. 25. Weekly Newsp. 26. Yellow Page Adv.

Fax: (281) 218-9332
Toll Free: (888) 867-7846
E-mail: ir@cyberonics.com
Web Site: www.cyberonics.com
Approx. Sls.: $190,464,398
Approx. Number Employees: 484
Year Founded: 1987
Business Description:
Epilepsy & Other Neurological Disorders Medical Devices Designer, Developer & Mfr
S.I.C.: 3845; 3842; 8733
N.A.I.C.S.: 334510; 339113; 541720
Media: 2
Personnel:
Hugh M. Morrison *(Chm)*
Daniel J. Moore *(Pres & CEO)*
Gregory H. Browne *(CFO & Sr VP-Fin)*
David S. Wise *(Chief Admin Officer, Sec & Sr VP)*
James A. Reinstein *(Chief Comml Officer & Sr VP)*
Darren W. Alch *(Corp Counsel, VP, Asst Sec & Compliance Officer)*
Mark Verratti *(VP-Sls-Americas, Asia & EMMEA)*
Shaun Comfort *(Sr Dir-Clinical Affairs)*
Ingrid Seymus *(Sr Dir-Mktg)*
Brands & Products:
CYBERONICS
NCP
NEUROCYBERNETIC PROSTHESIS
VNS THERAPY
Advertising Agency:
Schwartz Communications, Inc.
230 3rd Ave
Waltham, MA 02451
Tel.: (781) 684-0770
Fax: (781) 684-6500
— Helen Shik *(VP)*

CYBEX INTERNATIONAL, INC.
(Sub. of UM Holdings Limited)
10 Trotter Dr
Medway, MA 02053-2299
Tel.: (508) 533-4300
Fax: (508) 533-5500
Toll Free: (888) GOCYBEX
E-mail: info@cybexintl.com
Web Site: www.ecybex.com
Approx. Sls.: $122,961,000
Approx. Number Employees: 552
Business Description:
Strength, Fitness & Rehabilitation Equipment Marketer & Mfr
S.I.C.: 3949
N.A.I.C.S.: 339920
Export
Advertising Expenditures: $3,660,000
Media: 2-6-10
Distr.: Intl.
Budget Set: Dec.
Personnel:
John Aglialoro *(Chm & CEO)*
Arthur W. Hicks, Jr. *(Pres & CFO)*
James M. Ahearn *(Chief Acctg Officer & Treas)*
Raymond Giannelli *(Sr VP-R & D)*
Larry Gulko *(Sr VP-Bus Dev)*
Edward Kurzontkowski *(Sr VP-Mfg)*
Edward J. Pryts *(Sr VP-Sls-North America)*
John P. Young *(Sr VP-Sls-Intl)*
Heather Corbitt *(Mgr-Mktg)*
Brands & Products:
ARC TRAINER
CYBER EAGLE
TRAZER

CYCLACEL PHARMACEUTICALS, INC.
200 Connell Dr Ste 1500
Berkeley Heights, NJ 07922
Tel.: (908) 517-7330
Fax: (866) 271-3466
E-mail: info@cyclacel.com
Web Site: www.cyclacel.com
Approx. Rev.: $686,000
Approx. Number Employees: 18
Year Founded: 1996
Business Description:
Immune System Therapies Developer
S.I.C.: 2834; 8733
N.A.I.C.S.: 325412; 541710
Personnel:
Christopher S. Henney *(Vice Chm)*
Spiro Rombotis *(Pres & CEO)*
Paul McBarron *(COO, Sec & Exec VP-Fin)*
Gill Christie *(Dir-HR)*
Susan Davis *(Assoc Dir-Bus Dev)*
Brands & Products:
CYC116
CYCLACEL
SAPACITABINE
SELICICLIB
Advertising Agencies:
Feinstein Kean Healthcare
245 1st St 14th Fl
Cambridge, MA 02142-1292
Tel.: (617) 577-8110
Fax: (617) 577-8985
Pub Rels
— Kate Weiss *(Acct Exec)*

TS Communications LLC
37 Purchase
Rye, NY 10580
Tel.: (914) 921-5900

WCG
60 Francisco St
San Francisco, CA 94133
Tel.: (415) 362-5018
Fax: (415) 362-5019

CYNOSURE, INC.
5 Carlisle Rd
Westford, MA 01886
Tel.: (978) 256-4200
Fax: (978) 256-6556
Toll Free: (800) 886-2966
E-mail: info@cynosurelaser.com
Web Site: www.cynosurelaser.com
Approx. Rev.: $81,775,000
Approx. Number Employees: 259
Year Founded: 1991
Business Description:
Developer & Mfr of Light-Based Aesthetic & Medical Treatment Systems
S.I.C.: 3844; 3841; 3845
N.A.I.C.S.: 334517; 334510; 339112
Advertising Expenditures: $400,000
Media: 7-10
Personnel:
Michael R. Davin *(Chm, Pres & CEO)*
Timothy W. Baker *(CFO, Treas & Exec VP)*
Douglas J. Delaney *(Exec VP-Sls)*
David Mackie *(Exec VP-Ops)*
William T. Kelley *(Sr VP-Intl)*
Brands & Products:
ACCLAIM
AFFINITY QS
AFFIRM
APOGEE ELITE
BE TRANSFORMED
CYNERGY
CYNOSURE
CYNOSURESPA
ELITE MPX
LASERBODYSCULPTING
PHOTOSILK
SMARTLIPO
TRIACTIVE LASERDERMOLOGY

CYTRX CORPORATION
11726 San Vicente Blvd Ste 650
Los Angeles, CA 90049
Tel.: (310) 826-5648
Fax: (310) 826-6139
Web Site: www.cytrx.com
Approx. Rev.: $100,000
Approx. Number Employees: 15
Year Founded: 1985
Business Description:
Pharmaceutical Products
S.I.C.: 2836
N.A.I.C.S.: 325414
Media: 10-22
Personnel:
Max E. Link *(Chm)*
Steven A. Kriegsman *(Pres & CEO)*
John Y. Caloz *(CFO)*
Benjamin S. Levin *(Gen Counsel, Corp Sec & VP-Legal Affairs)*
Scott Geyer *(Sr VP-Mfg)*
Shi Chung Ng *(Sr VP)*
Scott Wieland *(Sr VP-Drug Dev)*
Brands & Products:
CREATING TOMMOROW TODAY
CYTRX
RNAI
TRANZFECT

DAIRY ASSOCIATION CO, INC.
91 Williams St
Lyndonville, VT 05851
Mailing Address:
PO Box 145
Lyndonville, VT 05851-0145
Tel.: (802) 626-3610
Fax: (802) 626-3433
Toll Free: (800) 232-3610
E-mail: info@bagbalm.com
Web Site: www.bagbalm.com
Approx. Number Employees: 9
Year Founded: 1899
Business Description:
Veterinary Pharmaceutical Products
S.I.C.: 2834
N.A.I.C.S.: 325412
Media: 2-6
Distr.: Natl.
Budget Set: Sept.
Personnel:
Barbara Allen *(Pres)*
Brands & Products:
BAG BALM
GREEN MOUNTAIN HOOF SOFTENER
TACKMASTER
Advertising Agency:
Paul Kaza Associates
1233 Shelburne Rd Ste C3
South Burlington, VT 05403-7753
Tel.: (802) 863-5956
Fax: (802) 864-8232
(All)

DARBY DENTAL SUPPLY, LLC
(Sub. of Darby Group Companies, Inc.)
300 Jericho Quadrangle
Jericho, NY 11753-2704
Tel.: (516) 683-1800
Fax: (800) 329-3272
Toll Free: (800) 645-2310
E-mail: info@darbydental.com
Web Site: www.darbydental.com
Approx. Number Employees: 350
Business Description:
Dental Supplies
S.I.C.: 5047
N.A.I.C.S.: 423450
Media: 4-7-10-13
Personnel:
Carl Ashkin *(CEO)*

DATASCOPE CORP.
(Sub. of MAQUET Cardiovascular LLC)
1300 MacArthur Blvd
Mahwah, NJ 07430
Tel.: (201) 995-8700
Fax: (201) 995-8910
Web Site: www.datascope.com
Approx. Sls.: $230,915,000
Approx. Number Employees: 765
Year Founded: 1964
Business Description:
Medical Electronic Instruments & Disposable Products Mfr, Sales & Distr
S.I.C.: 3841; 3845
N.A.I.C.S.: 339112; 334510
Import Export
Media: 2-7-10
Distr.: Intl.; Natl.
Budget Set: May -June
Personnel:
Christian Keller *(Pres & CEO)*
Henry M. Scaramelli *(CFO & VP-Fin)*
Gary Mohr *(Dir-Legal Affairs)*
Brands & Products:
ACCUCAP
ACCUTORR
ACCUTORR PLUS
ANESTAR
AUTOGRAFT EXPRESS
BENCHMARK
BIOPLEX
CARDIOSYNC
CLEARGUIDE
CS100
DATASCOPE
DUO
DURATHANE
ELITE
EZ-FLOW
FIDELITY
FLEXISENSOR
GAS MODULE SE
HEMATEX
INTELLISYNC
INTELLIVENT
INTERVASCULAR
LIFEGUARD
LINEAR
MULTINEX
PANORAMA
PASSPORT
PASSPORT 2
PATIENTNET
PERCLUDER
PERCOR
PERCOR STAT

Key to Media (For complete agency information see *The Advertising Red Books-Agencies* edition):
1. Bus. Publs. 2. Cable T.V. 3. Catalogs & Directories. 4. Co-op Adv. 5. Consumer Mags. 6. D.M. to Bus. Estab.7. D.M. to Consumers
8. Daily Newsp. 9. Exhibits/Trade Shows 10. Foreign 11. Infomercial 12. Internet Adv.13. Multimedia 14. Network Radio
15. Network T.V. 16. Newsp. Distr. Mags. 17. Other 18. Outdoor (Posters, Transit) 19. Point of Purchase20. Premiums, Novelties
21. Product Samples 22. Special Events Mktg. 23. Spot Radio 24. Spot T.V. 25. Weekly Newsp. 26. Yellow Page Adv.

Datascope Corp. — (Continued)

PERCOR STAT-DL
PROGUIDE
PROLUMEN
R-TRAC
RADICAL
SAFEGUARD
SENSATION
SENSOR GUARD
SPECTRUM
STATLOCK
SYSTEM 98XT
TRIO
VASOSEAL

DAUGHTERS OF CHARITY HEALTH SYSTEM

26000 Altamont Rd
Los Altos, CA 94022-4317
Tel.: (650) 917-4500
Web Site: www.dochs.org
Sales Range: $900-999.9 Million
Approx. Number Employees: 7,000
Year Founded: 2002
Business Description:
Hospital & Medical Center Operator
S.I.C.: 8741
N.A.I.C.S.: 561110
Media: 8-13-18
Personnel:
Robert Issai *(Pres & CEO)*
Mike Stuart *(CFO)*
Richard Hutsell *(CIO & VP)*
Stephanie Battles *(VP-HR)*

DAVOL INC.

(Sub. of C.R. Bard, Inc.)
100 Crossrings Blvd
Warwick, RI 02886
Tel.: (401) 463-7000
Fax: (800) 531-4124
Toll Free: (800) 856-6753
E-mail: info@davol.com
Web Site: www.davol.com
Sales Range: $75-99.9 Million
Approx. Number Employees: 300
Year Founded: 1874
Business Description:
Mfr. of Surgical Prosthetics & Irrigation Systems
S.I.C.: 3842; 8011
N.A.I.C.S.: 339113; 621111
Advertising Expenditures: $500,000
Media: 2-7-10-21-23-24
Distr.: Intl.; Natl.
Personnel:
John Groetelrf *(Pres)*
Brands & Products:
ARTHRO-FLO
ENDO-FLO
HYDRO-FLEX
SIMPULSE
X-STREAM
Advertising Agency:
Catalyst
275 Promenade St Ste 275
Warwick, RI 02908
Tel.: (401) 732-1886
Fax: (401) 732-5528

DAWE'S LABORATORIES

3355 N Arlington Hts Rd
Arlington Heights, IL 60004-7706
Tel.: (847) 577-2020
Fax: (847) 577-1898
Toll Free: (800) 323-4317
Web Site: www.dawesnutrition.com
Approx. Number Employees: 10
Year Founded: 1920
Business Description:
Mfr. of Vitamin Products for Animal Nutrition
S.I.C.: 2048; 8733
N.A.I.C.S.: 311119; 541710
Import Export
Advertising Expenditures: $300,000
Media: 2-7
Distr.: Natl.
Budget Set: Mar.
Personnel:
Charles R. Dawe *(Pres & CEO)*
Eileen Brockman *(Mgr-Pur)*
Brands & Products:
AQUA DEE
CALF-FORTE
CLOSE-UP PELLET
DAWE ACE
DAWELYTE
DAWE'S LABORATORIES
FIRM-O-SHELL
NITIL
PRYFERM
STRESEEZ

DAXOR CORPORATION

350 5th Ave Ste 7120
New York, NY 10118-7120
Tel.: (212) 330-8500
Fax: (212) 244-0806
E-mail: info@daxor.com
Web Site: www.daxor.com
Approx. Rev.: $17,326,939
Approx. Number Employees: 42
Year Founded: 1971
Business Description:
Medical Instrumentation & Biotechnology Services
S.I.C.: 3841; 8099
N.A.I.C.S.: 339112; 621999
Advertising Expenditures: $7,318
Media: 2-7-10
Personnel:
Joseph Feldschuh *(Chm, Pres & CEO)*
David Frankel *(CFO)*
Stephen Feldschuh *(COO)*
Everis Engstrom *(VP-Engrg)*
Donald Margouleff *(Dir-Nuclear Medicine)*
Brands & Products:
BVA 100

DC BRANDS INTERNATIONAL, INC.

9500 W 49th Ave Ste D-106
Wheat Ridge, CO 80033
Tel.: (303) 279-3800
Toll Free: (866) 432-2726
Web Site: www.hardnutrition.com
Approx. Rev.: $605,493
Approx. Number Employees: 17
Year Founded: 1998
Business Description:
Nutritional-Based Water Beverages & Other Specialized Nutritional Products Mfr & Distr
S.I.C.: 2086; 2099; 2833; 2836; 5122
N.A.I.C.S.: 312111; 311999; 325411; 325414; 424210
Advertising Expenditures: $586,828
Personnel:
Richard Pearce *(Chm, Pres & CEO)*
Bob Armstrong *(CFO)*
Jeremy J. Alcamo *(Chief Procurement Officer)*
Tom Vigil *(VP-Sls)*
Wade Brantley *(Dir-IR)*
Robert Nikkel *(Chief Herbalist)*
Brands & Products:
CHANGE YOUR LIFE
H.A.R.D. NUTRITION
HEALTH ADVANTAGE

DEN-MAT CORPORATION

2727 Skwy Dr PO Box 1729
Santa Maria, CA 93455-1413
Tel.: (805) 922-8491
Fax: (805) 922-6933
Toll Free: (800) 445-0345
E-mail: info@denmat.com
Web Site: www.denmat.com
Approx. Number Employees: 515
Year Founded: 1974
Business Description:
Dental & Oral Care Products Developer & Whslr
S.I.C.: 3843
N.A.I.C.S.: 339114
Media: 2-4-6-7-10
Distr.: Natl.
Personnel:
Noreen Freitas *(Exec VP)*
Eric Relyea *(VP-Mktg)*
Brands & Products:
ALLEGRO
BIO-CAP
C.B.V. TEMP
CERINATE
DECTOR
DEN-MAT
GERISTORE
GLOSS-N-SEAL
INFINITY
MARATHON
QUIK START
REMBRANDT
REMBRANDT ALLEGRO
REMBRANDT SAPPHIRE
SAPPHIRE
TENURE
TENURE QUIK
TENURE UNIBOND
ULTRA-BOND QUIK
VIRTUOSO

DENDREON CORPORATION

3005 1st Ave
Seattle, WA 98121-1035
Tel.: (206) 256-4545
Fax: (206) 256-0571
E-mail: busdev@dendreon.com
Web Site: www.dendreon.com
E-Mail For Key Personnel:
Public Relations: pr@denfreon.com
Approx. Rev.: $48,057,000
Approx. Number Employees: 1,497
Year Founded: 1992
Business Description:
Biotechnology Research & Services
S.I.C.: 2834; 8733
N.A.I.C.S.: 325412; 541720
Advertising Expenditures: $598,000
Media: 2
Personnel:
Richard B. Brewer *(Chm)*
Mitchell H. Gold *(Pres & CEO)*
Gregory T. Schiffman *(CFO, Treas & Exec VP)*
Mark W. Frohlich *(Chief Medical Officer & Exec VP-Clinical Affairs)*
David L. Urdal *(Exec VP & Chief Scientific Officer)*
John E. Osborn *(Gen Counsel, Sec & Exec VP)*
Richard F. Hamm, Jr. *(Exec VP-Corp Dev)*
Richard J. Ranieri *(Exec VP-HR)*
Varun Nanda *(Sr VP-Global Comml Ops)*
Brands & Products:
ANTIGEN CASSETTE
CA-9
CEA
DENDREON
LAPULEUCEL-T
MYEZENIUM
NEUVENGE
NEUZENIUM
PROVENGE
PROZENIUM
SIMPLESEP ENRICHMENT SYSTEM
SIPULEUCEL-T
TARGETING CANCER, TRANSFORMING LIVES
TRP-P8
Advertising Agency:
WCG
60 Francisco St
San Francisco, CA 94133
Tel.: (415) 362-5018
Fax: (415) 362-5019

DENTAL WORLD

900 Merchants Concourse
Westbury, NY 11590-5142
Tel.: (516) 683-9100
Fax: (516) 683-1232
E-mail: dentworld@aol.com
Web Site: www.dentworld.com
Approx. Number Employees: 30
Year Founded: 1987
Business Description:
Dental Services & Dental Centers Franchiser
S.I.C.: 8021
N.A.I.C.S.: 621210
Media: 1-2-5-7-8-9-10-16-23-25-26
Distr.: Reg.
Personnel:
Natalie Gambella *(Owner)*
Brands & Products:
DENTAL WORLD

DENTALCARE PARTNERS INC.

5875 Landerbrook Dr Ste 250
Cleveland, OH 44124-6502
Tel.: (440) 684-6940
Fax: (440) 684-6941
Toll Free: (800) 47-SMILE
E-mail: dentalworks@dcpartners.com
Web Site: www.dcpartners.com
Approx. Number Employees: 850
Year Founded: 1989
Business Description:
Dental Services
S.I.C.: 8021
N.A.I.C.S.: 621210
Advertising Expenditures: $1,300,000
Media: 7-8-24-26
Distr.: Reg.
Personnel:
Doug Brown *(CEO)*
Brands & Products:
DENTALCARE PARTNERS

DENTSPLY INTERNATIONAL INC.

Susquehanna Commerce Ctr 221 W Philadelphia St
York, PA 17404
Mailing Address:

PO Box 872
York, PA 17405-0872
Tel.: (717) 845-7511
Fax: (717) 849-4762
Toll Free: (800) 877-0020
E-mail: investor@dentsply.com
Web Site: www.dentsply.com
Approx. Sls.: $2,221,014,000
Approx. Number Employees: 9,700
Year Founded: 1899
Business Description:
Holding Company; Dental Equipment & Supplies Mfr & Whslr
S.I.C.: 3843; 3844
N.A.I.C.S.: 339114; 334517
Import Export
Media: 1-2-4-7-10-11-13-17-21
Distr.: Intl.; Natl.
Budget Set: Aug.
Personnel:
Bret W. Wise *(Chm & CEO)*
Christopher T. Clark *(Pres & COO)*
William R. Jellison *(CFO & Sr VP)*
Deborah Rasin *(Gen Counsel, Sec & VP)*
James G. Mosch *(Exec VP)*
Robert J. Size *(Sr VP)*
Albert J. Sterkenburg *(Sr VP)*
Chip Farnham *(Dir-Govt Div)*
Don Gronert *(Reg Mgr-Northeast & Intl)*
Terry Chennault *(Reg Mgr-Southwest)*
Randy DeMarco *(Reg Mgr-Mid-South)*
Ed Doyle *(Reg Mgr-Central)*
Leslie du Plooy *(Reg Mgr-Southeast)*
Kyle Morton *(Reg Mgr-West)*
Brands & Products:
ACCUJECT
AL-COTE
ALLSOLUTIONS
ANKYLOS
AQUASIL
AQUASIL ULTRA SMART WETTING
AUTOMATRIX
B4
BIOBLEND
BIOBOND II
BIOFORCE
BIOFORM
BIOPURE
BIOVEST
BIOWAX
CALIBRA
CASTONE
CAULK
CAULK FYNAL
CAVITRON
CAVITRON 30K SOFTIP
CAVITRON BOBCAT PRO
CAVITRON JET PLUS
CAVITRON STERIMATE
CERAMCO
CERAMPRESS
CERAMX
CERCON
COMSPAN
CRESCENT
CRISTOBAL
CUALK IRM
CURE RITE
CUTWELL
DELTON
DENTSPLY
DENTSPLY INTERNATIONAL
DENTSULATE
DETREY
DISPERSALLOY
DISPOSA-SHIELD
DUALINE
DUCERAGOLD
DUCERAM
DYCAL
DYRACT
ECLIPSE
EEZEE-GRIP
ELEPHANT
ENDOSONIC
ENHANCE
ESTHET X
EXCELSIOR
EZ-VIEW
FASKUT
FASTIPS
FINESSE
FIRST BITE
FLEXICHANGE
FLUOROCORE
FLUROSHIELD
FOR BETTER DENTISTRY
FRIALIT
FRIOS
GAC
GENIE
GLASTONE
GLOSS
HYDROSIL
ILLUMINE
IN-OVATION
INTEGRITY
INTERACTIVE MYSTIQUE
IRM
JELTRATE
KAOLINER
LASTING TOUCH
LUCI-SOF
MAILLEFER
MAX-I-PROBE
MEGALLOY
MIDWEST STYLUS
MULTI-VEST
MYSTIQUE
NEOWAX
NEYTECH
NRG
NUPRO
OPTALOY
ORAQIX
ORTHOWORKS
OSTEOGRAF
PALODENT
PEPGEN
PEPGEN P-15
POGO
POLYJEL NF
PRIME AND BOND
PRINCIPLE
PRISMA
PROBOND
PROFILE
PROMIX
PROTAPER
PUMICIDE
QHL75 LITE
QUIXX
R&R
RAINTREE
REGALLOY
REGISIL
REPROSIL
RESILINE
RIM-LOCK
RINN
ROLL-O-WAX
ROOT ZX
SANI-TIP
SEAL& PROTECT
SIMPLEX
SMARTLITE
SOOTHE-GUARD
SPECTRUM
SUCCESS
SUREFIL
THERMAFIL
TPH
TRANSHEET
TRAYBYTE
TRIAD
TRUBASE
TRUBLEND
TRUWAX
TYLOK PLUS
ULTRA
ULTRACROWN
ULTRASONIK
UNI-GRIP
UNISON
VIP FILM HOLDER
VITA
VULCAM
WHITE GOLD
WIG-L-BUG
XCP-DS
XIVE
XP BOND
ZHERMACK
ZIRCATE
ZOE B AND T
Advertising Agencies:
3H Communications Inc.
309 Church St
Oakville, ON L6J 1N9, Canada
Tel.: (905) 338-8177
Fax: (905) 338-1317

All Star Incentive Marketing, Inc.
660 Main St
Fiskdale, MA 01518
Tel.: (508) 347-7672
Fax: (508) 347-5404
Toll Free: (800) 526-8629

ANEW Marketing Group
811 W Jericho Tpke Ste 109E
Smithtown, NY 11787
Tel.: (631) 982-4000
Fax: (631) 434-1129

Blakeslee Advertising
916 N Charles St
Baltimore, MD 21201
Tel.: (410) 727-8800
Fax: (410) 752-1302

PowerAxle
c/ Sagasta 15-6 Izquda
28004
Madrid, Spain
Tel.: (34) 91 594 18 09
Fax: (34) 91 594 20 13

DEPOMED, INC.
1360 O'Brien Dr
Menlo Park, CA 94025-1436
Tel.: (650) 462-5900
Fax: (650) 462-9993
E-mail: investor@depomedinc.com
Web Site: www.depomedinc.com
Approx. Rev.: $80,764,000
Approx. Number Employees: 69
Business Description:
Drug Delivery Technologies Developer
S.I.C.: 2833; 2834; 8733
N.A.I.C.S.: 325411; 325412; 541710
Advertising Expenditures: $300,000
Personnel:
James A. Schoeneck *(Pres & CEO)*
Peter D. Staple *(CEO)*
Matthew M. Gosling *(Gen Counsel & VP)*
Thadd M. Vargas *(Sr VP-Bus Dev)*
Kera Alexander *(VP-Admin & HR)*
Tammy L. Cameron *(VP-Fin)*
Abid Rawn *(VP-Sls & Mktg)*
Kevin Weber *(VP-Mktg)*
Brands & Products:
ACUFORM
DEPOMED
ENHANCING PHARMACEUTICALS ENHANCING LIVES
GABAPENTIN GR
GLUMETZA
MAKING A DIFFERENCE WITH NOVEL THERAPIES
PROQUIN

DEPUY ORTHOPAEDICS
(Sub. of Johnson & Johnson)
700 Orthopaedic Dr
Warsaw, IN 46581
Tel.: (574) 267-8143
Fax: (574) 267-7196
Toll Free: (800) 366-8143
E-mail: info@dpyus.jnj.com
Web Site: www.depuy.com
E-Mail For Key Personnel:
Public Relations: mgibson2@dpyus.jnj.com
Sales Range: $650-699.9 Million
Approx. Number Employees: 3,500
Business Description:
Orthopedic Products Mfr & Whslr
S.I.C.: 3842
N.A.I.C.S.: 339113
Import Export
Media: 1-2-4-10-11-13
Distr.: Natl.
Personnel:
Peter Batesko, III *(CFO & VP-Fin)*
Lorie Gawreluk *(Pres-Worldwide)*
Michael A. Kaufman *(VP-Law)*
Kathleen McDaniel *(Worldwide VP-HR)*
Brands & Products:
AML HIP
DEPUY
GLOBAL TOTAL SHOULDER SYSTEM
LCS TOTAL KNEE SYSTEM
PFC SIGMA TOTAL KNEE SYSTEM
Advertising Agency:
ARRCO Medical Advertising Inc.
1 Edgewater Dr
Norwood, MA 02062-4674
Tel.: (781) 769-7190
Fax: (781) 769-9480

DERMA SCIENCES, INC.
214 Carnegie Ctr Ste 300
Princeton, NJ 08540-6237
Tel.: (609) 514-4744
Fax: (609) 514-0502
Toll Free: (800) 825-4325
E-mail: info@dermasciences.com
Web Site: www.dermasciences.com
Approx. Sls.: $56,474,056
Approx. Number Employees: 195
Year Founded: 1985

Key to Media (For complete agency information see *The Advertising Red Books-Agencies* edition):
1. Bus. Publs. 2. Cable T.V. 3. Catalogs & Directories. 4. Co-op Adv. 5. Consumer Mags. 6. D.M. to Bus. Estab.7. D.M. to Consumers 8. Daily Newsp. 9. Exhibits/Trade Shows 10. Foreign 11. Infomercial 12. Internet Adv.13. Multimedia 14. Network Radio 15. Network T.V. 16. Newsp. Distr. Mags. 17. Other 18. Outdoor (Posters, Transit) 19. Point of Purchase20. Premiums, Novelties 21. Product Samples 22. Special Events Mktg. 23. Spot Radio 24. Spot T.V. 25. Weekly Newsp. 26. Yellow Page Adv.

DERMA SCIENCES, INC. — (Continued)

Business Description:
Wound Closure & Catheter Securement Skin Products Supplier & Mfr
S.I.C.: 3841; 2834; 2844
N.A.I.C.S.: 339112; 325412; 325620
Advertising Expenditures: $1,197,309
Personnel:
Edward J. Quilty *(CEO)*
John E. Yetter *(CFO & VP)*
Robert C. Cole *(Exec VP-Sls)*
Frederic Eigner *(Exec VP-Ops)*
Bary J. Wolfenson *(Exec VP-Global Mktg & Bus Dev)*
Diane Maydick *(Dir-Clinical Affairs)*
Brands & Products:
ALGICELL
APRIVERA
AQUASITE
BATHE AWAY
CATH-STRIP
COMPDRESS
COMPRIBAND
DERMA SCIENCES
DERMAGRAN
DUBAN
DUCARE
DUDRESS
DUPAD
DUPAQUE
DUPRESS
DUSOFT
DUSOR
DUTEX
DUTOP
ELASTIVE
FLEXOPLAST
GAZETEX
GLEN-SLEEVE
HYDRO-SOFT
HYDROCELL
IN BETWEEN
INTEGRA
THE MARSUPIAL
MEDIHONEY
MOBILITY1
MYSOTROL
NG STRIP
PAK-ITS
PRIMACARE
PRIMACOL
PRIMADERM
PRIMAPAD
PRIMER
SHUR-CONFORM
SHUR STRIP
SILVERSEAL
SOFT WASH
SORBACELL
SORBAN
SURECARE
SURGIGRIP
SURGILAST
SURGITUBE
SUTURE STRIP
SWASH
SYSTENET
THERABATH
UC STRIP
ULTRAFIX
UNNA-PAK
UNNAPRESS
XTRASORB

DERMIK LABORATORIES, INC.
(Sub. of Sanofi-Aventis US LLC)
1050 Westlakes Dr
Berwyn, PA 19312-2421
Tel.: (484) 595-2700
Web Site: www.dermik.com
E-Mail For Key Personnel:
President: robert.bitterman@aventis.com
Marketing Director: keith.greathouse@aventis.com
Approx. Sls.: $200,000,000
Approx. Number Employees: 10
Year Founded: 1964
Business Description:
Mfr. of Dermatologicals
S.I.C.: 2834
N.A.I.C.S.: 325412
Export
Media: 3-6-8-9-10-13-16-20-21-22
Distr.: Natl.
Budget Set: Nov.
Brands & Products:
BENZAGEL
BENZAMYCIN
CARAC
DERMATOP
HY TONE
KLARON
NORITATE
PENLAC
PSORCON
PSORCON-E
SULFACET-R
VANAMIDE
ZETAR
Advertising Agency:
Photosound Communications
1000 Wyckoff Ave
Mahwah, NJ 08536
Tel.: (609) 514-5366
Fax: (609) 514-5377

DESIGNING HEALTH, INC.
28410 Witherspoon Pkwy
Valencia, CA 91355-4167
Tel.: (661) 257-1705
Fax: (661) 257-2189
E-mail: customerservice@designinghealth.com
Web Site: www.designinghealth.com
Approx. Number Employees: 25
Business Description:
Food, Vitamins & Nutritional Supplements
S.I.C.: 2833; 5961
N.A.I.C.S.: 325411; 454113
Media: 2-6-10-19-21-23-24
Personnel:
Robert Collett *(Pres)*
Nate Armstrong *(COO & VP)*
Brands & Products:
ALL IS WELL
AVIAN
CANINE
EQUINE
FELINE
MEGA FLAX
MISSING LINK
OMEGA 3 BASIC

THE DETROIT MEDICAL CENTER
(Sub. of Vanguard Health Systems, Inc.)
Orchestra Pl 3663 Woodward Ave
Detroit, MI 48201
Tel.: (313) 745-5111
Fax: (313) 887-5211
Toll Free: (888) 362-2500
E-mail: jobs@dmc.org
Web Site: www.dmc.org
Approx. Number Employees: 12,500
Year Founded: 1985
Business Description:
Hospital & Medical Center Operator
S.I.C.: 8062; 8011
N.A.I.C.S.: 622110; 621111
Advertising Expenditures: $1,400,000
Media: 2-3-4-6-7-8-9-10-13-18-19-20-22-23-24-25-26
Distr.: Reg.
Budget Set: Nov.-Dec.
Personnel:
Michael Duggan *(Pres & CEO)*
Jay B. Rising *(CFO & Exec VP)*
Mary Zuckerman *(COO & Exec VP)*
Michael LeRoy *(CIO)*
Safwan Badr *(Exec VP & Chief Medical Officer)*
Timothy Ryan *(Chief Bus Dev Officer & Sr VP)*
Floyd Allen *(Gen Counsel)*
Steven D. Grant *(Exec VP-Physician Partnerships)*
Linda Alexander *(Admin Dir-Post Acute Svcs & Physician Rel)*
Ken Bearden *(Dir-Mktg & Comm)*
Emery King *(Dir-Comm)*
Lori Mouton *(Dir-Corp Pub Rel & Mktg)*
Brands & Products:
DMC

DEXCOM INC
6340 Sequence Dr
San Diego, CA 92121
Tel.: (858) 200-0200
Fax: (858) 200-0201
E-mail: info@dexcom.com
Web Site: www.dexcom.com
Approx. Rev.: $48,631,000
Approx. Number Employees: 405
Business Description:
Glucose Monitoring System Designer & Developer
S.I.C.: 3821; 3841
N.A.I.C.S.: 339111; 339112
Advertising Expenditures: $1,000,000
Personnel:
Jonathan T. Lord *(Chm)*
Kevin Ronald Sayer *(Pres)*
Terrance H. Gregg *(CEO)*
Jess Roper *(CFO & VP)*
Steven R. Pacelli *(COO)*
Andrew K. Balo *(Sr VP-Clinical & Regulatory Affairs)*
Richard B. Doubleday *(VP-Sls)*
Brands & Products:
BETWEEN THE LINES
DEXCOM
DEXCOM DATA MANAGER
DEXCOM DM
LIVE UNINTERRUPTED
OPENCHOICE
SENSYNC
SEVEN PLUS
STAY BETWEEN THE LINES
STS
TAKE CONTROL - LIVE UNINTERRUPTED

DEY L.P.
(Sub. of Merck KGaA)
2751 Napa Vly Corporate Dr
Napa, CA 94558
Tel.: (707) 224-3200
Fax: (707) 224-0495
E-mail: info@dey.com
Web Site: www.dey.com
Approx. Sls.: $125,000,000
Approx. Number Employees: 900
Business Description:
Pharmaceutical Solutions Mfr
S.I.C.: 2834; 8733
N.A.I.C.S.: 325412; 541710
Media: 6
Personnel:
Caroline Myers *(Pres & CEO)*
Imtiaz Chaudry *(Sr VP)*
Al R. Erario *(Sr VP-Quality Sys)*
Gary Michaud *(Sr VP-Ops)*
Mailet Minassian *(Sr VP-HR)*
Ann Peets *(Grp Dir-Mktg)*
Brands & Products:
ACCUNEB
CUROSURF
DEY
DUONEB
EPIPEN

DIASORIN INC.
(Sub. of Biofin Holding International BV)
1951 Northwestern Ave
Stillwater, MN 55082-7536
Mailing Address:
PO Box 285
Stillwater, MN 55082-0285
Tel.: (651) 439-9710
Fax: (651) 351-5669
Toll Free: (800) 328-1482
E-mail: info@diasorin.com
Web Site: www.diasorin.com
Approx. Number Employees: 160
Year Founded: 1975
Business Description:
In-Vitro Diagnostics Mfr
S.I.C.: 2835
N.A.I.C.S.: 325413
Import Export
Media: 4-10
Personnel:
Carroll Streetman *(Pres)*
Brands & Products:
LIAISON

DIET CENTER WORLDWIDE, INC.
(Holding of The Health Management Group, Inc.)
395 Springside Dr
Akron, OH 44333
Tel.: (330) 665-5861
Fax: (330) 666-2197
Toll Free: (800) 656-3294
E-mail: info@dietcenter.com
Web Site: www.dietcenter.com
Year Founded: 1972
Business Description:
Franchised Weight Loss Centers
S.I.C.: 7299
N.A.I.C.S.: 812191
Media: 2-3-4-9-23-25
Distr.: Natl.
Budget Set: Nov.
Personnel:
Charles E. Sekeres *(Pres & CEO)*
Lori Duff *(Dir-Ops-Trng)*
Mike Zsely *(Dir-Admin)*
Brands & Products:
DIET CENTER
EXCLUSIVELY YOU

Key to Media (For complete agency information see *The Advertising Red Books-Agencies* edition):
1. Bus. Publs. 2. Cable T.V. 3. Catalogs & Directories. 4. Co-op Adv. 5. Consumer Mags. 6. D.M. to Bus. Estab.7. D.M. to Consumers 8. Daily Newsp. 9. Exhibits/Trade Shows 10. Foreign 11. Infomercial 12. Internet Adv.13. Multimedia 14. Network Radio 15. Network T.V. 16. Newsp. Distr. Mags. 17. Other 18. Outdoor (Posters, Transit) 19. Point of Purchase20. Premiums, Novelties 21. Product Samples 22. Special Events Mktg. 23. Spot Radio 24. Spot T.V. 25. Weekly Newsp. 26. Yellow Page Adv.

INSTANT SHAPE UP
THE WEIGHT-LOSS PROFESSIONALS

DIGIRAD CORPORATION

13950 Stowe Dr
Poway, CA 92046-8803
Tel.: (858) 726-1600
Fax: (858) 726-1700
Toll Free: (800) 947-6134
E-mail: info@digirad.com
Web Site: www.digirad.com
Approx. Rev.: $56,183,000
Approx. Number Employees: 349
Year Founded: 1985
Business Description:
Nuclear Medicine Imaging Equipment Mfr
S.I.C.: 3845; 3829
N.A.I.C.S.: 334510; 334519
Advertising Expenditures: $400,000
Personnel:
Todd P. Clyde *(Pres & CEO)*
Richard B. Slansky *(CFO)*
Vera P. Pardee *(Gen Counsel, Sec & VP)*
Randy L. Weatherhead *(Sr VP-Sls & Mktg)*
Brands & Products:
2020TC IMAGER
4D-MSPECT
CARDIUS
DIGIONE
DIGIRAD
DIGIRAD IMAGINIG SOLUTIONS
DIGIRENT
DIGITECH
FLEXIMAGING
IMAGER
MIRAGE
NUCLEAR
SOLIDIUM
SPECTOUR
SPECTPAK PLUS
ULTRASOUND

DIK DRUG COMPANY

160 Tower Dr
Burr Ridge, IL 60527-5720
Tel.: (630) 655-4000
Fax: (630) 655-4031
E-mail: sales@dikdrug.com
Web Site: www.dikdrug.com
E-Mail For Key Personnel:
Sales Director: sales@dikdrug.com
Approx. Number Employees: 110
Year Founded: 1917
Business Description:
Drug Wholesaler
S.I.C.: 5122
N.A.I.C.S.: 424210
Media: 4-5-16-17
Distr.: Reg.
Budget Set: Oct.
Personnel:
Edward A. Dik *(Owner)*
John H. Dik *(Chm & CEO)*
J. B. Howard *(CFO)*
Tim Melvin *(VP)*
Gary Prester *(VP-Sls & Mktg)*
Karen Barbahen *(Mgr-Accts Receivable)*
Brands & Products:
CENTSIBLE

DISCOUNT DRUG MART INC.

211 Commerce Dr
Medina, OH 44256-1331
Tel.: (330) 725-2340
Fax: (330) 722-2990
E-mail: info@discount-drugmart.com
Web Site: www.discount-drugmart.com
Sales Range: $550-599.9 Million
Approx. Number Employees: 4,000
Year Founded: 1969
Business Description:
Drug Store
S.I.C.: 5399; 5912
N.A.I.C.S.: 452990; 446110
Import
Media: 4-13-19-23-24-25
Personnel:
Parviz Boodjeh *(Founder)*
John Gans *(Pres)*

DISETRONIC MEDICAL SYSTEMS, INC.

(Sub. of Roche Diabetes Care AG)
11800 Exit 5 Pkwy Ste 120
Fishers, IN 46037
Tel.: (317) 570-5100
Fax: (888) 810-0758
Toll Free: (800) 280-7801
E-mail: info@disetronic-usa.com
Web Site: www.disetronic-usa.com
Approx. Number Employees: 150
Business Description:
Medical & Surgical Apparatus & Equipment Mfr
S.I.C.: 3841; 5047
N.A.I.C.S.: 339112; 423450
Export
Advertising Expenditures: $200,000
Media: 6-10-11-13-21
Budget Set: Dec.
Personnel:
Nancy Dean *(VP-Mktg)*
Brands & Products:
ACCU-CHEK
DISETRONIC

DIVERSEY HOLDINGS INC.

8310 16th St
Sturtevant, WI 53177-0902
Tel.: (262) 631-4001
Fax: (262) 631-4282
Web Site: www.diversey.com
Approx. Sls.: $3,127,677,000
Approx. Number Employees: 10,170
Year Founded: 2001
Business Description:
Holding Company
S.I.C.: 6719
N.A.I.C.S.: 551112
Advertising Expenditures: $1,655,000
Personnel:
Helen P. Johnson-Leipold *(Chm)*
Norman Clubb *(Exec VP & CFO)*
Scott D. Russell *(Gen Counsel, Sec & Sr VP)*
Advertising Agencies:
BJL Group Limited
Sunlight House Quay St
Manchester, M3 3JZ, United Kingdom
Tel.: (44) 161 831 7141
Fax: (44) 161 832 1289

Fikir Merkezi
Mevlut Pehlivan Sokak Yilmaz Han
No 24/1
34349
Istanbul, Turkey
Tel.: (90) 212 347 86 86
Fax: (90) 212 347 86 87

LuckyEye Group
Kaya Aldogan Sokak Serhan Apt 3/10
Istanbul, Turkey
Tel.: (90) 212 216 8251
Fax: (90) 212 216 8254

Mulberry Marketing Communications
Chicago
308 W Erie St Ste 701
Chicago, IL 60654
Tel.: (312) 664-1532
Fax: (312) 664-1532

Ogilvy Primary Contact Ltd.
21-141 W bourne Ter
London, SWW 0DH, United Kingdom
Tel.: (44) 207 468 6900
Fax: (44) 207 468 6950

SBC Advertising
333 W Nationwide Blvd
Columbus, OH 43215
Tel.: (614) 891-7070
Fax: (614) 255-2600
Toll Free: (866) 891-7001

DIXIE HEALTH, INC.

2161 New Market Pkwy SE Ste 222
Marietta, GA 30067-8768
Tel.: (770) 951-9232
Fax: (770) 951-9249
Toll Free: (800) 288-9232
E-mail: marcia@dixiehealth.com
Web Site: www.dixiehealth.com
Approx. Number Employees: 15
Year Founded: 1988
Business Description:
Healthcare Products Mfr
S.I.C.: 5122; 5192
N.A.I.C.S.: 424210; 424920
Import Export
Advertising Expenditures: $500,000
Media: 3-4-5-6-8-9-13-16-19
Distr.: Natl.
Budget Set: Jan.
Personnel:
Robert Jackson *(Gen Counsel)*
Brands & Products:
BETA YAM 900
BREASTIQUE
COCOTONIN
DERMAL C
DERMAL-E
DERMAL H3
DERMAL K
DERMAL XL
DIXIE HEALTH INC
ESTRO-GYNE
ESTROGYN
KH3/GHQ10
LENDING NATURE A HAND
MIRACLE THIGH
MIRACLE THIGH CREAM
PRO 10
PRO-ENDORPHIN
PRO-HGH
PROGESTONE
PROGESTONE-900
PROGESTONE HP
PROGESTONE TEN
RELASTYL
RELAXIN
ROYAL JELLY
ROYAL JELLY BOOSTER
ROYAL JELLY CAPSULES
RX-ERECT
RXERECT
SOFT TOUCH
SUPER TESTRON
VASO-PROPHIN
VASODERM
VASOPROPHIN RX
VIVAXL
ZORIASIS

DJO INCORPORATED

(Holding of The Blackstone Group L.P.)
1430 Decision St
Vista, CA 92081
Tel.: (760) 727-1280
Fax: (760) 734-3595
Toll Free: (800) 936-6569
E-mail: info@djortho.com
Web Site: www.djortho.com
Approx. Rev.: $413,058,000
Approx. Number Employees: 3,000
Business Description:
Functional Bracing, Rehabilitative Post Operative Bracing, Sports Medicine Bracing, Neoprene Products & Orthopedic Soft Goods
S.I.C.: 3842; 2676
N.A.I.C.S.: 339113; 322291
Advertising Expenditures: $1,100,000
Media: 10
Personnel:
Leslie H. Cross *(Chm)*
Michael P. Mogul *(CEO)*
Vickie L. Capps *(CFO, Treas & Exec VP)*
Donald M. Roberts *(Gen Counsel, Sec & Exec VP)*
Tom Capizzi *(Exec VP-HR)*
Michael R. McBrayer *(Sr VP)*
Brands & Products:
4TITUDE
ALP PLUS
ARCTICFLOW
ARMOR
ATLAS
BOOMERANG WRIST
CARTILAGE
CCMI MARK
CERVICAL
COMFORT
COMFORTFORM
CRADLE
DEFIANCE
DELUXE DONUT
DJ ORTHO
DONJOY
DONJOY VISTA
DRYTEX
DURA KOLD
DURA SOFT
DURAFO
FEMALE FOURCE
FLOAM
FOURCE POINT
HORSESHOE PATELLA
HUMERAL CUFF
ICEMAN
IROM
KNEE GUARANTEE
LATERAL
LEGEND
LUMBROSACRAL
MAXTRAX
MIAMI JR.
MONTANA
NEVER STOP GETTING BETTER
OADJUSTER
OFFICECARE
OL1000
OL1000 SC

Key to Media (For complete agency information see *The Advertising Red Books-Agencies* edition):
1. Bus. Publs. 2. Cable T.V. 3. Catalogs & Directories. 4. Co-op Adv. 5. Consumer Mags. 6. D.M. to Bus. Estab.7. D.M. to Consumers
8. Daily Newsp. 9. Exhibits/Trade Shows 10. Foreign 11. Infomercial 12. Internet Adv.13. Multimedia 14. Network Radio
15. Network T.V. 16. Newsp. Distr. Mags. 17. Other 18. Outdoor (Posters, Transit) 19. Point of Purchase20. Premiums, Novelties
21. Product Samples 22. Special Events Mktg. 23. Spot Radio 24. Spot T.V. 25. Weekly Newsp. 26. Yellow Page Adv.

DJO Incorporated — (Continued)

ONTRACK
OPAL
PATELLA DONUT
PATELLOFEMORA
PHILADELPHIA
PLAYMAKER
PODOUS
POST-OP
PROCARE
PROROM
QUADRANT
REGENTEK
REHAB
ROCKETSOC
ROM HIP
SHIN SPLINT
SIDEKICK
SPINALOGIC
STABILIZING
THUMB-O-PRENE
TIBIAL
TROM
TRU-PULL
ULTRASLING
ULTRASLING ER
UNIVERSAL SURROUND
VELOCITY
WALKABOUT
WRAP-ON
WRIST WRAPS

DJO SURGICAL

(Sub. of DJO Incorporated)
9800 Metric Blvd
Austin, TX 78758-5445
Tel.: (512) 832-9500
Fax: (512) 834-6300
Toll Free: (800) 456-8696
Web Site: www.reableinc.com
Sales Range: $125-149.9 Million
Approx. Number Employees: 1,300
Year Founded: 1992
Business Description:
Reconstructive Surgical Implants, Spinal Disorder Treatment Products & Physical Rehabilitation Devices, Products & Equipment Mfr
S.I.C.: 3841; 3842; 3845
N.A.I.C.S.: 339112; 334510; 339113
Advertising Expenditures: $3,100,000
Media: 2-7-10
Personnel:
Kenneth W. Davidson *(Chm & CEO)*
William W. Burke *(CFO & Exec VP)*
Craig L. Smith *(Chief Scientific Officer)*
Peter W. Baird *(Grp Pres-Therapeutic Devices)*
Jack F. Cahill *(Exec VP)*
Don Dumoulin *(Exec VP)*
Scott Klosterman *(Exec VP)*
Brands & Products:
3DKNEE
3DMATRIX
911 FIRST RESPONSE
ADAPTA
ALFA
AUTO-FLEX
AUTO-TRAC
B.A.T.H.
CELLEX
CHATTANOOGA
CHATTANOOGA EUROPE
CHIEFTAIN
CLEAR CUT
CLP
COLPAC
COVER-SLING
CPS
CYCLONE
CYCLONE ACP
DTS
DURA-STICK
DURA-STIM
E ENCORE
E2 FIX
EMG RETRAINER
EMPI
EPIK
ERGOBASIC
ERGOSTYLE
ERGOWAVE
ES 2000
EVER GREEN BECAUSE IT'S OUR WORLD TOO
EXCELERATOR
FLEXIPAC
FLUIDO
FLUIDOTHERAPY
FOUNDATION
FOUNDATION TOTAL HIP SYSTEM
HOTPAC
HYDROCOLLATOR
HYDROCOLLATOR COLPAC
INDUSTRY'S CHOICE
INSPIRING PEOPLE, ENRICHING LIVES
INTELECT
INTELECT LEGEND
ISOBAR
KALLASSY
KALLASSY ANKLE SUPPORT
KERAMOS
KEYSTONE
LINEAR
LINEAR HIP SYSTEM
MAXIMUM POLY
M.I.K.A
MYOSSAGE
NAVIGATOR
NYLATEX
OPTI-ICE
OPTIFLEX
OPTIFLEX S
OSTEOMILL
PARA-CARE
PASS
POWER FLEX
POWERPLAY
PRE-VENT
PRESSSION
QUICK-FIT
R120
RAM
REBOUND
REVELATION
REVELATION HIP SYSTEM
REVERSE
REVERSE SHOULDER PROSTHESIS
RSP
SECURE-ALL
SENSAFLEX
SPINALATOR
SPORTS SUPPORTS
STABILIZER
STAMINA
STEALTH
STEAM PACK
THERATHEM
TRIAX
TRITON
TRU-TRAC
TRUE/FIX
TRUE/FLEX
TRUE/LOK
TRUTLE NECK
TX
VARIGRIP
VECTRA
VECTRA GENISYS
VITALITY
VITALSTIM
WARM'N FORM
WELLNESS BY DESIGN
WRIGHTLOCK

DR. TATTOFF, INC.

8500 Wilshire Blvd Ste 105
Beverly Hills, CA 90211
Tel.: (310) 659-5101
Fax: (310) 659-4141
Toll Free: (888) TATT-OFF
Web Site: www.drtattoff.com
Approx. Number Employees: 12
Year Founded: 2004
Business Description:
Laser Tattoo Removal, Hair Removal & Other Laser-Based Skin Care Services
S.I.C.: 8071; 8093
N.A.I.C.S.: 621511; 621498
Advertising Expenditures: $301,898
Media: 3-6-8-9-10-13-23-25
Personnel:
John J. Klobnak *(Chm)*
John P. Keefe *(CEO)*
Mark A. Edwards *(CFO)*
Ian A. Kirby *(CMO)*
William T. Kirby *(Dir-Medical)*

DRAVON MEDICAL, INC.

11465 SE Hwy 212
Clackamas, OR 97015-0069
Tel.: (503) 656-6600
Fax: (503) 655-5229
Toll Free: (800) 654-1976
E-mail: dravon@mindstring.com
Web Site: www.dravon.com
Sales Range: $10-24.9 Million
Approx. Number Employees: 25
Year Founded: 1974
Business Description:
Disposable Medical Products & Custom Bags Mfr & Contract Services
S.I.C.: 3841; 2673
N.A.I.C.S.: 339112; 322223
Export
Media: 2-10
Distr.: Natl.
Personnel:
Michael P. Napoli *(Pres & CEO)*
Richard W. Parker *(VP-Fin)*
Brands & Products:
DRAVON MEDICAL
SQUEEZE BAG
TRUE BLUE A CLAMP
TRUE BLUE T CLAMP
Advertising Agency:
UBM Canon
11444 W Olympic Blvd
Los Angeles, CA 90064
Tel.: (310) 445-4200
Fax: (310) 445-4299

DUANE READE, INC.

(Sub. of Walgreen Co.)
440 9th Ave
New York, NY 10001-1620
Tel.: (212) 273-5700
Fax: (212) 244-6527
E-mail: hostmaster@duanereade.com
Web Site: www.duanereade.com
Approx. Sls.: $1,837,499,000
Approx. Number Employees: 7,000
Year Founded: 1960
Business Description:
Drugstore Chain Operator
S.I.C.: 5912
N.A.I.C.S.: 446110
Advertising Expenditures: $12,400,000
Media: 13-18-19-23
Personnel:
John K. Henry *(CFO & Sr VP)*
Michelle D. Bergman *(Gen Counsel & Sr VP)*
Charles R. Newsom *(Sr VP-Store Ops)*
Mark W. Scharbo *(Sr VP-Supply Chain)*
Paul Tiberio *(Sr VP-Mktg & Merchandising)*
Brands & Products:
APT.5
DUANE READE
ROCK BOTTOM
Advertising Agencies:
DeVito/Verdi
100 5th Ave 16th Fl
New York, NY 10011
Tel.: (212) 431-4694
Fax: (212) 431-4940
Drug Store

J. Hunter Advertising Inc.
(Division of J. Hunter Group)
1111 Broadhollow Rd Ste 211
Farmingdale, NY 11735
Tel.: (631) 777-3331
Fax: (631) 393-6788

DUSA PHARMACEUTICALS, INC.

25 Upton Dr
Wilmington, MA 01887
Tel.: (978) 657-7500
Fax: (978) 657-9193
E-mail: Investor-relations@dusapharma.com
Web Site: www.dusapharma.com
Approx. Rev.: $37,432,998
Approx. Number Employees: 85
Business Description:
Pharmaceuticals Mfr
S.I.C.: 2834
N.A.I.C.S.: 325412
Media: 10
Personnel:
Jay M. Haft *(Chm)*
Robert F. Doman *(Pres & CEO)*
Richard C. Christopher *(CFO & VP-Fin)*
William F. O'Dell *(Exec VP-Sls & Mktg)*
Scott L. Lundahl *(VP-Regulatory Affairs & Intellectual Property)*
Brands & Products:
BLU-U
CLINDAREACH
DELIVERING SOLUTIONS FOR DERMATOLOGY
DUSA
KERASTICK
LEVULAN
METED
NICOMIDE
NICOMIDE-T

Key to Media (For complete agency information see *The Advertising Red Books-Agencies* edition):
1. Bus. Publs. 2. Cable T.V. 3. Catalogs & Directories. 4. Co-op Adv. 5. Consumer Mags. 6. D.M. to Bus. Estab.7. D.M. to Consumers 8. Daily Newsp. 9. Exhibits/Trade Shows 10. Foreign 11. Infomercial 12. Internet Adv.13. Multimedia 14. Network Radio 15. Network T.V. 16. Newsp. Distr. Mags. 17. Other 18. Outdoor (Posters, Transit) 19. Point of Purchase20. Premiums, Novelties 21. Product Samples 22. Special Events Mktg. 23. Spot Radio 24. Spot T.V. 25. Weekly Newsp. 26. Yellow Page Adv.

PSORIATEC
Advertising Agency:
Spectrum
2000 K St NW 2nd Fl
Washington, DC 20006-1890
Tel.: (202) 955-6222
Fax: (202) 955-0044

DYAX CORP.

300 Technology Sq
Cambridge, MA 02139
Tel.: (617) 225-2500
Fax: (617) 225-2501
E-mail: webmaster@dyax.com
Web Site: www.dyax.com
Approx. Rev.: $51,399,000
Approx. Number Employees: 137
Year Founded: 1989
Business Description:
Biopharmaceutical Products Discovery, Development & Commercialization
S.I.C.: 8733; 2834
N.A.I.C.S.: 541710; 325412
Advertising Expenditures: $396,000
Media: 2
Personnel:
Henry E. Blair *(Chm)*
Gustav A. Christensen *(Pres & CEO)*
George Migausky *(CFO & Exec VP)*
Ivana Magovcevic-Liebisch *(Gen Counsel & Exec VP-Corp Dev)*
William E. Pullman *(Chief R&D Officer & Exec VP)*
Mark J. Sawyer *(Sr VP-Technical Ops)*
Brands & Products:
DYAX
WEBPHAGE

DYMATIZE ENTERPRISES, INC.

(Holding of TA Associates, Inc.)
13737 N Stemmons Fwy
Farmers Branch, TX 75234
Tel.: (972) 732-1990
Fax: (972) 732-1771
Toll Free: (800) 500-3069
E-mail: customerservice@dymatize.com
Web Site: www.dymatize.com
Sales Range: $1-9.9 Million
Approx. Number Employees: 20
Year Founded: 1994
Business Description:
Nutritional Supplement Mfr & Marketer
S.I.C.: 2834
N.A.I.C.S.: 325412
Media: 6-10-13
Advertising Agencies:
Click Here, Inc.
8750 N Central Expy Ste 100
Dallas, TX 75231-6430
Tel.: (214) 891-5325
Fax: (214) 346-4870
Digital Media
Dymatize Nutrition

The Richards Group, Inc.
8750 N Central Expy Ste 100
Dallas, TX 75231-6430
Tel.: (214) 891-5700
Fax: (214) 265-2933
Dymatize Nutrition
Media Planning & Buying

DYNACQ HEALTHCARE, INC.

10304 Interstate 10 E Ste 369
Houston, TX 77029
Tel.: (713) 378-2000
Fax: (713) 673-6416
E-mail: info@dynacq.com
Web Site: www.dynacq.com
E-Mail For Key Personnel:
Marketing Director: philipchan@dynacq.com
Approx. Rev.: $2,142,490
Approx. Number Employees: 159
Business Description:
Holding Company; Acute Care Hospital Management Services
S.I.C.: 8069; 8082
N.A.I.C.S.: 622310; 621610
Advertising Expenditures: $5,440,000
Media: 17
Personnel:
Chiu Moon Chan *(Founder, Chm & CEO)*
Philip S. Chan *(CFO, Treas & VP-Fin)*
Ringo Cheng *(Dir-IT)*

DYNATRONICS CORPORATION

7030 Park Centre Dr
Salt Lake City, UT 84121-6618
Tel.: (801) 568-7000
Fax: (801) 568-7711
Toll Free: (800) 874-6251
E-mail: info@dynatronics.com
Web Site: www.dynatronics.com
Approx. Sls.: $32,692,859
Approx. Number Employees: 153
Year Founded: 1983
Business Description:
Medical & Cosmetic Equipment & Supplies Mfr
S.I.C.: 3845; 3841
N.A.I.C.S.: 334510; 339112
Advertising Expenditures: $175,700
Media: 10
Personnel:
Kelvyn H. Cullimore, Jr. *(Chm, Pres & CEO)*
Terry M. Atkinson *(CFO)*
Larry K. Beardall *(Exec VP)*
Bryan D. Alsop *(VP-IT)*
Brands & Products:
ALGISITE
ALLEVYN
ANKLE TOUGH
AQUAFLEX
AQUASONIC
ARTIFLEX
BAPS
BASELINE
BIO-FREEZE
BODYICE
CALISSE
CAN-DO
CARPAL LOCK
CERES SECRET
CERVICAL PILLOW BY CORE
CHO-PAT
CO-FLEX
COMFY-TRAC
COMPRILAN
COVERLET
CRUTCH-MATE
CYROCUP
D-CORE
DIGI-FLEX
DIGITAL PAD
DISCIDE
DOUBLE CORE
DURELAST
DYNAFLEX
DYNAGEL
DYNAHEAT
DYNATRON
DYNATRON T3
DYNATRON T4
DYNATRON T4X
DYNATRON X3
DYNATRON X5
DYNATRONICS
EASY SEAT
ELASTO-GEL
ELASTOMULL
EPI-LOCK
EUCERIN
FLEXALL
FLEXIGRIP
FOAMFIGHTER
FORM-FIT
FORMFIT ANKLE
GRANSTAND
HAND HELPER
HEELBO
HYDROLIFT
HYPAFIX
IBOX
ION
ISOBAND
ISOTONER
JOBSKIN
JOBST
KINESIO
KLARITY
KOMPREX
LEUKOTAPE
LIGHTPLAST
MEDIC-AIR
MEDIC-AIR CERVIICAL SLEEP PILLO
MEDIC-AIR INFLATABLE BACK PILLO
MEDIC-AIR INFLATABLE LUMBAR ROLL PILLO
MEMORY PLUS
MID-CORE
MOLLELAST
NAUGAHYDE
NECK DOCTOR
NIGHT ROLL
OPSITE
PANOGAUZE
PARAFFIN BATH
PARATHERAPY
PELVIC BLOCKS BY CORE
PLYOBACK
PLYOTRAMP
POLAR
POLYS
POLYSORB
POSITION BLOCK
POWER WEB
PRIMAPORE
PRO FITTER
PROFORE
PROSTRETCH
REPLICARE
ROSIDAL
SANISTAT
SARATOGA
SCIFIT
SCOOT-GARD
SENSIFOOT
SILICORE
SILIPOS
SKILLBUILDERS
SLIM STYLE
SPENCO
SPORTBLOCKS
STEENS
STROOPS
STS
SWELL SPOTS
SYNERGIE
SYNERGIE AESTHETIC MASSAGE SYSTEM
THERA-BAND
THERA-P
THERMOPHORE
TRAVEL-CORE
TRI-CORE
ULTIMA
VELCRO
VELFOAM
VINYL
VISCOLAS

DYNISCO INSTRUMENTS LLC

(Sub. of Roper Industries, Inc.)
38 Forge Pkwy
Franklin, MA 02038
Tel.: (508) 541-9400
Fax: (508) 541-6206
E-mail: infoinst@dynisco.com
Web Site: www.dynisco.com
E-Mail For Key Personnel:
Sales Director: sales@dynisco.com
Sales Range: $50-74.9 Million
Approx. Number Employees: 150
Year Founded: 1953
Business Description:
Electronic Pressure Transducers Mfr
S.I.C.: 3829; 5084
N.A.I.C.S.: 334519; 423830
Personnel:
Ken Brown *(Pres)*
Rich Pavero *(VP-Sls & Mktg)*
Mary Costain *(Mgr-Mktg)*
Brands & Products:
DYNIPAK
SMARTLINK
VISCOSENSOR
Advertising Agency:
Blass Communications LLC
17 Drowne Rd
Old Chatham, NY 12136-3006
Tel.: (518) 766-2222
Fax: (518) 766-2446

EARL & LORAINE MILLER CHILDREN'S HOSPITAL

(Sub. of Memorial Health Services Inc.)
2801 Atlantic Ave
Long Beach, CA 90806
Tel.: (562) 933-2000
Fax: (562) 933-1266
Web Site: www.memorialcare.org
Year Founded: 1970
Business Description:
Hospital Services
S.I.C.: 8062
N.A.I.C.S.: 622110
Media: 3-9-10-15-18-22-25
Personnel:
Diana Hendel *(CEO)*

EAST ALABAMA MEDICAL CENTER

2000 Pepperell Pkwy
Opelika, AL 36801-5452
Tel.: (334) 749-3411
Fax: (334) 528-1509
Web Site: www.eamc.org
Sales Range: $200-249.9 Million
Approx. Number Employees: 2,200
Year Founded: 1952

Key to Media (For complete agency information see *The Advertising Red Books-Agencies* edition):
1. Bus. Publs. 2. Cable T.V. 3. Catalogs & Directories. 4. Co-op Adv. 5. Consumer Mags. 6. D.M. to Bus. Estab.7. D.M. to Consumers 8. Daily Newsp. 9. Exhibits/Trade Shows 10. Foreign 11. Infomercial 12. Internet Adv.13. Multimedia 14. Network Radio 15. Network T.V. 16. Newsp. Distr. Mags. 17. Other 18. Outdoor (Posters, Transit) 19. Point of Purchase20. Premiums, Novelties 21. Product Samples 22. Special Events Mktg. 23. Spot Radio 24. Spot T.V. 25. Weekly Newsp. 26. Yellow Page Adv.

East Alabama Medical Center — (Continued)

Business Description:
Hospital & Health Care Services
S.I.C.: 8062
N.A.I.C.S.: 622110
Media: 10
Personnel:
Terry W. Andrus *(Pres & CEO)*
Sam Price *(CFO & Exec VP)*

ECR PHARMACEUTICALS CO., INC.

(Sub. of Hi-Tech Pharmacal Co., Inc.)
3969 Deep Rock Rd
Richmond, VA 23233-1433
Mailing Address:
PO Box 71600
Richmond, VA 23255
Tel.: (804) 527-1950
Fax: (804) 527-1959
E-mail: contactecr@ecrpharma.com
Web Site: www.ecrpharma.com
Sales Range: $10-24.9 Million
Approx. Number Employees: 100
Year Founded: 1990
Business Description:
Pharmaceutical Products Mfr
S.I.C.: 2834; 5122
N.A.I.C.S.: 325412; 424210
Import
Media: 10-20-21
Distr.: Natl.
Budget Set: Nov. -Dec.
Personnel:
Janice H. Hardin *(Asst VP-Pharmaceutical Admin)*
Brands & Products:
BUPAP
DEXPAK TAPERPAKS
LODRANE
VOSOL
Advertising Agency:
Object9
4156 WE Heck Ct
Baton Rouge, LA 70816
Tel.: (225) 368-9899
Fax: (225) 368-9898

EISAI INC.

(Sub. of Eisai Corporation of North America)
100 Tice Blvd
Woodcliff Lake, NJ 07677
Tel.: (201) 692-1100
Fax: (201) 692-1804
Web Site: www.eisai.com
Sales Range: $1-4.9 Billion
Approx. Number Employees: 900
Year Founded: 1995
Business Description:
Pharmaceutical Prescriptions & Ethical Health Care Products Mfr & Sales
S.I.C.: 2834
N.A.I.C.S.: 325412
Personnel:
Cynthia Schwalm *(Pres)*
Steven Sembler *(Chief Comml Officer & Sr VP)*
Ann Miller *(Sr VP-Pharmaceutical Svcs)*
Louis C. Arp *(Gen Mgr & VP-Supply Ops)*
Sean Spears *(Sr Dir-Pharmacy & Trade Rels)*
Robert Fogleman *(Assoc Dir)*
Robert Gomez *(Assoc Dir-Sls & Mktg Info Sys)*
Suzanne Grogan *(Sr Mgr-Corp Comm)*
Brands & Products:
ACIPHEX
ALOXI
ARICEPT
BANZEL
DACOGEN
GLIADEL
HEXALEN
ONTAK
PANRETIN
SALAGEN
TARGRETIN
Advertising Agencies:
Centron
90 5th Ave
New York, NY 10011
Tel.: (646) 722-8900
Fax: (646) 722-8988
ONTAK
Targretin

Dentsu Communications, Inc.
32 Ave of Americas 16th Fl
New York, NY 10013
Tel.: (212) 660-6790
Fax: (212) 660-6797

JFK Communications Inc.
Princeton Corp Ctr 5 Independence Way Ste 300
Princeton, NJ 08540
Tel.: (609) 514-5117
Fax: (609) 514-5234
— Jennifer Lawson *(Acct Exec)*

LLNS
220 E 42nd St
New York, NY 10017-5806
Tel.: (212) 771-3000
Fax: (212) 771-3010

Ogilvy Healthworld GmbH
Darmstadter Landstrasse 112
60598
Frankfurt, Germany
Tel.: (49) 69 610 91 01 14

ELAN CORPORATION

(Sub. of Elan Corporation plc)
800 Gateway Blvd
South San Francisco, CA 94080
Tel.: (650) 877-0900
Fax: (650) 553-7138
Web Site: www.elan.com
Approx. Number Employees: 100
Business Description:
Drug Delivery Units Mfr
S.I.C.: 2834
N.A.I.C.S.: 325412
Media: 2-7-10
Personnel:
Kelly Martin *(CEO)*
Eliseo Oreste Salinas *(Chief Medical Officer & Head-Global Dev & Exec VP)*

ELECTRIC MOBILITY CORPORATION

(d/b/a The Rascal Company)
1 Mobility Plz
Sewell, NJ 08080-1031
Tel.: (856) 468-0270
Fax: (856) 468-3426
Toll Free: (800) 468-1000
E-mail: info@electricmobility.com
Web Site: www.electricmobility.com
Approx. Number Employees: 450
Year Founded: 1974
Business Description:
Wheelchairs Mfr
S.I.C.: 3842; 3751
N.A.I.C.S.: 339113; 336991
Import Export
Media: 3-4
Personnel:
Arthur Rea *(COO)*
Brands & Products:
AUTOGO
CONVERTABLE
FOLD AND GO
PEDALPOWER
RASCAL
TURNABOUT
ULTRALITE

ELECTROMED, INC.

500 6th Ave NW
New Prague, MN 56071
Tel.: (952) 758-9299
Fax: (866) 758-5077
Toll Free: (800) 462-1045
E-mail: info@electromed.com
Web Site: www.electromed.com
Approx. Rev.: $14,303,848
Approx. Number Employees: 66
Year Founded: 1992
Business Description:
Airway Clearance Healthcare Products Mfr
S.I.C.: 3841
N.A.I.C.S.: 339112
Advertising Expenditures: $642,000
Media: 10
Personnel:
Robert D. Hansen *(Co-Founder, Chm & CEO)*
Terry M. Belford *(CFO)*
William R. Grimm *(Reg Mgr-Western US)*
Sherie Wheeler *(Reg Mgr-Central US)*
Brad Blascziek *(Mgr-Mfg)*
Clara M. Buri *(Mgr-Patient Svcs)*
Martin J. Davig *(Mgr-Sls-Natl)*
Lonnie J. Helgeson *(Mgr-Product Ops)*
Gregory A. Spurlock *(Mgr-Quality Assurance)*
Brands & Products:
CREATING SUPERIOR CARE THROUGH INNOVATION.
SINGLE PATIENT USE VEST
SMARTVEST

ELI LILLY AND COMPANY

Lilly Corporate Ctr 893 S Delaware St
Indianapolis, IN 46225
Tel.: (317) 276-2000
Fax: (317) 277-6579
Telex: 276051
Web Site: www.lilly.com
Approx. Rev.: $23,076,000,000
Approx. Number Employees: 38,350
Year Founded: 1876
Business Description:
Pharmaceutical Products Mfr, Developer & Marketer
S.I.C.: 2834
N.A.I.C.S.: 325412
Import Export
Advertising Expenditures: $4,497,000,000
Media: 2-4-5-6-7-8-9-10-11-13-15-17-19-20-21-24
Distr.: Intl.; Natl.
Personnel:
John C. Lechleiter *(Chm, Pres & CEO)*
Derica W. Rice *(CFO & Exec VP-Global Svcs)*
Michael C. Heim *(CIO & Sr VP-IT)*
Timothy J. Garnett *(Chief Medical Officer & Sr VP-Drug Dev Center of Excellence)*
James A. Ward *(VP)*
Bryce D. Carmine *(Exec VP & Pres-Lilly Bio-Medicines)*
Susan Mahony *(Pres-Lilly Oncology & Sr VP)*
Jeffrey N. Simmons *(Pres-Elanco Animal Health & Sr VP)*
Jacques Tapiero *(Pres-Emerging Markets & Sr VP)*
Thomas F. Bumol *(VP-Biotechnology & Pres-AME)*
Frank M. Deane *(Pres-Mfg Ops)*
Thomas R. Verhoeven *(Pres-Global Product Dev)*
Robert A. Armitage *(Sr VP & Gen Counsel)*
Thomas W. Grein *(Treas & Sr VP)*
Jan M. Lundberg *(Exec VP-Science & Tech)*
E. Paul Ahern *(Sr VP-Global API Mfg)*
Steve Fry *(Sr VP-HR & Diversity)*
William F. Heath *(Sr VP-Product R&D)*
Barton R. Peterson *(Sr VP-Corp Affairs & Comm)*
Fionnuala Walsh *(Sr VP-Quality)*
W. Darin Moody *(VP-Corp Engrg)*
Jeffrey A. Winton *(VP-Comm)*
Patricia Martin *(Sr Dir-Lilly Diabetes)*
Mark Nagy *(Sr Dir Mktg)*
Lauren Cislak *(Mgr-Corp Comm)*
Brands & Products:
ALIMTA
BYETTA
CIALIS
CYMBALTA
DARVON
DOBUTREX
EVISTA
FORTEO
GEMZAR
GLUCAGON
HUMALOG
HUMATROPE
HUMULIN
INNOVATION IS PERSONAL
LILLY
POSILAC
PROZAC
REOPRO
STRATTERA
SYMBYAX
XIGRIS
ZYPREXA
Advertising Agencies:
Draftfcb New York
100 W 33rd St
New York, NY 10001
Tel.: (212) 885-3000
Fax: (212) 885-3300

Grey New York
777 3rd Ave
New York, NY 10017-1401
Tel.: (212) 546-2000
Fax: (212) 546-1495
Cialis

imc2
12404 Park Central Ste 400

Key to Media (For complete agency information see *The Advertising Red Books-Agencies* edition):
1. Bus. Publs. 2. Cable T.V. 3. Catalogs & Directories. 4. Co-op Adv. 5. Consumer Mags. 6. D.M. to Bus. Estab.7. D.M. to Consumers
8. Daily Newsp. 9. Exhibits/Trade Shows 10. Foreign 11. Infomercial 12. Internet Adv.13. Multimedia 14. Network Radio
15. Network T.V. 16. Newsp. Distr. Mags. 17. Other 18. Outdoor (Posters, Transit) 19. Point of Purchase20. Premiums, Novelties
21. Product Samples 22. Special Events Mktg. 23. Spot Radio 24. Spot T.V. 25. Weekly Newsp. 26. Yellow Page Adv.

Dallas, TX 75251
Tel.: (214) 224-1000
Fax: (214) 224-1100
(Cymbalta)

Jackson Integrated
5804 Churchman Bypass
Indianapolis, IN 46203-6109
Tel.: (317) 791-9000
Fax: (317) 791-9800
Toll Free: (888) JACKSON

OMD-USA
195 Broadway
New York, NY 10007
Tel.: (212) 590-7100
(Media Buying & Planning)

EMD SERONO, INC.

(Sub. of Merck Serono International SA)
1 Technology Pl
Rockland, MA 02370
Tel.: (781) 982-9000
Toll Free: (800) 283-8088
Web Site: www.emdserono.com
Approx. Number Employees: 700
Business Description:
Pharmaceutical & Biological Research Services
S.I.C.: 8733; 2834
N.A.I.C.S.: 541710; 325412
Personnel:
James Hoyes *(Pres)*
Lisa Costantino *(CFO)*
Tom Gunning *(Gen Counsel & Sr VP)*
David L. Stern *(Exec VP-Endocrinology)*
Steve Arkinstall *(Sr VP-Global Technologies & Head-Res Ops Site-US)*
Advertising Agency:
mono
(Partially Owned by MDC Partners)
3036 Hennepin Ave
Minneapolis, MN 55408
Tel.: (612) 822-4135
Fax: (612) 454-4950

EMERGENCY MEDICAL SERVICES CORPORATION

(Sub. of Onex Corporation)
6200 S Syracuse Way, Ste 200
Greenwood Village, CO 80111
Tel.: (303) 495-1200
Fax: (303) 495-1466
Fax: (303) 495-1611 (Inv Rels)
E-mail: information@emsc.net
Web Site: www.emsc.net
Approx. Rev.: $2,859,322,000
Approx. Number Employees: 12,674
Year Founded: 1972
Business Description:
Emergency Medical Services; Ambulance Services & Physicians
S.I.C.: 2329; 4119; 8049; 8322
N.A.I.C.S.: 315211; 621399; 621910; 624230
Media: 2-8-9-10-14-15-22-25
Personnel:
William A. Sanger *(Chm & CEO)*
Randel G. Owen *(CFO & Exec VP)*
R. Jason Standifird *(Sr VP, Chief Acctg Officer & Controller)*
Steve Ratton, Jr. *(Treas & Sr VP)*
Steve Murphy *(Sr VP-Govt & Natl Svcs)*
Kimberly Norman *(Sr VP-HR)*
Deborah Hileman *(VP-Corp Comm, Mktg & IR)*

EMERGENT GROUP, INC.

(Sub. of Universal Hospital Services, Inc.)
10939 Pendleton St
Sun Valley, CA 91352
Tel.: (818) 394-2800
Fax: (818) 394-2850
Web Site: www.primedical.net
Approx. Rev.: $29,604,522
Approx. Number Employees: 128
Business Description:
Holding Company; Surgical Equipment Supplier; Hospital Support Services
S.I.C.: 5047; 6719; 8322
N.A.I.C.S.: 423450; 551112; 624230
Advertising Expenditures: $36,628
Media: 17
Personnel:
Bruce J. Haber *(Chm & CEO)*
Louis Buther *(Pres)*
William M. McCay *(CFO)*

EMISPHERE TECHNOLOGIES, INC.

240 Cedar Knolls Rd Ste 200
Cedar Knolls, NJ 07927
Tel.: (973) 532-8000
Fax: (973) 532-8121
E-mail: jobs@emisphere.com
Web Site: www.emisphere.com
Approx. Rev.: $100,000
Approx. Number Employees: 16
Year Founded: 1986
Business Description:
Oral Drug Delivery Systems Mfr
S.I.C.: 2834; 8733
N.A.I.C.S.: 325412; 541720
Media: 2-4-10-18
Personnel:
Michael R. Garone *(Interim CEO)*
Laura Kragie *(VP-Clinical Dev & Chief Medical Officer)*
Ehud Arbit *(Dir-Res)*
Brands & Products:
ELAPRIN
ELIGEN
EMIGENT
EMISPHERE
EMISPHERE TECHNOLOGIES
Advertising Agency:
Adam Friedman Associates
11 E 44 St 5th Fl
New York, NY 10017
Tel.: (212) 981-2529
Fax: (212) 981-8174
Investor Relations

EMPI, INC.

(Sub. of DJO Surgical)
599 Cardigan Rd
Saint Paul, MN 55126-4099
Tel.: (651) 415-9000
Fax: (651) 415-7497
Toll Free: (800) 328-2536
Web Site: www.empi.com
Sales Range: $150-199.9 Million
Approx. Number Employees: 780
Year Founded: 1977
Business Description:
Nerve Stimulators, Muscle Stimulators, Orthopedic Rehabilitation Systems & Non-Invasive Drug Delivery Systems
S.I.C.: 3845; 3841; 3842
N.A.I.C.S.: 334510; 339112; 339113
Media: 2-4-6-7-9-10-17-20
Distr.: Intl.; Natl.
Budget Set: Jan.
Personnel:
Les Cross *(Pres)*
Brands & Products:
ADVANCE DYNAMIC ROM
DUPEL
ECLIPSE+
EMPI
EPIX VT
EPIX XL
FOCUS
INNOSENSE
INNOVA PFS
MINNOVA
PRONEX
RELION
SAUNDERS
Advertising Agency:
Lois Paul & Partners
150 Presidential Way
Woburn, MA 01801
Tel.: (781) 782-5000
Fax: (781) 782-5999

ENCISION INC.

6797 Winchester Cir
Boulder, CO 80301
Tel.: (303) 444-2600
Fax: (303) 444-2693
Toll Free: (800) 998-0986
E-mail: feedback@encision.com
Web Site: www.encision.com
Approx. Sls.: $11,616,657
Approx. Number Employees: 52
Business Description:
Surgical Instrument Developer & Mfr
S.I.C.: 3841
N.A.I.C.S.: 339112
Advertising Expenditures: $3,770,742
Media: 2-10-21
Personnel:
David W. Newton *(Co-Founder & VP)*
Vern D. Kornelsen *(Co-Founder)*
Roger C. Odell *(Chm)*
Fred Perner *(Pres & CEO)*
Todd Theis *(Dir-Sls)*
Kent Cherrey *(Mgr-Sls-Mountain West Reg)*
John Flaiz *(Mgr-Sls-Central Reg)*
Steve Koehler *(Mgr-Sls-Eastern Reg)*
Brands & Products:
AEM
ELECTROSHIELD
ENCISION
ENTOUCH
LAPROSCOPIC INSTRUMENTS

ENCORIUM GROUP, INC.

435 Devon Park Dr Bldg 500
Wayne, PA 19087
Tel.: (484) 588-5400
E-mail: hq@encorium.com
Web Site: www.encorium.com
Approx. Rev.: $21,166,675
Approx. Number Employees: 155
Year Founded: 1989
Business Description:
Contract Pharmaceutical Research Services
S.I.C.: 8733; 2834
N.A.I.C.S.: 541710; 325412
Import Export
Media: 2-13
Personnel:
Shahab Fatheazam *(Chm)*
Kai E. Lindevall *(Pres & CEO)*
Alison O'Neill *(Sr VP-Clinical Ops)*
Anna Minkkinen *(Sr Dir-Project Mgmt)*
Brands & Products:
DATAFAX
ENCORIUM
IDATAFAX
INTELLIGENCE AT THE CORE
ORACLE CLINICAL
ORACLE TMS
QUICKSILVER

ENDO PHARMACEUTICALS HOLDINGS, INC.

100 Endo Blvd
Chadds Ford, PA 19317
Tel.: (610) 558-9800
Fax: (610) 558-8979
Web Site: www.endo.com
Approx. Rev.: $1,716,229,000
Approx. Number Employees: 2,947
Year Founded: 1920
Business Description:
Holding Company for Pharmaceutical Mfr
S.I.C.: 2834; 2833; 8733
N.A.I.C.S.: 325412; 325411; 541710
Advertising Expenditures: $56,900,000
Personnel:
Roger H. Kimmel *(Chm)*
David P. Holveck *(Pres & CEO)*
Alan G. Levin *(CFO & Exec VP)*
Julie H. McHugh *(COO & Exec VP)*
Jim Maguire *(CIO & Sr VP)*
Caroline B. Manogue *(Chief Legal Officer, Sec & Exec VP)*
Edward J. Sweeney *(Principal Acctg Officer, VP & Controller)*
Ivan P. Gergel *(Exec VP-R & D)*
Larry Cunningham *(Sr VP-HR)*
Sandeep Gupta *(Sr VP-Discovery & Early Dev)*
Brands & Products:
DEPODUR
ENDO
ENDOCET
ENDODAN
FROVA
HYCODAN
HYCOTUSS
LIDODERM
MOBAN
MS CONTIN
NARCAN
NUMORPHAN
OPANA
OPANA ER
PERCOCET
PERCODAN
PROMISE
RAPINYL
SYMMETREL
THINK
TRANSDUR
ZYDONE
Advertising Agencies:
Accel Health
220 E 42nd St
New York, NY 10017
Tel.: (646) 428-2500
Fax: (646) 428-2501

The Corporate Communications Group
14 Henderson Dr
West Caldwell, NJ 07006-6608
Tel.: (973) 808-0009

Key to Media (For complete agency information see *The Advertising Red Books-Agencies* edition):
1. Bus. Publs. 2. Cable T.V. 3. Catalogs & Directories. 4. Co-op Adv. 5. Consumer Mags. 6. D.M. to Bus. Estab.7. D.M. to Consumers
8. Daily Newsp. 9. Exhibits/Trade Shows 10. Foreign 11. Infomercial 12. Internet Adv.13. Multimedia 14. Network Radio
15. Network T.V. 16. Newsp. Distr. Mags. 17. Other 18. Outdoor (Posters, Transit) 19. Point of Purchase20. Premiums, Novelties
21. Product Samples 22. Special Events Mktg. 23. Spot Radio 24. Spot T.V. 25. Weekly Newsp. 26. Yellow Page Adv.

Endo Pharmaceuticals Holdings, Inc. — (Continued)

Fax: (973) 808-9740

Dudnyk Healthcare Group
5 Walnut Grove Dr Ste 280
Horsham, PA 19044
Tel.: (215) 443-9406
Fax: (215) 443-0207

Euro RSCG Life LM&P
200 Madison Ave
New York, NY 10016
Tel.: (212) 532-1000
Fax: (212) 213-0449

Iris Global Clinical Trials Solutions
211 E Chicago Ave
Chicago, IL 60611
Tel.: (312) 664-5310
Fax: (312) 649-7232

Ogilvy CommonHealth Interactive Marketing
430 Interpace Pkwy
Parsippany, NJ 07054
Tel.: (973) 352-1400
Fax: (973) 352-1210

RTC Relationship Marketing
1055 Thomas Jefferson St NW # 200
Washington, DC 20007
Tel.: (202) 625-2111
Fax: (202) 424-7900

Saatchi & Saatchi Healthcare Advertising
375 Hudson St
New York, NY 10014
Tel.: (212) 463-3400

Web Ad.vantage
321 N Union Ave
Havre De Grace, MD 21078
Tel.: (410) 942-0488
Fax: (410) 942-0487

ENDOCARE, INC.

(Sub. of HealthTronics, Inc.)
201 Technology Dr
Irvine, CA 92618
Tel.: (949) 450-5400
Fax: (949) 450-5300
Toll Free: (800) 418-4677
Sales Range: $25-49.9 Million
Business Description:
Cryotherapy Technology Developer for Prostate Cancer & Renal Tumor Treatment
S.I.C.: 3841
N.A.I.C.S.: 339112; 541711
Advertising Expenditures: $200,000
Media: 2-8-10
Personnel:
James S.B. Whittenburg *(Pres)*
Brands & Products:
AUTOFREEZE
CRYOCARE
CRYOCARE CS
CRYOGRID
CRYOGUIDE
DIRECT ACCESS
ENDOCARE
EXTENDING LIFE EVERYDAY
FASTTRAC
FOCAL CRYO
PERCRYO
RIGISCAN
TCAP
V-PROBE

ENDOLOGIX, INC.

11 Studebaker
Irvine, CA 92618-2013
Tel.: (949) 595-7200
Fax: (949) 457-9561
Toll Free: (800) 983-2284
E-mail: investorrelations@endologix.com
Web Site: www.endologix.com
Approx. Rev.: $67,251,000
Approx. Number Employees: 297
Year Founded: 1997
Business Description:
Developer & Mfr of Treatments for Vascular Diseases
S.I.C.: 3841; 3842
N.A.I.C.S.: 339112; 339113
Advertising Expenditures: $8,794,000
Personnel:
Franklin D. Brown *(Chm)*
John McDermott *(Pres & CEO)*
Robert J. Krist *(CFO & Sec)*
Joseph A. Dejohn *(VP-Sls)*
Ruth Lyons *(VP-Global Mktg)*
Stefan G. Schreck *(VP-Tech)*
Brands & Products:
ENDOLOGIX
INTUITRAK
POWERLINK
VISIFLEX SUREPASS

ENPATH MEDICAL, INC.

(Sub. of Greatbatch, Inc.)
2300 Berkshire Ln N
Minneapolis, MN 55441
Tel.: (763) 951-8181
Fax: (763) 559-0148
Toll Free: (800) 559-2613
E-mail: info@enpathmed.com
Web Site: www.enpathmedical.com
E-Mail For Key Personnel:
Marketing Director: mkraus@medamicus.com
Sales Range: $25-49.9 Million
Approx. Number Employees: 260
Year Founded: 1985
Business Description:
Venous Vessel Introducers Developer, Mfr & Supplier
S.I.C.: 3841
N.A.I.C.S.: 339112
Advertising Expenditures: $1,696,000
Brands & Products:
AXIA
AXIA RSN
FASTAC
FLOWGUARD
INTERLOCK
MYOPORE
PTFE INTERLOCK

ENZO BIOCHEM INC.

527 Madison Ave
New York, NY 10022-4304
Tel.: (212) 583-0100
Tel.: (631) 755-5500
Fax: (631) 755-5561
E-mail: custsrv@enzobio.com
Web Site: www.enzo.com
Approx. Rev.: $97,082,000
Approx. Number Employees: 527
Year Founded: 1976
Business Description:
Biotechnology Research Services
S.I.C.: 8071; 8733
N.A.I.C.S.: 621511; 541720; 621512
Advertising Expenditures: $375,000
Personnel:
Elazar Rabbani *(Chm, CEO & Sec)*
Barry W. Weiner *(Pres, Treas & CFO)*
Carl Balezentis *(Pres-Enzo Life Sciences)*
Natalie Bogdanos *(Gen Counsel)*
Andrew R. Crescenzo *(Sr VP-Fin)*
Herbert B. Bass *(VP-Fin)*
Brands & Products:
ALEQUEL
ENZO
ENZODIRECT
GENEBEAM
HGTV43
OPTIQUEL
STEALTH VECTOR

ENZYMATIC THERAPY INC.

(Sub. of Nature's Way Holding Co.)
825 Challenger Dr
Green Bay, WI 54311
Tel.: (920) 469-1313
Fax: (920) 570-6460
Web Site: www.enzy.com
Sales Range: $50-74.9 Million
Approx. Number Employees: 290
Year Founded: 1981
Business Description:
Natural & Synthetic Vitamins Mfr
S.I.C.: 2833; 2834; 5499
N.A.I.C.S.: 325411; 325412; 446191
Media: 6-13
Personnel:
Randy Rose *(CEO)*
Cathy Stone *(Sr VP-Ops)*
Barb Braatz *(Mgr-Mktg (Associate))*
Brands & Products:
ACIDOPHILUS PEARLS
PMS ESCAPE
PREDICTEASE
REMIFEMIN
WHOLE BODY CLEANSE

EPOCRATES, INC.

1100 Park Pl Ste 300
San Mateo, CA 94403
Tel.: (650) 227-1700
Fax: (650) 227-2770
E-mail: pr@epocrates.com
Web Site: www.epocrates.com
Approx. Rev.: $103,988,000
Approx. Number Employees: 312
Year Founded: 1998
Business Description:
Interactive Clinical Information & Decision Support Tools for Healthcare Industry
S.I.C.: 2741; 7389
N.A.I.C.S.: 516110; 519190
Advertising Expenditures: $700,000
Media: 1-2-7-10-13-17
Personnel:
Patrick S. Jones *(Chm)*
Rosemary A. Crane *(Pres & CEO)*
Patrick Spangler *(CFO)*
David Burlington *(COO)*
MaryAnn Capritti *(CMO)*
Joseph B. Kleine *(Chief Comml Officer & Exec VP)*
Burt W. Podbere *(Chief Acctg Officer & Sr VP-Fin)*
Thomas C. Giannulli *(Chief Medical Info Officer)*
Matthew Kaminer *(Gen Counsel & Sec)*
Erica Sniad Morgenstern *(Dir-IR, PR & Comm)*
Estuardo Torres *(Brand Mgr)*
Brands & Products:
DOCALERT
DOCMEMO
EPOCRATES
EPOCRATES DX
EPOCRATES ESSENTIALS
EPOCRATES ESSENTIALS DELUXE
EPOCRATES HONORS
EPOCRATES ID
EPOCRATES LAB
EPOCRATES MEDINSIGHT
EPOCRATES MEDTOOLS
EPOCRATES ONLINE PLUS AHFS
EPOCRATES QUICKQUAL
EPOCRATES QUICKRECRUIT
EPOCRATES QUICKSURVEY
EPOCRATES RX
EPOCRATES RX FORMULARY
EPOCRATES RX PRO
EPOCRATES SXDX
ESSENTIALPOINTS
INTERACTIONCHECK
MOBILECME
MOBILEOUTCOMES
MULTICHECK
PHARMFLASH

ERLANGER HEALTH SYSTEM

975 E 3rd St
Chattanooga, TN 37403-2103
Tel.: (423) 778-7000
Fax: (423) 778-7650
E-mail: sharon.cahill@erlanger.org
Web Site: www.erlanger.org
Sales Range: $500-549.9 Million
Approx. Number Employees: 5,000
Year Founded: 1891
Business Description:
Healthcare & Medical Services
S.I.C.: 8062; 8011
N.A.I.C.S.: 622110; 621111
Media: 3-7-8-18-22-23-24-26
Personnel:
Dan R. Quarles *(Chm)*
Jim Brexler *(CEO)*
Charlesetta Woodard-Thompson *(COO & VP)*
Dan R. Quarles *(Trustees)*
Donna Bourdon *(Sr VP)*
Greg Gentry *(Sr VP-HR)*
Lynn Whisman *(Chief Nursing Officer & Sr VP)*
Chris Vaughn *(Dir-Clinical Mktg)*
Jeffrey A. Loy *(Mgr-Procurement)*

EUSA PHARMA (USA) INC.

(Sub. of EUSA Pharma, Inc.)
650 College Rd E Ste 3100
Princeton, NJ 08540
Mailing Address:
PO Box 5308
Princeton, NJ 08543-5308
Tel.: (609) 750-8200
Fax: (609) 452-2476
Toll Free: (800) 833-3533
Approx. Rev.: $20,218,000
Approx. Number Employees: 76
Year Founded: 1980
Business Description:
Cancer Treatment Pharmaceutical Developer & Mfr
S.I.C.: 2834
N.A.I.C.S.: 325412
Import Export
Advertising Expenditures: $4,500,000

Key to Media (For complete agency information see *The Advertising Red Books-Agencies* edition):
1. Bus. Publs. 2. Cable T.V. 3. Catalogs & Directories. 4. Co-op Adv. 5. Consumer Mags. 6. D.M. to Bus. Estab.7. D.M. to Consumers 8. Daily Newsp. 9. Exhibits/Trade Shows 10. Foreign 11. Infomercial 12. Internet Adv.13. Multimedia 14. Network Radio 15. Network T.V. 16. Newsp. Distr. Mags. 17. Other 18. Outdoor (Posters, Transit) 19. Point of Purchase20. Premiums, Novelties 21. Product Samples 22. Special Events Mktg. 23. Spot Radio 24. Spot T.V. 25. Weekly Newsp. 26. Yellow Page Adv.

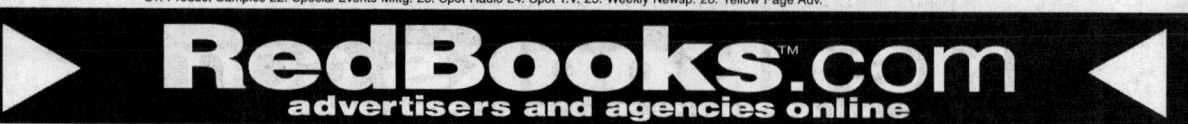

Media: 2-7-10-21
Distr.: Intl.; Natl.
Budget Set: Oct.
Personnel:
Stephen A. Ross *(Sr VP-Mktg & Sls)*
Pat McCloskey *(Sr Dir-Bus Dev)*

EXACT SCIENCES CORPORATION

441 Charmany Drive
Madison, WI 53719
Tel.: (608) 284-5700
Fax: (608) 284-5701
E-mail: info@exactsciences.com
Web Site: www.exactsciences.com/
Approx. Rev.: $5,344,000
Approx. Number Employees: 35
Year Founded: 1995
Business Description:
Cancer Screening Technology Research & Development Services
S.I.C.: 8733; 2835; 8071
N.A.I.C.S.: 541710; 325413; 621511
Advertising Expenditures: $68,100
Media: 10
Personnel:
Kevin T. Conroy *(Pres & CEO)*
Maneesh K. Arora *(CFO & Sr VP)*
John M. Krayacich *(Sr VP-Sls & Mktg)*
Brands & Products:
APPLYING GENOMICS TO ERADICATE CANCER
DNA INTEGRITY ASSAY
EFFIPURE
EXACTSCIENCES
KEEP IT SIMPLE. CATCH IT EARLY
PREGEN-PLUS
Advertising Agencies:
Captains of Industry
21 Union St
Boston, MA 02108
Tel.: (617) 725-1959
Fax: (617) 725-0089

Fleishman-Hillard Inc.
855 Boylston St 5th Fl
Boston, MA 02116
Tel.: (617) 267-8223
Fax: (617) 267-5905

EXACTECH, INC.

2320 NW 66th Ct
Gainesville, FL 32653-1630
Tel.: (352) 377-1140
Fax: (352) 378-2617
Toll Free: (800) 392-2832
E-mail: info@exac.com
Web Site: www.exac.com
Approx. Sls.: $190,483,000
Approx. Number Employees: 553
Year Founded: 1985
Business Description:
Orthopaedic Implant Devices & Related Surgical Instrumentation Developer, Marketer & Mfr
S.I.C.: 3841; 3842
N.A.I.C.S.: 339112; 339113
Advertising Expenditures: $27,046,000
Media: 2-10
Personnel:
R. William Petty *(Chm & CEO)*
David W. Petty *(Pres)*
Jody Phillips *(CFO)*
Gary J. Miller *(Exec VP-R&D)*
Bruce Thompson *(Sr VP & Gen Mgr-Biologics Div)*
Daniel Berdat *(VP-Intl Sls & Mktg)*
Raymond Cloutier *(VP-Engrg & Dev)*
Xavier Sarabia *(VP-Engrg & Dev, Large Joints)*
Brands & Products:
A GREAT DAY IN THE O.R.
ACUDRIVER
ACUMATCH
AURA
CEMEX
EQUINOXE
EXACTECH
INTERSPACE
MCS
NOVATION
OPTEFIL
OPTEFORM
OPTEON CEMENTED HIP
OPTETRAK

EXAMWORKS GROUP, INC.

3280 Peachtree Rd NE Ste 2625
Atlanta, GA 30305
Tel.: (404) 952-2400
Fax: (404) 846-1554
Toll Free: (877) 628-4703
E-mail: info@examworks.com
Web Site: www.examworks.com
Approx. Rev.: $163,511,000
Approx. Number Employees: 1,281
Business Description:
Holding Company; Independent Medical Examinations, Peer & Bill Reviews & Related Services
S.I.C.: 7389; 6719
N.A.I.C.S.: 561499; 551112
Advertising Expenditures: $448,000
Personnel:
Richard E. Perlman *(Chm)*
Wesley J. Campbell *(Pres)*
James K. Price *(CEO)*
J. Miguel Fernandez de Castro *(CFO & Sr VP)*
Kevin J. Kozlowski *(CIO & VP)*
Clare Y. Arguedas *(Gen Counsel, VP & Asst Sec)*
Crystal B. Patmore *(Sec & VP-HR)*
Joshua W. LeMaire *(VP-Sls & Mktg)*

EXPRESS SCRIPTS, INC.

1 Express Way
Saint Louis, MO 63121
Tel.: (314) 770-1666
Fax: (314) 702-7037
Toll Free: (800) 332-5455
Web Site: www.express-scripts.com
Approx. Rev.: $44,973,200,000
Approx. Number Employees: 13,170
Year Founded: 1986
Business Description:
Pharmacy Benefit Management Services
S.I.C.: 0762; 5912; 5961
N.A.I.C.S.: 115116; 446110; 454113
Media: 2-10
Personnel:
George Paz *(Chm, Pres & CEO)*
Jeffrey Hall *(CFO & Exec VP)*
Kelley Elliott *(Chief Acctg Officer, VP & Controller)*
Agnes Rey-Giraud *(Pres-Intl Ops)*
Michael Holmes *(Exec VP)*
Edward Ignaczak *(Exec VP-Sls & Mktg)*
Patrick Mcnamee *(Exec VP-Ops & Tech)*
Susan Lang *(Chief Supply Chain Officer & Sr VP)*
Joseph Federer *(Sr Dir)*
Renee Blake *(Sr Product Mgr)*
Brands & Products:
DRUG DIGEST
EXPRESS SCRIPTS
Advertising Agency:
Rodgers Townsend, LLC
1000 Clark Ave 5th Fl
Saint Louis, MO 63102
Tel.: (314) 436-9960
Fax: (314) 436-9961

EXTENDICARE HEALTH SERVICES INC.

(Sub. of Extendicare Real Estate Investment Trust)
111 W Michigan St
Milwaukee, WI 53203-2903
Tel.: (414) 908-8000
Fax: (414) 908-8059
Toll Free: (800) 395-5000
E-mail: info@extendicare.com
Web Site: www.extendicare.com
Approx. Number Employees: 450
Year Founded: 1985
Business Description:
Skilled Nursing Services
S.I.C.: 8059; 7389
N.A.I.C.S.: 623110; 561499
Media: 2-8-9-10-13-18-20-22-23-26
Distr.: Reg.
Personnel:
Tim Lukulda *(CEO)*
Roch Carter *(Gen Counsel & VP)*
Douglas J. Harris *(CFP, Sr VP & Treas)*
Tim Detary *(VP-HR)*
Advertising Agency:
JB Chicago
435 N LaSalle Ste 201
Chicago, IL 60654
Tel.: (312) 442-7223
Fax: (312) 264-0138

EXTENDICARE REAL ESTATE INVESTMENT TRUST

3000 Steeles Ave E Ste 700
Markham, ON L3R 9W2, Canada
Tel.: (905) 470-4000
Fax: (905) 470-5588
E-mail: invest@extendicare.com
Web Site: www.extendicare.com
Approx. Rev.: $2,108,043,518
Approx. Number Employees: 37,700
Year Founded: 1968
Business Description:
Long-Term Care Services
S.I.C.: 8059; 8082
N.A.I.C.S.: 623110; 621610
Advertising Expenditures: $750,000
Media: 2-7-16
Distr.: Natl.
Budget Set: June
Personnel:
Timothy L. Lukenda *(Pres & CEO)*
Douglas J. Harris *(CFO & Sr VP)*
Brands & Products:
EXTENDICARE
HEALTH CARE IS OUR BUSINESS

F&F FOODS, INC.

3501 W 48th Pl
Chicago, IL 60632-3028
Tel.: (773) 927-3737
Fax: (773) 927-3906
E-mail: webmasters@fffoods.com
Web Site: www.fffoods.com
Approx. Number Employees: 110
Business Description:
Confections, Cough Drops, Snacks & Vitamins Mfr
S.I.C.: 2099; 2834
N.A.I.C.S.: 311340; 325412
Export
Advertising Expenditures: $700,000
Media: 8-10-11-13-14-15-19-20-21
Distr.: Natl.
Brands & Products:
COMBATZ
DAILY C
F&F
F&F DIETARY SUPPLEMENTS
FAST DRY
FOXES
FRUTRIENTS
GREENIES
INTENSE MINTS
KING OF DENMARK
POLAR BLAST
SEN-SEN
SMITH BROTHERS
SUGARFREE INTENSE MINTS

THE F. DOHMEN CO.

W194 N11381 McCormick Dr
Germantown, WI 53022-3033
Mailing Address:
PO Box 9
Germantown, WI 53022-0009
Tel.: (262) 255-0022
Fax: (262) 255-0041
E-mail: hr@dohmen.com
Web Site: www.dohmen.com
Sales Range: $1-4.9 Billion
Approx. Number Employees: 200
Year Founded: 1858
Business Description:
Prescription Benefits Management, Healthcare Management Software Supplier & Health Insurance Management Services
S.I.C.: 5912; 6411; 7372; 8742
N.A.I.C.S.: 446110; 334611; 524298; 541611
Media: 2-5-8-10-21

FARNAM COMPANIES, INC.

(Sub. of Central Garden & Pet Company)
301 W Osborn Rd
Phoenix, AZ 85013-3921
Mailing Address:
PO Box 34820
Phoenix, AZ 85067-4820
Tel.: (602) 285-1660
Fax: (602) 207-2183
Toll Free: (800) 234-2269
E-mail: info@mail.farnam.com
Web Site: www.farnam.com
Sales Range: $400-449.9 Million
Approx. Number Employees: 400
Year Founded: 1946
Business Description:
Horse & Livestock Health Care Products Mfr & Distr
S.I.C.: 5154; 0752; 2834
N.A.I.C.S.: 424520; 115210; 325412
Import Export
Media: 1-7-8-10-20-21
Distr.: Intl.; Natl.
Budget Set: Aug.
Personnel:
Rick Blomquist *(Pres & CEO)*
Chris Jacobi *(Sr VP-Equine Products)*

Key to Media (For complete agency information see *The Advertising Red Books-Agencies* edition):
1. Bus. Publs. 2. Cable T.V. 3. Catalogs & Directories. 4. Co-op Adv. 5. Consumer Mags. 6. D.M. to Bus. Estab.7. D.M. to Consumers 8. Daily Newsp. 9. Exhibits/Trade Shows 10. Foreign 11. Infomercial 12. Internet Adv.13. Multimedia 14. Network Radio 15. Network T.V. 16. Newsp. Distr. Mags. 17. Other 18. Outdoor (Posters, Transit) 19. Point of Purchase20. Premiums, Novelties 21. Product Samples 22. Special Events Mktg. 23. Spot Radio 24. Spot T.V. 25. Weekly Newsp. 26. Yellow Page Adv.

Farnam Companies, Inc. — (Continued)

Christina Miller *(Mktg Mgr)*
Ron Akre *(Mgr-Mktg Svcs)*
Brands & Products:
ATTACK-ALL
DURAMARK
FLY TERMINATOR
MILK JUGG TRAP
NEWZ

THE FEMALE HEALTH COMPANY

515 N State St Ste 2225
Chicago, IL 60610
Tel.: (312) 595-9123
Fax: (312) 595-9122
Toll Free: (800) 884-1601
E-mail: info@femalehealthcompany.com
Web Site: www.femalehealth.com
Approx. Rev.: $22,221,955
Approx. Number Employees: 48
Year Founded: 1996
Business Description:
Female Condom Mfr
S.I.C.: 2844
N.A.I.C.S.: 325620
Advertising Expenditures: $220,181
Media: 2-6-8
Personnel:
O. B. Parrish *(Chm & CEO)*
Donna Felch *(CFO)*
Michael Pope *(VP & Gen Mgr)*
Lucie van Mens *(Dir-Program Dev & Support)*
Mary Ann Leeper *(Sr. Strategic Advisor)*
Brands & Products:
FC FEMALE CONDOM
FHC

FEMPRO INC.

1330 Rue Michaud
Drummondville, QC J2C 2Z5, Canada
Tel.: (819) 475-8900
Fax: (819) 475-1217
Toll Free: (800) 303-6635
E-mail: fempro@fempro.com
Web Site: www.fempro.com
Approx. Number Employees: 100
Year Founded: 1984
Business Description:
Feminine Hygiene Products Mfr
S.I.C.: 2676
N.A.I.C.S.: 322291
Media: 5-6-10-13-21
Personnel:
Jean Fleury *(CEO)*
Brands & Products:
FEMPRO
INCOGNITO
Advertising Agency:
Lemieux Bedard
Place des Congres
Sherbrooke, QC J1L 2G5, Canada
Tel.: (819) 823-0850
Fax: (819) 823-1484

FIBROCELL SCIENCE, INC.

405 Eagleview Blvd
Exton, PA 19341
Tel.: (484) 713-6000
Fax: (484) 713-6001
E-mail: info@fibrocellscience.com
Web Site: www.fibrocellscience.com
Approx. Rev.: $936,369
Approx. Number Employees: 23
Year Founded: 1995
Business Description:
Reconstructive Cosmetic Procedures Developer
S.I.C.: 2836; 2834; 8733
N.A.I.C.S.: 325414; 325412; 541720
Advertising Expenditures: $1,200,000
Media: 2-8-10-11
Personnel:
David M. Pernock *(Chm & CEO)*
Declan Daly *(CFO & COO)*
Brands & Products:
ISOLAGEN
ISOLAGEN PROCESS
ISOLAGEN THERAPY
THE SCIENCE OF CELLULAR REJUVENATION
Advertising Agency:
Sam Brown Inc.
7 Maplewood Dr
Newtown Square, PA 19073
Tel.: (610) 353-4545
Fax: (610) 353-5462

FIRST SURGICAL PARTNERS INC.

(Formerly Arkson Nutraceuticals Corp.)
411 1st St
Bellaire, TX 77401
Tel.: (713) 665-1111
Approx. Rev.: $46,165,361
Approx. Number Employees: 125
Year Founded: 1998
Business Description:
Investment Services; Pharmaceuticals
S.I.C.: 6289; 2834
N.A.I.C.S.: 523999; 325412
Advertising Expenditures: $377,833
Personnel:
Jacob Varon *(Chm)*
Anthony F. Rotondo *(Pres & CEO)*
Don Knight *(VP-Fin)*

FLEMING PHARMACEUTICALS

1733 Gilsinn Ln
Fenton, MO 63026-2000
Tel.: (636) 343-5306
Fax: (636) 343-5322
Toll Free: (800) 343-0164
E-mail: info@flemingpharma.com
Web Site: www.flemingpharma.com
Approx. Number Employees: 125
Year Founded: 1960
Business Description:
Ethical Pharmaceuticals Mfr
S.I.C.: 2834
N.A.I.C.S.: 325412
Media: 2-4-8-10-21
Distr.: Natl.
Budget Set: Nov.
Personnel:
Phillip Dritsas *(Pres)*
Sandy Barbercheck *(Mgr-Mktg)*
Mary Moss *(Mgr-Customer Svc)*
Brands & Products:
CALOMIST
FLEMING
MAGONATE
NEPHROCAPS
OBEGYN
OCEAN
OCEAN COMPLETE
OCEAN FOR KIDS
OCEAN GEL
OCEAN ULTRA
PROBARIMINQT
THYROSHIELD

FLORA MANUFACTURING & DISTRIBUTING LTD.

7400 Fraser Park Drive
Burnaby, BC V5J 5B9, Canada
Tel.: (604) 436-6000
Fax: (604) 436-6060
Toll Free: (888) 436-6697
E-mail: info@florahealth.com
Web Site: www.florahealth.com
Sales Range: $10-24.9 Million
Approx. Number Employees: 180
Business Description:
Herbal Remedies Mfr & Distr
S.I.C.: 2833; 2834
N.A.I.C.S.: 325411; 325412
Media: 6-11
Personnel:
Thomas Greither *(Owner & Pres)*

FLORIDA BLOOD SERVICES INC.

10100 Dr Martin Luther King Jr St N
Saint Petersburg, FL 33716
Tel.: (727) 568-5433
Tel.: (727) 568-2168 (Corp Rels)
Fax: (727) 568-1177
Web Site: www.fbsblood.org
Approx. Rev.: $75,000,000
Approx. Number Employees: 450
Year Founded: 1993
Business Description:
Blood Distribution & Services
S.I.C.: 8099
N.A.I.C.S.: 621991
Media: 9-23-24-25
Personnel:
Lawrence Stagg *(Chm)*
Jane Riley Leach *(Pres)*
Don Doddridge *(CEO)*

FOODSCIENCE CORPORATION

20 New England Dr
Essex Junction, VT 05452
Tel.: (802) 878-5508
Fax: (802) 878-0549
E-mail: info@foodsciencecorp.com
Web Site: www.foodsciencecorp.com
Sales Range: $25-49.9 Million
Approx. Number Employees: 150
Business Description:
Human & Animal Nutritional Food Supplements
S.I.C.: 5122
N.A.I.C.S.: 424210
Export
Media: 6
Personnel:
Dale Metz *(CEO)*
Brands & Products:
FOODSCIENCE
PET NATURALS

FOREST LABORATORIES, INC.

909 3rd Ave
New York, NY 10022-4731
Tel.: (212) 421-7850
Fax: (212) 750-9152
Toll Free: (800) 947-5227
E-mail: info@frx.com
Web Site: www.frx.com
Approx. Rev.: $4,419,700,000
Approx. Number Employees: 5,600
Year Founded: 1956
Business Description:
Branded & Generic Pharmaceuticals Mfr
S.I.C.: 2834
N.A.I.C.S.: 325412
Export
Media: 2-7-10-20-21
Distr.: Intl.; Natl.
Budget Set: Jan.
Personnel:
Howard Solomon *(Chm, Pres & CEO)*
Francis I. Perier, Jr. *(CFO, Exec VP-Fin & Admin)*
Elaine Hochberg *(Chief Comml Officer & Exec VP)*
Rita Weinberger *(Chief Acctg Officer, VP & Controller)*
Marco Taglietti *(Pres-Forest Res Institute, Sr VP-R&D)*
Herschel S. Weinstein *(Gen Counsel & VP)*
Kevin Walsh *(Sr VP & Dir-Ops)*
Gavin Corcoran *(Sr VP-Early Dev Internal Medicine)*
Jerome Lynch *(Sr VP-Sls)*
David F. Solomon *(Sr VP-Corp Dev & Strategic Plng)*
Bernard J. McGovern *(VP-HR)*
William J. Meury *(VP-Mktg)*
Brian Stevens *(Assoc Dir-E-Mktg)*
Brands & Products:
AEROBID
AEROCHAMBER PLUS
ARMOUR THYROID
BENICAR
BENICAR HCT
BYSTOLIC
CAMPRAL
CARBAMAZEPINE
CELEXA
CERVIDIL
COLOMYCIN
COMBUNOX
DALIRESP
ESGIC
ESGIC-PLUS
FOREST LABORATORIES, INC.
INFASURF
LEVOTHROID
LEXAPRO
LORCET PLUS
MONUROL
NAMENDA
SAVELLA
TEFLARO
TESSALON
THEOCHRON
THYROLAR
TIAZAC
Advertising Agency:
PointRoll Inc.
951 E Hector St
Conshohocken, PA 19428
Tel.: (267) 558-1300
Fax: (267) 285-1141
Toll Free: (800) 203-6956

FORM YOU 3 INTERNATIONAL, INC.

395 Springside Dr
Akron, OH 44333
Tel.: (330) 668-1461
Fax: (330) 666-2197
Toll Free: (800) 525-6315
E-mail: info@formyou3.com
Web Site: www.formyou3.com

Key to Media (For complete agency information see *The Advertising Red Books-Agencies* edition):
1. Bus. Publs. 2. Cable T.V. 3. Catalogs & Directories. 4. Co-op Adv. 5. Consumer Mags. 6. D.M. to Bus. Estab.7. D.M. to Consumers
8. Daily Newsp. 9. Exhibits/Trade Shows 10. Foreign 11. Infomercial 12. Internet Adv.13. Multimedia 14. Network Radio
15. Network T.V. 16. Newsp. Distr. Mags. 17. Other 18. Outdoor (Posters, Transit) 19. Point of Purchase20. Premiums, Novelties
21. Product Samples 22. Special Events Mktg. 23. Spot Radio 24. Spot T.V. 25. Weekly Newsp. 26. Yellow Page Adv.

Approx. Sls.: $4,000,000
Approx. Number Employees: 20
Year Founded: 1982
Business Description:
Full Service Weight Loss Centers Franchisor
S.I.C.: 5149; 7299
N.A.I.C.S.: 424490; 812191
Advertising Expenditures: $275,000
Media: 1-2-6-7-8-9-10-17-19-20-23-25-26
Distr.: Direct to Consumer; Intl.; Natl.
Budget Set: July
Personnel:
Charles E. Sekeres *(Pres & CEO)*
Pamela Zepp *(Dir-Mktg)*
Brands & Products:
FORM YOU 3
FORM YOU FAST
FORMU-3
WEIGHT LOSS CENTERS
Advertising Agency:
October-Design
2132 E 9th St Ste 210
Cleveland, OH 44115
Tel.: (216) 623-0995
Fax: (216) 623-0908

FRESENIUS MEDICAL CARE NORTH AMERICA
(Sub. of Fresenius Medical Care AG & Co. KGaA)
Reservoir Woods 920 Winter St
Waltham, MA 02451-1457
Tel.: (781) 402-9000
Fax: (781) 699-9715
Toll Free: (800) 662-1237
E-mail: corphr@fmcna.com
Web Site: www.fmcna.com
Approx. Number Employees: 1,135
Business Description:
Mfr & Marketer of Artificial Kidney Supplies & Treatment Centers, Respiratory Therapy Products Distribution, Infusion Therapy Services & Products
S.I.C.: 8092; 5047
N.A.I.C.S.: 621492; 423450
Advertising Expenditures: $450,000
Media: 2-4-7-10-17
Distr.: Natl.
Budget Set: Oct.
Personnel:
Ben Lips *(Chm & CEO)*
Rice Powell, Jr. *(Deputy Chm & CEO-North America)*
Ravi Kalathil *(CIO & VP)*
Linda Donald *(Pres-Fresenius Medical Svcs N/IRC Bus Unit)*
Ronald Kuerbitz *(Exec VP)*
Jose Diaz Buxo *(Sr VP)*
Deborah Harvey *(Sr VP-Opers)*
Todd Kerr *(Sr VP-Compliance)*
J. Michael Lazarus *(Sr VP)*
Robert McGorty *(Sr VP-Fin & Admin)*
Brian O'Connell *(Sr VP-HR)*
Jane A. Kramer *(VP-Pub Affairs & Comm)*
Brands & Products:
CHEK
COR
GRANUFLO 1000
LIA
NATURALYTE
POLYSULFONE
SOAR
STEP
TRAC
TRIPS

FUJIFILM MEDICAL SYSTEMS USA, INC.
(Sub. of FUJIFILM U.S.A., Inc.)
419 W Ave
Stamford, CT 06902-6300
Tel.: (203) 324-2000
Fax: (203) 327-6485
Toll Free: (800) 431-1850
E-mail: info_cr@fujimed.com
Web Site: www.fujimed.com
Approx. Number Employees: 750
Year Founded: 1965
Business Description:
Medical Digital Imaging Products & Film Distr
S.I.C.: 5047; 5043
N.A.I.C.S.: 423450; 423410
Advertising Expenditures: $1,000,000
Media: 1-2-4-7-10-22
Distr.: Natl.
Budget Set: May
Personnel:
John Weber *(Exec VP)*
Randy Nagel *(Dir-Coporate Comm)*
Brands & Products:
CLEARVIEW-CS
CLEARVIEW-D
CLEARVIEW-ES
DRYPIX1000
DRYPIX3000
DRYPIX5000
DRYPIX7000
FLASH LITE IIP
FLASH PLUS IIP
SMARTCR
SPEEDSUITE
SYNAPSE
VELOCITY-T
VELOCITY-U

FUJIREBIO DIAGNOSTICS INC.
(Sub. of Fujirebio Inc.)
201 Great Valley Pkwy
Malvern, PA 19355-1307
Tel.: (610) 240-3800
Fax: (610) 240-3803
E-mail: customerservice@fdi.com
Web Site: www.fdi.com
Approx. Number Employees: 100
Business Description:
Mfr. & Developer of Diagnostic Tests
S.I.C.: 5047; 8011
N.A.I.C.S.: 423450; 621111
Personnel:
Takeo Hayashi *(Chm)*
Paul T. Touhey, Jr. *(Pres, CEO & COO)*
Brands & Products:
FUJIREBIO
Advertising Agencies:
JFK Communications Inc.
Princeton Corp Ctr 5 Independence Way Ste 300
Princeton, NJ 08540
Tel.: (609) 514-5117
Fax: (609) 514-5234

Stern + Associates
11 Commerce Dr
Cranford, NJ 07016
Tel.: (908) 276-4344
Fax: (908) 276-7007

FUTUREDONTICS, INC.
6060 Ctr Dr 7th Fl
Los Angeles, CA 90045-1596
Tel.: (310) 215-6400
Fax: (310) 215-6401
Toll Free: (800) 222-5882
Web Site: www.1800dentist.com/
Approx. Number Employees: 225
Year Founded: 1986
Business Description:
Dental Referral Network
S.I.C.: 8742
N.A.I.C.S.: 541613
Advertising Expenditures: $15,000,000
Media: 2-3-6-9-10-13-14-15-18-22-23-24-25
Distr.: Natl.
Personnel:
Fred Joyal *(Founder & Partner)*
Gary Saint Denis *(Chm & Founding Partner)*
Larry Twersky *(Pres)*
Ron Joyal *(COO)*
David Call *(Exec VP-Membership)*
Karen Bengtson *(VP-Media)*
Brands & Products:
1-800-DENTIST
A GREAT DENTIST CAN CHANGE YOUR LIFE
DENTAL REFERRAL SERVICE
DENTISTRY.COM
GOASKFRED.COM
PATIENT ACTIVATOR
SMILEWORKS

G&W LABORATORIES INC.
111 Coolidge St
South Plainfield, NJ 07080-3801
Tel.: (908) 753-2000
Fax: (908) 753-5174
E-mail: info@gwlabs.com
Web Site: www.gwlabs.com
Approx. Number Employees: 250
Year Founded: 1918
Business Description:
Pharmaceutical Preparations
S.I.C.: 2834
N.A.I.C.S.: 325412
Import Export
Media: 2
Personnel:
Ronald Greenblatt *(Pres & COO)*
Joel Zaklin *(VP-Sls & Mktg)*
Brands & Products:
ACEPHEN
ANUCORT-HC
BACITRACIN
BISAC-EVAC
CARLESTA
CICLOPIROX
DOCUSOFT S
FLUCATISONE
FORMULATION R
FROM LABORATORY TO LIFE
G & W
HALOBETASOL
METRONIDAZOLE
MIGERGOT
MOMETASONE
PROCHLORPERAZINE
PROMETHEGAN
SANI-PADS
SANI SUPP
TOLNAFTATE

GAIAM, INC.
833 W South Boulder Rd
Louisville, CO 80027-2452
Tel.: (303) 222-3600
Fax: (303) 222-3700
Toll Free: (877) 989-6321
E-mail: investorrelations@gaiam.com
Web Site: www.gaiam.com
Approx. Rev.: $274,268,000
Approx. Number Employees: 557
Year Founded: 1988
Business Description:
Distr of Alternative Health Supplements & Environmentally-Friendly Household Goods
S.I.C.: 5961; 5499; 7822; 8399
N.A.I.C.S.: 454113; 446191; 512120; 813312
Advertising Expenditures: $37,700,000
Media: 4-6-8-10-12-13-19
Personnel:
Jirka Rysavy *(Chm)*
William S. Sondheim *(Pres)*
Lynn Powers *(CEO)*
Stephen J. Thomas *(CFO)*
Brands & Products:
BALANCE BALL
BUDOKON
DANCE
DAY FIT
THE FIRM
GAIAM
HARMONY
KICKBOX
MUDRA
PLANT GREEN
QIGONG
SHAPE
STRONGWOMEN
TAE BO
YOGAKIDS
Advertising Agency:
Krupp Kommunications, Inc
636 Ave of the Americas 4th Fl
New York, NY 10011
Tel.: (212) 886-6703
Fax: (212) 265-4708

GALDERMA LABORATORIES, L.P.
(Joint Venture of Nestle S.A. & L'Oreal S.A.)
14501 N Freeway
Fort Worth, TX 76177-3304
Tel.: (817) 961-5000
Fax: (817) 961-0035
E-mail: webmaster@galderma.com
Web Site: www.galdermausa.com
Approx. Number Employees: 250
Year Founded: 1981
Business Description:
Dermatology Product Mfr
S.I.C.: 2834
N.A.I.C.S.: 325412
Import Export
Media: 2-3-6-7-10-13-15-17-24
Personnel:
Francois Fournier *(Pres)*
Kevin Kriel *(Grp Prod Dir-Mktg)*
Brands & Products:
BENZAC AC
BENZAC AC WASH
BENZAC W
BENZAC W WASH
CAPEX TOPICAL SHAMPOO
CETAPHIL
CLINDAGEL
DES OWEN
DIFFERIN CREAM
DIFFERIN GEL
DIFFERIN SOLUTION

Key to Media (For complete agency information see *The Advertising Red Books-Agencies* edition):
1. Bus. Publs. 2. Cable T.V. 3. Catalogs & Directories. 4. Co-op Adv. 5. Consumer Mags. 6. D.M. to Bus. Estab.7. D.M. to Consumers 8. Daily Newsp. 9. Exhibits/Trade Shows 10. Foreign 11. Infomercial 12. Internet Adv.13. Multimedia 14. Network Radio 15. Network T.V. 16. Newsp. Distr. Mags. 17. Other 18. Outdoor (Posters, Transit) 19. Point of Purchase20. Premiums, Novelties 21. Product Samples 22. Special Events Mktg. 23. Spot Radio 24. Spot T.V. 25. Weekly Newsp. 26. Yellow Page Adv.

Galderma Laboratories, L.P. — (Continued)

DY-O-DERM
METROGEL
ROSANIL
SOLAGE
TRI-LUMA

Advertising Agency:
Red Door Communications, Ltd.
123 Mortlake High St
London, SW14 8SN, United Kingdom
Tel.: (44) 20 8392 8040
Fax: (44) 20 8392 8050
Cetaphil

GAMMEX RMI INC.

7600 Discovery Dr
Middleton, WI 53562-2610
Tel.: (608) 828-7000
Fax: (608) 828-7500
Toll Free: (800) 426-6391
E-mail: sales@gammex.com
Web Site: www.gammex.com
E-Mail For Key Personnel:
Sales Director: sales@gammex.com
Approx. Number Employees: 60
Year Founded: 1969
Business Description:
Mfr. of Laser Positioning Equipment & Quality Assurance Products
S.I.C.: 3829; 3844
N.A.I.C.S.: 334519; 334517
Export
Media: 1-2-4-6-10-13-20-26
Distr.: Intl.
Budget Set: Annually
Personnel:
Pamela Durden *(Coord-Adv/Show)*
Brands & Products:
BOLUFLEX
COMBIFIX
FEETFIX
GAMMEX
GAMMEX LASERS
GAMMEX RMI
KNEEFIX
PHANTORN
POSICAST
POSIFIX
POSIFRAME
POSIREST
POSITILT
RAD-CHECK
REPOVAC
SOLID WATER
THORAWEDGE

GANEDEN BIOTECH, INC.

5915 Landerbrook Dr Ste 304
Mayfield Heights, OH 44124
Tel.: (440) 229-5200
Fax: (440) 229-5240
Toll Free: (800) 406-4650
E-mail: info@ganedenbiotech.com
Web Site: www.ganedenbiotech.com
Approx. Number Employees: 19
Business Description:
Over-the-Counter Dietary Supplements
S.I.C.: 2834
N.A.I.C.S.: 325412
Media: 2-4-6-7-8-10-13-21-23-24
Personnel:
Andrew Lefkowitz *(Pres & CEO)*
Marshall Fong *(VP-Mktg)*
Brands & Products:
CLEARLY CONFIDENT
DIGESTIVE ADVANTAGE
GANEDEN
IMPROVING QUALITY OF LIFE

GARDEN OF LIFE, INC.

5500 Village Blvd Ste 202
West Palm Beach, FL 33407
Tel.: (561) 748-2477
Tel.: (561) 748-2478
Fax: (561) 741-8130
Fax: (561) 575-5488
Toll Free: (800) 365-7709
Toll Free: (800) 622-8986
Web Site: www.gardenoflife.com
Approx. Number Employees: 150
Year Founded: 2000
Business Description:
Nutritional & Herbal Supplement Mfr; Healthy Living Publisher
S.I.C.: 2834
N.A.I.C.S.: 325412
Media: 6-8-10-13
Personnel:
Jordan S. Rubin *(Founder, Chm & CEO)*
Brian Ray *(Pres)*
Jeff Brams *(Gen Counsel)*
Lianne de Moya *(VP-Product Dev)*
Jason Dewberry *(VP-Mktg & Media)*
Kent Keyser *(VP-Sls)*
Erik Schmitt *(VP-Fin)*
Teresa M. Miller *(Sr Dir-HR & Quality)*
Brands & Products:
ACID DEFENSE
ALPHA AROMA THERAPY
BEYOND OMEGA-3
BIOPROTECT
CLEAR ENERGY
CLENZOLOGY
CODMEGA
DETOXIFIBER
DHA CHEWABLES
EMPOWERING EXTRAORDINARY HEALTH
EXTRA VIRGIN COCONUT OIL
FRUITS OF LIFE
FUCOPROTEIN
FUCOTHIN
FUNGAL DEFENSE
FYI
GARDEN OF LIFE
GOATEIN
HOMEOSTATIC SOIL ORGANISMS
HORMONES
LIVING CALCIUM
LIVING FOODS
LIVING MULTI
LIVING VITAMIN C
THE MAKER'S DIET
OCEANS 3
OLDE WORLD
OMEGA PM
OMEGAXANTHIN
PERFECT CLEANSE
PERFECT FOOD
PERFECT MEAL
PERFECT WEIGHT
POTEN-ZYME
PRIMAL DEFENSE
PRO2GO
RADICAL FRUITS
RESTORE
RM-10
SUPER SEED
TEA TRIO
ULTRAZORBE
VITAMIN CODE
ZERO GRAVITY
ZYME

GC AMERICA, INC.

(Sub. of GC Corporation)
3737 W 127th St
Alsip, IL 60803
Tel.: (708) 597-0900
Fax: (800) 323-7063
Toll Free: (800) 323-7063
E-mail: gca_sales@gcamerica.com
Web Site: www.gcamerica.com
Sales Range: $25-49.9 Million
Approx. Number Employees: 130
Year Founded: 1992
Business Description:
Dental Materials & Supplies Mfr
S.I.C.: 3843
N.A.I.C.S.: 339114
Import Export
Advertising Expenditures: $2,000,000
Media: 1-8-10-22
Distr.: Intl.; Natl.
Budget Set: Apr.
Personnel:
Tom Sadler *(Dir-Mfg)*
Brands & Products:
ACRIDENSE
ACRON
COE-LOR
COE-SEP
COECAL
DUPLI-COE-LOID
EXAIMPLANT
FIT CHECKER
FUJIVEST
G-CERA
GC
GC CROWNTEK
GC FUJI ORTHO
GC FUJIROCK
GC STONE GLAZE
GC VEST
GRADIA
INITIAL
MULTI-SEP
ORBIT
PATTERN RESIN
PERMA-CRYL
POLYPOUR
SUPER-CAL
WAX-RITE

G.C. HANFORD MANUFACTURING CO

(d/b/a Hanford Pharmaceuticals)
304 Oneida St
Syracuse, NY 13202-3433
Tel.: (315) 476-7418
Fax: (315) 476-7434
Toll Free: (800) 234-4263
E-mail: info@hanford.com
Web Site: www.hanford.com
Approx. Number Employees: 200
Year Founded: 1846
Business Description:
Antibiotics & Health Care Products Mfr
S.I.C.: 2834
N.A.I.C.S.: 325412
Export
Advertising Expenditures: $275,000
Media: 2-4-7
Distr.: Natl.
Personnel:
George R. Hanford *(Chm)*
Brands & Products:
BALSAM OF MYRRH
GO-DRY
HAN-PEN B
HAN-PEN G
HANFORD
HANPAK
MASTI-CLEAR
MICROSUSPENSION
SHATTERGUARD
U.S.VET

GE HEALTHCARE TECHNOLOGIES

(Sub. of GE Healthcare)
3000 N Grandview Blvd
Waukesha, WI 53188
Tel.: (262) 544-3011
Toll Free: (800) 643-6439
Web Site: www.gehealthcare.com
Sales Range: $900-999.9 Million
Business Description:
Diagnostic Imaging Equipment & Accessories Mfr
S.I.C.: 3844; 3821; 3845
N.A.I.C.S.: 334517; 334510; 339111
Media: 2
Personnel:
John Dineen *(Pres & CEO)*
Russel P. Mayer *(CIO & Exec VP)*
Jean-Michel Cossery *(CMO & VP)*
Sean Burke *(CMO-Diagnostic Imaging)*
Lynne Gailey *(Exec VP-Global Comm)*
Paul Mirabella *(Exec VP-Devel)*
Robert Moore *(Sr VP-Sls-Mktg)*
Liz Blackwood *(General Mgr-QA)*
Ralph Strosin *(Gen Mgr-Opers)*
Paul Klein *(Dir-Comml COE)*
Brands & Products:
DISCOVERY ST
LIGHTSPEED RT
LOGIQ 3
LOGIQ 5
LOGIQ 7
LOGIQ 9
LOGIQ BOOK
MYOVIEW
OEC
OMNIPAQUE
OMNISCAN
OPTISON
REVOLUTION
SIGNA
VISIPAQUE
VIVID 3
VIVID 7
VOLUSON 730
Advertising Agency:
BBDO Worldwide Inc.
(Sub. of Omnicom Group, Inc.)
1285 Ave of the Americas
New York, NY 10019-6028
Tel.: (212) 459-5000
Fax: (212) 459-6645

GE WATER & PROCESS TECHNOLOGIES

(Sub. of GE Water & Process Technologies)
3239 Dundas St W
Oakville, ON L6M 4B2, Canada
Tel.: (905) 465-3030
Fax: (905) 465-3050
Web Site: www.zenon.com
Sales Range: $150-199.9 Million
Approx. Number Employees: 600
Year Founded: 1980

Key to Media (For complete agency information see *The Advertising Red Books-Agencies* edition):
1. Bus. Publs. 2. Cable T.V. 3. Catalogs & Directories. 4. Co-op Adv. 5. Consumer Mags. 6. D.M. to Bus. Estab.7. D.M. to Consumers 8. Daily Newsp. 9. Exhibits/Trade Shows 10. Foreign 11. Infomercial 12. Internet Adv.13. Multimedia 14. Network Radio 15. Network T.V. 16. Newsp. Distr. Mags. 17. Other 18. Outdoor (Posters, Transit) 19. Point of Purchase20. Premiums, Novelties 21. Product Samples 22. Special Events Mktg. 23. Spot Radio 24. Spot T.V. 25. Weekly Newsp. 26. Yellow Page Adv.

Business Description:
Developer of Membrane Technologies for Water Purification
S.I.C.: 2834; 9511
N.A.I.C.S.: 325412; 924110
Media: 2-7-10
Personnel:
John E. Barker *(CFO)*
Rafael Simon *(COO)*
Steve Watzeck *(VP-Domestic Sls)*
Brands & Products:
HOMESPRING
MEMBRANE MEDIA
PERMAFLOW
REINFORCED MEMBRANES
WATER FOR THE WORLD
ZEEDWEED
ZEEWEED
ZENOGEM
ZENON
ZENOPURE

GEISINGER HEALTH SYSTEM
100 N Academy Ave
Danville, PA 17822-0001
Tel.: (570) 271-6211
Fax: (570) 271-7498
Web Site: www.geisinger.org
Sales Range: $300-349.9 Million
Approx. Number Employees: 8,400
Year Founded: 1915
Business Description:
Hospital & Health Care Services
S.I.C.: 8742; 8071
N.A.I.C.S.: 541611; 621511
Media: 2-4-8-10-13-18-23-24-26
Personnel:
Glen Steele, Jr. *(Pres & CEO)*
Bruce H. Hamory *(Mng Partner & Exec VP)*
Kevin F. Brennan *(CFO, Treas & Exec VP)*
Frank Trembulak *(COO & Exec VP)*
Susan Alcorn *(Chief Comm Officer)*
Joanne Wade *(Chief Admin Officer & Exec VP-Strategic Program Dev)*
Howard Grant *(Chief Medical Officer & Exec VP)*
Peter B. Berger *(Assoc Chief Res Officer)*
Dudley Gerow *(Chief Govt Programs Officer)*
Andrew M. Deubler *(Exec VP-Integrated Resource Dev)*
Robert C. Spahr *(Sr VP-Svc Quallity)*
David Jolley *(Assoc VP-PR)*
Advertising Agencies:
Academy Avenue Group
100 N Academy Ave
Danville, PA 17822-3013
Tel.: (570) 271-7234

Aloysius Butler & Clark
819 Washington St
Wilmington, DE 19801-1509
Tel.: (302) 655-1552
Fax: (302) 655-3105
Toll Free: (800) 848-1552

dio, LLC
3111 Farmtrail Rd
York, PA 17406
Tel.: (717) 764-8288
Fax: (717) 764-1415

HavrillaGroup
22E E Roseville Rd
Lancaster, PA 17601
Tel.: (717) 569-6902
Fax: (717) 569-6930

GENELINK, INC.
317 Wekiva Springs Rd Ste 200
Longwood, FL 32779
Tel.: (609) 823-6991
Tel.: (407) 772-7164
Toll Free: (800) 558-GENE
E-mail: info@genelinkbio.com
Web Site: www.genelinkbio.com
Approx. Rev.: $7,839,972
Approx. Number Employees: 15
Business Description:
DNA Preservation Services for Inherited Disease Treatment
S.I.C.: 8071; 2834; 8733
N.A.I.C.S.: 621511; 325412; 541710
Advertising Expenditures: $47,947
Media: 6-14-15
Personnel:
Bernard L. Kasten, Jr. *(Chm, Acting Pres & Acting CEO)*
Robert P. Ricciardi *(Chief Science Officer)*
Sharon M. Tahaney *(Pres-GeneWiz Life Sciences Inc)*
Harold H. Harrison *(Dir-Medical)*
Brands & Products:
DERMAGENETICS
DNA ULTRACUSTOM
GENELINK
GENELINK HEALTHY AGING ASSESSMENT
GENELINK NUTRAGENETIC PROFILE
JUICEBOOST
LIFEMAP CUSTOM
LIFEMAP ESSENTIALS
LIFEMAP NUTRITION
LIFEMAP SKIN CARE
LIFEMAP WEALTH SYSTEM
SNPACTIVE
YOUR GENETIC COMPASS

GENENCOR INTERNATIONAL, INC.
(Div. of Danisco A/S)
925 Page Mill Rd
Palo Alto, CA 94304-1013
Tel.: (650) 846-7500
Fax: (650) 845-6500
E-mail: info@genencor.com
Web Site: www.genencor.com
Sales Range: $400-449.9 Million
Approx. Number Employees: 1,271
Business Description:
Genetically-Based Biotechnology Products
S.I.C.: 2834; 8733
N.A.I.C.S.: 325412; 541710
Media: 10
Personnel:
Tjerk de Ruiter *(CEO)*
Michael V. Arbige *(Exec VP-Tech)*

GENENTECH, INC.
(Sub. of Hoffmann-La Roche Inc.)
1 DNA Way
South San Francisco, CA 94080-4918
Tel.: (650) 225-1000
Fax: (650) 225-6000
Toll Free: (800) 821-8590
E-mail: medinfo@gene.com
Web Site: www.gene.com
Approx. Rev.: $13,418,000,000
Approx. Number Employees: 11,186
Year Founded: 1976
Business Description:
Researcher of Human Genetic Information to Discover, Develop, Manufacture & Market Human Pharmaceuticals
S.I.C.: 2833; 2834; 8733
N.A.I.C.S.: 325411; 325412; 541710
Export
Advertising Expenditures: $439,000,000
Media: 2-4-7-10-13-21
Distr.: Natl.
Budget Set: Nov.
Personnel:
Arthur D. Levinson *(Chm)*
Ian T. Clark *(CEO & Head-Comml Ops-North America)*
Hal V. Barron *(Exec VP-Global Dev & Chief Medical Officer)*
Richard H. Scheller *(Chief Scientific Officer & Exec VP-Res)*
Robert E. Andreatta *(Chief Acctg Officer, VP & Controller)*
Steve Krognes *(Sr VP, Reg Head-Fin & IT, CFO-Pharma North America)*
Sean A. Johnston *(Gen Counsel & Sr VP)*
Kenneth J. Hillan *(Sr VP-Product Dev, Head-Clinical Dev & Inflammation DBA)*
William N. Anderson *(Sr VP-Sls & Mktg-BioOncology)*
Andrew C. Chan *(Sr VP-Immunology)*
Jennifer E. Cook *(Sr VP-Genentech Immunology & Ophthalmology)*
Markus Gemuend *(Sr VP-Global Head Procurement & Contract Mfg Ops)*
Charles Calderaro, III *(VP & Gen Mgr-Ops)*
Khurem Farooq *(VP-Sls & Mktg)*
Alexander Hardy *(VP-Sls, Mktg & HER2 Franchise)*
Laura Sullivan *(Sr Mgr-Market Plng & Patient Insights)*
Brands & Products:
ACTIVASE
AVASTIN
CATHFLO
CATHFLO ACTIVASE
GENENTECH
HERCEPTIN
LUCENTIS
NUTROPIN
NUTROPIN AQ
NUTROPIN AQ PEN
NUTROPIN DEPOT
OMNITARG
PROTROPIN
RAPTIVA
TNKASE
Advertising Agencies:
Jel, Inc.
2117 28th St
Sacramento, CA 95818
Tel.: (916) 447-5463
Fax: (916) 447-5465

Vox Medica Inc.
601 Walnut St Ste 250-S
Philadelphia, PA 19106-3514
Tel.: (215) 238-8500
Fax: (215) 238-0881

Weber Shandwick
(Sub. of The Interpublic Group of Companies)
919 3rd Ave
New York, NY 10022
Tel.: (212) 445-8000
Fax: (212) 445-8001

GENERAL BANDAGES, INC.
8300 Lehigh Ave
Morton Grove, IL 60053-2616
Mailing Address:
PO Box 909
Morton Grove, IL 60053-0909
Tel.: (847) 966-8383
Fax: (847) 966-7733
Web Site: www.generalbandages.com
Sales Range: $100-124.9 Million
Approx. Number Employees: 30
Year Founded: 1977
Business Description:
Self-Adhering Gauze Tape, Safety Tape, First Aid Kits & Supplies
S.I.C.: 3842; 5047
N.A.I.C.S.: 339113; 423450
Media: 2-4-6-7-8-13-21
Distr.: Natl.
Budget Set: Dec.
Personnel:
Mignon de Clerk *(Dir-Mktg)*
Brands & Products:
GAUZTEX
GUARD-TEX

GENERAL CANNABIS, INC.
2183 Fairview Rd Ste 101
Costa Mesa, CA 92627
Toll Free: (888) 693-5219
Web Site: www.generalcannabis.com
Approx. Rev.: $7,699,634
Approx. Number Employees: 68
Year Founded: 2003
Business Description:
Medicinal Cannabis Information & Management Services
S.I.C.: 7389; 8748
N.A.I.C.S.: 519190; 541618; 561499
Advertising Expenditures: $1,036,000
Personnel:
James Pakulis *(Chm & CEO)*
Douglas Francis *(Pres & Chief Strategy Officer)*
Munjit S. Johal *(CFO, Treas & Sec)*
Tamara Bigham *(Dir-HR)*
Jerry Lotter *(Dir-Ops)*

GENERAL NUTRITION CENTERS, INC.
(Joint Venture of Ontario Teachers' Pension Plan & Ares Management LLC)
300 6th Ave
Pittsburgh, PA 15222
Tel.: (412) 288-4600
Fax: (412) 288-4764
E-mail: media@gnc-hq.com
Web Site: www.gnc.com
Approx. Rev.: $1,822,396,000
Approx. Number Employees: 5,308
Year Founded: 1935
Business Description:
Nutritional Supplements Mfr, Distr & Retailer
S.I.C.: 5499; 2833; 5999
N.A.I.C.S.: 446191; 325411; 445299; 446199
Import
Advertising Expenditures: $50,000,000

Key to Media (For complete agency information see *The Advertising Red Books-Agencies* edition):
1. Bus. Publs. 2. Cable T.V. 3. Catalogs & Directories. 4. Co-op Adv. 5. Consumer Mags. 6. D.M. to Bus. Estab.7. D.M. to Consumers
8. Daily Newsp. 9. Exhibits/Trade Shows 10. Foreign 11. Infomercial 12. Internet Adv.13. Multimedia 14. Network Radio
15. Network T.V. 16. Newsp. Distr. Mags. 17. Other 18. Outdoor (Posters, Transit) 19. Point of Purchase20. Premiums, Novelties
21. Product Samples 22. Special Events Mktg. 23. Spot Radio 24. Spot T.V. 25. Weekly Newsp. 26. Yellow Page Adv.

General Nutrition Centers, Inc. — (Continued)

Media: 1-3-5-6-8-14-15-22-23
Personnel:
Norman Axelrod *(Chm)*
Beth J. Kaplan *(Pres & CMO & Chief Mdsg Officer)*
Joseph M. Fortunato *(CEO)*
Michael M. Nuzzo *(CFO & Exec VP)*
David P. Berg *(COO & Exec VP-Global Bus Dev)*
Gerald J. Stubenhofer, Jr. *(Chief Legal Officer & Sr VP)*
Thomas Dowd *(Exec VP-Ops, Stores & Dev)*
Darryl Green *(Sr VP-Domestic Franchising)*
Lee Karayusuf *(Sr VP-Distr & Transportation)*
Robert M. Kral *(Sr VP-Mdsg)*
Michael Locke *(Sr VP-Mfg)*
Anthony Phillips *(Sr VP-Bus Analysis)*
Guru Ramanathan *(Chief Innovation Officer & Sr VP)*
Dennis Magulick *(Sr Dir-Treasury & IR)*
Brands & Products:
HERBAL PLUS
MEGA MEN
PREVENTIVE NUTRITION
PRO PERFORMANCE
SCAN DIET
THERMO BURST
TOTAL LEAN
TOTAL LEAN MRP
TRIPLE CLEANSE
ULTRA MEGA
WOMEN'S ARGINMAX
Advertising Agency:
Cramer-Krasselt
225 N Michigan Ave
Chicago, IL 60601-7601
Tel.: (312) 616-9600
Fax: (312) 616-3839

GENERAL SCIENTIFIC SAFETY EQUIPMENT CO.

2553 E Somerset St Fl 1
Philadelphia, PA 19134-5925
Tel.: (215) 739-7559
Fax: (215) 739-7441
Toll Free: (800) 523-0166
Approx. Number Employees: 2
Year Founded: 1988
Business Description:
Distr of First Aid, Medical & Personal Safety Supplies & Equipment
S.I.C.: 5047
N.A.I.C.S.: 423450
Media: 2-4-7-10-26
Distr.: Intl.; Natl.
Budget Set: Apr.
Personnel:
Angela D'Amico *(Owner)*
Brands & Products:
FILTAIRETTE
G.S.
IDS

GENEREX BIOTECHNOLOGY CORPORATION

33 Harbour Square Suite 202
Toronto, ON M5J 2G2, Canada
Tel.: (416) 364-2551
Fax: (416) 364-9363
Toll Free: (800) 391-6755
E-mail: info@generex.com
Web Site: www.generex.com
Approx. Rev.: $1,172,611
Approx. Number Employees: 43
Business Description:
Pharmaceutical Research & Development
S.I.C.: 2834
N.A.I.C.S.: 325412
Media: 2-7-10
Personnel:
John P. Barratt *(Chm)*
Mark Fletcher *(Pres & CEO)*
Rose C. Perri *(CFO & COO)*
Eric Von Hofe *(Pres-Antigen Express & VP)*
Roberto F. Cid *(VP-Mktg & Sls)*
Stephen Fellows *(VP-Fin)*
Jaime Davidson *(Dir-Medical)*
George Markus *(Mgr-Regulatory Affairs)*
Brands & Products:
BABOOM
CRAVE-NX
GENEREX BIOTECHNOLOGY
GLUCOBREAK
ORAL-LYN
RAPIDMIST
Advertising Agency:
Rubenstein Public Relations
1345 Ave of the Americas
New York, NY 10105
Tel.: (212) 843-8000
Fax: (212) 843-9200

GENESIS HEALTHCARE CORP.

(Joint Venture of J.E. Robert Company & Formation Capital LLC)
101 E State St
Kennett Square, PA 19348-3109
Tel.: (610) 444-6350
Fax: (610) 925-4000
E-mail: info@genesishcc.com
Web Site: www.genesishcc.com
Approx. Rev.: $1,770,298,000
Approx. Number Employees: 35,500
Year Founded: 2003
Business Description:
Skilled & Intermediate Nursing Care & Operator of Eldercare Facilities
S.I.C.: 8059; 8361
N.A.I.C.S.: 623110; 623220
Media: 2
Personnel:
George V. Hager, Jr. *(Chm & CEO)*
Robert A. Reitz *(COO & Exec VP)*
Richard L. Castor *(CIO & Sr VP)*
David C. Almquist *(Pres-Southern Area & Exec VP)*
Paul D. Bach *(Pres-Central Area & Exec VP)*
Richard P. Blinn *(Pres-Northeast Area & Exec VP)*
Dan Hirschfeld *(Pres-Genesis Rehab Svcs)*
Richard Pell, Jr. *(Sr VP-Admin)*
Brands & Products:
GENESIS HEALTHCARE
Advertising Agency:
TBC Inc.
900 S Wolfe St
Baltimore, MD 21231
Tel.: (410) 347-7500
Fax: (410) 986-1299

GENOMIC SOLUTIONS INC.

(Sub. of Harvard Bioscience, Inc.)
4355 Varsity Dr
Ann Arbor, MI 48108-5004
Tel.: (734) 975-4800
Fax: (734) 975-4808
Toll Free: (877) GENOMIC
E-mail: info@genomicsolutions.com
Web Site: www.genomicsolutions.com
Sales Range: $50-74.9 Million
Approx. Number Employees: 150
Year Founded: 1997
Business Description:
Genomic & Proteomic Instrumentation, Software, Consumables & Services Mfr, Designer, Developer & Marketer
S.I.C.: 3826; 2834
N.A.I.C.S.: 334516; 325412
Media: 2-4-10-19
Personnel:
Boris Deu *(Gen Mgr)*
Judy Thompson *(Mgr-Mktg Comm)*
Brands & Products:
GENETAC
GENOMIC SOLUTIONS
INVESTIGATOR
Advertising Agency:
FOURSIGHT Creative Group, Inc.
900 Starkweather
Plymouth, MI 48170
Tel.: (734) 453-6991
Fax: (734) 453-0337

GENOPTIX, INC.

(Sub. of Novartis AG)
2110 Rutherford Rd
Carlsbad, CA 92008
Tel.: (760) 268-6200
Fax: (760) 268-6201
Fax: (888) 755-1604
Toll Free: (800) 755-1605
E-mail: info@genoptix.com
Web Site: www.genoptix.com
Approx. Rev.: $184,378,000
Approx. Number Employees: 440
Business Description:
Medical Laboratory Services
S.I.C.: 8733; 8071
N.A.I.C.S.: 541710; 621511
Media: 10-19-21
Personnel:
Andrew E. Senyei *(Chm)*
Bashar Dabbas *(Pres & Chief Medical Officer-Cartesian Medical Grp)*
Tina S. Nova Bennett *(Pres)*
Douglas A. Schuling *(CFO & Exec VP)*
Samuel D. Riccitelli *(COO & Exec VP)*
Philippe J. Marchand *(CIO & Sr VP)*
Christian V. Kuhlen *(Chief Compliance Officer, Gen Counsel & VP)*
Cheri Caviness *(Sr VP-HR)*
Jonathan Diver *(Sr VP-Laboratory Ops)*
Mike Nerenberg *(Sr VP-Bus Dev & Medical Affairs)*
Walt Williams *(VP-Medical Reimbursement & Contract System Compliance)*
Marcy Graham *(Sr Dir-IR)*

GENTIVA HEALTH SERVICES, INC.

3350 Riverwood Pkwy Ste 1400
Atlanta, GA 30339-3314
Tel.: (770) 951-6450
Toll Free: (888) GENTIVA
E-mail: cbsresumes@gentiva.com
Web Site: www.gentiva.com
Approx. Rev.: $1,447,029,000
Approx. Number Employees: 15,350
Year Founded: 1970
Business Description:
Home Health Care Services
S.I.C.: 8082; 8059
N.A.I.C.S.: 621610; 623110
Media: 2-3-4-6-7-8-9-10-13-17-18-20-22-23-24-25-26
Distr.: Natl.
Personnel:
Ronald A. Malone *(Chm)*
Rodney D. Windley *(Vice Chm)*
Anthony H. Strange *(Pres & CEO)*
Eric R. Slusser *(CFO, Treas & Exec VP)*
John N. Camperlengo *(Chief Compliance Officer, Gen Counsel, Sec & Sr VP)*
David L. Gieringer *(Chief Acctg Officer, VP & Controller)*
Charlotte A. Weaver *(Chief Clinical Officer & Sr VP)*
Thomas M. Boelsen *(Sr VP-CareCentrix)*
Mike Cardone *(Reg VP)*
Dean Johnson *(VP-Sls)*
Brands & Products:
CARECENTRIX
GENTIVA
GREAT HEALTHCARE HAS COME HOME
HEALTHSHEETS
LIFESMART
REHAB WITHOUT WALLS
SAFE STRIDES
WOUND CARE PROTOCOLS
Advertising Agency:
Ciociola & Company Advertising, Inc.
914 Morgan Rd
Rydal, PA 19046
Tel.: (215) 887-5999
Fax: (215) 376-0496
(Home Health Care Services, Pharmaceutical Services & Distribution)

GENZYME CORPORATION

(Sub. of Sanofi-Aventis)
500 Kendall St
Cambridge, MA 02142
Tel.: (617) 252-7500
Fax: (617) 252-7600
Web Site: www.genzyme.com
Approx. Rev.: $4,048,708,000
Approx. Number Employees: 10,100
Year Founded: 1981
Business Description:
Pharmaceutical Developer
S.I.C.: 2836; 2834
N.A.I.C.S.: 325414; 325412
Export
Media: 2-10
Distr.: Direct to Consumer; Intl.; Natl.; Reg.
Budget Set: Aug.
Personnel:
Henri A. Termeer *(Chm, Pres & CEO)*
Michael S Wyzga *(CFO & Exec VP-Fin)*
David Meeker *(COO)*
Thomas J Desrosier *(Chief Legal Officer, Gen Counsel & Sr VP)*
Zoltan A. Csimma *(Chief HR Officer & Sr VP)*

Key to Media (For complete agency information see *The Advertising Red Books-Agencies* edition):
1. Bus. Publs. 2. Cable T.V. 3. Catalogs & Directories. 4. Co-op Adv. 5. Consumer Mags. 6. D.M. to Bus. Estab.7. D.M. to Consumers
8. Daily Newsp. 9. Exhibits/Trade Shows 10. Foreign 11. Infomercial 12. Internet Adv.13. Multimedia 14. Network Radio
15. Network T.V. 16. Newsp. Distr. Mags. 17. Other 18. Outdoor (Posters, Transit) 19. Point of Purchase20. Premiums, Novelties
21. Product Samples 22. Special Events Mktg. 23. Spot Radio 24. Spot T.V. 25. Weekly Newsp. 26. Yellow Page Adv.

Richard A. Moscicki *(Chief Medical Officer & Sr VP-Clinical Dev & Medical Affairs)*
Alan E. Smith *(Chief Scientific Officer & Sr VP-Res)*
Jason A. Amello *(Chief Acctg Officer & Corp Controller)*
Peter Wirth *(Exec VP-Legal & Corp Dev & Sec)*
Sandford D Smith *(Pres-Intl Grp & Exec VP)*
John P Butler *(Pres-Personalized Genetic Health & Sr VP)*
Mark J. Enyedy *(Pres-Oncology & Multiple Sclerosis, Sr VP)*
Donald E Pogorzelski *(Pres-Diagnostic Products & VP)*
Georges Gemayel *(Exec VP)*
Mary Mcgrane *(VP, Sr VP-Govt Rels)*
Alison Lawton *(Sr VP & Gen Mgr-Biosurgery)*
Caren Arnstein *(Sr VP-Corp Affairs)*
Ron Branning *(Sr VP-Global Product Quality)*
Richard H. Douglas *(Sr VP-Corp Dev)*
David D. Fleming *(Sr VP)*
James A. Geraghty *(Sr VP)*
Elliott D. Hillback *(Sr VP-Corp Affairs)*
Ann Merrifield *(Sr VP-Bus Excellence Initiative)*
Mark Gibson *(Dir-Mktg-Global)*

Brands & Products:
AFP4
ALDURAZYME
CAMPATH
CARTICEL
CEREDASE
CEREZYME
CHOLESTAGEL
CLOLAR
CONTRAST
DEKLENE
DIAMOND-FLEX
DIAMOND-LINE
DIAMOND-TOUCH
ENDOCABG
EPICEL
EVOLTRA
FABRAZYME
GENZYME
GENZYME-OPCAB ELITE DEEP STERNAL BLADES
GENZYME-OPCAB ELITE SUTURE STOPS
GLYPRO
HECTOROL
HYLAFORM
HYLUMED
IMMOBILIZER
INSIGHT
LUMIZYME
MABCAMPATH
MACI
MASDA
MOZOBIL
MYOZYME
N-GENEOUS HDL
NEXTSTITCH
OSOM
POLYDEK
QUICK TACK
SAGE
SAHARA
SAPHLITE
SEPRA
SEPRAFILM
SPHERE
SWITCH-BLADE
SYNVISC-ONE
TEVDEK
THORA-KLEX
THYMOGLOBULIN
THYROGEN

Advertising Agency:
The GMR Group
755 Business Ctr Dr Ste 250
Horsham, PA 19044-3444
Tel.: (215) 653-7401
Fax: (215) 653-7982

GENZYME GENETICS INC.

(Sub. of LABORATORY CORPORATION OF AMERICA HOLDINGS)
3400 Computer Dr
Westborough, MA 01581
Tel.: (508) 898-9001
Fax: (508) 389-5549
Toll Free: (800) 357-5744
Web Site: www.genzymegenetics.com
Sales Range: $300-349.9 Million
Approx. Number Employees: 700
Year Founded: 1981
Business Description:
Screening & Diagnosis of Genetic Disorders
S.I.C.: 2834
N.A.I.C.S.: 325412
Media: 2-7-10
Distr.: Intl.; Natl.
Budget Set: Nov.

GENZYME ONCOLOGY, INC.

(Sub. of Genzyme Corporation)
4545 Horizon Hill Blvd
San Antonio, TX 78229
Tel.: (210) 949-8200
Fax: (210) 949-8210
Toll Free: (888) 453-9062
Web Site:
www.genzymeoncology.com
Sales Range: $25-49.9 Million
Approx. Number Employees: 216
Year Founded: 1994
Business Description:
Cancer Drug Research, Development & Mfr
S.I.C.: 2834; 8733
N.A.I.C.S.: 325412; 541720
Media: 10
Personnel:
Mark J. Enyedy *(Pres & Sr VP)*
Brands & Products:
APOMINE
HOPE INTO REALITY
ILX-651

GEOPHARMA, INC.

(d/b/a Innovative Health Products)
(Filed Ch 11 Bankruptcy #1105210 on 03/23/11 in U.S. Bankruptcy Ct, Middle Dist of FL, Tampa)
6950 Bryan Dairy Rd
Largo, FL 33777-1608
Tel.: (727) 544-8866
Fax: (727) 544-4386
Toll Free: (800) 654-2347
E-mail: info@geopharmainc.com
Web Site: www.onlineihp.com
Approx. Sls.: $21,958,948
Approx. Number Employees: 271
Year Founded: 1985
Business Description:
Mfr of Dietary Supplements, Over-the-Counter Drugs & Health & Beauty Care Products
S.I.C.: 2834
N.A.I.C.S.: 325412
Advertising Expenditures: $391,141
Media: 2-4-8-10-13-16-25
Brands & Products:
GP
Advertising Agency:
RedChip Companies, Inc.
500 Winderely Pl Ste 100
Maitland, FL 32751
Tel.: (407) 644-4256
Fax: (407) 644-0758
Toll Free: (800) 733-2447

GETINGE USA, INC.

(Sub. of Getinge AB)
1777 E Henrietta Rd
Rochester, NY 14623
Tel.: (585) 475-1400
Fax: (585) 272-5033
Toll Free: (800) 475-9040
E-mail: webinfo@getingeusa.com
Web Site: www.getingeusa.com
Approx. Number Employees: 900
Year Founded: 1883
Business Description:
Sterility Assurance Systems
Examining & Operating Equipment & Related Accessories & Consumables Mfr
S.I.C.: 3842; 3841
N.A.I.C.S.: 339113; 339112
Export
Media: 2-4-7-8-10-11-17-20
Distr.: Natl. Intl.
Personnel:
Andrew Cserey *(Pres & CEO)*
Terry Cooke *(Sr VP)*
Brands & Products:
WILSON

GF HEALTH PRODUCTS, INC.

2935 NE Pkwy
Atlanta, GA 30360
Tel.: (770) 447-1609
Fax: (678) 291-3232
Fax: (800) 726-0601
Toll Free: (800) 347-5678
E-mail: info@grahamfield.com
Web Site: www.grahamfield.com
Approx. Number Employees: 330
Year Founded: 1946
Business Description:
Medical & Home Health Care Products Mfr & Distr
S.I.C.: 5047; 3841; 3845
N.A.I.C.S.: 423450; 334510; 339112
Import Export
Media: 1-2-4-5-7-8-10-13-19-21-22-23
Distr.: Intl.
Budget Set: Oct.
Personnel:
Kenneth Spett *(Pres & COO)*
Beatrice Scherer *(CEO)*
Cherie L. Antoniazzi *(Sr VP-Quality & Risk Mgmt)*
Marc Bernstein *(Sr VP-Consumer Sls)*
Ivan Bielik *(Sr VP-Bus Analysis)*
Lawrence de la Haba *(Sr VP-Bus Dev)*
David Walton *(Sr VP-Long-Term Care Div)*
Scott Lerner *(Dir-IT & Internet Mktg/Sls)*
Brands & Products:
ACCUMAX
AEROCELL
AEROCIDE
AKROS
AKROSAIR
ALTADYNE
AQUATHERM
AUTO STOP
BANDAGEGARD
BRISTOLINE
CASTGARD
COMPANION
EVEREST & JENNINGS
EZE-LOK
FEATHER
FERTILO-PAK
FLEX BED
FOR THE QUALITY OF LIFE
GOWLLANDS
GRAFCO
GRAFKETTE
HEALTHTEAM
ISHIHARA
JOHN BUNN
LABAC
LABSTAR
LABTRON
LUMEX
LUMEXAIR
MATRIX PLUS
MEDICOPASTE
MEGAVIEW
METRO
METRO LE
METRO POWER
NEBULITE
NM INDUSTRIES
OMNI MANUFACTURING
OPTIMAX
ORTHO-BIOTIC
ORTHO-EASE
PATRICIA
PREFERRED CARE
PROTAMATE
SAFESHIELD
SIMMONS
SIMMONS HEALTHCARE
SMITH & DAVIS
SORTHOEASE
SPIROPET
SUPERIOR
SURE-LIFT
SURE-SAFE
TENDERCLOUD
TENDERFLO
THERA-PUTTY
THERABATH
THERMALEEZE
TRAVELER
TRAVELER XD
TUB-GUARD
VACUTEC
VELCRO
VERSAMODE
VISTA
VISTA IC
WALLMAX
WHISPERLITE
ZENITH

GILEAD SCIENCES, INC.

333 Lakeside Dr
Foster City, CA 94404-1147
Tel.: (650) 574-3000
Fax: (650) 578-9264
Toll Free: (800) 445-3235
E-mail: public_affairs@gilead.com

Key to Media (For complete agency information see *The Advertising Red Books-Agencies* edition):
1. Bus. Publs. 2. Cable T.V. 3. Catalogs & Directories. 4. Co-op Adv. 5. Consumer Mags. 6. D.M. to Bus. Estab.7. D.M. to Consumers 8. Daily Newsp. 9. Exhibits/Trade Shows 10. Foreign 11. Infomercial 12. Internet Adv.13. Multimedia 14. Network Radio 15. Network T.V. 16. Newsp. Distr. Mags. 17. Other 18. Outdoor (Posters, Transit) 19. Point of Purchase20. Premiums, Novelties 21. Product Samples 22. Special Events Mktg. 23. Spot Radio 24. Spot T.V. 25. Weekly Newsp. 26. Yellow Page Adv.

Gilead Sciences, Inc. — (Continued)

Web Site: www.gilead.com
Approx. Rev.: $7,949,420,000
Approx. Number Employees: 4,000
Year Founded: 1987
Business Description:
Biopharmaceutical Product Mfr
S.I.C.: 2836; 2834; 8733
N.A.I.C.S.: 325414; 325412; 541710
Advertising Expenditures: $108,100,000
Media: 2-7-10-18
Personnel:
John C. Martin *(Chm & CEO)*
John F. Milligan *(Pres & COO)*
Robin L. Washington *(CFO & Sr VP)*
Norbert W. Bischofberger *(Chief Scientific Officer & Exec VP-R & D)*
Gregg H. Alton *(Exec VP-Corp & Medical Affairs)*
Kevin Young *(Exec VP-Comml Ops)*
Anthony D. Caracciolo *(Sr VP)*
Paul Carter *(Sr VP-Comml Ops-Intl)*
Andrew Cheng *(Sr VP-Dev Ops)*
Seigo Izumo *(Sr VP-Cardiovascular Therapeutics)*
William A. Lee *(Sr VP-Res)*
John G. McHutchison *(Sr VP-Liver Disease Therapeutics)*
Kristen M. Metza *(Sr VP-HR)*
James R. Meyers *(Sr VP-Comml Ops-North America)*
Alan Bruce Montgomery *(Sr VP)*
John J. Toole *(Sr VP-Corp Dev)*
Taiyin Yang *(Sr VP-Pharmaceutical Dev & Mfg)*
Brands & Products:
AMBISOME
EMTRIVA
GILEAD
GILEAD SCIENCES
HEPSERA
LETAIRIS
MACUGEN
TAMIFLU
TRUVADA
VIREAD
VISTIDE
Advertising Agencies:
Carol H. Williams Advertising
1400 65th St Ste 200
Emeryville, CA 94608
Tel.: (510) 763-5200
Fax: (510) 763-9266

Giant Creative/Strategy, LLC
60 Broadway St
San Francisco, CA 94111
Tel.: (415) 655-5200
Fax: (415) 655-5201
SpeakFromTheHeart.com

Ignite Health
8955 Research Dr
Irvine, CA 92618-4237
Tel.: (949) 861-3200
Fax: (949) 861-3750
SpeakFromTheHeart.com

GILLETTE
(Sub. of The Gillette Company)
Prudential Tower Bldg
Boston, MA 02199-8004
Tel.: (617) 421-7000
Fax: (617) 421-7123
Web Site: www.gillette.com
Sales Range: $1-4.9 Billion
Business Description:
Dental Care Products Mfr
S.I.C.: 2844; 2841
N.A.I.C.S.: 325620; 325611
Media: 2-5-6-7-8-9-11-13-15-19-20-23-24-25
Brands & Products:
ADVANTAGE
CRISSCROSS
CROSSACTION
INDICATOR
ORAL-B
ORAL-B 3D EXCEL
OXYJET
POWERHEAD
SATINFLOSS
STAGES
SUPER FLOSS
ULTRA FLOSS
Advertising Agencies:
BBDO Worldwide Inc.
(Sub. of Omnicom Group, Inc.)
1285 Ave of the Americas
New York, NY 10019-6028
Tel.: (212) 459-5000
Fax: (212) 459-6645

The Geppetto Group
95 Morton St 8th Fl
New York, NY 10014-3336
Tel.: (212) 462-8140
Fax: (212) 462-8197

GLAXO SMITH KLINE INC.
(Sub. of GlaxoSmithKline Plc)
7333 Mississauga Rd
Mississauga, ON L5N 6L4, Canada
Tel.: (905) 819-3000
Fax: (905) 819-3099
Telex: 6-967582
Web Site: www.gsk.ca
Approx. Number Employees: 1,800
Year Founded: 1903
Business Description:
Pharmaceuticals Mfr & Distr
S.I.C.: 2834
N.A.I.C.S.: 325412
Media: 7-15-17-18
Distr.: Natl.
Personnel:
Paul N. Lucas *(Pres & CEO)*
Raymond Castonguay *(CFO)*
Ruth Kemp *(VP-HR)*
Natasha Dias *(Coord-Media)*
Advertising Agencies:
Grey Canada
1881 Yonge St Ste 800
Toronto, ON M4S 3C4, Canada
Tel.: (416) 486-0700
Fax: (416) 486-8907
Sensodyne

Ogilvy & Mather
33 Yonge St
Toronto, ON M5E 1X6, Canada
Tel.: (416) 367-3573
Fax: (416) 363-2088

GLAXOSMITHKLINE
(Sub. of GlaxoSmithKline Plc)
5 Moore Drive PO Box 13398
Research Triangle Park, NC 27709-3398
Tel.: (919) 483-2100
Fax: (919) 315-6049
Toll Free: (800) 825-5249
Telex: 80-2813
Web Site: www.gsk.com
Approx. Number Employees: 4,500
Year Founded: 1977
Business Description:
Pharmaceuticals Mfr & Distr
S.I.C.: 2834; 8733
N.A.I.C.S.: 325412; 541710
Import
Media: 2-4-7-10-17
Distr.: Intl.; Natl.
Personnel:
Marc Dunoyer *(Pres-Asia Pacific & Japan)*
Abbas Hussain *(Pres-Emerging Markets & Asia Pacific)*
Rupert Bondy *(Gen Counsel & Sr VP)*
Terri Sherrill *(Dir-Natl Mkt Programs)*
Shannon Graham *(Mgr-State Advocacy & Alliance Dev)*
Advertising Agencies:
ArnoldNYC
110 5th Ave
New York, NY 10011
Tel.: (212) 463-1000
Fax: (212) 463-1080

Casanova Pendrill, LLC
275-A McCormick Ave Ste 100
Costa Mesa, CA 92626-3369
Tel.: (714) 918-8200
Fax: (714) 918-8295

Draftfcb
101 E Erie St
Chicago, IL 60611
Tel.: (312) 425-5000
Fax: (312) 425-5010

Footsteps
200 Varick St Ste 610
New York, NY 10014-7434
Tel.: (212) 924-6432
Fax: (212) 924-5669

HealthSTAR Communications, Inc.
1000 Wyckoff Ave
Mahwah, NJ 07430
Tel.: (201) 560-5370
Fax: (201) 891-2380

imc2
622 3rd Ave 11th Fl
New York, NY 10017
Tel.: (212) 430-3200
Fax: (212) 430-3220

GLAXOSMITHKLINE MDR-BOSTON FACILITY
(Sub. of GlaxoSmithKline Plc)
830 Winter St
Waltham, MA 02451-1420
Tel.: (781) 795-4100
Fax: (781) 890-7471
Web Site: www.gsk.com/research/about/about_locationsus.html
Approx. Number Employees: 78
Year Founded: 1994
Business Description:
Pharmaceutical Discovey & Development
S.I.C.: 2834
N.A.I.C.S.: 325412
Export
Advertising Expenditures: $500,000
Media: 4-7
Personnel:
Edward C. English *(CFO, Treas & VP)*
Brands & Products:
APAN
DIRECT SELECT
THE FUTURE IN DRUG DEVELOPMENT
LEAP
LOTESTROL
MASTRSCREEN
METAPRO
PLENAXIS
REL-EASE
Advertising Agency:
WHITTMANHART
150 North Michigan Ave Ste 300
Chicago, IL 60601
Tel.: (312) 981-6000
Fax: (312) 981-6100

GLOBAL HEALTHCARE EXCHANGE, LLC
(d/b/a GHX, LLC)
1315 W Century Dr
Louisville, CO 80027
Tel.: (720) 887-7000
Fax: (720) 887-7200
Toll Free: (800) 968-7449
E-mail: support@ghx.com
Web Site: www.ghx.com
Approx. Number Employees: 300
Year Founded: 2000
Business Description:
Healthcare Industry Business-to-Business Exchange & Supply Chain Management Services
S.I.C.: 5045; 8742
N.A.I.C.S.: 425110; 541614
Media: 2-8-10-13
Personnel:
Bruce Johnson *(CEO)*
Rob Gillespie *(CFO)*
Leigh Anderson *(Exec VP-Ops)*
Kurt W. Blasena *(Exec VP-Sls & Prof Svcs)*
Pete Nelson *(VP & Gen Mgr-Supply Chain Svcs)*
Cheryl Flury *(VP-Corp Comm)*
Thomas Griffin *(Gen Mgr-Bus Solutions & Dir)*
Nils Clausen *(Gen Mgr-Canada)*
Karen Conway *(Dir-Indus Rels)*
Paul Cronin *(Product Mgr)*
Brands & Products:
ALLSOURCE
AP CENTER
G-FAX
GHX
GHX METATRADE
GHX MISHARE
HEALTH CONNEXION
NUVIA
ONDEMAND AP
SALESACCELERATOR

GOLDEN LIVING
(Sub. of Fillmore Capital Partners, LLC)
1000 Fianna Way
Fort Smith, AR 72919
Tel.: (479) 201-2000
Fax: (479) 201-1101
Toll Free: (877) 823-8375
Web Site: www.goldenven.com
Approx. Number Employees: 34,300
Year Founded: 1963

Key to Media (For complete agency information see *The Advertising Red Books-Agencies* edition):
1. Bus. Publs. 2. Cable T.V. 3. Catalogs & Directories. 4. Co-op Adv. 5. Consumer Mags. 6. D.M. to Bus. Estab.7. D.M. to Consumers
8. Daily Newsp. 9. Exhibits/Trade Shows 10. Foreign 11. Infomercial 12. Internet Adv.13. Multimedia 14. Network Radio
15. Network T.V. 16. Newsp. Distr. Mags. 17. Other 18. Outdoor (Posters, Transit) 19. Point of Purchase20. Premiums, Novelties
21. Product Samples 22. Special Events Mktg. 23. Spot Radio 24. Spot T.V. 25. Weekly Newsp. 26. Yellow Page Adv.

Business Description:
Nursing Rehabilitation Facilities, Institutional & Mail Order Pharmaceuticals, Assisted Acute Long-Term Transitional Hospitals, Living Projects & Home Health Centers Operator
S.I.C.: 8059; 8051; 8361
N.A.I.C.S.: 623311; 623110; 623210; 623220; 623312; 623990
Media: 2-13-16-17-26
Distr.: Natl.
Personnel:
Neil Kurtz *(Pres & CEO)*
Ann Harmon *(CFO & Exec VP-Strategic Plng)*
Martha Schram *(Sr VP)*
Blair Jackson *(VP-Corp Comm)*
Brands & Products:
AEDON STAFFING
AEGIS THERAPIES
BEVERLY
CERES STRATEGIES
HOSPICE PREFERRED CHOICE
LARES CARE RESOURCE

GRANDPA BRANDS COMPANY
1820 Airport Exch Blvd
Erlanger, KY 41018-3192
Tel.: (859) 647-0777
Fax: (859) 647-0778
Toll Free: (800) 684-1468
E-mail: info@grandpabrands.com
Web Site: www.grandpabrands.com
Approx. Number Employees: 12
Year Founded: 1878
Business Description:
Pine Tar Soap & Dental Aids Mfr
S.I.C.: 2834; 2841
N.A.I.C.S.: 325412; 325611
Media: 4-5-6-10-13
Distr.: Natl.
Personnel:
Richard D. Oliver *(Chm, Pres & CEO)*
Brands & Products:
ALGOLI
ARGILE BLANCHE
ARGIMIEL
BAKING SODA
DENT'S
DENT'S EAR WAX DROPS
DENT'S EXTRA STRENGTH
DENT'S MAXI-STRENGTH
GRANDPA ALGOLI SAVON
GRANDPA ARGILE BLANCHE SAVON
GRANDPA ARGIMIEL SAVON
GRANDPA BRANDS
GRANDPA LE STICK
GRANDPA LOVE-MY-LOOFAH
GRANDPA OATMEAL
GRANDPA ORANGE ESSENCE
GRANDPA PATCHOULI
GRANDPA PINE TAR
GRANDPA SHEA BUTTER
GRANDPA'S
INDIAN CORN
LE STICK
LOVE-MY-LOOFAH
NATURE DE FRANCE
SHEA BUTTER
THYLOX
WITCH-HAZEL
WONDER PINE TAR

GRAYMARK HEALTHCARE, INC.
210 Park Ave Ste 1350
Oklahoma City, OK 73102
Tel.: (405) 601-5300
Fax: (405) 601-4550
Web Site:
www.graymarkhealthcare.com
Approx. Rev.: $22,764,089
Approx. Number Employees: 177
Business Description:
Holding Company; Pharmacies, Healthcare Services & Devices
S.I.C.: 5912; 3841; 6719; 8069; 8071
N.A.I.C.S.: 446110; 339112; 551112; 621511; 621512; 622310
Advertising Expenditures: $356,789
Media: 2-6-7-10-18-23
Personnel:
Stanton Nelson *(CEO)*
Grant A. Christianson *(CFO)*

GREEN PHARMACEUTICALS INC.
Ste A 591 Constitution Ave
Camarillo, CA 93012-9106
Tel.: (805) 388-0600
Fax: (805) 482-9054
Web Site: www.snorestop.com
Approx. Number Employees: 13
Business Description:
Herbal Vitamins & Mineral Supplements Whslr
S.I.C.: 5122
N.A.I.C.S.: 424210
Media: 6
Personnel:
Kenneth Rifkin *(Pres)*
Christian DeRivel *(Dir-Mktg)*
Brands & Products:
NASOSPRAY
SNORESTOP
SNORESTOP EXTINGUISHER
SNORESTOP FASTTABS
THE SNORING SPECIALISTS

GREENVILLE HOSPITAL SYSTEM INC.
701 Grove Rd
Greenville, SC 29605-5611
Tel.: (864) 455-7000
Fax: (864) 455-6218
Web Site: www.ghs.org
Sales Range: $750-799.9 Million
Approx. Number Employees: 7,300
Business Description:
Operates Hospital & Health Care Services
S.I.C.: 8062; 8069
N.A.I.C.S.: 622110; 622310
Media: 2-3-4-7-9-10-13-18-24-25
Personnel:
Michael Riordan *(Pres & CEO)*
Susan Bichel *(CFO & VP)*
Doran Dunaway *(CIO & VP)*
Douglas Dorman *(VP-HR)*
Paul V. Catalana *(Program Dir)*
Sally Foister *(Dir-Mktg Svcs)*

GRIFFIN HEALTH SERVICES CORPORATION
130 Division St
Derby, CT 06418-1326
Tel.: (203) 735-7421
Fax: (203) 732-7477
Toll Free: (800) 354-3094
E-mail: griffin@griffinhealth.org
Web Site: www.griffinhealth.org
Approx. Number Employees: 1,381
Year Founded: 1901
Business Description:
Hospital & Health Care Services
S.I.C.: 8062; 8011
N.A.I.C.S.: 622110; 621111
Media: 2-4-9-10-13-22-23-24-25
Personnel:
Patrick Charmel *(Pres & CEO)*
Susan Frampton *(Pres-Plaintree)*
Edward Berns *(VP-Legal Affairs)*
James Moylan *(VP-Fin)*
Christine Cooper *(Dir-Radiology, Cardiology & Neurology)*
Gene DeLaurentis *(Dir-Environ Svcs)*
Matthew Milardo *(Dir-Admitting & Bus Svcs)*
Lorie Pierce *(Dir-Clinical 2 NA & B)*
Mary Price *(Dir-Physical Medicine)*
Ken Roberts *(Dir-Comm & Pub Affairs)*
Jo Clare Wilson *(Dir-Pastoral Care)*
Royce York *(Dir-Respiratory Svcs)*
Sylvia Adams *(Supvr, Nursing Administration)*

GTX, INC.
175 Toyota Plaza 7th Fl
Memphis, TN 38103
Tel.: (901) 523-9700
Fax: (901) 644-8075
E-mail: investor.relations@gtxinc.com
Web Site: www.gtxinc.com
Approx. Rev.: $60,613,000
Approx. Number Employees: 111
Year Founded: 1997
Business Description:
Hormone-Targeting Drug Developer
S.I.C.: 2834
N.A.I.C.S.: 325412
Personnel:
Joseph R. Hyde, III *(Chm)*
Mitchell S. Steiner *(Vice Chm & CEO)*
Marc S. Hanover *(Pres & COO)*
Mark E. Mosteller *(CFO & VP)*
Henry P. Doggrell *(Gen Counsel, Sec & VP)*
Michael D. Brown *(VP-Mktg & Managed Care)*
Gregory A. Deener *(VP-Sls & Mktg)*
Christopher K. West *(VP-Sls)*
Michael K. Brawer *(Exec Dir-Medical Affairs & Clinical Dev)*
Gary T. Bird *(Dir-Corp Quality)*
McDavid Stilwell *(Dir-Corp Comm & Fin Analysis)*
Carney Duntsch *(Mgr-Corp Comm)*
Brands & Products:
ACAPODENE
FARESTON
GTX
NEW SCIENCE.ESTABLISHED PATHWAYS.BETTER MEDICINES
OSTARINE
Advertising Agency:
Medicus Life Brands
1675 Broadway 5th Fl
New York, NY 10019-5820
Tel.: (212) 468-3100
Fax: (212) 468-3187
— Lisa Ebert *(Acct Exec)*

THE GURWIN JEWISH GERIATRIC CENTER
68 Hauppauge Rd
Commack, NY 11725
Tel.: (631) 715-2000
Fax: (631) 715-2922
E-mail: info@gurwin.org
Web Site: www.gurwin.org
Approx. Number Employees: 1,000
Year Founded: 1988
Business Description:
Health Care Services
S.I.C.: 8082
N.A.I.C.S.: 621610
Media: 2
Personnel:
Lawrence Simon *(Chm)*
Berk Brotesky *(Pres)*
Dennine Cook *(Dir-Community & Media Rels)*

GUS COMMUNICATIONS, INC.
1006 Lonetree Ct
Bellingham, WA 98229
Tel.: (360) 715-8580
Fax: (360) 715-9633
Web Site: www.gusinc.com
Business Description:
Communication Solutions for Autism, ALS, Stroke, Aphasia & Others
S.I.C.: 8049
N.A.I.C.S.: 621340
Media: 10
Personnel:
Gordon Harris *(Pres)*

HAAG-STREIT USA INC
(Sub. of Haag-Streit Holding AG)
3535 Kings Mills Rd
Mason, OH 45040
Tel.: (513) 336-7255
Fax: (513) 336-7260
Web Site: www.haag-streit-usa.com
Business Description:
Medical Dental & Hospital Equipment & Supplies Whslr
S.I.C.: 5047
N.A.I.C.S.: 423450
Personnel:
Walter Inaebnit *(Owner)*
Advertising Agency:
Holland Advertising:Interactive
700 Walnut St Ste 205
Cincinnati, OH 45202-2011
Tel.: (513) 744-3000
Fax: (513) 721-1269

HAEMONETICS CORPORATION
400 Wood Rd
Braintree, MA 02184-9114
Tel.: (781) 848-7100
Fax: (781) 356-3558
Toll Free: (800) 225-5242
E-mail: investor@haemonetics.com
Web Site: www.haemonetics.com
E-Mail For Key Personnel:
Public Relations: investor@haemonetics.com
Approx. Rev.: $676,694,000
Approx. Number Employees: 2,201
Year Founded: 1971
Business Description:
Blood Processing Equipment & Disposables Mfr
S.I.C.: 3841; 3845
N.A.I.C.S.: 339112; 334510
Export
Advertising Expenditures: $2,800,000
Media: 7-10-11
Personnel:
Richard J. Meelia *(Chm)*
Brian Concannon *(Pres & CEO)*
Christopher J. Lindop *(CFO & VP-Bus Dev)*

Key to Media (For complete agency information see *The Advertising Red Books-Agencies* edition):
1. Bus. Publs. 2. Cable T.V. 3. Catalogs & Directories. 4. Co-op Adv. 5. Consumer Mags. 6. D.M. to Bus. Estab.7. D.M. to Consumers 8. Daily Newsp. 9. Exhibits/Trade Shows 10. Foreign 11. Infomercial 12. Internet Adv.13. Multimedia 14. Network Radio 15. Network T.V. 16. Newsp. Distr. Mags. 17. Other 18. Outdoor (Posters, Transit) 19. Point of Purchase20. Premiums, Novelties 21. Product Samples 22. Special Events Mktg. 23. Spot Radio 24. Spot T.V. 25. Weekly Newsp. 26. Yellow Page Adv.

Haemonetics Corporation — (Continued)

Peter Allen *(CMO)*
Sandra L. Jesse *(Chief Legal Officer & VP)*
Remi Corlin *(Pres-Asia)*
James O'Shaughnessy *(Gen Counsel & VP)*
Steven C. Swenson *(VP & Gen Mgr-Global Plasma Svcs)*
Joseph Forish *(VP-HR)*
Susan M. Hanlon *(VP-Fin)*

Brands & Products:
ACP
THE BLOOD MANAGEMENT COMPANY
BLOODTRACK
CARDIOPAT
CELL SAVER
CYMBAL
DONOR DOC
DYNAMIC DISK
EDGEBLOOD
EDGECELL
EL DORADO DONOR
ELYNX
EQUE
THE GLOBAL LEADER IN BLOOD MANAGEMENT SOLUTIONS
HAEMONETICS
HEMASPHERE
IMPACT
MCS
ORTHOPAT
PCS
SAFETRACE
SAFETRACE TX
SAPANET
SEBRASEBRA
SMARTSUCTION
SURROUND
TEG
TOTAL CONTAINMENT DEVICE

Advertising Agency:
Schwartz Communications, Inc.
230 3rd Ave
Waltham, MA 02451
Tel.: (781) 684-0770
Fax: (781) 684-6500

HALIFAX MEDICAL CENTER

303 N Clyde Morris Blvd
Daytona Beach, FL 32114
Fax: (386) 255-5528
Toll Free: (877) 8HALIFAX
Web Site: www.halifaxhealth.org
Sales Estimate: $40-59 Million
Approx. Number Employees: 5,000
Business Description:
Hospital
S.I.C.: 8062
N.A.I.C.S.: 622110
Media: 8-13-16-18-22-23-26
Personnel:
Jeff Feasel *(Pres & CEO)*
Harry Reese *(CFO)*
Lori Delone *(CIO)*
Al Alexander *(Chief HR Officer)*
David Davidson *(Gen Counsel)*
Joe Petrock *(Exec Dir-HMC Foundation & Govt Rels)*
William Griffin *(Dir-System Res & Plng)*
Advertising Agency:
Adworks, Inc.
1225 19th St NW Ste 500
Washington, DC 20036
Tel.: (202) 342-5585
Fax: (202) 739-8201

HALOZYME THERAPEUTICS, INC.

11388 Sorrento Valley Rd
San Diego, CA 92121
Tel.: (858) 794-8889
Fax: (858) 704-8311
E-mail: info@halozyme.com
Web Site: www.halozyme.com
Approx. Rev.: $13,624,115
Approx. Number Employees: 102
Year Founded: 1998
Business Description:
Recombinant Human Enzyme Mfr, Developer & Marketer
S.I.C.: 2834; 2835
N.A.I.C.S.: 325412; 325413; 541711
Media: 2-7-10-13-17
Personnel:
Kenneth J. Kelley *(Chm)*
Gregory I. Frost *(Pres & CEO)*
Kurt A. Gustafson *(CFO & VP)*
Michael J. LaBarre *(VP-Product Dev)*

HANGER ORTHOPEDIC GROUP, INC.

10910 Domain Dr Ste 300
Austin, TX 78758
Tel.: (512) 777-3800
E-mail: info@hanger.com
Web Site: www.hanger.com
Approx. Sls.: $817,379,000
Approx. Number Employees: 4,273
Year Founded: 1984
Business Description:
Orthotic & Prosthetic Patient-Care Centers Developer & Operator
S.I.C.: 8049; 3842; 8093
N.A.I.C.S.: 621399; 339113; 621498
Advertising Expenditures: $3,500,000
Media: 4-5-10-22
Personnel:
Vinit K. Asar *(Pres & COO)*
Thomas F. Kirk *(CEO)*
George E. McHenry *(CFO, Sec & Exec VP)*
Walt Meffert, Jr. *(CIO & VP)*
Thomas C. Hofmeister *(Chief Acctg Officer & VP-Fin)*
Thomas E. Hartman *(Gen Counsel & VP)*
Ronald N. May *(Exec VP)*
Richmond L. Taylor *(Exec VP)*
Andrew C. Morton *(VP-HR)*
Scott Klosterman *(Gen Mgr-Dosteon Solutions)*
Advertising Agency:
Ames Scullin O'Haire
245 Peachtree Center Ave 23rd Fl
Atlanta, GA 30303
Tel.: (404) 659-2769
Fax: (404) 659-7664
SureFit

HARRY J. BOSWORTH COMPANY

7227 N Hamlin Ave
Skokie, IL 60076-3901
Tel.: (847) 679-3400
Fax: (847) 679-2080
Toll Free: (800) 323-4352
E-mail: info@bosworth.com
Web Site: www.bosworth.com
Approx. Number Employees: 38
Year Founded: 1912
Business Description:
Dental Materials Mfr
S.I.C.: 3843; 8021
N.A.I.C.S.: 339114; 621210
Import Export
Media: 2-4-5-10-11-13-21-22
Distr.: Intl.; Natl.
Personnel:
Mildred M. Goldstein *(Pres)*
Herbert L. Pozen *(VP-Sls & Mktg)*
Brands & Products:
AEGIS
B-CROWNS
BIG BITE TRAYS
BO-BOX
BOSWORTH
BOTRAYS
CLEAR LINER
COMFORTCAINE
CONTACT
COPALINER
CORA-CAINE
CURE-ALL
DENTUSIL
DUZ-ALL
E-Z SQUEEZE
FASTRAY
FASTRAY LC
FLEXO
GLAZE
G.T.C.
HI-SPOT
HYDROX
IMPACT 1500
IMPACT 2000
IMPACT 750
LIGHT LINEAR
LIGHT LINER
MASQUE
MEGABOND
MY TOOTH BOXES
NATURAL
NEOCRYL
NEW RIMSEAL
NEW TRULINER
ORIGINAL TRULINER
ORTHOGLO
PLASTOGUM
PLASTOPASTE
PLASTOSIL
RE'CORD
SAPPHIRE
SILENE
SIMPLASTIC
SOFTONE
SUPERBITE
SUPEREBA
SUPERGEL
SUPERGEL FRESH
SUPERPASTE
SUPERSIL
TAC
TRAY AWAYS
TRIM
TRUREPAIR
TRUSOFT
ULTRA TRIM
VIGILANCE
WONDER WEDGES
ZMENT

HARVARD BIOSCIENCE, INC.

84 October Hill Rd
Holliston, MA 01746-1371
Tel.: (508) 893-8999
Fax: (508) 429-5732
Toll Free: (800) 272-2775
E-mail: info@harvardbioscience.com
Web Site: www.harvardbioscience.com
Approx. Rev.: $108,179,000
Approx. Number Employees: 389
Year Founded: 1901
Business Description:
Life Science Analytical Instrument Developer, Mfr & Marketer
S.I.C.: 3826
N.A.I.C.S.: 334516
Advertising Expenditures: $8,100,000
Media: 2-4-7-10-20-23
Personnel:
Chane Graziano *(Chm & CEO)*
David Green *(Pres)*
Thomas McNaughton *(CFO)*
Susan M. Luscinski *(COO)*
David Strack *(Pres-Genomic Solutions & Union Biometrica)*
Ron Sostek *(VP-Sls & Mktg)*

HARVARD PILGRIM HEALTH CARE, INC.

93 Worcester St
Wellesley, MA 02481
Tel.: (617) 745-1000
Tel.: (617) 509-7400 (Media Rels)
Fax: (617) 509-2042
Toll Free: (888) 888-4742
E-mail: info@harvardpilgrim.org
Web Site: www.harvardpilgrim.org
Approx. Number Employees: 1,400
Business Description:
HMO & Health Care Services
S.I.C.: 6321
N.A.I.C.S.: 524114
Media: 2-3-7-9-10-13-18-22-23-24-25
Distr.: Reg.
Personnel:
Eric H. Schultz *(Pres & CEO)*
Roberta Herman *(COO & Chief Medical Officer)*
Deborah A. Norton *(CIO)*
Laura S. Peabody *(Chief Legal Officer)*
Vincent Capozzi *(Sr VP-Sls & Customer Svc)*
Gary H. Lin *(Sr VP-Actuarial Svcs)*
Rick Weisblatt *(Sr VP-Provider Network & Product Dev)*
Beth-Ann Roberts *(VP-Ops-Northern New England)*
Lynn A. Bowman *(VP-Customer Svc & Sls Ops)*
Michael Blunck *(Dir-Fin)*
Karith Kristel-Smith *(Mgr-Adv)*
Brands & Products:
CELEBRATING 65
FIRST SENIORITY FREEDOM
HARVARD PILGRIM HEALTH CARE
HPHCONNECT
MAKING GREAT HEALTH CARE A LITTLE EASIER
NETWORK MATTERS
Advertising Agency:
Hill Holliday
53 State St
Boston, MA 02109
Tel.: (617) 366-4000

HCA HOLDINGS, INC.

(Formerly HCA Inc.)
1 Park Plz
Nashville, TN 37203-6527
Tel.: (615) 344-9551
Fax: (615) 344-2266
Web Site: www.hcahealthcare.com
Approx. Rev.: $30,683,000,000
Approx. Number Employees: 146,000
Year Founded: 1988

Key to Media (For complete agency information see *The Advertising Red Books-Agencies* edition):
1. Bus. Publs. 2. Cable T.V. 3. Catalogs & Directories. 4. Co-op Adv. 5. Consumer Mags. 6. D.M. to Bus. Estab.7. D.M. to Consumers 8. Daily Newsp. 9. Exhibits/Trade Shows 10. Foreign 11. Infomercial 12. Internet Adv.13. Multimedia 14. Network Radio 15. Network T.V. 16. Newsp. Distr. Mags. 17. Other 18. Outdoor (Posters, Transit) 19. Point of Purchase20. Premiums, Novelties 21. Product Samples 22. Special Events Mktg. 23. Spot Radio 24. Spot T.V. 25. Weekly Newsp. 26. Yellow Page Adv.

Business Description:
Holding Company; Hospital & Medical Facility Operator; Owned by Bain Capital, LLC, by KKR & Co. L.P. & by Banc of America Capital Investors, LP
S.I.C.: 6719; 8062
N.A.I.C.S.: 551112; 622110
Media: 25-26
Personnel:
Richard M. Bracken *(Chm & CEO)*
R. Milton Johnson *(Pres & CFO)*
Noel Brown Williams *(CIO & Sr VP)*
Alan R. Yuspeh *(Sr VP & Chief Ethics/ Compliance Officer)*
Jonathan B. Perlin *(Pres-Clinical/ Physician Svcs Grp & Chief Medical Officer)*
Robert A. Waterman *(Gen Counsel, Chief Labor Rels Officer & Sr VP)*
Charles J. Hall *(Pres-Eastern Grp)*
Samuel N. Hazen *(Pres-Ops)*
Michael P. Joyce *(Pres-Southeast Div)*
Margaret G. Lewis *(Pres-Div)*
A. Bruce Moore, Jr. *(Pres-Svc Line & Ops Integration)*
W. Paul Rutledge *(Pres-Central Grp)*
Beverly B. Wallace *(Pres-NewCo Bus Solutions)*
David G. Anderson *(Treas & Sr VP-Fin)*
Donald W. Stinnett *(Sr VP & Controller)*
Victor L. Campbell *(Sr VP-Govt Rels & IR)*
Jana J. Davis *(Sr VP-Comm)*
Joseph A. Sowell, III *(Sr VP-Dev)*
Joseph N. Steakley *(Sr VP-Internal Audit Svcs)*
John M. Steele *(Sr VP-HR)*
Juan Vallarino *(Sr VP-Strategic Pricing & Analytics)*
Mitzi G. Kent *(VP-Sls)*

HCA INC.
(Name Changed to HCA HOLDINGS, INC.)

HCR MANORCARE, INC.
(Holding of The Carlyle Group, LLC)
333 N Summit St
Toledo, OH 43604-2617
Mailing Address:
PO Box 10086
Toledo, OH 43699-0086
Tel.: (419) 252-5500
Fax: (419) 252-5554
E-mail: info@hcr-manorcare.com
Web Site: www.hcr-manorcare.com
E-Mail For Key Personnel:
Public Relations:
corporatecommunications@hcr-manorcare.com
Approx. Rev.: $3,613,185,000
Approx. Number Employees: 59,500
Year Founded: 1991
Business Description:
Short-Term Post-Acute Medical Care & Rehabilitation & Long-Term Skilled Nursing Care
S.I.C.: 8059; 8062
N.A.I.C.S.: 623110; 622110
Advertising Expenditures: $15,000,000
Media: 4-10-13
Personnel:
Paul A. Ormond *(CEO)*
Steven M. Cavanaugh *(CFO)*
Stephen L. Guillard *(COO & Exec VP)*
Richard A. Parr II *(Gen Counsel & VP)*
John K. Graham *(Grp VP)*
Marty Grabijas *(VP, Gen Mgr & Dir-Mktg)*
Nancy A. Edwards *(VP & Gen Mgr)*
Lynn M. Hood *(VP & Gen Mgr)*
Susan E. Morey *(VP & Gen Mgr)*
Michael J. Reed *(VP & Gen Mgr)*
Brands & Products:
ARDEN COURTS
CIRCLE OF CARE
HCR MANOR CARE
HEARTLAND
MANORCARE HEALTH SERVICES

HEALTH FITNESS CORPORATION
(Sub. of Trustmark Mutual Holding Company)
1650 W 82nd St Ste 1100
Bloomington, MN 55431
Tel.: (952) 831-6830
Fax: (952) 879-5173
Toll Free: (800) 639-7913
Web Site: www.hfit.com
Approx. Rev.: $77,676,409
Approx. Number Employees: 847
Year Founded: 1975
Business Description:
Health Improvement Services & Programs
S.I.C.: 9431; 7991; 8748
N.A.I.C.S.: 923120; 541618; 713940
Advertising Expenditures: $212,020
Personnel:
Paul Lotharius *(Pres & CEO)*
Brian J. Gagne *(COO)*
Sean Katz *(CIO)*
J. Mark McConnell *(Sr VP-Bus & Corp Dev)*
Debra Marshall *(VP-Mktg)*
Greg Siedschlag *(VP-Fin)*

HEALTH MANAGEMENT ASSOCIATES, INC.
5811 Pelican Bay Blvd Ste 500
Naples, FL 34108-2710
Tel.: (239) 598-3104
Fax: (239) 598-2705
E-mail: info@hma.org
Web Site: www.hma.com
Approx. Rev.: $5,114,997,000
Approx. Number Employees: 28,500
Year Founded: 1977
Business Description:
Operates Acute Care & Psychiatric Hospitals
S.I.C.: 8062
N.A.I.C.S.: 622110
Personnel:
William J. Schoen *(Chm)*
Gary D. Newsome *(Pres & CEO)*
Kelly E. Curry *(CFO & Exec VP)*
Ken Chatfield *(CIO)*
Ronald N. Riner *(Chief Medical Officer)*
Jon P. Vollmer *(Exec VP & CEO-Div 6)*
J. Dale Armour *(Sr VP & CEO-Div 4)*
Ann M. Barnhart *(Sr VP & CEO-Div 3)*
John R. Finnegan *(Sr VP & CEO-Div 7)*
Bradley E. Jones *(Sr VP & CEO-Div 8)*
Stephen L. Midkiff *(Sr VP & CEO-Div 1)*
Joshua S. Putter *(Sr VP & CEO-Div 2)*
Page H. Vaughan *(Sr VP & CEO-Div 5)*
Timothy R. Parry *(Gen Counsel & Sr VP)*
Kathleen K. Hollaway *(VP-Assoc Gen Counsel)*
Peter M. Lawson *(Exec VP-Dev)*
James A. Barber *(Sr VP)*
Frederick L Drow *(Sr VP-HR)*
Robert E. Farnham *(Sr VP-Fin)*
Lisa Gore *(Sr VP-Clinical Affairs)*
James L. Jordan *(Sr VP-MIS)*
Kenneth M. Koopman *(Sr VP-Reimbursement)*
Alan Levine *(Sr VP-Health Dev Ops & Govt Rel)*
Stanley D. McLemore *(Sr VP-Ops Fin)*
Johnny A. Owenby *(Sr VP-Support Svcs)*
John C. Merriwether *(VP-Fin Relations)*
Matthew F. Tormey *(VP-Audit & Compliance)*

Advertising Agency:
Franklin Street Marketing
9700 Farrar Ct
Richmond, VA 23236
Tel.: (804) 320-3838
Fax: (804) 320-1999
Toll Free: (800) 644-8555

HEALTH MANAGEMENT SYSTEMS, INC.
(Sub. of HMS Holdings Corp.)
401 Park Ave S
New York, NY 10016-8808
Tel.: (212) 685-4545
Fax: (212) 857-5010
Toll Free: (877) HMS-0184
E-mail: info@hmsy.com
Web Site: www.hmsy.com

Sales Range: $100-124.9 Million
Approx. Number Employees: 400
Year Founded: 1974

Business Description:
Proprietary Information Management & Data Processing Services to Hospitals & Other Healthcare Providers, Government Health Service Agencies & Other Healthcare Payers & Companies Providing Services to the Healthcare Industry
S.I.C.: 7374; 7372
N.A.I.C.S.: 518210; 511210

Media: 2-10
Personnel:
William C. Lucia *(Pres & CEO)*
Cynthia Nustad *(CIO)*
Sean Curtin *(Exec VP-Ops)*
Christina Dragonetti *(Exec VP-Comm Markets)*
Maria Perrin *(Exec VP-Govt Markets)*
Stephen Vaccaro *(Sr VP & Gen Mgr-Program Integrity Svcs)*
Kimberly Daub Glenn *(Sr VP-Govt Svcs East)*
Joseph Joy *(Sr VP)*
Donna J. Price *(Sr VP-Govt Svcs West)*
Thomas A. Baggett, Jr. *(VP-Project Mgmt Office)*
Francesca Marraro *(Dir-Mktg)*
Brands & Products:
ACP
CAMS
RCR
TPL

HEALTH NET, INC.
21650 Oxnard St
Woodland Hills, CA 91367-6607
Tel.: (818) 676-6000
Fax: (818) 676-8591
Toll Free: (800) 291-6911
E-mail: Investor.Relations@healthnet.com
Web Site: www.health.net
E-Mail For Key Personnel:
President: jay.m.gellert@health.net
Approx. Rev.: $13,619,852,000
Approx. Number Employees: 8,010
Business Description:
Managed Health Care Services
S.I.C.: 6321
N.A.I.C.S.: 524114
Media: 7-8-10
Personnel:
Roger F. Greaves *(Chm)*
Jay M. Gellert *(Pres & CEO)*
Joseph C. Capezza *(CFO & Exec VP)*
James E. Woys *(COO & Exec VP)*
Patricia T. Clarey *(Chief Compliance Officer, Chief Regulatory Officer & Sr VP)*
John P. Sivori *(Pres-Health Net Pharmaceutical Svcs & Sr VP)*
Steven Sell *(Pres-Health Plan-Western Reg)*
Angelee F. Bouchard *(Gen Counsel, Sec & Sr VP)*
Marie Montgomery *(Sr VP & Controller)*
Karin D. Mayhew *(Sr VP-Org Effectiveness)*
Suzana Weltken *(Product Mgr)*
Brands & Products:
A BETTER DECISION
DECISION POWER
HEALTH NET
HEALTH NET ELECT
HEALTH NET SELECT
HEALTH NET SENIORITY PLUS
PREGNANCY MATTERS
QUITTING MATTERS
RAPID ACCESS
Advertising Agencies:
Acento Advertising, Inc.
2254 S Sepulveda Blvd
Los Angeles, CA 90064
Tel.: (310) 943-8300
Fax: (310) 943-8310
Commercial Health Plan Division
Creative
Digital
Marketing
Media Planning
Strategic Planning

Horizon Media, Inc.
1940 Century Park E 3rd Fl
Los Angeles, CA 90067-1700
Tel.: (310) 282-0909
Fax: (310) 229-8104
Toll Free: (800) 282-0901

HEALTH PRODUCTS CORPORATION
1060 Nepperhan Ave
Yonkers, NY 10703-1432

Key to Media (For complete agency information see *The Advertising Red Books-Agencies* edition):
1. Bus. Publs. 2. Cable T.V. 3. Catalogs & Directories. 4. Co-op Adv. 5. Consumer Mags. 6. D.M. to Bus. Estab.7. D.M. to Consumers
8. Daily Newsp. 9. Exhibits/Trade Shows 10. Foreign 11. Infomercial 12. Internet Adv.13. Multimedia 14. Network Radio
15. Network T.V. 16. Newsp. Distr. Mags. 17. Other 18. Outdoor (Posters, Transit) 19. Point of Purchase20. Premiums, Novelties
21. Product Samples 22. Special Events Mktg. 23. Spot Radio 24. Spot T.V. 25. Weekly Newsp. 26. Yellow Page Adv.

Health Products Corporation — (Continued)

Tel.: (914) 423-2900
Fax: (914) 963-6001
Web Site: www.hpc7.com
Approx. Number Employees: 200
Year Founded: 1973
Business Description:
Beauty Aids, OTC Drugs & Vitamins Mfr
S.I.C.: 2833; 5122
N.A.I.C.S.: 325411; 424210
Import Export
Media: 2-7-8-9-19-23
Distr.: Intl.; Natl.
Personnel:
Joseph Lewin *(Pres)*
Bob Feinstein *(VP-Mktg)*
Brands & Products:
ASPI COR
CALCIKIDS
DHEA
FUNNY CHEW CHEWS
GRAPEFRUIT DIET TABS
HANGO
HEALTH EPA
HEALTH HAIR
IMUTABS
KHG-7
LACTALINS
MALPOTANE
MELATONICIN
MEMOR-X
OMEGA LASKA
PRO-OX
RETINYL A
STOP SMOKING NOW!!
STRESSFREE
TRUE WHITE GEL
VES
ZIKO
ZURION

HEALTH WATCH INC.
(Sub. of Health Watch Holdings, Inc.)
6400 Park of Commerce Blvd Ste 1
Boca Raton, FL 33487
Tel.: (561) 994-6699
Fax: (888) 994-1835
Toll Free: (800) 226-8100
E-mail: doug@healthwatchinc.com
Web Site: www.healthwatchinc.com/
Sales Range: $25-49.9 Million
Approx. Number Employees: 140
Year Founded: 1986
Business Description:
Home Healthcare Systems & Services
S.I.C.: 8082
N.A.I.C.S.: 621610
Media: 4-6
Personnel:
Richard Brooks *(Pres)*
Brands & Products:
HEALTH WATCH
PERSONAL RESPONSE SYSTEM (PRS)

HEALTHSOUTH CORPORATION
3660 Grandview Pkwy
Birmingham, AL 35243
Tel.: (205) 967-7116
Fax: (205) 969-3543
Toll Free: (888) 476-8849
E-mail: kristi.gilmore@healthsouth.com
Web Site: www.healthsouth.com
Approx. Rev.: $1,999,300,000
Approx. Number Employees: 23,000
Year Founded: 1984
Business Description:
Rehabilitation & Long-Term Acute Care Services
S.I.C.: 8059; 8049; 8093
N.A.I.C.S.: 623110; 621399; 621498
Advertising Expenditures: $4,700,000
Personnel:
Jay F. Grinney *(Pres & CEO)*
Douglas E. Coltharp *(CFO & Exec VP)*
Mark J. Tarr *(COO & Exec VP)*
John P. Whittington *(Gen Counsel, Sec & Exec VP)*
Edmund Fay *(Treas & Sr VP-Fin)*
Mary Ann Arico *(Sr VP-IR)*
Andy Price *(Sr VP-Acctg)*
Brands & Products:
FACILITIES OUTCOME SOFTWARE
LONGTERM CARE REHAB CONTRACTS
REHAB CONSULTING TO (LTC)
REHABILITY CENTERS
REHABILITY HEALTH SERVICE
Advertising Agency:
Ad Club
1304 W Roseburg Ave
Modesto, CA 95350-4855
Tel.: (209) 529-9067
Fax: (209) 529-5265
Toll Free: (800) 333-1228

HEALTHSPAN SOLUTIONS, LLC
2228 Cottondale Ln Ste 100
Little Rock, AR 72205
Tel.: (501) 663-3001
Fax: (501) 660-4007
E-mail: info@the-healthspan.com
Web Site: www.gobenevia.com
Business Description:
Nutritional Supplement Drinks Mfr & Distr
S.I.C.: 5499
N.A.I.C.S.: 446191
Media: 2-6-8-13-21-26
Personnel:
John Troup *(Pres & CEO)*
Nicolaas Deutz *(Chief Medical Officer)*
Robert Wolf *(Chief Scientific Officer)*

HEALTHSPORT, INC.
1620 Beacon Pl
Oxnard, CA 93033
Tel.: (818) 593-4880
Fax: (818) 593-4808
Toll Free: (866) 225-7548
E-mail: hankdurschlag@yahoo.com
Web Site: www.healthsportinc.com
Approx. Rev.: $2,602,581
Approx. Number Employees: 13
Business Description:
Nutritional Supplement Mfr, Marketer & Sales
S.I.C.: 2834; 5122
N.A.I.C.S.: 325412; 424210
Advertising Expenditures: $113,189
Media: 17
Personnel:
Robert Steven Davidson *(Pres)*
Kevin Taheri *(CEO)*
Mark Udell *(CFO & Chief Acctg Officer)*

HEALTHSPRING, INC.
9009 Carothers Parkway Ste 501
Franklin, TN 37067
Tel.: (615) 291-7000
Web Site: www.healthspring.com
Approx. Rev.: $3,135,709,000
Approx. Number Employees: 3,200
Year Founded: 1995
Business Description:
Managed Care Services
S.I.C.: 6321; 9431
N.A.I.C.S.: 524114; 923120
Advertising Expenditures: $23,100,000
Personnel:
Herbert A. Fritch *(Chm & CEO)*
Michael G. Mirt *(Pres)*
Karey L. Witty *(CFO & Exec VP)*
Mark A. Tulloch *(COO & Exec VP-Enterprise Ops)*
Sharad Mansukani *(Exec VP & Chief Strategy Officer)*
David L. Terry, Jr. *(Chief Actuary & Sr VP)*
Dirk O. Wales *(Sr VP & Chief Medical Officer)*
Scott C. Huebner *(Exec VP & Pres-Texas)*
Matthew Shawn Morris *(Exec VP & Pres-Tennessee)*
Thomas C. Rekart *(Exec VP & Pres-East Reg)*
James R. Hailey *(Sr VP & Pres-Pharmaceutical Ops)*
J. Gentry Barden *(Gen Counsel, Sec & Sr VP)*
J. Lankford Wade *(Treas & Sr VP)*

HEALTHTRONICS, INC.
(Sub. of Endo Pharmaceuticals Holdings, Inc.)
9825 Spectrum Dr Bldg 3
Austin, TX 78717
Tel.: (512) 328-2892
Fax: (512) 439-8303
Toll Free: (888) 252-6575
E-mail: info@healthtronics.com
Web Site: www.healthtronics.com
Approx. Rev.: $185,330,000
Approx. Number Employees: 619
Business Description:
Medical & Hospital Equipment Mfr
S.I.C.: 3845; 3841; 5047; 7352
N.A.I.C.S.: 334510; 339112; 423450; 532291
Advertising Expenditures: $803,000
Media: 4
Personnel:
James S.B. Whittenburg *(Pres & CEO)*
Richard A. Rusk *(CFO, Treas, Sec, VP & Controller)*
Brands & Products:
HEALTHTRONICS
LITHODIAMOND
REVOLIX
TOTAL UROLOGY. TOTAL CARE.
TOTALCARE

HEALTHWAYS, INC.
701 Cool Springs Blvd
Franklin, TN 37067
Tel.: (615) 614-4929
Fax: (615) 665-7697
Toll Free: (800) 327-3822
E-mail: info@healthways.com
Web Site: www.healthways.com
Approx. Rev.: $720,333,000
Approx. Number Employees: 2,800
Year Founded: 1981
Business Description:
Comprehensive Care & Disease Management Services for Health Plans & Hospitals
S.I.C.: 6321; 8011; 8092; 8099; 8742
N.A.I.C.S.: 524114; 541611; 621492; 621493; 621999
Advertising Expenditures: $5,000,000
Media: 1-2-7-8-9-10-22-25-26
Distr.: Natl.; Reg.
Budget Set: July
Personnel:
Thomas G. Cigarran *(Founder)*
Ben R. Leedle, Jr. *(Pres & CEO)*
Alfred Lumsdaine *(CFO & VP)*
Thomas F. Cox *(COO & Exec VP)*
Matthew E. Kelliher *(Pres-Intl Bus)*
James W. Elrod *(Gen Counsel, Sec & VP)*
Jeff Klem *(VP-HR)*
Charlie Moore *(Exec Dir)*
Brands & Products:
CARDIAC HEALTHWAYS
DIABETES HEALTHWAYS
GALLUPS-HEALTHWAY WELL-BEING INDEX
HEALTHWAYS
RESPIRATORY HEALTHWAYS

HEARUSA, INC.
1250 Northpoint Pkwy
West Palm Beach, FL 33407-1912
Tel.: (561) 478-8770
Fax: (561) 478-9603
Toll Free: (800) 323-3277
E-mail: info@hearusa.com
Web Site: www.hearusa.com
Approx. Rev.: $83,502,000
Approx. Number Employees: 427
Year Founded: 1986
Business Description:
Hearing Tests & Services
S.I.C.: 5999
N.A.I.C.S.: 453910; 446199; 453998
Advertising Expenditures: $6,900,000
Media: 6-8-9-10-13-19-20-25-26
Personnel:
Stephen J. Hansbrough *(Chm & CEO)*
Gino Chouinard *(Pres & COO)*
Francisco Punal *(CFO & Sr VP)*
Paige Brough *(Sr VP-Corp Comm)*
Brands & Products:
HEARUSA
HEARX
ITS CLEAR WE CARE.

HEEL CANADA INC.
11025 LH Lafontaine
Anjou, QC H1J 2Z4, Canada
Tel.: (514) 353-4335
Fax: (514) 353-4336
E-mail: info@heel.ca
Web Site: www.heel.ca
Sales Range: $1-9.9 Million
Approx. Number Employees: 40
Business Description:
Homeopathic Medicine Mfr
S.I.C.: 2834
N.A.I.C.S.: 325412
Media: 6-11

HELICOS BIOSCIENCES CORPORATION
1 Kendall Sq Bldg 200
Cambridge, MA 02139
Tel.: (617) 264-1800
Fax: (617) 264-1700
Toll Free: (877) 243-5426

Key to Media (For complete agency information see *The Advertising Red Books-Agencies* edition):
1. Bus. Publs. 2. Cable T.V. 3. Catalogs & Directories. 4. Co-op Adv. 5. Consumer Mags. 6. D.M. to Bus. Estab.7. D.M. to Consumers 8. Daily Newsp. 9. Exhibits/Trade Shows 10. Foreign 11. Infomercial 12. Internet Adv.13. Multimedia 14. Network Radio 15. Network T.V. 16. Newsp. Distr. Mags. 17. Other 18. Outdoor (Posters, Transit) 19. Point of Purchase20. Premiums, Novelties 21. Product Samples 22. Special Events Mktg. 23. Spot Radio 24. Spot T.V. 25. Weekly Newsp. 26. Yellow Page Adv.

E-mail: investorrelations@helicosbio.com
Web Site: www.helicosbio.com
Approx. Rev.: $4,397,000
Approx. Number Employees: 22
Business Description:
Genetic Sequencing Technology Developer & Mfr
S.I.C.: 3845; 2836; 3643; 3824; 3829
N.A.I.C.S.: 334510; 325414; 334514; 334519; 335931
Personnel:
Ivan D. Trifunovich *(Exec Chm, Pres & CEO)*
Jeffrey R. Moore *(CFO & Sr VP)*
Patrice Milos *(Chief Scientific Officer & Sr VP)*
Mark Solakian *(Gen Counsel & VP)*
Advertising Agency:
Racepoint Group, Inc.
404 Wyman St Ste 375
Waltham, MA 02451
Tel.: (781) 487-4600
Fax: (781) 890-5822
— Sally Bain *(Acct Exec)*

HEMACARE CORPORATION
15350 Sherman Way Ste 350
Van Nuys, CA 91406
Tel.: (818) 986-3883
Fax: (818) 251-5300
Toll Free: (877) 310-0717
E-mail: mailroom@hemacare.com
Web Site: www.hemacare.com
Approx. Rev.: $30,252,000
Approx. Number Employees: 159
Year Founded: 1978
Business Description:
Blood Products & Services Supplier
S.I.C.: 8099; 8071
N.A.I.C.S.: 621991; 621511
Import Export
Media: 7-11
Personnel:
Steven B. Gerber *(Chm)*
Peter C. van der Wal *(Pres & CEO)*
Lisa Beth Bacerra *(CFO)*
Anna Stock *(COO)*
David Ciavarella *(Medical Dir-Coral Blood Svcs)*
Jacquelyn Hedlund *(Medical Dir-Coral Blood Svcs)*
Melanie Osby *(Dir-Medical-Natl)*
Brands & Products:
CORAL
HEMACARE CORPORATION

HEMCON MEDICAL TECHNOLOGIES, INC.
10575 SW Cascade Ave Ste 130
Portland, OR 97223-4363
Tel.: (503) 245-0459
Fax: (503) 245-1326
Toll Free: (877) 247-0196
E-mail: info@hemcon.com
Web Site: www.hemcon.com
Sales Range: $100-124.9 Million
Approx. Number Employees: 86
Year Founded: 2002
Business Description:
Bandage & First Aid Product Mfr
S.I.C.: 3842
N.A.I.C.S.: 339113
Media: 10
Personnel:
William P. Wiesmann *(Co-Founder & Chm)*
John W. Morgan *(CEO)*
William Block *(Pres-US)*
Keith Real *(Exec VP-R & D)*
Advertising Agency:
Capstrat
1201 Edwards Mill Rd 1st Fl
Raleigh, NC 27607-3625
Tel.: (919) 828-0806
Fax: (919) 834-7959

HEMOPHILIA HEALTH SERVICES, INC.
(Unit of Accredo Health Group, Inc.)
201 Great Circle Rd
Nashville, TN 37228
Tel.: (615) 352-2500
Fax: (615) 261-6730
Toll Free: (800) 800-6606
E-mail: info@hemophiliahealth.com
Web Site: www.hemophiliahealth.com
Sales Range: $100-124.9 Million
Approx. Number Employees: 200
Year Founded: 1990
Business Description:
Pharmaceuticals, Therapeutic Supplies & Disease Management Services for People with Hemophilia
S.I.C.: 5122
N.A.I.C.S.: 424210
Media: 2-10
Personnel:
Craig Mears *(Pres)*

HEMOSENSE, INC.
(Sub. of ALERE INC.)
651 River Oaks Pkwy
San Jose, CA 95134
Tel.: (408) 719-1393
Fax: (408) 719-1184
Toll Free: (877) 436-6444
E-mail: moreinfo@hemosense.com
Web Site: www.hemosense.com
Approx. Rev.: $16,257,000
Approx. Number Employees: 79
Business Description:
Blood Coagulation Monitoring Device Developer & Mfr
S.I.C.: 3841
N.A.I.C.S.: 339112
Advertising Expenditures: $400,000
Personnel:
Ron Zwanziger *(Pres & CEO)*
William H. Dippel *(Exec VP-Ops & R & D)*
Brands & Products:
COUMADIN
HEMOSENSE
INRATIO

HENRY SCHEIN, INC.
135 Duryea Rd
Melville, NY 11747
Tel.: (631) 843-5500
Fax: (631) 843-5676
Toll Free: (800) 582-2702
E-mail: custserv@henryschein.com
Web Site: www.henryschein.com
Approx. Sls.: $7,526,790,000
Approx. Number Employees: 13,500
Year Founded: 1932
Business Description:
Healthcare Products Distr & Support Services
S.I.C.: 5047; 3843; 5122
N.A.I.C.S.: 423450; 339114; 424210
Import Export
Advertising Expenditures: $12,700,000
Media: 4-8-10
Personnel:
Stanley M. Bergman *(Chm & CEO)*
James P. Breslawski *(Pres & COO)*
Steven Paladino *(CFO & Exec VP)*
Grace Monahan *(CIO & VP)*
Gerald A. Benjamin *(Chief Admin Officer & Exec VP)*
Leonard A. David *(Chief Compliance Officer & Sr VP)*
James A. Harding *(CTO & Sr VP)*
Michael Racioppi *(Chief Mdsg Officer & Sr VP)*
David McKinley *(Pres-Henry Schein Medical)*
Lonnie Shoff *(Pres-Henry Schein Global Healthcare Specialties Grp)*
Michael Zack *(Pres-Intl Group)*
Mark E. Mlotek *(Exec VP-Corp Bus Dev)*
Gerard Metselaar *(VP-Sls, Mktg Intl Group & Corp Brand Dev)*
John Scano *(VP-Fin Ops-Global)*
Mark Mastroianni *(Dir-Mktg Comm & Programs)*
Pamela Winikoff *(Dir-Corp Comm)*
Brands & Products:
ARUBA
AVIMARK
DENTALVISION
DENTRIX
EASY DENTAL
EXACT
HENRY SCHEIN
MICROMD
OASIS
Advertising Agencies:
A. Lavin Communications
8 Haven Ave Ste 223
New York, NY 10001
Tel.: (212) 290-9540
Fax: (516) 944-4487

Murray Leff & Co., Inc.
8216 250th St
Jamaica, NY 11426-2524
Tel.: (718) 470-6729
Fax: (718) 347-8562

Rubenstein Associates, Inc.
1345 Ave of the Americas Fl 30
New York, NY 10105-0109
Tel.: (212) 843-8000
Fax: (212) 843-9200

HEPALIFE TECHNOLOGIES, INC.
(Name Changed to Alliqua, Inc.)

HERBALIFE INTERNATIONAL OF AMERICA, INC.
(Holding of Herbalife Ltd.)
800 W Olympic Blvd
Los Angeles, CA 90015
Mailing Address:
PO Box 80210
Los Angeles, CA 90080-0210
Tel.: (310) 410-9600
Fax: (310) 203-2478
E-mail: info@herbalife.com
Web Site: www.herbalife.com
Sales Range: $1-4.9 Billion
Approx. Number Employees: 2,450
Year Founded: 1980
Business Description:
Retailer of Nutritional Products, Weight Loss & Health Supplements, Skin Care, Hair Care & Suntan Products
S.I.C.: 5122; 5499
N.A.I.C.S.: 424210; 446191
Import Export
Advertising Expenditures: $11,300,000
Media: 3-6-9-11-14-15-20-22-23-24-26
Distr.: Intl.; Natl.
Budget Set: Nov.
Personnel:
Michael O. Johnson *(Chm & CEO)*
John DeSimone *(CFO)*
Richard P. Goudis *(COO)*
Brett R. Chapman *(Gen Counsel)*
John Purdy *(Sr VP-Asia Pacific)*
George Fischer *(VP-WW Corp Comm)*
Brands & Products:
AMINOGEN
CARDIO TOCONOX
FLORAFIBER
GARDEN 7
HEART
HERBALIFE
HERBALIFELINE
INNER NUTRITION
KINDERMINS
MALE FACTOR 1000
MAN
NATURE'S MIRROR
NITEWORKS
OUTER NUTRITION
PRELOX
RADIANT C
RELAX NOW
SCHIZANDRA PLUS
SHAPEWORKS
SKIN ACTIVATOR
SLEEP NOW
SOUL
TANG KUEI
THERMOJETICS
WOMAN
XTRA-CAL

HERBALIFE LTD.
800 W Olympic Blvd Ste 406
Los Angeles, CA 90015
Tel.: (213) 745-0500
Tel.: (213) 745-0474 (IR)
Toll Free: (866) 866-4744
E-mail: investorrelations@herbalife.com
Web Site: www.herbalife.com
Approx. Sls.: $2,734,226,000
Approx. Number Employees: 4,500
Year Founded: 1980
Business Description:
Weight Management, Nutritional Supplement, Energy, Fitness & Personal Care Products Sales
S.I.C.: 5122; 5499
N.A.I.C.S.: 424210; 446191
Advertising Expenditures: $2,600,000
Personnel:
Michael O. Johnson *(Chm & CEO)*
Desmond Walsh *(Pres)*
John DeSimone *(CFO)*
Richard P. Goudis *(COO)*
Bosco Shin-Shing Chiu *(Chief Acctg Officer)*
Brett R. Chapman *(Gen Counsel & Sec)*
Michael T. Yatcilla *(Sr Dir-Technical Ops)*
Manolis Leontzakos *(Dir-Greece & Cyprus)*

Key to Media (For complete agency information see *The Advertising Red Books-Agencies* edition):
1. Bus. Publs. 2. Cable T.V. 3. Catalogs & Directories. 4. Co-op Adv. 5. Consumer Mags. 6. D.M. to Bus. Estab.7. D.M. to Consumers 8. Daily Newsp. 9. Exhibits/Trade Shows 10. Foreign 11. Infomercial 12. Internet Adv.13. Multimedia 14. Network Radio 15. Network T.V. 16. Newsp. Distr. Mags. 17. Other 18. Outdoor (Posters, Transit) 19. Point of Purchase20. Premiums, Novelties 21. Product Samples 22. Special Events Mktg. 23. Spot Radio 24. Spot T.V. 25. Weekly Newsp. 26. Yellow Page Adv.

Herbalife Ltd. — (Continued)

Brands & Products:
AMINOGEN
CELL ACTIVATOR
CELL-U-LOSS
CORE COMPLEX
DINOMINS
FLORAFIBER
GARDEN 7
HERBAL CONCENTRATE
HERBALIFE
KINDERMINS
LIFTOFF
MALE FACTOR 1000
NITEWORKS
NOURIFUSION
OUTER NUTRITION
PRELOX
PROTEIN BAR
RADIANT C
RELAX NOW
ROSEOX
SCHIZANDRA PLUS
SHAPEWORKS
SKIN ACTIVATOR
SNACK DEFENSE
SOUP MIX
TANG KUEI PLUS
THERMO-BOND
TITLEIST
TOTAL CONTROL
TRI-SHIELD
XTRA-CAL

Advertising Agencies:
Hanson & Hanson Enterprises LLC
2099 S Pelzer Rd
Boonville, IN 47601
Tel.: (812) 897-7910
Fax: (812) 897-7911
Toll Free: (877) 302-0250

Taylor & Pond Corporate Communications
2970 5th Ave Ste 120
San Diego, CA 92103-5995
Tel.: (619) 297-3742
Fax: (619) 297-3743

HESKA CORPORATION

3760 Rocky Mountain Ave
Loveland, CO 80538
Tel.: (970) 493-7272
Fax: (970) 619-3003
Toll Free: (800) GOHESKA
E-mail: vetcareheska@heska.ch
Web Site: www.heska.com
Approx. Rev.: $65,451,000
Approx. Number Employees: 276
Year Founded: 1988
Business Description:
Develops, Manufactures & Markets Companion Animal Health Products
S.I.C.: 5122; 2834; 2836
N.A.I.C.S.: 424210; 325412; 325414
Import Export
Advertising Expenditures: $735,000
Media: 5-7-10-11
Personnel:
Robert B. Grieve *(Chm & CEO)*
Michael J. McGinley *(Pres & COO)*
Jason A. Napolitano *(CFO, Sec & Exec VP)*
Joe Aperfine *(Exec VP-Sls & Mktg)*
Donald L. Wassom *(Mng Dir-Heska Fribourg & Dir-Global Allergy)*
Mark D. Cicotello *(VP-HR)*
Malcolm A. Hammerton *(VP-IT)*
G. Lynn Snodgrass *(VP-Sls)*
Nancy Wisnewski *(VP-Product Dev & Tech Customer Svc)*

Brands & Products:
ALLERCEPT
CBC-DIFF
DRI-CHEM
E-SCREEN
E.R.D.-HEALTHSCREEN
EZ HEALTHCHECK
FELINE ULTRANASAL
G2 DIGITAL
HEMATRUE
HESKA
HESKAVIEW INTEGRATED SOFTWARE
IMMUCHECK
LAB REPORTING SYSTEM
SOLO STEP
THYROMED
TRUE20
VET/E-SIG
VET/IV
VET/OX
VET/OX G2 DIGITAL MONITOR

HI-TECH PHARMACAL CO., INC.

369 Bayview Ave
Amityville, NY 11701-2801
Tel.: (631) 789-8228
Fax: (631) 789-8429
Toll Free: (800) 262-9010
Web Site: www.hitechpharm.com
E-Mail For Key Personnel:
President: dseltzer@hitechpharm.com
Approx. Sls.: $163,691,000
Approx. Number Employees: 389
Year Founded: 1982
Business Description:
Specialty Pharmaceutical Products Developer, Mfr & Marketer
S.I.C.: 2834; 2833; 5122
N.A.I.C.S.: 325412; 325411; 424210
Advertising Expenditures: $3,968,000
Media: 2-6-7-13-19-21
Personnel:
David S. Seltzer *(Chm, Pres, CEO, Treas & Sec)*
William Peters *(CFO & VP)*
Gary M. April *(Pres-Health Care Products Div)*
Marlene Ross *(VP-Mktg)*

Brands & Products:
CHOICE
DIABETIC TUSSIN
DIABETIDERM
DIABETISWEET
HI-TECH
MULTI-BETIC
ZOSTRIX

HILL-ROM COMPANY, INC.

(Sub. of Hill-Rom Holdings, Inc.)
1069 State Rd 46 E
Batesville, IN 47006-7520
Tel.: (812) 934-7777
Fax: (812) 934-8189
Toll Free: (800) 445-3730
E-mail: webmaster@hill-rom.com
Web Site: www.hill-rom.com
Sales Range: $100-124.9 Million
Approx. Number Employees: 1,800
Year Founded: 1929
Business Description:
Mfr. of Patient Care Products & Specialized Rental Therapy Products
S.I.C.: 3842; 7352
N.A.I.C.S.: 339113; 532291
Import Export
Media: 2-7-10-13-22
Personnel:
Susan R. Lichtenstein *(Chief Legal Officer & Sr VP-Corp Affairs)*
Michael Oliver *(Chief HR Officer & Sr VP)*
Richard G. Keller *(Chief Acctg Officer, VP & Controller)*
Martha Goldberg Aronson *(Pres-North America & Sr VP)*
Alejandro Infante Saracho *(Pres-Intl & Sr VP)*
Alejandro Infante *(Pres-Intl & Surgical)*
Jeff Kao *(Pres-NAAC)*
John H. Dickey *(Sr VP-Corp Support Svcs)*
Scott Jeffers *(Sr VP-Global Supply Chain)*
Earl DeCarli *(Grp VP-Care Continuum Svcs)*
Mitch Tidman *(Dir-Intl Mktg)*
Leah Schoettmer *(Mgr-Mktg Comm)*

Brands & Products:
CAREPORTER
CLINITRON AT-HOME
COMLITE
COMPOSER
DURASTAR
ECLIPSE MATTRESS
EPICAREPORTER
ISOLETTE
MEDAES
ON 3
OSPREY
PRIMA
RESIDENT
RESUSCITAIRE
RITE-HITE
SILKAIR MATTRESS
V-CUE
YELLOFINS

HILL-ROM HOLDINGS, INC.

1069 State Rte 46 E
Batesville, IN 47006-8928
Tel.: (812) 934-7777
Fax: (812) 934-8189
Web Site: www.hill-rom.com
E-Mail For Key Personnel:
Public Relations: Christopher.feeney@hillenbrand.com
Approx. Rev.: $1,469,600,000
Approx. Number Employees: 6,350
Year Founded: 1884
Business Description:
Holding Company
S.I.C.: 6719; 3995
N.A.I.C.S.: 551112; 339995
Import Export
Advertising Expenditures: $4,300,000
Media: 2-7-8-17
Distr.: Natl.
Budget Set: Oct.
Personnel:
Rolf A. Classon *(Chm)*
John J. Greisch *(Pres & CEO)*
Mark Guinan *(CFO)*
Phillip Settimi *(CMO & Sr VP-Global Mktg & Corp Strategy)*
Susan R. Lichtenstein *(Chief Legal Officer & Sr VP-Corp Affairs)*
Michael Oliver *(Chief HR Officer & Sr VP)*
Richard G. Keller *(Chief Acctg Officer, VP & Controller)*
Martha Goldberg-Aronson *(Pres-North America & Sr VP)*
Alejandro Infante Saracho *(Pres-Intl & Sr VP)*
Abel Ang *(Pres-Asia Pacific Reg)*
John H. Dickey *(Sr VP-Corp Support Svcs)*
Scott Jeffers *(Sr VP-Supply Chain-Global)*
Earl Decarli *(Grp VP)*
Hinesh Patel *(VP-Bus Dev & Strategy)*
Lauren Green Caldwell *(Dir-Corp Comm & Pub Rel)*
Christopher Feeney *(Dir-Pub Affairs & Corp Comm)*

Brands & Products:
AVANTGUARD

Advertising Agencies:
Fahlgren Mortine
4030 Easton Station Ste 300
Columbus, OH 43219
Tel.: (614) 383-1500
Fax: (614) 383-1501

Fahlgren Mortine
4030 Easton Sta Ste 300
Columbus, OH 43219
Tel.: (614) 383-1500
Fax: (614) 383-1501

VantagePoint, Inc
80 Villa Rd
Greenville, SC 29615
Tel.: (864) 331-1240
Fax: (864) 331-1245

HILL TOP RESEARCH INC.

6088 Main & Mill Streets
Miamiville, OH 45147
Mailing Address:
PO Box 138
Miamiville, OH 45147-0138
Tel.: (513) 831-3114
Fax: (513) 831-1217
E-mail: info@hill-top.com
Web Site: www.hill-top.com
Approx. Number Employees: 250
Year Founded: 1947
Business Description:
Laboratory Services
S.I.C.: 8734
N.A.I.C.S.: 541380
Media: 2-7-10-13-20
Personnel:
John Murta *(Pres)*
Paul Briggs *(VP & Gen Mgr-Contract Res Org Svcs)*
John Lyssikatos *(VP-Sls & Mktg)*
Tati Bates *(Dir-Site)*
Kathy Baxter *(Dir-Quality Assurance)*
Jeff Berg *(Dir-Tech)*
Nalini Kaul *(Dir-IT)*
Gayle Mulberry *(Dir-Technical-Microbiology)*
Linda Oddo *(Dir-Tech)*
Stacey Risk *(Dir-Bus Dev & Clinical Feasibility)*
Jack Wild *(Dir-Tech)*

Brands & Products:
ACCELERATING SUCCESS

HOFFMANN-LA ROCHE INC.

(Sub. of F. Hoffmann-La Roche AG)
340 Kingsland St
Nutley, NJ 07110-1199
Tel.: (973) 235-5000
Fax: (973) 235-7605
Toll Free: (800))526-6367

Key to Media (For complete agency information see *The Advertising Red Books-Agencies* edition):
1. Bus. Publs. 2. Cable T.V. 3. Catalogs & Directories. 4. Co-op Adv. 5. Consumer Mags. 6. D.M. to Bus. Estab.7. D.M. to Consumers 8. Daily Newsp. 9. Exhibits/Trade Shows 10. Foreign 11. Infomercial 12. Internet Adv.13. Multimedia 14. Network Radio 15. Network T.V. 16. Newsp. Distr. Mags. 17. Other 18. Outdoor (Posters, Transit) 19. Point of Purchase20. Premiums, Novelties 21. Product Samples 22. Special Events Mktg. 23. Spot Radio 24. Spot T.V. 25. Weekly Newsp. 26. Yellow Page Adv.

E-mail: us.investor_relations@roche.com
Web Site: www.rocheusa.com
Approx. Number Employees: 6,600
Business Description:
Pharmaceuticals, Fine Chemicals, Vitamins & Diagnostics Mfr
S.I.C.: 2834; 3841
N.A.I.C.S.: 325412; 339112
Media: 2-10-15-19-21-24
Budget Set: Dec.
Personnel:
Frederick C. Kentz *(Gen Counsel, Sec & VP)*
Nancy Shore DiLella *(Gen Counsel)*
Tom Klein *(VP-Sls & Mktg-Virology)*
Barbara Senich *(VP-Sls & Mktg Svcs)*
Theresa Martinez *(Dir-Mktg-Pegasys)*
John Lyons *(Brand Dir-Boniva)*
John McLaughlin *(Brand Dir-HIV)*
Drake Parker *(Brand Dir-Xeloda)*
Chris Vales *(Brand Dir-New Products)*
Linda Lee-Mathieson *(Dir-Clinical Mgmt-Pharma Dev Ops)*
Brands & Products:
ACCUTANE
ANAPROX
BONIVA
BUMEX
CELLCEPT
COPEGUS
CYTOVENE
DEMADEX
EC-NAPROSYN
FORTOVASE
FUZEON
GANTRISIN
HIVID
INVIRASE
KLONOPIN
KYTRIL
LARIUM
NAPROSYN
PEGASYS
ROCALTROL
ROMAZICON
SORIATANE
TASMAR
TICLID
TORADOL
VALCYTE
VALIUM
VERSED
VESANOID
XELODA
XENICAL
ZENAPAX

HOFFMANN-LA ROCHE LIMITED
(Sub. of F. Hoffmann-La Roche AG)
(d/b/a Roche)
2455 Meadowpine Blvd
Mississauga, ON L5N 6L7, Canada
Tel.: (905) 542-5555
Fax: (905) 542-7130
Web Site: www.rochecanada.com
Approx. Number Employees: 700
Year Founded: 1931
Business Description:
Mfr & Sales of Pharmaceuticals
S.I.C.: 2834
N.A.I.C.S.: 325412
Export
Media: 2-6-8-10-13-18-20-21
Distr.: Intl.
Personnel:
Ronald Miller *(Pres & CEO)*
Jim Willoughby *(Gen Counsel, Corp Sec & VP)*
Brands & Products:
WE INNOVATE HEALTHCARE

HOME DIAGNOSTICS, INC.
(Sub. of Nipro Corporation)
2400 NW 55th Ct
Fort Lauderdale, FL 33309
Tel.: (954) 677-9201
Fax: (954) 677-9203
Toll Free: (800) 342-7226
Toll Free: (888) 777-7357
E-mail: professionals@hdidiabetes.com
Web Site: www.homediagnostics.com
Approx. Sls.: $123,582,443
Approx. Number Employees: 571
Year Founded: 1985
Business Description:
Diabetes Management & Blood Glucose Monitoring Systems
S.I.C.: 3821; 3826; 3845; 5047
N.A.I.C.S.: 339111; 334510; 334516; 423450
Import Export
Advertising Expenditures: $4,500,000
Media: 1-4-5-6-10-11-23-24
Distr.: Direct to Consumer; Intl.; Natl.; Reg.
Personnel:
George S. Godfrey *(Sr VP & Gen Mgr-Ops-Nipro Diagnostics)*
Lynne M. Brown *(Dir-Sls, Mktg-Latin America & Caribbean)*
Kim Zeltwanger *(Dir-HR)*
Brands & Products:
GENTLE DRAW
GOLDSENSOR
HOMEDIAGNOSTICS
KETONE CARE
PRESTIGE IQ
PRESTIGE LX
PRESTIGE SMART SYSTEM
SIDEKICK
THE SMART CHOICE
TRACKEASE
TRACKEASE SMART SYSTEM
TRACKRECORD
TRUE2GO
TRUEFILL
TRUEREAD
TRUERESULT
TRUETEST
TRUETRACK
TRUETRACK SMART SYSTEM

HOOPER HOLMES, INC.
170 Mount Airy Rd
Basking Ridge, NJ 07920
Tel.: (908) 766-5000
Fax: (908) 953-6304
E-mail: hholmes@hooperholmes.com
Web Site: www.hooperholmes.com
Approx. Rev.: $166,370,000
Approx. Number Employees: 900
Year Founded: 1899
Business Description:
Corporate Health Information Services; Insurance Exams
S.I.C.: 8049; 6411; 8099
N.A.I.C.S.: 621399; 524298; 621999
Advertising Expenditures: $300,000
Media: 2
Personnel:
Larry R. Ferguson *(Chm)*
Ransom J. Parker *(Pres & CEO)*
Michael J. Shea *(CFO, Treas & Sr VP)*
Lori E. Gorman *(COO)*
Burt R. Wolder *(CMO & Sr VP)*
Mark Patterson *(Pres-Heritage Labs Div)*
Mark Rosenblum *(Gen Counsel, Sec & Sr VP)*
Richard D'Alesandro *(Sr VP-Admin Svcs Grp)*
Susheel K. Jain *(Sr VP-Health Care)*
Anthony Mendicino *(Sr VP-Risk Assessment Sls)*
Richard Whitbeck, Jr. *(Sr VP)*
David K. Winsemius *(VP & Dir-Medical)*
Darla Carr *(Asst VP-Lab Ops-Heritage Labs Intl)*
Gurmukh Singh *(Dir-Lab-Heritage Labs Intl)*
Patricia A. Thomas *(Asst Dir-Lab-Heritage Labs Intl)*
Brands & Products:
HOOPER HOLMES
INFOLINK
PORTAMEDIC

HOSPIRA, INC.
275 N Field Dr
Lake Forest, IL 60045
Tel.: (224) 212-2000
Toll Free: (877) 946-7747
E-mail: shareholder@computershare.com
Web Site: www.hospira.com
Approx. Sls.: $3,917,200,000
Approx. Number Employees: 14,000
Business Description:
Specialty Pharmaceuticals & Delivery Systems
S.I.C.: 2834; 3841
N.A.I.C.S.: 325412; 339112
Media: 4
Personnel:
Christopher B. Begley *(Chm)*
F. Michael Ball *(CEO)*
Thomas E. Werner *(CFO & Sr VP-Fin)*
Daphne E. Jones *(CIO & Sr VP)*
Sumant Ramachandra *(Chief Scientific Officer & Sr VP-R & D)*
Ron Squarer *(Chief Comml Officer & Sr VP)*
Svend Andersen *(Pres-EMEA)*
Thomas G. Moore *(Pres-Global Pharmaceuticals)*
Timothy Oldham *(Pres-Asia-Pacific)*
Brian J. Smith *(Gen Counsel, Sec & Sr VP)*
Francois L. Dubois *(Sr VP-Quality)*
James H. Hardy, Jr. *(Sr VP-Ops)*
Brands & Products:
ABBO-VAC
ABBOCATH
ABBOJECT
ACCESS PLUS
ADD-VANTAGE
ADVANCING WELLNESS
ANSYR
CARPUJECT
CLAVE
CLC2000
CLEAR-CATH
DESIGN-A-SET
FIRSTCHOICE
GEMSTAR
HEXTEND
LIFECARE
LIFECARE PCA
LIFESHIELD
MAJORITY OF PLUMSETS
MEDNET
MICROCLAVE
MULTIFLEX
NUTRIMIX
OMNI-FLOW
OMNI-FLOW 4000
OPTICATH
OPTIQ
PENTALUMEN
PLUM A
PLUM A PLUS
PRECEDEX
PSARRAY
PUNCTUR-GUARD
SAFESET
SETSOURCE
SLIM-PAK
THERMOSET
TKO
TRANSPAC
VENICARE
VISV
Advertising Agency:
Kinect
211 E Chicago Ave
Chicago, IL 60611
Tel.: (312) 475-3610
Tel.: (646) 428-6050
Fax: (312) 475-2692

HOVEROUND CORP.
(Sub. of Jordan Industries, Inc.)
2151 Whitfield Industrial Way
Sarasota, FL 34243-4047
Tel.: (941) 739-6200
Fax: (941) 727-8686
E-mail: marketing@hoveround.com
Web Site: www.hoveround.com
Approx. Number Employees: 497
Year Founded: 1992
Business Description:
Mfr. Of Wheelchairs
S.I.C.: 3842; 5963
N.A.I.C.S.: 339113; 454390
Personnel:
Thomas E. Kruse *(Pres & CEO)*
George Kruse *(CFO)*
Jeff Hilton *(Dir-Mktg)*
Brands & Products:
HOVEROUND
Advertising Agencies:
Imarketing Ltd, Inc.
20 Nassau St Ste 250E
Princeton, NJ 08542
Tel.: (609) 921-0400
Digital Assignment

Mercury Media, Inc.
520 Broadway Ste 400
Santa Monica, CA 90401
Tel.: (310) 451-2900
Direct Response Assignment

HUMAN GENOME SCIENCES, INC.
14200 Shady Grove Rd
Rockville, MD 20850
Tel.: (301) 309-8504
Fax: (301) 309-8512
E-mail: Investor_Relations@hgsi.com
Web Site: www.hgsi.com

Human Genome Sciences, Inc. — (Continued)

Approx. Rev.: $157,351,000
Approx. Number Employees: 1,100
Year Founded: 1992
Business Description:
Gene-Based Therapies Developer
S.I.C.: 2835; 2834
N.A.I.C.S.: 325413; 325412
Media: 10
Personnel:
Argeris N. Karabelas *(Chm)*
H. Thomas Watkins *(Pres & CEO)*
David P. Southwell *(CFO & Exec VP)*
Barry A. Labinger *(Chief Comml Officer & Exec VP)*
James H. Davis *(Gen Counsel, Sec & Exec VP)*
David C. Stump *(Exec VP-R & D)*
Susan D. Bateson *(Sr VP-HR)*
Sally D. Bolmer *(Sr VP-Regulatory Affairs)*
Susan B. McKay *(Sr VP-HR)*
Craig C. Parker *(Sr VP-Strategy & Corp Dev)*
Curran M. Simpson *(Sr VP-Ops)*
Scott Habig *(VP-Sls)*
Kevin P. McRaith *(VP-Sls & Mktg)*
Joseph A. Morin *(VP-Engrg)*
Jerry Parrott *(VP-Corp Comm & Pub Policy)*
Michele M. Wales *(VP-Intellectual Property)*
Peter Vozzo *(Sr Dir-IR)*
Brands & Products:
ABTHRAX
ALBUFERON
HGS
HUMAN GENOME SCIENCES
LYMPHOSTAT-B
SYNCRIA

HYPERTENSION DIAGNOSTICS, INC.

10275 Wayzata Blvd Ste 310
Minnetonka, MN 55305
Tel.: (651) 687-9999
Fax: (651) 687-0485
Toll Free: (888) 785-7392
E-mail: infoteam@hdii.com
Web Site: www.hdi-pulsewave.com
E-Mail For Key Personnel:
President: gguettler@hdii.com
Approx. Rev.: $1,389,181
Approx. Number Employees: 4
Year Founded: 1988
Business Description:
Proprietary Devices Designer, Developer, Mfr & Marketer to Detect Changes Non-Invasively in Small & Large Artery Elasticity
S.I.C.: 3841
N.A.I.C.S.: 339112
Advertising Expenditures: $771,319
Media: 7-10
Personnel:
Mark N. Schwartz *(Chm, CEO & CFO)*
Greg H. Guettler *(Pres & Sec)*
Brands & Products:
CVPROFILOR
CVPROFILOR DO-2020
CVPROFILOR MD-3000
HDI/ PULSEWAVE CR-2000
HYPERTENSION DIAGNOSTICS

HYTHIAM, INC.
(Name Changed to CATASYS, INC.)

I-FLOW CORPORATION

(Sub. of Kimberly-Clark Corporation)
20202 Windrow Dr
Lake Forest, CA 92630
Tel.: (949) 206-2700
Fax: (949) 206-2600
Toll Free: (800) 448-3569
E-mail: information@iflo.com
Web Site: www.iflo.com
Approx. Rev.: $133,055,000
Approx. Number Employees: 430
Year Founded: 1985
Business Description:
Drug Delivery Systems Developer & Marketer
S.I.C.: 3841
N.A.I.C.S.: 339112
Advertising Expenditures: $7,800,000
Personnel:
Joanne B. Bauer *(Pres & CEO)*
Mark A. Buthman *(CFO)*
Thomas J. Mielke *(Exec VP)*
Brands & Products:
HOMEPUMP ECLIPSE
I-FLOW
ON-Q
ON-Q C-BLOC
ON-Q PAINBUSTER
ON-Q SOAKER
ONE-STEP KVO
PARAGON
REDEFINING RECOVERY
RELY-A-FLOW
SELECT-A-FLOW
SIDEKICK
SOAKER
VIP

IDENIX PHARMACEUTICALS, INC.

60 Hampshire St
Cambridge, MA 02139
Tel.: (617) 995-9800
Fax: (617) 995-9801
E-mail: idenix@idenix.com
Web Site: www.idenix.com
Approx. Rev.: $10,222,000
Approx. Number Employees: 109
Year Founded: 1998
Business Description:
Biopharmaceutical Mfr
S.I.C.: 2834; 2836
N.A.I.C.S.: 325412; 325414; 541711
Import Export
Media: 7-11
Personnel:
Ronald C. Renaud, Jr. *(Pres & CEO)*
Daniella Beckman *(Interim CFO & Controller)*
Douglas L. Mayers *(Chief Medical Officer & Exec VP)*
Maria Stahl *(Gen Counsel & Sr VP)*
David N. Standring *(Exec VP-Biology)*
Paul J. Fanning *(Sr VP-HR)*
Brands & Products:
IDX899
INDENIX
NNRTI

IDERA PHARMACEUTICALS, INC.

167 Sidney St
Cambridge, MA 02139
Tel.: (617) 679-5500
Fax: (617) 679-5592
E-mail: info@iderapharma.com
Web Site: www.iderapharma.com
Approx. Rev.: $16,110,000
Approx. Number Employees: 36
Year Founded: 1989
Business Description:
Pharmaceuticals
S.I.C.: 2836; 2834; 8733
N.A.I.C.S.: 325414; 325412; 541720
Media: 10
Personnel:
Sudhir Agrawal *(Chm, Pres & CEO)*
Youssef El-Zein *(Vice Chm)*
Louis J. Arcudi, III *(CFO, Treas & Sec)*
Steven J. Ritter *(VP-Intellectual Property & Contracts)*
David M. Lough *(Dir-Bus Dev & Alliance Mgmt)*
Brands & Products:
ACTILON
AMPLIVAX
AVASTIN
CAMPTOSAR
ERBITUX
IDERA
IMO
TARCEVA
Advertising Agency:
MacDougall Biomedical Communications, Inc.
888 Worcester St Ste 370
Wellesley, MA 02482
Tel.: (781) 235-3060
Fax: (781) 235-3061

IDEXX LABORATORIES, INC.

1 IDEXX Dr
Westbrook, ME 04092
Tel.: (207) 556-0300
Fax: (207) 556-4286
E-mail: investorrelations@idexx.com
Web Site: www.idexx.com
Approx. Rev.: $1,103,392,000
Approx. Number Employees: 4,800
Year Founded: 1984
Business Description:
Diagnostic Testing Materials & Drugs Mfr for Pets & Livestock
S.I.C.: 2835; 2834
N.A.I.C.S.: 325413; 325412
Advertising Expenditures: $1,700,000
Personnel:
Jonathan W. Ayers *(Chm, Pres & CEO)*
Merilee Raines *(CFO, Treas & Corp VP)*
Conan R. Deady *(Gen Counsel, Sec & Corp VP)*
Giovani Twigge *(Corp VP-HR)*
Brad Brazell *(Dir-IDEXX VetLab Station)*
Sharon Collin *(Dir-Mktg)*
Penny Maier *(Dir-Mktg-Digital)*
Brands & Products:
ACAREXX
ACUMEDIA
ADR COMBO
ADRCHEK
BETTER CHOICE
CARDIOPET
CATALYST DX
CHEKIT
COAG DX
COLILERT
COLILERT-18
COLISURE
CORNERSTONE
DIAGNOSTIC EDGE
DST
EBI
ENTEROLERT
EQUIVIEW
EZ-QC
FACILITATOR
FELINE TRIPLE
FILTA-MAX
FILTA-MAX XPRESS
FLEXTEST
FLOCKCHEK
HERDCHEK
IDEXX DIGITAL
IDEXX-DIRECT
IDEXX LABORATORIES
IDEXX SNAPSHOT DX
IDEXX VETVAULT
INTELLISHARE
IVS-CONNECT
LABREXX
LASERCYTE
NAVIGATOR
OPTI
OPTIRHYTHM
PACS
PATIENT ADVISOR
PETCHEK
POURQUIER
PRACTICE DEVELOPER
PRACTICE EXPLORER
PRACTICE PROFILE
PZI VET
QBC VETAUTOREAD
QUALIBEADS
QUANT C6
RESULTS PLUS
SNAP
SNAP 3DX
SNAP 4DX
SPEC CPL
SPEC FPL
VETAUTOREAD
VETERINARY PRACTICE-MANAGEMENT
VETLAB
VETLINK
VETLYTE
VETSTAT
VETTEST
WINPLATE
WISDOM
XCHEK

ILLUMINA, INC.-HAYWARD

(Sub. of Illumina, Inc.)
25861 Industrial Blvd
Hayward, CA 94545
Tel.: (510) 670-9300
Fax: (510) 670-9302
Web Site: www.illumina.com
Sales Range: $1-9.9 Million
Approx. Number Employees: 118
Year Founded: 1992
Business Description:
Genetic Analysis System & Technology Developer & Marketer
S.I.C.: 3826; 8733
N.A.I.C.S.: 334516; 541710
Export
Media: 2-10-13
Brands & Products:
LYNX
MEGACLONE
MEGATYPE
MPSS
SEQUENCING-BY-SYNTHESIS

Key to Media (For complete agency information see *The Advertising Red Books-Agencies* edition):
1. Bus. Publs. 2. Cable T.V. 3. Catalogs & Directories. 4. Co-op Adv. 5. Consumer Mags. 6. D.M. to Bus. Estab.7. D.M. to Consumers 8. Daily Newsp. 9. Exhibits/Trade Shows 10. Foreign 11. Infomercial 12. Internet Adv.13. Multimedia 14. Network Radio 15. Network T.V. 16. Newsp. Distr. Mags. 17. Other 18. Outdoor (Posters, Transit) 19. Point of Purchase20. Premiums, Novelties 21. Product Samples 22. Special Events Mktg. 23. Spot Radio 24. Spot T.V. 25. Weekly Newsp. 26. Yellow Page Adv.

SOLEXA

IMAGEWORKS

250 Clearbrook Rd Ste 240
Elmsford, NY 10523-1315
Tel.: (914) 592-6100
Fax: (914) 592-6148
Toll Free: (800) 592-6666
E-mail: custserv@imageworkscorporation.com
Web Site: www.imageworkscorporation.com
Sales Range: $10-24.9 Million
Approx. Number Employees: 122
Year Founded: 1978
Business Description:
Film Processor; Digital & Traditional X-Ray Systems Mfr
S.I.C.: 3861
N.A.I.C.S.: 333315
Import Export
Advertising Expenditures: $287,600
Media: 2-4-6-7-10-26
Distr.: Natl.
Budget Set: July
Personnel:
R. Scott Jones *(Chm & CEO)*
Elise Nissen *(CFO, Principal Acctg Officer, Treas, Sec & Exec VP-Fin)*
Daniel Fields *(Exec VP-Sls-NewTom)*
Aida McKinney *(Exec VP-Admin)*
Marc Irving *(VP-Production)*
Marc Thacher *(VP-Sls)*
Mark Diffenderfer *(Dir-Dental Sls-Southeast Reg)*
Michael Ellison *(Dir-3D Imaging Ops)*
Jim Johnson *(Dir-Engrg)*
Herb Clay *(Mgr-Veterinary Products)*
Cathy Helwig *(Mgr-Customer Center)*
Pamela Pegus *(Mgr-Intl Sls)*
Kimberly Gillman *(Coord-Sr Mktg Comm)*
Brands & Products:
810 BASIC
810 PLUS
DENT-X
DENT-X PROIMAGE
DIGITAL VETTEK
DIGIVET-1417CR
ENDOS
EVA
EVA-VET
IMAGE-VET 70
MEDI-PRO/MP
MINI-MEDICAL
MINI-NDT
PANOURA ULTRA
SENS-A-VIEW

IMAGING DIAGNOSTIC SYSTEMS, INC.

5307 NW 35th Ter
Fort Lauderdale, FL 33309
Tel.: (954) 581-9800
Fax: (954) 581-0555
E-mail: info@imds.com
Web Site: www.imds.com
Approx. Sls.: $181,172
Approx. Number Employees: 19
Year Founded: 1993
Business Description:
Computed Tomography Laser Breast Imaging System Development & Testing Services
S.I.C.: 2835; 8071
N.A.I.C.S.: 325413; 621511
Advertising Expenditures: $9,871
Media: 10-11
Personnel:
Linda B. Grable *(Chm & CEO)*
Allan L. Schwartz *(CFO & Exec VP)*
Deborah O'Brien *(Sr VP)*
Brands & Products:
CTLM
LILA
SCANNING FOR LIFE

IMCLONE SYSTEMS INCORPORATED

(Sub. of Eli Lilly and Company)
180 Varick St
New York, NY 10014
Tel.: (212) 645-1405
Fax: (212) 645-2054
E-mail: media@imclone.com
Web Site: www.imclone.com
Approx. Rev.: $590,833,000
Approx. Number Employees: 1,128
Year Founded: 1984
Business Description:
Oncology Pharmaceuticals Developer & Marketer
S.I.C.: 2834
N.A.I.C.S.: 325412
Media: 10
Personnel:
Bernhard Ehmer *(Pres)*
Richard P. Crowley *(Sr VP)*
Greg Plowman *(Sr VP-Res)*
Tim Talomie *(VP-Plng-New Products & Mktg-Global)*
Brands & Products:
ERBITUX

IMMUCOR, INC.

(d/b/a ImmucorGamma)
3130 Gateway Dr PO Box 5265
Norcross, GA 30091-5625
Tel.: (770) 441-2051
Fax: (770) 441-3807
Toll Free: (800) 829-2553
E-mail: info@immucor.com
Web Site: www.immucor.com
Approx. Sls.: $329,073,000
Approx. Number Employees: 760
Year Founded: 1982
Business Description:
Developer, Manufacturer & Retailer of Blood Testing Equipment
S.I.C.: 2834
N.A.I.C.S.: 325412
Import Export
Advertising Expenditures: $500,000
Media: 10
Personnel:
Joseph E. Rosen *(Chm)*
William A. Hawkins *(CEO)*
Richard A. Flynt *(CFO, Principal Acctg Officer & Exec VP)*
Phil Moise *(Gen Counsel, Sec & Exec VP)*
Brands & Products:
CAPTURE
DIAS PLUS
GALILEO
GALILEO-ECHO
IMMUCORGAMMA
MULTIREADER PLUS
ROSYS
SEGMENTSAMPLER

IMMUNOGEN, INC.

830 Winter St
Waltham, MA 02451
Tel.: (781) 895-0600
Fax: (781) 895-0611
E-mail: info@immunogen.com
Web Site: www.immunogen.com
Approx. Rev.: $19,305,000
Approx. Number Employees: 211
Year Founded: 1981
Business Description:
Cancer Therapeutics
S.I.C.: 2834; 8733
N.A.I.C.S.: 325412; 541710
Media: 5
Personnel:
Stephen C. McCluski *(Chm)*
Daniel M. Junius *(Pres & CEO)*
Gregory D. Perry *(CFO & Sr VP)*
John M. Lambert *(Chief Scientific Officer & Exec VP-R&D)*
Craig Barrows *(Gen Counsel, Sec & VP)*
Walter A. Blattler *(Exec VP-Science & Tech)*
Thomas Chittenden *(Exec Dir-Res)*
Carol Hausner *(Exec Dir)*
Thomas Lauzon *(Exec Dir-Ops)*
Linda Buono *(Sr Dir-HR)*

IMMUNOMEDICS, INC.

300 American Rd
Morris Plains, NJ 07950-2460
Tel.: (973) 605-8200
Fax: (973) 605-8282
E-mail: info@immunomedics.com
Web Site: www.immunomedics.com
Approx. Rev.: $14,709,479
Approx. Number Employees: 121
Year Founded: 1982
Business Description:
Developer & Mfr of Cancer Diagnostics & Drug Therapies
S.I.C.: 2834; 8733
N.A.I.C.S.: 325412; 541720
Media: 2-4-7-10
Distr.: Natl.
Personnel:
David M. Goldenberg *(Chm, Chief Medical Officer & Chief Scientific Officer)*
Cynthia L. Sullivan *(Pres & CEO)*
Gerard G. Gorman *(CFO & Sr VP-Fin & Bus Dev)*
Brands & Products:
AFP-CIDE
AFP-SCAN
CEA-CIDE
IMMUNOMEDICS
IMMUSTRIP
LEUKOSCAN
LYMPHOCIDE
LYMPHOSCAN
MYELOMASCAN

IMMUNOSYN CORPORATION

10815 Rancho Bernardo Road, Suite 101
San Diego, CA 92127
Tel.: (858) 200-2320
Fax: (888) 851-7143
Toll Free: (888) 853-3663
Web Site: www.immunosyn.com
Approx. Number Employees: 1
Year Founded: 2006
Business Description:
Biopharmaceutical Drug Products Marketer, Distr & Sales
S.I.C.: 5122
N.A.I.C.S.: 424210
Personnel:
Stephen D. Ferrone *(CEO)*
Douglas A. McClain, Jr. *(CFO, Chief Acctg Officer & Sec)*
Advertising Agency:
The Blaine Group
8665 Wilshire Blvd Ste 301
Beverly Hills, CA 90211-2932
Tel.: (310) 360-1499
Fax: (310) 360-1498

IMPAX LABORATORIES, INC.

30831 Huntwood Ave
Hayward, CA 94544
Tel.: (510) 476-2000
Fax: (510) 471-3200
E-mail: info@impaxlabs.com
Web Site: www.impaxlabs.com
Approx. Rev.: $879,509,000
Approx. Number Employees: 918
Year Founded: 1995
Business Description:
Pharmaceuticals Mfr & Marketer
S.I.C.: 2834; 8733
N.A.I.C.S.: 325412; 541710
Media: 2-7-10
Personnel:
Robert L. Burr *(Chm)*
Larry Hsu *(Pres & CEO)*
Arthur A. Koch, Jr. *(CFO & Exec VP-Fin)*
Suneel Gupta *(Chief Scientific Officer)*
Michael Nestor *(Pres-Pharmaceuticals Div)*
Mark A. Schlossberg *(Gen Counsel & Sr VP)*
Mark Fitch *(Sr VP-Global Ops)*
Jeff Nornhold *(Sr VP-Global Quality Affairs)*
Brands & Products:
ADDERALL XR
AGRYLIN
ALLEGRA-D
AMRIX
ANDROID
ARALEN
BETAPACE
BRETHINE
CLARITIN-D
CLARITIN-D 12-HR
CLARITIN REDITAB
COLESTID
CONCERTA
CYMBALTA
DECLOMYCIN
DEPAKOTE ER
DETROL LA
DIDREX
DITROPAN XL
DIVIDABLE MULTIPLE-ACTION DELIVERY SYSTEM
DORYX
EFFEXOR XR
FLOMAX
FLORINEF
FLUMADINE
GLUCOPHAGE XR
IMPAX
LOFIBRA
LOPID
MESTINON
MINOCIN
MYSOLINE
NORFLEX
OPANA ER
OXYCONTIN
PARTICLE DISPERSION SYSTEMS

Key to Media (For complete agency information see *The Advertising Red Books-Agencies* edition):
1. Bus. Publs. 2. Cable T.V. 3. Catalogs & Directories. 4. Co-op Adv. 5. Consumer Mags. 6. D.M. to Bus. Estab.7. D.M. to Consumers
8. Daily Newsp. 9. Exhibits/Trade Shows 10. Foreign 11. Infomercial 12. Internet Adv.13. Multimedia 14. Network Radio
15. Network T.V. 16. Newsp. Distr. Mags. 17. Other 18. Outdoor (Posters, Transit) 19. Point of Purchase20. Premiums, Novelties
21. Product Samples 22. Special Events Mktg. 23. Spot Radio 24. Spot T.V. 25. Weekly Newsp. 26. Yellow Page Adv.

IMPAX Laboratories, Inc. — (Continued)

PERSANTINE
PHARMACEUTICAL STABILIZATION SYSTEM
PHENERGAN
PRILOSEC
PROAMATINE
REDITABS
RILUTEK
RIMADYL
SALAGEN
SINEMETCR
SOLODYN
TIMED MULTIPLE-ACTION DELIVERY SYSTEM
TRENTAL
ULTRAM ER
ULTRASE
URECHOLINE
URISPAS
WELLBUTRIN SR
WELLBUTRIN XL
XANAX XR
ZYBAN

Advertising Agency:
Draftfcb HealthCare
100 W 33rd St
New York, NY 10001
Tel.: (212) 672-2300
Fax: (212) 672-2301

IMS HEALTH, INC.

(Holding of TPG Capital, L.P.)
901 Main Ave Ste 612
Norwalk, CT 06851-1187
Tel.: (203) 845-5200
Fax: (203) 845-5299
E-mail: service@imshealth.com
Web Site: www.imshealth.com
Approx. Rev.: $2,189,745,000
Approx. Number Employees: 7,250
Year Founded: 1954
Business Description:
Information Solutions for the Pharmaceutical & Health Care Industries
S.I.C.: 7372; 7374; 8732; 8742
N.A.I.C.S.: 511210; 518210; 541611; 541910
Advertising Expenditures: $541,645
Media: 2-7-10
Personnel:
Ari Bousbib *(Chm & CEO)*
David R. Carlucci *(Pres & COO)*
Seyed Mortazavi *(Pres-North Europe & Africa)*
William J. Nelligan *(Pres-Americas)*
Tatsuyuki Saeki *(Pres-Japan)*
Adel Al-Saleh *(Sr VP-Global Pharma Solutions)*
Kevin C. Knightly *(Sr VP-Supply Mgmt)*
Kevin S. McKay *(Sr VP-Global Ops)*
Karla L. Packer *(Sr VP-HR)*
John R. Walsh *(Sr VP-Payer & Govt Solutions)*
Darcie Peck *(VP-Fin)*
Murray L. Aitken *(Exec Dir)*
Brands & Products:
ANALOGUE PLANNER
COMPETITIVE INTELLIGENCE
DATAVIEW
EARLY INSIGHT
EARLYVIEW
HOSPITAL SUPPLY INDEX
IMS
IMS ATU ADVANTAGE
IMS NPA
INTEGRATED PROMOTIONAL SERVICES
INTELLIGENCE APPLIED
KNOWLEDGE LINK
MARKET DYNAMICS
MARKET PROGNOSIS
NATIONAL DISEASE AND THERAPEUTIC INDEX
NATIONAL PRESCRIPTION AUDIT
NATIONAL SALES PERSPECTIVES
NEW PRODUCT SPECTRA
PERFORMANCE TRACKER
PLANTRAK
RETAIL METHOD OF PAYMENT
RETAIL METHOD OF PAYMENT REPORT
THERAPY FORECASTER

INCYTE CORPORATION

Rte 141 & Henry Clay Rd Bldg E336
Wilmington, DE 19880
Tel.: (302) 498-6700
Fax: (302) 425-2750
E-mail: investor@incyte.com
Web Site: www.incyte.com
E-Mail For Key Personnel:
Sales Director: sales@incyte.com
Approx. Rev.: $169,878,000
Approx. Number Employees: 247
Business Description:
Enzyme-Inhibiting Drug Mfr
S.I.C.: 8733; 2834
N.A.I.C.S.: 541710; 325412
Media: 7-21
Personnel:
Richard U. de Schutter *(Chm)*
Paul A. Friedman *(Pres & CEO)*
David C. Hastings *(CFO & Exec VP)*
Patricia S. Andrews *(Chief Comml Officer & Exec VP)*
Patricia Schreck *(Gen Counsel & Exec VP)*
Paula J. Swain *(Exec VP-HR)*
Brands & Products:
BIOKNOWLEDGE LIBRARY
THE DRIVE TO DISCOVER. THE EXPERIENCE TO DELIVER.
DRUGMATRIX
ERBITUX
HERCEPTIN
INCYTE
LIFESEQ
PROTEOME BIOKNOWLEDGE
REVERSET
TARCEVA
ZOOSEQ

INFA-LAB INC.

11 Wall St
Rockaway, NJ 07866-2903
Mailing Address:
PO Box 691
Rockaway, NJ 07866-2903
Tel.: (973) 625-2265
Fax: (973) 625-5641
Toll Free: (800) 247-7527
E-mail: infalab@worldnet.att.net
Web Site: www.infalab.com
Approx. Sls.: $1,000,000
Approx. Number Employees: 5
Business Description:
Orthodontic Mfr
S.I.C.: 8072
N.A.I.C.S.: 339116
Media: 4-13
Distr.: Natl.
Budget Set: Feb.
Personnel:
George C. Rose *(Pres)*
Brands & Products:
BRACE GARD
INFALAB
MAGIC TOUCH

INGENIX, INC.

(Branch of Ingenix, Inc.)
2525 Lake Park Blvd
Salt Lake City, UT 84120
Tel.: (801) 982-3000
Fax: (801) 982-4040
Toll Free: (800) INGENIX
E-mail: info@ingenix.com
Web Site: www.ingenix.com
Sales Range: $50-74.9 Million
Business Description:
Phase I-IV Clinical Trials; Data Management & Biostatistics; Regulatory Consulting & Marketing Services
S.I.C.: 8742; 7371
N.A.I.C.S.: 541611; 541511
Media: 2-7-10-13-22
Personnel:
Shelby Solomon *(Pres)*
Melissa Fonnesbeck *(Product Mgr)*
Brands & Products:
CPT
DISRUPTIONANALYSIS
EFACT
ENCODER PRO
GEOACCESS
GEONETWORKS
ICES
INGENIX
INGENIX SCRIPTS
LABRX
MDR
PARALLAX I
PHCS
POWERTRAK
PROCISE
PROCISE METRIX
PROCISE PRACTICE
PROCISE PREDICT
PRO_SEARCH
R&A ACTUARIAL TOOLBOX
R&A MCURE
Advertising Agency:
Organic, Inc.
555 Market St 4th Fl
San Francisco, CA 94105
Tel.: (415) 581-5300
Fax: (415) 581-5400

INOVA HEALTH SYSTEM

2990 Telestar Ct
Falls Church, VA 22042-1207
Tel.: (703) 289-2000
Fax: (703) 205-2161
Web Site: www.inova.org
Sales Range: $600-649.9 Million
Approx. Number Employees: 14,911
Year Founded: 1956
Business Description:
Healthcare Services
S.I.C.: 8062
N.A.I.C.S.: 622110
Import Export
Advertising Expenditures: $12,100,000
Media: 10-13-22
Personnel:
John Knox Singleton *(CEO)*
Richard Magenheimer *(CFO)*
Ryan Bosch *(Chief Medical Info Officer)*
Paige Moses *(Sr Dir-Foundation Svcs)*
Linda Robertson *(Sr Dir-Dev Svcs)*
Tim Cronen *(Dir-Annual Programs)*
Dayna Kuhar *(Dir-Dev)*
Mary Myers *(Dir-Leadership Giving)*
Kim Perry *(Dir-Dev)*
Maureen Zutz *(Dir-Leadership Giving)*
Brands & Products:
INOVA HEALTH SYSTEM
INOVA SPORTSPLEX

INSPIRE PHARMACEUTICALS, INC.

8081 Arco Corporate Dr Ste 400
Raleigh, NC 27617
Tel.: (919) 941-9777
Fax: (919) 941-9797
E-mail: info@inspirepharm.com
Web Site: www.inspirepharm.com
Approx. Rev.: $106,399,000
Approx. Number Employees: 240
Year Founded: 1993
Business Description:
Drugs for the Treatment of Respiratory & Ocular Diseases Developer & Researcher
S.I.C.: 2834; 8733
N.A.I.C.S.: 325412; 541710
Advertising Expenditures: $9,463,000
Media: 8
Personnel:
Kenneth B. Lee, Jr. *(Chm)*
Adrian Adams *(Pres & CEO)*
Thomas R. Staab II *(CFO & Exec VP)*
Robert M. Savel, II *(Chief Tech Officer & Sr VP)*
Stephen D. Celestini *(Sr VP & Chief Compliance Officer)*
Charles A. Johnson *(Chief Medical Officer, Exec VP-R & D)*
Joseph M. Spagnardi *(Gen Counsel, Sr VP & Sec)*
R. Kim Brazzell *(Exec VP-Medical & Scientific Affairs)*
Andrew I. Koven *(Chief Administrative & Legal Officer, Exec VP)*
Joseph K. Schachle *(Exec VP-Pulmonary Bus)*
Gerald W. St. Peter *(Sr VP-Ophthalmology Bus)*
Francisca K. Yanez *(VP-HR)*
Sean K. Blake *(Sr Dir-IT)*
Darrin P. Bryan *(Sr Dir-Ops & Strategic Markets)*
Robert J. Dempsey *(Sr Dir-Ophthalmic Medical Dev)*
Carole Evans *(Sr Dir-CMC Ops)*
Advertising Agency:
BMC Communications Group, LLC
740 Broadway 9th Fl
New York, NY 10003
Tel.: (212) 477-9007
Fax: (212) 460-9028

INTEGRA LIFESCIENCES HOLDINGS CORPORATION

311 Enterprise Dr
Plainsboro, NJ 08536
Tel.: (609) 275-0500
Fax: (609) 275-5363
Toll Free: (800) 654-2873
E-mail: custsvcnj@integra-ls.com
Web Site: www.integra-ls.com

Key to Media (For complete agency information see *The Advertising Red Books-Agencies* edition):
1. Bus. Publs. 2. Cable T.V. 3. Catalogs & Directories. 4. Co-op Adv. 5. Consumer Mags. 6. D.M. to Bus. Estab.7. D.M. to Consumers
8. Daily Newsp. 9. Exhibits/Trade Shows 10. Foreign 11. Infomercial 12. Internet Adv.13. Multimedia 14. Network Radio
15. Network T.V. 16. Newsp. Distr. Mags. 17. Other 18. Outdoor (Posters, Transit) 19. Point of Purchase20. Premiums, Novelties
21. Product Samples 22. Special Events Mktg. 23. Spot Radio 24. Spot T.V. 25. Weekly Newsp. 26. Yellow Page Adv.

Approx. Rev.: $732,068,000
Approx. Number Employees: 3,000
Year Founded: 1989
Business Description:
Holding Company; Medical Devices, Implants & Biomaterials Developer & Mfr
S.I.C.: 6719; 2836; 3826; 3841
N.A.I.C.S.: 551112; 325414; 334516; 339112
Media: 2-4-6-7-8-9-10-11-25
Personnel:
Richard E. Caruso *(Chm)*
Peter J. Arduini *(Pres & COO)*
Stuart M. Essig *(CEO)*
John B. Henneman, III *(CFO & Exec VP-Fin & Admin)*
Eric Fourcault *(Pres-EMEA Div)*
Debbie Leonetti *(Pres-Instruments, Latin America, AsiaPacific & Canada)*
Robert D. Paltridge *(Pres-Extremity Reconstruction)*
Richard D. Gorelick *(Gen Counsel-HR, Sec & Sr VP)*
John Bostjancic *(Sr VP-Fin & VP-Corp Dev)*
Judith E. O'Grady *(Sr VP-Regulatory, Quality & Clinical)*
James A. Oti *(Sr VP-Global Ops)*
Karen Mroz-Bremner *(Sr Mgr)*
Brands & Products:
ACCU-DISC
ACCU DRAIN
ACHILLON
ADVANCED EXTREMITY SOLUTIONS
ANTI-SIPHON DEVICES
ATLAS
BIOBLOCK
BIOMEND
BIOPATCH
BOLD
BUDDE
CALCANEA
CAMINO
COLLACOTE
COLLAPLUG
COLLATAPE
CONTOUR-FLEX
CUSA ASPIRATOR
CUSA DISSECTRON
CUSA EXCEL
CUSA NXT
CUSA ULTRASONICS
DERIFIL
DISSECTRON
DURAGEN
DURAGEN PLUS
ELEKTROTOM
ELEKTROTOM HITT
ENDURA
EQUI-FLOW
HAKIM
HALLU
HALLU-FIX
HELISTAT
HELITENE
HERMETIC
HEYER-SCHULTE
HINTEGRA
HORIZONTAL-VERTICAL
I.CO.S
INTEGRA
INTEGRA EPILEPSY
INTEGRA MOZAIK
INTEGRA NEUROSUPPLIES
JARIT
K-FIX
K2
KALIX
KATALYST
KGTI
KOMPRESSOR
KRANIOS
LICOX
LPV II
LUMBAR TRACK
MAYFIELD
MBA
MISHLER
MOBIUS
NEURAGEN
NEURAWRAP
NEUROVIEW
NEWDEAL
NO-REACT
NOVUS
NPH
OMNISHUNT
OSTEOGUIDES
OSTEOJECT
OSV II
PAIN PAK
PAINPAK
PUDENZ
R&B
RUGGLES
SAFEGUARD
SAMY
SELECTOR
SMART VALVE
SOLUSTAPLE
SPARTA
SPETZLER
SPIDER
SPIN
SUNDT
SUTURABLE DURAGEN
SYNPLUG
T.A.C.PIN
TENOGLIDE
TRAUMACATH
TRIAD
ULTRA PURE
ULTRAVS
UNI-CLIP
UNIVERSAL 2
VENTRIX
VERSUS GORE-TEX
VIPER

INTEGRA RADIONICS INC.
(Sub. of Integra LifeSciences Holdings Corporation)
22 Terry Ave
Burlington, MA 01803-2516
Tel.: (781) 272-1233
Fax: (781) 272-2428
E-mail: info@radionics.com
Web Site: www.radionics.com
Approx. Sls.: $29,900,000
Approx. Number Employees: 150
Year Founded: 1938
Business Description:
Surgical Devices Mfr
S.I.C.: 3845; 3841
N.A.I.C.S.: 334510; 339112
Import Export
Media: 10
Brands & Products:
CRW
CUSA
OMNISIGHT
XKNIFE

INTEGRAMED AMERICA, INC.
2 Manhattanville Rd
Purchase, NY 10577-2113
Tel.: (914) 253-8000
Fax: (914) 253-8008
E-mail: info@integramed.com
Web Site: www.integramed.com
E-Mail For Key Personnel:
Marketing Director: j.higham@integramed.com
Approx. Rev.: $243,169,000
Approx. Number Employees: 1,177
Year Founded: 1985
Business Description:
Management Support to Reproductive Healthcare Specialists
S.I.C.: 7389; 8093; 8099; 8741
N.A.I.C.S.: 561499; 561110; 621410; 621999
Advertising Expenditures: $5,852,000
Personnel:
Jay Higham *(Chm & CEO)*
Andrew Mintz *(Pres)*
Timothy P. Sheehan *(CFO & Sr VP)*
Scott Soifer *(Exec VP & Chief Admin Officer)*
Claude E White *(Gen Counsel, Sec & VP)*
Donald S. Wood *(Chief & Sr VP)*
Jeffrey C. Futterman *(VP-IT)*
Angela Gizinski *(VP-HR)*
Brands & Products:
ARTWORKS
THE FERTILITY COMPANY
FERTILITYDIRECT
FERTILITYMARKIT
INTEGRAMED

INTEGRATED BIOPHARMA, INC.
225 Long Ave
Hillside, NJ 07205
Tel.: (973) 926-0816
Fax: (973) 926-1735
E-mail: c.alseika@chemintl.com
Web Site: www.dynamex.com
Approx. Sls.: $37,019,000
Approx. Number Employees: 117
Business Description:
Biopharmaceutical & Nutraceutical Mfr
S.I.C.: 2834
N.A.I.C.S.: 325412
Import Export
Advertising Expenditures: $3,173,000
Media: 10-18-21
Personnel:
Dina L. Masi *(CFO)*
Christina Kay *(Exec VP)*
Riva Kay Sheppard *(Exec VP)*
Brands & Products:
AGROLABS SPIRULINA
DELIVERS NOW
DXNOW
DYNAMEX
NATURALLY ALOE
NATURALLY MANGOSTEEN
NATURALLY NONI
NATURALLY POMEGRANATE
PHYTOCHROME
PHYTOSEL
WHEN OVERNIGHT JUST ISN'T FAST ENOUGH

INTEGREAT, INC.
14988 N 78th Way Ste 100
Scottsdale, AZ 85260
Tel.: (480) 778-1000
Fax: (480) 609-5379
Toll Free: (800) 676-1360
Web Site: www.igreat.com
Approx. Sls.: $2,500,000
Approx. Number Employees: 35
Year Founded: 1998
Business Description:
Medical Record Information Applications & Services
S.I.C.: 7371; 8742
N.A.I.C.S.: 541511; 541611
Media: 2-7-10
Personnel:
David Koeller *(Pres)*
Tom Hall *(CFO)*
Dan Murray *(VP-Sls & Mktg)*
Brands & Products:
IC-CHART
IC-MYHEALTHRECORD
INTEGREAT

INTELLIGENT HEARING SYSTEMS CORP.
6860 SW 81 St
Miami, FL 33143-7708
Tel.: (305) 668-6102
Fax: (305) 668-6103
Toll Free: (800) 447-9783
E-mail: ihsys@ihsys.com
Web Site: www.ihsys.com
Sales Range: $25-49.9 Million
Approx. Number Employees: 22
Year Founded: 1983
Business Description:
Hearing Diagnostic Equipment Mfr
S.I.C.: 3841; 5734
N.A.I.C.S.: 339112; 443120
Export
Media: 2-10
Distr.: Natl.
Personnel:
Jerome Cohen *(Owner)*
Edward Miskiel *(Pres)*
Carlos Lopez *(CFO)*
Rafael Delgato *(Exec VP)*
Marra Lashbrook *(VP-Mktg)*
Octavio Garrastacho *(Product Mgr)*
Brands & Products:
CHATS
INTELLIGENT HEARING SYSTEMS
INTELLIGENT VRA
IVRA
LIPP
MANUAL VRA
PET SCREENER
SMART AUDIOMETER
SMART SCREENER
SMARTDPOAE
SMARTEP
SMARTEP-ASSR
SMARTTROAE
VIDEO VRA

INTERLEUKIN GENETICS, INC.
135 Beaver St
Waltham, MA 02452
Tel.: (781) 398-0700
Fax: (781) 398-0720
Web Site: www.ilgenetics.com
Approx. Rev.: $1,997,173
Approx. Number Employees: 22
Business Description:
Genetic & Diagnostic Test Development Services
S.I.C.: 2835; 2834
N.A.I.C.S.: 325413; 325412
Advertising Expenditures: $19,000
Media: 22

Key to Media (For complete agency information see *The Advertising Red Books-Agencies* edition):
1. Bus. Publs. 2. Cable T.V. 3. Catalogs & Directories. 4. Co-op Adv. 5. Consumer Mags. 6. D.M. to Bus. Estab.7. D.M. to Consumers 8. Daily Newsp. 9. Exhibits/Trade Shows 10. Foreign 11. Infomercial 12. Internet Adv.13. Multimedia 14. Network Radio 15. Network T.V. 16. Newsp. Distr. Mags. 17. Other 18. Outdoor (Posters, Transit) 19. Point of Purchase20. Premiums, Novelties 21. Product Samples 22. Special Events Mktg. 23. Spot Radio 24. Spot T.V. 25. Weekly Newsp. 26. Yellow Page Adv.

Interleukin Genetics, Inc. — (Continued)

Personnel:
James M. Weaver *(Chm)*
Kenneth S. Kornman *(Pres & Chief Scientific Officer)*
Lewis H. Bender *(CEO)*
Eliot M. Lurier *(CFO)*
Todd Anthony Walker *(VP-Mktg)*
Brands & Products:
GENSONA
PST
Advertising Agency:
LaVoie Strategic Communications Group, Inc.
12 Derby Sq S1
Salem, MA 01970
Tel.: (978) 745-4200
Fax: (978) 745-4242

INTERMOUNTAIN HEALTH CARE INC.

36 S State St
Salt Lake City, UT 84111
Tel.: (801) 442-2000
Tel.: (801) 442-3325 (HR)
Fax: (801) 442-2857
E-mail: webmaster@ihc.com
Web Site: www.ihc.com
Approx. Number Employees: 30,000
Year Founded: 1975
Business Description:
Health Care Facilities; Health Care Plans
S.I.C.: 8062
N.A.I.C.S.: 622110
Media: 2-3-6-9-10-13-14-15-18-20-23-24-25
Distr.: Reg.
Personnel:
Kem C. Gardner *(Chm)*
Kent H. Murdock *(Vice Chm, Pres & CEO)*
Charles W. Sorenson *(Pres & CEO)*
Elizabeth Hammond *(Dir-Res)*
Janet Frank *(Mgr-Media)*
Advertising Agency:
Goodman Media International, Inc.
750 7th Ave 28th Fl
New York, NY 10016
Tel.: (212) 576-2700
Fax: (212) 576-2701

INTERMOUNTAIN HOSPITAL

(Sub. of Psychiatric Solutions, Inc.)
303 N Allumbaugh
Boise, ID 83704
Tel.: (208) 377-8400
Fax: (208) 377-8523
Toll Free: (800) 321-5984
Web Site:
www.intermountainhospital.com
Sales Range: $50-74.9 Million
Approx. Number Employees: 250
Business Description:
Psychiatric & Substance Abuse Hospital
S.I.C.: 8063
N.A.I.C.S.: 622210
Personnel:
Brent J. Bryson *(CEO)*
Jonathan MacDonald *(CFO)*
Chuck Christiansen *(Dir-Bus Dev)*
Lisa Enger *(Dir-Assessment & Referral)*
Jennifer Hunkovic *(Dir-Risk Mgmt Performance Improvement)*
Nancy Nelson *(Dir-HR)*
Charles Novak *(Dir-Medical)*
Kathy Windom *(Dir-Social Svcs)*
Advertising Agency:
CLM Marketing & Advertising
588 W Idaho St
Boise, ID 83702-5928
Tel.: (208) 342-2525
Fax: (208) 384-1906

INTERMUNE, INC.

3280 Bayshore Blvd
Brisbane, CA 94005
Tel.: (415) 466-2200
Fax: (415) 466-2300
E-mail: ir@intermune.com
Web Site: www.intermune.com
Approx. Rev.: $259,291,000
Approx. Number Employees: 105
Year Founded: 1998
Business Description:
Products for the Treatment of Serious Pulmonary, Infectious & Hepatic Diseases Developer
S.I.C.: 2834
N.A.I.C.S.: 325412
Personnel:
Daniel G. Welch *(CEO)*
John C. Hodgman *(CFO & Sr VP)*
Howard A. Simon *(Sr VP-HR/Corp Svcs, Chief Compliance Officer & Assoc Gen Counsel)*
Steven B. Porter *(Chief Medical Officer & Sr VP-Clinical Affairs)*
Bruce W. Tomlinson *(VP, Corp Controller & Chief Acctg Officer)*
Robin J. Steele *(Gen Counsel, Sec & Sr VP)*
Giacomo Nepi *(Mng Dir-Europe & Sr VP)*
Markus Leyck Dieken *(Sr VP & Gen Mgr-Germany)*
Marianne T. Armstrong *(Chief Regulatory & Drug Safety Officer, Sr VP)*
Williamson Z. Bradford *(Sr VP-Clinical Science & Biometrics)*
Frank T. Weber *(Sr VP)*
Erik Harris *(VP-Mktg)*
Manuela Maronati *(VP-Sls & Mktg-Europe)*
Terri Shoemaker *(VP-Sls)*
Brands & Products:
ACTIMMUNE
INFERGEN
INTERMUNE
Advertising Agency:
nitrogen
One S Broad St Fl 11
Philadelphia, PA 19107
Tel.: (215) 625-0111
Fax: (215) 625-9037

INTERPORE CROSS INTERNATIONAL, LLC

(Sub. of Biomet, Inc.)
181 Technology Dr
Irvine, CA 92618
Tel.: (949) 453-3200
Fax: (949) 453-3225
E-mail: biomet.interporecross@biomet.com
Web Site: www.interpore.com
Sales Range: $50-74.9 Million
Approx. Number Employees: 213
Year Founded: 1975
Business Description:
Synthetic Bone & Tissue Products & Spinal Implant Devices Designer, Mfr & Marketer
S.I.C.: 3845; 3843
N.A.I.C.S.: 334510; 339114
Export
Advertising Expenditures: $501,000
Personnel:
Philip A. Mellinger *(Principal Exec Officer)*
Brands & Products:
AGF
ALTIUS
BONEPLAST
C-TEK
CDO
GEO STRUCTURE
INTERGRO
LP2
PRO OSTEON
PRO OSTEON 500
SYNERGY
TPS-C
TPS-TL

INTUITIVE SURGICAL, INC.

1266 Kifer Rd
Sunnyvale, CA 94086
Tel.: (408) 523-2100
Fax: (408) 523-1390
E-mail: webmaster@intusurg.com
Web Site: www.intuitivesurgical.com
Approx. Rev.: $1,413,000,000
Approx. Number Employees: 1,660
Year Founded: 1995
Business Description:
Robotic Surgical Systems Mfr
S.I.C.: 3841; 3842
N.A.I.C.S.: 339112; 339113
Advertising Expenditures: $1,400,000
Media: 10
Personnel:
Lonnie M. Smith *(Chm)*
Gary S. Guthart *(Pres & CEO)*
Marshall L. Mohr *(CFO & Sr VP)*
Mark J. Meltzer *(Gen Counsel & Sr VP)*
Jerome J. McNamara *(Exec VP-Worldwide Sls & Mktg)*
Sal Brogna *(Sr VP-Engrg)*
Augusto V. Castello *(Sr VP-Product Ops)*
Colin Morales *(Sr VP-Customer Support Grp)*
Aleks Cukic *(VP-Strategy)*
Benjamin B. Gong *(VP-Fin)*
Gene Nagel *(VP-Trng & Dev)*
Frank D. Nguyen *(VP-Intellectual Property)*
William C. Nowlin *(VP-Product Quality)*
Dave Rosa *(VP-Product Dev)*
Brands & Products:
AESOP
ALPHA
BEYOND THE LIMITS OF THE HUMAN HAND
DA VINCI
ENDOWRIST
HERMES
INSITE
INTUITIVE
INTUITIVE SURGICAL
MICROWRIST
NAVIGATOR
PRECISE
PROGRASP
SNAP-FIT
SOCRATES
SOLO SURGERY
SURGICAL IMMERSION
ZEUS

INVACARE CANADA LP

(Holding of Invacare Corporation)
570 Matheson Blvd E Unit # 8
Mississauga, ON L4Z 4G4, Canada
Tel.: (905) 890-8300
Fax: (905) 890-5244
Toll Free: (800) 668-5324
Web Site: www.invacare.ca
Sales Range: $10-24.9 Million
Approx. Number Employees: 80
Year Founded: 1992
Business Description:
Home Medical Products
S.I.C.: 8082
N.A.I.C.S.: 621610
Media: 4-10
Personnel:
A. Malachi Mixon, III *(Chm & CEO)*
Gerald B. Blouch *(Pres & COO)*
Gregory C. Thompson *(CFO & Sr VP)*
Dale LaPorte *(Gen Counsel & Sr VP-Bus Dev)*
Joseph B. Richey, II *(Sr VP-Electronic & Design Engrg)*
Louis F. J. Slangen *(Sr VP)*
Joe Usaj *(Sr VP)*
Ben Morelli *(Gen Mgr)*
Sheila Clarke *(Mgr-Assoc Mktg)*

INVACARE CORPORATION

1 Invacare Way
Elyria, OH 44035-4190
Mailing Address:
PO Box 4028
Elyria, OH 44036-2028
Tel.: (440) 329-6000
Fax: (440) 329-6568
Toll Free: (800) 333-6900
E-mail: info@invacare.com
Web Site: www.invacare.com
Approx. Sls.: $1,722,081,000
Approx. Number Employees: 6,300
Year Founded: 1979
Business Description:
Mfr. & Distr of Non-Acute Health Care Products for Home Health Care, Retail & Extended Care Markets
S.I.C.: 3841; 2514; 2676; 3842
N.A.I.C.S.: 339112; 322291; 337124; 339113
Import Export
Advertising Expenditures: $20,119,000
Media: 2-4-5-6-7-8-10-11-15-16-19-20-22-26
Distr.: Intl.; Natl.
Personnel:
A. Malachi Mixon, III *(Chm)*
Gerald B. Blouch *(Pres & CEO)*
Robert K. Gudbranson *(CFO & Sr VP)*
Dave Mewes *(CIO)*
Joseph B. Richey, II *(Pres-Invacare Tech & Sr VP-Electronics & Design Engrg)*
Anthony C. LaPlaca *(Gen Counsel & Sr VP)*
Louis F. J. Slangen *(Chief Product Officer & Sr VP-Corp Mktg)*
Patricia A. Stumpp *(Sr VP-HR)*
Lara Mahoney *(Dir-Investor Rels & Corp Comm)*

Key to Media (For complete agency information see *The Advertising Red Books-Agencies* edition):
1. Bus. Publs. 2. Cable T.V. 3. Catalogs & Directories. 4. Co-op Adv. 5. Consumer Mags. 6. D.M. to Bus. Estab.7. D.M. to Consumers 8. Daily Newsp. 9. Exhibits/Trade Shows 10. Foreign 11. Infomercial 12. Internet Adv.13. Multimedia 14. Network Radio 15. Network T.V. 16. Newsp. Distr. Mags. 17. Other 18. Outdoor (Posters, Transit) 19. Point of Purchase20. Premiums, Novelties 21. Product Samples 22. Special Events Mktg. 23. Spot Radio 24. Spot T.V. 25. Weekly Newsp. 26. Yellow Page Adv.

Mary Caserta *(Mgr-Fin Svcs)*
Steve Hubeny *(Mgr-Fin Svcs)*
Sheri Thomas *(Coord-Adv)*

Brands & Products:
2GR
2GT
2GTR
3500S
3G ARROW RWD
3G TORQUE SP RWD
5 STAR SERVICE PLAN DESIGN
A-T
A4
ABSOLUTE
ADVENTURE
THE AFTERMARKET GROUP
AIRFLO
ALLEGRO
ANYTHING ELSE IS A COMPROMISE
APOLLO
ARROW
ARROW FWD
A'SURE
ATLAS
AT'M
AURORA
AX3
BARIATRIC SOLUTIONS DESIGN
BLEND2
BLUE MEDALLION
BLUE-RELEASE
BREATHE IN THE FREEDOM
BRUT
BUILDING RESPIRATORY USE TOGETHER
BUZZ HMV
CAREGUARD
CHECK O 2 PLUS
COMET
COMFORT COMES STANDARD
COMFORT FIRST
COMFORT-MATE
COMFORT SOLUTIONS
COMFORTSEAL
COMPASS
CONNECT O 2
CONTOURA
CONTOURU
CONTRACTURE PLATFORM
COURT-SIDE GLIDE DESIGN
CROSSFIRE
CRUISER
DEBONAIR
DPJ
DUALFLEX
EDLP
EFFORTLESS E XHALATION
ELAN SERIES
ELEMENT
ELEMENT C1
ELEMENT R1
ELIMINATOR
ELITE
ENVOY
ENVOY JR.
ESSENTIAL
EX
EXCEL
EXCELERATOR
FIRST ALERT
FLOVAIR
FLYER
FOR PEOPLE WHO CAN SIT WHEREVER THEY WANT
FORCE
FORMULA
FROM THE WORLD LEADER IN HOME CARE
FRONTIER LITE
G-TRAC
GB
GET-U-UP
GT
HEXAFLEX
HOME DELIVERY PLUS
HOMEFILL
I-CLASS
I-FIT
IMPOSSIBLE STOPS HERE
INFINITY
INTOUCH ZONE
INVACARE
INVACARE VIRTUAL PLUS
INVACARE VIRTUAL SERVICE
INVISIBLE SUPER LOW
IPARTNER SOLUTIONS
IVC
IVC 9000 XT
IVC TRACER IV
IVC TRACER SX5
JYMNI
K2000
K3000
K4000
K7000
KEEPING UP WITH YOU
LSS LIGHTWEIGHT SHOCK STOPPER
LYNX
LYNX SX-3
M50
M51
M61
M71
M91
M94
MAP-O-GRAM
MARINER
MICROAIR
MK 5
MK6I
MKIV
MOBIL-MIST
MOBILAID
MOBILAIRE
MPJ
MVP
MVP JR.
MX-4
NUTRON
NX
ONE STOP SHOPPING PLUS
ONE2ONE
ORBIT
OXYLOCK
P7E
P9000
PANTHER LX-4
PASSPORT
PATRIOT
PAXBAC
PERSONAL BACK 10
PERSONAL BACK 10 PLUS
PERSONAL SEAT VF
PHOENIX
PINDOT
PLATINUM
POLARIS
POSEIDON
POWER 9000
POWER LIFT
PRECISERX
PRO-SA
PRO-T
PRONTO
PROPEL
PROSPIN
QUICK CODE
QUICK SET
R2
R32
R50
R51
RANGER II
RANGER X
REHAB ASAP
REHAB JUST GOT EASIER
REHAB NOW
REHAB ONE
RELIANT
RELIANT 600
RELIANT PLUS
ROLLITE
ROLLS
SAFETY YOU CAN TRUST
SANDSTORM
SCOUT
SEATMAKER
SENSO 2
SERVICE6
SIEVE-GARD
SILHOUETTE
SMART ADJUSTABILITY
SMARTLEG
SOF-WAIRE
SOFTX
SOFTXHALE
SOLACE
SOLARA
SPARTAN
SPJ
SPORTRUNNER
SPREE GT
SPRINT
SPT
SPYDER
STABILITE
STARDUST
STARGAZER
STINGRAY
STORM SERIES
STRATOS
SUPER-PRO
SUPER PRO-T
SUREGLIDE
SURESTEP
T-3
T-4
TAG
TARGIT
TARSYS
TCD
TDX
TERMINATOR
THINAIR
THUMB SAVER
TIGER
TITAN
TOP END
TOPAZ
TORGUE
TORQUE
TOTAL EASE
TOTAL ONE STOP SHOPPING
TRACER
TRANSFORMER
TRUETRACK
TSS
TURN-Q
TWILIGHT
ULTI-MATE
UNIBACK
VENTURE
VERANDA
VISCOFOAM
WALKLITE
WEB OX
X4
XPO2
XTERRA
XTRA
YES, YOU CAN.
ZIPCHARGE

Advertising Agency:
Torch Group
30675 Solon Rd Ste 102
Cleveland, OH 44139-2942
Tel.: (440) 519-1822
Fax: (440) 519-1823

INVACARE SUPPLY GROUP, INC.

(Sub. of Invacare Corporation)
9 Industrial Rd
Milford, MA 01757
Tel.: (508) 634-5100
Fax: (508) 482-0201
Toll Free: (800) 225-4792
E-mail: gbosco@invacare.com
Web Site:
www.invacaresupplygroup.com
Sales Range: $50-74.9 Million
Approx. Number Employees: 135
Business Description:
Medical Supplies
S.I.C.: 5047
N.A.I.C.S.: 423450
Media: 4-7-10
Personnel:
Greg Bosco *(Dir-Mdsg & Mktg)*

INVERNESS MEDICAL PROFESSIONAL DIAGNOSTICS

(Sub. of ALERE INC.)
(d/b/a Inverness Medical Professional Diagnostics)
2 Research Way
Princeton, NJ 08540
Tel.: (609) 627-8000
Fax: (609) 627-8013
Toll Free: (800) 257-9525
Telex: 510-685-4443
Web Site:
www.invernessmedicalpd.com
Sales Range: $50-74.9 Million
Approx. Number Employees: 250
Business Description:
Pregnancy Tests & Diagnostic Assays
Mfr For Numerous Auto-Immune, Bacterial & Viral Diseases
S.I.C.: 3826
N.A.I.C.S.: 334516
Export
Advertising Expenditures: $500,000
Media: 2-4-7-10
Distr.: Natl.

Brands & Products:
ANA ELISA
ANALYST
BACTURCULT
BETA-SLIDE
BIO-TEK ELX
CLEARVIEW
CLEARVIEW C. DIFF A
CLEARVIEW HCG
CRYPTO-LA

Inverness Medical Professional Diagnostics — (Continued)

IMMUNEX CRP
ISOSTAT
LABOTECH
MACRA
MONO-DIFF
MONO TEST
MULTI-LYTE
PATHFINDER
PERSONALLAB
PREVUE
RHEUMATEX
RHEUMATON
ROTATEST
RUBELLA-PLUS
SOFTWARE
STATUS
STREPTONASE-B
STREPTOZYME
TPM-TEST
UCG BETA SLIDE
UCG SLIDE TEST
VIROGEN
WAMPOLE COLORCARD MONO
WAMPOLE IMPACT RPR
WAMPOLE PREVUE
WELLPREP
WELLWASH

IOWA HEALTH SYSTEM, INC.

1200 Pleasant St
Des Moines, IA 50309-1406
Tel.: (515) 241-6212
Fax: (515) 241-5059
E-mail: ihspublicaffairs@ihs.org
Web Site: www.ihs.org
Approx. Number Employees: 18,375
Year Founded: 1993
Business Description:
Health Care Services
S.I.C.: 8049
N.A.I.C.S.: 621399
Import Export
Media: 2-9-23-24-25
Personnel:
James E. Hoffman, III *(Chm)*
Bill Leaver *(Pres & CEO)*
Duncan Gallagher *(CFO & COO)*
Denny Drake *(Gen Counsel, VP & Compliance Officer)*
Cheri Bustos *(VP-PR & Comm)*
Advertising Agency:
ME&V
6711 Chancellor Dr
Cedar Falls, IA 50613-6969
Tel.: (319) 268-9151
Fax: (319) 268-0124
Toll Free: (877) WEBEASY

IPC THE HOSPITALIST COMPANY, INC.

4605 Lankershim Blvd Ste 617
North Hollywood, CA 91602
Tel.: (818) 766-3502
Fax: (818) 766-3999
Toll Free: (888) 447-2362
E-mail: information@ipcm.com
Web Site: www.hospitalist.com
Approx. Rev.: $363,402,000
Approx. Number Employees: 1,792
Year Founded: 1995
Business Description:
Hospital Management Services
S.I.C.: 9651; 8062; 8742
N.A.I.C.S.: 926150; 541611; 622110
Media: 2-13-22
Personnel:
Adam D. Singer *(Chm, CEO & Chief Medical Officer)*
R. Jeffrey Taylor *(Pres & COO)*
Devra G. Shapiro *(CFO)*
Kerry E. Weiner *(Chief Clinical Officer)*
Richard G. Russell *(Chief Dev Off & Exec VP)*
Sanford Peterson *(Exec Dir-Kansas City Reg)*
Isela Sotolongo *(Exec Dir)*
Advertising Agency:
The Ruth Group
141 5th Ave 5th Fl
New York, NY 10010
Tel.: (646) 536-7000

IRIS INTERNATIONAL, INC.

9158 Eton Ave
Chatsworth, CA 91311
Tel.: (818) 709-1244
Fax: (818) 700-9661
Toll Free: (800) PRO-IRIS
E-mail: irisinc@proiris.com
Web Site: www.proiris.com
Approx. Rev.: $107,672,000
Approx. Number Employees: 377
Year Founded: 1979
Business Description:
In Vitro Diagnostic Equipment & Imaging Automation Designer, Developer, Mfr & Marketer
S.I.C.: 3826; 2834; 3841
N.A.I.C.S.: 334516; 325412; 339112
Advertising Expenditures: $360,000
Media: 2-7-10-11-13
Personnel:
Cesar M. Garcia *(Chm)*
Amin I. Khalifa *(CFO & VP-Fin)*
Philip J. Ginsburg *(CMO-Iris Intl Inc)*
Thomas E. Warekois *(Pres-Iris Diagnostics Bus Unit & Corp VP)*
Vance R. White *(Pres-CLIA Laboratory Div & Corp VP)*
Veronica O. Tarrant *(VP-Fin & Controller)*
Richard A. O'Leary *(Corp VP-HR & Admin)*
Brands & Products:
900UDX
939UDX
AUCTION JET
AUCTION MAX
AUTION JET AJ-4270
AUTION MAX AX-4280
AUTO-PARTICLE RECOGNITION
CENSLIDE
CRITSPIN
CYTOFUGE
DIFFSPIN
ICHEM
IQ
IQ200
IRICELL
IRIS
LIPOCLEAR
MODEL 500
NADIA
PROSVUE
SPRINT
STATSAMPLER
STATSPIN
THERMOBRITE
UF-100
VELOCITY
THE YELLOW IRIS

ISIS PHARMACEUTICALS, INC.

1896 Rutherford Rd
Carlsbad, CA 92008-7326
Tel.: (760) 931-9200
Fax: (760) 603-2700
Fax: (760) 931-9639
E-mail: info@isisph.com
Web Site: www.isispharm.com
Approx. Rev.: $108,473,000
Approx. Number Employees: 370
Year Founded: 1989
Business Description:
Biopharmaceutical Drug Developer
S.I.C.: 2834; 8733
N.A.I.C.S.: 325412; 541710
Media: 10
Personnel:
Stanley T. Crooke *(Chm & CEO)*
B. Lynne Parshall *(CFO & COO)*
Martin Bedigian *(VP & Chief Medical Officer)*
C. Frank Bennett *(Sr VP-Res)*
Kristina Lemonidis *(Dir-IR)*
Brands & Products:
ISIS
TAXOTERE
VITRAVENE

ISORAY, INC.

350 Hills St Ste 106
Richland, WA 99354
Tel.: (509) 375-1202
Toll Free: (877) 447-6729
E-mail: info@isoray.com
Web Site: www.isoray.com
Approx. Sls.: $5,286,084
Approx. Number Employees: 36
Business Description:
Therapeutic Medical Isotope & Device Mfr
S.I.C.: 3841; 2834
N.A.I.C.S.: 339112; 325412
Advertising Expenditures: $376,319
Personnel:
Dwight Babcock *(Chm & CEO)*
Robert R. Kauffman *(Vice Chm)*
Donald R. Segna *(VP-Strategic Plng)*
Eric Knipfer *(Dir-Natl Sls)*
Brands & Products:
ISORAY MEDICAL

ISTA PHARMACEUTICALS, INC.

50 Technology Dr
Irvine, CA 92618-2315
Tel.: (949) 788-6000
Fax: (949) 788-6010
E-mail: info@istavision.com
Web Site: www.istavision.com
Approx. Rev.: $156,525,000
Approx. Number Employees: 326
Year Founded: 1992
Business Description:
Drug Products for Eye Diseases & Conditions Developer & Marketer
S.I.C.: 5122; 2834
N.A.I.C.S.: 424210; 325412
Media: 10
Personnel:
Richard C. Williams *(Chm)*
Vicente Anido, Jr. *(Pres & CEO)*
Lauren Silvernail *(CFO & VP-Corp Dev)*
Glenn E. Davis *(Chief Compliance Officer & VP-Legal)*
Brian G. Drazbav *(Chief Acctg Officer & VP-Fin)*
Chris Dax *(VP-Mktg)*
Kathleen Mcginley *(VP-HR & Corp Svcs)*
Thomas Mitro *(VP-Sls & Mktg)*
Brands & Products:
BEPREVE
BROMDAY
CAPROGEL
ISTA
ISTA PHARMACEUTICALS
ISTALOL
REMURA
T-PRED
VITRASE
XIBROM
XIBROM QD

JANSSEN PHARMACEUTICA PRODUCTS, L.P.

(Sub. of Johnson & Johnson)
1125 Trenton Harbourton Rd
Titusville, NJ 08560
Tel.: (609) 730-2000
Fax: (609) 730-2323
E-mail: info@janssen.com
Web Site: www.janssen.com
Sales Range: $200-249.9 Million
Approx. Number Employees: 1,600
Year Founded: 1953
Business Description:
Pharmaceutical Preparations Mfr
S.I.C.: 2833; 2834
N.A.I.C.S.: 325411; 325412
Media: 2-4-6-7-9
Distr.: Natl.
Brands & Products:
ACIPHEX
DURAGESIC
NIZORAL
PROPULSID
RISPERDAL
RISPERDAL CONSTA
SPORANOX

JAZZ PHARMACEUTICALS, INC.

3180 Porter Dr
Palo Alto, CA 94304
Tel.: (650) 496-3777
Fax: (650) 496-3781
E-mail: contact@jazzpharmaceuticals.com
Web Site:
www.jazzpharmaceuticals.com
Approx. Rev.: $173,781,000
Approx. Number Employees: 242
Year Founded: 2003
Business Description:
Neurological & Psychiatric Pharmaceutical Products Developer
S.I.C.: 2834
N.A.I.C.S.: 325412
Advertising Expenditures: $1,600,000
Personnel:
Bruce C. Cozadd *(Chm & CEO)*
Kathryn E. Falberg *(CFO & Sr VP)*
James L.T. Wissel *(Chief Regulatory/Compliance Officer & Sr VP)*
Jeffrey Tobias *(Chief Medical Officer & Sr VP-R & D)*
Karen J. Wilson *(Chief Acctg Officer)*
Carol A. Gamble *(Gen Counsel, Sec & Sr VP)*
Russell J. Cox *(Sr VP-Sls & Mktg)*
Michael Desjardin *(Sr VP-Product Dev)*

Key to Media (For complete agency information see *The Advertising Red Books-Agencies* edition):
1. Bus. Publs. 2. Cable T.V. 3. Catalogs & Directories. 4. Co-op Adv. 5. Consumer Mags. 6. D.M. to Bus. Estab.7. D.M. to Consumers 8. Daily Newsp. 9. Exhibits/Trade Shows 10. Foreign 11. Infomercial 12. Internet Adv.13. Multimedia 14. Network Radio 15. Network T.V. 16. Newsp. Distr. Mags. 17. Other 18. Outdoor (Posters, Transit) 19. Point of Purchase20. Premiums, Novelties 21. Product Samples 22. Special Events Mktg. 23. Spot Radio 24. Spot T.V. 25. Weekly Newsp. 26. Yellow Page Adv.

Mark G. Eller *(Sr VP-Res & Clinical Dev)*
Edwin W. Luker *(VP-Sls)*
Heather Mcgaughey *(VP-HR)*

Brands & Products:
ANTIZOL
CT STEPS
EXPERIENCE A NEW RELEASE
JAZZ PHARMACEUTICALS
JZP
LUVOX CR
SODAS
WAKE UPTO THE DIFFERENCE
XYREM
XYREM SUCESS PROGRAM

THE JEAN COUTU GROUP (PJC) INC.

530 Beriault St
Longueuil, QC J4G 1S8, Canada
Tel.: (450) 646-9760
Fax: (450) 646-5649
E-mail: info@jeancoutu.com
Web Site: www.jeancoutu.com
Approx. Rev.: $2,392,902,534
Approx. Number Employees: 1,044
Year Founded: 1969
Business Description:
Pharmaceutical, Health & Beauty Cosmetics & Food Retailer
S.I.C.: 5912; 5499
N.A.I.C.S.: 446110; 446191
Advertising Expenditures: $6,000,000
Media: 4-6-9-15-20-21-22-25
Personnel:
Jean Coutu *(Chm)*
Yvon Martineau *(Vice Chm)*
Francois J. Coutu *(Pres & CEO)*
Michel Boucher *(CIO & VP)*
Andre Belzile *(Exec VP-Fin & Corp Affairs)*
Alain Lafortune *(Exec VP-Pur & Mktg)*
Richard Mayrand *(Exec VP-Pharmacy & Govt Affairs)*
Normand Messier *(Exec VP-Network Ops)*
Helene Bisson *(VP-Comm)*
Denis Courcy *(VP-HR)*
Guy Franche *(VP-Control & Treasury)*
Jean H. Gagnon *(VP-Legal Affairs)*
Jean-Michel Coutu *(Asst VP-Pharmacy Sys)*
Guy Dubuc *(Asst VP-Retail Fin)*
Marc Dumas *(Asst VP-Construction)*
Serge Ouellet *(Asst VP-Pur & Mktg Dept)*
Nathalie Plante *(Asst VP-Pharmacy)*
Vronique Duval *(Asst Sec)*

Brands & Products:
AVENE
BROOKS
DERMABLEND
ECKERD
ECONOMIE
FIDELITY
HARVARD SQUARE
JEAN COUTU
PERSONNELLE
PERSONNELLE SHREK
PJC
VICHY LABORATORIES

Advertising Agency:
Draftfcb
1080 Cote du Beaver Hall Ste 1100
Montreal, QC H2Z 1S8, Canada
Tel.: (514) 938-4141
Fax: (514) 938-2022

JENNY CRAIG, INC.

(Sub. of Nestle Healthcare Nutrition)
5770 Fleet St
Carlsbad, CA 92008
Tel.: (760) 696-4000
Fax: (760) 696-4506
Toll Free: (800) 597-JENNY
Web Site: www.jennycraig.com
Sales Range: $350-399.9 Million
Approx. Number Employees: 3,420
Year Founded: 1983
Business Description:
Weight Management Centers
S.I.C.: 5499; 5149
N.A.I.C.S.: 446191; 424490
Advertising Expenditures: $25,000,000
Media: 1-3-6-9-11-22-23-24-25
Distr.: Natl.
Budget Set: Quarterly
Personnel:
Patti Larchet *(CEO)*
Jim Kelly *(CFO & VP)*
Shoukry Tiab *(CIO & VP-Info Sys)*
Chris Guglielmo *(VP-HR & Organizational Dev)*
Scott Parker *(VP-Mktg)*

Brands & Products:
JENNY CRAIG
JENNY CRAIG DIRECT
ULTIMATE CHOICE

Advertising Agencies:
Lippe Taylor
215 Park Ave S 16th Fl
New York, NY 10003
Tel.: (212) 598-4400
Fax: (212) 598-0620
Pub Rels

Zenith Media
2049 Century Park E Ste 1300
Los Angeles, CA 90067
Tel.: (310) 551-3500
Fax: (310) 551-4119
(Media Planning & Buying)

JEUNIQUE INTERNATIONAL INC.

19501 E Walnut Dr S
City of Industry, CA 91748
Tel.: (909) 598-8598
Fax: (909) 594-8961
E-mail: support@jeunique.com
Web Site: www.jeunique.com
Approx. Sls.: $23,800,000
Approx. Number Employees: 75
Year Founded: 1959
Business Description:
Health & Beauty Products
S.I.C.: 2833
N.A.I.C.S.: 325411
Media: 6
Personnel:
Mulford J. Nobbs *(Pres)*

Brands & Products:
ALOE BLAST
ALOE BRITE
ALOE VERA
ALPHACEUTICALS
ARTHOCARE
ARTHROCARE
AZULENE
BIOTECH 21
CELLO-GEL
CHLORO-LIFE
CLEANSING HERBS
COLORBIND
CONCEPT 2000
CONTROLA BROW
DELICAT
ECO-CLEAN
ELASTISHIELD
ENVIE
ENZYM-AID
FAT LASH
FEMININE CARE
FINELLE
FIRM N TONE
GINSENG
GOLDEN SUPREME
HI-GLOSS
HUNZA RICH
JEUNIQUE
LIP AMPLIFIER
LIPLIFE
LIPSTIX
LOOFAH
LYSIDOPHILUS
MAG-NI-SEL
MAINTENANCE PLUS
MARVELOUS MASCARA
MENTAL CARE
MIR'CLE
NATAL SUPPORT
NATURALBROWN
NEROLI
THE ONE DAY DIET
PEDICARE
PROSTATE CARE
REJEUVAMETICS
REJEUVENIQUE
ROLL-ON
SO-SHINE
WILD YAM

JEWISH HOME LIFECARE

120 W 106th St
New York, NY 10025
Tel.: (212) 870-5000
Fax: (212) 870-5742
E-mail: info@jewishhome.org
Web Site: www.jewishhome.org
Approx. Sls.: $80,000,000
Approx. Number Employees: 900
Business Description:
Geriatric, Rehabilitative & Home Health Services
S.I.C.: 8361; 8082
N.A.I.C.S.: 623312; 621610
Personnel:
David R. Haas *(Chm)*
Audrey S. Weiner *(Pres & CEO)*
Kenneth Sherman *(Sr VP & Administrator-Bronx Div)*
Audrey Wathen *(Sr VP-HR)*

Advertising Agency:
Geto & deMilly Inc.
276 5th Ave Ste 806
New York, NY 10001
Tel.: (212) 686-4551
Fax: (212) 213-6850

JOHNSON & JOHNSON

1 Johnson & Johnson Plz
New Brunswick, NJ 08933-0001
Mailing Address:
PO Box 726
Langhorne, PA 19047-0726
Tel.: (732) 524-0400
Web Site: www.jnj.com
Approx. Sls.: $61,587,000,000
Approx. Number Employees: 114,000
Year Founded: 1886
Business Description:
Surgical Dressings, Baby Products, Pharmaceuticals & Healthcare Products Mfr
S.I.C.: 5122; 2834; 2841; 3841; 3842
N.A.I.C.S.: 424210; 325412; 325611; 339112; 339113
Import Export
Advertising Expenditures: $2,400,000,000
Media: 1-2-3-4-6-7-8-9-10-11-13-14-15-16-18-19-20-21-22-23-24-25
Distr.: Intl.; Natl.
Personnel:
William C. Weldon *(Chm & CEO)*
Alex Gorsky *(Vice Chm)*
Sherilyn S. McCoy *(Vice Chm)*
Dominic J. Caruso *(CFO & VP-Fin)*
Laverne H. Council *(CIO & VP)*
Anthony Carter *(Chief Diversity Officer)*
Kaye I. Foster-Cheek *(Officer)*
Stefano Curti *(Pres-Global Skincare)*
Russell C. Deyo *(Gen Counsel & VP)*
Kim Kadlec *(Grp VP-Mktg-Global Worldwide)*
Gail Horwood *(VP-Digital Strategy & Ecommerce)*
Jeffrey Leebaw *(VP-Corp Comm)*
Helayna Minsk *(VP-Mktg-Women's Health-Worldwide)*
Daniel Weiss *(Grp Dir-HealthCare Products)*
Fred Tewell *(Grp Product Dir-Baby Bus)*
Tina Sabarre *(Dir-Mktg-Philippines)*
Katie Devine *(Product Dir-Aveeno)*
Rebecca Goberstein *(Assoc Product Dir-Digital Mktg)*
Elizabeth Kreul-Starr *(Assoc Product Dir)*
Charmaine Corney *(Dir-Media Leverage)*
Lori Dolginoff *(Dir-Comm)*
Alissa Lynch *(Dir-Global Franchise)*
Jennifer S. Nelson *(Dir-Strategy & Insight-Worldwide)*
Tina Pinto *(Dir-IR)*
Steve Weinstein *(Dir-New Venture & Innovation Sourcing)*
Christine Balingit *(Grp Mgr-Brand Johnson's Baby)*
Royce Carvalho *(Assoc Brand Mgr)*
Kirk Keel *(Brand Mgr-Bengay)*
Chad Mizee *(Sr Brand Mgr)*
Carmen Nestares *(Brand Mgr-Neosporin)*
Derek Sotto *(Brand Mgr)*

Brands & Products:
ACTISORB
ADAPTIC
AFFINITY
ALL-FLEX
AVEENO
BAND-AID
BENADRYL
BENECOL
BENGAY
BIOCLUSIVE
BIOPATCH
CAREFREE
CARTO
CELSIUS
CHARITE
CIDEX
CLEAN & CLEAR
CLEARGLIDE

Key to Media (For complete agency information see *The Advertising Red Books-Agencies* edition):
1. Bus. Publs. 2. Cable T.V. 3. Catalogs & Directories. 4. Co-op Adv. 5. Consumer Mags. 6. D.M. to Bus. Estab.7. D.M. to Consumers 8. Daily Newsp. 9. Exhibits/Trade Shows 10. Foreign 11. Infomercial 12. Internet Adv.13. Multimedia 14. Network Radio 15. Network T.V. 16. Newsp. Distr. Mags. 17. Other 18. Outdoor (Posters, Transit) 19. Point of Purchase20. Premiums, Novelties 21. Product Samples 22. Special Events Mktg. 23. Spot Radio 24. Spot T.V. 25. Weekly Newsp. 26. Yellow Page Adv.

Johnson & Johnson — (Continued)

CYPHER
DERMABOND
DITROPAN XL
DOLORMIN
DORIBAX
DOXIL
DURAGESIC
DYNA-FLEX
ELMIRON
EPREX
ETHIBOND EXCEL
FIBRACOL
FLEXERIL
FLOXIN
GYNECARE
GYNECARE VERISTAT
HALDOL
HARMONIC SCALPEL
HEALTHY WOMAN
IBOT
IMODIUM
INDEPENDENCE
INDIGO
INTERCEED
K-Y BRAND
LACTAID
LEUSTATIN
LEVAQUIN
LISTERINE
LIVOSTIN
LUBRIDERM
MAMMOTOME
MAXPRO
MONISTAT
MONISTAT-DERM
MONOCRYL
MOTILIUM
MOTRIN
MYLANTA
MYLICON
NATRECOR
NAVI-STAR
NEOSPORIN
NEUTROGENA
NEUTROGENA WAVE
NIZORAL
NU-GEL
OB
ONETOUCH
ORTHO
ORTHO-CEPT
ORTHO-CYCLEN
ORTHO EVRA
ORTHO MICRONOR
ORTHO TRI-CYCLEN
ORTHOCLONE OKT
PALMAZ-SCHATZ
PANCREASE
PARAFON FORTE
PARIET
PEPCID
PERSA-GEL
PIZ BUIN
PROCRIT
PROLENE
PRONOVA
PROXIMATE
PURELL
PURPOSE
RAZADYNE
REACH
REGRANEX
REMBRANDT
REMICADE
REMINYL
RENOVA
RETIN-A MICRO
RHOGAM
ROC
SIMPLY COUGH
SIMPLY STUFFY
SOF-FOAM
SPLENDA
SPORANOX
ST. JOSEPH
STAYFREE
STERRAD
SUDAFED
SULTRIN
TERAZOL
THERMACHOICE
TIELLE
TOLECTIN
TOPAMAX
TYLENOL
TYLOX
ULTRACET
ULTRAM
URISTAT
UVAR
VERMOX
VIACTIV
VICRYL
VISINE
VITROS
WATCHBAND INCISION

Advertising Agencies:

Aegis Group plc
10 Triton Street
London, NW1 3BF, United Kingdom
Tel.: (44) 2070707700
Fax: (44) 2070707800
Media Buying/Planning

DDB Chicago
200 E Randolph St
Chicago, IL 60601
Tel.: (312) 552-6000
Fax: (312) 552-2370
Aveeno
— Susan Lulich *(Acct Dir)*

DDB Worldwide Communications Group Inc.
(Sub. of Omnicom Group, Inc.)
(Corporate Headquarters)
437 Madison Ave 5nd Fl
New York, NY 10022-7001
Tel.: (212) 415-2000
Fax: (212) 415-3414

Deutsch, Inc.
(A Lowe & Partners Company)
111 8th Ave 14th Fl
New York, NY 10011-5201
Tel.: (212) 981-7600
Fax: (212) 981-7525
Imodium EZ Chews

Fuel Industries
7 Hinton Ave N Ste 100
Ottawa, ON K1Y 4P1, Canada
Tel.: (613) 224-6738
Fax: (613) 224-6802

hypernaked
159-173 Saint John St
London, EC1V 4QY, United Kingdom
Tel.: (44) 207 336 8084
Fax: (44) 207 336 8009

ID Media
(Part of the Interpublic Group of Companies)
100 W 33rd St
New York, NY 10001
Tel.: (212) 907-7011
Fax: (212) 907-7290

J. Walter Thompson Company (d/b/a JWT)
466 Lexington Ave
New York, NY 10017-3140
Tel.: (212) 210-7000
Fax: (212) 210-7299
Reach
Band-Aid

JWT
7th F Equitable Bank Tower 8751 Paseo de Roxas
Makati, 1227, Philippines
Tel.: (63) 2 864 8700
Tel.: (63) 2 864 8570
Tel.: (63) 2 864 8560
Fax: (63) 2 884 8563
(Benadryl, Sinutab, Listerine, Band-Aid, Reach, Bactidol)

JWT Advertising Co. Ltd.
25/F No 989 Chang Le Road The Center
Shanghai, 200031, China
Tel.: (86) 21 2405 0000
Fax: (86) 21 2405 0001
Tylenol

La Comunidad
6400 Biscayne Blvd
Miami, FL 33138
Tel.: (305) 993-5700
Tel.: (305) 865-9600
Fax: (305) 865-9609
Hispanic

The Martin Agency
One Shockoe Plz
Richmond, VA 23219-4132
Tel.: (804) 698-8000
Fax: (804) 698-8001
Motrin - Creative & Media Planning
Tylenol - Creative & Media Planning

McCann Erickson India
McCann House Dr SS Rao Road
Mumbai, 40012, India
Tel.: (91) 22 241 76601
Fax: (91) 22 241 6871

Mindshare
498 7th Ave
New York, NY 10018
Tel.: (212) 297-7000
Fax: (212) 297-7001

Mother Ltd.
Biscuit Bldg 10 Redchurch St
London, E2 7DD, United Kingdom
Tel.: (44) 20 7012 1999
Fax: (44) 20 7012 1989
K-Y

Mother New York
595 11th Ave
New York, NY 10036
Tel.: (212) 254-2800
Fax: (212) 254-6121

OgilvyOne Worldwide
636 11th Ave
New York, NY 10036
Tel.: (212) 237-4000
Fax: (212) 237-5123

OMD Beijing
Unit 502-505 5 Fl Tower 1 China Central Place
No 81 Jianguo Rd
Beijing, 100 025, China
Tel.: (86) 10 6561 2198
Fax: (86) 10 6561 3845
Xian Jansen Pharmaceuticals

Omnicom Group Inc.
437 Madison Ave 9th Fl
New York, NY 10022-7001
Tel.: (212) 415-3600
Fax: (212) 415-3530

Roberts + Langer DDB
437 Madison Ave 8th Fl
New York, NY 10022
Tel.: (646) 289-7300
Fax: (212) 593-1286
Lubriderm

Simms & McIvor Marketing Communications
3121 Rt 22 E Branch Estates
Branchburg, NJ 08876-3500
Tel.: (908) 722-8777
Fax: (908) 722-7833

TAXI New York
455 Broadway 3rd Fl
New York, NY 10013
Tel.: (212) 414-8294
Fax: (212) 414-8444

Universal McCann
100 33rd St 8th Fl
New York, NY 10001
Tel.: (212) 883-4700
Media Buying
Tylenol Rapid Release Tablets

Wax Communications Ltd.
90 Tottenham Ct Rd
London, W1T 4TJ, United Kingdom
Tel.: (44) 207 9273500
Fax: (44) 207 927 3501
Roc

JOHNSON & JOHNSON BABY PRODUCTS, INC.

(Sub. of Johnson & Johnson)
1 Johnson & Johnson Plz
New Brunswick, NJ 08933
Tel.: (732) 524-0400
Fax: (732) 524-3300
Web Site: www.jnj.com
Sales Range: $25-49.9 Million
Approx. Number Employees: 50

Business Description:
Baby Products Mfr
S.I.C.: 2834; 2676; 3821; 3842; 3845; 3999
N.A.I.C.S.: 325412; 322291; 334510; 339111; 339113; 339999

Personnel:
William C. Weldon *(Chm & CEO)*

Advertising Agencies:

BBDO New York
1285 Ave of the Americas 7th Fl
New York, NY 10019-6028
Tel.: (212) 459-5000

Key to Media (For complete agency information see *The Advertising Red Books-Agencies* edition):
1. Bus. Publs. 2. Cable T.V. 3. Catalogs & Directories. 4. Co-op Adv. 5. Consumer Mags. 6. D.M. to Bus. Estab.7. D.M. to Consumers
8. Daily Newsp. 9. Exhibits/Trade Shows 10. Foreign 11. Infomercial 12. Internet Adv.13. Multimedia 14. Network Radio
15. Network T.V. 16. Newsp. Distr. Mags. 17. Other 18. Outdoor (Posters, Transit) 19. Point of Purchase20. Premiums, Novelties
21. Product Samples 22. Special Events Mktg. 23. Spot Radio 24. Spot T.V. 25. Weekly Newsp. 26. Yellow Page Adv.

Global Creative Assignment

Omnicom Group Inc.
437 Madison Ave 9th Fl
New York, NY 10022-7001
Tel.: (212) 415-3600
Fax: (212) 415-3530

Roberts + Langer DDB
437 Madison Ave 8th Fl
New York, NY 10022
Tel.: (646) 289-7300
Fax: (212) 593-1286
Global Creative Duties
— Andy Langer *(Chief Creative Officer)*

JOHNSON & JOHNSON HEALTH CARE SYSTEMS INC.

(Sub. of Johnson & Johnson)
425 Hoes Ln PO Box 6800
Piscataway, NJ 08855-6800
Tel.: (732) 562-3000
Fax: (732) 214-0322
Toll Free: (800) 551-7690
Web Site: www.jnjgateway.com
Sales Range: $50-74.9 Million
Approx. Number Employees: 100
Business Description:
Account Management & Business Support Services for Large Managed Care Organizations, Hospitals & Government Customers
S.I.C.: 5047
N.A.I.C.S.: 423450
Advertising Agency:
Simms & McIvor Marketing Communications
3121 Rt 22 E Branch Estates
Branchburg, NJ 08876-3500
Tel.: (908) 722-8777
Fax: (908) 722-7833

JOHNSON & JOHNSON INC.

(Sub. of Johnson & Johnson)
7101 Notre-Dame East
Montreal, QC H1N 2G4, Canada
Tel.: (514) 251-5100
Fax: (514) 251-6233
Toll Free: (800) 361-8068
E-mail: info@jnjcanada.com
Web Site: www.jnjcanada.com
Sales Range: $150-199.9 Million
Approx. Number Employees: 700
Year Founded: 1919
Business Description:
Orthopedic Prosthetic Surgical Appliances, Perfumes, Cosmetics & Toilet Preparations Mfr
S.I.C.: 3821
N.A.I.C.S.: 339111
Media: 3-5-6-8-9-14-15-16-19-21-23-24-25
Distr.: Intl.
Budget Set: Aug.
Personnel:
Jeff Smith *(Pres)*
Michele M. Cotton *(Dir-Fin-Supply Chain & Logistics)*
Advertising Agencies:
DDB Canada
33 Bloor Street East Suite 1700
Toronto, ON M4W 3T4, Canada
Tel.: (416) 925-9819
Fax: (416) 925-4180

Lowe Roche
260 Queen St W Ste 301
Toronto, ON M5V 1Z8, Canada
Tel.: (416) 927-9794
Fax: (416) 927-1188

MacLaren McCann Canada Inc.
10 Bay St
Toronto, ON M5J 2S3, Canada
Tel.: (416) 594-6000
Fax: (416) 643-7030
Fax: (416) 643-7027

Marketel
(Assoc. with McCann Erickson WorldGroup)
1100 Rene-Levesque Boulevard West
19th Floor
Montreal, QC H3B 4N4, Canada
Tel.: (514) 935-9445
Fax: (514) 935-1964

JOHNSON & JOHNSON - MERCK CONSUMER PHARMACEUTICALS CO.

(Joint Venture of Johnson & Johnson & Merck & Co., Inc.)
7050 Camp Hill Rd
Fort Washington, PA 19034-2292
Tel.: (215) 273-7000
Fax: (215) 273-4193
Toll Free: (800) 755-4008
Web Site: www.pepcidac.com
Sales Range: $1-4.9 Billion
Approx. Number Employees: 2,000
Year Founded: 1989
Business Description:
Heartburn Relief Products Mfr; Owned 50% by Johnson & Johnson & 50% by Merck & Co. Inc.
S.I.C.: 2834
N.A.I.C.S.: 325412
Media: 3-4-6-13-16-18-21
Personnel:
Calvin Schmidt *(Gen Mgr)*
Jim Morris *(Assoc Brand Mgr)*
Brands & Products:
PEPCID AC
PEPCID COMPLETE

JOHNSON & JOHNSON VISION CARE, INC.

(Sub. of Johnson & Johnson)
7500 Centurion Pkwy
Jacksonville, FL 32256-0517
Tel.: (904) 443-1000
Fax: (904) 443-1297
Toll Free: (800) 843-2020
E-mail: info@jnjvision.com
Web Site: www.jnjvision.com
Sales Range: $650-699.9 Million
Approx. Number Employees: 3,500
Business Description:
Ophthalmic Products Mfr
S.I.C.: 3851
N.A.I.C.S.: 339115
Export
Media: 1-2-3-5-6-7-8-10-13-15-18-19-21-22
Distr.: Natl.
Personnel:
Iane. L. Davis *(Mng Dir)*
Robert Manning *(Dir-Digital Franchise-Global)*
Brands & Products:
1-DAY ACUVUE
ACUVUE
ACUVUE 2 COLOURS
SUREVUE

Advertising Agency:
Buzz Strategies
PO Box 6614
Chandler, AZ 85246
Tel.: (480) 926-2899
Fax: (480) 598-0253

K-V PHARMACEUTICAL COMPANY

1 Corporate Woods Dr
Bridgeton, MO 63044
Tel.: (314) 645-6600
Fax: (314) 644-2419
E-mail: cbiffignani@kvpharmaceutical.com
Web Site: www.kvpharmaceutical.com
Approx. Rev.: $27,300,000
Approx. Number Employees: 271
Year Founded: 1942
Business Description:
Pharmaceutical Research & Development Services
S.I.C.: 2834; 5122
N.A.I.C.S.: 325412; 424210
Import Export
Advertising Expenditures: $4,500,000
Media: 7-21
Personnel:
Gregory J. Divis, Jr. *(Pres & CEO)*
Thomas S. McHugh *(CFO, Chief Acctg Officer & Treas)*
Mark T. Hartman *(Pres-Generics Div)*
Patrick J. Christmas *(Gen Counsel & VP)*
Gregory S. Bentley *(Sec & Sr VP-Law)*
Brands & Products:
BIOSERT
CLINDESSE
DERMASITE
DESCOTE
DESTAB
EVAMIST
FLAVORTECH
GYNAZOLE-1
KV
KV/24
LIQUETTE
MAKENA
METER RELEASE
MICRO-K
MICRO RELEASE
MICROMASK
OCUSITE
ORASERT
ORASITE
PULMOSITE
SITE RELEASE
TRANSCELL
VAGISITE

KAISER PERMANENTE

1 Kaiser Plz Ste 2600
Oakland, CA 94612-3673
Tel.: (510) 271-5800
Fax: (510) 271-6493
Web Site: www.kaiserpermanente.org
Sales Range: $25-49.9 Billion
Approx. Number Employees: 136,511
Year Founded: 1945
Business Description:
Not-for-Profit Health & Medical Service Plans; Health Care Services
S.I.C.: 6321; 8011; 8049; 8093
N.A.I.C.S.: 524114; 621111; 621112; 621399; 621491; 621493; 621498
Personnel:
Bernard J. Tyson *(Pres & COO)*
Kathy Lancaster *(CFO & Exec VP)*
Tony Fiorello *(COO & Chief Nursing Officer-Kaiser Permanente Medical Center)*
Philip Fasano *(CIO & Exec VP)*
Steve Zatkin *(Gen Counsel & Sr VP)*
Arthur M. Southam *(Exec VP-Health Plan Ops)*
Raymond J. Baxter *(Sr VP-Community Benefit)*
Louise L. Liang *(Sr VP-Quality & Clinical Sys Support)*
Holly Potter *(VP-PR)*
David Jones *(Exec Dir-Laboratory SubPortolio-Care Delivery)*
Valerie Constable *(Dir-Market Intelligence, Brand Mktg & Adv)*
Angelique Vega *(Dir-Media)*
Maggie Soldano *(Assoc Dir-Brand Creative)*
Duyen Nguyen *(Product Mgr)*
Brands & Products:
KAISER PERMANENTE
Advertising Agencies:
Campbell-Ewald
30400 Van Dyke Ave
Warren, MI 48093-2368
Tel.: (586) 574-3400
Fax: (586) 575-9925

Digitas, Inc.
111 E Wacker Dr Ste 1500
Chicago, IL 60601-4501
Tel.: (312) 729-0100
Fax: (312) 729-0111
Online Creative & Offline Direct Marketing

GolinHarris
601 W 5th St 4th Fl
Los Angeles, CA 90071-2004
Tel.: (213) 623-4200
Fax: (213) 895-4746
Agency of Record

Initiative
1 Dag Hammarskjold Plz
New York, NY 10017
Tel.: (212) 605-7000
Fax: (917) 305-4003

TMP Worldwide
(Wholly-Owned by Veronis Suhler Stevenson)
205 Hudson St 5th Fl
New York, NY 10013
Tel.: (646) 613-2000
Fax: (646) 613-0649

KANEKA NUTRIENTS L.P.

(Sub. of Kaneka Corporation)
6250 Underwood Rd
Pasadena, TX 77507
Tel.: (281) 291-4489
Fax: (281) 291-4470
E-mail: info@kanekaqh.com
Web Site: www.kanekaqh.com
Approx. Number Employees: 70
Business Description:
Dietary Supplements Mfr
S.I.C.: 7299
N.A.I.C.S.: 812191
Media: 13
Personnel:
Tom Schrier *(Mgr-Natl Sls)*

Key to Media (For complete agency information see *The Advertising Red Books-Agencies* edition):
1. Bus. Publs. 2. Cable T.V. 3. Catalogs & Directories. 4. Co-op Adv. 5. Consumer Mags. 6. D.M. to Bus. Estab.7. D.M. to Consumers 8. Daily Newsp. 9. Exhibits/Trade Shows 10. Foreign 11. Infomercial 12. Internet Adv.13. Multimedia 14. Network Radio 15. Network T.V. 16. Newsp. Distr. Mags. 17. Other 18. Outdoor (Posters, Transit) 19. Point of Purchase20. Premiums, Novelties 21. Product Samples 22. Special Events Mktg. 23. Spot Radio 24. Spot T.V. 25. Weekly Newsp. 26. Yellow Page Adv.

KBD, INC.
2550 American Ct
Crescent Springs, KY 41017
Tel.: (859) 331-0800
Fax: (859) 331-0802
Toll Free: (800) 544-3757
E-mail: info@sperti.com
Web Site: www.sperti.com
Approx. Number Employees: 5
Year Founded: 1991
Business Description:
Personal Sunlamp Mfr
S.I.C.: 3641
N.A.I.C.S.: 335110
Export
Media: 10-13
Distr.: Intl.; Natl.
Budget Set: Sept.
Personnel:
James G. Shepherd *(Owner)*
Elaine Scherder *(Mgr-Plant)*
Brands & Products:
SPERTI

KENDLE INTERNATIONAL INC.
441 Vine St Ste 1200
Cincinnati, OH 45202
Tel.: (513) 381-5550
Fax: (513) 381-5870
Toll Free: (800) 733-1572
E-mail: info@kendle.com
Web Site: www.kendle.com
Approx. Rev.: $448,259,000
Approx. Number Employees: 3,105
Year Founded: 1981
Business Description:
Contract Biopharmaceutical Research & Development Services
S.I.C.: 8733
N.A.I.C.S.: 541711
Advertising Expenditures: $1,600,000
Personnel:
Candace Kendle *(Chm)*
Stephen A. Cutler *(Pres & CEO)*
Keith A. Cheesman *(CFO & Sr VP)*
Mark J. Roseman *(CMO & Sr VP-Sls)*
Jarrod Pontius *(Chief Legal Officer, Sec & VP)*
Doug Moehring *(Sr Dir-New Bus Dev)*
Jeffrey M. Zucker *(Sr Dir & Global Head-Patient Recruitment)*
Michael Lawson *(Dir-IR)*
Brands & Products:
KENDLE
REAL PEOPLE. REAL RESULTS
TRIALWEB

KENNEDY HEALTH SYSTEM
1099 White Horse Rd
Voorhees, NJ 08043
Tel.: (856) 566-5200
Fax: (856) 566-5277
Toll Free: (800) KHS-9007
E-mail: info@kennedyhealth.org
Web Site: www.kennedyhealth.org
Sales Range: $300-349.9 Million
Approx. Number Employees: 3,508
Year Founded: 1965
Business Description:
Health Care Services
S.I.C.: 8062; 8741
N.A.I.C.S.: 622110; 561110
Media: 1-3-4-8-13-23
Personnel:
John P. Silvestri *(Chm)*
Martin A. Bieber *(Pres & CEO)*
Gary Terrinoni *(CFO & Sr VP)*
Daniel Herriman *(Chief Medical Officer & Sr VP)*
Joseph W. Devine *(Sr VP-Admin & External Rels)*
Fran G. Atkinson *(VP-Mktg)*
Emilio DeCesaris *(VP-Fin Ops)*
Anneliese McMenamin *(VP-HR)*
Nicole Pensiero *(Dir-Comm)*
Advertising Agency:
LevLane Advertising/PR/Interactive
100 Penn Sq E
Philadelphia, PA 19107
Tel.: (215) 825-9600
Fax: (215) 809-1900
— Cortney Boothman *(Acct Coord-Center City District,)*

KENSEY NASH CORPORATION
735 Pennsylvania Dr
Exton, PA 19341
Tel.: (484) 713-2100
Fax: (484) 713-2900
Toll Free: (800) 524-1984
E-mail: info@kenseynash.com
Web Site: www.kenseynash.com
Approx. Rev.: $71,637,608
Approx. Number Employees: 307
Year Founded: 1984
Business Description:
Cardiovascular Medical Devices Mfr
S.I.C.: 3841; 3842; 8733
N.A.I.C.S.: 339112; 339113; 541710
Media: 4-7-10
Personnel:
John E. Nash *(Co-Founder & VP-New Tech)*
Kenneth Kensey *(Co-Founder)*
Joseph W. Kaufmann *(Pres & CEO)*
Michael Celano *(CFO)*
Douglas G. Evans *(COO & Asst Sec)*
William Fiehler *(VP-Product Dev)*
Jeffrey C. Kelly *(VP-Legal Affairs)*
James M. Elmer *(Sr Dir-Ops)*
Brands & Products:
ANGIO-SEAL
DRILAC
EPI-GUIDE
KENSEY NASH
PTM
SCAFFOLD FOAM
TRIACTIV
TRIACTIV FX
/VITOSS
Advertising Agency:
Northlight Advertising
1208 Kimberton Rd
Chester Springs, PA 19425
Tel.: (484) 202-8506
Fax: (484) 202-8510

KERR DRUG INC.
3220 Spring Forest Rd
Raleigh, NC 27616
Tel.: (919) 544-3896
Fax: (919) 544-3796
Web Site: www.kerrdrug.com
Approx. Sls.: $212,700,000
Approx. Number Employees: 90
Year Founded: 1997
Business Description:
Provider of Pharmacy Services
S.I.C.: 5912
N.A.I.C.S.: 446110
Import Export
Personnel:
Anthony Civello *(Pres & CEO)*
Bill Baxley *(Sr VP-Mdsg & Mktg)*
Ken Patterson *(Dir-Mdsg)*
Ken Jones *(Mgr-Point)*
Advertising Agencies:
919 Marketing Company
102 Avent Ferry Rd
Holly Springs, NC 27540
Tel.: (919) 557-7890
Fax: (919) 557-0041

StoreBoard Media
441 Lexington Ave 14th Fl
New York, NY 10017
Tel.: (212) 682-3300

KERYX BIOPHARMACEUTICALS, INC.
750 Lexington Ave 20th Fl
New York, NY 10022
Tel.: (212) 531-5965
Fax: (212) 531-5961
E-mail: ir@keryx.com
Web Site: www.keryx.com
Approx. Rev.: $764,000
Approx. Number Employees: 25
Year Founded: 1998
Business Description:
Acquisition, Development & Commercialization of Pharmaceutical Products for Treatment of Life-Threatening Diseases
S.I.C.: 2834; 8733
N.A.I.C.S.: 325412; 541710
Media: 10
Personnel:
Michael P. Tarnok *(Chm)*
Ron Bentsur *(CEO)*
James F. Oliviero *(CFO)*
Lauren Fischer *(Dir-IR)*
Advertising Agency:
Redington Inc.
49 Richmondville Ave Ste 108
Westport, CT 06880
Tel.: (203) 222-7399
Tel.: (212) 926-1733
Fax: (203) 222-1819
Pub Rels

KINDRED HEALTHCARE, INC.
680 S 4th St
Louisville, KY 40202-2407
Tel.: (502) 596-7300
Fax: (502) 596-4170
Toll Free: (800) 545-0749
E-mail: web_administrator@kindredhealthcare.com
Web Site: www.kindredhealthcare.com
Approx. Rev.: $4,359,697,000
Approx. Number Employees: 40,600
Year Founded: 1985
Business Description:
Hospitals, Nursing Centers & Rehabilitation Service Facilities Operator
S.I.C.: 8059; 7299; 8062; 8069
N.A.I.C.S.: 623110; 622110; 622310; 812199
Advertising Expenditures: $10,000,000
Personnel:
Edward L. Kuntz *(Chm)*
Paul J. Diaz *(Pres & CEO)*
Richard A. Lechleiter *(CFO & Exec VP)*
Benjamin A. Breier *(COO)*
Richard E. Chapman *(CIO, Chief Admin Officer & Exec VP)*
Kim Martin *(Chief Compliance Officer & Sr VP-Risk Mgmt)*
John J. Lucchese *(Chief Acctg Officer, Sr VP & Controller)*
Jack Shapiro *(Pres/CEO-Chicago Div)*
Lane M. Bowen *(Pres-Nursing Center Div & Exec VP)*
Jeffrey P. Winter *(Pres-Hospital Div & Exec VP)*
Christopher M. Bird *(Pres-Peoplefirst Rehabilitation Div)*
M. Suzanne Riedman *(Gen Counsel & Sr VP)*
Joseph L. Landenwich *(Sr VP-Corp Legal Affairs & Corp Sec)*
William M. Altman *(Sr VP-Strategy & Pub Poilcy)*
Gregory C. Miller *(Sr VP-Corp Dev & Fin Plng)*
Susan E. Moss *(VP-Corp Comm)*
Advertising Agency:
Neathawk Dubuque & Packett
417 Market St
Chattanooga, TN 37402
Tel.: (423) 752-4687
Fax: (423) 752-3697
Toll Free: (888) 619-8697

KINETIC CONCEPTS, INC.
8023 Vantage Dr
San Antonio, TX 78230-4769
Mailing Address:
PO Box 659508
San Antonio, TX 78265-9508
Tel.: (210) 524-9000
Fax: (210) 255-6998
Toll Free: (800) 275-4524
Web Site: www.kci1.com
Approx. Rev.: $2,017,752,000
Approx. Number Employees: 6,900
Year Founded: 1976
Business Description:
Wound Treatment Solution, Clinical Beds & Medical Devices Designer, Mfr & Marketer
S.I.C.: 3844; 3841; 3845; 5047
N.A.I.C.S.: 334517; 334510; 339112; 423450
Export
Advertising Expenditures: $13,300,000
Media: 1-2-7-10
Distr.: Natl.
Personnel:
Ronald W. Dollens *(Chm)*
Catherine M. Burzik *(Pres & CEO)*
Martin J. Landon *(CFO & Exec VP)*
David H. Ramsey *(CIO & Sr VP)*
Daniel G. Ciaburri *(CMO)*
Michael Genau *(Pres-Active Healing Solutions-Global)*
Patrick Loh *(Pres-Asia Pacific)*
Stephen D. Seidel *(Pres-Therapeutic Support Sys Bus)*
Lynne D. Sly *(Pres-Therapeutic Surfaces)*
David Lillback *(Sr VP-HR)*
Michael Schneider *(Sr VP-Mfg & Ops)*
Brian L. Robey *(Sr Dir-Product Dev)*
David Holmes *(Dir-IR)*
Rohit Kashyap *(Dir-Corp Dev)*
Brands & Products:
ACTIV A.C.
AIRMAXXIS
AIRPAL
ATMOSAIR
BARIAIR

Key to Media (For complete agency information see *The Advertising Red Books-Agencies* edition):
1. Bus. Publs. 2. Cable T.V. 3. Catalogs & Directories. 4. Co-op Adv. 5. Consumer Mags. 6. D.M. to Bus. Estab.7. D.M. to Consumers
8. Daily Newsp. 9. Exhibits/Trade Shows 10. Foreign 11. Infomercial 12. Internet Adv.13. Multimedia 14. Network Radio
15. Network T.V. 16. Newsp. Distr. Mags. 17. Other 18. Outdoor (Posters, Transit) 19. Point of Purchase20. Premiums, Novelties
21. Product Samples 22. Special Events Mktg. 23. Spot Radio 24. Spot T.V. 25. Weekly Newsp. 26. Yellow Page Adv.

BARIATRIC SUPPORT
BARIKARE
BARIMAXX
CARECHAIR
CHANGING THE STANDARD OF HEALING
THE CLINICAL ADVANTAGE
CRITICAL CARE THERAPIES
DYNAPULSE
EZ LIFT
FIRST STEP SELECT
FIRSTSTEP
FLUIDAIR
KCI EXPRESS
KINAIR
KINETIC THERAPHY
MAXAIR ETS
MAXXIS
PARADYNE
PEDIDYNE
PLEXIPULSE
RIK
ROTOPRONE
ROTOREST
THERAPULSE
THERAREST
TRIADYNE
V.A.C.
VAC CONNECT
VAC FREEDOM
VAC GRANUFOAM
VAC INSTILL
VAC SIMPLACE

Advertising Agency:
HC&B Healthcare Communications
701 Brazos St Ste 1450
Austin, TX 78701-2581
Tel.: (512) 320-8511
Fax: (512) 320-8990

KING PHARMACEUTICALS, INC.

(Sub. of Pfizer Inc.)
501 5th St
Bristol, TN 37620
Tel.: (423) 989-8000
Fax: (423) 989-8786
Fax: (866) 990-0545
Toll Free: (800) 776-3637
Approx. Rev.: $1,776,500,000
Approx. Number Employees: 2,640
Year Founded: 1994
Business Description:
Branded Prescription Pharmaceutical Products Mfr, Developer, Marketer & Retailer
S.I.C.: 2834
N.A.I.C.S.: 325412
Advertising Expenditures: $100,425,000
Media: 2-5-7-10-11
Personnel:
Brian A. Markison *(Chm, Pres & CEO)*
Joseph Squicciarino *(CFO)*
Michael H. Davis *(CIO)*
Eric Carter *(CMO & Chief Science Officer)*
Frederick Brouillette Jr. *(Corp Compliance Officer)*
Eric J. Bruce *(Chief Technical Ops Officer)*
Richard G. Buecheler *(Exec VP-Quality)*
Bradley Knoll *(Exec VP-Mfg)*
John Golubieski *(VP-Fin Plng & Analysis)*
Brands & Products:
ALTACE
AVINZA
BICILLIN
CORGARD
CORZIDE
CYTOMEL
FLORINEF
INTAL
KING PHARMACEUTICALS
LEVOXYL
LORABID
MENEST
NEOSPORIN
PEDIOTIC
PENICILLINN G PROCAINE
PROCANBID
SEPTRA
SILVADENE
SKELAXIN
SONATA
SYNERCID
TAPAZOLE
THALITONE
THROMBI-GEL
THROMBI-PAD
THROMBIN-JMI
TILADE
TUSSIGON
VIROPTIC
Advertising Agency:
The Tombras Group
630 Concord St
Knoxville, TN 37919-3305
Tel.: (865) 524-5376
Fax: (865) 524-5667

KMG CHEMICALS, INC.

9555 W Sam Houston Pkwy S Ste 600
Houston, TX 77099
Tel.: (713) 600-3800
Fax: (713) 600-3850
E-mail: info@kmgchemicals.com
Web Site: www.kmgb.com
Approx. Sls.: $208,628,000
Approx. Number Employees: 318
Year Founded: 1986
Business Description:
Specialty Chemicals Marketer, Mfr & Distr
S.I.C.: 2861; 2869; 2899; 5162; 5169
N.A.I.C.S.: 325191; 325199; 325998; 424610; 424690
Advertising Expenditures: $465,000
Personnel:
David L. Hatcher *(Chm)*
J. Neal Butler *(Pres & CEO)*
John V. Sobchak *(CFO)*
Roger C. Jackson *(Gen Counsel & Sec)*
Thomas H. Mitchell *(VP-Sls)*
Brands & Products:
ANSAR
ANSAR 6.6
BUENO
BUENO 6
KMG

KNIGHT-MCDOWELL LABS

(dba Airborne, Inc.)
20 Constitution Blvd S
Shelton, CT 06484
Tel.: (203) 922-7555
Fax: (203) 922-7555
Toll Free: (800) 590-9794
Web Site: www.airbornehealth.com
Year Founded: 1997
Business Description:
Mfr of Airborne Health Products Mfr
S.I.C.: 2834
N.A.I.C.S.: 325412
Media: 6-10-13-14-15-18-19-20-21-22-23
Personnel:
Victoria Knight-McDowell *(Pres)*
Brands & Products:
AIRBORNE
AIRBORNE JR.
ON-THE-GO LEMON LIME
TEACHER TRUST FUND

KYOWA HAKKO U.S.A., INC.

(Sub. of Kyowa Hakko Kirin Co., Ltd.)
767 3rd Ave 19th Fl
New York, NY 10017
Tel.: (212) 319-5353
Fax: (212) 421-1283
Telex: 6973541 KHK NYK
E-mail: info@kyowa-usa.com
Web Site: www.kyowa-usa.com
Approx. Number Employees: 25
Year Founded: 1969
Business Description:
Pharmaceutical, Food Additive & Chemical Mfr & Distr
S.I.C.: 2834; 2899
N.A.I.C.S.: 325412; 325998
Import Export
Media: 2-4-8-10-21
Personnel:
Toshikazu Kamiya *(Pres & CEO)*
Karen E. Todd *(Dir-Mktg)*

KYPHON, INC.

(Sub. of Medtronic, Inc.)
1221 Crossman Ave
Sunnyvale, CA 94089
Tel.: (408) 548-6500
Fax: (408) 548-6501
Web Site: www.kyphon.com
Approx. Sls.: $407,790,016
Approx. Number Employees: 1,200
Year Founded: 1994
Business Description:
Medical Device Developer & Mfr
S.I.C.: 3841
N.A.I.C.S.: 339112
Advertising Expenditures: $4,313,000
Brands & Products:
AHEAD OF THE CURVE
ELEVATE
EXACT
EXPRESS
IPD
KYPHON
KYPHX
KYPHX INFLATABLE BONE TAMP
KYPHX INFLATION SYRINGE
KYPHX XPANDER
LATITUDE
ONE-STEP
X-STOP
XPANDER
Advertising Agency:
Ameredia, Inc.
101 Howard St Ste 380
San Francisco, CA 94105
Tel.: (415) 788-5100
Fax: (415) 449-3411

LA JOLLA PHARMACEUTICAL COMPANY

4365 Executive Dr Ste 300
San Diego, CA 92121
Tel.: (858) 452-6600
Fax: (858) 626-2851
Web Site: www.ljpc.com
Approx. Rev.: $5,347,000
Approx. Number Employees: 3
Year Founded: 1989
Business Description:
Biopharmaceutical Product Developer
S.I.C.: 2836; 2834
N.A.I.C.S.: 325414; 325412
Media: 10
Personnel:
Deirdre Y. Gillespie *(Pres & CEO)*
Gail A. Sloan *(CFO & Sec)*
Andrew Wiseman *(Sr Dir-IR)*
Brands & Products:
LA JOLLA
RIQUENT
TOLERAGENS
TOLERANCE TECHNOLOGY
Advertising Agency:
The Communications Strategy Group, Inc.
42 Front St
Marblehead, MA 01945
Tel.: (781) 631-3117
Fax: (781) 631-3278

LABONE, INC.

(Sub. of Quest Diagnostics Incorporated)
10101 Renner Blvd
Lenexa, KS 66219
Mailing Address:
PO Box 2035
Shawnee Mission, KS 66201-1035
Tel.: (913) 888-1770
Fax: (913) 888-0771
E-mail: info@questdiagnostics.com
Web Site: www.labone.com
Sales Range: $450-499.9 Million
Approx. Number Employees: 2,900
Year Founded: 1972
Business Description:
Substance Abuse Testing
S.I.C.: 8071
N.A.I.C.S.: 621511
Media: 10
Personnel:
Peter Wilkinson *(Dir-Mktg & Investor Rels)*
Brands & Products:
CASEONE
CASEVIEW
LAB CARD PROGRAM
LABLINK
LABONE NET

LABORATORY CORPORATION OF AMERICA HOLDINGS

(d/b/a LabCorp)
358 S Main St
Burlington, NC 27215
Tel.: (336) 229-1127
Fax: (336) 436-1205
Toll Free: (800) 222-7566
E-mail: media@labcorp.com
Web Site: www.labcorp.com
Approx. Sls.: $5,003,900,000
Approx. Number Employees: 31,000
Year Founded: 1971
Business Description:
Clinical Laboratory Testing Services
S.I.C.: 8071; 8734
N.A.I.C.S.: 621511; 541380
Media: 10
Personnel:
David P. King *(Chm, Pres & CEO)*

Key to Media (For complete agency information see *The Advertising Red Books-Agencies* edition):
1. Bus. Publs. 2. Cable T.V. 3. Catalogs & Directories. 4. Co-op Adv. 5. Consumer Mags. 6. D.M. to Bus. Estab.7. D.M. to Consumers 8. Daily Newsp. 9. Exhibits/Trade Shows 10. Foreign 11. Infomercial 12. Internet Adv.13. Multimedia 14. Network Radio 15. Network T.V. 16. Newsp. Distr. Mags. 17. Other 18. Outdoor (Posters, Transit) 19. Point of Purchase20. Premiums, Novelties 21. Product Samples 22. Special Events Mktg. 23. Spot Radio 24. Spot T.V. 25. Weekly Newsp. 26. Yellow Page Adv.

LABORATORY CORPORATION OF AMERICA HOLDINGS — (Continued)

William B. Hayes *(CFO & Exec VP)*
James T. Boyle, Jr. *(COO & Exec VP)*
Andrew Scott Walton *(CIO, Exec VP-Strategic Plng & Corp Dev)*
Lidia L. Fonseca *(CIO & Sr VP)*
F. Samuel Eberts, III *(Chief Legal Officer, Sec & Sr VP-Corp Affairs)*
Andrew J. Conrad *(Exec VP & Chief Scientific Officer)*
Mark E. Brecher *(Sr VP & Chief Medical Officer)*
Lisa Hoffman Starr *(Sr VP-HR)*
Stephen Anderson *(Dir-IR)*
Shawn Weiss *(Dir-Tech)*
Donna F. Schuetz *(Mgr-Corp Comm)*

Brands & Products:
E-RESULTS
ELABCORP
FIBROSURE
GENOSURE
IGPAP-PLUS
INNOVATION QUALITY CONVENIENCE
LABCORP
LABDIRECT
MICROCYTEPLUS
QUANTASURE
THERASURE

LAHEY CLINIC
41 Mall Rd
Burlington, MA 01805
Tel.: (781) 744-5100
Fax: (781) 744-5212
Web Site: www.lahey.org
Sales Range: $650-699.9 Million
Approx. Number Employees: 4,500
Year Founded: 1923
Business Description:
Non-Profit Multi-Specialty Diagnostic Clinic & Hospital
S.I.C.: 8062; 8011
N.A.I.C.S.: 622110; 621111
Media: 8-9-23-25-26
Distr.: Reg.
Personnel:
David M. Barrett *(Pres & CEO)*
Timothy O'Connor *(CFO, Chief Admin Officer & Exec VP & Treas)*
Samford Kurtz *(COO)*
Nelson Gagnon *(CIO)*
Phillips Axten *(Chief Legal Officer & Sr VP)*
Lynn Malloy *(COO-Medical Center Ops & Sr VP)*
Stanley B. Bello *(Sr VP-Community Grp Practices)*
Linda Cagle *(Sr VP)*
Roger Cameron *(Sr VP-Patient Fin Svcs)*
Michael Gill *(Sr VP-Revenue Fin)*
Scott Hartman *(Sr VP-Comm & Mktg)*
Jeffrey Holden *(Sr VP-Fin Svcs)*
Rose Lewis *(Dir-Mktg Comm)*
Ron Bradley *(Mgr-Clinical Nutrition)*
Steve Danehy *(Mgr-Media Rels)*

LAKE CONSUMER PRODUCTS, INC.
(Sub. of Wisconsin Pharmacal Company, LLC)
1 Pharmacal Way
Jackson, WI 53037
Mailing Address:
PO Box 198
Jackson, WI 53037-0198
Tel.: (262) 677-7179
Fax: (262) 677-9006
Toll Free: (800) 635-3696
E-mail: info@lakeconsumer.com
Web Site: www.lakeconsumer.com
Approx. Number Employees: 22
Business Description:
Pharmaceuticals
S.I.C.: 2834
N.A.I.C.S.: 325412
Brands & Products:
BEYOND FRESH INTIMATES
ME AGAIN
PERSANI
PRE CONCEIVE PLUS
VAGI GARD
YEAST GARD
Advertising Agency:
Celtic, Inc.
330 S Executive Dr Ste 206
Brookfield, WI 53005-4215
Tel.: (262) 789-7630
Fax: (262) 789-9454
Lake Consumer Products
— Bill Bussler *(Dir-Acct Svcs)*

LANCER ORTHODONTICS INC.
2330 Cousteau Ct
Vista, CA 92081
Tel.: (760) 744-5585
Fax: (760) 744-5724
Toll Free: (800) 854-2896
E-mail: info@lancerortho.com
Web Site: www.lancerortho.com
Sales Range: $1-9.9 Million
Approx. Number Employees: 40
Year Founded: 1967
Business Description:
Orthodontic Appliances & Peripheral Products Mfr
S.I.C.: 3843; 5047
N.A.I.C.S.: 339114; 423450
Import Export
Media: 2-4-7-10-13-26
Distr.: Natl.
Budget Set: May
Brands & Products:
BLUVUE
INTRIGUE SILK
LANCER
OASI IMPLANT
PRAXIS GLIDE
REDI-PAK
WICK WEDGE

LANDAUER, INC.
2 Science Rd
Glenwood, IL 60425-1586
Tel.: (708) 755-7000
Fax: (708) 755-7016
Toll Free: (800) 323-8830
E-mail: custserv@landauerinc.com
Web Site: www.landauerinc.com
Approx. Rev.: $114,367,000
Approx. Number Employees: 540
Year Founded: 1954
Business Description:
Analytical Services to Determine Human Exposure to Radiation
S.I.C.: 3845; 3824; 8734
N.A.I.C.S.: 334510; 334514; 541380
Advertising Expenditures: $748,000
Media: 4-7-8-10-13
Personnel:
William E. Saxelby *(CEO)*
Jonathon M. Singer *(CFO & Sr VP)*
Richard E. Bailey *(Sr VP-Ops)*
R. Craig Yoder *(Sr VP-Mktg & Tech)*
Inid Deneau *(Dir-Mktg)*
Brands & Products:
HOMEBUYER'S PREFERRED
INLIGHT
LANDAUER
LUXEL
MICROSTAR
NANODOT
RADPRO
RADTRAK
THINKING OUTSIDE THE BADGE
TRIPLE I

LANELABS USA INC.
3 North St
Waldwick, NJ 07463
Tel.: (201) 661-6000
Fax: (201) 661-6001
Web Site: www.lanelabs.com
Year Founded: 1994
Business Description:
Mfr & Marketer Natural Supplements & Pharmaceuticals
S.I.C.: 5122; 2833
N.A.I.C.S.: 424210; 325411
Media: 4-6-10
Personnel:
Andrew J. Lane *(Pres)*
Beatrice Querel *(Mgr-Sls & Mktg)*
Brands & Products:
ADVACAL
ADVAJOINT
ANTI-AGING PHYSICIAN
BREATHE
CHOLESTERALL
ENERG
FERTIL MALE
GI48
GUM RELIEF
H2GO
HERBAL V
IMMUNOFIN
LANELABS
MSR MULTI
MY DAILY VEGGIES
MY SWEET REVENGE
NATURE'S LINING
NOXYLANE
OMEGA MULTI
PALMVITEE
SUNSPOT
TOKI
VIRACLE

LANNETT COMPANY, INC.
9000 State Rd
Philadelphia, PA 19136
Tel.: (215) 333-9000
Fax: (215) 333-9004
Toll Free: (800) 325-9994
E-mail: info@lannett.com
Web Site: www.lannett.com
E-Mail For Key Personnel:
Sales Director: sales@lannett.com
Approx. Sls.: $125,177,949
Approx. Number Employees: 305
Year Founded: 1942
Business Description:
Generic Pharmaceutical Product Mfr
S.I.C.: 2834
N.A.I.C.S.: 325412
Advertising Expenditures: $30,000
Media: 2-10
Personnel:
William Farber *(Chm)*
Ronald A. West *(Vice Chm)*
Arthur P. Bedrosian *(Pres & CEO)*
William F. Schreck *(COO)*
Kevin Smith *(VP-Sls & Mktg)*
Brands & Products:
ACETAZOLAMIDE
BUTALBITAL
CLINDAMYCIN
DANAZOL
DICYCLOMINE HCL
DIGOXIN
DILAUDID
DIPHENOXYLATE
HYDROMORPHONE HCL
LANNETT
LEVOTHYROXINE SODIUM
LEVOXYL
METHOCARBAMOL
MYSOLINE
PHENTERMINE HCL
PRIMIDONE
ROBAXIN
TERBUTALINE SULFATE
UNITHROID

LEAVITT MANAGEMENT GROUP, INC.
2600 Lake Lucien Dr Ste 180
Maitland, FL 32751-7217
Tel.: (407) 875-2080
Fax: (407) 875-1219
Approx. Number Employees: 200
Year Founded: 1989
Business Description:
Holding Company; Medical Hair Restoration, Advanced Dermatology & Cosmetic Surgery Consultation & Surgical Services
S.I.C.: 6719; 8049
N.A.I.C.S.: 551112; 621399
Media: 3
Personnel:
Matt L. Leavitt *(Owner-Mktg & Owner-Head-Ops Mgmt)*
Michael D. Leavitt *(Chm)*
Justin Kuperberg *(CFO)*
David Morrell *(Pres-Advanced Dermatology & Cosmetic Surgery)*
William Sutton *(Gen Counsel)*
Erica Novak *(Dir-HR)*
Advertising Agency:
Response Mine
3390 Peachtree Rd Ste 800
Atlanta, GA 30326
Tel.: (404) 233-0370
Fax: (404) 233-0302
Online Marketing

LECTEC CORPORATION
1407 S Kings Hwy
Texarkana, TX 75501
Tel.: (903) 832-0993
Fax: (903) 832-0994
E-mail: information@lectec.com
Web Site: www.lectec.com
Approx. Rev.: $91,273
Approx. Number Employees: 2
Year Founded: 1977
Business Description:
Intellectual Property Licensing Services
S.I.C.: 3845; 2834; 6719; 6794
N.A.I.C.S.: 334510; 325412; 533110; 551112
Advertising Expenditures: $231,000
Personnel:
Robert J. Rudelius *(Chm)*
Gregory G. Freitag *(CEO & CFO)*

Key to Media (For complete agency information see *The Advertising Red Books-Agencies* edition):
1. Bus. Publs. 2. Cable T.V. 3. Catalogs & Directories. 4. Co-op Adv. 5. Consumer Mags. 6. D.M. to Bus. Estab.7. D.M. to Consumers 8. Daily Newsp. 9. Exhibits/Trade Shows 10. Foreign 11. Infomercial 12. Internet Adv.13. Multimedia 14. Network Radio 15. Network T.V. 16. Newsp. Distr. Mags. 17. Other 18. Outdoor (Posters, Transit) 19. Point of Purchase20. Premiums, Novelties 21. Product Samples 22. Special Events Mktg. 23. Spot Radio 24. Spot T.V. 25. Weekly Newsp. 26. Yellow Page Adv.

Brands & Products:
LECTEC
THERAPATCH
THERAPATCH ANTI-ITCH FOR KIDS
THERAPATCH ANTI-ITCH OUTDOORS
THERAPATCH COLD SORE
THERAPATCH COOL
THERAPATCH FEVER
THERAPATCH HEADACHE
THERAPATCH PSORIASIS
THERAPATCH VAPOR CHERRY PATCH
THERAPATCH VAPOR CHEST
THERAPATCH VAPOR NOSE & CHIN
THERAPATCH WARM

LEE MEMORIAL HEALTH SYSTEM

PO Box 2218
Fort Myers, FL 33902
Tel.: (239) 332-1111
Fax: (239) 985-3542
Toll Free: (800) 936-5321
Web Site: www.leememorial.org
Approx. Number Employees: 5,700
Business Description:
Community Healthcare System
S.I.C.: 8062
N.A.I.C.S.: 622110
Media: 2-6
Personnel:
Linda L. Brown *(Vice Chm)*
James R. Nathan *(CEO & Pres-Sys)*
C.B. Rebsamen *(Chief Medical Officer-Ambulatory & Strategic Svcs)*
Donna Giannuzzi *(Chief Patient Care Officer)*
Chuck Krivenko *(Officer-Patient Safety & Clinical Svcs)*
Patti Chlipala *(Dir-Dev)*
Karen Krieger *(Dir-Pub Affairs)*
Ken Shoriak *(Dir-System Ops)*

LEE PHARMACEUTICALS

1434 Santa Anita Ave
South El Monte, CA 91733-3312
Tel.: (626) 442-3141
Fax: (626) 443-8745
Toll Free: (800) 950-5337
E-mail: rlee@leepharmaceuticals.com
Web Site:
www.leepharmaceuticals.com
Sales Range: $1-9.9 Million
Approx. Number Employees: 92
Year Founded: 1971
Business Description:
Polymeric Biomaterials & Consumer Products Developer, Mfr & Marketer
S.I.C.: 2834
N.A.I.C.S.: 325412
Export
Advertising Expenditures: $180,000
Media: 5
Distr.: Intl.; Natl.
Budget Set: Oct.
Personnel:
Ronald Lee *(Chm & CEO)*
Mike Agresti *(CFO)*
Roland Hernandez *(Pres-Consumer Products Div)*
John Ferguson *(Sr VP-Sls)*
Debra S. Hogan *(Mgr-Natl Accounts)*
Brands & Products:
666 COLD PREP
ACRYLINE
ALOE 99
AQUAFILTER
BIKINI BARE
BLACK DRAUGHT
BRUSH N' FLOSS
CANKAID
CEVI-BID
CHAP-EX
CHERACOL
CHERACOL D
CITROCARBONATE
COPE
CREO-TERPIN
DENTLOCK
DEWITTS
DR. HANDS
EVAC-U-GEN
FEMIRON
IODEX
LADY ESTHER
LEE
LIP-EX
LIPOMUL
LITE'N UP
MEDICONE
NICK-FIX
NORWICH
NORWICH ASPIRIN
NULLO
ONE STEP AT A TIME
ORASTAT
OTIX
P-A-C
PAIN-A-LAY
PERMA-GRIP
PETERSON'S
PLATE-WELD
PRESS-ON-NAILS
PROBEC-T
PYRROXATE
ROSE MILK
SAXON
SAYMAN
SERUTAN
SIGTAB
SIPPERS
SLOAN'S LINIMENT
SUNDANCE
TAKE-OFF
THEX FORTE
UNGENTINE
VENTURE
VINCE
WATE-ON
WAX FOR BRACES
ZIP
ZONITE
ZYMACAP
Advertising Agency:
Lee & Lee
1434 Santa Anita Ave
South El Monte, CA 91733-3312
Tel.: (626) 442-3141
Fax: (626) 443-8745
Toll Free: (800) 950-5337
(Pharmaceutical Products)

LEGACY HEALTH SYSTEM

1919 NW Lovejoy
Portland, OR 97209
Tel.: (503) 415-5600
Fax: (503) 415-5777
E-mail: info@lhs.com
Web Site: www.legacyhealth.org
Sales Range: $800-899.9 Million
Approx. Number Employees: 7,935
Year Founded: 1989
Business Description:
Hospitals & Home Health Agencies
S.I.C.: 8062; 8071; 8082
N.A.I.C.S.: 622110; 621511; 621610
Media: 4-6-10-22
Personnel:
Colleen A. Cain *(Chm)*
George Brown *(Pres & CEO)*
P. Campbell Groner, III *(Chief Legal Officer, Compliance Officer & Sr VP)*
Jack Cioffi *(Chief Medical Officer & Sr VP)*
Sonja Steves *(Sr VP-HR)*

LEMAITRE VASCULAR, INC.

63 2nd Ave
Burlington, MA 01803
Tel.: (781) 221-2266
Fax: (781) 221-2223
Web Site: www.lemaitre.com
Approx. Sls.: $56,060,000
Approx. Number Employees: 255
Year Founded: 1983
Business Description:
Vascular Devices & Medical Supplies Mfr
S.I.C.: 3841
N.A.I.C.S.: 339112
Advertising Expenditures: $300,000
Media: 2-7-10-22
Personnel:
George W. Lemaitre *(Chm & CEO)*
David B. Roberts *(Pres)*
Joseph P. Pellegrino, Jr. *(CFO)*
Peter R. Gebauer *(Pres-Intl Ops)*
Trent G. Kamke *(Sr VP-Ops)*
Robert V. Linden *(Sr VP-Sls-The Americas)*
Kimberly L. Cieslak *(VP-Mktg)*
Maik D. Helmers *(VP-Central Europe & Sls)*
Cornelia W. Lemaitre *(VP-HR)*
Jonathan W. Ngau *(VP-IT)*
Nobuhiro Okabe *(Mgr-Country)*
Brands & Products:
ALBOGRAFT
ANASTOCLIP
ASPIRE
ENDOFIT
ENDOHELIX
ENDORE
EXPANDABLE LEMAITRE VALVULOTOME
EXPEDIAL
F3
GLOW 'N TELL
INAHARA-PRUITT
INVISIGRIP
LEMAITRE
LEMAITRE VASCULAR
LEVEREDGE
MOLLRING CUTTER
NOVASIL
OPTILOCK
PERISCOPE
PRUITT
PRUITT-INAHARA
REDDICK
TAARGET
TT
UNIFIT
VASCUTAPE
VCS

LENOX HILL HOSPITAL

100 E 77th St
New York, NY 10075
Tel.: (212) 434-2000
Fax: (212) 434-2825
Web Site: www.lenoxhillhospital.org
Sales Range: $600-649.9 Million
Approx. Number Employees: 3,000
Year Founded: 1857
Business Description:
Hospital Operator
S.I.C.: 8062
N.A.I.C.S.: 622110
Media: 2-9-10-25
Personnel:
William O. Hiltz *(Chm)*
Gladys George *(Pres & CEO)*
Michael Breslin *(CFO & Exec VP)*
Louis Ajamy *(CIO & VP)*
Terence O'Brien *(Exec VP)*
Glenn Courounis *(VP-HR)*
Philip Rosenthal *(Exec Dir)*

LEXICON PHARMACEUTICALS, INC.

8800 Technology Forest Pl
The Woodlands, TX 77381-1160
Tel.: (281) 863-3000
Fax: (281) 863-8088
Toll Free: (800) 578-1972
Web Site: www.lexpharma.com
Approx. Rev.: $4,908,000
Approx. Number Employees: 290
Year Founded: 1995
Business Description:
Biopharmaceutical Research & Development
S.I.C.: 2834; 2836; 8733
N.A.I.C.S.: 325412; 325414; 541710
Media: 10
Personnel:
Samuel L. Barker *(Chm)*
Arthur T. Sands *(Pres & CEO)*
Jeffrey L. Wade *(CFO & Exec VP-Corp Dev)*
Brian P. Zambrowicz *(Chief Scientific Officer & Exec VP)*
Pablo Lapuerta *(Chief Medical Officer & Sr VP-Clinical Dev)*
Alan J. Main *(Exec VP-Pharmaceutical Res)*
Lance K. Ishimoto *(Sr VP-Corp Dev & Alliance Mgmt)*
Steven A. Tragash *(Chief of Staff & Sr VP-Corp Affairs)*
James F. Tessmer *(VP-Fin & Acctg)*
Elaine M. Clark *(Sr Dir-Regulatory Affairs)*
Kenny S. Frazier *(Sr Dir-Clinical Ops)*
D. Wade Walke *(Sr Dir-Corp Comm & IR)*
Joel P. Freiman *(Dir-Drug Safety)*
Brands & Products:
10TO10
E-BIOLOGY
GENOME5000
INTERNET UNIVERSAL
LEXGEN.COM
LEXGENE
LEXICON
LEXVISION
OMNIBANK

LIBERATOR MEDICAL HOLDINGS, INC.

2979 SE Gran Park Way
Stuart, FL 34997
Tel.: (772) 287-2414
Fax: (772) 286-7881
E-mail: info@liberatormedical.com
Web Site: www.liberatormedical.com
Approx. Sls.: $40,919,000
Approx. Number Employees: 214

Key to Media (For complete agency information see *The Advertising Red Books-Agencies* edition):
1. Bus. Publs. 2. Cable T.V. 3. Catalogs & Directories. 4. Co-op Adv. 5. Consumer Mags. 6. D.M. to Bus. Estab.7. D.M. to Consumers 8. Daily Newsp. 9. Exhibits/Trade Shows 10. Foreign 11. Infomercial 12. Internet Adv.13. Multimedia 14. Network Radio 15. Network T.V. 16. Newsp. Distr. Mags. 17. Other 18. Outdoor (Posters, Transit) 19. Point of Purchase20. Premiums, Novelties 21. Product Samples 22. Special Events Mktg. 23. Spot Radio 24. Spot T.V. 25. Weekly Newsp. 26. Yellow Page Adv.

Liberator Medical Holdings, Inc. — (Continued)

Business Description:
Holding Company; Direct-To-Consumer Medical Supplies
S.I.C.: 5047; 5961; 6719
N.A.I.C.S.: 454111; 423450; 454113; 551112
Advertising Expenditures: $4,629,000
Media: 4-6-8-12-13
Personnel:
Mark A. Libratore *(Pres & CEO)*
Robert J. Davis *(CFO)*
John Leger *(COO & Sr VP)*
Paul Levett *(CMO)*

LIBERTY MEDICAL SUPPLY, INC.

(Sub. of Medco Health Solutions, Inc.)
10400 S Federal Hwy
Port Saint Lucie, FL 34952
Tel.: (772) 398-5800
Fax: (772) 398-5886
Toll Free: (800) 376-1599
E-mail: corp@libertymedical.com
Web Site: www.libertymedical.com
Sales Range: $75-99.9 Million
Year Founded: 1989
Business Description:
Online Diabetic, Urological Disorder & Other Specialty Medical Supplies Distr
S.I.C.: 5961; 5912
N.A.I.C.S.: 454111; 446110
Advertising Expenditures: $500,000
Media: 3-8-13-23-24
Personnel:
Keith Jones *(Pres)*
Jonathan Starr *(CFO, VP & Asst Treas)*
Peter Gaylord *(Treas & Sr VP)*
Advertising Agencies:
A. Eicoff & Co.
(Div. of Ogilvy & Mather Worldwide)
401 N Michigan Ave 4th Fl
Chicago, IL 60611-4212
Tel.: (312) 527-7183
Fax: (312) 527-7188
Toll Free: (800) 333-6605

Response Mine
3390 Peachtree Rd Ste 800
Atlanta, GA 30326
Tel.: (404) 233-0370
Fax: (404) 233-0302

LIFE ALERT EMERGENCY RESPONSE INC.

16027 Ventura Blvd Ste 400
Encino, CA 91436
Tel.: (818) 700-7000
Fax: (818) 922-3362
Web Site: www.lifealert.com
Sales Range: $10-24.9 Million
Approx. Number Employees: 120
Business Description:
Provider of Burglary Protection Services
S.I.C.: 7381; 5731
N.A.I.C.S.: 561612; 443112
Brands & Products:
I'VE FALLEN AND I CAN'T GET UP!
LIFE ALERT 50+
LIFE ALERT CLASSIC
LIFE ALERT EMERGENCY
Advertising Agency:
E&M Advertising
462 7th Ave 8th Fl
New York, NY 10018-7606
Tel.: (212) 981-5900
Fax: (212) 981-2121

LIFE CARE CENTERS OF AMERICA

3570 Keith St NW
Cleveland, TN 37320
Mailing Address:
PO Box 3480
Cleveland, TN 37320-3480
Tel.: (423) 472-9585
Fax: (423) 339-8350
Toll Free: (800) 554-9585
Web Site: www.lcca.com
Sales Range: $1-4.9 Billion
Approx. Number Employees: 30,000
Year Founded: 1970
Business Description:
Retirement & Health Care Centers Operator
S.I.C.: 8059; 8082; 8322; 8361
N.A.I.C.S.: 623110; 621610; 623311; 623990; 624120
Media: 2-8-10-22-25-26
Personnel:
Forrest L. Preston *(Chm & CEO)*
Beecher Hunter *(Pres)*
Steve Ziegler *(CFO)*
Chris Mitchell *(COO)*
Carol Hulgan *(Sr VP-Life Care Home Health Inc)*
Dee McCarthy *(Sr VP-Clinical Svcs)*
Jennie McClaren *(Sr VP-HR)*
Peg Kennedy *(VP-Trng)*
Yuriy Lutsenko *(Exec Dir-Morgan County)*

LIFE CARE SERVICES LLC

(Sub. of LCS Holdings Inc.)
400 Locust St Ste 820
Des Moines, IA 50309-2334
Tel.: (515) 875-4500
Fax: (515) 875-4780
Web Site: www.lcsnet.com
Approx. Rev.: $22,000,000
Approx. Number Employees: 300
Business Description:
Retirement Communities Operator
S.I.C.: 6513
N.A.I.C.S.: 531110
Personnel:
Diane C. Bridgewater *(CFO, Treas & VP)*
Advertising Agency:
Zillner Marketing Communications
8725 Rosehill Rd Ste 200
Lenexa, KS 66215
Tel.: (913) 599-3230
Fax: (913) 599-0080
— Chelsea Krohe *(Acct Exec)*

LIFE PLUS INTERNATIONAL

15 Industrial Dr
Batesville, AR 72501-5512
Tel.: (870) 698-2311
Fax: (800) 959-2777
Toll Free: (800) 572-8446
E-mail: info@lifeplususa.com
Web Site: www.lifeplus.com
Approx. Number Employees: 150
Year Founded: 1992
Business Description:
Nutritional Supplements
S.I.C.: 5499
N.A.I.C.S.: 446191; 445299
Media: 4-8
Personnel:
Robert Christian *(Co-Founder)*
William T. Evans *(Co-Founder)*
Timothy A. Nolan *(Co-Founder)*
J. Robert Lemon *(Pres)*
Brands & Products:
BODYSMART
CALMAG PLUS
DAILY BIOBASICS
ENERXAN
FOREVER YOUNG
LIFE PLUS
OMEGOLD
PARACLEANSE
PROANTHENOLS
WONDER GEL

LIFE TECHNOLOGIES CORPORATION

5791 Van Allen Way
Carlsbad, CA 92008
Mailing Address:
PO Box 6482
Carlsbad, CA 92008
Tel.: (760) 603-7200
Fax: (760) 602-6500
Toll Free: (800) 955-6288
Web Site: www.lifetechnologies.com/
Approx. Rev.: $3,588,094,000
Approx. Number Employees: 11,000
Year Founded: 1987
Business Description:
Research Tools Mfr for Gene Cloning, Gene Expression & Gene Analysis; Sera, Cell & Tissue Culture Media & Reagents Mfr
S.I.C.: 2836; 3826
N.A.I.C.S.: 325414; 334516
Advertising Expenditures: $213,574
Media: 2-4-7-10-13-17
Personnel:
Gregory T. Lucier *(Chm & CEO)*
Mark Stevenson *(Pres & COO)*
David F. Hoffmeister *(CFO)*
Joe Beery *(CIO & Sr VP)*
Amanda Clardy *(CMO)*
John A. Cottingham *(Chief Legal Officer)*
Kelli A. Richard *(Chief Acctg Officer & VP-Fin)*
Nicolas M. Barthelemy *(Pres-Comml Ops)*
Bernd Brust *(Pres-Molecular Medicine)*
Peter Dansky *(Pres-Molecular & Cell Biology)*
John Miller *(Pres-Genetic Sys)*
Claude D. Benchimol *(Sr VP-Biological Info Sys)*
Peter M. Leddy *(Sr VP-HR)*
Mark O'Donnell *(Sr VP-Global Ops)*
Adam S. Taich *(VP-Fin & Leader-Global Comml)*
Eileen Pattinson *(Sr Dir-IR)*
Brands & Products:
ABSOLUTE-S
ACCUPRIME
ACTEV
ADENOVIRUS
ALAMARBLUE
ALBUMAX
ALEXA FLUOR
ALIGNFLOW
AMNIOMAX
AMPLEX
ANGIOSTATIN
ANTI-HIS
ANTI-HISG
ANTI-LEXA
ANTI-THIO
ANTI-XPRESS
ANTIBODY BEACON
APO-BRDU
APOTARGET
AQUALITE
ARES
ATTO-TAG
ATTOFLUOR
BAC-N-BLUE
BAC-TO-BAC
BACLIGHT
BACULODIRECT
BEADRETRIEVER
BENCHMARK
BIOCHARTER
BIOEASE
BIONICK
BIOPARTICLES
BIOPRIME
BIORELIANCE
BIOTIN
BLOCK-IT
BLOCKAID
BLUEJUICE
BO-PRO
BOBO
BOCILLIN
BODIPY
BP CLONASE
BRAINSTAIN
BSDCASSETTE
CALTAG
CANDYCANE
CAPTAVIDIN
CAPTIVATE
CASCADE BLUE
CASCADE YELLOW
CAT
CDNA CYCLE
CELLFECTIN
CELLTRACE
CELLTRACKER
CERTIFIED LUX
CHAMPION
CHARGESWITCH
CHROMATIDE
CLICK-IT
CLONASE
CLONECHECKER
CLONEMINER
CLONERANGER
CLONEWELL
COLCEMID
COLLOIDAL COOMASSIE
COMPENFLOW
CONCERT
CONSTELLATION
COOMASSIE
COOMASSIE FLUOR
COPY KIT
COT-1 DNA
COUNTBRIGHT
COVERWELL
CULTUREWELL
CUSTOM LUX
CYQUANT
CYTOSETS
D-LUX
D-TOPO
DAPOXYL
DETECTAGENE
DH10BAC
DH12S
DH5A
DIPSTICK

Key to Media (For complete agency information see *The Advertising Red Books-Agencies* edition):
1. Bus. Publs. 2. Cable T.V. 3. Catalogs & Directories. 4. Co-op Adv. 5. Consumer Mags. 6. D.M. to Bus. Estab.7. D.M. to Consumers
8. Daily Newsp. 9. Exhibits/Trade Shows 10. Foreign 11. Infomercial 12. Internet Adv.13. Multimedia 14. Network Radio
15. Network T.V. 16. Newsp. Distr. Mags. 17. Other 18. Outdoor (Posters, Transit) 19. Point of Purchase20. Premiums, Novelties
21. Product Samples 22. Special Events Mktg. 23. Spot Radio 24. Spot T.V. 25. Weekly Newsp. 26. Yellow Page Adv.

DISCOVERASE
DM-BODIPY
DNA MASS
DNAZOL
DQ
DRYEASE
DYECHROME
DYECYCLE
DYEMER
DYNABEADS
DYNAL
E-BASE
E-EDITOR
E-GEL
E-HOLDER
E-PAGE
EASY-DNA
EASYCOMP
ECHO
ECOR
EK-AWAY
EKMAX
ELECTRO-FAST
ELECTROCOMP
ELECTROMAX
ELISA
ELONGASE
ELUTATUBE
ENDOSTAIN
ENDOSTATIN
ENZCHEK
EPISERF
ER-TRACKER
EVOQUEST
EVOTRACK
EXPRESS FIVE
EXPRESSWAY
EZQ
FAST CAT
FASTTRACK
FECTIN
FLITRX
FLP-IN
FLUOCELLS
FLUOREPORTER
FLUOROCILLIN
FLUOROMYELIN
FLUOROPURE
FLUOROSCRIPT
FLUOSPHERES
FLUOZIN
FOAMAWAY
FOCALCHECK
FREESTYLE
FUN
FUNGALIGHT
FUNGIZONE
FURA RED
FURAZIN
GATEWAY
GELTREX
GENE POOL
GENECATCHER
GENEHOGS
GENEJUMPER
GENERACER
GENESTORM
GENETAILOR
GENETICIN
GENETRAPPER
GENICON
GIBCO
GIBCO FOAMAWAY
GLUTAMAX
GREENER
HG-LINK
HIGH FIVE
HIMARK
HIPERFORM
HYBRID HUNTER
HYBRISLIP
HYBRIWELL
I-SAGE
IBASE
IBLOT
ICAT
IMAGE-IT
IMAGENE GREEN
IMAGENE RED
IMMEDIA
INFLUX
INSECTSELECT
INSPECK
INVISION
INVITROGEN
INVITROLON
INVITROMASS
INVITROSOL
IPGRUNNER
ITK
JO-PRO
JOJO
KARYOMAX
KNOCKOUT
LABSHARE
LANTHASCREEN
LIBRARY EFFICIENCY
LINEARFLOW
LIPOFECTAMINE
LIPOFECTIN
LISSAMINE
LIVE/DEAD
LOLO
LR CLONASE
LUMIO
LUX
LYSOSENSOR
LYSOTRACKER
LYTICBLAZER
MACH1
MAGICMARK
MAGNA-SEP
MAGNARACK
MAGNESIUM
MAPPAIRS
MARINA BLUE
MARINER
MARK12
MARROWMAX
MAX EFFICIENCY
MEASURE-IT
MICRO-FASTTRACK
MICROHYB
MITO TRACKER
MITOFLUOR
MITOPROBE
MITOSOX
MITOTRACKER
MOLECULAR PROBES
MRNA CATCHER
MRNA DIRECT
MULTIPLEXED PROTEOMICS
MULTISHOT
MULTISITE GATEWAY
MULTISPECK
MYCOFLUOR
NANOGOLD
NANOORANGE
NATIVEMARK
NATIVEPAGE
NATIVEPURE
NEUROBASAL
NEUROTRACE
NEUTRAVIDIN
NEWPORT GREEN
NOVEX
NUPAGE
OLIGOFECTAMINE
OLIGOPERFECT
OMNIMAX
ONCYTE
ONE SHOT
OPTI-MEM
OPTIFECT
OPTIMAB
OPTIPRO
OREGON GREEN
ORGANELLE LIGHTS
OWL CENTIPEDE
OXYBURST
PACIFIC BLUE
PACIFIC ORANGE
PANOMER
PARAGON
PATHBLAZER
PATHCLONES
PB-MAX
PCDNA
PCR OPTIMIZER
PD-DIRECT
PDEST
PDISPLAY
PEAKFLOW
PENTA-HIS
PENTR
PEPPERMINTSTICK
PEPTIDESELECT
PHEN
PHRODO
PIP
PIPER
PLASMID
PLATINUM
PLURONIC
PLUS
PO-PRO
POPO
POSITOPE
POWEREASE
PRESS-TO-SEAL
PRO-Q
PROBOND
PROLONG
PROPLATE
PROQUEST
PROTOARRAY
PS-SPECK
PSHOOTER
PURELINK
PVAX
PZERO
QDOT
QUANT-IT
REACT
READY-LOAD
REDIPLATE
REDOXSENSOR
RELAY
RELI
REMBRANDT
RESGEN
RHINOHIDE
RHODAMINE GREEN
RHODAMINE RED
RHODOL GREEN
RHODZIN
RNAAQUEOUS
RNAI TOPO
RNASE
RNASE AWAY
RNASELECT
RNASEOUT
RNASEZAP
SAFE IMAGER
SAIVI
SECORE
SECURE-SEAL
SEEBLUE
SELECTFX
SELECTSCREEN
SENSIFLEX
SHARP
SHUTTLE PIP
SILVERQUEST
SILVERXPRESS
SIMPLYBLUE
SIZESELECT
SLOWFADE
S.N.A.P
SNARF
SOLID
SPECTRA
SPHINGOSTRIPS
ST-BODIPY
STAINEASE
STAR
STEALTH
SUPERSCRIPT
SYBR
SYBR SAFE
SYPRO
SYTO
SYTOX
T-REX
TA CLONING
TAG-ON-DEMAND
TC-FLASH
TC-REASH
TETRASPECK
TEXAS RED
THERMALACE
THERMO-X
THERMOSCRIPT
TO-PRO
TOPO
TOPO TA CLONING
TOTAL FOR AGILENT
TOTO
TOXBLAZER
TRACKIT
TRANSFIX
TRANSFLUOSPHERES
TRIZOL
TRYPLE
TS-LINK
TUBULINTRACKER
ULTIMATE
ULTRAMAX
ULTRAPURE
ULTRASENSE
ULYSIS
UNITRAY
V5-DEST
VECTOR NTI
VECTORDESIGNER
VERVE
VIAGRAM
VIRAPOWER
VIVID COLORS
VOYAGER
VYBRANT
WESTERNBREEZE
XCELL
XCELL SURELOCK
XPRESS
YO-PRO
YOYO
ZENON

Key to Media (For complete agency information see *The Advertising Red Books-Agencies* edition):
1. Bus. Publs. 2. Cable T.V. 3. Catalogs & Directories. 4. Co-op Adv. 5. Consumer Mags. 6. D.M. to Bus. Estab.7. D.M. to Consumers
8. Daily Newsp. 9. Exhibits/Trade Shows 10. Foreign 11. Infomercial 12. Internet Adv.13. Multimedia 14. Network Radio
15. Network T.V. 16. Newsp. Distr. Mags. 17. Other 18. Outdoor (Posters, Transit) 19. Point of Purchase20. Premiums, Novelties
21. Product Samples 22. Special Events Mktg. 23. Spot Radio 24. Spot T.V. 25. Weekly Newsp. 26. Yellow Page Adv.

Life Technologies Corporation —
(Continued)

ZEOCASSETTE
ZEOCIN
ZERO BACKGROUND
ZERO BLUNT
ZOOM

Advertising Agency:
Philip Johnson Associates
214 Grant Ave Ste 450
San Francisco, CA 94108-4628
Tel.: (415) 364-3100
Fax: (415) 200-0801

LIFE TECHNOLOGIES CORPORATION

(Div. of Life Technologies Corporation)
542 Flynn Rd
Camarillo, CA 93012-8027
Tel.: (805) 987-0086
Fax: (805) 383-5379
Toll Free: (800) 242-0607
E-mail: info@lifetechnologies.com
Web Site: www.lifetechnologies.com
Sales Range: $25-49.9 Million
Approx. Number Employees: 239
Year Founded: 1989
Business Description:
Cellular Pathway Exploration Tools, Protein Arrays, Antibodies & Recombinant Proteins Developer & Marketer
S.I.C.: 2835; 8733
N.A.I.C.S.: 325413; 541710
Import Export
Media: 2-4-7-10-20
Brands & Products:
ALAMARBLUE
BIOFLUIDS
CARTESIAN ARRAY
CHIPCLIP
CYTOSETS
FAST
IC BLOCK
IC FIX
MERCATOR
MESSAGESCREEN

LIFE TIME FITNESS INC

2902 Corporate Pl
Chanhassen, MN 55317
Tel.: (952) 947-0000
Fax: (952) 947-9137
E-mail: webmaster@lifetimefitness.com
Web Site: www.lifetimefitness.com
Approx. Rev.: $912,844,000
Approx. Number Employees: 12,500
Year Founded: 1990
Business Description:
Fitness Centers Operator
S.I.C.: 7991; 7999
N.A.I.C.S.: 713940; 611620
Import Export
Advertising Expenditures: $26,300,000
Media: 4-6-8-22
Personnel:
Bahram Akradi *(Founder, Chm, Pres & CEO)*
Michael R. Robinson *(CFO & Exec VP)*
Eric J. Buss *(Exec VP)*
Mark L. Zaebst *(Exec VP-Real Estate Dev)*
Marie Jacobsen *(Dir-Plng)*
David Schutz *(Dir-Race-Life Time Triathalon)*
Mark Neuman *(Coord-Mktg)*
Brands & Products:
A HEALTHY WAY OF LIFE COMPANY
EXPERIENCE LIFE
LIFE TIME FITNESS
Advertising Agency:
Mindframe, Inc.
212 3rd Ave N Ste 586
Minneapolis, MN 55401-1440
Tel.: (612) 204-0320

LIFECELL CORPORATION

(Div. of Kinetic Concepts, Inc.)
1 Millennium Way
Branchburg, NJ 08876
Tel.: (908) 947-1100
Fax: (908) 947-1200
Fax: (908) 947-1089
E-mail: corporatecommunications@lifecell.com
Web Site: www.lifecell.com
Approx. Rev.: $191,130,000
Approx. Number Employees: 443
Year Founded: 1986
Business Description:
Skin Graft Materials for Reconstructive, Urogynecologic & Orthopedic Surgery
S.I.C.: 2836; 3842
N.A.I.C.S.: 325414; 339113
Media: 10
Personnel:
Lisa N. Colleran *(Pres)*
Steven T. Sobieski *(CFO, VP-Fin & Admin)*
Bruce Lamb *(Sr VP-Dev & Regulatory Affairs)*
Advertising Agency:
Simms & McIvor Marketing Communications
3121 Rt 22 E Branch Estates
Branchburg, NJ 08876-3500
Tel.: (908) 722-8777
Fax: (908) 722-7833

LIFECORE BIOMEDICAL, LLC

(Holding of Warburg Pincus LLC)
3515 Lyman Blvd
Chaska, MN 55318-3050
Tel.: (952) 368-4300
Fax: (952) 368-3411
E-mail: info@lifecore.com
Web Site: www.lifecore.com
E-Mail For Key Personnel:
President: djallin@lifecore.com
Approx. Sls.: $69,629,000
Approx. Number Employees: 241
Year Founded: 1965
Business Description:
Dental Implant Systems, Tissue Regeneration Products & Medical Grade Hyaluronan Mfr
S.I.C.: 3842; 2833; 2836
N.A.I.C.S.: 339113; 325411; 325414
Advertising Expenditures: $670,000
Media: 2-4-7-10
Personnel:
Dennis J. Allingham *(Pres & CEO)*
Larry D. Hiebert *(VP & Gen Mgr)*
Brands & Products:
CALFORMA
CALMATRIX
CAPSET
DYNABLAST
DYNAGRAFT-D
LOCATOR
MEMBRANES
PRIMA CONNEX
PRIMA SOLO
QUICK-CAP
RENOVA
RESTORE
STAGE-1
TEFGEN REGENERATIVE MEMBRANE
ZEST

LIFELINE SYSTEMS, INC.

(Div. of Philips Medical Systems)
111 Lawrence St
Framingham, MA 01702-8156
Tel.: (508) 988-1000
Fax: (508) 988-1384
Toll Free: (800) 451-0525
E-mail: info@lifelinesys.com
Web Site: www.lifelinesys.com
Sales Range: $150-199.9 Million
Approx. Number Employees: 829
Year Founded: 1974
Business Description:
Personal Response Products & Services Mfr & Distr
S.I.C.: 3841; 3643; 3669
N.A.I.C.S.: 339112; 334290; 335931
Advertising Expenditures: $150,000
Media: 2-3-4-6-7-10-13-14-18-23-24-25-26
Distr.: Natl.
Personnel:
Mark T. Rutherford *(VP-Consumer Mktg)*
Brands & Products:
LIFELINE

LIFELOC TECHNOLOGIES, INC.

12441 W 49th Ave Unit 4
Wheat Ridge, CO 80033
Tel.: (303) 431-9500
Fax: (303) 431-1423
Toll Free: (800) 722-4872
E-mail: info@lifeloc.com
Web Site: www.lifeloc.com
Approx. Sls.: $4,287,597
Approx. Number Employees: 21
Year Founded: 1983
Business Description:
Portable Hand-Held Breathalyzers & Related Supplies Developer, Mfr & Marketer
S.I.C.: 3841; 5047
N.A.I.C.S.: 339112; 423450
Media: 13-17
Personnel:
Vern D. Kornelsen *(Chm, CFO & Sec)*
Barry R. Knott *(Pres, CEO & Treas)*
Kristie L. LaRose *(VP-Fin)*

LIFESCAN INC

(Sub. of Johnson & Johnson)
1000 Gibraltar Dr
Milpitas, CA 95035
Tel.: (408) 263-9789
Fax: (408) 942-6070
Toll Free: (800) 227-8862
Web Site: www.lifescan.com
Sales Range: $1-4.9 Billion
Approx. Number Employees: 3,000
Year Founded: 1981
Business Description:
Personal Blood Glucose Monitoring Kits & Blood Derivative Diagnostic Agents Mfr
S.I.C.: 2834; 3841
N.A.I.C.S.: 325412; 339112
Media: 2-3-4-5-6-7-8-10-11-13-15-19
Distr.: Intl.
Budget Set: Aug.
Personnel:
Alice Hsueh *(Product Dir-Digital Mktg)*
Brands & Products:
HARMONY
INDUO
ONETOUCH
ONETOUCH BASIC
ONETOUCH FASTTAKE
ONETOUCH PROFILE
ONETOUCH SURE STEP
ONETOUCH TEST STRIPS
ONETOUCH ULTRA
ONETOUCH ULTRASMART
Advertising Agencies:
Publicis Consultants
424 2nd Ave W
Seattle, WA 98119-4013
Tel.: (206) 285-5522
Fax: (206) 272-2497

Vox Medica Inc.
601 Walnut St Ste 250-S
Philadelphia, PA 19106-3514
Tel.: (215) 238-8500
Fax: (215) 238-0881

LIFEVANTAGE CORPORATION

11545 W Bernardo Ct Ste 301
San Diego, CA 92127
Tel.: (858) 312-8000
Fax: (801) 206-3800
E-mail: customerservice@lifevantage.com
Web Site: www.lifevantage.com
Approx. Sls.: $11,478,460
Approx. Number Employees: 33
Business Description:
Nutritional Supplement Mfr
S.I.C.: 2834; 2833
N.A.I.C.S.: 325412; 325411
Advertising Expenditures: $21,982
Media: 6-13-23
Personnel:
Garry P. Mauro *(Chm)*
Douglas C. Robinson *(Pres & CEO)*
Carrie E. Carlander *(CFO)*
Kirby Zenger *(COO)*
David W. Brown *(Pres/CEO-Network Mktg Ops)*
Ben Seeman *(VP-Sls)*
Brands & Products:
PROTANDIM

LIGAND PHARMACEUTICALS INCORPORATED

11085 N Torrey Pines Rd Ste 300
La Jolla, CA 92037
Tel.: (858) 550-7500
Fax: (858) 550-7506
E-mail: investors@ligand.com
Web Site: www.ligand.com
Approx. Rev.: $23,538,000
Approx. Number Employees: 31
Year Founded: 1987
Business Description:
Pharmaceutical Mfr, Researcher, Developer & Marketer
S.I.C.: 2834; 8733
N.A.I.C.S.: 325412; 541710
Media: 5-10
Personnel:
John W. Kozarich *(Chm)*

Key to Media (For complete agency information see *The Advertising Red Books-Agencies* edition):
1. Bus. Publs. 2. Cable T.V. 3. Catalogs & Directories. 4. Co-op Adv. 5. Consumer Mags. 6. D.M. to Bus. Estab.7. D.M. to Consumers
8. Daily Newsp. 9. Exhibits/Trade Shows 10. Foreign 11. Infomercial 12. Internet Adv.13. Multimedia 14. Network Radio
15. Network T.V. 16. Newsp. Distr. Mags. 17. Other 18. Outdoor (Posters, Transit) 19. Point of Purchase20. Premiums, Novelties
21. Product Samples 22. Special Events Mktg. 23. Spot Radio 24. Spot T.V. 25. Weekly Newsp. 26. Yellow Page Adv.

John L. Higgins *(Pres & CEO)*
John P. Sharp *(CFO & VP-Fin)*
Matthew W. Foehr *(COO & Exec VP)*
Charles S. Berkman *(Gen Counsel, Sec & VP)*
Audrey Warfield-Graham *(VP-HR)*
Rob McKay *(Sr Dir)*

Brands & Products:
AVINZA
LIGAND
TARGRETIN

Advertising Agencies:
Kane & Finkel Healthcare Communications
534 4th St
San Francisco, CA 94107
Tel.: (415) 777-4990
Fax: (415) 777-5019

Lippert/Heilshorn & Associates, Inc.
800 Third Ave 17th Fl
New York, NY 10022
Tel.: (212) 838-3777
Fax: (212) 838-4568

Regan Campbell Ward McCann
150 E 42nd St 16th Fl
New York, NY 10017-5642
Tel.: (646) 742-2100
Fax: (646) 742-2206

LIGHTHOUSE INTERNATIONAL

111 E 59th St
New York, NY 10022
Tel.: (212) 821-9200
Fax: (212) 821-9707
Toll Free: (800) 829-0500
E-mail: info@lighthouse.org
Web Site: www.lighthouse.org
Approx. Number Employees: 300
Year Founded: 1905

Business Description:
Vision Rehabilitation Services
S.I.C.: 8322; 8331
N.A.I.C.S.: 624120; 624310
Media: 2-6-8-10-13

Personnel:
Roger O. Goldman *(Chm)*
Mark G. Ackerman *(Pres & CEO)*
M. Stephen Soltis *(CFO & Chief Admin Officer)*
Ted Francavilla *(Exec VP-Corp Dev)*
Amy Horowitz *(Sr VP-Res & Evaluation)*
Cynthia Stuen *(Chief Pro Affairs Officer & Sr VP)*
Lisa Ferfoglia *(VP-HR)*
Leslie Jones *(Exec Dir-Music School)*
Tara Easter *(Project Dir)*
Eleanor E. Faye *(Dir-Medical)*
Leslie Gottlieb *(Dir-Comm)*

Brands & Products:
LIGHTHOUSE

LIPOSCIENCE, INC.

2500 Sumner Blvd
Raleigh, NC 27616
Tel.: (919) 212-1999
Fax: (919) 212-1998
Toll Free: (877) 547-6837
E-mail: customer.service@liposcience.com
Web Site: www.liposcience.com
Sales Range: $10-24.9 Million
Approx. Number Employees: 150
Year Founded: 1991

Business Description:
Clinical Diagnostic Applications
Developer & Marketer of Nuclear Magnetic Resonance (NMR) Spectroscopy Machines
S.I.C.: 3845
N.A.I.C.S.: 334510

Personnel:
James D. Otvos *(Founder, Exec VP & Chief Scientific Officer)*
Charles A. Sanders *(Chm)*
Richard O. Brajer *(Pres & CEO)*
Lucy G. Martindale *(CFO & Exec VP)*
Timothy J. Williams *(Gen Counsel, Sec & VP)*
Mark Kirtland *(VP-Strategy & Bus Dev)*

Advertising Agency:
Schwartz Communications, Inc.
230 3rd Ave
Waltham, MA 02451
Tel.: (781) 684-0770
Fax: (781) 684-6500

LORUS THERAPEUTICS INC.

2 Meridian Road
Toronto, ON M9W 4Z7, Canada
Tel.: (416) 798-1200
Fax: (416) 798-2200
E-mail: info@lorusthera.com
Web Site: www.lorusthera.com
Approx. Rev.: $128,207
Approx. Number Employees: 17
Year Founded: 1986

Business Description:
Antisense, Immunotherapy & Chemotherapy Technologies for Cancer Treatment
S.I.C.: 2834; 8733
N.A.I.C.S.: 325412; 541710

Personnel:
Denis R. Burger *(Chm)*
Aiping H. Young *(Pres & CEO)*
Elizabeth Williams *(Acting CFO, Dir-Fin & Admin)*
Peter Murray *(Dir-Clinical Dev)*

Brands & Products:
FOCUSSED-INNOVATIVE-EFFECTIVE
LORUS THERAPEUTICS
VIRULIZIN

Advertising Agency:
Mansfield Communications, Inc.
225 Richmond Street West Suite 302
Toronto, ON M5V 1W2, Canada
Tel.: (416) 599-0024
Fax: (416) 599-7484
Pub Rels

LUCILLE ROBERTS HEALTH SPA, INC.

4 E 80th St
New York, NY 10021
Tel.: (212) 734-0500
Fax: (212) 628-0809
Toll Free: (800) LUCILLE
E-mail: lucilleroberts@lucilleroberts.com
Web Site: www.lucilleroberts.com
Approx. Number Employees: 450
Year Founded: 1970

Business Description:
Women's Health Club Chain Owner & Operator
S.I.C.: 7991; 7299
N.A.I.C.S.: 713940; 812191
Advertising Expenditures: $2,000,000
Media: 8-9-16-17-25-26
Distr.: Direct to Consumer; Natl.
Budget Set: Nov.

Personnel:
Kirk Roberts *(VP-Adv)*

LUITPOLD PHARMACEUTICALS, INC.

1 Luitpold Dr
Shirley, NY 11967
Tel.: (631) 924-4000
Fax: (631) 924-8654
Toll Free: (800) 645-1706
Web Site: www.luitpold.com
E-Mail For Key Personnel:
Marketing Director: wtozzi@aol.com
Approx. Number Employees: 400

Business Description:
Developer & Mfr of Pharmaceuticals for Human & Veterinary Usage
S.I.C.: 2834; 5122
N.A.I.C.S.: 325412; 424210
Media: 2-4-5-6-7-8-10-13-19-20-21
Distr.: Natl.
Budget Set: Feb.

Personnel:
Mary Jane Helenek *(Pres & CEO)*
Fred Pratt *(VP-Ops, Production & Mfg)*
Walter Tozzi *(Dir-Prof Svcs)*

Brands & Products:
ADEQUAN
DEXFERRUM
EQUIPHEN
TARGACEUTICAL
TAXOPREXIN
VENOFER

LUNA INNOVATIONS INC.

(Filed Ch 11 Bankruptcy #971811 on 07/17/09 in U.S. Bankruptcy Ct, Western Dist of VA, Roanoke)
1 Riverside Cir Ste 400
Roanoke, VA 24016
Tel.: (540) 769-8400
Fax: (540) 769-8401
E-mail: solutions@lunainnovations.com
Web Site: www.lunainnovations.com
Approx. Rev.: $34,538,394
Approx. Number Employees: 187
Year Founded: 1990

Business Description:
Innovative Technologies Research & Development
S.I.C.: 8733; 3643; 3674; 3829
N.A.I.C.S.: 541710; 334413; 334519; 335931
Advertising Expenditures: $73,490
Media: 7-21

Personnel:
Richard W. Roedel *(Chm)*
Kent A. Murphy *(Vice Chm)*
My E. Chung *(Pres, CEO & COO)*
Dale E. Messick *(CFO & Chief Acctg Officer)*
Scott A. Graeff *(Chief Commercialization Officer & Treas)*

MAGELLAN HEALTH SERVICES, INC.

55 Nod Rd
Avon, CT 06001
Tel.: (860) 507-1900
Fax: (860) 507-1990
Fax: (410) 953-5200
Toll Free: (800) 410-8312
Web Site: www.magellanhealth.com
Approx. Rev.: $2,969,240,000
Approx. Number Employees: 4,900
Year Founded: 1969

Business Description:
Behavioral Health & Employee Assistance Services
S.I.C.: 3641; 8011; 8049; 8063; 8069; 8093; 8361; 8742
N.A.I.C.S.: 335110; 541611; 621112; 621330; 621399; 621420; 622210; 622310; 623220
Advertising Expenditures: $3,000,000
Media: 9-13-14-15-18
Distr.: Direct to Consumer; Intl.; Natl.

Personnel:
Rene Lerer *(Chm & CEO)*
Karen S. Rohan *(Pres)*
Jonathan N. Rubin *(CFO)*
Gary Anderson *(CIO)*
Alan Lotvin *(Pres-ICORE)*
Kim M. Mageau *(Pres-Pharmacy Solutions)*
Tina M. Blasi *(CEO-Natl Imaging Associates)*
Daniel N. Gregoire *(Gen Counsel)*
Jeffrey N. West *(Sr VP & Controller)*
David W. Carter *(Sr VP-Mktg & Comm)*
Suzanne Kunis *(Sr VP)*
Jay Youell *(Sr VP-Health Plans & Insurance Markets)*

Brands & Products:
CHARTER MEDICAL
GETTING BETTER ALL THE TIME
MAGELLAN HEALTH SERVICES

MAINE COAST REGIONAL HEALTH FACILITIES INC.

50 Union St
Ellsworth, ME 04605
Tel.: (207) 667-5311
Fax: (207) 664-5305
Web Site: www.mainehospital.org
E-Mail For Key Personnel:
Marketing Director: dbaril@mainehospital.org
Approx. Number Employees: 600
Year Founded: 1947

Business Description:
Operator of General Medical & Surgical Hospital
S.I.C.: 8062; 8011
N.A.I.C.S.: 622110; 621111
Import Export
Advertising Expenditures: $200,000
Media: 4-10-13-22

Personnel:
Karen W. Stanley *(Chm)*
John McCormack *(CEO)*
Kevin A. Sedgwick *(CFO & VP)*
Peter J. Ossanna *(Pres-Medical Staff)*

MAKO SURGICAL CORP.

2555 Davie Rd
Fort Lauderdale, FL 33317
Tel.: (954) 927-2044
Fax: (954) 927-0446
E-mail: contactus@makosurgical.com
Web Site: www.makosurgicalcorp.com
Approx. Rev.: $44,296,000
Approx. Number Employees: 315
Year Founded: 2004

Business Description:
Medical Devices Focusing on Orthopedic Knee Advanced Robotic Solutions & Implants
S.I.C.: 3842; 3841
N.A.I.C.S.: 339113; 339112
Advertising Expenditures: $1,600,000

Key to Media (For complete agency information see *The Advertising Red Books-Agencies* edition):
1. Bus. Publs. 2. Cable T.V. 3. Catalogs & Directories. 4. Co-op Adv. 5. Consumer Mags. 6. D.M. to Bus. Estab.7. D.M. to Consumers
8. Daily Newsp. 9. Exhibits/Trade Shows 10. Foreign 11. Infomercial 12. Internet Adv.13. Multimedia 14. Network Radio
15. Network T.V. 16. Newsp. Distr. Mags. 17. Other 18. Outdoor (Posters, Transit) 19. Point of Purchase20. Premiums, Novelties
21. Product Samples 22. Special Events Mktg. 23. Spot Radio 24. Spot T.V. 25. Weekly Newsp. 26. Yellow Page Adv.

MAKO Surgical Corp. — (Continued)

Personnel:
William F. Tapia *(Co-Founder & Dir-Regulatory Affairs)*
Rony A. Abovitz *(Co-Founder & Chief Visionary Officer)*
Maurice R. Ferre *(Chm, Pres & CEO)*
Fritz L. LaPorte *(CFO & Sr VP-Fin & Admin)*
Menashe R. Frank *(Gen Counsel, Sec & Sr VP)*
Ivan Delevic *(Sr VP-Strategic Mktg & Bus Dev)*
James E. Keller *(Sr VP-RA & QA)*
Richard Leparmentier *(Sr VP-Engrg)*
Duncan H. Moffat *(Sr VP-Ops)*
Steven J. Nunes *(Sr VP-Sls & Mktg)*
Benny Hagag *(Gen Mgr & VP-Intl Bus-Asia Pacific, MEA & Canada)*
Samantha C. Brodsky *(Dir-HR)*
Cynthia M. Kalb *(Dir-Mktg)*
Sue Siebert *(Mgr-Mktg Comm)*

MANATEE MEMORIAL HOSPITAL & HEALTH SYSTEM

(Sub. of UHS of Delaware, Inc.)
206 2nd St E
Bradenton, FL 34208
Tel.: (941) 746-5111
Fax: (941) 745-6862
E-mail: info@manateememorial.com
Web Site: www.manateememorial.com
Approx. Rev.: $60,000,000
Approx. Number Employees: 1,400
Year Founded: 1953
Business Description:
Medical Services
S.I.C.: 8062; 8011
N.A.I.C.S.: 622110; 621111
Media: 2-9-22-23-24-25
Personnel:
Hugh I. Miller *(Chm)*
Moody L. Chisholm *(CEO & VP-UHS Acute Care Div)*
Kevin DiLallo *(CEO)*
Richard S. Fletcher *(COO)*
Vernon DeSear *(VP-Mktg & Bus Dev)*
Betty Chambliss *(Dir-Adv & Community Events)*
Paula Jefferson *(Dir-Imaging Svcs)*
Steven Watsky *(Dir-Medical)*

MANNATECH, INCORPORATED

600 S Royal Ln Ste 200
Coppell, TX 75019-3823
Tel.: (972) 471-7400
Fax: (972) 471-8135
E-mail: ir@mannatech.com
Web Site: www.mannatech.com
Approx. Sls.: $228,088,000
Approx. Number Employees: 490
Year Founded: 1993
Business Description:
Proprietary Nutritional Supplements & Topical Products
S.I.C.: 2833
N.A.I.C.S.: 325411
Export
Advertising Expenditures: $5,600,000
Personnel:
J. Stanley Fredrick *(Chm)*
Stephen D. Fenstermacher *(Co-CEO & CFO)*
Robert A. Sinnott *(Co-CEO & Chief Science Officer)*
Claire Zevalkink *(Chief Global Mktg Officer & Sr VP)*
B. Keith Clark *(Chief Legal Officer & Exec VP)*
Randy S. Bancino *(Pres-Global Bus Ops & Expansion)*
Alfredo Bala *(Exec VP-Sls)*
Natalie Clark *(Sr VP-North American Sls & Ops)*
Ronald Norman *(Sr VP-Intl)*
Gary M. Spinell *(Sr VP-Fin & Admin)*
Brett Duncan *(VP-Mktg)*
Landen Fredrick *(VP-Sls-North America)*
Patrick Park *(Gen Mgr-Bus Ops-Korea)*
Patricia Yakesch *(Dir-Mktg-Skin Care)*
Brands & Products:
ACCELERATOR 3
ADVANCED
AMBRODERM
AMBROSTART
AMBROTOSE
AMBROTOSE AO
AMBROTOSE COMPLEX
BOUNCEBACK
CARDIO BALANCE
EM-PACT
EMPRIZONE
GI-PRO
GI-ZYME
GLYCENTIALS
GLYCO BEARS
GLYCOLEAN
GLYCOSLIM
HOPE. HEALTH. OPPURTUNITY.
IMMUNOSTART
MAN-ALOE CLASSIC
MANNA-BEARS
MANNA-C
MANNACLEANSE
MANNATECH
MANNATECH OPTIMAL SKIN CARE SYSTEM
OSOLEAN
PHYT-ALOE
PHYTOMATRIX
PLUS
SPORT
Advertising Agency:
Hospodka & White
350 N St Paul Ste 2895
Dallas, TX 75201
Tel.: (972) 421-0780
Fax: (972) 421-0783

MAQUET, INC.

(Sub. of MAQUET GmbH & Co. KG)
45 Barbour pond dr
Wayne, NJ 07470
Tel.: (908) 947-2300
Fax: (973) 709-6511
E-mail: info@maquet.com
Web Site: www.maquet.com
Approx. Number Employees: 75
Business Description:
Hospital Medical Equipment
S.I.C.: 5047
N.A.I.C.S.: 423450; 541711
Personnel:
Chima Abuba *(Pres & CEO)*
Nancy Werfel *(Product Mgr-Anesthesia)*
Advertising Agency:
R&J Public Relations
1140 Rte 22 E Ste 200
Bridgewater, NJ 08807
Tel.: (908) 722-5757
Fax: (908) 722-5776
(VARIOP)

MARIANJOY REHABILITATION HOSPITAL

(Sub. of Wheaton Franciscan Services Inc.)
26 W 171 Roosevelt Rd
Wheaton, IL 60187
Tel.: (630) 462-4000
Fax: (630) 462-4444
Toll Free: (800) 462-2366
Web Site: www.marianjoy.org
Approx. Number Employees: 800
Year Founded: 1972
Business Description:
Rehabilitation Hospital
S.I.C.: 8069; 8093
N.A.I.C.S.: 622310; 621498
Import Export
Advertising Expenditures: $172,000
Media: 2-9-10-22-23
Personnel:
Don Fischer *(Chm)*
John D. Oliverio *(Vice Chm)*
Kathleen C. Yosko *(Pres & CEO)*
Michael Hedderman *(CFO & VP-Fin)*
Denise LeBloch *(VP-Mktg & Comm, Exec Dir-Marianjoy Foundation)*
Teresa Chapman *(VP-HR)*

MARSHFIELD CLINIC

1000 N Oak Ave
Marshfield, WI 54449
Tel.: (715) 387-5511
Fax: (715) 387-5240
Toll Free: (800) 782-8581
Web Site: www.marshfieldclinic.org
Approx. Number Employees: 5,000
Year Founded: 1916
Business Description:
Medical Clinic, Research Foundation
S.I.C.: 8011
N.A.I.C.S.: 621111
Advertising Expenditures: $200,000
Media: 8-9-13-18-23-24
Distr.: Reg.
Personnel:
James S. Coleman *(COO)*
Barbara A. Kuhl *(Gen Counsel & Compliance Officer)*
Reed E. Hall *(Exec Dir)*
Robert Dums *(Dir-Sys & Processes)*
Robert K. Gribble *(Dir-Medical)*
David Keefe *(Dir-HR)*
Greg Nycz *(Dir-Health)*
Victoria L. Strobel *(Dir-Bus Dev & Insurance Ops)*
Kathleen Fons-Anderson *(Mgr-Pharmacy-Merrill Center)*
Brands & Products:
DON'T JUST LIVE. SHINE.
MARSHFIELD CLINIC

MARTEK BIOSCIENCES CORPORATION

(Sub. of Royal DSM N.V.)
6480 Dobbin Rd
Columbia, MD 21045-5825
Tel.: (410) 740-0081
Fax: (410) 740-2985
E-mail: contactus@martek.com
Web Site: www.martek.com
Approx. Rev.: $450,023,000
Approx. Number Employees: 592
Year Founded: 1985
Business Description:
Nutritional & Pharmaceutical Products
S.I.C.: 2834; 8733
N.A.I.C.S.: 325412; 541720
Advertising Expenditures: $14,300,000
Media: 6
Personnel:
Robert J. Flanagan *(Chm)*
David M. Abramson *(Pres)*
Steve Dubin *(CEO)*
Peter L. Buzy *(CFO, Treas, Exec VP-Fin & Admin)*
Peter A. Nitze *(COO & Exec VP)*
David M. Feitel *(Gen Counsel, Sec & Sr VP)*
Barney B. Easterling *(Sr VP-Mfg)*
Sarah Sullivan *(Dir-Strategy)*
Brands & Products:
ARASCO
BRIGHT BEGINNINGS
DHASCO
FORMULAID
LIFE ENRICHED.
LIFE'S ARA
LIFE'S DHA
MARTEK
NEUROMINS
SURELIGHT
Advertising Agency:
gkv Communications
The Cascade Bldg 1030 Hull St Ste 400
Baltimore, MD 21230
Tel.: (410) 539-5400
Fax: (410) 234-2441

MASIMO CORPORATION

40 Parker
Irvine, CA 92618
Tel.: (949) 297-7000
Fax: (949) 297-7001
Web Site: www.masimo.com
Approx. Rev.: $405,407,000
Approx. Number Employees: 2,397
Year Founded: 1989
Business Description:
Motion & Low Perfusion Tolerant Pulse Oximetry Mfr
S.I.C.: 3844; 3841
N.A.I.C.S.: 334517; 339112
Advertising Expenditures: $5,900,000
Personnel:
Joe E. Kiani *(Chm & CEO)*
Mark P. de Raad *(CFO & Exec VP)*
Anthony Allan *(COO)*
Yongsam Lee *(CIO & Exec VP-Regulatory Affairs)*
Michael O'Reilly *(Chief Medical Officer & Exec VP)*
Jon Coleman *(Pres-Worldwide Sls & Mktg & Clinical Res)*
Rick Fishel *(Pres-Worldwide OEM Bus & Corp Dev)*
Paul Jansen *(Exec VP-Mktg)*
Anand Sampath *(Exec VP-Engrg)*
Brands & Products:
CLEANSHIELD
CLOSER TO THE HEART
LNCS
LNOP
MASIMO
MASIMO SET
RADICAL
RAINBOW SET
SIGNAL EXTRACTION TECHNOLOGY

Key to Media (For complete agency information see *The Advertising Red Books-Agencies* edition):
1. Bus. Publs. 2. Cable T.V. 3. Catalogs & Directories. 4. Co-op Adv. 5. Consumer Mags. 6. D.M. to Bus. Estab.7. D.M. to Consumers 8. Daily Newsp. 9. Exhibits/Trade Shows 10. Foreign 11. Infomercial 12. Internet Adv.13. Multimedia 14. Network Radio 15. Network T.V. 16. Newsp. Distr. Mags. 17. Other 18. Outdoor (Posters, Transit) 19. Point of Purchase20. Premiums, Novelties 21. Product Samples 22. Special Events Mktg. 23. Spot Radio 24. Spot T.V. 25. Weekly Newsp. 26. Yellow Page Adv.

SIGNAL I.Q.

MASTEX INDUSTRIES, INC.
2035 Factory Ln
Petersburg, VA 23803-3694
Tel.: (804) 732-8300
Fax: (804) 732-8395
Approx. Number Employees: 8
Year Founded: 1947
Business Description:
Therapeutic Apparatus Mfr
S.I.C.: 3634; 3089
N.A.I.C.S.: 335211; 326199
Import Export
Advertising Expenditures: $380,000
Media: 2-3-4-6-10-11
Distr.: Natl.
Personnel:
Frank Mast *(Pres)*
Brands & Products:
FORMX
HEALTH STARTS WITH HEALING TOUCH
NORDIC
TEXTYLE
THERMALEEZE
THERMALFREEZE

MATERION MICROELECTRONICS & SERVICES
(Formerly Williams Advanced Materials Inc.)
(Sub. of BRUSH ENGINEERED MATERIALS INC.)
2978 Main St
Buffalo, NY 14214-1004
Tel.: (716) 837-1000
Fax: (716) 833-2926
Toll Free: (800) 327-1355
E-mail: microelectronics@materion.com
Web Site: www.materion.com/microelectronics
Sales Range: $50-74.9 Million
Approx. Number Employees: 200
Business Description:
Thin Film Deposition & Semiconductor Packaging Components Mfr
S.I.C.: 3679; 3341; 3479; 3499
N.A.I.C.S.: 334419; 331492; 332812; 332999
Export
Media: 2-7-10
Distr.: Intl.; Natl.
Budget Set: Sept. -Oct.
Personnel:
Richard W. Sager *(Pres)*
Matthew Willson *(VP & Gen Mgr)*
Derrick Brown *(VP-Mktg & Comml Dev)*
Scott Haluska *(VP-Sls & Mktg)*
George Wityak *(VP-Tech)*

MATRIXX INITIATIVES, INC.
(Holding of H.I.G. Capital, LLC)
8515 E Anderson Dr
Scottsdale, AZ 85255
Tel.: (602) 385-8888
Web Site: www.matrixxinc.com
Approx. Sls.: $67,317,239
Approx. Number Employees: 29
Business Description:
Nasally-Delivered Over-The-Counter Remedies Developers
S.I.C.: 2833; 2834; 6733
N.A.I.C.S.: 325411; 325412; 525920
Advertising Expenditures: $25,400,000
Media: 6-15
Personnel:
Dennis O'Donnell *(Pres & CEO)*
James A. Marini *(VP-Sls)*
Marla Bradbury *(Brand Mgr-Zicam)*
Brands & Products:
BETTER WAYS TO GET BETTER
MATRIXX
Advertising Agencies:
Cramer-Krasselt
225 N Michigan Ave
Chicago, IL 60601-7601
Tel.: (312) 616-9600
Fax: (312) 616-3839

Cramer-Krasselt
1850 N Central Ave Ste 1800
Phoenix, AZ 85004-4561
Tel.: (602) 417-0600
Fax: (602) 258-1446

GolinHarris
(Part of the Interpublic Group of Companies)
111 E Wacker Dr 11th Fl
Chicago, IL 60601-4306
Tel.: (312) 729-4000
Fax: (312) 729-4010

The Storch-Murphy Group
299 Stoughton Ave
Cranford, NJ 07016
Tel.: (908) 276-0777
Fax: (908) 276-0888
— Robert Murphy *(Pres)*

MAXIM HEALTHCARE SERVICES
7227 Lee Deforest Dr
Columbia, MD 21046
Tel.: (410) 910-1500
Fax: (410) 910-1600
E-mail: info@maxhealthcare.com
Web Site: www.maxhealthcare.com
Approx. Number Employees: 900
Business Description:
Medical Help Service
S.I.C.: 7363
N.A.I.C.S.: 561320
Media: 2
Personnel:
Stephen J. Bisciotti *(Pres)*
Brian Wynne *(Pres)*
Brad Bennett *(CEO)*
Brett Barlag *(CFO & Chief Strategy Officer)*
Gregory Ericson *(CIO)*
Paula Sotir *(COO-Homecare Div & Chief Clinical Officer)*
Kathy Ayres *(VP-HR)*

MAXIM HEALTHCARE SERVICES INC.
(Sub. of Maxim Healthcare Services)
4813 Jonestown Rd Ste 106
Harrisburg, PA 17109
Tel.: (717) 526-4555
Fax: (877) 339-7710
E-mail: antempoo@maxhealth.com
Web Site: www.maximhealthcare.com
Approx. Number Employees: 5
Year Founded: 2000
Business Description:
Homecare & Clinical Staffing Services
S.I.C.: 7363
N.A.I.C.S.: 561320
Media: 7-9

MAXIMUM HUMAN PERFORMANCE, INC.
21 Dwight Pl
Fairfield, NJ 07004
Tel.: (973) 785-9055
Fax: (973) 785-9159
Toll Free: (888) 783-8844
E-mail: info@maxperformance.com
Web Site: www.maxperformance.com
Approx. Number Employees: 15
Year Founded: 1997
Business Description:
Fitness & Health Enhancing Products Whslr
S.I.C.: 5149
N.A.I.C.S.: 424490
Media: 4-6-8-10-12-13-26
Personnel:
Gerard Dente *(CEO)*
Vincent Giampapa *(Dir-Medical Res)*
Lisa Passaretti *(Mgr-Office & Acctg)*
Brands & Products:
A-BOMB
ANADROX
CREATINE
CYCLIN-GF
DARK MATTER
DARK RAGE
DREN
MACROBOLIC
MHP
RELEVE
REMI
SARM-X
SECRETAGOGUE-ONE
SIMPLY WHEY
T-BOMB
T-BOMB II
TAKE OFF!
THYRO-SLIM
TRAC
TRAC EXTREME-NO
UP YOUR MASS
XPEL

MCKEON PRODUCTS, INC.
25460 Guenther
Warren, MI 48091
Tel.: (586) 427-7560
Fax: (586) 427-7204
Web Site: www.macksearplugs.com
E-Mail For Key Personnel:
Marketing Director: suzie@macksearplugs.com
Approx. Number Employees: 40
Year Founded: 1962
Business Description:
Earplugs Mfr & Distr
S.I.C.: 3842; 3949
N.A.I.C.S.: 339113; 339920
Media: 2-6-10
Personnel:
Devin Benner *(CEO)*
Pete Benner *(Mgr-Natl Sls)*
Marian L. Green *(Mgr)*
Jake Herman *(Mgr-Natl Sls)*
Brands & Products:
AQUA BLOCK
DREAMGIRL
DREAMPLUG
DREAMWEAVER
DRY-N-CLEAR
EAR SEALS
EARDRYER
EARPHONE ANCHORS
EARSAVER
HEAR PLUGS
MACK'S
PACK
PILLOW SOFT
ROCKIN ROLL-UPS
SAFE SOUND
SHOOTER'S PUTTY
SHUT-EYE SHADE
SNORE BLOCKERS
SOUND ASLEEP
WAX AWAY

MCKESSON CORPORATION
1 Post St
San Francisco, CA 94104
Tel.: (415) 983-8300
Fax: (415) 983-7160
Toll Free: (800) 482-3784
Telex: 170712
E-mail: corpcommunications@mckesson.com
Web Site: www.mckesson.com
E-Mail For Key Personnel:
Public Relations:
corpcommunications@mckesson.com
Approx. Rev.: $112,084,000,000
Approx. Number Employees: 36,400
Year Founded: 1833
Business Description:
Healthcare Products & Information Systems
S.I.C.: 5122; 5047
N.A.I.C.S.: 424210; 423450
Import Export
Advertising Expenditures: $1,000,000
Media: 1-2-3-4-5-6-7-8-9-10-11-14-15-16-18-19-20-21-22-23-24-25
Distr.: Intl.; Natl.
Personnel:
John H. Hammergren *(Chm, Pres & CEO)*
Jeffrey C. Campbell *(CFO & Exec VP)*
Randall N. Spratt *(CIO, CTO & Exec VP)*
Laureen E. Seeger *(Chief Compliance Officer, Gen Counsel & Exec VP)*
Patrick J. Blake *(Exec VP & Grp Pres-McKesson Tech Solutions)*
Paul C. Julian *(Exec VP & Grp Pres-Distr, Specialty Care Solutions & Retail)*
Jorge L. Figueredo *(Exec VP-HR)*
Paul E. Kirincic *(Exec VP-PR, Corp Mktg & Comm)*
Marc E. Owen *(Exec VP-Corp Strategy & Bus Dev)*
Anne-Marie Law *(Sr VP-HR Specialty & US Oncology)*
Jim Nemecek *(Sr VP-Mktg)*
James Larkin *(Dir-Pub Rel)*
Laura Green *(Mgr-Mktg)*
Brands & Products:
ACUDOSE-RX
ACUMAX PLUS
ANESTHESIA-RX
ASK-A-NURSE
AUTOMATIC DECISION SUPPORT
CONNECT-RX
CRMS
EMPOWERING HEALTHCARE
EPISODE PROFILER
FULFILL-RX
HEALTH MART
HEALTHQUEST
HORIZON MEDCOMM-RX
MCKKESON

Key to Media (For complete agency information see *The Advertising Red Books-Agencies* edition):
1. Bus. Publs. 2. Cable T.V. 3. Catalogs & Directories. 4. Co-op Adv. 5. Consumer Mags. 6. D.M. to Bus. Estab.7. D.M. to Consumers 8. Daily Newsp. 9. Exhibits/Trade Shows 10. Foreign 11. Infomercial 12. Internet Adv.13. Multimedia 14. Network Radio 15. Network T.V. 16. Newsp. Distr. Mags. 17. Other 18. Outdoor (Posters, Transit) 19. Point of Purchase20. Premiums, Novelties 21. Product Samples 22. Special Events Mktg. 23. Spot Radio 24. Spot T.V. 25. Weekly Newsp. 26. Yellow Page Adv.

McKesson Corporation — (Continued)

MEDCAROUSEL
NARCSTATION
PACMED
PARAGON
PATTERNS PROFILER
ROBOT-RX
SELFPACE
SERIES 2000
STAR 2000
SUPPLYSCAN
VALU-RITE

Advertising Agency:
EMG3
380 US Route 1
Falmouth, ME 04105
Tel.: (207) 828-4660
Fax: (207) 828-4704

MCNEIL-PPC, INC.

(Sub. of Johnson & Johnson)
(d/b/a McNeil Consumer & Specialty Pharmaceuticals)
7050 Camp Hill Rd
Fort Washington, PA 19034-2210
Tel.: (215) 273-7000
Fax: (215) 273-4193
Toll Free: (800) 962-5357
E-mail: info@brands2liveby.com
Web Site: www.brands2liveby.com
Sales Range: $900-999.9 Million
Approx. Number Employees: 1,500
Year Founded: 1879
Business Description:
Pain Reliever Drug Mfr
S.I.C.: 2834
N.A.I.C.S.: 325412
Media: 2-3-6-7-9-15-19-21-24
Distr.: Natl.
Budget Set: Sept.
Personnel:
Brenda S. Bass *(VP-Sls)*
Jeffrey Leebaw *(VP-Corp Comm)*
Carol Goodrich *(Dir-Corp Media Rels)*
Marc Monseau *(Dir-Corp Media Rels)*
Jennifer Salkeld Nelson *(Dir-Market Res-J&J Consumer Healthcare)*
Brands & Products:
ACTIFED
BENADRYL
BENYLIN
CHILDREN'S MOTRIN
CHILDREN'S TYLENOL
CHILDREN'S TYLENOL COLD
DOXIDAN
DRAMAMINE
EFFERDENT
EFFERGRIP
EMETROL
E.P.T
FLOXIN OTIC
FRESH 'N BRITE
GELUSIL
HEMORID
LAVACOL
LISTERINE
LISTERMINT
LUDEN'S
MAXIMUM STRENGTH TYLENOL SINUS MEDICATION
MICATIN
MOTRIN
MYADEC
NASALCROM
PEDIACARE
PLAX
PROGAINE
PROXACOL
ROGAINE
ROLAIDS
SIMPLY SLEEP
SINUTAB
ST. JOSEPH'S ASPIRIN
SUDACARE
SUDAFED
TUCKS
TYLENOL
TYLENOL COUGH/COLD/FLU
TYLENOL HEADACHE PLUS
TYLENOL PM
TYLENOL SINUS/ALLERGY SINUS
UNICAP
VISINE
WART-OFF
WOMEN'S TYLENOL

Advertising Agencies:
Edelman
250 Hudson St
New York, NY 10013
Tel.: (212) 768-0550
Fax: (212) 704-0128

JWT
Centro Banaven Torre C Piso 3 Ave
La Estancia Chuao
Caracas, 1061, Venezuela
Tel.: (58) 212 991 3544
Fax: (58) 212 902 3227
Dramamine

Universal McCann
100 33rd St 8th Fl
New York, NY 10001
Tel.: (212) 883-4700

MD SCIENTIFIC LLC

2815 Coliseum Centre Dr Ste 250
Charlotte, NC 28217-1468
Tel.: (704) 335-1300
Fax: (704) 335-1309
E-mail: info@mdsci.com
Web Site: www.mdscientific.com
Year Founded: 2003
Business Description:
Developer of Software Applications to Calculate Insulin Dosages for Critically Ill Patients
S.I.C.: 2834
N.A.I.C.S.: 325412
Export
Media: 4-7-11
Brands & Products:
ENDOTOOL
Advertising Agency:
Blue Nine Partners
809 West Hill St Ste D
Charlotte, NC 28208
Tel.: (704) 344-9191
Fax: (704) 358-3199
Fax: (704) 344-9710

MDS INC.

(Name Changed to Nordion Inc.)

MEAD JOHNSON NUTRITION COMPANY

(d/b/a Mead Johnson Nutritionals)
2701 Patriot Blvd
Glenview, IL 60026
Tel.: (847) 832-2420
Web Site: www.meadjohnson.com
Approx. Sls.: $3,141,600,000
Approx. Number Employees: 6,500
Year Founded: 1905
Business Description:
Infant Formulas, Vitamins & Other Nutritional Products Mfr
S.I.C.: 2834; 2099; 2836
N.A.I.C.S.: 325412; 311999; 325414
Import Export
Advertising Expenditures: $401,900,000
Media: 3-7-8-11-13-15-17-21
Personnel:
James M. Cornelius *(Chm)*
Stephen W. Golsby *(Pres & CEO)*
Peter G. Leemputte *(CFO & Sr VP)*
Peter Kasper Jakobsen *(Pres-Americas)*
William Pool *(Gen Counsel, Sec & Sr VP)*
Lynn H. Clark *(Sr VP-HR)*
Dirk Hondmann *(Sr VP-Global Res & Dev)*
James Jeffrey Jobe *(Sr VP-Global Supply Chain)*
Christopher Perille *(VP-Corp Comm & Pub Affairs)*
Robert Cleveland *(Dir-Mktg-Global)*
Brands & Products:
BOOST
CAL-C-TOSE
CASEC
CE-VI-SOL
CHOCOMILK
CRITICAL CARE NUTRITIONALS
ENFAMAMA A+
ENFAMIL
ENFAMIL HUMAN MILK FORTIFIER
FER-IN-SOL
ISOCAL HCN
LACTOFREE
LIPISORB
LOFENALAC
MCT OIL
MODUCAL
NURSETTE
NUTRAMENT
NUTRAMIGEN
POLY-VI-FLOR WITH IRON
POLY-VI-SOL
PORTAGEN
PREGESTIMIL
SUSTACAL
THERAGRAN
TRAUMACAL
TRI-VI-FLOR
TRI-VI-SOL
TRI-VI-SOL WITH IRON
ULTRACAL
Advertising Agencies:
Gray Loon Marketing Group, Inc.
300 SE Riverside Dr Ste 200
Evansville, IN 47713
Tel.: (812) 422-9999
Fax: (812) 422-3342
Toll Free: (888) GRAYLOON

HealthStar Public Relations
112 Madison Ave
New York, NY 10016
Tel.: (212) 532-0909
Fax: (212) 532-6907

Saatchi & Saatchi
25/F Sathorn City Tower 175 S Sathorn Rd Khwaeng Thungmahamek
Bangkok, 10120, Thailand
Tel.: (66) 2 640 4700
Fax: (66) 2 679 5210

Wishbone
245 5th Ave 12th Fl
New York, NY 10016
Tel.: (646) 486-9700
Tel.: (646) 486-9701
Fax: (212) 213-0659

MEDASSETS INC.

100 N Point Center E Ste 200
Alpharetta, GA 30022
Tel.: (678) 323-2500
Fax: (678) 323-2501
E-mail: info@medassets.com
Web Site: www.medassets.com
Approx. Rev.: $391,331,000
Approx. Number Employees: 3,100
Business Description:
Hospitals & Health Systems Margin & Cash Flow Improvement Solutions
S.I.C.: 6099; 5047; 7379; 7389
N.A.I.C.S.: 522320; 423450; 541519; 561499
Advertising Expenditures: $2,224,000
Personnel:
John A. Bardis *(Founder, Chm, Pres & CEO)*
Terrence J. Mulligan *(Vice Chm)*
Bruce F. Wesson *(Vice Chm)*
Charles O. Garner *(CFO & Exec VP)*
Rand A. Ballard *(COO, Chief Customer Officer & Sr Exec VP)*
Randall B. Sparkman *(CTO & CIO)*
Jonathan H. Glenn *(Chief Admin Officer, Chief Legal Officer & Exec VP)*
Nicholas J. Sears *(Chief Medical Officer)*
Lance M. Culbreth *(Chief Acctg Officer & Sr VP)*
Laurence Neil Hunn *(Pres-Revenue Cycle Tech & Exec VP)*
Stephanie Alexander *(Pres-Performance Analytics)*
Allen W. Hobbs *(Pres-Client Mgmt-Field Ops & Sls)*
Patrick T. Ryan *(Pres-Spend Mgmt Segment)*
Robert P. Borchert *(Sr VP-Investor & Corp Comm)*
R. Lynn Howard *(Sr VP-HR)*
Daniel H. James, Jr. *(Sr VP)*
Brands & Products:
CAREPRICER
CDM MASTER
CDQUICK
CROSSWALK
MEDASSETS
MEDASSETS NET REVENUE SYSTEMS
MERGE TECHNOLOGY
MYMENTOR
SELECT
Advertising Agency:
Three Atlanta
359 E Paces Ferry Rd Ste 300
Atlanta, GA 30305
Tel.: (404) 266-0899
Fax: (404) 266-3699

MEDCATH CORPORATION

10720 Sikes Pl Ste 300
Charlotte, NC 28277-8141
Tel.: (704) 708-6600
Fax: (704) 708-5035
E-mail: ir@medcath.com
Web Site: www.medcath.com
Approx. Rev.: $442,496,000
Approx. Number Employees: 1,678
Year Founded: 1988

Key to Media (For complete agency information see *The Advertising Red Books-Agencies* edition):
1. Bus. Publs. 2. Cable T.V. 3. Catalogs & Directories. 4. Co-op Adv. 5. Consumer Mags. 6. D.M. to Bus. Estab.7. D.M. to Consumers
8. Daily Newsp. 9. Exhibits/Trade Shows 10. Foreign 11. Infomercial 12. Internet Adv.13. Multimedia 14. Network Radio
15. Network T.V. 16. Newsp. Distr. Mags. 17. Other 18. Outdoor (Posters, Transit) 19. Point of Purchase20. Premiums, Novelties
21. Product Samples 22. Special Events Mktg. 23. Spot Radio 24. Spot T.V. 25. Weekly Newsp. 26. Yellow Page Adv.

Business Description:
Cardiovascular Healthcare Services & Hospital Operator
S.I.C.: 8062; 8011; 8069; 8093
N.A.I.C.S.: 622110; 621111; 621498; 622310
Advertising Expenditures: $2,200,000
Personnel:
James Arthur Parker *(CEO)*
Lora Ramsey *(CFO)*
Joan Mccanless *(Chief Compliance Officer, Chief Clinical Officer & Sr VP)*
Brands & Products:
MEDCATH
Advertising Agency:
Eric Mower and Associates
1001 Morehead Sq Dr 5th Fl
Charlotte, NC 28203
Tel.: (704) 375-0123
Fax: (704) 375-0222
Toll Free: (800) 968-0682
Pub Rels

MEDCO HEALTH SOLUTIONS, INC.

100 Parsons Pond Dr
Franklin Lakes, NJ 07417
Tel.: (201) 269-3400
Fax: (201) 269-1109
E-mail: solutions@medco.com
Web Site: www.medcohealth.com
Approx. Rev.: $65,968,300,000
Approx. Number Employees: 23,425
Business Description:
Pharmaceutical Products & Services
S.I.C.: 5122; 5912; 5961
N.A.I.C.S.: 424210; 446110; 454111
Personnel:
David B. Snow, Jr. *(Chm & CEO)*
Kenneth O. Klepper *(Pres & COO)*
Richard J. Rubino *(CFO & Sr VP-Fin)*
Jay Silverstein *(Chief Branding Officer & Sr VP)*
Jack A. Smith *(CMO & Sr VP)*
Glen D. Stettin *(Chief Medical Officer & Sr VP)*
Robert S. Epstein *(Chief Clinical R&D Officer & Pres-Advanced Clinical Science & Res)*
Brian T. Griffin *(Pres-Intl & CEO-Medco Celesio)*
Mary T. Daschner *(Pres-Govt PBM Grp)*
John P. Driscoll *(Pres-New Markets)*
Glenn C. Taylor *(Grp Pres-Health Plans)*
Timothy C. Wentworth *(Grp Pres-Employer & Key Accts)*
Thomas M. Moriarty *(Gen Counsel, Sec & Sr VP-Pharmaceutical Contracting)*
Gabriel R. Cappucci *(Sr VP & Controller)*
Karin Princivalle *(Sr VP-HR)*
Andrew Miller *(Sr Mgr-Corp Comm)*
Kevin Stanley *(Mgr-Diabetes TRC Specialty Pharmacist)*
Brands & Products:
ACCREDO
ACCU-CHEK
AT THE HEART OF HEALTH
EXPERXT ADVISOR
GENERICS FIRST
LIVE LIFE WELL
MEDCO
MEDCO MEDICARE PRESCRIPTION PLAN
ONETOUCH
RATIONALIQ
Advertising Agencies:
Coyne Public Relations
14 Walsh Dr 2nd Fl
Parsippany, NJ 07054
Tel.: (973) 316-1665
Fax: (973) 316-6568

Gotham Incorporated
150 E 42nd St 12th Fl
New York, NY 10017
Tel.: (212) 414-7000
Fax: (212) 414-7095

OgilvyOne Worldwide
636 11th Ave
New York, NY 10036
Tel.: (212) 237-4000
Fax: (212) 237-5123
Agency of Record
Medco Pharmacy Brand Campaign

RAPP
437 Madison Ave 3rd Fl
New York, NY 10022
Tel.: (212) 817-6800
Fax: (212) 590-8400
Direct Marketing
Interactive
Public Relations

MEDEX ASSISTANCE CORPORATION

(d/b/a MEDEX Gobal Group, Inc.)
8501 Lasalle Rd Ste 200
Towson, MD 21286
Tel.: (410) 453-6300
Fax: (410) 453-6331
E-mail: info@medexassist.com
Web Site: www.medexassist.com
E-Mail For Key Personnel:
President: bkirby@medexassist.com
Sales Range: $25-49.9 Million
Approx. Number Employees: 77
Year Founded: 1977
Business Description:
International Travel Assistance & Emergency Response Services
S.I.C.: 8322
N.A.I.C.S.: 624230
Personnel:
Bruce Kirby *(Pres & CEO)*
Ron Varlotta *(CFO)*
Susan Torroella *(COO)*
Mike Roban *(VP-Sls, Mktg & Client Rels)*
William Irwin *(Dir-Security)*
Eddie Jenkins *(Dir-IT)*
Walter B. Koppel *(Dir-Medical)*
Advertising Agency:
Crosby Marketing Communications
705 Melvin Ave Ste 200
Annapolis, MD 21401-1540
Tel.: (410) 626-0805
Fax: (410) 269-6547

MEDEXPRESS PHARMACY, LTD

650 Washington Rd
Ste 800
Pittsburgh, PA 15228
Tel.: (412) 344-7690
Fax: (412) 344-7693
Toll Free: (888) 344-7740
Web Site: www.symonscapital.com
Approx. Rev.: $2,600,000
Approx. Number Employees: 10
Year Founded: 1983
Business Description:
Management Services
S.I.C.: 8741
N.A.I.C.S.: 561110
Personnel:
Edward L. Symons Jr. *(Founder & Chm)*
Michael P. Czajka *(Pres & CEO)*
Chris D. Rickard *(COO & CTO)*
Colin E. Symons *(Chief Investment Officer & Portfolio Mgr)*
Advertising Agency:
Conover Tuttle Pace
77 N Washington St
Boston, MA 02114
Tel.: (617) 412-4000
Fax: (617) 412-4411

MEDEXPRESS URGENT CARE

(Joint Venture of Sequoia Capital & General Atlantic LLC)
1751 Earl Core Rd
Morgantown, WV 26505
Tel.: (304) 225-2500
Fax: (304) 225-2576
Web Site: www.medexpress.com
Approx. Number Employees: 1,300
Business Description:
Urgent Care Clinics
S.I.C.: 8093
N.A.I.C.S.: 621498
Media: 22
Personnel:
Bryan Stuchell *(Owner)*
Frank Alderman *(CEO)*
Dino Eliopoulos *(CFO)*
Michael Geldart *(COO)*
Robert Hiser *(CIO)*
Moe Rubenstein *(Gen Counsel)*
Russ Sullivan *(VP-HR)*

MEDICAL NUTRITION USA, INC.

(Sub. of Groupe Danone S.A.)
10 W Forest Ave
Englewood, NJ 07631-4020
Tel.: (201) 569-1188
Fax: (201) 596-3224
Toll Free: (800) 221-0308
E-mail: info@pro-stat.com
Web Site: www.mdnu.com
Approx. Sls.: $16,089,000
Approx. Number Employees: 37
Year Founded: 1981
Business Description:
Nutritional Supplement Developer & Distr
S.I.C.: 5122; 2834
N.A.I.C.S.: 424210; 325412
Media: 10
Personnel:
Arnold M. Gans *(Founder & Chief Scientific Officer)*
Robert Mathias *(Pres)*
Nigel P. Hughes *(CEO)*
Frank J. Kimmerling *(CFO & Exec VP)*
Jeffrey M. Janco *(COO-HR & Exec VP)*
Myra D. Gans *(Exec VP-Mktg)*
David Shapiro *(VP-Sls)*

MEDICAL RESOURCES INC.

1455 Broad St
Bloomfield, NJ 07003
Tel.: (973) 707-1100
Fax: (973) 707-1118
Toll Free: (800) 537-7272
E-mail: info@mrii.com
Web Site: www.mrii.com
Approx. Number Employees: 1,000
Year Founded: 1979
Business Description:
Diagnostic Imaging Centers
S.I.C.: 8071
N.A.I.C.S.: 621511
Personnel:
Amalia Faraclas *(VP-Admin Opers & Compliance Officer)*
Dave McCabe *(VP-Fin)*
Advertising Agency:
The Lazur Hoyvald Group - LHG
3121 Rt 22 E Ste 304
Branchburg, NJ 08876
Tel.: (908) 393-8500
Tel.: (908) 393-8501
Fax: (908) 450-1363

MEDICAL STAFFING NETWORK HOLDINGS INC.

(Filed Ch 11 Bankruptcy #10-29101 on 07/07/2010 in U.S. Bankruptcy Ct, Southern Dist of FL, West Palm Beach)
901 Yamato Rd Ste 110
Boca Raton, FL 33431
Tel.: (561) 322-1300
Fax: (561) 322-1200
Toll Free: (800) 633-1256
E-mail: webinfo@msnhealth.com
Web Site: www.msnhealth.com
Approx. Rev.: $340,877,000
Approx. Number Employees: 950
Year Founded: 1998
Business Description:
Temporary Nurses, Physicians & Medical Support Staff in Health Care Facilities
S.I.C.: 7363; 7361
N.A.I.C.S.: 561320; 561310
Advertising Expenditures: $3,600,000
Media: 2-10-13-22
Personnel:
Robert J. Adamson *(Chm & CEO)*
Kevin S. Little *(Pres & CFO)*
Jeffrey Yesner *(Chief Acctg Officer)*
Brands & Products:
MEDICAL STAFFING NETWORK
ONESOURCE
Advertising Agency:
Media Crew One, Inc.
901 Yamato Rd Ste 110
Boca Raton, FL 33431
Tel.: (561) 322-1335
Fax: (561) 322-1200
Toll Free: (800) 992-6699

MEDICINE SHOPPE INTERNATIONAL, INC.

(Sub. of Cardinal Health, Inc.)
1 Rider Trail Plz Dr Ste 300
Earth City, MO 63045
Tel.: (314) 993-6000
Fax: (314) 872-5500
Toll Free: (800) 325-1397
E-mail: contactus@medshoppe.com
Web Site: www.medshoppe.com
Sales Range: $75-99.9 Million
Approx. Number Employees: 250
Year Founded: 1970
Business Description:
Pharmaceutical Services

Key to Media (For complete agency information see *The Advertising Red Books-Agencies* edition):
1. Bus. Publs. 2. Cable T.V. 3. Catalogs & Directories. 4. Co-op Adv. 5. Consumer Mags. 6. D.M. to Bus. Estab.7. D.M. to Consumers
8. Daily Newsp. 9. Exhibits/Trade Shows 10. Foreign 11. Infomercial 12. Internet Adv.13. Multimedia 14. Network Radio
15. Network T.V. 16. Newsp. Distr. Mags. 17. Other 18. Outdoor (Posters, Transit) 19. Point of Purchase20. Premiums, Novelties
21. Product Samples 22. Special Events Mktg. 23. Spot Radio 24. Spot T.V. 25. Weekly Newsp. 26. Yellow Page Adv.

Medicine Shoppe International, Inc. — (Continued)

S.I.C.: 2834; 5122
N.A.I.C.S.: 325412; 424210
Media: 2-3-5-6-7-8-9-10-14-15-16-17-19-20-23-24-25-26
Distr.: Direct to Consumer; Natl.
Budget Set: July
Personnel:
Kim Myers *(Gen Counsel & VP)*
Scott Glover *(Sr VP-Sls & Mktg)*
Terry Burnside *(Gen Mgr)*
Brands & Products:
CARING BEYOND PRESCRIPTION
THE MEDICINE SHOPPE
Advertising Agency:
Weber Shandwick-Saint Louis
555 Washington Ave
Saint Louis, MO 63101
Tel.: (314) 436-6565
Fax: (314) 622-6212
Toll Free: (800) 551-5971
— Carrie Trammell *(Acct Exec)*

THE MEDICINES COMPANY
8 Sylvan Way
Parsippany, NJ 07054
Tel.: (973) 290-6000
Fax: (973) 656-9898
Toll Free: (800) 388-1183
E-mail: investor.relations@themedco.com
Web Site: www.themedicinescompany.com
Approx. Rev.: $437,645,000
Approx. Number Employees: 420
Year Founded: 1996
Business Description:
Biopharmaceutical Products Developer
S.I.C.: 2834; 2836
N.A.I.C.S.: 325412; 325414; 541711
Advertising Expenditures: $1,500,000
Personnel:
Clive A. Meanwell *(Chm, Pres & CEO)*
Glenn P. Sblendorio *(CFO, Exec VP & Treas)*
Bill O'Connor *(Chief Acctg Officer)*
Paul M. Antinori *(Gen Counsel & Sr VP)*
Leslie C. Rohrbacker *(Chief Human Strategy Officer & VP)*
Brands & Products:
ANGIOMAX
ANGIOX
CANGRELOR
CLEVIDIPINE
CLEVIPREX
THE MEDICINES COMPANY
Advertising Agency:
WCG
60 Francisco St
San Francisco, CA 94133
Tel.: (415) 362-5018
Fax: (415) 362-5019

MEDICIS PHARMACEUTICAL CORPORATION
7720 N Dobson Rd
Scottsdale, AZ 85256-2740
Tel.: (602) 808-8800
Fax: (602) 808-0822
E-mail: rd@medicis.com
Web Site: www.medicis.com
Approx. Rev.: $699,968,000
Approx. Number Employees: 679
Year Founded: 1988
Business Description:
Prescription, Over-the-Counter & Cosmetic Products Developer & Marketer for Treatment of Dermatological Conditions
S.I.C.: 2834; 5122
N.A.I.C.S.: 325412; 424210
Advertising Expenditures: $51,900,000
Media: 7-10-21-22
Personnel:
Jonah Shacknai *(Founder, Chm & CEO)*
Mark A. Prygocki, Sr. *(Pres)*
Richard D. Peterson *(CFO, Treas & Exec VP)*
Jason Hanson *(COO & Exec VP)*
Mitchell S. Wortzman *(Chief Scientific Officer & Exec VP)*
Joseph Cooper *(Exec VP-Corp & Product Dev)*
Vincent Ippolito *(Exec VP-Sls & Mktg)*
Kara J. Stancell *(Exec Dir-IR & Corp Comm)*
Brands & Products:
A/T/S
ALUSTRA
DYNACIN
LOPROX
LUSTRA
LUSTRA-AF
PLEXION
PLEXION-TS
RESTYLANE
SOLODYN
TRIAZ
VANOS
ZIANA
Advertising Agency:
Lippe Taylor
215 Park Ave S 16th Fl
New York, NY 10003
Tel.: (212) 598-4400
Fax: (212) 598-0620
Ziana

MEDICOOL, INC.
20460 Gramercy Pl
Torrance, CA 90501
Tel.: (310) 784-1200
Tel.: (310) 782-2200
Fax: (310) 427-7274
Fax: (310) 782-8900
Toll Free: (800) 433-2469
Web Site: www.medicool.com
Approx. Sls.: $1,500,000
Approx. Number Employees: 17
Year Founded: 1986
Business Description:
Medical Equipment Whslr
S.I.C.: 3841
N.A.I.C.S.: 339112
Media: 2-4-6-7-10-13-19-20-21
Brands & Products:
ADORN
AUTOCLAVE
BURR SANITIZER
CADEX ALARM WATCH
CALLUSAN CREME MOUSSE
COUNT-A-DOSE
CROCS RX CUSTOM CLOUD
CROCS RX SILVER CLOUDS
CYCLECHISER
DI CASE
DIA-PAK
DIA-PAK CLASSIC
DIA-PAK DAYMATE
DIA-PAK DELUXE
DIASOX
DIAVITE
DURASOX
EF-1
ENCORE
EXERCHIZER
EXTENDBAR
FEM AID
FILE SPRAY
FILE STREAM
FILEMASTER 520
FRIO
HEALSPA
IMPO-AID
INSTA GLUCOSE
INSTA-JECT
INSUL-GUIDE
INSULIN PROTECTOR
ISABEL CRISTINA
JOBST SOCKS
KOLINSKY BRUSHES
LET'S GO
LET'S TOUCH
MAGNI-GUIDE
MANICURE PEDICURE STATION
MEDI-FRIDGE
MEDICOOL
MEDICOOLER
MERINO LANOLIN
MERINO SKIN CREME
MINI CYCLE
MY BEAUTIFUL NAILS
MY LOVELY FEET
NAILGLIDE 2100
NAILPRO 2000
PEDINOVA III
PENPLUS CASE
PILLMINDER
POUCHO FOR INHALER
POUCHO FOR INSULIN
PRO POWER 20K
PRO POWER 30K
PRO POWER 35K
PROTECTALL
PROTOUCH 1000
ROHNER COMFORT SOCKS
SAFECLIP
SILVER KNIT
SLIPPERY STUFF
STEP HAPPY INSOLES
SWISS CARBIDE
THERALL
TURBO FILE 2400
TURBO FILE II
TWEEZLIGHT
VAC FILE
WIDE SOCKS
WRIGHT PREFILL

MEDIFAST, INC.
11445 Cronhill Dr
Owings Mills, MD 21117-2220
Tel.: (410) 581-8042
Fax: (410) 581-8070
Toll Free: (800) 638-7867
E-mail: info@medifastdiet.com
Web Site: www.medifast.net
E-Mail For Key Personnel:
President: brad@medifastdiet.com
Approx. Rev.: $257,552,000
Approx. Number Employees: 507
Year Founded: 1980
Business Description:
Weight & Disease Management Products Mfr & Distr
S.I.C.: 2833; 2834
N.A.I.C.S.: 325411; 325412
Advertising Expenditures: $23,000,000
Media: 2-3-5-6-10-16-19-23
Distr.: Natl.
Budget Set: Dec.
Personnel:
Bradley T. MacDonald *(Chm)*
Margaret E. MacDonald-Sheetz *(Pres & COO)*
Michael S. McDevitt *(CEO)*
Brendan N. Connors *(CFO)*
Leo V. Williams *(Exec VP)*
Jaime Elwood *(VP-Mktg)*
Brands & Products:
MEDIFAST

MEDIMMUNE LLC
(Sub. of AstraZeneca PLC)
One MedImmune Way
Gaithersburg, MD 20878-4021
Tel.: (301) 398-0000
Fax: (301) 398-9000
E-mail: info@medimmune.com
Web Site: www.medimmune.com
Sales Range: $1-4.9 Billion
Approx. Number Employees: 3,000
Year Founded: 1988
Business Description:
Pharmaceuticals, Biotechnologies & Medicinal Products Developer, Mfr & Marketer
S.I.C.: 8733; 2833; 2834; 2836
N.A.I.C.S.: 541720; 325411; 325412; 325414
Export
Advertising Expenditures: $11,000,000
Media: 10-22
Personnel:
Peter Greenleaf *(Pres)*
Timothy Pearson *(CFO & Exec VP)*
William C. Bertrand, Jr. *(Gen Counsel, Exec VP-Legal Affairs & Corp Compliance Officer)*
Scott Carmer *(Exec VP-Comml Ops)*
Max Donley *(Exec VP-HR)*
Peter A. Kiener *(Exec VP-R&D)*
Bernardus N.M. Machielse *(Exec VP)*
Andrew D. Skibo *(Exec VP-Ops)*
Shou-Bai Chao *(Sr VP-Mfg)*
Gail Folena-Wasserman *(Sr VP-Dev)*
Paul Williams *(VP-Infectious Disease Franchise)*
Tor Constantino *(Dir-PR-Infectious Disease)*
Ellen Thompson *(Dir-Corp Capability)*
Sidoney Atse *(Assoc Dir-Internal Comm)*
Brands & Products:
CYTOGAM
ETHYOL
FLUMIST
NEUTREXIN
RESPIGAM
Advertising Agencies:
Euro RSCG Worldwide
350 Hudson St
New York, NY 10014-4504
Tel.: (212) 886-2000
Fax: (212) 886-2016
Toll Free: (800) 937-0233
Professional

Fleishman-Hillard Inc.
200 N Broadway
Saint Louis, MO 63102-2730
Tel.: (314) 982-1700
Fax: (314) 982-0586

Key to Media (For complete agency information see *The Advertising Red Books-Agencies* edition):
1. Bus. Publs. 2. Cable T.V. 3. Catalogs & Directories. 4. Co-op Adv. 5. Consumer Mags. 6. D.M. to Bus. Estab.7. D.M. to Consumers
8. Daily Newsp. 9. Exhibits/Trade Shows 10. Foreign 11. Infomercial 12. Internet Adv.13. Multimedia 14. Network Radio
15. Network T.V. 16. Newsp. Distr. Mags. 17. Other 18. Outdoor (Posters, Transit) 19. Point of Purchase20. Premiums, Novelties
21. Product Samples 22. Special Events Mktg. 23. Spot Radio 24. Spot T.V. 25. Weekly Newsp. 26. Yellow Page Adv.

(Flu Vaccination)

HARTE-HANKS, INC.
9601 McAllister Freeway Ste 610
San Antonio, TX 78216
Tel.: (210) 829-9000
Fax: (210) 829-9403
Toll Free: (800) 456-9748
Flumist

MEDLINE INDUSTRIES, INC.

1 Medline Pl
Mundelein, IL 60060
Tel.: (847) 949-5500
Fax: (847) 643-3126
Toll Free: (800) 633-5463
E-mail: info@medline.com
Web Site: www.medline.com
Approx. Number Employees: 5,000
Year Founded: 1966
Business Description:
Medical & Surgical Products Mfr & Distr
S.I.C.: 3842; 5047
N.A.I.C.S.: 339113; 423450
Media: 2-4-5-7-10-19-22
Distr.: Natl.
Budget Set: Nov.
Personnel:
Andrew Mills *(Pres)*
Charles N. Mills *(CEO)*
Jim Abrams *(COO)*
Hunter Banks *(Pres-Preferred HealthCare Grp)*
Ray Swaback *(Pres-Sls)*
David Greenberg *(Exec VP-Strategy)*
Barbara Kallay *(Sr VP-Global HR)*
Rick Lee *(Sr VP-Fin)*
Stephen Burns *(VP-Sls)*
Marc Lessem *(VP-Mktg)*
Thomas Pawlik *(VP-Corp Mktg)*
Stu Schneider *(VP-Sls & Mktg)*
John Marks *(Dir-Corp Commun)*
Michael Dressler *(Acct Mgr-Hospital & Surgery Sls Consultation Div)*
Brands & Products:
ACCU-WRAP
AKROCLEN
ALOETOUCH
ARGLAES
ARMOR-NIT
AVANT GAUZE
BETTER PANT
BOOST
BRIGHT SPOT
CIDEX
CONTRO-BULB
CONTRO-PISTON
COOLSPOT
COTTON CLOUD
DERMA-GEL
DIAMOND DUO
DURA-NAP
DYNACOR
EAGLE MASTER TRAK
EASY CARE
ECLIPSE
ELITE TEX
EMS
EQUINOX
ETO CONTAINER-STERISET
EUDERMIC
FEELS LIKE HOME
FROSTLITE
GEMINI
GENIE II
GLEAMER
GLUCOLET 2
HALF-SIZE STERISET
HARVEY ELITE
ISOLEX
KANGAROO
KANGAROO ENTRIFLUSH
KONIG
KOOL'N KLEEN
LAKESIDE ERGO-ONE
LATEXFREE
MAXORB
MED-CHECK
MEDFIX
MEDI-WRAP
MEDLINE
MERITZ
MOLICARE
MY-CATH
NEOLON
OPTIFOAM
OUTPATIENT
POLY-CATH
PRESSURE ULCER PREVENTION
PRO-STAT
PROSOURCE
PROTECTION PLUS
QUICKSUITE
RADION-X
READYBATH
REMEDY
RESOURCE
SAF-T-BLEND
SENSICARE
SENSICARE ADVANTIX
SENTRY
SILVASORB
SKINTEGRITY
SLEEPSTRIP
SOFT-FIT
SOFT-SPAN
SOOTHE & COOL
SPECI-CATCH
SPECI-CATH
STAGE IV
SUPER NOVA
SURE-CHECK
SURE SET
TASKIT
TENDERWET
THICK-IT
THREE-QUARTER SIZE STERISET
ULTRAFLEX
ULTRASORBS
UNIVERSAL
VISIONARY
WAGIND
WIDE BAND

MEDPLUS, INC.

(Sub. of Quest Diagnostics Incorporated)
4690 Pkwy Dr
Mason, OH 45040
Tel.: (513) 229-5500
Fax: (513) 229-5505
Toll Free: (800) 444-6235
E-mail: info@medplus.com
Web Site: www.medplus.com
Sales Range: $100-124.9 Million
Approx. Number Employees: 210
Year Founded: 1991
Business Description:
Information Management Systems for Health Care Organizations
S.I.C.: 5045; 8711
N.A.I.C.S.: 423430; 541330
Media: 10
Personnel:
Richard A. Mahoney *(Pres & VP)*
Philip S. Present, II *(COO)*
Rebecca Hellmann *(VP-Mktg)*
Brands & Products:
CARE360
CHARTMAXX
EMAXX
MEDPLUS
OPTIMAXX
Advertising Agency:
Medicus Life Brands
1675 Broadway 5th Fl
New York, NY 10019-5820
Tel.: (212) 468-3100
Fax: (212) 468-3187

MEDPORT, LLC

23 Acorn St
Providence, RI 02903
Tel.: (401) 273-0444
Fax: (401) 273-0630
E-mail: info@medportllc.com
Web Site: www.medportllc.com
Approx. Sls.: $2,200,000
Approx. Number Employees: 20
Year Founded: 1996
Business Description:
Health Care Products Mfr
S.I.C.: 3842
N.A.I.C.S.: 339113
Media: 8-9
Personnel:
Larry Wesson *(CEO)*
Brands & Products:
MEDGLIDER
MEDPORT

MEDQUIST INC.

(Sub. of MEDQUIST HOLDINGS INC.)
9009 Carothers Pkwy
Franklin, TN 37067
Toll Free: (866) 295-4600
E-mail: solutions@medquist.com
Web Site: www.medquist.com
Approx. Rev.: $375,240,000
Approx. Number Employees: 6,500
Year Founded: 1970
Business Description:
Transcription & Information Management Services to Hospitals, Physicians & Other Health Care Organizations
S.I.C.: 7374; 7338; 7371; 7372
N.A.I.C.S.: 518210; 511210; 541511; 561410
Advertising Expenditures: $918,000
Personnel:
Robert M. Aquilina *(Chm)*
Peter Masanotti *(Pres & CEO)*
Anthony D. James *(CFO & Co-COO)*
Michael F. Clark *(Co-COO)*
Kevin Piltz *(CIO)*
Mark R. Sullivan *(Chief Compliance Officer, Gen Counsel & Sec)*
James Brennan *(Principal Acctg Officer)*
Brands & Products:
CODERUNNER
DOCQMINE
ESIGN
MEDQUIST
TALKSTATION

MEDRAD, INC.

(Sub. of Bayer HealthCare Pharmaceuticals Inc.)
100 Global View Dr
Warrendale, PA 15086
Tel.: (412) 767-2400
Fax: (412) 767-4120
Toll Free: (800) 633-7231
Toll Free: (800) MEDRAD1
Web Site: www.medrad.com
E-Mail For Key Personnel:
Sales Director: jtedeschi@medrad.com
Sales Range: $600-649.9 Million
Approx. Number Employees: 1,700
Year Founded: 1964
Business Description:
Diagnostic Imaging & Therapeutic Medical Device Mfr
S.I.C.: 3841; 3845
N.A.I.C.S.: 339112; 334510
Export
Media: 2-7-10-11
Distr.: Intl.; Natl.
Budget Set: July
Personnel:
Julio Rivera *(Chief Compliance Officer & Sr VP-Corp Compliance)*
Gary Bucciarelli *(Sr VP)*
Cliff Kress *(Sr VP)*
Jeff Owoc *(Sr VP-Ops)*
John Tedeschi *(Sr VP-Svcs-Intl)*
Doug Descalzi *(Exec Dir)*
Diane Watson *(Exec Dir)*
Luanne Radermacher *(Dir-Corp Affairs)*
Brands & Products:
ENVISION CT
THE LEADING IMAGE
MARK V PROVIS
MEDRAD VISTRON CT
MRINNERVU
QWIK FIT SYRINGE
SPECTRIS MR

MEDRAD INTERVENTIONAL/ POSSIS

(Sub. of MEDRAD, Inc.)
9055 Evergreen Blvd NW
Minneapolis, MN 55433-5833
Tel.: (763) 780-4555
Fax: (763) 783-8463
Toll Free: (888) 848-7677
E-mail: market@possis.com
Web Site: www.possis.com
Approx. Sls.: $66,654,592
Approx. Number Employees: 30
Year Founded: 1952
Business Description:
Catheter Systems & Other Medical Devices Mfr
S.I.C.: 3841; 3842
N.A.I.C.S.: 339112; 339113
Export
Personnel:
James D. Gustafson *(Sr VP-R & D & Engrg & Clinical Evaluation & Chief Quality Officer)*
Shawn McCarrey *(Exec VP-North American-Cardiovascular)*
Brands & Products:
ANGIOJET
AVX
BRINGING MEDICAL POSSIBILITIES TO LIFE
CROSS-STREAM
NEUROJET
PERMA-FLOW
PERMA-PASS
PERMA-SEAL
POSSIS
POWER PULSE

Key to Media (For complete agency information see *The Advertising Red Books-Agencies* edition):
1. Bus. Publs. 2. Cable T.V. 3. Catalogs & Directories. 4. Co-op Adv. 5. Consumer Mags. 6. D.M. to Bus. Estab.7. D.M. to Consumers
8. Daily Newsp. 9. Exhibits/Trade Shows 10. Foreign 11. Infomercial 12. Internet Adv.13. Multimedia 14. Network Radio
15. Network T.V. 16. Newsp. Distr. Mags. 17. Other 18. Outdoor (Posters, Transit) 19. Point of Purchase20. Premiums, Novelties
21. Product Samples 22. Special Events Mktg. 23. Spot Radio 24. Spot T.V. 25. Weekly Newsp. 26. Yellow Page Adv.

MEDRAD Interventional/Possis — (Continued)

RHEOLYTIC
SUR-PASS
XMI
XPEEDIOR
XVG

Advertising Agency:
TripleInk
60 S 6th St Ste 2800
Minneapolis, MN 55402
Tel.: (612) 342-9800
Fax: (612) 342-9745
Toll Free: (800) 632-1388

MEDSTAR HEALTH INC.

5565 Sterrett Pl 5th Fl
Columbia, MD 21044
Tel.: (410) 772-6500
Fax: (410) 715-3754
Toll Free: (877) 772-6505
Web Site: www.medstarhealth.org
E-Mail For Key Personnel:
Public Relations: john.a.marzano@medstar.net
Sales Range: $1-4.9 Billion
Approx. Number Employees: 22,000
Year Founded: 1987
Business Description:
Hospital Management Services
S.I.C.: 8741; 8621
N.A.I.C.S.: 561110; 813920
Import Export
Advertising Expenditures: $300,000
Media: 2-3-4-7-8-9-10-18-20-21-22-23-25
Personnel:
Edward S. Civera *(Chm)*
E.F. Shaw Wilgis *(Chm)*
Edward J. Brody *(Vice Chm)*
Kenneth A. Samet *(Pres & CEO)*
William L. Thomas *(Mng Dir, Chief Med Officer-Medical Affairs & Exec VP)*
Michael J. Curran *(CFO, Chief Admin Officer & Exec VP)*
Catherine Szenczy *(CIO & Sr VP)*
Oliver M. Johnson, II *(Gen Counsel & Exec VP)*
M. Joy Drass *(Exec VP-Ops-Washington)*
Carl Schindelar *(Exec VP-Ops-Baltimore)*
Christine M. Swearingen *(Exec VP-Plng, Mktg & Community Rels)*
Eric R. Wagner *(Exec VP-External Affairs & Diversified Ops)*
Steven S. Cohen *(Sr VP-Integrated Ops)*
Maureen McCausland *(Chief Nursing Officer & Sr VP)*
David P. Noe *(VP-HR)*
Phillip Farfel *(Sr Dir-Grant Dev)*
Curt McCormick *(Dir-Corp Comm)*
Phil Scharper *(Dir-Mktg)*
Denise M. Hobik *(Mgr-Operational Comm)*
Katrina D. Mitchell-Cooper *(Mgr-Dev Res)*
Brands & Products:
FRANKLIN SQUARE HOSPITAL CENTER
GEORGETOWN UNIVERSITY HOSPITAL
GOOD SAMARITAN HOSPITAL
HARBOR HOSPITAL
NATIONAL REHABILITATION HOSPITAL
UNION MEMORIAL HOSPITAL
WASHINGTON HOSPITAL CENTER

MEDTECH, INC.

(Sub. of Prestige Brands Holdings, Inc.)
90 N Brdwy
Irvington, NY 10533
Tel.: (914) 524-6810
Fax: (914) 524-6815
Toll Free: (800) 443-4908
Web Site: www.medtechinc.com
Approx. Number Employees: 20
Year Founded: 1955
Business Description:
Health & Beauty Aids Marketer
S.I.C.: 5122
N.A.I.C.S.: 424210
Media: 2-3-4-5-6-7-8-15-16-19-21-22-23-24
Distr.: Natl.
Brands & Products:
ARTHRITIS PAIN FORMULA-APF
CLOVERINE
COMPOZ
CUTEX
DENOREX
DERMOPLAST
EZO
FREEZONE
HEET
KERODEX
MOMENTUM
MOSCO
NEW SKIN
OUTGRO
OXIPOR
PERCOGESIC
ZINCON

MEDTRONIC

(Formerly Osteotech, Inc.)
(Div. of Medtronic, Inc.)
51 James Way
Eatontown, NJ 07724-2272
Tel.: (732) 542-2800
Web Site: www.osteotech.com
Approx. Rev.: $96,678,000
Approx. Number Employees: 297
Year Founded: 1986
Business Description:
Processor of Human Bone & Connective Tissue for Transplantation; Developer, Mfr & Marketer of Systems for Musculoskeletal Surgery
S.I.C.: 3841; 2834; 2836; 3842
N.A.I.C.S.: 339112; 325412; 325414; 339113
Personnel:
Christopher J. O'Connell *(Pres)*
Gary L. Ellis *(CFO & VP)*
Mark Phelps *(Sr Dir-Program, Diagnostics & Monitoring)*
Keyna P. Skeffington *(Asst Sec)*
Brands & Products:
GRAFTECH
GRAFTON
OSTEOACTIVE
OSTEOTECH
Advertising Agency:
Becker Guerry
107 Tindall Rd
Middletown, NJ 07748-2321
Tel.: (732) 671-6440
Fax: (732) 671-4350

MEDTRONIC, INC.

710 Medtronic Pkwy NE
Minneapolis, MN 55432-5604
Tel.: (763) 514-4000
Fax: (763) 514-4879
Toll Free: (800) 633-8766
E-mail: investor.relations@medtronic.com
Web Site: www.medtronic.com
Approx. Sls.: $15,933,000,000
Approx. Number Employees: 45,000
Year Founded: 1949
Business Description:
Therapeutic Electromedical Devices Mfr
S.I.C.: 3845; 3842
N.A.I.C.S.: 334510; 339113
Import Export
Advertising Expenditures: $16,000,000
Media: 1-2-7-10-13
Distr.: Intl.; Natl.
Personnel:
Omar S. Ishrak *(Chm & CEO)*
Brian D. Webster *(Pres)*
Gary L. Ellis *(CFO & Sr VP)*
Michael J. Coyle *(Exec VP & Grp Pres-Cardiology Bus)*
Christopher J. O'Connell *(Grp Pres-Restorative Therapies & Exec VP)*
Robert H. Blankemeyer *(Pres-Surgical Tech & Sr VP)*
James P. Mackin *(Pres-Cardiac Rhythm Disease Mgmt & Sr VP)*
Catherine M. Szyman *(Pres-Diabetes & Sr VP)*
Katie M. Szyman *(Pres-Neuromodulation & Sr VP)*
Tom Tefft *(Pres-Neuromodulation & Sr VP)*
D. Cameron Findlay *(Gen Counsel, Sec & Sr VP)*
Jean-Luc Butel *(Grp Pres-Intl & Exec VP)*
Susan Alpert *(Chief Regulatory Officer & Sr VP)*
H. James Dallas *(Sr VP-Quality & Ops)*
Richard E. Kuntz *(Chief Scientific, Clinical & Regulatory Officer & Sr VP)*
Stephen N. Oesterle *(Sr VP-Tech & Medicine)*
Caroline Stockdale *(Sr VP-HR)*
Eli B. Hamou *(Product Mgr-R&D)*
Brands & Products:
5F RF MARINR
ACT II
ACTIVA
ANEURX
AOA
AT500
BECKER
BIO-CONSOLE
BIO-MEDICUS
BIO-PROBE
BIOPLUS
BRIDGE
BRYAN
CAPSURE SP NOVUS
CARDIOBLATE
CARDIORHYTHM
CD HORIZON
CLOTTRAC
CODE-STAT
COLLECTION 3
CONTEGRA
CROSSPOINT
DELTA
DIGITRAPPER MKIII
DLP
DURAN ANCORE
ELITE
ELITE II
ENERTEC
ENTERRA
FIXATION
FLUORONAV
FRAMELINK
FREESTYLE
GEM DR
GEM II DR
GEM III
GUARDWIRE
GUNDRY
HALL EASY-FIT
HANCOCK
HANCOCK II
HANCOCK M.O. II
HEMOPUMP
HEPCON HMS PLUS
IMPORT
INDURA
INFUSE
INNERVISION
INSYNC
INSYNC.ICD
INTER FIX
INTERACT
INTERSTIM
ISOMED
ITREL
ITREL EZ
ITREL II
JEWEL
JEWEL PCD
JEWEL PLUS
KEYPOINT
KINETRA
LANDMARX
LEGACY
LEGEND PLUS
LIFEPAK
LIFEPAK 500
LT-CAGE
MARINR
MARKER CHANNEL
MATTRIX
MAXIMO
MEDTRONIC
MEDTRONIC CARDIOVASCULAR ALLIANCE
MEDTRONIC FIRST ALLIANCE
MEDTRONIC HALL
MEDTRONIC KAPPA
MEDTRONIC MOSAIC
MEDTRONIC NEURO
MEDTRONIC PREFERRED ALLIANCE
MICRO JEWEL
MICRO-REL
MINIMAX PLUS
NEUROPEN
OCTOPUS2
OCTUPUS
OPUS
PASYS
PBS
PERCUSURGE
POLESTAR
PROMEON
RF CONDUCTR
RF MARINR
RF PERFORMR
SE-4

Key to Media (For complete agency information see *The Advertising Red Books-Agencies* edition):
1. Bus. Publs. 2. Cable T.V. 3. Catalogs & Directories. 4. Co-op Adv. 5. Consumer Mags. 6. D.M. to Bus. Estab.7. D.M. to Consumers
8. Daily Newsp. 9. Exhibits/Trade Shows 10. Foreign 11. Infomercial 12. Internet Adv.13. Multimedia 14. Network Radio
15. Network T.V. 16. Newsp. Distr. Mags. 17. Other 18. Outdoor (Posters, Transit) 19. Point of Purchase20. Premiums, Novelties
21. Product Samples 22. Special Events Mktg. 23. Spot Radio 24. Spot T.V. 25. Weekly Newsp. 26. Yellow Page Adv.

SECURA
SELECTION AFM
SELECTSECURA
SENSIA
SEQUESTRA 1000
SILACURE
SILHOUET
SITESEER
SPECTRAFLEX
SPECTRAX
SPECTRAX SX
STARFISH
STEALTHSTATION
STEALTHSTATION TREON
TREATMENT GUIDANCE SYSTEM
SUREFIX
SYMBIOS
SYMMIX
SYNCHROMED
SYNERGY
TALENT
THERA
TORQR
TOWARD MAN'S FULL LIFE
TRANSFORM
TRANSVENE
TREON
TSRH-3D
VITATRON
WIKTOR
X-TREL
ZUMA

Advertising Agencies:
Barrie D'Rozario Murphy
400 1st Ave N Ste 220
Minneapolis, MN 55401
Tel.: (612) 279-1500
Fax: (612) 332-9995

Clarity Coverdale Fury Advertising, Inc.
120 S 6th St Ste 1300
Minneapolis, MN 55402-1810
Tel.: (612) 339-3902
Fax: (612) 359-4399

Richter7
280 S 400 W Ste 200
Salt Lake City, UT 84101
Tel.: (801) 521-2903
Fax: (801) 359-2420

MEMORIAL HEALTH SERVICES INC.

17360 Brookhurst St
Fountain Valley, CA 92708
Tel.: (714) 377-2900
Web Site: www.memorialcare.org
E-Mail For Key Personnel:
Marketing Director: ASternchak@memorialcarp.org
Approx. Number Employees: 7,500
Business Description:
Hospital Services
S.I.C.: 8062; 8011
N.A.I.C.S.: 622110; 621111
Media: 4-9-10-13-25
Personnel:
Barry Arbuckle *(Pres & CEO)*
Rick Graniere *(CFO)*
J. Scott Joslyn *(CIO & Sr VP)*
Anne Sternchak *(Mgr-Mktg & Comm)*
Brands & Products:
MEMORIALCARE

MEMORIAL HERMANN HEALTHCARE SYSTEM

6411 Fannin St
Houston, TX 77030
Tel.: (713) 448-5555
Fax: (713) 448-5760
E-mail: dan.wolter@memorialhermann.org
Web Site: www.memorialhermann.org
E-Mail For Key Personnel:
Public Relations: beth_sartori@mhhs.org
Sales Range: $350-399.9 Million
Approx. Number Employees: 19,500
Business Description:
Not-for-profit Health Care System
S.I.C.: 8062
N.A.I.C.S.: 622110
Media: 4-10-13-22
Personnel:
James R. Montague *(Chm)*
Craig Cordola *(CEO-Texas Medical Center Campus)*
Paul O'Sullivan *(CEO-Memorial Hermann Heart & Vascular Institute)*
Chuck Stokes *(COO)*
Daniel J. Wolterman *(Exec Officer)*
Erin Asprec *(CEO-Southeast)*
Amanda Spielman *(Exec VP)*
Brands & Products:
BREAKTHROUGHS EVERY DAY
MEMORIAL HERMANN

MEMORIAL SLOAN-KETTERING CANCER CENTER INC.

1275 York Ave
New York, NY 10065
Tel.: (212) 639-2000
Fax: (212) 639-5850
E-mail: publicaffairs@mskcc.org
Web Site: www.mskcc.org
Approx. Number Employees: 8,768
Year Founded: 1884
Business Description:
Hospital
S.I.C.: 8069; 8399
N.A.I.C.S.: 622310; 813319
Media: 2
Personnel:
Stephen D. Nimer *(Vice Chm-Faculty Dev)*
Harold Varmus *(Pres)*
John R. Gunn *(Exec VP)*
Michael P. Gutnick *(Sr VP-Fin & Asst Treas)*
David R. Artz *(Mng Dir-Info Sys)*
Ellen Sonet *(VP-Mktg)*
Christine Hickey *(Dir-Comm)*
Thomas J. Kelly *(Dir-Sloan-Kettering Institute)*
Andrew D. Maslow *(Dir-Indus Affairs)*
Douglas A. Warner III *(Mgr)*
Advertising Agency:
DiMassimo Goldstein
(d/b/a DIGO Brands)
220 E 23rd St
New York, NY 10010
Tel.: (212) 253-7500
Fax: (646) 507-5850

MEMRY CORPORATION

(Sub. of SAES Getters S.p.A.)
3 Berkshire Blvd
Bethel, CT 06801
Tel.: (203) 739-1100
Fax: (203) 798-6363
Toll Free: (866) 466-3679
E-mail: info@memry.com
Web Site: www.memry.com
Approx. Rev.: $51,677,000
Approx. Number Employees: 363
Year Founded: 1983
Business Description:
Shape Memory Alloy & Specialty Polymer-Extrusion Products Designer, Engineer & Developer
S.I.C.: 3841
N.A.I.C.S.: 339112
Media: 2-10-13
Personnel:
Nicola Di Bartolomeo *(CEO)*
James V. Dandeneau *(Pres-Putnam Plastics Division)*
Marcy MacDonald *(VP-HR & Corp Sec)*
Elizabeth Powers *(Sr Product Mktg Mgr-Memry Corporation)*
Brands & Products:
FLEXIUM

THE MENTHOLATUM COMPANY

(Sub. of Rohto Pharmaceutical Co. Ltd.)
707 Sterling Dr
Orchard Park, NY 14127-1557
Tel.: (716) 677-2500
Fax: (716) 674-3696
Fax: (716) 677-9528
Toll Free: (800) 688-7660
Web Site: www.mentholatum.com
Approx. Number Employees: 335
Year Founded: 1889
Business Description:
Proprietary Drugs Mfr
S.I.C.: 2834; 2844
N.A.I.C.S.: 325412; 325620
Import Export
Media: 2-6-9-15-21-23-24
Distr.: Natl.
Budget Set: May
Personnel:
Akiyoshi Yoshida *(Pres & CEO)*
John Ende *(VP-Sls, Mktg & Customer Svc)*
Todd Cantrell *(Brand Mgr-Oxy)*
Brands & Products:
DEEP HEATING
FLETCHERS CASTORIA
MENTHOLATUM
MENTHOLATUM ARTHRITIS PATCH
MENTHOLATUM CHERRY CHEST RUB FOR KIDS
MENTHOLATUM OINTMENT
MENTHOLATUM PAIN PATCH BRAND
MIGRAINE ICE
NATURAL ICE
RED CROSS
ROHTO V
ROHTO ZI
SNUG
SOFTLIPS
WELLPATCH
Advertising Agencies:
Campbell Associates
801 Beacon Park
Webster, MA 01570-1566
Tel.: (508) 949-6500
Fax: (508) 949-1099
Toll Free: (888) 422-8723

Media Pros
One Franklin Park N.
Buffalo, NY 14202
Tel.: (716) 885-6337
(Media Services)

Partners+Napier
192 Mill St Ste 600
Rochester, NY 14614-1022
Tel.: (585) 454-1010
Fax: (585) 454-1575
Toll Free: (800) 274-4954

Robin Leedy & Associates
118 N Bedford Rd Ste 302
Mount Kisco, NY 10549
Tel.: (914) 241-0086
Fax: (914) 242-2061

MENTOR CORPORATION

(Unit of Ethicon, Inc.)
(d/b/a Mentor Worldwide)
201 Mentor Dr
Santa Barbara, CA 93111
Tel.: (805) 879-6000
Fax: (805) 964-2712
Toll Free: (800) 525-0245
E-mail: investorrelations@mentorcorp.com
Web Site: www.mentorwwllc.com
Approx. Sls.: $373,208,000
Approx. Number Employees: 1,190
Year Founded: 1969
Business Description:
Cosmetic Surgery Products Mfr
S.I.C.: 3842; 3845
N.A.I.C.S.: 339113; 334510
Export
Advertising Expenditures: $3,100,000
Media: 6-9-25
Distr.: Natl.
Budget Set: Mar.
Personnel:
Joshua H. Levine *(Pres & CEO)*
Edward S. Northup *(COO)*
Joseph A. Newcomb *(Gen Counsel, Sec & VP)*
Vicki S. Chuck *(VP-HR)*
Brian E. Luedtke *(VP-Global Mktg & Sls)*
Ole S. Mikkelsen *(VP-IT)*
Sara Allison DeRousse *(Sr Dir-Pro Rels)*
Christopher Allman *(Dir-Corp Comm)*
Brands & Products:
ASK DIANE
BODYLOGIC
CAROMED
COMFORTMATE
CONTOUR PROFILE
FOLYSIL
GUIDE STRIPE
LYSONIX
MAKE LIFE MORE BEAUTIFUL
MEDFLEX
MEMORYGEL
NEOFORM
NIA 24
THE POWER TO TRANSFORM
RADOVAN
ROUND SPECTRUM
SILTEX
SPECTRUM
ULTRASCULPT
URO-TEX
WHILE SILTEX

Key to Media (For complete agency information see *The Advertising Red Books-Agencies* edition):
1. Bus. Publs. 2. Cable T.V. 3. Catalogs & Directories. 4. Co-op Adv. 5. Consumer Mags. 6. D.M. to Bus. Estab.7. D.M. to Consumers 8. Daily Newsp. 9. Exhibits/Trade Shows 10. Foreign 11. Infomercial 12. Internet Adv.13. Multimedia 14. Network Radio 15. Network T.V. 16. Newsp. Distr. Mags. 17. Other 18. Outdoor (Posters, Transit) 19. Point of Purchase20. Premiums, Novelties 21. Product Samples 22. Special Events Mktg. 23. Spot Radio 24. Spot T.V. 25. Weekly Newsp. 26. Yellow Page Adv.

MERA PHARMACEUTICALS, INC.
73-4460 Queen Ka'ahumanu Hwy
Ste 110
Kailua Kona, HI 96740-2639
Tel.: (808) 326-9301
Fax: (808) 326-9401
E-mail: info@merapharma.com
Web Site: www.merapharma.com
Approx. Sls.: $599,091
Approx. Number Employees: 5
Year Founded: 1998
Business Description:
Natural Products Researcher, Developer & Mfr
S.I.C.: 2833; 8733
N.A.I.C.S.: 541711; 325411; 541710
Media: 13-24
Personnel:
Gregory F. Kowal *(Chm & CEO)*
Michael F. Corcoran *(Pres & Dir Sls Mktg)*
Kenneth I. Crowder *(COO)*
Anthony E. Applebaum *(Principal Fin Officer & Principal Acctg Officer)*
Brands & Products:
ASTAFACTOR
BRINGING THE OCEAN TO LIFE
KONA SEA SALT
MERA PHARMACEUTICALS
SALMON ESSENTIALS

MERCK & CO., INC.
1 Merck Dr
Whitehouse Station, NJ 08889-0100
Tel.: (908) 423-1000
Web Site: www.merck.com
Approx. Sls.: $45,987,000,000
Approx. Number Employees: 94,000
Year Founded: 1928
Business Description:
Pharmaceuticals & Health Care Products Mfr
S.I.C.: 2834; 2836
N.A.I.C.S.: 325412; 325414
Import Export
Media: 2-3-6-9-14-15-16-18-21-23-24-25
Distr.: Natl.
Personnel:
Richard T. Clark *(Chm)*
Kenneth C. Frazier *(Pres & CEO)*
Peter N. Kellogg *(CFO & Exec VP)*
J. Chris Scalet *(CIO & Exec VP-Global Svcs)*
Richard S. Bowles, III *(Chief Compliance Officer & Exec VP)*
Mervyn Turner *(Chief Strategy Officer)*
Michael Rosenblatt *(Chief Medical Officer & Exec VP)*
Willie A. Deese *(Pres-Mfg Div & Exec VP)*
Bridgette P. Heller *(Pres-Consumer Health Care & Exec VP)*
Peter S. Kim *(Pres-Research Laboratories & Exec VP)*
Raul E. Kohan *(Pres-Animal Health & Exec VP)*
Michael Kamarck *(Pres-Merck BioVentures, Sr VP-Vaccines & Bio MMD)*
Julie Louise Gerberding *(Pres-Vaccine Div)*
Bruce N. Kuhlik *(Gen Counsel & Exec VP)*
Mirian M. Graddick-Weir *(Exec VP-HR)*
John Canan *(Sr VP & Controller)*
Gary Rosenthal *(Sr VP-Fin-Global Human Health)*
Joseph K. Schachle *(Gen Mgr)*
Audrey Belkin *(Dir-Claritin Mktg)*
Laurie Hekmat *(Dir-Mktg)*
Sumana Rajagopal *(Sr Mgr-Cross Channel Media-Global)*
Lynne Minter *(Mgr-Media & Adv-Global)*
Sarah Morgan *(Mgr-Comm)*
Brands & Products:
A&D OINTMENT
AEROLIZER
AFRIN
AQUAFLOR
ARCOXIA
ASAMANEX
AURIFLUSH
BANAMINE
BOVILIS
BRIDION
BUTOX
CAELYX
CERAZETTE
CHLOR-TRIMETON
CIPRO
CIRCUMVENT PCV2
CLARINEX
CLARITIN
COBACTAN
COCCIVAC
CONTINUUM
COPPERTONE
COPPERTONE KIDS
COPPERTONE SPORT
COPPERTONE ULTRAGUARD
CORICIDIN
CORICIDIN HBP
CORRECTOL
CUSHION GRIP
DEFEND
DIPROLENE
DR. SCHOLL'S
DRIXORAL
DUOFILM
ECLIPSE
ELOCON
EULEXIN
FOLLISTIM
FORADIL
GALAXY
GARDASIL
GYNE-LOTRIMIN
HOMEAGAIN
IMDUR
IMPLANON
INNOVAX ND-SB
INTEGRILIN
INTRON
JANUMET
K-DUR
LEVENTA
LEVITRA
LIVIAL
LOTRIMIN
LOTRISONE
M+PAC
MARVELON
MAXIVAC
MEXSANA
MIRALAX
MOMETAMAX
NASONEX
NITRO-DUR
NORCURON
NOXAFIL
NUFLOR
NUVARING
OPTIMMUNE
ORBAX
ORGARAN
OTOMAX
PANACUR
PARACOX
PEG-INTRON
PEGINTRON
PROVENTIL
RALGRO
REBETOL
REBETRON
RECEPTAL
REMERON
RESFLOR
ROTATEQ
SCALIBOR
SCHERING-PLOUGH
SINGULAIR
SLICE
SOLARCAINE
SOLTAB
SUBOXONE
SUBUTEX
TEMODAR
TINACTIN
TO EARN TRUST, EVERY DAY.
TRI-HEART
TRI-MERIT
TWISTHALER
VETSULIN
VYTORIN
WATER BABIES
ZEMURON
ZETIA
ZOCOR
ZOSTAVAX
ZUBRIN
Advertising Agencies:
Draftfcb
101 E Erie St
Chicago, IL 60611
Tel.: (312) 425-5000
Fax: (312) 425-5010

Draftfcb HealthCare
100 W 33rd St
New York, NY 10001
Tel.: (212) 672-2300
Fax: (212) 672-2301

Euro RSCG Worldwide
350 Hudson St
New York, NY 10014-4504
Tel.: (212) 886-2000
Fax: (212) 886-2016
Toll Free: (800) 937-0233
(Claritin, Levitra)

The Interpublic Group of Companies, Inc.
1114 Ave of the Americas 19th Fl
New York, NY 10036
Tel.: (212) 704-1200
Fax: (212) 704-1201

Oy Clay Network Ltd.
Kalevankatu 31
FI-00100
Helsinki, Finland
Tel.: (358) 9 686 6710
Fax: (358) 9 694 0170

MERCK FROSST CANADA LTD.
(Sub. of Merck & Co., Inc.)
16711 Trans Canada Highway
Kirkland, QC H9H 3L1, Canada
Tel.: (514) 428-8600
Fax: (514) 428-2670
Toll Free: (800) 567-2594
E-mail: servicesmt_customer@merck.com
Web Site: www.merck.ca
Sales Range: $1-4.9 Billion
Approx. Number Employees: 1,600
Business Description:
Pharmaceuticals Distr
S.I.C.: 5122
N.A.I.C.S.: 424210
Advertising Expenditures: $5,000,000
Media: 2-4-6-10
Distr.: Natl.
Personnel:
Carlos G. Dourado *(Pres)*
Heather Coleman *(Mgr-Direct Mktg-MCC)*
Advertising Agencies:
Anderson DDB Sante.Vie.Esprit.
3500 Blvd De Maisonneuve St W Ste 610
Montreal, QC H3Z 3C1, Canada
Tel.: (514) 844-9505
Fax: (514) 842-9871

Embryon Communication Design
276 36th Ave
Lachine, QC H8T 2A3, Canada
Tel.: (514) 890-1212
Fax: (514) 890-1216

kirshenbaum bond senecal + partners
Toronto
2 Bloor Street E 26th Fl
Toronto, ON M4W 3J4, Canada
Tel.: (416) 260-7000
Fax: (416) 260-7100

NATIONAL Public Relations
2001 McGill College Ave Ste 800
Montreal, QC H3A 1G1, Canada
Tel.: (514) 843-7171
Fax: (514) 843-6976

MERCK HUMAN HEALTH DIVISION
(Div. of Merck & Co., Inc.)
770 Sumneytown Pike
West Point, PA 19486
Tel.: (800) 347-9097
Web Site: www.merck.com
Sales Range: $1-4.9 Billion
Approx. Number Employees: 6,000
Business Description:
Prescription Pharmaceutical & Biological Products Mfr
S.I.C.: 2834
N.A.I.C.S.: 325412
Advertising Expenditures: $750,000
Media: 2-3-6-7-8-9-10-15-24-25
Distr.: Natl.
Budget Set: Oct.
Personnel:
Mark Timney *(Pres-US Ops)*
Brands & Products:
FLEXEVIL
HEPTAVAX
TONOCARD
VASERETIC
VASOTEC
Advertising Agencies:
Draftfcb New York
100 W 33rd St
New York, NY 10001

Key to Media (For complete agency information see *The Advertising Red Books-Agencies* edition):
1. Bus. Publs. 2. Cable T.V. 3. Catalogs & Directories. 4. Co-op Adv. 5. Consumer Mags. 6. D.M. to Bus. Estab.7. D.M. to Consumers 8. Daily Newsp. 9. Exhibits/Trade Shows 10. Foreign 11. Infomercial 12. Internet Adv.13. Multimedia 14. Network Radio 15. Network T.V. 16. Newsp. Distr. Mags. 17. Other 18. Outdoor (Posters, Transit) 19. Point of Purchase20. Premiums, Novelties 21. Product Samples 22. Special Events Mktg. 23. Spot Radio 24. Spot T.V. 25. Weekly Newsp. 26. Yellow Page Adv.

Tel.: (212) 885-3000
Fax: (212) 885-3300
Print

Initiative Worldwide
(Part of The Interpublic Group of Companies, Inc.)
1 Dag Hammerskjold Plz 5th Fl
New York, NY 10017
Tel.: (212) 605-7000
Fax: (212) 605-7200
Radio & TV

MERZ AESTHETICS
(Formerly BioForm Medical, Inc.)
(Sub. of Merz Pharma GmbH & Co. KGaA)
1875 S Grant St Ste 200
San Mateo, CA 94402
Tel.: (650) 286-4000
Fax: (650) 286-4090
Fax: (866) 862-1212
Toll Free: (866) 862-1221
Web Site: www.merzaesthetics.com
Approx. Rev.: $66,518,000
Approx. Number Employees: 310
Year Founded: 1999
Business Description:
Medical Aesthetics Products Mfr
S.I.C.: 2834
N.A.I.C.S.: 325412
Advertising Expenditures: $331,000
Media: 5-8
Personnel:
Dennis Condon *(Pres & Chief Bus Officer)*
Steve Basta *(CEO)*
Adam Gridley *(Sr VP-Product Dev)*
Dean Erickson *(VP-Mfg & Gen Mgr-WI Ops)*
Chris Holmes *(VP-Sls)*
Freddie Park *(VP-Legal Affairs)*
Brands & Products:
AETHOXYSKLEROL
BIOGLUE
COAPTITE
RADIESSE
VOICE RADIESSE

MESA LABORATORIES, INC.
12100 W 6th Ave
Lakewood, CO 80228-1252
Tel.: (303) 987-8000
Fax: (303) 987-8989
Telex: 821485 MESAMED
E-mail: investorrelations@mesalabs.com
Web Site: www.mesalabs.com
Approx. Sls.: $32,826,000
Approx. Number Employees: 177
Year Founded: 1982
Business Description:
Medical Products for Kidney Dialysis & Sensor Products Used in Industrial Processing & Transportation
S.I.C.: 3823; 3841
N.A.I.C.S.: 334513; 339112
Export
Advertising Expenditures: $315,000
Media: 7-10-13
Personnel:
Luke R. Schmieder *(Chm)*
John J. Sullivan *(Pres, CEO & Treas)*
Steven W. Peterson *(CFO, Chief Acctg Officer, Sec & VP-Fin)*
Glenn E. Adriance *(VP-Sls & Mktg)*
Brands & Products:
APEX
DATATRACE
ECHO
HYDRA WATER QUALITY INSTRUMENT
LOTEMP
MEDICAL
MESA
MESA LABS
NUSONICS
RAVEN
SGM BIOTECH
TORQO
WESTERN METERS

METROPOLITAN HEALTH NETWORKS, INC.
250 Australian Ave S Ste 400
West Palm Beach, FL 33401
Tel.: (561) 805-8500
Fax: (561) 805-8501
Toll Free: (888) 663-8227
E-mail: mearley@metcare.com
Web Site: www.metcare.com
Approx. Rev.: $368,185,734
Approx. Number Employees: 226
Business Description:
Health Service Network
S.I.C.: 6321
N.A.I.C.S.: 524114
Advertising Expenditures: $359,000
Personnel:
Michael M. Earley *(Chm & CEO)*
Jose A. Guethon *(Pres & COO)*
Robert J. Sabo *(CFO)*
Roman G. Fisher *(CIO & Sr VP)*
William H. McCoy, III *(Chief Medical Info Officer)*
Roberto L. Palenzuela *(Gen Counsel & Corp Sec)*
Maria A. Xirau *(Sr VP-Ops)*
Sharon Munroe *(VP-HR)*

METROPOLITAN JEWISH HEALTH SYSTEM
6323 7th Ave
Brooklyn, NY 11220
Tel.: (718) 921-7601
Fax: (718) 630-2565
E-mail: info@mjhs.org
Web Site: www.mjhs.org
Approx. Number Employees: 1,400
Business Description:
Health Care Services
S.I.C.: 8082
N.A.I.C.S.: 621610
Media: 2
Personnel:
Eli S. Feldman *(Pres & CEO)*
Alexander S. Balko *(Exc VP, COO & CFO)*
Susan Caputo *(Pres-Home Care & Hospice & Palliative Care)*
Robert E. Leamer *(Gen Counsel & Sr VP)*
Esther Spiegel *(Exec VP-Inpatient Ops)*
Elliot M. Brooks *(Sr VP-HR)*
Michael Yrigoyen *(Sr VP-Bus Dev)*
Advertising Agency:
gkv Communications
The Cascade Bldg 1030 Hull St Ste 400
Baltimore, MD 21230
Tel.: (410) 539-5400
Fax: (410) 234-2441

MIAMI CHILDREN'S HOSPITAL
3100 SW 62nd Ave
Miami, FL 33155
Tel.: (305) 666-6511
Tel.: (305) 543-1623 (Pub Rels)
Toll Free: (800) 432-6837
E-mail: info@mch.com
Web Site: www.mch.com
Approx. Number Employees: 2,000
Business Description:
Health Care Services
S.I.C.: 8069
N.A.I.C.S.: 622310
Media: 6
Personnel:
Narendra Kini *(Pres & CEO)*
April Andrews-Singh *(VP & Chief Ethics & Compliance Officer)*
Advertising Agencies:
Eisenberg & Associates
511 NE 3rd Ave
Fort Lauderdale, FL 33301-3235
Tel.: (954) 760-9500
Fax: (954) 760-9594

The MWW Group
700 13th St NW
Washington, DC 20006
Tel.: (202) 585-2270
Fax: (202) 585-2273

MICHAEL DATTOLI MD, LLC
(d/b/a Dattoli Cancer Center)
2803 Fruitville Rd
Sarasota, FL 34237
Tel.: (941) 957-4926
Fax: (941) 957-0038
Toll Free: (877) 328-8654
Web Site: www.dattoli.com
Approx. Rev.: $1,500,000
Approx. Number Employees: 21
Year Founded: 2000
Business Description:
Prostrate Cancer Treatment Center
S.I.C.: 8011
N.A.I.C.S.: 621111
Advertising Expenditures: $250,000
Media: 2-10-13-16-18-22-23-24
Personnel:
Michael J. Dattoli *(Owner)*
Ginya Carnahan *(Dir-Mktg, Dev-Dattoli Cancer Center & Foundation)*

MICROLINE SURGICAL INC.
(Sub. of Hoya Holdings, Inc.)
800 Cummings Ctr Ste 157 X
Beverly, MA 01915
Tel.: (978) 922-9810
Fax: (978) 922-9209
E-mail: info@microlinesurgical.com
Web Site: www.microlinepentax.com
Approx. Number Employees: 140
Year Founded: 1987
Business Description:
Laparoscopic, Cutting & Dissecting Medical Equipment Mfr
S.I.C.: 3841; 5047
N.A.I.C.S.: 339112; 423450
Personnel:
Jean-Luc Boulnois *(Chm, Pres & CEO)*
Advertising Agency:
Seidler Bernstein
700 Technology Sq 4th Fl
Cambridge, MA 02139
Tel.: (617) 225-0400
Fax: (617) 225-0011
(Logo)

MICROMET, INC.
6707 Democracy Blvd Ste 505
Bethesda, MD 20817-1100
Tel.: (240) 752-1420
Fax: (240) 752-1425
E-mail: info@micromet-inc.com
Web Site: www.micromet-inc.com
Approx. Rev.: $28,744,000
Approx. Number Employees: 170
Business Description:
Biological Products Research, Development & Commercialization Services for Cancer Treatment & Control
S.I.C.: 2836; 8733
N.A.I.C.S.: 325414; 541720
Personnel:
David F. Hale *(Chm)*
Christian Itin *(Pres & CEO)*
Barclay A. Phillips *(CFO & Sr VP)*
Patrick A. Baeuerle *(Chief Scientific Officer & Sr VP)*
Jan Fagerberg *(Chief Medical Officer & Sr VP)*
Matthias Alder *(Gen Counsel, Sec & Sr VP)*
Christian Neitzel *(Dir-HR)*
Brands & Products:
ADECATUMUMAB MT201
BITE
D93
EPIMET
MICROMET
MT103 MEDI 538
MT110
MT203
MT204
SCAGE
Advertising Agency:
Schwartz Communications, Inc.
230 3rd Ave
Waltham, MA 02451
Tel.: (781) 684-0770
Fax: (781) 684-6500

MIDWEST CENTER FOR STRESS & ANXIETY, LLC
(Holding of Transom Capital Group, LLC)
106 N Church St Ste 200
Oak Harbor, OH 43449
Mailing Address:
PO Box 205
Oak Harbor, OH 43449
Tel.: (419) 898-4357
Fax: (419) 898-0669
E-mail: support@stresscenter.com
Web Site: www.stresscenter.com
Sales Range: $1-9.9 Million
Approx. Number Employees: 35
Year Founded: 1989
Business Description:
Stress, Anxiety & Depression Self-Help Products & Support Services
S.I.C.: 8322; 5961; 5999
N.A.I.C.S.: 624190; 446199; 454111; 454113
Media: 3-7-8-14-15-23-24
Distr.: Intl.
Personnel:
Phillip H. Fisher *(Co-Founder)*
Lucinda Bassett *(Pres)*
Advertising Agencies:
Marketing Architects, Inc.
110 Cheshire Lane Ste 200
Minneapolis, MN 55305
Tel.: (952) 449-2500

Key to Media (For complete agency information see *The Advertising Red Books-Agencies* edition):
1. Bus. Publs. 2. Cable T.V. 3. Catalogs & Directories. 4. Co-op Adv. 5. Consumer Mags. 6. D.M. to Bus. Estab.7. D.M. to Consumers 8. Daily Newsp. 9. Exhibits/Trade Shows 10. Foreign 11. Infomercial 12. Internet Adv.13. Multimedia 14. Network Radio 15. Network T.V. 16. Newsp. Distr. Mags. 17. Other 18. Outdoor (Posters, Transit) 19. Point of Purchase20. Premiums, Novelties 21. Product Samples 22. Special Events Mktg. 23. Spot Radio 24. Spot T.V. 25. Weekly Newsp. 26. Yellow Page Adv.

Midwest Center for Stress & Anxiety, LLC — (Continued)

TargetCom, LLC
444 N Michigan Ave 33rd Fl
Chicago, IL 60611-3905
Tel.: (312) 822-1100
Fax: (312) 822-9628
Toll Free: (877) 423-7837

MILESTONE SCIENTIFIC, INC.

220 S Orange Ave
Livingston, NJ 07039
Tel.: (973) 535-2717
Fax: (973) 535-2829
Toll Free: (800) 862-1125
E-mail: info@milesci.com
Web Site: www.milesci.com
Approx. Rev.: $9,749,968
Approx. Number Employees: 16
Year Founded: 1989
Business Description:
Disposable Medical & Dental Products Developer, Mfr & Marketer
S.I.C.: 3842; 2676; 3841; 3843; 5047
N.A.I.C.S.: 339113; 322291; 339112; 339114; 423450
Advertising Expenditures: $107,011
Media: 2-7-8-10-22
Personnel:
Leslie Bernhard *(Chm)*
Leonard A. Osser *(CEO)*
Joseph D'Agostino *(CFO)*
Eugene Casagrande *(Dir-Intl & Prof Rels)*
Mark Hochman *(Dir-Clinical Affairs)*
Dale Johnson *(Dir-Intl Distr)*
Stephen Solomon *(Dir-Engrg & Regulatory Affairs)*
Marvin Terrell *(Dir-Domestic Distr)*
Brands & Products:
COMPUDENT
COMPUFLO
COMPUMED
COOL BLUE WAND
MILESTONE
MILESTONE SCIENTIFIC
THE SAFETYWAND
STA
THE WAND
THE WAND PLUS

MILLENNIUM: THE TAKEDA ONCOLOGY COMPANY

(Sub. of Takeda Pharmaceutical Company Limited)
40 Landsdowne St
Cambridge, MA 02139-4134
Tel.: (617) 679-7000
Fax: (617) 374-7000
E-mail: info@mlnm.com
Web Site: www.mlnm.com
Approx. Rev.: $527,525,000
Approx. Number Employees: 966
Year Founded: 1993
Business Description:
Treatments & Diagnostics for Asthma, Stroke, Colitis & Crohn's Disease
S.I.C.: 2834; 8733
N.A.I.C.S.: 325412; 541710
Advertising Expenditures: $43,100,000
Media: 4-10-21
Personnel:
Deborah L. Dunsire *(Pres & CEO)*
Nancy A. Simonian *(Chief Medical Officer-Clinical & Regulatory Affairs)*
Laurie Bartlet Keating *(Gen Counsel & Sr VP)*
Christophe M. Bianchi *(Exec VP)*
Stephen M. Gansler *(Sr VP-HR)*
Anna Protopapas *(Sr VP-Corp Dev & Strategy)*
Peter F. Smith *(Sr VP-Non-Clinical Dev Sciences)*
Claire Thom *(Sr VP-Portfolio Mgmt)*
Isabelle Mercier *(VP-Mktg)*
Brands & Products:
BREAKTHROUGH SCIENCE. BREAKTHROUGH MEDICINE
CAMPATH
INTEGRILIN
MILLENNIUM
VELCADE

MILTEX, INC.

589 Davies Dr
York, PA 17402-8630
Tel.: (717) 840-9335
Fax: (717) 840-9347
Fax: (866) 854-8400
Toll Free: (800) 645-8000
Toll Free: (866) 854-8300
E-mail: customerservice@miltex.com
Web Site: www.miltex.com
Sales Range: $10-24.9 Million
Approx. Number Employees: 250
Year Founded: 1890
Business Description:
Hand-Held Surgical Instruments Mfr & Supplier
S.I.C.: 5047
N.A.I.C.S.: 423450
Media: 10-13
Brands & Products:
CARB-N-SERT
CERAM-A-GRIP
GRIPLITE
MEISTERHAND
MILTEX
REDEFINING EXCELLENCE
THOMPSON
TIP-IT

MIRACLE-EAR, INC.

(Sub. of Amplifon USA)
5000 Cheshire Ln N
Minneapolis, MN 55446-3706
Tel.: (763) 268-4000
Fax: (763) 268-4295
Toll Free: (877) 268-4264
Web Site: www.miracle-ear.com
Approx. Number Employees: 100
Year Founded: 1948
Business Description:
Mfr. & Sales of Hearing Aids
S.I.C.: 3845; 5999
N.A.I.C.S.: 334510; 446199
Media: 1-2-3-6-8-14-15-24-26
Distr.: Intl.; Natl.
Budget Set: Sept.
Personnel:
Herns Runch *(Pres)*
Anne Gowen *(Dir-Mktg)*
Brands & Products:
AMPLIFIT
MIRACLE-EAR
Advertising Agency:
Zephyr Media Group
990 Grove St Ste 300
Evanston, IL 60201
Tel.: (847) 328-1519
Fax: (847) 328-3518

MISONIX INC.

1938 New Hwy
Farmingdale, NY 11735-1204
Tel.: (631) 694-9555
Fax: (631) 694-9412
Toll Free: (800) 645-9846
Web Site: www.misonix.com
Approx. Sls.: $14,440,061
Approx. Number Employees: 77
Year Founded: 1992
Business Description:
Ultrasonic Equipment & Medical Devices Mfr
S.I.C.: 3841; 3821; 3845
N.A.I.C.S.: 339112; 334510; 339111
Import Export
Advertising Expenditures: $105,000
Media: 10
Personnel:
Michael A. McManus, Jr. *(Pres & CEO)*
Richard Zaremba *(CFO & Sr VP)*
Michael C. Ryan *(Sr VP-Medical Div)*
Dan Voic *(VP-R&D & Engrg)*
E. Y. Denard *(Sr Dir-Sls)*
Brands & Products:
AURA
AUTOSONIX
HISONIC
LYSONIX
MISONIX
MYSTAIRE
PULSESELECT
SONICATORS
XL-2000

MISSION PHARMACAL COMPANY INC.

10999 IH 10 W Ste 1000
San Antonio, TX 78230-1355
Tel.: (210) 696-8400
Fax: (210) 696-6010
Web Site:
www.missionpharmacal.com
Approx. Number Employees: 461
Year Founded: 1946
Business Description:
Pharmaceutical Preparations
S.I.C.: 2834
N.A.I.C.S.: 325412
Import Export
Media: 2-7-11-13-14-21
Personnel:
Neill Walsdorf, Jr. *(Pres)*
Neill Walsdorf, Sr. *(CEO)*
Thomas Dooley *(CFO)*
Brands & Products:
CALCIBIND
CITRACAL
CITRACAL PRENATAL RX
CITRICAL ULTRADENSE
FOSFREE
LITHOSTAT
MAGTRATE
MISSION
STONECOMP
STONERISK
STONETRACK
THERA-GESIC
THIOLA
ULTRADENSE
UROCIT
UROCIT-K
URORISK
VED
Advertising Agencies:
Design North, Inc.
8007 Douglas Ave
Racine, WI 53402
Tel.: (262) 639-2080
Tel.: (262) 898-1090
Fax: (262) 639-5230
Toll Free: (800) 247-8494

Moroch Partners
3625 N Hall St Ste 1100
Dallas, TX 75219-5122
Tel.: (214) 520-9700
Fax: (214) 252-1724

Topin & Associates, Inc.
205 N Michigan Ave Ste 2315
Chicago, IL 60601-5923
Tel.: (312) 645-0100
Fax: (312) 645-0120

MODERN PRODUCTS, INC.

6425 W Executive Dr
Mequon, WI 53092-0248
Tel.: (262) 242-2400
Fax: (262) 242-2751
E-mail: modernfearn@aol.com
Web Site: www.modernfearn.com
Approx. Number Employees: 25
Year Founded: 1925
Business Description:
Special Diet Foods & Health Food Seasoning Mfr
S.I.C.: 2099
N.A.I.C.S.: 311942
Import Export
Advertising Expenditures: $625,000
Media: 2-5-6-7-9-10-16-19-21-22
Distr.: Intl.
Budget Set: Oct.
Personnel:
Gaylord G. Palermo *(Pres)*
Anthony A. Palermo *(CEO)*
Michele Palmero *(Dir-Adv)*
Brands & Products:
B-FAMILY
CLASSIQUE FARE
FEARN
GARLIC PLUS
GAYLORD HAUSER
HERBAL BOUQUET
INDO
LEMON PEPPER
NATURALLY CAJUN
NATURALLY SALT FREE
NATURFRESH
ONION MAGIC
SANTAY
SIPP
SPICE GARDEN
SPIKE
SWISS FORMULA
SWISS-KRISS
VEGE-SAL
VEGIT

MOLECULAR DEVICES CORPORATION

(Sub. of MDS Analytical Technologies)
1311 Orleans Dr
Sunnyvale, CA 94089-1136
Tel.: (408) 747-1700
Fax: (408) 747-3601
Toll Free: (800) 635-5577
E-mail: info@moldev.com
Web Site: www.moleculardevices.com
Sales Range: $150-199.9 Million
Approx. Number Employees: 300
Business Description:
Drug Measurement Systems Developer & Mfr

Key to Media (For complete agency information see *The Advertising Red Books-Agencies* edition):
1. Bus. Publs. 2. Cable T.V. 3. Catalogs & Directories. 4. Co-op Adv. 5. Consumer Mags. 6. D.M. to Bus. Estab.7. D.M. to Consumers
8. Daily Newsp. 9. Exhibits/Trade Shows 10. Foreign 11. Infomercial 12. Internet Adv.13. Multimedia 14. Network Radio
15. Network T.V. 16. Newsp. Distr. Mags. 17. Other 18. Outdoor (Posters, Transit) 19. Point of Purchase20. Premiums, Novelties
21. Product Samples 22. Special Events Mktg. 23. Spot Radio 24. Spot T.V. 25. Weekly Newsp. 26. Yellow Page Adv.

S.I.C.: 3826; 3841
N.A.I.C.S.: 334516; 339112
Advertising Expenditures: $1,200,000
Personnel:
Mark Verheyden *(Pres)*
Lisa English *(Dir-Mktg)*
Brands & Products:
ACQUEST
ACUITY
ACUITYXPRESS
ANALYST
AQUAMAX
CATCHPOINT
COMBI
DISCOVERY
EMAX
EMBLA
FLEXSTATION
FLIPR
FLIPR 384
FLIPRTETRA
GENEPIX PRO
IMAGEXPRESS
IONWORKS
LMAX
METAFLUOR
METAMORPH
METAVUE
METAXPRESS
MICRO
MINIDISC
OPUSXPRESS
PATCHXPRESS
QUATTRO
SCREENSTATION
SKANSTACKER
SKANWASHER
SOFTMAX
SPECTRAMAX
SPECTRAMAX GEMINI
SYNCHROMAX
THERMOMAX
THRESHOLD
TRANSFLUOR
TRANSIL
VERSAMAX
VMAX
Advertising Agency:
HiveMind Marketing Inc.
111 N Market St Ste 300
San Jose, CA 95113-1116
Tel.: (408) 418-4620
Fax: (408) 418-4621
Toll Free: (866) 781-8195

MOLINA HEALTHCARE, INC.
200 Oceangate Ste 100
Long Beach, CA 90802-4317
Tel.: (562) 435-3666
Fax: (562) 437-1335
Toll Free: (888) 562-5442
Web Site: www.molinahealthcare.com
Approx. Rev.: $4,085,977,000
Approx. Number Employees: 4,200
Business Description:
Healthcare Services
S.I.C.: 6321; 8011; 9441
N.A.I.C.S.: 524114; 621491; 923130
Media: 7-8
Personnel:
J. Mario Molina *(Pres & CEO)*
John C. Molina *(CFO)*
Terry P. Bayer *(COO)*
Mark L. Andrews *(Chief Legal Officer & Sec)*
Michael Steele *(Sr VP-Dual Eligible Strategies)*
Brands & Products:
BREATHE WITH EASE
FREE & CLEAR
HEDIS
MOLINA
MOLINA HEALTHCARE
MOLINA OPTIONS PLUS
MOTHERHOOD MATTERS
YOUR EXTENDED FAMILY

MOLNLYCKE
(Sub. of Molnlycke Health Care AB)
5550 Peachtree Pkwy Ste 500
Norcross, GA 30092
Tel.: (864) 260-5920
Fax: (888) 824-6435
Toll Free: (800) 843-8497
Web Site: www.molnlycke.com
Approx. Number Employees: 300
Business Description:
Cotton Drapes Surgical
S.I.C.: 2833
N.A.I.C.S.: 325411
Personnel:
Vivienne Heywood *(Dir-Pub Rel)*
Advertising Agency:
Luquire George Andrews, Inc.
(dba LGA)
4201 Congress St Ste 400
Charlotte, NC 28209
Tel.: (704) 552-6565
Fax: (704) 552-1972
— Lauren Sammerson *(VP-Pub Rel)*

MONOGRAM BIOSCIENCES, INC.
(Sub. of LABORATORY CORPORATION OF AMERICA HOLDINGS)
345 Oyster Point Blvd
South San Francisco, CA 94080-1913
Tel.: (650) 635-1100
Fax: (650) 624-4490
Web Site: www.monogrambio.com
Approx. Rev.: $62,193,000
Approx. Number Employees: 382
Year Founded: 1995
Business Description:
Biological Test Products Mfr
S.I.C.: 2836; 2834; 8733
N.A.I.C.S.: 325414; 325412; 541710
Advertising Expenditures: $6,500,000
Media: 10-16
Personnel:
Kathy L. Hibbs *(Gen Counsel & Sr VP)*
Tien T. Bui *(VP-Sls & Mktg)*
Lisa Spiro *(Sr Dir-Mktg)*
Brands & Products:
ETAG
ETAG PERFORMER
GENESEQ
HERMARK
PHENOSCREEN
PHENOSENSE
PHENOSENSE GT
REPLICATION CAPACITY
TROFILE
VERATAG
Advertising Agency:
Purohit Navigation
111 S Wacker Dr Ste 4700
Chicago, IL 60606-4303
Tel.: (312) 341-8100
Fax: (312) 341-8119

MONTEFIORE MEDICAL CENTER
111 E 210 St
Bronx, NY 10467-2662
Tel.: (718) 920-4321
Tel.: (718) 920-6400 (Admin Offices)
Fax: (718) 920-2240
E-mail: info@montefiore.org
Web Site: www.montefiore.org
Sales Range: $1-4.9 Billion
Approx. Number Employees: 10,000
Year Founded: 1884
Business Description:
Hospital & Health Care Services
S.I.C.: 8062
N.A.I.C.S.: 622110
Advertising Expenditures: $3,500,000
Media: 2-4-6-9-10-13-18-22-23-24-25
Personnel:
Steven M. Safyer *(Pres & CEO)*
Donald L. Ashkenase *(Exec VP-Corp Affairs)*
Robert B. Conaty *(Exec VP-Ops)*
Susan Green *(Sr VP-Ops)*
Stanley L. Jacobson *(Sr VP & Special Advisor-Bus Affairs)*
Joel A. Perlman *(Sr VP-Fin)*
Advertising Agency:
Walter F. Cameron Advertising Inc.
350 Motor Pkwy Ste 410
Hauppauge, NY 11788-5125
Tel.: (631) 232-3033
Fax: (631) 232-3111

MONTICELLO DRUG CO.
(Sub. of The Monticello Companies, Inc.)
1604 Stockton St
Jacksonville, FL 32204-4524
Tel.: (904) 384-3666
Fax: (904) 388-6307
Web Site:
www.monticellocompanies.com
Approx. Sls.: $3,500,000
Approx. Number Employees: 11
Year Founded: 1908
Business Description:
Cold Preparations, Liquid & Tablets Mfr
S.I.C.: 2834
N.A.I.C.S.: 325412
Export
Advertising Expenditures: $250,000
Media: 2-3-5-6-7-8-14-20-22-23-24-25
Distr.: Reg.
Budget Set: June
Personnel:
Henry E. Dean, III *(Pres & CEO)*
Thomas S. Dean *(Exec VP)*
Brands & Products:
666
DEWITTS
NULLO
OTIX
THROAT DISCS

MOORE MEDICAL CORP.
(Sub. of McKesson Corporation)
1690 New Erigain Ave
Farmington, CT 06032
Mailing Address:
PO Box 1500
New Britain, CT 06050-1500
Tel.: (860) 826-3600
Fax: (860) 225-4440
Toll Free: (800) 234-1464
E-mail: info@mooremedical.com
Web Site: www.mooremedical.com
E-Mail For Key Personnel:
Marketing Director: mflorence@mooremedical.com
Sales Range: $125-149.9 Million
Approx. Number Employees: 306
Year Founded: 1947
Business Description:
Health-Care Products Distr
S.I.C.: 5047; 5122
N.A.I.C.S.: 423450; 424210
Export
Advertising Expenditures: $1,676,000
Media: 4-7
Brands & Products:
MOORE
VALUMED

MORINDA HOLDINGS INC.
333 W River Prk Dr
Provo, UT 84604
Tel.: (801) 234-1000
Fax: (801) 234-1001
E-mail: generalenquiry@gni.com
Web Site: www.gni.com
Sales Range: $1-4.9 Billion
Approx. Number Employees: 444
Year Founded: 1996
Business Description:
Drugs, Proprietaries & Sundries Mfr
S.I.C.: 6719
N.A.I.C.S.: 551112
Import Export
Media: 3-6-9-10-13-14-15-18-19-20-21-22-23-24
Personnel:
John Wadsworth *(Pres)*
Richard Rife *(Gen Counsel)*
Brands & Products:
TAHITIAN NONI

MORTON GROVE PHARMACEUTICALS, INC.
(Sub. of Wockhardt Limited)
6451 W Main St
Morton Grove, IL 60053-2633
Tel.: (973) 257-4960
Fax: (847) 967-5607
Toll Free: (800) 346-6854
E-mail: contactusa@Wockhardt.com
Web Site: www.mgp-online.com
Sales Range: $50-74.9 Million
Approx. Number Employees: 200
Year Founded: 1995
Business Description:
Producer of Pharmaceutical Preparations
S.I.C.: 2834; 2844
N.A.I.C.S.: 325412; 325620
Import Export
Media: 2-4
Personnel:
Mark Hartman *(Pres)*
Prakash Chainiani *(CFO & VP)*

MOUNT SINAI MEDICAL CENTER
4300 Alton Rd
Miami Beach, FL 33140-2910
Tel.: (305) 674-2064
Tel.: (305) 674-2121
Fax: (305) 674-2007
Web Site: www.msmc.com
Sales Estimate: $10-19 Million
Approx. Number Employees: 3,000
Year Founded: 1946
Business Description:
Medical Center

Key to Media (For complete agency information see *The Advertising Red Books-Agencies* edition):
1. Bus. Publs. 2. Cable T.V. 3. Catalogs & Directories. 4. Co-op Adv. 5. Consumer Mags. 6. D.M. to Bus. Estab.7. D.M. to Consumers 8. Daily Newsp. 9. Exhibits/Trade Shows 10. Foreign 11. Infomercial 12. Internet Adv.13. Multimedia 14. Network Radio 15. Network T.V. 16. Newsp. Distr. Mags. 17. Other 18. Outdoor (Posters, Transit) 19. Point of Purchase20. Premiums, Novelties 21. Product Samples 22. Special Events Mktg. 23. Spot Radio 24. Spot T.V. 25. Weekly Newsp. 26. Yellow Page Adv.

Mount Sinai Medical Center — (Continued)

S.I.C.: 8062
N.A.I.C.S.: 622110
Media: 22
Personnel:
Steven Sonenreich *(Pres & CEO)*
Anne Marie Gothard *(CMO-Interim)*

MPI RESEARCH, INC.

54943 N Main St
Mattawan, MI 49071-9399
Tel.: (269) 668-3336
Fax: (269) 668-4151
Web Site: www.mpiresearch.com
Approx. Number Employees: 1,600
Year Founded: 1962
Business Description:
Independent Contract Research Services
S.I.C.: 8733
N.A.I.C.S.: 541710
Export
Media: 2-10-17-20
Distr.: Intl.
Budget Set: Nov.
Personnel:
William U. Parfet *(Chm & CEO)*
Tim Derrington *(Pres & COO)*
Tina Rogers *(Exec VP & Dir-Res)*
Jim Laveglia *(Exec VP-Drug Safety Evaluation)*
Ali S. Faqi *(Sr Dir-Developmental & Reproductive Toxicology)*
Dale M. Cooper *(Dir-Clinical Medicine)*
Motoko Boucher *(Mgr-Mktg)*

MUELLER SPORTS MEDICINE, INC.

1 Quench Dr
Prairie Du Sac, WI 53578-2100
Tel.: (608) 643-8530
Fax: (608) 643-2568
Toll Free: (800) 356-9522
E-mail: sportcare@muellersportsmed.com
Web Site: www.muellersportsmed.com
Approx. Sls.: $25,000,000
Approx. Number Employees: 90
Year Founded: 1961
Business Description:
Mfr of Pharmaceuticals for Athletes
S.I.C.: 2834; 3842
N.A.I.C.S.: 325412; 339113
Export
Media: 1-2-4-5-7-8-10-13-19-21-22
Distr.: Intl.; Natl.
Budget Set: Nov. -Dec.
Personnel:
Brett Mueller *(Pres)*
Curt Mueller *(CEO-Registered Pharmacist)*
Herb Raschka *(Sr VP-Sls & Mktg)*
John Swafford *(Sr VP)*
Dale Roper *(Mgr-Reg Sls-South Central)*
Brands & Products:
B SHARP
EUROTAPE
LITE
LITE ANKLE BRACE
M-TAPE
M-WRAP
MEDI-STAT
MUELLER
MUELLER GUARD
MUELLERGESIC
MUELLERHINGE
MUELLERKOLD
NO GLARE STRIPS
QUENCH GUM
SMILE SCRUB
SPORT CARE
TULI'S
ULTRALITE CARPAL TUNNEL WRIST BRACE
WHIZZER
WRAPONS
Advertising Agency:
JSJ Advertising Agency
1 Quench Dr PO Box 99
Prairie Du Sac, WI 53578
Tel.: (608) 643-8530
Fax: (608) 643-2568
(Sports Medicine)

MULTIPLAN, INC.

(Sub. of MultiPlan Inc.)
1100 Winter St
Waltham, MA 02451-1440
Tel.: (781) 895-7500
Fax: (781) 895-3458
Toll Free: (800) 253-4417
E-mail: info@multiplan.com
Web Site: www.multiplan.com
Sales Range: $125-149.9 Million
Approx. Number Employees: 1,100
Year Founded: 1985
Business Description:
Healthcare Management Services
S.I.C.: 6321
N.A.I.C.S.: 524114
Media: 8
Personnel:
Mark Tabak *(CEO)*
Brands & Products:
PHCS
Advertising Agency:
Gearon Hoffman Inc.
88 Broad St
Boston, MA 02110
Tel.: (617) 247-1522
Fax: (617) 247-6821

MULTISORB TECHNOLOGIES, INC.

325 Harlem Rd
Buffalo, NY 14224-1825
Tel.: (716) 824-8900
Fax: (716) 824-4128
Toll Free: (888) Sorbent
E-mail: info@multisorb.com
Web Site: www.multisorb.com
Sales Range: $50-74.9 Million
Approx. Number Employees: 350
Year Founded: 1961
Business Description:
Mfr. & Packager of Desiccant Products, Contract Packaging & Sterilization
S.I.C.: 3295; 2819
N.A.I.C.S.: 327992; 325188
Import Export
Media: 2-4-7-8-10-11-16
Distr.: Natl.
Budget Set: Jan.
Personnel:
John S. Cullen *(Founder, Chm & CEO)*
Jim Renda *(Pres, COO & Exec VP)*
Richard Burke *(Dir-Mktg)*
Adrian Possumato *(Dir-Global)*
Brands & Products:
CALCULATIONS THROUGH OPERATIONS
CRYOSORB
DESICAP
DESIFORM
DESIMAX
DESIMAX SLF
DRI-CAN
DRICAP
DRIKETTE
DRIMOP
ELECTROSTITCH
FRESHCARD
FRESHMAX
FRESHPAX
HI-DRY
HUMONITOR
MAPLOX
MINIPAX
MULTIFORM
MULTIFORM CSF
MULTISORB TECHNOLOGIES
NATRASORB
POLYSORB
SADDLEFORM
SANISORB
SANISORB X
SECUREFORM
SORBARING
SORBICAP
STABILOX
STRIPPAX
TRANSORB
TYVEK
Advertising Agency:
Eric Mower and Associates
Key Ctr at Fountain Plz 50 Fountain Plz Ste 1000
Buffalo, NY 14202
Tel.: (716) 842-2233
Fax: (716) 842-6676

MWI VETERINARY SUPPLY, INC.

651 S Stratford Dr Ste 100
Meridian, ID 83642
Mailing Address:
PO Box 910
Meridian, ID 83680-0919
Tel.: (208) 955-8930
Fax: (208) 955-8902
Toll Free: (800) 824-3703
E-mail: investorrelations@mwivet.com
Web Site: www.mwivet.com
Approx. Rev.: $1,229,342,000
Approx. Number Employees: 1,179
Year Founded: 1976
Business Description:
Animal Health Products Distr
S.I.C.: 5122; 0742; 5047
N.A.I.C.S.: 424210; 423450; 541940
Advertising Expenditures: $717,000
Media: 2
Personnel:
John F. McNamara *(Chm)*
James F. Cleary, Jr. *(Pres & CEO)*
Mary Patricia B. Thompson *(CFO)*
James S. Hay *(CIO)*
Jeffrey J. Danielson *(VP-Sls)*
John R. Ryan *(VP-Mktg)*

MYLAN, INC.

1500 Corporate Dr Ste 400
Canonsburg, PA 15222
Tel.: (724) 514-1800
Fax: (724) 514-1870
E-mail: patrick.fitzerald@mylan.com
Web Site: www.mylan.com
Approx. Rev.: $5,450,522,000
Approx. Number Employees: 13,000
Year Founded: 1961
Business Description:
Pharmaceutical Products Mfr
S.I.C.: 2834; 6321
N.A.I.C.S.: 325412; 524114
Import
Advertising Expenditures: $5,435,000
Distr.: Natl.
Personnel:
Robert J. Coury *(Chm & CEO)*
Heather Bresch *(Pres)*
John D. Sheehan *(CFO & Exec VP)*
Rajiv Malik *(COO & Exec VP)*
Joseph Haggerty *(Gen Counsel & Sr VP)*
Eric M. Leeds *(Sr VP & Head-Global IR)*
Gregory L. Sheldon *(Global CIO & Sr VP)*
Nina Devlin *(VP-Comm)*
Brands & Products:
APOKYN
DIGITEK
KRISTALOSE
MYLAN
ZAGAM
Advertising Agency:
Rienzi & Rienzi Communications
150 River Rd., Bldg. M
Montville, NJ 07045
Tel.: (973) 334-0300
Fax: (973) 334-9537

NABI BIOPHARMACEUTICALS

12276 Wilkins Ave
Rockville, MD 20852
Tel.: (301) 770-3099
Fax: (301) 770-3097
Toll Free: (800) 685-5579
Telex: 4949797 NABI
E-mail: irpr@nabi.com
Web Site: www.nabi.com
Approx. Rev.: $35,005,000
Approx. Number Employees: 35
Year Founded: 1969
Business Description:
Biopharmaceutical Products Developer & Marketer
S.I.C.: 2836
N.A.I.C.S.: 325414
Export
Advertising Expenditures: $2,700,000
Media: 4-13
Personnel:
Geoffrey F. Cox *(Chm)*
Raafat E.F. Fahim *(Pres & CEO)*
Ron Kocok *(CFO)*
Matthew W. Kalnik *(Sr VP-Strategic Plng & Bus Ops)*
Paul Kessler *(Sr VP-Clinical, Medical & Regulatory Affairs)*
Brands & Products:
ALOPRIM
ALTASTAPH
CIVACIR
ENTEROVAX
HEBIG
NABI BIOPHARMACEUTICALS
NABI-HB
NICVAX
PENTASTAPH
PHOSLO
POWERING THE IMMUNE SYSTEM
RENS
STAPHVAX

Key to Media (For complete agency information see *The Advertising Red Books-Agencies* edition):
1. Bus. Publs. 2. Cable T.V. 3. Catalogs & Directories. 4. Co-op Adv. 5. Consumer Mags. 6. D.M. to Bus. Estab.7. D.M. to Consumers
8. Daily Newsp. 9. Exhibits/Trade Shows 10. Foreign 11. Infomercial 12. Internet Adv.13. Multimedia 14. Network Radio
15. Network T.V. 16. Newsp. Distr. Mags. 17. Other 18. Outdoor (Posters, Transit) 19. Point of Purchase20. Premiums, Novelties
21. Product Samples 22. Special Events Mktg. 23. Spot Radio 24. Spot T.V. 25. Weekly Newsp. 26. Yellow Page Adv.

Advertising Agency:
Human Capital Management, Inc.
1000 Corporate Dr Ste 300
Fort Lauderdale, FL 33334
Tel.: (954) 318-2300
Fax: (954) 318-2301

NATIONAL DENTEX CORPORATION

(Holding of Welsh Carson Anderson & Stowe, LLC)
2 Vision Dr
Natick, MA 01760
Tel.: (508) 907-7800
Fax: (508) 907-6050
E-mail: webmaster@nationaldentex.com
Web Site: www.nationaldentex.com
Approx. Rev.: $161,195,204
Approx. Number Employees: 1,745
Year Founded: 1982
Business Description:
Dental Laboratories Operator
S.I.C.: 8071; 3843; 8072
N.A.I.C.S.: 621512; 339114; 339116
Advertising Expenditures: $2,468,000
Media: 2-4
Personnel:
John W. Green *(Pres & COO)*
Steven E. Casper *(CEO)*
Wayne M. Coll *(CFO, VP & Asst Treas)*
Richard F. Becker, Jr. *(Exec VP & Treas)*
Eloy V. Sepulveda *(Grp VP)*

NATIONAL HEALTHCARE EXCHANGE SERVICES, INC.

629 J St
Sacramento, CA 95814
Tel.: (916) 231-0670
Fax: (916) 231-0220
Toll Free: (800) 753-3638
E-mail: investorrelations@nhxs.com
Web Site: www.nhxs.com
Sales Range: $1-9.9 Million
Approx. Number Employees: 14
Business Description:
Medical Billing & Revenue Recovery Services
S.I.C.: 7372; 7389
N.A.I.C.S.: 511210; 561499
Personnel:
Mark W. Rieger *(CEO)*
Rose M. Laur *(Dir-Healthcare Solutions)*
Jeff Souza *(Dir-IT)*
Brands & Products:
ADMINISERVE
CONTRACTRESOLVE
EOBRESOLVE
MGMA
NHXS
NHXSPRICER
REIMBURSEMENT ACCURACY MADE SIMPLE
Advertising Agency:
ProAmericas
8174 South Holly #405
Centennial, CO 80122
Tel.: (303) 933-2626

NATIONAL HOME HEALTH CARE CORP.

(Holding of Angelo, Gordon & Co. L.P.)
700 White Plains Rd Ste 275
Scarsdale, NY 10583-5013
Tel.: (914) 722-9000
Fax: (914) 722-9239
E-mail: rheller@nhhc.net
Web Site: www.nhhc.net
Sales Range: $100-124.9 Million
Approx. Number Employees: 3,680
Year Founded: 1983
Business Description:
Home Health Care Services
S.I.C.: 8082; 8322
N.A.I.C.S.: 621610; 624120
Advertising Expenditures: $200,000
Media: 7-8-13-17-22
Personnel:
Steven Fialkow *(Pres)*
Robert P. Heller *(CFO)*

NATIONSHEALTH, INC.

(Holding of ComVest Group Holdings, Inc.)
13650 NW 8th St Ste 210
Sunrise, FL 33325
Tel.: (954) 903-5000
Fax: (954) 903-5850
Toll Free: (800) 977-0601
E-mail: Webmaster@NationsHealth.com
Web Site: www.nationshealth.com
Approx. Rev.: $100,376,000
Approx. Number Employees: 597
Business Description:
Mail Order Medical Supply Distr
S.I.C.: 5961; 5047; 6321
N.A.I.C.S.: 454113; 423450; 524114
Advertising Expenditures: $609,000
Media: 8-19-24
Personnel:
Glenn M. Parker *(Pres & CEO)*
Timothy Fairbanks *(CFO)*
Joshua B. Weingard *(Chief Legal Officer & Exec VP)*
Rodney Carson *(Exec VP-Ops)*
Brands & Products:
ACCUCHECK
ASCENSIA
FREESTYLE
NATIONSHEALTH

NATROL, INC.

(Sub. of Plethico Pharmaceuticals Ltd.)
21411 Prairie St
Chatsworth, CA 91311-5829
Tel.: (818) 739-6000
Fax: (818) 739-6001
Toll Free: (800) 326-1520
E-mail: info@natrol.com
Web Site: www.natrol.com
Approx. Sls.: $65,564,000
Approx. Number Employees: 251
Year Founded: 1980
Business Description:
Mfr & Marketer of Dietary Supplements, Herbal Teas & Sports Nutrition Products
S.I.C.: 2833; 2834
N.A.I.C.S.: 325411; 325412
Import Export
Advertising Expenditures: $7,056,000
Media: 3-4-5-6-10-12-13-14-15-18-19-20-22-23-24
Personnel:
Jenia G. Khudagulyan *(COO & Sr VP)*
Peter Gil *(Dir-Intl Sls)*
Lisa Sheppard *(Dir-Mktg)*
Brands & Products:
ACTIVIN
BENECARDIA
BIOBEADS
BONE PROTECTOR
BRAINSPEED ATTENTION
BRAINSPEED MEMORY
BRAINSPEED PERFORM
CARB INTERCEPT
CARDIO OMEGA SOLUTIONS
CETYLPURE
CHINA CHLORELLA
CHOLESTEROL BALANCE
CHROMEMATE
CITRIMAX
COMPLETE BALANCE
CRAN SUPPORT
CRAVEX
DHA NEUROMINS
ESSENTIALLY PURE INGREDIENTS
ESTER-C
FAT BURNER
FEELANEW
GLUCOSUPPORT
GUGULIPID
HOT FLASHEX
IMMUNENHANCER
KAVATROK
KAVATROL
KID'S COMPANION
LACI LAXATIV-A-TEA
LACI LE BEAU
LAXATIV-A-TEA
METABOFIRM
MY DEFENSE
MY FAVORITE MULTIPLE
NATROL
NATROL COMPLETE BALANCE
NEUROMINS
OCUSENSE
OMEGA
OSTEO OMEGA SOLUTIONS
PC CARE
PHASE 2 STARCH NEUTRALIZER
PMS CONTROL
PMS OMEGA SOLUTIONS
POWER TIME
PRO LAB
PROSTATEXCELL
PYCNOGENOL
SAF STRESS & ANXIETY FORMULA
SEROTAIN
SLEEP N RESTORE
TAKE ONE
TONALIN
TRIPLELEAN
TUMMY CARE
ULTRA CARB INTERCEPT
ZERO FLUSH

NATURAL ALTERNATIVES INTERNATIONAL, INC.

1185 Linda Vista Dr
San Marcos, CA 92069-3823
Tel.: (760) 744-7340
Fax: (760) 744-9589
E-mail: info@nai-online.com
Web Site: www.nai-online.com
Approx. Sls.: $55,882,000
Approx. Number Employees: 127
Year Founded: 1980
Business Description:
Mfr of Encapsulated & Tablet Vitamins & Related Nutrients, Including Phytochemicals Derived from Botanicals & Foods
S.I.C.: 2833
N.A.I.C.S.: 325411
Advertising Expenditures: $65,000
Media: 17
Personnel:
Mark A. LeDoux *(Chm & CEO)*
Kenneth E. Wolf *(CFO & COO)*
Marian Barker *(VP-New Product Introductions & Strategic Initiatives)*
Fausto Petrini *(Dir-Ops)*
Brands & Products:
ABSORBALEAN
CRYSTALTINE
HYDROMINS
NAI

NATURAL ORGANICS, INC.

548 Broadhollow Rd
Melville, NY 11747
Tel.: (631) 293-0030
Fax: (631) 293-0349
E-mail: info@naturesplus.com
Web Site: www.naturesplus.com
Approx. Number Employees: 355
Business Description:
Vitamin Products Development
S.I.C.: 2834
N.A.I.C.S.: 325412
Media: 6-18
Personnel:
Gerald Kessler *(Founder)*
James Gibbons *(Pres)*
Brands & Products:
ACTI-ZYME
ALGAE MAX
ALLER-7
ALPHASTAT
ANIMAL PARADE
ARA-LARIX
BABY PLEX
BETA-PRO
BIOPERINE
BIOPERINE 10
BOTANICLEANSE
C-ASCORBS
CAL/MAG
CANDIDA FORTE
CARDIOACTIN
CARROT-TEIN
CHILDREN'S VITA-GELS
CHONDROITIN
CITRIMAX
COLOSTRUM
COMMANDO
CONNECT-ALL
CRITICAL KETO-NUTRIENTS
DETOXYGEN
DHEA
DOPHILUS
DYNO-MINS
DYNO-VITES
ENERGY ELIXIR
THE ENERGY SUPPLEMENTS
ESPECIALLY YOURS
FIBERIFIC
FOLLIDERM
FRUITEIN
GARLITE
GINKGO-COMBO
GLUCOTRIM
GOLDEN YEARS
GREEN LIGHTING
HEMA-PLEX
HERBA-TEIN
HUPERZINE
HYPERTROL
IMMUNACE
IMMUNACTIN
IMMUNE-ACTION
IMMUNECTAR
INFLAMACTIN

Key to Media (For complete agency information see *The Advertising Red Books-Agencies* edition):
1. Bus. Publs. 2. Cable T.V. 3. Catalogs & Directories. 4. Co-op Adv. 5. Consumer Mags. 6. D.M. to Bus. Estab.7. D.M. to Consumers
8. Daily Newsp. 9. Exhibits/Trade Shows 10. Foreign 11. Infomercial 12. Internet Adv.13. Multimedia 14. Network Radio
15. Network T.V. 16. Newsp. Distr. Mags. 17. Other 18. Outdoor (Posters, Transit) 19. Point of Purchase20. Premiums, Novelties
21. Product Samples 22. Special Events Mktg. 23. Spot Radio 24. Spot T.V. 25. Weekly Newsp. 26. Yellow Page Adv.

Natural Organics, Inc. — (Continued)

ISOFLAVONE
KALM-ASSURE
KETOJUICE
KETOSLIM
KETOSNAX
KETOTROPIC
KETOZYME
L-ARGININE
L-GLUTAMINE
L-LYSINE
L-METHIONINE
L-ORNITHINE
L-TYROSINE
LACTOFERON
LIQUID BONE POWER
LOVE BUFFS
LOVITES
LUTEIN
MEGA CLA
MEGA-FORCE
MIGHTY LEAN
MIGRAACTIN
MIXED VEGETABLES
NATURE CLEANSE
NATURE'S PLUS
NEUROGENIC
NUTRI-GENIC
NUTRIGLOW
NUTRIZAC
OCTA-CAROTENE
OCU-CARE
OCUACTIN
OPTIFRESH
ORANGE JUICE JR
OSTIVONE
OXY-NECTAR
PARA SYSTEM
PHOSPHATIDYLSERINE
PROST-ACTIN
REGENERATION
RIBOSE
SAME
SAY YES TO BEANS
SAY YES TO DAIRY
SEROTAIN
SHOT-O
SKINNY MINI
SLEEP-ASSURE
SOURCE OF LIFE
SPIRU-TEIN
SUGAR CONTROL
THERMO TROPICS
TOCOTRIENOL
TRIM-PLEX
ULTRA-ACTIVIN
ULTRA-CHONDROITIN
ULTRA CRANBERRY
ULTRA EPO
ULTRA GINKGO
ULTRA-GLUCOSAMINE
ULTRA-HAIR
ULTRA-ISOFLAVONE
ULTRA-JUICE
ULTRA-LUTEIN
ULTRA-NAILS
ULTRA-ONE
ULTRA PRENATAL
ULTRA-SKIN
ULTRA-VIRILE-ACTIN
ULTRA-ZYME
WHEY-TEIN

NATURE'S SUNSHINE PRODUCTS, INC.

75 E 1700 S
Provo, UT 84606
Tel.: (801) 342-4300
Fax: (801) 342-4305
E-mail: questions@natr.com
Web Site: www.naturessunshine.com
Approx. Rev.: $349,918,000
Approx. Number Employees: 1,073
Year Founded: 1972
Business Description:
Herbal & Homeopathic Products, Vitamin & Mineral Supplements & Personal Care Products Mfr & Marketer
S.I.C.: 2834; 2833
N.A.I.C.S.: 325412; 325411
Export
Advertising Expenditures: $1,318,000
Media: 4-6-7-10-19-21
Distr.: Intl.; Natl.
Budget Set: Oct.
Personnel:
Kristine F. Hughes *(Chm)*
Michael D. Dean *(Pres & CEO)*
Stephen M. Bunker *(CFO, Treas & Exec VP)*
Jamon A. Jarvis *(Chief Compliance Officer, Gen Counsel & Exec VP)*
Bryant J. Yates *(Pres-Intl)*
John R DeWyze *(Exec VP-Ops)*
Efrain Villalobos *(Exec VP-Sls-United States)*
Craig Dalley *(VP-Sls-United States)*
Jim May *(VP-IT)*
Brands & Products:
ADAPTAMAX
ALJ
BIFIDOPHILUS FLORA FORCE
CARBO GRABBERS
CHOLESTER-REG
CLEANSTART
CORTISOL FORMULA
ENERG-V
EVERFLEX
FAT GRABBERS
FOOD ENZYMES
HISTABLOCK
MEGA-CHEL
METABOMAX
NATURAL CHANGES
NATURE'S SUNSHINE
NEXRUTINE
NONI
NUTRI-BURN
NUTRI-CALM
PAW PAW CELL-REG
PRO-G-YAM
PROACTAZYME
PROBIOTIC ELEVEN
RELORA
SINUS SUPPORT
TRIPLE RELIEF
ULTIMATE GREENZONE
VITAWAVE
VS-C
X-ACTION

NATURESTAR BIO-TEC INC.

1770 S Vineyard Ave 1270 E Acacia
Ontario, CA 91761
Tel.: (909) 930-1878
Fax: (909) 930-5438
Toll Free: (888) 882-2672
E-mail: sales@naturestarusa.com
Web Site: www.naturestarusa.com
E-Mail For Key Personnel:
Sales Director: sales@naturestarusa.com
Sales Range: $1-9.9 Million
Approx. Number Employees: 15
Business Description:
Health Supplement Mfr
S.I.C.: 2834
N.A.I.C.S.: 325412
Media: 6
Personnel:
Liquiong Fei *(Pres)*
Brands & Products:
IF YOU VALUE YOUR HEALTH
NATURESTAR
QUALITY YOU CAN COUNT ON!

NATUREWELL, INCORPORATED

110 W C St Ste 1300
San Diego, CA 92101
Tel.: (619) 234-0222
Toll Free: (800) 454-6790
E-mail: info@naturewell.com
Web Site: www.naturewell.com
Approx. Int. Income: $4,023
Year Founded: 1983
Business Description:
Healthcare Products Developer & Marketer
S.I.C.: 2834
N.A.I.C.S.: 325412
Advertising Expenditures: $22,546
Media: 4-10
Personnel:
James R. Arabia *(CEO)*
Brands & Products:
ALLERSPRAY
ANTI-OXY SPRAY
ARTHRISPRAY
MIGRASPRAY
MIGRASPRAY.COM
NATUREWELL
PMS SPRAY

NATUREX INC.

(Sub. of Naturex SA)
375 Huyler St
South Hackensack, NJ 07626
Tel.: (201) 440-5000
Fax: (201) 342-8000
E-mail: naturex@naturex.us
Web Site: www.naturex.com
Sales Range: $25-49.9 Million
Approx. Number Employees: 150
Business Description:
Solid, Liquid & Powdered Botanical Extracts Mfr
S.I.C.: 2833
N.A.I.C.S.: 325411
Import
Media: 2-8-10-11
Personnel:
Jacques Dikansky *(Pres & CEO)*

NATUS MEDICAL INCORPORATED

1501 Industrial Rd
San Carlos, CA 94070-4111
Tel.: (650) 802-0400
Fax: (650) 802-0401
Toll Free: (800) 255-3901
E-mail: InvestorRelations@Natus.com
Web Site: www.natus.com
Approx. Rev.: $218,655,000
Approx. Number Employees: 750
Business Description:
Hearing Screening & Diagnostic Systems, Jaundice Management Products, Newborn Care Products, Neurology Diagnostic Systems & Sleep Diagnostic Systems Developer & Mfr
S.I.C.: 3826; 3841
N.A.I.C.S.: 334516; 339112
Advertising Expenditures: $264,000
Media: 1-2-7-8-10-13
Personnel:
Robert A. Gunst *(Chm)*
John T. Buhler *(Pres & COO)*
James B. Hawkins *(CEO)*
Steven J. Murphy *(CFO & VP-Fin)*
Kenneth M. Traverso *(VP-Mktg & Sls)*
Brands & Products:
AABR
ACCUSCREEN
ALGO
ALGO 3I
ALGO 5
ALGO FLEXICOUPLER
ALGO PORTABLE
AOAE
BILIBAND
BRAINZ
CMS
COCHLEA-SCAN
EAR COUPLERS
ECHO-SCREEN
ECHOLINK
MINIMUFFS
MSDS
NATUS
NEOBLUE
NEOMETRICS
VRS
XLTEK

NBTY, INC.

(Holding of The Carlyle Group, LLC)
2100 Smithtown Ave
Ronkonkoma, NY 11779
Tel.: (631) 200-2000
Fax: (631) 567-7148
Web Site: www.nbty.com
Approx. Sls.: $2,581,950,000
Approx. Number Employees: 13,950
Year Founded: 1971
Business Description:
Natural Vitamins, Food Supplements & Cosmetics Mfr & Distr
S.I.C.: 2833; 2834
N.A.I.C.S.: 325411; 325412
Import Export
Advertising Expenditures: $10,195,000
Media: 1-2-4-5-6-7-8-9-10-18-19-20-23-24-25
Distr.: Natl.
Personnel:
Scott Rudolph *(Chm)*
Harvey Kamil *(Pres & CFO)*
Jeffrey A. Nagel *(CEO)*
Hans Lindgren *(Sec & Sr VP-Ops)*
James P. Flaherty *(Sr VP-Mktg & Adv)*
Joseph J. Looney *(VP-Fin)*
Brands & Products:
AMERICAN HEALTH
DETUINEN
ESTER-C
HOLLAND & BARRETT
LENATURISTE
MET-RX
NATURE'S BOUNTY
NBTY
NUTRITION HEADQUARTERS
OSTEO-BI-FLEX

Key to Media (For complete agency information see *The Advertising Red Books-Agencies* edition):
1. Bus. Publs. 2. Cable T.V. 3. Catalogs & Directories. 4. Co-op Adv. 5. Consumer Mags. 6. D.M. to Bus. Estab.7. D.M. to Consumers 8. Daily Newsp. 9. Exhibits/Trade Shows 10. Foreign 11. Infomercial 12. Internet Adv.13. Multimedia 14. Network Radio 15. Network T.V. 16. Newsp. Distr. Mags. 17. Other 18. Outdoor (Posters, Transit) 19. Point of Purchase20. Premiums, Novelties 21. Product Samples 22. Special Events Mktg. 23. Spot Radio 24. Spot T.V. 25. Weekly Newsp. 26. Yellow Page Adv.

PURITAN'S PRIDE
REXALL
SISU
SOLGAR
SUNDOWN
VITAMIN WORLD
WORLDWIDE SPORT NUTRITION

NCH HEALTHCARE SYSTEM, INC.

350 7th St N
Naples, FL 34102
Tel.: (239) 513-7000
Web Site: www.nchmd.org
Sales Range: $350-399.9 Million
Approx. Number Employees: 4,000
Business Description:
Health Care Services
S.I.C.: 8741
N.A.I.C.S.: 561110
Personnel:
Allen S. Weiss *(Pres & CEO)*
Vickie Hale *(CFO)*
Advertising Agency:
The David Group Inc.
526 Superior Ave E Ste 300
Cleveland, OH 44114-1983
Tel.: (216) 687-1818
Tel.: (216) 687-1890
Fax: (216) 687-0107
Fax: (216) 687-1482
Toll Free: (800) 686-1818

NEIGHBORCARE, INC.

(Sub. of Omnicare, Inc)
1800 Wasinton Blvd St 420
Baltimore, MD 21230
Tel.: (410) 752-2600
Fax: (410) 528-7447
Web Site: www.omnicare.com/intro.asp
Sales Range: $1-4.9 Billion
Approx. Number Employees: 6,100
Year Founded: 1985
Business Description:
Pharmacy & Medical Supply Services
S.I.C.: 5912
N.A.I.C.S.: 446110
Media: 2-7-8-23-24
Personnel:
Mary Lou Gradisek *(Dir-Mktg)*
Brands & Products:
NEIGHBORCARE

NEIGHBORLY CARE NETWORK

12425 28th St N Ste 200
Saint Petersburg, FL 33716
Tel.: (727) 573-9444
Fax: (727) 289-0029
E-mail: info@neighborly.org
Web Site: www.neighborly.org
Approx. Number Employees: 115
Business Description:
Health & Wellness Programs for Seniors & Their Families
S.I.C.: 9431
N.A.I.C.S.: 923120
Personnel:
Debra Shade *(Pres & CEO)*
Advertising Agency:
Paradise Advertising & Marketing
150 2nd Ave N Ste 800
Saint Petersburg, FL 33701
Tel.: (727) 821-5155
Fax: (727) 822-3722

NEKTAR THERAPEUTICS

455 Mission Bay Blvd S
San Francisco, CA 94158
Tel.: (415) 482-5300
E-mail: nektarsc@nektar.com
Web Site: www.nektar.com
Approx. Rev.: $159,039,000
Approx. Number Employees: 408
Year Founded: 1990
Business Description:
Mfr of Inhalers & Nebulizers & Developer of Pharmaceuticals for the Treatment of Diabetes & Respiratory Infections
S.I.C.: 2834; 3841; 8733
N.A.I.C.S.: 325412; 339112; 541710
Personnel:
Robert B. Chess *(Chm)*
Howard W. Robin *(Pres & CEO)*
John Nicholson *(CFO & Sr VP)*
Lorianne K. Masuoka *(Sr VP & Chief Medical Officer)*
Stephen K. Doberstein *(Sr VP & Chief Scientific Officer)*
Rinko Ghosh *(Chief Bus Officer & Sr VP)*
Jillian B. Thomsen *(Chief Acctg Officer & Sr VP-Fin)*
Gil M. Labrucherie *(Gen Counsel, Sec & Sr VP)*
Tim Warner *(Sr VP-IR & Corp Affairs)*
Stephan Herrera *(Sr Dir-IR & Corp Affairs)*
Jennifer Ruddock *(Sr Dir-IR & Corp Affairs)*
Brands & Products:
ADVANCED POLYMER CONJUGATE TECHNOLOGY
AERONEB
DURASEAL
EXUBERA
MIRCERA
NEKTAR
NEULASTA
NKTR
PULMOSOL
PULMOSPHERE
Advertising Agency:
S.A. Noonan Communications
27 N Moore St Ste 10C
New York, NY 10013
Tel.: (212) 966-3650

NEOSTEM, INC.

420 Lexington Ave Ste 450
New York, NY 10170
Tel.: (212) 584-4180
Fax: (212) 656-1933
E-mail: info@neostem.com
Web Site: www.neostem.com
Approx. Rev.: $69,821,294
Approx. Number Employees: 611
Year Founded: 1980
Business Description:
Stem Cell Collection & Processing Services
S.I.C.: 8071; 8733
N.A.I.C.S.: 621511; 541710
Advertising Expenditures: $180,758
Media: 17
Personnel:
Robin L. Smith *(Chm & CEO)*
Ian Zhang *(Pres & Mng Dir-China)*
Larry A. May *(CFO)*
Catherine M. Vaczy *(Gen Counsel & VP)*
Denis Rodgerson *(Dir-Stem Cell Science)*

NEOVASC INC.

13700 Mayfield Place Suite 2135
Richmond, BC V6V 2E4, Canada
Tel.: (604) 270-4344
Fax: (604) 270-4384
E-mail: info@neovasc.com
Web Site: www.neovasc.com
Approx. Sls.: $4,440,858
Approx. Number Employees: 55
Business Description:
Medical Products Developer & Mfr
S.I.C.: 3844; 3841; 3845
N.A.I.C.S.: 334517; 334510; 339112
Personnel:
Paul Geyer *(Chm)*
Alexei Marko *(CEO)*
Christopher Clark *(CFO)*
Brian McPherson *(COO)*
Schmuel Banai *(Dir-Medical)*
Mark Schwartz *(Dir-Clinical & Regulatory Affairs)*
Brands & Products:
METRICATH
PERIPATCH
REDUCER
Advertising Agency:
GendeLLindheim BioCom Partners, LLC
1375 Broadway 11th Floor
New York, NY 10018
Tel.: (212) 584-2276
Fax: (866) 214-9359
Toll Free: (866) 214-9359

NESTLE HEALTHCARE NUTRITION

(Formerly Novartis Nutrition Corporation)
(Sub. of Nestle Healthcare Nutrition)
1600 Utica Ave S Ste 600
Minneapolis, MN 55416
Mailing Address:
PO Box 370
Minneapolis, MN 55440-0370
Tel.: (952) 848-6000
Fax: (952) 848-6050
Toll Free: (800) 333-3785
Approx. Number Employees: 950
Business Description:
Mfr. of a Spectrum of Nutritional Products for Professional & Consumer Use
S.I.C.: 2099; 2032
N.A.I.C.S.: 311999; 311422
Media: 2-3-6-9
Distr.: Natl.
Personnel:
Sonya Hughes *(Dir)*
Bob Lang *(Dir-Ops)*
Terri Porter *(Dir)*
Samah Manzalawi *(Brand Mgr-Benefiber)*
Michael Polzin *(Mgr-Media Rels)*
Brands & Products:
ARGINAID
BENECALORIE
BENEFIBER
BENEPROTEIN
DAIRYTHICK
GLUTOSOLVE
ISOSOURCE
OPTISOURCE
OVALTINE
THICKENUP

NEUROGESX, INC.

2215 Bridgepointe Pkwy Ste 200
San Carlos, CA 94070-4117
Tel.: (650) 358-3300
Fax: (650) 649-1798
E-mail: inquiries@neurogesx.com
Web Site: www.neurogesx.com
Approx. Rev.: $8,266,000
Approx. Number Employees: 106
Year Founded: 2000
Business Description:
Biopharmaceutical Developer & Marketer of Pain Management Therapies
S.I.C.: 2834; 2836; 8733
N.A.I.C.S.: 325412; 325414; 541710
Advertising Expenditures: $5,800,000
Personnel:
Gary A. Lyons *(Chm)*
Anthony A. Ditonno *(Pres & CEO)*
Stephen F. Ghiglieri *(CFO, COO & Exec VP)*
Keith R. Bley *(Sr VP-Nonclinical R & D)*
Karen J. Harder *(Sr VP-Regulatory Affairs & Tech Ops)*
Michael E. Markels *(Sr VP-Comml Ops & Bus Dev)*
Timothy Arendt *(VP-Sls)*
Amy C. Cavers *(Sr Dir-Mktg)*
Christopher Panarites *(Sr Dir-Reimbursement)*
Linda L. Schock *(Dir-Comml Ops)*

NEUROMETRIX, INC.

62 4th Ave
Waltham, MA 02451
Tel.: (781) 890-9989
Fax: (781) 890-1556
Toll Free: (888) 786-7287
E-mail: info@neurometrix.com
Web Site: www.neurometrix.com
Approx. Rev.: $13,899,670
Approx. Number Employees: 69
Year Founded: 1996
Business Description:
Neurological Diagnostic Testing Device Mfr
S.I.C.: 3841; 8733
N.A.I.C.S.: 339112; 541710
Advertising Expenditures: $256,000
Media: 10
Personnel:
Shai N. Gozani *(Pres & CEO)*
Thomas T. Higgins *(CFO & Sr VP)*
Krishnamurthy Balachandran *(COO)*
Guy Daniello *(Sr VP-IT)*
Michael P. Williams *(Sr VP-Engrg)*
Brands & Products:
ADVANCE
DIGISCOPE
NC-STAT
NEUROMETRIX
ONCALL
TRANSFORMING PATIENT CARE THROUGH NEUROTECHNOLOGY

NEW CONCEPT ENERGY, INC.

1800 Valley View Ln Ste 300
Dallas, TX 75234
Tel.: (972) 407-8400
Fax: (972) 407-8436
E-mail: info@newconceptenergy.com
Web Site: www.newconceptenergy.com

Key to Media (For complete agency information see *The Advertising Red Books-Agencies* edition):
1. Bus. Publs. 2. Cable T.V. 3. Catalogs & Directories. 4. Co-op Adv. 5. Consumer Mags. 6. D.M. to Bus. Estab.7. D.M. to Consumers 8. Daily Newsp. 9. Exhibits/Trade Shows 10. Foreign 11. Infomercial 12. Internet Adv.13. Multimedia 14. Network Radio 15. Network T.V. 16. Newsp. Distr. Mags. 17. Other 18. Outdoor (Posters, Transit) 19. Point of Purchase20. Premiums, Novelties 21. Product Samples 22. Special Events Mktg. 23. Spot Radio 24. Spot T.V. 25. Weekly Newsp. 26. Yellow Page Adv.

New Concept Energy, Inc. — (Continued)

Approx. Rev.: $4,213,000
Approx. Number Employees: 26
Business Description:
Oil & Natural Gas Services;
Commercial Property Management
S.I.C.: 1311; 6289; 8059; 8361
N.A.I.C.S.: 211111; 523999; 623110; 623312
Media: 8-9-17-18-22-23-25-26
Personnel:
Gene S. Bertcher *(Chm, Pres, CEO, CFO & Treas)*

NEW YORK BLOOD CENTER, INC.

310 E 67th St
New York, NY 10065
Tel.: (212) 570-3000
Fax: (212) 570-3195
Web Site: www.nybloodcenter.org
Sales Range: $250-299.9 Million
Approx. Number Employees: 1,400
Business Description:
Blood Collection, Distribution & Services
S.I.C.: 8099
N.A.I.C.S.: 621991
Media: 9-25
Personnel:
Lawrence J. Hannigan *(CFO & VP)*
Margi Gandolfi *(VP-Mktg & Strategic Plng)*
Robert Purvis *(VP-Customer Svc)*
Advertising Agencies:
Finn Partners
8 Hartum Street
PO Box 45138
Jerusalem, 91450, Israel
Tel.: (972) 2 589 2000
Fax: (972) 2 581 8999

Rubenstein Associates, Inc.
1345 Ave of the Americas Fl 30
New York, NY 10105-0109
Tel.: (212) 843-8000
Fax: (212) 843-9200
Public Relations

The Ruder Finn Group
301 E 57th St
New York, NY 10022-2900
Tel.: (212) 593-6400
Fax: (212) 593-6397

NEW YORK-PRESBYTERIAN HEALTHCARE SYSTEM

525 E 68th St
New York, NY 10021-4870
Tel.: (212) 305-2500
Fax: (212) 746-8235
Web Site: www.nypsystem.org
Approx. Rev.: $8,940,000,000
Approx. Number Employees: 82,205
Business Description:
Hospital Operator
S.I.C.: 8062
N.A.I.C.S.: 622110
Personnel:
Herbert Pardes *(Pres & CEO)*
Aurelia G. Boyer *(CIO & Sr VP)*
David Alge *(VP-Strategy & Fin Plng)*
David A. Feinberg *(VP-Mktg)*
Advertising Agencies:
Greater Than One
395 Hudson St 5th Fl
New York, NY 10014
Tel.: (212) 252-1999
Fax: (212) 252-7364

Munn Rabot LLC
33 W 17th St Fl 3
New York, NY 10011-5511
Tel.: (212) 727-3900
Fax: (212) 604-9804
Toll Free: (888) 847-0290

Rubenstein Associates, Inc.
1345 Ave of the Americas Fl 30
New York, NY 10105-0109
Tel.: (212) 843-8000
Fax: (212) 843-9200

NEXMED, INC.

(Name Changed to APRICUS BIOSCIENCES, INC.)

NITROMED, INC.

(Holding of Deerfield Management Company L.P.)
6000 Fairview Rd Ste 610
Charlotte, NC 28210
Tel.: (704) 941-2020
E-mail: info@nitromed.com
Web Site: www.nitromed.com
Approx. Rev.: $14,920,000
Approx. Number Employees: 5
Business Description:
Pharmaceutical Research
S.I.C.: 2834; 8733
N.A.I.C.S.: 325412; 541720
Advertising Expenditures: $1,000,000
Personnel:
Argeris N. Karabelas *(Chm)*
Michael Sabolinski *(Chief Medical Officer)*
Brands & Products:
BIDIL
MAKING TODAY'S BEST MEDICINES BETTER
N
NITROMED
NITRX

NMT MEDICAL, INC.

27 Wormwood St
Boston, MA 02210-1619
Tel.: (617) 737-0930
Fax: (617) 737-0924
Toll Free: (800) 666-6484
E-mail: info@nmtmedical.com
Web Site: www.nmtmedical.com
Approx. Rev.: $13,220,117
Approx. Number Employees: 77
Business Description:
PFO Closures Implanted in Minimally Invasive Surgery to Treat Vascular Conditions
S.I.C.: 3841; 3842
N.A.I.C.S.: 339112; 339113
Advertising Expenditures: $1,000
Media: 10
Personnel:
Richard E. Davis *(Pres & CEO)*
Ron Seyffert *(VP-Intl Sls & Mktg)*
Brands & Products:
AT THE HEART OF BRAIN ATTACKS
BIOSTAR
CARDIOSEAL
STARFLEX

NON-INVASIVE MONITORING SYSTEMS, INC.

(d/b/a Nims Inc.)
4400 Biscayne Blvd
Miami, FL 33137
Tel.: (305) 575-4200
E-mail: info@nims-inc.com
Web Site: www.nims-inc.com
Approx. Rev.: $617,000
Approx. Number Employees: 6
Year Founded: 1985
Business Description:
Medical Equipment Mfr
S.I.C.: 3845; 8733
N.A.I.C.S.: 334510; 541710
Export
Media: 4-7-8-10-13
Distr.: Natl.
Budget Set: July
Personnel:
Jane H. Hsiao *(Chm)*
Marvin A. Sackner *(CEO)*
James J. Martin *(CFO)*
Steven B. Mrha *(COO)*
Brands & Products:
AT-101
EXER-REST
NIMS
RESPITRACE

NORDIC NATURALS, INC.

111 Jennings Dr
Watsonville, CA 95076
Tel.: (831) 724-6200
Fax: (831) 724-6600
E-mail: info@nordicnaturals.com
Web Site: www.nordicnaturals.com
Sales Range: $1-9.9 Million
Approx. Number Employees: 115
Business Description:
Health Supplements Mfr
S.I.C.: 2834
N.A.I.C.S.: 325412
Media: 6
Personnel:
Joar Opheim *(Pres)*
Meredith Greiner *(Dir-Mktg)*

NORDION INC.

(Formerly MDS Inc.)
447 March Road
Ottawa, ON K2K 1X8, Canada
Tel.: (613) 592-2790
Fax: (613) 592-6937
E-mail: service@nordion.com
Web Site: www.nordion.com
Approx. Rev.: $240,352,000
Approx. Number Employees: 643
Year Founded: 1969
Business Description:
Drug Development & Disease Management Products
S.I.C.: 8733; 2834; 3841
N.A.I.C.S.: 541710; 325412; 339112
Media: 2-4-7-10
Distr.: Natl.
Personnel:
William D. Anderson *(Chm)*
Steven M. West *(CEO)*
Peter Dans *(CFO)*
Kenneth L. Horton *(Gen Counsel & Exec VP-Corp Dev)*
Christopher Ashwood *(Sr VP-Corp Svcs)*
Kevin Brooks *(Sr VP-Sls & Mktg)*
Jill Chitra *(Sr VP-Quality & Regulatory Affairs)*
Peter Covitz *(Sr VP-Innovation)*
Tamra Benjamin *(VP-Pub & Govt Rels)*
Brands & Products:
ELAN
QUALITY ON TIME
SCIENCE ADVANCING HEALTH

NORTHSIDE HOSPITAL

1000 Johnson Ferry Rd NE
Atlanta, GA 30342-1606
Tel.: (404) 851-8000
Fax: (404) 851-6282
Web Site: www.northside.com
Approx. Number Employees: 10,000
Year Founded: 1970
Business Description:
Operator of Medical Hospital
S.I.C.: 8062; 8011
N.A.I.C.S.: 622110; 621111
Media: 8
Personnel:
Bob Quattrocchi *(CEO)*
Advertising Agency:
Moxie Interactive Inc.
The Northyards 384 Northyards Blvd NW Ste 290
Atlanta, GA 30313-2440
Tel.: (404) 601-4500
Fax: (404) 601-4505

NORTHWEST MEDICAL CENTER, INC.

(Sub. of HCA HOLDINGS, INC.)
6200 N La Cholla Blvd
Tucson, AZ 85741-3529
Tel.: (520) 742-9000
Fax: (520) 469-8181
Web Site:
www.northwestmedicalcenter.com
Approx. Number Employees: 1,700
Business Description:
Hospital
S.I.C.: 8062
N.A.I.C.S.: 622110
Personnel:
Kevin Stockton *(CEO)*
Ronald Patrick *(CFO)*
Advertising Agency:
Eisenberg & Associates
511 NE 3rd Ave
Fort Lauderdale, FL 33301-3235
Tel.: (954) 760-9500
Fax: (954) 760-9594

NORTHWEST NATURAL PRODUCTS INC.

6350 NE Campus Dr
Vancouver, WA 98661
Tel.: (360) 690-8527
Fax: (360) 737-2692
E-mail: info1@nwnaturalproducts.com
Web Site:
www.nwnaturalproducts.com
Approx. Number Employees: 500
Business Description:
Vitamins Mfr & Distr
S.I.C.: 5122
N.A.I.C.S.: 424210
Media: 2-6-10-13-17
Personnel:
Kathryn Jones *(Pres)*
Brands & Products:
ACCUFLORA
DETOX 7
L'IL CRITTERS
NORTHWEST NATURAL PRODUCTS
VITAFUSION
WE MAKE NUTRITION TASTE GOOD
Advertising Agency:
Lexicon Communications Corp.
520 Bellmore Way

Key to Media (For complete agency information see *The Advertising Red Books-Agencies* edition):
1. Bus. Publs. 2. Cable T.V. 3. Catalogs & Directories. 4. Co-op Adv. 5. Consumer Mags. 6. D.M. to Bus. Estab.7. D.M. to Consumers
8. Daily Newsp. 9. Exhibits/Trade Shows 10. Foreign 11. Infomercial 12. Internet Adv.13. Multimedia 14. Network Radio
15. Network T.V. 16. Newsp. Distr. Mags. 17. Other 18. Outdoor (Posters, Transit) 19. Point of Purchase20. Premiums, Novelties
21. Product Samples 22. Special Events Mktg. 23. Spot Radio 24. Spot T.V. 25. Weekly Newsp. 26. Yellow Page Adv.

Pasadena, CA 91103
Tel.: (626) 683-9200
Fax: (622) 628-1960
Public Relations

NORTHWESTERN MEMORIAL HEALTHCARE

251 E Huron St
Chicago, IL 60611-2908
Tel.: (312) 926-6363
Tel.: (312) 926-7432 (Media Rels)
Fax: (312) 926-5625
Web Site: www.nmh.org
Approx. Rev.: $1,100,000,000
Approx. Number Employees: 6,464
Business Description:
Hospital & Health Care Operations
S.I.C.: 8062; 8011; 8082
N.A.I.C.S.: 622110; 621111; 621610
Media: 18
Personnel:
Edward M. Liddy *(Chm)*
Dean M. Harrison *(Pres & CEO)*
Peter J. McCanna *(CFO & Exc VP-Admin)*
Dennis M. Murphy *(COO & Exec VP)*
Timothy R. Zoph *(CIO & VP)*
Carol M. Lind *(Gen Counsel & Sr VP)*
Michelle A. Janney *(Sr VP-Ops)*
Julie L. Creamer *(Sr VP)*
Dean L. Manheimer *(Sr VP-HR)*
Holli I. Salls *(VP-PR, Mktg & Physician Svcs)*
Ralph M. Weber *(VP-Community Rels)*
Kris Lathan *(Dir)*
William Spies *(Assoc Dir-Nuclear Medicine)*
Brands & Products:
NMH
Advertising Agency:
Young & Rubicam Chicago
233 N Michigan Ave 16th Fl
Chicago, IL 60601-5519
Tel.: (312) 596-3000
Fax: (312) 596-3130

NOVA BIOMEDICAL CORPORATION

200 Prospect St
Waltham, MA 02454
Tel.: (781) 894-0800
Fax: (781) 893-6998
Toll Free: (800) 458-5813
E-mail: info@novabiomedical.com
Web Site: www.novabiomedical.com
Sales Range: $50-74.9 Million
Approx. Number Employees: 500
Business Description:
Diagnostic Hematology, Electrolytes, Blood Gas Instruments & Supplies Mfr
S.I.C.: 3826; 2833
N.A.I.C.S.: 334516; 325411
Export
Advertising Expenditures: $300,000
Media: 1-4-6-7-8-10-11-20
Distr.: Intl.; Natl.
Budget Set: Sept.-Oct.
Personnel:
Franci C. Manganaro *(Pres & CEO)*
Cliff Larsson *(Dir-Creative Svcs)*
Brands & Products:
BIOPROFILE
CELLTRAK
MULTI-WELL
NOVA
NOVA MAX
NOVANET
NUCLEUS
PHOX
STAT PROFILE
STAT PROFILE PLUS
STATSENSOR

NOVANT HEALTH, INC.

2085 Frontis Plz Blvd
Winston Salem, NC 27103-3013
Tel.: (336) 718-5000
Fax: (336) 718-9258
Web Site: www.novanthealth.org
Sales Range: $1-4.9 Billion
Approx. Number Employees: 20,000
Year Founded: 1997
Business Description:
Health Care Services
S.I.C.: 8741
N.A.I.C.S.: 561110
Media: 4-10
Personnel:
Gregory J. Beier *(Pres & Exec VP)*
Paul M. Wiles *(Pres)*
Dean Swindle *(CFO & Pres-Ambulatory Svcs)*
Carl S. Armato *(COO & Sr Exec VP)*
Sallye Liner *(Chief Clinical Officer & Exec VP)*
Jannette Smith-Hill *(Sr VP-HR)*
Brands & Products:
NOVANT HEALTH

NOVAPRO

(Sub. of Cross Country Healthcare, Inc.)
1408 N Westshore Blvd Ste 300
Tampa, FL 33607
Tel.: (813) 636-5050
Fax: (888) 668-2762
Toll Free: (888) 668-2776
Web Site: www.novaprostaffing.com
Sales Range: $10-24.9 Million
Approx. Number Employees: 28
Business Description:
Temporary Staffing to Healthcare Industry
S.I.C.: 7361
N.A.I.C.S.: 561310
Media: 2
Personnel:
Lisa Lapina *(Dir-Recruitment)*

NOVARTIS CORPORATION

(Sub. of Novartis AG)
608 5th Ave
New York, NY 10020-2303
Tel.: (212) 307-1122
Fax: (212) 246-0185
Web Site: www.us.novartis.com
Approx. Number Employees: 52
Year Founded: 1983
Business Description:
Holding Company
S.I.C.: 2834; 3851
N.A.I.C.S.: 325412; 339115
Import Export
Personnel:
Meryl Zausner *(CFO)*
Praveen Tyle *(Sr VP & Head-BD&L-Global)*
Mickey McDermott *(VP Comm-Animal Health)*
Sheldon Jones *(VP-Comm)*
Brandy Robinson *(VP-Commun)*
Lisa Aglialoro *(Sr Brand Mgr)*
Cindi Holda *(Sr Brand Mgr)*
Advertising Agencies:
APCO Worldwide
700 12th St NW Ste 800
Washington, DC 20005
Tel.: (202) 778-1000
Fax: (202) 466-6002

Blast Radius
285 Madison Ave 12th Fl
New York, NY 10017
Tel.: (212) 925-4900
Fax: (212) 925-5247
Novartis OTC

Chamberlain Healthcare Public Relations
111 Broadway 19th Fl
New York, NY 10006
Tel.: (212) 884-0650
Fax: (212) 884-0628

Cline, Davis & Mann, Inc.
220 E 42nd St 8th Fl
New York, NY 10017-5806
Tel.: (212) 907-4300
Fax: (212) 557-7240

DDB New York
437 Madison Ave
New York, NY 10022-7001
Tel.: (212) 415-2000
Fax: (212) 415-3506

Deutsch, Inc.
(A Lowe & Partners Company)
111 8th Ave 14th Fl
New York, NY 10011-5201
Tel.: (212) 981-7600
Fax: (212) 981-7525
Exelon

Euro RSCG Worldwide HQ
350 Hudson St
New York, NY 10014-4504
Tel.: (212) 886-2000
Fax: (212) 886-2016

MEC - NA HQ, New York
825 7th Ave
New York, NY 10019-5818
Tel.: (212) 474-0000
Fax: (212) 474-0003
(Media Buying & Planning)

Regan Campbell Ward McCann
150 E 42nd St 16th Fl
New York, NY 10017-5642
Tel.: (646) 742-2100
Fax: (646) 742-2206

Saatchi & Saatchi New York
375 Hudson St
New York, NY 10014-3660
Tel.: (212) 463-2000
Fax: (212) 463-9855
Lamisil
Fenistil
Voltaren
Otrivin

NOVARTIS PHARMACEUTICALS CORP.

(Sub. of Novartis Corporation)
1 Health Plz
East Hanover, NJ 07936-1016
Tel.: (862) 778-8300
Fax: (973) 781-8265
Toll Free: (800) 277-2254
E-mail: info@pharma.us.novartis.com
Web Site: www.pharma.us.novartis.com
Approx. Number Employees: 300
Business Description:
Pharmaceutical Preparations
S.I.C.: 2834; 8733
N.A.I.C.S.: 325412; 541710
Media: 1-2-6-7-8-9-16-20-21-25
Distr.: Natl.
Personnel:
Jennifer McGovern *(Sr Product Mgr-Diovan)*
Sue Zibelli *(Mgr-Media Svcs, Agency Rels & Ops)*
Advertising Agencies:
Cline, Davis & Mann, Inc.
210 Carnegie Ctr Ste 200
Princeton, NJ 08540-6226
Tel.: (609) 936-5600
Fax: (609) 275-5060

Harrison and Star
(Subsidiary of Omnicom Group, Inc.)
16 W 22nd St
New York, NY 10010
Tel.: (212) 727-1330
Fax: (212) 822-6590

HealthSTAR Communications, Inc.
1000 Wyckoff Ave
Mahwah, NJ 07430
Tel.: (201) 560-5370
Fax: (201) 891-2380

The Lanmark Group Inc.
527 Industrial Way W
Eatontown, NJ 07724-2211
Tel.: (732) 389-4500
Fax: (732) 389-4998

Lopez Negrete Communications, Inc.
3336 Richmond Ave Ste 200
Houston, TX 77098
Tel.: (713) 877-8777
Fax: (713) 877-8796

Ogilvy Commonhealth Consumer Care
424 Interpace Pkwy
Parsippany, NJ 07054
Tel.: (973) 352-2300
Fax: (973) 352-1270

Ogilvy CommonHealth Scientific Communications
432 Interpace Pkwy
Parsippany, NJ 07054
Tel.: (973) 352-2900
Fax: (973) 352-1170

Porter Novelli
(Sub. of Omnicom Group, Inc.)
75 Varick St 6th Fl
New York, NY 10013
Tel.: (212) 601-8000
Fax: (212) 601-8101

NOVARTIS VACCINES & DIAGNOSTICS, INC.

(Div. of Novartis AG)
350 Massachusetts Ave
Cambridge, MA 02139
Tel.: (617) 871-7000
E-mail: nvd.communications@novartis.com
Web Site: www.novartis-vaccines.com

Key to Media (For complete agency information see *The Advertising Red Books-Agencies* edition):
1. Bus. Publs. 2. Cable T.V. 3. Catalogs & Directories. 4. Co-op Adv. 5. Consumer Mags. 6. D.M. to Bus. Estab.7. D.M. to Consumers 8. Daily Newsp. 9. Exhibits/Trade Shows 10. Foreign 11. Infomercial 12. Internet Adv.13. Multimedia 14. Network Radio 15. Network T.V. 16. Newsp. Distr. Mags. 17. Other 18. Outdoor (Posters, Transit) 19. Point of Purchase20. Premiums, Novelties 21. Product Samples 22. Special Events Mktg. 23. Spot Radio 24. Spot T.V. 25. Weekly Newsp. 26. Yellow Page Adv.

Novartis Vaccines & Diagnostics, Inc. — (Continued)

Business Description:
Vaccines & Blood Testing & Molecular Diagnostics Mfr
S.I.C.: 2834; 8733
N.A.I.C.S.: 325412; 541710

Personnel:
Andrin Oswald *(CEO)*
Nima Farzan *(VP-Mktg)*

Brands & Products:
FLUVIRIN

Advertising Agencies:
nitrogen
One S Broad St Fl 11
Philadelphia, PA 19107
Tel.: (215) 625-0111
Fax: (215) 625-9037
Fluvirin

Torre Lazur McCann
Waterview Corporate Ctr 20 Waterview Blvd
Parsippany, NJ 07054-1295
Tel.: (973) 263-9100
Fax: (973) 263-4113
Fluvirin

NOVEN PHARMACEUTICALS, INC.

(Sub. of Hisamitsu Pharmaceutical Co., Inc.)
11960 SW 144th St
Miami, FL 33186
Tel.: (305) 253-5099
Fax: (305) 251-1887
Web Site: www.noven.com
Approx. Rev.: $108,175,000
Approx. Number Employees: 610
Year Founded: 1987

Business Description:
Transdermal Drug Delivery
S.I.C.: 2834; 8733
N.A.I.C.S.: 325412; 541710
Advertising Expenditures: $21,701,000

Personnel:
Jeffrey F. Eisenberg *(Pres & CEO)*
Michael D. Price *(CFO & VP)*
Jeff T. Mihm *(Chief Admin Officer, Gen Counsel & VP)*
Joel S. Lippman *(Chief Medical Officer & Exec VP-Product Dev)*
Andrew Panagy *(VP-Mktg & Sls)*
Lance D. Williams *(VP-HR)*

Brands & Products:
COMBIPATCH
DAYTRANA
DEPAKOTE
DEPAKOTE ER
ESTALIS
ESTRADOT
LITHOBID
MENOREST
MESAFEM
NOVEN
NOVOGYNE
PEXEVA
STAVZOR
VIVELLE
VIVELLE-DOT

Advertising Agency:
FD U.S. - Chicago
227 W Monroe St Ste 900
Chicago, IL 60602
Tel.: (312) 553-6700
Fax: (312) 553-6740
Media Contact

NOW HEALTH GROUP, INC.

(d/b/a Now Foods)
395 Glen Ellyn Rd
Bloomingdale, IL 60108-2176
Tel.: (630) 545-9098
Fax: (630) 790-8019
Toll Free: (888) 669-3663
E-mail: sales@nowfoods.com
Web Site: www.nowfoods.com
E-Mail For Key Personnel:
Sales Director: sales@nowfoods.com
Approx. Number Employees: 550
Year Founded: 1963

Business Description:
Vitamins & Supplements Mfr
S.I.C.: 2023
N.A.I.C.S.: 311514
Import Export
Media: 6

Personnel:
Elwood Richard *(Chm)*
Al Powers *(Pres)*
Michael Lelah *(Dir-Tech)*
Jim Ritcheske *(Mgr-Mktg)*

Brands & Products:
AIR DEFENSE
ALPHASORB-C
AWE-SLIM
BERRYDOPHILUS
BONE STRENGTH
BRAIN ELEVATE
BROCCOLOGY
CELERY CIRCULATION
D-FLAME
DAILY VITS
DETOX SUPPORT
EASY CLEANSE
EFFER-C
ELECTRO PRO
FLEX MOBILITY
GR8-DOPHILUS
IMMUNE REVIEW
NATURAL BERRY FULL
NATURAL CITRUS MOISTURE
NATURAL HERBAL REVIVAL
NOW
OCU SUPPORT
POMERATROL
PRO-GH
PROBIOTIC DEFENSE
RED OMEGA
RESPIR-ALL
THYROID ENERGY
TRU-C BIOCOMPLEX
TRU HOODIA COMPLEX
TRUE BALANCE
TRUE FOCUS
ULCETROL
VEIN SUPREME
WATER OUT
XYLIWHITE

NPS PHARMACEUTICALS, INC.

550 Hills Dr 3rd Fl
Bedminster, NJ 07921
Tel.: (908) 450-5300
Fax: (908) 450-5351
E-mail: webmaster@npsp.com
Web Site: www.npsp.com
Approx. Rev.: $89,414,000
Approx. Number Employees: 63

Business Description:
Pharmaceuticals Mfr & Developer
S.I.C.: 2836; 2834
N.A.I.C.S.: 325414; 325412
Media: 10-21

Personnel:
Peter G. Tombros *(Chm)*
Francois E. Nader *(Pres & CEO)*
Luke M. Beshar *(CFO & Sr VP)*
Roger J. Garceau *(Chief Medical Officer & Sr VP)*
Eric Pauwels *(Chief Comml Officer & Sr VP)*
Edward Stratemeier *(Gen Counsel & Sr VP)*

Brands & Products:
CALCILYTICS
DELUCEMINE
GATTEX
IMAGINING LIFE'S POSSIBILITIES
ISOVALERIMIDE
MGLURS
NPS
NPS PHARMACEUTICALS
PREOS
PREOTACT
TEDUGLUTIDE

NUMARK LABORATORIES, INC.

164 Northfield Ave
Edison, NJ 08837-3855
Mailing Address:
PO Box 6321
Edison, NJ 08818-6321
Tel.: (732) 417-1870
Fax: (732) 225-0066
Toll Free: (800) 338-8079
Web Site: www.numarklabs.com
Sales Range: $10-24.9 Million
Approx. Number Employees: 20
Year Founded: 1987

Business Description:
Marketer of Over-the-Counter & Prescription Products
S.I.C.: 5122
N.A.I.C.S.: 424210

Personnel:
Moaiz F. Daya *(Co-Founder & VP-Mktg)*
Patrick M. Lonergan *(Co-Founder)*
Benjamin M. Deavenport *(VP-Fin)*
Robert C. Stites *(Asst Dir-Product)*

Brands & Products:
5 - DAY DEODORANT
ACNOMEL
ACRYLINE
AGORAL
ALBOLENE
ALOPHEN
AQUA CARE
B.F.I.
BROMO SELTZER
CERTAIN DRI
CONTI
CYSTEX
EQUALACTIN
HYDROCIL
LANOLOR
LIPOFLAVONOID
LIPOTRIAD
LYDIA PINKHAM
MELFIAT 105
NUMARK LABORATORIES
P-V-TUSSIN
PLATE WELD
SARATOGA
SPECTROCIN PLUS
ST-37
SWEETA
THERMOTABS
VERACOLATE
YODORA

Advertising Agency:
Chestnut Communications, Inc.
15 E Putnam Ave
Greenwich, CT 06830-7242
Tel.: (203) 629-9098
Fax: (203) 869-0416

NUNATURALS, INC.

2220 W 2nd Ave Ste 1
Eugene, OR 97402
Tel.: (541) 344-9785
Fax: (541) 683-5268
Toll Free: (800) 753-4372
E-mail: info@nunaturals.com
Web Site: www.nunaturals.com
Approx. Number Employees: 10

Business Description:
Vitamins & Herbal Products Whslr
S.I.C.: 5122
N.A.I.C.S.: 424210
Media: 4-6

Personnel:
Paula Sablosky *(Owner)*
Warren Sablosky *(CEO)*

NUTRACEUTICAL INTERNATIONAL CORPORATION

1400 Kearns Blvd Fl 2
Park City, UT 84060-7228
Tel.: (435) 655-6000
Toll Free: (800) 669-8877
E-mail: info@nutraceutical.com
Web Site: www.nutraceutical.com
Approx. Sls.: $180,052,000
Approx. Number Employees: 685
Year Founded: 1932

Business Description:
Dietary Supplements & Pharmaceutical Preparations
S.I.C.: 2833; 2834
N.A.I.C.S.: 325411; 325412
Import Export
Advertising Expenditures: $2,000,000
Media: 2-4-8-13-16-22-23-24

Personnel:
Frank W. Gay, II *(Chm & CEO)*
Bruce Hough *(Pres)*
Cory J. Mcqueen *(CFO & VP)*
Jeffrey A. Hinrichs *(COO, Sec & Exec VP)*
Gary M. Hume *(Exec VP)*
Stanley E. Soper *(VP-Legal Affairs & Asst Sec)*
Christopher B. Neuberger *(VP-Mktg & Sls)*
Andrew W. Seelos *(Controller & Asst VP)*

Brands & Products:
ACTION LABS
ACTIPET
ARTHRI-MEND
ARTHRIFIX
BEEPLEX
BEEVIVE
BRAIN PEP
CALCIFIBER
CARB-X
CARDIALL
CATUABA POWER MAX
CELLUMIN
CHAI SPIRIT
CHAMOMILE CALM
CHERRY BARK BLEND
CINNAMON ZYLICIOUS

Key to Media (For complete agency information see *The Advertising Red Books-Agencies* edition):
1. Bus. Publs. 2. Cable T.V. 3. Catalogs & Directories. 4. Co-op Adv. 5. Consumer Mags. 6. D.M. to Bus. Estab.7. D.M. to Consumers 8. Daily Newsp. 9. Exhibits/Trade Shows 10. Foreign 11. Infomercial 12. Internet Adv.13. Multimedia 14. Network Radio 15. Network T.V. 16. Newsp. Distr. Mags. 17. Other 18. Outdoor (Posters, Transit) 19. Point of Purchase20. Premiums, Novelties 21. Product Samples 22. Special Events Mktg. 23. Spot Radio 24. Spot T.V. 25. Weekly Newsp. 26. Yellow Page Adv.

COGNI-CLEAR
COLDFRONT
COX-2 CONTROL
CRANACTIN
CRYSTAL CALCIUM
DERMAQUIL
DIET 5
DINOSAURS
EGCG BOOST
ENERGY
ENHANCED ENERGY
ENZAPLEX
FAT MAGNET
FAT-X
FIPROFLAX
FITWOMAN MULTI
FIZZ C
FUN FRESH FOOD
GINSENG POWERMAX
GLYCONITRIC
HAWAIIAN BAMBOO
HEALTH FROM THE SUN
HEMORRHOL
HENZA MEAL
HERBS FOR KIDS
HOLY HEMP
INSURE
KAL
LIFEFLO
LIFESTYLE FORMULAS
LONG JACK POWER MAX 200
MINTY GINGER
MIZTIQUE
MONTANA BIG SKY
MULTI-MAX
MULTISAURUS
MY WHEY
NATRABIO
NATURAL BALANCE
NATURAL SPORT
NATURALCARE
NATURALMAX
NATURES LIFE
NIGHTIME FORMULA
NITROCARN
NUTRA
OMEGA SEED
ORGANIC SWEET MOOSE
PEACEFUL NITE
PEACEFUL PLANET
PEPTIC DEFENSE
PERFORMANCE
PIONEER NUTRITI
POLIPOM
POLLEN POWER
PREMIER
PREMIER ONE
PROGESTA-CARE
PURE ENERGY
PURELY MAGNESIUM
QUICK DIGEST
RAW ENERGY
REACTA-C
ROYAL JELLY
SKINNY FAST
SOLAR GREEN
SOLARAY
SOYTEIN
SPECTRO
SPRING DROPS
SUNNY GREEN
SUPER 5-HTP
SUPER FIT BURNERS
SUPER MELATONIN PLUS
SUPER SAW PALMETTO PLUS
SUPERTONE
TASTE WAVES
TEMP ASSURE
THOMPSON
THOMPSON NUTRIT
TOTAL GREEN
TRIM CORE
TURBO ENERGY
ULTIMATE NUTRIT
ULTIMATE NUTRITION
ULTRA OMEGA 3-6-9
VEGGIE COMPLETE
VEGLIFE
VERY BERRY
WIZARD
WOODLAND
WOODLAND PUBLISHING
YOHIMBE ACTION FOR MEN
ZAND

NUTRAMAX LABORATORIES, INC.

2208 Lakeside Blvd
Edgewood, MD 21040
Tel.: (410) 776-4000
Fax: (410) 776-4009
Toll Free: (800) 925-5187
Web Site: www.nutramaxlabs.com
Approx. Number Employees: 225
Year Founded: 1992
Business Description:
Mfr, Researcher, Developer & Marketer of Nutraceuticals & Pharmaceuticals
S.I.C.: 2834
N.A.I.C.S.: 325412
Media: 6-7
Personnel:
Todd Henderson *(Pres)*
Blake Whitney *(Dir-Sls & Mktg)*
Brands & Products:
COMAL
COMAX
CONSIL
COSAMIN
COSAMINDS
COSEQUIN
DENOSYL
DENOSYL SD4
FCHG49
MACRO-SORB
NUTRAMAX
QUELANT
SENIOR MOMENT
TRH122
WELACTIN
Advertising Agencies:
Ron Foth Advertising
8100 N High St
Columbus, OH 43235-6400
Tel.: (614) 888-7771
Fax: (614) 888-5933

SNS Marketing
400 Red Brook Blvd Ste 310
Owings Mills, MD 21117
Tel.: (410) 527-1800
Fax: (410) 527-1899

NUTRISYSTEM, INC.

600 Office Center Dr
Fort Washington, PA 19034
Tel.: (215) 706-5300
Fax: (215) 706-5388
Toll Free: (800) 321THIN
E-mail: info@nutrisystem.com
Web Site: www.nutrisystem.com
Approx. Rev.: $509,515,000
Approx. Number Employees: 573
Year Founded: 1972
Business Description:
Weight Loss Centers, Services & Products
S.I.C.: 7299; 5499; 5961; 5963
N.A.I.C.S.: 812191; 446191; 454111; 454390
Advertising Expenditures: $118,100,000
Media: 3-8-13-15-18-20-23-24
Distr.: Natl.
Budget Set: Monthly
Personnel:
Joseph M. Redling *(Chm & CEO)*
David D. Clark *(CFO)*
Brad Wilson *(Sr VP-Brand & Channel Mgmt)*
Meredith Bandy *(Head-PR, Blogger & Media)*
Bill Chase *(Head-Online Adv)*
Sean McCormick *(Head-TV & Radio Adv)*
Nicole Morrison *(Head-Print Adv)*
Brands & Products:
ADVANCED
NOURISH
NUCUISINE
NUTRI/SYSTEM
NUTRIHANCE
NUTRISYSTEM
NUTRISYSTEM NOURISH
PERSONALIZED PROFILE
SELECT
Advertising Agencies:
DonatWald+Haque
1316 Third St Ste 301
Santa Monica, CA 90401
Tel.: (310) 394-1717
Fax: (310) 394-1716

Gregory FCA
27 W Athens Ave Ste 200
Ardmore, PA 19003
Tel.: (610) 642-8253
Fax: (610) 642-1258
Fax: (610) 649-9029
Toll Free: (800) 499-4734
Investor Relations Agency of Record

ML Rogers
102 Madison Ave 10th Fl
New York, NY 10016
Tel.: (212) 213-3833
(Nu-Kitchen)

NUTRITION 21, INC.

4 Manhattanville Rd
Purchase, NY 10577-2139
Tel.: (914) 701-4500
Fax: (914) 696-0860
E-mail: mail@nutrition21.com
Web Site: www.nutrition21.com
Approx. Rev.: $8,763,000
Approx. Number Employees: 11
Year Founded: 1983
Business Description:
Nutrition Products Developer & Marketer
S.I.C.: 2833; 2834; 2836
N.A.I.C.S.: 325411; 325412; 325414
Advertising Expenditures: $200,000
Media: 3-4-6
Personnel:
John H. Gutfreund *(Chm)*
Michael A. Zeher *(Pres & CEO)*
Alan J. Kirschbaum *(CFO, Treas & VP-Fin)*
Benjamin T. Sporn *(Gen Counsel)*
Brands & Products:
ADVANCED MEMORY FORMULA
CHROMAX
CORE4LIFE ADVANCED MEMORY FORMULA
DIABETES ESSENTIALS
DIABETES ESSENTIALS NUTRITION TO GO
DIACHROME
ICELAND HEALTH
MAGNEMAX
NUTRITION 21
SELENOMAX
SELENOPURE
ZENERGEN
ZINMAX

NUVASIVE, INC.

7475 Lusk Blvd
San Diego, CA 92121
Tel.: (858) 909-1800
Fax: (858) 909-2000
Toll Free: (800) 455-1476
E-mail: info@nuvasive.com
Web Site: www.nuvasive.com
Approx. Rev.: $478,237,000
Approx. Number Employees: 789
Business Description:
Medical Devices Mfr for the Treatment of Spinal Disorders
S.I.C.: 3842; 3841; 8733
N.A.I.C.S.: 339113; 339112; 541710
Advertising Expenditures: $37,701,000
Media: 2-7-10
Personnel:
Alexis V. Lukianov *(Chm & CEO)*
Keith C. Valentine *(Pres & COO)*
Michael J. Lambert *(CFO & Exec VP)*
Mark Zecca *(CIO)*
Patrick S. Miles *(Pres-Americas)*
Jason M. Hannon *(Gen Counsel & Exec VP)*
Jeffrey P. Rydin *(Exec VP-Sls-Americas)*
G. Bryan Cornwall *(Sr VP-Res & Clinical Resources)*
Robin Evans Grandl *(Product Mgr)*
Brands & Products:
COROENT
CREATIVE SPINE TECHNOLOGY
MAS
MAXCESS
NEUROVISION
NUVASIVE
XLIF
Advertising Agency:
inferno
505 Tennessee St Ste 108
Memphis, TN 38103
Tel.: (901) 278-3773
Fax: (901) 278-3774

NUVIM, INC.

12 Rte 17 N Ste 212
Paramus, NJ 07652
Tel.: (201) 556-1010
Tel.: (201) 556-1013
Toll Free: (877) 850-8777
Web Site: www.nuvim.com
Sales Range: $1-9.9 Million
Approx. Number Employees: 5
Year Founded: 1999
Business Description:
Dietary Supplement Beverages Producer, Marketer & Distr
S.I.C.: 2037; 2836
N.A.I.C.S.: 311411; 325414

Key to Media (For complete agency information see *The Advertising Red Books-Agencies* edition):
1. Bus. Publs. 2. Cable T.V. 3. Catalogs & Directories. 4. Co-op Adv. 5. Consumer Mags. 6. D.M. to Bus. Estab.7. D.M. to Consumers
8. Daily Newsp. 9. Exhibits/Trade Shows 10. Foreign 11. Infomercial 12. Internet Adv.13. Multimedia 14. Network Radio
15. Network T.V. 16. Newsp. Distr. Mags. 17. Other 18. Outdoor (Posters, Transit) 19. Point of Purchase20. Premiums, Novelties
21. Product Samples 22. Special Events Mktg. 23. Spot Radio 24. Spot T.V. 25. Weekly Newsp. 26. Yellow Page Adv.

NuVim, Inc. — (Continued)

Advertising Expenditures: $477,000
Media: 8-13-19-24
Personnel:
Richard P. Kundrat *(Chm & CEO)*
Brands & Products:
FEEL THE DIFFERENCE
FRUIT SYMPHONY
LACTOACTIN
LACTOMUNE
NUTRAFLORA
NUVIM

NYCOMED US, INC.

(Sub. of Nycomed International Management GmbH)
60 Baylis Rd
Melville, NY 11747
Mailing Address:
PO Box 2006
Melville, NY 11747
Tel.: (631) 454-7677
Fax: (631) 454-6389
Web Site: www.nycomedus.com
Approx. Number Employees: 400
Business Description:
Pharmaceuticals Mfr
S.I.C.: 2834; 2851
N.A.I.C.S.: 325412; 325510
Media: 2-7-10-20-21
Personnel:
Stephen J. Andrzejewski *(CEO)*
Joseph J. LaRosa *(Gen Counsel & Sr VP)*
Ralph Landau *(Sr VP & Corp Officer-Ops, Res & Dev)*
Jeff Wasserstein *(Sr VP-Bus Dev & Strategy)*
Mindy Kirsch *(VP-HR)*

NYER MEDICAL GROUP, INC.

13 Water St
Holliston, MA 01746
Tel.: (508) 429-8506
E-mail: info@nyermedicalgroup.com
Web Site:
www.nyermedicalgroup.com
Sales Range: $50-74.9 Million
Approx. Number Employees: 190
Year Founded: 1991
Business Description:
Holding Company Focusing on Medical Products; Equipment, Supplies & Novelty Items Distr to Emergency Medical Services Companies, Fire Departments & Police Departments
S.I.C.: 5047; 5999
N.A.I.C.S.: 423450; 446199
Advertising Expenditures: $155,525
Media: 4-7-8-13-24-26
Personnel:
Mark Dumouchel *(Pres & CEO)*
Karen L. Wright *(Treas, Sec & VP-Fin)*

OAKWOOD HEALTHCARE, INC.

18101 Oakwood Blvd
Dearborn, MI 48124-4089
Tel.: (313) 593-7000
Fax: (313) 253-6033
Toll Free: (800) 543WELL
E-mail: webmaster@oakwood.org
Web Site: www.oakwood.org
Approx. Rev.: $2,000,000,000
Approx. Number Employees: 9,418
Year Founded: 1985
Business Description:
Healthcare Services
S.I.C.: 8062
N.A.I.C.S.: 622110
Media: 2-8-18-23-24
Personnel:
Brian Connolly *(Pres & CEO)*
Doug Welday *(CFO & Exec VP)*
J. Joseph Diederich *(COO & Exec VP)*
Nancy Gray *(Chief Dev Officer)*
Paul Conway *(Sr VP-HR)*
Brands & Products:
ARTS FOR THE SPIRIT
OAKWOOD
WE SPECIALIZE. IN YOU.
WINE FOR THE SPIRIT

OBAGI MEDICAL PRODUCTS, INC.

3760 Kilroy Airport Way Ste 500
Long Beach, CA 90806
Tel.: (562) 628-1007
E-mail: webmaster@obagi.com
Web Site: www.obagi.com
Approx. Sls.: $112,763,000
Approx. Number Employees: 203
Business Description:
Topical Skin Health Systems
S.I.C.: 2833; 2834
N.A.I.C.S.: 325411; 325412
Advertising Expenditures: $425,000
Media: 1-2-7-10-13-18-22
Personnel:
Albert J. Fitzgibbons, III *(Chm)*
Albert F. Hummel *(Pres & CEO)*
Preston S. Romm *(CFO & Exec VP-Fin, Admin & Ops)*
David Goldstein *(Exec VP-Global Sls & Field Mktg)*
Judith C. Hattendorf *(Sr VP-Product Dev)*
Brands & Products:
OBAG-C RX
OBAGI
ROSACLEAR
SUNFADER

O'CONNOR HOSPITAL

(Sub. of Daughters of Charity Health System)
2105 Forest Ave
San Jose, CA 95128
Tel.: (408) 947-2500
Fax: (408) 283-7776
Web Site: www.oconnorhospital.org
Approx. Number Employees: 1,000
Year Founded: 1889
Business Description:
Health Care Services
S.I.C.: 8062
N.A.I.C.S.: 622110
Media: 9-10-18-22-23-24-25
Personnel:
James Dover *(Pres & CEO)*
David Carroll *(CFO & Sr VP)*
Julie Hatcher *(VP-HR)*
Elizabeth Nikels *(VP-Comm)*
Bruce Blackfield *(Dir-Fin)*
Peter Schubart *(Dir)*

OCULUS INNOVATIVE SCIENCES

1129 N McDowell Blvd
Petaluma, CA 94954
Tel.: (707) 283-0550
Fax: (707) 283-0551
E-mail: info@oculusis.com
Web Site: www.oculusis.com
Approx. Rev.: $7,364,000
Approx. Number Employees: 43
Year Founded: 1999
Business Description:
Wound Infection Control
S.I.C.: 2834; 2836; 3841; 8733
N.A.I.C.S.: 325412; 325414; 339112; 541710
Advertising Expenditures: $246,000
Media: 7-10
Personnel:
Hojabr Alimi *(Chm, Pres & CEO)*
Robert E. Miller *(CFO)*
James Schutz *(COO, Gen Counsel, Corp Sec & Dir)*
Bruce Thornton *(Exec VP)*
Andres Gutierrez *(Dir-Medical Affairs)*
Dan McFadden *(Dir-IR)*
Robert Northey *(Dir-R & D)*

ODYSSEY HEALTHCARE, INC.

(Sub. of Gentiva Health Services, Inc.)
717 N Harwood St Ste 1500
Dallas, TX 75201-6519
Tel.: (214) 922-9711
Fax: (214) 922-9752
Toll Free: (888) 922-9711
E-mail: info@odsyhealth.com
Web Site: www.odyssey-healthcare.com
Approx. Rev.: $686,438,000
Approx. Number Employees: 5,891
Year Founded: 1996
Business Description:
Healthcare Services
S.I.C.: 4813; 8059; 8069; 8082
N.A.I.C.S.: 517110; 621610; 622310; 623110
Import Export
Advertising Expenditures: $1,000,000
Media: 17
Personnel:
Richard R. Burnham *(Chm)*
Robert A. Lefton *(Pres & CEO)*
Craig P. Goguen *(COO & Sr VP)*
Bradley W. Bickham *(Gen Counsel & VP)*
Sally A. Parnell *(Sr VP-Clinical & Regulatory Affairs)*
Brands & Products:
IMPROVING THE QUALITY OF LIFE
ODYSSEY

OHIOHEALTH

180 E Broad St
Columbus, OH 43201-3201
Tel.: (614) 544-4455
Web Site: www.ohiohealth.com
Sales Range: $1-4.9 Billion
Approx. Number Employees: 15,340
Year Founded: 1983
Business Description:
Non-Profit Hospital & Health Care Services
S.I.C.: 8062
N.A.I.C.S.: 622110
Media: 4-10-13
Personnel:
David P. Blom *(Pres & CEO)*
Michael W. Louge *(CFO & Exec VP)*
Robert P. Millen *(COO & Exec VP)*
Bob Gilbert *(Sr Ops Officer-OhioHealth Neighborhood Care)*
Karen Jefferson Morrison *(Pres-OhioHealth Foundation & Sr VP-External Affairs-OhioHealth)*
John Kowalski *(Sr VP-Fin)*
Mark Hopkins *(Dir-Media Rels)*
Jana Basham *(Mgr-CME)*
Amber DeBarr *(Mgr-Mktg)*
Paula Kobelt *(Mgr-Quality Assurance)*
Lexie Sines *(Mgr-Continuing Medical Education)*
Advertising Agencies:
Doner
The Diamond Bldg 1100 Superior Ave 10th Fl
Cleveland, OH 44114
Tel.: (216) 771-5700
Fax: (216) 771-1308

Doner
25900 Northwestern Hwy
Southfield, MI 48075
Tel.: (248) 354-9700
Fax: (248) 827-8440

OMEGA PROTEIN CORPORATION

2105 City West Blvd Ste 500
Houston, TX 77042-2838
Tel.: (713) 623-0060
Fax: (713) 940-6122
Toll Free: (800) 345-8805
E-mail: media@omegaproteininc.com
Web Site: www.omegaproteininc.com
Approx. Rev.: $167,704,000
Approx. Number Employees: 493
Business Description:
Omega-3 Fish Oil & Fish Meal Products Processor, Marketer & Distr
S.I.C.: 2092; 0919; 2079; 5499
N.A.I.C.S.: 311712; 114119; 311225; 446191
Personnel:
Joseph L. Von Rosenberg, III *(Chm)*
Bret D. Scholtes *(CFO & Exec VP)*
John D. Held *(Gen Counsel, Sec & Exec VP)*
Mark E. Griffin *(Sr VP-R&D, Sls & Mktg)*
Joseph E. Kadi *(Sr VP-Ops)*
Ben Landry *(Dir-Pub Affairs)*
Brands & Products:
HEALTHY PRODUCTS FOR A HEALTHY WORLD
NATURAL NAUTIC
NEPTUNE
OMEGA PROTEIN
OMEGAEQUIS
OMEGAGROW
OMEGAGROW PLUS
OMEGAPURE
SEACIDE
SEALAC
SPECIAL SELECT
VIRGINIA PRIME GOLD
VIRGINIA PRIME PLATINUM
Advertising Agency:
Paulsen Marketing Communications, Inc.
(d/b/a Paulsen AgriBranding)
3510 S 1st Ave Cir
Sioux Falls, SD 57105-5807
Tel.: (605) 336-1745
Fax: (605) 336-2305

OMNICARE CLINICAL RESEARCH, INC.

(Holding of Nautic Partners, LLC)
630 Allendale Rd
King of Prussia, PA 19406
Tel.: (484) 679-2400

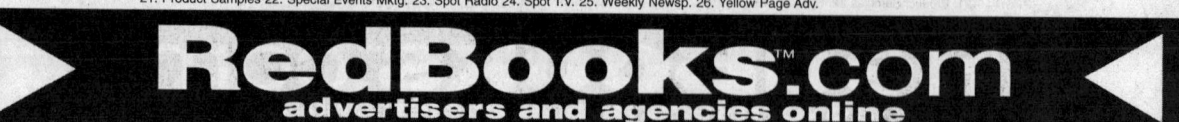

Key to Media (For complete agency information see *The Advertising Red Books-Agencies* edition):
1. Bus. Publs. 2. Cable T.V. 3. Catalogs & Directories. 4. Co-op Adv. 5. Consumer Mags. 6. D.M. to Bus. Estab.7. D.M. to Consumers
8. Daily Newsp. 9. Exhibits/Trade Shows 10. Foreign 11. Infomercial 12. Internet Adv.13. Multimedia 14. Network Radio
15. Network T.V. 16. Newsp. Distr. Mags. 17. Other 18. Outdoor (Posters, Transit) 19. Point of Purchase20. Premiums, Novelties
21. Product Samples 22. Special Events Mktg. 23. Spot Radio 24. Spot T.V. 25. Weekly Newsp. 26. Yellow Page Adv.

Fax: (484) 679-2410
Web Site: www.omnicarecr.com
Sales Range: $75-99.9 Million
Year Founded: 2000
Business Description:
Management Consulting Services
S.I.C.: 8748
N.A.I.C.S.: 541618
Personnel:
James M. Pusey *(Pres & CEO)*
Advertising Agency:
Backe Digital Brand Marketing
35 Cricket Ter Ctr
Ardmore, PA 19003-2203
Tel.: (610) 896-9260
Fax: (610) 896-9242

OMNICARE, INC

100 E River Ctr Blvd Ste 1600
Covington, KY 41011
Tel.: (859) 392-3300
Fax: (859) 392-3333
Toll Free: (800) 990-6664
E-mail: investor_relations@omnicare.com
Web Site: www.omnicare.com
Approx. Sls.: $6,146,212,000
Approx. Number Employees: 13,750
Year Founded: 1981
Business Description:
Pharmacy & Consulting Services for Geriatric Care Professionals
S.I.C.: 5912; 5047; 5122
N.A.I.C.S.: 446110; 423450; 424210
Media: 2-13
Personnel:
John L. Workman *(Pres & CFO)*
John G. Figueroa *(CEO)*
Randy Carpenter *(CIO & Sr VP)*
Tim Canning *(CMO & Sr VP)*
Kathleen McGuan *(Chief Compliance Officer & Sr VP)*
William A. Fitzpatrick *(Corp Compliance Officer)*
Jeffrey M. Stamps *(Pres-Long Term Care Ops & Exec VP)*
W. Gary Erwin *(Pres-Omnicare Senior Health Outcomes & Sr VP-Pro Svcs)*
Thomas W. Ludeke *(Pres-Omnicare Info Solutions & VP)*
Nitin Sahney *(Pres-Specialty Care Grp)*
Alexander M. Kayne *(Gen Counsel, Sec & Sr VP)*
Thomas R. Marsh *(Treas & VP-Fin Svcs)*
Priscilla Stewart-Jones *(Exec VP-HR)*
Erin E. Ascher *(Sr VP-HR)*
Leo P. Finn III *(Sr VP-Strategic Plng & Dev)*
Tracy Finn *(Sr VP)*
Timothy J. Hopkins *(Sr VP-Trade Rels)*
Robert Kraft *(Sr VP)*
Daniel J. Maloney *(Sr VP-Pharmaceutical Pur)*
Bradley S. Abbott *(VP, Controller & Grp Exec-Corp Fin Svcs Grp)*
Beth A. Kinerk *(Corp VP-Customer Renewal & Sls)*
D. Michael Laney *(VP-Mgmt Info Sys)*
Christopher J. Ross *(Dir-IR)*
Brands & Products:
ACCU-CARE
ADD ON
CYPRESS
MDS2GO
OMNICARE
OMNICARE GERIATRIC PHARMACEUTICAL CARE GUIDELINES
OMNIVIEW
ORCAS
ORDER ENTRY
THE PRESCRIPTION FOR POSITIVE OUTCOMES
PRO-TRACKING
Advertising Agency:
Deardorff Associates
319 E Lea Blvd
Wilmington, DE 19802
Tel.: (302) 764-7573
Fax: (302) 764-5451

OMNICELL INC.

1201 Charleston Rd
Mountain View, CA 94043-1337
Tel.: (650) 251-6100
Fax: (650) 251-6266
Toll Free: (800) 850-6664
E-mail: info@omnicell.com
Web Site: www.omnicell.com
Approx. Rev.: $222,407,000
Approx. Number Employees: 753
Year Founded: 1992
Business Description:
Pharmacy & Supply Systems to the Health Care Industry
S.I.C.: 8071; 2834; 7372; 7373
N.A.I.C.S.: 621511; 325412; 511210; 541512
Advertising Expenditures: $1,100,000
Media: 7-8-10
Personnel:
Randall A. Lipps *(Chm, Pres & CEO)*
Rob G. Seim *(CFO & VP-Fin)*
Dan S. Johnston *(Gen Counsel & VP)*
J. Christopher Drew *(Sr VP-Field Ops)*
Marga Ortigas-Wedekind *(VP-Global Mktg & Product Dev)*
Richard Caldwell *(Sr Product Mgr)*
Brands & Products:
ANYWHERE RN
DECISIONCENTER
MEDGUARD
OMNIBUYER
OMNICELL
OMNICELL PHARMACYCENTRAL
OMNICENTER
OMNIGATE
OMNILINKRX
OMNIRX
OMNISUPPLIER
OPTIFLEX
OPTIFLEX CL
OPTIFLEX MS
OPTIFLEX SS
PHARMACYCENTRAL
POINT-TO-POINT MEDICATION SAFETY
SAFETYMED
SAFETYMED RN
SAFETYPAK
SECUREVAULT
SURE-MED
WORKFLOWRX

ONCOGENEX PHARMACEUTICALS, INC.

1522 217th Pl SE Ste 100
Bothell, WA 98021
Tel.: (425) 686-1500
Fax: (425) 686-1600
Web Site: www.oncogenex.com
Approx. Rev.: $92,000
Approx. Number Employees: 27
Business Description:
Pharmaceutical Developer & Mfr
S.I.C.: 2834; 8733
N.A.I.C.S.: 325412; 541720
Media: 7-10-13
Personnel:
Jack Goldstein *(Chm)*
Scott Daniel Cormack *(Pres & CEO)*
Michelle G. Burris *(CFO & Exec VP-Ops)*
Cindy Jacobs *(Chief Medical Officer & Exec VP)*
Brands & Products:
BRINGING HOPE TO LIFE
ONCOGENEX
SONOGEN
TOCOSOL

ONCOTHYREON INC.

2601 4th Ave Ste 500
Seattle, WA 98121
Tel.: (206) 801-2100
Fax: (206) 801-2101
E-mail: IR@Oncothyreon.com
Web Site: www.oncothyreon.com/
Approx. Rev.: $18,000
Approx. Number Employees: 25
Year Founded: 1985
Business Description:
Cancer Treatment Biotechnology Services
S.I.C.: 2834; 2836; 8733
N.A.I.C.S.: 325412; 325414; 541710
Advertising Expenditures: $75,000
Media: 2-10
Personnel:
Christopher S. Henney *(Chm)*
Robert L. Kirkman *(Pres & CEO)*
Julie M. Eastland *(CFO & VP-Corp Dev)*
Gary Christianson *(COO)*
Jane Tulloch *(Dir-Investor Rels)*
Brands & Products:
BLP25
TAKING AIM AT CANCER
THERATOPE

ORAGENICS, INC.

3000 Bayport Dr Ste 685
Tampa, FL 33607
Tel.: (813) 286-7900
Fax: (813) 286-7904
E-mail: info@oragenics.com
Web Site: www.oragenics.com
Approx. Rev.: $1,308,910
Approx. Number Employees: 19
Business Description:
Biopharmaceutical Research Services
S.I.C.: 2834; 8733
N.A.I.C.S.: 325412; 541710
Advertising Expenditures: $1,615,268
Personnel:
Frederick W. Telling *(Chm)*
Brian Bohunicky *(CFO & Interim CEO)*
Jeffrey D. Hillman *(Chief Scientific Officer)*
Gerard David *(Exec VP-Sls & Mktg)*

ORASURE TECHNOLOGIES INC

220 E First St
Bethlehem, PA 18015-1338
Tel.: (610) 882-1820
Fax: (610) 882-1825
Toll Free: (800) 869-3538
E-mail: orasure@orasure.com
Web Site: www.orasure.com
Approx. Rev.: $75,014,836
Approx. Number Employees: 231
Year Founded: 1985
Business Description:
Oral Fluid Diagnostic Testing, Infectious Disease Testing & Substance Abuse Testing
S.I.C.: 8733; 2834; 2835
N.A.I.C.S.: 541720; 325412; 325413
Advertising Expenditures: $209,621
Media: 2-7-10-13-20
Personnel:
Douglas G. Watson *(Chm)*
Douglas A. Michels *(Pres & CEO)*
Ronald H. Spair *(CFO & COO)*
Stephen R. Lee *(Chief Science Officer & Exec VP)*
Jack E. Jerrett *(Gen Counsel, Sec & Sr VP)*
P. Michael Formica *(Exec VP & Gen Mgr-Cryosurgery Sys)*
Tony Zezzo *(Exec VP-Mktg & Sls)*
Mark L. Kuna *(Controller & Sr VP-Fin)*
Henry B. Cohen *(Sr VP-HR)*
Debra Fraser-Howze *(Sr VP-Govt & External Affairs)*
Robert A. Gregg *(Sr VP-Regulatory Affairs & Quality Assurance)*
Ron Ticho *(Sr VP-Corp Comm)*
Kenneth A. Adach *(VP-Global Consumer Mktg)*
Jeane Brunmark *(Dir-Latin America Sls)*
Joseph Oerson *(Dir-Sls-Africa)*
Michael Heath *(Reg Mgr-Corp Acct)*
Christina Werner *(Mgr-Natl Accounts, Criminal Justice & Forensic Toxicology)*
Brands & Products:
AUTO-LYTE
COMPOUND W
COMPOUND W FREEZE OFF
FREEZE 'N CLEAR SKIN CLINIC
HISTOFREEZER
INTERCEPT
MICRO-PLATE
ORAQUICK ADVANCE
ORASURE
ORASURE TECHNOLOGIES, INC.
POINTTS
Q.E.D.
UPLINK
UPT

ORE PHARMACEUTICALS INC.

One Main St Ste 300
Cambridge, MA 02142
Tel.: (617) 649-2001
Toll Free: (877) ORE-PHRM
Web Site: www.orepharma.com
Approx. Rev.: $1,950,000
Approx. Number Employees: 14
Year Founded: 1994
Business Description:
Drug Discovery & Development Genomic & Data Management Technologies
S.I.C.: 2834; 3826; 8733
N.A.I.C.S.: 325412; 334516; 541720
Media: 10
Personnel:
J. Stark Thompson *(Chm)*
Mark J. Gabrielson *(Pres & CEO)*
Benjamin L. Palleiko *(CFO, Treas, Sec & Sr VP)*
Stephen R. Donahue *(Sr VP)*

Key to Media (For complete agency information see *The Advertising Red Books-Agencies* edition):
1. Bus. Publs. 2. Cable T.V. 3. Catalogs & Directories. 4. Co-op Adv. 5. Consumer Mags. 6. D.M. to Bus. Estab.7. D.M. to Consumers
8. Daily Newsp. 9. Exhibits/Trade Shows 10. Foreign 11. Infomercial 12. Internet Adv.13. Multimedia 14. Network Radio
15. Network T.V. 16. Newsp. Distr. Mags. 17. Other 18. Outdoor (Posters, Transit) 19. Point of Purchase20. Premiums, Novelties
21. Product Samples 22. Special Events Mktg. 23. Spot Radio 24. Spot T.V. 25. Weekly Newsp. 26. Yellow Page Adv.

Ore Pharmaceuticals Inc. — (Continued)

Albert Risdorfer *(VP-HR)*
Chris T. Dunne *(Sr Dir-Fin)*
Kory Engelke *(Sr Dir-Gen Toxicology)*
Steven Godin *(Sr Dir-Gen Toxicology)*
Brands & Products:
ASCENTA
BIOEXPRESS
GENECHIP
GENEEXPRESS
GENESIS ENTERPRISE SYSTEM
ORE
PHASE R
SCIANTIS
SELECTION
TOXEDGE
TOXEXPRESS
TOXPLUS
TOXSCREEN
TOXSHIELD
TOXSUITE

ORJENE CO., INC.

(Sub. of Jason Natural Products Inc.)
(d/b/a Orjene Natural Cosmetics)
c/o Hain Celestial Group 58 S Service Rd
Melville, NY 11747-2342
Tel.: (631) 730-2200
Approx. Sls.: $2,700,000
Approx. Number Employees: 30
Business Description:
Mfr of Skin Treatment Cosmetics, Shampoos, Creams, Lotions & Oils
S.I.C.: 2844; 7231
N.A.I.C.S.: 325620; 812112
Media: 6-8-10-21-23
Distr.: Direct to Consumer; Natl.
Brands & Products:
ORJENE

ORTHO-CLINICAL DIAGNOSTICS, INC.

(Sub. of Johnson & Johnson)
1001 US Hwy 202
Raritan, NJ 08869-0606
Tel.: (908) 218-1300
Fax: (908) 704-3696
Toll Free: (800) 322-6374
Web Site: www.orthoclinical.com
Sales Range: $900-999.9 Million
Approx. Number Employees: 1,650
Business Description:
Diagnostic Substances Mfr
S.I.C.: 2834
N.A.I.C.S.: 325412
Export
Media: 4-6-7-8-10-11-21
Distr.: Natl.
Budget Set: Oct.-Nov.
Brands & Products:
ABO
AFFIRMAGEN
ANTI-HUMAN GLOBULIN REAGENTS
ANTIBODY ENHANCEMENT MEDIA
BIOCLONE
CHLAMYDIA ANTIGEN ELISA
CHROMOGENIC
COAGULATION CONTROLS
COOMBS CONTROL
CYTORONABSOLUTE
ELECTRA 1400C
ELECTRA 1600C
FACTOR ASSAY
FETALSCREEN
FIBRINDEX
HBC ELISA
HBSAG ELISA
HCV 3.0 ELISA
HIV-1 ELSIA
HSV ANTIGEN ELISA
HTLV-I/II
IMMUNOCOUNT
IMMUNOPHENOTYPING
MICRHOGAM RH (D)
MICROWELL ELISA
ORTHO
ORTHO DIMERKLONE
POOLED SCREENING CELLS
QUANTITATIVE FIBRINOGEN
REAGENT RED BLOOD CELLS
RECOMBIGEN HIV-1 EIA
RESOLVE PANELS A, B & C
RH-HR
RHOGAM RH (D)
RIBA HCV
RIBA HIV-1
RSV ANTIGEN ELISA
SELECTOGEN
SIMWASH
SURGISCREEN
THROMBOSIL APTT REAGENT
VITROS

ORTHO-MCNEIL PHARMACEUTICAL, INC.

(Sub. of Johnson & Johnson)
1000 US Hwy 202
Raritan, NJ 08869-0602
Tel.: (908) 218-6000
Fax: (908) 575-9224
Web Site: www.ortho-mcneil.com
Sales Range: $1-4.9 Billion
Approx. Number Employees: 3,500
Business Description:
Pharmaceuticals Mfr
S.I.C.: 2833; 2834
N.A.I.C.S.: 325411; 325412
Media: 1-4-5-10-11-18-19-20-21
Distr.: Natl.
Budget Set: Oct. -Nov.
Personnel:
Seth H.Z. Fischer *(Pres)*
Beatriz Mallory *(Dir-Mktg, Multicultural)*
Brands & Products:
AXERT
DITROPAN
DITROPAN XL
ELMIRON
FLOXIN
HALDOL
INVEGA
MODICON
ORTHO
ORTHO-CEPT
ORTHO EVRA
ORTHO MICRONOR
ORTHO-NOVUM
ORTHO TRI-CYCLEN
PANCREASE
PARAFLEX CAPLETS
PARAFON FORTE
PARAGARD
PROTOSTAT
TERAZOL
TOPAMAX
TYLENOL WITH CODEINE
TYLOX
ULTRACET
ULTRAM
VASCOR

ORTHOLOGIC CORP.

(Name Changed to CAPSTONE THERAPEUTICS CORP.)

OSCIENT PHARMACEUTICALS CORP.

(Filed Ch 11 Bankruptcy #916576 on 07/13/09 in U.S. Bankruptcy Ct, Dist of MA, Boston)
Ste 2200 1000 Winter St
Waltham, MA 02451
Tel.: (781) 398-2300
Fax: (781) 893-9535
Web Site:
www.oscientrestructuring.com
Approx. Rev.: $86,848,000
Approx. Number Employees: 316
Year Founded: 1961
Business Description:
Discovery & Development of Pharmaceutical & Diagnostics Products
S.I.C.: 2834; 8733
N.A.I.C.S.: 325412; 541710
Advertising Expenditures: $2,607,000
Media: 4-7-8-10-13-21
Personnel:
Christopher J. M. Taylor *(VP-IR & Corp Comm)*
Brands & Products:
FACTIVE
OSCIENT
PATHOGENOME DATABASE
TESTIM

OSF HEALTHCARE SYSTEM

(Group of The Sisters of the Third Order of St. Francis)
800 NE Glen Oak Ave
Peoria, IL 61603-3200
Tel.: (309) 655-2850
Fax: (309) 655-6869
Web Site: www.osfhealthcare.org
Approx. Rev.: $4,666,112,920
Approx. Number Employees: 12,254
Year Founded: 1989
Business Description:
Non-Profit Hospitals, Long-Term Care Facilities & Nursing Colleges Organization
S.I.C.: 8741; 8062; 8069; 8221
N.A.I.C.S.: 561110; 611310; 622110; 622310
Personnel:
Judith Ann Duvall *(Chm)*
Diane Marie McGrew *(Pres & Treas)*
James M. Moore *(CEO)*
James J. Mormann *(CIO)*
Susan Campbell *(Chief Nursing Officer & Sr VP)*
Darryl Long *(Chief Supply Chain Officer)*
Tara D. Canty *(Sr VP-Govt Rels)*
John R. Evancho *(Sr VP-Compliance & Privacy)*
Gerald J. McShane *(Sr VP-Medical Svcs)*
Bruce F. Mehl *(Sr VP-HR)*
Vance C. Parkhurst *(Sr VP-Legal Svcs)*
Robert Sawicki *(Sr VP-Supportive Care)*
James G. Farrell *(VP-Mktg & Comm)*
Advertising Agency:
Muller Bressler Brown
4739 Belleview Ave Ste 100
Kansas City, MO 64112-1316
Tel.: (816) 531-1992
Fax: (816) 531-6692

OTIX GLOBAL, INC.

(Sub. of William Demant Holding A/S)
4246 Riverboat Rd Ste 300
Salt Lake City, UT 84123
Tel.: (801) 312-1700
Fax: (801) 365-3000
Toll Free: (888) 678-4327
Web Site: www.otixglobal.com
Sales Range: $75-99.9 Million
Approx. Number Employees: 700
Business Description:
Digital Hearing Aids Mfr, Designer & Marketer
S.I.C.: 3845; 3841; 3842
N.A.I.C.S.: 334510; 339112; 339113
Advertising Expenditures: $6,779,000
Media: 7-16
Personnel:
Joseph A. Lugara *(Pres & COO)*
Trina Lucero *(Mgr-Sls Support-Intl Div)*
Brands & Products:
ALTAIR
APPLAUSE
BALANCE
DIRECTIONALPLUS
EXPRESSFIT
EXPRESSLINK
ION
NATURA
QUARTET
S.M.A.R.T. TECHNOLOGY
SONIC INNOVATIONS
SONICBLU
TOUCH
TRIBUTE
VELOCITY

Beatley Gravitt Communications
9A W Grace St
Richmond, VA 23220
Tel.: (804) 355-9151
Fax: (804) 359-5261

OXIS INTERNATIONAL, INC.

468 N Camden Dr Ste 200
Beverly Hills, CA 90210
Tel.: (310) 860-5184
Toll Free: (800) 547-3686
E-mail: corporate@oxis.com
Web Site: www.oxis.com
Approx. Rev.: $11,000
Year Founded: 1993
Business Description:
Therapeutic & Diagnostic Products Developer
S.I.C.: 2834
N.A.I.C.S.: 325412
Advertising Expenditures: $106,000
Media: 7-21
Personnel:
Anthony J. Cataldo *(Chm & CEO)*
Bernard M. Landes *(Pres)*
Randall Moeckli *(Sr Dir-Sls & Mktg)*

OXYSURE SYSTEMS, INC.

10880 John W Elliot Dr Ste 600
Frisco, TX 75034
Tel.: (972) 294-6450
E-mail: investors@oxysure.com
Web Site: www.oxysure.com
Approx. Rev.: $387,361
Approx. Number Employees: 8
Year Founded: 2004
Business Description:
Medical Grade Oxygen On Demand

Key to Media (For complete agency information see *The Advertising Red Books-Agencies* edition):
1. Bus. Publs. 2. Cable T.V. 3. Catalogs & Directories. 4. Co-op Adv. 5. Consumer Mags. 6. D.M. to Bus. Estab.7. D.M. to Consumers
8. Daily Newsp. 9. Exhibits/Trade Shows 10. Foreign 11. Infomercial 12. Internet Adv.13. Multimedia 14. Network Radio
15. Network T.V. 16. Newsp. Distr. Mags. 17. Other 18. Outdoor (Posters, Transit) 19. Point of Purchase20. Premiums, Novelties
21. Product Samples 22. Special Events Mktg. 23. Spot Radio 24. Spot T.V. 25. Weekly Newsp. 26. Yellow Page Adv.

S.I.C.: 3841; 2813; 2899
N.A.I.C.S.: 339112; 325120; 325998
Advertising Expenditures: $48,230
Media: 6-8
Personnel:
Julian T. Ross *(Chm & CEO)*
Brands & Products:
OXYSURE

PACIFICARE HEALTH SYSTEMS, LLC
(Div. of UnitedHealth Group Incorporated)
5995 Plaza Dr
Cypress, CA 90630
Mailing Address:
PO Box 25186
Santa Ana, CA 92799-5186
Tel.: (714) 952-1121
Fax: (714) 226-3581
Web Site: www.pacificare.com
Sales Range: $1-4.9 Billion
Approx. Number Employees: 9,800
Year Founded: 1975
Business Description:
Healthcare Services
S.I.C.: 6321
N.A.I.C.S.: 524114
Media: 1-7-8-13-14-15-18-22
Distr.: Reg.
Personnel:
Steven Hensley *(Chm & CEO)*
John Santelli *(CIO & Sr VP)*
Brands & Products:
AMS
EXECU-FIT
PACIFICARE
PRESCRIPTION SOLUTIONS
SECURE HORIZONS

PACIFICHEALTH LABORATORIES, INC.
100 Matawan Rd Ste 420
Matawan, NJ 07747
Tel.: (732) 739-2900
Fax: (732) 636-7410
E-mail: information@pacifichealthlabs.com
Web Site: www.pacifichealthlabs.com
Approx. Rev.: $7,200,960
Approx. Number Employees: 9
Year Founded: 1995
Business Description:
Researcher, Developer & Marketer of Nutritional & Natural Sports Nutrition, Weight Loss & Diabetes Products
S.I.C.: 2833; 2834; 5122
N.A.I.C.S.: 325411; 325412; 424210
Advertising Expenditures: $213,132
Media: 2-6-10-13-19-24
Personnel:
Robert Portman *(Chm)*
Frederick Duffner *(Pres & CEO)*
Stephen P. Kuchen *(CFO & COO)*
Brands & Products:
ACCEL GEL
ACCELERADE HYDRO
COUNTDOWN
ENDUROX RESTORE
FORZE GPS
SATIETROL
SATIETROL COMPLETE

PACIRA PHARMACEUTICALS, INC.
(Formerly Pacira, Inc.)
5 Silvay Way Ste 125
Parsippany, NJ 07054
Tel.: (973) 254-3560
E-mail: investor@pacira.com
Web Site: www.pacira.com
Approx. Rev.: $14,562,000
Approx. Number Employees: 83
Year Founded: 2007
Business Description:
Pharmaceutical Mfr
S.I.C.: 2834
N.A.I.C.S.: 325412
Personnel:
Fred A. Middleton *(Chm)*
David M. Stack *(Pres & CEO)*
James S. Scibetta *(CFO)*
William Lambert *(Sr VP-Pharmaceutical Dev)*
Mark Walters *(Sr VP-Technical Ops & Bus Dev)*
Lynette Bowman *(VP-HR)*
Vladimir Kharitonov *(VP-Product Dev & Tech Transfer)*
Taunia Markvicka *(VP-Mktg)*
Mary Beriont *(Dir-Mktg)*
Brands & Products:
DEPOBUPIVACAINE
DEPOCYT
DEPOCYTE
DEPODUR
DEPOFOAM
EXPAREL
PACIRA
Advertising Agency:
Pure Communications, Inc.
1015 Ashes Dr Ste 204
Wilmington, NC 28405
Tel.: (910) 509-3970

PAIN THERAPEUTICS, INC.
2211 Bridgepointe Pkway Ste 500
San Mateo, CA 94404
Tel.: (650) 624-8200
Fax: (650) 624-8222
Web Site: www.paintrials.com
Approx. Rev.: $16,809,000
Approx. Number Employees: 18
Business Description:
Opioid Painkiller Mfr
S.I.C.: 2834
N.A.I.C.S.: 325412
Advertising Expenditures: $4,100,000
Personnel:
Remi Barbier *(Chm, Pres & CEO)*
Peter S. Roddy *(CFO & VP)*
Nadav Friedmann *(COO & Chief Medical Officer)*
George Ben Thornton *(Sr VP-Tech)*
Michael Zamloot *(Sr VP-Tech Ops)*
Brands & Products:
OXYTREX
PAIN THERAPEUTICS
REMOXY

PALADIN LABS, INC.
6111 Royalmount Ave Ste 102
Montreal, QC H4P 2T4, Canada
Tel.: (514) 340-1112
Fax: (514) 344-4675
Toll Free: (888) 376-7830
E-mail: info@paladinlabs.com
Web Site: www.paladinlabs.com
Approx. Rev.: $130,397,753
Year Founded: 1996
Business Description:
Biotechnological & Pharmaceutical Products Mfr
S.I.C.: 2834
N.A.I.C.S.: 325412
Media: 2-10
Personnel:
Ted Wise *(Chm)*
Jonathan Ross Goodman *(Pres & CEO)*
Samira Sakhia *(CFO)*
Etan Jagermann *(COO)*
Mark Beaudet *(VP-Mktg & Sls)*
Brands & Products:
PALADIN

PALCO LABS INC.
360 El Pueblo Rd
Scotts Valley, CA 95066
Tel.: (831) 430-1600
Fax: (831) 430-1610
Toll Free: (800) 346-4488
E-mail: info@palcolabs.com
Web Site: www.palcolabs.com
Approx. Number Employees: 20
Year Founded: 1979
Business Description:
Surgical & Medical Instruments
S.I.C.: 3841; 5047
N.A.I.C.S.: 339112; 423450
Media: 6-10-13
Personnel:
Carolyn Hughes *(Dir-Mktg)*
Brands & Products:
AUTO-LANCET
EZ-LANCE
EZ-VAC
INJECT-EASE
INSUL-CAP
WET-STOP

PARAMOUNT HEALTH SYSTEMS
(Sub. of ProMedica Health System)
1901 Indian Wood Cir
Maumee, OH 43537-4055
Tel.: (419) 887-2500
Fax: (419) 887-2034
Web Site: www.paramounthealthcare.com
Approx. Number Employees: 360
Year Founded: 1987
Business Description:
Health Insurance Services
S.I.C.: 8011
N.A.I.C.S.: 621491
Import Export
Personnel:
Jack Randolf *(Pres)*
Jeff O'Connell *(Dir-Mktg)*
Advertising Agency:
Hart Associates, Inc.
1915 Indian Wood Cir
Maumee, OH 43537-4002
Tel.: (419) 893-9600
Fax: (419) 893-9070

PAREXEL INTERNATIONAL CORPORATION
195 West St
Waltham, MA 02451-1121
Tel.: (781) 487-9900
Fax: (781) 487-0525
Web Site: www.parexel.com
Approx. Rev.: $1,422,425,000
Approx. Number Employees: 10,550
Year Founded: 1983
Business Description:
Biopharmaceutical Information, Communications, Clinical Development, Technology & Consulting Services
S.I.C.: 8733; 4899; 7389; 8748
N.A.I.C.S.: 541710; 517910; 519190; 541690
Advertising Expenditures: $1,100,000
Media: 2-7-10-13
Personnel:
Josef H. Von Rickenbach *(Chm & CEO)*
James F. Winschel *(CFO & Sr VP)*
Mark A. Goldberg *(COO)*
Josephine Hoppe *(CIO)*
Ulf Schneider *(Chief Admin Officer & Sr VP)*
Kurt A. Brykman *(Pres-Consulting & Medical Comm Svcs)*
Steve Kent *(Pres-Perceptive Informatics)*
Andrew M. Smith *(Pres-Medical Mktg Svcs)*
Douglas A. Batt *(Gen Counsel, Sec & Sr VP)*
Anita Cooper *(Sr VP & Gen Mgr-Clinical Res Svcs)*
Joseph C. Avellone *(Sr VP-Clinical Res Svcs)*
Charles A. Stevens *(VP & Gen Mgr)*
Imogene Grimes *(VP-Biostatistics & Data Sciences Strategic Svcs)*
Jennifer Baird *(Sr Dir-PR)*
Brands & Products:
CLINBASE
EXPERTISE THAT MAKES THE DIFFERENCE
IMPACT
INITIATOR
INVESTIGATOR
PACE
PAREXEL
Advertising Agency:
Denneen & Company
222 Berkeley St Ste 1200
Boston, MA 02116
Tel.: (617) 236-1300
Fax: (617) 267-5001

PARTNERS HEALTHCARE SYSTEM, INC.
800 Boylston St Ste 1150 Prudential Twr
Boston, MA 02199
Tel.: (617) 278-1000
Fax: (617) 278-1049
Web Site: www.partners.org
Sales Range: $550-599.9 Million
Approx. Number Employees: 16,981
Year Founded: 1994
Business Description:
Hospital & Health Care Services
S.I.C.: 8062
N.A.I.C.S.: 622110
Media: 4-10-13
Personnel:
John M. Connors, Jr. *(Chm)*
James Noga *(CIO & VP)*
Peter K. Markell *(VP-Fin)*
Brands & Products:
PARTNERS
Advertising Agency:
Hill Holliday
53 State St
Boston, MA 02109
Tel.: (617) 366-4000

PATHEON INC.
(Holding of JLL Partners Inc.)
2100 Syntex Court
Mississauga, ON L5N 7K9, Canada

Key to Media (For complete agency information see *The Advertising Red Books-Agencies* edition):
1. Bus. Publs. 2. Cable T.V. 3. Catalogs & Directories. 4. Co-op Adv. 5. Consumer Mags. 6. D.M. to Bus. Estab.7. D.M. to Consumers
8. Daily Newsp. 9. Exhibits/Trade Shows 10. Foreign 11. Infomercial 12. Internet Adv.13. Multimedia 14. Network Radio
15. Network T.V. 16. Newsp. Distr. Mags. 17. Other 18. Outdoor (Posters, Transit) 19. Point of Purchase20. Premiums, Novelties
21. Product Samples 22. Special Events Mktg. 23. Spot Radio 24. Spot T.V. 25. Weekly Newsp. 26. Yellow Page Adv.

Patheon Inc. — (Continued)

Tel.: (905) 821-4001
Fax: (905) 812-6709
Toll Free: (888) PATHEON
E-mail: patheon@patheon.com
Web Site: www.patheon.com
Approx. Rev.: $671,200,000
Approx. Number Employees: 4,300
Year Founded: 1974
Business Description:
Prescription & Over-the-Counter Drugs Packaging & Mfr
S.I.C.: 5122
N.A.I.C.S.: 424210
Export
Personnel:
Ramsey A. Frank *(Chm)*
Terry S. Novak *(Pres & Chief Comml Officer)*
James C. Mullen *(CEO)*
Eric W. Evans *(CFO & Exec VP)*
Paul M. Garofolo *(CTO & Exec VP)*
Mark Kontny *(Chief Scientific Officer & Pres-Global Pharmaceutical Dev Svcs)*
Jonathan Arnold *(Chief Procurement Officer)*
Peter T. Bigelow *(Pres-North American Ops)*
Doaa A. Fathallah *(Sr VP, Gen Counsel-Europe & Global Pharmaceutical Dev Svcs)*
Geoffery M. Glass *(Exec VP-Global Strategy, Sls & Mktg)*
Antonella Mancuso *(Sr VP & Mng Dir-Ops-Europe)*
Andrew Kelley *(Sr VP-Comml Ops Europe & Asia Pacific)*
Brands & Products:
PERFORMANCE THE WORLD OVER
QUICK TO CLINIC
Advertising Agency:
Stonefly Communications Group
500 Olde Worthington Rd
Westerville, OH 43082
Tel.: (614) 543-6020
Fax: (614) 839-7373
Drug Development

PATHWORK DIAGNOSTICS
595 Penobscot
Redwood City, CA 94063
Tel.: (650) 366-1003
Fax: (650) 599-9083
Web Site: www.pathworkdx.com
Approx. Number Employees: 35
Year Founded: 2002
Business Description:
Technology for Identifying Protein Biomarker Patterns
S.I.C.: 8733
N.A.I.C.S.: 541710
Media: 2-4
Personnel:
Richard J. Bastiani *(Chm)*
Deborah J. Neff *(Pres & CEO)*
Fletcher Payne *(CFO)*
Shawn Becker *(VP-Mktg & Reimbursement)*

PATIENT CARE, INC.
(Sub. of Almost Family, Inc.)
100 Executive Dr Ste 130
West Orange, NJ 07052-3309
Tel.: (973) 243-5900
Fax: (973) 243-5901
Toll Free: (866) 728-2273
Web Site: www.patientcare.com
Sales Range: $25-49.9 Million
Approx. Number Employees: 4,304
Year Founded: 1975
Business Description:
Home Healthcare Services
S.I.C.: 8082
N.A.I.C.S.: 621610
Media: 6-9-13-25
Distr.: Natl.; Reg.
Personnel:
Greg Bellware *(COO)*
Annette Davis *(Mgr)*

PATIENT SAFETY TECHNOLOGIES, INC.
2 Venture Plz Ste 350
Irvine, CA 92618
Tel.: (949) 387-2277
E-mail: investor.relations@surgicountmedical.com
Web Site: www.surgicountmedical.com
Approx. Rev.: $14,797,013
Approx. Number Employees: 13
Year Founded: 1987
Business Description:
Surgical Appliance & Supplies Mfr
S.I.C.: 3841
N.A.I.C.S.: 339112
Advertising Expenditures: $83,000
Media: 10-17
Personnel:
Brian E. Stewart *(Pres & CEO)*
David C. Dreyer *(CFO, Sec & Exec VP)*
Brands & Products:
CITADEL
SAFETY SPONGE
SURGICOUNTER

PATTERSON COMPANIES, INC.
1031 Mendota Hts Rd
Saint Paul, MN 55120
Tel.: (651) 686-1600
Fax: (651) 686-9331
Toll Free: (800) 328-5536
E-mail: jobs@pattersondental.com
Web Site: www.pattersoncompanies.com
Approx. Sls.: $3,415,670,000
Approx. Number Employees: 7,100
Year Founded: 1877
Business Description:
Dental Equipment & Supplies Distr
S.I.C.: 5047; 5112
N.A.I.C.S.: 423450; 424120
Advertising Expenditures: $20,630,000
Media: 2-4-7-8-10
Personnel:
Peter L. Frechette *(Chm)*
Scott P. Anderson *(Pres & CEO)*
R. Stephen Armstrong *(CFO, Treas & Exec VP)*
Ranell M. Hamm *(CIO)*
Jerome E. Thygesen *(VP-HR)*

PC GROUP, INC.
419 Park Ave S Ste 500
New York, NY 10016
Tel.: (212) 687-3260
Fax: (212) 818-9873
Toll Free: (800) 645-5520
E-mail: ir@langercorporate.com
Web Site: www.pcgrpinc.com
Approx. Sls.: $44,989,046
Approx. Number Employees: 289
Year Founded: 1971
Business Description:
Orthopedic & Skincare Products Mfr
S.I.C.: 3842; 2676; 2841; 3149; 3841
N.A.I.C.S.: 339113; 316219; 322291; 325611; 339112
Export
Advertising Expenditures: $381,000
Media: 1-2-5-7-8-10-19-20-22
Distr.: Intl.; Natl.
Budget Set: Mar.
Personnel:
Warren B. Kanders *(Chm)*
W. Gray Hudkins *(Pres & CEO)*
Brands & Products:
ALLSPORT
ALLSPORT CLASSIC
ALLSPORT FLEXIBLE
ATP/TENNIS
BASKETBALL
CYCLIST
DESIGNLINE
DRESSFLEX
FOOTBALL
GOLF
HEALTHFLEX
HEEL FIT
LANGER BIOMECHANICS
LYTE FIT
MARATHONER
PPT
RUNNER'S MOULD
SILIPOS
SKI/SKATE
SOCCER
SPORTHOTICS
SPRINTER
SUPERFORM STYLOTIC
TENNIS
ULTRA SLIMS
WE'RE WITH YOU EVERY STEP OF THE WAY

PDI, INC.
Morris Corporate Ctr 1 Bldg A 300
Interpace Pkwy
Parsippany, NJ 07054
Tel.: (862) 207-7800
Toll Free: (800) 242-7494
E-mail: jesmith@pdi-inc.com
Web Site: www.pdi-inc.com
Approx. Rev.: $144,652,000
Approx. Number Employees: 870
Year Founded: 1988
Business Description:
Pharmaceutical Marketing & Sales Solutions
S.I.C.: 8742; 7389
N.A.I.C.S.: 541613; 561499
Advertising Expenditures: $378,000
Media: 2-7-10
Personnel:
Gerald P. Belle *(Chm)*
Nancy S. Lurker *(CEO)*
Jeffrey E. Smith *(CFO, Treas & Exec VP-Fin)*
Frank Arena *(Sr VP-Sls Ops)*
Kathy Marsico *(Sr VP-HR)*
Gerald R. Melillo, Jr. *(Sr VP-Bus Dev)*
Richard P. Micali *(Sr VP-Sls Svcs)*
Jo Ann Saitta *(Sr VP-IT)*
Brands & Products:
PDI ON DEMAND
PHARMAKON
SELECT ACCESS
TVG
VITAL ISSUES MEDICINE

PDL BIOPHARMA INC.
932 Southwood Blvd
Incline Village, NV 89451
Tel.: (775) 832-8500
Fax: (775) 832-8501
Web Site: www.pdl.com
Approx. Rev.: $344,975,000
Approx. Number Employees: 8
Year Founded: 1986
Business Description:
Researcher & Developer of Humanized Antibodies to Prevent or Treat Diseases
S.I.C.: 2836; 2834
N.A.I.C.S.: 325414; 325412
Advertising Expenditures: $19,600,000
Personnel:
John P. McLaughlin *(Pres & CEO)*
Christine Larson *(CFO & VP)*
Caroline Krumel *(Chief Acctg Officer & VP-Fin)*
Christopher L. Stone *(Gen Counsel & VP)*
Danny Hart *(Asst Sec & Assoc Gen Counsel)*
Brands & Products:
DACLIZUMAB
HUZAF
NUVION
PDL BIOPHARMA
TERLIPRESSIN
ULTRATIDE
VOLOCIXMAB

PEDIAMED PHARMACEUTICALS, INC.
(Sub. of Union Springs, LLC)
7310 Turfway Rd Ste 490
Florence, KY 41042
Tel.: (859) 282-8582
Fax: (859) 282-3105
E-mail: service@pediamedpharma.com
Web Site: www.pediamedpharma.com
Approx. Number Employees: 20
Year Founded: 2000
Business Description:
Children's Medicines Developer
S.I.C.: 2834
N.A.I.C.S.: 325412
Media: 2-4-10-13
Brands & Products:
ACCUHIST PDX
PEDIAMED
THE PEDIATRICS COMPANY
VIRAVAN

PEDIATRIC SERVICES OF AMERICA, INC.
(d/b/a PSA HealthCare)
310 Technology Pkwy Ste A
Norcross, GA 30092-2932
Tel.: (770) 441-1580
Fax: (770) 263-9340
Toll Free: (800) 897-6373
E-mail: info@psakids.com
Web Site: www.psakids.com
Sales Range: $100-124.9 Million
Approx. Number Employees: 3,388
Year Founded: 1989
Business Description:
Pediatric Health Care Services,

Key to Media (For complete agency information see *The Advertising Red Books-Agencies* edition):
1. Bus. Publs. 2. Cable T.V. 3. Catalogs & Directories. 4. Co-op Adv. 5. Consumer Mags. 6. D.M. to Bus. Estab.7. D.M. to Consumers 8. Daily Newsp. 9. Exhibits/Trade Shows 10. Foreign 11. Infomercial 12. Internet Adv.13. Multimedia 14. Network Radio 15. Network T.V. 16. Newsp. Distr. Mags. 17. Other 18. Outdoor (Posters, Transit) 19. Point of Purchase20. Premiums, Novelties 21. Product Samples 22. Special Events Mktg. 23. Spot Radio 24. Spot T.V. 25. Weekly Newsp. 26. Yellow Page Adv.

Equipment, Pharmaceutical Services, Infusion Therapy, Pediatric Rehabilitation & Case Management
S.I.C.: 8082
N.A.I.C.S.: 621610
Advertising Expenditures: $600,000
Media: 7-8-13
Personnel:
James McCurry *(Pres & CEO)*
Lori J. Reel *(CFO)*
Brands & Products:
PSA

PENINSULA COUNSELING CENTER

50 Hawthorne Ave
Valley Stream, NY 11580
Tel.: (516) 569-6600
Fax: (516) 374-2261
Web Site:
www.peninsulacounseling.org
Approx. Number Employees: 126
Year Founded: 1913
Business Description:
Nonprofit Mental Health Counselor
S.I.C.: 8093
N.A.I.C.S.: 621420
Media: 14-26
Personnel:
Gary Weiss *(Dir)*
Mark Weiss *(Dir)*
Advertising Agency:
G.S. Schwartz & Co. Inc.
470 Park Ave S 10th Fl S
New York, NY 10016-6819
Tel.: (212) 725-4500
Fax: (212) 725-9188

PENTAX MEDICAL COMPANY

(Div. of Pentax of America, Inc.)
102 Chestnut Ridge Rd
Montvale, NJ 07645-1856
Tel.: (201) 571-2300
Fax: (201) 391-4189
Toll Free: (800) 431-5880
E-mail: sales@pentaxmedical.com
Web Site: www.pentaxmedical.com
E-Mail For Key Personnel:
Sales Director: sales@pentaxmedical.com
Approx. Number Employees: 150
Year Founded: 1976
Business Description:
Medical Imaging & Endoscopy Equipment Mfr
S.I.C.: 3841
N.A.I.C.S.: 339112
Import Export
Advertising Expenditures: $500,000
Media: 1-2-4-7-8-10-20-22
Distr.: Intl.; Natl.
Budget Set: Mar.
Personnel:
David Woods *(Pres)*
Jack Adler *(Gen Counsel)*
Jene Merante *(VP-Fin)*
Brands & Products:
70K SERIES
FEESST
MINIVISION
PENTAX
PSV-4000

PFIZER INC.

235 E 42nd St
New York, NY 10017-5755
Tel.: (212) 733-2323
Fax: (212) 573-7851
Telex: 420440
Web Site: www.pfizer.com
Approx. Rev.: $67,809,000,000
Approx. Number Employees: 110,600
Year Founded: 1849
Business Description:
Diversified, Research-Based Health Care Company with Businesses in Pharmaceuticals, Hospital Products, Consumer Products & Animal Health
S.I.C.: 2834; 2833
N.A.I.C.S.: 325412; 325411
Import Export
Advertising Expenditures: $2,900,000,000
Media: 2-7-8-13-17
Distr.: Natl.
Budget Set: Sept.
Personnel:
George A. Lorch *(Chm)*
Ian C. Read *(Pres & CEO)*
Olivier Brandicourt *(Pres & Gen Mgr-Primary Care)*
Jeffrey E. Keisling *(CIO & Sr VP)*
Douglas M. Lanker *(Exec VP & Chief Compliance Officer)*
Freda C. Lewis-Hall *(Exec VP & Chief Medical Officer)*
Elizabeth Barrett *(Reg Pres-Oncology Bus Unit-US)*
Garry Nicholson *(Pres/Gen Mgr-Oncology Bus Unit)*
David S. Simmons *(Pres/Gen Mgr-Emerging Markets & Established Products)*
Mikael Dolsten *(Pres-R&D-Worldwide)*
Adele Gulfo *(Pres-Primary Care-United States)*
Frank A. D'Amelio *(Exec VP & CFO-Bus Ops)*
Amy Schulman *(Gen Counsel & Bus Unit Lead Nutritionals & Exec VP)*
Chuck Hill *(Exec VP-HR)*
Kristin Peck *(Exec VP-Worldwide Bus Dev & Innovation)*
Sally Susman *(Exec VP-Policy, External Affairs & Commun)*
Yvonne Greenstreet *(Sr VP & Head-Medicine Dev-Specialty Care Bus Unit)*
Robert E. Landry, Jr. *(Sr VP-Fin)*
Mary S. McLeod *(Sr VP)*
Anthony Principi *(Sr VP-Federal Govt Rels)*
Gregory Simon *(Sr VP-Policy-Worldwide)*
Anna Maria DeSalva *(VP-External Affairs & Comm, Science, Tech & Medicine)*
Martine J. George *(VP-Medical Affairs-Global)*
Jim Sage *(VP-Mktg-US Primary Care)*
John Santoro *(VP)*
Geno Germano *(Pres/Gen Mgr-Specialty Care & Oncology)*
Joan Campion *(Sr Dir)*
Ashley Gaines *(Sr Dir & Team Leader-US Geodon Mktg)*
Angela Hwang *(Sr Dir, Grp Leader-Neuroscience Mktg & Sls)*
Dave Cahill *(Dir-Mktg)*
Debbie Botwick *(Dir-Multi-Channel Plng & Team Leader)*
Linda Dyson *(Dir-Comml Comm-Pfizer Nutrition)*
Diana Farrell *(Dir-eMktg)*
Deborah Kogan *(Dir-Mktg-US)*
Wendy Lazarus *(Dir-Govt Rels & Pub Affairs)*
Valarie Leishman *(Dir-Vendor Mgmt)*
Michele Waits *(Dir-Mktg)*
Mary Cherubini *(Sr Mgr-Application Support)*
Dan Kramer *(Sr Mgr-Mktg-Animal Health)*
Moulay Skali *(Sr Brand Mgr-Antibacterial)*
Brands & Products:
A FEW SECONDS
ABRATEL
ACCUPRIL
ACCURETIC
ADAWNA
ADRISTES
ALDACTAZIDE
ALDACTONE
AMOXI-DROP
AMOXI-TABS
AMPHOCIN
ANSAID
ANTHELCIDE
ANTIROBE
ANTIVERT
ARICEPT
AROMASIN
ARTHROTEC
ASK ME 3
ATARAX
ATGAM
AZAVOR
AZULFIDINE
AZULFIDINE EN-TABS
BACITRACIN
BACTODERM
BAIN DE SOLEIL
BENEFOCUS
BINEXIS
BOVI-SHIELD FP
BOVI-SHIELD GOLD
BOVISHIELD
BRAMANT
BRIARA
BRIDGE PROGRAM
BRITESS
CADUET
CALAN
CALAN SR
CALFGUARD
C.A.L.M
CALOREG
CAMPTOSAR
CANISATE
CARATRI
CARDIOVULNERABLE
CARDURA
CARDURA XL
CARMILAX
CAVERJECT
CEFOBID
CEFSHOT
CELEBREX
CELONTIN
CENRAL
CEREBYX
CERENIA
CERVIGAM
CESAVESS
CESTEX
CHAMPIX
CHANTIX
CLASSIAV
CLAVAMOX
CLEOCIN
CLEOCIN HCL
CLEOCIN PEDIATRIC
CLEOCIN PHOSPHATE
CLEOCIN T
CMECENTER.COM
COLESTID
THE CONTROL TOWER
CONVENIA
CORTEF
CORVERT
COTY
COUGHGUARD
COVERA
COVERA-HS
CRESSENCE
CYKLOKAPRON
CYTOTEC
DAXAS
DAYPRO
DAYPRO ALTA
DECTOMAX
DEFENSOR
DEKRIA
DELTA ALBAPLEX
DEPO
DEPO-ESTRADIOL
DEPO-MEDROL
DEPO-PROVERA
DEPO-SUBQ PROVERA 104
DEPO-TESTOSTERONE
DERMA-CLENS
DETROL
DETROL LA
DIABINESE
DIAVIM
DIDREX
DIFLUCAN
DILANTIN
DILANTIN-125
DILANTIN INFATABS
DILANTIN KAPSEALS
DOMITOR
DOSTINEX
DOUBLETAKE
DRAXXIN
DUAFFEX
DURASECT
DYNASTAT
EAZI-BREED
EBREZA
EDOVIN
EGIRIO
ELIQUIS
ELLENCE
EMCYT
EMERAUDE DE COTY
EMSELEX
ENABLEX
ENTROLYTE
ENVACAR
EQIONZ
EQUELL
EQUITY
ER BAC
ER BAC PLUS
ERAXIS
ERUZENT
ESTRING
ETULSI
EXCENEL
EXTHERO
EZ MAX
FANSET
FARROWSURE
FELDENE
FELOCELL
FELOMUNE
FEM-VIAGRA

Key to Media (For complete agency information see *The Advertising Red Books-Agencies* edition):
1. Bus. Publs. 2. Cable T.V. 3. Catalogs & Directories. 4. Co-op Adv. 5. Consumer Mags. 6. D.M. to Bus. Estab.7. D.M. to Consumers 8. Daily Newsp. 9. Exhibits/Trade Shows 10. Foreign 11. Infomercial 12. Internet Adv.13. Multimedia 14. Network Radio 15. Network T.V. 16. Newsp. Distr. Mags. 17. Other 18. Outdoor (Posters, Transit) 19. Point of Purchase20. Premiums, Novelties 21. Product Samples 22. Special Events Mktg. 23. Spot Radio 24. Spot T.V. 25. Weekly Newsp. 26. Yellow Page Adv.

Pfizer Inc. — (Continued)

FILARIBITS
FINATHRO
FIRSTDOSE
FITFORUMS
FLAGYL
FLAVASURE
FLAVAVAC
FLORONE
FLUSURE
FONAMI
FORSOFEX
FORTRESS
FRAGMIN
GADALION
GANEQUEL
GARCEL
GARIZET
GELFILM
GELFOAM
GENOTROPIN
GENOTROPIN MIXER
GEOCILLIN
GEODON
GET BACK TO YOUR DAY
GLADORA
GLANVAC
GLUCOTROL
GLUCOTROL XL
GLYNASE
GLYSET
GRANULEX
GXL FOR LIVING
HALCION
HALOTESTIN CIII
HANDIHALER
HEMABATE
HERDSECURE
HYLARTIN
IDAMYCIN
IMMUFERON
IMMULAST
IMPROVOC
INFINAIR
INLOCEF
INLYTA
INPFORMED
INSPRA
ISOJECT
JETTIZO
KARIDEL
KIDSEARS
KIKITAR
KNOW YOUR CONDITION
KNOWING MORE
KOPIRA
LAX'AIRE
LEPTOFERM-5
LEUKOCELL
LEVENIA
LIFMIOR
LIFREON
LINCO-SPECTIN
LINCOCIN
LINCOCIN AQUADROPS
LINCOMIX
LIPITOR
LIQUAMYCIN
LITTERGUARD
LIXOTINIC
LOMOTIL
LOPID
LUCADIA
LUTALYSE
LYRICA
MACUVERSE
MARAX
MARAX-DF
MEDROL
MERISEF
MGA
MICRONASE
MINIPRESS
MINIQUICK
MITA-CLEAR
MITABAN
MYCITRACIN
MYCOBOVIS
MYCOBUTIN
MYCOPLUS
MYCOPRO
MYCOSURE
NADRION
NARDIL
NASAGUARD-B
NAVANE
NAXCEL
NCOMMAND
NECTIV
NEMEX
NEO-PREDEF
NEOCEF
NEOMIX
NEPLIN
NEURONTIN
NICOTROL
NICOTROL INHALER
NICOTROL NS
NILUXA
NITROSTAT
NORCALCIPHOS
NORLAP
NORPACE
NORPACE CR
NORVASC
NURESCA
OFORMA
ONE SHOT ULTRA
ONLY4VETS
OPOVAS
OPOVASC
ORBEOS
ORBESEAL
ORINASE DIAGNOSTIC
OTI-CLENS
OUTCOMES RESEARCH
PACTIVA
PAGENT
PAN-OTIC
PANATHRA
PANMYCIN AQUADROPS
PARACHEK
PARVO-VAC
PATREX
PERMAPEN
PET-CAL
PET-F.A.
PET TINIC
PFIZER FOR LIVING
PFIZER MEDNET
PFIZERPEN
PHS UNIVERSITY
PLEUROGUARD
PNEUMOSIS
PRANITA
PRECEDENCE
PREDEF
PREGGUARD
PREGGUARD FP
PREGUNTAME 3
PREPIDIL
PREZENT
PRIMOR
PROCARDIA
PROCARDIA XL
PROSTIN
PROSTIN VR PEDIATRIC
PROVERA
QSTED
QUESPRI
QUILTROL
R-GENE-10
RELASTRA
RELESTRA
RELNEU
RELPAX
RENESE
RENUAC
RESCRIPTOR
RESPISURE
RESPISURE-ONE
RESVAC
RETEEM
REVATIO
REVOLUTION
RHINOMUNE
RIMADYL
ROCCAL
SANA LA RANA
SAPREE
SATRINE
SAVGO
SAYANA
SELECT VAC
SELZENTRY
SERTIPHEX
SHARE CARD
SINEQUAN
SIRBO
SITEFOCUS
SLEEPGELS
SLEEPMELTS
SLEEPTABS
SLENTROL
SOLITUDE
SOLU-CORTEF
SOLU-DELTA-CORTEF
SOLU-MEDROL
SOMAVERT
SOMPOSURE
SOMUBAC
SPIRIVA HANDIHALER
SPIROVAC
SPRIESSE
STATHERZ
STAYBRED
STELTO
STIMUGEN
STOCKER VAC
STRENGTH IN THE FACE OF ALZHEIMER'S
STRONGID
SURALENE
SUROND
SUTENT
SYKILLSTOP
SYNAREL
TAPREA
TEFLIC
TEMARIL-P
TEOPSIS
TERRAMYCIN
TESCALA
THERABLOAT
THEROSCA
THRACURIA
TIKOSYN
TILANX
TINGUIS
TOLINASE
TOPOSAR
TORGENA
TORIANEX
TOVIAZ
TRAFION
TRELSTAR
TRELSTAR LA 11.25 MG
TRESCALA
TRIAMULOX
TRIMATRA
TRIOPTIC
TRIOPTIC-P
TRIOPTIC-S
TRIOSC
TRITOP
TRITORVIS
TRUSCIENT
TSHIELD
TSV-2
TUCOPRIM
ULTRABAC
ULTRACHOICE
UNASYN
UNIPET NUTRITABS
UNISOM
UROBIOTIC
V-MAX
VALBAZEN
VANTIN
VEQUIOR
VERAQUIS
VERASERA
VERVESS
VFACTS
VFEND
VIAGRA
VIBRAMYCIN
VIMERO
VIRACEPT
VISITINE
VISORBIN
VISORBITS
VISTARIL
VIZZABLE
VORCUM
VOYENE
VOYESE
VUSTEDRA
WEAN VAC
WHERE HEALTH MEETS REAL LIFE
WINSTROL
WORKING TOGETHER FOR A HEALTHIER WORLD
XALATAN
XALCOM
XANAX
XANAX XR
XATHERO
YEARLING VAC
Z-ONE
ZANNER
ZARONTIN
ZELDOX
ZENIQUIN
ZIMAXX
ZINECARD
ZITH
ZITH 1
ZITHRO
ZITHRO COMPLETE
ZITHROMAX
ZMAX
ZMAX SOLO
ZOLOFT
ZYLEXIS
ZYRTEC
ZYVOX

Key to Media (For complete agency information see *The Advertising Red Books-Agencies* edition):
1. Bus. Publs. 2. Cable T.V. 3. Catalogs & Directories. 4. Co-op Adv. 5. Consumer Mags. 6. D.M. to Bus. Estab.7. D.M. to Consumers 8. Daily Newsp. 9. Exhibits/Trade Shows 10. Foreign 11. Infomercial 12. Internet Adv.13. Multimedia 14. Network Radio 15. Network T.V. 16. Newsp. Distr. Mags. 17. Other 18. Outdoor (Posters, Transit) 19. Point of Purchase20. Premiums, Novelties 21. Product Samples 22. Special Events Mktg. 23. Spot Radio 24. Spot T.V. 25. Weekly Newsp. 26. Yellow Page Adv.

Advertising Agencies:
AM/PM Advertising Inc.
345 Claremont Ave Ste 26
Montclair, NJ 07042
Tel.: (973) 824-8600
Fax: (646) 366-1168

BVK
250 W Coventry Ct #300
Milwaukee, WI 53217-3972
Tel.: (414) 228-1990
Fax: (414) 228-7561
Toll Free: (888) 347-3212
Maraviroc
Public Relations

Carat
150 E 42nd St
New York, NY 10017
Tel.: (212) 689-6800
Fax: (212) 689-6005
Media Buying

Catalyst Online
320 Nevada St 1st Fl
Newton, MA 02460
Tel.: (617) 663-4100
Fax: (617) 663-4104

Cohn & Wolfe
200 Fifth Ave
New York, NY 10010
Tel.: (212) 798-9700
Fax: (212) 329-9900

Daniel J. Edelman, Inc.
(d/b/a Edelman)
200 E Randolph St Fl 63
Chicago, IL 60601-6705
Tel.: (312) 240-3000
Fax: (312) 240-2900
Chantix
Public Relations

Dieste
1999 Bryan St Ste 2700
Dallas, TX 75201
Tel.: (214) 259-8000
Fax: (214) 259-8040

Digitas Inc.
33 Arch St
Boston, MA 02110
Tel.: (617) 867-1000
Fax: (617) 867-1111
Direct Mktg & CRM
Viagra

Draftfcb HealthCare
100 W 33rd St
New York, NY 10001
Tel.: (212) 672-2300
Fax: (212) 672-2301

Euro RSCG Life LM&P
200 Madison Ave
New York, NY 10016
Tel.: (212) 532-1000
Fax: (212) 213-0449
Xalatan

Fathom Communications
(Part of Omnicom Group of Companies)
437 Madison Ave
New York, NY 10022
Tel.: (212) 817-6600
Fax: (212) 415-3514
Pfizer Health Solutions
"Balance it out Arkansas"

G2 Worldwide
200 5th Ave
New York, NY 10010
Tel.: (212) 537-3700
Fax: (212) 546-2425
Pfizer.com
Aromacin

The GMR Group
755 Business Ctr Dr Ste 250
Horsham, PA 19044-3444
Tel.: (215) 653-7401
Fax: (215) 653-7982

Gotham Incorporated
150 E 42nd St 12th Fl
New York, NY 10017
Tel.: (212) 414-7000
Fax: (212) 414-7095

Grey New York
777 3rd Ave
New York, NY 10017-1401
Tel.: (212) 546-2000
Fax: (212) 546-1495
Advil Cold & Sinus
Alavert
Dimetapp
Preparation H
Robitussin

HealthSTAR Communications, Inc.
1000 Wyckoff Ave
Mahwah, NJ 07430
Tel.: (201) 560-5370
Fax: (201) 891-2380

Holt & Germann Public Affairs LLC
172 W State St
Trenton, NJ 08608
Tel.: (908) 832-0557
Fax: (866) 379-4233

J. Walter Thompson Company
(d/b/a JWT)
466 Lexington Ave
New York, NY 10017-3140
Tel.: (212) 210-7000
Fax: (212) 210-7299
(Global Creative; Celebrex)

The Kaplan Thaler Group
825 8th Ave 34th Fl
New York, NY 10019
Tel.: (212) 474-5000
Fax: (212) 474-5702
Celebrex
Lyrica
Lipitor
Caduet

LaVoie Strategic Communications Group, Inc.
12 Derby Sq S1
Salem, MA 01970
Tel.: (978) 745-4200
Fax: (978) 745-4242

LLNS
220 E 42nd St
New York, NY 10017-5806
Tel.: (212) 771-3000
Fax: (212) 771-3010

Slentrol

Lowe
4th - 6th Floors Victoria Building Jl
Sultan Hasanuddin kav No 47-51
Jakarta, 12160, Indonesia
Tel.: (62) 21 725 4849
Fax: (62) 21 725 4850

Marina Maher Communications
830 3rd Ave
New York, NY 10022
Tel.: (212) 485-6800
Fax: (212) 355-6318
Detrol
Fesoterodine

McCann Erickson/New York
622 3rd Ave
New York, NY 10017
Tel.: (646) 865-2000
Fax: (646) 487-9610
Chantix
Viagra (Asia & EMEA)

McGarry Bowen, LLC
601 W 26th St Ste 1150
New York, NY 10001
Tel.: (212) 598-2900
Fax: (212) 598-2996
Advil
Advil PM
Children's Advil
ThermaCare

MGH, Inc.
100 Painters Mill Rd Ste 600
Owings Mills, MD 21117-7305
Tel.: (410) 902-5000
Fax: (410) 902-8712
Slentrol
BARC

Ogilvy PR/New York
636 11th Ave
New York, NY 10036
Tel.: (212) 880-5200
Fax: (212) 884-1997

Photosound Communications
1000 Wyckoff Ave
Mahwah, NJ 08536
Tel.: (609) 514-5366
Fax: (609) 514-5377

PointRoll Inc.
951 E Hector St
Conshohocken, PA 19428
Tel.: (267) 558-1300
Fax: (267) 285-1141
Toll Free: (800) 203-6956
Online/Banner Adv
Chantix

Porter Novelli
(Sub. of Omnicom Group, Inc.)
75 Varick St 6th Fl
New York, NY 10013
Tel.: (212) 601-8000
Fax: (212) 601-8101
Viagra

R/GA
350 W 39th St
New York, NY 10018-1402
Tel.: (212) 946-4000
Fax: (212) 946-4010

Digital Creative

RealTime Media, Inc.
1060 1st Ave Ste 201
King of Prussia, PA 19406
Tel.: (610) 337-3600
Fax: (610) 337-2300

Research Development & Promotions
(d/b/a RDP)
360 Menores Ave
Coral Gables, FL 33134
Tel.: (305) 445-4997
Fax: (305) 445-4221

Response Media, Inc.
3155 Medlock Bridge Rd
Norcross, GA 30071-1423
Tel.: (770) 451-5478
Fax: (770) 451-4929

Rosetta
100 American Metro Blvd
Hamilton, NJ 08619
Tel.: (609) 689-6100
Fax: (609) 631-0184
Toll Free: (800) 374-6008

Rosica Strategic Public Relations
95 Rt 17 S Ste 109
Paramus, NJ 07652
Tel.: (201) 843-5600
Fax: (201) 843-5680

TargetCast tcm
909 3rd Ave 31st Fl
New York, NY 10022
Tel.: (212) 500-6900
Fax: (212) 500-6880
Media Buying

TAXI
495 Wellington St W Ste 102
Toronto, ON M5V 1E9, Canada
Tel.: (416) 979-7001
Fax: (416) 979-7626

Tribal DDB Worldwide
437 Madison Ave 8th Fl
New York, NY 10022
Tel.: (212) 515-8600
Fax: (212) 515-8660
Digital Creative

Unit 7
30 Irving Pl 11th Fl
New York, NY 10003
Tel.: (212) 209-1600
Fax: (212) 209-1800

Vox Medica Inc.
601 Walnut St Ste 250-S
Philadelphia, PA 19106-3514
Tel.: (215) 238-8500
Fax: (215) 238-0881
Events Mngmt
Local Promotional Speaker Program

PFIZER POULTRY HEALTH
(Div. of Pfizer Animal Health)
1040 Swabia Ct
Durham, NC 27703-8481
Mailing Address:
PO Box 13989
Research Triangle Park, NC 27709-3989
Tel.: (919) 941-5185
Fax: (919) 941-5186

Key to Media (For complete agency information see *The Advertising Red Books-Agencies* edition):
1. Bus. Publs. 2. Cable T.V. 3. Catalogs & Directories. 4. Co-op Adv. 5. Consumer Mags. 6. D.M. to Bus. Estab.7. D.M. to Consumers 8. Daily Newsp. 9. Exhibits/Trade Shows 10. Foreign 11. Infomercial 12. Internet Adv.13. Multimedia 14. Network Radio 15. Network T.V. 16. Newsp. Distr. Mags. 17. Other 18. Outdoor (Posters, Transit) 19. Point of Purchase20. Premiums, Novelties 21. Product Samples 22. Special Events Mktg. 23. Spot Radio 24. Spot T.V. 25. Weekly Newsp. 26. Yellow Page Adv.

Pfizer Poultry Health — (Continued)

E-mail: customerservice@pfizer.com
Web Site:
www.pfizerpoultryhealth.com
Sales Range: $50-74.9 Million
Approx. Number Employees: 309
Year Founded: 1985
Business Description:
Poultry Health Vaccination Products & Services
S.I.C.: 2836
N.A.I.C.S.: 325414
Export
Advertising Expenditures: $200,000
Media: 2-4-7-10-11-21-25
Personnel:
David M. Baines *(VP-Sls)*
Brands & Products:
BURSAPLEX
EGG REMOVER
EGG REMOVER SYSTEM
EMBREX
THE IN OVO COMPANY
INOVOCOX
INOVOJECT
NEWPLEX
VACCINE SAVER
VNF

PHARMACEUTICAL PRODUCT DEVELOPMENT, INC.
(d/b/a PPD, Inc.)
929 N Front St
Wilmington, NC 28401
Tel.: (910) 251-0081
Fax: (910) 762-5820
E-mail: louise.caudle@rtp.ppdi.com
Web Site: www.ppdi.com
Approx. Rev.: $1,470,570,000
Approx. Number Employees: 11,000
Year Founded: 1989
Business Description:
Drug Discovery & Development Contract Research Services
S.I.C.: 8733; 2834; 2836
N.A.I.C.S.: 541710; 325412; 325414; 541711
Advertising Expenditures: $2,700,000
Media: 2-7-8-10-13-22
Personnel:
Raymond Hill *(CEO)*
Daniel G. Darazsdi *(CFO, Treas & Asst Sec)*
William J. Sharbaugh *(COO)*
Michael O. Wilkinson *(CIO & EVP-Tech, Innovation & Performance)*
Christine A. Dingivan *(Exec VP & Chief Medical Officer)*
Peter Wilkinson *(Chief Acctg Officer-Treasury, Tax, Ops Fin & VP-Fin)*
B. Judd Hartman *(Gen Counsel & Sec)*
Lee E. Babiss *(Exec VP-Global Laboratory Svcs)*
Paul D. Colvin *(Exec VP-Global Clinical Dev)*
Henrietta Ukwu *(Sr VP & Head-Global Regulatory Affairs)*
Elena Logan *(Sr VP-Global Central Labs)*
William W. Richardson *(Sr VP-Global Bus Dev)*
Louise Caudle *(Dir-Corp Comm)*
Ned Glascock *(Assoc Dir-Pub Affairs & Investor Comm)*
Sue Ann Pentecost *(Mgr-Corp Comm)*
Brands & Products:
PPD

PHARMANET DEVELOPMENT GROUP, INC.
(Holding of JLL Partners Inc.)
504 Carnegie Ctr
Princeton, NJ 08540
Tel.: (609) 951-6800
Fax: (609) 514-0390
E-mail: info@pharmanet.com
Web Site: www.pharmanet.com
Approx. Rev.: $451,453,000
Approx. Number Employees: 2,400
Year Founded: 1999
Business Description:
Holding Company; Clinical Research & Drug Development Services
S.I.C.: 6719
N.A.I.C.S.: 551112; 541711
Advertising Expenditures: $3,400,000
Media: 10
Personnel:
Thomas J. Newman *(Pres)*
Jeffrey P. McMullen *(CEO)*
George McMillan *(CFO & Exec VP)*
Stephen Kasay *(CIO)*
Riaz Bandali *(Pres-Early Stage Dev)*
Paul A. Taylor *(Pres-Taylor Tech Inc)*
Christopher S. Brennan *(Gen Counsel)*
Gregory M. Hockel *(Exec VP-Regulatory Affairs)*
Mary F. Johnson *(Exec VP-Biostatistics)*
Ian B. Holmes *(Sr VP-Corp Dev)*
Valerie Palumbo *(Sr VP-Corp Quality Assurance)*
Robin C. Sheldrick *(Sr VP-HR)*
Anthony E. Maida, III *(VP-Clinical Res & Gen Mgr-Oncology-World-wide)*
Anne-Marie Hess *(VP-Mktg & Corp Comm)*

PHARMASAVE DRUGS (NATIONAL) LTD.
8411 200th Street Ste 201
Langley, BC V2Y 1L9, Canada
Tel.: (604) 532-2250
Fax: (604) 533-0628
Toll Free: (800) 661-6106
Web Site: www.pharmasave.com
Approx. Number Employees: 55
Year Founded: 1981
Business Description:
Drug Store Operator
S.I.C.: 5912
N.A.I.C.S.: 446110
Advertising Expenditures: $3,000,000
Media: 4-9-13-16-19-22-23-24-26
Brands & Products:
LIVE WELL WITH PHARMASAVE
PHARMASAVE

PHARMAVITE LLC
(Sub. of Otsuka Pharmaceutical Co., Ltd.)
8510 Balboa Blvd Ste 300
Northridge, CA 91325
Tel.: (818) 221-6200
Fax: (818) 221-6393
Toll Free: (800) 276-2878
Web Site: www.pharmavite.com
Approx. Number Employees: 832
Year Founded: 1971
Business Description:
Mfr. of Dietary Supplement Products & Skin Care Products
S.I.C.: 2833; 2834
N.A.I.C.S.: 325411; 325412
Import Export
Advertising Expenditures: $5,000,000
Media: 2-6-14-17
Distr.: Natl.
Budget Set: Mar.
Personnel:
Michael Settsu *(Chm & CEO)*
Connie Barry *(Pres & Co-CEO)*
Steve Chopp *(CFO)*
Mark Walsh *(COO)*
Bill Tullis *(Exec VP-Sls)*
Lisa Reavlin *(Dir-Innovation)*
Sheryl Biesman *(Mgr-Digital Mktg)*
Josh Minnick *(Brand Mgr)*
Brands & Products:
ADVANTRUM
AGE DEFENSE
CALMPOWER
CLEARBLEND
CRANASSURE
CRANEZE
CRANSOLUTIONS
DIET NUTRITION PACK
THE EASY WAY TO BETTER HEALTH
ELEMAT
ESSENTIAL BALANCED OMEGA 3/6
ESSENTIALBALANCED ENERGY PACK FOR WOMEN
EVEN COMPLEXION
EYE DEFENSE
EYE ESSENTIALS
FIBERCLEAR...CLEARLY BETTER
GARLIFE
GO SLIM
HERBAL ABCS
INSTAFIBER
INTERNAL HEALTH EXTERNAL BEAUTY
LEAN ADVANTAGE
MADE FOR HER
MEMORY ON DEMAND
MOOD PLUS
MULTILEAN
MY WELLNESS REWARDS
NATURE MADE
NATURE MADE ADVANCE
NATURE MADE DIET WISE
NATURE MADE HEALTHSOLUTIONS
NATURE'S SOLUTION FOR BETTER HEALTH
OPTIMIZE
PHARMAVITE
PRO-2-GEL
REKINDLE
SAM-E
SNAP PACK
SOY BALANCE
STRESS EEZ
TRIMUNE
TRIPLE FLEX
WEIGHT ASSIST
WELLNESS 101
WELLNESS REWARDS
WINTER WELLNESS
WOMEN'S CIRCLE
YOUR BODY'S OWN MOOD ENHANCER
Advertising Agencies:
Ogilvy & Mather
3530 Hayden Ave
Culver City, CA 90232
Tel.: (310) 280-2200
Fax: (310) 280-9473

Porter Novelli
(Sub. of Omnicom Group, Inc.)
75 Varick St 6th Fl
New York, NY 10013
Tel.: (212) 601-8000
Fax: (212) 601-8101

PHC, INC.
(d/b/a Pioneer Behavioral Health)
200 Lake St Ste 102
Peabody, MA 01960-4781
Tel.: (978) 536-2777
Fax: (978) 536-2677
Toll Free: (800) 543-2447
E-mail: info@phc-inc.com
Web Site: www.phc-inc.com
Approx. Rev.: $62,007,879
Approx. Number Employees: 394
Year Founded: 1976
Business Description:
Behavioral Health Treatment Centers
S.I.C.: 8063
N.A.I.C.S.: 622210
Advertising Expenditures: $136,183
Media: 8
Personnel:
Bruce A. Shear *(Chm, Pres & CEO)*
Paula C. Wurts *(CFO)*
Alexander Nelson Luvall *(Exec VP)*
Robert A. Boswell *(Sr VP)*
Advertising Agency:
HC International
Graybar Bldg 420 Lexington Ave
New York, NY 10017
Tel.: (561) 245-5155
Fax: (858) 408-1808

PHILIPS MEDICAL SYSTEMS
(Div. of Philips Medical Systems)
595 Miner Rd
Cleveland, OH 44143-2131
Tel.: (440) 483-3000
Web Site: www.careers.philips.com
Approx. Number Employees: 5,300
Year Founded: 1915
Business Description:
Mfr. & Retailer of Medical Imaging Equipment; Distributor of Radiologic Supplies & Accessories
S.I.C.: 3844; 5047
N.A.I.C.S.: 334517; 423450
Export
Advertising Expenditures: $1,500,000
Media: 2-3-4-7-10-11-13-20
Distr.: Intl.; Natl.
Budget Set: Mar.
Brands & Products:
QLAB

PHILIPS RESPIRONICS
(Div. of Philips Medical Systems)
1010 Murry Ridge Ln
Murrysville, PA 15668-8525
Tel.: (724) 387-5200
Fax: (724) 387-5010
Toll Free: (800) 345-6443
Web Site: www.respironics.com
Approx. Sls.: $1,195,035,000
Approx. Number Employees: 4,900
Year Founded: 1976
Business Description:
Patient Ventilation Products Designer, Mfr & Marketer
S.I.C.: 3842; 3845
N.A.I.C.S.: 339113; 334510
Import Export

Key to Media (For complete agency information see *The Advertising Red Books-Agencies* edition):
1. Bus. Publs. 2. Cable T.V. 3. Catalogs & Directories. 4. Co-op Adv. 5. Consumer Mags. 6. D.M. to Bus. Estab.7. D.M. to Consumers
8. Daily Newsp. 9. Exhibits/Trade Shows 10. Foreign 11. Infomercial 12. Internet Adv.13. Multimedia 14. Network Radio
15. Network T.V. 16. Newsp. Distr. Mags. 17. Other 18. Outdoor (Posters, Transit) 19. Point of Purchase20. Premiums, Novelties
21. Product Samples 22. Special Events Mktg. 23. Spot Radio 24. Spot T.V. 25. Weekly Newsp. 26. Yellow Page Adv.

Advertising Expenditures: $3,198,000
Media: 1-2-4-6-7-10-17-22
Distr.: Natl.
Budget Set: Apr. -May
Personnel:
Craig Gruchacz *(CFO & Sr VP)*
Craig B. Reynolds *(COO & Exec VP)*
Derek Smith *(Pres-Hospital Grp)*
Maryellen Bizzack *(Dir-Mktg & Comm)*
Advertising Agencies:
Brunner
11 Stanwix St 5th Fl
Pittsburgh, PA 15222-1312
Tel.: (412) 995-9500
Fax: (412) 995-9501

FSC Marketing Communications
Gulf Tower 707 Grant St, Ste 2900
Pittsburgh, PA 15222
Tel.: (412) 471-3700
Fax: (412) 471-9323

Gotham Incorporated
150 E 42nd St 12th Fl
New York, NY 10017
Tel.: (212) 414-7000
Fax: (212) 414-7095

PHONAK LLC

(Sub. of Sonova Holding AG)
4520 Weaver Pkwy
Warrenville, IL 60555-3927
Tel.: (630) 821-5000
Fax: (630) 393-6797
Web Site: www.phonak-us.com
Approx. Number Employees: 200
Business Description:
Hearing Instruments Mfr
S.I.C.: 3845; 5999
N.A.I.C.S.: 334510; 446199
Media: 2-6
Advertising Agency:
Chandler Group, Inc.
604 Davis St Fl 2
Evanston, IL 60201-4419
Tel.: (847) 475-7900
Fax: (847) 475-4498

PHYSICIANS FORMULA HOLDINGS, INC.

1055 W 8th St
Azusa, CA 91702
Tel.: (626) 334-3395
Fax: (626) 812-9462
E-mail: inquiry@physiciansformula.com
Web Site: www.physiciansformula.com
Approx. Sls.: $78,523,000
Approx. Number Employees: 147
Year Founded: 1937
Business Description:
Cosmetics Mfr & Whslr
S.I.C.: 2844; 5122
N.A.I.C.S.: 325620; 446120
Advertising Expenditures: $8,600,000
Personnel:
Ingrid Jackel *(Chm & CEO)*
Jeffrey P. Rogers *(Pres & Dir)*
Jeff M. Berry *(CFO)*
Vivian Durra *(Dir-Mktg & Comm)*
Advertising Agencies:
Looney Advertising and Design
7 N Mountain Ave
Montclair, NJ 07042
Tel.: (973) 783-0017
Tel.: (973) 220-0335
Fax: (973) 783-0613

Women's Marketing Inc.
1221 Post Rd E Ste 201
Westport, CT 06880-5430
Tel.: (203) 256-0880
Fax: (203) 256-0883

PHYSICIANS GREATSKIN CLINICS

(d/b/a Greatskin.com)
118 Walnut St
Clayton, NM 88415
Tel.: (575) 374-8366
Fax: (877) 500-4414
Toll Free: (800) 700-4414
E-mail: info@greatskinabq.com
Web Site: www.greatskin.com
Approx. Number Employees: 10
Year Founded: 1996
Business Description:
Prescription Strength Face & Body Products & Treatments
S.I.C.: 8011
N.A.I.C.S.: 621111
Media: 13
Personnel:
Lori Van Wormer *(CEO)*
Brands & Products:
GREAT PRODUCTS. GREAT PRICES.
GREATSKIN
PEPTOXYL
RETEXTUREYES2
Advertising Agency:
Net Man
1103 Canyon Rd
Santa Fe, NM 87501
Tel.: (505) 984-9879

PHYSICIANS WEIGHT LOSS CENTERS, INC.

(Holding of The Health Management Group, Inc.)
395 Springside Dr
Akron, OH 44333
Tel.: (330) 666-7952
Fax: (330) 666-2197
Toll Free: (800) 205-7887
E-mail: info@pwlc.com
Web Site: www.pwlc.com
Approx. Number Employees: 30
Year Founded: 1979
Business Description:
Franchised Weight Loss Centers
S.I.C.: 7299
N.A.I.C.S.: 812191
Advertising Expenditures: $4,000,000
Media: 3-8-9-10-17-23-24-25-26
Distr.: Intl.
Budget Set: Dec.
Personnel:
Charles E. Sekeres *(Pres & CEO)*
Kristyn Austriaco *(Dir-Nutritional Svcs)*
Victoria de los Santos *(Dir-Franchise Dev)*
Tammy DeHarpart *(Dir-Product Dev & Distr)*
Mike Zsely *(Dir-Admin)*
Linda Maksim *(Mgr-Internet Website)*
Brands & Products:
PHYSICIANS WEIGHT LOSS CENTERS
THERMOGENICS
WITH YOU EVERY DAY, EVERY POUND OF THE WAY

PLANTATION GENERAL HOSPITAL

(Sub. of HCA HOLDINGS, INC.)
401 NW 42nd Ave
Plantation, FL 33317-2835
Tel.: (954) 587-5010
Fax: (954) 587-3220
Web Site: www.plantationgeneral.com
Approx. Number Employees: 1,000
Year Founded: 1966
Business Description:
Hospital
S.I.C.: 8062
N.A.I.C.S.: 622110
Personnel:
Barbara J. Simmons *(CEO)*
Advertising Agency:
Eisenberg & Associates
511 NE 3rd Ave
Fort Lauderdale, FL 33301-3235
Tel.: (954) 760-9500
Fax: (954) 760-9594

PLIVA, INC.

(Sub. of PLIVA d.d.)
72 Eagle Rock Ave
East Hanover, NJ 07936-2822
Tel.: (973) 386-5566
Fax: (973) 386-9280
Toll Free: (800) 922-0547
E-mail: administrator@plivainc.com
Web Site: www.plivainc.com
Sales Range: $150-199.9 Million
Approx. Number Employees: 500
Year Founded: 1979
Business Description:
Mfr & Marketer of Generic Pharmaceutical Products
S.I.C.: 2834
N.A.I.C.S.: 325412
Import Export
Media: 4-6-8-11
Personnel:
Jeffery Smith *(CFO, Treas & Exec VP)*
Rena Defranci *(VP-HR)*

PONIARD PHARMACEUTICALS, INC.

750 Battery St Ste 330
South San Francisco, CA 94111
Tel.: (650) 583-3774
Fax: (650) 583-3789
E-mail: info@poniard.com
Web Site: www.poniard.com
Approx. Number Employees: 12
Year Founded: 1984
Business Description:
Monoclonal Antibody Based Pharmaceutical Mfr
S.I.C.: 2834
N.A.I.C.S.: 325412
Advertising Expenditures: $500,000
Media: 2-4-7-10
Distr.: Natl.
Personnel:
Gerald McMahon *(Chm)*
Michael S. Perry *(Pres & Chief Medical Officer)*
Ronald A. Martell *(CEO)*
Michael K. Jackson *(Interim CFO)*
Anna Lewak Wight *(VP-Legal & Corp Sec)*
Cheni Kwok *(Sr VP-Corp Dev)*
Brands & Products:
PONIARD
PONIARD PHARAMACEUTICALS

POST GLOVER RESISTORS INC.

(Sub. of Telema S.p.A)
4750 Olympic Blvd
Erlanger, KY 41018-3141
Tel.: (859) 283-0778
Tel.: (859) 282-2900
Fax: (859) 283-2978
Fax: (859) 282-2904
Toll Free: (800) 537-6144
Toll Free: (800) 208-7915
E-mail: sales@postglover.com
Web Site: www.postglover.com
E-Mail For Key Personnel:
Sales Director: sales@postglover.com
Year Founded: 1893
Business Description:
High Power Electrical Resistors Mfr
S.I.C.: 3676; 3679
N.A.I.C.S.: 334415; 334419
Export
Advertising Expenditures: $300,000
Media: 2-4-7-10-11-17
Distr.: Intl.; Natl.
Budget Set: Oct.
Personnel:
Richard Field *(Pres)*
Scott Fuller *(VP-Sls & Mktg)*
Steve Fisher *(Mgr-Inside Sls)*
Dan Kobida *(Mgr-Engrg)*
Jeremy Lieland *(Mgr-Application)*
Karl Larsson *(Engr)*

POWERBAR INC.

(Sub. of Nestle USA, Inc.)
800 N Brand Blvd
Glendale, CA 91203-1245
Tel.: (973) 593-7500
Web Site: www.powerbar.com
Approx. Number Employees: 300
Business Description:
Mfr. of Energy & Protein Bars
S.I.C.: 2099
N.A.I.C.S.: 311340
Advertising Expenditures: $200,000
Media: 2-3-6-9-14-15-16-18-21-25
Distr.: Natl.
Budget Set: Sept. -Oct.
Brands & Products:
LAYERED PROTEINPLUS
POWERBAR ENERGY BITES
POWERBAR HARVEST
POWERBAR PERFORMANCE
POWERBAR POWER GEL
POWERBAR PROTEINPLUS
PRIA
PRIA CARB SELECT
PROTEINPLUS CARB SELECT
SUGARFREE PROTEINPLUS

PRA INTERNATIONAL INC.

(Holding of Genstar Capital, LLC)
4140 Park Lake Ave Ste 400
Raleigh, NC 27612
Tel.: (919) 786-8200
Fax: (919) 786-8201
E-mail: info@praintemational.com
Web Site: www.prainternational.com
E-Mail For Key Personnel:
Public Relations: publicrelations@praintl.com
Approx. Rev.: $338,166,016
Approx. Number Employees: 3,000
Year Founded: 1981
Business Description:
Clinical Drug Development
S.I.C.: 8733; 8071

Key to Media (For complete agency information see *The Advertising Red Books-Agencies* edition):
1. Bus. Publs. 2. Cable T.V. 3. Catalogs & Directories. 4. Co-op Adv. 5. Consumer Mags. 6. D.M. to Bus. Estab.7. D.M. to Consumers
8. Daily Newsp. 9. Exhibits/Trade Shows 10. Foreign 11. Infomercial 12. Internet Adv.13. Multimedia 14. Network Radio
15. Network T.V. 16. Newsp. Distr. Mags. 17. Other 18. Outdoor (Posters, Transit) 19. Point of Purchase20. Premiums, Novelties
21. Product Samples 22. Special Events Mktg. 23. Spot Radio 24. Spot T.V. 25. Weekly Newsp. 26. Yellow Page Adv.

PRA International Inc. — (Continued)

N.A.I.C.S.: 541710; 621511
Import Export
Media: 2-7-10-22
Personnel:
Melvin D. Booth *(Chm)*
Colin Shannon *(Pres & CEO)*
Linda Baddour *(CFO & Exec VP)*
David W. Dockhorn *(Exec VP-Product Registration-Americas)*
Susan C. Stansfield *(Exec VP-Product Registration)*
Bruce A. Teplitzky *(Exec VP-Strategic Drug Dev)*
Bucky Walsh *(Exec VP-Corp Svcs)*
Tami Klerr-Naivar *(Sr VP-Bus Dev)*
Steve Powell *(Sr VP-Clinical Informatics & Late Phase Svcs)*
Hani S. Zaki *(Sr VP-Late Phase Svcs)*
Brands & Products:
PRA E-TMF
PROJECT ASSURANCE
Advertising Agency:
LLNS
220 E 42nd St
New York, NY 10017-5806
Tel.: (212) 771-3000
Fax: (212) 771-3010
— Kim Thompson *(Media Supvr)*

PREMIER CARESCIENCE

(Div. of Premier Inc.)
3600 Market St 7th Fl
Philadelphia, PA 19104
Tel.: (215) 387-9401
Fax: (215) 387-9406
Toll Free: (888) 223-8247
Web Site: www.carescience.com
Approx. Number Employees: 105
Business Description:
Healthcare Technology
S.I.C.: 7371; 8742
N.A.I.C.S.: 541511; 541611
Media: 4-10
Personnel:
Suzan Devore *(Pres & CEO)*
Pamela M. Howard *(VP-Sls & Mktg)*
Brands & Products:
CARESCIENCE

PRESBYTERIAN HEALTHCARE SERVICES

2501 Buena Vista SE
Albuquerque, NM 87106
Tel.: (505) 841-1234
Fax: (505) 923-6141
Toll Free: (800) 672-8880
E-mail: info@phs.org
Web Site: www.phs.org
Approx. Number Employees: 6,000
Year Founded: 1908
Business Description:
Hospital & Health Care Services
S.I.C.: 8062
N.A.I.C.S.: 622110
Advertising Expenditures: $20,000,000
Media: 10-13-18-22
Personnel:
James H. Hinton *(Pres, CEO & Chm-PHP)*
Paul Briggs *(CFO & Sr VP)*
Diane Fisher *(Sr VP-Legal Svcs)*
Renee Reimer *(VP-HR)*
Sunah Jung *(Dir-Provider Svcs)*
Tammy Nelson *(Mgr-Medical Staff Affairs)*
Advertising Agency:
McKee Wallwork Cleveland
1030 18th St NW
Albuquerque, NM 87104
Tel.: (505) 821-2999
Fax: (505) 821-0006
Toll Free: (888) 821-2999

PRESSURE BIOSCIENCES, INC.

14 Norfolk Ave
South Easton, MA 02375
Tel.: (508) 230-1828
E-mail: info@pressurebioscience.com
Web Site: www.pressurebiosciences.com
Approx. Rev.: $1,340,032
Approx. Number Employees: 14
Year Founded: 1986
Business Description:
Proprietary Pressure Cycling Technology (PCT) for Nucleic Acid & Protein Extractions Developer & Marketer
S.I.C.: 3873; 2834; 3821
N.A.I.C.S.: 334518; 325412; 339111
Export
Advertising Expenditures: $8,853
Media: 2-7-10-13
Personnel:
Richard T. Schumacher *(Founder)*
R. Wayne Fritzsche *(Chm)*
Edmund Ting *(Sr VP-Engrg)*
Nathan P. Lawrence *(VP-Mktg & Bus Dev)*
Jose Q. Lanuza *(Dir-Sls)*
Brands & Products:
ACCUCHART
ACCURUN
BAROCYCLER
DISCOVERY STARTS WITH SAMPLE PREPARATION
MICROTUBE
PBI
PROTEOSOLVE-SB
PULSE
VERIF-EYE
Advertising Agency:
RedChip Companies, Inc.
500 Winderely Pl Ste 100
Maitland, FL 32751
Tel.: (407) 644-4256
Fax: (407) 644-0758
Toll Free: (800) 733-2447

PRITIKIN LONGEVITY CENTER & SPA

8755 NW 36th St
Miami, FL 33178
Tel.: (305) 935-7131
Fax: (305) 935-7111
E-mail: info@pritikin.com
Web Site: www.pritikin.com
Sales Range: $1-9.9 Million
Approx. Number Employees: 75
Year Founded: 1975
Business Description:
Provides Nutritional & Medical Services; Lodging on Premises
S.I.C.: 7011
N.A.I.C.S.: 721110
Media: 2-6-8-9-10-18-23-24-25-26
Distr.: Direct to Consumer; Intl.; Natl.
Personnel:
Paul Lehr *(Co-Owner)*
Brands & Products:
PRITIKIN
PRITIKIN EDGE
PRITIKIN LONGEVITY CENTER
PRITIKIN PROGRAMS

PRO-DEX, INC.

2361 McGaw Ave
Irvine, CA 92614
Tel.: (949) 769-3200
Fax: (714) 513-7755
Toll Free: (800) 562-6204
E-mail: investor.relations@pro-dex.com
Web Site: www.pro-dex.com
Approx. Sls.: $27,109,000
Approx. Number Employees: 115
Year Founded: 1978
Business Description:
Dental Products Mfr
S.I.C.: 5047; 3823; 3843; 7359
N.A.I.C.S.: 423450; 334513; 339114; 532490
Advertising Expenditures: $102,000
Media: 8-22-26
Personnel:
William L. Healey *(Chm)*
Mark P. Murphy *(Pres & CEO)*
Harold A. Hurwitz *(CFO)*
Paul Rudzinski *(VP-Sls)*
Brands & Products:
ACCELERATING POSSIBILITIES
ASTROMEC
CANALIGATOR
THE COMPANY IN MOTION
MAXP
MICRO MOTORS
OMS-EZ
OREGON MICRO SYSTEMS
PRO-DEX

PROGRESSIVE MEDICAL, INC.

(Joint Venture of Fiserv, Inc. & Stone Point Capital LLC)
250 Progressive Way
Westerville, OH 43082
Tel.: (614) 794-3300
Fax: (614) 923-7650
Toll Free: (800) 777-3574
Web Site: www.progressive-medical.com
Approx. Number Employees: 480
Year Founded: 1986
Business Description:
Medical Equipment & Pharmacy Services
S.I.C.: 5999; 5047
N.A.I.C.S.: 446199; 423450
Personnel:
David Bianconi *(Chm)*
Kevin Banion *(Pres & CEO)*
Tron Emptage *(Chief Clinical & Compliance Officer)*
Mark T. Brower *(Mgr-Info Svcs)*
Shane Fordham *(Acct Coord)*
Brands & Products:
FIRST FILL
INSTANT ACTIVATION
INTERVENTION RX
PROGRESSIVE MEDICAL
PROVANT
Advertising Agency:
Marketing Works, Inc.
740 Lakeview Plz Blvd Ste 100
Worthington, OH 43085
Tel.: (614) 540-5520
Fax: (614) 540-5524

PROMETHEUS LABORATORIES, INC.

9410 Carrol Pk Dr
San Diego, CA 92121-4203
Tel.: (858) 824-0895
Fax: (858) 824-0896
Toll Free: (888) 423-5227
E-mail: contactus@prometheuslabs.com
Web Site: www.prometheuslabs.com
Approx. Sls.: $68,000,000
Approx. Number Employees: 200
Year Founded: 1995
Business Description:
Mfr & Marketer of Pharmaceutical Products
S.I.C.: 2834
N.A.I.C.S.: 325412
Personnel:
Tim Sear *(Chm)*
Joseph M. Limber *(Pres & CEO)*
Mark Spring *(CFO & Sr VP)*
Bill Zondler *(CIO & VP-Info Svcs)*
Declan Doogan *(Exec VP & Chief Medical Officer)*
Ron Rocca *(VP-Sls & Mktg)*
Toni L. Wayne *(VP-HR)*
Tony Goosmann *(Gen Mgr-Oncology)*
Brands & Products:
BREATH TEK
FIBROSPECT
HELIDAC
IBD FIRST STEP
IMURAN
PRO-GENOLOGIX
PRO-PREDICTRX
RIDAURA
TRANDATE
ZYLOPRIM
Advertising Agency:
Pacific Communications
575 Anton Blvd Ste 900
Costa Mesa, CA 92626-7665
Tel.: (714) 427-1900
Fax: (714) 796-3039

PROPHASE LABS, INC.

(Formerly The Quigley Corporation)
621 N Shady Retreat Rd
Doylestown, PA 18901
Tel.: (215) 345-0919
Fax: (267) 880-1153
E-mail: ir@prophaselabs.com
Web Site: www.prophaselabs.com
Approx. Sls.: $14,502,000
Approx. Number Employees: 44
Year Founded: 1989
Business Description:
Cold-Remedy, Nutrition & Weight Management Products Mfr, Marketer & Developer
S.I.C.: 2834
N.A.I.C.S.: 325412
Advertising Expenditures: $6,900,000
Personnel:
Ted Karkus *(Chm & CEO)*
Robert V. Cuddihy, Jr. *(COO & CFO)*
Michael Petteruti *(Exec Dir-Science & Tech)*
Fiona Augar *(Coord-Mktg)*
Brands & Products:
BODYMATE
COLD-EEZE
THE NATURE OF HUMAN HEALTH
ZIGG

Key to Media (For complete agency information see *The Advertising Red Books-Agencies* edition):
1. Bus. Publs. 2. Cable T.V. 3. Catalogs & Directories. 4. Co-op Adv. 5. Consumer Mags. 6. D.M. to Bus. Estab.7. D.M. to Consumers
8. Daily Newsp. 9. Exhibits/Trade Shows 10. Foreign 11. Infomercial 12. Internet Adv.13. Multimedia 14. Network Radio
15. Network T.V. 16. Newsp. Distr. Mags. 17. Other 18. Outdoor (Posters, Transit) 19. Point of Purchase20. Premiums, Novelties
21. Product Samples 22. Special Events Mktg. 23. Spot Radio 24. Spot T.V. 25. Weekly Newsp. 26. Yellow Page Adv.

PROPPER MANUFACTURING COMPANY, INC.

36-04 Skillman Ave
Long Island City, NY 11101-1730
Tel.: (718) 392-6650
Fax: (718) 482-8909
Toll Free: (800) 832-4300
E-mail: Marketing@proppermfg.com
Web Site: www.proppermfg.com
E-Mail For Key Personnel:
Marketing Director: marketing@proppermfg.com
Approx. Number Employees: 75
Year Founded: 1935
Business Description:
Mfr. & Importer of Medical & Laboratory Supplies & Diagnostic Instruments
S.I.C.: 3841; 6512
N.A.I.C.S.: 339112; 531120
Import Export
Advertising Expenditures: $100,000
Consumer Mags.: $30,000; Exhibits/Trade Shows: $40,000; Other: $30,000
Distr.: Intl.; Natl.
Budget Set: June
Personnel:
Kevin Davis *(Sr Mgr-Territory)*
Kevin Donovan *(Mgr-Territory)*
Bryce Lister *(Mgr-Territory)*
Mike McNulty *(Mgr-Territory)*
Wayne Schultz *(Mgr-Territory)*
Cris Theriault *(Mgr-Territory)*
Bob Woodring *(Mgr-Territory)*
Brands & Products:
ALERT-O.A.D
AUTOSFIG
BEV-L-EDGE
BI-O.K.
BIO-CHALLENGE TEST-PAK
CARDIOQUET
CHEX-ALL
CLICKSTOP
DUO-FLASH
DUO RECORD
DUO-SPORE
EO EASY READ
F/O
GAS-CHEX
HI-DRI
HI-SPEED
IRRIGO
LUMICYTE
O.K.
O.K. STRIPS
ONCE-A-DAY
PASS/FAIL
PROPPER
PROPPER PLUS
PROPPER STAR
THE PUSHER
QUICK CHALLENGE
SELECT
SERA-SHARP
SERACULT
SERAKET
SERATURE
SMALSTRIP
STEAM-DOT
STERI-DOT
STERI-WRAP
STRATE-LINE
SUPERLUME
SWANN MORTON
TEMPTUBE
TEST-PAK
TIMECARD
TWIN-FROST
TWINDICATOR
ULTRA
VAPOR LINE
VELKET
WATS

PROVENA HEALTH INC.

19065 Hickory Creek Dr Ste 300
Mokena, IL 60448
Tel.: (708) 478-7678
Fax: (708) 478-5960
Web Site: www.provena.org
Approx. Number Employees: 20,000
Year Founded: 1997
Business Description:
Hospital Operator
S.I.C.: 8062; 8059
N.A.I.C.S.: 622110; 623311
Import Export
Advertising Expenditures: $300,000
Media: 2-6-10-13
Personnel:
Bob Biedron *(Chm)*
Guy R. Wiebking *(Pres & CEO)*
James D. Witt *(Pres & CEO-Provena Mercy Medical Center)*
Anthony J. Filer *(CFO & Sr VP-Sys)*
John P. Lynch *(CIO & VP-System)*
Margaret A. Gavigan *(Sr VP-System & Chief Clinical Officer)*
Beth Hughes *(Pres/CEO-Provena Saint Joseph Medical Center)*
Terry S. Solem *(Sr VP-System-HR)*
Lisa M. Lagger *(VP-System, PR & Mktg)*

PROVIDENCE HEALTH SYSTEM

1801 Lind ave SW
Renton, WA 98057
Tel.: (425) 525-3355
Fax: (425) 525-3338
Web Site: www.providence.org
Approx. Number Employees: 32,240
Year Founded: 1859
Business Description:
Hospital & Health Care Services
S.I.C.: 8062; 8742
N.A.I.C.S.: 622110; 541611
Advertising Expenditures: $3,000,000
Media: 17-25
Personnel:
John F. Koster *(Pres & CEO)*
Jan Jones *(Chief Admin Officer & Sr VP)*
Michael Butler *(Exec VP-Fin & Strategy)*
Jack Mudd *(Sr VP-Mission Leadership)*
Claudia Haglund *(VP-Strategic Dev)*
Steve Brennan *(Mgr-System Advocacy)*

PROXYMED, INC.

(Name Changed to Anx E-Business Corp.)

PURDUE PHARMA LP

1 Stamford Forum 201 Tresser Blvd
Stamford, CT 06901-3431
Tel.: (203) 588-8000
Tel.: (203) 588-8069
Fax: (203) 588-8850
Toll Free: (800) 745-7445
Toll Free: (877) PURDUE1
E-mail: info@concordcustomcleaners.com
Web Site: www.purduepharma.com
Sales Range: $1-4.9 Billion
Approx. Number Employees: 1,150
Year Founded: 1892
Business Description:
Pharmaceuticals Mfr & Distr
S.I.C.: 2834; 5122
N.A.I.C.S.: 325412; 424210
Media: 4-6-14-21-25
Personnel:
Edward B. Mahony *(CFO & Exec VP)*
James W. Heins *(Sr Dir-Pub Affairs)*
Peter Justason *(Dir-eMktg)*
Brands & Products:
IN THE FACE OF PAIN
MS CONTIN
MSIR
OXYCONTIN
OXYFAST
OXYIR
PALLADONE
PURDUE
Advertising Agency:
Della Femina Rothschild Jeary & Partners
902 Broadway 15th Fl
New York, NY 10010
Tel.: (212) 506-0700
Fax: (212) 506-0751
(Senokot, Betadine & New Over-the-Counter Product Development)

PURE FRUIT TECHNOLOGIES, LLC

1276 S 820 E Ste 150
American Fork, UT 84003
Tel.: (801) 216-8300
Toll Free: (866) 464-6738
E-mail: cs@pft.com
Web Site: www.purefruittechnologies.com
Sales Range: $1-9.9 Million
Approx. Number Employees: 11
Year Founded: 2002
Business Description:
Botanical Products Mfr & Marketer
S.I.C.: 2833; 5961; 5963
N.A.I.C.S.: 325411; 454113; 454390
Media: 6-10
Brands & Products:
GOJI ZEN
MANGO-XAN
PURE FRUIT. NOTHING ELSE
PURE FRUIT TECHNOLOGIES
SEABUCK 7

PURETEK CORPORATION

1245 Aviation Pl
San Fernando, CA 91340
Tel.: (818) 361-3316
Fax: (818) 361-8722
Web Site: www.d-care.com
Approx. Number Employees: 300
Year Founded: 1992
Business Description:
Pharmaceuticals Mfr
S.I.C.: 2834; 2833; 2836
N.A.I.C.S.: 325412; 325411; 325414
Import Export
Media: 2-6
Personnel:
Stephen Pressman *(Exec VP)*
Carla Dunn *(Mgr-Mktg)*
Brands & Products:
BREATH RELIEF
CARDIOLINK
D-CARE
DELIGHTS
MEITE
PHARMAFLEX
PHARMAPURE
SPA LOGIX

QIAGEN GAITHERSBURG INC.

(Sub. of QIAGEN North American Holdings, Inc.)
1201 Clopper Rd
Gaithersburg, MD 20878-4000
Tel.: (301) 944-7000
Fax: (301) 944-7121
Toll Free: (800) 344-3631
Web Site: www.digene.com
Approx. Rev.: $152,888,000
Approx. Number Employees: 490
Year Founded: 1985
Business Description:
Gene-Based Testing Systems Developer & Mfr
S.I.C.: 2834
N.A.I.C.S.: 325412
Advertising Expenditures: $7,730,000
Media: 2-6-8-15-24
Personnel:
Peer M. Schatz *(CEO)*
Attila T. Lorincz *(Chief Scientific Officer)*
Vincent J. Napoleon *(Gen Counsel, Sec & Sr VP)*
James H. Godsey *(Sr VP-R & D)*
Belinda O. Patrick *(Sr VP)*
Pamela A. Rasmussen *(VP-Corp Comm)*
Brands & Products:
DIGENE
DNAWITHPAP
HPV DNA TEST
HYBRID CAPTURE
RAPID CAPTURE
Advertising Agency:
Gotham Incorporated
150 E 42nd St 12th Fl
New York, NY 10017
Tel.: (212) 414-7000
Fax: (212) 414-7095

QLT USA, INC.

(Sub. of QLT, Inc.)
2579 Midpoint Dr
Fort Collins, CO 80525-4417
Tel.: (970) 482-5868
Fax: (970) 482-9735
Sales Range: $25-49.9 Million
Approx. Number Employees: 158
Year Founded: 1986
Business Description:
Drug Delivery Systems
S.I.C.: 2834
N.A.I.C.S.: 325412
Export
Media: 2-5-7-10-11
Brands & Products:
ATRIDOX
ATRIGEL
ATRISONE
ATRISORB-D
ATRISORB-FREE FLOW
BCP
BEMA
DOXIROBE
MCA
SMP

QUADRAMED CORPORATION

(Holding of Francisco Partners Management, LLC)
12110 Sunset Hills Rd Ste 600

Key to Media (For complete agency information see *The Advertising Red Books-Agencies* edition):
1. Bus. Publs. 2. Cable T.V. 3. Catalogs & Directories. 4. Co-op Adv. 5. Consumer Mags. 6. D.M. to Bus. Estab.7. D.M. to Consumers 8. Daily Newsp. 9. Exhibits/Trade Shows 10. Foreign 11. Infomercial 12. Internet Adv.13. Multimedia 14. Network Radio 15. Network T.V. 16. Newsp. Distr. Mags. 17. Other 18. Outdoor (Posters, Transit) 19. Point of Purchase20. Premiums, Novelties 21. Product Samples 22. Special Events Mktg. 23. Spot Radio 24. Spot T.V. 25. Weekly Newsp. 26. Yellow Page Adv.

QuadraMed Corporation — (Continued)

Reston, VA 20190
Tel.: (703) 709-2300
Fax: (703) 709-2490
Toll Free: (800) 393-0278
E-mail: investorrelations2@quadramed.com
Web Site: www.quadramed.com
E-Mail For Key Personnel:
Public Relations: BKane@quadramed.com
Approx. Rev.: $150,435,000
Approx. Number Employees: 613
Year Founded: 1993
Business Description:
Software, Web-Enabled Solutions & Professional Consulting Services to Hospitals & Healthcare Providers for Information Management
S.I.C.: 7371; 8748
N.A.I.C.S.: 541511; 541618
Advertising Expenditures: $2,800,000
Media: 7-10
Personnel:
Duncan W. James *(Pres & CEO)*
David L. Piazza *(CFO & Exec VP)*
Brook A. Carlon *(Sr VP-HR & Admin Svcs)*
Thomas J. Dunn *(Sr VP-Sls & Mktg)*
Lora Zalewski *(VP-Fin)*
Brands & Products:
AFFINITY
CHANCELLOR
COMPLYSOURCE
MPISPY
QUADRAMED
QUALITY CARE. FINANCIAL HEALTH.
QUANTIM
QUANTUM
SMARTID
SMARTMERGE
SMARTSCAN
TEMPUS
WINPFS

QUALITY KING DISTRIBUTORS INC.

2060 9th Ave
Ronkonkoma, NY 11779-6253
Tel.: (631) 737-5555
Fax: (631) 439-2388
Toll Free: (800) 676-5554
E-mail: custserv@qkd.com
Web Site: www.qkd.com
Approx. Rev.: $2,450,000,000
Approx. Number Employees: 1,400
Year Founded: 1955
Business Description:
Health & Beauty Aids Distr
S.I.C.: 5122
N.A.I.C.S.: 424210
Media: 16
Personnel:
Glenn Nussdorf *(CEO)*
Mike Anderson *(CFO)*
Marc Garrett *(VP-DP)*
Jane Midgal *(VP-HR)*

QUALITY SYSTEMS, INC.

18111 Von Karman Ave, Ste 700
Irvine, CA 92612
Tel.: (949) 255-2600
Fax: (949) 255-2605
Toll Free: (800) 888-7955
E-mail: qsi@qsii.com
Web Site: www.qsii.com/
Approx. Rev.: $353,363,000
Approx. Number Employees: 1,537
Year Founded: 1974
Business Description:
Health Care Information System Services
S.I.C.: 7373; 7372
N.A.I.C.S.: 541512; 511210
Advertising Expenditures: $7,122,000
Media: 2-7-10
Personnel:
Sheldon Razin *(Founder & Chm)*
Patrick B. Cline *(Pres)*
Steven T. Plochocki *(CEO)*
Paul A. Holt *(CFO)*
James J. Sullivan *(Gen Counsel, Sec & Exec VP)*
Donn E. Neufeld *(Exec VP-EDI & Dental)*
Steve Puckett *(Exec VP-NextGen Inpatient Solution)*
Monte Sandler *(Exec VP-NextGen Practice Solutions)*
Brands & Products:
NEXTGEN EMR
NEXTGEN EPM
NEXTGEN HEALTHCARE
QSI DENTAL SYSTEM
QUIC NETWORK
Advertising Agency:
Stratagem Healthcare Communications, LLC
450 Sansome St 12th Fl
San Francisco, CA 94111
Tel.: (415) 397-3667
Fax: (415) 397-3668

QUANTROS, INC.

690 N McCarthy Blvd Ste 200
Milpitas, CA 95035
Tel.: (408) 957-3300
Fax: (408) 957-3320
Toll Free: (877) Quantros
E-mail: info@quantros.com
Web Site: www.quantros.com
Approx. Number Employees: 50
Business Description:
Health Care Information Technology Services
S.I.C.: 7371
N.A.I.C.S.: 541511
Media: 10
Personnel:
Keith Hagen *(Pres & CEO)*
Chris Rasmussen *(Gen Counsel, Sec & VP)*
Thomas C. Leahy *(Exec VP-Sls & Mktg)*
Chris Bethell *(VP-Mktg)*
Venky Vaddineni *(VP-Engrg & System Design)*
Monica Berry *(Dir-Patient Safety Svcs)*

QUANTUM, INC.

PO Box 2791
Eugene, OR 97402
Tel.: (541) 345-5556
Fax: (541) 345-4825
Toll Free: (800) 448-1448
E-mail: info@quantumhealth.com
Web Site: www.quantumhealth.com
Sales Range: $25-49.9 Million
Approx. Number Employees: 24
Business Description:
Vitamins & Herbal Supplement Mfr
S.I.C.: 2833
N.A.I.C.S.: 325411
Media: 6
Personnel:
Eve McClure *(Pres)*

QUEST DIAGNOSTICS INCORPORATED

3 Giralda Farms
Madison, NJ 07940
Tel.: (973) 520-2700
Toll Free: (800) 222-0446
E-mail: investor@questdiagnostics.com
Web Site: www.questdiagnostics.com
Approx. Rev.: $7,368,925,000
Approx. Number Employees: 42,000
Year Founded: 1928
Business Description:
Medical Testing Laboratories
S.I.C.: 8071
N.A.I.C.S.: 621511; 621512
Media: 7-8-11
Personnel:
Surya N. Mohapatra *(Chm & CEO)*
Robert A. Hagemann *(CFO & Sr VP)*
Jon R. Cohen *(Chief Medical Officer & Sr VP)*
Stephen C. Suffin *(Chief Laboratory Officer & VP)*
Michael E. Prevoznik *(Gen Counsel & Sr VP)*
William R. Grant *(Sr VP)*
Joan E. Miller *(Sr VP-Pathology & Hospital Svcs)*
David Evans *(VP-IT)*
David W. Norgard *(VP-HR)*
Laure E. Park *(VP-Comm & IR)*
Barry Sample *(Dir-Science & Tech-Employer Solutions)*
Kathleen Valentine *(Dir-IR)*
Brands & Products:
CARDIO CRP
CELLSEARCH
HEPTIMAX
HERPESELECT
IMMUNOCAP
LEUMETA
QUEST DIAGNOSTICS
UROVYSION
VYSIS
Advertising Agencies:
Lorel Marketing Group LLC
590 N Gulth Rd
King of Prussia, PA 19406
Tel.: (610) 337-2343
Fax: (610) 768-9511

Marketing Edge Group
1555 Ruth Rd Units 1 & 2
North Brunswick, NJ 08902
Tel.: (732) 658-1540
Fax: (732) 745-1990

Topin & Associates, Inc.
205 N Michigan Ave Ste 2315
Chicago, IL 60601-5923
Tel.: (312) 645-0100
Fax: (312) 645-0120

QUESTCOR PHARMACEUTICALS, INC.

1300 N Kellogg Dr Ste D
Anaheim, CA 92807
Tel.: (714) 786-4200
E-mail: sales@questcor.com
Web Site: www.questcor.com
E-Mail For Key Personnel:
Sales Director: sales@questcor.com
Approx. Sls.: $115,131,000
Approx. Number Employees: 152
Year Founded: 1999
Business Description:
Central Nervous System Treatment Developer
S.I.C.: 2834
N.A.I.C.S.: 325412
Media: 10-13-18-21
Personnel:
Virgil D. Thompson *(Chm)*
Don M. Bailey *(Pres & CEO)*
Michael H. Mulroy *(CFO, Gen Counsel, Sec & Sr VP)*
Stephen L. Cartt *(Chief Bus Officer & Exec VP)*
David J. Medeiros *(Sr VP-Pharmaceutical Ops)*
Brands & Products:
H.P. ACTHAR GEL
QUESTCOR
Advertising Agency:
Kane & Finkel Healthcare Communications
534 4th St
San Francisco, CA 94107
Tel.: (415) 777-4990
Fax: (415) 777-5019

QUIDEL CORPORATION

10165 McKellar Ct
San Diego, CA 92121-4201
Tel.: (858) 552-1100
Fax: (858) 453-4338
Toll Free: (800) 874-1517
E-mail: ir@quidel.com
Web Site: www.quidel.com
Approx. Rev.: $113,339,000
Approx. Number Employees: 532
Year Founded: 1979
Business Description:
Rapid Immuno-Diagnostic Products Mfr
S.I.C.: 2835; 2834; 3841
N.A.I.C.S.: 325413; 325412; 339112
Export
Advertising Expenditures: $1,000,000
Media: 2-4-5-7-9-10-13-21
Personnel:
Mark A. Půlido *(Chm)*
Douglas C. Bryant *(Pres & CEO)*
John M. Radak *(CFO)*
David R. Scholl *(Sr VP-Comml Ops & Pres-DHI)*
Robert J. Bujarski *(Gen Counsel, Sec & Sr VP)*
Scott M. Mcleod *(Sr VP-Ops)*
John D. Tamerius *(Sr VP-Clinical & Regulatory Affairs)*
Brands & Products:
H. PYLORI GII
IN-LINE
METRA
MICROVUE
QUICKVUE
QUICKVUE ADVANCE
QUICKVUE IN-LINE
QUICKVUE+
QUIDEL
SEMI-Q

THE QUIGLEY CORPORATION

(Name Changed to ProPhase Labs, Inc.)

RADIANT RESEARCH INC.

(Sub. of ICICI Bank Limited)
11500 Northlake Dr Ste 320

Key to Media (For complete agency information see *The Advertising Red Books-Agencies* edition):
1. Bus. Publs. 2. Cable T.V. 3. Catalogs & Directories. 4. Co-op Adv. 5. Consumer Mags. 6. D.M. to Bus. Estab.7. D.M. to Consumers 8. Daily Newsp. 9. Exhibits/Trade Shows 10. Foreign 11. Infomercial 12. Internet Adv.13. Multimedia 14. Network Radio 15. Network T.V. 16. Newsp. Distr. Mags. 17. Other 18. Outdoor (Posters, Transit) 19. Point of Purchase20. Premiums, Novelties 21. Product Samples 22. Special Events Mktg. 23. Spot Radio 24. Spot T.V. 25. Weekly Newsp. 26. Yellow Page Adv.

Cincinnati, OH 45249
Tel.: (513) 247-5500
Fax: (513) 247-5510
E-mail: info@radiantresearch.com
Web Site: www.radiantresearch.com
Approx. Number Employees: 400
Year Founded: 1998
Business Description:
Research Services
S.I.C.: 8732
N.A.I.C.S.: 541910
Media: 6-8-9-10-13-23-24
Personnel:
Julie L. McHugh *(CEO)*
Leslie Moldauer *(Dir)*
Brands & Products:
RADIANT
RADIANT RESEARCH
Advertising Agency:
Radiant Media
1120 112th Ave NE Ste 480
Bellevue, WA 98004
Tel.: (425) 468-6200

RADIATION THERAPY SERVICES, INC.
(Holding of Vestar Capital Partners, Inc.)
(d/b/a 21st Century Oncology)
2234 Colonial Blvd
Fort Myers, FL 33907
Tel.: (239) 931-7333
Fax: (239) 931-7380
Toll Free: (800) 437-1619
Web Site: www.rtsx.com
Sales Range: $25-49.9 Million
Approx. Number Employees: 1,240
Business Description:
Radiation Therapy Services for Cancer Patients
S.I.C.: 8011
N.A.I.C.S.: 621111
Media: 10
Personnel:
Daniel E. Dosoretz *(Pres & CEO)*
Kerrin E. Gillespie *(CFO & Sr VP)*

RADIOEAR CORP.
205 Main St
New Eagle, PA 15067-1120
Tel.: (724) 258-5353
Fax: (724) 258-8342
Approx. Number Employees: 30
Year Founded: 1924
Business Description:
Mfr. of Hearing Instruments
S.I.C.: 3825; 3829
N.A.I.C.S.: 334515; 334519
Media: 2-6-7-8
Distr.: Natl.
Budget Set: Aug.
Personnel:
Andrew Kriceri *(VP)*
Brands & Products:
RADIOEAR

RADIOMETER AMERICA INC.
(Sub. of Radiometer A/S)
810 Sharon Dr
Westlake, OH 44145-1521
Tel.: (440) 871-8900
Fax: (440) 871-2633
Toll Free: (800) 736-0600
E-mail: info@radiometeramerica.com
Web Site:
www.radiometeramerica.com
Sales Range: $75-99.9 Million
Approx. Number Employees: 200
Year Founded: 1960
Business Description:
Medical & General Laboratory Equipment Mfr, Seller & Marketer
S.I.C.: 5047
N.A.I.C.S.: 423450
Import Export
Advertising Expenditures: $55,000
Media: 1-2-4-7-10-13-20
Distr.: Natl.
Budget Set: Feb.
Personnel:
Jan Weaver *(Mktg Mgr-Svc)*
Brands & Products:
AUTOCHECK
PICO 50
QUALICHECK +
RADIANCE
TCM4
TCM400
WORLDWIDE DATACHECK

RAINBOW LIGHT NUTRITIONAL SYSTEMS, INC.
125 McPherson St
Santa Cruz, CA 95060
Tel.: (831) 429-9089
Fax: (831) 429-0189
E-mail: info@rlns.com
Web Site: www.rainbowlight.com
Approx. Sls.: $6,000,000
Approx. Number Employees: 50
Year Founded: 1981
Business Description:
Mfr. of Medicinal & Botanical Products
S.I.C.: 2833; 5961
N.A.I.C.S.: 325411; 454113
Media: 6
Brands & Products:
3-WAY STRESS MANAGEMENT SYSTEM
40+ MULTIVITAMIN
ACTIVE HEALTH TEEN MULTIVITAMIN
ACTIVE SENIOR
ADVANCED ENZYME SYSTEM
ADVANCED NUTRITIONAL SYSTEM
ADVANCED NUTRITIONAL SYSTEM IRON-FREE
ALL-ZYME
ALL-ZYME DOUBLE STRENGTH
ALLERGY RESCUE
B-COMPLETE
BIO-BALANCED
BLACK COHOSH MENO-RELIEF 1650
BONES 4 LIFE
CALCIUM +
CANDIDA CLEANSE
COMPLETE B-COMPLEX
COMPLETE IRON SYSTEM
COMPLETE MENOPAUSE MULTIVITAMIN
COMPLETE NUTRITIONAL SYSTEM
COMPLETE PRENATAL SYSTEM
CONGEST-AWAY
DEEP DEFENSE
DERMACOMPLEX
DHA 250 SMART ESSENTIALS
ECHINACEA SUPERCOMPLEX
ECOCRAFTED
ENERGIZER
ENERGY B-COMPLEX
ENZYMEND DIGESTIVE AID
EVERYDAY CALCIUM
EVERYDAY FIBER SYSTEM
FEMAGEN
FOOD-BASED C-1000
FOOD-BASED CALCIUM
FOOD FOR MEN
FOOD FOR WOMEN
FOOD GROWN
GET WELL SOON
GINGKO-GOTU KOLA SUPERCOMPLEX
GINKGO-BACOPA QUICK THINKING
GOLDEN C
GUMMY BEAR ESSENTIALS
GUMMY OMEGALICIOUS
GUMMY POWER SOURS
GUMMY VITAMIN C SLICES
HEALTHY FAMILY
HEALTHY MOTION
HERBAL EXTRAS
IMMUNO-BUILD
JUST ONCE
KID'S ONE MULTISTARS
LACTO-ZYME DAIRY-EZE
MASTER NUTRIENT SYSTEM PLUS
MEDGUM
MENOPAUSE ONE MULTIVITAMIN
MEN'S ONE
MIGRASOLVE
MILK THISTLE HEPATO-GUARD 10K
MINTASURE
MULTI-MINS
NAIL, HAIR & SKIN CONNECTION
NUTRI STARS
NUTRISTARS
NUTRISTART MULTIVITAMIN POWDER
OMEGA GLO-COAT 3-6-9
PERFORMANCE ENERGY
PETADOLEX
PMS RELIEF
PRENATAL ONE
PROTEIN ENERGIZER
PROTEIN ENERGIZER ACAI
PROTEIN ENERGIZER CHOCOLATE
PROTEIN ENERGIZER VANILLA
PROTEIN ENERGIZER WHEY
RAINBOW LIGHT
RAINBOW LIGHT NUTRITIONAL SYSTEMS
RAINBOW NECTAR
REJUVENAGE
RELAX
RESPIRTONE
SPIRULINA
SUNNY GUMMIES
SUPER C
SUPER C 1000
SUPRACLEAR
VITEX-BLACK COHOSH SUPERCOMPLEX
VITEX SUPERCOMPLEX
WHERE HOLISTIC NUTRITION IS A SCIENCE
WHOLE DOG DAILY
WOMEN'S ANSWER MULTIVITAMIN
WOMEN'S NUTRITIONAL SYSTEM
WOMEN'S ONE

RBC LIFE SCIENCES, INC.
2301 Crown Ct
Irving, TX 75038-4305
Tel.: (972) 893-4000
Fax: (972) 893-4111
E-mail: info@rbclifesciences.com
Web Site: www.rbclifesciences.com
Approx. Sls.: $28,157,010
Approx. Number Employees: 72
Year Founded: 1991
Business Description:
Drugs, Proprietaries & Sundries
S.I.C.: 8733; 2844; 5122; 5199
N.A.I.C.S.: 541710; 325620; 424210; 424990
Import Export
Advertising Expenditures: $57,000
Media: 17
Personnel:
Clinton H. Howard *(Chm)*
Steven E. Brown *(CFO, Sec & VP-Fin)*
Don Clark *(CIO)*
Kenneth L. Sabot *(Sr VP-Ops)*
Mickey Stroud *(Dir-Creative)*
Brands & Products:
10 DAYS OF CHOCOLATE
24 SEVEN
ALOE CREME
ALOE GELEE
ALOEMANNAN
ARTICHOKE NANOCLUSTERS
BATH SALTS
BIOSHAPE
CELLUTION
CHOCOLATE SLIM SHAKE
CITRUS MINT
COENZYME
COLO-VADA-PLUS
DIGESTION FORMULA
DIOSIN
ELECTRONMETER
FIRSTFOOD
GREEN PHYTO POWER
HYDRACEL
IMMUNE
IMMUNE360
I.Q.
LIP THERAPY
MAGICAL
MELATONIN PLUS
MICROBRITE
MICROHYDRIN
MOISTURE BALANCE
MSM WITH MICROHYDRIN
MULTI-ACTIVE
NANOCEUTICALS
NUTRAFIRM
OMEGA BOOST ONE
OPC PLUS
ORA KEY
OVER 30
PHYCOTENE CREME
PHYTO POWER
PROTIVITY
PURIFYING
ROYAL BODYCARE
SANGO CORAL CALCIUM
SILVER
SKIN THERAPY MIST
SLIM SHAKE
SPIRULINA
TRIPLE FX
TRU ALOE
VANILLA SLIM SHAKE
VITAMIN E CLUSTERS

REGENERON PHARMACEUTICALS, INC.
777 Old Saw Mill River Rd
Tarrytown, NY 10591-6717
Tel.: (914) 345-7400
Fax: (914) 347-2113
E-mail: communications@regeneron.com
Web Site: www.regeneron.com

Key to Media (For complete agency information see *The Advertising Red Books-Agencies* edition):
1. Bus. Publs. 2. Cable T.V. 3. Catalogs & Directories. 4. Co-op Adv. 5. Consumer Mags. 6. D.M. to Bus. Estab.7. D.M. to Consumers 8. Daily Newsp. 9. Exhibits/Trade Shows 10. Foreign 11. Infomercial 12. Internet Adv.13. Multimedia 14. Network Radio 15. Network T.V. 16. Newsp. Distr. Mags. 17. Other 18. Outdoor (Posters, Transit) 19. Point of Purchase20. Premiums, Novelties 21. Product Samples 22. Special Events Mktg. 23. Spot Radio 24. Spot T.V. 25. Weekly Newsp. 26. Yellow Page Adv.

Regeneron Pharmaceuticals, Inc. — (Continued)

Approx. Rev.: $459,074,000
Approx. Number Employees: 1,395
Year Founded: 1988
Business Description:
Developer of Protein-Based Drugs for Treatment of Diseases & Conditions
S.I.C.: 2834; 8733
N.A.I.C.S.: 325412; 541720
Personnel:
P. Roy Vagelos *(Chm)*
Leonard S. Schleifer *(Pres & CEO)*
Murray A. Goldberg *(CFO, Treas, Sr VP-Fin, Asst Sec & Admin)*
George D. Yancopoulos *(Pres-Regeneron Res Laboratori, Exec VP & Chief Scientific Officer)*
Stuart A. Kolinski *(Gen Counsel, Sec & Sr VP)*
Valeta A. Gregg *(VP & Asst Gen Counsel)*
Douglas S. McCorkle *(VP, Controller & Asst Treas)*
Beverly C. Dubs *(Asst Treas & Admin Controller)*
Daniel Van Plew *(Sr VP & Gen Mgr-Indus Ops & Prod Supply)*
Peter Powchik *(Sr VP-Clinical Dev)*
Neil Stahl *(Sr VP-R & D)*
Robert J. Terifay *(Sr VP-Comml)*
Michael Aberman *(VP-Strategy & IR)*
Peter G. Dworkin *(VP-Corp Comm)*
Kremena Simitchieva *(VP-Mktg)*
Brands & Products:
ARCALYST
AXOKINE
DESIGNER PROTEIN THERAPEUTICS
RILONACEPT
VEGF TRAP
VELOCIGENE
VELOCIIMMUNE
VELOCIMAB
VELOCIMOUSE
Advertising Agencies:
WCG
114 5th Ave 10th Fl
New York, NY 10011
Tel.: (212) 301-7200
Fax: (212) 867-3249

WCG
60 Francisco St
San Francisco, CA 94133
Tel.: (415) 362-5018
Fax: (415) 362-5019

RELIANCE MEDICAL PRODUCTS, INC.
(Sub. of Haag-Streit Holding US Inc.)
3535 Kings Mills Rd
Mason, OH 45040-2303
Tel.: (513) 398-3937
Fax: (513) 398-0256
Toll Free: (800) 735-0357
E-mail: webmaster@reliance-medical.com
Web Site: www.reliance-medical.com
Approx. Sls.: $50,000,000
Approx. Number Employees: 100
Year Founded: 1898
Business Description:
Medical & Optical Equipment Mfr
S.I.C.: 3841; 3845
N.A.I.C.S.: 339112; 334510
Media: 2-4-7-10
Distr.: Natl.
Budget Set: Oct.
Personnel:
Domonic Beck *(Pres & COO)*
Steve Juenger *(Dir-Mktg)*

RELIV INTERNATIONAL, INC.
136 Chesterfield Industrial Blvd
Chesterfield, MO 63005-1220
Tel.: (636) 537-9715
Fax: (636) 537-9753
E-mail: intlinfo@relivinc.com
Web Site: www.reliv.com
Approx. Sls.: $78,748,388
Approx. Number Employees: 246
Year Founded: 1988
Business Description:
Nutritional Supplements, Weight-Management Products, Sports Drink Mixes, Nutritional Bars, Dietary Fiber Products, Functional Foods & Skin Care Products Mfr & Marketer
S.I.C.: 2833
N.A.I.C.S.: 325411
Advertising Expenditures: $55,000
Media: 8-9-13-25
Personnel:
Sandra S. Montgomery *(Co-Founder)*
Carl W. Hastings *(Vice Chm & Chief Scientific Officer)*
Steven D. Albright *(CFO & Sr VP-Fin)*
Robert L. Montgomery Jr. *(COO, Chm-Reliv Kalogris Foundation & Exec VP)*
R. Scott Montgomery *(COO & Exec VP)*
Stephen M. Merrick *(Gen Counsel & Sr VP)*
Ryan Montgomery *(Exec VP-Worldwide Sls)*
Don Gibbons *(Sr VP-Distributor Success)*
Steve Hastings *(Sr VP)*
Brett Hastings *(VP-Legal)*
Barry Murov *(VP-Corp Comm)*
Kurt Wulff *(VP-Mktg)*
Khairul Abdul Karim *(Gen Mgr-Four Southeast Asian Markets)*
Jim Lahm *(Dir-IT)*
Jennie Santhuff *(Dir-Distributor Svcs)*
Lori Sauerwein *(Dir-Strategic Dev)*
Mark Malott *(Mgr-Intl Mktg)*
Brands & Products:
ADVANTRA Z
ARTHAFFECT
ARTHRED
CARDIOSENTIALS
CELLEBRATE
CITRIMAX
DELIGHT
FIBRESTORE
GLUCAFFECT
INNERGIZE
NUTRITION MADE SIMPLE LIFE MADE RICH
OPTIBERRY
PROVANTAGE
RELIV
RELIV CLASSIC
RELIV NOW
REVERSAGE
SLIMPLICITY
SOYSENSE
SOYSENTIALS
ULTRIM PLUS

THE RENFREW CENTERS INC.
475 Spring Ln
Philadelphia, PA 19128
Tel.: (215) 482-5353
Fax: (215) 482-7390
Toll Free: (800) RENFREW
Web Site: www.renfrewcenter.com
Approx. Rev.: $19,000,000
Approx. Number Employees: 750
Business Description:
Women's Mental Health Services
S.I.C.: 8069; 8361
N.A.I.C.S.: 622310; 623990
Media: 1-6-13-18-22
Personnel:
Samuel E. Menaged *(Founder & Pres)*

REPLIGEN CORPORATION
41 Sayon St Bldg 1 Ste 100
Waltham, MA 02453
Tel.: (781) 250-0111
Fax: (781) 250-0115
Toll Free: (800) 622-2259
E-mail: info@repligen.com
Web Site: www.repligen.com
E-Mail For Key Personnel:
President: wherlihy@repligen.com
Approx. Rev.: $27,291,024
Approx. Number Employees: 66
Year Founded: 1981
Business Description:
Drugs for Autoimmune & Neurological Disorder Treatment
S.I.C.: 2836; 2834; 8733
N.A.I.C.S.: 325414; 325412; 541710
Export
Media: 2-7
Personnel:
Karen A. Dawes *(Co-Chm)*
Alexander Rich *(Co-Chm)*
Walter C. Herlihy *(Pres & CEO)*
William J. Kelly *(CFO)*
Michael M. Hall *(CMO & Sr VP-Clinical & Regulatory Affairs)*
Robert A. Spurr *(Chief Comml Officer & Sr VP-Sls & Mktg)*
James R. Rusche *(Sr VP-R&D)*
Brands & Products:
OPUS
RPROTEIN A
SECREFLO
SURE

Power Creative
11701 Commonwealth Dr
Louisville, KY 40299-2358
Tel.: (502) 267-0772
Fax: (502) 267-1727

RESMED INC.
9001 Spectrum Center Blvd
San Diego, CA 92123
Tel.: (858) 836-5000
Fax: (858) 746-2900
Toll Free: (800) 424-0737
E-mail: reception@resmed.com
Web Site: www.resmed.com
Approx. Sls.: $1,243,148,000
Approx. Number Employees: 3,450
Year Founded: 1984
Business Description:
Medical Equipment to Treat Sleep-Disordered Breathing
S.I.C.: 3841; 5047
N.A.I.C.S.: 339112; 423450
Media: 7-10
Personnel:
Peter C. Farrell *(Founder, Chm, Pres & CEO)*
Brett A. Sandercock *(CFO)*
Robert D. Douglas *(COO)*
Michael Zill *(CIO)*
David Pendarvis *(Chief Admin Officer & Global Gen Counsel)*
Jim Hollingshead *(Chief Strategy Officer)*
Don Darkin *(Pres-Strategic Bus Unit)*
Michael J. Farrell *(Pres-Americas)*
Stein Jacobsen *(Pres-Europe)*
Geoff Neilson *(Pres-Respiratory Care Strategic Bus Unit)*
Shannon Burgess *(Mgr-Sls)*
Brands & Products:
ACTIVA
ACTIVECELL
ADAPT SV
AERIAL
AERO-CLICK
AERO-FIX
APNEAL
APNEALINK
AUTOSCAN
AUTOSET
AUTOSET ADVANTAGE
AUTOSET CS
AUTOSET CS 2
AUTOSET RESPOND
AUTOSET SPIRIT
AUTOSET T
AUTOSET VANTAGE
AUTOVIEW
AUTOVPAP
BOOMERANG
BUBBLE CUSHION
BUBBLE MASK
ELISEE
EMBLA
EMBLETTA
EOLE
EPR
ESCAPE
HELIA
HUMIDAIRE
IPAP MAX
IPAP MIN
KIDSTA
MAGELLAN
MALIBU
MAP
MEPAL
MERIDIAN
MESAM
MIRAGE
MIRAGE ACTIVA
MIRAGE MICRO
MIRAGE MIRAGE LIBERTY
MIRAGE QUATTRO
MIRAGE SWIFT
MIRAGE VISTA
MORITZ BILEVEL
PAPILLON
POLY-MESAM
RESALARM
RESCAP
RESCONTROL
RESCONTROL II
RESLINK
RESMED
RESSCAN
RESTRAXX
RESVIEW
S7 ELITE
S7 LIGHTWEIGHT

Key to Media (For complete agency information see *The Advertising Red Books-Agencies* edition):
1. Bus. Publs. 2. Cable T.V. 3. Catalogs & Directories. 4. Co-op Adv. 5. Consumer Mags. 6. D.M. to Bus. Estab.7. D.M. to Consumers 8. Daily Newsp. 9. Exhibits/Trade Shows 10. Foreign 11. Infomercial 12. Internet Adv.13. Multimedia 14. Network Radio 15. Network T.V. 16. Newsp. Distr. Mags. 17. Other 18. Outdoor (Posters, Transit) 19. Point of Purchase20. Premiums, Novelties 21. Product Samples 22. Special Events Mktg. 23. Spot Radio 24. Spot T.V. 25. Weekly Newsp. 26. Yellow Page Adv.

S8 AUTOSCORE
S8 AUTOSET SPIRIT
S8 AUTOSET VANTAGE
S8 COMPACT
S8 ELITE
S8 ESCAPE
S8 LIGHTWEIGHT
S8 PRIMA
SELFSET
SILENT PAPILLON
SLEEP 4A HEALTHY LIFE
SLEEPKIT SOLUTIONS
SLEEPVANTAGE
SMART DATA
SMARTSTART
SPIRIT
SULLIVAN
SWIFT
TANGO
TICONTROL
TRAXX
ULTRA MIRAGE
VENTIAL
VISTA
VPAP
VPAP ADAPT SV
VPAP AUTO
VPAP MALIBU
VPAP MAX
VS EASYFIT
VS INTEGRA
VS SERENA
VS ULTRA
VSYNC
VSYNC WITH TICONTROL

RESPONSE GENETICS, INC.

1640 Marengo St 6th Fl
Los Angeles, CA 90033
Tel.: (323) 224-3900
Fax: (323) 224-3096
E-mail: investor@responsegenetics.com
Web Site: www.responsegenetics.com
Approx. Rev.: $21,277,415
Approx. Number Employees: 95
Year Founded: 1999
Business Description:
Diagnostic Cancer Testing
S.I.C.: 8734
N.A.I.C.S.: 541380
Advertising Expenditures: $657,697
Personnel:
Kathleen Danenberg *(Founder)*
Kirk K. Calhoun *(Chm)*
David W. Smith *(Vice Chm)*
Christine Meda *(Pres)*
Denise Mcnairn *(Interim CEO)*
David D. O'Toole *(CFO & VP)*
Brands & Products:
DTP
RESPONSE DX COLON
RESPONSE DX LUNGS
RESPONSE GENETICS
RESPONSEDX

RETRACTABLE TECHNOLOGIES INC.

511 Lobo Ln
Little Elm, TX 75068
Tel.: (972) 294-1010
Fax: (972) 292-3600
Toll Free: (888) 806-2626
E-mail: rti@vanishpoint.com
Web Site: www.vanishpoint.com
Approx. Sls.: $36,219,562
Approx. Number Employees: 154
Year Founded: 1994
Business Description:
Safety Needle Devices Designer, Developer, Mfr & Marketer
S.I.C.: 3841; 5047
N.A.I.C.S.: 339112; 423450
Media: 2
Personnel:
Thomas J. Shaw *(Chm, Pres & CEO)*
Douglas W. Cowan *(CFO & VP)*
Steven R. Wisner *(Exec VP)*
Russell B. Kuhlman *(VP-Sls)*
Kathryn M. Duesman *(Exec Dir-Global Health)*
Shayne Blythe *(Dir-Sls & Mktg Logistics)*
John W. Fort, III *(Dir-Acctg)*
James A. Hoover *(Dir-Quality Assurance)*
Jules Millogo *(Dir-Medical)*
Lawrence G. Salerno *(Dir-Ops)*
R. John Maday *(Production Mgr)*
Judy Ni Zhu *(Mgr-R&D)*
Brands & Products:
PATIENT SAFE
VANISHPOINT

REXALL SUNDOWN, INC.

(Sub. of NBTY, Inc.)
851 Broken Sound Pkwy NW
Boca Raton, FL 33487-3693
Tel.: (561) 241-9400
Fax: (561) 999-0005
Toll Free: (800) 327-0908
E-mail: webmaster@rexallsundown.com
Web Site: www.rexallsundown.com
Sales Range: $400-449.9 Million
Approx. Number Employees: 1,400
Year Founded: 1976
Business Description:
Vitamins, Nutritional Supplements & Consumer Health Products Mfr & Distr
S.I.C.: 5122; 2834
N.A.I.C.S.: 424210; 325412
Import Export
Media: 1-4-5-6-7-8-10-11-13-15-18-19-20-21-22-23-25-26
Distr.: Intl.; Natl.
Brands & Products:
CARBSOLUTIONS
MET-RX
OSTEO-BI-FLEX
POKEMON VITAMINS
RICHARDSON LABS
SUNDOWN
WORLDWIDE

RICOLA USA, INC.

(Sub. of Ricola AG)
51 Gibraltar Dr
Morris Plains, NJ 07950-1254
Tel.: (973) 984-6811
Fax: (973) 984-6814
Toll Free: (800) 323-9073
E-mail: info@ricolausa.com
Web Site: www.ricolausa.com
Approx. Number Employees: 15
Business Description:
Natural Herbal Products Mfr & Marketer
S.I.C.: 5122
N.A.I.C.S.: 424210
Import
Advertising Expenditures: $8,000,000
Media: 2-3-4-10-14-15-18-19-21-23-24
Distr.: Intl.
Personnel:
Peter Burke *(VP-Mktg)*
Advertising Agency:
KH Advertising
245 Main St Ste 202
Chester, NJ 07930
Tel.: (908) 879-3757
Fax: (908) 879-5811
(Website, Herbal Throat Drops & Herbal Breath Mints)

RITE AID CORPORATION

30 Hunter Ln
Camp Hill, PA 17011-2400
Mailing Address:
PO Box 3165
Harrisburg, PA 17105-3165
Tel.: (717) 761-2633
Fax: (717) 975-5871
Toll Free: (800) RITE-AID
E-mail: info@riteaid.com
Web Site: www.riteaid.com
Approx. Rev.: $25,214,907,000
Approx. Number Employees: 51,408
Year Founded: 1962
Business Description:
Retail Drug Store Chains
S.I.C.: 5912
N.A.I.C.S.: 446110
Advertising Expenditures: $367,412,000
Media: 4-5-6-8-9-16-18-23-25-26
Distr.: Reg.
Budget Set: Mar.
Personnel:
Mary F. Sammons *(Chm)*
John T. Standley *(Pres & CEO)*
Frank G. Vitrano *(CFO, Chief Admin Officer & Sr Exec VP)*
Kenneth A. Martindale *(COO)*
Don P. Davis *(CIO & Sr VP)*
Anthony J. Bellezza *(Sr VP-Internal Assurance & Chief Compliance Officer)*
Susan Henderson *(Chief Comm Officer & Sr VP)*
Douglas E. Donley *(Chief Acctg Officer & Sr VP)*
Marc A. Strassler *(Gen Counsel & Exec VP)*
Brian Fiala *(Exec VP-HR)*
Tony Montini *(Exec VP-Mdsg)*
Robert I. Thompson *(Exec VP-Pharmacy)*
Robert K. Thompson *(Exec VP-Store Ops)*
Scott Bernard *(Sr VP-Ops)*
Gerald P. Cardinale *(Sr VP-Procurement)*
Derek Griffith *(Sr VP-Northeast Div)*
Christopher Hall *(Sr VP-Pharmacy Bus Dev)*
John Learish *(Sr VP-Mktg)*
Wilson A. Lester, Jr. *(Sr VP-Supply Chain)*
Matt Miles *(Sr VP-Central Div)*
Daniel Miller *(Sr VP-Pharmacy Ops)*
Jon Olson *(Sr VP-Southern Div)*
Bill Romine *(Sr VP-Western Div)*
Bryan Shirtliff *(Sr VP-Mdsg)*
Bill Wolfe *(Sr VP-Managed Care & Govt Affairs)*
Ken Black *(Grp VP-Compensation, Benefits & Shared Svcs)*
Robert Blickley *(Grp VP-Construction Svcs)*
Bob Oberosler *(Grp VP-Loss Prevention)*
Ernie Richardsen *(Grp VP-Pharmaceutical Pur & Clinical Svcs)*
Matt Schroeder *(Grp VP-Strategy & IR)*
Karen Smith *(Grp VP-Real Estate)*
Ted W. Armstrong *(Dir-HR & Distr Centers)*
Brands & Products:
BROOKS
C.BOOTH DERMA
ECKERD
LIFE CHECK
OWNER'S CHOICE
PHOTO RITE
PURE SPRING
RITE AID
WITH US, IT'S PERSONAL
Advertising Agency:
Parker Advertising Service, Inc.
101 N Pointe Blvd 2nd Fl
Lancaster, PA 17601
Tel.: (717) 581-1966
Fax: (717) 581-1566
Toll Free: (800) 396-3306

ROCHE DIAGNOSTICS CORPORATION

(Sub. of F. Hoffmann-La Roche AG)
9115 Hague Rd
Indianapolis, IN 46250
Mailing Address:
PO Box 50457
Indianapolis, IN 46256
Tel.: (317) 521-2000
Fax: (317) 521-2090
Web Site: www.roche-diagnostics.us
Approx. Number Employees: 100
Year Founded: 1965
Business Description:
Diagnostic Instruments & Reagents, Orthopedic Implants & Biochemicals Distributer & Mfr
S.I.C.: 3826; 3841
N.A.I.C.S.: 334516; 339112
Distr.: Intl.; Natl.
Budget Set: Aug.
Personnel:
Steve A. Oldham *(Gen Counsel, Sec & VP-Law & Ethics Compliance)*
H. J. Crowley *(Sr VP-Pro Diagnostics)*
Susan Zienowicz *(Sr VP-Applied Science)*
Randy Pritchard *(VP-Mktg-Centralized Diagnostics)*
Advertising Agency:
Jackson Integrated
5804 Churchman Bypass
Indianapolis, IN 46203-6109
Tel.: (317) 791-9000
Fax: (317) 791-9800
Toll Free: (888) JACKSON

ROCHESTER MEDICAL CORPORATION

1 Rochester Medical Dr NW
Stewartville, MN 55976-1647
Tel.: (507) 533-9600
Fax: (507) 533-4232
Toll Free: (800) 243-3315
Web Site: www.rocm.com
Approx. Sls.: $41,442,680
Approx. Number Employees: 268

Key to Media (For complete agency information see *The Advertising Red Books-Agencies* edition):
1. Bus. Publs. 2. Cable T.V. 3. Catalogs & Directories. 4. Co-op Adv. 5. Consumer Mags. 6. D.M. to Bus. Estab.7. D.M. to Consumers 8. Daily Newsp. 9. Exhibits/Trade Shows 10. Foreign 11. Infomercial 12. Internet Adv.13. Multimedia 14. Network Radio 15. Network T.V. 16. Newsp. Distr. Mags. 17. Other 18. Outdoor (Posters, Transit) 19. Point of Purchase20. Premiums, Novelties 21. Product Samples 22. Special Events Mktg. 23. Spot Radio 24. Spot T.V. 25. Weekly Newsp. 26. Yellow Page Adv.

Rochester Medical Corporation — (Continued)

Business Description:
Urinary Incontinence & Retention Treatment Products Mfr
S.I.C.: 3841; 3842
N.A.I.C.S.: 339112; 339113
Export
Advertising Expenditures: $1,600,000
Media: 2-4-10-21
Personnel:
Anthony J. Conway *(Pres & COO)*
Philip J. Conway *(CEO)*
David A. Jonas *(CFO & Sec)*
Jim Carper *(VP-Mktg)*
Brands & Products:
FEMSOFT
MAGIC(CUBE)
NATURAL
ONE FOCUS, ONE MISSION: IMPROVING LIVES
PERSONAL CATHETER
POP-ON
RELEASENF
ROCHESTER
ROCHESTER MEDICAL
SECURE GLIDE
ULTRAFLEX
WIDEBAND

ROCKWELL MEDICAL TECHNOLOGIES, INC.

30142 S Wixom Rd
Wixom, MI 48393-3440
Tel.: (248) 960-9009
Fax: (248) 960-9119
Toll Free: (800) 449-3353
E-mail: invest@rockwellmed.com
Web Site: www.rockwellmed.com
Approx. Sls.: $59,554,592
Approx. Number Employees: 300
Year Founded: 1995
Business Description:
Mfr. of Hemodialysis, Concentrates, Dialysis Kits & Other Hemodialysis Products
S.I.C.: 3829; 3845
N.A.I.C.S.: 334519; 334510
Export
Media: 10
Personnel:
Robert L. Chioini *(Founder, Chm, Pres & CEO)*
Thomas E. Klema *(CFO, Treas, Sec & VP)*
Brands & Products:
DRI-SATE
RENALPURE
STERILYTE

ROCKWIN CORPORATION

(d/b/a Hearing Help Express)
105 N 1st St
Dekalb, IL 60115-0586
Mailing Address:
PO Box 586
Dekalb, IL 60115-3201
Tel.: (815) 756-1471
Fax: (815) 748-0945
Toll Free: (800) 221-2099
Web Site:
www.hearinghelpexpress.com
Approx. Number Employees: 20
Year Founded: 1980
Business Description:
Mail Order Hearing Aids
S.I.C.: 5999
N.A.I.C.S.: 446199
Import
Media: 2-6-8-9-25
Distr.: Natl.
Personnel:
James E. Hovis *(Chm & CEO)*
Advertising Agency:
Sunman Direct
307 N Michigan Ave Ste 1012
Chicago, IL 60601
Tel.: (312) 726-3141

THE ROHO GROUP

100 N Florida Ave
Belleville, IL 62221-5429
Tel.: (618) 277-9150
Fax: (618) 277-9510
Toll Free: (800) 851-3449
E-mail: marketing@therohogroup.com
Web Site: www.therohogroup.com
Approx. Number Employees: 210
Year Founded: 2001
Business Description:
Holding Company
S.I.C.: 5047; 2822
N.A.I.C.S.: 423450; 325212
Media: 4-7-8-10-13
Personnel:
Tom Borcherding *(Pres)*
Jeffrey W. Bakert *(CFO)*
Pat Chelf *(Sr VP-Sls & Bus Dev)*
Brands & Products:
ADAPTOR
AIRLITE
BARISELECT
CONTOUR SELECT
DRY FLOATATION
ENHANCER
HARMONY
HEAL PAD
HEALFLOAT
HIGH PROFILE
HYBRIDSELECT
JETSTREAM PRO
LOW PROFILE
LTV
MERLIN
MID PROFILE
MINI-MAX
MOSAIC
NEXUS SPIRIT
PACK-IT
PRODIGY MATTRESS OVERLAY
QUADTRO
QUADTRO SELECT
RETROBACK
ROHO
THE ROHO GROUP
ROHO MOJO
SELECTAIR
SELECTPROTECT
SHAPE FITTING TECHNOLOGY
TRIUMPH
TRIUMPH CONTOUR
XSENSOR

ROTECH HEALTHCARE, INC.

2600 Technology Dr Ste 300
Orlando, FL 32804
Tel.: (407) 822-4600
Fax: (407) 297-6217
Toll Free: (877) 603-7840
E-mail: investor@rotech.com
Web Site: www.rotech.com
Approx. Rev.: $496,426,000
Approx. Number Employees: 3,800
Year Founded: 1981
Business Description:
Home Medical Equipment & Related Products & Services; Infusion Therapy, Home Respiratory Care & Other Medical Services & Equipment Marketer & Distr
S.I.C.: 8082; 3841; 7352
N.A.I.C.S.: 621610; 339112; 532291
Advertising Expenditures: $425,000
Personnel:
Arthur J. Reimers *(Chm)*
Philip L. Carter *(Pres & CEO)*
Steven P. Alsene *(CFO & Treas)*
Michael R. Dobbs *(COO)*
Rebecca L. Myers *(Chief Legal Officer & Sec)*

ROXANE LABORATORIES, INC.

(Sub. of Boehringer Ingelheim Corp.)
1809 Wilson Rd
Columbus, OH 43228
Mailing Address:
PO Box 16532
Columbus, OH 43216-6532
Tel.: (614) 276-4000
Fax: (614) 308-3540
Toll Free: (800) 962-8364
Web Site: www.roxane.com
Approx. Number Employees: 1,029
Year Founded: 1982
Business Description:
Ethical Pharmaceuticals Mfr
S.I.C.: 2834
N.A.I.C.S.: 325412
Export
Advertising Expenditures: $300,000
Media: 2-4-10
Distr.: Natl.
Budget Set: Dec.
Brands & Products:
DEXAMETHASONE INTENSOL
DHT
DIAZEPAM INTENSOL
DOLOPHINE
LORAZEPAM INTENSOL
ORLAAM
PREDNISONE INTENSOL
PRELU-2
PROPRANOLOL HCL INTENSOL
ROXANE LABORATORIES
ROXICET
TORECAN

RURAL/METRO CORPORATION

9221 E Via de Ventura
Scottsdale, AZ 85258
Tel.: (480) 994-3886
Fax: (480) 606-3328
Toll Free: (800) 352-2309
Web Site: www.ruralmetro.com
Approx. Rev.: $530,754,000
Approx. Number Employees: 5,966
Year Founded: 1948
Business Description:
Emergency & Non-Emergency Medical Transportation Services, Fire Protection & Other Safety-Related Services
S.I.C.: 8099; 4119; 9224
N.A.I.C.S.: 485991; 621910; 621999; 922160
Advertising Expenditures: $400,000
Media: 2-10
Personnel:
Michael P. DiMino *(Pres & CEO)*
Kristine B. Ponczak *(CFO, Treas, Sec & Sr VP)*
M. Bryan Gibson *(COO & Exec VP)*
Jeffrey D. Perry *(CIO & Sr VP)*
Donna Berlinski *(Principal Acctg Officer, VP & Controller)*
Brands & Products:
RURAL/METRO

SAGE SOFTWARE HEALTHCARE, INC.

(Div. of Sage Software, Inc.)
2202 N West Shore Blvd Ste 300
Tampa, FL 33607
Tel.: (813) 202-5000
Fax: (813) 289-6420
Toll Free: (877) 932-6301
Web Site: www.sagehealth.com
Approx. Number Employees: 200
Year Founded: 1996
Business Description:
Supplier of Healthcare Software & Services
S.I.C.: 7372
N.A.I.C.S.: 511210
Media: 2-7-10-13
Personnel:
Betty Otter Nickerson *(Pres)*
Jeanne Walters *(CFO & Sr VP)*
Lee Horner *(Sr VP-Sls-North America)*
Janet Livengood *(Sr VP-Div Counsel)*
Brands & Products:
MEDICAL MANAGER

SAGENT HOLDING CO.

1901 N Roselle Rd Ste 700
Schaumburg, IL 60195
Tel.: (847) 908-1600
Fax: (847) 908-1601
E-mail: ir@sagentpharma.com
Web Site: www.sagentpharma.com
Approx. Rev.: $74,056,000
Approx. Number Employees: 85
Year Founded: 2006
Business Description:
Holding Company; Pharmaceutical Mfr
S.I.C.: 2834; 6719
N.A.I.C.S.: 325412; 551112
Advertising Expenditures: $515,000
Personnel:
Jeffrey Yordon *(CEO)*
Ronald Pauli *(CFO)*
Michael Logerfo *(Chief Legal Officer, VP & Sec)*
Albert Patterson *(Sr VP-Ops)*
Lorin Drake *(VP-Sls & Mktg)*
Dave Hebeda *(VP-Fin)*

SAINT BARNABAS HEALTH CARE SYSTEM

99 Hwy 37 W
Toms River, NJ 08755
Tel.: (732) 557-8000
Fax: (732) 923-8087
Toll Free: (888) 724-7123
E-mail: info@sbhcs.com
Web Site: www.sbhcs.com
Approx. Number Employees: 23,000
Year Founded: 1982
Business Description:
Statewide Hospital System
S.I.C.: 8062
N.A.I.C.S.: 622110
Import Export
Media: 2-6-23-24
Personnel:
Ronald Delmauro *(Pres & CEO)*
Ellen Greene *(VP-Pub Rels & Mktg)*
Denise Clark *(Mgr-Mktg)*

Key to Media (For complete agency information see *The Advertising Red Books-Agencies* edition):
1. Bus. Publs. 2. Cable T.V. 3. Catalogs & Directories. 4. Co-op Adv. 5. Consumer Mags. 6. D.M. to Bus. Estab.7. D.M. to Consumers
8. Daily Newsp. 9. Exhibits/Trade Shows 10. Foreign 11. Infomercial 12. Internet Adv.13. Multimedia 14. Network Radio
15. Network T.V. 16. Newsp. Distr. Mags. 17. Other 18. Outdoor (Posters, Transit) 19. Point of Purchase20. Premiums, Novelties
21. Product Samples 22. Special Events Mktg. 23. Spot Radio 24. Spot T.V. 25. Weekly Newsp. 26. Yellow Page Adv.

Advertising Agency:
Aloysius Butler & Clark
819 Washington St
Wilmington, DE 19801-1509
Tel.: (302) 655-1552
Fax: (302) 655-3105
Toll Free: (800) 848-1552
Community Medical Center; Toms River, NJ

SAINT PETERSBURG GENERAL HOSPITAL
(Sub. of HCA HOLDINGS, INC.)
6500 38th Ave N
Saint Petersburg, FL 33710
Tel.: (727) 384-1414
Fax: (727) 341-4889
Web Site: www.stpetegeneral.com
Approx. Number Employees: 490
Business Description:
Hospital
S.I.C.: 8062
N.A.I.C.S.: 622110
Media: 22-24
Personnel:
Robert Conroy *(Pres & CEO)*
JoAnne Cattell *(Chief Nursing Officer)*

SALIX PHARMACEUTICALS, INC.
1700 Perimeter Park Dr
Morrisville, NC 27560-8404
Tel.: (919) 862-1000
Fax: (919) 862-1095
E-mail: investor.relations@salix.com
Web Site: www.salix.com
Approx. Rev.: $336,973,000
Approx. Number Employees: 390
Business Description:
Specialty Pharmaceuticals Mfr
S.I.C.: 2834
N.A.I.C.S.: 325412
Advertising Expenditures: $6,700,000
Personnel:
Randy W. Hamilton *(Founder)*
Lorin K. Johnson *(Founder & Chief Scientific Liaison)*
John F. Chappell *(Chm)*
Carolyn J. Logan *(Pres & CEO)*
Adam C. Derbyshire *(CFO, Exec VP-Fin & Admin)*
William P. Forbes *(Chief Dev Officer, Exec VP-R&D)*
G. Michael Freeman *(Assoc VP-IR & Corp Comm)*
Brands & Products:
ANUSOL-HC
APSIRO
AZASAN
BALSALAZIDE
COLAZAL
COLAZIDE
DIURIL
INTELLICOR
MOVIPREP
OSMOPREP
PEPCID
PREMID
PROCTOCORT
SALIX
VISICOL
XIFAXAN
Advertising Agencies:
MedThink Communications
3301 Benson Dr Ste 400
Raleigh, NC 27609
Tel.: (919) 786-4918
Fax: (919) 786-4926

Resolute Communications
276 5th Ave
New York, NY 10001
Tel.: (212) 213-8181
Fax: (212) 213-8484

Strategic Domain, Inc.
307 7th Ave 24th Fl
New York, NY 10001-6007
Tel.: (212) 812-1900
Fax: (212) 924-4393

THE SALK COMPANY
320 Washington St
Brooklyn, MA 02445
Tel.: (617) 782-4030
Fax: (800) 343-0243
Toll Free: (800) 343-4497
E-mail: info@salkcompany.com
Web Site: www.salkcompany.com
Approx. Sls.: $2,500,000
Approx. Number Employees: 30
Year Founded: 1950
Business Description:
Mfr of Waterproof Protective Undergarments & Reusable Incontinence Systems
S.I.C.: 3842; 2326
N.A.I.C.S.: 339113; 315225
Media: 2-4-5-6-7-10-13-18-19-21-25
Distr.: Natl.
Personnel:
Lawrence Salk *(Owner)*
Brands & Products:
AQUA-GEL
CAREFOR
COMFORT COLLECTION
COMPANION
DIABETICARE
THE FLANNELETTE
FLANNELETTE PLUS
HALO SHIELD
HEALTHDRI
HOLOFIBER
THE I.V. GOWN
KEEPING YOU COMFORTABLE EVERYDAY
LADYLACE
LIGHT & DRY
PREMIER
PRIMACARE
PRIMAPAD
SALK
SANI-PANT
SANIPAD
SIMPLYDRI
THE SLEEP SHIRT
SLEEPDRI
SNAPWRAP
SUREGRIP
THERMAGOWN
TIEBACK

SAN CORPORATION
716 N Ventura Rd Ste 431
Oxnard, CA 93030
Tel.: (805) 988-0640
Fax: (805) 278-0862
Toll Free: (888) 519-9300
E-mail: info@sann.net
Web Site: www.sann.net
Year Founded: 1996
Business Description:
Supplements
S.I.C.: 6531
N.A.I.C.S.: 531210
Media: 6
Personnel:
Matthias Boldt *(Pres)*
Ricardo Holden *(Dir-Art)*
Brands & Products:
BCAA-PRO
ESTRODEX
INNOVATIONS FOR THE SERIOUS MINDED ATHLETE
LIPIDEX
MYODRIVE
MYOTEIN
MYOTEST
NA-R-ALA
SAN
TIGHT FEM
WE DELIVER RESULTS

SANOFI-AVENTIS U.S. LLC.
(Sub. of Sanofi-Aventis)
55 Corporate Dr
Bridgewater, NJ 08807
Tel.: (908) 981-5000
Fax: (908) 981-7870
Toll Free: (800) 981-2491
Web Site: www.sanofi-aventis.us
Approx. Number Employees: 15,000
Business Description:
Pharmaceuticals Research, Developer, Mfr & Marketer
S.I.C.: 2834; 5122
N.A.I.C.S.: 325412; 424210
Media: 2
Distr.: Natl.
Budget Set: Nov.
Personnel:
Paul Chew *(CMO)*
John Durso *(Chief Comml Officer & Sr VP)*
Gregory Irace *(Sr VP-Global Svcs)*
Matthew E. Ros *(Asst VP-Comml Lead-Global)*
Stefanie Perna Nacar *(Sr Product Mgr-Oncology Mktg)*
Brands & Products:
ALLEGRA
AMBIEN CIV
COPAXONE
ELOXATIN
LANTUS
LOVENOX
PLAVIX
TAXOTERE
Advertising Agencies:
LaVoie Strategic Communications Group, Inc.
12 Derby Sq S1
Salem, MA 01970
Tel.: (978) 745-4200
Fax: (978) 745-4242

MCS
1420 US Hwy 206 N Ste 100
Bedminster, NJ 07921-2652
Tel.: (908) 234-9900
Fax: (908) 470-4490

MSLGROUP
1675 Broadway 9th Floor
New York, NY 10019-5865
Tel.: (212) 468-4200
Fax: (212) 468-3007

Optimedia International U.S.
375 Hudson St 7th Fl
New York, NY 10014
Tel.: (212) 820-3200
Fax: (212) 820-3300

Publicis New York
4 Herald Sq 950 6th Ave
New York, NY 10001
Tel.: (212) 279-5550
Fax: (212) 279-5560

Vigilante Advertising
345 Hudson Street
New York, NY 10014
Tel.: (212) 545-2850
Fax: (212) 444-6061

SANOFI PASTEUR, INC
(Sub. of Sanofi Pasteur SA)
Discovery Dr
Swiftwater, PA 18370-0187
Tel.: (570) 839-7187
Fax: (570) 839-0955
Web Site: www.sanofipasteur.us.com
Approx. Number Employees: 4,000
Year Founded: 1978
Business Description:
Vaccines & Immunology Products Mfr
S.I.C.: 2834
N.A.I.C.S.: 325412
Import Export
Advertising Expenditures: $600,000
Media: 2-3-4-8-10-16
Distr.: Intl.; Natl.
Budget Set: July-Aug.
Personnel:
Damian Braga *(Pres-US & Americas)*
Brands & Products:
ACTHIB
CANOIN
DAPTACEL
DT
FLUZONE
IMOGAM
IMOVAX
IPOL
JE-VAX
MENOMUNE
MSTA
TD
THERACYS
TRIHIBIT
TRIPEDIA
TUBERSOL
TYPHIM VI
VAXSERVE
YF-VAX
Advertising Agencies:
directDeutsch
111 8th Ave
New York, NY 10011-5201
Tel.: (212) 981-7600
Fax: (212) 981-7525

PRP-Public Relations Partners
Avenue Roger Vandendriessche 5
1150
Brussels, Belgium
Tel.: (32) 2 762 0485
Fax: (32) 2 771 1959

Publicis Health GmbH
Bruckenstrasse 21
50667
Kolin, Germany
Tel.: (49) 69 97 14 70 0
Fax: (49) 69 97 14 70 620

SANTARUS, INC.
3721 Valley Centre Dr
San Diego, CA 92130
Tel.: (858) 314-5700
Fax: (858) 314-5701

Key to Media (For complete agency information see *The Advertising Red Books-Agencies* edition):
1. Bus. Publs. 2. Cable T.V. 3. Catalogs & Directories. 4. Co-op Adv. 5. Consumer Mags. 6. D.M. to Bus. Estab.7. D.M. to Consumers 8. Daily Newsp. 9. Exhibits/Trade Shows 10. Foreign 11. Infomercial 12. Internet Adv.13. Multimedia 14. Network Radio 15. Network T.V. 16. Newsp. Distr. Mags. 17. Other 18. Outdoor (Posters, Transit) 19. Point of Purchase20. Premiums, Novelties 21. Product Samples 22. Special Events Mktg. 23. Spot Radio 24. Spot T.V. 25. Weekly Newsp. 26. Yellow Page Adv.

Santarus, Inc. — (Continued)

E-mail: contact@santarus.com
Web Site: www.santarus.com
Approx. Rev.: $125,351,000
Approx. Number Employees: 223
Business Description:
Pharmaceutical Mfr
S.I.C.: 2869; 2834; 8733
N.A.I.C.S.: 325199; 325412; 541720
Advertising Expenditures: $2,600,000
Personnel:
David F. Hale *(Chm)*
Gerald T. Proehl *(Pres & CEO)*
Debra P. Crawford *(CFO, Treas, Sec & Sr VP)*
Carey J. Fox *(Gen Counsel & Sr VP)*
E. David Ballard *(Sr VP-Clinical Res & Medical Affairs)*
Julie A. DeMeules *(Sr VP-HR)*
William C. Denby, III *(Sr VP-Comml Ops)*
Warren E. Hall *(Sr VP-Mfg & Product Dev)*
Michael D. Step *(Sr VP-Corp Dev)*
Blake A. Boland *(VP-Sls)*
Martha L. Hough *(VP-Fin & IR)*
Thomas J. Joyce *(VP-Mktg & Natl Accts)*
Brands & Products:
GLUMETZA
OTC ZEGERID
SANTARUS
SANTARUS,INC.
ZEGERID

SAVA SENIOR CARE LLC

1 Ravinia Dr Ste 1500
Atlanta, GA 30346-2115
Tel.: (678) 443-7000
Fax: (770) 393-8054
Web Site: www.savaseniorcare.com
Approx. Rev.: $3,106,700,000
Approx. Number Employees: 35,000
Year Founded: 1997
Business Description:
Operation of Long-term Health Care Centers & Nursing Home Facilities
S.I.C.: 8059
N.A.I.C.S.: 623110
Media: 2-4-8-10-22
Personnel:
Tony Oglesby *(Pres & CEO)*
Stefano M. Miele *(Gen Counsel & Exec VP)*

SAVARIA CONCORD LIFTS INC.

(Sub. of Savaria Corporation)
107 Alfred Kuehne Blvd
Brampton, ON L6T 4K3, Canada
Tel.: (905) 791-5555
Fax: (905) 791-2222
Toll Free: (800) 661-5112
E-mail: info@savaria.com
Web Site: www.concordelevator.com
Sales Range: $50-74.9 Million
Approx. Number Employees: 180
Year Founded: 1993
Business Description:
Elevators & Moving Stairways Mfr
S.I.C.: 3534
N.A.I.C.S.: 333921
Import Export
Media: 10
Personnel:
Marcel Bourassa *(Pres)*
Bill Richardson *(Exec VP)*
Robert Berthiaume *(VP-Engrg)*
Rob DeRooy *(VP-Customer Svc)*
Dawn Rethoret *(Mgr-Mktg)*
Brands & Products:
COMMANDER
CONCORD
HANDLIFT
INFINITY
INFINITY SRE
IPL
ORION
PAL
PROLIFT SCL
PROLIFT VOYAGER

SAVARIA CORPORATION

2724 Etienne-Lenoir Street
Laval, QC H7R 0A3, Canada
Tel.: (450) 681-5655
Fax: (450) 624-1349
Toll Free: (800) 931-5655
E-mail: info@savaria.com
Web Site: www.savaria.com
Approx. Sls.: $66,463,512
Approx. Number Employees: 331
Business Description:
Stairlift, Inclined & Vertical Wheelchair Platform Lift & Residential Elevator Mfr
S.I.C.: 3534
N.A.I.C.S.: 333921
Media: 2-4-5-10
Personnel:
Marcel Bourassa *(Chm, Pres & CEO)*
Jean-Marie Bourassa *(CFO)*
Sebastien Bourassa *(Pres-China)*
Bill Richardson *(Exec VP-Elevators & Lifts)*
Pierre Tiernan *(Exec VP-Vehicles)*
Helene Bernier *(VP-Fin)*
Robert Berthiaume *(VP-Engrg)*
Rob DeRooy *(VP-Customer Svc)*
Alison Fraser *(VP-Mktg)*
Pierre Cote *(Dir-Tech)*
Bruce Hayes *(Dir-HR)*
Eric Perron *(Dir-Production Engrg)*
Gary Ross *(Dir-Sls)*

SCANDINAVIAN FORMULAS, INC.

140 E Church St
Sellersville, PA 18960
Tel.: (215) 453-2507
Fax: (215) 257-9781
Toll Free: (800) 688-2276
E-mail: info@scandinavianformulas.com
Web Site: www.scandinavianformulas.com
Approx. Number Employees: 4
Business Description:
Sale & Marketing of Natural Health Care Products
S.I.C.: 5122
N.A.I.C.S.: 424210
Media: 4-6
Personnel:
Catherine Peklak *(Pres & CEO)*
Advertising Agency:
Allebach Advertising
117 N Main St
Souderton, PA 18964
Tel.: (215) 721-7693
Fax: (215) 721-7694

SCHICK-WILKINSON SWORD

(Sub. of Energizer Holdings, Inc.)
10 Leighton Rd
Milford, CT 06460-3552
Mailing Address:
PO Box 537
Neenah, WI 54957
Tel.: (203) 882-2100
Fax: (203) 882-2114
Toll Free: (800) SHAVERS
Web Site: www.shaving.com
Sales Range: $1-4.9 Billion
Approx. Number Employees: 4,000
Business Description:
Shaving Products Mfr
S.I.C.: 2834
N.A.I.C.S.: 325412
Media: 6-9-14-15-19-20-21-23-24
Distr.: Natl.
Personnel:
David P. Hatfield *(Pres & CEO)*
Jeffery Chapman *(Dir-Brand Commun-Global)*
Adel Mekhail *(Dir-Mktg)*
Wendy Salustro *(Sr Brand Mgr)*
Suma Nagaraj *(Brand Mgr-Schick Xtreme3)*
Brands & Products:
GET READY
INTUITION
SCHICK QUATTRO
SCHICK QUATTRO POWER ST
Advertising Agencies:
COLANGELO
120 Tokeneke Rd
Darien, CT 06820
Tel.: (203) 662-6600
Fax: (203) 662-6601
— Kelly Peraino *(Acct Dir)*
— Joe Raimo, Sr. *(Sr Acct Exec)*

J. Walter Thompson Company (d/b/a JWT)
466 Lexington Ave
New York, NY 10017-3140
Tel.: (212) 210-7000
Fax: (212) 210-7299

SCHIFF NUTRITION INTERNATIONAL, INC.

(Sub. of Weider Health & Fitness Inc.)
2002 S 5070 W
Salt Lake City, UT 84104-4726
Tel.: (801) 975-5000
Fax: (801) 972-2223
E-mail: international@weider.com
Web Site: www.schiffnutrition.com
Approx. Sls.: $213,648,000
Approx. Number Employees: 414
Business Description:
Mfr. & Marketer of Health Foods, Nutritional Supplements, Vitamins & Personal Care Products
S.I.C.: 2833; 2834; 5141; 8049
N.A.I.C.S.: 325411; 325412; 424410; 621399
Export
Advertising Expenditures: $14,514,000
Media: 5-6-19
Distr.: Intl.; Natl.
Personnel:
Eric Weider *(Chm)*
Tarang P. Amin *(Pres & CEO)*
Joseph W. Baty *(CFO & Exec VP)*
Jennifer Steeves-Kiss *(CMO & Sr VP)*
Scott K. Milsten *(Gen Counsel, Sec & Sr VP)*
Shane Durkee *(Sr VP-R & D)*
Jon Fieldman *(Sr VP-Ops)*
Raquel Hinz *(VP-Sls & Mktg)*
Brands & Products:

Lippert/Heilshorn & Associates, Inc.
800 Third Ave 17th Fl
New York, NY 10022
Tel.: (212) 838-3777
Fax: (212) 838-4568
Investor Relations

PHD Los Angeles
10960 Wilshire Blvd
Los Angeles, CA 90024
Tel.: (310) 405-8700
Fax: (310) 405-8797

SCICLONE PHARMACEUTICALS, INC.

950 Tower Ln Ste 900
Foster City, CA 94404-2125
Tel.: (650) 358-3456
Fax: (650) 358-3469
Toll Free: (800) 724-2566
E-mail: investorrelations@sciclone.com
Web Site: www.sciclone.com
Approx. Rev.: $85,112,000
Approx. Number Employees: 261
Business Description:
Pharmaceuticals Mfr
S.I.C.: 2834
N.A.I.C.S.: 325412
Advertising Expenditures: $200,000
Personnel:
Jon S. Saxe *(Chm)*
Friedhelm Blobel *(Pres & CEO)*
Gary S. Titus *(CFO)*
Cynthia W. Tuthill *(Sr VP-Scientific Affairs & Chief Scientific Officer)*
Mark Lotter *(CEO-China Ops)*
Eric J. Hoechstetter *(VP-Legal Affairs)*
Randy J. McBeath *(VP-Mktg)*
Ivan B. Hui *(Asst VP-Fin)*
Brands & Products:
DC BEAD
RP101
SCICLONE
SCV-07
ZADAXIN

SCIENTIFIC PROTEIN LABORATORIES, INC.

(Holding of AMERICAN CAPITAL, LTD.)
700 E Main St
Waunakee, WI 53597-1440
Mailing Address:
PO Box 158
Waunakee, WI 53597-0158
Tel.: (608) 849-5944
Fax: (608) 849-4053
Toll Free: (800) 334-4775
Telex: 26-5479
Sales Range: $50-74.9 Million
Approx. Number Employees: 150
Year Founded: 1967
Business Description:
Pharmaceuticals, Pancreatins, Heparins & Blood Protein Products Mfr
S.I.C.: 2834; 2833
N.A.I.C.S.: 325412; 325411
Import Export
Media: 2-7
Distr.: Intl.; Natl.
Budget Set: Oct.

Key to Media (For complete agency information see *The Advertising Red Books-Agencies* edition):
1. Bus. Publs. 2. Cable T.V. 3. Catalogs & Directories. 4. Co-op Adv. 5. Consumer Mags. 6. D.M. to Bus. Estab.7. D.M. to Consumers
8. Daily Newsp. 9. Exhibits/Trade Shows 10. Foreign 11. Infomercial 12. Internet Adv.13. Multimedia 14. Network Radio
15. Network T.V. 16. Newsp. Distr. Mags. 17. Other 18. Outdoor (Posters, Transit) 19. Point of Purchase20. Premiums, Novelties
21. Product Samples 22. Special Events Mktg. 23. Spot Radio 24. Spot T.V. 25. Weekly Newsp. 26. Yellow Page Adv.

Personnel:
David Strunce *(Pres & CEO)*
Kathy Lynch *(Dir-HR)*

Brands & Products:
SPL

SCOLR PHARMA, INC.
19204 North Creek Pkwy Ste 100
Bothell, WA 98011
Tel.: (425) 368-1050
Fax: (425) 373-0181
E-mail: info@scolr.com
Web Site: www.scolr.com
Approx. Rev.: $618,000
Approx. Number Employees: 6
Year Founded: 1983
Business Description:
Controlled Drug-Delivery Technology Developer
S.I.C.: 2834
N.A.I.C.S.: 325412
Advertising Expenditures: $30,000
Media: 17
Personnel:
Stephen J. Turner *(Pres & CEO)*
Richard M. Levy *(CFO & Exec VP-Fin)*

Brands & Products:
CDT

THE SCOOTER STORE, INC.
(Sub. of Harrison Worldwide Enterprises, Inc.)
1650 Independence Dr
New Braunfels, TX 78132
Mailing Address:
PO Box 310709
New Braunfels, TX 78131-0709
Tel.: (830) 626-5600
Fax: (800) 877-7266
Toll Free: (800) 391-7237
E-mail: info@thescooterstore.com
Web Site: www.thescooterstore.com
Approx. Number Employees: 1,500
Year Founded: 1991
Business Description:
Mobility Services
S.I.C.: 5999
N.A.I.C.S.: 446199
Media: 3-8
Personnel:
Doug Harrison *(Founder, Pres & CEO)*
Fred Stepan *(CFO)*
Robert Berger *(CMO)*
Dan Gibbens *(Exec VP-Healthcare Rels)*
Mike Pfister *(Exec VP-External Rels & Govt Affairs)*
Bill Sisoian *(Exec VP-Sls)*
Mark Allen *(Sr VP-Ops)*
Jay Greene *(Sr VP-IT & HIPAA Security Officer)*
Tim Zipp *(Sr VP-Corp Compliance)*
Mark B. Leita *(Sr Dir-Govt Rels)*

Advertising Agency:
Zimmerman Advertising
2200 W Commercial Blvd Ste 300
Fort Lauderdale, FL 33309-3064
Tel.: (954) 644-4000
Fax: (954) 731-2977
Toll Free: (800) 248-8522

SCRIPNET
1050 Banburry Cross Dr Ste 290
Las Vegas, NV 89144
Tel.: (702) 365-6979
Fax: (702) 248-2688
Toll Free: (888) 880-8562
E-mail: helpdesk@scripnet.com
Web Site: www.scripnet.com
Approx. Number Employees: 25
Year Founded: 1997
Business Description:
Pharmacy Management Services
S.I.C.: 7374
N.A.I.C.S.: 518210
Personnel:
Dennis Sponer *(CEO)*
Sharon Planchunas *(Dir-HR)*

Brands & Products:
MAKING WORKER'S COMPENSATION WORK BETTER
SCRIPTNET

Advertising Agency:
ProAmericas
8174 South Holly #405
Centennial, CO 80122
Tel.: (303) 933-2626

SCRIPPS
4275 Campus Point Ct
San Diego, CA 92121-1513
Tel.: (858) 678-7000
Fax: (858) 678-6558
Toll Free: (800) SCRIPPS
Web Site: www.scrippshealth.org
Approx. Number Employees: 10,000
Year Founded: 1924
Business Description:
Hospital & Clinic Owner & Operator
S.I.C.: 8062; 8082
N.A.I.C.S.: 622110; 621610
Media: 1-13-22
Personnel:
Chris Van Gorder *(Pres & CEO)*
Richard K. Rothberger *(CFO & Corp Exec VP)*
A. Brent Eastman *(Chief Medical Officer & Sr VP)*
Richard R. Sheridan *(Gen Counsel, Sec & Sr VP)*
Victor V. Buzachero *(Sr VP-HR)*
June Komar *(Sr VP-Strategic Plng & Bus Dev)*

Advertising Agency:
Cone
(A Member of Omnicom Group)
855 Boylston St
Boston, MA 02116
Tel.: (617) 227-2111
Fax: (617) 523-3955

SCRIPPS MERCY HOSPITAL
(Sub. of Scripps)
4077 5th Ave
San Diego, CA 92103
Tel.: (619) 294-8111
Web Site: www.scripps.org
Approx. Number Employees: 2,000
Year Founded: 1890
Business Description:
Health Care Services
S.I.C.: 8062
N.A.I.C.S.: 622110
Media: 8-23
Personnel:
Tom Gammiere *(CEO & Sr VP)*

SECHRIST INDUSTRIES, INC.
4225 E La Palma Ave
Anaheim, CA 92807
Tel.: (714) 579-8400
Fax: (714) 579-0814
Toll Free: (800) SECHRIST
E-mail: info@sechristusa.com
Web Site: www.sechristusa.com
Approx. Number Employees: 100
Year Founded: 1972
Business Description:
Mfr. of Medical Products & Industrial Measuring Instruments
S.I.C.: 3841; 8011
N.A.I.C.S.: 339112; 621111
Import Export
Media: 2-6-7-10-13-20
Distr.: Natl.
Personnel:
Edward Pulwer *(Pres & CEO)*
John Razzano *(CFO)*
William I. Preuit *(Sr VP-Intl Sls & Mktg)*

Brands & Products:
MILLENNIUM
MONOPLACE
SAVI
SECHRIST
SMARTSYNC

SECUREALERT, INC.
150 W Civic Center Dr Ste 400
Sandy, UT 84070
Tel.: (801) 908-5132
Tel.: (801) 451-6141
Fax: (801) 451-6281
Toll Free: (866) 451-6141
E-mail: ir@securealert.com
Web Site: www.securealert.com
Approx. Rev.: $12,450,971
Approx. Number Employees: 186
Year Founded: 1997
Business Description:
Wireless Monitoring & Surveillance Products & Services Developer & Marketer
S.I.C.: 7382; 4812; 8099
N.A.I.C.S.: 561621; 517212; 621999
Advertising Expenditures: $87,567
Media: 17
Personnel:
David G. Derrick *(Chm & CEO)*
John L. Hastings, III *(Pres, COO & Dir)*
Chad D. Olsen *(CFO)*

SENETEK PLC
51 New Orleans Ct Ste 1A
Hilton Head Island, SC 29928
Tel.: (404) 418-6203
E-mail: ir@senetek.net
Web Site: www.senetekplc.com
Approx. Rev.: $1,693,920
Approx. Number Employees: 4
Year Founded: 1983
Business Description:
Metal, Oil & Gas Exploration Services; Pharmaceuticals & Skincare Mfr
S.I.C.: 1099; 1311; 2834; 2844
N.A.I.C.S.: 212299; 211111; 325412; 325620
Advertising Expenditures: $108,000
Media: 17
Personnel:
Anthony Williams *(Vice Chm & Sec)*
Howard Mattes Crosby *(Pres & CFO)*
John Patric Ryan *(CEO)*

SENTARA HEALTHCARE
6015 Poplar Hall Dr Ste 300
Norfolk, VA 23502
Tel.: (757) 455-7000
Fax: (757) 455-7964
Fax: (757) 455-7164
Toll Free: (800) 736-8272
Toll Free: (800) 552-7200
Web Site: www.sentara.com
Approx. Number Employees: 15,000
Business Description:
Operates Hospital & Health Care Services
S.I.C.: 8062; 6321
N.A.I.C.S.: 622110; 524114
Advertising Expenditures: $700,000
Media: 3-4-7-8-9-10-13-23-24-25-26
Personnel:
Howard P. Kern *(Pres & COO)*
David L. Bernd *(CEO)*
Robert A. Broerman *(CFO & Sr VP)*

Brands & Products:
EICU
SENTARA
SENTARA ECARE
YOUR COMMUNITY, NOT-FOR-PROFIT HEALTH CENTER

SEQUENOM, INC.
3595 John Hopkins Ct
San Diego, CA 92121-1331
Tel.: (858) 202-9000
Fax: (858) 202-9001
E-mail: sequenom@sequenom.com
Web Site: www.sequenom.com
Approx. Rev.: $47,459,000
Approx. Number Employees: 237
Business Description:
Gene Sequencing Research & Pharmaceutical Preparations
S.I.C.: 8733; 7371
N.A.I.C.S.: 541710; 541511; 541720
Advertising Expenditures: $400,000
Media: 10
Personnel:
Harry F. Hixson, Jr. *(Chm & CEO)*
Paul V. Maier *(CFO)*
Clarke Neumann *(Gen Counsel & VP)*
Ronald M. Lindsay *(Exec VP-R&D)*
Michael Monko *(Sr VP-Sls & Mktg)*
Robin G. Weiner *(Sr VP-Quality & Regulatory Affairs)*
William J. Welch *(Sr VP-Diagnostics)*
Alisa Judge *(VP-HR)*

Brands & Products:
CANCER EPIPANEL
EPIBROWSER
EPIDESIGNER
EPITYPER
FUSIO CHIP
IMPRINTING EPIPANEL
IPLEX
IPLEX GOLD
ISEQ
MASSARRAY
MASSARRAY EPITYPER
MASSARRAY MALDI TOF MS
MASSARRAY NANODISPENSER RS1000
MASSARRAY OLIGOCHECK
MASSARRAY QGE
MASSARRAY SNP DISCOVERY
MASSARRAY TYPER
MASSCLEAVE
MOUSE EPIPANEL
ONOCARTA
REAL SNP
REALSNP.COM
SECUREDX
SEQUENOM
SNP CREDITS
SPECTRO CHIP
STANDARD EPIPANEL
TYPEPLEX

Key to Media (For complete agency information see *The Advertising Red Books-Agencies* edition):
1. Bus. Publs. 2. Cable T.V. 3. Catalogs & Directories. 4. Co-op Adv. 5. Consumer Mags. 6. D.M. to Bus. Estab.7. D.M. to Consumers 8. Daily Newsp. 9. Exhibits/Trade Shows 10. Foreign 11. Infomercial 12. Internet Adv.13. Multimedia 14. Network Radio 15. Network T.V. 16. Newsp. Distr. Mags. 17. Other 18. Outdoor (Posters, Transit) 19. Point of Purchase20. Premiums, Novelties 21. Product Samples 22. Special Events Mktg. 23. Spot Radio 24. Spot T.V. 25. Weekly Newsp. 26. Yellow Page Adv.

SERACARE LIFE SCIENCES, INC.
37 Birch St
Milford, MA 01757
Tel.: (508) 244-6400
Fax: (508) 634-3394
Toll Free: (800) 676-1881
E-mail: info@seracare.com
Web Site: www.seracare.com
E-Mail For Key Personnel:
Sales Director: sales@seracare.net
Approx. Rev.: $50,380,140
Approx. Number Employees: 241
Year Founded: 2001
Business Description:
Plasma Collection for the Pharmaceutical Industry
S.I.C.: 2834
N.A.I.C.S.: 325412
Advertising Expenditures: $100,000
Media: 7-10
Personnel:
Susan L.N. Vogt *(Pres & CEO)*
Gregory A. Gould *(CFO)*
Kathi Benjamin *(VP-HR)*
Sean O'Connor *(VP-Sls & Mktg)*

SHAKLEE CORPORATION
(Joint Venture of Ripplewood Holdings LLC & Activated Holdings LLC)
4747 Willow Rd
Pleasanton, CA 94588-2763
Tel.: (925) 924-2000
Fax: (925) 924-2862
Toll Free: (800) SHAKLEE
E-mail: fieldcomm@shaklee.com
Web Site: www.shaklee.com
Approx. Number Employees: 400
Year Founded: 1956
Business Description:
Vitamins & Nutritional Products Distr; Jointly Owned by Ripplewood Holdings LLC (40.5%) & Activated Holdings LLC (40.5%)
S.I.C.: 5122
N.A.I.C.S.: 424210
Import Export
Media: 8
Distr.: Intl.; Natl.
Budget Set: Sept.
Personnel:
Roger Barnett *(Chm & CEO)*
Ken Harris *(CIO)*
Marjorie Fine *(Gen Counsel, Sec & Exec VP)*
Laura Hughes *(Sr VP-Sls & Field Dev)*
Cindy Latham *(Sr VP-Mktg)*
Craig Mansfield *(Sr VP-Mktg Svcs)*
Jim Greene *(VP-Product Dev)*
Brands & Products:
ACNE CLARIFYING COMPLEX
ACUITY PLUS
BESTWATER
C+E REPAIR P.M.
CALMING COMPLEX
CREATING HEALTHIER LIVES
DTX
ENFUSELLE
ENFUTOX
ESSENTIALS
FORMULA I
GARLIC
GTA PLUS
MOODLIFT
OPTIFLORA
OSTEOKINETIC
PEPPERMINT-GINGER PLUS
PHYTO FEM
SAW PALMETTO PLUS
SHAKLEE
SHAKLEE CLASSICS
SHAKLEE CORENERGY
SHAKLEE DR
SHAKLEE PERFORMANCE
SLIM PLAN GOLD
VALERIAN
Advertising Agency:
Lippe Taylor
215 Park Ave S 16th Fl
New York, NY 10003
Tel.: (212) 598-4400
Fax: (212) 598-0620

SHIONOGI PHARMA, INC.
(Sub. of Shionogi & Co., Ltd.)
5 Concourse Pkwy Ste 1800
Atlanta, GA 30328
Tel.: (770) 442-9707
Fax: (770) 442-9594
Toll Free: (800) 461-3696
E-mail: ir@sciele.com
Web Site: www.shionogipharma.com/default.aspx
Approx. Rev.: $382,255,000
Approx. Number Employees: 920
Year Founded: 1992
Business Description:
Brand Name Prescription Drugs Marketer & Sales to High-Prescribing Primary Care & Specialty Physicians
S.I.C.: 2834; 5122
N.A.I.C.S.: 325412; 424210
Advertising Expenditures: $32,100,000
Media: 2
Personnel:
Joseph J. Ciaffoni *(Pres)*
Darrell Borne *(CFO)*
Leslie Zacks *(Gen Counsel)*
Brands & Products:
ALTOPREV
COGNEX
FENOGLIDE
FORTAMET
FOSTEUM
FURADANTIN
MESCOLOR
METHYLIN CHEWABLE TABLETS
METHYLIN ORAL SOLUTION
OPTINATE
ORAPRED ODT
PONSTEL
PRENATE DHA
PRENATE ELITE
PRENATE GT
PROTUSS
ROBINUL
ROBINUL FORTE
RONDEC SYRUP
SCIELE
SULAR
TANAFED DMX
TANAFED DP
TRIGLIDE
TWINJECT
ZEBUTAL

SHOPPERS DRUG MART CORPORATION
243 Consumers Road
Toronto, ON M2J 4W8, Canada
Tel.: (416) 493-1220
Fax: (416) 491-7316
Web Site: www.shoppersdrugmart.ca
Approx. Sls.: $9,772,707,008
Approx. Number Employees: 1,100
Year Founded: 1962
Business Description:
Licensed & Company-Owned Drug Stores
S.I.C.: 5912
N.A.I.C.S.: 446110
Media: 4-6-8-9-13-14-18-19-21-22-25-26
Personnel:
Holger Kluge *(Chm)*
Domenic Pilla *(Pres & CEO)*
Bradley Lukow *(CFO & Exec VP)*
Mary-Alice Vuicic *(Chief Admin Officer & Exec VP-HR)*
Frank Pedinelli *(Gen Counsel & Sr VP-Legal)*
John Caplice *(Treas & Sr VP-IR & Corp Affairs)*
Adam Grabowski *(VP-Legal Affairs & Corp Sec)*
Mary Kelly *(Exec VP-Mdsg & Category Mgmt)*
Dorian Lo *(Exec VP-Pharmacy & Healthcare)*
Michael Motz *(Exec VP-Ops)*
Loreen Paananen *(Exec VP-Retail Dev)*
Mark Valesano *(Exec VP-Pharmacy)*
Chong Bang *(Sr VP-Mdsg & Global Sourcing)*
Erik Botines *(Sr VP-Peers Rels)*
Paul Damiani *(Sr VP-Healthcare Bus)*
Terry Landry *(Sr VP-Corp Infinity)*
Geoffrey Martin *(Sr VP-Bus Dev)*
Susanne Priest *(Sr VP-Pharmacy)*
Kevin Whibbs *(Sr VP-Logistics & Supply Chain)*
Becky Hong *(Dir-Front Store Pricing)*
Brands & Products:
HEALTHWATCH
PHARMAPRIX
SHOPPERS DRUG MART
SHOPPERS HOME HEALTH CARE
SHOPPERS OPTIMUM

SHRINERS HOSPITALS FOR CHILDREN
2900 Rocky Point Dr
Tampa, FL 33607-1460
Tel.: (813) 281-0300
Toll Free: (800) 237-5055
E-mail: shrinepr@shrinenet.org
Web Site: www.shrinershq.org
Approx. Rev.: $500,000,000
Approx. Number Employees: 6,100
Year Founded: 1922
Business Description:
Hospital Owner & Operator
S.I.C.: 8069
N.A.I.C.S.: 622310
Media: 7-8-13-20-22
Personnel:
Gene Bracewell *(Pres & CEO)*
Douglas Maxwel *(Pres)*
Advertising Agency:
tomsheehan worldwide
645 Penn St
Reading, PA 19601-3408
Tel.: (610) 478-8448
Fax: (610) 478-8449

SIEMENS MEDICAL SOLUTIONS DIAGNOSTICS
(Sub. of Siemens Healthcare Diagnostics)
511 Benedict Ave
Tarrytown, NY 10591-5005
Tel.: (914) 631-8000
Fax: (914) 524-2132
Telex: 219-264-8649
Web Site: diagnostics.siemens.com/
Approx. Number Employees: 815
Business Description:
Laboratory Testing, Test Instruments, Reagents & Diagnostic Telemedicine Systems
S.I.C.: 3826; 8733
N.A.I.C.S.: 334516; 541710
Export
Advertising Expenditures: $25,000,000
Media: 2-4-7-10-11-21
Distr.: Intl.; Natl.
Budget Set: June

SIEMENS, MOUNTAIN VIEW BRANCH
(Sub. of Siemens Corporation)
1230 Shorebird Way
Mountain View, CA 94039-7393
Mailing Address:
PO Box 7393
Mountain View, CA 94039-7393
Tel.: (650) 969-9112
Fax: (650) 968-1833
Fax: (650) 943-7006
Toll Free: (800) 422-8766
E-mail: webmaster@siemens.com
Web Site: www.acuson.com
Sales Range: $800-899.9 Million
Approx. Number Employees: 300
Year Founded: 1981
Business Description:
Mfr., Designer & Marketer of Medical Diagnostic Ultrasound Imaging Systems
S.I.C.: 3844; 3845; 5999
N.A.I.C.S.: 334517; 334510; 446199
Export
Media: 1-2-4-7-10-11-17-18-20-22
Distr.: Intl.
Personnel:
Norbert Gaus *(CEO)*
Brands & Products:
ASPEN ADVANCED ECHOCARDIOGRAPHY SYSTEM
ASPEN ADVANCED ULTRASOUND SYSTEM
ASPEN ECHOCARDIOGRAPHY SYSTEM
ASPEN ULTRASOUND SYSTEM
CYPRESS ECHOCARDIOGRAPHY SYSTEM
CYPRESS ULTRASOUND SYSTEM
DI-200
DICOM
KINET DX PACS SOLUTION
SEQUOIA 512
SEQUOIA C256
SONOLINE
SONOLINE ADARA
SONOLINE OMNIA
SONOLINE SIENNA
WEBPRO

SIGA TECHNOLOGIES, INC.
35 E 62nd St
New York, NY 10065
Tel.: (212) 672-9100
Fax: (212) 697-3130
E-mail: info@siga.com
Web Site: www.siga.com

Key to Media (For complete agency information see *The Advertising Red Books-Agencies* edition):
1. Bus. Publs. 2. Cable T.V. 3. Catalogs & Directories. 4. Co-op Adv. 5. Consumer Mags. 6. D.M. to Bus. Estab.7. D.M. to Consumers
8. Daily Newsp. 9. Exhibits/Trade Shows 10. Foreign 11. Infomercial 12. Internet Adv.13. Multimedia 14. Network Radio
15. Network T.V. 16. Newsp. Distr. Mags. 17. Other 18. Outdoor (Posters, Transit) 19. Point of Purchase20. Premiums, Novelties
21. Product Samples 22. Special Events Mktg. 23. Spot Radio 24. Spot T.V. 25. Weekly Newsp. 26. Yellow Page Adv.

Approx. Rev.: $19,215,837
Approx. Number Employees: 65
Year Founded: 1995
Business Description:
Infectious Disease Prevention & Treatment Pharmaceutical Developer & Mfr
S.I.C.: 2834
N.A.I.C.S.: 325412
Media: 17
Personnel:
Eric A. Rose *(Chm & CEO)*
Daniel J. Luckshire *(CFO & Exec VP)*
Dennis E. Hruby *(Chief Scientific Officer)*
Brands & Products:
HUMAN BIOARMOR
SIGA
ST-246
Advertising Agency:
KCSA Strategic Communications (Kanan, Corbin, Schupak & Aronow, Inc.)
880 3rd Ave 6th Fl
New York, NY 10022
Tel.: (212) 682-6300
Fax: (212) 697-0910

SIGNPATH PHARMA INC.
1375 California Rd
Quakertown, PA 18951
Tel.: (215) 538-9996
Fax: (215) 538-1245
Web Site: www.signpathpharma.com
Approx. Rev.: $40,783
Year Founded: 2006
Business Description:
Curcumin-Based Pharmaceuticals Researcher, Developer & Mfr
S.I.C.: 2834; 2836
N.A.I.C.S.: 325412; 325414
Advertising Expenditures: $49,175
Media: 17
Personnel:
Lawrence Helson *(CEO)*

SIMILASAN CORPORATION
(Div. of Similasan AG)
1745 Shea Center Dr
Highlands Ranch, CO 80129-1537
Tel.: (303) 539-4060
Fax: (303) 539-4061
Toll Free: (800) 426-1644, ext. 1
Web Site: www.similasanusa.com
Approx. Number Employees: 10
Business Description:
Over-the-Counter Homeopathic Medications Importer & Distr
S.I.C.: 2834
N.A.I.C.S.: 325412
Media: 2-3-6-10-13-14-15
Brands & Products:
ACTIVE RESPONSE FORMULA
EARACHE RELIEF
HEALTHY RELIEF

SIMPLEXITY HEALTH
565 Century Ct
Klamath Falls, OR 97601
Mailing Address:
PO Box 609
Klamath Falls, OR 97601-0329
Tel.: (541) 882-5406
Tel.: (541) 883-8848 (Customer Svc)
Fax: (541) 884-1869
Fax: (800) 797-8228
Toll Free: (800) 800-1300
E-mail: info@simplexityhealth.com
Web Site: www.simplexityhealth.com
Sales Range: $10-24.9 Million
Approx. Number Employees: 100
Business Description:
Nutritional Supplements Mfr & Distr
S.I.C.: 2834; 2833
N.A.I.C.S.: 325412; 325411
Media: 2-4-6-10-12-13
Personnel:
Jerry Anderson *(Pres & COO)*
Charlotte Carreira *(VP-Mktg & Sls)*
Brands & Products:
ALPHA GOLD
ALPHA SUN
ANIMAL MATRIX
ANTIOXIDANT ESSENTIALS
BG BAR
BIFIDUS
CONTAIN
COQSKIN
E-12 SUPER ENZYMES
ENERGY FOR LIFE
ENZYMES
ESSENTIAL MATRIX
ESSENTIALS
GOLDEN LILY
GRAPE SYNERGY
IMMUSUN
NATURAL BEAUTY ESSENTIALS
NATURALIGHT
NEW SEASONS
OMEGA GOLD
OMEGA SUN
ORIGINAL ESSENTIALS
ORIGINAL FORMULA ENZYMES
OSTEOSUN
OUR GREEN DRINK
PLANET FOOD
REALITY
RESISTANCE
SBGANYTIME
SIMPLE SOLUTION FOR TODAY'S COMPLEX LIFESTYLES
SIMPLEXITY HEALTH
SIMPLY SBGA
SPECTRABIOTIC
STEMPLEX
SUPER BLUE GREEN
SUPER Q10
SUPER SPROUTS AND ALGAE
SUPER SUN SMOOTHIE
VISION
VISION ESSENTIALS

SKLAR CORPORATION
889 S Matlack St
West Chester, PA 19382-4971
Tel.: (610) 430-3200
Fax: (610) 429-0500
Fax: (610) 696-9007 (Sales)
Toll Free: (800) 221-2166
E-mail: surgi@sklarcorp.com
Web Site: www.sklarcorp.com
Approx. Number Employees: 70
Year Founded: 1892
Business Description:
Surgical Instruments Mfr
S.I.C.: 5047
N.A.I.C.S.: 423450
Import
Media: 2-4-10
Distr.: Intl.; Natl.
Budget Set: Nov.
Personnel:
Donald Taylor *(Pres)*
Brands & Products:
ECONO
MERIT
SKLAR
SKLAR DISINFECTANT
SKLAR ENZYMATIC
SKLAR FRESH
SKLAR HAND SANITIZING GEL
SKLAR INSTRU-GUARD LUBE
SKLAR INSTRU-GUARD ONE-STEP
SKLAR INSTRUMENTS
SKLAR KLEEN LF
SKLAR KLEEN LIQUID
SKLAR KLEEN POWDER
SKLAR POLISH
SKLAR SOAK
SKLAR-ZYME
SKLARCUT
SKLARGRIP
SKLARHONE
SKLARLITE
SKLARTIP
SKLARTITE
SKLARTOUCH
SURGI-OR

SMILE BRANDS GROUP INC.
(Holding of Freeman Spogli & Co.)
201 E Sandpointe Ave Ste 800
Santa Ana, CA 92707-5778
Tel.: (714) 668-1300
Fax: (714) 428-1300
Web Site: www.smilebrands.com
Approx. Rev.: $445,024,000
Approx. Number Employees: 1,797
Business Description:
Dental Management Services
S.I.C.: 8742
N.A.I.C.S.: 541611
Advertising Expenditures: $9,500,000
Media: 6-8-9-13-18-23-24-25
Personnel:
Steve C. Bilt *(Pres & CEO)*
Bradley E. Schmidt *(CFO)*
Roy D. Smith *(COO)*
George J. Suda *(CIO)*
Neal Crowly *(Gen Counsel & Sr VP)*
Richard N. Brown *(Sr VP-Mktg & Sls)*
Dennis R. Fratt *(Sr VP-Ops Svcs Grp)*
Beth R. Goldstein *(Sr VP-HR)*
William P. McCarthy *(Sr VP-Real Estate & Facility Dev)*
Andrea Epstein *(VP-Mktg)*
Heidi Fisher *(VP-HR)*
Brands & Products:
BRIGHT NOW!
MONARCH DENTAL
NEWPORT DENTAL
SMILE BRANDS
SMILES FOR EVERYONE

SMITH & NEPHEW, INC., ENDOSCOPY DIVISION
(Div. of Smith & Nephew plc)
150 Minuteman Rd
Andover, MA 01810-5885
Tel.: (978) 749-1000
Fax: (800) 554-6105
Toll Free: (800) 343-5717
E-mail: endo.inquiry@smith-nephew.com
Web Site: www.endo.smith-nephew.com
Approx. Number Employees: 500
Business Description:
Mfr of Orthopedic Arthroscopy Products Including Television Cameras & Monitors, Endoscopes, Arthroscopes, Orthopedic Hand & Powered Instruments, Fiber Optic Illumination Systems, Laparoscopes & Surgical Instruments
S.I.C.: 3841
N.A.I.C.S.: 339112
Import Export
Media: 2-3-7-10-11
Personnel:
Mike Frazzette *(Pres)*
Joe Metzger *(Sr VP-Comm)*
Todd Usen *(Sr VP-Sls-US)*
Don A. Young *(Sr VP-Corp Sustainability)*
Sean Gallimore *(VP-Global Mktg)*

SMITHS MEDICAL MD, INC.
(Sub. of Smiths Medical)
1265 Grey Fox Rd
Saint Paul, MN 55112-6929
Tel.: (651) 633-2556
Fax: (651) 628-7153
Toll Free: (800) 426-2448
Web Site: www.smiths-medical.com
Approx. Number Employees: 100
Business Description:
Laboratory & Medical Equipment Mfr
S.I.C.: 3841; 8011
N.A.I.C.S.: 339112; 621111
Media: 2-6-7-10
Personnel:
Martha Sewall *(VP-Mktg)*
Brands & Products:
CADD
CADD-LEGACY
CADD-MICRO
CADD-PCA
CADD-PLUS
CADD-PRIZM
CADD TPN
DELTEC COZMO
P.A.S. PORT
PORT-A-CATH
VENTRA
Advertising Agency:
Simms & McIvor Marketing Communications
3121 Rt 22 E Branch Estates
Branchburg, NJ 08876-3500
Tel.: (908) 722-8777
Fax: (908) 722-7833

SOLTA MEDICAL, INC.
25881 Industrial Blvd
Hayward, CA 94545
Tel.: (510) 782-2286
Fax: (510) 782-2287
Toll Free: (877) 782-2286
E-mail: info@solta.com
Web Site: www.solta.com
Approx. Rev.: $110,932,000
Approx. Number Employees: 287
Year Founded: 1995
Business Description:
Develops, Manufactures & Markets Medical Devices for Non-Invasive Skin Treatment
S.I.C.: 3845; 3841; 3842
N.A.I.C.S.: 334510; 339112; 339113
Advertising Expenditures: $397,000
Personnel:
Stephen J. Fanning *(Chm, Pres & CEO)*
John Glenn *(CFO)*
Brands & Products:
NXT
RELIANT

SOLTA MEDICAL, INC. — (Continued)

RESULTS YOU CAN SEE & FEEL
SOLTAMEDICAL
THERMACOOL

SOMANETICS CORPORATION

(Sub. of Covidien Inc.)
2600 Troy Center Dr
Troy, MI 48084-4771
Tel.: (248) 244-1400
Fax: (248) 244-0978
Toll Free: (800) 359-7662
E-mail: customerservice@somanetics.com
Web Site: www.somanetics.com
Approx. Rev.: $50,013,734
Approx. Number Employees: 133
Year Founded: 1982
Business Description:
Noninvasive Patient Monitoring Systems Mfr & Sales
S.I.C.: 3841; 3845
N.A.I.C.S.: 339112; 334510
Media: 2-13
Personnel:
Bruce J. Barrett *(Pres & CEO)*
William M. Iacona *(CFO, Treas, VP & Controller)*
Arik Allan Anderson *(Sr VP-Ops/R & D)*
Dominic J. Spadafore *(Sr VP-Sls & Mktg)*
Brands & Products:
AREA UNDER THE CURVE
AUC
CORRESTORE
ENLIGHTENING MEDICINE
ICURO
INVOS
OXYALERT
OXYALERT NIRSENSOR
REFLECTING THE COLOR OF LIFE
SCR
SOMANETICS
SOMANETICS ALLIANCE
SOMASENSOR
WINDOW TO THE BRAIN

SONA MEDSPA INTERNATIONAL, INC.

(Holding of Carousel Capital Partners)
(d/b/a Sona MedSpa)
10740 Sikes Pl Ste 120
Charlotte, NC 28277
Tel.: (980) 233-3200
Fax: (615) 591-5041
E-mail: info@sonamedspa.com
Web Site: www.sonamedspa.com
Approx. Number Employees: 80
Year Founded: 1997
Business Description:
Laser Medical Spa Services Franchisor
S.I.C.: 8093
N.A.I.C.S.: 621498
Media: 6-7-8-9-10-13-18-19-21-22-23-24-26
Personnel:
Heather Rose *(Chm)*
Pat Fox *(CFO)*
Kurt Schusterman *(CMO)*
Brands & Products:
SONA
SONA CONCEPT

SOURCE NATURALS

(Sub. of Threshold Enterprises, Ltd.)
23 Janis Way
Scotts Valley, CA 95066
Tel.: (831) 438-6851
Fax: (831) 438-7410
Toll Free: (800) 815-2333
E-mail: csp1@thresholdent.com
Web Site: www.sourcenaturals.com
Year Founded: 1982
Business Description:
Nutritional Formulations Mfr
S.I.C.: 2834
N.A.I.C.S.: 325412
Media: 2-3-4-5-6-7-8-9-13-17-18-20-21-24-25
Personnel:
Ira Goldberg *(CEO)*
Todd Williams *(Mgr-Mktg Programs)*
Brands & Products:
ALLER-RESPONSE
ALLERCETIN
ATTENTIVE CHILD
CHOLES-RESPONSE
CHOLESTREX
ELAN VITAL
ESSENTIAL ENZYMES
FIBRO-RESPONSE
GLUCO-SCIENCE
GLUCOSAMEND
HEART SCIENCE
HIGHER MIND
LIFE FORCE
LIVER GUARD
LUSTRE
MALE RESPONSE
MEGAMIND
MENOPAUSE MULTIPLE
MENTAL EDGE
MONTHLY COMFORT
MOOD BALANCE
MUSCLE MASS
NIGHTREST
POLICOSANOL CHOLESTEROL COMPLEX
POSITIVE THOUGHTS
PROSTA-RESPONSE
SKIN ETERNAL PLUS
ULTRA BONE BALANCE
ULTRA-CAL NIGHT
ULTRA JOINT RESPONSE
VISUAL EYES
WELLNESS COLD & FLU
WELLNESS COUGH SYRUP
WELLNESS EARACHE
WELLNESS FORMULA
WELLNESS MULTIPLE

SOUTH BROWARD HOSPITAL DISTRICT

(d/b/a Memorial Healthcare System)
3501 Johnson St
Hollywood, FL 33021
Tel.: (954) 987-2000
Fax: (954) 265-3412
E-mail: info@mhs.net
Web Site: www.mhs.net
Sales Range: $700-749.9 Million
Approx. Number Employees: 7,000
Business Description:
Public Healthcare Services
S.I.C.: 8062
N.A.I.C.S.: 622110
Personnel:
Shane Strum *(Chm)*
Frank V. Sacco *(CEO)*
Matthew J. Muhart *(CFO)*

Advertising Agency:
ME&V
6711 Chancellor Dr
Cedar Falls, IA 50613-6969
Tel.: (319) 268-9151
Fax: (319) 268-0124
Toll Free: (877) WEBEASY

SPACELABS MEDICAL, INC.

(Sub. of OSI Systems, Inc.)
5150 220th Ave SE
Issaquah, WA 98029
Mailing Address:
PO Box 7018
Issaquah, WA 98027-7018
Tel.: (425) 657-7200
Fax: (425) 657-7212
Toll Free: (800) 522-7025
Web Site: www.spacelabs.com
Sales Range: $450-499.9 Million
Approx. Number Employees: 1,177
Year Founded: 1958
Business Description:
Mfr. of Healthcare Information Technologies Including Information Systems, Patient Monitoring Equipment, Diagnostic & Consumer Monitoring Products & Supplies
S.I.C.: 3845; 3841
N.A.I.C.S.: 334510; 339112
Export
Media: 2-4-7-8-10
Distr.: Intl.; Natl.
Budget Set: Oct.
Personnel:
Gary Grenter *(Pres & CEO)*
Alen Edrick *(CFO)*
Joseph Davin *(Pres-Global Sls & Mktg)*
Nicholas Ong *(Pres-Anesthesia Delivery & Ventilation)*
Victor Sze *(Gen Counsel & Sec)*
Roy Davin *(VP-Product Dev)*

SPAN-AMERICA MEDICAL SYSTEMS, INC.

70 Commerce Ctr
Greenville, SC 29615-5814
Mailing Address:
PO Box 5231
Greenville, SC 29606-5231
Tel.: (864) 288-8877
Fax: (864) 288-8692
Toll Free: (800) 888-6752
E-mail: info@spanamerica.com
Web Site: www.spanamerica.com
Approx. Sls.: $52,355,662
Approx. Number Employees: 218
Year Founded: 1975
Business Description:
Mfr of Medical Mattress Products, Foam Pads & Pillows; Packaging Services for Consumer & Medical Products
S.I.C.: 3086; 2676
N.A.I.C.S.: 326150; 322291
Export
Advertising Expenditures: $1,801,000
Personnel:
James D. Ferguson *(Pres & CEO)*
Richard C. Coggins *(CFO, Sec & VP-Fin)*
James R. O'Reagan *(VP-R&D & Engrg)*
Clyde A. Shew *(VP-Medical Sls & Mktg)*
Jim Ross *(Mgr-Sls)*

Brands & Products:
ATLAS
CFT
EASY AIR
THE EQUALIZER
EZ-DISH
GEL-T
GEO-MATT
GEO-MATTRESS
GEO-WAVE
HEEL SLOPE
INNOVATIVE SOLUTIONS.
ISCH-DISH
PRESSUREGUARD
PRESSUREGUARD RENEW
RING-OF-AIR
SACRAL DISH
SAFETY EDGE
SECURE I.V.
SELAN
SPAN AMERICA
SPAN+AIDS
THERA-FOAM
TURN SELECT
WINGS

THE SPECTRANETICS CORPORATION

9965 Federal Dr
Colorado Springs, CO 80921
Tel.: (719) 633-8333
Fax: (719) 633-8791
Fax: (719) 447-2022
E-mail: webmaster@spectranetics.com
Web Site: www.spectranetics.com
Approx. Rev.: $117,917,000
Approx. Number Employees: 470
Year Founded: 1984
Business Description:
Medical Appliances & Equipment Mfr
S.I.C.: 3845; 3841
N.A.I.C.S.: 334510; 339112
Advertising Expenditures: $300,000
Media: 2-10
Personnel:
Scott Drake *(Pres & CEO)*
Guy A. Childs *(CFO & VP)*
Roger W. Wertheimer *(Gen Counsel, Sec & VP-HR)*
Jason D. Hein *(Sr VP-Sls, Mktg & Exec Council Member)*
Shahriar Matin *(Sr VP-Ops, Product Dev, Intl & Exec Council Member)*
Jennifer Vaughan *(Dir-Sls-US)*
Brands & Products:
CLIRPATH TURBO
CROSS-PILOT
CVX-300
ELCA
EXTREME
LEAD LOCKING DEVICE
LLD EZ
POINT 9
QUICK-CROSS
SPECTRANETICS
SPECTRANETICS LASER SHEATH
THROMCAT
TURBO-BOOSTER
TURBO ELITE
VITESSE
WE GET YOUR BLOOD FLOWING

SPECTRASCIENCE, INC.

11568 Sorrento Valley Rd Ste 11
San Diego, CA 92121
Tel.: (858) 847-0200
Fax: (858) 847-0880

Key to Media (For complete agency information see *The Advertising Red Books-Agencies* edition):
1. Bus. Publs. 2. Cable T.V. 3. Catalogs & Directories. 4. Co-op Adv. 5. Consumer Mags. 6. D.M. to Bus. Estab.7. D.M. to Consumers 8. Daily Newsp. 9. Exhibits/Trade Shows 10. Foreign 11. Infomercial 12. Internet Adv.13. Multimedia 14. Network Radio 15. Network T.V. 16. Newsp. Distr. Mags. 17. Other 18. Outdoor (Posters, Transit) 19. Point of Purchase20. Premiums, Novelties 21. Product Samples 22. Special Events Mktg. 23. Spot Radio 24. Spot T.V. 25. Weekly Newsp. 26. Yellow Page Adv.

E-mail: info@spectrascience.com
Web Site: www.spectrascience.com
Approx. Rev.: $23,650
Approx. Number Employees: 6
Business Description:
Non-Invasive Cancer Detection Products Mfr
S.I.C.: 3841
N.A.I.C.S.: 339112
Media: 10
Personnel:
Michael P. Oliver *(Pres & CEO)*
James W. Dorst *(CFO)*
Mike Brady *(Dir-Engrg)*
Todd Pinkowski *(Dir-Ops)*
Michael V. Vaudry *(Dir-Sls-Intl)*
Brands & Products:
WAVSTAT

SPECTRUM LABORATORIES INC.
18617 S Broadwick St
Compton, CA 90220
Tel.: (310) 885-4600
Fax: (310) 885-3330
E-mail: customerservice@spectrumlabs.com
Web Site: www.spectrumlabs.com
Sales Range: $10-24.9 Million
Approx. Number Employees: 116
Business Description:
Surgical & Medical Instruments
S.I.C.: 3841; 3821
N.A.I.C.S.: 339112; 339111
Advertising Expenditures: $171,000
Media: 4-8-10-19
Personnel:
Roy T. Eddleman *(Chm & CEO)*
Anthony J. Macdonald *(Pres)*
Brian A. Watts *(CFO & VP-Fin)*
Brands & Products:
CELLFLO
CELLGAS
CELLMAX
CHROM
CLEAR BATH
CULTUREGARD
DISPODIALYZER
DRAWER/GANIZERS
DYNAFIBRE
DYNAGARD
FLEAKER
FLOAT-A-LYZER
GANIZERS
GLENCO
HY N DRY
KROSFLO
LEADING THE WAY IN BIOSEPARATION
MEDIAKAP
MEDIDROPPERS
MESH
MICRO DISPODIALYZER
MICRO-PRODICON
MICROGON
MICROKROS
MIDIKROS
MINIKAP
MINIKROS
MOLECULAR
MOLECULAR/POR
PHARMFLO
RAPID WRAP
REFRIG/ARRANGERS
SELEXTRAC
SILENT SWIRL
SPECTRA/CHROM
SPECTRA/GEL
SPECTRA MESH
SPECTRA/POR
SPECTRUM
SPECTRUMLABS.COM
STROLL
SUPERFLO
TRANSFERTUBE
TRIAC
VACU/TROL
ZYMAX

SPECTRUM ORGANIC PRODUCTS, INC.
(Sub. of The Hain Celestial Group, Inc.)
5341 Old Redwood Hwy Ste 400
Petaluma, CA 94954
Tel.: (631) 730-2200
Fax: (707) 765-8470
E-mail: spectrumnaturals@netdex.com
Web Site:
www.spectrumorganics.com
Sales Range: $25-49.9 Million
Approx. Number Employees: 25
Year Founded: 1980
Business Description:
Organic & Natural Culinary & Nutritional Oils Mfr
S.I.C.: 2079; 2099
N.A.I.C.S.: 311225; 311942
Media: 2-4-6
Personnel:
Jethren Phillips *(Founder & Chm)*
Advertising Agency:
Foerstel Design
753 Walnut St
Boise, ID 83712
Tel.: (208) 345-6656

SPERIAN EYE & FACE PROTECTION INC.
(Sub. of Sperian Protection SA)
900 Douglas Pkwy
Smithfield, RI 02917
Tel.: (401) 233-0333
Fax: (401) 232-2230
E-mail: eosley@bacou-dalloz.com
Web Site: www.sperian.com/Americas/Product_Catalog/Gloves.aspx
Business Description:
Chemical Product & Preparation Mfr
S.I.C.: 2899
N.A.I.C.S.: 325998
Personnel:
Erica L. Osley, Sr. *(Dir-Global Mktg)*
Advertising Agency:
Nail Communications
63 Eddy St
Providence, RI 02903
Tel.: (401) 331-6245
Fax: (401) 331-2987

SPHERIX INC.
6430 Rockledge Dr #503
Bethesda, MD 20817
Tel.: (301) 897-2540
Fax: (301) 897-2567
Toll Free: (866) SPHERIX
E-mail: info@spherix.com
Web Site: www.spherix.com
Approx. Rev.: $1,432,452
Approx. Number Employees: 9
Year Founded: 1967
Business Description:
Pharmaceutical Products Mfr; Regulatory & Technical Consulting Services
S.I.C.: 2834; 8748
N.A.I.C.S.: 325412; 541690
Advertising Expenditures: $300,000
Media: 2-7-10
Distr.: Intl.; Natl.
Personnel:
Gilbert V. Levin *(Founder)*
Robert J. Vander Zanden *(Chm)*
Robert A. Lodder, Jr. *(Pres)*
Claire L. Kruger *(CEO & COO)*
Robert L. Clayton *(CFO & Treas)*
Y. Lu *(Mgr-R&D)*
Brands & Products:
NATURLOSE

S.S.S. COMPANY
71 University Ave
Atlanta, GA 30315
Tel.: (404) 521-0857
Fax: (404) 880-0383
Toll Free: (800) 237-3843
Web Site:
www.ssspharmaceuticals.com
Approx. Number Employees: 40
Year Founded: 1826
Business Description:
Over-the-Counter Drugs Mfr
S.I.C.: 2834
N.A.I.C.S.: 325412
Media: 2-4-5-6-11-14-19-21
Distr.: Intl.; Natl.
Budget Set: Oct. -Dec.
Personnel:
Charles M. Bentley *(Chm & Pres)*
Brands & Products:
20/20
BURN-O JEL
CURASORE
FUNG-O
HDA TOOTHACHE GEL
MOTHER'S FRIEND
NUMOL
PFEIFFER
SSS
TETTERINE
THROTO-CEPTIC
WASSER

ST. ALPHONSUS REGIONAL MEDICAL CENTER
(Unit of Trinity Health)
1055 N Curtis Rd
Boise, ID 83706-1352
Tel.: (208) 367-2121
Fax: (208) 367-3123
Web Site: www.saintalphonsus.org
Sales Range: $75-99.9 Million
Approx. Number Employees: 3,000
Business Description:
Health Care
S.I.C.: 8062
N.A.I.C.S.: 622110
Personnel:
Kristen Micheletti *(Dir-Mktg & Comm)*
Advertising Agency:
Stoltz Marketing Group
615 W Main St 2nd Fl
Boise, ID 83702
Tel.: (208) 388-0766
Fax: (208) 388-0764

ST. JOHN HEALTH
(Sub. of Ascension Health, Inc.)
28000 Dequindre Rd
Warren, MI 48092-2468
Tel.: (586) 753-1911
Fax: (586) 753-0745
Web Site: www.stjohn.org
Approx. Number Employees: 900
Business Description:
Hospital Operator
S.I.C.: 8062
N.A.I.C.S.: 622110
Personnel:
Patricia Maryland *(Pres & CEO)*
Patrick McGuire *(CFO)*
Paul Van Tiem *(COO & Exec VP)*
Daniela Scholl *(Mgr-PR)*
Advertising Agencies:
Airfoil Public Relations
1000 Town Ctr Dr Ste 600
Southfield, MI 48075
Tel.: (248) 304-1400
Fax: (248) 304-1401
Toll Free: (866) AIRFOIL
Inpatient Care

Publicis in Mid America
200 S Meridian St Ste 500
Indianapolis, IN 46225-1076
Tel.: (317) 639-5135
Fax: (317) 639-5134

ST. JUDE CHILDREN'S RESEARCH HOSPITAL
332 N Lauderdale St
Memphis, TN 38105-2729
Tel.: (901) 495-3300
Fax: (901) 495-3103
E-mail: info@stjude.org
Web Site: www.stjude.org
Sales Range: $75-99.9 Million
Approx. Number Employees: 3,200
Business Description:
Pediatric Childrens Cancer Research
S.I.C.: 8733; 8062
N.A.I.C.S.: 541720; 622110
Media: 1-6-7-8-9-11-13-14-15-18-22-26
Distr.: Intl.
Personnel:
Emily Callahan *(CMO)*
George Shadroui *(Sr VP)*
Advertising Agencies:
Alianda
11579 Vicolo Loop
Windermere, FL 34786
Tel.: (407) 694-5210

FAME
60 S Sixth St Ste 2600
Minneapolis, MN 55402
Tel.: (612) 746-3263
Fax: (612) 746-3333

Russ Reid Company, Inc.
2 N Lake Ave Ste 600
Pasadena, CA 91101-1868
Tel.: (626) 449-6100
Fax: (626) 449-6190
Toll Free: (800) 275-0430

ST. JUDE MEDICAL, INC.
1 Lillehei Plz
Saint Paul, MN 55117-9983
Tel.: (651) 483-2000
Fax: (651) 756-3301
Toll Free: (800) 328-9634
Web Site: www.sjm.com
Approx. Sls.: $5,164,771,000
Approx. Number Employees: 15,000
Year Founded: 1976

St. Jude Medical, Inc. — (Continued)

Business Description:
Cardiovascular Medical Devices Mfr, Distr & Marketer
S.I.C.: 3821; 2676; 3842; 3844; 3845; 3999
N.A.I.C.S.: 339111; 322291; 334510; 334517; 339113; 339999
Import Export
Media: 2-4
Personnel:
Daniel J. Starks *(Chm, Pres & CEO)*
Michael T. Rousseau *(Grp Pres)*
John C. Heinmiller *(CFO & Exec VP)*
Thomas R. Northenscold *(CIO & VP-IT)*
Mark D. Carlson *(Chief Medical Officer & Sr VP-Res, Clinical Affairs)*
Denis M. Gestin *(Pres-Intl)*
Pamela S. Krop *(Gen Counsel, Sec & VP)*
Angela D. Craig *(VP-Corp Rel & HR)*
Brands & Products:
ACAP
ACCENT
ACROSS
ACTIVE BALANCING
AESCULA
AF SUPPRESSION
AFFINITY
AGILIS
ANALYST ACEL
ANGIO-SEAL
ANTHEM
APEEL
ATLAS
ATLAS II
ATTUNE
AUTOCAPTURE
AV PLUS
BICOR
BIVCAP
BRK
COMFORT GRIP
CONTOUR
COOL PATH
COOL POINT
CPS AIM
CPS COURIER
CPS DIRECT
CPS DUO
CPS LUMINARY
CPS VENTURE
CURRENT
CURRENT ACCEL
DEFT RESPONSE
DIRECT TO TARGET
DIRECTALERTS
DIRECTCALL
DUAL-8
DURAL-REACH
DURATA
ENSITE ARRAY
ENSITE CONNECT
ENSITE FUSION
ENSITE NAVX
ENSITE SYSTEM
ENSITE VERISMO
ENTITY
EP-4
EP-WORKMATE
EPIC
EPICOR
EVALUATOR
FAST-CATH
FAST-PASS
FLEXFIT
FRONTIER
GUIDERIGHT
HOUSECALL PLUS
HP
HYDROSTEER
IDENTITY
INQUIRY
INTEGRITY
ISOFLEX
LINKMATE
LIVEWIRE
LIVEWIRE TC
LOCATOR
LUMA-CATH
MAXIMUM
MERLIN
MERLIN HOME
MERLIN.NET
MICRONY
MORE CONTROL LESS RISK
NURSEMATE
OMNISENSE
OPTIM
OPTISENSE
PACEL
PASSIVE PLUS
PREMERE
PROMOTE
PROMOTE ACCEL
PROXIS
QUICKFLEX
QUICKOPT
QUICKSITE
REFLEXION
REFLEXION SPIRAL
REFLEXION SPIRAL X
REGENCY
RESPONSE
RIATA
SAFIRE
SJM
SJM BIOCOR
SJM CONFIRM
SJM ENCAP
SJM REGENT
SJM TAILOR
SMARTSCHEDULE
SPL
ST. JUDE MEDICAL
SUPREME
SUTURE
SWARTZ
TAILORED THERAPY
TEN TEN
TENDRIL
THERAPY
TIGERWIRE
TVL
ULTIMUM
ULTRACINCH
ULTRAVAND
VECT SELECT
VENTURE
VERITY
VICTORY
VIEWFLEX
VIEWMATE
VIP
ZEPHYR
Advertising Agency:
TripleInk
60 S 6th St Ste 2800
Minneapolis, MN 55402
Tel.: (612) 342-9800
Fax: (612) 342-9745
Toll Free: (800) 632-1388

ST. VINCENT MEDICAL CENTER

(Sub. of Daughters of Charity Health System)
2131 W 3rd St
Los Angeles, CA 90057-1901
Tel.: (213) 484-7111
Fax: (213) 484-9304
Web Site:
www.stvincentmedicalcenter.org
Approx. Number Employees: 1,500
Business Description:
Medical Center
S.I.C.: 8062
N.A.I.C.S.: 622110
Media: 6-17
Personnel:
Catherine Fickes *(CFO)*

STAAR SURGICAL COMPANY

1911 Walker Ave
Monrovia, CA 91016-4846
Tel.: (626) 303-7902
Fax: (626) 303-2962
E-mail: info@staar.com
Web Site: www.staar.com
E-Mail For Key Personnel:
President: execoffices@staar.com
Approx. Sls.: $54,958,000
Approx. Number Employees: 279
Year Founded: 1982
Business Description:
Ophthalmic Devices & Vision Implants Mfr
S.I.C.: 3842; 3841; 3851
N.A.I.C.S.: 339113; 339112; 339115
Import Export
Media: 13
Personnel:
Don M. Bailey *(Chm)*
Barry G. Caldwell *(Pres & CEO)*
Deborah J. Andrews *(CFO & VP)*
Donald J. Todd *(Pres-Asia Pacific)*
William W. Goodmen *(VP-HR-Global)*
Robin Hughes *(VP-Mktg)*
Brands & Products:
ACRYLIC
AFINITY
AQUAFLOW
AUTO-CORRELATION
COLLAMER
CRUISE CONTROL
ELASTIMIDE
MICRO TIP CARTRIDGE
MICROSTAAR
PERIVENT
RANDOM PULSE
SILICONE
SONIC WAVE
STAAR
STAAR ELASTIC LENS
STAAR ELASTIMIDE
STAAR TORIC
STAARVISC
TORIC
TORIC ICL
ULTRAVAC
VISIAN ICL
VISIAN TORIC ICL
VISION OF THE FUTURE

STAMFORD HEALTH SYSTEM INC.

30 Shelbourne Rd
Stamford, CT 06904
Tel.: (203) 276-1000
Web Site: www.stamhealth.org
Sales Range: $250-299.9 Million
Approx. Number Employees: 1,900
Business Description:
Health Care Services
S.I.C.: 8741
N.A.I.C.S.: 561110
Personnel:
Brian Grissler *(Pres & CEO)*
Scott Orstad *(Mgr-Comm)*
Advertising Agency:
Catalyst Marketing Communications Inc.
2777 Summer St Ste 301
Stamford, CT 06905
Tel.: (203) 348-7541
Fax: (203) 348-5688

STARKEY LABORATORIES, INC.

6700 Washington Ave S
Eden Prairie, MN 55344
Tel.: (952) 941-6401
Fax: (952) 828-9262
Toll Free: (800) 328-8602
Web Site: www.starkey.com
Sales Range: $250-299.9 Million
Approx. Number Employees: 3,300
Year Founded: 1967
Business Description:
Customized Hearing Aids Mfr
S.I.C.: 3845; 7629
N.A.I.C.S.: 334510; 811211
Import Export
Media: 2-4-7-10-17
Distr.: Natl.
Personnel:
William F. Austin *(Founder & CEO)*
Scott Nelson *(CFO)*
Keith Guggenberger *(Sr VP-Ops)*
Larry Miller *(Sr VP-HR)*
Lisa Kagel *(Sr Dir-Customer Relations)*
Chris McCormick *(Sr Dir- Mktg & Comm)*
Lisa Richard *(Sr Dir-Customer Rels)*
Thomas Victorian *(Dir-Continuation Engrg)*
Brands & Products:
BLUWAVE
DAVINCI
DESTINY
DRIVE ARCHITECTURE
ELI
LEXIS
LISTENHEAR
S SERIES
SOUNDPORT
STARKEY

STEN CORPORATION

10275 Wayzata Blvd Ste 310
Hopkins, MN 55305-1661
Tel.: (952) 545-2776
Fax: (952) 545-2795
E-mail: info@stencorporation.com
Web Site: www.stencorporation.com
Sales Range: $10-24.9 Million
Approx. Number Employees: 14
Year Founded: 1978
Business Description:
Automobile Finance Services
S.I.C.: 6371
N.A.I.C.S.: 525990
Advertising Expenditures: $177,563
Media: 4-13-19
Personnel:
Kenneth W. Brimmer *(CEO)*

Key to Media (For complete agency information see *The Advertising Red Books-Agencies* edition):
1. Bus. Publs. 2. Cable T.V. 3. Catalogs & Directories. 4. Co-op Adv. 5. Consumer Mags. 6. D.M. to Bus. Estab.7. D.M. to Consumers
8. Daily Newsp. 9. Exhibits/Trade Shows 10. Foreign 11. Infomercial 12. Internet Adv.13. Multimedia 14. Network Radio
15. Network T.V. 16. Newsp. Distr. Mags. 17. Other 18. Outdoor (Posters, Transit) 19. Point of Purchase20. Premiums, Novelties
21. Product Samples 22. Special Events Mktg. 23. Spot Radio 24. Spot T.V. 25. Weekly Newsp. 26. Yellow Page Adv.

Brands & Products:
STEN

THE STEPHAN COMPANY
1850 W McNab Rd
Fort Lauderdale, FL 33309-1012
Tel.: (954) 971-0600
Fax: (954) 971-2633
E-mail: information@thestephanco.com
Web Site: www.thestephanco.com
Sales Range: $10-24.9 Million
Approx. Number Employees: 90
Year Founded: 1897
Business Description:
Hair, Cosmetic & Ethnic Products
S.I.C.: 2844; 2841; 5999
N.A.I.C.S.: 325620; 325611; 446199
Media: 5
Personnel:
Frank F. Ferola *(Chm, Pres & CEO)*
Robert C. Spindler *(CFO)*
Tyler Kiester *(Asst Sec)*
Brands & Products:
BALM BARR
CASHMERE BOUQUET
FRANCES DENNEY
MODERN & IMAGE
NATURE'S PET
PROTEIN 29
QUINSANA
SENSITIVE
THE STEPHAN COMPANY
STEPHAN'S
STIFF STUFF
STRETCH MARK
TREVOR SORBIE OF AMERICA
WILDROOT

STEREOTAXIS, INC.
4320 Forest Park Ave Ste 100
Saint Louis, MO 63108
Tel.: (314) 678-6172
Fax: (314) 678-6159
Toll Free: (866) 646-2346
E-mail: jstolze@sterotaxis.com
Web Site: www.stereotaxis.com
Approx. Rev.: $54,051,237
Approx. Number Employees: 204
Year Founded: 1990
Business Description:
Cardiology Instrument Control System Designer, Mfr & Marketer
S.I.C.: 3845; 3841
N.A.I.C.S.: 334510; 339112
Import Export
Media: 7-8-10-18
Personnel:
Fred A. Middleton *(Chm)*
Michael P. Kaminski *(Pres & CEO)*
Samuel W. Duggan *(CFO)*
Douglas M. Bruce *(COO & CTO)*
J. David Burkhardt *(Chief Medical Officer)*
Melissa C. Walker *(Sr VP-Regulatory, Quality, Clinical & Compliance)*
David A. Griffin *(VP-HR)*
Brands & Products:
ASSERT
CARDIODRIVE
CRONUS
GENTLETOUCH
HELIOS
NAVIGANT
NIOBE
STEREOTAXIS
STEREOTAXIS SYSTEM
TITAN

Advertising Agency:
Dovetail
12 Maryland Plz
Saint Louis, MO 63108-1502
Tel.: (314) 361-9800
Fax: (314) 361-9801

STERIS CORPORATION
5960 Heisley Rd
Mentor, OH 44060-1834
Tel.: (440) 354-2600
Fax: (440) 639-4450
Toll Free: (800) JIT-4-USE
E-mail: webmaster@steris.com
Web Site: www.steris.com
E-Mail For Key Personnel:
President: Les_Vinney@steris.com
Approx. Rev.: $1,207,448,000
Approx. Number Employees: 5,000
Year Founded: 1987
Business Description:
Mfr of Infection Prevention, Contamination Prevention, Microbial Reduction & Surgical Support Products & Services to Healthcare, Scientific, Research, Food & Industrial Customers
S.I.C.: 3842; 3841
N.A.I.C.S.: 339113; 339112
Export
Advertising Expenditures: $6,013,000
Media: 2-13
Personnel:
John P. Wareham *(Chm)*
Walter M. Rosebrough, Jr. *(Pres & CEO)*
Michael J. Tokich *(CFO & Sr VP)*
Peter A. Burke *(CTO & Sr VP)*
Timothy L. Chapman *(Pres-Healthcare & Sr VP)*
Robert E. Moss *(Pres-Isomedix Svcs & Life Sciences & Sr VP)*
Mark D. McGinley *(Gen Counsel, Sec & Sr VP)*
Gerard J. Reis *(Sr VP-Govt Affairs)*
Dan Carestio *(VP-Sls & Mktg)*
Mark Fraser *(Dir-Midwest Plant Ops)*
Dennis Kanupp *(Dir-Ops)*
Stephen Norton *(Dir-Corp Comm)*
Robin Baum *(Mgr-Media Rels)*
Kevin Cmiel *(Mgr-Corp Sls)*
Brands & Products:
1-STROKE ENVIRON
ACUTE-KARE
ADI-ZYME
ALCARE
ALCARE PLUS
AMERSE
AMSCO
AMSCO CENTURY
AMSCRUB
AQUAGEL
BACTOSHIELD
BASIL
CAGE-KLENZ
CAL STAT
CENTURY
CHEMDI
CHEMEXPRESS
CIP
CMAX
COVERAGE
COVERAGE PLUS NPD
CRIT-KLENZ
DART
DEEPSITE
EAGLEPAC
ECOCYCLE 10
ECOLINE
ENVIROSYSTEMS
ENZYCARE
EO STEL SCAN
EXAMINER
FINN-AQUA
FLEXMATIC
FOAM 140
GASTAPE
GLASS-KLENZ
HAMO
HARMONY
HAUSTED
HERMES-READY
HINGE-FREE
KINDEST KARE
KLENZYME
LABKLENZ
LYOVAC
MANU-KLENZ
MAXLIFE
MILLENIUM
ONE SOLUTION
ORTHOVISION
PRE-KLENZ
PRIMA-KARE
PROCESS KLENZ
PROKLENZ
PROLYSTICA
RELIANCE
SAFECYCLE
SCRUBMATE
SEPTIHOL
SEPTISOL
SOFT N SURE
SPLIT
SPOR-KLENZ
SPORDEX
SPORDI
STANDARD SIDERAIL
STAPHENE
STEAM TAPE
STERAFFIRM
STERIS
STERIS-ZYME
SURGIGRAPHIC
SYNERGY
SYSTEM 1
SYSTEM 1E
TEMP-A-SURE
VAPROX
VERIFY
VESPHENE
VESTA-SYDE
VHP
VIS-U-ALL
WEINBERGER
WESCODYNE
ZOLVSTAT
Advertising Agencies:
APCO Worldwide
700 12th St NW Ste 800
Washington, DC 20005
Tel.: (202) 778-1000
Fax: (202) 466-6002

Stevens Strategic Communications, Inc.
Gemini Towers, Ste 500, 1991 Crocker Rd
Westlake, OH 44115-1900
Tel.: (440) 617-0100
Fax: (440) 614-0529

STIEFEL LABORATORIES, INC.
(Sub. of GlaxoSmithKline Plc)
255 Alhambra Cir Ste 1000
Coral Gables, FL 33134-7412
Tel.: (305) 443-3800
Fax: (305) 443-3467
Toll Free: (888) 784-3335
E-mail: custserv@stiefel.com
Web Site: www.stiefel.com
Sales Range: $900-999.9 Million
Approx. Number Employees: 3,500
Year Founded: 1847
Business Description:
Pharmaceuticals Mfr
S.I.C.: 2834
N.A.I.C.S.: 325412
Import Export
Media: 2-4-7-10-24
Distr.: Intl.; Natl.
Personnel:
William D. Humphries *(Pres)*
Brands & Products:
ACNE-AID
BENOXYL
BIOPSY PUNCH
BRASIVOL
BREVOXYL
BURO-SOL
CLARIPEL
CLINDAPAK
CLINDETS
CLINDOXYL
CLOBEVATE
CURETTE
CYCLOCORT
DANGARD
DERMAVITE
DOAK
DRICLOR
DUAC
DUOFLIM
DUOFORTE
DUOPLANT
EMO-CORT
EPILYT
ERYSOL
EVOCLIN
GELUNGEL
HIDRAFIL
IMPRUV
ISOTREX
LACTICARE
LUXIQ
MIMYX
MINOCIN
NERISALIC
NERISONE
NUBEVITAL
OILATUM
OLUX
OLUX-E
PANOXYL
PHYSIOGEL
POLYTAR
PREVEX
REJUVA-A
RETISOL-A
REVALESKIN
ROSAC
SARNA
SARNOL
SASTID
SOLAGE
SOLUGEL
SORIATANE
STIEPROX
STIEVA-A
STIEVAMYCIN
SULFOXYL
SULFUR SOAP
TERSA-TAR

Key to Media (For complete agency information see *The Advertising Red Books-Agencies* edition):
1. Bus. Publs. 2. Cable T.V. 3. Catalogs & Directories. 4. Co-op Adv. 5. Consumer Mags. 6. D.M. to Bus. Estab.7. D.M. to Consumers
8. Daily Newsp. 9. Exhibits/Trade Shows 10. Foreign 11. Infomercial 12. Internet Adv.13. Multimedia 14. Network Radio
15. Network T.V. 16. Newsp. Distr. Mags. 17. Other 18. Outdoor (Posters, Transit) 19. Point of Purchase20. Premiums, Novelties
21. Product Samples 22. Special Events Mktg. 23. Spot Radio 24. Spot T.V. 25. Weekly Newsp. 26. Yellow Page Adv.

Stiefel Laboratories, Inc. — (Continued)

TERSASEPTIC
TINAMED
UREMOL
VERDESO
VUSION
WARTEC
XOLEGEL
XOLOGEL
ZEASORB
ZETACET
ZNP

STRYKER CORPORATION

2825 Airview Blvd
Kalamazoo, MI 49002
Tel.: (269) 385-2600
Fax: (269) 385-1062
Web Site: www.strykercorp.com
Approx. Sls.: $7,320,000,000
Approx. Number Employees: 20,036
Year Founded: 1964
Business Description:
Specialty Surgical & Medical Products Developer, Mfr & Marketer
S.I.C.: 3841; 3842
N.A.I.C.S.: 339112; 339113
Import Export
Media: 6-24
Personnel:
Stephen P. MacMillan *(Chm, Pres & CEO)*
Ramesh Subrahmanian *(Grp Pres-Intl)*
Curt Hartman *(CFO & VP)*
Tony M. McKinney *(Chief Acctg Officer & VP)*
Lonny J. Carpenter *(Pres-Global Quality & Ops)*
Kevin Lobo *(Pres-Neurotechnology & Spine Grp)*
Timothy J. Scannell *(Grp Pres-MedSurg)*
Curtis E. Hall *(Gen Counsel, Sec & VP)*
Edward B. Lipes *(Exec VP)*
Marcia S. Kaminsky *(VP-Comm & Pub Affairs)*
Katherine A. Owen *(VP-Strategy & IR)*
Michael W. Rude *(VP-HR)*
Teresa Hess *(Dir-Reporting)*
Brands & Products:
ACCOLADE
AIRES
ALLOCRAFT
APEX
ASNIS III
AVS
BIOSTEON
BIOZIP
BIXCUT
BONESOURCE
CERVICORE
COLORADO MICRODISSECTION NEEDLE
COLORADO NEEDLE
CONSTAVAC
CORDLESS DRIVER
CORE
CRANIOFIX 2
CROSSFIRE
DALL-MILES
DEKOMPRESSOR
DIAPASON
DJD II
DURACON
DURAMATRIX
DYNAMIC JOINT DISTRACTOR II
EDIT ELITE
EIUS
ENDOSUITE
EPIC
EXETER
FLEXICORE
FLEXVISION
FORMULA
GAMMA
HERCULES
HOFFMAN II COMPACT
HOFFMANN II
HOWMEDICA
HUMMER
HYDROSET
I-SUITE
I.M. SAW
INFRAVISION
INION
INTERPULSE
ISOFLEX
KNIFELIGHT
LEIBINGER
MAINSTAY
MATTA PELVIC
MIXEVAC
MONOTUBE TRIAX
MULTI-GUIDE II
MX-RPO
NAVSUITE
NEPTUNE
NEUROCLIP
NUMELOCK
OASYS
OFFICEPACS
OMEGA
OP-1
ORTHINOX
ORTHOPAD
OSTEONICS
PACS
PAINPUMP
PAL
POWER PRO
PUREFIX
RAY THREADED FUSION CAGE
REFLEX
REM
REVOLUTION
RUGGED
SCORPIO
SECUR-FIT
SECURE
SERFAS
SIDNE
SIMPLEX
SKELETAL ANCHORAE
SMARTLOAD
SMARTLOCK
SOLAR
SPINEPLEX
SPIRAL RADIUS
STAIR PRO
STRYKECAM
STRYKER
STRYKEVAC
SUPRACONDYLAR NAIL
SWITCHPOINT INFINITY
SYMMETRIC
TISSUEMEND
TMZF
TRIATHLON
TRIDENT
TRIO
TRU-FIT
TWINFIX
UNIVERSAL NEURO
VBOSS
VISUM
WICHITA
XCEL
XIA
XPRT
Advertising Agencies:
Duffey Petrosky
39303 Country Club Dr Ste A18
Farmington Hills, MI 48331-3482
Tel.: (248) 489-8300
Fax: (248) 994-1600

Trimention Advertising
2200 S Dixie Hwy Ste 500
Coconut Grove, FL 33133
Tel.: (305) 858-3155
Fax: (305) 858-3154

Wallwork Curry McKenna
10 City Sq 5th Fl
Charlestown, MA 02129
Tel.: (617) 266-8200
Fax: (617) 266-8270

STRYKER ORTHOPAEDICS

(Div. of Stryker Corporation)
325 Corporate Dr
Mahwah, NJ 07430
Tel.: (201) 831-5000
Fax: (201) 831-4000
Web Site: www.stryker.com
Sales Range: $450-499.9 Million
Approx. Number Employees: 1,500
Business Description:
Orthopedic Implants, Trauma Products & Bone Cement Mfr
S.I.C.: 3842
N.A.I.C.S.: 339113
Import Export
Advertising Expenditures: $5,000,000
Media: 3-4-6-11-20-22
Distr.: Intl.; Natl.
Personnel:
Kien Nguyen *(VP & Gen Mgr-OtisMed)*
Brian Lurie *(VP-IT)*
Yin Becker *(Exec Dir-Homer Stryker Center)*
Peg Bradshaw *(Dir-Medical Education & Mktg Svcs)*

SUCAMPO PHARMACEUTICALS, INC.

4520 East West Hwy 3rd Fl
Bethesda, MD 20814
Tel.: (301) 961-3400
Fax: (301) 961-3440
E-mail: info@sucampo.com
Web Site: www.sucampo.com
Approx. Rev.: $61,870,000
Approx. Number Employees: 93
Year Founded: 1996
Business Description:
Pharmaceutical Research & Mfr
S.I.C.: 2834; 8733
N.A.I.C.S.: 325412; 541710
Advertising Expenditures: $650,000
Personnel:
Ryuji Ueno *(Chm, CEO & Chief Scientific Officer)*
Cary J. Claiborne *(Interim CFO)*
James J. Egan *(COO)*
Andrew P. Smith *(Chief Acctg Officer)*
Stanley G. Miele *(Pres-Sucampo Pharma Americas, Inc. & Sr VP-Sls & Mktg)*
Thomas J. Knapp *(Gen Counsel, Sec & Sr VP)*
Gayle R. Dolecek *(Sr VP-R&D)*
Kathryn de Santis *(VP-IR & Corp Comm)*
Greg Deener *(VP-Mktg, Strategy & Implementation-Sucampo Pharma Americas, Inc.)*
Kathryn DeSantis *(Dir-IR & PR)*
Brands & Products:
AMITIZA

SUMITOMO CORPORATION OF AMERICA

(Sub. of Sumitomo Corporation of America)
600 3rd Ave Ste 39
New York, NY 10016
Tel.: (212) 207-0379
Fax: (212) 207-0826
E-mail: info@sumitomo.com
Web Site: www.sumitomo.com
Approx. Number Employees: 15
Year Founded: 1989
Business Description:
Import & Export of Specialty Chemical Products
S.I.C.: 5169; 5045
N.A.I.C.S.: 424690; 423430
Import Export
Media: 17
Distr.: Natl.
Personnel:
Barbara Hasson *(Product Mgr)*
Tyler D. Schinto *(Mgr)*

SUMMIT INDUSTRIES, INC.

839 Pickens Industrial Dr
Marietta, GA 30062-3100
Tel.: (770) 590-0600
Fax: (770) 590-0714
Toll Free: (800) 241-6996
Web Site: www.summitinds.com
Sales Range: $10-24.9 Million
Approx. Number Employees: 30
Year Founded: 1920
Business Description:
Mfr & Distr of Pharmaceutical, Automotive Aftermarket & Equestrian Products
S.I.C.: 2834; 2842
N.A.I.C.S.: 325412; 325612
Export
Media: 2-4-5-6-7-8-10-13-19
Distr.: Intl.; Natl.
Personnel:
Mark Jaggei *(Pres & CEO)*
Mark Moffit *(Exec VP-VP Sls & Mktg)*
Brands & Products:
CORONA
CREOMULSION
KOZAK
LANTISEPTIC
LEXOL
SUMMIT INDUSTRIES
VINYLEX
Advertising Agency:
McCulloch & Company
85 Mill St Ste C200
Roswell, GA 30075
Tel.: (770) 643-2848
Fax: (770) 643-2802

SUNBRIDGE HEALTHCARE CORPORATION

(Div. of Sun Healthcare Group Inc.)
101 Sun Ave NE

Key to Media (For complete agency information see *The Advertising Red Books-Agencies* edition):
1. Bus. Publs. 2. Cable T.V. 3. Catalogs & Directories. 4. Co-op Adv. 5. Consumer Mags. 6. D.M. to Bus. Estab.7. D.M. to Consumers 8. Daily Newsp. 9. Exhibits/Trade Shows 10. Foreign 11. Infomercial 12. Internet Adv.13. Multimedia 14. Network Radio 15. Network T.V. 16. Newsp. Distr. Mags. 17. Other 18. Outdoor (Posters, Transit) 19. Point of Purchase20. Premiums, Novelties 21. Product Samples 22. Special Events Mktg. 23. Spot Radio 24. Spot T.V. 25. Weekly Newsp. 26. Yellow Page Adv.

Albuquerque, NM 87109
Tel.: (505) 821-3355
Fax: (505) 468-8013
Toll Free: (866) 758-2512
Web Site: www.sunh.com
Sales Range: $75-99.9 Million
Approx. Number Employees: 300
Year Founded: 1989
Business Description:
Long-Term & Subacute Care Facilities, Nursing Homes & Acute Rehab
S.I.C.: 8059
N.A.I.C.S.: 623110
Media: 2-6-8-9-10-20-23-25-26
Distr.: Natl.
Personnel:
Bill Mathies *(Chm & CEO)*
Logan Sexton *(Pres)*
L. Bryan Shaul *(CFO & Exec VP)*
Michael Newman *(Gen Counsel & Exec VP)*
Sue Coppola *(Sr VP-Clinical Ops)*
Chauncey J. Hunker *(Chief Compliance & Risk Officer & Sr VP)*

SUNOVION PHARMACEUTICALS INC.

(Formerly Sepracor, Inc.)
(Sub. of Dainippon Sumitomo Pharma Co., Ltd.)
84 Waterford Dr
Marlborough, MA 01752
Tel.: (508) 481-6700
Fax: (508) 357-7490
E-mail: info@sunovion.com
Web Site: www.sunovion.com/index.html
Approx. Rev.: $1,292,289,000
Approx. Number Employees: 2,400
Business Description:
Researcher, Developer & Commercializer of Pharmaceutical & Biopharmaceutical Compounds
S.I.C.: 2834
N.A.I.C.S.: 325412; 541711
Advertising Expenditures: $216,400,000
Media: 8
Personnel:
Saburo Hamanaka *(Chm & CEO)*
Mark Iwicki *(Pres & COO)*
Jay Smith *(Sr VP-Sls & Mktg-CNS Respiratory)*
Brands & Products:
ALLEGRA
BROVANA
CLARINEX
IMPROVING HEALTH THROUGH INNOVATION
LUNESTA
OMNARIS
SEPRACOR
STEDESA
XOPENEX
XOPENEX HFA
XUSAL
XYZAL

SUNRISE MEDICAL INC.

(Div. of Sunrise Medical Inc.)
7477 E Dry Creek Pkwy
Longmont, CO 80503-8009
Tel.: (303) 218-4500
Fax: (303) 218-4590
Web Site: www.sunrisemedical.com
Approx. Number Employees: 2,000
Business Description:
Wheelchairs & Accessories Mfr
S.I.C.: 3842
N.A.I.C.S.: 339113
Media: 1-2-4-7-8-10-13-18-19-22

SUNRISE SENIOR LIVING, INC.

7900 Westpark Drive
McLean, VA 22102
Tel.: (703) 273-7500
Fax: (703) 744-1601
Toll Free: (888) 4DIGNITY
E-mail: marketingdesign@sunriseseniorliving.com
Web Site: www.sunriseseniorliving.com
Approx. Rev.: $1,406,701,000
Approx. Number Employees: 31,700
Year Founded: 1981
Business Description:
Assisted Living Services for Seniors
S.I.C.: 8059; 8361
N.A.I.C.S.: 623311; 623110; 623990
Advertising Expenditures: $4,400,000
Media: 8-9-10-14-18-23-26
Personnel:
Paul J. Klaassen *(Chm)*
Mark S. Ordan *(CEO)*
C. Marc Richards *(CFO & Chief Acctg Officer)*
D. Gregory Neeb *(Chief Investment Officer & Chief Admin Officer)*
Teresa M. Klaassen *(Chief Cultural Officer)*
David Haddock *(Gen Counsel & Sec)*
Tiffany L. Tomasso *(Exec VP-European Ops)*
Michael J. Rodis *(Sr VP-HR)*
Brands & Products:
THE BEST MOVE FOR YOUR LIFE
COMPANION LIVING
EDNA'S PLACE
THE FOUNTAINS
SUNRISE SENIOR LIVING
TERRACE CLUB
Advertising Agency:
Tierney Communications
(A Div. of the Interpublic Group of Companies)
The Bellevue 200 S Broad St
Philadelphia, PA 19102-3803
Tel.: (215) 790-4100
Fax: (215) 790-4363

SUNSTAR AMERICAS INC.

(Sub. of Sunstar Suisse S.A .)
4635 W Foster Ave
Chicago, IL 60630-1709
Tel.: (773) 777-4000
Fax: (773) 777-5101
Web Site: www.gumbrand.com
Approx. Number Employees: 750
Year Founded: 1923
Business Description:
Preventive Dentistry & Oral Hygiene Products Mfr
S.I.C.: 3991; 3843
N.A.I.C.S.: 339994; 339114
Import Export
Advertising Expenditures: $2,000,000
Media: 1-2-4-5-6-7-10-20-21
Distr.: Intl.; Natl.
Budget Set: Oct.
Personnel:
Anne Foppe *(Dir-Pro Mktg)*
Brands & Products:
BUTLER
BUTLER GUM ANGLE
BUTLER SMILE CENTER
BUTLER SMILE FACTORY
BUTLERWEAVE
CLEAR DIP
DOME-TRIM
EEZ-THRU
EXPANDING
FLOSBRUSH
FLOSSMATE
FRESH-R
G-U-M
GELCLAIR
GO-BETWEENS
GUM-CRITTERS
GUM POSTCARE
GUM PULSE
HEALTHY GUMS HEALTHY LIFE
L'IL SAFARI FRIENDS
MICRO TIP
PERIO PIC
PERIOGLAS
PROTECT
PROXABRUSH
PROXAPIC
QUAD-GRIP
RED-COTE
RIGHT KIND
RINCINOL
SEA FRIENDS
SHAPE 1
SUB-G
SUPER TIP
TECHNIQUE
TRAV-LER
TUFF-SPUN

SUPERGEN INC.

4140 Dublin Blvd Ste 200
Dublin, CA 94568-7757
Tel.: (925) 560-0100
Fax: (925) 560-0101
E-mail: info@supergen.com
Web Site: www.supergen.com
Approx. Rev.: $52,972,000
Approx. Number Employees: 97
Year Founded: 1991
Business Description:
Pharmaceuticals Mfr
S.I.C.: 2834
N.A.I.C.S.: 325412
Advertising Expenditures: $19,000
Media: 7-10
Personnel:
James S. J. Manuso *(Chm, Pres & CEO)*
Michael Molkentin *(CFO & Corp Sec)*
Timothy L. Enns *(Sr VP-Corp Comm & Bus Dev)*
Michael V. Mccullar *(Sr VP-Strategy & Discovery Ops)*
Shu Lee *(VP-Intellectual Property & Legal Affairs)*
Brands & Products:
AVICINE
CLIMB
DECITABINE
MITOMYCIN
NIPENT
PACLITAXEL
SAVING LIVES IS OUR GOAL
SUPERGEN
SURFACE SAFE
Advertising Agency:
Cadent Medical Communications
1707 Market Pl Blvd Ste 350
Irving, TX 75063
Tel.: (972) 929-1900
Fax: (972) 929-1901

SUPERVALU PHARMACIES, INC.

(Sub. of SUPERVALU, Inc.)
19011 Lk Dr E
Chanhassen, MN 55317-9322
Mailing Address:
PO Box 59004
Minneapolis, MN 55459-0004
Tel.: (952) 294-7186
Tel.: (952) 828-4640
Tel.: (847) 916-4244
Fax: (952) 294-7190
Web Site: www.supervalu.com
Sales Range: $50-74.9 Million
Approx. Number Employees: 30
Year Founded: 1985
Business Description:
Drug Stores
S.I.C.: 5912
N.A.I.C.S.: 446110
Advertising Expenditures: $79,200,000
Media: 3-13-17-18-21-25
Personnel:
Duncan MacNaughton *(Exec VP-Mdsg & Mktg)*

SURMODICS, INC.

9924 W 74th St
Eden Prairie, MN 55344-3523
Tel.: (952) 829-2700
Fax: (952) 829-2743
Toll Free: (866) SURMODX
E-mail: info@surmodics.com
Web Site: www.surmodics.com
Approx. Rev.: $69,898,000
Approx. Number Employees: 215
Year Founded: 1979
Business Description:
Surface Modification Solutions to the Medical Device Industry
S.I.C.: 2836; 2891
N.A.I.C.S.: 325414; 325520
Export
Media: 2-10
Personnel:
Robert C. Buhrmaster *(Chm)*
Gary R. Maharaj *(Pres & CEO)*
Timothy J. Arens *(Interim CFO & VP-Fin)*
Bryan K. Phillips *(Gen Counsel, Sec & Sr VP-Legal & HR)*
Charles W. Olson *(Sr VP & Gen Mgr-Medical Device)*
Arthur J. Tipton *(Sr VP & Gen Mgr-Pharmaceuticals)*
Joseph J. Stich *(VP-Bus Ops & Gen Mgr-In-Vitro Diagnostics)*
Brands & Products:
ACCOLADE
BIOFX
BRAVO
BRINGING INNOVATION TOGETHER
CODELINK
ENCORE
EUREKA
I-VATION
IN VITRO
INNORX
PHOTOLINK
POLYACTIVE
PROTEX
RETINAJECT
STABILCOAT
STABILGUARD
STABILZYME
SURMODICS

Key to Media (For complete agency information see *The Advertising Red Books-Agencies* edition):
1. Bus. Publs. 2. Cable T.V. 3. Catalogs & Directories. 4. Co-op Adv. 5. Consumer Mags. 6. D.M. to Bus. Estab.7. D.M. to Consumers
8. Daily Newsp. 9. Exhibits/Trade Shows 10. Foreign 11. Infomercial 12. Internet Adv.13. Multimedia 14. Network Radio
15. Network T.V. 16. Newsp. Distr. Mags. 17. Other 18. Outdoor (Posters, Transit) 19. Point of Purchase20. Premiums, Novelties
21. Product Samples 22. Special Events Mktg. 23. Spot Radio 24. Spot T.V. 25. Weekly Newsp. 26. Yellow Page Adv.

SurModics, Inc. — (Continued)

SYNBIOSYS

SUTTER HEALTH
2200 River Plz Dr
Sacramento, CA 95833-4134
Tel.: (916) 733-8800
Fax: (916) 733-7038
E-mail: webmaster@sutterhealth.org
Web Site: www.sutterhealth.org
Approx. Rev.: $7,258,000,000
Approx. Number Employees: 43,139
Year Founded: 1981
Business Description:
Hospital Management
S.I.C.: 6719; 8062
N.A.I.C.S.: 551112; 622110
Advertising Expenditures: $500,000
Media: 4-10-13-24
Personnel:
Patrick Fry *(Pres & CEO)*
Robert D. Reed *(CFO & Sr VP)*
Jonathan Manis *(CIO)*
Gordon Hunt *(CMO & Sr VP)*
Florence L. Di Benedetto *(Gen Counsel & Sr VP)*
Joel Grey *(Sr VP-Admin Svcs)*
Sarah Krevans *(Sr VP-Managed Care)*
Bill Gleeson *(VP-Comm)*
Karen Garner *(Dir-Comm)*
Brands & Products:
SUTTER HEALTH
WITH YOU. FOR LIFE.
Advertising Agency:
Glass McClure
2700 J St 2nd Fl
Sacramento, CA 95816
Tel.: (916) 448-6956
Fax: (916) 448-2049

SWANSON HEALTH PRODUCTS INC.
4075 40th Ave SW
Fargo, ND 58104-3912
Tel.: (701) 356-2700
Fax: (701) 356-2708
E-mail: swansonretail@swansonvitamins.com
Web Site: www.swansonvitamins.com
Approx. Number Employees: 400
Year Founded: 1971
Business Description:
Catalog & Mail-Order Houses
S.I.C.: 5961; 5499
N.A.I.C.S.: 454113; 446191
Import Export
Media: 4-6-8-13
Personnel:
Leland Swanson, Jr. *(Pres)*
Brands & Products:
AYURVEDIC
BEST GARLIC SUPPLEMENTS
BEST WEIGHT-CONTROL FORMULAS
BODY RESCUE
BOIRON
COMPLEMENTS
CONDITION SPECIFIC FORMULAS
EFAS
FALK'S
GREENFOODS FORMULAS
HEALTHY HOME
HOMEOPATHY
KYOTO BRAND
LEE SWANSON SIGNATURE LINE
NATURE'S SECRET
ORGANIC
OTC
PASSION
PH BALANCE
PINNACLE
PREMIUM
PROBIOTICS
SELECT
SHEN MIN
SOLGAR
SUN CHLORELLA
SUPERIOR HERBS
SWANSON
SWANSON HEALTH PRODUCTS
SYSTEMS
TRACE MINERALS
ULTRA
VEGETARIAN
WISDOM

SWISHER INTERNATIONAL, INC.
(Sub. of Swisher Hygiene Inc.)
4725 Piedmont Row Dr Ste 400
Charlotte, NC 28210
Tel.: (704) 364-7707
Fax: (800) 444-4565
Toll Free: (877) 7SWISHER
E-mail: contact@swisheronline.com
Web Site: www.swisherhygiene.com
Sales Range: $25-49.9 Million
Approx. Number Employees: 60
Year Founded: 1986
Business Description:
Cleaning Products & Facility Cleaning Services
S.I.C.: 7349; 5169; 7359
N.A.I.C.S.: 561720; 424690; 532490
Media: 9-13
Personnel:
H. Wayne Huizenga *(Chm)*
Steven R. Berrard *(Pres & CEO)*
Hugh H. Cooper *(CFO & Treas)*
Michael Kipp *(Chief Acctg Officer & VP)*
Thomas E. Aucamp *(Exec VP)*
Thomas C. Byrne *(Exec VP)*
Brands & Products:
SWISHER

SXC HEALTH SOLUTIONS CORP.
2441 Warrenville Rd Ste 610
Lisle, IL 60532-3642
Tel.: (630) 577-3100
Fax: (630) 577-3101
Toll Free: (800) 282-3232
Web Site: www.sxc.com
Approx. Rev.: $1,948,389,000
Approx. Number Employees: 1,216
Year Founded: 1993
Business Description:
Pharmaceutical Industry Benefit Management & Information Technology Services
S.I.C.: 7372; 7371
N.A.I.C.S.: 334611; 541511
Media: 10
Personnel:
Mark A. Thierer *(Chm & CEO)*
Jeffrey Park *(CFO & Exec VP)*
John Romza *(CTO & Exec VP-R&D)*
Cliff Berman *(Gen Counsel & Sr VP)*
B. Greg Buscetto *(Sr VP & Gen Mgr)*
Mark A. Adkison *(Sr VP-Mail & Specialty)*
Jeff Jensen *(Sr VP-Healthcare Tech)*
Michael Zaslav *(Sr VP-Provider Dev)*
Brands & Products:
RXCLAIM
RXEXPRESS
RXMAX
RXPORTAL
RXSERVER
RXTRACK
Advertising Agency:
S.A. Noonan Communications
27 N Moore St Ste 10C
New York, NY 10013
Tel.: (212) 966-3650

SYBRON DENTAL SPECIALTIES, INC.
(Sub. of Danaher Corporation)
1717 W Collims Ave
Orange, CA 92687
Tel.: (714) 516-7400
Fax: (714) 516-7953
Toll Free: (800) 537-7824
Web Site: www.sybrondental.com
Sales Range: $600-649.9 Million
Approx. Number Employees: 4,117
Business Description:
Orthodontic Supplies & Dental Products Mfr
S.I.C.: 3843
N.A.I.C.S.: 339114
Advertising Expenditures: $6,765,000
Personnel:
Mark C. Yorba *(CIO & Exec VP)*
Brands & Products:
A COMPANY ORTHODONTICS
ADAPT
ALGINOT
BEAVERS
BELLE DE ST. CLAIRE
BELLEWAX
BICORTICAL
BIOPLANT
BIORESORB
BODYGUARD
CANISTER EXPRESS
CAVICIDE
CAVITEC
CAVIWIPES
CENTRIFICO
COMPOROLLER
CONTOUR
CORERESTORE
CYTOPLAST
DAMON
DEMETRON
DETERGEZYME
DIMENSION
DISPENS-IT-ALL
DISPOS-A-BITE
DISPOS-A-TRAP
DOWEL PIN INDEXER
EASY TRAY
EMPOWER
ENDOPORE
ENTEGRA
ENVIROCIDE
EVAC-U-TRAP
EXPA-SYL
EXTRUDE
EYEMAX
FILL-IN
GUARDINA SEAL
HANDLE COVER
HERBST
HERCULITE
HIRES
HP SLEEVE
INJECTOMATIC
INSPIRE ICE
INTEGRA
K-FLEX
KERR
KLEEN DIP
KLEENASEPTIC
LIFE
MARA
MASTERTOUCH
MAXCEM
METREX
METRICIDE
METRICLEAN
METRIDRY
METRIGUARD
METRILUBE
METRIMIST
METRISHINE
METRISPONGE
METRITEST
METRIWASH
METRIZYME
MICROMATIC
MINIENDO
NEXUS
OCCLUBRUSH
OPTIBOND
OPTIBULB
OPTICLEAN
OPTIDAM
OPTIDISC
OPTIGUARD
OPTILUX
OPTIMIX
OPTIVIEW
ORMCO
ORTHOS
OSTEOPLATE
PATHFINDER
PERIOSTAR
PERMLASTIC
PINNACLE COVER ALL
PITT-EASY
PREMICIDE
PREMIDEX
PREMISE
PROCIDE
PRODIGY
PURETEX
QUANTEC
QUIK SPRUES
READY SPRUES
REALSEAL
REVOLUTION
SAFE-TIPS
SEAL-TIGHT
SLICK LUBE
SLIP-NOTS
SMEARCLEAR
SMOOTHY
SOFTISSUE MOULAGE
SOFTLINE
THE SOLIDIFIER
SPREE
STANDOUT
SUPER-SEP
SUPERMAT
SYBRALOY
TAKE 1
TEMPBOND
TEMPFIL
TEMPHASE
TOOTHPRINTS
TOUCHSONIC
TURBO VAC
TYTIN
ULTRA-WAXER

Key to Media (For complete agency information see *The Advertising Red Books-Agencies* edition):
1. Bus. Publs. 2. Cable T.V. 3. Catalogs & Directories. 4. Co-op Adv. 5. Consumer Mags. 6. D.M. to Bus. Estab.7. D.M. to Consumers
8. Daily Newsp. 9. Exhibits/Trade Shows 10. Foreign 11. Infomercial 12. Internet Adv.13. Multimedia 14. Network Radio
15. Network T.V. 16. Newsp. Distr. Mags. 17. Other 18. Outdoor (Posters, Transit) 19. Point of Purchase20. Premiums, Novelties
21. Product Samples 22. Special Events Mktg. 23. Spot Radio 24. Spot T.V. 25. Weekly Newsp. 26. Yellow Page Adv.

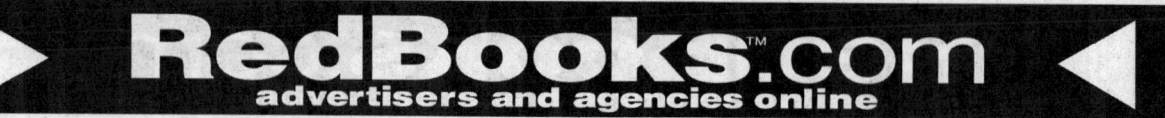

VIONEX
VIONEXUS
VITAL 1
WET-WAXER
ZEON

SYMMETRY MEDICAL INC.

3724 N State Rd 15
Warsaw, IN 46582
Tel.: (574) 268-2252
Fax: (574) 267-7306
Web Site: www.symmetrymedical.com
Approx. Rev.: $360,830,000
Approx. Number Employees: 2,797
Year Founded: 1986
Business Description:
Surgical & Medical Instruments Mfr
S.I.C.: 3841; 3842; 3845
N.A.I.C.S.: 339112; 334510; 339113
Import Export
Advertising Expenditures: $490,000
Personnel:
Craig B. Reynolds *(Chm)*
Thomas J. Sullivan *(Pres & CEO)*
Fred L. Hite *(Sr VP, CFO & IR Officer)*
John J. Hynes *(COO)*
Ronda L. Harris *(Chief Acctg Officer)*
Brian S. Moore *(Pres-Bus Dev)*
David C. Milne *(Gen Counsel, Sec & Sr VP-HR)*
Jose Fernandez *(Sr VP-New Product Dev)*
D. Darin Martin *(Sr VP-Quality Assurance, Regulatory Affairs & Compliance Officer)*
Brands & Products:
POLYPRINT
SYMMETRY MEDICAL
TOTAL SOLUTIONS

SYNBIOTICS CORPORATION

(Sub. of Pfizer Animal Health)
12200 NW Ambassador Dr Ste 101
Kansas City, MO 64163
Tel.: (816) 464-3500
Fax: (816) 464-3521
Toll Free: (800) 228-4305
E-mail: Customerservice1@synbiotics.com
Web Site: www.synbiotics.com
Sales Range: $10-24.9 Million
Approx. Number Employees: 100
Year Founded: 1982
Business Description:
Veterinary Diagnostics, Vaccines & Other Animal Health Related Products Mfr, Developer & Marketer
S.I.C.: 2836; 5122
N.A.I.C.S.: 325414; 424210
Media: 10
Personnel:
Paul R. Hays *(Pres & CEO)*
Dan O'Rourke *(CFO & Controller)*
Clifford Frank *(VP-Strategic Projects)*
Brands & Products:
ASSURE
CANINE RHEUMATOID FACTOR
DIROCHEK
FLUDETECT
FRESH A.I.
FRESH EXPRESS
FUNGASSAY
ICG STATUS-LH
ICG STATUS-PRO
LAB-EZ
OVASSAY
OVUCHECK
PROFILE
PROFLOK
REPROCHEK
SCA2000
SYNBIOTICS CORPORATION
TITERCHEK
TUBERCULIN
VIRACHEK
WITNESS

SYNTHES INC.

1302 Wrights Ln E
West Chester, PA 19380
Tel.: (610) 71-9 5000
E-mail: ir.info@synthes.com
Web Site: www.synthes.com
Approx. Sls.: $3,192,544,000
Approx. Number Employees: 9,947
Year Founded: 1974
Business Description:
Implants & Biomaterial Medical Devices Developer & Mfr
S.I.C.: 3842; 3841
N.A.I.C.S.: 339113; 339112
Advertising Expenditures: $38,000,000
Media: 10
Personnel:
Hansjorg Wyss *(Chm & CEO)*
Charles Hedgepeth *(Vice Chm)*
Michel Orsinger *(Pres & CEO)*
Robert Donohue *(CFO)*
Alfredo Granai *(Pres-Latin America)*
Judy Mitchell *(Pres-Asia Pacific)*
Brands & Products:
AXON
CHRONOS
CLICK'X
COMPACT
COMPACT HAND
COMPACT MF
CRANIOFACIAL REPAIR SYSTEM
DBX
FLAPFIX
LOCKING COMPRESSION PLATE
PHILOS
PLIVIOPURE
SKELETAL REPAIR SYSTEM
SYNFIX-LR
TRAVIOS
UNILOCK
VECTRA
VEPTR

SYNTHETECH, INC.

(Sub. of W. R. GRACE & CO.)
1290 Industrial Way SW
Albany, OR 97322
Mailing Address:
PO Box 646
Albany, OR 97321
Tel.: (541) 967-6575
Fax: (541) 967-9424
E-mail: corp@synthetech.com
Web Site: www.synthetech.com
Approx. Rev.: $15,244,000
Approx. Number Employees: 63
Year Founded: 1981
Business Description:
Peptide Building Blocks & Specialty Amino Acids Mfr
S.I.C.: 2879; 2836; 2899; 5169
N.A.I.C.S.: 325320; 325414; 325998; 424690
Import Export
Media: 10-11-13
Personnel:
Gregory R. Hahn *(Pres & CEO)*
Gary A. Weber *(CFO & VP-Fin)*
Brett Reynolds *(VP-Sls & Mktg)*
Joseph Murphy *(Dir-Bus Dev)*
Michael C. Standen *(Dir-Tech)*

SYNUTRA INTERNATIONAL, INC.

2275 Research Blvd Ste 500
Rockville, MD 20850
Tel.: (301) 840-3888
Web Site: www.synutra.com
Approx. Sls.: $248,516,000
Approx. Number Employees: 5,200
Business Description:
Infant Formula Product Mfr
S.I.C.: 2023
N.A.I.C.S.: 311514
Advertising Expenditures: $41,420,000
Personnel:
Liang Zhang *(Chm & CEO)*
Weiguo Zhang *(Pres, Interim CFO & COO)*
William W. Wu *(Head-Mktg)*
Brands & Products:
SHENGYUAN
SYNUTRA

TAKEDA PHARMACEUTICALS NORTH AMERICA, INC.

(Sub. of Takeda America Holdings, Inc.)
1 Decatur Pkwy
Deerfield, IL 60015-4832
Tel.: (847) 582-2000
Toll Free: (800) 621-1020
Web Site: www.tap.com
Approx. Number Employees: 1,600
Year Founded: 1977
Business Description:
Pharmaceutical Mfr; Owned 50% by Takeda Chemical Industries, Ltd. & 50% by Abbott Laboratories
S.I.C.: 2834; 8733
N.A.I.C.S.: 325412; 541710
Media: 17
Personnel:
Alan MacKenzie *(Chief Admin Officer & Exec VP-Ops)*
Edward J. Fiorentino *(Exec VP)*
Glenn Warner *(Exec VP)*
Denise Kitchen *(VP-HR)*
Daniel Gandor *(Product Mgr-Uloric Sls & Payer Strategies)*
Brands & Products:
CREACID

TALECRIS BIOTHERAPEUTICS HOLDINGS CORP.

4101 Research Commons 79 TW Alexander Dr
Research Triangle Park, NC 27709
Tel.: (919) 316-6300
Fax: (919) 316-6316
E-mail: info@talecris.com
Web Site: www.talecris.com
Approx. Rev.: $1,601,619,000
Approx. Number Employees: 5,400
Business Description:
Immunology, Pulmonology & Hemostasis Critical Care Treatments Developer & Mfr
S.I.C.: 2834; 2836
N.A.I.C.S.: 541711; 325412; 325414
Advertising Expenditures: $11,300,000
Media: 13-21
Personnel:
Lawrence D. Stern *(Chm & CEO)*
John M. Hanson *(CFO & Exec VP)*
John F. Gaither, Jr. *(Gen Counsel, Sec & Exec VP)*
Mary J. Kuhn *(Exec VP-Ops)*
John R. Perkins *(Exec VP-Global Comml Ops)*
Stephen R. Petteway *(Exec VP-Res & Dev)*
Joel Abelson *(Sr VP & Gen Mgr-Portfolio Mgmt & Intl Bus)*
Bruce Nogales *(Sr VP & Gen Mgr-Talecris Plasma Resources)*
Jim Engle *(Sr VP-IT)*
Kari Heerdt *(Sr VP-HR)*
Thomas L. Lynch *(Sr VP-Corp Compliance & Regulatory Affairs)*
Dan Menichella *(Sr VP-Bus Dev)*
Drayton Virkler *(Sr Dir-IR)*
Advertising Agency:
Draftfcb HealthCare
100 W 33rd St
New York, NY 10001
Tel.: (212) 672-2300
Fax: (212) 672-2301

TARGACEPT, INC.

200 E 1st St Ste 300
Winston Salem, NC 27101-4165
Tel.: (336) 480-2100
Fax: (336) 480-2107
E-mail: alan.musso@targacept.com
Web Site: www.targacept.com
Approx. Rev.: $85,713,000
Approx. Number Employees: 132
Year Founded: 1997
Business Description:
Pharmaceutical Treatments for Disorders & Diseases of the Nervous System
S.I.C.: 2834
N.A.I.C.S.: 325412
Media: 10-18
Personnel:
Mark B. Skaletsky *(Chm)*
J. Donald deBethizy *(Pres & CEO)*
Alan A. Musso *(CFO, Treas, Sr VP-Fin & Admin)*
Geoffrey C. Dunbar *(Sr VP-Clinical Dev, Regulatory Affairs & Chief Medical Officer)*
Peter A. Zorn *(Gen Counsel, Sec & Sr VP-Legal Affairs)*
William S. Caldwell *(Sr VP-Drug Discovery & Dev)*
Mauri K. Hodges *(VP-Fin, Controller & Corp Sys)*
Karen A. Hicks *(VP-HR)*
Brands & Products:
AMPLIXA
INVERSINE
NNR THERAPEUTICS
TARGACEPT
TRIDMAC

TEAM HEALTH HOLDINGS, INC.

(Holding of The Blackstone Group L.P.)
(d/b/a TeamHealth Group)
265 Brookview Town Centre Way Ste 400
Knoxville, TN 37919
Tel.: (865) 693-1000
Fax: (865) 539-3073
Toll Free: (800) 342-2898
E-mail: media_relations@teamhealth.com
Web Site: www.teamhealth.com

Key to Media (For complete agency information see *The Advertising Red Books-Agencies* edition):
1. Bus. Publs. 2. Cable T.V. 3. Catalogs & Directories. 4. Co-op Adv. 5. Consumer Mags. 6. D.M. to Bus. Estab.7. D.M. to Consumers
8. Daily Newsp. 9. Exhibits/Trade Shows 10. Foreign 11. Infomercial 12. Internet Adv.13. Multimedia 14. Network Radio
15. Network T.V. 16. Newsp. Distr. Mags. 17. Other 18. Outdoor (Posters, Transit) 19. Point of Purchase20. Premiums, Novelties
21. Product Samples 22. Special Events Mktg. 23. Spot Radio 24. Spot T.V. 25. Weekly Newsp. 26. Yellow Page Adv.

Team Health Holdings, Inc. — (Continued)

Approx. Rev.: $2,671,374,000
Approx. Number Employees: 5,700
Year Founded: 1979
Business Description:
Holding Company; Outsourced Healthcare Professional Staffing & Administrative Services
S.I.C.: 6719; 7389; 8741
N.A.I.C.S.: 551112; 561110; 561311; 561499
Media: 2-7-10-13
Personnel:
H. Lynn Massingale *(Chm)*
Greg Roth *(Pres & CEO)*
David P. Jones *(CFO & Exec VP)*
Stephen Sherlin *(Chief Compliance Officer)*
Joseph B. Carman *(Chief Admin Officer)*
Heidi Solomon Allen *(Gen Counsel & Sr VP)*
Kent Bristow *(Sr VP-Ops)*
Dan Wilbanks *(Sr VP-Bus Dev & Mktg)*
Advertising Agencies:
DS Tombras
4017 Hillsboro Pike Ste 408
Nashville, TN 37215
Tel.: (615) 321-0080
Fax: (615) 321-0080

The Tombras Group
4718 Lake Park Dr Ste 2
Johnson City, TN 37615
Tel.: (423) 915-1266

TECHNE CORPORATION
614 McKinley Pl NE
Minneapolis, MN 55413-2610
Tel.: (612) 379-8854
Fax: (612) 379-6580
E-mail: techinfo@techne-corp.com
Web Site: www.techne-corp.com
Approx. Sls.: $289,962,000
Approx. Number Employees: 763
Year Founded: 1981
Business Description:
Holding Company; Biotechnology Products; Genes, Cytokines & Polyclonal & Monoclonal Antibodies, Clinical Research Diagnostics Kits & Hematology Controls Developer & Producer
S.I.C.: 2836; 2834; 6719; 8733
N.A.I.C.S.: 325414; 325412; 541710; 551112
Export
Advertising Expenditures: $2,800,000
Media: 2-4-7-8-13
Personnel:
Thomas E. Oland *(Chm, Pres & CEO)*
Roger C. Lucas *(Vice Chm)*
Gregory J. Melsen *(CFO, Treas & VP-Fin)*
Tim Manning *(Dir-Mktg Comm)*
Sarah Roettger *(Coord-Adv)*
Brands & Products:
DUOSET
FLUOROKINE
MAGCELLECT
PROTEOME PROFILER
QUANTIKINE
RD SYSTEMS

TEMPLE UNIVERSITY HEALTH SYSTEM
3401 N Broad St
Philadelphia, PA 19140
Tel.: (215) 707-2000
Fax: (215) 707-1472
E-mail: tuhs@temple.edu
Web Site: tuh.templehealth.org/content/default.htm
Approx. Rev.: $850,000,000
Approx. Number Employees: 8,000
Year Founded: 1892
Business Description:
University Hospital & Healthcare Network
S.I.C.: 8399; 8059
N.A.I.C.S.: 813212; 623110
Advertising Expenditures: $1,000,000
Media: 2-3-4-6-8-9-10-18-23-24-25-26
Distr.: Natl.
Personnel:
Robert H. Lux *(CFO, Treas & VP)*
Arthur C. Papacostas *(CIO)*
Charles C. Soltoff *(Assoc VP-Mktg)*
Rebecca Harmon *(Dir-PR)*
Brands & Products:
CRADLE TO GRAVE
TEMPLE
Advertising Agency:
Tierney Communications
(A Div. of the Interpublic Group of Companies)
The Bellevue 200 S Broad St
Philadelphia, PA 19102-3803
Tel.: (215) 790-4100
Fax: (215) 790-4363
(Hospitals)

TENDER CORPORATION
106 Burndy Rd
Littleton, NH 03561
Tel.: (603) 444-5464
Fax: (603) 444-6735
Toll Free: (800) 258-4696
E-mail: info@tendercorp.com
Web Site: www.tendercorp.com
Approx. Number Employees: 40
Year Founded: 1975
Business Description:
First Aid Kits, Insect Repellants & After Bite Treatments Mfr
S.I.C.: 2834; 7389
N.A.I.C.S.: 325412; 561910
Export
Advertising Expenditures: $860,000
Media: 2-4-5-6-8-10-11-16-19-20-21-23
Distr.: Intl.; Natl.
Budget Set: July
Personnel:
Jason Cartwright *(CEO)*
Leslie Lindberg *(CFO)*
John Gaulin *(COO)*
Simon Ashdown *(Dir-PR)*
Naomi Reinhard *(Mgr-Mktg)*
Steve Berard *(Product Mgr)*
Brands & Products:
AFTER BITE
AFTER CUTS & SCRAPES
AFTER STING
BEN'S
DRY HANDS
EASY CARE
NATRAPEL

TENET HEALTHCARE CORPORATION
1445 Ross Ave Ste 1400
Dallas, TX 75202
Mailing Address:
PO Box 809088
Dallas, TX 75380-9088
Tel.: (469) 893-2200
Fax: (469) 893-8600
Toll Free: (800) 421-7470
E-mail: feedback@tenethealth.com
Web Site: www.tenethealth.com
Approx. Rev.: $9,205,000,000
Approx. Number Employees: 56,605
Year Founded: 1969
Business Description:
Owner & Operator of General Hospitals & Related Healthcare Facilities
S.I.C.: 8062; 8069
N.A.I.C.S.: 622110; 622310
Advertising Expenditures: $6,000,000
Media: 6-9-17-21-25
Distr.: Natl.
Budget Set: Apr.
Personnel:
Trevor Fetter *(Pres)*
Jason Alexander *(CEO)*
Biggs C. Porter *(CFO)*
Stephen L. Newman *(COO)*
Stephen F. Brown *(CIO & Exec VP)*
Kelvin A. Baggett *(Chief Medical Officer & Sr VP)*
William J. Masterton *(CEO-Coastal Carolina Hospital)*
Mark O'Neil, Jr. *(CEO-Hilton Head Reg Healthcare)*
Gary K. Ruff *(Gen Counsel & Sr VP)*
Cathy Kusaka Fraser *(Sr VP-HR)*
John Holland *(Sr VP)*
Cyler Murphy *(Sr VP-Fin Ops)*
Thomas Rice *(Sr VP)*
J. Scott Richardson *(Sr VP-Fin Ops)*
Robert L. Smith *(Sr VP)*
Joe Gage *(VP-HR & Hospital Ops)*
Kimberly Clark *(Asst Brand Mgr)*
Jennifer Beard *(Mgr-PR)*
Brands & Products:
TENET
TENETCARE
Advertising Agency:
Joele Frank, Wilkinson Brimmer Katcher
140 E 45th St 37th Fl
New York, NY 10017
Tel.: (212) 355-4449
Fax: (212) 355-4554

THERADYNE HEALTHCARE PRODUCTS DIV.
(Div. of Kurt Manufacturing Co. Inc.)
395 Ervin Industrial Blvd
Jordan, MN 55352-1062
Tel.: (763) 502-6199
Fax: (763) 492-3443
Toll Free: (800) 328-4014
Web Site: www.theradyne.com
Approx. Number Employees: 175
Year Founded: 1968
Business Description:
Wheelchairs for Hospitals & Nursing Homes; Home Health Care Equipment Mfr
S.I.C.: 3599; 3842
N.A.I.C.S.: 332710; 339113
Import Export
Advertising Expenditures: $250,000
Media: 6-8-10-19-21
Distr.: Natl.
Budget Set: July
Brands & Products:
AVIATOR AISLE TRANSPORT CHAIRS
ENVOY
INTEGRA
MAXIM
MICROSHELL
POGON
ROVER EXPRESS
ROVER LWF
ROVER LWF-PLUS
ROVER PS
THERADYE
VENTURE
VENTURE PLUS

THERATIVE, INC.
6248 Preston Ave
Livermore, CA 94551
Tel.: (925) 371-3900
Fax: (925) 371-3903
E-mail: information@therative.com
Web Site: www.therative.com
Approx. Number Employees: 10
Business Description:
Medical Products & Solutions Developer
S.I.C.: 2834; 3841
N.A.I.C.S.: 325412; 339112
Media: 1-5-13-24
Brands & Products:
THERMACLEAR
Advertising Agencies:
Euro RSCG Worldwide PR
(Corporate Headquarters)
200 Madison Ave
New York, NY 10016
Tel.: (212) 367-6800
Fax: (212) 367-7154

GolinHarris/Panache
430 Pacific Ave
San Francisco, CA 94133
Tel.: (415) 333-9991
Fax: (415) 274-7933
ThermaClear

TLC VISION CORPORATION
5280 Solar Dr Ste 100
Mississauga, ON L4W 5M8, Canada
Tel.: (905) 602-2020
Fax: (905) 602-2025
Toll Free: (800) 852-1033
Toll Free: (888) 225-5852
E-mail: tlc.info@tlcvision.com
Web Site: www.tlcv.com
Approx. Rev.: $275,668,000
Approx. Number Employees: 1,000
Year Founded: 1993
Business Description:
Laser Vision Correction Facilities Operator
S.I.C.: 8049; 3851; 8093
N.A.I.C.S.: 621399; 339115; 621498
Advertising Expenditures: $21,700,000
Media: 4-8-10-13-25
Personnel:
Warren S. Rustand *(Chm)*
James B. Tiffany *(Pres & COO)*
Henry Lynn *(CIO)*
Michael Gries *(Chief Restructuring Officer)*
William J. McManus *(CFO-Interim)*

Key to Media (For complete agency information see *The Advertising Red Books-Agencies* edition):
1. Bus. Publs. 2. Cable T.V. 3. Catalogs & Directories. 4. Co-op Adv. 5. Consumer Mags. 6. D.M. to Bus. Estab.7. D.M. to Consumers
8. Daily Newsp. 9. Exhibits/Trade Shows 10. Foreign 11. Infomercial 12. Internet Adv.13. Multimedia 14. Network Radio
15. Network T.V. 16. Newsp. Distr. Mags. 17. Other 18. Outdoor (Posters, Transit) 19. Point of Purchase20. Premiums, Novelties
21. Product Samples 22. Special Events Mktg. 23. Spot Radio 24. Spot T.V. 25. Weekly Newsp. 26. Yellow Page Adv.

Brands & Products:
A LIFETIME OF VISION
TLC LIFETIME COMMITMENT
TLC VISION CORPORATION
TLCVISION

TLC VISION CORPORATION
(Sub. of TLC Vision Corporation)
16305 Swingley Ridge Rd Ste 300
Chesterfield, MO 63017-1777
Tel.: (636) 534-2300
Fax: (636) 534-2301
Toll Free: (877) TLC2388
Web Site: www.tlcvision.com
Approx. Rev.: $230,190,000
Approx. Number Employees: 800
Business Description:
Provider of Corrective Laser Eye Surgery Services
S.I.C.: 8011
N.A.I.C.S.: 621111
Advertising Expenditures: $10,400,000

TOMOTHERAPY INCORPORATED
1240 Deming Way
Madison, WI 53717-2911
Tel.: (608) 824-2800
Fax: (608) 824-2996
Web Site: www.tomotherapy.com
Approx. Rev.: $195,363,000
Approx. Number Employees: 636
Year Founded: 2002
Business Description:
Radiation Therapy Systems Developer, Mfr & Sales
S.I.C.: 3844; 3841; 5047
N.A.I.C.S.: 334517; 339112; 423450
Export
Advertising Expenditures: $300,000
Media: 10
Personnel:
Thomas Rockwell Mackie *(Co-Founder & Chm)*
Frederick A. Robertson *(CEO)*
Thomas E. Powell *(CFO & Treas)*
Brenda S. Furlow *(Gen Counsel, Sec & VP)*
Delwin T. Coufal *(VP-Mktg)*
Paul J. Pienkowski *(VP-Product Dev)*
Alison Sparks *(VP-HR)*
Jeff Spielman *(Dir-Sls-Northeast Reg)*
Harry Tschopik *(Dir-Asia Pacific Sls)*

TOTAL NUTRACEUTICAL SOLUTIONS, INC.
80 Columbia St
Stevenson, WA 98648
Mailing Address:
PO Box 910
Stevenson, WA 98648
Tel.: (509) 427-5132
Fax: (509) 427-5142
E-mail: info@totalnutraceutical.com
Web Site: www.totalnutraceutical.com
Approx. Rev.: $67,608
Year Founded: 2007
Business Description:
Pharmaceutical Researcher, Marketer & Distr
S.I.C.: 5122; 2099; 8733
N.A.I.C.S.: 424210; 311999; 541710
Advertising Expenditures: $184,000
Media: 17
Personnel:
Marvin S. Hausman *(Chm & CEO)*
Devin Andres *(VP-Sls & Mktg)*

TRANS1 INC.
301 Government Ctr Dr
Wilmington, NC 28403
Tel.: (910) 332-1700
Fax: (910) 332-1701
Toll Free: (866) 256-1206
E-mail: info@trans1.com
Web Site: www.trans1.com
Approx. Rev.: $26,154,000
Approx. Number Employees: 129
Year Founded: 2000
Business Description:
Lower Back Surgical Device Designer, Mfr & Marketer
S.I.C.: 3841
N.A.I.C.S.: 339112
Advertising Expenditures: $1,800,000
Media: 10
Personnel:
Richard D. Randall *(Chm)*
Kenneth Reali *(Pres & CEO)*
Joseph P. Slattery *(CFO & Exec VP)*
Rick Feiler *(VP-Mktg)*
Dwayne Montgomery *(VP-Sls)*
Brands & Products:
AXIALIF
AXIALIF 2L
AXIALIF 360
TRANS1

TRANSCEND SERVICES, INC.
1 Glenlake Pkwy Ste 1325
Atlanta, GA 30328
Tel.: (404) 364-8000
Fax: (678) 808-0601
Toll Free: (800) 205-7047
E-mail: investorrelations@trcr.com
Web Site: www.transcendservices.com
E-Mail For Key Personnel:
Sales Director: salesandmarketing@trcr.com
Approx. Rev.: $94,307,000
Approx. Number Employees: 1,955
Year Founded: 1976
Business Description:
Patient Information Services
S.I.C.: 7389
N.A.I.C.S.: 561499
Advertising Expenditures: $893,000
Media: 2-6-7-8-10-16
Personnel:
Larry G. Gerdes *(Founder & CEO)*
Susan Mcgrogan *(Pres & COO)*
Lance Cornell *(CFO)*

TRANSCEPT PHARMACEUTICALS, INC.
1003 W Cutting Blvd Ste 110
Point Richmond, CA 94804
Tel.: (510) 215-3500
Fax: (510) 215-3535
E-mail: info@transcept.com
Web Site: www.transcept.com/
Approx. Rev.: $12,500,000
Approx. Number Employees: 31
Year Founded: 2003
Business Description:
Specialty Pharmaceutical Company
S.I.C.: 2834; 8733
N.A.I.C.S.: 325412; 541710
Advertising Expenditures: $125,000
Media: 17
Personnel:
Nikhilesh Singh *(Founder, Chief Scientific Officer & Sr VP)*
G. Kirk Raab *(Chm)*
Glenn A. Oclassen, Sr. *(Pres & CEO)*
Thomas P. Soloway *(CFO & Sr VP)*
Joseph T. Kennedy *(Gen Counsel, Sec & VP)*
Terrence Moore *(VP-Sls & Mktg)*
Marilyn E. Wortzman *(VP-Fin)*
Brands & Products:
INTERMEZZO

TRUE NORTH NUTRITION LTD.
88 E Beaver Creek Rd Bldg A Unit 1
Richmond Hill, ON L4B 4A8, Canada
Tel.: (905) 762-7070
Fax: (905) 762-7099
Fax: (888) 446-8783
Toll Free: (800) 261-4223
Web Site: www.truenorthnutrition.com
Sales Range: $10-24.9 Million
Approx. Number Employees: 50
Year Founded: 1997
Business Description:
Health Supplements Sales, Marketing & Distribution
S.I.C.: 5963
N.A.I.C.S.: 454390
Media: 4-5-6-10
Personnel:
Sam DeSimone *(Pres & CEO)*
Lana Abreu *(Mgr-Key Accounts)*

TWINLAB CORPORATION
(Sub. of IdeaSphere Inc.)
632 Broadway Fl 11
New York, NY 10012
Tel.: (212) 651-8500
Fax: (212) 505-5462
Fax: (631) 630-3490 (Sales)
Toll Free: (800) 645-5626
E-mail: product@twinlab.com
Web Site: www.twinlab.com
E-Mail For Key Personnel:
Sales Director: sales@twinlab.com
Approx. Number Employees: 300
Year Founded: 1931
Business Description:
Mfr of Nutritional Supplements, Including Vitamins, Minerals, Nutriceuticals, Herbs & Sports Nutrition Products
S.I.C.: 2833; 2834
N.A.I.C.S.: 325411; 325412
Media: 4-8-10-13
Personnel:
Tom Tolworthy *(Pres & CEO)*
Joseph Sinicropi *(CFO & COO)*
Kate Pastor *(Exec VP-Retail Sls)*
Stephen Welling *(VP & Gen Mgr)*
Brands & Products:
ANSWERS FOR LIFE
IRONMAN TRIATHOLON
TWINLAB

THE TYLENOL COMPANY
(Sub. of Johnson & Johnson)
1 Johnson & Johnson Plz
New Brunswick, NJ 08933
Tel.: (732) 524-0400
Fax: (732) 524-3300
Toll Free: (877) 895-3665
Web Site: www.j&j.com
Sales Range: $25-49.9 Million
Approx. Number Employees: 100
Business Description:
Pharmaceuticals Mfr
S.I.C.: 2834
N.A.I.C.S.: 325412
Advertising Expenditures: $135,000,000
Personnel:
William C. Weldon *(Chm & CEO)*
Patrick Conroy *(Brand Mgr)*

UCB MANUFACTURING, INC.
(Sub. of UCB S.A.)
755 Jefferson Rd
Rochester, NY 14623-3233
Mailing Address:
PO Box 31710
Rochester, NY 14603-1710
Tel.: (585) 475-9000
Fax: (585) 475-1016
Toll Free: (800) 234-5535
Web Site: www.ucb.com
Approx. Number Employees: 500
Year Founded: 1886
Business Description:
Pharmaceutical Research & Development
S.I.C.: 2834; 2833
N.A.I.C.S.: 325412; 325411
Media: 2-4-6-10-12-21
Distr.: Natl.
Budget Set: Oct.
Personnel:
Daniel Greenleaf *(Pres)*

UDL LABORATORIES, INC.
(Sub. of Mylan, Inc.)
1718 Northrock Ct
Rockford, IL 61103
Tel.: (815) 282-1201
Fax: (815) 282-9391
Toll Free: (800) 848-0462
Web Site: www.udllabs.com
Sales Range: $200-249.9 Million
Approx. Number Employees: 400
Year Founded: 1980
Business Description:
Repackager & Marketer of Multi Source & Single Source of Pharmaceutical Products & Unit Dose for Institutions
S.I.C.: 2834; 5122
N.A.I.C.S.: 325412; 424210
Media: 2-4-7-10-21
Distr.: Natl.
Budget Set: Oct.
Personnel:
Jodi Eichelberger *(VP & Gen Mgr)*
Brands & Products:
EMERGI-SCRIPT

ULURU INC.
4452 Beltway Dr
Addison, TX 75001
Tel.: (214) 905-5145
Fax: (214) 905-5130
E-mail: kgray@uluruinc.com
Web Site: www.uluruinc.com
Approx. Rev.: $1,557,357
Approx. Number Employees: 9
Business Description:
Wound Management, Plastic Surgery & Oral Care Products Developer
S.I.C.: 2834
N.A.I.C.S.: 325412
Media: 5-11-12
Personnel:
Kerry P. Gray *(Pres, CEO & Dir)*
Terrance K. Wallberg *(CFO, Treas, Sec & VP)*
Christopher J. Stergion *(Dir-Sls & Mktg)*
Brands & Products:
ADVANCING TOPICAL DELIVERY
ALTRAZEAL

Key to Media (For complete agency information see *The Advertising Red Books-Agencies* edition):
1. Bus. Publs. 2. Cable T.V. 3. Catalogs & Directories. 4. Co-op Adv. 5. Consumer Mags. 6. D.M. to Bus. Estab.7. D.M. to Consumers
8. Daily Newsp. 9. Exhibits/Trade Shows 10. Foreign 11. Infomercial 12. Internet Adv.13. Multimedia 14. Network Radio
15. Network T.V. 16. Newsp. Distr. Mags. 17. Other 18. Outdoor (Posters, Transit) 19. Point of Purchase20. Premiums, Novelties
21. Product Samples 22. Special Events Mktg. 23. Spot Radio 24. Spot T.V. 25. Weekly Newsp. 26. Yellow Page Adv.

ULURU Inc. — (Continued)

ORADISC
RESIDERM
ULURU

UNILIFE CORPORATION

633 Lowther Rd
Lewisberry, PA 17339
Tel.: (717) 938-9323
E-mail: info@unilife.com.au
Web Site: www.unilife.com.au
Approx. Rev.: $6,650,000
Approx. Number Employees: 129
Business Description:
Safety Syringe Developers
S.I.C.: 3841
N.A.I.C.S.: 339112
Advertising Expenditures: $500,000
Personnel:
Alan Shortall *(CEO)*
R. Richard Wieland, II *(CFO & Exec VP)*
Ramin Mojdehbakhsh *(COO & Exec VP)*
J. Christopher Naftzger *(Chief Compliance Officer, Gen Counsel & Sec)*
Bernhard Opitz *(Sr VP-Ops)*
Stephen Allan *(VP-Mktg & Comm)*
Jack J. Kelley, III *(VP-Strategic Mktg)*
David Watson *(VP-Engrg)*
Cynthia Lighty *(Dir-HR & Legal Svcs & Asst Sec)*
Dan Adlon *(Dir-Design Engrg)*
Ian Hanson *(Dir-Advanced Drug Delivery Sys)*
Mark Hassett *(Dir-Sls & Mktg)*
Deborah Karlak *(Dir-SEC Reporting)*
Lisa MacKenzie *(Dir-Clinical Affairs & Product Mgmt)*
Graham Purches *(Dir-Ops-RTFS)*
Tom Westbye *(Dir-Product Dev)*

UNITED AMERICAN HEALTHCARE CORP.

300 River Pl Ste 4950
Detroit, MI 48207-4291
Tel.: (313) 393-4571
Fax: (313) 393-3394
Web Site: www.uahc.com
Approx. Rev.: $3,818,000
Approx. Number Employees: 30
Business Description:
HMO Management Services
S.I.C.: 6411; 8742; 8748
N.A.I.C.S.: 524210; 541611; 541618
Media: 13-26
Personnel:
John M. Fife *(Chm, Pres & CEO)*
Robert Sullivan *(CFO & Treas)*
Stephanie M. Dowell *(CEO-Health Plan)*

UNITED SURGICAL PARTNERS INTERNATIONAL, INC.

(Holding of Welsh Carson Anderson & Stowe, LLC)
15305 Dallas Pkwy Ste 1600
Addison, TX 75001
Tel.: (210) 826-7366
Fax: (972) 713-3550
Web Site: www.unitedsurgical.com
Approx. Rev.: $576,665,000
Approx. Number Employees: 6,100
Year Founded: 1998
Business Description:
Surgical Hospitals & Centers Owner, Manager & Operator
S.I.C.: 8062; 8011
N.A.I.C.S.: 622110; 621493
Media: 6
Personnel:
Donald E. Steen *(Chm)*
William H. Wilcox *(Pres & CEO)*
Mark A. Kopser *(CFO & Exec VP)*
Neils P. Vernegaard *(COO & Exec VP)*
Brett P. Brodnax *(Chief Dev Officer & Exec VP)*
James A. Jackson *(Chief Petty Officer)*
Corey Ridgway *(Pres-Mktg)*
Jason B. Cagle *(Gen Counsel)*
John J. Wellik *(Sec, Sr VP-Acctg & Admin)*
Jonathan R. Bond *(Sr VP-Ops)*
Monica Cintado-Scokin *(Sr VP-Dev)*
Mark C. Garvin *(Sr VP-Ops)*
Jot Hollenbeck *(Sr VP-Dev)*
Luke D. Johnson *(Sr VP)*
Andrew H. Johnston *(Sr VP-Dev)*
Patrick Murphy *(Sr VP)*

UNITED THERAPEUTICS CORPORATION

1040 Spring St
Silver Spring, MD 20910
Tel.: (301) 608-9292
Fax: (301) 608-9291
E-mail: afisher@unither.com
Web Site: www.unither.com/
Approx. Rev.: $603,831,000
Approx. Number Employees: 520
Year Founded: 1996
Business Description:
Chronic & Life-Threatening Cardiovascular, Cancer & Infectious Diseases Biopharmaceutical Mfr
S.I.C.: 2834; 2836
N.A.I.C.S.: 325412; 325414
Advertising Expenditures: $1,600,000
Media: 17
Personnel:
Martine A. Rothblatt *(Chm & CEO)*
Roger A. Jeffs *(Pres & COO)*
John M. Ferrari *(CFO & Treas)*
Paul A. Mahon *(Gen Counsel, Sec & Exec VP)*
David Walsh *(Exec VP-Ops & Medicinal Chemistry)*
Christopher Patusky *(Dir-Real Estate)*

UNIVERSAL HEALTH SERVICES INC.

367 S Gulph Rd PO Box 61558
King of Prussia, PA 19406
Mailing Address:
PO Box 61558
King of Prussia, PA 19406-0958
Tel.: (610) 768-3300
Fax: (610) 768-3336
Toll Free: (800) 347-7750
Web Site: www.uhsinc.com
Approx. Rev.: $5,568,185,000
Approx. Number Employees: 49,700
Year Founded: 1978
Business Description:
Hospital Management & Services
S.I.C.: 8062; 8063
N.A.I.C.S.: 622110; 622210
Media: 2-3-4-8-9-13-18-20-22-23-24-25
Distr.: Natl.; Reg.
Personnel:
Alan B. Miller *(Chm & CEO)*
Marc D. Miller *(Pres)*
Steve G. Filton *(CFO, Sec & Sr VP)*
Marvin G. Pember *(Pres-Acute Care Div & Sr VP)*
Matthew D. Klein *(Gen Counsel & VP)*
Debra K. Osteen *(Sr VP)*
Martin C. Schappell *(Sr VP)*
John Paul Christen *(VP-Fin)*
Brands & Products:
UHS

UNIVERSAL HOSPITAL SERVICES, INC.

(Holding of Irving Place Capital Management, L.P.)
7700 France Ave S Ste 275
Edina, MN 55435
Tel.: (952) 893-3200
Fax: (952) 893-0704
Toll Free: (800) 847-7368
Web Site: www.uhs.com
Approx. Rev.: $317,422,000
Approx. Number Employees: 1,472
Business Description:
Medical Equipment Leasing
S.I.C.: 7352; 5047
N.A.I.C.S.: 532291; 423450
Media: 2-7
Personnel:
Gary D. Blackford *(Chm & CEO)*
Rex T. Clevenger *(CFO & Exec VP)*
Scott M. Madson *(Chief Acctg Officer, VP & Controller)*
Timothy W. Kuck *(Exec VP-Strategy & Bus Dev)*
Jeffrey L. Singer *(Exec VP-Sls & Mktg)*
Diana J. Vance-Bryan *(Exec VP-Ops)*
Robert Brooks *(Sr VP-Field Ops)*
Walter T. Chesley *(Sr VP-HR & Dev)*
David G. Lawson *(Sr VP-Info & Strategic Res)*
Robert Zdon *(Sr VP-Corp Ops)*
Kenneth Harvey *(VP-Sls-Long Term Care)*

UNIVERSITY HOSPITAL & MEDICAL CENTER

(Sub. of HCA HOLDINGS, INC.)
7201 N University Dr
Tamarac, FL 33321-2913
Tel.: (954) 721-2200
Fax: (954) 724-6444
Web Site: www.hca.com
Approx. Number Employees: 500
Business Description:
Hospital
S.I.C.: 8062
N.A.I.C.S.: 622110
Personnel:
Mark Rader *(CEO)*
Advertising Agency:
Eisenberg & Associates
511 NE 3rd Ave
Fort Lauderdale, FL 33301-3235
Tel.: (954) 760-9500
Fax: (954) 760-9594

UPSTREAM BIOSCIENCES INC.

71130 198 - 8060 Silver Spring Blvd
Calgary, AB T3B 5K2, Canada
Tel.: (403) 537-2516
Toll Free: (800) 539-0289
E-mail: info@upstreambio.com
Web Site: www.upstreambio.com
Approx. Int. Income: $3,927
Year Founded: 2002
Business Description:
Biopharmaceutical Mfr
S.I.C.: 2834
N.A.I.C.S.: 325412
Personnel:
Mike McFarland *(Pres, CEO, CFO, Treas & Sec)*
Advertising Agency:
GendeLLindheim BioCom Partners, LLC
1375 Broadway 11th Floor
New York, NY 10018
Tel.: (212) 584-2276
Fax: (866) 214-9359
Toll Free: (866) 214-9359

UROLOGIX, INC.

14405 21st Ave N
Minneapolis, MN 55447-4685
Tel.: (763) 475-1400
Fax: (763) 475-1443
Toll Free: (800) 475-1403
E-mail: customerservice@urologix.com
Web Site: www.urologix.com
Approx. Sls.: $12,571,000
Approx. Number Employees: 88
Year Founded: 1991
Business Description:
Non-Surgical, Catheter-Based Therapies Developer & Marketer
S.I.C.: 3845
N.A.I.C.S.: 334510
Media: 9-25
Personnel:
Mitchell Dann *(Chm)*
Stryker Warren, Jr. *(CEO)*
Brian J. Smrdel *(CFO)*
Gregory J. Fluet *(COO & Exec VP)*
Lisa Ackermann *(VP-Sls & Mktg)*
Charles Lehman *(Dir-Ops)*
Rebecca J. Weber *(Dir-Fin)*
Jennifer Wilner *(Dir-Regulatory & Quality)*
Brands & Products:
COOLED THERMO THERAPY
COOLED THERMOCATH
COOLWAVE
FLOMAX
PROSTATRON
RECTAL THERMAL SENSING UNIT
TARGIS
TUMT
UROLOGIX
UROLOGIX MOBILE

UROPLASTY, INC.

5420 Feltl Rd
Minnetonka, MN 55343
Tel.: (952) 426-6140
Fax: (952) 426-6199
Toll Free: (866) 255-4522
E-mail: info.usa@uroplasty.com
Web Site: www.uroplasty.com
Approx. Sls.: $13,787,032
Approx. Number Employees: 83
Business Description:
Urinary Incontinency Implant Mfr
S.I.C.: 3841
N.A.I.C.S.: 339112
Advertising Expenditures: $181,000
Media: 7-10
Personnel:
R. Patrick Maxwell *(Chm)*
David B. Kaysen *(Pres & CEO)*
Mahedi A. Jiwani *(CFO, Treas & VP)*
Susan Hartjes Holman *(COO & Sec)*

Key to Media (For complete agency information see *The Advertising Red Books-Agencies* edition):
1. Bus. Publs. 2. Cable T.V. 3. Catalogs & Directories. 4. Co-op Adv. 5. Consumer Mags. 6. D.M. to Bus. Estab.7. D.M. to Consumers 8. Daily Newsp. 9. Exhibits/Trade Shows 10. Foreign 11. Infomercial 12. Internet Adv.13. Multimedia 14. Network Radio 15. Network T.V. 16. Newsp. Distr. Mags. 17. Other 18. Outdoor (Posters, Transit) 19. Point of Purchase20. Premiums, Novelties 21. Product Samples 22. Special Events Mktg. 23. Spot Radio 24. Spot T.V. 25. Weekly Newsp. 26. Yellow Page Adv.

Brands & Products:
BIOPLASTIQUE
MACROPLASTIQUE
PTQ
URGENT
UROPLASTY
VOX

US ONCOLOGY, INC.

(Sub. of McKesson Corporation)
10101 Woodloch Forrest Dr
The Woodlands, TX 77380
Tel.: (281) 863-1000
Toll Free: (800) 381-2637
E-mail: oncology.info@usoncology.com
Web Site: www.usoncology.com/home/
E-Mail For Key Personnel:
Public Relations: jennifer.horspool@usoncology.com
Approx. Rev.: $3,511,680,000
Approx. Number Employees: 4,400
Year Founded: 1992
Business Description:
Oncology Practice Management Services
S.I.C.: 3845; 8049; 8093
N.A.I.C.S.: 334510; 621399; 621498
Media: 2-13
Personnel:
Bruce D. Broussard *(Chm & CEO)*
Lloyd K. Everson *(Vice Chm)*
David W. Young *(CFO)*
Glen Laschober *(COO & Exec VP)*
Kevin F. Krenzke *(Chief Acctg Officer)*
Roy A. Beveridge *(Exec VP & Dir-Medical)*
Grant Bogle *(Sr VP-Reg Ops)*
David B. Bronsweig *(Sr VP-HR)*
Khristin Wierman *(VP-Mktg)*

U.S. PHYSICAL THERAPY, INC.

1300 W Sam Houston Pkwy S Ste 300
Houston, TX 77042
Tel.: (713) 297-7000
Fax: (713) 297-7090
Toll Free: (800) 580-6285
E-mail: pking@usphysicaltherapy.com
Web Site: www.usph.com
Approx. Rev.: $211,233,000
Approx. Number Employees: 1,876
Year Founded: 1990
Business Description:
Outpatient Physical & Occupational Therapy Clinics Operator
S.I.C.: 8049; 1522; 6321; 8082; 8093; 8099; 8331
N.A.I.C.S.: 621340; 236220; 524114; 621498; 621610; 621999; 624310
Media: 2-10
Personnel:
Daniel C. Arnold *(Chm)*
Mark J. Brookner *(Vice Chm)*
Christopher J. Reading *(Pres & CEO)*
Lawrance W. McAfee *(CFO & Exec VP)*
Bill Johnston *(Coord-Mktg)*

USANA HEALTH SCIENCES, INC.

(Holding of Gull Holdings, Ltd.)
3838 W Parkway Blvd
Salt Lake City, UT 84120-6336
Tel.: (801) 954-7100
Fax: (801) 956-9486
E-mail: dist.serv@us.usana.com
Web Site: www.usana.com
Approx. Sls.: $517,644,000
Approx. Number Employees: 1,240
Year Founded: 1992
Business Description:
Nutritional, Personal Care & Weight Management Product Developer & Mfr
S.I.C.: 2833
N.A.I.C.S.: 325411
Advertising Expenditures: $3,842,000
Personnel:
Myron W. Wentz *(Founder & Chm)*
David A. Wentz *(CEO)*
G. Douglas Hekking *(CFO)*
Roy W. Truett *(COO)*
Kevin G. Guest *(Pres-North America)*
James Bramble *(Gen Counsel & Corp Sec)*
Bill Duncan *(Exec VP-Australasia)*
Timothy E. Wood *(Exec VP-R & D)*
Alan Bergstrom *(VP-Customer Svc)*
Paul Jones *(VP-HR)*
Dan Macuga *(VP-Mktg & PR)*
Shawn Mclelland *(VP-Media & Events)*
Riley Timmer *(VP-Fin)*
Brands & Products:
BIOMEGA
BODY ROX
COQUINONE
E-PRIME
ESSENTIALS
FIBERGY
FIBERGY BARS
GINKO-PS
HEALTHPAK
MAGA AO
NATURAL
NUTRIMEAL
NUTRITION BAR
OPTOMEGA
PALMETTO PLUS
PHYTOESTRIN
POLY C
PROCOSA
PROFLAVANOL
PROFLAVANOL-T
PROTEO-C
SOYAMAX
USANA
USANIMALS
VISIONEX

UTAH MEDICAL PRODUCTS, INC.

7043 S 300 W
Midvale, UT 84047-1048
Tel.: (801) 566-1200
Fax: (801) 566-7305
Toll Free: (866) 754-9789
Toll Free: (800) 533-4984
E-mail: info@utahmed.com
Web Site: www.utahmed.com
E-Mail For Key Personnel:
President: kcornwell@utahmed.com
Public Relations: prichins@utahmed.com
Approx. Sls.: $25,121,000
Approx. Number Employees: 160
Year Founded: 1978
Business Description:
Specialty Medical Devices for Obstetrics, Gynecology, Urology, Electrosurgery, Neonatal Intensive Care & Blood Pressure Monitoring
S.I.C.: 3842; 3841
N.A.I.C.S.: 339113; 339112
Import Export
Advertising Expenditures: $2,272,000
Media: 2-10
Personnel:
Kevin L. Cornwell *(CEO)*
Paul O. Richins *(Chief Admin Officer)*
Marcena H. Clawson *(VP-Corp Sls)*
Brands & Products:
ABCORP
ARMO-COT
AROM-COT
BT-CATH
C-LETZ
CMI
CORDGUARD
DELTA-CAL
DELTA-FLOW
DELTRAN
DIALY-NATE
DISPOSA-HOOD
ENDOCURETTE
EPITOME
FILTRESSE
FINESSE
FLEX CUP
GESCO
HEMO-NATE
HEMO-TAP
INTRAN
LETZ
LIBERTY
LUMIN
MUC-X
MYELO-NATE
NUTRI-CATH
NUTRI-LOK
OPTIMICRO
OPTISPEC
PALA-NATE
PATHFINDER
PATHFINDER PLUS
PICC-NATE
QWIK CONNECT PLUS
SAFE-T-GAUGE
SECURE CUP
SOFT TOUCH
TENDER TOUCH
THORA-CATH
TVUS/HSG-CATH
UMBILI-CATH
URI-CATH
UTAH MEDICAL PRODUCTS INC
UTAHBALL
UTAHLOOP
VAC-U-NATE
VELVET TOUCH
VERI-CAL
WORKING TO SAVE LIVES

VALEANT PHARMACEUTICALS INTERNATIONAL

(Div. of Valeant Pharmaceuticals International, Inc.)
1 Enterprise
Aliso Viejo, CA 92656-2606
Tel.: (949) 461-6000
Fax: (949) 461-6609
Toll Free: (800) 548-5100
Web Site: www.valeant.com
Year Founded: 1959
Business Description:
Pharmaceutical Products Mfr & Distr
S.I.C.: 2834
N.A.I.C.S.: 325412
Export
Advertising Expenditures: $215,000
Media: 2-6-8-10-13-14
Distr.: Intl.; Natl.
Budget Set: Nov.
Personnel:
Rajiv De Silva *(Pres-Valeant Pharm Intl Inc & COO-Specialty Pharma)*
Richard K. Masterson *(Pres-Biovail Laboratories-Intl)*
Brands & Products:
AMOXIVET
ANCOBON
ANCOTIL
ANDROID
ANXIRON
ARRETIN
BEDOYECTA
BENEDORM
BISOCARD
BONTRIL
CATRIX
CERAVE
CESAMET
CITAXIN
CLOPAMID
DALMANE
DELAGIL
DERMADRATE
DERMATIX
DERMAVEEN
DIAMIN
EFUDEX
ELDOQUIN
ENI
GLYQUIN
HYROTONE MAX
ISOFACE
KINERASE
KONADERM
LIBRAX
MACROMAX
MESTINON
MICROKA
NIACIN
NYAL
OTINUM
OXSORALEN-ULTRA
PERMAX
PHRENILIN
PRINORM
SOLAQUIN
UNICARE
UNIFER
VALEANT
VIRAMIDINE
VIRAZOLE
ZELAPAR
Advertising Agency:
CDM West
10960 Wilshire Blvd Ste 1750
Los Angeles, CA 90024
Tel.: (212) 907-6919
Fax: (310) 444-7041

VALEANT PHARMACEUTICALS INTERNATIONAL, INC.

7150 Mississauga Road
Mississauga, ON L5N 8M5, Canada
Tel.: (905) 286-3000
Fax: (905) 286-3050
Web Site: www.valeant.com
Approx. Rev.: $1,181,237,000
Approx. Number Employees: 4,300
Year Founded: 1994
Business Description:
Pharmaceuticals & Drug Delivery Systems Mfr

Key to Media (For complete agency information see *The Advertising Red Books-Agencies* edition):
1. Bus. Publs. 2. Cable T.V. 3. Catalogs & Directories. 4. Co-op Adv. 5. Consumer Mags. 6. D.M. to Bus. Estab.7. D.M. to Consumers 8. Daily Newsp. 9. Exhibits/Trade Shows 10. Foreign 11. Infomercial 12. Internet Adv.13. Multimedia 14. Network Radio 15. Network T.V. 16. Newsp. Distr. Mags. 17. Other 18. Outdoor (Posters, Transit) 19. Point of Purchase20. Premiums, Novelties 21. Product Samples 22. Special Events Mktg. 23. Spot Radio 24. Spot T.V. 25. Weekly Newsp. 26. Yellow Page Adv.

Valeant Pharmaceuticals International, Inc. — (Continued)

S.I.C.: 2834; 2833
N.A.I.C.S.: 325412; 325411
Advertising Expenditures: $29,900,000
Media: 2-6-10-21
Personnel:
J. Michael Pearson *(Chm & CEO)*
Rajiv De Silva *(Pres & COO-Specialty Pharmaceuticals)*
Philip W. Loberg *(CFO & Exec VP)*
Robert Chai-Onn *(Gen Counsel, Sec & Exec VP)*
Jennifer Tindale *(VP & Assoc Gen Counsel)*
Mark Durham *(Sr VP-HR)*
Christopher Bovaird *(VP-Corp Fin)*
Nelson F. Isabel *(VP-IR & Corp Comm)*
Rochelle Seide *(VP-Intellectual Property)*
Brands & Products:
ATIVAN
GLUMETZA
ISORDIL
MONOCOR
NITOMAN
RALIVIA
TEVETEN
TIAZAC
ULTRAM
VALEANT
VASERETIC
VASOTEC
WELLBUTRIN
ZOVIRAX
ZYBAN

VCA ANTECH, INC.

12401 W Olympic Blvd
Los Angeles, CA 90064-1022
Tel.: (310) 571-6500
Fax: (310) 571-6700
Toll Free: (800) 966-1822
E-mail: webmaster@vcamail.com
Web Site: www.vcaantech.com
Approx. Rev.: $1,381,468,000
Approx. Number Employees: 9,400
Business Description:
Animal Health Care Services
S.I.C.: 8734; 0711; 0742; 0752
N.A.I.C.S.: 541380; 115112; 541940; 812910
Advertising Expenditures: $11,200,000
Media: 2-7-10-19
Personnel:
Robert L. Antin *(Co-Founder, Chm, Pres & CEO)*
Arthur J. Antin *(Co-Founder, COO, Sec, Dir & Sr VP)*
Neil Tauber *(Co-Founder & Sr VP-Dev)*
Alexis Nahama *(Chm & VP-Mktg)*
Tomas W. Fuller *(CFO & VP)*
Advertising Agency:
Ketchum Directory Advertising/Kansas City
7015 College Blvd Ste 700
Overland Park, KS 66211-1524
Tel.: (913) 344-1900
Fax: (913) 344-1960
Toll Free: (800) 922-6977

VENTURI, INC.

2299 Traversefield Dr
Traverse City, MI 49686
Tel.: (231) 929-7732
Fax: (231) 929-7735
E-mail: info@venturi-inc.com
Web Site: www.venturi-inc.com
Sales Range: $10-24.9 Million
Approx. Number Employees: 6
Year Founded: 1963
Business Description:
Cigarette Filter Holders, 4-Week Stop-Smoking System, Disposable Toothbrushes, Safety Mats & Bath Accessories Mfr
S.I.C.: 5099; 5199
N.A.I.C.S.: 423990; 424990
Import Export
Media: 2-5-7-8-10-20-21
Distr.: Intl.; Natl.
Budget Set: Monthly
Personnel:
Tim Dutmers *(Owner)*
Brands & Products:
AMBERWARE
SLIP-X
SMILESAVER
SNUG PLUG
SOLUTIONS
STOP-A-CLOG
TARGARD
TUB TATTOOS
VENTURI

VERTEX PHARMACEUTICALS INCORPORATED

130 Waverly St
Cambridge, MA 02139-4252
Tel.: (617) 444-6100
Fax: (617) 444-6680
E-mail: investorinfo@vrtx.com
Web Site: www.vpharm.com
Approx. Rev.: $143,370,000
Approx. Number Employees: 1,691
Year Founded: 1989
Business Description:
Pharmaceutical Mfr
S.I.C.: 2834; 8733
N.A.I.C.S.: 325412; 541720
Advertising Expenditures: $4,300,000
Personnel:
Matthew W. Emmens *(Chm, Pres & CEO)*
Ian F. Smith *(CFO & Exec VP)*
Kenneth S. Boger *(Chief Legal Officer & Sr VP)*
Peter Mueller *(Chief Scientific Officer, Exec VP-Global R & D)*
Nancy J. Wysenski *(Chief Comml Officer & Exec VP)*
Amit K. Sachdev *(Sr VP & Gen Mgr)*
Lisa Kelly-Croswell *(Sr VP-HR)*
Lora Pike *(Dir-IR)*
Zachry Barber *(Assoc Dir-Corp Comm)*
Brands & Products:
AGENERASE
LEXIVA
TELZIR
VERTEX
Advertising Agency:
LaVoie Strategic Communications Group, Inc.
12 Derby Sq S1
Salem, MA 01970
Tel.: (978) 745-4200
Fax: (978) 745-4242

VHA INC.

220 Las Colinas Blvd E
Irving, TX 75039-5503
Tel.: (972) 830-0626
Tel.: (972) 830-0798 (Media Rels)
Fax: (972) 830-0000
Toll Free: (800) 842-5146
E-mail: feedback@vha.com
Web Site: www.vha.com
Approx. Rev.: $451,451,000
Approx. Number Employees: 3,500
Year Founded: 1977
Business Description:
Supply Chain Management & Hospital Consulting Services
S.I.C.: 8748
N.A.I.C.S.: 541618
Advertising Expenditures: $3,000,000
Media: 2-4-10-13
Personnel:
Curtis W. Nonomaque *(Pres & CEO)*
Peter P. Csapo *(CFO)*
Michael Cummins *(CIO & Sr VP)*
Gail Rigler *(Chief Mktg Officer, Chief Comm Officer, Sr VP-Mktg & Comm)*
Michael Regier *(Gen Counsel & Sr VP-Legal & Corp Affairs)*
Michael J. Daly *(Exec VP)*
K. Jeffrey Hayes *(Sr VP-Strategic Svcs)*
Jeff McLaren *(Sr VP-Natl Supply Chain)*
Doug Guziec *(VP-Strategy)*
Samantha Keyes *(VP-Corp Mktg)*
John Fassnacht *(Sr Dir)*
Lynn Gentry *(Sr Dir-PR)*
Edwin C. Streeter *(Sr Dir-Logistics)*
Brands & Products:
A BLUEPRINT FOR DELIVERING BETTER HEALTH CARE
RESULTS ARE JUST THE BEGINING
SUPPLY LYNX
VHA

VIA PHARMACEUTICALS, INC.

750 Battery St Ste 330
San Francisco, CA 94111
Tel.: (415) 283-2200
Fax: (415) 283-2201
E-mail: info@viapharmaceuticals.com
Web Site: www.viapharmaceuticals.com
Approx. Number Employees: 6
Year Founded: 2004
Business Description:
Pharmaceutical Developer & Mfr for the Treatment of Cardiovascular Disease
S.I.C.: 8733; 2834
N.A.I.C.S.: 541710; 325412
Personnel:
Douglass B. Given *(Chm)*
Lawrence K. Cohen *(Pres & CEO)*
James G. Stewart *(CFO & Sr VP)*
Brands & Products:
STILETTO
VGEF-2
VIA
Advertising Agency:
WCG
60 Francisco St
San Francisco, CA 94133
Tel.: (415) 362-5018
Fax: (415) 362-5019

VIACELL, INC.

(Sub. of PerkinElmer Life & Analytical Sciences, Inc.)
245 1st St
Cambridge, MA 02142
Tel.: (617) 914-3400
Toll Free: (866) 668-4895
Web Site: www.viacellinc.com
Approx. Rev.: $54,426,000
Approx. Number Employees: 254
Year Founded: 1994
Business Description:
Cancer, Infertility, Genetic & Cardiac Disease Cellular Therapies
S.I.C.: 8093; 7335; 8099; 8733
N.A.I.C.S.: 621410; 541720; 541922; 621999
Advertising Expenditures: $3,100,000
Media: 6-8-13
Personnel:
Jim Corbett *(Pres)*
Nadia Altomare *(VP-Sls, Svc & Ops)*
Christopher Stump *(VP-Sls & Training)*
Brands & Products:
CORD BLOOD BANKING + RESEARCH
VIACORD

VIACORD

(Div. of ViaCell, Inc.)
245 1st St
Cambridge, MA 02142
Tel.: (617) 914-3900
Fax: (781) 663-6052
Toll Free: (866) 688-4895
E-mail: info@viacord.com
Web Site: www.viacord.com
Sales Range: $25-49.9 Million
Approx. Number Employees: 100
Year Founded: 1993
Business Description:
Biological Research Services
S.I.C.: 8733
N.A.I.C.S.: 541710
Media: 6
Personnel:
David Blackett *(Mktg Dir)*

VICTUS, INC.

4918 SW 74th Ct
Miami, FL 33155
Tel.: (305) 663-2129
Fax: (305) 663-1843
E-mail: info@victusinc.com
Web Site: www.victusinc.com
Sales Range: $1-9.9 Million
Approx. Number Employees: 50
Business Description:
Medical Products Mfr & Distr
S.I.C.: 2834; 3069
N.A.I.C.S.: 325412; 326299
Media: 2-6-10-11-13-18-21
Personnel:
Enrique Lopez *(Owner)*
Mariano Macias *(Owner)*
Rolando Sierra *(Dir-Mktg)*
Brands & Products:
CLAVE
CORPAK
ENTEREX
ENTEREX DIABETIC
ENTEREX RENAL
GLUTAPAK
GLUTAPAK-10
INMUNEX
PROTEINEX
SECURE-FLOW
VICTUS

VIOQUEST PHARMACEUTICALS, INC.

PO Box 2287
Minneapolis, MN 55402
Tel.: (612) 220-3237

Key to Media (For complete agency information see *The Advertising Red Books-Agencies* edition):
1. Bus. Publs. 2. Cable T.V. 3. Catalogs & Directories. 4. Co-op Adv. 5. Consumer Mags. 6. D.M. to Bus. Estab. 7. D.M. to Consumers 8. Daily Newsp. 9. Exhibits/Trade Shows 10. Foreign 11. Infomercial 12. Internet Adv. 13. Multimedia 14. Network Radio 15. Network T.V. 16. Newsp. Distr. Mags. 17. Other 18. Outdoor (Posters, Transit) 19. Point of Purchase 20. Premiums, Novelties 21. Product Samples 22. Special Events Mktg. 23. Spot Radio 24. Spot T.V. 25. Weekly Newsp. 26. Yellow Page Adv.

Sales Range: Less than $1 Million
Approx. Number Employees: 3
Year Founded: 2000
Business Description:
Late Pre-Clinical & Early Clinical Stage Therapies Acquirer, Developer & Marketer
S.I.C.: 2834
N.A.I.C.S.: 325412
Advertising Expenditures: $29,681
Media: 10-21
Brands & Products:
LENOCTA
VIOQUEST
VQD-001 SODIUM STIBOGLUCONATE
VQD-002 TRICIRIBINE
XYFID

VIRBAC CORPORATION

(Sub. of Virbac S.A.)
3200 Meacham Blvd
Fort Worth, TX 76137
Tel.: (817) 831-5030
Fax: (817) 831-8327
Toll Free: (800) 338-3659
Web Site: www.virbaccorp.com
Approx. Number Employees: 269
Year Founded: 1999
Business Description:
Mfr & Distr of Health, Grooming, Dental & Parasiticide Products for Pets
S.I.C.: 2834; 0752
N.A.I.C.S.: 325412; 812910
Advertising Expenditures: $2,400,000
Media: 5
Personnel:
Erik R. Martinez *(Pres & CEO)*
Laurent Cesar *(Exec VP-Indus Ops)*
Michael S. O'Bryan *(Exec VP-Bus Ops)*
Brands & Products:
ALLERDERM
CET HOME DENTAL CARE
IVERHART PLUS FLAVORED CHEWABLES
PREVENTIC
SOLOXINE
Advertising Agency:
Calise & Sedei
501 Elm St, Ste 500
Dallas, TX 75202
Tel.: (469) 385-4790
Fax: (214) 760-7094

VIROPHARMA INCORPORATED

730 Stockton Dr
Exton, PA 19341
Tel.: (610) 458-7300
Fax: (610) 458-7380
E-mail: questions@viropharma.com
Web Site: www.viropharma.com
Approx. Rev.: $439,012,000
Approx. Number Employees: 232
Year Founded: 1994
Business Description:
Pharmaceuticals Product Developer
S.I.C.: 2834; 2833
N.A.I.C.S.: 325412; 325411
Media: 10
Personnel:
Vincent J. Milano *(Chm, Pres & CEO)*
Charles A. Rowland, Jr. *(CFO & VP)*
Daniel B. Soland *(COO & VP)*
Richard S. Morris *(Chief Acctg Officer & VP)*
Will Roberts *(VP-Corp Comm)*
Robert Doody *(Asst Dir-IR)*
Brands & Products:
CINRYZE
CINRYZESOLUTIONS
MAIRBAVIR
VANCOCIN
VIROPHARMA INCORPORATED

VIRTUAL RADIOLOGIC CORPORATION

(Holding of Providence Equity Partners LLC)
11995 Singletree Ln Ste 500
Eden Prairie, MN 55344
Tel.: (952) 392-1100
Fax: (952) 942-3361
Toll Free: (800) 737-0610
E-mail: info@vrad.com
Web Site: www.virtualrad.com
Approx. Rev.: $120,736,000
Approx. Number Employees: 244
Year Founded: 2001
Business Description:
Remote Digital Diagnostic Imaging Services
S.I.C.: 8071
N.A.I.C.S.: 621512
Advertising Expenditures: $30,000
Media: 2-7-13-17
Personnel:
Robert C. Kill *(Pres & CEO)*
Justin Roth *(CFO)*
Mike Kolar *(Gen Counsel, Sec & VP)*
Sandy Schmitt *(Sr VP-Strategy & Dev)*
Jim Tierney *(Sr VP-Ops-vRad Radiology Alliance)*
Julie Shaffrey *(Dir-Quality Assurance)*

VISITING NURSE ASSOCIATION OF CENTRAL JERSEY

(Affil. of Visiting Nurse Service of New York)
176 Riverside Ave
Red Bank, NJ 07701-1014
Tel.: (732) 224-6760
Fax: (732) 747-2822
Web Site: www.vnacj.org
Approx. Number Employees: 1,000
Year Founded: 1912
Business Description:
Home Healthcare Services
S.I.C.: 7389
N.A.I.C.S.: 561990
Media: 2-23
Personnel:
Stanley Coleman *(Chm)*
Mary Ann Christopher *(Pres & CEO)*
Kevin Rogers *(CFO)*
John Harz *(VP-HR)*
Nancy Montserrat *(Dir-Bus Dev)*
Patricia Rusca *(Dir-Quality & Regulatory Compliance)*
Eileen H. Toughill *(Dir-Health)*

VISITING NURSE ASSOCIATION OF FLORIDA

2400 SE Monterey Rd
Stuart, FL 34996
Tel.: (772) 286-1844
Fax: (772) 286-8753
Toll Free: (800) 318-0399
Web Site: www.vnaflorida.org
Business Description:
Home Health Care Agency
S.I.C.: 8082
N.A.I.C.S.: 621610
Media: 22
Personnel:
Don Crow *(Dir-Ops)*

VISITING NURSE ASSOCIATION OF SOMERSET HILLS INC.

200 Mount Airy Rd
Basking Ridge, NJ 07920
Tel.: (908) 766-0180
Fax: (908) 766-5492
E-mail: mail@visitingnurse.org
Web Site: www.visitingnurse.org
Approx. Rev.: $6,000,000
Approx. Number Employees: 135
Year Founded: 1904
Business Description:
Home Health Care Services
S.I.C.: 8082; 8322
N.A.I.C.S.: 621610; 624190
Media: 2
Personnel:
Ann Painter *(CEO)*
Mary Chipparulo *(CFO)*
Marie Sperber *(Dir-Dev & Mktg)*
Karen Ellis *(Mgr-Volunteers)*

VISITING NURSE ASSOCIATION OF STATEN ISLAND

400 Lake Ave
Staten Island, NY 10303
Tel.: (718) 720-2245
Fax: (718) 816-3534
Web Site: www.vnasi.org
Approx. Sls.: $20,823,699
Approx. Number Employees: 155
Year Founded: 1917
Business Description:
Home Health-Care Services
S.I.C.: 7389
N.A.I.C.S.: 561990
Media: 2
Personnel:
Calvin M. Sprung *(Pres & CEO)*
William A. Bloom *(CFO)*

VISITING NURSE SERVICE OF NEW YORK

107 E 70th St
New York, NY 10021-5006
Tel.: (212) 609-1500
Fax: (212) 794-6610
Toll Free: (888) VNS-1-CALL
E-mail: careers@vnsny.org
Web Site: www.vnsny.org
Sales Range: $700-749.9 Million
Approx. Number Employees: 1,178
Year Founded: 1893
Business Description:
Home & Community-Based Health Care
S.I.C.: 8082
N.A.I.C.S.: 621610
Media: 2-13-18-24
Personnel:
Carol Raphael *(Pres & CEO)*
Joan Marren *(COO)*
Michael Bernstein *(CMO)*
Roger Harris *(Mgr)*
Brands & Products:
VNS CHOICE
VNSNY
WE BRING THE CARING HOME
Advertising Agency:
Rubenstein Associates, Inc.
1345 Ave of the Americas Fl 30
New York, NY 10105-0109
Tel.: (212) 843-8000
Fax: (212) 843-9200

VISITING NURSE SERVICES IN WESTCHESTER, INC.

360 Mamaroneck Ave
White Plains, NY 10605
Tel.: (914) 682-1480
Fax: (914) 684-0937
Toll Free: (888) FOR-VNSW
E-mail: info@vns.org
Web Site: www.vns.org
Approx. Rev.: $12,000,000
Approx. Number Employees: 125
Year Founded: 1901
Business Description:
Healthcare Services
S.I.C.: 8082
N.A.I.C.S.: 621610
Media: 2-13
Personnel:
Nicholas D'Angelo *(Chm)*
Carol L. Weber *(Pres & CEO)*
Albert L. DeMartino *(Dir-Medical)*
Suzanne Moses *(Dir-Patient Svcs)*

VITACOST.COM, INC.

5400 Broken Sound Blvd NW Ste 500
Boynton Beach, FL 33487
Tel.: (561) 982-4180
Web Site: www.vitacost.com
Approx. Sls.: $191,807,029
Approx. Number Employees: 290
Business Description:
Vitamins & Nutraceuticals Online Retailer & Catalog Sales
S.I.C.: 5961; 5122
N.A.I.C.S.: 454111; 424210; 454113
Advertising Expenditures: $8,690,000
Media: 1-13
Personnel:
Jeffrey J. Horowitz *(CEO)*
Stephen E. Markert, Jr. *(Interim CFO)*
Robert Wegner *(COO)*
Robert D. Hirsch *(CIO & VP-IT)*
David Zucker *(CMO)*
Mary L. Marbach *(Gen Counsel)*
Ellen Finnerty *(VP-HR)*
Brands & Products:
LIVE LONGER & SAVE MONEY
TOP BRAND VITAMINS AT WHOLESALE COST
VITACOST.COM

VITAL IMAGES, INC.

5850 Opus Parkway Ste 300
Minnetonka, MN 55343-4411
Tel.: (952) 487-9500
Fax: (952) 487-9510
Web Site: www.vitalimages.com
Approx. Rev.: $59,709,000
Approx. Number Employees: 238
Business Description:
Develops, Markets & Supports Medical Visualization & Analysis Software for Use Primarily in Clinical Diagnosis, Surgical Planning & Medical Screening
S.I.C.: 2834
N.A.I.C.S.: 325412
Import Export
Advertising Expenditures: $2,796,000
Personnel:
Vincent J. Argiro *(Founder & CTO)*

Key to Media (For complete agency information see *The Advertising Red Books-Agencies* edition):
1. Bus. Publs. 2. Cable T.V. 3. Catalogs & Directories. 4. Co-op Adv. 5. Consumer Mags. 6. D.M. to Bus. Estab.7. D.M. to Consumers 8. Daily Newsp. 9. Exhibits/Trade Shows 10. Foreign 11. Infomercial 12. Internet Adv.13. Multimedia 14. Network Radio 15. Network T.V. 16. Newsp. Distr. Mags. 17. Other 18. Outdoor (Posters, Transit) 19. Point of Purchase20. Premiums, Novelties 21. Product Samples 22. Special Events Mktg. 23. Spot Radio 24. Spot T.V. 25. Weekly Newsp. 26. Yellow Page Adv.

Vital Images, Inc. — (Continued)

James B. Hickey, Jr. *(Chm)*
Michael H. Carrel *(Pres & CEO)*
Peter J. Goepfrich *(CFO)*
Steven P. Canakes *(Exec VP-Sls)*
Cindy J. Edwards *(VP-HR)*

Brands & Products:
AUTOGATE
FUSION7D
THE IMAGE OF UNDERSTANDING
SUREPLAQUE
VITAL
VITAL CONNECT
VITALCARDIA
VITALPERFORMANCE
VITREA
VITREA 2
VITREAACCESS
VOXELVIEW
VSCORE

VITAL PHARMACEUTICALS, INC.

(d/b/a VPX Sports)
15751 SW 41st St Ste 300
Fort Lauderdale, FL 33331
Tel.: (954) 641-0570
Fax: (954) 641-4960
Toll Free: (800) 954-7904
E-mail: info@vpxsports.com
Web Site: www.vpxsports.com
Sales Range: $1-9.9 Million
Approx. Number Employees: 110
Year Founded: 1993
Business Description:
Dietary Supplement Mfr & Marketer
S.I.C.: 2834
N.A.I.C.S.: 325412
Media: 6-10
Personnel:
Jack Owoc *(Pres)*

VITAL SIGNS, INC.

(Div. of GE Healthcare Clinical Systems)
20 Campus Rd
Totowa, NJ 07512-1210
Tel.: (973) 790-1330
Fax: (973) 956-5436
Toll Free: (800) 932-0760
Web Site: www.vital-signs.com
Approx. Rev.: $205,257,000
Approx. Number Employees: 1,257
Year Founded: 1988
Business Description:
Anethesia & Respiratory Medical Products & Related Critical Care Applications Designer, Mfr & Marketer
S.I.C.: 3841; 3842
N.A.I.C.S.: 339112; 339113
Media: 2-7-10-21
Personnel:
Robert Ladd *(Gen Counsel & VP-HR)*
Mark Jefferson *(VP-Sls & Mktg)*

Brands & Products:
ACCU-PEEP
ACORN II
ACTAR-DFIB
ASPIRATOR
BABY BLUE II
BABYSAFE
BEAR I
BEAR II
BREAS
BREATHE-EASY
C-CO2
CLEEN-ABLE
CODE BLUE
CODE BLUE II
CUFF-ABLE
DISPOSA-VIEW
ENFLOW
FLOW-TROL
G.A.S.
GIN BABY
GREENLIGHT
GREENLIGHT II
HYDROGARD
INFUSABLE
INFUSASCAN
ISOCATH
KURTIS MSD
LIGHT WAND
LIMB-O
MICRO ABG
MISTY-OX
MISTY OX MULTIFIT
OXYGARD
PEDI BLUE II
QUIK ABG
RESPIRGARD II
SAFE SAC
SPIROGARD
T-WALL
THERMADRAPE
TURBO HEATER
ULTRA-SLIP
VITAL GAUGE
VITAL SEAL
VITAL SIGNS
VITAL TEMP
VITAL VIEW
VITAL VIEW II
WHISPER JET

VITAMIN SHOPPE, INC.

(Holding of Irving Place Capital Management, L.P.)
2101 91st St
North Bergen, NJ 07047-6446
Tel.: (201) 868-5959
Fax: (800) 852-7153
Toll Free: (800) 223-1216
Web Site: www.vitaminshoppe.com
Approx. Sls.: $751,482,000
Approx. Number Employees: 2,220
Year Founded: 1977
Business Description:
Holding Company; Vitamins & Other Health Related Products Retailer & Direct Marketer
S.I.C.: 5961; 5499; 5912; 6719
N.A.I.C.S.: 454113; 446110; 446191; 551112
Advertising Expenditures: $13,000,000
Media: 3-6-13-14-15-23-24
Personnel:
Richard L. Markee *(Chm & CEO)*
Michael G. Archbold *(Pres & COO)*
Anthony N. Truesdale *(CEO)*
Louis H. Weiss *(CMO)*
James M. Sander *(Gen Counsel, Sec & VP)*
Susan McLaughlin *(Dir-Corp Comm)*

Brands & Products:
VITAMINSHOPPE.COM

Advertising Agency:
Allison & Partners
505 Sansome St 7th Fl
San Francisco, CA 94111-3310
Tel.: (415) 217-7500
Fax: (415) 217-7503
(Vitamin Shoppe)

VITAMIN WORLD, INC.

(Sub. of NBTY, Inc.)
4320 Veterans Hwy
Holbrook, NY 11741
Tel.: (631) 567-9500
Fax: (631) 471-5693
Web Site: www.vitaminworld.com
Sales Range: $75-99.9 Million
Approx. Number Employees: 200
Business Description:
Nutritional Supplements
S.I.C.: 5499
N.A.I.C.S.: 446191
Advertising Expenditures: $500,000
Media: 4-5-6-8-13-19-20
Personnel:
Scott Rudolph *(CEO)*
Karen McCutcheon *(Dir-Mktg & Adv)*

Brands & Products:
VITAMIN WORLD
VITAMINWORLD.COM
WE MAKE QUALITY VITAMINS A PART OF YOUR LIFE

VITATECH INTERNATIONAL, INC.

2832 Dow Ave
Tustin, CA 92780-7212
Tel.: (714) 832-9700
Fax: (714) 731-8482
E-mail: wolfmfg@calpha.com
Web Site: www.vitatech.com
Approx. Number Employees: 140
Year Founded: 1954
Business Description:
Provider of Vitamin Preparations
S.I.C.: 2834; 2833
N.A.I.C.S.: 325412; 325411
Media: 10
Personnel:
Thomas T. Tierney *(Pres & CEO)*

Brands & Products:
VITA-TECH

VIVUS, INC.

1172 Castro St
Mountain View, CA 94040-2552
Tel.: (650) 934-5200
Fax: (650) 934-5389
E-mail: corpdev@vivus.com
Web Site: www.vivus.com
Approx. Rev.: $468,000
Approx. Number Employees: 43
Year Founded: 1991
Business Description:
Erectile & Sexual Dysfunction Pharmaceutical Products Developer & Mfr
S.I.C.: 2834; 3841; 8733
N.A.I.C.S.: 325412; 339112; 541710
Advertising Expenditures: $34,000
Media: 17
Personnel:
Peter Y. Tam *(Pres)*
Leland F. Wilson *(CEO)*
Timothy E. Morris *(CFO & Sr VP-Fin)*
Michael P. Miller *(Chief Comml Officer & Sr VP)*
Lee B. Perry *(Chief Acctg Officer & VP)*
Guy P. Marsh *(VP-US Ops & Gen Mgr)*

Brands & Products:
ACTIS
ALISTA
INNOVATIVE THERAPIES. NOVEL PRODUCTS
LURAMIST
MUSE
QNEXA
TESTOSTERONE MDTS

VNUS MEDICAL TECHNOLOGIES, INC.

(Sub. of Covidien Inc.)
5799 Fontanoso Way
San Jose, CA 95138-1015
Tel.: (408) 473-1100
Tel.: (408) 360-7200
Tel.: (408) 360-7400
Fax: (408) 365-8480
Fax: (408) 944-0292
Toll Free: (888) 797-8346
E-mail: info@vnus.com
Web Site: www.vnus.com
E-Mail For Key Personnel:
President: bfarley@vnus.com
Approx. Rev.: $101,151,000
Approx. Number Employees: 318
Year Founded: 1995
Business Description:
Medical Device Mfr
S.I.C.: 3845; 3841
N.A.I.C.S.: 334510; 339112
Advertising Expenditures: $558,000
Personnel:
Jon Kitahara *(Coord-Media)*

Brands & Products:
CLOSURE
CLOSUREFAST
CLOSUREPLUS
CLOSURERFS
LEGLINE
LOGIQ
LOGIQ BOOK
LOGIQ E
LYCRA
RFGPLUS
TACTEL
ULTRALINE
VAREX
VAREX VPH-CH1
VAREX VPH-M1L
VAREX VPH-M1R
VAREX VPH-M2L
VAREX VPH-M2R
VAREX VPH-M3L
VAREX VPH-M3R
VAREX VPH-M4L
VAREX VPH-M4R
VAREX VPH-MOS1
VAREX VPH-MOS2
VAREX VPH-R1R
VAREX VPH-R2L
VAREX VPH-VA1
VAREX VPH-VA2
VAREX VPH-VA3
VAREX VPH-VA4
VAREX VPH-VA5
VAREX VPH-VA6
VEINLITE
VEINLITE I
VEINLITE II
VEINLITE LED
VNUS
VNUS RFG2

VWR FUNDING, INC.

(Holding of Madison Dearborn Partners, LLC)
100 Matsonford Rd PO Box 6660
Radnor, PA 19087
Tel.: (610) 431-1700
Fax: (610) 429-5569
E-mail: info@vwr.com

Key to Media (For complete agency information see *The Advertising Red Books-Agencies* edition):
1. Bus. Publs. 2. Cable T.V. 3. Catalogs & Directories. 4. Co-op Adv. 5. Consumer Mags. 6. D.M. to Bus. Estab.7. D.M. to Consumers
8. Daily Newsp. 9. Exhibits/Trade Shows 10. Foreign 11. Infomercial 12. Internet Adv.13. Multimedia 14. Network Radio
15. Network T.V. 16. Newsp. Distr. Mags. 17. Other 18. Outdoor (Posters, Transit) 19. Point of Purchase20. Premiums, Novelties
21. Product Samples 22. Special Events Mktg. 23. Spot Radio 24. Spot T.V. 25. Weekly Newsp. 26. Yellow Page Adv.

Web Site: www.vwr.com
Approx. Sls.: $3,638,700,000
Approx. Number Employees: 7,000
Year Founded: 2004
Business Description:
Holding Company; Laboratory Supplies Distr
S.I.C.: 6719; 5047
N.A.I.C.S.: 551112; 423450
Advertising Expenditures: $21,800,000
Personnel:
John M. Ballbach *(Chm, Pres & CEO)*
Gregory L. Cowan *(CFO & Sr VP)*
Matthew C. Malenfant *(Pres-Lab Distribution & Svcs-North America & Sr VP)*
Eddy Ming Kei Wu *(Pres-Asia Pacific & Sr VP)*
George Van Kula *(Gen Counsel, Sec & Sr VP)*
Manuel Brocke-Benz *(Sr VP & Mng Dir-Europe, Lab Distr & Svcs)*
Paul A. Dumas *(Sr VP-HR)*
Theodore C. Pulkownik *(Sr VP-Strategy & Corp Dev)*
Jon Michael Colyer *(VP & Gen Mgr-Science Education)*

WAKUNAGA OF AMERICA CO., LTD.
(Sub. of Wakunaga Pharmaceutical Co., Ltd.)
23501 Madera
Mission Viejo, CA 92691
Tel.: (949) 855-2776
Fax: (949) 458-2764
Toll Free: (800) 421-2998
E-mail: info@wakunaga.com
Web Site: www.kyolic.com
Approx. Number Employees: 75
Business Description:
Pharmaceutical Mfr
S.I.C.: 2834
N.A.I.C.S.: 325412
Media: 6
Personnel:
Kenro Nakamura *(Chm)*
Brands & Products:
KYOLIC

WARNER CHILCOTT CORPORATION
(Corporate Headquarters of WARNER CHILCOTT PUBLIC LIMITED COMPANY)
100 Enterprise Dr
Rockaway, NJ 07866
Tel.: (973) 442-3200
Fax: (973) 442-3283
E-mail: ir@wcrx.com
Web Site: www.wcrx.com
Approx. Number Employees: 582
Year Founded: 1986
Business Description:
Women's Healthcare & Dermatology Pharmaceuticals Mfr
S.I.C.: 2834
N.A.I.C.S.: 325412
Import Export
Media: 2-7-8-10-13-15-20-21-22-24
Distr.: Natl.
Personnel:
Roger M. Boissonneault *(Pres & CEO)*
Paul Herendeen *(CFO & Exec VP)*
W. Carlton Reichel *(Pres-Pharmaceuticals)*
Izumi Hara *(Gen Counsel, Sec & Sr VP)*
Anthony D. Bruno *(Exec VP-Corp Dev)*
Leland H. Cross *(Sr VP-Tech Ops)*
Herman Ellman *(Sr VP-Clinical Dev)*
Alvin Howard *(Sr VP-Regulatory Affairs)*
William J. Poll *(Sr VP-Fin)*
Dave Domzalski *(VP-Sls & Mktg)*
Advertising Agencies:
Concentric Communications
1285 6th Ave Fl #3
New York, NY 10019
Tel.: (212) 209-4550
Fax: (212) 209-4543

Euro RSCG Life Adrenaline
200 Madison Ave 2nd Fl
New York, NY 10016
Tel.: (212) 251-2750
Fax: (212) 251-8819

Regan Campbell Ward McCann
150 E 42nd St 16th Fl
New York, NY 10017-5642
Tel.: (646) 742-2100
Fax: (646) 742-2206

WATAUGA MEDICAL CENTER
PO Box 2600
Boone, NC 28607-2600
Tel.: (828) 262-4100
Fax: (828) 262-4169
Toll Free: (800) 443-7385
E-mail: webmaster@apprhs.org
Web Site: www.apprhs.org
Approx. Number Employees: 1,500
Year Founded: 1932
Business Description:
Health Care Center
S.I.C.: 8062; 8011
N.A.I.C.S.: 622110; 621111
Media: 6-24
Personnel:
Clayton Dean *(Chm)*
Richard Sparks *(Pres & CEO)*
Herman A. Godwin *(Sr VP & Dir-Medical)*
Mary Etta Long *(Sr VP-Medical Staff)*

WATER PIK, INC.
(Holding of The Carlyle Group, LLC)
1730 E Prospect Rd
Fort Collins, CO 80553-0001
Tel.: (970) 484-1352
Fax: (970) 221-8715
Toll Free: (800) 525-2774
Web Site: www.waterpik.com
Approx. Number Employees: 600
Business Description:
Dental Care & Pool Products Mfr
S.I.C.: 3843
N.A.I.C.S.: 339114
Import Export
Distr.: Intl.; Natl.
Personnel:
Richard Bisson *(Pres & CEO)*
Brands & Products:
WATERPIK SHOWERHEADS
Advertising Agency:
Ketchum
(Part of Omnicom)
1285 Ave of the Americas
New York, NY 10019
Tel.: (646) 935-3900
Fax: (646) 935-4482

WATSON PHARMACEUTICALS, INC.
311 Bonnie Cir
Corona, CA 92880
Tel.: (951) 493-5300
Fax: (951) 270-1429
Fax: (951) 493-5836
Toll Free: (800) 249-5499
E-mail: patty.eisenhaur@watson.com
Web Site: www.watsonpharm.com
Approx. Rev.: $3,566,900,000
Approx. Number Employees: 6,030
Year Founded: 1984
Business Description:
Brand & Generic Pharmaceuticals
S.I.C.: 2834; 8733
N.A.I.C.S.: 325412; 541710
Import
Advertising Expenditures: $9,400,000
Media: 6
Personnel:
Andrew L. Turner *(Chm)*
Paul M. Bisaro *(Pres & CEO)*
R. Todd Joyce *(CFO & Exec VP)*
Thomas R. Giordano *(CIO & Sr VP)*
Edward F. Heimers *(Pres-Brands Div & Exec VP)*
Albert Paonessa, III *(COO-Anda Inc & Exec VP)*
David A. Buchen *(Gen Counsel, Sec & Exec VP)*
Sigurdur Oli Olafsson *(Exec VP-Generics-Global)*
Robert A. Stewart *(Exec VP-Ops-Global)*
George Frederick Wilkinson *(Exec VP-Global Brands)*
Clare Carmichael *(Sr VP-HR)*
Francois A. Menard *(Sr VP-Generics R & D)*
Gordon Munro *(Sr VP-Quality Assurance)*
Eric Pluckhorn *(Dir-Mktg)*
Brands & Products:
ACETA-GESIC
AFEDITAB
ALLER-CHLOR
ALLERFRIM
ALMACONE
ALORA
ANDRX
BREVICON
BROMALINE
CALCI-CHEW
CALCI-MIX
CONDYLOX
CORDRAN
CORMAX
DILACOR
DIPHENHIST
FERRLECIT
GELNIQUE
HYDROSKIN
INFED
JOLIVETTE
KIDKARE
L-CARNITINE
LEENA
LOW OGESTREL
LOXITANE
LUTERA
MAXIDONE
MONODOX
MONONESSA
NECON
NEPHRO-CALCI
NEPHRO-FER
NEPHRO-VITE
NOR-QD
NORCO
NORINYL
NRS
OXYTROL
RAPAFLO
REPREXAIN
SEA OMEGA
TRI-NORINYL
TRINESSA
WATSON
ZOVIA
Advertising Agency:
Fallon Medica LLC
620 Shrewsbury Ave
Tinton Falls, NJ 07701
Tel.: (732) 345-3500
Fax: (732) 212-1926

WATSON PHARMACEUTICALS, INC.
(Sub. of Watson Pharmaceuticals, Inc.)
4955 Orange Dr
Davie, FL 33314
Tel.: (954) 585-1400
Fax: (954) 217-4327
Toll Free: (800) 621-7143
E-mail: andrxinfo@watsonandandrx.com
Web Site: www.watson.com
Sales Range: $1-4.9 Billion
Approx. Number Employees: 1,600
Year Founded: 1992
Business Description:
Generic Pharmaceuticals Mfr
S.I.C.: 2834; 5122
N.A.I.C.S.: 325412; 424210
Advertising Expenditures: $11,771,000
Media: 2-10
Personnel:
Thomas R. Giordano *(CIO & Sr VP)*
Charles M. Mayr *(Sr VP-Corp Affairs)*
Steve Sost *(Dir)*
Brands & Products:
ALTOCOR
ANDRX
ANEXSIA
CARTIA XT
DILTIA XT
EMBREX
ENTEX
FILMTAB
TAZTIA XT

WEBMD HEALTH SERVICES GROUP
(Branch of WebMD Health Corporation)
2701 NW Vaughn St Ste 700
Portland, OR 97210
Tel.: (503) 279-9010
Fax: (503) 279-1632
E-mail: info@webmd.com
Web Site: www.webmd.com
Sales Range: $75-99.9 Million
Approx. Number Employees: 230
Business Description:
Communications Platforms Services for the Healthcare Industry
S.I.C.: 9431; 6371
N.A.I.C.S.: 923120; 525120
Media: 6-7-8-10-13

Key to Media (For complete agency information see *The Advertising Red Books-Agencies* edition):
1. Bus. Publs. 2. Cable T.V. 3. Catalogs & Directories. 4. Co-op Adv. 5. Consumer Mags. 6. D.M. to Bus. Estab.7. D.M. to Consumers 8. Daily Newsp. 9. Exhibits/Trade Shows 10. Foreign 11. Infomercial 12. Internet Adv.13. Multimedia 14. Network Radio 15. Network T.V. 16. Newsp. Distr. Mags. 17. Other 18. Outdoor (Posters, Transit) 19. Point of Purchase20. Premiums, Novelties 21. Product Samples 22. Special Events Mktg. 23. Spot Radio 24. Spot T.V. 25. Weekly Newsp. 26. Yellow Page Adv.

WebMD Health Services Group —
(Continued)

Personnel:
Heidi Anderson *(VP-Sls & Publr)*
Craig Froude *(Exec VP)*
Mark Merner *(Dir-Strategic Dev)*

WEIGHT WATCHERS INTERNATIONAL, INC.

(Holding of Artal Luxembourg S.A.)
11 Madison Ave 17th Fl
New York, NY 10010
Tel.: (212) 589-2700
Fax: (212) 589-2601
Toll Free: (800) 651-6000
Web Site:
www.weightwatchersinternational.com
Approx. Rev.: $1,452,037,000
Approx. Number Employees: 26,000
Year Founded: 1961
Business Description:
Weight-Control Classes & Related Services
S.I.C.: 7299
N.A.I.C.S.: 812990; 812191
Advertising Expenditures:
$190,999,000
Media: 2-3-6-7-8-9-14-15-16-18-19-23-24-25-26
Distr.: Intl.; Natl.
Personnel:
Raymond Debbane *(Chm)*
David P. Kirchoff *(Pres & CEO)*
Ann M. Sardini *(CFO)*
Cheryl Callan *(CMO)*
Dave Burwick *(Pres-North America)*
Melanie Stubbing *(Pres-Intl)*
Jeffrey A. Fiarman *(Gen Counsel, Sec & Exec VP)*
Maurice Kelly *(VP-Strategy-Opers-Continental Europe)*
Lee Hurley *(Dir-Online Mktg)*
Brands & Products:
1.2.3 SUCCESS
JUST 2 POINTS
JUST 3 POINTS
PERSONAL CHOICE PROGRAM
POINTS
SMART ONES
WATCH YOURSELF CHANGE
WEIGHT WATCHERS
Advertising Agencies:
The A Team, LLC
232 Madison Ave
New York, NY 10016
Tel.: (212) 239-0499
Fax: (212) 239-0575

Ferrara & Company
29 Airpark Rd
Princeton, NJ 08540
Tel.: (609) 924-4932
Fax: (609) 945-8700

G2 USA
200 5th Ave
New York, NY 10010
Tel.: (212) 537-3700
Fax: (212) 537-3737
Analytics
CRM
Direct Mail
ECRM
Marketing Campaign
Strategic Planning

Horizon Media, Inc.
75 Varick St
New York, NY 10013
Tel.: (212) 220-5000
Toll Free: (800) 633-4201
Media Buying
Media Planning

McCann Erickson/New York
622 3rd Ave
New York, NY 10017
Tel.: (646) 865-2000
Fax: (646) 487-9610
Creative
Social Media Agency of Record

Razorfish New York
1440 Broadway 19th Fl
New York, NY 10018
Tel.: (212) 798-6600
Fax: (212) 798-6601
Social Media Analytics

Weber Shandwick
(Sub. of The Interpublic Group of Companies)
919 3rd Ave
New York, NY 10022
Tel.: (212) 445-8000
Fax: (212) 445-8001
Public Relations

Young & Rubicam Inc.
285 Madison Ave
New York, NY 10017-6401
Tel.: (212) 210-3000
Fax: (212) 490-9073

WELLQUEST INTERNATIONAL, INC.

230 5th Ave Ste 800
New York, NY 10001
Tel.: (212) 689-9094
Fax: (212) 689-9093
Toll Free: (800) 608-5569
Web Site: www.wellquestintl.com
Business Description:
Vitamins & Health Care Products
S.I.C.: 2833; 5122
N.A.I.C.S.: 325411; 424210
Media: 3-6-8-12
Personnel:
Al Mishan *(Pres)*
Brands & Products:
BLOUSSANT
CELEBRITY WHITE
CLEAN BETWEEN MACHINE
D-SNORE
ENER-X
EUROLIPSTYQUE
MAGNA BLUE
MEMORY PURE
MIAMI 48 HOUR DIET
O-GEL
QUICK & SMOOTHE
STRETCHAWAY
THERACEL
TRIMEGA
VEINISH
VITAL SOLUTIONS
WELLQUEST
YOH

WELLQUEST MEDICAL & WELLNESS CORPORATION

3400 SE Macy Rd Ste 18
Bentonville, AR 72712
Tel.: (479) 845-0880
Web Site: www.wellquest.md/
Approx. Rev.: $3,823,994
Approx. Number Employees: 23
Business Description:
Medical Spa, Skincare & Nutraceutical Product Store Owner & Operator; Medical Practice Management Services
S.I.C.: 7231; 5122; 8011
N.A.I.C.S.: 812112; 446120; 621111
Advertising Expenditures: $45,000
Media: 17
Personnel:
Steve Swift *(Founder, Chm & Pres)*
Curtis Rice *(Co-Founder, VP & Dir)*
John O'Connor *(Sec & Dir)*

WEXFORD HEALTH SOURCES INC.

45 Holiday Dr Foster Plz Two
Pittsburgh, PA 15220
Tel.: (412) 937-8590
Fax: (412) 937-8599
E-mail: sales@wexfordhealth.com
Web Site: www.wexfordhealth.com
E-Mail For Key Personnel:
Sales Director: sales@wexfordhealth.com
Approx. Number Employees: 650
Year Founded: 1992
Business Description:
Health Care Services
S.I.C.: 8742
N.A.I.C.S.: 541611
Import Export
Media: 10
Personnel:
Kevin C. Halloran *(Pres)*
Martell Hill *(CEO)*

W.F. YOUNG, INC.

302 Benton Dr
East Longmeadow, MA 01028-5990
Tel.: (413) 526-9999
Fax: (413) 526-8990
Toll Free: (800) 628-9653
Web Site: www.absorbine.com
E-Mail For Key Personnel:
President: tyoung@absorbine.com
Sales Director: rwallace@absorbine.com
Approx. Number Employees: 30
Year Founded: 1892
Business Description:
Consumer Health Products & Veterinary Products Mfr
S.I.C.: 2834
N.A.I.C.S.: 325412
Export
Media: 2-4-5-6-7-8-9-10-11-13-14-15-16-18-19-20-21-22-23-24-25
Distr.: Natl.
Personnel:
Adam D. Raczkowski *(Pres & COO)*
Tyler F. Young *(CEO)*
Rob Wallace *(VP-Sls & Mktg)*
Brands & Products:
ABSORBINE
ABSORBINE JR.
ABSORBINE PRO CMC
ABSORBINE VETPATCH
ANTIPHLOGISTINE
BIGELOIL
BUG BLOCK
BUG BLOCK EASY SWIPE
DURAGUARD
FLEX+
FLYS-X
HOOFLEX
HOOFLEX+
HORSE LOVER'S BULLETIN
THE HORSE WORLD'S MOST TRUSTED NAME
HORSEMAN'S ONE STEP
MIRACLE GROOM
PASTURE PROTECTION
REFRESHMINT
ROLL-ON RELIEF
SANTA FE
SHOWCLEAN
SHOWSHEEN
STALL SAFE
SUPERPOO
SUPERSHIELD
SUPERSHIELD GREEN
SUPERSHINE
ULTRASHIELD
ULTRASPOT

WHATMAN INC.

(Sub. of Whatman International Ltd.)
800 Centennial Ave
Piscataway, NJ 08854
Tel.: (973) 245-8300
Fax: (973) 245-8301
Toll Free: (800) 942-8626
E-mail: info@whatman.com
Web Site: www.whatman.com
Sales Range: $50-74.9 Million
Approx. Number Employees: 60
Business Description:
Medical Laboratory Sample Preparation & Filtration Equipment Mfr
S.I.C.: 3821; 3841; 5049
N.A.I.C.S.: 339111; 339112; 423490
Advertising Expenditures: $1,500,000
Media: 1-2-4-7-10-11
Distr.: Intl.; Natl.
Personnel:
Helen Evans *(VP-Mktg)*
Lynn Nelson *(Mgr-Mktg)*
Brands & Products:
AUTOVIAL
CLINIPREP
CONZ
ONE-SHOT
PROCESSOR
UNIPREP

WHITEWING LABS, INC.

1815 Flower St
Glendale, CA 91201
Tel.: (818) 241-1913
Fax: (818) 240-2785
Toll Free: (800) 950-3030
E-mail: service@whitewing.com
Web Site: www.whitewing.com
E-Mail For Key Personnel:
President: cynthia@whitewing.com
Approx. Number Employees: 5
Year Founded: 1993
Business Description:
Nutritional Supplements Developer & Marketer to the Over Forty Market
S.I.C.: 2834
N.A.I.C.S.: 325412
Advertising Expenditures: $100,000
Media: 3-4-6-8-9-15-16-24-25
Personnel:
C. Kolke *(Pres)*
Brands & Products:
ANTI-GLOOM
ARTHRIVIVE
ARTHRIVIVE BLUE
CHOCO-THIN
CHOLEST-LESS

Key to Media (For complete agency information see *The Advertising Red Books-Agencies* edition):
1. Bus. Publs. 2. Cable T.V. 3. Catalogs & Directories. 4. Co-op Adv. 5. Consumer Mags. 6. D.M. to Bus. Estab.7. D.M. to Consumers 8. Daily Newsp. 9. Exhibits/Trade Shows 10. Foreign 11. Infomercial 12. Internet Adv.13. Multimedia 14. Network Radio 15. Network T.V. 16. Newsp. Distr. Mags. 17. Other 18. Outdoor (Posters, Transit) 19. Point of Purchase20. Premiums, Novelties 21. Product Samples 22. Special Events Mktg. 23. Spot Radio 24. Spot T.V. 25. Weekly Newsp. 26. Yellow Page Adv.

CIRC-ELATION
COLON PURE
DE-STRESS
ENERG-EYES
EVENING GLOW
IMMUNE DEFENSE
JOINT AIDE
NZ GESTION
OSTEO SAFE
POWER MIND
PRESSURE CONTROL
PROPAUSE
PROSTSAFE
PROSTSAFE PLUS
PROTRANS CREAM
RESTPIRATION
SEXHILARATE
SKIN ELATION CREAM
SLEEP SAFE
VITAMIN AND MINERAL SYSTEM
WHITEWING LABS

WILLIAMS ADVANCED MATERIALS INC.
(Name Changed to Materion Microelectronics & Services)

WISCONSIN PHARMACAL COMPANY, LLC
1 Pharmacal Way
Jackson, WI 53037-9583
Tel.: (262) 677-4121
Fax: (262) 677-9006
Toll Free: (800) 558-6614
E-mail: info@pharmacalway.com
Web Site: www.pharmacalway.com
Sales Range: $10-24.9 Million
Approx. Number Employees: 60
Year Founded: 1896
Business Description:
Insect Repellent, Insect Bite Lotion, Water Purification Tablets, Fishing Chemicals, Hand Cleaner, Sunscreen Products, First Aid Kits & Camp & Travel Accessories Mfr & Marketer
S.I.C.: 2879; 2899; 3842
N.A.I.C.S.: 325320; 325998; 339113
Import Export
Advertising Expenditures: $1,500,000
Media: 2-3-4-6-8-9-10-19-22-23-24
Distr.: Intl.; Natl.
Personnel:
Jeff Potts *(Owner)*
John Wundrock *(CEO)*
Andy Wundrock *(VP-Sls)*
Brands & Products:
ATWATER CAREY
BACKPACKER
BAITMATE
CHLORAZENE
DAYHIKER
EXPEDITION
FAMILY
LIGHT AND DRY
NON SCENTS
PERSONAL
POTABLE AQUA
REFLECT
REPEL
SPORT PAK
STING-EZE

XANGO, LLC
2889 Ashton Blvd
Lehi, UT 84043
Tel.: (801) 816-8000
Fax: (801) 816-8001
E-mail: info@xango.com
Web Site: www.xango.com
Sales Range: $550-599.9 Million
Approx. Number Employees: 450
Business Description:
Nutritional Supplement Mfr & Direct Seller
S.I.C.: 2833; 2037; 2836; 5963
N.A.I.C.S.: 325411; 311411; 325414; 454390
Media: 10-20
Personnel:
Bryan Davis *(Co-Founder)*
Gordon Morton *(Co-Founder)*
Joe Morton *(Co-Founder)*
Kent Wood *(Co-Founder)*
Robert S. Conlee *(Pres & CEO)*
Beverly Hollister *(Sr VP)*
Brands & Products:
3SIXTY5
GLIMPSE
XANGO

XANODYNE PHARMACEUTICALS, INC.
(Sub. of Union Springs, LLC)
1 Riverfront Pl
Newport, KY 41071-4563
Tel.: (859) 371-6383
Fax: (859) 371-6391
Toll Free: (877) XANODYNE
E-mail: contact@xanodyne.com
Web Site: www.xanodyne.com
Approx. Rev.: $66,923,000
Approx. Number Employees: 177
Year Founded: 2001
Business Description:
Specialty Pharmaceuticals Developer & Mfr
S.I.C.: 2834
N.A.I.C.S.: 325412
Advertising Expenditures: $454,000
Media: 2-4-7-10-13
Personnel:
Rolf A. Classon *(Chm)*
Natasha Giordano *(Pres & CEO)*
Rita O'Connor *(CFO & CIO)*
Kevin T. Anderson *(Chief Compliance Officer & VP-HR)*
Gary A. Shangold *(Chief Medical Officer & Exec VP-R&D)*
Thomas P. Jennings *(Chief Regulatory Officer, Gen Counsel & Sec)*
Daniel W. Docherty *(VP-Mktg)*
Brands & Products:
AMICAR
DEXALONE
DUET
HYCET
LUCIDEX
STUART PRENATAL
STUARTNATAL PLUS 3
XANODYNE

XELR8 HOLDINGS, INC.
(Name Changed to BAZI INTERNATIONAL, INC.)

XOMA LTD.
2910 7th St
Berkeley, CA 94710-2700
Tel.: (510) 204-7200
Fax: (510) 644-2011
Toll Free: (800) 246-9662
E-mail: info@xoma.com
Web Site: www.xoma.com
Approx. Rev.: $33,641,000
Approx. Number Employees: 230
Year Founded: 1981
Business Description:
Mfr of Biopharmaceuticals
S.I.C.: 2834; 2836; 8733
N.A.I.C.S.: 325412; 325414; 541710
Import Export
Personnel:
W. Denman Van Ness *(Chm)*
John W. Varian *(Interim CEO)*
Fred Kurland *(CFO & VP-Fin)*
Patrick J. Scannon *(Exec VP & Chief Medical Officer)*
Christopher J. Margolin *(Gen Counsel, Sec & VP)*
Charles C. Wells *(VP-HR & IT)*
Brands & Products:
CIMZIA
HUMAN ENGINEERING
LUCENTIS
NEUPREX
XOMA
Advertising Agency:
Canale Communications
4010 Goldfinch
San Diego, CA 92103
Tel.: (619) 849-6000

YOUNG INNOVATIONS, INC.
13705 Shoreline Ct E
Earth City, MO 63045-1202
Tel.: (314) 344-0010
Fax: (314) 344-0021
Toll Free: (800) 325-1881
E-mail: info@youngdental.com
Web Site: www.youngdental.com
Approx. Rev.: $102,842,000
Approx. Number Employees: 400
Year Founded: 1996
Business Description:
Dental Products Designer, Mfr & Marketer
S.I.C.: 3843; 5047
N.A.I.C.S.: 339114; 423450
Advertising Expenditures: $3,645,000
Personnel:
Alfred E. Brennan *(Chm & CEO)*
George E. Richmond *(Vice Chm)*
Brands & Products:
YOUNG INNOVATIONS, INC.

Z TRIM HOLDINGS, INC.
1011 Campus Dr
Mundelein, IL 60060
Tel.: (847) 549-6002
Fax: (847) 549-6028
Toll Free: (877) MY-ZTRIM
E-mail: info@ztrim.com
Web Site: www.ztrim.com
Approx. Rev.: $903,780
Approx. Number Employees: 24
Business Description:
All-Natural Agricultural-Based Fat Replacement Product
S.I.C.: 2836
N.A.I.C.S.: 325414
Export
Advertising Expenditures: $13,953
Media: 5-7
Personnel:
Steven J. Cohen *(CEO)*
Brian Chaiken *(CFO)*
Therese Malundo *(VP-Science & Tech)*

ZEE MEDICAL, INC.
(Div. of McKesson Corporation)
22 Corporate Pk
Irvine, CA 92606-3112
Mailing Address:
PO Box 19527
Irvine, CA 92623-9527
Tel.: (949) 252-9500
Fax: (949) 252-9649
Toll Free: (800) 841-8417
E-mail: careers@zeemedical.com
Web Site: www.zeemedical.com
Sales Range: $250-299.9 Million
Approx. Number Employees: 800
Year Founded: 1959
Business Description:
Distr of Occupational First Aid & Safety Products & Services
S.I.C.: 5122; 7389
N.A.I.C.S.: 424210; 541990
Import Export
Advertising Expenditures: $954,000
Media: 1-2-4-5-10-13-19-20-21-26
Distr.: Natl.
Personnel:
Cara Swank *(VP-Fin)*
Brands & Products:
IBUTAB
PAINAID
ZEE
ZEE ADVANTAGE

ZEPTOMETRIX CORPORATION
872 Main St
Buffalo, NY 14202-1403
Tel.: (716) 882-0920
Fax: (716) 882-0959
Toll Free: (800) 274-5478
E-mail: sales@zeptometrix.com
Web Site: www.zeptometrix.com
E-Mail For Key Personnel:
Sales Director: sales@zeptometrix.com
Approx. Number Employees: 25
Year Founded: 1999
Business Description:
Integrated Biotechnology Company that Manufactures & Distributes Products for the Research & Biotechnology Communities Worldwide
S.I.C.: 2836
N.A.I.C.S.: 325414
Media: 2-4-7
Personnel:
James Hengst *(CEO)*
Ron Urmson *(CFO)*

ZILA, INC.
(Div. of TOLMAR Inc.)
5227 N Seventh St
Phoenix, AZ 85014-2800
Tel.: (602) 266-6700
Fax: (602) 234-2264
E-mail: info@zila.com
Web Site: www.zila.com
Approx. Rev.: $45,060,801
Approx. Number Employees: 367
Year Founded: 1980
Business Description:
Pharmaceuticals Developer & Mfr
S.I.C.: 2834; 5047
N.A.I.C.S.: 325412; 423450
Advertising Expenditures: $9,700,000
Media: 2-6-8-10
Personnel:
Diane E. Klein *(Treas & VP-Fin)*
Brands & Products:
ORATEST
PDT SENSOR
PRO-SELECT PLATINUM
PRO-TIES
PRODENRX
ROTADENT

Key to Media (For complete agency information see *The Advertising Red Books-Agencies* edition):
1. Bus. Publs. 2. Cable T.V. 3. Catalogs & Directories. 4. Co-op Adv. 5. Consumer Mags. 6. D.M. to Bus. Estab.7. D.M. to Consumers
8. Daily Newsp. 9. Exhibits/Trade Shows 10. Foreign 11. Infomercial 12. Internet Adv.13. Multimedia 14. Network Radio
15. Network T.V. 16. Newsp. Distr. Mags. 17. Other 18. Outdoor (Posters, Transit) 19. Point of Purchase20. Premiums, Novelties
21. Product Samples 22. Special Events Mktg. 23. Spot Radio 24. Spot T.V. 25. Weekly Newsp. 26. Yellow Page Adv.

Zila, Inc. — (Continued)

SMOOTHIE
TBLUE
VIZILITE
ZILA
ZTC

ZIMMER ORTHOPAEDICS
(Unit of Zimmer Orthopaedic Implant Division)
1800 W Center St
Warsaw, IN 46580-2304
Tel.: (512) 432-9900
Fax: (512) 432-9014
Web Site: www.zimmer-orthopedics.ch/z/ctl/op/global/action/3/id/143/template/CP/navid/7079
Sales Range: $25-49.9 Million
Approx. Number Employees: 100
Business Description:
Mfr. & Distributor of Orthopedic Implants for Hips, Knees & Shoulders
S.I.C.: 3841; 5047
N.A.I.C.S.: 339112; 423450
Brands & Products:
HIPS, SHOULDERS AND ORTHOPEDIC PRODUCTS
Advertising Agency:
Abelson-Taylor, Inc.
33 W Monroe St
Chicago, IL 60603
Tel.: (312) 894-5500
Fax: (312) 894-5526
Fax: (312) 894-5528

ZOGENIX, INC.
12671 High Bluff Dr Ste 200
San Diego, CA 92130
Tel.: (858) 259-1165
Fax: (858) 259-1166
Toll Free: (866) 964-3649
E-mail: info@zogenix.com
Web Site: www.zogenix.com
Approx. Rev.: $23,442,000
Approx. Number Employees: 144
Year Founded: 2006
Business Description:
Pharmaceutical Mfr
S.I.C.: 2834
N.A.I.C.S.: 325412
Advertising Expenditures: $1,072,000
Personnel:
Cam L. Garner *(Chm)*
Stephen J. Farr *(Pres, COO & Dir)*
Roger L. Hawley *(CEO)*
Ann D. Rhoads *(CFO & Exec VP)*
John J. Turanin *(VP & Gen Mgr)*
Stephen H. Jenner *(VP-Mktg)*
Mark Thompson *(VP-Sls & Managed Market)*
Brands & Products:
INTRAJECT
SUMAVEL DOSEPRO
WHERE MEDICINE MEETS TECHNOLOGY
ZOGENIX
ZX002

ZOLL MEDICAL CORPORATION
269 Mill Rd
Chelmsford, MA 01824-4105
Tel.: (978) 421-9655
Fax: (978) 421-0025
Toll Free: (800) 348-9011
E-mail: info@zoll.com
Web Site: www.zoll.com
Approx. Sls.: $443,989,000
Approx. Number Employees: 1,679
Year Founded: 1980
Business Description:
Mfr & Producer of Cardiac Resuscitation Devices Combining Noninvasive Temporary Pacing, Defibrillation, Monitoring & Cardioversion
S.I.C.: 3845
N.A.I.C.S.: 334510
Advertising Expenditures: $2,272,000
Media: 2-4-7-8-10-11-13
Distr.: Intl.
Budget Set: July
Personnel:
Benson F. Smith *(Chm)*
Jonathan Rennert *(Pres)*
Richard A. Packer *(CEO)*
Patrice Blechet *(Mng Dir)*
A. Ernest Whiton *(CFO & VP-Admin)*
Stephen Korn *(Gen Counsel, Sec & VP)*
Ward M. Hamilton *(Sr VP & VP-Mktg)*
Steven K. Flora *(Sr VP-North America Sls)*
Susan Schumacher *(Dir-Mktg Comm)*
Brands & Products:
ADVANCING RESUSCITATION. TODAY.
AED PLUS
AED PRO
AUTOPULSE
CODE-READY
CODENET
CODENET CENTRAL
CODENET WRITER
LIFEVEST
M SERIES
PD 1200
PD 1400
PD 2000
PEDI PADZ
POCKET CPR
POWER CHARGER
POWER INFUSER
PRO PADZ
R SERIES
REAL CPR HELP
RESCUENET
RESQPOD
SEE-THRU CPR
STAT PADZ
SUREPOWER
V PAK
XTREME PACK
ZOLL
ZOLL E SERIES
Advertising Agency:
Publicis Consultants
1675 Broadway 3rd Fl
New York, NY 10019
Tel.: (212) 527-8895
Fax: (212) 527-8850
Public Relations

ZONARE MEDICAL SYSTEMS, INC.
420 N Bernardo Ave
Mountain View, CA 94043-5209
Tel.: (650) 230-2800
Fax: (650) 230-2828
Toll Free: (877) 966-2731
E-mail: info@zonare.com
Web Site: www.zonare.com
Sales Range: $25-49.9 Million
Approx. Number Employees: 176
Year Founded: 1999
Business Description:
Compact Ultrasound Systems Developer, Mfr & Marketer
S.I.C.: 3841
N.A.I.C.S.: 339112
Advertising Expenditures: $353,000
Personnel:
Jay D. Miller *(Pres & CEO)*
Timothy A. Marcotte *(CFO & VP)*
Glen W. McLaughlin *(CTO & VP-Engrg)*
Mark M. Miller *(VP-Sls & Mktg)*
Brands & Products:
CHANNEL DOMAIN PROCESSING
CONVERTIBLE ULTRASOUND
ZONARE
Z.ONE
ZONE SONOGRAPHY

ZYMOGENETICS, INC.
(Sub. of Bristol-Myers Squibb Company)
1201 Eastlake Ave E
Seattle, WA 98102-3702
Tel.: (206) 442-6600
Fax: (206) 442-6608
Toll Free: (800) 775-6686
E-mail: info@zgi.com
Web Site: www.zymogenetics.com
Approx. Rev.: $136,972,000
Approx. Number Employees: 323
Year Founded: 1981
Business Description:
Biochemical Research & Development
S.I.C.: 2836; 8733
N.A.I.C.S.: 325414; 541710
Media: 2
Personnel:
James A. Johnson *(CFO, Treas & Exec VP)*
Eleanor Ramos *(Chief Medical Officer & Sr VP)*
Brands & Products:
PEG-IFN
RECOTHROM
ZYMOGENETICS

Key to Media (For complete agency information see *The Advertising Red Books-Agencies* edition):
1. Bus. Publs. 2. Cable T.V. 3. Catalogs & Directories. 4. Co-op Adv. 5. Consumer Mags. 6. D.M. to Bus. Estab.7. D.M. to Consumers 8. Daily Newsp. 9. Exhibits/Trade Shows 10. Foreign 11. Infomercial 12. Internet Adv.13. Multimedia 14. Network Radio 15. Network T.V. 16. Newsp. Distr. Mags. 17. Other 18. Outdoor (Posters, Transit) 19. Point of Purchase20. Premiums, Novelties 21. Product Samples 22. Special Events Mktg. 23. Spot Radio 24. Spot T.V. 25. Weekly Newsp. 26. Yellow Page Adv.

Public Utilities

Gas — Electric — Telephone — Telegraph — Water

8X8, INC.
810 W Maude Ave
Sunnyvale, CA 94085
Tel.: (408) 727-1885
Fax: (408) 980-0432
E-mail: jcitelli@8x8.com
Web Site: www.8x8.com
Approx. Rev.: $70,163,000
Approx. Number Employees: 254
Business Description:
Digital Telecommunications Products Mfr
S.I.C.: 3669; 3651; 3674; 7372
N.A.I.C.S.: 334290; 334310; 334413; 511210
Advertising Expenditures: $5,900,000
Personnel:
Bryan R. Martin *(Chm, CEO & Pres)*
Daniel Weirich *(CFO)*
Debbie Jo Severin *(CMO)*
Kim Niederman *(Sr VP-Sls)*
Don Trimble *(VP-Channel Sls)*
Joan Citelli *(Dir-Corp Comm)*
Jessica Walia Weimer *(Sr Mgr-Mktg-Demand Generation)*
Brands & Products:
8X8
PACKET8
PACKET8 VIRTUAL OFFICE

AASTRA TECHNOLOGIES LTD.
155 Snow Boulevard
Concord, ON L4K 4N9, Canada
Tel.: (905) 760-4200
Fax: (905)-760-4233
Web Site: www.aastra.com
E-Mail For Key Personnel:
Sales Director: sales@aastra.com
Approx. Sls.: $734,426,585
Approx. Number Employees: 2,200
Year Founded: 1970
Business Description:
Telecommunication Services & Equipment Whslr
S.I.C.: 4899; 3661
N.A.I.C.S.: 517910; 334210
Media: 10
Personnel:
Francis N. Shen *(Chm & Co-CEO)*
Anthony P. Shen *(Pres, Co-CEO & COO)*
Allan J. Brett *(CFO & VP-Fin)*
Hugues Scholaert *(Reg Pres & Exec VP)*
John Tobia *(Gen Counsel, Sec & VP-Legal)*
Yves Laliberte *(Exec VP)*
Brands & Products:
AASTRA
ASCOTEL
CENTERGY
CLEARSPAN
DECTOVERIP
DETEWE
INTECOM
INTEGRATED CONFERENCE MANAGER
INTELLIGATE
MATRA
MD EVOLUTION
MERIDIAN
MX-ONE
NEXSPAN
OFFICE
OPENATTENDANT
OPENCOM
OPENCTI
OPENPHONE
OPENVOICE
POINTSPAN
POWERTOUCH
SOFTPHONE
SOLIDUS ECARE
TAPI
UNIFIED COMMUNICATION PLATFORM
VENTURE
VENTUREIP
VIDEORUNNER
VIDIEM
VIPR
VISION
VISTA

ADVANCED TELECOM SERVICES
996 Old Eagle School Rd Ste 1105
Wayne, PA 19087
Tel.: (610) 688-6000
Fax: (610) 964-9117
Toll Free: (800) 247-1287
E-mail: sales@advancedtele.com
Web Site: www.advancedtele.com
E-Mail For Key Personnel:
Sales Director: sales@advancedtele.com
Approx. Number Employees: 15
Year Founded: 1989
Business Description:
Inbound Telemarketing Services
S.I.C.: 4813
N.A.I.C.S.: 517310
Media: 2-7
Personnel:
Robert Jay Bentz *(Pres)*
Paul Hehn *(CFO)*
Brands & Products:
ADVANCED TELECOM SERVICES
INTERACTIVITY FOR THE WORLD
MATCHLINK
MONSTERTONES.COM
RINGINGPHONE.COM
VOICETONE

AEP OHIO
(Sub. of American Electric Power Company, Inc.)
850 Tech Ctr Dr
Gahanna, OH 43230
Tel.: (614) 883-7999
Web Site: www.aepohio.com
Sales Range: $1-4.9 Billion
Business Description:
Electric Power Generation
S.I.C.: 4939; 4911; 4924; 4931
N.A.I.C.S.: 221122; 221119; 221121; 221210
Media: 3-15
Personnel:
Joseph Hamrock *(Pres & COO-AEP Ohio)*
Selwyn J. Dias *(VP-Regulatory & Fin)*
Matthew D. Kyle *(Dir-Bus Ops Support)*
Karen L. Sloneker *(Dir-Customer Svcs & Mktg)*
David A. Varwig *(Mgr-Safety & Health)*

AGL RESOURCES INC.
10 Peachtree Pl NE
Atlanta, GA 30309
Tel.: (404) 584-4000
Fax: (404) 584-3714
E-mail: corpcomm@aglresources.com
Web Site: www.aglresources.com
Approx. Rev.: $2,373,000,000
Approx. Number Employees: 2,621
Year Founded: 1856
Business Description:
Natural Gas Distr
S.I.C.: 4924
N.A.I.C.S.: 221210
Advertising Expenditures: $3,169,000
Media: 8
Distr.: Reg.
Personnel:
John W. Somerhalder, II *(Chm, Pres & CEO)*
Andrew W. Evans *(CFO & Exec VP)*
Donna N. Peeples *(CMO & VP-Corp Comm)*
Bryan E. Seas *(Chief Acctg Officer & Sr VP)*
Jodi Gidley *(Pres-Elizabethtown Gas, Elkton Gas & Sr VP-Mid-Atlantic Ops)*
James A. Gillis *(Pres-AGL Networks)*
Dana A. Grams *(Pres-Pivotal Energy Dev)*
Paul R. Shlanta *(Chief Ethics/Compliance Officer, Gen Counsel & Exec VP)*
Steve Cave *(Treas & VP-Fin)*
Henry P. Linginfelter *(Exec VP)*
Jeffrey P. Brown *(Sr VP & Deputy Gen Counsel)*
Bryan Batson *(Sr VP-Govt & Regulatory Affairs)*
Darilyn Jones *(Sr VP-Risk Control-Sequent Energy Mgmt)*
Melanie M. Platt *(Sr VP-HR, Mktg & Comm)*
Robert Duvall *(VP & Gen Mgr-Ops-Virginia & Maryl&)*
Scott E. Maddox *(VP-Info Sys & Tech-Sequent Energy Mgmt)*
Ira G. Pearl *(VP-Tech & Environmental Sustainability)*
Elizabeth W. Reese *(VP-Fin)*
Sarah M. Stashak *(Dir-IR)*
Advertising Agency:
Macquarium Intelligent Communications
1800 Peachtree St NW Ste 250
Atlanta, GA 30309
Tel.: (404) 554-4000
Fax: (404) 554-4001

ALABAMA GAS CORPORATION
(Sub. of Energen Corporation)
605 Richard Arrington Jr Blvd N
Birmingham, AL 35203-2707
Tel.: (205) 326-2700
Tel.: (205) 326-8100
Fax: (205) 326-2704
Toll Free: (800) 292-4005

Key to Media (For complete agency information see *The Advertising Red Books-Agencies* edition):
1. Bus. Publs. 2. Cable T.V. 3. Catalogs & Directories. 4. Co-op Adv. 5. Consumer Mags. 6. D.M. to Bus. Estab.7. D.M. to Consumers 8. Daily Newsp. 9. Exhibits/Trade Shows 10. Foreign 11. Infomercial 12. Internet Adv.13. Multimedia 14. Network Radio 15. Network T.V. 16. Newsp. Distr. Mags. 17. Other 18. Outdoor (Posters, Transit) 19. Point of Purchase20. Premiums, Novelties 21. Product Samples 22. Special Events Mktg. 23. Spot Radio 24. Spot T.V. 25. Weekly Newsp. 26. Yellow Page Adv.

Alabama Gas Corporation — (Continued)

Web Site: www.alagasco.com/About-Alagasco/Newsroom/Media-Center/Quick-Facts-754.html
Approx. Rev.: $619,772,000
Approx. Number Employees: 1,100
Year Founded: 1852
Business Description:
Natural Gas Distr
S.I.C.: 4924
N.A.I.C.S.: 221210
Media: 2
Personnel:
James T. McManus II *(Chm & CEO)*
Dudley C. Reynolds *(Pres & COO)*
J. David Woodruff, Jr. *(Gen Counsel, VP & Sec)*
William K. Bibb *(VP-HR)*
Joe E. Cook *(Asst Sec)*

ALABAMA POWER COMPANY

(Sub. of Southern Company)
600 N 18th St
Birmingham, AL 35291-0001
Mailing Address:
PO Box 2641
Birmingham, AL 35291-0001
Tel.: (205) 257-1000
Fax: (331) 407-6140
Web Site: www.alabamapower.com
Approx. Rev.: $5,976,000,000
Approx. Number Employees: 6,552
Year Founded: 1927
Business Description:
Electric Utility
S.I.C.: 4911; 4931; 4939
N.A.I.C.S.: 221121; 221111; 221119
Personnel:
Charles D. McCrary *(Pres & CEO)*
Phil Raymond *(CFO, Treas & Exec VP)*
J. Barnie Beasley, Jr. *(Pres/CEO-Southern Nuclear)*
William E. Zales *(Sec, VP & Asst Treas)*
Dwight H. Evans *(ExecVP)*
Anthony R. James *(Exec VP)*
Steven R. Spencer *(Exec VP-External Affairs)*
Greg Barker *(Sr VP-Bus Dev & Customer Support)*
Robin Hurst *(Sr VP-Power Delivery)*
Theodore J. McCullough *(Sr VP & Sr Production Officer)*
Advertising Agencies:
Lawler Ballard Van Durand
31 Inverness Center Pkwy Ste 110
Birmingham, AL 35242-4822
Tel.: (205) 995-1775
Fax: (205) 991-5141

Luckie & Company
600 Luckie Dr Ste 150
Birmingham, AL 35223-2429
Tel.: (205) 879-2121
Fax: (205) 877-9855
(Media Buying)

ALLETE, INC.

30 W Superior St
Duluth, MN 55802
Tel.: (218) 279-5000
Fax: (218) 720-2502
Toll Free: (800) 535-3056
E-mail: arutledge@allete.com
Web Site: www.allete.com
Approx. Rev.: $907,000,000
Approx. Number Employees: 1,401
Year Founded: 1906
Business Description:
Utility Operations Including Electric, Water, Wastewater & Gas Operations; Utility-Related Businesses Which Include Coal Mining, Paper & Pulp Production & Manufacturing of Truck-Mounted Lifting Equipment; Investments
S.I.C.: 4911; 1222; 4924; 4931; 4939; 4941; 6531
N.A.I.C.S.: 221122; 212112; 221111; 221119; 221210; 221310; 531390
Advertising Expenditures: $490,000
Media: 2-7-10-17
Distr.: Direct to Consumer; Reg.
Budget Set: July
Personnel:
Donald J. Shippar *(Chm)*
Alan R. Hodnik *(Pres & CEO)*
Mark A. Schober *(CFO & Sr VP)*
Deborah A. Amberg *(Gen Counsel, Sec & Sr VP)*
David J. McMillan *(Sr VP-Mktg, Regulatory & Pub Affairs)*
Michael Evans *(Sr Mgr-Bus Dev)*
Brands & Products:
ALLETE
MINNESOTA POWER
Advertising Agency:
Black & Veatch Corporate Marketing & Branding
11401 Lamar Ave
Overland Park, KS 66211
Tel.: (913) 458-2000
Fax: (913) 458-2934

ALLIANT ENERGY CORPORATION

4902 N Biltmore Ln
Madison, WI 53718
Mailing Address:
PO Box 77007
Madison, WI 53707-1007
Tel.: (608) 458-3311
Fax: (608) 458-4824
Toll Free: (800) 255-4628
E-mail: customercare@alliantenergy.com
Web Site: www.alliantenergy.com
Approx. Rev.: $3,416,100,000
Approx. Number Employees: 4,704
Year Founded: 1981
Business Description:
Public Utility Holding Company; Regulated Electricity & Natural Gas Services
S.I.C.: 6719; 4911; 4924; 4931; 4939
N.A.I.C.S.: 551112; 221111; 221112; 221113; 221119; 221121; 221122; 221210
Media: 22
Personnel:
William D. Harvey *(Chm & CEO)*
Patricia L. Kampling *(Pres & COO)*
Thomas L. Hanson *(CFO, Treas & VP)*
Robert J. Durian *(Chief Acctg Officer & Controller)*
Thomas L. Aller *(Sr VP-Energy Resource Dev)*
Dundeana K. Doyle *(Sr VP-Energy Delivery)*
John O. Larsen *(Sr VP-Generation)*
Peggy Howard Moore *(VP-Fin)*
Wayne Reschke *(VP-HR)*
Bob Bartlett *(Dir-Pub & Community Affairs)*
Enrique Bacalao *(Asst Treas)*
Brands & Products:
ALLIANT ENERGY
POWERCURE
SECOND NATURE

ALLTEL CORPORATION

(Joint Venture of Verizon Communications Inc. & Vodafone Group Plc)
1 Allied Dr
Little Rock, AR 72202
Tel.: (501) 905-8000
Fax: (501) 905-5444
Toll Free: (877) 446-3628
E-mail: lucie.pathmann@verizonwireless.com
Web Site: www.verizonwireless.com
Sales Range: $1-4.9 Billion
Approx. Number Employees: 16,104
Year Founded: 1954
Business Description:
Wireless Voice & Data Telecommunications Products & Services
S.I.C.: 4812; 4813
N.A.I.C.S.: 517212; 517310
Advertising Expenditures: $364,000,000
Media: 2-3-4-5-6-7-8-9-10-18-19-20-22-23-24-25-26
Distr.: Intl.; Natl.
Budget Set: Nov.
Personnel:
Jack D. Plating *(Pres)*
Brands & Products:
ALLTEL

AMEREN CORPORATION

1 Ameren Plz 1901 Chouteau Ave
Saint Louis, MO 63103-3003
Tel.: (314) 621-3222
Fax: (314) 554-3801
E-mail: marketing@ameren.com
Web Site: www.ameren.com
Approx. Rev.: $7,638,000,000
Approx. Number Employees: 9,474
Year Founded: 1997
Business Description:
Holding Company; Supplier of Electric & Gas Services
S.I.C.: 4939; 4924; 4931
N.A.I.C.S.: 221111; 221119; 221210
Advertising Expenditures: $4,000,000
Media: 2-7-8-18
Personnel:
Thomas R. Voss *(Chm, Pres & CEO)*
Warner L. Baxter *(Pres & CEO-Missouri)*
Martin J. Lyons *(CFO & Sr VP)*
Michael G. Mueller *(Pres-Fuel Co.)*
Andrew M. Serri *(Pres-Energy Mktg)*
Gregory L. Nelson *(Gen Counsel & Sr VP)*
Richard J. Mark *(Sr VP-Customer Ops-Missouri)*
Charles D. Naslund *(Sr VP-Generation & Environmental Projects-Missouri)*
Charles A. Bremer *(VP-ASC-IT)*
David A. Whiteley *(Exec Dir)*
Mark E. Blair *(Mgr-Insurance Risk Mgmt)*
Jeff L. Dodd *(Mgr-Back Office)*
Jeffrey Hackman *(Mgr-Transmission Ops)*
Thomas B. Leigh *(Mgr-Sls & Mktg-Ameren Energy Mktg)*
Mark Nealon *(Mgr-Reliability Improvement)*
Greg Ringkamp *(Mgr-Distr Plng & Asset Performance)*
Joseph Solari *(Mgr-Dev-ED)*
Advertising Agencies:
The Bivings Group
2201 Wisconsin Ave NW Ste 310
Washington, DC 20007
Tel.: (202) 741-1500
Fax: (202) 741-1501

Rodgers Townsend, LLC
1000 Clark Ave 5th Fl
Saint Louis, MO 63102
Tel.: (314) 436-9960
Fax: (314) 436-9961

AMEREN ILLINOIS COMPANY

(Formerly Central Illinois Public Service Company)
(Sub. of Ameren Corporation)
300 Liberty St
Peoria, IL 61602
Tel.: (309) 677-5271
Fax: (877) 226-3736
Toll Free: (888) 789-2477
Approx. Rev.: $3,014,000,000
Approx. Number Employees: 2,752
Year Founded: 1902
Business Description:
Electricity & Gas Distr
S.I.C.: 4911; 4924; 4931; 4939
N.A.I.C.S.: 221122; 221119; 221210
Media: 10-23-24-25
Distr.: Direct to Consumer; Reg.
Personnel:
Scott A. Cisel *(Chm, Pres & CEO)*
Warner L. Baxter *(CFO & Exec VP)*
Martin J. Lyons *(Chief Acctg Officer & Sr VP)*
Leigh Morris *(Dir-Corp Commun)*
Advertising Agency:
Rodgers Townsend, LLC
1000 Clark Ave 5th Fl
Saint Louis, MO 63102
Tel.: (314) 436-9960
Fax: (314) 436-9961

AMERICAN ELECTRIC POWER

(Sub. of AEP Ohio)
1 Riverside Plaza
Columbus, OH 43215
Tel.: (614) 716-1000
Fax: (614) 716-1823
Web Site: www.aepohio.com
Approx. Rev.: $2,208,101,000
Approx. Number Employees: 1,323
Year Founded: 1937
Business Description:
Electric Power Distribution & Generation Services
S.I.C.: 4939; 4911; 4931
N.A.I.C.S.: 221111; 221119; 221121; 221122
Advertising Expenditures: $6,000,000
Personnel:
Michael G. Morris *(Chm & CEO)*
Joseph M. Buonaiuto *(Sr VP)*
Advertising Agency:
Advantage Agency
223 Albemarle Ave
Roanoke, VA 24016
Tel.: (540) 400-0979
Fax: (540) 400-7385

Key to Media (For complete agency information see *The Advertising Red Books-Agencies* edition):
1. Bus. Publs. 2. Cable T.V. 3. Catalogs & Directories. 4. Co-op Adv. 5. Consumer Mags. 6. D.M. to Bus. Estab.7. D.M. to Consumers
8. Daily Newsp. 9. Exhibits/Trade Shows 10. Foreign 11. Infomercial 12. Internet Adv.13. Multimedia 14. Network Radio
15. Network T.V. 16. Newsp. Distr. Mags. 17. Other 18. Outdoor (Posters, Transit) 19. Point of Purchase20. Premiums, Novelties
21. Product Samples 22. Special Events Mktg. 23. Spot Radio 24. Spot T.V. 25. Weekly Newsp. 26. Yellow Page Adv.

AMERICAN ELECTRIC POWER COMPANY, INC.

1 Riverside Plz
Columbus, OH 43215-2372
Tel.: (614) 716-1000
Fax: (614) 716-1823
E-mail: mediarelations@aep.com
Web Site: www.aep.com
Approx. Rev.: $14,427,000,000
Approx. Number Employees: 18,712
Year Founded: 1906
Business Description:
Electric Utility Holding Company
S.I.C.: 4939; 4911
N.A.I.C.S.: 221111; 221122
Advertising Expenditures: $25,000,000
Media: 2-3-6-9-10-23-24-25-26
Distr.: Reg.
Budget Set: Oct.
Personnel:
Michael G. Morris *(Chm & CEO)*
Carl L. English *(Vice Chm)*
Nicholas K. Akins *(Pres)*
Brian X. Tierney *(CFO & Exec VP)*
Pablo A. Vegas *(CIO & VP)*
Dennis E. Welch *(Chief Admin Officer & Exec VP)*
Venita McCellon-Allen *(Pres/COO-Southwestern Electric Power Co)*
Keith Darling *(Pres-AEP River Ops LLC)*
Robert P. Powers *(Pres-AEP Utilities)*
Susan Tomasky *(Pres-AEP Transmission)*
D. Michael Miller *(Gen Counsel, Sec & Sr VP)*
Charles E. Zebula *(Treas & Sr VP)*
Lisa Barton *(Exec VP-Transmission)*
Mark C. McCullough *(Exec VP-Generation)*
J. Craig Baker *(Sr VP-Regulatory Svcs)*
Coulter R. Boyle *(Sr VP-Comml Ops)*
Joel P. Gebbie *(Sr VP)*
Michael Heyeck *(Sr VP-Transmission)*
Timothy K. Light *(Sr VP-Fuels, Emissions & Logistics)*
Richard E. Munczinski *(Sr VP-Regulatory Svcs)*
Barbara D. Radous *(Sr VP-Shared Svcs)*
Bill Sigmon *(Sr VP-Engrg, Projects & Field Svcs)*
Lawrence J. Weber *(Chief Nuclear Officer & Sr VP)*
Dale Heydlauff *(VP-Corp Comm)*
Genevieve Tuchow *(VP-HR)*
Pat D. Hemlepp *(Dir-Corp Media Rels)*
Julie Sherwood *(Dir-IR)*
Melissa Mchenry *(Sr Mgr-Media Rels & Policy Comm)*
Matthew Dryden *(Mgr-IR)*
Quinton Lies *(Mgr-Cook Nuclear Plant)*
Dave Tabata *(Mgr-Mktg)*
Brands & Products:
AEP
AMERICAN ELECTRIC POWER
AMERICA'S ENERGY PARTNER
GRID SMART
Advertising Agency:
Advantage Agency
223 Albemarle Ave
Roanoke, VA 24016
Tel.: (540) 400-0979
Fax: (540) 400-7385

AMERICAN ELECTRIC POWER SERVICE CORPORATION

(Sub. of American Electric Power Company, Inc.)
(d/b/a AEPSC)
1 Riverside Plz
Columbus, OH 43215-2355
Tel.: (614) 716-1000
Fax: (614) 716-1823
Web Site: www.aep.com
Sales Range: $1-4.9 Billion
Approx. Number Employees: 2,300
Year Founded: 1937
Business Description:
Public Utilities Management Services
S.I.C.: 4931; 8711
N.A.I.C.S.: 221119; 541330
Advertising Expenditures: $1,703,000
Personnel:
Michael G. Morris *(Chm, Pres & CEO)*
Carl English *(Vice Chm)*
Joseph Hamrock *(Pres & COO)*
Brian X. Tierney *(Exec VP & CFO)*
Michael Miller *(Sr VP, Gen Counsel & Sec)*
Mark McCullough *(Exec VP-Generation)*
Todd Busby *(Sr VP-Commerical Ops)*
Richard E. Munczinski *(Sr VP-Regulatory Svcs)*
Barbaba Radous *(Sr VP-Shared Svcs)*
William L. Sigmon, Jr. *(Sr VP-Engrg, Projects & Field Svcs)*
Stephen P. Smith *(Sr VP-Acctg, Plng & Strategy)*
Bruce H. Braine *(VP)*
Dale E. Heydlauff *(VP-Corp Comm)*

AMERICAN WATER WORKS COMPANY, INC.

(d/b/a American Water)
1025 Laurel Oak Rd
Voorhees, NJ 08043-3506
Tel.: (856) 346-8200
Fax: (856) 346-8360
Web Site: www.amwater.com
Approx. Rev.: $2,710,677,000
Approx. Number Employees: 7,600
Year Founded: 1886
Business Description:
Water Utility Holding Company
S.I.C.: 4941
N.A.I.C.S.: 221310
Media: 5-10-17
Personnel:
George MacKenzie, Jr. *(Chm)*
Jeffry E. Sterba *(Pres & CEO)*
Ellen C. Wolf *(CFO & Sr VP)*
Kellye Walker *(Chief Admin Officer & Gen Counsel)*
Walter J. Lynch *(Pres/COO-Regulated Ops)*
Sharon C. Cameron *(Pres-American Water Enterprises)*
John R. Bigelow *(Sr VP-Bus Svcs)*
Nick O. Rowe *(Sr VP-Eastern Div)*
Mark F. Strauss *(Sr VP-Corp Strategy & Bus Dev)*
Barbara Boyarsky *(VP & Gen Mgr-American Water Resources)*
Sean G. Burke *(VP-HR)*
Advertising Agencies:
The MWW Group
111 E Wacker Dr 10th Fl
Chicago, IL 60601
Tel.: (312) 853-3131
Fax: (312) 853-0955

MWW Group
One McKinney Plz 3232 McKinney Ave
Dallas, TX 75204
Tel.: (972) 231-2990
Fax: (972) 231-9442

APACHE CORPORATION

2000 Post Oak Blvd Ste 100
Houston, TX 77056-4400
Tel.: (713) 296-6000
Fax: (713) 296-6496
E-mail: webmaster@apachecorp.com
Web Site: www.apachecorp.com
Approx. Rev.: $12,092,000,000
Approx. Number Employees: 4,449
Year Founded: 1954
Business Description:
Independent Energy Company Engaged in Exploration, Development & Production of Natural Gas & Crude Oil
S.I.C.: 1321; 1311
N.A.I.C.S.: 211112; 211111
Media: 8-11
Personnel:
G. Steven Farris *(Chm & CEO)*
Rodney J. Eichler *(Co-Pres & COO)*
Roger B. Plank *(Co-Pres & Chief Corp Officer)*
Thomas P. Chambers *(CFO & Exec VP)*
Michael S. Bahorich *(CTO & Exec VP)*
Rebecca A. Hoyt *(Chief Acctg Officer, Controller & VP)*
P. Anthony Lannie *(Gen Counsel & Exec VP)*
Jon A. Jeppesen *(Exec VP-Gulf Coast Reg)*
W. Kregg Olson *(Exec VP-Corp Reservoir Engrg)*
Matthew W. Dundrea *(Sr VP-Treasury & Admin)*
Robert J. Dye *(Sr VP-Global Comm & Corp Affairs)*
Margery M. Harris *(Sr VP-HR)*
Janine J. McArdle *(Sr VP-Gas Monetization)*
Sarah B. Teslik *(Sr VP-Policy & Governance)*
Paul McKinney *(Reg VP-Gulf Coast Onshore)*
Alex C. de Alvarez *(VP-Security)*
Alfonso Leon *(VP-Plng, Strategy & IR)*
Aaron Merrick *(VP-IT)*
David Higgins *(Dir-Pub Affairs)*
Anne Hedrich *(Mgr-e-Comm)*
Kenny McMinn *(Mgr-Production-Gulf Coast Reg)*

AQUA AMERICA, INC.

762 W Lancaster Ave
Bryn Mawr, PA 19010-3402
Tel.: (610) 527-8000
Fax: (610) 525-7658
E-mail: investorrelations@aquaamerica.com
Web Site: www.aquaamerica.com
Approx. Rev.: $726,072,000
Approx. Number Employees: 1,632
Year Founded: 1968
Business Description:
Holding Company; Water & Waste Water Services
S.I.C.: 4941
N.A.I.C.S.: 221310
Media: 2-23
Personnel:
Nicholas DeBenedictis *(Chm, Pres & CEO)*
David P. Smeltzer *(CFO)*
Roy H. Stahl *(Chief Admin Officer, Gen Counsel & Sec)*
Robert A. Rubin *(Chief Acctg Officer, VP & Controller)*
Thomas Bruns *(Pres-Aqua Indiana, Inc.)*
Richard S. Fox *(Pres-Aqua Utilities Florida, Inc.)*
Robert G. Liptak, Jr. *(Pres-Northern Ops-Aqua America)*
Christopher P. Luning *(VP-Corp Dev & Corp Counsel)*
Brian Dingerdissen *(Dir-IR)*
Brands & Products:
AQUA
Advertising Agency:
Braithwaite Communications
100 Penn Sq E Ste 480
Philadelphia, PA 19107
Tel.: (215) 564-3200
Fax: (215) 564-3455

AQUARION WATER COMPANY

(Sub. of Macquarie Bank Limited)
200 Monroe Tpke
Monroe, CT 06468
Tel.: (203) 445-7310
Fax: (203) 330-4613
Web Site: www.aquarion.com
Year Founded: 1991
Business Description:
Public Water Supply & Utility Management Services
S.I.C.: 4941; 2421
N.A.I.C.S.: 221310; 321113
Advertising Expenditures: $300,000
Media: 8-9-10-17-25-26
Personnel:
Charles V. Firlotte *(Pres & CEO)*
Donald J. Morrissey *(CFO & Corp Sec)*
Leendert DeJong *(Dir-Water Quality & Environ Mgmt)*
John J. Herlihy *(Dir-Water Quality & Regulations)*

ARIZONA PUBLIC SERVICE COMPANY

(Sub. of Pinnacle West Capital Corporation)
400 N 5th St
Phoenix, AZ 85004-3902
Mailing Address:
PO Box 53999
Phoenix, AZ 85072-3999
Tel.: (602) 250-1000
Fax: (602) 250-3007
Toll Free: (800) 253-9405
E-mail: aps@aps.com
Web Site: www.aps.com
Approx. Rev.: $3,180,807,000
Approx. Number Employees: 6,600
Year Founded: 1920
Business Description:
Generator & Electricity Supplier
S.I.C.: 1623; 4911; 4931; 4939
N.A.I.C.S.: 237130; 221119; 221122
Advertising Expenditures: $6,500,000
Media: 2-7-8-9-10-13-14-15-18-19-24-26
Distr.: Reg.
Budget Set: Sept.

Key to Media (For complete agency information see *The Advertising Red Books-Agencies* edition):
1. Bus. Publs. 2. Cable T.V. 3. Catalogs & Directories. 4. Co-op Adv. 5. Consumer Mags. 6. D.M. to Bus. Estab.7. D.M. to Consumers
8. Daily Newsp. 9. Exhibits/Trade Shows 10. Foreign 11. Infomercial 12. Internet Adv.13. Multimedia 14. Network Radio
15. Network T.V. 16. Newsp. Distr. Mags. 17. Other 18. Outdoor (Posters, Transit) 19. Point of Purchase20. Premiums, Novelties
21. Product Samples 22. Special Events Mktg. 23. Spot Radio 24. Spot T.V. 25. Weekly Newsp. 26. Yellow Page Adv.

Arizona Public Service Company —
(Continued)

Personnel:
Donald G. Robinson *(Pres & COO)*
Edward Z. Fox *(Chief Sustainability Officer & VP)*
Tammy McLeod *(Chief Customer Officer & VP)*
David Falck *(Gen Counsel, Sec & Sr VP)*
Randall K. Edington *(Exec VP & Chief Nuclear Officer)*
Steven M. Wheeler *(Exec VP)*
Bob Bement *(Sr VP-Ops-Palo Verde Nuclear Generating Station)*
Dwight Mims *(Sr VP-Regulatory & Oversight-Palo Verde Nuclear Station)*
Mark A. Schiavoni *(Sr VP-Fossil Ops)*
Lori S. Sundberg *(Sr VP-HR & Ethics)*
John Hesser *(VP-Engrg-Palo Verde Nuclear Generating Station)*
Brad Albert *(Gen Mgr-Strategic Plng & Resource Acquisition)*
Becky Hickman *(Dir-IR)*
Conrad Spencer *(Dir-Design Engrg & Special Projects)*
David Bentler *(Mgr-APS Community & Economic Dev)*
Jim McDonald *(Mgr-PR)*

Brands & Products:
APS

Advertising Agencies:
Media Buying Services, Inc.
4545 E Shea Blvd Ste 162
Phoenix, AZ 85028-6008
Tel.: (602) 996-2232
Fax: (602) 996-5658
Toll Free: (888) 996-2232

MichaelsWilder
7773 W Golden Ln
Peoria, AZ 85345-7977
Tel.: (623) 334-0100
Fax: (623) 334-0200
Toll Free: (800) 423-6468

AT&T

(Div. of AT&T Inc.)
2600 Camino Ramon
San Ramon, CA 94583-4328
Tel.: (925) 823-5388
Toll Free: (800) 333-9519
Web Site: www.att.com
Sales Range: $1-4.9 Billion
Approx. Number Employees: 7,000
Year Founded: 1983
Business Description:
Regional Holding Company; Telecommunications Products & Services
S.I.C.: 4813
N.A.I.C.S.: 517310
Media: 2-6-9-16-17-18-23-24-31
Distr.: Reg.
Personnel:
LJ Kobe *(Dir-Emerging Media Platforms)*
Connie Mertens *(Dir-Online Mktg)*
Erin Petty *(Dir-Interactive & Innovation)*
Jerry Lynch *(Reg Mgr-Sls)*
Jacob Pearson *(Sr Mgr-Media-Interactive & Innovation)*
Jennifer Fisher *(Mgr-Program-Network Engrg)*

Advertising Agencies:
BBDO Worldwide Inc.
(Sub. of Omnicom Group, Inc.)
1285 Ave of the Americas
New York, NY 10019-6028
Tel.: (212) 459-5000
Fax: (212) 459-6645

Rodgers Townsend, LLC
1000 Clark Ave 5th Fl
Saint Louis, MO 63102
Tel.: (314) 436-9960
Fax: (314) 436-9961

AT&T COMMUNICATIONS CORP.

(Div. of AT&T Inc.)
1 AT&T Way
Bedminster, NJ 07921
Tel.: (908) 221-4191
Fax: (908) 532-1675
Web Site: www.att.com
Sales Range: $200-249.9 Million
Year Founded: 1885
Business Description:
Voice, Data & Video Communications Services
S.I.C.: 4813
N.A.I.C.S.: 517110
Import Export
Media: 3-6-8-9-13-14-15-16-18-23-24-25-31
Distr.: Direct to Consumer; Natl.
Personnel:
Randall L. Stephenson *(Chm, Pres & CEO)*
Cathy Martine *(Exec VP-Small Bus Solutions & Alternate Channels)*
John C. Petrillo *(Exec VP-Corp Strategy & Bus Dev)*
Linda Rogers *(VP-Enterprise Sls-Southeast)*
Dean Harvey *(Gen Mgr-Visual Commun)*
Mike Song *(Product Mgr-Remote Access)*
Verdi Chang *(Mgr-Sls & Mktg)*
Brands & Products:
BUSINESSDIRECT
CALLVANTAGE
ONE RATE USA
SOLUTION ASSISTANT
UNLIMITED
VOICE DNA
WORLDNET
THE WORLD'S NETWORKING COMPANY
Advertising Agencies:
Alexander & Richardson
161 Washington Valley Rd Ste 205
Warren, NJ 07059-7121
Tel.: (732) 302-1223
Fax: (732) 356-9574

Bandujo Donker & Brothers
22 W 21st St 8th Fl
New York, NY 10011
Tel.: (212) 332-4100
Fax: (212) 366-6068

Beanstalk
220 E 42nd St 15th Fl
New York, NY 10017
Tel.: (212) 421-6060
Fax: (212) 421-6388

The Bravo Group HQ
285 Madison Ave 12th Fl
New York, NY 10017
Tel.: (212) 780-5800

Devaney & Associates
606 Providence Rd
Towson, MD 21286
Tel.: (410) 296-0800
Fax: (410) 296-5437

Dieste
1999 Bryan St Ste 2700
Dallas, TX 75201
Tel.: (214) 259-8000
Fax: (214) 259-8040

DMNA
97 S Second St Ste 300
San Jose, CA 95113-2512
Tel.: (408) 512-2110
Fax: (408) 297-8020

Gogerty Marriott
2900 Century Sq 1501 4th Ave Ste 2900
Seattle, WA 98101
Tel.: (206) 292-3000

Gotham Incorporated
150 E 42nd St 12th Fl
New York, NY 10017
Tel.: (212) 414-7000
Fax: (212) 414-7095

interTrend Communications, Inc.
555 E Ocean Blvd
Long Beach, CA 90802-5003
Tel.: (562) 733-1888
Fax: (562) 733-1889

Maslansky, Luntz & Partners
1101 King St Ste 110
Alexandria, VA 22314
Tel.: (703) 358-0080
Fax: (703) 358-0089

MAX Advertising
3190 NE Expy Ste 120
Atlanta, GA 30341
Tel.: (770) 454-7100
Fax: (770) 454-7100

PointRoll Inc.
951 E Hector St
Conshohocken, PA 19428
Tel.: (267) 558-1300
Fax: (267) 285-1141
Toll Free: (800) 203-6956

RealTime Media, Inc.
1060 1st Ave Ste 201
King of Prussia, PA 19406
Tel.: (610) 337-3600
Fax: (610) 337-2300

Schifino Lee Advertising
511 W Bay St Ste 400
Tampa, FL 33606
Tel.: (813) 258-5858
Fax: (813) 254-1146

Sloane & Company LLC
(d/b/a Sloane & Company)
7 Times Sq Tower 17th Fl
New York, NY 10036
Tel.: (212) 486-9500
Fax: (212) 486-9094

Thunder Factory
27 Maiden Ln Ste 525
San Francisco, CA 94108
Tel.: (415) 992-3276
Fax: (415) 956-0604

AT&T INC.

208 S Akard St
Dallas, TX 75202
Tel.: (210) 821-4105
Fax: (210) 351-2071
Web Site: www.att.com
Approx. Rev.: $124,280,000,000
Approx. Number Employees: 265,590
Year Founded: 1984
Business Description:
Broadband Internet, Cable Television, Landline & Wireless Telecommunication Services & Phone Directories
S.I.C.: 4813; 2741; 4812; 7375
N.A.I.C.S.: 517310; 511140; 517110; 517212; 518111
Advertising Expenditures: $2,797,000,000
Media: 2-6-7-8-9-13-18-22-23-24-31
Distr.: Direct to Consumer; Reg.
Budget Set: Aug.
Personnel:
Randall L. Stephenson *(Chm, Pres & CEO)*
Richard G. Lindner *(CFO & Sr Exec VP)*
Charlene Lake *(Chief Sustainability Officer & Sr VP-Pub Affairs)*
Ralph de la Vega *(Pres/CEO-Mobility & Consumer Markets)*
John T. Stankey *(Pres/CEO-AT&T Bus Solutions)*
Glenn Lurie *(Pres-Emerging Devices)*
Forrest E. Miller *(Grp Pres-Corp Strategy & Dev)*
Rayford Wilkins, Jr. *(CEO-Diversified Bus)*
Wayne Watts *(Gen Counsel & Sr Exec VP)*
William A. Blase, Jr. *(Sr Exec VP-HR)*
John J. Stephens *(Sr VP & Controller)*
Don Cain *(Sr VP)*
Anne Chow *(Sr VP-Premier Client Grp)*
Esther Lee *(Sr VP-Brand Mktg & Adv)*
Larry Solomon *(Sr VP-Corp Comm)*
Michael J. Viola *(Sr VP-Corp Fin)*
Brad Bridges *(VP-Corp Strategy)*
Maria Mandel *(VP-Media & Mktg Innovation-Advanced Adv Solutions)*
Mark Wright *(VP-Media Svc)*
Brent Olson *(Asst VP-Pub Policy)*
Laura Zuckerman *(Asst VP)*
Adrian Quintanilla *(Gen Mgr)*
Steve Governale *(Exec Dir-Interactive & Innovation)*
John Schinter *(Exec Dir-Energy)*
Cindy Matthews *(Mktg Dir)*
Gavin McCarty *(Dir-Sls Ops)*
Marisa Shockley *(Assoc Dir-Media Innovation)*
Keith Bryan *(Area Mgr-Retail Sls)*
Brooks McCorcle *(Mgr-Institutional Investors)*
Brands & Products:
AT&T
AT&T 1-800-YELLOWPAGES
AT&T CONNECTECH
AT&T FAST ACCESS
AT&T U-VERSE
GO PHONE

Key to Media (For complete agency information see *The Advertising Red Books-Agencies* edition):
1. Bus. Publs. 2. Cable T.V. 3. Catalogs & Directories. 4. Co-op Adv. 5. Consumer Mags. 6. D.M. to Bus. Estab.7. D.M. to Consumers
8. Daily Newsp. 9. Exhibits/Trade Shows 10. Foreign 11. Infomercial 12. Internet Adv.13. Multimedia 14. Network Radio
15. Network T.V. 16. Newsp. Distr. Mags. 17. Other 18. Outdoor (Posters, Transit) 19. Point of Purchase20. Premiums, Novelties
21. Product Samples 22. Special Events Mktg. 23. Spot Radio 24. Spot T.V. 25. Weekly Newsp. 26. Yellow Page Adv.

QUICKSOURCE
YOUR WORLD. DELIVERED

Advertising Agencies:
BBDO New York
1285 Ave of the Americas 7th Fl
New York, NY 10019-6028
Tel.: (212) 459-5000
Birthday
Go Phone

BBDO Worldwide Inc.
(Sub. of Omnicom Group, Inc.)
1285 Ave of the Americas
New York, NY 10019-6028
Tel.: (212) 459-5000
Fax: (212) 459-6645

The Bravo Group HQ
285 Madison Ave 12th Fl
New York, NY 10017
Tel.: (212) 780-5800

DDB Chicago
200 E Randolph St
Chicago, IL 60601
Tel.: (312) 552-6000
Fax: (312) 552-2370

Initiative
1 Dag Hammarskjold Plz
New York, NY 10017
Tel.: (212) 605-7000
Fax: (917) 305-4003
Southern Region

MEC - NA HQ, New York
825 7th Ave
New York, NY 10019-5818
Tel.: (212) 474-0000
Fax: (212) 474-0003
Media Buying & Planning
Wireless
— Dennis Donlin *(Pres-AT&T)*

Rodgers Townsend, LLC
1000 Clark Ave 5th Fl
Saint Louis, MO 63102
Tel.: (314) 436-9960
Fax: (314) 436-9961

Zugara Inc.
8536 National Blvd Ste B
Culver City, CA 90232
Tel.: (310) 945-4950
Fax: (310) 945-4951
Digital

AT&T INC.
(Div. of AT&T Inc.)
(d/b/a AT&T East)
310 Orange St
New Haven, CT 06510
Tel.: (203) 771-5200
Fax: (203) 498-9402
Web Site: www.att.com

Sales Range: $800-899.9 Million
Approx. Number Employees: 6,790
Year Founded: 1878
Business Description:
Telecommunication Services
S.I.C.: 4813
N.A.I.C.S.: 517110; 517310

Media: 1-2-3-4-5-6-8-9-10-14-15-18-19-20-22-23-24-25-26
Distr.: Direct to Consumer; Reg.
Budget Set: Nov.

Personnel:
Margaret McIntyre *(Exec Dir-Consumer Products Media)*
Charles Rogers *(Sr Mgr-Tech Support)*

AT&T SOUTHEAST
(Div. of AT&T Inc.)
472 Ivy Park Ln NE
Atlanta, GA 30342-4554
Tel.: (404) 249-2000
Fax: (404) 249-2071
E-mail: investor@bellsouth.com
Web Site: www.bellsouth.com
Sales Range: $150-199.9 Million
Approx. Number Employees: 500
Year Founded: 1983
Business Description:
International Telecommunications Holding Company; Local Telephone Service; Mobile Communications Services Including Cellular, Nationwide Paging & Mobile Data; Advertising & Publishing Services; Market & Maintain Stand-Alone & Fully-Integrated Communications Systems
S.I.C.: 4812; 4813
N.A.I.C.S.: 517110; 517212; 517310
Advertising Expenditures: $298,000,000
Media: 3-5-7-8-10-14-15-23-24-26
Distr.: Intl.; Natl.
Personnel:
Scott Frank *(Pres & CEO-Intellectual Property)*
Pat Shannon *(CFO, Principal Acctg Officer & Sr VP-Fin-BellSouth)*
William L. Smith *(Pres-Local Network Ops)*
Krista S. Tillman *(Pres-North Carolina-Ops)*
William C. Pate *(VP-Adv & PR)*
Scott Finney *(Dir-Mktg)*
Alan Pate *(Dir-Mktg)*
Matt Jackson *(Sr Mgr-Mktg)*
Kathy Adams *(Sr Mgr-Mktg)*
Kathy Boughey *(Mgr-Lead Product Mktg)*
Harry Coleman *(Mgr-Product)*
Stefanie Elder *(Mgr-Market Res)*
Brands & Products:
1-800-GET-REAL
1-877-GO-DIGITAL
9-1-1 PINPOINT
ACCUPULSE
ADREACH
ADREACH IMPRESSIONS
ADTELLIGENCE
ADWATCH
ALIANZA
ALREADY IN TOUCH WITH THE FUTURE
AMERICAST
AMERICAST ADVANTAGE
AMERICAST PREMIERCAST
AMERICAST VIEWCAST
AREA PLUS
BACK-UP
BELL
BELLSOUTH
BELLSOUTH 411 NATIONWIDE
BELLSOUTH AMIGO
BELLSOUTH ANSWERS
BELLSOUTH BEYOND PROTECTION PLAN
BELLSOUTH BUSINESS ADVANTAGE
BELLSOUTH BUSINESS CHOICE
BELLSOUTH BUSINESS PLUS
BELLSOUTH CLASSIC
BELLSOUTH CONNECTED COMMUNITY
BELLSOUTH ENHANCED SOLUTIONS
BELLSOUTH. ESCUCHAMOS. RESPONDEMOS.
BELLSOUTH ESSENTIALS
BELLSOUTH GEAR
BELLSOUTH INSITE
BELLSOUTH INTELLIGENT WIRELESS NETWORK
BELLSOUTH INTERACTIVE PAGING
BELLSOUTH. LISTENING. ANSWERING.
BELLSOUTH MAKES YOU FEEL AT HOME WHEN YOU'RE NOT
BELLSOUTH MOBILITY
BELLSOUTH POWERTOOL
BELLSOUTH PREMIUM SYSTEMS
BELLSOUTH PREPAID TO GO
BELLSOUTH PROFESSIONAL SERVICES
BELLSOUTH PSP REWARD
BELLSOUTH SELECT
BELLSOUTH SELECT BUSINESS
BELLSOUTH SELECT LIVING
BELLSOUTH SOLUTIONS
BELLSOUTH TELECOMMUNICATIONS
BELLSOUTH.NET
BERRIWORX
BERRY OPTIMIZER
BERRYPRO
BERRYQUEST
BETTER CONNECTIONS
BRAND GOLD
BUSINESS BUZZ
BUSINESS EX CHOICE
BUSINESS GUARDIAN
BUSINESS ONE
BUSINESS WINNING AWARDS
BUSY CONNECT
BUZZ
CALL LOGIX
CALL ON US
CELLEMETRY
CELLULINK
CINGULAR
CLICK, PAY AND SAIL AWAY
THE COMPANY THAT CONNECTS YOU, NOW PROTECTS YOU
COMPLETE CHOICE
COPYRIGHT GOLD
COUNTRY SELECT
COURTESYCOMPLETE
CRISISLINK
DATA ANSWERS
DCS MINUTE MANAGER
DELIVERS MORE
DIGITAL ESSX
DIRECT TO DOOR MEDIA
ESSX
EVERYTHING YOU EXPECT FROM A LEADER
EXPRESS CINEMA
FASTACCESS
FIXED RATE ULTRA
FLEXSERV
THE GOLDEN BULB
THE GOLDIE
IDEAS TO PROFITS
INTEGRATION PLUS
IT'S FOR YOU
LEARNING ALIVE TEACHERS
LET YOUR FINGER DO THE WALKING
LIFEREACH
LIFE'S CALLING. WHY WAIT?
LIGHTGATE
LINEONE
MEGALINK
MEMENTO
MEMORYCALL
MINUTE MANAGER
MOVEXPRESS
MOVING IS QUICK WHEN YOU CLICK
MYBIZ
NETWORK EXPRESS
NEVADA BELL
ONDACOM
THE ORIGINAL SEARCH ENGINE
PACIFIC BELL
PATENT GOLD
PRESS BLUE TO GET THROUGH
PRI ADVANTAGE ONE
PRIVACY DIRECTOR
PULL, PROD AND PUSH IP
PULSELINK
REAL CALL
REAL PAGES
REAL TALKING ADS
THE REAL WHITE PAGES
REALPAGES.COM
REGIONSERV
RESPUESTAS BELLSOUTH
RIGHTTOUCH
RINGMASTER
ROBOTAG
SABER
SEE IT. BUY IT AND MORE @ BELLSOUTH.COM
SIMPLE SELECT
SMALL BUSINESS BLUEPRINT
SMALL BUSINESS SELECT
SMARTLINE
SMARTPATH
SMARTVIEW
SOFTWARE GOLD
SOLUTION ADVISOR
SOUTH CENTRAL BELL
SOUTHERN BELL
STAR LINES
STATE TALK
STEVEN GRAPHICS
SUNLINK
SUPERVIEW
SYNCHRONET
TEAMTELEWORK
TEAMTELEWORK CONNECTIONS
TOUCHSTAR
TRADEMARK GOLD
TRANSPORT ADVANTAGE
TV THE WAY IT SHOULD BE
UNLIMITED ANSWERS
VISUAL DIRECTOR
WATCHALERT
WATTSAVER
WINCENTER
WINCONNECT
WINLOGIC
WINNING VALUE
WORLD CLASS CAMPUS
YELLOWVISION
YOU CAN'T GET FROM I TO P WITHOUT IP
YOUR INTERCONNECTION ADVANTAGE
ZIPCONNECT
Advertising Agencies:
G2 Worldwide
200 5th Ave
New York, NY 10010

Key to Media (For complete agency information see *The Advertising Red Books-Agencies* edition):
1. Bus. Publs. 2. Cable T.V. 3. Catalogs & Directories. 4. Co-op Adv. 5. Consumer Mags. 6. D.M. to Bus. Estab.7. D.M. to Consumers
8. Daily Newsp. 9. Exhibits/Trade Shows 10. Foreign 11. Infomercial 12. Internet Adv.13. Multimedia 14. Network Radio
15. Network T.V. 16. Newsp. Distr. Mags. 17. Other 18. Outdoor (Posters, Transit) 19. Point of Purchase20. Premiums, Novelties
21. Product Samples 22. Special Events Mktg. 23. Spot Radio 24. Spot T.V. 25. Weekly Newsp. 26. Yellow Page Adv.

AT&T Southeast — (Continued)

Tel.: (212) 537-3700
Fax: (212) 546-2425

Initiative Atlanta
5909 Peachtree-Dunwoody Rd Ste 600
Atlanta, GA 30328
Tel.: (678) 441-7100
Fax: (678) 441-7263

Response Media, Inc.
3155 Medlock Bridge Rd
Norcross, GA 30071-1423
Tel.: (770) 451-5478
Fax: (770) 451-4929

Solar Velocity
3300 Highland Pkwy Ste 260
Smyrna, GA 30082
Tel.: (404) 978-2240
Fax: (404) 978-2241

THINK, Inc.
1375 Peachtree St NE Ste 600
Atlanta, GA 30309
Tel.: (404) 962-8900
Fax: (404) 962-8901

AT&T WEST

(Div. of AT&T Inc.)
525 Market St
San Francisco, CA 94105
Tel.: (415) 778-1231
E-mail: hgdiamond@att.com
Web Site: www.att.com
Sales Range: $75-99.9 Million
Business Description:
Telecommunications & Internet Services
S.I.C.: 4813; 7375
N.A.I.C.S.: 517110; 518111
Advertising Expenditures: $140,000,000
Personnel:
Steve Dimmitt *(Pres)*
William R. Drexel *(Sr VP & Asst Gen Counsel)*
Robin Greenway MacGillivray *(Sr VP)*
Brands & Products:
PACIFIC BELL

ATCO LTD.

909 11th Ave SW Ste 1500
Calgary, AB T2R 1N6, Canada
Tel.: (403) 292-7500
Fax: (403) 292-7532
Web Site: www.atco.com
Approx. Rev.: $3,510,242,428
Approx. Number Employees: 7,700
Year Founded: 1947
Business Description:
Electric & Natural Gas Distr; Electrical Generation & Transmission
S.I.C.: 4911; 4924; 4931; 4939
N.A.I.C.S.: 221122; 221119; 221210
Advertising Expenditures: $2,600,000
Media: 1-2-6-8-9-10-16-17-18-20-22-23-24-25-26
Distr.: Intl.; Natl.
Budget Set: Oct.
Personnel:
Ronald D. Southern *(Chm)*
Nancy C. Southern *(Deputy Chm, Pres & CEO)*
Brian R. Bale *(CFO & Sr VP)*
Susan R. Werth *(Chief Admin Officer & Sr VP)*
Owen G. Edmondson *(Exec VP-Fin & Regulatory)*
Kevin J. Cumming *(Sr VP-Northern Dev)*
Robert J. Myles *(Sr VP-Corp Dev & Plng)*
Carson J. Ackroyd *(VP-Mktg & Comm)*
Erhard M. Kiefer *(VP-HR & Corp Svcs)*
Catherine M. Widdoes *(VP-HR Svcs)*
Paul G. Wright *(VP-Fin & Treasury)*
Carol Gear *(Asst Sec)*

ATMOS ENERGY CORPORATION

3 Lincoln Centre Ste 1800 5430 LBJ Fwy
Dallas, TX 75240-2615
Mailing Address:
PO Box 650205
Dallas, TX 75265-0205
Tel.: (972) 934-9227
Fax: (972) 855-3040
E-mail: gerald.hunter@atmosenergy.com
Web Site: www.atmosenergy.com
Approx. Rev.: $4,789,690,000
Approx. Number Employees: 4,913
Year Founded: 1906
Business Description:
Natural Gas Distr; Natural Gas Transportation & Storage Services; Energy Management & Gas Marketing Services
S.I.C.: 4924; 4911; 4922; 5172
N.A.I.C.S.: 221210; 221121; 424720; 486210
Media: 7-8-9-25
Distr.: Reg.
Budget Set: May
Personnel:
Robert W. Best *(Chm)*
Kim R. Cocklin *(Pres & CEO)*
Fred E. Meisenheimer *(CFO & Sr VP)*
Richard J. Gius *(CIO & VP)*
J. Kevin Akers *(Pres-Kentucky & MidStates Div)*
Mark S. Bergeron *(Pres-Atmos Energy Holdings Inc)*
Richard A. Erskine *(Pres-Atmos Pipeline-Texas)*
David E. Gates *(Pres-Mississippi Div)*
Gary W. Gregory *(Pres-West Texas Div)*
Tom S. Hawkins, Jr. *(Pres-Louisiana Div)*
John A. Paris *(Pres-Mid-Tex Div)*
Gary L. Schlessman *(Pres-Colorado Kansas Div)*
Louis P. Gregory *(Gen Counsel & Sr VP)*
Ron W. McDowell *(Exec VP-Bus Dev)*
Michael E. Haefner *(Sr VP-HR)*
Jeff Hardgrave *(VP-Customer Svc)*
Gary G. Rehm *(VP-Mktg)*
Trey Hill *(Dir-Pub Affairs)*
Gerald Hunter *(Dir-Corp Comm)*
Scott Powell *(Dir-Safety, Security & Compliance)*
Gary L. Smith *(Dir-Rates)*
Jeanette Moser *(Reg Mgr-Pub Affairs)*
Shelley Burnett *(Mgr-Pub Affairs)*
Randy Hartford *(Mgr-Pub Affairs)*
Doug Hill *(Mgr-Pub Affairs)*
James Johnson *(Mgr-Pub Affairs)*
Mike Schweikhard *(Mgr-Pub Affairs)*
Terry Tombaugh *(Mgr-Pub Affairs)*
Karl Weber *(Mgr-Pub Affairs)*
Randy West *(Mgr-Pub Affairs)*
Advertising Agencies:
Garza Creative Group
2601 Hibernia St Ste 200
Dallas, TX 75204
Tel.: (214) 720-3888
Fax: (214) 720-3889

RBMM
7007 Twin Hills Ave Ste 200
Dallas, TX 75231
Tel.: (214) 987-6500
Fax: (214) 987-3662

SKSW Advertising
1255 W 15th St Ste 800
Plano, TX 75075
Tel.: (972) 424-3000
Fax: (972) 424-3011

AVISTA CORPORATION

1411 E Mission Ave
Spokane, WA 99202-2600
Mailing Address:
PO Box 3727
Spokane, WA 99220-3727
Tel.: (509) 489-0500
Tel.: (509) 495-4817
Tel.: (509) 495-4174 (Corp Comm)
Fax: (509) 495-8725
E-mail: corpcomm@avistacorp.com
Web Site: www.avistacorp.com
Approx. Rev.: $1,558,740,000
Approx. Number Employees: 2,499
Year Founded: 1889
Business Description:
Energy & Energy Related Businesses
S.I.C.: 4939; 4924; 4931
N.A.I.C.S.: 221112; 221111; 221119; 221210
Import
Advertising Expenditures: $1,500,000
Media: 1-2-3-5-6-7-8-9-10-12-13-18-19-20-22-23-24-25-26
Distr.: Direct to Consumer
Budget Set: July
Personnel:
Scott L. Morris *(Chm, Pres & CEO)*
Mark T. Thies *(CFO & Sr VP)*
James M. Kensok *(CIO & VP)*
Marian M. Durkin *(Chief Compliance Officer, Gen Counsel & Sr VP)*
Roger D. Woodworth *(Chief Strategy Officer & VP-Sustainable Energy Solutions)*
Stuart A. Stiles *(Pres/CEO-Advantage IQ)*
Ann M. Wilson *(Treas & VP-Fin)*
Karen S. Feltes *(Corp Sec & Sr VP-HR)*
Dennis P. Vermillion *(Sr VP)*
Jessie Wuerst *(Comm Mgr)*
Kelly Conley *(Mgr-Product Mktg)*
Jason Lang *(Mgr-IR)*
Patty Shea *(Mgr-Reg Bus)*
Brands & Products:
AVISTA
AVISTA COMMUNICATIONS
AVISTA ENERGY
AVISTA VENTURES
Advertising Agency:
Gard Communications
711 SW Alder St 4th Fl
Portland, OR 97205
Tel.: (503) 221-0100
Fax: (503) 226-4854
Toll Free: (800) 800-7132

BALTIMORE GAS AND ELECTRIC COMPANY

(Sub. of CONSTELLATION ENERGY GROUP, INC.)
110 W Fayette St Ste 2
Baltimore, MD 21201-3708
Mailing Address:
PO Box 1475
Baltimore, MD 21203-1475
Tel.: (410) 470-2800
Fax: (410) 234-7406
Toll Free: (800) 685-0123
Approx. Rev.: $3,461,700,000
Approx. Number Employees: 10,000
Year Founded: 1816
Business Description:
Natural Gas & Electric Distr
S.I.C.: 4939; 4911; 4924; 4931
N.A.I.C.S.: 221122; 221119; 221210
Media: 2-3-4-5-6-7-8-9-10-18-20-23-24-25-26
Distr.: Reg.
Personnel:
Mayo A. Shattuck, III *(Chm)*
Kenneth W. DeFontes Jr. *(Pres & CEO)*
Paul J. Allen *(Chief Environmental Officer & Sr VP)*
A. Christopher Burton *(Sr VP-Gas, Electric Ops & Plng)*
Mark Case *(Sr VP-Strategy & Regulatory Affairs)*
Brian Daschbach *(Sr VP-Integrated Field Svcs)*
Carol Dodson *(Sr VP-Asset Mgmt Svcs)*
Jeannette M. Mills *(Chief Customer Officer & Sr VP)*
Thomas Valenti *(Sr VP-Logistics Mgmt Svcs)*
Stephen J. Woerner *(Sr VP)*
Malinda Small *(VP-Comm)*
David Vosvick *(VP-HR)*
Brands & Products:
CONSTELLATION POWER
CONSTELLATION POWER SOURCE

BASIN ELECTRIC POWER COOPERATIVE

1717 E Interstate Ave
Bismarck, ND 58503
Tel.: (701) 223-0441
Fax: (701) 557-5142
Web Site: www.basinelectric.com
Approx. Number Employees: 2,000
Year Founded: 1961
Business Description:
Electric Power Generation, Transmission & Distribution; Coal Gasification; Bituminous Coal & Lignite Surface
S.I.C.: 4931; 1311
N.A.I.C.S.: 221119; 211111
Personnel:
Cliff Gjellstad *(Pres)*
Ronald R. Harper *(CEO & Gen Mgr)*
Clifton Hudgins *(CFO & Sr VP-Fin Svcs)*
Paul Sukut *(CFO & Sr VP-Fin Svcs)*
Claire Olson *(Gen Counsel & Sr VP)*
Wayne Backman *(Sr VP-Generation)*
Mike Eggl *(Sr VP-External Rels & Comm)*
Wayne Bachman *(VP-Ops-Engrg)*

Key to Media (For complete agency information see *The Advertising Red Books-Agencies* edition):
1. Bus. Publs. 2. Cable T.V. 3. Catalogs & Directories. 4. Co-op Adv. 5. Consumer Mags. 6. D.M. to Bus. Estab.7. D.M. to Consumers 8. Daily Newsp. 9. Exhibits/Trade Shows 10. Foreign 11. Infomercial 12. Internet Adv.13. Multimedia 14. Network Radio 15. Network T.V. 16. Newsp. Distr. Mags. 17. Other 18. Outdoor (Posters, Transit) 19. Point of Purchase20. Premiums, Novelties 21. Product Samples 22. Special Events Mktg. 23. Spot Radio 24. Spot T.V. 25. Weekly Newsp. 26. Yellow Page Adv.

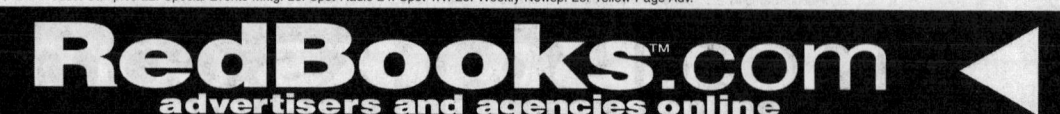

Floyd Robb *(VP-Comm & Mktg Support)*
Shawn Deisz *(Mgr-Acctg)*
David Raatz *(Mgr-Mktg & Power Supply Plng)*
Ron Rebenitsch *(Mgr-Alternative Tech)*
Gary Drost *(Asst Sec)*
Advertising Agency:
Odney
1400 W Century Ave
Bismarck, ND 58503
Tel.: (701) 222-8721
Fax: (701) 222-8172
Toll Free: (888) 500-8721

B.C. HYDRO

333 Dunsmuir St 16th Fl
Vancouver, BC V6B 5R3, Canada
Tel.: (604) 528-1600
Fax: (604) 623-3937
Toll Free: (800) 224-9376
Web Site: www.bchydro.com
Approx. Number Employees: 4,406
Year Founded: 1945
Business Description:
Electric Utility Services
S.I.C.: 9631
N.A.I.C.S.: 926130
Personnel:
Dan Doyle *(Chm)*
David Cobb *(Pres & CEO)*
Bev van Ruyven *(Deputy CEO & Exec VP)*
Charles Reid *(CFO & Exec VP-Fin)*
Don Stuckert *(CIO)*
Debbie Nagle *(Chief HR Officer & Sr VP)*
Lisa Seppala *(Chief Safety, Health & Environment Officer)*
Raymond A. Aldeguer *(Gen Counsel & Sr VP)*
Chris O'Riley *(Exec VP-Generation)*
Susan Yurkovich *(Exec VP)*
Michele Morgan *(Sr VP-Smart Metering Infrastructure Project)*
Leigh Ann Shoji-Lee *(Sr VP-Field Ops)*
Jim Nelson *(Mgr-Mktg)*
Patrick Mathot *(Product Mgr)*
Brands & Products:
BC HYDRO
FOR GENERATIONS
POWERSMART
Advertising Agencies:
DDB Vancouver
1600-777 Hornby St
Vancouver, BC V6Z 2T3, Canada
Tel.: (604) 687-7911
Fax: (604) 640-4343

OMD Canada
67 Richmond St W 2nd Fl
Toronto, ON M5H 1Z5, Canada
Tel.: (416) 681-5600
Fax: (416) 681-5620
Media Buying

Tribal DDB Vancouver
1600-777 Hornby St
Vancouver, BC V6Z 2T3, Canada
Tel.: (604) 608-4451
Fax: (604) 640-4343

BCE INC.

(d/b/a Bell Canada Enterprises)
1 Carrefour Alexander Graham Bell
Building A 6th Floor
Verdun, QC H3E 3B3, Canada
Tel.: (514) 870-8777
Tel.: (514) 870-4619
Fax: (514) 786-3970
Toll Free: (888) 339-6353
Toll Free: (888) 932-6666
E-mail: investor.relations@bce.ca
Web Site: www.bce.ca
E-Mail For Key Personnel:
Public Relations: investor.relations@bce.ca
Approx. Rev.: $18,069,000,000
Approx. Number Employees: 50,200
Year Founded: 1880
Business Description:
Telecommunication Services
S.I.C.: 4899; 4812; 4813
N.A.I.C.S.: 517910; 517110; 517212
Export
Media: 22
Personnel:
Thomas Charles O'Neill *(Chm)*
George A. Cope *(Pres & CEO)*
Siim A. Vanaselja *(CFO & Exec VP)*
Michael Cole *(CIO & Exec VP)*
Stephen Howe *(CTO & Exec VP)*
Martine Turcotte *(Chief Legal Officer & Exec VP)*
Stephane Boisvert *(Pres-Bell Bus Markets)*
Charles Brown *(Pres-The Source)*
Ron Close *(Pres-Bell New Ventures)*
Kevin W. Crull *(Pres-Residential Svcs)*
Wade Oosterman *(Chief Brand Officer & Pres-Bell Mobility-Channels)*
John Sweeney *(Pres-Wholeslae)*
William J. Fox *(Exec VP-Comm & Dev)*
Scott L. Thomson *(Exec VP-Corp Dev & Plng)*
Mary Anne Turcke *(Exec VP-Field Svcs)*
David Wells *(Exec VP-Corp Svcs)*
Karyn A. Brooks *(Sr VP & Controller)*
Alain Bilodeau *(Sr VP)*
Bernard le Duc *(Sr VP-Investor Rels,FIN)*
Wayne L. Tunney *(Sr VP)*
Stephan Argent *(VP-Digital Media)*
Thane Fotopoulos *(Sr Dir-IR)*
Brands & Products:
BCE
BCE MOBILE
BCE NEXXIA
BELL EXPRESSVU
BELL MOBILITY
BELL SYMPATICO
MAKING IT SIMPLE
Advertising Agency:
Zulu Alpha Kilo
512 King St E
Toronto, ON Canada M5A 1M1
Tel.: (416) 777-9858

BEACON POWER CORPORATION

65 Middlesex Rd
Tyngsboro, MA 01879
Tel.: (978) 694-9121
Fax: (978) 694-9127
Toll Free: (888) 938-9112
E-mail: beacon@beaconpower.com
Web Site: www.beaconpower.com
Approx. Rev.: $895,703
Approx. Number Employees: 73
Year Founded: 1997
Business Description:
Flywheel Energy Storage Systems Developer
S.I.C.: 4939; 3612
N.A.I.C.S.: 221111; 335311
Advertising Expenditures: $7,000
Personnel:
Virgil G. Rose *(Chm)*
F. William Capp *(Pres & CEO)*
James M. Spiezio *(CFO & VP-Fin)*
Brands & Products:
BEACON POWER
RIM TECHNOLOGY
SMART ENERGY MATRIX
SMART POWER
Advertising Agency:
The Investor Relations Group, Inc.
11 Stone St
New York, NY 10004
Tel.: (212) 825-3210
Fax: (212) 825-3229

BELL CANADA

(Sub. of Bell Canada International, Inc.)
1 Carrefour Alexander Graham Bell
Building A 4th Fl
Verdun, QC H3E 3B3, Canada
Tel.: (514) 391-5263
Fax: (514) 766-5735
Toll Free: (888) 932-6666
E-mail: bcecomms@bce.ca
Web Site: www.bce.ca/en/contact/
Year Founded: 1880
Business Description:
Telecommunications Services; Voice, Data & Image Transmissions
S.I.C.: 4813
N.A.I.C.S.: 517110
Media: 2-7-17
Distr.: Intl.
Personnel:
Thomas Little *(Pres)*
Siim A. Vanaselja *(CFO & Exec VP)*
Wade Oosterman *(Chief Brand Officer & Pres-Bell Mobility & BDI)*
Leo W. Houle *(Chief Talent Officer)*
Martine Turcotte *(Chief Legal & Regulatory Officer & Exec VP)*
Heather Tulk *(Sr VP-Mktg & Sls)*
Rajat Chopra *(Assoc Dir-Brand & Strategy-Interactive Mktg)*
Advertising Agency:
Grip Ltd.
179 John St 6th Fl
Toronto, ON M5T 1X4, Canada
Tel.: (416) 340-7111
Fax: (416) 340-7776

THE BERRY COMPANY LLC

(Sub. of Local Insight Media, LP)
3170 Kettering Blvd
Dayton, OH 45439-1924
Mailing Address:
PO Box 6000
Dayton, OH 45401-6000
Tel.: (937) 296-2121
Fax: (937) 296-4945
Web Site:
www.berrymeansbusiness.com
Sales Range: $150-199.9 Million
Approx. Number Employees: 600
Year Founded: 1910
Business Description:
Telephone Directory Advertising
S.I.C.: 7311; 2741
N.A.I.C.S.: 541810; 511199
Media: 2-8
Personnel:
Dan Graham *(Chief Admin Officer)*

BOOST MOBILE, LLC

(Sub. of Sprint Nextel Corp.)
8845 Irvine Center Dr Ste 200
Irvine, CA 92618
Tel.: (949) 748-3200
Fax: (949) 789-4888
E-mail: sales@boostmobile.com
Web Site: www.boostmobile.com
E-Mail For Key Personnel:
Sales Director: sales@boostmobile.com
Sales Range: $25-49.9 Million
Approx. Number Employees: 145
Business Description:
Communication Products & Services
S.I.C.: 4812
N.A.I.C.S.: 517212
Media: 6-10-13-17-22-23-24-31
Personnel:
Carlene Robinson *(Dir-Brand Mktg & Entertainment)*
Chris Jones *(Sr Brand Mgr)*
Brands & Products:
BOOST
RE-BOOST
Advertising Agencies:
180 Los Angeles
1733 Ocean Ave 4th fl
Santa Monica, CA 90401
Tel.: (310) 382-1400
Fax: (310) 382-1401
Marketing Agency of Record
— Matthew Elhardt *(Creative Dir-Boost Mobile & Sony)*

Attik
85 2nd St 6th Fl
San Francisco, CA 94105
Tel.: (415) 284-2600
Fax: (415) 284-2650

iNSPIRE!
3625 N Hall St Ste 1100
Dallas, TX 75219
Tel.: (214) 521-7373
Fax: (214) 252-1722
Hispanic Advertising
Sin Abusos Campaign

Mindshare
498 7th Ave
New York, NY 10018
Tel.: (212) 297-7000
Fax: (212) 297-7001
Media

The Vidal Partnership
228 E 45th St 11th Fl
New York, NY 10017-3303
Tel.: (646) 356-6600
Fax: (212) 661-7650

CALPINE CORPORATION

717 Texas Ave Ste 1000
Houston, TX 77002
Tel.: (713) 830-2000
Fax: (713) 830-2001
Toll Free: (800) 359-5115
E-mail: Public-Relations@calpine.com
Web Site: www.calpine.com
Approx. Rev.: $6,545,000,000
Approx. Number Employees: 2,142
Year Founded: 1984

Key to Media (For complete agency information see *The Advertising Red Books-Agencies* edition):
1. Bus. Publs. 2. Cable T.V. 3. Catalogs & Directories. 4. Co-op Adv. 5. Consumer Mags. 6. D.M. to Bus. Estab.7. D.M. to Consumers
8. Daily Newsp. 9. Exhibits/Trade Shows 10. Foreign 11. Infomercial 12. Internet Adv.13. Multimedia 14. Network Radio
15. Network T.V. 16. Newsp. Distr. Mags. 17. Other 18. Outdoor (Posters, Transit) 19. Point of Purchase20. Premiums, Novelties
21. Product Samples 22. Special Events Mktg. 23. Spot Radio 24. Spot T.V. 25. Weekly Newsp. 26. Yellow Page Adv.

Calpine Corporation — (Continued)

Business Description:
Owns, Leases & Operates Integrated Systems of Fuel-Efficient Natural Gas-Fired & Renewable Geothermal Power Plants
S.I.C.: 4931; 4939
N.A.I.C.S.: 221119; 221111
Media: 7-8
Personnel:
J. Stuart Ryan *(Chm)*
Jack A. Fusco *(Pres & CEO)*
Zamir Rauf *(CFO)*
Dennis Fishback *(CIO & Sr VP)*
W. Thaddeus Miller *(Chief Legal Officer, Sec & Exec VP)*
Kevin G. McMahon *(Chief Compliance Officer & Sr VP-Internal Audit)*
Kenneth A. Graves *(VP & Controller & Interim Chief Acctg Officer)*
Gary M. Germeroth *(Chief Risk Officer & Exec VP)*
Jim D. Deidiker *(Chief Acctg Officer & Sr VP)*
Stephen J. Muscato *(Sr VP-Comml Ops)*
Sarah Novosel *(Sr VP-Govt Affairs)*
Joseph E. Ronan, Jr. *(Sr VP-Govt & Regulatory Affairs)*
Norma F. Dunn *(VP-Corp Comm)*
Craig Martin *(Dir)*
Christine Parker *(Dir-IR)*
Gevan Reeves *(Dir-Western)*
Brands & Products:
CALPINE
REPOWERING AMERICA

CAMERON COMMUNICATION LLC
153 W Dave Dugas Rd
Sulphur, LA 70665
Tel.: (337) 583-2111
Fax: (337) 583-2026
E-mail: info@camtel.com
Web Site: www.camtel.com
Approx. Number Employees: 200
Year Founded: 1928
Business Description:
Telephone Communication, Except Radio
S.I.C.: 4813
N.A.I.C.S.: 517310
Personnel:
William L. Henning, Sr. *(Chm)*
Advertising Agency:
The O'Carroll Group
300 E McNeese Ste 2B
Lake Charles, LA 70605
Tel.: (337) 478-7396
Fax: (337) 478-0503

CASS COUNTY ELECTRIC COOPERATIVE, INC.
491 Elm St
Kindred, ND 58051-4001
Tel.: (701) 277-4400
Fax: (701) 356-4500
Web Site: www.kwh.com
Sales Range: $75-99.9 Million
Approx. Number Employees: 95
Year Founded: 1937
Business Description:
Electric Services
S.I.C.: 4939; 4911
N.A.I.C.S.: 221122
Import Export
Personnel:
Scott Handy *(Pres & CEO)*
Chad Sapa *(CFO & VP-Corp Svcs)*
Tim Sanden *(CIO & VP-IT)*
Brad Schmidt *(Sr VP-Transmission & Distr Svcs)*
Advertising Agency:
Odney
1400 W Century Ave
Bismarck, ND 58503
Tel.: (701) 222-8721
Fax: (701) 222-8172
Toll Free: (888) 500-8721

CELL-TEL GOVERNMENT SYSTEMS, INC.
8226 Phillips Hwy Ste 290
Jacksonville, FL 32256
Tel.: (904) 363-1111
Fax: (904) 363-0032
Toll Free: (800) 737-7545
E-mail: mstarling@cell-tel.com
Web Site: www.cell-tel.com
E-Mail For Key Personnel:
President: ewilson@cell-tel.com
Approx. Number Employees: 18
Year Founded: 1990
Business Description:
After Market Cellular Systems & Equipment
S.I.C.: 5731
N.A.I.C.S.: 443112
Export
Media: 1
Distr.: Intl.; Natl.
Budget Set: Oct.
Personnel:
Elizabeth A. Wilson *(Founder & Pres)*

CELLCO PARTNERSHIP
(Joint Venture of Verizon Communications Inc. & Vodafone Group Plc)
(d/b/a Verizon Wireless)
1 Verizon Way
Basking Ridge, NJ 07920
Tel.: (908) 306-7000
Web Site: www.verizonwireless.com
Sales Range: $25-49.9 Billion
Approx. Number Employees: 83,100
Year Founded: 1984
Business Description:
Holding Company; Wireless Voice & Data Services; Owned 55% by Verizon Communications Inc. & by 45% by Vodafone Group Plc
S.I.C.: 6719; 4812
N.A.I.C.S.: 551112; 517212
Media: 2-3-4-5-6-7-8-9-10-12-13-15-16-17-18-19-23-24-25-26-31
Personnel:
Daniel S. Mead *(Pres & CEO)*
John Townsend *(CFO & VP)*
Ajay Waghray *(CIO)*
Mike Lanman *(CMO & VP)*
Steven E. Zipperstein *(Gen Counsel, Sec & VP-Legal & External Affairs)*
John Harrobin *(Sr VP-Digital Media & Mktg)*
Martha Delehanty *(VP-HR)*
Charlie Falco *(VP-Customer Svc Ops)*
James J. Gerace *(VP-Corp Comm)*
Mark Harris *(VP-Natl Govt Sls & Ops)*
Rose M. Kirk *(VP-Natl Enterprise Sls & Dist)*
Suzy Deering *(Exec Dir-Corp Mktg)*
Advertising Agency:
Erwin-Penland
(Owned by Hill, Holliday, Connors, Cosmopulos, Inc., Member of the Interpublic Group)
125 E Broad St
Greenville, SC 29601
Tel.: (864) 271-0500
Fax: (864) 235-5941

CENTRAL HUDSON GAS & ELECTRIC CORPORATION
(Sub. of CH Energy Group, Inc.)
284 South Ave
Poughkeepsie, NY 12601
Tel.: (845) 452-2700
Fax: (845) 486-5544
Toll Free: (800) 527-2714
Web Site: www.centralhudson.com
Approx. Rev.: $719,934,000
Approx. Number Employees: 856
Year Founded: 1926
Business Description:
Public Electric & Gas Utility
S.I.C.: 1731; 4911; 4924; 4931; 4939
N.A.I.C.S.: 238210; 221119; 221122; 221210
Advertising Expenditures: $11,115,000
Personnel:
Steven V. Lant *(Chm, Pres & CEO)*
Christopher M. Capone *(CFO & Exec VP)*
John E. Gould *(Gen Counsel & Exec VP)*
Denise D. VanBuren *(Corp Sec & VP-Corp Comm)*
James P. Laurito *(Exec VP)*
Charles A. Freni *(Sr VP-Customer Svc & Dir)*
Thomas C. Brocks *(VP-HR)*
Paul E. Haering *(VP-Engrg & Environ Affairs)*
John P. Glusko *(Dir-Govt Affairs & Economic Dev)*
Paul Tesoro *(Dir-Corp Comm)*
Brian N. Dimisko *(Mgr-Customer Acct Svcs)*
Brands & Products:
CENTRAL HUDSON

CENTRAL ILLINOIS COMPANY
(Name Changed to Ameren Illinois Company)

CENTRAL MAINE POWER COMPANY
(Sub. of Iberdrola USA, Inc.)
83 Edison Dr
Augusta, ME 04336
Tel.: (207) 623-3521
Fax: (207) 623-5908
Toll Free: (800) 565-0121
E-mail: corpcomm@cmpco.com
Web Site: www.cmpco.com
Approx. Number Employees: 1,400
Year Founded: 1899
Business Description:
Electric Utility
S.I.C.: 4939; 4911; 4931
N.A.I.C.S.: 221122; 221119; 221121
Import Export
Advertising Expenditures: $2,500,000
Media: 2-3-5-6-7-8-9-10-16-17-19-22-23-24-25
Distr.: Direct to Consumer; Reg.
Budget Set: Aug.
Personnel:
Sara J. Burns *(Pres & CEO)*

CENTURYLINK, INC.
(Formerly CenturyTel, Inc.)
100 CenturyLink Dr
Monroe, LA 71203
Mailing Address:
PO Box 4065
Monroe, LA 71211-4065
Tel.: (318) 388-9000
Fax: (318) 388-9064
Toll Free: (800) 831-1733
Web Site: www.centurylink.com
E-Mail For Key Personnel:
Public Relations: pcameron@CenturyTel.com
Approx. Rev.: $7,041,534,000
Approx. Number Employees: 20,300
Year Founded: 1946
Business Description:
Telecommunications Services
S.I.C.: 4813; 4899
N.A.I.C.S.: 517110; 517910
Advertising Expenditures: $2,000,000
Media: 2-3-5-7-8-9-18-19-22-23-24-25-26
Distr.: Natl.; Reg.
Personnel:
Harvey P. Perry *(Vice Chm)*
Glen F. Post, III *(Pres & CEO)*
R. Stewart Ewing, Jr. *(CFO, Exec VP & Asst Sec)*
Karen A. Puckett *(COO & Exec VP)*
John Knies *(Chief Info Security Officer)*
William E. Cheek *(Pres-Wholesale Ops)*
Stacey W. Goff *(Gen Counsel, Sec & Exec VP)*
Dennis G. Huber *(Exec VP-Network Svcs)*
David D. Cole *(Sr VP-Ops Support & Controller)*
Advertising Agency:
Butler/Till Media Services, Inc.
2349 Monroe Ave
Rochester, NY 14618
Tel.: (585) 473-3740
Fax: (585) 473-3862
Media Agency of Record

CENTURYTEL, INC.
(Name Changed to CenturyLink, Inc.)

CHANNELL COMMERCIAL CORP.
26040 Ynez Rd
Temecula, CA 92591-6033
Mailing Address:
PO Box 9022
Temecula, CA 92589-9022
Tel.: (951) 719-2600
Fax: (951) 296-2322
Toll Free: (800) 423-1863
E-mail: uscustsrv@channellcorp.com
Web Site: www.channellcomm.com
Sales Range: $125-149.9 Million
Approx. Number Employees: 618
Year Founded: 1922
Business Description:
Telecommunications Equipment Designer & Mfr & Thermoplastic Enclosures Mfr
S.I.C.: 3669; 3089; 3661
N.A.I.C.S.: 334290; 326199; 334210
Export
Advertising Expenditures: $596,000
Personnel:
Jacqueline M. Channell *(Interim Chm & Sec)*

Key to Media (For complete agency information see *The Advertising Red Books-Agencies* edition):
1. Bus. Publs. 2. Cable T.V. 3. Catalogs & Directories. 4. Co-op Adv. 5. Consumer Mags. 6. D.M. to Bus. Estab.7. D.M. to Consumers
8. Daily Newsp. 9. Exhibits/Trade Shows 10. Foreign 11. Infomercial 12. Internet Adv.13. Multimedia 14. Network Radio
15. Network T.V. 16. Newsp. Distr. Mags. 17. Other 18. Outdoor (Posters, Transit) 19. Point of Purchase20. Premiums, Novelties
21. Product Samples 22. Special Events Mktg. 23. Spot Radio 24. Spot T.V. 25. Weekly Newsp. 26. Yellow Page Adv.

Guy Marge *(Pres)*
William H. Channell, Jr. *(CEO)*
Edward J. Burke *(CTO & VP-Corp Engrg)*

Brands & Products:
ADSL
AEMR
BET
BMST
BMT
BPH
BROADBAND TUBING
CHANNELL
CIT
CON
CPT
DSL
ECONOMY HEAT-SHRINKABLE END CAPS
FIBERMARK 1
FTTP
GLB
HDC
HEAT-SHRINKABLE CABLE BREAKOUTS
HEAT-SHRINKABLE CABLE SEALING GLANDS
HEAT-SHRINKABLE END CAPS
HEAT-SHRINKABLE SLEEVES
HEAT-SHRINKABLE WRAPAROUND CLOSURES
HEAT-SHRINKABLE WRAPAROUND REPAIR KITS
MAH
MINI-ROCKER
MRA
MRB
MRF
MRT
MWT
OFK
OJK
PWT
RHINO

CHESAPEAKE UTILITIES CORPORATION

909 Silver Lake Blvd
Dover, DE 19904-2409
Mailing Address:
PO Box 615
Dover, DE 19903-0615
Tel.: (302) 734-6799
Fax: (302) 734-6750
Toll Free: (888) 742-5275
Web Site: www.chpk.com
Approx. Rev.: $427,546,000
Approx. Number Employees: 734
Year Founded: 1859
Business Description:
Propane & Natural Gas Distr
S.I.C.: 4924; 5984
N.A.I.C.S.: 221210; 454312
Media: 2-17
Personnel:
Ralph J. Adkins *(Chm)*
John R. Schimkaitis *(Vice Chm)*
Michael P. McMasters *(Pres & COO)*
Beth W. Cooper *(CFO, Treas, Sec & Sr VP)*
Stephen C. Thompson *(Sr VP & Pres-Eastern Shore Natural Gas)*
Matthew Kim *(Asst VP)*

CINCINNATI BELL INC.

221 E 4th St Ste 700
Cincinnati, OH 45202-4137
Mailing Address:
PO Box 2301
Cincinnati, OH 45201-2301
Tel.: (513) 397-9900
Fax: (513) 397-5092
Web Site: www.cincinnatibell.com
Approx. Rev.: $1,377,000,000
Approx. Number Employees: 3,000
Year Founded: 1873
Business Description:
Local Phone Service & Regional Wireless Voice & Data Communications
S.I.C.: 4813; 4812
N.A.I.C.S.: 517110; 517212
Advertising Expenditures: $22,800,000
Media: 9-15-18-23-25
Distr.: Reg.
Personnel:
Phillip R. Cox *(Chm)*
John F. Cassidy *(Pres & CEO)*
Gary J. Wojtaszek *(CFO)*
Tara L. Khoury *(CMO & Sr VP)*
Theodore H. Torbeck *(Pres/Gen Mgr-Cincinnati Bell Comm Group)*
Christopher J. Wilson *(Gen Counsel & VP)*
Dennis P. Hinkel *(VP & Gen Mgr)*
Brian G. Keating *(VP-HR & Admin)*
Brands & Products:
CINCINNATI BELL
Advertising Agency:
Northlich
Sawyer Point Bldg 720 Pete Rose Way
Cincinnati, OH 45202
Tel.: (513) 421-8840
Fax: (513) 455-4749
(Consumer Market)

CITIZENS ENERGY GROUP

2020 N Meridian St
Indianapolis, IN 46202
Tel.: (317) 924-3341
Fax: (317) 713-0056
E-mail: customercare@cgcu.com
Web Site: www.citizensgas.com
Approx. Number Employees: 1,150
Year Founded: 1935
Business Description:
Gas Distribution Company; Foundry Coke & Blast Furnace Coke Mfr
S.I.C.: 4924; 2999
N.A.I.C.S.: 221210; 324199
Media: 1-2-5-6-8-9-10-18-19-20-23-24-25-26
Distr.: Reg. (Gas)
Budget Set: Oct.
Personnel:
Carey B. Lykins *(Pres & CEO)*
John Brehm *(CFO & Sr VP)*
M. Jean Richcreek *(Chief Admin Officer & Sr VP)*
William A. Tracy *(Sr VP-Ops)*
John R. Whitaker *(Sr VP-Corp & Legal Affairs)*
Robert Hummel *(VP-HR)*
Jeff S. Brown *(Dir-Sls & Mktg)*
Advertising Agency:
Bandy Carroll Hellige Advertising
307 W Muhammad Ali Blvd
Louisville, KY 40202
Tel.: (502) 589-7711
Fax: (502) 589-0390

CLECO CORPORATION

2030 Donahue Ferry Rd
Pineville, LA 71360
Mailing Address:
PO Box 5000
Pineville, LA 71361-5000
Tel.: (318) 484-7400
Toll Free: (800) 622-6537
E-mail: info@cleco.com
Web Site: www.cleco.com
Approx. Rev.: $1,158,262,000
Approx. Number Employees: 1,277
Year Founded: 1934
Business Description:
Electric Power & Energy Services
S.I.C.: 4911; 4924; 4931; 4939
N.A.I.C.S.: 221122; 221119; 221121; 221210
Media: 2-3-7-8-9-10-13-18-19-20-23-24-25
Distr.: Direct to Consumer; Reg.
Budget Set: Sept.
Personnel:
J. Patrick Garrett *(Chm)*
Michael H. Madison *(Pres & CEO)*
Darren J. Olagues *(CFO & Sr VP)*
R. Russell Davis *(Chief Acctg Officer & VP-IR)*
George W. Bausewine *(Pres/COO-Cleco Power)*
Wade A. Hoefling *(Gen Counsel, Sr VP, Asst Sec & Dir-Regulatory Compliance)*
Jeffrey W. Hall *(Sr VP-Govt Affairs & Chief Diversity Officer)*
Keith D. Crump *(Grp VP)*
Susan Broussard *(Mgr-Corp Comm)*
Terry L. Taylor *(Asst Controller)*
Advertising Agencies:
Dresner Corporate Services
20 N Clark St Ste 3550
Chicago, IL 60602
Tel.: (312) 780-7211
Fax: (312) 726-7448
Toll Free: (800) 373-7637

Morgan + Company
3527 Canal St
New Orleans, LA 70119
Tel.: (504) 523-7734
Fax: (504) 523-7737

CMS ENERGY CORPORATION

One Energy Plaza
Jackson, MI 49201
Tel.: (517) 788-0550
Fax: (517) 788-1859
E-mail: info@cmsenergy.com
Web Site: www.cmsenergy.com
Approx. Rev.: $6,432,000,000
Approx. Number Employees: 7,822
Year Founded: 1886
Business Description:
Holding Company; Owner of Energy Companies
S.I.C.: 4931; 4924; 4939; 6712
N.A.I.C.S.: 221119; 221112; 221210; 551111
Media: 1-2-3-7-8-9-10-20-23-24-25
Distr.: Reg.
Budget Set: Aug.
Personnel:
David W. Joos *(Chm, Co-Pres & CEO)*
John G. Russell *(Pres & CEO)*
Thomas J. Webb *(CFO & Exec VP)*
Mamatha Chamarthi *(CIO & VP)*
Joseph P. Tomasik *(Chief Dev Officer & VP)*
David G. Mengebier *(Chief Compliance Officer & Sr VP)*
Michael Shore *(VP & Chief Risk Officer)*
Glenn P. Barba *(Chief Acctg Officer, VP & Controller)*
James E. Brunner *(Gen Counsel & Sr VP)*
John M. Butler *(Sr VP)*
William E. Garrity *(Sr VP-Consumers Energy Company)*
Frank Johnson *(Sr VP-Consumers Energy Company)*
Paul N. Preketes *(Sr VP-Energy Delivery)*
Advertising Agency:
Kolt Communications, Inc.
2104 Jolly Rd Ste 200
Okemos, MI 48864
Tel.: (517) 706-0001

COLUMBIA GAS OF MARYLAND, INC.

(Sub. of NiSource Inc.)
501 Technology Dr
Canonsburg, PA 15317-9585
Tel.: (724) 416-6300
Fax: (724) 461-6380
Toll Free: (888) 460-4332
Web Site: www.columbiagasmd.com
Sales Range: $25-49.9 Million
Approx. Number Employees: 80
Business Description:
Gas Utility
S.I.C.: 4924; 1711
N.A.I.C.S.: 221210; 238220
Personnel:
M. Carol Fox *(Pres)*
Thomas E. Cuddy *(Dir-Comm & Community Rels)*
Advertising Agency:
Elias Savion Advertising, Public Relations & Interactive
Dominion Tower 24th Fl
Pittsburgh, PA 15206
Tel.: (412) 642-7700
Fax: (412) 642-2277

COLUMBIA GAS OF OHIO, INC.

(Sub. of NiSource Inc.)
200 Civic Ctr Dr
Columbus, OH 43215
Tel.: (614) 460-6000
Fax: (614) 460-6986
Web Site: www.columbiagasohio.com
Sales Range: $1-4.9 Billion
Approx. Number Employees: 900
Business Description:
Gas Utility Services
S.I.C.: 4924
N.A.I.C.S.: 221210
Advertising Expenditures: $300,000
Bus. Publs.: $120,000; D.M. to Bus. Estab.: $30,000; D.M. to Consumers: $30,000; Daily Newsp.: $60,000; Exhibits/Trade Shows: $60,000
Personnel:
Jack Partridge *(Pres)*
Jack Laverty *(Mgr-Demand Side Mgmt (DSM))*
Advertising Agency:
Hart Associates, Inc.
1915 Indian Wood Cir
Maumee, OH 43537-4002
Tel.: (419) 893-9600
Fax: (419) 893-9070

Key to Media (For complete agency information see *The Advertising Red Books-Agencies* edition):
1. Bus. Publs. 2. Cable T.V. 3. Catalogs & Directories. 4. Co-op Adv. 5. Consumer Mags. 6. D.M. to Bus. Estab.7. D.M. to Consumers
8. Daily Newsp. 9. Exhibits/Trade Shows 10. Foreign 11. Infomercial 12. Internet Adv.13. Multimedia 14. Network Radio
15. Network T.V. 16. Newsp. Distr. Mags. 17. Other 18. Outdoor (Posters, Transit) 19. Point of Purchase20. Premiums, Novelties
21. Product Samples 22. Special Events Mktg. 23. Spot Radio 24. Spot T.V. 25. Weekly Newsp. 26. Yellow Page Adv.

COLUMBIA GAS OF PENNSYLVANIA, INC.
(Sub. of NiSource Inc.)
501 Technology Dr
Canonsburg, PA 15317-9585
Tel.: (724) 416-6300
Fax: (412) 572-7162
Toll Free: (888) 460-4332
Web Site:
www.columbiagaspamd.com
Sales Range: $750-799.9 Million
Approx. Number Employees: 983
Business Description:
Gas Utility
S.I.C.: 4924
N.A.I.C.S.: 221210
Personnel:
M. Carol Fox *(Pres)*
Mark Kempic *(Dir-Rates & Regulatory Policy)*
Mike Marcus *(Mgr-Comm & Community Affairs)*
Advertising Agency:
Elias Savion Advertising, Public Relations & Interactive
Dominion Tower 24th Fl
Pittsburgh, PA 15206
Tel.: (412) 642-7700
Fax: (412) 642-2277

COMMERCE ENERGY, INC.
(Sub. of Universal Energy Group Ltd.)
575 Anton Blvd Ste 650
Costa Mesa, CA 92626
Tel.: (714) 259-2500
Fax: (714) 259-2501
Toll Free: (800) 962-4655
E-mail: contactus@commerceenergy.com
Web Site: www.commerceenergy.com
Approx. Rev.: $459,801,000
Approx. Number Employees: 200
Year Founded: 1997
Business Description:
Electric & Natural Gas Marketing Services
S.I.C.: 1311; 4911; 4939
N.A.I.C.S.: 211111; 221111; 221122
Import Export
Advertising Expenditures: $1,153,000
Media: 2-4-7-8-18
Personnel:
C. Douglas Mitchell *(CFO & Sec)*
Brands & Products:
1-800-ELECTRIC
COMMERCE ENERGY
ELECTRIC AMERICA
GREEN SMART
SURE CHOICE

COMMONWEALTH TELEPHONE ENTERPRISES, INC.
(Sub. of Frontier Communications Corporation)
(d/b/a Frontier Communications)
100 CTE Dr
Dallas, PA 18612-9745
Tel.: (570) 631-2700
Fax: (570) 675-6058
Toll Free: (866) 931-5256
E-mail: info@frontieronline.com
Web Site: www.frontieronline.com
Sales Range: $300-349.9 Million
Approx. Number Employees: 1,110
Year Founded: 1897
Business Description:
Communications, Information & Entertainment Services
S.I.C.: 4813
N.A.I.C.S.: 517110; 517310
Advertising Expenditures: $3,080,000
Media: 25-26
Personnel:
Patricia Amendola *(Reg Mgr-Comm & PR)*
Stephanie Beasly *(Mgr-Comm)*
Karen C. Miller *(Mgr-Comm)*
Brands & Products:
EPIX
JACK FLASH

THE CONNECTICUT LIGHT AND POWER COMPANY
(Sub. of NORTHEAST UTILITIES)
107 Selden St
Berlin, CT 06037
Mailing Address:
PO Box 270
Hartford, CT 06141-0270
Tel.: (860) 665-5000
Tel.: (860) 947-2000
Fax: (860) 665-5457
Toll Free: (800) 286-5000
E-mail: clpwebmaster@nu.com
Web Site: www.cl-p.com
Approx. Rev.: $2,999,102,000
Approx. Number Employees: 1,847
Year Founded: 1917
Business Description:
Electric Power Distribution & Generation Services
S.I.C.: 4911; 4931; 4939
N.A.I.C.S.: 221122; 221119; 221121
Advertising Expenditures: $2,000,000
Media: 2-8-9-10-23-24-25
Distr.: Direct to Consumer; Reg.
Budget Set: Oct.
Personnel:
Charles W. Shivery *(Chm)*
Jeff Butler *(Pres & COO)*
Leon J. Olivier *(CEO)*
David R. McHale *(CFO & Exec VP)*

CONNECTICUT WATER SERVICE, INC.
93 W Main St
Clinton, CT 06413
Tel.: (860) 669-8630
Fax: (860) 669-5579
Toll Free: (800) 286-5700 (Customer Service)
E-mail: info@ctwater.com
Web Site: www.ctwater.com
Approx. Rev.: $66,408,000
Approx. Number Employees: 204
Year Founded: 1956
Business Description:
Holding Company; Water Supplier
S.I.C.: 4941; 6719
N.A.I.C.S.: 221310; 551112
Media: 8
Distr.: Reg.
Personnel:
Eric W. Thornburg *(Chm)*
David C. Benoit *(CFO, Treas & VP-Fin)*
Kristen A. Johnson *(Corp Sec & VP-HR)*
Peter J. Bancroft *(Dir-Rates-Forecasting & Asst Treas)*
Daniel J. Meaney *(Dir-Corp Comm)*
Brands & Products:
CONNECTICUT WATER
LINEBACKER

CONSOLIDATED COMMUNICATIONS, INC.
(Holding of Consolidated Communications Holdings, Inc.)
4008 Gibsonia Rd
Gibsonia, PA 15044-9311
Tel.: (724) 443-9600
Fax: (724) 443-9431
Web Site: www.consolidated.com/
Approx. Rev.: $103,465,000
Approx. Number Employees: 357
Year Founded: 1985
Business Description:
Telecommunication Services & Equipment
S.I.C.: 4813; 5065
N.A.I.C.S.: 517110; 423690; 517310
Import Export
Advertising Expenditures: $1,567,000
Media: 7-13-23

CONSOLIDATED COMMUNICATIONS OPERATOR SERVICES, INC.
(Holding of Consolidated Communications Holdings, Inc.)
121 S 17th St
Mattoon, IL 61938
Tel.: (217) 235-3311
Fax: (217) 234-2810
Web Site: www.penntele.com
Sales Range: $50-74.9 Million
Approx. Number Employees: 225
Year Founded: 1985
Business Description:
Alternate Operator Services & Directory Assistance
S.I.C.: 4813
N.A.I.C.S.: 517110; 517310
Media: 4-10-19-20-22-26
Personnel:
Rick Hall *(Exec VP)*

CONSOLIDATED EDISON, INC.
(d/b/a Con Ed)
4 Irving Pl
New York, NY 10003-3502
Tel.: (212) 460-4600
Fax: (212) 982-7816
E-mail: corpcom@coned.com
Web Site: www.conedison.com
Approx. Rev.: $13,325,000,000
Approx. Number Employees: 15,180
Year Founded: 1998
Business Description:
Energy Holding Company
S.I.C.: 4939; 4911; 4931; 6719
N.A.I.C.S.: 221111; 221119; 221122; 551112
Media: 2-7-8-9-16-18-19-22-23-24-25
Distr.: Direct to Consumer; Reg.
Personnel:
Robert N. Hoglund *(CFO & Sr VP)*
Robert Muccilo *(Chief Acctg Officer, VP & Controller)*
Marilyn Caselli *(Sr VP)*
John F. Miksad *(Sr VP-Electric Ops)*
Luther Tai *(Sr VP-Enterprise Shared Svcs)*
Jan C. Childress *(Dir-IR)*
Henry Kolenovsky *(Coord-Mktg)*
Advertising Agency:
Rubenstein Associates, Inc.
1345 Ave of the Americas Fl 30
New York, NY 10105-0109
Tel.: (212) 843-8000
Fax: (212) 843-9200

CONSTELLATION ENERGY GROUP, INC.
100 Constellation Way
Baltimore, MD 21202
Tel.: (410) 470-2800
Fax: (410) 234-5220
E-mail: communications@constellation.com
Web Site: www.constellation.com
Approx. Rev.: $14,340,000,000
Approx. Number Employees: 7,600
Year Founded: 1817
Business Description:
Energy, Electricity & Natural Gas Distr
S.I.C.: 4911; 4924; 4931; 4939
N.A.I.C.S.: 221113; 221111; 221119; 221121; 221122; 221210
Media: 6-10-24
Personnel:
Mayo A. Shattuck, III *(Chm, Pres & CEO)*
Michael J. Wallace *(Vice Chm, COO & Exec VP)*
Jonathan W. Thayer *(CFO & Sr VP)*
Bruce J. Stewart *(CMO & Mng Dir-Retail Energy Bus)*
Charles A. Berardesco *(Chief Compliance Officer, Gen Counsel, Sec & Sr VP)*
Brenda L. Boultwood *(Chief Risk Officer & Sr VP)*
Mary L. Lauria *(Chief HR Officer & Sr VP)*
Bryan P. Wright *(Controller & Chief Acctg Officer)*
Henry B. Barron, Jr. *(Pres/CEO-Nuclear Grp, Chief Nuclear Officer & Exec VP)*
Kathleen W. Hyle *(COO-Constellation Energy Resources & Sr VP)*
James L. Connaughton *(Exec VP-Corp Affairs, Pub & Environ Policy)*
Paul J. Allen *(Chief Environmental Officer & Sr VP-Corp Affairs)*
Kenneth W. DeFontes *(Sr VP)*
Andrew L. Good *(Sr VP-Corp Strategy & Dev)*
Robert L. Gould *(VP-Corp Comm)*
Brands & Products:
BGE
CONSTELLATION ENERGY
Advertising Agency:
Alexander & Tom
3500 Boston St Ste 225
Baltimore, MD 21224-5275
Tel.: (410) 327-7400
Fax: (410) 327-7403

CONSUMERS ENERGY COMPANY
(Sub. of CMS Energy Corporation)
1 Energy Plz
Jackson, MI 49201
Tel.: (517) 788-0550
Fax: (517) 788-6911
Toll Free: (800) 477-5050
E-mail: info@cmsenergy.com
Web Site:
www.consumersenergy.com
Approx. Rev.: $6,156,000,000
Approx. Number Employees: 7,522
Year Founded: 1886
Business Description:
Electric & Natural Gas Distr & Generator
S.I.C.: 4939; 4924; 4931

Key to Media (For complete agency information see *The Advertising Red Books-Agencies* edition):
1. Bus. Publs. 2. Cable T.V. 3. Catalogs & Directories. 4. Co-op Adv. 5. Consumer Mags. 6. D.M. to Bus. Estab.7. D.M. to Consumers 8. Daily Newsp. 9. Exhibits/Trade Shows 10. Foreign 11. Infomercial 12. Internet Adv.13. Multimedia 14. Network Radio 15. Network T.V. 16. Newsp. Distr. Mags. 17. Other 18. Outdoor (Posters, Transit) 19. Point of Purchase20. Premiums, Novelties 21. Product Samples 22. Special Events Mktg. 23. Spot Radio 24. Spot T.V. 25. Weekly Newsp. 26. Yellow Page Adv.

N.A.I.C.S.: 221112; 221111; 221119; 221210
Media: 2-8-9-23-24-25
Distr.: Reg.
Budget Set: Aug.
Personnel:
John G. Russell *(Pres & CEO)*
Thomas J. Webb *(CFO & Exec VP)*
David G. Mengebier *(Chief Compliance Officer & Sr VP-Governmental & Pub Affairs)*
Glenn P. Barba *(Chief Acctg Officer, VP & Controller)*
James E. Brunner *(Gen Counsel & Sr VP)*
John M. Butler *(Sr VP)*
William E. Garrity *(Sr VP)*
Jackson L. Hanson *(Sr VP)*
Frank Johnson *(Sr VP)*
Daniel J. Malone *(Sr VP)*
Theodore J. Vogel *(Chief Tax Counsel & VP)*
Jeff Holyfield *(Exec Dir-Corp Comm)*
Pramada Reddy *(Exec Dir-Strategic Comm)*
Dan Bishop *(Dir-Pub Info)*
Valerie Guttowsky *(Mgr-Field Ops-Lakeshore Energy)*
Brands & Products:
HOUSECALL

CPS ENERGY
145 Navarro St
San Antonio, TX 78205
Tel.: (210) 353-2000
Fax: (210) 353-0000
Web Site: www.cpsenergy.com
Approx. Sls.: $1,266,502,000
Approx. Number Employees: 4,000
Business Description:
Electric & Natural Gas Utility
S.I.C.: 4931; 4924
N.A.I.C.S.: 221119; 221210
Media: 7-8-10-13-18-22-23-24-26
Personnel:
Charles E. Foster *(Chm)*
Derrick Howard *(Vice Chm)*
Doyle N. Beneby, Jr. *(Pres & CEO)*
Jelynne LeBlanc-Burley *(Chief Admin Officer & Exec VP)*
Carolyn E. Shellman *(Gen Counsel & Exec VP)*
Lawanda Parnell *(Sr Dir-Enterprise Application Delivery)*
Brands & Products:
AUTOPAY
CPS ENERGY
ENERGY CONNECTION
FIRST CONNECTIONS
WINDTRICITY
Advertising Agencies:
The Atkins Group
501 Soledad
San Antonio, TX 78205
Tel.: (210) 444-2500
Fax: (210) 824-8236

Taylor West Advertising
4040 Broadway St Ste 302
San Antonio, TX 78209-6353
Tel.: (210) 805-0320
Fax: (210) 805-9371

DAIRYLAND POWER COOPERATIVE
3200 E Ave S
La Crosse, WI 54601-0218
Tel.: (608) 788-4000
Fax: (608) 787-1420
E-mail: info@dairynet.com
Web Site: www.dairynet.com
Approx. Number Employees: 530
Year Founded: 1941
Business Description:
Generation & Transmission of Electrical Energy
S.I.C.: 4931
N.A.I.C.S.: 221119
Media: 2-4-5-10-23-24
Distr.: Reg.
Budget Set: Oct.
Personnel:
William L. Berg *(Pres & CEO)*
Phil Moilien *(CFO & VP)*
Mary Lund *(VP-HR)*

DAKOTA ELECTRIC ASSOCIATION
4300 220th St W
Farmington, MN 55024
Tel.: (651) 463-6212
Fax: (651) 463-6256
Toll Free: (800) 874-3409
E-mail: info@dakotaelectric.com
Web Site: www.dakotaelectric.com
E-Mail For Key Personnel:
Marketing Director: mfosse@dakotaelectric.com
Sales Director: mfosse@dakotaelectric.com
Sales Range: $125-149.9 Million
Approx. Number Employees: 220
Year Founded: 1937
Business Description:
Electric Services; Electric Distribution Cooperative
S.I.C.: 4911; 4939; 8611
N.A.I.C.S.: 221122; 813910
Media: 2-3-4-9-10-13-22
Distr.: Reg.
Personnel:
James F. Sheldon *(Chm)*
William F. Holton *(Vice Chm)*
Greg Miller *(Pres & CEO)*
Lou Weflen *(CFO)*
Randy Poulson *(VP-Engrng Svcs)*
Peggy Johnson *(Dir-Community Rels)*
Brands & Products:
DAKOTA ELECTRIC
POWER QUICK PLUS!
Advertising Agency:
JAM Advertising Inc.
7270 Forestview Ln N Ste 200
Maple Grove, MN 55369
Tel.: (763) 898-3794
Fax: (763) 898-3804

DELMARVA POWER
(Sub. of Calpine Corporation)
PO Box 6066
Newark, DE 19714
Mailing Address:
PO Box 6066
Newark, DE 19714-6066
Tel.: (302) 451-5564
Fax: (302) 451-5264
Web Site: www.delmarva.com
Approx. Rev.: $8,000,000
Approx. Number Employees: 115
Year Founded: 1998
Business Description:
Gas & Other Services Combined - Utility Company
S.I.C.: 4924; 4931
N.A.I.C.S.: 221210; 221119
Personnel:
Gary J. Morsches *(Pres & CEO)*
Art Agra *(CFO & Sr VP)*
Joseph M. Rigby *(CFO)*
Advertising Agency:
Tipton Communications
220 Continental Dr Ste 211
Newark, DE 19713
Tel.: (302) 454-7901
Fax: (302) 454-7903
Employee Communications

DOMINION EAST OHIO ENERGY
(Sub. of Dominion Resources, Inc.)
120 Tredegar St
Richmond, VA 23219
Tel.: (800) 362-7557
Fax: (216) 736-5115
Toll Free: (800) 990-4090
E-mail: customer_service@dom.com
Web Site: www.dom.com
Sales Range: $1-4.9 Billion
Approx. Number Employees: 1,700
Year Founded: 1898
Business Description:
Gas Utility
S.I.C.: 4924; 4922
N.A.I.C.S.: 221210; 486210
Media: 7-8-18
Distr.: Direct to Consumer; Reg.
Personnel:
Thomas F. Ferrell *(Chm, Pres & CEO)*
Mark F. McGettrick *(CFO & Exec VP)*
Brands & Products:
EAST OHIO DOMINION
EAST OHIO GAS
NATURAL

DOMINION PITTSBURGH POWER
(Sub. of Dominion Resources, Inc.)
625 Liberty Ave
Pittsburgh, PA 15222-3199
Tel.: (412) 224-2626
Fax: (412) 690-1136
Toll Free: (800) 764-0111
E-mail: customer_service@dom.com
Web Site: www.dom.com
Sales Range: $200-249.9 Million
Year Founded: 1942
Business Description:
Gas & Electric Transmission
S.I.C.: 4924
N.A.I.C.S.: 221210
Advertising Expenditures: $4,500,000
Media: 2-3-5-7-8-9-10-13-14-15-18-19-23-24-25-26
Distr.: Reg.
Budget Set: Oct.
Personnel:
Dan Donovan *(Mgr-Media Rels)*
Brands & Products:
CNG

DOMINION RESOURCES, INC.
120 Tredegar St
Richmond, VA 23219-4306
Mailing Address:
PO Box 26532
Richmond, VA 23261-6532
Tel.: (804) 819-2000
Fax: (804) 819-2233
E-mail: investor.relations@dom.com
Web Site: www.dom.com
Approx. Rev.: $15,197,000,000
Approx. Number Employees: 15,800
Year Founded: 1983
Business Description:
Electric Power, Natural Gas Transmission & Oil Development
S.I.C.: 4939; 4911; 4924; 4931
N.A.I.C.S.: 221122; 221119; 221121; 221210
Media: 2-3-6-7-8-10-13-14-15-18-23-24
Personnel:
Thomas F. Farrell, II *(Chm, Pres & CEO)*
Steven A. Rogers *(Pres & Chief Admin Officer-Dominion Resources Svcs)*
Mark F. McGettrick *(CFO & Exec VP)*
Margaret E. McDermid *(CIO & Sr VP)*
Carter M. Reid *(Chief Compliance Officer, Gen Counsel, Sec & VP)*
Pamela F. Faggert *(Chief Environmental Officer & VP)*
Paul D. Koonce *(CEO-Dominion Virginia Power)*
James L. Stutts *(Gen Counsel & Sr VP)*
G. Scott Hetzer *(Treas & Sr VP-Tax)*
Robert Blue *(Sr VP-Law, Pub Policy & Environment)*
Mary C. Doswell *(Sr VP-Alternative Energy Solutions)*
Diane G. Leopold *(Sr VP-Bus Dev & Generation Construction)*
Chet Wade *(Mng Dir-Corp Comm)*
William C. Hall, Jr. *(VP-External Affairs & Corp Comm)*
Hunter Applewhite *(Dir-Adv & PR)*
Mark Lazenby *(Dir-Exec Comm & Editorial Svcs)*
Jim Norvelle *(Dir-Media Rels)*
Patricia G. Shell *(Dir)*
David Botkins *(Mgr-Media Rels)*
Elmore Lockley *(Mgr-Media Rels)*
Lora Spiller *(Mgr-Adv)*
Advertising Agency:
Penn Schoen & Berland
1110 Vermont Ave NW Ste 1200
Washington, DC 20005
Tel.: (202) 842-0500
Fax: (202) 842-0511

DOMINION VIRGINIA POWER
(Sub. of Dominion Resources, Inc.)
120 Tredegar St
Richmond, VA 23219
Mailing Address:
PO Box 26666
Richmond, VA 23261
Tel.: (804) 771-3000
Toll Free: (888) 667-3000
Toll Free: (877) 244-0459
E-mail: customer_service@dom.com
Web Site: www.dom.com
Approx. Number Employees: 9,631
Year Founded: 1909
Business Description:
Electric Power Transmission Services
S.I.C.: 4931
N.A.I.C.S.: 221119
Media: 2-6-9-16-23-24-25-26
Distr.: Reg.
Budget Set: Nov.
Personnel:
Paul D. Koonce *(CEO-Dominion Virginia Power)*
David W. Green *(Sr VP-Customer Svc)*
Brands & Products:
COMFORT ASSURED
ENERGY SAVER HOME

Key to Media (For complete agency information see *The Advertising Red Books-Agencies* edition):
1. Bus. Publs. 2. Cable T.V. 3. Catalogs & Directories. 4. Co-op Adv. 5. Consumer Mags. 6. D.M. to Bus. Estab.7. D.M. to Consumers 8. Daily Newsp. 9. Exhibits/Trade Shows 10. Foreign 11. Infomercial 12. Internet Adv.13. Multimedia 14. Network Radio 15. Network T.V. 16. Newsp. Distr. Mags. 17. Other 18. Outdoor (Posters, Transit) 19. Point of Purchase20. Premiums, Novelties 21. Product Samples 22. Special Events Mktg. 23. Spot Radio 24. Spot T.V. 25. Weekly Newsp. 26. Yellow Page Adv.

Dominion Virginia Power — (Continued)

NORTH CAROLINA POWER
VIRGINIA POWER

Advertising Agency:
Siegel+Gale
625 Ave of the Americas 4th Fl
New York, NY 10011
Tel.: (212) 453-0400
Fax: (212) 453-0401

DPL INC.

1065 Woodman Dr
Dayton, OH 45432
Mailing Address:
PO Box 1247
Dayton, OH 45401-1247
Tel.: (937) 224-6000
Toll Free: (800) 322-9244
Web Site: www.dplinc.com
Approx. Rev.: $1,833,100,000
Approx. Number Employees: 1,321
Year Founded: 1985
Business Description:
Holding Company; Electric Power Generation; 25% Owned by Kohlberg Kravis Roberts & Co.
S.I.C.: 3355; 3356; 3357; 4911; 4924; 4931; 4939
N.A.I.C.S.: 331319; 221119; 221121; 221122; 221210; 331422; 331491; 335921; 335929
Media: 7-8-9
Distr.: Reg.
Budget Set: July
Personnel:
Glenn E. Harder *(Chm)*
Paul R. Bishop *(Vice Chm)*
Paul M. Barbas *(Pres & CEO)*
Frederick J. Boyle *(CFO & Sr VP)*
Daniel J. McCabe *(Chief Admin Officer & Sr VP)*
Joseph W. Mulpas *(Chief Acctg Officer, VP & Controller)*
Timothy G. Rice *(Sec, VP & Asst Gen Counsel)*
Arthur G. Meyer *(Gen Counsel & Sr VP)*
Gary G. Stephenson *(Exec VP-Ops)*
Scott J. Kelly *(Sr VP-Retail Ops & DPLER)*
Teresa F. Marrinan *(Sr VP-Bus Plng & Dev)*
Dennis A. Lantzy *(VP-Power Production)*
Tom Raga *(Dir-Govt Rels)*
Advertising Agency:
Fahlgren Mortine
4030 Easton Station Ste 300
Columbus, OH 43219
Tel.: (614) 383-1500
Fax: (614) 383-1501

DTE ENERGY COMPANY

1 Energy Plz
Detroit, MI 48226-1279
Tel.: (313) 235-4000
Fax: (313) 235-8055
Toll Free: (800) 551-5009
Web Site: www.dteenergy.com
Approx. Rev.: $8,557,000,000
Approx. Number Employees: 9,800
Year Founded: 1996
Business Description:
Holding Company; Electric & Gas Utilities Owner
S.I.C.: 4911; 4924; 4939; 6719
N.A.I.C.S.: 221113; 221111; 221122; 221210; 551112
Media: 2-9-14-15-18
Distr.: Reg.
Budget Set: Sept.
Personnel:
Gerard M. Anderson *(Chm, Pres & CEO)*
David E. Meador *(CFO & Exec VP)*
Lynne Ellyn *(CIO & Sr VP)*
David Ruud *(Exec VP & Pres-DTE Energy Svcs)*
Steven Mabry *(Pres-DTE Energy Trading)*
Richard L. Redmond *(Pres-DTE Gas & Oil)*
Bruce D. Peterson *(Gen Counsel & Sr VP)*
J. Chris Brown *(Exec VP-DTE Energy Resources)*
Jack Davis *(Chief Nuclear Officer & Sr VP)*
Joyce V. Hayes-Giles *(Sr VP-Customer Svc)*
Paul C. Hillegonds *(Sr VP-Corp Affairs)*
Advertising Agency:
BERLINE
70 E Long Lk Rd
Bloomfield Hills, MI 48304
Tel.: (248) 593-4744
Fax: (248) 593-4740

DUKE ENERGY INDIANA, INC.

(Sub. of Duke Energy Corporation)
1000 E Main St
Plainfield, IN 46168
Tel.: (317) 839-9611
Fax: (317) 838-2292
Toll Free: (800) 521-2232
Approx. Rev.: $2,520,000,000
Approx. Number Employees: 1,607
Year Founded: 1942
Business Description:
Electric Utility Services
S.I.C.: 4911; 4939
N.A.I.C.S.: 221122
Advertising Expenditures: $500,000
Media: 7-8-9-23-25
Distr.: Reg.
Budget Set: Aug.-Sept.
Personnel:
David L. Hauser *(CFO & Grp Exec)*
Marc E. Manly *(Chief Legal Officer, Corp Sec & Grp Exec)*
Doug Esamann *(Pres-Duke Energy Indiana)*
Steven K. Young *(Sr VP & Controller)*

DUKE ENERGY CORPORATION

526 S Church St
Charlotte, NC 28202-1904
Tel.: (704) 594-6200
Tel.: (704) 382-3853
Fax: (704) 382-3814
Toll Free: (800) USEDUKE
E-mail: ContactUs@duke-energy.com
Web Site: www.duke-energy.com
E-Mail For Key Personnel:
Public Relations: publicaffairs@duke-energy.com
Approx. Rev.: $14,272,000,000
Approx. Number Employees: 18,440
Year Founded: 1904
Business Description:
Power Plants & Natural Gas Pipelines Operator & Electricity & Natural Gas Distr
S.I.C.: 4939; 4911; 4922; 4931
N.A.I.C.S.: 221122; 221112; 221119; 221121; 486210
Import
Media: 2-7-10
Distr.: Reg.
Personnel:
James E. Rogers, Jr. *(Chm, Pres & CEO)*
Lynn J. Good *(CFO & Grp Exec)*
Christopher C. Rolfe *(Chief Admin Officer & Grp Exec)*
Marc E. Manly *(Chief Legal Officer, Corp Sec & Grp Exec)*
Virginia S. Mackin *(Chief Comm Officer & Sr VP)*
David W. Mohler *(CTO & Sr VP)*
Jennifer L. Weber *(Chief HR Officer)*
Dhiaa M. Jamil *(Chief Nuclear Officer, Grp Exec & Chief Generation Officer)*
Brett C. Carter *(Pres-Duke Energy North Carolina)*
Julia S. Janson *(Pres-Ohio & Kentucky Ops)*
Sandra P. Meyer *(Pres-Duke Energy Ohio & Duke Energy Kentucky)*
Jim L. Stanley *(Pres-Duke Energy Indiana)*
B. Keith Trent *(Grp Exec & Pres-Comml Bus)*
Stephen G. De May *(Treas & Sr VP-IR)*
Steven K. Young *(Sr VP & Controller)*
Roberta B. Bowman *(Sr VP & Chief Sustainablility Officer)*
Richard W. Haviland *(Sr VP-Construction & Major Projects)*
Gianna M. Manes *(Chief Customer Officer & Sr VP)*
Ronald R. Reising *(Chief Procurement Officer & Sr VP)*
Christopher Heck *(VP-Sls-Mktg)*
John Haysbert *(Dir-Federal Govt Affairs)*
Leah Moss *(Mktg Project Dir)*
William Baker *(Mgr-Load Rsch)*
Advertising Agency:
Northlich
Sawyer Point Bldg 720 Pete Rose Way
Cincinnati, OH 45202
Tel.: (513) 421-8840
Fax: (513) 455-4749
Retail Sales

DUQUESNE LIGHT COMPANY

(Holding of Duquesne Light Holdings, Inc.)
411 7th Ave
Pittsburgh, PA 15219-1919
Tel.: (412) 393-6000
Fax: (412) 393-1263
Web Site: www.duquesnelight.com
Approx. Rev.: $723,200,000
Approx. Number Employees: 1,400
Year Founded: 1912
Business Description:
Electrical Utility Services
S.I.C.: 4911; 4931; 4939
N.A.I.C.S.: 221122; 221111; 221119
Media: 9-16-18-23-24-25-26
Distr.: Direct to Consumer; Reg.
Personnel:
Richard Riazzi *(Pres & CEO)*
Mark E. Kaplan *(CFO, Sr VP & Treas)*
Maureen L. Hogel *(COO)*
James E. Wilson *(Chief Strategic Officer & Sr VP)*
William F. Fields *(Treas, VP & Pres-DQE Fin)*
Darrin K. Duda *(Mgr)*
Advertising Agency:
Dymun + Company
200 1st Ave
Pittsburgh, PA 15222-1512
Tel.: (412) 281-2345
Fax: (412) 281-3493

EDISON ELECTRIC INSTITUTE

701 Pennsylvania Ave NW
Washington, DC 20004-2696
Tel.: (202) 508-5000
Fax: (202) 508-5015
Web Site: www.eei.org
Approx. Number Employees: 200
Year Founded: 1933
Business Description:
Investor-Owned Electric Utility Association
S.I.C.: 8611
N.A.I.C.S.: 813910
Media: 9-10-18
Distr.: Natl.
Budget Set: June
Personnel:
Richard Kelly *(Chm & CEO-Xcel Energy)*
Thomas R. Kuhn *(Pres)*
Jim Owen *(Exec Dir-Member Rels & Meeting Svcs)*
Brian Farrell *(Sr Dir-Member Rels)*
Louis Jahn *(Sr Dir)*
John Kinsman *(Sr Dir-Environment)*
David Dworzak *(Dir-Reliability)*
Eric Holdsworth *(Dir-Climate Programs)*
Gregory Obenchain *(Mgr-Distr Ops & Standards)*
Raj Patel *(Mgr-Transmission Ops)*
Advertising Agency:
The Bivings Group
2201 Wisconsin Ave NW Ste 310
Washington, DC 20007
Tel.: (202) 741-1500
Fax: (202) 741-1501

EDISON INTERNATIONAL

2244 Walnut Grove Ave Ste 369
Rosemead, CA 91770-3714
Mailing Address:
PO Box 800
Rosemead, CA 91770-0800
Tel.: (626) 302-1212
Fax: (626) 302-2517
Toll Free: (800) 621-8516
E-mail: edison.gifts@sce.com
Web Site: www.edison.com
Approx. Rev.: $12,409,000,000
Approx. Number Employees: 20,117
Year Founded: 1987
Business Description:
Holding Company; Electric Utilities Owner
S.I.C.: 4939; 4911; 4931; 6512
N.A.I.C.S.: 221111; 221112; 221119; 221121; 531120
Advertising Expenditures: $3,044,000
Media: 2-10-23-25
Distr.: Direct to Consumer; Reg.
Budget Set: May -June
Personnel:
Theodore F. Craver, Jr. *(Chm, Pres & CEO)*
Jim Scilacci *(CFO, Treas & Exec VP)*
Mahvash Yazdi *(CIO & Sr VP-Bus Integration)*

Key to Media (For complete agency information see *The Advertising Red Books-Agencies* edition):
1. Bus. Publs. 2. Cable T.V. 3. Catalogs & Directories. 4. Co-op Adv. 5. Consumer Mags. 6. D.M. to Bus. Estab.7. D.M. to Consumers 8. Daily Newsp. 9. Exhibits/Trade Shows 10. Foreign 11. Infomercial 12. Internet Adv.13. Multimedia 14. Network Radio 15. Network T.V. 16. Newsp. Distr. Mags. 17. Other 18. Outdoor (Posters, Transit) 19. Point of Purchase20. Premiums, Novelties 21. Product Samples 22. Special Events Mktg. 23. Spot Radio 24. Spot T.V. 25. Weekly Newsp. 26. Yellow Page Adv.

Barbara E. Mathews *(Chief Governance Officer, Sec, VP & Assoc Gen Counsel)*
Cecil R. House *(Chief Procurement Officer & Sr VP-Safety & Ops Support)*
Robert L. Adler *(Gen Counsel & Exec VP)*
Polly L. Gault *(Exec VP-Pub Affairs)*
Janet Clayton *(Sr VP-Corp Comm)*
Daryl D. David *(Sr VP-HR)*
Bruce Foster *(Sr VP-Regulatory Affairs)*
James D. Kelly *(Sr VP-TDBU)*
Harry B. Hutchison *(VP-Customer Svc)*
R. W. Krieger *(VP-Production)*

Brands & Products:
EDISON
LEADING THE WAY IN ELECTRICITY

Advertising Agency:
Grey Los Angeles
3500 W Olive Ave Ste 700
Burbank, CA 91505
Tel.: (818) 531-0800
Fax: (818) 531-0701

EL PASO CORPORATION

El Paso Bldg 1001 Louisiana St
Houston, TX 77002-5089
Mailing Address:
PO Box 2511
Houston, TX 77252-2511
Tel.: (713) 420-2600
Fax: (713) 420-4417
E-mail: InvestorRelations@elpaso.com
Web Site: www.elpaso.com

Approx. Rev.: $4,616,000,000
Approx. Number Employees: 4,937
Year Founded: 1928
Business Description:
Natural Gas Transporter, Producer & Extractor
S.I.C.: 4922; 1311
N.A.I.C.S.: 486210; 211111
Media: 2-9

Personnel:
John R. Sult *(CFO, Sr VP & Controller)*
Susan B. Ortenstone *(Chief Admin Officer & Exec VP)*
D. Mark Leland *(Pres-Midstream Grp & Exec VP)*
James C. Yardley *(Pres-Pipeline Grp & Exec VP)*
James J. Cleary *(Pres-Western Pipeline Grp)*
Brent J. Smolik *(Pres-El Paso Exploration & Production Co)*
Robert W. Baker *(Gen Counsel & Exec VP)*
Alan Bishop *(Dir-Shareholder Rels)*
William Baerg *(Mgr-IR)*

Advertising Agencies:
The Leslie Corporation
15110 Mintz Ln
Houston, TX 77014
Tel.: (281) 591-0915
Fax: (281) 591-0921

Rosica Strategic Public Relations
95 Rt 17 S Ste 109
Paramus, NJ 07652
Tel.: (201) 843-5600
Fax: (201) 843-5680

THE EMPIRE DISTRICT ELECTRIC COMPANY

602 Joplin St
Joplin, MO 64801
Mailing Address:
PO Box 127
Joplin, MO 64802-0127
Tel.: (417) 625-5100
Fax: (417) 625-5173
Fax: (417) 625-5146
Toll Free: (800) 206-2300
E-mail: corp.communications@empiredistrict.com
Web Site: www.empiredistrict.com
Approx. Rev.: $541,276,000
Approx. Number Employees: 750
Year Founded: 1909
Business Description:
Generator, Purchaser, Transmitter, Distr & Seller of Electricity
S.I.C.: 4911; 4931; 4939; 4941
N.A.I.C.S.: 221122; 221119; 221310
Advertising Expenditures: $225,000
Media: 8-9-17-23-24-25-26
Distr.: Direct to Consumer; Reg.
Budget Set: Aug.
Personnel:
William L. Gipson *(Pres & CEO)*
Laurie A. Delano *(CFO & VP-Fin)*
Rob Sager *(Chief Acctg Officer, Controller, Asst Sec & Asst Treas)*
Bradley P. Beecher *(Exec VP)*
Blake Mertens *(Gen Mgr-Energy Supply)*
Elizabeth Dumm *(Dir-Governmental Affairs)*
George Thullesen *(Dir-Environ Policy)*
Brands & Products:
EDE

ENERGEN CORPORATION

605 Richard Arrington Jr Blvd N
Birmingham, AL 35203-2707
Tel.: (205) 326-2700
Fax: (205) 326-2704
Toll Free: (800) 654-3206
E-mail: info@energen.com
Web Site: www.energen.com
Approx. Rev.: $1,578,534,000
Approx. Number Employees: 1,530
Year Founded: 1979
Business Description:
Natural Gas & Oil Exploration
S.I.C.: 4924; 1321; 1389
N.A.I.C.S.: 221210; 211112; 213112
Media: 2-4-13-26
Distr.: Reg.
Budget Set: Sept.
Personnel:
James T. McManus II *(Chm & CEO)*
Charles W. Porter Jr. *(CFO, Treas & VP)*
J. David Woodruff, Jr. *(Gen Counsel, VP & Sec)*
L. Brunson White *(Sr VP-Mktg-Alagasco)*
Joe E. Cook *(Asst Sec & VP-Legal)*
William K. Bibb *(VP-HR)*
Brands & Products:
ENERGEN

ENERGY FUTURE HOLDINGS CORP.

(Joint Venture of The Goldman Sachs Group, Inc., KKR & CO. L.P. & TPG Capital, L.P.)
1601 Bryan St
Dallas, TX 75201-3411
Tel.: (214) 812-4600
Fax: (214) 812-7077
Web Site: www.energyfutureholdings.com
Approx. Rev.: $8,235,000,000
Approx. Number Employees: 9,200
Year Founded: 1945
Business Description:
Energy Services Holding Company; Owned by KKR & Co. L.P., TPG Capital, L.P. & The Goldman Sachs Group, Inc.
S.I.C.: 6719; 4911; 4939
N.A.I.C.S.: 551112; 221112; 221122
Media: 2-6-7-8-9-10-22-23-24-25
Distr.: Reg.
Personnel:
John F. Young *(Pres & CEO)*
David A. Campbell *(CEO-Luminant)*
Charles R. Enze *(CEO-Luminant Construction)*
Paul M. Keglevic *(CFO & Exec VP)*
Linda P. Jojo *(CIO & Sr VP)*
Mac McFarland *(Chief Comml Officer & Exec VP)*
Robert C. Walters *(Gen Counsel & Exec VP)*
Stanley J. Szlauderbach *(Sr VP & Controller)*
M. Rizwan Chand *(Sr VP)*
Advertising Agencies:
Firehouse, Inc.
14860 Landmark Blvd No 247
Dallas, TX 75254
Tel.: (972) 692-0911
Fax: (972) 692-0912

Garza Creative Group
2601 Hibernia St Ste 200
Dallas, TX 75204
Tel.: (214) 720-3888
Fax: (214) 720-3889
(Hispanic Advertising)
— Vicki Garza *(Chief Exec. Officer)*

ENERGY TRANSFER EQUITY, L.P.

3738 Oak Lawn Ave
Dallas, TX 75219
Tel.: (214) 981-0700
Fax: (214) 981-0706
E-mail: investorrelations@energytransfer.com
Web Site: www.energytransfer.com
Approx. Rev.: $6,598,132,000
Approx. Number Employees: 6,229
Business Description:
Natural Gas Midstream, Transportation & Storage Services; Propane Retailer
S.I.C.: 5984; 4922; 4924
N.A.I.C.S.: 454312; 221210; 486210
Media: 2-7-8
Personnel:
Kelcy L. Warren *(Chm & CEO)*
John W. McReynolds *(Pres, CFO & Dir)*
Marshall S. McCrea, III *(Pres & COO)*
Jerry J. Langdon *(Chief Admin & Compliance Officer)*
Thomas P. Mason *(Gen Counsel, Sec & VP)*

ENERGY UNITED ELECTRIC MEMBERSHIP CORPORATION

567 Mocksville Hwy
Statesville, NC 28625-8269
Tel.: (704) 873-5241
Fax: (704) 878-0161
E-mail: info@energyunited.com
Web Site: www.energyunited.com
Approx. Number Employees: 212
Year Founded: 1969
Business Description:
Electrical Services
S.I.C.: 4939; 4911
N.A.I.C.S.: 221122
Personnel:
Wayne H. Wilkins *(CEO)*
Alec Natt *(CFO & VP-Corp Svcs)*
Kathleen Hart *(CIO & VP-Customer Care)*
Tim Holder *(VP-Sls)*
Joe Leach *(VP-Engrg)*
Tom Tedrow *(VP-HR)*
Brands & Products:
ENERGY UNITED
YOUR LOCAL CONNECTION
Advertising Agency:
Eric Mower and Associates
1001 Morehead Sq Dr 5th Fl
Charlotte, NC 28203
Tel.: (704) 375-0123
Fax: (704) 375-0222
Toll Free: (800) 968-0682

ENERGYSOLUTIONS INC.

423 W 300 S Ste 200
Salt Lake City, UT 84101
Tel.: (801) 649-2000
E-mail: info@energysolutions.com
Web Site: www.energysolutions.com
Approx. Rev.: $1,752,042,000
Approx. Number Employees: 500
Business Description:
Nuclear Material Recycling, Processing & Disposal Services
S.I.C.: 4212; 4953
N.A.I.C.S.: 562112; 562211
Advertising Expenditures: $5,000,000
Personnel:
Val John Christensen *(Pres & CEO)*
William R. Benz *(CFO & Exec VP)*
Carol Fineagan *(CIO & Sr VP)*
John A. Christian *(Pres-Long-Term Stewardship Grp)*
Mark Morant *(Pres-Global Comml Grp)*
Alan M. Parker *(Pres-Govt Grp)*
Raul A. Deju *(Exec VP)*
Mark A. Walker *(Dir-Mktg & Media Rels)*

ENTERGY CORPORATION

639 Loyola Ave
New Orleans, LA 70113
Mailing Address:
PO Box 61000
New Orleans, LA 70161
Tel.: (504) 576-4000
Fax: (504) 569-4063
Toll Free: (800) ENTERGY
E-mail: mlopicc@entergy.com
Web Site: www.entergy.com
Approx. Rev.: $11,487,577,000
Approx. Number Employees: 14,958
Year Founded: 1914
Business Description:
Electric Utilities Holding Company
S.I.C.: 4911; 4924; 4931; 4939
N.A.I.C.S.: 221122; 221111; 221113; 221119; 221210
Media: 2-6-8-9-16-23-24
Distr.: Reg.
Budget Set: Sept.

Key to Media (For complete agency information see *The Advertising Red Books-Agencies* edition):
1. Bus. Publs. 2. Cable T.V. 3. Catalogs & Directories. 4. Co-op Adv. 5. Consumer Mags. 6. D.M. to Bus. Estab.7. D.M. to Consumers 8. Daily Newsp. 9. Exhibits/Trade Shows 10. Foreign 11. Infomercial 12. Internet Adv.13. Multimedia 14. Network Radio 15. Network T.V. 16. Newsp. Distr. Mags. 17. Other 18. Outdoor (Posters, Transit) 19. Point of Purchase20. Premiums, Novelties 21. Product Samples 22. Special Events Mktg. 23. Spot Radio 24. Spot T.V. 25. Weekly Newsp. 26. Yellow Page Adv.

Entergy Corporation — (Continued)

Personnel:
J. Wayne Leonard *(Chm & CEO)*
Leo P. Denault *(CFO & Exec VP)*
Mark T. Savoff *(COO & Exec VP)*
Roderick K. West *(Chief Admin Officer & Exec VP)*
Richard J. Smith *(Pres-Entergy Wholesale Commodity Bus)*
Gary J. Taylor *(Pres-Utility Ops)*
Robert S. Sloan *(Gen Counsel & Exec VP)*
Kimberly H. Despeaux *(Sr VP-Federal Policy, Regulatory & Governmental Affairs)*
Terry Seamons *(Sr VP-Organizational Dev Entergy Corporation)*
Toni Beck *(Grp VP-Corp Comm)*
Barrett Green *(VP-Risk & Fin)*
Ed Melendreras *(VP-Sls & Mktg)*
Doug Mader *(Dir-IT Infrastructure & Enterprise Svcs)*
Michael Dupre *(Mgr-IR)*

Brands & Products:
ENTERGY
THE POWER OF PEOPLE

Advertising Agencies:
Meyers + Partners
833 W Jackson Blvd Ste 600
Chicago, IL 60607
Tel.: (312) 733-9999
Fax: (312) 226-0526

Object9
4156 WE Heck Ct
Baton Rouge, LA 70816
Tel.: (225) 368-9899
Fax: (225) 368-9898

The Ramey Agency
1322 Hardwood Trail
Cordova, TN 38016
Tel.: (901) 761-3685
Fax: (901) 761-3688

Stone Ward
225 E Markham St Ste 450
Little Rock, AR 72201-1629
Tel.: (501) 375-3003
Fax: (501) 375-8314

ENTERGY NEW ORLEANS, INC.

(Sub. of Entergy Corporation)
1600 Perdido St
New Orleans, LA 70112
Tel.: (504) 670-3700
Web Site: www.entergy-neworleans.com
Approx. Rev.: $659,266,000
Approx. Number Employees: 345
Business Description:
Electricity & Natural Gas Distr
S.I.C.: 4911; 4924; 4939
N.A.I.C.S.: 221122; 221210
Media: 2-4-7-8-9-10-11-14-15-18-24-25
Distr.: Direct to Consumer; Reg.
Budget Set: Oct.
Personnel:
Charles Rice *(Pres & CEO)*
Rick Vogler *(Mgr-Adv & Creative Svcs)*
Chad Brumfield *(Mgr-Mktg Comm)*
Brands & Products:
NEW ORLEANS PUBLIC SERVICE

Advertising Agency:
Stone Ward
225 E Markham St Ste 450
Little Rock, AR 72201-1629
Tel.: (501) 375-3003
Fax: (501) 375-8314

ENVIROGEN TECHNOLOGIES, INC.

(Holding of Amplio Partners)
Two Kingwood Pl 700 Rockmead Dr Ste 105
Kingwood, TX 77339
Fax: (281) 358-2443
Toll Free: (877) 312-8950
E-mail: info@basinwater.com
Web Site: www.envirogen.com
Approx. Rev.: $11,778,000
Approx. Number Employees: 103
Business Description:
Design, Build & Implement Systems for the Treatment of Contaminated Water
S.I.C.: 4941
N.A.I.C.S.: 221310
Media: 5-7-8
Personnel:
Scott A. Katzmann *(Chm)*
W. Christopher Chisholm *(CFO & Exec VP)*
Richard A. Reese *(COO & VP)*
Scott B. Hamilton *(Gen Counsel & Sec)*
James C. Spain *(Reg VP-Southern Region)*

E.ON U.S. LLC

(Name Changed to LG&E and KU Energy LLC)

EXELON CORPORATION

10 S Dearborn St 48th Fl
Chicago, IL 60680
Mailing Address:
PO Box 805398
Chicago, IL 60680-5398
Tel.: (312) 394-7398
Fax: (312) 394-7945
Toll Free: (800) 483-3220
Web Site: www.exeloncorp.com
Approx. Rev.: $18,644,000,000
Approx. Number Employees: 19,214
Year Founded: 2000
Business Description:
Holding Company; Electric & Natural Gas Distr
S.I.C.: 4939; 4924; 6719
N.A.I.C.S.: 221111; 221210; 551112
Media: 5-6-9-10-18-22-23-25
Personnel:
John W. Rowe *(Chm & CEO)*
Christopher M. Crane *(Pres & COO)*
Matthew F. Hilzinger *(CFO & Sr VP)*
Ronald J. DeGregorio *(COO & Sr VP-Exelon Transmission Company)*
Susan Landahl *(COO & Sr VP-Nuclear)*
Dan Hill *(CIO & Sr VP)*
Douglas J. Brown *(Chief Investment Officer & Sr VP)*
Ruth Ann M. Gillis *(Chief Diversity Officer, Pres-Exelon Bus & Exec VP)*
Sunil Garg *(Pres-Power)*
Darryl M. Bradford *(Gen Counsel & Sr VP)*
Denis P. O'Brien *(Exec VP)*
William A. Von Hoene, Jr. *(Exec VP-Fin & Legal)*
Calvin Butler, Jr. *(Sr VP-HR)*
Kenneth W. Cornew *(Sr VP)*
Christopher H. Mudrick *(Sr VP-Ops Support)*
John Samolis *(Sr VP-Employee & Labor Rels)*
JaCee M. Burnes *(VP-Treasury Ops & Asst Treas)*
Michael Campbell *(VP-Talent Mgmt & Organizational Effectiveness)*
Ellen Caya *(VP-Physical & Cyber Security)*
Tabrina Davis *(VP-Comm)*
Craig Nesbit *(VP-Comm)*
Kathleen Cantillon *(Dir-External Comm)*
Jackie Carney *(Dir-Federal Govt Affairs)*
Valencia McClure *(Dir-Comm)*
Michael Wood *(Sr Mgr-Comm)*
Jennifer Medley *(Mgr-External Comm)*
April Schilpp *(Mgr-Comm)*
Brands & Products:
ENERGY FOR THE COMMUNITY
EXELON
EXELON 2020
THAT'S OUR PROMISE. THAT'S OUR WAY

Advertising Agencies:
The San Jose Group
233 N Michigan Ave 24 Fl
Chicago, IL 60601
Tel.: (312) 565-7000
Fax: (312) 565-7500

Star Group Communications, Inc.
(d/b/a The Star Group)
220 Laurel Rd
Voorhees, NJ 08043
Tel.: (856) 782-7000
Fax: (856) 782-5699

FAIRPOINT COMMUNICATIONS, INC.

521 E Morehead St Ste 250
Charlotte, NC 28202
Tel.: (704) 344-8150
Fax: (704) 344-8121
E-mail: information@fairpoint.com
Web Site: www.fairpoint.com
Approx. Rev.: $1,070,986,000
Approx. Number Employees: 4,032
Year Founded: 1991
Business Description:
Local & Long Distance Telecommunications Services
S.I.C.: 4813
N.A.I.C.S.: 517110; 517310
Personnel:
Edward D. Horowitz *(Chm)*
Peter G. Nixon *(Pres)*
Paul H. Sunu *(CEO)*
Ajay Sabherwal *(CFO & Exec VP)*
Kathleen McLean *(CIO & Exec VP)*
Michael C. Reed *(Pres-Maine)*
Shirley J. Linn *(Gen Counsel & Exec VP)*
Patrick C. McHugh *(VP & Asst Gen Counsel)*
Walter E. Leach Jr. *(Exec VP-Corp Dev)*
Gary C. Garvey *(Sr VP-HR)*
Lisa R. Hood *(Sr VP-Fin Initiatives)*
Louise Merriman *(Mgr-Digital Mktg)*
Advertising Agency:
Hill Holliday
53 State St
Boston, MA 02109
Tel.: (617) 366-4000

FIRST CHOICE POWER

(Sub. of TNP Enterprises, Inc.)
4001 International Plz
Fort Worth, TX 76109
Mailing Address:
Box 901088
Fort Worth, TX 76101
Tel.: (817) 731-0099
Fax: (817) 735-5731
Toll Free: (866) 469-2464
Web Site: www.firstchoicepower.com
Sales Range: $200-249.9 Million
Year Founded: 2000
Business Description:
Electrical Utility Services
S.I.C.: 4931
N.A.I.C.S.: 221119
Personnel:
Brian Hayduk *(Pres)*
Mark Faulkner *(Mktg Mgr)*
Advertising Agency:
SKM Group
6350 Transit Rd
Depew, NY 14043
Tel.: (716) 989-3200
Fax: (716) 989-3220

FIRSTENERGY CORP.

76 S Main St
Akron, OH 44308-1812
Tel.: (330) 384-5100
Tel.: (330) 761-7837
Fax: (330) 384-3772
Toll Free: (800) 736-3402
E-mail: turoskyk@firstenergycorp.com
Web Site: www.firstenergycorp.com
Approx. Rev.: $13,339,000,000
Approx. Number Employees: 13,330
Year Founded: 1997
Business Description:
Holding Company; Electric Utility Services
S.I.C.: 4911; 4931; 4939; 6719
N.A.I.C.S.: 221122; 221111; 221119; 551112
Media: 2-3-7-8-9-10-13-17-22-23-24-25-26
Distr.: Direct to Consumer; Reg.
Budget Set: Sept.
Personnel:
Anthony J. Alexander *(Pres & CEO)*
Mark T. Clark *(CFO & Exec VP)*
Harvey L. Wagner *(Chief Acctg Officer, VP & Controller)*
John W. Judge *(Chief Procurement Officer)*
Charles Edward Jones, Jr. *(Pres-FirstEnergy Utilities)*
Leila L. Vespoli *(Gen Counsel & Exec VP)*
Gary R. Leidich *(Exec VP)*
Richard J. Horak *(Asst Controller)*
Gary Benz *(Dir-Bus Dev)*
James E. Graf *(Dir-Harrison Power Station-FirstEnergy Generation Corp.)*
Jeffrey R. Kalata *(Dir-Tax)*
Randy Scilla *(Asst Treas)*
Edward J. Udovich *(Asst Sec)*
Brands & Products:
FIRSTENERGY
OUR ENERGY IS WORKING FOR YOU.

Key to Media (For complete agency information see *The Advertising Red Books-Agencies* edition):
1. Bus. Publs. 2. Cable T.V. 3. Catalogs & Directories. 4. Co-op Adv. 5. Consumer Mags. 6. D.M. to Bus. Estab.7. D.M. to Consumers
8. Daily Newsp. 9. Exhibits/Trade Shows 10. Foreign 11. Infomercial 12. Internet Adv.13. Multimedia 14. Network Radio
15. Network T.V. 16. Newsp. Distr. Mags. 17. Other 18. Outdoor (Posters, Transit) 19. Point of Purchase20. Premiums, Novelties
21. Product Samples 22. Special Events Mktg. 23. Spot Radio 24. Spot T.V. 25. Weekly Newsp. 26. Yellow Page Adv.

FLORIDA POWER & LIGHT COMPANY

(Sub. of NEXTERA ENERGY, INC.)
700 Universe Blvd
Juno Beach, FL 33408-2657
Mailing Address:
PO Box 14000
North Palm Beach, FL 33408-0420
Tel.: (561) 694-4000
Tel.: (561) 691-7171
Fax: (561) 694-4999
Fax: (561) 694-3865
E-mail: experiments@fpl.com
Web Site: www.fpl.com

Approx. Rev.: $10,485,000,000
Year Founded: 1925

Business Description:
Electric Utility
S.I.C.: 4911; 4931; 4939; 6282
N.A.I.C.S.: 221122; 221111; 221119; 523920
Advertising Expenditures: $6,300,000

Media: 1-2-3-6-7-8-9-10-18-19-20-23-24-26
Distr.: Direct to Consumer; Reg.
Budget Set: Aug.

Personnel:
Edward F. Tancer *(Vice Chm & Sr VP-Governmental Affairs-State)*
Armando J. Olivera *(Pres & CEO)*
Lewis Hay, III *(CEO)*
Armando Pimentel, Jr. *(CFO & Exec VP-Fin)*
Lakshman Charanjiva *(CIO & VP)*
Christopher A. Bennett *(Exec VP & Chief Strategy Officer)*
Kimberly Ousdahl *(Chief Acctg Officer, VP & Controller)*
F. Mitchell Davidson *(Pres/CEO-NextEra Energy Resources)*
John A. Stall *(Pres-Nuclear Div-FPL Grp)*
R. Wade Litchfield *(Gen Counsel & VP)*
Michael O'Sullivan *(Sr VP-Dev)*
Robert L. McGrath *(Exec VP-Engrg, Construction & Corp Svcs)*
Antonio Rodriguez *(Exec VP-Power Generation Div)*
Robert H. Escoto *(Sr VP-HR, VP & Asst Sec)*
Eric E. Silagy *(Sr VP-Regulatory & State Govt Affairs)*
Robert E. Barrett, Jr. *(VP-Fin)*
Timothy Fitzpatrick *(VP-Mktg & Comm)*
Lawrence Kelleher *(VP-HR)*
Mary Lou Kromer *(VP-Corp Commun)*
John Franklin *(Gen Mgr-Quality)*
John Haney *(Dir-Demand Side Mgmt)*

Advertising Agencies:
Pantin/Beber Silverstein Public Relations
(Part of the Beber Silverstein Group)
3361 SW 3rd Ave
Miami, FL 33145-3911
Tel.: (305) 856-9800
Fax: (305) 857-0027

rbb Public Relations
355 Alhambra Cir Ste 800
Miami, FL 33134
Tel.: (305) 448-7450
Fax: (305) 448-5027

FLORIDA POWER CORPORATION

(Name Changed to Progress Energy Florida)

FLORIDA PUBLIC UTILITIES COMPANY

(Sub. of Chesapeake Utilities Corporation)
401 S Dixie Hwy
West Palm Beach, FL 33401-5807
Mailing Address:
PO Box 3395
West Palm Beach, FL 33402-3395
Tel.: (561) 832-0872
Fax: (561) 833-8579
Toll Free: (800) 427-7712
E-mail: corporate@fpuc.com
Web Site: www.fpuc.com
E-Mail For Key Personnel:
President: jenglish@fpuc.com
Approx. Rev.: $168,548,000
Approx. Number Employees: 385
Year Founded: 1924
Business Description:
Natural & Propane Gas, Electricity & Water Services
S.I.C.: 4939; 4911; 4924; 4931
N.A.I.C.S.: 221111; 221119; 221122; 221210
Advertising Expenditures: $249,000
Personnel:
John R. Schimkaitis *(Chm & CEO)*
Jeff Householder *(Pres)*
Charles L. Stein *(COO & Sr VP)*
Mark Cutshaw *(Gen Mgr-Northeast)*
Don Kitner *(Gen Mgr)*
Terry Knowles *(Dir-IT)*
Julia Petty *(Dir-Customer Relations)*

FRONTIER COMMUNICATIONS CORPORATION

3 High Ridge Park
Stamford, CT 06905-1328
Tel.: (203) 614-5600
Fax: (203) 614-4602
Toll Free: (800) 757-5755
Web Site: www.frontier.com
E-Mail For Key Personnel:
Public Relations: bsmith@czn.com
Approx. Rev.: $3,797,675,000
Approx. Number Employees: 14,800
Year Founded: 1935
Business Description:
Telecommunications, Internet & Satellite Television Services
S.I.C.: 4813; 4841; 7375
N.A.I.C.S.: 517110; 515210; 518111
Advertising Expenditures: $4,500,000
Personnel:
Mary Agnes Wilderotter *(Chm & CEO)*
Donald R. Shassian *(CFO & Exec VP)*
Daniel J. McCarthy *(COO & Exec VP)*
Kathleen Quinn Abernathy *(Chief Legal Officer & Exec VP)*
Susana D'Emic *(Chief Acctg Officer, Sr VP & Controller)*
Ken Arndt *(Pres-Southeast Reg)*
David R. Whitehouse *(Treas & Sr VP)*
Peter B. Hayes *(Exec VP-Comml Sls)*
Cecilia K. McKenney *(Exec VP-HR & Call Center Sls)*
Melinda White *(Exec VP-Revenue Dev)*
Robert J. Larson *(Sr VP)*
Dana E. Waldo *(Sr VP)*
Brigid M. Smith *(Asst VP-Corp Comm)*
Karen C. Miller *(Mgr-Comm)*

Brands & Products:
FRONTIER

Advertising Agencies:
Campbell Mithun, Inc.
Campbell Mithun Tower 222 S 9th St
Minneapolis, MN 55402-3389
Tel.: (612) 347-1000
Fax: (612) 347-1515

Nemer Fieger
6250 Excelsior Blvd Ste 203
Minneapolis, MN 55416-2735
Tel.: (952) 925-4848
Fax: (952) 925-1907

o2kl
10 W 18th St 6th Fl
New York, NY 10011
Tel.: (646) 829-6239
Fax: (646) 839-6254

GAINESVILLE REGIONAL UTILITIES INC.

301 SE 4th Ave
Gainesville, FL 32601-6857
Tel.: (352) 334-3400
Fax: (352) 334-3149
Toll Free: (800) 818-3436
Web Site: www.gru.com
Approx. Number Employees: 762
Year Founded: 1912
Business Description:
Combination Utility Services
S.I.C.: 4931; 4941
N.A.I.C.S.: 221119; 221310
Personnel:
Jennifer L. Hunt *(CFO)*
Robert Hunzinger *(Gen Mgr-Utilities)*
David E. Beaulieu *(Asst Gen Mgr-Energy Delivery)*
David M. Richardson *(Asst Gen Mgr-Water Waste Water Sys)*

Brands & Products:
GRU
MORE THAN ENERGY

Advertising Agency:
The MWW Group
700 13th St NW
Washington, DC 20006
Tel.: (202) 585-2270
Fax: (202) 585-2273

THE GAS COMPANY LLC

(Sub. of MACQUARIE INFRASTRUCTURE COMPANY LLC)
515 Kamakee St
Honolulu, HI 96814
Mailing Address:
PO Box 3000
Honolulu, HI 96802-3000
Tel.: (808) 535-5933
Fax: (808) 594-5522
Web Site: www.hawaiigas.com
Approx. Number Employees: 300
Year Founded: 1904
Business Description:
Natural Gas Distr
S.I.C.: 4924
N.A.I.C.S.: 221210
Import
Advertising Expenditures: $500,000
Media: 2-3-5-6-8-10-13-24-26
Distr.: Reg.
Budget Set: Sept.
Personnel:
Jeffrey M. Kissel *(Pres & CEO)*
Thomas K.L.M. Young *(COO & Sr VP)*
George T. Aoki *(Gen Counsel, Sec & VP)*
Greg Toth *(VP-Mktg)*
Kenneth T. Yamamoto *(VP-HR)*

Brands & Products:
GASCO

Advertising Agency:
interTrend Communications, Inc.
555 E Ocean Blvd
Long Beach, CA 90802-5003
Tel.: (562) 733-1888
Fax: (562) 733-1889

GAZ METRO LIMITED PARTNERSHIP

(Sub. of Gaz Metro Inc.)
1717 rue du Havre
Montreal, QC H2K 2X3, Canada
Tel.: (514) 598-3321
Fax: (514) 598-3725
Toll Free: (800) 361-4005
E-mail: info@gazmetro.com
Web Site: www.gazmetro.com
Sales Range: $1-4.9 Billion
Approx. Number Employees: 1,400
Year Founded: 1957
Business Description:
Natural Gas Distr
S.I.C.: 4924
N.A.I.C.S.: 221210
Export
Advertising Expenditures: $2,800,000
Media: 1-2-4-5-7-9-10-13-17-18-22-25
Distr.: Intl.; Natl.
Budget Set: Aug. -Sept.
Personnel:
Sophie Brochu *(Pres & CEO)*
Pierre Despars *(CFO & Exec VP)*
Jocelyn Lajoie *(Dir-Risk Assessment & Internal Audit)*

Advertising Agency:
SID LEE
75 Queen Street Ofc 1400
Montreal, QC H3C 2N6, Canada
Tel.: (514) 282-2200
Fax: (514) 282-0499

GENERAL COMMUNICATION, INC.

2550 Denali St Ste 1000
Anchorage, AK 99503-2751
Tel.: (907) 265-5600
Fax: (907) 868-5676
Toll Free: (800) 770-7886
E-mail: careers@gci.com
Web Site: www.gci.com
E-Mail For Key Personnel:
President: rduncan@gci.com
Approx. Rev.: $651,250,000
Approx. Number Employees: 1,655
Year Founded: 1979
Business Description:
Telecommunications Services
S.I.C.: 4841; 4813
N.A.I.C.S.: 517110; 515210; 517310
Advertising Expenditures: $4,300,000
Media: 3-4-5-8-9-13-23-24-25
Personnel:
Ronald A. Duncan *(Co-Founder, Pres & CEO)*
Stephen M. Brett *(Chm)*
John M. Lowber *(CFO & Sr VP)*

Key to Media (For complete agency information see *The Advertising Red Books-Agencies* edition):
1. Bus. Publs. 2. Cable T.V. 3. Catalogs & Directories. 4. Co-op Adv. 5. Consumer Mags. 6. D.M. to Bus. Estab.7. D.M. to Consumers
8. Daily Newsp. 9. Exhibits/Trade Shows 10. Foreign 11. Infomercial 12. Internet Adv.13. Multimedia 14. Network Radio
15. Network T.V. 16. Newsp. Distr. Mags. 17. Other 18. Outdoor (Posters, Transit) 19. Point of Purchase20. Premiums, Novelties
21. Product Samples 22. Special Events Mktg. 23. Spot Radio 24. Spot T.V. 25. Weekly Newsp. 26. Yellow Page Adv.

General Communication, Inc. — (Continued)

Lynda L. Tarbath *(Chief Acctg Officer & VP)*
G. Wilson Hughes *(Exec VP & Gen Mgr)*
William C. Behnke *(Sr VP-Strategic Initiatives)*
Richard P. Dowling *(Sr VP-Corp Dev)*
Tina Pidgeon *(Sr Counsel & Sr VP-Governmental Affairs)*
Paul Landes *(Gen Mgr & VP)*
Bruce Broquet *(VP-Fin)*
Michael Kirk *(Dir-Machine-to-Machine Markets-Cycle30, Inc.)*

GENON ENERGY, INC.

(Formerly RRI Energy, Inc.)
1000 Main St
Houston, TX 77002
Mailing Address:
PO Box 148
Houston, TX 77001-0148
Tel.: (832) 357-3000
Web Site: www.genon.com
Approx. Rev.: $2,270,000,000
Approx. Number Employees: 3,487
Year Founded: 1906
Business Description:
Electricity & Energy Services
S.I.C.: 4931; 4911; 4939; 5172; 6221
N.A.I.C.S.: 221111; 221112; 221119; 221121; 221122; 424720; 523130
Advertising Expenditures: $95,000,000
Personnel:
Edward R. Muller *(Chm, Pres & CEO)*
J. William Holden, III *(CFO & Exec VP)*
Michael L. Jines *(Chief Compliance Officer, Gen Counsel, Corp Sec & Exec VP)*
Robert Gaudette *(Chief Comml Officer & Sr VP)*
Rogers Daniel Herndon *(Exec VP-Strategic Plng & Bus Dev)*
Thomas C. Livengood *(Sr VP & Controller)*
Anne M. Cleary *(Sr VP-Asset Mgmt)*
David S. Freysinger *(Sr VP-Plant Ops)*
Albert H. Myres *(Sr VP-Govt & Pub Affairs)*
Karen D. Taylor *(Chief Diversity Officer & Sr VP-HR)*
Pat Hammond *(Dir-Comm)*
Scott Burns *(Product Mgr-SmartEnergy)*
Advertising Agencies:
DMN3
2010 N Loop W Ste 240
Houston, TX 77018
Tel.: (713) 868-3000
Fax: (713) 868-1388
Toll Free: (800) 625-8320

Lopez Negrete Communications, Inc.
3336 Richmond Ave Ste 200
Houston, TX 77098
Tel.: (713) 877-8777
Fax: (713) 877-8796

Parker Advertising Service, Inc.
101 N Pointe Blvd 2nd Fl
Lancaster, PA 17601
Tel.: (717) 581-1966
Fax: (717) 581-1566
Toll Free: (800) 396-3306

Possible Worldwide
5780 W Jefferson Blvd
Los Angeles, CA 90016
Tel.: (310) 202-2900
Fax: (310) 202-2910

The Richards Group, Inc.
8750 N Central Expy Ste 100
Dallas, TX 75231-6430
Tel.: (214) 891-5700
Fax: (214) 265-2933
(Energy Related-Non Regulated & Telecommunications)

GEORGIA POWER COMPANY

(Sub. of Southern Company)
241 Ralph McGill Blvd NE
Atlanta, GA 30308-3374
Mailing Address:
PO Box 4545
Atlanta, GA 30302-4545
Tel.: (404) 506-6526
Tel.: (404) 506-7676 (Media Rels)
Fax: (404) 506-3771
E-mail: corpcomm@georgiapower.com
Web Site: www.georgiapower.com
Approx. Rev.: $8,349,000,000
Approx. Number Employees: 8,330
Year Founded: 1883
Business Description:
Electric Power Distr
S.I.C.: 4911; 4931; 4939
N.A.I.C.S.: 221122; 221119; 221121
Import
Media: 17
Personnel:
William Paul Bowers *(Pres & CEO)*
Cliff S. Thrasher *(CFO, Treas & Exec VP)*
G. Edison Holland, Jr. *(Gen Counsel, Sec, Exec VP & Chief Compliance Officer)*
Ann P. Daiss *(Chief Acctg Officer, VP & Comptroller)*
Andrew J. Dearman III *(Chief Transmission Officer & Exec VP)*
W. Craig Barrs *(Exec VP-External Affair)*
Mickey A. Brown *(Exec VP-Customer Svc Org)*
C.B. Mike Harreld *(Exec VP)*
Charles D. McCrary *(Exec VP)*
Judy M. Anderson *(Sr VP-Charitable Giving)*
E. Lamont Houston *(Sr VP-Customer Svcs & Sls)*
Chris Bell *(VP-Energy Plng & Sls)*
Ellen N. Lindemann *(VP-HR)*
Jeffrey Wallace *(VP-Cust Svcs)*
Jennifer Zeller *(Dir-Res)*
Brands & Products:
THE CHOICE
GOOD CENTS HOME
Advertising Agencies:
Fitzgerald+CO
3060 Peachtree Rd NW
Atlanta, GA 30305
Tel.: (404) 504-6900
Fax: (404) 239-0548
(Brand & Media)

Grey Atlanta
191 Peachtree St NE Ste 4025
Atlanta, GA 30309
Tel.: (404) 261-2360
Fax: (404) 261-9360

Lattimer Communications
934 Glenwood Ave Ste 260
Atlanta, GA 30316
Tel.: (404) 526-9321
Fax: (404) 526-9324

Response Media, Inc.
3155 Medlock Bridge Rd
Norcross, GA 30071-1423
Tel.: (770) 451-5478
Fax: (770) 451-4929

The Richards Group, Inc.
8750 N Central Expy Ste 100
Dallas, TX 75231-6430
Tel.: (214) 891-5700
Fax: (214) 265-2933

GLENTEL INC.

8501 Commerce Ct
Burnaby, BC V5A 4M3, Canada
Tel.: (604) 415-6500
Fax: (604) 415-7007
Toll Free: (800) GLEN-TEL
E-mail: customer_service@glentel.com
Web Site: www.glentel.com
Approx. Sls.: $420,066,618
Approx. Number Employees: 300
Year Founded: 1963
Business Description:
Wireless Communication, Mobile Satellite & Personal Communication Solutions
S.I.C.: 3663
N.A.I.C.S.: 334220
Advertising Expenditures: $2,000,000
Personnel:
Thomas E. Skidmore *(Chm, Pres & CEO)*
Jas Boparai *(CFO)*
David M. Hartman *(VP-Ops-Retail Div)*
Cary T. Skidmore *(VP-Mktg)*
Damon A. Jones *(Gen Mgr-Retail Div)*
Brands & Products:
GLENTEL
Advertising Agency:
James Hoggan & Associates, Inc.
#510-1125 Howe St
Vancouver, BC V6Z 2K8, Canada
Tel.: (604) 739-7500
Fax: (604) 736-9902

GRANDE COMMUNICATIONS NETWORKS LLC

(Holding of ABRY Partners LLC)
401 Carlson Cir
San Marcos, TX 78666
Tel.: (512) 878-4600
Fax: (512) 878-4010
Web Site: www.grandecom.com
Approx. Rev.: $205,271,000
Approx. Number Employees: 785
Year Founded: 1999
Business Description:
Telecommunications; Broadband Network Services for Cable Television, Telephone & Internet
S.I.C.: 4899; 4841; 7375
N.A.I.C.S.: 517910; 515210; 517510; 518111
Advertising Expenditures: $2,700,000
Personnel:
Duncan T. Butler, Jr. *(Chm)*
Matthew M. Murphy *(Pres)*
Walter K.L. Ferguson, Jr. *(COO)*
Harris Bass *(VP & Gen Mgr-Austin)*
Dottie Lane *(VP & Gen Mgr-Corpus Christi)*
Matt Rohre *(VP & Gen Mgr-Waco)*
Tracy Brutcher *(VP-HR)*
Lamar Horton *(VP-Network Ops & Engrg)*
Steven Knouse *(VP-Fin)*
Kip Simonson *(VP-Sls & Mktg)*

GREAT PLAINS ENERGY INCORPORATED

1200 Main St
Kansas City, MO 64105
Tel.: (816) 556-2200
Fax: (816) 556-2418
E-mail: ir@kcpl.com
Web Site: www.greatplainsenergy.com
Approx. Rev.: $2,255,500,000
Approx. Number Employees: 3,188
Year Founded: 2001
Business Description:
Holding Company; Electric Power Distribution & Generation Services
S.I.C.: 6719; 4911; 4931; 4939
N.A.I.C.S.: 551112; 221112; 221113; 221119; 221121; 221122
Personnel:
Michael J. Chesser *(Chm & CEO)*
William H. Downey *(Pres & COO)*
Heather A. Humphrey *(Gen Counsel & VP-HR)*
Terry Bassham *(Exec VP-Utility Ops, KCP & L)*
Mark G. English *(Asst Gen Counsel & Asst Sec)*
Advertising Agency:
Kuhn & Wittenborn, Inc.
2405 Grand Blvd Ste 600
Kansas City, MO 64108-2519
Tel.: (816) 471-7888
Fax: (816) 471-7530

GREEN MOUNTAIN ENERGY COMPANY

(Sub. of NRG Energy, Inc.)
300 W Sixth St Ste 900
Austin, TX 78701-6635
Mailing Address:
PO Box 689008
Austin, TX 78768-9008
Tel.: (512) 691-6100
Fax: (512) 691-6151
Toll Free: (888) 246-6730
E-mail: info@greenmountain.com
Web Site: www.greenmountain.com
Sales Range: $400-449.9 Million
Approx. Number Employees: 190
Year Founded: 1997
Business Description:
Energy Services
S.I.C.: 4911; 4939
N.A.I.C.S.: 221122
Media: 22
Personnel:
Paul D. Thomas *(Pres & CEO)*
Robert Thomas *(Chief Legal Officer)*
Scott Hart *(Pres-Comml Svcs)*
Paul N. Markovich *(Pres-Residential Svcs)*
Ronald E. Prater *(Sr VP-Supply)*
John T. Savage *(Sr VP-Mktg)*
Helen Brauner *(VP-Strategic Plng)*
Michael Current *(VP-Fin, Acctg & Compliance)*
Kimberlee Flores *(Dir-HR)*

Key to Media (For complete agency information see *The Advertising Red Books-Agencies* edition):
1. Bus. Publs. 2. Cable T.V. 3. Catalogs & Directories. 4. Co-op Adv. 5. Consumer Mags. 6. D.M. to Bus. Estab.7. D.M. to Consumers 8. Daily Newsp. 9. Exhibits/Trade Shows 10. Foreign 11. Infomercial 12. Internet Adv.13. Multimedia 14. Network Radio 15. Network T.V. 16. Newsp. Distr. Mags. 17. Other 18. Outdoor (Posters, Transit) 19. Point of Purchase20. Premiums, Novelties 21. Product Samples 22. Special Events Mktg. 23. Spot Radio 24. Spot T.V. 25. Weekly Newsp. 26. Yellow Page Adv.

Brands & Products:
BEGREEN
BIG TEXAS SUN CLUB
GREEN MOUNTAIN ENERGY

GREEN MOUNTAIN POWER CORPORATION

(Sub. of Northern New England Energy Corporation)
163 Acorn Ln
Colchester, VT 05446-6612
Tel.: (802) 864-5731
Fax: (802) 655-8445
Toll Free: (888) 835-4672
E-mail: callcenter@gmpvt.com
Web Site:
www.greenmountainpower.biz
Approx. Rev.: $240,476,000
Approx. Number Employees: 192
Year Founded: 1893
Business Description:
Electricity Supplier
S.I.C.: 4911; 4931; 4939
N.A.I.C.S.: 221122; 221111; 221119
Advertising Expenditures: $250,000
Media: 2-8-9-23-24
Distr.: Reg.
Budget Set: Sept.
Personnel:
Mary G. Powell *(Pres & CEO)*
Dawn D. Bugbee *(CFO & VP)*
Donald J. Rendall, Jr. *(Gen Counsel, Sec & VP)*
Dorothy Schnure *(Mgr-Corp Rels)*
Brands & Products:
ON. EVERY DAY.

GREENHOUSE HOLDINGS, INC.

5171 Santa Fe St Ste 1
San Diego, CA 92109
Tel.: (858) 273-2626
Fax: (858) 430-2790
Web Site: www.greenhouseintl.com
Approx. Rev.: $6,731,986
Approx. Number Employees: 30
Year Founded: 2004
Business Description:
Energy Efficient Products
S.I.C.: 4931; 1389
N.A.I.C.S.: 221119; 213112
Advertising Expenditures: $34,058
Media: 17
Personnel:
John Galt *(Chm)*
Robert Russ Earnshaw *(Pres)*
Justin Farry *(CFO & Treas)*

GULF POWER COMPANY

(Sub. of Southern Company)
1 Energy Pl
Pensacola, FL 32520-0001
Tel.: (850) 444-6111
Fax: (850) 444-6476
E-mail: info@gulfpower.com
Web Site: www.gulfpower.com
Approx. Rev.: $1,590,209,000
Approx. Number Employees: 1,330
Year Founded: 1926
Business Description:
Electric Power Utility Company
S.I.C.: 4939; 4911; 4931
N.A.I.C.S.: 221111; 221119; 221122
Media: 2-3-4-6-14-15-23-24
Personnel:
J. Barnie Beasley, Jr. *(Chm & Pres/CEO-Southern Nuclear)*
Anthony J. Topazi *(Pres & CEO-Mississippi Power)*
Scott Teel *(CFO & VP)*
W. Ron Hinson *(Controller & Chief Acctg Officer)*
G. Edison Holland, Jr. *(Gen Counsel, Sec & Exec VP)*
James H. Miller *(Gen Counsel & Sr VP)*
Cliff S. Thrasher *(Treas & Exec VP)*
Mickey A. Brown *(Exec VP)*
Andrew J. Dearman III *(Exec VP)*
Charles D. McCrary *(Exec VP)*
Chris Womack *(Exec VP)*
Judy M. Anderson *(Sr VP)*
Ellen L. Allen *(VP & Loans Ops Mgr)*
Francis M. Fisher *(VP-Customer Ops)*
Sandy Sims *(Mgr-Pub Affairs)*
Lynn Erickson *(Specialist-Comm)*
Advertising Agency:
Fitzgerald+CO
3060 Peachtree Rd NW
Atlanta, GA 30305
Tel.: (404) 504-6900
Fax: (404) 239-0548

HAWAIIAN ELECTRIC COMPANY, INC.

(Holding of Hawaiian Electric Industries, Inc.)
(d/b/a HECO)
900 Richards St
Honolulu, HI 96813-2919
Mailing Address:
PO Box 3978
Honolulu, HI 96840-0001
Tel.: (808) 548-7311
Fax: (808) 543-4747
Web Site: www.heco.com
Approx. Rev.: $2,382,366,000
Approx. Number Employees: 2,318
Year Founded: 1891
Business Description:
Electric Power Distribution & Generation Services
S.I.C.: 4939; 4911; 4931
N.A.I.C.S.: 221122; 221119
Media: 2-6-7-8-9-10-22-23-24
Distr.: Reg.
Budget Set: Sept.
Personnel:
Constance H. Lau *(Chm)*
Richard M. Rosenblum *(Pres & CEO)*
Tayne S.Y. Sekimura *(CFO & Sr VP)*
Susan A. Li *(Gen Counsel & VP)*
Robert A. Alm *(Exec VP-Pub Affairs)*

HAWAIIAN TELCOM COMMUNICATIONS, INC.

(Sub. of Hawaiian Telcom Holdco, Inc.)
1177 Bishop St
Honolulu, HI 96813
Tel.: (808) 546-4511
Tel.: (808) 643-3456
Fax: (808) 546-6194
E-mail: customer.relations@hawaiiantel.com
Web Site: www.hawaiiantel.com
Sales Range: $450-499.9 Million
Approx. Number Employees: 1,504
Business Description:
Telecommunications Products & Services
S.I.C.: 4813; 4812; 4899; 7375
N.A.I.C.S.: 517310; 517110; 517212; 517910; 518111
Advertising Expenditures: $9,300,000
Personnel:
James A. Attwood, Jr. *(Vice Chm)*
Stephen C. Gray *(Vice Chm)*
Eric K. Yeaman *(Pres & CEO)*
Robert F. Reich *(CFO)*
Rose Hauser *(CIO & Sr VP)*
John Komeiji *(Gen Counsel & Sr VP)*
Michael Edl *(Sr VP-Network Svcs)*
Craig T. Inouye *(Sr VP-Sls)*
Geoffrey Loui *(Sr VP)*
Brian Tanner *(Dir-IR)*
Ann Nishida *(Sr Mgr-Corp Comm)*
John K. Duncan *(Accountant)*

HECTOR COMMUNICATIONS CORPORATION

(Joint Venture of Arvig Enterprises Inc., Blue Earth Valley Communications & New Ulm Telecom, Inc.)
27 N Minneota St
New Ulm, MN 56073
Tel.: (507) 354-2500
Fax: (507) 359-4650
Toll Free: (866) 451-8601
E-mail: unisupport@newulmtel.net
Web Site: www.hectorcom.com
Sales Range: $25-49.9 Million
Approx. Number Employees: 125
Year Founded: 1990
Business Description:
Holding Company; Local Telecommunication Services
S.I.C.: 6719; 4813; 4841
N.A.I.C.S.: 551112; 515210; 517110; 517310
Advertising Expenditures: $4,108,218
Media: 8-9-23-24-25
Personnel:
Bill Otis *(Chm & Pres)*

HITACHI COMMUNICATIONS AMERICA INC.

(Formerly Hitachi Telecom (USA), Inc.)
(Sub. of Hitachi America, Ltd.)
3617 Pkwy Ln
Norcross, GA 30092-2829
Tel.: (770) 446-8820
Fax: (770) 242-1414
E-mail: info@hitel.com
Web Site: www.hitachi-cta.com
Approx. Number Employees: 90
Business Description:
Telecommunications Solutions Mfr & Developer
S.I.C.: 3661
N.A.I.C.S.: 334210
Media: 10
Personnel:
Geomokazu Waguri *(VP-Fin)*
Pete Westafer *(Mgr-Mktg Comm)*
Advertising Agency:
Calysto Communications
861 Sapphire Ln Sugar Hill
Atlanta, GA 30518
Tel.: (404) 266-2060
Fax: (404) 266-2041

HOOSIER ENERGY RURAL ELECTRIC COOPERATIVE INC.

7398 N State Rd 37
Bloomington, IN 47404-9424
Tel.: (812) 876-2021
Fax: (812) 876-3476
Web Site: www.hepn.com
Approx. Number Employees: 450
Year Founded: 1935
Business Description:
Electricity Services
S.I.C.: 4931
N.A.I.C.S.: 221119
Personnel:
J. Steven Smith *(Pres & CEO)*
Mike Rampley *(Sr VP-Mktg & Bus Dev)*
Randy Haymaker *(Dir-Pub Affairs)*
Advertising Agency:
St. Claire Group
716 Adams St Ste C
Carmel, IN 46032
Tel.: (317) 816-8810
Fax: (317) 816-8820

HYDRO-QUEBEC

75 Rene Levesque Blvd W
Montreal, QC H2Z 1A4, Canada
Tel.: (514) 289-2211
Fax: (514) 289-3158
Web Site: www.hydroquebec.com
Approx. Rev.: $12,570,201,160
Approx. Number Employees: 19,521
Year Founded: 1944
Business Description:
Public Utility; Energy Supplier
S.I.C.: 4939; 4911
N.A.I.C.S.: 221111; 221122
Media: 2-6-11
Personnel:
Michael L. Turcotte *(Chm)*
Thierry Vandal *(Pres & CEO)*
Isabelle Thellen *(Officer-Pub Affairs)*
Andre Boulanger *(Pres-Hydro-Quebec TransEnergie)*
Richard Cacchione *(Pres-Hydro-Quebec Generation)*
Isabelle Courville *(Pres-Hydro-Quebec Distr)*
Real Laporte *(Pres-Hydro-Quebec Equipment & Shared Svcs)*
Marie Jose Nadeau *(Exec VP-Corp Affairs & Sec Gen)*
Elie Saheb *(Exec VP-Tech)*
Jean-Hugues Lafleur *(VP-Fin, Treasury & Pension Fund)*
Michel Martinez *(VP-HR)*
Joanne Chevrier *(Mgr-Mktg)*

IDACORP, INC.

1221 W Idaho St
Boise, ID 83702-5627
Mailing Address:
PO Box 70
Boise, ID 83707-0070
Tel.: (208) 388-2200
Fax: (208) 388-6955
E-mail: iwebster@idahopower.com
Web Site: www.idacorpinc.com
Approx. Rev.: $1,036,029,000
Approx. Number Employees: 2,032
Year Founded: 1998
Business Description:
Energy Holding Company
S.I.C.: 6719; 4911; 4931; 4939
N.A.I.C.S.: 551112; 221111; 221119; 221122
Advertising Expenditures: $500,000
Media: 1-5-8-9-17-23-24-25
Distr.: Reg.
Budget Set: Oct.
Personnel:
J. LaMont Keen *(Pres & CEO)*
Darrel T. Anderson *(CFO & Sr VP-Admin Svcs)*
Dennis C. Gribble *(CIO & VP)*

Key to Media (For complete agency information see *The Advertising Red Books-Agencies* edition):
1. Bus. Publs. 2. Cable T.V. 3. Catalogs & Directories. 4. Co-op Adv. 5. Consumer Mags. 6. D.M. to Bus. Estab.7. D.M. to Consumers
8. Daily Newsp. 9. Exhibits/Trade Shows 10. Foreign 11. Infomercial 12. Internet Adv.13. Multimedia 14. Network Radio
15. Network T.V. 16. Newsp. Distr. Mags. 17. Other 18. Outdoor (Posters, Transit) 19. Point of Purchase20. Premiums, Novelties
21. Product Samples 22. Special Events Mktg. 23. Spot Radio 24. Spot T.V. 25. Weekly Newsp. 26. Yellow Page Adv.

IDACORP, Inc. — (Continued)

Ken W. Petersen *(Chief Acctg Officer & Corp Controller)*
Rex Blackburn *(Gen Counsel & Sr VP)*
Steven R. Keen *(Treas & VP-Fin)*
Daniel B. Minor *(Exec VP-Ops)*
John R. Gale *(Sr VP-Corp Responsibility)*
Warren Kline *(VP-Customer Svc & Reg Ops)*
Luci K. McDonald *(VP-HR & Corp Svcs)*
Lawrence Spencer *(Dir-IR)*
Brands & Products:
IDACORP

INDIANAPOLIS POWER & LIGHT COMPANY

(Sub. of The AES Corporation)
1 Monument Cir
Indianapolis, IN 46206
Mailing Address:
PO Box 1595
Indianapolis, IN 46206-1595
Tel.: (317) 261-8261
Fax: (703) 528-4510
E-mail: publicaffairs.ipl@aes.com
Web Site: www.iplpower.com
Approx. Rev.: $1,079,113,000
Approx. Number Employees: 1,500
Year Founded: 1983
Business Description:
Electric Power Distribution & Generation Services
S.I.C.: 4931; 4911; 4939
N.A.I.C.S.: 221119; 221122
Media: 9-18-22-25
Distr.: Reg.
Personnel:
William P. Marsan *(Gen Counsel, Sec & VP)*
Ronald E. Talbot *(Sr VP-Power Supply)*
Ken Zagzebski *(Sr VP-Customer Ops)*
Geoffrey M. Gailey *(VP-HR)*
Jim Sadtler *(VP-Supply & Tech)*
Crystal Livers-Powers *(Dir-Corp Comm)*
Advertising Agency:
Borshoff
47 S Pennsylvania St Ste 500
Indianapolis, IN 46204
Tel.: (317) 631-6400
Fax: (317) 631-6499

INTEGRYS ENERGY GROUP, INC.

130 E Randolph Dr
Chicago, IL 60601
Tel.: (312) 228-5400
Toll Free: (800) 669-1269
Web Site: www.integrysgroup.com
E-Mail For Key Personnel:
President: lweyers@wpsr.com
Public Relations: tmeinz@wpsr.com
Approx. Rev.: $5,203,200,000
Approx. Number Employees: 4,612
Year Founded: 1993
Business Description:
Holding Company; Electric Power Generation & Distribution Services
S.I.C.: 6719; 4911; 4924; 4931; 4939
N.A.I.C.S.: 551112; 221119; 221122; 221210
Media: 7-8-13
Personnel:
Charles A. Schrock *(Chm, Pres & CEO)*
Joseph P. O'Leary *(CFO & Sr VP)*
Charles A. Cloninger *(CMO)*
Barth J. Wolf *(Chief Legal Officer, Sec & VP)*
Lawrence T. Borgard *(Pres/COO-Utilities)*
Daniel J. Verbanac *(Pres-Integrys EnergySvcs)*
Phillip M. Mikulsky *(Exec VP-Bus Performance & Shared Svcs)*
Barbara A. Nick *(Sr VP-Energy Delivery & Customer Svc)*
David W. Harpole *(VP-IT & Project Svcs)*
William D. Laakso *(VP-HR)*
Advertising Agency:
Ellingsen Brady Advertising (EBA)
207 E Buffalo St Ste 400
Milwaukee, WI 53202
Tel.: (414) 224-9424
Fax: (414) 224-9432

INTERACTIVE COMMUNICATIONS INC

(d/b/a InComm)
250 Williams St Ste M-100
Atlanta, GA 30303
Tel.: (770) 240-6100
Fax: (404) 601-1000
Toll Free: (888) USSOUTH
E-mail: info@incomm.com
Web Site: www.incomm.com
Approx. Number Employees: 270
Year Founded: 1992
Business Description:
Holding Company; Phone Cards, ISPs & Telecommunications Services; Switch-Based Carrier
S.I.C.: 7389
N.A.I.C.S.: 561421
Advertising Expenditures: $200,000
Media: 2-4-6-7-8-9-17
Distr.: Natl.
Personnel:
M. Brooks Smith *(Pres & CEO)*
Daniel M. Kahrs *(COO)*
Phil Graves *(Exec VP)*
Brenda Agee *(VP-Admin & Fin)*
Edward Vargo *(Mgr-Mktg Svcs)*
Brands & Products:
INTERACTIVE COMMUNICATIONS

INTERDIGITAL, INC.

781 3rd Ave
King of Prussia, PA 19406
Tel.: (610) 878-7800
Fax: (610) 992-7842
E-mail: webmaster@interdigital.com
Web Site: www.interdigital.com
Approx. Rev.: $394,545,000
Approx. Number Employees: 300
Year Founded: 1972
Business Description:
Digital Wireless Telephone Systems Mfr
S.I.C.: 3674; 3661; 7373
N.A.I.C.S.: 334413; 334210; 541512
Export
Advertising Expenditures: $7,914,000
Media: 9-14-15-23-24-25
Distr.: Intl.; Natl.
Budget Set: Nov.
Personnel:
Steven Terrell Clontz *(Chm)*
William J. Merritt *(Pres & CEO)*
Scott A. McQuilkin *(CFO)*
Gary D. Isaacs *(Chief Admin Officer)*
Richard J. Brezski *(VP, Controller & Chief Acctg Officer)*
Stephen W. Sprecher *(Gen Counsel & Sec)*
Mark A. Lemmo *(Exec VP-Bus Dev & Product Mgmt)*
Janet Meenehan Point *(Exec VP-Comm & IR)*
Lawrence F. Shay *(Exec VP-Intellectual Property & Intellectual Property Counsel)*
Jack Indekeu *(Dir-Mktg)*
Brett Attebery *(Sr Mgr-Strategic Plng)*
Brands & Products:
B CDMA
INTERDIGITAL
SLIMCHIP
ULTRAPHONE
WIRELESS TECHNOLOGIES TO MOVE YOUR IDEAS

INTERMOUNTAIN GAS COMPANY

(Sub. of MDU Resources Group, Inc.)
555 S Cole Rd
Boise, ID 83709-0940
Mailing Address:
PO Box 7608
Boise, ID 83707-1608
Tel.: (208) 377-6000
Tel.: (208) 377-6840
Fax: (208) 377-6097
Web Site: www.intgas.com
Sales Range: $350-399.9 Million
Approx. Number Employees: 332
Year Founded: 1950
Business Description:
Natural Gas Distr
S.I.C.: 4924
N.A.I.C.S.: 221210
Media: 5-8-24
Distr.: Reg.
Budget Set: Oct.
Personnel:
David L. Goodin *(Pres & CEO)*
Eldon Book *(COO & Exec VP)*
Brent Wilde *(Dir-Mktg & Indus Svcs)*
Advertising Agency:
DaviesMoore
277 N Sixth St Ste 3B
Boise, ID 83702
Tel.: (208) 472-2129
Fax: (208) 472-7450
(Natural Gas)

ITC HOLDINGS CORP.

27175 Energy Way
Novi, MI 48377
Tel.: (248) 946-3000
Fax: (248) 374-7140
Web Site: www.itc-holdings.com
Approx. Rev.: $696,843,000
Approx. Number Employees: 433
Year Founded: 2002
Business Description:
Holding Company; Electric Power Transmission Services
S.I.C.: 6719; 4911
N.A.I.C.S.: 551112; 221121
Personnel:
Joseph L. Welch *(Chm, Pres & CEO)*
Cameron M. Bready *(CFO, Treas & Exec VP)*
Jon E. Jipping *(COO & Exec VP)*
Denis Y. DesRosiers *(CIO & VP-IT)*
Linda H. Blair *(Chief Bus Officer & Exec VP)*
Gregory Ioanidis *(Pres-ITC Michigan & VP-ITC Holdings Corp)*
Daniel J. Oginsky *(Gen Counsel & Sr VP)*
Christine Mason Soneral *(VP & Gen Counsel-Utility Ops)*
Patricia A. Wenzel *(Dir-Treasury & Risk Mgmt)*
Advertising Agency:
Barkley Public Relations
1740 Main St
Kansas City, MO 64108
Tel.: (816) 842-1500

JERSEY CENTRAL POWER & LIGHT COMPANY

(Sub. of FirstEnergy Corp.)
c/o FirstEnergy Corp 76 S Main St
Akron, OH 44308
Toll Free: (800) 736-3402
Approx. Rev.: $3,027,088,000
Approx. Number Employees: 1,434
Year Founded: 1946
Business Description:
Electric Power Distr
S.I.C.: 4939; 4911; 4931
N.A.I.C.S.: 221122; 221111; 221119
Media: 17
Distr.: Natl.
Personnel:
Donald Lynch *(Pres)*

KANSAS CITY POWER & LIGHT COMPANY

(Holding of Great Plains Energy Incorporated)
1200 Main St
Kansas City, MO 64105
Mailing Address:
PO Box 418679
Kansas City, MO 64141-9679
Tel.: (816) 556-2200
Fax: (816) 556-2661
E-mail: custserv@kcpl.com
Web Site: www.kcpl.com
E-Mail For Key Personnel:
Public Relations: investor.info@kcpl.com
Approx. Rev.: $1,517,100,000
Year Founded: 1882
Business Description:
Electric Power Generation & Distribution Services
S.I.C.: 4911; 4939
N.A.I.C.S.: 221122; 221112; 221113
Media: 2-7-8-9-10-13-15-18-20-22-23-25
Distr.: Reg.
Budget Set: Sept.
Personnel:
Michael J. Chesser *(Chm & CEO)*
William H. Downey *(Pres & COO)*
Terry Bassham *(CFO & Exec VP-Fin & Strategic Dev)*
Heather A. Humphrey *(Gen Counsel & VP-HR)*
Michael L. Deggendorf *(Sr VP)*
Scott H. Heidtbrink *(Sr VP-Corp Svcs)*
Chuck Tickles *(VP-IT)*
Brands & Products:
ACCOUNTLINK
Advertising Agency:
Kuhn & Wittenborn, Inc.
2405 Grand Blvd Ste 600
Kansas City, MO 64108-2519

Key to Media (For complete agency information see *The Advertising Red Books-Agencies* edition):
1. Bus. Publs. 2. Cable T.V. 3. Catalogs & Directories. 4. Co-op Adv. 5. Consumer Mags. 6. D.M. to Bus. Estab.7. D.M. to Consumers 8. Daily Newsp. 9. Exhibits/Trade Shows 10. Foreign 11. Infomercial 12. Internet Adv.13. Multimedia 14. Network Radio 15. Network T.V. 16. Newsp. Distr. Mags. 17. Other 18. Outdoor (Posters, Transit) 19. Point of Purchase20. Premiums, Novelties 21. Product Samples 22. Special Events Mktg. 23. Spot Radio 24. Spot T.V. 25. Weekly Newsp. 26. Yellow Page Adv.

Tel.: (816) 471-7888
Fax: (816) 471-7530

KENTUCKY UTILITIES COMPANY
(Sub. of LG&E and KU Energy LLC)
1 Quality St
Lexington, KY 40507-1428
Tel.: (859) 255-2100
Fax: (859) 367-1185
Toll Free: (800) 981-0600
Web Site: www.kuenergy.com
Sales Range: $1-4.9 Billion
Approx. Number Employees: 895
Year Founded: 1912
Business Description:
Regulated Electric Utility
S.I.C.: 4939; 4931
N.A.I.C.S.: 221111; 221119
Media: 2-7-8-9-17-23-24-25
Distr.: Direct to Consumer; Reg.
Budget Set: Sept.
Personnel:
Victor A. Staffieri *(Pres & CEO)*
Brands & Products:
KU

LACLEDE GAS COMPANY
(Sub. of The Laclede Group, Inc.)
720 Olive St
Saint Louis, MO 63101
Tel.: (314) 342-0500
Fax: (314) 641-2166
Toll Free: (800) 887-4173
E-mail: customerservice@lacledegas.com
Web Site: www.lacledegas.com
Approx. Number Employees: 1,697
Year Founded: 1857
Business Description:
Natural Gas Distr
S.I.C.: 4924; 4922
N.A.I.C.S.: 221210; 486210
Media: 3-7-8-9-14-23-24-25
Distr.: Direct to Consumer; Reg.
Budget Set: Sept.
Personnel:
Douglas H. Yaeger *(Chm, Pres & CEO)*
Mary Caola Kullman *(Chief Governance Officer & Sec)*
Mark C. Darrell *(Gen Counsel)*
Lynn D. Rawlings *(Treas & Asst Sec)*
Richard A. Skau *(Sr VP-HR)*
Michael R. Spotanski *(Sr VP-Ops & Mktg)*
Ellen L. Theroff *(Asst VP-Admin & Assoc Gen Counsel)*
Craig R. Hoeferlin *(Asst VP-Engrg & Field Svcs)*
Advertising Agency:
Barkley
304 N Broadway
Saint Louis, MO 63102
Tel.: (314) 727-9500
Fax: (314) 727-0561
Toll Free: (800) 886-0561

LAPP INSULATOR COMPANY, LLC
130 Gilbert St
Le Roy, NY 14482
Tel.: (585) 768-6221
Fax: (585) 768-6219
Telex: 6854129 LAPINS
E-mail: info@lappinsulator.com
Web Site: www.lappinsulator.com
Approx. Number Employees: 350
Year Founded: 1916
Business Description:
Mfr of High Voltage Insulators
S.I.C.: 3264; 3644
N.A.I.C.S.: 327113; 335932
Advertising Expenditures: $200,000
Bus. Publs.: $50,000; Catalogs & Directories: $30,000; D.M. to Bus. Estab.: $10,000; Exhibits/Trade Shows: $50,000; Foreign: $5,000; Other: $35,000; Premiums, Novelties: $10,000; Product Samples: $10,000
Distr.: Intl.; Natl.
Budget Set: Oct.
Personnel:
Rob Johnson *(COO & VP)*
Brands & Products:
LAPP INSULATORS
LINE POST
OUR CUSTOMERS POWER THE FUTURE
RG
RODURFLEX
STATION POST

LATTICE INC.
7150 N Park Dr Ste 500
Pennsauken, NJ 08109
Tel.: (856) 910-1166
Fax: (856) 910-1811
E-mail: info@latticeincorporated.com
Web Site: www.latticeincorporated.com
E-Mail For Key Personnel:
Sales Director: sales@scidyn.com
Approx. Sls.: $13,538,319
Approx. Number Employees: 44
Year Founded: 1973
Business Description:
Designs, Mfr & Markets Modular Microprocessor Based Instruments & Systems Used by the Telephone Operating Companies & Other Suppliers of Telecommunication Services
S.I.C.: 3661; 3663
N.A.I.C.S.: 334210; 334220
Export
Advertising Expenditures: $300,000
Media: 2-4-7-10-20
Distr.: Intl.
Budget Set: Dec.
Personnel:
Paul Burgess *(Pres & CEO)*
Joe Noto *(CFO)*
Thomas R. Spadaro *(VP-Engrg)*
Brands & Products:
THE FABRIC OF SECURE COMMUNICATIONS
LATTICE INCORPORATED
SCIDYN
VFX-250S

LG&E AND KU ENERGY LLC
(Formerly E.ON U.S. LLC)
(Sub. of PPL Corporation)
220 W Main St
Louisville, KY 40232
Tel.: (502) 627-2000
Fax: (502) 627-3609
Web Site: www.lge-ku.com
Sales Range: $900-999.9 Million
Approx. Number Employees: 3,500
Year Founded: 1989
Business Description:
Electric & Natural Gas Distr
S.I.C.: 4911; 4924; 4931; 4939
N.A.I.C.S.: 221122; 221119; 221210
Media: 1-2-7-8-9-10-13-17-20-22-23-24-25-26
Distr.: Direct to Consumer; Reg.
Personnel:
Victor A. Staffieri *(Chm, Pres & CEO)*
S. Bradford Rives *(CFO)*
John R. McCall *(Gen Counsel, Sec, Exec VP & Chief Compliance Officer)*
Dorothy O'Brien *(VP-Legal & Environ & Deputy Gen Counsel)*
Chris Hermann *(Sr VP-Energy Delivery)*
Paula H. Pottinger *(Sr VP-HR)*
Paul W. Thompson *(Sr VP-Energy Svcs)*
R.W. Chip Keeling *(VP-Comm)*

LINCOLN ELECTRIC SYSTEM
1040 O St
Lincoln, NE 68508-3609
Tel.: (402) 475-4211
Fax: (402) 475-9759
E-mail: info@les.com
Web Site: www.les.com
Sales Range: $150-199.9 Million
Approx. Number Employees: 450
Year Founded: 1966
Business Description:
Electric Utility Services
S.I.C.: 4931
N.A.I.C.S.: 221119
Personnel:
Douglas Curry *(CEO)*
Debbra Hoy *(VP-HR)*
Advertising Agency:
Bailey Lauerman
1248 O St Ste 900
Lincoln, NE 68508-1460
Tel.: (402) 475-2800
Fax: (402) 475-5115

LIVETV AIRFONE, INC.
(Sub. of LiveTV LLC)
2809 Butterfield Rd
Oak Brook, IL 60522-9000
Tel.: (630) 572-1800
Fax: (800) 909-7249
Toll Free: (800) AIRFONE
Sales Range: $50-74.9 Million
Approx. Number Employees: 175
Business Description:
Airborne Voice & Data Communications Services
S.I.C.: 4812
N.A.I.C.S.: 517212
Media: 2-6-7-8-10-13-18-19
Brands & Products:
AIRFONE SERVICE

LONG ISLAND POWER AUTHORITY
333 Earle Ovington Blvd Ste 403
Uniondale, NY 11553
Tel.: (516) 222-7700
Fax: (516) 222-9137
Toll Free: (800) 490-0025
E-mail: lipacustomerservice@lipower.org
Web Site: www.lipower.org
Approx. Number Employees: 5,187
Year Founded: 1998
Business Description:
Electrical Transmission & Distribution Systems
S.I.C.: 4931
N.A.I.C.S.: 221119
Media: 2-13
Personnel:
Howard Steinberg *(Chm)*
Herb Hogue *(CFO)*
Michael D. Hervey *(COO)*
Bruce Germano *(VP-Customer Svc)*

MCI, LLC
(Sub. of Verizon Communications Inc.)
22001 Loudoun County Pkwy
Ashburn, VA 20147
Tel.: (601) 460-5600
Fax: (601) 460-8269
Toll Free: (877) 624-1000
Web Site: www.mci.com
Sales Range: $75-99.9 Million
Year Founded: 1983
Business Description:
Long-Distance Voice, Data & Video Services
S.I.C.: 4813; 8721
N.A.I.C.S.: 517310; 541219
Advertising Expenditures: $400,000,000
Media: 3-6-13-14-15-22-23
Personnel:
Grace Trent *(Sr VP-Comm)*
Brands & Products:
MCI
UUNET

MEMPHIS LIGHT, GAS & WATER
220 S Main St
Memphis, TN 38103-3917
Mailing Address:
PO Box 430
Memphis, TN 38101-0430
Tel.: (901) 544-6549
Fax: (901) 528-4547
E-mail: corpcomm@mlgw.com
Web Site: www.mlgw.com
Approx. Number Employees: 5,100
Year Founded: 1939
Business Description:
Municipal Utility Services
S.I.C.: 4931
N.A.I.C.S.: 221119
Advertising Expenditures: $250,000
Media: 3-9-15-18-23-24-25
Distr.: Direct to Consumer
Budget Set: Jan.
Personnel:
Jerry Collins *(Pres & CEO)*
John McCullough *(CFO, Treas, Sec & VP)*
Mark Heuberger *(Chief Comm Officer)*
Cheryl W. Patterson *(Gen Counsel & VP)*
Alonzo Weaver *(VP-Ops & Engrg)*
Gale Jones Carson *(Dir-Corp Comm)*
Cliff DeBerry *(Dir-Analysis & Strategy & Performance)*
Jozelle Booker *(Mgr-Contracts)*

MERCURY SOLAR SYSTEMS INC.
36 Midland Ave
Port Chester, NY 10573
Tel.: (914) 637-9700
Fax: (914) 637-9713
Toll Free: (877) 6GETSUN
E-mail: gogreen@mercurysolarsystems.com
Web Site: www.mercurysolarsystems.com
Sales Range: $25-49.9 Million
Approx. Number Employees: 100
Year Founded: 2006

Key to Media (For complete agency information see *The Advertising Red Books-Agencies* edition):
1. Bus. Publs. 2. Cable T.V. 3. Catalogs & Directories. 4. Co-op Adv. 5. Consumer Mags. 6. D.M. to Bus. Estab.7. D.M. to Consumers
8. Daily Newsp. 9. Exhibits/Trade Shows 10. Foreign 11. Infomercial 12. Internet Adv.13. Multimedia 14. Network Radio
15. Network T.V. 16. Newsp. Distr. Mags. 17. Other 18. Outdoor (Posters, Transit) 19. Point of Purchase20. Premiums, Novelties
21. Product Samples 22. Special Events Mktg. 23. Spot Radio 24. Spot T.V. 25. Weekly Newsp. 26. Yellow Page Adv.

Mercury Solar Systems Inc. — (Continued)
Business Description:
Solar & Thermal Energy Systems Designer & Installer
S.I.C.: 4931
N.A.I.C.S.: 221119
Media: 8-9-10-13-22-23-25
Personnel:
J. Jared Haines *(Pres)*
Frank J. Alfano *(CEO)*
Anthony Coschigano, III *(Sr VP-Ops)*
Lloyd Hoffstatter *(VP-Engrg)*
Robert Stickney *(VP-Sls)*

METROPCS COMMUNICATIONS, INC.
2250 Lakeside Blvd
Richardson, TX 75082-4304
Tel.: (214) 570-5800
Toll Free: (888) 863-8768
E-mail: metropcs@metropcs.com
Web Site: www.metropcs.com
Approx. Rev.: $4,069,353,000
Approx. Number Employees: 3,600
Year Founded: 1994
Business Description:
Wireless Broadband Personal Communication Services
S.I.C.: 4812; 4899
N.A.I.C.S.: 517212; 517910
Advertising Expenditures: $150,800,000
Personnel:
Roger D. Linquist *(Chm, Pres & CEO)*
J. Braxton Carter *(CFO & Exec VP)*
Thomas C. Keys *(COO)*
John J. Olsen *(CIO & Sr VP)*
Malcolm M. Lorang *(CTO & Sr VP)*
Christine B. Kornegay *(Chief Acctg Officer, Sr VP & Controller)*
Mark A. Stachiw *(Gen Counsel, Sec & Exec VP)*
Keith D. Terreri *(Treas & VP-Fin)*
Ed Chao *(Sr VP-Engrg & Network Ops)*
Douglas S. Glen *(Sr VP-Corp Dev)*
Phillip T. Terry *(Sr VP-Corp Mktg)*
Tom Currier *(VP-HR)*
Jim Mathias *(Dir-IR)*
Dick Elpers *(Product Mgr)*
Brands & Products:
METROPCS
PERMISSION TO SPEAK FREELY
UNLIMIT YOURSELF.
Advertising Agencies:
The Richards Group, Inc.
8750 N Central Expy Ste 100
Dallas, TX 75231-6430
Tel.: (214) 891-5700
Fax: (214) 265-2933

Springbox, Ltd.
706 Congress Ave Ste A
Austin, TX 78701
Tel.: (512) 391-0065
Fax: (512) 391-0064

MIDAMERICAN ENERGY HOLDINGS COMPANY
(Holding of Berkshire Hathaway Inc.)
666 Grand Ave Ste 500
Des Moines, IA 50309-2580
Mailing Address:
PO Box 657
Des Moines, IA 50303-0657
Tel.: (515) 242-4300
Fax: (515) 281-2389
Toll Free: (888) 427-5632
E-mail: info@midamerican.com
Web Site: www.midamerican.com
E-Mail For Key Personnel:
Public Relations: mareinders@midamerican.com
Approx. Rev.: $11,127,000,000
Approx. Number Employees: 15,800
Year Founded: 1999
Business Description:
Holding Company; Electric & Gas Distribution & Generation Services
S.I.C.: 4939; 4911; 4924; 4931; 6719
N.A.I.C.S.: 221122; 221119; 221210; 551112
Advertising Expenditures: $850,000
Media: 1-2-3-5-6-7-8-9-10-13-18-20-22-23-24-25-26
Distr.: Reg.
Budget Set: Aug.
Personnel:
Gregory E. Abel *(Chm, Pres & CEO)*
Patrick J. Goodman *(CFO & Sr VP)*
Maureen E. Sammon *(Chief Admin Officer & Sr VP)*
Douglas L. Anderson *(Gen Counsel & Sr VP)*
A. Robert Lasich *(Gen Counsel & VP)*
Ann Thelen *(Dir-Comm & Media Rels)*
Mark Reinders *(Comm Mgr)*
Brands & Products:
SAFETY LINK
Advertising Agency:
Parker Advertising Service, Inc.
101 N Pointe Blvd 2nd Fl
Lancaster, PA 17601
Tel.: (717) 581-1966
Fax: (717) 581-1566
Toll Free: (800) 396-3306

MIDDLESEX WATER COMPANY
1500 Ronson Rd
Iselin, NJ 08830-3049
Mailing Address:
PO Box 1500
Iselin, NJ 08830-0452
Tel.: (732) 634-1500
Fax: (732) 750-5981
E-mail: info@middlesexwater.com
Web Site: www.middlesexwater.com
Approx. Rev.: $102,735,000
Approx. Number Employees: 292
Year Founded: 1897
Business Description:
Water & Wastewater System
S.I.C.: 4941; 4959
N.A.I.C.S.: 221310; 562998
Media: 1-10-25
Personnel:
J. Richard Tompkins *(Chm)*
Dennis W. Doll *(Pres & CEO)*
A. Bruce O'Connor *(CFO & VP)*
Kenneth J. Quinn *(Gen Counsel, Treas, Sec & VP)*
James P. Garrett *(VP-HR)*

MINNESOTA POWER
(Sub. of Allete, Inc.)
30 W Superior St
Duluth, MN 55802-2030
Tel.: (218) 722-2641
Fax: (218) 723-3983
Toll Free: (800) 228-4966
E-mail: customerservice@mnpower.com
Web Site: www.mnpower.com
Sales Range: $1-9.9 Million
Approx. Number Employees: 1,300
Business Description:
Generator, Transmitter & Distributor of Electricity
S.I.C.: 6519
N.A.I.C.S.: 531190
Personnel:
Alan Hodnik *(COO)*
Eric Norberg *(Sr VP-Strategy & Plng)*
Advertising Agency:
Black & Veatch Corporate Marketing & Branding
11401 Lamar Ave
Overland Park, KS 66211
Tel.: (913) 458-2000
Fax: (913) 458-2934

MITEL NETWORKS, INC.
(Sub. of Mitel Networks Corporation)
7300 W boston st
Chandler, AZ 85226
Tel.: (480) 858-9600
Fax: (480) 894-4012
Web Site: www.mitel.com
Approx. Sls.: $458,364,000
Approx. Number Employees: 1,949
Year Founded: 1969
Business Description:
Communication Solutions to Small & Medium Sized Businesses; Digital Communication Platforms & Software; Computer Telephone Integration; Unified Messaging Software; Network Services; Network & Data Products; Internet Connectivity Products; Long Distance Call Services; Maintenance & Leasing & Support Services
S.I.C.: 3661; 5045
N.A.I.C.S.: 334210; 423430
Import Export
Advertising Expenditures: $605,000
Media: 1-2-5-7-10-13-18-20-22-26
Distr.: Intl.
Budget Set: Sept.
Personnel:
Steve Spooner *(CFO)*
Brands & Products:
ATTENDANT CONSOLE
AXXESS
COMMSOURCE
CONNECTION ASSISTANT
ENCORE
ENCORECX
ENTERPRISE
IDS/MEDLEY
INTER-TEL
INTERPRISE
NETSOLUTIONS
UNIFIED COMMUNICATOR
THE VOICE OF THE INTERNET

MOMENTUM TELECOM, INC.
2700 Corp Dr Ste 200
Birmingham, AL 35242
Tel.: (205) 978-4400
Fax: (205) 978-4401
Web Site: www.momentumtelecom.com
Approx. Number Employees: 250
Year Founded: 1996
Business Description:
Telephone Communication Services
S.I.C.: 9631
N.A.I.C.S.: 926130
Personnel:
Alan Creighton *(Pres & CEO)*
Auri Vizgaitis *(VP-IT)*
Advertising Agency:
Blanc & Otus Public Relations
60 Green St
San Francisco, CA 94111
Tel.: (415) 856-5100
Fax: (415) 856-5193

MTS ALLSTREAM, INC.
(Sub. of Manitoba Telecom Services, Inc.)
200 Wellington St W
Toronto, ON M5V 3G2, Canada
Tel.: (416) 345-2000
Fax: (416) 345-2840
Toll Free: (888) 288-2273
Web Site: www.allstream.com
Sales Range: $700-749.9 Million
Approx. Number Employees: 4,000
Year Founded: 1999
Business Description:
Telecommunication Services
S.I.C.: 4813
N.A.I.C.S.: 517110
Media: 7-8
Personnel:
Thomas E. Stefanson *(Chm)*
Dean Prevost *(Pres)*
Pierre J. Blouin *(CEO)*
Chris Peirce *(Chief Corp Officer)*
Mark Welch *(Head-Sls)*
Jocelyne M. Cote-O'Hara *(Dir-Corp)*
Gregory J. Hanson *(Dir-Corp)*
Lesley McFarlane *(Dir-Bus Plng & Operational Performance)*
Angie Specic *(Dir-Customer Experience Strategy)*

MUNICIPAL ELECTRIC AUTHORITY OF GEORGIA
1470 Riveredge Pkwy
Atlanta, GA 30328-4686
Tel.: (770) 563-0300
Fax: (770) 953-3141
Toll Free: (800) 333-6324
Web Site: www.meagpower.org
Sales Range: $700-749.9 Million
Approx. Number Employees: 100
Year Founded: 1975
Business Description:
Public Power Joint Action Agency
S.I.C.: 9631
N.A.I.C.S.: 926130
Advertising Expenditures: $1,144,000
Media: 2-7-8-10-13-26
Personnel:
Kerry S. Waldron *(Vice Chm)*
Robert P. Johnston *(Pres & CEO)*
James E. Fuller *(CFO & Sr VP)*
Mary G. Jackson *(Chief Acctg Officer & VP)*
Paul Warfel *(Reg Mgr)*
Doug Moore *(Project Mgr)*

MXENERGY HOLDINGS INC.
595 Summer St Ste 300
Stamford, CT 06901
Mailing Address:
PO Box 8127
Stamford, CT 06905-8127
Tel.: (203) 356-1318
Fax: (203) 425-9562
Toll Free: (800) 785-4373
E-mail: mediarelations@mxenergy.com
Web Site: www.mxenergy.com
Approx. Sls.: $561,206,000
Approx. Number Employees: 203
Business Description:
Gas & Electricity Distr

Key to Media (For complete agency information see *The Advertising Red Books-Agencies* edition):
1. Bus. Publs. 2. Cable T.V. 3. Catalogs & Directories. 4. Co-op Adv. 5. Consumer Mags. 6. D.M. to Bus. Estab.7. D.M. to Consumers 8. Daily Newsp. 9. Exhibits/Trade Shows 10. Foreign 11. Infomercial 12. Internet Adv.13. Multimedia 14. Network Radio 15. Network T.V. 16. Newsp. Distr. Mags. 17. Other 18. Outdoor (Posters, Transit) 19. Point of Purchase20. Premiums, Novelties 21. Product Samples 22. Special Events Mktg. 23. Spot Radio 24. Spot T.V. 25. Weekly Newsp. 26. Yellow Page Adv.

S.I.C.: 4924; 4911; 4939
N.A.I.C.S.: 221210; 221122
Advertising Expenditures: $4,546,000
Media: 1-8
Personnel:
Jeffery A. Mayer *(CEO)*
Chaitu Parikh *(CFO & Exec VP)*
Gina Goldberg *(Sr VP-Sls & Mktg)*
Brands & Products:
MAX
MURPHY
MXENERGY
MXENERGY SAVERSGUIDE
MXENERGY WIZARD

NATIONAL FUEL GAS DISTRIBUTION CORP.

(Sub. of National Fuel Gas Company)
6363 Main St
Williamsville, NY 14221
Tel.: (716) 857-7000
Fax: (716) 857-6500
Toll Free: (800) 365-3234
E-mail: info@nationalfuelgas.com
Web Site: www.nationalfuelgas.com
Sales Range: $750-799.9 Million
Approx. Number Employees: 1,547
Year Founded: 1902
Business Description:
Natural Gas Public Utility
S.I.C.: 4924
N.A.I.C.S.: 221210
Media: 2-3-5-6-7-8-9-10-14-15-22-23-24-25
Distr.: Direct to Consumer; Reg.
Budget Set: Aug.
Personnel:
Anna Marie Cellino *(Pres)*
Carl M. Carlotti *(Sr VP)*
James D. Ramsdell *(Sr VP)*
Jeff Hart *(Asst VP-Utility Bus)*
Amy Shiley *(Gen Mgr-HR & Payroll Dept)*

NATIONAL GRID USA

(Sub. of National Grid plc)
40 Sylvin Rd
Waltham, MA 02451
Tel.: (781) 907-1520
Fax: (781) 522-1052
Web Site: www.nationalgridus.com
Sales Range: $1-4.9 Billion
Approx. Number Employees: 2,000
Year Founded: 1947
Business Description:
Holding Company; Owner of Public Utilities
S.I.C.: 4931
N.A.I.C.S.: 221119
Export
Media: 2-3-4-7-8-9-10-19-20-23-24-25
Distr.: Reg.
Budget Set: Oct.
Personnel:
Ellen Smith *(COO)*
Thomas King *(Exec Dir)*
Advertising Agencies:
Firstborn
630 9th Ave Ste 910
New York, NY 10036
Tel.: (212) 581-1100
Fax: (212) 765-7605

Impressions-A.B.A. Industries, Inc.
393 Jericho Tpk
Mineola, NY 11501
Tel.: (516) 739-3210
Fax: (516) 739-9246

NEBRASKA PUBLIC POWER DISTRICT

1414 15th St
Columbus, NE 68601-5226
Mailing Address:
PO Box 499
Columbus, NE 68602-0499
Tel.: (402) 564-8561
Fax: (402) 563-5527
E-mail: webeditor@nppd.com
Web Site: www.nppd.com
Approx. Rev.: $752,372,000
Approx. Number Employees: 2,300
Year Founded: 1970
Business Description:
Electric Utility Company
S.I.C.: 4931
N.A.I.C.S.: 221119
Advertising Expenditures: $700,000
Media: 10-17-22
Distr.: Reg.
Personnel:
Traci Bender *(CFO, VP-Fin, Risk Mgmt & Rates)*
Pat Pope *(COO & VP)*
Jeanne Schieffer *(Specialist-PR & Adv)*

NEUSTAR, INC.

46000 Center Oak Plz
Sterling, VA 20166
Tel.: (571) 434-5400
Fax: (571) 434-5786
E-mail: webmaster@neustar.com
Web Site: www.neustar.biz
Approx. Rev.: $526,812,000
Approx. Number Employees: 1,022
Year Founded: 1999
Business Description:
Communications Clearing House & Interconnectivity Services; Administrator of North American Telephone Numbering Plan
S.I.C.: 8742; 3661; 4899; 7375
N.A.I.C.S.: 541611; 334210; 517910; 518111
Advertising Expenditures: $5,300,000
Personnel:
James G. Cullen *(Chm)*
Lisa A. Hook *(Pres & CEO)*
Paul S. Lalljie *(CFO & Sr VP)*
Mark Pilipczuk *(CMO)*
Martin K. Lowen *(Gen Counsel, Sec & Sr VP)*
Douglas Arnold *(Sr VP-HR)*
Alex Berry *(Sr VP-Internet Infrastructure Svcs)*
Steven J. Edwards *(Sr VP-Carrier Svcs & Carrier Svcs North America Sls)*
Gerald J. Kovach *(Sr VP-External Affairs)*
Guenter H. Krauss *(Sr VP-Intl Div-Carrier Svcs)*
Matthew C. Levin *(Sr VP-Bus Affairs)*
Alex Tulchinsky *(Sr VP-Shared Svcs)*
Timothy Dodd *(VP/Gen Mgr-Neustar Media)*
Steve Boyce *(Corp Treas & VP-Fin)*
Brands & Products:
CARE
CLEARING HOUSE
INTERNET ADDRESS
LSREXPRESS
NEULEVEL
NEUSTAR
TRUSTED TO BRING NETWORKS TOGETHER

NEW BRUNSWICK POWER CORPORATION

515 King St
PO Box 2000
Fredericton, NB E3B 4X1, Canada
Tel.: (506) 458-4444
Tel.: (506) 458-4448
Fax: (506) 458-4000
Toll Free: (800) 663-6272
E-mail: nbpowergrandfalls@nbpower.com
Web Site: www.nbpower.com
E-Mail For Key Personnel:
Public Relations: mloisier@nbpower.com
Sales Range: $1-4.9 Billion
Approx. Number Employees: 2,500
Year Founded: 1920
Business Description:
Electrical Utility Services
S.I.C.: 4911; 4939
N.A.I.C.S.: 221122
Import Export
Media: 2-3-6-7-8-9-10-11-13-15-23-24-25
Distr.: Canada
Personnel:
Derek H. Burney *(Chm)*
Wanda Harrison *(Gen Counsel & Sec)*
Darrell Bishop *(Exec VP-Strategic Plng)*
Bob Crawford *(VP-Customer Svc)*
Sharon MacFarlane *(VP-Fin)*
Paul H. Theriault *(VP-HR)*

NEW YORK POWER AUTHORITY, INC.

30 S Pearl St
Albany, NY 12207-3425
Tel.: (518) 433-6700
Fax: (518) 433-6781
Web Site: www.nypa.gov
Sales Range: $50-74.9 Million
Approx. Number Employees: 1,500
Year Founded: 1931
Business Description:
Electric Services
S.I.C.: 9199
N.A.I.C.S.: 921190
Import Export
Media: 10-16-18-20
Personnel:
Gil Quiniones *(Acting Pres & Acting CEO)*
Elizabeth McCarthy *(CFO & Exec VP)*
Janis E. Archer *(Officer-Strategy Mgmt)*
Judith McCarthy *(Gen Counsel & Exec VP)*
Angelo S. Esposito *(Sr VP-Technology)*
Paul Finnegan *(Sr VP-Governmental Affairs)*
James Pasquale *(Sr VP-Mktg & Economic Dev)*
Michael Huvane *(VP-Mktg)*
Michael Saltzman *(Dir-Media Rels)*
Steve Ramsey *(Mgr-Community Rels)*
Brands & Products:
POWER FOR JOBS

NICOR INC.

1844 W Ferry Rd
Naperville, IL 60563-9600
Mailing Address:
PO Box 3014
Naperville, IL 60566-7014
Tel.: (630) 305-9500
Web Site: www.nicor.com
Approx. Rev.: $2,709,800,000
Approx. Number Employees: 3,800
Year Founded: 1976
Business Description:
Holding Company; Natural Gas Distribution & Containerized Freight Transportation Services
S.I.C.: 6719; 4412
N.A.I.C.S.: 551112; 483111
Advertising Expenditures: $140,000
Media: 26
Personnel:
Russ M. Strobel *(Chm, Pres & CEO)*
Richard L. Hawley *(CFO & Exec VP)*
Paul C. Gracey, Jr. *(Gen Counsel, Sec & Sr VP)*
Daniel R. Dodge *(Exec VP-Diversified Ventures)*
Claudia J. Colalillo *(Sr VP-HR & Corp Comm)*
Gerald P. O'Connor *(Sr VP-Fin & Stategic Plng)*
Barbara A. Zeller *(VP-IT)*
Kary D. Brunner *(Dir-IR)*
Steve Grzenia *(Specialist-Comm)*
Brands & Products:
NICOR

NOKIA CANADA CORPORATION

(Sub. of Nokia Corporation)
601 Westney Rd S
Ajax, ON L1S 4N7, Canada
Tel.: (905) 427-6654
Fax: (905) 427-6725
Web Site: www.nokia.ca
Approx. Number Employees: 60
Business Description:
Sales of Cellular Mobile Phones
S.I.C.: 4812
N.A.I.C.S.: 517212
Personnel:
Richard White *(Gen Mgr)*
Myles Donald *(Sr Mgr-Mktg-Partner Mktg-Global)*
Advertising Agency:
Ketchum Canada
33 Bloor St E Ste 1607
Toronto, ON M4W 3H1, Canada
Tel.: (416) 355-7400
Fax: (416) 355-7420

NORTEL NETWORKS CORPORATION

(Filed for Chapter 11 Bankruptcy 1/14/09)
5495 Airport Road Suite 360
Mississauga, ON L4V 1R9, Canada
Tel.: (905) 863-7000
Tel.: (905) 863-6049 (IR)
Fax: (905) 863-2496
E-mail: investor@nortel.com
Web Site: www.nortel.com
Approx. Rev.: $620,000,000
Approx. Number Employees: 30,300
Business Description:
Digital Telecommunications Systems & Information Management Systems
S.I.C.: 3669; 3661; 4812; 4899
N.A.I.C.S.: 334290; 334210; 517212; 517910
Advertising Expenditures: $14,800,000

Key to Media (For complete agency information see *The Advertising Red Books-Agencies* edition):
1. Bus. Publs. 2. Cable T.V. 3. Catalogs & Directories. 4. Co-op Adv. 5. Consumer Mags. 6. D.M. to Bus. Estab.7. D.M. to Consumers 8. Daily Newsp. 9. Exhibits/Trade Shows 10. Foreign 11. Infomercial 12. Internet Adv.13. Multimedia 14. Network Radio 15. Network T.V. 16. Newsp. Distr. Mags. 17. Other 18. Outdoor (Posters, Transit) 19. Point of Purchase20. Premiums, Novelties 21. Product Samples 22. Special Events Mktg. 23. Spot Radio 24. Spot T.V. 25. Weekly Newsp. 26. Yellow Page Adv.

Nortel Networks Corporation — (Continued)

Media: 2-3-6-9-10-11-13-15-22-23-24-26
Distr.: Intl.
Personnel:
David I. Richardson *(Chm)*
Samih Elhage *(Pres)*
Anna Ventresca *(Chief Compliance Officer, Gen Counsel & Corp Sec)*
George Andrew Riedel *(Chief Strategy Officer)*
Darryl Edwards *(Pres-Europe, Middle East & Africa)*
Joel Hackney *(Pres-Enterprise Solutions)*
Richard Lowe *(Pres-Wireless Networks)*
Christopher Simon Ricaurte *(Pres-Bus Svcs)*
Chuck Saffell *(CEO-Nortel Govt Solutions)*
Dennis J. Carey *(Exec VP-Corp Ops)*
William J. Donovan *(Sr VP-Bus Transformation Office)*
John Marshall Doolittle *(Sr VP)*
Elena Soldera King *(Sr VP-HR)*
Brands & Products:
ALTEON
BAYSTACK
BUSINESS MADE SIMPLE
CALLPILOT
CONTIVITY
DMS
DMS-HLR
DMS-MSC
DMS-MTX
EPICON
LINKPLEXER
MERIDIAN
MERIDIAN 1
METRO ETHERNET MANAGER
NORSTAR
NORTEL
NORTEL NETWORKS
OPTIVITY
PASSPORT
PERIPHONICS
POLYCOM
PRESIDE
S/DMS TRANSPORTNODE
SHASTA
SOUNDPOINT
SUCCESSION
SYMPOSIUM
TRAPEZE NETWORKS
UNIFIED MESSAGING 2000
Advertising Agencies:
Euro RSCG Skybridge
6 Briset St
London, Surrey EC1M 5NR, United Kingdom
Tel.: (44) 20 8661 8200
Fax: (44) 28 661 8201

Primate Marketing Consultants (PMC)
8/F Guang Hai Tower 308 Bin Jiang Road Central
Guangzhou, 510200, China
Tel.: (86) 20 8356 9288
Fax: (86) 20 8356 9277

Quarry Integrated Communications
180 King St S
Waterloo, ON N2J 1P8, Canada
Tel.: (519) 570-2020
Fax: (519) 743-3053

Weber Shandwick
(Sub. of The Interpublic Group of Companies)
919 3rd Ave
New York, NY 10022
Tel.: (212) 445-8000
Fax: (212) 445-8001

NORTHEAST UTILITIES

One Federal Street Building 111-4
Springfield, MA 01105
Mailing Address:
PO Box 270
Hartford, CT 06141-0270
Tel.: (413) 785-5871
Toll Free: (800) 286-5000
E-mail: nucommunications@nu.com
Web Site: www.nu.com
Approx. Rev.: $4,898,167,000
Approx. Number Employees: 6,182
Year Founded: 1966
Business Description:
Electric & Gas Utilities Services
S.I.C.: 4911; 4924; 4939
N.A.I.C.S.: 221121; 221111; 221122; 221210
Advertising Expenditures: $1,700,000
Personnel:
Charles W. Shivery *(Chm)*
David R. McHale *(CFO & Exec VP)*
Leon J. Olivier *(COO & Exec VP)*
James A. Muntz *(Pres-Transmission)*
Gregory B. Butler *(Gen Counsel & Sr VP)*
Laurie E. Aylsworth *(VP-Transmission Projects, Engrg & Maintenance)*
Marie van Luling *(VP-Corp Comm)*
Karen Samide *(Mgr-Yankee Gas Comm)*
O. Kay Comendul *(Asst Sec)*
Michael DiPietro *(Asst Controller-Acctg Svcs)*
Timothy J. Griffin *(Asst Controller-Corp Budgeting & Reporting)*
Susan B. Weber *(Asst Treas-Fin)*
Advertising Agencies:
Bauza & Associates
11 Asylum St
Hartford, CT 06103
Tel.: (860) 246-2100
Fax: (860) 246-2101

Cronin & Company, Inc.
50 Nye Rd
Glastonbury, CT 06033-1280
Tel.: (860) 659-0514
Fax: (860) 659-3455

NORTHERN ILLINOIS GAS COMPANY

(Sub. of Nicor Inc.)
(d/b/a Nicor Gas Company)
1844 W Ferry Rd
Naperville, IL 60563-9600
Mailing Address:
PO Box 190
Aurora, IL 60507-0190
Tel.: (630) 983-8888
Fax: (630) 983-9183
Toll Free: (888) NICOR4U
E-mail: info@nicor.com
Approx. Rev.: $2,204,400,000
Approx. Number Employees: 2,200
Year Founded: 1954
Business Description:
Natural Gas Distr
S.I.C.: 4924; 1389
N.A.I.C.S.: 221210; 213112
Advertising Expenditures: $2,300,000
Media: 1-2-6-7-8-9-10-13-18-20-22-23-24-25
Distr.: Direct to Consumer; Reg.
Budget Set: Aug.
Personnel:
Russ M. Strobel *(Chm, Pres & CEO)*
Richard L. Hawley *(CFO & Exec VP)*
Paul C. Gracey, Jr. *(Gen Counsel, Sec & Sr VP)*
Rocco J. D'Alessandro *(Exec VP-Ops)*
Claudia J. Colalillo *(Sr VP-HR & Customer Care)*
Daniel R. Dodge *(Sr VP-Diversified Ventures & Corp Plng)*
Kris Nichols *(VP-Engrg)*
Gerald P. O'Connor *(VP-Admin & Fin)*

NORTHERN INDIANA PUBLIC SERVICE COMPANY

(Sub. of NiSource Inc.)
801 E 86th Ave
Merrillville, IN 46410-6271
Tel.: (219) 853-5200
Fax: (219) 647-5589
Web Site: www.nipsco.com
Sales Range: $1-4.9 Billion
Approx. Number Employees: 2,498
Year Founded: 1912
Business Description:
Natural Gas Distr & Electric Company
S.I.C.: 4939; 4924; 4931
N.A.I.C.S.: 221111; 221119; 221210
Advertising Expenditures: $5,500,000
Media: 14-15-18-23-24
Distr.: Direct to Consumer; Reg.
Personnel:
Jeffrey W. Grossman *(CFO)*
Mike Finissi *(COO)*
Tim Caister *(Dir-Electric Regulatory Policy)*

NORTHWEST NATURAL GAS COMPANY

220 NW 2nd Ave
Portland, OR 97209-3943
Tel.: (503) 226-4211
Fax: (503) 721-2506
Telex: 4667220-2584
Web Site: www.nwnatural.com
Approx. Rev.: $367,581,000
Approx. Number Employees: 1,028
Year Founded: 1859
Business Description:
Natural Gas Distr
S.I.C.: 4924
N.A.I.C.S.: 221210
Media: 2-7
Distr.: Natl.
Personnel:
Gregg S. Kantor *(Pres & CEO)*
David Hugo Anderson *(CFO & Sr VP)*
David A. Weber *(CIO)*
Richard Daniel *(Pres-NW Natural Gas Storage)*
Margaret D. Kirkpatrick *(Gen Counsel & VP)*
MardiLyn Saathoff *(Chief Governance Officer, Corp Sec & Deputy Gen Counsel)*
Lea Anne Doolittle *(Sr VP)*
C Alex Miller *(VP-Fin & Regulation)*
Robert S. Hess *(Dir-IR)*
Brands & Products:
NW NATURAL
WE GREW UP HERE
Advertising Agency:
Gard Communications
711 SW Alder St 4th Fl
Portland, OR 97205
Tel.: (503) 221-0100
Fax: (503) 226-4854
Toll Free: (800) 800-7132

NORTHWESTEL INC.

(Sub. of Bell Canada)
301 Lambert St
PO Box 2727
Whitehorse, YT Y1A 4Y4, Canada
Tel.: (867) 668-5300
Fax: (867) 668-7079
E-mail: info@nwtel.ca
Web Site: www.nwtel.ca
Sales Range: $100-124.9 Million
Approx. Number Employees: 650
Business Description:
Telephone, Telecommunications, Mobile Communications & Cable Television Services
S.I.C.: 4813
N.A.I.C.S.: 517110
Media: 2-7-8-10-18-21-22-26
Personnel:
Terry Mosey *(Chm)*
Paul Flaherty *(Pres & CEO)*
Advertising Agency:
Aasman Design Inc.
201-402 Hansen St
Whitehorse, YT Y1A 1Y8, Canada
Tel.: (867) 668-5248
Fax: (867) 633-6959

NORTHWESTERN CORPORATION

3010 W 69th St
Sioux Falls, SD 57108
Tel.: (605) 978-2900
Fax: (605) 978-2910
Toll Free: (800) 245-6977
E-mail: nor@northwestern.com
Web Site:
www.northwesternenergy.com
Approx. Rev.: $1,110,720,000
Approx. Number Employees: 1,363
Year Founded: 1923
Business Description:
Electricity & Natural Gas Services
S.I.C.: 4939; 4911; 4924; 4931
N.A.I.C.S.: 221111; 221119; 221122; 221210
Advertising Expenditures: $2,000,000
Media: 3-8-9-10-13-14-18-19-20-23-24-25-26
Distr.: Reg.
Budget Set: Oct.
Personnel:
E. Linn Draper, Jr. *(Chm)*
Robert C. Rowe *(Pres & CEO)*
Brian B. Bird *(CFO, Treas & VP)*
Bobbi L. Schroeppel *(VP-Customer Care & Comm)*
Claudia Rapkoch *(Dir-Comm)*
Dan Rausch *(Dir-IR)*
Tom Glanzer *(Coord-Comm)*
Brands & Products:
NORTHWESTERN
Advertising Agency:
Flying Horse Communications
602 Ferguson Ave Ste 1
Bozeman, MT 59718
Tel.: (406) 586-9654

Key to Media (For complete agency information see *The Advertising Red Books-Agencies* edition):
1. Bus. Publs. 2. Cable T.V. 3. Catalogs & Directories. 4. Co-op Adv. 5. Consumer Mags. 6. D.M. to Bus. Estab.7. D.M. to Consumers 8. Daily Newsp. 9. Exhibits/Trade Shows 10. Foreign 11. Infomercial 12. Internet Adv.13. Multimedia 14. Network Radio 15. Network T.V. 16. Newsp. Distr. Mags. 17. Other 18. Outdoor (Posters, Transit) 19. Point of Purchase20. Premiums, Novelties 21. Product Samples 22. Special Events Mktg. 23. Spot Radio 24. Spot T.V. 25. Weekly Newsp. 26. Yellow Page Adv.

NORTHWESTERN ENERGY
(Sub. of NorthWestern Corporation)
40 E Broadway St
Butte, MT 59701
Tel.: (406) 497-3000
Fax: (406) 497-2535
Toll Free: (888) 467-2669
E-mail: econdev@northwesternenergy.com
Web Site: www.northwesternenergy.com
Sales Range: $75-99.9 Million
Approx. Number Employees: 100
Year Founded: 1912
Business Description:
Electric & Gas Utility
S.I.C.: 4939; 4911; 4924
N.A.I.C.S.: 221122; 221210
Import
Advertising Expenditures: $800,000
Media: 1-3-6-7-8-9-16-17-23-24-25-26
Distr.: Direct to Consumer; Reg.
Budget Set: Nov.
Personnel:
Brian B. Bird *(CFO)*
Frank Spangler *(Dir-Customer Interaction)*
Brands & Products:
NORTHWESTERN ENERGY

NV ENERGY
(Formerly Sierra Pacific Power Company)
(Sub. of NV Energy, Inc.)
6100 Neil Rd
Reno, NV 89511-1132
Mailing Address:
PO Box 10100
Reno, NV 89520-0400
Tel.: (775) 834-4011
Fax: (775) 834-4202
Toll Free: (800) 962-0399
E-mail: nmedia@nvenergy.com
Web Site: www.nvenergy.com
Approx. Rev.: $1,027,822,000
Approx. Number Employees: 1,113
Year Founded: 1860
Business Description:
Electric & Gas Utility Services
S.I.C.: 4931; 4911; 4924; 4939
N.A.I.C.S.: 221119; 221121; 221122; 221210
Advertising Expenditures: $350,000
Media: 1-3-6-8-9-10-13-15-18-20-22-23-24-25
Distr.: Reg.
Budget Set: Oct.
Personnel:
Dilek L. Samil *(CFO, Treas & Sr VP-Fin)*
E. Kevin Bethel *(Chief Acctg Officer, VP & Controller)*
Paul L. Kaleta *(Corp Sec, Sr VP & Gen Counsel-Shared Svcs)*
Jeffrey L. Ceccarelli *(Sr VP-Energy Supply)*
Roberto R. Denis *(Sr VP-Energy Supply)*
Brands & Products:
SIERRA PACIFIC POWER

NV ENERGY, INC.
6226 W Sahara Ave
Las Vegas, NV 89146
Tel.: (702) 402-5000
Toll Free: (800) 962-0399
E-mail: mediarelations@sppc.com
Web Site: www.sierrapacificresources.com
Approx. Rev.: $3,280,222,000
Approx. Number Employees: 2,916
Year Founded: 1984
Business Description:
Holding Company; Electric Power & Gas Distr
S.I.C.: 4924; 4911; 4931; 4939; 6719
N.A.I.C.S.: 221210; 221111; 221119; 221122; 551112
Media: 1-2-3-6-7-8-9-10-18-22-23-24-25
Distr.: Direct to Consumer; Reg.
Personnel:
Philip G. Satre *(Chm)*
Dilek L. Samil *(Pres & CEO)*
Michael W. Yackira *(Pres & CEO)*
E. Kevin Bethel *(Chief Acctg Officer, VP & Controller)*
Paul J. Kaleta *(Gen Counsel, Sec & Sr VP)*
Jeffrey L. Ceccarelli *(Sr VP-Energy Supply)*
Roberto R. Denis *(Sr VP-Energy Supply)*
Tony F. Sanchez, III *(Sr VP-Govt & Community Strategy)*
Rob Stillwell *(Head-Corp Comm)*
Britta Carlson *(Mgr-IR)*
Brands & Products:
A VISION FOR OUR ENERGY FUTURE
E-THREE
NEVADA POWER
NVENERGY
SIERRA PACIFIC
SIERRA PACIFIC COMMUNICATIONS
SIERRA PACIFIC RESOURCES
TUSCARORA GAS PIPELINE CO

OCEAN POWER TECHNOLOGIES, INC.
1590 Reed Rd
Pennington, NJ 08534
Tel.: (609) 730-0400
Fax: (609) 730-0404
E-mail: info@oceanpowertech.com
Web Site: www.oceanpowertechnologies.com
Approx. Rev.: $6,691,082
Approx. Number Employees: 51
Business Description:
Wave Energy Electricity Generating Systems
S.I.C.: 5063; 4939
N.A.I.C.S.: 423610; 221111
Personnel:
George W. Taylor *(Chm)*
Seymour S. Preston, III *(Vice Chm)*
Charles Frederick Dunleavy *(CEO)*
Brian M. Posner *(CFO)*
Deborah A. Montagna *(VP & Gen Mgr-Govt Sys)*
Robert F. Lurie *(VP-Bus Dev & Mktg-North Amercia)*
David B. Stewart *(VP-Advanced Engrg)*
Brands & Products:
CELLBUOY
MAKING WAVES IN POWER
OPT
POWERBUOY
TALK ON WATER
Advertising Agency:
Edelman
250 Hudson St
New York, NY 10013
Tel.: (212) 768-0550
Fax: (212) 704-0128

OGE ENERGY CORP.
321 N Harvey Ave
Oklahoma City, OK 73102-3405
Mailing Address:
PO Box 321
Oklahoma City, OK 73101-0321
Tel.: (405) 553-3000
Fax: (405) 553-3567
Web Site: www.oge.com
Approx. Rev.: $3,716,900,000
Approx. Number Employees: 3,416
Year Founded: 1902
Business Description:
Public Utility Holding Company
S.I.C.: 4939; 4922; 4931; 6719
N.A.I.C.S.: 221111; 221112; 221119; 486210; 551112
Advertising Expenditures: $9,000,000
Media: 2-3-4-6-9-15-22-23-24-25
Distr.: Direct to Consumer
Budget Set: Nov.
Personnel:
Peter B. Delaney *(Chm & CEO)*
Danny P. Harris *(Pres & COO-OGE Energy Corp, OG & E Electric Svcs)*
Sean Trauschke *(CFO & VP)*
Reid V. Nuttall *(CIO & VP-IT)*
H. Scott Forbes *(Chief Acctg Officer & Controller)*
John D. Rhea *(Asst Corp Sec & Compliance Officer)*
Max J. Myers *(Treas, Mng Dir-Corp Dev & Fin)*
S. Craig Johnston *(VP-Strategy & Mktg)*
Stephen E. Merrill *(VP-HR)*
Richard Clements *(Mgr-Economic Dev)*
Richard Cornelison *(Dev Project Mgr)*
Susan P. Harkness *(Mgr-Adv, Brand & Event)*
Donald G. Ives *(Dev Project Mgr)*
William J. Bullard *(Asst Gen Counsel)*
Brands & Products:
ENOGEX
OG&E ELECTRIC SERVICES
OG+E
OGE
POWERPLUS
SYSTEM WATCH
Advertising Agency:
Ackerman McQueen, Inc.
1100 The Tower 1601 NW Expy
Oklahoma City, OK 73118
Tel.: (405) 843-7777
Fax: (405) 848-1932
(Electric Utility Service)

OHIO GAS COMPANY
200 W High St
Bryan, OH 43506-0528
Tel.: (419) 636-1117
Fax: (419) 636-9837
Toll Free: (800) 331-7396
Web Site: www.ohiogas.com
Approx. Number Employees: 120
Year Founded: 1914
Business Description:
Natural Gas Utility
S.I.C.: 4924
N.A.I.C.S.: 221210
Media: 5-8-9-10-23-24
Distr.: Reg.
Budget Set: Dec.
Personnel:
Richard P. Hallett *(Pres)*
Doug Westhoven *(Mgr-Adv)*

OMAHA PUBLIC POWER DISTRICT
OPPD Energy Plz 444 S 16th St Mall
Omaha, NE 68102-2247
Tel.: (402) 636-2000
Fax: (402) 636-3914
Toll Free: (800) 554-OPPD
E-mail: webmaster@oppd.com
Web Site: www.oppd.com
Sales Range: $650-699.9 Million
Approx. Number Employees: 2,364
Year Founded: 1946
Business Description:
Electric Utility Company Providing Services for Southeast Nebraska
S.I.C.: 4939; 4911
N.A.I.C.S.: 221122
Advertising Expenditures: $7,000,000
Media: 2-3-5-9-10-19-23-24-25-26
Distr.: Reg.
Budget Set: Dec.
Personnel:
N. Phillips Dodge, Jr. *(Vice Chm)*
W. Gary Gates *(Pres & CEO)*
Timothy J. Burke *(VP-Customer Svc & Pub Affairs)*
Douglas Collins *(Mgr-Energy Mktg)*
James Krist *(Mgr-Key Acct Sls & Svc)*
Steven Schmitz *(Mgr-IT Div)*

ORANGE & ROCKLAND UTILITIES, INC.
(Sub. of Consolidated Edison, Inc.)
1 Blue Hill Plz
Pearl River, NY 10965
Tel.: (845) 352-6000
Fax: (845) 577-2726
Toll Free: (877) 434-4100
Web Site: www.oru.com
Sales Range: $700-749.9 Million
Approx. Number Employees: 1,045
Year Founded: 1926
Business Description:
Electric & Gas Utility Services
S.I.C.: 4911; 4924; 4939
N.A.I.C.S.: 221122; 221210
Personnel:
William G. Longhi *(Pres & CEO)*
Robert T. Kosior *(Ethics Officer)*
Edwin J. Ortiz *(VP-Customer Svc)*
Tom L Brizzolara *(Dir-Pub Affairs)*
Joan S. Jacobs *(Dir-HR)*
Advertising Agency:
S3
718 Main St
Boonton, NJ 07005
Tel.: (973) 257-5533
Fax: (973) 257-5543

PACIFICORP
(Sub. of MidAmerican Energy Holdings Company)
825 NE Multnomah St
Portland, OR 97232
Tel.: (503) 813-5000
Fax: (503) 813-7247
Toll Free: (888) 221-7070
E-mail: webmaster@pacificorp.com
Web Site: www.pacificorp.com

Key to Media (For complete agency information see *The Advertising Red Books-Agencies* edition):
1. Bus. Publs. 2. Cable T.V. 3. Catalogs & Directories. 4. Co-op Adv. 5. Consumer Mags. 6. D.M. to Bus. Estab.7. D.M. to Consumers
8. Daily Newsp. 9. Exhibits/Trade Shows 10. Foreign 11. Infomercial 12. Internet Adv.13. Multimedia 14. Network Radio
15. Network T.V. 16. Newsp. Distr. Mags. 17. Other 18. Outdoor (Posters, Transit) 19. Point of Purchase20. Premiums, Novelties
21. Product Samples 22. Special Events Mktg. 23. Spot Radio 24. Spot T.V. 25. Weekly Newsp. 26. Yellow Page Adv.

PacifiCorp — (Continued)

Approx. Rev.: $4,432,000,000
Approx. Number Employees: 6,300
Year Founded: 1984
Business Description:
Electric Power Transmission & Distribution Services
S.I.C.: 4939; 4931
N.A.I.C.S.: 221111; 221119
Media: 2-4-7-8-9-10-14-18-19-20-23-24-25-26
Distr.: Reg.
Personnel:
Gregory E. Abel *(Chm & CEO)*
Micheal G. Dunn *(Pres-PacifiCorp Energy)*
Brands & Products:
PACIFIC POWER
UTAH POWER
Advertising Agencies:
Hallock Agency
2445 NW Irving St
Portland, OR 97210
Tel.: (503) 224-1711
Fax: (503) 224-3026

Parker Advertising Service, Inc.
101 N Pointe Blvd 2nd Fl
Lancaster, PA 17601
Tel.: (717) 581-1966
Fax: (717) 581-1566
Toll Free: (800) 396-3306

PECO ENERGY COMPANY

(Sub. of Exelon Corporation)
2301 Market St
Philadelphia, PA 19101
Mailing Address:
PO Box 8699
Philadelphia, PA 19101-8699
Tel.: (215) 841-4000
Toll Free: (800) 494-4000
Web Site: www.exeloncorp.com/ourcompanies/peco
Approx. Rev.: $5,519,000,000
Approx. Number Employees: 2,423
Year Founded: 1881
Business Description:
Electric & Gas Utility
S.I.C.: 4939; 4911; 4924
N.A.I.C.S.: 221122; 221111; 221112; 221210
Advertising Expenditures: $6,000,000
Media: 1-2-3-6-7-8-9-10-22-23-24-25
Distr.: Reg.
Budget Set: Monthly
Personnel:
Paul R. Bonney *(Gen Counsel & VP-Regulatory Affairs)*
Denis P. O'Brien *(Exec VP)*
Elizabeth A. Murphy *(Dir-Governmental & External Affairs)*
Advertising Agency:
Tierney Communications
(A Div. of the Interpublic Group of Companies)
The Bellevue 200 S Broad St
Philadelphia, PA 19102-3803
Tel.: (215) 790-4100
Fax: (215) 790-4363
(Corp. Identity-Electric & Gas Services)

PEPCO HOLDINGS, INC.

701 9th St NW
Washington, DC 20068
Tel.: (202) 872-2000
Fax: (202) 331-6750
E-mail: trwelle@pepco.com
Web Site: www.pepcoholdings.com
Approx. Rev.: $7,039,000,000
Approx. Number Employees: 50,141,632
Year Founded: 1896
Business Description:
Holding Company; Electric Power Distr
S.I.C.: 4911; 4899; 4924; 4931; 4939
N.A.I.C.S.: 221122; 221111; 221119; 221210; 517910
Media: 7-8-13-23-24-25
Personnel:
Joseph M. Rigby *(Chm, Pres & CEO)*
Anthony J. Kamerick *(CFO & Sr VP)*
Kenneth J. Parker *(VP-Public Policy)*
Vincent Maione *(Pres-Atlantic City Electric)*
Kirk Emge *(Gen Counsel & Sr VP)*
David M. Velazquez *(Exec VP)*
Beverly L. Perry *(Sr VP)*
Laura L. Monica *(VP-Corp Comm)*
Karen Lefkowitz *(Dir-Customer Relations)*
Michael J. Sullivan, Sr. *(Mgr-Compensation & Benefits)*
Tom R. Welle *(Mgr-Brand Adv)*
Advertising Agencies:
FD Americas Public Affairs
1101 K St NW 9th Fl
Washington, DC 20005
Tel.: (202) 346-8800
Fax: (202) 346-8804

Radio Direct Response
1400 N Providence Rd Ste 4000
Media, PA 19063
Tel.: (610) 892-7300
Fax: (610) 892-1899
Toll Free: (800) 969-AMFM

Stanton Communications, Inc.
1150 Connecticut Ave NW Ste 810
Washington, DC 20036
Tel.: (202) 223-4933
Fax: (202) 223-1375

PG&E CORPORATION

1 Market Plz Spear Tower Ste 2400
San Francisco, CA 94105
Tel.: (415) 267-7000
Tel.: (415) 973-7000
Fax: (415) 267-7268
Toll Free: (800) 743-5000
E-mail: invrel@pge-corp.com
Web Site: www.pgecorp.com
Approx. Rev.: $13,841,000,000
Approx. Number Employees: 19,424
Year Founded: 1852
Business Description:
Holding Company; Energy Services
S.I.C.: 4911; 4924; 4931; 4939
N.A.I.C.S.: 221122; 221119; 221121; 221210
Media: 2-6-8-9-18-23-24-25
Distr.: Natl.
Personnel:
Anthony F. Earley, Jr. *(Chm, Pres & CEO)*
Kent M. Harvey *(CFO & Sr VP)*
John S. Keenan *(COO & Sr VP)*
Karen A. Austin *(CIO & Sr VP)*
Steven L. Kline *(VP & Chief Sustainability Officer)*
Christopher P. Johns *(Pres-Pacific Gas & Electric Company)*
Hyun Park *(Gen Counsel & Sr VP)*
Nicholas M. Bijur *(Treas & Sr Dir)*
Nancy E. Mcfadden *(Sr VP)*
Greg S. Pruett *(Sr VP-Corp Rels)*
Rand L. Rosenberg *(Sr VP-Corp Strategy & Dev)*
John R. Simon *(Sr VP-HR)*
Fong Wan *(Sr VP-Energy Procurement)*
Rob Parkhurst *(Mgr-Climate Protection & Analysis)*
Greg Snapper *(Mgr-External Comm)*
Brands & Products:
PGE
Advertising Agencies:
Barnett Cox & Associates
711 Tank Farm Rd Ste 210
San Luis Obispo, CA 93401
Tel.: (805) 545-8887
Fax: (805) 545-0860

Venables, Bell & Partners
201 Post St Ste 200
San Francisco, CA 94108
Tel.: (415) 288-3300
Fax: (415) 421-3683

PIEDMONT NATURAL GAS COMPANY, INC.

4720 Piedmont Row Dr
Charlotte, NC 28210
Mailing Address:
PO Box 33068
Charlotte, NC 28233
Tel.: (704) 364-3120
Fax: (704) 365-8515
Toll Free: (800) 752-7508
E-mail: investorrelations@piedmontng.com
Web Site: www.piedmontng.com
Approx. Rev.: $1,552,295,000
Approx. Number Employees: 1,788
Year Founded: 1950
Business Description:
Natural Gas Distr
S.I.C.: 4924; 1321
N.A.I.C.S.: 221210; 211112
Media: 2-6-7-8-9-10-19-20-22-26
Distr.: Direct to Consumer; Reg.
Budget Set: Nov.
Personnel:
Thomas E. Skains *(Chm, Pres & CEO)*
David J. Dzuricky *(CFO & Sr VP)*
Jane R. Lewis-Raymond *(Chief Compliance Officer, Gen Counsel, Sec & VP)*
Robert O. Pritchard *(Chief Risk Officer, Treas & VP)*
Karl W. Newlin *(Sr VP-Corp Plng & Bus Dev)*
Kevin M. O'Hara *(Sr VP-Corp & Community Affairs)*
Franklin H. Yoho *(Sr VP-Comml Ops)*
Michael H. Yount *(Sr VP-Utility Ops)*
Ranelle Q. Warfield *(VP-Customer Svc)*
Bill Williams *(VP-Sls & Delivery Svcs)*
Brands & Products:
THE ENERGY WITHIN
NASHVILLE GAS
NCNG
PIEDMONT NATURAL GAS
Advertising Agency:
Media Power Advertising
5009 Monroe Rd Ste 101
Charlotte, NC 28205-7847
Tel.: (704) 567-1000
Fax: (704) 567-8193

PINELLAS COUNTY UTILITIES

14 S Ft Harrison Ave
Clearwater, FL 33756-5146
Tel.: (727) 464-4000
Fax: (727) 464-3576 4643717
E-mail: custsrv@co.pinellas.fl.us
Web Site: www.pinellascounyt.org/utilities
Approx. Number Employees: 600
Year Founded: 1937
Business Description:
Utilities
S.I.C.: 9532
N.A.I.C.S.: 925120
Advertising Expenditures: $500,000
Media: 2-4-6-9-13-14-16-18-19-20-21-22-23-24-25
Personnel:
Tim Wiley *(Dir-Customer Svcs)*
David Baker *(Mgr-Public Info Div & Comm Dept)*

PNM RESOURCES, INC.

Alvarado Sq
Albuquerque, NM 87158-0001
Tel.: (505) 241-2700
Fax: (505) 241-2367
Web Site: www.pnmresources.com
Approx. Rev.: $1,673,517,000
Approx. Number Employees: 2,134
Business Description:
Holding Company; Electric Utility Services
S.I.C.: 6719; 4911; 4939
N.A.I.C.S.: 551112; 221122
Media: 2-3-4-5-6-7-8-9-10-13-18-19-22-23-24-25-26
Distr.: Reg.
Budget Set: Dec.
Personnel:
Jeffry E. Sterba *(Chm)*
Patricia K. Vincent-Collawn *(Pres, CEO & COO)*
Charles Eldred *(CFO & Exec VP)*
Alice Cobb *(Chief Admin Officer & Sr VP)*
Jim Ferland *(Sr VP-Utility Ops)*
Brands & Products:
PNM RESOURCES
Advertising Agency:
Rick Johnson & Company, Inc.
1120 Pennsylvania St NE
Albuquerque, NM 87110-7408
Tel.: (505) 266-1100
Fax: (505) 262-0525
(Full Service, Print, Broadcast)
— Pam Schneider *(Acct. Exec.)*

PORTLAND GENERAL ELECTRIC COMPANY

121 SW Salmon St
Portland, OR 97204-2901
Mailing Address:
PO Box 4404
Portland, OR 97208-4404
Tel.: (503) 464-8000
Fax: (503) 464-2676
Toll Free: (800) 542-8818
Web Site: www.portlandgeneral.com
Approx. Rev.: $1,783,000,000
Approx. Number Employees: 2,671
Year Founded: 1889
Business Description:
Electric Power Distribution Services

Key to Media (For complete agency information see *The Advertising Red Books-Agencies* edition):
1. Bus. Publs. 2. Cable T.V. 3. Catalogs & Directories. 4. Co-op Adv. 5. Consumer Mags. 6. D.M. to Bus. Estab.7. D.M. to Consumers
8. Daily Newsp. 9. Exhibits/Trade Shows 10. Foreign 11. Infomercial 12. Internet Adv.13. Multimedia 14. Network Radio
15. Network T.V. 16. Newsp. Distr. Mags. 17. Other 18. Outdoor (Posters, Transit) 19. Point of Purchase20. Premiums, Novelties
21. Product Samples 22. Special Events Mktg. 23. Spot Radio 24. Spot T.V. 25. Weekly Newsp. 26. Yellow Page Adv.

S.I.C.: 4911; 4924; 4939
N.A.I.C.S.: 221122; 221111; 221210
Media: 7-8-23
Distr.: Direct to Customer; Natl.
Budget Set: Dec.-Jan.
Personnel:
Corbin A. McNeill, Jr. *(Chm)*
James J. Piro *(Pres & Co-CEO)*
Maria M. Pope *(CFO, Treas & Sr VP-Fin)*
Campbell A. Henderson *(CIO & VP-IT)*
Jay Jeffrey Dudley *(Gen Counsel, VP & Corp Compliance Officer)*
Bill Valach *(Dir-IR)*
Advertising Agency:
North
1515 NW 19th Ave
Portland, OR 97209
Tel.: (503) 222-4117
Fax: (503) 222-4118

POTOMAC ELECTRIC POWER COMPANY

(Sub. of Pepco Holdings, Inc.)
(d/b/a Pepco)
701 9th St NW
Washington, DC 20068-0001
Tel.: (202) 872-2000
Fax: (202) 331-6750
E-mail: info@pepco.com
Web Site: www.pepco.com
Approx. Rev.: $2,288,000,000
Approx. Number Employees: 1,375
Year Founded: 1896
Business Description:
Electric Power & Services
S.I.C.: 4931
N.A.I.C.S.: 221119
Media: 4-10-23-24-26
Distr.: Reg.
Budget Set: Nov.
Personnel:
Joseph M. Rigby *(Chm, Pres & CEO)*
Anthony J. Kamerick *(CFO & Sr VP)*
Kirk Emge *(Sr VP & Gen Counsel-Pepco Holdings, Inc.)*
Ellen Sheriff Rogers *(Sec & Asst Treas)*
Beverly L. Perry *(Sr VP)*
Tom Welle *(Mgr-Adv)*
Advertising Agency:
Maya Advertising & Communications
1819 L St NW Ste 100
Washington, DC 20036
Tel.: (202) 337-0566
Fax: (202) 337-0548

PPL CORPORATION

2 N 9th St
Allentown, PA 18101-1179
Tel.: (610) 774-5151
Fax: (610) 774-4198
E-mail: invrel@pplweb.com
Web Site: www.pplweb.com
Approx. Rev.: $8,521,000,000
Approx. Number Employees: 13,809
Year Founded: 1920
Business Description:
Electric Power Distr
S.I.C.: 4931; 4911; 4939
N.A.I.C.S.: 221119; 221111; 221122
Advertising Expenditures: $500,000
Media: 2-8-9-10-18-23-24-25-26
Distr.: Direct to Consumer; Intl.
Budget Set: Aug.
Personnel:
James H. Miller *(Chm & CEO)*
William H. Spence *(Pres)*
Paul A. Farr *(CFO & Exec VP)*
James Schinski *(CIO & VP)*
Victor N. Lopiano *(Sr VP-PPL Fossil & Hydro Generation, Pres-PPL Nuclear Dev)*
Robert J. Grey *(Gen Counsel, Sec & Sr VP)*
James E. Abel *(Treas & Sr VP-Fin)*
Michael Wood *(Sr Mgr-Corp Comm)*
Advertising Agency:
BCN Communications
900 N Franklin St Ste 800
Chicago, IL 60610
Tel.: (312) 787-2783
Fax: (312) 787-6097

PROGRESS ENERGY FLORIDA

(Formerly Florida Power Corporation)
(Sub. of Progress Energy, Inc.)
299 First Ave N
Saint Petersburg, FL 33701-3324
Mailing Address:
PO Box 33199
Saint Petersburg, FL 33733-8199
Tel.: (727) 820-5151
Tel.: (727) 443-2641
Fax: (727) 820-5026
Toll Free: (866) 520-6397
Web Site: www.progress-energy.com
Approx. Rev.: $5,254,000,000
Approx. Number Employees: 4,000
Year Founded: 1899
Business Description:
Electric Power Generation & Distribution
S.I.C.: 4931; 4911; 4939
N.A.I.C.S.: 221119; 221122
Media: 23-24
Personnel:
Vincent M. Dolan *(Pres & CEO)*
James Scarola *(Sr VP & Chief Nuclear Officer)*
Michael A. Lewis *(Sr VP-Energy Delivery)*
Paula J. Sims *(Sr VP-Power Ops)*
Martha W. Barnwell *(VP-North Coastal Reg)*
Laura M. Boisvert *(VP-South Central Reg)*
David J. Maxson *(VP-North Coastal Reg)*
Mark Wimberly *(VP-South Coastal Reg)*
Robert J. Duncan *(Mgr-Vegitation Mgmt)*
Anne M. Huffman *(VP-HR)*
Peter E. Toomey *(VP-Fin)*
Sandra S. Wyckoff *(VP-Audit)*
Advertising Agencies:
Center Line
310 S Harrington St
Raleigh, NC 27603
Tel.: (919) 821-2921
Fax: (919) 821-2922

Clean Design, Inc.
10 Laboratory Dr Bldg 2 Ste 200
Research Triangle Park, NC 27709
Tel.: (919) 544-2193
Fax: (919) 473-2200

PROGRESS ENERGY, INC.

410 S Wilmington St
Raleigh, NC 27601
Mailing Address:
PO Box 1551
Raleigh, NC 27602-1551
Tel.: (919) 546-6111
Fax: (919) 546-2920
Toll Free: (800) 452-2777
Web Site: www.progress-energy.com/
Approx. Rev.: $10,190,000,000
Approx. Number Employees: 11,000
Year Founded: 1908
Business Description:
Public Utility Holding Company; Electric Energy Generation & Distr
S.I.C.: 4939; 4911
N.A.I.C.S.: 221111; 221122
Advertising Expenditures: $4,000,000
Media: 1-2-3-5-6-7-8-9-10-13-19-20-22-23-24-25-26
Distr.: Direct to Consumer; Reg.
Budget Set: Aug.
Personnel:
William D. Johnson *(Chm, Pres & CEO)*
Lloyd M. Yates *(Pres & CEO-Progress Energy Carolinas, Inc)*
Mark F. Mulhern *(CFO & Sr VP)*
Jeffrey M. Stone *(Chief Acctg Officer & Controller)*
John R. McArthur *(Gen Counsel, Sec & Sr VP-Corp Rels)*
Jeffrey J. Lyash *(Exec VP-Energy Supply)*
James Scarola *(Sr VP & Chief Nuclear Officer-Carolinas & Florida)*
Paula J. Sims *(Sr VP-Corp Dev)*
Advertising Agency:
Clean Design, Inc.
10 Laboratory Dr Bldg 2 Ste 200
Research Triangle Park, NC 27709
Tel.: (919) 544-2193
Fax: (919) 473-2200

PUBLIC SERVICE COMPANY OF NEW HAMPSHIRE

(Sub. of NORTHEAST UTILITIES)
780 N Commercial St
Manchester, NH 03101-1134
Mailing Address:
PO Box 330
Manchester, NH 03105-0330
Tel.: (603) 669-4000
Tel.: (603) 634-2228 (Media Rels)
Fax: (866) 482-0461
Toll Free: (800) 662-7764
E-mail: psnhcorpcommun@psnh.com
Web Site: www.psnh.com
Approx. Rev.: $1,033,439,000
Approx. Number Employees: 1,240
Year Founded: 1926
Business Description:
Electric Power Distribution & Generation Services
S.I.C.: 4931; 4911; 4924; 4939
N.A.I.C.S.: 221119; 221121; 221122; 221210
Media: 1-8-13-18-23
Personnel:
Charles W. Shivery *(Chm)*
Gary A. Long *(Pres & COO)*
Leon J. Olivier *(CEO)*
David R. McHale *(CFO & Exec VP)*
Gregory B. Butler *(Gen Counsel & Sr VP)*
Advertising Agency:
Rumbletree
170 W Rd
Portsmouth, NH 03801
Tel.: (603) 433-6214
Fax: (603) 433-6269

PUBLIC SERVICE COMPANY OF NORTH CAROLINA, INC.

(Sub. of SCANA Corporation)
(d/b/a PSNC Energy)
800 Gaston Rd
Gastonia, NC 28056
Mailing Address:
PO Box 100256
Columbia, SC 29202
Tel.: (704) 864-6731
Fax: (704) 834-6553
Toll Free: (866) 546-5369
Toll Free: (877) 776-2627
Web Site: www.psncenergy.com
Sales Range: $600-649.9 Million
Approx. Number Employees: 800
Year Founded: 1938
Business Description:
Natural Gas Distr
S.I.C.: 4924
N.A.I.C.S.: 221210
Advertising Expenditures: $500,000
Media: 1-2-3-5-6-7-8-9-10-15-18-19-20-22-23-24-25-26
Distr.: Direct to Consumer; Reg.
Budget Set: Oct.
Personnel:
Sharon D. Boone *(Controller & Asst Sec)*

PUBLIC SERVICE COMPANY OF OKLAHOMA

(Sub. of American Electric Power Company, Inc.)
1 Riverside Plz
Columbus, OH 43215
Tel.: (614) 716-1000
Web Site: www.psoklahoma.com
Approx. Rev.: $1,273,662,000
Approx. Number Employees: 1,150
Year Founded: 1913
Business Description:
Electric Power Distr
S.I.C.: 4939; 4911; 4931
N.A.I.C.S.: 221122; 221119
Advertising Expenditures: $1,215,000
Media: 1-2-3-6-7-8-9-10-11-18-19-20-22-23-24-25-26
Distr.: Reg.
Budget Set: Sept.
Personnel:
Michael G. Morris *(Chm & CEO)*
Stuart Solomon *(Pres & COO)*
Brian X. Tierney *(CFO & VP)*
Joseph M. Buonaiuto *(Controller & Chief Acctg Officer)*
David Sartin *(VP-Regulatory & Fin)*
Andrea Chancellor *(Dir-Corp Comm)*
Alan Decker *(Dir-Regulatory Svcs)*
Bobby Mouser *(Dir-Mktg & Customer Svc)*
Debbie Arwood *(Reg Mgr-HR)*
Floyd Schulte *(Mgr-Safety & Health)*
Brands & Products:
GROWING AND PROTECTING YOUR WEALTH
Advertising Agency:
Inventiva
522 E Borgfeld Dr
San Antonio, TX 78260-1622
Tel.: (830) 438-7599
Fax: (830) 438-7566

Key to Media (For complete agency information see *The Advertising Red Books-Agencies* edition):
1. Bus. Publs. 2. Cable T.V. 3. Catalogs & Directories. 4. Co-op Adv. 5. Consumer Mags. 6. D.M. to Bus. Estab.7. D.M. to Consumers 8. Daily Newsp. 9. Exhibits/Trade Shows 10. Foreign 11. Infomercial 12. Internet Adv.13. Multimedia 14. Network Radio 15. Network T.V. 16. Newsp. Distr. Mags. 17. Other 18. Outdoor (Posters, Transit) 19. Point of Purchase20. Premiums, Novelties 21. Product Samples 22. Special Events Mktg. 23. Spot Radio 24. Spot T.V. 25. Weekly Newsp. 26. Yellow Page Adv.

PUBLIC SERVICE ENTERPRISE GROUP INCORPORATED

80 Park Plaza
Newark, NJ 07101
Tel.: (973) 456-3500
Tel.: (973) 430-6397
Fax: (973) 824-7056
E-mail: webmaster@pseg.com
Web Site: www.pseg.com
Approx. Rev.: $11,793,000,000
Approx. Number Employees: 9,965
Year Founded: 1903
Business Description:
Diversified Energy & Energy Services Holding Company
S.I.C.: 4924; 4911; 4931; 4939
N.A.I.C.S.: 221210; 221119; 221121; 221122
Media: 1-2-3-4-6-7-8-9-10-16-18-22-23-24-25
Distr.: Reg.
Budget Set: Jan.
Personnel:
Ralph Izzo *(Chm, Pres & CEO)*
Ralph A. LaRossa *(Pres, COO-PSE & G)*
Caroline D. Dorsa *(CFO & Exec VP)*
Margaret M. Pego *(Chief HR Officer & Sr VP-HR)*
Randall E. Mehrberg *(Pres-Energy Holdings, Exec VP-Plng & Strategy)*
Thomas P. Joyce *(Pres-Nuclear Div & Chief Nuclear Officer)*
Richard P. Lopriore *(Pres-PSEG Fossil)*
Advertising Agencies:
The Bivings Group
2201 Wisconsin Ave NW Ste 310
Washington, DC 20007
Tel.: (202) 741-1500
Fax: (202) 741-1501

GraficaGroup
525 E Main St
Chester, NJ 07930-2627
Tel.: (908) 879-2169
Fax: (908) 879-2569

PUGET ENERGY, INC.

(Joint Venture of Canada Pension Plan Investment Board, British Columbia Investment Management Corporation, Macquarie Group Limited & Alberta Investment Management Corporation)
10885 NE 4th St Ste 1200
Bellevue, WA 98004-5515
Mailing Address:
PO Box 97034
Bellevue, WA 98009-9734
Tel.: (425) 454-6363
Fax: (425) 424-6537
Toll Free: (888) 225-5773
E-mail: durga.waite@pse.com
Web Site: www.pugetenergy.com
Approx. Rev.: $3,122,217,000
Year Founded: 1999
Business Description:
Holding Company; Electric Power & Gas Distr
S.I.C.: 4939; 4911; 4924; 6719
N.A.I.C.S.: 221122; 221210; 551112
Media: 1-6-8-9-10-23-24-25-26
Distr.: Reg.
Budget Set: Dec.
Personnel:
William S. Ayer *(Chm, Pres & CEO)*
Kimberly J. Harris *(Pres & CEO-Puget Sound Energy)*
Don E. Gaines *(Treas & VP-Fin)*

QUALCOMM INCORPORATED

5775 Morehouse Dr
San Diego, CA 92121-1714
Tel.: (858) 587-1121
Fax: (858) 658-2100
E-mail: corpcomm@qualcomm.com
Web Site: www.qualcomm.com
Approx. Rev.: $10,991,000,000
Approx. Number Employees: 17,500
Year Founded: 1985
Business Description:
Digital Wireless Communications Products, Technologies & Services
S.I.C.: 4812; 3661; 4899
N.A.I.C.S.: 517212; 334210; 517910
Export
Media: 2-6-7-9-10-13-25
Personnel:
Paul E. Jacobs *(Chm & CEO)*
Steven R. Altman *(Vice Chm)*
Richard Sulpizio *(Pres/CEO-Qualcomm Enterprise Svcs)*
Derek K. Aberle *(Grp Pres & Exec VP)*
William E. Keitel *(CFO & Exec VP)*
Steve Mollenkopf *(COO)*
Norm Fjeldheim *(CIO & Sr VP)*
Matt Grob *(CTO & Exec VP)*
Margaret L. Johnson *(Pres-Global Market Dev & Exec VP)*
Jing Wang *(Pres-Global Bus Ops & Exec VP)*
Young Koo Cha *(Pres-Qualcomm Korea & Sr VP)*
Kimberly M. Koro *(Pres-Govt Tech & Sr VP)*
Rafael Steinhauser *(Pres-Latin America & Sr VP)*
Rob Chandhok *(Pres-Qualcomm Innovation Center Inc & Internet Svcs)*
John Stefanac *(Pres-SEA/Pacific)*
Donald J. Rosenberg *(Gen Counsel, Sec & Exec VP)*
James Lederer *(Exec VP & Gen Mgr-Qualcomm CDMA Technologies)*
Andrew Gilbert *(Exec VP-European Innovation Dev)*
Roberto Padovani *(Exec VP)*
Daniel L. Sullivan *(Exec VP-HR)*
William Bold *(Sr VP-Govt Affairs)*
William F. Davidson, Jr. *(Sr VP-IR & Global Mktg)*
Anastassia Lauterbach *(Sr VP-Global Bus Ops-Europe)*
Norman L. Ellis *(VP-Sls, Mktg & Svcs-Enterprise Svcs)*
Thomas N. Flies *(Sr Dir-Product Mgmt)*
John Sinnott *(Sr Dir-IR)*
Sayeed Choudhury *(Dir-Product Mgmt-Web Technologies)*
Amy Berguson *(Sr Mgr-IR)*
Jonathan Leibo *(Sr Mgr-Mktg)*
Todd Schak *(Sr Mgr-IR)*
Eric Witty *(Product Mgr)*
Bill Stone *(Mgr & Sr Staff Engr)*
Xiang Wang *(Engr)*
Brands & Products:
BREW
CDMA2000
CMX
DELIVERYONE
FLUENCE
GLOBALSTAR
GLOBALTRACS
GPSONE
LAUNCHPAD
MIRASOL
MSM6100
MSM6225
MSM6250
MSM6300
MSM6500
MSM7500
OMNITRACS
OMNIVISION
OPENGL
Q3DIMENSION
QCAMCORDER
QCAMERA
QCHAT
QPOINT
QSEC
QUALCOMM
QVIDEOPHONE
SNAPDRAGON
Advertising Agencies:
Magner Sanborn
111 N Post Ste 400
Spokane, WA 99201
Tel.: (509) 688-2200
Fax: (509) 688-2299

Rizzuti/Austin Marketing Group
1846 Rosemeade Pkwy Ste 150
Carrollton, TX 75007
Tel.: (972) 394-5116
Fax: (972) 394-5272

QUEST RESOURCE CORPORATION

(Sub. of PostRock Energy Corporation)
Oklahoma Tower 210 Park Ave Ste 2750
Oklahoma City, OK 73102
Tel.: (405) 600-7704
Fax: (405) 600-7722
E-mail: info@qrcp.net
Web Site: www.qrcp.net
Approx. Rev.: $176,113,000
Approx. Number Employees: 309
Year Founded: 1982
Business Description:
Producer, Transporter & Developer of Natural Gas
S.I.C.: 1311; 1381; 1389
N.A.I.C.S.: 211111; 213111; 213112
Media: 17
Personnel:
David C. Lawler *(Pres & CEO)*

QWEST COMMUNICATIONS INTERNATIONAL INC.

(Sub. of CenturyLink, Inc.)
1801 California St
Denver, CO 80202
Tel.: (303) 992-1400
Fax: (303) 896-8515
Toll Free: (800) 899-7780
Toll Free: (800) 567-7296 (IR)
E-mail: qnews@qwest.com
Web Site: www.qwest.com
Approx. Rev.: $11,730,000,000
Approx. Number Employees: 28,343
Year Founded: 1996
Business Description:
Holding Company; Wired Data, Internet, Video & Voice Telecommunications Carrier
S.I.C.: 6719; 4813; 7374; 7375
N.A.I.C.S.: 551112; 517110; 517919; 518111; 518210
Advertising Expenditures: $296,000,000
Media: 2-3-6-7-9-13-15-23
Distr.: Natl.; Reg.
Personnel:
Edward A. Mueller *(Chm & CEO)*
Teresa Taylor *(COO)*
Christopher K. Ancell *(Pres-Bus Markets Grp)*
Stephanie G. Comfort *(Exec VP-Corp Strategy)*
Roland R. Thornton *(Exec VP)*
Robert D. Tregemba *(Exec VP-Network Ops)*
Dan Yost *(Exec VP-Mass Markets)*
R. Steven Davis *(Sr VP-Pub Policy & Govt Rels)*
Kurt Fawkes *(Sr VP-IR)*
Stephen E. Brilz *(VP, Deputy Gen Counsel & Asst Sec)*
Brant Krisewicz *(Mgr-Lead Digital Media)*
Brands & Products:
10 10 056
60 MINUTE CANADA SAVINGS
60 MINUTE MEXICO SAVINGS
800 CONNECT
800 PAGELINE
ABSOLUTE DATA INTEGRITY
ADVANTAGE SELECT U.S.
AFFORD-A-CALL
AFTERCARE
ANALOG TRUNK SAFETY PLUS
ANYWHERE VOICEMAIL
AQCB
ASIALINK
AWARENESS BUILDER PACKAGE
BARGAIN CALL
BILLMATE
BRNA
BROADBAND ACCESS AGGREGATION SERVICE
BROADBAND BY QWEST
BROWSENOW
C4PM
CALLER ID WITH PRIVACY +
CITYWIDE REPLY
COME HOME TO QWEST AND BRING YOUR NUMBER WITH YOU
COMPLETE-A-CALL
COMPLETE COVERAGE PACKAGE
CONNECTED SCHOOLS
CONVENIENCEPAK
COUNTDOWN
CUSTOMCHOICE
CUSTOMCHOICE COMPLETE
CYBERCENTER
DATASTOP
DENVER TASTE
DEX
DID
DIGITAL ANYWHERE
DIRECTQUEST
DIRECTV
DOMESTIC NETWORK DIVERSITY SERVICES
DR. TELEWORK
DVL
E-FERRAL
EASY START THREE
EBILL COMPANION
ED CENTRO DE QWEST, DONDE LE BRINDAMOS EN SU IDIOM
EL CENTRO

Key to Media (For complete agency information see *The Advertising Red Books-Agencies* edition):
1. Bus. Publs. 2. Cable T.V. 3. Catalogs & Directories. 4. Co-op Adv. 5. Consumer Mags. 6. D.M. to Bus. Estab.7. D.M. to Consumers 8. Daily Newsp. 9. Exhibits/Trade Shows 10. Foreign 11. Infomercial 12. Internet Adv.13. Multimedia 14. Network Radio 15. Network T.V. 16. Newsp. Distr. Mags. 17. Other 18. Outdoor (Posters, Transit) 19. Point of Purchase20. Premiums, Novelties 21. Product Samples 22. Special Events Mktg. 23. Spot Radio 24. Spot T.V. 25. Weekly Newsp. 26. Yellow Page Adv.

EL CENTRO DE QWEST
ELPASOTEL
ESPIRITU DE SERVICIO
EVERY STUDENT. EVERY SCHOOL. CONNECTED.
EVERYWHERE LINE
EWS
EWS EXTENDED WORKPLACE SOLUTIONS
EXPANDED COVERAGE
EXPERIENCE CHOICE
FAMILYLINE
FASTFACTS
FINDME
FLEXIBLE CHOICE
FREEDOM FOR HOSTED APPLICATIONS
GEOMAX
GEOPLUS
GET CONNECTED, STAY CONNECTED. WORLDWIDE!
GET IN THE Q
GET IT IN GEAR
HIGHWAY Q
HOME LINK
HOMERECEPTIONIST
THE INCREDIBLE INTERNET GUY
INFOQWEST
INTERNET POINTER
INTRACALL
IQ NETWORKING
IT'S ALL ABOUT CHOICE
IT'S ALL ABOUT CHOICE QWEST CHOICE TV & ONLINE
IVRQUEST
JUST ONE DESTINATION
KIDZQWEST
LCI ALTERNATIVE
LIFE'S BETTER HERE
LITEL
LONG DISTANCE TO GO
MARCO CAPACITY
MARKET EXPANSION LINE
MEDIA EXPRESS
MEGABIT 256 DELUXE
MEGABIT 256 SELECT
MEGABIT SPOKENHERE
MEGACENTRAL
MONITORPARTNER
MOUNTAIN BELL
MOVING WORK TO THE WORKERS
MY BUSINESS PARTNERS
MYQWEST
N@KED DSL
NAKED DSL
NON-STOP
NORTHWESTERN
OFFICE LINK
ON-THE-GO
ONEFLEX
ONLINE CALL ALERT
THE ORIGINAL SEARCH ENGINE
PEAQ
PENNIES PER CALL!
PENNY PLUS
PHONE BACKER
PHONE NET
PLUG 'N' PLAY
POPULARCHOICE
PORT PAC
THE POWER TO STAY CONNECTED ANYTIME, ANYWHERE
POWERWEB
PREFERREDCHOICE
PREMEIRCHOICE
PREMIER CIRCLE
PRESENTING WIRELESS THE WAY YOU WANT IT.
PRIVACY SCREEN
PRIVACYPAK
PROMISE OF VALUE
PUSHCASTER
Q
Q BY QWEST
Q. INTEGRITY
Q QWEST CENTER OMAHA
Q QWEST DIGITAL MEDIA
Q SEARCH
Q.ASP
Q.BIZ
Q.COLLECT
Q.CONTRACTOR
Q.GUARANTEED
Q.HOME
Q.MARKETPLACE
Q.MEMBER
QNC
Q.PARTNER
Q.PORT
QPP
Q.PREMIER
Q'S JOOK JOINT
Q.TALK
QUE TAL
Q.UNIVERSAL COLLECT
QWAVE
QWCC
QWEST
QWEST 411
QWEST ADVANTAGE
QWEST ALLIANCE
QWEST APPTIMUM
QWEST ARENA
QWEST CENTER OMAHA
QWEST CHOICE
QWEST CHOICE ONLINE
QWEST CONNECT
QWEST CONNECTQ
QWEST CONTROL
QWEST CYBER.SOLUTIONS
QWEST DEX
QWEST DEX ADVANTAGE
QWEST DSL
QWEST DSL 256
QWEST DSL PRO
QWEST DSL PRO DELUXE
QWEST ENTERPRISE
QWEST EXPRESS
QWEST EXPRESS UK
QWEST FREEDOM
QWEST HIGH-SPEED INTERNET
QWEST HOSTING...CHOICE-DRIVEN SOLUTIONS
QWEST INTERNATIONAL ANYTIME SAVINGS PLAN
QWEST IQ
QWEST IQ NETWORKING
QWEST LIGHTSPEED
QWEST LINK
QWEST LINKED
QWEST LOYAL ADVANTAGE
QWEST PASSPORT
QWEST PLATFORM PLUS
QWEST PROMISE OF VALUE
QWEST REWARDS
QWEST RIDE THE LIGHT
QWEST ROLLBACK
QWEST SELECT SOLUTIONS
QWEST TOTAL ADVANTAGE
QWEST TOTAL CARE
QWEST VOICE ADVANTAGE
QWEST VOICE BROWSING
QWEST WEB CONTACT CENTER
QWEST WIRELESS
QWESTAIR
QWESTLINKED
QWEST.NET
QWESTREWARDS
QWESTSOURCE
Q.WORLD
THE REAL DEAL
REFER2QWEST
REMOTE CONTROL
REPORT PARTNER
REQWEST
SECURITY 800
SECURITY SCREEN
SIMPLY BUSINESS
SIMPLY GUARANTEED
SOLUTIONS THAT ARE OUT OF THE BOX.
SPARQ
SPIRIT OF SERVICE
SPIRIT OF SERVICE EXPERIENCE
SPIRIT OF SERVICE IN ACTION
STAND-BY-LINE
STEALTH
STORE ON THE GO
TELEMAREXPRESS
THINK QWEST FIRST
TNR
TOTAL LINK
TOTAL PACKAGE
TRU QWEST
ULTIMATE CHOICE
ULTIMATE FREEDOM
U.S. LONG DISTANCE
US WEST
US WEST CHOICE ONLINE
US WEST CHOICE TV
US WEST CHOICE TV & ONLINE
US WEST COMPLETE COVERAGE
US WEST DEX INTERNET POINTER
US WEST ONLINE AVENUE
US WEST POWERWEB
USLD
USLD SELECT
USWEST DEX ON-THE-GO
VERTICAL DESTINATION
WEBWORLDCAFE & COFFEEHOUSE
WEBWORLDCAFE & COFFEEHOUSE POWERED BY US WEST
WERCS COMMUNICATIONS
WHERE YOU RECEIVE PERSONAL ATTENTION
WIDENING OUR WORLD WOW
YOU CAN
YOU RATE THE CALL

Advertising Agency:
Aspen Marketing Services
1240 N Ave
West Chicago, IL 60185
Tel.: (630) 293-9600
Fax: (630) 293-9609
Toll Free: (800) 848-0212

RGC RESOURCES, INC.

519 Kimball Ave NE
Roanoke, VA 24016-2103
Mailing Address:
PO Box 13007
Roanoke, VA 24030-3007
Tel.: (540) 777-4427
Fax: (540) 777-2636
E-mail: info@rgcresources.com
Web Site: www.rgcresources.com
Approx. Rev.: $73,823,914
Approx. Number Employees: 122
Business Description:
Holding Company; Natural Gas Distr
S.I.C.: 4924; 6719
N.A.I.C.S.: 221210; 551112
Media: 3-16
Personnel:
John B. Williamson, III *(Chm, Pres & CEO)*
Howard T. Lyon *(CFO, Treas & VP)*
Robert L. Wells *(VP-IT, Asst Sec & Asst Treas)*

ROCHESTER GAS & ELECTRIC CORPORATION

(Sub. of Iberdrola USA, Inc.)
89 East Ave
Rochester, NY 14649-0001
Mailing Address:
PO Box 5300
Ithaca, NY 14852-5300
Tel.: (585) 771-4444
Tel.: (585) 771-4802 (media relations)
Fax: (585) 771-4600
Toll Free: (800) 743-2110
Web Site: www.rge.com
Approx. Rev.: $1,116,293,000
Approx. Number Employees: 1,078
Year Founded: 1904
Business Description:
Electric & Gas Utility Services
S.I.C.: 4931; 4911; 4924; 4939
N.A.I.C.S.: 221119; 221121; 221122; 221210
Advertising Expenditures: $300,000
Media: 2-5-7-8-9-10-23-24-25
Distr.: Direct to Consumer
Budget Set: Aug. -Sept.
Personnel:
Mark S. Lynch *(Pres-NYSEG and RG&E)*

RRI ENERGY INC.

(Name Changed to GenOn Energy, Inc.)

RURAL CELLULAR CORPORATION

(Joint Venture of Verizon Communications Inc. & Vodafone Group Plc)
(d/b/a Unicel)
3905 Dakota St SW
Alexandria, MN 56308
Mailing Address:
PO Box 2000
Alexandria, MN 56308
Tel.: (320) 762-2000
Fax: (320) 808-2120
Toll Free: (800) 450-2000
Toll Free: (800) GO-CELLULAR
Web Site: www.rccwireless.com
Approx. Rev.: $635,315,000
Approx. Number Employees: 1,132
Year Founded: 1990
Business Description:
Wireless Communication Services
S.I.C.: 4813; 4812
N.A.I.C.S.: 517310; 517211
Media: 5-13-19
Personnel:
Wesley E. Schultz *(CFO & Exec VP)*
Scott G. Donlea *(Sr VP-Network & Product Dev)*
Karen C. Henrikson *(VP-HR)*
William M. Johnson, III *(VP-Customer Equipment & Pur)*

Key to Media (For complete agency information see *The Advertising Red Books-Agencies* edition):
1. Bus. Publs. 2. Cable T.V. 3. Catalogs & Directories. 4. Co-op Adv. 5. Consumer Mags. 6. D.M. to Bus. Estab.7. D.M. to Consumers 8. Daily Newsp. 9. Exhibits/Trade Shows 10. Foreign 11. Infomercial 12. Internet Adv.13. Multimedia 14. Network Radio 15. Network T.V. 16. Newsp. Distr. Mags. 17. Other 18. Outdoor (Posters, Transit) 19. Point of Purchase20. Premiums, Novelties 21. Product Samples 22. Special Events Mktg. 23. Spot Radio 24. Spot T.V. 25. Weekly Newsp. 26. Yellow Page Adv.

SAN ANTONIO WATER SYSTEM

2800 US Hwy 281 N
San Antonio, TX 78212-3106
Tel.: (210) 704-7297
Fax: (210) 704-7297
E-mail: info@saws.org
Web Site: www.saws.org
Sales Range: $200-249.9 Million
Approx. Number Employees: 1,500
Year Founded: 1992
Business Description:
Water Supply
S.I.C.: 4941
N.A.I.C.S.: 221310
Personnel:
Willie A. Mitchell *(Vice Chm)*
Robert Puente *(Pres & CEO)*
Advertising Agency:
Taylor West Advertising
4040 Broadway St Ste 302
San Antonio, TX 78209-6353
Tel.: (210) 805-0320
Fax: (210) 805-9371

SANTEE COOPER

1 Riverwood Dr
Moncks Corner, SC 29461
Tel.: (843) 761-8000
Fax: (843) 761-7060
E-mail: info@santeecooper.com
Web Site: www.santeecooper.com
Approx. Number Employees: 1,800
Business Description:
Electric Power & Water Utility Distr
S.I.C.: 4911; 4939
N.A.I.C.S.: 221122
Media: 6-10-18-20-22-26
Personnel:
Lonnie N. Carter *(Pres & CEO)*
Elaine G. Peterson *(CFO & Exec VP)*
Bill McCall, Jr. *(COO & Exec VP)*
Jim Brogdon, Jr. *(Exec VP & Gen Counsel)*
Rennie M. Singletary, III *(Exec VP-Corp Svcs)*
Laura Varn *(VP-Corp Comm)*
C. Samuel Bennett, II *(Mgr-Economic Dev)*

SASKATCHEWAN POWER CORPORATION

(Sub. of Crown Investments Corporation of Saskatchewan)
(d/b/a SaskPower)
2025 Victoria Ave
Regina, SK S4P 0S1, Canada
Tel.: (306) 566-2121
Fax: (306) 566-2548
Toll Free: (888) 757-6937
E-mail: info@saskpower.com
Web Site: www.saskpower.com
Approx. Rev.: $1,188,222,000
Year Founded: 1929
Business Description:
Public Utility & Electricity Supplier
S.I.C.: 4911; 4939
N.A.I.C.S.: 221122
Media: 2-3-4-6-8-9-10-14-15-16-18-19-20-23-24-25-26
Distr.: Reg.
Budget Set: Nov.
Personnel:
Joel Teal *(Chm)*
Bill Wheatley *(Vice Chm)*
Patricia Youzwa *(Pres & CEO)*
Sandeep Kalra *(CFO, VP-Fin & Enterprise Risk Mgmt)*
Tom Kindred *(CIO & VP-Corp IT)*
Philip H. Davies *(VP-Legal, Land & Regulatory Affairs)*
Garner Mitchell *(VP-Power Production)*
Advertising Agency:
Brown Communications Group
2275 Albert St
Regina, SK S4P 2V5, Canada
Tel.: (306) 352-6625
Fax: (306) 757-1980
Toll Free: (877) 202-7696

SCANA CORPORATION

100 SCANA Pkwy
Cayce, SC 29033
Tel.: (803) 217-9000
Web Site: www.scana.com
Approx. Rev.: $4,601,000,000
Approx. Number Employees: 5,877
Year Founded: 1846
Business Description:
Electric, Natural Gas & Public Transportation Services
S.I.C.: 4939; 4119; 4911; 4924; 4931
N.A.I.C.S.: 221111; 221119; 221122; 221210; 485999
Advertising Expenditures: $66,163
Media: 1-2-5-6-7-8-9-10-15-16-18-19-20-22-23-24-25
Distr.: Natl.
Budget Set: Jan.
Personnel:
William B. Timmerman *(Chm & CEO)*
Kevin B. Marsh *(Pres & COO)*
Paul V. Fant *(Pres & COO-Carolina Gas Transmission)*
Jimmy E. Addison *(CFO & Sr VP)*
Ronald T. Lindsay *(Gen Counsel & Sr VP)*
Gina S. Champion *(Sec, Dir-Corp Governance & Assoc Gen Counsel)*
Pat Hutson *(Sr VP-HR)*
Charles B. McFadden *(Sr VP-Govt Affairs & Economic Dev)*
Cathy Love *(VP-Comm & Plng)*
Eric Boomhower *(Mgr-Pub Affairs)*
Brands & Products:
ENERGETIC MINDS
POWER FOR LIVING
SCANA
Advertising Agency:
McCrae Communications
107 Stonewall Ave
Fayetteville, GA 30214
Tel.: (770) 460-7277

SEATTLE CITY LIGHT

700 Fifth Ave Ste 3200
Seattle, WA 98104-5031
Mailing Address:
PO Box 34023
Seattle, WA 98124-4023
Tel.: (206) 684-3000
Tel.: (206) 684-3508
Fax: (206) 233-2757
E-mail: webteam.scl@seattle.gov
Web Site: www.ci.seattle.wa.us/light
Sales Range: $800-899.9 Million
Approx. Number Employees: 1,560
Year Founded: 1905
Business Description:
Municipal Electric Utility; Conservation Loans, Grants & Services
S.I.C.: 4939; 4911
N.A.I.C.S.: 221122
Advertising Expenditures: $259,694
Media: 9-13-16-18-23-24-26
Distr.: Direct to Consumer
Personnel:
Roy Lum *(CIO & Interim CFO)*
Darwyn Anderson *(Dir-HR)*
Suzanne Hartman *(Dir-Comm & Pub Affairs)*
Michael Mann *(Interim Dir-Office Sustainability & Environ)*
Julie Tobin *(Office Mgr)*
Brands & Products:
ENERGY SMART SERVICES
SEATTLE CITY LIGHT

SEMPRA ENERGY

101 Ash St
San Diego, CA 92101-3017
Tel.: (619) 696-2034
Fax: (619) 696-2374
Toll Free: (877) 736-7721
E-mail: careers.sr@sempra.com
Web Site: www.sempra.com
Approx. Rev.: $9,003,000,000
Approx. Number Employees: 13,504
Year Founded: 1998
Business Description:
Energy Services Holding Company; Provider of Electricity, Natural Gas & Value-Added Products & Services
S.I.C.: 4924; 4931; 6719
N.A.I.C.S.: 221210; 221119; 551112
Personnel:
Donald E. Felsinger *(Chm)*
Neal E. Schmale *(Pres & COO)*
Jeff Martin *(Pres & CEO-Sempra Generation)*
Debra Reed *(CEO)*
Mark A. Snell *(CFO & Exec VP)*
Joseph A. Householder *(Chief Acctg Officer, Sr VP & Controller)*
Javade Chaudhri *(Gen Counsel & Exec VP)*
Charles A. Mcmonagle *(Treas & Sr VP)*
G. Joyce Rowland *(Sr VP-HR)*
Erin Koch *(Mgr-Govt Rels)*
Brands & Products:
SEMPRA ENERGY
Advertising Agency:
al Punto Advertising, Inc.
730 El Camino Way Ste 200
Tustin, CA 92780-7733
Tel.: (714) 544-0888
Fax: (714) 544-0830

SHAW ENVIRONMENTAL

(Sub. of The Shaw Group Inc.)
13 British American Blvd
Latham, NY 12110
Tel.: (518) 783-1996
Fax: (518) 783-8397
E-mail: environmental@shawgrp.com
Web Site: www.shawgrp.com
Sales Range: $75-99.9 Million
Business Description:
Integrated Solid Waste Services
S.I.C.: 8748
N.A.I.C.S.: 541690
Advertising Expenditures: $750,000
Media: 10
Personnel:
Cornelius Murphy *(Sr VP-Federal Div)*

SIERRA PACIFIC POWER COMPANY

(Name Changed to NV Energy)

SKYTEL COMMUNICATIONS INC.

(Sub. of Velocita Wireless LLC)
500 Clinton Center Dr
Clinton, MS 39056
Tel.: (601) 292-8035 (HR)
Tel.: (601) 292-8800 (Customer Svc)
Toll Free: (800) 552-6835
E-mail: skyinfo@skytel.com
Web Site: www.skytel.com
Approx. Rev.: $100,000,000
Approx. Number Employees: 375
Year Founded: 1988
Business Description:
Wireless Paging Services
S.I.C.: 4812; 7389
N.A.I.C.S.: 517212; 561421
Advertising Expenditures: $200,000
Media: 2-3-8-9-13-17-24-26
Distr.: Natl.
Personnel:
Martin Grillo *(CEO)*
Wendy Mullins *(Gen Counsel)*
Molly McCardle *(VP-Strategic Bus Dev)*
Brands & Products:
SKYFAX
SKYPAGER
SKYTALK
SKYTEL 2-WAY
SKYWORD
SKYWORD PLUS
SKYWRITER

SOUTH JERSEY GAS COMPANY

(Sub. of South Jersey Industries, Inc.)
1 S Jersey Plz
Folsom, NJ 08037
Tel.: (609) 561-9000
Fax: (609) 561-8225
Toll Free: (888) 766-9900
E-mail: sjindustries@sjindustries.com
Web Site: www.sjindustries.com
Approx. Rev.: $475,982,000
Approx. Number Employees: 407
Year Founded: 1910
Business Description:
Natural Gas Distr
S.I.C.: 4924
N.A.I.C.S.: 221210
Media: 8-9-18-23-24-25
Distr.: Reg.
Budget Set: Aug. -Sept.
Personnel:
Edward J. Graham *(Chm, Pres & CEO)*
David A. Kindlick *(CFO & VP)*
Jeffrey E. Dubois *(COO, Sr VP & VP)*

SOUTHERN CALIFORNIA EDISON COMPANY

(Sub. of Edison International)
2244 Walnut Grove Ave
Rosemead, CA 91770-3714
Mailing Address:
PO Box 800
Rosemead, CA 91770-0800
Tel.: (626) 302-1212
Fax: (626) 302-2517
Web Site: www.sce.com
Approx. Rev.: $9,983,000,000
Approx. Number Employees: 18,230
Year Founded: 1886
Business Description:
Electric Utility Services
S.I.C.: 4911; 4931; 4939
N.A.I.C.S.: 221122; 221111; 221119
Advertising Expenditures: $5,000,000

Key to Media (For complete agency information see *The Advertising Red Books-Agencies* edition):
1. Bus. Publs. 2. Cable T.V. 3. Catalogs & Directories. 4. Co-op Adv. 5. Consumer Mags. 6. D.M. to Bus. Estab.7. D.M. to Consumers 8. Daily Newsp. 9. Exhibits/Trade Shows 10. Foreign 11. Infomercial 12. Internet Adv.13. Multimedia 14. Network Radio 15. Network T.V. 16. Newsp. Distr. Mags. 17. Other 18. Outdoor (Posters, Transit) 19. Point of Purchase20. Premiums, Novelties 21. Product Samples 22. Special Events Mktg. 23. Spot Radio 24. Spot T.V. 25. Weekly Newsp. 26. Yellow Page Adv.

Media: 9-14-15
Distr.: Reg.
Budget Set: Dec.
Personnel:
Ronald L. Litzinger *(Pres)*
Linda G. Sullivan *(CFO & Sr VP)*
Mahvash Yazdi *(CIO & Sr VP-Bus Integration)*
Barbara E. Mathews *(Chief Governance Officer, Sec, VP & Assoc Gen Counsel)*
Cecil R. House *(Chief Procurement Officer & Sr VP-Safety & Ops Support)*
Polly L. Gault *(Exec VP-Pub Affairs)*
Stephen E. Pickett *(Exec VP)*
Lynda L. Ziegler *(Exec VP)*
James A. Kelly *(Sr VP & Head-Transmission/Distr Bus)*
Peter T. Dietrich *(Sr VP & Chief Nuclear Officer)*
Bruce C. Foster *(Sr VP-Regulatory Ops)*
Stuart R. Hemphill *(Sr VP-Power Procurement)*
Patricia Miller *(VP-HR)*
Tammy Tumbling *(Dir-Philanthropy & Community Involvement)*
Gail Malone *(Mgr)*
Advertising Agencies:
DDB Los Angeles
340 Main St
Venice, CA 90291
Tel.: (310) 907-1500
Fax: (310) 907-1571

Lagrant Communications
600 Wilshire Blvd Ste 1520
Los Angeles, CA 90017-2920
Tel.: (323) 469-8680
Fax: (323) 469-8683

Sensis
811 W 7th St Ste 300
Los Angeles, CA 90017
Tel.: (213) 861-7427
Fax: (323) 861-7436
Toll Free: (866) 434-2443

Valencia, Perez & Echeveste
1605 Hope St Ste 250
South Pasadena, CA 91030
Tel.: (626) 403-3200
Fax: (626) 403-1700

SOUTHERN CALIFORNIA GAS COMPANY

(Sub. of Sempra Energy)
555 W 5th St
Los Angeles, CA 90013-1010
Mailing Address:
PO Box 513249
Los Angeles, CA 90051-1249
Tel.: (213) 244-1200
Fax: (213) 244-8292
Web Site: www.socalgas.com
Approx. Rev.: $3,822,000,000
Approx. Number Employees: 7,067
Year Founded: 1867
Business Description:
Natural Gas Distr
S.I.C.: 4924; 4922
N.A.I.C.S.: 221210; 486210
Advertising Expenditures: $5,355,000
Bus. Publs.: $50,000; Cable T.V.: $105,000; Consumer Mags.: $220,000; Daily Newsp.: $352,000; Other: $100,000; Outdoor (Posters, Transit): $143,000; Spot Radio: $2,350,000; Spot T.V.: $2,020,000; Weekly Newsp.: $115,000
Distr.: Direct to Consumer; Reg.
Budget Set: Oct.
Personnel:
Michael W. Allman *(Pres & CEO)*
Robert M. Schlax *(CFO, VP & Controller)*
Anne S. Smith *(COO)*
Steven D. Davis *(Sr VP)*
William L. Reed *(Sr VP-Strategic Plng)*
Richard M. Morrow *(VP-Customer Svcs & Mktg)*
Brands & Products:
SOUTHERN CALIFORNIA GAS
Advertising Agencies:
al Punto Advertising, Inc.
730 El Camino Way Ste 200
Tustin, CA 92780-7733
Tel.: (714) 544-0888
Fax: (714) 544-0830

interTrend Communications, Inc.
555 E Ocean Blvd
Long Beach, CA 90802-5003
Tel.: (562) 733-1888
Fax: (562) 733-1889

Lexicon Communications Corp.
520 Bellmore Way
Pasadena, CA 91103
Tel.: (626) 683-9200
Fax: (622) 628-1960

SOUTHERN COMPANY

30 Ivan Allen Jr Blvd NW
Atlanta, GA 30308
Tel.: (404) 506-5000
Fax: (404) 506-0455
Web Site:
www.southerncompany.com
Approx. Rev.: $17,456,000,000
Approx. Number Employees: 25,940
Year Founded: 1945
Business Description:
Electric Power Utility Holding Company
S.I.C.: 4939; 4911; 4931; 6141
N.A.I.C.S.: 221112; 221111; 221113; 221119; 221121; 522220
Media: 2-3-7-8-10-13-15-24
Distr.: Natl.
Budget Set: Jan. -Dec.
Personnel:
Thomas A. Fanning *(Chm, Pres & CEO)*
C. Alan Martin *(CEO-Southern Svcs & Exec VP)*
Arthur P. Beattie *(CFO & Exec VP)*
Anthony J. Topazi *(COO & Exec VP)*
Kenneth E. Coleman *(CIO & Sr VP)*
W. Ron Hinson *(Chief Acctg Officer & Comptroller)*
William O. Ball *(Exec VP & Chief Transmission Officer)*
Douglas E. Jones *(Chief Production Officer)*
Susan N. Story *(Pres/CEO-Svcs & Exec VP)*
William Paul Bowers *(Pres/CEO-Georgia Power)*
Christopher C. Womack *(Pres-External Affairs & Exec VP)*
Oscar C. Harper *(Pres-Southern Power & Sr VP-Svcs)*
G. Edison Holland *(Gen Counsel, Sec & Exec VP)*
Anthony R. James *(Exec VP)*
Charles D. McCrary *(Exec VP)*
Chris Hobson *(Sr VP-Res & Environ Affairs)*
Theodore J. McCullough *(Sr VP-Svcs)*
Carrie Kurlander *(VP-Comm)*
Stacy Kilcoyne *(Dir-HR)*
Brands & Products:
SOUTHERN COMPANY
Advertising Agencies:
Fitzgerald+CO
3060 Peachtree Rd NW
Atlanta, GA 30305
Tel.: (404) 504-6900
Fax: (404) 239-0548
(Brand & Media)

Grey Atlanta
191 Peachtree St NE Ste 4025
Atlanta, GA 30309
Tel.: (404) 261-2360
Fax: (404) 261-9360

Lattimer Communications
934 Glenwood Ave Ste 260
Atlanta, GA 30316
Tel.: (404) 526-9321
Fax: (404) 526-9324

SOUTHERN UNION COMPANY

5444 Westheimer Rd
Houston, TX 77056
Tel.: (713) 989-2000
Fax: (713) 989-1121
E-mail: info@southernunionco.com
Web Site: www.southernunionco.com
Approx. Rev.: $2,489,913,000
Approx. Number Employees: 2,437
Year Founded: 1932
Business Description:
Natural Gas Transportation, Storage, Gathering, Processing & Distr
S.I.C.: 4924
N.A.I.C.S.: 221210
Media: 2-4-7-8-10-23
Distr.: Direct to Consumer; Reg.
Budget Set: June
Personnel:
George L. Lindemann *(Chm & CEO)*
Eric D. Herschmann *(Vice Chm, Pres & COO)*
Roger A. Farrell *(Pres & COO-Southern Union Gas Svcs)*
Richard N. Marshall *(CFO & Sr VP)*
Daniel W. Bishop, II *(Chief Ethics Officer)*
Robert M. Kerrigan III *(Sec, VP & Asst Gen Counsel)*
Monica M. Gaudiosi *(Gen Counsel & Sr VP)*
George E. Aldrich *(Sr VP & Controller)*
Robert O. Bond *(Sr VP-Pipeline Ops)*
Michael German *(Sr VP-Utility Ops)*
John Barnett *(Dir-External Affairs)*
Brands & Products:
SOUTHERN UNION COMPANY
SUC

SPRINT NEXTEL CORP.

6200 Sprint Pkwy
Overland Park, KS 66251
Tel.: (703) 433-4000
Fax: (703) 433-4343
Toll Free: (800) 829-0965
E-mail: investor.relations@sprint.com
Web Site: www.sprint.com
Approx. Rev.: $32,563,000,000
Approx. Number Employees: 40,000
Year Founded: 1899
Business Description:
Holding Company; Wireless, Long Distance & Local Telecommunication Services
S.I.C.: 4813; 4812; 4899; 6719; 7382
N.A.I.C.S.: 517110; 517212; 517310; 517910; 551112; 561621
Advertising Expenditures: $1,400,000,000
Media: 3-6-9-15-18-23-24-31
Distr.: Intl.; Natl.
Budget Set: Nov.
Personnel:
James H. Hance, Jr. *(Chm)*
Matt Carter *(Pres)*
Daniel R. Hesse *(CEO)*
Joseph J. Euteneuer *(CFO)*
Ryan H. Siurek *(Principal Acctg Officer, VP & Controller)*
Robert S. Foosaner *(Sr VP-Govt Affairs & Chief Regulatory Officer)*
Kathryn A. Walker *(Chief Network Officer)*
Paget L. Alves *(Pres-Bus Markets Grp)*
Danny L. Bowman *(Pres-Integrated Solutions Grp)*
Keith O. Cowan *(Pres-Strategy & Corp Dev)*
Steven L. Elfman *(Pres-Network Ops & Wholesale)*
John D. Feehan, Jr. *(Sr VP & CFO-Sprint Prepaid Group)*
Charles Wunsch *(Gen Counsel & Sec)*
William Morgan *(Sr VP-Corp Mktg)*
Sandra J. Price *(Sr VP-HR)*
Bill White *(Sr VP-Corp Comm)*
Mike Goff *(VP-Natl Adv, Adv & Corp Brand Mgmt)*
Anita Bajaj Newton *(VP-Media & Digital Mktg)*
Randy Ritter *(VP-Mktg)*
Bob Stohrer *(VP-Mktg)*
Nikki Kiekbusch *(Gen Mgr-Mobile Ad Svcs)*
Nancy Beaton *(Dir-Consumer Mktg)*
Joe Mandacina *(Dir-Analyst Rels & Exec Comm)*
Stephanie Wilroy *(Sr Mgr-Digital Strategy & Social Media)*
Amy Pickerill *(Mgr-Email & Mobile Mktg)*
Aggie Sabala *(Mgr-Mktg)*
Kymber Umana *(Mgr-Hispanic Mktg)*
Candice Wolken *(Mgr-Digital Adv)*
Brands & Products:
BUSINESS MOBILITY FRAMEWORK
DIGILINK
EMPOWERED EDUCATION
LINE GUARD
NEXTEL
PCS CLEAR WIRELESS WORKPLACE
PCS VISION
SPRINT
SPRINT PCS
TRANSLINK
XOHM
Advertising Agencies:
Berlin Cameron United
100 Ave of the Americas 2nd Fl
New York, NY 10013
Tel.: (212) 824-2000

Key to Media (For complete agency information see *The Advertising Red Books-Agencies* edition):
1. Bus. Publs. 2. Cable T.V. 3. Catalogs & Directories. 4. Co-op Adv. 5. Consumer Mags. 6. D.M. to Bus. Estab.7. D.M. to Consumers
8. Daily Newsp. 9. Exhibits/Trade Shows 10. Foreign 11. Infomercial 12. Internet Adv.13. Multimedia 14. Network Radio
15. Network T.V. 16. Newsp. Distr. Mags. 17. Other 18. Outdoor (Posters, Transit) 19. Point of Purchase20. Premiums, Novelties
21. Product Samples 22. Special Events Mktg. 23. Spot Radio 24. Spot T.V. 25. Weekly Newsp. 26. Yellow Page Adv.

Sprint Nextel Corp. — (Continued)

Fax: (212) 268-8454
— Tamara Goodman *(Acct Dir)*

Callahan Creek, Inc.
805 New Hampshire St
Lawrence, KS 66044-2739
Tel.: (785) 838-4774
Fax: (785) 838-4033

CRT/tanaka
101 W Commerce Rd
Richmond, VA 23224
Tel.: (804) 675-8100
Fax: (804) 675-8183

Euro RSCG 4D
36 E Grand Ave Stes 3 & 4
Chicago, IL 60610
Tel.: (312) 640-6800
Fax: (312) 640-6801

Goodby, Silverstein & Partners, Inc.
(Part of Omnicom Group, Inc.)
720 California St
San Francisco, CA 94108-2404
Tel.: (415) 392-0669
Fax: (415) 788-4303
"Now Network" Campaign

Mindshare
498 7th Ave
New York, NY 10018
Tel.: (212) 297-7000
Fax: (212) 297-7001

Soho Square
636 11th Ave
New York, NY 10036
Tel.: (212) 237-7646
Xohm

The Vidal Partnership
228 E 45th St 11th Fl
New York, NY 10017-3303
Tel.: (646) 356-6600
Fax: (212) 661-7650

STARTEC GLOBAL COMMUNICATIONS CORPORATION

(Holding of Platinum Equity, LLC)
7361 Calhoun Pl Ste 650
Derwood, MD 20855-2775
Tel.: (301) 610-4300
Fax: (301) 610-4301
Toll Free: (800) 827-3374
E-mail: webmaster@startec.com
Web Site: www.startec.com
E-Mail For Key Personnel:
Marketing Director: tjmaster@startec.net
Approx. Rev.: $100,000,000
Approx. Number Employees: 270
Year Founded: 1989
Business Description:
International & Long Distance Telecommunications Services
S.I.C.: 4813; 4899
N.A.I.C.S.: 517310; 517910
Media: 7-13-17
Personnel:
Thomas Perez-Ducy *(Pres & CEO)*
Brands & Products:
STARTEC

SUNPOWER CORPORATION

3939 N 1st St
San Jose, CA 95134-1506
Tel.: (408) 240-5500
Fax: (408) 240-5400
Toll Free: (877) SUN-0123
E-mail: information@sunpowercorp.com
Web Site: www.sunpowercorp.com
Approx. Rev.: $2,219,230,000
Approx. Number Employees: 5,150
Business Description:
Solar Electric Power Products Designer, Mfr & Whslr
S.I.C.: 4931; 4911; 4939
N.A.I.C.S.: 221119; 221122
Advertising Expenditures: $3,300,000
Media: 10-17
Personnel:
Thomas Dinwoodie *(Founder & Chief Technical Officer)*
Thomas H. Werner *(Pres & CEO)*
Howard J. Wenger *(Pres-Utility & Power Plants Bus Grp)*
Dennis V. Arriola *(CFO & Exec VP)*
Marty Neese *(COO)*
David Henry *(Chief Mktg Officer)*
James S. Pape *(Pres-Residential & Comml Bus Grp)*
Bruce R. Ledesma *(Gen Counsel, Corp Sec & Exec VP)*
Julie Blunden *(Exec VP-Pub Policy & Corp Comm)*
Douglas J. Richards *(Exec VP-HR & Corp Svcs)*
Gian Maria Ferrero *(VP & Gen Mgr-Utilities & Power Plants)*
Peter Aschenbrenner *(VP-Corp Strategy)*
Gary Aranjo *(Sr Dir-Fin Acctg)*
E. Thomas Atchison *(Sr Dir-Quality & Reliability Assurance)*
Helen Kendrick *(Mgr-Corp Comm)*
Advertising Agency:
Ogilvy Public Relations Worldwide
636 11th Ave
New York, NY 10036
Tel.: (212) 880-5200
Fax: (212) 370-4636

SUREWEST COMMUNICATIONS

8150 Industrial Ave Bldg A
Roseville, CA 95678
Mailing Address:
PO Box 969
Roseville, CA 95678
Tel.: (916) 786-6141
Tel.: (916) 786-1799 (IR)
E-mail: media@surewest.com
Web Site: www.surw.com
Approx. Rev.: $243,499,000
Approx. Number Employees: 818
Year Founded: 1996
Business Description:
Holding Company; Telecommunications, Digital Video, Internet & Other Related Services
S.I.C.: 4813; 4812; 4833; 4841; 6719; 7375
N.A.I.C.S.: 517110; 515120; 515210; 517212; 518111; 551112
Import Export
Advertising Expenditures: $6,548,000
Media: 10
Personnel:
Kirk C. Doyle *(Chm)*
Steven C. Oldham *(Pres & CEO)*
Dan T. Bessey *(CFO & VP)*
Scott K. Barber *(COO & VP)*
Timothy J. Dotson *(CIO & VP)*
L. Scott Sommers *(Sr VP-Fin & Corp Dev)*
Kenneth E. Johnson *(VP & Gen Mgr-Ops-Kansas)*
Peter C. Drozdoff *(VP-Mktg)*
Matt Zuschlag *(Gen Mgr-Ops-Kansas City)*
Ron Rogers *(Dir-Corp Comm)*
Misty Wells *(Mgr-IR)*
Kerri Bessey *(Asst Sec & Legal Sec)*
William E. Peterson *(Asst Sec)*
Brands & Products:
SUREWEST

T-SYSTEMS NORTH AMERICA INC.

(Sub. of T-Systems Enterprise Services GmbH)
701 Warrenville Rd Ste 100
Lisle, IL 60532
Tel.: (630) 493-6100
Fax: (630) 493-6111
E-mail: info@t-systemsus.com
Web Site: www.t-systemsus.com
Approx. Number Employees: 350
Business Description:
Communication Technology Solutions
S.I.C.: 4899
N.A.I.C.S.: 517910
Personnel:
Heike Auerbach *(Mng Dir & Member-Mgmt Bd)*
Jeff Siansky *(Chief Sls & Svc Officer)*
Jordan Kanfer *(VP, Gen Counsel-HR & Member-Mgmt Board)*
Advertising Agency:
Lambert Edwards & Associates
755 W Big Beaver Rd Ste 1100
Troy, MI 48084
Tel.: (248) 362-4200
Fax: (248) 362-3428

TAMPA ELECTRIC COMPANY

(Sub. of TECO Energy, Inc.)
702 N Franklin St
Tampa, FL 33602-4429
Mailing Address:
PO Box 111
Tampa, FL 33601-0111
Tel.: (813) 228-1111
Fax: (813) 228-4644
Web Site: www.tampaelectric.com
Approx. Rev.: $2,673,600,000
Approx. Number Employees: 2,300
Business Description:
Electric Power Distribution & Generation Services
S.I.C.: 4911; 4931; 4939
N.A.I.C.S.: 221122; 221111; 221119
Media: 2-6-9-10-23-24-25-26
Distr.: Reg.
Personnel:
Sherrill W. Hudson *(Chm)*
Gordon L. Gillette *(Pres)*
John B. Ramil *(CEO)*
Sandra W. Callahan *(CFO, Treas, VP-Fin & Acctg)*
Charles A. Attal, III *(Chief Legal Officer, Gen Counsel & Sr VP)*
Clinton E. Childress *(Chief HR Officer & Sr VP)*

TEKELEC

5200 Paramount Parkway
Morrisville, NC 27560
Tel.: (919) 460-5500
Fax: (919) 460-0877
Toll Free: (888) 628-5521
E-mail: info@tekelec.com
Web Site: www.tekelec.com
E-Mail For Key Personnel:
Sales Director: sales@tekelec.com
Approx. Rev.: $423,963,000
Approx. Number Employees: 1,291
Year Founded: 1979
Business Description:
Develops Network Switching & Diagnostic Solutions for Traditional & Converging Communications Networks & Provides Call Center Products & Solutions
S.I.C.: 3663; 3661; 3825
N.A.I.C.S.: 334220; 334210; 334515
Export
Advertising Expenditures: $500,000
Media: 2-4-10-11-13-17-20-22
Distr.: Natl.
Budget Set: Dec.
Personnel:
Mark A. Floyd *(Chm)*
Ronald J. de Lange *(Pres & CEO)*
Gregory S. Rush *(CFO & Sr VP)*
J. Scott Weidenfeller *(CMO & Principal)*
Susie Kim Riley *(CMO)*
Stuart H. Kupinsky *(Gen Counsel & Sr VP-Corp Affairs)*
David K. Rice *(Sr VP-Ops)*
Luis Pajares *(VP-Sls-Americas)*
Boudewijn Pesch *(VP-Sls-Europe & Asia)*
Brands & Products:
ASI
BUILDING SMART NETWORKS
EAGLE
IP7
IX7000
SXI 500 SIP SERVER
TEKCORE
TEKELEC
TEKSERVER
TEKWARE
TOTALVIEW
Advertising Agency:
Hanft Raboy & Partners
205 Hudson St 7th Fl
New York, NY 10013
Tel.: (212) 674-3100
Fax: (212) 228-7679

TELEPHONE & DATA SYSTEMS, INC.

30 N LaSalle St Ste 4000
Chicago, IL 60602-2590
Tel.: (312) 630-1900
Fax: (312) 630-1908
Fax: (312) 630-1922
E-mail: TDSinfo@teldta.com
Web Site: www.teldta.com
E-Mail For Key Personnel:
Public Relations: Tom.Catani@teldta.com
Approx. Rev.: $4,986,829,000
Approx. Number Employees: 12,400
Year Founded: 1969
Business Description:
Diversified Teleommunications Services Company
S.I.C.: 4813; 4812

Key to Media (For complete agency information see *The Advertising Red Books-Agencies* edition):
1. Bus. Publs. 2. Cable T.V. 3. Catalogs & Directories. 4. Co-op Adv. 5. Consumer Mags. 6. D.M. to Bus. Estab.7. D.M. to Consumers 8. Daily Newsp. 9. Exhibits/Trade Shows 10. Foreign 11. Infomercial 12. Internet Adv.13. Multimedia 14. Network Radio 15. Network T.V. 16. Newsp. Distr. Mags. 17. Other 18. Outdoor (Posters, Transit) 19. Point of Purchase20. Premiums, Novelties 21. Product Samples 22. Special Events Mktg. 23. Spot Radio 24. Spot T.V. 25. Weekly Newsp. 26. Yellow Page Adv.

N.A.I.C.S.: 517310; 517110; 517212
Advertising Expenditures: $266,500,000
Media: 7-9-10-25
Distr.: Natl.
Personnel:
Walter C.D. Carlson *(Chm)*
LeRoy T. Carlson, Jr. *(Pres & CEO)*
Kenneth R. Meyers *(CFO & Exec VP)*
Kurt Thaus *(CIO & Sr VP)*
Douglas D. Shuma *(Sr VP & Controller)*
Scott H. Williamson *(Sr VP-Acq & Corp Dev)*
C. Theodore Herbert *(VP-HR)*
James R. Jenkins *(VP-Legal & External Affairs-US Cellular Corp)*
Julie Mathews *(Mgr-IR)*
Brands & Products:
TDS
TELEPHONE & DATA SYSTEMS
Advertising Agencies:
Mercury Mambo
1107 S 8th St
Austin, TX 78704
Tel.: (512) 447-4440
Fax: (512) 447-5787

Outdoor24
288 Seik Rd
Washington, PA 15301
Tel.: (724) 228-2040
Fax: (724) 228-2490

TELSCAPE COMMUNICATIONS, INC.
606 E Huntington Dr
Monrovia, CA 91016
Tel.: (626) 415-1000
Fax: (626) 415-0104
E-mail: info@telscape.com
Web Site: www.telscape.com
Approx. Number Employees: 233
Year Founded: 1995
Business Description:
Telecommunications Services
S.I.C.: 4813
N.A.I.C.S.: 517310
Import Export
Media: 6-8
Advertising Agency:
al Punto Advertising, Inc.
730 El Camino Way Ste 200
Tustin, CA 92780-7733
Tel.: (714) 544-0888
Fax: (714) 544-0830

TELUS CORPORATION
555 Robson Street
Vancouver, BC V6B 3K9, Canada
Tel.: (604) 697-8044
Fax: (604) 432-9681
Toll Free: (800) 667-4871
E-mail: info@telus.com
Web Site: www.telus.com
Approx. Rev.: $9,570,511,720
Approx. Number Employees: 34,800
Year Founded: 1904
Business Description:
Telecommunications & Internet Services
S.I.C.: 4813; 4812; 4899; 7375
N.A.I.C.S.: 517110; 517212; 517910; 518111
Advertising Expenditures: $313,000,000
Personnel:
Brian A. Canfield *(Chm)*
Judy A. Shuttleworth *(Vice Chm-HR)*
Darren Entwistle *(Pres & CEO)*
Kevin A. Salvadori *(Pres & Exec VP)*
Robert G. McFarlane *(CFO & Exec VP)*
Audrey T. Ho *(Gen Counsel, Sec & VP)*
Robert S. Gardner *(Sr VP & Treas)*
Josh Blair *(Exec VP-HR)*
Eros Spadotto *(Exec VP-Tech Strategy)*
Paul Lepage *(Sr VP-TELUS Health & Fin Solutions)*
Rachael Mens *(Dir-Mktg Comm)*
Darrell Rae *(Mgr-IR)*
Brands & Products:
THE FUTURE IS FRIENDLY
IROOM
MIKE
MOBILE CUSTOMER SELF SERVICE
TELUS
TELUS AGENTANYWHERE
TELUS ASSET TRACKER
TELUS BUSINESS ONE
TELUS FLEET TRACKER
TELUS MOBILITY
TELUS NAVIGATOR
TELUS RESOURCE TRACKER
TELUS SAFETYNET
TELUS XPRESS
Advertising Agencies:
Agency59 Response
1910 Yonge Street 4th Fl
Toronto, ON M4S 1Z5, Canada
Tel.: (416) 484-1959
Fax: (416) 484-9846

Media Experts
495 Wellington St W Ste 250
Toronto, ON M5V 1E9, Canada
Tel.: (416) 597-0707
Fax: (416) 597-9927

TAXI
495 Wellington St W Ste 102
Toronto, ON M5V 1E9, Canada
Tel.: (416) 979-7001
Fax: (416) 979-7626

TOUCHSTONE ENERGY COOPERATIVES
4301 Wilson Blvd
Arlington, VA 22203
Tel.: (703) 907-5500
Fax: (703) 907-5554
E-mail: nrica@corp.com
Web Site: www.touchstoneenergy.cooperative.com
Approx. Number Employees: 600
Business Description:
Business & Publicity Services for Energy Cooperatives
S.I.C.: 7389
N.A.I.C.S.: 561499
Media: 3-6-10-18
Personnel:
Jim Bausell *(COO)*
Ann Maggard *(Dir-Comm & Media Rels)*
Brands & Products:
THE POWER OF HUMAN CONNECTIONS
TOUCHSTONE ENERGY
Advertising Agency:
Odney
1400 W Century Ave
Bismarck, ND 58503
Tel.: (701) 222-8721
Fax: (701) 222-8172
Toll Free: (888) 500-8721

TRANSALTA CORPORATION
110 12th Ave SW
Calgary, AB T2P 2M1, Canada
Mailing Address:
P O Box 1900
Calgary, AB T2P 2M1, Canada
Tel.: (403) 267-7110
Fax: (403) 267-2590
Toll Free: (800) 387-3598
E-mail: investor_relations@transalta.com
Web Site: www.transalta.com
Approx. Rev.: $2,758,898,920
Approx. Number Employees: 2,389
Year Founded: 1911
Business Description:
Power Generation & Distribution Services
S.I.C.: 4931; 4911; 4939
N.A.I.C.S.: 221112; 221111; 221119; 221122
Export
Media: 2-6-7-8
Distr.: Reg.
Budget Set: Nov. -Dec.
Personnel:
Donna Soble Kaufman *(Chm)*
Stephen G. Snyder *(Pres & CEO)*
Brett Gellner *(CFO)*
Dawn Farrell *(COO)*
Kenneth S. Stickland *(Chief Legal Officer)*
Mark B. Mackay *(VP-Tech & Innovation)*
Alex R. McFadden *(VP-Tech & Controls)*
Parviz Mohamed *(VP-IT)*
Gregory P. Reinhart *(VP-HR)*
Jess Nieukerk *(Mgr-IR)*
Brands & Products:
TRANSALTA

TRANSCANADA ENERGY LTD.
(Sub. of TRANSCANADA CORPORATION)
450 1st St SW
Calgary, AB T2P 5H1, Canada
Tel.: (403) 920-2000
Fax: (403) 920-2200
E-mail: webmaster_e@transcanada.com
Web Site: www.transcanada.com
Year Founded: 1986
Business Description:
Energy Marketing Services
S.I.C.: 4911; 4939
N.A.I.C.S.: 221122
Export
Media: 2
Distr.: Intl.
Personnel:
Harold N. Kvisle *(Pres & CEO)*
Shela Shapiro *(Sr Mgr-Comm)*

TUCSON ELECTRIC POWER COMPANY
(Sub. of UniSource Energy Corporation)
1 S Church Ave Ste 100
Tucson, AZ 85701-1612
Mailing Address:
PO Box 711
Tucson, AZ 85702-0711
Tel.: (520) 571-4000
Fax: (520) 571-4000
Web Site: www.tep.com
Approx. Rev.: $1,124,979,000
Approx. Number Employees: 1,384
Year Founded: 1892
Business Description:
Electric Power Distribution & Generation Services
S.I.C.: 4911; 4931; 4939
N.A.I.C.S.: 221122; 221111; 221119
Advertising Expenditures: $1,800,000
Media: 1-2-3-5-6-7-8-9-10-13-18-19-20-22-23-24-25-26
Distr.: DM; Local
Budget Set: Aug.
Personnel:
Paul J. Bonavia *(Chm, Pres & CEO)*
Kevin P. Larson *(CFO, Treas & Sr VP)*
Raymond S. Heyman *(Gen Counsel)*
Kentton C. Grant *(Treas & VP-Fin)*
Michael J. DeConcini *(Sr VP-Ops)*
David G. Hutchens *(VP-Wholesale Energy)*
Thomas A. McKenna *(VP-Engrg & UniSource Energy Svcs)*
Catherine E. Ries *(VP-HR)*
Brands & Products:
WE'RE THERE WHEN YOU NEED US.

TXU ENERGY RETAIL COMPANY LLC
(Joint Venture of The Goldman Sachs Group, Inc., KKR & CO. L.P. & TPG Capital, L.P.)
1601 Bryan St
Dallas, TX 75201
Mailing Address:
PO Box 100001
Dallas, TX 75310
Tel.: (214) 812-4600
Toll Free: (800) 242-9113
Web Site: www.txuenergy.com
Approx. Rev.: $16,500,000
Approx. Number Employees: 72
Year Founded: 1993
Business Description:
Electricity
S.I.C.: 4939; 4911
N.A.I.C.S.: 221122
Media: 13
Personnel:
Michael Grasso *(CMO)*
Jim Burke *(CEO-TXU Energy)*
Cecily Gooch *(Gen Counsel & VP)*
Advertising Agencies:
The Richards Group, Inc.
8750 N Central Expy Ste 100
Dallas, TX 75231-6430
Tel.: (214) 891-5700
Fax: (214) 265-2933
Creative

TracyLocke
1999 Bryan St Ste 2800
Dallas, TX 75201
Tel.: (214) 259-3500
Fax: (214) 259-3550
— Ashley Fick *(Grp Acct Dir)*

UGI CORPORATION
460 N Gulph Rd
King of Prussia, PA 19406
Mailing Address:
PO Box 965
Valley Forge, PA 19482-0965
Tel.: (610) 337-1000
Fax: (610) 992-3254
Web Site: www.ugicorp.com

Key to Media (For complete agency information see *The Advertising Red Books-Agencies* edition):
1. Bus. Publs. 2. Cable T.V. 3. Catalogs & Directories. 4. Co-op Adv. 5. Consumer Mags. 6. D.M. to Bus. Estab.7. D.M. to Consumers
8. Daily Newsp. 9. Exhibits/Trade Shows 10. Foreign 11. Infomercial 12. Internet Adv.13. Multimedia 14. Network Radio
15. Network T.V. 16. Newsp. Distr. Mags. 17. Other 18. Outdoor (Posters, Transit) 19. Point of Purchase20. Premiums, Novelties
21. Product Samples 22. Special Events Mktg. 23. Spot Radio 24. Spot T.V. 25. Weekly Newsp. 26. Yellow Page Adv.

UGI Corporation — (Continued)

E-Mail For Key Personnel:
Public Relations: investorrelations@ugicorp.com
Approx. Rev.: $5,591,400,000
Approx. Number Employees: 9,400
Year Founded: 1882
Business Description:
Holding Company; Natural Gas, Propane & Electric Power Distr
S.I.C.: 4924; 4911; 4939; 6719
N.A.I.C.S.: 221210; 221122; 551112
Media: 2-5-6-7-8-9-18-23-25-26
Distr.: Reg.
Budget Set: Sept.
Personnel:
Lon R. Greenberg *(Chm & CEO)*
John L. Walsh *(Pres & COO)*
Robert C. Flexon *(CFO)*
Davinder Athwal *(Chief Acctg Officer, Chief Risk Officer, VP-Acctg & Fin Control)*
Francois Varagne *(Chm/CEO-Antargaz)*
Eugene V.N. Bissell *(Pres/CEO-AmeriGas Propane)*
Margaret M. Calabrese *(Sec & Assoc Gen Counsel)*
William D. Katz *(VP-HR)*
William G. Robey *(VP-Sls Ops)*
Thomas A. Barry *(Auditor)*
Brands & Products:
UGI CORPORATION
UGI ENTERPRISES
UGI UTILITIES INC
Advertising Agency:
Reese
955 Berkshire Blvd
Wyomissing, PA 19610-1229
Tel.: (610) 378-1835
Fax: (610) 378-1676

UIL HOLDINGS CORPORATION

157 Church St
New Haven, CT 06510-2100
Mailing Address:
PO Box 1564
New Haven, CT 06506-0901
Tel.: (203) 499-2000
Fax: (203) 499-2414
Fax: (203) 499-3624
E-mail: uil@uinet.com
Web Site: www.uil.com
Approx. Rev.: $997,666,000
Approx. Number Employees: 1,824
Year Founded: 1899
Business Description:
Holding Company; Owner of Electricity & Energy Related Services
S.I.C.: 4939; 1731; 4931
N.A.I.C.S.: 221112; 221111; 221119; 238210
Advertising Expenditures: $500,000
Media: 1-2-3-5-7-8-9-10-13-14-15-18-25-26
Distr.: Reg.
Budget Set: Sept.
Personnel:
James P. Torgerson *(Pres & CEO)*
Richard J. Nicholas *(CFO & Exec VP)*
Anthony J. Vallillo *(COO & Exec VP)*
Linda L. Randell *(Gen Counsel & Sr VP)*
Richard J. Reed *(VP-Engrg & Project Excellence-UI)*
Brands & Products:
UIL
UIL HOLDINGS CORPORATION

UNISOURCE ENERGY CORPORATION

1 S Church Ave Ste 100
Tucson, AZ 85702-0711
Mailing Address:
PO Box 711
Tucson, AZ 85702
Tel.: (520) 571-4000
Fax: (520) 884-3602
Fax: (520) 884-3601
Toll Free: (866) 537-8709
E-mail: ir@unisourceenergy.com
Web Site: www.unisourceenergy.com
Approx. Rev.: $1,453,677,000
Approx. Number Employees: 1,976
Business Description:
Holding Company; Public Utility
S.I.C.: 4931; 4911; 4924; 4939
N.A.I.C.S.: 221119; 221111; 221112; 221122; 221210
Media: 8-23-24
Personnel:
Paul J. Bonavia *(Chm, Pres & CEO)*
Kevin P. Larson *(CFO, Treas & Sr VP)*
Raymond S. Heyman *(Gen Counsel & Sr VP)*
Kentton C. Grant *(Treas & VP-Fin)*
David G. Hutchens *(Exec VP)*
Michael J. DeConcini *(Sr VP-Ops)*
Thomas A. McKenna *(VP-Engrg)*
Catherine E. Ries *(VP-HR)*
Jo Smith *(Dir-IR)*

UNITED STATES CELLULAR CORPORATION

(Sub. of Telephone & Data Systems, Inc.)
8410 W Bryn Mawr Ave Ste 700
Chicago, IL 60631-3463
Tel.: (773) 399-8900
Fax: (773) 399-8936
E-mail: info@uscellular.com
Web Site: www.uscellular.com
Approx. Rev.: $4,177,681,000
Approx. Number Employees: 9,000
Business Description:
Cellular Telephone Service
S.I.C.: 4812; 4813
N.A.I.C.S.: 517212; 517211; 517310
Advertising Expenditures: $258,200,000
Personnel:
LeRoy T. Carlson, Jr. *(Chm)*
Mary N. Dillon *(Pres & CEO)*
Steven T. Campbell *(CFO, Treas & Exec VP-Fin)*
Jay M. Ellison *(COO & Exec VP)*
Michael S. Irizarry *(CTO & Exec VP-Engrg)*
Jeffrey J. Childs *(Chief HR Officer & Exec VP)*
Alan D. Ferber *(Chief Strategy & Brand Officer & Exec VP)*
Carter S. Elenz *(Exec VP-Sls & Customer Svc)*
Nick B. Wright *(Sr VP-Sls)*
Thomas P. Catani *(VP-Ops-East Reg & Sls)*
R. Lynn Costlow *(VP-Customer Svc)*
John M. Cregier *(VP-IT)*
John C. Gockley *(VP-Legal & Regulatory Affairs)*
Katherine L. Hust *(VP-Mid-Central Reg & Sls)*
Edward C. Perez *(VP-Mktg & Sls Ops)*
Grant Spellmeyer *(Sr Dir-Legislative & Regulatory Affairs)*
Janet Rose *(Mgr-Sls)*
Brands & Products:
EASYEDGE
SPEEDTALK
TALKTRACKER
Advertising Agencies:
L.C. Williams & Associates, LLC
150 N Michigan Ave 38th Fl
Chicago, IL 60601-7558
Tel.: (312) 565-3900
Fax: (312) 565-1770
Toll Free: (800) 837-7123

Publicis & Hal Riney
2001 The Embarcadero
San Francisco, CA 94133-5200
Tel.: (415) 293-2001
Fax: (415) 293-2620

UNITED WATER RESOURCES INC.

(Sub. of SUEZ Environnement SA)
200 Old Hook Rd
Harrington Park, NJ 07640-1716
Tel.: (201) 767-9300
Fax: (201) 767-7142
Toll Free: (800) 230-2685
E-mail: rich.henning@unitedwater.com
Web Site: www.unitedwater.com
Sales Range: $800-899.9 Million
Approx. Number Employees: 2,600
Year Founded: 1869
Business Description:
Water Treatment Utility
S.I.C.: 6035; 4941
N.A.I.C.S.: 522120; 221310
Media: 6-8-9-22-25
Distr.: Reg.
Personnel:
Anthony J. Harding *(Chm)*
Robert Iacullo *(Pres)*
Bertrand Camus *(CEO)*
Edward J. Imparato *(CFO & Sr VP-Fin)*
Thomas P. Brown *(Pres-Contract Svcs)*
Robert Gerber *(Gen Counsel & Sr VP)*
Richard Henning *(Sr VP-Comm)*
Charles T. Wall *(Sr VP-HR)*
Advertising Agencies:
Kron & Associates Advertising Inc.
1849 Broad Ripple Ave
Indianapolis, IN 46220-2339
Tel.: (317) 253-9050
Fax: (317) 253-9010

Messer & Susslin & Others, Inc.
274 N Middletown Rd
Pearl River, NY 10965-1216
Tel.: (845) 735-3030
Fax: (845) 735-2270

Zeta Interactive
99 Pk Ave 23rd Fl
New York, NY 10016
Tel.: (646) 834-9400
Fax: (646) 834-9390

USA MOBILITY, INC.

6850 Versar Ctr Ste 420
Springfield, VA 22151-4148
Toll Free: (800) 611-8488
E-mail: customer.care@usamobility.com
Web Site: www.usamobility.com
Approx. Rev.: $233,254,000
Approx. Number Employees: 519
Year Founded: 2004
Business Description:
Wireless Messaging Services
S.I.C.: 4813; 4812
N.A.I.C.S.: 517310; 517110; 517211; 517212
Advertising Expenditures: $100,000
Media: 17
Personnel:
Royce G. Yudkoff *(Chm)*
Vincent D. Kelly *(Pres & CEO)*
Shawn E. Endsley *(CFO & Chief Acctg Officer)*
Thomas Saine *(CIO)*
James H. Boso *(Exec VP)*
Bonnie Culp *(Exec VP-HR)*
Paul Grandfield *(Exec VP-Ops)*
Brands & Products:
USA MOBILITY

UTILX CORPORATION

(Sub. of InfrastruX Group, Inc.)
22820 Russell Rd
Kent, WA 98032-4892
Mailing Address:
PO Box 97009
Kent, WA 98064-9709
Tel.: (253) 395-0200
Fax: (253) 395-1040
Toll Free: (800) 252-0556
E-mail: marketing@utilx.com
Web Site: www.utilx.com
E-Mail For Key Personnel:
Marketing Director: marketing@utilx.com
Approx. Number Employees: 800
Year Founded: 1984
Business Description:
Underground Power & Telecommunications Cable Renovation, Maintenance & Replacement Services
S.I.C.: 7629; 3357
N.A.I.C.S.: 811213; 335929
Export
Media: 2-10
Distr.: Direct to Consumer; Intl.; Natl.
Budget Set: Apr.
Personnel:
Jack Stel *(Pres & CEO)*
James Derezes *(VP-Sls & Mktg)*
Jason French *(VP-Fin & Acctg)*
Steven Maasch *(VP-HR)*
Nagu N. Srinivas *(VP)*
William Stagi *(VP-Engrg)*

VERENDRYE ELECTRIC COOPERATIVE

615 Hwy 52 W
Velva, ND 58790
Tel.: (701) 338-2855
Fax: (701) 624-0353
Web Site: www.verendrye.com
Approx. Number Employees: 63
Business Description:
Distribution, Electric Power
S.I.C.: 4939; 4911
N.A.I.C.S.: 221122
Personnel:
Bruce Carlson *(Gen Mgr)*
Randy Hauck *(Member & Mgr-Energy Svcs)*
Tom Rafferty *(Mgr-Comm)*

Key to Media (For complete agency information see *The Advertising Red Books-Agencies* edition):
1. Bus. Publs. 2. Cable T.V. 3. Catalogs & Directories. 4. Co-op Adv. 5. Consumer Mags. 6. D.M. to Bus. Estab.7. D.M. to Consumers
8. Daily Newsp. 9. Exhibits/Trade Shows 10. Foreign 11. Infomercial 12. Internet Adv.13. Multimedia 14. Network Radio
15. Network T.V. 16. Newsp. Distr. Mags. 17. Other 18. Outdoor (Posters, Transit) 19. Point of Purchase20. Premiums, Novelties
21. Product Samples 22. Special Events Mktg. 23. Spot Radio 24. Spot T.V. 25. Weekly Newsp. 26. Yellow Page Adv.

Jackie Schmaltz *(Mgr-Billing)*
Cindy Shattuck *(Mgr-Credit)*
John Westby *(Mgr-Engrg & Ops)*

Advertising Agency:
Odney
1400 W Century Ave
Bismarck, ND 58503
Tel.: (701) 222-8721
Fax: (701) 222-8172
Toll Free: (888) 500-8721

VERIZON COMMUNICATIONS INC.

140 West St
New York, NY 10007
Tel.: (212) 395-1000
Fax: (212) 869-3265
Toll Free: (800) 621-9900
Toll Free: (800) 555-1212
Web Site: www.verizon.com

Approx. Rev.: $106,565,000,000
Approx. Number Employees: 194,400
Year Founded: 2000

Business Description:
Communications Services
S.I.C.: 4813; 4812; 4899
N.A.I.C.S.: 517110; 517212; 517310; 517910
Advertising Expenditures: $2,483,700,000
Media: 1-2-3-4-5-6-7-8-9-10-11-13-14-15-16-18-19-20-22-23-24-25-26-31

Personnel:
Ivan G. Seidenberg *(Chm)*
Lowell C. McAdam *(Pres & CEO)*
Francis J. Shammo *(CFO & Exec VP)*
John G. Stratton *(CMO-Wireless)*
Anthony Melone *(CTO & Exec VP)*
Carl Erhart *(Pres-Central Reg)*
Keith Fulton *(Pres-Verizon West)*
Jim Gerace *(Pres-New York)*
Virginia P. Ruesterholz *(Pres-Svcs Ops)*
Robert Toohey *(Pres-Global Enterprise)*
Randal S. Milch *(Exec VP & Gen Counsel)*
Catherine T. Webster *(Treas & Sr VP)*
Marianne Drost *(Sec, Deputy Gen Counsel & Sr VP)*
John W. Diercksen *(Exec VP-Strategy, Dev & Plng)*
Marc C. Reed *(Exec VP-HR)*
Thomas J. Tauke *(Exec VP-Pub Affairs, Policy & Comm)*
Kathleen Grillo *(Sr VP-Federal Regulatory Affairs)*
Robert J. Barish *(Sr VP & Controller)*
Eric Bruno *(Sr VP-Consumer Product Mgmt)*
John N. Doherty *(Sr VP-IR)*
John Harrobin *(Sr VP-Digital Media & Mktg)*
Ronald H. Lataille *(Sr VP-IR)*
Kathleen H. Leidheiser *(Sr VP-Internal Auditing)*
Martha Delehanty *(VP-HR)*
Emilio Gonzalez *(VP-Pub Policy & Strategic Alliances)*
Brian Hinman *(VP-Intellectual Property & Licensing)*
Rose Stuckey Kirk *(VP-Pub Affairs, Policy & Comm)*
Torod Neptune *(Corp VP-Comm)*
Jeff McFarland *(Exec Dir & Dir-Multicultural Mktg)*
Jennifer Byrne *(Exec Dir-Bus Dev, Partnership Mgmt & Innovation)*
Faizun Kamal *(Exec Dir)*
Bob Varettoni *(Exec Dir-Corp Comm)*
Trudy Adams *(Dir-livesource)*
John Bonomo *(Dir-Media Rels)*
Alberto Canal *(Dir-Media Rels)*
Sharon Cohen-Hagar *(Dir-Media Rels)*
Bobbi Henson *(Dir-Media Rels)*
Oscar Madrid *(Dir-Multicultural Mktg)*
Debra J. Speed *(Dir-Strategic Alliances)*
Helen Ulan *(Dir-Creative)*
Kevin Laverty *(Sr Mgr-Media Rels)*
Prentice Parrish *(Sr Mgr-Multicultural Mktg)*
Jim Smith *(Fin Mgr)*
Margo Howell *(Product Mgr)*
Sandra Arnette *(Mgr-PR)*
Jon Davies *(Mgr-Media Rels)*
Bob Elek *(Mgr-Media Rels)*
Ruth Farley *(Mgr-Entertainment Portal)*
Lee Gierczynski *(Mgr-PR & Corp Comm)*
Phyllis Lopes *(Mgr)*
Sharon Shaffer *(Mgr-Media Rels)*
Heather Wilner *(Mgr-Media Rels)*
John Adams *(Engr-Solutions)*

Brands & Products:
CHOICE
DIRECTV
FIOS
IOBI HOME
NFL SUNDAY TICKET
OUR PEOPLE. OUR WORK. OUR VALUES.
PLUS DVR
PLUS HD DVR
VERIZON
VERIZON FIVE CENTS PLAN
VERIZON FREEDOM
VERIZON WIRELESS
VOICEWING

Advertising Agencies:
AdAsia Communications, Inc.
85 Fifth Ave 7th Fl
New York, NY 10003
Tel.: (212) 871-6886
Fax: (212) 871-6883

Erwin-Penland
(Owned by Hill, Holliday, Connors, Cosmopulos, Inc., Member of the Interpublic Group)
125 E Broad St
Greenville, SC 29601
Tel.: (864) 271-0500
Fax: (864) 235-5941

Huntington Advertising, Inc.
4575 Weaver Pkwy Ste 500
Warrenville, IL 60555
Tel.: (630) 836-1850
Fax: (630) 836-1171

Kyp Plc
Meridien House 42-43 Upper Berkeley Street
London, W1H 5QL, United Kingdom
Tel.: (44) 20 7535 3000
Fax: (44) 20 7535 3001

Landor Associates
230 Park Ave S 6th Fl
New York, NY 10003
Tel.: (212) 614-5050
Fax: (212) 614-3966

Lopez Negrete Communications, Inc.
3336 Richmond Ave Ste 200
Houston, TX 77098
Tel.: (713) 877-8777
Fax: (713) 877-8796
U.S. Hispanic Account (Creative Assignment)

Matter Communications
50 Water St, Mill #3, The Tannery
Newburyport, MA 01950
Tel.: (978) 499-9250
Fax: (978) 499-9253

McCann Erickson/New York
622 3rd Ave
New York, NY 10017
Tel.: (646) 865-2000
Fax: (646) 487-9610
Verizon Wireless
FiOS
Blackberry Storm

McGarry Bowen
515 N State St 29th Fl
Chicago, IL 60654
Tel.: (312) 239-6370
Fax: (312) 840-8396

McGarry Bowen, LLC
601 W 26th St Ste 1150
New York, NY 10001
Tel.: (212) 598-2900
Fax: (212) 598-2996
Droid Smartphone
Verizon Wireless
— Lisa Kang *(Acct Supvr)*

Momentum Worldwide
250 Hudson St
New York, NY 10013
Tel.: (646) 638-5400
Fax: (646) 638-5401
National Events & Sponsorship

Moxie Interactive Inc.
The Northyards 384 Northyards Blvd NW Ste 290
Atlanta, GA 30313-2440
Tel.: (404) 601-4500
Fax: (404) 601-4505

R/GA
350 W 39th St
New York, NY 10018-1402
Tel.: (212) 946-4000
Fax: (212) 946-4010
— Tara Wayner *(Exec Dir-Creative)*

Tierney Communications
(A Div. of the Interpublic Group of Companies)
The Bellevue 200 S Broad St
Philadelphia, PA 19102-3803
Tel.: (215) 790-4100
Fax: (215) 790-4363
(Consumer, Informative)

Universal McCann
100 33rd St 8th Fl
New York, NY 10001
Tel.: (212) 883-4700
Media Planning

Zenith Media Services
(Regional Headquarters for ZenithOptimedia, the Americas)
299 W Houston St 10th Fl
New York, NY 10014-4806
Tel.: (212) 859-5100
Fax: (212) 727-9495
(Media Buying)

VIRGIN MEDIA INC.

909 Third Ave Ste 2863
New York, NY 10022
Mailing Address:
NTL House Bartley Wood Business Park
Hook, United Kingdom
Tel.: (212) 906-8440
Web Site: www.virginmedia.co.uk

Approx. Rev.: $5,650,625,169
Approx. Number Employees: 11,300

Business Description:
Telecommunications & Broadband Internet Services
S.I.C.: 7375; 4812; 4813; 4841
N.A.I.C.S.: 518111; 515210; 517110; 517212
Export
Advertising Expenditures: $197,204,826

Personnel:
Neil A. Berkett *(CEO & COO)*
Tony Harris *(Mng Dir-Bus Div)*
Eamonn Francis O'Hare *(CFO)*
Andrew Barron *(COO)*
Martin Wyke *(CIO)*
Nigel Gilbert *(CMO)*
Paul Buttery *(Chief Customer & Networks Officer)*
Scott Dresser *(Gen Counsel & Sec)*
Pete Taddeo *(Exec Dir-Sls)*
Eric Craig *(Dir-Indirect Distr)*
Robert C. Gale *(Dir-Fin Control & Tax)*
Bob Foss *(Mktg Mgr-Solutions)*
Carol Maybury *(Product Mgr)*

Advertising Agencies:
DDB London
12 Bishop's Bridge Road
London, W2 6AA, United Kingdom
Tel.: (44) 207 258 3979
Fax: (44) 207 402 4871

Manning Gottlieb OMD
Seymour Mews House
London, W1H 6BN, United Kingdom
Tel.: (44) 207 470 5300
Fax: (44) 207 412 0244
Media Planning & Buying

Spike/DDB
55 Washington St Ste 650
Brooklyn, NY 11201
Tel.: (718) 596-5400
Fax: (212) 415-3101

WARWICK VALLEY TELEPHONE CO.

(d/b/a WVT Communications)
47 Main St
Warwick, NY 10990
Tel.: (845) 986-8080
Fax: (845) 986-6699
Toll Free: (800) 952-7642
E-mail: service@warwick.net
Web Site: www.wvtc.com

Approx. Rev.: $24,426,000
Approx. Number Employees: 96
Year Founded: 1902

Key to Media (For complete agency information see *The Advertising Red Books-Agencies* edition):
1. Bus. Publs. 2. Cable T.V. 3. Catalogs & Directories. 4. Co-op Adv. 5. Consumer Mags. 6. D.M. to Bus. Estab.7. D.M. to Consumers 8. Daily Newsp. 9. Exhibits/Trade Shows 10. Foreign 11. Infomercial 12. Internet Adv.13. Multimedia 14. Network Radio 15. Network T.V. 16. Newsp. Distr. Mags. 17. Other 18. Outdoor (Posters, Transit) 19. Point of Purchase20. Premiums, Novelties 21. Product Samples 22. Special Events Mktg. 23. Spot Radio 24. Spot T.V. 25. Weekly Newsp. 26. Yellow Page Adv.

Warwick Valley Telephone Co. — (Continued)

Business Description:
Telephone Communications, Video & Internet Services
S.I.C.: 4813; 7375
N.A.I.C.S.: 517310; 517110; 518111
Advertising Expenditures: $471,000
Personnel:
Robert J. DeValentino *(Chm)*
Duane W. Albro *(Pres & CEO)*
Ralph Martucci *(CFO, Treas & Exec VP)*
Joyce A. Stoeberl *(Sec & Sr VP)*
David Denapoli *(Sr VP-Bus Mktg & Sls)*
Kevin Schofield *(Sr VP-Ops)*
Meg Walsh *(Sr VP-Consumer Mktg & Sls)*

WASHINGTON GAS LIGHT CO.
(Sub. of WGL Holdings, Inc.)
101 Constitution Ave NW
Washington, DC 20080
Tel.: (703) 750-1000
Fax: (703) 750-5533
E-mail: webmaster@washgas.com
Web Site: www.washgas.com
E-Mail For Key Personnel:
President: jdegraffenreidt@washgas.com
Approx. Rev.: $1,321,521,000
Year Founded: 1848
Business Description:
Natural Gas & Electric Distr
S.I.C.: 4924; 4911; 4939
N.A.I.C.S.: 221210; 221122
Advertising Expenditures: $750,000
Media: 2-5-7-8-9-10-13-23-24-25-26
Distr.: Direct to Consumer; Reg.
Budget Set: Oct.
Personnel:
Terry D. McCallister *(Chm & CEO)*
Adrian P. Chapman *(Pres & COO)*
Vincent L. Ammann, Jr. *(CFO & VP)*
Beverly J. Burke *(Gen Counsel & VP)*
Douglas A. Staebler *(VP-Engrg, Ops & Mktg)*
William Zeigler, Jr. *(VP-HR & Org Dev)*
Brands & Products:
WASHINGTON GAS
Advertising Agency:
SRB Communications
1819 L St NW 7th Fl
Washington, DC 20036
Tel.: (202) 775-7721
Fax: (202) 777-7421

WASTE CONNECTIONS, INC.
2295 Iron Point Rd Ste 200
Folsom, CA 95630
Tel.: (916) 608-8200
Fax: (916) 608-8291
E-mail: hr@wasteconnections.com
Web Site:
www.wasteconnections.com
Approx. Rev.: $1,319,757,000
Approx. Number Employees: 5,510
Year Founded: 1997
Business Description:
Solid Waste Collection, Transfer, Disposal & Recycling Services
S.I.C.: 4212; 4953
N.A.I.C.S.: 562111; 562211; 562212
Advertising Expenditures: $4,171,000
Media: 7-10-26
Personnel:
Steven F. Bouck *(Pres)*
Ronald J. Mittelstaedt *(CEO)*
Worthing F. Jackman *(CFO & Exec VP)*
Darrell W. Chambliss *(COO & Exec VP)*
Eric O. Hansen *(CIO & VP)*
David G. Eddie *(Chief Acctg Officer & Sr VP)*
Patrick J. Shea *(Gen Counsel, Sec & VP)*
David M. Hall *(Sr VP-Sls & Mktg)*
James M. Little *(Sr VP-Engrg & Disposal)*
Eric M. Merrill *(Sr VP-People, Safety & Dev)*
Advertising Agency:
Jel, Inc.
2117 28th St
Sacramento, CA 95818
Tel.: (916) 447-5463
Fax: (916) 447-5465

WASTE MANAGEMENT, INC.
1001 Fannin St Ste 4000
Houston, TX 77002-6711
Tel.: (713) 512-6200
Fax: (713) 512-6299
Web Site: www.wm.com
Approx. Rev.: $12,515,000,000
Approx. Number Employees: 42,800
Year Founded: 1971
Business Description:
Solid Waste Management & Environmental Services
S.I.C.: 4212; 4953; 4959
N.A.I.C.S.: 562111; 562112; 562119; 562211; 562212; 562213; 562219; 562998
Media: 2-7
Personnel:
David P. Steiner *(Pres & CEO)*
Steven Preston *(CFO & Exec VP-Fin, Recycling & Energy Svcs)*
Puneet Bhasin *(CIO & Sr VP)*
Rick L. Wittenbraker *(Chief Compliance Officer, Gen Counsel, Sr VP)*
Greg A. Robertson *(Chief Acctg Officer & VP)*
Cherie C. Rice *(Treas & VP-Fin)*
James E. Trevathan *(Exec VP-Growth, Innovation & Field Support)*
David A. Aardsma *(Sr VP-Sls & Mktg)*
Barry H. Caldwell *(Sr VP-Govt Affairs & Corp Comm)*
James C. Fish, Jr. *(Sr VP-Eastern Grp)*
Brett W. Frazier *(Sr VP-Southern Grp)*
Michael J. Romans *(Sr VP-People)*
Charles E. Williams *(Sr VP-Ops)*
Duane C. Woods *(Sr VP-Western Grp)*
Lynn C. Brown *(VP-Corp Comm)*
Greg Nikkel *(VP-Fin)*
Brands & Products:
BIO-IN-A-BOX
BIOSITE
CYCLER
GREEN SQUAD
INSTA-BIN
M2Z
PORT-O-LET
THE SERVICE MACHINE
STREAMLINE
THINK GREEN
TOSS
UPSTREAM
WASTE MANAGEMENT
WASTE WATCH
WASTEROUTE
Advertising Agencies:
Cookerly Public Relations
3500 Lenox Rd 1 Alliance Ctr Ste 510
Atlanta, GA 30326
Tel.: (404) 816-2037
Fax: (404) 816-3037
(Electronics Recycling Awareness)

FKM
1800 W Loop S Ste 2100
Houston, TX 77027
Tel.: (713) 862-5100
Fax: (713) 869-6560
Waste & Environmental Services

WESTERN WIND ENERGY CORPORATION
885 W George St Ste 1326
Vancouver, BC V6C 3E8, Canada
Tel.: (604) 685-9463
Fax: (604) 685-9441
E-mail: info@westernwindenergy.com
Web Site:
www.westernwindenergy.com
Approx. Rev.: $2,738,832
Approx. Number Employees: 2
Year Founded: 1981
Business Description:
Wind Power Services
S.I.C.: 4939; 4911
N.A.I.C.S.: 221111; 221122
Advertising Expenditures: $35,214
Media: 17
Personnel:
Jeffrey J. Ciachurski *(CEO)*
Keven Craig *(CFO)*
T. Alana Steele *(COO & Gen Counsel)*
J. Michael Boyd *(Exec VP-Bus Dev)*
Steven R. Mendoza *(Exec VP & Chief Engrg)*
Chris Thompson *(Sr VP-Project Fin)*

WESTMORELAND COAL COMPANY
Two N Cascade Ave 14th Fl
Colorado Springs, CO 80903
Tel.: (719) 442-2600
Fax: (719) 448-5825
Web Site: www.westmoreland.com
E-Mail For Key Personnel:
Public Relations: diane.jones@westmoreland.com
Approx. Rev.: $506,057,000
Approx. Number Employees: 1,081
Year Founded: 1854
Business Description:
Production & Sale of Coal; Owner & Operator of Independent Power Plants
S.I.C.: 1221; 4931
N.A.I.C.S.: 212111; 221119
Media: 2-7-9-10-13
Distr.: Intl.; Natl.
Personnel:
Keith E. Alessi *(Pres & CEO)*
Kevin A. Paprzycki *(CFO & Treas)*
Douglas P. Kathol *(Exec VP-Colorado Springs)*
Diane S. Jones *(VP-Corp Rel & Asst Sec)*
Thomas G. Durham *(VP-Plng & Engrg)*
Mary A. Hauck *(VP-HR)*
Bruno LeCrampe *(Dir-Internal Controls)*
Russ Werner *(Dir-Acctg)*
Brands & Products:
WESTMORELAND
WESTMORELAND ENERGY
WESTMORELAND POWER

WISCONSIN ENERGY CORPORATION
231 W Michigan St
Milwaukee, WI 53203
Mailing Address:
PO Box 1331
Milwaukee, WI 53201-1331
Tel.: (414) 221-2345
Fax: (414) 221-2554
E-mail: Contact@wisconsinenergy.com
Web Site: www.wisconsinenergy.com
Approx. Rev.: $4,202,500,000
Approx. Number Employees: 4,596
Year Founded: 1987
Business Description:
Holding Company; Electricity & Natural Gas Utilities Owner & Operator
S.I.C.: 6719; 4924; 4931; 4939
N.A.I.C.S.: 551112; 221111; 221112; 221119; 221210
Advertising Expenditures: $2,000,000
Media: 2-6-9-18-23-25
Distr.: Reg.
Personnel:
Gale E. Klappa *(Chm, Pres & CEO)*
Frederick D. Kuester *(CFO & Exec VP)*
Kristine A. Rappe *(Chief Admin Officer & Sr VP)*
Allen L. Leverett *(Pres/CEO-We Generation & Exec VP)*
James C. Fleming *(Gen Counsel & Exec VP)*
Charles R. Cole *(Sr VP-Customer Ops)*
Robert M. Garvin *(Sr VP-External Affairs)*
Barry McNulty *(Mgr-External Comm)*
Keith H. Ecke *(Asst Sec)*
David L. Hughes *(Asst Treas)*
James A. Schubilske *(Asst Treas)*
Brands & Products:
WISCONSIN ENERGY

WORLD ENERGY SOLUTIONS, INC.
446 Main St
Worcester, MA 01608
Tel.: (508) 459-8100
Fax: (508) 459-8101
Toll Free: (800) 578-0718
E-mail: info@worldenergy.com
Web Site: www.worldenergy.com
Approx. Rev.: $17,984,662
Approx. Number Employees: 60
Business Description:
Online Energy Brokerage Services
S.I.C.: 6221; 7389
N.A.I.C.S.: 523140; 425120
Advertising Expenditures: $166,667
Personnel:
Edward T. Libbey *(Chm)*
Philip V. Adams *(Pres & COO)*
Richard Domaleski *(CEO)*
James F. Parslow *(CFO)*
Rob Hartwell *(CIO)*
Andrew Thomas *(Sr VP-Ops)*
Advertising Agencies:
AMP Agency
295 Devonshire St
Boston, MA 02110
Tel.: (617) 542-5587
Fax: (617) 896-1311

Key to Media (For complete agency information see *The Advertising Red Books-Agencies* edition):
1. Bus. Publs. 2. Cable T.V. 3. Catalogs & Directories. 4. Co-op Adv. 5. Consumer Mags. 6. D.M. to Bus. Estab.7. D.M. to Consumers
8. Daily Newsp. 9. Exhibits/Trade Shows 10. Foreign 11. Infomercial 12. Internet Adv.13. Multimedia 14. Network Radio
15. Network T.V. 16. Newsp. Distr. Mags. 17. Other 18. Outdoor (Posters, Transit) 19. Point of Purchase20. Premiums, Novelties
21. Product Samples 22. Special Events Mktg. 23. Spot Radio 24. Spot T.V. 25. Weekly Newsp. 26. Yellow Page Adv.

Horn Group
45 Braintree Hill Office Park Ste 100
Braintree, MA 02184
Tel.: (617) 431-1020
Fax: (781) 794-9944
— Julie Crotty *(Acct Exec)*

XCEL ENERGY INC.
414 Nicollet Mall
Minneapolis, MN 55401-1993
Tel.: (612) 330-5500
Fax: (612) 330-2900
Toll Free: (800) 328-8226
Web Site: www.xcelenergy.com
Approx. Rev.: $10,310,947,000
Approx. Number Employees: 11,290
Year Founded: 1909
Business Description:
Electricity & Natural Gas Products & Services
S.I.C.: 4911; 4924; 4931; 4939
N.A.I.C.S.: 221121; 221111; 221119; 221122; 221210
Media: 2-3-4-7-8-9-15-18-23-24-25
Personnel:
Benjamin G.S. Fowke, III *(Chm & CEO)*
David M. Sparby *(Grp Pres & Sr VP)*
Teresa S. Madden *(CFO)*
Marvin McDaniel, Jr. *(Chief Admin Officer & VP)*
Dennis L. Koehl *(Chief Nuclear Officer & VP)*
David L. Eves *(Pres/CEO-Pub Svc Company-Colorado)*
Riley Hill *(Pres/CEO-Southwestern Pub Svc Company)*
Judy M. Poferl *(Pres/CEO-Northern States Power Company-Minnesota)*
Michael L. Swenson *(Pres/CEO-Northern States Power Company-Wisconsin)*
Scott Wilensky *(Gen Counsel & VP)*
Jerome Davis *(Reg VP-Colorado)*
Jay Hermann *(VP-Mktg)*
Scott L. Weatherby *(VP & Chief Audit Exec)*
Nikki Lewis *(Dir-Compliance)*
Jack Nielsen *(Dir-IR)*
John Welch *(Dir-Power Ops)*
Brands & Products:
BILLWISE
BUDGETSMART
CONNECTSMART
ENERGY MAKEOVER
HOME PERFORMANCE REBATE
HOMESMART
INFOSMART
INFOWISE
OPERATIONWISE
PAYSMART
RESPONSIBLE BY NATURE
SITEWISE
XCEL ENERGY
Advertising Agency:
Texas Press Association
718 W 5th St Ste 100
Austin, TX 78701-2799
Tel.: (512) 477-6755
Fax: (512) 477-6759
Toll Free: (800) 749-4793

XFONE, INC.
5307 W Loop 289
Lubbock, TX 79414
Tel.: (806) 771-5212
Fax: (806) 788-3398
Web Site: www.xfone.com
Approx. Rev.: $58,943,709
Approx. Number Employees: 294
Business Description:
Long Distance Voice & Data Communications Services
S.I.C.: 4899; 4813
N.A.I.C.S.: 517910; 517110
Advertising Expenditures: $412,697
Media: 2-7-8-13
Personnel:
Itzhak Almog *(Chm)*
Guy Nissenson *(Pres, CEO & Dir)*
Niv Krikov *(CFO)*
Alon Reisser *(Gen Counsel & Sec)*
Gilad Amozeg *(Exec VP)*
Iddo Keinan *(Dir-Comml)*

YANKEE GAS SERVICES COMPANY
(Sub. of Yankee Energy System, Inc.)
107 Selden St PO Box 270
Berlin, CT 06037
Tel.: (203) 639-4000
Fax: (860) 665-6276
Toll Free: (800) 989-0900
Web Site: www.yankeegas.com
Sales Range: $500-549.9 Million
Approx. Number Employees: 500
Year Founded: 1989
Business Description:
Natural Gas Distribution
S.I.C.: 4911; 4939
N.A.I.C.S.: 221122
Media: 2-7-10-17-23-24
Distr.: Reg.
Personnel:
Rod Powell *(Pres & COO)*

Key to Media (For complete agency information see *The Advertising Red Books-Agencies* edition):
1. Bus. Publs. 2. Cable T.V. 3. Catalogs & Directories. 4. Co-op Adv. 5. Consumer Mags. 6. D.M. to Bus. Estab.7. D.M. to Consumers
8. Daily Newsp. 9. Exhibits/Trade Shows 10. Foreign 11. Infomercial 12. Internet Adv.13. Multimedia 14. Network Radio
15. Network T.V. 16. Newsp. Distr. Mags. 17. Other 18. Outdoor (Posters, Transit) 19. Point of Purchase20. Premiums, Novelties
21. Product Samples 22. Special Events Mktg. 23. Spot Radio 24. Spot T.V. 25. Weekly Newsp. 26. Yellow Page Adv.

Publishers, Printers, Engravers, Etc.

Artists' Materials — Books — Book Stores — Engraving — Greeting Cards — Lithographers — Music Publishers — Newspapers — Printing — Publications

21ST CENTURY NEWSPAPERS, INC.
(Sub. of Journal Register Company)
48 W Huron St
Pontiac, MI 48342
Tel.: (248) 745-4793
Fax: (248) 332-0830
Web Site:
www.21stcenturynewspapers.com
Approx. Number Employees: 200
Year Founded: 1995
Business Description:
Newspapers & Magazine Publisher
S.I.C.: 2711; 2721
N.A.I.C.S.: 511110; 511120
Media: 9-13-25
Personnel:
William Ging *(Dir-IT)*
Kim Klein *(Dir-Mktg)*
Tom Perkins *(Dir-HR)*

AARP PUBLICATIONS
(Div. of AARP)
780 3rd Ave
New York, NY 10017
Tel.: (646) 521-2500
Fax: (212) 319-5849
E-mail: adsales@aarp.org
Web Site: www.aarpmedia.org
Approx. Number Employees: 35
Business Description:
Magazine Publisher
S.I.C.: 8399
N.A.I.C.S.: 813212
Media: 2-8-10-11-13
Personnel:
James H. Fishman *(Publr & VP)*
Nancy Perry Graham *(VP & Editor)*
Shelagh Daly Miller *(VP-Adv)*
Ina S. Josephson *(Dir-Special Accts)*
Laurie Levitt *(Assoc Dir-Integrated Mktg)*

ABBEVILLE PRESS INC.
137 Varick St Ste 504
New York, NY 10013
Tel.: (212) 366-5585
Fax: (212) 366-6966
E-mail: abbeville@abbeville.com
Web Site: www.abbeville.com
Approx. Sls.: $3,500,000
Approx. Number Employees: 15
Year Founded: 1977
Business Description:
Art & Illustrated Books, Stationery & Printed Gift Items
S.I.C.: 2731
N.A.I.C.S.: 511130
Media: 8-10
Personnel:
Robert E. Abrams *(Publr)*

ABEBOOKS INC.
(Sub. of Amazon.com, Inc.)
410 Garbally Rd Ste 4
Victoria, BC V8T 2K1, Canada
Tel.: (250) 475-6013
Fax: (250) 475-6014
Web Site: www.abebooks.com
Sales Range: $75-99.9 Million
Approx. Number Employees: 130
Year Founded: 1995
Business Description:
Online Marketplace For New & Used Books
S.I.C.: 5942
N.A.I.C.S.: 451211
Media: 6-13
Personnel:
John Chase *(CFO & VP)*
Shaun Jamieson *(Dir-Sls & Acct Mgmt)*
Thomas Nicol *(Dir-Mktg)*

ABILENE REPORTER NEWS
(Sub. of The E.W. Scripps Company)
101 Cypress St
Abilene, TX 79601-5816
Mailing Address:
PO Box 30
Abilene, TX 79601
Tel.: (325) 673-4271
Fax: (325) 670-6797
Toll Free: (800) 588-6397
E-mail: citydesk@reporternews.com
Web Site: www.reporternews.com
Sales Range: $50-74.9 Million
Approx. Number Employees: 220
Business Description:
Morning & Sunday Newspaper Publisher
S.I.C.: 2711
N.A.I.C.S.: 511110
Media: 2-4-7-8-9-10-13-18-19-20-21-22-23-24
Personnel:
Dave Hedge *(Chief Revenue Officer & Publr)*
Mike Hall *(Dir-Ops)*

ACADEMIC COMMUNICATION ASSOCIATES, INC.
Bldg 102 4001 Avenida de la Plata
Oceanside, CA 92052-4279
Mailing Address:
PO Box 4279
Oceanside, CA 92052
Tel.: (760) 722-9593
Fax: (760) 722-1625
Toll Free: (888) 758-9558
E-mail: acom@acadcom.com
Web Site: www.acadcom.com
Business Description:
Instructional Resources & Assessment Tools Publisher for Children & Adults with Speech & Language Disorders, Learning Disabilities & Other Special Learning Needs
S.I.C.: 2731; 8049
N.A.I.C.S.: 511130; 621340
Media: 4-13
Personnel:
Larry Mattes *(Founder & Pres)*

ACADEMIC INNOVATIONS
281 S Magnolia Ave
Santa Barbara, CA 93117
Tel.: (805) 967-8015
Fax: (805) 967-5357
E-mail: sales@academicinnovations.com
Web Site:
www.academicinnovations.com
E-Mail For Key Personnel:
Sales Director: sales@academicinnovations.com
Approx. Number Employees: 8
Year Founded: 1990
Business Description:
Educational Materials Publisher
S.I.C.: 2731; 8742
N.A.I.C.S.: 511130; 541611
Media: 4-7-10-13
Personnel:
Melinda Bingham *(CEO)*
Brands & Products:
CAREER CHOICES
CAREERCHOICES.COM
INSTRUCTOR'S GUIDE
LIFESTYLE MATH
LIFESTYLEMATH.COM
POSSIBILITIES

ACTIVE PARENTING PUBLISHERS
1955 Vaughn Rd NW Ste 108
Kennesaw, GA 30144-7808
Tel.: (770) 429-0565
Fax: (770) 429-0334
Toll Free: (800) 825-0060
E-mail: cservice@activeparenting.com
Web Site: www.activeparenting.com
Approx. Number Employees: 15
Year Founded: 1980
Business Description:
Educational Materials Publisher
S.I.C.: 2731; 7812
N.A.I.C.S.: 511130; 512110
Media: 1-4-7-10
Personnel:
Michael H. Popkin *(Pres)*
Marian Adair *(Mgr-Pur & Distributor Sls)*
Cathy Daughtridge *(Mgr-Online Grps)*
Erica Mclean Haynes *(Mgr-Acctg)*
Virginia Murray *(Mgr-Mktg)*
Brands & Products:
ACTIVE CHRISTIAN PARENTING
ACTIVE PARENTING NOW
ACTIVE PARENTING OF TEENS
ACTIVE PARENTING PUBLISHERS
ACTIVE PARENTING TODAY
ACTIVE TEACHING
CONNECTING WITH KIDS
COOPERATIVE PARENTING AND DIVORCE
FAMILIES IN ACTION
FREE THE HORSES: A CHARACTER EDUCATION ADVENTURE
PARENTS ON BOARD
WINDOWS - HEALING AND HELPING THROUGH LOSS

ADDISON-WESLEY
(Sub. of Pearson Education)
75 Arlington St Ste 300
Boston, MA 02116-3936
Tel.: (617) 848-7500
Fax: (617) 848-6016
E-mail: info@aw-bc.com
Web Site: www.aw-bc.com
Approx. Number Employees: 800
Business Description:
Textbooks, Professional & Reference Books
S.I.C.: 2731

Key to Media (For complete agency information see *The Advertising Red Books-Agencies* edition):
1. Bus. Publs. 2. Cable T.V. 3. Catalogs & Directories. 4. Co-op Adv. 5. Consumer Mags. 6. D.M. to Bus. Estab.7. D.M. to Consumers
8. Daily Newsp. 9. Exhibits/Trade Shows 10. Foreign 11. Infomercial 12. Internet Adv.13. Multimedia 14. Network Radio
15. Network T.V. 16. Newsp. Distr. Mags. 17. Other 18. Outdoor (Posters, Transit) 19. Point of Purchase20. Premiums, Novelties
21. Product Samples 22. Special Events Mktg. 23. Spot Radio 24. Spot T.V. 25. Weekly Newsp. 26. Yellow Page Adv.

N.A.I.C.S.: 511130
Advertising Expenditures: $1,000,000
Media: 2-4-7-10-13-14-23
Distr.: Intl.; Natl.
Budget Set: Sept.
Brands & Products:
ADDISON-WESLEY
BENJAMIN CUMMINGS
CELEBRATION PRESS
CUISENAINE
DALE SEYMOUR
GOOD YEAR BOOKS
LONGMAN
SCOTT FORESMAN

ADNET DIRECT PRINTING
(Unit of GateHouse Media, Inc.)
73 Buffalo St
Canandaigua, NY 14424
Tel.: (585) 394-0770
Fax: (585) 394-8786
E-mail: design@messengerpostmedia.com
Web Site: www.adnetdirect.net
Sales Range: $75-99.9 Million
Approx. Number Employees: 100
Business Description:
Commercial Printing & Design Services
S.I.C.: 7336; 2759
N.A.I.C.S.: 541430; 323119
Media: 25
Personnel:
William Rumsey *(Dir-Comml Printing)*
Cathy Buksar *(Mgr-Mailing & Distr)*
Brian Ellis *(Mgr-Production)*

ADVANCE PUBLICATIONS, INC.
950 W Fingerboard Rd
Staten Island, NY 10305-1453
Tel.: (718) 981-1234
Tel.: (212) 286-2860
Fax: (718) 981-1456
Web Site: www.advance.net
Sales Range: $5-14.9 Billion
Approx. Number Employees: 27,585
Year Founded: 1886
Business Description:
Newspaper, Magazine, Book & Internet Publisher
S.I.C.: 2721; 2711; 2731; 2741
N.A.I.C.S.: 511120; 511110; 511130; 511199; 516110
Media: 6-9-24
Distr.: Natl.
Personnel:
Donald E. Newhouse *(Pres)*
Tom Summer *(CFO)*
Randolph Siegel *(Pres-Local Digital Strategy)*
Samuel I. Newhouse, Jr. *(Publr)*
Andrew D. Siegel *(Sr VP-Strategy & Corp Dev)*

ADVANSTAR COMMUNICATIONS INC.
(Holding of Veronis Suhler Stevenson Partners LLC)
641 Lexington Ave Fl 8
New York, NY 10022
Tel.: (212) 951-6600
Fax: (212) 951-6666
E-mail: info@advanstar.com
Web Site: www.advanstar.com
Approx. Sls.: $323,721,984
Approx. Number Employees: 1,000
Business Description:
Trade & Business Journal Publisher & Trade Show Organizer
S.I.C.: 2721
N.A.I.C.S.: 511120
Personnel:
Joseph Loggia *(CEO)*
Theodore S. Alpert *(CFO & Exec VP-Fin)*
J. Vaughn *(CIO)*
Thomas W. Ehardt *(Chief Admin Officer & Exec VP)*
Ward Hewins *(Gen Counsel & VP)*
Tony Calanca *(Exec VP-Exhibitions)*
Georgiann Decenzo *(Exec VP-Licensing, Market Dev & Europe)*
Eric I. Lisman *(Exec VP-Corp Dev)*
Ron Wall *(Exec VP-Pharmaceutical & Science)*
Mike Alic *(VP-Electronic Media)*
Sherrie Krantz *(VP-Mktg-Fashion Grp-MAGIC Marketplace)*
Nancy Nugent *(VP-HR)*
Ken Schnepf *(Editor-Products)*
Teresa McNulty *(Mgr-Specialty Medicine, Womens & Childrens Health)*
Brands & Products:
AMERICAN SALON
COSMETIC SURGERY TIMES
TRAVEL AGENT
VIDEO STORE
Advertising Agency:
5W Public Relations
888 7th Ave 12th Fl
New York, NY 10106
Tel.: (212) 999-5585
Fax: (646) 328-1711
Licensing International Expo 2008

ADVANTAGE BUSINESS MEDIA
100 Enterprise Dr Ste 600
Rockaway, NJ 07866-0912
Tel.: (973) 920-7000
Fax: (973) 920-7542
E-mail: advantagecommunications@advantagemedia.com
Web Site: www.advantagebusinessmedia.com
Sales Range: $10-24.9 Million
Approx. Number Employees: 99
Year Founded: 2006
Business Description:
Trade Magazines & Website Publisher
S.I.C.: 2721; 2741
N.A.I.C.S.: 511120; 511140; 516110
Media: 4-13
Personnel:
George Fox *(Pres)*
Richard Reiff *(CEO)*
Thomas Lynch *(Publr)*
Brands & Products:
BIOPERFORM.COM
BIOSCIENCE TECHNOLOGY
BROADBAND-TODAY.COM
CED
CHEM.INFO
DRUG DISCOVERY & DEVELOPMENT
EITD
FOOD MANUFACTURING
GENOMICS & PROTEOMICS
INDUSTRIAL MAINTENANCE & PLANT OPERATION
LABORATORY EQUIPMENT
MANUFACTURING.NET
MEDICAL DESIGN TECHNOLOGY
PHARMACEUTICAL PROCESSING
THE PROCESS ENGINEER
PRODUCT DESIGN & DEVELOPMENT
PRODUCTION TECHNOLOGY NEWS
PRODUCTS FOR INDUSTRY
R&D
SCIENTIFIC COMPUTING
SURGICAL PRODUCTS
WIRELESS DESIGN & DEVELOPMENT
WIRELESS WEEK

ADVERTISING AGE
(Unit of Crain Communications, Inc. - New York)
711 3rd Ave
New York, NY 10017
Tel.: (212) 210-0100
Fax: (212) 210-0200
E-mail: editor@adage.com
Web Site: www.adage.com
Approx. Number Employees: 100
Year Founded: 1930
Business Description:
Advertising, Marketing & Media Newspaper & Internet Publisher
S.I.C.: 2711; 2741
N.A.I.C.S.: 511110; 516110
Media: 7-8-10-18
Distr.: Natl.
Budget Set: Oct.
Personnel:
Allison Price Arden *(Publr)*
Rance E. Crain *(Editor-in-Chief)*
Ann Marie Kerwin *(Editor)*
Abbey Klaassen *(Editor)*
Jennifer Rooney *(Editor)*
Brian Steinberg *(Editor-TV)*
Laurel Wentz *(Editor-Intl & Multicultural)*
Jesper Goransson *(Dir-Art)*
John LaMarca *(Dir-Audience Dev)*

ADVISOR-SOURCE NEWSPAPERS
(Sub. of Journal Register Company)
48075 Van Dyke Ave
Utica, MI 48317-3258
Tel.: (586) 731-1000
Fax: (586) 731-8172
E-mail: chris.troszak@advisorsource.com
Web Site: www.sourcenewspapers.com
Approx. Number Employees: 45
Business Description:
Weekly Newspaper Publisher
S.I.C.: 2711; 2721
N.A.I.C.S.: 511110; 511120
Media: 25
Personnel:
Chris Troszak *(Gen Mgr)*
Jody Mcveigh *(Editor)*

THE ADVOCATE
(Sub. of Newspaper Network of Central Ohio)
22 N 1st St
Newark, OH 43055-5608
Tel.: (740) 345-4053
Fax: (740) 328-8581
Fax: (740) 328-8580
E-mail: info@newarkadvocate.com
Web Site: www.newarkadvocate.com
Sales Range: $50-74.9 Million
Approx. Number Employees: 175
Year Founded: 1820
Business Description:
Newspaper Publisher
S.I.C.: 2711; 2721
N.A.I.C.S.: 511110; 511120
Advertising Expenditures: $300,000
Media: 3-5-9-10-13-18-20-23-24-25
Distr.: Direct to Consumer; Reg.
Budget Set: Sept.
Personnel:
Bill Albrecht *(Pres & Publr)*
Randy Green *(Mgr-Sls-Adv)*
Mike Kimble *(Mgr-Maintenance)*
Beth McHenry *(Mgr-Platemaking)*
Jennye Struckman *(Mgr-Fin)*

AGAINST ALL ODDS PRODUCTIONS INC.
PO Box 1189
Sausalito, CA 94966
Tel.: (415) 331-6300
Web Site: www.againstallodds.info
Business Description:
Internet & Book Publishing
S.I.C.: 2741; 2731
N.A.I.C.S.: 516110; 511130
Media: 1-9-14-15-25
Personnel:
Rick Smolan *(CEO)*
Katya Able *(COO)*

A.H. BELO CORPORATION
400 S Record St
Dallas, TX 75202-4806
Mailing Address:
PO Box 224866
Dallas, TX 75222-4866
Tel.: (214) 977-8200
Fax: (214) 977-8201
Web Site: www.ahbelo.com
Approx. Rev.: $487,308,000
Approx. Number Employees: 2,200
Year Founded: 2007
Business Description:
Newspaper Publisher
S.I.C.: 2711
N.A.I.C.S.: 511110
Advertising Expenditures: $7,768,000
Personnel:
Robert W. Decherd *(Chm, Pres & CEO)*
Alison K. Engel *(CFO, Treas & Sr VP)*
Michael J. O'Hara *(CIO & Sr VP)*
Daniel J. Blizzard *(Sec & Sr VP)*
James M. Moroney, III *(Exec VP)*

AIIM INTERNATIONAL
(Div. of AIIM International)
1100 Wayne Ave Ste 1100
Silver Spring, MD 20910-5616
Tel.: (301) 587-8202
Fax: (301) 587-2711
E-mail: aiim@aiim.org
Web Site: www.edocmagazine.com
Approx. Number Employees: 19
Business Description:
Publisher of Magazine for Information Management Professionals & Enterprise Content Management
S.I.C.: 8621
N.A.I.C.S.: 813920
Advertising Expenditures: $1,500,000
Media: 2-4-7-10-11
Distr.: Intl.
Budget Set: Jan.

Key to Media (For complete agency information see *The Advertising Red Books-Agencies* edition):
1. Bus. Publs. 2. Cable T.V. 3. Catalogs & Directories. 4. Co-op Adv. 5. Consumer Mags. 6. D.M. to Bus. Estab.7. D.M. to Consumers
8. Daily Newsp. 9. Exhibits/Trade Shows 10. Foreign 11. Infomercial 12. Internet Adv.13. Multimedia 14. Network Radio
15. Network T.V. 16. Newsp. Distr. Mags. 17. Other 18. Outdoor (Posters, Transit) 19. Point of Purchase20. Premiums, Novelties
21. Product Samples 22. Special Events Mktg. 23. Spot Radio 24. Spot T.V. 25. Weekly Newsp. 26. Yellow Page Adv.

AIIM International — (Continued)

Personnel:
Bryant Duhon *(Editor)*

THE ALDERMAN COMPANY
325 Model Farm Rd
High Point, NC 27263-1825
Mailing Address:
PO Box 2046
High Point, NC 27261-2046
Tel.: (336) 889-6121
Fax: (336) 889-7717
E-Mail For Key Personnel:
Sales Director: sales@aldermancompany.com
Approx. Number Employees: 100
Year Founded: 1898
Business Description:
Photography, Design, Photo Labwork, Advertising, Public Relations & Publicity for Manufacturers, Retailers & Advertising Agencies
S.I.C.: 7335; 7311; 7384; 7389
N.A.I.C.S.: 541922; 541410; 541810; 812921
Media: 2-4-10
Distr.: Natl.
Budget Set: Jan.
Personnel:
Eugene Johnston *(Chm)*
Jeffrey B. Williams *(Pres)*
Sharon K. Allen *(Gen Counsel)*

ALEX WILSON COLDSTREAM LTD.
32 Colonization Ave
PO Box 3009
Dryden, ON P8N 2Y9, Canada
Tel.: (807) 223-2381
Fax: (807) 223-2907
Toll Free: (800) 465-7230
E-mail: awcl@awcoldstream.com
Web Site: www.awcoldstream.com
Approx. Sls.: $15,000,000
Approx. Number Employees: 34
Year Founded: 1940
Business Description:
Stock Products & Custom Orders Printers
S.I.C.: 2752
N.A.I.C.S.: 323114
Import Export
Media: 2-4-6-7-8-25
Budget Set: Nov. -Dec.
Personnel:
Roy Wilson *(Pres & CEO)*

ALFRED A. KNOPF, INC.
(Affil. of Random House, Inc.)
1745 Broadway
New York, NY 10019
Tel.: (212) 782-9000
E-mail: alfred@randomhouse.com
Web Site:
www.knopf.knopfdoubleday.com
Approx. Number Employees: 85
Year Founded: 1915
Business Description:
Publishers of Fiction, Nonfiction, Juvenile Books
S.I.C.: 2731
N.A.I.C.S.: 511130
Import Export
Media: 2-5-6-8-9-25
Distr.: Direct to Consumer; Natl.
Personnel:
Paul Bogaards *(Sr VP-Publicity)*

Brands & Products:
BORZOI
EVERYMAN LIBRARY
Advertising Agency:
Verso Advertising, Inc.
50 W 17th St 5th Fl
New York, NY 10011-5702
Tel.: (212) 292-2990
Fax: (212) 557-2592

ALLEGRA NETWORK LLC
47585 Galleon Dr
Plymouth, MI 48170
Tel.: (248) 596-8600
Fax: (248) 596-8601
Web Site: www.allegranetwork.com
Sales Range: $250-299.9 Million
Approx. Number Employees: 45
Year Founded: 1976
Business Description:
Quick Printing Services
S.I.C.: 7389; 2752
N.A.I.C.S.: 541990; 323110
Advertising Expenditures: $1,300,000
Media: 1-2-3-5-7-8-9-10-11-18-19-20-23-24-25-26
Distr.: Natl.
Budget Set: Nov.
Personnel:
Thomas S. Monaghan *(Founder)*
William D. McIntyre Jr. *(Chm)*
Carl Gerhardt *(Pres & CEO)*
Brands & Products:
ALLEGRA NETWORK
ALLEGRA PRINT & IMAGING
AMERICAN SPEEDY PRINTING
INSTANT COPY
INSTY-PRINTS
QUIK PRINT
SPEEDY PRINTING
ZIPPY PRINT

ALLEN PRESS INC.
810 E Tenth St
Lawrence, KS 66044-3018
Tel.: (785) 843-1235
Fax: (785) 843-1244
E-mail: info@allenpress.com
Web Site: www.allenpress.com
Approx. Sls.: $26,000,000
Approx. Number Employees: 275
Year Founded: 1935
Business Description:
Scientific Periodicals Publisher
S.I.C.: 2721
N.A.I.C.S.: 511120
Import Export
Media: 2-13
Brands & Products:
LOGICAL SOCIETY OF NORTH AMERICA

ALLSTON-BRIGHTON TAB
(Unit of GateHouse Media New England)
254 2nd Ave
Needham, MA 02494
Tel.: (781) 433-8200
Fax: (781) 433-8202
Web Site: www.wickedlocal.com/allston
Sales Range: $100-124.9 Million
Business Description:
Newspaper Publisher
S.I.C.: 2711
N.A.I.C.S.: 511110
Media: 25

Personnel:
Chuck Goodrich *(VP-Adv)*
Valentina Zic *(Editor-News)*
Harriet Steinberg *(Mgr-Display Adv)*
Richard Whippen *(Mgr-Adv-Natl)*

ALPHA MEDIA GROUP INC.
(Holding of Quadrangle Group LLC)
1040 6th Ave Fl 14
New York, NY 10018
Tel.: (212) 302-2626
Web Site: www.maxim.com/movies/dvd-reviews/31550/south-park-passion-jew.html
Year Founded: 1997
Business Description:
Magazine Publisher & Printer
S.I.C.: 2721
N.A.I.C.S.: 511120
Media: 4-6-8-13-19-21-22
Personnel:
Kent Brownridge *(Chm & CEO)*
Glenn Rosenbloom *(Pres & Co-CEO)*
Joseph Mangione *(CEO)*
Joe Levy *(Editor-in-Chief-Blender Magazine)*
Karen Wartell *(Dir-Fashion & Beauty-Maxim)*
Brands & Products:
BLENDER
MAXIM
STUFF
Advertising Agency:
Steak
648 Broadway Ste 703
New York, NY 10012
Tel.: (646) 556-6585
Fax: (917) 591-9389
(Blender, Maxim)

A.M. BEST COMPANY
Ambest Rd
Oldwick, NJ 08858
Tel.: (908) 439-2200
Fax: (908) 439-3296
E-mail: customer_service@ambest.com
Web Site: www.ambest.com
Year Founded: 1899
Business Description:
Insurance Company Rating Agency; Insurance Industry Information Publisher
S.I.C.: 2731; 2721
N.A.I.C.S.: 511130; 511120
Export
Advertising Expenditures: $1,000,000
Media: 2-4-7-10
Distr.: Intl.; Natl.
Budget Set: Dec.
Personnel:
Arthur Snyder *(Chm, Pres & Publr)*
Jeffrey A. Oster *(Pres-Client Preservation & Mktg)*
Arthur Snyder, III *(COO & Exec VP)*
Larry Mayewski *(Chief Rating Officer & Exec VP)*
Paul Tinnirello *(Exec VP)*
Lee McDonald *(Grp VP-Comm)*
Jim Fowler *(Mgr-Bus Dev)*
Matthew Josefowicz *(Mgr-Client Comm)*
Brands & Products:
A.M. BEST
BEST RATINGS
BESTDAY
BESTESP
BESTLINK
BESTMARK
BEST'S REVIEW
BESTWEEK
BESTWIRE
THE INSURANCE INFORMATION SOURCE

AMARILLO GLOBE-NEWS
(Unit of Morris Publishing Group, LLC)
PO Box 2091
Amarillo, TX 79166
Tel.: (806) 376-4488
Fax: (806) 376-9217
E-mail: info@amarillo.com
Web Site: www.amarillo.com
Approx. Number Employees: 200
Year Founded: 1951
Business Description:
Newspaper Publisher
S.I.C.: 2711; 2721
N.A.I.C.S.: 511110; 511120
Media: 8-9
Personnel:
Lester T. Simpson *(Publr)*
Michael Distelhorst *(Dir-Adv)*
Mike O'Connor *(Dir-Production)*

AMERICAN BABY MAGAZINE
(Div. of Meredith Publishing Group)
375 Lexington Ave
New York, NY 10017-5529
Tel.: (212) 499-2000
Fax: (212) 455-1463
Toll Free: (800) 678-1208
E-mail: support@americanbaby.com
Web Site: www.americanbaby.com
Sales Range: $10-24.9 Million
Approx. Number Employees: 50
Business Description:
Magazine Publisher
S.I.C.: 2721
N.A.I.C.S.: 511120
Media: 8-10-13
Personnel:
Lauren Wiener *(Mng Dir-Interactive Sls & Media)*
Chuck Hajj *(Mng Dir)*
Dana Points *(Editor-in-Chief)*

AMERICAN BANKNOTE CORPORATION
(d/b/a ABnote Group)
2200 Fletcher Ave
Fort Lee, NJ 07024
Tel.: (201) 592-3400
Fax: (201) 224-2762
E-mail: info@americanbanknote.com
Web Site:
www.americanbanknote.com
Sales Range: $150-199.9 Million
Approx. Number Employees: 2,520
Year Founded: 1795
Business Description:
Engraving & Printing Securities, Food Coupons, Travellers Cheques, Postage Stamps, Stock & Bond Gift Certificates, State Vital Documents, Gift Certificates, Business Checks
S.I.C.: 2759; 2752; 2754; 6719
N.A.I.C.S.: 323119; 323110; 323111; 551112
Export
Advertising Expenditures: $500,000
Media: 2-7
Distr.: Intl.; Natl.
Personnel:
Steven G. Singer *(Chm & CEO)*
Patrick J. Gentile *(COO & Exec VP)*

Key to Media (For complete agency information see *The Advertising Red Books-Agencies* edition):
1. Bus. Publs. 2. Cable T.V. 3. Catalogs & Directories. 4. Co-op Adv. 5. Consumer Mags. 6. D.M. to Bus. Estab.7. D.M. to Consumers 8. Daily Newsp. 9. Exhibits/Trade Shows 10. Foreign 11. Infomercial 12. Internet Adv.13. Multimedia 14. Network Radio 15. Network T.V. 16. Newsp. Distr. Mags. 17. Other 18. Outdoor (Posters, Transit) 19. Point of Purchase20. Premiums, Novelties 21. Product Samples 22. Special Events Mktg. 23. Spot Radio 24. Spot T.V. 25. Weekly Newsp. 26. Yellow Page Adv.

Justin D'Angelo *(COO & Sr VP)*
Stuart Blank *(Pres-Cards Div)*
Miguel Santisteban *(Pres-ABN Argentina)*
Joseph Caffarella *(CEO-North America)*
Philippe Delanoue *(CEO-Europe)*
Sidney Levy *(CEO-South America)*
David M. Kober *(Exec VP & Gen Counsel)*
Thomas Ziemkus *(Sr VP)*

AMERICAN EXPRESS PUBLISHING CORPORATION

(Sub. of American Express Travel Related Services Company, Inc.)
1120 Ave Of The Americas
New York, NY 10036-6700
Tel.: (212) 382-5600
Fax: (212) 768-1568
Web Site: www.amexpub.com
Sales Range: $25-49.9 Million
Approx. Number Employees: 350
Business Description:
Publisher of Magazines
S.I.C.: 2721
N.A.I.C.S.: 511120
Media: 6
Budget Set: Dec.
Personnel:
Mark Stanich *(CMO, Pres-Digital Media & Sr VP)*
Marshall A. Corey *(VP, Pres-Books, Products & Svcs)*
Christina Grdovic Baltz *(Publr-Food & Wine & VP)*
J.P. Kyrillos *(Publr-Travel + Leisure)*
Nancy Novogrod *(Sr VP, Editor-in-Chief-Travel + Leisure & Editorial Dir)*
Cara David *(Sr VP-Strategic Insights, Mktg & Sls)*
Richard David Story *(Sr VP)*
Dana Corwin *(VP & Editor-in-Chief-Food & Wine)*
Jordana Pransky *(VP & Dir-Ad)*
Jill S. Davison *(VP-Corp Comm)*
Jill Rudnick *(VP-Mktg-Departures)*
Laura Begley *(Dir)*
Elizabeth Marsh *(Dir-Corp Comm-Travel & Leisure Brand)*
Jennifer Sommer *(Dir-Los Angeles)*
Frederica Wald *(Dir-Custom Solutions)*
Tanisa Williams *(Dir-HR)*
Kristy M. Bauer *(Sr Mgr-Corp Mktg Svcs)*
Brands & Products:
ALTITUDE
CENTURION-THE MAGAZINE
DEPARTURES
EXECUTIVE TRAVEL
EXECUTIVE TRAVEL SKYGUIDE
FOOD & WINE MAGAZINE
LIFESTYLE & TRAVEL FOR PHYSICIANS
TRAVEL + LEISURE FAMILY
TRAVEL + LEISURE GOLF
TRAVEL + LEISURE MAGAZINE
TRAVEL + ROMANCE
Advertising Agency:
AGENCYSACKS
345 7th Ave 7th Fl
New York, NY 10001-5006
Tel.: (212) 826-4004
Fax: (212) 593-7824

AMERICAN FUTURE SYSTEMS INC.

(d/b/a Progressive Business Publications)
370 Technology Dr
Malvern, PA 19355
Tel.: (610) 695-8600
Fax: (610) 647-8089
Toll Free: (800) 220-5000
E-mail: customer_service@pbp.com
Web Site: www.pbp.com
Approx. Number Employees: 400
Year Founded: 1989
Business Description:
Newsletter Publishing
S.I.C.: 2741
N.A.I.C.S.: 511199
Media: 7-10
Personnel:
Len Fesi *(Dir-HR)*
Brands & Products:
PROGRESSIVE BUSINESS

AMERICAN GREETINGS CORPORATION

1 American Rd
Cleveland, OH 44144-2398
Tel.: (216) 252-7300
Fax: (216) 252-6778
Telex: 980371 AGC CLV
E-mail: investor.relations@amgreetings.com
Web Site:
www.corporate.americangreetings.com
Approx. Rev.: $1,592,568,000
Approx. Number Employees: 7,400
Year Founded: 1906
Business Description:
Greeting Card, Gift Wrap, Stationery & Giftware Mfr & Distr
S.I.C.: 2771; 2678
N.A.I.C.S.: 511191; 322233
Import
Advertising Expenditures: $17,434,000
Distr.: Intl.; Natl.
Budget Set: Dec.
Personnel:
Morry Weiss *(Chm)*
James C. Spira *(Vice Chm)*
Stephen J. Smith *(CFO & Sr VP)*
Douglas W. Rommel *(Sr VP & CIO)*
Sally Schriner *(Pres-AG Interactive)*
Catherine M. Kilbane *(Gen Counsel, Sec & Sr VP)*
Gregory M. Steinberg *(Treas & Dir-IR)*
John W. Beeder *(Sr VP & Exec Sls & Mktg Officer)*
John S.N. Charlton *(Sr VP)*
Michael L. Goulder *(Sr VP & Exec Supply Chain Officer)*
Thomas H. Johnston *(Sr VP-Creative & Mdsg)*
Brian T. McGrath *(Sr VP-HR)*
Erwin Weiss *(Sr VP-Enterprise Resource Plng)*
Dawn Wayt *(VP-Mktg-AG Interactive)*
Carol Miller *(Exec Dir-New Product Concepts)*
Matt Schweitzer *(Brand Mgr)*
Maureen Meidenbauer *(Brand Mgr-Taylor Swift)*
Barbara Eifel *(Product Mgr)*
Brands & Products:
AMERICAN GREETINGS
AMERICAN GREETINGS SAYS IT BEST
CARLTON
CARLTON CARDS
CREATABLES
DATEWORKS
DESIGNERS' COLLECTION
DESIGNWARE
GIBSON
PLUSMARK
SOFT TOUCH
Advertising Agency:
Northlich
Sawyer Point Bldg 720 Pete Rose Way
Cincinnati, OH 45202
Tel.: (513) 421-8840
Fax: (513) 455-4749

AMERICAN HERITAGE PUBLISHING

416 Hungerford Dr Ste 216
Rockville, MD 20850-4127
Tel.: (240) 453-0900
Fax: (240) 453-0902
Toll Free: (800) 777-1222
E-mail: mail@americanheritage.com
Web Site: www.americanheritage.com
Sales Range: Less than $1 Million
Approx. Number Employees: 9
Year Founded: 1954
Business Description:
Magazine Publisher
S.I.C.: 2741
N.A.I.C.S.: 511199
Media: 6-13
Distr.: Natl.
Budget Set: Dec.
Personnel:
Robert L. Jenkins *(Dir-Adv)*
Jenni Rodibaugh *(Mgr-Permissions)*
Brands & Products:
AMERICAN HERITAGE
INVENTION & TECHNOLOGY

AMERICAN LAWYER MEDIA, INC.

(Sub. of Incisive Media Limited)
120 Broadway 5th Fl
New York, NY 10271
Tel.: (212) 457-9400
Fax: (646) 417-7705
Toll Free: (800) 888-8300
Web Site: www.alm.com
E-Mail For Key Personnel:
President: wpollak@amlaw.com
Approx. Number Employees: 777
Year Founded: 1978
Business Description:
Legal & Business Publishing
S.I.C.: 2721; 2711
N.A.I.C.S.: 511120; 511110
Advertising Expenditures: $76,682,000
Personnel:
Eric F. Lundberg *(CFO & Sr VP)*
Allison C. Hoffman *(Gen Counsel & Sr VP)*
Ron Spinner *(Publr-Verdictsearch & ALM Experts)*
Jack Berkowitz *(Sr VP)*
Kevin Vermeulen *(Sr VP)*
Aric Press *(VP-Editor In Chief)*
Sara Diamond *(VP-Books & Directory Publr-Legal)*
Tim Kennelty *(VP-Product Strategy & Dev-Substantive Law Grp)*
Brands & Products:
THE AMERICAN LAWYER
CORPORATE COUNSEL
GLOBEST.COM
LAW.COM
THE NATIONAL LAW JOURNAL
NEW YORK LAW JOURNAL
REAL ESTATE FORUM

THE AMERICAN LEGION MAGAZINE

700 N Pennsylvania St
Indianapolis, IN 46204-1129
Tel.: (317) 630-1200
Fax: (317) 630-1280
E-mail: dandretti@legion.org
Web Site: www.legion.org
Sales Range: $50-74.9 Million
Approx. Number Employees: 281
Year Founded: 1919
Business Description:
Magazine Publisher
S.I.C.: 2721; 5961
N.A.I.C.S.: 511120; 454113
Advertising Expenditures: $200,000
Media: 4
Distr.: Natl.
Personnel:
Diane Andretti *(Dir-Adv)*
Brands & Products:
THE AMERICAN LEGION

AMERICAN LIBRARY ASSOCIATION

50 E Huron St
Chicago, IL 60611-2729
Tel.: (312) 944-6780
Fax: (312) 440-9374
Toll Free: (800) 545-2433
E-mail: ala@ala.org
Web Site: www.ala.org
Approx. Number Employees: 250
Year Founded: 1876
Business Description:
Library Association
S.I.C.: 8621
N.A.I.C.S.: 813920
Import Export
Advertising Expenditures: $400,000
Media: 2-4-6-7-8-10-11-13
Distr.: Intl.; Natl.
Budget Set: Jan.
Personnel:
Gregory Calloway *(CFO)*
Keith Michael-Fields *(Exec Dir)*
Cathleen Bourdon *(Assoc Dir-Mktg)*
Deborah Robertson *(Dir-Pub Programs)*
Cyntia Vivian *(Dir-HR)*
Donald E. Chatham *(Assoc Dir-Publ)*
Mary Davis Fournier *(Project Mgr)*
Brands & Products:
ALA TECHSOURCE
AMERICAN LIBRARIES
BOOK LINKS
BOOKLIST
BOOKLIST ONLINE
GIVEALA

AMERICAN MEDIA, INC.

1000 American Media Way
Boca Raton, FL 33464
Tel.: (561) 997-7733
Fax: (561) 989-1298
Web Site:
www.americanmediainc.com

Key to Media (For complete agency information see *The Advertising Red Books-Agencies* edition):
1. Bus. Publs. 2. Cable T.V. 3. Catalogs & Directories. 4. Co-op Adv. 5. Consumer Mags. 6. D.M. to Bus. Estab.7. D.M. to Consumers
8. Daily Newsp. 9. Exhibits/Trade Shows 10. Foreign 11. Infomercial 12. Internet Adv.13. Multimedia 14. Network Radio
15. Network T.V. 16. Newsp. Distr. Mags. 17. Other 18. Outdoor (Posters, Transit) 19. Point of Purchase20. Premiums, Novelties
21. Product Samples 22. Special Events Mktg. 23. Spot Radio 24. Spot T.V. 25. Weekly Newsp. 26. Yellow Page Adv.

American Media, Inc. — (Continued)

Sales Range: $450-499.9 Million
Approx. Number Employees: 1,000
Year Founded: 1952
Business Description:
Publishing & Printing
S.I.C.: 2721; 2711; 2741
N.A.I.C.S.: 511120; 511110; 511199
Export
Advertising Expenditures: $20,000,000
Media: 2-8-10-11-13-14-15-18-19-23-24
Distr.: Natl.
Budget Set: Apr.
Personnel:
David J. Pecker *(Chm, Pres & CEO)*
Chris Polimeni *(CFO)*
Kevin Hyson *(CMO & Exec VP)*
Michael B. Kahane *(Gen Counsel, Sec & Exec VP)*
Larry Menkes *(Publr-Men's Fitness)*
Chris Scardino *(Exec VP & Grp Dir-Publ)*
David Perel *(Exec VP & Mng Editor-Radar Online)*
Dave Leckey *(Exec VP-Consumer Mktg)*
Daniel Rotstein *(Exec VP-HR & Admin)*
Michael Esposito *(Sr VP-Ops & Digital Production)*
Robin Keller *(VP & Gen Mgr-Digital Media)*
Ron Minutella *(VP-Fin Plng & Analysis)*
Chris Lockwood *(Editor-in-Chief)*
Tara Kraft *(Editor-in-Chief-Shape)*
Mark Eisner *(Dir-Supply Mgmt)*
Seth Kelly *(Dir-Editorial)*
Stephen Romeo *(Dir-Production)*
Brands & Products:
AMI SPECIALS
AUTO WORLD MAGAZINE
COUNTRY WEEKLY
FIT PREGNANCY
FLEX
GLOBE
GLOBE DIGESTS
LIVING FIT
MEN'S FITNESS
MICRO MAGAZINES
MINIMAGS
MIRA!
MPH
MUSCLE & FITNESS
MUSCLE & FITNESS HERS
THE NATIONAL ENQUIRER
NATIONAL EXAMINER
NATURAL HEALTH
NOPI STREET PERFORMANCE COMPACT
QUICK
SHAPE EN ESPANOL
SHAPE MAGAZINE
STAR MAGAZINE
SUN
WEEKLY WORLD NEWS

AMERICAN METEOROLOGICAL SOCIETY

(d/b/a AMS)
45 Beacon St
Boston, MA 02108-3693
Tel.: (617) 227-2425
Fax: (617) 742-8718
E-mail: amspubs@ametsoc.org
Web Site: www.ametsoc.org
Approx. Number Employees: 72
Year Founded: 1920
Business Description:
Trade Journal Publisher
S.I.C.: 2721; 8621
N.A.I.C.S.: 511120; 813920
Media: 10
Personnel:
Thomas R. Karl *(Pres)*
Keith L. Seitter *(Exec Dir)*
Joyce Annese *(Dir-Exec Programs)*
Stephanie Armstrong *(Dir-Dev)*
Jim Brey *(Dir-Education Program)*
Beth Farley *(Dir-Member Svcs)*
Claudia Gorski *(Dir-Meetings)*
Ken Heideman *(Dir-Publ)*
William H Hooke *(Dir-AMS Policy Program & Sr Policy Fellow)*
Corinne Kazarosian *(Dir-Infor Technologies)*
Joseph M Moran *(Assoc Dir-Education Program)*
Kelly Savoie *(Mgr-Mktg & Special Programs)*
Brands & Products:
PUBLISH TECHNICAL JOURNALS

AMERICAN REPROGRAPHICS COMPANY

1981 N Broadway Ste 385
Walnut Creek, CA 94596
Tel.: (925) 949-5100
Fax: (925) 949-5101
E-mail: info@e-arc.com
Web Site: www.e-arc.com
Approx. Sls.: $441,639,000
Approx. Number Employees: 3,200
Year Founded: 1997
Business Description:
Photocopying & Duplicating Services
S.I.C.: 2791; 2752; 7336; 7338; 7372; 7389
N.A.I.C.S.: 323122; 323114; 511210; 541430; 561410; 561439
Advertising Expenditures: $1,892,000
Personnel:
Kumarakulasingam Suriyakumar *(Chm, Pres & CEO)*
John E.D. Toth *(CFO)*
Dilantha Wijesuriya *(COO)*
Joe Abeyesinhe *(Sr VP-Pur)*
Ted Buscaglia *(Sr VP-Global Svcs)*
Theodore J. Carson *(Sr VP-Mergers & Acq)*
Ken Gini *(Sr VP-Integration)*
David Stickney *(VP-Corp Comm)*
Janine Brandel *(Dir-Integration)*
Jonathan F. Styrlund *(Dir-Integration)*
Kumar Wiratunga *(Dir-Digital Ops)*
Brands & Products:
ABACUS PCR
AMERICAN REPROGRAPHICS COMPANY
ARC
ISHIPDOCS
METAPRINT
ONEVIEW
PEIR
PLANWELL
PLANWELL BIDCASTER
PLANWELL ENTERPRISE
PLANWELL EWO
PLANWELL PDS
SUB-HUB
Advertising Agency:
The Ruth Group
141 5th Ave 5th Fl
New York, NY 10010
Tel.: (646) 536-7000

AMERICAN SOCIETY OF CINEMATOGRAPHERS

1782 N Orange Dr
Hollywood, CA 90028-4307
Tel.: (323) 969-4333
Fax: (323) 882-6391
Toll Free: (800) 448-0145
E-mail: office@theasc.com
Web Site: www.theasc.com
Approx. Number Employees: 70
Year Founded: 1919
Business Description:
Professional Organization of Cinematographers
S.I.C.: 8621; 7812
N.A.I.C.S.: 813920; 512110
Media: 2-4-10
Personnel:
Martha Winterhalter *(Publr-ASC Holding Corp)*
Sonja Pierce *(Coord-Classified Adv)*
Brands & Products:
AMERICAN CINEMATOGRAPHER
THE AMERICAN SOCIETY OF CINEMATOGRAPHERS
LOYALTY. PROGRESS. ARTISTRY

AMERICAN TECHNICAL PUBLISHERS, INC.

10100 Orland Pkwy Ste 200
Orland Park, IL 60467
Tel.: (708) 957-1100
Fax: (708) 957-1101
Toll Free: (800) 323-3471
E-mail: service@americantech.net
Web Site: www.go2atp.com
Approx. Number Employees: 50
Year Founded: 1898
Business Description:
Publisher of Vocational & Technical Textbooks
S.I.C.: 2731
N.A.I.C.S.: 511130
Export
Media: 2-7-8-10
Distr.: Direct to Consumer; Natl.
Budget Set: Oct.
Personnel:
Robert D. Deisinger *(Pres)*
David J. Holloway *(Sr VP)*
Jonathan F. Gosse *(Editor-in-Chief)*
Brands & Products:
AMERICAN TECHNICAL PUBLISHER
MASTER MATH
QUICK QUIZZES

AMESBURY NEWS

(Unit of GateHouse Media New England)
72 Cherry Hill Dr
Beverly, MA 01915
Tel.: (978) 388-2406
Fax: (978) 739-8501
E-mail: amesbury@cnc.com
Web Site: www.wickedlocal.com/amesbury
Sales Range: $25-49.9 Million
Approx. Number Employees: 60
Business Description:
Newspaper Publisher
S.I.C.: 2711
N.A.I.C.S.: 511110
Media: 8-21-25
Personnel:
Charles Goodrich *(Publr)*
Robin Lorenzen *(VP-Mktg)*
Janet Mackay-Smith *(Editor-News)*
Nancy Bentley-Porter *(Mgr-Display Adv)*
Peter Chianca *(Mgr-Website)*
Pat Coen *(Mgr-Production)*
Jeff McEvoy *(Mgr-Adv-Natl)*
Brands & Products:
AMESBURY NEWS

AMOS CRAFT PUBLISHING

(Div. of Amos Press, Inc.)
2400 Devon Ave Ste 292
Des Plaines, IL 60018-4618
Tel.: (847) 635-5800
Fax: (847) 635-6311
Toll Free: (800) 272-3871
Web Site: www.craftideas.com
Approx. Number Employees: 30
Year Founded: 1951
Business Description:
Craft Magazines Publisher
S.I.C.: 2721
N.A.I.C.S.: 511120
Media: 4-7-8-13
Distr.: Natl.
Personnel:
Williams Say *(Pres & CEO)*
Brands & Products:
AMOS CRAFT PUBLISHING
CRAFTING 101
CRAFTS' N THINGS
CROSS STITCHER
PACK-O-FUN
PAINTING
PAPER MADE EASY

AMOS PRESS, INC.

911 Vandemark Rd
Sidney, OH 45365
Mailing Address:
PO Box 4129
Sidney, OH 45365
Tel.: (937) 498-2111
Fax: (937) 498-0888
Web Site: www.amospress.com
Sales Range: $50-74.9 Million
Approx. Number Employees: 370
Business Description:
Periodical Publisher
S.I.C.: 2721; 2711
N.A.I.C.S.: 511120; 511110
Media: 4-13
Personnel:
Bruce Daniel Boyd *(Pres)*
Jerry Osmus *(Sr Dir-Digital)*
Brands & Products:
AMOS PUBLISHING
CARS & PARTS
COIN WORLD
CORVETTE ENTHUSIAST
CRAFTS' N THINGS
CROSS STITCHER
LINN'S STAMP NEWS
MOPAR ENTHUSIAST
MUSCLECAR ENTHUSIAST
MUSTANG ENTHUSIAST
PACK-O-FUN
PAINTING
PONTIAC ENTHUSIAST
SCOTT STAMP MONTHLY

ANCIENT AMERICAN

PO Box 370
Colfax, WI 54730
Tel.: (715) 962-3299
Fax: (715) 962-3296
Toll Free: (877) 494-0044

Key to Media (For complete agency information see *The Advertising Red Books-Agencies* edition):
1. Bus. Publs. 2. Cable T.V. 3. Catalogs & Directories. 4. Co-op Adv. 5. Consumer Mags. 6. D.M. to Bus. Estab.7. D.M. to Consumers
8. Daily Newsp. 9. Exhibits/Trade Shows 10. Foreign 11. Infomercial 12. Internet Adv.13. Multimedia 14. Network Radio
15. Network T.V. 16. Newsp. Distr. Mags. 17. Other 18. Outdoor (Posters, Transit) 19. Point of Purchase20. Premiums, Novelties
21. Product Samples 22. Special Events Mktg. 23. Spot Radio 24. Spot T.V. 25. Weekly Newsp. 26. Yellow Page Adv.

E-mail: wayne@ancientamerican.com
Web Site: www.ancientamerican.com
Sales Range: Less than $1 Million
Approx. Number Employees: 9
Year Founded: 1993
Business Description:
Magazine
S.I.C.: 2721
N.A.I.C.S.: 511120
Media: 2-4-6-8
Distr.: Natl.
Personnel:
Roger Grawe *(Mgr-Fulfillment)*
Ephraim James *(Mgr-Production)*
Kristine May *(Mgr-Circulation)*
Wayne N. May *(Mgr-Adv)*
Roger Waller *(Webmaster)*
Brands & Products:
ANCIENT AMERICAN
ARCHAEOLOGY OF THE AMERICAS BEFORE COLUMBUS

ANDERSON & VREELAND, INC.
8 Evans St
Fairfield, NJ 07004-2210
Mailing Address:
PO Box 1246
West Caldwell, NJ 07007-1246
Tel.: (973) 227-2270
Fax: (973) 882-6621
E-mail: info@aveast.com
Web Site:
www.andersonvreeland.com
Approx. Number Employees: 135
Year Founded: 1961
Business Description:
Supplier of Flexographic Platemaking Equipment & Materials for the Graphic Arts
S.I.C.: 3555; 5084
N.A.I.C.S.: 333293; 423830
Import Export
Advertising Expenditures: $180,000
Media: 2-5-10-20
Distr.: Intl.; Natl.
Personnel:
Howard Vreeland, Jr. *(Chm)*
Thomas O. Gavin *(Pres)*
Joseph K. Anderson *(Reg Mgr-Sls-Eastern)*
Lonnie Grieser *(Mgr-Warehouse)*
Garin Lions *(Mgr-Sls & Field Mgr)*
Brands & Products:
A & V
ANDERSON & VREELAND
ARTPRO
DIGITAL COSMOLIGHT
DOTSPY
MOUNT-O-MATIC
MOUNT-O-MATIC PLUS
NEXUS
OPTI-MOUNT
PREDICTION
SOFT-TOUCH
ULTRAMATIC
Advertising Agency:
Knudsen, Gardner & Howe, Inc.
2103 Saint Clair Ave NE
Cleveland, OH 44114-4018
Tel.: (216) 781-5000
Fax: (216) 781-5004

ANDREWS MCMEEL UNIVERSAL
1130 Walnut St
Kansas City, MO 64106
Tel.: (816) 581-7500
Fax: (816) 932-6600
Toll Free: (800) 255-6734
Web Site: www.amuniversal.com
Approx. Number Employees: 110
Year Founded: 1970
Business Description:
Books, Calendars, Greeting Cards & Stationery Products Mfr & Distr
S.I.C.: 2731; 2741
N.A.I.C.S.: 511130; 511199
Media: 5-6-7-8-9-10-19-21-25
Distr.: Direct to Consumer; Natl.
Budget Set: Dec. -May
Personnel:
John P. McMeel *(Chm & Pres)*
Kathleen W. Andrews *(Vice Chm)*
Bridget McMeel *(Partner)*
Les Hinmon *(CFO & VP)*
Kerry Slagle *(Pres/CEO-Atlantic Syndication-Universal Uclick)*
Lee Salem *(Pres/Editor-Universal Uclick)*
Hugh T. Andrews *(Exec VP)*
Michael Stewart *(VP-HR)*
John Vivona *(VP-Sls)*
Patty Adams *(Mgr-Editorial Svcs)*
Kathy Hilliard *(Dir-Publicity)*
Bill Weir *(Sls Mgr)*
Staci Hobson *(Mgr-Grp & Special Sls)*

ANTARCTIC PRESS
7272 Wurzbach Rd Ste 204
San Antonio, TX 78240
Tel.: (210) 614-0396
Fax: (210) 593-0692
E-mail: apcog1@gmail.com
Web Site: www.antarctic-press.com
Approx. Number Employees: 6
Year Founded: 1984
Business Description:
Comic Books Publisher & Action Figures Mfr
S.I.C.: 2721; 5092
N.A.I.C.S.: 511120; 423920
Media: 10-13
Personnel:
Ben Dunn *(Founder)*
Jochen Weltjens *(Editor-in-Chief)*
Rod Espinosa *(Editor)*
Robby Bevard *(Coord-Production)*

ANTELOPE VALLEY NEWSPAPER INC.
37404 Sierra Hwy
Palmdale, CA 93550
Tel.: (661) 273-2700
Fax: (661) 947-4870
E-mail: editor@avpress.com
Web Site: www.avpress.com
Sales Range: $10-24.9 Million
Approx. Number Employees: 200
Business Description:
Newspapers, Publishing & Printing
S.I.C.: 2711
N.A.I.C.S.: 511110
Media: 3-7-8-9-10-18-19-20-21-22-23-24-26
Personnel:
William C. Markham *(Pres)*
Cherie Bryant *(VP & Gen Mgr)*
Cheryl Fletcher *(Mgr-Mktg)*

ANTICOSTI, LLC
41 Prospect St
Midland Park, NJ 07432-1645
Tel.: (201) 689-8222
Fax: (201) 891-7104
Approx. Sls.: $1,100,000
Approx. Number Employees: 7
Year Founded: 1997
Business Description:
Printing & Writing Paper
S.I.C.: 5111
N.A.I.C.S.: 424110
Media: 4-6

ANTRIM COUNTY NEWS
(Sub. of Journal Register Company)
206 N Bridge St
Bellaire, MI 49615-9589
Tel.: (231) 533-8523
Fax: (231) 533-6803
E-mail: info@antrimcountynews.com
Web Site:
www.antrimcountynews.com
Approx. Number Employees: 12
Business Description:
Weekly Newspaper Publishing
S.I.C.: 2711; 2721
N.A.I.C.S.: 511110; 511120
Media: 25

APPEAL-DEMOCRAT
(Unit of Freedom Newspapers, Inc.)
1530 Ellis Lk Dr
Marysville, CA 95901
Tel.: (530) 741-2345
Fax: (530) 741-0140
E-mail: adnewsroom@appealdemocrat.com
Web Site: www.appealdemocrat.com
Approx. Number Employees: 100
Year Founded: 1851
Business Description:
Newspaper
S.I.C.: 2711
N.A.I.C.S.: 511110
Media: 8-9-13
Personnel:
Dave Schmall *(Publr)*
Debbie Baggett *(Dir-Adv & Mktg)*

ARCHITECTURAL DIGEST
(Unit of Conde Nast Publications, Inc.)
4 Times Square 18th Fl
New York, NY 10036
Tel.: (323) 965-3700
E-mail: subscriptions@archdigest.com
Web Site:
www.architecturaldigest.com
Approx. Number Employees: 50
Year Founded: 1972
Business Description:
Architecture Magazine
S.I.C.: 2721
N.A.I.C.S.: 511120
Media: 2-6-7-8-19
Distr.: Intl.; Natl.
Personnel:
Giulio Capua *(Publr & VP)*
Paige Rense *(Editor-in-Chief)*
Anne Holliday-Woodard *(Assoc Dir-Integrated Mktg)*

ARCHROMA GLOBAL SERVICES
(Sub. of Clariant International Ltd.)
4331 Chesapeake Dr
Charlotte, NC 28216
Tel.: (704) 395-6569
E-mail: archroma.services@clariant.com
Web Site: www.archroma.com
Business Description:
Printing Services
S.I.C.: 2281; 5961
N.A.I.C.S.: 313111; 454113
Media: 1-2-4-10-11
Personnel:
Brad McClanahan *(Bus Mgr-Global)*
Brands & Products:
COLORPROSE

THE ARIZONA REPUBLIC
(Unit of Phoenix Newspapers, Inc.)
200 E Van Buren St
Phoenix, AZ 85004
Tel.: (602) 444-8000
Fax: (602) 444-8044
Toll Free: (800) 331-9303
E-mail: info@azcentral.com
Web Site: www.azcentral.com
Sales Range: $450-499.9 Million
Approx. Number Employees: 3,000
Year Founded: 1880
Business Description:
Newspaper Publisher
S.I.C.: 2711
N.A.I.C.S.: 511110
Advertising Expenditures: $1,000,000
Media: 3-8-9-15-23
Distr.: Direct to Consumer; Reg.
Personnel:
John Zidich *(Pres & Publr)*
Jon Held *(CFO & Exec VP)*
Randy Lovely *(Editor & VP-News)*
Robert Kotwasinski *(VP-Production)*
Mark Faller *(Editor-Sports Center)*
Kathy Tulumello *(Bus Dir-Center)*
Jill Cassidy *(Mgr-Travel Content)*
Heather McKie *(Mgr-Automotive)*

THE ARKANSAS CITY TRAVELER
(Sub. of Winfield Publishing Co.)
200 E 5th Ave
Arkansas City, KS 67005
Tel.: (620) 442-4200
Fax: (620) 442-7483
E-mail: news@arkcity.net
Web Site: www.arkcity.net
Approx. Number Employees: 32
Business Description:
Newspaper Publisher
S.I.C.: 2711
N.A.I.C.S.: 511110
Media: 8-9
Personnel:
Lloyd Craig *(Gen Mgr)*
Joey Sprinkle *(Editor-Sports)*
Micah Mitchell *(Dir-Adv)*
Marilyn Coury *(Mgr-Circulation)*
Susie Kincaid *(Mgr-Bus)*

THE ARLINGTON ADVOCATE
(Unit of GateHouse Media New England)
9 Meriam St
Lexington, MA 02420
Tel.: (781) 674-7726
Fax: (781) 674-7735
E-mail: arlington@cnc.com
Web Site: www.wickedlocal.com
Sales Range: $10-24.9 Million
Approx. Number Employees: 45
Business Description:
Newspaper Publisher

The Arlington Advocate — (Continued)
S.I.C.: 2711
N.A.I.C.S.: 511110
Media: 19-25
Personnel:
Chuck Goodrich *(Publr)*
Anne Eisenmenger *(Mgr-Website)*
Nicole Laskowski *(Mgr-Website)*
Christin Pineau *(Mgr-Display Adv)*
Linda Vahey *(Mgr-Circulation)*

ARMADA TIMES
(Sub. of Journal Register Company)
23061 E Main St
Armada, MI 48005
Tel.: (586) 784-5551
Fax: (586) 784-8710
E-mail: editor@voicenews.com
Approx. Number Employees: 2
Business Description:
Weekly Newspaper
S.I.C.: 2711; 2721
N.A.I.C.S.: 511110; 511120
Media: 25
Brands & Products:
ARMADA TIMES

ARTYPE, INC.
3530 Work Dr
Fort Myers, FL 33916-7533
Tel.: (239) 332-1174
Fax: (239) 332-5378
Toll Free: (800) 237-4474
E-mail: artype@att.net
Web Site: www.artypeinc.com
Approx. Number Employees: 35
Year Founded: 1942
Business Description:
High Quality Plastics Signs, Scratch Off Game Cards, Stickers, Coroplast, Political, Real Estate, & Outdoor Signs, Door Hangers, Bumper Stickers & Banners Mfr
S.I.C.: 3993
N.A.I.C.S.: 339950
Export
Media: 4-7
Distr.: Natl.
Personnel:
John Hunt *(Owner)*
Steve Hunt *(Pres)*

ASBURY PARK PRESS INC.
(Sub. of Gannett Co., Inc.)
3601 Hwy 66
Neptune, NJ 07754
Mailing Address:
PO Box 1550
Neptune, NJ 07754
Tel.: (732) 922-6000
Fax: (732) 643-3719
Toll Free: (800) 883-7737
E-mail: national@app.com
Web Site: www.app.com
Sales Range: $400-449.9 Million
Approx. Number Employees: 1,500
Year Founded: 1879
Business Description:
Newspaper Publisher
S.I.C.: 2711
N.A.I.C.S.: 511110
Media: 2-3-7-8-10-18-19-20-21-22-23-26
Distr.: Reg.
Personnel:
Thomas M. Donovan *(Pres & Publr)*
Sam Siciliano *(Reg VP-Customer Dev)*
Hollis R. Towns *(Exec Dir & VP-News)*
Judith Dorsey *(VP-HR)*
Wayne L. Peragallo *(VP-Info Sys)*
Erik Statler *(VP-Fin)*
Dennis Carmody *(Editor-Bus)*
Kathy Dzielak *(Editor-Entertainment & Dining)*
Andrew Prendimano *(Art Dir-Photo)*
Brands & Products:
THE ASBURY PARK PRESS
HOME NEWS TRIBUNE
IN-JERSEY
ISLANDER
OCEAN COUNTY OBSERVER

ASHLAND DAILY TIDINGS
(Unit of Ottaway Newspapers, Inc.)
1661 Siskiyou Blvd
Ashland, OR 97520
Mailing Address:
PO Box 7
Ashland, OR 97520-0061
Tel.: (541) 482-3456
Fax: (541) 482-3688
E-mail: news@dailytidings.com
Web Site: www.dailytidings.com
Sales Range: $10-24.9 Million
Approx. Number Employees: 10
Business Description:
Newspaper Publisher
S.I.C.: 2711
N.A.I.C.S.: 511110
Media: 8-9
Personnel:
Grady Singletary *(Publr)*
Myles Murphy *(Editor-City)*
Joe Zavala *(Editor)*

ASHLAND TAB
(Unit of GateHouse Media New England)
33 New York Ave
Framingham, MA 01701
Tel.: (508) 626-3800
Fax: (508) 626-4400
E-mail: ashland@cnc.com
Web Site: www.wickedlocal.com
Sales Range: $10-24.9 Million
Approx. Number Employees: 2
Business Description:
Newspaper Publisher
S.I.C.: 2711
N.A.I.C.S.: 511110
Media: 25
Personnel:
Nicole Simmons *(Editor-New Media)*

ASIAN WEEK FOUNDATION
(Sub. of Pan Asia Venture Capital Corporation)
564 Market St Ste 320
San Francisco, CA 94104
Tel.: (415) 397-0220
Tel.: (415) 373-4003
Fax: (415) 397-7258
E-mail: asianweek@asianweek.com
Web Site: www.asianweek.com
Approx. Number Employees: 15
Business Description:
Online Newspaper Focusing on Asian Pacific American Community
S.I.C.: 2741; 2711
N.A.I.C.S.: 516110; 511110
Media: 8-13-22-23
Personnel:
Ted Fang *(Pres, Publr & Editor)*
Jesus Coronel *(Mgr-Ops & Accountant)*
Carrolyn Kubota *(Mgr-Comm)*
Brands & Products:
ASIANWEEK

ASIMOV'S SCIENCE FICTION MAGAZINE
(Div. of Penny Publications, LLC)
475 Park Ave S 11th Fl
New York, NY 10016
Tel.: (212) 686-7188
Fax: (212) 686-7414
E-mail: asimovs@dellmagazines.com
Web Site: www.asimovs.com
Business Description:
Science Fiction Magazine
S.I.C.: 2721
N.A.I.C.S.: 511120
Media: 8-10
Personnel:
Peter Kanter *(Publr)*
Bruce W. Sherbow *(VP-Mktg & Sls)*
Sheila Williams *(Editor)*
Victoria Green *(Dir-Art)*
June Levine *(Asst Dir-Art)*
Abigail Browning *(Mgr-Subsidiary Rights & Mktg)*

ASTARA, INC.
10700 Jersey Blvd Ste 450
Rancho Cucamonga, CA 91730
Tel.: (909) 948-7412
Fax: (909) 948-2016
E-mail: mail@astara.org
Web Site: www.astara.org
Approx. Number Employees: 9
Year Founded: 1951
Business Description:
Religious & Educational Book Publisher
S.I.C.: 2731; 8661
N.A.I.C.S.: 511130; 813110
Export
Media: 2-3-4-7-8-10-16-20-21-23-26
Distr.: Intl.; Natl.
Budget Set: Dec.
Personnel:
Dean Zakich *(Gen Mgr)*
Sally Fleck *(Mgr-Member Records)*
Elizabeth Hickerson *(Mgr-Mktg)*
Brands & Products:
ASTARA

ASTRO COMMUNICATIONS SERVICES, INC.
334 Calef Hwy
Epping, NH 03042
Tel.: (603) 734-4300
Fax: (603) 734-4311
Toll Free: (800) 514-5070
E-mail: astrosales@astrocom.com
Web Site: www.astrocom.com
Sales Range: Less than $1 Million
Approx. Number Employees: 4
Year Founded: 1973
Business Description:
Astrology Services; Publisher of Books, Charts, Reports & Software
S.I.C.: 7299; 2731
N.A.I.C.S.: 812990; 511130
Export
Media: 4-7-11-13-21

ASYLUM RECORD
(Sub. of Warner Music Group Corp.)
1290 Ave of the Americas
New York, NY 10104
Tel.: (212) 707-3020
Fax: (212) 405-5408
E-mail: asylum2006@gmail.com
Web Site: www.asylumrecords.com
Sales Range: $10-24.9 Million
Approx. Number Employees: 50
Business Description:
Records, Tapes & Music Publisher
S.I.C.: 2741
N.A.I.C.S.: 512230
Media: 8-13-21
Personnel:
Julie Manda *(Mgr)*

ATHENS BANNER-HERALD
(Unit of Morris Publishing Group, LLC)
1 Press Pl
Athens, GA 30601
Tel.: (706) 549-0123
Fax: (706) 722-0011
E-mail: info@onlineathens.com
Web Site: www.onlineathens.com
Approx. Number Employees: 250
Year Founded: 1832
Business Description:
Newspaper Publisher
S.I.C.: 2711; 2721
N.A.I.C.S.: 511110; 511120
Media: 8-9
Personnel:
Greg Williamson *(Controller)*
Don Nelson *(Editor-Community)*
Julie Phillips *(Editor-Arts & Entertainment)*
Bill Stewart *(Editor-News)*
Jim Heady *(Dir-Circulation)*
George James *(Mgr-Retail Adv)*

ATHLON SPORTS, INC.
220 25th Ave N Ste 200
Nashville, TN 37203
Tel.: (615) 327-0747
Fax: (615) 327-1149
E-mail: info@athlonsports.com
Web Site: www.athlonsports.com
Approx. Number Employees: 65
Year Founded: 1967
Business Description:
Periodicals, Publishing Only
S.I.C.: 2721
N.A.I.C.S.: 511120
Media: 6-8-13-14-15-18-19
Personnel:
Stephen Duggan *(Pres & CEO)*
Mary Dunn *(CFO)*
Scott Garrett *(Pres-Natl Sls)*
Richard Beck *(Reg VP)*
Doris Kyle *(Dir-Finance)*
Brands & Products:
ATHLON SPORTS
SCENES FROM RACEDAY
SCENES FROM SATURDAY
SCENES FROM SUNDAY
SIDELINE SPIRIT

THE ATLANTA JOURNAL-CONSTITUTION
(Sub. of Cox Newspapers, Inc.)
223 Perimeter Ctr Pkwy NE
Atlanta, GA 30346
Mailing Address:
PO Box 4689
Atlanta, GA 30302-4689
Tel.: (404) 526-5151
Fax: (404) 526-5746
Toll Free: (800) 846-6672
Web Site: www.ajc.com
Year Founded: 1868

Key to Media (For complete agency information see *The Advertising Red Books-Agencies* edition):
1. Bus. Publs. 2. Cable T.V. 3. Catalogs & Directories. 4. Co-op Adv. 5. Consumer Mags. 6. D.M. to Bus. Estab.7. D.M. to Consumers
8. Daily Newsp. 9. Exhibits/Trade Shows 10. Foreign 11. Infomercial 12. Internet Adv.13. Multimedia 14. Network Radio
15. Network T.V. 16. Newsp. Distr. Mags. 17. Other 18. Outdoor (Posters, Transit) 19. Point of Purchase20. Premiums, Novelties
21. Product Samples 22. Special Events Mktg. 23. Spot Radio 24. Spot T.V. 25. Weekly Newsp. 26. Yellow Page Adv.

Business Description:
Newspaper
S.I.C.: 2711; 2721
N.A.I.C.S.: 511110; 511120
Advertising Expenditures: $1,000,000
Media: 9-13-18-23-24
Personnel:
Jim Kennedy *(CEO)*
Todd Cregar *(CFO & Sr VP)*
Michael Joseph *(Publr)*
Robert W. Eickhoff *(Sr VP-Ops & VP-Circulation)*
Susan Davidson *(Sr VP-HR)*
Moya Neville *(Sr VP-Adv Sls)*
Amy Chown *(VP-Mktg)*
Booker Izell *(VP-Community Affairs & Work Force Diversity)*
Leon Levitt *(VP-Digital Media)*
Charles Parker *(VP-Legal Affairs)*
Kevin Riley *(Editor-in-Chief-Dayton Daily News)*
Todd Duncan *(Editor-OTP assignment)*
Andre Jackson *(Editor-Editorial)*
Shawn McIntosh *(Editor-Pub & Administrator-Blog)*
Barbara Senftleber *(Editor-Newsroom Dev)*
Eric Myers *(Sr Dir-Adv)*
Mindy Buckalew *(Sr Mgr-Sls & Product Plng)*

THE ATLANTIC MONTHLY GROUP

(Sub. of National Journal Group)
600 New Hampshire Ave NW Ste 400
Washington, DC 20037
Tel.: (202) 266-6000
Fax: (202) 266-6001
E-mail: web@theatlantic.com
Web Site: www.theatlantic.com
Approx. Number Employees: 55
Year Founded: 1857
Business Description:
Magazine Publishing Services
S.I.C.: 2721
N.A.I.C.S.: 511120
Media: 6-8-13-22
Distr.: Natl.
Personnel:
David G. Bradley *(Chm)*
Elaine Erchak *(CFO)*
John Kefferstan *(Dir)*
Jason Treat *(Dir-Art)*
Brands & Products:
THE ATLANTIC MONTHLY MAGAZINE
Advertising Agency:
Euro RSCG Worldwide HQ
350 Hudson St
New York, NY 10014-4504
Tel.: (212) 886-2000
Fax: (212) 886-2016

ATLAS PEN & PENCIL CORPORATION

408 Madison St Ste 126
Shelbyville, TN 37160
Tel.: (954) 920-4444
Fax: (954) 920-8899
Fax: (800) 342-8889
Toll Free: (800) 327-3232
E-mail: sales@atlaspen.com
Web Site: www.atlaspen.com
E-Mail For Key Personnel:
Sales Director: sales@atlaspen.com
Sales Range: $25-49.9 Million
Approx. Number Employees: 200
Year Founded: 1948
Business Description:
Pens & Pencils Custom Engraving & Imprinting for Advertising & Promotion
S.I.C.: 3479; 2759; 3952
N.A.I.C.S.: 332812; 323119; 339942
Advertising Expenditures: $2,000,000
Media: 2-4-6-7-8-13
Distr.: Natl.
Budget Set: Jan.
Personnel:
Dave Thomas *(Pres)*
Brands & Products:
COMET
EZ GRIPPER
HIDE-A-PEN
IMPERIAL
MONTE MARCO
SIGNIA
STARDUST
VISTA GRIPPER

AUBURN JOURNAL INC.

(Sub. of Brehm Communications Inc.)
1030 High St
Auburn, CA 95603-4707
Tel.: (530) 885-5656
Fax: (530) 885-4902
E-mail: auburnjournal@goldcountrymedia.com
Web Site: www.auburnjournal.com
Approx. Number Employees: 100
Year Founded: 1963
Business Description:
Newspapers
S.I.C.: 2711
N.A.I.C.S.: 511110
Import Export
Media: 9-25
Personnel:
Tony Hazarian *(Publr)*

AUBURN TRADER

(Sub. of Brehm Communications Inc.)
11899 Edgewood Rd Ste C
Auburn, CA 95603
Tel.: (530) 888-7653
Fax: (530) 268-3326
Web Site: www.auburntrader.com
Approx. Number Employees: 5
Year Founded: 1981
Business Description:
Publisher of Daily Except Saturday Newspaper
S.I.C.: 2711
N.A.I.C.S.: 511110
Import Export
Media: 9
Brands & Products:
THE AUBURN TRADER

THE AUDIO PARTNERS PUBLISHING CORPORATION

1133 High St
Auburn, CA 95603-5135
Tel.: (530) 888-7804
Fax: (530) 888-7805
Toll Free: (888) 480-7803
E-mail: info@audiopartners.com
Web Site: www.audiopartners.com
Approx. Number Employees: 35
Year Founded: 1987
Business Description:
Audio Books Mfr
S.I.C.: 3652
N.A.I.C.S.: 334612
Advertising Expenditures: $150,000
Media: 2-4-6-7-8-10
Personnel:
Linda D. Olsen *(Pres)*
Grady Hesters *(CEO)*
Brands & Products:
AUDIO EDITIONS

AUDUBON MAGAZINE

(Sub. of National Audubon Society)
225 Varick St 7 Fl
New York, NY 10014-9536
Tel.: (212) 979-3102
Tel.: (212) 979-3000
Fax: (212) 979-3166
E-mail: education@audubon.org
Web Site: www.audubon.org
E-Mail For Key Personnel:
President: jflicker@audubon.org
Sales Estimate: $20-39 Million
Approx. Number Employees: 235
Year Founded: 1882
Business Description:
National Audubon Society Publisher
S.I.C.: 2721
N.A.I.C.S.: 511120
Media: 2-6-20
Distr.: Direct to Consumer; Intl.; Natl.
Budget Set: June
Personnel:
Ed Whitaker *(Mng Dir-Mktg & Publ)*
Nancy Severance *(Dir-Mktg & Comm)*
Brands & Products:
AUDUBON
Advertising Agency:
Bergman Group
4880 Sadler Rd Ste 220
Glen Allen, VA 23060
Tel.: (804) 225-0600
Fax: (804) 225-0900

AUGSBURG FORTRESS

Ste 600 100 S 5th St PO Box 1209
Minneapolis, MN 55402-1242
Tel.: (612) 330-3300
Fax: (612) 330-3455
Fax: (800) 722-7766
Toll Free: (800) 328-4648
E-mail: info@augsburgfortress.org
Web Site: www.augsburgfortress.org
Sales Range: $25-49.9 Million
Approx. Number Employees: 304
Year Founded: 1891
Business Description:
Mfr. of Ecclesiastic Garments; Altar Supplies; Religious Music; Publisher of Religious Books & Periodicals
S.I.C.: 2731; 5942
N.A.I.C.S.: 511130; 451211
Import Export
Media: 4-10
Distr.: Direct to Consumer; Intl.; Natl.
Budget Set: Apr.
Personnel:
Beth A. Lewis *(Pres & CEO)*
John Rahja *(CFO)*
Sandy Middendorf *(VP-HR & Organizational Dev)*
Brands & Products:
AUGSBURG FORTRESS
FRIAR TUCK SHIRTS

AUTHOR SOLUTIONS, INC.

(Holding of Bertram Capital Management LLC)
(d/b/a AuthorHouse)
1663 Liberty Dr Ste 200
Bloomington, IN 47403
Tel.: (812) 339-6000
Fax: (812) 339-6554
Toll Free: (888) 519-5121
E-mail: info@authorhouse.com
Web Site: www.authorsolutions.com
Business Description:
Self-Publishing Service for Authors
S.I.C.: 2741; 2731
N.A.I.C.S.: 511199; 511130
Media: 10
Personnel:
Kevin Weiss *(Pres & CEO)*
Joe Bayern *(Mng Dir & SVP)*
Kevin G. Gregory *(CFO)*
Randy Davis *(CIO)*
Bill Becher *(Sr VP-Production Svcs & Output Ops)*
Keith Ogorek *(Sr VP-Mktg)*
Don Seitz *(Sr VP-Sls-Worldwide)*
Joe Steinbach *(VP & Gen Mgr)*
Bruce Bunner *(VP-Sls & Mktg)*
Christopher Schrader *(VP-HR)*
Dave Weinman *(VP-Production)*
Jeffrey M. Drazan *(Dir-Mng)*
Shelley Rogers *(Mktg Mgr)*
Brands & Products:
AUTHORHOUSE

AUTOMOTIVE NEWS

(Unit of Crain Communications, Inc.)
1155 Gratiot Ave
Detroit, MI 48207-2997
Tel.: (313) 446-6000
Fax: (313) 446-8030
E-mail: autonews@crain.com
Web Site: www.automotivenews.com
E-Mail For Key Personnel:
Sales Director: lschlagh@crain.com
Public Relations: kpecar@crain.com
Approx. Number Employees: 300
Year Founded: 1925
Business Description:
Automotive Industry Newspaper & Internet Publisher
S.I.C.: 2711; 2741
N.A.I.C.S.: 511110; 516110
Media: 2-4-7-10-17-20-21-22
Distr.: Intl.; Natl.
Budget Set: Dec.
Personnel:
Peter Brown *(Publr & Editorial Dir)*
Keith E. Crain *(Editor-in-Chief)*
Charles Child *(Editor-Intl)*
Victor Galvan *(Editor-Web)*
Rick Kranz *(Editor-Product)*
Karen Faust O'Rourke *(Editor-Insight)*
James B. Treece *(Editor-Indus)*
David Versical *(Editor-Online)*
Rick Greer *(Dir-Sls)*

AUTOROLL PRINT TECHNOLOGIES

11 River St
Middleton, MA 01949-2421
Tel.: (978) 777-2160
Fax: (978) 777-7940
Toll Free: (800) 786-6598
E-mail: donna_cannatelli@autoroll.com
Web Site: www.autoroll.com
Approx. Number Employees: 15
Year Founded: 1970
Business Description:
Mfr of Printing Pads & Ink Products
S.I.C.: 3555; 2893
N.A.I.C.S.: 333293; 325910
Import Export
Advertising Expenditures: $312,500
Media: 1-2-4-7-10-11-21

Key to Media (For complete agency information see *The Advertising Red Books-Agencies* edition):
1. Bus. Publs. 2. Cable T.V. 3. Catalogs & Directories. 4. Co-op Adv. 5. Consumer Mags. 6. D.M. to Bus. Estab.7. D.M. to Consumers
8. Daily Newsp. 9. Exhibits/Trade Shows 10. Foreign 11. Infomercial 12. Internet Adv.13. Multimedia 14. Network Radio
15. Network T.V. 16. Newsp. Distr. Mags. 17. Other 18. Outdoor (Posters, Transit) 19. Point of Purchase20. Premiums, Novelties
21. Product Samples 22. Special Events Mktg. 23. Spot Radio 24. Spot T.V. 25. Weekly Newsp. 26. Yellow Page Adv.

Autoroll Print Technologies — (Continued)
Distr.: Intl.
Budget Set: Dec.
Personnel:
Clif Treco *(Exec VP)*
Mike Hess *(Mgr-Reg Sls)*
Mike Lavezzorio *(Mgr-Reg Sls)*
Brands & Products:
AUTOROLL
EXACTRA
PADFLEX

AVALON PUBLISHING GROUP, INC.
1700 4th St
Berkeley, CA 94710
Tel.: (510) 595-3664
Fax: (510) 595-4228
E-mail: info@pgw.com
Web Site: www.avalonpub.com
Sales Estimate: $20-39 Million
Approx. Number Employees: 45
Year Founded: 1994
Business Description:
Publishing
S.I.C.: 2731
N.A.I.C.S.: 511130
Advertising Expenditures: $200,000
Media: 4-13
Brands & Products:
AVALON TRAVEL
CARROLL & GRAF
FIELD PRESS
MARLOWE & CO
NATION BOOKS
SEAL PRESS
SHOEMAKER & HOARD
THUNDER'S MOUTH

B&W PRESS, INC.
401 E Main St
Georgetown, MA 01833
Tel.: (978) 352-6100
Fax: (978) 352-5955
E-mail: csr@bwpress.com
Web Site: www.bwpress.com
Sales Range: $75-99.9 Million
Approx. Number Employees: 100
Year Founded: 1966
Business Description:
Mfr. of Direct Mail Bind-in Order Form Envelopes for Catalogs, Magazines & Direct Response Specialty Format Mailers
S.I.C.: 2677; 2752
N.A.I.C.S.: 322232; 323110
Media: 2-4-13
Personnel:
Paul Beegan *(Owner)*

B. DALTON BOOKSELLER, INC.
(Div. of Barnes & Noble, Inc.)
122 5th Ave
New York, NY 10011-5605
Tel.: (212) 633-3300
Fax: (212) 675-0413
Web Site: www.barnesandnoble.com
Sales Range: $1-4.9 Billion
Approx. Number Employees: 14,000
Business Description:
Bookstores
S.I.C.: 5942
N.A.I.C.S.: 451211
Media: 9-17-18-24-26-31
Distr.: Natl.
Budget Set: July
Personnel:
Leonard Riggio *(Founder & Chm)*
Stephen Riggio *(Vice Chm & CEO)*
Joe Lombardi *(CFO)*
Chirs Troia *(CIO)*
Mark Bottini *(VP & Dir-Stores)*
Brands & Products:
B. DALTON

BABCOX PUBLICATIONS INC.
3550 Embassy Pkwy
Akron, OH 44333
Tel.: (330) 670-1234
Fax: (330) 670-0874
Web Site: www.babcox.com
Approx. Sls.: $20,000,000
Approx. Number Employees: 67
Business Description:
Publisher of Automotive Magazines
S.I.C.: 2721; 7375
N.A.I.C.S.: 511120; 518111
Media: 2-7-10
Personnel:
William E. Babcox *(Pres)*
Greg Cira *(CFO, VP & Publr)*
Dean Martin *(Reg Mgr-Sls & Assoc Publr)*
Brendan Baker *(Mng Editor-Motorcycle Product News & Sr Editor-Engine Builder)*
Amy Antenora *(Editor-aftermarketNews.com)*
Jason Stahl *(Editor)*
Brad Mitchell *(Dir-Circulation & IT)*
Jim Merle *(Reg Mgr-Sls)*
Doug Basford *(Reg Sls Mgr)*
John Hirnikl *(Production Mgr)*
Karen Kaim *(Sls Mgr-Classified)*
Chuck Balazs *(Mgr-Info Sys)*
Bob Roberts *(Mgr-Mktg Res)*
John Zick *(Mgr-West Coast)*

BAKER & TAYLOR, INC.
(Holding of Castle Harlan, Inc.)
2550 W Tyvola Rd Ste 300
Charlotte, NC 28217
Tel.: (704) 998-3100
Fax: (704) 998-3316
Toll Free: (800) 775-1800
E-mail: btinfo@btol.com
Web Site: www.btol.com
Approx. Number Employees: 2,600
Year Founded: 1828
Business Description:
Wholesale Distr of Books & Value-Added Services to Libraries & Bookstores; DVDs, Videocassettes & Audio CDs & Cassettes; Computer Software
S.I.C.: 5192; 7822
N.A.I.C.S.: 424920; 512120
Export
Media: 2-4-7
Personnel:
Thomas I. Morgan *(Chm & CEO)*
Arnie Wight *(Pres & COO)*
Jeff Leonard *(CFO)*
Matt Carroll *(CIO & Exec VP)*
David Cully *(Pres-Retail Markets & Exec VP-Mdsg & Digital Media Svcs)*
George Coe *(Pres-Library & Education)*
Robert Nelson *(Pres-Digital Grp)*
Amy Baldwin *(Mgr-Comm)*
Brian Lahlum *(Mgr-Creative Svcs)*
True Sims *(Mgr-Production-Publishing Grp)*

BAKER PUBLISHING GROUP
6030 Fulton St E
Ada, MI 49301-9106
Tel.: (616) 676-9185
Fax: (616) 676-9573
E-mail: permissions@bakerbooks.com
Web Site: www.bakerpublishinggroup.com
Approx. Number Employees: 200
Year Founded: 1939
Business Description:
Book Publishing Services
S.I.C.: 2731; 5942
N.A.I.C.S.: 511130; 451211
Import Export
Media: 10-22
Personnel:
Richard Baker *(Chm)*

THE BALTIMORE SUN COMPANY
(Sub. of Tribune Publishing Company)
(d/b/a Baltimore Sun Media Group)
501 N Calvert St
Baltimore, MD 21278
Mailing Address:
PO Box 1377
Baltimore, MD 21278-1377
Tel.: (410) 332-6000
Fax: (410) 323-2898
Toll Free: (888) 539-1280
Web Site: www.baltimoresun.com
Approx. Number Employees: 1,000
Year Founded: 1837
Business Description:
Newspaper Publisher
S.I.C.: 2711
N.A.I.C.S.: 511110
Import
Media: 1-2-3-4-5-7-8-9-10-18-19-20-21-22-23-24
Distr.: Direct to Consumer; Reg.
Budget Set: Various
Personnel:
Timothy E. Ryan *(Pres, CEO & Publr)*
J. Montgomery Cook *(Sr VP & Editor)*
Judy Berman *(Sr VP-Mktg)*
Trish Carroll *(Sr VP-Targeted Print)*
Stephen G. Seidl *(Sr VP-Ops & Tech)*
Linda Hastings *(VP-Adv)*
Michael Cross-Barnet *(Editor-OP/ED Page)*
Sarah Kelber *(Editor-Food & Blogger-Reality TV)*
Paul Krakovsky *(Dir-Interactive Sls)*
Renee Mutchnik *(Dir-Mktg & Comm)*
Brent Betts *(Mgr-Online Classified Sls)*
Anne C. Burger *(Mgr-Interactive Mktg)*
John E. McIntyre *(Mgr-Night Content Production)*
Brands & Products:
THE SUN
Advertising Agency:
MGH, Inc.
100 Painters Mill Rd Ste 600
Owings Mills, MD 21117-7305
Tel.: (410) 902-5000
Fax: (410) 902-8712

BANNER DIRECT
222 W 83rd St Ste 7G
New York, NY 10024
Tel.: (212) 737-0700
Fax: (646) 454-1124
E-mail: bdirect@bannerdirect.com
Web Site: www.bannerdirect.com
E-Mail For Key Personnel:
President: Christine@bannerdirect.com
Approx. Number Employees: 5
Year Founded: 1975
Business Description:
Publishing & Advertising Services
S.I.C.: 7389
N.A.I.C.S.: 541930
Media: 7-8-13-22
Distr.: Intl.; Natl.
Budget Set: Nov.
Personnel:
Michael Walsh *(VP-Strategy)*
Trudy Maus *(Creative Dir)*

BANTAM DELL PUBLISHING GROUP
(Group of Random House, Inc.)
1745 Broadway
New York, NY 10019
Tel.: (212) 782-9000
Fax: (212) 782-8374
Toll Free: (800) 223-6834
E-mail: webmaster@randomhouse.com
Web Site: www.randomhouse.com
Approx. Number Employees: 200
Year Founded: 1951
Business Description:
Publisher of Hardcover, Mass Market & Trade Paperback Books, General Fiction & Non-Fiction for Adults & Young Readers
S.I.C.: 2731
N.A.I.C.S.: 511130
Export
Media: 2-4-6-8-9-10-11-13-14-20-23-25
Distr.: Natl.
Personnel:
Betsey Hulsebosch *(VP, Dir-Creative Mktg & Bantam Dell)*
Brands & Products:
BANTAM DOUBLEDAY DELL
CRIMELINE
DELACORTE PRESS
DELL
DELTA
THE DIAL PRESS
DOMAIN
DTP
FANFARE
ISLAND
SPECTRA

BARKER CREEK PUBLISHING INC.
5889 State Hwy 303
Bremerton, WA 98383
Mailing Address:
PO Box 2610
Poulsbo, WA 98370
Tel.: (360) 782-9300
Fax: (877) 933-1035
Toll Free: (800) 692-5833
E-mail: customerservice@barkercreek.com
Web Site: www.barkercreek.com
E-Mail For Key Personnel:
Marketing Director: marketing@barkercreek.com
Approx. Number Employees: 10
Business Description:
Children's Educational Materials Publisher & Retailer
S.I.C.: 2731; 5961
N.A.I.C.S.: 511130; 454111

Key to Media (For complete agency information see *The Advertising Red Books-Agencies* edition):
1. Bus. Publs. 2. Cable T.V. 3. Catalogs & Directories. 4. Co-op Adv. 5. Consumer Mags. 6. D.M. to Bus. Estab.7. D.M. to Consumers 8. Daily Newsp. 9. Exhibits/Trade Shows 10. Foreign 11. Infomercial 12. Internet Adv.13. Multimedia 14. Network Radio 15. Network T.V. 16. Newsp. Distr. Mags. 17. Other 18. Outdoor (Posters, Transit) 19. Point of Purchase20. Premiums, Novelties 21. Product Samples 22. Special Events Mktg. 23. Spot Radio 24. Spot T.V. 25. Weekly Newsp. 26. Yellow Page Adv.

Media: 4-13
Personnel:
Carolyn Hurst *(CEO)*
Candy Thoresen *(Mgr-Sls & Customer Svc)*
Brands & Products:
ALL-AROUND BORDERS
BARKER CREEK
DRAW WRITE NOW
E-RACE AWAY
E-Z EDIT
EASY-2-DRAW
FARM-TASTIC
FUNCTIONAL
HAPPY HANDWRITING
KIDABC'S
KIDMATH
KIDPHONICS
KIDREAD
KIDSHAPES
KIDUSA
KIDWORDS
LASTINGLESSONS
LEARNING MAGNETS
MAGNETIC KIDBOARDS
MY RED CARRYING CASE
MY RED SORT 'N STORE CASE
MY SORT 'N STORE 5-PACK
PICK-A-POCKET
REMEMBER ME
STICKER SCHOOLHOUSE
STICKERUSA
WOWER
ZOOBILEE

BARNES & NOBLE, INC.
122 5th Ave 2nd Fl
New York, NY 10011-5605
Tel.: (212) 633-3300
Fax: (201) 559-6910
Toll Free: (800) 962-6177
E-mail: customerservice@bn.com
Web Site:
www.barnesandnobleinc.com
Approx. Sls.: $6,998,565,000
Approx. Number Employees: 35,835
Year Founded: 1971
Business Description:
Book Store Owner & Operator
S.I.C.: 5942; 2731; 5961
N.A.I.C.S.: 451211; 454111; 454113; 511130
Advertising Expenditures: $70,013,000
Media: 4-5-6-7-8-9-19-22-25
Distr.: Direct to Consumer; Reg.
Budget Set: July
Personnel:
Leonard Riggio *(Founder & Chm)*
Stephen Riggio *(Vice Chm)*
William J. Lynch, Jr. *(CEO)*
Joseph J. Lombardi *(CFO)*
Christopher Grady-Troia *(CIO)*
Jaime Carey *(Chief Mdsg Officer)*
John Foley *(Pres-E-Commerce)*
Jamie Iannone *(Pres-Digital Products)*
Mitchell S. Klipper *(CEO-Retail Grp)*
Eugene V. DeFelice *(Gen Counsel, Sec & VP)*
Mary Ellen Keating *(Sr VP-Corp Comm & Pub Affairs)*
Mark Bottini *(VP & Dir-Stores)*
Sasha Norkin *(VP-Acq Mktg, Corp & Gift Card Sls)*
Michelle Smith *(VP-HR)*
Jonathan Shar *(Gen Mgr-Digital Newsstand)*
Bob Kessler *(Reg Dir)*
Carolyn Brown *(Dir-Corp Comm)*
Miwa Messer *(Dir-Discover Great New Writers Programme)*
Andy Milevoj *(Dir-IR)*
Brands & Products:

JWT U.S.A., Inc.
(d/b/a JWT-Team Detroit)
550 Town Ctr Dr
Dearborn, MI 48126
Tel.: (313) 615-3100
Tel.: (313) 615-2000 (Team Detroit)
Fax: (313) 964-3191
Fax: (212) 615-4600

Merkley + Partners
(Sub. of Omnicom Group, Inc.)
200 Varick St
New York, NY 10014-4810
Tel.: (212) 366-3500
Fax: (212) 805-7445
Agency of Record

Mullen
40 Broad St
Boston, MA 02109
Tel.: (617) 226-9000
Fax: (617) 226-9100
Creative
Media

BARNESANDNOBLE.COM LLC
(Sub. of Barnes & Noble, Inc.)
76 9th Ave
New York, NY 10011-5201
Tel.: (212) 414-6000
Fax: (212) 414-6140
Fax: (212) 414-6171
Web Site: www.bn.com
Sales Range: $400-449.9 Million
Approx. Number Employees: 1,001
Year Founded: 1998
Business Description:
Books & Related Products Online Retailer & Marketer
S.I.C.: 5942
N.A.I.C.S.: 451211
Import
Media: 2-5-6-8-9-19-25-31
Distr.: Natl.
Budget Set: Nov.
Personnel:
Leonard Riggio *(Chm)*
Kevin M. Frain *(CFO)*
Brands & Products:
DORSET PRESS

BARRON'S
(Sub. of Dow Jones Consumer Media)
1155 Avenue of the Americas 8th Fl
New York, NY 10036-2711
Tel.: (212) 597-5945
Tel.: (212) 416-2700
Fax: (212) 597-5948
Toll Free: (800) 227-0245
E-mail: editors@barrons.com
Web Site: www.barronsmag.com
E-Mail For Key Personnel:
President: ed.finn@dowjones.com
Marketing Director: donald.black@dowjones.com
Sales Director: gary.holland@dowjones.com
Sales Range: $25-49.9 Million
Approx. Number Employees: 100
Year Founded: 1921
Business Description:
Business & Financial Publication
S.I.C.: 2721
N.A.I.C.S.: 511120
Advertising Expenditures: $4,000,000
Media: 1-2-3-6-7-8-9-10-11-13-14-15-18-19-21-22-23-24-25
Distr.: Intl.
Budget Set: Oct.
Personnel:
Edwin A. Finn, Jr. *(Pres & Editor)*
Sterling T. Shea *(Managing Director)*
Gary Holland *(Publr & VP-Adv)*
Donald E. Black *(VP-Mktg)*
Gail Griffin *(Gen Mgr-Barron's Online)*
Robin G. Blumenthal *(Editor)*
Thomas G. Donlan *(Editor-Editorial Page)*
Gene Epstein *(Editor-Economics)*
Jay Palmer *(Editor)*
Lauren R. Rublin *(Asst Mng-Editor)*
Michael Santoli *(Editor)*
Lawrence C. Strauss *(Editor)*
Sandra Ward *(Editor)*
Patricia R. Kasner *(Exec Dir)*
Paul Martin, Jr. *(Art Dir-Mktg)*
Mark Wauben *(Dir-Art)*
Diane Sipprelle *(Asst Dir-Art)*
Robert Connolly *(Assoc Dir-Art)*
James H. Balmer *(Mgr-Adv Svcs)*
Ward McGuiness *(Mgr-Adv Svcs)*
Brands & Products:
BARRON'S
Advertising Agency:
Lawrence Butner Adv., Inc.
228 E 45th St
New York, NY 10017
Tel.: (212) 338-5060
Fax: (212) 682-4586

BARRON'S EDUCATIONAL SERIES, INC.
250 Wireless Blvd
Hauppauge, NY 11788
Tel.: (631) 434-3311
Fax: (631) 434-3723
Toll Free: (800) 645-3476
E-mail: info@barronseduc.com
Web Site: www.barronseduc.com
Sales Range: $75-99.9 Million
Approx. Number Employees: 125
Year Founded: 1941
Business Description:
Book Publishing
S.I.C.: 2731; 5942
N.A.I.C.S.: 511130; 451211
Media: 10
Personnel:
Manuel H. Barron *(Chm)*
Ellen Sibley *(Pres)*

BASIC BOOKS, INC.
(Sub. of The Perseus Books Group)
387 Park Ave S 12th Fl
New York, NY 10016
Tel.: (212) 340-8164
E-mail: perseus.promos@perseusbooks.com
Web Site: www.basicbooks.com
Approx. Number Employees: 20
Year Founded: 1952
Business Description:
Publisher of Nonfiction Books
S.I.C.: 2759
N.A.I.C.S.: 323119
Media: 2-4-5-6-8-9-10-25
Distr.: Direct to Consumer; Intl.; Natl.
Budget Set: Apr.
Advertising Agency:
Verso Advertising, Inc.
50 W 17th St 5th Fl
New York, NY 10011-5702
Tel.: (212) 292-2990
Fax: (212) 557-2592

BAUER PUBLISHING USA
(Sub. of H. Bauer Publishing Ltd.)
270 Sylvan Ave
Englewood Cliffs, NJ 07632
Tel.: (201) 569-6699
Fax: (201) 569-5303
E-mail: gwelch@bauerpublishing.com
Web Site: www.bauerpublishing.com
Sales Range: $25-49.9 Million
Approx. Number Employees: 300
Business Description:
Magazine Publisher
S.I.C.: 2721
N.A.I.C.S.: 511120
Media: 6-8
Personnel:
Hubert Boehle *(Pres & CEO)*
Richard Buchert *(Sr VP-Production)*
Dennis Cohen *(Sr VP-Subscriptions & Licensing)*
Richard Teehan *(Sr VP-Fin & Admin)*

BAYARD INC.
(Holding of Bayard-Presse S.A.)
(d/b/a 23rd Publications)
(d/b/a Catholic Digest)
1 Montauk Ave Ste 200
New London, CT 06320
Mailing Address:
PO Box 6015
New London, CT 06320
Tel.: (860) 437-3012
Fax: (860) 437-3013
Toll Free: (800) 321-0411
Web Site: www.bayard-inc.com
Approx. Number Employees: 50
Year Founded: 1936
Business Description:
Publisher of Magazines & Books
S.I.C.: 7371
N.A.I.C.S.: 541511
Advertising Expenditures: $3,500,000
Media: 4-8-10-13-21
Distr.: Direct to Consumer; Natl.
Budget Set: June
Personnel:
Daniel Connors *(Editor-in-Chief)*
Thomas M. Rickert *(Dir-Adv Sls)*
Karen Reed *(Dir-Customer Svc)*
Brands & Products:
CATHOLIC DIGEST
CATHOLIC DIGEST LARGE PRINT READER
GODS WORD TODAY
Advertising Agency:
Rickert Media
2632 W 44th Ste 4
Minneapolis, MN 55410
Tel.: (612) 920-0050
Fax: (612) 920-0051

THE BEACON
(Unit of GateHouse Media New England)
150 Baker Ave Ext Ste 101
Concord, MA 01742
Tel.: (978) 263-4736
Fax: (978) 371-5711
E-mail: beacon@cnc.com

Key to Media (For complete agency information see *The Advertising Red Books-Agencies* edition):
1. Bus. Publs. 2. Cable T.V. 3. Catalogs & Directories. 4. Co-op Adv. 5. Consumer Mags. 6. D.M. to Bus. Estab.7. D.M. to Consumers
8. Daily Newsp. 9. Exhibits/Trade Shows 10. Foreign 11. Infomercial 12. Internet Adv.13. Multimedia 14. Network Radio
15. Network T.V. 16. Newsp. Distr. Mags. 17. Other 18. Outdoor (Posters, Transit) 19. Point of Purchase20. Premiums, Novelties
21. Product Samples 22. Special Events Mktg. 23. Spot Radio 24. Spot T.V. 25. Weekly Newsp. 26. Yellow Page Adv.

The Beacon — (Continued)

Web Site: www.wickedlocal.com/acton
Sales Range: $25-49.9 Million
Approx. Number Employees: 60
Business Description:
Newspaper Publisher
S.I.C.: 2711
N.A.I.C.S.: 511110
Media: 25
Personnel:
Chuck Goodrich *(Publr)*
Brian Briggs *(VP-Adv)*
Anne Marie Magerman *(Dir-Adv)*
Mike Bentle *(Mgr-Sls)*
Pamela Calder *(Mgr-Display Adv)*
Linda Vahey *(Mgr-Circulation)*
Brands & Products:
THE BEACON

THE BEACON JOURNAL PUBLISHING COMPANY
(Sub. of Black Press Group Ltd.)
44 E Exchange St
Akron, OH 44309
Tel.: (330) 996-3000
Fax: (330) 996-3033
Fax: (330) 572-2830
Web Site: www.ohio.com
Approx. Number Employees: 624
Year Founded: 1839
Business Description:
Newspaper Publisher
S.I.C.: 2711
N.A.I.C.S.: 511110
Media: 2-3-9-16-18-20-22-23-24-26
Distr.: Direct to Consumer; Reg.
Personnel:
Black David *(Pres)*

BEDFORD MINUTEMAN
(Unit of GateHouse Media New England)
150 Baker Ave Ext Ste 101
Concord, MA 01742
Tel.: (781) 275-7204
Fax: (978) 371-5220
E-mail: bedford@cnc.com
Web Site: www.wickedlocal.com
Sales Range: $10-24.9 Million
Approx. Number Employees: 50
Business Description:
Newspaper Publisher
S.I.C.: 2711
N.A.I.C.S.: 511110
Media: 25
Personnel:
Chris Klingenberg *(Editor-Sports)*
Mike Murphy *(Mgr-Display Adv)*
Linda Vahey *(Mgr-Circulation)*

BELL-MARK CORPORATION
331 Changebridge Rd
Pine Brook, NJ 07058
Tel.: (973) 882-0202
Fax: (973) 882-4910
E-mail: info@bell-mark.com
Web Site: www.bell-mark.com
Sales Range: $75-99.9 Million
Approx. Number Employees: 100
Business Description:
Coding, Printing & Marking Solutions for Packaging & Converting Industries Designer & Mfr
S.I.C.: 5084; 5112
N.A.I.C.S.: 423830; 424120
Media: 2-10-13
Personnel:
John Marozzi *(Pres)*
James Pontrella *(CFO)*
Doug Duch *(Mgr-Mktg)*
Brands & Products:
BELL-MARK
EASYPRINT
FLEXO
FLEXPRINT
INTELIJET
KWIKLOK

BELMONT CITIZEN-HERALD
(Unit of GateHouse Media New England)
9 Meriam St
Lexington, MA 02420
Tel.: (617) 484-2633
Fax: (781) 674-7735
E-mail: belmont@cnc.com
Web Site: www.wickedlocal.com/belmont
Sales Range: $10-24.9 Million
Approx. Number Employees: 40
Business Description:
Newspaper Publisher
S.I.C.: 2711
N.A.I.C.S.: 511110
Media: 19-25
Personnel:
Chuck Goodrich *(Publr)*
Mike Liuzza *(Editor-Sports)*
Anne Eisenmenger *(Mgr-Website)*
Linda Vahey *(Mgr-Circulation)*

BELVOIR PUBLICATIONS INC.
800 Connecticut Ave
Norwalk, CT 06854
Tel.: (203) 857-3100
Fax: (203) 857-3103
E-mail: customer_service@belvoir.com
Web Site: www.belvoir.com
Approx. Number Employees: 348
Year Founded: 1971
Business Description:
Publisher of Books, Videos & Web Sites
S.I.C.: 2721; 2731
N.A.I.C.S.: 511120; 511130
Import Export
Media: 2-6-8-10
Personnel:
Robert Englander *(Chm, CEO & Principal)*
Ron Goldberg *(CFO)*
Tom Canfield *(Principal & VP-Circulation)*
Timothy H. Cole *(Exec VP)*
Greg King *(Sr VP-Circulation)*
Brands & Products:
ANTIQUES ROADSHOW INSIDER
ARTHRITIS ADVISOR
AVWEB
BOATBUILDER
CATWATCH
DOGWATCH
HEART ADVISOR
KITCHEN & COOK
MARY ENGELBREIT'S HOME COMPANION
MARYJANESFARM
SPIN TO WIN
THE TRAIL RIDER
WHOLE DOG JOURNAL

THE BENNINGTON BANNER
(Unit of MediaNews Group, Inc.)
425 Main St
Bennington, VT 05201
Tel.: (802) 447-2025
Fax: (802) 442-3413
E-mail: news@benningtonbanner.com
Web Site:
www.benningtonbanner.com
Approx. Number Employees: 60
Business Description:
Newspaper Publisher
S.I.C.: 2711
N.A.I.C.S.: 511110
Media: 8-9
Personnel:
Jim Therrien *(Editor)*
Cris Oldham *(Dir-Cust Svcs)*

BERNARD C. HARRIS PUBLISHING CO., INC.
2500 Westchester Ave Ste 400
Purchase, NY 10577
Tel.: (914) 641-3500
Toll Free: (800) 326-6600
E-mail: moreinfo@bcharrispub.com
Web Site: www.bcharrispub.com
Sales Range: $100-124.9 Million
Approx. Number Employees: 2,000
Year Founded: 1963
Business Description:
Alumni Directories
S.I.C.: 2741
N.A.I.C.S.: 511140; 511199
Advertising Expenditures: $1,000,000
Media: 4-8-13-20
Personnel:
Thomas K. Burke *(CFO)*
Susan L. D'Agostino *(Sr VP-Ops & Admin)*
Don Ross *(Sr VP)*
Al Phipps *(VP-Controller-Gen Mgr-Ops)*

BEST PERSONALIZED BOOKS, INC.
Best Plz 4201 Airborn Dr
Addison, TX 75001
Tel.: (972) 250-1000
Fax: (972) 930-1010
E-mail: admin@bestpress.com
Web Site:
www.bestpersonalizedbooks.com
Sales Range: $10-24.9 Million
Approx. Number Employees: 100
Business Description:
Book Publisher
S.I.C.: 2731
N.A.I.C.S.: 511130
Media: 6
Personnel:
Jack Kalisher *(Pres)*

BETTER HOMES & GARDENS BOOKS
(Div. of Meredith Publishing Group)
1716 Locust St
Des Moines, IA 50309-3023
Tel.: (515) 284-3000
Fax: (515) 284-2700
Web Site: www.bhg.com
Sales Range: $25-49.9 Million
Approx. Number Employees: 90
Business Description:
Magazine Publisher
S.I.C.: 2721
N.A.I.C.S.: 511120
Media: 2-6-8-13-14-15-25
Personnel:
Gayle Butler *(Editor-in-Chief)*

BEVERLY CITIZEN
(Unit of GateHouse Media New England)
72 Cherry Hill Dr
Beverly, MA 01915
Tel.: (978) 739-8543
Fax: (978) 739-8501
E-mail: beverly@cnc.com
Web Site: www.wickedlocal.com/beverly
Sales Range: $10-24.9 Million
Approx. Number Employees: 4
Business Description:
Newspaper Publisher
S.I.C.: 2711
N.A.I.C.S.: 511110
Media: 9
Personnel:
Charles Goodrich *(Publr)*
Chris Hurley *(Editor-Sports)*
Peter Chiana *(Mgr-Website)*
Dena Lisle *(Mgr-Display Adv)*
Brands & Products:
BEVERLY CITIZEN NEWSPAPER

BILLERICA MINUTEMAN
(Unit of GateHouse Media New England)
150 Baker Ave Ext Ste 101
Concord, MA 01742
Tel.: (978) 667-2156
Fax: (978) 371-5212
E-mail: billerica@cnc.com
Web Site: www.wickedlocal.com/billerica
Sales Range: $10-24.9 Million
Approx. Number Employees: 50
Business Description:
Newspaper Publisher
S.I.C.: 2711
N.A.I.C.S.: 511110
Media: 8-9-25
Personnel:
Chuck Goodrich *(Publr)*
Max Bowen *(Editor-News)*
Doug Hastings *(Editor-Sports)*
Linda Vahey *(Mgr-Circulation)*

THE BIOGRAPHY CHANNEL
(Joint Venture of Comcast Corporation, The Walt Disney Company, General Electric Company & The Hearst Corporation)
235 E 45th St Ste 1104
New York, NY 10017-3303
Tel.: (212) 649-4099
Tel.: (212) 210-1400
Fax: (212) 210-1326
Web Site: www.biography.com
Sales Range: $10-24.9 Million
Approx. Number Employees: 30
Business Description:
Biographical Programming Cable Network
S.I.C.: 4841
N.A.I.C.S.: 515210
Media: 3-6-10-13
Personnel:
Robert DeBitetto *(Pres & Gen Mgr)*
Thomas Moody *(Sr VP-Programming Plng & Acq)*
John Hartinger *(Head-Mktg)*
Peter Tarshis *(Head-Programming)*
Ronald Gross *(Dir-Art)*
Scott Monte *(Dir-Adv-Eastern)*

Key to Media (For complete agency information see *The Advertising Red Books-Agencies* edition):
1. Bus. Publs. 2. Cable T.V. 3. Catalogs & Directories. 4. Co-op Adv. 5. Consumer Mags. 6. D.M. to Bus. Estab.7. D.M. to Consumers 8. Daily Newsp. 9. Exhibits/Trade Shows 10. Foreign 11. Infomercial 12. Internet Adv.13. Multimedia 14. Network Radio 15. Network T.V. 16. Newsp. Distr. Mags. 17. Other 18. Outdoor (Posters, Transit) 19. Point of Purchase20. Premiums, Novelties 21. Product Samples 22. Special Events Mktg. 23. Spot Radio 24. Spot T.V. 25. Weekly Newsp. 26. Yellow Page Adv.

Brands & Products:
BIOGRAPHY

BIZBASH MEDIA INC.
21 W 38th St 13th Fl
New York, NY 10018
Tel.: (646) 638-3600
Fax: (646) 638-3601
Web Site: www.bizbash.com
Approx. Rev.: $8,900,000
Approx. Number Employees: 56
Year Founded: 2000
Business Description:
Trade Media for The Event Industry
S.I.C.: 2721; 2741
N.A.I.C.S.: 511120; 511199
Media: 10-22
Personnel:
David Adler *(Founder & CEO)*
Richard Aaron *(Pres)*
Robert Fitzgerald *(Sr VP-Sls & Mktg)*
Lisa Cericola *(Editor-Style)*
Ted Kruckel *(Editor-Large & Columnist)*
Anna Sekula *(Assoc Editor)*
Courtney Thompson *(Editor-News)*
Joey Bouchard *(Dir-Art)*
Sheryl Olaskowitz *(Dir-Events & Tradeshows)*

THE BLADE CO.
(Div. of Block Communications, Inc.)
541 N Superior St
Toledo, OH 43660-1000
Tel.: (419) 724-6000
Fax: (419) 724-6080
Toll Free: (800) 245-3311
E-mail: circulation@toledoblade.com
Web Site: www.toledoblade.com
Approx. Number Employees: 650
Year Founded: 1835
Business Description:
Newspaper Publishing
S.I.C.: 2711
N.A.I.C.S.: 511110
Media: 3-7-8-10-13-18-19-20-21-22-23-24-26
Distr.: Direct to Consumer; Reg.
Personnel:
William Block *(Chm)*
Joseph Zerbey *(Pres & Gen Mgr)*
John R. Block *(Editor-in-Chief)*
Kendall Downs *(Editor-Copy)*
Dennis Bova *(Editor-News)*
Greg Braknis *(Editor-Bus)*
Sue Brickey *(Editor-Copy)*
Bob Cunningham *(Web Editor)*
Heather Dennis *(Editor-Copy)*
Brian Dugger *(Editor-Copy)*
Tony Durham *(Editor-News)*
Barbara Hendel *(Editor-Society)*
Dennis Horger *(Editor-Copy)*
Doug Koerner *(Editor-Copy)*
Martin Kruse *(Editor-Picture)*
Jim Kwiatkowski *(Editor-Copy)*
Alan Ponzio *(Editor-Copy)*
Tom Quinn *(Editor-Copy)*
Rose Russell *(Editor)*
Jim Sielicki *(Editor-Copy)*
Chet Sullwold *(Editor-Copy)*
Elisa Tomaszewski *(Editor-Copy)*
Chip Towns *(Asst Editor-Sports)*
Todd Wetzler *(Editor-Copy)*
David Yonke *(Editor-Religion)*
Wes Booher *(Dir-Art)*
John Crisp *(Dir-Sls, Mktg & New Media)*
Malcolm Edge *(Dir-IT)*
Richard Fuller *(Dir-Circulation)*
Michael Mori *(Dir-Adv)*
David Shutt *(Dir-Editorial)*
Tom Sutherland *(Mgr-Adv Svcs & Supvr-PrePress)*
Jeff Cole *(Mgr-City Home Delivery)*
Betsy Kenniston *(Mgr-Single Copy)*
Shelly Kowalski *(Mgr-Adv Ops & Dev)*
Mark Peddicord *(Mgr-Mktg)*
Jeff Pezzano *(Mgr-Retail Adv)*
Ron Shnider *(Mgr-Sls Devel)*
Brad Vriezelaar *(Mgr-New Media)*
Brands & Products:
THE BLADE

BLISS COMMUNICATIONS INC.
1 S Parker Dr
Janesville, WI 53545-3928
Tel.: (608) 755-8220
E-mail: sbliss@gazettextra.com
Web Site: www.gazetteextra.com
Sales Range: $25-49.9 Million
Approx. Number Employees: 525
Year Founded: 1845
Business Description:
Newspapers
S.I.C.: 2711; 4832
N.A.I.C.S.: 511110; 515112
Media: 8-9-13-18-23-24
Personnel:
Sidney H. Bliss *(Pres & Chm)*
Robert Lisser *(CFO, Sec & VP)*

BLOCK COMMUNICATIONS, INC.
405 Madison Ave, Ste 2100
Toledo, OH 43604
Tel.: (419) 724-6448
Tel.: (419) 724-6212
Fax: (419) 724-6167
Web Site:
www.blockcommunications.com
Sales Range: $400-449.9 Million
Approx. Number Employees: 2,000
Year Founded: 1900
Business Description:
Newspaper Publisher; Television Broadcasting; Advertising Distr
S.I.C.: 2711; 4841
N.A.I.C.S.: 511110; 515210
Media: 8-9-16-17-18
Distr.: Direct to Consumer; Reg.
Personnel:
John R. Block *(Vice Chm & Dir-Editorial)*
Jodi L. Miehls *(CFO)*
Brands & Products:
THE BLADE
PITTSBURGH POST-GAZETTE

BLOOMBERG BUSINESSWEEK
(Sub. of Bloomberg L.P.)
1221 Ave of the Americas Ste C3A
New York, NY 10020-1001
Tel.: (212) 512-6704
Web Site: www.businessweek.com
Sales Range: $50-74.9 Million
Approx. Number Employees: 200
Year Founded: 1929
Business Description:
Business Magazine
S.I.C.: 2721
N.A.I.C.S.: 511120
Advertising Expenditures: $2,000,000
Media: 2-7-9-17
Distr.: Natl.
Personnel:
Paul Bascobert *(Pres)*
Norman Pearlstine *(Chief Content Officer)*
Geoffrey A. Dodge *(VP-Publr-North America)*
Hugh Wiley *(Publr)*
Josh Tyrangiel *(Editor)*
Hugo Lindgren *(Exec Editor)*
James E. Ellis *(Asst Mng Editor)*
Aida Rosario *(Editorial Office Mgr)*
Ken Machlin-Lockwood *(Mgr-Editorial Ops)*
Robin Ajello *(Assoc Editor)*
Spencer A. Ante *(Editor-Computers)*
Adam Aston *(Editor-Energy & Environment)*
Susan Berfield *(Assoc Editor)*
Rose Brady *(Editor)*
Adrienne Carter *(Editor-Fin)*
Maria Chapin *(Copy Editor)*
Gail Fowler *(Copy Editor)*
Mark Hyman *(Editor-Sports)*
Frederick F. Jespersen *(Editor-Scoreboards)*
Mindy Katzman *(Photo Editor)*
Louis Lavelle *(Editor)*
Cristina Lindblad *(Editor)*
Harry Maurer *(Editor-Latin America Economy-Bloomberg LP)*
Marc Miller *(Deputy Copy Editor)*
Kathleen Moore *(Sr Photo Editor)*
Anne Newman *(Editor-Copy)*
Peter K. Niceberg *(Editor-Production)*
Bruce Nussbaum *(Editor-Innovation)*
Eric Pooley *(Editor)*
David Purcell *(Editor)*
David Rocks *(Sr Editor)*
Doug Royalty *(Sr Copy Editor)*
Jim Taibi *(Deputy Copy Editor)*
Steven Taylor *(Editor-Bloomberg News)*
Anne Tergesen *(Assoc Editor)*
Don Besom *(Assoc Art Dir)*
Dan Beucke *(Dir-News)*
Christian Corser *(Dir-Sls Dev-Special Ad Sections)*
Susan Fingerhut *(Dir-Editorial Ops)*
Susannah Harte *(Dir-Events & Brand Dev)*
Patrice Serret *(Dir-Market Dev-Education Sls)*
Ronnie Weil *(Dir-Photo)*
Ron Plyman *(Assoc Dir-Art)*
Patti Straus *(Assoc Dir-Comm)*
Heather Carpenter *(Sr Mgr-Comm)*
Susann Rutledge *(Deputy Mgr-Info Svcs)*
Maryanne Ventrice *(Mgr-Sls Dev)*
Veronica Wronski *(Coord-Integrated Sls)*

BOBIT BUSINESS MEDIA
3520 Challenger St
Torrance, CA 90503
Tel.: (310) 533-2400
Fax: (310) 533-2500
E-mail: webmaster@bobit.com
Web Site: www.bobit.com
Approx. Number Employees: 150
Year Founded: 1961
Business Description:
Business Magazine Publishing Services
S.I.C.: 2721; 7231
N.A.I.C.S.: 511120; 812112
Media: 2-10
Personnel:
Ed Bobit *(Chm)*
Ty F. Bobit *(Pres & CEO)*
Richard Johnson *(CFO)*
Christine Strain *(Dir-Acctg)*
Katie Fillingame *(Mgr-Audience Mktg)*
Brands & Products:
AUTO RENTAL NEWS
AUTO TRIM & RESTYLING
AUTOMOTIVE FLEET
BUSINESS DRIVER
BUSINESS FLEET
DEATH ROW
FLEET ASSOCIATION DIRECTORY
FLEET FINANCIALS
GOVERNMENT FLEET
LIMOUSINE AND CHAUFFEURED TRANSPORTATION
METRO
MOBILE ELECTRONICS
MODERN TIRE DEALER
NAILS
POLICE
SCHOOL BUS FLEET
SECURITY PRESS
SECURITY SALES & INTEGRATION
Advertising Agency:
Newman Grace Inc.
6133 Fallbrook Ave
Woodland Hills, CA 91367
Tel.: (818) 713-1678
Fax: (818) 999-6314

BON APPETIT MAGAZINE
(Unit of Conde Nast Publications, Inc.)
6300 Wilshire Blvd
Los Angeles, CA 90048
Mailing Address:
Four Times Sq
New York, NY 10036-6518
Tel.: (323) 965-3600
Fax: (323) 937-1206
Web Site: www.bonappetit.com
Approx. Number Employees: 1,500
Business Description:
Food & Entertaining Magazine
S.I.C.: 2721
N.A.I.C.S.: 511120
Media: 6-8-22
Distr.: Direct to Consumer; Natl.
Personnel:
Heather John *(Sr Editor)*
Martha Lipman Simon *(Editor-Online)*
Eileen M. McCarthy *(Exec Dir-Mktg & Strategic Plng)*
Mayellen W. Mooney *(Dir-Creative Mktg)*
Thomas Kramer *(Dir-Adv Svcs)*
Dara O'Brien *(Dir-Mktg)*
Laurie Keller *(Sr Mgr-Mktg)*
Lauren Saunders *(Coord-Adv)*
Cat Cora *(Exec Chef)*
Advertising Agency:
M. Young Communications
77 5th Ave 2nd Fl
New York, NY 10003
Tel.: (212) 620-7027
Fax: (212) 645-3654

BONITA BANNER NEWPAPER INC.
(Sub. of The E.W. Scripps Company)
26381 S Tamiami Trl Ste 116
Bonita Springs, FL 34134-4214
Mailing Address:
PO Box 40
Bonita Springs, FL 34133-0040
Tel.: (239) 213-6000
Fax: (239) 263-4816
E-mail: info@bonitanews.com

Key to Media (For complete agency information see *The Advertising Red Books-Agencies* edition):
1. Bus. Publs. 2. Cable T.V. 3. Catalogs & Directories. 4. Co-op Adv. 5. Consumer Mags. 6. D.M. to Bus. Estab.7. D.M. to Consumers 8. Daily Newsp. 9. Exhibits/Trade Shows 10. Foreign 11. Infomercial 12. Internet Adv.13. Multimedia 14. Network Radio 15. Network T.V. 16. Newsp. Distr. Mags. 17. Other 18. Outdoor (Posters, Transit) 19. Point of Purchase20. Premiums, Novelties 21. Product Samples 22. Special Events Mktg. 23. Spot Radio 24. Spot T.V. 25. Weekly Newsp. 26. Yellow Page Adv.

Bonita Banner Newpaper Inc. — (Continued)

Web Site: www.bonitanews.com
Sales Range: $25-49.9 Million
Approx. Number Employees: 40
Business Description:
Daily Newspaper Publishing
S.I.C.: 2711; 2741
N.A.I.C.S.: 511110; 511199
Media: 7-8-9
Personnel:
Dave O'Neil *(Acting Publr)*

BONNIER ACTIVE MEDIA, INC.
(Div. of Bonnier Corporation)
2 Park Ave 9th Fl
New York, NY 10016-5675
Tel.: (212) 779-5000
Fax: (212) 779-5599
Web Site: www.bonniercorp.com
E-Mail For Key Personnel:
Sales Director: bruce.revman@tmm.com
Approx. Number Employees: 700
Business Description:
Magazine & Internet Publisher
S.I.C.: 2721; 2741
N.A.I.C.S.: 511120; 516110
Media: 2-6-7-8-10-13-18-19-20
Distr.: Natl.
Personnel:
Wendi S. Berger *(Assoc Publr-Publications)*
George Sass, Jr. *(Editor-in-Chief)*
Slaton L. White *(Editor-SHOT Business)*
Brands & Products:
BMXONLINE.COM
FIELD & STREAM
FIELDANDSTREAM.COM
FREEZE
FREEZEONLINE.COM
GOLF MAGAZINE
GOLF MAGAZINE.COM
GOLFONLINE.COM
MOTORBOATING
MOTORBOATING.COM
OUTDOOR LIFE
OUTDOORLIFE.COM
POPSCI.COM
POPULAR SCIENCE
RIDE BMX
SALT WATER SPORTSMAN
SALTWATERSPORTSMAN.COM
SKATEBOARDING.COM
SKI
SKIING
SKIINGMAG.COM
SKIMAG.COM
SKINET.COM
THIS OLD HOUSE
THISOLDHOUSE.ORG
TIME4 MEDIA
TODAYSHOMEOWNER.COM
TRANSWORLD BMX
TRANSWORLD MOTOCROSS
TRANSWORLD SKATEBOARDING
TRANSWORLD SNOWBOARDING
TRANSWORLD SURF
TRANSWORLDMOTOCROSS.COM
TRANSWORLDSNOWBOARDING.COM
TRANSWORLDSURF.COM
YACHTING
YACHTINGNET.COM

BONNIER CORPORATION
(Sub. of Bonnier Magazine Group AB)
460 N Orlando Ave Ste 200
Winter Park, FL 32789
Tel.: (407) 628-4802
Fax: (407) 628-7061
Web Site: www.bonniercorp.com
Sales Range: $350-399.9 Million
Approx. Number Employees: 1,200
Business Description:
Magazine Publisher
S.I.C.: 2721; 2741
N.A.I.C.S.: 511120; 516110
Media: 6-8
Personnel:
Jonas Bonnier *(Chm)*
Terry Snow *(CEO)*
Randall Koubek *(CFO)*
Dan Altman *(COO)*
Jeremy Thompson *(Gen Counsel)*
Eric Zinczenko *(VP & Grp Publr-Outdoor)*
Scott Salyers *(Publr-Fishing)*
Mark Wildman *(Sr VP-Corp Sls & Mktg)*
Gregg Hano *(VP & Grp Publr-Tech)*
Cathy Hertz *(VP-HR)*
Dean Turcol *(VP-Corp Comm)*
Lori Barbely *(Editor-Photo)*
John Miller *(Brand Dir)*
Leigh Bingham *(Dir-Subscription)*
Diane G. Potter *(Dir-Consumer Mktg)*
Dean Psarakis *(Dir-Bus-Consumer Mktg)*
David Weaver *(Dir-Art)*
Peter Winn *(Dir-Plng & Dev & Consumer Mktg)*
Brands & Products:
BABYTALK
BOATING LIFE
CARIBBEAN TRAVEL & LIFE
CRUISING WORLD
DESTINATION WEDDINGS & HONEYMOONS
FIELD & STREAM
FLORIDA TRAVEL & LIFE
FLY FISHING IN SALT WATERS
GARDEN DESIGN
HOME FT. LAUDERDALE
HOME MIAMI
ISLANDS
KITEBOARDING
MARLIN
MEETING TRAVELER
MOTOCROSS
MOTOR BOATING
NEWBOATS.COM
OUTDOOR LIFE
PARENTING
POPULAR SCIENCE
POWER CRUISING
QUAD OFF ROAD
RESORTS & GREAT HOTELS
RIDEBMX
SAILING WORLD
SALT WATER SPORTSMAN
SAVEUR
SCIENCE ILLUSTRATED
SHOT BUSINESS
SKI
SKIING
SNOW
SPA
SPORT DIVER
SPORT FISHING
TRANSWORLD BUSINESS
TRANSWORLD MOTOCROSS
TRANSWORLD RIDE BMX
TRANSWORLD SKATEBOARDING
TRANSWORLD SNOWBOARDING
TRANSWORLD SURF
USEDBOATS.COM
WAKEBOARDING
WARREN MILLER ENTERTAINMENT
WATERSKI
WINDSURFING
WORLD ENTERTAINMENT SERVICES
WORLD SPORTS & MARKETING
YACHTBROKER.COM
YACHTING

BOOK-OF-THE-MONTH CLUB, INC.
(Sub. of Bookspan)
501 Franklin Ave
Garden City, NY 11530
Tel.: (516) 490-4561
Fax: (516) 490-4714
Web Site: www.bomc.com
Approx. Sls.: $200,000,000
Approx. Number Employees: 850
Year Founded: 1926
Business Description:
Book Publishing & Production
S.I.C.: 5961
N.A.I.C.S.: 454113
Media: 2-6-7-8-9-25
Distr.: Direct to Consumer; Natl.
Budget Set: Sept.
Personnel:
Linda Andersen *(Sr VP-Mktg)*
Brands & Products:
COOKING & CRAFTS BOOK CLUB
FORTUNE BOOK CLUB

BOOKAZINE COMPANY, INC.
75 Hook Rd
Bayonne, NJ 07002-5006
Tel.: (201) 339-7777
Fax: (201) 339-7778
Toll Free: (800) 221-8112
E-mail: inquire@bookazine.com
Web Site: www.bookazine.com
Approx. Number Employees: 170
Year Founded: 1928
Business Description:
Book & Catalog Publisher
S.I.C.: 5192; 2741
N.A.I.C.S.: 424920; 511199
Media: 4-8-10-13-22
Personnel:
Robert Kallman *(Pres & CEO)*
Andrew Collings *(VP-Mdsg)*
Cindy Raiton *(VP, Sls)*
Kathleen Willoughby *(VP-Mktg & Online Dev)*
Brands & Products:
BOOKAZINE

BOOKS-A-MILLION, INC.
402 Industrial Ln
Birmingham, AL 35211-4465
Mailing Address:
PO Box 19768
Birmingham, AL 35219-9768
Tel.: (205) 942-3737
Fax: (205) 942-6601
Toll Free: (800) 201-3550
Web Site: www.bamm.com
Approx. Rev.: $494,963,000
Approx. Number Employees: 2,600
Year Founded: 1917
Business Description:
Book Retailer
S.I.C.: 5942
N.A.I.C.S.: 451211
Import
Advertising Expenditures: $3,500,000
Media: 2-4-5-8-9-18-19-22-23-25-26
Distr.: Reg.
Budget Set: Oct.
Personnel:
Clyde B. Anderson *(Chm & CEO)*
Terrance G. Finley *(Pres & COO)*
Brian W. White *(CFO)*
Douglas G. Markham *(Chief Admin Officer, Sec & Exec VP)*
Tyler Novak *(Gen Counsel)*
James F. Turner *(Exec VP-Real Estate & Bus Dev)*
Aaron Jarrells *(Gen Mgr-Blacksburg)*
Brands & Products:
BAMM
BOOKLAND
BOOKS-A-MILLION
BOOKS & CO
HOLD THAT THOUGHT
JOE MUGGS
KIDS-A-MILLION
MILLIONAIRES' CLUB
SWEET WATER PRESS
THANKS A MILLION

BOOKSPAN
(Div. of Direct Brands, Inc.)
501 Franklin Ave
Garden City, NY 11530-5945
Tel.: (516) 490-4561
Fax: (516) 490-4714
Web Site: www.bookspan.com
E-Mail For Key Personnel:
President: markus.wilhelm@bookspan.com
Marketing Director: lucia.coffey@bookspan.com
Approx. Sls.: $401,900,000
Approx. Number Employees: 2,300
Year Founded: 1930
Business Description:
Mail Order Book Club Operator; Owned 50% by Bertelsmann AG & 50% by Time Warner Inc.
S.I.C.: 5961
N.A.I.C.S.: 454113
Media: 2-3-5-6-8-9-13-14-16-22-23-25
Distr.: Natl.
Personnel:
Brigitte Weeks *(Pres)*
Carole Baron *(Sr VP & Dir-Publ)*
Walter Gross *(Sr VP-Distr)*
Sean Buckley *(Dir-Credit)*
Brands & Products:
AMERICAN COMPASS
ARCHITECTS & DESIGNERS BOOK SERVICE
BEHAVIORAL SCIENCE BOOK SERVICE
BLACK EXPRESSIONS
BOOK-OF-THE-MONTH CLUB
CHILDREN'S BOOK-OF-THE-MONTH CLUB
CIRCULO
COMPUTER BOOKS DIRECT
CRAFTER'S CHOICE
THE DISCOVERY CHANNEL
DOUBLEDAY BOOK CLUB
DOUBLEDAY LARGE PRINT HOME LIBRARY

Key to Media (For complete agency information see *The Advertising Red Books-Agencies* edition):
1. Bus. Publs. 2. Cable T.V. 3. Catalogs & Directories. 4. Co-op Adv. 5. Consumer Mags. 6. D.M. to Bus. Estab.7. D.M. to Consumers 8. Daily Newsp. 9. Exhibits/Trade Shows 10. Foreign 11. Infomercial 12. Internet Adv.13. Multimedia 14. Network Radio 15. Network T.V. 16. Newsp. Distr. Mags. 17. Other 18. Outdoor (Posters, Transit) 19. Point of Purchase20. Premiums, Novelties 21. Product Samples 22. Special Events Mktg. 23. Spot Radio 24. Spot T.V. 25. Weekly Newsp. 26. Yellow Page Adv.

EARLY CHILDHOOD TEACHER'S CLUB
EQUESTRIAN'S EDGE
THE GOOD COOK
HISTORY BOOK CLUB
HOMESTYLE BOOKS
INSIGHTOUT BOOK CLUB
KIDS BOOK PLANET
THE LIBRARY OF SPEECH-LANGUAGE PATHOLOGY
THE LITERARY GUILD
THE MILITARY BOOK CLUB
MOSAICO
MYSTERY GUILD
NURSE'S BOOK SOCIETY
ONE SPIRIT
OUTDOORSMAN'S EDGE
PRIMARY TEACHERS' BOOK CLUB
QUALITY PAPERBACK BOOK CLUB
THE READERS' SUBSCRIPTION
RHAPSODY
THE SCIENCE FICTION BOOK CLUB
SCIENTIFIC AMERICAN BOOK CLUB
SMART READER REWARDS
STEPHEN KING LIBRARY
ZOOBA

BOOTH NEWSPAPERS, INC.

(Sub. of Advance Publications, Inc.)
St 155 Michigan NW
Grand Rapids, MI 49503
Mailing Address:
PO Box 2168
Grand Rapids, MI 49501
Tel.: (616) 222-5825
Fax: (616) 222-5390
Web Site:
www.boothnewspapers.com
Sales Range: $10-24.9 Million
Approx. Number Employees: 25
Business Description:
Newspapers Publisher
S.I.C.: 2711
N.A.I.C.S.: 511110
Media: 7-8-9-10-18
Distr.: Reg.
Budget Set: Oct.
Personnel:
Tricia Berkompas *(Coord-Adv-Sls)*
Michael Ply *(Controller, Dir-Fin & HR)*
Larry Dodge *(Dir-Sls & Mktg)*
Kim Brown *(Sls Mgr-Adv)*
Vicki McReynolds *(Mgr-Recruitment Adv)*
Dan Sippel *(Mgr-Travel Adv)*
Tanya Fair *(Supvr-Adv Support)*
Brands & Products:
THE ANN ARBOR NEWS
THE BAY CITY TIMES
THE FLINT JOURNAL
THE GRAND RAPIDS PRESS
THE JACKSON CITIZEN PATRIOT
THE KALAMAZOO GAZETTE
THE MUSKEGON CHRONICLE
THE SAGINAW NEWS

BORDERS, INC.

(Sub. of Borders Group, Inc.)
100 Phoenix Dr
Ann Arbor, MI 48108-2202
Tel.: (734) 477-1100
Fax: (734) 477-1633
Web Site: www.borders.com
Sales Range: $1-4.9 Billion
Approx. Number Employees: 800
Year Founded: 1971
Business Description:
Book, Music & Video Superstores
S.I.C.: 5942; 5192
N.A.I.C.S.: 451211; 424920
Advertising Expenditures: $10,000,000
Media: 6-8-9-13-14-19-23-25-31
Advertising Agency:
Brierley & Partners
8401 N Central Expy Ste 1000 LB-37
Dallas, TX 75225-4403
Tel.: (214) 760-8700
Fax: (214) 743-5511

BOSTON COMMON PRESS, L.P.

(d/b/a America's Test Kitchen)
17 Station St
Brookline, MA 02445
Tel.: (617) 232-1000
Fax: (617) 232-1572
Web Site:
www.americastestkitchen.com
Business Description:
Publisher of Cooking Related Materials
S.I.C.: 2741; 2721; 2731
N.A.I.C.S.: 516110; 511120; 511130
Media: 15
Personnel:
Christopher Kimball *(Founder)*
Eliot Wadsworth *(Mng Partner & Dir)*
Sharyn Shabot *(CFO)*
Brands & Products:
COOK'S COUNTRY MAGAZINE
COOK'S ILLUSTRATED

THE BOSTON GLOBE

(Sub. of Affiliated Publications, Inc.)
135 William T Morrissey Blvd
Boston, MA 02125-3310
Mailing Address:
PO Box 55819
Boston, MA 02205-5819
Tel.: (617) 929-2000
Fax: (617) 929-3192
E-mail: realestate@globe.com
Web Site: www.boston.com
Sales Range: $350-399.9 Million
Approx. Number Employees: 2,500
Year Founded: 1872
Business Description:
Newspaper Publishing
S.I.C.: 2711
N.A.I.C.S.: 511110
Advertising Expenditures: $2,190,000
Bus. Publs.: $212,000; D.M. to Bus. Estab.: $160,000; D.M. to Consumers: $400,000; Outdoor (Posters, Transit): $168,000; Spot Radio: $680,000; Spot T.V.: $500,000; Yellow Page Adv.: $70,000
Distr.: Reg.
Budget Set: Oct.
Personnel:
Christopher Mayer *(Publr)*
Chris Pircio *(CFO)*
Christopher Hall *(VP-HR & Labor Rels)*
Jason Kissell *(VP-Adv)*
Robert L. Powers *(VP-Mktg & Comm)*
Wade Sendall *(VP-IT)*
Lisa M. DeSisto *(Chief Adv Officer & Gen Mgr-Boston.com)*
Martin Baron *(Editor)*
Renee Loth *(Editor-Editorial Page)*
Marjorie Pritchard *(Editor-Op-Ed)*
Dan Bunker *(Dir-Sys Architecture)*
Averil Capers *(Dir-Community Mktg & Res)*
Peter Doucette *(Dir-Consumer Mktg)*
Teresa M. Hanafin *(Dir-User Engagement)*
Mary Kelly *(Mgr-Sls)*
Tim Borton *(Mgr-Supplements)*
Rajae Bouganza *(Mgr-Adv Ops)*
Andrew Donovan *(Mgr-Divisional Sls-Non-Traditional Revenue)*
Tom Drislane *(Mgr-Automotive Sls)*
Ed Foley *(Mgr-Preprint)*
Barbara Gibson *(Mgr-Sls)*
Scott Halstead *(Mgr-Mktg Events)*
Tom Furdon *(Supvr-Adv Control Unit)*
Michael Kingsley *(Supvr-Sls Coordination)*
Mary Surro *(Supvr-Customer Svc)*
Daryl Alger *(Coord-Sls)*
Mike Devlin *(Coord-Info Sys)*
Janel Quiroz *(Coord-Sls)*
Christine Stapleton *(Coord-Adv)*
Maria Tack *(Coord-Sls)*
David Thayer *(Coord-Sls)*
Chris Zito *(Coord-Sls)*
Advertising Agency:
Hill Holliday
53 State St
Boston, MA 02109
Tel.: (617) 366-4000

BOSTON HERALD INC.

(Sub. of Herald Media Inc.)
1 Herald Sq
Boston, MA 02106
Mailing Address:
PO Box 55843
Boston, MA 02205
Tel.: (617) 619-6893
Fax: (617) 426-1869
Toll Free: (800) 882-1211
Web Site: www.bostonherald.com
Sales Range: $250-299.9 Million
Approx. Number Employees: 860
Year Founded: 1846
Business Description:
Publisher & Printer of Newspapers
S.I.C.: 7383
N.A.I.C.S.: 519110
Media: 8-9-10-13-18-19-20-21-22-23-25-26
Personnel:
Patrick J. Purcell *(Owner, Pres & Publr)*
Joe Scieacca *(Editor-in-Chief)*
Rachelle Cohen *(Editor)*
Frank Quaratiello *(Editor-Bus)*

BOWTIE INC.

(Formerly Fancy Publications Inc.)
2401 Beverly Blvd
Los Angeles, CA 90057-1001
Tel.: (213) 385-2222
Fax: (213) 385-8565
Web Site: www.bowtieinc.com
Approx. Number Employees: 350
Business Description:
Magazine Publishing
S.I.C.: 2721
N.A.I.C.S.: 511120
Media: 2-7-13
Personnel:
Norman Ridker *(Pres)*
Patrick Trowbridge *(Publr)*
Jeff Scharf *(Sr VP-Sls)*
Nikki Dutra *(List Mgr)*
Brands & Products:
AQUARIUM FISH MAGAZINE
AUTO RESTORER
BIRD TALK
BIRDS USA
CAT FANCY
CATS USA
CRITTERS USA
DOG FANCY
DOGS USA
FERRETS
FERRETS USA
HAWAII
HOBBY FARMS
HORSE ILLUSTRATED
HORSES USA
KITTENS USA
KOI WORLD & WATER GARDENS
MOTORCYCLE CONSUMER NEWS
PET PRODUCT NEWS
THE PET PRODUCT NEWS BUYING GUIDE DIRECTORY
PONDS MAGAZINE
PONDS USA AND WATER GARDENS
POPULAR DOGS SERIES
PUPPIES USA
RABBITS
REPTILES MAGAZINE
VETERINARY PRACTICE NEWS
WATER GARDEN NEWS
WILDBIRD
YOUNG RIDER
Advertising Agency:
The Richards Organization
(Sub. of MSRI)
14 Calvert St
Harrison, NY 10528-3213
Tel.: (914) 835-3111
Fax: (914) 835-3698
Toll Free: (800) 4ALLADS

BOYDS MILLS PRESS, INC.

(Sub. of Highlights for Children, Inc.)
815 Church St
Honesdale, PA 18431
Tel.: (570) 253-1164
Fax: (570) 253-0179
E-mail: admin@boydsmillspress.com
Web Site: www.boydsmillspress.com
Approx. Number Employees: 50
Year Founded: 1990
Business Description:
Children's Books
S.I.C.: 2731
N.A.I.C.S.: 511130
Media: 7-8-10
Personnel:
Clay Winters *(Pres)*
Kent L. Brown, Jr. *(Publr)*
Tim Gillner *(Dir-Art)*
Larry Rosler *(Dir-Editorial)*

BOYS' LIFE MAGAZINE

(Div. of Boy Scouts of America)
271 Madison Ave Ste 401
New York, NY 10016-1001
Tel.: (212) 532-0985
Fax: (212) 889-4513
Toll Free: (877) 929-LIFE
E-mail: info@boyslife.org
Web Site: www.boyslife.org
Approx. Sls.: $15,000,000
Approx. Number Employees: 7
Year Founded: 1912
Business Description:
Magazine Operations
S.I.C.: 2721
N.A.I.C.S.: 511120
Media: 2-4-6-7-8-10-13-17
Distr.: Natl.
Budget Set: Oct.
Personnel:
J. Warren Young *(Publr)*

Key to Media (For complete agency information see *The Advertising Red Books-Agencies* edition):
1. Bus. Publs. 2. Cable T.V. 3. Catalogs & Directories. 4. Co-op Adv. 5. Consumer Mags. 6. D.M. to Bus. Estab.7. D.M. to Consumers 8. Daily Newsp. 9. Exhibits/Trade Shows 10. Foreign 11. Infomercial 12. Internet Adv.13. Multimedia 14. Network Radio 15. Network T.V. 16. Newsp. Distr. Mags. 17. Other 18. Outdoor (Posters, Transit) 19. Point of Purchase20. Premiums, Novelties 21. Product Samples 22. Special Events Mktg. 23. Spot Radio 24. Spot T.V. 25. Weekly Newsp. 26. Yellow Page Adv.

Boys' Life Magazine — (Continued)

Jim Wilson *(Assoc Publr)*
J.D. Owen *(Editor-in-Chief)*
Paula Murphey *(Assoc Editor)*
Belia Rangel Freedman *(Editor-Copy)*
Bryan Wursten *(Editor-Online)*
Barry Brown *(Dir-Adv)*
Brenda Brown *(Dir-Adv)*
Scott Feaster *(Dir-Design)*
Craig J. Vander Ploeg *(Dir-Adv)*
Bob Wiemers *(Dir-Ops)*
Mark J. Adeszko *(Reg Mgr-Adv)*
Lois Ann Roethel *(Bus Mgr)*
Judy Bramlett *(Mgr-Customer Rels)*
Eugene Handon *(Mgr-Natl Traffic)*
Lisa Hott *(Mgr-Adv Production)*

Brands & Products:
BOYS' LIFE
SCOUTING MAGAZINE

BRAINERD DAILY DISPATCH

(Unit of Morris Publishing Group, LLC)
506 James St
Brainerd, MN 56401-0974
Mailing Address:
PO Box 974
Brainerd, MN 56401-0974
Tel.: (218) 829-4705
Fax: (218) 829-7735
Toll Free: (800) 432-3703
Web Site: www.brainerddispatch.com
Approx. Number Employees: 107
Business Description:
Newspaper Publisher
S.I.C.: 2721; 8742
N.A.I.C.S.: 511120; 541611
Media: 8-9
Personnel:
Terry J. McCollough *(Publr)*
Kari Lake *(Controller & Dir-HR)*
Mike Bialka *(Editor-Sports)*
Roy Miller *(Editor)*
Kathi Nagorski *(City Editor)*
Mike O'Rourke *(Opinions Editor)*
Brian Peterson *(Editor-Outdoors)*
Diana Kiehlbauch *(Dir-Production-Comml Printing)*
Denton Newman, Jr. *(Dir-Audience Dev)*
Sam Swanson *(Mgr-Adv)*

BRANT PUBLICATIONS, INC.

575 Broadway 5th Fl
New York, NY 10012-3230
Tel.: (212) 941-2800
Fax: (212) 941-2932
Toll Free: (800) 925-9271
E-mail: info@themagazineantiques.com
Web Site:
www.themagazineantiques.com
E-Mail For Key Personnel:
Sales Director: jmorton@brantpub.com
Approx. Number Employees: 100
Year Founded: 1922
Business Description:
Publisher of Art Magazines
S.I.C.: 2721
N.A.I.C.S.: 511120
Media: 2-4-6-7-8-9-10
Distr.: Natl.
Budget Set: Apr.
Personnel:
Peter Brant *(Owner-Brant ELECTRIC)*
Cynthia Zabel *(Publr)*
Debbie Blasucci *(VP-Fin)*
Christopher Bollen *(Editor-in-Chief-Interview)*

Brands & Products:
ART IN AMERICA
INTERVIEW
THE MAGAZINE ANTIQUES

BREHM COMMUNICATIONS INC.

16644 W Bernardo Dr Ste 300
San Diego, CA 92127-1901
Tel.: (858) 451-6200
Fax: (858) 451-3814
Web Site:
www.brehmcommunications.com
Approx. Number Employees: 13
Year Founded: 1919
Business Description:
Newspaper Publisher
S.I.C.: 2752; 2711
N.A.I.C.S.: 323110; 511110
Media: 1-8-9-10
Personnel:
W. J. Brehm, Sr. *(Chm)*
Bill Brehm, Jr. *(Pres)*
Tom Taylor *(VP & Gen Mgr)*

BRENTWOOD-BENSON MUSIC PUBLISHING, INC.

(Sub. of Provident Music Group)
(d/b/a Brentwood Records)
2555 Meridian Blvd Ste 100
Franklin, TN 37067
Tel.: (615) 261-3300
Fax: (615) 261-3386
Toll Free: (800) 846-7664
E-mail: sales@brentwoodbenson.com
Web Site:
www.brentwoodbenson.com
E-Mail For Key Personnel:
Sales Director: sales@brentwoodbenson.com
Approx. Number Employees: 60
Business Description:
Recorded Music & Entertainment Producer & Mfr
S.I.C.: 2741; 3652
N.A.I.C.S.: 512230; 334612
Media: 6-19
Distr.: Intl.; Natl.
Budget Set: Oct. -Nov.
Personnel:
Dale Matthews *(Pres)*
Robyn Lehman *(CEO)*
Brands & Products:
PROVIDENT MUSIC

BRIDGE PUBLICATIONS INC.

5600 E Olympic Blvd
Los Angeles, CA 90022
Tel.: (323) 953-3320
Fax: (323) 888-6201
E-mail: info@bridgepub.com
Web Site: www.bridgepub.com
Approx. Sls.: $13,000,000
Approx. Number Employees: 65
Business Description:
Book Publishing
S.I.C.: 2731; 3652
N.A.I.C.S.: 511130; 334612
Media: 10-22
Personnel:
Lucia Winther *(VP-Sls)*
Don Arnow *(Dir-Sls)*

BRINKER DISPLAYS

545 N Arlington Ave
East Orange, NJ 07017-4000
Tel.: (973) 678-1200
Approx. Number Employees: 35
Business Description:
Point of Purchase Displays Mfr
S.I.C.: 2531; 3993; 7319
N.A.I.C.S.: 337127; 339950; 541850; 541890
Media: 2-4-8-10-26
Budget Set: Nov.

BROADVIEW PRESS INC.

815 First St SW Ste 412
Calgary, AB T2P 1N3, Canada
Tel.: (705) 743-8990
Fax: (519) 767-1643
E-mail: customerservice@broadviewpress.com
Web Site: www.broadviewpress.com
Approx. Sls.: $2,556,077
Approx. Number Employees: 30
Year Founded: 2003
Business Description:
Academic Publisher
S.I.C.: 2731
N.A.I.C.S.: 511130
Media: 4
Personnel:
Don Le Pan *(Pres & CEO)*
Carol Richardson *(CFO & Comptroller)*

BROWN & BIGELOW, INC.

345 Plato Blvd E
Saint Paul, MN 55107-1211
Tel.: (651) 293-7000
Fax: (651) 222-3874
Toll Free: (800) 628-1749
E-mail: customer-service@brownandbigelow.com
Web Site: www.brownandbigelow.com
Approx. Number Employees: 225
Year Founded: 1896
Business Description:
Mfr. of Calendars & Advertising Specialties
S.I.C.: 7319; 2752
N.A.I.C.S.: 541890; 323110
Import Export
Media: 1-2-4-5-6-7-8-9-10-19-21-26
Distr.: Direct to Consumer; Natl.
Budget Set: Aug.
Personnel:
William D. Smith *(Pres)*
Garry P. Hoden *(CFO)*
Robert L. Petschke *(Exec VP)*
William D. Smith, Jr. *(Exec VP)*
Brands & Products:
ACTION TECH
ADAMS
ADVANTAGE
ADVANTAGE TIMBER
ANVIL
AUGUSTA
BADGER
BANNERS DEN
BELLA
BENDEEZ
BEST
BEVERAGE WRENCH
BLU
THE BOSS
BROWN & BIG
BROWN & BIGELOW
BROWN & BIGGER
BUSHNELL
BUXTON
CAN KEY
CHAMPION
CLASSIC LINE
CLIC STIC
CLIP CUP
CLIPPABLES
COMFORT BLEND
COMP-U-FOLIO
COOLMAX
COORDINATOR
CORDURA
COTTON DELUXE
CUSTOM CRYSTAL
CUSTOM-MEMO
CUTTER AND BUCK
CYBER BRUSH
CYBERCLIP
DOPP
DYMONDWOOD
EAGLE CREEK
ECOSTONE
ELITE
EMAIL SERIES
ESQUIRE
ESSENTIAL
FASTBINDERS
FIXXERS
FLEXABLES
FLYING COASTER
FREQUENT FLYERS
FRESHGUARD
FUNCAP
THE FUNKYLINE
GARRISON
GILDON
HARDTOP KOOZIE
HARDWOOD
HARDWOOD GREEN
HEADSWEATS
HEMPTOWN
HOTLINE
HYP
ICE
ICU
IZOD
JONATHAN COREY
KEEP-IT-COOL
KLEEN SWEEPS
KLIPPER KING
KOOZIE
LA LOVING
LAL
LEE
LIP TONOC
LOCK JAWS
MAXI MINDER
MAXIM
MAZE PEN
MEMOIR COLLECTION
MINI MINDER
OBELISK
OBSESSION
OUTER BANK
PENNANTS
PERFCARD SMARTLINE
PING
PINNACLE
POCKET HOLDER
PORT AND COMPANY
PORT COLLECTION
PRINTPRO
PROMOCLIP
QUIK FLIP
QUIKOIN
RABBIT SKINS
REMEMBRANCE ADVERTISING
RIVERS END

Key to Media (For complete agency information see *The Advertising Red Books-Agencies* edition):
1. Bus. Publs. 2. Cable T.V. 3. Catalogs & Directories. 4. Co-op Adv. 5. Consumer Mags. 6. D.M. to Bus. Estab.7. D.M. to Consumers
8. Daily Newsp. 9. Exhibits/Trade Shows 10. Foreign 11. Infomercial 12. Internet Adv.13. Multimedia 14. Network Radio
15. Network T.V. 16. Newsp. Distr. Mags. 17. Other 18. Outdoor (Posters, Transit) 19. Point of Purchase20. Premiums, Novelties
21. Product Samples 22. Special Events Mktg. 23. Spot Radio 24. Spot T.V. 25. Weekly Newsp. 26. Yellow Page Adv.

ROBOT SERIES
ROMBE
SCRUBBY
SHANNON
SINCERELY VISIONS
SMARTLINE
SOF-TOUCH
SPEED ZONE
SPORT TEK
STEDMAN
STEDMAN FOR HER
STEEL
STRESS GLOOP
SUPERB

BROWN CITY BANNER
(Unit of JAMS Media LLC)
4241 Main St
Brown City, MI 48416-0250
Tel.: (810) 346-2753
Fax: (810) 346-2579
Web Site:
browncitybanner.mihomepaper.com/
Approx. Number Employees: 3
Business Description:
Newspaper Publisher
S.I.C.: 2711
N.A.I.C.S.: 511110
Media: 25
Personnel:
Dawn Diller *(Office Mgr)*
Brands & Products:
BROWN CITY BANNER

THE BROWNSVILLE HERALD
(Unit of Freedom Newspapers, Inc.)
1135 E Van Buren St
Brownsville, TX 78520
Tel.: (956) 542-4301
Fax: (956) 982-4201
Web Site: www.brownsvilleherald.com
Approx. Number Employees: 63
Year Founded: 1892
Business Description:
Newspaper
S.I.C.: 2711
N.A.I.C.S.: 511110
Media: 6-8-9-13-22-23
Personnel:
Daniel Cavazos *(Publr)*
Jaime Galvan *(Editor-City)*
Santos Garcia *(Editor-Spanish)*
Carlos Rodriquez *(Editor)*
Juan Carlos Sanchez *(Editor-Spanish Sports)*
Zulema Baez *(Dir-Spanish Publ)*
Odie Carden *(Dir-Internet Svcs)*
Sandy McGehee *(Dir-Educational Svcs)*
Speedy Aldape *(Mgr-Building OPS)*
Odie Cardem *(Mgr-Svcs)*
Max Gajowski *(Mgr)*
Irma Rubio *(Mgr-Customer Svc)*

THE BUREAU OF NATIONAL AFFAIRS, INC.
1801 S Bell St
Arlington, VA 22202
Tel.: (703) 341-3000
Fax: (800) 253-0332
Toll Free: (800) 372-1033
E-mail: customercare@bna.com
Web Site: www.bna.com
Approx. Rev.: $331,009,000
Approx. Number Employees: 1,506
Year Founded: 1929
Business Description:
Print, Electronic News, Analysis & Reference Products Publisher
S.I.C.: 2711; 2721; 2741
N.A.I.C.S.: 511110; 511120; 516110
Advertising Expenditures: $5,724,000
Media: 2-4-7-10-13-21-25
Distr.: Intl.; Natl.
Budget Set: Sept.
Personnel:
Paul N. Wojcik *(Chm & CEO)*
Gregory C. McCaffery *(Vice Chm, Pres & COO)*
Robert P. Ambrosini *(CFO)*
Carol A. Clark *(CIO & Exec VP)*
Eunice F. Lin *(Gen Counsel & Exec VP)*
Cynthia J. Bolbach *(Corp Sec & Exec VP)*
Brands & Products:
ALTERNATIVE INVESTMENT LAW REPORT
BANKING DAILY
BANKING REPORT
BANKRUPTCY LAW DAILY
BANKRUPTCY LAW REPORTER
BIOTECH WATCH
BNA
BNACOMPANYDASH
BNACONVERGENCE
BNACUSTOMCLIP
BNAINFODASH
CHEMCITE RESEARCH SUITE
CHEMICAL REGULATION REPORTER
CLASS ACTION LITIGATION REPORT
COMPUTER TECHNOLOGY LAW REPORT
CORPORATE ACCOUNTABILITY REPORT
DAILY LABOR REPORT
DAILY REPORTS FOR EXECUTIVES
DAILY TAX REPORT
EMPLOYEE BENEFITS LIBRARY
ERISA COMPLIANCE & ENFORCEMENT LIBRARY
EXPERT EVIDENCE REPORT
FAMILY LAW REPORTER
HOMELAND SECURITY BRIEFING
IMPORT REFERENCE GUIDE
INFRASTRUCTURE INVESTMENT & POLICY REPORT
INTERNATIONAL TRADE REPORTER DECISIONS
LABOR RELATIONS REPORTER
LABORPLUS
MEDICAL DEVICES LAW & INDUSTRY REPORT
PHARMACEUTICAL LAW & INDUSTRY REPORT
TAXCORE
WEB WATCH
WTO REPORTER
Advertising Agency:
Gardner Keaton, Inc.
3536 East Forest Lk Dr
Sarasota, FL 34232
Tel.: (941) 924-7216
Fax: (941) 924-7194

BURLINGTON UNION
(Unit of GateHouse Media New England)
150 Baker Ave Ext Ste105
Concord, MA 01742
Tel.: (781) 229-0918
Fax: (978) 371-5711
E-mail: burlington@cnc.com
Web Site: www.wickedlocal.com/burlington
Sales Range: $10-24.9 Million
Approx. Number Employees: 52
Business Description:
Newspaper Publisher
S.I.C.: 2711
N.A.I.C.S.: 511110
Media: 9
Personnel:
Chuck Goodrich *(Publr)*
Bruce Coulter *(Editor-News & Mgr-Website)*
Anne Eisenmenger *(Mgr-Website)*
Linda Vahey *(Mgr-Circulation)*

BUSINESS & LEGAL REPORTS INC.
141 Mill Rock Rd E
Old Saybrook, CT 06475-4217
Tel.: (860) 510-0100
Fax: (860) 510-7225
E-mail: service@blr.com
Web Site: www.blr.com
Sales Range: $25-49.9 Million
Approx. Number Employees: 150
Year Founded: 1977
Business Description:
Magazine Publishing Services
S.I.C.: 2721; 2731
N.A.I.C.S.: 511120; 511130
Media: 7
Personnel:
Robert L. Brady *(Founder, CEO & Chm)*
Brian Gurnham *(COO)*
Susan Prince *(Mng Editor)*
Brands & Products:
BLR
COMPENSATION.BLR.COM
ENVIRO.BLR.COM
HR.BLR.COM
SAFETY.BLR.COM

BUSINESS NEWS PUBLISHING COMPANY INC.
2401 W Big Beaver Rd Ste 700
Troy, MI 48084
Tel.: (248) 362-3700
Tel.: (248) 244-6400
Fax: (248) 362-0317
E-mail: webmaster@bnp.com
Web Site: www.bnp.com
Approx. Number Employees: 180
Year Founded: 1926
Business Description:
Publisher of Periodicals & Newspapers
S.I.C.: 2711
N.A.I.C.S.: 511110
Import Export
Media: 2-10-13-17-22
Personnel:
James E. Henderson *(Chm)*
Harper Henderson *(Co-CEO)*
Mitchell Henderson *(Co-CEO)*
Taggart Henderson *(Co-CEO)*
Doug Siwek *(Dir-Mktg)*

BUTTERICK, MCCALL & VOGUE PATTERN COMPANY
(Div. of Butterick, McCall & Vogue Pattern Company)
11 Penn Plz 121 broad way 34th Fl
New York, NY 10271
Tel.: (212) 465-6800
Fax: (212) 465-6805
Web Site: www.butterick.com
Approx. Number Employees: 350
Year Founded: 1863
Business Description:
Patterns, Magazines & Catalogs
S.I.C.: 2741; 2721
N.A.I.C.S.: 511199; 511120
Export
Advertising Expenditures: $675,000
Media: 2-4-5-6-7-8-10-17-18-19
Distr.: Intl.
Budget Set: Oct.
Personnel:
Joan Campbell *(Dir-Adv)*
Brands & Products:
BUTTERICK
SEE & SEW
VOGUE

CABLE NEWS NETWORK LP
(Sub. of Turner Broadcasting System, Inc.)
1271 Ave Of The Americas
New York, NY 10020
Tel.: (212) 275-8200
Tel.: (212) 522-5618
Web Site: www.money.com
Sales Range: $10-24.9 Million
Approx. Number Employees: 36
Year Founded: 1972
Business Description:
Cable Television Network
S.I.C.: 4841
N.A.I.C.S.: 515210
Media: 2-6-7-8-9-18-21
Distr.: Direct to Consumer; Intl.; Natl.
Personnel:
Janet Rolle *(CMO & Exec VP-Worldwide)*
Greg D'Alba *(COO-Adv Sls & Exec VP)*
Jed Hartman *(Grp Publr-Fortune & CNNMoney)*
Susan Bunda *(Exec VP-Content Dev & Strategy-Worldwide)*
Ken Jautz *(Exec VP-US)*
Katrina Cukaj *(Sr VP)*
William Hsu *(VP-Adv Sls-Asia Pacific)*
Marybeth Strobel *(VP & Mgr-Sls)*
Stacey Rabsatt *(Dir-Sls-South East Asia)*

THE CADMUS PUBLISHER SERVICES GROUP
(Sub. of Cenveo Inc.)
2901 Byrdhill Rd
Richmond, VA 23228
Mailing Address:
PO Box 27367
Richmond, VA 23261-7367
Tel.: (804) 287-5680
Tel.: (804) 261-3000
Fax: (804) 287-6267
Fax: (804) 515-5720
Toll Free: (877) 422-3687
Toll Free: (800) 888-2973
E-mail: info@kwglobal.com
Web Site: www.cenveo.com
Approx. Sls.: $451,223,000
Approx. Number Employees: 3,300
Year Founded: 1984
Business Description:
Printing, Publishing & Packaging Solutions
S.I.C.: 2759; 2721; 2752
N.A.I.C.S.: 323119; 323110; 511120
Media: 2-8-10

Key to Media (For complete agency information see *The Advertising Red Books-Agencies* edition):
1. Bus. Publs. 2. Cable T.V. 3. Catalogs & Directories. 4. Co-op Adv. 5. Consumer Mags. 6. D.M. to Bus. Estab.7. D.M. to Consumers
8. Daily Newsp. 9. Exhibits/Trade Shows 10. Foreign 11. Infomercial 12. Internet Adv.13. Multimedia 14. Network Radio
15. Network T.V. 16. Newsp. Distr. Mags. 17. Other 18. Outdoor (Posters, Transit) 19. Point of Purchase20. Premiums, Novelties
21. Product Samples 22. Special Events Mktg. 23. Spot Radio 24. Spot T.V. 25. Weekly Newsp. 26. Yellow Page Adv.

The Cadmus Publisher Services Group — (Continued)

Brands & Products:
MEDIAWORKS
RAPID EDIT

CADMUS SPECIALTY PUBLICATIONS

(Div. of The Cadmus Publisher Services Group)
1991 Northampton St
Easton, PA 18042-3173
Tel.: (610) 258-9111
Fax: (610) 250-7202
Web Site: www.cadmus.com
Sales Range: $25-49.9 Million
Approx. Number Employees: 400
Year Founded: 1901
Business Description:
Offset Printing of Magazines & Catalogs, Publishing
S.I.C.: 2752
N.A.I.C.S.: 323110
Media: 2-7
Brands & Products:
CADMUS 3PATH
CADMUS DELIVERYWORKS
CADMUS MEDIAWORKS

THE CALGARY SUN

(Sub. of Sun Media Corporation)
2615 12th St NE
Calgary, AB T2E 7W9, Canada
Tel.: (403) 250-4200
Fax: (403) 250-4258
Telex: 38-22734
E-mail: dal.lewis@sunmedia.ca
Web Site: www.calgarysun.com
Approx. Number Employees: 250
Year Founded: 1980
Business Description:
Daily Newspaper Publisher
S.I.C.: 2711
N.A.I.C.S.: 511110
Import
Media: 10-13-18-22-23-24
Personnel:
Terry Birch *(Pres)*
Gordon Norrie *(CEO & Publr)*
Ed Huculak *(Gen Mgr & Dir-Adv)*
Jose Rodriguez *(Editor-in-Chief)*
Bruce Mapherson *(Dir-Circulation)*
Svend Mortensen *(Dir-Production)*
Diane Wensel *(Dir-Mktg)*
Dal Lewis *(Asst Dir-Adv)*
Brands & Products:
THE CALGARY SUN

CALIFORNIA OFFSET PRINTERS, INC.

(Sub. of COP Communications)
620 W Elk Ave
Glendale, CA 91204
Tel.: (818) 291-1100
Fax: (818) 291-1192
E-mail: info@copprints.com
Web Site: www.copprints.com
Approx. Number Employees: 100
Year Founded: 1962
Business Description:
Publication Printers: Tabloids, Magazines, Directories
S.I.C.: 2752; 2741
N.A.I.C.S.: 323110; 511199
Import
Media: 2-4-8-10-13-16-17-20-22-26
Distr.: Natl.; Reg.

Personnel:
William R. Rittwage *(Pres & CEO)*

CALKINS MEDIA INC.

8400 Rt 13
Levittown, PA 19057
Tel.: (215) 949-4011
Fax: (215) 949-4177
Web Site: www.phillyburbs.com
Approx. Number Employees: 2,035
Year Founded: 1976
Business Description:
Newspapers
S.I.C.: 2711
N.A.I.C.S.: 511110
Import Export
Media: 8-9
Personnel:
Steve Todd *(Gen Mgr & Dir-Circulation)*
Dave Koehler *(Dir-Design)*
Jennifer Schultz *(Mgr-Adv)*

CAMBRIDGE CHRONICLE

(Unit of GateHouse Media New England)
20 Holland St Ste 404
Somerville, MA 02144
Tel.: (617) 629-3387
Fax: (617) 629-3381
E-mail: cambridge@cnc.com
Web Site: www.wickedlocalcambridge.com
Sales Range: $100-124.9 Million
Approx. Number Employees: 2
Business Description:
Newspaper Publisher
S.I.C.: 2711
N.A.I.C.S.: 511110
Media: 9

CAMBRIDGE INFORMATION GROUP, INC.

7200 Wisconsin Ave Ste 601
Bethesda, MD 20814-4837
Tel.: (301) 961-6700
Fax: (301) 961-6790
E-mail: info@cambridgeinformationgroup.com
Web Site: www.cambridgeinformationgroup.com
Approx. Sls.: $75,000,000
Approx. Number Employees: 2,000
Year Founded: 1971
Business Description:
Investment Holding Company; Education, Research & Information Services
S.I.C.: 6719; 2741; 6289; 7389; 8299
N.A.I.C.S.: 551112; 511140; 516110; 519190; 523999; 541712; 611710
Media: 4-7-8-10-11
Personnel:
Robert N. Snyder *(Founder & Chm)*
Andrew M. Snyder *(Pres)*
Michael K. Chung *(COO)*
Jill Snyder Granader *(Principal)*
Barbara Inkellis *(Gen Counsel, Sec & Sr VP)*
Larisa Avner Trainor *(Gen Counsel)*
Delores Snowden *(VP-HR)*

CAMBRIDGE UNIVERSITY PRESS, NORTH AMERICAN BRANCH

(Sub. of Cambridge University Press)
32 Avenue of the Americas
New York, NY 10013-2473
Tel.: (212) 924-3900
Fax: (212) 691-3239
Toll Free: (800) 221-4512
E-mail: information@cup.org
Web Site: www.cup.org
Approx. Number Employees: 150
Business Description:
Publisher of Books, Publications & Journals
S.I.C.: 2731; 2721
N.A.I.C.S.: 511130; 511120
Media: 8-10
Distr.: Intl.; Natl.
Personnel:
Liza Muphury *(Dir-Mktg)*

CAMDEN NEWS PUBLISHING COMPANY

(Holding of Wehco Media, Inc.)
121 E Capitol Ave
Little Rock, AR 72201-3819
Tel.: (501) 378-3400
Fax: (501) 376-8949
Web Site: www.camdenarknews.com
Year Founded: 1929
Business Description:
Newspapers
S.I.C.: 2711; 4841
N.A.I.C.S.: 511110; 515210
Import Export
Media: 8-9-13
Personnel:
Walter E Hussman *(Pres & CEO)*
Allen Berry *(CFO)*
John Mobbs *(Dir-Adv)*

CANSON INC.

(Sub. of ArjoWiggins SAS)
21 Industrial Dr
South Hadley, MA 01075
Tel.: (413) 538-9250
Fax: (413) 533-6554
Web Site: www.canson-us.com
E-Mail For Key Personnel:
Marketing Director: rtoth@canson-us.com
Sales Range: $25-49.9 Million
Approx. Number Employees: 100
Business Description:
Marketer & Distr Artists' Materials
S.I.C.: 2679
N.A.I.C.S.: 322299
Advertising Expenditures: $2,000,000
Media: 2-5-7-10-18-19-21
Distr.: Natl.
Budget Set: Aug.
Personnel:
James Allery *(Pres)*
Bob Toth *(VP-Mktg)*
Giulia Biagi *(Product Mgr)*
Luis Pedro *(Mgr-Ops)*

CANTON JOURNAL

(Unit of GateHouse Media New England)
370 Paramount Dr
Raynham, MA 02767
Tel.: (508) 967-3515
Fax: (508) 967-3501
E-mail: canton@cnc.com
Web Site: www.wickedlocal.com/canton
Sales Range: $25-49.9 Million
Approx. Number Employees: 2
Business Description:
Newspaper Publisher
S.I.C.: 2711
N.A.I.C.S.: 511110
Media: 9
Personnel:
Mark Olivieri *(Publr)*
Anne Eisenmenger *(Mgr-Website)*
Art Geisinger *(Mgr-Display Adv)*
Linda Vahey *(Mgr-Circulation)*
Brands & Products:
CANTON JOURNAL

THE CANTON REPOSITORY

(Unit of GateHouse Media, Inc.)
500 Market Ave S
Canton, OH 44702
Tel.: (330) 580-8300
Tel.: (330) 580-8400
Tel.: (330) 580-8500
Fax: (330) 580-2122
Toll Free: (877) 580-8500
E-mail: info@cantonrep.com
Web Site: www.cantonrep.com
Sales Range: $25-49.9 Million
Approx. Number Employees: 300
Business Description:
Newspaper Publishing Services
S.I.C.: 2711
N.A.I.C.S.: 511110
Media: 8-9-13-18-22-26
Personnel:
Kevin M. Kampman *(Vice Chm & Publr)*
Dan Kane *(Editor-Entertainment)*
Dave Sereno *(Editor)*
Jeff Verbus *(Copy Editor)*
Ryan Sander *(Dir-Online Products)*
Gail Valli *(Sls Mgr-Classifieds)*
Ray Scarnecchia *(Pressroom Mgr)*
Scott Whitman *(Mgr-IT)*

CAPE COD TIMES

(Unit of Ottaway Newspapers, Inc.)
319 Main St
Hyannis, MA 02601
Tel.: (508) 775-1200
E-mail: news@capecodonline.com
Web Site: www.capecodonline.com
Sales Range: $100-124.9 Million
Business Description:
Newspaper Publisher
S.I.C.: 2711
N.A.I.C.S.: 511110
Media: 7-8-9-13-22-25
Personnel:
Peter Meyer *(Pres & Publr)*
Paul Pronovost *(Editor-in-Chief)*
Gregory Bryant *(Editor-Online)*
Meg Burton *(Editor-Features)*
Chris Cheney *(Editor-Night)*
Linda Corcoran *(Editor-Sunday)*
Kathi Scrizzi Driscoll *(Editor-Home & Family)*
Gwenn Friss *(Editor-Food)*
Erin Healy *(Editor-PrimeTime)*
Bill Higgins *(Editor-Sports)*
Richard Holmes *(Editor-Features Design)*
Ann Humphrey *(Editor-Lifestyle)*
Bryan Lantz *(Editor-Bus)*
Melanie Lauwers *(Editor-Book, Health & Travel)*
Wendy Lopata *(Editor-Community News)*
Michael Medwar *(Editor-Community)*
Tim Miller *(Editor-Entertainment & CapeWeek)*
William Mills *(Editor-Editorial Page)*
Susan Moeller *(Editor-News)*
Dhyana Sansoucie *(Editor-Presentation)*

Key to Media (For complete agency information see *The Advertising Red Books-Agencies* edition):
1. Bus. Publs. 2. Cable T.V. 3. Catalogs & Directories. 4. Co-op Adv. 5. Consumer Mags. 6. D.M. to Bus. Estab.7. D.M. to Consumers
8. Daily Newsp. 9. Exhibits/Trade Shows 10. Foreign 11. Infomercial 12. Internet Adv.13. Multimedia 14. Network Radio
15. Network T.V. 16. Newsp. Distr. Mags. 17. Other 18. Outdoor (Posters, Transit) 19. Point of Purchase20. Premiums, Novelties
21. Product Samples 22. Special Events Mktg. 23. Spot Radio 24. Spot T.V. 25. Weekly Newsp. 26. Yellow Page Adv.

Ron Sikora *(Editor-News/Sports Design)*
Lisa Maiden *(Dir-Retail & Natl Adv)*
Kate McMahon *(Dir-Internet)*
James Preston *(Dir-Photo)*
Robert Sypek *(Dir-Member Svcs)*
Joseph Allen *(Mgr-Member Svcs)*
Ben Emery *(Mgr-Preprint Major Accounts)*
Mike Fabia *(Mgr-Print Ops)*
Jeffrey H. Rixon *(Mgr-Adv)*
Susan Scott-Mabile *(Mgr-Adv)*
Kevin Wright *(Mgr-Adv Svcs)*
Robin Smith-Johnson *(Librarian)*

CAPE CODDER
(Unit of GateHouse Media New England)
5 Namskaket Rd
Orleans, MA 02653
Tel.: (508) 255-2121
Fax: (508) 247-3202
E-mail: capecodder@cnc.com
Web Site: www.wickedlocalcapecodd.com/brewster
Sales Range: $10-24.9 Million
Approx. Number Employees: 40
Business Description:
Newspaper Publisher
S.I.C.: 2711
N.A.I.C.S.: 511110
Media: 25
Personnel:
Mark Skala *(Publr)*
Carol K. Dumas *(Mng Editor)*
Matt Rice *(Editor-Sports)*
Anne Eisenmenger *(Mgr-Website)*
Susan Gaulin *(Mgr-Display Adv)*
Philip G. Ouellette *(Mgr-Circulation)*
Brands & Products:
CAPE CODDER

CAPITAL CITY PRESS
(d/b/a The Advocate)
7290 Bluebonnet Blvd
Baton Rouge, LA 70810-1611
Tel.: (225) 383-1111
Fax: (225) 388-0348
Toll Free: (800) 960-6397
Web Site: www.2theadvocate.com
Approx. Number Employees: 375
Year Founded: 1842
Business Description:
Morning Daily Newspaper
S.I.C.: 2711; 2752
N.A.I.C.S.: 511110; 323110
Media: 9-13-18-20-23-24-26
Distr.: Direct to Consumer; Reg.
Budget Set: Nov.
Personnel:
Richard F. Manship *(Pres & CEO)*
Douglas L. Manship, Jr. *(COO & Publr)*
Richard Shurley *(CTO & Dir-Facilities & Ops)*
Ralph Bender *(VP-Fin)*
Dean Blanchard *(Dir-Circulation)*
Judy Jumonville *(Dir-Library)*
Linda Wunstel *(Dir-Mktg)*
Mike Nola *(Mgr-Classified Adv)*
Jason Gele *(Coord-Online Adver)*
Brands & Products:
THE ADVOCATE

CAPITAL GAZETTE COMMUNICATIONS INC.
(Sub. of Landmark Media Enterprises LLC)
2000 Capital Dr
Annapolis, MD 21401
Tel.: (410) 268-5000
Fax: (410) 268-4643
E-mail: capstaff@capitalgazette.com
Web Site: www.hometownannapolis.com
Approx. Number Employees: 400
Business Description:
Newspaper Publisher
S.I.C.: 2711
N.A.I.C.S.: 511110
Media: 8-9
Personnel:
Kathy Flynn *(Mng Dir)*
Charles Feeney *(CFO)*
Tom Marquardt *(Publr & Editor)*
Mark Barebo *(Dir-Adv)*
Rob Pryor *(Dir-Circulation)*
Doris Burgess *(Mgr-Circulation)*
Brands & Products:
THE BOWIE BLADE-NEWS
THE CAPITAL
THE CROFTON NEWS-CRIER
HOMETOWNANNAPOLIS.COM
MARYLAND GAZETTE
THE WASHINGTONIAN MAGAZINE
THE WEST COUNTY GAZETTE

CAPSTONE PRESS, INC.
(Sub. of Coughlan Companies, Inc.)
151 Good Counsel Dr
Mankato, MN 56001
Tel.: (507) 388-6650
Fax: (888) 262-0705
Web Site: www.capstonepress.com
Sales Range: $100-124.9 Million
Approx. Number Employees: 173
Business Description:
Books Publisher
S.I.C.: 2731
N.A.I.C.S.: 511130
Media: 2-4-10-13-18-20
Personnel:
Robert J. Coughlan *(Chm & Co-Owner)*
G. Thomas Ahern *(CEO)*
Matthew A. Keller *(CMO)*
Eric S. Fitzgerald *(VP-Sls-Direct)*
Lisa Hanson *(Dir-HR)*

CARL FISCHER, LLC
65 Bleecker St
New York, NY 10012-2420
Tel.: (212) 777-0900
Fax: (212) 477-6996
Toll Free: (800) 762-2328 (Natl.)
E-mail: cf-info@carlfischer.com
Web Site: www.carlfischer.com
Approx. Number Employees: 25
Year Founded: 1872
Business Description:
Music Publishers, Dealers, Distributors
S.I.C.: 2741; 5736
N.A.I.C.S.: 512230; 451140
Import Export
Media: 2-4-6-7-8-9-10-11-13-22
Distr.: Natl.
Personnel:
Hayden Connor *(Pres)*
Larry Clark *(VP & Editor-in-Chief)*
Brands & Products:
ABCS OF STRINGS
ALL THAT JAZZ
ALL TIME FAVORITES
CARL FISCHER
CARL FISCHER PERFORMANCE SERIES
THE GUITAR GRIMOIRE
MUSIC PATHWAYS
SOUNDS SPECTACULAR

CARLTON CARDS RETAIL, INC.
(Div. of American Greetings U.S. Greeting Card Division)
1 American Rd
Cleveland, OH 44144-2301
Tel.: (216) 252-7300
Fax: (216) 252-6778
E-mail: support@americangreetings.com
Web Site: www.americangreetings.com
Sales Range: $900-999.9 Million
Approx. Number Employees: 2,000
Business Description:
Retail Card & Gift Stores
S.I.C.: 5947; 2754; 2759; 2771
N.A.I.C.S.: 453220; 323111; 323112; 323113; 323119; 511191
Media: 6-8-13-22
Personnel:
Tom Johnston *(Pres)*
Dennis Beckstrom *(VP-Fin)*
Brands & Products:
CARLTONCARDS.COM

CARROLL COUNTY TIMES
(Unit of Landmark Community Newspapers, LLC)
201 Railroad Ave
Westminster, MD 21157
Mailing Address:
PO Box 346
Westminster, MD 21158
Tel.: (410) 875-5400
Tel.: (410) 848-4400
Fax: (410) 751-5906
Toll Free: (877) 228-4637
E-mail: kim.pooe@carrollcountytimes.com
Web Site: www.carrollcountytimes.com
Approx. Number Employees: 200
Business Description:
Daily Newspaper
S.I.C.: 2711; 2752
N.A.I.C.S.: 511110; 323110
Media: 9-13
Personnel:
Joe McClure *(Copy Editor)*
Kim Stenley *(Copy Editor)*
Nick Wood *(Copy Editor)*
Bob Blubaugh *(Editor-Sports)*
Jim Lee *(Editor)*
Brian Patterson *(Editor-Night News)*
Patti Ritter *(Editor-Neighborhoods)*
Charles Baker *(Dir-Adv)*
Jerry Blizzard *(Dir-Homes Magazines & Classified)*
Patrick Stoetzer *(Coord-Writing)*
Aaron Wilson *(Writing Coord-Ravens)*

CARUS PUBLISHING COMPANY
30 Grove St
Peterborough, NH 03458
Tel.: (815) 224-5803
Fax: (603) 371-9026
Toll Free: (800) 588-8585
E-mail: info@cricketmag.com
Web Site: www.cricketmag.com
Sales Range: $25-49.9 Million
Approx. Number Employees: 50
Business Description:
Magazine & Book Publisher
S.I.C.: 2731
N.A.I.C.S.: 511130
Media: 8
Personnel:
Jason Patenaude *(Pres & COO)*
Andre Carus *(CEO)*
Mark Fagiano *(VP-Mktg)*

CASTLE CONNOLLY MEDICAL LTD.
42 W 24th St 2nd Fl
New York, NY 10010
Tel.: (212) 367-8400
Fax: (212) 367-0964
Toll Free: (800) 399-3627
E-mail: info@castleconnolly.com
Web Site: www.castleconnolly.com
E-Mail For Key Personnel:
President: jconnolly@castleconnolly.com
Marketing Director: liss-levinson@castleconnolly.com
Sales Range: $25-49.9 Million
Approx. Number Employees: 20
Year Founded: 1992
Business Description:
Internet & Publishing Company in Consumer Health
S.I.C.: 2731; 2741
N.A.I.C.S.: 511130; 511199
Media: 2-4-6-9-13-23
Distr.: Natl.
Personnel:
John K. Castle *(Chm)*
John J. Connolly *(Pres & CEO)*
William Liss-Levinson *(Chief Strategy Officer, Chief Ops Officer & VP)*

THE CAXTON PRINTERS LTD.
312 Main St
Caldwell, ID 83605-3235
Tel.: (208) 459-7421
Fax: (208) 459-7450
E-mail: info@caxtonprinters.com
Web Site: www.caxtonprinters.com
Approx. Number Employees: 55
Year Founded: 1907
Business Description:
Distr of Commercial Printers, Textbook & School Supplies
S.I.C.: 5192; 2752
N.A.I.C.S.: 424920; 323110
Media: 2-8-25
Distr.: Reg.
Budget Set: Jan.
Personnel:
Dave Gipson *(Pres)*
Scott Gipson *(Publr & VP)*
Ron Gipson *(VP & Mgr-Printing)*
Brands & Products:
CAXTON

CCH
(Unit of Wolters Kluwer Financial & Compliance Services)
4025 W Peterson Ave
Chicago, IL 60646
Tel.: (773) 866-6000
Web Site: www.cch.com
Approx. Number Employees: 20
Business Description:
Publishing
S.I.C.: 2741
N.A.I.C.S.: 511199
Media: 2

Key to Media (For complete agency information see *The Advertising Red Books-Agencies* edition):
1. Bus. Publs. 2. Cable T.V. 3. Catalogs & Directories. 4. Co-op Adv. 5. Consumer Mags. 6. D.M. to Bus. Estab.7. D.M. to Consumers 8. Daily Newsp. 9. Exhibits/Trade Shows 10. Foreign 11. Infomercial 12. Internet Adv.13. Multimedia 14. Network Radio 15. Network T.V. 16. Newsp. Distr. Mags. 17. Other 18. Outdoor (Posters, Transit) 19. Point of Purchase20. Premiums, Novelties 21. Product Samples 22. Special Events Mktg. 23. Spot Radio 24. Spot T.V. 25. Weekly Newsp. 26. Yellow Page Adv.

CCH — (Continued)

Personnel:
Mike Sabbatis *(Pres & CEO)*
Jerry Pruitt *(VP-Customer Svc & Ops)*
Christian Wolfe *(VP-Bus Intelligence & Strategy)*

Advertising Agency:
Stackpole & Partners Advertising
222 Merrimac St
Newburyport, MA 01950
Tel.: (978) 463-6600
Fax: (978) 463-6610

CCH INC.

(Sub. of Wolters Kluwer Tax & Accounting)
2700 Lk Cook Rd
Riverwoods, IL 60015-3867
Tel.: (847) 267-7000
Fax: (847) 267-2873
Toll Free: (888) 224-7377
Web Site: www.cch.com
Approx. Number Employees: 900
Year Founded: 1913
Business Description:
Tax, Legal, Securities, Human Resources, Health Care & Small Business Information & Software
S.I.C.: 2721; 2731; 7389
N.A.I.C.S.: 511120; 511130; 561499
Import Export
Media: 2-7-10-21
Distr.: Direct to Consumer; Natl.
Budget Set: Aug.
Personnel:
Norman Plaistow *(Exec VP)*
Jerry Pruitt *(VP-Customer Svc & Ops)*
Sharon Kube *(Product Mgr)*
Leslie Bonacum *(Mgr-Corp Comm)*
Brands & Products:
1040 EXPRESS ANSWERS
1040 PREPARATION & PLANNING GUIDE
1041 EXPRESS ANSWEERS
1041 PREPARATION & PLANNING GUIDE
1065 & 1120S EXPRESS ANWSERS
1065 EXPRESS ANSWERS
CCH HAND
CCH ONLINE PAY AS YOU GO
CCH SWORD
CCH TEAMMATE
CORPSYSTEM
KLEINROCK
PRACTICAL TAX PROFESSIONAL
PROSYSTEM FX
PROSYSTEM FX OFFICE
TAX PREP PARTNER SERIES
TAXSCRIPTS TAXPRO

CCPRESS.NET INC.

7110 Golden Ring Rd Ste 114
Baltimore, MD 21221-3136
Tel.: (410) 574-0780
Fax: (410) 574-0793
Toll Free: (877) 999-8969
E-mail: info@ccpress.net
Web Site: www.ccpress.net
Approx. Number Employees: 7
Year Founded: 1999
Business Description:
Commercial Printing Services
S.I.C.: 2752
N.A.I.C.S.: 323110
Media: 7-13

Personnel:
Patti Woodworth *(Pres)*
Ben Woodworth *(VP-Sls)*

CENGAGE LEARNING

(Sub. of Cengage Higher Education)
20 Davis Dr
Belmont, CA 94002
Tel.: (650) 595-2350
Fax: (650) 637-7544
Fax: (800) 487-8488
Toll Free: (800) 354-9706
Web Site:
www.academic.cengage.com
Year Founded: 1956
Business Description:
Educational Software & Textbook Publisher
S.I.C.: 2731; 8299
N.A.I.C.S.: 511130; 611710
Advertising Expenditures: $1,538,000
Media: 4-10
Distr.: Intl.; Natl.
Budget Set: May-June
Personnel:
Sean Wakely *(Pres)*
Dean D. Durbin *(CFO)*
John Barnes *(Exec VP-Consumer Markets)*
David Guttman *(Sr VP & Gen Mgr-Web Research Products Grp)*
John Wong *(Mgr-Bus)*

CENVEO INC.

1 Canterbury Green
Stamford, CT 06901
Tel.: (203) 595-3000
Fax: (203) 595-3071
E-mail: info@cenveo.com
Web Site: www.cenveo.com
Approx. Sls.: $1,814,716,000
Approx. Number Employees: 8,700
Year Founded: 1994
Business Description:
Printing & Printing-Related Products & Services
S.I.C.: 2621; 2653; 2752
N.A.I.C.S.: 322121; 322211; 323110
Advertising Expenditures: $2,800,000
Media: 1-2-4-7-10-20-22
Personnel:
Robert G. Burton, Sr. *(Chm & CEO)*
Mark S. Hiltwein *(CFO & Exec VP)*
Dean E. Cherry *(Pres-Envelope Product Grp)*
Cappy Childs *(Pres-Comml Print Grp)*
Harry R. Vinson *(Pres-Cenveo Print)*
Kenneth P. Viret *(Sr VP & Controller)*
Robert J. Muma *(Sr VP-Corp Dev)*
Brands & Products:
3B2
CONVEO
ECENERGY
INDESIGN
MAIL-WELL
QUARK
TEX
VISION DELIVERED
WISCO
XPP

CFQ MEDIA, LLC

(Sub. of Mindfire Entertainment)
3740 Overland Ave Ste E
Los Angeles, CA 90034
Tel.: (310) 204-2029
Fax: (310) 204-5882
E-mail: mail@cfq.com
Web Site: www.cfq.com
E-Mail For Key Personnel:
President: dwilliams@cfq.com
Sales Range: Less than $1 Million
Approx. Number Employees: 10
Business Description:
Genre Film Magazines Publisher
S.I.C.: 2721
N.A.I.C.S.: 511120
Media: 4-6-8-10-13
Brands & Products:
CINEFANTASTIQUE
FEMME FATALES

CHAMPION AMERICA

20 Flax Mill Rd
Branford, CT 06405
Tel.: (203) 315-1181
Fax: (203) 315-1106
Toll Free: (800) 521-7000
Toll Free: (800) 336-3707
E-mail: teamca@champion-america.com
Web Site: www.champion-america.com
Approx. Number Employees: 150
Year Founded: 1989
Business Description:
All Types of Identification Products Including Signs, Tags, Labels & Pipemarkers Mfr
S.I.C.: 3479; 3993
N.A.I.C.S.: 332812; 339950
Advertising Expenditures: $5,000,000
Media: 2-4-7-21
Distr.: Natl.
Budget Set: June
Personnel:
Frank Jarhnett *(CEO)*
Donna J. Canestri *(Dir-Mktg Admin)*
Janice Fowler *(Mgr-Adv)*

CHAMPION INDUSTRIES, INC.

2450 1st Ave
Huntington, WV 25728
Mailing Address:
PO Box 2968
Huntington, WV 25728-2968
Tel.: (304) 528-2700
Fax: (304) 528-2765
Toll Free: (800) 624-3431
E-mail: champion@champion-industries.com
Web Site: www.champion-industries.com
Approx. Rev.: $129,933,571
Approx. Number Employees: 700
Year Founded: 1992
Business Description:
Commercial Printer, Business Forms Mfr & Office Products & Office Furniture Supplier
S.I.C.: 2752; 2522; 2759; 2761; 5021
N.A.I.C.S.: 323110; 323116; 323119; 337214; 423210
Advertising Expenditures: $598,000
Media: 2
Personnel:
Marshall T. Reynolds *(Chm & CEO)*
Toney K. Adkins *(Pres & COO)*
Todd R. Fry *(CFO & Sr VP)*
J. Mac Aldridge *(Sr VP)*
R. Douglas McElwain *(Sr VP)*
James A. Rhodes *(Sr VP)*

CHANNING BETE CO., INC.

1 Community Pl
South Deerfield, MA 01373
Tel.: (413) 665-7611
Fax: (413) 665-2671
Toll Free: (800) 628-7733
E-mail: custsvcs@channing-bete.com
Web Site: www.channing-bete.com
Approx. Number Employees: 300
Year Founded: 1946
Business Description:
Publisher & Printer of Scriptographic Informational & Educational Booklets & Related Materials
S.I.C.: 2731; 7812
N.A.I.C.S.: 511130; 512110
Personnel:
Michael Bete *(Pres & CEO)*
Kim Canuel *(CFO)*
Robert L. Underwood *(Exec VP)*
Carol W. Bete *(Sr VP-Adv)*
Daniel E. Carmody *(Sr VP)*
Brands & Products:
CHANNING BETE
COMMUNITIES THAT CARE
FAMILIES THAT CARE
GUIDING GOOD CHOICES
PARENTS WHO CARE
PATHS
PREPARING FOR SCHOOL SUCCESS
SOAR
Advertising Agency:
Signaltree Marketing & Advertising
160 Emerald St Ste 201
Keene, NH 03431
Tel.: (603) 358-5100
Fax: (603) 358-5109

THE CHARLOTTE OBSERVER PUBLISHING CO.

(Sub. of McClatchy Newspapers, Inc.)
(d/b/a The Charlotte Observer)
600 S Tryon St
Charlotte, NC 28202-1880
Mailing Address:
PO Box 32188
Charlotte, NC 28232
Tel.: (704) 358-5000
Fax: (704) 358-5036
Toll Free: (800) 532-5350
E-mail: localnews@charlotteobserver.com
Web Site: www.charlotteobserver.com
Sales Range: $350-399.9 Million
Approx. Number Employees: 1,200
Business Description:
Newspaper Publisher
S.I.C.: 2711
N.A.I.C.S.: 511110
Media: 8-9-13-25
Personnel:
Ann Caulkins *(Pres & Publr)*
Brands & Products:
THE CHARLOTTE OBSERVER
CHARLOTTE.COM

CHELMSFORD INDEPENDENT

(Unit of GateHouse Media New England)
150 Baker Ave Ext Ste 105
Concord, MA 01742
Tel.: (978) 256-7196
Fax: (978) 371-5711
E-mail: chelmsford@cnc.com
Web Site: www.wickedlocal.com/chelmsford
Sales Range: $50-74.9 Million
Approx. Number Employees: 200

Key to Media (For complete agency information see *The Advertising Red Books-Agencies* edition):
1. Bus. Publs. 2. Cable T.V. 3. Catalogs & Directories. 4. Co-op Adv. 5. Consumer Mags. 6. D.M. to Bus. Estab.7. D.M. to Consumers 8. Daily Newsp. 9. Exhibits/Trade Shows 10. Foreign 11. Infomercial 12. Internet Adv.13. Multimedia 14. Network Radio 15. Network T.V. 16. Newsp. Distr. Mags. 17. Other 18. Outdoor (Posters, Transit) 19. Point of Purchase20. Premiums, Novelties 21. Product Samples 22. Special Events Mktg. 23. Spot Radio 24. Spot T.V. 25. Weekly Newsp. 26. Yellow Page Adv.

Business Description:
Newspaper Publisher
S.I.C.: 2711
N.A.I.C.S.: 511110
Media: 9-16
Personnel:
Chuck Goodrich *(Publr)*
Jesse Floyd *(Editor-Chelmsford)*
Steve Tobey *(Editor-Sports)*
Tracey DeLorey *(Mgr-Display Adv)*
Kevin Zimmerman *(Website Mgr)*

CHICAGO READER, INC.
(Sub. of Creative Loafing, Inc.)
11 E Illinois St
Chicago, IL 60611
Tel.: (312) 828-0350
Fax: (312) 828-9926
E-mail: mail@chicagoreader.com
Web Site: www.chicagoreader.com
Sales Range: $10-24.9 Million
Approx. Number Employees: 51
Year Founded: 1971
Business Description:
Newspaper Publisher
S.I.C.: 2711
N.A.I.C.S.: 511110
Media: 13-18
Personnel:
Alison Draper *(Publr)*
Mary Jo Madden *(Gen Mgr)*
Tony Adler *(Assoc Editor)*
Michael Miner *(Editor)*
Philip Montoro *(Editor)*
Julia Thiel *(Editor)*
David Wilcox *(Asst Editor)*
Kristen Kaza *(Dir-Mktg)*
Perry A. Kim *(Mgr-Circulation)*
Brett Murpht *(Mgr-Online Prod)*
Brad Winckler *(Mgr-Digital Sls)*
Brands & Products:
HOT TYPE
READER

CHICAGO SUN TIMES
(Sub. of Sun-Times Media Group, Inc.)
350 N Orleans Ste 9 10
Chicago, IL 60654
Tel.: (312) 321-3000
Fax: (312) 321-9655
Web Site: www.suntimes.com
Approx. Number Employees: 2,600
Year Founded: 1941
Business Description:
Daily Newspaper
S.I.C.: 2711; 2752
N.A.I.C.S.: 511110; 323110
Media: 2-7-8-9-16-19-22-23-24-25
Distr.: Direct to Consumer
Budget Set: Nov.
Personnel:
Jeremy Halbreich *(Chm)*
Fred Lebolt *(Pres & Gen Mgr)*
Art Redmond *(CMO)*
John Barron *(Publr)*
John Martin *(VP-Adv)*
Don Hayner *(Editor-in-Chief)*
Thomas Conner *(Editor-Online Features)*
Eric White *(Dir-Design)*
James Burklow *(Mgr-Production)*
John Nocita *(Mgr-Electronic Adv)*
Alejandro Escalona *(Columnist-Latino Affairs)*

CHICAGO TRIBUNE COMPANY
(Sub. of Tribune Publishing Company)
(d/b/a Chicago Tribune Media Group)
435 N Michigan Ave
Chicago, IL 60611-4066
Tel.: (312) 222-3232
Toll Free: (800) TRIBUNE
E-mail: info@chicagotribune.com
Web Site: www.chicagotribune.com
Approx. Number Employees: 3,000
Year Founded: 1847
Business Description:
Newspaper & Magazine Publisher; News Syndication Services
S.I.C.: 2711; 2721; 7383
N.A.I.C.S.: 511110; 511120; 519110
Advertising Expenditures: $6,000,000
Media: 8-13-21
Distr.: Reg.
Budget Set: Sept.
Personnel:
Tony Hunter *(Pres, CEO & Publr)*
Philip B. Doherty *(CFO & VP)*
Gerould W. Kern *(Sr VP & Editor)*
Rebecca Brubaker *(Sr VP-Mfg & Distr)*
Robert Fleck *(Sr VP-Adv)*
Janice Jacobs *(VP-HR)*
Jonathon S. Berlin *(Editor-Graphics)*
Bruce Dold *(Editor)*
Ben Estes *(Editor-ChicagoTribunecom)*
Tran Ha *(Editor-RedEye)*
Louise Kiernan *(Editor)*
George Knue *(Editor-Chicago Breaking News Center)*
Michael A. Lev *(Editor-Bus-Chicago Tribune)*
Meg Theno *(Editor-Multimedia & Web Photo)*
Randall Weissman *(Editor-News Admin)*
Michael Cahan *(Dir-Mobile Sls & Strategy)*
Jim Rotche *(Dir-Strategy & Dev)*
Brands & Products:
CHICAGO TRIBUNE
CHICAGOSPORTS.COM
CHICAGOTRIBUNE.COM
HOLAHOY.COM
HOY CHICAGO

CHRISTIAN HERALD ASSOCIATION
(d/b/a The Bowery Mission)
132 Madison Ave
New York, NY 10016-7004
Tel.: (212) 684-2800
Fax: (212) 684-3740
Toll Free: (800) BOWERY1
E-mail: info@chaonline.org
Web Site: www.bowery.org
Approx. Number Employees: 180
Year Founded: 1879
Business Description:
Religious Services; Periodical Publisher
S.I.C.: 5961; 2721
N.A.I.C.S.: 454113; 511120
Import Export
Media: 17
Distr.: Natl.
Personnel:
Edward H. Morgan, Jr. *(Pres & CEO)*
Robert Depue *(CFO)*
Tom Basile *(Dir-The Bowery Mission)*

CHRISTIANITY TODAY INTERNATIONAL
465 Gundersen Dr
Carol Stream, IL 60188-2415
Tel.: (630) 260-6200
Fax: (630) 260-0114
E-mail: ctiad@christianitytoday.com
Web Site: www.christianitytoday.com
E-Mail For Key Personnel:
President: probbins@christianitytoday.com
Marketing Director: cthompson@christianitytoday.com
Sales Director: BOndracek@christianitytoday.com
Approx. Number Employees: 110
Year Founded: 1955
Business Description:
Christian Magazines Publisher
S.I.C.: 2721; 8661
N.A.I.C.S.: 511120; 813110
Advertising Expenditures: $1,000,000
Media: 6-8-13
Distr.: Direct to Consumer; Intl.; Natl.
Budget Set: Feb.
Personnel:
Harold B. Smith *(Pres & CEO)*
Carol Thompson *(COO)*
Keith Stonehocker *(Chief Strategy Officer)*
Kevin A. Miller *(Exec VP)*
Terumi Echols *(Sr VP-Adv & Circulation)*
Vicki Howard *(Sr VP)*
David Neff *(Editor-in-Chief)*
Julie Kaminski *(Dir-Mktg & Comm)*
Brands & Products:
BOOKS & CULTURE
CAMPUS LIFE
CHRISTIAN HISTORY
CHRISTIAN PARENTING TODAY
CHRISTIANITY TODAY
LEADERSHIP
MARRIAGE PARTNERSHIP
MEN OF INTEGRITY
PREACHING TODAY
TODAY'S CHRISTIAN WOMAN
YOUR CHURCH

CINCINNATI BUSINESS COURIER
(Unit of American City Business Journals, Inc.)
101 W 7th St
Cincinnati, OH 45202-2411
Tel.: (513) 621-6665
Fax: (513) 621-2462
E-mail: cincinnati@bizjournals.com
Web Site:
www.cincinnati.bizjournals.com
Approx. Number Employees: 40
Business Description:
Weekly Newspaper Publisher
S.I.C.: 2711; 2741
N.A.I.C.S.: 511110; 511199
Media: 7-13-25
Personnel:
Douglas Bolton *(Publr)*
Jamie Smith *(Publr)*
Karen Bells *(Editor)*
Rob Daumeyer *(Editor)*
Andrea Tortora *(Editor & Writer)*
Gigi Verna *(Editor-Daily News)*
Kevin Cox *(Dir-Art)*
Kristin Davenport *(Dir-Creative)*
Joe Hoffecker *(Dir-Mktg & Subscriber Svcs)*
Kelly Tassos *(Assoc Dir-Adv)*
Wende Powell *(Mgr-Classified Sls)*
Liz Folz *(Designer-Adv)*
Steve Lanier *(Designer-Adv)*

THE CINCINNATI ENQUIRER, INC.
(Sub. of Gannett Co., Inc.)
312 Elm St
Cincinnati, OH 45202-2739
Tel.: (513) 768-8000
Fax: (513) 768-8340
E-mail: business@cincinnati.com
Web Site: www.Cincinnati.com
Sales Range: $350-399.9 Million
Approx. Number Employees: 1,200
Year Founded: 1841
Business Description:
Newspaper Publisher
S.I.C.: 2711
N.A.I.C.S.: 511110
Media: 1-2-4-6-7-8-9-10-13-18-20-23-24
Distr.: Direct to Consumer; Reg.
Personnel:
Margaret Buchanan *(Pres & Publr)*
James Jackson *(VP-New Media & Product Dev)*
Carolyn Washburn *(Editor)*
Mike Gleason *(Dir-Retail Adv)*
Mark Woodruf *(Dir-Market Dev)*
Brands & Products:
THE CINCINNATI ENQUIRER

THE CINCINNATI POST
(Sub. of The E.W. Scripps Company)
125 E Ct St
Cincinnati, OH 45202-1212
Tel.: (513) 352-2000
Fax: (513) 621-3962
E-mail: postedits@cincypost.com
Sales Range: $25-49.9 Million
Approx. Number Employees: 88
Business Description:
Publisher of Daily Newspapers
S.I.C.: 2711
N.A.I.C.S.: 511110
Media: 9

CISION US INC.
(Sub. of Cision AB)
(d/b/a Cision North America)
332 S Michigan Ave Ste 900
Chicago, IL 60604-4393
Tel.: (312) 922-2400
Fax: (312) 922-3126
Toll Free: (866) 639-5087
E-mail: info.us@cision.com
Web Site: www.bacons.com
Approx. Number Employees: 346
Year Founded: 1995
Business Description:
Business Communication Media Planning, Connection, Monitoring & Analysis Products & Services
S.I.C.: 7389; 7372
N.A.I.C.S.: 561499; 511210
Personnel:
Joseph Bernardo *(CEO)*
Mike Czlonka *(CFO & Sr VP)*
K.C. Brown *(Sr VP-Analysis Svcs)*
Steven Brown *(Sr VP-Sls-North America)*
Vanessa Bugasch *(Sr VP-Global Mktg & Product Mktg)*
Wayne Bullock *(Sr VP-Analysis Ops)*
Brett Safron *(Sr VP-Product Mgmt)*
Scott Thompson *(Sr VP-IT)*
Randy Zierfuss *(Sr VP-HR)*
Advertising Agency:
Impressions-A.B.A. Industries, Inc.
393 Jericho Tpk
Mineola, NY 11501

Key to Media (For complete agency information see *The Advertising Red Books-Agencies* edition):
1. Bus. Publs. 2. Cable T.V. 3. Catalogs & Directories. 4. Co-op Adv. 5. Consumer Mags. 6. D.M. to Bus. Estab.7. D.M. to Consumers 8. Daily Newsp. 9. Exhibits/Trade Shows 10. Foreign 11. Infomercial 12. Internet Adv.13. Multimedia 14. Network Radio 15. Network T.V. 16. Newsp. Distr. Mags. 17. Other 18. Outdoor (Posters, Transit) 19. Point of Purchase20. Premiums, Novelties 21. Product Samples 22. Special Events Mktg. 23. Spot Radio 24. Spot T.V. 25. Weekly Newsp. 26. Yellow Page Adv.

Cision US Inc. — (Continued)

Tel.: (516) 739-3210
Fax: (516) 739-9246

CITRUS COUNTY CHRONICLE
(Unit of Landmark Community Newspapers, LLC)
1624 N Meadowcrest Blvd
Crystal River, FL 34429-5760
Tel.: (352) 563-6363
Fax: (352) 563-5665
Toll Free: (888) 852-2340
E-mail: newsdesk@chronicleonline.com
Web Site: www.chronicleonline.com
Approx. Sls.: $170,700,000
Approx. Number Employees: 150
Business Description:
Newspapers
S.I.C.: 2711
N.A.I.C.S.: 511110
Media: 13
Personnel:
Gerald Mulligan *(Publr)*
Claire Laxton *(Editor)*
Trina Murphy *(Dir-Ops)*
John Provost *(Dir-Adv)*
Kathy Stewart *(Dir-Circulation)*
Thomas Feeney *(Mgr-Production)*
Brands & Products:
CITRUS PUBLISHING

CITY GUIDE MAGAZINE
Empire State Bldg 350 5th Ave Ste 2420
New York, NY 10118
Tel.: (212) 315-0800
Fax: (212) 271-2239
E-mail: info@cityguidemagazine.com
Web Site: www.cityguidemagazine.com
E-Mail For Key Personnel:
Sales Director: sales@cityguidemagazine.com
Approx. Rev.: $5,500,000
Approx. Number Employees: 24
Year Founded: 1982
Business Description:
Weekly Tourist Magazine
S.I.C.: 2721
N.A.I.C.S.: 511120
Media: 5-6-22
Distr.: Direct to Consumer; Intl.; Natl.
Budget Set: Oct.
Personnel:
David Miller *(CEO)*
Janet Barbash *(Dir-Commun Rels)*
Brands & Products:
CITY GUIDE

CLEMENT COMMUNICATIONS INC.
(Sub. of Brady Corporation)
10 La Crue Ave
Concordville, PA 19331
Tel.: (610) 459-1700
Tel.: (610) 459-4200
Fax: (610) 459-0936
Fax: (800) 459-1933
Toll Free: (888) 358-5858
E-mail: customerservice@clement.com
Web Site: www.clement.com
Approx. Sls.: $12,900,000
Approx. Number Employees: 85
Year Founded: 1919
Business Description:
Book Publishing & Print
S.I.C.: 2731
N.A.I.C.S.: 511130
Media: 7

CLIPPER MAGAZINE INC.
3708 Hempland Rd
Mountville, PA 17554
Tel.: (717) 569-5100
Fax: (717) 569-5101
Toll Free: (888) 569-5100
E-mail: info@clippermagazine.com
Web Site: www.clippermagazine.com
Sales Range: $75-99.9 Million
Approx. Number Employees: 1,000
Year Founded: 1983
Business Description:
Coupon Distribution Services
S.I.C.: 2754; 2721
N.A.I.C.S.: 323111; 511120
Media: 8-16
Personnel:
Steven Zuckerman *(CEO)*
Jeff Hartman *(CFO)*
Ian Ruzow *(COO)*
Bob Zuckerman *(Publr)*
Dave Anderson *(Dir-HR)*
Mark Carbonetta *(Dir-Recruit)*
Sue Killian *(Mgr-Adv)*
Brands & Products:
CLIPPERMAGAZINE
MY CLIPPER.COM

CLOVIS NEWS JOURNAL
(Unit of Freedom Newspapers, Inc.)
521 Pile St
Clovis, NM 88101
Tel.: (575) 763-3431
Fax: (575) 762-3879
E-mail: info@cnjonline.com
Web Site: www.cnjonline.com
Approx. Number Employees: 80
Year Founded: 1929
Business Description:
Newspaper
S.I.C.: 2711; 4833
N.A.I.C.S.: 511110; 515120
Media: 9
Personnel:
Ray Sullivan *(Publr)*
David Stevens *(Editor)*

COBOURG DAILY STAR
(Div. of Osprey Media Group, Inc.)
99 King St W
PO Box 400
Cobourg, ON K9A 4L1, Canada
Tel.: (905) 372-0131
Fax: (905) 372-4966
E-mail: dmacleod@northumberlandtoday.com
Web Site: www.northumberlandtoday.com
Approx. Number Employees: 40
Business Description:
Daily Newspaper
S.I.C.: 2711
N.A.I.C.S.: 511110
Media: 13-25
Personnel:
Dan MacLeod *(Publr)*

COLLECTORS EDITIONS
9002 Eton Ave
Canoga Park, CA 91304-1616
Tel.: (818) 700-8431
Fax: (818) 700-9324
Toll Free: (800) 736-0001
E-mail: contact@collectorseditions.com
Web Site: www.collectorseditions.com
Approx. Number Employees: 50
Business Description:
Fine Art Publisher
S.I.C.: 2741
N.A.I.C.S.: 511199
Media: 6-10
Personnel:
Michael Young *(CEO)*
Eric Lange *(CFO)*

COLORADO COMMUNITY NEWSPAPERS
(Unit of ASP Westward, L.P.)
125 Stephanie Pl
Castle Rock, CO 80109
Tel.: (303) 688-3128
Fax: (303) 660-4826
E-mail: jbangs@ccnewspapers.com
Web Site: www.coloradocommunitynewspapers.com
Approx. Sls.: $40,600,000
Approx. Number Employees: 200
Business Description:
Newspaper Publisher
S.I.C.: 2711
N.A.I.C.S.: 511110
Media: 8-13-25
Personnel:
Asa Cole *(Pres & Publr)*
Erin Addenbrooke *(Mgr-Sls)*

COLUMBIA UNIVERSITY PRESS
61 W 62nd St
New York, NY 10023
Tel.: (212) 459-0600
Fax: (212) 459-3678
E-mail: cup_book@columbia.edu
Web Site: www.columbia.edu
Sales Range: $10-24.9 Million
Approx. Number Employees: 50
Year Founded: 1893
Business Description:
Publishing
S.I.C.: 2731; 5192
N.A.I.C.S.: 511130; 424920
Import Export
Media: 4-5-6-8-9-10-11-13-20-23-25
Distr.: Intl.; Natl.
Personnel:
James D. Jordan *(Pres)*
Meredith Howard *(Dir-Publicity)*
Brands & Products:
COLUMBIA UNIVERSITY PRESS
EAST EUROPEAN MONOGRAPHS
EDINBURGH UNIVERSITY PRESS
UNIVERSITY OF TOKYO PRESS
WALLFLOWER PRESS
Advertising Agency:
Columbia University Press Advertising Group
61 W 62nd St
New York, NY 10023-7015
Tel.: (212) 459-0600
Fax: (212) 459-3678
Toll Free: (800) 944UNIV

COMMENTARY
165 E 56th St
New York, NY 10022-2709
Tel.: (212) 891-1400
Fax: (212) 891-6700
Toll Free: (800) 829-6270
E-mail: mail@commentarymagazine.com
Web Site: www.commentarymagazine.com
Approx. Number Employees: 13
Year Founded: 1945
Business Description:
Magazine Publisher
S.I.C.: 8661; 2759
N.A.I.C.S.: 813110; 323119
Export
Advertising Expenditures: $100,000
Media: 6-8-10-13
Distr.: Direct to Consumer; Natl.
Budget Set: Jan.
Personnel:
David Billet *(Asst Editor)*
John Podhoretz *(Editor)*
Ilya Leyzerzon *(Dir-Bus Assoc)*
Sarah M. Stern *(Dir-Bus)*
Brands & Products:
COMMENTARY

COMMUNITY NEWSPAPERS INC.
297 Prince Ave #14
Athens, GA 30601
Tel.: (706) 548-0010
Fax: (706) 548-0808
Toll Free: (800) 226-0692
Web Site: www.cninewspapers.com
Sales Range: $25-49.9 Million
Approx. Number Employees: 10
Business Description:
Newspapers, Publishing & Printing
S.I.C.: 2711
N.A.I.C.S.: 511110
Media: 8-9
Personnel:
Tom Wood *(Chm)*
W. H. NeSmith, Jr. *(Pres)*
Mark Major *(CFO)*
Joel Jenkins *(Dir-Mktg)*
Bob Oliver *(Accountant)*
Gary Snow *(Asst Controller)*

COMPASSLEARNING, INC.
(Holding of Marlin Equity Partners, LLC)
203 Colorado St
Austin, TX 78701
Tel.: (512) 478-9600
Fax: (858) 587-1629
Toll Free: (800) 232-9556
E-mail: info@compasslearning.com
Web Site: www.compasslearning.com
Sales Range: $150-199.9 Million
Approx. Number Employees: 300
Year Founded: 1969
Business Description:
Computer Based Educational Products & Services
S.I.C.: 7379; 7372
N.A.I.C.S.: 541519; 511210
Media: 7-10
Personnel:
Eric Loeffel *(CEO)*
Trey Chambers *(CFO)*
Rick Perez *(VP-Sls)*
Brands & Products:
EXPLORER
ODYSSEY

COMPLEX MEDIA, INC.
40 W 23rd St
New York, NY 10010
Tel.: (917) 262-3147
Tel.: (917) 262-4000

Key to Media (For complete agency information see *The Advertising Red Books-Agencies* edition):
1. Bus. Publs. 2. Cable T.V. 3. Catalogs & Directories. 4. Co-op Adv. 5. Consumer Mags. 6. D.M. to Bus. Estab.7. D.M. to Consumers
8. Daily Newsp. 9. Exhibits/Trade Shows 10. Foreign 11. Infomercial 12. Internet Adv.13. Multimedia 14. Network Radio
15. Network T.V. 16. Newsp. Distr. Mags. 17. Other 18. Outdoor (Posters, Transit) 19. Point of Purchase20. Premiums, Novelties
21. Product Samples 22. Special Events Mktg. 23. Spot Radio 24. Spot T.V. 25. Weekly Newsp. 26. Yellow Page Adv.

Web Site: www.complexmedianetwork.com
Sales Range: $10-24.9 Million
Approx. Number Employees: 80
Year Founded: 2002
Business Description:
Music, Style & Lifestyle Media Network & Magazine Publisher
S.I.C.: 2721
N.A.I.C.S.: 519130; 511120
Media: 10-18-19-21-22
Personnel:
Rich Antoniello *(CEO)*
Moksha Fitzgibbons *(VP-Sls & Assoc Publr)*
Brian Kelley *(Gen Mgr)*
Parry Moss *(Sr Dir-Sls-West Coast)*
Aleksey Baksheyev *(Dir-Tech)*
Cheryl LoMaglio Carvajal *(Dir-Admin)*
Brendan Frederick *(Deputy Dir-Content Dev)*
Edgar Hernandez *(Dir-Natl Sls)*
Rachel Shapiro *(Assoc Dir-Promos & Mktg-Complex Magazine)*
Brands & Products:
COMPLEX MAGAZINE

COMPUTERWORLD, INC.
(Sub. of IDG)
492 Old Connecticut Path
Framingham, MA 01701
Tel.: (508) 879-0700
Fax: (508) 872-2364
E-mail: circulation@computerworld.com
Web Site: www.computerworld.com
Approx. Number Employees: 250
Year Founded: 1967
Business Description:
Magazine Publishers
S.I.C.: 2721
N.A.I.C.S.: 511120
Media: 2-7-10-22
Distr.: Natl.
Personnel:
Matthew Smith *(COO & Exec VP)*
Ron Milton *(Exec VP-Strategic Programs)*
Gregg Pinsky *(Sr VP & Gen Mgr-Online)*
Guy J. Russo *(Sr VP)*
Martha Connors *(VP & Gen Mgr-Online)*
James E. Hull *(VP-Engrg Svcs)*
Sarah Dyck *(VP-Mktg)*
Paul T. Higday *(VP-IT & Program Dev)*
Maria C. Suarez *(Asst VP-Security)*
Ellen Fanning *(Editor-Special Projects)*
Bob Rawson *(Mng Editor-Production)*
Brands & Products:
IT CAREERS MAGAZINE

COMPUTYPE INC.
(d/b/a Castcal Idntification Concepts)
2285 W County Rd C
Saint Paul, MN 55113
Tel.: (651) 633-0633
Fax: (651) 633-7122
Toll Free: (800) 328-0852
Web Site: www.computype.com
Approx. Number Employees: 180
Year Founded: 1975
Business Description:
Commercial Printing
S.I.C.: 2759; 2672
N.A.I.C.S.: 323119; 322222
Personnel:
William E. Roach *(Chm)*
Bruce R. Wray *(Mgr-Mktg)*
Brands & Products:
COMPUTYPE
DATAMAX
DEMAND
DENSEI
DOLPHIN
FALCON
FLAP
LAP4000
MICROSCAN
N.D.L.
SYMBOL
TEKLYNX
TOPGUN
YOU CAN COUNT ON IT
ZEBRA
Advertising Agency:
Gabriel deGrood Bendt
608 2nd Ave S Ste 129
Minneapolis, MN 55402
Tel.: (612) 547-5000
Fax: (612) 547-5090

CONCORD JOURNAL
(Unit of GateHouse Media New England)
150 Baker Ave Ext Ste 101
Concord, MA 01742
Tel.: (978) 369-2800
Fax: (978) 371-5711
E-mail: concord@cnc.com
Web Site: www.wickedlocal.com
Sales Range: $25-49.9 Million
Approx. Number Employees: 75
Business Description:
Newspaper Publisher
S.I.C.: 2711
N.A.I.C.S.: 511110
Media: 9
Personnel:
Chuck Goodrich *(Publr)*
Cheryl Lecesse *(Editor)*
Steve Tobey *(Editor-Sports)*
Pamela Calder *(Mgr-Display Adv)*
Sheryl Lecesse *(Mgr-Website)*
Brands & Products:
BEACON
CONCORD JOURNAL
LEXINGTON MINUTEMAN

CONCORD PUBLISHING HOUSE INC.
(Div. of Rust Communications)
301 Broadway St
Cape Girardeau, MO 63701
Tel.: (573) 334-7100
Fax: (573) 334-4454
E-mail: info@semissourian.com
Web Site: www.southeastmissourian.com
Approx. Number Employees: 100
Business Description:
Multi-Color Printing & Copying Graphic Design Services
S.I.C.: 2759
N.A.I.C.S.: 323119
Media: 8-9-13-18
Personnel:
Gary W. Rust *(Chm)*
Rex D. Rust *(Co-Pres)*
Wally Lage *(COO)*
Brands & Products:
SOUTHEAST MISSOURIAN

CONCORDIA PUBLISHING HOUSE
3558 S Jefferson Ave
Saint Louis, MO 63118-3968
Tel.: (314) 268-1000
Fax: (314) 268-1329
Toll Free: (800) 325-3040
Web Site: www.cph.org
Sales Range: $25-49.9 Million
Approx. Number Employees: 250
Year Founded: 1869
Business Description:
Publisher of Religious Books, Magazines & Music
S.I.C.: 2731; 7331
N.A.I.C.S.: 511130; 541860
Import Export
Advertising Expenditures: $3,000,000
Media: 1-2-4-5-6-7-8-10-13-16-19-20-21-26
Distr.: Natl.
Budget Set: Oct.
Personnel:
Bruce G. Kintz *(Pres & CEO)*
Jonathan D. Schultz *(Corp Counsel & VP)*
Peggy Anderson *(Exec Dir-Fin)*
Steve Harris *(Exec Dir-IT)*
Brands & Products:
ARCH BOOKS
THE CHRISTIAN EDUCATION SPECIALIST
CONCORDIA
LEARNING ABOUT SEX
LITTLE VISITS
VOYAGES

CONDE NAST PUBLICATIONS, INC.
(Div. of Advance Publications, Inc.)
4 Times Sq
New York, NY 10036-6518
Tel.: (212) 286-2860
E-mail: magpr@condenast.com
Web Site: www.condenet.com
Sales Range: $1-4.9 Billion
Approx. Number Employees: 3,000
Year Founded: 1909
Business Description:
Magazine Publisher
S.I.C.: 2721; 2741
N.A.I.C.S.: 511120; 516110
Media: 2-6-7-8-9-10-11-18-23
Distr.: Intl.; Natl.
Budget Set: Nov. -Dec.
Personnel:
Robert A. Sauerberg, Jr. *(Pres)*
Charles H. Townsend *(CEO)*
John W. Bellando *(COO)*
Jill Bright *(Chief Admin Officer)*
Jonathan Newhouse *(CEO-Conde Nast Intl)*
Drew Schutte *(Sr VP & Chief Revenue Officer)*
Nancy Berger Cardone *(Publr & VP)*
Howard Mittman *(Publr-Wired & VP)*
Gina Sanders *(Publr-Lucky & VP)*
Beth Brenner *(Publr)*
Jason Wagenheim *(Publr-Glamour)*
Monica Ray *(Exec VP-Consumer Mktg)*
Bill Wackerman *(Exec VP)*
Peter Armour *(Sr VP-Circulation)*
Kevin Hickey *(Sr VP)*
David Orlin *(Sr VP-Ops & Strategic Sourcing)*
Maurie Perl *(Sr VP-Brand Comm)*
Robert Silverstone *(Sr VP-Fin)*
Anna Harvey *(VP & Editorial Dir-Conde Nast Intl)*
Brandon Holley *(Editor-in-Chief-Lucky)*
Ruth Reichl *(Editor-in-Chief-Gourmet)*
Mark McClusky *(Sr Editor-Products-Wired Magazine)*
Tammy Laspalakis *(Dir-Consumer Mktg)*
Erica Boeke *(Brand Dir-Arch Digest)*
Linda Kennedy *(Dir-Adv)*
Patty Oppenheimer *(Dir-Mktg)*
Samuel I. Newhouse, Jr. *(Mgr-Mktg)*
Brands & Products:
ALLURE
ARCHITECTURAL DIGEST
BON APPETIT
BRIDES
BRIDES.COM
CONCIERGE.COM
CONDE NAST PORTFOLIO
CONDE NAST TRAVELER
COOKIE
DETAILS
DOMINO
ELEGANT BRIDE
EPICURIOUS.COM
GENTLEMEN'S QUARTERLY
GLAMOUR
GOLF DIGEST
GOLF WORLD
GOURMET
LUCKY
MEN'S VOGUE
MEN.STYLE.COM
MODERN BRIDE
THE NEW YORKER
PORTFOLIO
SELF
SHOPVOGUE.TV
STYLE.COM
TEEN VOGUE
VANITY FAIR
VOGUE
W
WIRED
Advertising Agency:
Hurrell Moseley Dawson & Grimmer
Exmouth House 3 11 Pine St
London, EC1R OJH, United Kingdom
Tel.: (44) 20 7278 6655
Fax: (44) 20 7278 6688
(Wired)

CONDE NAST PUBLICATIONS, INC.
(Branch of Conde Nast Publications, Inc.)
6300 Wilshire Blvd
Los Angeles, CA 90048-5204
Tel.: (323) 965-3400
Fax: (323) 930-2420
Web Site: www.condenast.com
Approx. Number Employees: 210
Year Founded: 1965
Business Description:
Publisher of Magazines
S.I.C.: 2721
N.A.I.C.S.: 511120
Media: 2-6-8-24
Distr.: Intl.; Natl.
Budget Set: Oct.
Personnel:
Keryn Howarth *(Coord-Adv)*

Key to Media (For complete agency information see *The Advertising Red Books-Agencies* edition):
1. Bus. Publs. 2. Cable T.V. 3. Catalogs & Directories. 4. Co-op Adv. 5. Consumer Mags. 6. D.M. to Bus. Estab.7. D.M. to Consumers 8. Daily Newsp. 9. Exhibits/Trade Shows 10. Foreign 11. Infomercial 12. Internet Adv.13. Multimedia 14. Network Radio 15. Network T.V. 16. Newsp. Distr. Mags. 17. Other 18. Outdoor (Posters, Transit) 19. Point of Purchase20. Premiums, Novelties 21. Product Samples 22. Special Events Mktg. 23. Spot Radio 24. Spot T.V. 25. Weekly Newsp. 26. Yellow Page Adv.

CONDE NAST TRAVELER
(Unit of Conde Nast Publications, Inc.)
4 Times Sq
New York, NY 10036-6518
Tel.: (212) 286-2860
Fax: (212) 286-2190
Web Site: www.cntraveler.com
Approx. Number Employees: 80
Year Founded: 1987
Business Description:
Travel Magazine Publisher
S.I.C.: 2721; 7011
N.A.I.C.S.: 511120; 721199
Media: 6-8-19
Distr.: Direct to Consumer; Natl.
Personnel:
Susan Harrington *(Assoc Publr-Mktg)*
Klara Glowczewska *(Editor-in-Chief)*
John Hillock *(Exec Dir)*
Mark Connolly *(Dir-Style)*
John Grimwade *(Dir-Graphics)*
Wendy Perrin *(Dir-Consumer News & Digital Community)*
Kara Rosen *(Dir-Creative Svcs)*
Ty Trippet *(Dir-Comm)*
Brands & Products:
CONDE NAST TRAVELER MAGAZINE

CONGRESSIONAL QUARTERLY, INC.
(Sub. of The Economist Group Limited)
1255 22nd St NW
Washington, DC 20037
Tel.: (202) 887-8500
Tel.: (202) 419-8500
Fax: (202) 419-8760
Toll Free: (800) 432-2250
E-mail: classdept@rolocall.com
Web Site: www.cq.com
Approx. Number Employees: 300
Year Founded: 1945
Business Description:
Books, Magazines, Daily Newspapers & E-Newsletters with Information Relating to Events on Capitol Hill, Congressional Activity & Background Information on Political Figures
Publisher
S.I.C.: 2721; 2711; 2731
N.A.I.C.S.: 511120; 511110; 511130
Media: 2-7-13
Personnel:
Douglas A. Wallen *(CFO & Sr VP)*
Dennis Arndt *(CTO & Sr VP)*
Mark Walters *(Sr VP & Publr)*
Mike Mills *(Sr VP & Editorial Dir)*
Arnie Thomas *(Sr VP-Client Rel)*
Jim Gale *(VP-Sls)*
Karen Whitman *(VP-Adv)*
David Hawkings *(Editor)*
Lori Bone *(Sr Dir-Ops-CQ StateTrack)*
Sean F. Doyle *(Sr Dir-Natl Sls)*
Kenny Ames *(Dir-Client Relationships)*
Caroline Coghil *(Dir-Fin Mgmt)*
Cynthia Cunningham *(Dir-HR)*
Rebecca Danzenbaker *(Dir-Acct Mgmt)*
David Glickstein *(Dir-Circulation)*
Jeff Steinman *(Dir-Product Dev)*
Paul Zurawski *(Dir-Bus Strategy)*
Lara Wystra Perkins *(Sr Mgr-Mktg)*
Mark Brazier *(Mgr-Resellers & Affiliates)*
Julie S. Kimbro *(Mgr-Product Mktg)*
Lisa McAvoy *(Mgr-Product Dev)*
Deidre Miller *(Mgr-Circulation Sls Mktg)*
Charles Morrell *(Mgr-Product Dev)*
Brands & Products:
CQ HOMELAND SECURITY
CQ HOUSE ACTION REPORTS
CQ PRESS
CQ TODAY
CQ WEEKLY
CQ.COM

CONSOLIDATED GRAPHICS, INC.
5858 Westheimer Ste 200
Houston, TX 77057
Tel.: (713) 787-0977
Fax: (713) 787-5013
E-mail: smcclanahan@cgx.com
Web Site: www.cgx.com
Approx. Sls.: $1,054,040,000
Approx. Number Employees: 5,333
Year Founded: 1985
Business Description:
Sheetfed, Web & Digital Commercial Printing Services
S.I.C.: 2759; 2752
N.A.I.C.S.: 323119; 323110
Media: 2-10
Personnel:
Joe R. Davis *(Chm & CEO)*
Jon C. Biro *(CFO, Chief Acctg Officer, Sec & Exec VP)*
Paul M. Garner *(CTO & Exec VP)*
James H. Cohen *(Exec VP-Mergers & Acq)*
Richard A. Davis *(Exec VP-Pur & Ops)*
M. Grae Griffin *(Exec VP-HR)*
Aaron T. Grohs *(Exec VP-Sls & Mktg)*
Rody Grant *(Dir-Recruiting, Trng & Dev)*
Sheila McClanahan *(Dir-IR)*
Brands & Products:
CGX SOLUTIONS
CGXMEDIA
COIN
CONSOLIDATED GRAPHICS
OPAL

CONSUMERS UNION OF THE UNITED STATES, INC.
101 Truman Ave
Yonkers, NY 10703-1044
Tel.: (914) 378-2000
Fax: (914) 378-2900
Web Site: www.consumerreport.org
Approx. Number Employees: 650
Year Founded: 1972
Business Description:
Non Profit Consumer Reports Publisher
S.I.C.: 2741
N.A.I.C.S.: 511199
Media: 6-8
Personnel:
Walter D. Bristol, Jr. *(Vice Chm)*
James Guest *(Pres & CEO)*
Richard Gannon *(CFO-Consumers Union, Publr-Consumer Report & VP)*
Kimberly Kleman *(Editor-in-Chief-Consumer Reports Magazine & Deputy Dir-Editorial)*
Jean M. Halloran *(Dir-Food Policy Initiatives)*
Urvashi Rangan *(Dir-Technical Policy)*
Steve Findlay *(Sr Health Policy Analyst)*
Brands & Products:
CONSUMER REPORTS
CONSUMERSUNION.ORG

COOK COMMUNICATIONS MINISTRIES
4050 Lee Vance View
Colorado Springs, CO 80918-7102
Tel.: (719) 536-0100
Fax: (719) 536-3265
Toll Free: (800) 708-5550
E-mail: sandy.roy@davidccook.com
Web Site: www.davidccook.com
Approx. Number Employees: 300
Year Founded: 1875
Business Description:
Publishers of Christian Educational Materials & Christian Trade Books
S.I.C.: 8661; 2721
N.A.I.C.S.: 813110; 511120
Export
Advertising Expenditures: $250,000
Media: 4-5-6-8-10-13-14-16-19-21-23
Distr.: Direct to Consumer; Natl.
Budget Set: Jan. -Apr.
Personnel:
Cris Doornbos *(Pres & CEO)*
Brands & Products:
BEST TO YOU
CHARIOT
CHARIOT VICTOR
CHURCH CURRICULUM
FAITH KIDZ
HONOR
LIFE JOURNEY
NEXGEN
RIVER OAK
VICTOR

CORNELL UNIVERSITY PRESS
512 E State St
Ithaca, NY 14850-4412
Tel.: (607) 277-2338
Fax: (607) 277-2374
Web Site: www.cornell.edu
Approx. Number Employees: 80
Year Founded: 1868
Business Description:
General Non-Fiction & Scholarly Books Publisher
S.I.C.: 2731
N.A.I.C.S.: 511130
Media: 5-6-8-17
Distr.: Intl.; Natl.
Budget Set: Monthly
Personnel:
Priscilla L. Hurdle *(Asst Dir & Mng Editor)*
John G. Ackerman *(Dir-Press-NY-Ithaca)*
Mahinder S. Kingra *(Mgr-Mktg)*
Mark Lawrence *(Mgr-Web & Comm-CCSF)*
Brands & Products:
CORNELL PAPERBACKS
Advertising Agency:
Roberts Advertising
(c/o Cornell University Press-Sage House)
512 E State St
Ithaca, NY 14850-4412
Tel.: (607) 277-2338
Fax: (607) 277-2397
(Books)

CORNWALL STANDARD-FREEHOLDER
(Div. of Osprey Media Group, Inc.)
1150 Montreal Rd
Cornwall, ON K6H 1E2, Canada
Tel.: (613) 933-3160
Fax: (613) 933-7521
E-mail: publisher@standard-freeholder.com
Web Site: www.standard-freeholder.com
Approx. Number Employees: 100
Business Description:
Daily Newspaper
S.I.C.: 2711
N.A.I.C.S.: 511110
Media: 13-25
Personnel:
Milton Ellis *(Publr)*
Peter Padbury *(Mgr-Adv)*

CORPUS CHRISTI CALLER-TIMES
(Sub. of The E.W. Scripps Company)
820 N Lower Broadway St
Corpus Christi, TX 78401
Mailing Address:
PO Box 9136
Corpus Christi, TX 78469
Tel.: (361) 884-2011
Fax: (361) 886-3777
E-mail: info@caller.com
Web Site: www.caller.com
Sales Range: $75-99.9 Million
Approx. Number Employees: 250
Business Description:
Morning & Sunday Newspaper Publisher
S.I.C.: 2711; 2721
N.A.I.C.S.: 511110; 511120
Media: 1-6-8-9-13
Personnel:
Darrell G. Coleman *(Pres & Publr)*
Steve Arnolds *(VP-Mktg)*
Libby Averyt *(VP-Adv)*

COSMOPOLITAN
(Unit of Hearst Magazines)
300 W 57th St
New York, NY 10019-3212
Tel.: (212) 649-3570
Tel.: (212) 649-2000
Fax: (212) 265-1849
Fax: (212) 307-6563
Web Site: www.cosmopolitan.com
Approx. Number Employees: 100
Year Founded: 1886
Business Description:
Publisher of Women's Magazine
S.I.C.: 2759; 2721
N.A.I.C.S.: 323119; 511120
Media: 6-8-10-16-17-19
Distr.: Direct to Consumer; Intl.; Natl.
Budget Set: Oct.
Personnel:
Kate White *(Editor-in-Chief)*
Robert Conway *(Editor-Photo Res)*
Esther Crain *(Editor-Articles)*
Brooke Elder *(Sr Editor-Fashion)*
Molly Fahner *(Assoc Editor)*
Rebecca Hessel *(Sr Editor-Fashion)*
Jane Katz *(Deputy Editor-Articles)*
Andrea Lavinthal *(Editor-Beauty)*
Amri Ryan Leever *(Editor-Fashion Market)*
Cara Litke *(Assoc Editor)*
Cara Mischel *(Editor-Photo & Res)*
Lesley Rotchford *(Editor-Features)*

Key to Media (For complete agency information see *The Advertising Red Books-Agencies* edition):
1. Bus. Publs. 2. Cable T.V. 3. Catalogs & Directories. 4. Co-op Adv. 5. Consumer Mags. 6. D.M. to Bus. Estab.7. D.M. to Consumers 8. Daily Newsp. 9. Exhibits/Trade Shows 10. Foreign 11. Infomercial 12. Internet Adv.13. Multimedia 14. Network Radio 15. Network T.V. 16. Newsp. Distr. Mags. 17. Other 18. Outdoor (Posters, Transit) 19. Point of Purchase20. Premiums, Novelties 21. Product Samples 22. Special Events Mktg. 23. Spot Radio 24. Spot T.V. 25. Weekly Newsp. 26. Yellow Page Adv.

Riann Smith *(Deputy Editor-Articles)*
John Lanuza *(Art Dir)*
Ann Bacon Wright *(Dir-Copy & Res)*
Molly Catlin-Triffin *(Dir-Features)*
Ann P. Kwong *(Dir-Design)*
Karen Larrain *(Dir-Fashion Market)*
Brooke Rosen Lucks *(Dir-Accessories)*
Michelle M. McCool *(Dir-Fashion)*
Brands & Products:
BAZAAR
Advertising Agency:
LPNY Ltd.
135 E 65th St
New York, NY 10021
Tel.: (212) 288-5676
Fax: (212) 288-5679

COUNTRY GAZETTE
(Unit of GateHouse Media New England)
159 S Main St
Milford, MA 01757
Tel.: (508) 634-7562
Fax: (508) 634-7568
E-mail: gazette@cnc.com
Web Site: www.wickedlocal.com/bellingham
Sales Range: $10-24.9 Million
Approx. Number Employees: 7
Business Description:
Newspaper Publisher
S.I.C.: 2711
N.A.I.C.S.: 511110
Media: 9
Personnel:
Art Davidson *(Editor-Sports)*
Heather McCarrom *(Editor-News)*
Nicole Simmons *(Mgr-Website)*

COUNTRY HOME MAGAZINE
(Div. of Meredith Publishing Group)
1716 Locust St
Des Moines, IA 50309-3023
Tel.: (515) 284-2015
Fax: (515) 284-3684
Toll Free: (800) 374-9431
E-mail: countryh@mdp.com
Web Site: www.countryhome.com
Sales Range: $100-124.9 Million
Year Founded: 1979
Business Description:
Magazine Publisher
S.I.C.: 2721
N.A.I.C.S.: 511120
Media: 6-13-17
Distr.: Natl.
Personnel:
Carol Sheehan *(Editor-in-Chief)*
Dennis Wedlick *(Dir-Creative)*
Grace Chung *(Dir-Adv)*
Marc Rebucci *(Dir-Adv-Country Home)*

COUNTRY SAMPLER INC.
(Sub. of Emmis Publishing, L.P.)
707 Kautz Rd
Saint Charles, IL 60174
Tel.: (630) 377-8000
Fax: (630) 377-8194
E-mail: info@sampler.com
Web Site: www.sampler.com
Sales Range: $50-74.9 Million
Approx. Number Employees: 70
Year Founded: 1984
Business Description:
Magazine Publisher
S.I.C.: 2721
N.A.I.C.S.: 511120
Advertising Expenditures: $800,000
Media: 2-6-7-8-10-13-19-20
Distr.: Natl.
Personnel:
Margaret B. Kernan *(COO)*
Brands & Products:
COUNTRY BUSINESS
COUNTRY MARKETPLACE
COUNTRY SAMPLER
COUNTRY SAMPLER DECORATING IDEAS

COUNTRY WEEKLY, INC.
(Sub. of American Media, Inc.)
118 16th Ave S Ste 230
Nashville, TN 37203-3140
Tel.: (615) 259-1111
Fax: (615) 255-1110
Web Site: www.countryweekly.com
Approx. Number Employees: 25
Business Description:
Periodical Publisher
S.I.C.: 2721
N.A.I.C.S.: 511120
Media: 8-25
Personnel:
Larry Holden *(Founder & Partner)*

THE COUNTY LINE REMINDER
(Sub. of Journal Register Company)
48 S St
Ortonville, MI 48462-8673
Mailing Address:
PO Box 560
Ortonville, MI 48462
Tel.: (248) 627-2843
Fax: (248) 627-3473
E-mail: reminder@lapeergroup.com
Web Site: www.lapeergroup.com
Approx. Number Employees: 2
Business Description:
Weekly Newspaper Publishing
S.I.C.: 2711; 2721
N.A.I.C.S.: 511110; 511120
Media: 25
Personnel:
Deanna Sera *(Gen Mgr)*
Brands & Products:
THE COUNTY LINE REMINDER

THE COURIER
(Unit of GateHouse Media, Inc.)
2201 Woodlawn Rd
Lincoln, IL 62656
Mailing Address:
PO Box 740
Lincoln, IL 62656-0740
Tel.: (217) 732-2101
Fax: (217) 732-7039
E-mail: courier@lincolncourier.com
Web Site: www.lincolncourier.com
Sales Range: $25-49.9 Million
Approx. Number Employees: 20
Business Description:
Newspaper
S.I.C.: 2711; 2752
N.A.I.C.S.: 511110; 323110
Media: 9-13
Personnel:
Michele Long *(Publr)*
Dan Tackett *(Editor)*
Brands & Products:
THE COURIER

COURIER CORPORATION
15 Wellman Ave
North Chelmsford, MA 01863-1334
Tel.: (978) 251-6000
Fax: (978) 251-8228
E-mail: marketing@courier.com
Web Site: www.courier.com
Approx. Sls.: $257,140,000
Approx. Number Employees: 1,662
Year Founded: 1824
Business Description:
Books Publishing, Printing & Binding
S.I.C.: 2732; 2741
N.A.I.C.S.: 323117; 511140
Export
Media: 10
Distr.: Natl.
Budget Set: Jan.
Personnel:
James F. Conway, III *(Chm, Pres & CEO)*
Peter M. Folger *(CFO & Sr VP)*
Robert P. Story, Jr. *(COO & Exec VP)*
Rajeev Balakrishna *(Gen Counsel, Sec, VP & Clerk)*
Christopher Kuppig *(VP-Bus Dev & Publ)*
Eric J. Zimmerman *(VP-Publ)*
Terry French *(Mgr-Mktg)*

CPP, INC.
1055 Joaquin Rd 2nd Fl
Mountain View, CA 94043
Tel.: (650) 969-8901
Fax: (650) 969-8608
Toll Free: (800) 624-1765
E-mail: custserv@cpp.com
Web Site: www.cpp.com
Approx. Number Employees: 97
Year Founded: 1956
Business Description:
Miscellaneous Publishing
S.I.C.: 2741
N.A.I.C.S.: 511199
Media: 4-7-10
Personnel:
Jeffrey Hayes *(Pres & CEO)*
Calvin W. Finch *(CFO & Sr VP)*
Steven Waldo *(Chief Legal Officer, Sec & VP)*
Leah Walling *(Dir-Mktg Comm & Product Mktg-FIRO)*
Brands & Products:
CPI
CPI 260
CPP
FIRO-B
THE PEOPLE DEVELOPMENT PEOPLE
SKILLSONE
STRONG
Advertising Agency:
MSR Communications
832 Sansome St 2nd Fl
San Francisco, CA 94111-1558
Tel.: (415) 989-9000
Fax: (415) 989-9002
Toll Free: (866) 247-6172

C.R. GIBSON, LLC
(Sub. of CSS Industries, Inc.)
402 BNA Dr Bldg 100 Ste 600
Nashville, TN 37217
Tel.: (615) 724-2900
Fax: (615) 724-3199
Toll Free: (800) 243-6004
E-mail: customerservice@crgibson.com
Web Site: www.crgibson.com
Approx. Sls.: $50,000,000
Approx. Number Employees: 350
Year Founded: 1870
Business Description:
Stationery Items, Gift Books & Photo Albums
S.I.C.: 5943; 5947
N.A.I.C.S.: 453210; 453220
Import Export
Advertising Expenditures: $2,000,000
Media: 1-2-4-9-10-19-21-23-25
Distr.: Direct to Consumer; Intl.; Natl.
Personnel:
Laurie Gilner *(Pres)*
Steve Wash *(Sr VP-Fin)*
Ann Cummings *(VP-Creative)*
Meryl Taylor *(Mktg Dir)*
Dennis O'Brien *(Dir-Product Devel)*
Brands & Products:
C.R. GIBSON
CREATIVE PAPERS
MARKINGS
STEPPING STONES
Advertising Agency:
GoConvergence
4545 36th St
Orlando, FL 32811
Tel.: (407) 235-3210
Fax: (407) 299-9907

CRAIN COMMUNICATIONS, INC.
1155 Gratiot Ave
Detroit, MI 48207-2997
Tel.: (313) 446-6000
Fax: (313) 446-0383
Fax: (313) 446-1680 (Accounting)
E-mail: info@crain.com
Web Site: www.crain.com
Approx. Number Employees: 1,000
Year Founded: 1916
Business Description:
Business, Trade & Consumer Magazines, Newspapers & Internet Publisher
S.I.C.: 2721; 2711; 2741
N.A.I.C.S.: 511120; 511110; 516110
Export
Media: 2-6-7-8-9-11-13-18-20-22-23-25
Distr.: Direct to Consumer; Intl.; Natl.
Budget Set: Oct.
Personnel:
Keith E. Crain *(Chm)*
Rance E. Crain *(Pres)*
Paul Dalpiaz *(CIO)*
Mary Kay Crain *(Treas & Asst Sec)*
Merrilee P. Crain *(Sec & Asst Treas)*
Peter Brown *(VP-Publr & Editorial Dir-Automotive News)*
K.C. Crain, Jr. *(VP & Group Publisher)*
Mary L. Kramer *(Publr-Detroit Bus & VP)*
William A. Morrow *(Exec VP-Ops)*
Gloria Scoby *(Sr VP & Grp Publr)*
Robert C. Adams *(Grp VP-Tech & Mfg & Circulation)*
Laura Anger *(VP-HR)*
David Kamis *(VP-Mfg & Production)*
Thomas M. Marantette, Jr. *(VP-Fin)*
Amy Crossman *(Dir-Mktg-CrainsNewYork.com)*
Donald D. Eagle *(Dir-Corp Facilities)*
Elayne Glick *(Dir-Audience Dev Pensions)*
Peter K. Grantz *(Dir-Tax)*
Kathy Henry *(Dir-Circulation & Audience Dev)*

Key to Media (For complete agency information see *The Advertising Red Books-Agencies* edition):
1. Bus. Publs. 2. Cable T.V. 3. Catalogs & Directories. 4. Co-op Adv. 5. Consumer Mags. 6. D.M. to Bus. Estab.7. D.M. to Consumers
8. Daily Newsp. 9. Exhibits/Trade Shows 10. Foreign 11. Infomercial 12. Internet Adv.13. Multimedia 14. Network Radio
15. Network T.V. 16. Newsp. Distr. Mags. 17. Other 18. Outdoor (Posters, Transit) 19. Point of Purchase20. Premiums, Novelties
21. Product Samples 22. Special Events Mktg. 23. Spot Radio 24. Spot T.V. 25. Weekly Newsp. 26. Yellow Page Adv.

Crain Communications, Inc. — (Continued)

Trish Henry *(Dir-Adv-CrainsNewYork.com)*
Colleen M. Robar *(Dir-Corp Comm)*

Brands & Products:
ADVERTISING AGE
AMERICAN COIN-OP
AMERICAN DRYCLEANER
AMERICAN LAUNDRY NEWS
AUTOMOBILWOCHE
AUTOMOTIVE NEWS
AUTOWEEK
BTOB
BUSINESS INSURANCE
CRAIN'S CHICAGO BUSINESS
CRAIN'S CLEVELAND BUSINESS
CRAIN'S DETROIT BUSINESS
CRAIN'S MANCHESTER BUSINESS
CRAIN'S NEW YORK BUSINESS
CREATIVITY
EUROPEAN RUBBER JOURNAL
FINANCIAL WEEK
INVESTMENTNEWS
MODERN HEALTHCARE
MODERN PHYSICIAN
PENSIONS & INVESTMENTS
PLASTICS & RUBBER WEEKLY
PLASTICS NEWS
RUBBER & PLASTICS NEWS
STAFFING INDUSTRY ANALYSTS
TELEVISIONWEEK
TIRE BUSINESS
URETHANES TECHNOLOGY INTERNATIONAL
WASTE & RECYCLING NEWS
WASTE NEWS
WORKFORCE MANAGEMENT

CRAIN'S CHICAGO BUSINESS
(Unit of Crain Communications, Inc. - Chicago)
360 N Michigan Ave
Chicago, IL 60601-3806
Tel.: (312) 649-5200
Fax: (312) 649-5415
Web Site: www.chicagobusiness.com
Approx. Number Employees: 52
Business Description:
Business Newspaper & Internet Publisher
S.I.C.: 2711; 2741
N.A.I.C.S.: 511110; 516110
Media: 23-24
Personnel:
David Snyder *(Publr)*
Gabrielle Tompkins *(Assoc Dir-Res & Mgr-Social Media)*

CRAIN'S NEW YORK BUSINESS
(Unit of Crain Communications, Inc. - New York)
711 3rd Ave
New York, NY 10017-4036
Tel.: (212) 210-0100
Fax: (212) 210-0799
E-mail: nyweb@crainsnewyork.com
Web Site: www.crainsnewyork.com
Approx. Number Employees: 40
Year Founded: 1985
Business Description:
Business Newspaper & Internet Publisher
S.I.C.: 2711; 2741
N.A.I.C.S.: 511110; 516110
Media: 2-4-7-10-13-16
Personnel:
Amy Crossman *(Dir-Mktg)*
Steve Krupinski *(Dir-Art)*
Catherine Evans Gittens *(Product Mgr-Newsletter)*
Sabra Harrison *(Asst Mgr-Mktg)*

CREATIVE COMMUNICATION CONCEPTS CORP.
(d/b/a Alternatives News Magazine)
(d/b/a Coast Magazine)
721 Seaboard St Pella Plz Ste 15
Myrtle Beach, SC 29578
Tel.: (843) 444-5556
Fax: (843) 444-5558
Toll Free: (800) 968-5819
E-mail: altnews@sccoast.net
Web Site: www.myrtlebeachalternatives.com
Approx. Number Employees: 14
Year Founded: 1985
Business Description:
Publisher of Magazines
S.I.C.: 7311
N.A.I.C.S.: 541810
Advertising Expenditures: $400,000
Media: 2-6-8-9-13-26
Distr.: Natl.
Budget Set: Various
Personnel:
William E. Darby *(CEO & Publr)*
Dariel Bendin *(Editor)*
Michella Woods *(Dir-Creative)*
Brands & Products:
ALTERNATIVES NEWS MAGAZINE
COAST MAGAZINE

CREATIVE LOAFING, INC.
(Holding of Atalaya Capital Management LP)
19011 N 13th St Ste W200
Tampa, FL 33605
Tel.: (813) 739-4800
Fax: (813) 739-4801
Web Site: www.creativeloafing.com
Approx. Sls.: $24,000,000
Approx. Number Employees: 45
Business Description:
Newspaper Publisher
S.I.C.: 2711
N.A.I.C.S.: 511110
Media: 8-25
Personnel:
Marty Petty *(CEO)*
James Howard *(Publr)*
Sharry Smith *(Publr)*
Tony DiSalvo *(VP-Sls)*
Shawn Alff *(Editor-Sex & Love)*
Joe Bardi *(Assoc Editor-Ops)*
Katie Machol *(Editor-Food & Green Community Co-Editor)*
Mitch Perry *(Editor-News & Politics)*
Leilani Polk *(Editor-Music)*
David Warner *(Editor)*
Franki Weddington *(Editor-Arts & Entertainment)*
Patrick Mersinger *(Sr Dir-Interactive)*
Paul Clark *(Dir-Art)*
Jane Earle *(Dir-Mktg Art)*
Julie Garisto *(Dir-Art)*
Murray Grevious *(Dir-MIS)*
Joran Oppelt *(Dir-Mktg & Promotions)*
Chris Herring *(Sr Mgr-Interactive)*
Nick Tipton *(Mgr-AD Design)*
Edward Adams *(Mgr-Online)*
London Fajkus *(Mgr-Ops)*
Marsha Smoot *(Mgr-Credit)*

CREDITRISKMONITOR.COM, INC.
704 Executive Blvd Ste A
Valley Cottage, NY 10989
Tel.: (845) 230-3000
Fax: (845) 267-4110
Toll Free: (877) 468-6276
E-mail: info@creditriskmonitor.com
Web Site: www.creditriskmonitor.com
Approx. Rev.: $9,343,011
Approx. Number Employees: 64
Business Description:
Online Financial Information Services
S.I.C.: 2741
N.A.I.C.S.: 516110
Media: 13
Personnel:
Jerome S. Flum *(Chm & CEO)*
William B. Danner *(Pres)*
Lawrence Fensterstock *(CFO & Sr VP)*

CRM MEDIA, LLC
(Sub. of Information Today Inc.)
237 W 35th St 14th Fl
New York, NY 10001-2509
Tel.: (212) 251-0608
Fax: (212) 779-1152
Web Site: www.destinationcrm.com
Approx. Number Employees: 8
Business Description:
Periodical
S.I.C.: 2721
N.A.I.C.S.: 511120
Media: 2-10-13
Personnel:
Bob Fernekees *(Publr)*
Dennis Sullivan *(Acct Dir)*
David Myron *(Dir-Editorial)*

THE CROWN PUBLISHING GROUP
(Group of Random House, Inc.)
1745 Broadway
New York, NY 10019
Tel.: (212) 782-9000
Fax: (212) 940-7381
Web Site: www.crownpublishing.com
Approx. Number Employees: 400
Business Description:
Book Publisher
S.I.C.: 2731
N.A.I.C.S.: 511130
Media: 6-10-13-19-20
Distr.: Direct to Consumer; Natl.
Brands & Products:
BELL TOWER
CLARKSON POTTER
CROWN
CROWN BUSINESS
CROWN FORUM
CROWN JOURNEYS
HARMONY
SHAYE AREHEART
THREE RIVERS PRESS
Advertising Agency:
Verso Advertising, Inc.
50 W 17th St 5th Fl
New York, NY 10011-5702
Tel.: (212) 292-2990
Fax: (212) 557-2592

CSS INDUSTRIES, INC.
1845 Walnut St Ste 800
Philadelphia, PA 19103-4755
Tel.: (215) 569-9900
Toll Free: (800) 4900CSS
Web Site: www.cssindustries.com
Approx. Sls.: $450,700,000
Approx. Number Employees: 1,830
Year Founded: 1923
Business Description:
Holding Company; Seasonal Consumer Products
S.I.C.: 2771; 2678
N.A.I.C.S.: 511191; 322233
Import Export
Media: 4-5-8-9-19-23
Distr.: Natl.
Personnel:
Jack Farber *(Chm)*
Christopher J. Munyan *(Pres & CEO)*
Vincent A. Paccapaniccia *(CFO & VP-Fin)*
William G. Kiesling *(Gen Counsel & VP-Legal & HR)*
Stefanie L. Smoke *(Treas, Controller & Asst Sec)*
Michael A. Santivasci *(Corp Sec & Asst Gen Counsel)*
Candice B. Cohen *(Asst Sec)*
Brands & Products:

CYNTHIANA PUBLISHING CO.
(Sub. of Landmark Media Enterprises LLC)
302 Webster Ave
Cynthiana, KY 41031-1660
Mailing Address:
PO Box 160
Cynthiana, KY 41031-0160
Tel.: (859) 234-1035
Fax: (859) 234-8096
E-mail: bbarnes@cynthianademocrat.com
Web Site: www.cynthianademocrat.com
Approx. Number Employees: 40
Year Founded: 1973
Business Description:
Commercial Printing & Newspaper Publishing Combined
S.I.C.: 2711; 2721; 2791
N.A.I.C.S.: 511110; 323122; 511120
Media: 8-9-25
Personnel:
Beckey Barnes *(Editor)*
Patricia Jenkins *(Mgr-Adv)*
Brands & Products:
THE CYNTHIANA DEMOCRAT
THE HARRISON SHOPPER

DAEDALUS BOOKS, INC.
9645 Gerwig Ln
Columbia, MD 21046
Tel.: (410) 309-2700
Fax: (410) 309-2701
Toll Free: (800) 395-2665
Web Site: www.daedalusbooks.com
Approx. Number Employees: 150
Year Founded: 1980
Business Description:
Retailer of Books & Music
S.I.C.: 5192; 5942
N.A.I.C.S.: 424920; 451211
Media: 4-6-9-18-25
Personnel:
Robin Moody *(Pres)*
Tony Clemmons *(Mgr-Facilities)*
Cheryl Gant *(Mgr-Sls)*

THE DAILY ARDMOREITE
(Unit of GateHouse Media, Inc.)
117 W Broadway
Ardmore, OK 73401
Tel.: (580) 223-2200
Fax: (580) 226-2363

Key to Media (For complete agency information see *The Advertising Red Books-Agencies* edition):
1. Bus. Publs. 2. Cable T.V. 3. Catalogs & Directories. 4. Co-op Adv. 5. Consumer Mags. 6. D.M. to Bus. Estab.7. D.M. to Consumers
8. Daily Newsp. 9. Exhibits/Trade Shows 10. Foreign 11. Infomercial 12. Internet Adv.13. Multimedia 14. Network Radio
15. Network T.V. 16. Newsp. Distr. Mags. 17. Other 18. Outdoor (Posters, Transit) 19. Point of Purchase20. Premiums, Novelties
21. Product Samples 22. Special Events Mktg. 23. Spot Radio 24. Spot T.V. 25. Weekly Newsp. 26. Yellow Page Adv.

Toll Free: (800) 873-0211
E-mail: info@ardmoreite.com
Web Site: www.ardmoreite.com
Sales Range: $10-24.9 Million
Approx. Number Employees: 48
Year Founded: 1893
Business Description:
Daily Newspaper Publisher
S.I.C.: 2711
N.A.I.C.S.: 511110
Media: 3-9-14-15-23-24-26
Personnel:
Kim Benedict *(Publr)*
Joe Hornback *(Dir-Circulation)*
Melissa Mangham *(Dir-Online)*
Lisa Wilkinson *(Dir-Adv)*
Kathy Worley *(Office Mgr)*

THE DAILY BREEZE
(Unit of Los Angeles Newspaper Group)
(d/b/a Torrance Daily Breeze)
21250 Hawthorne Blvd Ste 170
Torrance, CA 90503
Tel.: (310) 540-5511
Fax: (310) 540-6272
E-mail: marketing@dailybreeze.com
Web Site: www.dailybreeze.com
Approx. Number Employees: 284
Year Founded: 1894
Business Description:
Newspaper Publishers
S.I.C.: 2711
N.A.I.C.S.: 511110
Media: 8
Personnel:
Gregg Bertness *(VP-Adv)*
Jeannie Bolio *(Mgr-Sls)*
Marilyn James *(Mgr-Sls Dev)*
Brands & Products:
THE DAILY BREEZE
Advertising Agency:
Vertis Inc.
2004 McGaw Ave
Irvine, CA 92614
Tel.: (949) 476-0893
Fax: (949) 476-2381

DAILY GAZETTE CO. INC.
2345 Maxon Rd
Schenectady, NY 12308
Tel.: (518) 374-4141
Fax: (518) 395-3084
E-mail: gazette@dailygazette.com
Web Site: www.dailygazette.com
Approx. Sls.: $25,000,000
Approx. Number Employees: 235
Business Description:
Newspapers
S.I.C.: 2711; 2752
N.A.I.C.S.: 511110; 323110
Media: 8-9
Personnel:
John Hume, III *(Pres)*
Daniel T. Beck *(Gen Mgr)*

THE DAILY HERALD CO.
(Sub. of The Washington Post Company)
1213 California St
Everett, WA 98201
Mailing Address:
PO Box 930
Everett, WA 98206
Tel.: (425) 339-3000
Fax: (425) 339-3435
E-mail: webfeedback@heraldnet.com
Web Site: www.heraldnet.com
Sales Range: $25-49.9 Million
Approx. Number Employees: 400
Business Description:
Newspaper Publishing
S.I.C.: 2711
N.A.I.C.S.: 511110
Media: 7-8-13-25
Personnel:
Charles Lyons *(CEO)*
David Dadisman *(Gen Mgr)*
Mike Benbow *(Editor-Bus)*
Steve Hawes *(Dir-Adv)*
Kelly Hulin *(Dir-Mktg & Interactive Media)*
Calvin James *(Dir)*
Rob Schwertley *(Adv Dir)*
Casey Ditton *(Mgr-Home Delivery)*
Sean Flaherty *(Mgr-Retail Adv)*
Kate McCullough *(Mgr-Classified Advertising)*
Robin Prendergast *(Mgr-Digital Bus Dev)*
Tracie Leese *(Supvr-Mktg)*
Brands & Products:
HERALDNET.COM

THE DAILY ITEM
38 Exchange St
Lynn, MA 01901
Tel.: (781) 593-7700
Fax: (781) 595-0035
E-mail: info@itemlive.com
Web Site: www.itemlive.com
Approx. Number Employees: 100
Business Description:
Publisher of News Media
S.I.C.: 2711
N.A.I.C.S.: 511110
Media: 3-13-18-23
Personnel:
Tara Cleary *(Dir-Adv & New Media)*

THE DAILY ITEM
(Sub. of Community Newspaper Holdings, Inc.)
200 Market St
Sunbury, PA 17801
Tel.: (570) 286-5671
Fax: (570) 286-2570
Toll Free: (800) 792-2303
E-mail: info@dailyitem.com
Web Site: www.dailyitem.com
Approx. Number Employees: 200
Business Description:
Newspaper
S.I.C.: 2711
N.A.I.C.S.: 511110
Media: 7-8-9-13-18
Personnel:
Gary Grossman *(Publr)*
Joanne Arbogast *(Editor-Mng, Features & Weekend)*
Paul Boyer *(Editor-Community)*
John Finnerty *(Editor-Editorial)*
Leonard M. Ingrassia *(Editor)*
Patricia Bennett *(Dir-Adv)*
Fred Scheller *(Dir-Circulation)*
Richard Haas *(Mgr-Adv Svcs)*
Lori Seebold *(Mgr-Adv Svcs)*

DAILY JOURNAL CORPORATION
915 E 1st St
Los Angeles, CA 90012-4050
Mailing Address:
355 S Grand Ave 34th Fl
Los Angeles, CA 90071-1560
Tel.: (213) 229-5300
Fax: (213) 680-3682
E-mail: info@dailyjournal.com
Web Site: www.dailyjournal.com
Approx. Rev.: $37,580,000
Approx. Number Employees: 195
Year Founded: 1986
Business Description:
Legal Newspaper Publishers
S.I.C.: 2711; 7313
N.A.I.C.S.: 511110; 541840
Advertising Expenditures: $17,553,000
Media: 9
Personnel:
Charles T. Munger *(Chm)*
J. P. Guerin *(Vice Chm)*
Gerald L. Salzman *(Pres, CEO, CFO, Treas & Asst Sec)*
Jake Flaherty *(Dir-Design)*
Ellen Ireland *(Dir-Mktg)*
Audrey Miller *(Dir-Adv)*

THE DAILY NEWS
(Unit of Freedom Newspapers, Inc.)
724 Bell Fork Rd 28540 PO Box 196
Jacksonville, NC 28541
Tel.: (910) 353-1171
Fax: (910) 353-7316
E-mail: info@thedailynews.com
Web Site: www.thedailynews.com
Year Founded: 2002
Business Description:
Newspaper
S.I.C.: 2711
N.A.I.C.S.: 511110
Media: 8-9-10-13-25

DAILY NEWS, L.P.
(d/b/a New York Daily News)
450 W 33rd St
New York, NY 10001
Tel.: (212) 210-6336
Fax: (212) 643-7831
Toll Free: (800) 223-1660
E-mail: news@nydailynews.com
Web Site: www.nydailynews.com
Approx. Number Employees: 1,500
Year Founded: 1919
Business Description:
Daily & Sunday General Circulation Newspaper
S.I.C.: 2711
N.A.I.C.S.: 511110
Media: 2-3-4-9-11-18-23-24
Distr.: Reg.
Personnel:
Mark Karmer *(CEO)*
Brands & Products:
DAILY NEWS
HORA HISPANA
NYDAILYNEWS.COM
SCRATCH N' MATCH
YOUR DRIVE EN ESPANOL

DAILY NEWS TRIBUNE
(Unit of GateHouse Media New England)
738A Main St
Waltham, MA 02451
Tel.: (781) 398-8002
Fax: (781) 398-8010
E-mail: newstribune@cnc.com
Web Site: www.dailynewstribune.com
Sales Range: $10-24.9 Million
Approx. Number Employees: 7
Business Description:
Newspaper Publisher
S.I.C.: 2711
N.A.I.C.S.: 511110
Media: 9-13
Personnel:
Kirk Davis *(Pres)*
Scott Souza *(Editor-Sports)*
Nicole Simmons *(Mgr-Website)*
Cris Warren *(Mgr-Display Adv)*
Brands & Products:
DAILY NEWS TRIBUNE

DAILY NEWS TRIBUNE INC.
(d/b/a News Tribune)
426 2nd St
La Salle, IL 61301
Tel.: (815) 223-3200
Fax: (815) 223-2543
E-mail: delivery@newstrib.com
Web Site: www.newstrib.com
Approx. Sls.: $10,200,000
Approx. Number Employees: 142
Business Description:
Newspapers, Publishing & Printing
S.I.C.: 2711
N.A.I.C.S.: 511110
Media: 8-9
Personnel:
Joyce McCullough *(Publr)*
Scott Stavrakas *(VP-Sls & Mktg)*
Robert Vickrey *(VP-Sls & Mktg)*

THE DAILY OAKLAND PRESS
(Sub. of 21st Century Newspapers, Inc.)
48 W Huron St
Pontiac, MI 48342
Mailing Address:
PO Box 436009
Pontiac, MI 48343-6009
Tel.: (248) 332-8181
Fax: (248) 332-6480
Toll Free: (800) 686-2754
E-mail: class@oakpress.com
Web Site: www.theoaklandpress.com
Approx. Number Employees: 100
Business Description:
Daily Newspaper
S.I.C.: 2711; 2721
N.A.I.C.S.: 511110; 511120
Media: 2-3-9-13-15-23-24-25
Distr.: Natl.
Budget Set: Oct.
Personnel:
Kevin Haezebroeck *(Publr & Sr VP-Ops-Michigan)*
Allan P. Adler *(Editor-Editorial Page)*
Lee Dryden *(Metro Editor)*
Steve Frye *(Editor-Online)*
Julie Jacobson-Hines *(Editor-Local News)*
Rick Kessler *(Editor-Good Life)*
Jeff Kuehn *(Editor-Sports)*
Alissa Malerman *(Editor-Food)*
Matt Myftiu *(Metro Editor)*
Nicole Robertson *(Editor-Metro)*
Joseph Szczesny *(Automotive Editor)*
Tim Thompson *(Editor-Photo Res)*
Roger Wingelaar *(Editor-Presentation)*
John Lazzeri *(Dir-Circulation)*
Joe Hildebrand *(Mgr-Promos)*
Joann Powell *(Mgr-Customer Satisfaction)*
Noelle Klomp *(Supvr-Classified)*
Sarah Probert *(Supvr-Retail Sls)*
Brands & Products:
THE BIG DRIVE
THE BIG LIST
THE BIG ONE

Key to Media (For complete agency information see *The Advertising Red Books-Agencies* edition):
1. Bus. Publs. 2. Cable T.V. 3. Catalogs & Directories. 4. Co-op Adv. 5. Consumer Mags. 6. D.M. to Bus. Estab.7. D.M. to Consumers 8. Daily Newsp. 9. Exhibits/Trade Shows 10. Foreign 11. Infomercial 12. Internet Adv.13. Multimedia 14. Network Radio 15. Network T.V. 16. Newsp. Distr. Mags. 17. Other 18. Outdoor (Posters, Transit) 19. Point of Purchase20. Premiums, Novelties 21. Product Samples 22. Special Events Mktg. 23. Spot Radio 24. Spot T.V. 25. Weekly Newsp. 26. Yellow Page Adv.

DAILY PRESS
(Unit of Freedom Newspapers, Inc.)
13891 Pk Ave
Victorville, CA 92392
Mailing Address:
PO Box 1389
Victorville, CA 92393
Tel.: (760) 241-7744
Fax: (760) 241-7145
Web Site: www.vvdailypress.com
Year Founded: 1937
Business Description:
Newspaper
S.I.C.: 2711; 2752
N.A.I.C.S.: 511110; 323110
Media: 8-9
Personnel:
Stephan Wingert *(Publr)*
Don Holland *(Editor)*
Steve Williams *(Editor-Editorial Page)*
Angie Callahan *(Dir-Adv)*
Susan Drake *(Mgr-Classified Adv)*
Raul Gutierrez *(Mgr-Mailroom)*
Jane Rowan *(Mgr-New Media)*
Brands & Products:
DAILY PRESS
DESERT DISPATCH
HESPERIA STAR

DAILY RACING FORM, LLC
(Sub. of Sports Information Group LLC)
315 Hudson St Fl 9
New York, NY 10013
Tel.: (212) 366-7600
Fax: (212) 366-7773
Toll Free: (800) 306-3676
E-mail: cservice@drf.com
Web Site: www.drf.com
E-Mail For Key Personnel:
President: BDiamond@drf.com
Marketing Director: mminger@drf.com
Sales Director: rmarks@drf.com
Approx. Number Employees: 150
Year Founded: 1894
Business Description:
Horse Racing Information Newspaper
S.I.C.: 2711
N.A.I.C.S.: 511110
Media: 3-6-13-15-17-19-26
Personnel:
Steven Crist *(Chm & Publr)*
John Harkij *(CEO)*
Vic Sauerhoff *(CFO)*
Logan Bailey *(VP & Gen Mgr-Kentucky)*
Jeffrey Burch *(VP-Adv)*
Mandy Minger *(VP-Mktg)*
Rich Rosenbush *(Editor-in-Chief)*
Fritz Widaman *(Dir-Sls & Bus Dev)*
William J. Allen *(Mgr-Circulation-West)*
Steve Marcinak *(Mgr-Circulation-Midwest)*
Harry McAlpin *(Mgr-Circulation-East)*
Brands & Products:
DAILY RACING FORM
DRF.COM

DAILY RECORD
(Unit of Gannett Co., Inc.)
6th Century Dr
Parsippany, NJ 07054
Mailing Address:
PO Box 217
Parsippany, NJ 07054
Tel.: (973) 428-6200
Fax: (973) 428-6529
Toll Free: (800) 398-8993
E-mail: newsroom@dailyrecord.com
Web Site: www.dailyrecord.com
Sales Range: $25-49.9 Million
Approx. Number Employees: 100
Year Founded: 1898
Business Description:
Newspaper Publisher
S.I.C.: 2711
N.A.I.C.S.: 511110
Media: 2-8-9-13-23
Distr.: Direct to Consumer; Reg.
Personnel:
Karen Guarasi *(Reg VP-Adv)*
James A. Flachsenhaar *(Gen Mgr & Editor)*
Frank DiLeo *(Editor-Sports)*
Keith Muccilli *(Editor-Photo)*
Bill Ditty *(Dir-Adv)*
Brands & Products:
DAILY RECORD

DAILY REPUBLICAN REGISTER
(Sub. of Brehm Communications Inc.)
115 E 4th St
Mount Carmel, IL 62863-2110
Tel.: (618) 262-5144
Fax: (618) 263-4437
Web Site: www.tristate-media.com
Approx. Number Employees: 15
Year Founded: 1975
Business Description:
Newspaper Publisher
S.I.C.: 2711; 2752
N.A.I.C.S.: 511110; 323110
Export
Media: 9-23
Personnel:
Phillip Summers *(Pres & Publr)*
William Brehm *(Pres)*
Brands & Products:
MOUNT CARMEL DAILY REPUBLICAN REGISTER

THE DAILY STAR
(Sub. of Community Newspaper Holdings, Inc.)
102 Chestnut St
Oneonta, NY 13820
Tel.: (607) 432-1000
Fax: (607) 432-5847
E-mail: webmaster@thedailystar.com
Web Site: www.thedailystar.com
Approx. Number Employees: 50
Year Founded: 1890
Business Description:
Newspaper Publisher
S.I.C.: 2711
N.A.I.C.S.: 511110
Media: 7-8-9-13-18
Personnel:
Sam Pollak *(Editor)*
Emily Popek *(Editor-Community News)*
Dean Russin *(Editor-Sports)*
Danielle Ziemba *(Editor-Weekend & Special Editions)*
Matt Lyons *(Dir-Art & Mgr-Circulation)*
Fred Schmidt *(Dir-Circulation & Mktg)*
Olin Benedict *(Mgr-Composing)*
Karen Chichester *(Mgr-Acctg)*
Terry LaPointe *(Mgr-Classifieds & Customer Svc)*

THE DAILY TELEGRAM
(Sub. of Forum Communications Company)
1226 Ogden Ave Ste 1
Superior, WI 54880
Tel.: (715) 395-5000
Fax: (715) 395-0002
E-mail: editotrial@superiortelegram.com
Web Site: www.superiortelegram.com
Approx. Sls.: $55,500,000
Approx. Number Employees: 13
Business Description:
Newspaper Distr
S.I.C.: 2711
N.A.I.C.S.: 511110
Media: 13
Personnel:
Erin Makela *(Gen Mgr)*

DAILY TIMES LEADER
(Sub. of Horizon Publications Inc.)
227 Ct St
West Point, MS 39773-2926
Mailing Address:
PO Box 1176
West Point, MS 39773-1176
Tel.: (662) 494-1422
Fax: (662) 494-1414
E-mail: dtlnews@dailytimesleader.com
Web Site: www.dailytimesleader.com
Approx. Number Employees: 18
Business Description:
Commercial Printing & Newspaper Publishing
S.I.C.: 2711
N.A.I.C.S.: 511110
Media: 8-9-13
Personnel:
Don Norman *(Publr)*
Donna Harris *(Dir-Retail Adv)*
Brands & Products:
DAILY TIMES LEADER

THE DAILY TRIBUNE
(Sub. of 21st Century Newspapers, Inc.)
210 E 3rd St
Royal Oak, MI 48067-2638
Tel.: (248) 541-3000
Fax: (248) 541-7903
E-mail: info@dailytribune.com
Web Site: www.dailytribune.com
Approx. Number Employees: 40
Business Description:
Daily Newspaper Publishing
S.I.C.: 2711; 2721
N.A.I.C.S.: 511110; 511120
Media: 9
Brands & Products:
24/7
DAILY TRIBUNE

THE DALLAS MORNING NEWS CO.
(Sub. of A.H. Belo Corporation)
508 Young St
Dallas, TX 75202-4808
Mailing Address:
PO Box 655237
Dallas, TX 75265-5237
Tel.: (214) 977-8222
Fax: (214) 977-8319
Toll Free: (800) 431-0010
Web Site: www.dallasnews.com
Sales Range: $500-549.9 Million
Approx. Number Employees: 2,000
Year Founded: 1885
Business Description:
Newspaper Publisher
S.I.C.: 2711
N.A.I.C.S.: 511110
Media: 3-7-8-9-13-16-18-19-20-23-24-25-26
Distr.: Reg.
Budget Set: Aug.
Personnel:
John McKeon *(Pres)*
Jim Moroney *(CEO & Publr)*
Fran Wills *(CMO)*
Cyndy Carr *(Sr VP-Sls)*
James T. Berry, Jr. *(VP-Strategy & Plng)*
Grant Moise *(Gen Mgr-Briefing)*
Robert W. Mong *(Editor)*
Sara Miller *(Dir-Art)*
Brands & Products:
DALLASNEWS.COM
Advertising Agency:
The Richards Group, Inc.
8750 N Central Expy Ste 100
Dallas, TX 75231-6430
Tel.: (214) 891-5700
Fax: (214) 265-2933

DANCE MAGAZINE
(Div. of MacFadden Communications Group, LLC)
333 7th Ave 11th Fl
New York, NY 10001
Tel.: (212) 979-4800
Toll Free: (800) 331-1750
E-mail: jpetrov@dancemedia.com
Web Site: www.dancemagazine.com
Business Description:
Magazine
S.I.C.: 2721
N.A.I.C.S.: 511120
Media: 6-8
Personnel:
Karla Johnson *(Pres)*
Wendy Perron *(Editor-in-Chief)*
Hanna Rubin *(Mng Editor)*
Jessie Petrov *(Dir-Mktg)*
Laura Moffat *(Mgr-Adv Sls-Western States, Midwest States, CT & PA)*
Maureen Boston *(Mgr-Adv Sls-Dance Magazine & Young Dancer Marketplace)*
Dee Dee Castro *(Mgr-Sls-Classified Adv & Dance Finder)*

DANVERS HERALD
(Unit of GateHouse Media New England)
72 Cherry Hill Dr
Beverly, MA 01915
Tel.: (978) 774-0505
Fax: (978) 739-8501
E-mail: danvers@cnc.com
Web Site: www.wickedlocal.com/danvers
Sales Range: $25-49.9 Million
Approx. Number Employees: 75
Year Founded: 1870
Business Description:
Newspaper Publisher
S.I.C.: 2711
N.A.I.C.S.: 511110
Media: 8-25
Personnel:
Janes Piasecki *(CFO)*
Chuck Goodrich *(Publr)*
Joe McConnell *(Editor-Sports)*
Cathryn O'Hare *(Editor-News)*
Pat Coen *(Mgr-Production)*
Jane Welch *(Mgr-Display Adv)*

Key to Media (For complete agency information see *The Advertising Red Books-Agencies* edition):
1. Bus. Publs. 2. Cable T.V. 3. Catalogs & Directories. 4. Co-op Adv. 5. Consumer Mags. 6. D.M. to Bus. Estab.7. D.M. to Consumers 8. Daily Newsp. 9. Exhibits/Trade Shows 10. Foreign 11. Infomercial 12. Internet Adv.13. Multimedia 14. Network Radio 15. Network T.V. 16. Newsp. Distr. Mags. 17. Other 18. Outdoor (Posters, Transit) 19. Point of Purchase20. Premiums, Novelties 21. Product Samples 22. Special Events Mktg. 23. Spot Radio 24. Spot T.V. 25. Weekly Newsp. 26. Yellow Page Adv.

DARK HORSE COMICS, INC.
10956 SE Main St
Milwaukie, OR 97222-7644
Tel.: (503) 652-8815
Fax: (503) 654-9440
E-mail: dhc@darkhorse.com
Web Site: www.darkhorse.com
Approx. Number Employees: 80
Year Founded: 1986
Business Description:
Comic Books & Multimedia Publisher
S.I.C.: 2721
N.A.I.C.S.: 511120
Media: 4-5-6-10-19-20
Distr.: Intl.; Natl.
Personnel:
Mike Richardson *(Publr & Producer)*
Neil Hankerson *(Exec VP)*
Anita Nelson *(VP-Sls, Mktg & Licensing)*
David Scroggy *(VP-Product Devel)*
Micha Hershman *(Dir-Mktg)*
Mark Bernardi *(Mgr-Sls)*
Rachelle Callaway *(Mgr-Distributed Product & Intl Sls)*
Amy Huey *(Mgr-Adv & Clearances)*
Brands & Products:
DARK HORSE
DARK HORSE COMICS

THE DARTNELL CORP.
(Sub. of LRP Publications)
360 Hiatt Dr
Palm Beach Gardens, FL 33418-7106
Tel.: (561) 622-6520
Fax: (561) 622-2423
Toll Free: (800) 621-5463
E-mail: custserv@lrp.com
Web Site: www.dartnellcorp.com
Approx. Number Employees: 189
Year Founded: 1917
Business Description:
Publisher of Business Books; Newsletters, Training Films & Seminars
S.I.C.: 2721; 7389
N.A.I.C.S.: 511120; 711410
Export
Advertising Expenditures: $6,000,000
Media: 2-3-4-5-6-7-8-9-10-13-23
Distr.: Direct to Consumer; Intl.; Natl.
Budget Set: Dec.
Brands & Products:
CUSTOMERS FIRST

DATAMAX CORPORATION
(Sub. of Dover Engineered Systems, Inc.)
4501 Pkwy Commerce Blvd
Orlando, FL 32808-1013
Tel.: (407) 578-8007
Fax: (407) 578-8377
Toll Free: (800) 816-9649
E-mail: info@datamax-oneil.com
Web Site: www.datamax-oneil.com
Sales Range: $100-124.9 Million
Approx. Number Employees: 350
Year Founded: 1977
Business Description:
Bar Code Software, Label Printing Devices & Labels Mfr
S.I.C.: 3577; 2754
N.A.I.C.S.: 334119; 323111
Export
Media: 2-5-7-10
Personnel:
Carter Williams *(CFO)*
Theo Bielowicz *(Dir-Distr Mgmt)*
Brands & Products:
A-CLASS
E-CLASS
I-CLASS
I-CLASS-RFID
M-CLASS
S-CLASS
W-CLASS
Advertising Agency:
Dayner Hall Marketing + Advertising
(d/b/a DaynerHall)
621 E Pine St
Orlando, FL 32801
Tel.: (407) 428-5750
Fax: (407) 426-9896

DAUGHTERS OF ST. PAUL
(d/b/a Pauline Books and Media)
50 Saint Pauls Ave
Boston, MA 02130-3491
Tel.: (617) 522-8911
Fax: (617) 541-9805
Web Site: www.paulinemedia.com
Approx. Number Employees: 80
Business Description:
Book Publishing & Printing
S.I.C.: 2731; 7812
N.A.I.C.S.: 511130; 512110
Media: 4-10

DC COMICS, INC.
(Sub. of Warner Bros. Entertainment Inc.)
1700 Brdwy
New York, NY 10019-5905
Tel.: (212) 636-5400
Fax: (212) 636-5979
E-mail: publicity@dccomics.com
Web Site: www.dccomics.com
E-Mail For Key Personnel:
Marketing Director:
dccomicsadvertising@dccomics.com
Sales Range: $75-99.9 Million
Approx. Number Employees: 250
Year Founded: 1935
Business Description:
Comic Book Publishing, Syndication & Product Licensing Services
S.I.C.: 2721
N.A.I.C.S.: 511120
Media: 5-6-19-21
Distr.: Natl.
Personnel:
Paul Levitz *(Pres & Publ)*
Geoff Johns *(Chief Creative Officer-DC Entertainment)*
Diane Nelson *(Pres-DC Entertainment)*
Jim Lee *(Co-Publr)*
Patrick Caldon *(Exec VP-Fin & Ops)*
John Rood *(Exec VP-Sls, Bus Dev & Mktg-DC Entertainment)*
Dan DiDio *(Sr VP & Exec Editor)*
Richard Bruning *(Sr VP & Dir-Creative)*
Amy Genkins *(Sr VP-Legal & Bus Affairs)*
Amy Jenkins *(Sr VP-Legal)*
Gregory Noveck *(Sr VP-Creative Affairs)*
Steve Rotterdam *(Sr VP-Sls & Mktg)*
Cheryl Rubin *(Sr VP-Brand Mgmt)*
Georg Brewer *(VP-Design & Creative)*
Chris Caramalis *(VP-Fin)*
John Cunningham *(VP-Mktg)*
Ron Perazza *(VP-Online-DC Entertainment)*
Alysse Soll *(VP-Adv & Custom Publ)*
Bob Wayne *(VP-Sls)*
Bob Harras *(Editor-in-Chief)*
Gary Kleinman *(Dir-Sls-Natl)*
Dave McCullough *(Dir-DC Online)*
Brands & Products:
ALAN SCOTT
ALFRED PENNYWORTH
AQUAMAN
BARBARA GORDON
BARRY ALLEN
BATGIRL
BATMAN
BEAST BOY
BLACK ADAM
BLOODHOUND
BLUE BEETLE
BOOSTER GOLD
BRAINIAC
BRUCE WAYNE
CAPTAIN COLD
CAPTAIN COMET
CAPTAIN MARVEL
CATWOMAN
CLARK KENT
CYBORG
DC COMICS
DICK GRAYSON
DOOM PATROL
FIRESTORM
THE FLASH
GREEN ARROW
GREEN LANTERN
GUY GARDNER
IMPULSE
JIM GORDON
JIMMY OLSEN
JLA
JOKER
JSA
JUSTICE LEAGUE OF AMERICA
JUSTICE SOCIETY OF AMERICA
KRYPTO
KYLE RAYNER
LEX LUTHOR
LOBO
LOIS LANE
THE MARTIAN MANHUNTER
MR. MXYZPTLK
NIGHTWING
OMAC
THE OUTSIDERS
PARADOX PRESS
PARASITE
THE PENGUIN
PERRY WHITE
PLASTIC MAN
PROFESSOR ZOOM
RA'S AL GHUL
ROBIN
SANDMAN
THE SCARECROW
SCARECROW
SENTINEL
SHAZAM
STARMAN
SUICIDE SQUAD
SUPERBOY
SUPERGIRL
SUPERMAN
SUPERWOMAN
TEEN TITANS
TIM DRAKE
VERTIGO
WALLY WEST
WILDSTORM
WONDER GIRL
WONDER WOMAN
ZOOM

DELTA FARM PRESS
(Joint Venture of MidOcean Partners, LLP & Wasserstein & Co., LP)
14920 US Hwy 61
Clarksdale, MS 38614
Mailing Address:
PO Box 1420
Clarksdale, MS 38614-1420
Tel.: (662) 624-8503
Fax: (662) 627-1977
Toll Free: (800) 253-3160
E-mail: info@deltafarmpress.com
Web Site: www.deltafarmpress.com
Approx. Number Employees: 55
Year Founded: 1943
Business Description:
Newspaper Publisher
S.I.C.: 2711
N.A.I.C.S.: 511110
Advertising Expenditures: $200,000
Media: 2-6-17
Distr.: Natl.
Budget Set: Nov.
Personnel:
Richard A. Wright *(Dir-Adv)*
Darrah Parker *(Mgr-Mktg)*
Brands & Products:
DELTA AGRICULTURAL DIGEST
FARM PRESS PUBLICATIONS
SOUTHEAST AGRICULTURAL DIGEST

DELUXE CORPORATION
3680 Victoria St N
Shoreview, MN 55126
Mailing Address:
PO Box 64235
Saint Paul, MN 55164-0235
Tel.: (651) 483-7111
Fax: (651) 481-4163
E-mail: feedback@deluxe.com
Web Site: www.deluxe.com
Approx. Rev.: $1,402,237,000
Approx. Number Employees: 5,765
Year Founded: 1915
Business Description:
Fraud Prevention, Customer Loyalty & Brand Building Products & Services
S.I.C.: 7389; 2759
N.A.I.C.S.: 561499; 323119
Advertising Expenditures: $93,500,000
Media: 2-4-5-7-10-19
Distr.: Natl.
Budget Set: May
Personnel:
Lee J. Schram *(CEO)*
Terry D. Peterson *(CFO & Sr VP)*
Thomas L. Morefield *(Pres-Fin Svcs & Sr VP)*
Anthony C. Scarfone *(Gen Counsel, Sec & Sr VP)*
Julie M. Loosbrock *(Sr VP-HR)*
Malcolm J. McRoberts *(Sr VP-Small Bus Svcs)*
Lynn R. Koldenhoven *(VP-Sls & Mktg-Direct to Consumer)*
Laura L. Radewald *(VP-Enterprise Brand, Customer Experience & Media Relations)*

Key to Media (For complete agency information see *The Advertising Red Books-Agencies* edition):
1. Bus. Publs. 2. Cable T.V. 3. Catalogs & Directories. 4. Co-op Adv. 5. Consumer Mags. 6. D.M. to Bus. Estab.7. D.M. to Consumers 8. Daily Newsp. 9. Exhibits/Trade Shows 10. Foreign 11. Infomercial 12. Internet Adv.13. Multimedia 14. Network Radio 15. Network T.V. 16. Newsp. Distr. Mags. 17. Other 18. Outdoor (Posters, Transit) 19. Point of Purchase20. Premiums, Novelties 21. Product Samples 22. Special Events Mktg. 23. Spot Radio 24. Spot T.V. 25. Weekly Newsp. 26. Yellow Page Adv.

Deluxe Corporation — (Continued)

Steve Morse *(Exec Dir-Mktg Solutions & Product Mgmt)*
Jennifer Anderson *(Dir-Foundations & Community Affairs)*
Brands & Products:
DELUXE
DELUXE BUSINESS ADVANTAGE
DELUXE DETECT
DELUXE ID THEFTBLOCK
DELUXE KNOWLEDGE EXCHANGE
DELUXE SECUREMAIL
DELUXECALLING
DELUXECARD
DELUXESELECT
LOYALTY THROUGH EXPERIENCE
NEBS
PARTNERUP
REFERRAL EXPRESS!
YOUR PARTNER IN GROWTH.
Advertising Agency:
Risdall Marketing Group
550 Main St
New Brighton, MN 55112-3271
Tel.: (651) 286-6700
Fax: (651) 631-2561
Toll Free: (888) RISDALL

THE DEMOCRAT CO.

(Sub. of Brehm Communications Inc.)
1226 Ave H
Fort Madison, IA 52627-4544
Tel.: (319) 372-6421
Fax: (319) 372-3867
E-mail: democrats@interl.net
Web Site: www.dailydem.com
Approx. Number Employees: 40
Year Founded: 1906
Business Description:
Newspapers
S.I.C.: 2711; 2791
N.A.I.C.S.: 511110; 323122
Import Export
Media: 9-22-25
Personnel:
Mark Smidt *(Publr)*
Brands & Products:
DAILY DEMOCRAT
DAILY GATE CITY
HANCOCK COUNTY JOURNAL PILOT

DENTON PUBLISHING COMPANY

(Sub. of A.H. Belo Corporation)
314 E Hickory St
Denton, TX 76201-4272
Mailing Address:
PO Box 369
Denton, TX 76202-0369
Tel.: (940) 387-3811
Fax: (940) 566-6846
E-mail: drc@dentonrc.com
Web Site: www.dentonrc.com
Sales Range: $25-49.9 Million
Approx. Number Employees: 70
Year Founded: 1903
Business Description:
Newspaper Publishing
S.I.C.: 2711
N.A.I.C.S.: 511110
Media: 9-13
Personnel:
Bill Patterson *(Publr)*
Sandra Kelly *(Dir-Adv)*
Cody Robinson *(Dir-Production)*
Brands & Products:
THE DENTON RECORD CHRONICLE

THE DENVER NEWSPAPER AGENCY

(Joint Venture of The E.W. Scripps Company & MediaNews Group, Inc.)
101 W coosas st
Denver, CO 80204
Tel.: (303) 820-1010
Fax: (303) 820-1369
Toll Free: (800) 336-7678
E-mail: fdixon@denverpost.com
Web Site: www.denverpost.com
Sales Range: $350-399.9 Million
Approx. Number Employees: 1,200
Year Founded: 1893
Business Description:
Newspaper Advertising & Promotional Services; Owned by The E.W. Scripps Company & by MediaNews Group Inc.
S.I.C.: 7311; 7319
N.A.I.C.S.: 541810; 541890
Advertising Expenditures: $4,000,000
Media: 2-3-4-6-7-8-10-13-23-24-26
Distr.: Reg.
Budget Set: June
Personnel:
Gerald Grilly *(Pres & CEO)*
Frank Dixon *(COO)*
Missy Miller *(Sr VP-HR & Labor Rels)*
Bob Kinney *(VP-IT & PrePubl)*
Rich Bradley *(Dir-Circulation)*
Larry Charest *(Dir-Production)*
Tim Dubus *(Dir-Creative-Mktg)*
Bernie Gitt *(Dir-Circulation Consumer Rels)*
Steve Johansson *(Dir-Circulation Ops)*
Kathy Maaliki *(Dir-Benefit & HR Admin)*
Vernon Mallinen *(Dir-Consumer Mktg)*
Katie McManus *(Dir-Pkgng)*
Tracy Ulmer *(Dir-Promos & Community Rels)*
Robyn Davenport *(Mgr-Recruitment-Online Product)*
Brands & Products:
THE DENVER POST
ROCKY MOUNTAIN NEWS
Advertising Agencies:
Bradley Reid & Associates
900 W 5th Ave Ste 100
Anchorage, AK 99501
Tel.: (907) 276-6353
Fax: (907) 276-1042

Karsh & Hagan Communications, Inc.
2399 Blake St Ste 160
Denver, CO 80205-2108
Tel.: (303) 296-8400
Fax: (303) 296-2015

DERRICK PUBLISHING CO.

1510 W 1st St
Oil City, PA 16301
Tel.: (814) 676-7444
Fax: (814) 677-8347
E-mail: info@thederrick.com
Web Site: www.thederrick.com
Approx. Sls.: $14,000,000
Approx. Number Employees: 130
Business Description:
Newspapers, Publishing & Printing
S.I.C.: 2711; 4832
N.A.I.C.S.: 511110; 515112
Media: 8-9-13
Personnel:
Patrick C. Boyle *(Owner)*
Paul Hess *(Mgr-Adv Sls)*

DERRY PUBLISHING CO. INC.

(Sub. of Eagle-Tribune Publishing Company Inc.)
(d/b/a The Derry News)
46 W Broadway
Derry, NH 03038-2329
Tel.: (603) 437-7000
Fax: (603) 432-4510
Web Site: www.derrynews.com
Approx. Number Employees: 17
Year Founded: 1984
Business Description:
Newspaper Publisher
S.I.C.: 2711
N.A.I.C.S.: 511110
Media: 8-9
Personnel:
L. Getler *(Publr)*
Bruce Slichko *(Mgr-Circulation)*
Nancy Wimmer *(Coord-Adv)*

DERYCZ SCIENTIFIC, INC.

1524 Cloverfield Blvd Ste E
Santa Monica, CA 90404
Tel.: (310) 477-0354
Tel.: (707) 658-1931
E-mail: investors@deryczscientific.com
Web Site: www.deryczscientific.com
Approx. Sls.: $24,935,473
Approx. Number Employees: 10
Year Founded: 2006
Business Description:
Holding Company; Printing Services
S.I.C.: 6719; 2759; 7389
N.A.I.C.S.: 551112; 323119; 519190
Advertising Expenditures: $40,437
Media: 2-10-22
Personnel:
Peter V. Derycz *(Chm, Pres & CEO)*
Richard McKilligan *(CFO & Gen Counsel)*
Ian Palmer *(Head-Mktg)*
Jan Peterson *(Head-PR)*

DESERT DISPATCH

(Unit of Freedom Newspapers, Inc.)
130 Coolwater Ln
Barstow, CA 92311
Tel.: (760) 256-2257
Fax: (760) 256-0685
E-mail: blint@desertdispatch.com
Web Site: www.desertdispatch.com
Approx. Number Employees: 12
Year Founded: 1910
Business Description:
Newspaper
S.I.C.: 2711; 7313
N.A.I.C.S.: 511110; 541840
Media: 8-9
Personnel:
Scott Shackford *(Editor-in-Chief)*
Bea Lint *(Dir-Adv)*

DESERT PUBLICATIONS INC.

303 N Indian Cyn Dr
Palm Springs, CA 92262
Tel.: (760) 325-2333
Fax: (760) 325-7008
E-mail: milt@palmspringslife.com
Web Site: www.desertpublications.com
Approx. Number Employees: 65
Business Description:
Publisher of Magazines
S.I.C.: 2721
N.A.I.C.S.: 511120
Media: 6-13
Personnel:
Milton W. Jones *(Pres & Publr)*
Frank W. Jones *(Assoc Publr)*
Brands & Products:
GUESTLIFE
PALM SPRINGS LIFE
Advertising Agency:
The Jones Agency
303 N Indian Canyon Dr
Palm Springs, CA 92262-6015
Tel.: (760) 325-1437
Fax: (760) 778-0320

DETAILS MAGAZINE

(Unit of Conde Nast Publications, Inc.)
750 3rd Ave 3rd Fl
New York, NY 10017
Tel.: (212) 630-4000
Fax: (212) 630-4830
Toll Free: (800) 234-3071
Web Site: www.details.com
Approx. Number Employees: 120
Business Description:
Magazine Publisher
S.I.C.: 2721
N.A.I.C.S.: 511120
Media: 6-8-10
Personnel:
Bill Wackermann *(Publr & VP)*
Daniel Peres *(Editor-in-Chief)*
Julia Fry *(Dir-Adv)*
Timothy Hodler *(Dir-Res)*
Jennifer Kiffer *(Dir-Mktg Dev)*

DETROIT LEGAL NEWS PUBLISHING LLC

2001 W Lafayette Blvd
Detroit, MI 48216
Tel.: (313) 961-3949
Fax: (313) 961-3082
Web Site: www.legalnews.com
Approx. Number Employees: 75
Year Founded: 1895
Business Description:
Commercial Printing & Newspaper Publishing Combined
S.I.C.: 2711; 2721
N.A.I.C.S.: 511110; 511120
Media: 7-9
Personnel:
Bradley L. Thompson, II *(CEO-Detroit Legal News Co)*

DETROIT MEDIA PARTNERSHIP

(Formerly Detroit Newspaper Partnership, L.P.)
(Sub. of Gannett Co., Inc.)
615 W Lafayette Blvd
Detroit, MI 48226
Tel.: (313) 222-6400
Toll Free: (800) 395-3300
Web Site: www.detroitmedia.com
Sales Range: $750-799.9 Million
Approx. Number Employees: 2,600
Year Founded: 1989
Business Description:
Holding Company; Newspaper Publisher
S.I.C.: 6719; 2711
N.A.I.C.S.: 551112; 511110
Media: 6-7-8-9-10-13-18-19-23-25
Distr.: Reg.
Personnel:
Joyce Jenereaux *(Exec VP)*

Key to Media (For complete agency information see *The Advertising Red Books-Agencies* edition):
1. Bus. Publs. 2. Cable T.V. 3. Catalogs & Directories. 4. Co-op Adv. 5. Consumer Mags. 6. D.M. to Bus. Estab.7. D.M. to Consumers
8. Daily Newsp. 9. Exhibits/Trade Shows 10. Foreign 11. Infomercial 12. Internet Adv.13. Multimedia 14. Network Radio
15. Network T.V. 16. Newsp. Distr. Mags. 17. Other 18. Outdoor (Posters, Transit) 19. Point of Purchase20. Premiums, Novelties
21. Product Samples 22. Special Events Mktg. 23. Spot Radio 24. Spot T.V. 25. Weekly Newsp. 26. Yellow Page Adv.

Kristi B. Bowden *(VP-HR)*
Rebecca Steckler *(VP-Adv)*
Tim Brower *(Dir-Digital Dev)*
Joanne Krause *(Dir-Automotive Adv)*
David Richards *(Dir-Integrated Client Solutions)*

Advertising Agency:
BERLINE
70 E Long Lk Rd
Bloomfield Hills, MI 48304
Tel.: (248) 593-4744
Fax: (248) 593-4740
(Newspaper)

THE DETROIT NEWS, INC.

(Sub. of MediaNews Group, Inc.)
615 W Lafayette Blvd
Detroit, MI 48226-3124
Tel.: (313) 222-6400
Fax: (313) 222-2190
E-mail: metro@detnews.com
Web Site: www.detnews.com
Sales Range: $25-49.9 Million
Approx. Number Employees: 350
Business Description:
Newspaper Publisher
S.I.C.: 2711
N.A.I.C.S.: 511110
Advertising Expenditures: $750,000
Media: 2-6-7-8-9-10-11-13-14-18-19-21-22-23-24
Distr.: Natl.
Budget Set: Sept.
Personnel:
Nick Assendelft *(Editor-Govt)*
Arthur Brooks *(Editor-Copy)*
Michael Brown *(Asst Mng Editor-Info Tech)*
Susan Carney *(Editor-Bus)*
Leslie Crutchfield *(Editor-Copy)*
Marlene Davenport *(Deputy Editor-News)*
Lawrence Davis *(Editor-Copy)*
Judy Diebolt *(Asst Features Editor-Homestyle)*
Rick Epps *(Editor-Presentation)*
Chris Farina *(Editor-Photo Assignment)*
Nolan Finley *(Editor-Editorial Page)*
Don Frost *(Asst Editor-News)*
Rita Holt *(Editor-Features)*
Robert L'Heureux *(Editor-Online Graphics)*
Ruben Luna *(Deputy Editor-Sports)*
Kathleen Niezurawski *(Editor-Copy)*
Don Ramsey *(Editor-Copy)*
Chris Rizk *(Editor-Night City)*
Leslie Rotan *(Editor-Copy)*
James Russ *(Editor-Online Sports)*
Sandra Silfven *(Editor-Copy)*
Timothy Summers *(Editor-Graphic)*
Steve Wilkinson *(Editor-Copy)*
Craig Yuhas *(Editor-Copy)*
Tom Gromak *(Dir-News & Tech)*

DETROIT NEWSPAPER PARTNERSHIP, L.P.

(Name Changed to Detroit Media Partnership)

DEX ONE CORPORATION

1001 Winstead Dr
Cary, NC 27513
Tel.: (919) 297-1600
Toll Free: (866) 527-4550
E-mail: info@dexone.com
Web Site: www.dexone.com
Approx. Rev.: $991,259,000
Approx. Number Employees: 3,200
Year Founded: 1886
Business Description:
Marketing Services
S.I.C.: 2752; 2741; 7319; 8742
N.A.I.C.S.: 541890; 323110; 511140; 541613; 541870
Advertising Expenditures: $52,200,000
Media: 13-22
Personnel:
Alfred T. Mockett *(CEO)*
Gregory W. Freiberg *(CFO & Exec VP)*
Margaret Le Beau *(CMO & Sr VP)*
Atish Banerjea *(CTO & Sr VP)*
Sylvester J. Johnson *(Chief Acctg Officer)*
David W. Sharman *(Chief Strategist Officer & Sr VP)*
Mark W. Hianik *(Gen Counsel, Sec & Sr VP)*
Richard J. Hanna *(Exec VP-Sls & Mktg)*
Sean W. Greene *(Sr VP-Interactive)*
Tyler D. Gronbach *(Sr VP-Corp Comm & Admin)*
Donna Towles *(Sr VP-Ops)*
Gretchen Zech *(Sr VP-HR)*
Brands & Products:
DEX
DEX ONE
Advertising Agency:
Cramer-Krasselt
225 N Michigan Ave
Chicago, IL 60601-7601
Tel.: (312) 616-9600
Fax: (312) 616-3839

DIAMOND COMIC DISTRIBUTORS, INC.

1966 Greenspring Dr Ste 300
Lutherville Timonium, MD 21093-4161
Tel.: (410) 560-7100
Fax: (410) 560-7151
E-mail: service@diamondcomics.com
Web Site: www.diamondcomics.com
Approx. Number Employees: 540
Year Founded: 1982
Business Description:
Comic Books & Related Products Distr
S.I.C.: 5192
N.A.I.C.S.: 424920
Export
Media: 4-8-10-13-22
Personnel:
Steve Geppi *(Founder & Pres)*
Charles A. Parker *(COO & Exec VP)*
Roger Fletcher *(VP-Mktg)*
Bill Schanes *(VP-Pur)*
Larry R. Swanson *(VP-Fin)*
Joe Shanley *(Brand Mgr)*
Eric Watson *(Brand Mgr)*
Cindy Anderson *(Mgr-Mktg Production)*

DIRECT HOLDINGS AMERICAS INC.

(Sub. of The Reader's Digest Association, Inc.)
8280 Willow Oaks Corporate Dr Ste 800
Fairfax, VA 22031-4511
Tel.: (703) 663-4500
Fax: (703) 663-4545
Web Site: www.timelife.com
Sales Range: $400-449.9 Million
Approx. Number Employees: 150
Year Founded: 1961
Business Description:
Book, Music & Video Product Direct Marketing & Retail Services
S.I.C.: 7389; 5735; 5942; 5961
N.A.I.C.S.: 541990; 451211; 451220; 454111; 454113
Media: 3-5-6-7-8-11-14-23-24
Distr.: Intl.; Natl.
Personnel:
Chris Hearing *(Pres)*
Randy Elkins *(Sr VP)*
Jennifer Smith *(Dir-Mktg)*
Brands & Products:
AMERICAN COUNTRY
CHILDS FIRST LIBRARY OF LEARNING
GARDENER'S GUIDE
LITTLE PEOPLE, BIG BOOKS
MYSTERIES OF THE UNKNOWN
ROCK N' ROLL
SOUNDS OF THE SEVENTIES
THE THIRD REICH
TIME-LIFE VIDEO RECORDINGS
VICTORY AT SEA VIDEO
VIETNAM VIDEO
VOYAGE THROUGH THE UNIVERSE
WORLD WAR II VIDEO
Advertising Agencies:
Hawthorne Direct Inc.
300 N 16th St
Fairfield, IA 52556-2604
Tel.: (641) 472-3800
Fax: (641) 472-4553

RJ Lauren, Inc.
23679 Calabasas Rd Ste 552
Calabasas, CA 91302
Tel.: (818) 879-2200
Fax: (818) 879-2215

DISCOVER MAGAZINE

(Sub. of The Walt Disney Company)
90 5th Ave
New York, NY 10011-7629
Tel.: (212) 624-4800
E-mail: editorial@discovermagazine.com
Web Site: www.discovermagazine.com
Sales Range: $100-124.9 Million
Business Description:
Magazine Publisher
S.I.C.: 2721
N.A.I.C.S.: 511120
Advertising Expenditures: $1,000,000
Media: 6-8-17
Distr.: Direct to Consumer; Natl.
Personnel:
Bob Guccione, Jr. *(Chm)*
Henry Donahue *(CEO)*
William C. Hostetter *(Publr)*
Corey S. Powell *(Editor-in-Chief)*
Jennifer Barone *(Editor-News)*
Advertising Agency:
Goodman Media International, Inc.
750 7th Ave 28th Fl
New York, NY 10016
Tel.: (212) 576-2700
Fax: (212) 576-2701

THE DISPATCH PRINTING COMPANY

34 S 3rd St
Columbus, OH 43215-4201
Tel.: (614) 461-5000
Fax: (614) 461-5533
Web Site: www.dispatch.com
Approx. Number Employees: 2,300
Year Founded: 1871
Business Description:
Publisher of Newspapers
S.I.C.: 2711; 4833
N.A.I.C.S.: 511110; 515120
Import
Media: 2-7-8-9-10-18-20-22-23-24
Distr.: Natl.
Personnel:
John F. Wolfe *(Chm, CEO & Publr)*
Michael J. Fiorile *(Pres & COO)*
Poe A. Timmons *(CFO & VP)*
Joe Gallo *(CIO & VP)*
Abby Clark *(VP-Sls)*
Gary Kiefer *(Mng Editor-New Media)*
Karl Kuntz *(Editor-Photo)*
Ben Marrison *(Editor)*
Jean Nemeti *(Dir-Mktg)*
Don Wentz *(Dir-Mktg-Art)*
Eric Wygle *(Mgr-Mktg & Promos)*
Brands & Products:
CNS THIS WEEK
THE COLUMBUS DISPATCH
DCS "THE BAG"
DISPATCH CONSUMER SERVICES

DK PUBLISHING

(Unit of Penguin Group (USA) Inc.)
375 Hudson St
New York, NY 10014
Tel.: (212) 366-2000
Fax: (212) 689-4828
E-mail: web@dk.com
Web Site: www.us.dk.com
Approx. Number Employees: 120
Year Founded: 1991
Business Description:
Nonfiction Books, CD-ROMs & Videos Publisher
S.I.C.: 2731
N.A.I.C.S.: 511130
Import Export
Advertising Expenditures: $1,000,000
Media: 2-3-4-6-9-10-13-14-15-18-19-20-21-22-23-24-25
Personnel:
Anita Bloom *(Assoc Dir-eBook & Publ Bus Mgmt)*
Tanya Reynolds *(Publicist)*
Brands & Products:
EYEWITNESS BOOKS
EYEWITNESS TRAVEL
KISS

DODGE CITY DAILY GLOBE

(Unit of GateHouse Media, Inc.)
705 N 2nd Ave
Dodge City, KS 67801-0820
Mailing Address:
PO Box 820
Dodge City, KS 67801-0820
Tel.: (620) 225-4151
Fax: (620) 225-4154
Toll Free: (800) 279-8795
E-mail: dcnews@dodgeglobe.com
Web Site: www.dodgeglobe.com
Sales Range: $10-24.9 Million
Approx. Number Employees: 50
Year Founded: 1878
Business Description:
Daily Newspaper Publisher
S.I.C.: 2711
N.A.I.C.S.: 511110
Media: 8-9

Key to Media (For complete agency information see *The Advertising Red Books-Agencies* edition):
1. Bus. Publs. 2. Cable T.V. 3. Catalogs & Directories. 4. Co-op Adv. 5. Consumer Mags. 6. D.M. to Bus. Estab.7. D.M. to Consumers 8. Daily Newsp. 9. Exhibits/Trade Shows 10. Foreign 11. Infomercial 12. Internet Adv.13. Multimedia 14. Network Radio 15. Network T.V. 16. Newsp. Distr. Mags. 17. Other 18. Outdoor (Posters, Transit) 19. Point of Purchase20. Premiums, Novelties 21. Product Samples 22. Special Events Mktg. 23. Spot Radio 24. Spot T.V. 25. Weekly Newsp. 26. Yellow Page Adv.

Dodge City Daily Globe — (Continued)

Personnel:
Darrel Adams *(Publr)*
Shawn Cannon *(Mgr-New Media)*
Rebecca Gerber *(Mgr-Classified Ads)*

THE DOLAN COMPANY

222 S 9th St Ste 230
Minneapolis, MN 55402
Tel.: (612) 317-9420
Fax: (612) 321-0563
Fax: (612) 317-9434
Web Site: www.dolanmedia.com
Approx. Rev.: $311,309,000
Approx. Number Employees: 2,034
Year Founded: 1992
Business Description:
Holding Company; Business & Professional Publisher
S.I.C.: 6719; 2711; 2741; 7389
N.A.I.C.S.: 551112; 511110; 511199; 516110; 519190
Media: 4-7-8-10-25
Personnel:
James P. Dolan *(Chm, Pres & CEO)*
Vicki J. Duncomb *(CFO & VP-Fin)*
Scott J. Pollei *(COO & Exec VP)*
Renee L. Jackson *(Gen Counsel & VP)*
Mark W.C. Stodder *(Exec VP-Bus Info)*
Vince Swartout *(VP-Tech)*
Robert J. Evans *(Dir-IR)*

DOME PUBLISHING COMPANY, INC.

10 New England Way
Warwick, RI 02886-6904
Tel.: (401) 738-7900
Fax: (401) 732-5377
Toll Free: (800) 432-4352
E-mail: sales@domeind.com
Web Site: www.domeproducts.com
E-Mail For Key Personnel:
Sales Director: sales@domeind.com
Approx. Number Employees: 60
Year Founded: 1940
Business Description:
Publisher of Payroll Books; Travel Expense Records; Medical Expense Logs & Related Products
S.I.C.: 2789; 8721
N.A.I.C.S.: 323121; 541219
Export
Advertising Expenditures: $1,225,000
Bus. Publs.: $1,000,000; Consumer Mags.: $200,000; Premiums, Novelties: $25,000
Distr.: Natl.
Brands & Products:
DOME
HANDEZE
IDEAL SYSTEMS
SELFGRIP

DOMINION ENTERPRISES

(Sub. of Landmark Media Enterprises LLC)
150 Granby St
Norfolk, VA 23510
Mailing Address:
PO Box 2576
Norfolk, VA 23501-2576
Tel.: (757) 351-7000
Fax: (757) 314-2500
Web Site:
www.dominionenterprises.com
Approx. Rev.: $850,000,000
Approx. Number Employees: 6,600
Year Founded: 1991
Business Description:
Media & Information Services
S.I.C.: 7389; 2721; 2731; 2741; 7319
N.A.I.C.S.: 561499; 511120; 511130; 511140; 511199; 541870; 561439; 561990
Export
Media: 2-6-7-8-10-13
Distr.: Natl.
Personnel:
Teresa F. Blevins *(CFO & Exec VP)*
Joe C. Fuller *(CIO & VP)*
Robert M. Berndt *(Pres-Dominion Dealer Solutions)*
Jeff T. Littlejohn *(Pres-Dominion Adv Media & Dominion Innovations)*
Jack J. Ross *(Pres-Adv Media)*
Terry M. Slattery *(Pres-For Rent Media Solutions)*
George P. Brooks *(Exec VP)*
Guy R. Friddell, III *(Exec VP)*
Sunny R. Sonner *(Exec VP-HR)*
Brands & Products:
123 MOVERS.COM
123CONTRACTORQUOTES.COM
AERO TRADER
@UTO REVENUE
ATVTRADERONLINE.COM
AUTO TRADER ON-LINE
AUTOTRADER.COM
BARGAIN TRADER
BIG TRUCK TRADER
BOAT TRADER
BOATS.COM
CAREERS IN GEAR
COMPUTER HOTLINE
CORPORATE HOUSING
CYCLE TRADER
DEALER SPECIALTIES
DEALERSKINS
DISTINCTIVE HOMES
THE EMPLOYMENT GUIDE
EQUIPMENT TRADER
FOR RENT
HARMON HOMES
HARMONHOMES.COM
HEALTHCAREERWEB.COM
HOME SOLUTIONS
HOMES.COM
HOTELCOUPONS.COM
JOBALOT.COM
JUST AUTOMOTIVE
KATABAT
MAILMARK
NATIONAL RV TRADER
NEW HOMES & LIVING
NOR'EASTER
NUMBER1EXPERT.COM
PARA RENTAR
PARENTHOOD
PASSAGE MAKER
PAYLOAD
PRESTIGE COLLECTION
PWCTRADERONLINE.COM
RENTJILLSHOUSE.COM
RJHRESORTS.COM
ROOMSAVER.COM
RV TRADER
SELECTQU
SENIOR OUTLOOK
SNOWMOBILETRADERONLINE.COM
SOUNDINGS
SOUNDINGS TRADE ONLY
TARGET MARKETING MAINE
TELECOM GEAR
TIMESHARESAVER.COM
TOWING & RECOVERY FOOTNOTES
TRADERONLINE.COM
TRAVEL COUPON GUIDE
TRAVEL SAVER GUIDE
TRAVELER DISCOUNT GUIDE
US TRAVEL GUIDE
VACATIONSAVER.COM
WALNECK'S CLASSIC MOTORCYCLE
WOODSHOP NEWS
XI GROUP
YACHT TRADER
YACHTWORLD.COM

DORCHESTER PUBLISHING CO., INC.

200 Madison Ave Ste 2000
New York, NY 10016
Tel.: (212) 725-8811
Fax: (212) 532-1054
Toll Free: (800) 481-9191
E-mail: dorchpub@dorchpub.com
Web Site: www.dorchesterpub.com
Sales Range: $10-24.9 Million
Approx. Number Employees: 50
Year Founded: 1971
Business Description:
Book Publisher
S.I.C.: 2731
N.A.I.C.S.: 511130
Media: 4-8-10-13
Personnel:
John Predich *(Pres)*

DOUBLEDAY

(Sub. of Bantam Dell Publishing Group)
1745 Broadway
New York, NY 10019
Tel.: (212) 782-9000
Fax: (212) 302-7985
Fax: (212) 782-8911 (Adv.)
Web Site: www.doubleday.com
Approx. Number Employees: 100
Year Founded: 1897
Business Description:
Book Publishers; Mail Order Book Club
S.I.C.: 2731
N.A.I.C.S.: 511130
Media: 2-3-6-9-13-14-18-23-24
Distr.: Intl.; Natl.
Budget Set: Jan.
Personnel:
Sonny Mehta *(Chm)*
Markus Dohle *(Pres & CEO)*
Judy Jacoby *(Dir-Adv)*
Brands & Products:
ANCHOR BIBLE
BROADWAY
CURRENCY
DOUBLEDAY
MAIN STREET BOOKS
NAN A. TALESE
THE NEW JERUSALEM BIBLE

DOVER PUBLICATIONS, INC.

(Sub. of Massachusetts National Publishing Business Trust)
31 E 2nd St
Mineola, NY 11501
Tel.: (516) 294-7000
Fax: (516) 742-6953
E-mail: info@doverpublications.com
Web Site: store.doverpublications.com/
Sales Range: $75-99.9 Million
Approx. Number Employees: 200
Business Description:
Publisher
S.I.C.: 2731
N.A.I.C.S.: 511130
Media: 4-6-19
Personnel:
Christopher J. Kuppig *(Pres)*
Ken Katzman *(VP-Mktg)*

DOVER-SHERBORN PRESS

(Unit of GateHouse Media New England)
254 2nd Ave
Needham, MA 02494
Tel.: (781) 433-8250
Fax: (781) 433-8202
E-mail: dover-sherborn@cnc.com
Web Site: www.wickedlocal.com/dover
Sales Range: $50-74.9 Million
Approx. Number Employees: 150
Business Description:
Newspaper Publisher
S.I.C.: 2711
N.A.I.C.S.: 511110
Media: 8-25
Personnel:
Kirk Davis *(Pres & COO)*
Greg Reibman *(Publr)*
Brian Briggs *(VP-Adv)*
Valentina Zic *(Editor-News)*
Anne Eisenmenger *(Mgr-Website)*
Carlo Petrillo *(Mgr-Adv Sls)*

DOW JONES & COMPANY, INC.

(Sub. of News Corporation)
1211 Avenue of the Americas
New York, NY 10036
Tel.: (212) 416-2000
Fax: (212) 416-4348
Telex: 7607743
E-mail: djcom@dowjones.com
Web Site: www.dj.com
Approx. Rev.: $1,783,870,000
Approx. Number Employees: 7,400
Year Founded: 1882
Business Description:
Business Information Services & News Publisher
S.I.C.: 2711; 2721; 2741; 7383; 7389
N.A.I.C.S.: 511110; 511120; 516110; 519110; 519190
Media: 2-3-6-7-8-9-13-14-15-16-17-18-23-24
Distr.: Intl.; Natl.
Budget Set: Nov.
Personnel:
Todd H. Larsen *(Pres)*
Leslie Hinton *(CEO & Publr-The Wall Street Journal)*
Martin Murtland *(Mng Dir & VP)*
Kevin P. Halpin *(CFO)*
Bethany B. Sherman *(Chief Comm Officer & Sr VP)*
Gregory Giangrande *(Chief HR Officer & Sr VP)*
Michael F. Rooney *(Chief Revenue Officer)*
Mark H. Jackson *(Gen Counsel & Exec VP)*
Kelly Leach *(Sr VP-Strategy)*
Ian Weston *(Sr VP-Special Projects)*
John N. Wilcox *(Sr VP)*

Key to Media (For complete agency information see *The Advertising Red Books-Agencies* edition):
1. Bus. Publs. 2. Cable T.V. 3. Catalogs & Directories. 4. Co-op Adv. 5. Consumer Mags. 6. D.M. to Bus. Estab.7. D.M. to Consumers
8. Daily Newsp. 9. Exhibits/Trade Shows 10. Foreign 11. Infomercial 12. Internet Adv.13. Multimedia 14. Network Radio
15. Network T.V. 16. Newsp. Distr. Mags. 17. Other 18. Outdoor (Posters, Transit) 19. Point of Purchase20. Premiums, Novelties
21. Product Samples 22. Special Events Mktg. 23. Spot Radio 24. Spot T.V. 25. Weekly Newsp. 26. Yellow Page Adv.

Kenneth Herts *(VP & Gen Mgr-Fin Markets)*
Robert J. Thomson *(Editor-in-Chief-Dow Jones & Mng Editor-The Wall Street Journal)*
Joseph Rosenfeld *(Sr Dir-Fin)*
Andrew Eberle *(Reg Dir-Sls-Corp Markets Grp)*
Colin Doody *(Sr Mgr-Bus Dev-WSJ Digital)*
Emily J. Edmonds *(Mgr-PR)*
Daniel Hennessey *(Mgr-Interim IT)*
Ted Muhindi *(Graphic Designer-Mktg)*
Brands & Products:
THE ASIAN WALL STREET JOURNAL
BALANCING THE BOOKS
BARRON'S
CHARTING THE MARKET
COMMODITIES CORNER
CURRENT YIELD
D.C. CURRENT
DJIA
THE DOW
DOW JONES
THE DOW JONES AVERAGES
DOW JONES INDEXES
DOW JONES INDUSTRY GROUPS
DOW JONES NEWSWIRES
FACTIVA
FAR EASTERN ECONOMIC REVIEW
FUND OF INFORMATION
THE GROUND FLOOR
HEARD ON THE STREET
MARKET LABORATORY
MARKET WATCH
MARKET WEEK
OFFERINGS IN THE OFFING
OTHER VOICES
PULSE OF THE ECONOMY
REFRESHER COURSE
REVIEW AND PREVIEW
SIZING UP SMALL CAPS
THE STRIKING PRICE
THE TRADER
TRADING POINTS
UP AND DOWN WALL STREET
THE WALL STREET JOURNAL
THE WALL STREET JOURNAL SUNDAY
WHAT'S NEWS
WHO'S NEWS
WSJ.COM
Advertising Agencies:
Ogilvy Public Relations Worldwide
636 11th Ave
New York, NY 10036
Tel.: (212) 880-5200
Fax: (212) 370-4636

TBC Inc.
900 S Wolfe St
Baltimore, MD 21231
Tel.: (410) 347-7500
Fax: (410) 986-1299

DRG TEXAS LP
(Sub. of Dynamic Resource Group)
(d/b/a Strategic Fulfillment Group)
111 Corporate Dr
Big Sandy, TX 75755
Tel.: (903) 636-4011
Fax: (903) 636-9009
Web Site: www.anniesattic.com
Approx. Sls.: $35,000,000
Approx. Number Employees: 200
Business Description:
Magazine Publishing Services
S.I.C.: 5961
N.A.I.C.S.: 454113
Media: 2-6-8-10-13
Personnel:
Roger Muselman *(Owner & Chm)*
Tony Pyplak *(Pres)*
Eric Wilson *(Dir-Mktg)*

THE DUN & BRADSTREET CORP.
103 JFK Pkwy
Short Hills, NJ 07078-2708
Tel.: (973) 921-5500
Toll Free: (800) 234-3867
E-mail: custserv@dnb.com
Web Site: www.dnb.com
Approx. Rev.: $1,676,600,000
Approx. Number Employees: 5,200
Year Founded: 1841
Business Description:
Business Information, Publishing & Marketing Services
S.I.C.: 7389; 2741
N.A.I.C.S.: 519190; 516110
Advertising Expenditures: $24,300,000
Media: 2-4-7-10-13-26
Distr.: Direct to Consumer; Intl.; Natl.
Personnel:
Sara Mathew *(Chm & CEO)*
Anastasios G. Konidaris *(CFO & Sr VP)*
Walter S. Hauck, III *(CIO & Sr VP-Tech)*
Joshua L. Peirez *(CMO & Pres-Innovation)*
Emanuele A. Conti *(Chief Admin Officer)*
Patricia A. Clifford *(Chief HR Officer & Sr VP)*
James H. Delaney *(Pres-Global Sls & Mktg Solutions)*
George Stoeckert *(Pres-North America)*
Byron C. Vielehr *(Pres-Global Risk & Analytics)*
Jeffrey S. Hurwitz *(Gen Counsel, Sec & Sr VP)*
Stacy A. Cashman *(Sr VP)*
Brands & Products:
BUSINESS INFORMATION REPORT
D & B
D&B MARKET SPECTRUM
D&B SPEND ANALYSIS
D-U-N-S NUMBER
DECIDE WITH CONFIDENCE
DUNSRIGHT
RISK ASSESSMENT MANAGER
Advertising Agencies:
Alexander & Richardson
161 Washington Valley Rd Ste 205
Warren, NJ 07059-7121
Tel.: (732) 302-1223
Fax: (732) 356-9574

Allen & Gerritsen
The Arsenal on the Charles 311 Arsenal St 4th Fl
Watertown, MA 02472
Tel.: (617) 926-4005
Fax: (617) 926-0133

International Robotics, Inc.
(Pioneers of Techno-Marketing)
2001 Palmer Ave
Larchmont, NY 10538
Tel.: (914) 630-1060
Fax: (914) 630-1733
Toll Free: (800) 826-8001

Zeta Interactive
716 Main St
Boonton, NJ 07005
Tel.: (973) 316-9696
Fax: (973) 316-8006

DUNDAS STAR NEWS INC.
(Div. of Hamilton Community News)
333 Arvin Ave
Stoney Creek, ON L8E 2M6, Canada
Tel.: (905) 523-5800
Fax: (905) 523-4014
E-mail: editor@dundasstarnews.com
Web Site: www.dundasstarnews.com
Approx. Number Employees: 30
Year Founded: 1996
Business Description:
Newspaper Publisher
S.I.C.: 2711
N.A.I.C.S.: 511110
Media: 8-25
Personnel:
Debra Downey *(Editor-News)*
Jennifer McKie *(Mgr-Retail Adv)*
Brands & Products:
DUNDAS STAR NEWS

DUPONT PUBLISHING, INC.
3051 Tech Dr
Saint Petersburg, FL 33716
Tel.: (727) 573-9339
Fax: (727) 489-0202
Toll Free: (800) 746-3975
Web Site: www.dupontregistry.com
Approx. Number Employees: 80
Business Description:
Magazine Publisher
S.I.C.: 2721
N.A.I.C.S.: 511120
Media: 6-8-10-13
Personnel:
Steven B. Chapman *(CEO)*
J. Douglas Baldridge *(Gen Counsel)*
Thomas L. duPont *(Publr)*
Brands & Products:
A BUYERS GALLERY OF FINE AUTOMOBILES
A BUYERS GALLERY OF FINE BOATS
A BUYERS GALLERY OF FINE HOMES
CELEBRITY CAR
DUPONT REGISTRY
DUPONT REGISTRY TAMPA BAY
DUPONTREGISTRY.COM

DUPONT REGISTRY
(Div. of duPont Publishing, Inc.)
3051 Tech Dr
Saint Petersburg, FL 33716
Tel.: (727) 573-9339
Fax: (727) 489-0202
Toll Free: (800) 233-1731
E-mail: comments@dupontregistry.com
Web Site: www.dupontregistry.com
Approx. Number Employees: 100
Business Description:
Magazine Publisher
S.I.C.: 2721
N.A.I.C.S.: 511120
Media: 6-8-10-13
Personnel:
Thomas L. duPont *(Chm)*
Kit Jeerapaet *(Pres-A Buyers Gallery of Fine Automobiles)*
Tim Breaux *(VP-Sls)*
Danielle Kesten *(VP-Sls)*
Sherri L. Norris *(VP-Sls)*
Hal Reddick *(VP-Sls)*
Brands & Products:
A BUYER'S GALLERY OF FINE AUTOMOBILES
A BUYER'S GALLERY OF FINE BOATS
A BUYER'S GALLERY OF FINE HOMES

THE DURHAM HERALD CO.
(Unit of Paxton Media Group LLC)
2828 Pickett Rd
Durham, NC 27705
Tel.: (919) 419-6500
Fax: (919) 419-6878
E-mail: webadmin@heraldsun.com
Web Site: www.heraldsun.com
Approx. Number Employees: 400
Year Founded: 1889
Business Description:
Newspapers
S.I.C.: 2711
N.A.I.C.S.: 511110
Media: 8-9
Personnel:
David Paxton *(Founder, CEO & CFO)*
Rick Bean *(Publr)*
Bob Ashley *(Editor)*
Nancy Wykle *(Editor)*
Elaine Morgan *(Dir-Adv & Mktg)*
Thomas Tuttle *(Dir-Adv & Mktg)*
Brands & Products:
THE HERALD-SUN
HERALD.COM

DYNAMIC RESOURCE GROUP
306 E Parr Rd
Berne, IN 46711
Tel.: (260) 589-4075
Fax: (260) 589-8093
E-mail: webmaster@drgnetwork.com
Web Site: www.drgnetwork.com
Sales Range: $25-49.9 Million
Approx. Number Employees: 90
Year Founded: 1925
Business Description:
Printer of Catalogs & Magazines
S.I.C.: 2741
N.A.I.C.S.: 516110
Media: 4-6-7-8-10-13-18-19-20
Personnel:
Roger Muselman *(Chm)*
Thomas C. Muselman *(Pres)*
Mike Klansek *(CFO & Publr)*
Greg Deily *(VP-Mktg)*
Sally Allen *(Dir-Bus Dev)*
Brenda Wendling *(Dir-Product Ops)*
Angie Wheeler *(Dir-HR)*
Nancy Brown *(Mgr-PR)*

EAGLE-TRIBUNE PUBLISHING COMPANY INC.
(Sub. of Community Newspaper Holdings, Inc.)
100 Turnpike St
North Andover, MA 01845-5033
Tel.: (978) 946-2000
Fax: (978) 685-1588
Web Site: www.eagletribune.com
Sales Range: $25-49.9 Million
Approx. Number Employees: 522
Year Founded: 1940

Key to Media (For complete agency information see *The Advertising Red Books-Agencies* edition):
1. Bus. Publs. 2. Cable T.V. 3. Catalogs & Directories. 4. Co-op Adv. 5. Consumer Mags. 6. D.M. to Bus. Estab.7. D.M. to Consumers
8. Daily Newsp. 9. Exhibits/Trade Shows 10. Foreign 11. Infomercial 12. Internet Adv.13. Multimedia 14. Network Radio
15. Network T.V. 16. Newsp. Distr. Mags. 17. Other 18. Outdoor (Posters, Transit) 19. Point of Purchase20. Premiums, Novelties
21. Product Samples 22. Special Events Mktg. 23. Spot Radio 24. Spot T.V. 25. Weekly Newsp. 26. Yellow Page Adv.

Eagle-Tribune Publishing Company Inc. — (Continued)

Business Description:
Newspaper Publisher
S.I.C.: 2711; 2752
N.A.I.C.S.: 511110; 323110
Import Export
Media: 8-9
Personnel:
Al Getler *(Pres & Publr)*
Karen Andreas *(Publr)*
William B. Ketter *(Sr VP)*
Laure D'amore *(VP-HR)*
Daniel J. Griffin *(VP-Mktg)*
Ellen K. Zappala *(VP-Adv)*
John S. Gregory *(Dir-IT)*
Steven A. Milone *(Dir-Circulation)*

EAST OREGONIAN PUBLISHING CO.

211 SE Byers Ave
Pendleton, OR 97801
Tel.: (541) 276-2211
Fax: (541) 278-2688
Toll Free: (800) 522-0255
E-mail: classifieds@eastoregonian.com
Web Site: www.eastoregonian.com
Sales Range: $10-24.9 Million
Approx. Number Employees: 75
Business Description:
Commercial Printing & Newspaper Publishing Services
S.I.C.: 2711
N.A.I.C.S.: 511110
Media: 8-9
Personnel:
Kathryn Brown *(Owner)*
Steve Forrester *(Pres)*

EAST VALLEY TRIBUNE

(Unit of Freedom Newspapers, Inc.)
120 W 1st Ave
Mesa, AZ 85210-1312
Mailing Address:
PO Box 1547
Mesa, AZ 85211-1547
Tel.: (480) 898-6500
Fax: (480) 898-5606
E-mail: info@eastvalleytribune.com
Web Site: www.eastvalleytribune.com
Approx. Number Employees: 35
Business Description:
Newspaper Publishing
S.I.C.: 2711
N.A.I.C.S.: 511110
Media: 8-9
Personnel:
Terry Horne *(Publr & Editor)*
Lawn Griffiths *(Editor-Religion)*
Cheryl Kushner *(Deputy Editor-Features)*
Ted Brown *(Dir-Sls)*
Jim Dickey *(Dir-Production)*
Diane Snoble *(Office Mgr)*
Brands & Products:
EAST VALLEY TRIBUNE
SCOTTSDALE TRIBUNE
SCOTTSDALE VIEWS
TRIBUNE CONNECTION

EASTON JOURNAL

(Unit of GateHouse Media New England)
370 Paramount Dr
Raynham, MA 02767
Tel.: (508) 967-3510
Fax: (508) 967-3501
E-mail: easton@cnc.com
Web Site: www.wickedlocal.com
Sales Range: $100-124.9 Million
Year Founded: 1993
Business Description:
Newspaper Publisher
S.I.C.: 2711
N.A.I.C.S.: 511110
Media: 8-25

EAU CLAIRE PRESS COMPANY

(d/b/a Leader Telegram)
701 S Farwell St
Eau Claire, WI 54701
Tel.: (715) 833-9200
Fax: (715) 833-9244
Web Site: www.leadertelegram.com
Approx. Sls.: $17,000,000
Approx. Number Employees: 283
Business Description:
Newspapers, Publishing & Printing
S.I.C.: 2711
N.A.I.C.S.: 511110
Media: 5-8-9-22
Personnel:
Pieter Graaskamp *(Pres)*
Dan Graaskamp *(VP-Sls)*

EBSCO INDUSTRIES, INC.

5724 Hwy 280 E
Birmingham, AL 35242-6818
Mailing Address:
PO Box 1943
Birmingham, AL 35201-1943
Tel.: (205) 991-6600
Fax: (205) 995-1636
Web Site: www.ebscoind.com
Sales Range: $1-4.9 Billion
Approx. Number Employees: 6,200
Year Founded: 1944
Business Description:
Furniture & Fixtures; Printing & Publishing; Fabricated Metal Products; Miscellaneous Manufacturing Industries; Information Management Services; Traditional & Electronic Journal & Periodical Subscription Management; Real Estate Development Services
S.I.C.: 2732; 7389
N.A.I.C.S.: 323117; 561499
Import Export
Advertising Expenditures: $15,000,000
Media: 1-2-4-7-10-11-19-20-26
Distr.: Intl.
Personnel:
James T. Stephens *(Chm, Pres & CEO)*
David Walker *(CFO & VP)*
Elton B. Stephens, Jr. *(Gen Mgr-Real Estate)*
Sheri C. Thompson *(Dir-Internal Comm)*
Brands & Products:
EBSCO
KNIGHT & HALE

EBSCO INDUSTRIES WESTWOOD

(Div. of EBSCO Industries, Inc.)
249 Vanderbilt Ave
Norwood, MA 02062
Tel.: (781) 501-7000
Fax: (781) 501-7070
Approx. Sls.: $35,100,000
Approx. Number Employees: 250
Year Founded: 1881
Business Description:
Wholesale Periodical Subscriptions
S.I.C.: 5192
N.A.I.C.S.: 424920
Advertising Expenditures: $200,000
Media: 2-7
Distr.: Direct to Consumer; Natl.

EDITORIAL TELEVISA INTERNATIONAL

(Div. of Editorial Televisa S.A. de C.V.)
(d/b/a Editorial America)
6355 NW 36th St
Miami, FL 33166
Tel.: (305) 871-6400
Fax: (305) 871-0922
Web Site: www.editorialtelevisa.com
Sales Range: $500-549.9 Million
Approx. Number Employees: 100
Business Description:
Magazine Publishing
S.I.C.: 2721; 2731
N.A.I.C.S.: 511120; 511130
Media: 2-6-8-10-14-15-18-22
Personnel:
Eduardo Michelsen *(CEO)*

EDMONTON JOURNAL GROUP INC.

(Unit of Postmedia Network Inc.)
10006 101st St
Edmonton, AB T5J0S1, Canada
Mailing Address:
PO Box 2421
Edmonton, AB T5J 2S6, Canada
Tel.: (780) 429-5100
Fax: (780) 498-5659
Fax: (780) 429-5500 (Newsroom)
E-mail: jnero@thejournal.canwest.com
Web Site: www.edmontonjournal.com
E-Mail For Key Personnel:
Sales Director: connolly@thejournal.southam.ca
Approx. Number Employees: 645
Year Founded: 1903
Business Description:
Cybergraphics Services
S.I.C.: 7336
N.A.I.C.S.: 541430
Media: 2-3-4-7-9-13-17-18-19-20-23-24-26
Distr.: Direct to Consumer
Budget Set: Aug.
Personnel:
John Connolly *(Publr)*
Joe Celino *(VP-Production, Sys, Reader Sls & Svc)*
Advertising Agency:
Atkinson Media Marketing
4050 Sea Grape Circle, Ste. 100
Delray Beach, FL 33445
Tel.: (561) 637-6200
Fax: (561) 637-1099

EDUCATIONAL DEVELOPMENT CORPORATION

10302 E 55th Pl
Tulsa, OK 74146-6515
Mailing Address:
PO Box 470663
Tulsa, OK 74147-0663
Tel.: (918) 622-4522
Fax: (918) 665-7919
Fax: (800) 747-4509
Toll Free: (800) 475-4522
E-mail: edc@edcpub.com
Web Site: www.edcpub.com
E-Mail For Key Personnel:
President: rwhite@edcpub.com
Sales Director: rmcdaniel@edpub.com
Approx. Sls.: $39,630,700
Approx. Number Employees: 70
Year Founded: 1965
Business Description:
Children's Books Publisher & Distr
S.I.C.: 5192; 2731; 5942
N.A.I.C.S.: 424920; 451211; 511130
Import
Advertising Expenditures: $162,800
Media: 2-4-5-8-10
Distr.: Natl.
Personnel:
Randall W. White *(Chm, Pres & Treas)*
Craig M. White *(VP-IT)*
Todd R. White *(Mgr-School & Library Educational Svcs)*

EDUCATIONAL GUIDANCE AFRO AMERICAN PRESS

(Div. of Eastern Guild)
1234 Wood St
Philadelphia, PA 19107-1111
Tel.: (215) 568-3838
Fax: (215) 568-3106
Approx. Number Employees: 15
Year Founded: 1940
Business Description:
Publisher of Encyclopedias; Afro American Press
S.I.C.: 2741
N.A.I.C.S.: 511199
Advertising Expenditures: $200,000
Media: 2-6-8-9
Distr.: Direct to Consumer; Natl.
Brands & Products:
BLACK HISTORY LIBRARY
EDUCATIONAL GUIDANCE
ENCYCLOPEDIA OF BLACK AMERICANS
REFERENCE LIBRARY OF HISPANIC AMERICANS
REFERENCE LIBRARY OF NORTHERN NATIVE AMERICANS

ELEMENT K JOURNALS

(Div. of Element K LLC)
500 Canal View Blvd
Rochester, NY 14623-2800
Tel.: (585) 240-7500
Fax: (585) 292-4392
Toll Free: (800) 223-8720
Toll Free: (877) 203-5248 (Canada)
E-mail: bizdev@eliresearch.com
Web Site: www.elijournals.com
Business Description:
Newsletters for Users of Various PC Software
S.I.C.: 7371
N.A.I.C.S.: 541511
Media: 2-17

ELEMENT K ONLINE LLC

(Sub. of Element K LLC)
500 Canal View Blvd
Rochester, NY 14623-2800
Tel.: (585) 240-7500
E-mail: jobs@elementk.com
Web Site: www.elementk.com
Business Description:
Internet-Based Training

Key to Media (For complete agency information see *The Advertising Red Books-Agencies* edition):
1. Bus. Publs. 2. Cable T.V. 3. Catalogs & Directories. 4. Co-op Adv. 5. Consumer Mags. 6. D.M. to Bus. Estab.7. D.M. to Consumers
8. Daily Newsp. 9. Exhibits/Trade Shows 10. Foreign 11. Infomercial 12. Internet Adv.13. Multimedia 14. Network Radio
15. Network T.V. 16. Newsp. Distr. Mags. 17. Other 18. Outdoor (Posters, Transit) 19. Point of Purchase20. Premiums, Novelties
21. Product Samples 22. Special Events Mktg. 23. Spot Radio 24. Spot T.V. 25. Weekly Newsp. 26. Yellow Page Adv.

S.I.C.: 7373; 7371
N.A.I.C.S.: 541512; 541511
Media: 13
Personnel:
Lesley Darling *(Chief Learning Officer)*
Brands & Products:
YOUR LEARNING SOLUTIONS PARTNER

ELSEVIER HEALTH SCIENCES
(Joint Venture of Reed Elsevier NV & Reed Elsevier plc)
1600 John F Kennedy Blvd Ste 1800
Philadelphia, PA 19103-2899
Tel.: (215) 239-3900
Fax: (215) 239-3990
Web Site: www.us.elsevierhealth.com
Approx. Number Employees: 550
Business Description:
Publishers of Medical Books & Journals
S.I.C.: 2721; 2731; 2741
N.A.I.C.S.: 511199; 511120; 511130; 516110
Personnel:
Frank Reid, III *(Chief HR Officer-RE Tech & Sr VP)*
Michael Hansen *(CEO-Health Sciences)*
Linda C. Belfus *(Sr VP)*
David Goldmann *(VP & Editor-in-Chief)*
Brands & Products:
NETTER ANATOMY
Advertising Agency:
AMP Agency (Alloy Marketing & Promotion)
77 N Washington St
Boston, MA 02114
Tel.: (617) 723-8929
Fax: (617) 723-2188
Media Agency of Record-Netter Anatomy

ENCYCLOPAEDIA BRITANNICA, INC.
331 N La Salle St
Chicago, IL 60654
Tel.: (312) 347-7000
Fax: (312) 294-2104
Toll Free: (800) 323-1229
Telex: 190203 EBINCUT
E-mail: media@us.britannica.com
Web Site: www.britannica.com
Sales Range: $400-449.9 Million
Approx. Number Employees: 200
Year Founded: 1768
Business Description:
Encyclopedia Publisher
S.I.C.: 2731
N.A.I.C.S.: 511130
Media: 4-6-8-10-13-16-20
Distr.: Direct to Consumer; Natl.
Budget Set: July
Personnel:
Jorge Cauz *(Pres)*
William J. Bowe *(Gen Counsel & Exec VP)*
Michael Ross *(Sr VP & Gen Mgr)*
Tom Panelas *(Dir-Comm)*
Brands & Products:
BRITANNICA
GREAT BOOKS OF THE WESTERN WORLD

ENTERTAINMENT PUBLICATIONS, INC.
(Sub. of MH Private Equity Fund LLC)
1414 E Maple Rd
Troy, MI 48083
Tel.: (248) 404-1000
Fax: (248) 404-1941
Fax: (248) 404-1915
Toll Free: (800) 450-8114
E-mail: mktgsolutions@entertainment.com
Web Site: www.entertainment.com
Sales Range: $75-99.9 Million
Approx. Number Employees: 800
Year Founded: 1962
Business Description:
Discount Programs & Coupon Book Publisher
S.I.C.: 2731
N.A.I.C.S.: 511130
Export
Advertising Expenditures: $1,000,000
Media: 2-6-7-8-9-10-13-16-17-19
Distr.: Natl.
Budget Set: July -June
Personnel:
Michael Periard *(CFO)*
Ann Atkinson *(COO)*
Melissa Fisher *(CMO)*
Angela Aufdemberge *(Exec VP-Ops)*
Brands & Products:
THE CROWN DESIGN
ENTERTAINMENT
FREQUENT VALUES
GOLD C
NATIONAL VALUES
ONE FOR THE COMMUNITY
SALLY FOSTER
SAVING SPREE
SUMMER VACATION
TRAVEL NORTH AMERICA AT HALF PRICE
THE ULTIMATE SAVINGS MEMBERSHIP
VALUES

ENTERTAINMENT WEEKLY INC.
(Sub. of Time Inc.)
135 W 50th St 3 Fl
New York, NY 10020
Tel.: (212) 522-5600
Fax: (212) 522-0074
Web Site: www.ew.com
Sales Range: $100-124.9 Million
Approx. Number Employees: 250
Year Founded: 1990
Business Description:
Weekly Magazine Publisher
S.I.C.: 2721
N.A.I.C.S.: 511120
Media: 6-7
Personnel:
Nancy Ryan *(Gen Mgr)*
Christine Gibson *(Sr Dir-Integrated Mktg)*
Carol A. Mazzarella *(Dir-Production & Tech)*

ENTREPRENEUR MEDIA, INC.
2445 McCabe Way Ste 400
Irvine, CA 92614-4293
Tel.: (949) 261-2325
Fax: (949) 261-7729
E-mail: memberservices@entrepreneur.com
Web Site: www.entrepreneur.com
Sales Range: $25-49.9 Million
Approx. Number Employees: 80
Year Founded: 1987
Business Description:
Information & Services for Small & Mid-Sized Businesses
S.I.C.: 2721
N.A.I.C.S.: 511120
Media: 2-4-7-8-10-13-18-20-22
Personnel:
Neil Pearlman *(Pres & COO)*
Ryan Shea *(Pres & Corp Publr)*
Peter J. Shea *(CEO)*
Joseph Goodman *(CFO & Sr VP)*
Lisa Murray *(VP-Mktg)*
Paul Fishback *(Mgr-Adv & Director-Production)*
Lori Flynn *(Dir-Adv-Midwest)*
Glen Harn *(Dir-Adv)*
Wendy Hidenrick *(Mgr-Online Sls-Midwest Reg)*
Brands & Products:
ENTREPRENEUR
ENTREPRENEUR CONNECT
ENTREPRENEUR MAGAZINE
ENTREPRENEUR PRESS
ENTREPRENEUR.COM
ENTREPRENEUR'S STARTUPS
FRANCHISE 500
SMALLBIZSEARCH.COM
WOMENENTREPRENEUR.COM

EP COMMUNICATIONS
(d/b/a Exceptional Parent)
416 Main St
Johnstown, PA 15901
Tel.: (814) 361-3860
Fax: (814) 361-3861
Web Site: www.eparent.com
Approx. Sls.: $3,000,000
Business Description:
Magazine Publisher
S.I.C.: 2721
N.A.I.C.S.: 511120
Media: 6
Personnel:
Joseph M. Valenzano, Jr. *(Pres, CEO & Publr)*
Bob Salluzzo *(COO)*
Matt Valenzano *(Publr)*
Vanessa B. Ira *(Mgr-Sls-Western Reg)*
Kendra Kelly *(Mgr-Adv Traffic)*

ESSENCE MAGAZINE
(Sub. of Essence Communications Inc.)
135 W 50th St 4th Fl
New York, NY 10020
Tel.: (212) 522-1634
Fax: (212) 921-5173
E-mail: info@essence.com
Web Site: www.essence.com
Sales Range: $50-74.9 Million
Approx. Number Employees: 180
Year Founded: 1970
Business Description:
Magazine Publisher
S.I.C.: 2721
N.A.I.C.S.: 511120
Media: 2-3-5-6-7-8-11-15-22-24-26
Distr.: Natl.
Personnel:
Michelle Ebanks *(Pres)*
Angela Burt-Murray *(Editor-in-Chief)*
Sheryl Hilliard Tucker *(Editor-in-Chief)*
Pamela M. Edwards *(Editor-Fashion & Beauty Features)*
Lynya Floyd *(Editor-Health & Relationships)*
Jonell Nash *(Editor-Food)*
Tasha Turner *(Editor-Beauty)*
Dana Baxter *(Dir-Pub Rels)*
Elliana Placas *(Dir-Fashion)*
Susan L. Taylor *(Dir-Editorial-Essence Magazine)*
Brands & Products:
ESSENCE
ESSENCE BRINGS YOU GREAT COOKING
IN THE SPIRIT

EVAN-MOOR CORPORATION
(d/b/a Evan-Moor Educational Publishers)
18 Lower Reagsdale Dr
Monterey, CA 93940-5746
Tel.: (831) 649-5901
Tel.: (831) 649-6256
Fax: (800) 777-4332
Toll Free: (800) 777-4362
E-mail: sales@evan-moor.com
Web Site: www.evan-moor.com
E-Mail For Key Personnel:
Sales Director: sales@evan-moor.com
Approx. Number Employees: 40
Year Founded: 1979
Business Description:
Educational Materials Publisher
S.I.C.: 8299
N.A.I.C.S.: 611710
Media: 4-7-13
Personnel:
Bill Evans *(Founder & CEO)*
Audrey Ciccone *(Dir-Mktg)*
Brands & Products:
EVAN-MOOR

THE EVANSVILLE COURIER & PRESS
(Sub. of The E.W. Scripps Company)
300 E Walnut St
Evansville, IN 47713
Mailing Address:
PO Box 268
Evansville, IN 47702
Tel.: (812) 464-7459
Fax: (812) 464-7422
Fax: (812) 422-8196
E-mail: info@courierpress.com
Web Site: www.courierpress.com
Sales Range: $100-124.9 Million
Approx. Number Employees: 300
Business Description:
Publisher of Morning & Sunday Newspapers
S.I.C.: 2711; 2791
N.A.I.C.S.: 511110; 323122
Media: 8-9
Personnel:
Jack Pate *(Pres & Publr)*
Mizell Stewart *(Editor)*
Kathryn Gieneart *(Dir-Mktg)*
Tim Hayden *(Dir-Ops)*
Jim Michels *(Dir-New Media)*
Thom Mominee *(Dir-HR)*

THE E.W. SCRIPPS COMPANY
312 Walnut St
Cincinnati, OH 45202-4024
Mailing Address:
PO Box 5380
Cincinnati, OH 45201-5380
Tel.: (513) 977-3000
Fax: (513) 977-3721

The E.W. Scripps Company — (Continued)

Toll Free: (800) 888-3000
E-mail: corpcomm@scripps.com
Web Site: www.scripps.com
Approx. Rev.: $776,890,000
Approx. Number Employees: 4,600
Year Founded: 1878
Business Description:
Diversified Media Company
S.I.C.: 2711; 4833
N.A.I.C.S.: 511110; 515120
Import
Media: 3-9-13-15-24-25-26
Distr.: Natl.
Budget Set: Jan.
Personnel:
Nackey E. Scagliotti *(Chm)*
Richard A. Boehne *(Pres & CEO)*
Timothy M. Wesolowski *(CFO, Treas & Sr VP)*
Lisa A. Knutson *(Chief Admin Officer)*
David M. Giles *(VP & Deputy Gen Counsel)*
William Appleton *(Gen Counsel & Sr VP)*
Brian Lawlor *(Sr VP-Television Div)*
Timothy E. Stautberg *(Sr VP-Newspaper Div)*
Bruce Hartmann *(VP-Sls & Mktg)*
Timothy King *(VP-Corp Comm & IR)*
Jessica Rappaport *(VP-Mktg-Television Div)*
Deanene Catani *(Reg Dir-Mktg)*
Krista McDivitt *(Reg Dir-IT-West Reg)*
David Francois *(Dir-New Media)*
Josh Friedman *(Dir-Maria Moors Cabot Prizes)*
Jack Lail *(Dir-News Innovation)*
Julie Moos *(Dir-Poynter Online)*
Brands & Products:
THE ABILENE REPORTER-NEWS
THE ALBUQUERQUE TRIBUNE
ANDERSON INDEPENDENT-MAIL
BIRMINGHAM POST-HERALD
BONITA DAILY NEWS
BREMERTON SUN
COLORADO DAILY
THE COMMERCIAL APPEAL
CORPUS CHRISTI CALLER-TIMES
DAILY CAMERA (BOULDER)
DENVER ROCKY MOUNTAIN NEWS
DO IT YOURSELF NETWORK
THE EVANSVILLE COURIER & PRESS
THE FOOD NETWORK
FT. PIERCE NEWS
THE GLEANER
GREAT AMERICAN COUNTRY
HOME & GARDEN TELEVISION
THE JUPITER COURIER
THE KITSAP SUN
KJRH, CHANNEL 2 (TULSA)
THE KNOXVILLE NEWS-SENTINEL
KNXV, ABC (PHOENIX)
KSHB, NBC (KANSAS CITY)
KYPOST.COM
NAPLES DAILY NEWS
THE PORT ST. LUCIE NEWS
RECORD SEARCHLIGHT
REDDING RECORD SEARCHLIGHT
ROCKY MOUNTAIN NEWS
SAN ANGELO STANDARD-TIMES
SCRIPPS
SCRIPPS MEDIA CENTER
SCRIPPS PRODUCTIONS
SEBASTIAN SUN
THE STUART NEWS
THE TRIBUNE (FT. PIERCE)
VENTURA COUNTRY STAR
VENTURA COUNTY STAR
VERO BEACH PRESS JOURNAL
WCPO, ABC (CINCINNATI)
WEWS, ABC (CLEVELAND)
WFTS, ABC (TAMPA)
WICHITA FALLS TIMES RECORD NEWS
WMAR, ABC (BALTIMORE)
WPTV, NBC (WEST PALM BEACH)
WXYZ, ABC (DETROIT)
Advertising Agencies:
Media Storm LLC
99 Washington St
South Norwalk, CT 06854
Tel.: (203) 852-8001
Fax: (203) 852-5592
Fine Living Network
DIY Network
Food Network
HGTV

Northlich Public Relations
720 E Pete Rose Way Ste 120
Cincinnati, OH 45202-3579
Tel.: (513) 421-8840
Fax: (513) 287-1858

THE EXAMINER
(Unit of GateHouse Media, Inc.)
410 S Liberty St
Independence, MO 64050
Mailing Address:
PO Box 459 64051
Independence, MO 64050
Tel.: (816) 254-8600
Fax: (816) 836-3805
Web Site: www.examiner.net
Sales Range: $25-49.9 Million
Approx. Number Employees: 75
Year Founded: 1898
Business Description:
Daily Newspaper Publisher
S.I.C.: 2711
N.A.I.C.S.: 511110
Media: 2-5-8-9-13-20-21-22-23
Personnel:
Steve Curd *(Publr)*
Sharon Dankenbring *(Dir-Mktg)*
Sharon Hall *(Dir-Bus & HR)*
Ginger Kuftack *(Dir-Production)*
David Lammers *(Dir-Adv)*
Ginger Kustack *(Mgr-Production)*
Brands & Products:
THE EXAMINER

THE EXPOSITOR
(Div. of Osprey Media Group, Inc.)
53 Dalhousie St
Brantford, ON N3T 5S8, Canada
Tel.: (519) 756-2020
Fax: (519) 756-3285
Fax: (519) 756-4911
Toll Free: (866) 541-6757
E-mail: comp@theexpositor.com
Web Site: www.brantfordexpositor.com
Approx. Number Employees: 65
Business Description:
Daily Newspaper
S.I.C.: 2711
N.A.I.C.S.: 511110
Media: 8-9

F.A. DAVIS PUBLISHING COMPANY
1915 Arch St
Philadelphia, PA 19103
Tel.: (215) 568-2270
Fax: (215) 440-3016
E-mail: orders@fadavis.com
Web Site: www.fadavis.com
Approx. Number Employees: 150
Year Founded: 1879
Business Description:
Textbook Publisher
S.I.C.: 2731
N.A.I.C.S.: 511130
Media: 10
Personnel:
Robert H. Craven, Jr. *(Pres)*
David G. White *(Mgr-Digital Mktg)*
Brands & Products:
F.A. DAVIS
PUBLISHER OF TABER'S

FAIRCHILD FASHION GROUP
(Div. of Conde Nast Publications, Inc.)
Fl 7 750 3rd Ave
New York, NY 10017-2703
Tel.: (212) 630-4000
Fax: (212) 630-4295
Approx. Number Employees: 900
Year Founded: 1892
Business Description:
Publisher of Fashion Related Books, Magazines & Electronic Media
S.I.C.: 2721; 2741
N.A.I.C.S.: 511120; 516110
Media: 2-6-9-10-13-25
Distr.: Intl.; Natl.
Personnel:
Patrick McCarthy *(Chm-Editorial)*
Gina Sanders *(Pres & CEO)*
Lis Ryan Howard *(Sr VP & Chief Revenue Officer)*
Will Schenck *(Chief Revenue Officer & VP)*
Nina Lawrence *(VP& Publr-W Magazine)*
Chris Mitchell *(VP-Publr-Details)*
Ed Nardoza *(Editor-in-Chief)*
Peter Kaplan *(Dir-Editorial)*
Brands & Products:
BEAUTY BIZ
BEAUTY REPORT INTERNATIONAL
DAILY NEWS RECORD
FAIRCHILD
FOOTWEAR NEWS
VITALS
WWD
WWDLUXURY

FAIRWAY OUTDOOR ADVERTISING
(Div. of Morris Communications Company LLC)
713 Broad St
Augusta, GA 30901
Tel.: (706) 724-8987
Fax: (706) 724-6308
E-mail: info@fairwayoutdoor.com
Web Site: www.fairwayoutdoor.com
Approx. Number Employees: 50
Business Description:
Outdoor Advertising Services
S.I.C.: 7311; 7319
N.A.I.C.S.: 541810; 541850
Media: 13-17-18
Personnel:
Mark E. Moyer *(CEO)*
Tom Burgess *(VP-Fin)*
Ken Guy *(Dir-Ops-Natl)*
Maria Suarez *(Dir-Corp Sls & Mktg)*

FAIRWAY OUTDOOR ADVERTISING OF GEORGIA-ALABAMA
(Branch of Fairway Outdoor Advertising)
3420 Jefferson Rd
Athens, GA 30607-1476
Tel.: (706) 543-0380
Fax: (706) 354-0991
Web Site: www.fairwayoutdoor.com
Approx. Number Employees: 50
Business Description:
Outdoor Advertising Services
S.I.C.: 7311; 7319
N.A.I.C.S.: 541810; 541850
Media: 13-17-18
Personnel:
Thomas H. Burgess *(VP-Fin)*
Marshall Henderson *(Mgr-Sls)*

FAIRWAY OUTDOOR ADVERTISING OF THE GSA
(Branch of Fairway Outdoor Advertising)
814 Duncan Reidville Rd
Duncan, SC 29334-1900
Mailing Address:
PO Box 1900
Duncan, SC 29334-1900
Tel.: (864) 439-6371
Fax: (864) 439-7482
Web Site: www.fairwayoutdoor.com
Approx. Number Employees: 60
Business Description:
Outdoor Advertising Services
S.I.C.: 7311; 7319
N.A.I.C.S.: 541810; 541850
Media: 13-17-18
Personnel:
Terry Graves *(Gen Mgr)*
Glenn Coker *(Dir-Art)*
Erskine Thomason *(Mgr-Sls)*

FAIRWAY OUTDOOR ADVERTISING OF THE PIEDMONT TRIAD
(Branch of Fairway Outdoor Advertising)
1920 W Lee St
Greensboro, NC 27403
Tel.: (336) 292-4242
Fax: (336) 294-2085
Web Site: www.fairwayoutdoor.com
Approx. Number Employees: 25
Business Description:
Outdoor Advertising Services
S.I.C.: 7311; 7319
N.A.I.C.S.: 541810; 541850
Media: 13-17-18
Personnel:
Dan O'Shea *(Gen Mgr)*
Eddie Jones *(Mgr-Sls)*

FAIRWAY OUTDOOR ADVERTISING OF THE TRIANGLE EAST
(Branch of Fairway Outdoor Advertising)
508 Capital Blvd
Raleigh, NC 27605
Tel.: (919) 755-1900
Fax: (919) 832-3802
E-mail: deana.morris@fairwayoutdoor.com

Key to Media (For complete agency information see *The Advertising Red Books-Agencies* edition):
1. Bus. Publs. 2. Cable T.V. 3. Catalogs & Directories. 4. Co-op Adv. 5. Consumer Mags. 6. D.M. to Bus. Estab.7. D.M. to Consumers
8. Daily Newsp. 9. Exhibits/Trade Shows 10. Foreign 11. Infomercial 12. Internet Adv.13. Multimedia 14. Network Radio
15. Network T.V. 16. Newsp. Distr. Mags. 17. Other 18. Outdoor (Posters, Transit) 19. Point of Purchase20. Premiums, Novelties
21. Product Samples 22. Special Events Mktg. 23. Spot Radio 24. Spot T.V. 25. Weekly Newsp. 26. Yellow Page Adv.

Web Site: www.fairwayoutdoor.com
Sales Range: $50-74.9 Million
Approx. Number Employees: 50
Business Description:
Outdoor Advertising Services
S.I.C.: 7311; 7319
N.A.I.C.S.: 541810; 541850
Media: 13-18
Personnel:
Paul Hickman *(Gen Mgr)*
Todd Allen *(Dir-Real Estate)*
Lisa Rondina *(Mgr-Sls)*
Mike Russell *(Mgr-Mktg)*

THE FAMILY CIRCLE, INC.
(Div. of Meredith Publishing Group)
375 Lexington Ave
New York, NY 10017
Tel.: (212) 499-2000
Fax: (212) 499-1987
E-mail: fcfeedback@familycircle.com
Web Site: www.familycircle.com
Sales Range: $50-74.9 Million
Approx. Number Employees: 200
Year Founded: 1931
Business Description:
Magazine Publisher
S.I.C.: 2721
N.A.I.C.S.: 511120
Media: 10
Personnel:
Joanne Lopinto *(Assoc Publr-Mktg)*
Linda Fears *(Editor-in-Chief)*
Jonna Gallo Weppler *(Dir-Articles)*
Laura Rosenblatt *(Assoc Dir-Mktg)*
Rebecca Benner *(Assoc Mgr-Mktg)*
Brands & Products:
FAMILY CIRCLE

FARGO ELECTRONICS INC.
(Sub. of HID Global Corporation)
6533 Flying Cloud Dr
Eden Prairie, MN 55344
Tel.: (952) 941-9470
Fax: (952) 941-7836
Toll Free: (800) 459-5636
Web Site: www.fargo.com
E-Mail For Key Personnel:
Sales Director: sales@fargo.com
Public Relations: pr@fargo.com
Sales Range: $75-99.9 Million
Approx. Number Employees: 168
Year Founded: 1974
Business Description:
Mfr. Developer & Supplier of Printing Systems & Consumable Supplies
S.I.C.: 3571; 2759; 7371
N.A.I.C.S.: 334111; 323119; 541511
Media: 10
Personnel:
Dennis Hebert *(Pres)*
Thomas C. Platner *(VP-Engrng-Mfg)*
Brands & Products:
BUILD-A-BADGE
CARDJET
DIRECT TO CARD
FARGO
HIGH-DEFINITION PRINTING
HOLOMARK
MIFARE
PERSONA
PERSONA SERIES
POLYGUARD
PRINT SECURITY MANAGER
PRINT SECURITY SUITE
PROFESSIONAL SERIES
RIBBONTRAQ
SECURE
SECUREMARK
SECUREVAULT
SMARTGUARD
SMARTLOAD
SMARTSCREEN
SMARTSHIELD
ULTRACARD
VERIMARK
VISUAL SECURITY

FARM JOURNAL MEDIA
110 One Penn Sq W 30 S 15 St Ste 900
Philadelphia, PA 19102
Tel.: (215) 557-8900
Fax: (215) 568-5012
Toll Free: (800) 523-1538
E-mail: aginfo@agweb.com
Web Site: www.agweb.com
Approx. Number Employees: 40
Year Founded: 1877
Business Description:
Publisher of Agricultural Magazines
S.I.C.: 2721
N.A.I.C.S.: 511120
Media: 2-6-7-8-10-13-18-24
Distr.: Natl.
Personnel:
Andrew J. Weber *(CEO)*
Jeff Pence *(Pres-Digital Media)*
Stephen J. Custer *(Publr & Exec VP)*
Will Murphy *(Sr VP-Sls)*

FARM PROGRESS COMPANIES
(Sub. of Rural Press Limited)
255 38th Ave Ste P
Saint Charles, IL 60174-2095
Tel.: (630) 690-5600
Fax: (630) 462-2869
E-mail: don-tourte@farmprogress.com
Web Site: www.farmprogress.com
Approx. Number Employees: 100
Year Founded: 1841
Business Description:
Publisher & Printer of Agricultural Magazine
S.I.C.: 2721
N.A.I.C.S.: 511120
Advertising Expenditures: $400,000
Media: 2-4-7-10
Distr.: Reg.
Budget Set: Nov. -Jan.
Personnel:
Chuck Latin *(Pres)*
Michael Barb *(CFO)*
Scott Fisher *(Dir-IT)*
Rosemary Schimek *(Dir-Mktg)*
Don Tourte *(Dir-Natl Sls, Adv & Events)*
Jeffrey Tennant *(Mgr-Special Projects & Publ Grp-Natl)*

FARRAR, STRAUS & GIROUX, INC.
(Div. of Holtzbrinck Publishers, LLC)
19 Union Sq W
New York, NY 10003-3304
Tel.: (212) 741-6900
Fax: (212) 633-9385
Web Site: www.fsgbooks.com
Approx. Number Employees: 120
Year Founded: 1946
Business Description:
Publisher of Books
S.I.C.: 2731
N.A.I.C.S.: 511130
Advertising Expenditures: $400,000
Media: 2-6-7-8-9-10-25
Distr.: Natl.
Budget Set: Various
Personnel:
Jonathan Galassi *(Pres & Publr)*
Jeff Seroy *(Sr VP-Publicity and Mktg)*
Rodrigo Corral *(Dir-Creative)*
Vicki Genna *(Adv Dir)*
Brands & Products:
FARRAR, STRAUS & GIROUX
SUNBURST
Advertising Agency:
Verso Advertising, Inc.
50 W 17th St 5th Fl
New York, NY 10011-5702
Tel.: (212) 292-2990
Fax: (212) 557-2592

FASTLINE PUBLICATIONS INC.
4900 Fox Run Rd
Buckner, KY 40010
Tel.: (502) 222-0146
Web Site: www.fastline.com
Approx. Sls.: $20,000,000
Approx. Number Employees: 200
Year Founded: 1978
Business Description:
Magazines Publisher
S.I.C.: 2721
N.A.I.C.S.: 511120
Media: 7-10
Personnel:
William G. Howard *(Founder & CEO)*
Joe McWilliams *(Pres)*
Tim Hess *(CFO & Exec VP)*
Jim Hughey *(VP-Production)*
Brands & Products:
FASTLINE

FAYETTEVILLE PUBLISHING CO.
(d/b/a The Fayetteville Observer)
458 Whitfield St
Fayetteville, NC 28306
Tel.: (910) 323-4848
Fax: (910) 486-3544
Toll Free: (800) 682-3476
E-mail: customerservice@fayobserver.com
Web Site: fayobserver.com/
Approx. Number Employees: 400
Business Description:
Newspapers, Publishing & Printing
S.I.C.: 2711; 2791
N.A.I.C.S.: 511110; 323122
Media: 2-8-9-18-20-23-26
Personnel:
Kim Krast *(CFO)*
Charles Broadwell *(Publr-The Fayetteville Observer)*
Michael Arnholt *(Exec Editor)*
Tim White *(Editor-Editorial Page)*
Ron Cartledge *(Dir-Production)*
Trevor Collins *(Dir-Mktg & Sls)*
Jim Sills *(Sr Acct Mgr-Adv)*
Brands & Products:
FAYETTEVILLE ONLINE
FAYOBSERVER.COM

FHM
(Sub. of Bauer Consumer Media Ltd.)
110 5th Ave
New York, NY 10011
Tel.: (212) 201-6700
Fax: (212) 201-6965
Web Site: www.fhmus.com
Approx. Number Employees: 50
Business Description:
Online Magazine Publisher
S.I.C.: 2721
N.A.I.C.S.: 519130; 511120
Media: 13
Brands & Products:
FHM

FILM SCORE MONTHLY
6311 Romaine St Ste 7109
Hollywood, CA 90038-2617
Tel.: (323) 461-2240
E-mail: lukas@filmscoremonthly.com
Web Site: www.filmscoremonthly.com
E-Mail For Key Personnel:
President: lukas@filmscoremonthly.com
Sales Range: Less than $1 Million
Approx. Number Employees: 1
Year Founded: 1990
Business Description:
Record Label & Publisher of Online Motion Picture & Television Music Appreciation Magazine
S.I.C.: 2741; 8999
N.A.I.C.S.: 511199; 512210
Media: 4-6-8-10-13
Brands & Products:
FILM SCORE MONTHLY

FILMFAX, INC.
1320 Oakton St
Evanston, IL 60202
Tel.: (847) 866-7155
E-mail: filmfax@speedsite.com
Web Site: www.filmfax.com
Sales Range: $50-74.9 Million
Approx. Number Employees: 2
Year Founded: 1986
Business Description:
Movie & Television Magazines Publisher
S.I.C.: 2721
N.A.I.C.S.: 511120
Media: 4-6-8-10-13-22
Personnel:
Michael Stein *(Editor & Publr)*
Brands & Products:
FILMFAX

FINDLAW
(Sub. of Thomson Legal)
800 W California Ave 2nd Fl
Sunnyvale, CA 94086-4834
Tel.: (408) 524-4799
Fax: (408) 524-4798
E-mail: webmaster@findlaw.com
Web Site: www.findlaw.com
Year Founded: 1995
Business Description:
Legal Research Web Site
S.I.C.: 9222; 8111
N.A.I.C.S.: 922130; 541110
Media: 2-7-8-13
Personnel:
Karl Florida *(VP-Strategy & Bus Dev)*
Wlodek Kubalski *(Chief Architect & VP-Tech)*
Brands & Products:
FINDLAW.COM

FITNESS RX
(Div. of Advanced Research Press, Inc.)
690 Rt 25A
Setauket, NY 11733
Tel.: (631) 751-9696
Fax: (631) 751-9699

Key to Media (For complete agency information see *The Advertising Red Books-Agencies* edition):
1. Bus. Publs. 2. Cable T.V. 3. Catalogs & Directories. 4. Co-op Adv. 5. Consumer Mags. 6. D.M. to Bus. Estab.7. D.M. to Consumers
8. Daily Newsp. 9. Exhibits/Trade Shows 10. Foreign 11. Infomercial 12. Internet Adv.13. Multimedia 14. Network Radio
15. Network T.V. 16. Newsp. Distr. Mags. 17. Other 18. Outdoor (Posters, Transit) 19. Point of Purchase20. Premiums, Novelties
21. Product Samples 22. Special Events Mktg. 23. Spot Radio 24. Spot T.V. 25. Weekly Newsp. 26. Yellow Page Adv.

Fitness Rx — (Continued)

E-mail: editor@fitnessrxmag.com
Web Site: www.fitnessrxmag.com
Approx. Number Employees: 10
Business Description:
Magazine
S.I.C.: 5912
N.A.I.C.S.: 446110
Consumer Mags.: 100%
Personnel:
Steve Blechman *(Editor-in-Chief)*
Elyse Blechman *(Dir-Design)*
Alan Dittrich, Jr. *(Assoc Dir-Art)*
Brands & Products:
FITNESS RX FOR MEN
FITNESS RX FOR WOMEN

FLASHES PUBLISHERS
(Unit of GateHouse Media, Inc.)
595 Jenner Dr
Allegan, MI 49010
Tel.: (269) 673-1562
Fax: (269) 673-4761
Toll Free: (800) 968-4415
E-mail: publish@flashespublishers.com
Web Site: www.flashespublishers.com
Sales Range: $25-49.9 Million
Approx. Number Employees: 90
Year Founded: 1934
Business Description:
Shopping Guides Publisher & Commercial Printing Services
S.I.C.: 2721; 2741
N.A.I.C.S.: 511120; 511199
Media: 2-8-10-13-20-21-22-23-26
Personnel:
Pete Esser *(Publr)*
Michele Arthur *(Dir-HR)*
Janet Johnson *(Mgr-Classifieds)*
Debbie Lunsford *(Mgr-Circulation)*
Brands & Products:
FLASHES PUBLISHERS

FLORIDA FAMILY MAGAZINE
1840 Glengary St
Sarasota, FL 34231
Tel.: (941) 922-5437
Fax: (941) 923-6613
E-mail: info@floridafamilyliving.com
Web Site: www.floridafamilyliving.com
Approx. Number Employees: 8
Business Description:
Magazine Publisher
S.I.C.: 2721
N.A.I.C.S.: 511120
Media: 8-13
Personnel:
Beth Winkle *(Publr)*

THE FLORIDA TIMES-UNION
(Unit of Morris Publishing Group, LLC)
1 Riverside Ave
Jacksonville, FL 32202
Tel.: (904) 359-4111
Fax: (904) 359-4400
Web Site: www.jacksonville.com
Approx. Number Employees: 900
Year Founded: 1864
Business Description:
Newspaper Publisher
S.I.C.: 2711; 2721
N.A.I.C.S.: 511110; 511120
Media: 8-9-10-13
Personnel:
William S Morris *(Owner)*
Robert Martin *(Gen Mgr)*
Carole Fader *(Editor)*
Carol Holmes *(Dir-HR)*
Karen Brashear *(Mktg Mgr-FL-Jacksonville)*
Del Jones *(Mgr-Sls & Mktg)*
Beth Wardlaw *(Mgr-Inside Sls & Customer Svc)*

FLORIDA TRAVEL, INC.
2310 Townline Rd N1T 2J2
Cambridge, ON Canada
Tel.: (519) 658-8105
Fax: (519) 658-5045
Toll Free: (800) 430-2435
E-mail: sun@floridatravelusa.com
Web Site: www.floridatravelusa.com
Business Description:
Magazine Publisher
S.I.C.: 2721
N.A.I.C.S.: 511120
Media: 4-6-8-13
Personnel:
Anita Geddes *(Pres, Publr & Editor)*
Ron Keleher *(VP-Mktg)*
Brands & Products:
FLORIDA TRAVEL
FLORIDA TRAVEL MAGAZINE

FODOR'S TRAVEL PUBLICATIONS, INC.
(Sub. of Random House, Inc.)
1745 Broadway
New York, NY 10019
Tel.: (212) 751-2600
Fax: (212) 572-2248
Toll Free: (800) 755-7244
E-mail: editors@fodors.com
Web Site: www.fodors.com
Approx. Number Employees: 40
Year Founded: 1936
Business Description:
Travel Guides Publisher
S.I.C.: 2731
N.A.I.C.S.: 511130
Media: 2-6-20
Distr.: Natl.
Budget Set: Nov.
Brands & Products:
AROUND THE CITY WITH KIDS
CITYGUIDES
CITYPACKS
COMPASS AMERICAN GUIDES
EXPLORING GUIDES
FLASHMAPS
FODOR'S
FODOR'S GOLD GUIDES
FODORS.COM
LANGUAGES FOR TRAVELERS
POCKET GUIDES
TRAVEL HISTORIC AMERICA
WHERE TO WEEKEND
Advertising Agency:
Winstar Interactive Media
307 7th Ave Ste 2003
New York, NY 10001
Tel.: (212) 916-0713
Fodors.com

FOLLETT CORPORATION
2233 W St
River Grove, IL 60171
Tel.: (708) 583-2000
Fax: (708) 452-9347
Toll Free: (800) 621-4345
Web Site: www.follett.com
Sales Range: $1-4.9 Billion
Approx. Number Employees: 8,300
Year Founded: 1873
Business Description:
Contract Management of Bookstores; Wholesale Distributor of Textbooks, Library Books, Paper Products & School Supplies
S.I.C.: 5942
N.A.I.C.S.: 451211
Import Export
Personnel:
R. Mark Litzsinger *(Chm)*
Christopher D. Traut *(Pres & CEO)*
Richard Hooper *(CFO)*
Scott Deaton *(Exec VP-Mktg)*
Kathryn Stanton *(Exec VP-Fin)*
Brands & Products:
FOLLETT
POWERING EDUCATION. WORLDWIDE.
Advertising Agencies:
GSP Marketing Services, Inc.
320 W Ohio St
Chicago, IL 60654
Tel.: (312) 944-3000
Fax: (312) 944-8587

Tech Image Ltd.
1130 W Lake Cook Rd Ste 250
Buffalo Grove, IL 60089
Tel.: (847) 279-0022
Fax: (847) 279-8922
Toll Free: (888) 4-TECH-PR
Follett Digital Resources

FORBES, INC.
60 5th Ave
New York, NY 10011-8802
Tel.: (212) 620-2200
Fax: (212) 620-2245
Toll Free: (800) 242-8786
Telex: 235948-FMNYUR
E-mail: subscriber@forbes.com
Web Site: www.forbesinc.com
Approx. Sls.: $410,000,000
Approx. Number Employees: 700
Year Founded: 1917
Business Description:
Magazines Publisher; Investor In Real Estate
S.I.C.: 2721; 6282
N.A.I.C.S.: 511120; 523930
Export
Advertising Expenditures: $13,800,000
Media: 1-2-7-9-13-18-22
Distr.: Intl.; Natl.
Budget Set: Nov.
Personnel:
Malcolm Stevenson Forbes, Jr. *(Chm & CEO-Forbes, Editor-in-Chief)*
Christopher Forbes *(Vice Chm)*
Timothy C. Forbes *(Pres & COO)*
William Adamopoulos *(Pres & Publr-Forbes Asia)*
Sean Hegarty *(CFO)*
Kendall Crolius *(CMO)*
Robert L. Forbes *(Pres-ForbesLife & VP)*
Moira Forbes *(Publr-ForbesLife Executive Woman)*
Monie Begley Feury *(Sr VP-Comm)*
Chris Pagano *(Sr VP)*
Bruce Rogers *(VP-Mktg)*
Carol Hymowitz *(Editorial Dir-ForbesLife Executive Woman)*
Gary Walther *(Editor-ForbesLife)*
Brands & Products:
FORBES
FORBES ASIA
FORBESLIFE
FORBESWOMAN
Advertising Agencies:
Fletcher Media Group
94 Grove St
Peterborough, NH 03458
Tel.: (603) 924-6383
Fax: (603) 924-6562

Jaffe & Partners
148 Madison Ave 12th Fl
New York, NY 10016-5109
Tel.: (212) 696-5555
Fax: (212) 696-4998

FORRESTER RESEARCH, INC.
400 Technology Sq
Cambridge, MA 02139-3583
Tel.: (617) 613-6000
Fax: (617) 613-5000
E-mail: press@forrester.com
Web Site: www.forrester.com
Approx. Rev.: $250,726,000
Approx. Number Employees: 1,078
Year Founded: 1983
Business Description:
Market Research Services
S.I.C.: 8732; 8733
N.A.I.C.S.: 541910; 541720
Media: 10-13
Personnel:
George F. Colony *(Chm & CEO)*
Michael A. Doyle *(CFO & Treas)*
Charles Rutstein *(COO)*
George M. Orlov *(CTO & CIO)*
Gail S. Mann *(Chief Legal Officer & Sec)*
Scott Chouinard *(Chief Acctg Officer)*
Steven Peltzman *(Chief Bus Tech Officer)*
Megan Burns *(Principal & Analyst)*
Josh Bernoff *(Sr VP)*
Dennis van Lingen *(Mng Dir-Mktg & Strategy Client Grp)*
Harly Manning *(VP & Dir-Res)*
Paula Figueiredo *(Mgr)*
Andreas Lohner *(Mgr)*
Steve Noble *(Sr Analyst)*
Brands & Products:
FORRESTER
FORRESTER OVAL PROGRAM
FORRESTER WAVE
FORRTEL
MAKING LEADERS SUCCESSFUL EVERY DAY
TECHNOGRAPHICS
TECHRANKINGS
TEI
TOTAL ECONOMIC IMPACT
WHOLEVIEW 2

THE FORT MORGAN TIMES
(Joint Venture of The E.W. Scripps Company & MediaNews Group, Inc.)
329 Main St
Fort Morgan, CO 80701-2108
Mailing Address:
PO Box 4000
Fort Morgan, CO 80701-4000
Tel.: (970) 867-5651
Fax: (970) 867-7448
E-mail: fmtimes@fmtimes.com
Web Site: www.fortmorgantimes.com
Approx. Number Employees: 11

Key to Media (For complete agency information see *The Advertising Red Books-Agencies* edition):
1. Bus. Publs. 2. Cable T.V. 3. Catalogs & Directories. 4. Co-op Adv. 5. Consumer Mags. 6. D.M. to Bus. Estab.7. D.M. to Consumers
8. Daily Newsp. 9. Exhibits/Trade Shows 10. Foreign 11. Infomercial 12. Internet Adv.13. Multimedia 14. Network Radio
15. Network T.V. 16. Newsp. Distr. Mags. 17. Other 18. Outdoor (Posters, Transit) 19. Point of Purchase20. Premiums, Novelties
21. Product Samples 22. Special Events Mktg. 23. Spot Radio 24. Spot T.V. 25. Weekly Newsp. 26. Yellow Page Adv.

Business Description:
Newspapers Publisher
S.I.C.: 2711
N.A.I.C.S.: 511110
Media: 8-9
Personnel:
Julie Tonsing *(Gen Mgr)*

FORT WORTH STAR-TELEGRAM
(Sub. of McClatchy Newspapers, Inc.)
400 W 7th St
Fort Worth, TX 76102-4793
Tel.: (817) 390-7400
Fax: (817) 390-7789
Toll Free: (800) 776-STAR
E-mail: info@dfw.com
Web Site: www.dfw.com
E-Mail For Key Personnel:
Marketing Director: jescott@star-telegram.com
Sales Range: $500-549.9 Million
Approx. Number Employees: 2,000
Business Description:
Newspaper Publisher
S.I.C.: 2711
N.A.I.C.S.: 511110
Media: 8-9-18-19-20-22-23-24
Distr.: Reg.
Budget Set: Oct.
Personnel:
Gary Wortel *(Pres & Publr)*
Jim Witt *(Sr VP & Exec Editor)*
Chet Wakefield *(Sr VP-Ops)*
Mike Winter *(Sr VP-Adv)*
Bob Ray Sanders *(VP & Assoc Editor)*
Lois Norder *(Mng Editor-News)*
Kathy Vetter *(Mng Editor-Enterprise)*
Jim Fuquay *(Editor-Bus)*
John Gravois *(Asst Mng Editor-Govt Affairs)*
Paul K. Harral *(Editor-Editorial Page)*
David Humphrey *(Editor-Sports)*
Tom Johanningmeier *(Editor-Sports)*
Scott Nishimura *(Editor-Bus)*
Ann Thompson *(Editor-Metro)*
Lee Williams *(Editor-Metro)*
Brands & Products:
STAR-TELEGRAM

FORTUNE
(Unit of Time Inc.)
1271 Avenue Of The Americas
New York, NY 10020
Tel.: (212) 522-1212
Fax: (212) 467-0455
Toll Free: (800) 621-8000
Web Site: www.fortune.com
Sales Range: $100-124.9 Million
Business Description:
Business Magazine Publisher
S.I.C.: 2721
N.A.I.C.S.: 511120
Media: 2-6-7-8-9-13-18-20-24
Distr.: Direct to Consumer; Intl.; Natl.
Personnel:
Franklin L. Terkelsen *(Treas & Employee-Corp Devel)*
Douglas Beighle *(Sr VP)*
John D. Bergen *(Sr VP-Corp Affairs)*
John Huey *(Editor-in-Chief)*
Andy Serwer *(Mng Editor-Magazine's)*
Geoffrey Colvin *(Editor)*
Leigh Gallagher *(Sr Editor)*
Peter Gumbel *(Editor-Europe)*
Stephanie Mehta *(Editor-Global)*
Jeffrey O'Brien *(Sr Editor)*
Andrew Butcher *(Dir-Publ)*

FORUM COMMUNICATIONS COMPANY
101 5th St N
Fargo, ND 58102-4826
Tel.: (701) 235-7311
Fax: (701) 241-5406
E-mail: news@forumcomm.com
Web Site: www.forumcomm.com
Approx. Number Employees: 1,300
Year Founded: 1917
Business Description:
Newspaper Publishing & Communications Services
S.I.C.: 2711
N.A.I.C.S.: 511110
Import
Media: 8-9
Personnel:
William C. Marcil *(Chm)*
John Hajostek *(VP-Fin & CFO)*
Aaron Becher *(Dir-Adv)*

FRANK MAYBORN ENTERPRISES
(d/b/a Temple Daily Telegram)
10 S 3rd St
Temple, TX 76501
Tel.: (254) 778-4444
Fax: (254) 774-9391
Web Site: www.tdtnews.com
Approx. Number Employees: 105
Business Description:
Newspapers
S.I.C.: 2711
N.A.I.C.S.: 511110
Media: 8-9-13
Personnel:
Anyse Sue Mayborn *(Pres)*
Jerry Prickett *(Mng Editor)*
Brands & Products:
THE FT HOOD SENTINAL
TDTNEWS.COM
TEMPLE DAILY TELEGRAM

FRANKLIN COVEY CANADA, LTD.
(Sub. of Franklin Covey Company)
60 Struck Ct
Cambridge, ON N1R 8L2, Canada
Tel.: (519) 740-2580
Fax: (519) 740-6848
Web Site: www.franklincovey.ca
Sales Range: $25-49.9 Million
Approx. Number Employees: 100
Business Description:
Business Services
S.I.C.: 7389
N.A.I.C.S.: 561499
Media: 1-2-4-7-8-10-13-18-19-20-22-23-24-26
Personnel:
Deborah Szczepko *(Dir-Consumer Sls & Mktg)*

FRANKLIN COVEY COMPANY
2200 W Parkway Blvd
Salt Lake City, UT 84119-2099
Tel.: (801) 975-1776
Fax: (801) 817-6447
Toll Free: (800) 827-1776
E-mail: comments@franklincovey.com
Web Site: www.franklincovey.com
E-Mail For Key Personnel:
Public Relations: debra.lund@franklincovey.com
Approx. Sls.: $136,874,000
Approx. Number Employees: 600
Year Founded: 1983
Business Description:
Training, Productivity Tools & Performance Solutions
S.I.C.: 8742; 5112; 8299; 8748
N.A.I.C.S.: 541611; 424120; 541618; 611699
Import Export
Advertising Expenditures: $3,300,000
Media: 1-4-7-8-13
Personnel:
Robert A. Whitman *(Chm & CEO)*
Stephen R. Covey *(Vice Chm)*
Stephen D. Young *(CFO)*
Michael Sean Covey *(Chief Innovation Officer & Exec VP)*
Robert William Bennett, Jr. *(Pres-Org Strategic Bus)*
Shawn D. Moon *(Exec VP)*
Jeff Anderson *(Sr VP-Porduct Mgmt)*
Debra S. Lund *(Dir-PR)*
Matt Murdoch *(Dir-Sls & Mktg)*
Brands & Products:
THE 4 DISCIPLINES OF EXECUTION
THE 4 ROLES OF LEADERSHIP
THE 6 MOST IMPORTANT DECISIONS YOU'LL EVER MAKE
THE 7 HABITS FOR MANAGERS
THE 7 HABITS OF HIGHLY EFFECTIVE FAMILIES
THE 7 HABITS OF HIGHLY EFFECTIVE PEOPLE
THE 7 HABITS OF HIGHLY EFFECTIVE TEENS
THE 8TH HABIT: FROM EFFECTIVENESS TO GREATNESS
EVERYDAY GREATNESS
FIRST THINGS FIRST
FOCUS: ACHIEVING YOUR HIGHEST PRIORITIES
FRANKLIN PLANNER
FRANKLINCOVEY
INTRO TO THE 7 HABITS FOR HEALTHCARE
MEETING ADVANTAGE
PLANPLUS
THE POWER PRINCIPLE: INFLUENCE WITH HONOR
PRESENTATION ADVANTAGE
PRINCIPLE-CENTERED LEADERSHIP
PRINCIPLE-CENTERED LEADERSHIP WEEK
PROJECT MANAGEMENT - AN APPROACH THAT REALLY WORKS
RETHINKING STRESS
TECHNICAL WRITING ADVANTAGE
WRITING ADVANTAGE
THE XQ

FRAWLEY CORPORATION
5737 Kanan Rd PMB 188
Agoura Hills, CA 91301
Tel.: (818) 735-6640
Fax: (818) 735-6647
Sales Range: Less than $1 Million
Approx. Number Employees: 1
Year Founded: 1970
Business Description:
Holding Company; Real Estate Development
S.I.C.: 6552; 6519; 6719
N.A.I.C.S.: 237210; 531190; 551112
Media: 2-9-17-24-25-26
Distr.: Intl.; Natl.
Budget Set: Sept.
Personnel:
Michael P. Frawley *(Chm, Pres, CEO & Treas)*

FREDERICK FELL PUBLISHERS, INC.
1403 Shoreline Way
Hollywood, FL 33019
Tel.: (954) 925-5242
Fax: (954) 455-4243
Toll Free: (800) 771-3355
E-mail: fellpub@aol.com
Web Site: www.fellpub.com
Sales Range: $10-24.9 Million
Approx. Number Employees: 45
Year Founded: 1943
Business Description:
Book Publisher
S.I.C.: 2731
N.A.I.C.S.: 511130
Export
Advertising Expenditures: $250,000
Media: 2-5-6-9-13
Distr.: Intl.; Natl.
Personnel:
Donald L. Lessne *(Publr)*
Brands & Products:
FELL'S
OFFICIAL-KNOW-IT-ALL-GUIDE
Advertising Agency:
Fell Advertising
1403 Shoreline Way
Hollywood, FL 33019
Tel.: (954) 925-5242
Fax: (954) 455-4243

THE FREE LANCE-STAR PUBLISHING CO.
616 Amelia St
Fredericksburg, VA 22401
Tel.: (540) 374-5000
Fax: (540) 373-8450
Web Site: www.fredericksburg.com
Approx. Number Employees: 435
Year Founded: 1885
Business Description:
Newspaper Publishers; Radio Broadcasting; Internet Service
S.I.C.: 2711; 4832
N.A.I.C.S.: 511110; 515112
Import
Media: 8-9-13-20-22-23
Personnel:
Mildred C. Cavin *(CFO)*
Josiah P. Rowe, III *(Publr)*
Bill Smith *(Dir-Adv)*

THE FREE PRESS
(Unit of Freedom Newspapers, Inc.)
2103 N Queen St
Kinston, NC 28501-1622
Mailing Address:
PO Box 129
Kinston, NC 28502-0129
Tel.: (252) 527-3191
Fax: (252) 527-8838
E-mail: freepressuse@freedomenc.com
Web Site: www.kinston.com
Approx. Rev.: $4,220,256
Approx. Number Employees: 50
Year Founded: 1882
Business Description:
Newspapers Publishing & Printing
S.I.C.: 2711
N.A.I.C.S.: 511110

Key to Media (For complete agency information see *The Advertising Red Books-Agencies* edition):
1. Bus. Publs. 2. Cable T.V. 3. Catalogs & Directories. 4. Co-op Adv. 5. Consumer Mags. 6. D.M. to Bus. Estab.7. D.M. to Consumers
8. Daily Newsp. 9. Exhibits/Trade Shows 10. Foreign 11. Infomercial 12. Internet Adv.13. Multimedia 14. Network Radio
15. Network T.V. 16. Newsp. Distr. Mags. 17. Other 18. Outdoor (Posters, Transit) 19. Point of Purchase20. Premiums, Novelties
21. Product Samples 22. Special Events Mktg. 23. Spot Radio 24. Spot T.V. 25. Weekly Newsp. 26. Yellow Page Adv.

The Free Press — (Continued)

Media: 8-9
Personnel:
Vernon Debolt *(Pres)*
Patrick Holmes *(Publr)*
Billy Moore *(Adv Dir)*

FREEDOM COMMUNICATIONS, INC.

17666 Fitch
Irvine, CA 92614-6022
Tel.: (949) 253-2300
Fax: (949) 474-7675
E-mail: info@link.freedom.com
Web Site: www.freedom.com
Approx. Number Employees: 8,000
Year Founded: 1905
Business Description:
Holding Company; Newspaper Publishing & Television Broadcasting
S.I.C.: 6719; 2711; 4833
N.A.I.C.S.: 551112; 511110; 515120
Media: 1-2-3-4-6-7-8-9-10-13-18-20-22-23-24-25-26
Distr.: Direct to Consumer; Reg.
Personnel:
Mitchell Stern *(Pres & CEO)*
Douglas S. Bennett *(Pres-Freedom Interactive)*
Marcy Bruskin *(VP-HR & Org Dev)*
Brian Wolf *(VP-HR & Organizational Dev)*
Stephen C. Kelley *(Dir-Enterprise Fin Plng & Analysis)*
Patrick Rice *(Dir-Content-Florida Freedom)*
Brands & Products:
APPEAL-DEMOCRAT
THE BROWNSVILLE HERALD
CLOVIS NEWS JOURNAL
THE DAILY NEWS
DAILY PRESS
DESERT DISPATCH
EAST VALLEY TRIBUNE
THE FREE PRESS
FREEDOM COMMUNICATIONS
THE GASTON GAZETTE
HAVELOCK NEWS
HESPERIA STAR
HICKORY NEWS
JACKSONVILLE JOURNAL-COURIER
JONES POST
THE LIMA NEWS
MID VALLEY TOWN CRIER
THE MONITOR
MYORANGECOUNTY.COM
NEWS HERALD
NORTHWEST FLORIDA DAILY NEWS
ODESSA AMERICAN
THE ORANGE COUNTY REGISTER
PORTERVILLE RECORDER
QUAY COUNTY SUN
THE SEDALIA DEMOCRAT
THE STAR
SUN JOURNAL
THE TELEGRAPH
THE TIMES-NEWS
THE TOPSAIL ADVERTISER
THE TRIBUNE
VALLEY MORNING STAR
THE WALTON SUN
THE YUMA DAILY SUN

THE FREELANCE-STAR RADIO GROUPS

(Div. of The Free Lance-Star Publishing Co.)
616 Amelia St
Fredericksburg, VA 22401-3887
Tel.: (540) 373-1500
Fax: (540) 374-5525
E-mail: wfls@flstarweb.com
Web Site: www.wfls.com
Approx. Number Employees: 44
Year Founded: 1960
Business Description:
Radio Broadcasting
S.I.C.: 2711; 4832
N.A.I.C.S.: 511110; 515112
Media: 8-13-20-22-23
Personnel:
John Moen *(Gen Mgr)*
Shelly Bynum *(Dir-Production)*
Frank Hammon *(Dir-News)*
Paul Johnson *(Mgr-Ops)*

FRIENDFINDER NETWORKS INC.

6800 Broken Sound Pkwy Ste 100
Boca Raton, FL 33487
Tel.: (561) 912-7000
Fax: (561) 912-7038
Web Site: www.ffn.com
Sales Range: $300-349.9 Million
Approx. Number Employees: 350
Year Founded: 1965
Business Description:
Social Networking & Multimedia Entertainment Services
S.I.C.: 2741; 2721; 7999
N.A.I.C.S.: 516110; 511120; 713990
Advertising Expenditures: $500,000
Media: 1-3-5-8-9-13-19-20-22-23-24
Distr.: Natl.
Budget Set: Nov.
Personnel:
Daniel C. Staton *(Chm)*
Marc H. Bell *(Pres & CEO)*
Ezra Shashoua *(CFO)*
Anthony Previte *(COO)*
Rob Brackett *(Pres-Internet Grp)*
Carmela Monti *(VP-HR)*
Brian M. Prenoveau *(Dir-IR)*
Brands & Products:
FORUM
FRIENDFINDER NETWORKS
GIRLS OF PENTHOUSE
PENTHOUSE
PENTHOUSE LETTERS
VARIATIONS

GALE GROUP INC.

(Sub. of Cengage Learning Inc.)
27500 Drake Rd
Farmington Hills, MI 48331-3535
Tel.: (248) 699-4253
Fax: (248) 699-8064
Fax: (800) 414-5043
Toll Free: (800) 877-4253
Web Site: www.gale.com
Approx. Number Employees: 1,000
Year Founded: 1954
Business Description:
Reference Book & Electronic Reference Materials Publisher
S.I.C.: 2741; 2721; 2731; 3679; 8299
N.A.I.C.S.: 511140; 334419; 511120; 511130; 611710
Import Export
Media: 2-4-6-7-10-17-21-22
Distr.: Intl.; Natl.
Budget Set: Oct.
Personnel:
Dennis Stepaniak *(COO)*
Frank Menchaca *(Exec VP-Publ)*
Jill Lectka *(Sr VP-Circulating & Trade Publ)*
Stephen Abram *(VP-Strategic Partnerships & Mkts)*
Brands & Products:
BLACKBIRCH PRESS
CHARLES SCRIBNER'S SONS
FIVE STAR
G.K. HALL & CO.
GRAHAM & WHITESIDE
GREENHAVEN PRESS
K.G. SAUR
KIDHAVEN PRESS
LARGE PRINT PRESS
LUCENT BOOKS
MACMILLAN REFERENCE USA
OCEANO GRUPO EDITORIAL
PRIMARY SOURCE MICROFILM
SCHIRMER REFERENCES
SCHOLARLY RESOURCES
SLEEPING BEAR PRESS
ST. JAMES PRESS
THE TAFT GROUP
THOMSON GALE
THORNDIKE PRESS
TWAYNE PUBLISHERS
UXL
WHEELER PUBLISHING

THE GALLUP ORGANIZATION-PRINCETON

(Sub. of The Gallup Organization)
502 Carnegie Ctr Ste 300
Princeton, NJ 08540
Tel.: (609) 924-9600
Fax: (609) 279-2541
Toll Free: (800) 888-5493
E-mail: info@gallup.com
Web Site: www.gallup.com
Sales Range: $1-9.9 Million
Approx. Number Employees: 50
Year Founded: 1935
Business Description:
Management Consulting, Public Opinion Services & Periodical Publisher
S.I.C.: 8732; 2721; 8742
N.A.I.C.S.: 541910; 511120; 541611
Media: 2-7-8-13-22
Personnel:
James K. Clifton *(CEO)*

GANNETT CO., INC.

7950 Jones Branch Dr
McLean, VA 22107-0001
Tel.: (703) 854-6000
Fax: (703) 854-2046
Telex: 170934 GANCOM
E-mail: gcishare@gannett.com
Web Site: www.gannett.com
Approx. Rev.: $5,438,678,000
Approx. Number Employees: 32,600
Year Founded: 1906
Business Description:
Holding Company; Newspaper, Broadcasting & Internet Services
S.I.C.: 2711; 4833; 7319
N.A.I.C.S.: 511110; 515120; 541850; 541890
Import Export
Advertising Expenditures: $4,937,000,000
Personnel:
Gracia C. Martore *(Pres & CEO)*
Paul N. Saleh *(CFO & Sr VP)*
Maryam Banikarim *(CMO & Sr VP)*
David A. Payne *(Chief Digital Officer & Sr VP)*
Bill Albrecht *(Pres-Media Network of Central Ohio)*
Robert J. Dickey *(Pres-US Community Publ)*
Laura Hollingsworth *(Pres-MidWest Grp)*
Carol Hudler *(Pres-South Grp-USCP Div)*
Dave Lougee *(Pres-Gannett Brdcst)*
Karen R. Moreno *(Pres-Gannett Supply)*
Mary P. Stier *(Pres-Midwest Newspaper Grp)*
John A. Williams *(Pres-Gannett Digital Ventures)*
Todd A. Mayman *(Gen Counsel, Sec & Sr VP)*
William A. Behan *(Sr VP-Labor Rel)*
Philip R. Currie *(Sr VP-News-Newspaper Div)*
Daniel J. Donaghy *(Sr VP-Sls-Gannett Digital Ventures)*
Roxanne V. Horning *(Sr VP-HR)*
Steve Silberman *(Reg VP)*
Peter Lundquist *(VP & Gen Mgr-Gannett High School Sports)*
Jennifer Carroll *(VP-Digital Content)*
Craig Etheridge *(VP-Mobile Adv Sls-Gannett Digital)*
Debra Goetz *(VP-Mktg)*
Kate Marymont *(VP-Info Center Content)*
Carla Wojnaroski *(Gen Mgr)*
Jeffrey Heinz *(Dir-IR)*
Eric Hertting *(Asst Treas)*
Erik Faigh *(Coord-Digital)*
Advertising Agency:
Ad2Pro Media Solutions
23371 Mulholland Dr Ste 132
Woodland Hills, CA 91364
Tel.: (818) 591-7713
Fax: (818) 267-5511

GANNETT HEALTHCARE GROUP

(Div. of Gannett Co., Inc.)
1721 Moon Lake Blvd Ste 540
Hoffman Estates, IL 60169-2170
Tel.: (847) 839-1700
Fax: (847) 839-1711
E-mail: info@nursingspectrum.com
Web Site: www.nurse.com
Sales Range: $25-49.9 Million
Approx. Number Employees: 60
Business Description:
Healthcare Magazine & Website Publisher
S.I.C.: 2721
N.A.I.C.S.: 511120
Media: 2-8-10-22
Personnel:
Steve Hauber *(CEO & Publr)*
Eric Katler *(CFO & Exec VP-Fin)*
Andy Baldwin *(Exec VP-Bus Dev)*
Fred J. DiCostanzo *(Exec VP-HR)*
Robert G. Hess, Jr. *(Exec VP-Global Programming)*
John Leggett *(Exec VP)*
Ray Riordan *(Exec VP-Sls & Mktg)*
Melyni Serpa *(Exec VP-Circulation & Production)*

Key to Media (For complete agency information see *The Advertising Red Books-Agencies* edition):
1. Bus. Publs. 2. Cable T.V. 3. Catalogs & Directories. 4. Co-op Adv. 5. Consumer Mags. 6. D.M. to Bus. Estab.7. D.M. to Consumers 8. Daily Newsp. 9. Exhibits/Trade Shows 10. Foreign 11. Infomercial 12. Internet Adv.13. Multimedia 14. Network Radio 15. Network T.V. 16. Newsp. Distr. Mags. 17. Other 18. Outdoor (Posters, Transit) 19. Point of Purchase20. Premiums, Novelties 21. Product Samples 22. Special Events Mktg. 23. Spot Radio 24. Spot T.V. 25. Weekly Newsp. 26. Yellow Page Adv.

Doug Houser *(VP-Professional Svcs-Adv)*
Paul Murray *(VP-IT)*
Brands & Products:
CAREER FITNESS
NURSING SPECTRUM

GARDNER PUBLICATIONS, INC.
6915 Vly Ave
Cincinnati, OH 45244-3029
Tel.: (513) 527-8800
Fax: (513) 527-8801
Toll Free: (800) 950-8020
E-mail: info@gardnerweb.com
Web Site: www.gardnerweb.com
Approx. Sls.: $23,000,000
Approx. Number Employees: 110
Year Founded: 1928
Business Description:
Trade Journals & Books Publisher
S.I.C.: 2721; 2731
N.A.I.C.S.: 511120; 511130
Import Export
Media: 2-7-10
Personnel:
Richard G. Kline *(Pres)*
Fred M. Rzezak *(Reg VP)*
Steven R. Kline *(Dir-Market Intelligence)*
Melissa Skaulem *(Dir-Mktg)*
Brands & Products:
AUTOMOTIVE MANUFACTURING & PRODUCTION
GARDNER
MODERN MACHINE SHOP
PRODUCTS FINISHING

GARLINGHOUSE COMPANY
2121 Boundary St Ste 208 Burnside Bldg
Beaufort, SC 29902
Tel.: (843) 271-6107
Fax: (866) 454-9101
Toll Free: (800) 235-5700
Toll Free: (800) 895-3715
E-mail: info@garlinghouse.com
Web Site: www.garlinghouse.com
Approx. Sls.: $10,000,000
Approx. Number Employees: 25
Year Founded: 1907
Business Description:
Home & Residential Building Plans Publisher
S.I.C.: 5961; 2721
N.A.I.C.S.: 454113; 511120
Export
Media: 2-4-6-7-8-9-11-13-26
Distr.: Direct to Consumer; Intl.; Natl.
Budget Set: Sept.
Personnel:
Jarret Magbee *(Pres & CEO)*
Brands & Products:
THE GARLINGHOUSE HOME PLANS

THE GASTON GAZETTE
(Unit of Freedom Newspapers, Inc.)
1893 Remount Rd
Gastonia, NC 28054
Tel.: (704) 869-1700
Fax: (704) 867-5751
E-mail: gastongazette@link.freedom.com
Web Site: www.gastongazette.com
Approx. Number Employees: 250,000
Year Founded: 1880
Business Description:
Newspaper
S.I.C.: 2711
N.A.I.C.S.: 511110
Media: 8-9-13-22
Personnel:
Jennie Lambert *(Publr)*
Sherry Collins *(Dir-Promo)*
Brent Powers *(Dir-New Media & Internet Sls)*
Christopher T. Workman *(Bus Mgr)*
Crystal Armstrong *(Mgr-Creative Svcs)*
Jamey Jenkins *(Mgr-Adv)*

GATEHOUSE MEDIA, INC.
350 Willowbrook Office Pk
Fairport, NY 14450
Tel.: (585) 598-0030
Fax: (585) 248-2631
E-mail: investorrelations@gatehousemedia.com
Web Site: www.gatehousemedia.com
Approx. Rev.: $558,588,000
Approx. Number Employees: 5,239
Business Description:
Print & Online Publisher
S.I.C.: 2711; 2721; 2741
N.A.I.C.S.: 511110; 511120; 516110
Advertising Expenditures: $4,397,000
Media: 9-16-18-25
Personnel:
Wesley Robert Edens *(Chm)*
Kirk A. Davis *(Pres & COO)*
Michael E. Reed *(CEO)*
Melinda A. Janik *(CFO & Sr VP)*
Rick Daniels *(COO)*
Paul Ameden *(CIO)*
Polly G. Sack *(Gen Counsel)*
O. Rourke *(Exec VP-Atlantic Reg)*

GATEHOUSE MEDIA SUBURBAN NEWSPAPERS, INC.
(Sub. of GateHouse Media, Inc.)
1101 W 31st St Ste 100
Downers Grove, IL 60515-5581
Tel.: (630) 368-1100
Tel.: (630) 368-1144
Fax: (630) 969-0228
Web Site: www.mysuburbanlife.com
Sales Range: $500-549.9 Million
Approx. Number Employees: 3,200
Business Description:
Newspaper Publisher
S.I.C.: 2711
N.A.I.C.S.: 511110
Media: 9

THE GAZETTE
(Unit of Freedom Newspapers, Inc.)
30 S Prospect St
Colorado Springs, CO 80903
Tel.: (719) 632-5511
Fax: (719) 636-0118
E-mail: customercare@gazette.com
Web Site: www.gazette.com
Approx. Number Employees: 450
Business Description:
Newspaper Publisher
S.I.C.: 2711
N.A.I.C.S.: 511110
Media: 8-9
Personnel:
Steven Pope *(Pres & Publr)*
Dena Rosenberry *(Editor-Section)*
Jeff Thomas *(VP & Editor)*
Pula Davis *(Editor-Sys)*
Warren Epstein *(Editor-Arts & Culture)*
Teresa J. Farney *(Editor-Food)*
Sue Millman *(Editor-City)*
Ginny Greene *(Dir-Internet)*
Sean Paige *(Dir-Local Liberty Action)*
Brad Shaw *(Dir-IT)*
Stuart Wong *(Dir-Photo)*

GAZETTE COMMUNICATIONS, INC.
500 3rd Ave SE
Cedar Rapids, IA 52401-1608
Tel.: (319) 398-8211
Fax: (319) 398-8395
Toll Free: (800) 397-8222
Web Site: www.gazetteonline.com
Sales Range: $200-249.9 Million
Approx. Number Employees: 600
Year Founded: 1883
Business Description:
Newspaper, Online & Multimedia Publisher; TV Station Owner
S.I.C.: 2711
N.A.I.C.S.: 511110
Media: 2-5-7-8-9-13-22-24
Distr.: Direct to Consumer; Reg.
Personnel:
Joe Hladky *(Chm & CEO)*
Ken Slaughter *(CFO)*
Tim McDougall *(VP-Products & Publr)*
Lyle Muller *(Editor-The Gazette)*
Richard Pratt *(Editor-Online)*
Jeff Tecklenburg *(Editor-Opinion Page-The Gazette)*
Chris Edwards *(Dir-Adv)*
Joe Wise *(Mgr-Prepress)*
Kevin Zacek *(Mgr-Production)*
Brands & Products:
COMMUNITY NEWS ADVERTISER
THE GAZETTE
GAZETTEONLINE.COM
PENNYSAVER

GEORGE BRAZILLER PUBLISHERS, INC.
174 E 74th St
New York, NY 10016-5110
Tel.: (212) 889-0909
Fax: (212) 689-5405
E-mail: info@georgebraziller.com
Web Site: www.georgebraziller.com
Sales Range: $75-99.9 Million
Approx. Number Employees: 7
Year Founded: 1955
Business Description:
Art, Architectural, Literature, Fiction, Non-Fiction & Poetry Book Publisher
S.I.C.: 2731
N.A.I.C.S.: 511130
Media: 2-4-5-6-9-10-16-21-22-25
Distr.: Intl.; Natl.
Budget Set: Jan. -June
Personnel:
George Braziller *(Publr)*

GEORGE F. CRAM CO., INC.
(Sub. of Herff Jones, Inc.)
4719 W 62nd St
Indianapolis, IN 46268-2593
Mailing Address:
PO Box 68596
Indianapolis, IN 46206-0426
Tel.: (317) 635-5564
Fax: (317) 329-3305
Toll Free: (800) 227-4199
E-mail: info@maps-globe.com
Web Site: www.maps-globes.com/
Approx. Number Employees: 90
Year Founded: 1867
Business Description:
Mfr. of Maps, Atlases, Globes & Teaching Aids
S.I.C.: 2741
N.A.I.C.S.: 511199
Import Export
Media: 2-4-7-8-10-13-26
Distr.: Natl.
Budget Set: Nov.
Personnel:
Arthur Thomas *(Pur Agent)*
Brands & Products:
CRAM
GEORGE F. CRAM

GEORGE J. FOSTER CO. INC.
(d/b/a Foster's Daily Democrat)
150 Venture Dr
Dover, NH 03820
Tel.: (603) 742-4455
Fax: (603) 740-3464
Web Site: www.fosters.com
Approx. Sls.: $13,800,000
Approx. Number Employees: 100
Business Description:
Newspapers, Publishing & Printing
S.I.C.: 2711
N.A.I.C.S.: 511110
Media: 8-9
Personnel:
Robert H. Foster *(Pres & Publr)*
Simeon Broughton *(Dir-IT)*
Wayne Chick *(Dir-Pub Rels & Major Accts)*

GETTY IMAGES, INC.
(Holding of Hellman & Friedman LLC)
601 N 34th St
Seattle, WA 98103-8694
Tel.: (206) 925-5000
Fax: (206) 925-5001
E-mail: feedback@gettyimages.com
Web Site: www.gettyimages.com
Sales Range: $800-899.9 Million
Approx. Number Employees: 1,935
Year Founded: 1995
Business Description:
Stock Photograph Archiving & Sales
S.I.C.: 7335; 7319; 7336
N.A.I.C.S.: 541922; 541430; 541890
Advertising Expenditures: $21,700,000
Media: 2-4-7-13
Personnel:
Mark H. Getty *(Co-Founder & Chm)*
Jonathan D. Klein *(Co-Founder & CEO)*
Bart Catalane *(CFO & Sr VP)*
Nicholas Evans-Lombe *(COO)*
John Lapham *(Gen Counsel & Sr VP)*
Lisa Calvert *(Sr VP-HR & Facilities)*
Jim Gurke *(Sr VP-Mktg)*
Steve Heck *(Sr VP-Tech)*
Lee Martin *(Sr VP-Sls-Europe)*
Adrian Murrell *(Sr VP-Global Editorial)*
Craig Peters *(Sr VP-Bus Dev)*
Rebecca Rockafellar *(Sr VP-Ecommerce Platform Mgmt)*
Michael Teaster *(Sr VP-Sls-North America & Asia Pacific)*
Brands & Products:
GETTY IMAGES

GLAMOUR
(Unit of Conde Nast Publications, Inc.)
4 Times Sq 16th Fl
New York, NY 10036
Tel.: (212) 286-2860

Key to Media (For complete agency information see *The Advertising Red Books-Agencies* edition):
1. Bus. Publs. 2. Cable T.V. 3. Catalogs & Directories. 4. Co-op Adv. 5. Consumer Mags. 6. D.M. to Bus. Estab.7. D.M. to Consumers 8. Daily Newsp. 9. Exhibits/Trade Shows 10. Foreign 11. Infomercial 12. Internet Adv.13. Multimedia 14. Network Radio 15. Network T.V. 16. Newsp. Distr. Mags. 17. Other 18. Outdoor (Posters, Transit) 19. Point of Purchase20. Premiums, Novelties 21. Product Samples 22. Special Events Mktg. 23. Spot Radio 24. Spot T.V. 25. Weekly Newsp. 26. Yellow Page Adv.

Glamour — (Continued)

Fax: (212) 286-6922
Web Site: www.glamour.com
Business Description:
Women's Magazine Publisher
S.I.C.: 2721; 2741
N.A.I.C.S.: 511120; 516110
Media: 4-8-10-11-13
Personnel:
Jason Wagenheim *(Publr)*
Pamela Drucker Mann *(Assoc Publr-Adv)*
William Wackermann *(Exec VP & Dir-Publ)*
Cynthia Leive *(Editor-in-Chief)*
Theresa Griggs *(Art Dir)*
Grace Dawson *(Dir-Adv)*
Jason Scneider *(Dir-Adv)*

GLENCOE/MCGRAW-HILL

(Div. of McGraw-Hill Education)
8787 Orion Pl
Columbus, OH 43240-4027
Tel.: (614) 430-4000
Fax: (614) 430-4168
Toll Free: (800) 334-7344
E-mail: customer.service@mcgraw-hill.com
Web Site: www.glencoe.com
Sales Range: $75-99.9 Million
Approx. Number Employees: 508
Business Description:
Publishers of Teaching & Learning Aid Materials
S.I.C.: 2731; 2741
N.A.I.C.S.: 511130; 511199
Import Export
Media: 1-2-4-7-8-10
Distr.: Natl.
Personnel:
Tom Bruce *(VP-Dir Sls)*

THE GLOBE PEQUOT PRESS, INC.

(Sub. of Morris Communications Company LLC)
246 Goose Ln
Guilford, CT 06437
Mailing Address:
PO Box 480
Guilford, CT 06437-0480
Tel.: (203) 458-4500
Fax: (203) 458-4601
Fax: (800) 820-2329
Toll Free: (888) 249-7586
E-mail: info@globe-pequot.com
Web Site: www.globepequot.com
E-Mail For Key Personnel:
Marketing Director: lForland@globe-pequot.com
Public Relations: publicity@globepequot.com
Approx. Number Employees: 125
Year Founded: 1947
Business Description:
Travel, Outdoor & Recreation Books Publisher
S.I.C.: 2731
N.A.I.C.S.: 511130
Import Export
Media: 2-4-5-6-7-8-10-11-19-20-21-22
Distr.: Intl.
Personnel:
James Joseph *(Pres)*
Inger Forland *(Exec Dir-Mktg, Design & PR)*
Gail Blackhall *(Dir-Subsidiary Rights)*
Max Phelps *(Dir-Mktg & Sls Dev-Outdoor Industry)*
Chris Grimm *(Mgr-Natl Acct)*
Brands & Products:
CADOGAN GUIDES
FALCON GUIDES
GLOBE PEQUOT
INSIDER'S GUIDE
THE LYONS PRESS

GOOD HOUSEKEEPING

(Unit of Hearst Magazines)
300 W 57th St
New York, NY 10019
Tel.: (212) 649-2551
Fax: (212) 649-2441
E-mail: info@goodhousekeeping.com
Web Site:
www.goodhousekeeping.com
Approx. Number Employees: 100
Year Founded: 1901
Business Description:
Publisher of Women's Magazine
S.I.C.: 2721; 2731
N.A.I.C.S.: 511120; 511130
Media: 6-8-10-13-14-15-19-23-24
Distr.: Direct to Consumer; Intl.; Natl.
Budget Set: Dec.
Personnel:
Patricia Haegele *(Publr & Sr VP)*
Mary Hayes *(VP & Dir-Direct Response)*
Rosemary Ellis *(Editor-in-Chief)*
Jane Bianchi *(Editor)*
Kate Coyne *(Editor-Entertainment)*
Clare Ellis *(Assoc Editor-Res)*
Patricia Greco *(Assoc Editor)*
Alyssa Kolsky Hertzig *(Editor-Beauty)*
Laura Mathews *(Editor-Literary)*
Jordan Ross *(Editor-Copy)*
Nicole Stagg *(Exec Dir-Content & Product Strategy)*
Theresa B. Salimbene *(Dir-Mktg Res)*
Kristi Lane *(Designer)*
Marley Israel *(Sr Designer)*
Trent Johnson *(Art Dir)*
Esther Levy *(Mktg Dir)*
Toni Gerber Hope *(Dir-Health)*
John P. Kupsch *(Dir-Technical-Research Institute)*
Sara Lyle *(Dir-Lifestyle)*
Sara Rad *(Dir-Brand Devel)*
Benay R. Bubar *(Assoc Dir-Production)*
Joseph Cavallieri *(Assoc Dir-Art)*
Christine Batraville *(Sr Mgr-Mktg-Food & Packaged Goods)*
Clinton Finn *(Mgr-Adv Svcs)*
Tara Torino *(Mgr-Direct Response Adv Sls)*

THE GOODHEART-WILLCOX CO., INC.

18604 W Creek Dr
Tinley Park, IL 60477-6243
Tel.: (708) 687-5000
Fax: (708) 687-0315
Fax: (888) 409-3900
Toll Free: (800) 323-0440
E-mail: custserv@g-w.com
Web Site: www.g-w.com
Sales Range: $10-24.9 Million
Approx. Number Employees: 65
Year Founded: 1921
Business Description:
Mechanical, Technical & Home Economics Textbooks Publisher
S.I.C.: 2731
N.A.I.C.S.: 511130
Media: 2-4-5-6-8-10-13-22
Distr.: Intl.
Budget Set: June
Personnel:
John F. Flanagan *(Pres)*
Todd J. Scheffers *(VP-Sls)*
Zak Semens *(Coord-Adv)*

THE GRAND ISLAND DAILY INDEPENDENT

(Sub. of Omaha World Herald Company)
422 W 1st St
Grand Island, NE 68801
Mailing Address:
PO Box 1208
Grand Island, NE 68802-1208
Tel.: (308) 382-1000
Fax: (308) 382-8129
Toll Free: (800) 658-3160
Web Site: www.theindependent.com
Approx. Number Employees: 100
Business Description:
Newspaper Publisher
S.I.C.: 2711
N.A.I.C.S.: 511110
Media: 8-9
Personnel:
Donald S. Smith *(Publr)*
Bill Dunn *(Editor)*
Terri Hahn *(Editor-Features)*
John Lilly *(Dir-Ops)*
Sonya Schultz *(Dir-Adv)*
Jack Sheard *(Dir-New Media)*
Pat Bell *(Mgr-Classifieds)*
Kimberly Sweetser *(Mgr-Retail Adv)*
Brands & Products:
THE GRAND ISLAND DAILY INDEPENDENT

GREAT LAKES PUBLISHING COMPANY

(d/b/a Cleveland Magazine)
1422 Euclid Ave Ste 730
Cleveland, OH 44115
Tel.: (216) 771-2833
Fax: (216) 781-6318
E-mail: information@clevelandmagazines.com
Web Site: www.glpublishing.com
Approx. Sls.: $11,000,000
Approx. Number Employees: 70
Business Description:
Magazine Publisher
S.I.C.: 2721; 2731
N.A.I.C.S.: 511120; 511130
Media: 2-6-7-8-10-13
Personnel:
Lute Harmon, Sr. *(Chm)*
Lute Harmon, Jr. *(Pres)*
Brands & Products:
CINCY LIFE
CINCYBUSINESS
CLEVELAND HOME DECOR
CLEVELAND MAGAZINE
FEAST!MAGAZINE
INSIDE BUSINESS MAGAZINE
LONGWEEKENDS
MYOHIOWINE.COM
OHIO BUSINESS MAGAZINE
OHIO ENTREPRENEUR
OHIO MAGAZINE

GREAT SOURCE

(Div. of Houghton Mifflin Harcourt Publishing Company)
181 Ballardvale St
Wilmington, MA 01887-1024
Tel.: (978) 661-1300
Fax: (800) 289-3994
Web Site: www.greatsource.com
Business Description:
Textbook Publishing Company
S.I.C.: 2731; 2732
N.A.I.C.S.: 511130; 323117
Media: 4-10

GREATER MEDIA NEWSPAPERS, INC.

(Sub. of Greater Media, Inc.)
3499 US Hwy 9 Ste 1B
Freehold, NJ 07728-3281
Mailing Address:
PO Box 5001
Freehold, NJ 07728-5001
Tel.: (732) 358-5200
Fax: (732) 780-4257
E-mail: gmntnews@gmnews.com
Web Site: www.gmnews.com
Approx. Number Employees: 125
Business Description:
Newspapers - Publishing & Printing
S.I.C.: 2711
N.A.I.C.S.: 511110
Media: 14-25
Distr.: Reg.
Personnel:
Peter Smyth *(Pres & CEO)*
Ben S. Cannizzaro *(Publr & Gen Mgr)*
Daniel A. Finn, Jr. *(Sr VP & Reg Gen Mgr)*
John Fullam *(VP)*
Gene Lennon *(Dir-Interactive, IT & Production)*
Bob Waitt *(Dir-Adv)*
Robert Waitt *(Dir-Adv)*
Brands & Products:
ATLANTICVILLE
BRICK TOWNSHIP BULLETIN
THE EXAMINER
THE HUB
INDEPENDENT
NEWS TRANSCRIPT
SENTINEL
SUBURBAN
TRI-TOWN NEWS

GRESHAM OUTLOOK

1190 NE Division st
Gresham, OR 97030-0185
Mailing Address:
PO Box 747
Gresham, OR 97030
Tel.: (503) 665-2181
Fax: (503) 665-2187
E-mail: news@theoutlookonline.com
Web Site: www.theoutlookonline.com
Approx. Number Employees: 150
Business Description:
Weekly Newspaper
S.I.C.: 2711
N.A.I.C.S.: 511110
Media: 8-9
Personnel:
Steve Clark *(Pres)*
Brands & Products:
GRESHAM OUTLOOK

GREY HOUSE PUBLISHING CORP.

PO Box 56
Amenia, NY 12501
Tel.: (518) 789-8700
Fax: (518) 789-0556
Toll Free: (800) 562-2139

Key to Media (For complete agency information see *The Advertising Red Books-Agencies* edition):
1. Bus. Publs. 2. Cable T.V. 3. Catalogs & Directories. 4. Co-op Adv. 5. Consumer Mags. 6. D.M. to Bus. Estab.7. D.M. to Consumers
8. Daily Newsp. 9. Exhibits/Trade Shows 10. Foreign 11. Infomercial 12. Internet Adv.13. Multimedia 14. Network Radio
15. Network T.V. 16. Newsp. Distr. Mags. 17. Other 18. Outdoor (Posters, Transit) 19. Point of Purchase20. Premiums, Novelties
21. Product Samples 22. Special Events Mktg. 23. Spot Radio 24. Spot T.V. 25. Weekly Newsp. 26. Yellow Page Adv.

E-mail: books@greyhouse.com
Web Site: www.greyhouse.com
Approx. Number Employees: 25
Business Description:
Book Publishing
S.I.C.: 2731; 2741
N.A.I.C.S.: 511130; 511199
Media: 4-8-10-13
Personnel:
Richard Gottlieb *(Pres)*
Leslie Mackenzie *(Publr)*
Jessica Moody *(VP-Mktg)*

GROVE/ATLANTIC, INC.

841 Broadway
New York, NY 10003-4704
Tel.: (212) 614-7850
Fax: (212) 614-7886
Toll Free: (800) 521-0178
E-mail: publicity@groveatlantic.com
Web Site: www.groveatlantic.com
Sales Range: $25-49.9 Million
Approx. Number Employees: 50
Year Founded: 1993
Business Description:
Publisher of Books
S.I.C.: 2731
N.A.I.C.S.: 511130
Media: 4-5-6-8-9-10-19-25
Distr.: Intl.; Natl.
Personnel:
Eric Price *(COO, Exec VP & Assoc Publr)*
Morgan Entrekin *(Publr)*
Horn Purg *(Mng Editor)*
Brands & Products:
GROVE/ATLANTIC

GUARD PUBLISHING COMPANY

(d/b/a The Register Guard)
3500 Chad Dr
Eugene, OR 97408
Tel.: (541) 485-1234
Fax: (541) 683-7631
E-mail: info@registerguard.com
Web Site: www.registerguard.com
Approx. Sls.: $25,900,000
Approx. Number Employees: 400
Business Description:
Newspapers; Publishing & Printing
S.I.C.: 2711
N.A.I.C.S.: 511110
Media: 8-9
Personnel:
Alton F. Baker, III *(Pres)*
Gail Whighting *(Dir-Adv)*
Donovan Mack *(Mgr-Adv & Mgr-Retail Adv)*

GULF PUBLISHING COMPANY

2 Green Way Plz Ste 1020
Houston, TX 77046
Tel.: (713) 529-4301
Fax: (713) 520-4433
E-mail: publications@gulfpub.com
Web Site: www.gulfpub.com
Sales Range: $50-74.9 Million
Approx. Number Employees: 230
Year Founded: 1916
Business Description:
Magazine & Book Publishers
S.I.C.: 2721; 2731; 2741
N.A.I.C.S.: 511120; 511130; 511199
Advertising Expenditures: $50,000
Media: 2-4-7-10-11-13
Distr.: Intl.; Natl.
Budget Set: Jan.
Personnel:
John Royall *(Pres & CEO)*
Sheryl Stone *(Mgr-Production)*
Brands & Products:
COMPOSITE CATALOG
GENNET M
GPC
HPI CONSTRUCTION BOXSCORE
HYDPRO
HYDROCARBON PROCESSING
INSTRUCALC
NATASHA
OIL & GAS TECHNOLOGY
PATHVIEW
PEPAC
PETROCALC
S H E AUDITOR
SUPERSMITH
WINHEAT
WINSMITH
WORLD OIL
WORLD PETROLEUM INDUSTRY
XPSIM

GULFSHORE BUSINESS

(Sub. of Gulfshore Media LLC)
3560 Craft Rd Ste 301
Naples, FL 34105
Tel.: (239) 594-9980
Fax: (239) 449-4163
Web Site:
www.gulfshorebusiness.com
Approx. Number Employees: 35
Business Description:
Magazine Publisher
S.I.C.: 2721
N.A.I.C.S.: 511120
Media: 6-8
Personnel:
Phil Borchmann *(Editor)*
Tessa Tilden-Smith *(Dir-Creative)*
Sara Clements *(Mgr-Credit)*
Kathleen Peckham *(Mgr-Adv Svcs & Reprint Sls)*
Tracy Heaslip Ross *(Mgr-Opers)*
Brands & Products:
GULFSHORE BUSINESS

GULFSHORE LIFE

(Sub. of Gulfshore Media LLC)
3560 Kraft Rd Ste 301
Naples, FL 34105
Tel.: (239) 449-4111
Tel.: (239) 594-9980
Fax: (239) 449-4163
E-mail: info@gulfshorelifemag.com
Web Site: www.gulfshorelife.com
Approx. Number Employees: 40
Business Description:
Magazine Publisher
S.I.C.: 2721
N.A.I.C.S.: 511120
Media: 6-8
Personnel:
Pam Daniel *(Dir-Editorial)*
David Sandoer *(Chief-Editor)*
Tessa Tilden-Smith *(Dir-Creative)*
Kathleen Peckham *(Mgr-Adv Svcs & Reprint Sls)*
Brands & Products:
GULFSHORE LIFE

GULFSHORE MEDIA LLC

(Formerly Curtco/Gulfshore Media LLC)
3560 Kraft Rd Ste 301
Naples, FL 34105
Tel.: (239) 449-4111
Fax: (239) 449-4163
Fax: (239) 594-9986
Toll Free: (800) 220-4853
E-mail: info@gulshorelifemag.com
Web Site: www.gulfshorelife.com
Approx. Number Employees: 25
Business Description:
Magazine Publisher
S.I.C.: 2721
N.A.I.C.S.: 511120
Media: 6-8
Personnel:
Dan Denton *(Pres & Publr)*
Pam Daniel *(Dir-Editorial & VP)*
David Sendler *(Editor-in-Chief)*
Kerri Nolan *(Dir-Circulation)*
Kris Richards *(Dir-Online Adv-Robb Report)*
Tessa Tilden-Smith *(Dir-Creative)*
Catherine Kane *(Acct Mgr-Online Adv)*
Kathleen Peckham *(Mgr-Adv Svcs & Reprint Sls)*
Tracy Heaslip Ross *(Mgr-Ops)*
Amy Thompson *(Mgr-Production)*
Brands & Products:
GULFSHORE BUSINESS
GULFSHORE HOMEBUYER
GULFSHORE LIFE
SARASOTA MAGAZINE
SARASOTA/MANATEE BUSINESS

GULL COMMUNICATIONS INC

(Sub. of Brehm Communications Inc.)
65 W Ctr St
Richfield, UT 84701-2546
Tel.: (435) 896-5476
Fax: (435) 896-8123
E-mail: info@richfieldreaper.com
Web Site: www.richfieldreaper.com
Approx. Number Employees: 30
Year Founded: 1990
Business Description:
Weekly Newspaper
S.I.C.: 2711
N.A.I.C.S.: 511110
Import Export
Media: 25
Personnel:
Roger Barney *(Comptroller)*
Sandy Ehillith *(Exec Dir)*

HAIGHTS CROSS COMMUNICATIONS, INC.

(Filed Ch 11 Bankruptcy #1010062 on 01/11/2010 in U.S. Bankruptcy Ct, Dist of DE, Wilmington)
136 Madison Ave 8th Fl
New York, NY 10016
Tel.: (212) 209-0500
Fax: (212) 209-0501
E-mail: info@haightscross.com
Web Site: www.haightscross.com
Sales Range: $150-199.9 Million
Approx. Number Employees: 542
Year Founded: 1996
Business Description:
Educational Books, Periodicals, Audio Products, Software & Online Products Publisher
S.I.C.: 2721; 2731; 7372
N.A.I.C.S.: 511120; 511130; 511210
Advertising Expenditures: $900,000
Media: 4-7-10-13
Personnel:
Eugene I. Davis *(Chm)*
Ronald Schlosser *(Pres & CEO)*
Melissa L. Linsky *(Treas & Sr VP-Fin & Plng)*
Brands & Products:
AUDIO ADVENTURES
CHELSEA HOUSE
NEWBRIDGE
OAKSTONE
RECORDED BOOKS
SUNDANCE
TRIUMPH LEARNING

HAINES & COMPANY, INC.

8050 Freedom Ave NW
North Canton, OH 44720-6912
Mailing Address:
PO Box 2117
North Canton, OH 44720-6912
Tel.: (330) 494-9111
Fax: (330) 494-0378
Toll Free: (800) 843-8452
E-mail: criscros@haines.com
Web Site: www.haines.com
Approx. Number Employees: 300
Year Founded: 1932
Business Description:
Publisher of Cross References, Tradename Directories, Mailing Lists & CD Roms; Printing, Design & Mailing Services
S.I.C.: 2741; 7331
N.A.I.C.S.: 511140; 541860
Media: 4-7-10-13-26
Personnel:
William K. Haines, Sr. *(Chm)*
William K. Haines, Jr. *(Pres)*
Brands & Products:
CRISS+CROSS
CRISS+CROSS PLUS
HAINES & COMPANY

HALLMARK CARDS, INC.

2501 McGee Trafficway
Kansas City, MO 64108-2615
Tel.: (816) 274-5111
Fax: (816) 274-7276
Toll Free: (800) 425-5627
Telex: 6841027 Hall UW
Web Site: www.hallmark.com
Sales Range: $1-4.9 Billion
Approx. Number Employees: 16,000
Year Founded: 1910
Business Description:
Greeting Cards, Stationery & Related Products
S.I.C.: 2771; 3952
N.A.I.C.S.: 511191; 339942
Import Export
Media: 2-3-4-6-7-8-9-11-13-14-15-18-20-22-23-24-25
Distr.: Natl.
Personnel:
Donald J. Hall *(Chm)*
Donald J. Hall, Jr. *(Vice Chm, Pres & CEO)*
Jack Moore *(Pres)*
David E. Hall *(Pres-Personal Expression Grp)*
William Hall *(Pres-Hall Family Foundations)*
Brian E. Gardner *(Gen Counsel & Exec VP)*
Steve Doyal *(Sr VP-Pub Affairs & Comm)*
Margaret Keating *(Grp VP-Ops)*
Tara Morrow *(VP-Creative)*
Lindsey Roy *(Gen Mgr-Product Mgr)*
Sabrina Wiewel *(Gen Mgr-Chain Drug)*
Marn Jensen *(Dir-Creative)*
Rosemary Arroyo *(Mgr-Administration-Public Affairs & Comm)*

Key to Media (For complete agency information see *The Advertising Red Books-Agencies* edition):
1. Bus. Publs. 2. Cable T.V. 3. Catalogs & Directories. 4. Co-op Adv. 5. Consumer Mags. 6. D.M. to Bus. Estab.7. D.M. to Consumers
8. Daily Newsp. 9. Exhibits/Trade Shows 10. Foreign 11. Infomercial 12. Internet Adv.13. Multimedia 14. Network Radio
15. Network T.V. 16. Newsp. Distr. Mags. 17. Other 18. Outdoor (Posters, Transit) 19. Point of Purchase20. Premiums, Novelties
21. Product Samples 22. Special Events Mktg. 23. Spot Radio 24. Spot T.V. 25. Weekly Newsp. 26. Yellow Page Adv.

Hallmark Cards, Inc. — (Continued)

Tom Brailsford *(Mgr-Consumer Understanding & Insights)*
Kristi Ernsting *(Mgr-Media Rel)*
Kim Newton *(Mgr-Bus)*

Brands & Products:
EXPRESSIONS
GIFT BOOKS FROM HALLMARK
HALLMARK
HALLMARK GOLD CROWN
INTERART
KEEPSAKE ORNAMENTS
PARTY EXPRESS FROM HALLMARK
THE PICTURE PEOPLE

Advertising Agencies:
Fleishman-Hillard Inc.
2405 Grand Blvd Ste 700
Kansas City, MO 64108-2522
Tel.: (816) 474-9407
Fax: (816) 474-7783

Leo Burnett Worldwide, Inc.
35 W Wacker Dr
Chicago, IL 60601-1723
Tel.: (312) 220-5959
Fax: (312) 220-3299
— Robin Broder *(Acct Exec)*

Paulsen Marketing Communications, Inc.
(d/b/a Paulsen AgriBranding)
3510 S 1st Ave Cir
Sioux Falls, SD 57105-5807
Tel.: (605) 336-1745
Fax: (605) 336-2305

VML, Inc.
250 Richards Rd
Kansas City, MO 64116-4279
Tel.: (816) 283-0700
Fax: (816) 283-0954
Toll Free: (800) 990-2468

HAMILTON COMMUNITY NEWS
(Div. of Metroland Media Group Ltd.)
333 Arvin Avenue
Stoney Creek, ON L8E 2M6, Canada
Tel.: (905) 523-5800
Fax: (905) 523-4014
Web Site: www.hamiltonnews.com/
Approx. Number Employees: 45
Business Description:
Newspaper Publisher
S.I.C.: 2711; 2721
N.A.I.C.S.: 511110; 511120
Media: 8-10-23-25-26

Brands & Products:
ANCASTER NEWS
HAMILTON MOUNTAIN NEWS
STAR NEWS
STONEY CREEK NEWS

THE HAMILTON SPECTATOR
(Sub. of Torstar Corporation)
44 Frid St
PO Box 300
Hamilton, ON L8N 3G3, Canada
Tel.: (905) 526-3333
Fax: (905) 526-0147
Telex: 6-18349
Web Site: www.thespec.com
Approx. Number Employees: 500
Business Description:
Newspaper Publishing
S.I.C.: 2711
N.A.I.C.S.: 511110
Media: 8-9

Personnel:
Ian Oliver *(Exec VP)*
Derek Fleming *(VP-Fin)*
Ian McMeekin *(VP-HR)*
Kelly Montague *(VP-Adv)*
Gary Myers *(VP-Circulation & Mktg)*
Dean Zavarise *(VP-Production)*
Nancy Kimmins *(Controller-Bus Office)*
Bob Hutton *(Dir-Art)*
Susan Azzopardi *(Dir-Adv)*
Mark Dills *(Dir-Production)*
Jamie Poehlman *(Dir-HR)*
Danette McGibney *(Sls Mgr)*
Jane Allison *(Mgr-Community Partnerships)*
Cathryn Easterbrook *(Mgr-Classified Sls)*
Jim McArthur *(Mgr-Circulation Ops)*
Morgan McCormack *(Mgr-Mktg & Branding)*
Chris Switalski *(Mgr-Circulation)*

HAMILTON-WENHAM CHRONICLE
(Unit of GateHouse Media New England)
72 Cherry Hill Dr
Beverly, MA 01915
Tel.: (978) 739-8542
Fax: (978) 739-8501
E-mail: hamilton-wenham@cnc.com
Web Site: www.wickedlocal.com/hamilton
Sales Range: $100-124.9 Million
Business Description:
Newspaper Publisher
S.I.C.: 2711
N.A.I.C.S.: 511110
Media: 8-9-13-18
Personnel:
Charles Goodrich *(Publr)*
Chris Hurley *(Editor-Sports)*
Peter Chianca *(Mgr-Website)*
Pat Coen *(Mgr-Production)*
Joan Gould *(Mgr-Display Adv)*

HANNIBAL COURIER-POST
(Unit of GateHouse Media, Inc.)
200 N 3rd St
Hannibal, MO 63401-3504
Tel.: (573) 221-2800
Fax: (573) 221-1568
Toll Free: (800) 748-7025
E-mail: newsroom@courierpost.com
Web Site: www.hannibal.net
Sales Range: $10-24.9 Million
Approx. Number Employees: 48
Year Founded: 1838
Business Description:
Newspaper Publisher
S.I.C.: 2711
N.A.I.C.S.: 511110
Media: 8-9-13-22-25
Personnel:
Mary Lou Montgomery *(Editor-News)*
Tina Kopecky *(Dir-Sls & Mktg)*
Janet Willett *(Bus Mgr)*
Travis Givan *(Mgr-Online Ads)*

HARLAND CLARKE HOLDINGS CORP.
(Sub. of M & F Worldwide Corp.)
10931 Laureate Dr
San Antonio, TX 78249
Tel.: (210) 694-8888
Toll Free: (800) 723-3690
E-mail: info@harlandclarke.com
Web Site: www.harlandclarke.com
Approx. Rev.: $1,671,200,000
Approx. Number Employees: 7,900
Year Founded: 1923
Business Description:
Printed Forms & Software for Financial Institutions Mfr
S.I.C.: 2782; 2752; 2761; 3555; 3577; 5084; 7372
N.A.I.C.S.: 323118; 323110; 323116; 333293; 334119; 423830; 511210
Export
Advertising Expenditures: $19,600,000
Media: 2-5-7-10
Distr.: Intl.; Natl.
Personnel:
Charles T. Dawson *(Pres & CEO)*
Peter A. Fera, Jr. *(CFO & Exec VP)*
Judy Norris *(Gen Counsel & Sr VP)*
Advertising Agency:
Modern Climate
800 Hennepin 8th Fl
Minneapolis, MN 55403
Tel.: (612) 343-8180
Fax: (612) 343-8178

HARLEQUIN ENTERPRISES LIMITED
(Sub. of Torstar Corporation)
225 Duncan Mills Rd
Toronto, ON M3B 3K9, Canada
Tel.: (416) 445-5860
Fax: (416) 445-8655
Telex: 6-966697
Web Site: www.eharlequin.com
Approx. Sls.: $485,000,000
Approx. Number Employees: 350
Year Founded: 1949
Business Description:
Book Publishing
S.I.C.: 2731
N.A.I.C.S.: 511130
Export
Media: 4-6-9-12-13-19-23-24
Distr.: Intl.; Natl.
Budget Set: Jan.
Personnel:
Donna Hayes *(CEO)*
Christine Clifford *(Exec VP-Direct Mail & Reader Service)*
Loriana Sacilotto *(Exec VP-Global Publishing & Strategy)*
Brands & Products:
GOLD EAGLE
HARLEQUIN
MIRA
SILHOUETTE
WORLDWIDE
Advertising Agency:
Westover Media
11578 SW Riverwood Rd
Portland, OR 97219
Tel.: (503) 675-2580
Fax: (503) 675-2581

HARLEQUIN MAGAZINES INC
(Sub. of Harlequin Enterprises Limited)
233 Brdwy Rm 1001 10th Fl
New York, NY 10279-0001
Tel.: (212) 553-4200
Fax: (212) 227-8969
Web Site: www.eharlequin.com
Approx. Number Employees: 50
Year Founded: 1979
Business Description:
Publishing
S.I.C.: 2721
N.A.I.C.S.: 511120
Import Export
Advertising Expenditures: $15,000,000
Media: 2-6-8-10-16-19-20-21-24-25
Distr.: Direct to Consumer; Natl.
Budget Set: Oct.
Personnel:
Lorianna Sacilotto *(Exec VP-Global Publishing & Strategy)*
Katherine Orr *(VP-PR)*
Anita Sultmanis *(Dir-Mktg)*
Brands & Products:
HARLEQUIN HISTORICALS
SILHOUETTE DESIRE
SILHOUETTE INTIMATE MOMENTS
SILHOUETTE ROMANCE
SILHOUETTE SPECIAL EDITIONS

HARPERCOLLINS PUBLISHERS INC.
(Sub. of News America Incorporated)
10 E 53rd St
New York, NY 10022-5244
Tel.: (212) 207-7000
Fax: (212) 207-7145
Telex: 12-5741 (Domestic)
E-mail: erin.crum@harpercollins.com
Web Site: www.harpercollins.com
Sales Range: $1-4.9 Billion
Approx. Number Employees: 900
Year Founded: 1817
Business Description:
General Trade & Children's Book Publisher
S.I.C.: 2731; 5942
N.A.I.C.S.: 511130; 451211
Media: 2-4-6-7-8-9-18-25
Distr.: Natl.
Personnel:
Brian Murray *(Pres & CEO)*
Janet Gervasio *(CFO)*
Richard Schwartz *(CIO & Sr VP)*
Josh Marwell *(Pres-Sls)*
Jeanette Zwart *(VP-Sls)*
Kristin Bowers *(VP-Sls-W Reg)*
Erin Crum *(VP-Corp Comm)*
Suzanne Daghlian *(Dir-Mktg)*
Brands & Products:
ACCESS
AMISTAD
AVON
CAEDMON
DARK ALLEY
ECCO
EOS
FOURTH ESTATE
GREENWILLOW BOOKS
HARPER DESIGN INTERNATONAL
HARPERAUDIO
HARPERBUSINESS
HARPERCOLLINS
HARPERCOLLINS CHILDREN'S BOOKS
HARPERENTERTAINMENT
HARPERFESTIVAL
HARPERLARGEPRINT
HARPERRESOURCE
HARPERSANFRANCISCO
HARPERTEMPEST
HARPERTORCH
HARPERTROPHY
JOANNA COTLER BOOKS
KATHERINE TEGEN
LAURA GERINGER BOOKS
PERENNIAL
PERFECTBOUND

Key to Media (For complete agency information see *The Advertising Red Books-Agencies* edition):
1. Bus. Publs. 2. Cable T.V. 3. Catalogs & Directories. 4. Co-op Adv. 5. Consumer Mags. 6. D.M. to Bus. Estab.7. D.M. to Consumers
8. Daily Newsp. 9. Exhibits/Trade Shows 10. Foreign 11. Infomercial 12. Internet Adv.13. Multimedia 14. Network Radio
15. Network T.V. 16. Newsp. Distr. Mags. 17. Other 18. Outdoor (Posters, Transit) 19. Point of Purchase20. Premiums, Novelties
21. Product Samples 22. Special Events Mktg. 23. Spot Radio 24. Spot T.V. 25. Weekly Newsp. 26. Yellow Page Adv.

QUILL
RAYO
REGANBOOKS
WILLIAM MORROW
ZONDERVAN

Advertising Agencies:
Centra360
1400 Old Country Rd Ste 420
Westbury, NY 11590-5119
Tel.: (516) 997-3147
Fax: (516) 334-7798

Walker Media
Middlesex House 34-42 Cleveland St
London, W1T 4JE, United Kingdom
Tel.: (44) 20 7447 7500
Fax: (44) 20 7447 7501

HARPER'S MAGAZINE FOUNDATION
666 Broadway 11th Fl
New York, NY 10012-2317
Tel.: (212) 420-5720
Fax: (212) 228-5889
E-mail: letters@harpers.org
Web Site: www.harpers.org
Approx. Number Employees: 30
Year Founded: 1850
Business Description:
Harper's Magazine Publisher
S.I.C.: 2721
N.A.I.C.S.: 511120
Media: 8-13-18
Distr.: Natl.
Personnel:
John R. MacArthur *(Pres & Publr)*
Lynn Carlson *(VP & Gen Mgr)*
Giulia Melucci *(VP-Pub Rels)*
Kathy Park Price *(VP-PR)*
Benjamin Austen *(Asst Editor)*
Christopher Cox *(Editor)*
Ben Metcalf *(Editor-Literary)*
Ellen Rosenbush *(Editor)*
Jennifer Szalai *(Editor)*
Jennifer Adams *(Dir-Production)*
Stacey D. Clarkson *(Dir-Art)*
Alyssa Coppelman *(Asst Dir-Art)*
Irene M. Castagliola *(Mgr-Classified Sls)*
Kim Lau *(Accountant)*
Brands & Products:
HARPER'S INDEX
HARPER'S MAGAZINE

HARRIS ENTERPRISES INC.
1 N Main St Ste 520
Hutchinson, KS 67501-5251
Mailing Address:
PO Box 748
Hutchinson, KS 67504-0748
Tel.: (620) 694-5830
Fax: (620) 694-5837
Toll Free: (877) 930-5830
Web Site: www.hgbc.com
Approx. Number Employees: 500
Year Founded: 1950
Business Description:
Holding Company for Daily & Weekly Newspapers
S.I.C.: 2711
N.A.I.C.S.: 511110
Media: 2-17
Personnel:
Bruce Buchanan *(Pres)*

HARVARD BUSINESS REVIEW
(Sub. of Harvard Business School Publishing Corporation)
Ste 1501 75 Rockefeller Plz
New York, NY 10019-6908
Tel.: (212) 872-9280
Fax: (212) 956-0933
Web Site: www.hp.org
Approx. Number Employees: 15
Business Description:
Publisher of Business Management Magazine
S.I.C.: 5192
N.A.I.C.S.: 424920
Media: 2-8-13
Personnel:
David Wan *(CEO)*
Karen Dillon *(Editor)*
Erin Brown *(Dir-Mktg Comm)*
Sarah Cliffe *(Dir-Editorial)*
Gwen Gulick *(Sr Mgr-Mktg & Comm)*
Julie Devoll *(Mgr-Publicity)*

HARVARD UNIVERSITY PRESS
79 Garden St
Cambridge, MA 02138-1423
Tel.: (617) 495-2600
Fax: (617) 495-5898
Toll Free: (800) 405-1619
E-mail: contact_hup@harvard.edu
Web Site: www.hup.harvard.edu
Approx. Number Employees: 80
Year Founded: 1913
Business Description:
Publisher of Scholarly Books for the General Reader
S.I.C.: 2741; 2731
N.A.I.C.S.: 511199; 511130
Advertising Expenditures: $200,000
Media: 2-4-6-7-8-9-10-11-13-25
Distr.: Intl.; Natl.
Budget Set: Various
Personnel:
William Lindsey *(CFO)*
Ben Sharbaugh *(Mgr-Digital Dissemination)*
Brands & Products:
HARVARD UNIVERSITY PRESS
LOEB CLASSICAL LIBRARY

HAVELOCK NEWS
(Unit of Freedom Newspapers, Inc.)
230 Stonebridge Sq
Havelock, NC 28532
Tel.: (252) 444-1999
Fax: (252) 447-0897
E-mail: kbuday@freedomenc.com
Web Site: www.havenews.com
Approx. Number Employees: 3
Year Founded: 1986
Business Description:
Newspaper
S.I.C.: 2711
N.A.I.C.S.: 511110
Media: 8-25
Personnel:
Ken Buday *(Gen Mgr & Editor)*
Brands & Products:
HAVELOCK NEWS
WINDSOCK

HAVERHILL GAZETTE
(Sub. of Eagle-Tribune Publishing Company Inc.)
181 Merrimack St
Haverhill, MA 01832-3598
Tel.: (978) 556-8500
Fax: (978) 521-6790
Toll Free: (800) 370-0321
E-mail: info@hgazette.com
Web Site: www.hgazette.com
Approx. Number Employees: 15
Business Description:
Newspaper Publisher
S.I.C.: 2711
N.A.I.C.S.: 511110
Media: 8-9
Personnel:
Al Getler *(Publr)*

HAWORTH PRESS INC.
10 Alice St
Binghamton, NY 13904
Tel.: (607) 722-5857
Fax: (607) 722-1424
Toll Free: (800) 429-6784
E-mail: getinfo@haworthpress.com
Web Site: www.haworthpressinc.com
Sales Range: $10-24.9 Million
Approx. Number Employees: 280
Year Founded: 1978
Business Description:
Publisher of Periodicals & Books
S.I.C.: 2721; 2731
N.A.I.C.S.: 511120; 511130
Media: 2-4-7-10
Personnel:
Roger Hall *(Sr VP)*
Margaret Tatich *(VP-Mktg)*
Brands & Products:
HAWORTH
SOCIAL WORK IN HEALTH CARE

HBG BOOKS, INC.
(Sub. of Hachette Livre SA)
(d/b/a Hachette Book Group, USA)
237 Park Ave
New York, NY 10017
Tel.: (212) 364-1100
Fax: (212) 522-7989
Toll Free: (800) 759-0190
Web Site:
www.hachettebookgroup.com
Approx. Number Employees: 120
Business Description:
Paperback & Hardcover Book Publishers
S.I.C.: 2731
N.A.I.C.S.: 511130
Advertising Expenditures: $5,000,000
Media: 2-3-4-5-6-7-8-9-10-11-13-14-15-16-18-19-21-23-24-25
Distr.: Natl.
Personnel:
David Young *(Chm & CEO)*
Thomas Maciag *(CFO & Exec VP)*
Kenneth Michaels *(COO)*
Carol Ross *(Gen Counsel & Exec VP)*
Michael Pietsch *(Exec VP & Publr)*
Jamie Raab *(Exec VP & Publr-Grand Central Publ)*
Megan Tingley *(Sr VP & Publr)*
Rolf Zettersten *(Sr VP & Publr-FaithWords & Center Street)*
Tim Holmn *(VP & Publr-Orbit)*
Christine Barba *(Exec VP-Sls & Mktg)*
Maja Thomas *(Sr VP-Digital & Audio Publ)*
Sophie Cottrell *(VP & Dir-Comm)*
Andrea Weinzimer *(VP-HR)*
Brands & Products:
CENTER STREET
MYSTERIOUS PRESS
WARNER ASPECT
WARNER BUSINESS BOOKS
WARNER FAITH

HEALTH MAGAZINE
(Unit of Time Inc. Health)
1271 Ave Of The Americas 20th Fl
New York, NY 10020-1300
Tel.: (212) 522-9400
Fax: (212) 522-9088
Web Site: www.health.com
Sales Range: $25-49.9 Million
Approx. Number Employees: 75
Year Founded: 1987
Business Description:
Publishing
S.I.C.: 2721
N.A.I.C.S.: 511120
Media: 2-6-7-8-10-13-18-19-20-21-22-23
Distr.: Natl.
Personnel:
Dave Watt *(Publr)*
Zovig Garboushian *(Dir-Integrated Mktg)*
Mila Sorsonsen *(Dir-Art)*
Brands & Products:
HEALTH

HEALTHSTREAM, INC.
209 10th Ave S Ste 450
Nashville, TN 37203
Tel.: (615) 301-3100
Fax: (615) 301-3200
E-mail: contact@healthstream.com
Web Site: www.healthstream.com
Approx. Rev.: $65,754,263
Approx. Number Employees: 356
Business Description:
Education & Training for Health Care Professionals
S.I.C.: 7373; 7372; 7376; 8299
N.A.I.C.S.: 541512; 511210; 541513; 611430
Advertising Expenditures: $130,000
Media: 4-8-10-13-17
Personnel:
Robert A. Frist, Jr. *(Chm, Pres & CEO)*
Gerard M. Hayden, Jr. *(CFO & Sr VP)*
J. Edward Pearson *(COO & Sr VP)*
Jeffrey Doster *(CTO & Sr VP)*
Michael M. Collier *(Gen Counsel & VP)*
Arthur E. Newman *(Exec VP)*
Leuther Cale *(Sr Dir-Mktg)*
Brands & Products:
ABMS
AUTHORING CENTER
COMPETENCY COMPASS
HEALTHSTREAM
HEALTHSTREAM AUTHORING CENTER
HEALTHSTREAM EXPRESS
HEARTCODE
HEATLHSTREAM LEARNING CENTER
HOSPITALDIRECT
WEBEVENT

HEALTHY DIRECTIONS LLC
(Joint Venture of A.C. Israel Enterprises Inc. & American Securities LLC)
7811 Montrose Rd Ste 2
Potomac, MD 20854-3359
Tel.: (301) 340-2100
Tel.: (301) 340-7788
Fax: (301) 424-2588
Web Site: www.healthydirections.com
Approx. Number Employees: 240

Key to Media (For complete agency information see *The Advertising Red Books-Agencies* edition):
1. Bus. Publs. 2. Cable T.V. 3. Catalogs & Directories. 4. Co-op Adv. 5. Consumer Mags. 6. D.M. to Bus. Estab.7. D.M. to Consumers
8. Daily Newsp. 9. Exhibits/Trade Shows 10. Foreign 11. Infomercial 12. Internet Adv.13. Multimedia 14. Network Radio
15. Network T.V. 16. Newsp. Distr. Mags. 17. Other 18. Outdoor (Posters, Transit) 19. Point of Purchase20. Premiums, Novelties
21. Product Samples 22. Special Events Mktg. 23. Spot Radio 24. Spot T.V. 25. Weekly Newsp. 26. Yellow Page Adv.

Healthy Directions LLC — (Continued)

Business Description:
Publisher of Health Newsletter
S.I.C.: 2741; 5122
N.A.I.C.S.: 511199; 424210
Media: 7-8-13
Personnel:
Roger Difato *(COO)*

HEALTHY PLANET PRODUCTS PUBLISHING, INC.
51 Moraga Way Ste 4
Orinda, CA 94963
Tel.: (925) 253-9595
Tel.: (925) 254-9112
Toll Free: (800) 424-4422
E-mail: customersvc@healthyplanet.com
Web Site: www.healthyplanet.com
Sales Range: $1-9.9 Million
Approx. Number Employees: 13
Year Founded: 1978
Business Description:
Greeting Cards, Gifts & Stationery Marketer & Distr
S.I.C.: 2771
N.A.I.C.S.: 511191
Advertising Expenditures: $250,000
Media: 13-19-20
Brands & Products:
HEALTHY PLANET

THE HEARST CORPORATION
300 W 57th St
New York, NY 10019
Tel.: (212) 649-2000
Fax: (212) 541-4133
E-mail: hearstbusinessmedia@hearst.com
Web Site: www.hearst.com
Sales Range: $1-4.9 Billion
Approx. Number Employees: 20,000
Year Founded: 1887
Business Description:
Holding Company; Newspaper, Magazine, Book, Directory & Internet Publisher; Radio & Television Broadcasting; Motion Picture & Television Programming Production Services
S.I.C.: 6719; 2711; 2721; 2731; 2741; 4832; 4833; 4841; 7812; 7822
N.A.I.C.S.: 551112; 511110; 511120; 511130; 511140; 512110; 512120; 515112; 515120; 515210; 517510; 519130
Export
Media: 2-3-5-6-7-8-9-10-11-13-15-19-23-24-25
Distr.: Natl.
Personnel:
George R. Hearst Jr. *(Chm)*
Frank A. Bennack, Jr. *(Vice Chm & CEO)*
Mitchell Scherzer *(CFO)*
Steven R. Swartz *(COO)*
James M. Asher *(Chief Legal Officer, Chief Dev Officer & Sr VP)*
Richard P. Malloch *(Pres-Hearst Bus Media)*
Scott M. Sassa *(Pres-Hearst Entertainment & Syndication)*
Ronald J. Doerfler *(Sr VP-Fin & Admin)*
Brands & Products:
ALBANY TIMES UNION
ASSOCIATED PUBLISHING CO.
CLASSIC AMERICAN HOME
COMAG
COMAG MARKETING GROUP
COMMUNICATIONS DATA SERVICES, INC.
COSMOGIRL!
COSMOPOLITAN
COSMOPOLITAN TELEVISION
COUNTRY LIVING
COUNTRY LIVING GARDENER
ESQUIRE
FIRST DATABANK
GOOD HOUSEKEEPING
HARPER'S BAZAAR
HEARST
HEARST ANIMATION PRODUCTIONS
HEARST ARGYLE TELEVISION PRODUCTIONS
HEARST BOOKS
HEARST EAGLE AWARDS
HEARST ENTERTAINMENT DISTRIBUTION
HEARST ENTERTAINMENT PRODUCTIONS
HEARST INTERACTIVE MEDIA
HEARST NEWS SERVICE
HOUSE BEAUTIFUL
HOUSTON CHRONICLE
HURON DAILY TRIBUNE
LAREDO MORNING TIMES
LOCOMOTION
MARIE CLAIRE
MISQUINCEMAG.COM
MOBILITY TECHNOLOGIES
O THE OPRAH MAGAZINE
POPULAR MECHANICS
QUICK & SIMPLE
REDBOOK
SAN FRANCISCO CHRONICLE
SEVENTEEN
SMARTMONEY
STARMEDIA
TOWN & COUNTRY
TOWN & COUNTRY TRAVEL
VERANDA

HEARST MAGAZINES
(Div. of The Hearst Corporation)
300 W 57th St
New York, NY 10019
Tel.: (212) 649-2000
Fax: (212) 977-4148
Approx. Number Employees: 18,300
Year Founded: 1846
Business Description:
Magazine, Book & Internet Publisher
S.I.C.: 2721; 2731
N.A.I.C.S.: 511120; 511130; 519130
Media: 2-6-7-8-9-10-14-15-24
Distr.: Intl.; Natl.
Personnel:
David Carey *(Pres)*
Debra Robinson *(CIO & Sr VP)*
Michael A. Clinton *(Pres-Mktg & Dir-Publ)*
Jennifer Levene Bruno *(Publr-Veranda & Assoc Publr-Adv-House Beautiful)*
John P. Loughlin *(Exec VP & Gen Mgr)*
Scherri Roberts *(VP & Dir-HR)*
Jessica Kleiman *(VP-PR)*
David Rockefeller *(Gen Mgr)*
Paul Luthringer *(Exec Dir-Mktg Comm)*
Sage Edson *(Dir-Natl Lifestyle-House Beautiful)*
Ellen R. Levine *(Dir-Editorial)*

HEARTLAND PUBLICATIONS LLC
1 W Main St
Clinton, CT 06413
Tel.: (860) 664-1075
Fax: (860) 664-1085
Web Site: www.heartlandpublications.com
Year Founded: 2004
Business Description:
Newspaper Publisher
S.I.C.: 2711
N.A.I.C.S.: 511110
Media: 7-8-9
Personnel:
Michael Bush *(Pres & CEO)*
Gary Lawrence *(COO)*

HELM, INC.
(Sub. of Helm Holding Company)
14310 Hamilton Ave
Highland Park, MI 48203-3776
Tel.: (313) 865-5000
Fax: (313) 865-2457
Toll Free: (800) 782-4356
Web Site: www.helm.com
Approx. Number Employees: 150
Year Founded: 1946
Business Description:
Provider of Auto Repair Publications
S.I.C.: 7389; 7319
N.A.I.C.S.: 561910; 541890
Personnel:
Dennis Gusick *(Pres)*
Bob Malkiewicz *(Partner & Exec VP)*
Chuck Stocks *(Sr VP-Ops)*
Advertising Agency:
Budco Creative Services
13700 Oakland Ave
Highland Park, MI 48203
Tel.: (313) 957-5100
Fax: (313) 957-5522
Toll Free: (888) BUDCO-40
— Paula Biskup *(Dir-Corp Comm)*

THE HENNEGAN COMPANY
(Sub. of Consolidated Graphics, Inc.)
7455 Empire Dr
Florence, KY 41042-2923
Tel.: (859) 282-3600
Fax: (859) 282-3601
E-mail: sales@hennegan.com
Web Site: www.hennegan.com
E-Mail For Key Personnel:
President: bottjr@hennegan.com
Sales Director: sales@hennegan.com
Sales Range: $100-124.9 Million
Approx. Number Employees: 275
Year Founded: 1886
Business Description:
Lithographic Printing Services
S.I.C.: 2752; 2789
N.A.I.C.S.: 323110; 323121
Import Export
Media: 4
Personnel:
Robert B. Ott, Sr. *(Chm)*
Daniel Bailey *(Pres)*
Robert B. Ott, Jr. *(CEO)*
Michael Fleury *(Exec VP-Natl Sls)*
Dennis Purcell *(Exec VP-Admin)*
Gary Briney *(VP & Dir-Quality)*
Mike Butler *(VP-Production)*
Greg Trachsel *(VP-HR)*
Michael Vandenburg *(VP-Production)*
Greg Chapman *(Dir-Estimating)*
Joe Eglseder *(Dir-Web Opers)*
Todd Ivy *(Dir-Finishing Ops)*
Rob Nielsen *(Dir-Prepress Ops)*
Greg Wallace *(Dir-Mailing Svcs)*
Mark Weyhe *(Dir-MIS)*
Jennie Diedrichs *(Mgr-Customer Svc)*
Gary Greis *(Mgr-Digital Print Opers)*
Brands & Products:
MICRO-TONE

HESPERIA STAR
(Unit of Freedom Newspapers, Inc.)
17045 Main St
Hesperia, CA 92345
Tel.: (760) 956-7827
Fax: (760) 956-6803
E-mail: editor@hesperiastar.com
Web Site: www.hesperiastar.com
Approx. Number Employees: 4
Business Description:
Newspaper
S.I.C.: 7313
N.A.I.C.S.: 541840
Media: 8-22-25
Personnel:
Peter Day *(Editor)*

HI-DESERT PUBLISHING CO. INC.
(Sub. of Brehm Communications Inc.)
56445 29 Palms Hwy
Yucca Valley, CA 92284-2861
Tel.: (760) 365-3315
Fax: (760) 365-8686
Web Site: www.hidesertstar.com
Sales Range: $25-49.9 Million
Approx. Number Employees: 70
Year Founded: 1990
Business Description:
Publisher of Newspapers
S.I.C.: 2711
N.A.I.C.S.: 511110
Import Export
Media: 8-9
Personnel:
Cindy Melland *(Mgr-Adv & Publr)*

HICKORY PRINTING SOLUTIONS
(Sub. of Consolidated Graphics, Inc.)
725 Reese Dr
Conover, NC 28613-2935
Mailing Address:
PO Box 69
Hickory, NC 28603
Tel.: (828) 465-3431
Fax: (828) 465-2517
Toll Free: (800) 442-5679
E-mail: hphr@hickoryprinting.com
Web Site: www.hickoryprinting.com
E-Mail For Key Personnel:
Sales Director: sales@hickoryprinting.com
Approx. Number Employees: 225
Year Founded: 1917
Business Description:
Commercial Web, Sheetfed & Package Printing Services
S.I.C.: 2752; 2759
N.A.I.C.S.: 323110; 323119
Media: 2-4-7-10-21-26
Distr.: Natl.
Personnel:
Stephen Patton *(Pres)*
George B. Glisan *(CEO)*
Jeffrey A. Hale *(CFO)*
Ola Tornerud *(Dir-Mktg)*
Brands & Products:
BIG ENOUGH, SMALL ENOUGH

Key to Media (For complete agency information see *The Advertising Red Books-Agencies* edition):
1. Bus. Publs. 2. Cable T.V. 3. Catalogs & Directories. 4. Co-op Adv. 5. Consumer Mags. 6. D.M. to Bus. Estab.7. D.M. to Consumers 8. Daily Newsp. 9. Exhibits/Trade Shows 10. Foreign 11. Infomercial 12. Internet Adv.13. Multimedia 14. Network Radio 15. Network T.V. 16. Newsp. Distr. Mags. 17. Other 18. Outdoor (Posters, Transit) 19. Point of Purchase20. Premiums, Novelties 21. Product Samples 22. Special Events Mktg. 23. Spot Radio 24. Spot T.V. 25. Weekly Newsp. 26. Yellow Page Adv.

EMPOWERING YOUR VISUAL MARKETING
HICKORYPRINTENGINE

HIGHLIGHTS FOR CHILDREN, INC.
1800 Watermark Dr
Columbus, OH 43215-1060
Tel.: (614) 486-0631
Fax: (614) 487-2700
Toll Free: (800) 848-8922
E-mail: jobs@highlights.com
Web Site: www.highlights.com
Approx. Number Employees: 584
Year Founded: 1946
Business Description:
Magazines & Educational Materials for Children
S.I.C.: 2721
N.A.I.C.S.: 511120
Import Export
Advertising Expenditures: $20,000,000
Media: 1-2-3-4-5-6-7-8-9-10-12-13-15-16-19-20-21-24-25
Distr.: Natl.
Personnel:
Kent S. Johnson *(CEO)*
Eric Myers *(Dir-Interactive Mktg & Media)*
Brands & Products:
FUN WITH A PURPOSE
THE FUN ZONE
HIDDEN PICTURE
HIGHLIGHTS
HIGHLIGHTS FOR CHILDREN
HIGHLIGHTSKIDS
INKLINGS
MATH MANIA
PUZZLE MANIA
STENCIL FACTORY
STIGGLES
TEACHING
TOP SECRET ADVENTURES
WHICH WAY USA

HILLSDALE DAILY NEWS
(Unit of GateHouse Media, Inc.)
33 McCollum St
Hillsdale, MI 49242-0287
Tel.: (517) 437-7351
Fax: (517) 437-3963
E-mail: webmaster@hillsdale.net
Web Site: www.hillsdale.net
Sales Range: $10-24.9 Million
Approx. Number Employees: 27
Year Founded: 1839
Business Description:
Newspaper Publisher
S.I.C.: 2711
N.A.I.C.S.: 511110
Media: 8-9
Personnel:
David Ferro *(Publr)*
Tony Van Buren *(Dir-Adv)*
RoxAnne Morgret *(Mgr-Circulation)*

HISPANIC BUSINESS INC.
425 Pine Ave
Santa Barbara, CA 93117-3709
Tel.: (805) 964-4554
Fax: (805) 964-5539
E-mail: info@hispanicbusiness.com
Web Site: www.hispanicbusiness.com
Sales Range: $10-24.9 Million
Approx. Number Employees: 60
Year Founded: 1979
Business Description:
Business Magazine Publisher
S.I.C.: 2721
N.A.I.C.S.: 511120
Media: 6-7-8
Personnel:
Jesus Chavarria *(Pres, CEO & Publr)*

THE HOLLAND SENTINEL
(Unit of GateHouse Media, Inc.)
54 W 8th St
Holland, MI 49423
Tel.: (616) 392-2311
Fax: (616) 392-3526
Toll Free: (800) 968-3497
E-mail: rwallace@sentinelnet.com
Web Site: www.thehollandsentinel.net
E-Mail For Key Personnel:
Marketing Director: JMulder@sentinelnet.com
Sales Range: $25-49.9 Million
Approx. Number Employees: 110
Year Founded: 1896
Business Description:
Newspaper Publisher
S.I.C.: 2711
N.A.I.C.S.: 511110
Media: 2-8-9-21-22-26
Personnel:
Peter Esser *(Publr)*

THE HOLLYWOOD REPORTER INC.
(Joint Venture of Guggenheim Partners, LLC & Pluribus Capital Management LLC)
5055 Wilshire Blvd
Los Angeles, CA 90036-4396
Tel.: (323) 525-2000
Fax: (323) 525-2372
E-mail: info1@hollywoodreporter.com
Web Site: www.hollywoodreporter.com
Approx. Number Employees: 300
Year Founded: 1930
Business Description:
Entertainment News Publisher
S.I.C.: 2721; 2711
N.A.I.C.S.: 511120; 511110
Media: 2-6-8-10-13
Personnel:
Steve Brennan *(Editor-Intl)*
Gregg Kilday *(Editor-Film)*
Lasey Rose *(Editor-TV)*
Carrie Smith *(Editor-Contributing Photo)*
Georg Szalai *(Editor-Bus & Chief-New York Bureau)*
Kelly Jones *(Dir-Production)*
Janice Min *(Dir-Editorial)*
Alex Moore *(Dir-Mktg)*

HOLT MCDOUGAL
(Div. of Houghton Mifflin Harcourt Publishing Company)
909 Davis St
Evanston, IL 60201
Tel.: (847) 869-2300
Fax: (847) 869-0841
Toll Free: (800) 727-3009
Web Site: www.mcdougallittell.com
Approx. Number Employees: 150
Year Founded: 1969
Business Description:
School Text Book Publisher
S.I.C.: 2731
N.A.I.C.S.: 511130
Export
Media: 1-2-7-10
Distr.: Intl.; Natl.
Brands & Products:
MCDOUGAL LITTELL

HOLYOKE NEWS CO. INC.
720 Main St
Holyoke, MA 01040
Tel.: (413) 534-4537
Fax: (413) 538-7161
Toll Free: (800) 628-8372
Web Site: www.holyoke-news.com
Approx. Sls.: $21,100,000
Approx. Number Employees: 99
Business Description:
Magazines, Books, & Newspapers Distr
S.I.C.: 5192
N.A.I.C.S.: 424920
Media: 8-9
Personnel:
Amir Evan *(Pres)*

HOMETOWN COMMUNICATIONS NETWORK, INC.
(Sub. of Gannett Co., Inc.)
41304 Concept Dr
Plymouth, MI 48170
Tel.: (734) 591-2300
Fax: (734) 591-9424
Web Site: www.hometownlife.com
E-Mail For Key Personnel:
President: raginian@oeonline.com
Sales Range: $350-399.9 Million
Approx. Number Employees: 1,100
Year Founded: 1974
Business Description:
Holding Company; Publisher of Community Newspapers & Telephone Directories
S.I.C.: 2711
N.A.I.C.S.: 511110
Media: 4-8-9
Personnel:
Susan Rosiek *(Publr & Mgr)*
Grace Perry *(Dir-Adv)*
Frank Cibor *(Mgr-Retail Adv)*
Brands & Products:
THE ECCENTRIC
THE OBSERVER

THE HONOLULU ADVERTISER
(Name Changed to The Honolulu Star-Advertiser)

THE HONOLULU STAR-ADVERTISER
(Formerly The Honolulu Advertiser)
(Sub. of Oahu Publications, Inc.)
Restaurant Row 7 Waterfront Plz Ste 210 500 Ala Moana Blvd
Honolulu, HI 96813
Mailing Address:
PO Box 3110
Honolulu, HI 96802-3110
Tel.: (808) 525-8000
Tel.: (808) 529-4700
Fax: (808) 525-8037
E-mail: citydesk@staradvertiser.com
Web Site: www.staradvertiser.com
Sales Range: $150-199.9 Million
Approx. Number Employees: 900
Year Founded: 1856
Business Description:
Newspaper
S.I.C.: 2711
N.A.I.C.S.: 511110
Advertising Expenditures: $500,000
Media: 9-10-13-23-24
Distr.: Reg.
Personnel:
Dennis Francis *(Pres)*
Roger R. Forness *(VP-Tech)*
Marsha McFadden *(Mng Editor-Content)*
Stephen J. Downes *(Asst Mng Editor)*
Brands & Products:
THE HONOLULU STAR-ADVERTISER

HOOVER'S, INC.
(Sub. of The Dun & Bradstreet Corp.)
5800 Airport Blvd
Austin, TX 78752-4204
Tel.: (512) 374-4500
Fax: (512) 374-4501
E-mail: salesinfo@hoovers.com
Web Site: www.hoovers.com
E-Mail For Key Personnel:
Sales Director: salesinfo@hoovers.com
Sales Range: $50-74.9 Million
Approx. Number Employees: 231
Year Founded: 1990
Business Description:
Publisher of Business Information
S.I.C.: 7389; 2741
N.A.I.C.S.: 541990; 511199; 516110
Advertising Expenditures: $6,000,000
Media: 2-7-10-13-20-22-24
Personnel:
David Mather *(Pres)*
Thomas M. Ballard *(CTO & VP-Engrg)*
Edward Garana *(Dir-User Experience & Design)*
Amy Crow *(Mgr-Brand & PR)*
Brands & Products:
THE BUSINESS INFORMATION AUTHORITY
HOOVER'S
HOOVER'S BUSINESS RECORDS
HOOVER'S COMPANY INFORMATION
HOOVER'S HANDBOOK
HOOVER'S ONLINE

HORIZON HOUSE PUBLICATIONS INC.
685 Canton St
Norwood, MA 02062
Tel.: (781) 769-9750
Fax: (781) 762-9230
E-mail: info@horizonhouse.com
Web Site: www.horizonhouse.com
Approx. Sls.: $25,000,000
Approx. Number Employees: 75
Business Description:
Trade Journals Publishing
S.I.C.: 2721; 2731
N.A.I.C.S.: 511120; 511130
Media: 2-8-10-13
Personnel:
William Bazzy *(Chm)*
Ivar Bazzy *(Pres)*
William M. Bazzy *(CEO)*
Dan Campbell *(Dir-Admin)*
Brands & Products:
HORIZON HOUSE

HOT OFF THE PRESS, INC.
1250 NW 3rd Ave
Canby, OR 97013
Tel.: (503) 266-9102

Key to Media (For complete agency information see *The Advertising Red Books-Agencies* edition):
1. Bus. Publs. 2. Cable T.V. 3. Catalogs & Directories. 4. Co-op Adv. 5. Consumer Mags. 6. D.M. to Bus. Estab.7. D.M. to Consumers 8. Daily Newsp. 9. Exhibits/Trade Shows 10. Foreign 11. Infomercial 12. Internet Adv.13. Multimedia 14. Network Radio 15. Network T.V. 16. Newsp. Distr. Mags. 17. Other 18. Outdoor (Posters, Transit) 19. Point of Purchase20. Premiums, Novelties 21. Product Samples 22. Special Events Mktg. 23. Spot Radio 24. Spot T.V. 25. Weekly Newsp. 26. Yellow Page Adv.

Hot Off the Press, Inc. — (Continued)
Fax: (503) 266-8749
Toll Free: (800) 227-9595
Web Site: www.paperwishes.com
Approx. Number Employees: 60
Year Founded: 1980
Business Description:
Craft Books & Supplies
S.I.C.: 2731; 5945
N.A.I.C.S.: 511130; 451120
Media: 4-13
Personnel:
Paulette Jarvey *(Pres)*
Sara Naumann *(Head-Product Dev)*

HOUGHTON MIFFLIN HARCOURT PUBLISHING COMPANY
(Sub. of Houghton Mifflin Riverdeep Group Plc)
222 Berkeley St
Boston, MA 02116
Tel.: (617) 351-5000
Fax: (617) 351-1100
Web Site: www.hmco.com
Sales Range: $1-4.9 Billion
Approx. Number Employees: 3,113
Year Founded: 1832
Business Description:
Book Publisher
S.I.C.: 2731
N.A.I.C.S.: 511130
Advertising Expenditures: $6,300,000
Media: 2-4-6-20
Distr.: Natl.
Personnel:
Lawrence K. Fish *(Chm)*
Linda K. Zecher *(Pres & CEO)*
Michael Muldowney *(CFO)*
Ciara Smyth *(Chief HR Officer & Exec VP)*
Mike Lavelle *(Pres-Houghton Mifflin Harcourt Education Grp)*
Mark Schumacher *(CFO-K12 & Exec VP)*
Eric Shuman *(COO-Education Grp & Exec VP)*
Bill Bayers *(Gen Counsel & Exec VP)*
Greg Dumont *(Exec VP-Corp Dev & Ops)*
Rita H. Schaefer *(Exec VP-Comprehensive Curriculum & Education Grp)*
Sanj Kharbanda *(VP-Digital Mktg Strategy)*
Brands & Products:
ASSESS2LEARN
BASIC EARLY ASSESSMENT OF READING
BATERIA III WOODCOCK-MUNOZ
BEST AMERICAN SERIES
BEST AMERICAN SHORT STORIES
EAROBICS LITERACY LAUNCH
EDUCATION PLACE
EDUSOFT
EDUSPACE
EVERY DAY COUNTS
GATES-MACGINITIE READING TESTS
HOUGHTON MIFFLIN
HOUGHTON MIFFLIN MATH
IOWA TESTS OF BASIC SKILLS
KNOWLEDGE BEYOND DOUBT
NEW WAYS TO KNOW
SMARTHINKING
SUMMER SUCCESS
UNIVERSAL NONVERBAL INTELLIGENCE TEST
WOODCOCK-JOHNSON
WRITE SOURCE

HOUGHTON MIFFLIN HARCOURT PUBLISHING COMPANY
(Sub. of Houghton Mifflin Harcourt School Publishers)
9400 S Park Cr Loop
Orlando, FL 32819
Tel.: (407) 345-2000
Fax: (407) 363-6917
Telex: 568373
Web Site: www.harcourt.com
Approx. Rev.: $1,113,000,000
Approx. Number Employees: 1,200
Year Founded: 1919
Business Description:
Educational Publisher
S.I.C.: 2731
N.A.I.C.S.: 511130
Import Export
Advertising Expenditures: $200,000
Media: 2-6-8-9-10
Distr.: Intl.; Natl.
Personnel:
Richard Blake *(VP-Commun-Govt Rels)*

HOUR PUBLISHING COMPANY
1 Selleck St
Norwalk, CT 06855
Tel.: (203) 846-3281
Fax: (203) 846-9897
Fax: (203) 840-1802
E-mail: news@wiltonvillager.com
Web Site: www.wiltonvillager.com
Approx. Sls.: $11,400,000
Approx. Number Employees: 70
Business Description:
Newspapers
S.I.C.: 2711; 2741
N.A.I.C.S.: 511110; 511199
Media: 8-9
Personnel:
Brent Whitton *(Pres)*
John Brosz *(VP-Sls & Mktg)*

HOUSE BEAUTIFUL
(Unit of Hearst Magazines)
300 W 57th St 24th Fl
New York, NY 10019
Tel.: (212) 903-5103
Fax: (212) 765-8292
Web Site: www.housebeautiful.com
Approx. Number Employees: 45
Year Founded: 1896
Business Description:
Magazine
S.I.C.: 2721
N.A.I.C.S.: 511120
Media: 8-19-21
Distr.: Intl.; Natl.
Budget Set: Nov.
Personnel:
Stephen Drucker *(Editor-in-Chief)*
Wendi Horowitz *(Dir-Art)*
Lisa A. Lachowetz *(Dir-Mktg Svcs)*

HOUSE OF WHITE BIRCHES, INC.
(Sub. of Dynamic Resource Group)
306 E Parr Rd
Berne, IN 46711-1138
Tel.: (260) 589-4000
Fax: (260) 589-8093
E-mail: customer_service@drgnetwork.com
Web Site: www.whitebirches.com
E-Mail For Key Personnel:
Sales Director: john_boggs@whitebirches.com
Sales Range: $25-49.9 Million
Approx. Number Employees: 80
Year Founded: 1947
Business Description:
Publisher of Craft, Hobby Magazines, Books & Novelties
S.I.C.: 2721; 2741
N.A.I.C.S.: 511120; 511199
Advertising Expenditures: $8,000,000
D.M. to Consumers: $8,000,000
Distr.: Natl.
Personnel:
David McKee *(CEO)*
John Rosswurm *(Dir-Internet Mktg)*
Brands & Products:
CROCHET WORLD
GOOD OLD DAYS
GOOD OLD DAYS SPECIAL ISSUES
HOME COOKING
KNITTING DIGEST
PAPERWORKS
QUILTERS WORLD

HOUSTON CHRONICLE
(Unit of Hearst Newspapers)
801 Texas Ave
Houston, TX 77002-2904
Tel.: (713) 362-7171
Tel.: (713) 220-3565 (Adv)
Fax: (713) 362-6677
Toll Free: (800) 735-3800
E-mail: info@chron.com
Web Site: www.chron.com
E-Mail For Key Personnel:
Marketing Director: joycelyn.marek@chron.com
Public Relations: lainie.gordon@chron.com
Approx. Number Employees: 2,000
Year Founded: 1901
Business Description:
Daily & Sunday Paper
S.I.C.: 5192
N.A.I.C.S.: 424920
Advertising Expenditures: $2,500,000
Media: 2-3-4-5-6-8-9-10-11-13-14-15-18-20-21-22-23-24-25-26
Distr.: Reg.
Budget Set: Oct.
Personnel:
John W. Sweeney *(Pres)*
Robert Carlquist *(Exec VP & Gen Mgr)*
Jeff Cohen *(Exec VP & Editor)*
Mary Ann Wendt *(VP-HR)*
Laura Goldberg *(Editor-Bus)*
George Haj *(Editor-News)*
David Langworthy *(Editor)*
Judy Minshew *(Editor-Viewpoints)*
John Wilburn *(Editor)*
Lainie Gordon *(Dir-Pub Rels)*
Milton Wilson *(Dir)*
Kay Lewis *(Office Mgr-Washington Bureau)*
Howard Decker *(Mgr-Neighborhood Newsroom)*
Anitura Joseph *(Mgr-Gen Acctg)*
Brands & Products:
HOUSTON CHRONICLE
Advertising Agency:
Richards/Carlberg
1900 W Loop S Ste 1100
Houston, TX 77027
Tel.: (713) 965-0764
Fax: (713) 965-0135

H.S. CROCKER CO., INC.
12100 Smith Dr
Huntley, IL 60142-9618
Tel.: (847) 669-3600
Fax: (847) 669-1170
Web Site: www.hscrocker.com
Approx. Number Employees: 200
Year Founded: 1856
Business Description:
Pharmaceutical & Pressure Sensitive Labels Printers & Folding Cartons & Portion Pack Lids Mfr.
S.I.C.: 2671; 2672
N.A.I.C.S.: 322221; 322222
Advertising Expenditures: $600,000
Media: 2-4-10
Distr.: Natl.
Budget Set: Jan.
Personnel:
Ron Giordano *(Chm & CEO)*
John Dai *(Sec, Controller & Dir-Fin)*
Norbert Suarez *(VP-Sls)*
Brands & Products:
CROCKERBRITE

HUMAN KINETICS PUBLISHERS INC.
1607 N Market St
Champaign, IL 61820
Tel.: (217) 351-5076
Fax: (217) 351-2674
Toll Free: (800) 747-4457
E-mail: info@hkusa.com
Web Site: www.humankinetics.com
E-Mail For Key Personnel:
President: rainer@hkusa.com
Approx. Number Employees: 350
Year Founded: 1974
Business Description:
Books Publishing
S.I.C.: 2731; 3652
N.A.I.C.S.: 511130; 334612
Media: 10-13
Personnel:
Rainer Martens *(Founder & Pres)*
Brian Holding *(CEO)*
Julie Martens *(Exec VP)*
Kim L. Brown *(Dir-Mktg)*

HURON COUNTY VIEW
(Formerly The Thumb Blanket)
(Unit of JAMS Media LLC)
55 Westland Dr
Bad Axe, MI 48413-7741
Tel.: (989) 269-9918
Fax: (989) 269-8109
Approx. Number Employees: 11
Business Description:
Weekly Newspaper Publishing
S.I.C.: 2711; 2721
N.A.I.C.S.: 511110; 511120
Media: 25
Personnel:
Jane Vanderpoel *(Gen Mgr)*

THE H.W. WILSON CO.
950 University Ave
Bronx, NY 10452-4224
Tel.: (718) 588-8400
Fax: (718) 590-1617
Fax: (800) 590-1617

Key to Media (For complete agency information see *The Advertising Red Books-Agencies* edition):
1. Bus. Publs. 2. Cable T.V. 3. Catalogs & Directories. 4. Co-op Adv. 5. Consumer Mags. 6. D.M. to Bus. Estab.7. D.M. to Consumers
8. Daily Newsp. 9. Exhibits/Trade Shows 10. Foreign 11. Infomercial 12. Internet Adv.13. Multimedia 14. Network Radio
15. Network T.V. 16. Newsp. Distr. Mags. 17. Other 18. Outdoor (Posters, Transit) 19. Point of Purchase20. Premiums, Novelties
21. Product Samples 22. Special Events Mktg. 23. Spot Radio 24. Spot T.V. 25. Weekly Newsp. 26. Yellow Page Adv.

Toll Free: (800) 367-6770
E-mail: hwwmsg@info.hwwilson.com
Web Site: www.hwwilson.com
E-Mail For Key Personnel:
President: hregan@info.hwwilson.com
Marketing Director: ESutter@hwwilson.com
Public Relations: dloeding@wlb.hwwilson.com
Approx. Number Employees: 350
Year Founded: 1898
Business Description:
Publisher of Indexes, Abstracts, Full-Text & Reference Works for Libraries in Print & Electronic Form
S.I.C.: 2721; 2731
N.A.I.C.S.: 511120; 511130
Advertising Expenditures: $2,000,000
Media: 2-4-7-10-20
Distr.: Direct to Consumer; Intl.; Natl.
Budget Set: Apr. -Mar.
Personnel:
Harold Regan *(Pres & CEO)*
Deborah Voigt Loeding *(VP-Sls & Mktg)*
Lucian A. Parziale *(VP-Info Sys)*
Frank Daly *(Dir-Mktg)*
John Tavaska *(Dir-Database Licensing)*
Bernie Seiler *(Product Mgr-WilsonWeb)*
Debbie Jackson *(Mgr-HR)*
Deirdre Simmons *(Mgr-Sls-Mktg-Admin)*
Brands & Products:
H.W. WILSON
WILSONDISC
WILSONWEB

HYPERION BOOKS
(Sub. of The Walt Disney Company)
77 W 66th St
New York, NY 10023
Tel.: (212) 456-0113
Fax: (212) 456-0112
E-mail: info@hyperionbooks.com
Web Site: www.hyperionbooks.com
Sales Range: $100-124.9 Million
Year Founded: 1991
Business Description:
Publisher of Fiction & Non-Fiction Books
S.I.C.: 2731
N.A.I.C.S.: 511130
Media: 5-8-10-13
Personnel:
Ellen Archer *(Pres & Publr)*
Joan Lee *(Mgr-Mktg)*
Brands & Products:
HYPERION AUDIOBOOKS
HYPERION EAST

I.D. MAGAZINE
(Sub. of F&W Publications, Inc.)
38 E 29th St 3rd Fl
New York, NY 10016-8942
Tel.: (212) 447-1400
Fax: (212) 447-5231
E-mail: idedit@fwpubs.com
Web Site: www.idonline.com
Approx. Sls.: $7,000,000
Approx. Number Employees: 25
Year Founded: 1965
Business Description:
Publisher of Magazine, ID Products & Handbook of Foodservice Distr
S.I.C.: 2721
N.A.I.C.S.: 511120
Advertising Expenditures: $700,000
Media: 2-10-19-20
Distr.: Natl.
Budget Set: Oct.
Brands & Products:
HANDBOOK OF FOODSERVICE DISTRIBUTION
INSTITUTIONAL DISTRIBUTION

IDEARC MEDIA CORP.
(Sub. of SUPERMEDIA INC.)
2200 W Airfield Dr
Dallas, TX 75261
Mailing Address:
PO Box 619810
Dallas, TX 75261-9810
Tel.: (972) 453-7100
Tel.: (972) 453-7000
Fax: (972) 453-6668
Fax: (972) 453-3969
Web Site: www.idearcmedia.com
Sales Range: $1-4.9 Billion
Approx. Number Employees: 9,000
Year Founded: 1936
Business Description:
Publisher & Printer of Telephone Directories & Electronic Databases
S.I.C.: 7375; 8721
N.A.I.C.S.: 518111; 541219
Media: 2-4-7-9-10-23-24-25
Distr.: Intl.; Natl.
Budget Set: Jan.
Personnel:
Lester Chu *(VP-Mktg)*
Randy Roush *(Exec Dir-Strategic Mktg & Plng)*
Mary de la Garza *(Dir-Media Rels)*
Jennifer Stelling *(Product Mgr-Superpages.com)*
Brands & Products:
SUPERPAGES
Advertising Agency:
Sullivan Perkins
2811 McKinney Ave Ste 320
Dallas, TX 75204-8566
Tel.: (214) 922-9080
Fax: (214) 922-0044

IHS INC.
15 Inverness Way E
Englewood, CO 80112
Tel.: (303) 790-0600
Toll Free: (800) 525-7052
E-mail: info@ihs.com
Web Site: www.ihs.com
Approx. Rev.: $1,075,460,000
Approx. Number Employees: 4,400
Year Founded: 1959
Business Description:
Technical & Business Information Content Services
S.I.C.: 7373; 2741; 7371
N.A.I.C.S.: 541512; 511199; 541511
Media: 2-7-10
Personnel:
Jerre L. Stead *(Chm & CEO)*
Scott Key *(Pres & COO)*
Michael J. Sullivan *(CFO & Exec VP)*
Richard G. Walker *(Chief Strategy Officer & Sr VP)*
Jeffrey D. Sisson *(Chief HR Officer & Sr VP)*
Heather Matzke-Hamlin *(Chief Acctg Officer)*
Jane Okun Bomba *(Chief Customer Process Officer & Sr VP)*
Stephen Green *(Gen Counsel, Sec & Sr VP)*
Daniel Yergin *(Exec VP)*
Brian Sweeney *(Sr VP-Global Sls)*

THE ILE CAMERA
(Sub. of Heritage Newspapers, Inc.)
1 Heritage Pl
South Gate, MI 48195
Tel.: (734) 676-0515
Fax: (734) 246-2727
E-mail: editor@ilecamera.com
Web Site: www.ilecamera.com
Approx. Number Employees: 25
Business Description:
Publisher of Newspapers
S.I.C.: 2711; 2721
N.A.I.C.S.: 511110; 511120
Media: 25
Personnel:
Karl Ziomek *(Editor)*

IMAGE CHECKS INC.
(Sub. of Custom Direct Income Fund)
1802 Fashion Ct
Little Rock, AR 21085
Mailing Address:
PO Box 548
Little Rock, AR 72203-0548
Tel.: (410) 679-3300
Fax: (918) 669-2071
Toll Free: (800) 562-8768
Web Site: www.cdi-us.com
Approx. Rev.: $8,200,000
Approx. Number Employees: 160
Year Founded: 1997
Business Description:
Personal Checks & Related Products Mfr
S.I.C.: 2679
N.A.I.C.S.: 322299
Media: 4-8-13
Brands & Products:
IMAGE CHECKS

IMAGE COMICS INC.
2134 Allston Way 2nd Flr
Berkeley, CA 94704
Tel.: (510) 644-4980
Fax: (510) 644-4988
E-mail: info@imagecomics.com
Web Site: www.imagecomics.com
Approx. Number Employees: 10
Year Founded: 1993
Business Description:
Comic Books & Related Items Publisher & Mfr
S.I.C.: 2721; 5942
N.A.I.C.S.: 511120; 451211
Media: 10-11
Personnel:
Todd McFarlane *(Partner)*
Marc Silvestri *(Partner)*
Eric Stephenson *(Publr)*
Tyler Shainline *(Mgr-Production)*
Brands & Products:
COMIC BOOKS
IMAGE COMICS

IMAS PUBLISHING (USA) INC.
810 Seventh Ave 27th Fl
New York, NY 10019
Tel.: (212) 378-0400
Fax: (212) 378-0470
Web Site: www.nbmedia.com
Approx. Number Employees: 55
Year Founded: 1976
Business Description:
Magazine Publisher
S.I.C.: 2711; 2721
N.A.I.C.S.: 511110; 511120
Media: 2-10

IN STYLE MAGAZINE
(Unit of Time Inc.)
1271 Ave of the Americas Ste 18-38B2
New York, NY 10020
Tel.: (212) 522-4455
Tel.: (212) 522-1212
Fax: (212) 522-3684
E-mail: imadvertising@aol.com
Web Site: www.instyle.com
Sales Range: $100-124.9 Million
Year Founded: 1994
Business Description:
Magazine
S.I.C.: 2721
N.A.I.C.S.: 511120
Media: 6-8-10-13-18-20-22
Personnel:
Ann S. Moore *(Chm & CEO)*
Stephanie George *(Pres)*
Katherine Rizzuto *(VP & Assoc Publr-Adv)*
Ron Prince *(Assoc Publr-Mktg)*
Connie Anne Phillips *(Publr)*
Sylvia Auton *(Exec VP)*
John Squires *(Exec VP)*
David Geithner *(VP & Grp Gen Mgr)*
Nancy Valentino *(VP-Comm)*
John Huey *(Editor-in-Chief)*
Kahlana Barfield *(Asst Editor)*
Bronwyn Barnes *(Entertainment-Editor)*
Annie Baron *(Editor-Photo-Instylecom)*
Amy Barton *(Assoc Editor-Instylecom)*
Donna Bulseco *(Deputy Editor)*
Kassidy Gala *(Assoc Editor-Photo-Instylecom)*
Meg Hemphill *(Asst Editor)*
James Patrick Herman *(Sr Editor)*
Nicole Hyatt *(Editor-Photo)*
Marcia Lawther *(Chief-Copy)*
Robin Sayers *(Sr Editor)*
Ariela Suster *(Assoc Editor-Market)*
Sandra Vernet *(Deputy Chief-Copy)*
Cyd Wilson *(Dir-Creative Devel)*
Mariya Ivankovitser *(Asst Dir-Art)*
Ashley Atiyeh *(Dir-Beauty)*
Jessica Blickstein *(Dir-Beauty)*
Tom Colaprico *(Dir-Production)*
Andrea Damast *(Dir-Fashion & Retail-Instylecom)*
Tim Hanley *(Dir-Midwest)*
John Korpics *(Dir-Creative)*
Hal Rubenstein *(Dir-Fashion)*
Erin Sumwalt *(Dir-Market)*
Amy Synnott-D'Annibale *(Dir-Beauty)*
Cynthia Weber Cleary *(Dir-Fashion)*
Celine Wojtala *(Deputy Dir-Res Center)*
Brooke Caruso *(Assoc Brand Mgr)*
George Woods, Jr. *(Mgr-Production)*
Teresa Granda *(Mgr-Adv Svcs)*
Arleen F. O'Brien *(Mgr-Makeup)*
Nikki Zila *(Mgr-Integrated Mktg)*
DeLora E. Jones *(Chief-Reporters)*
Brands & Products:
IN STYLE

IN TOUCH WEEKLY
(Div. of Bauer Publishing USA)
270 Sylvan Ave Ste 4
Englewood Cliffs, NJ 07632
Tel.: (201) 569-6699

Key to Media (For complete agency information see *The Advertising Red Books-Agencies* edition):
1. Bus. Publs. 2. Cable T.V. 3. Catalogs & Directories. 4. Co-op Adv. 5. Consumer Mags. 6. D.M. to Bus. Estab.7. D.M. to Consumers
8. Daily Newsp. 9. Exhibits/Trade Shows 10. Foreign 11. Infomercial 12. Internet Adv.13. Multimedia 14. Network Radio
15. Network T.V. 16. Newsp. Distr. Mags. 17. Other 18. Outdoor (Posters, Transit) 19. Point of Purchase20. Premiums, Novelties
21. Product Samples 22. Special Events Mktg. 23. Spot Radio 24. Spot T.V. 25. Weekly Newsp. 26. Yellow Page Adv.

In Touch Weekly — (Continued)

Fax: (201) 569-5303
E-mail: contactintouch@intouchweekly.com
Web Site: www.intouchweekly.com
Business Description:
Magazine
S.I.C.: 2731
N.A.I.C.S.: 511130
Media: 6-8-13
Personnel:
Garry Wasko *(Editor-in-Chief-Articles)*
Michelle Lee *(Editor-in-Chief)*
Richard Spencer *(Editor-in-Chief)*
Jim Loffredo *(Mgr-Art Production)*

INDEPENDENT PUBLISHERS GROUP

814 N Franklin St Fl 1
Chicago, IL 60610
Tel.: (312) 337-0747
Fax: (312) 337-5985
E-mail: frontdesk@ipgbook.com
Web Site: www.ipgbook.com
Approx. Number Employees: 50
Business Description:
Books
S.I.C.: 5192
N.A.I.C.S.: 424920
Media: 10
Personnel:
Mark Suchomel *(Pres)*
Curt Matthews *(CEO)*
Teresa Gamboa *(CFO)*
Cynthia Murphy *(Mgr-Mktg)*
Mary Rowles *(Mgr-Title Dev)*

INDIANAPOLIS STAR

(Unit of Indiana Newspapers Inc.)
307 N Pennsylvania St
Indianapolis, IN 46204-1819
Mailing Address:
PO Box 145
Indianapolis, IN 46206-0145
Tel.: (317) 444-4000
Fax: (317) 444-7222
Fax: (317) 444-8200
Toll Free: (800) 669-7827
E-mail: info@indystar.com
Web Site: www.indystar.com
Sales Range: $450-499.9 Million
Approx. Number Employees: 1,500
Year Founded: 1903
Business Description:
Newspaper Publisher
S.I.C.: 2711; 2752
N.A.I.C.S.: 511110; 323110
Advertising Expenditures: $1,500,000
Media: 2-4-6-7-8-9-10-13-18-23
Distr.: Reg.
Budget Set: Nov.
Personnel:
Michael G. Kane *(Pres & Publr)*
Dennis R. Ryerson *(VP & Editor)*
Bill Bolger *(VP-Ops & Info Tech)*
James Keough *(VP-HR)*
Bruce Klink *(Grp Controller & VP-Fin)*
Patrick Peregrin *(VP-Adv)*
D. Todd Moore *(Editor-Admin)*
John Anderson *(Dir-Ops)*
John Cherba *(Dir-Retail Adv)*
Jennifer Gombach *(Dir-Audience Dev)*
Lisa Hite-Wadler *(Dir-Adv Ops)*
Yasha Holmes *(Dir-Classified Adv)*
Patricia Franks Miller *(Dir-Interactive Sls)*
Greg Erbeck *(Mgr-Sls & Mtkg)*
Leigh Hedger *(Mgr-Custom Publ)*
Tim Newbrough *(Mgr-Creative Svcs)*
Dolores Record *(Mgr-Admin)*
Karen Sensback *(Mgr-Bus Dev)*

INFOGROUP INC.

(Holding of CCMP Capital Advisors, LLC)
5711 S 86th Cir
Omaha, NE 68127-4146
Tel.: (402) 593-4500
Fax: (402) 596-8902
E-mail: ir@infousa.com
Web Site: www.infogroup.com
Approx. Sls.: $499,913,000
Approx. Number Employees: 3,146
Year Founded: 1972
Business Description:
Holding Company; Business & Consumer Database Publisher
S.I.C.: 6719; 2741; 7389; 8732
N.A.I.C.S.: 551112; 511140; 519190; 541910
Export
Advertising Expenditures: $19,600,000
Media: 2-3-4-7-8-10-12-13-17-26
Distr.: Intl.; Natl.
Budget Set: Nov.
Personnel:
Richard F. Zannino *(Chm)*
Clare Hart *(Pres & CEO)*
Richard Hanks *(CFO & Exec VP)*
Slade Kobran *(CMO)*
Gemma Postlethwaite *(Chief Product Officer)*
John Copenhaver *(Pres-Small Bus Grp)*
Jim DeRouchey *(Pres-Licensing)*
Philip J. Garlick *(Pres-OneSource)*
Mike Hilts *(Pres-Interactive)*
Marc Litvinoff *(Pres-Res Grp & Opinion Res)*
Franklin Rios *(Pres-Enterprise Solutions Grp)*
Winston King *(Gen Counsel & Sec)*
Ann Kennedy *(Sr VP-Product & Data Innovation)*
Lisa Olson *(Sr VP)*
Susie Robinson *(Sr VP-HR)*
Christian Ward *(Sr VP-Data Strategy, Analytics & Capabilities)*
Dana Hayman *(VP-Mktg Strategy & Insights)*
Brands & Products:
A WORLD OF SOLUTIONS
AMERICAN BUSINESS DIRECTORIES
CREDIT.NET
INFOGROUP
LISTBAZAAR.COM
NEWLEADSUSA
SALESGENIE.COM
Advertising Agency:
infoGROUP Inc.
5711 S 86th Cir
Omaha, NE 68127-4146
Tel.: (402) 593-4500
Fax: (402) 596-0475
Toll Free: (800) 336-8349

INFORMATION TODAY INC.

143 Old Marlton Pike
Medford, NJ 08055-8750
Tel.: (609) 654-6266
Fax: (609) 654-4309
Toll Free: (800) 300-9868
E-mail: custserv@infotoday.com
Web Site: www.infotoday.com
Approx. Number Employees: 114
Business Description:
Book, Periodical, & Internet Publisher & Business Services
S.I.C.: 2721; 2731; 2741; 7389
N.A.I.C.S.: 511120; 511130; 516110; 561920
Media: 2-10-13
Personnel:
Roger R. Bilboul *(Chm)*
Thomas H. Hogan *(Pres & Publr)*
Jim Pitkow *(CEO)*
John Brokenshire *(CFO)*
John Bryans *(Publr & Editor-in-Chief-Books)*
M. Heide Dengler *(VP-Graphics & Production)*
Thomas Hogan, Jr. *(VP-Mktg & Bus Dev)*
William C. Spence *(VP-IT)*
Susan M. Stearns *(Dir-Mktg)*
Meredith Browning *(Dir-Accts)*
Sue Hogan *(Dir-HR)*
Arnoud Kemp *(Dir-Sls-Mktg)*
Michael V. Zarrello *(Dir-Exhibits & Adv Sls)*
Inge Coffey *(Mgr-Circulation)*
Walter McQuillan *(Mgr-Sls)*
David Panara *(Mgr-Adv Sls)*
Janeen Welsh *(Mgr-Circulation)*

INNER TRADITIONS INTERNATIONAL

1 Park St
Rochester, VT 05767
Tel.: (802) 767-3174
Fax: (802) 767-3726
E-mail: sales@innertraditions.com
Web Site: www.innertraditions.com
E-Mail For Key Personnel:
Sales Director: sales@innertraditions.com
Approx. Sls.: $6,000,000
Approx. Number Employees: 40
Year Founded: 1975
Business Description:
Publisher of Books
S.I.C.: 2731
N.A.I.C.S.: 511130
Media: 4-6-8-10-13
Personnel:
Ehud Sperling *(Founder & Pres)*
John Hays *(Dir-Sls)*

THE INQUIRER & MIRROR

(Unit of Ottaway Newspapers, Inc.)
1 Old S Rd
Nantucket, MA 02554-6029
Mailing Address:
PO Box 1198
Nantucket, MA 02554-1198
Tel.: (508) 228-0001
Fax: (508) 325-5089
E-mail: newsroom@inkym.com
Web Site: www.ack.net/
Sales Range: $10-24.9 Million
Approx. Number Employees: 14
Year Founded: 1821
Business Description:
Newspaper Publisher
S.I.C.: 2711
N.A.I.C.S.: 511110
Media: 8-9
Personnel:
Marianne R. Stanton *(Publr & Editor)*
Joshua H. Balling *(Mng Editor)*
Nicole Harnishfeger *(Dir-Visual Content)*
Brands & Products:
INQUIRER & MIRROR
NANTUCKET TODAY

INSIDE BUSINESS INC.

(Sub. of Landmark Media Enterprises LLC)
150 W Brambleton Ave
Norfolk, VA 23510
Tel.: (757) 222-5353
Fax: (757) 222-5359
E-mail: info@insidebiz.com
Web Site: www.insidebiz.com
Approx. Number Employees: 12
Year Founded: 1995
Business Description:
Newspapers Publishing
S.I.C.: 2711
N.A.I.C.S.: 511110
Media: 2-7
Personnel:
Mike Herron *(Gen Mgr & Assoc Publr)*
Carol Lichti *(Editor)*
Bill Blake *(Dir-Sls)*
Rawles Magee *(Mgr-Legal Adv)*
John Kinsley *(Sr Acct Exec)*
Robin Simmons *(Sr Acct Exec)*
Brands & Products:
INSIDE BUSINESS

INSIGHT ON THE NEWS

(Sub. of News World Communications Inc)
3600 New York Ave Northeast
Washington, DC 20002-1947
Tel.: (202) 636-3000
Fax: (202) 269-1862
E-mail: advertising@insightmag.com
Web Site: www.insightmag.com
Approx. Number Employees: 31
Year Founded: 1985
Business Description:
Publisher of Current Events Magazine
S.I.C.: 2711; 7383
N.A.I.C.S.: 511110; 519110
Advertising Expenditures: $500,000
Media: 8-10-13-23-24-25
Distr.: Direct to Consumer; Natl.
Budget Set: Nov.
Brands & Products:
INSIGHT ON THE NEWS

INSPIRATION SOFTWARE, INC.

9400 SW Beaverton-Hillsdale Hwy
Ste 300
Beaverton, OR 97005
Tel.: (503) 297-3004
Fax: (503) 297-4676
E-mail: marketing@inspiration.com
Web Site: www.inspiration.com
Approx. Sls.: $17,000,000
Approx. Number Employees: 55
Year Founded: 1982
Business Description:
Publisher of Visual-Learning Software
S.I.C.: 7371
N.A.I.C.S.: 541511
Media: 13
Personnel:
Mona Westhaver *(Co-Founder & Pres)*
Donald Helfgott *(Co-Founder & CEO)*
Brian L. McKean *(VP-Sls)*
Amy Chan *(Dir-Mktg)*

Key to Media (For complete agency information see *The Advertising Red Books-Agencies* edition):
1. Bus. Publs. 2. Cable T.V. 3. Catalogs & Directories. 4. Co-op Adv. 5. Consumer Mags. 6. D.M. to Bus. Estab.7. D.M. to Consumers 8. Daily Newsp. 9. Exhibits/Trade Shows 10. Foreign 11. Infomercial 12. Internet Adv.13. Multimedia 14. Network Radio 15. Network T.V. 16. Newsp. Distr. Mags. 17. Other 18. Outdoor (Posters, Transit) 19. Point of Purchase20. Premiums, Novelties 21. Product Samples 22. Special Events Mktg. 23. Spot Radio 24. Spot T.V. 25. Weekly Newsp. 26. Yellow Page Adv.

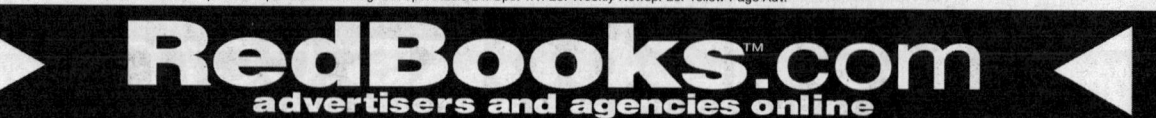

Nancy Martell *(Dir-HR)*
Sid Snyder *(Dir-Software Dev)*

Brands & Products:
INSPIRATION
INSPIRATION SOFTWARE
INSPIRED LEARNING COMMUNITY
INSPIREDATA
KIDSPIRATION
THE LEADER IN VISUAL THINKING AND LEARNING
WEBSPIRATION

INSTITUTIONAL INVESTOR, INC.

(Sub. of Euromoney Institutional Investor PLC)
225 Park Ave S 8th Fl
New York, NY 10003-1605
Tel.: (212) 224-3300
Telex: 671391
E-mail: ideas@institutionalinvestor.com
Web Site: www.institutionalinvestor.com
Approx. Number Employees: 50
Business Description:
Business Periodicals Publisher
S.I.C.: 2721; 2741
N.A.I.C.S.: 511120; 511199
Media: 6-13
Personnel:
Allison Adams *(Mng Dir & Grp Publr)*
David E. Antin *(COO-Magazine)*
Ernest S. McCrary *(Editor & Publr-Special Projects)*
Christine Cavolina *(Publr-Magazine)*
Steven Weiss *(VP-Fin)*
Mike Carroll *(Editor-Magazine)*
Tom Lamont *(Editor-News)*
Fred R. Bleakley *(Dir-Editorial-Membership)*
Nick Ferris *(Mgr-Community & Social Networking)*

INTEGRATED SOLUTIONS MAGAZINE, INC.

(Sub. of Jameson Publishing Inc.)
5340 Frylind Rd Ste300
Erie, PA 16510
Tel.: (814) 897-9000
Fax: (814) 899-5580
E-mail: corrypub@corrypub.com
Web Site: www.fieldtechnologiesonline.com
Approx. Rev.: $3,200,000
Approx. Number Employees: 55
Business Description:
Trade Journal Publisher
S.I.C.: 2721
N.A.I.C.S.: 511120
Media: 2-7
Personnel:
Jim Roddy *(Pres & Gen Mgr)*
Rich Ranus *(Sr Dir-Sls)*
Carrie Brocious *(Dir-Mktg)*
Ed Hess *(Dir-Publ)*
Melinda Reed-Fadden *(Dir-Circulation)*

INTERNATIONAL CENTER FOR ENTREPRENEURIAL DEVELOPMENT, INC.

12715 Telge Rd
Cypress, TX 77429-2164
Tel.: (281) 256-4100
Fax: (281) 373-4450
E-mail: info@iced.net
Web Site: www.iced.net
Approx. Number Employees: 175
Year Founded: 1967
Business Description:
Franchiser of Instant Printing, Thermography, Pack & Ship & Computer Education Centers
S.I.C.: 6794; 7331
N.A.I.C.S.: 533110; 541860
Advertising Expenditures: $300,000
Media: 2-4-6-7-8-9-13-19-20-22-25-26
Distr.: Intl.; Natl.
Budget Set: Dec.
Personnel:
Steve Hammerstein *(Pres & CEO)*
Perry Hillegeist *(COO & VP)*

Brands & Products:
AWT
COMPUTER TOTS
COPY CLUB
FRANKLIN'S PRINTING
THE INK WELL
KKBC
KWIK KOPY PRINTING
PARCEL PLUS
WOMEN'S HEALTH BOUTIQUE

INTERNATIONAL DATA GROUP

1 Exeter Plz 15th Fl
Boston, MA 02116
Mailing Address:
3 Post Office Sq 4th Fl
Boston, MA 02109
Tel.: (617) 534-1200
Fax: (617) 423-0240
E-mail: questions@idg.com
Web Site: www.idg.com
Approx. Rev.: $3,200,000,000
Approx. Number Employees: 13,640
Year Founded: 1964
Business Description:
Computer Newspapers, Magazines & Books; Computer Industry Research & Analysis
S.I.C.: 2721; 8732
N.A.I.C.S.: 511120; 541910
Media: 10
Personnel:
Patrick J. McGovern *(Founder & Chm)*
Ted Bloom *(CFO & Treas)*
Bob Carrigan *(CEO-IDG Comm-Worldwide)*
Mike Romoff *(Gen Mgr-IDG TechNetwork)*
Susanna Hinds *(Dir-Corp Comm)*

Brands & Products:
ANSWERS FOR THE INFORMATION AGE
CIO
COMPUTERWORLD
CSO
GAMEPRO
IDG.NET
THE INDUSTRY STANDARD
INFOWORLD
LINUXWORLD
MACWORLD
NETWORK WORLD
PC WORLD

INTERNATIONAL TICKET CO.

24 Beechwood Rd
Summit, NJ 07901
Tel.: (908) 918-1122
Fax: (973) 887-2277
Toll Free: (800) 635-5468
Web Site: www.itcpromotions.com
Approx. Number Employees: 3
Year Founded: 1898
Business Description:
Mfr. of Tickets, Tags, Labels, Large Numbering, Printed Products & Business Forms, Premium Novelties
S.I.C.: 2759
N.A.I.C.S.: 323119
Export
Advertising Expenditures: $50,000
Media: 2-4-6-7-8-10-20-21-26
Distr.: Natl.
Personnel:
Larry Manshel *(Owner)*
Roger L. Manshel *(Owner)*

INVESTORS BUSINESS DAILY, INC.

(Sub. of Data Analysis, Inc.)
12655 Beatrice St
Los Angeles, CA 90066
Tel.: (310) 448-6000
Fax: (310) 448-6803
E-mail: ibdnews@investors.com
Web Site: www.investors.com
Approx. Number Employees: 200
Year Founded: 1984
Business Description:
Newspaper & Book Publisher
S.I.C.: 2711; 6282
N.A.I.C.S.: 511110; 523930
Media: 3-6-10-13
Personnel:
William O'Neil *(Founder & Chm)*
Kathleen Sherman *(VP-Corp Commun)*
Chris Gessel *(Exec Editor)*
Jonathan Hahn *(Mgr-Media Rels)*
Janice Janendo *(Mgr-Adv Mktg)*

Brands & Products:
CAN SLIM
EIBD
IBD 100
IBD 100 SMARTLINK
IBD EXTRA!
INVESTORS BUSINESS DAILY
INVESTORS.COM

IOWA FARMER TODAY

(Unit of Lee Enterprises, Incorporated)
1065 Sierra Court NE Ste B
Cedar Rapids, IA 52402-6585
Tel.: (319) 398-2640
Fax: (319) 398-2696
Toll Free: (800) 475-6655
E-mail: sales@iowafarmertoday.com
Web Site: www.iowafarmertoday.com
E-Mail For Key Personnel:
Sales Director: sales@iowafarmertoday.com
Sales Range: $25-49.9 Million
Approx. Number Employees: 36
Year Founded: 1984
Business Description:
Specialty Newspaper Publisher
S.I.C.: 2711; 2721
N.A.I.C.S.: 511110; 511120
Media: 7
Personnel:
Steve DeWitt *(Publr)*
Robert Davis *(Dir-Internet)*
Brad Steffens *(Mgr-Inside Sls)*

Brands & Products:
EQUIPMENT CONNECTION
IOWA FARMER TODAY
MIDWEST MARKETER

IPSWICH CHRONICLE

(Unit of GateHouse Media New England)
72 Cherry Hill Dr
Beverly, MA 01935
Tel.: (978) 412-1800
Fax: (978) 412-1801
E-mail: ipswich@cnc.com
Web Site: www.wickedlocal.com/ipswich
Sales Range: $100-124.9 Million
Year Founded: 1872
Business Description:
Newspaper Publisher
S.I.C.: 2711
N.A.I.C.S.: 511110
Media: 8-25
Personnel:
Joshua Boyd *(Editor-Sports)*
Wendall Waters *(Editor)*
Pat Coen *(Mgr-Production)*
Joan Gould *(Mgr-Display Adv)*

ISLANDS MAGAZINE

(Unit of Bonnier Corporation)
460 N Orlando Ave Ste 200
Winter Park, FL 32789
Tel.: (407) 628-4802
Fax: (407) 628-7061
Web Site: www.islands.com
Business Description:
Travel Magazine & Internet Publisher
S.I.C.: 2721; 2741
N.A.I.C.S.: 511120; 516110
Media: 6-8
Personnel:
Ken G. Leandro *(Publr)*
Ashley Knaus *(Editor-Res)*
Michael Bessire *(Dir-Art)*
Chris Tauber *(Mgr-Content)*
Amanda Harris *(Coord-Online Bus)*
Lindsey Parry *(Coord-Adv)*

JACKSONVILLE BUSINESS JOURNAL

(Unit of American City Business Journals, Inc.)
1200 Riverplace Blvd Ste 201
Jacksonville, FL 32207-1899
Tel.: (904) 396-3502
Fax: (904) 396-5706
E-mail: jacksonville@bizjournals.com
Web Site: www.jacksonville.bizjournals.com
Approx. Number Employees: 30
Business Description:
Local Business Newspaper Publisher
S.I.C.: 2711
N.A.I.C.S.: 511110
Media: 7-8-22
Personnel:
David Sillick *(Publr)*
Andy Brennan *(Dir-Circulation & Mktg)*
Eleanor Snite *(Dir-Res)*

THE JACKSONVILLE DAILY NEWS CO.

(Unit of Freedom Newspapers, Inc.)
724 Bell Fork Rd
Jacksonville, NC 28540-6311
Mailing Address:
PO Box 196
Jacksonville, NC 28541-0196
Tel.: (910) 353-1171
Fax: (910) 353-7316
Web Site: www.jdnews.com
Sales Range: $1-9.9 Million
Approx. Number Employees: 173
Year Founded: 1953
Business Description:
Newspapers

Key to Media (For complete agency information see *The Advertising Red Books-Agencies* edition):
1. Bus. Publs. 2. Cable T.V. 3. Catalogs & Directories. 4. Co-op Adv. 5. Consumer Mags. 6. D.M. to Bus. Estab.7. D.M. to Consumers
8. Daily Newsp. 9. Exhibits/Trade Shows 10. Foreign 11. Infomercial 12. Internet Adv.13. Multimedia 14. Network Radio
15. Network T.V. 16. Newsp. Distr. Mags. 17. Other 18. Outdoor (Posters, Transit) 19. Point of Purchase20. Premiums, Novelties
21. Product Samples 22. Special Events Mktg. 23. Spot Radio 24. Spot T.V. 25. Weekly Newsp. 26. Yellow Page Adv.

The Jacksonville Daily News Co. — (Continued)

S.I.C.: 2711; 2721
N.A.I.C.S.: 511110; 511120
Media: 8-9
Personnel:
Elliott Potter *(Publr & Exec Editor)*
Ken Warren *(VP-Adv)*
Brands & Products:
THE HOMEPLACE
THE JACKSONVILLE DAILY NEWS

JACKSONVILLE JOURNAL-COURIER

(Unit of Freedom Newspapers, Inc.)
235 W State St
Jacksonville, IL 62650
Tel.: (217) 245-6121
Fax: (217) 245-1226
E-mail: news@myjournalcourier.com
Web Site: www.myjournalcourier.com
Approx. Number Employees: 150
Year Founded: 1830
Business Description:
Newspaper
S.I.C.: 2711
N.A.I.C.S.: 511110
Media: 8-9
Personnel:
David Bauer *(Editor)*
Jeff Lonergan *(Dir-Production)*

JAMESON PUBLISHING INC.

Knowledge Park 5340 Fryling Rd Ste 300
Erie, PA 16510
Tel.: (814) 897-9000
Fax: (814) 899-5583
E-mail: jamesonpublishing@jamesonpublishing.com
Web Site:
www.jamesonpublishing.com
Approx. Sls.: $11,444,921
Approx. Number Employees: 70
Year Founded: 1980
Business Description:
Publisher of Trade Journals
S.I.C.: 2721
N.A.I.C.S.: 511120
Media: 2-8-10-13
Personnel:
Rick Peterson *(Co-Founder & Co-Owner)*
Terry C. Peterson *(Founder)*
Jim Roddy *(Pres & Gen Mgr)*
John Howland *(VP-Sls & Mktg)*

JAPS-OLSON COMPANY

7500 Excelsior Blvd
Saint Louis Park, MN 55426
Tel.: (952) 932-9393
Fax: (952) 912-1900
Toll Free: (800) 548-2897
Web Site: www.japsolson.com
Approx. Number Employees: 750
Year Founded: 1907
Business Description:
Printing, Packaging & Mailing Services
S.I.C.: 2752; 7331
N.A.I.C.S.: 323110; 541860
Media: 2
Personnel:
Robert E. Murphy *(Chm)*
Michael R. Murphy *(Pres)*
Michael W. Beddor *(CEO)*
Gary Petrangelo *(CFO)*
Kevin J. Beddor *(Pres-JO Direct)*

J.B. DOLLAR STRETCHER MAGAZINE

3105 Farnham Rd
Richfield, OH 44286
Tel.: (330) 659-3590
Fax: (330) 659-6741
Toll Free: (800) 673-2531
Web Site: www.jbdollar.com
Approx. Sls.: $18,000,000
Approx. Number Employees: 150
Year Founded: 1985
Business Description:
Publisher of Direct Mail Advertising Magazine
S.I.C.: 2752
N.A.I.C.S.: 323110
Media: 6-8-10-13-18-20-23-24
Distr.: Direct Mail to Consumer; Reg.
Personnel:
Joan Minchak *(Co-Owner & Co-Publisher)*
Robert J. Minchak *(Owner)*
Mark Kozer *(Pres-Sls)*
Brands & Products:
J.B. DOLLAR STRETCHER

JENKINS GROUP, INC.

1129 Woodmere Dr Ste B
Traverse City, MI 49686
Tel.: (231) 933-0445
Fax: (231) 933-0448
Toll Free: (800) 706-4636
E-mail: jrj@bookpublishing.com
Web Site: www.bookpublishing.com
Approx. Number Employees: 10
Year Founded: 1988
Business Description:
Publishing & Promotional Services
S.I.C.: 2721; 2732
N.A.I.C.S.: 511120; 323117
Advertising Expenditures: $50,000
Internet Adv.: $50,000
Personnel:
Jerrold Jenkins *(Owner)*
James J. Kalajian *(Pres & COO)*
Andrew Parvel *(Dir-Mktg)*

JERSEY JOURNAL NEWSPAPER

(Sub. of Advance Publications, Inc.)
30 Journal Sq
Jersey City, NJ 07306-4101
Tel.: (201) 653-1000
Fax: (201) 217-2455
Web Site: www.thejerseyjournal.com
Approx. Number Employees: 150
Business Description:
Job Printing & Newspaper Publishing
S.I.C.: 2711
N.A.I.C.S.: 511110
Media: 8-9
Personnel:
Judy Locorriere *(Editor)*
Harvey Zucker *(Mng Editor-Production)*
Denise Copeland *(Dir-Ops)*
Sharon Pizzutiello *(Dir-Mktg)*
Brands & Products:
THE JERSEY JOURNAL

J.J. KELLER & ASSOCIATES, INC.

3003 W Breezewood Ln
Neenah, WI 59456
Tel.: (920) 722-2848
Fax: (920) 727-7516
Toll Free: (800) 327-6868
E-mail: servicesales@jjkeller.com
Web Site: www.jjkeller.com
E-Mail For Key Personnel:
Sales Director: sales@jjkeller.com
Approx. Number Employees: 1,400
Year Founded: 1953
Business Description:
Publisher Workplace Compliance Materials
S.I.C.: 2741; 8742
N.A.I.C.S.: 511199; 541614
Export
Media: 2-4-5-7-10-13-19-20-21-22-26
Distr.: Direct to Consumer; Intl.; Natl.
Budget Set: Jan.
Personnel:
Robert L. Keller *(Chm & CEO)*
James J. Keller *(Pres)*
Terrance Quirk *(Sr VP)*
Janice Reh Hamblin *(VP-Sls)*
Kim Riebau *(VP-Sls)*
Thomas Hines *(Mgr-Corp Creative & Promo)*
Brands & Products:
DRIVER MANAGEMENT ONLINE
FUEL TAX MASTER
HUMAN RESOURCE TRAINING CUSTOMIZER
J .J. KELLER'S DRIVER FILE
KELLER-SOFT
KELLERONLINE
KELLER'S FOOD BIOTERRORISM INFORMATION CENTER
KELLER'S INCIDENT INVESTIGATOR
KELLER'S INFORMATION CENTERS
KELLER'S JOB SAFETY ANALYZER
KELLER'S MAINTENANCE MANAGER
KELLER'S MSDS VIEWER
KELLER'S NAFTA RESOURCE CENTER
KELLER'S SECURITY RESOURCE CENTER
KELLERSCAN
KELLERSTAR
SAFETY TRAINING CUSTOMIZER

JOBSON MEDICAL INFORMATION LLC

(Holding of The Wicks Group of Companies, LLC)
100 Ave of the Americas 9th Fl
New York, NY 10013-1689
Tel.: (212) 274-7000
Fax: (212) 431-0500
Web Site: www.jobson.com
Approx. Sls.: $35,000,000
Approx. Number Employees: 150
Year Founded: 1971
Business Description:
Periodicals
S.I.C.: 2721; 2741
N.A.I.C.S.: 511120; 511199
Import Export
Media: 10-13
Personnel:
Jeffrey MacDonald *(CEO)*

JOHN WILEY & SONS, INC.

111 River St
Hoboken, NJ 07030-5774
Tel.: (201) 748-6000
Fax: (201) 748-6088
Toll Free: (800) 225-5945
E-mail: info@wiley.com
Web Site: www.wiley.com
E-Mail For Key Personnel:
Public Relations: sspilka@wiley.com
Approx. Rev.: $1,742,551,000
Approx. Number Employees: 5,100
Year Founded: 1807
Business Description:
Educational, Scientific, Technical, Medical, Professional, Reference & Trade Books, Journals & Multimedia Products Publisher
S.I.C.: 2731; 2721; 2741; 7372
N.A.I.C.S.: 511130; 511120; 511199; 511210
Import Export
Advertising Expenditures: $27,100,000
Media: 2-3-4-5-6-7-8-9-10-13-14-15-18-19-20-22-23-25
Distr.: Natl.
Budget Set: Dec.
Personnel:
Peter Booth Wiley *(Chm)*
William J. Pesce *(Pres & CEO)*
Ellis E. Cousens *(CFO & Exec VP)*
Stephen M. Smith *(COO & Exec VP)*
Warren C. Fristensky *(CIO & Sr VP-IT)*
Edward J. Melando *(Chief Acctg Officer, VP & Controller)*
Stephen A. Kippur *(Pres-Pro, Trade Publ & Exec VP)*
Gary M. Rinck *(Gen Counsel & Sr VP)*
Matt Holt *(Publr, VP & Exec Editor)*
Mark Allin *(Sr VP-Pro & Trade)*
William J. Arlington *(Sr VP-HR)*
Clifford Kline *(Sr VP-Customer Svc & Distr)*
Bonnie E. Lieberman *(Sr VP-Global Higher Education)*
Steve Miron *(Sr VP-Scientific, Tech & Medical & Scholarly)*
Eric A. Swanson *(Sr VP-Govt Rel & Public Policy)*
Patrick Kelly *(VP & Dir-Publ)*
Gwenyth Jones *(VP-Digital Publ)*
Marc Mikulich *(VP-Brand Mgmt & Intl Rights)*
Margie Schustack *(VP-Mktg Ops)*
Susan Spilka *(VP-Corp Comm)*
Andrew Bilbao *(Dir-Plng & Dev)*
Alida Setford *(Dir-Adv & Promo)*
Brands & Products:
CLIFFSNOTES
DUMMIES
FROMMER'S
JOSSEY-BASS
KNOWLEDGE FOR GENERATIONS
MCGUFFEY
PFEIFFER
SYBEX
WILEY
WILEY INTERSCIENCE
WILEY-VCH
Advertising Agency:
Signature Advertising
409 Canal St
Milldale, CT 06467-0698
Tel.: (860) 426-2144
Fax: (860) 426-2149

THE JOHNS HOPKINS UNIVERSITY PRESS

(Sub. of The Johns Hopkins University)
2715 N Charles St
Baltimore, MD 21218
Tel.: (410) 516-6900
Fax: (410) 516-6968

Key to Media (For complete agency information see *The Advertising Red Books-Agencies* edition):
1. Bus. Publs. 2. Cable T.V. 3. Catalogs & Directories. 4. Co-op Adv. 5. Consumer Mags. 6. D.M. to Bus. Estab.7. D.M. to Consumers
8. Daily Newsp. 9. Exhibits/Trade Shows 10. Foreign 11. Infomercial 12. Internet Adv.13. Multimedia 14. Network Radio
15. Network T.V. 16. Newsp. Distr. Mags. 17. Other 18. Outdoor (Posters, Transit) 19. Point of Purchase20. Premiums, Novelties
21. Product Samples 22. Special Events Mktg. 23. Spot Radio 24. Spot T.V. 25. Weekly Newsp. 26. Yellow Page Adv.

E-mail: kk@press.jhu.edu
Web Site: www.press.jhu.edu
Approx. Number Employees: 110
Year Founded: 1878
Business Description:
Scholarly Books & Journals Publisher
S.I.C.: 2731; 2741
N.A.I.C.S.: 511130; 511199
Media: 2-4-6-7-8-9-10-11-16-17-19-25
Distr.: Intl.; Natl.
Budget Set: Sept.
Personnel:
Karen Willmes *(Mgr-Adv & Direct Mail)*
Becky Brasington Clark *(Dir-Mktg & Online Book Publ)*
John Holmes *(Dir-Devel)*
Stacey Armstead *(Mgr-Info Sys)*

JOHNSON NEWSPAPER CORPORATION
260 Washington St
Watertown, NY 13601-3301
Tel.: (315) 782-1000
Fax: (315) 661-2523
Toll Free: (800) 642-6222 (NY Only)
Web Site: www.wdt.net
Approx. Number Employees: 250
Year Founded: 1870
Business Description:
Newspaper Publishing
S.I.C.: 2711; 2752
N.A.I.C.S.: 511110; 323110
Media: 8-9-19-20-21-22
Personnel:
John B. Johnson, Jr. *(Chm & CEO)*
Harold B. Johnson *(Pres)*
Barbara Peck *(Mgr-Adv)*
Brands & Products:
WATERTOWN DAILY TIMES

JOHNSON PUBLISHING COMPANY, INC.
820 S Michigan Ave
Chicago, IL 60605-2103
Tel.: (312) 322-9200
Fax: (312) 322-1099
E-mail: help@fcc.com
Web Site:
www.johnsonpublishing.com
Sales Range: $450-499.9 Million
Approx. Number Employees: 2,000
Year Founded: 1942
Business Description:
Publisher of Magazines/Books; Radio Broadcasting; Television Production; Mfr. of Cosmetics
S.I.C.: 2721; 2731
N.A.I.C.S.: 511120; 511130
Advertising Expenditures: $1,000,000
Media: 2-4-6-7-8-9-10-13-18-19-20-21-25
Distr.: Intl.; Natl.
Budget Set: Aug.
Personnel:
Linda Johnson Rice *(Chm)*
Desiree Rogers *(CEO)*
Nijole Yutkowitz *(Dir-Sls)*
Brands & Products:
EBONE
EBONY
EBONY FASHION FAIR
FASHION FAIR
FASHION FAIR COSMETICS
JET
JOHNSON PUBLISHING COMPANY
JPC BOOK DIVISION

JOMIRA/ADVANCE
470 3rd St Ste 211
San Francisco, CA 94107
Tel.: (415) 356-7801
Fax: (415) 356-7804
Toll Free: (800) 600-2777
E-mail: kamdeemah@jomirabooks.com
Web Site: www.jomirabooks.com
Sales Range: $10-24.9 Million
Approx. Number Employees: 10
Year Founded: 1985
Business Description:
Book Publisher
S.I.C.: 2731
N.A.I.C.S.: 511130
Advertising Expenditures: $401,288
Media: 6-7-8-9-16-25
Distr.: Natl.
Budget Set: July
Personnel:
Gerardo Joffe *(Pres)*
Brands & Products:
JOMIRA
JOMIRA/ADVANCE
Advertising Agency:
Jomira Advertising
470 Third St Ste 211
San Francisco, CA 94107
Tel.: (415) 356-7801
Fax: (415) 356-7804
Toll Free: (800) 600-2777

JOURNAL COMMUNICATIONS, INC.
333 W State St
Milwaukee, WI 53203-1305
Mailing Address:
PO Box 661
Milwaukee, WI 53201-0661
Tel.: (414) 224-2000
Fax: (414) 224-2469
Toll Free: (800) 388-2291
Web Site: www.jc.com
Approx. Rev.: $376,759,000
Approx. Number Employees: 1,800
Year Founded: 1882
Business Description:
Communications Company; Publications, Broadcasting, Printing & Telecommunications
S.I.C.: 2711; 4833
N.A.I.C.S.: 511110; 515120
Import Export
Advertising Expenditures: $2,677,000
Media: 17
Distr.: Natl.
Budget Set: Oct.
Personnel:
Steven J. Smith *(Chm, Pres & CEO)*
Mary Hill Leahy *(Chief Compliance Officer, Gen Counsel, Sec & Sr VP)*
Kenneth L. Kozminski *(Pres-IPC Print Svcs & VP-Journal Comm)*
James P. Prather *(Exec VP-TV & Radio Ops-Journal Brdcst Grp & VP)*
Steven H. Wexler *(Exec VP-TV & Radio Ops-Journal Brdcst Grp & VP)*
Elizabeth Brenner *(Exec VP)*
Matt O'Malley *(Mgr-Procurement & Sourcing)*

THE JOURNAL GAZETTE
(Sub. of Fort Wayne Newspapers, Inc.)
600 W Main St
Fort Wayne, IN 46802
Tel.: (260) 461-8519
Toll Free: (800) 324-0505
E-mail: info@fortwayne.com
Web Site: www.fortwayne.com
Approx. Number Employees: 15
Business Description:
Newspaper
S.I.C.: 2711
N.A.I.C.S.: 511110
Media: 13
Personnel:
Julie Inskeep *(Publr)*

JOURNAL OF COMMERCE, INC.
(Sub. of UBM Global Trade)
33 Washington St 13th Fl
Newark, NJ 07102
Tel.: (973) 848-7000
Fax: (973) 848-7165
Toll Free: (800) 223-0243
E-mail: editor@joc.com
Web Site: www.joc.com
Approx. Number Employees: 160
Year Founded: 1827
Business Description:
Journals for the Shipping & the Airline Industries
S.I.C.: 2721; 2741
N.A.I.C.S.: 511120; 516110
Media: 2-9-10-13
Distr.: Direct to Consumer; Natl.
Personnel:
Christine Oldenbrook *(Publr)*
Joseph Bonney *(Editor)*
William B. Cassidy *(Editor-Trucking & Domestic Transportation)*
Alan M. Field *(Editor-Intl Trade)*
Peter T. Leach *(Editor)*
Marsha Salisbury *(Editor-Res)*
Thomas L. Gallagher *(Webmaster)*

JOURNAL PUBLISHING CO. INC.
(Sub. of CREATE Foundation)
(d/b/a NE Mississippi Daily Journal)
1242 S Green St
Tupelo, MS 38804
Tel.: (662) 842-2611
Fax: (662) 842-2233
Web Site: www.nems360.com
Approx. Sls.: $16,461,889
Approx. Number Employees: 200
Year Founded: 1972
Business Description:
Newspapers, Publishing & Printing
S.I.C.: 2711; 6512
N.A.I.C.S.: 511110; 531120
Media: 8-9
Personnel:
William L. Crews *(Chm)*
Clay Foster *(Pres)*
John Pitts *(Editor-Sports)*
Cindy Carr *(Mgr Classified Adv)*
Brands & Products:
NEWSPAPERS

JOURNAL REGISTER COMPANY
(Filed for Ch 11 Bankruptcy on 2/21/09)
790 Township Line Rd Ste 300
Yardley, PA 19067
Tel.: (215) 504-4200
Fax: (215) 867-2173
E-mail: ir@journalregister.com
Web Site: www.journalregister.com
Sales Range: $450-499.9 Million
Approx. Number Employees: 3,400
Year Founded: 1755
Business Description:
Newspaper Publisher
S.I.C.: 2741; 2711
N.A.I.C.S.: 516110; 511110
Media: 2-8-9-18-19-20-23-25-26
Distr.: Direct to Consumer; Reg.
Personnel:
Joseph A. Ripp *(Chm)*
William J. Higginson *(Pres & COO)*
John Paton *(CEO)*
Jeff Bairstow *(CFO)*
Edward Condra *(Publr)*
Daniel Sarko *(Sr VP-Integrated Sls)*
Jerry Bammel *(VP & Gen Mgr)*
Jim Brady *(Editor-in-Chief)*
Ryan Adams *(Dir-Corp Natl Digital Sls)*
Teresa Goodrich *(Dir-Retail Adv)*
Gena Hamilton *(Dir-Digital Bus Dev)*

JOURNAL SENTINEL, INC.
(Sub. of Journal Communications, Inc.)
333 W State St
Milwaukee, WI 53203-1305
Mailing Address:
PO Box 661
Milwaukee, WI 53201-0661
Tel.: (414) 224-2000
Fax: (414) 224-2047
E-mail: jsmetro@journelsentinel.com
Web Site: www.jsonline.com
Sales Range: $400-449.9 Million
Approx. Number Employees: 1,400
Year Founded: 1882
Business Description:
Publisher of Newspaper
S.I.C.: 2711
N.A.I.C.S.: 511110
Advertising Expenditures: $1,000,000
Media: 6-9-20
Distr.: Reg.
Personnel:
Steven Smith *(Chm)*
Elizabeth Brenner *(Pres & Publr)*
Ken Mcnamee *(CFO & Sr VP)*
Royce Miles *(Exec VP)*
Martin Kaiser *(Sr VP & Editor)*
Daniel Harmsen *(Sr VP-HR)*
Pamela Henson *(Sr VP-Adv)*
Hugh Mcgarry *(Sr VP-Sls)*
O. Ricardo Pimentel *(VP & Editor-Editorial Page)*
Jandell Herum *(VP-Adv)*
Dennis Black *(Copy Editor)*
Michael Juley *(Editor-Crime, Courts, Social Svcs)*
Thomas Koetting *(Asst Mng Editor)*
Gary Krentz *(Editor-Local News)*
Becky Lang *(Editor-Health, Science, Environment & Religion)*
Gary D. Miller *(Sr Editor-Bus)*
Michael Mulvey *(Editor-Govt, Politics & Columnists)*
James B. Nelson *(Deputy Bus Editor)*
Ron Smith *(Sr Editor-News Ops)*
Nancy Stohs *(Editor-Food)*
David Vogel *(Editor-News)*
Jill Williams *(Asst Mng Editor)*
Bill Windler *(Editor-Sports)*
James Conigliaro *(Dir-Interactive Tech)*
Mark Thomas *(Dir-Adv)*

Key to Media (For complete agency information see *The Advertising Red Books-Agencies* edition):
1. Bus. Publs. 2. Cable T.V. 3. Catalogs & Directories. 4. Co-op Adv. 5. Consumer Mags. 6. D.M. to Bus. Estab.7. D.M. to Consumers
8. Daily Newsp. 9. Exhibits/Trade Shows 10. Foreign 11. Infomercial 12. Internet Adv.13. Multimedia 14. Network Radio
15. Network T.V. 16. Newsp. Distr. Mags. 17. Other 18. Outdoor (Posters, Transit) 19. Point of Purchase20. Premiums, Novelties
21. Product Samples 22. Special Events Mktg. 23. Spot Radio 24. Spot T.V. 25. Weekly Newsp. 26. Yellow Page Adv.

Journal Sentinel, Inc. — (Continued)

Brands & Products:
MILWAUKEE JOURNAL SENTINEL

JOURNAL STAR, INC.
(Unit of GateHouse Media, Inc.)
1 News Plz
Peoria, IL 61643-0001
Tel.: (309) 686-3000
Fax: (309) 686-3143
E-mail: info@pjstar.com
Web Site: www.pjstar.com
Sales Range: $50-74.9 Million
Approx. Number Employees: 450
Business Description:
Newspapers Publisher
S.I.C.: 2711
N.A.I.C.S.: 511110
Media: 8-9-22
Personnel:
Ken Mauser *(Publr)*
Justin McConnell *(Asst Gen Mgr)*
Phil Jordan *(Dir-Mktg)*
Crag Rogers *(Dir-Adv)*
Gretchen Piper *(Mgr-Classified Advertising)*
Brian Porter *(Mgr-Bus Dev)*
Janelle Martel *(Coord-Adv)*

JOURNAL-STAR PRINTING CO.
(Sub. of Lee Enterprises, Incorporated)
(d/b/a Lincoln Group)
926 P St
Lincoln, NE 68508-3615
Tel.: (402) 475-4200
Fax: (402) 475-4211
Web Site: www.journalstar.com
Sales Range: $50-74.9 Million
Approx. Number Employees: 450
Business Description:
Newpaper Publisher
S.I.C.: 2711
N.A.I.C.S.: 511110
Media: 14-16-18-22-23-26
Personnel:
John Maher *(Publr)*
Advertising Agency:
Ayres Kahler + Sacco
6800 Normal Blvd
Lincoln, NE 68506-2814
Tel.: (402) 450-7530
Fax: (402) 441-4739

JUNEAU EMPIRE
(Unit of Morris Publishing Group, LLC)
3100 Channel Dr
Juneau, AK 99801
Tel.: (907) 523-2295
Fax: (907) 586-9097
E-mail: nrclerk@juneauempire.com
Web Site: www.juneauempire.com
Approx. Number Employees: 80
Business Description:
Newspaper Publisher
S.I.C.: 2711; 2721
N.A.I.C.S.: 511110; 511120
Media: 8-9
Personnel:
Mark Bryan *(Publr)*
Paul Hay *(Dir-Adv)*

THE JUPITER COURIER JOURNAL
(Sub. of The E.W. Scripps Company)
1939 S Federal Hwy
Stuart, FL 34994
Tel.: (561) 746-5111
Fax: (561) 745-2403
Web Site: www.tcpalm.com/tcp/jupiter_courier
Sales Range: $10-24.9 Million
Approx. Number Employees: 21
Business Description:
Newspaper Publishers
S.I.C.: 2711
N.A.I.C.S.: 511110
Media: 25
Personnel:
Brightman Brock *(Editor-Community Publ)*

KAESER & BLAIR INCORPORATED
4236 Grissom Dr
Batavia, OH 45103
Tel.: (513) 732-6400
Fax: (513) 732-1753
Fax: (800) 630-9878
Toll Free: (800) 642-9790
E-mail: prospectus@kaeser-blair.com
Web Site: www.kaeser-blair.com
Sales Range: $75-99.9 Million
Approx. Number Employees: 140
Year Founded: 1894
Business Description:
Promotional Advertising Products Distr
S.I.C.: 7319
N.A.I.C.S.: 541890
Import
Advertising Expenditures: $2,000,000
Media: 2-6-7-10-13-14-21-22
Personnel:
Richard E. Kaeser *(Owner & Chm)*
Kurt R. Kaeser *(Owner, Pres & CEO)*
Christy Kaeser *(Owner & Dir-Special Projects)*
Scott Graber *(CFO)*
Robert Lewellen *(COO)*
Gregg Emmer *(CMO)*
Advertising Agency:
Concept 80 Advertising
4236 Grissom Dr
Batavia, OH 45103
Tel.: (513) 732-6400
Fax: (513) 732-1573

KALMBACH PUBLISHING CO.
21027 Crossroads Cir
Waukesha, WI 53186
Mailing Address:
PO Box 1612
Waukesha, WI 53187-1612
Tel.: (262) 796-8776
Fax: (262) 796-1615
Toll Free: (888) 558-1544
E-mail: webmaster@kalmbach.com
Web Site: www.kalmbach.com
E-Mail For Key Personnel:
President: gboettcher@kalmbach.com
Sales Range: $50-74.9 Million
Approx. Number Employees: 300
Year Founded: 1934
Business Description:
Book & Magazine Publisher
S.I.C.: 2721; 2731
N.A.I.C.S.: 511120; 511130
Export
Media: 2-6-10
Distr.: Intl.; Natl.
Budget Set: May -June
Personnel:
Gerald B. Boettcher *(Pres)*
Kevin Keefe *(VP-Editorial & Publr)*
Connie Bradley *(VP-HR)*
James Schweder *(VP-Tech)*
Christa Laubusch *(Supvr-Adv Promotion)*
Brands & Products:
AMERICAN SNOWMOBILER
ASTRONOMY
ASTRONOMY.COM
BEAD & BUTTON
BEADSTYLE
BIRDERS WORLD
CLASSIC TOY TRAINS
CLASSIC TRAINS
DOLLHOUSE MINIATURES
FINESCALE MODELER
GARDEN RAILWAYS
MODEL RAILROADER
MODEL RETAILER
PLAYS
SCALE AUTO
TRAINS
TRAINS.COM
THE WRITER

THE KANSAS CITY STAR COMPANY
(Sub. of McClatchy Newspapers, Inc.)
1729 Grand Blvd
Kansas City, MO 64108-1413
Tel.: (816) 234-4636
Fax: (816) 234-4926
E-mail: starinfo@kcstar.com
Web Site: www.kansascity.com
Sales Range: $450-499.9 Million
Approx. Number Employees: 1,910
Year Founded: 1880
Business Description:
Newspaper Publisher
S.I.C.: 2711
N.A.I.C.S.: 511110
Media: 1-2-7-9-10-20-23-24
Distr.: Reg.
Personnel:
Mark Zieman *(Pres & Publr)*
Bryan Harbison *(CFO & VP)*
Mike Fannin *(VP & Editor)*
Timothy Doty *(VP-Adv)*
Dan Peak *(Gen Mgr)*
Julie Adam *(Editor-Kansas)*
Jeff Goldsmith *(Editor-News)*
Helen Gray *(Editor-Religion)*
Greg Hack *(Editor-Daily Bus Pages)*
Cindy Hoedel *(Editor-Star Magazine)*
Sharon Hoffmann *(Editor-Copy-Features)*
Darryl Levings *(Editor-Natl)*
Chris Ochsner *(Editor-Weekend Photo)*
Steve Rosen *(Editor-Dollars & Sense)*
Jill Silva *(Editor-Food)*

KCI COMMUNICATIONS, INC.
(Sub. of Newsletter Holdings)
7600A Leesburg Pk W Bldg Ste 300
Falls Church, VA 22043
Tel.: (703) 905-8000
Tel.: (703) 394-4931
Fax: (703) 905-8001
Toll Free: (800) 832-2330
E-mail: info@kciinvesting.com
Web Site: www.kciinvesting.com
E-Mail For Key Personnel:
Marketing Director: marketing@kci-com.com
Approx. Sls.: $20,000,000
Approx. Number Employees: 35
Year Founded: 1984
Business Description:
Publisher of Financial Newsletters
S.I.C.: 2721; 2731
N.A.I.C.S.: 511120; 511130
Advertising Expenditures: $1,000,000
Media: 8-13
Distr.: Natl.
Budget Set: Monthly
Personnel:
Roger Conrad *(Editor-Analyst)*
Elliott H. Gue *(Editor-Wall Street Winners & Trading Floor Pro)*
George Kleinman *(Editor-Futures Market Forecaster)*
Ivan D. Martchev *(Editor-Wall Street Winners & Trading Floor Pro)*
Yiannis G. Mostrous *(Editor-Wall Street Winners & Trading Floor Pro)*
Andrea Prendergast *(Mgr-Customer Svc)*
Brands & Products:
PERSONAL FINANCE
ROGER CONRAD'S POWER PLAYS
TRADING FLOOR PRO
UTILITY FORECASTER
WALL STREET WINNERS
Advertising Agency:
Media Mart
7600A Leesburg Pike W Bldg Ste 300
Falls Church, VA 22043
Tel.: (703) 905-4532
Tel.: (703) 905-8000
Fax: (703) 905-8097
(Financial Newsletter)

KELLEY BLUE BOOK CO., INC.
195 Technology Dr
Irvine, CA 92618-2402
Tel.: (949) 770-7704
Fax: (949) 727-3400
Web Site: www.kbb.com
Approx. Number Employees: 500
Year Founded: 1926
Business Description:
Vehicle Pricing Information
S.I.C.: 2721; 2741
N.A.I.C.S.: 511120; 511199
Media: 7-8-13
Personnel:
Paul Johnson *(Pres & CEO)*
Leo Drew *(Exec VP-OEM, Partner-Sls & Strategy)*
John Morrison *(CFO)*
Mike Romano *(Sr VP-Dealer Strategy)*
Dan Ingle *(VP-Analytic Insights Tech)*
Tim Hand *(Dir-Sls-West Coast)*
Michele Everett *(Mgr-Adv Sls-kbb.com)*

KENSINGTON PUBLISHING CORP.
119 W Forty St 21st Fl
New York, NY 10018
Tel.: (212) 407-1500
Fax: (212) 935-0699
E-mail: customerservice@kensingtonbooks.com
Web Site: www.kensingtonbooks.com
Approx. Number Employees: 75
Year Founded: 1972
Business Description:
Book Publisher
S.I.C.: 2731; 5942
N.A.I.C.S.: 511130; 451211
Media: 2-4-6-10-19
Personnel:
Steven Zacharius *(Pres & CEO)*

Key to Media (For complete agency information see *The Advertising Red Books-Agencies* edition):
1. Bus. Publs. 2. Cable T.V. 3. Catalogs & Directories. 4. Co-op Adv. 5. Consumer Mags. 6. D.M. to Bus. Estab.7. D.M. to Consumers 8. Daily Newsp. 9. Exhibits/Trade Shows 10. Foreign 11. Infomercial 12. Internet Adv.13. Multimedia 14. Network Radio 15. Network T.V. 16. Newsp. Distr. Mags. 17. Other 18. Outdoor (Posters, Transit) 19. Point of Purchase20. Premiums, Novelties 21. Product Samples 22. Special Events Mktg. 23. Spot Radio 24. Spot T.V. 25. Weekly Newsp. 26. Yellow Page Adv.

Mike Rosamilia *(CFO & VP)*
Laurie Parkin *(VP & Publr)*
Michaela Hamilton *(Editor-in-Chief-Citadel & Exec Editor-Kensington)*
Audrey LaFehr *(Dir-Editorial)*
Douglas A. Mendini *(Dir-Sls)*
Leslie Underwood *(Dir-Mktg & Online Media)*
Brands & Products:
BRAVA
DAFINA
ENCANTO
KENSINGTON
PINNACLE
TWIN STREAMS
ZEBRA

THE KENTUCKY POST
(Sub. of The E.W. Scripps Company)
125 E Ct St
Cincinnati, OH 45202
Mailing Address:
PO Box 2678
Covington, KY 41012
Tel.: (859) 292-2600
Fax: (859) 291-2525
Web Site: www.kypost.com
Sales Range: $25-49.9 Million
Approx. Number Employees: 100
Business Description:
Evening & Saturday Morning Paper
S.I.C.: 2711
N.A.I.C.S.: 511110
Media: 9

THE KIPLINGER WASHINGTON EDITORS, INC.
1729 H St NW
Washington, DC 20006-3904
Tel.: (202) 887-6400
Tel.: (212) 398-6320 (Advertising)
Fax: (202) 331-1206
Toll Free: (800) 544-0155
E-mail: webmaster@kiplinger.com
Web Site: www.kiplinger.com
Approx. Number Employees: 125
Year Founded: 1920
Business Description:
Publisher of Newsletters & Magazines
S.I.C.: 2721; 2752
N.A.I.C.S.: 511120; 323110
Advertising Expenditures: $20,000,000
Media: 2-7-8-14-21-23-24-25
Distr.: Direct to Consumer; Natl.
Budget Set: Oct.
Personnel:
Corbin M. Wilkes *(CFO & Sr VP)*
Alex J. McKenna *(Publr-Kiplinger's Personal Finance)*
Denise Elliott *(VP-Sls & Mktg)*
Janet Bodnar *(Editor)*
Douglas Harbrecht *(Dir-New Media-Kiplingercom)*
Kevin McCormally *(Dir-Editorial)*
Frances Blowers *(Coord-Adv Production)*
Brands & Products:
KIPLINGER AGRICULTURAL LETTER
KIPLINGER CALIFORNIA LETTER
THE KIPLINGER LETTER
KIPLINGER PERSONAL FINANCE
KIPLINGER TAX LETTER
KIPLINGER TAXCUT
KIPLINGERFORCAST.COM
KIPLINGER'S HOME LEGAL ADVISOR
KIPLINGER'S MUTUAL FUNDS
KIPLINGER'S PERSONAL FINANCE
KIPLINGER'S RETIREMENT REPORT
KIPLINGER'S SMALL BUSINESS ATTORNEY
Advertising Agency:
Trylon SMR
41 East 11th St
New York, NY 10003
Tel.: (212) 725-2295
Fax: (212) 725-2243
Kiplinger.com

KITSAP SUN
(Sub. of The E.W. Scripps Company)
545 5th St
Bremerton, WA 98337-1413
Mailing Address:
PO Box 259
Bremerton, WA 98337-0053
Tel.: (360) 377-3711
Fax: (360) 377-9237
Toll Free: (888) 377-3711
E-mail: webmaster@kitsapsun.com
Web Site: www.kitsapsun.com
Sales Range: $50-74.9 Million
Approx. Number Employees: 200
Business Description:
Morning & Sunday Newspaper Publisher
S.I.C.: 2711
N.A.I.C.S.: 511110
Media: 2-8-9
Personnel:
Carol Horton *(Publr)*
David Nelson *(Editor)*

KMWORLD
(Div. of Information Today Inc.)
22 Bayview St
Camden, ME 04843
Mailing Address:
PO Box 1358
Camden, ME 04843
Tel.: (207) 236-8524
Fax: (207) 236-6452
E-mail: editor@kmworld.com
Web Site: www.kmworld.com
Sales Range: $10-24.9 Million
Approx. Number Employees: 5
Business Description:
Periodical
S.I.C.: 2721
N.A.I.C.S.: 511120
Media: 2-10-13
Personnel:
Andy Moore *(Publr)*
Hugh McKellar *(Editor-in-Chief)*
Brands & Products:
E CONTENT MAGAZINE
EVENT DV MAGAZINE
KM WORLD MAGAZINE

KNOXVILLE NEWS-SENTINEL COMPANY
(Sub. of The E.W. Scripps Company)
2332 News Sentinel Dr
Knoxville, TN 37921-5761
Mailing Address:
PO Box 59038
Knoxville, TN 37950-9038
Tel.: (865) 523-3131
Tel.: (865) 342-6858
Fax: (865) 673-3478
E-mail: ads@knews.com
Web Site: www.knoxnews.com
E-Mail For Key Personnel:
President: hartmann@knews.com
Marketing Director: murphy@knews.com
Sales Range: $50-74.9 Million
Approx. Number Employees: 500
Year Founded: 1886
Business Description:
Newspaper Publisher
S.I.C.: 2711
N.A.I.C.S.: 511110
Media: 2-9-10-20-23-24
Distr.: Direct to Consumer; Reg.
Budget Set: Oct.
Personnel:
Bruce Hartmann *(Pres & Publr)*
Brands & Products:
GOVOLS.COM
HOMEMARKETONLINE
KNOXAPARTMENTS.COM
KNOXCARS.COM
KNOXNEWS.COM
KNOXVILLE NEWS-SENTINEL

KODAK GRAPHIC COMMUNICATIONS
(Sub. of Kodak Graphic Communications Group)
3700 Gilmore Way
Burnaby, BC V5G 4M1, Canada
Tel.: (060) 445-12700
Fax: (060) 443-79891
E-mail: info@graphics.kodak.com
Web Site: www.graphics.kodak.com
Sales Range: $650-699.9 Million
Approx. Number Employees: 3,900
Year Founded: 1983
Business Description:
Prepress Systems & Digital Solutions Developer & Mfr
S.I.C.: 3555; 2759
N.A.I.C.S.: 333293; 323119
Media: 2-4-7-8-9-10-11-13-22-25
Personnel:
Robert L. Berman *(Chief HR Officer & Sr VP)*
Laurence L. Hickey *(Sec & Chief Governance Officer)*
Essie L. Calhoun *(Chief Diversity Officer)*
Brad W. Kruchten *(Sr VP, Pres-Film, Photofinishing & Entertainment Grp)*
Mary Jane Hellyar *(Pres-FPEG)*
John Blake *(VP & Gen Mgr-Digital Capture & Devices)*
Victor Cho *(VP-Consumer Digital Imaging Grp & Gen Mgr-Internet Svcs)*
Steven B. Decker *(VP-Consumer Digital Imaging Grp & Gen Mgr-Cameras, Accessories)*
Diane McCue *(VP & Gen Mgr-Plates Bus)*
Gerard K. Meuchner *(VP & Dir-Comm, Pub Affairs)*
Stephen Green *(Reg Mng Dir-Sls, Customer Ops & VP-Asia Pacific)*
Hezy Rotman *(Gen Mgr)*
Roger Lines *(Dir-Strategy & Bus Dev)*
N. David Brown *(Mgr-Imaging Informatics)*
Doris Cheng *(Mgr-Reg Mktg Comm)*
Brands & Products:
AGFA
APOGEE
APTUS
BRISQUE
BRISQUE 5.0
CLARUS PL
CLARUS WL
DOLEV
EVERSMART
HARLEQUIN
HARMONY
IMAGINE CREATE BELIEVE
IQ SMART
LEAF
LOTEM
MAGNUS VLF
NEXUS
PANDORA
POSTSCRIPT
PREPS
PREPS 5.1
PRINERGY
PRINERGY EVO
PROOFSETTER SPECTRUM
RAMPAGE
SPIRE
SPIRE CXP8000
SPOTLESS 4
SPOTLESS X
SQUARESPOT
STACCATO
SYNAPSE
SYNAPSE DIRECTOR
THERMOFLEX
TRENDSETTER
TRENDSETTER SPECTRUM
TRUEFLOW
VERIS

KODANSHA AMERICA LLC
(Sub. of Kodansha Ltd.)
451 Park Ave S 7th Fl
New York, NY 10016
Tel.: (917) 322-6200
Fax: (212) 935-6929
E-mail: info@kodanshaamerica.com
Web Site: www.kodansha-intl.com
Approx. Number Employees: 8
Year Founded: 1966
Business Description:
Publisher
S.I.C.: 2731; 5192
N.A.I.C.S.: 511130; 424920
Import Export
Advertising Expenditures: $200,000
Personnel:
Sawako Noma *(Chm)*
Yoichi Kimata *(Sr VP)*
Laura Shaptkin *(Dir-Sls & Mktg)*
Brands & Products:
KODANSHA
KODANSHA AMERICA
KODANSHA GLOBE
KODANSHA INT'L

KRAUSE PUBLICATIONS, INC.
(Sub. of F&W Publications, Inc.)
700 E State St
Iola, WI 54990-0001
Tel.: (715) 445-2214
Fax: (715) 445-4087
Toll Free: (800) 272-5233
E-mail: info@krause.com
Web Site: www.krause.com
Sales Range: $75-99.9 Million
Approx. Number Employees: 200
Year Founded: 1952
Business Description:
Publisher of Books & Magazines Focusing on Hobbies, Collectibles, Crafts, Sewing, Hunting, Fishing & The Construction Trade
S.I.C.: 2721; 2731
N.A.I.C.S.: 511120; 511130

Key to Media (For complete agency information see *The Advertising Red Books-Agencies* edition):
1. Bus. Publs. 2. Cable T.V. 3. Catalogs & Directories. 4. Co-op Adv. 5. Consumer Mags. 6. D.M. to Bus. Estab.7. D.M. to Consumers
8. Daily Newsp. 9. Exhibits/Trade Shows 10. Foreign 11. Infomercial 12. Internet Adv.13. Multimedia 14. Network Radio
15. Network T.V. 16. Newsp. Distr. Mags. 17. Other 18. Outdoor (Posters, Transit) 19. Point of Purchase20. Premiums, Novelties
21. Product Samples 22. Special Events Mktg. 23. Spot Radio 24. Spot T.V. 25. Weekly Newsp. 26. Yellow Page Adv.

Krause Publications, Inc. — (Continued)

Export
Media: 6-8-10-13
Personnel:
David Nussbaum *(Pres)*
Scott Tappa *(Publr-Numismatics)*
Phil Graham *(VP-Production)*
Amy Myer *(VP-HR)*
Brands & Products:
DISCOVERIES
GOLDMINE
GUN LIST

LADIES' HOME JOURNAL
(Div. of Meredith Publishing Group)
125 Park Ave
New York, NY 10017
Tel.: (212) 557-6600
E-mail: info@lhj.com
Web Site: www.lhj.com
Sales Range: $25-49.9 Million
Approx. Number Employees: 100
Business Description:
Magazine
S.I.C.: 2721
N.A.I.C.S.: 511120
Media: 6-8
Personnel:
Diane Mallory *(Publr)*
Alicesa Vongluekiat *(Assoc Publr-Mktg)*
Sally Lee *(Editor-in-Chief)*
Tara Bench *(Editor-Food & Entertaining)*
Lorraine Goennon *(Editor-Articles)*
Susan Pocharski *(Editor-Entertainment)*
Amanda Wolfe *(Editor)*
Julie Bain *(Dir-Health)*
Lindsay Davis *(Mgr-Mktg)*

LAKE CITY REPORTER
(Sub. of Community Newspapers Inc.)
180 E Duval St
Lake City, FL 32055-4083
Mailing Address:
PO Box 1709
Lake City, FL 32056-1709
Tel.: (386) 752-1293
Fax: (386) 752-9400
Web Site: www.lakecityreporter.com
Approx. Number Employees: 38
Business Description:
Newspaper
S.I.C.: 2711
N.A.I.C.S.: 511110
Media: 8-9
Personnel:
Tom Wood *(Chm)*
Dink Nesmith *(Pres)*
Todd Wilson *(Publr)*
Tim Kirby *(Editor-Sports)*
Dave Kimler *(Dir-Tech)*
Brands & Products:
LAKE CITY

LANCASTER NEWSPAPERS INC.
8 W Can Ste
Lancaster, PA 17608-1328
Tel.: (717) 291-8681
Fax: (717) 291-2304
E-mail: insidesales@lnpnews.com
Web Site: www.lnpnews.com
Approx. Number Employees: 450
Year Founded: 1928
Business Description:
Newspaper Publishing Services
S.I.C.: 2711
N.A.I.C.S.: 511110
Media: 8-25
Personnel:
Nancy Fisher *(Dir-Fin)*
Robert W. Magel, Jr. *(Dir-Mktg)*

LAPEER COUNTY PRESS
(Unit of JAMS Media LLC)
1521 Imlay City Rd
Lapeer, MI 48446-3175
Mailing Address:
PO Box 220
Lapeer, MI 48446-0220
Tel.: (810) 664-0811
Fax: (810) 667-6309
E-mail: editor@countypress.com
Web Site: www.countypress.com
Approx. Number Employees: 123
Business Description:
Newspaper Publisher
S.I.C.: 2711
N.A.I.C.S.: 511110
Media: 8-25
Personnel:
Jeff Hogan *(Editor)*
Peter Neill *(Mgr)*
Theresa Richey *(Mgr-Circulation)*

LAS VEGAS SUN, INC.
2360 Corporate Cir 3rd Fl
Henderson, NV 89074
Tel.: (702) 385-3111
Fax: (702) 383-7264
Web Site: www.lasvegassun.com
Approx. Number Employees: 130
Year Founded: 1950
Business Description:
Newspaper Publisher
S.I.C.: 2711
N.A.I.C.S.: 511110
Media: 2-7-9-13-18-22-23-24-25-26
Distr.: Direct to Consumer; Natl.; Reg.
Budget Set: Jan.
Personnel:
Daniel Greenspun *(Publr & Editor)*
Brian Greenspun *(Editor)*
Brands & Products:
LAS VEGAS SUN

LATINA MEDIA VENTURES, LLC
625 Madison Ave 3rd Fl
New York, NY 10022
Tel.: (212) 642-0200
Fax: (917) 777-0861
E-mail: info@latina.com
Web Site: www.latina.com
Approx. Number Employees: 35
Year Founded: 1996
Business Description:
Magazine Publisher
S.I.C.: 2721
N.A.I.C.S.: 511120
Media: 6-8-13
Personnel:
Christy Haubegger *(Founder)*
Lauren Michaels *(Co-Pres & Publr)*
Mathew Fox *(Dir-IT & Digital Media)*
Brands & Products:
LATINA

LAURA DAMIANO DESIGNS
500 Pondside Dr
White Plains, NY 10607
Tel.: (914) 760-6909
E-mail: info@lauradamianodesigns.com
Web Site:
www.lauradamianodesigns.com
Approx. Number Employees: 2
Business Description:
Custom Hand-Made Invitations for Weddings, Birthdays, Christenings; Logo Designs, Brochures, Flyers & Postcards
S.I.C.: 2741
N.A.I.C.S.: 511199
Media: 17-29
Personnel:
Laura Damiano *(Owner)*
John Wool *(VP-Mktg & Sls)*

LAURIN PUBLISHING CO., INC.
2 S St
Pittsfield, MA 01201
Tel.: (413) 499-0514
Fax: (413) 442-3180
E-mail: photonics@laurin.com
Web Site: www.photonics.com
Approx. Number Employees: 70
Year Founded: 1954
Business Description:
Publisher of Trade Journals
S.I.C.: 2721; 2741
N.A.I.C.S.: 511120; 511199
Media: 10
Personnel:
Teddi C. Laurin *(Chm & CEO)*
Bob Briere *(Dir-Sls)*
Heidi Miller *(Mgr-Circulation)*
Brands & Products:
BIOPHOTONICS INTERNATIONAL
EUROPHOTONICS
PHOTONICS DIRECTORY
THE PHOTONICS PRODUCT & RESOURCE SHOWCASE
PHOTONICS SPECTRA
PHOTONICS.COM
PHOTONICSFIBER.COM
PHOTONICSWEB DIRECTORY

LAW BULLETIN PUBLISHING COMPANY
415 N State St
Chicago, IL 60610
Tel.: (312) 644-7800
Fax: (312) 644-4255
E-mail: info@lbpc.com
Web Site: www.lawbulletin.com
Sales Range: $100-124.9 Million
Approx. Number Employees: 150
Business Description:
Legal Publishing Services
S.I.C.: 2741
N.A.I.C.S.: 511199
Media: 2-4-7-10-13
Personnel:
Jim Banich *(CEO)*

LEADER & KALKASKIAN
(Sub. of 21st Century Newspapers, Inc.)
318 N Cedar St
Kalkaska, MI 49646-8424
Tel.: (231) 258-4600
Fax: (231) 258-4603
E-mail: leader@torchlake.com
Web Site:
www.leaderandkalkaskian.com
Approx. Number Employees: 7
Business Description:
Weekly Newspaper Publishing
S.I.C.: 2711; 2721
N.A.I.C.S.: 511110; 511120
Media: 25
Personnel:
Chris Tredway *(Editor)*
Brands & Products:
THE LEADER & THE KALKASKIAN

LEANIN' TREE, INC.
6055 Longbow Dr
Boulder, CO 80301
Tel.: (303) 530-1442
Fax: (303) 530-7283
Toll Free: (800) 777-8716
E-mail: info@leanintree.com
Web Site: www.leanintree.com
Approx. Number Employees: 250
Year Founded: 1949
Business Description:
Greeting Cards, Prints, Notes & Christmas Cards Publisher & Retailer
S.I.C.: 2771
N.A.I.C.S.: 511191
Export
Advertising Expenditures: $750,000
Media: 2-4-8
Personnel:
Edward P Trumble *(Founder & Chm)*
Tom Trumble *(Pres & CEO)*
Pete Mahlstedt *(CFO & COO)*
Jane Trumble *(Sr VP-Product Mgmt)*
Pat Wallace *(Dir-Mktg)*
Brands & Products:
THE ART OF JOSEPHINE WALL
BERGSMA GALLERY
BEST WISHES
BRIDGES
CELEBRATION GREETINGS
CONTEMPO
ENCHANTED UNIVERSE
ENCUENTROS
GALLERY OF HORSES
GALLERY OF THE WEST
GROWING EXPRESSIONS
JUDY BUSWELL
LEANIN'TREE
LIFE IS CRAP
NOTIONSTM
QUBES
SCRAPBOOK CARDS
SEA COVE GALLERY
TIMES REMEMBERED
TRUMBLE GREETINGS
WESTERN TRADITIONS
WILDLIFE GALLERY
Advertising Agency:
Leanin' Tree, Inc.
6055 Longbow Dr
Boulder, CO 80301
Tel.: (303) 530-1442
Fax: (303) 530-7283
Toll Free: (800) 777-8716

LEBHAR-FRIEDMAN INC.
425 Pk Ave
New York, NY 10022
Tel.: (212) 756-5000
Fax: (212) 756-5290
Toll Free: (800) 453-2427
E-mail: info@lf.com
Web Site: www.lf.com
E-Mail For Key Personnel:
President: rfriedma@lf.com
Approx. Number Employees: 500
Year Founded: 1925
Business Description:
Publisher Retailing Resources; Retail & Foodservice Advertising & Marketing Services

Key to Media (For complete agency information see *The Advertising Red Books-Agencies* edition):
1. Bus. Publs. 2. Cable T.V. 3. Catalogs & Directories. 4. Co-op Adv. 5. Consumer Mags. 6. D.M. to Bus. Estab.7. D.M. to Consumers
8. Daily Newsp. 9. Exhibits/Trade Shows 10. Foreign 11. Infomercial 12. Internet Adv.13. Multimedia 14. Network Radio
15. Network T.V. 16. Newsp. Distr. Mags. 17. Other 18. Outdoor (Posters, Transit) 19. Point of Purchase20. Premiums, Novelties
21. Product Samples 22. Special Events Mktg. 23. Spot Radio 24. Spot T.V. 25. Weekly Newsp. 26. Yellow Page Adv.

S.I.C.: 2721; 2711
N.A.I.C.S.: 511120; 511110
Advertising Expenditures: $500,000
Media: 2-4-7-9-10-19-20-21-25
Distr.: Intl.; Natl.
Budget Set: Nov.
Personnel:
J. Roger Friedman *(Pres)*
Daniel J. Mills *(CFO & Exec VP)*
Brands & Products:
APC TODAY
CHAIN STORE AGE
CONTEMPORARY SURGERY
CONVERGENT HEALTH SOLUTIONS
CURRENT PSYCHIATRY
DIAMOND CHAIN STORE AGE
DIAMOND HOME CENTER
DIAMOND RETAILTECHNOLOGY
DOWDEN CUSTOM MEDIA
DRUG STORE NEWS
EDICIONES Y ESTUDIOS
FSA GROUP
HOME CHANNEL NEWS
THE JOURNAL OF FAMILY PRACTICE
MAYO CLINIC PROCEEDINGS
MEDICAL DECISION POINT
NATION'S RESTURANT NEWS
OBG MANAGEMENT
RESTAURANT NEWS

LEE ENTERPRISES, INCORPORATED
201 N Harrison St Ste 600
Davenport, IA 52801-1924
Tel.: (563) 383-2100
Fax: (563) 323-9609
E-mail: information@lee.net
Web Site: www.lee.net
Approx. Rev.: $780,648,000
Approx. Number Employees: 6,098
Year Founded: 1890
Business Description:
Newspaper Publisher
S.I.C.: 2711; 2721
N.A.I.C.S.: 511110; 511120
Media: 9-17-25
Personnel:
Mary E. Junck *(Chm, Pres & CEO)*
Carl G. Schmidt *(CFO, Treas & VP)*
Brian E. Kardell *(CIO & VP-Production)*
Karen J. Guest *(Chief Legal Officer & VP-Law)*
Manuel Collazo *(Pres/Publr-Lee Central California Newspapers)*
Paul M. Farrell *(VP-Sls & Mktg)*
Michael R. Gulledge *(VP-Publ)*
Daniel K. Hayes *(VP-Corp Comm)*
Vytenis P. Kuraitis *(VP-HR)*
Kevin D. Mowbray *(VP-Publ)*
Gregory P. Schermer *(VP-Interactive Media)*
Greg R. Veon *(VP-Publ)*

LEHMAN COMMUNICATIONS CORPORATION
(Joint Venture of The E.W. Scripps Company & MediaNews Group, Inc.)
350 Terry St
Longmont, CO 80501-5440
Tel.: (303) 776-2244
Fax: (303) 772-8339
Toll Free: (800) 796-8201
Web Site: www.timescall.com
Approx. Number Employees: 250
Year Founded: 1957
Business Description:
Newspapers Publishing Services
S.I.C.: 2711
N.A.I.C.S.: 511110
Import Export
Media: 8-9-18-22
Personnel:
Edward Lehman *(Chm & CEO)*
Dean Lehman *(Pres)*
Brands & Products:
CANON CITY DAILY RECORD
COLORADO HOMETOWN WEEKLY
REPORTER-HERALD

LET'S GO PUBLICATIONS, INC.
(Sub. of Harvard Student Agencies, Inc.)
67 Mount Auburn St
Cambridge, MA 02138-4961
Tel.: (617) 495-9659
Fax: (617) 496-7070
E-mail: publicity@letsgo.com
Web Site: www.letsgo.com
Approx. Number Employees: 40
Business Description:
International Travel Guides Publisher
S.I.C.: 2741
N.A.I.C.S.: 511199
Media: 13-19
Personnel:
Sara Plana *(Dir-Publ)*
Brands & Products:
LET'S GO

LEWISTON DAILY SUN
(d/b/a Sun Journal)
104 Pk St
Lewiston, ME 04240
Tel.: (207) 784-5411
Fax: (207) 777-3436
Web Site: www.sunjournal.com
Sales Range: $10-24.9 Million
Approx. Number Employees: 300
Business Description:
Newspapers, Publishing & Printing
S.I.C.: 2711
N.A.I.C.S.: 511110
Media: 8-9
Personnel:
James R. Costello, Sr. *(Pres & Publr)*
Steve Costello *(VP-Mktg)*

LEWTAN INDUSTRIES CORP.
30 High St
Hartford, CT 06103
Tel.: (860) 278-9800
Fax: (860) 278-9019
E-mail: lewtan@snet.net
Web Site: www.lewtan8.com
Approx. Sls.: $7,000,000
Approx. Number Employees: 70
Year Founded: 1947
Business Description:
Promotional Products Mfr
S.I.C.: 3993
N.A.I.C.S.: 339950
Media: 2-7-10
Personnel:
Marvin Lewtan *(Founder)*
Douglas Lewtan *(Pres)*
Brands & Products:
BIG CUSHION
CLASSIC CUSHION
LEW-TEX
LEWTAN INDUSTRIES
MIGHTY GRIP

LEXISNEXIS CORPORATE AFFILIATIONS
(Joint Venture of Reed Elsevier NV & Reed Elsevier plc)
121 Chanlon Rd N Bldg
New Providence, NJ 07974
Tel.: (908) 665-6687
Fax: (908) 665-3572
Toll Free: (800) 340-3244
E-mail: corporateaffiliations@lexisnexis.com
Web Site: www.corporateaffiliations.com
Sales Range: $1-9.9 Million
Approx. Number Employees: 20
Business Description:
Corporate Information Directory Publisher
S.I.C.: 2741
N.A.I.C.S.: 511140; 519130
Media: 2-4-7-8-10-13-20
Personnel:
Michael J. Browning *(Dir-Product Plng)*
Thomas M. Bachmann *(Dir-Client Dev Data Svcs)*
Tanya Hurst *(Sr Mgr-Ops)*
Laura L. Tarnofsky *(Project Mgr)*
Gregory D. Schraft *(Mgr-Reg Sls)*
Russel Hymowitz *(Sr Acct/Fin Analyst)*
Brands & Products:
CORPORATE AFFILIATIONS

LEXISNEXIS GROUP
(Joint Venture of Reed Elsevier NV & Reed Elsevier plc)
9443 Springboro Pike
Miamisburg, OH 45342
Mailing Address:
PO Box 933
Dayton, OH 45401-0933
Tel.: (937) 865-6800
Fax: (937) 847-3090
Toll Free: (800) 227-4908
E-mail: pr@lexisnexis.com
Web Site: www.lexisnexis.com
E-Mail For Key Personnel:
Sales Director: newsales@lexisnexis.com
Approx. Rev.: $3,920,114,660
Approx. Number Employees: 14,700
Business Description:
Legal, Tax, Regulatory, Risk Management, Information Analytics & Business Information Solutions
S.I.C.: 2741; 2731; 7389
N.A.I.C.S.: 511199; 511130; 511140; 519130; 519190
Personnel:
Michael F. Walsh *(Chief Exec Officer-Legal & Production)*
Carolyn S. Ullerick *(CFO)*
Barbara J. Cooperman *(CMO-Global & Sr VP)*
Kenneth R. Thompson, II *(Chief Legal Officer & Sr VP)*
James M. Peck *(CEO-Risk Solutions)*
Kumsal Bayazit *(Sr VP-Global Strategy & Practice Mgmt)*
John C. Birch *(Sr VP-Fin)*
Dawn Conway *(Sr VP-Corp Responsibility)*
Michael E. S. Frankel *(Sr VP-Bus Dev, Mergers & Acq)*
Suzanne Petren-Moritz *(Sr VP-Strategic Projects)*
Jeff R. Reihl *(Sr VP-Tech & Ops-New Lexis)*
Richard G. Schwalm *(Sr VP-Ops-Reed Elsevier Tech Svcs)*
Alexander N. Watson *(Sr VP-Editorial & Content Dev-Global)*
Ian Koenig *(VP & Chief Architect-Product Delivery Platforms)*
Brad Sidwell *(VP & Gen Mgr)*
Nancy A. Nash *(VP-Deputy Gen Counsel & Lead Litigation Counsel)*
Ketan Ambani *(VP-Strategic Sourcing)*
Gerald D. Barton *(VP-Product Dev-Global)*
Michael Daley *(VP-Global Customer Svc & Support)*
Mark Gilmore *(VP-Reward-HR Svcs)*
Katherine A. Lagana *(VP-New Lexis Application Dev-Global Solutions Dev)*
Eric Roberts *(VP-Global Content/ Editorial Shared Svcs)*
Scott Sessler *(VP-Strategic Bus Dev-Risk Data Solutions)*
Harry R. Silver *(VP-Legal R&D-Global Solutions Dev)*
Thomas A. Smith *(VP-HR Policy & Compliance-US)*
Edward Spaeth *(VP & Lead Content Acq Counsel)*
Richard W. Van Vleck *(VP-Strategic Bus Dev)*
James W. Wanke *(VP-Content Architecture-Global)*
Steven Wildfeuer *(VP & Lead Intellectual Property Counsel)*
James E. Byrd *(Sr Dir & Assoc Gen Counsel)*
Tracy Bennett *(Sr Dir-HR)*
Courtney Brinkman *(Sr Dir-VOC & Market Res)*
Terence J. Casey *(Sr Dir-GCDEPS)*
Phillip R. Jacobs *(Sr Dir-Global Product Dev)*
Tony R. Kemp *(Sr Dir-HR, Fin & Backoffice Solutions)*
Dean Ketring *(Sr Dir-Sls Ops)*
Ronald J. Meyer *(Sr Dir-Strategic Tech)*
Cynthia L. Niekamp *(Sr Dir)*
David B. Oakley *(Sr Dir-Licensing)*
Rodney C. Player *(Sr Dir-Shared Svcs)*
Silvian Rosario *(Sr Dir-Web Strategy)*
Mary Kay D. Schieltz *(Sr Dir-Global Product Dev)*
Deborah Silcox *(Sr Dir-Product Mgmt & Product Plng)*
Ann T. Taylor *(Sr Dir-Strategy & Innovation)*
Hope A. Thackery *(Sr Dir-Security Policy & Programs)*
Cheri L. Williams *(Sr Dir)*
Carolyn D. Young *(Sr Dir-Customer Experience)*
David E. Ciolli *(Sr Corp Counsel & Dir)*
Jennifer N. Elleman *(Sr Corp Counsel & Dir)*
Douglas Conn *(Dir-IT-Reed Elsevier Tech Svcs)*
Jonathan Hoy *(Dir-Global Content Mgmt & Sourcing)*
Melissa Jones *(Dir-Global Product Dev)*
Selene K. Edmunds Martin *(Dir-LexisNexis Cares)*
Nigel H. Roberts *(Dir-Global Associations)*
Julie Anne Walch *(Dir-HR)*

Key to Media (For complete agency information see *The Advertising Red Books-Agencies* edition):
1. Bus. Publs. 2. Cable T.V. 3. Catalogs & Directories. 4. Co-op Adv. 5. Consumer Mags. 6. D.M. to Bus. Estab.7. D.M. to Consumers 8. Daily Newsp. 9. Exhibits/Trade Shows 10. Foreign 11. Infomercial 12. Internet Adv.13. Multimedia 14. Network Radio 15. Network T.V. 16. Newsp. Distr. Mags. 17. Other 18. Outdoor (Posters, Transit) 19. Point of Purchase20. Premiums, Novelties 21. Product Samples 22. Special Events Mktg. 23. Spot Radio 24. Spot T.V. 25. Weekly Newsp. 26. Yellow Page Adv.

LexisNexis Group — (Continued)

Martin Judge *(Mgr-Client)*
Steve Noble *(Mgr)*
Kermit F. Lowery *(Asst Gen Counsel)*

Advertising Agencies:
BRC Marketing Inc.
7051 Corporate Way
Dayton, OH 45459
Tel.: (937) 384-0515
Fax: (937) 384-0522
Toll Free: (888) 905-0515

Cone
(A Member of Omnicom Group)
855 Boylston St
Boston, MA 02116
Tel.: (617) 227-2111
Fax: (617) 523-3955

Gerard Design
15 W. Jefferson Ave.
Naperville, IL 60540
Tel.: (630) 355-0775

Wunderman
(Worldwide Headquarters)
285 Madison Ave
New York, NY 10017
Tel.: (212) 941-3000
Fax: (212) 210-5454

LEXISNEXIS U.S. LEGAL MARKETS

(Joint Venture of Reed Elsevier NV & Reed Elsevier plc)
9443 Springboro Pike
Miamisburg, OH 45342
Mailing Address:
PO Box 933
Dayton, OH 45401-0933
Tel.: (937) 865-6800
Fax: (937) 865-1351
Toll Free: (800) 253-5624
Web Site: www.law.lexisnexis.com
Approx. Number Employees: 3,000
Business Description:
Legal Information Products & Solutions
S.I.C.: 7389; 2741
N.A.I.C.S.: 541199; 516110; 519190
Personnel:
Michael F. Walsh *(Pres & CEO-US Legal Markets)*
Ethan Eisner *(VP & Mng Dir)*
Philip B. Livingston *(CEO-Martindale-Hubbell)*
Robert C. Romeo *(Sr VP & Gen Mgr-Res & Litigation Solutions)*
Dean Keith Hawk, Jr. *(Acting Sr VP-Sls)*
Linda M. Hlavac *(Sr VP-HR)*
Elizabeth K. Rector *(Sr VP-Customer Experience)*
Amy Minnick *(VP & Mng Dir-Sls Ops, Tools, Training & Strategy)*
Thomas E. Ogburn *(VP & Gen Mgr-Bus Insight Solutions)*
Matthew D. Mitchell *(VP-Specialist Sls-Global Practice Mgmt)*
Jean Bright *(VP-Sls)*
Ellen Campbell-Kaminski *(VP-Mktg-US Markets)*
Rex Caswell *(VP)*
Alyce Clark *(VP-HR)*
Elizabeth J. Fess *(VP-Fin)*
David M. Flynn *(VP-Sls-MBS)*
Luke B. Gaffney *(VP-Corp Sls)*
Kelly J. Kitchen *(VP-Sls Ops)*
Karin B. Lieber *(VP-Sls & Strategic Accounts)*
David J. Markham *(VP-Sls Plng & Strategy)*
Bryan G. Miller *(VP-Sls)*
Phyllis M. Millikan *(VP-Specialized Law Solution Consulting)*
Rick D. Neitenbach *(VP-Sls-Corp Legal Natl)*
Thomas P. Osif *(VP-Sls & Mktg)*
Andrea E. Popovecz *(VP-Sls)*
Krista Albaugh *(Sr Dir-Mktg)*
Terry Williams *(Sr Dir-Program)*
James C. Bangs *(Sr Dir-Sls Ops)*
Deborah Krintzline-Ball *(Sr Dir-Bus Mgt)*
Sherri M. Markowski *(Sr Dir-Bus Mgmt)*
Leslie S. Oaks *(Sr Dir-Fin)*
Nickolaus A. Schoeffler *(Sr Dir)*
June G. Doyal *(Dir-User Experience)*
Jonathan M. Dull *(Dir-MH Fulfillment Operation & Fulfillment Shared Svcs)*
Steven J. Hess *(Dir-Client Engagements)*
Jeffrey J. Johnson *(Dir-Enterprise Bus Processes & Sys-New Lexis)*
Deana Sparling *(Dir-Law School Market Plng)*
Debra Ulrich *(Mgr-Sls Plng & Strategy)*
Jacob Yanes *(Mgr-Editorial Sys)*

Advertising Agencies:
AMP Agency (Alloy Marketing & Promotion)
77 N Washington St
Boston, MA 02114
Tel.: (617) 723-8929
Fax: (617) 723-2188
Media Agency of Record

Ogilvy Public Relations Worldwide
636 11th Ave
New York, NY 10036
Tel.: (212) 880-5200
Fax: (212) 370-4636
Lawyers.com

LIBERATION PUBLICATIONS INC.

(d/b/a The Advocate)
6380 Wilshire Blvd Ste 1400
Los Angeles, CA 90028
Tel.: (323) 871-1225
Fax: (323) 467-0173
E-mail: letters@advocate.com
Web Site: www.advocate.com
Approx. Number Employees: 85
Business Description:
Magazines Publishers
S.I.C.: 2721
N.A.I.C.S.: 511120
Media: 6-8

THE LIMA NEWS

(Unit of Freedom Newspapers, Inc.)
3515 Elida Rd
Lima, OH 45807
Tel.: (419) 223-1010
Fax: (419) 229-2926
E-mail: news@limanews.com
Web Site: www.limaoasi.com
Approx. Number Employees: 100
Year Founded: 1884
Business Description:
Newspaper
S.I.C.: 2711
N.A.I.C.S.: 511110
Media: 8-9
Personnel:
James Shine *(Publr)*
J.D. Bruewer *(Editor-Internet Content)*
Jim Krumel *(Editor)*
Ron Lederman *(Editor-Editorial Page)*
Craig Orosz *(Editor-Photo)*
Bill Clinger *(Dir-Mktg)*
Leila Osting *(Dir-HR)*
Ed Eichler *(Bus Mgr)*
Travis L. Sibold *(Mgr-Web Production & Tech)*
Steve Beck *(Mgr-Display Adv)*
Natalie Buzzard *(Mgr-Local Display)*
Eric Germann *(Mgr-Info Sys)*
Bob Rodi *(Mgr-Opers)*
Susie Rosengarten *(Mgr-Ad Graphics)*
Brands & Products:
THE LIMA NEWS

LINCOLN NEWS MESSENGER

(Sub. of Brehm Communications Inc.)
553 F St
Lincoln, CA 95648-1849
Tel.: (916) 645-7733
Fax: (916) 645-2776
E-mail: tarol@goldcountrymedia.com
Web Site:
www.lincolnnewsmessenger.com
Approx. Number Employees: 7
Year Founded: 1891
Business Description:
Weekly Newspaper Publisher
S.I.C.: 2711
N.A.I.C.S.: 511110
Media: 13-25
Personnel:
Jean Lund *(Gen Mgr)*

LINE PUBLICATIONS, INC.

10537 Santa Monica Blvd Ste 250
Los Angeles, CA 90025
Tel.: (310) 234-9501
Fax: (310) 234-0332
Web Site: www.movieline.com
Approx. Number Employees: 20
Year Founded: 1989
Business Description:
Magazine Publisher
S.I.C.: 2721
N.A.I.C.S.: 511120
Media: 2-3-6-10-13-20
Personnel:
Anne Volokh *(Chm & CEO)*
John Evans *(Pres)*
Brands & Products:
MOVIELINE'S HOLLYWOOD LIFE

LIPPINCOTT WILLIAMS & WILKINS, INC.

(Sub. of Wolters Kluwer Health & Pharma Solutions)
530 Walnut St
Philadelphia, PA 19106-3619
Tel.: (215) 521-8300
Fax: (215) 521-8902
E-mail: orders@lww.com
Web Site: www.lww.com
Approx. Sls.: $19,757,032
Approx. Number Employees: 350
Year Founded: 1998
Business Description:
Medical Books Publisher
S.I.C.: 2731; 2721
N.A.I.C.S.: 511130; 511120
Media: 4-7-10-13
Personnel:
Susan Driscoll *(Exec VP & Gen Mgr)*
Matthew Cahill *(VP-Journal Publ)*
Brands & Products:
ACSM'S HEALTH AND FITNESS JOURNAL
ALCOHOLISM
AMERICAN JOURNAL OF NURSING
AMERICAN JOURNAL OF THERAPEUTICS
THE COMPLETE GUIDE TO HERBAL MEDICINES
SPRINGHOUSE
STEDMAN'S MEDICAL DICTIONARIES

LITERARY CLASSICS OF THE UNITED STATES, INC.

(d/b/a Library of America)
14 E 60th St
New York, NY 10022-1006
Tel.: (212) 308-3360
Fax: (212) 750-8352
E-mail: info@loa.org
Web Site: www.loa.org
Approx. Number Employees: 18
Year Founded: 1979
Business Description:
Publisher of Books
S.I.C.: 2731; 2732
N.A.I.C.S.: 511130; 323117
Media: 6-10
Personnel:
Cheryl Hurley *(Pres)*
Dan Baker *(CFO & VP)*
Advertising Agency:
Goldberg McDuffie Communications, Inc.
444 Madison Ave Ste 3300
New York, NY 10022
Tel.: (212) 446-5100
Fax: (212) 980-5228

LITTLE, BROWN & COMPANY

(Sub. of HBG Books, Inc.)
237 Park Ave
New York, NY 10017
Tel.: (212) 364-1100
Fax: (212) 364-0934
E-mail: publicity@littlebrown.com
Web Site:
www.hachettebookgroup.com/publishing_little-brown-and-company.aspx
E-Mail For Key Personnel:
Sales Director: sales@twbookmark.com
Approx. Number Employees: 300
Year Founded: 1837
Business Description:
Book Publishers
S.I.C.: 2731
N.A.I.C.S.: 511130
Import Export
Media: 2-3-4-5-6-7-8-9-10-13-14-15-18-19-22-23-24-25
Distr.: Intl.; Natl.
Personnel:
Michael Pietsch *(Publr)*
Megan Tingley *(Publr-Books for Young Readers)*
Miriam Parker *(Dir-Mktg)*
Brands & Products:
BACK BAY BOOKS
BULFINCH PRESS

Key to Media (For complete agency information see *The Advertising Red Books-Agencies* edition):
1. Bus. Publs. 2. Cable T.V. 3. Catalogs & Directories. 4. Co-op Adv. 5. Consumer Mags. 6. D.M. to Bus. Estab.7. D.M. to Consumers
8. Daily Newsp. 9. Exhibits/Trade Shows 10. Foreign 11. Infomercial 12. Internet Adv.13. Multimedia 14. Network Radio
15. Network T.V. 16. Newsp. Distr. Mags. 17. Other 18. Outdoor (Posters, Transit) 19. Point of Purchase20. Premiums, Novelties
21. Product Samples 22. Special Events Mktg. 23. Spot Radio 24. Spot T.V. 25. Weekly Newsp. 26. Yellow Page Adv.

Advertising Agency:
Publishers Advertising Associates
237 Park Ave 15Fl
New York, NY 10017
Tel.: (212) 364-1100

LLEWELLYN WORLDWIDE LIMITED
2143 Wooddale Dr
Woodbury, MN 55125-2989
Tel.: (651) 291-1970
Fax: (651) 291-1908
Toll Free: (800) THE-MOON
E-mail: info@llewellyn.com
Web Site: www.llewellyn.com
E-Mail For Key Personnel:
President: carl@llewellyn.com
Sales Director: rhondao@llewellyn.com
Approx. Number Employees: 100
Year Founded: 1901
Business Description:
Book & Magazine Publisher
S.I.C.: 2731; 2721
N.A.I.C.S.: 511130; 511120
Import Export
Media: 4-6-10-26
Distr.: Intl.; Natl.
Personnel:
Carl L Weschcke *(Owner)*
Lynne Menturweck *(Dir-Art)*
Erika Carry *(Dir-HR)*
Nanette Peterson *(Production Mgr)*
Brands & Products:
FATE MAGAZINE
NEW WORLDS

LOCALTEL, INC.
360 Merrimack St Ste 216
Lawrence, MA 01843
Tel.: (978) 332-8000
Fax: (888) 441-8100
Toll Free: (888) 562-2583
Web Site: www.localtel.com
Approx. Sls.: $10,973,411
Approx. Number Employees: 20
Business Description:
Advertising Directory Publisher
S.I.C.: 2741; 7311
N.A.I.C.S.: 511199; 541810
Media: 13
Personnel:
Donald C. Flanders *(Dir-Reg Sls North)*
Brands & Products:
LOCAL TEL
WE'RE IN YOUR NEIGHBORHOOD.

LOCKWOOD PUBLICATIONS INC.
26 Broadway Fl 9M
New York, NY 10004
Tel.: (212) 391-2060
Fax: (212) 827-0945
Web Site:
www.lockwoodpublications.com
Approx. Number Employees: 40
Business Description:
Publishing Magazines
S.I.C.: 5192
N.A.I.C.S.: 424920
Media: 2-10
Personnel:
Sam Kowalski *(CFO & Controller)*
Fred Lockwood *(Publr)*
Robert Lockwood *(Exec Dir)*
Brands & Products:
MAGAZINES

LOG CABIN DEMOCRAT, LLC
(Sub. of Morris Publishing Group, LLC)
1058 Front St
Conway, AR 72032
Mailing Address:
PO Box 969
Conway, AR 72033-0969
Tel.: (501) 327-6621
Fax: (501) 327-6787
Toll Free: (800) 678-4523
E-mail: editorial@thecabin.net
Web Site: www.thecabin.net
Approx. Number Employees: 90
Year Founded: 1879
Business Description:
Newspaper Publisher
S.I.C.: 2711
N.A.I.C.S.: 511110
Media: 2-9-10-13-20-21-22-23-26
Personnel:
Rick Fahr *(Editor & Acting Publr)*
Nick Stahl *(Dir-Online Svcs)*
Advertising Agency:
Morris Digital Works, LLC
725 Broad St
Augusta, GA 30901
Tel.: (706) 724-0851
Tel.: (202) 903-6665
Tel.: (703) 333-5895
Tel.: (706) 828-2955
Fax: (706) 722-7403
Toll Free: (800) 622-6358

LOS ANGELES DAILY NEWS PUBLISHING COMPANY
(Sub. of Los Angeles Newspaper Group)
(d/b/a Daily News of Los Angeles)
PO Box 4200
Woodland Hills, CA 91365-4200
Tel.: (818) 713-3000
Fax: (818) 713-0058
Toll Free: (800) 346-6397
Web Site: www.dailynews.com
Approx. Number Employees: 1,000
Year Founded: 1911
Business Description:
Newspaper Publishing
S.I.C.: 2711
N.A.I.C.S.: 511110
Media: 8-9
Personnel:
Liz Gaier *(Acting Publr)*
Bill Van Laningham *(Dir-Mktg)*
Brands & Products:
THE DAILY NEWS

LOS ANGELES MAGAZINE
(Sub. of Emmis Publishing, L.P.)
5900 Wilshire Blvd 10th Fl
Los Angeles, CA 90036
Tel.: (323) 801-0100
Tel.: (323) 801-0040 (Adv)
Fax: (323) 801-0104
E-mail: lagmarketing@lamag.com
Web Site: www.lamag.com
Sales Range: $25-49.9 Million
Approx. Number Employees: 55
Business Description:
Magazine Publisher
S.I.C.: 2721
N.A.I.C.S.: 511120
Media: 6-8-13-22
Personnel:
Barbara Burden *(VP & Gen Mgr)*
Mary Melton *(Editor-in-Chief)*
Kari Mozena *(Editor)*

LOS ANGELES TIMES COMMUNICATIONS, LLC
(Sub. of Tribune Publishing Company)
(d/b/a Los Angeles Times Media Group)
202 W First St
Los Angeles, CA 90012
Tel.: (213) 237-5000
Fax: (213) 237-7355
Toll Free: (800) LATIMES
E-mail: feedback@latimes.com
Web Site: www.latimes.com
Year Founded: 1881
Business Description:
Newspaper & Magazine Publisher; News Syndication Services
S.I.C.: 2711; 2721; 7383
N.A.I.C.S.: 511110; 511120; 519110
Advertising Expenditures: $5,000,000
Media: 1-2-3-6-7-8-9-10-11-18-19-20-21-22-23-24-26
Distr.: Natl.
Personnel:
Kathy Thomson *(Pres & COO)*
Eddy W. Hartenstein *(CEO & Publr)*
Chris Avetisian *(CFO)*
Scott McKibben *(Chief Revenue Officer & Exec VP)*
Jack D. Klunder *(Pres-Los Angeles Times Newspaper)*
Julie K. Xanders *(Gen Counsel & Sr VP)*
Robertson Barrett *(Sr VP-Interactive & Gen Mgr)*
John T. O'Loughlin *(Exec VP-Adv & Chief Revenue Officer)*
Gwen P. Murakami *(Sr VP-Admin)*
Russell Newton *(Sr VP-Ops)*
Scott Pompe *(Sr VP-Adv & Targeted Media)*
Emily Smith *(Sr VP-Digital)*
Donna Stokley *(Mng DirAdv Sls)*
Kim McCleary LaFrance *(VP-Pub Affairs)*
Karlene W. Goller *(VP-Legal & Deputy Gen Counsel)*
Juliana Jaoudi *(VP-Sls Online)*
Anna Magzanyan *(VP-Mktg)*
Michelle Manzo-Lembo *(VP-Adv)*
Lynne A. Segall *(VP-Entertainment Adv)*
Nancy M. Sullivan *(VP-Comm)*
Annie Gilbar *(Editor-in-Chief-LA Magazine)*
Davan Maharaj *(Mng Editor-Los Angeles Times Newspaper)*
Catharine Hamm *(Editor-Travel)*
Russ Stanton *(Editor-Los Angeles Times Newspaper)*
Leslie Lindeman *(Dir-Real Estate)*
Norma Gonzalez *(Mgr-Field)*
Brands & Products:
BURBANK LEADER
DAILY PILOT
GLENDALE-NEWS PRESS
LA
LA CANADA VALLEY SUN
LA CRESCENTA VALLEY SUN
LAGUNA BEACH COASTLINE PILOT
LATIMES.COM
LOS ANGELES TIMES
TIMES COMMUNITY NEWS
Advertising Agencies:
Draftfcb
17600 Gillette Ave
Irvine, CA 92614-5702
Tel.: (949) 851-3050
Fax: (949) 567-9465

HEILBrice
9840 Irvine Center Dr
Irvine, CA 92618
Tel.: (949) 336-8800
Fax: (949) 336-8819

Reality2
11661 San Vicente Blvd Ste 900
Los Angeles, CA 90049
Tel.: (310) 826-5662
Fax: (310) 826-5606

Round2 Communications, LLC
10866 Wilshire Blvd Ste 900
Los Angeles, CA 90024
Tel.: (310) 481-8040
Fax: (310) 571-1827

LOZANO ENTERPRISES, LP
700 S Flowers St Ste 3000
Los Angeles, CA 90017
Tel.: (213) 622-8332
Fax: (213) 896-2309
Web Site: www.laopinion.com
Approx. Number Employees: 250
Year Founded: 1926
Business Description:
Newspapers
S.I.C.: 7389
N.A.I.C.S.: 561499
Import Export
Media: 8-9-13
Personnel:
Jose I. Lozano *(Principal)*
Steve Bentz *(VP-Adv)*
Mary Zerafa *(VP-Mktg)*
Jim Pellegrino *(Dir-Circulation)*
Mark Andrews *(Mgr-Accts)*
Brands & Products:
LOZANO

LRP PUBLICATIONS
747 Dresher Rd
Horsham, PA 19044-2247
Mailing Address:
PO Box 980
Horsham, PA 19044-0980
Tel.: (215) 784-0860
Tel.: (215) 658-0938
Fax: (215) 784-9639
Toll Free: (800) 341-7874
E-mail: custserve@lrp.com
Web Site: www.lrp.com
Approx. Number Employees: 300
Year Founded: 1977
Business Description:
Publisher of Business-to-Business Newsletters, Magazines, Books, Software & On-line Services
S.I.C.: 2721; 8111
N.A.I.C.S.: 511120; 541110
Media: 2-7-10-13
Personnel:
Kenneth Kahn *(Pres)*
Todd Lutz *(CFO)*
Jana Shellington *(VP-Mktg & Customer Svc)*
Stephen Bevilacqua *(Dir-Special Education Grp)*
Stephen LaRue *(Dir-Dev)*
John Norlin *(Dir-Education Ancillaries)*
Brands & Products:
HUMAN RESOURCE EXEC MAGAZINE
RISK MANAGEMENT

Key to Media (For complete agency information see *The Advertising Red Books-Agencies* edition):
1. Bus. Publs. 2. Cable T.V. 3. Catalogs & Directories. 4. Co-op Adv. 5. Consumer Mags. 6. D.M. to Bus. Estab.7. D.M. to Consumers 8. Daily Newsp. 9. Exhibits/Trade Shows 10. Foreign 11. Infomercial 12. Internet Adv.13. Multimedia 14. Network Radio 15. Network T.V. 16. Newsp. Distr. Mags. 17. Other 18. Outdoor (Posters, Transit) 19. Point of Purchase20. Premiums, Novelties 21. Product Samples 22. Special Events Mktg. 23. Spot Radio 24. Spot T.V. 25. Weekly Newsp. 26. Yellow Page Adv.

THE LUBBOCK AVALANCHE-JOURNAL
(Unit of Morris Publishing Group, LLC)
710 Ave J
Lubbock, TX 79401
Tel.: (806) 762-8844
Fax: (806) 744-9603
Web Site: www.lubbockonline.com
Approx. Number Employees: 300
Year Founded: 1900
Business Description:
Newspaper Publisher
S.I.C.: 2711; 2721
N.A.I.C.S.: 511110; 511120
Media: 8-9
Personnel:
Stephen A. Beasley *(Publr)*
David Daniel *(News Editor)*
Patrick Gonzales *(Editor-Sports)*
Joe Hughes *(Editorial Page Editor)*
William Kerns *(Editor-Entertainment)*
Beth Pratt *(Religion Editor)*
Lloyd Strong *(Editor-Copy)*
Shelby Caballero *(Dir-HR)*
Steve Davis *(Dir-Music)*
Brandon Hughes *(Dir)*
Michael Messerly *(Dir-Online Adv)*
Bob Barth *(Mgr)*
Chris Berry *(Mgr-Online Sls)*

LUXURY SPAFINDER MAGAZINE
(Div. of Spa Finder, Inc.)
257 Park Ave S
New York, NY 10010
Tel.: (212) 924-6800
Web Site: www.spafinder.com/day-spas/United+States_New+York/Hammam/N=51+1567+12006
Business Description:
Magazine
S.I.C.: 2721
N.A.I.C.S.: 511120
Personnel:
Patricia Steele *(Dir-Mktg)*
Brands & Products:
LUXURY SPAFINDER
Advertising Agency:
Della Femina Rothschild Jeary & Partners
902 Broadway 15th Fl
New York, NY 10010
Tel.: (212) 506-0700
Fax: (212) 506-0751

MACDERMID PRINTING SOLUTIONS, LLC
(Joint Venture of Weston Presidio Capital & Court Square Capital Partners, L.P.)
5210 Phillip Lee Dr
Atlanta, GA 30336
Tel.: (404) 696-4565
Fax: (404) 699-3354
Toll Free: (800) 348-7201
E-mail: mpsproductinfo@macdermid.com
Web Site: www.macdermid.com
E-Mail For Key Personnel:
Marketing Director: gbarba@macdermid.com
Approx. Number Employees: 1,100
Year Founded: 1995
Business Description:
General Printing Products & Packaging Systems
S.I.C.: 3555
N.A.I.C.S.: 333293
Import Export
Advertising Expenditures: $1,000,000
Media: 2-4-7-10
Distr.: Intl.; Natl.
Personnel:
Heather Perkinson *(Mgr-Mktg)*
Brands & Products:
ENDURA
EPIC
FLEX-LIGHT
MERIGRAPH
NAPPFLEX
NAPPLATE
POLYCELL
POLYFIBRON
PRISM
SPLASH
TYPE 50
XT555
XT750

MACFADDEN COMMUNICATIONS GROUP, LLC
333 7th Ave
New York, NY 10001
Tel.: (212) 979-4800
Fax: (646) 674-0103
E-mail: info@macfad.com
Web Site: www.macfad.com
Approx. Number Employees: 50
Year Founded: 1900
Business Description:
Magazine & Website Publisher
S.I.C.: 2721; 1389
N.A.I.C.S.: 511120; 213112
Media: 4-6-10-13-19
Distr.: Natl.
Budget Set: Oct.
Personnel:
Jeffrey Schaeffer *(Vice Chm)*
Peter J. Callahan *(CEO)*
Jerald J. Cerza, Jr. *(CFO)*
Michelle David *(Dir-Grp Mktg)*
Brands & Products:
CHICAGO PIZZA EXPO
DANCE MAGAZINE
DANCE MAGAZINE COLLEGE GUIDE
DANCE MAGAZINE STERN'S DIRECTORY
INTERNATIONAL PIZZA EXPO
LA COCINA MEXICANA
NATIONAL ASSOCIATION OF PIZZA OPERATORS
NORTHEAST PIZZA EXPO
PET AISLE
PET BUSINESS MAGAZINE
PIZZA TODAY MAGAZINE

MACOMB COUNTY LEGAL NEWS
(Sub. of Detroit Legal News Publishing LLC)
148 S Main St Ste 100
Mount Clemens, MI 48043
Mailing Address:
PO Box 707
Mount Clemens, MI 48046-0707
Tel.: (586) 463-4300
Fax: (586) 463-4554
Web Site:
www.macomblegalnews.com
E-Mail For Key Personnel:
President: bthompson@legalnews.com
Approx. Number Employees: 2
Year Founded: 1927
Business Description:
Weekly Legal Newspaper Publisher
S.I.C.: 2711
N.A.I.C.S.: 511110
Media: 25
Personnel:
Brad Thompson *(Pres)*
Melanie Deeds *(Editor)*

MADISON NEWSPAPERS, INC.
(Joint Venture of Lee Enterprises, Incorporated & The Capital Times Company)
(d/b/a Capital Newspapers)
1901 Fish Hatchery Rd
Madison, WI 53713-1248
Mailing Address:
PO Box 8056
Madison, WI 53708-8056
Tel.: (608) 252-6200
Fax: (608) 252-6333
Web Site:
www.capitalnewspapers.com
Sales Range: $50-74.9 Million
Approx. Number Employees: 500
Year Founded: 1948
Business Description:
Newspaper Publisher; Owned by 50% Lee Enterprises, Incorporated & 50% by The Capital Times Company
S.I.C.: 2711
N.A.I.C.S.: 511110
Media: 1-2-4-5-7-8-9-10-18-19-20-21-23-24-25-26
Distr.: Reg.
Budget Set: Sept.
Personnel:
John H. Lussier *(Pres & CEO)*
Pam Wells *(CFO)*
Jennifer Hefty *(Dir-Mktg)*
Debbie Reed *(Dir-HR)*
Todd Sears *(Dir-Adv)*
Phil Stoddard *(Dir-Circulation)*
Rob Strabala *(Dir-Production & Building Svcs)*
Jon Denk *(Mgr-Retail Adv)*
Sue Halverson-Natvig *(Mgr-Sls Dev)*
Julie Johnson *(Mgr-Classified Sls)*
Kerin Rue *(Mgr-Customer Svc)*
Jeff Schroeter *(Mgr-Natl Adv)*
Phil Simon *(Mgr-Direct Mktg)*
Brands & Products:
AD WORLD
AGRI-VIEW
APARTMENT SHOWCASE
BARABOO NEWS REPUBLIC
THE CAPITAL TIMES
JUNEAU COUNTY REMINDER
JUNEAU COUNTY STAR TIMES
NURSINGMATTERS
PORTAGE DAILY REGISTER
RACK EXPRESS
REEDSBURG TIMES PRESS
SHOPPER STOPPER
WHEELS FOR YOU
WISCONSIN DELLS EVENTS
WISCONSIN STATE JOURNAL

MAITLAND PRIMROSE GROUP
7220 N 16th St Ste C
Phoenix, AZ 85020
Tel.: (602) 944-0046
Fax: (602) 944-9946
E-mail: info@maitlandprimrosegroup.com
Web Site: www.maitlandprimrose.com
Sales Range: $10-24.9 Million
Approx. Number Employees: 12
Business Description:
Publisher
S.I.C.: 2731; 2721; 2741
N.A.I.C.S.: 511130; 511120; 511199
Personnel:
Margaret Tritch *(Pres)*
Advertising Agency:
Goldstein Communications
231 W 29th St
New York, NY 10001
Tel.: (212) 838-0822
Fax: (212) 838-0855

MANUFACTURERS' NEWS, INC.
1633 Central St
Evanston, IL 60201
Tel.: (847) 864-7000
Fax: (847) 332-1100
Toll Free: (888) 752-5200
E-mail: info@manufacturersnews.com
Web Site:
www.manufacturersnews.com
E-Mail For Key Personnel:
Sales Director: sales@mninfo.com
Approx. Number Employees: 120
Year Founded: 1912
Business Description:
Directories & Databases Mfr
S.I.C.: 2741
N.A.I.C.S.: 511140
Import Export
Media: 2-4-7-10-21
Distr.: Direct to Consumer; Natl.
Budget Set: Jan.
Personnel:
Howard S. Dubin *(Chm)*
Thomas G. Dubin *(Pres & CEO)*
George Kartsounes *(COO)*
Scott Kartsounes *(VP-Tech)*
Brands & Products:
DIRECTORY
MNI
MNI LEADS

MARCO ISLAND EAGLE
(Sub. of Naples Daily News)
579 Elkcam Cir
Marco Island, FL 34146
Mailing Address:
PO Box 579
Marco Island, FL 34146
Tel.: (239) 213-5300
Fax: (239) 213-5390
E-mail: editor@marcoeagle.com
Web Site: www.marcoeagle.com
Sales Range: $10-24.9 Million
Approx. Number Employees: 35
Business Description:
Newspaper Publisher
S.I.C.: 2711
N.A.I.C.S.: 511110
Media: 13-20-25
Personnel:
Mary Quinton *(Mgr-Naples News Media Grp Events)*
Brands & Products:
MARCO ISLAND EAGLE
MARCO ISLANDER

MARIAH MEDIA INC.
(d/b/a Outside Magazine)
Outside Plz 400 Market St
Santa Fe, NM 87501
Tel.: (505) 989-7100

Key to Media (For complete agency information see *The Advertising Red Books-Agencies* edition):
1. Bus. Publs. 2. Cable T.V. 3. Catalogs & Directories. 4. Co-op Adv. 5. Consumer Mags. 6. D.M. to Bus. Estab.7. D.M. to Consumers
8. Daily Newsp. 9. Exhibits/Trade Shows 10. Foreign 11. Infomercial 12. Internet Adv.13. Multimedia 14. Network Radio
15. Network T.V. 16. Newsp. Distr. Mags. 17. Other 18. Outdoor (Posters, Transit) 19. Point of Purchase20. Premiums, Novelties
21. Product Samples 22. Special Events Mktg. 23. Spot Radio 24. Spot T.V. 25. Weekly Newsp. 26. Yellow Page Adv.

Fax: (505) 989-4700
Web Site: www.outside.away.com
Approx. Sls.: $10,100,000
Approx. Number Employees: 60
Business Description:
Magazine Publisher
S.I.C.: 2721
N.A.I.C.S.: 511120
Media: 6-8
Personnel:
Lawrence J. Burke, II *(Chm & Editor-in-Chief)*
Scott Parmeley *(Dir-Publ)*
Paul Rolnick *(Dir-Consumer Mktg)*
Brands & Products:
BODYWORK
OUTSIDE

MARIAN HEATH GREETING CARDS
9 Kendrick Rd
Wareham, MA 02571
Tel.: (508) 291-0766
Fax: (508) 291-2976
Toll Free: (800) 338-3740
E-mail: talktous@rencards.com
Web Site: www.marianheath.com
Approx. Number Employees: 50
Business Description:
Greeting Card Company
S.I.C.: 2771
N.A.I.C.S.: 511191
Media: 4
Personnel:
Kimberley Lehrman *(Sr VP-Sls & Mktg)*

MARIN INDEPENDENT JOURNAL
(Unit of Bay Area News Group)
150 Alameda Del Prado
Novato, CA 94949
Mailing Address:
PO Box 6150
Novato, CA 94948-6150
Tel.: (415) 883-8600
Fax: (415) 382-0549
Web Site: www.marinij.com
Approx. Number Employees: 275
Business Description:
Newspaper Publisher
S.I.C.: 2711
N.A.I.C.S.: 511110
Media: 8
Personnel:
Chuck O'Daniel *(VP-Adv & Mktg)*
Ron Thayer *(Dir-Adv)*

MARKET DATA RETRIEVAL
(Sub. of The Dun & Bradstreet Corp.)
6 Armstrong Rd
Shelton, CT 06484
Tel.: (203) 926-4800
Fax: (203) 929-5253
Toll Free: (800) 333-8802
E-mail: mdrinfo@dnb.com
Web Site: www.schooldata.com
E-Mail For Key Personnel:
Marketing Director: msubrizi@dnb.com
Sales Range: $25-49.9 Million
Approx. Number Employees: 166
Year Founded: 1969
Business Description:
School Marketing Information & Services
S.I.C.: 8732
N.A.I.C.S.: 541910
Media: 2-4-7-10-22
Distr.: Intl.; Natl.
Budget Set: Oct.
Personnel:
Fady Khairallah *(Pres)*
Moyra McArdle *(Dir-Mktg)*
Brands & Products:
DIRECT RESPONSE INDEX
SCHOOL CONSTRUCTION ALERT

MARKETING MAGAZINE
(Unit of Rogers Publishing Limited)
1 Mount Pleasant Road
Toronto, ON M4Y 2Y5, Canada
Tel.: (416) 764-2000
Fax: (416) 764-1519
Web Site: www.marketingmag.ca
Approx. Number Employees: 30
Business Description:
Trade Magazine Publisher
S.I.C.: 2721
N.A.I.C.S.: 511120; 519130
Media: 2-7-10-13
Personnel:
Peter Zaver *(Art Dir)*
Lucy Collin *(Dir-Sls)*
Lida Kudla *(Dir-Production Svcs)*
Brands & Products:
MARKETING MAGAZINE

MARQUIS WHO'S WHO, LLC
300 Connell Dr Ste 2000
Berkeley Heights, NJ 07922
Tel.: (908) 673-1000
Fax: (908) 673-1189
Toll Free: (800) 473-7020
E-mail: marquisinfo@marquiswhoswho.com
Web Site: www.marquiswhoswho.com
Approx. Number Employees: 70
Year Founded: 1898
Business Description:
Publisher of Biographical Reference Materials
S.I.C.: 2741
N.A.I.C.S.: 511199
Advertising Expenditures: $40,000
Media: 2-10-13
Distr.: Direct to Consumer; Intl.; Natl.
Budget Set: Aug.
Personnel:
Jeanne Gottfried *(CEO)*
Vincent Papa *(CFO)*
Fred Marks *(COO)*
Judy Weiss-Brown *(SVP-Mktg)*
Kelli MacKinnon *(Dir-Sls)*
Anne Collins *(Sls Mgr)*
Judy Weiss *(Mgr-Mktg)*
Brands & Products:
WHO WAS WHO IN AMERICA
WHO'S WHO IN AMERICA
WHO'S WHO IN AMERICAN ART
WHO'S WHO IN AMERICAN LAW
WHO'S WHO IN AMERICAN POLITICS
WHO'S WHO IN ASIA
WHO'S WHO IN FINANCE AND INDUSTRY
WHO'S WHO IN MEDICINE AND HEALTHCARE
WHO'S WHO IN SCIENCE AND ENGINEERING
WHO'S WHO IN THE EAST
WHO'S WHO IN THE MIDWEST
WHO'S WHO IN THE SOUTH AND SOUTHWEST
WHO'S WHO IN THE WEST
WHO'S WHO IN THE WORLD
WHO'S WHO OF AMERICAN WOMEN

MARSHALL & SWIFT/BOECKH, LLC
(Holding of TPG Capital, L.P.)
350 S Grand Ave Ste 3400
Los Angeles, CA 90071
Tel.: (213) 683-9000
Fax: (213) 683-9010
Toll Free: (800) 421-8042
Web Site: www.msbinfo.com
Approx. Sls.: $48,972,880
Approx. Number Employees: 120
Business Description:
Supplier of Residential & Commercial Property Valuation Products & Services
S.I.C.: 6531
N.A.I.C.S.: 531390
Media: 4-7-10-13
Personnel:
Salil Donde *(CEO)*
Peter M. Wells *(Pres/Bus Mgr-Comml Solutions)*
Jennifer Fisher *(Gen Counsel)*
Robert Blythe *(Sr VP-Sls)*
Geoff Garlow *(Sr VP-Product Dev & IT)*
Todd Eyler *(VP-Mktg)*
Kayla Merker *(Mktg Mgr)*
Brands & Products:
MSB

MARTHA STEWART LIVING OMNIMEDIA, INC.
601 W 26th St
New York, NY 10001
Tel.: (212) 827-8000
Fax: (212) 827-8204
Web Site: www.marthastewart.com
Approx. Rev.: $230,813,000
Approx. Number Employees: 615
Year Founded: 1996
Business Description:
How-To Publishing, Television Broadcasting, Internet Production & Merchandising Services
S.I.C.: 2741; 2721; 2731; 3663; 4833; 5961; 7812
N.A.I.C.S.: 516110; 334220; 454113; 511120; 511130; 512110; 515120
Advertising Expenditures: $14,300,000
Media: 6-8-13
Personnel:
Charles A. Koppelman *(Chm)*
Lisa Gersh *(Pres & COO)*
Ken West *(CFO)*
Daniel Taitz *(Chief Admin Officer, Gen Counsel & Sec)*
Gael A. Towey *(Chief Creative Officer & Dir-Editorial)*
Robin Marino *(CEO-Mdsg)*
Peter Hurwitz *(Gen Counsel & Sec)*
Sally Preston *(Exec VP & Publr-Sls)*
Amy P. Wilkins *(Sr VP & Publr-Martha Stewart Weddings)*
Patsy Pollack *(Exec VP-Mdsg)*
Allison Jacques *(Sr VP & Controller)*
Missy Foristall *(Sr VP-Digital Programming & Strategy)*
Sarah Gormley *(Sr VP-Comm & Mktg)*
Inna Kern *(Sr VP-Sls Mktg)*
Jeanne Meyer *(Sr VP-Comm)*
Diana Pearson *(Sr VP-Media Rels)*
Darcy Miller *(VP & Editor-Weddings)*
Viktoria Degtar *(Dir-Digital Adv Sls & Asst VP)*
Nicole McCormack *(Asst VP-Integrated Sales)*
Geoffrey A. Darby *(Gen Mgr-Television)*
Pilar Guzman *(Editor-in-Chief)*
Dave Grove *(Editor)*
Katherine Hottinger *(Editor)*
Hannah Milman *(Editor-Holidays & Crafts)*
Rhonda Bitterman *(Dir-Sls)*
Brands & Products:
BODY + SOUL
EMERIL'S & BAM!
EVERYDAY FOOD
MARTHA STEWART
MARTHA STEWART BABY
MARTHA STEWART COLLECTION
MARTHA STEWART EVERYDAY
MARTHA STEWART FLOWERS
MARTHA STEWART KIDS
MARTHA STEWART LIVING
MARTHA STEWART SHOW
MARTHA STEWART SIGNATURE
MARTHA STEWART: THE CATALOG FOR LIVING
MARTHA STEWART WEDDINGS
MARTHASTEWART.COM
PETKEEPING WITH MARC MORRONE
Advertising Agencies:
Centra360
1400 Old Country Rd Ste 420
Westbury, NY 11590-5119
Tel.: (516) 997-3147
Fax: (516) 334-7798

Susan Magrino Agency
641 Lexington Ave 28th Fl
New York, NY 10022
Tel.: (212) 957-3005
Fax: (212) 957-4071
Public Relations

MARTIN SASS INC.
(d/b/a U.S. Monitor)
86 Maple Ave
New City, NY 10956-5092
Tel.: (845) 634-1331
Fax: (845) 634-9618
Toll Free: (800) 767-7967
E-mail: contactus@usmonitor.com
Web Site: www.usmonitor.com
Approx. Number Employees: 25
Year Founded: 1973
Business Description:
Mailing List Services
S.I.C.: 7331
N.A.I.C.S.: 541860
Media: 2
Personnel:
Anita Sass *(Co-Founder & Pres)*
Paul Ercolino *(VP-Sls & Mktg)*

MARTINDALE-HUBBELL, INC.
(Joint Venture of Reed Elsevier NV & Reed Elsevier plc)
(d/b/a LexisNexis Martindale-Hubbell)
121 Chanlon Rd
New Providence, NJ 07974-1541
Tel.: (908) 464-6800
Fax: (908) 464-3553
Toll Free: (800) 526-4902
E-mail: info@martindale.com
Web Site: www.martindale.com
Approx. Number Employees: 500
Year Founded: 1868

Key to Media (For complete agency information see *The Advertising Red Books-Agencies* edition):
1. Bus. Publs. 2. Cable T.V. 3. Catalogs & Directories. 4. Co-op Adv. 5. Consumer Mags. 6. D.M. to Bus. Estab.7. D.M. to Consumers
8. Daily Newsp. 9. Exhibits/Trade Shows 10. Foreign 11. Infomercial 12. Internet Adv.13. Multimedia 14. Network Radio
15. Network T.V. 16. Newsp. Distr. Mags. 17. Other 18. Outdoor (Posters, Transit) 19. Point of Purchase20. Premiums, Novelties
21. Product Samples 22. Special Events Mktg. 23. Spot Radio 24. Spot T.V. 25. Weekly Newsp. 26. Yellow Page Adv.

Martindale-Hubbell, Inc. — (Continued)

Business Description:
Legal Directories Publisher, Online Marketing & Advertising Services
S.I.C.: 2741; 2731; 7389
N.A.I.C.S.: 511140; 511130; 516110; 519190
Media: 2-4-7-10-13
Budget Set: Aug.
Personnel:
Philip B. Livingston *(CEO & Sr VP-Client Dev/Practice Mgmt-LexisNexis US Legal Markets)*
David A. Palmieri *(VP & Mng Dir)*
Linda M. Hlavac *(Sr VP-HR-US Legal Markets)*
Brian Douty *(VP-Fin-LexisNexis US Legal Markets)*
Patrik U. Dyberg *(VP-Global Product Dev-Client Dev)*
Leonard Gilbert *(VP-Online Adv & Promo Solutions)*
Alfredo Sciascia *(VP-Strategic Plng-USLM Mktg & Bus Solutions)*
Aidan T. McManus *(Acting Head-Reed Elsevier Tech Svcs)*
Ruth J. Davis *(Sr Dir-Ops & Bus Dev)*
Sharon L. Lubrano *(Sr Dir-Online Svcs)*
Mark H. Van Orman *(Sr Dir-Editorial Ops)*
Erin L. Martin *(Dir-Mktg)*
Anand A. Pandya *(Product Dir-Pay Per Lead)*
Thomas M. Bachmann *(Dir-Client Dev Data Svcs)*
James Clay Cazier *(Dir-Web Svcs)*
Phylis J. Peotter *(Dir-Customer Relations)*
Christopher J. Thomas *(Dir-Program Mgmt-Global Enterprise Info Solutions)*
Christine Geitner *(Reg Mgr-New Jersey/Massachusetts-Global Real Estate & Corp Svcs)*
Matthew O'Connell *(Mgr-Production)*
Fran V. Nanni *(Mgr-Events)*

MARVEL ENTERTAINMENT, LLC

(Sub. of The Walt Disney Company)
417 5th Ave 11th Fl
New York, NY 10016
Tel.: (212) 576-4000
Fax: (212) 576-8517
E-mail: infomvl@jcir.com
Web Site: www.marvel.com
Approx. Sls.: $676,177,000
Approx. Number Employees: 300
Year Founded: 1988
Business Description:
Comic Book Publisher, Movie Studio & Entertainment
S.I.C.: 2731; 2721; 6794; 7812
N.A.I.C.S.: 511130; 511120; 512110; 533110
Import
Advertising Expenditures: $1,400,000
Media: 3-4-5-6-9-10-15-19-24-25
Distr.: Intl.; Natl.
Budget Set: Oct.
Personnel:
Morton E. Handel *(Chm)*
Alan Fine *(Pres, CEO, CMO & Exec VP)*
Dan Buckley *(Pres & Publr)*
Louis D'Esposito *(Co-Pres)*
Kevin Feige *(Co-Pres-Production)*
Isaac Perlmutter *(CEO)*
Mark D. Plotkin *(Chief Acctg Officer)*
Simon Philips *(Pres-Marvel Intl)*
John Turitzin *(Gen Counsel & Exec VP)*
Dan Phillips *(Sr VP & Gen Mgr-Digital Media)*
Axel Alonso *(Editor-in-Chief)*
Brands & Products:
MARVEL

MASSACHUSETTS LAWYERS WEEKLY, INC.

(Sub. of The Dolan Company)
10 Milk St Ste 1000
Boston, MA 02108
Tel.: (617) 451-7300
Fax: (617) 451-7324
Toll Free: (800) 451-9998
Web Site:
www.masslawyersweekly.com
Sales Range: $10-24.9 Million
Approx. Number Employees: 50
Year Founded: 1972
Business Description:
Legal Newspapers Publisher
S.I.C.: 2711
N.A.I.C.S.: 511110
Media: 7-25
Personnel:
James P. Dolan *(Pres & CEO)*
David L. Yas *(Publr & Editor-in-Chief)*
Thomas E. Egan *(Editor-Opinion)*
Paul E. Lamoureux *(Sr Opinion Editor)*
Matt Yas *(Assoc Editor)*
Terry Driscoll *(Dir-Art)*
David E. Frank *(Sr News Coord)*
Noah Schaffer *(News Coord)*
Brands & Products:
ATLANTIC COAST IN-HOUSE
LAWYERS USA
MASSACHUSETTS LAWYERS WEEKLY
MASSACHUSETTS MEDICAL LAW REPORT
MICHIGAN LAWYERS WEEKLY
MIDWEST IN-HOUSE
MISSOURI LAWYERS WEEKLY
NEW ENGLAND IN-HOUSE
NORTH CAROLINA LAWYERS WEEKLY
RHODE ISLAND LAWYERS WEEKLY
SOUTH CAROLINA LAWYERS WEEKLY
VIRGINIA LAWYERS WEEKLY

MATTHEWS INTERNATIONAL CORPORATION

2 N Shore Ctr
Pittsburgh, PA 15212-5851
Tel.: (412) 442-8200
Fax: (412) 442-8290
E-mail: investorrelations@matw.com
Web Site: www.matw.com
Approx. Sls.: $821,829,000
Approx. Number Employees: 4,900
Year Founded: 1850
Business Description:
Industrial Marking Products, Bronze, Aluminum & Plastic Tablets, Signs & Memorials, Rubber Printing Plates, Rubber Stamps & Projects, Machinery for Product Identification & Cutting Dies Mfr
S.I.C.: 3364; 3995
N.A.I.C.S.: 331522; 339995
Media: 1-2-4-7-10-13-19
Distr.: Intl.; Natl.
Budget Set: Oct.
Personnel:
John D. Turner *(Chm)*
Joseph C. Bartolacci *(Pres & CEO)*
Steven F. Nicola *(CFO, Treas & Sec)*
James P. Doyle *(Grp Pres-Memorialization)*
Brian J. Dunn *(Grp Pres-Graphics & Marking Products)*
Franz J. Schwarz *(Pres-Graphics Europe)*
Brian D. Walters *(Gen Counsel & VP)*
Jennifer A. Ciccone *(VP-HR)*
Brands & Products:
A HISTORY OF MAKING OUR MARK
AIRGRIT
CREMORIAL
EDGEWOOD
THE GOLD STANDARD OF QUALITY & CRAFTSMANSHIP
GORHAM BRONZE
MATTHEWS INTERNATIONAL
THE POINT OF VICTORY
POWER-PAK
RICHMOND
ROCKEDGE
Advertising Agency:
Drake Advertising, Inc.
4141 Brownsville Rd Ste 1
Pittsburgh, PA 15227
Tel.: (412) 882-4700
Fax: (412) 882-4702
Toll Free: (877) 583-7253

MCBOOKS PRESS INC.

I D Booth Bldg 520 N Meadow St
Ithaca, NY 14850
Tel.: (607) 272-2114
Fax: (607) 273-6068
Toll Free: (888) 266-5711
E-mail: mcbooks@mcbooks.com
Web Site: www.mcbooks.com
Approx. Number Employees: 4
Business Description:
Publisher of History & Special Interest Books
S.I.C.: 2731
N.A.I.C.S.: 511130
Media: 4-6-8
Personnel:
Alexander Skutt *(Publr)*
Panda Musgrove *(Art Dir)*
Jackie Swift *(Dir-Editorial)*

THE MCCLATCHY COMPANY

2100 Q St
Sacramento, CA 95816-6816
Tel.: (916) 321-1846
Fax: (916) 321-1964
E-mail: contact@mcclatchy.com
Web Site: www.mcclatchy.com
Approx. Rev.: $1,375,232,000
Approx. Number Employees: 7,773
Year Founded: 1857
Business Description:
Newspaper Publisher
S.I.C.: 2711
N.A.I.C.S.: 511110
Advertising Expenditures: $910,628,000
Personnel:
Gary B. Pruitt *(Chm, Pres & CEO)*
Patrick J. Talamantes *(CFO & VP-Fin)*
Karole Morgan-Prager *(Gen Counsel, Corp Sec & VP)*
Stephen Bernard *(VP-Adv)*
Heather L. Fagundes *(VP-HR)*
Jim York *(VP-IT-Newspaper Div)*

MCCLATCHY INTERACTIVE

(Sub. of The McClatchy Company)
1100 Situs Ct
Valley, NC 27606
Tel.: (919) 861-1200
Fax: (919) 861-1300
E-mail: info@mcclatchyinteractive.com
Web Site:
www.mcclatchyinteractive.com
Sales Range: $50-74.9 Million
Approx. Number Employees: 200
Business Description:
Multimedia News Delivery
S.I.C.: 2711
N.A.I.C.S.: 511110
Personnel:
Fraser Van Asch *(Exec VP & Gen Mgr)*
Brian Kirlik *(Sr VP-Market Svcs)*
Advertising Agency:
Ad2Pro Media Solutions
23371 Mulholland Dr Ste 132
Woodland Hills, CA 91364
Tel.: (818) 591-7713
Fax: (818) 267-5511

MCCLATCHY NEWSPAPERS, INC.

(Div. of The McClatchy Company)
2100 Q St
Sacramento, CA 95816-6816
Mailing Address:
PO Box 15779
Sacramento, CA 95852-0779
Tel.: (916) 650-2847
Fax: (916) 321-1954
Fax: (916) 321-1869
Web Site: www.mcclatchy.com
Sales Range: $1-4.9 Billion
Approx. Number Employees: 9,850
Year Founded: 1857
Business Description:
Printing, Newspaper Publishing; Operation of On-line Database Services
S.I.C.: 2711; 2759
N.A.I.C.S.: 511110; 323119
Import
Advertising Expenditures: $3,000,000
Media: 2-8-10-13-18-23-24-26
Distr.: Natl.
Personnel:
Gary B. Pruitt *(Chm, Pres & CEO)*
Cheryl Dell *(Pres/Publr-The Sacramento Bee)*
Heather L. Fagundes *(VP-HR)*
Jill Threde *(Dir-Major Accts)*
Brands & Products:
SACRAMENTO BEE

MCFARLAND & COMPANY, INC.

960 Hwy 88 W
Jefferson, NC 28640
Tel.: (336) 246-4460
Fax: (336) 246-5018
E-mail: info@mcfarlandpub.com
Web Site: www.mcfarlandpub.com
Approx. Number Employees: 32
Year Founded: 1979
Business Description:
Reference Book Publisher
S.I.C.: 2731

Key to Media (For complete agency information see *The Advertising Red Books-Agencies* edition):
1. Bus. Publs. 2. Cable T.V. 3. Catalogs & Directories. 4. Co-op Adv. 5. Consumer Mags. 6. D.M. to Bus. Estab.7. D.M. to Consumers 8. Daily Newsp. 9. Exhibits/Trade Shows 10. Foreign 11. Infomercial 12. Internet Adv.13. Multimedia 14. Network Radio 15. Network T.V. 16. Newsp. Distr. Mags. 17. Other 18. Outdoor (Posters, Transit) 19. Point of Purchase20. Premiums, Novelties 21. Product Samples 22. Special Events Mktg. 23. Spot Radio 24. Spot T.V. 25. Weekly Newsp. 26. Yellow Page Adv.

N.A.I.C.S.: 511130
Media: 2-4-6-7-8-10-13
Personnel:
Robert Franklin *(Publr)*
Rhonda Herman *(Publr)*

THE MCGRAW-HILL COMPANIES INC.

1221 Ave of the Americas
New York, NY 10020-1001
Tel.: (212) 512-2000
Tel.: (212) 904-2000
Fax: (212) 512-3840
Toll Free: (866) 436-8502
Telex: 127960
E-mail: customer.service@mcgraw-hill.com
Web Site: www.mcgraw-hill.com
E-Mail For Key Personnel:
Public Relations: mary_skafidas@mcgraw-hill.com
Approx. Rev.: $6,168,331,000
Approx. Number Employees: 21,000
Year Founded: 1888
Business Description:
Book Publisher & Business Solutions Services
S.I.C.: 2731; 2721
N.A.I.C.S.: 511130; 511120
Import Export
Advertising Expenditures: $51,900,000
Media: 1-2-6-10-13-14-17-24-25
Distr.: Natl.
Personnel:
Harold W. McGraw, III *(Chm, Pres & CEO)*
Jack F. Callahan, Jr. *(CFO & Exec VP)*
Jonathan Miller *(CIO)*
Emmanuel Korakis *(Principal Acctg Officer, Sr VP & Controller)*
Robert J. Bahash *(Pres-McGraw-Hill Education)*
Glenn S. Goldberg *(Pres-Info & Media Svcs)*
Gregory Hamilton *(Pres-Aviation Week)*
Kenneth M. Vittor *(Gen Counsel & Exec VP)*
John Berisford *(Exec VP-HR)*
D. Edward Smyth *(Exec VP-Corp Affairs)*
Charles L. Teschner, Jr. *(Exec VP-Global Strategy)*
Bruce D. Marcus *(Sr VP-Enterprise Sys)*
Patricia M. Walsh *(Sr VP-Mktg & Comm-McGraw-Hill Fin)*
Mary Skafidas *(VP-Comm & Mktg)*
Frank Briamonte *(Sr Dir-Corp Comm)*
William Jordan *(Sr Dir-Govt Affairs & Comm)*
Hitesh Chitalia *(Dir-eBusiness)*
Jason Feuchtwanger *(Dir-Corp Media Rels)*
Lisa Gottschalk *(Dir-Mktg)*
Tom Stanton *(Dir-Comm-McGraw-Hill Education)*
Celeste Hughes *(Sr Mgr-Comm & Shareholder Relations)*
Lisa Nicks *(Sr Mgr-Mktg)*
Heather Wagner *(Mgr-Mktg)*
Brands & Products:
APPLETON & LANGE
AVIATION WEEK
BUSINESSWEEK
MCGRAW-HILL
THE MCGRAW-HILL COMPANIES
PLATTS
STANDARD & POOR'S
Advertising Agencies:
Impressions-A.B.A. Industries, Inc.
393 Jericho Tpk
Mineola, NY 11501
Tel.: (516) 739-3210
Fax: (516) 739-9246

Mass Transmit
453 W17th St
New York, NY 10011
Tel.: (704) 706-2670
Fax: (704) 447-7262

MEDIANEWS GROUP, INC.

101 W Colfax Ave Ste 1100
Denver, CO 80202
Tel.: (303) 954-6360
Fax: (303) 954-6320
E-mail: contact@medianewsgroup.com
Web Site: www.medianewsgroup.com
E-Mail For Key Personnel:
Sales Director: sales@medianewsgroup.com
Public Relations: probinson@medianewsgroup.com
Sales Range: $1-4.9 Billion
Approx. Number Employees: 10,500
Year Founded: 1984
Business Description:
Newspaper Publisher; Radio & Television Station Operator
S.I.C.: 2711; 4832; 4833
N.A.I.C.S.: 511110; 515112; 515120
Media: 8-9
Personnel:
William Dean Singleton *(Founder & Chm)*
Gordon A. Paris *(Interim Pres)*
John Paton *(CEO)*
Ronald A. Mayo *(CFO & VP)*
Michael Sileck *(Interim Chief Revenue Officer)*
Oliver Knowlton *(Pres-Interactive)*
Howell E. Begle Jr. *(Gen Counsel)*
Stephen M. Hesse *(Sr VP-Circulation)*
Alison Kane *(Chief Digital Officer & Sr VP)*
Anthony F. Tierno *(Sr VP-Ops)*
Barbary Brunner *(VP-Mktg & Product Innovations)*
Charles M. Kamen *(VP-HR)*
Michael R. Petrak *(VP-Sls)*

MEDICINE HAT NEWS

(Div. of Alberta Newspaper Group)
3257 Dunmore Road Southeast
Medicine Hat, AB T1B 3R2, Canada
Tel.: (403) 527-1101
Fax: (403) 527-7244
Web Site: www.medicinehatnews.com
Sales Range: $10-24.9 Million
Approx. Number Employees: 350
Business Description:
Newspaper Publishing
S.I.C.: 2711
N.A.I.C.S.: 511110
Media: 8-9-13
Personnel:
Ron W. Turner *(CFO)*
Michael J. Hertz *(Grp Publr)*
Gord Derouin *(Dir-Adv)*
Tom Peterson *(Dir-Mfg)*
Alan Poirier *(Dir-Readership Dev)*
Gorden Waterhouse *(Dir-Circulation)*
Danette Nutley *(Mgr-New Bus & Media Dev)*

MEMPHIS PUBLISHING COMPANY

(Sub. of The E.W. Scripps Company)
(d/b/a The Commercial Appeal)
495 Union Ave
Memphis, TN 38103-3217
Tel.: (901) 529-2345
Fax: (901) 529-5879
Toll Free: (800) 444-6397
Web Site: www.commercialappeal.com
Sales Range: $75-99.9 Million
Approx. Number Employees: 840
Business Description:
Newspaper Publishing
S.I.C.: 2711
N.A.I.C.S.: 511110
Media: 9-18-23
Personnel:
Chris Peck *(Editor)*

MEN'S JOURNAL

(Sub. of Wenner Media LLC)
1290 Ave of The Americas 2nd Fl
New York, NY 10104
Tel.: (212) 484-1616
Fax: (212) 484-3429
Web Site: www.mensjournal.com
Approx. Sls.: $550,000
Approx. Number Employees: 30
Year Founded: 1992
Business Description:
Publisher of Men's Magazine
S.I.C.: 2741
N.A.I.C.S.: 511199
Media: 2-4-6-8-10-11-13-20-22
Distr.: Natl.
Personnel:
Stephanie Freeman *(Mgr-Integrated Mktg)*
Advertising Agency:
Fletcher Media Group
94 Grove St
Peterborough, NH 03458
Tel.: (603) 924-6383
Fax: (603) 924-6562

MEREDITH CORPORATION

1716 Locust St
Des Moines, IA 50309-3038
Tel.: (515) 284-3000
Fax: (515) 284-2700
Toll Free: (800) 284-4236
E-mail: shareholderhelp@meredith.com
Web Site: www.meredith.com
E-Mail For Key Personnel:
Public Relations: art.slusark@meredith.com
Approx. Rev.: $1,400,480,000
Approx. Number Employees: 3,150
Year Founded: 1902
Business Description:
Publishing & Broadcasting Services
S.I.C.: 2741; 2721; 2731; 4833
N.A.I.C.S.: 516110; 511120; 511130; 515120
Advertising Expenditures: $90,700,000
Media: 2-6-7-8-10-13-14-18-19-20-21-23-24
Distr.: Intl.; Natl.
Personnel:
Stephen M. Lacy *(Chm, Pres & CEO)*
Dianna Mell Meredith Frazier *(Vice Chm)*
Joseph H. Ceryanec *(CFO & VP)*
Nancy Weber *(CMO & Exec VP)*
John S. Zieser *(Chief Dev Officer, Gen Counsel & Sec)*
Jack Goldenberg *(CTO & Sr VP)*
Thomas H. Harty *(Pres-Natl Media Grp)*
Paul A. Karpowicz *(Pres-Local Media Grp)*
Pete Snyder *(Pres-Emerging Markets Grp)*
Liz Schimel *(Exec VP-Digital & CRM)*
Michael Brownstein *(Sr VP-Corp Sls)*
James T. Carr *(VP-Publ)*
Art Slusark *(VP-Corp Comm & Govt Rels)*
Susan Fletcher *(Exec Dir-Digital Innovation)*
Brendan Smyth *(Exec Dir-Media Solutions)*
Jean Crowley *(Sls Dir-Natl)*
Bunny Fensterheim *(Sls Dir-Dev)*
Ann Baird *(Dir-Mktg)*
Grace Chung-Mui *(Dir-Adv)*
Jeannine Shao Collins *(Dir-Publ)*
Warren Milich *(Dir-Strategic Mktg)*
Barbara Moses *(Dir-Sls-Los Angeles-Parents Magazine)*
Bill Shaner *(Dir-Media Solution)*
Kimberly Schelpf *(Sr Mgr-Mktg)*
Amy Macauley *(Mgr-Fitness Magazine-Western)*
Peter Senseney *(Mgr-Natl Sls)*
Brands & Products:
12 MESES
AMERICAN BABY
AMERICAN PATCHWORK & QUILTING
BETTER HOMES
BETTER HOMES AND GARDENS
COUNTRY LIFE
COUNTRYHOME
DECORATING
DIABETIC LIVING
DREAM DECKS & PATIOS
EASY FAMILY FOOD
ESPERA
FAMILY CIRCLE
FITNESS
GARDEN, DECK, & LANDSCAPE
HEALTHY KIDS EN ESPANOL
HEART-HEALTHY LIVING
KITCHEN AND BATH IDEAS
KITCHENS
LADIES' HOME JOURNAL
LIVING THE COUNTRY LIFE
MEREDITH
MIDWEST LIVING
MORE
PARENTS
QUILTING
READYMADE
REMODEL
RENOVATION STYLE
SCRAPBOOKS ETC.
SER PADRES
SIEMPRE MUJER
STORAGE
SUCCESSFUL FARMING
TRADITIONAL HOME
WE INSPIRE. SHE MAKES IT HAPPEN
WOOD

Key to Media (For complete agency information see *The Advertising Red Books-Agencies* edition):
1. Bus. Publs. 2. Cable T.V. 3. Catalogs & Directories. 4. Co-op Adv. 5. Consumer Mags. 6. D.M. to Bus. Estab.7. D.M. to Consumers
8. Daily Newsp. 9. Exhibits/Trade Shows 10. Foreign 11. Infomercial 12. Internet Adv.13. Multimedia 14. Network Radio
15. Network T.V. 16. Newsp. Distr. Mags. 17. Other 18. Outdoor (Posters, Transit) 19. Point of Purchase20. Premiums, Novelties
21. Product Samples 22. Special Events Mktg. 23. Spot Radio 24. Spot T.V. 25. Weekly Newsp. 26. Yellow Page Adv.

Meredith Corporation — (Continued)

Advertising Agencies:
Strategic America
6600 Westown Pkwy Ste 100
West Des Moines, IA 50266-7708
Tel.: (888) 898-6400
Fax: (515) 224-4181

Trylon SMR
41 East 11th St
New York, NY 10003
Tel.: (212) 725-2295
Fax: (212) 725-2243
BHG.com

MERGENT, INC.
(Holding of Carousel Capital Partners)
580 Kingsley Park Dr
Fort Mill, SC 29715-6403
Tel.: (704) 527-2700
Fax: (704) 559-6960
Toll Free: (800) 937-1398
E-mail: customerservice@mergent.com
Web Site: www.mergent.com
Sales Range: $50-74.9 Million
Approx. Number Employees: 250
Year Founded: 1900
Business Description:
Corporate & Financial Data Processor & Publisher
S.I.C.: 2741; 7374
N.A.I.C.S.: 511140; 516110; 518210
Media: 2-10
Personnel:
Jonathan Worrall *(CEO)*
John Pedernales *(Exec Mng Dir)*
Kimberly Pyle *(Exec Mng Dir-HR)*
Chris Henry *(Mng Dir)*
Jeff Zazzaro *(Mng Dir)*
Charles E. Miller, Jr. *(CFO)*
Timothy Roche *(CFO)*
Fred Jenkins *(Exec VP-Sls)*
Karen Peterson *(Mng Dir-Fixed Income)*
Neil Gandhai *(Sr Mgr-Product)*
Brands & Products:
MERGENT
MERGENT ACTIVE
MERGENT ANNUAL REPORTS
MERGENT BONDVIEWER
MERGENT EVENTSDATA
MERGENT EX-DATE SERVICE
MERGENT FIXED INCOME DATA MANAGEMENT PLATFORM
MERGENT FIXED INVESTMENT SECURITIES DATABASE
MERGENT GLOBAL COMPANY DATA
MERGENT HISTORICAL SECURITIES EQUITIES DATA
MERGENT HORIZON
MERGENT INDICATED ANNUAL DIVIDEND DATA
MERGENT ONLINE
MERGENT RETAIL NOTES
MERGENT SHORT INTEREST MONITOR DATA
MERGENT UNIT INVESTMENT TRUST DATA
MERGENT WEBREPORTS

MERION PUBLICATIONS, INC.
2900 Horizon Dr
King of Prussia, PA 19406-0956
Tel.: (610) 278-1400
Fax: (610) 278-1425
Toll Free: (800) 355-5627
E-mail: lley@advanceweb.com
Web Site: www.advanceweb.com
Approx. Number Employees: 400
Year Founded: 1975
Business Description:
News & Information for Nurses
S.I.C.: 2721
N.A.I.C.S.: 511120
Media: 2-8-10
Personnel:
Ann Wiest Kielinski *(Pres)*
Susan Basile *(VP & Dir-Creative Svcs)*
Jaci Nicely *(VP & Dir-HR)*
W. M. Kielinski *(Gen Mgr)*
David Gorgonzola *(Dir-Natl Sls)*
Christina Allmer *(Dir-Mktg Svcs)*
Todd Gerber *(Dir-Multimedia)*
Linda Jones *(Dir-Editorial)*
Maria Lowe *(Dir-Pub Rels)*
Doris Mohr *(Dir-Art)*
Ken Nicely *(Dir-IT & Bus Sys)*
Walt Saylor *(Dir-Design)*
Scott Sundy *(Dir-Mktg)*
Carla Frehn *(Mgr-Design & Production)*
Eleanor Kuchma *(Mgr-Recruitment & Web Ad Quality Control)*
Maryann Kurkowski *(Mgr-List)*
Laura Ley *(Mgr-HR-Adv)*
Christine Marvel *(Mgr-Billing)*
Brands & Products:
ADVANCE FOR ADMINISTRATORS OF THE LABORATORY
ADVANCE FOR AUDIOLOGISTS
ADVANCE FOR CAREERS
ADVANCE FOR DIRECTORS IN REHABILITATION
ADVANCE FOR HEALTH INFORMATION EXECUTIVES
ADVANCE FOR HEALTH INFORMATION PROFESSIONALS
ADVANCE FOR IMAGING AND ONCOLOGY ADMINISTRATORS
ADVANCE FOR LPNS
ADVANCE FOR MANAGERS OF RESPIRATORY CARE
ADVANCE FOR MEDICAL LABORATORY PROFESSIONALS
ADVANCE FOR NURSE PRACTITIONERS
ADVANCE FOR NURSES
ADVANCE FOR OCCUPATIONAL THERAPY PRACTITIONERS
ADVANCE FOR PHYSICAL THERAPISTS AND PT ASSISTANTS
ADVANCE FOR PHYSICIAN ASSISTANTS
ADVANCE FOR PROVIDERS OF POST-ACUTE CARE
ADVANCE FOR RESPIRATORY CARE PRACTITIONERS
ADVANCE FOR SLEEP.COM
ADVANCE FOR SPEECH LANGUAGE PATHOLOGISTS AND AUDIO
ADVANCE JOB FAIRS & CE EVENTS

MERRIAM-WEBSTER, INC.
(Sub. of Encyclopaedia Britannica, Inc.)
47 Federal St
Springfield, MA 01105-1127
Mailing Address:
PO Box 281
Springfield, MA 01102-0281
Tel.: (413) 734-3134
Fax: (413) 731-5979
E-mail: permission@m-w.com
Web Site: www.m-w.com
Approx. Number Employees: 110
Year Founded: 1831
Business Description:
Printer & Publisher of Books
S.I.C.: 2731; 2741
N.A.I.C.S.: 511130; 511199
Export
Advertising Expenditures: $2,000,000
Media: 2-4-6-7-9-10-11-19-20-22-23
Distr.: Intl.
Budget Set: May
Personnel:
John M. Morse *(Pres & Publr)*
Miles Kronby *(Chief Product Officer-Digital)*
Stephen Perrault *(Editor-in-Chief)*
Michael Guzzi *(Dir-Electronic Product Dev)*
Gerald Wick *(Tech Supvr)*
Brands & Products:
MERRIAM-WEBSTER
Advertising Agency:
Planned Television Arts
1110 2nd Ave
New York, NY 10022-2021
Tel.: (212) 583-2718

MERRILL CORPORATION
(Holding of DLJ Merchant Banking Partners)
1 Merrill Cir
Saint Paul, MN 55108
Tel.: (651) 646-4501
Fax: (651) 646-5332
Toll Free: (800) 688-4400
E-mail: info@merrillcorp.com
Web Site: www.merrillcorp.com
E-Mail For Key Personnel:
Public Relations: investorrelations@merrillcorp.com
Sales Range: $750-799.9 Million
Approx. Number Employees: 5,200
Year Founded: 1968
Business Description:
Business Communication & Information Management Outsourcing Services
S.I.C.: 7338; 2759
N.A.I.C.S.: 561410; 323119
Media: 4-7-8-10-20-25-26
Distr.: Natl.
Budget Set: Jan.
Personnel:
John W. Castro *(Chm & CEO)*
Robert H. Nazarian *(CFO, Treas & Exec VP)*
Katherine L. Miller *(Chief Acctg Officer & Controller)*
Rick R. Atterbury *(Pres-Transaction & Compliance Svcs & Legal Solutions)*
Roy Gross *(Pres-Mktg & Comm Solutions)*
Steven J. Machov *(Gen Counsel, Sec & Exec VP)*
Brenda J. Vale *(Sec & Exec VP)*
Craig Levinsohn *(Exec VP)*
Mark Rossi *(Sr VP & Gen Mgr-Sls)*
Jim Garippa *(Sr VP-Sls)*
Ken Lambert *(Sr VP-Mktg)*
Nancy Moeller *(Dir-Mktg & Creative Svcs)*
Brands & Products:
CETARA WORDSHARE
MERRILL DISCOVERY NAVIGATOR
MERRILL NET:PROSPECT
MERRILLCONNECT
MERRILLREPORTS

METRO LIFE MEDIA, INC.
3902 Henderson Blvd Ste 100
Tampa, FL 33629
Tel.: (813) 251-8600
Fax: (813) 251-8622
Web Site: www.tampabaymetro.com
Business Description:
Magazine Publisher
S.I.C.: 2721
N.A.I.C.S.: 511120
Media: 2-6-8-13
Personnel:
Stephen Parag, II *(Publr & Editor-in-Chief)*
Ronda M. Parag *(Publr & Mng Editor)*
Brands & Products:
METROBIZ
METROHOME
METROLIFE
METROLISTING
METRO'S BEST
METROSTOP
METROSTYLE
SUNCOAST LIFE
TAMPA BAY METRO CHARITY REGISTER
TAMPA BAY METRO GUIDE
TAMPA BAY METRO MAGAZINE

METRO NEWSPAPER ADVERTISING SERVICES, INC.
(Sub. of Gemini Communications)
8th W 38th St 4th Fl
New York, NY 10018
Tel.: (212) 576-9502
Fax: (212) 532-1710
E-mail: getinfo@metrosn.com
Web Site: www.metrosn.com
Approx. Sls.: $80,000,000
Approx. Number Employees: 100
Year Founded: 1932
Business Description:
Sales & Marketing of Newspapers
S.I.C.: 5192
N.A.I.C.S.: 424920
Media: 2-7-9-16-17-25
Distr.: Natl.; Reg.
Budget Set: Nov.
Personnel:
Michael Baratoff *(Owner)*
Phyllis Cavaliere *(Chm & CEO)*
Kim Aiello *(Sr VP-Ops)*
Nili DeBono *(Sr VP-Fin-Admin)*
Bill Huck *(Sr VP-Eastern Sls Reg)*
Tack Prashad *(Sr VP-Client Svcs)*
Brands & Products:
METRO TV BOOK NETWORK
ROP NETWORKS
SUNDAY MAGAZINE NETWORK

METRO NEWSPAPERS ADVERTISING SERVICES, INC.
(Sub. of Metro Newspaper Advertising Services, Inc.)
160 Spear St Ste 1875
San Francisco, CA 94105
Tel.: (415) 227-8857
Fax: (415) 227-0995
E-mail: infosf@metrosn.com
Web Site: www.metrosn.com
Approx. Number Employees: 20
Business Description:
Newspaper Planning & Buying Resource

Key to Media (For complete agency information see *The Advertising Red Books-Agencies* edition):
1. Bus. Publs. 2. Cable T.V. 3. Catalogs & Directories. 4. Co-op Adv. 5. Consumer Mags. 6. D.M. to Bus. Estab.7. D.M. to Consumers
8. Daily Newsp. 9. Exhibits/Trade Shows 10. Foreign 11. Infomercial 12. Internet Adv.13. Multimedia 14. Network Radio
15. Network T.V. 16. Newsp. Distr. Mags. 17. Other 18. Outdoor (Posters, Transit) 19. Point of Purchase20. Premiums, Novelties
21. Product Samples 22. Special Events Mktg. 23. Spot Radio 24. Spot T.V. 25. Weekly Newsp. 26. Yellow Page Adv.

S.I.C.: 5192
N.A.I.C.S.: 424920
Media: 2-9-16-25
Personnel:
Ali Nazem *(Sr VP-Western Sls Reg & Digital Bus Dev-Natl)*

METRO PUBLISHING INC.

550 S 1st St
San Jose, CA 95113
Tel.: (408) 200-1300
Fax: (408) 271-3520
E-mail: sales@metronews.com
Web Site: www.metronews.com
E-Mail For Key Personnel:
Sales Director: sales@metronews.com
Approx. Sls.: $22,500,000
Approx. Number Employees: 70
Year Founded: 1978
Business Description:
Publisher of Newspapers
S.I.C.: 2711
N.A.I.C.S.: 511110
Media: 8-9-13
Personnel:
Dan Pulcrano *(CEO)*

METRO-PUCK COMICS NETWORK

(Sub. of Metro Newspaper Advertising Services, Inc.)
8 W 38th St
New York, NY 10018
Tel.: (212) 689-8200
Fax: (212) 532-1710
Web Site: www.metrosn.com/contact.html
Sales Range: $1-9.9 Million
Approx. Number Employees: 55
Year Founded: 1932
Business Description:
Publisher of Sunday Comics Sections for Newspapers
S.I.C.: 7313
N.A.I.C.S.: 541840
Advertising Expenditures: $300,000
Media: 2-7-9-20-25
Distr.: Natl.
Budget Set: Oct.
Personnel:
Phyllis Cavaliere *(Pres & CEO)*
Michael Baratoff *(COO & Exec VP)*
Bill Huck *(Sr VP)*
Nili DeBono *(VP-Fin & Admin)*
Brands & Products:
METRO-PUCK COMICS NETWORK
METRO ROP NETWORKS
SUNDAY MAGAZINE NETWORK

METROWEST DAILY NEWS

(Unit of GateHouse Media New England)
33 New York Ave
Framingham, MA 01701
Tel.: (508) 626-4412
Fax: (508) 626-4400
E-mail: metrowest@cnc.com
Web Site: www.metrowestdailynews.com
Sales Range: $100-124.9 Million
Business Description:
Newspaper Publisher
S.I.C.: 2711
N.A.I.C.S.: 511110
Media: 9
Personnel:
Kirk Davis *(Publr)*
Richard Lodge *(Editor-in-Chief)*
Art Davidson *(Editor-Sports)*
Jenifer Lipson *(Editor-Entertainment)*
Nancy Olesin *(Editor-Lifestyles)*
Cheryl Robinson *(Mgr-Display Ads)*

THE MIAMI HERALD

(Sub. of The Miami Herald Media Company)
1 Herald Plz
Miami, FL 33132
Tel.: (305) 350-2111
Fax: (305) 376-4550
Fax: (305) 376-5287
Toll Free: (800) 437-2535
E-mail: eabad@miamiherald.com
Web Site: www.miami.com
Sales Range: $300-349.9 Million
Approx. Number Employees: 1,000
Year Founded: 1903
Business Description:
Newspaper Publisher
S.I.C.: 2711
N.A.I.C.S.: 511110
Media: 2-4-5-6-7-8-9-18-23-24-26
Distr.: Direct to Consumer; Natl.
Personnel:
David Landsberg *(Pres & Publr)*
Susan A. Rosenthal *(CFO & VP-Fin)*
Alexandra Villoch *(Sr VP-Adv & Mktg)*
Cesar Mendoza *(VP-IT)*
Raul Lopez *(Gen Mgr-Interactive)*
Anders Gyllenhaal *(Editor)*
Elaine Pasekoff *(Mgr-Mktg Promo)*
Brands & Products:
EL NUEVO HERALD
ELNUEVOHERALD.COM
Advertising Agency:
Media Counselors
7700 N Kendall Dr #801
Miami, FL 33156
Tel.: (305) 596-2806
Fax: (305) 598-4973

MIDNIGHT MARQUEE PRESS, INC.

9721 Britinay Ln
Baltimore, MD 21234-1863
Tel.: (410) 665-1198
Fax: (410) 665-9207
E-mail: mmaquee@aol.com
Web Site: www.midmar.com
Approx. Number Employees: 2
Year Founded: 1963
Business Description:
Books & Magazines On Movies Publisher
S.I.C.: 2731
N.A.I.C.S.: 511130
Media: 4-6-8-10
Personnel:
Susan Svehla *(VP & Editor & Co-Owner)*
Gary J. Svehla *(Owner)*
Linda J. Walter *(Copy Editor)*
Brands & Products:
MAD ABOUT MOVIES
MIDNIGHT MARQUEE

THE MILL POND PRESS COMPANIES, INC.

(Sub. of Mill Pond Holdings LLC)
250 Ctr Ct Unit A
Venice, FL 34285
Tel.: (941) 497-6020
Fax: (941) 497-6026
Approx. Number Employees: 35
Year Founded: 1973
Business Description:
Publishers of Fine Art
S.I.C.: 2752
N.A.I.C.S.: 323110
Media: 2-4-10
Personnel:
Linda Schaner *(Pres)*
Linda Sthaner *(Dir-Mktg)*

MILLIGAN NEWS CO. INC.

150 N Autumn St
San Jose, CA 95110
Tel.: (408) 298-3322
Fax: (408) 293-5669
Toll Free: (800) 873-2387
E-mail: ed-dept@milligannews.com
Web Site: www.milligannews.com
Approx. Number Employees: 10
Business Description:
Book Whslr
S.I.C.: 5192; 5942
N.A.I.C.S.: 424920; 451211
Media: 8-9
Personnel:
Patton H. Milligan *(Pres)*

MOD-PAC CORP.

1801 Elmwood Ave
Buffalo, NY 14207-2496
Tel.: (716) 873-0640
Fax: (716) 447-9201
Fax: (800) 873-1269
Toll Free: (800) 666-3722
E-mail: sales@modpac.com
Web Site: www.modpac.com
E-Mail For Key Personnel:
Sales Director: sales@modpac.com
Approx. Rev.: $48,721,000
Approx. Number Employees: 347
Year Founded: 1881
Business Description:
Paperboard Packaging Printer, Designer & Mfr
S.I.C.: 7389; 2657
N.A.I.C.S.: 561910; 322212
Advertising Expenditures: $86,000
Media: 17
Personnel:
Kevin T. Keane *(Chm)*
Daniel G. Keane *(Pres & CEO)*
David B. Lupp *(CFO & COO)*
Daniel J. Geary *(VP-Fin)*
Philip C. Rechin *(VP-Sls)*

MONARCH SERVICES, INC.

4517 Harford Rd
Baltimore, MD 21214
Tel.: (410) 254-9200
Fax: (410) 254-0991
Web Site: www.monarchservices.net
Sales Range: $1-9.9 Million
Approx. Number Employees: 59
Year Founded: 1958
Business Description:
Magazine Publisher
S.I.C.: 2721
N.A.I.C.S.: 511120
Export
Advertising Expenditures: $1,265,000
Media: 8-10-11-13
Distr.: Direct to Consumer; Intl.; Natl.; Reg.
Budget Set: Dec.
Personnel:
Jackson Y. Dott *(Pres)*
Marshall Chadwell *(CFO, Treas, Sec & Controller)*
Andrea Thompson *(Dir-Adv Sls-Natl)*
Brands & Products:
GIRLS' LIFE

THE MONITOR

(Unit of Freedom Newspapers, Inc.)
1400 E Nolana
McAllen, TX 78501
Tel.: (956) 683-4000
Fax: (956) 686-4201
Toll Free: (800) 366-4343
E-mail: info@themonitor.com
Web Site: www.themonitor.com
Sales Range: $10-24.9 Million
Approx. Number Employees: 250
Year Founded: 1909
Business Description:
Publishing Newspaper
S.I.C.: 2711; 7313
N.A.I.C.S.: 511110; 541840
Media: 8-9
Personnel:
Jenise Diaz *(CFO)*
Benita Mendell *(Gen Mgr)*
Stephan Fagan *(Editor)*
Marc Geller *(Editor-Metro)*
Ernie Rodriguez *(Dir-Internet Ops)*
Becky Solis *(Dir-Adv)*
Chris Castillo *(Mgr-Retail Adv Sls)*
Sheri Dease *(Mgr-Creative Svcs)*
Robin Torres *(Mgr-Natl Adv Sls)*
Audra Green *(Coord-Mktg)*
Brands & Products:
THE MONITOR

MOODY PUBLISHERS

(Sub. of Moody Bible Institute)
820 N La Salle Blvd
Chicago, IL 60610-3214
Tel.: (312) 329-2101
Fax: (312) 329-2019
Toll Free: (800) 678-8812
E-mail: publicity@moody.edu
Web Site: www.moodypublishers.com
Approx. Number Employees: 40
Year Founded: 1894
Business Description:
Publisher of Books & Bibles
S.I.C.: 8741; 2721
N.A.I.C.S.: 561110; 511120
Media: 1-2-4-5-6-7-10-14-19-20-21-23-24
Distr.: Intl.; Natl.
Budget Set: July
Personnel:
Greg Thornton *(VP-Publ)*
Brands & Products:
MOODY PRESS, THE NAME YOU CAN TRUST
NORTHFIELD PUBLISHING

THE MORNING CALL, INC.

(Sub. of Tribune Publishing Company)
101 N 6th St
Allentown, PA 18105
Mailing Address:
PO Box 1260
Allentown, PA 18105
Tel.: (610) 820-6500
Fax: (610) 770-3706
Web Site: www.mcall.com
Approx. Number Employees: 900
Year Founded: 1883
Business Description:
Newspaper Publisher
S.I.C.: 2711; 2621
N.A.I.C.S.: 511110; 322122
Media: 2-3-6-7-8-10-13-18-19-20-21-22-23-24

Key to Media (For complete agency information see *The Advertising Red Books-Agencies* edition):
1. Bus. Publs. 2. Cable T.V. 3. Catalogs & Directories. 4. Co-op Adv. 5. Consumer Mags. 6. D.M. to Bus. Estab.7. D.M. to Consumers 8. Daily Newsp. 9. Exhibits/Trade Shows 10. Foreign 11. Internet Adv.12. Internet Adv.13. Multimedia 14. Network Radio 15. Network T.V. 16. Newsp. Distr. Mags. 17. Other 18. Outdoor (Posters, Transit) 19. Point of Purchase20. Premiums, Novelties 21. Product Samples 22. Special Events Mktg. 23. Spot Radio 24. Spot T.V. 25. Weekly Newsp. 26. Yellow Page Adv.

The Morning Call, Inc. — (Continued)

Personnel:
Thomas Brown *(CFO & VP)*
David Erdman *(VP & Editor)*
Mike Miorelli *(Mgr-Digital Topic & Editor-Metro)*
Jodi Duckett *(Editor-Arts & Entertainment)*
Michael Hirsch *(Editor-Features)*
William Kline *(Editor-Sports)*
Irene Kraft *(Editor-Lifestyle)*
Peter Leffler *(Editor-State)*
Steve Boyle *(Dir-Retail Adv)*
William Childs *(Dir-Creative)*
George Figueroa *(Dir-HR)*
Steve Lauber *(Dir-Major & Natl Adv)*
Paul J. Lynch *(Dir-Mfg)*
Linda McDonald *(Dir-Sls & Mktg)*
Bob Brown *(Mgr-Natl Sls-Retail)*
Paul Fernandez *(Mgr-Circulation Retail Sls)*
Heather Hawn *(Mgr-Circulation Admin)*
Dave Houser *(Mgr-Interactive Sls)*
Christine Schiavo *(Mgr-Topic)*
Gene Travagline *(Mgr-Facility Ops)*

THE MORNING SUN

(Unit of GateHouse Media, Inc.)
701 N Locust St
Pittsburg, KS 66762-0570
Mailing Address:
PO Box H
Pittsburg, KS 66762
Tel.: (620) 231-2600
Fax: (620) 231-0645
E-mail: submissions@morningsun.net
Web Site: www.morningsun.net
Sales Range: $25-49.9 Million
Approx. Number Employees: 35
Year Founded: 1895
Business Description:
Newspaper Publisher
S.I.C.: 2711
N.A.I.C.S.: 511110
Media: 8-9-13
Personnel:
Stephen M. Wade *(Publr & Editor)*
Nikki Patrick *(Editor-Family Living)*
Mike Dalton *(Dir-Circulation)*
Andrew Nash *(Dir-Online)*
Kaycie Brown *(Bus Mgr)*
Jeremy Parvin *(Mgr-Prepress & Design)*

MORRIS COMMUNICATIONS COMPANY LLC

(Holding of Shivers Trading & Operating Co.)
725 Broad St
Augusta, GA 30901-1336
Tel.: (706) 724-0851
Fax: (706) 722-0011
Toll Free: (800) 662-6358
Web Site: www.morris.com
Year Founded: 1945
Business Description:
Books, Newspapers, Magazines & Shopping Guides Publisher; Outdoor Advertising Services; Radio Station Broadcasting Services
S.I.C.: 2711; 7319
N.A.I.C.S.: 511110; 541850
Media: 2-4-5-7-8-9-10-13-14-17-18-20-21-22-23-25-26
Distr.: Reg.
Budget Set: Nov.
Personnel:
William S. Morris, III *(Chm & CEO)*
William S. Morris, IV *(Pres)*
Steve K. Stone *(CFO & Sr VP)*
Paul V. Buckley *(CIO)*
Craig S. Mitchell *(Treas, Sec & Sr VP-Fin)*
James C. Currow *(Exec VP-Newspapers)*
Martha Jean McHaney *(VP-HR)*
Terry K. House, Jr. *(Asst Sec & Dir-Tax)*

MORRIS MULTIMEDIA, INC.

27 Abercorn
Savannah, GA 31401
Tel.: (912) 233-1281
Fax: (912) 232-4639
Web Site: www.morrismultimedia.com
Approx. Number Employees: 900
Year Founded: 1970
Business Description:
Newspaper Publishing & Television Broadcasting Services
S.I.C.: 2711; 4833
N.A.I.C.S.: 511110; 515120
Media: 8-9
Personnel:
Charles H. Morris *(Chm & CEO)*
Jeffrey R. Samuels *(CFO & VP)*
H. Dean Hinson *(Pres-Morris Network)*
Jackie Haynes *(Administrator & Coord-HR)*

MORRIS PUBLISHING GROUP, LLC

(Holding of Shivers Trading & Operating Co.)
725 Broad St
Augusta, GA 30901
Tel.: (706) 724-0851
Tel.: (706) 823-3236 (Sr VP-Fin)
Web Site: www.morris.com/divisions/morris_publishing_group
Approx. Rev.: $243,191,000
Approx. Number Employees: 1,668
Year Founded: 2001
Business Description:
Holding Company; Newspaper, Magazine & Shopping Guide Publisher
S.I.C.: 6719; 2711; 2721; 2741
N.A.I.C.S.: 551112; 511110; 511120; 511199; 516110
Advertising Expenditures: $172,686,000
Personnel:
William S. Morris, IV *(CEO)*
Steve K. Stone *(CFO & Sr VP)*
Craig S. Mitchell *(Treas, Sec & Sr VP-Fin)*
Derek J. May *(Exec VP)*

MOTHER EARTH NEWS

(Sub. of Ogden Publications, Inc.)
1503 SW 42nd St
Topeka, KS 66609
Tel.: (785) 274-4300
Fax: (785) 274-4305
Toll Free: (800) 234-3368
Web Site: www.motherearthnews.com
Approx. Number Employees: 100
Year Founded: 1970
Business Description:
Magazine Publisher
S.I.C.: 2721
N.A.I.C.S.: 511120
Import Export
Media: 2-8-13-20
Distr.: Natl.
Personnel:
Bryan Welch *(Publr & Dir-Editorial)*
Cheryl Long *(Editor-in-Chief)*
Brandy Ernzen *(Brand Mgr)*
Brands & Products:
MOTHER EARTH
THE ORIGINAL GUIDE TO LIVING WISELY

MOTOR BOATING MAGAZINE

(Unit of Bonnier Corporation)
460 N Orlando Ave Ste 200
Winter Park, FL 32789
Tel.: (407) 628-4802
Fax: (407) 628-7061
E-mail: info@motorboating.com
Web Site: www.motorboating.com
Sales Range: $100-124.9 Million
Year Founded: 1907
Business Description:
Motor Boating Magazine Publisher
S.I.C.: 2721
N.A.I.C.S.: 511120
Media: 6-8
Distr.: Direct to Consumer; Natl.
Personnel:
John McEver *(Publr)*
Peter A. Janssen *(Dir-Editorial)*
Dave Ritchie *(Dir-Editorial-Marine Grp)*
Emilie Whitcomb *(Dir-Art)*
Brands & Products:
MOTOR BOATING

MOUNT AIRY GAZETTE

(Div. of The Gazette)
218 S Main St
Mount Airy, MD 21771
Mailing Address:
PO Box 298
Damascus, MD 20872-0298
Tel.: (301) 831-0047
Fax: (301) 829-9101
E-mail: carroll@gazette.net
Web Site: www.gazette.net
Sales Range: Less than $1 Million
Approx. Number Employees: 5
Business Description:
Newspaper Publisher
S.I.C.: 2711
N.A.I.C.S.: 511110
Media: 13
Personnel:
Dennis Wilson *(Publr)*

MULTI-AD, INC.

1720 W Detweiller Dr
Peoria, IL 61615-1612
Tel.: (309) 692-1530
Fax: (309) 692-6566
E-mail: corporate@multiad.com
Web Site: www.multi-ad.com
E-Mail For Key Personnel:
President: jdouglas@multi-ad.com
Sales Range: $25-49.9 Million
Approx. Number Employees: 220
Year Founded: 1945
Business Description:
Retail Advertising Materials & Programs Mfr; Contract Printing
S.I.C.: 2741; 7374
N.A.I.C.S.: 511199; 518210
Advertising Expenditures: $300,000
Media: 2-7-10
Distr.: Intl.
Budget Set: Oct.
Personnel:
James Douglas *(Pres & CEO)*
Shelby Vaughan *(CFO)*
John Kocher *(Exec VP)*
Jim Garner *(Sr VP)*
Amy Williamson *(Product Mgr)*
Brands & Products:
AD-BUILDER
KWIKEE
KWIKEE KOLOR
KWIKEE RECAS
KWIKEE SYSTEMS
MULTI-AD
MULTI-AD CREATOR
MULTI-AD SEARCH

MUSIC SALES CORPORATION

257 Pk Ave S Fl 20
New York, NY 10010-7304
Tel.: (212) 254-2100
Fax: (212) 254-2013
Toll Free: (800) 431-7187
E-mail: info@musicsales.com
Web Site: www.musicsales.com
Approx. Number Employees: 80
Year Founded: 1935
Business Description:
Music Publishing
S.I.C.: 2741
N.A.I.C.S.: 512230
Import Export
Media: 1-2-4-5-6-8-10-19-21
Distr.: Natl.
Budget Set: June
Personnel:
Barrie Edwards *(Pres)*
Tomas Wise *(Dir-Digital Publ)*
Philip Black *(Mgr-Pro)*

NAPLES DAILY NEWS

(Sub. of The E.W. Scripps Company)
1100 Immokalee Rd
Naples, FL 34110-6237
Tel.: (239) 262-3161
Fax: (239) 263-4816
E-mail: info@naplesnews.com
Web Site: www.naplesnews.com
E-Mail For Key Personnel:
Sales Director: sales@naplesnews.com
Sales Range: $100-124.9 Million
Approx. Number Employees: 280
Business Description:
Daily Newspaper Publisher
S.I.C.: 2711
N.A.I.C.S.: 511110
Advertising Expenditures: $500,000
Media: 3-8-9-23
Personnel:
David Neill *(Pres & Publr)*
Deb Trinka *(Dir-HR)*
Brands & Products:
NAPLES DAILY NEWS
NAPLESNEWS.COM

NATIONAL ASSOCIATION OF REALTORS

430 N Michigan Ave
Chicago, IL 60611-4011
Tel.: (800) 874-6500
Fax: (312) 329-5978
Toll Free: (800) 874-6500
E-mail: infocencral@realtors.org
Web Site: www.realtor.org
E-Mail For Key Personnel:
President: fsibley@realtors.org
Marketing Director: jthom@realtors.org
Sales Range: $10-24.9 Million
Approx. Number Employees: 300

Key to Media (For complete agency information see *The Advertising Red Books-Agencies* edition):
1. Bus. Publs. 2. Cable T.V. 3. Catalogs & Directories. 4. Co-op Adv. 5. Consumer Mags. 6. D.M. to Bus. Estab.7. D.M. to Consumers 8. Daily Newsp. 9. Exhibits/Trade Shows 10. Foreign 11. Infomercial 12. Internet Adv.13. Multimedia 14. Network Radio 15. Network T.V. 16. Newsp. Distr. Mags. 17. Other 18. Outdoor (Posters, Transit) 19. Point of Purchase20. Premiums, Novelties 21. Product Samples 22. Special Events Mktg. 23. Spot Radio 24. Spot T.V. 25. Weekly Newsp. 26. Yellow Page Adv.

Business Description:
Magazine Publisher
S.I.C.: 8611; 2721
N.A.I.C.S.: 813910; 511120
Advertising Expenditures: $200,000
Media: 2-4-6-7-10-20-22
Distr.: Natl.
Budget Set: Oct.
Personnel:
Dale A. Stinton *(CEO)*
Frank Sibley *(Sr VP-Comm & Conventions)*
Kathy Marusarz *(Mgr-Bus)*
Brands & Products:
E-PRO
ENTERTAINMENT
LISTNINGLOCK
NAR IS THE VOICE FOR REAL ESTATE
NATIONAL ASSOCIATION OF REALTORS
REALTOR
REALTOR BENEFITS
REALTOR.COM
Advertising Agencies:
MOST Brand Development + Advertising
25 Enterprise Ste 250
Aliso Viejo, CA 92656
Tel.: (949) 475-4050
Fax: (949) 475-4051

TargetCom, LLC
444 N Michigan Ave 33rd Fl
Chicago, IL 60611-3905
Tel.: (312) 822-1100
Fax: (312) 822-9628
Toll Free: (877) 423-7837

THE NATIONAL ENQUIRER

(Div. of American Media, Inc.)
1000 American Media Way
Boca Raton, FL 33464-1000
Tel.: (561) 989-1221
Fax: (561) 989-1377
Web Site: www.nationalenquirer.com
Year Founded: 1952
Business Description:
Publishing
S.I.C.: 2731
N.A.I.C.S.: 511130
Media: 8-25
Personnel:
David Becker *(CEO)*
David Jackson *(Publr)*
Mary Beth Wright *(Publr)*
Jane Watson Malan *(Dir-Mktg, American Media)*

NATIONAL GEOGRAPHIC SOCIETY

1145 17th St NW
Washington, DC 20036-4701
Tel.: (202) 857-7000
Fax: (202) 828-6679
Toll Free: (800) 647-5463
E-mail: education@nationalgeographic.com
Web Site:
www.nationalgeographic.com
Approx. Number Employees: 1,300
Year Founded: 1888
Business Description:
Publishers of Books & Magazines, Producers of Television Documentaries
S.I.C.: 2721; 2731
N.A.I.C.S.: 511120; 511130
Advertising Expenditures: $1,000,000
Bus. Publs.: $670,000; D.M. to Bus. Estab.: $180,000; Special Events Mktg.: $150,000
Distr.: Natl.
Budget Set: Jan.
Personnel:
John M. Fahey, Jr. *(CEO)*
Christopher Liedel *(CFO & Exec VP)*
Edward M. Prince, Jr. *(COO-National Geographic Global Media)*
Declan Moore *(Pres-Publ & Exec VP-Natl Geographic Society)*
John Caldwell *(Pres-Digital Media)*
John Griffin *(Pres-Publ)*
Tim Kelly *(Pres-Global Media)*
Terry Adamson *(Exec VP-Govt Affairs)*
Linda Berkeley *(Exec VP)*
Terry D. Garcia *(Exec VP)*
Elizabeth J. Hudson *(Exec VP)*
Eric Brodnax *(Sr VP-Ecommerce & Mktg)*
Jenifer Berman *(VP-Mktg)*
Brendan A. Hart *(VP-Mktg & Bus Intelligence)*
Jim Hoos *(VP-Digital Sls)*
Sheila F. Buckmaster *(Sr Editor-National Geographic Traveler)*
Bryan Kinkade *(Dir-NGA, Travel & Tourism)*
Thomas Lundell *(Dir-Southeast-Digital Adv Sls-NationalGeographic.com)*
Laurin Ensslin *(Travel Brand Mgr-Natl Geographic Global Media-NG Magazine)*
Brands & Products:
NATIONAL GEOGRAPHIC
NATIONAL GEOGRAPHIC ADVENTURE
NATIONAL GEOGRAPHIC KIDS MAGAZINE
NATIONAL GEOGRAPHIC TRAVELER
Advertising Agencies:
Allscope Media
230 W 41st St
New York, NY 10036
Tel.: (212) 253-1300

Bodden Partners
102 Madison Ave
New York, NY 10016-7417
Tel.: (212) 328-1111
Fax: (212) 328-1100
Digital/Online Content

Mediasmith
274 Brannan St Ste 601
San Francisco, CA 94107-2000
Tel.: (415) 252-9339
Fax: (415) 252-9854

NATIONAL JOURNAL GROUP

600 New Hampshire Ave NW Fl 4
Washington, DC 20037-2403
Tel.: (202) 739-8400
Fax: (202) 266-7053
Web Site: www.nationaljournal.com
Approx. Number Employees: 350
Year Founded: 1969
Business Description:
Magazines, Newsletters, Books & Directories Publisher Concerning Government Policy & Politics
S.I.C.: 2721
N.A.I.C.S.: 511120
Media: 2-4-7-9
Personnel:
Andy Sareyan *(Pres & Exec VP-Atlantic Media Co.)*
Elaine Erchak *(CFO)*
Victoria Lion Monroe *(Sr VP)*
David Beard *(Deputy Editor-in-Chief & Editor-Digital)*
Andrea White *(Editor)*
Will Colston *(Dir-Mktg)*
Advertising Agency:
Arnold D.C.
1310 N Courthouse Rd
Arlington, VA 22201
Tel.: (703) 399-3600
Fax: (703) 399-3601

NATIONAL LAMPOON, INC.

8228 W Sunset Blvd
West Hollywood, CA 90046-2414
Tel.: (310) 474-5252
Fax: (310) 474-1219
E-mail: feedback@nationallampoon.com
Web Site: www.nationallampoon.com
Sales Range: $1-9.9 Million
Approx. Number Employees: 24
Year Founded: 1967
Business Description:
Holding Company; Brand Lessor for Feature Films, Television Programming, Interactive Entertainment, Home Video, Audio Recordings & Books
S.I.C.: 6719; 6794
N.A.I.C.S.: 551112; 533110
Advertising Expenditures: $1,762,467
Media: 6-13
Personnel:
James P. Jimirro *(Chm)*
Justin Kanew *(VP-Production & Dev)*
Brands & Products:
NATIONAL LAMPOON
Advertising Agency:
Bender/Helper Impact, Inc.
11500 W Olympic Blvd Ste 655
Los Angeles, CA 90064-1530
Tel.: (310) 473-4147
Fax: (310) 478-4727

NATIONAL REVIEW, INC.

215 Lexington Ave
New York, NY 10016-6023
Tel.: (212) 679-7330
Fax: (212) 849-2835
E-mail: letters@nationalreview.com
Web Site: www.nationalreview.com
Approx. Number Employees: 40
Year Founded: 1955
Business Description:
Political Opinion Magazine Publisher
S.I.C.: 2721
N.A.I.C.S.: 511120
Advertising Expenditures: $250,000
Media: 3-8-9-13-18-21-25
Distr.: Natl.
Budget Set: Nov.
Personnel:
James X. Kilbridge *(CFO)*
Scott Budd *(Publr)*
Richard Lowry *(Editor)*
Brands & Products:
NATIONAL REVIEW

NATURAL HEALTH MAGAZINE

(Div. of Weider Publications, LLC)
21100 Erwin St
Woodland Hills, CA 91367
Tel.: (212) 545-4800
Fax: (818) 992-6895
Web Site: www.naturalhealthmag.com
Approx. Number Employees: 20
Business Description:
Magazine
S.I.C.: 2721
N.A.I.C.S.: 511120
Media: 6-8-22
Personnel:
Peg Moline *(Editor-in-Chief)*

NEBRASKA BOOK COMPANY, INC.

(Sub. of NBC Acquisition Corp.)
4700 S 19th St
Lincoln, NE 68512-1216
Tel.: (402) 421-7300
Fax: (402) 421-0510
Toll Free: (800) 869-0366
E-mail: info@nebook.com
Web Site: www.nebook.com
Year Founded: 1915
Business Description:
Book Store Owner & Operator
S.I.C.: 5942; 5192
N.A.I.C.S.: 451211; 424920
Advertising Expenditures: $7,000,000
Personnel:
Barry S. Major *(Pres & COO)*
Mark W. Oppegard *(CEO)*
Alan G. Siemek *(CFO)*
Larry R. Rempe *(Sr VP-VP-IT & Mgr-Data Processing)*
Steven A. Clemente *(Sr VP-Retail Div)*
Michael J. Kelly *(Sr VP-Textbook Div)*
Advertising Agency:
Bernstein-Rein Advertising, Inc.
4600 Madison Ave Ste 1500
Kansas City, MO 64112-3016
Tel.: (816) 756-0640
Fax: (816) 399-6000
Toll Free: (800) 571-6246

NEUMEDIA, INC.

2000 Ave of the Stars Ste 410
Los Angeles, CA 90067
Tel.: (310) 601-2500
Fax: (310) 277-2741
E-mail: info@mandalaymediainc.com
Web Site:
www.mandalaymediainc.com
Approx. Rev.: $14,037,000
Approx. Number Employees: 196
Year Founded: 1998
Business Description:
Entertainment Content Including Images, Video, TV Programming & Games Publisher & Distr
S.I.C.: 7999; 2741
N.A.I.C.S.: 713990; 511199; 516110
Advertising Expenditures: $1,072,000
Personnel:
Robert S. Ellin *(Co-Chm)*
Peter Guber *(Co-Chm)*
Paul M. Schaeffer *(Vice Chm)*
James Lefkowitz *(Pres)*
Russell Burke *(CFO)*
David Mandell *(Gen Counsel, Sec-Twistbox & Exec VP)*

THE NEW ENGLAND JOURNAL OF MEDICINE

(Div. of Massachusetts Medical Society)
10 Shattuck St
Boston, MA 02115

Key to Media (For complete agency information see *The Advertising Red Books-Agencies* edition):
1. Bus. Publs. 2. Cable T.V. 3. Catalogs & Directories. 4. Co-op Adv. 5. Consumer Mags. 6. D.M. to Bus. Estab.7. D.M. to Consumers
8. Daily Newsp. 9. Exhibits/Trade Shows 10. Foreign 11. Infomercial 12. Internet Adv.13. Multimedia 14. Network Radio
15. Network T.V. 16. Newsp. Distr. Mags. 17. Other 18. Outdoor (Posters, Transit) 19. Point of Purchase20. Premiums, Novelties
21. Product Samples 22. Special Events Mktg. 23. Spot Radio 24. Spot T.V. 25. Weekly Newsp. 26. Yellow Page Adv.

The New England Journal of Medicine — (Continued)

Tel.: (617) 734-9800
Fax: (617) 739-9864
Toll Free: (800) 445-8080
Web Site: www.nejm.org
Sales Range: $10-24.9 Million
Approx. Number Employees: 200
Year Founded: 1812
Business Description:
Medical Journal Published by the Massachusetts Medical Society
S.I.C.: 2721; 8621
N.A.I.C.S.: 511120; 813920
Media: 2-4-8-13
Personnel:
Corinne Broderick *(Exec VP)*
Christopher R. Lynch *(VP-Publ)*
Jeffrey M. Drazen *(Editor-in-Chief)*
Gale Burdett *(Mgr-Sls-Mktg)*
Brands & Products:
THE NEW ENGLAND JOURNAL OF MEDICINE

NEW JERSEY MONTHLY
55 Park Pl
Morristown, NJ 07963
Mailing Address:
PO Box 920
Morristown, NJ 07963-0920
Tel.: (973) 539-8230
Fax: (973) 538-2953
E-mail: info@njmonthly.com
Web Site: www.njmonthly.com
Sales Range: $1-9.9 Million
Approx. Number Employees: 50
Year Founded: 1976
Business Description:
News & Information on New Jersey Publisher
S.I.C.: 2721
N.A.I.C.S.: 511120
Media: 6-10-19-23
Personnel:
Kate S. Tomlinson *(Owner)*
Frank Visconti *(Dir-Sls & Adv)*
Brands & Products:
NEW JERSEY MONTHLY

THE NEW LEADER
535 W 114 St
New York, NY 10027-6708
Tel.: (212) 854-1640
Fax: (212) 854-9099
E-mail: editor@thenewleader.com
Web Site: www.thenewleader.com
Sales Range: Less than $1 Million
Approx. Number Employees: 2
Year Founded: 1924
Business Description:
Magazine Publisher
S.I.C.: 2721
N.A.I.C.S.: 511120
Media: 6-7-8
Distr.: Intl.; Natl.
Personnel:
Mitchel Levitas *(Chm)*

THE NEW REPUBLIC INC.
1331 H St NW Ste 700
Washington, DC 20005-4737
Tel.: (202) 508-4444
Fax: (202) 628-9383
Toll Free: (800) 827-1289
E-mail: online@tnr.com
Web Site: www.tnr.com
Sales Range: $10-24.9 Million
Approx. Number Employees: 65
Year Founded: 1914
Business Description:
Weekly Magazine Publisher
S.I.C.: 2721
N.A.I.C.S.: 511120
Media: 2-6-8-9
Distr.: Natl.
Personnel:
Katherine Marsh *(Mng Editor)*
Franklin Foer *(Editor)*
Richard Just *(Editor)*
Leon Wieseltier *(Literary Editor)*
June Lough *(Dir-Mktg)*
Paula Kapacinskas *(Mgr-Online Adv-Midwest)*
Shannon McAndrews *(Mgr-Online Adv)*
Bob Wagner *(Mgr-Adv-East Coast)*
Bob Washburn *(Mgr-Print Adv-West Coast)*
Brands & Products:
THE NEW REPUBLIC

THE NEW YORK LAW PUBLISHING COMPANY
(Sub. of American Lawyer Media, Inc.)
120 Broadway 5th Fl
New York, NY 10271
Tel.: (212) 457-9545
Fax: (212) 696-4514
Toll Free: (866) 305-3058
Web Site: www.nylj.com
Sales Range: $100-124.9 Million
Approx. Number Employees: 250
Business Description:
Newspaper Publisher for Legal Topics
S.I.C.: 2711; 2732
N.A.I.C.S.: 511110; 323117
Media: 2-8-9-10-13-16-25-26
Distr.: Direct to Consumer; Natl.
Personnel:
William L. Pollak *(Pres & CEO)*
Eric Lundberg *(CFO)*
Stephen P. Lincoln *(Publr)*
Brands & Products:
NEW YORK LAW JOURNAL

NEW YORK MAGAZINE
(Sub. of New York Media Holdings, LLC)
75 Variveck St
New York, NY 10013
Tel.: (212) 508-0700
Fax: (212) 508-0617
E-mail: kathrine.ward@nymag.com
Web Site: www.nymag.com
Approx. Number Employees: 100
Year Founded: 1968
Business Description:
Magazine Publisher
S.I.C.: 2721
N.A.I.C.S.: 511120
Media: 2-7-8-9-18-22
Distr.: Reg.
Budget Set: Annually
Personnel:
Kit Taylor *(COO)*
Lawrence C. Burstein *(Publr)*
Adam Moss *(Editor-in-Chief)*
Jon Gluck *(Editor)*
Robin Raisfeld *(Editor-Food)*
Sona Hacherian Hofstede *(Exec Dir-Creative & Mktg Svcs)*
Ron Stokes *(Exec Dir-Sls & Mktg)*
Chris Dixon *(Dir-Design)*
Sona Hacherin *(Mgr-Mktg)*

THE NEW YORK POST
(Sub. of News America Incorporated)
1211 Ave of the Americas
New York, NY 10036-8701
Tel.: (212) 930-8000
Fax: (212) 930-8540
Web Site: www.nypost.com
Sales Range: $300-349.9 Million
Approx. Number Employees: 1,000
Year Founded: 1801
Business Description:
Publisher of Newspaper
S.I.C.: 2711
N.A.I.C.S.: 511110
Media: 2-3-7-8-9-10-13-18-19-21-22-23-24
Distr.: Direct to Consumer; Natl.
Personnel:
Patrick Judge *(VP-Adv)*
Aimee Rametta *(VP-Mktg)*
Col Allan *(Editor-in-Chief)*
Ralph D'Onofrio *(Dir-Adv)*
James Reilly *(Dir-Sls & Fin)*
Brands & Products:
NEW YORK POST
NYPOST.COM
Advertising Agency:
Young & Rubicam Inc.
285 Madison Ave
New York, NY 10017-6401
Tel.: (212) 210-3000
Fax: (212) 490-9073

THE NEW YORK TIMES
(Sub. of NYT Management Services, Inc.)
620 8th Ave
New York, NY 10018
Tel.: (212) 556-7652
Fax: (212) 556-7088
Toll Free: (800) NYTIMES
E-mail: publisher@nytimes.com
Web Site: www.nytimes.com
Sales Range: $600-649.9 Million
Approx. Number Employees: 3,000
Year Founded: 1851
Business Description:
Newspaper
S.I.C.: 2711; 2721; 4832
N.A.I.C.S.: 511110; 511120; 515111; 515112
Advertising Expenditures: $4,500,000
Media: 2-7-8-9-11-18-21-23-24
Distr.: Natl.
Budget Set: Dec.
Personnel:
Arthur O. Sulzberger, Jr. *(Chm & Publr)*
Scott Heekin-Canedy *(Pres & Gen Mgr)*
Roland A. Caputo *(CFO)*
Kenneth A. Richieri *(Gen Counsel & Sr VP)*
R. Anthony Benten *(Controller & Sr VP-Fin)*
Alexis Buryk *(Sr VP-Adv)*
James C. Lessersohn *(Sr VP-Corp Dev)*
Murray Gaylord *(VP-Mktg)*
Judy E. Gross *(VP-Sys & Tech)*
Mark W. Herlyn *(VP-Adv)*
Alyse Myers *(VP-Brand Programs)*
Eliot Pierce *(VP-Strategy, Bus Dev & Ad Ops)*
Jill Abramson *(Mng Editor)*
John M. Geddes *(Co-Mng Editor)*
Patricia Cohen *(Editor-Ideas)*
Mary Ann Giordano *(Deputy Editor-Styles)*
Jonathan I. Landman *(Deputy Mng Editor)*
Andrew M. Rosenthal *(Editor-Editorial Page)*
William E. Schmidt *(Editor)*
Teresa Tritch *(Editor-Tax & Fin & Economics)*
Pete Wells *(Editor-Dining)*
Diane McNulty *(Exec Dir-Community Affairs & Media Rels)*
Helen Seligman *(Dir-Sls Dev Grp)*
Devon Tighe *(Dir-Customer Insight Grp)*
Paula Schwartz *(Asst Dir-IR & Online Comm)*
Kristin A. Campbell *(Mktg Mgr-Adv & Promo)*
Advertising Agency:
Horn Group
55 Broad St Fl 29
New York, NY 10004
Tel.: (646) 202-9750
Fax: (646) 826-0022

THE NEW YORK TIMES COMPANY
620 8th Ave
New York, NY 10018
Tel.: (212) 556-1234
Fax: (212) 556-7389
E-mail: news-tips@nytimes.com
Web Site: www.nytco.com
Approx. Rev.: $2,393,463,000
Approx. Number Employees: 7,414
Year Founded: 1896
Business Description:
Newspaper, Broadcast & Cable TV
S.I.C.: 2711; 4832
N.A.I.C.S.: 511110; 515112
Media: 2-3-7-8-9-11-13-18-21-23-24-26
Distr.: Natl.
Budget Set: Oct.
Personnel:
Arthur O. Sulzberger, Jr. *(Chm & Publr)*
Michael Golden *(Vice Chm)*
Janet L. Robinson *(Pres & CEO)*
James M. Follo *(CFO & Sr VP)*
Joseph N. Seibert *(CIO & Sr VP)*
Kenneth A. Richieri *(Gen Counsel & Sr VP)*
Diane Brayton *(Sec & Asst Gen Counsel)*
R. Anthony Benten *(Controller & Sr VP-Fin)*
Namini Yasmin *(Sr VP-Mktg & Circulation & Gen Mgr-Reader Applications)*
Alexis Buryk *(Sr VP-Adv)*
Robert H. Christie *(Sr VP-Corp Comm)*
Terry L. Hayes *(Sr VP-Ops & Labor)*
Todd C. McCarty *(Sr VP-HR)*
Martin A. Nisenholtz *(Sr VP-Digital Ops)*
Denise Warren *(Chief Adv Officer & Sr VP)*
Vincenzo Dimaggio *(VP & Asst Controller)*
Desiree Dancy *(Chief Diversity Officer & VP-HR)*
Kerrie Gillis *(VP-Adv)*
Todd Haskell *(VP-Adv, Digital Sls & Ops)*
Seth Rogin *(VP-Adv)*
Michael Valentine *(VP-HR)*

Key to Media (For complete agency information see *The Advertising Red Books-Agencies* edition):
1. Bus. Publs. 2. Cable T.V. 3. Catalogs & Directories. 4. Co-op Adv. 5. Consumer Mags. 6. D.M. to Bus. Estab.7. D.M. to Consumers 8. Daily Newsp. 9. Exhibits/Trade Shows 10. Foreign 11. Infomercial 12. Internet Adv.13. Multimedia 14. Network Radio 15. Network T.V. 16. Newsp. Distr. Mags. 17. Other 18. Outdoor (Posters, Transit) 19. Point of Purchase20. Premiums, Novelties 21. Product Samples 22. Special Events Mktg. 23. Spot Radio 24. Spot T.V. 25. Weekly Newsp. 26. Yellow Page Adv.

Terrance Williams *(VP-HR)*
Sandra Kelder *(Exec Dir-Corp Comm)*
Abbe Serphos *(Exec Dir-Corp Comm)*
Paula Schwartz *(Dir-IR)*

Brands & Products:
THE NEW YORK TIMES

Advertising Agency:
Opto Design
153 W 27th St Ste 1201
New York, NY 10001
Tel.: (212) 254-4470
Fax: (212) 254-5266

THE NEW YORKER MAGAZINE, INC.

(Sub. of Conde Nast Publications, Inc.)
4 Times Sq
New York, NY 10036-6518
Tel.: (212) 286-5400
Fax: (212) 286-4168
Toll Free: (800) 690-6115
E-mail: mediarequests@newyorker.com
Web Site: www.newyorker.com
Sales Range: $75-99.9 Million
Approx. Number Employees: 225
Year Founded: 1925
Business Description:
Magazine Publisher
S.I.C.: 2721
N.A.I.C.S.: 511120
Export
Media: 8
Distr.: Natl.
Budget Set: Nov.
Personnel:
Lisa Hughes *(Publr & VP)*
David Remnick *(Editor)*
Terese Cunningham *(Dir-Adv)*
Jennifer Swanciger *(Dir-Mktg)*
Maria Tenaglia *(Dir-Adv)*

NEWS AMERICA INCORPORATED

(Sub. of News Corporation)
1211 Ave of the Americas
New York, NY 10036-8701
Tel.: (212) 852-7000
Fax: (212) 852-7159
Web Site: www.newscorp.com
Sales Range: $350-399.9 Million
Approx. Number Employees: 6,000
Year Founded: 1923
Business Description:
Publisher of Newspapers, Magazines & Books
S.I.C.: 2711; 2721; 2731
N.A.I.C.S.: 511110; 511120; 511130
Media: 2-6-9-13-14-15-16-18-23-24-25
Personnel:
Keith Rupert Murdoch *(Chm & CEO)*
Chase Carey *(Deputy Chm, Pres & COO)*
David F. DeVoe *(CFO)*
Anthea Disney *(Exec VP-Content)*
John Nallen *(Exec VP & Deputy CFO)*
Haggerty Paul *(Exec VP-Global Tax & Benefits)*
Martin Pompadur *(Exec VP)*
Michael Regan *(Exec VP-Govt Affairs)*
Reed Nolte *(Sr VP-IR)*
Mary Mattimore *(VP-Mktg)*
James Rupert Murdoch *(Deputy COO-News Corp & Dir)*

Brands & Products:
THE BOSTON HERALD

NEWS & RECORD

(Sub. of Landmark Media Enterprises LLC)
200 E Market St
Greensboro, NC 27420-0848
Tel.: (336) 373-7000
Fax: (336) 373-7183
Toll Free: (800) 553-6880
Web Site: www.news-records.com
Approx. Number Employees: 450
Business Description:
Daily Newspaper Publisher; Contract Printing
S.I.C.: 2711; 2721; 2791
N.A.I.C.S.: 511110; 323122; 511120
Media: 9-25
Personnel:
Robin Saul *(Pres & Publr)*
Dennis Shelton *(Editor-in-Chief)*
Allen Johnson *(Editor-Editorial Page)*
John Robinson *(Editor)*
Regina Glaspie *(Dir-Circulation)*
Catherine Kernels *(Dir-Adv)*
Brands & Products:
FOR YOUR LIFE

NEWS CHIEF

(Sub. of Lakeland Ledger Publishing Corporation)
455 6th St SW
Winter Haven, FL 33881
Tel.: (863) 401-6900
Fax: (863) 294-2008
E-mail: news@newschief.com
Web Site: www.newschief.com
Sales Range: $25-49.9 Million
Approx. Number Employees: 80
Year Founded: 1911
Business Description:
Newspaper Publisher
S.I.C.: 2711
N.A.I.C.S.: 511110
Media: 8-9
Personnel:
Jeff Amero *(Dir-Audience)*
Scott Girouard *(Mgr-Online Adv)*
Debra Parker *(Mgr-Classifieds)*
Nanay Pittman *(Mgr-Adv)*
Paul Crate *(Chief Photographer)*
Brands & Products:
CENTRAL SHOPPER
LAKELAND SHOPPER
THE NEWS CHIEF

NEWS CORPORATION

1211 Ave of the Americas
New York, NY 10036
Tel.: (212) 852-7000
Fax: (212) 852-7145
Web Site: www.newscorp.com
Approx. Rev.: $33,405,000,000
Approx. Number Employees: 51,000
Year Founded: 1923
Business Description:
Holding Company; Newpapers, Magazine & Book Publishing, Radio & TV Stations, Motion Picture & TV Program Production & Distribution
S.I.C.: 2711; 2721; 2731; 4832; 4833; 7812
N.A.I.C.S.: 511110; 511120; 511130; 512110; 515112; 515120
Advertising Expenditures: $2,500,000,000
Personnel:
Keith Rupert Murdoch *(Chm & CEO)*
Chase Carey *(Deputy Chm, Pres & COO)*
David F. DeVoe *(CFO & Sr Exec VP)*
James Murdoch *(Deputy COO)*
Katie Vanneck-Smith *(CMO)*
John McKinley *(CTO & Pres-Tech-Digital Media Grp)*
Beryl Cook *(Chief HR Officer & Exec VP)*
Jonathan F. Miller *(Chm/CEO-Digital Media Grp & Chief Digital Officer)*
Jon Housman *(Pres-Digital Journalism Initiatives)*
Lawrence A. Jacobs *(Gen Counsel & Sr Exec VP)*
Jorge Espinel *(Exec VP-Strategy & Corp. Dev-News Digital Media)*
Jack Kennedy *(Exec VP-Ops-News Corp Digital Media)*
Joel Klein *(Exec VP)*
John Nallen *(Exec VP & Deputy CFO)*
Michael Regan *(Exec VP-Govt Affairs)*
Genie Gavenchak *(Chief Compliance & Ethics Officer, Sr VP & Deputy Gen Counsel)*
Christine C. Cook *(Sr VP-Adv Sls-The Daily)*
Teri Everett *(Sr VP-Corp Affairs & Comm)*
Julie Henderson *(Sr VP-Comm & Corp Strategy)*
Reed Nolte *(Sr VP-IR)*
Jack Horner *(VP-Corp Affairs & Comm)*
Tony Santabarbara *(VP-Fin)*
Brands & Products:
FARSI1
SMARTSOURCE
ZEMZEMEH

THE NEWS-ENTERPRISE

(Unit of Landmark Community Newspapers, LLC)
408 W Dixie Ave
Elizabethtown, KY 42701-2455
Tel.: (270) 769-1200
Fax: (270) 765-7318
E-mail: info@thenewsenterprise.com
Web Site: www.newsenterprise.com
Approx. Number Employees: 110
Year Founded: 1974
Business Description:
Daily Newspaper
S.I.C.: 2711; 2721
N.A.I.C.S.: 511110; 511120
Media: 13
Personnel:
Chris Ordway *(Publr)*
Ben Sheroan *(Editor)*
Lisa D'Alessio *(Mgr-HR)*

NEWS GAZETTE INC.

15 E Main St
Champaign, IL 61820
Tel.: (217) 351-5252
Fax: (217) 351-5374
E-mail: news@news-gazette.com
Web Site: www.news-gazette.com
Approx. Number Employees: 400
Business Description:
Newspapers, Publishing & Printing
S.I.C.: 2711
N.A.I.C.S.: 511110
Media: 8-9-22

NEWS HERALD

(Unit of Freedom Newspapers, Inc.)
501 W 11th St
Panama City, FL 32401-1940
Mailing Address:
PO Box 1940
Panama City, FL 32402
Tel.: (850) 747-5000
Fax: (850) 747-5097
E-mail: news@pcna.com
Web Site: www.newsherald.com
Approx. Number Employees: 125
Year Founded: 1936
Business Description:
Newspaper Publishing
S.I.C.: 2711; 2752
N.A.I.C.S.: 511110; 323110
Advertising Expenditures: $80,000
Media: 3-8-9-10-13-19-21-22-23-24
Personnel:
Karen Hanes *(Publr)*
Mike Cazalas *(Editor)*
Pam Gregory *(Dir-Adv)*
Brands & Products:
THE NEWS HERALD

THE NEWS-HERALD

(Sub. of Heritage Newspapers, Inc.)
1 Heritage Pl Ste 100
Southgate, MI 48195
Tel.: (734) 246-0800
Fax: (734) 246-2727
E-mail: editor@heritage.com
Web Site: www.heritage.com
Approx. Number Employees: 45
Business Description:
Newspaper Publisher
S.I.C.: 2711; 2721
N.A.I.C.S.: 511110; 511120
Media: 25
Personnel:
Jeff Schell *(Dir-Adv)*
Tim Ingle *(Mgr-Adv)*
Stacey Mastascusa *(Mgr-Sls & Mktg)*

NEWS-LEADER

(Sub. of Community Newspapers Inc.)
511 Ash St
Fernandina Beach, FL 32034-3930
Mailing Address:
PO Box 766
Fernandina Beach, FL 32035-0766
Tel.: (904) 261-3696
Fax: (904) 261-3698
Web Site: www.fbnewsleader.com
Approx. Number Employees: 25
Business Description:
Newspaper Publishing
S.I.C.: 2711
N.A.I.C.S.: 511110
Media: 8-9-18
Personnel:
Foy Maloy *(Publr)*
Beth Jones *(Editor-Sports)*
Sian Perry *(Editor)*
Robert Fiege *(Dir-Production)*
Mike Hankins *(Dir-Adv)*
Bob Timpe *(Dir-Circulation)*
Angeline Mudd *(Mgr-Bus)*

NEWS MEDIA CORPORATION

211 Hwy 38 E
Rochelle, IL 61068
Tel.: (815) 562-2061
Fax: (815) 562-2161
E-mail: info@newsmediacorporation.com
Web Site:
www.newsmediacorporation.com
Sales Range: $25-49.9 Million
Approx. Number Employees: 650
Year Founded: 1975

Key to Media (For complete agency information see *The Advertising Red Books-Agencies* edition):
1. Bus. Publs. 2. Cable T.V. 3. Catalogs & Directories. 4. Co-op Adv. 5. Consumer Mags. 6. D.M. to Bus. Estab.7. D.M. to Consumers
8. Daily Newsp. 9. Exhibits/Trade Shows 10. Foreign 11. Infomercial 12. Internet Adv.13. Multimedia 14. Network Radio
15. Network T.V. 16. Newsp. Distr. Mags. 17. Other 18. Outdoor (Posters, Transit) 19. Point of Purchase20. Premiums, Novelties
21. Product Samples 22. Special Events Mktg. 23. Spot Radio 24..Spot T.V. 25. Weekly Newsp. 26. Yellow Page Adv.

News Media Corporation — (Continued)

Business Description:
Newspapers
S.I.C.: 2711
N.A.I.C.S.: 511110
Media: 8-9
Personnel:
John C. Tompkins *(Pres)*
John Shank *(Gen Mgr)*
Brands & Products:
DESERT TIMES
NEWS MEDIA CORPORATION

NEWS PUBLISHING COMPANY

305 E 6th Ave
Rome, GA 30162
Tel.: (706) 291-6397
Fax: (706) 290-5228
Web Site: www.romenews-tribune.com
Sales Range: $10-24.9 Million
Approx. Number Employees: 225
Business Description:
Newspapers, Publishing & Printing
S.I.C.: 2711
N.A.I.C.S.: 511110
Media: 8-9
Personnel:
Burgett H. Mooney, III *(Pres)*
Otis Raybon *(Publr)*
Joe Morgan *(Mgr-Bus)*
Brands & Products:
NEWSPAPERS

THE NEWS-SENTINEL

(Sub. of Fort Wayne Newspapers, Inc.)
600 W Main St
Fort Wayne, IN 46802
Tel.: (260) 461-8444
Fax: (260) 461-8817
E-mail: nsmetro@news-sentinel.com
Web Site: www.news-sentinel.com
Approx. Number Employees: 55
Business Description:
Newspaper
S.I.C.: 2711
N.A.I.C.S.: 511110
Media: 13
Personnel:
Michael Christman *(Publr)*
Kerry Hubartt *(Editor)*
Tracy Kelley *(Dir-Adv)*

NEWS-SUN, INC.

(Sub. of Harbor Point Media)
2227 US Hwy 27 S
Sebring, FL 33870
Tel.: (863) 386-5625
Fax: (863) 385-1954
Web Site: www.newssun.com
Sales Range: $1-9.9 Million
Approx. Number Employees: 45
Year Founded: 1920
Business Description:
Newspaper Publications
S.I.C.: 2711
N.A.I.C.S.: 511110
Media: 8-9

THE NEWS-TIMES

(Unit of Hearst Newspapers)
(d/b/a The Danbury News-Times)
333 Main St
Danbury, CT 06810-5818
Tel.: (203) 744-5100
Fax: (203) 792-2163
Web Site: www.newstimes.com
Year Founded: 1883
Business Description:
Newspaper Publisher
S.I.C.: 2711
N.A.I.C.S.: 511110
Advertising Expenditures: $50,000
Media: 5-6-7-8-9-10-13-18-20-22-25-26
Personnel:
Mark Aldam *(Exec VP-Hearst Newspapers)*
Art Cummings *(Editor)*
Linda Tuccio-Koonz *(Editor-Features)*
Keith Whamond *(Editor-Online)*
Robbin Jorgensen Plouffe *(Reg Dir-Sls)*
Erin Youngquist *(Reg Dir-Sls & Recruitment)*
Tony Fasanella *(Sls Dir-Automotive & Real Estate)*
Elliott Huron *(Sls Dir-Major Acct)*
Ron Darr *(Dir-Ops)*
Christopher Bell *(Mgr-Interactive Sls)*
Suzanne Gallagher *(Mgr-Sls)*
Rich Joudy *(Mgr-Info Tech)*
Loraine Marshall *(Mgr-Retail Adv)*
Nancy Mengler *(Mgr-Creative Svcs)*
Adam Ramli *(Mgr-Interactive Sls)*
Matt Soper *(Mgr-Adv Automotive)*
Teresa Rousseau *(Copy Editor & Coord)*

THE NEWS TRIBUNE

(Sub. of News Tribute)
1950 S State St
Tacoma, WA 98405
Mailing Address:
PO Box 11000
Tacoma, WA 98411-0008
Tel.: (253) 597-8742
Fax: (253) 597-8274
Web Site: www.tribnet.com
Sales Range: $50-74.9 Million
Approx. Number Employees: 200
Year Founded: 1880
Business Description:
Publisher of Newspapers
S.I.C.: 2711
N.A.I.C.S.: 511110
Media: 3-8-9-13-16-18-23-24-26
Distr.: Reg.
Budget Set: Nov. -Dec.
Personnel:
David A. Zeeck *(Pres & Publr)*
Rodney W. Robinson *(Dir-IT)*
Gary Standridge *(Mgr-Brand Mktg)*
Brands & Products:
THE NEWS TRIBUNE

NEWS TRIBUNE CO.

210 Monroe St
Jefferson City, MO 65101
Tel.: (573) 636-3131
Fax: (573) 761-0235
E-mail: nt@newstribune.com
Web Site: www.newstribune.com
Approx. Sls.: $10,000,000
Approx. Number Employees: 120
Business Description:
Newspapers, Publishing & Printing
S.I.C.: 2711; 3555
N.A.I.C.S.: 511110; 333293
Media: 8-9-13
Personnel:
Mike Vivion *(Gen Mgr)*
Jane Haslag *(Mgr)*
Brands & Products:
NEWS TRIBUNE

NEWS WEST PUBLISHING COMPANY INC.

(Sub. of Brehm Communications Inc.)
2435 S Miracle Mile
Bullhead City, AZ 86442-7311
Tel.: (928) 763-2505
Fax: (928) 763-2369
E-mail: mvdnews@mohavedailynews.com
Web Site: www.mohavedailynews.com
Approx. Number Employees: 100
Year Founded: 1963
Business Description:
Daily Except Saturday Paper Publisher
S.I.C.: 2711; 2721
N.A.I.C.S.: 511110; 511120
Media: 9
Personnel:
Gary Milks *(Pres & Publr)*

NEWS WORLD COMMUNICATIONS INC

(Sub. of Family Federation for World Peace & Unification)
3600 New York Ave NE
Washington, DC 20002-1947
Tel.: (202) 636-3000
Fax: (202) 636-8906
Toll Free: (888) 927-4846
Web Site: www.washingtontimes.com
Approx. Number Employees: 100
Year Founded: 1982
Business Description:
Publisher of Daily Newspaper
S.I.C.: 7313; 2752
N.A.I.C.S.: 541840; 323110
Advertising Expenditures: $3,000,000
Media: 1-7-8-9-13-17-20-23-24
Distr.: Reg.
Budget Set: Mar.
Personnel:
Curt Sheel *(Gen Mgr)*
Joseph W. Scopin *(Asst Mng Editor)*
Maria Stainer *(Asst Mng Editor)*
Marjorie O'Donnell *(Dir-Special Sls Grp)*
Brands & Products:
THE WASHINGTON TIMES

NEWSDAY LLC

(Sub. of Cablevision Systems Corporation)
235 Pinelawn Rd
Melville, NY 11747
Tel.: (631) 843-2020
Fax: (631) 843-2375
Web Site: www.newsday.com
Sales Range: $250-299.9 Million
Year Founded: 2008
Business Description:
Holding Company; Newspaper & Online Media Publisher
S.I.C.: 6719; 2711
N.A.I.C.S.: 551112; 511110; 519130
Personnel:
Terry Jimenez *(Pres-Media Grp)*
Fred Groser *(Publr)*
Kenneth J. DePaoloa *(Exec VP-Sls & Mktg)*
Tim Martin *(VP-HR & Labor Rels)*
Bill Miller *(Editor-Metro)*
Frank Czuchan *(Dir-Consumer Mktg & Brand Strategy)*
Erik Zenhausern *(Dir-Circulation & Subscription)*
Advertising Agency:
The Brooklyn Brothers
18 E 17th St 6th Fl
New York, NY 10003
Tel.: (212) 242-0200
Fax: (212) 242-0217

NEWSWEEK, INC.

(Sub. of The Washington Post Company)
395 Hudson St
New York, NY 10014
Tel.: (212) 445-4000
Web Site: www.newsweek.com
Sales Range: $100-124.9 Million
Approx. Number Employees: 350
Year Founded: 1933
Business Description:
Magazine Publisher
S.I.C.: 2721
N.A.I.C.S.: 511120
Export
Advertising Expenditures: $1,000,000
Media: 1-6-8-11-22
Distr.: Natl.
Budget Set: Dec.
Personnel:
Thomas Ascheim *(CEO)*
Patrick Hagerty *(Publr-US)*
John M. Ernst *(Dir-Sls Opers)*
Brands & Products:
NEWSWEEK
Advertising Agencies:
Fletcher Media Group
94 Grove St
Peterborough, NH 03458
Tel.: (603) 924-6383
Fax: (603) 924-6562

Marketing Communications International Inc.
(d/b/a AdMarket International)
105 Woodrow Ave
Southport, CT 06890
Tel.: (203) 319-1000
Fax: (203) 319-1004

Sparxoo
4400 W Spruce St # 333
Tampa, FL 44607
Tel.: (646) 345-1800

THE NEWTON KANSAN

(Unit of GateHouse Media, Inc.)
121 W 6th St
Newton, KS 67114-0268
Tel.: (316) 283-1500
Fax: (316) 283-2471
Toll Free: (888) 526-7261
E-mail: news@thekansan.com
Web Site: www.thekansan.com
Sales Range: $10-24.9 Million
Approx. Number Employees: 35
Year Founded: 1872
Business Description:
Newspaper Publisher
S.I.C.: 2711
N.A.I.C.S.: 511110
Media: 8-9
Personnel:
Ken Knepper *(Publr)*
Shelly Drake *(Controller & Bus Dir)*
Mark Schnabel *(Editor)*

Key to Media (For complete agency information see *The Advertising Red Books-Agencies* edition):
1. Bus. Publs. 2. Cable T.V. 3. Catalogs & Directories. 4. Co-op Adv. 5. Consumer Mags. 6. D.M. to Bus. Estab.7. D.M. to Consumers
8. Daily Newsp. 9. Exhibits/Trade Shows 10. Foreign 11. Infomercial 12. Internet Adv.13. Multimedia 14. Network Radio
15. Network T.V. 16. Newsp. Distr. Mags. 17. Other 18. Outdoor (Posters, Transit) 19. Point of Purchase20. Premiums, Novelties
21. Product Samples 22. Special Events Mktg. 23. Spot Radio 24. Spot T.V. 25. Weekly Newsp. 26. Yellow Page Adv.

NIELSEN BUSINESS MEDIA
(Group of The Nielsen Company (US), LLC)
770 Broadway
New York, NY 10003-9595
Tel.: (646) 654-4500
Fax: (646) 654-7272
E-mail: bmcomm@nielsen.com
Web Site: www.nielsenbusinessmedia.com
Approx. Number Employees: 600
Business Description:
Books & Book Clubs, Research & Information Services & Marketing Services; Publisher of Annual Directories & Magazines
S.I.C.: 2721; 2741; 7389
N.A.I.C.S.: 511120; 516110; 519190; 561920
Import Export
Media: 2-4-7-8-9-10-11-13-19-20-22-26
Distr.: Intl.; Natl.
Budget Set: Nov.
Personnel:
Sabrina Crow *(Mng Dir & Sr VP)*
John Burbank *(Pres-Nielsen Strategic Initiatives)*
David Loechner *(Pres-Nielsen Expositions)*
Linda McCutcheon *(Sr VP)*
Michael Alicea *(Sr VP-Global HR)*
Gerry Byrne *(Sr VP-Media & Entertainment Grp)*
Mark Hosbein *(Sr VP-Adv Solutions)*
Joe Randall *(Sr VP-Building Design)*
Mary Kay Sustek *(Sr VP-Central Svcs)*
Karen Benezra *(VP & Exec Dir)*
Susan Tremblay *(Dir-Bus Dev-Mktg & Media Grp)*
Brands & Products:
AMPHOTO
ARCHITECTURE
BACK STAGE
BACK STAGE WEST
BILLBOARD
BILLBOARD BULLETIN
BILLBOARD INFORMATION NETWORK
BPI ENTERTAINMENT NEWS WIRE
INTERIORS
INTERNATIONAL MUSIC & MEDIA CONFERENCE
MARKETING COMPUTERS
MUSIC & MEDIA
MUSIC VIDEO CONFERENCE AWARDS
PHOTO DISTRICT NEWS
PIX
THE PRODUCER'S MASTERGUIDE
ROSS REPORTS
TV INDEX
WATERCOLOR
WATSON-GUPTILL
WHITNEY LIBRARY OF DESIGN

NJBIZ
(Sub. of Journal Publications Inc.)
220 Davidson Ave Ste 302
Somerset, NJ 08873
Tel.: (732) 246-7677
Fax: (732) 846-0421
Fax: (732) 249-8886
Toll Free: (888) NJNEWS1
E-mail: info@njbiz.com
Web Site: www.njbiz.com
Approx. Number Employees: 35
Year Founded: 1988
Business Description:
Business Information Publisher Specific to New Jersey
S.I.C.: 2711
N.A.I.C.S.: 511110
Media: 2-7-10-13-16-22
Personnel:
Lawrence M. Kluger *(Pres)*
David Schankweiler *(CEO)*
Penelope Spencer *(Sr Acct Exec)*
Brands & Products:
NJBIZ
NJBIZADVERTISING
NJBIZ.COM
NJBIZDAILY
NJBIZDATA
NJBIZEVENTS

NORTH AMERICAN PUBLISHING COMPANY
1500 Spring Gdn St Ste 1200
Philadelphia, PA 19130
Tel.: (215) 238-5300
Fax: (215) 238-5457
Toll Free: (800) 777-8074
E-mail: customerservice@napco.com
Web Site: www.napco.com
Approx. Number Employees: 125
Year Founded: 1944
Business Description:
Business, Professional & Consumer Magazine Publisher
S.I.C.: 2721
N.A.I.C.S.: 511120
Advertising Expenditures: $500,000
Media: 6-8-9-13-14-17-23-25
Distr.: Direct to Consumer; Intl.; Natl.; Reg.
Budget Set: Nov.
Personnel:
Irvin J. Borowsky *(Founder & Chm)*
Ned S. Borowsky *(Pres & CEO)*
Bob Gibbons *(Sr VP)*
Ernie Kollias *(VP-Fin & Controller)*
Alexis Luciano *(Dir-eLearning)*
Brands & Products:
BUSINESS FORMS & SYSTEMS
BUSINESS FORMS LABELS & SYSTEMS
DEALERSCOPE MERCHANDISING
INPLANT GRAPHIC
MAGAZINE & BOOKSELLER
PRINTING IMPRESSIONS
PUBLISH & PRODUCTION EXECUTIVE
TARGET MARKETING
TELEVISION PROGRAMMING SOURCEBOOK

THE NORTH BAY NUGGET
(Div. of Osprey Media Group, Inc.)
259 Worthington St W
North Bay, ON P1B 3B5, Canada
Mailing Address:
PO Box 570
North Bay, ON P1B 8J6, Canada
Tel.: (705) 472-3200
Fax: (705) 472-1438
Telex: 705-472-1438
E-mail: news@nugget.ca
Web Site: www.nugget.ca
Approx. Number Employees: 89
Year Founded: 1907
Business Description:
Daily Newspaper
S.I.C.: 2711
N.A.I.C.S.: 511110
Media: 8-9
Personnel:
Dan Johnson *(Publr)*
Steve Page *(Dir-Adv)*
Ken Ferance *(Mgr)*

NORTH JERSEY MEDIA GROUP INC.
150 River St
Hackensack, NJ 07601-7110
Tel.: (201) 646-4000
Fax: (201) 457-2520
E-mail: marketing@northjersey.com
Web Site: www.northjersey.com
Approx. Rev.: $248,000,000
Approx. Number Employees: 1,500
Year Founded: 1921
Business Description:
Owns & Operates Newspapers & Television Stations
S.I.C.: 2711
N.A.I.C.S.: 511110
Media: 8-9-20-22-23
Personnel:
Malcolm A. Borg *(Chm)*
Steven A. Borg *(Pres)*
Andy Eick *(VP-Consumer Sls & Circulation)*
Brands & Products:
RECORD

THE NORTHERN NEWS
(Div. of Osprey Media Group, Inc.)
8 Duncan Avenue
Kirkland Lake, ON P2N 3L4, Canada
Mailing Address:
P.O. Box 1030
Kirkland Lake, ON P2N 3L4, Canada
Tel.: (705) 567-5321
Fax: (705) 567-5377
E-mail: news@northernnews.ca
Web Site: www.northernnews.ca
Approx. Number Employees: 12
Business Description:
Daily Newspaper
S.I.C.: 2711
N.A.I.C.S.: 511110
Media: 13-25
Personnel:
Tim Creswell *(Gen Mgr & Mgr-Adv)*

NORTHSTAR TRAVEL MEDIA LLC
(Holding of Boston Ventures Management, Inc.)
100 Lighting Way
Secaucus, NJ 07094-3619
Tel.: (201) 902-2000
Fax: (201) 902-1822
Web Site: www.northstartravelmedia.com
Approx. Number Employees: 200
Year Founded: 2001
Business Description:
Publisher of Periodicals
S.I.C.: 2721
N.A.I.C.S.: 511120
Personnel:
Thomas Kemp *(Chm & CEO)*
Linda Li Davachi *(CFO)*
Robert G. Sullivan *(VP & Publr-Travel Weekly)*
Lori Cioffi *(VP, Dir-Meetings Grp, Editor-in-Chief-M & C)*
Arnie Weissmann *(VP, Dir-Editorial & Editor-in-Chief-Travel Weekly)*
Janine L. Bavoso *(VP-HR)*
Michelle M. Rosenberg *(VP-Mktg Solutions)*
Kenneth Shapiro *(Editor-in-Chief-TravelAge West)*
Roberta Bianchi-Muller *(Dir-Internet Production)*
Beth Koesser *(Dir-Database Content)*
Rich Mastropietro *(Dir-Info Tech Infrastructure & Ops)*
Cindy D. Sheaffer *(Dir-NC Ops, Editorial Dir-Electronic Products Grp)*
Advertising Agency:
PlattForm Advertising
708 3rd Ave 12th Fl
New York, NY 10017
Tel.: (212) 684-4800
Fax: (212) 576-1129
Toll Free: (866) 671-4429

NORTHWEST FLORIDA DAILY NEWS
(Unit of Freedom Newspapers, Inc.)
200 NW Racetrack Rd PO Box 2949
Fort Walton Beach, FL 32547
Tel.: (850) 863-1111
Fax: (850) 862-5230
Web Site: www.nwfdailynews.com
Sales Range: $1-9.9 Million
Approx. Number Employees: 125
Year Founded: 1946
Business Description:
Newspaper Publishing
S.I.C.: 2711
N.A.I.C.S.: 511110
Media: 8-9
Personnel:
Tom Conner *(Publr)*
Jason Mobley *(Gen Mgr)*
Colin Lipnicky *(Editor)*
Craig Hatcher *(Dir-Adv)*
April Gaffka *(Mgr-Adv & Sls)*
Brands & Products:
NORTHWEST FLORIDA DAILY NEWS

NOVO 1, INC.
20825 Swenson Dr Ste 200
Waukesha, WI 53186
Tel.: (262) 827-6400
Fax: (262) 827-6440
Toll Free: (877) 810-7171
Web Site: www.novo1.com
Sales Range: $75-99.9 Million
Approx. Number Employees: 2,500
Business Description:
Direct Marketing Tools & Services
S.I.C.: 7389
N.A.I.C.S.: 561499
Media: 2-10
Personnel:
George D. Dalton *(Chm & CEO)*
Terrence O'Reilly *(Gen Counsel, Sec & Sr Exec VP-Fin)*
Michael Hennen *(Exec VP-Ops & Controller)*
Kevin Kasper *(Sr VP-Mktg)*
Brands & Products:
NOVO 1

THE NPD GROUP, INC.
900 W Shore Rd
Port Washington, NY 11050-4624
Tel.: (516) 625-0700
Fax: (516) 625-4888
E-mail: info@npd.com
Web Site: www.npd.com
Approx. Number Employees: 950
Year Founded: 1953

Key to Media (For complete agency information see *The Advertising Red Books-Agencies* edition):
1. Bus. Publs. 2. Cable T.V. 3. Catalogs & Directories. 4. Co-op Adv. 5. Consumer Mags. 6. D.M. to Bus. Estab.7. D.M. to Consumers 8. Daily Newsp. 9. Exhibits/Trade Shows 10. Foreign 11. Infomercial 12. Internet Adv.13. Multimedia 14. Network Radio 15. Network T.V. 16. Newsp. Distr. Mags. 17. Other 18. Outdoor (Posters, Transit) 19. Point of Purchase20. Premiums, Novelties 21. Product Samples 22. Special Events Mktg. 23. Spot Radio 24. Spot T.V. 25. Weekly Newsp. 26. Yellow Page Adv.

The NPD Group, Inc. — (Continued)

Business Description:
Market Information Services
S.I.C.: 8732
N.A.I.C.S.: 541910
Media: 13
Personnel:
Tod Johnson *(Chm & CEO)*
Karyn Schoenbart *(Pres & COO)*
Tom Lynch *(CFO & COO)*
Dennis Brown *(Pres-Beauty/Home/Fashion Grp)*
Diane Nicholson *(Pres-Beauty)*
Mark Turim *(Pres-Asia Pacific)*
Tim Bush *(Gen Mgr)*

NUARC COMPANY, INC.
(Sub. of M&R Printing Equipment Inc.)
6200 W Howard St
Niles, IL 60714
Tel.: (847) 967-4400
Tel.: (847) 967-4465 (International)
Fax: (847) 967-9664
Fax: (847) 967-0417 (International)
Toll Free: (800) 962-8883
E-mail: info@nuarc.com
Web Site: www.mrprint.com/en/Home.aspx
Approx. Number Employees: 300
Year Founded: 1946
Business Description:
Mfr. of Graphic Arts Equipment
S.I.C.: 3861; 3555
N.A.I.C.S.: 333315; 333293
Export
Advertising Expenditures: $200,000
Media: 2-4-7-10-11-13-26
Distr.: Intl.; Natl.
Budget Set: Nov.
Brands & Products:
FLIP-TOP
NUARC

NURSING2008
(Unit of Lippincott Williams & Wilkins, Inc.)
323 Norristown Rd Ste 200
Ambler, PA 19002
Tel.: (215) 646-8700
Fax: (215) 367-2155
E-mail: nursing@wolterskluwer.com
Web Site: www.nursing2008.com
Approx. Number Employees: 80
Business Description:
Nursing Journal
S.I.C.: 5113
N.A.I.C.S.: 424130
Media: 6-7-8-10-13
Personnel:
Linda Lafkowski Jones *(Editor-in-Chief)*
Jan Corwin Enger *(Editor)*
Denise D. Hayes *(Editor-Clinical)*
Keith Follweiler *(Exec Dir-Mktg)*
Lisa Whelan *(Assoc Dir-Direct Mktg)*
Pat Wendelken *(Mgr-Recruitment Adv Sls)*

OAG WORLDWIDE LIMITED
(Sub. of OAG Worldwide Limited)
3025 Highland Pkwy Ste 200
Downers Grove, IL 60515-5561
Tel.: (630) 515-5300
Fax: (630) 515-5301
Toll Free: (800) 342-5624
E-mail: custsvc@oag.com
Web Site: www.oag.com
Approx. Number Employees: 50
Year Founded: 1929
Business Description:
Publisher of Travel & Transportation Guides, Online Information & Magazines
S.I.C.: 2741
N.A.I.C.S.: 511199
Media: 2-4-6-7-8-10-13-20
Distr.: Intl.; Natl.
Personnel:
Stephen Bray *(Mng Dir)*
Brent Albrecht *(Dir-Global Mktg)*
Brands & Products:
FREQUENT FLYER MAGAZINE
OAG CARGO EXPRESS
OAG EXECUTIVE FLIGHT GUIDE
OAGEXPRESS

THE OAK RIDGER, LLC
(Unit of GateHouse Media, Inc.)
785 Oak Ridge Tpke
Oak Ridge, TN 37830-7076
Tel.: (865) 482-1021
Fax: (865) 220-5460
Web Site: www.oakridger.com
Sales Range: $10-24.9 Million
Year Founded: 1949
Business Description:
Newspaper Publisher
S.I.C.: 2711
N.A.I.C.S.: 511110
Media: 8-9-13
Personnel:
Darrell Richardson *(Publr & Editor)*
Tank Johnson *(Editor-Sports)*
Christopher Lamm *(Mgr-Online Ads & Webmaster)*
Sonya Isabell *(Mgr-Classified Ads)*
Janet Wood *(Mgr-Display Ads)*
Brands & Products:
THE OAK RIDGER

OBSERVER PUBLISHING COMPANY
122 S Main St
Washington, PA 15301
Tel.: (724) 222-2200
Fax: (724) 229-2754
Web Site: www.observer-reporter.com
Approx. Sls.: $17,000,000
Approx. Number Employees: 300
Business Description:
Newspapers
S.I.C.: 2711; 2759
N.A.I.C.S.: 511110; 323119
Media: 8-9
Personnel:
David Lyle *(CFO)*
Thomas P. Northrop *(Publr)*
Brands & Products:
THE ALMANAC
OBSERVER REPORTER

OCONEE PUBLISHING INC.
(Sub. of Edwards Publications Inc.)
(d/b/a Messenger, The)
210 W N 1st St
Seneca, SC 29678
Tel.: (864) 882-2375
Fax: (864) 882-2381
E-mail: newsed@dailyjm.com
Web Site: www.upstatetoday.com
Approx. Rev.: $3,100,000
Approx. Number Employees: 52
Business Description:
Newspapers, Publishing & Printing
S.I.C.: 2711; 2721
N.A.I.C.S.: 511110; 511120
Media: 8-9
Personnel:
Diana Augustine *(Dir-Adv)*
Brands & Products:
DAILY JOURNAL
GOLDEN CORNERS SHOPPER'S GUIDE
UPSTATE THIS WEEK

ODESSA AMERICAN
(Unit of Freedom Newspapers, Inc.)
222 E Fourth St
Odessa, TX 79760
Tel.: (432) 337-4661
Fax: (432) 334-8671
E-mail: info@oaoa.com
Web Site: www.oaoa.com
Approx. Number Employees: 70
Year Founded: 1940
Business Description:
Newspaper
S.I.C.: 2711
N.A.I.C.S.: 511110
Media: 6-8-9-13-22-23-24
Personnel:
Patrick Canty *(Publr)*
John Kerr *(Exec Editor)*
Lynn Van Amburgh *(Dir-Ops)*
Laura Denn *(Adv Dir)*
Arleene Loyd *(Dir-Bus Retention & Expansion)*
Stacey Ream *(Dir-Adv & Mktg)*
Linda Sweatt *(Dir-Convention & Visitors Bureau)*
Eve Flores-Gamboa *(Mgr-Mktg)*
Angie Fuentes *(Mgr-Classified Sls)*
Coye S. Kerley *(Mgr-Adv Sls)*
Sean Maggio *(Mgr-Interactive)*
Stacy Reeves *(Coord-Natl Adv)*

OGDEN NEWSPAPERS, INC.
1500 Main St
Wheeling, WV 26003
Tel.: (304) 233-0100
Fax: (304) 233-0327
E-mail: myer@new-register.net
Web Site: www.oweb.com
Approx. Number Employees: 5,000
Year Founded: 1890
Business Description:
Newspaper & Magazine Publisher
S.I.C.: 2711; 2721
N.A.I.C.S.: 511110; 511120
Media: 8-9-13
Personnel:
Robert Nutting *(CEO)*
Duane Wittman *(CFO)*
Pam Bennett *(Dir-Adv)*

OGDEN PUBLICATIONS, INC.
(Sub. of Ogden Newspapers, Inc.)
1503 SW 42nd St
Topeka, KS 66609-1265
Tel.: (785) 274-4300
Fax: (785) 274-4305
Toll Free: (800) 678-5779
E-mail: advertising@ogdenpubs.com
Web Site: www.ogdenpubs.com
Approx. Sls.: $29,900,000
Approx. Number Employees: 125
Business Description:
Magazine Publisher
S.I.C.: 2721
N.A.I.C.S.: 511120
Media: 6-8-13
Personnel:
Jessica Kellner *(Mng Editor)*
Rod Peterson *(Dir-Adv)*
Brandy Ernzen *(Brand Mgr)*
Brands & Products:
BRAVE HEARTS
CAPPER'S
EARTHMOMENT.COM
FARM COLLECTOR
GAS ENGINE MAGAZINE
GOOD THINGS TO EAT
GRIT
HERB COMPANION
HERBS FOR HEALTH
MOTHER EARTH NEWS
NATURAL HOME
STEAM TRACTION
UTNE READER

OGDEN PUBLISHING CORPORATION
(Sub. of Sandusky Newspapers Inc.)
332 S Standard Way
Ogden, UT 84404-1306
Mailing Address:
PO Box 12790
Ogden, UT 84412-2790
Tel.: (801) 625-4554
Fax: (801) 625-4508
E-mail: lcarter@standard.net
Web Site: www.standard.net
Approx. Number Employees: 325
Year Founded: 1888
Business Description:
Newspaper Publishing & Printing
S.I.C.: 2711; 2741
N.A.I.C.S.: 511110; 516110
Media: 8-9
Personnel:
David Rau *(Pres)*
Lee Carter *(VP & Publr)*
David Greiling *(Asst Mng Editor)*
Brad Roghaar *(Dir-Sls)*
Bart Wade *(Dir-Production)*
Vaughn Jacobsen *(Bus Mgr)*
Jared W. Bird *(Mgr-Retail Adv)*
David H. Newman *(Mgr-Adv)*
Mark Shenefelt *(Mgr)*
Brands & Products:
STANDARD EXAMINER

OKLAHOMA PUBLISHING COMPANY
9000 N Broadway Ext 25125
Oklahoma City, OK 73114-3708
Tel.: (405) 475-3311
Fax: (405) 475-3996
Web Site: www.newsok.com
Sales Range: $25-49.9 Million
Approx. Number Employees: 1,000
Year Founded: 1903
Business Description:
Publisher
S.I.C.: 2711
N.A.I.C.S.: 511110
Advertising Expenditures: $800,000
Media: 2-9-10-14-18-20-21
Distr.: Reg.
Budget Set: Nov.
Personnel:
Christine Gaylord Everest *(Chm & CEO)*
Advertising Agency:
Ackerman McQueen, Inc.
1100 The Tower 1601 NW Expy
Oklahoma City, OK 73118
Tel.: (405) 843-7777
Fax: (405) 848-1932

Key to Media (For complete agency information see *The Advertising Red Books-Agencies* edition):
1. Bus. Publs. 2. Cable T.V. 3. Catalogs & Directories. 4. Co-op Adv. 5. Consumer Mags. 6. D.M. to Bus. Estab.7. D.M. to Consumers
8. Daily Newsp. 9. Exhibits/Trade Shows 10. Foreign 11. Infomercial 12. Internet Adv.13. Multimedia 14. Network Radio
15. Network T.V. 16. Newsp. Distr. Mags. 17. Other 18. Outdoor (Posters, Transit) 19. Point of Purchase20. Premiums, Novelties
21. Product Samples 22. Special Events Mktg. 23. Spot Radio 24. Spot T.V. 25. Weekly Newsp. 26. Yellow Page Adv.

THE OKLAHOMAN
(Div. of Oklahoma Publishing Company)
9000 N Broadway
Oklahoma City, OK 73114
Mailing Address:
PO Box 25125
Oklahoma City, OK 73125-0125
Tel.: (405) 475-3311
Fax: (405) 475-3183
Web Site: www.oklahoman.com
Approx. Number Employees: 1,200
Year Founded: 1903
Business Description:
Publishers of Newspaper
S.I.C.: 2711; 1311
N.A.I.C.S.: 511110; 211111
Advertising Expenditures: $750,000
Media: 1-2-3-7-8-9-10-17-19-20-21-23-24
Distr.: Direct to Consumer; Reg.
Personnel:
David L. Thompson *(Publr)*
Brands & Products:
THE OKLAHOMAN
Advertising Agency:
Ackerman McQueen, Inc.
1100 The Tower 1601 NW Expy
Oklahoma City, OK 73118
Tel.: (405) 843-7777
Fax: (405) 848-1932

O'MEARA-BROWN PUBLICATIONS, INC.
(d/b/a Lakeland Boating Magazine)
727 S Dearborn Ste 812
Chicago, IL 60605
Tel.: (312) 276-0610
Fax: (312) 276-0619
Toll Free: (800) 331-0132
E-mail: info@lakelandboating.com
Web Site: www.lakelandboating.com
Sales Range: $10-24.9 Million
Approx. Number Employees: 15
Year Founded: 1942
Business Description:
Boating Magazine Publisher
S.I.C.: 2721
N.A.I.C.S.: 511120
Media: 3-8-10-13
Distr.: Natl.
Budget Set: Dec.
Personnel:
Walter B. O'Meara *(Publr)*
Sharon P. O'Meara *(VP-Mktg)*
Kirsten Moxley *(Reg Mgr-Sls)*
Brands & Products:
GREAT LAKES ANGLER
LAKE HURON
LAKE MICHIGAN
LAKE ONTARIO
LAKE SUPERIOR
LAKELAND BOATING

ONLINE
(Div. of Information Today Inc.)
88 Danbury Rd Ste 1D
Wilton, CT 06897
Tel.: (203) 761-1466
Fax: (203) 761-1444
Web Site: www.onlineinc.com/contacts.shtml
Business Description:
Product Reviews, Case Studies, Electronic, Industry, & Online Databases Periodicals
S.I.C.: 2721
N.A.I.C.S.: 511120
Media: 2-10-13
Personnel:
Michelle Manafy *(Editor-in-Chief)*
Renee Fortin *(Dir-Art)*
Walter McQuillan *(Mgr-Sls)*

OPTIMIZERX CORPORATION
407 Sixth St
Rochester, MI 48307
Tel.: (248) 651-6568
Toll Free: (877) 568-3840
E-mail: info@optimizerx.com
Web Site: www.optimizerx.com
Approx. Rev.: $71,065
Approx. Number Employees: 5
Year Founded: 2006
Business Description:
Website Publisher & Marketing Services That Creates, Promotes & Fulfills Custom Marketing & Advertising Programs
S.I.C.: 2741; 7319; 8742
N.A.I.C.S.: 516110; 541613; 541890
Advertising Expenditures: $130,061
Media: 17
Personnel:
David A. Harrell *(Founder & Chm)*
H. David Lester *(CEO)*
Terence J. Hamilton *(Dir & VP-Sls)*

THE ORANGE COUNTY REGISTER
(Unit of Freedom Newspapers, Inc.)
625 N Grand Ave
Santa Ana, CA 92701-4347
Tel.: (714) 796-7000
Fax: (714) 796-2222
E-mail: sales@ocregister.com
Web Site: www.ocregister.com
E-Mail For Key Personnel:
Sales Director: sales@ocregister.com
Approx. Number Employees: 2,600
Year Founded: 1905
Business Description:
Daily Newspaper
S.I.C.: 2711
N.A.I.C.S.: 511110
Advertising Expenditures: $1,000,000
Media: 1-2-3-4-6-7-8-10-23
Distr.: Direct to Consumer; Reg.
Budget Set: Oct.
Personnel:
Terry Horne *(Pres & Publr)*
Ken Brusic *(Sr VP-Content & Editor)*
Ken Nelson *(Sr VP-Adv & Interactive Dev)*
Michael Henry *(Gen Mgr & VP-Fin)*
Brands & Products:
ORANGE COUNTY REGISTER

OREGONIAN PUBLISHING CO.
(Sub. of Advance Publications, Inc.)
1320 SW Broadway
Portland, OR 97201-3411
Tel.: (503) 221-8327
Fax: (503) 294-4199
E-mail: info@oregonian.com
Web Site: www.oregonlive.com
Approx. Number Employees: 900
Year Founded: 1850
Business Description:
Newspaper Publisher
S.I.C.: 2711
N.A.I.C.S.: 511110
Media: 2-5-8-9-10-18-19-20-21-22-23-24-25
Distr.: Direct to Consumer; Reg.
Personnel:
Debi Walery *(Gen Mgr-Adv)*
Therese Bottomly *(Mng Editor-Readership & Standards)*
Peter Bhatia *(Editor)*
Randy Cox *(Editor)*
Ryan Courtney *(Dir-Classified Adv)*
Denice Williams *(Mgr-Adv)*
Brands & Products:
THE OREGONIAN

O'REILLY MEDIA, INC.
1005 Gravenstein Hwy N
Sebastopol, CA 95472-3858
Tel.: (707) 827-7000
Fax: (707) 829-0104
Toll Free: (800) 998-9938
E-mail: nuts@oreilly.com
Web Site: www.oreilly.com
Approx. Number Employees: 270
Year Founded: 1978
Business Description:
Technical Writing & Publishing Services
S.I.C.: 2731; 2741
N.A.I.C.S.: 511130; 511199
Advertising Expenditures: $100,000
Media: 2-4-6-7-8-10-13-19-21-22
Personnel:
Timothy F. O'Reilly *(Founder, Pres & CEO)*
Laura Baldwin *(Pres)*
Gina Blaber *(Dir-Conferences)*
Betsy Waliszewski *(Sr Mgr-Mktg)*
Brands & Products:
THE HACKS SERIES
THE "IN A NUTSHELL" SERIES
O'REILLY
SAFARI

OSPREY MEDIA GROUP, INC.
(Sub. of Quebecor Media Inc.)
100 Renfrew Dr Ste 110
Markham, ON L3R 9R6, Canada
Tel.: (905) 752-1132
Fax: (905) 752-1138
Web Site: www.ospreymedialp.com
Approx. Number Employees: 50
Business Description:
Newspaper, Magazine & Specialty Publications Publisher
S.I.C.: 2721; 2711
N.A.I.C.S.: 511120; 511110
Media: 6-8-9-10-13-25
Personnel:
Blair Mackenzie *(Gen Counsel, Sec & VP)*
Julia Kamula *(Sr VP-Ops)*
Jack Mulchinock *(VP-Tech)*
Donna Glasspoole *(Dir-Classifieds & Application Sys)*
Paul Haigh *(Dir-Treasury)*
Penny Whitehead *(Dir-Payroll, Pension & Benefits)*
Corrie Hynes *(Mgr-Adv)*

THE OTTAWA CITIZEN
(Unit of Postmedia Network Inc.)
1101 Baxter Rd
Ottawa, ON K2C 3M4, Canada
Tel.: (613) 829-9100
Tel.: (613) 596-3744
Fax: (613) 726-1198
Toll Free: (800) 267-6100
Web Site: www.ottawacitizen.com
Approx. Number Employees: 300
Business Description:
Newspaper Publisher
S.I.C.: 2711
N.A.I.C.S.: 511110
Media: 8-9
Personnel:
Deborah Bennett *(VP-HR & Fin)*
Jeery Nott *(Editor)*
Lynne Clark *(Dir-Mktg)*

OUR SUNDAY VISITOR, INC.
200 Noll Plz
Huntington, IN 46750-4310
Tel.: (260) 356-8400
Fax: (260) 356-8472
Toll Free: (800) 348-2440
E-mail: oursunvis@osv.com
Web Site: www.osv.com
Approx. Number Employees: 300
Year Founded: 1912
Business Description:
Religious Books & Materials Publisher
S.I.C.: 2721; 2759
N.A.I.C.S.: 511120; 323119
Advertising Expenditures: $800,000
Media: 2-4-6-7-8-10-13-20-21-25
Distr.: Natl.
Budget Set: Feb. -Mar.
Personnel:
Greg Erlandson *(Pres & Publr)*
Kyle Hamilton *(Pres-Envelopes)*
Therese Calouette *(Mgr-Adv)*
Brands & Products:
BRINGING YOUR CATHOLIC FAITH TO LIFE
THE CATHOLIC ANSWER
GRACE IN ACTION
MY DAILY VISITOR
OSV.COM
OUR SUNDAY VISITOR
PAMPHLET
THE PRIEST
TAKE OUT

OXFORD UNIVERSITY PRESS, INC.
(Sub. of Oxford University Press)
198 Madison Ave
New York, NY 10016-4308
Tel.: (212) 726-6000
Fax: (212) 726-6440
Toll Free: (800) 334-4249
E-mail: webmaster@oup.com
Web Site: www.oup-usa.org
Approx. Number Employees: 400
Business Description:
Publisher of Books
S.I.C.: 2731; 5961
N.A.I.C.S.: 511130; 454113
Import Export
Advertising Expenditures: $4,300,000
Media: 2-4-7-8-9-10-13-19-20-21-22-23-25
Distr.: Intl.; Natl.
Personnel:
Colleen Scollans *(VP & Dir-Sls & Mktg)*
Kurt Hettler *(Dir-Distr)*
Scott Beebe *(Mgr-Online Publ)*

PACIFIC PALISADES POST INC.
(Sub. of Small Newspaper Group Inc.)
839 Via De La Paz PO Box 725
Pacific Palisades, CA 90272-3618
Tel.: (310) 454-1321
Fax: (310) 454-1078
E-mail: editor@palipost.com
Web Site: www.palisadespost.com

Key to Media (For complete agency information see *The Advertising Red Books-Agencies* edition):
1. Bus. Publs. 2. Cable T.V. 3. Catalogs & Directories. 4. Co-op Adv. 5. Consumer Mags. 6. D.M. to Bus. Estab.7. D.M. to Consumers 8. Daily Newsp. 9. Exhibits/Trade Shows 10. Foreign 11. Infomercial 12. Internet Adv.13. Multimedia 14. Network Radio 15. Network T.V. 16. Newsp. Distr. Mags. 17. Other 18. Outdoor (Posters, Transit) 19. Point of Purchase20. Premiums, Novelties 21. Product Samples 22. Special Events Mktg. 23. Spot Radio 24. Spot T.V. 25. Weekly Newsp. 26. Yellow Page Adv.

Pacific Palisades Post Inc. — (Continued)

Approx. Number Employees: 30
Business Description:
Newspaper Services
S.I.C.: 2711
N.A.I.C.S.: 511110
Media: 8-9-18-25
Personnel:
Tom Small *(Pres)*
Steve Galluzzo *(Editor-Sports)*
Ed Lowe *(Dir-Graphics)*
Cheryel Kanan *(Mgr-Bus)*
Jim Reynolds *(Mgr-Production)*

PACIFIC PRESS PUBLISHING ASSOCIATION

1350 N Kings Rd
Nampa, ID 83687
Tel.: (208) 465-2500
Fax: (208) 465-2531
E-mail: dalgal@pacificpress.com
Web Site: www.pacificpress.com
Approx. Sls.: $29,378,153
Approx. Number Employees: 180
Business Description:
Periodicals, Publishing & Printing
S.I.C.: 2721; 2731
N.A.I.C.S.: 511120; 511130
Media: 6-8-10-13
Personnel:
Dale Galusha *(Pres)*
Chuck Bobst *(VP-Production)*
Doug Church *(VP-Mktg & Sls)*

PADDOCK PUBLICATIONS, INC.

155 E Algonquin Rd
Arlington Heights, IL 60005
Tel.: (847) 427-4300
Fax: (847) 427-1550
E-mail: sales@dailyherald.com
Web Site: www.dailyherald.com
E-Mail For Key Personnel:
President: dbaumann@dailyherald.com
Sales Director: sales@dailyherald.com
Approx. Number Employees: 250
Year Founded: 1872
Business Description:
Publisher of Newspapers
S.I.C.: 2711
N.A.I.C.S.: 511110
Media: 1-2-3-4-5-9-10-18-19-20-21-23-26
Distr.: Direct to Consumer; Reg.
Budget Set: Dec.
Personnel:
Douglas K. Ray *(Chm, Pres, CEO & Publr)*
Daniel E. Baumann *(Chm)*
Robert Y. Paddock *(Vice Chm & Exec VP)*
John Lampinen *(Sr VP & Editor)*
Colin O'Donnell *(VP & Dir-Ops-Plng)*
Betsy Kmiecik *(VP-HR)*
Madeleine Doubek *(Asst VP & Exec Editor)*
Kelly Casalino *(Asst VP & Dir)*
James Cook *(Asst VP-Mktg & Mgr-Promo)*
Scott Stones *(Asst VP-Daily Herald)*
John Graham *(Mgr-Mktg & Res)*
Brands & Products:
DAILY HERALD
REFLEJOS

PAISANO PUBLICATIONS, LLC

28210 Dorothy Dr
Agoura Hills, CA 91301
Tel.: (818) 889-8740
Fax: (818) 889-4726
E-mail: kjohnson@easyriders.net
Web Site: www.easyriders.com
Approx. Number Employees: 135
Business Description:
Magazine Publisher
S.I.C.: 2721
N.A.I.C.S.: 511120
Media: 4-6-8-10-13-20
Personnel:
Joseph Teresi *(Chm)*
Cathy Gibson *(VP-Production)*
Tammy Porter *(Dir-Adv)*
Brands & Products:
BIKER
EASYRIDERS
FLASH
HIBEAMZ
IN THE WIND
SAVAGE
STREET CUSTOMS
TAILGATE
TATTOO
V-TWIN
V-TWIN NEWS

PALATKA DAILY NEWS

(Sub. of Community Newspapers Inc.)
1825 Saint Johns Ave
Palatka, FL 32177-4442
Mailing Address:
PO Box 777
Palatka, FL 32178
Tel.: (386) 312-5200
Fax: (386) 312-5209
Web Site: www.palatkadailynews.com
Approx. Number Employees: 58
Business Description:
Daily Newspaper
S.I.C.: 2711
N.A.I.C.S.: 511110
Media: 8-9-13-22
Personnel:
Rusty Starr *(Publr)*
Mary Kaye Wells *(Dir-Adv)*
Brands & Products:
PALATKA DAILY NEW NEWSPAPER

PALM BEACH MEDIA GROUP INC.

PO Box 3344
Palm Beach, FL 33480
Tel.: (561) 659-0210
Fax: (561) 659-1736
E-mail: info@palmbeachmedia.com
Web Site: www.palmbeachmedia.com
Approx. Number Employees: 29
Business Description:
Magazine Publisher
S.I.C.: 2721
N.A.I.C.S.: 511120
Media: 6-7-8-10-13
Personnel:
Ronald J. Woods *(Owner & Publr)*
Jason Davis *(Editor)*
Allison Reckson *(Exec Dir-Mktg & Special Projects)*
Deidre Wade *(Sr Mgr-Acct)*
Mirian Baldes *(Mgr-Acctg)*
Marjorie Leiva *(Mgr-Circulation)*
Donna Lewis *(Mgr-Acct)*
Bridget Meyer *(Mgr-Acct)*
Kathy Nelson *(Mgr-Acct)*
Nicole Ruth *(Mgr-Acct)*
Brands & Products:
EDGEWATER BEACH HOTEL & CLUB
FI MAGAZINE: FISHER ISLAND
THE JEWEL OF PALM BEACH: THE MAR-A-LAGO CLUB
LEGACY: PONTE VEDRA INN & CLUB
NAPLES CHARITY REGISTER
NAPLES ILLUSTRATED
NEOPOLITAN: REGISTRY RESORT & CLUB
PALM BEACH CHARITY REGISTER
PALM BEACH ILLUSTRATED
REFLECTIONS: LONGBOAT KEY CLUB
TAMPA BAY CHARITY REGISTER
TAMPA BAY ILLUSTRATED
TRADITIONS: THE BREAKERS
TURNBERRY: TURNBERRY ISLE RESORT & CLUB

PANTHEON BOOKS, INC.

(Sub. of Random House, Inc.)
1745 Broadway
New York, NY 10019
Tel.: (212) 751-2600
Fax: (212) 572-6030
Telex: 126-575
E-mail: pantheonpublicity@randomhouse.com
Web Site: www.randomhouse.com/pantheon
Approx. Number Employees: 22
Business Description:
Book Publisher
S.I.C.: 2731
N.A.I.C.S.: 511130
Media: 2-4-6-9-25
Distr.: Natl.
Brands & Products:
PANTHEON
Advertising Agency:
Verso Advertising, Inc.
50 W 17th St 5th Fl
New York, NY 10011-5702
Tel.: (212) 292-2990
Fax: (212) 557-2592

THE PAPER MAGIC GROUP, INC.

(Sub. of CSS Industries, Inc.)
401 Adams Ave
Scranton, PA 18501
Mailing Address:
PO Box 977
Scranton, PA 18501-0977
Tel.: (570) 961-3863
Fax: (570) 961-3930
Toll Free: (800) 278-1085
Web Site: www.papermagic.com
Sales Range: $50-74.9 Million
Approx. Number Employees: 150
Business Description:
Mfr. of Greeting Cards, Gift Tags, Decor, Valentine & Educational Products
S.I.C.: 2771; 2678
N.A.I.C.S.: 511191; 322233
Advertising Expenditures: $240,000
Media: 4-5-7-10-13-19
Distr.: Natl.
Budget Set: Oct.
Personnel:
Paul Quick *(Pres)*
Brands & Products:
COLOR-CLINGS
DON POST STUDIOS
DUDLEY'S
EUREKA
HOLIDAY SPICE
JOYFUL GREETINGS
LEARNING PLAYGROUND
PAPER MAGIC
PAPER MAGIC VALENTINES
PINE HOLLOW
PMG HOLLOWEEN

PARACHUTE PROPERTIES, LLC

322 8th Ave Ste 500
New York, NY 10001
Tel.: (212) 691-1422
E-mail: info@parachutepublishing.com
Web Site:
www.parachutepublishing.com
Approx. Number Employees: 10
Year Founded: 1983
Business Description:
Book Packager
S.I.C.: 7389
N.A.I.C.S.: 561910
Media: 1-4-22
Personnel:
Joan Waricha *(Pres & CEO)*

PARADE MAGAZINE

(Div. of Parade Publications Inc.)
711 3rd Ave
New York, NY 10017
Tel.: (212) 450-7000
Fax: (212) 450-7200
Web Site: www.parade.com
Approx. Number Employees: 5
Business Description:
Magazine
S.I.C.: 2721
N.A.I.C.S.: 511120
Media: 6-8-9-25
Personnel:
Jack Haire *(Pres & CEO-Parade Publ)*
Brett Wilson *(Publr)*
David Barber *(Exec VP-Newspaper Rels)*
Jim Hackett *(Sr VP-Mktg & Res)*
Ira Yoffe *(VP & Dir-Creative)*
Lee Kravitz *(Editor in Chief)*
Sara Brzowsky *(Editor)*
Fran Carpentier *(Editor)*
David H. Levy *(Editor-Science)*
Isadore Rosenfeld *(Editor-Health)*
Alexis Collado *(Mgr-Publicity)*

PARADE PUBLICATIONS INC.

(Sub. of Advance Publications, Inc.)
711 3rd Ave
New York, NY 10017-4014
Tel.: (212) 450-7000
Fax: (212) 450-7287
E-mail: ny_sales@parade.com
Web Site: www.parade.com
Approx. Number Employees: 180
Year Founded: 1941
Business Description:
Magazine Publisher
S.I.C.: 2721; 2711
N.A.I.C.S.: 511120; 511110
Media: 8-13-16-25
Distr.: Natl.
Budget Set: Oct.
Personnel:
John J. Beni *(Vice Chm)*

Key to Media (For complete agency information see *The Advertising Red Books-Agencies* edition):
1. Bus. Publs. 2. Cable T.V. 3. Catalogs & Directories. 4. Co-op Adv. 5. Consumer Mags. 6. D.M. to Bus. Estab.7. D.M. to Consumers
8. Daily Newsp. 9. Exhibits/Trade Shows 10. Foreign 11. Infomercial 12. Internet Adv.13. Multimedia 14. Network Radio
15. Network T.V. 16. Newsp. Distr. Mags. 17. Other 18. Outdoor (Posters, Transit) 19. Point of Purchase20. Premiums, Novelties
21. Product Samples 22. Special Events Mktg. 23. Spot Radio 24. Spot T.V. 25. Weekly Newsp. 26. Yellow Page Adv.

Jack Haire *(Pres & CEO-Parade Publ)*
Allison Werder *(CMO & Exec VP)*
Mike DeBartolo *(Publr & Exec VP)*
David Barber *(Exec VP-Newspaper Rels)*
Jim Hackett *(Sr VP-Mktg)*
Alex Baxter *(VP & Gen Mgr-Digital)*
Ira Yoffe *(VP & Dir-Creative)*
Christy Emden *(VP-Comm)*
Brands & Products:
PARADE
PARADE.COM

PARENTS MAGAZINE

(Div. of Meredith Publishing Group)
375 Lexington Ave
New York, NY 10017-5514
Tel.: (212) 499-2000
Fax: (212) 499-2159
Web Site: www.parents.com
E-Mail For Key Personnel:
Marketing Director: JDake@gjusa.com
Sales Range: $50-74.9 Million
Approx. Number Employees: 200
Year Founded: 1926
Business Description:
Magazine Publisher
S.I.C.: 2721
N.A.I.C.S.: 511120
Export
Media: 2-4-10-18-19-20-23
Distr.: Natl.
Budget Set: Feb.
Personnel:
Brian Kightlinger *(Assoc Publr)*
Sally Lee *(Editor-in-Chief)*
Jeffrey Saks *(Creative Dir)*
Andrea Amadio *(Art Dir-Parents)*
Nancy Welch *(Dir-Health)*
Veronica DaCosta *(Coord-Adv Sls, Parents Magazine)*
Brands & Products:
PARENTS EXPECTING
PARENTS MAGAZINE

PATCH COMMUNICATIONS

5211 S Washington Ave
Titusville, FL 32780
Tel.: (321) 268-5010
Fax: (321) 267-1894
Web Site: www.sportingclays.com
Approx. Number Employees: 30
Year Founded: 1978
Business Description:
Sports & Hobby Magazines
S.I.C.: 2721; 2741
N.A.I.C.S.: 511120; 511199
Advertising Expenditures: $200,000
Media: 2-6-7-8-13
Personnel:
Ken Wood *(Mgr-Adv)*
Brands & Products:
SPORTING CLAYS MAGAZINE

PAZDUR PUBLISHING CO.

2171 Campus Dr Ste 330
Irvine, CA 92612-1422
Tel.: (949) 752-6474
Fax: (949) 752-0398
Toll Free: (800) 367-8653
Web Site:
www.executivegolfermagazine.com
Approx. Number Employees: 26
Year Founded: 1972
Business Description:
Magazine For Private Country Club Golfers
S.I.C.: 2721
N.A.I.C.S.: 511120
Export
Advertising Expenditures: $400,000
Media: 5-6-22
Distr.: Direct to Consumer; Natl.
Budget Set: Dec.
Personnel:
Edward F. Pazdur *(Chm & CEO)*
Mark Pazdur *(Publr)*
Theda Pazdur *(Exec VP)*
Brands & Products:
EXECUTIVE GOLFER
PRIVATE COUNTRY CLUB GUEST POLICY DIRECTORY

PC MAGAZINE

(Unit of Ziff Davis Media Inc.)
28 E 28th St
New York, NY 10016
Tel.: (212) 503-5100
Fax: (212) 503-5000
Toll Free: (800) 336-2423
Web Site: www.pcmagmedia.com
Approx. Number Employees: 500
Business Description:
Computer Related Magazine Publisher
S.I.C.: 7372; 2721
N.A.I.C.S.: 511210; 511120
Media: 2-7-8-9-10-18
Personnel:
Ken Detlet *(VP-Digital Sls-PCMag Network)*
Lance Ulanoff *(Editor-in-Chief)*
Ashley Kinley *(Dir-Mktg)*
Mark Pope *(Mgr-Mktg)*
Brands & Products:
GOODCLEANTECH.COM
MOBILE.PCMAG.COM
PCMAG.COM
SECURITYWATCH.COM

PEARSON ASSESSMENT & INFORMATION

(Sub. of Pearson Assessments)
19500 Bulverde Rd
San Antonio, TX 78259
Tel.: (210) 339-5000
Fax: (800) 232-1223
Toll Free: (800) 211-8378
Web Site:
www.pearsonassessments.com
Sales Range: $350-399.9 Million
Approx. Number Employees: 950
Business Description:
Educational, Occupational Therapy, Psychological, Speech & Language Assessment Products Publisher
S.I.C.: 2741; 8299
N.A.I.C.S.: 511199; 611710
Advertising Expenditures: $500,000
Media: 2-4-7-10-17-20-21
Distr.: Natl.
Personnel:
Kevin Brueggeman *(Pres-Education Div)*
Aurelio Prifitera *(Pres-Clinical)*

PEARSON ASSESSMENTS

(Sub. of Pearson Education)
5601 Green Vly Dr
Bloomington, MN 55437-1187
Tel.: (952) 681-3000
Fax: (952) 681-3406
Toll Free: (800) 328-6172
Web Site:
www.pearsonassessments.com
Approx. Number Employees: 900
Year Founded: 1962
Business Description:
Integrated Systems & Support Services
S.I.C.: 3577; 2761
N.A.I.C.S.: 334119; 323116
Export
Media: 4-7-10
Distr.: Intl.; Natl.
Budget Set: Dec.
Personnel:
Douglas Kubach *(Pres & CEO)*
Brands & Products:
EXAMVIEW TEST GENERATOR
EZDATA
NCS DESIGNEXPERT
NCS DOCUSCAN PATIENT ENCOUNTER SYSTEM
OPSCAN INSIGHT 70
PEARSON PASERIES
PEARSON TEST ITEM BANKS
PERCEPTION
PROSPER
PROSPER ASSESSMENT SYSTEM
REMARK CLASSIC OMR
SCANTOOLS PLUS
SCANTOOLS PLUS SDK
SURVEYTRACKER
SURVEYTRACKER PLUS 5.0
SURVEYTRACKER PLUS EMAIL WEB 5.0
XTENDER IMAGING

PEARSON EDUCATION

(Sub. of Pearson, Inc.)
1 Lk St
Upper Saddle River, NJ 07458-1813
Tel.: (201) 236-7000
Fax: (201) 236-3381
E-mail: Communications@pearsoned.com
Web Site: www.pearsoned.com
Approx. Number Employees: 18,460
Year Founded: 1998
Business Description:
Educational Publishing
S.I.C.: 2721; 2731
N.A.I.C.S.: 511120; 511130
Media: 2-4-7-10
Personnel:
Peter Jovanovich *(Pres & CEO)*
Peter J. Cohen *(CEO-School Grp)*
Allen Wheatcroft *(Sr VP-Product Dev Svcs)*
Hillary Hoffman *(Product Mgr-Mktg)*
Brands & Products:
SCOTT FORESMAN

PEARSON EDUCATION

(Formerly Allyn & Bacon)
(Sub. of Pearson Education)
75 Arlington St Ste 300
Boston, MA 02116-3936
Tel.: (617) 848-6000
Fax: (617) 848-6018
E-mail: exam.copies@ablongman.com
Web Site: www.pearsoned.com
Approx. Sls.: $150,000,000
Approx. Number Employees: 250
Year Founded: 1868
Business Description:
Textbooks & Electronic Media Educational Products for the Humanities, Education & Social Services
S.I.C.: 2731
N.A.I.C.S.: 511130
Export
Advertising Expenditures: $1,560,000
D.M. to Bus. Estab.: $700,000; D.M. to Consumers: $800,000; Exhibits/Trade Shows: $60,000
Distr.: Intl.; Natl.
Personnel:
Sandi Kirshner *(Pres)*
Nancy Forsyth *(Dir-Editorial)*
Kevin Stone *(Sr VP)*
John Owen *(VP & Mgr-Bus)*
Priscilla McGeehon *(Exec Editor)*
Frank Morelli *(Dir)*
Laura L. Manley *(Mgr-Mktg)*

PEARSON TECHNOLOGY GROUP

(Sub. of Pearson Education)
800 E 96th St
Indianapolis, IN 46240
Tel.: (317) 428-3500
Web Site: www.pearsoned.com
Approx. Number Employees: 900
Year Founded: 1981
Business Description:
Information Services, Electronic Publishing, General & Educational Publishing, Exhibitions, Scientific, Medical & Technical Publishing; Reference Materials, Translation Services
S.I.C.: 2731
N.A.I.C.S.: 511130
Media: 2-4-5-7-9-10-17
Distr.: Intl.; Natl.
Personnel:
Steven A. Dowling *(Exec VP-Corp Dev)*

PEMMICAN PUBLICATIONS INC.

150 Henry Ave
Winnipeg, MB Canada
Tel.: (204) 589-6346
Fax: (204) 589-2063
E-mail: rlynch@pemmican.mb.ca
Web Site: www.pemmican.mb.ca
Approx. Number Employees: 3
Year Founded: 1980
Business Description:
Books on Metis & Canadian Aboriginal Culture & Issues Publisher
S.I.C.: 2731
N.A.I.C.S.: 511130
Media: 2-3-8-10-13-25

PENGUIN GROUP (USA) INC.

(Sub. of The Penguin Publishing Co. Ltd.)
375 Hudson St
New York, NY 10014-3658
Tel.: (212) 366-2000
Fax: (212) 414-3366
Web Site: www.penguin.com
Sales Range: $1-4.9 Billion
Approx. Number Employees: 1,200
Business Description:
Book Publisher
S.I.C.: 2731
N.A.I.C.S.: 511130
Import Export
Media: 2-4-6-7-8-9-18-23
Distr.: Natl.
Personnel:
Susan Petersen Kennedy *(Pres)*
David Shanks *(CEO)*
Anthony J. Laurino *(CFO)*
Clare Ferraro *(Pres-Viking, Plume & Studio Books Imprints)*

Key to Media (For complete agency information see *The Advertising Red Books-Agencies* edition):
1. Bus. Publs. 2. Cable T.V. 3. Catalogs & Directories. 4. Co-op Adv. 5. Consumer Mags. 6. D.M. to Bus. Estab.7. D.M. to Consumers
8. Daily Newsp. 9. Exhibits/Trade Shows 10. Foreign 11. Infomercial 12. Internet Adv.13. Multimedia 14. Network Radio
15. Network T.V. 16. Newsp. Distr. Mags. 17. Other 18. Outdoor (Posters, Transit) 19. Point of Purchase20. Premiums, Novelties
21. Product Samples 22. Special Events Mktg. 23. Spot Radio 24. Spot T.V. 25. Weekly Newsp. 26. Yellow Page Adv.

Penguin Group (USA) Inc. — (Continued)
Lauri Hornik *(VP-Publr)*
Franceso Sedita *(Publr-Price Stern Sloan)*
Doug Whiteman *(Exec VP-Bus Ops)*
Tim McCall *(VP & Dir-Online Sls & Mktg)*
Brands & Products:
COBBLEHILL
DIAL
DUTTON & NAL
DUTTON CHILDRENS
LODESTAR
ONYX
PLUME & MERIDIAN
ROC
SIGNET
TOPAZ
VIKING
VIKING KESTREL
WARNE
Advertising Agency:
Goodman Media International, Inc.
750 7th Ave 28th Fl
New York, NY 10016
Tel.: (212) 576-2700
Fax: (212) 576-2701
(Penguin Books, Madeline & the Cats of Rome)

THE PENINSULA CLARION
(Unit of Morris Publishing Group, LLC)
150 Trading Bay Dr Ste 1
Kenai, AK 99611
Tel.: (907) 283-7551
Fax: (907) 283-3299
Web Site: www.peninsulaclarion.com
E-Mail For Key Personnel:
Sales Director: sales@peninsulaclarion.com
Approx. Number Employees: 43
Year Founded: 1970
Business Description:
Newspaper Publisher
S.I.C.: 2711; 2721
N.A.I.C.S.: 511110; 511120
Media: 8-9
Personnel:
Stan W. Pitlo *(Publr)*
Evy Gebhardt *(Dir-Mktg)*

PENNWELL PUBLISHING COMPANY INC.
1421 S Sheridan Rd
Tulsa, OK 74112-6619
Tel.: (918) 835-3161
Fax: (918) 831-9497
E-mail: webmaster@pennwell.com
Web Site: www.pennwell.com
Approx. Number Employees: 360
Year Founded: 1932
Business Description:
Publisher of Periodicals & Books
S.I.C.: 2721; 2731
N.A.I.C.S.: 511120; 511130
Import Export
Media: 2-10-13
Personnel:
Robert Biolchini *(Pres & CEO)*
Robert H. Kelly *(Publr)*
Wendy Lissau *(Mktg Mgr)*

PENTON MEDIA, INC.
(Joint Venture of MidOcean Partners, LLP & Wasserstein & Co., LP)
249 W 17th St
New York, NY 10011
Tel.: (212) 204-4200
Fax: (212) 206-3622
E-mail: sharon.rowlands@penton.com
Web Site: www.penton.com
Approx. Number Employees: 150
Year Founded: 1886
Business Description:
Trade Publications, Websites, Trade Shows & Other Proprietary Business Information Media Products & Services; Owned 50% by Wasserstein & Co., LP & 50% by MidOcean Partners, LLP
S.I.C.: 2741; 2721; 2731; 7389
N.A.I.C.S.: 511199; 511120; 511130; 511140; 516110; 561920
Personnel:
Nicola Allais *(CFO & Exec VP)*
Jasmine Alexander *(CIO & Sr VP)*
Andrew Schmolka *(Gen Counsel & Sr VP)*
Randall Friedman *(Grp Publr)*
Dan Bagan *(Sr VP-Agriculture & Mktg & Food Grp)*
Warren N. Bimblick *(Sr VP-Strategy & Bus Dev)*
Fred Linder *(Sr VP-Lifestyle Grp)*
Bob MacArthur *(Sr VP-Indus Grp)*
Kim Paulsen *(Sr VP-Tech Grp)*
Bill Baumann *(VP-Design Engrg & Electronics Markets)*
Mike Hancock *(VP-Intl Sls)*
Wayne Madden *(VP-Sls Dev)*
Kurt Nelson *(VP-HR)*
Rick Stewart *(VP-Fin)*
Jill Baldassano *(Mgr-Corp Comm)*
Advertising Agency:
Meritdirect, Llc.
333 Westchester Ave
White Plains, NY 10604
Tel.: (914) 368-1000
Fax: (914) 368-1150

PENTON MEDIA, INC.
(Joint Venture of MidOcean Partners, LLP & Wasserstein & Co., LP)
9800 Metcalf Ave
Overland Park, KS 66212-2216
Mailing Address:
PO Box 12901
Overland Park, KS 66282-2901
Tel.: (913) 341-1300
Fax: (913) 967-1898
Web Site: www.penton.com
Sales Range: $25-49.9 Million
Approx. Number Employees: 200
Year Founded: 2005
Business Description:
Proprietary Business Information Media Products & Services
S.I.C.: 2741; 2721; 7389
N.A.I.C.S.: 511199; 511120; 511140; 516110; 561920
Advertising Expenditures: $500,000
Media: 2-4-7-8-10-11-20
Distr.: Natl.
Budget Set: Dec.

PENTON MEDIA, INC.
(Joint Venture of MidOcean Partners, LLP & Wasserstein & Co., LP)
The Penton Media Bldg 1300 E 9th St
Cleveland, OH 44114-1503
Tel.: (216) 931-9709
Fax: (216) 696-1752
Web Site: www.penton.com
Sales Range: $150-199.9 Million
Approx. Number Employees: 200
Year Founded: 1886
Business Description:
Proprietary Business Information Media Products & Services
S.I.C.: 2721; 2741; 7389
N.A.I.C.S.: 511120; 511140; 511199; 516110; 561920
Import Export
Advertising Expenditures: $3,700,000
Media: 2-7-10-13
Personnel:
Rick Seibt *(Dir-Online Project Mgmt)*
Jane Cooper *(Dir-Mktg)*
Jacquie Niemiec *(Dir-Online Sls)*
J. Basil Dannebohm *(Product Mgr-Digital)*
Bethany Weaver *(Mgr-Corp Comm)*
Brands & Products:
WHERE MEDIA IS GOING

PEOPLE MAGAZINE
(Unit of Time Inc.)
Time Life Bldg Rockefeller Ctr
New York, NY 10020
Tel.: (212) 522-2028
Fax: (212) 522-0883
E-mail: peopleinfo@timeinc.com
Web Site: www.people.com
Sales Range: $100-124.9 Million
Year Founded: 1974
Business Description:
Weekly News & Features Magazine
S.I.C.: 2721
N.A.I.C.S.: 511120
Media: 6-8
Distr.: Natl.
Personnel:
Ann S. Moore *(Chm & CEO)*
Karen Kovacs *(Publr)*
Jack Haire *(Exec VP)*
David Geithner *(VP & Gen Mgr)*
John L. Brown *(VP-Consumer Mktg People Grp)*
Ellie Duque *(Dir-Adv-West)*
John J. Gallagher *(Dir-Adv)*
Laura Schroff *(Mgr-Adv-StyleWatch)*
Brands & Products:
PEOPLE MAGAZINE

PEOPLE2PEOPLE GROUP INC.
(Div. of The Phoenix Media/ Communications Group)
126 Brookline Ave
Boston, MA 02215
Tel.: (617) 450-8671
Fax: (617) 425-2615
E-mail: asegel@tpigroup.com
Web Site: www.people2people.com
Approx. Sls.: $18,000,000
Approx. Number Employees: 50
Year Founded: 1996
Business Description:
Online Personal Ad & Dating Services
S.I.C.: 2741
N.A.I.C.S.: 516110
Media: 8-9-13-25

THE PERSEUS BOOKS GROUP
387 Park Ave S 12th Fl
New York, NY 10016
Tel.: (212) 340-8100
Fax: (212) 340-8105
Web Site: www.perseusbooksgroup.com
Sales Range: $25-49.9 Million
Approx. Number Employees: 1,100
Business Description:
Books Publisher & Distr
S.I.C.: 2731; 2732; 5192
N.A.I.C.S.: 511130; 323117; 424920
Export
Media: 10
Personnel:
David Steinberger *(CEO)*
Rick Joyce *(Chief Mktg Officer)*
Jon Anderson *(VP & Dir-Creative)*
Sarah Wolf *(Dir-Sls Special)*

PERSONAL SELLING POWER INC.
1140 Intl Pkwy
Fredericksburg, VA 22406-1126
Tel.: (540) 752-7000
Fax: (540) 752-7001
Toll Free: (800) 752-7355
E-mail: info@sellingpower.com
Web Site: www.sellingpower.com
Approx. Sls.: $9,000,000
Approx. Number Employees: 38
Business Description:
Customer Relationship Manangement Information Magazine Publisher
S.I.C.: 2721; 2731
N.A.I.C.S.: 511120; 511130
Media: 2-7-13
Personnel:
Gerhard Gschwandtner *(Founder & CEO)*

PETER LI EDUCATION GROUP
2621 Dryden Rd Ste 300
Dayton, OH 45439
Tel.: (937) 293-1415
Fax: (937) 293-1310
Toll Free: (800) 523-4625
E-mail: service@peterli.com
Web Site: www.peterli.com
E-Mail For Key Personnel:
Marketing Director: tperkins@peterli.com
Approx. Number Employees: 80
Year Founded: 1971
Business Description:
Publisher of Educational Magazines & Periodicals
S.I.C.: 2721
N.A.I.C.S.: 511120
Advertising Expenditures: $200,000
Media: 2-4-6-7-8-10-20-21
Distr.: Intl.; Natl.
Budget Set: June
Personnel:
Peter J. Li *(Pres & Publr)*
Pam Gibson *(VP-Fin & Admin)*
Terry Perkins *(VP-Mktg)*
Patty James *(Dir-Publ)*
Kevin Jensen *(Mgr-Production)*
Brands & Products:
PETER LI

PHANMEDIA L.L.C.
77 Franklin Ave
Ocean Grove, NJ 07756
Mailing Address:
PO Box 216
Ocean Grove, NJ 07756
Tel.: (732) 988-6264
Fax: (732) 988-9180
E-mail: phanmedia@aol.com
Web Site: www.videoscopemag.com
Approx. Number Employees: 2
Business Description:
Magazine Publisher
S.I.C.: 2721

Key to Media (For complete agency information see *The Advertising Red Books-Agencies* edition):
1. Bus. Publs. 2. Cable T.V. 3. Catalogs & Directories. 4. Co-op Adv. 5. Consumer Mags. 6. D.M. to Bus. Estab.7. D.M. to Consumers
8. Daily Newsp. 9. Exhibits/Trade Shows 10. Foreign 11. Infomercial 12. Internet Adv.13. Multimedia 14. Network Radio
15. Network T.V. 16. Newsp. Distr. Mags. 17. Other 18. Outdoor (Posters, Transit) 19. Point of Purchase20. Premiums, Novelties
21. Product Samples 22. Special Events Mktg. 23. Spot Radio 24. Spot T.V. 25. Weekly Newsp. 26. Yellow Page Adv.

N.A.I.C.S.: 511120
Media: 6-8-10
Personnel:
Joe Kane *(Editor)*
Nancy Naglin *(Mgr-Adv)*
Brands & Products:
THE PHANTOM OF THE MOVIES VIDEOSCOPE

PHILADELPHIA DAILY NEWS
(Div. of Philadelphia Newspapers, LLC)
400 N Broad St
Philadelphia, PA 19101-4099
Mailing Address:
PO Box 7788
Philadelphia, PA 19101
Tel.: (215) 854-2000
Fax: (215) 854-5954
Web Site: www.philly.com
Approx. Number Employees: 3,065
Year Founded: 1925
Business Description:
Newspaper Publisher
S.I.C.: 2711
N.A.I.C.S.: 511110
Media: 2-4-7-8-9-10-13-18-19-20-21-23
Distr.: Reg.
Budget Set: Nov.
Personnel:
Brian P. Tierney *(CEO)*
Alejandro Alvarez *(Editor)*
Jenice Armstrong *(Editor)*
William Bunch *(Editor)*
Bill Conlin *(Editor)*
Laurie Conrad *(Editor)*
Paul Domowitch *(Editor)*
Sam Donnellon *(Editor)*
Howard Gensler *(Editor-Entertainment)*
Daniel Geringer *(Editor)*
Marcus Hayes *(Editor)*
David Maialetti *(Editor)*
Regina Medina *(Editor)*
Kevin Mulligan *(Editor)*
Don Russell *(Editor)*
John Smallwood *(Editor)*
Jim Smith *(Editor)*
Jonathan Takiff *(Editor)*
Gary Thompson *(Editor)*
Debbie Woodell *(Editor)*

THE PHILADELPHIA INQUIRER
(Div. of Philadelphia Newspapers, LLC)
400 N Broad St
Philadelphia, PA 19130
Mailing Address:
PO Box 8263
Philadelphia, PA 19101
Tel.: (215) 854-2000
Fax: (215) 854-4216
E-mail: abennett@phillynews.com
Web Site: www.philly.com
Approx. Number Employees: 2,500
Year Founded: 1829
Business Description:
Newspaper Publisher
S.I.C.: 2711
N.A.I.C.S.: 511110
Media: 2-4-7-8-9-10-13-18-19-20-21-23
Distr.: Direct to Consumer
Personnel:
Brian P. Tierney *(CEO)*
William K. Marimow *(Exec VP & Editor)*
Michael Rozansky *(Deputy Editor-Arts & Features)*
Chris Satullo *(Editor-Editorial)*
Brian Toolan *(Editor-Bus)*
Helene Glowienka *(Mgr-Budget & Admin)*
Advertising Agency:
Quaker City Mercantile
114-120 S 13th St
Philadelphia, PA 19107
Tel.: (215) 922-5220
Fax: (215) 922-5228

PHILADELPHIA MEDIA HOLDINGS LLC
(Filed Ch 11 Bankruptcy #911206 on 02/22/09 in U.S. Bankruptcy Ct, Eastern Dist of PA, Philadelphia)
400 N Broad St
Philadelphia, PA 19130-4015
Tel.: (215) 854-2000
Fax: (215) 854-5572
E-mail: info@philly.com
Web Site: www.philly.com
Approx. Number Employees: 3,800
Year Founded: 2006
Business Description:
Holding Company
S.I.C.: 6719; 2711
N.A.I.C.S.: 551112; 511110
Personnel:
Greg Osberg *(CEO & Publr)*
Advertising Agency:
Razorfish Philadelphia
417 N 8th St Fl 2
Philadelphia, PA 19123-3916
Tel.: (267) 295-7100
Fax: (267) 295-7101

PIP PRINTING, INC.
(Sub. of Franchise Services, Inc.)
26722 Plaza Dr Ste 200
Mission Viejo, CA 92691
Tel.: (949) 282-3800
Fax: (949) 282-3899
E-mail: corporate@pip.com
Web Site: www.pip.com
Sales Range: $200-249.9 Million
Approx. Number Employees: 50
Year Founded: 1965
Business Description:
Business Printing Franchises
S.I.C.: 2761
N.A.I.C.S.: 323116
Advertising Expenditures: $5,000,000
Media: 2-3-4-5-6-7-10-14-19-20-23-24-26
Distr.: Natl.
Budget Set: May
Personnel:
David Rovivoux *(VP-Mktg)*

PLAIN DEALER PUBLISHING CO.
(Sub. of Advance Publications, Inc.)
(d/b/a The Plain Dealer)
1801 Superior Ave Plain Dealer Plz
Cleveland, OH 44114
Tel.: (216) 999-4800
Tel.: (216) 999-5000
Fax: (216) 999-6354
Web Site: www.plaindealer.com
Approx. Number Employees: 1,800
Year Founded: 1842
Business Description:
Newspaper Publishing
S.I.C.: 2711
N.A.I.C.S.: 511110
Distr.: Local
Personnel:
Alex Machaskee *(Pres-Publr)*
Robert M. Long *(Exec VP)*
Joseph J. Bowman *(VP & Dir-Ops Tiedeman Production & Distr Center)*
William Calaiacovo *(VP & Dir-Labor Rels & HR)*
Robert Perona *(VP & Dir-Circulation)*
David Breen *(Dir-Ops)*
Joseph T. DeAngelo *(Dir-Building & Transportation Svcs)*
Shirley D. Stineman *(Dir-Comm Affairs & Mktg)*
Jeff Ganor *(Mgr-Automotive)*
Jim Trutko *(Mgr-Market Res)*
Pamela Wagner *(Mgr-Recruitment)*
Brands & Products:
THE PLAIN DEALER
Advertising Agency:
Stern Advertising, Inc.
29125 Chagrin Blvd
Cleveland, OH 44122-4622
Tel.: (216) 464-4850
Fax: (216) 464-7859

THE PLANNING SHOP
555 Bryant St Ste 180
Palo Alto, CA 94301
Tel.: (650) 289-9120
Fax: (650) 289-9125
E-mail: info@planningshop.com
Web Site: www.planningshop.com
Sales Range: Less than $1 Million
Approx. Number Employees: 3
Business Description:
Publisher & Producer of Books & Software for Entrepreneurs
S.I.C.: 7372; 2731
N.A.I.C.S.: 511210; 511130
Media: 2-8-10-13
Personnel:
Rhonda Abrams *(Founder & CEO)*
Bryan Murray *(Mgr-Academic Mktg)*

PLAYBILL INCORPORATED
525 7th Ave Ste 1801
New York, NY 10018-4918
Tel.: (212) 557-5757
Fax: (212) 682-2932
Toll Free: (800) 437-7456
E-mail: frontdesk@playbill.com
Web Site: www.playbill.com
Approx. Number Employees: 30
Year Founded: 1884
Business Description:
Publisher of Theater Guides, Programs & Information
S.I.C.: 2721
N.A.I.C.S.: 511120
Media: 2-4-8-10-13-23
Personnel:
Arthur T. Birsch *(Chm)*
Philip S. Birsh *(Pres & Publr-Playbill)*
Glen A. Asciutto *(Sr Acct Mgr)*
Brands & Products:
PLAYBILL
SHOWBILL

PLAYBOY ENTERPRISES, INC.
680 N Lake Shore Dr
Chicago, IL 60611
Tel.: (312) 751-8000
Fax: (312) 751-2818
E-mail: ir@playboy.com
Web Site:
www.playboyenterprises.com
Approx. Rev.: $240,353,000
Approx. Number Employees: 547
Year Founded: 1953
Business Description:
Holding Company; Adult Magazine, Calendar & Internet Media Publisher; Adult Entertainment Programming & Home Video Production & Distribution
S.I.C.: 6719; 2721; 2731; 2741; 4841; 5961; 7812; 7822
N.A.I.C.S.: 551112; 454111; 511120; 511130; 511199; 512110; 512120; 517510; 519130
Export
Advertising Expenditures: $22,900,000
Media: 2-3-4-5-6-7-8-9-10-11-12-16-17-19-20-21-22-23-24-25-26
Distr.: Intl.; Natl.
Budget Set: June
Personnel:
Alex L. Vaickus *(Pres)*
Scott N. Flanders *(CEO)*
Christoph M. Pachler *(CFO & Exec VP)*
Hugh M. Hefner *(Editor-in-Chief & Chief Creative Officer)*
Howard Shapiro *(Gen Counsel, Sec & Exec VP-Admin & Law)*
Jeremy S. Westin *(Exec VP & Gen Mgr-Video Products & Digital Distr)*
Jeffrey M. Jenest *(Exec VP)*
Richard S. Rosenzweig *(Exec VP)*
Rachel Sagan *(Executive Vice President, Business Affairs, and General Counsel)*
Scott G. Stephen *(Exec VP-Print/Digital Grp)*
Gary Rosenson *(Sr VP & Gen Mgr-Playboy Entertainment Group)*
Carol A. Devine *(Sr VP-HR)*
Martha O. Lindeman *(Sr VP-Corp Comm & IR)*
Matthew Doyle *(Dir-Photo)*
Rob Wilson *(Dir-Art)*
Joel T Bennett *(Sr Product Mgr-Mktg)*
Scott Liss *(Sls Mgr-Midwest Adv-Playboy Magazine & Playboycom)*
Amy Williamson *(Asst Treas)*
Brands & Products:
7 LIVES XPOSED
A DAY OF SEX IN AMERICA
A NIGHT AT THE PLAYBOY MANSION
ADULTVISION
THE BACHELOR PAD
BETTING BUNNY
BUNNY COSTUME
BUNNYPASS
CC MUSIC
CELEBRITY CENTERFOLD
CENTERFOLD
CENTERFOLD COLLECTOR CARDS
CLASSIC CENTERFOLDS
CLIMAX 3
COMPETE
CRITICS' CHOICE VIDEO
CYBER CLUB
EDEN
ENTERTAINMENT FOR MEN
EROS COLLECTION
EYEBALL BENDERS
FAST SERVE
FEMLIN
FOR COUPLES ONLY
GIRLS OF THE INTERNET

Key to Media (For complete agency information see *The Advertising Red Books-Agencies* edition):
1. Bus. Publs. 2. Cable T.V. 3. Catalogs & Directories. 4. Co-op Adv. 5. Consumer Mags. 6. D.M. to Bus. Estab.7. D.M. to Consumers
8. Daily Newsp. 9. Exhibits/Trade Shows 10. Foreign 11. Infomercial 12. Internet Adv.13. Multimedia 14. Network Radio
15. Network T.V. 16. Newsp. Distr. Mags. 17. Other 18. Outdoor (Posters, Transit) 19. Point of Purchase20. Premiums, Novelties
21. Product Samples 22. Special Events Mktg. 23. Spot Radio 24. Spot T.V. 25. Weekly Newsp. 26. Yellow Page Adv.

Playboy Enterprises, Inc. — (Continued)

HEF'S SUPERBUNNIES
HMH
HOME BODIES
HOT NET
HUGH HEFNER
HUGH M. HEFNER
INSIDE OUT
INSTANT ACCESS
JAZZ
MAN TRACK
THE MANSION
MISS APRIL
MISS AUGUST
MISS DECEMBER
MISS FEBRUARY
MISS JANUARY
MISS JULY
MISS JUNE
MISS MARCH
MISS MAY
MISS NOVEMBER
MISS OCTOBER
MISS SEPTEMBER
THE MOST VISITED GLOBAL ENTERTAINMENT SITE FOR MEN
MS. PLAYBOY
MUSIC
NIGHT CALLS 411
NIGHT CALLS RADIO
NO BOYS ALLOWED
PASSION COVE
PLAY4FUN
PLAYBEAR
PLAYBOY
PLAYBOY AUDIO
PLAYBOY BACHELOR PARTY
PLAYBOY CASINO
PLAYBOY CENTERFOLD
THE PLAYBOY CLUB
PLAYBOY CYBER CLUB
THE PLAYBOY EDGE
PLAYBOY EXPOSED
THE PLAYBOY FOUNDATION
PLAYBOY FUNNIES
PLAYBOY HOT HD
PLAYBOY JAZZ
PLAYBOY JAZZ FESTIVAL
PLAYBOY LOUNGE
PLAYBOY MANSION
PLAYBOY NEWS DESK
PLAYBOY ONLINE
PLAYBOY PLAYMATE ALUMNI ASSOCIATION
PLAYBOY POKER
PLAYBOY RACING
PLAYBOY SPA
PLAYBOY SPORTSBOOK.COM
PLAYBOY TV
PLAYBOY TV JUKEBOX
PLAYBOY TV NETWORKS
PLAYBOY X-TREME TEAM
PLAYBOY.COM
PLAYBOY.COMVERSATION
PLAYBOYNET
PLAYBOYPLUS
PLAYBOYRACINGUSA
PLAYBOY'S BATHING BEAUTIES
PLAYBOY'S BOOK OF LINGERIE
PLAYBOY'S CASTING CALLS
PLAYBOY'S COLLEGE GIRLS
PLAYBOY'S CYBER GIRLS
PLAYBOY'S NUDES
PLAYBOY'S PLAYMATE OF THE MONTH
PLAYBOY'S PLAYMATE REVIEW
PLAYBOYSTORE
PLAYBOYSTORE.COM
PLAYBOYTV CLUB
PLAYMATE OF THE MONTH
PLAYMATE OF THE YEAR
PLAYMATE PROFILE
PMOY
PRIVATE CALLS
PROWL
RABBIT HEAD DESIGN
REBOOT
REDHEADS
ROAM
ROUZE
SCAN
SCRAWL
SEX COURT
SEXCETERA
STRIP SEARCH
SUNSUAL
TECHCHICK
TOTALLY BUSTED
TV CLUB
UNIQUELY PLAYMATES
VIDEO CENTERFOLD
VIP
THE WEEKEND FLASH
WET AND WILD
WORLD OF PLAYBOY
THE WORLD'S MOST ORNERY CROSSWORD PUZZLE
X X-TREME TEAM

Advertising Agency:
Gorilla Nation Media, LLC
5140 W Goldleaf Cir Fl 3
Los Angeles, CA 90056
Tel.: (310) 449-1890
Fax: (310) 449-1891
Playboy Online

PLM GROUP LTD.
(Sub. of Transcontinental Inc.)
210 Duffield Dr
Markham, ON L6G 1C9, Canada
Tel.: (416) 848-8500
Fax: (041) 684-88501
E-mail: contact_us@plmgroup.com
Web Site: www.plmgroup.com
Approx. Number Employees: 470
Year Founded: 1987
Business Description:
Business Visual Communications & Commercial Printing
S.I.C.: 2759
N.A.I.C.S.: 323119
Media: 10
Personnel:
Warren Eddy *(VP-Mktg)*

POLYSORT CORPORATION
4000 Embassy Pkwy Ste 400
Akron, OH 44333-8391
Tel.: (330) 665-5918
Fax: (330) 665-5152
Toll Free: (800) 326-8666
E-mail: polysort@polysort.com
Web Site: www.polysort.com
E-Mail For Key Personnel:
President: acharles@polysort.com
Approx. Number Employees: 20
Year Founded: 1995
Business Description:
Online Community for the Plastics & Rubber Industries
S.I.C.: 7375
N.A.I.C.S.: 518111
Media: 2-10-13
Personnel:
Angela Charles *(Mng Dir)*
Brands & Products:
POLYSORT
THE POWER OF MANY. TOGETHER WE MAKE BUSINESS BETTER.

POPULAR MECHANICS
(Unit of Hearst Magazines)
300 W 57th St
New York, NY 10019
Tel.: (212) 649-2000
Fax: (646) 280-1081
E-mail: popularmechanics@hearst.com
Web Site:
www.popularmechanics.com
E-Mail For Key Personnel:
President: jmcgill@hearst.com
Approx. Number Employees: 75
Year Founded: 1902
Business Description:
Publisher of Automotive Magazine
S.I.C.: 2759; 7539
N.A.I.C.S.: 323119; 811118
Media: 2-6-8-10-13-19
Distr.: Natl.
Budget Set: Oct.
Personnel:
Bruce A. Mitnick *(Gen Mgr)*
Jim Meig *(Editor-in-Chief)*
Jerry Beilinson *(Editor)*
Roy Berendsohn *(Assoc Editor-Home)*
Mike Kresch *(Exec Dir-Mktg)*
Glen Suenmayor *(Creative Dir)*
Jane Wladar *(Adv Dir)*
Advertising Agency:
McNeil Group, Inc.
385 Oxford Valley Rd Ste 420
Yardley, PA 19067
Tel.: (215) 321-9662

PORT HOPE EVENING GUIDE
(Div. of Osprey Media Group, Inc.)
99 King St
Cobourg, ON K9A 2M2, Canada
Tel.: (905) 885-2471
Fax: (905) 370-4966
E-mail: mmartin@northumberlandtoday.com
Web Site:
www.northumberlandtoday.com
Approx. Number Employees: 20
Business Description:
Daily Newspaper
S.I.C.: 2711
N.A.I.C.S.: 511110
Media: 13-21-22-25
Personnel:
Gerry Drage *(Dir-Adv)*

PORTERVILLE RECORDER
(Unit of Freedom Newspapers, Inc.)
115 E Oak Ave
Porterville, CA 93257
Tel.: (559) 784-5000
Fax: (559) 784-5245
E-mail: recorderads@portervillerecorder.com
Web Site: www.recorderonline.com
Approx. Number Employees: 65
Business Description:
Newspaper
S.I.C.: 2711
N.A.I.C.S.: 511110
Advertising Expenditures: $25,000
Media: 8-9-18-22-23
Personnel:
Gunter Copeland *(Dir-Adv)*
Craig Dimmitt *(Bus Mgr)*
Martha Gomaz *(Mgr-Acctg)*
Brands & Products:
PORTERVILLE RECORDER

THE POST COMPANY
(d/b/a Post Register)
333 Northgate Mile
Idaho Falls, ID 83401
Tel.: (208) 522-1800
Fax: (208) 529-3142
Web Site: www.postregister.com
Approx. Number Employees: 175
Business Description:
Newspapers, Publishing & Printing
S.I.C.: 2711
N.A.I.C.S.: 511110
Media: 8-9-22-24-25
Personnel:
Jerry Brady *(Owner)*
Roger Plothow *(Publr & Editor)*
Ken Clements *(Dir-Adv)*
Ivy Berry *(Mgr-Bus)*

POST INDEPENDENT
(Sub. of Swift Newspapers, Inc.)
2014 Grand Ave
Glenwood Springs, CO 81601-4116
Tel.: (970) 945-8515
Fax: (970) 945-8518
E-mail: news@postindependent.com
Web Site: www.postindependent.com
Approx. Number Employees: 65
Business Description:
Newspaper Publishing
S.I.C.: 2721; 2752
N.A.I.C.S.: 511120; 323110
Media: 2-8-13
Distr.: Reg.
Budget Set: Nov.
Personnel:
Dale Shrull *(Editor)*

POWELL'S BOOKS INC.
7 NW 9th Ave
Portland, OR 97209
Tel.: (503) 228-0540
Fax: (503) 228-1142
Toll Free: (800) 291-9676
E-mail: press@powells.com
Web Site: www.powells.com
Approx. Sls.: $45,287,846
Approx. Number Employees: 500
Year Founded: 1971
Business Description:
Book Stores
S.I.C.: 5942; 5932
N.A.I.C.S.: 451211; 453310
Media: 6-13
Personnel:
Michael Powell *(Founder & Pres)*
Emily Powell *(Owner & VP)*
Miriam Sontz *(CEO)*

PR NEWSWIRE ASSOCIATION LLC
(Sub. of United Business Media Limited)
350 Hudson Ste 300
New York, NY 10014
Tel.: (201) 360-6776
Fax: (800) 793-9313
Toll Free: (800) 793-9313
Toll Free: (866) 641-4636
E-mail: information@prnewswire.com
Web Site: www.prnewswire.com
Approx. Number Employees: 800

Key to Media (For complete agency information see *The Advertising Red Books-Agencies* edition):
1. Bus. Publs. 2. Cable T.V. 3. Catalogs & Directories. 4. Co-op Adv. 5. Consumer Mags. 6. D.M. to Bus. Estab.7. D.M. to Consumers 8. Daily Newsp. 9. Exhibits/Trade Shows 10. Foreign 11. Infomercial 12. Internet Adv.13. Multimedia 14. Network Radio 15. Network T.V. 16. Newsp. Distr. Mags. 17. Other 18. Outdoor (Posters, Transit) 19. Point of Purchase20. Premiums, Novelties 21. Product Samples 22. Special Events Mktg. 23. Spot Radio 24. Spot T.V. 25. Weekly Newsp. 26. Yellow Page Adv.

Business Description:
Electronic Transmission of Press Releases to News Media
S.I.C.: 7383
N.A.I.C.S.: 519110
Media: 2-13
Personnel:
Ninan Chacko *(CEO)*
Ken Dowell *(Exec VP)*
Scott Mozarsky *(Global Chief Comml Officer & Exec VP)*
Liam Power *(Sr VP-Compliance Svcs)*
Bob Seiler *(Sr VP-Sls & Mktg)*
Rachel Meranus *(VP-Mktg & Comm)*
Garry Durston *(Dir-Mktg Comm-Europe, Middle East, Africa & India)*
Tom Miale *(Mgr-Natl Acct)*
Brands & Products:
EWATCH
MEDIATLAS
MULTIVU
PROFNET
Advertising Agency:
Impressions-A.B.A. Industries, Inc.
393 Jericho Tpk
Mineola, NY 11501
Tel.: (516) 739-3210
Fax: (516) 739-9246

PRESBYTERIAN PUBLISHING CORPORATION

100 Witherspoon St
Louisville, KY 40202-1396
Tel.: (502) 569-5052
Fax: (502) 569-8308
Toll Free: (800) 227-2872
E-mail: customer_service@presbypub.com
Web Site: www.wjkbooks.com
Approx. Number Employees: 35
Year Founded: 1861
Business Description:
Publisher of Religious Books
S.I.C.: 2731; 2721
N.A.I.C.S.: 511130; 511120
Import Export
Advertising Expenditures: $800,000
Media: 2-4-5-6-7-8-10-11-13-18-19-20-21-22-26
Distr.: Natl.
Budget Set: July -Nov.
Personnel:
Marc Lewis *(Pres & Publr)*
Monte Anderson *(COO)*
David Dobson *(Exec Dir-Publ & Editorial Dir)*
Bill Falvey *(Dir-Sls)*
Sarah Foreman *(Dir-Customer Svc & Distr)*
Brands & Products:
GENEVA PRESS
WESTMINSTER JOHN KNOX PRESS
Advertising Agency:
Roth Advertising, Inc.
PO Box 96
Sea Cliff, NY 11579-0096
Tel.: (516) 674-8603
Fax: (516) 674-8606

PRESS & GUIDE

(Sub. of Heritage Newspapers, Inc.)
One Heritage Dr
Southgate, MI 48195
Tel.: (734) 243-2100
Fax: (734) 282-7942
Web Site: www.pressandguide.com
Business Description:
Newspaper Publisher
S.I.C.: 2711; 2721
N.A.I.C.S.: 511110; 511120
Media: 25
Personnel:
Jim Williams *(Pres)*

THE PRESS-ENTERPRISE COMPANY

(Sub. of A.H. Belo Corporation)
2415 14th St
Riverside, CA 92501-3814
Mailing Address:
PO Box 792
Riverside, CA 92502-0792
Tel.: (951) 684-1200
Fax: (951) 368-9021
E-mail: info@press-enterprise.com
Web Site: www.pe.com
Sales Range: $75-99.9 Million
Approx. Number Employees: 600
Year Founded: 1878
Business Description:
Newspaper Publishing
S.I.C.: 2711
N.A.I.C.S.: 511110
Media: 10
Personnel:
Ronald Redfern *(CEO & Publr)*
Frank Escobedo *(Publisher-La Prensa & Gen Mgr-Hispanic Media)*
Karen Kokiko *(VP-Mktg)*

PRESS-REPUBLICAN

(Sub. of Community Newspaper Holdings, Inc.)
170 Margaret St
Plattsburgh, NY 12901
Mailing Address:
PO Box 459
Plattsburgh, NY 12901
Tel.: (518) 561-2300
Fax: (518) 562-3361
E-mail: news@pressrepublican.com
Web Site: www.pressrepublican.com
Approx. Number Employees: 125
Year Founded: 1811
Business Description:
Newspaper Publisher
S.I.C.: 2711
N.A.I.C.S.: 511110
Media: 8-9
Personnel:
Bob Parks *(Publr)*
Joshua Cameron *(Editor-Design)*
Lois Clermont *(Editor-News)*
Bob Grady *(Editor)*
Bruce Rowland *(Editor)*
George Rock *(Dir-Mktg)*
Dan Thayer *(Dir-Production)*

THE PRESS-TRIBUNE

(Sub. of Brehm Communications Inc.)
188 Cirby Way
Roseville, CA 95678-6420
Tel.: (916) 786-8746
Fax: (916) 786-0332
E-mail: emezzetti@goldcountrymedia.com
Web Site: www.rosevillept.com
Approx. Number Employees: 25
Year Founded: 1995
Business Description:
Publisher of Daily Newspapers
S.I.C.: 2711
N.A.I.C.S.: 511110
Import Export
Media: 9-13-16
Personnel:
Erin Mezzetti *(Bus Mgr)*
Brands & Products:
THE EL DORADO HILLS TELEGRAPH
THE FOLSOM TELEGRAPH
THE GRANITE BAY PRESS TRIBUNE
THE GRANITE BAY VIEW
LINCOLN NEWS MESSENGER
THE PLACER HERALD
THE PRESS-TRIBUNE

PRESSTEK, INC.

10 Glenville St
Greenwich, CT 06831
Tel.: (203) 769-8056
Tel.: (203) 769-8054 (IR)
Fax: (203) 769-8099
E-mail: kmakrakis@presstek.com
Web Site: www.presstek.com
E-Mail For Key Personnel:
Public Relations: blabaugh@presstek.com
Approx. Rev.: $128,577,000
Approx. Number Employees: 503
Year Founded: 1987
Business Description:
Direct Imaging Technology for the Printing Industry
S.I.C.: 3555; 3577
N.A.I.C.S.: 333293; 334119
Import Export
Advertising Expenditures: $200,000
Media: 2-7-8-10-18-20-22
Budget Set: Annually
Personnel:
Jeffrey Jacobson *(Chm, Pres & CEO)*
Jeffrey A. Cook *(CFO & Exec VP)*
Kathleen McHugh *(CMO & VP)*
Guy Sasson *(Pres-EMEA)*
James R. Van Horn *(Gen Counsel, Sec & VP)*
Peter A. Bouchard *(VP & Gen Mgr)*
Cathleen V. Cavanna *(VP-HR)*
Joseph A. Demharter *(VP-Sls)*
Hakan Elmali *(VP-Engrg & Res)*
Peter Banks *(Dir-Sls)*
Debbie Galonsky *(Dir-Accts-Natl)*
Kurt Hamlin *(Dir-Strategic Accts)*
Tim Sawyer *(Dir-Sls-Asia Pacific Rim)*
Daniel Victory *(Dir-Global Technical-Digital Plates)*
Brian Wolfenden *(Dir-Mktg Comm)*
Axel Thien *(Bus Mgr-Germany, Austria & Switzerland)*
Brands & Products:
A SMARTER WAY TO PRINT
ANTHEM
APPLAUSE
COMPASS
DI
DIMENSION EXCEL
DIMENSION PRO 800
DIMENSION SERIES
PEARLDRY
PRESSTEK
PROFIRE DIGITAL PLATE MEDIA
PROFIRE EXCEL
VECTOR FL52

PRIMEDIA INC.

3585 Engineering Dr
Norcross, GA 30092
Tel.: (678) 421-3000
E-mail: information@primedia.com
Web Site: www.primedia.com
Approx. Rev.: $232,218,000
Approx. Number Employees: 745
Year Founded: 1989
Business Description:
Magazine, Book & Online Publisher; Television Programming; Educational Video Producer
S.I.C.: 2741; 2721; 2731; 4833; 7812
N.A.I.C.S.: 516110; 511120; 511130; 512110; 515120
Advertising Expenditures: $41,500,000
Media: 2-4-6-7-8
Personnel:
Dean B. Nelson *(Chm)*
Charles J Stubbs *(Pres & CEO)*
Kim Payne *(CFO & Sr VP)*
J. Michael Barber *(Chief Acctg Officer & Sr VP-Acctg)*
Keith L. Belknap *(Gen Counsel, Sec & Sr VP)*
Carl F. Salas *(Treas & Sr VP)*
Steve R. Aster *(Sr VP)*
George Kang *(VP & Gen Mgr-Automotive Digital Network)*
Christine Searight *(VP-Mktg-Apartment Guide)*
Shawn Higgins *(Dir-Mktg-Automotive Grp)*
Cindy Karamitis *(Dir-List Mgmt)*
Brands & Products:
4X4 GARAGE
APARTMENT GUIDE
AQUA-VISION
AUTOMOBILE
AUTOMOBILE REDBOOK
BANK OF KNOWLEDGE
BOATWORKS
BROADWAY LIGHTING MASTER
BROADWAY SOUND MASTER
CATERED ARTS
CHANNEL ONE NEWS
CHEVY HIGH PERFORMANCE
CODEWATCH
CONNECTED LIVING
CRAFTS
DIRECTTIPS
DIRT RIDER
DISRIBUTECH
DOLL READER
DOTY
EDIGITALPHOTO.COM
FEDERAL OUTLOOK
FEELING FIT
FLIPLETTES
FOUR WHEELER
GARDEN STYLE
GREEN GUIDE
HANDGUNS
I-SECURITY
IN-FISHERMAN
INTRAPRIME
JOY OF SCENTS
KIT CAR
THE LAST BID
NEW HOME GUIDE
NEW YORK MAGAZINE SHOP
THE OFFICIAL TRACTOR BLUE BOOK
PRIMEED
PRO FOOTBALL THIS WEEK
PULSE
REALITY CHECK
RENTALS.COM
REPLINKTV
SCRAPLIFTABLES
SHALLOW WATER ANGLER

Key to Media (For complete agency information see *The Advertising Red Books-Agencies* edition):
1. Bus. Publs. 2. Cable T.V. 3. Catalogs & Directories. 4. Co-op Adv. 5. Consumer Mags. 6. D.M. to Bus. Estab.7. D.M. to Consumers
8. Daily Newsp. 9. Exhibits/Trade Shows 10. Foreign 11. Infomercial 12. Internet Adv.13. Multimedia 14. Network Radio
15. Network T.V. 16. Newsp. Distr. Mags. 17. Other 18. Outdoor (Posters, Transit) 19. Point of Purchase20. Premiums, Novelties
21. Product Samples 22. Special Events Mktg. 23. Spot Radio 24. Spot T.V. 25. Weekly Newsp. 26. Yellow Page Adv.

PRIMEDIA Inc. — (Continued)

SHOOTING TIMES
SLAM
SNOWBOARDER
SOAP OPERA WEEKLY
SPORTUTILITY OF THE YEAR
SSTUNER
STAMP IT!
STATE OF THE STATES
STICKBOW HUNTING
SUPER STREET
SURFER
TOBY
TRIBAL
THE ULTIMATE DOLL AUTHORITY
WHEELS AFIELD
WILDFIRE
WILDFOWL
THE WORLD'S #1 AUTOMOBILE AUTHORITY

Advertising Agency:
Gravitas Communications
900 Broadway Ste 1002
New York, NY 10003
Tel.: (212) 924-9500
Fax: (646) 224-8342
— Jocelyn Johnson *(Acct Exec)*

THE PRINCE GEORGE CITIZEN

(Sub. of Glacier Media Inc.)
150 Brunswick St
PO Box 5700
Prince George, BC V2L 5K9, Canada
Tel.: (250) 562-2441
Fax: (250) 562-7453
E-mail: news@princegeorgecitizen.com
Web Site: www.princegeorgecitizen.com
Approx. Number Employees: 100
Business Description:
Newspaper Publishing
S.I.C.: 2711
N.A.I.C.S.: 511110
Media: 8-9
Personnel:
Hugh Nicholson *(Publr)*
Dave Paulson *(Mng Editor)*
Mick Kearns *(Editor-City)*
Jim Swanson *(Editor-Sports)*
Lu Verticchio *(Dir-Adv)*
Matthew Altizer *(Mgr-Sys)*
Colleen Sparrow *(Mgr-Circulation)*

THE PRINCETON REVIEW, INC.

111Speen St
Framingham, MA 01701
Tel.: (508) 663-5050
E-mail: editorialsupport@review.com
Web Site: www.princetonreview.com
Approx. Rev.: $214,426,000
Approx. Number Employees: 898
Year Founded: 1981
Business Description:
Online & Offline Test Preparation Software, Books & Magazines Publisher; College Admissions Help & Financial Advice; Classroom Base & Online Test Preparation Courses
S.I.C.: 8299; 2721; 2731; 7372
N.A.I.C.S.: 611710; 511120; 511130; 511210; 611691
Advertising Expenditures: $33,600,000
Media: 2-6-8-9-10-13-18-20-25-26
Personnel:
David Lowenstein *(Chm)*
John M. Connolly *(Interim Pres & Interim CEO)*
Scott Kirkpatrick *(Pres)*
H. Scott Kirkpatrick, Jr. *(Pres-Test Preparation Svcs Div)*
Robert Franek *(Publr & Sr VP)*
Kevin A. Howell *(Exec VP & Gen Mgr)*
Linda Nessim-Rubin *(Exec VP-Comm & HR)*
Harriet Brand *(Dir-PR)*
Brands & Products:
BEST 351 COLLEGES
HOMEROOM.COM
MATHSMART
THE PRINCETON REVIEW
Advertising Agency:
Earthquake Media, LLC
15 E 26th St Ste 802
New York, NY 10010-1505
Tel.: (212) 204-9200
Fax: (212) 967-1210

PRINCETON UNIVERSITY PRESS

41 William St
Princeton, NJ 08540-5237
Tel.: (609) 258-4900
Fax: (609) 258-6305
E-mail: info@press.princeton.edu
Web Site: www.press.princeton.edu
Approx. Number Employees: 90
Year Founded: 1905
Business Description:
Publisher of Scholarly Books
S.I.C.: 2721; 2731
N.A.I.C.S.: 511120; 511130
Advertising Expenditures: $400,000
Media: 2-6-7-8-9-10-11-13-16-25
Distr.: Intl.; Natl.
Budget Set: Mar.
Personnel:
Patrick Carroll *(Controller & Assoc Dir)*
Maia Coven Reim *(Art Dir-Adv)*
Peter Dougherty *(Dir)*
Adam Fortgang *(Dir-Asst Press & Dir-Mktg)*
Neil Litt *(Dir-Editing, Design & Production)*
Eric Rohmann *(Dir-Sls)*
Brands & Products:
PRINCETON
Advertising Agency:
The Caslon Agency
41 William St
Princeton, NJ 08540-5237
Tel.: (609) 258-4924
Fax: (609) 258-1335
(Books Scholarly & General Interest)

PRITZKER MILITARY LIBRARY

104 S Michigan Ave Ste 400
Chicago, IL 60603
Tel.: (312) 374-9333
Fax: (312) 374-9314
E-mail: info@pritzkermilitarylibrary.net
Web Site: www.pritzkermilitarylibrary.org
Sales Range: $25-49.9 Million
Approx. Number Employees: 15
Business Description:
Military Library
S.I.C.: 8231
N.A.I.C.S.: 519120
Advertising Agency:
Zapwater Communications
1165 N Clark St Ste 313
Chicago, IL 60610
Tel.: (312) 771-1271
Tel.: (312) 943-0333
Fax: (312) 943-0852

THE PROVIDENCE JOURNAL CO.

(Sub. of A.H. Belo Corporation)
75 Fountain St
Providence, RI 02902
Tel.: (401) 277-7000
Fax: (401) 277-7346
Web Site: www.projo.com
Sales Range: $100-124.9 Million
Year Founded: 1829
Business Description:
Newspaper Publishing & TV Broadcasting
S.I.C.: 2711
N.A.I.C.S.: 511110
Advertising Expenditures: $1,500,000
Media: 2-3-6-8-10-19-20-21-22-23-24
Distr.: Natl.
Budget Set: Sept. -Oct.
Personnel:
Steven Sinofsky *(Pres)*
Howard G. Sutton *(Publr)*
Mark T. Ryan *(Exec VP & Gen Mgr)*
Joel P. Rawson *(Sr VP & Exec Editor)*
Scott C. Connolly *(Sr VP)*
Wayne D. Pelland *(Sr VP-Ops)*
Sandra J. Radcliffe *(Sr VP-Fin)*
Robert B. Whitcomb *(VP & Editor-Edit Page)*
Maura Brodeur *(VP-Adv)*
Tori Provost *(Mktg Dir)*
Dotty Craig *(Mgr-Mktg)*
Brands & Products:
PROJO.COM

PRUDENT PUBLISHING COMPANY, INC.

65 Challenger Rd Fl 1
Ridgefield Park, NJ 07660
Tel.: (201) 641-7900
Fax: (201) 641-1401
E-mail: info@prudentpub.com
Web Site: www.gallerycollection.com
Approx. Sls.: $16,000,000
Approx. Number Employees: 85
Year Founded: 1929
Business Description:
Business-To-Business Mail Order Publisher of Greeting Cards
S.I.C.: 2741
N.A.I.C.S.: 511199
Media: 4-7-8-13-21
Personnel:
Bernard J. D'avella, Jr. *(Pres)*
Allen Greenwald *(CFO)*
H. L. Devore *(CMO)*
Brands & Products:
THE GALLERY COLLECTION
PREMIUM QUALITY CARDS FOR A LASTING IMPRESSION

PUBLIC UTILITIES REPORTS, INC.

8229 Boone Blvd Ste 400
Vienna, VA 22182-2623
Tel.: (703) 847-7720
Fax: (703) 917-6964
Toll Free: (800) 368-5001
E-mail: pur@pur.com
Web Site: www.pur.com
Sales Range: Less than $1 Million
Approx. Number Employees: 15
Business Description:
Public Utilities Reports
S.I.C.: 2731; 2721
N.A.I.C.S.: 511130; 511120
Media: 7
Personnel:
Bruce Radford *(Pres & CEO)*
Louis Turner *(Treas & Accountant)*
Joseph Paparello *(Dir-Sls)*
Jean Cole *(Mgr-Mktg)*

PUBLICATIONS & COMMUNICATIONS, INC.

(d/b/a PCI)
13581 Pond Springs Rd 450
Austin, TX 78729-4108
Tel.: (512) 250-9023
Fax: (512) 331-3950
Toll Free: (800) 678-9724
Web Site: www.pcinews.com
Sales Range: Less than $1 Million
Approx. Number Employees: 15
Year Founded: 1980
Business Description:
Computer Trade Publications
S.I.C.: 2721
N.A.I.C.S.: 511120
Export
Media: 2-6-7-13
Personnel:
Gary Pittman *(Mng Partner)*
Larry Storer *(Dir-Editorial Svcs)*
Brands & Products:
PCI
SOFTWARE
WILSON PUBLICATIONS

PUBLICATIONS INTERNATIONAL, LTD.

7373 N Cicero Ave
Lincolnwood, IL 60712-1613
Tel.: (847) 676-3470
Fax: (847) 676-3671
Web Site: www.pubint.com
Approx. Number Employees: 225
Year Founded: 1967
Business Description:
Book Publishing Company
S.I.C.: 2731; 2721
N.A.I.C.S.: 511130; 511120
Import Export
Media: 10-13
Personnel:
Lou Weber *(Founder)*

PUBLISHERS CIRCULATION FULFILLMENT INC.

502 Washington Ave Ste 500
Towson, MD 21204-5017
Tel.: (410) 821-8614
Fax: (410) 583-1578
Web Site: www.pcfcorp.com
Approx. Number Employees: 5,000
Year Founded: 1980
Business Description:
Newspaper Circulation Services
S.I.C.: 7389
N.A.I.C.S.: 561499
Import Export
Media: 8
Personnel:
Gerard Giordana *(CEO)*
Thomas D. Foard *(CFO & Exec VP)*
Kevin Daly *(Exec VP-Distr Svcs)*

Key to Media (For complete agency information see *The Advertising Red Books-Agencies* edition):
1. Bus. Publs. 2. Cable T.V. 3. Catalogs & Directories. 4. Co-op Adv. 5. Consumer Mags. 6. D.M. to Bus. Estab.7. D.M. to Consumers
8. Daily Newsp. 9. Exhibits/Trade Shows 10. Foreign 11. Infomercial 12. Internet Adv.13. Multimedia 14. Network Radio
15. Network T.V. 16. Newsp. Distr. Mags. 17. Other 18. Outdoor (Posters, Transit) 19. Point of Purchase20. Premiums, Novelties
21. Product Samples 22. Special Events Mktg. 23. Spot Radio 24. Spot T.V. 25. Weekly Newsp. 26. Yellow Page Adv.

PUBLISHERS GROUP WEST
(Sub. of The Perseus Books Group)
1700 4th St
Berkeley, CA 94710
Tel.: (510) 809-3700
Fax: (510) 809-3777
Toll Free: (800) 788-3123
E-mail: info@pgw.com
Web Site: www.pgw.com
Approx. Number Employees: 300
Year Founded: 1976
Business Description:
Books Distr
S.I.C.: 5192
N.A.I.C.S.: 424920
Media: 2-4
Personnel:
Suk Lee *(Dir-Intl Sls)*

PUTMAN MEDIA, INC.
555 W Pierce Rd Ste 301
Itasca, IL 60143-2666
Tel.: (630) 467-1300
Fax: (630) 467-1179
Toll Free: (800) 984-7644
E-mail: info@putman.net
Web Site: www.putman.net
E-Mail For Key Personnel:
President: jcappelletti@putman.net
Approx. Number Employees: 60
Year Founded: 1938
Business Description:
Trade Journal Publisher
S.I.C.: 2721; 2731
N.A.I.C.S.: 511120; 511130
Media: 2-10
Personnel:
John M. Cappelletti, Jr. *(Pres & CEO)*
Russ Kratowicz *(Exec Editor-Plant Svcs Magazine)*
Michele Vaccarello Wagner *(Sr Editor)*
Dave Fisher *(Reg Mgr-Northeast & Mid-Atlantic)*
Laura Martinez *(Reg Mgr-Western & Mountain)*
Greg Zamin *(Reg Mgr-Midwest & Southeast)*
Rita Fitzgerald *(Production Mgr)*
Jeanne Freedland *(Sls Mgr)*
Anneta Gauthier *(Production Mgr)*
Faith Dalton *(District Mgr)*
Christy Dickman *(Mgr-HR)*

QUANTURO PUBLISHING, INC.
4141 NE 2nd Ave Ste 205
Miami, FL 33137
Tel.: (305) 373-3700
Fax: (305) 373-3708
E-mail: info@floridainternationalmag.com
Web Site:
www.floridainternationalmag.com
Approx. Number Employees: 15
Business Description:
Magazine Publisher
S.I.C.: 2721
N.A.I.C.S.: 511120
Media: 6-8
Personnel:
Esther Q. Jackson *(Owner)*
Phyllis Pesaturo *(VP & Dir-Creative)*
Brands & Products:
FLORIDA INTERNATIONAL MAGAZINE

QUAY COUNTY SUN
(Unit of Freedom Newspapers, Inc.)
902 S 1st St
Tucumcari, NM 88401
Mailing Address:
PO Box 1408
Tucumcari, NM 88401-1408
Tel.: (575) 461-1952
Fax: (575) 461-1965
E-mail: cnjonline@qcsunonline.com
Web Site: www.qcsunonline.com
Approx. Number Employees: 4
Year Founded: 1975
Business Description:
Newspaper
S.I.C.: 2711
N.A.I.C.S.: 511110
Media: 8-9
Personnel:
Ray Sullivan *(Publr)*
Russell Anglin *(Editor)*
Brands & Products:
QUAY COUNTY SUN

QUEBECOR MEDIA INC.
(Sub. of Quebecor, Inc.)
612 Rue Saint-Jacques
Montreal, QC H3C 4M8, Canada
Tel.: (514) 380-1999
Fax: (514) 985-8515
Toll Free: (866) 380-1999
E-mail: qi_reshum@quebecor.com
Web Site: www.quebecor.com
Approx. Rev.: $3,914,817,868
Approx. Number Employees: 16,360
Year Founded: 1995
Business Description:
Printing & Media Services
S.I.C.: 4841; 2711; 2741; 4812; 5192; 7375
N.A.I.C.S.: 515210; 424920; 511110; 511140; 516110; 517212; 518111
Advertising Expenditures: $11,968,601
Media: 6-9-13-15-25
Personnel:
Serge Gouin *(Chm)*
Erik Peladeau *(Vice Chm)*
Pierre Karl Peladeau *(Pres & CEO)*
Louis Morin *(CFO & VP)*
Luc Lavoie *(Exec VP-Corp Affairs)*
Hugues Simard *(Sr VP-Dev & Strategy)*
Sylvie Cordeau *(VP-Comm)*
Roger Martel *(VP-Internal Audit)*
Jean-Francois Pruneau *(VP-Fin)*
Marc Tremblay *(VP-Legal Affairs)*
Wade Hynes *(Gen Mgr-Community Digital Products & Svcs)*
Christian Marcoux *(Asst Sec)*

QUEBECOR WORLD
(Sub. of Quad/Graphics, Inc.)
2000 Arthur Ave
Elk Grove Village, IL 60007-6007
Tel.: (847) 640-6000
Fax: (847) 640-6029
E-mail: global.sales@quebecorworld.com
Web Site: www.quebecorworld.com
Approx. Number Employees: 250
Year Founded: 1946
Business Description:
Offset Printing; General Commercial Catalogs; Web Printing
S.I.C.: 2752
N.A.I.C.S.: 323110
Advertising Expenditures: $3,400,000
Media: 6-10-17-23
Distr.: Natl.

QUESTAR ASSESSMENT, INC.
4 Hardscrabble Hts
Brewster, NY 10509-0382
Mailing Address:
PO Box 382
Brewster, NY 10509-0382
Tel.: (845) 277-8100
Fax: (845) 277-8115
E-mail: generalinquiries@questarai.com
Web Site: www.questarai.com
Sales Range: $25-49.9 Million
Approx. Number Employees: 136
Year Founded: 1976
Business Description:
Educational Reading Assessment Tests Publisher
S.I.C.: 8299; 2741
N.A.I.C.S.: 611710; 511199
Advertising Expenditures: $650,000
Media: 7-10-16
Personnel:
Andrew L. Simon *(Chm)*
Roy Lipner *(Pres & CEO)*
David Vail *(CFO)*
Steve Mesmer *(COO)*
Dennis Anest *(Sr VP-Tech & Ops)*
Michael D. Beck *(Sr VP-Res & Assesment Svcsv)*
Linda G. Straley *(Sr VP)*
Brands & Products:
CORE KNOWLEDGE
DEGREES OF READING POWER
DRP-BOOKLINK
DRP EZCONVERTER
MAC II TEST
READING POWER ESSENTIALS
SIGNPOSTS EARLY LITERACY
SSSMART
SUCCESS BY YOUR STANDARDS
TEXTSENSE
WRITEQUEST

RAND MCNALLY & COMPANY
(Holding of Patriarch Partners, LLC)
8255 N Central Park Ave
Skokie, IL 60076
Mailing Address:
PO Box 7600
Chicago, IL 60680-7600
Tel.: (847) 329-8100
Fax: (800) 934-3479
Toll Free: (800) 678-7263
Web Site: www.randmcnally.com
E-Mail For Key Personnel:
Public Relations: Elsberg@randmcnally.com
Approx. Number Employees: 400
Year Founded: 1856
Business Description:
Map & Travel Guide Publisher
S.I.C.: 2741
N.A.I.C.S.: 511199
Media: 2-4-5-6-7-8-9-10-13-18-19-20-23
Distr.: Direct to Consumer; Intl.; Natl.
Budget Set: Nov.
Personnel:
Dave Muscatel *(CEO)*
Jim Rodi *(Sr VP-Mobile Comm)*
Brands & Products:
INTELLIROUTE
MILEMAKER
RAND MCNALLY FOR KIDS
STREETFINDER
THE THOMAS GUIDE
TRIP MAKER

RANDALL-REILLY PUBLISHING COMPANY LLC
(Holding of Investcorp International, Inc.)
3200 Rice Mine Rd NE
Tuscaloosa, AL 35406-1510
Tel.: (205) 349-2990
Fax: (205) 345-0958
Toll Free: (800) 633-5953
E-mail: rhoffham@rrpub.com
Web Site: www.rrpub.com
Approx. Number Employees: 380
Year Founded: 1934
Business Description:
Publishing Services
S.I.C.: 2721
N.A.I.C.S.: 511120
Import Export
Media: 2-6-10-13
Personnel:
F. Michael Reilly *(Chm, Pres & CEO)*
Shane Elmore *(CFO & Treas)*
David R. Wright *(COO & VP)*
Chip Wisdom *(Publr)*
Robert Lake *(Sr VP-Acq)*
Linda Longton *(Sr VP-Editorial & Res)*
Jeff Mason *(Sr VP-Trucking Media Grp)*
Dan Tidwell *(Sr VP-Construction Div)*
Brent Reilly *(Gen Mgr-Ops)*
Alan K. Sims *(Dir-Sls & Mktg)*
Brands & Products:
CONSTRUCTION
POP BID
TRUCKING
WHO'S WHO AMOUNG STUDENTS
WOODWORKING

RANDOM HOUSE CHILDREN'S BOOKS
(Sub. of Random House, Inc.)
1745 Broadway
New York, NY 10019
Tel.: (212) 782-9000
Fax: (212) 782-9484
Web Site: www.randomhouse.com
Business Description:
Children's Books Publr
S.I.C.: 2731
N.A.I.C.S.: 511130
Media: 4
Personnel:
Chip Gibson *(Pres & Publr)*
Kate Klimo *(Dir-Editorial)*
Melissa Zar *(Coord-Mktg)*
Brands & Products:
BANTAM BOOKS FOR YOUNG READERS
BEGINNER BOOKS
CROWN CHILDREN'S BOOKS
DELACORTE PRESS BOOKS
DRAGONFLY
GOLDEN BOOKS
KNOPF CHILDREN'S BOOKS
LAUREL-LEAF
RANDOM HOUSE
SESAME STREET
SKYLARK
STARFIRE
YEARLING

RANDOM HOUSE, INC.
(Div. of Bertelsmann AG)
1745 Broadway
New York, NY 10019
Tel.: (212) 782-9000
Fax: (212) 302-7985

Random House, Inc. — (Continued)

Toll Free: (800) 726-0600
Web Site: www.randomhouse.com
Approx. Rev.: $2,588,082,400
Approx. Number Employees: 5,264
Year Founded: 1927
Business Description:
Book Publisher
S.I.C.: 2731; 5942
N.A.I.C.S.: 511130; 451211
Media: 2-6-9-23
Distr.: Direct to Consumer; Natl.
Budget Set: Jan.-July
Personnel:
Gail Rebuck *(Chm & CEO-UK)*
Markus Dohle *(Deputy Chm & COO)*
Sonny Mehta *(Pres-Alfred A Knopf & Publr)*
Chip Gibson *(Publr)*
Stuart Applebaum *(Exec VP-Comm)*
Jaci Updike *(Sr VP & Dir-Sls)*
Debbie Aroff *(Sr Mgr-Brand Mktg)*
Brands & Products:
CHILDREN'S CLASSICS
CRESCENT BOOKS
DERRYDALE
GRAMERCY BOOKS
HOUSE COLLECTIBLES
KOVEL'S
LIVING LANGUAGE
PANTHEON BOOKS
PRINCETON REVIEW
RANDOM HOUSE PUZZLES & GAMES
RANDOM HOUSE REFERENCE
SHOCKEN BOOKS
TESTAMENT BOOKS
VINTAGE ANCHOR
WINGS BOOKS

THE READER'S DIGEST ASSOCIATION, INC.

(Holding of Ripplewood Holdings LLC)
Reader's Digest Rd
Pleasantville, NY 10570
Tel.: (914) 238-1000
Fax: (914) 238-4559
Toll Free: (800) 234-9000
E-mail: william.adler@rd.com
Web Site: www.rd.com
Approx. Rev.: $2,786,400,000
Approx. Number Employees: 4,700
Year Founded: 1922
Business Description:
Magazines, Books, Music, Videos, Electronic Publishing & New Media Publisher
S.I.C.: 2721; 2731; 2741
N.A.I.C.S.: 511120; 511130; 511199; 516110
Advertising Expenditures: $23,000,000
Media: 2-6-8-9-10-13-14-19-20-24
Distr.: Direct to Consumer; Intl.; Natl.
Budget Set: May
Personnel:
Randal Curran *(Chm)*
Robert Guth *(Pres & CEO)*
Liz Vaccariello *(Chief Content Officer & Editor-in-Chief-Reader's Digest Community)*
Neil Wertheimer *(Chief Content Officer-Intl & Editor-in-Chief-Reader's Digest Book)*
Suzanne M. Grimes *(Pres-Lifestyle Communities & Exec VP-RDA)*
Dan Lagani *(Pres-Reader's Digest Community & Exec VP)*
Lisa W.A. Sharples *(Pres-Allrecipes.com & Exec VP-RDA)*
Dawn M. Zier *(Pres-Intl)*
Andrea R. Newborn *(Gen Counsel, Sec & Sr VP)*
Heddy Pierson *(Assoc Publr)*
Anne Balaban *(Publr-Everyday With Rachel Ray & VP)*
Jan Studin *(Publr-Taste of Home & VP)*
Harold Clarke *(Publr-Books, Music & Trade Publ)*
Cynthia Hack *(Publr-Selecciones)*
Albert L. Perruzza *(Sr VP-Global Ops & IT)*
Elaine Alimonti *(VP-Mktg & Sls Dev)*
Lora Gier *(VP Integreated Partnerships)*
Cara Schlanger *(VP-Mktg & Promo-Global)*
Steven Schwartz *(Gen Mgr-Digital-RD Community)*
Barbara O'Dair *(Exec Editor)*
Theresa O'Rourke *(Exec Editor-Every Day With Rachel Ray)*
Tom Prince *(Exec Editor-Reader's Digest Magazine)*
Terri Smith *(Exec Dir-Integrated & Brand Mktg)*
Brands & Products:
ALLRECIPES.COM
BOOKS ARE FUN
THE DIGEST
EVERY DAY WITH RACHEL RAY
THE FAMILY HANDYMAN
PEGASUS
QSP
READER'S DIGEST
REIMAN PUBLICATIONS
SELECCIONES
SELECT EDITIONS
TODAY'S BEST NONFICTION
Advertising Agencies:
Agency212, LLC
(The Tucker Partnership, Inc. (Parent Company))
112 W 20th St 7th Fl
New York, NY 10011
Tel.: (212) 994-6700
Fax: (212) 994-6699

Blue Sky Agency
950 Lowery Blvd Ste 30
Atlanta, GA 30318
Tel.: (404) 876-0202
Fax: (404) 876-0212
North America Agency of Record
Taste of Home
The Family Handyman

Chase/Temkin & Associates, LLC
168 Sawmill River Rd PO Box 224
Hawthorne, NY 10532
Tel.: (914) 449-6962
Fax: (914) 769-7974

Dan Klores Communications
(d/b/a dkc)
386 Park Ave S 10th Fl
New York, NY 10016
Tel.: (212) 685-4300
Fax: (212) 685-9024
Public Relations

G.S. Schwartz & Co. Inc.
470 Park Ave S 10th Fl S
New York, NY 10016-6819
Tel.: (212) 725-4500
Fax: (212) 725-9188
Integrated Public Relations Program
Your Life. . .The Reader's Digest Version

LDMI
13936 Gold Cir
Omaha, NE 68144-2359
Tel.: (402) 334-9446
Fax: (402) 334-9622
Toll Free: (800) 366-7686

Susan Magrino Agency
641 Lexington Ave 28th Fl
New York, NY 10022
Tel.: (212) 957-3005
Fax: (212) 957-4071

THE RECORD

(Unit of Ottaway Newspapers, Inc.)
530 E Market St
Stockton, CA 95202-3009
Mailing Address:
PO Box 900
Stockton, CA 95202
Tel.: (209) 943-6397
Fax: (209) 943-6565
Web Site: www.recordnet.com
Sales Range: $100-124.9 Million
Approx. Number Employees: 300
Business Description:
Newspaper Publisher
S.I.C.: 2711
N.A.I.C.S.: 511110
Media: 7-8-9-13-25
Personnel:
Roger Coover *(Pres & Publr)*
Brandye Alexander *(Editor-Night News)*
Deborah Blankenberg *(Copy Editor)*
Frankie Bozem *(Copy Editor-Day Desk)*
Ann Breitler *(Copy Editor-Day Desk)*
Bill Cauble *(Copy Editor)*
Mark Donaldson *(Copy Editor)*
Michael Gillaspy *(Editor-Sports)*
Eric Grunder *(Editor-Opinion Page)*
Kevin Hecteman *(Editor-Copy)*
Bob Highfill *(Editor-Sports)*
Robin Nichols *(Editor-Lens)*
Craig Sanders *(Editor-Photos)*
Peter Gutierrez *(Dir-Circulation)*
Rick Henning *(Dir-IT)*
Sandi Johnson *(Dir-HR)*
Deitra R. Kenoly *(Dir-Adv)*
Judy Sheelar *(Dir-Innovation & Mktg)*
Harry Coleman *(Mgr-Consumer Rels)*
Ken Damilano *(Mgr-Tech Svcs)*
Claudine Dunham *(Mgr-Credit)*
Jim Frankel *(Mgr-Ops & Safety)*
Joey Givens *(Mgr-Pressroom)*
Hilary Height *(Mgr-Adv Sls)*
Rick Oliveri *(Mgr-Home Delivery)*
Lisa C. Perry *(Mgr-Adv sls)*
Patsy Prato *(Mgr-Classified Phone)*
Gwen Toschi *(Mgr-Single Copy)*
Carol Wanner *(Mgr-Admin)*
Ral Weekly *(Mgr-Adv Production)*
Carol Bradley *(Coord-New Bus Sls & Education)*

THE RECORD

(Sub. of Torstar Corporation)
160 King St E
Kitchener, ON N2G 4E5, Canada
Tel.: (519) 894-2231
Fax: (519) 894-3912
Web Site: www.therecord.com
Approx. Number Employees: 200
Business Description:
Daily Newspaper
S.I.C.: 2711
N.A.I.C.S.: 511110
Media: 13-25
Personnel:
Donna Luelo *(Dir-Adv)*
Gray Myers *(Interim Dir)*
John Thompson *(Sls Mgr)*
Marion Parsons *(Asst Mgr-Sys & Admin)*
Craig Campbell *(Mgr-Sys & Data)*
Helen Exley *(Mgr-Mktg)*
Shelley Haney *(Mgr-Reg Adv Admin)*
Dan Patterson *(Mgr-Distr & Home Delivery)*
Bill Stoody *(Mgr-Adv)*

THE RECORD-JOURNAL PUBLISHING COMPANY

11 Crown St
Meriden, CT 06450-5713
Tel.: (203) 235-1661
Fax: (203) 235-3482
E-mail: newsroom@record-journal.com
Web Site: www.record-journal.com
Sales Range: $10-24.9 Million
Approx. Number Employees: 200
Year Founded: 1867
Business Description:
Newspaper Publishing Services
S.I.C.: 2711
N.A.I.C.S.: 511110
Media: 8-9
Personnel:
Kathy Merry *(CFO)*
Alison W. Muschinsky *(Sec & Sr VP)*
Eliot C. White *(Publr)*
Tim Ryan *(Exec VP & Gen Mgr-The Westerly Sun)*
Michael F. Killian *(Sr VP, Gen Mgr & Dir-Sls & Mktg)*
Raymond Roy *(VP-Westerly Sun & Gen Mgr)*
Kimberly Boose *(Dir-Svcs & Mgr-Adv)*
Sandra T. Blodgett *(Dir-Svcs)*
Doug Bevins *(Mgr)*
Kimberley Boath *(Mgr-Adv)*
Brands & Products:
BERLIN CITIZEN
RECORD JOURNAL
RECORD-JOURNAL
TIEMPO
WESTERLY SUN

THE RECORD SEARCHLIGHT

(Sub. of The E.W. Scripps Company)
1101 Twin View Blvd
Redding, CA 96003-1531
Mailing Address:
PO Box 492397
Redding, CA 96049-2397
Tel.: (530) 225-8315
Fax: (530) 225-8375
Fax: (530) 225-8212
Web Site: www.redding.com
Sales Range: $100-124.9 Million
Approx. Number Employees: 200
Year Founded: 1938
Business Description:
Morning & Sunday Newspapers Publisher

Key to Media (For complete agency information see *The Advertising Red Books-Agencies* edition):
1. Bus. Publs. 2. Cable T.V. 3. Catalogs & Directories. 4. Co-op Adv. 5. Consumer Mags. 6. D.M. to Bus. Estab.7. D.M. to Consumers
8. Daily Newsp. 9. Exhibits/Trade Shows 10. Foreign 11. Infomercial 12. Internet Adv.13. Multimedia 14. Network Radio
15. Network T.V. 16. Newsp. Distr. Mags. 17. Other 18. Outdoor (Posters, Transit) 19. Point of Purchase20. Premiums, Novelties
21. Product Samples 22. Special Events Mktg. 23. Spot Radio 24. Spot T.V. 25. Weekly Newsp. 26. Yellow Page Adv.

S.I.C.: 5192
N.A.I.C.S.: 424920
Media: 8-9
Personnel:
Shanna Cannon *(Pres & Publr)*
Kathy Thurber *(Dir-HR)*
Sterling Yeaman *(Dir-Production)*
Michelle Martin-Streeby *(Mgr-Mktg)*

RECORDED BOOKS, LLC
(Sub. of Haights Cross Communications, Inc.)
270 Skipjack Rd
Prince Frederick, MD 20678-3410
Tel.: (410) 535-5590
Fax: (410) 535-5499
Toll Free: (800) 638-1304
E-mail: customerservice@recordedbooks.com
Web Site: www.recordedbooks.com
Sales Range: $1-9.9 Million
Approx. Number Employees: 250
Year Founded: 1979
Business Description:
Unabridged Audio Books Retailer on Cassettes & Compact Discs
S.I.C.: 7389
N.A.I.C.S.: 512290
Advertising Expenditures: $250,000
Media: 6-8-13
Personnel:
Rich Freese *(Pres & CEO)*
Neil Tress *(CFO & COO)*

RECORDER PUBLISHING CO.
17 19 Morristown Rd
Bernardsville, NJ 07924
Tel.: (908) 766-3900
Fax: (908) 766-6365
Web Site: www.recordernewspapers.com
Sales Range: $10-24.9 Million
Approx. Number Employees: 30
Business Description:
Newspapers; Publishing & Printing
S.I.C.: 2711
N.A.I.C.S.: 511110
Media: 8-9
Personnel:
Steven Parker *(Co-Publisher & Mgr-Bus)*
Diane Howard *(Office Mgr)*

REDBOOK
(Unit of Hearst Magazines)
224 W 57th St
New York, NY 10019-3212
Tel.: (212) 649-3450
Tel.: (212) 649-3363
Fax: (212) 581-7605
Approx. Number Employees: 250
Year Founded: 1903
Business Description:
Women's Magazine
S.I.C.: 2759
N.A.I.C.S.: 323119
Media: 7-8-9-19-21
Distr.: Natl.
Budget Set: Oct.
Personnel:
Mary E. Morgan *(VP-Publr)*
Terrence Day *(VP & Sr Grp Dir-Circulation)*
Mary Hayes *(VP-Mail Order)*
Sara Anderson *(Sr Editor)*
Andrea Bauman *(Deputy Editor)*
Jessica Brown *(Editor-Sr Health)*
Barbara Chernetz *(Editor-Food)*
Judy Dutton *(Sr Editor)*
Jean H. Rodie *(Copy Chief Editor)*
Lori Berger *(Dir-Entertainment)*
Bruce Perez *(Dir-Photography)*
Lauren Rockwell *(Dir-Fashion)*
Drew Weicker *(Dir-New York Sls)*
Candie L. Patterson *(Sr Mgr-Mktg)*

THE REGISTER MAIL
(Unit of GateHouse Media, Inc.)
140 S Prairie St
Galesburg, IL 61401-4605
Mailing Address:
PO Box 310
Galesburg, IL 61401
Tel.: (309) 343-7181
Fax: (309) 343-7607
Web Site: www.galesburg.com
Sales Range: $25-49.9 Million
Approx. Number Employees: 120
Business Description:
Newspaper
S.I.C.: 2711
N.A.I.C.S.: 511110
Media: 8-9
Personnel:
Carol Uhlmann *(Mgr-Classified Adv)*
Brands & Products:
THE REGISTER MAIL

REIMAN MEDIA GROUP, INC.
(Sub. of The Reader's Digest Association, Inc.)
(d/b/a Reiman Publications)
5400 S 60th St
Greendale, WI 53129
Tel.: (414) 423-0100
Fax: (414) 423-8463
Fax: (414) 423-3912 (HR)
Toll Free: (800) 344-6913
Web Site: www.reimanpub.com
Sales Range: $300-349.9 Million
Approx. Number Employees: 500
Year Founded: 1965
Business Description:
Magazine Publisher
S.I.C.: 2721
N.A.I.C.S.: 511120
Media: 8-13
Personnel:
Catherine Cassidy *(Editor-in-Chief-Taste of Home)*
Brands & Products:
BACKYARD LIVING
BIRDS & BLOOMS
COOKING FOR TWO
COUNTRY
COUNTRY DISCOVERIES
COUNTRY WOMAN
FARM & RANCH LIVING
HEALTHY COOKING
QUICK COOKING
REMINISCE
TASTE OF HOME
TASTE OF HOME'S MENU$AVER

RESPONSE MAIL EXPRESS INC.
(Sub. of Direct Mail Express Inc.)
4910 Savarese Cir
Tampa, FL 33634-2403
Tel.: (813) 885-8200
Fax: (813) 885-8201
Toll Free: (800) 273-8866
E-mail: info@responsemail.com
Web Site: www.responsemail.com
Approx. Number Employees: 160
Business Description:
Direct Mail Advertising Services
S.I.C.: 7331; 2741
N.A.I.C.S.: 541860; 511140
Media: 2-6-10-13
Personnel:
Tom Panaggio *(CEO)*

REUTERS RESEARCH
(Sub. of Thomson Reuters Markets)
3 Times Sq
New York, NY 10036-6564
Tel.: (212) 607-2500
Fax: (646) 836-5110
Toll Free: (800) 721-2225
Web Site: www.reuters.com
Sales Range: $75-99.9 Million
Approx. Number Employees: 560
Business Description:
Investment Research Company
S.I.C.: 7375; 6282
N.A.I.C.S.: 518111; 523930
Media: 13
Personnel:
Gregg Amonette *(Sr VP-Bus Dev)*
Frank DeMaria *(Sr VP-Corp Pub Rels)*
Brooks Gibbins *(Sr VP-Sls)*
Ed Kitain *(Sr VP-Opers)*
Ric Camacho *(VP-Digital Syndication-Reuters Media)*
Paul Geraghty *(Product Mgr)*
George Racine *(Product Mgr)*
Jeff Saville *(Mgr-Mktg)*
Alexandra Honeysett *(Corp Comm Exec)*

REVENUE
(Div. of Montgomery Media International, LLC)
55 New Montgomery St Ste 617
San Francisco, CA 94105
Tel.: (415) 371-8800
E-mail: info@mthink.com
Web Site: mthink.com/contact
Business Description:
Magazine
S.I.C.: 2721
N.A.I.C.S.: 511120
Media: 7-13
Personnel:
Julienne Riveong *(Comptroller)*
Yvonne Schellerup *(Dir-Mktg)*
Tobias Siegel *(Dir-Sls)*

R.L. POLK & CO.
26955 Northwestern Hwy
Southfield, MI 48033-4716
Tel.: (248) 728-7000
Fax: (248) 728-2001
Toll Free: (800) 464-7655
Toll Free: (800) GO-4-POLK
E-mail: info@polk.com
Web Site: www.polk.com
Sales Range: $250-299.9 Million
Approx. Number Employees: 1,400
Year Founded: 1870
Business Description:
Automotive Industry Information Supplier for Automakers, Dealers & the Aftermarket
S.I.C.: 2741; 7389; 8732; 8733
N.A.I.C.S.: 511140; 519190; 541710; 541910
Advertising Expenditures: $200,000
Media: 2-7-8-10-13-22-26
Distr.: Natl.
Budget Set: Nov. -Dec.
Personnel:
Stephen R. Polk *(Chm, Pres & CEO)*
Michelle Goff *(CFO & Sr VP)*
Tim Rogers *(Pres-Polk Bus Unit)*
Steve Flinker *(VP-Sls & Client Svcs, Mng Dir-Asia Pacific)*
Mike Gingell *(VP-Sls & Client Svcs)*
Deborah Young *(VP-HR)*
Jack Smith *(Dir-Mktg)*
Brands & Products:
AUTOMOTIVE INTELLIGENCE
COVERS
CVINA
FOCAL POINTS
INTELLIGENCE. INSIGHT. IMPACT.
NVPP
PART LIFECYCLE
POLK
POLK INSIGHT
POLK TOTAL MARKET PREDICTOR
TELESTAT
TIP
TIP ACCESS
TIP NET
VINA
VINTELLIGENCE
Advertising Agency:
Lambert Edwards & Associates
755 W Big Beaver Rd Ste 1100
Troy, MI 48084
Tel.: (248) 362-4200
Fax: (248) 362-3428

THE ROANOKE TIMES
(Sub. of Landmark Media Enterprises LLC)
201 W Campbell Ave
Roanoke, VA 24011
Mailing Address:
PO Box 2491
Roanoke, VA 24010-2491
Tel.: (540) 981-3100
Fax: (540) 981-3194
Fax: (540) 981-3340
Toll Free: (800) 346-1234
E-mail: info@roanoke.com
Web Site: www.roanoke.com
Approx. Number Employees: 400
Business Description:
Newspaper Publisher
S.I.C.: 2711
N.A.I.C.S.: 511110
Media: 8-9-22
Personnel:
Debbie Meade *(Pres & Publr)*
Tonia Hart *(CFO)*
Carole Tarrant *(Editor)*
Stefan Babich *(Dir-Adv)*
Brands & Products:
ROANOKE TIMES NESWPAPER
ROANOKE.COM

ROBB REPORT
(Sub. of Curtco Media Labs LLC)
(Owned by CurtCo Media Labs, LLC)
29160 Heathercliff Rd Ste 200
Malibu, CA 90265
Tel.: (310) 589-7700
Fax: (310) 589-7701
Web Site: www.robbreport.com
Business Description:
Magazine
S.I.C.: 2721
N.A.I.C.S.: 511120
Media: 6-8-10-22
Personnel:
David Arnold *(Sr VP & Grp Publr)*
Colette Kronick *(Sr VP-Sls)*
Ken Debie *(VP-Design Dir)*
Melinda Lyon *(VP-HR)*

Key to Media (For complete agency information see *The Advertising Red Books-Agencies* edition):
1. Bus. Publs. 2. Cable T.V. 3. Catalogs & Directories. 4. Co-op Adv. 5. Consumer Mags. 6. D.M. to Bus. Estab.7. D.M. to Consumers
8. Daily Newsp. 9. Exhibits/Trade Shows 10. Foreign 11. Infomercial 12. Internet Adv.13. Multimedia 14. Network Radio
15. Network T.V. 16. Newsp. Distr. Mags. 17. Other 18. Outdoor (Posters, Transit) 19. Point of Purchase20. Premiums, Novelties
21. Product Samples 22. Special Events Mktg. 23. Spot Radio 24. Spot T.V. 25. Weekly Newsp. 26. Yellow Page Adv.

Robb Report — (Continued)

Karen E. Nicolas *(Dir-Production)*
Ed Cortese *(Dir-Fashion)*
Keith Fletcher *(Dir-Corp IT)*
Amy Jacobs Duca *(Dir-Circulation)*
Marion Lowry *(Dir-Adv-Western)*
Linda McShane *(Dir-Events)*
Kris Richards *(Dir-Online Adv)*
Virginia Pickel *(Sr Mgr-Adv Svcs)*
Marilyn Scott *(Office Mgr & Asst to CFO)*
Annette Echon *(Mgr-HR)*

RODALE, INC.

33 E Minor St
Emmaus, PA 18098-0099
Tel.: (610) 967-5171
Fax: (610) 967-8963
E-mail: info@rodale.com
Web Site: www.rodaleinc.com
Approx. Sls.: $629,000,000
Approx. Number Employees: 1,200
Year Founded: 1943
Business Description:
Publisher of Consumer Lifestyle Magazines & Books
S.I.C.: 2721; 2731
N.A.I.C.S.: 511120; 511130
Media: 1-2-3-4-5-6-7-8-9-10-11-12-13-14-15-16-17-19-20-22-23-24-25
Distr.: Direct to Consumer; Natl.
Budget Set: Oct.
Personnel:
Maria Rodale *(Chm & CEO)*
Thomas A. Pogash *(CFO)*
Ken Citron *(CIO & Exec VP-Publ Ops)*
Gregg Michaelson *(Pres-Integrated Mktg & Sls & CMO)*
Paul A. McGinley *(Chief Admin Officer, Gen Counsel & Exec VP)*
Christopher Cormier *(Assoc Publr-Prevention)*
Jack Essig *(Sr VP & Publr-Mens Health)*
Laura Frerer-Schmidt *(Publr-Women's Health)*
Eric Johnson *(Assoc Publr-Mktg)*
Michael Kuntz *(Assoc Publr-Integrated Sls-Prevention)*
Mary Murcko *(Grp Publr & Exec VP)*
Karen Rinaldi *(Exec VP & Publ Dir-Rodale Books)*
David Kang *(Sr VP & Gen Mgr-Subscription Svcs)*
Valerie Valente *(Sr VP & Dir-Publ)*
Todd Leiser *(Sr VP-Bus Intelligence Grp)*
John McCarthy *(Sr VP-Rodale Circulation & Online Ops)*
Sean Nolan *(VP & Gen Mgr-Rodale Digital)*
Allison Hobson Falkenberry *(VP-Brand & Digital Comm)*
Matt Bean *(Assoc VP-Mobile, Social & Emerging Media)*
Timothy R. Kennedy *(Gen Mgr-Rodale.com & Rodale News Network)*
David Zinczenko *(Editor-in-Chief-Mens Health/Editorial Dir-BestLife/Womens Health)*
Michele Promaulayko *(Editor-In-Chief)*
Allison Keane *(Exec Dir-Women's Health)*
Jennifer Chatham *(Dir-Sls Dev)*
Paul Collins *(Dir-Sports Mktg & Events)*
Cary Silvers *(Dir-Consumer Insights)*
Tanja Sullivan *(Dir-Corp Comm)*
Bethridge Toovell *(Dir-Comm)*
Ellie Prezant *(Assoc Dir-Mktg)*
Lauren Paul *(Mgr-Comm)*
Lynn Donches *(Librarian)*
Brands & Products:
BELLY OFF! DIET
BICYCLING
BICYCLING.COM
BIGGEST LOSER 30-DAY JUMP START
THE DAILY FIX
EAT THIS, NOT THAT!
ENCYCLOPEDIA OF ORGANIC GARDENING
THE END OF OVEREATING
FLAT BELLY DIET!
MEN'S HEALTH
MENSHEALTH.COM
MOUNTAIN BIKE
ORGANIC GARDENING
ORGANICGARDENING.COM
PREVENTION
PREVENTION.COM
RODALE
THE RUNNERS BODY
RUNNER'S WORLD
RUNNERSWORLD.COM
RUNNING TIMES
RUNNINGTIMES.COM
WOMEN'S HEALTH
WOMENSHEALTHMAG.COM
YOUNGER (THINNER) YOU DIET
Advertising Agency:
A. Eicoff & Co.
(Div. of Ogilvy & Mather Worldwide)
401 N Michigan Ave 4th Fl
Chicago, IL 60611-4212
Tel.: (312) 527-7183
Fax: (312) 527-7188
Toll Free: (800) 333-6605

RODALE MAGAZINE

(Unit of Rodale Magazines)
733 3rd Ave
New York, NY 10017-3293
Tel.: (212) 697-2040
Fax: (212) 682-2237
Toll Free: (800) 666-2303
E-mail: info@menshealth.com
Web Site: www.menshealth.com
Approx. Number Employees: 450
Business Description:
Magazine Publisher
S.I.C.: 2721
N.A.I.C.S.: 511120
Media: 4-6-8-22
Distr.: Natl.
Personnel:
Jack Essig *(Publr & Sr VP)*
Ronan Gardiner *(Publr)*
Dave Zinczenko *(Editor-in-Chief)*
Allison Keane *(Exec Dir)*
Ellen Cummings *(Exec Dir-Beauty & Grooming)*
Eric Hunter *(Exec Dir-Mktg)*
Mike Owen *(Dir-Online Adv)*
Advertising Agency:
Trylon SMR
41 East 11th St
New York, NY 10003
Tel.: (212) 725-2295
Fax: (212) 725-2243

ROGERS MEDIA INC.

(Div. of Rogers Communications Inc.)
333 Bloor St E 6th Fl
Toronto, ON M4y 3b7, Canada
Tel.: (416) 935-8200
Fax: (416) 935-8203
Telex: 6219547 MACPUBCO-TOR
Web Site: www.rogers.com
Sales Range: $600-649.9 Million
Approx. Number Employees: 3,000
Year Founded: 1887
Business Description:
Business Publications, Consumer Magazines, Trade & Consumer Shows
S.I.C.: 2721
N.A.I.C.S.: 511120
Media: 2-3-6-8-9-20-25
Distr.: Natl.
Budget Set: Sept.-Nov.
Personnel:
Keith Pelley *(Pres)*
Jason Tafler *(Chief Digital Officer)*
John Milne *(Sr VP)*
Jamie Hagarty *(VP-Fin Ops)*
Navaid Mansuri *(VP-Fin & Sports Programming)*
Heather Armstrong *(Asst VP-Commun)*

ROLLING STONE MAGAZINE

(Sub. of Wenner Media LLC)
1290 Ave Of The Americas 2nd Fl
New York, NY 10104
Tel.: (212) 484-1616
Fax: (212) 484-1621
E-mail: info@rollingstone.com
Web Site: www.rollingstone.com
Approx. Number Employees: 200
Year Founded: 1967
Business Description:
Magazine Publisher
S.I.C.: 2721; 2731; 2741
N.A.I.C.S.: 511120; 511130; 511199
Advertising Expenditures: $600,000
Media: 1-2-3-6-8-10-13-20-21-22
Distr.: Natl.
Budget Set: July
Personnel:
John A. Gruber *(COO)*
Dana Rosen *(Gen Counsel)*
Alatia Bradley *(Assoc Publr)*
Michael Provus *(Assoc Publr)*
Jann S. Wenner *(Publr & Editor)*
Will Schenck *(Publr)*
Timothy Walsh *(VP-Tax & Fin)*
Jason Fine *(Editor)*
Kurt Demars *(Dir-West Coast Adv)*
Joseph Hutchinson *(Dir-Art)*
Jodi Peckman *(Dir-Photography)*
Erik Yates *(Dir-Adv)*
Advertising Agency:
La Comunidad
Avenida Del Libertador 13548
B1640 A0T
Buenos Aires, Argentina
Tel.: (54) 11 4792 0251
Fax: (54) 11 4792 0251

ROSEBUD ENTERTAINMENT LLC

(d/b/a Baltimore Magazine)
1000 Lancaster St Ste 400
Baltimore, MD 21202
Tel.: (410) 752-4200
Fax: (410) 625-0280
Toll Free: (800) 935-0838
Web Site:
www.baltimoremagazine.net
Approx. Sls.: $22,900,000
Business Description:
Magazines: Publishing Only, Not Printed On Site
S.I.C.: 2721; 2731
N.A.I.C.S.: 511120; 511130
Media: 6-8
Personnel:
Richard Basoco *(COO & Editor)*
Lori Birney *(Dir-Circulation)*
Jessie Peterson *(Dir-Mktg)*
Brands & Products:
BALTIMORE MAGAZINE

ROTADYNE

(Plant of Rotation Dynamics Corp.)
9126 Industrial Blvd NE
Covington, GA 30014-1473
Tel.: (770) 784-0787
Fax: (770) 385-9868
Toll Free: (800) 448-7205
E-mail: covington@rotadyne.com
Web Site: www.rotadyne.com
Approx. Number Employees: 20
Year Founded: 1917
Business Description:
Industrial Printer Rollers, Machinery & Equipment Mfr
S.I.C.: 3555
N.A.I.C.S.: 333293
Export
Media: 2-4-5-7-8-10-13-20-21
Distr.: Intl.; Natl.
Budget Set: Dec.
Personnel:
Len Kruizenga *(Gen Mgr)*
Ed Nykiel *(Gen Mgr)*
Joe Sheridan *(Plant Mgr)*
Ruben Cabral *(Sls Mgr)*
Eric Adlersfuegel *(Mgr-Sls)*
John Walshe *(Mgr-Ops)*
Brands & Products:
COLORMASTER
FEEDMASTER
IMAGE MASTER
LITHO MASTER
PRINT MASTER
TASK MASTER
UV MASTER

THE ROTARIAN MAGAZINE

(Div. of Rotary International)
One Rotary Ctr 1560 Sherman Ave
Evanston, IL 60201
Tel.: (847) 866-3000
Tel.: (847) 866-3196 (Adv)
Fax: (847) 866-9732
Telex: 724-465
E-mail: rotarian@rotaryintl.org
Web Site: www.rotary.org
Sales Range: $1-9.9 Million
Year Founded: 1911
Business Description:
Magazine Publisher
S.I.C.: 2721
N.A.I.C.S.: 511120
Media: 2-4-7
Distr.: Intl.
Budget Set: July
Personnel:
Janice Chambers *(Sr Editor)*
Deborah Lawrence *(Dir-Design-Canada)*
Marc Dukes *(Coord-Adv)*
Brands & Products:
THE ROTARIAN

Key to Media (For complete agency information see *The Advertising Red Books-Agencies* edition):
1. Bus. Publs. 2. Cable T.V. 3. Catalogs & Directories. 4. Co-op Adv. 5. Consumer Mags. 6. D.M. to Bus. Estab.7. D.M. to Consumers 8. Daily Newsp. 9. Exhibits/Trade Shows 10. Foreign 11. Infomercial 12. Internet Adv.13. Multimedia 14. Network Radio 15. Network T.V. 16. Newsp. Distr. Mags. 17. Other 18. Outdoor (Posters, Transit) 19. Point of Purchase20. Premiums, Novelties 21. Product Samples 22. Special Events Mktg. 23. Spot Radio 24. Spot T.V. 25. Weekly Newsp. 26. Yellow Page Adv.

Advertising Agency:
Rotary International
1560 Sherman Ave
Evanston, IL 60201-4818
Tel.: (847) 866-3000
Fax: (847) 328-8554
(Monthly Association Magazine)

THE ROUGH NOTES COMPANY, INC.

11690 Technology Dr
Carmel, IN 46032-5600
Tel.: (317) 582-1600
Fax: (317) 816-1000
Fax: (800) 321-1909
Toll Free: (800) 428-4384
E-mail: rnc@roughnotes.com
Web Site: www.roughnotes.com
Approx. Number Employees: 20
Year Founded: 1878
Business Description:
Insurance Magazines & Insurance Information Services Publisher
S.I.C.: 2721; 2741
N.A.I.C.S.: 511120; 511199
Import Export
Media: 2-4-7-8-10
Distr.: Intl.; Natl.
Personnel:
Walter J. Gdowski *(Pres & CEO)*
Sam Berman *(COO & Exec VP)*
Eric Hall *(VP-Adv & Dir-Natl Sls)*
Dick Schoeninger *(VP-Adv)*
Georgianna Quinn *(Coord-Adv & Production)*
Brands & Products:
THE INSURANCE MARKETPLACE
THE PRODUCER ONLINE
RONOCO CALCULATOR WHEELS
ROUGH NOTES
THE ROUGH NOTES COMPANY

R.R. BOWKER LLC

(Holding of Cambridge Information Group, Inc.)
630 Central Ave
New Providence, NJ 07974-1541
Tel.: (908) 286-1090
Fax: (908) 219-0185
Toll Free: (888) 269-5372
E-mail: info@bowker.com
Web Site: www.bowker.com
Approx. Number Employees: 100
Year Founded: 1872
Business Description:
Database Publisher; Bibliographic Information & Searching, Analytical Promotional & Ordering Services for Booksellers, Libraries & Patrons
S.I.C.: 2731; 2741
N.A.I.C.S.: 511130; 516110
Advertising Expenditures: $30,000
Media: 2-4-7-10-13-22
Budget Set: Aug.
Personnel:
Andrew M. Snyder *(Chm)*
Phil Evans *(CFO)*
Gary Aiello *(COO & Sr VP-Publishing Svcs)*
Mark Heinzelman *(CIO)*
Sy Inwentarz *(Sr VP)*
Ann Roycroft *(VP-HR)*
Prabu Desikan *(Exec Dir-North American Sls)*
Paul Palumbo *(Sr Dir-Library Sls-US)*
Charlie Friscia *(Dir-Retail & Publ Svcs)*
Randy Boecker *(Sr Mgr-Strategic Accts)*
Peter Ashekian *(Mgr-Data Sls)*
Denise DiMaria *(Exec Asst & Mgr-Corp Events)*
Jacob Drill *(Mgr-Bus Dev)*
Natalie Piccotti *(Mgr-Mktg Supply Chain Svcs)*
Brands & Products:
A TO ZOO
AMERICAN BOOK TRADE DIRECTORY
AMERICAN LIBRARY DIRECTORY
AMERICAN MEN & WOMEN OF SCIENCE
ANNUAL REGISTER OF GRANT SUPPORT
AQUABROWSER
BEST BOOKS FOR CHILDREN
BOOK ANALYSIS SYSTEM
BOOKS IN PRINT
BOOKS IN PRINT INTELLIMARKET
BOOKWIRE
BOWKER ISBN
BOWKERLINK
CLICK OPEN TO THE WORLD
FACULTYONLINE
FICTION CONNECTION
GLOBAL BOOKS IN PRINT
GLOBALBOOKSINPRINT.COM
MIR
NON-FICTION CONNECTION
PATRONBOOKSINPRINT.COM
PUBEASY
PUBLISHERS WEEKLY
PUBNET
PUBTRACK
RCLWEB
RESOURCES FOR COLLEGE LIBRARIES
SIMBA
SPANISHBOOKSINPRINT.COM
SYNDETIC SOLUTIONS
SYNDETICS ICE
ULRICH SERIALS ANALYSIS SYSTEM
ULRICH'S INTERNATIONAL PERIODICALS DIRECTORY
ULRICHSWEB.COM
WORDS ON CASSETTE
YEARBOOK OF INTERNATIONAL ORGANIZATIONS
Advertising Agency:
Teague Communication
28005 Smyth Dr Ste 112
Valencia, CA 91355
Tel.: (661) 297-5292
Fax: (661) 702-9705

R.R. DONNELLEY

(Formerly Bowne & Co., Inc.)
(Branch of R.R. Donnelley & Sons Company)
55 Water St
New York, NY 10041-0017
Tel.: (212) 924-5500
Fax: (212) 658-5871
Web Site: www.rrdonnelley.com
Sales Range: $650-699.9 Million
Approx. Number Employees: 2,800
Year Founded: 1775
Business Description:
Financial, Marketing & Business Communications Services
S.I.C.: 7389; 2759; 6371; 8742
N.A.I.C.S.: 561499; 323119; 525990; 541613
Advertising Expenditures: $500,000
Media: 2-4-7-10-13-22-26
Distr.: Natl.
Personnel:
William P. Penders *(Pres)*
Erika Craven *(Pres-Investment Mgmt)*
Rob Blake *(Sr Dir-Interactive Svcs-Denver)*
Brands & Products:
BITS
BOWNE
BOWNE 6-K EXPRESS
BOWNE COMPLIANCE DRIVER
BOWNE DESK
BOWNE ENTERPRISE SOLUTIONS
BOWNE EPOD
BOWNE VIRTUAL DATAROOM
BOWNE8-K EXPRESS
BOWNEFAX
BOWNEIMPRESSIONS
BOWNELINK
BOWNFILE16
DEAL ROOM EXPRESS
DEALTRANS
DIGITAL LITIGATION SOLUTIONS
E2EXPRESS
EMPOWERING YOUR INFORMATION
EXPRESS START
FUNDALIGN
FUNDSMITH
LITIGATION LIFECYCLE
PROSPECTUSPRO
PURE COMPLIANCE
QUICKPATH
RAPIDVIEW
SECURITIESCONNECT
SMARTAPPS
SMARTFORUM
XMARK
Advertising Agency:
Renegade, LLC
75 9th Ave 8th Fl
New York, NY 10011
Tel.: (646) 486-7700
Fax: (646) 486-7800

R.R. DONNELLEY & SONS COMPANY

111 S Wacker Dr
Chicago, IL 60606-4301
Tel.: (312) 326-8000
Fax: (312) 326-8543
E-mail: info@rrd.com
Web Site: www.rrdonnelley.com
E-Mail For Key Personnel:
Marketing Director: Doug.Fitzgerald@rrd.com
Approx. Sls.: $10,018,900,000
Approx. Number Employees: 58,700
Year Founded: 1864
Business Description:
Pre-Media, Digital Photography, Content Management, Printing, Internet Consulting & Logistics
S.I.C.: 2754; 2759
N.A.I.C.S.: 323111; 323119
Media: 2-7-10-19
Distr.: Natl.
Budget Set: Oct.
Personnel:
Thomas J. Quinlan III *(Pres & CEO)*
Daniel N. Leib *(CFO)*
John R. Paloian *(COO)*
Suzanne S. Bettman *(Gen Counsel, Sec, Exec VP & Chief Compliance Officer)*
Andrew B. Coxhead *(Chief Acctg Officer, Sr VP & Controller)*
John C. Campanelli *(Pres-Print Bus)*
John Coyle *(Pres-Catalog, Retail & Direct Svcs)*
Edward E. Lane *(Pres-Book Directory Mfg Bus)*
Richard F. Marcoux *(Pres-Sls)*
James T. Mauck *(Pres-Asia)*
Doug Fitzgerald *(Exec VP-Mktg & Comm)*
Rebecca J. Bruening *(Sr VP-Ops & Bus Integration)*
Michael Manzella *(Sr VP-Environmental)*
Gian-Carlo Peressutti *(Sr VP-Pub Affairs)*
Brands & Products:
ADSPRING
BOOKTRACK
CUSTOMPOINT
DATASELECT
DEMANDSELECT
DIGIMAG
DIGITAL SWATCH MATCH
DOCUMENT PATHWAYS
DOCUMENTDIRECTOR
DYNAMAIL
E-MERGE
E.SOURCE
FACTNET
IMAGEMERCHANT
IVIEWXT
MOORE WALLACE
NET.DISTRO
NET.FILTER
NET.WORK
PAGEFLOW
PAGEPLANNER
PHOTO-FLOW
PIPELINE
PRINT MANAGEMENT
PROSPECTUS BUILDER
PUBSELECT
PUBSPRING
REPORTBUILDER
RIGHTMIX
RR DONNELLEY
SENDD
SHARESTREAM
SPEEDISET
STUDIOSTREAM
SYNC
TRAK
Advertising Agencies:
The David Group
PO Box 115
Lockport, IL 60441
Tel.: (815) 838-3000
Fax: (630) 257-9408
Fax: (800) 447-0729 (Outside IL)
Toll Free: (800) 548-8189 (Outside IL)

The Edelman Group
110 W 40th St Ste 2302
New York, NY 10018
Tel.: (212) 825-9200
Fax: (212) 825-1900

Marcel Media
445 W Erie Ste 211
Chicago, IL 60654
Tel.: (312) 255-8044
Fax: (866) 643-7506

Key to Media (For complete agency information see *The Advertising Red Books-Agencies* edition):
1. Bus. Publs. 2. Cable T.V. 3. Catalogs & Directories. 4. Co-op Adv. 5. Consumer Mags. 6. D.M. to Bus. Estab.7. D.M. to Consumers
8. Daily Newsp. 9. Exhibits/Trade Shows 10. Foreign 11. Infomercial 12. Internet Adv.13. Multimedia 14. Network Radio
15. Network T.V. 16. Newsp. Distr. Mags. 17. Other 18. Outdoor (Posters, Transit) 19. Point of Purchase20. Premiums, Novelties
21. Product Samples 22. Special Events Mktg. 23. Spot Radio 24. Spot T.V. 25. Weekly Newsp. 26. Yellow Page Adv.

RUNNING PRESS
(Sub. of The Perseus Books Group)
23 chescnut st
Philadelphia, PA 19103-4399
Tel.: (215) 567-5080
Fax: (215) 568-2919
Web Site: www.runningpress.com
Approx. Number Employees: 150
Business Description:
Book Publishers
S.I.C.: 2731
N.A.I.C.S.: 511130
Media: 10-13
Personnel:
Stuart David Teacher *(Pres)*
Brands & Products:
MINIATURE EDITIONS
SPECIAL FAVORS

SAFETYTOTS INTERNATIONAL, LTD.
PO Box 1641
Commack, NY 11725
Tel.: (631) 462-7592
Fax: (631) 462-1589
Toll Free: (866) 4SAFETOT
E-mail: info@safetytots.com
Web Site: www.safetytots.com
Business Description:
Educational Products
S.I.C.: 2731
N.A.I.C.S.: 511130
Media: 4-13
Personnel:
Paula Geonie *(Pres & CEO)*

SAIL MAGAZINE
(Sub. of Source Interlink Media)
98 N Washington St
Boston, MA 02114-2202
Tel.: (617) 720-8600
Fax: (617) 723-0911
E-mail: sailmail@sailmagazine.com
Web Site: www.sailmagazine.com
Approx. Number Employees: 25
Business Description:
Periodical
S.I.C.: 2721
N.A.I.C.S.: 511120
Advertising Agency:
Brewster Strategies
21 Eliot St
Natick, MA 01760-6085
Tel.: (508) 647-6282
Fax: (508) 647-0651

SAN ANGELO STANDARD, INC.
(Sub. of The E.W. Scripps Company)
(d/b/a San Angelo Standard-Times)
34 W Harris Ave
San Angelo, TX 76903-5838
Mailing Address:
PO Box 5111
San Angelo, TX 76903
Tel.: (325) 653-1221
Fax: (325) 659-8171
Toll Free: (800) 588-1884
E-mail: standard@gosanangelo.com
Web Site: www.gosanangelo.com
Sales Range: $25-49.9 Million
Approx. Number Employees: 85
Business Description:
Publisher of Morning & Sunday Newspapers
S.I.C.: 2711; 2721
N.A.I.C.S.: 511110; 511120
Media: 8-9
Personnel:
Jeff DeLoach *(Publr)*
Tim Archuleta *(Editor)*
Monty Stanley *(Dir-HR)*
Jamie Aikin *(Coord)*

SAN ANTONIO EXPRESS NEWS
(Unit of Hearst Newspapers)
Ave E At 3rd St
San Antonio, TX 78205
Tel.: (210) 250-3000
Fax: (210) 250-3105
Toll Free: (800) 555-1551
E-mail: marketing@railserveinc.com
Web Site: www.mysanantonio.com
Approx. Number Employees: 1,500
Year Founded: 1865
Business Description:
Newspaper Publishing
S.I.C.: 2711; 2721
N.A.I.C.S.: 511110; 511120
Media: 2-5-6-8-13-18-23-24
Distr.: Reg.
Budget Set: Sept.
Personnel:
Tom Stevenson *(Chm)*
Thomas A. Stephenson *(Pres & Publr)*
Susan Ehrman *(VP-HR)*
Kyrie O'Connor *(Interim Editor)*
Linda Case *(Dir-Creative Svcs)*
Rebecca Chavez-Becker *(Dir-Retail Sls-Territories & Hispanic Publ)*

SAN DIEGO BUSINESS JOURNAL
4909 Murphy Canyon Rd Ste 200
San Diego, CA 92123
Tel.: (858) 277-6359
Fax: (858) 277-2149
E-mail: sdbj@sdbj.com
Web Site: www.sdbj.com
Approx. Number Employees: 40
Business Description:
Publisher of Weekly Business Newspaper
S.I.C.: 2721; 2741
N.A.I.C.S.: 511120; 511199
Media: 8-10-21-22-25
Personnel:
Armon Mills *(Pres & Publr)*
Reo Carr *(Editor-in-Chief)*
Dale Ganzow *(Mgr-Sls)*
Brands & Products:
SAN DIEGO BUSINESS JOURNAL

THE SAN DIEGO UNION-TRIBUNE, LLC
(Holding of Platinum Equity, LLC)
350 Camino de la Reina
San Diego, CA 92108-3003
Mailing Address:
PO Box 120191
San Diego, CA 92112-0191
Tel.: (619) 299-3131
Fax: (619) 293-1896
Fax: (619) 260-5081
Toll Free: (800) 533-8830
E-mail: paul.bridwell@uniontrib.com
Web Site: www.signonsandiego.com
E-Mail For Key Personnel:
President: gene.bell@uniontrib.com
Public Relations: Drew.Schlosberg@uniontrib.com
Approx. Number Employees: 1,800
Year Founded: 1868
Business Description:
Newpaper Publisher
S.I.C.: 2711
N.A.I.C.S.: 511110
Advertising Expenditures: $750,000
Media: 1-2-4-8-9-10-18-19-22-23
Distr.: Direct to Consumer; Reg.
Budget Set: Oct.
Personnel:
Jaime Muldoon *(Editor-Copy)*
George Bonaros *(Dir-Mktg)*
Jody Vanden Heuvel *(Dir-Sls)*
Rita Jurczyk *(Dir-Major Media Sls)*
Philip Malavenda *(Dir-Ops & Bus Dev)*
Ann Radosevich *(Dir-HR Svcs)*
Drew Schlosberg *(Dir-Community & PR)*
Brands & Products:
ENLACE
THE SAN DIEGO UNION-TRIBUNE
SIGN ON SAN DIEGO

SAN FRANCISCO CHRONICLE
(Unit of Hearst Newspapers)
901 Mission St
San Francisco, CA 94103-2905
Tel.: (415) 777-1111
Tel.: (415) 777-7018 (Editorial)
Tel.: (415) 777-7100 (Main News)
Fax: (415) 543-4816
E-mail: metro@sfchronicle.com
Web Site: www.sfgate.com
Approx. Number Employees: 3,000
Business Description:
Newspaper Publisher
S.I.C.: 2711
N.A.I.C.S.: 511110
Advertising Expenditures: $2,500,000
Media: 8-9-19-20-23-24
Distr.: Reg.
Budget Set: Dec.
Personnel:
Frank J. Vega *(Chm & Publr)*
Mark Adkins *(Pres)*
Elizabeth Cain *(CFO)*
John Sillers *(Fin Dir)*
Ward H. Bushee *(Exec VP & Editor)*
Jeff Bergin *(Sr VP-Adv)*
Michael C. LaBonia *(Sr VP-Adv)*
Kelly Harville *(VP-Mktg)*
Calvin Siemer *(VP-Legal Affairs)*
Andrea Behr *(Editor-Copy Desk)*
Lois Kazakoff *(Editor-Editorial Page)*
Frank Mina *(Art Dir)*
Reid Sams *(Dir-Art)*
Advertising Agency:
Draftfcb West
1160 Battery St Ste 250
San Francisco, CA 94111
Tel.: (415) 820-8000
Fax: (415) 820-8087

SAN JOSE MERCURY NEWS
(Unit of Bay Area News Group)
750 Ridder Park Dr
San Jose, CA 95190
Tel.: (408) 920-5000
Fax: (408) 288-8060
E-mail: sgoldberg@mercurynews.com
Web Site: www.mercurynews.com
Approx. Number Employees: 700
Year Founded: 1851
Business Description:
Newspaper Publisher
S.I.C.: 2711
N.A.I.C.S.: 511110
Media: 7-8-9-10-13-19-20
Distr.: Reg.
Personnel:
Michael Tully *(Pres & Publr)*
David J. Butler *(VP & Editor)*
Jim Janiga *(VP-HR)*
Michael Turpin *(VP-Adv & Mktg)*
David Karabhg *(Gen Mgr-Online)*
Herschel Kenner *(Asst Mng Editor-News)*
Brands & Products:
MERCURY CENTER
MERCURYNEWS.COM

SANDUSKY NEWSPAPERS INC.
(d/b/a The Sandusky Register)
314 W Market St
Sandusky, OH 44870
Tel.: (419) 625-5500
Fax: (419) 625-7211
Toll Free: (800) 466-1243
Web Site: www.sanduskyregister.com
Approx. Sls.: $28,800,000
Approx. Number Employees: 140
Business Description:
Newspapers
S.I.C.: 2711; 4832
N.A.I.C.S.: 511110; 515112
Media: 8-9
Personnel:
Dudley A. White, Jr. *(Chm)*
Doug Phares *(Pres-Midwest Div)*
Mark Yocum *(Dir-Adv)*
Brands & Products:
SANDUSKY NEWPAPER

SANTA CRUZ SENTINEL
(Unit of Bay Area News Group)
1800 Green Hills Rd Ste 210
Scotts Valley, CA 95066
Tel.: (831) 423-4242
Fax: (831) 423-1154
E-mail: news@santacruzsentinel.com
Web Site: www.santacruzsentinel.com
Approx. Number Employees: 25
Business Description:
Newspaper Publisher
S.I.C.: 2711
N.A.I.C.S.: 511110
Media: 7-8-9-13-25
Personnel:
Julie Copeland *(Editor-City)*
Don Miller *(Editor)*
Tom Moore *(Editor-Online)*
Mike Blaesser *(Dir-Internet)*
Mardi Browning *(Mgr-Circulation & Mktg)*

SATURDAY EVENING POST SOCIETY
1100 Waterway Blvd
Indianapolis, IN 46202-2156
Tel.: (317) 634-1100
Tel.: (317) 636-8881
Fax: (317) 637-0126
Toll Free: (800) 558-2376
E-mail: firstinitiallastname@satevepost.org
Web Site:
www.saturdayeveningpost.com
Sales Range: $75-99.9 Million
Approx. Number Employees: 45
Year Founded: 1976
Business Description:
Health, Medical & Literary Magazines
S.I.C.: 2721; 2791
N.A.I.C.S.: 511120; 323122
Advertising Expenditures: $100,000
Media: 2-4-6-7-8-13-19-20-21

Key to Media (For complete agency information see *The Advertising Red Books-Agencies* edition):
1. Bus. Publs. 2. Cable T.V. 3. Catalogs & Directories. 4. Co-op Adv. 5. Consumer Mags. 6. D.M. to Bus. Estab.7. D.M. to Consumers
8. Daily Newsp. 9. Exhibits/Trade Shows 10. Foreign 11. Infomercial 12. Internet Adv.13. Multimedia 14. Network Radio
15. Network T.V. 16. Newsp. Distr. Mags. 17. Other 18. Outdoor (Posters, Transit) 19. Point of Purchase20. Premiums, Novelties
21. Product Samples 22. Special Events Mktg. 23. Spot Radio 24. Spot T.V. 25. Weekly Newsp. 26. Yellow Page Adv.

Distr.: Natl.
Budget Set: Jan.
Personnel:
Joan Servaas *(CEO)*
Robert Silvers *(Sec-Exec Publr)*
Dwight Lamb, Sr. *(Assoc Publr-Production)*
Trent Hackett *(Coord-Mktg & Sls)*
Brands & Products:
SATURDAY EVENING POST

THE SAULT STAR
(Div. of Osprey Media Group, Inc.)
145 Old Garden River Rd
Sault Sainte Marie, ON P6A 5M5, Canada
Mailing Address:
PO Box 460
Sault Sainte Marie, ON P6A 5M5, Canada
Tel.: (705) 759-3030
Fax: (705) 942-8690
E-mail: ssmstar@saultstar.com
Web Site: www.saultstar.com
Business Description:
Daily Newspaper
S.I.C.: 2711
N.A.I.C.S.: 511110
Media: 8-9
Personnel:
Lou Maulucci *(Publr)*

SAVANNAH MORNING NEWS
(Unit of Morris Publishing Group, LLC)
1375 Chatham Pkwy
Savannah, GA 31405
Mailing Address:
PO Box 1088
Savannah, GA 31402
Tel.: (912) 236-9511
Fax: (912) 525-0796
Web Site: www.savannahnow.com
Approx. Number Employees: 50
Year Founded: 1850
Business Description:
Newspaper Publisher
S.I.C.: 2711; 2721
N.A.I.C.S.: 511110; 511120
Media: 8-9
Personnel:
Michael Traynor *(Publr)*
Anita Sue Hagin *(Asst Mng Editor)*
Gale Baldwin *(Editor)*
Tom Barton *(Editor-Editorial Page)*
Arlinda Broady *(Editor-Bus)*
Steve Corrigan *(Editor-Closeups)*
Laura McAbee *(Editor-Wire)*
Tony Stastny *(Editor-Sports)*
Stacy Jennings *(Dir-Mktg)*
Sean Ruth *(Dir-Production)*
Robert Todd *(Dir-Ops)*
Chris White *(Mgr-Digital Media)*

SCARECROW PRESS, INC.
(Sub. of The Rowman & Littlefield Publishing Group)
4501 Forbes Blvd Ste 200
Lanham, MD 20706-4310
Tel.: (301) 459-3366
Fax: (301) 429-5748
Toll Free: (800) 462-6460
Web Site: www.scarecrowpress.com
Approx. Number Employees: 140
Business Description:
Reference & Professional Books
S.I.C.: 2731
N.A.I.C.S.: 511130
Export
Media: 4-10
Personnel:
Edward Kurdyla *(VP & Publr)*
Corinne Burton *(Mng Editor)*
Cathy MacRae *(Editor-VOYA)*
Stephen Ryan *(Editor-Arts & Literature)*
Dean Roxanis *(Dir-Mktg)*
Jared Hughes *(Coord-Mktg)*
Brands & Products:
THE STEINBECK REVIEW
TEACHER LIBRARIAN
VOYA

SCHAWK CANADA INC.
(Sub. of Schawk, Inc.)
1620 Tech Ave
Mississauga, ON L4W 5P4, Canada
Tel.: (905) 219-1600
Fax: (905) 219-1668
E-mail: info@schawk.com
Web Site: www.schawk.com
E-Mail For Key Personnel:
President: bcockerill@battengraphics.com
Sales Range: $25-49.9 Million
Approx. Number Employees: 145
Year Founded: 1971
Business Description:
Digital Imaging Services
S.I.C.: 7374; 7336
N.A.I.C.S.: 518210; 541430
Media: 8-22-26
Distr.: Intl.
Budget Set: Jan.
Personnel:
Robert Cockerill *(Pres & COO)*
Jim McLean *(Pres-Toronto)*
Jason Green *(VP-Fin-North America)*

SCHAWK, INC.
1695 S River Rd
Des Plaines, IL 60018-2205
Tel.: (847) 827-9494
Fax: (847) 827-1264
Toll Free: (800) 621-1909
E-mail: information@schawk.com
Web Site: www.schawk.com
Approx. Sls.: $460,626,000
Approx. Number Employees: 3,200
Year Founded: 1953
Business Description:
Digital Imaging Prepress Services for the Consumer Products Industry; Graphics Services & Brand Point Management
S.I.C.: 7336; 2791; 5084; 7319; 7389
N.A.I.C.S.: 541430; 323122; 423830; 541890; 561499
Advertising Expenditures: $200,000
Media: 1-2-4-7-10-20-26
Distr.: Natl.
Budget Set: Aug.
Personnel:
Clarence W. Schawk *(Chm)*
David A. Schawk *(Pres & CEO)*
Raymond Kieser *(Grp Mng Dir-European Ops)*
Timothy J. Cunningham *(CFO & Exec VP)*
A. Alex Sarkisian *(COO & Exec VP)*
Gary Rietz *(CIO)*
Eric Ashworth *(Chief Strategy Officer)*
Lor Gold *(Global Chief Creative Officer)*
Ronald J. Vittorini *(Gen Counsel)*
Chuck Dale *(Exec VP-Global Ops)*
Christopher Splan *(Exec VP-Bus Dev)*
Scott Strong *(Sr VP & Mng Dir-Schawk Digital Solutions)*
John Bittner *(Sr VP & Mgr-Global Bus)*
Carol G. Campagnolo *(Sr VP-HR)*
Mark Silva *(Sr VP-Emerging Platforms-Anthem Worldwide)*
Jerry Drury *(Mgr-Color)*
John T. McEnroe *(Asst Sec)*

SCHOLASTIC CORPORATION
557 Broadway
New York, NY 10012-3902
Tel.: (212) 343-6100
Fax: (212) 343-6934
E-mail: custserv@scholastic.com
Web Site: www.scholastic.com
Approx. Rev.: $1,912,900,000
Approx. Number Employees: 5,500
Year Founded: 1920
Business Description:
Children's Books, Magazines, Technology-Based Products, Teacher Materials, Television Programming, Film, Video & Toys
S.I.C.: 2731; 2721
N.A.I.C.S.: 511130; 511120
Advertising Expenditures: $163,400,000
Personnel:
Richard Robinson *(Chm, Pres & CEO)*
Maureen O'Connell *(CFO, Chief Admin Officer & Exec VP)*
Dani Nadel *(Chief Digital Mktg Officer-Book Clubs & ECommerce)*
Shane Armstrong *(Pres-Scholastic Intl Growth Markets & Exec VP)*
Deborah A. Forte *(Pres-Scholastic Media & Exec VP)*
Margery W. Mayer *(Pres-Education & Exec VP)*
Ellie Berger *(Pres-Trade Publ)*
Judith A. Newman *(Pres-Book Clubs & ECommerce)*
Andrew S. Hedden *(Gen Counsel, Sec & Exec VP)*
Francie Alexander *(Chief Academic Officer & Sr VP)*
Thomas P. Burke *(Sr VP-E Commerce)*
Anne Boynton-Trigg *(VP-Export-Scholastic Intl)*
Kyle Good *(VP-Corp Comm & Media Rels)*
Edie Perkins *(VP-Intl Product Dev-Scholastic Intl)*
Jennifer Slackman *(Dir-Mktg)*
Advertising Agency:
CCM Marketing Communications
11 E 47th St Fl 3
New York, NY 10017-7916
Tel.: (212) 689-8225
Fax: (212) 889-7388

SCHOLASTIC INC.
(Sub. of Scholastic Corporation)
557 Broadway
New York, NY 10012-3919
Tel.: (212) 343-6100
Fax: (212) 343-7811
Toll Free: (800) SCHOLASTIC
Web Site: www.scholastic.com
Sales Range: $50-74.9 Million
Approx. Number Employees: 150
Year Founded: 1920
Business Description:
Educational Materials Publisher
S.I.C.: 2721; 2731
N.A.I.C.S.: 511120; 511130
Media: 8-10-13-22
Personnel:
Richard Robinson *(Chm, Pres & CEO)*
Greg Worrell *(Pres-Classroom & Library Group)*
Faye Edwards *(VP & Gen Mgr-NSO Ops)*
Jocelyn Forman *(VP-Mktg)*
Brands & Products:
1-800-SCHOLASTIC
1-800-WIGGLE-1
100% KLUTZ CERTIFIED
100% KLUTZ EN ESPANOL
3D DINOSAURS
A JIGSAW JONES MYSTERY
A KID'S SCIENCE MUSEUM IN A BOOK
A ROOKIE READER
A TRUE BOOK
ACADEMIC AMERICAN
ACTION
THE ADVENTURES OF THE BAILEY SCHOOL KIDS
AGENT USA
AHORA
AKTUELL
ALGEBRA SHOP
ALL YOU CAN READ
ALLONS-Y
ALPHABET FUN BLOCKS
ALWAYS FRIENDS
THE AMAZING DAYS OF ABBY HAYES
AMERICAN ADVENTURES
AMERICAN OBSERVER
AMERICANA ANNUAL
AMERICA'S CLASSROOM NEWSPAPER
AMERICA'S HORRIBLE HISTORIES
ANIMORPHS
APPLE
APPLE PAPERBACKS
ARROW
THE BABY-SITTERS CLUB
BABY-SITTERS LITTLE SISTER
THE BAILEY CITY MONSTERS
THE BAILEY SCHOOL KIDS MAGAZINE
BEADIMALS
BEADLINGS
BEFORE I MADE HISTORY
THE BEST ME I CAN BE
BIG SCIENCE COMICS
THE BIGGEST CHILDREN'S BOOK IN THE WORLD
BLUE RIBBON
THE BLUE SKY PRESS
BONJOUR
BOOK FACTORY
BOOKS IN A CUP
BOOKS ON BREAK
BRAIN JAM
BRAIN PLAY
BRIDGES
BUBBLEARIUM
THE BUG BUNCH
BUILDING LANGUAGE FOR LITERACY
BUMPTZ SCIENCE CARNIVAL
CA VA?
CALIFORNIA CLUB MYSTERIES
CALIFORNIA DIARIES
CAPTAIN MIDNIGHT
CARD FACTORY
CARTWHEEL BOOKS
CATS CRADLE
CC
CECE

Key to Media (For complete agency information see *The Advertising Red Books-Agencies* edition):
1. Bus. Publs. 2. Cable T.V. 3. Catalogs & Directories. 4. Co-op Adv. 5. Consumer Mags. 6. D.M. to Bus. Estab.7. D.M. to Consumers 8. Daily Newsp. 9. Exhibits/Trade Shows 10. Foreign 11. Infomercial 12. Internet Adv.13. Multimedia 14. Network Radio 15. Network T.V. 16. Newsp. Distr. Mags. 17. Other 18. Outdoor (Posters, Transit) 19. Point of Purchase20. Premiums, Novelties 21. Product Samples 22. Special Events Mktg. 23. Spot Radio 24. Spot T.V. 25. Weekly Newsp. 26. Yellow Page Adv.

Scholastic Inc. — (Continued)

CHECKERBOARD
CHEERLEADERS
CHEZ NOUS
CHICKEN SOCKS
CHILDREN'S CIRCLE
CHILDREN'S PRESS
CHOICES
CHOICES, CHOICES
CHRONICLE OF AMERICA
CITIES OF THE WORLD
CLASSIC SCHOOL BOOK FAIRS
CLICK INTERACTIVE LEARNING CLUB
COLECCION IGUANA
COMMUNITY CONSTRUCTION KIT
CORNERSTONES OF FREEDOM
CP
CRITTERLAND ADVENTURES
CUENTOS FONETICOS DE SCHOLASTIC
CURRICULUM CONNECTIONS SCHOLASTIC
DARK FALLS
DAS RAD
DEAR AMERICA
DECISIONS, DECISIONS
DEEP INK
DETECTIVE ACADEMY
DIADEM
DIAL WITH STYLE
DINOFOURS
DINOSITOS
DIORAMA DESIGNER
DISASTER SCIENCE
DOLL HOSPITAL
DON'T EAT PETE
DOWNLOADS2GO
DRAWBREAKERS
DYNAMATH
EARTHSEARCH
EL AUTOBUS MAGICO
EL SOL
ELECTRONIC LEARNING
ENCHANTED TREE TREASURES
ENCYCLOPEDIA AMERICA
ESCHOLASTIC
EXPLORABOOK
EXTENDED DAY READING
FASTMATH
FIREFLY
FIRST DRAFT
FIRST GRADE FRIENDS
FIZZ
FLASHLIGHT READERS
FLUENCY FORMULA
FLUFFY THE CLASSROOM GUINEA PIG
FLYING PAGES
FOXTAIL
FRANKLIN WATTS
FRITZTV
FUNNY BONE BOOKS
FURRYTALE FRIENDS
FUTURES
G
GELLY BAND
GEOGRAPHY SEARCH
GETTING TO KNOW...NATURE'S CHILDREN
GHOSTVILLE ELEMENTARY
THE GIRLS OF CANBY HALL
GLOVE COMPARTMENT GAMES
GO SOLVE
GOOGLY EYES
GRAPH ACTION!
THE GRAPH CLUB
GRAPHIX
GREAT AMERICAN BOOK FAIRS
THE GREAT OCEAN RESCUE
THE GREAT SOLAR SYSTEM RESCUE
GREAT TEACHING IN THE ONE COMPUTER CLASSROOM
GREENIE
GROLIER
HELLO MATH READER
HELLO READER!
HELLO WRITER
HOLA, LECTOR!
HOLLYWOOD HIGH
HOME BOOK PACK
HOME MOVIES LOGO I
HOME MOVIES LOGO II
HONEYBEE
HORRIBLE HISTORIES
HORRIBLE SCIENCE
HORRORS
HOW TO SURVIVE ANYTHING CLUB
ICKY POO
THE INCREDIBLE CLAY BOOK
INFORMATIONAL INNOVATIONS
INNERBODYWORKS
INNOVACIONES
INNOVATIONS EXPERIENCING LITERATURE
INSTRUCTOR
INTERACTIVE KIDS
INTERACTIVE PHONICS READERS
INTERNATIONAL INSPIRER
IREACH
IREACH READ ACHIEVE
ITEACH
ITEACH.COM
ITTY-BITTY TEENY-TINY LEARNING BOOK
JIGSAW JONES MYSTERY
JUGGLING FOR THE COMPLETE KLUTZ
JUNIOR SCHOLASTIC
JUST SCHOOLIN' AROUND
KIDS ARE AUTHORS
KIDS ARE AUTHORS AWARD
KIDS TRAVEL
KIDSKETCH
KLUTZ
KLUTZ BOOK FACTORY
KLUTZ GALACTIC HEADQUARTERS
KLUTZ KWIZ
KLUTZ TO GO
LANTERN LOGO (ARTHUR A. LEVINE BOOKS)
LEE Y SERAS
LEMON DROP PRESS
LEO THE LETTER LOVING LOBSTER
LET'S FIND OUT
LET'S START
LITERARY CAVALCADE
LITERATURE TO THINK ABOUT
LITTLE APPLE
LITTLE RED TOOL BOX
LUCKY
LUCKY STAR
THE MAGIC SCHOOL BUS
MAGIC SPOON
MAGIC UNIVERSITY
MAKEOVER FUN 101
MANY VOICES
MAPMAKER'S TOOLKIT
MAPMAN
MARIPOSA
MARIPOSA SCHOLASTIC EN ESPANOL
MARTINA
MATH 180
MATH MAN
MATH MYSTERIES
MATH SHOP
MATH TUTOR
MOOSHKINS
THE MOST TRUSTED
THE MOST TRUSTED NAME IN LEARNING
MURPHY AND MYRTLE
MY FIRST HELLO READER!
MY FIRST STEPS TO LEARNING
MY FIRST STEPS TO READING
MY LIFE ACCORDING TO ME
MY NAME IS AMERICA
MYSTERY SENTENCES
NATIONAL INSPIRER
NBK NEWS
NEIGHBORHOOD MAPMACHINE
THE NEW BOOK OF KNOWLEDGE
NINA THE NAMING NEWT
OPERATION: FROG
ORCHARD BOOKS
PAPER, SCISSORS, ROCK
PARENT BAG BOOK
PARENT'S FRIEND
PEN & PAINTBRUSH
PICTURE BOOK PARADE
PLACEMARK
PLANET ZOO
PLAY! SCHOLASTIC
POINT
PONY PALS
POP ZONE
POPPEOPLE
PRE-K TODAY
PRIME TIME MATH
PUMPING PLASTIC
QED
QUALITY EDUCATION DATA
QUE TAL?
RAINFOREST DESIGNER
RAINFOREST RESEARCHERS
REACHING OUT
READ 180
READ ABOUT
READ AND RISE
READ STREET BOOK FAIRS
READING CHANGES EVERYTHING
READING DISCOVERY
READING FOR MEANING
READING IS BIG
READING MAGIC
READING STARTS WITH US
READY TO WRITE
REAL LIFE
THE REAL MOTHER GOOSE
RED HOUSE
REGGIE THE RHYMING RHINO
RHYME TIME READERS
ROCKET
ROCKIN' RHYTHM BAND BOARD BOOKS
ROOKIE BIOGRAPHIES
ROOKIE CHOICES
ROOKIE READ-ABOUT
SCHOLASTIC
SCHOLASTIC - THE MOST TRUSTED NAME IN LEARNING
SCHOLASTIC ACTION
SCHOLASTIC ADMINISTRATOR
SCHOLASTIC A.I.
SCHOLASTIC AND FLYING PAGES
SCHOLASTIC ART
SCHOLASTIC BANNERS
SCHOLASTIC BOOK FAIRS
SCHOLASTIC BOOKS ON TOUR
SCHOLASTIC CASSETTES
SCHOLASTIC CHOICES
SCHOLASTIC DECODABLE READERS
THE SCHOLASTIC EARLY CHILDHOOD WORKSHOP
SCHOLASTIC EXPLAINS
SCHOLASTIC EXPLORASTORY BOOK FAIR
SCHOLASTIC FAMILY BOOKSHELF
SCHOLASTIC HARDCOVER
SCHOLASTIC INTERACTIVE PHONICS READERS BOOSTER
SCHOLASTIC INTERNATIONAL
SCHOLASTIC LEARNING SIDE BY SIDE
SCHOLASTIC LITERACY FESTIVAL
SCHOLASTIC LITERACY PLACE
SCHOLASTIC MATH
SCHOLASTIC MATH PLACE
SCHOLASTIC MY FIRST LIBRARY
SCHOLASTIC NETWORK
SCHOLASTIC NEWS
SCHOLASTIC NEWS-EL PERIODICO
SCHOLASTIC PARENT & CHILD
SCHOLASTIC PHONICS CLUBHOUSE
SCHOLASTIC PHONICS READERS
SCHOLASTIC PRODUCTIONS
SCHOLASTIC READ XL
SCHOLASTIC READING COUNTS
SCHOLASTIC READING JAMBOREE
SCHOLASTIC READING LINE
SCHOLASTIC RECORDS
SCHOLASTIC RED
SCHOLASTIC REFERENCE
SCHOLASTIC SCIENCE PLACE
SCHOLASTIC SCOPE
SCHOLASTIC SHOWCASE
SCHOLASTIC SIDE BY SIDE
SCHOLASTIC SIDEKICKS
SCHOLASTIC SMART BOOKS
SCHOLASTIC SOLARES
SCHOLASTIC SOUND AND LETTER TIME
SCHOLASTIC SPELLING
SCHOLASTIC SPELLING STUDIO
SCHOLASTIC SPRINT READING
THE SCHOLASTIC STORE
SCHOLASTIC STORYBOOK COLLECTIBLES
SCHOLASTIC SUPERPRINT!
SCHOLASTIC TEACHER
SCHOLASTIC TESTING
SCHOLASTIC TIME-TO-TIME DISCOVER READERS
SCHOLASTIC TRANSITION PROGRAM
SCHOLASTIC UPDATE
SCHOLASTIC VIDEO COLLECTION
SCHOLASTIC VOZ DEL LECTOR
SCHOLASTIC ZIP ZOOM
SCHUSS
SCICLOPEDIA
SCIENCE DARES YOU!
SCIENCE PLACEMATS
SCIENCE SEEKERS
SCIENCE THINKMATS
SCIENCE WORLD
SCRIBBLE STUDIO
SECRET RINGS
SEE SAW
SENIOR SCHOLASTIC
SHOEBOX LIBRARY
SING AND READ STORYBOOK
SLAPPIES

SLIDE SHOP
SLINGCHUTE
SMART PLACE
SNOOTZ MATH TREK
SOCCER JR.
SOUP2NUTS
SPACE SHIP
SPECKLE
SPEEDY FACTS
SPY FIVE
SPY UNIVERSITY
SPY X
SPYLER
SQUARE PAIRS
STAR BOOK CLUB
STOP THE WATCH
STORY TREE
STORYTELLING CIRCLE
STORYWORKS
STRING AND BOOK
STRUGGLES FOR JUSTICE
SUCCESS WITH TYPING
SUCCESS WITH WRITING
SUNFIRE
SUPERFABULOSO
SUPERSCIENCE
TAB
TAB BOOK CLUB
TALES OF FANTASY
TALKING TEXT WRITER
TANGERINE PRESS
TEACHER FREEBIES
THE TEACHER STORE
TELENOVEL
TESSELLATION EXPLORATION
THEATRIX
THINKING READER
THREE TREES
TOM SNYDER PRODUCTIONS
TRC TEEN READERS CLUB
TREASURES OF THE EARTH
TREE
TREE OF KNOWLEDGE
TRUMPET
TRUMPET CLUB SPECIAL EDITION
TURTLE TRACKS
TWO BEST FRIENDS
UNDERSEA UNIVERSITY
UPFRONT
VOZ DEL LECTOR
WESTON WOODS
WIGGLEWORKS
WIGGLEWORKS SCHOLASTIC BEGINNING LITERACY SYSTEM
WILDLIFE ADVENTURE CARDS
WIREBOUND BOOK
WORD BY WORD FIRST READERS
WORD FAMILY TALES
WORD GIRL
THE WORLD ACCORDING TO KLUTZ
WORLD DISCOVERY SCIENCE READERS
WORLD WEEK
WRAPS
WRITE 180
WRITE LYRICS
YOU CAN SCRATCH OFF
ZAP SCIENCE
ZOOMATES

SCHROEDER PUBLISHING COMPANY

5801 Kentucky Dam Rd
Paducah, KY 42003-9323
Tel.: (270) 898-6211
Fax: (270) 898-8890
Toll Free: (800) 626-5420
E-mail: info@collectorbooks.com
Web Site: www.collectorbooks.com
E-Mail For Key Personnel:
President: billy@collectorbooks.com
Marketing Director: rick@collectorbooks.com
Public Relations: editor@collectorbooks.com
Approx. Number Employees: 65
Year Founded: 1974
Business Description:
Publisher of Collector Books & Quilting; Price Guides to Antiques & Collections
S.I.C.: 2731; 2721
N.A.I.C.S.: 511130; 511120
Import Export
Advertising Expenditures: $400,000
Media: 4-6-7-8-10-13
Distr.: Natl.
Budget Set: Nov.
Personnel:
William T. Schroeder *(Pres & CEO)*
Rick Lloyd *(VP-Adv)*
Gail Ashburn *(Editor)*
Brands & Products:
AMERICAN QUILTERS SOCIETY
COLLECTOR BOOKS
SCHROEDER

SCIENTIFIC AMERICAN, INC.

(Sub. of Georg von Holtzbrinck GmbH & Co. KG)
415 Madison Ave
New York, NY 10017-1111
Tel.: (212) 451-8200
Fax: (212) 754-1138
Toll Free: (800) 333-1199
Web Site: www.sciam.com
E-Mail For Key Personnel:
Marketing Director: lsalant@sciam.com
Sales Range: $50-74.9 Million
Approx. Number Employees: 100
Year Founded: 1845
Business Description:
Magazine Publisher
S.I.C.: 2721; 2731
N.A.I.C.S.: 511120; 511130
Import Export
Advertising Expenditures: $300,000
Media: 2-9
Distr.: Intl.; Natl.
Budget Set: Sept.
Personnel:
Steven Yee *(Pres)*
Bruce Brandfon *(VP & Publr)*
Michael Florek *(VP-Fin & Bus Dev)*
Jeremy A. Abbate *(Dir-Global Media Solutions)*
Catherine Bussey *(Sr Mgr-Retention Mktg)*
Marie Maher *(Bus Mgr)*
Brands & Products:
SCIENTIFIC AMERICAN
SCIENTIFIC AMERICAN MIND
Advertising Agency:
Trylon SMR
41 East 11th St
New York, NY 10003
Tel.: (212) 725-2295
Fax: (212) 725-2243

SCOUT MEDIA, INC.

(Sub. of Fox Interactive Media, Inc.)
Ste 700 2003 Western Ave
Seattle, WA 98121-2111
Tel.: (206) 728-7200
Fax: (206) 728-7744
E-mail: bizdev@scout.com
Web Site: www.scout.com
Sales Range: $50-74.9 Million
Approx. Number Employees: 200
Business Description:
Online Sports Information & Magazine Publisher
S.I.C.: 2741
N.A.I.C.S.: 516110
Media: 6-13
Personnel:
Alan Mcdonald *(Gen Mgr-Scout Publ)*
Joel Cox *(Exec Dir-Network Dev & Mktg)*
Stephan Miller *(Dir-Network Devel)*
Keith Haynes *(Product Mgr)*
Brands & Products:
SCOUT.COM

SCRANTON GILLETTE COMMUNICATIONS

3030 W Saltcreel Ln Ste 201
Arlington Heights, IL 60005
Tel.: (847) 391-1000
Fax: (847) 390-0408
E-mail: bfreiler@stcmail.com
Web Site: www.sgcpubs.com
Approx. Number Employees: 60
Business Description:
Business-to-Business Communications Publisher
S.I.C.: 2721
N.A.I.C.S.: 511120
Media: 6-8-13
Personnel:
Karla Gillette *(Chm)*
Edward Gillette *(Pres & CEO)*

SEATTLE POST-INTELLIGENCER

(Unit of Hearst Newspapers)
101 Elliott Ave W
Seattle, WA 98119-4236
Mailing Address:
PO Box 1909
Seattle, WA 98111-1909
Tel.: (206) 448-8000
Tel.: (206) 464-2121
Fax: (206) 448-8166
Toll Free: (800) 542-0820
E-mail: newsmedia@seattlepi.com
Web Site: www.seattlepi.com
Approx. Number Employees: 20
Year Founded: 1863
Business Description:
Newspaper Publishing
S.I.C.: 2711
N.A.I.C.S.: 511110
Media: 2-8-13-20-22
Distr.: Reg.
Budget Set: Sept.
Personnel:
Roger Oglesby *(Publr)*
Bob Swearingen *(Gen Mgr-Acctg & Facilities)*
David McCumber *(Mng Editor)*
Glenn Ericksen *(Copy Editor-Features)*
Duston Harvey *(Editor-Arts & Entertainment)*
Maren Hunt *(Copy Editor-News)*
Nick Rousso *(Editor-Sports)*
Scott Sunde *(Asst Editor)*
Jim Beatty *(Dir-Tech)*
Katherine White *(Coord-Pub Affairs)*
Brands & Products:
SEATTLE P-I.COM
SEATTLE POST-INTELLIGENCER

SEATTLE TIMES COMPANY

(Joint Venture of The McClatchy Company & Blethen Corporation)
1120 John St
Seattle, WA 98109
Mailing Address:
PO Box 70
Seattle, WA 98111
Tel.: (206) 464-2111
Fax: (206) 464-2009
E-mail: corporatecommunications@seattletimes.com
Web Site:
www.seattletimescompany.com
Sales Range: $500-549.9 Million
Approx. Number Employees: 3,020
Year Founded: 1896
Business Description:
Newspaper Publisher; Owned 50.5% by Blethen Corporation & 49.5% by The McClatchy Company
S.I.C.: 2711
N.A.I.C.S.: 511110
Advertising Expenditures: $20,000,000
D.M. to Consumers: $7,000,000; Daily Newsp.: $8,000,000; Other: $5,000,000
Distr.: Reg.
Budget Set: Nov.
Personnel:
Frank A. Blethen *(CEO & Publr)*
William D. Yearous *(CIO & VP)*
Alayne Fardella *(Sr VP)*
David Boardman *(Sr VP & Exec Editor)*
Alan Fisco *(Sr VP-Sls & Mktg)*
Greg Crosby *(Mgr-Network Svcs)*
Matthew Pferschy *(Mgr-Online Ad Ops & Analytics)*
Brands & Products:
THE SEATTLE POST-INTELLIGENCER
THE SEATTLE TIMES

THE SEDALIA DEMOCRAT

(Unit of Freedom Newspapers, Inc.)
700 S Massachusetts Ave
Sedalia, MO 65301
Tel.: (660) 826-1000
Fax: (660) 826-2413
E-mail: advertising@sedaliademocrat.com
Web Site: www.sedaliademocrat.com
Sales Range: $100-124.9 Million
Approx. Number Employees: 100
Year Founded: 1868
Business Description:
Newspaper
S.I.C.: 2711
N.A.I.C.S.: 511110
Media: 8-9-10-16-18-22-26
Personnel:
Dave Phillips *(Publr)*
Roger Hooker *(Editor-Copy)*
Bob Satnan *(Editor)*
Sharon Hall *(Dir-Fin)*
Eddie Crouch *(Mgr-Classifieds)*

SELF MAGAZINE

(Unit of Conde Nast Publications, Inc.)
4 Times Sq 5th Fl
New York, NY 10036-6518
Tel.: (212) 286-3970
Fax: (212) 286-6174
Web Site: www.condenast.com
Approx. Number Employees: 100

Self Magazine — (Continued)

Year Founded: 1979
Business Description:
Beauty & Health Magazine
S.I.C.: 2721; 2741
N.A.I.C.S.: 511120; 516110
Media: 6-8-13-19
Distr.: Intl.; Natl.
Personnel:
Laura McEwen *(VP & Publr)*
Lucy S. Danziger *(Editor-in-Chief)*
Dana Points *(Exec Editor)*
Katherine Lewis *(Mng Editor)*
Lindsay T. Huggins *(Editor-Fashion Market)*
Lida Moore Musso *(Sr Editor-Style)*
Robin Page *(Sr Editor-Fashion)*
Cynthia Walsh *(Dir-Mktg)*
Sara Austin *(Dir-News & Health Features)*
Meaghan Buchan *(Dir-Fitness)*
Paula Derrow *(Dir-Articles)*
Petra Kobayashi *(Dir-Art)*
Evyan Metzner *(Dir-Fashion)*
Wendy Nanus *(Dir-Adv)*
Cynthia Hall Seawright *(Dir-Creative)*

SENIOR MARKET ADVISOR
(Div. of Wiesner Publishing, LLC)
7009 S Potomac St Ste 200
Centennial, CO 80112
Tel.: (303) 397-7600
Fax: (303) 397-7619
Web Site:
www.seniormarketadvisor.com
Approx. Number Employees: 80
Business Description:
Business Magazine
S.I.C.: 2721
N.A.I.C.S.: 511120
Media: 2-7-8-13-22
Personnel:
Amy C. Cosper *(Grp Dir-Editorial)*
Astrid Solis *(Dir-Art)*

SERIGRAPH, INC.
3801 E Decorah Rd
West Bend, WI 53095-9597
Tel.: (262) 335-7200
Fax: (262) 335-7699
E-mail: info@serigraph.com
Web Site: www.serigraph.com
Sales Range: $100-124.9 Million
Approx. Number Employees: 950
Year Founded: 1949
Business Description:
Specialty Offset & Screen Printing: Decals, Decorative Trim
S.I.C.: 2759; 2752
N.A.I.C.S.: 323113; 323110
Export
Media: 4-7-10-17
Distr.: Natl.
Budget Set: Apr.-May
Personnel:
Sean Torinus *(CEO)*
Jeffrey J. Siemers *(CFO)*
Ken Crass *(Mgr-Program)*
Brands & Products:
3D-LUX
GEMINI IN-MOLD DECORATING
IMD1
LENTICULAR
LIQUID INK
MICROMOTION
SELECT METALIZATION
SERIGLAZE
SERIGRAPH
SERILLUSION

SEVEN STORIES PRESS INC.
140 Watts St
New York, NY 10013
Tel.: (212) 226-8760
Fax: (212) 226-1411
Toll Free: (800) 663-5714
Toll Free: (800) 283-3572
E-mail: info@sevenstories.com
Web Site: www.sevenstories.com
Approx. Number Employees: 12
Business Description:
Book Publisher
S.I.C.: 2731
N.A.I.C.S.: 511130
Media: 6-13
Personnel:
Daniel Simon *(Publr)*

SEVENTEEN MAGAZINE
(Unit of Hearst Magazines)
300 W 57th St 17Fl
New York, NY 10019
Tel.: (212) 649-3100
Fax: (212) 204-3972
Toll Free: (800) 388-1749
E-mail: ask17@seventeen.com
Web Site: www.seventeen.com
Approx. Number Employees: 115
Year Founded: 1944
Business Description:
Periodical Publisher
S.I.C.: 2721
N.A.I.C.S.: 511120
Advertising Expenditures: $300,000
Media: 9-11-22
Distr.: Natl.
Budget Set: Oct.
Personnel:
Linda C. Jenkins *(CFO & Sr VP)*
Ann Shoket *(Editor-in-Chief)*
Jasmine Snow *(Editor-Accessories)*
Yesenia Almonte *(Dir-Beauty)*
Julie Hochheiser *(Dir-Site)*
Gina Kelly *(Dir-Fashion)*
Jeff Carter *(Mgr-Natl Adv)*

SF NEWSPAPER COMPANY, LLC
(Sub. of Clarity Media Group, Inc.)
(d/b/a The San Francisco Examiner)
71 Stevenson St 2nd Fl
San Francisco, CA 94105
Tel.: (415) 359-2600
Fax: (415) 359-2626
Web Site: www.sfexaminer.com
Business Description:
Newspaper Publisher
S.I.C.: 2711; 2741
N.A.I.C.S.: 511110; 516110
Media: 6-9
Personnel:
John Wilcox *(Pres-Publr)*
Jim Pimentel *(Editor-in-Chief)*
Deirdre Hussey *(Mng Editor)*
Albert C. Pacciorini *(Bus Editor)*
Vivienne Sosnowski *(Exec Editor)*
Lulu Feliciano *(Dir-Mktg)*

SHAMBHALA PUBLICATIONS INC.
300 Massachusetts Ave
Boston, MA 02115
Mailing Address:
PO Box 308
Boston, MA 02117
Tel.: (617) 424-0030
Fax: (617) 236-1563
Toll Free: (888) 424-2329
E-mail: publicity@shambhala.com
Web Site: www.shambhala.com
Sales Range: $10-24.9 Million
Approx. Number Employees: 20
Business Description:
Publisher of Books
S.I.C.: 2731
N.A.I.C.S.: 511130
Media: 4-6-8-10-13
Personnel:
Nikko Odiseos *(Pres)*
Diane McCormick *(VP-Fin)*

SHAREDBOOK INC.
14 Wall St
New York, NY 10005
Tel.: (646) 442-8840
Fax: (646) 442-8841
E-mail: info@sharedbook.com
Web Site: www.sharedbook.com
Approx. Number Employees: 25
Business Description:
Custom Published Commemorative Albums
S.I.C.: 2741
N.A.I.C.S.: 511199
Personnel:
Josef Hollander *(Chm)*
Caroline Vanderlip *(CEO)*
Dave Brown *(VP-IT Ops)*
Rick Hunt *(VP-Mktg)*
Advertising Agency:
104 degrees West Partners
1925 Blake St Ste 200
Denver, CO 80202
Tel.: (720) 407-6060
Fax: (720) 407-6061

SHAWNEE NEWS-STAR
(Unit of GateHouse Media, Inc.)
215 N Bell
Shawnee, OK 74801
Tel.: (405) 273-4200
Fax: (405) 273-4207
Toll Free: (800) 332-2305
E-mail: newsroom@news-star.com
Web Site: www.news-star.com
Sales Range: $10-24.9 Million
Approx. Number Employees: 54
Year Founded: 1894
Business Description:
Newspaper Publisher
S.I.C.: 2711
N.A.I.C.S.: 511110
Media: 8-9
Personnel:
Brian Blansett *(Publr)*
Reita Easley *(Creative Dir)*
Stacie Harris *(Dir-Classified)*
Sherry Lankford *(Dir-Adv)*
Jeri McEntire *(Bus Mgr)*
Denis Westerman *(Mgr-Comml Print)*
Brands & Products:
SHAWNEE NEWS STAR

THE SHERIDAN GROUP, INC.
11311 McCormick Rd Ste 260
Hunt Valley, MD 21031-8676
Tel.: (410) 785-7277
Fax: (410) 785-7217
Web Site: www.sheridan.com
Approx. Sls.: $266,187,753
Approx. Number Employees: 1,450
Year Founded: 1915
Business Description:
Sheet Fed Offset & Web Printing
S.I.C.: 2752; 2732; 2759
N.A.I.C.S.: 323110; 323117; 323119
Advertising Expenditures: $200,000
Personnel:
John A. Saxton *(Pres & CEO)*
Robert M. Jakobe *(CFO)*
Douglas R. Ehmann *(CTO & Exec VP)*
J. Kenneth Garner *(VP-Bus Dev-Magazine Svcs)*
Dale A. Tepp *(VP-HR)*

SHOWCASE PUBLICATIONS INC.
(d/b/a Auto Shopper)
810 Hooper Ave
Toms River, NJ 08753
Tel.: (732) 349-7775
Fax: (732) 349-9020
E-mail: webads@autoshop.com
Web Site: www.showpubs.net
Approx. Number Employees: 10
Business Description:
Publishing & Printing Trade Journals
S.I.C.: 2721
N.A.I.C.S.: 511120
Media: 2-13
Personnel:
Bob Draper *(Pres)*

SIMMONS-BOARDMAN PUBLISHING CORP.
345 Hudson St 12 Fl
New York, NY 10014-4502
Tel.: (212) 620-7200
Fax: (212) 633-1165
E-mail: marinelog@sbpub.com
Web Site:
www.simmonsboardman.com
Approx. Sls.: $12,000,000
Approx. Number Employees: 75
Year Founded: 1928
Business Description:
Publisher of Industrial & Trade Magazines
S.I.C.: 2721; 2731
N.A.I.C.S.: 511120; 511130
Media: 2-4-7-10
Distr.: Intl.; Natl.
Budget Set: Nov.
Personnel:
Arthur J. Mcginnis *(Chm & Pres)*
Robert P. DeMarco *(Sr VP & Grp Publr)*
Jane Poterala *(Dir-Conference)*
Wendy Williams *(Dir-Art)*
Brands & Products:
MARINE LOG
RAILWAY AGE
SBP

SIMON & SCHUSTER CHILDREN'S PUBLISHING
(Div. of Simon & Schuster, Inc.)
1230 Ave of the Americas
New York, NY 10020
Tel.: (212) 698-2809
Fax: (212) 698-4350
Web Site:
www.simonandschuster.com
Business Description:
Juvenile Picture Books, Fiction & Non-Fiction Publisher
S.I.C.: 2731
N.A.I.C.S.: 511130
Media: 2-7-10
Distr.: Natl.

Key to Media (For complete agency information see *The Advertising Red Books-Agencies* edition):
1. Bus. Publs. 2. Cable T.V. 3. Catalogs & Directories. 4. Co-op Adv. 5. Consumer Mags. 6. D.M. to Bus. Estab.7. D.M. to Consumers 8. Daily Newsp. 9. Exhibits/Trade Shows 10. Foreign 11. Infomercial 12. Internet Adv.13. Multimedia 14. Network Radio 15. Network T.V. 16. Newsp. Distr. Mags. 17. Other 18. Outdoor (Posters, Transit) 19. Point of Purchase20. Premiums, Novelties 21. Product Samples 22. Special Events Mktg. 23. Spot Radio 24. Spot T.V. 25. Weekly Newsp. 26. Yellow Page Adv.

Personnel:
Rick Richter *(Pres & Publr)*
Brenda Bowen *(Exec VP-Publr)*
Suzanne Harper *(Sr VP-Publr-Hardcover)*
Lee Wade *(VP & Dir-Creative)*
Paul Crichton *(VP & Dir-Publicity)*
Alexandra Cooper *(Editor)*
Michelle Montague *(Exec Dir-Adv, Promo & Mktg)*
Elke Villa *(Dir-Mktg, Retail & Mass Market)*
Orly Sigal *(Asst Mgr-Publ)*
Brands & Products:
SIMON & SCHUSTER BOOKS FOR YOUNG READERS
SIMON PULSE
SIMON SPOTLIGHT

SIMON & SCHUSTER, INC.
(Sub. of CBS Corporation)
1230 Avenue of the Americas
New York, NY 10020
Tel.: (212) 698-7000
Fax: (212) 698-7099
Web Site:
www.simonandschuster.com
Sales Range: $750-799.9 Million
Approx. Number Employees: 1,500
Year Founded: 1924
Business Description:
Fiction, Non-Fiction, Trade Reference, Educational & Professional Information, Soft & Hardbound Books, Textbooks, Travel Guides, Children's Books, Computer Books & Software, College Guides, Test Preparation Guides, Legal & Financial Reports & Audio & Video Publisher; Film & Video Distr
S.I.C.: 2731; 2741; 7822
N.A.I.C.S.: 511130; 511199; 512120
Media: 1-2-3-5-6-7-8-9-10-11-13-14-15-16-19-21-22-23-24-25
Distr.: Natl.
Personnel:
Carolyn Reidy *(Pres & CEO)*
Elisa Rivlin *(Gen Counsel & Sr VP)*
Stacy Creamer *(VP & Publr-Touchstone Fireside)*
Dennis Eulau *(Exec VP-Ops)*
Michael Selleck *(Exec VP-Sls & Mktg)*
Carolyn Connolly *(Sr VP-HR)*
Joe D'Onofrio *(Sr VP-Supply Chain Ops)*
Adam Rothberg *(Sr VP-Corp Comm)*
Priscilla Painton *(Editor-in-Chief)*
Alice Mayhew *(Dir-Editorial)*
Brands & Products:
ALADDIN PAPERBACKS
ATHENEUM BOOKS FOR YOUNG READERS
ATRIA BOOKS
FIRESIDE BOOKS
THE FREE PRESS
KAPLAN
LITTLE SIMON
PIMSLEUR
POCKET BOOKS
RABBIT EARS BOOK & AUDIO
SCRIBNER
SIMON & SCHUSTER
SIMON & SCHUSTER AUDIOWORKS
SIMON & SCHUSTER SOUND IDEAS

SIR SPEEDY, INC.
(Sub. of Franchise Services, Inc.)
26722 Plz Dr
Mission Viejo, CA 92691
Tel.: (949) 348-5000
Fax: (949) 348-5066
Toll Free: (800) 747-7733
E-mail: corporateopportunities@sirspeedy.com
Web Site: www.sirspeedy.com
Approx. Number Employees: 70
Business Description:
Franchisor of Printing & Digital Networking Centers
S.I.C.: 6794; 2752
N.A.I.C.S.: 533110; 323110
Media: 1-2-3-6-7-8-9-11-13-14-19-20-25-26
Distr.: Natl.
Personnel:
Richard Lowe *(Pres & COO)*
Don F. Lowe *(CEO)*
David Robidoux *(VP-Mktg)*
Denise Denton *(Dir-Commun)*
Brands & Products:
SIR SPEEDY
Advertising Agency:
Summit Marketing Communications
7112 W. Jefferson Ave., Ste. 305
Lakewood, CO 80235-2328
Tel.: (303) 987-9030
(Printing Services)

SMARTMONEY
(Joint Venture of Dow Jones & Company, Inc.)
1211 Ave of the Americas
New York, NY 10036
Tel.: (212) 416-2000
Web Site: www.smartmoney.com
Sales Range: $25-49.9 Million
Approx. Number Employees: 100
Business Description:
Financial Magazine
S.I.C.: 2721; 2741
N.A.I.C.S.: 511120; 516110
Media: 2-7-8-10-13
Personnel:
Edwin A. Finn, Jr. *(Chm & Dir-Editorial)*
Michael Le Du *(CTO & Gen Mgr)*
Donald Luskin *(Chief Investment Officer)*
Jonathan Dahl *(Editor-in-Chief)*
Igor Greenwald *(Editor)*
James B. Stewart *(Editor)*
Dawn Gibbons *(Mktg Dir)*
Matt Wager *(Art Dir)*
Alfredo Castrillon *(Dir-Tech Ops)*
Dominique Boucher *(Dir-Product Dev)*
Bill Breen *(Dir-Web Dev)*
Steven Kutz *(Dir-Production)*
Linda Arunamata-Huang *(Ops Mgr)*
Ana Genao *(Mgr-Search Engine Optimization)*
Steve Moynihan *(Mgr-Texas)*
Frank Ruso *(Mgr-Adv Ops)*
Kevin Sheehan *(Mgr-Reprints)*
Sharone Peker *(Coord-Adv Traffic)*

SMITHSONIAN MAGAZINE
600 Maryland Ave SW Ste 6001 MRC 513
Washington, DC 20024
Tel.: (202) 633-6090
Tel.: (212) 916-1300 (advertising)
Fax: (202) 275-1972
Toll Free: (877) 240-1183
E-mail: info@si.edu
Web Site: www.smithsonianmag.com
Approx. Number Employees: 100
Year Founded: 1970
Business Description:
Magazine Publisher
S.I.C.: 2721; 9411
N.A.I.C.S.: 511120; 923110
Media: 5-7-8
Distr.: Natl.
Personnel:
Thomas Ott *(Pres)*
Alan Chu *(Gen Mgr)*
Diane M. Bolz *(Editor)*
Kathleen M. Burke *(Editor)*
T. A. Frail *(Editor)*
Laura Helmuth *(Editor)*
Jeanne Maglaty *(Editor)*
Mark Strauss *(Editor)*
Carey Winfrey *(Editor)*
Lisa Dunham *(Dir-Consumer Mktg)*
Maria G. Keehan *(Dir-Art)*
Rosie Walker *(Dir-Mktg)*
Laurie A. Corson *(Mgr-Mktg)*
Marilyn Cruz *(Mgr-Adv Svcs)*
Brands & Products:
SMITHSONIAN
SMITHSONIAN.COM

SNOWMASS VILLAGE SUN
(Sub. of Swift Newspapers, Inc.)
16 Kearns Rd Unit 211
Snowmass Village, CO 81615
Mailing Address:
PO Box 5770
Snowmass Village, CO 81615-5770
Tel.: (970) 923-5829
Fax: (970) 923-2571
Web Site: www.snowmasssun.com
Approx. Number Employees: 4
Year Founded: 1978
Business Description:
Newspaper
S.I.C.: 2711
N.A.I.C.S.: 511110
Media: 2-8-10-20-21-22-23
Personnel:
Madeleine Osberger *(Gen Mgr & Editor)*
Louise Walker *(Mgr-Adv Sls)*
Brands & Products:
SNOWMASS SUN

SOAP OPERA DIGEST
(Sub. of Source Interlink Media)
261 Madison Ave
New York, NY 10016
Tel.: (212) 915-4249
Fax: (212) 915-4261
Web Site: www.soapdigest.com
Approx. Number Employees: 60
Year Founded: 1975
Business Description:
Periodical
S.I.C.: 2721; 2731
N.A.I.C.S.: 511120; 511130
Media: 1-2-15-17-19-23
Distr.: Intl.; Natl.
Budget Set: Oct.
Personnel:
Daria Rivera *(Mgr-Online Adv)*
Advertising Agency:
Fletcher Media Group
94 Grove St
Peterborough, NH 03458
Tel.: (603) 924-6383
Fax: (603) 924-6562

SOBE LIFE, LLC
(d/b/a Trump World)
825 N Cass Ave Ste 209
Westmont, IL 60559
Tel.: (630) 986-5896
Fax: (630) 986-1581
Business Description:
Magazine Publisher
S.I.C.: 2721
N.A.I.C.S.: 999990
Media: 6-8
Personnel:
Michael A. Jacobson *(Chm & Pres)*
Lee Fry *(CEO)*
Robert Rorke *(Dir-Editorial)*
Kristen Ball *(Asst Editor)*
Jordan Stein *(Editor-Production)*

SOLAR COMMUNICATIONS, INC.
1120 Frontenac Rd
Naperville, IL 60563-1749
Tel.: (630) 983-1400
Fax: (630) 983-1494
Fax: (630) 983-6125
Toll Free: (800) 323-2751
Web Site:
www.solarcommunications.com
Approx. Number Employees: 225
Year Founded: 1961
Business Description:
Offset Printing, Specialized Packaging & Consumer Publishing
S.I.C.: 2759; 7389
N.A.I.C.S.: 323119; 561910
Export
Media: 2-10
Personnel:
John Henderlite *(CFO)*
Barbara L. Gunning *(VP-HR)*

SOUND PUBLISHING, INC.
(Sub. of Black Press Group Ltd.)
19351 8th Ave NE Ste 106
Poulsbo, WA 98370
Tel.: (360) 394-5800
Fax: (360) 394-5841
E-mail: classified@soundpublishing.com
Web Site: www.soundpublishing.com
Sales Range: $10-24.9 Million
Approx. Number Employees: 50
Year Founded: 1987
Business Description:
Newspaper Publishers
S.I.C.: 2711
N.A.I.C.S.: 511110
Media: 8-9
Personnel:
Deb Grigg *(Dir-Customer & Credit Svcs)*
Brands & Products:
PRINT NEWSPAPERS

SOURCE INTERLINK COMPANIES INC.
27500 Riverview Center Blvd Ste 400
Bonita Springs, FL 34134
Tel.: (239) 949-4450
Fax: (239) 949-7623
Toll Free: (866) 888-5389
E-mail: dheine@sourceinterlink.com
Web Site: www.sourceinterlink.com
Sales Range: $1-4.9 Billion
Approx. Number Employees: 4,400
Year Founded: 1995

Key to Media (For complete agency information see *The Advertising Red Books-Agencies* edition):
1. Bus. Publs. 2. Cable T.V. 3. Catalogs & Directories. 4. Co-op Adv. 5. Consumer Mags. 6. D.M. to Bus. Estab.7. D.M. to Consumers
8. Daily Newsp. 9. Exhibits/Trade Shows 10. Foreign 11. Infomercial 12. Internet Adv.13. Multimedia 14. Network Radio
15. Network T.V. 16. Newsp. Distr. Mags. 17. Other 18. Outdoor (Posters, Transit) 19. Point of Purchase20. Premiums, Novelties
21. Product Samples 22. Special Events Mktg. 23. Spot Radio 24. Spot T.V. 25. Weekly Newsp. 26. Yellow Page Adv.

Source Interlink Companies Inc. — (Continued)

Business Description:
Magazine Publication & Entertainment Distribution
S.I.C.: 2721; 2741; 3652; 5192; 7822; 7829
N.A.I.C.S.: 511120; 424920; 512120; 512199; 512220; 516110
Media: 2-6-7-10-19
Personnel:
Gregory Mays *(Chm)*
Michael L. Sullivan *(Pres & CEO)*
Marc Fierman *(CFO & Exec VP)*
Stephanie S. Justice *(Chief Admin Officer & Exec VP)*
Cynthia Beauchamp *(Gen Counsel)*
Jason Adams *(Dir-Corp Fin, Treasury & IR)*

SOURCE INTERLINK MEDIA
(Sub. of Source Interlink Companies Inc.)
261 Madison Ave 6th Fl
New York, NY 10016
Tel.: (212) 915-4000
Fax: (212) 915-4001
E-mail: info@sourceinterlink.com
Web Site: www.sourceinterlink.com
Sales Range: $500-549.9 Million
Approx. Number Employees: 500
Year Founded: 2000
Business Description:
Print & Digital Media Publisher
S.I.C.: 2731; 2721; 2741
N.A.I.C.S.: 511130; 511120; 516110
Media: 2-3-6-8-10-19-20-22-24
Distr.: Natl.
Budget Set: Apr.
Personnel:
Chris Argentieri *(Pres)*
Alan Alpanian *(Chief Creative Officer)*
Doug Evans *(Sr VP)*
Brad Gerber *(Chief Revenue Officer & Sr VP)*
Tom Slater *(VP-Consumer Mktg)*

SOUTH FLORIDA CEO
(Div. of CEO Publishing Group, Inc.)
299 SE 1st St Ste 601
Miami, FL 33131
Tel.: (305) 379-1118
Fax: (305) 379-1119
E-mail: subscriptions@southfloridaceo.com
Web Site: www.southfloridaceo.com
Business Description:
Magazine
S.I.C.: 2721
N.A.I.C.S.: 511120
Media: 8
Personnel:
Ron Mann *(Pres)*
Vivian Fried *(Publr)*
Elizabeth Carlisle *(Dir-Creative)*

SOUTHEASTERN PRINTING COMPANY INC.
3601 SE Dixie Hwy
Stuart, FL 34997-5246
Tel.: (772) 287-2141
Fax: (772) 288-3988
Toll Free: (800) 226-8221
E-mail: info@seprint.com
Web Site: www.seprint.com
Approx. Number Employees: 200
Year Founded: 1924
Business Description:
Full Service Commercial Printing
S.I.C.: 2752; 2759
N.A.I.C.S.: 323110; 323112
Media: 2-4-7-13
Personnel:
Don Mader *(CEO)*

SPAR GROUP, INC.
560 White Plains Rd
Tarrytown, NY 10591-5198
Tel.: (914) 332-4100
Fax: (914) 332-0741
E-mail: info@sparinc.com
Web Site: www.sparinc.com
Approx. Rev.: $63,154,000
Approx. Number Employees: 10,000
Business Description:
Merchandising & Marketing Services Supplier
S.I.C.: 5399; 7373; 8732
N.A.I.C.S.: 452990; 541512; 541910
Media: 2-4-7-10-20
Personnel:
Robert G. Brown *(Chm)*
William H. Bartels *(Vice Chm)*
Gary S. Raymond *(Pres & CEO)*
James R. Segreto *(CFO)*
Kori G. Belzer *(COO)*
Patricia Franco *(CIO & Pres-Intl Div)*
Mary Smith *(Sr VP-Sls & Mktg)*
Advertising Agency:
PondelWilkinson Inc.
1880 Century Park E Ste 350
Los Angeles, CA 90067
Tel.: (310) 279-5980
Fax: (310) 279-5988

THE SPOKESMAN-REVIEW
(Sub. of Cowles Publishing Co. Inc.)
999 W Riverside Ave
Spokane, WA 99201-1006
Mailing Address:
PO Box 2160
Spokane, WA 99210-2160
Tel.: (509) 459-5000
Fax: (509) 459-3941
Toll Free: (800) 338-8801
E-mail: editor@spokesman.com
Web Site: www.spokesman.com
E-Mail For Key Personnel:
Marketing Director: shaunh@spokesman.com
Approx. Number Employees: 650
Year Founded: 1883
Business Description:
Newspapers Publisher
S.I.C.: 2711
N.A.I.C.S.: 511110
Media: 3-7-8-9-10-18-19-20-21-22-24
Distr.: Direct to Consumer; Reg.
Personnel:
Robert B. Thomas *(Founder & Dir-Audience Dev)*
William Stacey Cowles *(Publr)*
Gary Graham *(Editor)*
Mike Dixon *(Dir-Adv)*
Shaun Higgins *(Dir-Sls & Mktg)*
Brands & Products:
SPOKANE.NET
THE SPOKESMAN-REVIEW
Advertising Agency:
Hanna & Associates Inc.
1100 E Lakeshore Dr Ste 201
Coeur D'Alene, ID 83814
Tel.: (208) 667-2428
Fax: (208) 765-8044

THE SPORTING NEWS
(Unit of American City Business Journals, Inc.)
475 Park Ave S 27th Fl
New York, NY 10016
Tel.: (212) 500-0650
Fax: (646) 424-2232
Toll Free: (800) 777-6785
Toll Free: (800) 443-1886
E-mail: warroom@sportingnews.com
Web Site: www.sportingnews.com
Approx. Number Employees: 122
Year Founded: 1886
Business Description:
Magazine Publisher
S.I.C.: 2711; 2731
N.A.I.C.S.: 511110; 511130
Advertising Expenditures: $200,000
Media: 2-4-5-6-7-8-10-20-21
Distr.: Natl.
Budget Set: Jan.
Personnel:
Jeff Price *(Pres & Publr)*
Ed Baker *(Publr)*
Stuart Marvin *(VP-Integrated Mktg & Sls)*
Brands & Products:
THE SPORTING NEWS
Advertising Agency:
Four Corners Communications, Inc.
215 Park Ave S Ste 1901
New York, NY 10003
Tel.: (212) 849-8250
Public Relations

SPORTS ILLUSTRATED
(Unit of Time Inc.)
1271 Ave Of The Americas
New York, NY 10020-1393
Tel.: (212) 522-1212
Tel.: (212) 522-4044
Tel.: (212) 522-8473 (Pub Rels)
Fax: (212) 522-4543
Web Site: www.si.com
Sales Range: $100-124.9 Million
Business Description:
Publisher of Weekly Magazine Devoted To Sports, Recreation & Active Leisure
S.I.C.: 2721
N.A.I.C.S.: 511120
Media: 3-6-8-9-13-15-25
Distr.: Natl.
Personnel:
Ann S. Moore *(Chm & CEO)*
Mark Ford *(Pres)*
Andrew R. Judelson *(CMO)*
John Squires *(Exec VP-Opers)*
Stacy Vollman Warwick *(VP & Gen Mgr-SI Digital)*
Kim Kelleher *(VP-Global Sls)*
David Bauer *(Deputy Mng Editor)*
Stefanie Kaufman *(Editor-Ops)*
Terry McDonell *(Editor)*
Rick Tetzeli *(Editor at Large)*
Christine Rosa *(Exec Dir-Event Mktg & Talent Rels)*
Amy S. Steiner *(Exec Dir-Brand Mktg)*
Steve Fine *(Dir-Photography)*
Dino Bernacchi *(Mgr-Adv)*
Advertising Agencies:
Big Chair Creative Group
157 W 111th St
New York, NY 10026
Tel.: (212) 399-3150
Fax: (212) 399-3165

PlattForm Advertising
708 3rd Ave 12th Fl
New York, NY 10017
Tel.: (212) 684-4800
Fax: (212) 576-1129
Toll Free: (866) 671-4429

SPRINGER SCIENCE+BUSINESS MEDIA, LLC
(Sub. of Springer Verlag GmbH)
233 Spring St
New York, NY 10013
Tel.: (212) 460-1500
Fax: (212) 460-1575
Toll Free: (800) SPRINGER
E-mail: service-ny@springer.com
Web Site: www.springer.com
E-Mail For Key Personnel:
Marketing Director: pmanning@springer-ny.com
Approx. Number Employees: 200
Year Founded: 1964
Business Description:
Scientific & Business Book & Journal Publisher
S.I.C.: 2731; 2721
N.A.I.C.S.: 511130; 511120
Consumer Mags.: 15%; D.M. to Consumers: 50%; Exhibits/Trade Shows: 35%
Distr.: Natl.
Budget Set: Oct.
Personnel:
Syed Hasan *(Pres-STM Sls Academic & Govt)*
Paul Manning *(VP-Sls)*
Monica Ciba-Lucas *(Dir-Mktg & Direct Response)*

SPS STUDIOS, INC.
(d/b/a Blue Mountain Arts Inc.)
2905 Wilderness Pl
Boulder, CO 80301-5402
Tel.: (303) 449-0536
Fax: (303) 417-6496
E-mail: info@sps.com
Web Site: www.sps.com
Approx. Number Employees: 4
Year Founded: 1996
Business Description:
Publisher & Distr of Greeting Cards, Poetry Books & Stationery
S.I.C.: 2771
N.A.I.C.S.: 511191
Import
Media: 1-2-5-6-9-10-23
Personnel:
Stephen Schutz *(Co-Chm)*
Susan Polis Schutz *(Co-Chm)*
Jared Schutz *(Exec Dir)*
Brands & Products:
CHILDREN OF THE INNER LIGHT
OCCASION GALLERIE
SPS
THOUGHTS OF LIFE

SRDS, INC.
(Sub. of Media Solutions)
1700 Higgins Rd
Des Plaines, IL 60018-5621
Tel.: (847) 375-5000
Fax: (847) 375-5001
Toll Free: (800) 851-7737
E-mail: contact@srds.com
Web Site: www.srds.com

Key to Media (For complete agency information see *The Advertising Red Books-Agencies* edition):
1. Bus. Publs. 2. Cable T.V. 3. Catalogs & Directories. 4. Co-op Adv. 5. Consumer Mags. 6. D.M. to Bus. Estab.7. D.M. to Consumers
8. Daily Newsp. 9. Exhibits/Trade Shows 10. Foreign 11. Infomercial 12. Internet Adv.13. Multimedia 14. Network Radio
15. Network T.V. 16. Newsp. Distr. Mags. 17. Other 18. Outdoor (Posters, Transit) 19. Point of Purchase20. Premiums, Novelties
21. Product Samples 22. Special Events Mktg. 23. Spot Radio 24. Spot T.V. 25. Weekly Newsp. 26. Yellow Page Adv.

Sales Range: $25-49.9 Million
Approx. Number Employees: 150
Year Founded: 1919
Business Description:
Media Rates & Marketing Data Information Services
S.I.C.: 2741; 7389; 8732; 8742
N.A.I.C.S.: 511140; 519190; 541613; 541910
Media: 2-4-7-10-13-17
Distr.: Intl.; Natl.
Personnel:
George L. Carens *(Pres)*
Glen A. Markowski *(CFO)*
Kevin McNally *(CFO)*
Bernadette Cognac *(VP & Dir-Agency Rels)*
Brands & Products:
INTERNATIONAL MEDIA GUIDE
LIFESTYLE MARKET ANALYST
SRDA OUT-OF-HOME ADVERTISING SOURCE
SRDS BUSINESS PUBLICATION ADVERTISING SOURCE
SRDS CIRCULATION
SRDS COMMUNITY PUBLICATION ADVERTISING SOURCE
SRDS CONSUMER MAGAZINE ADVERTISING SOURCE
SRDS DIRECT MARKETING LIST SOURCE
SRDS DIRECT NET
SRDS HISPANIC MEDIA & MARKET SOURCE
SRDS INTERACTIVE ADVERTISING SOURCE
SRDS MEDIA SOLUTIONS
SRDS NEWSPAPER ADVERTISING SOURCE
SRDS PRINT MEDIA PRODUCTION SOURCE
SRDS RADIO ADVERTISING SOURCE
SRDS TECHNOLOGY MEDIA SOURCE
SRDS TV & CABLE SOURCE

THE ST. AUGUSTINE RECORD
(Unit of Morris Publishing Group, LLC)
1 News Pl
Saint Augustine, FL 32086
Tel.: (904) 829-6562
Fax: (904) 819-3558
E-mail: info@staugustine.com
Web Site: www.staugustine.com
Year Founded: 1894
Business Description:
Newspaper Publisher
S.I.C.: 2711; 2721
N.A.I.C.S.: 511110; 511120
Media: 8-9-13
Personnel:
William S. Morris, III *(Pres-Morris Comm)*
Peter Alice *(Editor)*
Justin Barney *(Editor-Sports)*
Peter Ellis *(Editor)*
Peter T. Guinta *(Assignment Editor)*
Derek Hembd *(Editor-Design)*
Anne C. Heymen *(Editor-Features)*
Margo C. Pope *(Editor-Editorial Page)*
Melissa Pracht *(Compass Editor)*
Diane Rodgers *(Special Projects & Res Editor)*
Lauren Sonis *(Online News Editor)*
Peter Willott *(Editor-Photo)*
Steve Carswell *(Dir-Production)*
Gail Cumiskey *(Dir-Special Projects)*
Bill Mitchell *(Dir-Circulation)*
Lawrence Peck *(Dir-Online)*
Joyce Kraft *(Reg Mgr)*
Jan Holt *(Office Mgr)*
John Gagliano *(District Mgr-Circulation)*
Michelle Robinson *(District Mgr)*
Tom Rodish *(Mgr-Circulation)*
Kimberly Reese *(Coord-Layout)*

THE ST. CATHARINES STANDARD
(Div. of Osprey Media Group, Inc.)
17 Queen St
Saint Catharines, ON L2R 5G5, Canada
Tel.: (905) 684-7251
Fax: (905) 684-6032
E-mail: standard@stcatharinesstandard.ca
Web Site: www.stcatharinesstandard.ca
Approx. Number Employees: 120
Business Description:
Daily Newspaper
S.I.C.: 2711
N.A.I.C.S.: 511110
Media: 9-13
Personnel:
Judie Bullif *(Publr)*
Andrea Kriluck *(Mng Editor)*
Bernie Puchalski *(Editor-Sports)*

ST. LOUIS COUNTIAN
(Div. of Missouri Lawyers Media, Inc.)
319 N 4th St 5th Fl
Saint Louis, MO 63102
Tel.: (314) 421-1880
Fax: (314) 436-2718
E-mail: mail@thedailyrecord.com
Web Site: www.thedailyrecord.com
Sales Range: $10-24.9 Million
Approx. Number Employees: 30
Year Founded: 1881
Business Description:
Weekly Legal Newspapers
S.I.C.: 2711
N.A.I.C.S.: 511110
Media: 8-13-25
Personnel:
Amanda Passomore *(Mgr-Bus)*
Brands & Products:
THE COUNTIAN

ST. LOUIS POST-DISPATCH LLC
(Sub. of Lee Enterprises, Incorporated)
900 N Tucker Blvd
Saint Louis, MO 63101
Tel.: (314) 340-8000
Fax: (314) 340-3125
Toll Free: (800) 365-0820
Web Site: www.stltoday.com
Sales Range: $300-349.9 Million
Approx. Number Employees: 850
Business Description:
Daily Newspaper
S.I.C.: 2711
N.A.I.C.S.: 511110
Advertising Expenditures: $1,000,000
Media: 2-4-7-8-9-10-18-20-23-24
Distr.: Direct to Consumer; Reg.
Budget Set: Oct.
Personnel:
Kevin Mowbray *(Pres & Publr)*
Steven A. Schumm *(CFO)*
John E. Jacob *(Exec VP-Comm-Global)*
Jen Wood *(Sr VP-Adv)*
Nancy Long *(VP-Mktg)*
Christine Bertelson *(Asst Mng Editor & Features Editor)*
Arnie Robbins *(Editor)*
Mandy St. Amand *(Editor-Continuous News)*
Angie Nagy *(Dir-Real Estate Adv)*
Brian Walsh *(Dir-Local Retail)*
Susan Eckert *(Mgr-Media)*
Tracy Rouch *(Mgr-Pub Rels)*

ST. MARTINS PRESS, INC.
(Sub. of MacMillan Ltd.)
175 5th Ave
New York, NY 10010-7703
Tel.: (212) 674-5151
Fax: (212) 420-9314
Toll Free: (800) 221-7945
E-mail: webmaster@stmartins.com
Web Site: www.stmartins.com
Approx. Number Employees: 600
Year Founded: 1952
Business Description:
Book Publisher
S.I.C.: 2731; 5192
N.A.I.C.S.: 511130; 424920
Import Export
Advertising Expenditures: $1,200,000
Media: 1-2-3-4-5-6-8-9-10-13-14-15-16-18-19-20-22-23-24-25
Distr.: Direct to Consumer; Natl.
Budget Set: Nov.
Personnel:
John Sargent *(Pres & CEO)*
Tom Doherty *(Pres & Publ-Books)*
Alison Lazarus *(Pres-Trade Sls)*
Sally Richardson *(Pres-Trade Division)*
Philip Schwartz *(Exec VP)*
Kerry Nordling *(Dir-Subsidiary Rights)*
Bob Podrasky *(Sr Mgr-Domestic Rights)*
Brands & Products:
FORGE
MINOTAUR
PICADOR USA
TOR BOOKS

ST. PETERSBURG TIMES
(Sub. of The Times Publishing Co.)
490 1st Ave S
Saint Petersburg, FL 33701-4204
Mailing Address:
PO Box 1121
Saint Petersburg, FL 33731-1121
Tel.: (727) 893-8111
Fax: (727) 892-2378
Toll Free: (800) 333-7505
E-mail: local@sptimes.com
Web Site: www.tempabay.com
E-Mail For Key Personnel:
President: ptash@sptimes.com
Sales Director: rreeves@sptimes.com
Sales Range: $250-299.9 Million
Approx. Number Employees: 2,223
Year Founded: 1884
Business Description:
Publisher of Newspapers
S.I.C.: 2711; 2721
N.A.I.C.S.: 511110; 511120
Media: 3-6-8-9-10-13-18-19-20-21-22-23-24-26
Distr.: Reg.
Budget Set: Sept.
Personnel:
Paul C. Tash *(Chm, Pres & CEO)*
Jana L. Jones *(CFO & VP)*
Janet H. Woods *(CIO)*
Neil Brown *(Editor & VP)*
Martin A. Dyckman *(Editor-in-Chief)*
Joseph Childs *(Mng Editor-Tampa Bay)*
Keisha Clark *(Editor-Online News)*
Sebastian Dortch *(Editor-Metro)*
Philip L. Gailey *(Editor-Editorials)*
Jeanne Grinstead *(Deputy Mng Editor)*
Tim Nickens *(Editor-Editorials)*
Steve Spears *(Editor-Online Entertainment)*
Bill Stevens *(Editor-North Suncoast)*
Roger Fischer *(Dir-Online)*
Craig Holley *(Dir-Consumer Mktg)*
Nancy Waclawek *(Dir-Corp Giving)*
Brands & Products:
SPTIMES.COM
TAMPABAY.COM
WHEELFINDER.COM

STAGESTEP INC.
Ste 4 4701 Bath St
Philadelphia, PA 19137-2235
Tel.: (215) 636-9000
Fax: (267) 672-2912
Toll Free: (800) 523-0960
E-mail: stagestep@stagestep.com
Web Site: www.stagestep.com
E-Mail For Key Personnel:
President: randy@stagestep.com
Sales Range: $50-74.9 Million
Approx. Number Employees: 20
Year Founded: 1969
Business Description:
Specialty Flooring Products Dealer
S.I.C.: 5713
N.A.I.C.S.: 442210
Import Export
Media: 2-4-6-10-13-20-21
Distr.: Direct to Consumer; Intl.; Natl.
Budget Set: June
Personnel:
F. Randolph Swartz *(Pres)*
Sandi Brandon *(Controller)*
Sam Jamison *(Dir-Ops)*
Brands & Products:
THE COMPASS FLOORING SYSTEM
DANCESTEP
ENCORE
ENCORE ELITE
FOOTNOTES
PLYOROBICS
PROCLEAN
QUIETSTEP
QUIETSTEP & DANCESTEP
RAVE
RE-USE-IT
SLIP NOMOR
SLIP/NOMOR
SPRINGSTEP
STAGESTEP
SUPER BRAVO B
SUPER BRAVO CLASSIC
TIMESTEP
TIMESTEP T
WIPEOUT
WOODSTEP
WOODSTEP PLUS
WOODSTEP ULTRA
Advertising Agency:
GDG Consulting, Inc.
Cherry Hill Plaza Ste 500 1415 Rte 70 E

Key to Media (For complete agency information see *The Advertising Red Books-Agencies* edition):
1. Bus. Publs. 2. Cable T.V. 3. Catalogs & Directories. 4. Co-op Adv. 5. Consumer Mags. 6. D.M. to Bus. Estab.7. D.M. to Consumers
8. Daily Newsp. 9. Exhibits/Trade Shows 10. Foreign 11. Infomercial 12. Internet Adv.13. Multimedia 14. Network Radio
15. Network T.V. 16. Newsp. Distr. Mags. 17. Other 18. Outdoor (Posters, Transit) 19. Point of Purchase20. Premiums, Novelties
21. Product Samples 22. Special Events Mktg. 23. Spot Radio 24. Spot T.V. 25. Weekly Newsp. 26. Yellow Page Adv.

Stagestep Inc. — (Continued)

Cherry Hill, NJ 08034
Tel.: (856) 427-6144
Fax: (856) 427-6155

STANDARD EDUCATIONAL CORPORATION

900 N Shore Dr Ste 252
Lake Bluff, IL 60044
Mailing Address:
PO Box 68348
Portland, OR 97268
Tel.: (847) 283-0301
Fax: (847) 283-0295
E-mail: customerservice@standardeducational.com
Approx. Number Employees: 4
Year Founded: 1939
Business Description:
Publishing Company
S.I.C.: 2731; 7371
N.A.I.C.S.: 511130; 541511
Advertising Expenditures: $50,000
Media: 7
Personnel:
Cindy Giovenco *(Coord-Customer Svc)*
Brands & Products:
CHILD HORIZONS
WORLD PROGRESS QUARTERLY YEARBOOK

STANDARD PUBLISHING GROUP LLC

(Holding of The Wicks Group of Companies, LLC)
8805 Governor's Dr Ste 400
Cincinnati, OH 45249
Tel.: (513) 931-4050
Fax: (513) 931-0904
Toll Free: (800) 543-1353
Toll Free: (800) 543-1301
E-mail: customerservice@standardpub.com
Web Site: www.standardpub.com
Approx. Number Employees: 125
Year Founded: 1866
Business Description:
Publishes, Prints & Distributes Religious & Educational Materials
S.I.C.: 2731; 2721; 2732; 2741
N.A.I.C.S.: 511130; 323117; 511120; 511199
Import Export
Advertising Expenditures: $500,000
Media: 1-4-6-7-8-10-19-20-21
Distr.: Natl.
Budget Set: May
Personnel:
Jeff Ray *(VP-Sls & Mktg)*

THE STAR

(Unit of Freedom Newspapers, Inc.)
315 E Graham St
Shelby, NC 28151-5452
Mailing Address:
PO Box 48
Shelby, NC 28151-0048
Tel.: (704) 484-7000
Fax: (704) 484-0805
E-mail: shelby_star@link.freedom.com
Web Site: www.shelbystar.com
Approx. Number Employees: 60
Year Founded: 1884
Business Description:
Newspapers: Publishing Only Not Printed On Site
S.I.C.: 2711
N.A.I.C.S.: 511110
Media: 8-9
Personnel:
Skip Foster *(Publr)*
Jackie Bridges *(Editor-Lifestyles)*
Alan Ford *(Editor-Sports)*
Brent Powers *(Dir-Adv)*
Brands & Products:
NEWSPAPER

STAR COURIER

(Unit of GateHouse Media, Inc.)
105 E Central Blvd
Kewanee, IL 61443-2245
Tel.: (309) 852-2181
Fax: (309) 852-0010
Toll Free: (800) 397-7827
E-mail: info@starcourier.com
Web Site: www.starcourier.com
Sales Range: $10-24.9 Million
Approx. Number Employees: 26
Business Description:
Newspaper Publishing
S.I.C.: 2711
N.A.I.C.S.: 511110
Media: 8-9
Personnel:
Dee Evans *(Publr)*
Brands & Products:
STAR COURIER

STAR MAGAZINE

(Div. of American Media, Inc.)
1 Park Ave
New York, NY 10016
Tel.: (212) 545-4800
Fax: (212) 448-9509
E-mail: webmaster@starmagazine.com
Web Site: www.starmagazine.com
Year Founded: 1973
Business Description:
Magazine Publishing
S.I.C.: 2721
N.A.I.C.S.: 511120
Media: 6-13-15-18
Personnel:
David Pecker *(Pres & CEO)*
Bobbie Halfin *(VP & Dir-Interactive Ops)*
David Perel *(Editor-in-Chief)*
Cheryl Kramer *(Dir-Beauty & Fashion)*
Marc Richards *(Dir-Adv)*
Brands & Products:
STAR MAGAZINE

THE STAR TRIBUNE COMPANY

(Holding of Avista Capital Holdings, LP)
(Filed for Chapter 11 Bankruptcy 1/15/09)
425 Portland Ave
Minneapolis, MN 55488
Tel.: (612) 673-4000
Fax: (612) 673-4359
Toll Free: (800) 829-8742
E-mail: opinion@startribune.com
Web Site: www.startribune.com
E-Mail For Key Personnel:
Marketing Director: btaylor@startribune.com
Sales Range: $350-399.9 Million
Approx. Number Employees: 1,400
Year Founded: 1867
Business Description:
Publisher of Daily Newspapers
S.I.C.: 2711
N.A.I.C.S.: 511110
Advertising Expenditures: $900,000
Media: 2-3-6-7-8-9-13-18-19-20-22-23-24
Distr.: Direct to Consumer; Reg.
Personnel:
Nancy Barnes *(Sr VP & Editor)*
Anders Gyllenhaal *(Sr VP & Editor)*
Steve Alexander *(Sr VP-Circulation)*
Patricia Jones *(Sr VP-Legal & HR)*
Helen Wainwright *(Sr VP-HR & Labor Rel)*
Charles Hoag *(VP & Dir-Sls)*
Paul Kasbohm *(VP-Sls)*
Benjamin Taylor *(VP-Sls & Dev)*
Kristie Alberty *(Dir-Post Press Ops)*
Tracy Sinopoli *(Dir-Direct Mktg)*
Melissa Watson *(Product Mgr-Digital Project)*
Patrick Soli *(Mgr-Reg Sls)*
Brands & Products:
THE STAR TRIBUNE

STARLOG GROUP, INC.

475 Park Ave S
New York, NY 10016-6901
Tel.: (212) 689-2830
Fax: (212) 889-7933
E-mail: rita@starloggroup.com
Web Site: www.fangoria.com
Approx. Number Employees: 11
Year Founded: 1975
Business Description:
Publisher of Science Fiction, Horror & Other Fan Magazines
S.I.C.: 2721; 5942
N.A.I.C.S.: 511120; 451211
Media: 6-8-10-13-18-19-20-21-22
Brands & Products:
FANGORIA
STARLOG

THE STARPHOENIX

(Unit of Postmedia Network Inc.)
204 Fifth Ave N
Saskatoon, SK S7K 2P1, Canada
Tel.: (306) 657-6231
Fax: (306) 657-6437
E-mail: spnews@sp.canwest.com
Web Site: www.thestarphoenix.com
Approx. Number Employees: 250
Business Description:
Newspapers Publisher
S.I.C.: 2711
N.A.I.C.S.: 511110
Media: 8-9
Personnel:
Shannon Simpson *(Dir-Adv)*
Wendy Davies *(Mgr-Classified)*
Craig Peterson *(Mgr-Promos)*

STAT RESOURCE GROUP, INC.

(d/b/a Statlistics)
69 Kenosia Ave
Danbury, CT 06810
Tel.: (203) 778-8700
Fax: (203) 778-4839
E-mail: info@statlistics.com
Web Site: www.statlistics.com
Approx. Number Employees: 35
Year Founded: 1983
Business Description:
List Management & List Brokerage Services
S.I.C.: 7331
N.A.I.C.S.: 541860
Media: 2
Personnel:
John Papalia *(Pres & CEO)*
Donna Buckner *(CFO & COO)*
Brian Manning *(VP-Sls)*
Isabel Arvoy *(Sr Mgr-Accts)*
Mary Bleil *(Mgr-Accts)*
Turker Hassan *(Mgr-Interactive Dept-Email List Mgmt Turker Hassan)*
Barbara McGuire *(Mgr-Mktg)*
Nancy Spielmann *(Sr Acct Exec-Consumer)*

THE STATE JOURNAL-REGISTER

(Unit of GateHouse Media, Inc.)
1 Copley Plz
Springfield, IL 62701-1927
Tel.: (217) 788-1300
Fax: (217) 788-1551
Web Site: www.sj-r.com
Sales Range: $50-74.9 Million
Approx. Number Employees: 400
Business Description:
Publishing & Editing Newspapers
S.I.C.: 2711; 2791
N.A.I.C.S.: 511110; 323122
Media: 8
Personnel:
Gary Schieffer *(Editor-Metro)*
Shan Bailey *(Mgr)*
Connie Runkel *(Mgr-Credit)*
Robert Titone *(Mgr)*
Brands & Products:
STATE JOURNAL REGISTER

STENHOUSE PUBLISHERS

(Sub. of Highlights for Children, Inc.)
Fl 2 480 Congress St PO Box 11020
Portland, ME 04101-3400
Tel.: (207) 253-1600
Fax: (207) 253-5121
Fax: (207) 253-5773
Fax: (800) 833-9164
Toll Free: (800) 988-9812
E-mail: cusomerservice@stenhouse.com
Web Site: www.stenhouse.com
Approx. Number Employees: 15
Year Founded: 1993
Business Description:
Text Books & Materials
S.I.C.: 2731
N.A.I.C.S.: 511130
Media: 4-8-10-13
Personnel:
Dan Tobin *(Gen Mgr)*
William Varner *(Editor)*
Philippa Stratton *(Dir-Editorial)*
Elaine Cyr *(Mgr-Ops & Customer Svc)*
Chuck Lerch *(Mgr-Mktg)*

STERLING PUBLISHING CO., INC.

(Sub. of Barnes & Noble, Inc.)
387 Park Ave S
New York, NY 10016-8810
Tel.: (212) 532-7160
Fax: (212) 213-2495
Toll Free: (800) 367-9692
E-mail: info@sterlingpublishing.com
Web Site: www.sterlingpub.com
Sales Range: $25-49.9 Million
Approx. Number Employees: 100
Year Founded: 1949
Business Description:
Non-Fiction Books Publishers & Distr
S.I.C.: 2731; 5192
N.A.I.C.S.: 511130; 424920

Key to Media (For complete agency information see *The Advertising Red Books-Agencies* edition):
1. Bus. Publs. 2. Cable T.V. 3. Catalogs & Directories. 4. Co-op Adv. 5. Consumer Mags. 6. D.M. to Bus. Estab.7. D.M. to Consumers 8. Daily Newsp. 9. Exhibits/Trade Shows 10. Foreign 11. Infomercial 12. Internet Adv.13. Multimedia 14. Network Radio 15. Network T.V. 16. Newsp. Distr. Mags. 17. Other 18. Outdoor (Posters, Transit) 19. Point of Purchase20. Premiums, Novelties 21. Product Samples 22. Special Events Mktg. 23. Spot Radio 24. Spot T.V. 25. Weekly Newsp. 26. Yellow Page Adv.

Advertising Expenditures: $1,000,000
Media: 2-4-5-6-7-8-9-18-19-21
Distr.: Intl.; Natl.
Budget Set: June -July
Personnel:
Marcus Leaver *(Pres)*
Harold Lee *(VP-Fin)*
Rick Willet *(VP-Production)*
Leigh Ann Ambrosi *(Dir-Publicity)*
Judi Powers *(Dir-Mktg & Publicity-Sterling Children's Books)*
Christopher Vaccari *(Dir-Library Mktg)*

STRANG COMMUNICATIONS COMPANY
600 Rinehart Rd
Lake Mary, FL 32746-4898
Tel.: (407) 333-0600
Fax: (407) 333-7100
E-mail: webmaster@strang.com
Web Site: www.strang.com
E-Mail For Key Personnel:
President: sstrang@strang.com
Approx. Sls.: $6,000,000
Approx. Number Employees: 150
Year Founded: 1975
Business Description:
Religious Services & Publisher of Religious Materials
S.I.C.: 2721; 2731
N.A.I.C.S.: 511120; 511130
Advertising Expenditures: $250,000
Media: 2-6-8-10-13-23
Distr.: Natl.
Budget Set: June
Personnel:
Joy F. Strang *(Co-Owner & CFO)*
Stephen E. Strang *(Owner)*
David Condiff *(Publr)*
Tessie Devore *(Exec VP)*
Wendy Leech *(VP-Production & Design-Magazines)*
Lee Grady *(Editor)*
Brands & Products:
CHARISMA
CHARISMA & CHRISTIAN LIFE
CHRISTIAN LIFE
CHRISTIAN RETAILING
THE CHURCH BOOKSTORE
CREATION HOUSE
EXCEL
FRONTLINE
INSPIRATIONAL GIFT TRENDS
MINISTRIES TODAY
NEW MAN
REALMS
SILOAM
SPIRITLED WOMAN
STRANG
VIDA CRISTIANA

STREAMING MEDIA, INC.
(Sub. of Information Today Inc.)
88 Danbury Rd Ste 1D
Wilton, CT 06897
Tel.: (203) 761-1466
Fax: (203) 761-1444
Web Site: www.streamingmedia.com
Business Description:
Media Services
S.I.C.: 7375
N.A.I.C.S.: 518111
Media: 2-10-13
Personnel:
Dan Rayburn *(Exec VP)*
Advertising Agencies:
Schwartz Public Relations Associates, Inc.
444 Park Ave S 12th Fl
New York, NY 10016-7321
Tel.: (212) 677-8700
Fax: (212) 254-2507

Tyson Associates, Inc.
246 Federal Rd Ste D23
Brookfield, CT 06804-2650
Tel.: (203) 775-9465
Fax: (203) 775-0563

STRUCTURAL GRAPHICS, LLC
38 Plains Rd
Essex, CT 06426
Tel.: (860) 767-2661
Fax: (860) 767-2451
Toll Free: (800) 207-6787
E-mail: info@structuralgraphics.com
Web Site: www.structuralgraphics.com
Approx. Sls.: $12,000,000
Approx. Number Employees: 80
Year Founded: 1985
Business Description:
Graphic Arts & Related Design Services
S.I.C.: 7336; 7311
N.A.I.C.S.: 541430; 541810
Media: 2-10
Personnel:
Mike Maguire *(CEO)*
Ethan Goller *(Pres)*
Julie A. Abraham *(CFO)*
Tom Saltonstall *(VP & Dir-Sls-Pharmaceutical)*
Paula Baylis *(VP-Production)*
Kevin Gilligan *(VP-Mktg)*
Erik Hluchan *(Dir-Creative)*
Heather Ertel Mucha *(Dir-Strategy)*
Brands & Products:
4-WINDOW PULL
BOOK-CUBE
THE EXTENDO
FLAPPER
THE FLAPPER
GAME ON
MAGNAPOP
STRUCTURAL GRAPHICS

STYLE WEEKLY INC.
(Sub. of Landmark Media Enterprises LLC)
1313 E Main St Ste 103
Richmond, VA 23219
Tel.: (804) 358-0825
Fax: (804) 358-1079
Fax: (804) 355-9089
E-mail: allstyle@styleweekly.com
Web Site: www.styleweekly.com
Approx. Rev.: $1,700,000
Approx. Number Employees: 35
Year Founded: 1984
Business Description:
Newspaper Publishing
S.I.C.: 2711
N.A.I.C.S.: 511110
Media: 6-8
Personnel:
Lori Waran *(Publr)*
Brent Baldwin *(Editor & Creatvie Dir)*
Scott Bass *(Editor)*
Mike Hilleary *(Editor)*
Gordon Poindexter *(Editor)*
Jason Roop *(Editor)*
Deveron Timberlake *(Editor-Food & Drink)*
Tonie Stevens *(Dir-Display Adv)*
Martha Anderson *(Mgr-Distr)*
Hannah Huber *(Mgr-Non-Traditional Revenue)*
Dana Tavel *(Mgr-Recruitment Adv)*
Jennifer Waldbauer *(Asst Mgr-Sls)*
Brands & Products:
STYLE WEEKLY

SUCCESSORIES, INC.
(Holding of TWS Partnership LLC)
1040 Holland Dr
Boca Raton, FL 33487
Tel.: (561) 962-3507
Fax: (561) 998-7716
Toll Free: (800) 535-2773
Web Site: www.successories.com
Year Founded: 1985
Business Description:
Inspirational Calendars, Posters & Accessories Mfr
S.I.C.: 2752; 5199
N.A.I.C.S.: 323110; 424990
Media: 2-4-7-10-13-17
Distr.: Natl.

THE SUDBURY STAR
(Div. of Osprey Media Group, Inc.)
33 MacKenzie St
Sudbury, ON P3C 4Y1, Canada
Tel.: (705) 674-5271
Fax: (705) 674-0624
E-mail: editorial@thesudburystar.com
Web Site: www.thesudburystar.com
Approx. Number Employees: 50
Business Description:
Daily Newspaper
S.I.C.: 2711
N.A.I.C.S.: 511110
Media: 13-25
Personnel:
David Kilgour *(Publr)*
Ray Lavigne *(Dir-Adv)*

SUMNER COMMUNICATIONS INC.
24 Stony Hill Rd
Bethel, CT 06801
Tel.: (203) 748-2050
Fax: (203) 748-5932
Toll Free: (800) 999-8281
Web Site: www.sumnercom.com
Sales Range: $10-24.9 Million
Approx. Number Employees: 30
Business Description:
Publisher of Trade Magazine & Directories
S.I.C.: 2721; 2741; 7389
N.A.I.C.S.: 511120; 511140; 516110; 519190
Advertising Expenditures: $1,200,000
Media: 2-4-7-10-13
Personnel:
E. Scott Sumner *(CEO)*
Ronald A. Fisher *(Publr)*
Amber Lautier *(Dir-Adv)*
Brands & Products:
CLOSEOUTCENTRAL.COM
COVER MAGAZINE
COVERMAG.COM
DIRECTORY OF DOLLARS & C-STORE DIRECTORY
DIRECTORY OF WHOLESALERS, IMPORTERS & LIQUIDATORS
EAST COAST MERCHANDISER
GUIDE TO ACTIVE FLEAMARKETS & SWAP MEETS
MERCHANDISERGROU.COM
MIDWEST MERCHANDISER
SUMNERCOM.COM
SUMNERHOST.COM
TRADE SHOWS USA DIRECTORY
WEB WHOLESALER MAGAZINE
WEBWHOLESALERMAGAZINE.COM
WESTERN MERCHANDISER
WHOLESALECENTRAL.COM

THE SUN
(Unit of Freedom Newspapers, Inc.)
2055 Arizona Ave
Yuma, AZ 85364-6549
Mailing Address:
PO Box 271
Yuma, AZ 85366-0271
Tel.: (949) 253-2300
Fax: (928) 329-2753
E-mail: newsroom@yumasun.com
Web Site: www.yumasun.com
Approx. Number Employees: 150
Year Founded: 1876
Business Description:
Newspaper Publishing
S.I.C.: 2711
N.A.I.C.S.: 511110
Media: 8-9
Personnel:
Patrick Norris *(Controller)*
Randy Hoeft *(Editor-Specialized Content)*
Duvi Rodriguez *(Editor-Content)*
Doug Flynn *(Dir-Interactive)*
David Fornof *(Dir-Production)*
Lisa Miller *(Dir-Adv)*
Bob Roeser *(Dir-Circulation)*
Terry Ross *(Dir-NIC)*
Adrianne Wagner *(Dir-Mktg)*
Justin Cook *(Mgr-HR)*
John Courtis *(Mgr-Adv)*

THE SUN
(Unit of California Newspapers Partnership)
(d/b/a San Bernadino Sun)
4030 N Georgia Blvd
San Bernardino, CA 92407
Tel.: (909) 889-9666
Fax: (909) 885-8159
Web Site: www.sbsun.com
Approx. Number Employees: 500
Year Founded: 1894
Business Description:
Newspaper Publishing
S.I.C.: 2711
N.A.I.C.S.: 511110
Media: 8-9-13
Personnel:
Steve Lambert *(Owner)*
Nancy White *(Pres)*
Bob Balzer *(CEO & Publr)*
John Hoeft *(VP-Interactive)*
Frank Pine *(Gen Mgr & Editor)*
Louis Amestoy *(Asst Mng Editor)*
Jim Steinberg *(Editor-Health)*
Mirjam Swanson *(Editor-Sports)*
John Weeks *(Editor-Features)*
Gene Pearlman *(Dir-Adv)*
Joseph Tripp *(Dir-Online Adv)*
Jay Tuten *(Dir-Online Content)*
Norma Sapp *(Sls Mgr-Voice)*
Craig Bringhurst *(Adv Mgr)*
Ian Cooke *(Mgr-Classified Sales)*
Sandra Gray *(Mgr-Retail Sls)*
Brands & Products:
THE SUN NEWSPAPER

SUN JOURNAL
(Unit of Freedom Newspapers, Inc.)
3200 Wellon Blvd

Key to Media (For complete agency information see *The Advertising Red Books-Agencies* edition):
1. Bus. Publs. 2. Cable T.V. 3. Catalogs & Directories. 4. Co-op Adv. 5. Consumer Mags. 6. D.M. to Bus. Estab.7. D.M. to Consumers
8. Daily Newsp. 9. Exhibits/Trade Shows 10. Foreign 11. Infomercial 12. Internet Adv.13. Multimedia 14. Network Radio
15. Network T.V. 16. Newsp. Distr. Mags. 17. Other 18. Outdoor (Posters, Transit) 19. Point of Purchase20. Premiums, Novelties
21. Product Samples 22. Special Events Mktg. 23. Spot Radio 24. Spot T.V. 25. Weekly Newsp. 26. Yellow Page Adv.

Sun Journal — (Continued)

New Bern, NC 28562-5234
Mailing Address:
PO Box 1149
New Bern, NC 28563-1149
Tel.: (252) 638-8101
Fax: (252) 638-4664
E-mail: sunjournal@freedomenc.com
Web Site: www.newbernsj.com
Approx. Number Employees: 85
Year Founded: 1914
Business Description:
Newspapers Publishing & Printing
S.I.C.: 2711
N.A.I.C.S.: 511110
Advertising Expenditures: $150,000
Media: 8-9-10-18-21-22-23-24
Personnel:
Veron D. Bolt *(Pres)*
Judy Avery *(Gen Mgr & VP-Mktg)*
Scott Embry *(Dir-Adv)*
Sheila Meadows *(Dir-Circulation)*
Mike Credle *(Mgr-Creative Svcs)*

THE SUN TIMES
(Div. of Osprey Media Group, Inc.)
290 9th St E
Owen Sound, ON N4K 5P2, Canada
Mailing Address:
P.O. Box 200
Owen Sound, ON N4K 5P2, Canada
Tel.: (519) 376-2250
Fax: (519) 372-1861
E-mail: adds@suntimes.ca
Web Site:
www.owensoundsuntimes.com
Approx. Number Employees: 65
Year Founded: 1853
Business Description:
Daily Newspaper
S.I.C.: 2711
N.A.I.C.S.: 511110
Media: 8-9
Personnel:
Cheryl A. McMenemy *(Publr)*
Michael Dentand *(Mng Editor)*
Louise Kazarian *(Mgr-Adv)*

SUN-TIMES MEDIA GROUP, INC.
(Filed for Ch. 11 Bankruptcy on 3/31/09)
350 N Orleans St 10-S
Chicago, IL 60654
Tel.: (312) 321-2299
Web Site: www.suntimes.com
Sales Range: $300-349.9 Million
Approx. Number Employees: 2,169
Year Founded: 1990
Business Description:
Publishing, Printing & Distribution of Newspapers
S.I.C.: 2741; 2711
N.A.I.C.S.: 516110; 511110
Advertising Expenditures:
$287,198,000
Personnel:
Jeremy L. Halbreich *(Chm & Interim CEO)*
Rick Surkamer *(Pres & COO)*
Brian Linscott *(CFO & Sr VP-Fin)*
James R. McDonough *(Chief Admin Officer, Gen Counsel, Sec & Sr VP)*
Barbara Swanson *(Sr VP-Adv & Mktg)*
Matthew A. Saleski *(VP-Mktg)*
Tony Triner *(VP-Production)*

SUNSET PUBLISHING CORPORATION
(Sub. of Time Inc.)
80 Willow Rd
Menlo Park, CA 94025-3661
Tel.: (650) 321-3600
Fax: (650) 327-7537
E-mail: corporate@sunset.com
Web Site: www.sunset.com
E-Mail For Key Personnel:
President: lynchk@sunset.com
Marketing Director: whiteleyb@sunset.com
Sales Range: $75-99.9 Million
Approx. Number Employees: 80
Year Founded: 1898
Business Description:
Publisher of Magazines & Books
S.I.C.: 2721; 2731
N.A.I.C.S.: 511120; 511130
Media: 2-6-7-8-9-10-13-22-23
Distr.: Intl.; Natl.
Budget Set: Sept.
Personnel:
Katie Tamony *(VP & Editor-in-Chief)*
Brands & Products:
SUNSET

SUPERIOR PUBLISHING, INC.
(Sub. of American Consolidated Media LP)
1105 Tower Ave
Superior, WI 54880
Tel.: (715) 395-5725
Approx. Number Employees: 585
Year Founded: 1996
Business Description:
Newspaper Publishing & Printing Services
S.I.C.: 2711
N.A.I.C.S.: 511110
Import Export
Media: 8-9

SUPERMARKET NEWS
(Joint Venture of MidOcean Partners, LLP & Wasserstein & Co., LP)
249 W 17th St
New York, NY 10011
Tel.: (212) 204-4359
Fax: (913) 514-9136
Web Site:
www.supermarketnews.com
Approx. Number Employees: 20
Business Description:
Trade & Newspaper Publications
S.I.C.: 2721
N.A.I.C.S.: 511120
Media: 7-10-22
Personnel:
Jerry Rymont *(Publr)*
David Bagan *(Sr VP-Adv)*
David Merrefield *(VP & Dir-Editorial)*
David Orgel *(Editor-in-Chief)*
Michael Garry *(Editor-Tech)*
Mark Hamstra *(Editor-Retail & Fin)*
Jon Springer *(Editor)*
Bob Vosburgh *(Editor)*
Bill Dooley *(Adv Dir)*

SUPERMEDIA INC.
2200 W Airfield Dr PO Box 619810
Dallas, TX 75261
Tel.: (972) 453-7000
Fax: (972) 453-3969
Toll Free: (800) 555-4833
Web Site: www.supermedia.com
Approx. Rev.: $1,176,000,000
Approx. Number Employees: 4,400
Year Founded: 2006
Business Description:
Domestic Print & Internet Yellow Page Directories; Website Development Services
S.I.C.: 2741
N.A.I.C.S.: 511140; 516110
Advertising Expenditures:
$23,000,000
Personnel:
Douglas D. Wheat *(Chm)*
Peter J. McDonald *(Pres & CEO)*
Samuel D. Jones *(CFO, Treas & Exec VP)*
Matthew J. Stover *(CMO & Exec VP)*
Briggs Ferguson *(Pres-Internet)*
Cody Wilbanks *(Gen Counsel, Sec & Exec VP)*
Frank Gatto *(Exec VP-Ops)*
Georgia Scaife *(Exec VP-HR & Employee Admin)*
Robyn Rose *(VP-Product Mktg)*
Shayne Bryant *(Mgr)*
Andy Shane *(Mgr-External Comm)*
Brands & Products:
FAIR POINT YELLOW PAGES
FAIR POINT YELLOW PAGES COMPANION DIRECTORIES
IDEARC
IDEARC MEDIA
LOCALSEARCH.COM
SOLUTIONS DIRECT
SOLUTIONS DIRECT EXCLUSIVE MAILER
SOLUTIONS ON THE MOVE
SUPERGUARANTEE
SUPERPAGES
SUPERPAGES MOBILE
SUPERPAGES.COM
SWITCHBOARD
SWITCHBOARD.COM
VERIZON
VERIZON WHITE PAGES
VERIZON YELLOW PAGES
VERIZON YELLOW PAGES COMPANION DIRECTORIES
Advertising Agency:
TM Advertising
1717 Main St Ste 2000
Dallas, TX 75201
Tel.: (972) 556-1100
Fax: (972) 830-2619

SURVEY SAMPLING INTERNATIONAL LLC
6 Research Dr
Shelton, CT 06484
Tel.: (203) 567-7200
Fax: (203) 257-7367
E-mail: info@surveysampling.com
Web Site: www.surveysampling.com
Approx. Number Employees: 150
Year Founded: 1977
Business Description:
Supplier of Market Research Samples
S.I.C.: 8732
N.A.I.C.S.: 541910
Import Export
Advertising Expenditures: $100,000
Media: 2-10-13
Distr.: Bus.-to-Bus; Intl.
Personnel:
Dennis J Beckingham *(Pres & CFO)*
Kees de Jong *(CEO)*
Mark Hardy *(Mng Dir & Chief Strategy Officer)*
Christopher DeAngelis *(VP-Sls)*
Craig Lansley *(Dir-Client Svcs)*
Michelle Mosher *(Mgr-Offline Client Svc)*
Sandy Panza *(Mgr-Data Products Grp)*
Brands & Products:
CHOOZZ
OPINIONWORLD
RESPONDENT PRESERVATION INITIATIVE
SSI COMPASS
SSI-LITE
SSI-SNAP
SSI VERIFY
SUPERIOR DATA WRAPPED IN AN ENGAGING EXPERIENCE
SURVEY SAMPLING INTERNATIONAL
SURVEYSPOT

SWIFT NEWSPAPERS, INC.
500 Double Eagle Court
Reno, NV 89521
Tel.: (775) 850-7676
Fax: (775) 850-7677
E-mail: dns@swiftnews.com
Web Site: www.swiftcom.com
Approx. Number Employees: 20
Business Description:
Newspaper Publisher
S.I.C.: 2711
N.A.I.C.S.: 511110
Media: 8-9
Personnel:
Arne Hoel *(Chm)*

SYRACUSE UNIVERSITY PRESS
621 Skytop Rd Ste 110
Syracuse, NY 13244-5290
Tel.: (315) 443-5535
Fax: (315) 443-5545
Toll Free: (800) 365-8929
E-mail: supress@syr.edu
Web Site:
www.syracuseuniversitypress.syr.edu
E-Mail For Key Personnel:
Marketing Director: talitz@syr.edu
Sales Range: $10-24.9 Million
Approx. Number Employees: 14
Year Founded: 1943
Business Description:
Scholarly & Regional Books Retailer
S.I.C.: 2731; 5942
N.A.I.C.S.: 511130; 451211
Import Export
Media: 2-4-7-8-10-13-18-22
Distr.: Intl.; Natl.
Budget Set: June -Dec.
Brands & Products:
SYRACUSE UNIVERSITY PRESS

SYS-CON MEDIA, INC.
577 Chestnut Ridge Rd
Woodcliff Lake, NJ 07677
Tel.: (201) 802-3000
Fax: (201) 782-9601
Toll Free: (888) 303-5282
E-mail: info@sys-con.com
Web Site: www.sys-con.com
Approx. Number Employees: 10
Year Founded: 1994
Business Description:
IT Magazines Publisher; Trade Shows Producer

Key to Media (For complete agency information see *The Advertising Red Books-Agencies* edition):
1. Bus. Publs. 2. Cable T.V. 3. Catalogs & Directories. 4. Co-op Adv. 5. Consumer Mags. 6. D.M. to Bus. Estab.7. D.M. to Consumers 8. Daily Newsp. 9. Exhibits/Trade Shows 10. Foreign 11. Infomercial 12. Internet Adv.13. Multimedia 14. Network Radio 15. Network T.V. 16. Newsp. Distr. Mags. 17. Other 18. Outdoor (Posters, Transit) 19. Point of Purchase20. Premiums, Novelties 21. Product Samples 22. Special Events Mktg. 23. Spot Radio 24. Spot T.V. 25. Weekly Newsp. 26. Yellow Page Adv.

S.I.C.: 2721; 8243
N.A.I.C.S.: 511120; 611420
Media: 2-8-10
Personnel:
Fuat Kircaali *(Founder & CEO)*
Carmen Gonzalez *(Sr VP-Sls & Mktg)*

TAMPA BAY BUSINESS JOURNAL

(Unit of American City Business Journals, Inc.)
4350 W Cypress St Ste 800
Tampa, FL 33607-4176
Tel.: (813) 873-8225
Fax: (813) 876-1827
E-mail: tampabay@bizjournals.com
Web Site: www.tampabay.bizjournals.com
Approx. Number Employees: 33
Business Description:
Local Business Weekly Publisher
S.I.C.: 2711
N.A.I.C.S.: 511110
Media: 6
Personnel:
Angie Joseph *(Dir-Mktg & Circulation)*
Brands & Products:
TAMPA BAY BUSINESS JOURNAL

TAMPA BAY ILLUSTRATED

(Sub. of Palm Beach Media Group Inc.)
5110 Isnehover Blvd Ste 165
Tampa, FL 33634
Tel.: (727) 456-0400
Fax: (727) 456-0401
Web Site: www.tampabayillustrated.com
Approx. Number Employees: 15
Business Description:
Magazine
S.I.C.: 3841
N.A.I.C.S.: 339112
Media: 8
Personnel:
Ronald J. Woods *(Publr)*
Elizabeth Harrell *(Dir-Art)*
Allison Reckson *(Dir-Mktg)*
Sonya Cashner Meurer *(Dir-Fashion)*
Carolyn Ferris *(Dir-Art)*
Katherine Lande *(Dir-Adv)*

TAMPA BAY MAGAZINE

(Div. of Tampa Bay Publications, Inc.)
2531 Landmark Dr Ste 101
Clearwater, FL 33761
Tel.: (727) 791-4800
Fax: (727) 796-0527
Business Description:
Magazine
S.I.C.: 2721
N.A.I.C.S.: 511120
Media: 6-8
Personnel:
Margaret Word Burnside *(Co-Editor & Co-Publr)*
Martha Margolis *(Editor-Home & Garden)*
Tony Chaplinski, Jr. *(Exec Dir-Art & Mgr-Production)*
Lilo Barnes *(Dir-Mktg)*

TAMPA BAY NEWSPAPERS, INC.

9911 Seminole Blvd
Seminole, FL 33772
Tel.: (727) 397-5563
Fax: (727) 397-5900
E-mail: sales@tbnweekly.com
Web Site: www.tbnweekly.com
E-Mail For Key Personnel:
Sales Director: sales@tbnweekly.com
Approx. Number Employees: 30
Business Description:
Newspaper Publisher
S.I.C.: 2711
N.A.I.C.S.: 511110
Media: 8-9
Personnel:
Dan Autrey *(Pres & Publr)*
Suzette Porter *(Editor-Online & Mgr-Internet Svcs)*
Alexandra Caldwell *(Editor-Clearwater Beacon)*
David Brown *(Mgr-Production)*
Jay Rey *(Mgr-Adv Sls)*
Brands & Products:
BEACH BEACON
BELLEAIR BEE
CLEARWATER CITIZEN
ENTERTAINMENT EXTRA!
LARGO LEADER
SAFETY HARBOR JOURNAL
SEMINOLE BEACON
TBN WEEKLY ONLINE

TAMPA BAY PUBLICATIONS, INC.

2531 Landmark Dr
Clearwater, FL 33761
Tel.: (727) 791-4800
Fax: (727) 796-0527
E-mail: tbsub@tampabay.rr.com
Web Site: www.tampabaymagazine.com
Sales Range: $1-9.9 Million
Approx. Number Employees: 18
Business Description:
Magazine Publisher
S.I.C.: 2721
N.A.I.C.S.: 511120
Media: 6-7-8-10-13
Personnel:
Aaron R. Fodiman *(Pres & Publr)*
Margaret Word Burnside *(Editor)*
Brands & Products:
TAMPA BAY MAGAZINE

TAMPA MARKETING COMPANY

1906 N Armenia Ave Ste 1306
Tampa, FL 33607
Tel.: (813) 283-0760
E-mail: bill@southtampatoday.com
Web Site: www.southtampatoday.com
Approx. Number Employees: 10
Business Description:
Newspaper Publisher
S.I.C.: 2711
N.A.I.C.S.: 511110
Media: 9-25
Personnel:
Bill Sharp *(Pres)*

THE TAMPA TRIBUNE

(Unit of Media General, Inc.)
200 S Parker St
Tampa, FL 33606-2308
Mailing Address:
PO Box 191
Tampa, FL 33601-0191
Tel.: (813) 259-7711
Fax: (813) 259-7498
Web Site: www.tampatrib.com/
Sales Range: $400-449.9 Million
Approx. Number Employees: 1,500
Business Description:
Newspaper Publisher
S.I.C.: 2711
N.A.I.C.S.: 511110
Media: 2-3-7-8-9-13-14-15-18-21-22-23-24-25-26
Distr.: Reg.
Personnel:
Bob Geiger *(VP-Adv)*
Brands & Products:
THE TAMPA TRIBUNE

TAYLOR CORPORATION

1725 Roe Crest Dr
North Mankato, MN 56003
Mailing Address:
PO Box 3728
Mankato, MN 56002-3728
Tel.: (507) 625-2828
Fax: (507) 625-2988
Toll Free: (800) 545-6620
E-mail: communications@taylorcorp.com
Web Site: www.taylorcorp.com
Sales Range: $1-4.9 Billion
Approx. Number Employees: 12,500
Year Founded: 1948
Business Description:
Holding Company; Specialty Print, Media & Marketing Services
S.I.C.: 6719; 2677; 2752; 2754; 2759; 2771; 2789; 7331; 7336
N.A.I.C.S.: 323119; 322232; 323110; 323111; 323115; 323121; 511191; 541430; 541860; 551112
Import Export
Media: 4-8-13
Personnel:
Glen A. Taylor *(Chm & CEO)*
Thomas A. Johnson *(CFO & Treas)*
Jeff Eccles *(CIO)*
Gregory W. Jackson *(Chief Admin Officer, Gen Counsel & VP)*
Ron Hoffmeyer *(Exec VP)*
Steven Singer *(Exec VP)*
Colleen Whillhite *(Exec VP)*
Rick Barbieri *(Dir-Bus Dev-Amsterdam Printing Div)*

TECHNOLOGY MARKETING CORP.

(d/b/a TMCnet)
800 Connecticut Ave 1st Fl E
Norwalk, CT 06854
Tel.: (203) 852-6800
Fax: (203) 295-3773
E-mail: tmc@tmcnet.com
Web Site: www.tmcnet.com
Approx. Number Employees: 65
Year Founded: 1972
Business Description:
Periodical & Website Publisher
S.I.C.: 2721; 2741; 7389
N.A.I.C.S.: 511120; 516110; 561920
Media: 10-13
Personnel:
Nadji Tehrani *(Chm & CEO)*
Rich Tehrani *(Pres & Grp Editor-in-Chief)*
Frank Coppola *(Exec Dir-Confrence Sls)*
Karl Sundstrom *(Exec Dir-Bus Dev)*
Joe Fabiano *(Dir-Worldwide Events Accounts)*
Greg Galitzine *(Dir-Editorial)*
Shirley A. Russo *(Dir-Circulation)*
Jan Pierret *(Mgr-Mktg)*
Brands & Products:
ALTERNATIVE POWER
BIOMETRITECH
CUSTOMER INTER@CTION SOLUTIONS
INTERNET TELEPHONY
NGN
PLANET PDA
SIP MAGAZINE
SPEECH-WORLD
TMCNET.COM
VOIP DEVELOPER MAGAZINE
VOIPSWITCH
WIFI REVOLUTION
WIFI TELEPHONY MAGAZINE
WIMAX MAGAZINE

TEKNO BOOKS

(Sub. of Hollywood Media Corp.)
1524 University Ave Ste 305
Green Bay, WI 54302-1878
Tel.: (920) 437-6711
Fax: (920) 437-6721
E-mail: tekno@new.rr.com
Sales Range: $10-24.9 Million
Approx. Number Employees: 6
Year Founded: 1994
Business Description:
Books & Periodicals Publishing
S.I.C.: 2731
N.A.I.C.S.: 511130
Advertising Expenditures: $200,000
Media: 2-3-4-6-14-15-16-19-20-21-22-23-24-25
Distr.: Direct to Consumer; Intl.; Natl.; Reg.
Personnel:
Martin H. Greenberg *(CEO)*
John Helfers *(Editor)*

THE TELEGRAM

(Div. of Transcontinental Media)
430 Topsail Road
PO Box 5970
Saint John's, NL A1C 5X7, Canada
Tel.: (709) 364-6300
Fax: (709) 364-6029
E-mail: telegram@thetelegram.com
Web Site: www.thetelegram.com
Approx. Number Employees: 220
Business Description:
Daily Newspaper
S.I.C.: 2711
N.A.I.C.S.: 511110
Media: 8-13-25
Personnel:
Charlie Stacy *(Publr)*
Paul Newhook *(Comptroller-Telegram)*
Kerry Hann *(Mng Editor)*
Keith Connolly *(Mgr-Adv)*

THE TELEGRAPH

(Unit of Freedom Newspapers, Inc.)
111 E Broadway
Alton, IL 62002
Tel.: (618) 463-2500
Fax: (618) 463-9829
E-mail: webmaster@thetelegraph.com
Web Site: www.thetelegraph.com
Approx. Number Employees: 100
Year Founded: 1836
Business Description:
Newspaper
S.I.C.: 2711
N.A.I.C.S.: 511110
Media: 8-9-13
Personnel:
Jim Shrader *(Publr)*

Key to Media (For complete agency information see *The Advertising Red Books-Agencies* edition):
1. Bus. Publs. 2. Cable T.V. 3. Catalogs & Directories. 4. Co-op Adv. 5. Consumer Mags. 6. D.M. to Bus. Estab.7. D.M. to Consumers
8. Daily Newsp. 9. Exhibits/Trade Shows 10. Foreign 11. Infomercial 12. Internet Adv.13. Multimedia 14. Network Radio
15. Network T.V. 16. Newsp. Distr. Mags. 17. Other 18. Outdoor (Posters, Transit) 19. Point of Purchase20. Premiums, Novelties
21. Product Samples 22. Special Events Mktg. 23. Spot Radio 24. Spot T.V. 25. Weekly Newsp. 26. Yellow Page Adv.

TENNIS MAGAZINE
(Sub. of Miller Sports Group)
79 Madison Ave 8th Fl
New York, NY 10016-7802
Tel.: (212) 636-2700
Fax: (212) 636-2720
E-mail: jwilliams@tennis.com
Web Site: www.tennis.com
Approx. Number Employees: 100
Business Description:
Sports Magazine
S.I.C.: 2721
N.A.I.C.S.: 511120
Media: 6-8
Personnel:
Dave Morgan *(Chm & Partner)*
Chris Evert *(Publr)*
Jeff Williams *(Publr)*
Deepak Sharma *(Dir-Digital Adv Sls)*
Lisa Buco *(Sr Mgr-Digital Mktg)*

TEXAS MONTHLY
(Sub. of Emmis Publishing, L.P.)
701 Brazos Ste 1600
Austin, TX 78701
Mailing Address:
PO Box 1569
Austin, TX 78767
Tel.: (512) 320-6900
Fax: (512) 476-9007
Web Site: www.texasmonthly.com
Sales Range: $25-49.9 Million
Approx. Number Employees: 117
Year Founded: 1973
Business Description:
Magazine Publisher
S.I.C.: 2721
N.A.I.C.S.: 511120
Media: 2-4-6-7-8-9-13-19-21-23-25
Distr.: Reg.
Budget Set: Nov. -Aug.
Personnel:
Elynn J. Russell *(Pres)*
David Barr Dunham *(Publr-Texas Monthly Dev)*
Amy Banner Saralegui *(Publr)*
Shelly Brown Broussard *(Sr VP & Controller)*
Cathy S. Casey *(VP-Editorial Licensing & Comm)*
Roy Leamon, III *(VP-Production & Tech)*
Lorelei Calvert *(Gen Mgr)*
S. C. Gwynne *(Exec Editor)*
Gary Cartwright *(Editor)*
Pamela Colloff *(Editor)*
Michael Hall *(Editor)*
Christopher Keyes *(Editor-Articles)*
Patricia Busa McConnico *(Editor)*
Brian D. Sweany *(Editor-Articles)*
Elda Arellano *(Dir-Bus Ops)*
Nancy Brown *(Dir-Sls-Texas)*
Libby Farris *(Dir-Creative Svcs)*
Jennifer R. Garcia *(Dir-Mktg Svcs)*
Charlie Llewellin *(Dir-Digital Dev)*
Sara McCabe *(Dir-Custom Publ)*
Leslie A. Shelton *(Dir-Accts-Natl)*
T.J. Tucker *(Dir-Creative)*
Stacey Van Landingham *(Sr Mgr-Production)*
Karen Burke *(Mgr-Sls Resource)*
Missy Colbert *(Sr Project Mgr)*
Marilyn Plummer *(Mgr-Adv Projects)*
Jason Swedberg *(Mgr-Adv Ops)*
Brands & Products:
TEXAS MONTHLY

TFP DATA SYSTEMS
(Affil. of Taylor Corporation)
3451 Jupiter Ct
Oxnard, CA 93030-8957
Mailing Address:
PO Box 9012
Oxnard, CA 93031-9012
Tel.: (805) 981-0992
Fax: (805) 981-7161
Toll Free: (800) 482-9367
E-mail: info@tfpdata.com
Web Site: www.tfpdata.com
Approx. Number Employees: 60
Year Founded: 1973
Business Description:
Business Forms Mfr
S.I.C.: 2761; 2759
N.A.I.C.S.: 323116; 323119
Import Export
Media: 2-4-6-7-10
Distr.: Natl.
Budget Set: Nov.
Personnel:
Rick Rodiff *(Pres & COO)*

THAYER PUBLISHING
(Sub. of Corporate Graphics International)
150 Kingswood Rd
Mankato, MN 56001
Tel.: (507) 388-8647
Toll Free: (800) 257-8276
Web Site: www.cordialgreetings.com
Approx. Rev.: $3,500,000
Approx. Number Employees: 50
Business Description:
Greeting Card & Calendar Publishers
S.I.C.: 2752; 2771
N.A.I.C.S.: 323110; 511191
Media: 4
Personnel:
Leslie Stoltenberg *(Pres)*

THEODORE PRESSER CO.
588 N Gulph Rd
King of Prussia, PA 19406
Tel.: (610) 592-1222
Fax: (610) 592-1229
E-mail: presser@presser.com
Web Site: www.presser.com
Approx. Number Employees: 50
Year Founded: 1883
Business Description:
Distr & Publisher of Printed Music
S.I.C.: 2741
N.A.I.C.S.: 512230
Import Export
Media: 4-6-7-8-10-26
Distr.: Direct To Business; Natl.
Budget Set: Mar.
Personnel:
Sonya Kim *(Pres & CEO)*
John Howell *(CFO)*
Dewight Munroe *(Dir-Mktg)*
Brands & Products:
THEODORE PRESSER CO

THOMAS NELSON INC.
(Holding of Kohlberg & Company, LLC)
501 Nelson Pl
Nashville, TN 37214
Mailing Address:
PO Box 141000
Nashville, TN 37214
Tel.: (615) 889-9000
Fax: (615) 391-5225
Toll Free: (800) 933-9673
E-mail: rights@thomasnelson.com
Web Site: www.thomasnelson.com
Approx. Rev.: $253,056,992
Approx. Number Employees: 650
Year Founded: 1798
Business Description:
Bible & Religious Book Publisher
S.I.C.: 2731
N.A.I.C.S.: 511130
Import Export
Media: 2-4-5-6-7-8-10-11-14-15-19-20-21-23-24-26
Distr.: Natl.
Budget Set: Apr. -Mar.
Personnel:
Michael S. Hyatt *(Chm)*
Mark Schoenwald *(Pres & CEO)*
Stuart Bitting *(CFO & Exec VP)*
Gary Davidson *(Sr VP & Publr-Bible Grp)*
Brian Hampton *(Publr & Sr VP)*
Joe L. Powers *(Exec VP)*
Rick Proctor *(VP-IT)*
David Schroeder *(Sr Dir-Mktg)*
Claudia Duncan *(Dir-Mktg-Spanish Div)*
Brands & Products:
CARIBE
CONTOURS
COOL SPRINGS PRESS
GRAPHOMANIA
GRUPO NELSON
INTEGRITY
J. COUNTRYMAN
MARKINGS
NATURAL ENCOUNTERS
NELSON
REGENCY ENTERTAINMENT
RUTLEDGE HILL PRESS
SPINECHILLERS
SPIRIT-FILLED LIFE
THOMAS NELSON BIBLE
THOMAS NELSON BOOKS
TOCCATA
TOMMY NELSON
W PUBLISHING GROUP
WESTBOW PRESS
WOMEN OF FAITH

THOMAS NELSON PUBLISHERS
(Sub. of Thomas Nelson Inc.)
PO Box 141000
Nashville, TN 37214-1000
Tel.: (615) 889-9000
Web Site: www.thomasnelson.com
E-Mail For Key Personnel:
Marketing Director: JLoper@wordpublishing.com
Year Founded: 1953
Business Description:
Religious Book Publisher
S.I.C.: 2731
N.A.I.C.S.: 511130
Import Export
Advertising Expenditures: $1,500,000
Media: 2-3-4-5-6-7-8-9-10-13-18-19-20-23-24-25
Distr.: Direct to Consumer; Natl.
Budget Set: Aug.
Personnel:
David L. Moberg *(Sr VP & Grp Publ-Non-Fiction Trade)*

THOMAS PUBLISHING COMPANY LLC
5 Penn Plz
New York, NY 10001-1810
Tel.: (212) 695-0500
Fax: (212) 290-7362
E-mail: contact@thomaspublishing.com
Web Site: www.thomaspublishing.com
Approx. Number Employees: 300
Year Founded: 1898
Business Description:
Trade Reference Sources
S.I.C.: 2741; 2721
N.A.I.C.S.: 511140; 511120
Export
Media: 7-10-13
Personnel:
Jose E. Andrade *(Chm)*
Carl T. Holst-Knudsen *(Pres)*
Ivy Molofsky *(VP-HR)*
Linda Rigano *(Exec Dir-Strategic Svcs)*

THOMAS REGISTER OF AMERICAN MANUFACTURERS
(Div. of Thomas Publishing Company LLC)
5 Penn Plz
New York, NY 10001-1810
Tel.: (212) 695-0500
Fax: (212) 695-0500
E-mail: info@thomasnet.com
Web Site: www.thomasnet.com
Approx. Number Employees: 400
Year Founded: 1905
Business Description:
Thomas Register Publishing
S.I.C.: 8732
N.A.I.C.S.: 541910
Advertising Expenditures: $1,000,000
Media: 7-10-20
Budget Set: Aug. -Sept.
Personnel:
Jose E. Andrade *(Chm)*
Carl T. Holst-Knudsen *(Pres)*
Edmond V. Dillon *(VP Mktg)*
Ivy Molofsky *(VP-HR)*
Jana Tarzia *(Exec Dir-Mktg)*
Rita Lieberman *(Dir-Mktg Comm)*
Brands & Products:
CAD BLOCKS
INDUSTRY. ANSWERS. RESULTS.
PARTSPEC
PLANTSPEC
THOMAS REGISTER
THOMAS REGISTER. COM
THOMAS REGISTER ORDER ON LINE
THOMASSPEC

THOMSON HEALTHCARE
(Unit of Thomson Reuters - Corporate Headquarters)
777 E Eisenhower Pkwy
Ann Arbor, MI 48108
Tel.: (734) 913-3000
Web Site: home.thomsonhealthcare.com
Approx. Rev.: $452,000,000
Approx. Number Employees: 2,600
Business Description:
Healthcare Database, Analysis & Research Services
S.I.C.: 2741; 7389; 8733
N.A.I.C.S.: 511140; 516110; 519190; 541710
Media: 1-2-4-7-10-13-20-22
Distr.: Natl.
Budget Set: Oct.
Brands & Products:
AMERICAN HEALTH CONSULTANTS
BUSINESS AND HEALTH

Key to Media (For complete agency information see *The Advertising Red Books-Agencies* edition):
1. Bus. Publs. 2. Cable T.V. 3. Catalogs & Directories. 4. Co-op Adv. 5. Consumer Mags. 6. D.M. to Bus. Estab.7. D.M. to Consumers
8. Daily Newsp. 9. Exhibits/Trade Shows 10. Foreign 11. Infomercial 12. Internet Adv.13. Multimedia 14. Network Radio
15. Network T.V. 16. Newsp. Distr. Mags. 17. Other 18. Outdoor (Posters, Transit) 19. Point of Purchase20. Premiums, Novelties
21. Product Samples 22. Special Events Mktg. 23. Spot Radio 24. Spot T.V. 25. Weekly Newsp. 26. Yellow Page Adv.

CONTEMPORARY OB/GYN
CONTEMPORARY PEDIATRICS
CONTEMPORARY UROLOGY
DRUG TOPICS
DRUG TOPICS RED BOOK
HOSPITAL PHARMACIST REPORT
JAAPA
MEDEC DENTAL COMMUNICATIONS
MEDICAL ECONOMICS
MEDICAL ECONOMICS-OBGYN EDITION
MEDICAL ECONOMICS-PEDIATRICS EDITION
MICROMEDEX
PATIENT CARE
PATIENT CARE FOR THE NURSE PRACTITIONER
PDR
PHYSICIANS' DESK REF. FOR NON-PRESCRIPTION DRUGS
PHYSICIANS' DESK REFERENCE
PHYSICIANS' DESK REFERENCE FOR HERBAL MEDICINES
PHYSICIANS' DESK REFERENCE FOR OPTHALMOLOGY
THE RESEARCH GROUP
RN CAREER SEARCH
RN MAGAZINE
VETERINARY HEALTHCARE COMMUNICATIONS

THOMSON REUTERS CORPORATION

(Holding of The Woodbridge Company Limited)
Toronto Dominion Bank Tower 66 Wellington Street West
PO Box 24
Toronto, ON M5K 1A1, Canada
Tel.: (416) 360-8700
E-mail: general.info@thomsonreuters.com
Web Site: www.thomsonreuters.com
Approx. Rev.: $13,070,000,000
Approx. Number Employees: 57,900
Year Founded: 2008
Business Description:
Holding Company; Financial, Legal, Tax, Accounting, Scientific & Healthcare News & Information Publisher
S.I.C.: 6719; 2721; 2731; 2741; 7372; 7383; 7389
N.A.I.C.S.: 551112; 511120; 511130; 511140; 511210; 519110; 519130; 519190
Media: 2-4-7-10-13
Personnel:
David K.R. Thomson *(Chm)*
W. Geoffrey Beattie *(Co-Deputy Chm)*
Niall W. FitzGerald *(Co-Deputy Chm)*
Thomas H. Glocer *(CEO)*
Robert D. Daleo *(CFO & Exec VP)*
Gustav Carlson *(CMO & Exec VP)*
Abel Clark *(Chief Strategy Officer & Exec VP)*
James Powell *(CTO & Exec VP)*
Stephen G. Dando *(Chief HR Officer & Exec VP)*
James C. Smith *(CEO-Prof Div)*
Deirdre Stanley *(Gen Counsel & Exec VP)*
Stephen J. Adler *(Exec VP-News & Editor-in-Chief-News)*
Marc E. Gold *(Sr VP & Assoc Gen Counsel)*

Brands & Products:
AUTEX
AUTEX BLOCKDATA
BETA
CREATIVE SOLUTIONS
CURRENT DRUGS
DATASTREAM
DELMAR
DIALOG
ELITE
FIRST CALL
GALE
IR CHANNEL
MEDSTAT
MOROMEDEX
NETG
PATENT INDEX
PDR
PORTIA
PROMETRIC
QUANTEC
RIA
SDC
SDC PLATINUM
SOUTHWESTERN
SWEET & MAXWELL
THOMSON ONE
THOMSON RESEARCH
THOMSON REUTERS
TREASURA
TREASURY MANAGER
VENTUREXPERT
WADSWORTH
WEB OF SCIENCE
WEST GROUP
WESTLAW
WORLDSCOPE
Advertising Agency:
Impressions-A.B.A. Industries, Inc.
393 Jericho Tpk
Mineola, NY 11501
Tel.: (516) 739-3210
Fax: (516) 739-9246

THOMSON REUTERS TAX & ACCOUNTING

(Sub. of Thomson Tax & Accounting)
195 Broadway
New York, NY 10007
Tel.: (212) 367-6300
Fax: (212) 367-6305
E-mail: ria@thomson.com
Web Site: www.ria.thomson.com
Sales Range: $125-149.9 Million
Approx. Number Employees: 400
Year Founded: 1935
Business Description:
Publisher of Professional Books, Looseleaf Services, Newsletters, Journals & Directories, Primarily in the Fields of Tax Law Accounting, & Tax Software
S.I.C.: 8748; 2731
N.A.I.C.S.: 541618; 511130
Export
Media: 2-4-7-10-17
Personnel:
Boyd Gackle *(Product Mgr-GoSystem Tax RS)*
Brands & Products:
CHECKPOINT
E-FORM
GOSYSTEM
INSOURCE
TAX ALERTS
WG&L

THOMSON WEST

(Sub. of West Publishing Corporation)
50 Broad St Aqueduct Bldg
Rochester, NY 14694-0001
Tel.: (585) 546-5530
Fax: (585) 258-3718
Web Site: www.thomson.com
Approx. Number Employees: 1,000
Business Description:
Writing, Printing, Publishing & Binding of Legal Materials & Reference Works
S.I.C.: 2731; 2789
N.A.I.C.S.: 511130; 323121
Advertising Expenditures: $100,000
Media: 2-4-5-7-10-11-26
Distr.: Intl.
Personnel:
Steve Buege *(Pres & CEO-Thomson Elite)*
Kenneth M. Ross *(CTO & Sr VP)*
Scott Kinney *(Sr VP-Sls & Acct Mgmt)*
Andy Martens *(Sr VP)*
Tom Moran *(Sr VP-HR)*
Brands & Products:
CASEBASE
LAWDESK
PROLAW
WESTLAW

TIME INC.

(Sub. of Time Warner Inc.)
Time Life Bldg Rockefeller Ctr 1271 Ave of The Americas
New York, NY 10020-1393
Tel.: (212) 522-1212
Fax: (212) 522-0555
Web Site: www.timeinc.com
Sales Range: $1-4.9 Billion
Approx. Number Employees: 25,000
Year Founded: 1923
Business Description:
Periodicals Publisher
S.I.C.: 2721
N.A.I.C.S.: 511120
Media: 3-6-8-11-13-14-15-17-19-23-24
Distr.: Direct to Consumer; Intl.; Natl.
Budget Set: Dec.
Personnel:
Howard Averill *(CFO)*
John Squires *(COO)*
Stephanie George *(CMO & Exec VP)*
Ellin Martens *(Copy Chief)*
John Cantarella *(Pres-Digital, News & Sports Grp)*
Paul Greenberg *(Pres-Digital-Lifestyle Grp)*
Fran Hauser *(Pres-Digital Style, Entertainment & Lifestyle Grp)*
Howard Rosen *(Pres-Production & Fulfillment Ops)*
Maurice Edelson *(Gen Counsel)*
Kerry Bessey *(Exec VP-HR)*
Paul Caine *(Chief Revenue Officer & Exec VP)*
Jeffrey Fulton *(Exec VP)*
Steven Sachs *(Exec VP-Consumer Mtkg & Sls)*
Evelyn Webster *(Exec VP)*
Mary Haskin *(VP-Mktg & Sls Dev)*
Roberta Kapp *(VP-Mktg)*
John Huey *(Editor-in-Chief)*
James Kelly *(Mng Editor)*
Camille Chatterjee *(Deputy Editor-Health Magazine)*
Michael Elliott *(Editor-Time-Intl)*
Romesh Ratnesar *(Editor-Contributing)*
Bill Shapiro *(Editor)*
Samantha Fennell *(Exec Dir-Corp Sls)*
Mark Gallops *(Exec Dir)*
Arthur Hochstein *(Dir-Art)*
Deb Kadetsky *(Dir-Audience Dev-Lifestyle Grp)*
Martha Nelson *(Dir-Editorial)*
Justin Oborne *(Dir-Sls-Natl)*
Lauren Evans *(Mgr-Integrated Mktg)*

TIMES HERALD-RECORD

(Unit of Ottaway Newspapers, Inc.)
40 Mulberry St
Middletown, NY 10940
Mailing Address:
PO Box 2046
Middletown, NY 10940
Tel.: (845) 341-1100
Fax: (845) 343-2170
Toll Free: (800) 295-2181
Web Site: www.recordonline.com
Sales Range: $25-49.9 Million
Approx. Number Employees: 100
Business Description:
Newspaper Publisher
S.I.C.: 2711
N.A.I.C.S.: 511110
Media: 7-8-9-13-18
Personnel:
Genie Abrams *(Editor-Copy)*
Dick Bayne *(Editor-Copy)*
Mike Carey *(Editor-Local News)*
Phil Colangelo *(Editor-Copy)*
Marc Davis *(Editor-Copy)*
John DeSanto *(Editor-Multimedia)*
Joe Dowd *(Editor-Hudson Valley)*
Gittel Evangelist *(Editor-Copy)*
Linda Fite *(Editor-Copy)*
Brenda Gilhooly *(Editor-Custom Publ)*
Erik Gliedman *(Editor-Online)*
Ken Hall *(Editor-Opinion Page)*
Jim Hunyadi *(Editor-Production)*
Donna Kessler *(Editor-Sys)*
Tom Leek *(Editor-Gazette)*
Barry Lewis *(Editor-Sunday & Columnist-Sullivan County)*
Chris Mele *(Editor-Sunday/Enterprise)*
Tim Michaels *(Editor-Copy)*
Moe Mitterling *(Editor-Copy)*
Doug Mohart *(Editor-Sports)*
Matt Pepin *(Editor-Sports)*
Carol Reif *(Editor-Copy)*
Adrianne Reilly *(Editor-Local News)*
Dennis Sprick *(Editor-Copy)*
Kathi Hammer *(Dir-Adv)*
Patrick Mullen *(Dir-New Media)*
Amy Berkowitz *(Coord-Community News)*
Carmen Ramos *(Coord-Community News)*

TIMES JOURNAL INC.

(d/b/a Marietta Daily Journal)
580 S Fairground St SE
Marietta, GA 30060
Tel.: (770) 428-9411
Fax: (770) 428-7945
E-mail: advertising@mdjonline.com
Web Site: www.mdjonline.com
E-Mail For Key Personnel:
President: tsmith@mdjonline.com
Approx. Number Employees: 160
Business Description:
Publisher of Newspapers
S.I.C.: 2711

Key to Media (For complete agency information see *The Advertising Red Books-Agencies* edition):
1. Bus. Publs. 2. Cable T.V. 3. Catalogs & Directories. 4. Co-op Adv. 5. Consumer Mags. 6. D.M. to Bus. Estab.7. D.M. to Consumers
8. Daily Newsp. 9. Exhibits/Trade Shows 10. Foreign 11. Infomercial 12. Internet Adv.13. Multimedia 14. Network Radio
15. Network T.V. 16. Newsp. Distr. Mags. 17. Other 18. Outdoor (Posters, Transit) 19. Point of Purchase20. Premiums, Novelties
21. Product Samples 22. Special Events Mktg. 23. Spot Radio 24. Spot T.V. 25. Weekly Newsp. 26. Yellow Page Adv.

Times Journal Inc. — (Continued)

N.A.I.C.S.: 511110
Media: 8-9
Personnel:
Otis A. Brumby, Jr. *(Publr)*

THE TIMES-NEWS
(Unit of Freedom Newspapers, Inc.)
707 S Main St
Burlington, NC 27215
Tel.: (336) 227-0131
Fax: (336) 229-2466
E-mail: thetimesnews@lin.freedom.com
Web Site: www.thetimesnews.com
Sales Range: $125-149.9 Million
Approx. Number Employees: 175
Year Founded: 1887
Business Description:
Newspaper
S.I.C.: 2711; 8661
N.A.I.C.S.: 511110; 813110
Media: 8-9-13-22-23-26
Personnel:
Mike Little *(Gen Mgr)*
Joe Jurney *(Editor-Copy)*
Brent Lancaster *(Editor-City)*
Bob Sutton *(Editor-Sports)*
Madison Taylor *(Editor)*
Darryl Ayers *(Dir-Production)*
Linda Bowden *(Dir-Art)*
Roger Creasy *(Dir-Interactive Ops)*
Joyce Beasley *(Mgr-Customer Svc)*
Frances Woody *(Mgr-Admin)*
Brands & Products:
THE TIMES-NEWS

THE TIMES-PICAYUNE PUBLISHING CORP.
(Sub. of Advance Publications, Inc.)
3800 Howard Ave
New Orleans, LA 70125-1429
Tel.: (504) 822-6660
Tel.: (504) 826-3279
Fax: (504) 826-3800
Web Site: www.timespicayune.com
Approx. Number Employees: 900
Year Founded: 1837
Business Description:
Newspaper Publisher
S.I.C.: 2711
N.A.I.C.S.: 511110
Advertising Expenditures: $1,000,000
Media: 9
Distr.: Reg.
Budget Set: Nov.
Personnel:
Ashton Phelps, Jr. *(Publr)*
Ray Massett *(VP & Gen Mgr)*
Nygel Gibson *(VP & Mgr-Credit)*
P. Beth Adams *(VP-HR)*
Wayne Benjamin *(VP-Pur)*
Renee Bigelow *(VP-Mktg)*
Patrick Hinrichs *(VP-Pur & Transportation)*
Kelly Rose *(VP-Adv)*
Jim Amoss *(Editor)*
Terri Troncale *(Editor-Editorial Page)*
Brands & Products:
THE TIMES-PICAYUNE

THE TIMES PUBLISHING CO.
(Sub. of Times Holding Company Inc.)
490 1st Ave S
Saint Petersburg, FL 33701-4204
Tel.: (727) 893-8726
Fax: (727) 893-8675
Toll Free: (800) 333-7505
E-mail: local@sptimes.com
Web Site: www.tampabay.com
E-Mail For Key Personnel:
Public Relations: apenrose@sptimes.com
Sales Range: $250-299.9 Million
Approx. Number Employees: 1,098
Year Founded: 1884
Business Description:
Publisher of Newspapers
S.I.C.: 2711; 2721
N.A.I.C.S.: 511110; 511120
Media: 2-6-8-9-13-18-19-20-21-22-23-24-26
Distr.: Direct to Consumer; Reg.
Budget Set: Sept.
Personnel:
Paul Tash *(CEO)*
Jana Jones *(CFO, Treas & VP)*
Brands & Products:
CQ MONITOR
CQ RESEARCHER
CQ WEEKLY
CQ.COM
FLORIDA TREND
GOVERNING MAGAZINE
ST. PETERSBURG TIMES

TIMES PUBLISHING CO. INC.
205 W 12th St
Erie, PA 16534
Tel.: (814) 870-1606
Tel.: (814) 870-1600
Fax: (814) 870-1600
Toll Free: (800) 352-0043
Web Site: www.goerie.com
Approx. Sls.: $15,500,000
Approx. Number Employees: 240
Business Description:
Newspapers, Publishing & Printing
S.I.C.: 2711; 2752
N.A.I.C.S.: 511110; 323110
Media: 8-9
Personnel:
Edward Mead *(Chm)*
Richard Starr *(Sr VP-Res)*
Rick Sayers *(Exec Editor)*
Terry Casciolo *(Dir-Adv)*
Bill Dietz *(Mgr-Bus Dev)*
Devin Hamilton *(Mgr-Adv)*
Lisa Shade *(Mgr-Market Dev)*
Advertising Agency:
Engel O'Neill Advertising & Public Relations
2124 Sassafras St
Erie, PA 16502
Tel.: (814) 454-3111
Fax: (814) 456-7879

TIMES RECORD NEWS
(Sub. of The E.W. Scripps Company)
1301 Lamar St
Wichita Falls, TX 76301-7032
Mailing Address:
PO Box 120
Wichita Falls, TX 76307
Tel.: (940) 767-8341
Fax: (940) 720-1741
Toll Free: (800) 627-1646
Web Site: www.timesrecordnews.com
Sales Range: $50-74.9 Million
Approx. Number Employees: 200
Business Description:
Morning & Sunday Newspapers Publisher
S.I.C.: 2711
N.A.I.C.S.: 511110
Media: 9-25
Personnel:
Becky Schroeder *(CFO)*
Stacy Horany *(Editor-Copy)*
Bridget Knight *(Editor-Features)*
Lana Sweeten Shults *(Editor-Entertainment)*
Christy Ridinger *(Dir-Adv)*
Jackie Riley *(Dir-Mktg)*
Nita Stennett *(Dir-HR)*
Missy Seay *(Mgr-Retail Adv)*

TIMMINS DAILY PRESS
(Div. of Osprey Media Group, Inc.)
187 Cedar St S
Timmins, ON P4N 7G1, Canada
Mailing Address:
P.O. Box 560
Timmins, ON P4N 7G1, Canada
Tel.: (705) 268-5050
Fax: (705) 268-7373
E-mail: production@thedailypress.ca
Web Site: www.timminspress.com
Approx. Number Employees: 45
Business Description:
Daily Newspaper
S.I.C.: 2711
N.A.I.C.S.: 511110
Media: 13-25
Personnel:
Bruce Cowan *(Publr)*
Lisa Wilson *(Dir-Adv)*

TMP INTERNATIONAL, INC.
1711 W Greentree Dr Ste 208
Tempe, AZ 85284
Tel.: (480) 491-7070
Fax: (480) 491-4010
Web Site: www.spawn.com
Approx. Number Employees: 100
Year Founded: 1994
Business Description:
Comic Books & Related Items Publisher; Toys Mfr; Filmed Entertainment
S.I.C.: 3944
N.A.I.C.S.: 339932
Media: 4-6-8-10-13
Personnel:
Todd McFarlane *(Founder)*

TOM'S GUIDES PUBLISHING LLC
10559 Jefferson Blvd Ste A
Culver City, CA 90232
Tel.: (310) 279-5500
Fax: (310) 279-5522
E-mail: pr@tomshardware.com
Web Site: www.tomshardware.com
Year Founded: 1996
Business Description:
Resource for PC Hardware Reviews & News
S.I.C.: 2741
N.A.I.C.S.: 511199
Media: 13
Personnel:
Stephanie Dale *(VP-Sls)*
Patrica Hsu *(Dir-Mktg-Asia Pacific)*
Brands & Products:
TOM'S HARDWARE

THE TOPEKA CAPITAL-JOURNAL
(Unit of Morris Publishing Group, LLC)
616 SE Jefferson St
Topeka, KS 66607-1137
Tel.: (785) 295-1111
Fax: (785) 295-1230
Toll Free: (800) 777-7171
Web Site: www.cjonline.com
Approx. Number Employees: 276
Year Founded: 1879
Business Description:
Newspaper Publisher
S.I.C.: 2721; 7375
N.A.I.C.S.: 511120; 518111
Advertising Expenditures: $50,000
Media: 3-8-9-10-13-18-19-21-22-23
Personnel:
Mark E. Nusbaum *(Publr)*
Jeff Davis *(Design Editor)*
Fred Johnson *(City Editor)*
Steve Thompson *(Sys Editor)*
Eric Turner *(Editor-Sports)*
Bob Barth *(Dir-Print & Digital Adv)*
Robert Barth *(Dir-Print & Digital Adv)*
Terri Benson *(Dir-Mktg)*
Heather Johanning *(Dir-HR)*
Cheryl Austin *(Coord-Admin Svcs)*

TORONTO STAR NEWSPAPERS LTD.
(Sub. of Torstar Corporation)
1 Yonge St
Toronto, ON M5E 1E6, Canada
Tel.: (416) 367-2000
Fax: (416) 865-3606
Toll Free: (800) 268-8323
Telex: 6-23201
Web Site: www.thestar.com
Sales Range: $400-449.9 Million
Approx. Number Employees: 800
Year Founded: 1892
Business Description:
Newspaper Publishing
S.I.C.: 2711
N.A.I.C.S.: 511110
Advertising Expenditures: $1,000,000
Media: 2-6-11-15-18-19-23-24-25-26
Distr.: Natl.
Budget Set: June
Personnel:
John Cruickshank *(Publr)*
Michael Cooke *(Editor)*
Andrew Phillips *(Editor-Bus)*

TORSTAR CORPORATION
1 Yonge St
Toronto, ON M5E 1P9, Canada
Tel.: (416) 869-4010
Fax: (416) 869-4183
E-mail: torstar@torstar.ca
Web Site: www.torstar.ca
Approx. Rev.: $1,507,433,846
Approx. Number Employees: 6,600
Business Description:
Holding Company; Newspaper & Book Publishing
S.I.C.: 6719
N.A.I.C.S.: 551112
Media: 4-7-8-10-18-19
Personnel:
John A. Honderich *(Chm)*
David P. Holland *(Pres & CEO)*
Lorenzo Demarchi *(CFO & Exec VP)*
John Cruickshank *(Pres-Star Media Grp)*
Tomer Strolight *(Pres-Torstar Digital)*
Marie E. Beyette *(Gen Counsel, Sec & Sr VP)*
Patricia Hewitt *(Sr VP-HR)*
Gail Martin *(Sr VP-Fin)*
Joan Blastorah *(Dir-Art)*
Lorne Silver *(Dir-Creative)*

Key to Media (For complete agency information see *The Advertising Red Books-Agencies* edition):
1. Bus. Publs. 2. Cable T.V. 3. Catalogs & Directories. 4. Co-op Adv. 5. Consumer Mags. 6. D.M. to Bus. Estab.7. D.M. to Consumers
8. Daily Newsp. 9. Exhibits/Trade Shows 10. Foreign 11. Infomercial 12. Internet Adv.13. Multimedia 14. Network Radio
15. Network T.V. 16. Newsp. Distr. Mags. 17. Other 18. Outdoor (Posters, Transit) 19. Point of Purchase20. Premiums, Novelties
21. Product Samples 22. Special Events Mktg. 23. Spot Radio 24. Spot T.V. 25. Weekly Newsp. 26. Yellow Page Adv.

Advertising Agencies:
Dashboard
355 Adelaide St W Ste 200
Toronto, ON M5V 1S2, Canada
Tel.: (416) 504-4422
Fax: (416) 504-6644
Website Development
Winefox

JWT Company Ltd.
160 Bloor St E
Toronto, ON M4W 3P7, Canada
Tel.: (416) 926-7300
Fax: (416) 926-7389
(Weekly Scoop)

TOWN & COUNTRY
(Unit of Hearst Magazines)
300 W 57th St
New York, NY 10019-3794
Tel.: (212) 903-5000
Tel.: (212) 903-5321
Fax: (212) 262-7107
Toll Free: (800) 289-8696
E-mail: tnc@hearst.com
Web Site:
www.townandcountrymag.com
Approx. Number Employees: 50
Year Founded: 1846
Business Description:
Luxury Lifestyle Magazine Publisher
S.I.C.: 2721
N.A.I.C.S.: 511120
Media: 6-7-8-10-17-21-22
Distr.: Intl.; Natl.
Budget Set: Nov.
Personnel:
Valerie Salembier *(Chief Revenue Officer, Publr & Sr VP)*
Freeda Fawal-Farah *(Assoc Publr-Mktg)*
Rae M. Cazzola *(Gen Mgr)*
Pamela Fiori *(Editor-in-Chief)*
Andrew Sessa *(Assoc Editor-Arts, Culture & Design)*
Zoe G. Settle *(Editor)*
Beth Ifcher *(Dir-Grp Consumer Mktg)*
Lisa Schwartz Golodner *(Mktg Dir-Hearst Magazines)*
Dianne E. Athey *(Dir-Design)*
Linda Crowley *(Dir-Res)*
Sarah Medford *(Dir-Arts, Culture & Design)*
Stefanie Rapp *(Dir-Adv)*
Jamie Rosen *(Dir-Beauty)*
Effie Tsu *(Assoc Dir-Art)*
Alana M. Newton *(Mgr-Mktg)*
Delia C. Alvarado *(Mgr-Adv Svcs)*

TRADE PRESS PUBLISHING CORP.
2100 W Florist Ave
Milwaukee, WI 53209
Tel.: (414) 228-7701
Fax: (414) 228-1134
Web Site: www.tradepress.com
Approx. Sls.: $16,000,000
Approx. Number Employees: 58
Business Description:
Trade Journals Publisher
S.I.C.: 2721; 2791
N.A.I.C.S.: 511120; 323122
Media: 2-7-10
Personnel:
Robert Wisniewski *(Pres & CEO)*
Tim Rowe *(VP-Mktg)*
Wendy Melnick *(Mgr-Production)*

TRAFFIC WORLD, INC.
(Sub. of UBM Global Trade)
1270 National Press Bldg
Washington, DC 20045
Tel.: (202) 355-1150
Fax: (202) 355-1151
Toll Free: (888) 215-6084
E-mail: editor@trafficworld.com
Web Site: www.trafficworld.com
Approx. Number Employees: 20
Year Founded: 1907
Business Description:
Periodical
S.I.C.: 2721
N.A.I.C.S.: 511120
Media: 2-13
Personnel:
Steven Prince *(Publr)*
John Gallagher *(Assoc Editor-Trucking)*
India Jackson *(Mgr-Telecom)*

TRAFFORD HOLDINGS LTD.
2333 Government St Ste 6E
Victoria, BC V8T 4P4, Canada
Tel.: (250) 383-6864
Fax: (250) 383-6804
Toll Free: (888) 232-4444
E-mail: info@trafford.com
Web Site: www.trafford.com
Approx. Number Employees: 70
Year Founded: 1991
Business Description:
Book Publisher
S.I.C.: 2731
N.A.I.C.S.: 511130
Media: 10-13
Personnel:
John Norris *(Co-Founder)*
Martin Waterman *(Chm)*
Kingstone Reed *(CFO & VP)*
Jason Zimmel *(Controller)*

TRANSACTION PUBLISHERS, INC.
35 Berrue Cir
Piscataway, NJ 08854
Tel.: (732) 445-2280
Fax: (732) 748-9801
Toll Free: (888) 999-6778
E-mail: trans@transactionpub.com
Web Site: www.transactionpub.com
Approx. Number Employees: 27
Year Founded: 1962
Business Description:
Publishes Scholarly Books, Annuals & Journals In Various Social Sciences Disciplines Including International Relations, Economics, Government & Public Policy, Psychology, Ethnic & Urban Studies & Communications
S.I.C.: 2721; 5961
N.A.I.C.S.: 511120; 454113
Import Export
Media: 2-4-6-7-8-9-10-11-13-16-23
Distr.: Intl.; Natl.
Budget Set: July-Aug.
Personnel:
Mary E. Curtis *(Pres)*
Michael Celletto *(Mgr-Acctg)*
Brands & Products:
EXPRESS BOOK FREIGHT
SOCIETY
TRANSACTION
TRANSACTION PERIODICALS CONSORTIUM
TRANSACTION PUBLISHERS
TRANSACTION PUBLISHERS DISTRIBUTION

TRANSCONTINENTAL INC.
1 Place Ville Marie Bureau 3315
Montreal, QC H3B 3N2, Canada
Tel.: (514) 954-4000
Fax: (514) 954-4016
E-mail: info@transcontinental.ca
Web Site: www.transcontinental.com
Approx. Rev.: $2,130,963,912
Approx. Number Employees: 10,500
Year Founded: 1978
Business Description:
Newspapers, Magazines, Websites, Flyers & Catalogs Publishing & Printing Services
S.I.C.: 2711; 2721; 2741; 2759
N.A.I.C.S.: 511110; 323119; 511120; 516110
Media: 2-13
Personnel:
Remi Marcoux *(Founder & Chm)*
Isabelle Marcoux *(Vice Chm & VP-Corp Dev)*
Francois Olivier *(Pres & CEO)*
Benoit Huard *(CFO & VP)*
Natalie Lariviere *(Pres-Media)*
Brian Reid *(Pres-Printing)*
Christian Trudeau *(Pres-Mktg Comm)*
Pierre Marcoux *(Sr VP-Bus & Consumer Solutions Grp-Transcontinental Media)*
Rene Poirier *(Sr VP-Technologies)*
James Aziz *(VP-Fin & Acctg)*
Jean Denault *(VP-Procurement & Tech)*
Katya Laviolette *(Corp VP-HR)*
Sylvain Morissette *(VP-Corp Comm)*
Andre Bolduc *(Dir-Internal Audit)*
Nancy Bouffard *(Dir-External Comm)*
Jennifer F. McCaughey *(Dir-IR & Corp Comm)*
Brands & Products:
CANADIAN LIVING
ELLE CANADA
GOOD TIMES
THE HOCKEY NEWS
LES AFFAIRES
PUBLI-SAC
TRANSCONTINENTAL

TRANSPORT TOPICS PUBLISHING GROUP
2200 Mill Rd
Alexandria, VA 22314-4654
Tel.: (703) 838-1770
Fax: (703) 548-3662
Toll Free: (800) 259-0470
E-mail: tteditor@trucking.org
Web Site: www.ttnews.com
Approx. Number Employees: 39
Year Founded: 1933
Business Description:
National Weekly Business Newspaper of Trucking Industry
S.I.C.: 2711; 2721
N.A.I.C.S.: 511110; 511120
Media: 2-7-10-13-25
Distr.: Intl.; Natl.
Budget Set: Aug.
Personnel:
Howard S. Abramson *(Publr & Dir-Editorial)*
James Galligan *(Editor-Light-Medium Truck Publication)*
Carolyn Cason *(Mgr-Classified Adv)*
Brands & Products:
LIGHT & MEDIUM TRUCK
TRANSPORT TOPICS
TRANSPORT TOPICS 100
TRANSPORT TOPICS' LOGISTICS 50
UTILITY FLEET MANAGEMENT

TRAVELHOST, INC.
10701 N Stemmons Fwy
Dallas, TX 75220-2419
Tel.: (972) 556-0541
Fax: (972) 432-8729
E-mail: info@travelhost.com
Web Site: www.travelhost.com
Approx. Number Employees: 60
Year Founded: 1967
Business Description:
Publisher of Travel Information Online & Offline
S.I.C.: 2741
N.A.I.C.S.: 511199
Advertising Expenditures: $200,000
Media: 2-6-7-9-10-13
Distr.: Natl.
Budget Set: Oct.
Personnel:
James E. Buerger *(Founder & Chm)*
Sherry Buerger Carr *(Vice Chm & COO)*
Jim W. South *(CFO)*
Brenda Freeman Cantrell *(VP-Mktg)*
Patricia L. Nuss *(VP-Production)*
Kirk Smith *(Exec Dir-Mktg)*
Brands & Products:
CLUBHOUSE LIVING
CONDO CONCIERGE
HAPPY CAMPER
MARINE CONCIERGE
MY TRAVELHOST
TH
TRAVELHOST
TRAVELHOST TRAVEL REGISTRY
Advertising Agency:
TMP Worldwide/Advertising & Communications
4055 Valley View Ln Ste 600
Dallas, TX 75244-5074
Tel.: (972) 340-7400
Fax: (972) 340-7760

TRAVERSE CITY RECORD-EAGLE
(Sub. of Community Newspaper Holdings, Inc.)
120 W Front St
Traverse City, MI 49684
Tel.: (231) 946-2000
Fax: (231) 946-8273
E-mail: webmaster@record-eagle.com
Web Site: www.record-eagle.com
Business Description:
Newspaper Publisher
S.I.C.: 2711
N.A.I.C.S.: 511110
Media: 7-8-9-13-18
Personnel:
Michael Casuscelli *(Publr)*
Dennis Chase *(Editor-Sports)*
Garret Leiva *(Editor-Community News)*
Dave Miller *(Editor-Editorial Page)*
Bill O'Brien *(Editor-Bus)*
Brian Steele *(Editor-News)*
Jodee Taylor *(Editor-Features)*
Bill Thomas *(Editor)*
Mike Tyree *(Editor-News)*
Rich Roxbury *(Dir-Circulation)*

Key to Media (For complete agency information see *The Advertising Red Books-Agencies* edition):
1. Bus. Publs. 2. Cable T.V. 3. Catalogs & Directories. 4. Co-op Adv. 5. Consumer Mags. 6. D.M. to Bus. Estab.7. D.M. to Consumers 8. Daily Newsp. 9. Exhibits/Trade Shows 10. Foreign 11. Infomercial 12. Internet Adv.13. Multimedia 14. Network Radio 15. Network T.V. 16. Newsp. Distr. Mags. 17. Other 18. Outdoor (Posters, Transit) 19. Point of Purchase20. Premiums, Novelties 21. Product Samples 22. Special Events Mktg. 23. Spot Radio 24. Spot T.V. 25. Weekly Newsp. 26. Yellow Page Adv.

Traverse City Record-Eagle — (Continued)

Loraine Anderson *(Mgr-Photo)*
Dan Roach *(Mgr-Internet Vertical Sls)*
Chuck Staske *(Mgr-Home Delivery Sls)*
Tom Wyatt *(Mgr-Retail Adv)*
Yvonne Haywood *(Supvr-Customer Svc)*
Jeanne Hubbard *(Webmaster)*

TREND MAGAZINES, INC.

(Sub. of The Times Publishing Co.)
490 1st Ave S 8th Fl
Saint Petersburg, FL 33701-4204
Tel.: (727) 821-5800
Fax: (727) 822-5083
Web Site: www.floridatrends.com
Approx. Number Employees: 36
Year Founded: 1958
Business Description:
Statewide Business & Financial Publication
S.I.C.: 2721
N.A.I.C.S.: 511120
Media: 2-22
Personnel:
Andrew P. Corty *(Pres & Publr)*
Mark R. Howard *(Exec Editor)*
John Annunziata *(Mng Editor)*
Gary Bernloehr *(Dir-Art)*
Jill South *(Dir-Production)*
Lynn Lotkowictz *(Dir-Natl Sls)*
Karen Tyson *(Dir-Circulation & TopRank Florida)*
Barbara Goodman *(Bus Mgr)*
Joyce Edmondson *(Mgr-Online Project)*
Leslie Vasbinder *(Coord-Mktg & Special Projects)*
Brands & Products:
FLORIDA TRENDS

THE TRIBUNE

(Unit of Freedom Newspapers, Inc.)
100 Saint Louis Ave
Seymour, IN 47274
Mailing Address:
PO Box 447
Seymour, IN 47274
Tel.: (812) 522-4871
Fax: (812) 522-7691
Toll Free: (800) 800-8212
E-mail: info@millerheiman.com
Web Site: www.tribtown.com
Approx. Number Employees: 70
Year Founded: 1877
Business Description:
Newspaper
S.I.C.: 2711
N.A.I.C.S.: 511110
Daily Newsp.: 100%
Personnel:
Richard Davis *(Publr)*
Joanne Persinger *(Editor-Copy & Community)*
Tom Kesterson *(Dir-Circulation)*
Dondra Brown *(Mgr-Creative Svcs)*
Nancy Combs *(District Mgr)*
Robert Holbrook *(Mgr-Classified)*
Brands & Products:
THE TRIBUNE

TRIBUNE COMPANY

(Holding of Tribune Employee Stock Ownership Plan)
(Filed Ch 11 Bankruptcy #813241 on 12/08/2008 in U.S. Bankruptcy Ct, Dist of DE, Wilmington)
435 N Michigan Ave
Chicago, IL 60611
Tel.: (312) 222-9100
Fax: (312) 222-1573
E-mail: corp.info@tribune.com
Web Site: www.tribune.com
E-Mail For Key Personnel:
Marketing Director: ljones@tribune.com
Public Relations: gweitman@tribune.com
Approx. Rev.: $5,062,984,000
Approx. Number Employees: 20,000
Year Founded: 1847
Business Description:
Holding Company; Newspaper Publisher, Television & Radio Broadcasting
S.I.C.: 6719; 2711; 4832; 4833
N.A.I.C.S.: 551112; 511110; 515112; 515120
Import Export
Advertising Expenditures: $2,861,000,000
Media: 2-4-8-9-10-13-15-17-18-19-21-22-23-24-25
Distr.: Natl.; Reg.
Personnel:
Samuel Zell *(Chm)*
Eddy W. Hartenstein *(Pres & CEO)*
Nils E. Larsen *(Co-Pres & CIO)*
Donald J. Liebentritt *(Co-Pres & Chief Restructuring Officer)*
Chandler Bigelow *(CFO)*
Steve Gable *(CTO & Exec VP)*
Lee Abrams *(Chief Innovation Officer)*
David Eldersveld *(Gen Counsel, Sec & Sr VP)*
Carolyn Gilbert *(Exec VP)*
John Hendricks *(Exec VP-Interactive & Brdcst Sls)*
Doug Thomas *(Exec VP-Natl Sls)*
Harry Amsden *(Sr VP-Fin Ops)*
Sean Compton *(Sr VP-Programming & Entertainment)*
Bob Fleck *(CRO & Sr VP-Adv)*
Lee Jones *(Sr VP)*
Daniel G. Kazan *(Sr VP-Dev)*
Naomi Sachs *(Sr VP-Strategy)*
Gary Weitman *(Sr VP-Corp Rels)*
Anne Kelly *(VP-Adv)*
Ann Casey *(Dir-Brdcst Metrics)*
Brands & Products:
TRIBUNE
Advertising Agencies:
24/7 Real Media, Inc.
132 W 31st St 9th Fl
New York, NY 10001
Tel.: (212) 231-7100
Fax: (212) 760-1774
Toll Free: (877) 247-2477

Tribune Direct Marketing, Inc.
505 NW Ave
Northlake, IL 60164-1662
Tel.: (708) 836-2700
Fax: (708) 836-0605
Toll Free: (800) 545-9657

TRIBUNE-REVIEW PUBLISHING COMPANY

622 Cabin Hill Dr
Greensburg, PA 15601-1657
Tel.: (724) 834-1151
Fax: (724) 838-5171
E-mail: cmortimer@tribweb.com
Web Site: www.tribune-review.com
Approx. Number Employees: 1,500
Year Founded: 1924
Business Description:
Publisher of Newspapers
S.I.C.: 2711
N.A.I.C.S.: 511110
Media: 8-9
Personnel:
Richard M. Scaife *(Owner & Publr)*
Ralph Martin *(Pres & CEO)*
Jennifer Walter *(CFO & Dir-Corp Acct)*

TRUCKER PUBLICATIONS INC.

(Sub. of Target Media Partners)
1123 S University Ave Ste 320
Little Rock, AR 72204-1609
Mailing Address:
PO Box 3413
Little Rock, AR 72203-3413
Tel.: (501) 666-0500
Fax: (501) 666-0700
Toll Free: (800) 666-2770
E-mail: admin@thetrucker.com
Web Site: www.thetrucker.com
Approx. Number Employees: 10
Year Founded: 1999
Business Description:
Newspaper Publishing
S.I.C.: 2721; 2711
N.A.I.C.S.: 511120; 511110
Media: 2-9-10-13-14-22-25
Personnel:
Earb Kampbell *(Reporting Coord)*
Micah Jackson *(Publr)*
Laura Stacks *(Gen Mgr)*
Lyndon Finney *(Editor)*
Christine Kitchens *(Coord-Adv)*
Robin Nelson *(Coord-Production)*
Brands & Products:
WHERE THE NEWS IS FIRST

TUFCO TECHNOLOGIES, INC.

PO Box 23500
Green Bay, WI 54305-3500
Tel.: (920) 336-0054
Fax: (920) 336-9041
Toll Free: (800) 558-8145
E-mail: contact@tufco.com
Web Site: www.tufco.com
Approx. Sls.: $90,613,851
Approx. Number Employees: 305
Year Founded: 1992
Business Description:
Converted Paper Products Mfr; Specialty Printing Services; Business Imaging Paper Products Mfr & Distr
S.I.C.: 2679; 2671; 2676; 2759; 7336
N.A.I.C.S.: 322299; 322291; 323119; 326112; 541430
Export
Media: 2-5-10
Personnel:
Robert J. Simon *(Chm)*
Louis LeCalsey, III *(Pres & CEO)*
Michael B. Wheeler *(CFO, COO & Exec VP)*
James F. Robinson *(Sr VP-Sls & Mktg)*
George Hare *(Gen Mgr)*
John Michaud *(Dir-Bus Dev-Contract Mfg Div)*

TV GUIDE MAGAZINE GROUP, INC.

(Holding of OpenGate Capital LLC)
11 W 42nd St
New York, NY 10036
Tel.: (212) 852-7500
Fax: (212) 852-7323
Toll Free: (800) 866-1400
E-mail: contactus@tvguidemagazine.com
Web Site: www.tvguide.com/
Approx. Sls.: $70,700,000
Approx. Number Employees: 60
Year Founded: 1953
Business Description:
Online & Print Entertainment Periodical Publisher
S.I.C.: 2721; 2741
N.A.I.C.S.: 511120; 511140; 516110
Advertising Expenditures: $30,000,000
Media: 2-3-5-7-8-10-13-15-19-20-22-24
Distr.: Direct to Consumer; Natl.
Budget Set: May -June
Personnel:
Michael Clayton *(Exec VP & Gen Mgr)*
Diane L. Robina *(Exec VP-Dev, Acq & Pr)*
Brandon DiMassa *(Sr VP-Digital Media Syndication)*
Sasha Eysymontt *(Sr VP-Engrg)*
Christine Georgakakis *(Sr VP-Direct Response-TV Guide Network)*
Tim Russell *(Sr VP & VP/Mgr-Natl Sls)*
Ian Wallin *(Sr VP-Digital Ad Sls)*
Keith Bockus *(VP-Sls-East Coast)*
Adam Nash *(VP-Reg Sls)*
Christy Tanner *(Gen Mgr-TV Guide Online)*
Debra Birnbaum *(Editor-in-Chief)*
Carrie Hoffman *(Sr Dir-Mktg)*
Brands & Products:
CABLE GUIDE
TV GUIDE NETWORK
TV GUIDE ULTIMATE CABLE

TWELVE SIGNS, INC.

3369 S Robertson Blvd
Los Angeles, CA 90034-0069
Tel.: (310) 553-8000
Fax: (310) 836-0110
Web Site: www.starmatch.com
Approx. Number Employees: 100
Year Founded: 1967
Business Description:
Magazine Publisher
S.I.C.: 2721; 2741
N.A.I.C.S.: 511120; 511199
Media: 8-13
Personnel:
Richard Housman *(Chm & Creator)*
Valerie Jansen *(CFO)*
Brands & Products:
TWELVE SIGNS

TYNDALE HOUSE PUBLISHERS, INC.

351 Exec Dr
Carol Stream, IL 60188
Tel.: (630) 668-8300
Fax: (630) 668-3245
Fax: (800) 684-0247
Toll Free: (800) 323-9400
E-mail: catalogs@tyndale.com
Web Site: www.tyndale.com
E-Mail For Key Personnel:
Public Relations: pr_director@tyndale.com
Approx. Number Employees: 250
Year Founded: 1962
Business Description:
Bibles, Religious Books, Videos, Audios, Periodicals & Calendars

Key to Media (For complete agency information see *The Advertising Red Books-Agencies* edition):
1. Bus. Publs. 2. Cable T.V. 3. Catalogs & Directories. 4. Co-op Adv. 5. Consumer Mags. 6. D.M. to Bus. Estab.7. D.M. to Consumers
8. Daily Newsp. 9. Exhibits/Trade Shows 10. Foreign 11. Infomercial 12. Internet Adv.13. Multimedia 14. Network Radio
15. Network T.V. 16. Newsp. Distr. Mags. 17. Other 18. Outdoor (Posters, Transit) 19. Point of Purchase20. Premiums, Novelties
21. Product Samples 22. Special Events Mktg. 23. Spot Radio 24. Spot T.V. 25. Weekly Newsp. 26. Yellow Page Adv.

S.I.C.: 2731; 7812
N.A.I.C.S.: 511130; 512110
Export
Advertising Expenditures: $3,000,000
Distr.: Direct to Consumer; Intl.; Natl.
Budget Set: Mar.
Personnel:
Mark D. Taylor *(Pres & CEO)*
Paul Matthews *(CFO)*
Jeff Johnson *(COO)*
Brands & Products:
BIBLE ALIVE!
FOR THOSE WHO THIRST
HEART TO HEART
HEARTQUEST
HOW NOW SHALL WE LIVE?
ILUMINA
KID'S APPLICATION
LEATHERLIKE
LEFT BEHIND
LIFE APPLICATION
LITTLE BLESSINGS
LIVING BOOKS
MCGEE AND ME!
NEW BELIEVER'S
NEW LIVING TRANSLATION
NLT
ONE YEAR
SALTRIVER
SISTER CIRCLE
SPIRITUAL RENEWAL
STILLWATER
THIRSTY
TOUCHPOINT
TUTONE
TYNDALE
TYNDALE AUDIO
YOUNG BELIEVER

UBM GLOBAL TRADE
(Sub. of United Business Media Limited)
400 Windsor Corp Pk 50 Millstone Rd Ste 200
East Windsor, NJ 08520-1415
Tel.: (609) 371-7700
Tel.: (609) 371-7701
Fax: (609) 371-7712
Toll Free: (800) 221-5488
Web Site: www.ubmglobaltrade.com
Year Founded: 2000
Business Description:
Periodicals & Directories Publisher
S.I.C.: 2721
N.A.I.C.S.: 511120
Media: 4-7
Personnel:
John Day *(CEO)*
Peter Spinelli *(CFO)*
Steve Casley *(Pres/COO-BACK Aviation Solutions)*
Brendan McCahill *(Pres/COO-PIERS Info Svcs)*
Richard Rivera *(Sr VP-IT)*
Paul Page *(Dir-Editorial-The Journal Commerce)*
Brands & Products:
AIR CARGO WORLD
CANADIAN SAILINGS
DIRECTORY OF IMPORTERS & EXPORTERS
THE FLORIDA SHIPPER
THE FORWARDERS LIST OF ATTORNEYS
GULF SHIPPER
JOURNAL OF COMMERCE
JOURNAL OF COMMERCE ONLINE
MUSICAL AMERICA INTERNATIONAL
PACIFIC SHIPPER
SHIPPING DIGEST
TRAFFIC WORLD
TRANSPORTATION TELEPHONE TICKLER
U.S. CUSTOM HOUSE GUIDE

UNITED BUSINESS MEDIA LLC
(Sub. of United Business Media Limited)
600 Community Dr
Manhasset, NY 11030-3847
Tel.: (516) 562-5000
Fax: (516) 562-7830
Web Site: ubmtechnology.com
Sales Range: $750-799.9 Million
Approx. Number Employees: 3,376
Year Founded: 1971
Business Description:
High-Tech Publishing, Marketing & Information Services
S.I.C.: 8748
N.A.I.C.S.: 541618
Import Export
Advertising Expenditures: $450,000,000
Bus. Publs.: $270,000,000; Exhibits/ Trade Shows: $180,000,000
Distr.: Natl.
Personnel:
Kate Spellman *(Mng Dir)*
Patrick Nohilly *(CFO)*
Marie Myers *(Sr VP-Mfg)*
Mike Grover *(Dir-Content Ops & Syndication)*
Brands & Products:
CHANNEL CUSTOM PUBLISHING
CHANNELWEB
COMMWEB
COMPUTER RESELLER NEWS
COMPUTER TECHNOLOGY
COMPUTER TELEPHONY EXPO
CUSTOM MARKETING SOLUTIONS
EBUSINESS CONFERENCE & EXPO
EDTN
EE TIMES
ELECTRONIC BUYERS' NEWS
INFORMATIONWEEK
INTERNETWEEK
MSDN MAGAZINE
NETWORK COMPUTING
PC EXPO
PC FAB-PRINTED CIRCUIT FABRICATION
PCB DESIGN CONFERENCE
REALITY RESEARCH
SOFTWARE DEVELOPMENT
SYS ADMIN
TECHNOLOGY & LEARNING
TECHNOLOGY & LEARNING SCHOOL TECH
TECHWEB
TELE.COM
TELECONNECT MAGAZINE
VARBUSINESS
WALL STREET & TECHNOLOGY
WEB TECHNIQUES
WEBREVIEW.COM NETWORK
WINDOWS DEVELOPER'S JOURNAL
XCHANGE

UNITED PRESS INTERNATIONAL, INC.
(Sub. of News World Communications Inc)
1133 19th St NW Ste 800
Washington, DC 20036
Tel.: (202) 898-8000
Fax: (202) 898-8057
E-mail: sales@upi.com
Web Site: www.upi.com
E-Mail For Key Personnel:
Sales Director: sales@upi.com
Approx. Number Employees: 80
Year Founded: 1907
Business Description:
News & Information Services
S.I.C.: 7383; 2711
N.A.I.C.S.: 519110; 511110
Export
Media: 2-7-10-11-13
Personnel:
Michael Marshall *(Editor-in-Chief)*
Brands & Products:
ARABIA 2000
UPI ARABIC SERVICE
UPI NEWSTRACK
UPI PERSPECTIVES
UPI PHOTOS
UPI SPANISH

UNIVERSITY OF CHICAGO PRESS
(Sub. of University of Chicago)
1427 E 60th St
Chicago, IL 60637-2902
Tel.: (773) 702-7740
Fax: (773) 702-9756
Toll Free: (800) 621-2736
E-mail: marketing@press.uchicago.edu
Web Site: www.press.uchicago.edu
Approx. Number Employees: 200
Year Founded: 1892
Business Description:
Publisher of Academic Works
S.I.C.: 2741; 2731
N.A.I.C.S.: 511199; 511130
Advertising Expenditures: $300,000
Media: 2-4-5-6-7-9-10-23
Distr.: Intl.; Natl.
Budget Set: May-Nov.
Personnel:
Donald A. Collins *(Pres-Chicago Distr Svcs)*
Carol Kasper *(Dir-Mktg & Books Div)*
John Kessler *(Dir-Sls)*
Jill Shimabukuro *(Dir-Design & Production)*
Sylvia Hecimovich *(Mgr-Design)*
Levi Stahl *(Mgr-Publicity)*
Brands & Products:
CHICAGO ORIGINALS
Advertising Agency:
Tom, Dick & Harry Advertising
350 W Erie 2nd Fl
Chicago, IL 60654
Tel.: (312) 327-9500
Fax: (312) 327-9501

UNZ & COMPANY, INC.
333 Cedar Ave Bldg B Ste #2
Middlesex, NJ 08846
Tel.: (732) 667-1020
Fax: (732) 868-0260
Toll Free: (800) 631-3098
E-mail: marketing@unzco.com
Web Site: www.unzco.com
Approx. Number Employees: 16
Year Founded: 1879
Business Description:
Trainer of International Trade Compliance & Hazardous Materials; Publisher of Import/Export Forms, Placards & Software
S.I.C.: 8299; 2731
N.A.I.C.S.: 611699; 511130
Advertising Expenditures: $500,000
Media: 2-4-10-26
Distr.: Natl.
Budget Set: Oct.
Personnel:
Daniel T. Scott *(Pres)*
Jo-Ellen Beotsch-Yuhas *(Mgr-Mktg)*
Brands & Products:
CANADEK
EASI-SLI
MEXIDEK
UNIDEK
UNZ&CO

UP NORTH PUBLICATIONS
(Sub. of 21st Century Newspapers, Inc.)
711 W Pickard St
Mount Pleasant, MI 48858
Tel.: (989) 779-6000
Fax: (989) 779-6051
Web Site: www.themorningsun.com
Approx. Number Employees: 3
Business Description:
Weekly Newspaper Publisher
S.I.C.: 2711; 2721
N.A.I.C.S.: 511110; 511120
Media: 25
Personnel:
Al Frattura *(Pres & Publr)*
Brands & Products:
THE MORNING SUN

THE UPPER ROOM
1908 Grand Ave
Nashville, TN 37212-2129
Tel.: (615) 340-7200
Fax: (615) 340-7006
E-mail: info@upperroom.org
Web Site: www.upperroom.org
Sales Range: $10-24.9 Million
Approx. Number Employees: 200
Year Founded: 1935
Business Description:
Publisher of Spiritual Formation Resources
S.I.C.: 2721; 8661
N.A.I.C.S.: 511120; 813110
Advertising Expenditures: $800,000
D.M. to Consumers: $640,000; Exhibits/Trade Shows: $80,000; Other: $80,000
Distr.: Intl.; Natl.
Budget Set: Aug.
Personnel:
Charles Carahan *(CFO)*
Sarah Wilke *(Editor & Publr)*
Beth Richardson *(Editor-Alive)*
Sherry Elliott *(Dir-Admin Svcs)*
Chris McCormick *(Dir-Dev)*
Dale Rust Waymack *(Dir-Intl Ministries)*
Brands & Products:
ALIVE NOW
DEVO'ZINE
EL APOSENTO ALTO
POCKETS
THE UPPER ROOM

Key to Media (For complete agency information see *The Advertising Red Books-Agencies* edition):
1. Bus. Publs. 2. Cable T.V. 3. Catalogs & Directories. 4. Co-op Adv. 5. Consumer Mags. 6. D.M. to Bus. Estab.7. D.M. to Consumers
8. Daily Newsp. 9. Exhibits/Trade Shows 10. Foreign 11. Infomercial 12. Internet Adv.13. Multimedia 14. Network Radio
15. Network T.V. 16. Newsp. Distr. Mags. 17. Other 18. Outdoor (Posters, Transit) 19. Point of Purchase20. Premiums, Novelties
21. Product Samples 22. Special Events Mktg. 23. Spot Radio 24. Spot T.V. 25. Weekly Newsp. 26. Yellow Page Adv.

The Upper Room — (Continued)

WEAVINGS

U.S. BRONZE SIGN CO., INC.
811 2nd Ave
New Hyde Park, NY 11040
Tel.: (516) 352-5155
Fax: (516) 352-1761
Toll Free: (800) 872-5155
E-mail: customerservice@usbronze.com
Web Site: www.usbronze.com
Approx. Number Employees: 25
Year Founded: 1933
Business Description:
Tablets, Bronze & Aluminum Signs, Individual Building Letters & Plaques Mfr
S.I.C.: 3993; 3953
N.A.I.C.S.: 339950; 339943
Export
Media: 2-4-6-8-16-26
Distr.: Direct to Consumer; Intl.; Natl.
Personnel:
George T. Barbeosch *(Pres)*
Alan Kasten *(VP-Mktg)*
Brands & Products:
UNITED STATES BRONZE
U.S. BRONZE

U.S. HOSPITALITY CORPORATION
1940 Elm Hill Pike
Nashville, TN 37210
Tel.: (615) 259-4500
Fax: (615) 777-5500
Toll Free: (800) 467-1218
E-mail: judy.bourne@ushospitality.com
Web Site: www.ushospitality.com
Sales Range: $100-124.9 Million
Approx. Number Employees: 40
Year Founded: 1986
Business Description:
Directory Publisher
S.I.C.: 2741; 2752
N.A.I.C.S.: 511140; 323110
Media: 6
Personnel:
Mark Oldham *(Pres)*
John Bearden *(CEO)*
Judy Bourne *(Mgr-Sls)*
Jeni Moore *(Mgr-Design)*
Leevetta Ralston *(Mgr-Bindery)*

U.S. NAVAL INSTITUTE
291 Wood Rd
Annapolis, MD 21402
Tel.: (410) 268-6110
Fax: (410) 571-1703
Toll Free: (800) 233-8764
E-mail: circulation@usni.org
Web Site: www.usni.org
Approx. Number Employees: 100
Business Description:
Proceedings & Naval History Magazines & Books Publisher; Seminars for the Advancement of Issues Related to National Security
S.I.C.: 2731; 2721
N.A.I.C.S.: 511130; 511120
Media: 2-10
Personnel:
Rick Russell *(Dir-Naval Institute Press)*
Thomas L. Wilkerson *(CEO)*
Thomas Cutler *(Dir-Prof Publ)*
George Keating *(Dir-Sls-Mktg)*
Christine Onrubia *(Dir-Design & Production Svcs)*
Prospero Hernandez *(Bus Mgr)*
Lick Russell *(Mgr-Naval Institute Press)*
Brands & Products:
USNI

U.S. NEWS & WORLD REPORT, L.P.
450 W 33rd St
New York, NY 10001-2603
Tel.: (212) 716-6800
Fax: (212) 716-6976
Toll Free: (800) 436-6520
E-mail: webmaster@usnews.com
Web Site: www.usnews.com
Approx. Number Employees: 500
Year Founded: 1933
Business Description:
Weekly News Magazine of National & International Affairs
S.I.C.: 2721
N.A.I.C.S.: 511120
Media: 2-6-8-9-10-13-18-23-24
Distr.: Natl.
Budget Set: Dec.
Personnel:
Mortimer B. Zuckerman *(Chm & Editor-in-Chief)*
Peter M. Dwoskin *(Gen Counsel & Sr VP)*
Karen S. Chevalier *(Sr VP-Ops)*
Nancy Morrissey *(VP-Mktg)*
Margaret Mannix *(Exec Editor)*
Peter Cary *(Editor-Newsletter Grp)*
David Gergen *(Editor-at-Large)*
Brian Kelly *(Editor)*
Phyllis A. Panza *(Dir-Adv Svcs)*
Diane Watters *(Mktg Mgr)*
Susan Headden *(Mgr-Adv)*
Brands & Products:
U.S. NEWS
U.S. NEWS & WORLD REPORT
U.S. NEWS ONLINE
U.S. NEWS WASHINGTON BUSINESS REPORT
Advertising Agency:
Kwittken & Company
360 Lexington Ave 15th Fl
New York, NY 10017
Tel.: (646) 277-7111
Fax: (646) 658-0880

US WEEKLY LLC
(Joint Venture of The Walt Disney Company & Wenner Media LLC)
1290 Ave Of The Americas 2nd Fl
New York, NY 10104
Tel.: (212) 484-1616
Fax: (212) 651-7890
Web Site: www.usmagazine.com
Sales Range: $10-24.9 Million
Approx. Number Employees: 40
Year Founded: 1977
Business Description:
Magazine; Owned 50% by Wenner Media LLC & 50% by The Walt Disney Company
S.I.C.: 2721
N.A.I.C.S.: 511120
Media: 1-2-6-8-16-18-20-22
Distr.: Natl.
Personnel:
Mike Steel *(Editor-in-Chief)*
Gwen Flamberg *(Dir-Beauty)*

VAGABOND CREATIONS, INC.
2560 Lance Dr
Dayton, OH 45409-1512
Tel.: (937) 298-1124
Fax: (937) 298-1124
Toll Free: (800) 738-7237
E-mail: sales@vagabondcreations.com
Web Site: www.vagabondcreations.net
E-Mail For Key Personnel:
Sales Director: sales@vagabondcreations.net
Approx. Number Employees: 6
Year Founded: 1955
Business Description:
Greeting Cards, Illustrated Stationery Tablets & Coloring Pads with Attached Crayons Mfr & Publisher
S.I.C.: 2759; 2771
N.A.I.C.S.: 323119; 511191
Export
Media: 2-4-7
Distr.: Natl.
Budget Set: Monthly
Personnel:
George F. Stanley, Jr. *(Pres)*
Brands & Products:
SOPHISTICATE
VAGABOND CREATIONS

VALASSIS
(Sub. of Valassis Communications, Inc.)
1 Targeting Centre
Windsor, CT 06095
Mailing Address:
PO Box 755
Windsor, CT 06095-0755
Tel.: (860) 285-6100
Fax: (860) 298-5597
Web Site: www.valassis.com
Sales Range: $1-4.9 Billion
Approx. Number Employees: 3,800
Year Founded: 1929
Business Description:
Direct Mail Marketing Services
S.I.C.: 2741; 7331
N.A.I.C.S.: 511140; 541860
Advertising Expenditures: $2,000,000
Media: 2-5-7-8-10-18
Distr.: Natl.
Personnel:
Donald S. Schneider *(Exec VP & Chief HR Officer)*
Donald E. McCombs *(Pres-Opers & Exec VP)*
Ronald L. Goolsby *(Sr VP-Client Svcs)*
Dan Sherr *(Gen Mgr-IMO Grp)*
Brands & Products:
ADVO
MICROTARGETING
SHOPWISE

VALLEY MORNING STAR
(Unit of Freedom Newspapers, Inc.)
1310 S Commerce
Harlingen, TX 78550
Tel.: (956) 430-6200
Fax: (956) 430-6231
Web Site: www.valleystar.com
Approx. Number Employees: 125
Year Founded: 1909
Business Description:
Newspaper
S.I.C.: 2711
N.A.I.C.S.: 511110
Media: 4-8-9-13-18-19-20-21-22-25
Personnel:
Tyler Patton *(Publr)*
Ramon Rodriguez *(Editor-Online)*
Charlene Vandini *(Editor-City)*
Richard Guerrero *(Dir-Adv)*
Jill Stout *(Bus Mgr)*
Peggy Elder *(Mgr-Adv Ops)*
Rusty Hall *(Mgr-Circulation)*
Melva C. Juarez *(Mgr-Acctg)*
Marcia B. Kitten *(Mgr-Mktg & Sls Promos)*
Brands & Products:
VALLEY MORNING STAR

VALPAK DIRECT MARKETING SYSTEMS, INC.
(Sub. of Cox Newspapers, Inc.)
8605 Largo Lks Dr
Largo, FL 33773
Tel.: (727) 399-3000
Fax: (727) 399-3011
Toll Free: (800) 237-6266
Web Site: www.valpak.com
Approx. Rev.: $303,462,912
Approx. Number Employees: 1,000
Year Founded: 1968
Business Description:
Direct Mail Advertising Services
S.I.C.: 7331
N.A.I.C.S.: 541860
Personnel:
Jim Sampey *(Pres & CEO)*
Jeff Heinicka *(CFO & Exec VP)*
Todd Leiser *(VP & Gen Mgr)*
Janet Guyler *(VP-HR)*
Jim Sanpey *(VP-Sls)*
Deanna Willsey *(Dir-Corp Comm)*
Marsha Strickhouser *(Mgr-Pub Rels)*
Advertising Agency:
Finn Partners
211 E Ontario St Ste 1600
Chicago, IL 60611-3297
Tel.: (312) 644-8600
Fax: (312) 932-0367

VALUE LINE, INC.
(Holding of Arnold Bernhard & Co.)
220 E 42nd St
New York, NY 10017-5806
Tel.: (212) 907-1500
Tel.: (212) 907-1610 (Corp Comm)
Fax: (212) 818-9747
Toll Free: (800) 634-3583
E-mail: vlcr@valueline.com
Web Site: www.valueline.com
Approx. Rev.: $48,667,000
Approx. Number Employees: 175
Year Founded: 1931
Business Description:
Investment Advisory Service; Investment Service
S.I.C.: 6282; 2721
N.A.I.C.S.: 523920; 511120; 523930
Export
Advertising Expenditures: $10,874,000
Media: 2-6-7-8-9-25
Distr.: Intl.; Natl.
Personnel:
Howard A. Brecher *(Acting Chm/CEO)*
John A. McKay *(CFO)*
Brands & Products:
CONVERTIBLE SURVEYS
MOST TRUSTED NAME IN INVESTMENT RESEARCH
OPTIONS

Key to Media (For complete agency information see *The Advertising Red Books-Agencies* edition):
1. Bus. Publs. 2. Cable T.V. 3. Catalogs & Directories. 4. Co-op Adv. 5. Consumer Mags. 6. D.M. to Bus. Estab.7. D.M. to Consumers
8. Daily Newsp. 9. Exhibits/Trade Shows 10. Foreign 11. Infomercial 12. Internet Adv.13. Multimedia 14. Network Radio
15. Network T.V. 16. Newsp. Distr. Mags. 17. Other 18. Outdoor (Posters, Transit) 19. Point of Purchase20. Premiums, Novelties
21. Product Samples 22. Special Events Mktg. 23. Spot Radio 24. Spot T.V. 25. Weekly Newsp. 26. Yellow Page Adv.

VALUE LINE
VALUE LINE ASSET MANAGEMENT
VALUE LINE INVESTMENT ANALYZER 3.0
VALUE LINE INVESTMENT SURVEY
VALUE LINE MUTUAL FUND SURVEY
VALUE LINE PERFORMANCE
VALUE LINE RESEARCH CENTER
VALUE LINE SAFETY
VALUE LINE TIMELINESS
VALUELINE.COM
Advertising Agency:
Vanderbilt Advertising Inc.
(House Agency)
220 East 42 St
New York, NY 10017
Tel.: (212) 907-1500
Fax: (212) 907-1914

VANCE PUBLISHING CORPORATION
400 Knightsbridge Pkwy
Lincolnshire, IL 60069
Tel.: (847) 634-2600
Fax: (847) 634-4379
E-mail: info@vancepublishing.com
Web Site: www.vancepublishing.com
E-Mail For Key Personnel:
President: pwalker@vancepublishing.com
Approx. Number Employees: 150
Business Description:
Publish & Print Trade Journals
S.I.C.: 2721
N.A.I.C.S.: 511120
Media: 2
Personnel:
William C. Vance *(Chm)*
Peggy Walker *(Pres)*
Donald P. Ransdell *(VP & Dir-Publ)*
Steve Reiss *(VP-Publ, Dir-Salon & Wood Interiors)*
Tim L. Tobeck *(VP & Dir-Publ-Protein Div)*
Lori Eppel *(VP-Fin)*
Tom Fogarty *(Dir-Production)*
Philip Donahoo *(Mgr-Bus Dev-The Greenbook Grp)*
Connie Dudziak *(Mgr-Adv Ops)*
Brands & Products:
ACCESSORY MERCHANDISING
BOVINE VETERINARIAN
CITRUS & VEGETABLE MAGAZINE
COMMUNICATIONS FOR BUSINESS
COTTON FARMING
CUSTOM WOODWORKER'S ILLUSTRATED BUYING GUIDE
CUSTOM WOODWORKING BUSINESS
DAIRY HERD MANAGEMENT
DEALER & APPLICATOR
DROVERS
FURNITURE STYLE
THE GROWER
MEAT & SEAFOOD MERCHANDISING
MODERN SALON
THE PACKER
PEANUT GROWER
PORK
PROCESS
PRODUCE CONCEPTS
PRODUCE MERCHANDISING
RESIDENTIAL LIGHTING
RICE FARMING
SALON TODAY
SWINE PRACTITIONER
VANCE
WOOD & WOOD PRODUCTS
WOOD & WOOD PRODUCTS RED BOOK

VANITY FAIR
(Unit of Conde Nast Publications, Inc.)
4 Times Sq Fl 22
New York, NY 10036
Tel.: (212) 286-2860
Fax: (212) 286-7636
E-mail: vfmail@vanityfair.com
Web Site: www.vanityfair.com
Approx. Number Employees: 40
Business Description:
Magazine
S.I.C.: 2721
N.A.I.C.S.: 511120
Media: 6-8
Personnel:
Edward Menicheschi *(VP & Publr)*
Peter Devine *(Editor-Copy)*
Graydon Carter *(Editor)*
David Friend *(Editor-Creative Devel)*
Bruce Handy *(Sr Editor-Articles)*
Punch Hutton *(Editor)*
Jane Sarkin *(Editor)*
Ann Schneider *(Sr Editor-Photo Res)*
Ingrid Sischy *(Editor)*
Anderson Tepper *(Editor-Online)*
Julie Weiss *(Dir-Art)*
John Banta *(Dir-Res)*
Mary F. Braeunig *(Dir-Market)*
Sunhee C. Grinnell *(Dir-Beauty)*
David Harris *(Dir-Design)*
Sara Marks *(Dir-Special Projects)*
David Sorrano *(Dir-Mktg)*
Susan White *(Dir-Photography)*
Brands & Products:
VANITY FAIR MAGAZINE

VANTAGE PRESS, INC.
419 Pk Ave S
New York, NY 10016
Tel.: (212) 736-1767
Fax: (212) 736-2273
E-mail: vantagepub@aol.com
Web Site: www.vantagepress.com
Approx. Number Employees: 20
Year Founded: 1949
Business Description:
Publisher of Fiction & Non-fiction Books
S.I.C.: 2731
N.A.I.C.S.: 511130
Advertising Expenditures: $500,000
Media: 4-6-7-8-9-25
Distr.: Natl.
Budget Set: Nov.
Personnel:
Martin Littlefield *(Chm & Pres)*
Brands & Products:
VANTAGE PRESS
Advertising Agency:
Murray Leff & Co., Inc.
8216 250th St
Jamaica, NY 11426-2524
Tel.: (718) 470-6729
Fax: (718) 347-8562

VENTURA COUNTY STAR
(Sub. of The E.W. Scripps Company)
PO Box 6006
Camarillo, CA 93011
Tel.: (805) 437-0000
Fax: (805) 650-2950
E-mail: feedback@venturacountystar.com
Web Site: www.venturacountystar.com
Sales Range: $25-49.9 Million
Approx. Number Employees: 420
Business Description:
Publisher of Morning & Sunday Newspapers
S.I.C.: 2711
N.A.I.C.S.: 511110
Media: 8-9-13
Personnel:
George H. Cogswell, III *(Pres & Publr)*
Mike Blackwell *(Editor-Sports)*
Marty Bonvechio *(Editor-County)*
Timm Herdt *(Editor-State)*
Karen Hibdon *(Editor-Community)*
Joe R. Howry *(Editor)*
Jim Medina *(Editor)*
Marianne Ratcliff *(Editor-Opinion Page)*
Rick Welch *(Editor-Arts & Living)*
Mark Wyckoff *(Editor-Entertainment)*
Denice Atcheson *(Dir-Fin)*
Steven Guzzo *(Dir-IT)*
Ernie Reyes *(Dir-Ops)*
Mary Scott *(Mgr-Editorial Ops)*

VERO BEACH PRESS JOURNAL
(Sub. of The E.W. Scripps Company)
1801 US Hwy 1
Vero Beach, FL 32960
Tel.: (772) 562-2315
Tel.: (772) 569-7100
Fax: (772) 978-2365
E-mail: info@tcpalm.com
Web Site: www.tcpalm.com
Sales Range: $25-49.9 Million
Approx. Number Employees: 30
Business Description:
Morning & Sunday Newspapers Publisher
S.I.C.: 2711
N.A.I.C.S.: 511110
Media: 8-9
Personnel:
Laura Lucas *(Mgr-Mktg)*

VERTIS COMMUNICATIONS INC.
(Sub. of Vertis Inc.)
100 Winners Cir
Brentwood, TN 37027-5012
Tel.: (615) 377-0377
Fax: (615) 377-0370
Toll Free: (800) 621-7746
Web Site: www.vertisinc.com
Approx. Number Employees: 46
Year Founded: 1926
Business Description:
Newspaper Advertising Inserts, Comic Books, Sunday Color Comics, Large Format Publications Printing Services
S.I.C.: 2752; 2759
N.A.I.C.S.: 323110; 323112
Media: 2-7-10-13-22-25
Distr.: Natl.
Personnel:
Laurie Oswald *(Mgr-Mktg)*
Brands & Products:
COLOREXPRESS
COLORLOCK
COLORRIGHT
COLORSPACE
COLORSTOR
COLORVUE

VERTIS DIRECT MARKETING SERVICES
(Sub. of Vertis Inc.)
1980 Rte 1
North Brunswick, NJ 08902-4418
Mailing Address:
PO Box 6023
North Brunswick, NJ 08902-6023
Tel.: (732) 297-5100
Fax: (732) 821-3761
Toll Free: (800) 955-0545
Web Site: www.vertisinc.com
Approx. Number Employees: 500
Year Founded: 1969
Business Description:
Direct Response Printing Services
S.I.C.: 2759
N.A.I.C.S.: 323119
Import
Media: 1-8-10-13-20
Distr.: Intl.; Natl.
Budget Set: Dec.

VERTIS INC.
(Sub. of Vertis Holdings, Inc.)
(d/b/a Vertis Communications)
250 W Pratt Ste 1800
Baltimore, MD 21201
Mailing Address:
PO Box 17102
Baltimore, MD 21297-1102
Tel.: (410) 528-9800
Fax: (410) 528-9287
Toll Free: (800) 577-8371
E-mail: info@vertisinc.com
Web Site: www.vertisinc.com
Approx. Rev.: $1,365,154,000
Approx. Number Employees: 5,800
Year Founded: 1967
Business Description:
Newspaper Inserts Producer; Direct Mail, Package Design, Interactive Marketing & Media Planning Services
S.I.C.: 7319; 2741; 2759; 7331
N.A.I.C.S.: 541890; 323119; 516110; 541860
Media: 10-22
Personnel:
Ken Kaisen *(CIO & CTO)*
Richard Guetzloff *(CIO & Sr VP)*
Jeff Pritchett *(Treas & VP-Fin)*
John Colarossi *(Sr VP & Gen Mgr-Vertis Comm)*
Oscar Padilla *(Dir-Interactive Svcs)*
Advertising Agency:
Formula PR
810 Parkview Dr N
El Segundo, CA 90245
Tel.: (310) 578-7050
Fax: (310) 578-7077

VICTORIA ADVOCATE PUBLISHING COMPANY
311 E Constitution St
Victoria, TX 77901
Tel.: (361) 575-1451
Fax: (361) 574-1225
Web Site: www.victx.com
Approx. Sls.: $15,588,251
Approx. Number Employees: 131
Business Description:
Newspaper Publisher
S.I.C.: 2711
N.A.I.C.S.: 511110
Media: 8-9
Personnel:
John M. Roberts *(Owner & Pres)*

Key to Media (For complete agency information see *The Advertising Red Books-Agencies* edition):
1. Bus. Publs. 2. Cable T.V. 3. Catalogs & Directories. 4. Co-op Adv. 5. Consumer Mags. 6. D.M. to Bus. Estab.7. D.M. to Consumers 8. Daily Newsp. 9. Exhibits/Trade Shows 10. Foreign 11. Infomercial 12. Internet Adv.13. Multimedia 14. Network Radio 15. Network T.V. 16. Newsp. Distr. Mags. 17. Other 18. Outdoor (Posters, Transit) 19. Point of Purchase20. Premiums, Novelties 21. Product Samples 22. Special Events Mktg. 23. Spot Radio 24. Spot T.V. 25. Weekly Newsp. 26. Yellow Page Adv.

Victoria Advocate Publishing Company — (Continued)

Dan Easton *(Co-Publr & VP-Interactive)*
Brenda Miller-Fergerson *(Sr VP & Gen Mgr)*

VILLAGE SOUP
301 Pk St
Rockland, ME 04841
Tel.: (207) 594-4401
Fax: (207) 596-6981
Web Site: www.knox.villagesoup.com
Approx. Number Employees: 110
Business Description:
Newspapers, Publishing & Printing
S.I.C.: 2711
N.A.I.C.S.: 511110
Media: 8-9
Personnel:
Donna Culbertson *(Dir)*
Terri Mahoney *(Dir-Adv)*
Brands & Products:
NEWSPAPER

VILLARD BOOKS
(Unit of Random House Adult Trade Group)
1745 Broadway
New York, NY 10019
Tel.: (212) 782-9000
Web Site: www.randomhouse.com
Approx. Number Employees: 100
Year Founded: 1983
Business Description:
Book Publisher
S.I.C.: 2731
N.A.I.C.S.: 511130
Advertising Expenditures: $200,000
Media: 2-4-6-7-8-9-10-14-23-25-26
Distr.: Intl.
Brands & Products:
STRIVERS ROW
VILLARD

THE VIRGINIAN-PILOT
(Sub. of Landmark Media Enterprises LLC)
150 W Varmvaltom Ave
Norfolk, VA 23510
Tel.: (757) 446-2000
Fax: (757) 446-2414
Toll Free: (800) 446-2004
E-mail: info@pilotonline.com
Web Site: www.pilotonline.com
Approx. Number Employees: 2,500
Business Description:
Publishing
S.I.C.: 2711; 4833
N.A.I.C.S.: 511110; 515120
Media: 9-13-25
Personnel:
Carl A. Fincke, Jr. *(Sr Editor)*
Brands & Products:
HAMPTONROADS.COM
PILOTONLINE.COM
VIRGINIAN PILOT

VIRGO PUBLISHING, LLC
(Holding of Arlington Capital Partners)
3300 N Central Ave Ste 300
Phoenix, AZ 85012
Mailing Address:
PO Box 40079
Phoenix, AZ 85067-0079
Tel.: (480) 990-1101
Fax: (480) 990-0819
E-mail: info@vpico.com
Web Site: www.vpico.com
Approx. Sls.: $35,239,408
Approx. Number Employees: 100
Year Founded: 1986
Business Description:
Trade Magazine Publisher
S.I.C.: 2721; 2741
N.A.I.C.S.: 511120; 516110
Media: 2-10-22
Personnel:
John Siefert *(CEO)*
Dana Armitstead *(Publr)*
Bill Eikost *(Publr)*
Bob Weeks *(Publr)*
Peggy Jackson *(Exec VP-Health & Nutrition Network)*
Tim McElligott *(Editor in Chief-B/OSS)*
Brands & Products:
BILLING & OSS WORLD
CHURCH SOLUTION
CORPORATE LOGO
CULINOLOGY ONLINE
ENDONURSE
FOOD PRODUCT DESIGN
IMMEDIATE CARE BUSINESS
INFECTION CONTROL TODAY
INSIDE SELF-STORAGE
LOOKING FIT
MODERN CAR CARE
NATURAL PRODUCT INSIDER
PHONE+
PROFESSIONAL DOOR DEALER
RENTAL BUSINESS TODAY
SUPPLYSIDE INSIDE COSMECEUTICALS
TODAY'S SURGICENTER
XCHANGE

VOGUE MAGAZINE
(Unit of Conde Nast Publications, Inc.)
4 Times Sq Fl 12
New York, NY 10036-6518
Tel.: (212) 286-2860
Tel.: (212) 880-8800
Fax: (212) 286-6921
Web Site: www.style.com
Approx. Number Employees: 120
Business Description:
Publisher of Women's Magazine
S.I.C.: 2721; 2741
N.A.I.C.S.: 511120; 516110
Media: 6-8-10-13-18-19-22
Distr.: Intl.; Natl.
Personnel:
Lottie Oakley *(Co-Assoc Publr)*
David Stuckey *(Co-Assoc Publr)*
Susan Plagemann *(VP & Publr)*
Diego Scotti *(Exec Dir & Head-Mktg)*
Anna Wintour *(Editor-in-Chief)*
Phyllis Posnick *(Exec Editor-Fashion)*
Jillian Demling *(Editor-Entertainment)*
Filipa Fino *(Sr Editor-Accessories)*
Eve MacSweeney *(Assoc Editor)*
Meredith Melling Burke *(Sr Editor-Market)*
Ethel Park *(Asst Editor-Fashion)*
Valerie Steiker *(Sr Editor-Special Projects)*
Abigail Walch *(Sr Editor-Special Projects)*
Grace Coddington *(Dir-Creative)*
Sarah Brown *(Dir-Beauty)*
Tonne Goodman *(Dir-Fashion)*
Megan Salt *(Dir-Pub Rel)*
Ivan Shaw *(Dir-Photo)*
Virginia Smith *(Dir-Fashion Market & Accessories)*
Stephanie Winston Wolkoff *(Dir-Special Events)*

VOICE COMMUNICATIONS CORP.
(Sub. of 21st Century Newspapers, Inc.)
(d/b/a Voice Newspapers)
51180 Bedford St
New Baltimore, MI 48047-2533
Mailing Address:
PO Box 760
New Baltimore, MI 48047
Tel.: (586) 716-8100
Fax: (586) 716-8918
Toll Free: (800) 561-2248
E-mail: thevoice@voicenews.com
Web Site: www.voicenews.com
Approx. Number Employees: 42
Business Description:
Weekly Newspaper Publishing
S.I.C.: 2711; 2721
N.A.I.C.S.: 511110; 511120
Media: 8-25
Personnel:
Debbie Loggins *(Gen Mgr-Adv)*
Jeff Payne *(Editor)*
Rene Allard *(Mgr-Circulation)*
Brands & Products:
DOWN RIVER NEWS
MACOMB TOWNSHIP VOICE
WEEKEND VOICE

WALDEN BOOK COMPANY, INC.
(Sub. of Borders Group, Inc.)
100 Phoenix Dr
Ann Arbor, MI 48108-2202
Tel.: (734) 477-1100
Fax: (734) 477-1643
Toll Free: (800) 335-5885
Web Site: www.waldenbooks.com
Sales Range: $800-899.9 Million
Approx. Number Employees: 1,500
Business Description:
Book Retailer
S.I.C.: 5942
N.A.I.C.S.: 451211
Media: 3-7-8-15-16-19-26
Distr.: Natl.
Advertising Agency:
KSL Media, Inc.
367 Park Ave S 4th Fl
New York, NY 10016
Tel.: (212) 352-5800
Fax: (212) 352-5935
Media Buying Agency

WALKER PUBLISHING COMPANY, INC.
(Div. of Bloomsbury Publishing plc)
(d/b/a Walker & Company)
104 5th Ave 7th Fl
New York, NY 10011
Tel.: (212) 727-8300
Fax: (800) 218-9367
Fax: (212) 727-0984
Toll Free: (800) 289-2553
E-mail: publicity@walkerbooks.com
Web Site: www.walkerbooks.com
Approx. Number Employees: 30
Year Founded: 1959
Business Description:
Book Publisher
S.I.C.: 2731; 2741
N.A.I.C.S.: 511130; 511199
Advertising Expenditures: $200,000
Media: 2-6-7-8-9-25
Distr.: Natl.
Brands & Products:
WALKER & COMPANY

THE WALL STREET JOURNAL
(Sub. of Dow Jones Consumer Media)
1211 Ave Americas
New York, NY 10036
Tel.: (212) 416-2000
Web Site: www.wsj.com
Sales Range: $100-124.9 Million
Year Founded: 1889
Business Description:
Business Newspaper
S.I.C.: 2711
N.A.I.C.S.: 511110
Media: 2-6-7-8-9-13-18-20-23
Distr.: Natl.
Budget Set: Jan.
Personnel:
Keith Rupert Murdoch *(Chm)*
Todd H. Larsen *(Pres)*
Leslie Hinton *(CEO & Publr)*
Paul Bascobert *(CMO)*
Daniel Bernard *(Chief Product Officer)*
Michael F. Rooney *(Chief Revenue Officer)*
Lynne Brennen *(Sr VP-Circulation)*
Matthew A. Goldberg *(Sr VP-Digital Strategy & Ops-WSJ Digital Network)*
Joseph B. Vincent *(Sr VP-Ops)*
Sandra Baez *(VP-Adv Ops)*
Chris Collins *(VP-Multi Media Sls-US, Europe & The Americas)*
Matt Ellsworth *(VP-Mktg)*
Larry L. Hoffman *(VP-Production)*
Imtiaz Patel *(VP-Strategic Plng & Analysis)*
Don Reis *(VP)*
Andrew T. Rost *(VP-Strategic & Group Circulation)*
Alisa Bowen *(Gen Mgr)*
Gail Griffin *(Gen Mgr)*
Almar Latour *(Editor-in-Chief-Asia)*
Brian Tong *(Sls Dir-Classified Adv-Asia)*
Robert H. Christie *(Dir-Comm)*
Advertising Agency:
TBC Direct, Inc.
900 S Wolfe St
Baltimore, MD 21231
Tel.: (410) 347-7500
Fax: (410) 986-1299

THE WALTON SUN
(Unit of Freedom Newspapers, Inc.)
5597 Hwy 98 W Ste 203
Santa Rosa Beach, FL 32459
Mailing Address:
PO Box 2363
Santa Rosa Beach, FL 32459
Tel.: (850) 267-4555
Fax: (850) 267-0929
E-mail: news@waltonsun.com
Web Site: www.waltonsun.com
Approx. Number Employees: 75
Year Founded: 1997
Business Description:
Newspaper
S.I.C.: 2711
N.A.I.C.S.: 511110
Media: 8-13-25
Personnel:
William Hatfield *(Editor)*
Joan Kirkland *(Mgr-Bus)*

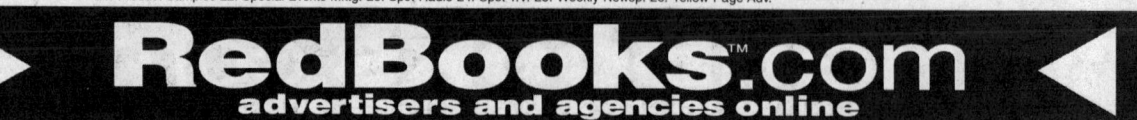

Key to Media (For complete agency information see *The Advertising Red Books-Agencies* edition):
1. Bus. Publs. 2. Cable T.V. 3. Catalogs & Directories. 4. Co-op Adv. 5. Consumer Mags. 6. D.M. to Bus. Estab.7. D.M. to Consumers
8. Daily Newsp. 9. Exhibits/Trade Shows 10. Foreign 11. Infomercial 12. Internet Adv.13. Multimedia 14. Network Radio
15. Network T.V. 16. Newsp. Distr. Mags. 17. Other 18. Outdoor (Posters, Transit) 19. Point of Purchase20. Premiums, Novelties
21. Product Samples 22. Special Events Mktg. 23. Spot Radio 24. Spot T.V. 25. Weekly Newsp. 26. Yellow Page Adv.

WARNER PRESS, INC.

1201 E 5th St
Anderson, IN 46012-3472
Tel.: (765) 644-7721
Fax: (765) 640-8005
Toll Free: (800) 741-7721
E-mail: wporders@warnerpress.org
Web Site: www.warnerpress.com
Approx. Number Employees: 55
Year Founded: 1881
Business Description:
Religious Materials Publisher
S.I.C.: 2731; 5049
N.A.I.C.S.: 511130; 423490
Import Export
Advertising Expenditures: $168,000
Bus. Publs.: $15,000; Catalogs & Directories: $20,000; Consumer Mags.: $5,000; D.M. to Bus. Estab.: $60,000; D.M. to Consumers: $10,000; Exhibits/Trade Shows: $12,000; Internet Adv.: $5,000; Other: $10,000; Point of Purchase: $20,000; Product Samples: $5,000; Special Events Mktg.: $5,000; Yellow Page Adv.: $1,000
Distr.: Natl.
Budget Set: Oct.
Personnel:
C. Eric King *(Pres)*
Regina Jackson *(Dir-Mktg)*
Michael Meadows *(Mgr-Mktg & Comm)*
Brands & Products:
CHRISTIAN ART
CONNECT EQUIP INSPIRE
EGERMEIER'S
HERITAGE COLLECTION
REFLECTION
WARNER PRESS

WARRICK PUBLISHING CO. INC.

(Sub. of Brehm Communications Inc.)
204 W Locust St
Boonville, IN 47601-1594
Tel.: (812) 897-2330
Fax: (812) 897-3703
Web Site: www.tristate-media.com/warricknews/aboutus
Approx. Number Employees: 9
Year Founded: 1985
Business Description:
Newspaper Publisher
S.I.C.: 2711; 2721
N.A.I.C.S.: 511110; 511120
Import Export
Media: 13-25
Personnel:
Gary Neal *(Publr)*
Brands & Products:
BOONVILLE STANDARD
NEWBURGH REGISTER

THE WASHINGTON NEWSPAPER PUBLISHING COMPANY, LLC

(Sub. of Clarity Media Group, Inc.)
(d/b/a The Washington Examiner)
1015 15th St NW Ste 500
Washington, DC 20005
Tel.: (202) 903-2000
Fax: (202) 459-4994
E-mail: editor@washingtonexaminer.com
Web Site: www.dcexaminer.com
Sales Range: $200-249.9 Million
Approx. Number Employees: 500
Business Description:
Newspapers Publisher
S.I.C.: 2711; 2741
N.A.I.C.S.: 511110; 516110
Media: 8-9
Personnel:
Michael E. Phelps *(Pres, CEO & Publr)*
Charlene Stewart *(VP-Adv)*
Brands & Products:
WASHINGTON EXAMINER

THE WASHINGTON POST

(Div. of The Washington Post Company)
1150 15th St NW
Washington, DC 20071
Tel.: (202) 334-6000
Fax: (202) 334-7126
Toll Free: (800) 627-1150
Web Site: www.washingtonpost.com
Sales Range: $450-499.9 Million
Approx. Number Employees: 3,000
Year Founded: 1877
Business Description:
Newspaper
S.I.C.: 2711
N.A.I.C.S.: 511110
Advertising Expenditures: $2,532,000
Media: 2-5-7-9-10-13-16-18-20-22-25
Distr.: Reg.
Budget Set: July
Personnel:
Donald E. Graham *(Chm & CEO)*
Stephen P. Hills *(Pres & Gen Mgr)*
Katharine Weymouth *(CEO-Washington Post Media)*
Diana Daniels *(Gen Counsel, Sec & VP)*
Ann McDaniel *(Sr VP)*
Gerald Rosberg *(Sr VP-Plng & Dev)*
Marcus Brauchli *(Exec Editor)*
Keith Tomatore *(VP-HR-Opers)*
David Griffin *(Editor-Visuals)*
Fred Hiatt *(Editor-Editorial Page)*
Bonnie Jo Mount *(Editor-Photography)*
Vanessa Ampolini *(Mgr-Mktg Projects)*
Nicolle Devenish *(Dir-Commun)*
David E. Seldin *(Dir-Commun)*
Wes Tyeryar *(Dir-Sls-Washington Post Digital)*
Marc H. Rosenberg *(Sr Mgr-Adv)*
Tracy Williams *(Sr Mgr-Mktg)*
Brands & Products:
THE WASHINGTON POST

THE WASHINGTON POST COMPANY

1150 15th St NW
Washington, DC 20071-0001
Tel.: (202) 334-6000
Web Site: www.washpostco.com
Approx. Rev.: $4,723,573,000
Approx. Number Employees: 20,000
Year Founded: 1947
Business Description:
Newspapers, Magazines, Broadcasting, Cable, Educational & Career Service Centers, Database Publishing & Electronic Information Services
S.I.C.: 2711; 2741; 4833
N.A.I.C.S.: 511110; 515120; 516110
Advertising Expenditures: $1,346,870,000
Media: 8-9-14-15-19
Personnel:
Donald E. Graham *(Chm & CEO)*
Boisfeuillet Jones, Jr. *(Vice Chm)*
Hal S. Jones *(CFO & Sr VP-Fin)*
Wallace R. Cooney *(Chief Acctg Officer & VP-Fin)*
Katharine Weymouth *(CEO-Washington Post Media)*
Veronica Dillon *(Gen Counsel, Sec & VP)*
Christopher Ma *(Sr VP)*
Ann McDaniel *(Sr VP)*
Pinkie Dent Mayfield *(VP-Corp Solutions & Asst Treas-Corp Solutions)*
Rima Calderon *(VP-Corp Comm & External Rels)*
Jane Elizabeth *(Editor-Digital)*
Kevin Merida *(Editor-Natl)*
Greg Schneider *(Business Editor)*
Sandy Sugawara *(Editor-Universal News)*
Scott Vance *(Editor-News)*
Matt Vita *(Editor-Sports)*
Aloma L. Myers *(Asst Treas)*
Brands & Products:
BUDGET TRAVEL
EL TIEMPO LATINO
NEWSWEEK
THE WASHINGTON POST
Advertising Agencies:
Adworks, Inc.
1225 19th St NW Ste 500
Washington, DC 20036
Tel.: (202) 342-5585
Fax: (202) 739-8201

ML Rogers
102 Madison Ave 10th Fl
New York, NY 10016
Tel.: (212) 213-3833
(Arthur Frommer Budget Travel Magazine)

WASHINGTONPOST.NEWSWEEK INTERACTIVE

(Unit of The Washington Post)
1515 N Courthouse Rd
Arlington, VA 22216
Mailing Address:
PO Box 17370
Arlington, VA 22216-7370
Tel.: (703) 469-2500
Fax: (703) 469-2995
E-mail: webnews@washingtonpost.com
Web Site: www.washingtonpost.com
Sales Range: $75-99.9 Million
Approx. Number Employees: 250
Business Description:
Online News Publication
S.I.C.: 2741; 2731
N.A.I.C.S.: 511140; 511130; 511199
Media: 13
Personnel:
Mark Whitaker *(VP & Editor-in-Chief)*
Jennifer Moyer *(VP-Fin)*
Anthony DeMaio *(Dir-Sls-East Coast)*

WATT PUBLISHING COMPANY

303 North Main Street Ste 500
Rockford, IL 61101
Tel.: (815) 996-5400
Fax: (815) 966-6416
Web Site: www.wattnet.com
Approx. Number Employees: 65
Year Founded: 1917
Business Description:
Magazines Publisher
S.I.C.: 2721
N.A.I.C.S.: 511120
Export
Advertising Expenditures: $400,000
Media: 2-7-10-17
Distr.: Intl.; Natl.
Budget Set: Nov.
Personnel:
Gregory A. Watt *(Pres & COO)*
Brands & Products:
EGG INDUSTRY
FEED INT'L
FEED MANAGEMENT
INDUSTRIA AVICOLA
MEAT PROCESSING
MEATNEWS.COM
PETFOOD FORUM
PETFOOD INDUSTRY
PIG INT'L
POULTRY INT'L
WATT
WATT POULTRY U.S.A.

WEBSITE MAGAZINE INCORPORATED

999 E Touhy Ave
Des Plaines, IL 60018
Tel.: (773) 628-2779
Fax: (773) 272-0920
Toll Free: (800) 817-1518
E-mail: info@websitemagazine.com
Web Site: www.websitemagazine.com
Approx. Number Employees: 10
Year Founded: 2007
Business Description:
Magazine & Website Publisher
S.I.C.: 2721; 2741
N.A.I.C.S.: 511120; 516110
Media: 7-8-13
Personnel:
Peter Prestipino *(Editor-in-Chief)*
Jesse Erbach *(Dir-Art)*
Brands & Products:
WEBSITE MAGAZINE

WEIDER PUBLICATIONS, LLC

(Sub. of American Media, Inc.)
21100 Erwin St
Woodland Hills, CA 91367-3712
Tel.: (818) 884-6800
Fax: (818) 884-0113
E-mail: info@fitnessonline.com
Web Site: www.fitnessonline.com
Sales Range: $150-199.9 Million
Approx. Number Employees: 75
Year Founded: 1939
Business Description:
Publisher of Health & Fitness Magazines
S.I.C.: 2721
N.A.I.C.S.: 511120
Import Export
Media: 2-3-4-5-6-13-19-21-22
Distr.: Intl.
Budget Set: May
Personnel:
David Pecker *(Chm)*
Paco Acosta *(Dir-Consumer Mktg)*

WENNER MEDIA LLC

1290 Ave of the Americas 2nd Fl
New York, NY 10104
Tel.: (212) 484-1616
Fax: (212) 484-3435
Web Site: www.rollingstone.com
Sales Range: $350-399.9 Million
Approx. Number Employees: 490
Year Founded: 1967
Business Description:
Periodicals & Books Publisher

Key to Media (For complete agency information see *The Advertising Red Books-Agencies* edition):
1. Bus. Publs. 2. Cable T.V. 3. Catalogs & Directories. 4. Co-op Adv. 5. Consumer Mags. 6. D.M. to Bus. Estab. 7. D.M. to Consumers 8. Daily Newsp. 9. Exhibits/Trade Shows 10. Foreign 11. Infomercial 12. Internet Adv. 13. Multimedia 14. Network Radio 15. Network T.V. 16. Newsp. Distr. Mags. 17. Other 18. Outdoor (Posters, Transit) 19. Point of Purchase 20. Premiums, Novelties 21. Product Samples 22. Special Events Mktg. 23. Spot Radio 24. Spot T.V. 25. Weekly Newsp. 26. Yellow Page Adv.

Wenner Media LLC — (Continued)
S.I.C.: 2721
N.A.I.C.S.: 511120
Advertising Expenditures: $1,000,000
Media: 2-6
Personnel:
Jann S. Wenner *(Owner & Chm)*
John Gruber *(COO)*
Matt Mastrangelo *(Publr-Rolling Stone)*
Michael Wolfe *(Publr-Men's Journal)*
Timothy Walsh *(VP-Fin)*
Alwyn Ling *(Dir-IT)*
Stephanie Freeman *(Mgr-Integrated Mktg-Men's Journal)*
Brands & Products:
MEN'S JOURNAL
ROLLING STONE
US WEEKLY

WESTERN COMMUNICATIONS INC.
1777 SW Chandler Ave
Bend, OR 97702
Tel.: (541) 382-1811
Fax: (541) 385-5802
Web Site: www.bendbulletin.com
Approx. Number Employees: 380
Year Founded: 1953
Business Description:
Newspaper Publisher
S.I.C.: 2711; 2741
N.A.I.C.S.: 511110; 511199
Media: 8-9
Personnel:
Elizabeth C. McCool *(Chm)*
Gordon Black *(Pres & Publr-Bulletin)*
Karen Anderson *(CFO)*
Brands & Products:
THE BAKER CITY HERALD
THE BULLETIN
BURNS TIMES-HERALD
CURRY COASTAL PILOT
THE DAILY TRIPLICATE
HERMISTON HERALD
LA GRANDE OBSERVER
UNION-DEMOCRAT

WESTERN NEWSPAPERS, INC.
1748 S Arizona Ave
Yuma, AZ 85364-5727
Tel.: (928) 783-3311
Fax: (928) 783-3313
Web Site: www.westernnews.com
Approx. Number Employees: 320
Year Founded: 1978
Business Description:
Publisher of Newspapers
S.I.C.: 2711; 7319
N.A.I.C.S.: 511110; 541850
Import Export
Media: 8-9
Personnel:
Blake Dewitt *(Sr VP)*
Dave Montgomery *(VP-Fin)*

W.H. FREEMAN AND WORTH PUBLISHERS, INC
(Sub. of Georg von Holtzbrinck GmbH & Co. KG)
41 Madison Ave
New York, NY 10010-2202
Tel.: (212) 576-9400
Fax: (212) 689-2383
Web Site: www.bfwpub.com
Approx. Sls.: $130,000,000
Approx. Number Employees: 100
Business Description:
Book Publishing Services
S.I.C.: 2731
N.A.I.C.S.: 511130
Media: 7-10
Personnel:
Elizabeth Widdicombe *(Pres)*
John Britch *(Dir-Mktg)*

WHERE INTERNATIONAL LP
(Sub. of Miller Publishing Group, LLC)
(d/b/a Where Magazines International)
11100 Santa Monica Blvd
Los Angeles, CA 90025
Tel.: (310) 893-5400
Web Site: www.wheremagazine.com
Approx. Sls.: $21,000,000
Business Description:
Magazines: Publishing & Printing
S.I.C.: 2721
N.A.I.C.S.: 511120
Media: 6-8

WHITE HOUSE HISTORICAL ASSOCIATION
740 Jackson Pl NW
Washington, DC 20038
Tel.: (202) 737-8292
Fax: (202) 789-0440
E-mail: webmaster@whha.org
Web Site: www.whitehousehistory.org
Approx. Number Employees: 100
Year Founded: 1961
Business Description:
Gifts & Educational Materials Related to the White House
S.I.C.: 2731; 5942
N.A.I.C.S.: 511130; 451211
Media: 10-13-18-20
Personnel:
Frederick J. Ryan, Jr. *(Chm)*
John F.W. Rogers *(Vice Chm)*
Neil W. Horstman *(Pres)*
Maria Downs *(Mgr-PR)*

THE WICHITA EAGLE
(Sub. of McClatchy Newspapers, Inc.)
825 E Douglas Ave
Wichita, KS 67202
Tel.: (316) 268-6000
Fax: (316) 268-6627
E-mail: schisenhall@witchitaeagle.com
Web Site: www.kansas.com
Sales Range: $25-49.9 Million
Approx. Number Employees: 400
Year Founded: 1872
Business Description:
Newspaper Publisher
S.I.C.: 2711
N.A.I.C.S.: 511110
Media: 9-10-18-20-22-23-24-26
Distr.: Direct to Consumer; Reg.
Budget Set: Sept.
Personnel:
Kim Nussbaum *(Pres & Publr)*
Dale Seiwert *(VP-CFO)*
Sherry Chisenhall *(Editor)*
Marcia Werts *(Editor)*

WIESNER PUBLISHING, LLC
7009 S Potomac St Ste 200
Englewood, CO 80112
Tel.: (303) 397-7600
Fax: (303) 397-7619
Web Site:
www.wiesnerpublishing.com
Approx. Number Employees: 135
Business Description:
Publisher of Magazines
S.I.C.: 2721
N.A.I.C.S.: 511120
Media: 2-6-7-10-13-22
Personnel:
E. Patrick Wiesner *(Pres)*
Dan Wiesner *(CEO)*
John Rich *(CFO)*
Betsy Kominsky *(VP & Grp Publr)*
John Wiesner *(VP-IT)*
Brands & Products:
BENEFITS SELLING
COLORADO BIZ
SENIOR MARKET ADVISOR
TRUCKING TIMES & SPORT UTILITY

WILLIAM H. SADLIER, INC.
9 Pine St
New York, NY 10005-1002
Tel.: (212) 227-2120
Fax: (212) 312-6080
Toll Free: (800) 221-5175
E-mail: webmaster@sadlier.com
Web Site: www.sadlier.com
Sales Range: $25-49.9 Million
Approx. Number Employees: 220
Year Founded: 1832
Business Description:
Textbook Publishing-Elementary & High School
S.I.C.: 2731
N.A.I.C.S.: 511130
Export
Media: 4-6-8-10-20-21-25
Distr.: Direct to Consumer; Intl.; Natl.
Budget Set: Aug.
Personnel:
William Sadlier Dinger *(Pres)*
Frank Sadlier Dinger, Jr. *(COO)*
Angela Dinger *(Gen Counsel)*
Rosemary Calicchio *(Publr & Exec VP)*
Carol Eipeis *(Exec VP-Creative Ops & Publr)*
John Bonenberger *(VP-Sls & Mgr-Natl Sls)*
Kevin O'Donnell *(VP & Administrator-Sls-Natl)*
Melissa Dinger Gibbons *(Dir-Program Res & Dev)*
Brands & Products:
SADLIER

WILLIAM S. HEIN & CO., INC.
1285 Main St
Buffalo, NY 14209-1911
Tel.: (716) 882-2600
Fax: (716) 883-8100
E-mail: mail@wshein.com
Web Site: www.wshein.com
Approx. Number Employees: 120
Year Founded: 1961
Business Description:
Book Publishing
S.I.C.: 2731; 5942
N.A.I.C.S.: 511130; 451211
Import Export
Media: 4-10-22
Personnel:
William S. Hein *(Chm)*
Kevin Marmion *(Pres)*
Bonnie Morton *(Treas & Asst Sec)*
Richard Spinelli *(Exec VP)*
Daniel P. Rosati *(Sr VP)*
Shane Marmion *(VP-Product Dev)*
Sylvia Bertot *(Asst Controller)*
Dale Missert *(Mgr-Acct Svcs/Royalty Admin)*
Lynne Zona *(Mgr-Customer Svcs)*

WINN DEVON ART GROUP
(Div. of Encore Art Group)
110-6311 Westminster Hwy
Richmond, BC V7C 4V4, Canada
Tel.: (206) 763-9544
Fax: (206) 762-1389
Web Site: www.winndevon.com
Approx. Number Employees: 50
Business Description:
Fine Art Reproductions, Limited Edition Prints, Imprints, Monoprints & Upscale Posters Publisher
S.I.C.: 2741
N.A.I.C.S.: 511199
Media: 10-13

WOODALL PUBLICATIONS CORP.
(Sub. of Affinity Group, Inc.)
2575 Vista Del Mar Dr
Ventura, CA 93002-8600
Tel.: (805) 667-2001
Fax: (805) 667-4468
Toll Free: (800) 323-9076
E-mail: info@woodalls.com
Web Site: www.woodalls.com
Approx. Number Employees: 50
Year Founded: 1935
Business Description:
Camping & RV Magazines Publisher
S.I.C.: 2741; 2721
N.A.I.C.S.: 511140; 511120
Media: 6-7-8-10-13-19-20-21
Distr.: Intl.; Natl.
Personnel:
Genevieve Branco *(Dir-Mktg & Consumer Experience)*
Brands & Products:
CAMPERWAYS
FLORIDA RV TRAVELER
MIDWEST RV TRAVELER
NORTHEAST OUTDOORS
SOUTHERN RV
SOUTHWEST RV TRAVELER
SUMMER DESTINATIONS
SUNNY DESTINATIONS
WOODALL

WORCESTER TELEGRAM & GAZETTE CORP.
(Sub. of NYT Management Services, Inc.)
20 Franklin St
Worcester, MA 01608-1904
Mailing Address:
PO Box 15012
Worcester, MA 01615-0012
Tel.: (508) 793-9100
Fax: (508) 793-9281
Web Site: www.telegram.com
Sales Range: $100-124.9 Million
Approx. Number Employees: 700
Year Founded: 1999
Business Description:
Newspaper Publisher
S.I.C.: 2711
N.A.I.C.S.: 511110
Media: 8-9
Personnel:
Bruce Gaultney *(Publr)*
Natalie Bradley *(Dir-Fin)*
Susan E. Burtchell *(Dir-Adv Sls)*
Averil Capers *(Dir-Community Mktg & Res)*

Key to Media (For complete agency information see *The Advertising Red Books-Agencies* edition):
1. Bus. Publs. 2. Cable T.V. 3. Catalogs & Directories. 4. Co-op Adv. 5. Consumer Mags. 6. D.M. to Bus. Estab.7. D.M. to Consumers
8. Daily Newsp. 9. Exhibits/Trade Shows 10. Foreign 11. Infomercial 12. Internet Adv.13. Multimedia 14. Network Radio
15. Network T.V. 16. Newsp. Distr. Mags. 17. Other 18. Outdoor (Posters, Transit) 19. Point of Purchase20. Premiums, Novelties
21. Product Samples 22. Special Events Mktg. 23. Spot Radio 24. Spot T.V. 25. Weekly Newsp. 26. Yellow Page Adv.

Victor A. DiNardo *(Dir-HR)*
Kathlene Donahue *(Dir-Consumer Mktg)*
Kurt E. Parent *(Dir-Opers)*
Anthony J. Simollardes *(Dir-Readership & Circulation)*
Karen Aloia *(Reg Mgr)*
Kim McLean *(Office Mgr)*
Lynne Ahlberg *(Mgr)*
Ronald Anger *(Mgr-Acctg)*
Edward J. Bauer *(Mgr-Classified)*
Mary Brytowski *(Mgr-TeleMarketing)*
Jason Derr *(Mgr-Sys Support)*
Bob Kusz *(Mgr-Classified Display)*
Paul V. LaCava *(Mgr-Services)*
Robert McCarthy *(Mgr-Sys Support)*
Jackie Phelps *(Mgr-Adv)*
Steve Pitocchelli *(Mgr-Sls)*
Wayne P. Shepard *(Mgr-Mailroom)*
Jane Sheppard *(Mgr-Sls)*
Kelly Tolman *(Mgr-Consumer Svcs)*
Liz Vadenais *(Mgr-Retail)*
Jay Valencourt *(Mgr-Adv Sls Ops)*
Ron Wolfram *(Mgr-Display Adv)*
Brands & Products:
WORCESTER TELEGRAM & GAZETTE

WORKING MOTHER MEDIA, INC.
(Holding of MCG Capital Corporation)
60 E 42nd St 27th Fl
New York, NY 10165
Tel.: (212) 351-6400
Fax: (212) 351-6487
E-mail: privacy@workingmother.com
Web Site: www.workingmother.com
E-Mail For Key Personnel:
President: carolevans@workingmother.com
Public Relations: bettyspence@workingmother.com
Sales Range: $50-74.9 Million
Approx. Number Employees: 150
Year Founded: 2001
Business Description:
Business Association, Conferences Organizer, Magazine Publisher & Internet Portal
S.I.C.: 2721; 7375
N.A.I.C.S.: 511120; 518111
Media: 6-13
Personnel:
Carol Evans *(Pres)*
Joan Sheridan Labarge *(VP & Grp Publr-Working Mother Media)*
Janet Wigfield *(VP & Exec Dir-Conferences + Events)*
Suzanne Riss *(Editor-in-Chief-Working Mother Magazine)*
Jennifer Owens *(Sr Dir-Editorial Res & Initiatives)*
Talyn Chaglasian *(Dir-Mktg & Promos)*
Lucia Knight *(Dir-Conferences)*
Robert Bernbach *(Mgr-Direct Response)*
Kelli Daley *(Mgr-Online Svcs)*
Brands & Products:
WORKING MOTHER

WORKMAN PUBLISHING COMPANY
225 Barick St
New York, NY 10014
Tel.: (212) 254-5900
Fax: (212) 254-8098
E-mail: info@workman.com
Web Site: www.workman.com
Approx. Number Employees: 160
Year Founded: 1967
Business Description:
Book Publisher
S.I.C.: 2731; 2759
N.A.I.C.S.: 511130; 323119
Media: 8-10-21-22
Personnel:
Peter Workman *(Pres & CEO)*
Brands & Products:
WORKMAN

WORLD BOOK/SCOTT FETZER COMPANY, INC.
(Sub. of The Scott Fetzer Company)
233 N Michigan Ave Ste 2000
Chicago, IL 60601-5519
Tel.: (312) 729-5800
Fax: (312) 729-5600
Toll Free: (800) 255-1750
Web Site: www.worldbook.com
Sales Range: $50-74.9 Million
Approx. Number Employees: 180
Year Founded: 1917
Business Description:
Book Publisher
S.I.C.: 2731; 2741
N.A.I.C.S.: 511130; 511199
Media: 2-4-6-8-10-24-26
Distr.: Direct to Consumer; Natl.
Budget Set: Dec.
Personnel:
Ben Hinton *(Mng Dir)*
Donald Keller *(CFO & VP)*
Patti Ginnis *(Chief Mktg Officer & VP)*
Paul Kobasa *(VP-Editorial & Editor-in-Chief)*
Robert Hall *(VP-Sls)*
Michael Noren *(Mgr-Editorial Regions)*
Shawn Brennan *(Editor)*
Nicholas Kilzer *(Editor)*
Dawn Krajcik *(Editor)*
Pete Kulak *(Editor)*
S. Thomas Richardson *(Editor)*
Kenneth J. Shenkman *(Editor)*
Sara Dreyfuss *(Dir-Editorial)*
Bev Ecker *(Dir-HR)*
Richard Flower *(Dir-US Rights)*
Adam Zoghlin *(Dir-Digital Dev)*
Jennifer Parello *(Assoc Dir-Mktg)*
Michael B. Schuldt *(Sr Mgr-Editorial Humanities)*
Ed Birchall *(Mgr-Sys Dev)*
Jeff De la Rosa *(Mgr-Sciences)*
Michael Lewis *(Mgr-Editing)*
Brands & Products:
CHILDCRAFT
THE WORLD BOOK DICTIONARY
WORLD BOOK ENCYCLOPEDIA
THE WORLD BOOK STUDENT DISCOVERY ENCYCLOPEDIA
THE WORLDBOOK ENCYCLOPEDIA OF PEOPLE AND PLACES
THE WORLDBOOK ENCYCLOPEDIA OF SCIENCE

WORLD PUBLISHING COMPANY INC.
315 S Boulder
Tulsa, OK 74103-3672
Tel.: (918) 583-2161
Fax: (918) 581-8353
E-mail: sales@tulsaworld.com
Web Site: www.tulsaworld.com
E-Mail For Key Personnel:
Sales Director: sales@tulsaworld.com
Approx. Number Employees: 725
Year Founded: 1905
Business Description:
Newspaper & Online Information Publisher
S.I.C.: 2711; 2741
N.A.I.C.S.: 511110; 516110
Media: 13
Personnel:
Robert E. Lorton *(Chm & CEO)*
Robert E. Lorton, III *(Pres & Publr)*
John R. Bair *(VP & Gen Mgr)*
Gene Curtis *(Writer-Tulsa World)*

WORTH
(Sub. of Curtco Media Labs LLC)
1177 Avenue Of The Americas 10th Fl
New York, NY 10036
Tel.: (212) 230-0200
Fax: (212) 230-0202
Web Site: www.worth.com
Approx. Sls.: $25,597,000
Approx. Number Employees: 57
Business Description:
Magazines
S.I.C.: 2721
N.A.I.C.S.: 511120
Media: 2-13
Personnel:
Richard Santulli *(Chm & CEO)*
David Ross *(Pres)*
David Small *(VP)*
Alison Parks *(Gen Mgr)*

W.W. NORTON & COMPANY, INC.
500 5th Ave
New York, NY 10110-0002
Tel.: (212) 354-5500
Fax: (212) 869-0856
Toll Free: (800) 223-2584
E-mail: publicity@wwnorton.com
Web Site: www.wwnorton.com
Sales Range: $100-124.9 Million
Approx. Number Employees: 180
Year Founded: 1923
Business Description:
Books Publisher & Whslr
S.I.C.: 2731; 5192
N.A.I.C.S.: 511130; 424920
Advertising Expenditures: $500,000
Media: 5-9-10-13-19-21-23
Distr.: Natl.
Budget Set: July
Personnel:
W. Drake McFeely *(Chm & Pres)*
Stephen King *(CFO)*
Roby Harrington *(VP & Dir-College Dept)*
Genevieve Luciano *(VP & Dir-Trade Publ)*
William F. Rusin *(VP & Dir-Sls)*
Sterling Lawrence *(Editor-in-Chief)*
Pearl Axson *(Office Mgr)*
Nomi Victor *(Mgr-Adv)*
Brands & Products:
W.W. NORTON
Advertising Agency:
Verso Advertising, Inc.
50 W 17th St 5th Fl
New York, NY 10011-5702
Tel.: (212) 292-2990
Fax: (212) 557-2592
(Books)

XERIUM TECHNOLOGIES, INC.
(Holding of Apax Partners LLP)
8537 Six Forks Rd
Raleigh, NC 27615
Tel.: (919) 526-1400
E-mail: ir@xerium.com
Web Site: www.xerium.com
Approx. Sls.: $548,334,000
Approx. Number Employees: 3,404
Business Description:
Paper Production
S.I.C.: 2211; 3069
N.A.I.C.S.: 313210; 326299
Advertising Expenditures: $1,108,000
Personnel:
Stephen R. Light *(Chm, Pres & CEO)*
Clifford E. Pietrafitta *(CFO)*
John Badrinas Ardevol *(CTO & Pres-Xerium Europe Rolls)*
Eduardo Fracasso *(Pres-Xerium South America)*
Thomas C. Johnson *(Pres-Xerium Asia)*
David Pretty *(Pres-Xerium Europe PMC & Xerium North America)*
Peter Williamson *(Pres-Europe)*
Kevin McDougall *(Corp Counsel & Exec VP)*
Josef Mayer *(Exec VP-Bus Dev)*

YALE UNIVERSITY PRESS
302 Temple St
New Haven, CT 06511-8909
Mailing Address:
PO Box 209040
New Haven, CT 06520-9040
Tel.: (203) 432-0960
Fax: (203) 432-0948
Fax: (800) 406-9145
Toll Free: (800) 405-1619
E-mail: customer.care@triliteral.org
Web Site: www.yalepress.yale.edu
Approx. Number Employees: 120
Year Founded: 1908
Business Description:
Publisher of Books
S.I.C.: 8221
N.A.I.C.S.: 611310
Advertising Expenditures: $800,000
Media: 2-4-5-6-7-8-9-10-13-14-16-22-23-25
Distr.: Direct to Consumer; Natl.
Budget Set: July
Personnel:
Richard C. Levin *(Pres)*
Thomas G. Mattia *(Chief Comm Officer & Special Advisor to Pres)*
John D. Rollins *(Dir-Fin)*
Brands & Products:
YALE NOTA BENE
YALE PRESS LOG
YALE PRESS PODCAST
YALE UNIVERSITY PRESS

YANKEE PUBLISHING INC.
1121 Main St
Dublin, NH 03444
Tel.: (603) 563-8111
Fax: (603) 563-8252
Toll Free: (800) 736-1100
E-mail: info@yankeemagazine.com
Web Site: www.yankeemagazine.com
Sales Range: $50-74.9 Million
Approx. Number Employees: 50
Year Founded: 1935
Business Description:
Publisher of Magazines & Periodicals
S.I.C.: 2721; 2741
N.A.I.C.S.: 511120; 511199
Media: 3-6-7-8-10-13-14-22-23-24
Distr.: Direct to Consumer; Natl.

Key to Media (For complete agency information see *The Advertising Red Books-Agencies* edition):
1. Bus. Publs. 2. Cable T.V. 3. Catalogs & Directories. 4. Co-op Adv. 5. Consumer Mags. 6. D.M. to Bus. Estab.7. D.M. to Consumers
8. Daily Newsp. 9. Exhibits/Trade Shows 10. Foreign 11. Infomercial 12. Internet Adv.13. Multimedia 14. Network Radio
15. Network T.V. 16. Newsp. Distr. Mags. 17. Other 18. Outdoor (Posters, Transit) 19. Point of Purchase20. Premiums, Novelties
21. Product Samples 22. Special Events Mktg. 23. Spot Radio 24. Spot T.V. 25. Weekly Newsp. 26. Yellow Page Adv.

Yankee Publishing Inc. — (Continued)

Budget Set: May
Personnel:
Judson D. Hale, Sr. *(Publr & VP)*
Jody Bugbee *(VP-HR)*
Mel Allen *(Editor)*
Brands & Products:
NEW ENGLAND.COM
THE OLD FARMER'S ALMANAC
YANKEE
YANKEE MAGAZINE TRAVEL GUIDE TO NEW ENGLAND

YANKTON DAILY PRESS & DAKOTAN

(Unit of GateHouse Media, Inc.)
319 Walnut St
Yankton, SD 57078-0056
Tel.: (605) 665-7811
Fax: (605) 665-1721
E-mail: webteam@yankton.net
Web Site: www.yankton.net
Sales Range: $10-24.9 Million
Approx. Number Employees: 30
Year Founded: 1861
Business Description:
Newspaper Publisher
S.I.C.: 2711
N.A.I.C.S.: 511110
Media: 8-9
Personnel:
Gary L. Wood *(Publr & Editor)*
Randy Dockendorf *(Editor-Reg)*
Heidi Henson *(Editor-Special Sections)*
Nathan Johnson *(Editor-City)*
David Jeffcoat *(Dir-Circulation)*
Beth Rye *(Dir-New Media)*
Micki Schievelbein *(Dir-Adv)*
Tonya Schild *(Bus Mgr)*
Kathy Larson *(Mgr-Composing)*
Noelle Schlechter *(Mgr-Distr & Customer Svc)*
Brands & Products:
YANKTON DAILY PROCESSING & DAKOTAN

YELLOW BOOK USA, INC.

(Sub. of Yell Group plc)
398 RXR Plz
Uniondale, NY 11556
Tel.: (516) 730-1900
Fax: (516) 730-1910
Toll Free: (800) YB-YELLOW
E-mail: info@yellowbook.com
Web Site: www.yellowbook.com
Sales Range: $750-799.9 Million
Approx. Number Employees: 180
Year Founded: 1930
Business Description:
Telephone Directory Publisher
S.I.C.: 2741
N.A.I.C.S.: 511140
Media: 13-23-24
Personnel:
Joseph A. Walsh *(Pres & CEO)*
Bryan Turner *(CFO)*
Gary Shaw *(CIO)*
Mark Cairns *(Chief Publ Officer)*
Patrick Marshall *(Chief New Media Officer)*
John Butler *(Gen Counsel)*
Brands & Products:
WEFORIA.COM
YELLOW BOOK
YELLOW BOOK USA
YELLOWBOOK.COM

Advertising Agency:
Roska Direct
211B Progress Dr
Montgomeryville, PA 18936-9618
Tel.: (215) 699-9200
Fax: (215) 699-9240

THE YORK NEWS-TIMES

(Sub. of Omaha World Herald Company)
327 Platte Ave
York, NE 68467
Mailing Address:
PO Box 279
York, NE 68467-0279
Tel.: (402) 362-4478
Fax: (402) 362-6748
Toll Free: (800) 334-4530
E-mail: classifieds@yorknewstimes.com
Web Site: www.yorknewstimes.com
Approx. Number Employees: 22
Year Founded: 1880
Business Description:
Newspaper Publisher
S.I.C.: 2711
N.A.I.C.S.: 511110
Media: 8-9
Personnel:
Greg Awtry *(Publr)*
Kathy Larson *(Mgr-Adv)*
Corey Mann *(Mgr-Circulation)*

YOUNG MONEY

10950 Gilroy Rd Ste D
Hunt Valley, MD 21031
Toll Free: (888) 788-4335
Web Site: www.youngmoney.com
Business Description:
Magazine Publishing Financial Advice for Young Adults
S.I.C.: 2721
N.A.I.C.S.: 511120
Media: 13
Personnel:
Ben Levy *(Pres)*

ZAGAT SURVEY, LLC

4 Columbus Cir
New York, NY 10019-1100
Tel.: (212) 977-6000
Fax: (212) 977-9760
E-mail: zagat@zagat.com
Web Site: www.zagat.com
Sales Range: $1-9.9 Million
Approx. Number Employees: 100
Year Founded: 1979
Business Description:
Surveys for the Food & Travel Industry
S.I.C.: 2741
N.A.I.C.S.: 511199
Personnel:
Tim Zagat *(Co-Founder, Co-Chm & CEO)*
Nina S. Zagat *(Co-Founder & Co-Chm)*
Tiffany Barbalato *(Dir-Corp Comm)*
Tami Zonenshine *(Dir-Mktg)*
Brands & Products:
ZAGAT
Advertising Agency:
Winstar Interactive Media
307 7th Ave Ste 2003
New York, NY 10001
Tel.: (212) 916-0713

THE ZONDERVAN CORPORATION

(Sub. of HarperCollins Publishers Inc.)
5300 Patterson SE
Grand Rapids, MI 49530-0001
Tel.: (616) 698-6900
Fax: (616) 698-3235
Web Site: www.zondervan.com
Approx. Sls.: $106,000,000
Approx. Number Employees: 500
Year Founded: 1931
Business Description:
Publisher & Distributor of Religious Books & Music, Children & Adult Publications & Gifts
S.I.C.: 2731; 8661
N.A.I.C.S.: 511130; 813110
Personnel:
Maureen Girkins *(Pres & CEO)*
Gary Wicker *(CFO & Exec VP)*
Arthur Brown *(Publr-Bibles & Sr VP)*
Verne Kenney *(Exec VP-Sls)*
Al Kerkstra *(Exec VP-Support Ops & HR)*
Steve Sammons *(Exec VP-Consumer Engagement)*
Rachel Barach *(Gen Mgr-Bible GatewayCom)*
Don Gates *(Dir-Internet Mktg)*
Carolyn Weidmayer *(Dir-Subsidiary & Intl Rights)*
Brands & Products:
HALLEY'S BIBLE HANDBOOK
NIV CHILDREN'S BIBLE
NIV PULPIT BIBLE
NIV STUDY BIBLE
Advertising Agency:
Deodandum Marketing Communications
18-5 E Dundee Rd Ste 204
Barrington, IL 60010
Tel.: (847) 842-6848

ZUMA PRESS, INC.

408 N El Camino Real
San Clemente, CA 92672
Tel.: (949) 494-7704
Fax: (949) 481-3941
E-mail: info@zumapress.com
Web Site: www.zumapress.com
Approx. Number Employees: 45
Year Founded: 1995
Business Description:
Picture Agency & News Wire Service
S.I.C.: 7335
N.A.I.C.S.: 541922
Media: 8-13
Personnel:
Julie Mason *(CFO)*
Scott McKiernan *(Publr, Photojournalist, Agent & Designer)*
Ruaridh Stewart *(Mgr-Picture Desk)*

Key to Media (For complete agency information see *The Advertising Red Books-Agencies* edition):
1. Bus. Publs. 2. Cable T.V. 3. Catalogs & Directories. 4. Co-op Adv. 5. Consumer Mags. 6. D.M. to Bus. Estab.7. D.M. to Consumers
8. Daily Newsp. 9. Exhibits/Trade Shows 10. Foreign 11. Infomercial 12. Internet Adv.13. Multimedia 14. Network Radio
15. Network T.V. 16. Newsp. Distr. Mags. 17. Other 18. Outdoor (Posters, Transit) 19. Point of Purchase20. Premiums, Novelties
21. Product Samples 22. Special Events Mktg. 23. Spot Radio 24. Spot T.V. 25. Weekly Newsp. 26. Yellow Page Adv.

Recreational Vehicles

Bicycles — Boats — Canoes — Marine Engines — Marine Oils — Mopeds — Motor Boats — Motorcycles — Sail Boats — Snowmobiles — Surfboards — Wind Surfers — Yachting Supplies

ACCURATE MOTORCARS
915 NE 3rd Ave Ste 5
Fort Lauderdale, FL 33304
Tel.: (954) 712-9322
Web Site:
www.cashforcarsonline.com
Business Description:
Automobile Buyer & Seller
S.I.C.: 5961
N.A.I.C.S.: 454111
Media: 13
Personnel:
Lior Sebag *(Mgr)*

AFFINITY GROUP HOLDING, INC.
(Sub. of AGI Holding Corp.)
2575 Vista Del Mar
Ventura, CA 93001
Tel.: (805) 667-4100
Fax: (805) 667-4419
Web Site: www.affinitygroup.com/contact.cfm
Approx. Rev.: $471,781,000
Approx. Number Employees: 1,541
Business Description:
Holding Company; RV Direct Marketer, Publisher & Merchandiser
S.I.C.: 6719; 2721; 5561; 5963
N.A.I.C.S.: 551112; 441210; 454390; 511120
Advertising Expenditures:
$25,100,000
Personnel:
Stephen Adams *(Chm)*
Thomas F. Wolfe *(CFO)*
Brands & Products:
AGI PUBLICATIONS
AMERICAN RIDER
ARCHERY BUSINESS
ATV MAGAZINE
ATV SPORT
BLACKS ARCHERY/BOWHUNTING
BLACKS FLYFISHING
BLACKS WING & CLAY
BOATING INDUSTRY
BOW HUNTING WORLD
CAMPERWAYS
CAMPING WORLD
COAST TO COAST
COAST TO COAST RESORTS
CRUISING RIDER
FLORIDA RV TRAVELER
GOLF CARD
GOOD SAM CLUB
HIGHWAYS
MOTORHOME
NORTHEAST OUTDOORS
POWERSPORTS BUSINESS
PRESIDENTS CLUB
REV
RIDER
RV BUSINESS
RV BUYERS GUIDE
RV PUBLICATIONS
RVTODAY
RVVIEW
SNOW WEEK
SNOWGOER
SNOWMOBILE
SOUTHERN RV
SOUTHWEST RV TRAVELER
SUMMER DESTINATIONS
SUNNY DESTINATIONS
THUNDER PRESS
TL BOOKS
TRAILER LIFE
TRAILER LIFE CAMPGROUNDS
WATERCRAFT WORLD
WOMAN RIDER
WOODALLS CAMPGROUND
Advertising Agency:
Allison & Partners
505 Sansome St 7th Fl
San Francisco, CA 94111-3310
Tel.: (415) 217-7500
Fax: (415) 217-7503
— Megan Dyer *(VP)*

AFFINITY GROUP, INC.
(Sub. of Affinity Group Holding, Inc.)
2575 Vista Del Mar
Ventura, CA 93001
Tel.: (805) 667-4100
Fax: (805) 667-4100
E-mail: info@affinitygroup.com
Web Site: www.affinitygroup.com
Approx. Rev.: $471,781,000
Approx. Number Employees: 1,541
Business Description:
Recreational Vehicle Sales, Periodical Publisher & Insurance Services
S.I.C.: 5561; 2721; 2741
N.A.I.C.S.: 441210; 511120; 516110
Advertising Expenditures:
$37,300,000
Personnel:
Stephen Adams *(Chm)*
Thomas F. Wolfe *(CFO)*
Laura A. James *(Sr VP-HR)*
Patel Prabhuling *(Sr VP)*

ALL AMERICAN GROUP, INC.
2831 Dexter Dr
Elkhart, IN 46514
Mailing Address:
PO Box 30
Elkhart, IN 46515
Tel.: (574) 266-2500
Fax: (574) 266-3042
E-mail: info@coachmen.com
Web Site:
www.allamericangroupinc.com
Approx. Sls.: $60,623,000
Approx. Number Employees: 172
Year Founded: 1964
Business Description:
Recreational Vehicles, RV Parts & Accessories & Modular Homes Mfr
S.I.C.: 3716; 3792
N.A.I.C.S.: 336213; 336214
Export
Media: 1-2-4-5-6-7-8-9-10-18-19-20-22
Distr.: Intl.; Natl.
Budget Set: Sept. -Oct.
Personnel:
William P. Johnson *(Chm)*
Richard M. Lavers *(Pres & CEO)*
Colleen A. Zuhl *(CFO)*
Rick J. Bedell *(Pres-Building & Housing Group)*
Leslie G. Thimlar *(VP-HR)*
Brands & Products:
ALL AMERICAN BUILDING SYSTEMS
ALL AMERICAN HOMES
COACHMEN
CRUISE AIR
GBM
GEORGIE BOY
MILLER BUILDING SYSTEMS
SPORTSCOACH

ALUMACRAFT BOAT COMPANY
315 W St Julien St
Saint Peter, MN 56082
Tel.: (507) 931-1050
Fax: (507) 931-9056
E-mail: sales@alumacraft.com
Web Site: www.alumacraft.com
E-Mail For Key Personnel:
Sales Director: sales@alumacraft.com
Approx. Number Employees: 200
Year Founded: 1946
Business Description:
Mfr. of Aluminum Fishing Boats & Canoes
S.I.C.: 3732
N.A.I.C.S.: 336612
Export
Advertising Expenditures: $250,000
Media: 4-8-13-18-19
Distr.: Intl.; Natl.
Budget Set: Oct.
Personnel:
David Benbow *(Owner & Chm)*
Jim Hobson *(Reg Mgr-Sls)*
Brands & Products:
ALUMACRAFT
CLASSIC
CO-17 CAMPER
DOMINATOR
FISHERMAN
LUNKER
NAVIGATOR
QUETICO
TOURNAMENT
TROPHY
YUKON

ARCTIC CAT INC.
505 Hwy 169 N Ste 1000
Plymouth, MN 55441
Tel.: (763) 354-1800
Web Site: www.arctic-cat.com
Approx. Sls.: $464,651,000
Approx. Number Employees: 1,323
Year Founded: 1982
Business Description:
Snowmobiles, All-Terrain Vehicles, Garments & Accessories Mfr & Sales
S.I.C.: 3799; 3751
N.A.I.C.S.: 336999; 336991
Import Export
Advertising Expenditures:
$15,507,000
Media: 4-5-6-10-13-16-18-19-22
Distr.: Natl.
Personnel:
Christopher A. Twomey *(Chm)*
Claude J. Jordan *(Pres & CEO)*
Timothy C. Delmore *(CFO & Sec)*
Brad Darling *(VP & Gen Mgr-Snowmobile Div)*

Key to Media (For complete agency information see *The Advertising Red Books-Agencies* edition):
1. Bus. Publs. 2. Cable T.V. 3. Catalogs & Directories. 4. Co-op Adv. 5. Consumer Mags. 6. D.M. to Bus. Estab.7. D.M. to Consumers
8. Daily Newsp. 9. Exhibits/Trade Shows 10. Foreign 11. Infomercial 12. Internet Adv.13. Multimedia 14. Network Radio
15. Network T.V. 16. Newsp. Distr. Mags. 17. Other 18. Outdoor (Posters, Transit) 19. Point of Purchase20. Premiums, Novelties
21. Product Samples 22. Special Events Mktg. 23. Spot Radio 24. Spot T.V. 25. Weekly Newsp. 26. Yellow Page Adv.

Arctic Cat Inc. — (Continued)

Mary Ellen Walker *(VP & Gen Mgr-Parts, Garments & Accessories)*
William J. Nee *(VP-HR)*
Ole E. Tweet *(VP-New Product Dev)*
John Tranby *(Mgr-Mktg)*
Brands & Products:
ACT
ARCTIC CAT
ARCTICWEAR
AWS
BEARCAT
CAT
CAT COMM
CATMASTER
CATS PRIDE
CROSSFIRE
F SERIES
FASTRACK
FIRECAT
INFINITE RIDER POSITIONING
IRP
JAGUAR
PANTERA
PANTHER
PRIDE
SHARE OUR PASSION.
SLIDE-ACTION REAR SUSPENSION
SNO PRO
T660
TWIN SPAR
WORLD CLASS SNOWMOBILES
Z
Z1
ZR
Advertising Agency:
Periscope
921 Washington Ave S
Minneapolis, MN 55415
Tel.: (612) 399-0500
Fax: (612) 399-0600
Toll Free: (800) 339-2103
(Snowmobiles, Personal Watercraft & All-Terrain Vehicles)

ATTWOOD CORPORATION

(Sub. of Brunswick Boat Group)
1016 N Monroe St
Lowell, MI 49331
Tel.: (616) 897-9241
Fax: (616) 897-8358
E-mail: customersupport@attwoodmarine.com
Web Site: www.attwoodmarine.com
Sales Range: $75-99.9 Million
Approx. Number Employees: 170
Year Founded: 1906
Business Description:
Marine Accessories & Hardware Mfr
S.I.C.: 3429
N.A.I.C.S.: 332510
Media: 1-4-5-10-11-19-20-21-24
Distr.: Intl.; Natl.
Budget Set: Dec.
Personnel:
Kevin Fletcher *(Dir-Sls & Mktg)*
Brands & Products:
AVENIR
CENTRIC
PERFORMANCE THAT'S BUILT TO LAST
WE KEEP THE FUN IN BOATING

BLUE BIRD CORPORATION

(Holding of Cerberus Capital Management, L.P.)
402 Blue Bird Blvd
Fort Valley, GA 31030
Mailing Address:
PO Box 937
Fort Valley, GA 31030
Tel.: (478) 825-2021
Fax: (478) 822-2457
Toll Free: (800) 486-7122
E-mail: info@blue-bird.com
Web Site: www.blue-bird.com
Approx. Sls.: $536,000,000
Approx. Number Employees: 800
Year Founded: 1932
Business Description:
School Bus Mfr
S.I.C.: 3711
N.A.I.C.S.: 336111; 336211
Export
Advertising Expenditures: $2,000,000
Media: 2-4-7-10-17
Distr.: Natl.
Budget Set: Sept.
Personnel:
Greg Zenneth *(CEO)*
Travis Kelly *(VP-Fin)*
Brands & Products:
BLUE BIRD
BLUE BIRD VISION
Advertising Agency:
Jackson Marketing Group
2 Task Ct
Greenville, SC 29607
Tel.: (864) 272-3000
Fax: (864) 272-3040

BOSTON WHALER, INC.

(Sub. of Brunswick Boat Group)
100 Whaler Way
Edgewater, FL 32141
Tel.: (386) 428-0057
Fax: (386) 423-8589
Fax: (386) 409-8559
Toll Free: (877) 294-5645
Toll Free: (800) WHALER-9
Web Site: www.whaler.com
Sales Range: $200-249.9 Million
Approx. Number Employees: 521
Year Founded: 1958
Business Description:
Fiberglass Power Boats Mfr
S.I.C.: 3732
N.A.I.C.S.: 336612
Media: 1-3-4-5-6-8-10-19-20-22-26
Distr.: Intl.; Natl.
Budget Set: Aug.
Personnel:
John Ward *(Pres)*
Ken Riopel *(VP-Fin)*

BRISTOL MARINE

99 Poppasquash Rd
Bristol, RI 02809
Tel.: (401) 253-2200
Fax: (401) 253-0007
E-mail: info@bristolmarine.com
Web Site: www.bristolmarine.com
Approx. Number Employees: 12
Year Founded: 1998
Business Description:
Owner & Operator of Boat Yard & Marina
S.I.C.: 3732; 5551
N.A.I.C.S.: 336612; 441222
Media: 4-6-7-8-10-13
Distr.: Natl.
Personnel:
Andy Tyska *(Owner)*
Brands & Products:
BRISTOL MARINE
BRISTOL YACHTS
QUALITY SERVICE THROUGHOUT THE YEAR

BWHC LLC

(d/b/a Bluewater)
811 E Maple Ave
Mora, MN 55051
Tel.: (320) 679-3811
Fax: (320) 679-3820
E-mail: bluewater@ncis.com
Web Site: www.bluewateryacht.com
Approx. Number Employees: 50
Year Founded: 1954
Business Description:
Luxury Yachts
S.I.C.: 3732; 5551
N.A.I.C.S.: 336612; 441222
Advertising Expenditures: $500,000
Media: 6-8-10
Distr.: Intl.; Natl.
Budget Set: Aug.
Personnel:
Steve Klapmeier *(Pres)*
Allen O. Hagen *(Sr VP-Sls)*
Cathy Cole *(Dir-Mktg)*
Brands & Products:
5200
5200 CUSTOM
5600 CUSTOM
5800 CUSTOM
6000 CUSTOM
7000 CUSTOM
BLUEWATER
Advertising Agency:
Bluewater
811 E Maple Ave
Mora, MN 55051
Tel.: (320) 679-3811
Fax: (320) 679-3820
(Bluewater Yachts)

CANNONDALE BICYCLE CORPORATION

(Sub. of Dorel Industries, Inc.)
172 Friendship Rd
Bedford, PA 15522-6600
Tel.: (814) 623-9073
Fax: (814) 623-6173
Toll Free: (800) BIKE-USA
E-mail: custserv@cannondale.com
Web Site: www.cannondale.com
Approx. Rev.: $200,000,000
Approx. Number Employees: 75
Year Founded: 1971
Business Description:
Aluminum Bicycles, Cycling Accessories & Apparel
S.I.C.: 3751; 2329
N.A.I.C.S.: 336991; 315228
Export
Advertising Expenditures: $1,526,000
Media: 6-8-9-17-19-25-26
Distr.: Intl.; Natl.
Budget Set: June
Personnel:
Bob Burbank *(Gen Mgr)*
Frank Hwang *(Dir-Mktg (Global))*
Patricia Wintermuth *(Dir-Mktg, Digital (Global))*
Advertising Agency:
Mangos
10 Great Valley Pkwy
Malvern, PA 19355-1316
Tel.: (610) 296-2555
Fax: (610) 640-9291

CATALINA YACHTS, INC.

21200 Victory Blvd
Woodland Hills, CA 91367-2522
Tel.: (818) 884-7700
Fax: (818) 884-3810
E-mail: info@catalinayachts.com
Web Site: www.catalinayachts.com
Approx. Number Employees: 260
Year Founded: 1970
Business Description:
Builder & Repairer of Yachts
S.I.C.: 3732; 5551
N.A.I.C.S.: 336612; 441222
Media: 7-10-13
Personnel:
Frank Butler *(Founder & Pres)*
Gerry Douglas *(VP-Engrg)*
Sharon Day *(Mgr-Natl Sls)*
Brands & Products:
CATALINA
THE SAILORS' CHOICE

CHRIS-CRAFT CORPORATION

8161 15th St E
Sarasota, FL 34243
Tel.: (941) 351-4900
Fax: (941) 358-3776
Web Site: www.chriscraft.com
Sales Range: $50-74.9 Million
Approx. Number Employees: 350
Year Founded: 1874
Business Description:
Runabouts, Fish Boats, Cruisers & Fiberglass Sportboats Mfr
S.I.C.: 3732; 5551
N.A.I.C.S.: 336612; 441222
Advertising Expenditures: $1,000,000
Media: 2-4-6-9-10-11-18-19-20
Distr.: Intl.; Natil
Budget Set: Mar.-Apr.
Personnel:
Stephen M. Julius *(Chm)*
Stephen Heese *(Pres & CEO)*
Mark Poncin *(CFO & VP)*
Chris Collier *(VP-Product Dev, Engrg & Quality)*
Jeff Ellis *(VP-Sls)*
Brands & Products:
BOWRIDER
CATALINA
CATALINA DOUBLE CABIN
CHRIS-CRAFT
CONCEPT 90
CONSTELLATION
CORSAIR
EXPRESS CRUISERS
LAUNCH
ROAMER
SPEEDSTER
SPORTDECK

THE COAST DISTRIBUTION SYSTEM, INC.

350 Woodview Ave
Morgan Hill, CA 95037-2823
Mailing Address:
PO Box 1750
Morgan Hill, CA 95038-1449
Tel.: (408) 782-6686
Fax: (408) 782-7790
Toll Free: (800) 538-7973
E-mail: customerservice@coastdist.com
Web Site: www.coastdistribution.com

Key to Media (For complete agency information see *The Advertising Red Books-Agencies* edition):
1. Bus. Publs. 2. Cable T.V. 3. Catalogs & Directories. 4. Co-op Adv. 5. Consumer Mags. 6. D.M. to Bus. Estab.7. D.M. to Consumers
8. Daily Newsp. 9. Exhibits/Trade Shows 10. Foreign 11. Infomercial 12. Internet Adv.13. Multimedia 14. Network Radio
15. Network T.V. 16. Newsp. Distr. Mags. 17. Other 18. Outdoor (Posters, Transit) 19. Point of Purchase20. Premiums, Novelties
21. Product Samples 22. Special Events Mktg. 23. Spot Radio 24. Spot T.V. 25. Weekly Newsp. 26. Yellow Page Adv.

Approx. Sls.: $108,600,000
Approx. Number Employees: 265
Year Founded: 1977
Business Description:
Boat & Recreational Vehicle Parts & Accessories Whslr
S.I.C.: 5551; 5013; 5091
N.A.I.C.S.: 441222; 423120; 423910; 441310
Media: 4-7-8-10
Distr.: Intl.; Natl.
Budget Set: Sept.
Personnel:
Thomas R. McGuire *(Chm)*
James I. Musbach *(Pres & CEO)*
Sandra A. Knell *(CFO, Sec & Exec VP-Fin)*
David A. Berger *(Exec VP-Ops)*
Dennis A. Castagnola *(Exec VP-Mfg & New Product Dev)*

CONFLUENCE WATERSPORTS CO. INC.
111 Kayaker Way
Easley, SC 29642-2433
Tel.: (888) 525-2925
Fax: (888) 884-0544
Web Site:
www.confluencewatersports.com
Approx. Number Employees: 200
Business Description:
Boats, Rigid: Plastics
S.I.C.: 3732
N.A.I.C.S.: 336612
Personnel:
Sue Rechner *(CEO)*
Shane Cobb *(VP-HR)*
Barbara Deaver *(Dir-Strategic Sourcing & Supply Chain Mgmt)*
Tim Jamison *(Dir-Product Mgmt)*
Craig Ray *(Mgr-Mktg Communications)*
Brands & Products:
CONFLUENCE
MAD RIVER
WAVE SPORT
WILDERNESS
Advertising Agency:
Erwin-Penland
(Owned by Hill, Holliday, Connors, Cosmopulos, Inc., Member of the Interpublic Group)
125 E Broad St
Greenville, SC 29601
Tel.: (864) 271-0500
Fax: (864) 235-5941
(Web Site Development & Redesign)

CORRECT CRAFT, INC.
14700 Aerospace Pkwy
Orlando, FL 32832
Tel.: (407) 855-4141
Fax: (407) 851-7844
Toll Free: (800) 346-2092
E-mail: info@correctcraft.com
Web Site: www.nautiques.com/contact/corporation
Approx. Number Employees: 400
Year Founded: 1925
Business Description:
Boat Building & Repairing
S.I.C.: 3732
N.A.I.C.S.: 336612
Export
Media: 1-2-4-5-6-7-8-9-10-14-18-19-20-22-23-24
Distr.: Intl.; Natl
Budget Set: Oct.
Personnel:
Ken Meloon *(Chm)*
Bill Yergon *(Pres & CEO)*
Don Bostick *(Mgr-Export)*
Brands & Products:
AIR NAUTIQUE
FASHION NAUTIQUE
NAUTIQUE NEWS
NAUTIQUE SUPERSPORT
NAUTIQUES
SKI NAUTIQUE
SKI NAUTIQUE OPEN BOW
SPORT NAUTIQUE

CYCLE COUNTRY ACCESSORIES CORPORATION
1701 38th Ave W PO Box 257
Spencer, IA 51301
Tel.: (712) 262-4191
Fax: (712) 262-0248
Toll Free: (800) 841-2222
E-mail: ccac@cyclecountry.com
Web Site: www.cyclecountry.com
Approx. Rev.: $12,112,633
Approx. Number Employees: 105
Year Founded: 1981
Business Description:
ATV Accessories Mfr
S.I.C.: 3751
N.A.I.C.S.: 336991
Advertising Expenditures: $170,000
Media: 1-2-3-4-6-7-8-9-10-13-15-24-25

DUTCHMEN MANUFACTURING, INC.
(Div. of Thor Industries, Inc.)
2164 Carangana Ct
Goshen, IN 46526
Tel.: (574) 534-1224
Fax: (574) 534-3807
Web Site: www.dutchmen.com
Sales Range: $100-124.9 Million
Approx. Number Employees: 800
Business Description:
Mfr. of Recreational Vehicles
S.I.C.: 3792
N.A.I.C.S.: 336214
Advertising Expenditures: $300,000
Media: 2-4-6-10-17-18
Distr.: Natl.
Budget Set: Sept.-Oct.
Personnel:
Don Clerk *(Pres)*
Joe Hosinski *(Dir-Mktg)*

E-Z-GO TEXTRON
(Sub. of Textron Inc.)
1451 Marvin Griffin Rd
Augusta, GA 30906-3852
Tel.: (706) 798-4311
Fax: (706) 771-4605
Toll Free: (800) 241-5855
E-mail: ezgo@textron.com
Web Site: www.ezgo.com
Sales Range: $400-449.9 Million
Approx. Number Employees: 1,100
Year Founded: 1954
Business Description:
Golf Cart & Utility Vehicle Mfr
S.I.C.: 3799; 3949
N.A.I.C.S.: 336999; 339920
Export
Media: 1-2-4-5-7-10-13-20-22-24-26
Distr.: Intl.; Natl.
Personnel:
Kevin Holleran *(Pres)*
Branbon Haddock *(Mgr-Mktg Comm)*
Brands & Products:
CLAYS CAR
CUSHMAN
THE #1 GOLF CAR IN THE WORLD
SHUTTLE
Advertising Agencies:
Swanson Russell Associates
1222 P St
Lincoln, NE 68508-1425
Tel.: (402) 437-6400
Fax: (402) 437-6401

TM Advertising
1717 Main St Ste 2000
Dallas, TX 75201
Tel.: (972) 556-1100
Fax: (972) 830-2619

EASTSIDE POWERSPORTS
2409 Old St Rt 32
Batavia, OH 45103
Tel.: (513) 732-0419
Fax: (513) 732-0724
E-mail: eastsidepowersports@yahoo.com
Web Site:
www.eastsidepowersports.com
Business Description:
Full Service Dealership for ATV's, UTV's, Dirt Bikes, Scooters, Go Carts & Other Similar Items
S.I.C.: 5571; 5599
N.A.I.C.S.: 441221; 441229
Media: 13-26-29
Personnel:
Dale Lusby *(Owner)*
Tonya Lusby *(Owner)*
Elizabeth Mayne *(Owner)*

ELMWOOD MARINE SERVICES, INC.
(Sub. of Memco Barge Line, Inc.)
50 Harvey Canal
Harvey, LA 70057
Mailing Address:
PO Box 1148
Harvey, LA 70059
Tel.: (504) 394-6230
Fax: (504) 392-8439
E-mail: info@elmwoodmarine.com
Web Site: www.elmwoodmarine.com
Sales Range: $50-74.9 Million
Approx. Number Employees: 100
Year Founded: 1990
Business Description:
Commercial Ship Building & Related Services
S.I.C.: 3731; 3732; 4499; 7699
N.A.I.C.S.: 336611; 336612; 488390; 811490
Media: 2-7-13
Distr.: Intl.; Natl.

FEATHERLITE, INC.
(Sub. of Universal Trailer Corporation)
(d/b/a Featherlite Trailers)
Hwy 63 & Hwy 9 PO Box 320
Cresco, IA 52136
Tel.: (563) 547-6000
Fax: (563) 547-6100
Toll Free: (800) 800-1230
E-mail: salesinfo@fthr.com
Web Site: www.fthr.com
E-Mail For Key Personnel:
Sales Director: salesinfo@fthr.com
Approx. Number Employees: 700
Year Founded: 1988
Business Description:
Specialty Trailer Mfr
S.I.C.: 3792
N.A.I.C.S.: 336214
Import Export
Media: 4-6-7-8-10-13-14-15-18-22
Personnel:
Eric P. Clement *(Gen Mgr & VP-Sls & Mktg)*
Brands & Products:
FEATHERLITE

FLEETWOOD ENTERPRISES INC.
(Filed Ch 11 Bankruptcy #914407 on 03/10/09 in U.S. Bankruptcy Ct, Central Dist of CA, Riverside)
3125 Myers St
Riverside, CA 92503-5527
Mailing Address:
PO Box 7638
Riverside, CA 92513-7638
Tel.: (951) 351-3500
E-mail: kathy.munson@fleetwood.com
Web Site: www.fleetwood.com
Sales Range: $1-4.9 Billion
Approx. Number Employees: 6,400
Year Founded: 1950
Business Description:
Manufactured Housing Retailer
S.I.C.: 2452; 3448
N.A.I.C.S.: 321992; 332311
Import Export
Advertising Expenditures: $390,000
Media: 2-3-4-8-10-13-17-19-20-26
Distr.: Direct to Consumer; Natl.; Reg.
Budget Set: Apr.
Brands & Products:
FLEETWOOD
Advertising Agency:
Ervin Advertising & Design, Inc.
(d/b/a Ervin AD)
130 McCormick Ave Ste 100
Costa Mesa, CA 92626
Tel.: (949) 251-1166
Fax: (714) 966-2371

FOUNTAIN POWERBOAT INDUSTRIES INC.
(Filed Ch 11 Bankruptcy #907132 on 08/24/09 in U.S. Bankruptcy Ct, Eastern Dist of North Carolina, Wilmington)
1653 Whichards Beach Rd
Washington, NC 27889-0457
Tel.: (252) 975-2000
Fax: (252) 975-6793
Toll Free: (800) 438-2055
E-mail: contact@fountainpowerboats.com
Web Site:
www.fountainpowerboats.com
Sales Range: $50-74.9 Million
Approx. Number Employees: 322
Year Founded: 1979
Business Description:
High Performance Deepwater Sport & Sport Fishing Boats & Cruisers Mfr, Designer & Marketer
S.I.C.: 3732; 3731
N.A.I.C.S.: 336612; 336611
Export
Advertising Expenditures: $2,013,740
Media: 2-6-10-11

Key to Media (For complete agency information see *The Advertising Red Books-Agencies* edition):
1. Bus. Publs. 2. Cable T.V. 3. Catalogs & Directories. 4. Co-op Adv. 5. Consumer Mags. 6. D.M. to Bus. Estab.7. D.M. to Consumers
8. Daily Newsp. 9. Exhibits/Trade Shows 10. Foreign 11. Infomercial 12. Internet Adv.13. Multimedia 14. Network Radio
15. Network T.V. 16. Newsp. Distr. Mags. 17. Other 18. Outdoor (Posters, Transit) 19. Point of Purchase20. Premiums, Novelties
21. Product Samples 22. Special Events Mktg. 23. Spot Radio 24. Spot T.V. 25. Weekly Newsp. 26. Yellow Page Adv.

Fountain Powerboat Industries Inc. — (Continued)

Personnel:
Reginald M. Fountain, Jr. *(Chm Pres & CEO)*
John DeLong *(CFO)*

Brands & Products:
CIRCULAR LIGHTNING BOLT
FOUNTAIN
SPORT CRUISER
SPORT FISHING

FTCA, INC

(Holding of Blackstreet Capital Management, LLC)
258 Beacon St
Somerset, PA 15501-0111
Mailing Address:
PO Box 111
Somerset, PA 15501
Tel.: (814) 445-9661
Fax: (814) 443-7320
Web Site: www.colemantrailers.com
Approx. Sls.: $75,000,000
Approx. Number Employees: 594
Year Founded: 1966
Business Description:
Folding Camping Trailer Mfr
S.I.C.: 3792
N.A.I.C.S.: 336214
Media: 13-17
Budget Set: Mar.
Personnel:
Allan Reeping *(Mgr-Sls)*

G. JOANNOU CYCLE CO. INC.

151 Ludlow Ave
Northvale, NJ 07647-2305
Tel.: (201) 768-9050
Fax: (201) 768-9520
Toll Free: (800) 222-0570
E-mail: info@jamisbikes.com
Web Site: www.jamisbikes.com
Sales Range: $10-24.9 Million
Approx. Number Employees: 80
Year Founded: 1937
Business Description:
Bicycle Whslr
S.I.C.: 5091
N.A.I.C.S.: 423910
Media: 2-4-8-9-10-13-16-17-19-25-26
Distr.: Natl.
Personnel:
Carine Joannou *(Pres & CEO)*
Dave Rosen *(Dir-Adv & Mktg)*

Brands & Products:
ARAGON
AURORA
BOSS CRUISER 7
BOSS CRUISER COASTER
CAPRI
CITIZEN
CODA COMP
CODA ELITE
CODA SPORT
COMET
COMMUTER
CROSS COUNTRY 1.0
CROSS COUNTRY 2.0
DAKAR
DAKAR SPORT
DAKAR XC COMP
DAKAR XC EXPERT
DAKAR XC PRO
DAKAR XLT 1.0
DAKAR XLT 2.0
DAKAR XLT 3.0
DAKOTA AL
DAKOTA XC
DRAGON
DURANGO SPORT
DURANGO SX
EARTH CRUISER 1
EARTH CRUISER 4
ECLIPSE
EXILE
EXPLORER 1.0
EXPLORER 2.0
EXPLORER 3.0
EXPLORER 4.0
FESTER
HOT ROD
JAMIS
JAMIS BICYCLES
KOMODO FX
LADY BUG
LASER
LURCH 1.0
LURCH 2.0
MISS DAISY
NOVA
QUEST
RANGER SX
RANGER XR
SATELLITE
STARLITE
TANGIER
TAXI
TRILOGY
VENTURA
VENTURA COMP
VENTURA SPORT
XENITH
XENITH PRO
XENITH TEAM

GEORGIE BOY MANUFACTURING, LLC

(Sub. of Coachmen Recreational Vehicle Company)
21888 Beck Dr
Elkhart, IN 46516
Mailing Address:
PO Box 30
Middlebury, IN 46540-0030
Tel.: (574) 295-7344
Fax: (574) 389-0823
Toll Free: (877) 876-9024
E-mail: gbinfo@georgieboy.com
Web Site: www.georgieboy.com
Sales Range: $75-99.9 Million
Approx. Number Employees: 500
Year Founded: 1967
Business Description:
Motorhome Mfr
S.I.C.: 3716; 3792
N.A.I.C.S.: 336213; 336214
Media: 1-2-3-4-5-6-8-9-10-11-14-15-19-22-23-24
Distr.: Intl.; Natl.
Budget Set: Sept.
Personnel:
Pat Terveer *(Pres)*
Mike Skibbe *(Controller)*

Brands & Products:
BELLAGIO
CRUISE AIR
CRUISE AIR III
CRUISE MASTER
GBM
LANDAU
THE MOTORHOME PEOPLE
PURSUIT
VELOCITY

GILMAN YACHT SALES, INC.

1212 US Hwy 1 Ste A
North Palm Beach, FL 33408-3536
Tel.: (561) 626-1790
Fax: (561) 626-5870
E-mail: info@gilmanyachts.com
Web Site: www.gilmanyachts.com
Sales Range: $50-74.9 Million
Approx. Number Employees: 16
Year Founded: 1968
Business Description:
Seller of Yachts
S.I.C.: 5551
N.A.I.C.S.: 441222
Media: 2-4-6-8-9-10-13-26
Personnel:
David Gilman *(Pres)*
Don Gilman *(VP & Broker)*

Brands & Products:
BRUCKMAN
GILMAN YACHTS
HORIZON
MJM

GILMAN YACHTS OF FORT LAUDERDALE, INC.

(Sub. of Gilman Yacht Sales, Inc.)
1510 SE 17th St Ste 300
Fort Lauderdale, FL 33316-1737
Tel.: (954) 525-8112
Fax: (954) 459-9997
E-mail: lauderdale@gilmanyachts.com
Web Site: www.gilmanyachts.com
Approx. Number Employees: 10
Year Founded: 2000
Business Description:
Builder & Brokerage of Luxury World Class Yachts
S.I.C.: 5551
N.A.I.C.S.: 441222
Media: 2-4-6-8-9-10-13-26
Distr.: Intl.; Natl.
Personnel:
Jeffrey W. Stanley *(Owner)*
Joe Majcherek *(Partner)*

Advertising Agency:
Laser Advertising
1500 Cordova Rd Ste 205
Fort Lauderdale, FL 33316
Tel.: (954) 760-4667
Fax: (954) 760-7049

GLASTRON BOATS INC.

(Holding of Platinum Equity, LLC)
700 Paul Larson Memorial Dr
Little Falls, MN 56345
Mailing Address:
PO Box 460
Little Falls, MN 56345-0460
Tel.: (320) 632-8395
Fax: (320) 632-1438
Sales Range: $150-199.9 Million
Approx. Number Employees: 870
Year Founded: 1956
Business Description:
Fiberglass Boats Mfr.
S.I.C.: 3732; 5551
N.A.I.C.S.: 336612; 441222
Export
Media: 2-6-7-10-17-19-24
Distr.: Natl.
Budget Set: June

Advertising Agency:
Kleckner Advertising
464 2nd St, Ste 105
Wayzata, MN 55331
Tel.: (952) 473-9944
Fax: (952) 473-1181
(Boats)

GRADY-WHITE BOATS, INC.

PO Box 1527
Greenville, NC 27835-1527
Tel.: (252) 752-2111
Fax: (252) 830-8462
Web Site: www.gradywhite.com
Sales Range: $75-99.9 Million
Approx. Number Employees: 150
Business Description:
Boats Mfr
S.I.C.: 3732
N.A.I.C.S.: 336612
Media: 4-6-10-24
Distr.: Natl.
Budget Set: Aug.
Personnel:
Kris Carroll *(Pres)*
Eddie Smith *(CEO)*
Joey Weller *(VP-Sls)*
Gwen Edwards *(Supvr-Sls Admin)*

Brands & Products:
ADVANCE
ADVENTURE
BIMINI
CHASE
ESCAPE
EXPRESS
FISHERMAN
GULFSTREAM
JOURNEY
MARLIN
RELEASE
SAILFISH
SEAFARER
SPORTSMAN
TOURNAMENT

Advertising Agency:
Adams & Longino Advertising, Inc.
605 Lynndale Ct Ste F
Greenville, NC 27858
Tel.: (252) 355-5566
Fax: (252) 355-7363

GREAT DANE TRAILERS

(Sub. of CC Industries, Inc.)
602 E Lathrop Ave
Savannah, GA 31415-1062
Mailing Address:
PO Box 67
Savannah, GA 31402-0067
Tel.: (912) 644-2100
Fax: (912) 644-2171
E-mail: advertising@greatdanetrailers.com
Web Site: www.greatdanetrailers.com
Approx. Number Employees: 4,000
Year Founded: 1900
Business Description:
Truck Trailers Mfr
S.I.C.: 3715
N.A.I.C.S.: 336212
Export
Advertising Expenditures: $3,000,000
Media: 1-2-4-7-10-13-22
Distr.: Intl.
Budget Set: Dec.
Personnel:
Sam Gupta *(Sr VP-Mfg)*
Brandie Fuller *(VP-Mktg)*
Dan McCormack *(Product Mgr)*

Brands & Products:
GREAT DANE

Advertising Agency:
Ketchum Directory Advertising/Kansas City
7015 College Blvd Ste 700
Overland Park, KS 66211-1524
Tel.: (913) 344-1900
Fax: (913) 344-1960
Toll Free: (800) 922-6977

GUARANTY RV CENTERS

20 Hwy 99 S
Junction City, OR 97448-9714
Tel.: (541) 998-2333
Fax: (541) 998-4263
Toll Free: (800) 766-9231
E-mail: info@guaranty.com
Web Site: www.guaranty.com
Sales Range: $300-349.9 Million
Approx. Number Employees: 320
Year Founded: 1966
Business Description:
New & Pre-owned RVs Retailers
S.I.C.: 5561; 5511
N.A.I.C.S.: 441210; 441110
Media: 2-3-5-6-8-9-10-13-14-15-16-18-22-23-24-25-26
Personnel:
Herb Nill *(Founder)*
Ed Morgan *(CFO)*
Shannon Nill *(Gen Mgr)*
Becky Smith *(Mgr-Guarantys Mktg)*

HARBORMASTER MARINE, INC.

37654 Amrhein Rd
Livonia, MI 48150-1821
Tel.: (734) 425-1080
Fax: (734) 425-1850
Toll Free: (800) 898-5387
E-mail: sales@harbormastermarine.com
Web Site:
www.harbormastermarine.com
E-Mail For Key Personnel:
Sales Director: sales@harbormastermarine.com
Sales Estimate: $5-9.9 Million
Approx. Number Employees: 10
Year Founded: 1947
Business Description:
Marine Propulsion & Steering Systems; Out-Board Drives & Thrusters
S.I.C.: 5088
N.A.I.C.S.: 423860
Export
Media: 2
Distr.: Intl.; Natl.
Budget Set: Nov.
Personnel:
Matthew Bradford *(Pres & CEO)*
Jason Pfander *(Mgr-Pur & Cust Svc)*
Brands & Products:
HARBORMASTER
MURRAY AND TREGURTHA

HATTERAS YACHTS

(Sub. of Brunswick Boat Group)
110 N Glenburnie Rd
New Bern, NC 28560
Tel.: (252) 633-3101
Tel.: (252) 634-4895 (sales & mktg)
Fax: (252) 634-4819
E-mail: info@hatterasyachts.com
Web Site: www.hatterasyachts.com
Sales Range: $75-99.9 Million
Approx. Number Employees: 200
Business Description:
Yachts Mfr
S.I.C.: 3732
N.A.I.C.S.: 336612
Media: 6-8-10-11-13-18-19-20
Distr.: Intl.; Natl.
Personnel:
Eric Cashion *(Dir-Mktg-Hatteras Collection)*
Brands & Products:
HATTERAS

HOBIE CAT COMPANY

4925 Oceanside Blvd
Oceanside, CA 92056-3044
Tel.: (760) 758-9100
Fax: (760) 758-1841
E-mail: info@hobiecat.com
Web Site: www.hobiecat.com
Approx. Number Employees: 200
Year Founded: 1968
Business Description:
Catamaran Sailboats, Kayaks, Parts & Accessories Mfr
S.I.C.: 3732
N.A.I.C.S.: 336612
Media: 1-6-8-10-13
Distr.: Intl.; Natl.
Personnel:
Greg Ketterman *(Owner)*
Doug Skidmore *(Pres)*
Bill Baldwin *(VP-Fin)*
Ruth Triglia *(VP-Sls)*
Dan Mangus *(Dir-Mktg)*
Brands & Products:
HOBIE
HOBIE CAT
LANAI
MAUI
MIRAGE CLASSIC
MIRAGE OUTBACK
MIRAGE OUTBACK FISHERMAN
MIRAGE SPORT
MIRAGE TANDEM
ODYSSEY
PURSUIT

HUCKINS YACHT CORPORATION

3482 Lake Shore Blvd
Jacksonville, FL 32210-5391
Tel.: (904) 389-1125
Fax: (904) 388-2281
E-mail: info@huckinsyacht.com
Web Site: www.huckinsyacht.com
Approx. Number Employees: 60
Year Founded: 1928
Business Description:
Yacht Sales, Building & Repairing Services
S.I.C.: 3732
N.A.I.C.S.: 336612
Export
Media: 2-4-6-7-8-10-13-18-22
Distr.: Intl.; Natl.
Personnel:
Cindy Purcell *(Owner)*
Dale B. Purcell *(Pres & CEO)*
Brands & Products:
FAIRFORM FLYER
HUCKINS
Advertising Agency:
Anson-Stoner Inc.
111 E Fairbanks Ave
Winter Park, FL 32789-7004
Tel.: (407) 629-9484
Fax: (407) 629-9480

HUNTER MARINE CORPORATION

(Sub. of Luhrs Marine Group)
14700 441 NW U.S. Hwy
Alachua, FL 32615
Mailing Address:
PO Box 1030
Alachua, FL 32616-1030
Tel.: (386) 462-3077
Fax: (386) 462-4077
Toll Free: (800) 771-5556
E-mail: info@huntermarine.com
Web Site: www.huntermarine.com
Approx. Number Employees: 350
Year Founded: 1974
Business Description:
Mfr of Sailboats
S.I.C.: 3732
N.A.I.C.S.: 336612
Import Export
Media: 4-5-6-8-10-13
Distr.: Intl.; Natl.
Budget Set: July -Aug.
Personnel:
Warren R. Luhrs *(Chm)*
Mike Williams *(Pres)*
Brands & Products:
ALURA
CLUB TRAINER
CRUISE PAL
HUNTER
LEGEND
LIBERTY
PASSAGE
VISION
XCITE

IMTRA CORPORATION

30 Samuel Barnet Blvd
New Bedford, MA 02745
Tel.: (508) 995-7000
Fax: (508) 998-5359
Toll Free: (800) 989-2580
E-mail: info@imtra.com
Web Site: www.imtra.com
Approx. Sls.: $11,400,000
Approx. Number Employees: 40
Year Founded: 1962
Business Description:
Distributor of Marine Crafts & Supplies
S.I.C.: 5088; 5091
N.A.I.C.S.: 423860; 423910
Personnel:
William H. Farnham, Jr. *(Chm)*
Nat Bishop *(Pres)*
Brands & Products:
ALBA
ALFO
ARGENTA
ARGO
ASTRO
ATHENA
BERMUDA
BLINK
BOB
BOSTON
CABIN
CABIN ANNE
CABIN MIA
CAROLINE
CHARLY BOY
CHIARA
CHIP
CIRCE
CLEO
CLOSET
CLUSETER
CONCORDE ALLOY
CUPIDO
DANY
DAVID
DEDALO
DELTA
DEMETRA
DIANA
DISCO
EGEO
ENEA
EOLO
ERMES
EROS
FARO
FLEX
FRED
FRIDA
GAIA
GHIBI
GIOVE
GLASS
ICARO
IMTRA
ITACA
JAZZ
JENY
LEDA
LEO B
LIFE
LIGHTHOUSE
LINARA
LUISELLA
MAIA
MALUA
MARY
MAX
MEDEA
MIDA
MIKE
MIMMA
MINOR
NAFISA
NARA
NEW CLASSIC
NEW LINE
NINFE
OCEAN
OMEGA
ONDINE
ORLANDO
OYSTER
PACIFIC
PATTY
PEGASUS
PENELOPE
PERSEO
PIER
POLARIS
POLIFEMO
PUMA
QUEEN
RAGNO
RECESSED
RENO
RESOLUX
ROGER
RONDETTO
SAMPEI
SARA
SHADES
SHELL
SIRIO
SKY
SPILLO
STAR
STORM

Key to Media (For complete agency information see *The Advertising Red Books-Agencies* edition):
1. Bus. Publs. 2. Cable T.V. 3. Catalogs & Directories. 4. Co-op Adv. 5. Consumer Mags. 6. D.M. to Bus. Estab.7. D.M. to Consumers
8. Daily Newsp. 9. Exhibits/Trade Shows 10. Foreign 11. Infomercial 12. Internet Adv.13. Multimedia 14. Network Radio
15. Network T.V. 16. Newsp. Distr. Mags. 17. Other 18. Outdoor (Posters, Transit) 19. Point of Purchase20. Premiums, Novelties
21. Product Samples 22. Special Events Mktg. 23. Spot Radio 24. Spot T.V. 25. Weekly Newsp. 26. Yellow Page Adv.

Imtra Corporation — (Continued)

SUSY
SYDNEY LED
TEBE
TIME
TONY
TOUCHLED
TUNA
TYPHOON
VENERE
VENUS
VIAREGGIO
VIENNA
VIOLA
VULCANO
WALTER
YACO
ZARA
ZEUS

Advertising Agency:
Brewster Strategies
21 Eliot St
Natick, MA 01760-6085
Tel.: (508) 647-6282
Fax: (508) 647-0651

JACOBSEN TEXTRON
(Sub. of Textron Inc.)
11108 Quality Drive
Charlotte, NC 28273
Tel.: (704) 504-6600
Fax: (704) 504-6661
Toll Free: (800) 848-1636
Web Site: www.jacobsen.com/
Sales Range: $800-899.9 Million
Approx. Number Employees: 4,000
Year Founded: 1921
Business Description:
Turf Maintenance Equipment & Industrial Vehicles Mfr
S.I.C.: 3524
N.A.I.C.S.: 333112
Export
Media: 2-4-5-7-8-10-18-19-20-22
Distr.: Natl.
Budget Set: Oct.
Personnel:
Dan Wilkinson *(Pres)*
Deanna Griffith *(Mgr-Mktg & Comm)*

JAYCO INC.
903 S Main St
Middlebury, IN 46540-9706
Tel.: (574) 825-5861
Fax: (574) 825-7354
Toll Free: (800) RV-JAYCO
E-mail: kyoder@jayco.com
Web Site: www.jayco.com
Approx. Number Employees: 1,200
Year Founded: 1968
Business Description:
Mfr of Recreational Vehicles
S.I.C.: 3792; 3716
N.A.I.C.S.: 336214; 336213
Export
Media: 1-2-4-5-6-10-13-15-18-19-20-24
Distr.: Intl.
Budget Set: July
Personnel:
Wilbur Bontrager *(Chm & CEO)*
Derald Bontrager *(Pres & COO)*
Kent A. Yoder *(CFO & Sr VP)*
Celina Tyler *(Gen Counsel)*
David L. Eash *(VP-Sls & Mktg)*
John Ganyard *(Dir-HR)*
Sid Johnson *(Dir-Mktg)*
Paul Gardner *(Sr Mgr-Product)*
Brands & Products:
DESIGNER
EAGLE
EAGLE SELECT
ESCAPADE
GRANITE RIDGE
GREYHAWK
JAY FEATHER EXP
JAY FEATHER LGT
JAY FEATHER SPORT
JAY FLIGHT
LEGACY
QWEST
QWEST BAJA
TALON ZX

KAWASAKI MOTORS CORP., U.S.A.
(Sub. of Kawasaki Heavy Industries, Ltd.)
9950 Jeronimo Rd
Irvine, CA 92618-2014
Mailing Address:
PO Box 25252
Santa Ana, CA 92799-5252
Tel.: (949) 770-0400
Fax: (949) 460-5600
Web Site: www.kawasaki.com
Approx. Number Employees: 400
Year Founded: 1966
Business Description:
Motorcycles, Parts & Accessories, Jet Ski Watercraft, Generators, All Terrain Vehicles, Engines, Utility Vehicles
S.I.C.: 5012; 5013
N.A.I.C.S.: 423110; 423120
Import Export
Media: 3-4-5-6-8-10-13-19-22-26
Distr.: Natl.
Budget Set: Oct.
Brands & Products:
BAYOU
BRUT FORCE
JET SKI
KAWASAKI MOUNTAIN BIKES
KFX
LET THE GOOD TIMES ROLL
MOJAVE
MULE
NINJA
PRAIRIE
TECATE
VULCAN
Advertising Agency:
O'Leary and Partners
5000 Birch St Ste 1000
Newport Beach, CA 92660
Tel.: (949) 833-8006
Fax: (949) 833-9155

KING OF THE ROAD
(Div. of Chief Industries, Inc.)
2318 Kent Ave
Grand Island, NE 68803
Mailing Address:
PO Box 99
York, NE 68467-0099
Tel.: (308) 382-3866
Fax: (308) 384-0162
Toll Free: (866) 400-9840
Web Site: www.eaglecrestrv.com
Approx. Number Employees: 200
Business Description:
Mfr Recreational Vehicles
S.I.C.: 3792
N.A.I.C.S.: 336214
Export
Advertising Expenditures: $1,300,000
Bus. Publs.: $390,000; Consumer Mags.: $325,000; D.M. to Bus. Estab.: $65,000; Exhibits/Trade Shows: $520,000
Distr.: Intl.; Natl.
Budget Set: July
Brands & Products:
CROWN MARQUIS
GENESIS
LS
ROYALITE
SLIDEDECK

LEHMAN TRIKES INC.
125 Industrial Dr
Spearfish, SD 57783
Tel.: (780) 423-3661
Fax: (780) 426-1293
Toll Free: (888) 3WHEELS
E-mail: info@lehmantrikes.com
Web Site: www.lehmantrikes.com
Approx. Rev.: $33,384,233
Approx. Number Employees: 65
Year Founded: 1998
Business Description:
Motorcycle Trike Conversion Mfr
S.I.C.: 3751
N.A.I.C.S.: 336991
Media: 6-10-22
Personnel:
John F. Lehman, Jr. *(Founder & Sr VP)*
Marc S. Rose *(Chm)*
Kennon D. Hines *(Pres & CEO)*
Timothy C. Kling *(CFO)*
Brands & Products:
LEADER OF THE THREE WORLD

LOOK COMMUNICATIONS INC.
1755 Rene Levesque Blvd East Suite 201
Montreal, QC H2K 4P6, Canada
Tel.: (514) 526-6645
Fax: (514) 526-6678
Toll Free: (877) 296-5665
E-mail: investorinfo@look.ca
Web Site: www.look.ca
Approx. Rev.: $424,747
Approx. Number Employees: 135
Year Founded: 1999
Business Description:
Digital Television Distribution & High-Speed & Dial-Up Internet Access Services
S.I.C.: 4812; 7375
N.A.I.C.S.: 517212; 518111
Media: 8
Personnel:
James Grant McCutcheon *(CEO & Acting CFO)*
Anthony Schultz *(VP-Network-Engrg)*

LOWE BOATS
(Sub. of Brunswick Boat Group)
2900 Industrial Dr
Lebanon, MO 65536
Tel.: (417) 532-9101
Fax: (417) 532-8979
Web Site: www.lowe.com
Sales Range: $125-149.9 Million
Approx. Number Employees: 325
Year Founded: 1971
Business Description:
Boat Mfr
S.I.C.: 3732
N.A.I.C.S.: 336612
Export
Media: 2-4-6-10-18-19
Distr.: Intl.; Natl.
Budget Set: Aug. -Sept.
Personnel:
Les Crawford *(Pres)*
John Metcalf *(VP-Mktg)*
Brands & Products:
LOWE
SEA NYMPH
SUNCRUISER

LUHRS CORPORATION
(Sub. of Luhrs Marine Group)
301 Riverside Dr
Millville, NJ 08332
Tel.: (856) 825-4117
Fax: (856) 825-2729
Toll Free: (800) 524-2804
E-mail: info@luhrs.com
Web Site: www.luhrs.com
Approx. Number Employees: 400
Year Founded: 1986
Business Description:
Sportfishing Boats Mfr
S.I.C.: 3732
N.A.I.C.S.: 336612
Export
Media: 4-5-6-8-10-20
Personnel:
Brett Marshall *(VP-Sls & Mktg)*

LUHRS MARINE GROUP
(Sub. of Morgan Industries Corp.)
255 Diesel Rd
Saint Augustine, FL 32084
Tel.: (856) 825-4117
Fax: (904) 827-2156
Toll Free: (800) 882-4343
E-mail: customerservice@luhrs.com
Web Site: www.luhrs.com
Approx. Number Employees: 80
Year Founded: 1985
Business Description:
Pleasure Boats Mfr
S.I.C.: 3732
N.A.I.C.S.: 336612
Media: 4-9-10-13-22
Personnel:
Brett Marshall *(VP-Sls & Mktg)*
Brands & Products:
GLENDINNING
LUHRS

MAINSHIP CORPORATION
(Sub. of Luhrs Marine Group)
548 Industrial Blvd
Midway, GA 31320
Tel.: (912) 884-9595
Fax: (912) 880-2132
Toll Free: (800) 578-0852
E-mail: info@mainship.com
Web Site: www.mainship.com
Sales Range: $25-49.9 Million
Approx. Number Employees: 400
Year Founded: 1975
Business Description:
Pleasure Boats Mfr
S.I.C.: 3732
N.A.I.C.S.: 336612
Import Export
Media: 4-5-6-8-10-20
Personnel:
Brian Dingler *(Treas & VP-Fin)*
Brands & Products:
PILOT

Key to Media (For complete agency information see *The Advertising Red Books-Agencies* edition):
1. Bus. Publs. 2. Cable T.V. 3. Catalogs & Directories. 4. Co-op Adv. 5. Consumer Mags. 6. D.M. to Bus. Estab.7. D.M. to Consumers 8. Daily Newsp. 9. Exhibits/Trade Shows 10. Foreign 11. Infomercial 12. Internet Adv.13. Multimedia 14. Network Radio 15. Network T.V. 16. Newsp. Distr. Mags. 17. Other 18. Outdoor (Posters, Transit) 19. Point of Purchase20. Premiums, Novelties 21. Product Samples 22. Special Events Mktg. 23. Spot Radio 24. Spot T.V. 25. Weekly Newsp. 26. Yellow Page Adv.

TROLLERS

MARINEMAX, INC.
18167 US Hwy 19 N Ste 300
Clearwater, FL 33764-6572
Tel.: (727) 531-1700
Fax: (727) 524-3954
Web Site: www.marinemax.com
Approx. Rev.: $450,340,000
Approx. Number Employees: 1,158
Business Description:
Recreational Boat Retailer
S.I.C.: 5551; 5013
N.A.I.C.S.: 441222; 441310
Advertising Expenditures: $8,500,000
Media: 5-6-8-10
Personnel:
William H. McGill, Jr. *(Chm, Pres & CEO)*
Michael H. McLamb *(CFO, Sec & Exec VP)*
Edward A. Russell *(COO & Exec VP)*
Michael J. Aiello *(Reg Pres)*
Paulee C. Day *(Gen Counsel, VP & Asst Sec)*
Kurt M. Frahn *(Treas & VP-Fin)*
Jay J. Avelino *(VP-HR & Team Dev)*
Greta Andrew *(Coord-Mktg & Event Plng)*
Advertising Agency:
Pyper Paul + Kenney, Inc.
1102 N Florida Ave
Tampa, FL 33602
Tel.: (813) 496-7000
Fax: (813) 496-7003

MARWI USA, INC.
724 W Clem Ste
Olney, IL 62450
Tel.: (618) 395-2200
Fax: (618) 395-4711
Toll Free: (800) 448-3876
E-mail: info@marwiusa.com
Web Site: www.marwiusa.com
E-Mail For Key Personnel:
Sales Director: sales@marwiusa.com
Approx. Number Employees: 12
Business Description:
Bicycle Components & Accessories Mfr & Sales
S.I.C.: 3751
N.A.I.C.S.: 336991
Advertising Expenditures: $200,000
Media: 4-6-7-10-22
Distr.: Natl.
Brands & Products:
MARWI
NIGHTPRO
TI-DYE
UNION
XERAMA

MASTERCRAFT BOAT COMPANY LLC
(Holding of Charlesbank Capital Partners, LLC)
100 Cherokee Cove Dr
Vonore, TN 37885-2129
Tel.: (423) 884-2221
Fax: (423) 884-2295
E-mail: john.dortan@mastercraft.com
Web Site: www.mastercraft.com
Sales Range: $200-249.9 Million
Approx. Number Employees: 200
Year Founded: 1968
Business Description:
Ski Boats & Skis Mfr & Retailer
S.I.C.: 3732; 3792
N.A.I.C.S.: 336612; 336214
Media: 1-2-4-5-7-8-10-13-18-21-22
Personnel:
John R. Dorton *(Pres, CEO & Dir)*
Scott Crutchfield *(Sr VP-Sls)*
Ian Birdsall *(VP-Sls & Mktg & Customer Svc-Intl)*
Jason Boertje *(Dir-Mktg)*
Brands & Products:
MARISTAR
POWERSTAR
PROSTAR

MERCURY MARINE
(Div. of Brunswick Corporation)
6250 W Pioneer Rd
Fond Du Lac, WI 54935-1939
Mailing Address:
PO Box 1939
Fond Du Lac, WI 54936-1939
Tel.: (920) 929-5000
Tel.: (920) 929-5040
Fax: (920) 929-5893
Fax: (920) 924-1724
E-mail: public.relations@mercmarine.com
Web Site: www.mercurymarine.com
Sales Range: $1-4.9 Billion
Approx. Number Employees: 6,200
Year Founded: 1939
Business Description:
Marine Propulsion Systems Mfr
S.I.C.: 3519; 3511
N.A.I.C.S.: 333618; 333611
Media: 2-4-6-7-8-9-10-11-14-18-19-20-23-24-25-26
Distr.: Intl.; Natl.
Budget Set: July -Aug.
Personnel:
Mark D. Schwabero *(Pres)*
Steve Cramer *(CFO, Chief Admin Officer & VP)*
Kevin Grodzki *(Pres-MerCruiser Bus Unit)*
Todd C. Lemke *(Gen Counsel)*
Ray Caruana *(VP-Sls-Americas)*
Stephan Cloutier *(VP-Procurement)*
Michael Shedivy *(VP-Mktg)*
Steve Fleming *(Dir-Comm)*
Brands & Products:
MERCURY MERCRUISER
MERCURY OUTBOARDS
MERCURY PRECISION PARTS
MERCURY SMARTCRAFT
Advertising Agency:
Jacobson Rost
233 N Water St 6th Fl
Milwaukee, WI 53202
Tel.: (414) 220-4888
Fax: (414) 220-4889
(All)

MICHIGAN WHEEL CORPORATION
(Holding of The Anderson Group, LLC)
(d/b/a Michigan Wheel Marine)
1501 Buchanan Ave SW
Grand Rapids, MI 49507-1697
Tel.: (616) 452-6941
Fax: (616) 247-0227
E-mail: info@miwheel.com
Web Site: www.miwheel.com
Sales Range: $1-9.9 Million
Approx. Number Employees: 85
Year Founded: 1903
Business Description:
Inboard & Outboard Boat Propeller Mfr & Distr
S.I.C.: 3714; 3324
N.A.I.C.S.: 336399; 331512
Import Export
Media: 2-4-6-7-8-10-13-18
Distr.: Intl.; Natl.
Budget Set: Oct.
Personnel:
Stanley J. Heide *(Pres & CEO)*
Kenneth Creech *(CFO)*
Marty Ronis *(VP-Mktg & Sls)*
Brands & Products:
AMBUSH
BALLISTIC
MICHIGAN MATCH
MICHIGAN PROPELLERS
MICHIGAN WHEEL CORPORATION
RAPTURE
VORTEX
XHS

MILLER YACHT SALES, INC.
200 State Hwy 166
Toms River, NJ 08757
Tel.: (732) 349-6800
Fax: (732) 349-6649
E-mail: mys1919@aol.com
Sales Range: $1-9.9 Million
Approx. Number Employees: 25
Business Description:
Mfr & Retailer of Yachts
S.I.C.: 5551; 3732
N.A.I.C.S.: 441222; 336612
Import Export
Media: 1-4-6-8-9-10-13-16-20-22
Distr.: Natl.
Personnel:
Donald Miller *(Pres)*
Ed Trengrove *(Mgr-Svcs)*
Brands & Products:
MARINE TRADER
MED YACHTS

OLD TOWN CANOE CO.
(Sub. of Johnson Outdoors Inc.)
125 Gilman Salls Ave Bldg B
Old Town, ME 04468
Tel.: (207) 827-5513
Tel.: (207) 827-5514
Fax: (207) 827-3647
E-mail: feedback@oldtowncanoe.com
Web Site: www.oldtowncanoe.com
Sales Range: $25-49.9 Million
Approx. Number Employees: 150
Year Founded: 1898
Business Description:
Mfr. of Kayaks and Accessories
S.I.C.: 3732
N.A.I.C.S.: 336612
Media: 2-4-5-6-26
Distr.: Natl.
Budget Set: Mar.
Personnel:
Tim Nagoon *(Gen Mgr)*
Brands & Products:
ALLAGASH
APPALACHIAN
DISCOVERY SCOUT
GUIDE
JOLT
MOLITOR
OLD TOWN
OT SPORT
OTCA
OTTER
POLYLINK3
PREDATOR SERIES
TRAPPER
TRIPPER
TWIN OTTER
Advertising Agency:
Hammerquist Nebeker
15230 NE 92nd St
Redmond, WA 98052
Tel.: (425) 869-3361

PACIFIC CYCLE INC.
(Div. of Dorel Industries, Inc.)
4902 Hammersley Rd
Madison, WI 53711-2614
Tel.: (608) 268-2468
Fax: (608) 268-8955
E-mail: info@pacific-cycle.com
Web Site: www.pacific-cycle.com
Sales Range: $400-449.9 Million
Approx. Number Employees: 100
Business Description:
Mfr. & Distr of Bicycles & Accessories
S.I.C.: 5091; 3751
N.A.I.C.S.: 423910; 336991
Media: 11-22
Personnel:
Alice Tillett *(Pres)*
Bob Kmoch *(CFO)*
Tim Staton *(Mgr-Mktg-Schwinn)*
Brands & Products:
DYNO
GT
INSTEP
KUSTOM KRUISER
MONGOOSE
PACIFIC
PACIFIC OUTDOORS
POWERLITE
ROADMASTER
SCHWINN
SCHWINN MOTOR SCOOTERS

PALMER JOHNSON INCORPORATED
128 Kentucky St
Sturgeon Bay, WI 54235-0109
Mailing Address:
PO Box 109
Sturgeon Bay, WI 54235-0109
Tel.: (920) 743-4412
Fax: (920) 743-9185
E-mail: info@palmerjohnson.com
Web Site: www.palmerjohnson.com
Approx. Number Employees: 600
Year Founded: 1918
Business Description:
Builder of Custom Yachts
S.I.C.: 3732; 4493
N.A.I.C.S.: 336612; 713930
Media: 10
Distr.: Intl.
Personnel:
Mike Kelsey, Jr. *(Pres)*
Tom Kuffel *(CFO & VP-Fin)*
Brands & Products:
PALMER JOHNSON

POLARIS INDUSTRIES, INC.
2100 Hwy 55
Medina, MN 55340-9770
Tel.: (763) 542-0500
Fax: (763) 542-0599
Toll Free: (800) POLARIS
Telex: 247355 PLRS UR
E-mail: richard.edwards@polarisind.com
Web Site: www.polarisindustries.com

Key to Media (For complete agency information see *The Advertising Red Books-Agencies* edition):
1. Bus. Publs. 2. Cable T.V. 3. Catalogs & Directories. 4. Co-op Adv. 5. Consumer Mags. 6. D.M. to Bus. Estab.7. D.M. to Consumers 8. Daily Newsp. 9. Exhibits/Trade Shows 10. Foreign 11. Infomercial 12. Internet Adv.13. Multimedia 14. Network Radio 15. Network T.V. 16. Newsp. Distr. Mags. 17. Other 18. Outdoor (Posters, Transit) 19. Point of Purchase20. Premiums, Novelties 21. Product Samples 22. Special Events Mktg. 23. Spot Radio 24. Spot T.V. 25. Weekly Newsp. 26. Yellow Page Adv.

Polaris Industries, Inc. — (Continued)

Approx. Sls.: $1,991,139,000
Approx. Number Employees: 3,000
Year Founded: 1954
Business Description:
All-Terrain Vehicles, Snowmobiles & Motorcycles Mfr & Marketer
S.I.C.: 3711; 2396; 3732; 3751; 3799
N.A.I.C.S.: 336112; 336360; 336612; 336991; 336999
Import Export
Advertising Expenditures: $37,433,000
Media: 1-2-3-4-5-6-7-8-9-10-13-14-15-18-19-20-22-23-24-25-26
Distr.: Intl.; Natl.
Budget Set: Nov.
Personnel:
Bennett J. Morgan *(Pres & COO)*
Scott W. Wine *(CEO)*
Michael W. Malone *(CFO & VP-Fin)*
William C. Fisher *(CIO & VP)*
David C. Longren *(CTO & VP-ORV & ORV Engrg-Off-Road Vehicle Bus)*
Steve Kemp *(CTO-Engrg)*
Stacy L. Bogart *(Gen Counsel, Sec, VP & Compliance Officer)*
Steve Menneto *(VP-Motorcycles)*
Michael P. Jonikas *(VP-Snowmobiles Bus, Sls & Corp Mktg)*
Jim Williams *(VP-HR)*
Steve Cohoon *(Gen Mgr-Powertrain & Sr Dir-Snow Engrg)*
Cassey Murphy *(Mgr-Mktg-Snowmobile Div)*
Jan Rintamaki *(Mgr-Mktg)*
Brands & Products:
GLACIER
LOCK & RIDE
POLARIS
PURE POLARIS
VICTORY MOTORCYCLES
THE WORLD'S TOUGHEST ATVS
Advertising Agencies:
The Integer Group, LLC
7245 W Alaska Dr
Lakewood, CO 80226
Tel.: (303) 393-3000
Fax: (303) 393-3730

Nelson Schmidt
600 E Wisconsin Ave
Milwaukee, WI 53202
Tel.: (414) 224-0210
Fax: (414) 224-9463
Global Electric Motorcars
Marketing
Sales

Weber Shandwick-Minneapolis
8000 Norman Ctr Dr Ste 400
Minneapolis, MN 55437
Tel.: (952) 832-5000
Fax: (952) 831-8241

REXHALL INDUSTRIES, INC.
46147 7th St W
Lancaster, CA 93534-7601
Tel.: (661) 726-0565
Fax: (661) 726-5811
Toll Free: (800) 765-7500
E-mail: executives@rexhall.com
Web Site: www.rexhall.com
E-Mail For Key Personnel:
President: bill@rexhall.com
Sales Director: sales@rexhall.com
Sales Range: $25-49.9 Million
Approx. Number Employees: 100
Year Founded: 1986
Business Description:
Self-Contained Motorhomes Used Primarily for Leisure Travel Mfr
S.I.C.: 3716
N.A.I.C.S.: 336213
Export
Media: 2-10-13-18-19
Personnel:
William Rex *(Chm, Pres & CEO)*
James C. Rex *(VP & Gen Mgr)*
Brands & Products:
AERBUS
AMERICAN CLIPPER
ANTHEM
CONCORD
ENTRYSLIDE
MINIBUS
REXAIR
REXHALL
REXHALL INDUSTRIES
ROSEAIR
STRENGTH, INTEGRITY & VALUE
T-REX DOUBLE & WIDE
VISION

S2 YACHTS, INC.
725 E 40th St
Holland, MI 49423
Tel.: (616) 392-7163
Fax: (616) 394-7466
Web Site: www.tiarayachts.com
Approx. Number Employees: 750
Year Founded: 1974
Business Description:
Yachts Mfr
S.I.C.: 3732
N.A.I.C.S.: 336612
Media: 6
Distr.: Intl.; Natl.; Reg.
Personnel:
Leon Slikkers *(Chm)*
Bob Slikkers *(Pres)*
David Slikkers *(CEO)*
Brands & Products:
S2 YACHTS
TIARA
Advertising Agency:
Biggs Gilmore Communications
261 E Kalamazoo Ave Ste 300
Kalamazoo, MI 49007-3841
Tel.: (269) 349-7711
Fax: (269) 349-3051

SABRE CORPORATION
12 Hawthorne Rd
Raymond, ME 04071
Tel.: (207) 655-3831
Fax: (207) 655-5050
E-mail: sabre@sabreyachts.com
Web Site: www.sabreyachts.com
E-Mail For Key Personnel:
Marketing Director: bentley@sabreyachts.com
Sales Director: brenda@sabreyacht.com
Sales Range: $100-124.9 Million
Approx. Number Employees: 150
Year Founded: 1971
Business Description:
Fiberglass Sailing Yachts & Motor Yachts Mfr
S.I.C.: 3732
N.A.I.C.S.: 336612
Export
Advertising Expenditures: $200,000
Media: 2-4-5-10
Distr.: Natl.
Personnel:
Ed Miller *(Chm)*
Daniel Zilkha *(Pres & CEO)*
Nancy J. Basselet *(CFO)*
Bentley Collins *(Mgr-Mktg)*
Brands & Products:
SABRE
SABRE SPIRIT
SABRELINE

SEA EAGLE DIVISION OF HARRISON HOGE INDUSTRIES, INC.
(Div. of Harrison-Hoge Industries, Inc.)
19 N Columbia St Ste 1
Port Jefferson Station, NY 11777-2165
Tel.: (631) 473-7308
Fax: (631) 473-7398
Toll Free: (800) 852-0925
E-mail: staff@seaeagle.com
Web Site: www.seaeagle.com
Year Founded: 1952
Business Description:
Inflatable Canoes & Dinghies Importer & Mfr
S.I.C.: 5091; 5961
N.A.I.C.S.: 423910; 454113
Advertising Expenditures: $1,000,000
Media: 2-4-5-6-7-8-9-13-20-25
Distr.: Natl.
Budget Set: Jan.

SEA RAY BOATS, INC.
(Sub. of Brunswick Boat Group)
2600 Sea Ray Blvd Bldg 1
Knoxville, TN 37914
Tel.: (865) 522-4181
Toll Free: (800) SRBOATS
Web Site: www.searay.com
Sales Range: $250-299.9 Million
Approx. Number Employees: 2,385
Year Founded: 1951
Business Description:
Fiberglass Boats Mfr
S.I.C.: 3732
N.A.I.C.S.: 336612
Media: 6-8-10-16-22-23
Distr.: Intl.; Natl.
Budget Set: July
Personnel:
Rob Parmentier *(Pres)*
Terry D. McNew *(Sr VP-Product Dev & Engrg)*
Mike Burke *(VP-Sls & Mktg)*
Rob Noyes *(VP-Mktg)*
Barry Slade *(Exec Dir-Global Brand Mngmt)*
Brands & Products:
A WORLD BEYOND THE MAIN STREAM
AMBERJACK
IF IT ISN'T A SEA RAY, YOU'VE MISSED THE BOAT.
LAGUNA
OVERNIGHTER
PACHANGA
RAY-TECH
RAY TEL
RAYNET
SEA RAY
SEA RAY LEGACY
SEA RAY LIVING
SEA RAY NAVIGATOR
SEA RAY YACHT RENDEZVOUS
SORRENTO
THE STANDARD OF EXCELLENCE
SUN-SPORT
SUNDANCER
SUNDECK
Advertising Agency:
AVALA Marketing Group
1078 Headquarters Park Dr
Fenton, MO 63026
Tel.: (636) 343-9988
Fax: (636) 326-3282

SILVERTON MARINE CORPORATION
(Sub. of Luhrs Marine Group)
301 Riverside Dr
Millville, NJ 08332-6798
Tel.: (856) 825-4117
Fax: (856) 825-2064
Toll Free: (877) 863-5298
E-mail: sales@silverton.com
Web Site: www.silverton.com
E-Mail For Key Personnel:
Sales Director: sales@silverton.com
Approx. Number Employees: 100
Year Founded: 1969
Business Description:
Mfr of Pleasure Boats
S.I.C.: 3732
N.A.I.C.S.: 336612
Export
Media: 4-5-6-8-10
Personnel:
Rick Cerami *(Pres)*
Brett Marshall *(VP-Sls & Mktg)*

SKIER'S CHOICE INC.
1717 Henry G Lane St
Maryville, TN 37801
Tel.: (865) 983-9924
Fax: (865) 983-9950
Web Site: www.skierschoice.com/
Sales Range: $350-399.9 Million
Approx. Number Employees: 355
Business Description:
Power Boat Mfr.
S.I.C.: 3732
N.A.I.C.S.: 336612
Media: 2-6-7-8-10-17-20-22
Personnel:
Rick Tinker *(Pres)*
Matt Brown *(Product Dev Mgr-Supra)*
Amy Mauzy *(Mgr-Mktg)*
Mike Shirley *(Mgr-Engrg)*
Brands & Products:
MOOMBA
SKIER'S CHOICE
SUPRA
Advertising Agency:
The Harmon Group
807 3rd Ave S
Nashville, TN 37210
Tel.: (615) 256-3393
Fax: (615) 256-3464

SKYLINE CORPORATION
2520 By-Pass Rd
Elkhart, IN 46515
Mailing Address:
PO Box 743
Elkhart, IN 46515-0743
Tel.: (574) 294-6521
Fax: (574) 293-7574
Toll Free: (800) 348-7469
E-mail: consumerrelations@skylinecorp.com
Web Site: www.skylinecorp.com

Key to Media (For complete agency information see *The Advertising Red Books-Agencies* edition):
1. Bus. Publs. 2. Cable T.V. 3. Catalogs & Directories. 4. Co-op Adv. 5. Consumer Mags. 6. D.M. to Bus. Estab.7. D.M. to Consumers 8. Daily Newsp. 9. Exhibits/Trade Shows 10. Foreign 11. Infomercial 12. Internet Adv.13. Multimedia 14. Network Radio 15. Network T.V. 16. Newsp. Distr. Mags. 17. Other 18. Outdoor (Posters, Transit) 19. Point of Purchase20. Premiums, Novelties 21. Product Samples 22. Special Events Mktg. 23. Spot Radio 24. Spot T.V. 25. Weekly Newsp. 26. Yellow Page Adv.

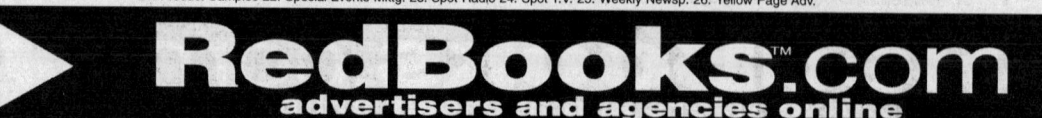

Approx. Sls.: $162,327,000
Approx. Number Employees: 1,300
Year Founded: 1951
Business Description:
Manufactured Housing & Recreational Vehicles Mfr & Distr
S.I.C.: 2451
N.A.I.C.S.: 321991
Advertising Expenditures: $5,000,000
Media: 5-13
Personnel:
Thomas G. Deranek *(Chm & CEO)*
Jon S. Pilarski *(CFO, Treas & VP-Fin)*
Charles W. Chambliss *(VP-Product Dev & Engrg)*
Terrence M. Decio *(VP-Mktg & Sls)*
Thomas Mcgillicuddy *(Dir-HR)*
Brands & Products:
ALJO
BRINGING AMERICA HOME. BRINGING AMERICA FUN.
CELEBRITY
CENTURY
LAYTON
NOMAD
SKYLINE

TAYLOR MADE GROUP
66 Kingsboro Ave
Gloversville, NY 12078
Tel.: (518) 725-0681
Fax: (518) 725-4335
Web Site: www.taylormadegroup.com
Approx. Number Employees: 16
Year Founded: 1908
Business Description:
Accessories for Boats, Windshields, Mirrors, Flags, Tempered Glass, Portable Toilets for RVs & Marine Vehicles, Air Conditioning & Refrigeration for Boats & Awnings Mfr
S.I.C.: 2394; 3732
N.A.I.C.S.: 314912; 336612
Import Export
Media: 2-4-6-7-8-9-10-11-19-20-21-23-25
Distr.: Intl.; Natl.
Budget Set: June
Personnel:
James W. Taylor *(Owner)*
John E. Taylor *(Owner)*
Dennis Flint *(Chm & CEO)*
Andy Jobbins *(Pres & COO)*
Tom Peters *(Mng Dir)*
Robert Khalife *(CFO)*
Mike Oathout *(VP-Sls & Mktg)*
Brands & Products:
AER-O-BUOY
BOAT GUARD
BOATOPS
MOOR 'N STOR
TAYLOR
TAYLOR MADE GROUP
TAYLOR MADE TECHNOLOGIES
TAYLORBRITE
TAYLOR*MADE
TRAILERITE

THOR INDUSTRIES, INC.
419 W Pike St
Jackson Center, OH 45334
Mailing Address:
PO Box 629
Jackson Center, OH 45334-9728
Tel.: (937) 596-6849
Fax: (937) 596-6539
Web Site: www.thorindustries.com
Approx. Sls.: $2,755,508,000
Approx. Number Employees: 8,250
Year Founded: 1980
Business Description:
Recreational Vehicles, Small & Mid-Sized Buses Mfr
S.I.C.: 3792; 3716
N.A.I.C.S.: 336214; 336213
Advertising Expenditures: $8,139,000
Media: 2-6-8-10-13
Personnel:
Peter B. Orthwein *(Chm, Pres & CEO)*
Christian G. Farman *(CFO, Treas & Sr VP)*
Tim J. Howard *(Pres-Breckenridge)*
Andrew Imanse *(Pres-Comml Bus)*
Richard E. Riegel, III *(Sr Grp Pres-Bus Grp & IR)*
George J. Lawrence *(Gen Counsel, Sec & Sr VP)*
Walter L. Bennett *(Exec VP)*
Rolf Nykamp *(Dir-Strategic Sourcing)*
Brands & Products:
AIRSTREAM
CHAMPION BUS
DAMON
DRIVING FOR EXCELLENCE
DUTCHMEN
ELDORADO NATIONAL
FOUR WINDS
GENERAL COACH
INFINITY
KEYSTONE
LAND YACHT
THOR INDUSTRIES

THURSTON SAILS, INC.
112 Tupelo St
Bristol, RI 02809
Tel.: (401) 254-0970
Fax: (401) 253-7830
E-mail: sthurston@quantumsails.com
Web Site: www.thurstonsails.com
E-Mail For Key Personnel:
President: sthurston@quantumsails.com
Approx. Number Employees: 20
Year Founded: 1950
Business Description:
Yacht Sails Mfr
S.I.C.: 2394
N.A.I.C.S.: 314912
Media: 2-6-10-20
Distr.: Natl.
Budget Set: Aug.
Personnel:
Steven K. Thurston *(Pres)*
Brands & Products:
BOATCOVERS
THURSTON

TRINITY YACHTS, LLC
13085 Seaway Rd
Gulfport, MS 39503-4607
Tel.: (228) 276-1000
Fax: (228) 276-1001
Web Site: www.trinityyachts.com
Sales Range: $100-124.9 Million
Approx. Number Employees: 425
Business Description:
Yacht Builder & Retailer
S.I.C.: 3732; 5551
N.A.I.C.S.: 336612; 441222
Media: 6-10-11
Personnel:
Felix Sabates, Jr. *(Chm)*
John Dane, III *(Pres & CEO)*
Wayne Bourgeois *(COO)*

ULTRA MOTORCYCLE COMPANY, INC.
42180 Sarah Way
Temecula, CA 92590
Tel.: (951) 699-4700
Fax: (951) 699-4701
Web Site: www.ultracycles.com
Approx. Sls.: $4,000,000
Approx. Number Employees: 80
Year Founded: 1985
Business Description:
V-Twin Powered Cruisers Mfr
S.I.C.: 5571
N.A.I.C.S.: 441221
Media: 2-10-22-25
Brands & Products:
APACHE PRO-STREET
CALIFORNIA KID
GROUND POUNDER
GROUNDPOUNDER ST
INTIMIDATOR
IT'S IN THE RIDE
LOWDOWN
UMC

UTILITY TRAILER MANUFACTURING COMPANY
17295 E Railroad St
City of Industry, CA 91748
Tel.: (626) 965-1541
Fax: (626) 965-2790
Web Site: www.utilitytrailer.com
Sales Range: $600-649.9 Million
Approx. Number Employees: 3,000
Year Founded: 1914
Business Description:
Commercial Trailers; Refrigerated Trailers; Flatbed Trailers; Dry Freight Vans; Tautliner Curtain Vans & Aftermarket Parts & Truck Bodies Mfr
S.I.C.: 3715; 3714
N.A.I.C.S.: 336212; 336399
Import Export
Advertising Expenditures: $650,000
Media: 2-5-7-10-11-13-26
Distr.: Intl.; Natl.; Reg.
Budget Set: Nov.
Personnel:
Harold C. Bennett *(Pres)*
Paul F. Bennett *(CEO)*
Craig Bennett *(Sr VP-Sls & Mktg)*
Jeffrey Bennett *(VP-Engrg)*
Brands & Products:
2000A
3000R
4000 D-X
TAUTLINER
UTILITY
UTILITY TRAILER
VERTA-LOCK

VIKING YACHT COMPANY
Rte 9
New Gretna, NJ 08224
Tel.: (609) 296-6000
Fax: (609) 296-3956
E-mail: sales@vikingyachts.com
Web Site: www.vikingyachts.com
E-Mail For Key Personnel:
Sales Director: sales@vikingyachts.com
Approx. Number Employees: 1,300
Year Founded: 1964
Business Description:
Yacht Mfr
S.I.C.: 3732
N.A.I.C.S.: 336612
Import Export
Advertising Expenditures: $350,000
Media: 5-6-8-10-17
Distr.: Intl.; Natl.
Budget Set: Aug.
Personnel:
Robert T. Healey *(Chm)*
William J. Healey *(Pres)*
Gerard D. Straub *(CFO & Exec VP)*
Patrick J. Healey *(Exec VP)*
John E. Kasinski *(VP & Controller)*
Joe Schwab *(VP-Sls)*
Pete Fredriksen *(Dir-Mktg)*
Brands & Products:
VALHALLA
VIKING
VIKING SPORT CRUISERS
VIKING WEAR

VIPER MOTORCYCLE COMPANY
(Sub. of Viper Powersports Inc.)
10895 Excelsior Blvd Ste 203
Hopkins, MN 55343
Tel.: (952) 938-2481
Fax: (952) 938-5138
E-mail: info@vipermotorcycle.com
Web Site: www.vipermotorcycle.com
Business Description:
Designer, Mfr & Marketer of Custom Heavyweight Motorcycles
S.I.C.: 3751; 5012
N.A.I.C.S.: 336991; 423110
Media: 2-4-5-6-8-10-13-17-22
Personnel:
John Lai *(Pres)*
Brands & Products:
DIABLO
DIAMONDBACK
VIPER

VOLVO PENTA OF THE AMERICAS, INC.
(Sub. of AB Volvo Penta)
1300 Volvo Penta Dr
Chesapeake, VA 23320
Tel.: (757) 436-2800
Fax: (757) 436-5150
Web Site: www.volvopenta.com
Approx. Number Employees: 200
Year Founded: 1907
Business Description:
Distributor of Marine, Diesel & Industrial Engines
S.I.C.: 5088; 3511
N.A.I.C.S.: 423860; 333611
Import Export
Advertising Expenditures: $1,000,000
Media: 1-2-3-4-5-6-7-10-11-16-19-20-22
Distr.: Intl.; Natl.
Budget Set: Dec.
Personnel:
Clint Moore *(Pres & CEO-Volvo Penta of the Americas)*
Brands & Products:
2 PLUS 4
DPX
DUOPROP
DURAPLUS
SX COBRA
SX DIESEL
XACT

WEST MARINE, INC.
500 Westridge Dr
Watsonville, CA 95076-4171

Key to Media (For complete agency information see *The Advertising Red Books-Agencies* edition):
1. Bus. Publs. 2. Cable T.V. 3. Catalogs & Directories. 4. Co-op Adv. 5. Consumer Mags. 6. D.M. to Bus. Estab.7. D.M. to Consumers 8. Daily Newsp. 9. Exhibits/Trade Shows 10. Foreign 11. Infomercial 12. Internet Adv.13. Multimedia 14. Network Radio 15. Network T.V. 16. Newsp. Distr. Mags. 17. Other 18. Outdoor (Posters, Transit) 19. Point of Purchase20. Premiums, Novelties 21. Product Samples 22. Special Events Mktg. 23. Spot Radio 24. Spot T.V. 25. Weekly Newsp. 26. Yellow Page Adv.

West Marine, Inc. — (Continued)

Tel.: (831) 728-2700
Fax: (831) 768-5000
E-mail: CatIntl@westmarine.com
Web Site: www.westmarine.com

Approx. Rev.: $622,802,000
Approx. Number Employees: 1,807
Year Founded: 1968

Business Description:
Boating Supplies Retailer
S.I.C.: 5551; 5961
N.A.I.C.S.: 441222; 454113
Advertising Expenditures: $5,600,000
Media: 2-3-4-6-7-8-9-10-18-22-23-26
Distr.: Intl.

Personnel:
Randolph K. Repass *(Chm)*
Geoffrey A. Eisenberg *(Pres & CEO)*
Thomas Moran *(CFO & Sr VP-Fin)*
Ashlee Aldridge *(CIO & Sr VP-Direct Sls)*
Ron Japinga *(Exec VP-Mdsg & Mktg)*
Christopher Bolling *(Sr VP-Bus Dev)*
Bruce Edwards *(Sr VP-Stores)*
Larry Smith *(Sr VP-Plng & Replenishment)*

Brands & Products:
WE MAKE BOATING MORE FUN

Advertising Agency:
Kelly, Scott & Madison
35 E Wacker Dr 14th Fl
Chicago, IL 60601-2314
Tel.: (312) 977-0772
Fax: (312) 977-0874

WINNEBAGO INDUSTRIES, INC.

605 W Crystal Lake Rd
Forest City, IA 50436
Mailing Address:
PO Box 152
Forest City, IA 50436-0152
Tel.: (641) 585-3535
Fax: (641) 585-6966
Toll Free: (800) 537-1885
E-mail: sdavis@winnebagoind.com
Web Site: www.winnebagoind.com
E-Mail For Key Personnel:
Sales Director: sales@winnebagoind.com
Public Relations: pr@winnebagoind.com

Approx. Rev.: $449,484,000
Approx. Number Employees: 1,950
Year Founded: 1958

Business Description:
Mfr. of Recreational Vehicles & Motor Homes
S.I.C.: 3716; 3714
N.A.I.C.S.: 336213; 336399
Import Export
Media: 1-2-5-6-8-10-13-18-19-20
Distr.: Intl.; Natl.
Budget Set: May

Personnel:
Robert J. Olson *(Chm)*
Randy J. Potts *(Pres & CEO)*
Sarah N. Nielsen *(CFO & VP)*
Raymond M. Beebe *(Gen Counsel, Sec & VP)*
Roger W. Martin *(VP-Sls & Mktg)*
William J. O'Leary *(VP-Product Dev)*
Sheila M. Davis *(Mgr-IR & Pub Rel)*

Brands & Products:
ABILITY EQUIPPED
ACCESS
ADVENTURER
ASPECT
CAMBRIA
DESTINATION
ELLIPSE
ERA
IMPULSE
ITASCA
ITASCA HORIZON
JOURNEY
LATITUDE
MED ONE
MERIDIAN
MINNIE
MINNIE WINNIE
NAVION
NAVION IQ
ONEPLACE SYSTEMS CENTER
OUTLOOK
PROTECTOR
RESTEASY MULTI-POSITION LOUNGE
RIALTA
SIGHTSEER
SPIRIT
STOREMORE
SUNCRUISER
SUNDANCER
SUNOVA
SUNRISE
SUNSTAR
THERMO-PANEL
TOUR
ULTI-BAY
ULTIMATE
VECTRA
VIEW
VISTA
WINNEBAGO
WINNEBAGO INDUSTRIES

Advertising Agencies:
D K & Y
6009 Penn Ave. S.
Minneapolis, MN 55419
Tel.: (612) 798-4070
Fax: (612) 798-4071
(Itasca, Ultimate)

Peterson Probst
9201 E Bloomington Fwy
Minneapolis, MN 55420
Tel.: (952) 884-6836

YAMAHA MOTOR CANADA LTD.

(Sub. of Yamaha Motor Co., Ltd.)
480 Gordon Baker Rd
Toronto, ON M2H 3B4, Canada
Tel.: (416) 498-1911
Fax: (416) 491-3122
Telex: 6986760
Web Site: www.yamaha-motor.ca
Approx. Number Employees: 150
Year Founded: 1973

Business Description:
Distr of Motorcycles, Snowmobiles, All-Terrain Vehicles, Power Products, Outboard Motors, Parts & Accessories, Golf Carts
S.I.C.: 5571
N.A.I.C.S.: 441221
Import
Media: 2-4-5-6-8-10-11-13-18-19-20-22-23-24-26
Distr.: Intl.; Natl.

Personnel:
Peter Smallman *(VP-Sls & Mktg)*
John Bayliss *(Mgr-Motorcycle Brand)*
Jon Blaicher *(Product Mgr)*
Tim Kennedy *(Mgr-Mktg)*
Chris Reid *(Mgr-Plng & Res-Natl)*
Bryan Hudgin *(Specialist-PR)*

YAMAHA MOTOR CORPORATION USA

(Sub. of Yamaha Motor Co., Ltd.)
6555 Katella Ave
Cypress, CA 90630
Tel.: (714) 761-7300
Fax: (714) 761-7302
Web Site: www.yamaha-motor.com
Approx. Number Employees: 375
Year Founded: 1977

Business Description:
Yamaha Motorized Products Distr
S.I.C.: 5088; 5013
N.A.I.C.S.: 423860; 423120
Media: 2-3-5-6-7-9-10-14-15-18-19-26
Distr.: Intl.; Natl.

Personnel:
Masato Adachi *(Pres & Exec Officer)*
Andrew Cullen *(Mgr-Mktg Comm)*
Bob Starr *(Mgr-Corp Comm)*
Tom Halverson *(Supvr)*

Brands & Products:
BANSHEE
ROAD STAR
ROAD STAR MIDNIGHT
ROAD STAR SILVERADO
ROAD STAR WARRIOR
ROYAL STAR VENTURE
WARRIOR
WAVERUNNER

Advertising Agency:
Marshall Design Associates
4940 Campus Dr.
Newport Beach, CA 92660
Tel.: (949) 440-0706
(Media)

ZODIAC OF NORTH AMERICA, INC.

(Sub. of Zodiac Marine & Pool)
540 Thompson Creek Rd
Stevensville, MD 21666-2508
Tel.: (410) 643-4141
Fax: (410) 643-4491
Web Site: www.zodiacmilpro.com/contact.php
Approx. Number Employees: 100
Year Founded: 1970

Business Description:
Consumer, Military & Commercial Rigid-Hull Inflatable Boat Mfr & Distr
S.I.C.: 3732; 3949; 5091
N.A.I.C.S.: 336612; 339920; 423910

Personnel:
Steven Seigel *(Pres & Gen Mgr)*
Matthew Bolt *(VP-Publicity & Adv)*
Bob Beck *(Sls Mgr-MilitaryFederal)*
Vincent Palmeri *(Sls Mgr-Law Enforcement)*

Advertising Agency:
Dougherty Tombras Advertising LLC
825 Sylvan Lake Road
Eagle, CO 81631
Tel.: (970) 328-9923

Key to Media (For complete agency information see *The Advertising Red Books-Agencies* edition):
1. Bus. Publs. 2. Cable T.V. 3. Catalogs & Directories. 4. Co-op Adv. 5. Consumer Mags. 6. D.M. to Bus. Estab.7. D.M. to Consumers 8. Daily Newsp. 9. Exhibits/Trade Shows 10. Foreign 11. Infomercial 12. Internet Adv.13. Multimedia 14. Network Radio 15. Network T.V. 16. Newsp. Distr. Mags. 17. Other 18. Outdoor (Posters, Transit) 19. Point of Purchase20. Premiums, Novelties 21. Product Samples 22. Special Events Mktg. 23. Spot Radio 24. Spot T.V. 25. Weekly Newsp. 26. Yellow Page Adv.

Restaurants

A&W ALL-AMERICAN FOOD RESTAURANTS, INC.
(Sub. of YUM! Brands, Inc.)
1900 Colonel Sanders Ln
Louisville, KY 40213
Tel.: (502) 874-3000
Fax: (502) 874-8848
Web Site: www.awrestaurants.com
Sales Range: $150-199.9 Million
Approx. Number Employees: 2,000
Year Founded: 1919
Business Description:
Quick-Service Restaurants Operator & Franchiser
S.I.C.: 5812
N.A.I.C.S.: 722211
Personnel:
Ben Butler *(Pres)*
Brands & Products:
A&W
A&W ROOT BEER
BABY BURGER
BACON N' EGGER
CHICKEN GRILL
CHUBBY CHICKEN
CHUBBY DINNER
CHUBBY 'JUNIOR'
MAMA BURGER
MOZZA BURGER
SAUSAGE N' EGGER
TEEN BURGER
UNCLE BURGER
WHISTLE DOG
Advertising Agency:
Ogilvy & Mather
Plaza Bapindo Bank Mandiri Tower
26 Fl
PO Box 2580
Jakarta, 12190, Indonesia
Tel.: (62) 21 526 626 1
Fax: (62) 21 526 626 3
Advertising Agency:
Rethink
700-470 Granvill St
Vancouver, BC V6C 1V5, Canada
Tel.: (604) 685-8911
Fax: (604) 685-9004
— Tom Shepansky *(Acct. Exec.)*

A&W FOOD SERVICES OF CANADA INC.
171 W Esplanade Ste 300
North Vancouver, BC V7M 3K9, Canada
Tel.: (604) 988-2141
Fax: (604) 988-5531
Web Site: www.aw.ca
E-Mail For Key Personnel:
President: jmooney@aw.ca
Sales Range: $400-449.9 Million
Approx. Number Employees: 100
Year Founded: 1956
Business Description:
Restaurant Operator
S.I.C.: 5812
N.A.I.C.S.: 722110
Import
Media: 1-5-8-9-14-15-16-18-19-20-23-24-25-26
Distr.: Natl.
Personnel:
Jefferson J. Mooney *(Chm)*
Paul F.B. Hollands *(Pres & CEO)*
Donald T. Leslie *(CFO)*
David Waterfall *(Dir-Adv-Promo)*

ABP CORPORATION
(d/b/a Au Bon Pain)
1 Au Bon Pain Way
Boston, MA 02210
Tel.: (617) 423-2100
Fax: (617) 423-7879
Web Site: www.aubonpain.com
Business Description:
Bakery & Cafe
S.I.C.: 5812
N.A.I.C.S.: 722211
Personnel:
Susan Morelli *(CEO)*
Maria Feicht *(Chief Brand Officer)*
Ed Frechette *(Sr VP-Mktg)*
Melissa Cook *(Dir-Mktg)*
Advertising Agency:
Conventures, Inc.
1 Design Ctr Pl Ste 718
Boston, MA 02210-2335
Tel.: (617) 439-7700
Fax: (617) 439-7701

ADVANCEPIERRE FOODS, INC.
(Formerly Pierre Foods, Inc.)
(Holding of Oaktree Capital Management, L.P.)
9990 Princeton Rd
Cincinnati, OH 45246
Tel.: (513) 874-8741
Fax: (513) 874-8395
Toll Free: (800) 969-2747
Web Site: www.pierrefoods.com
Sales Range: $1-4.9 Billion
Approx. Number Employees: 2,629
Year Founded: 1970
Business Description:
Processed Foods Mfr, Marketer & Distr
S.I.C.: 5147; 2015; 2099
N.A.I.C.S.: 311612; 311615; 311999
Advertising Expenditures: $538,000
Media: 2-8-10-20-25
Distr.: Direct to Consumer; Natl.
Budget Set: Oct.
Personnel:
Steven Kaplan *(Chm)*
William D. Toler *(CEO)*
Cynthia S. Hughes *(CFO, Principal Acctg Officer & VP)*
Rob Marlow *(Chief Info Officer)*
Anthony J. Schroder *(Pres-Convenience Channel)*
Sally Miller *(VP-IT)*
Brands & Products:
BIG AZ
BLUE STONE GRILL
CHIX-B-Q
CHOP HOUSE
COMMODITY MAGIC
DELI BREAK
DELIGHT BITES
DINE'N WITH
EL PUESTO DE PEDRO
FAST BITES
FAST CHOICE
FAT CHECK
GLOBAL GRILL
GOLDDIGGERS
HEARTHSIDE SELECT
HOT 'N' READY
LINK-N-DOG
MIA PIZZA BELLA
MOM 'N' POPS
PIAZZA'S
PIERRE
PIERRE CLASSICS
PIERRE CREATIONS
PIERRE CUISINE
PIERRE MAIN STREET DINER
PIERRE SELECT
PIERRE SIGNATURES
PIZZA PARLOR
PRIME SIRLOIN BUFFET BAKERY STEAKS
PRIME SIRLOIN FAMILY STEAK HOUSE
RIB-B-Q
RIB NIBBLERS
SAUS-A-RAGE
SMOKIE GRILL

AFC ENTERPRISES, INC.
5555 Glenridge Connector NE Ste 300
Atlanta, GA 30342-4741
Tel.: (404) 459-4450
Fax: (770) 353-3074
E-mail: investor.relations@afce.com
Web Site: www.afce.com
Approx. Rev.: $146,400,000
Approx. Number Employees: 1,245
Year Founded: 1992
Business Description:
Franchiser of Food & Beverage Services
S.I.C.: 5812
N.A.I.C.S.: 722211
Advertising Expenditures: $2,300,000
Media: 3-8-9-15-18-19-23-24
Personnel:
John M. Cranor, III *(Chm)*
Cheryl A. Bachelder *(Pres & CEO)*
H. Melville Hope, III *(CFO)*
Ralph Bower *(COO)*
Richard Lynch *(CMO)*
Harold M. Cohen *(Gen Counsel, Sec & Sr VP)*
Cheryl Fletcher *(Dir-Fin & IR)*
Brands & Products:
AFC
BONAFIDE
CRAVE APPEAL
THE FRANCHISER OF CHOICE
NEW AGE OF OPPORTUNITY

AMERICAN BLUE RIBBON HOLDINGS, LLC
(Joint Venture of Fidelity National Financial, Inc. & Newport Global Advisors, L.P.)
400 W 48th Ave
Denver, CO 80216
Mailing Address:
PO Box 16601
Denver, CO 80216-0601
Tel.: (303) 296-2121
Fax: (303) 672-2668
Toll Free: (800) 800-3644
E-mail: abrhcustomerservice@abrholdings.com
Web Site: www.abrholdings.com

Key to Media (For complete agency information see *The Advertising Red Books-Agencies* edition):
1. Bus. Publs. 2. Cable T.V. 3. Catalogs & Directories. 4. Co-op Adv. 5. Consumer Mags. 6. D.M. to Bus. Estab.7. D.M. to Consumers 8. Daily Newsp. 9. Exhibits/Trade Shows 10. Foreign 11. Infomercial 12. Internet Adv.13. Multimedia 14. Network Radio 15. Network T.V. 16. Newsp. Distr. Mags. 17. Other 18. Outdoor (Posters, Transit) 19. Point of Purchase20. Premiums, Novelties 21. Product Samples 22. Special Events Mktg. 23. Spot Radio 24. Spot T.V. 25. Weekly Newsp. 26. Yellow Page Adv.

American Blue Ribbon Holdings, LLC — (Continued)

Sales Range: $450-499.9 Million
Approx. Number Employees: 12,789
Year Founded: 1958
Business Description:
Restaurant Operator; Owned by Newport Global Advisors L.P. & Fidelity National Financial, Inc.
S.I.C.: 5812; 2051
N.A.I.C.S.: 722110; 311812
Advertising Expenditures: $12,700,000
Media: 8-9-13-18-22-23-24-25
Distr.: Reg.
Budget Set: Sept. -Oct.
Personnel:
Hazem Ouf *(Pres & CEO)*
Jennifer Sanning *(CMO)*
Timothy Kanaly *(Pres-Legendary Baking)*
Scott Chavkin *(Dir-Mktg-Legendary Baking)*
Leland Smith *(Dir-Sls & Mktg)*
Rick Spellman *(Sls Mgr-Natl-Grocery)*
Tim Moss *(Mgr-Sls-Natl-Foodservice)*
Brands & Products:
BAKERS SQUARE
BEST PIE IN AMERICA
LEGENDARY BAKING
MAX & ERMA'S
VILLAGE INN

AMERICAN DAIRY QUEEN CORPORATION
(Sub. of International Dairy Queen, Inc.)
7505 Metro Blvd
Minneapolis, MN 55439-3020
Mailing Address:
PO Box 39286
Minneapolis, MN 55439-0286
Tel.: (952) 830-0200
Fax: (952) 830-0480
Web Site: www.dairyqueen.com
Sales Range: $100-124.9 Million
Approx. Number Employees: 530
Year Founded: 1962
Business Description:
Hard Ice Cream, Soft Serve Treats, Hot Foods, Novelties, Frozen Cakes & Logs
S.I.C.: 2024; 5812
N.A.I.C.S.: 311520; 722211
Advertising Expenditures: $63,500,000
Cable T.V.: $5,000,000; D.M. to Consumers: $3,000,000; Daily Newsp.: $1,000,000; Newsp. Distr. Mags.: $2,000,000; Outdoor (Posters, Transit): $1,000,000; Point of Purchase: $2,000,000; Premiums, Novelties: $5,000,000; Spot Radio: $3,000,000; Spot T.V.: $40,500,000; Weekly Newsp.: $1,000,000
Distr.: Intl.; Natl.
Budget Set: July
Personnel:
John Gainor *(Pres & CEO)*
Charles J. Chapman, III *(COO)*
O. Michael Rinke *(VP, Asst Sec & Asst Gen Counsel)*
Russ L. Grundhauser *(VP-Fin Svcs)*
Dean Peters *(Dir-Comm)*
Brands & Products:
BLIZZARD
DQ
Advertising Agencies:
Charleston/Orwig, Inc.
515 W North Shore Dr
Hartland, WI 53029-8312
Tel.: (262) 563-5100
Fax: (262) 563-5101

Wong, Doody, Crandall, Wiener
8500 Steller Dr Ste 5
Culver City, CA 90232-2427
Tel.: (310) 280-7800
Fax: (310) 280-7780

AMERICAN RESTAURANT CONCEPTS, INC.
14476 Duval Pl W Ste 103
Jacksonville, FL 32218
Tel.: (904) 741-5500
Web Site:
www.dickswingsandgrill.com
Approx. Rev.: $372,062
Approx. Number Employees: 3
Year Founded: 2000
Business Description:
Restaurant Franchisor
S.I.C.: 5812
N.A.I.C.S.: 722110
Advertising Expenditures: $45,726
Media: 9-16-23-24-25
Personnel:
Michael Rosenberger *(Pres, CEO, CFO & Chief Acctg Officer)*

AMERICAN RESTAURANT PARTNERS, L.P.
3020 N Cypress Dr Ste 100
Wichita, KS 67226
Tel.: (316) 634-1190
Fax: (316) 634-1662
Sales Range: $50-74.9 Million
Approx. Number Employees: 2,700
Year Founded: 1987
Business Description:
Pizza Restaurant Operator
S.I.C.: 5812
N.A.I.C.S.: 722211
Advertising Expenditures: $4,600,000
Personnel:
Hal McCoy *(Pres & CEO)*
Terry Freund *(CFO)*
Lynda Barrier-Metz *(Dir-Mktg)*

APPLEBEE'S INTERNATIONAL, INC.
(Sub. of DineEquity, Inc.)
11201 Renner Blvd
Lenexa, KS 66219
Tel.: (913) 890-0100
Toll Free: (888) 59APPLE
E-mail: ca.diraimo@applebees.com
Web Site: www.applebees.com
Approx. Rev.: $1,337,921,000
Approx. Number Employees: 32,600
Year Founded: 1987
Business Description:
Franchise Management Services
S.I.C.: 8742
N.A.I.C.S.: 541611
Import
Advertising Expenditures: $56,731,000
Media: 3-9-18-19-23-24-26
Distr.: Reg.
Budget Set: Dec.
Personnel:
Julia A. Stewart *(Chm & CEO)*
Michael J. Archer *(Pres)*
Rebecca R. Tilden *(VP & Gen Counsel)*
Philip R. Crimmins *(Sr VP-Dev)*
Beverly O. Elving *(Sr VP-Fin)*
Kurt Hankins *(Sr VP-Menu Dev & Innovation)*
Caroline O'Keefe *(Sr VP-Mktg)*
Dawn Bullen *(VP-Mktg)*
Nancy E. Culbertson *(VP-Mktg & Innovation)*
Bridget Moen *(Brand Mgr)*
Brands & Products:
APPLEBEE'S
APPLEBEE'S NEIGHBORHOOD GRILL & BAR
EATIN' GOOD IN THE NEIGHBORHOOD
EATIN' RIGHT NEVER TASTED SO GOOD
VEGGIE PATCH
Advertising Agencies:
EastWest Marketing Group
401 5th Ave 4th Fl
New York, NY 10016
Tel.: (212) 951-7220
Fax: (212) 951-7201

McCann Erickson/New York
622 3rd Ave
New York, NY 10017
Tel.: (646) 865-2000
Fax: (646) 487-9610

MRM Worldwide
622 3rd Ave
New York, NY 10017-6707
Tel.: (646) 865-6230
Fax: (646) 865-6264

Restaurant Recruit, Inc.
(d/b/a R&R Advertising)
3409 Executive Ctr Dr Ste 202
Austin, TX 78731
Tel.: (512) 342-0110
Fax: (512) 342-0142
Toll Free: (800) 266-6996

Specialized Media Services, Inc.
741 Kenilworth Ave Ste 204
Charlotte, NC 28204
Tel.: (704) 333-3111
Fax: (704) 332-7466

Summit Marketing
Three Cityplace Dr Ste 350
Saint Louis, MO 63141-7091
Tel.: (314) 569-3737
Fax: (314) 569-0037
Toll Free: (866) 590-6000

APPLECREEK MANAGEMENT CO., INC.
6620 McGinnis Ferry Rd
Duluth, GA 30097
Tel.: (770) 623-0360
Fax: (770) 623-0557
Web Site: www.applecreekusa.com
Business Description:
Franchisee of Applebee's Restaurants & Developer & Franchisor of Up The Creek Grill Restaurants
S.I.C.: 5812
N.A.I.C.S.: 722110
Personnel:
William Palmer *(Founder & Pres)*
Advertising Agency:
The Hauser Group
530 Means St Ste G1
Atlanta, GA 30318
Tel.: (404) 222-0600
Fax: (404) 222-0580

ARBY'S CANADA, INC.
(Sub. of Arby's Restaurant Group, Inc.)
7045 Edwards Blvd Ste 304
Mississauga, ON L5S 1X2, Canada
Tel.: (905) 672-2729
Fax: (905) 672-2755
E-mail: info@arbys.com
Web Site: www.arbys.ca
Sales Range: $10-24.9 Million
Approx. Number Employees: 10
Business Description:
Fast Food Roast Beef Restaurant
S.I.C.: 5812
N.A.I.C.S.: 722110
Advertising Expenditures: $1,800,000
Media: 3-5-8-9-14-15-18-20-23-24
Distr.: Reg.
Budget Set: Sept.
Personnel:
Tracy Fletcher *(VP-Mktg)*
Wendy Spence *(Mgr-Natl Mktg)*

ARK RESTAURANTS CORP.
85 5th Ave 14th Fl
New York, NY 10003-3019
Tel.: (212) 206-8800
Fax: (212) 206-8814
E-mail: info@arkrestaurants.com
Web Site: www.arkrestaurants.com
Approx. Rev.: $117,768,000
Approx. Number Employees: 1,343
Year Founded: 1985
Business Description:
Restaurants Owner, Operator & Manager
S.I.C.: 5812; 5813
N.A.I.C.S.: 722110; 722410
Advertising Expenditures: $2,000,000
Media: 4-18-23-26
Distr.: Direct to Consumer
Personnel:
Michael S. Weinstein *(Chm & CEO)*
Robert Towers *(Pres, COO & Treas)*
Robert J. Stewart *(CFO)*
Michael Buck *(Gen Counsel & Sec)*
Vincent Pascal *(Sec & Sr VP-Ops)*
Paul Gordon *(Sr VP & Dir-Ops-Las Vegas)*
Walter Rauscher *(VP-Corp Sls & Catering)*
Linda Clous *(Dir-Facilities Mgmt)*
Marilyn Guy *(Dir-HR)*
John Oldweiler *(Dir-Pur)*
Evyette Ortiz *(Dir-Mktg)*
Jennifer Sutton *(Dir-Ops-Washington)*
Brands & Products:
AMERICA
ARK
BRYANT PARK GRILL
CANYON ROAD
CENTER CAFE
COLUMBUS BAKERY
EL RIO GRANDE
GALLAGHER'S
GALLAGHER'S BURGER BAR
GALLAGHER'S STEAKHOUSE
GONZALEZ Y GONZALEZ
THE GRILL AT TWO TREES
THE GRILL ROOM
JACK ROSE

Key to Media (For complete agency information see *The Advertising Red Books-Agencies* edition):
1. Bus. Publs. 2. Cable T.V. 3. Catalogs & Directories. 4. Co-op Adv. 5. Consumer Mags. 6. D.M. to Bus. Estab.7. D.M. to Consumers 8. Daily Newsp. 9. Exhibits/Trade Shows 10. Foreign 11. Infomercial 12. Internet Adv.13. Multimedia 14. Network Radio 15. Network T.V. 16. Newsp. Distr. Mags. 17. Other 18. Outdoor (Posters, Transit) 19. Point of Purchase20. Premiums, Novelties 21. Product Samples 22. Special Events Mktg. 23. Spot Radio 24. Spot T.V. 25. Weekly Newsp. 26. Yellow Page Adv.

LA RAMBLA
LUCKY SEVEN
LUTECE
THE METROPOLITAN CAFE
MGM GRAND CASINO
RED
SALOON BAR & GRILL
SEQUOIA
THUNDER GRILL
TSUNAMI GRILL
V BAR
VENUS

A.S. MANAGEMENT CORPORATION
888 Park Ave
New York, NY 10021-0235
Tel.: (203) 967-4003
Fax: (203) 967-4229
E-mail: rcallan@attglobal.net
Approx. Number Employees: 650
Year Founded: 1990
Business Description:
Operator of Restaurant Chain
S.I.C.: 8748
N.A.I.C.S.: 541618
Media: 9-18-19-23-25
Distr.: Natl.
Budget Set: Feb.
Brands & Products:
VICTORIA STATION

THE ATLANTA BREAD COMPANY
(d/b/a Atlanta Bread)
1955 Lake Park Dr Ste 400
Smyrna, GA 30080
Tel.: (770) 432-0933
Web Site: www.atlantabread.com/
Approx. Rev.: $1,100,000
Approx. Number Employees: 24
Year Founded: 2002
Business Description:
Bakery & Cafe
S.I.C.: 5812; 2051
N.A.I.C.S.: 722211; 311812
Personnel:
Jeff Massey *(Pres)*
Chris Campagna *(VP-Mktg)*
Advertising Agency:
Brunner
260 Peachtree St NW Ste 1100
Atlanta, GA 30303
Tel.: (404) 479-2200
Fax: (404) 479-9850

BAB, INC.
(d/b/a Big Apple Bagels)
500 Lake Cook Rd Ste 475
Deerfield, IL 60015
Tel.: (847) 948-7520
Fax: (847) 405-8140
Toll Free: (800) 251-6101
E-mail: bab@babcorp.com
Web Site: www.babcorp.com
Approx. Rev.: $2,913,741
Approx. Number Employees: 14
Year Founded: 1993
Business Description:
Bagel, Muffin & Coffee Retail Store Operator & Franchisor
S.I.C.: 5461; 2051; 5812
N.A.I.C.S.: 311811; 311812; 722211; 722213
Advertising Expenditures: $69,356
Media: 5-9-19-26
Personnel:
Michael W. Evans *(Pres & CEO)*
Jeffrey M. Gorden *(CFO)*
Michael K. Murtaugh *(Gen Counsel & VP)*
Brands & Products:
BAB
BIG APPLE BAGELS
BREWSTER'S
MY FAVORITE MUFFIN
THREE GREAT BRANDS. ONE GREAT PLACE
YOUR ALL DRY BAKERY CAFE
Advertising Agency:
Ebel, Signorelli & Welke LLC
(d/b/a ESW Partners)
600 W Fulton St
Chicago, IL 60661
Tel.: (312) 762-7400
Fax: (312) 762-7449

BACK BAY RESTAURANT GROUP, INC.
284 Newbury St
Boston, MA 02115-2801
Tel.: (617) 536-2800
Fax: (617) 236-4175
E-mail: eminer@backbayrestaurantgroup.com
Web Site: www.backbayrestaurantgroup.com
Sales Range: $100-124.9 Million
Approx. Number Employees: 2,600
Business Description:
Owner & Operator of Full Service Restaurants
S.I.C.: 5812
N.A.I.C.S.: 722110
Media: 6-13-18-19
Personnel:
Charles F. Sarkis *(Founder)*
Robert J. Ciampa *(CFO, Treas & VP)*
Brands & Products:
ABE & LOUIE'S
ATLANTIC FISH CO
CHARLEY'S
COACH GRILL
JOE'S AMERICAN BAR & GRILL
PAPA RAZZI

BACK YARD BURGERS, INC.
(Sub. of BBAC, LLC)
500 Church St Ste 200
Nashville, TN 37219
Tel.: (615) 620-2300
Fax: (615) 620-2301
Web Site: www.backyardburgers.com
Sales Range: $25-49.9 Million
Year Founded: 1987
Business Description:
Quick-Serve Restaurants Operator & Franchisor
S.I.C.: 5812; 6794
N.A.I.C.S.: 722211; 533110
Advertising Expenditures: $2,547,000
Media: 19
Personnel:
C. Stephen Lynn *(CEO)*
Michael G. Webb *(CFO)*
Brands & Products:
BACK YARD
BACK YARD BURGERS
Advertising Agencies:
Bohan
124 12th Ave S
Nashville, TN 37203
Tel.: (615) 327-1189
Fax: (615) 327-8123
Agency of Record (Advertising, Marketing & Promotional)

Paramore Redd Online Marketing
124 12th Ave S
Nashville, TN 37203
Tel.: (615) 386-9012
Social Media

BAKERS SQUARE
(Joint Venture of Fidelity National Financial, Inc. & Newport Global Advisors, L.P.)
400 W 48th Ave
Denver, CO 80216-1806
Mailing Address:
PO Box 16601
Denver, CO 80216-0601
Tel.: (303) 296-2121
Fax: (303) 672-2677
Web Site: www.bakerssquarerestaurants.com
Sales Range: $200-249.9 Million
Approx. Number Employees: 130
Year Founded: 1983
Business Description:
Restaurants
S.I.C.: 5812
N.A.I.C.S.: 722110
Advertising Expenditures: $9,230,000
Media: 3-8-9-13-19-23-24-26
Distr.: Natl.
Personnel:
Hazem Ouf *(CEO)*
Brands & Products:
THE BEST PIE IN AMERICA
UNBELIEVABLE PIE

BARLEYCORN'S
1073 Industrial Rd
Cold Spring, KY 41076-9097
Tel.: (859) 442-3400
Fax: (859) 442-3419
E-mail: barleycorns@fuse.net
Web Site: www.barleycorns.com
Approx. Number Employees: 210
Business Description:
Operator of Casual Restaurant
S.I.C.: 5812; 5813
N.A.I.C.S.: 722110; 722410
Advertising Expenditures: $50,000
Media: 7-8-13-18-19
Distr.: Direct to Consumer; Reg.
Personnel:
Kenneth Heil *(Pres)*
Brands & Products:
ANYTIME!
BARLEYCORN'S
YOUR REAL NEIGHBOR!

BENIHANA INC.
8685 NW 53rd Terrace
Miami, FL 33166
Tel.: (305) 593-0770
Fax: (305) 592-6371
Toll Free: (800) 327-3369
E-mail: contact@benihana.com
Web Site: www.benihana.com
E-Mail For Key Personnel:
President: president@benihana.com
Marketing Director: marketing@benihana.com
Public Relations: pr@benihana.com
Approx. Rev.: $327,640,000
Approx. Number Employees: 6,700
Year Founded: 1964
Business Description:
Restaurant Owner & Operator
S.I.C.: 5812
N.A.I.C.S.: 722110
Import
Advertising Expenditures: $6,800,000
Media: 2-3-5-6-7-8-9-10-11-15-18-19-20-22-23-24-25-26
Distr.: Direct to Consumer; Natl.
Budget Set: Mar.
Personnel:
Richard C. Stockinger *(Chm, CEO & Pres-Benihana)*
John E. Abdo *(Vice Chm)*
David Flanery *(CFO)*
Christopher P. Ames *(COO)*
Jennifer Evans *(Dir-Mktg)*
Brands & Products:
AN EXPERIENCE AT EVERY TABLE
BENIHANA
HARU
HIBACHI
RA
SAMURAI
Advertising Agency:
Cramer-Krasselt
225 N Michigan Ave
Chicago, IL 60601-7601
Tel.: (312) 616-9600
Fax: (312) 616-3839
Creative & Media Agency of Record
Digital
Direct Marketing
National & Local Market Advertising, Media Buying & Planning
Search

BERTUCCI'S CORP.
155 Otis St
Northborough, MA 01532
Tel.: (508) 351-2500
Fax: (508) 393-1231
Web Site: www.bertuccis.com
Sales Range: $200-249.9 Million
Approx. Number Employees: 6,500
Year Founded: 1981
Business Description:
Italian Restaurants
S.I.C.: 5812
N.A.I.C.S.: 722110
Media: 16-23
Personnel:
Stephen Clark *(Vice Chm & CEO)*
David Lloyd *(CEO)*
Jamie Moore *(Dir-Mktg)*
Kelly Chamberlin *(Brand Mgr)*
Brands & Products:
BERTUCCI'S
WHAT'S NOT TO LOVE?
Advertising Agency:
Connelly Partners
46 Waltham St Fl 4
Boston, MA 02118
Tel.: (617) 956-5050
Fax: (617) 956-5054
Grill Menu

BICKFORD'S FAMILY RESTAURANTS
(Sub. of Elxsi Corporation)
1330 Soldiers Field Rd
Brighton, MA 02135-1020
Tel.: (617) 782-4010
Fax: (617) 783-2554
Toll Free: (800) 969-5653
E-mail: info@bickfordsrestaurants.com
Web Site: www.bickfordsrestaurants.com

Key to Media (For complete agency information see *The Advertising Red Books-Agencies* edition):
1. Bus. Publs. 2. Cable T.V. 3. Catalogs & Directories. 4. Co-op Adv. 5. Consumer Mags. 6. D.M. to Bus. Estab.7. D.M. to Consumers
8. Daily Newsp. 9. Exhibits/Trade Shows 10. Foreign 11. Infomercial 12. Internet Adv.13. Multimedia 14. Network Radio
15. Network T.V. 16. Newsp. Distr. Mags. 17. Other 18. Outdoor (Posters, Transit) 19. Point of Purchase20. Premiums, Novelties
21. Product Samples 22. Special Events Mktg. 23. Spot Radio 24. Spot T.V. 25. Weekly Newsp. 26. Yellow Page Adv.

Bickford's Family Restaurants — (Continued)

Sales Range: $10-24.9 Million
Approx. Number Employees: 5
Business Description:
Operator of Restaurants
S.I.C.: 5812
N.A.I.C.S.: 722110
Media: 3-9-13-14-15-22-23-24-25
Distr.: Reg.
Budget Set: Dec.
Personnel:
Alexander Milley *(Pres)*
Brands & Products:
BICKFORD GRILLE

BIG BOY RESTAURANTS INTERNATIONAL, LLC
1 Big Boy Dr
Warren, MI 48091-1733
Tel.: (586) 759-6000
Fax: (586) 755-8551
E-mail: rardagna@bigboy.com
Web Site: www.bigboy.com
Approx. Number Employees: 1,000
Year Founded: 1938
Business Description:
Restaurants
S.I.C.: 5812; 2099
N.A.I.C.S.: 722110; 311999
Media: 5-9-18-19-20-22
Distr.: Direct to Consumer; Reg.
Personnel:
Robert G. Liggett, Jr. *(Chm)*
Keith E. Sirois *(CEO)*
Joe Kulczycki *(CFO)*
Debra Murphy *(Dir-HR & Trng)*
Brands & Products:
OHHH BOY!

BJ'S RESTAURANTS, INC.
7755 Center Ave Ste 300
Huntington Beach, CA 92647
Tel.: (714) 500-2400
Web Site: www.bjsrestaurants.com
Approx. Rev.: $513,860,000
Approx. Number Employees: 12,100
Year Founded: 1978
Business Description:
Family Restaurant & Brewhouse Owner & Operator
S.I.C.: 5812; 2082; 5813
N.A.I.C.S.: 722110; 312120; 722410
Advertising Expenditures: $4,200,000
Media: 5-10-13-18-19-23
Personnel:
Gerald W. Deitchle *(Chm, Pres & CEO)*
Gregory S. Levin *(CFO & Exec VP)*
Matthew W. Hood *(CMO)*
Wayne Jones *(Chief Restaurant Ops Officer & Exec VP)*
John D. Allegretto *(Chief Supply Chain Officer)*
Robert DeLiema *(Pres-BJ's Restaurants Foundation)*
Gregory S. Lynds *(Exec VP)*
Lon F. Ledwith *(Sr VP-Ops Talent Dev)*
Alexander M. Puchner *(Sr VP-Brewing Ops)*
Michele Maerz *(Reg VP-Ops)*
Steven Mintzer *(Reg VP-Ops)*
Christopher Pinsak *(Reg VP)*
Melanie Bruno-Carbone *(VP-Mktg)*
Jeff Preston *(VP-Pur)*
Brands & Products:
BJ'S
BJ'S BERRY BURST CIDER
BJ'S CHICAGO PIZZERIA
BJ'S FAMOUS PIZOOKIE
BJ'S JEREMIAH RED
BJ'S PIZZA & GRILL
BJ'S P.M. PORTER
BJ'S RESTAURANT & BREWERY
BJ'S RESTAURANT & BREWHOUSE
GREAT WHITE
HARVEST HEFEWEIZEN
NITWIT
NUTTY BREWNETTE
PIRANHA
PIZOOKIE
POOKS
TATONKA
Advertising Agency:
Restaurant Recruit, Inc.
(d/b/a R&R Advertising)
3409 Executive Ctr Dr Ste 202
Austin, TX 78731
Tel.: (512) 342-0110
Fax: (512) 342-0142
Toll Free: (800) 266-6996

BLACKEYED PEA RESTAURANTS INC.
(Sub. of Dynamic Management Company LLC)
313 E Main St Ste 2
Hendersonville, TN 37075
Tel.: (615) 277-1234
Fax: (615) 277-1220
Web Site: www.theblackeyedpea.com
Year Founded: 1986
Business Description:
Full-Service Restaurant
S.I.C.: 5812
N.A.I.C.S.: 722110
Media: 9-20-23-24-25-26
Distr.: Direct to Consumer; Reg.
Budget Set: Nov.
Personnel:
Bob Langford *(Chm-Owner)*
Brands & Products:
DIXIE HOUSE

BOB EVANS RESTAURANTS, INC.
(Sub. of Bob Evans Farms, Inc.)
3776 S High St
Columbus, OH 43207
Tel.: (614) 491-2225
Fax: (614) 492-4949
Toll Free: (800) 272-7675
Web Site: www.bobevans.com
Sales Range: $1-4.9 Billion
Approx. Number Employees: 300
Year Founded: 1953
Business Description:
Family Restaurants
S.I.C.: 5812
N.A.I.C.S.: 722110
Advertising Expenditures: $14,000,000
Media: 9-18-19-23-24
Distr.: Reg.
Budget Set: Jan.
Personnel:
Randall L. Hicks *(Pres & Chief Concept Officer)*
Paul Desantis *(CFO, Treas & Asst Corp Sec)*
Kathy North *(Sr VP-Restaurant Ops)*
Brands & Products:
BOB EVANS RESTAURANTS
OWENS FAMILY RESTAURANTS

BODDIE-NOELL ENTERPRISES, INC.
1021 Noell Ln
Rocky Mount, NC 27802
Tel.: (252) 937-2800
Fax: (252) 937-6991
Web Site: www.bneinc.com
Approx. Number Employees: 14,500
Year Founded: 1962
Business Description:
Restaurant Franchiser
S.I.C.: 5812
N.A.I.C.S.: 722110
Personnel:
Ben Mayo Boddie *(Chm)*
Michael W. Boddie *(Pres & CEO)*
W. Craig Worthy *(CFO)*
Jerry Allsbrook *(CMO)*
Michael Hancock *(Exec VP)*
William L. Boddie *(Mgr-District)*
Brands & Products:
BNE LAND AND DEVELOPMENT
BODDIE-NOELL ENTERPRISES
CAFE CAROLINA & BAKERY
THE HIGHWAY DINER
MOE'S SOUTHWEST GRILL
ROSE HILL CONFERENCE CENTER
TEXAS STEAKHOUSE & SALOON
WE BELIEVE IN PEOPLE
Advertising Agencies:
Lewis Advertising, Inc.
1050 Country Club Rd
Rocky Mount, NC 27804
Tel.: (252) 443-5131
Fax: (252) 443-9340

Rick Rountree Communications
2900 Highwoods Blvd, Ste 202
Raleigh, NC 27604
Tel.: (919) 878-1144
Fax: (919) 872-6599

BOJANGLES' RESTAURANTS, INC.
(Holding of Falfurrias Capital Partners)
9432 Southern Pine Blvd
Charlotte, NC 28273
Mailing Address:
PO Box 240239
Charlotte, NC 28224-0239
Tel.: (704) 527-2675
Fax: (704) 523-6803
Toll Free: (888) 300-4265
Web Site: www.bojangles.com
E-Mail For Key Personnel:
Marketing Director: rpoindexter@bojangles.com
Sales Range: $500-549.9 Million
Approx. Number Employees: 4,500
Year Founded: 1977
Business Description:
Franchised Fast Food Restaurants
S.I.C.: 5812
N.A.I.C.S.: 722211
Media: 2-3-5-8-9-10-13-18-19-20-22-23-24-25
Distr.: Direct to Consumer; Reg.
Budget Set: Sept.
Personnel:
Randy Kibler *(Pres & CEO)*
John Jordon *(CFO & Sr VP-Fin)*
Eric H. Newman *(Gen Counsel & Exec VP)*
Mike Bearss *(Sr VP-Pur, R & D)*
Randy Poindexter *(Sr VP-Mktg)*
Brands & Products:
BOJANGLES
BOJANGLES' FAMOUS CHICKEN N' BISCUITS
Advertising Agency:
BooneOakley
1445 S Mint St
Charlotte, NC 28203
Tel.: (704) 333-9797
Fax: (704) 348-2834
Agency of Record

BOMBAY PALACE COMPANY
30 W 52nd St
New York, NY 10019-6103
Tel.: (212) 541-7777
Fax: (212) 262-9664
E-mail: contact@bombaypalacenyc.com
Web Site: www.bombaypalacenyc.com
Approx. Number Employees: 100
Year Founded: 1979
Business Description:
Restaurant Operator
S.I.C.: 5812
N.A.I.C.S.: 722110
Media: 2-4-6-8-9-10-14-18-20-22-23-24-25-26
Distr.: Direct to Consumer; Natl.
Budget Set: Feb.
Personnel:
Mohan Ahluwalia *(Gen Mgr)*
Brands & Products:
PIRTI SINGH DILER

BONANZA RESTAURANTS
(Div. of Homestyle Dining LLC)
3701 W Plano Pkwy Ste 200
Plano, TX 75075
Tel.: (972) 244-8900
Fax: (972) 588-5866
Web Site: www.bonanzasteakhouses.com
Sales Range: $250-299.9 Million
Approx. Number Employees: 127
Year Founded: 1963
Business Description:
Family Restaurants
S.I.C.: 5812; 5813
N.A.I.C.S.: 722110; 722410
Advertising Expenditures: $25,000,000
Media: 1-2-3-5-9-11-16-17-18-19-20-21-23-24
Distr.: Natl.
Budget Set: Nov.
Personnel:
Sheryl Randolph *(Sr Dir-Mktg)*

BOSTON MARKET CORPORATION
(Holding of Sun Capital Partners, Inc.)
14103 Denver W Pkwy
Golden, CO 80401-3116
Tel.: (303) 278-9500
Fax: (303) 216-5678
Toll Free: (800) 365-7000
E-mail: info@bostonmarket.com
Web Site: www.bostonmarket.com
Approx. Number Employees: 13,000
Year Founded: 1985
Business Description:
Restaurant Operator
S.I.C.: 5812
N.A.I.C.S.: 722211
Advertising Expenditures: $48,000,000
Media: 3-5-7-8-9-15-18-19-21-22-23-24-25-26

Key to Media (For complete agency information see *The Advertising Red Books-Agencies* edition):
1. Bus. Publs. 2. Cable T.V. 3. Catalogs & Directories. 4. Co-op Adv. 5. Consumer Mags. 6. D.M. to Bus. Estab.7. D.M. to Consumers 8. Daily Newsp. 9. Exhibits/Trade Shows 10. Foreign 11. Infomercial 12. Internet Adv.13. Multimedia 14. Network Radio 15. Network T.V. 16. Newsp. Distr. Mags. 17. Other 18. Outdoor (Posters, Transit) 19. Point of Purchase20. Premiums, Novelties 21. Product Samples 22. Special Events Mktg. 23. Spot Radio 24. Spot T.V. 25. Weekly Newsp. 26. Yellow Page Adv.

Distr.: Natl.
Personnel:
George Michel *(Pres & CEO)*
Gregory S. Uhing *(CFO & Sr VP)*
Gerard C. Lewis *(Chief Concept Officer)*
J. Randal Miller *(Gen Counsel & Sr VP)*
Gretchen Miller Paules *(VP-Mktg)*
Brands & Products:
BOSTON MARKET
Advertising Agency:
Zimmerman Advertising
2200 W Commercial Blvd Ste 300
Fort Lauderdale, FL 33309-3064
Tel.: (954) 644-4000
Fax: (954) 731-2977
Toll Free: (800) 248-8522

BOSTON RESTAURANT ASSOCIATES, INC.

6 Kimball Ln Ste 210
Lynnfield, MA 01940
Tel.: (339) 219-0466
Fax: (339) 219-0467
E-mail: amy@raii.com
Web Site: www.pizzeriaregina.com
Sales Range: $10-24.9 Million
Approx. Number Employees: 425
Year Founded: 1926
Business Description:
Pizzerias & Full-Service Italian Restaurants Owner & Franchiser
S.I.C.: 5812
N.A.I.C.S.: 722110
Advertising Expenditures: $413,000
Media: 8-10-13-18-21-23-24-26
Personnel:
Robert C. Taft *(CEO)*
Fran V. Ross *(CFO & VP)*
Robert Fabrizio *(Chief Acctg Officer)*
Brands & Products:
BOSTON'S BRICKOVEN PIZZA
PIZZERIA REGINA
POLCARI'S

BRAVO BRIO RESTAURANT GROUP, INC.

(Joint Venture of Castle Harlan, Inc. & Bruckmann, Rosser, Sherrill & Co., LLC)
777 Goodale Blvd Ste 100
Columbus, OH 43212
Tel.: (614) 326-7944
Fax: (614) 326-7943
Toll Free: (888) 452-7286
Web Site: www.bbrg.com
Approx. Rev.: $343,025,000
Approx. Number Employees: 8,000
Year Founded: 1987
Business Description:
Restaurant Owner & Operator
S.I.C.: 5812
N.A.I.C.S.: 722110
Advertising Expenditures: $3,100,000
Personnel:
Alton F. Doody, III *(Chm)*
Saed Mohseni *(CEO)*
James J. O'Connor *(CFO & Treas)*
Brian O'Malley *(COO & Sr VP-Ops-BRIO)*
Ronald F. Dee *(Sr VP)*
Brands & Products:
BON VIE
BRAVO!
BRAVO! CUCINA ITALIANA
BRAVO! ITALIAN KITCHEN
BRIO
BRIO TUSCAN GRILLE
CUCINA BRAVO! ITALIANA

BRIDGEMAN'S RESTAURANTS INC.

6201 Brooklyn Blvd
Brooklyn Center, MN 55429-4035
Tel.: (763) 971-2947
Fax: (763) 971-2950
Toll Free: (800) 297-5050
E-mail: info@bridgemans.com
Web Site: www.bridgemans.com
E-Mail For Key Personnel:
President: steve@bridgemans.com
Sales Range: Less than $1 Million
Approx. Number Employees: 4
Year Founded: 1932
Business Description:
Ice Cream Parlors & Soda Fountains Operator
S.I.C.: 5812
N.A.I.C.S.: 722211
Advertising Expenditures: $700,000
Media: 2-10
Distr.: Direct to Consumer
Budget Set: Apr.
Personnel:
Steve Lampi *(Pres & COO)*
Brands & Products:
BRIDGEMAN'S ICE CREAM SHOPPE
THREE GALLON

BRIGHAM'S, INC.

(Holding of Grotech Ventures)
30 Mill St
Arlington, MA 02476-4700
Tel.: (781) 648-9000
Fax: (781) 646-0507
Toll Free: (800) BRIGHAMS
E-mail: brighams-mail@brighams.com
Web Site: www.brighams.com
Approx. Number Employees: 600
Year Founded: 1914
Business Description:
Ice Cream & Sandwich Shops
S.I.C.: 2024; 5143
N.A.I.C.S.: 311520; 424430
Advertising Expenditures: $800,000
Media: 5-18-19-22-23-24-25
Distr.: Reg.
Budget Set: Nov.
Personnel:
Bob Carlson *(VP-Sls)*
Brands & Products:
BRIGHAM'S
ELAN

BRINKER INTERNATIONAL, INC.

6820 LBJ Fwy
Dallas, TX 75240-6511
Tel.: (972) 980-9917
Fax: (972) 770-9593
Toll Free: (800) 775-7290
E-mail: investor.relations@brinker.com
Web Site: www.brinker.com
Approx. Rev.: $2,761,386,000
Approx. Number Employees: 60,322
Year Founded: 1975
Business Description:
Restaurant Operator & Franchisor
S.I.C.: 5812
N.A.I.C.S.: 722110
Advertising Expenditures: $80,600,000
Media: 3-8-9-13-14-15-18-19-21-22-23-24-25-26
Distr.: Reg.
Budget Set: May
Personnel:
Douglas H. Brooks *(Chm, Pres & CEO)*
Guy J. Constant *(CFO & Exec VP)*
Roger F. Thomson *(Chief Admin Officer, Gen Counsel, Sec & Exec VP)*
Valerie L. Davisson *(Chief People Works Officer & Exec VP)*
Carin L. Stutz *(Pres-Global Bus Dev & Sr VP)*
Steve D. Provost *(Pres-Maggiano's Little Italy)*
Wyman T. Roberts *(Pres-Chili's Grill & Bar)*
David Roy Doyle *(Sr VP & Controller)*
Jeffrey A. Hoban *(Sr VP & Asst Gen Counsel)*
Ian Baines *(Sr VP-Strategic Innovation)*
John R. Hosea *(Sr VP-People Svcs & IS)*
David R. Parsley *(Sr VP-Supply Chain Mgmt)*
Claudia Schaefer *(VP-Mktg, Culinary & Global Bus Dev)*
Terry W. Stephenson *(VP-Pur)*
Joseph A. Taylor *(VP-Comm & Pub Affairs)*
Bryan D. McCrory *(Asst Gen Counsel)*
Brands & Products:
BRINKER INTERNATIONAL
CHILI'S GRILL & BAR
MAGGIANO'S LITTLE ITALY
ON THE BORDER MEXICAN GRILL & CANTINA
ROMANO'S MACARONI GRILL
Advertising Agencies:
Barkley
1740 Main St
Kansas City, MO 64108
Tel.: (816) 842-1500
Agency of Record On the Border Mexican Grill & Cantina

Firehouse, Inc.
14860 Landmark Blvd No 247
Dallas, TX 75254
Tel.: (972) 692-0911
Fax: (972) 692-0912
Romano's Macaroni Grill
Maggiano's Little Italy

Prism Marketing Partners
400 E Royal Ln Ste 215
Irving, TX 75039
Tel.: (214) 254-3800
Fax: (214) 254-3801

BRINKER RESTAURANT CORPORATION

(Sub. of Brinker International, Inc.)
6820 LBJ Freeway
Dallas, TX 75240
Tel.: (972) 980-9917
Fax: (972) 770-9593
E-mail: info@brinker.com
Web Site: www.blinker.com
Sales Range: $200-249.9 Million
Approx. Number Employees: 1,300
Business Description:
Restaurant Owner and Operator
S.I.C.: 5812
N.A.I.C.S.: 722110
Personnel:
Douglas H. Brooks *(Chm, Pres & CEO)*
Advertising Agency:
Firehouse, Inc.
14860 Landmark Blvd No 247
Dallas, TX 75254
Tel.: (972) 692-0911
Fax: (972) 692-0912

BROWN'S CHICKEN & PASTA, INC.

489 W Fullerton Ave
Elmhurst, IL 60126
Tel.: (630) 617-8800
Fax: (630) 617-5900
Web Site: www.brownscatering.com
Sales Range: $50-74.9 Million
Approx. Number Employees: 12
Year Founded: 1949
Business Description:
Fast Food Services
S.I.C.: 5812
N.A.I.C.S.: 722211
Advertising Expenditures: $2,500,000
Media: 7-8-9-23-24
Distr.: Reg.
Budget Set: Aug.
Personnel:
Toni Portillo *(Owner)*
Mark Smith *(Dir-Mktg)*
Brands & Products:
BROWN'S CATERING
BROWN'S CHICKEN

BRUEGGER'S CORPORATION

(Holding of Sun Capital Partners, Inc.)
159 Bank St
Burlington, VT 05402-4420
Tel.: (802) 660-4020
Fax: (802) 660-4034
E-mail: info@brueggers.com
Web Site: www.brueggers.com
Approx. Number Employees: 50
Year Founded: 1983
Business Description:
Eating Place
S.I.C.: 5461; 6794
N.A.I.C.S.: 445291; 533110
Import Export
Personnel:
David T. Austin *(Pres)*
James J. Greco *(CEO)*
Robert D. Parette *(CFO)*
Scott D. Berkman *(VP-Pur, Mktg & Distr)*
Kim A. Nastri *(VP-Trng & Franchise Ops)*
Matt Riley *(Dir-HR)*
Advertising Agencies:
ClickCulture
3739 National Dr Ste 210
Raleigh, NC 27612
Tel.: (919) 420-7736
Fax: (919) 420-7758
Bagels
— Pam Guthrie *(VP & Dir-Acct Svcs)*

SPM Communications
2030 Main St Ste 325
Dallas, TX 75201
Tel.: (214) 379-7000 (Main)
Tel.: (817) 329-3257 (24 Hour Media Line)
Fax: (214) 379-7007

Key to Media (For complete agency information see *The Advertising Red Books-Agencies* edition):
1. Bus. Publs. 2. Cable T.V. 3. Catalogs & Directories. 4. Co-op Adv. 5. Consumer Mags. 6. D.M. to Bus. Estab.7. D.M. to Consumers
8. Daily Newsp. 9. Exhibits/Trade Shows 10. Foreign 11. Infomercial 12. Internet Adv.13. Multimedia 14. Network Radio
15. Network T.V. 16. Newsp. Distr. Mags. 17. Other 18. Outdoor (Posters, Transit) 19. Point of Purchase20. Premiums, Novelties
21. Product Samples 22. Special Events Mktg. 23. Spot Radio 24. Spot T.V. 25. Weekly Newsp. 26. Yellow Page Adv.

BUBBA GUMP SHRIMP COMPANY RESTAURANT & MARKET
(Sub. of Landry's Restaurants Inc.)
(d/b/a Bubba Gump Shrimp)
209 Avenida Fabricante 2nd Fl Ste 200
San Clemente, CA 92672-7544
Tel.: (949) 366-6260
Fax: (949) 366-6261
E-mail: forrest@bubbagump.com
Web Site: www.bubbagump.com
Sales Range: $200-249.9 Million
Approx. Number Employees: 50
Year Founded: 1996
Business Description:
Seafood Restaurant
S.I.C.: 5812; 5813
N.A.I.C.S.: 722110; 722410
Personnel:
Tim Busald *(Pres & CEO)*
Rob Ham *(Mng Dir & VP-Intl Ops)*
Dan Bylund *(CFO & VP-Fin)*
Gail Taggart *(Chief Strategic Officer & Exec VP)*
Lisa Bates *(Reg VP-Ops)*
Jim DuFault *(Reg VP-Ops)*
Brands & Products:
BUBBA GUMP SHRIMP
Advertising Agency:
Nemer Fieger
6250 Excelsior Blvd Ste 203
Minneapolis, MN 55416-2735
Tel.: (952) 925-4848
Fax: (952) 925-1907

BUCA, INC.
(Sub. of Planet Hollywood International, Inc.)
1300 Nicollet Mall Ste 5003
Minneapolis, MN 55403-2606
Tel.: (612) 225-3400
Fax: (612) 827-6446
E-mail: famiglia@bucainc.com
Web Site: www.bucainc.com
Approx. Sls.: $245,552,000
Approx. Number Employees: 5,650
Year Founded: 1993
Business Description:
Family-Style Italian Restaurants Operator
S.I.C.: 5812
N.A.I.C.S.: 722110
Advertising Expenditures: $7,800,000
Media: 1-8-9-10-13-16-18-21-23-24
Personnel:
Jason Kieser *(Chief Acctg Officer & VP-Fin)*
Tony Jones *(Sr VP-HR)*
Brands & Products:
BUCA DI BEPPO
BUCA LARGE
BUCA SMALL
Advertising Agency:
Periscope
921 Washington Ave S
Minneapolis, MN 55415
Tel.: (612) 399-0500
Fax: (612) 399-0600
Toll Free: (800) 339-2103

BUFFALO WILD WINGS, INC.
5500 Wayzata Blvd Ste 1600
Minneapolis, MN 55416
Tel.: (952) 593-9943
Fax: (952) 593-9787
Toll Free: (800) 499-9586
Web Site: www.buffalowildwings.com
Approx. Rev.: $613,256,000
Approx. Number Employees: 1,500
Year Founded: 1982
Business Description:
Casual Restaurant Operating & Franchising Services
S.I.C.: 5812
N.A.I.C.S.: 722110
Advertising Expenditures: $17,758,000
Media: 9-15-22-23-24-25
Personnel:
James M. Damian *(Chm)*
Sally J. Smith *(Pres & CEO)*
Mary J. Twinem *(CFO)*
James M. Schmidt *(COO)*
Judith A. Shoulak *(Sr VP-Ops, Exec VP-Global Ops & HR)*
Kathleen M. Benning *(Exec VP-Global Mktg & Brand Dev)*
Mounir N. Sawda *(Sr VP)*
Brands & Products:
BETTER-BE-READY BLAZIN
BUFFALO WILD WINGS
BUFFALO WILD WINGS GRILL & BAR
GET IT TO GO
SOMETHING WILD HAS COME TO TOWN
WE CAN'T START BLEND
WINGS BEERS SPORTS ALL THE ESSENTIALS
YOU HAVE TO BE HERE
Advertising Agencies:
22squared
1170 Peachtree St NE 15th Fl
Atlanta, GA 30309-7649
Tel.: (404) 347-8700
Fax: (404) 347-8800

Campbell-Ewald
30400 Van Dyke Ave
Warren, MI 48093-2368
Tel.: (586) 574-3400
Fax: (586) 575-9925
(Local Market Media Planning & Buying)

BUFFET PARTNERS LP
2701 E Plano Pkwy Ste 200
Plano, TX 75074
Tel.: (214) 291-2900
Fax: (214) 291-2467
Toll Free: (888) 626-6636
E-mail: contactus@furrs.net
Web Site: www.furrs.net
Sales Range: $125-149.9 Million
Approx. Number Employees: 4,500
Year Founded: 1947
Business Description:
Food Service
S.I.C.: 5812
N.A.I.C.S.: 722110
Advertising Expenditures: $4,000,000
Media: 6-7-8-9-13-18-20-23-24-26
Distr.: Reg.
Budget Set: Dec.
Personnel:
Raymond C. Hemmig *(Chm)*
Thomas M. Blasdell *(Pres & Gen Mgr-Dynamic Foods)*
David Siebert *(CFO)*
Jill Gouge Laird *(Dir-Mktg)*
Brands & Products:
FURR'S
Advertising Agency:
The Loomis Agency
17120 Dallas Pkwy Ste 200
Dallas, TX 75248-1189
Tel.: (972) 331-7000
Fax: (972) 331-7001

BUFFETS HOLDINGS, INC.
(Holding of CI Capital Partners LLC)
1020 Discovery Rd 100
Eagan, MN 55121
Tel.: (651) 994-8608
Fax: (651) 365-2356
Web Site: www.buffet.com
Approx. Sls.: $1,588,450,000
Approx. Number Employees: 33,000
Year Founded: 1983
Business Description:
Buffet-Style Restaurants Owner & Operator
S.I.C.: 5812
N.A.I.C.S.: 722110
Advertising Expenditures: $33,896,000
Media: 2-3-4-8-9-10-13-18-19-23-24-25-26
Distr.: Direct to Consumer; Natl.
Budget Set: Apr.
Personnel:
Frederick J. Iseman *(Chm)*
R. Michael Andrews, Jr. *(CEO)*
A. Keith Wall *(CFO & Exec VP)*
Steven R. Layt *(COO)*
M. Richard Kirk *(Exec VP-Ops-Ryan's Div)*
Fred P. Williams *(Exec VP-Concept Dev)*
Mario O. Lee *(Reg VP)*
Brands & Products:
COUNTRY BUFFET
FIRE MOUNTAIN
GRANNY'S BUFFET
HOMETOWN BUFFET
OLD COUNTRY BUFFET
RYAN'S
TAHOE JOE'S FAMOUS STEAKHOUSE

BUFFETS INC.
(Sub. of Buffets Holdings, Inc.)
1020 Discovery Rd Ste 100
Eagan, MN 55121
Tel.: (651) 994-8608
Fax: (651) 365-2356
Web Site: www.buffetsinc.com
Approx. Number Employees: 100
Business Description:
Buffet Restaurant Owner & Operator
S.I.C.: 5812
N.A.I.C.S.: 722110
Personnel:
R. Michael Andrews, Jr. *(CEO)*
Steven R. Layt *(COO)*
Advertising Agency:
TracyLocke
131 Danbury Rd
Wilton, CT 06897
Tel.: (203) 762-2400
Fax: (203) 762-2229

BURGER KING HOLDINGS INC.
(Holding of 3G Capital Management Inc.)
5505 Blue Lagoon Dr
Miami, FL 33126
Tel.: (305) 378-3000
E-mail: investor@whopper.com
Web Site: www.burgerking.com
Approx. Rev.: $2,502,200,000
Approx. Number Employees: 38,884
Year Founded: 1954
Business Description:
Restaurant Operator
S.I.C.: 5812
N.A.I.C.S.: 722211
Advertising Expenditures: $91,300,000
Media: 9-10-14-15-19-20-23-24
Distr.: Natl.
Personnel:
Bernardo Vieira Hees *(CEO)*
Daniel Schwartz *(CFO & Exec VP)*
Heitor Goncalves *(CIO & Chief Performance Officer)*
Flavia Faugeres *(Global CMO)*
Jacqueline Friesner *(Chief Acctg Officer, VP & Controller)*
Greg Ryan *(Pres-Latin America & Caribbean & Exec VP)*
Peter Tan *(Pres-Asia Pacific & Exec VP)*
Jose Tomas *(Chief HR/Comm Officer, Pres-Latin America, Caribbean & Exec VP)*
Steve Wiborg *(Pres-North America & Exec VP)*
Jonathan Fitzpatrick *(Exec VP & Chief Brand & Ops Officer)*
Peter B. Robinson *(Exec VP)*
Amy E. Wagner *(Sr VP-IR)*
Tia Lang *(Dir-Interactive & Media)*
Patricia Trevino *(Dir-Promotions & Multicultural Mktg)*
Brands & Products:
BK
BK BIG FISH
BK BREAKFAST SHOTS
BK BURGER SHOTS
BK FUSION
BK JOE
BK STACKER
BK VEGGIE
BK WRAPPER
BURGER KING
CHEESY TOTS
CHICKEN TENDERS
CHICK'N CRISP
CLUB BK
CROISSAN'WICH
DOUBLE CROISSAN'WICH
DOUBLE WHOPPER
HAVE IT YOUR WAY
KIDS CLUB
TENDERCRISP
TENDERGRILL
TRIPLE WHOPPER
WHOPPER
WHOPPER JR
Advertising Agencies:
Buntin Out-of-Home Media
1001 Hawkins St
Nashville, TN 37203-4758
Tel.: (615) 244-5720
Fax: (615) 244-6511

Coyne Public Relations
14 Walsh Dr 2nd Fl
Parsippany, NJ 07054
Tel.: (973) 316-1665
Fax: (973) 316-6568
Communications
Issues-Management Counsel
Marketing
Public Relations Agency of Record

Key to Media (For complete agency information see *The Advertising Red Books-Agencies* edition):
1. Bus. Publs. 2. Cable T.V. 3. Catalogs & Directories. 4. Co-op Adv. 5. Consumer Mags. 6. D.M. to Bus. Estab.7. D.M. to Consumers
8. Daily Newsp. 9. Exhibits/Trade Shows 10. Foreign 11. Infomercial 12. Internet Adv.13. Multimedia 14. Network Radio
15. Network T.V. 16. Newsp. Distr. Mags. 17. Other 18. Outdoor (Posters, Transit) 19. Point of Purchase20. Premiums, Novelties
21. Product Samples 22. Special Events Mktg. 23. Spot Radio 24. Spot T.V. 25. Weekly Newsp. 26. Yellow Page Adv.

EMAK Worldwide, Inc.
6330 San Vicente Blvd
Los Angeles, CA 90048-5425
Tel.: (323) 932-4300
Fax: (323) 932-4400
(Promotional Products for Big Kids Meal)

Initiative Worldwide
(Part of The Interpublic Group of Companies, Inc.)
1 Dag Hammerskjold Plz 5th Fl
New York, NY 10017
Tel.: (212) 605-7000
Fax: (212) 605-7200
Media Buying & Planning Agency

McGarry Bowen, LLC
601 W 26th St Ste 1150
New York, NY 10001
Tel.: (212) 598-2900
Fax: (212) 598-2996
Creative
Marketing

Nitro Ltd.
31/F Lan Sheng Bldg 2-8 Huai Hai Rd
Shanghai, 200021, China
Tel.: (86) 21 6391 0011
Fax: (86) 21 63190 366

The Pitch Agency
8825 National Blvd
Culver City, CA 90232
Tel.: (310) 838-7300
Youth & Family Agency of Record

Publicis Asia/Pacific Pte. Ltd.
(Headquarters)
80 Anson Road #33-00
Singapore, 079907, Singapore
Tel.: (65) 6 836 3488
Fax: (65) 6836 3588

Republica
2153 Coral Way
Miami, FL 33145
Tel.: (305) 442-0977
Fax: (305) 443-1631
Diversity Initiatives

Starcom MediaVest Group
35 W Wacker Dr
Chicago, IL 60601-1723
Tel.: (312) 220-3535
Fax: (312) 220-6530
Media Planning & Buying

Tapestry Partners
35 W Wacker Dr
Chicago, IL 60601
Tel.: (312) 220-3535
Fax: (312) 220-6561
Multicultural Media Agency of Record

TONIC
gold & diamond park, phase 2, building 3, floor 2
office 3203 po box 117668
Dubai, United Arab Emirates
Tel.: (971) 14 341 3868
Fax: (971) 971143413869

VML, Inc.
250 Richards Rd
Kansas City, MO 64116-4279
Tel.: (816) 283-0700
Fax: (816) 283-0954
Toll Free: (800) 990-2468
(Interactive Marketing)

Zehnder Communications
4311 Blue Bonnet Blvd
Baton Rouge, LA 70809
Tel.: (225) 243-5302
Fax: (225) 243-5307

ZenithOptimedia
1-4/F900 Huai Hai Zhong Road
Shanghai, China
Tel.: (86) 21 6133 8399
Fax: (86) 21 6133 8398
(Burger King China; Media Buying & Planning)

BURGER KING RESTAURANT OF CANADA, INC.

(Sub. of Burger King Holdings Inc.)
401 The W Mall Ste 700
Etobicoke, ON M9C 5J4, Canada
Tel.: (416) 626-6464
Fax: (416) 626-6464
Toll Free: (877) 271-0493
Web Site: www.burgerking.ca
Sales Range: $10-24.9 Million
Approx. Number Employees: 20
Year Founded: 1989
Business Description:
Fast Food Restaurant
S.I.C.: 5812
N.A.I.C.S.: 722211
Advertising Agency:
TAXI
495 Wellington St W Ste 102
Toronto, ON M5V 1E9, Canada
Tel.: (416) 979-7001
Fax: (416) 979-7626

BURGERVILLE USA

(Sub. of The Holland, Inc.)
109 W 17th St
Vancouver, WA 98660
Tel.: (866) 264-2313
Fax: (360) 694-9114
Toll Free: (888) TASTENW
E-mail: servicedesk@burgerville.com
Web Site: www.burgerville.com
Approx. Number Employees: 1,200
Year Founded: 1969
Business Description:
Fast Food Restaurants
S.I.C.: 5812
N.A.I.C.S.: 722211
Import Export
Media: 8-13-20-23
Personnel:
Jeff Harvey *(Pres & CEO)*
Kyle Dean *(CFO)*
Janice Williams *(COO)*
Brands & Products:
BURGERVILLE

CALIFORNIA PIZZA KITCHEN INC.

6053 W Century Blvd 11th Fl
Los Angeles, CA 90045-6438
Tel.: (310) 342-5000
Fax: (310) 342-4640
Toll Free: (800) 919-3227
Web Site: www.cpk.com
Approx. Rev.: $642,231,000
Approx. Number Employees: 14,000
Year Founded: 1985
Business Description:
Restaurant Operator
S.I.C.: 5812
N.A.I.C.S.: 722110; 722211
Advertising Expenditures: $7,400,000
Personnel:
Larry S. Flax *(Co-Founder)*
Richard L. Rosenfield *(Co-Founder)*
Gerard Johan Hart *(Chm, Pres & CEO)*
Susan M. Collyns *(CFO, COO & Exec VP)*
Sarah G. Grover *(Chief Comm Officer & Sr VP-Mktg & PR)*
Thomas Beck *(Sr VP-Construction)*
Clint Coleman *(Sr VP-Dev)*
Karen M. Settlemyer *(Sr VP-Procurement)*
Rudy Sugueti *(Sr VP-ASAP Ops)*
Brands & Products:
CALIFORNIA PIZZA KITCHEN
CPK ASAP

CAPTAIN D'S, LLC

(Holding of Sun Capital Partners, Inc.)
1717 Elm Hill Pike Ste A1
Nashville, TN 37210-3633
Tel.: (615) 391-5461
Fax: (615) 231-2309
Toll Free: (800) 314-4819
E-mail: dscomments@captainds.com
Web Site: www.captainds.com
Sales Range: $500-549.9 Million
Approx. Number Employees: 700
Year Founded: 1969
Business Description:
Quick Service Seafood Restaurants
S.I.C.: 5812
N.A.I.C.S.: 722211
Media: 3-9-18-19-23-24
Distr.: Reg.
Budget Set: Oct.
Personnel:
Philip M. Greifeld *(Pres & CEO)*
Mike Payne *(CFO)*
Michael T. Folks *(Gen Counsel & Sr VP)*
Monte Jump *(Exec VP-Mktg)*
Michael Lippert *(Exec VP-Ops)*
Sandy Clingan Smith *(Sr VP-Mktg)*
Paula Vissing *(Sr VP-Pur, QA, R & D)*
Janet Duckham *(VP-Procurement)*
Peter Gibbons *(VP-Product Dev)*
Jeff B. Suber *(VP-Pur)*
Margo Mize *(Sr Dir-Local Store Mktg)*
Joanne Kemp *(Dir-Quality Assurance)*
Advertising Agencies:
Euro RSCG Dallas
2800 N. Dallas Pkwy, Ste 300
Plano, TX 75093
Tel.: (972) 473-5600
Fax: (972) 473-5601

RPM-Right Place Media
437 Lewis Hargett Cir Ste 130
Lexington, KY 40503
Tel.: (859) 685-3800
Fax: (859) 685-3801

Sprokkit
333 S Grand Ave Ste 1600
Los Angeles, CA 90071
Tel.: (213) 626-2076
Fax: (231) 232-3739

CARA OPERATIONS LIMITED

6303 Airport Rd
199 Four Valley Dr
Vaughan, ON L4V 1R8, Canada
Tel.: (905) 760-2244
Fax: (186) 632-21188
E-mail: info@cara.com
Web Site: www.cara.com
Sales Range: $800-899.9 Million
Approx. Number Employees: 31,000
Year Founded: 1883
Business Description:
In-Flight Catering, Airport Restaurants, Gift Shops, Multi-Unit Restaurants, Institutional Catering, & Food Distribution
S.I.C.: 5812
N.A.I.C.S.: 722320
Import
Advertising Expenditures: $30,000,000
Media: 1-2-3-4-6-7-8-9-10-11-13-14-15-16-18-19-20-21-22-23-24-25-26
Distr.: Intl.; Natl.
Budget Set: Dec. -Jan.
Personnel:
M. Bernard Syron *(Chm)*
Arjen A. Melis *(Pres & Corp Dev)*
Steven Smith *(CFO)*
Rob Ramage *(Pres-Cara Airline Solutions)*
Ian C. Wilkie *(Gen Counsel, Sec & Sr VP)*
Sean Regan *(Sr VP)*
Brands & Products:
CARA
HARVEY'S
KELSEY'S
MONTANA'S
OUTBACK
SECOND CUP
SUMMIT
SWISS CHALET

CARL KARCHER ENTERPRISES, INC.

(Sub. of CKE Restaurants Inc.)
(d/b/a Carl's Jr)
6307 Carpinteria Ave Ste A
Carpinteria, CA 93013-2901
Tel.: (805) 745-7500
Fax: (602) 870-8477
Toll Free: (800) 422-4141
Web Site: www.carlsjr.com
Sales Range: $25-49.9 Million
Approx. Number Employees: 150
Year Founded: 1941
Business Description:
Operator of Restaurants
S.I.C.: 5812
N.A.I.C.S.: 722211
Advertising Expenditures: $50,000
Media: 1-3-4-7-8-9-10-13-14-15-16-19-20-23-24-25
Distr.: Natl.
Personnel:
Andrew F. Puzder *(CEO)*
Bradford R. Haley *(Exec VP-Mktg-Carls Jr-Hardees Brands)*
Advertising Agencies:
ADWizz Inc.
2620 Carmichael Way
Turlock, CA 95382
Tel.: (209) 656-1323
Fax: (209) 633-2277
Recruitment

Initiative Worldwide
(Part of The Interpublic Group of Companies, Inc.)
1 Dag Hammerskjold Plz 5th Fl

Key to Media (For complete agency information see *The Advertising Red Books-Agencies* edition):
1. Bus. Publs. 2. Cable T.V. 3. Catalogs & Directories. 4. Co-op Adv. 5. Consumer Mags. 6. D.M. to Bus. Estab.7. D.M. to Consumers
8. Daily Newsp. 9. Exhibits/Trade Shows 10. Foreign 11. Infomercial 12. Internet Adv.13. Multimedia 14. Network Radio
15. Network T.V. 16. Newsp. Distr. Mags. 17. Other 18. Outdoor (Posters, Transit) 19. Point of Purchase20. Premiums, Novelties
21. Product Samples 22. Special Events Mktg. 23. Spot Radio 24. Spot T.V. 25. Weekly Newsp. 26. Yellow Page Adv.

Carl Karcher Enterprises, Inc. — (Continued)

New York, NY 10017
Tel.: (212) 605-7000
Fax: (212) 605-7200

Mendelsohn Zien Advertising LLC
11111 Santa Monica Blvd 21st Fl
Los Angeles, CA 90025-3356
Tel.: (310) 444-1990
Fax: (310) 444-9888
(Monster Breakfast Sandwich)

Spacedog
11111 Santa Monica Blvd Ste 2110
Los Angeles, CA 90025
Tel.: (310) 274-7650
Fax: (310) 444-9384

Sprokkit
333 S Grand Ave Ste 1600
Los Angeles, CA 90071
Tel.: (213) 626-2076
Fax: (231) 232-3739

Weber Shandwick-Los Angeles
8687 Melrose Ave 7th Fl
Los Angeles, CA 90069
Tel.: (310) 854-8200
Fax: (310) 854-8201

CARRABBA'S ITALIAN GRILL, LLC

(Sub. of OSI Restaurant Partners LLC)
2202 NW Shore Blvd
Tampa, FL 33607
Tel.: (813) 282-1225
Fax: (813) 282-1209
Web Site: www.carrabbas.com
Approx. Number Employees: 400
Business Description:
Casual Dining Italian Restaurants
S.I.C.: 5812
N.A.I.C.S.: 722110
Media: 3
Personnel:
Steve T. Shlemon *(Pres)*

CARROLS CORPORATION

(Sub. of Carrols Restaurant Group, Inc.)
968 James St
Syracuse, NY 13203-2503
Mailing Address:
PO Box 6969
Syracuse, NY 13217-6969
Tel.: (315) 424-0513
Fax: (315) 425-8874
E-mail: contact@carrols.com
Web Site: www.carrols.com
Business Description:
Quick-Service Restaurants & Franchises Operator
S.I.C.: 5812
N.A.I.C.S.: 722211
Advertising Expenditures: $30,362,000
Media: 1-3-8-9-10-13-18-19-20-21-23-25
Distr.: Direct to Consumer; Distr.; Natl.
Budget Set: Various
Personnel:
Alan Vituli *(Chm & CEO)*
Daniel T. Accordino *(Pres & COO)*
Paul R. Flanders *(CFO, Treas & VP)*
Joseph A. Zirkman *(Chief Ethics, Compliance Officer, VP, Gen Counsel & Sec)*

Advertising Agency:
Quanta Advertising
968 James St
Syracuse, NY 13217
Tel.: (315) 472-2809
Fax: (315) 425-8874
(Fast Food)

CARROLS RESTAURANT GROUP, INC.

968 James St
Syracuse, NY 13203
Tel.: (315) 424-0513
Toll Free: (800) 348-1074
E-mail: investorrelations@carrols.com
Web Site: www.carrols.com
Approx. Rev.: $796,144,000
Approx. Number Employees: 16,300
Year Founded: 1960
Business Description:
Fast-Food Restaurants
S.I.C.: 5812
N.A.I.C.S.: 722110; 722211
Advertising Expenditures: $30,362,000
Personnel:
Alan Vituli *(Chm & CEO)*
Daniel T. Accordino *(CFO, Treas & VP)*
Paul R. Flanders *(CFO, Treas & VP)*
Timothy Tatt *(CEO-Fiesta Restaurant Grp)*
Joseph A. Zirkman *(Chief Ethics & Compliance Officer, Gen Counsel, Sec & VP)*

CASSANO'S INC.

1700 E Stroop Rd
Kettering, OH 45429-5040
Tel.: (937) 294-5464
Fax: (937) 294-8107
Web Site: www.cassanos.com
Approx. Number Employees: 775
Year Founded: 1953
Business Description:
Mfr. of Dough; Operator of Fast Food Pizza Chain
S.I.C.: 5812; 5149
N.A.I.C.S.: 722211; 424490
Advertising Expenditures: $500,000
Media: 3-8-13-19-20-24
Distr.: Direct to Consumer; Reg.
Personnel:
Chip Cassano *(CEO)*
Laura Hammons *(Coord-Mktg)*
Brands & Products:
CASSANO'S
PIZZA KING
Advertising Agency:
Penny/Ohlmann/Neiman, Inc.
1605 N Main St
Dayton, OH 45405-4141
Tel.: (937) 278-0681
Fax: (937) 277-1723

CBOCS, INC.

(Sub. of Cracker Barrel Old Country Store, Inc.)
305 Hartmann Dr
Lebanon, TN 37087
Mailing Address:
PO Box 787
Lebanon, TN 37088-0787
Tel.: (615) 444-5533
Fax: (615) 443-9818
Toll Free: (800) 333-9566
Web Site: www.crackerbarrelocs.com
E-Mail For Key Personnel:
Public Relations: mediarequests@crackerbarrel.com
Sales Range: $200-249.9 Million
Approx. Number Employees: 900
Year Founded: 1969
Business Description:
Restaurants & Gift Shops Operator
S.I.C.: 5812; 5947
N.A.I.C.S.: 722110; 453220
Import
Media: 9-13-17-18-19-22-23-26
Distr.: Direct to Consumer; Reg.
Budget Set: June
Personnel:
Michael A. Woodhouse *(Chm & CEO)*
Douglas E. Barber *(COO & Exec VP)*
Michael J. Zylstra *(Gen Counsel, Sec & VP)*
P. Doug Couvillion *(Sr VP-Fin)*
Nicholas V. Flanagan *(Sr VP-Restaurant Ops)*
Robert J. Harig *(Sr VP-HR)*
Terry A. Maxwell *(Sr VP-Retail Ops)*
William H. Crayton *(VP-Retail Plng & Allocation)*
Robert F. Doyle *(VP-Product Dev & Quality Assurance)*
Peter Keiser *(VP-Mktg)*
Advertising Agencies:
The Buntin Group
1001 Hawkins St
Nashville, TN 37203-4758
Tel.: (615) 244-5720
Fax: (615) 244-6511
(Outdoor)

Buntin Out-of-Home Media
1001 Hawkins St
Nashville, TN 37203-4758
Tel.: (615) 244-5720
Fax: (615) 244-6511

CEC ENTERTAINMENT, INC.

4441 W Airport Fwy
Irving, TX 75062-5834
Mailing Address:
PO Box 152077
Irving, TX 75015-2077
Tel.: (972) 258-8507
Fax: (972) 258-5524
E-mail: investor@cecentertainment.com
Web Site: www.chuckecheese.com
Approx. Rev.: $817,248,000
Approx. Number Employees: 17,300
Year Founded: 1979
Business Description:
Operator of Chain of Restaurant & Entertainment Centers
S.I.C.: 5812; 6794; 7993
N.A.I.C.S.: 722211; 533110; 713120
Advertising Expenditures: $35,282,000
Media: 3-5-8-15-18-20-25-26
Distr.: Natl.
Budget Set: Nov.
Personnel:
Richard M. Frank *(Chm)*
Michael H. Magusiak *(Pres & CEO)*
Tiffany B. Kice *(CFO, Treas & Exec VP)*
Michael L. Furlow *(CIO & Sr VP-IT)*
Scott A. McDaniel *(CMO & Exec VP)*
John R. Cardinale *(Exec VP-Dev & Pur)*
Richard T. Huston *(Exec VP-Mktg & Entertainment)*
Nikki Thompkinson *(Coord-Mktg)*
Brands & Products:
CHUCK E CHEESE'S
CHUCK E-CLUB
WHERE A KID CAN BE A KID
Advertising Agency:
M/C/C
8131 Lyndon B Johnson Fwy Ste 275
Dallas, TX 75251-1352
Tel.: (972) 480-8383
Fax: (972) 669-8447

CHAMPPS ENTERTAINMENT, INC.

(Sub. of Fox & Hound Restaurant Group)
10375 Park Meadows Dr Ste 560
Littleton, CO 80124
Tel.: (303) 804-1333
Fax: (303) 804-8477
Toll Free: (800) 461-5965
E-mail: info@champps.com
Web Site: www.champps.com
Sales Range: $150-199.9 Million
Approx. Number Employees: 5,400
Year Founded: 1987
Business Description:
Franchising & Operation of Champps Restaurants
S.I.C.: 5812; 6794
N.A.I.C.S.: 722110; 533110
Advertising Expenditures: $3,400,000
Media: 7-8-9-18-22-23-25
Brands & Products:
CHAMPPS

CHEF'S INTERNATIONAL, INC.

62 Broadway
Point Pleasant Beach, NJ 08742-2606
Tel.: (732) 295-0350
Fax: (732) 899-2522
E-mail: webmaster@jackbakerslobstershanty.com
Web Site: www.chefsinternationalnj.com/
Sales Range: $10-24.9 Million
Approx. Number Employees: 500
Year Founded: 1975
Business Description:
Restaurants
S.I.C.: 5812
N.A.I.C.S.: 722110
Advertising Expenditures: $421,500
Media: 2-3-4-6-7-8-9-13-14-16-18-19-20-22-23-25-26
Distr.: Reg.
Budget Set: Jan.
Personnel:
Robert M. Lombardi *(Chm)*
Martin W. Fletcher *(CFO)*
Brands & Products:
JACK BAKER'S LOBSTER SHANTY & WHARFSIDE

CHICK-FIL-A, INC.

5200 Buffington Rd
Atlanta, GA 30349-2945
Tel.: (404) 765-8000
Fax: (404) 765-8140
E-mail: philip.barrett@chick-fil-a.com
Web Site: www.chick-fil-a.com
Sales Range: $1-4.9 Billion
Approx. Number Employees: 50,000
Year Founded: 1967
Business Description:
Fast Food Restaurants
S.I.C.: 5812
N.A.I.C.S.: 722211

Key to Media (For complete agency information see *The Advertising Red Books-Agencies* edition):
1. Bus. Publs. 2. Cable T.V. 3. Catalogs & Directories. 4. Co-op Adv. 5. Consumer Mags. 6. D.M. to Bus. Estab.7. D.M. to Consumers
8. Daily Newsp. 9. Exhibits/Trade Shows 10. Foreign 11. Infomercial 12. Internet Adv.13. Multimedia 14. Network Radio
15. Network T.V. 16. Newsp. Distr. Mags. 17. Other 18. Outdoor (Posters, Transit) 19. Point of Purchase20. Premiums, Novelties
21. Product Samples 22. Special Events Mktg. 23. Spot Radio 24. Spot T.V. 25. Weekly Newsp. 26. Yellow Page Adv.

Advertising Expenditures: $6,000,000

Media: 5-8-9-18-19-21-23-26
Distr.: Natl.
Budget Set: Dec.

Personnel:
S. Truett Cathy *(Founder, Chm & CEO)*
Dan T. Cathy *(Pres & COO)*
James B. McCabe *(CFO & Sr VP-Fin)*
Janet Bridges *(Fin Dir-Svcs & Treasury)*
Kathy Buckley *(Fin Dir-Svcs)*
Donna W. Kirbow *(Fin Dir-Svcs)*
H. Allen Smith *(Fin Dir-Plng)*
Michael F. Erbrick *(CIO & VP-Info Tech)*
Steve A. Robinson *(CMO & Sr VP-Mktg)*
Donald M. Cathy *(Sr VP)*
Perry Ragsdale *(Sr VP-Real Estate, Design & Construction)*
Timothy P. Tassopoulos *(Sr VP-Field Ops)*
B. Lynn Chastain *(VP & Asst Gen Counsel)*
S. Tammy Pearson *(VP & Asst Gen Counsel)*
T. Mark Miller *(VP-Trng & Dev)*
Donald A. Perry *(VP-PR)*
David Salyers *(VP-Mktg-Natl & Reg)*
Barry V. White *(VP-Local Mktg & Comm)*
Howard Baker *(Sr Dir-Field Ops)*
Mark L. Brackett *(Sr Dir-People & BI Sys-Fin)*
Alex Dominguez *(Sr Dir-Real Estate)*
John E. Featherston, Jr. *(Sr Dir-Real Estate)*
Michael S. Garrison *(Sr Dir-Info Tech Client Svcs)*
Todd Grubbs *(Sr Dir-Franchisee Selection)*
C. Steve Hester *(Sr Dir-Distr)*
T. Wayne Hoover *(Sr Dir-Field Ops)*
Sandi T. Moody *(Sr Dir-Bus Analysis)*
Philip Orazi, III *(Sr Dir)*
Brent Ragsdale *(Sr Dir-Fin Plng)*
R. David Turner *(Sr Dir-Field Ops)*
Tim Boggs *(Dir-Admin)*
Saleitha L. Champion *(Dir-Fin Svcs-Restaurants)*
Thomas E. Childers *(Dir-Menu Innovation & Quality)*
Don Crocker *(Dir-Real Estate)*
Steve L. DeVane *(Dir-Real Estate Strategy & Res)*
Cheryl B. Dick *(Dir-Field Ops & Licensing)*
William J. Dunphy, Jr. *(Dir-Field Ops)*
Kevin R. Fannin *(Dir-Corp Svcs)*
Colin Gromley *(Dir-Real Estate)*
Glenn H. Hewitt *(Dir-Tax Acctg)*
Betty Hoffman *(Dir-Tax Acctg)*
Jay Kimsey *(Dir-Field Ops)*
Gregory E. Lollis *(Dir-Dev & Construction)*
Kelly D. Ludwick *(Dir-Corp Legal)*
Rich Matherne *(Dir-Field Ops)*
Robert Mclaughlin *(Dir-Sponsorships & Event Mktg)*
Kimberly M. McMillian *(Dir-Fin Svcs)*
Mark Moraitakis *(Dir-Svc Innovations)*
Tom Morder *(Dir-Customer Insights)*
Jodee W. Morgan *(Dir-HR)*
Tom A. Nolan *(Dir-Facilities & Reinvestment)*
Onoma Okuma *(Dir-Bus Growth & Supply Chain Solutions)*
Amy G. Rooks *(Dir-Real Estate)*
Roger H. Shealy *(Dir-Production Design)*
Dan Strain *(Dir-Product, Facilities, Ordering & Software Lifecycle)*
Chris Taylor *(Dir-Tech Architecture & Ops)*
Gregory B. Thompson *(Dir-Corp Comm)*
W. Timothy Yancey *(Dir-Supply Chain Sys)*

Brands & Products:
CHICK-FIL-A
CHICK-FIL-A WAFFLE POTATO FRIES
CHICK-N-STRIPS
HAND-SPUN MILKSHAKES

Advertising Agencies:
Engauge Communications
375 N Front St Ste 400
Columbus, OH 43215
Tel.: (614) 573-1010
Fax: (614) 573-1011

The Foundry Agency
2400 Lake Park Dr Ste 110
Smyrna, GA 30080
Tel.: (770) 874-5804
Fax: (770) 874-5807

The Richards Group, Inc.
8750 N Central Expy Ste 100
Dallas, TX 75231-6430
Tel.: (214) 891-5700
Fax: (214) 265-2933

CHILI'S, INC.

(Sub. of Brinker International, Inc.)
6820 LBJ Freeway
Dallas, TX 75240
Tel.: (972) 980-9917
Fax: (972) 770-9593
Sales Range: $50-74.9 Million

Business Description:
Restaurant Operator
S.I.C.: 5812
N.A.I.C.S.: 722110

Personnel:
Krista Gibson *(Sr VP-Brand Strategy)*
Kevin J. Carroll *(Reg VP)*
Nicola Cochran *(Dir-Mktg)*

Advertising Agencies:
Digitas Inc.
33 Arch St
Boston, MA 02110
Tel.: (617) 867-1000
Fax: (617) 867-1111
Analytics & Measurement
Customer Relationship Marketing
Digital Agency of Record
Digital Media Planning & Buying
Display
Mobile
Search Marketing
Social Media
Website Design

Hill Holliday
53 State St
Boston, MA 02109
Tel.: (617) 366-4000
Broadcast Advertising
Strategy

Millsport
1999 Bryan St Ste 1800
Dallas, TX 75201
Tel.: (214) 259-3200
Fax: (214) 259-3201

CHIPOTLE MEXICAN GRILL, INC.

1401 Wynkoop St Ste 500
Denver, CO 80202
Tel.: (303) 595-4000
Fax: (303) 595-4014
Fax: (303) 222-2500
E-mail: mediarelations@chipotle.com
Web Site: www.chipotle.com
Approx. Rev.: $1,835,922,000
Approx. Number Employees: 26,500
Year Founded: 1993

Business Description:
Mexican Restaurant Operator
S.I.C.: 5812
N.A.I.C.S.: 722110; 722211
Advertising Expenditures: $26,190,000
Media: 3-6-8-9-14-15-18-22-23

Personnel:
M. Steven Ells *(Chm & CEO)*
Montgomery F. Moran *(Co-CEO & Sec)*
John R. Hartung *(CFO)*
Mark Crumpacker *(CMO)*
Robert N. Blessing, Jr. *(Restaurant Support Officer)*
Rex A. Jones *(Exec Dir-Intl)*
Kevin Gick *(Dir-Mktg)*
William Espey *(Mgr-Creative)*

Advertising Agencies:
Compass Point Media
222 S 9th St
Minneapolis, MN 55402-3362
Tel.: (612) 347-6900
Fax: (612) 347-6969

Rokkan
176 Grand St 2nd Fl
New York, NY 10012-4003
Tel.: (212) 835-9300
Fax: (212) 251-9393

TDA Advertising & Design
1500 Pearl St Ste 300
Boulder, CO 80302
Tel.: (303) 247-1180
Fax: (303) 247-1214

CHURCH'S CHICKEN, INC.

(Holding of Arcapita, Inc.)
980 Hammond Dr NE Ste 1100
Atlanta, GA 30328-8187
Tel.: (770) 350-3800
Fax: (770) 512-3920
E-mail: info@churchs.com
Web Site: www.churchs.com
Sales Range: $1-4.9 Billion
Approx. Number Employees: 75
Year Founded: 1952

Business Description:
Fast Food Restaurants Operator
S.I.C.: 5812
N.A.I.C.S.: 722211
Advertising Expenditures: $23,000,000
Media: 3-8-9-11-18-19-20-23-24
Distr.: Intl.; Natl.
Budget Set: Oct.

Personnel:
Tully Friedman *(Chm)*
John Bowie *(Pres)*
James F. Hyatt *(CEO)*
Louis J. Profumo *(CFO & Exec VP)*
Tony Lavely *(CMO & Exec VP)*
Andy Bonaparte *(VP-Adv)*

Brands & Products:
HONEY BUTTER BISCUITS
JALAPENO CHEESE BOMBERS
WEVE GOT THE CRUNCH

Advertising Agencies:
The Media Kitchen
160 Varick St
New York, NY 10013
Tel.: (212) 633-0080
Fax: (212) 633-0080
Eastern Region Media

Trend Influence
303 Peachtree Center Ave Ste 625
Atlanta, GA 30303
Tel.: (404) 221-1188
Fax: (404) 720-8200
Creative Agency of Record

CICI ENTERPRISES INC.

(d/b/a CiCi's Pizza)
1080 W Bethel Rd
Coppell, TX 75019
Tel.: (972) 745-4200
Fax: (972) 745-4203
Web Site: www.cicispizza.com
E-Mail For Key Personnel:
Marketing Director: marketing@cicispizza.com
Approx. Number Employees: 700
Year Founded: 1985

Business Description:
All-You-Can-Eat Pizza Buffet Restaurant Operator
S.I.C.: 5812
N.A.I.C.S.: 722110
Media: 13-16

Personnel:
Joe Croce *(Founder)*
Mike Shumsky *(CEO)*
Tim Alba *(CFO)*
Nancy Hampton *(CMO)*
J. Forbes Anderson *(Chief Strategy Officer)*
Bob Kulick *(Pres-JMC Restaurant Distr)*
Deb Chappell *(Dir-Real Estate Svcs & Support)*

Advertising Agency:
Publicis Dallas
7300 Lonestar Dr
Plano, TX 75024
Tel.: (972) 628-7500
Fax: (972) 628-7864
Agency of Record
Creative
Digital
Media Buying & Planning

CKE RESTAURANTS INC.

(Holding of Apollo Management, L.P.)
6307 Carpinteria Ave Ste A
Carpinteria, CA 93013
Tel.: (805) 745-7500
Toll Free: (800) 422-4141
E-mail: pr@ckr.com
Web Site: www.ckr.com
E-Mail For Key Personnel:
Public Relations: pr@ckr.com
Approx. Number Employees: 21,300
Year Founded: 1941

Business Description:
Restaurants Operator & Franchisor
S.I.C.: 5812
N.A.I.C.S.: 722110; 722211

Key to Media (For complete agency information see *The Advertising Red Books-Agencies* edition):
1. Bus. Publs. 2. Cable T.V. 3. Catalogs & Directories. 4. Co-op Adv. 5. Consumer Mags. 6. D.M. to Bus. Estab.7. D.M. to Consumers
8. Daily Newsp. 9. Exhibits/Trade Shows 10. Foreign 11. Infomercial 12. Internet Adv.13. Multimedia 14. Network Radio
15. Network T.V. 16. Newsp. Distr. Mags. 17. Other 18. Outdoor (Posters, Transit) 19. Point of Purchase20. Premiums, Novelties
21. Product Samples 22. Special Events Mktg. 23. Spot Radio 24. Spot T.V. 25. Weekly Newsp. 26. Yellow Page Adv.

CKE Restaurants Inc. — (Continued)

Advertising Expenditures:
$64,443,000
Media: 8-10-13-20-21
Personnel:
Peter P. Copses *(Chm)*
E. Michael Murphy *(Pres & Chief Legal Officer)*
Andrew F. Puzder *(CEO)*
Theodore Abajian *(CFO & Exec VP)*
Jeffrey P. Chasney *(CIO & Exec VP-Strategic Plng)*
Brad R. Haley *(CMO)*
Ned Lyerly *(Exec VP-Global Franchise Developmen & Sr VP-Global Franchise Dev)*
Richard Buxton *(Exec VP-Real Estate Dev)*
John J. Dunion *(Exec VP-Supply Chain Mgmt)*
Richard E. Fortman *(Exec VP-Carls Jr Ops)*
Robert Starke *(Exec VP-Ops-Hardees)*
Brands & Products:
CARL'S JR.
CKE
GREEN BURRITO
HARDEE'S
LA SALSA FRESH MEXICAN GRILL
RED BURRITO
Advertising Agencies:
72andSunny
6300 Arizona Cir
Los Angeles, CA 90045
Tel.: (310) 215-9009
Fax: (310) 215-9012

David & Goliath
909 N Sepulveda Blvd Ste 700
El Segundo, CA 90245
Tel.: (310) 445-5200
Fax: (310) 445-5201

Mendelsohn Zien Advertising LLC
11111 Santa Monica Blvd 21st Fl
Los Angeles, CA 90025-3356
Tel.: (310) 444-1990
Fax: (310) 444-9888
Patty Melt Burger

COCO PAZZO OF ILLINOIS LLC

(d/b/a Coco Pazzo Restaurant)
300 W Hubbard St
Chicago, IL 60610
Tel.: (312) 836-0900
Fax: (312) 836-0257
E-mail: admin@cocopazzochicago.com
Web Site:
www.cocopazzochicago.com
Sales Range: $400-449.9 Million
Approx. Number Employees: 80
Business Description:
Italian Restaurant Franchiser
S.I.C.: 5812
N.A.I.C.S.: 722110
Media: 23
Personnel:
Jack Weiss *(Owner)*
Advertising Agency:
RR Public Relations, Inc.
2220 W Dickens Ave
Chicago, IL 60647
Tel.: (773) 252-8550
Tel.: (847) 914-9125
Fax: (773) 252-8552
Fax: (847) 914-9152

COLUMBIA RESTAURANT GROUP

2025 E 7th Ave
Tampa, FL 33605
Tel.: (813) 248-3000
Fax: (813) 247-5881
E-mail: info@columbiarestaurant.com
Web Site:
www.columbiarestaurant.com
Sales Range: $10-24.9 Million
Approx. Number Employees: 500
Business Description:
Restaurant Owner & Operator
S.I.C.: 5812
N.A.I.C.S.: 722110
Media: 6
Personnel:
Richard Gonzmart *(Pres)*
Candido Ferreira *(Gen Mgr-Celebration)*
Jim Hanratty *(Gen Mgr-Clearwater Beach)*
John Monetti *(Gen Mgr-Sarasota)*
Elisabete Silva *(Gen Mgr-St Petersburg)*
Jim Garris *(Mgr-Ops-Ybor City)*
Angela Geml *(Mgr-Mktg & Pub Rel)*

CORKY'S BAR-B-Q

5255 Poplar Ave
Memphis, TN 38119-3513
Tel.: (901) 685-9344
Toll Free: (800) 926-7597
E-mail: bbqinfo@corkysbbq.com
Web Site: www.corkysbbq.com
Approx. Number Employees: 120
Year Founded: 1984
Business Description:
Barbeque Cuisine Restaurants & Mail Order Gift Packages
S.I.C.: 5812
N.A.I.C.S.: 722110
Media: 6-8-9-18-21-22
Distr.: Natl.
Personnel:
Barry Pelts *(Co-Owner & Pres)*
Andrew L. Woodman *(CFO)*
Brands & Products:
CORKY'S

COSI, INC.

1751 Lake Cook Rd
Deerfield, IL 60015
Tel.: (847) 597-8800
Tel.: (847) 444-3200
Fax: (847) 597-8884
E-mail: contactus@getcosi.com
Web Site: www.getcosi.com
Approx. Rev.: $109,699,000
Approx. Number Employees: 2,038
Year Founded: 1996
Business Description:
Sandwich Deli, Restaurant, Delivery & Catering Services
S.I.C.: 5812
N.A.I.C.S.: 722110; 722211
Advertising Expenditures: $2,400,000
Media: 2-17
Personnel:
Mark S. Demilio *(Interim CEO)*
William Koziel *(CFO)*
Vicki Baue *(Chief Compliance/Legal Officer, Gen Counsel & VP)*
Steve Scrima *(VP-Pur & Distr)*
Advertising Agency:
XPR LLC
217 N Main St Ste 200
Santa Ana, CA 92701
Tel.: (714) 881-2310
Fax: (714) 881-2443

COUNTRY KITCHEN INTERNATIONAL, INC.

(Sub. of Kitchen Investment Group)
801 Deming Way
Madison, WI 53717-1918
Mailing Address:
PO Box 44434
Madison, WI 53744-4434
Tel.: (608) 833-9633
Fax: (608) 833-8329
Toll Free: (888) 359-3235
E-mail: info@countrykitchen.net
Web Site:
www.countrykitchenrestaurants.com/
Approx. Number Employees: 25
Year Founded: 1939
Business Description:
Country Kitchen Restaurant & Franchiser
S.I.C.: 5812; 8741
N.A.I.C.S.: 722310; 561110
Media: 3-5-8-9-10-13-18-19-20-22-23-24-25-26
Distr.: Natl.
Budget Set: Sept.
Personnel:
Charles Myers *(Pres & CEO)*
Chris McGrath *(VP-Mktg)*
Kevin Tormey *(Dir-Pur)*
Brands & Products:
COME HOME TO THE GOOD STUFF
COUNTRY HOSPITALITY

CRACKER BARREL OLD COUNTRY STORE, INC.

305 Hartmann Dr
Lebanon, TN 37087-2519
Mailing Address:
PO Box 787
Lebanon, TN 37088-0787
Tel.: (615) 444-5533
Fax: (615) 443-9476
Fax: (888) 263-4304
Toll Free: (800) 333-9566
E-mail: jdavis@crackerbarrel.com
Web Site: www.crackerbarrel.com
Approx. Rev.: $2,434,435,000
Approx. Number Employees: 67,000
Year Founded: 1998
Business Description:
Restaurant Holding Company
S.I.C.: 5812
N.A.I.C.S.: 722110
Advertising Expenditures:
$45,539,000
Media: 6-9-18-23-25
Personnel:
Michael A. Woodhouse *(Chm)*
Sandra Brophy Cochran *(Pres & CEO)*
Lawrence E. Hyatt *(CFO & Sr VP)*
N. B. Forrest Shoaf *(Chief Legal Officer, Sec & Sr VP)*
Douglas E. Barber *(Chief People Officer & Exec VP)*
P. Douglas Couvillion *(Chief Acctg Officer, VP & Controller)*
Christopher A. Ciavarra *(Sr VP-Mktg)*
Nicholas V. Flanagan *(Sr VP-Restaurant Ops)*
Edward A. Greene *(Sr VP-Strategic Initiatives)*
Robert J. Harig *(Sr VP-HR)*
Terry A. Maxwell *(Sr VP-Retail)*
Diana S. Wynne *(Sr VP-Corp Affairs)*
Bob Doyle *(VP-Product Dev & Quality Assurance)*
Kelly Flynt *(Gen Mgr-Baytown)*
Bobbi Fultz *(Gen Mgr-Morristown)*
David Kobylarz *(Gen Mgr-Adairsville)*
Matthew Lochiatto *(Gen Mgr-Zanesville)*
Craig Rickett *(Gen Mgr-Ringgold)*
Julie K. Davis *(Sr Dir-Corp Comm)*
Barbara A. Gould *(Mgr-IR)*
Tara Hubbard *(Mgr-Retail-Ottawa)*
Brands & Products:
CRACKER BARREL OLD COUNTRY STORE
Advertising Agencies:
The Buntin Group
1001 Hawkins St
Nashville, TN 37203-4758
Tel.: (615) 244-5720
Fax: (615) 244-6511
Outdoor
Planning & Buying

Buntin Out-of-Home Media
1001 Hawkins St
Nashville, TN 37203-4758
Tel.: (615) 244-5720
Fax: (615) 244-6511

Euro RSCG 4D
36 E Grand Ave Stes 3 & 4
Chicago, IL 60610
Tel.: (312) 640-6800
Fax: (312) 640-6801
Agency of Record
Creative

CURTIS RESTAURANT SUPPLY & EQUIPMENT CO.

6577 E 40th St
Tulsa, OK 74145-4516
Tel.: (918) 622-7390
Fax: (918) 665-0990
Web Site: www.curtisequipment.com
Sales Estimate: $20-39 Million
Approx. Number Employees: 35
Year Founded: 1946
Business Description:
Restaurant Supplies & Equipment Marketer
S.I.C.: 5046; 5021
N.A.I.C.S.: 423440; 423210
Media: 4-7-21
Personnel:
Jay Gulick *(Owner)*

DAIRY QUEEN CORPORATE STORE

(Sub. of International Dairy Queen, Inc.)
9656 Bluegrass Pkwy Ste 200
Louisville, KY 40299-1902
Tel.: (502) 499-6100
Fax: (502) 499-5164
Web Site: www.dairyqueen.com
Sales Range: $150-199.9 Million
Approx. Number Employees: 2,200
Business Description:
Eating Places Franchiser
S.I.C.: 5812
N.A.I.C.S.: 722110
Export
Advertising Expenditures: $4,500,000
Media: 3-8-9-18-19-20-23-24-25
Distr.: Reg.

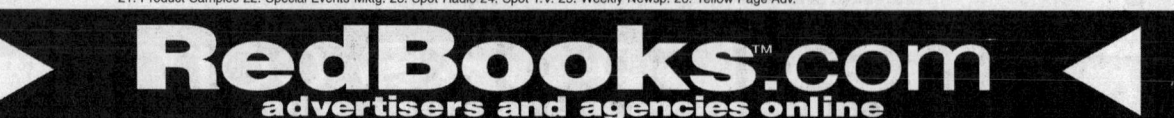

Key to Media (For complete agency information see *The Advertising Red Books-Agencies* edition):
1. Bus. Publs. 2. Cable T.V. 3. Catalogs & Directories. 4. Co-op Adv. 5. Consumer Mags. 6. D.M. to Bus. Estab.7. D.M. to Consumers
8. Daily Newsp. 9. Exhibits/Trade Shows 10. Foreign 11. Infomercial 12. Internet Adv.13. Multimedia 14. Network Radio
15. Network T.V. 16. Newsp. Distr. Mags. 17. Other 18. Outdoor (Posters, Transit) 19. Point of Purchase20. Premiums, Novelties
21. Product Samples 22. Special Events Mktg. 23. Spot Radio 24. Spot T.V. 25. Weekly Newsp. 26. Yellow Page Adv.

Budget Set: Nov.-Dec.

Brands & Products:
DQ

DAMON'S INTERNATIONAL INC.

(Sub. of Alliance Development Group)
4645 Executive Dr
Columbus, OH 43220-3601
Tel.: (614) 442-7900
Fax: (614) 442-7787
E-mail: info@damons.com
Web Site: www.damons.com
E-Mail For Key Personnel:
President: CHoward@damons.com
Approx. Number Employees: 3,350
Year Founded: 1979
Business Description:
Owner & Franchiser of Casual Dining Restaurants
S.I.C.: 5812; 8741
N.A.I.C.S.: 722211; 561110
Media: 2-3-7-8-9-10-13-17-18-23-24-25-26
Distr.: Intl.
Personnel:
Gary Reinhart *(Pres)*
Brands & Products:
DAMON'S
DAMON'S CLUBHOUSE
THE GRILL IS ON
IT ALL COMES TOGETHER AT DAMON'S

DARDEN RESTAURANTS, INC.

1000 Darden Ctr Dr
Orlando, FL 32837
Tel.: (407) 245-4000
Fax: (407) 245-5389
Toll Free: (800) 832-7336
E-mail: dardeninfo@darden.com
Web Site:
www.dardenrestaurants.com
Approx. Sls.: $7,113,100,000
Approx. Number Employees: 174,000
Year Founded: 1938
Business Description:
Restaurant Owner & Operator
S.I.C.: 5812; 6794
N.A.I.C.S.: 722110; 533110
Advertising Expenditures: $340,200,000
Media: 2-4-7-13-15-22
Personnel:
Clarence Otis, Jr. *(Chm & CEO)*
Andrew H. Madsen *(Pres & COO)*
C. Bradford Richmond *(CFO & Sr VP)*
Valerie K. Collins *(CIO, Sr VP & Controller)*
John Caron *(CMO & Sr VP)*
Kim A. Lopdrup *(Pres-Red Lobster & Sr VP)*
David T. Pickens *(Pres-Olive Garden & Sr VP)*
David C. George *(Pres-LongHorn Steakhouse)*
Eugene I. Lee, Jr. *(Pres-Specialty Restaurant Grp)*
Teresa Mosley Sebastian *(Gen Counsel, Sec & Sr VP)*
James J. Buettgen *(Sr VP-Bus Dev)*
Robert S. McAdam *(Sr VP-Govt & Community Affairs)*
Barry B. Moullet *(Sr VP-Supply Chain)*
Daisy Ng *(Sr VP-HR)*
Suk Singh *(Sr VP-Dev)*
Richard J. Walsh *(Sr VP-Corp Affairs)*
Jennifer Payne *(Mgr-Interactive Mktg)*
Scott Peters *(Mgr-Media)*
Brands & Products:
BAHAMA BREEZE
THE CAPITAL GRILLE
DARDEN
DARDEN RESTAURANTS
LONGHORN STEAKHOUSE
OLIVE GARDEN
RED LOBSTER
SEASONS 52
Advertising Agencies:
Grey New York
777 3rd Ave
New York, NY 10017-1401
Tel.: (212) 546-2000
Fax: (212) 546-1495
Creative Agency of Record

Starcom MediaVest Group
35 W Wacker Dr
Chicago, IL 60601-1723
Tel.: (312) 220-3535
Fax: (312) 220-6530
Longhorn Steaks
Media Agency
Olive Garden
Red Lobster

DAVCO RESTAURANTS INC.

(Sub. of DavCo Acquisition Holding Inc.)
1657 Crofton Blvd
Crofton, MD 21114-1305
Tel.: (410) 721-3770
Fax: (410) 793-0754
Web Site: www.davcorestaurants.com
Approx. Number Employees: 5,000
Year Founded: 1976
Business Description:
Fast-Food Restaurant Owner & Operator
S.I.C.: 5812
N.A.I.C.S.: 722211
Media: 13-15-18-19
Personnel:
Harvey Rothstein *(Chm & CEO)*
David J. Norman *(Pres & Gen Counsel)*
Charles C. McGuire, III *(CFO, Treas & Sr VP-Fin)*
Richard H. Borchers *(COO & Exec VP)*
Stacey Jackson *(Deputy Gen Counsel & Sr VP-HR)*
Dave Carpenter *(VP-HR)*

DAVE & BUSTER'S INC.

(Holding of Oak Hill Capital Partners, L.P.)
2481 Manana Dr
Dallas, TX 75220-1203
Tel.: (214) 357-9588
Fax: (214) 350-0941
Web Site: www.daveandbusters.com
Approx. Rev.: $521,539,000
Approx. Number Employees: 6,586
Year Founded: 1982
Business Description:
Entertainment Complex & Restaurant Builder & Operator
S.I.C.: 5812; 5813; 7999
N.A.I.C.S.: 722110; 713990; 722410
Advertising Expenditures: $26,588,000
Media: 3-13-23
Personnel:
Tyler Wolfram *(Chm)*
Dolf Berle *(Pres & COO)*
Stephen M. King *(CEO)*
Brian A. Jenkins *(CFO & Sr VP)*
Sean Gleason *(CMO)*
Jeffrey C. Wood *(Chief Dev Officer & Sr VP)*
Jay L. Tobin *(Gen Counsel, Sec & Sr VP)*
Margo Manning *(Sr VP-HR)*
J. Michael Plunkett *(Sr VP-Pur & Intl-Ops)*
Greg Clore *(VP-Info Tech)*
April Spearman *(VP-Mktg)*
Jennifer DeMarco Herskind *(Asst VP-Mktg)*
Remi Wellborn *(Sr Dir-Strategic Initiatives)*
Dave Curtis *(Dir-Recruiting)*
Kathryn Rainey *(Dir-Compensation)*
Ty Watson *(Dir-Sls)*
Jennifer Yarbrough *(Dir-HR)*
Lesley Madsen *(Reg Mgr-Mktg)*
Diana Rhodes *(Mgr-Loyalty & Online Mktg)*
Brands & Products:
RECESS IS CALLING
Advertising Agencies:
MediaCom
498 7th Ave
New York, NY 10018
Tel.: (212) 912-4200
Fax: (212) 508-4386
National Media Planning & Buying

Merkley + Partners
(Sub. of Omnicom Group, Inc.)
200 Varick St
New York, NY 10014-4810
Tel.: (212) 366-3500
Fax: (212) 805-7445
(Creative)

Young & Rubicam Chicago
233 N Michigan Ave 16th Fl
Chicago, IL 60601-5519
Tel.: (312) 596-3000
Fax: (312) 596-3130
Agency of Record
Creative

DEL TACO LLC

(Joint Venture of Leonard Green & Partners, L.P., Grotech Ventures & Charlesbank Capital Partners, LLC)
25521 Commercentre Dr Ste 200
Lake Forest, CA 92630
Tel.: (949) 462-9300
Fax: (949) 462-7444
Toll Free: (800) 852-7204
E-mail: customercommentline@deltaco.com
Web Site: www.deltaco.com
Sales Range: $300-349.9 Million
Approx. Number Employees: 80
Year Founded: 1961
Business Description:
Quick Service Mexican Restaurant Franchisor
S.I.C.: 5812
N.A.I.C.S.: 722211
Advertising Expenditures: $10,000,000
Media: 3-5-8-9-18-19-23-24-25
Distr.: Natl.
Personnel:
Shirlene Lopez *(Pres & COO)*
Paul J.B. Murphy, III *(CEO)*
Steven Brake *(CFO)*
John Capitola *(CMO)*
Janet Erickson *(Exec VP-Supply Chain, R&D)*
Peter Honer *(VP-Fin)*
David Snyder *(VP-IT)*
Stephanie Stroull *(Dir-Field Mktg & Mgr)*
Stephanie Sproull *(Sr Mgr-Field Mktg)*
Brands & Products:
DEL TACO
Advertising Agencies:
Doner
25900 Northwestern Hwy
Southfield, MI 48075
Tel.: (248) 354-9700
Fax: (248) 827-8440
Fast Food

LatinoLandia
17595 Harvard Ave Ste C5000
Irvine, CA 92614
Tel.: (949) 502-8822
Fax: (949) 502-8855

Sprokkit
333 S Grand Ave Ste 1600
Los Angeles, CA 90071
Tel.: (213) 626-2076
Fax: (231) 232-3739

DENNY'S CORPORATION

203 E Main St
Spartanburg, SC 29319-9966
Tel.: (864) 597-8000
Fax: (864) 597-8780
E-mail: ir@dennys.com
Web Site: www.dennys.com
Approx. Rev.: $548,466,000
Approx. Number Employees: 11,500
Year Founded: 1989
Business Description:
Food Service & Restaurant Franchise Owner & Operator
S.I.C.: 6794; 5812
N.A.I.C.S.: 722110; 533110; 722211
Advertising Expenditures: $17,400,000
Media: 2-3-5-6-14-15-18-23-24
Distr.: Natl.
Budget Set: Aug.
Personnel:
Debra Smithart-Oglesby *(Chm)*
John C. Miller *(Pres & CEO)*
F. Mark Wolfinger *(CFO, Chief Admin Officer & Exec VP)*
Roberto Rodriguez *(COO)*
S. Alex Lewis *(CIO & VP-IT)*
Frances Allen *(CMO & Exec VP)*
Timothy E. Flemming *(Chief Legal Officer, Gen Counsel & Sr VP)*
Jay C. Gilmore *(Chief Acctg Officer, VP & Controller)*
J. Scott Melton *(Sec, Asst Gen Counsel & Corp Goverance Officer)*
John W. Dillon *(VP-Mktg & Product Innovation)*
Jill A. Van Pelt *(VP-HR)*
Brands & Products:
CARROWS RESTAURANTS
COCO'S RESTAURANTS
DENNY'S
GRAND SLAM BREAKFAST
ORIGINAL GRAND SLAM

Key to Media (For complete agency information see *The Advertising Red Books-Agencies* edition):
1. Bus. Publs. 2. Cable T.V. 3. Catalogs & Directories. 4. Co-op Adv. 5. Consumer Mags. 6. D.M. to Bus. Estab.7. D.M. to Consumers
8. Daily Newsp. 9. Exhibits/Trade Shows 10. Foreign 11. Infomercial 12. Internet Adv.13. Multimedia 14. Network Radio
15. Network T.V. 16. Newsp. Distr. Mags. 17. Other 18. Outdoor (Posters, Transit) 19. Point of Purchase20. Premiums, Novelties
21. Product Samples 22. Special Events Mktg. 23. Spot Radio 24. Spot T.V. 25. Weekly Newsp. 26. Yellow Page Adv.

Denny's Corporation — (Continued)

Advertising Agencies:
Casanova Pendrill, LLC
275-A McCormick Ave Ste 100
Costa Mesa, CA 92626-3369
Tel.: (714) 918-8200
Fax: (714) 918-8295
Creative
Hispanic Agency of Record
Strategic Counsel

Gotham Incorporated
150 E 42nd St 12th Fl
New York, NY 10017
Tel.: (212) 414-7000
Fax: (212) 414-7095
Creative

Hill & Knowlton, Inc.
(Member of WPP)
825 3rd Ave 24th Fl
New York, NY 10022
Tel.: (212) 885-0300
Fax: (212) 885-0570

Odney
1400 W Century Ave
Bismarck, ND 58503
Tel.: (701) 222-8721
Fax: (701) 222-8172
Toll Free: (888) 500-8721

Optimedia International U.S.
375 Hudson St 7th Fl
New York, NY 10014
Tel.: (212) 820-3200
Fax: (212) 820-3300

Publicis Dallas
7300 Lonestar Dr
Plano, TX 75024
Tel.: (972) 628-7500
Fax: (972) 628-7864

Sprokkit
333 S Grand Ave Ste 1600
Los Angeles, CA 90071
Tel.: (213) 626-2076
Fax: (231) 232-3739

DENNY'S, INC.

(Div. of Denny's Corporation)
203 E Main St
Spartanburg, SC 29319
Tel.: (864) 597-8000
Fax: (864) 597-8780
E-mail: info@dennys.com
Web Site: www.dennys.com

Sales Range: $900-999.9 Million
Approx. Number Employees: 300
Year Founded: 1953
Business Description:
Operator of Family Style Restaurants
S.I.C.: 5812; 6794
N.A.I.C.S.: 722110; 533110

Media: 6-14-15-17-18-19-23
Distr.: Natl.
Budget Set: Aug.

Personnel:
F. Mark Wolfinger *(CFO & Exec VP)*
Frances Allen *(CMO)*
Timothy E. Flemming *(Gen Counsel & Sr VP)*

Advertising Agencies:
Erwin-Penland
(Owned by Hill, Holliday, Connors, Cosmopulos, Inc., Member of the Interpublic Group)
125 E Broad St
Greenville, SC 29601
Tel.: (864) 271-0500
Fax: (864) 235-5941
Local Advertising
Menus
Merchandising

Gotham Incorporated
150 E 42nd St 12th Fl
New York, NY 10017
Tel.: (212) 414-7000
Fax: (212) 414-7095
Lead Creative Agency

Optimedia International U.S.
375 Hudson St 7th Fl
New York, NY 10014
Tel.: (212) 820-3200
Fax: (212) 820-3300
Media Duties

Publicis Dallas
7300 Lonestar Dr
Plano, TX 75024
Tel.: (972) 628-7500
Fax: (972) 628-7864

DICK CLARK RESTAURANTS, INC.

(Joint Venture of Six Flags Entertainment Corp. & Red Zone LLC)
2900 Olympic Blvd
Santa Monica, CA 90404
Tel.: (310) 255-4600
Fax: (310) 255-4601
E-mail: reception@dickclark.com
Web Site:
www.dickclarkproductions.com
Sales Range: $10-24.9 Million
Approx. Number Employees: 20
Business Description:
Casual Dining Restaurants Owner & Operator
S.I.C.: 5812; 5813
N.A.I.C.S.: 722110; 722410
Import Export
Advertising Expenditures: $3,000,000
Media: 2-3-4-6-13-22-23-24-26
Brands & Products:
BANDSTAND TO GO-GO
DICK CLARK'S AB DINER
DICK CLARK'S AB GRILL
DICK CLARK'S BANDSTAND

DINEEQUITY, INC.

450 N Brand Blvd FL 7
Glendale, CA 91203-2347
Tel.: (818) 240-6055
Fax: (818) 637-3131
E-mail: info@ihopcorp.com
Web Site: www.dineequity.com
Approx. Rev.: $1,333,085,000
Approx. Number Employees: 650
Year Founded: 1958
Business Description:
Holding Company for Restaurants & Restaurant Franchising
S.I.C.: 5812; 6794
N.A.I.C.S.: 722110; 533110
Advertising Expenditures: $1,100,000
Media: 5-7-8-9-15-18-19-22-23-24-25-26
Distr.: Natl.
Budget Set: Nov.
Personnel:
Julia A. Stewart *(Chm & CEO)*
Tom Emrey *(CFO)*
Michael J. Archer *(Pres-Applebee's)*
Jean Birch *(Pres-IHOP Restaurants)*
Greggory Kalvin *(Sr VP & Controller)*
John Jakubek *(Sr VP-HR)*
Rebeca M. Johnson *(Sr VP-Mktg)*
Tod MacKenzie *(Sr VP-Comm & Pub Affairs)*
Carolyn P. O'Keefe *(Sr VP-Mktg)*
Patrick Lenow *(Exec Dir-Corp Comm)*
Stacy Roughan *(Dir-IR)*
Jennifer Pendergrass *(Mgr-Comm)*
Brands & Products:
ANY TIME'S A GOOD TIME FOR IHOP
APPLEBEE'S
COME HUNGRY. LEAVE HAPPY
DINEEQUITY
GREAT FRANCHISEES. GREAT BRAND.
IHOP
INTERNATIONAL HOUSE OF PANCAKES
Advertising Agency:
VITRO
(An MDC Partners Company)
625 Broadway Fl 4
San Diego, CA 92101-5403
Tel.: (619) 234-0408
Fax: (619) 234-4015
IHOP

DOCTOR'S ASSOCIATES INC.

(d/b/a Subway)
325 Bic Dr
Milford, CT 06461-3072
Tel.: (203) 877-4281
Fax: (203) 876-6674
Fax: (203) 876-6695
Toll Free: (800) 888-4848
Web Site: www.subway.com
Sales Range: $5-14.9 Billion
Approx. Number Employees: 730
Year Founded: 1965
Business Description:
Holding Company; Fast Food Restaurants Franchiser
S.I.C.: 6719; 5812
N.A.I.C.S.: 551112; 722211
Advertising Expenditures: $80,000,000
Media: 2-3-6-8-11-13-15-18-22-24
Distr.: Intl.; Natl.
Personnel:
Fred DeLuca *(Founder & Pres)*
William J. Schettini *(CMO)*
Suzanne Greco *(Dir-R & D)*
Eddie Lindley *(Sr Mgr-Multicultural Mktg)*
Michelle Cordial *(Brand Mgr-Subway)*
Advertising Agency:
MMB
580 Harrison Ave
Boston, MA 02118
Tel.: (617) 670-9700
Fax: (617) 670-9711
Agency of Record

DOMINO'S PIZZA, INC.

30 Frank Lloyd Wright Dr
Ann Arbor, MI 48106
Mailing Address:
PO Box 997
Ann Arbor, MI 48106-0997
Tel.: (734) 930-3030
Fax: (734) 747-6210
Toll Free: (888) 366-4667
E-mail: investorrelations@dominos.com
Web Site: www.dominos.com
Approx. Rev.: $1,570,894,000
Approx. Number Employees: 10,900
Year Founded: 1960
Business Description:
Pizza Restaurants & Delivery Services
S.I.C.: 5812
N.A.I.C.S.: 722211
Advertising Expenditures: $35,300,000
Media: 5-6-8-9-11-14-15
Distr.: Intl.; Natl.
Personnel:
David A. Brandon *(Chm)*
J. Patrick Doyle *(Pres & CEO)*
Michael T. Lawton *(CFO & Exec VP-Fin)*
Christopher K. McGlothlin *(CIO)*
Russell J. Weiner *(CMO)*
Ken Rollin *(Gen Counsel & Exec VP)*
Richard E. Allison, Jr. *(Exec VP-Intl)*
Scott Hinshaw *(Exec VP-Fran Ops)*
Lynn M. Liddle *(Exec VP-Comm & IR)*
John Macksood *(Exec VP-Supply Chain Svcs)*
Asi Sheikh *(Exec VP-Team USA)*
James G. Stansik *(Exec VP-Franchise Relations)*
Patricia A. Wilmot *(Exec VP-PeopleFirst)*
Tim McIntyre *(VP-Corp Comm)*
Julia Oswald *(VP-Strategy & Insights)*
Brandon Solano *(VP-Brand Innovation)*
Jane Roberts *(Dir-HR)*
Jim Zimmer *(Mgr-Natl Mktg)*
Stacie Barrett *(Mgr-Internal Comm)*
Brands & Products:
DOMINO'S AMERICAN LEGENDS
DOMINO'S PIZZA
HEATWAVE
YOU GOT 30 MINUTES
Advertising Agencies:
CP+B
3390 Mary St Ste 300
Coconut Grove, FL 33133
Tel.: (305) 859-2070
Fax: (305) 854-3419

CP+B Boulder
6450 Gunpark Dr
Boulder, CO 80301
Tel.: (303) 628-5100
Fax: (303) 516-0227
Show Us Your Pizza

JWT U.S.A., Inc.
(d/b/a JWT-Team Detroit)
550 Town Ctr Dr
Dearborn, MI 48126
Tel.: (313) 615-3100
Tel.: (313) 615-2000 (Team Detroit)
Fax: (313) 964-3191
Fax: (212) 615-4600

LatinWorks Marketing, Inc.
206 E 9th St Capital Tower Fl 13
Austin, TX 78701
Tel.: (512) 479-6200
Fax: (512) 479-6024
— Karin Clarke *(Asst Acct Exec)*

McCann Erickson Corp. Publicidad S.A.

Key to Media (For complete agency information see *The Advertising Red Books-Agencies* edition):
1. Bus. Publs. 2. Cable T.V. 3. Catalogs & Directories. 4. Co-op Adv. 5. Consumer Mags. 6. D.M. to Bus. Estab.7. D.M. to Consumers 8. Daily Newsp. 9. Exhibits/Trade Shows 10. Foreign 11. Infomercial 12. Internet Adv.13. Multimedia 14. Network Radio 15. Network T.V. 16. Newsp. Distr. Mags. 17. Other 18. Outdoor (Posters, Transit) 19. Point of Purchase20. Premiums, Novelties 21. Product Samples 22. Special Events Mktg. 23. Spot Radio 24. Spot T.V. 25. Weekly Newsp. 26. Yellow Page Adv.

Finlandia 345 y Suecia Edificio
McCann Erickson
Quito, Ecuador
Tel.: (593) 2 396 6800
Fax: (593) 2 246 8403

Mindshare
498 7th Ave
New York, NY 10018
Tel.: (212) 297-7000
Fax: (212) 297-7001
Media Buying

New Media Strategies
1100 Wilson Blvd Ste 1400
Arlington, VA 22209
Tel.: (703) 253-0050
Fax: (703) 253-0065
(Consumer Relationships, Pizza Tracker, Bread Bowl Pasta)

DONATOS PIZZERIA CORPORATION

935 Taylor Station Rd
Columbus, OH 43230-6657
Tel.: (614) 416-7700
Fax: (614) 416-7705
Toll Free: (800) DONATOS
Web Site: www.donatos.com
Sales Range: $150-199.9 Million
Approx. Number Employees: 5,000
Year Founded: 1963
Business Description:
Pizza Restaurant Owner, Operator & Franchisor
S.I.C.: 5812
N.A.I.C.S.: 722211
Media: 23-24
Personnel:
James E. Grote *(Founder & CEO)*
Jane Grote Abell *(Pres & COO)*
Doug Kourie *(CFO)*
Brands & Products:
ALLA CASA
BIG DON
CHICKEN VEGY MEDLEY
CLASSIC TRIO
DONATOS
FOUNDER'S FAVORITE
FRESH VEGY
HAWAIIAN
MARIACHI
MARIACHI BEEF
MARIACHI CHICKEN
SERIOUS CHEESE
SERIOUS MEAT
VEGY
WHAT PIZZA SHOULDBE
THE WORKS
Advertising Agency:
Engauge Communications
375 N Front St Ste 400
Columbus, OH 43215
Tel.: (614) 573-1010
Fax: (614) 573-1011

DORAKU CORP.

1104 Lincoln Rd
Miami Beach, FL 33139-2425
Tel.: (305) 695-8383
Fax: (305) 675-1441
E-mail: dorakusushi@gmail.com
Web Site: www.dorakusushi.com
Approx. Number Employees: 40
Business Description:
Sushi Restaurant & Entertainment
S.I.C.: 5812; 7999
N.A.I.C.S.: 722110; 713990
Media: 11
Personnel:
Kevin Aoki *(Owner)*

DUNKIN' BRANDS GROUP, INC.

(Formerly Dunkin' Brands, Inc.)
(Joint Venture of Carlyle Holding Corporation, Bain Capital, LLC & Thomas H. Lee Partners, L.P.)
130 Royall St
Canton, MA 02021
Mailing Address:
PO Box 317
Randolph, MA 02368-0317
Tel.: (781) 737-3000
Tel.: (781) 737-5200 (Media Rels)
Fax: (781) 737-4000
Fax: (718) 737-4360
E-mail: info@dunkinbrands.com
Web Site: www.dunkinbrands.com
Approx. Rev.: $577,135,000
Approx. Number Employees: 1,075
Year Founded: 1950
Business Description:
Donut, Ice Cream & Sandwich Shop Owner & Franchisor; Owned by Bain Capital Partners, Thomas H. Lee Partners & Carlyle Group
S.I.C.: 5461; 2095; 5812
N.A.I.C.S.: 311811; 311920; 722211
Advertising Expenditures: $65,000,000
Media: 3-8-9-15-18-19-20-23-24-25
Distr.: Direct to Consumer; Natl.
Budget Set: Mar.
Personnel:
Jon L. Luther *(Chm)*
Nigel Travis *(CEO)*
Neil Moses *(CFO)*
Daniel J. Sheehan *(CIO)*
John Costello *(CMO & Chief Inoviation Officer)*
Paul Reynish *(CMO-Dunkin' Brands Intl)*
Stephen J. Caldeira *(Chief Global Comm & Pub Affairs Officer)*
Paul Leech *(Chief Admin Officer)*
Bill Mitchell *(Sr VP & Brand Officer-Baskin-Robbins-US)*
Joe Scafido *(Chief Creative & Innovation Officer)*
Srinivas Kumar *(Pres/COO-Baskin-Robbins-Intl)*
Richard Emmett *(Gen Counsel & Sr VP)*
Steve Bratspies *(Sr VP-Dry Grocery)*
Christine Deputy *(Sr VP-HR)*
Karen Raskopf *(Sr VP-Corp Comm)*
Weldon Spangler *(Reg VP)*
Paul Carbone *(VP-Fin Mgmt)*
Ken Chaisson *(VP-IT, Deployment & Support Svcs)*
Brian O'Mara *(VP-Mktg-Baskin-Robbins)*
Nick Dunham *(Dir-Media)*
Stan Frankenthaler *(Dir-Culinary Dev)*
Jessica Schlueter *(Dir-Field Learning)*
Nick Spencer *(Mgr-Mktg-Dunkin Donuts)*
Brands & Products:
BASKIN-ROBBINS
DUNKIN' DONUTS
TOGO'S
WAKE-UP WRAP
Advertising Agencies:
22squared
1170 Peachtree St NE 15th Fl
Atlanta, GA 30309-7649
Tel.: (404) 347-8700
Fax: (404) 347-8800
Baskin Robbins Agency of Record

Hill Holliday
53 State St
Boston, MA 02109
Tel.: (617) 366-4000
(Digital Media Buying/Planning)

Sprokkit
333 S Grand Ave Ste 1600
Los Angeles, CA 90071
Tel.: (213) 626-2076
Fax: (231) 232-3739

Studiocom
191 Peachtree St NE Ste 4025
Atlanta, GA 30303
Tel.: (404) 541-9555
Digital Marketing (Agency of Record)

DUNKIN' BRANDS, INC.

(Name Changed to Dunkin' Brands Group, Inc.)

DYNAMIC MANAGEMENT COMPANY LLC

313 East Main St
Hendersonville, TN 37075
Tel.: (615) 277-1234
Fax: (615) 277-1220
Web Site: www.dynamicusa.com/
Approx. Number Employees: 6,300
Business Description:
Restaurant Owner & Operator
S.I.C.: 5812
N.A.I.C.S.: 722110
Media: 2-4-7-17-22
Personnel:
Robert Langford *(Chm/CEO-Dynamic Hospitality, LLC)*
Mark Francisco *(Dir-Res & Devel)*
Kori Langford *(Dir-Brand Dev)*
Ivan Peraza *(Dir-IT)*
Brands & Products:
BLACK EYED PEA
DENNY'S

EAT'N PARK HOSPITALITY GROUP

285 E Waterfront Dr
Homestead, PA 15230
Tel.: (412) 461-2000
Fax: (412) 461-6000
E-mail: comments@eatnpark.com
Web Site: www.eatnpark.com
Sales Range: $150-199.9 Million
Approx. Number Employees: 100
Year Founded: 1949
Business Description:
Family Restaurants
S.I.C.: 5812
N.A.I.C.S.: 722110
Advertising Expenditures: $5,000,000
Media: 8-13-17-18-19-20-22-23-24
Distr.: Reg.
Budget Set: Oct.
Personnel:
Jim Broadhurst *(Chm)*
Jeff Broadhurst *(Pres)*
Karen Bolden *(Chief People Officer & Sr VP)*
Mitch Possinger *(Pres-Onsite Brands Div)*
David Wohleber *(Exec VP)*
Brooks Broadhurst *(Sr VP)*
Kevin O. Connell *(Sr VP-Mktg)*
Adam Golomb *(Dir-E Commerce)*
Brands & Products:
AMERICA'S FAVORITE FAMILY RESTAURANT
BIGGER BETTER BURGERS
BREAKFAST SMILE
BREAKFAST'N FRUIT BUFFET
EAT 'N PARK
HOME SMILE COOKIN'
LIGHT 'N DELIGHTFUL
MIDNITE BUFFET
SENIORS ESPECIALLY
SMILEY
SUPERBURGER
Advertising Agencies:
Harmelin Media
525 Righters Ferry Rd
Bala Cynwyd, PA 19004-1315
Tel.: (610) 668-7900
Fax: (610) 668-9548

Think, Inc.
2818 Smallman St
Pittsburgh, PA 15222
Tel.: (412) 281-9228
Fax: (412) 281-9243

EL CHICO RESTAURANTS, INC.

(Sub. of Consolidated Restaurant Operations, Inc.)
12200 N Stemmons Fwy Ste 100
Dallas, TX 75234-5877
Tel.: (972) 238-0011
Fax: (972) 888-8198
Web Site: www.elchico.com
Business Description:
Full-Service Mexican Restaurants Operator & Franchiser
S.I.C.: 4011; 5812
N.A.I.C.S.: 482111; 722110
Advertising Expenditures: $2,000,000
Media: 5-6-8-9-18-19-20-23-24-25-26
Distr.: Reg.
Budget Set: Oct.
Personnel:
John Harkey *(Pres & CEO)*
Bill Watson *(VP-Mktg)*
Brands & Products:
EL CHICO
TOP SHELF

EL POLLO LOCO INC.

(Holding of Trimaran Capital Partners, LLC)
3535 Harbor Blvd Ste 100
Costa Mesa, CA 92626
Tel.: (714) 599-5000
Fax: (949) 399-2084
Toll Free: (877) 375-4968
E-mail: jweeks@elpolloloco.com
Web Site: www.elpolloloco.com
Approx. Number Employees: 3,600
Year Founded: 1975
Business Description:
Mexican Food Restaurant Operator
S.I.C.: 5812
N.A.I.C.S.: 722211
Advertising Expenditures: $1,000,000
Media: 1-5-7-8-9-10-16-19-21-22-24-25

El Pollo Loco Inc. — (Continued)

Distr.: Natl.
Personnel:
Samuel N. Borgese *(Chm)*
Steven J. Sather *(Pres & CEO)*
Gary Campanaro *(CFO & Sr VP-Fin)*
Dennis Farrow *(COO)*
Jeanne Scott *(Sr VP-HR & Training)*
Mark Hardison *(VP-Mktg)*
Julie L. Weeks *(VP-Comm)*
Brands & Products:
EL POLLO LOCO
Advertising Agencies:
Goodness Mfg.
6922 Hollywood Blvd 12th Fl
Los Angeles, CA 90028
Tel.: (310) 845-3035
Fax: (310) 845-3470
Communication
Strategic Marketing

V2 Media Tools Inc.
671 W Broadway
Glendale, CA 91205
Tel.: (818) 545-1581
Tel.: (818) 720-6403
Fax: (818) 545-1580

EL TORITO RESTAURANTS, INC.
(Sub. of Real Mex Restaurants, Inc.)
5660 Katella Ave
Cypress, CA 90630
Tel.: (562) 346-1200
Toll Free: (800) 858-6512
E-mail: webmaster@eltorito.com
Web Site: www.eltorito.com
Approx. Number Employees: 6,000
Business Description:
Restaurant Franchiser
S.I.C.: 5812
N.A.I.C.S.: 722110
Advertising Expenditures: $200,000
Media: 2-6-7-8-9-10-11-14-15-18-21-23-24-25
Distr.: Natl.
Personnel:
Rick Dutkiewicz *(Pres)*

ELMER'S RESTAURANTS, INC.
11802 SE Stark St
Portland, OR 97216-3762
Mailing Address:
PO Box 16938
Portland, OR 97292-0938
Tel.: (503) 252-1485
Fax: (503) 257-7448
Toll Free: (800) 325-5188
E-mail: comments@elmers-restaurants.com
Web Site: www.elmers-restaurants.com
E-Mail For Key Personnel:
President: brucedavis@elmers-restaurants.com
Sales Director: jerryscott@elmers-restaurant.com
Approx. Int. Income: $33,491,570
Approx. Number Employees: 290
Year Founded: 1960
Business Description:
Family Oriented Restaurants Franchiser & Operator
S.I.C.: 5812
N.A.I.C.S.: 722310; 722110
Media: 8-9-13-18-19-22-23-24-25
Personnel:
Bruce N. Davis *(Chm)*
Gerald Scott *(VP-Opers & Gen Mgr)*
Brands & Products:
ELMER'S
MITZEL'S AMERICAN KITCHEN
NORTHWEST FRESH!

ELXSI CORPORATION
3600 Rio Vista Ave Ste A
Orlando, FL 32805-6605
Tel.: (407) 849-1090
Fax: (407) 849-0625
Sales Range: $750-799.9 Million
Approx. Number Employees: 2,119
Year Founded: 1979
Business Description:
Holding Company; Restaurant Owner & Operator
S.I.C.: 6719; 5812
N.A.I.C.S.: 551112; 722110
Advertising Expenditures: $1,110,000
Personnel:
David M. Doolittle *(CFO, Treas, Sec & VP)*
Brands & Products:
ABDOW'S RESTAURANTS
BICKFORD'S RESTAURANTS

FAMIGLIA - DEBARTOLO, LLC
(Holding of DeBartolo Holdings, LLC)
(d/b/a Famous Famiglia Pizzeria)
199 Main St 8th Fl
White Plains, NY 10601
Tel.: (914) 328-4444
Fax: (914) 328-4479
E-mail: info@famousfamiglia.com
Web Site: www.famousfamiglia.com
Approx. Number Employees: 400
Business Description:
Pizza Restaurant Franchise
S.I.C.: 5812
N.A.I.C.S.: 722110
Media: 2-5
Personnel:
Paul Kolaj *(Co-Founder, Pres & CEO)*
John Kolaj *(Co-Founder, COO & Exec VP)*
Giorgio Kolaj *(Co-Founder, Exec VP-Global Bus Dev)*
Tony Kolaj *(Founder & Dir-Quality Control)*
Brands & Products:
FAMOUS FAMIGLIA
NEW YORK'S FAVORITE PIZZA

FAMILY SPORTS CONCEPTS, INC.
(d/b/a Beef 'O' Brady's)
5510 W LaSalle St Ste 200
Tampa, FL 33607
Tel.: (813) 226-2333
Fax: (813) 226-0030
Toll Free: (800) 728-8878
Web Site: www.beefobradys.com
Sales Range: $75-99.9 Million
Approx. Number Employees: 7,000
Year Founded: 1985
Business Description:
Operator of Franchised Chain of Family-Style Eateries
S.I.C.: 5812
N.A.I.C.S.: 722110
Media: 28
Personnel:
Jim Humboldt *(CFO)*
Brands & Products:
BEEF O'BRADY'S
Advertising Agency:
Ad Partners Inc.
9800 4th St N Ste 200
Saint Petersburg, FL 33702
Tel.: (727) 289-8900
Fax: (727) 289-8999

FAMOUS DAVE'S OF AMERICA, INC.
12701 Whitewater Dr Ste 200
Hopkins, MN 55343-4165
Tel.: (952) 294-1300
Fax: (952) 294-1301
E-mail: investorrelations@famousdaves.com
Web Site: www.famousdaves.com
Approx. Rev.: $148,268,000
Approx. Number Employees: 340
Year Founded: 1995
Business Description:
Restaurant Operator
S.I.C.: 5812
N.A.I.C.S.: 722110
Advertising Expenditures: $4,200,000
Media: 3-4-9-13-14-15-16-17-18-22-26
Personnel:
K. Jeffrey Dahlberg *(Chm)*
Christopher O'Donnell *(Pres & CEO)*
Diana Garvis Purcel *(CFO)*
Aric Nissen *(VP-Mktg & R & D)*
Jackie Kane Ottoson *(VP-HR)*
Jim Macchitelli *(Dir-Mktg Innovation)*
Brands & Products:
DEVIL'S SPIT
FAMOUS DAVE'S
GEORGIA MUSTARD
HOT FUDGE KAHLUA BROWNIES
LEGENDARY PIT BAR-B-QUE
RICH & SASSY
SHACK FRIES
SWEET & ZESTY
TEXAS PIT
WILBUR BEANS
Advertising Agencies:
The Aristos Group
750 E Lake St
Wayzata, MN 55391
Tel.: (952) 449-4100
Fax: (952) 449-4119

BBDO Minneapolis
150 S 5th St Ste 3500
Minneapolis, MN 55402-4200
Tel.: (612) 338-8401
Fax: (612) 656-0602

FAZOLI'S MANAGEMENT INC.
(Holding of Sun Capital Partners, Inc.)
(d/b/a Fazoli's Restaurants)
2470 Palumbo Dr
Lexington, KY 40509
Tel.: (859) 268-1668
Fax: (859) 268-2263
E-mail: rodney.lee@fazolis.com
Web Site: www.fazolis.com
Sales Range: $300-349.9 Million
Approx. Number Employees: 1,300
Year Founded: 1988
Business Description:
Operator of Italian Restaurants
S.I.C.: 5812
N.A.I.C.S.: 722110
Advertising Expenditures: $10,936,000
Media: 3-9-15-18-19-20-22-23-24-25-26
Distr.: Direct to Consumer; Reg.
Budget Set: Aug.
Personnel:
Carol Haward *(Pres & CEO)*
Rodney Lee *(CFO)*
Cathy Hull *(CMO)*
Dave Craig *(VP-HR)*
Brands & Products:
FAZOLI'S
Advertising Agencies:
Brokaw Inc.
425 W Lakeside Ave
Cleveland, OH 44113-1029
Tel.: (216) 241-8003
Fax: (216) 241-8033

RPM-Right Place Media
437 Lewis Hargett Cir Ste 130
Lexington, KY 40503
Tel.: (859) 685-3800
Fax: (859) 685-3801
Media Placement

FLORIDA WEST COAST CRUISES, INC.
(d/b/a StarLite Cruises)
25 Causeway Blvd
Clearwater, FL 33767
Tel.: (727) 462-2628
Fax: (727) 446-4814
Toll Free: (800) 444-4814
Web Site: www.starlitecruises.com
Approx. Number Employees: 100
Business Description:
Dinner Cruises
S.I.C.: 5812
N.A.I.C.S.: 722110
Media: 6-19
Personnel:
Phil M. Henderson, Jr. *(Pres)*

FOX & HOUND RESTAURANT GROUP
(Sub. of Newcastle Partners LP)
1551 N Waterfront Pkwy Ste 310
Wichita, KS 67206-6611
Tel.: (316) 634-0505
Fax: (316) 634-6060
E-mail: investorrelations@fhrg.com
Web Site: www.tentcorp.com
Approx. Number Employees: 10,000
Year Founded: 1997
Business Description:
Owns & Operates Entertainment Restaurants
S.I.C.: 5812
N.A.I.C.S.: 722110
Advertising Expenditures: $1,181,471
Media: 2-4-9-13-16-19-22-23-24-25-26
Personnel:
Jennifer Kurth *(Mgr-HR)*
Brands & Products:
BAILEY'S
BAILEY'S PUB & GRILLE
BAILEY'S SMOKEHOUSE & TAVERN
BAILEY'S SPORTS GRILLE
FOX & HOUND
FOX & HOUND ENGLISH PUB AND GRILLE
FOX & HOUND SMOKEHOUSE AND TAVERN
TOTAL ENTERTAINMENT

FRESH CHOICE RESTAURANTS, LLC
8371 Central Ave Ste A
Newark, CA 94560-3433

Key to Media (For complete agency information see *The Advertising Red Books-Agencies* edition):
1. Bus. Publs. 2. Cable T.V. 3. Catalogs & Directories. 4. Co-op Adv. 5. Consumer Mags. 6. D.M. to Bus. Estab.7. D.M. to Consumers 8. Daily Newsp. 9. Exhibits/Trade Shows 10. Foreign 11. Infomercial 12. Internet Adv.13. Multimedia 14. Network Radio 15. Network T.V. 16. Newsp. Distr. Mags. 17. Other 18. Outdoor (Posters, Transit) 19. Point of Purchase20. Premiums, Novelties 21. Product Samples 22. Special Events Mktg. 23. Spot Radio 24. Spot T.V. 25. Weekly Newsp. 26. Yellow Page Adv.

Tel.: (408) 776-0799
Fax: (408) 776-0788
Toll Free: (800) 859-8693
E-mail: info@freshchoice.com
Web Site: www.freshchoice.com
Sales Range: $75-99.9 Million
Approx. Number Employees: 1,115
Year Founded: 1986
Business Description:
Self-Service, Casual Dining Restaurants Featuring Specialty & Traditional Salads, Hot Pasta, Pizza, Soup, Bakery Items & Dessert
S.I.C.: 5812
N.A.I.C.S.: 722110
Advertising Expenditures: $245,000
Media: 8-9-19-22-23-24-25
Distr.: Natl.
Personnel:
James Howell *(VP-HR)*
Brands & Products:
FRESH CHOICE
FRESH CHOICE EXPRESS
JUST HOW YOU LIKE IT
ZOOPA
Advertising Agency:
Fuel Agency, Inc.
1300 Clay St 6th Fl
Oakland, CA 94612
Tel.: (510) 834-1400
Fax: (510) 482-5593

FRESH ENTERPRISES, LLC
(d/b/a Baja Fresh Mexican Grill)
5900 A Katella Ave Ste 101
Cypress, CA 90630
Tel.: (805) 495-4704
Fax: (562) 391-2401
E-mail: customercare@bajafresh.com
Web Site: www.bajafresh.com
Approx. Number Employees: 50
Year Founded: 1990
Business Description:
Mexican Food Restaurants Operator
S.I.C.: 5812
N.A.I.C.S.: 722211
Media: 3-9-13-15-17-18-24-25
Personnel:
Chuk Rink *(Pres)*
David Kim *(CEO)*
Jerry de Lucia *(Dir-Mktg)*
Brands & Products:
BAJA FRESH MEXICAN GRILL
Advertising Agencies:
EvansHardy & Young, Inc.
829 De La Vina St Ste 100
Santa Barbara, CA 93101-3238
Tel.: (805) 963-5841
Fax: (805) 564-4279

WorkPlace Media
9325 Progress Pkwy
Mentor, OH 44060-1855
Tel.: (440) 639-9100
Fax: (440) 639-9190
Toll Free: (800) 435-7576

FRISCH'S RESTAURANTS, INC.
2800 Gilbert Ave
Cincinnati, OH 45206-1206
Tel.: (513) 961-2660
Fax: (513) 559-5160
Web Site: www.frischs.com
Approx. Sls.: $303,540,552
Approx. Number Employees: 3,800
Year Founded: 1947
Business Description:
Restaurants Operator
S.I.C.: 5812
N.A.I.C.S.: 722110; 722211
Advertising Expenditures: $7,500,000
Media: 3-9-19-20-23-24-25
Distr.: Reg.
Budget Set: Feb.
Personnel:
Daniel W. Geeding *(Chm)*
Craig F. Maier *(Pres & CEO)*
Donald H. Walker *(CFO, Chief Acctg Officer & VP)*
Rinzy J. Nocero *(COO & VP)*
Michael E. Conner *(VP-HR)*
Karen F. Maier *(VP-Mktg)*
Brands & Products:
BIG BOY
BRAWNY LAD
BUDDIE BOY
FIRE & ICE
FRISCH-LY MADE
FRISCH'S
FRISCH'S BIG BOY
GOLDEN CORRAL
PIE BABY
WHAT'S YOUR FAVOURITE THING?
Advertising Agency:
Powers Agency
1 W 4th St 5th Fl
Cincinnati, OH 45202-3623
Tel.: (513) 721-5353
Fax: (513) 721-0086
(Frisch's Big Boy Restaurants)

GALARDI GROUP, INC.
4440 Von Karman Ave Ste 222
Newport Beach, CA 92660-2088
Tel.: (949) 892-2699
Tel.: (949) 851-2639
Fax: (949) 851-2615
Toll Free: (800) 764-9339
E-mail: lboemia@galardigroup.com
Web Site: www.wienerschnitzel.com
Sales Range: $200-249.9 Million
Approx. Number Employees: 48
Year Founded: 1961
Business Description:
Fast Food Restaurants
S.I.C.: 6794
N.A.I.C.S.: 533110
Advertising Expenditures: $5,870,000
Media: 8-16-17-23-24
Distr.: Reg.
Budget Set: Nov.
Personnel:
Dennis Tase *(Pres & COO)*
Tom Amberger *(VP-Mktg)*
Brands & Products:
WIENERSCHNITZEL
Advertising Agencies:
DGWB
217 N Main St Ste 200
Santa Ana, CA 92701
Tel.: (714) 881-2300
Fax: (714) 881-2442
(Quick Service Restaurants)

Morgan Marketing & Public Relations LLC
78 Discovery
Irvine, CA 92618
Tel.: (949) 261-2216
Fax: (949) 261-2272

GARDEN FRESH RESTAURANT CORP.
(Holding of Sun Capital Partners, Inc.)
15822 Bernardo Ctr Dr Ste A
San Diego, CA 92127-2320
Tel.: (858) 675-1600
Fax: (858) 675-1616
Web Site: www.souplantation.com
Approx. Number Employees: 80
Year Founded: 1983
Business Description:
Salad Buffet Restaurant Operator
S.I.C.: 5812
N.A.I.C.S.: 722110
Advertising Expenditures: $6,662,000
Media: 16-24
Personnel:
Michael P. Mack *(CEO)*
Eric Rosenzweig *(CIO)*
Brands & Products:
LOTS TO FEEL GOOD ABOUT!
SOUPLANTATION
SWEET TOMATOES
Advertising Agency:
Chemistry
1660 Union St 4th Fl
San Diego, CA 92101
Tel.: (619) 236-8397
Fax: (619) 236-8497
— Audrey Doherty *(Acct Exec-West Coast)*
— Jennifer Barry *(Acct Exec-Mid West)*
— Carolyn Izzo *(Acct Exec-East Coast)*

GIORDANO'S ENTERPRISES, INC.
308 W Randolph St
Chicago, IL 60606-1710
Tel.: (312) 641-6500
Fax: (312) 641-0016
E-mail: giordano@giordanos.com
Web Site: www.giordanos.com
Sales Range: $75-99.9 Million
Approx. Number Employees: 1,000
Year Founded: 1974
Business Description:
Restaurants
S.I.C.: 5812; 2099
N.A.I.C.S.: 722211; 311991
Media: 6-8-13-23-24
Distr.: Natl.
Personnel:
John Apostolou *(Pres)*
Dan Hull *(Dir-Mktg)*
Brands & Products:
GIORDANO'S

GODFATHER'S PIZZA, INC.
2808 N 108th St
Omaha, NE 68164
Tel.: (402) 391-1452
Fax: (402) 255-2687
Toll Free: (800) 456-8347
E-mail: webmaster@godfathers.com
Web Site: www.godfathers.com
Approx. Number Employees: 2,500
Year Founded: 1973
Business Description:
Operator of Pizza Restaurants
S.I.C.: 5812
N.A.I.C.S.: 722110
Media: 3-8-9-19-23-24-25-26
Distr.: Reg.
Budget Set: May
Personnel:
Ronald B. Gartlan *(Pres & CEO)*
Connie Cajka *(Dir-Sls)*
Jan Sammons *(Dir-Mktg)*
Ginny Allumbaugh *(Mgr-Franchise Mktg)*
Brands & Products:
GODFATHER'S PIZZA

GOLDEN CORRAL CORPORATION
(Sub. of Investors Management Corp.)
5151 Glenwood Ave
Raleigh, NC 27612-3267
Mailing Address:
PO Box 29502
Raleigh, NC 27626-0502
Tel.: (919) 781-9310
Fax: (919) 881-4485
E-mail: support@goldencorral.net
Web Site: www.goldencorral.net
Approx. Number Employees: 200
Year Founded: 1973
Business Description:
Operator of Family Style Restaurant
S.I.C.: 5812; 5046
N.A.I.C.S.: 722110; 423440
Media: 9-10-18-19-23-24-25
Personnel:
Ted M. Fowler *(Pres & CEO)*
Robert M. McDevitt *(Sr VP-Franchising)*
Judy Irwin *(VP-HR & Trng)*
Brands & Products:
BRASS BELL BAKERY
GOLDEN CHOICE BUFFET
GOLDEN CORRAL
MAKING PLEASURABLE DINING AFFORDABLE

GOOD TIMES RESTAURANTS, INC.
601 Corporate Cir
Golden, CO 80401-5622
Tel.: (303) 384-1400
Fax: (303) 273-0177
E-mail: goodtimes@gtrestaurants.com
Web Site:
www.goodtimesburgers.com
Approx. Rev.: $20,863,000
Approx. Number Employees: 64
Year Founded: 1987
Business Description:
Fast Food Restaurants Owner & Operater
S.I.C.: 5812
N.A.I.C.S.: 722211
Advertising Expenditures: $1,156,000
Media: 5-8-13-18-19-23-24
Personnel:
Eric W. Reinhard *(Chm)*
Boyd E. Hoback *(Pres & CEO)*
Susan M. Knutson *(Controller)*
Brands & Products:
GOOD TIMES BURGERS & FROZEN CUSTARD
Advertising Agency:
Shift 1
620 16th St Ste 200
Denver, CO 80202
Tel.: (303) 296-8011
Fax: (303) 296-9037

GRANDY'S
(Sub. of Souper Salad, Inc.)
401 E Corporate Dr

Key to Media (For complete agency information see *The Advertising Red Books-Agencies* edition):
1. Bus. Publs. 2. Cable T.V. 3. Catalogs & Directories. 4. Co-op Adv. 5. Consumer Mags. 6. D.M. to Bus. Estab.7. D.M. to Consumers
8. Daily Newsp. 9. Exhibits/Trade Shows 10. Foreign 11. Infomercial 12. Internet Adv.13. Multimedia 14. Network Radio
15. Network T.V. 16. Newsp. Distr. Mags. 17. Other 18. Outdoor (Posters, Transit) 19. Point of Purchase20. Premiums, Novelties
21. Product Samples 22. Special Events Mktg. 23. Spot Radio 24. Spot T.V. 25. Weekly Newsp. 26. Yellow Page Adv.

Grandy's — (Continued)

Lewisville, TX 75057
Tel.: (972) 434-9225
Fax: (972) 434-9244
Web Site: www.grandys.com
Approx. Number Employees: 20
Year Founded: 1973
Business Description:
Family Dining Restaurant Chain
S.I.C.: 5812
N.A.I.C.S.: 722211; 722110
Advertising Expenditures: $6,000,000
Media: 3-5-8-9-17-18-19-20-22-23-24-25-26
Distr.: Direct to Consumer; Reg.
Budget Set: Nov.
Personnel:
Danny Meisenheimer *(COO)*
Vivien Horton *(Dir-HR)*
Brands & Products:
GRANDY'S

GRANITE CITY FOOD & BREWERY LTD

5402 Parkdale Dr Ste 101
Minneapolis, MN 55416-1609
Tel.: (952) 215-0660
Fax: (952) 525-2021
E-mail: corporate@gcfb.net
Web Site: www.gcfb.net
Approx. Rev.: $89,330,387
Approx. Number Employees: 2,322
Year Founded: 1999
Business Description:
Restaurant & Brewery Owner & Operator
S.I.C.: 5812; 5813
N.A.I.C.S.: 722110; 722410
Advertising Expenditures: $1,025,450
Media: 2-16-18-26
Personnel:
Steven J. Wagenheim *(Founder, Pres & CEO)*
Joel C. Longtin *(Chm)*
Amy Knealing *(Mng Partner)*
James G. Gilbertson *(CFO)*
Darius Gilanfar *(COO)*
Eric LaClair *(Sr VP-Ops)*
Liz Severance *(VP-HR)*
Monica A. Underwood *(VP-Fin)*
Brands & Products:
BROAD AXE STOUT
BROTHER BENEDICT'S BOCK
DUKE OF WELLINGTON
FERMENTUS INTERRUPTUS
FOOD & BREWERY
GC
GRANITE CITY FOOD & BREWERY
NORTHERN LIGHT LAGER
TWO-PULL

GRILL CONCEPTS, INC.

6300 Canoga Ave Ste 600
Woodland Hills, CA 91367
Tel.: (818) 251-7000
Fax: (818) 999-4745
E-mail: info@thegrill.com
Web Site: grillconcepts.com
Approx. Rev.: $87,148,000
Approx. Number Employees: 2,100
Year Founded: 1988
Business Description:
Owner & Manager of Fine & Casual Dining Restaurants
S.I.C.: 5812; 7922
N.A.I.C.S.: 722310; 711110; 722211
Advertising Expenditures: $859,000
Media: 4-5-8-9-13-19-22-25
Personnel:
Michael Weinstock *(Chm & Exec VP)*
Robert Spivak *(Pres & CEO)*
John Bayley *(CFO)*
Louie Feinstein *(Sr VP-Ops)*
John Sola *(Sr VP-Culinary)*
Michelle Feinstein *(VP-Legal Affairs)*
Chris Gehrke *(VP-HR)*
Terri Henry *(VP-Mktg)*
Thomas Kachani *(VP-Pur & Distr)*
Bart McPhail *(Reg Dir)*
Jim Snodgrass *(Reg Dir)*
Steve Grant *(Dir-Area)*
Brands & Products:
DAILY GRILL
GRILL ON THE ALLEY
Advertising Agency:
Joan Luther & Associates
PO Box 17538
Beverly Hills, CA 90209
Tel.: (310) 273-4936
(Public Relations)

GRISANTI, INC.

Ste 304 333 E Main St
Louisville, KY 40202-1281
Tel.: (502) 429-0341
Fax: (502) 426-1236
Approx. Number Employees: 300
Year Founded: 1980
Business Description:
Italian Restaurant Chain
S.I.C.: 5812
N.A.I.C.S.: 722110
Media: 9-17-18-23-24-26
Distr.: Direct to Consumer; Reg.
Personnel:
Michael J. Grisanti *(Owner)*
Brands & Products:
GRISANTI'S

GUCKENHEIMER ENTERPRISES, INC.

3 Lagoon Dr Ste 325
Redwood City, CA 94065-5167
Tel.: (650) 592-3800
Fax: (650) 592-1670
Web Site: www.guckenheimer.com
Sales Range: $200-249.9 Million
Approx. Number Employees: 2,700
Year Founded: 1963
Business Description:
Holding Company; Corporate Food Service Contractors
S.I.C.: 6719; 5812
N.A.I.C.S.: 551112; 722310
Advertising Expenditures: $1,000,000
Media: 13-16-17-22-26
Personnel:
Jeanie S. Ritchie *(Founder, Chm & CEO)*
Frank Lapetina *(Pres & COO)*
Joe Alouf *(CFO & Exec VP)*
Jack Silk *(Sr VP)*

H. SALT OF SOUTHERN CALIFORNIA, INC.

2540 Corporate Pl Ste B102
Monterey Park, CA 91754
Tel.: (323) 264-8766
Fax: (323) 264-7262
Web Site: www.hsalt.com
Approx. Number Employees: 3
Year Founded: 1965
Business Description:
Fast Food Restaurant Owner & Franchisor
S.I.C.: 5812
N.A.I.C.S.: 722211
Advertising Expenditures: $500,000
Media: 5-9-16-25
Distr.: Reg.
Personnel:
Tom Chang *(Pres)*
Brands & Products:
H. SALT
H. SALT ESQ.

HARD ROCK CAFE FOUNDATION, INC.

(Sub. of Seminole Hard Rock Entertainment, Inc.)
6100 Old Park Ln
Orlando, FL 32835
Tel.: (407) 445-7625
Fax: (407) 445-9709
E-mail: customer_care@hardrock.com
Web Site: www.hardrock.com
Sales Range: $500-549.9 Million
Approx. Number Employees: 160
Year Founded: 1971
Business Description:
Theme Restaurant & Hotel Operator
S.I.C.: 5812; 5813; 7011; 7999
N.A.I.C.S.: 722110; 713210; 721120; 722410
Personnel:
Hamish A. Dodds *(Pres & CEO)*
John Galloway *(CMO & VP)*
Jay Wolszczak *(Gen Counsel & VP-Bus Affairs)*
Michael Shindler *(Exec VP-Hotel & Casinos)*
Kim Creighton *(VP-HR)*
Thomas Gispanski *(VP-Fin)*
Vickie Kunkle *(VP-Mdse)*
Brands & Products:
HARD ROCK CAFE
Advertising Agencies:
Coyne Public Relations
14 Walsh Dr 2nd Fl
Parsippany, NJ 07054
Tel.: (973) 316-1665
Fax: (973) 316-6568
— Kristen Hauser *(Acct Exec)*

Dan Klores Communications
(d/b/a dkc)
386 Park Ave S 10th Fl
New York, NY 10016
Tel.: (212) 685-4300
Fax: (212) 685-9024

HARDEES FOOD SYSTEMS, INC.

(Sub. of CKE Restaurants Inc.)
100 N Broadway Ste 1200
Saint Louis, MO 63102
Tel.: (314) 259-6200
Fax: (314) 259-6200
Toll Free: (800) 711-4274
Web Site: www.hardees.com
Sales Range: $1-4.9 Billion
Approx. Number Employees: 120
Year Founded: 1961
Business Description:
Fast Food Restaurant Chain
S.I.C.: 5812
N.A.I.C.S.: 722211
Advertising Expenditures: $60,000,000
Media: 3-6-8-18-22-23-24
Distr.: Intl.; Natl.
Budget Set: Oct.
Personnel:
Andrew F. Puzder *(Pres & CEO)*
Bradford R. Haley *(Exec VP-Mktg)*
Steve Lemley *(VP-Mktg)*
Brands & Products:
CINNAMON N' RAISIN
CRISPY CURLS
FRISCO BREAKFAST
FRISCO BURGER
HASH ROUNDS
HOT HAM N CHEESE
THICKBURGER
Advertising Agencies:
Action PR
49-51 Ypsilantou Str
11521
Athens, Greece
Tel.: (30) 210 724 0160
Fax: (30) 210 722 3417

ADWizz Inc.
2620 Carmichael Way
Turlock, CA 95382
Tel.: (209) 656-1323
Fax: (209) 633-2277
Recruitment

David & Goliath
909 N Sepulveda Blvd Ste 700
El Segundo, CA 90245
Tel.: (310) 445-5200
Fax: (310) 445-5201
— Phil Covitz *(Dir-Art & Assoc Dir-Creative)*

Mendelsohn Zien Advertising LLC
11111 Santa Monica Blvd 21st Fl
Los Angeles, CA 90025-3356
Tel.: (310) 444-1990
Fax: (310) 444-9888

Spacedog
11111 Santa Monica Blvd Ste 2110
Los Angeles, CA 90025
Tel.: (310) 274-7650
Fax: (310) 444-9384

Sprokkit
333 S Grand Ave Ste 1600
Los Angeles, CA 90071
Tel.: (213) 626-2076
Fax: (231) 232-3739

Weber Shandwick-Saint Louis
555 Washington Ave
Saint Louis, MO 63101
Tel.: (314) 436-6565
Fax: (314) 622-6212
Toll Free: (800) 551-5971

HMS STEAKHOUSE OF TAMPA INC.

(d/b/a Sam Seltzer Steakhouse)
4744 N Dale Mabry Hwy
Tampa, FL 33614
Tel.: (813) 873-7267
Fax: (813) 879-4744
E-mail: info@samseltzers.com
Web Site: www.samseltzers.com
Approx. Sls.: $17,000,000
Approx. Number Employees: 40
Business Description:
Steak & Barbecue Restaurants
S.I.C.: 5812; 5813
N.A.I.C.S.: 722110; 722410
Media: 8-16-24-25

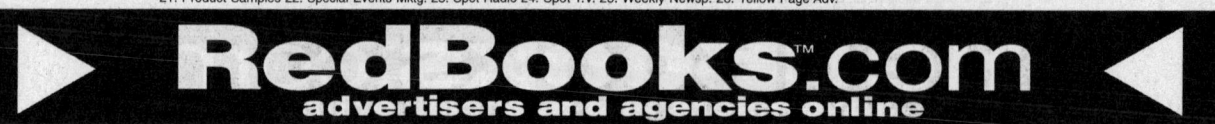

Key to Media (For complete agency information see *The Advertising Red Books-Agencies* edition):
1. Bus. Publs. 2. Cable T.V. 3. Catalogs & Directories. 4. Co-op Adv. 5. Consumer Mags. 6. D.M. to Bus. Estab.7. D.M. to Consumers
8. Daily Newsp. 9. Exhibits/Trade Shows 10. Foreign 11. Infomercial 12. Internet Adv.13. Multimedia 14. Network Radio
15. Network T.V. 16. Newsp. Distr. Mags. 17. Other 18. Outdoor (Posters, Transit) 19. Point of Purchase20. Premiums, Novelties
21. Product Samples 22. Special Events Mktg. 23. Spot Radio 24. Spot T.V. 25. Weekly Newsp. 26. Yellow Page Adv.

HONEY DEW ASSOCIATES, INC.
(d/b/a Honey Dew Donuts)
2 Taunton St
Plainville, MA 02762
Tel.: (508) 699-3900
Fax: (508) 699-3949
Toll Free: (800) 946-6393
Web Site: www.honeydewdonuts.com
Approx. Number Employees: 20
Year Founded: 1973
Business Description:
Doughnut Shops Operator & Franchiser
S.I.C.: 5812
N.A.I.C.S.: 722211
Advertising Expenditures: $500,000
Personnel:
Richard J. Bowen *(Founder & Pres)*
Brands & Products:
ENJOY THE LOCAL FLAVOR
HONEY DEW
HONEY DEW DONUTS
Advertising Agency:
PriMedia Inc.
1775 Bald Hill Rd
Warwick, RI 02886-4210
Tel.: (401) 826-3600
Fax: (401) 826-3644
Toll Free: (800) 397-5804

HOOTERS OF AMERICA INC.
1815 The Exchange SE
Atlanta, GA 30339-2027
Tel.: (770) 951-2040
Fax: (770) 618-7032
Web Site: www.hooters.com
Approx. Number Employees: 100
Year Founded: 1983
Business Description:
Restaurant Owner & Franchiser
S.I.C.: 5812; 6794
N.A.I.C.S.: 722110; 533110
Advertising Expenditures: $4,000,000
Media: 8-13-14-15-16-18-20-22-23-24
Personnel:
Coby Brooks *(Pres & CEO)*
Joe Hummel *(Exec VP-Ops & Pur)*
John Webber *(Exec VP-Franchising Ops)*
Mike McNeil *(VP-Mktg)*
Noela Cartagena *(Dir-Mktg)*
Alexis Aleshire *(Mgr-PR)*
Advertising Agency:
MP Media & Promotions Inc.
10608 Flickinger Lane Ste 101
Knoxville, TN 37922
Tel.: (865) 966-6767
Fax: (865) 966-6883

HOSS'S STEAK & SEA HOUSE, INC.
170 Patchway Rd
Duncansville, PA 16635
Tel.: (814) 695-7600
Fax: (814) 695-3865
Toll Free: (800) 992-4677
E-mail: comments@hosscorp.com
Web Site: www.hosss.com
Sales Range: $75-99.9 Million
Approx. Number Employees: 3,000
Year Founded: 1983
Business Description:
Provider of Dining Services
S.I.C.: 5812; 5146
N.A.I.C.S.: 722110; 424460
Advertising Expenditures: $2,000,000
Media: 4-13-22
Personnel:
Willard E. Campbell *(Chm & CEO)*
John Brown *(Pres)*
Carl Raup *(CFO)*
Billy Jo Walls *(Dir-Mktg)*
Brands & Products:
HOSS'S
WHERE YOUR FAMILY WANTS TO EAT!

HOULIHAN'S RESTAURANTS, INC.
8700 State Line Rd Ste 100
Leawood, KS 66206
Tel.: (913) 901-2500
Fax: (913) 901-2666
E-mail: comments@houlihans.com
Web Site: www.houlihans.com
Sales Range: $250-299.9 Million
Approx. Number Employees: 3,500
Year Founded: 1972
Business Description:
Casual Dining Restaurants
S.I.C.: 5812; 5813
N.A.I.C.S.: 722110; 722410
Advertising Expenditures: $2,000,000
Media: 1-2-4-5-6-7-8-9-10-14-16-17-19-21-22-23-25-26
Distr.: Natl.
Budget Set: Jan.
Personnel:
Robert Hartnett *(CEO)*
Robert Ellis *(CFO & Chief Dev Officer)*
Jennifer Gulvik *(VP-Mktg)*
Brands & Products:
BRAXTON
BRISTOL BAR & GRILL
CHEQUERS
DARRYL'S
DEVON
HOULIHAN'S
J. GILBERTS WOOD-FIRED STEAKS

IL FORNAIO (AMERICA) CORPORATION
(Sub. of Bruckmann, Rosser, Sherrill & Co., LLC)
770 Tamalpais Dr Ste 400
Corte Madera, CA 94925
Tel.: (415) 945-0500
Fax: (415) 924-0906
E-mail: info@ilfornaio.com
Web Site: www.ilfornaio.com
Approx. Number Employees: 3,000
Year Founded: 1959
Business Description:
Full-Service Italian Restaurants, Bakeries & Retail Markets Owner & Operator
S.I.C.: 5812
N.A.I.C.S.: 722110
Advertising Expenditures: $1,000,000
Media: 2-4-13-18
Personnel:
Michael J. Hislop *(Chm & CEO)*
Michael Beatrice *(Pres & COO)*
Mike Hislob *(CEO)*
Michael Mindel *(Sr VP-Mktg)*
Demetri Gill *(Controller & VP-Fin)*
Mim McNulty *(VP-HR)*
Brands & Products:
CANALETTO
IL FORNAIO
RISOTTERIA
Advertising Agency:
Sprokkit
333 S Grand Ave Ste 1600
Los Angeles, CA 90071
Tel.: (213) 626-2076
Fax: (231) 232-3739

IN-N-OUT BURGERS, INC.
4199 Campus Dr Ste 900
Irvine, CA 92612
Tel.: (949) 509-6200
Fax: (949) 509-6200
Fax: (949) 854-3675
Toll Free: (800) 786-1000
E-mail: feedback@in-n-out.com
Web Site: www.innout.com
Sales Range: $300-349.9 Million
Approx. Number Employees: 4,000
Year Founded: 1948
Business Description:
Hamburger Chain Restaurants
S.I.C.: 5812
N.A.I.C.S.: 722211
Advertising Expenditures: $5,000,000
Media: 17-18-23
Distr.: Natl.
Personnel:
Lynsi Martinez *(Pres)*
Roger Kotch *(CFO)*
Mark Taylor *(COO)*
Ken Iriart *(Exec VP-HR)*
Carl Arena *(Dir-Dev)*
Michelle Guzman *(Dir-Mktg)*
Katherine Sauls *(Dir-HR)*
Brands & Products:
2X2
3X3
4X4
5X5
ANIMAL
BTV
BURGER TELEVISION
DOUBLE-DOUBLE
ENTRADA-Y-SALIDA
FOUR BY FOUR
IN-N-OUT BURGER FOUNDATION
IN-N-OUT BURGERS
INO
PROTEIN
QUAD-QUAD
QUALITY YOU CAN TASTE. THAT'S WHAT A HAMBURGER'S ALL ABOUT
THREE BY THREE
TRIPLE TRIPLE
TWO BY TWO
Advertising Agencies:
Initiative Los Angeles
5700 Wilshire Blvd Ste 400
Los Angeles, CA 90036-3648
Tel.: (323) 370-8000
Fax: (323) 370-8950

O'Leary and Partners
5000 Birch St Ste 1000
Newport Beach, CA 92660
Tel.: (949) 833-8006
Fax: (949) 833-9155

INTERNATIONAL DAIRY QUEEN, INC.
(Holding of Berkshire Hathaway Inc.)
7505 Metro Blvd
Minneapolis, MN 55439-0286
Tel.: (952) 830-0200
Fax: (952) 830-0498
Web Site: www.dairyqueen.com
Sales Range: $1-4.9 Billion
Approx. Number Employees: 2,000
Year Founded: 1962
Business Description:
Softserve Treats, Hot Foods, Manufactured Novelties, Premium Hard Ice Cream/Frozen Cakes & Logs
S.I.C.: 5145
N.A.I.C.S.: 424450
Import Export
Advertising Expenditures: $45,000,000
Media: 3-8-9-10-13-18-19-20-23-24-25-26
Distr.: Intl.; Natl.
Budget Set: July
Personnel:
John Gainor *(Pres & CEO)*
Chuck Chapman *(COO)*
Troy Bader *(Chief Dev & Legal Officer)*
Michael Keller *(Chief Brand Officer)*
Russ Grundhauser *(VP-Fin Svcs)*
Dean Peters *(Dir-Comm)*
Brands & Products:
BARBECUE RANCH
BIG SCOOP
BLIZZARD FLAVOR TREAT
BUSTER BAR
THE CONE WITH THE CURL ON TOP
DAIRY QUEEN
DILLY BAR
DILLYWICH
DQ
DQ CHIPPER SANDWICH
DQ HOMESTYLE ULTIMATE BURGER
DQWICH
FULL MEAL DEAL
HOMESTYLE
HOMESTYLE DOUBLE BURGER
IRON GRILLED
MR. MISTY
QUEEN'S CHOICE
WAFFLE BOWL
Advertising Agencies:
Alliance Agency
200 5th Ave 4th Fl
New York, NY 10010
Tel.: (212) 546-1800
Fax: (212) 546-5549

Fishbowl Marketing
44 Canal Ctr Plz Ste 500
Alexandria, VA 22314
Tel.: (703) 836-3421
Fax: (703) 836-3422
Toll Free: (800) 836-2818

Henry Gill Communications
(d/b/a Henry Gill Advertising)
900 S Broadway Ste 300
Denver, CO 80209
Tel.: (303) 296-4100
Fax: (303) 296-3410

INTERNATIONAL HOUSE OF PANCAKES, INC.
(Sub. of DineEquity, Inc.)
450 N Brand Blvd 7th Fl
Glendale, CA 91203-2347
Mailing Address:
PO Box 29018
Glendale, CA 91209-9018
Tel.: (818) 240-6055
Fax: (818) 637-4730
Web Site: www.ihop.com

Key to Media (For complete agency information see *The Advertising Red Books-Agencies* edition):
1. Bus. Publs. 2. Cable T.V. 3. Catalogs & Directories. 4. Co-op Adv. 5. Consumer Mags. 6. D.M. to Bus. Estab.7. D.M. to Consumers
8. Daily Newsp. 9. Exhibits/Trade Shows 10. Foreign 11. Infomercial 12. Internet Adv.13. Multimedia 14. Network Radio
15. Network T.V. 16. Newsp. Distr. Mags. 17. Other 18. Outdoor (Posters, Transit) 19. Point of Purchase20. Premiums, Novelties
21. Product Samples 22. Special Events Mktg. 23. Spot Radio 24. Spot T.V. 25. Weekly Newsp. 26. Yellow Page Adv.

International House of Pancakes, Inc. — (Continued)

E-Mail For Key Personnel:
Public Relations: plenow@ihopcorp.com
Sales Range: $50-74.9 Million
Approx. Number Employees: 300
Year Founded: 1958
Business Description:
Restaurants Owners & Lessors
S.I.C.: 5812; 6794
N.A.I.C.S.: 722110; 533110
Media: 5-7-8-9-15-19-22-23-24-25-26
Distr.: Intl.; Natl.
Budget Set: Dec.
Personnel:
Jean M. Birch *(Pres)*
Carolyn O'Keefe *(CMO)*
Natalia Franco *(Sr VP-Mktg)*
John Jakubek *(Sr VP-HR)*
Michael Mendelsohn *(VP-Fin)*
Patrick Lenow *(Exec Dir-Corp Commun)*
Jennifer Pendergrass *(Mgr-Comm)*
Advertising Agency:
McCann Erickson/Los Angeles
5700 Wilshire Blvd Ste 225
Los Angeles, CA 90036
Tel.: (323) 900-7100
Fax: (323) 900-7111
Creative
Restaurants

J. ALEXANDER'S CORPORATION

3401 W End Ave Ste 260
Nashville, TN 37203
Tel.: (615) 269-1900
Fax: (615) 269-1999
Web Site: www.jalexanders.com
Approx. Sls.: $149,018,000
Approx. Number Employees: 2,750
Year Founded: 1971
Business Description:
Restaurant Operator
S.I.C.: 5812
N.A.I.C.S.: 722310; 722110
Advertising Expenditures: $79,000
Media: 13
Budget Set: Jan.
Personnel:
Lonnie J. Stout, II *(Chm, Pres & CEO)*
R. Gregory Lewis *(CFO & VP)*
Christopher P Conlon *(Reg Dir)*
Joseph D Davi *(Reg Dir)*
Fred A Anderson *(Dir-Acctg)*
Ralph G Carnevale *(Dir-Ops)*
James A Filaroski *(Dir-Product Dev)*
Jason S Parks *(Dir-Info Sys)*
Robert C Raleigh *(Dir-Construction)*
Christine Miles *(Mgr-Mktg)*
Janice Jackson *(Mgr-Investor Rels)*
Brands & Products:
J. ALEXANDER'S

JACK IN THE BOX INC.

9330 Balboa Ave
San Diego, CA 92123-1516
Tel.: (858) 571-2121
Fax: (858) 571-2101
Toll Free: (800) 955-5225
E-mail: franchise.sales@jackinthebox.com
Web Site: www.jackinthebox.com
Approx. Rev.: $2,297,531,000
Approx. Number Employees: 29,300
Year Founded: 1951
Business Description:
Fast Food Restaurant Owner, Operator & Franchisor; Convenience Store Operator
S.I.C.: 5812; 5411
N.A.I.C.S.: 722211; 445120
Advertising Expenditures: $89,800,000
Media: 3-5-8-9-15-18-19-20-22-23-24
Distr.: Reg.
Personnel:
Linda A. Lang *(Chm, Pres & CEO)*
Jerry P. Rebel *(CFO & Exec VP)*
Lenny A. Comma *(COO & Exec VP)*
Michael E. Verdesca *(CIO, VP & Div VP-Sys Dev)*
Terri F. Graham *(CMO & Sr VP-Mktg)*
Mark H. Blankenship *(Chief Admin Officer & Sr VP)*
Charles E. Watson *(Chief Dev Officer & Sr VP)*
Phillip H. Rudolph *(Gen Counsel, Corp Sec & Exec VP)*
Carol DiRaimo *(VP-IR & Corp Comm)*
Patti Foley *(Dir-Mktg Comm & Mdsg)*
Teka O'Rourke *(Dir-Strategic Mktg)*
Brands & Products:
BREAKFAST JACK
CARNIVORES & DESIGN
CLOWNHEAD DESIGN
EXTREME SAUSAGE
JACK
JACK CASH
JACK IN THE BOX
JACK JR.
JACK'S BACK
JACK'S GEAR
JACK'S KID'S MEAL
JACK'S SPICY CHICKEN
JACK'S WORLD
JUMBO JACK
LATE NIGHT & DESIGN
MEATY CHEESY BOYS
MONSTER TACO
OUR BEST BURGERS EVER
PANNIDO
PITA SNACKS
QDOBA MEXICAN GRILL
QUICK STUFF
SOURDOUGH JACK
WE DON'T MAKE IT 'TIL YOU ORDER IT.
Advertising Agencies:
Apollo Interactive, Inc.
8556 Hayden Pl
Culver City, CA 90232
Tel.: (310) 836-9777
Fax: (310) 836-6261
Toll Free: (800) 599-7499

Secret Weapon Marketing
1658 10th St
Santa Monica, CA 90404
Tel.: (310) 656-5999
Fax: (310) 656-6999
(Television Commercials)

JACKIES DINER

5758 S Tamiami Trl
Sarasota, FL 34231
Tel.: (941) 926-0909
Fax: (941) 926-0908
E-mail: jackiesdiner@comcast.net
Web Site: www.jackiesdiner.com
Business Description:
Restaurant
S.I.C.: 5812
N.A.I.C.S.: 722110
Media: 8-16
Personnel:
John Herlihy *(Owner)*

JACMAR COMPANIES, INC.

2200 W Vly Blvd
Alhambra, CA 91803-1928
Tel.: (626) 576-0737
Fax: (626) 576-2114
Toll Free: (800) 540-0737
Web Site: www.jacmar.com
Sales Range: $10-24.9 Million
Approx. Number Employees: 900
Year Founded: 1973
Business Description:
Franchiser of Restaurants
S.I.C.: 5141; 5147; 5812
N.A.I.C.S.: 424410; 424470; 722110; 722211
Advertising Expenditures: $250,000
Media: 2-3-4-5-7-10-19-23
Distr.: Intl.; Natl.
Budget Set: Oct.
Personnel:
William H. Tilley *(Chm)*
Jim A. Dal Pozzo *(Pres)*
David Reid *(CFO)*
Randy Hill *(Pres-Restaurant Div)*
Frank Visvikis *(Pres-Jacmar Food Svc Distr)*
Robert R. Hill *(Exec VP)*
Cindy Staats *(Dir-Mktg)*
Brands & Products:
JACMAR

JERRY'S FAMOUS DELI, INC.

12711 Ventura Blvd Ste 400
Studio City, CA 91604
Tel.: (818) 766-8311
Fax: (818) 766-8315
Web Site: www.jerrysfamousdeli.com
Approx. Number Employees: 1,200
Year Founded: 1978
Business Description:
Owner & Operator of New York Deli-Style Restaurants
S.I.C.: 5812
N.A.I.C.S.: 722110
Advertising Expenditures: $4,000,000
Media: 2-4-13-14-15-16-26
Personnel:
Isaac Starkman *(Chm, CEO & Sec)*
Guy Starkman *(Pres)*
Christina Sterling *(CFO)*
Ami Saffron *(VP & Dir-Dev)*
Connie Mendes *(Dir-HR)*
Brands & Products:
JERRY'S
JERRY'S FAMOUS DELI
RASCAL HOUSE
SOLLEYS

THE JOHNNY ROCKETS GROUP, INC.

(Holding of Red Zone LLC)
25550 Commercentre Dr Ste 200
Lake Forest, CA 92630-8855
Tel.: (949) 643-6100
Fax: (949) 643-6200
Web Site: www.johnnyrockets.com
Sales Range: $100-124.9 Million
Year Founded: 1986
Business Description:
Diner Style Hamburger Restaurant Chain Operator & Franchisor
S.I.C.: 5812; 6794
N.A.I.C.S.: 722110; 533110
Media: 6-7-8-10-13-18-22-24
Personnel:
Christopher J. Ainley *(Chm)*
John Christopher Fuller *(CEO)*
Tim Hackbardt *(Sr VP-Mktg)*
Cozette Phifer Koerber *(VP-Brand Mktg & Corp Comm)*
Chad Bailey *(Dir-Brand Mktg)*
Cozette Phifer *(Dir-Comm)*
Brands & Products:
JOHNNY ROCKETS
Advertising Agency:
Northten Inc.
21088 Bake Pkwy Ste 100
Lake Forest, CA 92630
Tel.: (949) 837-8272

JRN, INC.

209 W 7th St
Columbia, TN 38401-3233
Tel.: (931) 381-3000
Fax: (931) 490-4801
Sales Range: $1-4.9 Billion
Approx. Number Employees: 5,000
Year Founded: 1970
Business Description:
Restaurants & Motels Owner & Operator
S.I.C.: 5812
N.A.I.C.S.: 722211
Media: 8-9-18-24-25
Distr.: Natl.
Personnel:
John R. Neal *(Chm & Pres)*
Dick Moore *(CFO)*
Wally Herbert *(VP-Mktg)*
Debbie Follis *(Supvr-Accts)*

KER, INC.

7491 Ulmerton Rd
Largo, FL 33771
Tel.: (727) 535-2939
Fax: (727) 535-2827
E-mail: info@winghouse.com
Web Site: www.winghouse.com
Sales Range: $25-49.9 Million
Approx. Number Employees: 1,300
Business Description:
Restaurants
S.I.C.: 5812
N.A.I.C.S.: 722110
Media: 3-18-20-22
Personnel:
Crawford Ker *(Founder, Owner & Pres)*
Brands & Products:
KER'S WINGHOUSE

KETTLE RESTAURANTS, INC.

350 Oaks Trl Ste 142
Garland, TX 75043
Tel.: (972) 771-5982
Fax: (240) 282-7609
E-mail: comments@kettle.com
Web Site: www.kettle.com
Approx. Number Employees: 8
Year Founded: 1968
Business Description:
Restaurant Franchisor
S.I.C.: 5812
N.A.I.C.S.: 722110
Advertising Expenditures: $200,000
Media: 3-8-9-14-18-19-23-25
Distr.: Natl.
Personnel:
Mark Shackelford *(CEO & CFO)*
Nathan Shackelford *(VP-Mktg)*

Key to Media (For complete agency information see *The Advertising Red Books-Agencies* edition):
1. Bus. Publs. 2. Cable T.V. 3. Catalogs & Directories. 4. Co-op Adv. 5. Consumer Mags. 6. D.M. to Bus. Estab.7. D.M. to Consumers
8. Daily Newsp. 9. Exhibits/Trade Shows 10. Foreign 11. Infomercial 12. Internet Adv.13. Multimedia 14. Network Radio
15. Network T.V. 16. Newsp. Distr. Mags. 17. Other 18. Outdoor (Posters, Transit) 19. Point of Purchase20. Premiums, Novelties
21. Product Samples 22. Special Events Mktg. 23. Spot Radio 24. Spot T.V. 25. Weekly Newsp. 26. Yellow Page Adv.

KFC CORPORATION
(Sub. of YUM! Brands, Inc.)
1441 Gardiner Ln
Louisville, KY 40213
Mailing Address:
PO Box 32070
Louisville, KY 40232-2070
Tel.: (502) 874-1000
Fax: (502) 874-8291
Web Site: www.kfc.com
Sales Range: $1-4.9 Billion
Approx. Number Employees: 88,000
Year Founded: 1952
Business Description:
Kentucky Fried Chicken Restaurant Franchisor
S.I.C.: 5812; 6794
N.A.I.C.S.: 722211; 533110
Advertising Expenditures: $282,000,000
Media: 3-5-8-9-11-13-15-18-19-20-21-23-24-25-26
Distr.: Intl.; Natl.
Budget Set: June
Personnel:
Roger Eaton *(Pres & Chief Concept Officer)*
Laurence Roberts *(COO)*
Doug Hasselo *(Chief Food Innovation Officer)*
Javier Benito *(Exec VP-Mktg & Food Innovation)*
Jonathan Blum *(Sr VP)*
Sandy Chastain-Brough *(Sr Dir-Quality Assurance)*
Deva Bronson *(Mgr-Mktg)*
Mike Morris *(Mgr-Animal Welfare)*
Brands & Products:
APPLE PIE MINIS
BLT SALAD
CAESAR SALAD
CHICKEN CAPITAL USA
COLONEL'S CRISPY STRIPS
EXTRA CRISPY
FRIED WITH PRIDE
HONEY BBQ SANDWICH
HOT & SPICY
KFC SNACKER
LIFE TASTES BETTER WITH KFC
LITTLE BUCKET
ORIGINAL RECIPE
POPCORN CHICKEN
SMOKY CHIPOTLE CRISPY SNACKER
TENDER ROAST SANDWICH
THERE'S FAST FOOD..THEN THERE'S KFC!
TWISTER
WINGS
Advertising Agencies:
Bartle Bogle Hegarty Limited
(Global Headquarters)
60 Kingly Street
London, W1B 5DS, United Kingdom
Tel.: (44) 20 7734 1677
Fax: (44) 20 7437 3666
UK Marketing

Draftfcb
101 E Erie St
Chicago, IL 60611-2812
Tel.: (312) 425-5000
Fax: (312) 425-5010
Toasted Wraps
Smoky Chipotle Crispy

LevLane Advertising/PR/Interactive
100 Penn Sq E
Philadelphia, PA 19107
Tel.: (215) 825-9600
Fax: (215) 809-1900

McCann Erickson (Malaysia) Sdn. Bhd.
5-01 & 5-02 Wisma LYL No 12 Jalan 51A/223 Petaling Jaya
46100
Kuala Lumpur, Malaysia
Tel.: (60) 3 7841 2898
Fax: (60) 3 2712 6668

McCann Erickson (Singapore) Private Limited
40A Orchard Road #06-00 the MacDonald House
Singapore, 238838, Singapore
Tel.: (65) 6737 9911
Fax: (65) 6737 1455
— Christopher Yong *(Acct Exec)*

MEC, Global HQ, New York
825 7th Ave
New York, NY 10019-6014
Tel.: (212) 474-0000
Fax: (212) 474-0020
Fax: (212) 474-0003
(Media)

Weber Shandwick
(Sub. of The Interpublic Group of Companies)
919 3rd Ave
New York, NY 10022
Tel.: (212) 445-8000
Fax: (212) 445-8001

Williams/Crawford & Associates
415 N 5th St PO Box 789
Fort Smith, AR 72902
Tel.: (479) 782-5230
Fax: (479) 782-6970

KON TIKI AT TAHITIAN INN
601 S Dale Mabry Hwy
Tampa, FL 33609
Toll Free: (800) 876-1397
E-mail: marketing@kontikitampa.com
Web Site: www.kontikitampa.com
Business Description:
Restaurant & Inn
S.I.C.: 5812
N.A.I.C.S.: 722110
Media: 6-8-9-13-25-29
Personnel:
Chandra Lofton *(Dir-Mktg)*

KONA GRILL INC.
7150 E Camelback Rd Ste 220
Scottsdale, AZ 85251
Tel.: (480) 922-8100
Fax: (480) 991-6811
Toll Free: (866) 328-5662
E-mail: information@konagrill.com
Web Site: www.konagrill.com
Approx. Sls.: $87,589,000
Approx. Number Employees: 1,986
Business Description:
Restaurant Operations
S.I.C.: 7922; 5812
N.A.I.C.S.: 711110; 722110
Advertising Expenditures: $1,063,000
Media: 8-9-23-24-25
Personnel:
Mark S. Robinow *(CFO)*
Larry Ryback *(COO)*
Rachel Phillips-Luther *(VP-Mktg & Brand)*

KRISPY KREME DOUGHNUTS INC.
370 Knollwood St Ste 500
Winston Salem, NC 27103-1880
Mailing Address:
PO Box 83
Winston Salem, NC 27102
Tel.: (336) 725-2981
Fax: (336) 733-3791
Toll Free: (800) 457-4779
E-mail: blittle@krispykreme.com
Web Site: www.krispykreme.com
Approx. Rev.: $361,955,000
Approx. Number Employees: 3,700
Year Founded: 1937
Business Description:
Doughnuts Producer & Sales;
Doughnut Shops Owner & Operator
S.I.C.: 5461
N.A.I.C.S.: 311811; 445291
Advertising Expenditures: $197,321
Media: 3-7-8-9-18-19-20-23-24-25
Personnel:
James H. Morgan *(Chm, Pres & CEO)*
Douglas R. Muir *(CFO, Treas & Exec VP)*
Dwayne Chambers *(CMO & Sr VP)*
Stephen F. Cooper *(Chief Restructuring Officer)*
Sandra K. Michel *(Gen Counsel & Exec VP)*
Cindy Bay *(Sr VP-US Franchises & Company Stores)*
Kenneth J. Hudson *(Sr VP-HR & Organizational Dev)*
M. Bradley Wall *(Sr VP-Supply Chain & Off-Premises Ops)*
Brian K. Little *(Dir-Corp Comm)*
Brands & Products:
HOT KRISPY KREME ORIGINAL GLAZED NOW
KRISPY KREME
KRISPY KREME DOUGHNUT
KRISPY KREME ORIGINAL GLAZED
Advertising Agencies:
Barkley
1740 Main St
Kansas City, MO 64108
Tel.: (816) 842-1500
Media Planning
PR
Social Media

BBDO Guerrero
11th Floor Insular Life Building Ayala Avenue corner
Makati, 1226, Philippines
Tel.: (63) 2 892 701
Fax: (63) 892 7501
(Creative)

David Saint Germain LLC
580 County Rd B2 East
Saint Paul, MN 55117
Tel.: (952) 210-6962
Fax: (651) 244-9583

Intermark Group, Inc.
101 25th St N
Birmingham, AL 35203
Tel.: (205) 803-0000
Fax: (205) 870-3843
Toll Free: (800) 554-0218
Inside Scoop Facebook Application
Interactive Marketing
Social Media

Mullen
101 N Cherry St Ste 600
Winston Salem, NC 27101-4035
Tel.: (336) 765-3630
Fax: (336) 774-9550
Lead Agency

THE KRYSTAL COMPANY
1 Union Sq
Chattanooga, TN 37402
Tel.: (423) 757-1550
Fax: (423) 757-5610
Toll Free: (800) 458-5841
E-mail: info@krystalco.com
Web Site: www.krystal.com
Sales Range: $200-249.9 Million
Approx. Number Employees: 7,616
Year Founded: 1932
Business Description:
Fast Food Restaurant Operator
S.I.C.: 5812
N.A.I.C.S.: 722211
Media: 13-17-18-19-23-24
Personnel:
Andrew G. Cope *(Chm)*
James F. Exum *(Pres & CEO)*
Bob Marshall *(CFO)*
Michael G. Bass *(Sr VP)*
Robert Craigo *(Dir-Learning & Dev)*
Jeffrey R. Krause *(Dir-R&D)*
Brad Wahl *(Dir-Mktg)*
Advertising Agency:
The Johnson Group
436 Market St
Chattanooga, TN 37402-1203
Tel.: (423) 756-2608
Fax: (423) 267-0475

KYOTO PALACE JAPANESE STEAKHOUSE
1875 S Bascom Ave Ste 2500
Campbell, CA 95008
Tel.: (408) 377-6456
Web Site: www.kyotopalace.com
Approx. Rev.: $2,000,000
Approx. Number Employees: 35
Year Founded: 1998
Business Description:
Japanese Restaurant & Bar
S.I.C.: 5812
N.A.I.C.S.: 722110
Media: 9-13-25
Personnel:
Chuck Reynolds *(Pres)*

LA ROSA'S, INC.
2334 Boudinot Ave
Cincinnati, OH 45238
Tel.: (513) 347-5660
Fax: (513) 922-2710
E-mail: contact_us@larosas.com
Web Site: www.larosas.com
Sales Range: $25-49.9 Million
Approx. Number Employees: 1,500
Year Founded: 1954
Business Description:
Pizzeria Chain Franchisor
S.I.C.: 6794; 5812
N.A.I.C.S.: 533110; 722211
Advertising Expenditures: $4,000,000
Media: 3-8-13-17-18-19-20-21-22-23-24-25-26
Distr.: Direct to Consumer
Personnel:
Tillman D. Hughes, Jr. *(Chm)*

La Rosa's, Inc. — (Continued)

Mark La Rosa *(Pres & Chief Culinary Officer)*
Michael La Rosa *(CEO)*
Suzie Pheifer *(Mng Dir)*
Michael Selker *(CFO)*
Kevin Burrill *(COO)*
Pete Buscani *(Exec VP-Mktg)*
Cathy Shondel *(Dir-Mktg)*

Brands & Products:
LAROSA'S

Advertising Agency:
Brunner
11 Stanwix St 5th Fl
Pittsburgh, PA 15222-1312
Tel.: (412) 995-9500
Fax: (412) 995-9501

LA SALSA, INC.

(Sub. of Fresh Enterprises, LLC)
5900 Ketella Ave Ste A101
Cypress, CA 90630
Tel.: (805) 495-4704
Fax: (562) 391-2402
Web Site: www.lasalsa.com
Approx. Sls.: $81,600,000
Approx. Number Employees: 22
Year Founded: 1988

Business Description:
Fast Food Franchise
S.I.C.: 5812
N.A.I.C.S.: 722211
Import Export

Personnel:
Chuck Rink *(Pres)*

Advertising Agency:
EvansHardy & Young, Inc.
829 De La Vina St Ste 100
Santa Barbara, CA 93101-3238
Tel.: (805) 963-5841
Fax: (805) 564-4279

LAMP POST FRANCHISE CORPORATION

3002 Dow Ave Ste 320
Tustin, CA 92780
Tel.: (714) 731-6171
Fax: (714) 731-0951
Toll Free: (800) 731-9675
E-mail: lpfc@aol.com
Web Site: www.lamppostpizza.com
Approx. Number Employees: 500
Year Founded: 1976

Business Description:
Restaurant Franchisor
S.I.C.: 6794
N.A.I.C.S.: 533110
Media: 7-8-9
Distr.: Reg.
Budget Set: July

Personnel:
Tom Barro *(Pres)*

Brands & Products:
BACK STREET BREWERY
LAMPPOST PIZZA

LANDRY'S RESTAURANTS INC.

1510 West Loop S
Houston, TX 77027
Tel.: (713) 850-1010
Tel.: (713) 386-7000 (Exec)
Fax: (713) 386-7070
Toll Free: (800) 552-6379
E-mail: smyoung@ldry.com
Web Site: www.landrysrestaurants.com
Approx. Rev.: $1,123,797,394
Approx. Number Employees: 26,000
Year Founded: 1980

Business Description:
Restaurant Owner & Operator
S.I.C.: 5812
N.A.I.C.S.: 722110
Advertising Expenditures: $12,700,000
Media: 6-9-18-23-24-25
Distr.: Natl.

Personnel:
Tilman J. Fertitta *(Chm, Pres & CEO)*
Richard H. Liem *(CFO & Exec VP)*
Scott Sheinfeld *(Mgr-Brand Mktg)*

Brands & Products:
CHARLEYS CRAB
THE CHART HOUSE
THE CRAB HOUSE
KEMAH BOARDWALK
LANDRY'S
LANDRY'S SEAFOOD HOUSE
RAINFOREST CAFE

Advertising Agency:
Stoner Bunting Advertising
210 W Grant St
Lancaster, PA 17603-3707
Tel.: (717) 291-1491
Fax: (717) 399-8197

LAWRY'S RESTAURANTS, INC.

234 E Colorado Blvd Ste 500
Pasadena, CA 91101
Tel.: (626) 440-5234
Fax: (626) 440-5232
E-mail: info@lawrysonline.com
Web Site: www.lawrysonline.com
Approx. Number Employees: 650
Year Founded: 1938

Business Description:
Restaurant Owner & Franchise Operator
S.I.C.: 5812; 5813
N.A.I.C.S.: 722110; 722410
Media: 3-4-6-7-8-9-22-25-26
Distr.: Natl.
Budget Set: Nov. -Dec.

Personnel:
Richard Frank *(Pres & CEO)*
David E. Stockman *(Sr VP)*
Phil Crowley *(VP-Admin & Fin)*
Angela Kibodeaux *(Gen Mgr)*
Chris Szechenyi *(Gen Mgr)*
Ed Lepere *(Gen Mgr)*
Wayne Wood *(Gen Mgr)*
Rich Cope *(Dir-Mktg)*
Margo Brask *(Mgr-Mktg)*
Nancy Brosseit *(Mgr-Mktg)*
Sharon Fine *(Mgr-Mktg)*
Ellen Fremaux *(Mgr-Mktg)*
Michael Yager *(Mgr-Carvery Dev)*

Brands & Products:
CELEBRATING SPECIAL OCCASIONS FOR GENERATIONS
FIVE CROWNS
LAWRY 'S CRAVERY
LAWRY 'S RESTAURANTS
LAWRY'S THE PRIME RIB
TAM O'SHANTER

Advertising Agency:
JS2 Communications
661 N Harper Ave Ste 208
Los Angeles, CA 90048
Tel.: (323) 866-0880
Fax: (323) 866-0882
Lawry's The Prime Rib

LEE'S FAMOUS RECIPES INC.

171 Brook St SE Ste F
Fort Walton Beach, FL 23548
Tel.: (850) 244-6575
Fax: (850) 244-6131
Web Site: www.leesfamouschicken.net
Approx. Number Employees: 5
Year Founded: 2003

Business Description:
Restaurant Operator
S.I.C.: 5812
N.A.I.C.S.: 722211
Media: 7-8-9-18-20-23-24

Personnel:
Jeff Miller *(Pres)*
Laurie Seering *(VP-Mktg)*

LEGAL SEA FOODS INC.

1 Sea Food Wy
Boston, MA 02210
Tel.: (617) 530-9000
Fax: (617) 530-9021
Web Site: www.legalseafoods.com
Sales Range: $125-149.9 Million
Approx. Number Employees: 150

Business Description:
Seafood Restaurants
S.I.C.: 5812; 5146
N.A.I.C.S.: 722110; 424460
Media: 4-6-17

Personnel:
Roger S. Berkowitz *(Pres & CEO)*
Alan Dempsey *(Sr VP)*
Kate Shehan *(VP-HR)*
Ida Faber *(Dir-Mktg)*

Brands & Products:
IF IT ISN'T FRESH IT ISN'T LEGAL!
LEGAL SEA FOODS

Advertising Agency:
DeVito/Verdi
100 5th Ave 16th Fl
New York, NY 10011
Tel.: (212) 431-4694
Fax: (212) 431-4940
(Creative, Media Buying, New England Clam Chowder)

LETTUCE ENTERTAIN YOU ENTERPRISES, INC.

5419 N Sheridan Rd
Chicago, IL 60640-1964
Tel.: (773) 878-7340
Fax: (773) 878-7667
Web Site: www.leye.com
Approx. Number Employees: 4,500
Year Founded: 1971

Business Description:
Restaurant Owner & Operator
S.I.C.: 5812
N.A.I.C.S.: 722110; 722310
Media: 2-6-7-8-9-13-18-20-22-23-25-26
Distr.: Reg.
Budget Set: Sept.

Personnel:
Richard Melman *(Founder & Chm)*
Gabino Sotelino *(Founder-Mon Ami Gabi & Cafe Ba-Ba-Reeba!)*
Kevin Brown *(Pres & CEO)*
Christopher Meers *(Pres & Mng Partner)*
Howard Katz *(Pres)*
Geoff Alexander *(Mng Partner & VP)*
Charles Haskell *(Founding Partner)*
Fred Joast *(Founding Partner)*
Bob Wattel *(Founding Partner)*
John Buchanan *(Pres-Lettuce Consulting Grp & Sr VP-LEYE)*
Don Carson *(Pres-Don & Charlies)*
Jay Stieber *(Gen Counsel & Exec VP)*
Steve LaHaie *(Sr VP)*
Thomas Muno *(Sr VP-Acctg & Operational Analysis)*
Mark Dorian *(VP-Pur)*
Carrol Symank *(VP-Food Safety & Trng)*
Ann Johnson *(Dir-Artistic & Creative)*

Brands & Products:
AMBRIA
ANTICO POSTO
BEN PAO
BIG BOWL
BIG BOWL CHINESE EXPRESS
BRASSERIE JO
CAFE BA-BA-REEBA!
CHICAGO FLAT SAMMIES
COMMUNITY CANTEEN
DI PESCARA
DON & CHARLIE'S
EIFFEL TOWER
EVEREST
FOODLIFE
FRANKIES 5TH FLOOR PIZZERIA
FRANKIES SCALOPPINE
HUB 51
JOE'S
L. WOODS
L2O
LA GRANDE ORANGE
LETTUCE ENTERTAIN YOU
MAGGIANO'S LITTLE ITALY
MAGIC PAN CREPE STAND
MITY NICE GRILL
MON AMI GABI
NACIONAL 27
OSTERIA VIA STATO
PAPAGUS
PETTERINO'S
PIZZERIA VIA STATO
REEL CLUB
R.J. GRUNTS
SCOOZI!
SHAW'S CRAB HOUSE
STRIPBURGERS AT CAFE BA-BA-REEBA!
TRU
TUCCHETTI
TUCCI BENUCCH
TWIN CITY GRILL
VONG'S THAI KITCHEN
WILDFIRE
WOW BAO

Advertising Agencies:
Bullfrog & Baum
133 W 19th St 7th Fl
New York, NY 10011
Tel.: (212) 255-6717
Fax: (646) 763-8910

Margie Korshak Inc.
875 N Michigan Ave Ste 1535
Chicago, IL 60611
Tel.: (312) 751-2121
Fax: (312) 751-1422

LETTUCE SOUPRISE YOU, INC.

2470 Briarcliff Rd NE Ste 47A
Atlanta, GA 30329-3012
Tel.: (404) 636-8549
Fax: (404) 636-8621
E-mail: chieu_soka@yahoo.com
Approx. Number Employees: 3

Key to Media (For complete agency information see *The Advertising Red Books-Agencies* edition):
1. Bus. Publs. 2. Cable T.V. 3. Catalogs & Directories. 4. Co-op Adv. 5. Consumer Mags. 6. D.M. to Bus. Estab.7. D.M. to Consumers
8. Daily Newsp. 9. Exhibits/Trade Shows 10. Foreign 11. Infomercial 12. Internet Adv.13. Multimedia 14. Network Radio
15. Network T.V. 16. Newsp. Distr. Mags. 17. Other 18. Outdoor (Posters, Transit) 19. Point of Purchase20. Premiums, Novelties
21. Product Samples 22. Special Events Mktg. 23. Spot Radio 24. Spot T.V. 25. Weekly Newsp. 26. Yellow Page Adv.

Business Description:
Restaurant Services
S.I.C.: 5812
N.A.I.C.S.: 722110
Media: 2-4-5-6-7-8-9-10-21-25-26
Distr.: Natl.
Budget Set: Nov.
Personnel:
Juardy Juardy *(Pres)*

LEVY RESTAURANTS, INC.
(Sub. of Compass Group USA, Inc.)
980 N Michigan Ave
Chicago, IL 60611-4518
Tel.: (312) 664-8200
Fax: (312) 280-2739
Web Site: www.levyrestaurants.com
Approx. Number Employees: 170
Year Founded: 1976
Business Description:
Restaurant & Sports Arena Dining Services
S.I.C.: 5812
N.A.I.C.S.: 722110
Media: 6-8-9-10-23-25
Distr.: Reg.
Budget Set: July
Personnel:
Lawrence F. Levy *(Founder & Chm)*
Andrew J. Lansing *(Pres & CEO)*
Robert Seiffert *(CFO & Exec VP)*
Allison Webber *(Chief Innovation Officer)*
Jeffery Wineman *(Exec VP-New Bus Dev)*
Ann Pendleton *(Dir-Mktg)*
Brands & Products:
BISTRO 100
BISTRO 110
BISTRO TOUJOURS
CAFE CHICAGO
CAFE SPAGGIA
CHEFS EXPRESS
DOS HERMANOS
EADIE'S KITCHEN & MARKET
FOUNDERS HALL
FULTON'S CRABHOUSE
PORTOBELLO YACHT CLUB
SPIAGGIA
SPRATT'S KITCHEN & MARKET

LITTLE CAESARS ENTERPRISES, INC.
(Sub. of Ilitch Holdings, Inc.)
2211 Woodward Ave
Detroit, MI 48201
Tel.: (313) 983-6000
Fax: (313) 983-6390
E-mail: webmaster@littlecaesars.com
Web Site: www.littlecaesars.com
Sales Range: $400-449.9 Million
Approx. Number Employees: 9,000
Year Founded: 1959
Business Description:
Carry-Out Pizza Restaurant Operator & Franchiser
S.I.C.: 5812
N.A.I.C.S.: 722211
Advertising Expenditures: $18,000,000
Media: 8-14-15-23-24
Distr.: Natl.
Personnel:
Michael Ilitch *(Founder)*
David Scrivano *(Pres)*
Brands & Products:
BABY PAN!PAN
CAESAR WINGS
CRAZY BREAD
CRAZY SAUCE
LITTLE CAESAR'S
PIZZA BY THE SLICE
Advertising Agency:
Mars Advertising Group
(d/b/a UNIQUE CONCEPTS INTERNATIONAL)
25200 Telegraph Rd
Southfield, MI 48034
Tel.: (248) 936-2200
Fax: (248) 936-2760
Toll Free: (800) 521-9317

LOGAN'S ROADHOUSE, INC.
(Sub. of LRI HOLDINGS, INC.)
3011 Armory Dr Ste 300
Nashville, TN 37204
Tel.: (615) 885-9056
Fax: (615) 885-9057
Toll Free: (800) 815-9056
Web Site: www.logansroadhouse.com
Sales Range: $500-549.9 Million
Approx. Number Employees: 250
Year Founded: 1991
Business Description:
Full Service Casual Dining Restaurant Operator & Franchiser
S.I.C.: 5812
N.A.I.C.S.: 722110
Advertising Expenditures: $3,275,000
Personnel:
Tom Vogel *(Pres & COO)*
Amy L. Bertauski *(CFO)*
Paul Pendleton *(Sr VP-Ops)*
David Cavallin *(VP-Fin)*
Lynn D. Wildman *(VP-Pur)*

LONE STAR STEAKHOUSE & SALOON, INC.
(Holding of Lone Star Funds)
125 N Market St Ste 1300
Wichita, KS 67202
Tel.: (316) 264-8899
Fax: (316) 264-3282
Web Site: www.lonestarsteakhouse.com
Sales Range: $650-699.9 Million
Approx. Number Employees: 19,750
Year Founded: 1989
Business Description:
Owner & Operator of Restaurant Chain Specializing in Steaks, Ribs, Chicken & Fish
S.I.C.: 5812
N.A.I.C.S.: 722110
Advertising Expenditures: $19,782,000
Media: 6-7-18-20-22
Personnel:
Patrick Droesch *(Pres & COO)*
Mark Mednansky *(CEO)*
John D. White *(CFO, Treas & Exec VP)*
Brands & Products:
DEL FRISCO'S DOUBLE EAGLE STEAK HOUSE
FRANKIE'S ITALIAN GRILLE
LONE STAR
SULLIVAN'S STEAKHOUSE
TEXAS LAND & CATTLE COMPANY STEAK HOUSE

LONG JOHN SILVER'S, INC.
(Sub. of YUM! Brands, Inc.)
1441 Gardiner Ln
Louisville, KY 40213
Tel.: (502) 874-3000
Tel.: (502) 874-2101 (Media)
Fax: (502) 874-3050
Web Site: www.ljsilvers.com
Sales Range: $25-49.9 Million
Approx. Number Employees: 150
Year Founded: 1969
Business Description:
Quick-Service Restaurants Operator & Franchiser
S.I.C.: 5812
N.A.I.C.S.: 722211
Advertising Expenditures: $25,000,000
Personnel:
Ben Butler *(Pres)*
John Villanueva *(CMO)*
Anne Byerlein *(Chief People Officer)*
Advertising Agency:
Empower MediaMarketing
(MEDIA THAT WORKS)
1111 Saint Gregory St
Cincinnati, OH 45202
Tel.: (513) 871-9454
Fax: (513) 871-1804

LOUIS PAPPAS RESTAURANT GROUP, LLC
731 Wesley Ave
Tarpon Springs, FL 34689
Tel.: (727) 937-1770
Fax: (727) 937-1788
Web Site: www.louispappas.com
Sales Range: $1-9.9 Million
Approx. Number Employees: 100
Business Description:
Restaurant Owner & Operator
S.I.C.: 5812
N.A.I.C.S.: 722110
Media: 6
Personnel:
Louis L. Pappas *(Owner)*

LUBY'S FUDDRUCKERS RESTAURANTS, LLC
(Sub. of Luby's, Inc.)
13111 NW Freeway Ste 600
Houston, TX 77040
Tel.: (512) 275-0400
Fax: (512) 275-0670
Toll Free: (866) 891-1300
E-mail: feedback@fuddruckers.com
Web Site: www.fuddruckers.com
Approx. Number Employees: 5,100
Year Founded: 1980
Business Description:
Hamburger Restaurant Owner, Operator & Franchisor
S.I.C.: 5812
N.A.I.C.S.: 722110
Advertising Expenditures: $2,975,000
Cable T.V.: $50,000; D.M. to Consumers: $250,000; Daily Newsp.: $75,000; Outdoor (Posters, Transit): $35,000; Point of Purchase: $50,000; Spot T.V.: $2,500,000; Weekly Newsp.: $5,000; Yellow Page Adv.: $10,000
Distr.: Natl.
Personnel:
Peter Large *(CEO)*
Brands & Products:
FUDDRUCKERS

LUBY'S, INC.
13111 Northwest Fwy Ste 600
Houston, TX 77040
Tel.: (713) 329-6800
Fax: (713) 329-6809
Toll Free: (800) 886-4600
E-mail: info@lubys.com
Web Site: www.lubys.com
Approx. Sls.: $244,933,000
Approx. Number Employees: 5,826
Year Founded: 1947
Business Description:
Cafeteria & Restaurant Owner & Operator
S.I.C.: 5812
N.A.I.C.S.: 722110; 722212
Advertising Expenditures: $3,100,000
Media: 3-8-9-18-19-23-24-25-26
Distr.: Reg.
Budget Set: Sept.
Personnel:
Gasper Mir, III *(Chm & Exec Gen Mgr-Strategic Partnerships)*
Judith L. Craven *(Vice Chm)*
Christopher J. Pappas *(Pres & CEO)*
Scott Gray *(CFO & Sr VP)*
Peter Tropoli *(COO)*
Benjamin Coutee *(Sr VP-Ops)*
Thomas Guerrero *(Dir-Creative & Brand Mgr)*
Brands & Products:
LUBY'S
Advertising Agency:
Love Advertising Inc.
770 S Post Oak Ln Ste 101
Houston, TX 77056-1913
Tel.: (713) 552-1055
Fax: (713) 552-9155
Toll Free: (800) 544-5683

LUNDY ENTERPRISES, INC.
14112 Greenwell Springs Rd
Central, LA 70739
Tel.: (225) 262-1015
Fax: (225) 262-0200
E-mail: pizzahutcorp@bellsouth.net
E-Mail For Key Personnel:
President: harold@lundy-pizzahut.com
Public Relations: caryn@lundy-pizzahut.com
Sales Range: $25-49.9 Million
Approx. Number Employees: 1,200
Year Founded: 1992
Business Description:
Fast-Food Restaurant Franchise Owner
S.I.C.: 5812
N.A.I.C.S.: 722211
Advertising Expenditures: $2,300,000
Media: 3-5-8-9-15-16-19-20-22-23-24-26
Distr.: Direct to Consumer
Budget Set: Feb. -Dec.

LYON'S OF CALIFORNIA, INC.
8121 Glen Canyon Ct
Citrus Heights, CA 95610
Tel.: (916) 722-3825
Sales Range: $100-124.9 Million
Approx. Number Employees: 2,700
Year Founded: 1953
Business Description:
Restaurant Owner, Operator & Franchisor
S.I.C.: 5812
N.A.I.C.S.: 722110
Advertising Expenditures: $150,000

Key to Media (For complete agency information see *The Advertising Red Books-Agencies* edition):
1. Bus. Publs. 2. Cable T.V. 3. Catalogs & Directories. 4. Co-op Adv. 5. Consumer Mags. 6. D.M. to Bus. Estab.7. D.M. to Consumers 8. Daily Newsp. 9. Exhibits/Trade Shows 10. Foreign 11. Infomercial 12. Internet Adv.13. Multimedia 14. Network Radio 15. Network T.V. 16. Newsp. Distr. Mags. 17. Other 18. Outdoor (Posters, Transit) 19. Point of Purchase20. Premiums, Novelties 21. Product Samples 22. Special Events Mktg. 23. Spot Radio 24. Spot T.V. 25. Weekly Newsp. 26. Yellow Page Adv.

Lyon's of California, Inc. — (Continued)

Media: 8-9-18-19-20-26
Distr.: Reg.
Budget Set: July
Brands & Products:
LYONS

MAMA FU'S
(Sub. of Raving Brands, Inc.)
1935 Peachtree Rd
Atlanta, GA 30309
Tel.: (404) 367-5443
Fax: (404) 603-8070
E-mail: pr@mamafus.com
Web Site: www.mamafus.com
Approx. Number Employees: 30
Year Founded: 2003
Business Description:
Fast-Food Restaurants
S.I.C.: 5812
N.A.I.C.S.: 722110; 722211
Personnel:
Manny Galvec *(Gen Mgr)*
Advertising Agency:
Trevelino/Keller Communications Group
949 W Marietta St NW Ste X106
Atlanta, GA 30318-5275
Tel.: (404) 214-0722
Fax: (404) 214-0729

MAMMA ILARDO'S CORP.
110 W Rd Ste 201
Towson, MD 21204
Tel.: (410) 296-9104
Fax: (410) 296-9156
E-mail: pizza@mammailardos.com
Web Site: www.mammailardos.com
E-Mail For Key Personnel:
President: harry@mammailardos.com
Marketing Director: rob@mammailardos.com
Year Founded: 1976
Business Description:
Pizzeria Franchisor & Operator
S.I.C.: 5812
N.A.I.C.S.: 722110
Media: 5-18-19-20
Distr.: Natl.
Budget Set: Sept.
Personnel:
Harry Ilardo *(Pres & CEO)*
Robert Hittle *(Dir-Mktg)*
Brands & Products:
MAMMA ILARDO'S

MARCOS PIZZA INC.
5252 Monroe St
Toledo, OH 43623
Tel.: (419) 885-4844
Fax: (419) 885-1125
Toll Free: (800) 2MARCOS
Web Site: www.marcos.com
Approx. Number Employees: 1,000
Business Description:
Operator of Pizza Restaurants
S.I.C.: 5812
N.A.I.C.S.: 722211
Personnel:
Pasquale Giammarco *(Founder)*
Jack Butorac *(Pres & CEO)*
David Black *(Exec VP-Ops)*
Mike Jaynes *(VP-Sls & Product Integrity)*
Peter Wise *(VP-Mktg)*
Brands & Products:
MARCOS PIZZA
PEPPERONI MAGNIFICO
Advertising Agency:
MGH, Inc.
100 Painters Mill Rd Ste 600
Owings Mills, MD 21117-7305
Tel.: (410) 902-5000
Fax: (410) 902-8712

MAX & ERMA'S RESTAURANTS, INC.
(Joint Venture of Fidelity National Financial, Inc. & Newport Global Advisors, L.P.)
739 S Third St
Columbus, OH 43206
Mailing Address:
PO Box 297830
Columbus, OH 43229-7830
Tel.: (614) 431-5800
Fax: (614) 431-4100
E-mail: maxanderma@max-ermas.com
Web Site: www.maxandermas.com
E-Mail For Key Personnel:
President: todd@max-ermas.com
Sales Range: $125-149.9 Million
Year Founded: 1972
Business Description:
Restaurant Operator
S.I.C.: 5812
N.A.I.C.S.: 722110
Advertising Expenditures: $4,310,000
Media: 3-5-7-8-9-13-18-19-20-22-23-24-25-26
Distr.: Reg.
Budget Set: Nov. -Dec.
Personnel:
Jeff Neely *(Pres)*
Vack Tsambis *(VP-HR-IT)*
Jenifer Gulling *(Sr Dir-Trng & Dev)*

MAZZIO'S CORPORATION
4441 S 72nd E Ave
Tulsa, OK 74145-4692
Tel.: (918) 663-8880
Fax: (918) 641-1200
Web Site: www.mazzios.com
Sales Range: $200-249.9 Million
Approx. Number Employees: 4,100
Year Founded: 1961
Business Description:
Pizzeria & Italian Restaurant Owner, Operator & Franchiser
S.I.C.: 6794; 5812
N.A.I.C.S.: 533110; 722211
Media: 1-5-8-9-10-19-20-22-23-24-26
Distr.: Natl.
Budget Set: Jan.
Personnel:
Ken Selby *(Founder & Chm)*
Gregory R. Lippert *(Pres & CEO)*
Brands & Products:
CALZONE RING
DIPPIN' ZONE
MAZZIOS
MAZZIOS ITALIAN EATERY
QUESAPIZZA

MCCOLLA ENTERPRISES LTD.
(d/b/a Street Corner News)
2945 SW Wanamaker Dr
Topeka, KS 66614
Tel.: (785) 272-8529
Fax: (785) 272-2384
Toll Free: (800) 789-6397
E-mail: general@streetcorner.com
Web Site: www.streetcorner.com
Sales Range: $10-24.9 Million
Approx. Number Employees: 8
Year Founded: 1988
Business Description:
Mini-Convenience Store Franchiser
S.I.C.: 5994; 6794
N.A.I.C.S.: 451212; 533110
Advertising Expenditures: $25,000
Media: 2-4-7-9-10-13
Distr.: Natl.
Budget Set: Feb.
Personnel:
Peter La Colla *(CEO)*
Augie Meier *(Dir-Site Location)*
Brands & Products:
STREET CORNER

MCCORMICK & SCHMICK'S SEAFOOD RESTAURANTS, INC.
1414 NW Northrup St Ste 700
Portland, OR 97209
Tel.: (503) 226-3440
Fax: (503) 228-5074
E-mail: PreferredGuest@msmg.com
Web Site: www.mccormickandschmicks.com
Approx. Rev.: $351,056,000
Approx. Number Employees: 6,582
Year Founded: 1979
Business Description:
Seafood Restaurant Chain
S.I.C.: 5812
N.A.I.C.S.: 722110
Advertising Expenditures: $3,200,000
Media: 2-6-17-22
Personnel:
Douglas L. Schmick *(Co-Founder & Chm)*
William T. Freeman *(CEO)*
Michelle Lantow *(CFO)*
Michael B. Liedberg *(Exec VP-Ops)*
Martin P. Gardner *(VP-Fin)*
William H. P. King *(VP-Trng & Culinary Dev)*
Larry Summerton *(Exec Dir)*
Brands & Products:
MCCORMICK & SCHMICK'S
MCCORMICK & SCHMICK'S SEAFOOD RESTAURANT
Advertising Agencies:
CMD
1631 NW Thurman St
Portland, OR 97209-2558
Tel.: (503) 223-6794
Fax: (503) 223-2430

Tamara Wilson Public Relations
1809 7th Ave Ste 1403
Seattle, WA 98101
Tel.: (206) 838-8977
Fax: (206) 838-8980

MCDONALD'S CORPORATION
1 McDonald's Plaza
Oak Brook, IL 60523
Tel.: (630) 623-3000
Fax: (630) 623-5004
Web Site: www.mcdonalds.com
Approx. Rev.: $24,074,600,000
Approx. Number Employees: 400,000
Year Founded: 1955
Business Description:
Fast Food Restaurants
S.I.C.: 5812
N.A.I.C.S.: 722211
Import Export
Advertising Expenditures: $650,800,000
Media: 3-6-9-11-14-15-16-18-23-24-31
Distr.: Direct to Consumer; Intl.; Natl.
Budget Set: Nov.
Personnel:
James A. Skinner *(Vice Chm & CEO)*
Donald Thompson *(Pres & COO)*
Peter J. Bensen *(CFO & Exec VP)*
Neil Golden *(CMO & Sr VP)*
Marlena Peleo-Lazar *(Chief Creative Officer)*
Richard Floersch *(Chief HR Officer & Exec VP)*
Kevin Newell *(Exec VP & Global Chief Brand Officer)*
Jeffrey P. Stratton *(Chief Restaurant Officer & Exec VP)*
Jose Armario *(Grp Pres-Canada & Latin America)*
Timothy J. Fenton *(Pres-Asia, Middle East & Africa)*
Janice L. Fields *(Pres-USA)*
Doug Goare *(Pres-Europe)*
J.C. Gonzalez-Mendez *(Pres-Latin America)*
Karen King *(Pres-East Div-US)*
Steve Plotkin *(Pres-West Div-US)*
James Johannesen *(COO-USA & Exec VP)*
Gloria Santona *(Gen Counsel, Sec & Exec VP)*
Dean Barrett *(Sr VP-Global Mktg)*
David Fairhurst *(Sr VP)*
Terry Reese *(VP & Gen Mgr-Michigan Region)*
Mason Smoot *(VP & Gen Mgr-New York Metro Reg)*
Edgardo A. Navarro Linares *(VP-Multicultural Mktg)*
Walt Riker *(VP-Corp Media Rels)*
Dan Ryan *(VP-Field Mktg)*
Bill Whitman *(VP-Comm-US)*
Andrew Hipsley *(Head-Mktg-Asia/Pacific, Middle East & Africa)*
Heidi Barker *(Sr Dir-Corp Media Relation)*
Mark Carlson *(Sr Dir-Creative)*
Priscila Aviles Jamison *(Sr Dir-Creative-US Mktg)*
John Lewicki *(Sr Dir)*
Anja Carroll *(Dir-Media-US)*
Douglas Freeland *(Dir-Mktg-US)*
Kelly Hoyman *(Dir-Mktg-McDonald's USA-Northwest Region)*
Elizabeth Campbell *(Dir-Category & US Mktg)*
Cheryll O. Forsatz *(Dir-Comm-New York Metro Reg)*
Lisa Howard *(Dir-Corp Media Rels)*
Danielle Paris *(Dir-Product Innovation & Development & Menu Mgmt)*
Diane Pomierski *(Dir-Creative)*
Raul Reyes *(Dir-Natl Category)*
Cristina Vilella *(Dir-Mktg)*
Rick Wion *(Dir-Social Media)*
Tara McLaren Handy *(Sr Mgr-Comm)*
Lisa Mccomb *(Sr Mgr-Corp Media Rels)*
Danya Proud *(Sr Mgr-US Media Rels)*
Brands & Products:
1-800-MC1-STCK
AUTOMAC
BIG BREAKFAST
BIG MAC

BIG N' TASTY
BIRDIE
CHICKEN MCGRILL
CHICKEN MCNUGGETS
CHICKEN SELECTS
CINNAMON MELTS
CUARTO DE LIBRA
EGG MCMUFFIN
EMAC DIGITAL
EXTRA VALUE MEAL
FILET-O-FISH
FOOD FOLKS & FUN
FRUIT BUZZ
GE OP MAC
GO ACTIVE
GOLDEN ARCHES
GOOD TIMES
GOSPELFEST
GREAT BREAKS
GREAT TASTE
GRILLED CHICKEN SALAD DELUXE
GROENTEBURGER
HAMBURGER UNIVERSITY
HAPPY MEAL
HEALTHY GROWING UP
I'M LOVIN' IT
KIWIBURGER
MCBABY
MCBACON
MCBURGER
MCBUS
MCCAFE
MCCHICKEN
MCDIRECT SHARES
MCDONALDLAND
MCDONALD'S
MCDONALD'S HAMBURGERS
MCDOUBLE
MCDRIVE
MCEXPRESS
MCFLURRY
MCGRIDDLES
MCHERO
MCKIDS
MCKROKET
MCLEAN DELUXE
MCMEMORIES
MCMENU
MCMUFFIN
MCMUSIC
MCNIFICA
MCNUGGETS
MCNUGGETS KIP
MCOZ
MCPLANE
MCPOLLO
MCPREP
MCRIB
MCROYAL
MCSALAD SHAKER
MCSCHOLAR
MCSCHOLAR OF THE YEAR
MCSKILLET BURRITO
MCSWING
MIGHTY KIDS MEAL
MORNING MAC
QUARTER POUNDER
RMCC
RMHC
RONALD MCDONALD
RONALD MCDONALD CHILDREN'S CHARITIES
RONALD MCDONALD HOUSE
RONALD MCDONALD HOUSE CHARITIES
SAUSAGE MCMUFFIN
SNACK WRAP
VEGI MAC
YOU DESERVE A BREAK TODAY

Advertising Agencies:

5W Public Relations
888 7th Ave 12th Fl
New York, NY 10106
Tel.: (212) 999-5585
Fax: (646) 328-1711

Admerasia, Inc.
159 W 25th St 6th Fl
New York, NY 10001-7203
Tel.: (212) 686-3333
Fax: (212) 686-8998

AKQA, Inc.
118 King St 6th Fl
San Francisco, CA 94107
Tel.: (415) 645-9400
Fax: (415) 645-9420

Alma DDB
2601 S Bayshore Dr 4th Fl
Coconut Grove, FL 33133
Tel.: (305) 662-3175
Fax: (305) 662-8043
McCafe
Oatmeal

Arc Worldwide
(Sub. of Publicis Groupe S.A.)
35 W Wacker Dr 15th Fl
Chicago, IL 60601
Tel.: (312) 220-3200
Fax: (312) 220-1995

Arc Worldwide, Asia Pacific
Level 5 Menara Olympia
50200
Kuala Lumpur, Malaysia
Tel.: (60) 3 2031 0998
Fax: (60) 3 2031 0995

Arnold Worldwide
101 Huntington Ave
Boston, MA 02199-7603
Tel.: (617) 587-8000
Fax: (617) 587-8004

Burrell
233 N Michigan Ave Ste 2900
Chicago, IL 60601
Tel.: (312) 297-9600
Fax: (312) 297-9601
(African-American Consumer Public Relations & Mktg.)
— Linda Jefferson *(V.P.-Media)*

d exposito & Partners, LLC
875 Ave of the Americas 25th Fl
New York, NY 10001
Tel.: (646) 747-8800
Fax: (212) 273-0778
Angus Third Pounder

DDB Sydney Pty. Ltd.
46-52 Mountain Street Level 3
Ultimo, NSW 2007, Australia
Tel.: (61) 2 8260 2222
Fax: (61) 2 8260 2444

DDB Worldwide Communications Group Inc.
(Sub. of Omnicom Group, Inc.)
(Corporate Headquarters)
437 Madison Ave 5nd Fl
New York, NY 10022-7001
Tel.: (212) 415-2000
Fax: (212) 415-3414
Lead Agency

The Game Agency
18 E 16th St 7th Fl
New York, NY 10003
Tel.: (877) 986-4263
Fax: (347) 695-1270

Holt & Germann Public Affairs LLC
172 W State St
Trenton, NJ 08608
Tel.: (908) 832-0557
Fax: (866) 379-4233

Huntington Advertising, Inc.
4575 Weaver Pkwy Ste 500
Warrenville, IL 60555
Tel.: (630) 836-1850
Fax: (630) 836-1171

Leo Burnett
Leo Burnett House 3 Simba Road
Private Bag X19
2157
Sandton, South Africa
Tel.: (27) 11 235 4000
Fax: (27) 11 235 4001

Leo Burnett Worldwide, Inc.
35 W Wacker Dr
Chicago, IL 60601-1723
Tel.: (312) 220-5959
Fax: (312) 220-3299
Chicken Burger
Coffee
Fast Food
Fresh Salads
Happy Meal Choices
Lead Agency
Proud Papa
Snack Size Menu
— Bob Raidt *(Acct Exec)*

The Marketing Store
701 E 22nd St
Lombard, IL 60148
Tel.: (630) 693-1400
Fax: (630) 932-5200

Moroch
901 NE Loop 410 Ste 826
San Antonio, TX 78209-1310
Tel.: (210) 822-4840
Fax: (210) 822-8092
— Monique Davila *(Sr Acct Exec)*

Moroch Partners
3625 N Hall St Ste 1100
Dallas, TX 75219-5122
Tel.: (214) 520-9700
Fax: (214) 252-1724
Every Morning
McDonald's San Antonio Co-op
— April Morin *(Acct Exec)*
— Mary Cota *(Acct Coord)*

TBWA Chiat Day New York
488 Madison Ave
New York, NY 10022
Tel.: (212) 804-1000
Fax: (212) 804-1200

TBWA/Worldwide
(Sub. of Omnicom Group, Inc.)
488 Madison Ave 5th Fl
New York, NY 10022-5702
Tel.: (212) 804-1300
Fax: (212) 804-1333
Lead Agency

MCDONALD'S RESTAURANTS OF CANADA LTD.

(Sub. of McDonald's Corporation)
1 McDonalds Pl
Toronto, ON M3C 3L4, Canada
Tel.: (416) 443-1000
Fax: (416) 446-3376
E-mail: info@mcdonalds.ca
Web Site: www.mcdonalds.ca
Sales Range: $1-4.9 Billion
Approx. Number Employees: 77,000
Business Description:
Fast Food Restaurants
S.I.C.: 5812
N.A.I.C.S.: 722110
Media: 5-6-15-18-22-31
Personnel:
George A. Cohon *(Founder)*
John Betts *(Pres)*
David J. Hederson *(CFO & Sr VP)*
Dave J. Allen *(COO)*
Len Jillard *(Chief People Officer & Sr VP-People Resources)*
Richard Ellis *(Sr VP-Comm & Pub Affairs)*
Dave Simsons *(VP-Shared Svcs & IT)*

Advertising Agencies:

Cossette Communication-Marketing
502 King St W
Toronto, ON M5V 1L7, Canada
Tel.: (416) 922-2727
Fax: (416) 922-9450
Big Mac
Buttermilk Biscuits
Dollar Drink Days

Cossette Inc.
801 Grande Allee Ouest Ste 200
Quebec, QC G1S 1C1, Canada
Tel.: (418) 647-2727
Fax: (418) 647-2564

Cossette West
1085 Homer Street 5th Floor
Vancouver, BC V6B 1J4, Canada
Tel.: (604) 669-2727
Fax: (604) 687-1243
Premium Roast Coffee

NATIONAL Public Relations
2001 McGill College Ave Ste 800
Montreal, QC H3A 1G1, Canada
Tel.: (514) 843-7171
Fax: (514) 843-6976

OMD Canada
67 Richmond St W 2nd Fl
Toronto, ON M5H 1Z5, Canada
Tel.: (416) 681-5600
Fax: (416) 681-5620

Weber Shandwick
130 Albert St Ste 802
Ottawa, ON K1P 5G4, Canada
Tel.: (613) 230-2220
Fax: (613) 230-3874

MCGONIGAL'S PUB

105 S Cook St
Barrington, IL 60010-4311
Tel.: (847) 277-7400
Fax: (847) 842-7600

Key to Media (For complete agency information see *The Advertising Red Books-Agencies* edition):
1. Bus. Publs. 2. Cable T.V. 3. Catalogs & Directories. 4. Co-op Adv. 5. Consumer Mags. 6. D.M. to Bus. Estab.7. D.M. to Consumers 8. Daily Newsp. 9. Exhibits/Trade Shows 10. Foreign 11. Infomercial 12. Internet Adv.13. Multimedia 14. Network Radio 15. Network T.V. 16. Newsp. Distr. Mags. 17. Other 18. Outdoor (Posters, Transit) 19. Point of Purchase20. Premiums, Novelties 21. Product Samples 22. Special Events Mktg. 23. Spot Radio 24. Spot T.V. 25. Weekly Newsp. 26. Yellow Page Adv.

McGonigal's Pub — (Continued)

Web Site: www.mcgonigalspub.com
Business Description:
Local Pub
S.I.C.: 5812
N.A.I.C.S.: 722110
Media: 8-9-13-18-22-23-24-25
Personnel:
Brian McGonigal *(Owner)*

MCGUFFEY'S RESTAURANTS, INC.

Ste H2 370 N Louisiana Ave
Asheville, NC 28806-3659
Tel.: (828) 252-3300
Fax: (828) 254-3907
Approx. Number Employees: 500
Year Founded: 1983
Business Description:
Theme Restaurant Operator
S.I.C.: 5812
N.A.I.C.S.: 722110
Media: 8-23-24-26
Distr.: Reg.
Budget Set: Dec.
Personnel:
George M. Hill *(Pres)*

MERITAGE HOSPITALITY GROUP, INC.

3310 Eagle Prk Dr Ste 205
Grand Rapids, MI 49525
Tel.: (616) 776-2600
Fax: (616) 776-2776
Web Site:
www.meritagehospitality.com
Approx. Rev.: $69,095,340
Approx. Number Employees: 2,500
Year Founded: 1986
Business Description:
Fast Food Restaurant Franchise Owner
S.I.C.: 5812
N.A.I.C.S.: 722211
Advertising Expenditures: $2,164,000
Media: 9-22-23-24-25
Personnel:
Robert E. Schermer, Sr. *(Chm)*
Robert E. Schermer, Jr. *(Pres & CEO)*
Gary A. Rose *(CFO, COO, Treas, Sec & VP)*

MEXICAN RESTAURANTS, INC.

12000 Aerospace Ave Ste 400
Houston, TX 77034-5576
Tel.: (832) 300-5858
E-mail: comments@mexicanrestaurantsinc.com
Web Site:
www.mexicanrestaurantsinc.com
Approx. Rev.: $72,017,901
Approx. Number Employees: 1,950
Year Founded: 1996
Business Description:
Mexican Restaurant Operator
S.I.C.: 5812
N.A.I.C.S.: 722110
Advertising Expenditures: $1,630,285
Media: 7-8-18-19-23-24
Distr.: Direct to Consumer; Reg.
Personnel:
Michael D. Domec *(Chm)*
Larry N. Forehand *(Vice Chm)*
Curt Glowacki *(Pres & CEO)*
Andrew J. Dennard *(CFO, Sec & Exec VP)*
Loic M. Porry *(COO)*

Brands & Products:
CASA OLE
CRAZY JOSE'S
LA SENORITA
MISSION BURRITO
MONTEREY'S LITTLE MEXICO
MONTEREY'S TEX MEX CAFE
MRI
TURTOGA MEXICAN KITCHEN
Advertising Agency:
Stan & Lou Advertising
504 W 9th St
Houston, TX 77007
Tel.: (713) 683-8000
Fax: (713) 683-8090

MIAMI SUBS CORPORATION

(Sub. of Nathan's Famous Inc.)
6300 NW 31st Ave
Fort Lauderdale, FL 33309-1633
Tel.: (954) 973-0000
Fax: (954) 973-7616
E-mail: bpp@miamisubs.com
Web Site: www.miamisubs.com
Sales Range: $10-24.9 Million
Approx. Number Employees: 25
Year Founded: 1990
Business Description:
Operates & Franchises Miami Subs Restaurants
S.I.C.: 5812
N.A.I.C.S.: 722211
Advertising Expenditures: $2,000,000
Media: 3-5-8-9-10-18-19-20-21-22-23-25-26
Distr.: Direct to Consumer; Reg.
Budget Set: June
Personnel:
Donald L. Perlyn *(Exec VP-Franchise Dev)*
Brands & Products:
MIAMI SUBS
Advertising Agency:
Zimmerman Advertising
2200 W Commercial Blvd Ste 300
Fort Lauderdale, FL 33309-3064
Tel.: (954) 644-4000
Fax: (954) 731-2977
Toll Free: (800) 248-8522

MIMI'S CAFE, LLC

(Sub. of Bob Evans Farms, Inc.)
17852 E 17th St South Bldg Ste 108
Tustin, CA 92780
Tel.: (714) 544-4826
Web Site: www.mimiscafe.com
Sales Range: $10-24.9 Million
Approx. Number Employees: 30
Business Description:
Holding Company; Restaurants
S.I.C.: 5812; 6719
N.A.I.C.S.: 722110; 551112
Personnel:
Mark Mears *(Pres & Chief Concept Officer)*
Herbert Billinger *(Exec VP-Ops)*
Advertising Agency:
Sprokkit
333 S Grand Ave Ste 1600
Los Angeles, CA 90071
Tel.: (213) 626-2076
Fax: (231) 232-3739

MORGAN'S FOODS, INC.

4829 Galaxy Pkwy Ste S
Cleveland, OH 44128
Tel.: (216) 359-9000
Fax: (216) 359-2151
E-mail: investor.relations@morgansfoods.com
Web Site: www.morgansfoods.com
Approx. Rev.: $89,891,000
Approx. Number Employees: 1,722
Year Founded: 1925
Business Description:
Fast Food Restaurant Franchise Owner & Operator
S.I.C.: 5812
N.A.I.C.S.: 722211
Advertising Expenditures: $5,493,000
Media: 1-13-18-19-20-21-22
Personnel:
Leonard R. Stein-Sapir *(Chm & CEO)*
James J. Liguori *(Pres & COO)*
Kenneth L. Hignett *(CFO, Sec & Sr VP)*
Barton J. Craig *(Gen Counsel & Sr VP)*

MORTON'S OF CHICAGO, INC.

(Sub. of Morton's Restaurant Group, Inc.)
325 N La Salle Dr Ste 500
Chicago, IL 60654
Tel.: (312) 923-0030
Fax: (312) 923-0090
E-mail: info@mortons.com
Web Site: www.mortons.com
Sales Range: $200-249.9 Million
Approx. Number Employees: 1,500
Year Founded: 1978
Business Description:
Restaurant Chain
S.I.C.: 5812; 8742
N.A.I.C.S.: 722110; 541611
Advertising Expenditures: $1,500,000
Media: 1-6-10-22
Distr.: Natl.
Budget Set: Oct.
Personnel:
Patty Pleuss *(VP-Mktg & Sls)*

MORTON'S RESTAURANT GROUP, INC.

325 N LaSalle St Ste 500
Chicago, IL 60610
Tel.: (312) 923-0030
Web Site: www.mortons.com
Approx. Rev.: $296,126,000
Approx. Number Employees: 4,154
Year Founded: 1978
Business Description:
Owns & Operates Restaurants
S.I.C.: 5812
N.A.I.C.S.: 722110
Advertising Expenditures: $1,385,000
Media: 9-25
Distr.: Reg.
Personnel:
Klaus W. Fritsch *(Co-Founder & Vice Chm)*
Christopher J. Artinian *(Pres & CEO)*
Ronald M. DiNella *(CFO, Treas & Sr VP)*
Scott D. Levin *(Gen Counsel, Sec & Sr VP)*
Roger J. Drake *(Sr VP-Mktg & Comm)*
James W. Kirkpatrick *(Sr VP-Dev)*
Kevin E. Weinert *(Sr VP-Ops)*
Brands & Products:
BERTOLINIS AUTHENTIC TRATTORIAS
EXTENDED & ENHANCED
MORTON'S THE STEAKHOUSE

Advertising Agency:
Nevins & Associates
10946 Golden West Dr Ste 130
Hunt Valley, MD 21031
Tel.: (410) 568-8800
Fax: (410) 568-8804

MR. GATTI'S, LP

(Holding of Blue Sage Capital LP)
5912 Balcones Dr
Austin, TX 78731-5919
Tel.: (512) 459-2222
Fax: (512) 380-9540
Web Site: www.gattispizza.com
Sales Range: $125-149.9 Million
Approx. Number Employees: 25
Year Founded: 1964
Business Description:
Operator of Pizza Restaurants & Arcades
S.I.C.: 5812; 7993
N.A.I.C.S.: 722211; 713120
Advertising Expenditures: $1,800,000
Media: 9-16-17-23-26
Distr.: Direct to Consumer; Reg.
Budget Set: July
Personnel:
Michael J. Mrlik, II *(Pres & CEO)*
Ed Cohen *(VP-Mktg)*
Granya Gormley *(VP-HR & Trng)*
James S. Barclay *(Dir-Franchise Ops)*
Michael D. Glenn *(Dir-Ops)*
Brands & Products:
GATTILAND
GATTI'S-TO-GO
GATTITOWN
MR. GATTI'S

NATHAN'S FAMOUS INC.

1 Jericho Plz
Jericho, NY 11753
Tel.: (516) 338-8500
Fax: (516) 338-7220
E-mail: cs@nathansfamous.com
Web Site: www.nathansfamous.com
E-Mail For Key Personnel:
President: wnorbitz@nathansfamous.com
Approx. Rev.: $57,255,000
Approx. Number Employees: 219
Year Founded: 1916
Business Description:
Fast Food Franchiser
S.I.C.: 5812
N.A.I.C.S.: 722211
Advertising Expenditures: $233,000
Media: 2-3-8-9-10-19-20-21-22-23-25-26
Distr.: Reg.
Budget Set: Nov. -Dec.
Personnel:
Howard M. Lorber *(Chm)*
Wayne Norbitz *(Pres & COO)*
Eric Gatoff *(CEO)*
Ronald G. DeVos *(CFO)*
Donald L. Perlyn *(Exec VP)*
Karen Brown *(Sr Dir-HR)*
David Kalish *(Dir-Purchasing)*
Jerry Krevans *(Sr Product Dir)*
Mary Hyland *(Mgr-Mktg)*
Brands & Products:
ARTHUR TREACHER'S
KENNY ROGERS
KENNY ROGERS ROASTERS
MIAMI GRILL
MIAMI SUBS
NATHAN'S

Key to Media (For complete agency information see *The Advertising Red Books-Agencies* edition):
1. Bus. Publs. 2. Cable T.V. 3. Catalogs & Directories. 4. Co-op Adv. 5. Consumer Mags. 6. D.M. to Bus. Estab.7. D.M. to Consumers 8. Daily Newsp. 9. Exhibits/Trade Shows 10. Foreign 11. Infomercial 12. Internet Adv.13. Multimedia 14. Network Radio 15. Network T.V. 16. Newsp. Distr. Mags. 17. Other 18. Outdoor (Posters, Transit) 19. Point of Purchase20. Premiums, Novelties 21. Product Samples 22. Special Events Mktg. 23. Spot Radio 24. Spot T.V. 25. Weekly Newsp. 26. Yellow Page Adv.

Advertising Agency:
Manhattan Marketing Ensemble
443 Park Ave S 4th Fl
New York, NY 10016-7322
Tel.: (212) 779-2233
Fax: (212) 779-0825
(Nathan's Products)

NOBLE ROMAN'S, INC.

1 Virginia Ave Ste 300
Indianapolis, IN 46204-3669
Tel.: (317) 634-3377
Fax: (317) 636-3207
Toll Free: (800) 585-0669
Web Site: www.nobleromans.com
Approx. Rev.: $7,271,103
Approx. Number Employees: 20
Year Founded: 1972
Business Description:
Pizza Restaurant Operator
S.I.C.: 5812
N.A.I.C.S.: 722211; 722110
Advertising Expenditures: $2,500,000
Media: 2-9-23-25
Distr.: Natl.
Budget Set: Nov. -Dec.
Personnel:
Paul W. Mobley *(Chm, CEO & CFO)*
A. Scott Mobley *(Pres & Sec)*
Troy Branson *(Exec VP)*
Michael B. Novak *(VP-Product Dev & Pur & Distr)*
Brands & Products:
THE BETTER PIZZA PEOPLE
NOBLE ROMAN'S
NOBLE ROMAN'S PIZZA
TUSCANO'S ITALIAN STYLE SUBS

NOODLES & COMPANY

(Holding of Catterton Partners)
520 Zang St D
Broomfield, CO 80021
Tel.: (720) 214-1900
Fax: (720) 214-1934
Web Site: www.noodles.com
Sales Range: $100-124.9 Million
Approx. Number Employees: 100
Year Founded: 1995
Business Description:
Restaurant Operator
S.I.C.: 5812
N.A.I.C.S.: 722110
Personnel:
Kevin Reddy *(Pres & CEO)*
Keith Kinsey *(CFO & COO)*
Dawn Voss *(Chief Admin Officer)*
Paul Strassen *(Gen Counsel)*
Brands & Products:
NOODLES AND COMPANY
Advertising Agency:
Carmichael Lynch
110 N 5th St
Minneapolis, MN 55403
Tel.: (612) 334-6000
Fax: (612) 334-6090
(Creative/Media)

NORTHCOTT HOSPITALITY INTERNATIONAL, LLC

250 Lk Dr E
Chanhassen, MN 55317-9364
Tel.: (952) 294-5000
Fax: (952) 294-5101
Web Site:
www.northcotthospitality.com
Sales Range: $25-49.9 Million
Approx. Number Employees: 1,395
Year Founded: 1994
Business Description:
Restaurants & Motels Owner & Operator
S.I.C.: 5812; 7011
N.A.I.C.S.: 722110; 721110
Import Export
Media: 4-16-22-26
Personnel:
Paul Kirwin *(Pres, CEO & Dir)*
Brian Schwen *(CFO)*
Ron Burgett *(Exec VP)*
Brands & Products:
AMERICINN

NPC INTERNATIONAL, INC.

(Holding of Banc of America Capital Investors, LP)
7300 W 129th St
Overland Park, KS 66213
Tel.: (913) 327-5555
Fax: (913) 327-5850
E-mail: comments@npcinternational.com
Web Site: www.npcinternational.com
Approx. Sls.: $978,284,000
Approx. Number Employees: 26,000
Year Founded: 1962
Business Description:
Restaurant Franchise Owner & Operator
S.I.C.: 5812
N.A.I.C.S.: 722211
Advertising Expenditures: $55,600,000
Media: 5-9-17-19-23-24-25-26
Personnel:
James K. Swartz *(Chm, Pres, CEO & COO)*
Troy D. Cook *(CFO & Exec VP)*
Michael J. Woods *(CIO & VP-IT)*
Susan G. Dechant *(Chief Acctg Officer & VP-Admin)*
D. Blayne Vaughn *(Sr VP & Head-Ops)*
Linda L. Sheedy *(VP-Mktg)*
Lavonne K. Walbert *(VP-HR)*
Advertising Agency:
Euro RSCG Dallas
2800 N. Dallas Pkwy, Ste 300
Plano, TX 75093
Tel.: (972) 473-5600
Fax: (972) 473-5601

NUTRITION MANAGEMENT SERVICES COMPANY

2071 Kimberton Rd
Kimberton, PA 19442-0725
Tel.: (610) 935-2050
Fax: (610) 935-8287
E-mail: company@nmsc.com
Web Site: www.nmsc.com
Approx. Rev.: $20,013,903
Approx. Number Employees: 289
Year Founded: 1979
Business Description:
Food Management Services to Hospitals & Retirement Communities
S.I.C.: 5812; 7922; 8748
N.A.I.C.S.: 722310; 541618; 711110
Advertising Expenditures: $4,647
Media: 2-7-10
Distr.: Bus.-to-Bus
Personnel:
Kathleen A. Hill *(Pres, COO & Sec)*
Joseph V. Roberts *(CEO)*
Brands & Products:
NUTRITION MANAGEMENT SERVICE COMPANY
NUTRITION MANAGEMENT SERVICES COMPANY
Advertising Agency:
The Richards Organization
(Sub. of MSRI)
14 Calvert St
Harrison, NY 10528-3213
Tel.: (914) 835-3111
Fax: (914) 835-3698
Toll Free: (800) 4ALLADS

OCEANAIRE RESTAURANT CO. INC.

Hyatt Regency 1300 Nicollet Mall
Minneapolis, MN 55403
Tel.: (612) 333-2277
Fax: (612) 305-1923
Web Site: www.theoceanaire.com
Approx. Number Employees: 50
Business Description:
Restaurant Operator
S.I.C.: 5812; 5813
N.A.I.C.S.: 722110; 722410
Media: 6-8-9-22-23

O'CHARLEY'S INC.

3038 Sidco Dr
Nashville, TN 37204
Tel.: (615) 256-8500
Fax: (615) 782-5044
E-mail: info@ocharleys.com
Web Site: www.ocharleys.com
Approx. Rev.: $830,109,000
Approx. Number Employees: 22,000
Year Founded: 1982
Business Description:
Restaurant Operator
S.I.C.: 5812
N.A.I.C.S.: 722110
Advertising Expenditures: $32,700,000
Media: 9-14-15-19
Personnel:
Philip J. Hickey, Jr. *(Chm)*
David W. Head *(Pres & CEO)*
R. Jeffrey Williams *(Interim CFO, Chief Acctg Officer, Treas, Controller & Asst Sec)*
Leon M. de Wet *(CIO)*
Colin M. Daly *(Gen Counsel, Sec & Chief Compliance Officer)*
Lawrence D. Taylor *(Chief Supply Chain Officer)*
Marc A. Buehler *(Pres-Concept)*
Wilson L. Craft *(Pres-OCharleys Restaurants)*
John R. Grady *(Pres-Ninety Nine Concept)*
Anthony J. Halligan, III *(Pres-Stoney River Legendary Steaks Concept)*
Bob F. Luz *(VP-HR)*
Wade Breaux *(Dir-Creative Svcs)*
Brands & Products:
O'CHARLEY'S
Advertising Agencies:
BrightWave Marketing
1718 Peachtree St Ste 1090
Atlanta, GA 30309
Tel.: (404) 253-3797
E-Mail Agency of Record
E-Mail Enrollment
Guest Acquisition
Visit Frequency

The Buntin Group
1001 Hawkins St
Nashville, TN 37203-4758
Tel.: (615) 244-5720
Fax: (615) 244-6511

Merkley + Partners
(Sub. of Omnicom Group, Inc.)
200 Varick St
New York, NY 10014-4810
Tel.: (212) 366-3500
Fax: (212) 805-7445
Agency of Record
Creative
Media

OLIVE GARDEN ITALIAN RESTAURANT

(Div. of Darden Restaurants, Inc.)
1000 Darden Ctr Dr
Orlando, FL 32837
Tel.: (407) 245-4000
Fax: (407) 245-5389
Toll Free: (800) 832-7336
Web Site: www.olivegarden.com
Sales Range: $50-74.9 Million
Year Founded: 1982
Business Description:
Italian Food Restaurants Operator
S.I.C.: 5812
N.A.I.C.S.: 722110
Media: 14-15-23
Distr.: Natl.
Personnel:
David T. Pickens *(Pres)*
Valerie Insignares *(Exec VP-Ops)*
Steve Coe *(Dir-Media Rels)*
Matt Drewes *(Dir-Mktg Brand Mgmt Team)*
Stephanie Gutierrez *(Dir-Mktg)*
Mara Frazier *(Mgr-Media Rels)*
Advertising Agencies:
Grey New York
777 3rd Ave
New York, NY 10017-1401
Tel.: (212) 546-2000
Fax: (212) 546-1495

Zubi Advertising Services, Inc.
355 Alhambra Cir 10th Fl
Coral Gables, FL 33134-5006
Tel.: (305) 448-9824
Fax: (305) 460-6393

ORANGE JULIUS OF AMERICA

(Sub. of International Dairy Queen, Inc.)
7505 Metro Blvd
Minneapolis, MN 55439-3020
Mailing Address:
PO Box 39286
Minneapolis, MN 55439-0286
Tel.: (952) 830-0200
Fax: (952) 830-0480
E-mail: info@orangejulius.com
Web Site: www.orangejulius.com
Sales Range: $25-49.9 Million
Approx. Number Employees: 50
Year Founded: 1962
Business Description:
Fast Food Franchiser
S.I.C.: 5812; 5149
N.A.I.C.S.: 722211; 424490; 722213
Media: 5-9-19-21
Distr.: Intl.; Natl.

Key to Media (For complete agency information see *The Advertising Red Books-Agencies* edition):
1. Bus. Publs. 2. Cable T.V. 3. Catalogs & Directories. 4. Co-op Adv. 5. Consumer Mags. 6. D.M. to Bus. Estab.7. D.M. to Consumers
8. Daily Newsp. 9. Exhibits/Trade Shows 10. Foreign 11. Infomercial 12. Internet Adv.13. Multimedia 14. Network Radio
15. Network T.V. 16. Newsp. Distr. Mags. 17. Other 18. Outdoor (Posters, Transit) 19. Point of Purchase20. Premiums, Novelties
21. Product Samples 22. Special Events Mktg. 23. Spot Radio 24. Spot T.V. 25. Weekly Newsp. 26. Yellow Page Adv.

Orange Julius of America — (Continued)

Personnel:
John Gainor *(Pres & CEO)*
Kathy Heller *(Dir-Admin Svcs)*
Dean Peters *(Dir-Commun)*

Brands & Products:
JULIUS CREATIONS
JULIUS SMOOTHIE
JULIUS SUPREME
ORANGE JULIUS

Advertising Agency:
Grey New York
777 3rd Ave
New York, NY 10017-1401
Tel.: (212) 546-2000
Fax: (212) 546-1495

OSI RESTAURANT PARTNERS LLC

(Holding of Bain Capital, LLC)
2202 N West Shore Blvd 5th Fl
Tampa, FL 33607
Tel.: (813) 282-1225
Fax: (813) 286-2247
Toll Free: (877) 733-6774
E-mail: customerservice@outback.com
Web Site: www.osirestaurantpartners.com
Approx. Rev.: $3,628,466,000
Approx. Number Employees: 96,000
Year Founded: 1988
Business Description:
Restaurant Operators
S.I.C.: 5812
N.A.I.C.S.: 722110
Advertising Expenditures: $140,033,000
Media: 3-13-15-18-22-23-24
Distr.: Direct to Consumer; Reg.
Budget Set: Sept.
Personnel:
A. William Allen, III *(Co-Founder & CEO)*
Trudy I. Cooper *(Co-Founder & Sr VP-Trng, Dev, Outback Steakhouse)*
Elizabeth A. Smith *(CEO)*
Dirk A. Montgomery *(CFO & Sr VP)*
Charles M. Weston *(CIO & Sr VP)*
Richard Renninger *(Chief Dev Officer & Exec VP)*
Jody Bilney *(Chief Brand Officer & Exec VP)*
Irene Wenzel *(Chief Procurement Officer &Sr VP)*
Michael W. Coble *(Pres-Outback Steakhouse-Intl)*
Jeff Smith *(Pres-Outback Steakhouse)*
Joseph J. Kadow *(Sec, Exec VP, Chief Officer-Legal & Corp Affairs)*
Lindon Richardson *(Sr VP-Equipment & Design)*
Steven C. Stanley *(Sr VP-Construction)*
Stephanie L. Amberg *(VP-Pub Rel)*
Veronica Swiatek *(VP-Brand Mktg-Cheeseburger in Paradise)*
Richard Turer *(VP-Mktg)*
Lisa Hathcoat *(Mgr-IR)*

Brands & Products:
BLUE CORAL SEAFOOD & SPIRITS
BONEFISH GRILL
CARRABBA'S
FLEMING'S PRIME STEAKHOUSE & WINE BAR
LEE ROY SELMON'S
OUTBACK STEAKHOUSE
ROY'S

Advertising Agencies:
Carat
150 E 42nd St
New York, NY 10017
Tel.: (212) 689-6800
Fax: (212) 689-6005
Outback Steakhouse
Carrabba's Italian Grill

Carat North America Inc.
150 E 52nd St
New York, NY 10017
Tel.: (212) 252-0050
Fax: (212) 252-1250

David & Goliath
909 N Sepulveda Blvd Ste 700
El Segundo, CA 90245
Tel.: (310) 445-5200
Fax: (310) 445-5201

Deutsch New York
111 8th Ave 14th Fl
New York, NY 10011
Tel.: (212) 605-8000

Initiative
1 Dag Hammarskjold Plz
New York, NY 10017
Tel.: (212) 605-7000
Fax: (917) 305-4003
Bonefish Grill

The Kaplan Thaler Group
825 8th Ave 34th Fl
New York, NY 10019
Tel.: (212) 474-5000
Fax: (212) 474-5702

McCann Erickson, Inc.
W Building 7/F 813-4
Yeoksam-dong
Seoul, 1335-931, Korea (South)
Tel.: (82) 2 2186 9700
Fax: (82) 2 2051 3649
Outback Steakhouse Korea

Night Agency
307 Canal St Fl 2
New York, NY 10013
Tel.: (212) 431-1945
Fax: (917) 677-8327
Fleming's Prime Steak House & Wine Bar

Rawle Murdy Associates, Inc.
2 Beaufain St
Charleston, SC 29401
Tel.: (843) 577-7327
Fax: (843) 722-3960
Cheeseburger in Paradise

Young & Rubicam Chicago
233 N Michigan Ave 16th Fl
Chicago, IL 60601-5519
Tel.: (312) 596-3000
Fax: (312) 596-3130
(Bonefish Grill, Creative)

PAPA GINOS-DEANGELO HOLDING CORPORATION, INC.

600 Providence Hwy
Dedham, MA 02026-6804
Tel.: (781) 461-1200
Fax: (781) 461-1896
Toll Free: (800) PAPAGINO
Web Site: www.papaginos.com
Approx. Sls.: $135,000,000
Approx. Number Employees: 100
Year Founded: 1963
Business Description:
Holding Company; Pizzeria & Sandwich Shop Restaurants Owner, Operator & Franchisee
S.I.C.: 6719; 5812; 6794
N.A.I.C.S.: 551112; 533110; 722211
Advertising Expenditures: $7,325,000
D.M. to Bus. Estab.: $50,000; D.M. to Consumers: $300,000; Daily Newsp.: $400,000; Other: $725,000; Point of Purchase: $450,000; Premiums, Novelties: $100,000; Special Events Mktg.: $100,000; Spot Radio: $2,000,000; Spot T.V.: $2,800,000; Weekly Newsp.: $300,000; Yellow Page Adv.: $100,000
Budget Set: Feb.
Personnel:
Thomas J. Galligan, III *(Chm)*
Rick Wolf *(Pres & CEO)*
Kathy Tirrell *(Exec VP-Ops)*
Lori Whelan *(Exec VP-Fin & Strategic Plng)*
Celeste Contois *(Sr VP-HR)*
Michael McManama *(Sr VP-Brand Dev)*
Bruce Archambault *(VP-Pur)*

Brands & Products:
D'ANGELO
PAPA GINO'S

PAPA JOHN'S INTERNATIONAL, INC.

2002 Papa Johns Blvd
Louisville, KY 40299-2367
Mailing Address:
PO Box 99900
Louisville, KY 40269-0900
Tel.: (502) 261-7272
Fax: (502) 266-2925
Toll Free: (888) 777-7272
Web Site: www.papajohns.com
Approx. Rev.: $1,126,397,000
Approx. Number Employees: 16,000
Year Founded: 1985
Business Description:
Restaurant Operator
S.I.C.: 5812
N.A.I.C.S.: 722211
Advertising Expenditures: $47,174,000
Media: 5-8-11-14-15-20-22
Distr.: Natl.
Budget Set: Aug. -Sept.
Personnel:
John H. Schnatter *(Chm & CEO)*
J. David Flanery *(CFO, Treas & Sr VP)*
Lance Tucker *(CFO, Treas & Sr VP)*
Andrew Varga *(CMO & Sr VP)*
Christopher J. Sternberg *(Gen Counsel & Sr VP-Corp Comm)*
Annette Calhoun *(Sr VP-HR)*
Tim North *(Sr VP-Ops-North America)*
Timothy C. O'Hern *(Sr VP-Dev)*
Steve Ritchie *(Sr VP-Ops)*
Tom Sterrett *(Sr VP-Intl)*
Melissa Richards-Person *(Sr Dir-Adv & Promos)*

Brands & Products:
BETTER INGREDIENTS.BETTER PIZZA
PAPA JOHN'S
PIZZA PAPA JOHN'S

Advertising Agencies:
Brunner
11 Stanwix St 5th Fl
Pittsburgh, PA 15222-1312
Tel.: (412) 995-9500
Fax: (412) 995-9501
Papa J's Centro

MZD Advertising
8425 Woofield Crossing Blvd Ste 200 W
Indianapolis, IN 46240
Tel.: (317) 924-6271
Fax: (317) 925-3854

PARASOLE RESTAURANT HOLDINGS, INC.

5032 France Ave S
Edina, MN 55410
Tel.: (612) 822-0016
Fax: (612) 822-0705
Web Site: www.parasole.com
Sales Range: $10-24.9 Million
Approx. Number Employees: 22
Year Founded: 1986
Business Description:
Holding Company; Restaurants Developer & Operator
S.I.C.: 6719; 5812
N.A.I.C.S.: 551112; 722110
Consumer Mags.: 34%; Outdoor (Posters, Transit): 33%; Weekly Newsp.: 33%
Personnel:
Philip Roberts *(CEO & Partner)*

THE PASTA HOUSE CO.

1143 Macklind Ave
Saint Louis, MO 63110-1440
Tel.: (314) 535-6644
Fax: (314) 531-2499
Web Site: www.pastahouse.com
Approx. Sls.: $54,200,000
Approx. Number Employees: 2,500
Year Founded: 1974
Business Description:
Owns & Operates Restaurants
S.I.C.: 5812
N.A.I.C.S.: 722110
Import Export
Personnel:
J. Kim Tucci *(Co-Founder & Pres)*
Joe Fresta *(Co-Founder)*
John Harris *(CFO & VP)*
Sam Garanzini *(Sr VP)*
Mike Niewoehner *(Dir-Ops)*

Advertising Agency:
Kochan & Company Marketing Communications
800 Geyer Ave
Saint Louis, MO 63104-4048
Tel.: (314) 621-4455
Fax: (314) 621-1777

PATINA RESTAURANT GROUP LLC

120 W 45th St 16th Fl
New York, NY 10036
Tel.: (212) 789-8100
Fax: (212) 302-8032
Web Site: www.patinagroup.com
Sales Range: $200-249.9 Million
Year Founded: 2006
Business Description:
Restaurant Operator
S.I.C.: 5812

Key to Media (For complete agency information see *The Advertising Red Books-Agencies* edition):
1. Bus. Publs. 2. Cable T.V. 3. Catalogs & Directories. 4. Co-op Adv. 5. Consumer Mags. 6. D.M. to Bus. Estab.7. D.M. to Consumers 8. Daily Newsp. 9. Exhibits/Trade Shows 10. Foreign 11. Infomercial 12. Internet Adv.13. Multimedia 14. Network Radio 15. Network T.V. 16. Newsp. Distr. Mags. 17. Other 18. Outdoor (Posters, Transit) 19. Point of Purchase20. Premiums, Novelties 21. Product Samples 22. Special Events Mktg. 23. Spot Radio 24. Spot T.V. 25. Weekly Newsp. 26. Yellow Page Adv.

N.A.I.C.S.: 722110
Personnel:
Nick Valenti *(CEO)*
Tim OShea *(COO)*
Jennifer Shurdut *(Gen Counsel)*
Advertising Agency:
Verse Communications
13807 Ventura Blvd
Los Angeles, CA 91423
Tel.: (818) 981-3023
Fax: (818) 981-9250
Agency of Record
Brand Positioning
Media Relations
Social Media Outreach
Strategic Public Relations
The Black Truffle Dinner

PEPE'S INC.
1325 W 15th St
Chicago, IL 60608-2107
Tel.: (312) 733-2500
Fax: (312) 733-2564
E-mail: info@pepes.com
Web Site: www.pepes.com
Sales Range: $1-9.9 Million
Approx. Number Employees: 40
Year Founded: 1967
Business Description:
Franchisor of Mexican Restaurants
S.I.C.: 5149; 5143
N.A.I.C.S.: 424490; 424430
Export
Advertising Expenditures: $500,000
Media: 9-17-23-24-25
Distr.: Reg.
Budget Set: Nov.
Personnel:
Mario Dovalina *(Co-Founder & Chm)*
Edwin A. Ptak *(Co-Founder & Gen Counsel)*
Robert Ptak *(Pres)*

PERKINS & MARIE CALLENDER'S INC.
(Sub. of TRC Holdings LLC)
6075 Poplar Ave Ste 800
Memphis, TN 38119
Tel.: (901) 766-6400
Fax: (901) 766-6482
Toll Free: (800) 877-7375
Approx. Rev.: $536,068,000
Approx. Number Employees: 7,124
Business Description:
Restaurant Franchise & Operation Services
S.I.C.: 5812
N.A.I.C.S.: 722110
Advertising Expenditures: $26,712,000
Personnel:
Joseph F. Trungale *(CEO)*
Sred Grant *(CFO)*
Richard K. Arras *(Pres/COO-Perkins Restaurants & Bakeries)*
Cheryl Ahlbrandt *(Exec VP-Mktg & R & D)*
Toni Quist *(VP-HR & Trng)*
Glenn Drasher *(Sr Dir-Mktg-Perkins)*
Advertising Agency:
Doner
25900 Northwestern Hwy
Southfield, MI 48075
Tel.: (248) 354-9700
Fax: (248) 827-8440
Agency of Record
Digital
Event Suppport
Point of Sale
Print
Promotions
Social Media
TV

PETER PIPER, INC.
(Holding of ACON Investments, LLC)
950 W Behrend Dr Ste 102
Phoenix, AZ 85027
Tel.: (480) 609-6400
Fax: (480) 609-6520
E-mail: feedback@peterpiperpizza.com
Web Site: www.peterpiperpizza.com
Sales Range: $50-74.9 Million
Approx. Number Employees: 1,700
Year Founded: 1973
Business Description:
Pizza Restaurants Owner, Operator & Franchiser
S.I.C.: 5812; 7993
N.A.I.C.S.: 722110; 713120
Media: 24
Personnel:
Joe Luongo *(Pres & CEO)*
Rich Kerley *(CFO & Sr VP)*
Charles Bruce *(CMO & Sr VP-Mktg)*
Greg Palmer *(VP-HR)*
Jason Greenwood *(Dir-Mktg)*

PETRO STOPPING CENTERS L.P.
(Sub. of TravelCenters of America, LLC)
6080 Surety Dr
El Paso, TX 79905-2009
Mailing Address:
PO Box 26808
El Paso, TX 79926-6808
Tel.: (915) 779-4711
Fax: (915) 774-7382
E-mail: dmcclure@petrotruckstops.com
Web Site: www.petrotruckstops.com
Approx. Rev.: $1,800,000,000
Approx. Number Employees: 5,071
Year Founded: 1975
Business Description:
Retail Truck Stops & Restaurants
S.I.C.: 7538; 5541
N.A.I.C.S.: 447110; 447190; 811111
Advertising Expenditures: $500,000
Other: $500,000
Distr.: Natl.; Reg.
Budget Set: June
Personnel:
James A. Cardwell, Sr. *(Pres, COO & Sr VP-Mktg & Plng)*
James A. Cardwell, Jr. *(CFO, Chief Acctg Officer & Treas)*
Edward Escudero *(CFO, Chief Acctg Officer & Treas)*
Lisa Budtke *(Dir-Plng & Asst Treas)*
Stan Culpepper *(Dir-Fleet Sls)*
John Ponczoch *(Dir-Iron Skillet Ops)*
Brands & Products:
THE CHOICE OF AMERICA'S DRIVERS
THE DRIVER'S GENERAL STORE
FAST LANE
IRON SKILLET
PETRO LUBE
PETRO PASSPORT
PETRO POWER PLUS
THE QUALITY DIFFERENCE
TRUCKERS MOVE PETRO AMERICA
Advertising Agency:
Mithoff Burton Partners
123 W Mills Ave Ste 500
El Paso, TX 79901
Tel.: (915) 544-9400
Fax: (915) 544-9426
Toll Free: (877) 335-2322

PICCADILLY RESTAURANTS, LLC
(Holding of The Yucaipa Companies)
3232 Sherwood Forest Blvd
Baton Rouge, LA 70816-2218
Mailing Address:
PO Box 2467
Baton Rouge, LA 70821-2467
Tel.: (225) 296-8351
Fax: (225) 296-8370
Toll Free: (800) 552-7422
Web Site: www.piccadilly.com
Sales Range: $300-349.9 Million
Approx. Number Employees: 7,153
Year Founded: 1944
Business Description:
Cafeteria-Style Restaurant Operator
S.I.C.: 5812
N.A.I.C.S.: 722212
Advertising Expenditures: $6,000,000
Media: 17-18-19-23-24
Distr.: Direct to Consumer; Natl.
Personnel:
David Green *(CEO)*
Tom Sandman *(CFO)*
Brands & Products:
PICCADILLY EXPRESS
Advertising Agency:
Peter A. Mayer Advertising, Inc.
324 Camp St
New Orleans, LA 70130-2804
Tel.: (504) 581-7191
Fax: (504) 581-3009

PINKBERRY INC.
6310 San Vicente Blvd
Los Angeles, CA 90048
Tel.: (323) 932-6800
Fax: (323) 932-6805
E-mail: info@pinkberry.com
Web Site: www.pinkberry.com
Sales Range: $25-49.9 Million
Approx. Number Employees: 35
Business Description:
Frozen Yogurt Store Operator
S.I.C.: 5812
N.A.I.C.S.: 722211
Personnel:
Young Lee *(Co-Founder & Chief Creative Officer)*
Shelly Hwang *(Co-Founder & Chief Product Officer)*
Ron Graves *(CEO)*
Michael Dixon *(CFO)*
Mark Friedman *(Gen Counsel & Sr VP-Bus Dev)*
Todd Putman *(VP-Mktg)*
Glenn Lord *(Dir-Ops-Intl)*
Advertising Agency:
Bulldog Drummond, Inc.
2741 4th Ave
San Diego, CA 92103
Tel.: (619) 528-8404
Fax: (619) 528-8403

PIZZA HUT, INC.
(Sub. of YUM! Brands, Inc.)
14841 Dallas Pkwy
Dallas, TX 75254-7552
Tel.: (972) 338-7700
Tel.: (972) 338-7844 (Media Rels)
Fax: (972) 338-6869
E-mail: info@pizzahut.com
Web Site: www.pizzahut.com
Sales Range: $150-199.9 Million
Approx. Number Employees: 600
Year Founded: 1958
Business Description:
Franchiser of Pizza Hut Restaurants
S.I.C.: 5812
N.A.I.C.S.: 722211
Advertising Expenditures: $250,000,000
Media: 5-8-9-11-14-15-23-24
Distr.: Natl.
Personnel:
Scott O. Bergren *(Pres & Chief Concept Officer)*
Patrick C. Murtha *(COO)*
Kurt Kane *(CMO)*
Corri Reichert *(Head-Media-Natl)*
Doug Willmarth *(Brand Dir)*
Tressie Lieberman *(Sr Mgr-Digital Mktg)*
Jessyca Gonzalez *(Assoc Mgr-CRM)*
Brands & Products:
PIZZA HUT
Advertising Agencies:
Dieste
1999 Bryan St Ste 2700
Dallas, TX 75201
Tel.: (214) 259-8000
Fax: (214) 259-8040
(Hispanic Account)

J. Walter Thompson Company (d/b/a JWT)
466 Lexington Ave
New York, NY 10017-3140
Tel.: (212) 210-7000
Fax: (212) 210-7299

The Martin Agency
One Shockoe Plz
Richmond, VA 23219-4132
Tel.: (804) 698-8000
Fax: (804) 698-8001
Lead Creative Duties

Optimedia International U.S.
375 Hudson St 7th Fl
New York, NY 10014
Tel.: (212) 820-3200
Fax: (212) 820-3300
Media Planning & Buying

PIZZA INN, INC.
3551 Plano Pkwy
The Colony, TX 75056
Tel.: (469) 384-5000
Fax: (469) 384-5059
Toll Free: (800) 880-9955
E-mail: comments@pizzainn.com
Web Site: www.pizzainn.com
Approx. Rev.: $43,036,000
Approx. Number Employees: 57
Year Founded: 1958
Business Description:
Pizza Restaurant Operator & Franchisor
S.I.C.: 5812
N.A.I.C.S.: 722110
Import Export
Advertising Expenditures: $9,000,000
Media: 3-5-8-9-14-15-18-19-20-21-23-24-25-26
Distr.: Reg.

Key to Media (For complete agency information see *The Advertising Red Books-Agencies* edition):
1. Bus. Publs. 2. Cable T.V. 3. Catalogs & Directories. 4. Co-op Adv. 5. Consumer Mags. 6. D.M. to Bus. Estab.7. D.M. to Consumers
8. Daily Newsp. 9. Exhibits/Trade Shows 10. Foreign 11. Infomercial 12. Internet Adv.13. Multimedia 14. Network Radio
15. Network T.V. 16. Newsp. Distr. Mags. 17. Other 18. Outdoor (Posters, Transit) 19. Point of Purchase20. Premiums, Novelties
21. Product Samples 22. Special Events Mktg. 23. Spot Radio 24. Spot T.V. 25. Weekly Newsp. 26. Yellow Page Adv.

Pizza Inn, Inc. — (Continued)

Budget Set: Sept.
Personnel:
Mark E. Schwarz *(Chm)*
Ramon D. Phillips *(Vice Chm)*
Charles R. Morrison *(Pres & CEO)*
Madison Jobe *(COO & Sr VP)*
Nancy Ellefson *(Principal Acctg Officer, Sec & VP-Fin)*
Kendra Shier *(VP-Mktg)*
Scott Richter *(Sr Dir-Mktg)*
Dino Chavez *(Dir-Franchise Dev)*
Andy Wittman *(Mgr-Culinary Ops)*
Brands & Products:
ITALIAN CRUST
NEW YORK PAN
ORIGINAL THIN
PEPPERONI WRAPS
PIE FIVE
PIZZA INN
PIZZERT
STUFFED CRUST
Advertising Agency:
TDA Advertising & Design
1500 Pearl St Ste 300
Boulder, CO 80302
Tel.: (303) 247-1180
Fax: (303) 247-1214

POLLO TROPICAL INC.

(Div. of Carrols Corporation)
7300 N Kendall Dr Fl 8
Miami, FL 33156-7840
Tel.: (305) 670-7696
Fax: (305) 670-6403
Toll Free: (888) 778-7696
E-mail: contact@pollotropical.com
Web Site: www.pollotropical.com
Sales Range: $100-124.9 Million
Approx. Number Employees: 3,000
Year Founded: 1988
Business Description:
Fast Food Restaurant Owner, Operator & Franchisor
S.I.C.: 5812
N.A.I.C.S.: 722211
Advertising Expenditures: $3,000,000
Media: 3-8-9-17-19-21-22-23-24-25
Distr.: Reg.
Budget Set: Nov.
Personnel:
Vivian Lopez-Blanco *(CFO & VP)*
Jason Abelkop *(CMO)*
James Tunnessen *(Exec VP)*
Brands & Products:
POLLO TROPICAL
TROPIGRILL

PONDEROSA STEAKHOUSE

(Div. of Homestyle Dining LLC)
3701 W Plano Pkwy Ste 200
Plano, TX 75075
Tel.: (972) 244-8900
Telex: 288060
Web Site:
www.ponderosasteakhouses.com
Approx. Number Employees: 1,800
Year Founded: 1965
Business Description:
Full Service Restaurants
S.I.C.: 5812; 5813
N.A.I.C.S.: 722110; 722410
Advertising Expenditures: $9,000,000
Media: 8-9-17-18-19-20-23-24-25-26
Distr.: Natl.
Budget Set: Jan. -Dec.

POPEYE'S CHICKEN & BISCUITS

(Sub. of AFC Enterprises, Inc.)
5555 Glenridge Connector NE Ste 300
Atlanta, GA 30342-4741
Tel.: (404) 459-4450
Fax: (404) 459-4533
Toll Free: (800) 222-5857
E-mail: popeyescommunications@popeyes.com
Web Site: www.popeyes.com
Sales Range: $150-199.9 Million
Approx. Number Employees: 1,700
Year Founded: 1972
Business Description:
Operator of Fast Food Restaurants
S.I.C.: 5812
N.A.I.C.S.: 722211
Advertising Expenditures: $30,000,000
Bus. Publs.: $4,500,000; Catalogs & Directories: $3,000,000; Other: $22,500,000
Distr.: Reg.
Personnel:
Cheryl A. Bachelder *(Pres)*
H. Melville Hope, III *(CFO)*
Ralph Bower *(COO)*
Richard Lynch *(CMO)*
Harold Cohen *(VP-Legal)*
Alicia Thompson *(VP-Commun & PR)*
Brands & Products:
POPEYE'S
POPEYE'S CHICKEN & BISCUITS
THRILLSEEKERS
Advertising Agencies:
CooperKatz & Company
205 Lexington Ave 5th Fl
New York, NY 10016
Tel.: (917) 595-3030
Fax: (917) 326-8997

GSD&M
828 W 6th St
Austin, TX 78703-5420
Tel.: (512) 242-4736
Fax: (512) 242-4700
(Creative, Media Buying & Planning)

PRET A MANGER

(Sub. of Pret A Manger (Europe) Ltd)
11 W 42nd St
New York, NY 10017
Tel.: (212) 997-5520
Fax: (646) 728-0858
Web Site: www.pret.com
Sales Range: $10-24.9 Million
Approx. Number Employees: 40
Year Founded: 2000
Business Description:
Sandwich Shop
S.I.C.: 5812
N.A.I.C.S.: 722110
Media: 10-21
Personnel:
Martin Bates *(Pres)*

QIP HOLDER, LLC

(d/b/a Quiznos Sub)
1001 17th St Ste 200
Denver, CO 80202
Tel.: (720) 359-3300
Fax: (720) 359-3399
Web Site: www.quiznos.com
Sales Range: $125-149.9 Million
Approx. Number Employees: 450
Year Founded: 1981
Business Description:
Sandwich Restaurants Operator
S.I.C.: 5812
N.A.I.C.S.: 722211
Media: 3-6-8-14-16-18-19-23-24
Personnel:
Gregory D. Brenneman *(Exec Chm)*
Richard E. Schaden *(CEO)*
Brandon Turner *(CFO & Exec VP)*
Clyde Rucker *(COO & Exec VP)*
Jason Robson *(CMO & Exec VP)*
Pat Meyers *(Gen Counsel)*
John Teza *(Exec VP-Dev)*
Curt Bourg *(Sr VP-American Food Distr)*
Brands & Products:
MMMM...TOASTY!
QUIZ KIDZ
QUIZNOS
QUIZNOS SUB
TOASTY
TOASTY BULLETS
TOASTY TORPEDO
TOASTY TORPEDOES
Advertising Agencies:
Horizon Media, Inc.
75 Varick St
New York, NY 10013
Tel.: (212) 220-5000
Toll Free: (800) 633-4201
Quiznos (Media Duties)

pohMedia
1000 Sawgrass Pkwy Ste 110
Sunrise, FL 33323
Tel.: (954) 845-9454
Media Agency

Wong, Doody, Crandall, Wiener
1011 Western Ave Ste 900
Seattle, WA 98104
Tel.: (206) 624-5325
Fax: (206) 624-2369
Marketing Agency of Record
Quiznos

QUALITY DINING, INC.

4220 Edison Lks Pkwy
Mishawaka, IN 46545-1420
Tel.: (574) 271-4600
Fax: (574) 271-4612
Web Site: www.qdi.com
Sales Range: $200-249.9 Million
Approx. Number Employees: 7,200
Year Founded: 1981
Business Description:
Restaurant Franchiser
S.I.C.: 5812; 5813
N.A.I.C.S.: 722110; 722410
Advertising Expenditures: $8,528,000
Media: 2-4-13-22
Personnel:
Daniel B. Fitzpatrick *(Chm & CEO)*
John C. Firth *(Pres, Gen Counsel & Sec)*
James K. Fitzpatrick *(Chief Dev Officer & Sr VP)*
Lindley E. Burns *(Sr VP-Full Svc Dining Div)*
Gerald O. Fitzpatrick *(Sr VP-Burger King Div)*
Christopher L. Collier *(VP-Fin)*
Thomas D. Hanson *(VP-Mktg)*
Brands & Products:
PAPA VINO'S
PORTERHOUSE STEAKS & SEAFOOD

RA SUSHI PARTNERS

(Sub. of Benihana Inc.)
6263 N Scottsdale Rd Ste 285
Scottsdale, AZ 85250
Tel.: (480) 222-0191
Fax: (480) 222-0192
E-mail: office@rasushi.com
Web Site: www.rasushi.com
Sales Range: $10-24.9 Million
Approx. Number Employees: 500
Year Founded: 1964
Business Description:
Full Service Japanese Restaurant
S.I.C.: 5812
N.A.I.C.S.: 722110
Advertising Expenditures: $100,000
Media: 1-13-20-22-23-24
Personnel:
Scott Kilpatrick *(Co-Founder & VP-RA Sushi)*
Brands & Products:
RA SUSHI
Advertising Agencies:
The PR Boutique
3000 Weslayan Ste 280
Houston, TX 77027
Tel.: (713) 599-1271
Fax: (713) 599-1281

Zapwater Communications
1165 N Clark St Ste 313
Chicago, IL 60610
Tel.: (312) 771-1271
Tel.: (312) 943-0333
Fax: (312) 943-0852

RAMMKERR, INC.

(d/b/a Topsy's Popcorn)
221 W 74th Ter
Kansas City, MO 64114-5730
Tel.: (816) 523-5555
Fax: (816) 523-4747
Toll Free: (800) 722-1930
E-mail: info@topsyspopcorn.com
Web Site: www.topsyspopcorn.com
Approx. Number Employees: 40
Year Founded: 1981
Business Description:
Food Service & Franchise Company; Topsy's Shoppes Popcorn Franchise
S.I.C.: 5441
N.A.I.C.S.: 445292
Advertising Expenditures: $200,000
Media: 3-7-9-19-23-24-25
Distr.: Intl.; Natl.
Budget Set: Aug.
Personnel:
Robert Ramm *(Pres)*
Julie Winkert *(Office Mgr)*
Brands & Products:
TOPSY'S
Advertising Agency:
Gragg Advertising
450 E 4th St Ste 100
Kansas City, MO 64106
Tel.: (816) 931-0050
Fax: (816) 931-0051
Toll Free: (800) 649-4225
(Popcorn & Ice Cream)
— Gregory Gragg *(Acct. Exec.)*

RAVING BRANDS, INC.

1801 Peachtree Rd Ste 160
Atlanta, GA 30309
Tel.: (404) 355-5400
Web Site: www.ravingbrands.com
Year Founded: 2003

Key to Media (For complete agency information see *The Advertising Red Books-Agencies* edition):
1. Bus. Publs. 2. Cable T.V. 3. Catalogs & Directories. 4. Co-op Adv. 5. Consumer Mags. 6. D.M. to Bus. Estab.7. D.M. to Consumers 8. Daily Newsp. 9. Exhibits/Trade Shows 10. Foreign 11. Infomercial 12. Internet Adv.13. Multimedia 14. Network Radio 15. Network T.V. 16. Newsp. Distr. Mags. 17. Other 18. Outdoor (Posters, Transit) 19. Point of Purchase20. Premiums, Novelties 21. Product Samples 22. Special Events Mktg. 23. Spot Radio 24. Spot T.V. 25. Weekly Newsp. 26. Yellow Page Adv.

Business Description:
Fast-Food Franchiser
S.I.C.: 5812
N.A.I.C.S.: 722110; 722211
Media: 2-4-10-18-22-25
Personnel:
Daryl Dollinger *(Co-Founder & Pres)*
Martin Sprock *(Founder & CEO)*
Brands & Products:
BONEHEAD'S
DOC GREEN'S GOURMET SALADS
MAMA FU'S ASIAN HOUSE
MOE'S SOUTHWEST
PJ'S COFFEE & WINE BAR
PLANET SMOOTHIE
SHANE'S RIB SHACK
Advertising Agency:
Trevelino/Keller Communications Group
949 W Marietta St NW Ste X106
Atlanta, GA 30318-5275
Tel.: (404) 214-0722
Fax: (404) 214-0729

REAL MEX RESTAURANTS, INC.

(Holding of Sun Capital Partners, Inc.)
5660 Katella Ave Ste 100
Cypress, CA 90630
Tel.: (562) 346-1200
Fax: (562) 346-1470
Toll Free: (800) 735-3501
E-mail: carla.rodriguez@realmexrestaurants.com
Web Site: www.realmexrestaurants.com
Approx. Rev.: $227,907,000
Approx. Number Employees: 11,236
Year Founded: 1960
Business Description:
Mexican Restaurant Operator
S.I.C.: 5812
N.A.I.C.S.: 722110
Advertising Expenditures: $14,325,000
Media: 8-9-13-14-22-25
Distr.: Reg.
Personnel:
Anthony G. Polazzi *(Chm)*
Richard P. Dutkiewicz *(Interim Pres/ CEO, CFO & Exec VP)*
Lowel Petrie *(CMO & Sr VP)*
Carlos Angulo *(Pres-Real Mex Foods)*
Raymond Garcia *(Sr VP-Ops)*
Roberto Lopez *(Sr VP-R&D & Exec Chef)*
Steve Wallace *(Sr VP-HR)*
John Kuntz *(VP-IT)*
Madelaine Morrow *(VP-Fin)*
Mike Repetti *(VP-IT)*
Brands & Products:
ACAPULCO MEXICAN RESTAURANT
CASA GALLARDO
CHEVY'S FRESH MEX
EL PASO CANTINA
EL TORITO
EL TORITO GRILL
GUADALAHARRY'S
HOLA AMIGOS
KEYSTONE GRILL
LAS BRISAS
SINIGUAL
WHO-SONG & LARRY'S
Advertising Agencies:
Duke Marketing
4040 Civic Center Dr Ste 200
San Rafael, CA 94903
Tel.: (415) 492-4534
Local Store Marketing
PR

Hub Strategy and Communication
39 Mesa St Ste 212
San Francisco, CA 94129
Tel.: (415) 561-4345
Fax: (415) 771-5965
Advertising
Branding
Creative Dev
Socia Media

RED HOT & BLUE RESTAURANTS, INC.

1701 Clarendon Blvd Ste 105
Arlington, VA 22209-2700
Tel.: (703) 276-8833
Fax: (703) 528-4789
E-mail: operations@redhotandblue.com
Web Site: www.redhotandblue.com
Approx. Number Employees: 300
Business Description:
Restaurant Chain
S.I.C.: 5812
N.A.I.C.S.: 722110
Media: 3-5-7-8-9-16-18-19-20-21-22-23-24-25-26
Distr.: Reg.
Budget Set: Mar.
Personnel:
Jeanne Ormsby *(VP-Fin & Admin)*
Brands & Products:
RED HOT AND BLUE

RED LOBSTER

(Div. of Darden Restaurants, Inc.)
1000 Darden Ctr Dr
Orlando, FL 32837
Tel.: (407) 245-4000
Fax: (407) 245-5733
Toll Free: (800) 832-7336
Toll Free: (800) LOBSTER
E-mail: careers@redlobster.com
Web Site: www.redlobster.com
Sales Range: $25-49.9 Million
Approx. Number Employees: 100
Year Founded: 1968
Business Description:
Seafood Restaurants Operator
S.I.C.: 5812
N.A.I.C.S.: 722110
Media: 3-8-15-18-23-24-26
Distr.: Natl.
Budget Set: May
Personnel:
Kim A. Lopdrup *(Pres)*
Salli Setta *(Exec VP-Mktg)*
Jane Diange *(Sr VP-HR)*
John Fadool *(Sr VP-Culinary)*
Bill Lambert *(Sr VP-Fin)*
Brands & Products:
GET TOGETHER AT RED LOBSTER
LIGHTHOUSE SELECTIONS
RED CLAW LAGER
RED LOBSTER TO GO
Advertising Agencies:
Anthem Worldwide
77 Maiden Ln 4th Fl
San Francisco, CA 94108
Tel.: (415) 896-9399
Fax: (415) 896-9387

Buntin Out-of-Home Media
1001 Hawkins St
Nashville, TN 37203-4758
Tel.: (615) 244-5720
Fax: (615) 244-6511

Grey New York
777 3rd Ave
New York, NY 10017-1401
Tel.: (212) 546-2000
Fax: (212) 546-1495

ZenithOptimedia
299 W Houston St 11th Fl
New York, NY 10014
Tel.: (212) 859-5100
Fax: (212) 727-9495

RED MANGO INC.

2811 McKinney Ave Ste 18
Dallas, TX 75204
Tel.: (214) 302-5910
Fax: (214) 302-5980
Web Site: www.redmangousa.com
Business Description:
Frozen Yogurt Store Operator
S.I.C.: 5812
N.A.I.C.S.: 722211
Personnel:
Daniel J. Kim *(Founder & Chief Concept Officer & Member-Board-Dir)*
Jim Notarnicola *(Dir-Licensing)*
Sara McKee *(Coord-Mktg)*
Advertising Agency:
The Richards Group, Inc.
8750 N Central Expy Ste 100
Dallas, TX 75231-6430
Tel.: (214) 891-5700
Fax: (214) 265-2933

RED ROBIN GOURMET BURGERS, INC.

6312 S Fiddlers Green Cir #200N
Greenwood Village, CO 80111
Tel.: (303) 846-6000
E-mail: relations@redrobin.com
Web Site: www.redrobin.com/
Approx. Rev.: $864,269,000
Approx. Number Employees: 23,198
Year Founded: 1969
Business Description:
Hamburger Restaurant Chain
S.I.C.: 5812
N.A.I.C.S.: 722110
Advertising Expenditures: $17,200,000
Media: 16-18-23-24
Personnel:
Pattye L. Moore *(Chm)*
Eric C. Houseman *(Pres & COO)*
Stephen E. Carley *(CEO)*
Stuart B. Brown *(CFO & Sr VP)*
Denny Marie Post *(CMO & Sr VP)*
Annita M. Menogan *(Chief Legal Officer, Sec & Sr VP)*
Todd A. Brighton *(Chief Dev Officer & Sr VP)*
Jonathon W. James *(Sr VP-Enterprise Svcs)*
Katherine L. Scherping *(Sr VP)*
Jennifer Rivas *(Dir-Mktg-Natl)*
Brands & Products:
BOTTOMLESS STEAK FRIES
INSANELY DELICIOUS
MAD MIXOLOGY
RED ROBIN
Advertising Agencies:
Cultivator Advertising & Design
2737 Larimer St Ste B
Denver, CO 80205
Tel.: (303) 444-4134
Fax: (800) 783-4152

Periscope
921 Washington Ave S
Minneapolis, MN 55415
Tel.: (612) 399-0500
Fax: (612) 399-0600
Toll Free: (800) 339-2103
Agency of Record
Red Robin...YUMMM Campaign

RESTAURANT ASSOCIATES CORPORATION

(Sub. of Compass Group USA, Inc.)
330 Fifth Ave 5th Fl
New York, NY 10001
Tel.: (212) 613-5500
E-mail: info@restaurantassociates.com
Web Site: www.restaurantassociates.com
Sales Range: $450-499.9 Million
Approx. Number Employees: 11,000
Year Founded: 1919
Business Description:
Restaurant Management Services
S.I.C.: 5812; 5813
N.A.I.C.S.: 722110; 722410
Advertising Expenditures: $2,000,000
Media: 2-4-6-7-8-9-13-18-22-23-24-26
Distr.: Natl.
Personnel:
Edward J. Sirhal *(Pres)*
Dick Cattani *(CEO)*
Charles LaMonica *(Exec VP-FoodSvc Ops)*
Michael Gallagher *(Sr VP-Special Projects & Support Svcs)*
Andrew Ziobro *(Sr VP-Ops-Cultural Centers & Catering Div)*
Gina Zimmer *(VP-Mktg & Comm)*

RESTAURANT DEVELOPERS CORP.

7010 Engle Rd Ste 100
Cleveland, OH 44130
Tel.: (440) 625-3080
Fax: (440) 625-3081
Toll Free: (888) 860-5082
Web Site: www.mrhero.com
Approx. Number Employees: 30
Year Founded: 1973
Business Description:
Operator & Franchiser of Mr. Hero Restaurants & Arabica Coffee Houses
S.I.C.: 5812; 6794
N.A.I.C.S.: 722211; 533110
Advertising Expenditures: $1,500,000
Media: 2-3-6-7-9-10-13-14-18-19-24-25
Distr.: Direct to Consumer; Natl.
Budget Set: Nov. -Dec.
Personnel:
Michael Nasr *(Pres & CEO)*
Brands & Products:
ARIBICA COFFEE HOUSE
FRESH FOR YOU
HOT BUTTERED CHEESESTEAK
MR. HERO
ROMANBURGER

Key to Media (For complete agency information see *The Advertising Red Books-Agencies* edition):
1. Bus. Publs. 2. Cable T.V. 3. Catalogs & Directories. 4. Co-op Adv. 5. Consumer Mags. 6. D.M. to Bus. Estab.7. D.M. to Consumers 8. Daily Newsp. 9. Exhibits/Trade Shows 10. Foreign 11. Infomercial 12. Internet Adv.13. Multimedia 14. Network Radio 15. Network T.V. 16. Newsp. Distr. Mags. 17. Other 18. Outdoor (Posters, Transit) 19. Point of Purchase20. Premiums, Novelties 21. Product Samples 22. Special Events Mktg. 23. Spot Radio 24. Spot T.V. 25. Weekly Newsp. 26. Yellow Page Adv.

RESTAURANT GROUP INC.
745 S Garfield Ave Ste A
Traverse City, MI 49686
Tel.: (231) 941-5052
Fax: (231) 941-2369
E-mail: info@hrgonline.net
Web Site: www.hrgonline.net
Approx. Number Employees: 15
Business Description:
Fast-Food Restaurant Chain
S.I.C.: 5812; 5813
N.A.I.C.S.: 722110; 722410
Advertising Agency:
Winfield & Associates Marketing & Advertising
3221 Blue Ridge Rd Ste 105
Raleigh, NC 27612
Tel.: (919) 861-0620
Fax: (919) 861-0625

RESTAURANTS UNLIMITED, INC.
(Holding of Sun Capital Partners, Inc.)
1818 N Northlake Way
Seattle, WA 98103-9097
Tel.: (206) 634-3082
Fax: (206) 547-4829
Web Site: www.r-u-i.com
Approx. Sls.: $149,000,000
Approx. Number Employees: 3,500
Year Founded: 1969
Business Description:
Owns & Operates Restaurants
S.I.C.: 5812
N.A.I.C.S.: 722110
Advertising Expenditures: $4,000,000
Bus. Publs.: $800,000; Consumer Mags.: $1,600,000; Exhibits/Trade Shows: $400,000; Other: $1,200,000
Distr.: Direct to Consumer; Reg.
Personnel:
Norman Abdallah *(CEO)*
Don Adams *(Chief Creative Officer)*
Pat Irwin *(VP-IT)*
Will Powers *(VP-Mktg)*
Brands & Products:
CUTTER'S BAYHOUSE
HORATIO'S
KINCAID'S FISH, CHOP & STEAK HOUSE
PALOMINO RESTAURANT ROTISSERIA BAR
SKATES ON THE BAY
Advertising Agencies:
Lane PR
905 SW 16th Ave
Portland, OR 97205
Tel.: (503) 221-0480
Fax: (503) 221-9765

Tamara Wilson Public Relations
1809 7th Ave Ste 1403
Seattle, WA 98101
Tel.: (206) 838-8977
Fax: (206) 838-8980

RIB CITY GRILL, INC.
2122 Second St
Fort Myers, FL 33901
Tel.: (239) 334-8634
Fax: (239) 332-7232
Web Site: www.ribcity.com
Approx. Number Employees: 100
Year Founded: 1989
Business Description:
Restaurant
S.I.C.: 5812
N.A.I.C.S.: 722110
Media: 6
Personnel:
Craig Peden *(Pres)*
Paul Peden *(CEO)*
Beth Watson *(District Mgr)*

ROCK BOTTOM RESTAURANTS, INC.
(Sub. of CraftWorks Restaurants & Breweries Inc.)
248 Centennial Pkwy
Louisville, CO 80027-1675
Tel.: (303) 664-4000
Fax: (303) 664-4199
Toll Free: (800) 273-9827
E-mail: webmaster@rockbottom.com
Web Site: www.rockbottom.com
Sales Range: $150-199.9 Million
Approx. Number Employees: 100
Year Founded: 1994
Business Description:
Restaurant Chain
S.I.C.: 5812
N.A.I.C.S.: 722110
Advertising Expenditures: $500,000
Media: 2-4-6-7-8-9-10-23-25-26
Distr.: Natl.
Personnel:
Frank B. Day *(Chm)*
Gary B. Foreman *(Sr VP-Brand Mgmt)*
Buck Warfield *(Sr VP-Dev)*
Brands & Products:
CHOP HOUSE
OLD CHICAGO
ROCK BOTTOM RESTAURANT & BREWERY
THE WALNUT BREWERY

ROCKY ROCOCO CORPORATION
105 E Wisconsin Ave Ste 101
Oconomowoc, WI 53066
Tel.: (262) 569-5580
Fax: (262) 569-5591
Toll Free: (800) 888-ROCKY
Web Site: www.rockyrococo.com
E-Mail For Key Personnel:
President: president@rockyrococo.com
Approx. Rev.: $55,000,000
Approx. Number Employees: 650
Year Founded: 1974
Business Description:
Franchised Pizza Restaurants
S.I.C.: 5812; 6794
N.A.I.C.S.: 722211; 533110
Advertising Expenditures: $1,000,000
Media: 5-8-9-18-19-21-23-24-25-26
Distr.: Reg.
Personnel:
Tom Hester *(Pres)*
Brands & Products:
ROCKY ROCOCO

ROMACORP, INC.
1700 Alma Dr Ste 400
Plano, TX 75075-6964
Tel.: (214) 343-7800
Fax: (214) 343-9203
E-mail: customersupport@tonyromas.com
Web Site: www.tonyromas.com
Sales Range: $100-124.9 Million
Approx. Number Employees: 1,000
Year Founded: 1972
Business Description:
Owner & Franchiser of Restaurants
S.I.C.: 5812
N.A.I.C.S.: 722110
Media: 3-5-6-8-9-13-14-15-18-20-21-26
Distr.: Intl.; Natl.
Personnel:
Ken Myres *(Pres)*
David Short *(Exec VP-Legal)*
Brands & Products:
BLUE RIDGE SMOKIES
CAROLINA HONEYS
TONY ROMA'S
TONY ROMA'S RED HOTS

ROUND TABLE PIZZA
1320 Willow Pass Rd Ste 600
Concord, CA 94520
Tel.: (925) 969-3900
Fax: (925) 969-3978
Web Site: www.roundtablepizza.com
Sales Range: $25-49.9 Million
Approx. Number Employees: 15
Year Founded: 1959
Business Description:
Pizzerias Owner & Operator
S.I.C.: 5812
N.A.I.C.S.: 722211
Personnel:
Amy Lucas *(Mgr-Mktg)*
Brands & Products:
ROUND TABLE PIZZA
Advertising Agency:
ID Media-Los Angeles
8687 Melrose Ave 8th Fl
West Hollywood, CA 90069
Tel.: (310) 360-5700
Fax: (310) 360-5711
Round Table Pizza

RUBIO'S RESTAURANTS, INC.
(Holding of Mill Road Capital, L.P)
1902 Wright Pl Ste 300
Carlsbad, CA 92008-6583
Tel.: (760) 929-8226
Fax: (760) 929-8203
Toll Free: (800) 354-4199
Web Site: www.rubios.com
Approx. Rev.: $188,878,000
Approx. Number Employees: 3,800
Year Founded: 1983
Business Description:
Restaurant Operator
S.I.C.: 5812
N.A.I.C.S.: 722110
Advertising Expenditures: $5,200,000
Media: 13-18-19
Personnel:
Ralph Rubio *(Chm)*
Daniel E. Pittard *(Pres & CEO)*
Frank E. Henigman *(CFO & Sr VP)*
Marc S. Simon *(COO)*
Kenneth C. Hull *(Sr VP-Dev)*
Brands & Products:
FRESH MEXICAN GRILL
OUR FOOD.YOUR PLACE
RUBIO'S
RUBIO'S A-GO-GO
WORLD FAMOUS FISH TACO

RUBY TUESDAY, INC.
150 W Church Ave
Maryville, TN 37801-4936
Tel.: (865) 379-5700
Fax: (865) 379-6817
E-mail: investorrelations@rubytuesday.com
Web Site: www.rubytuesday.com
Approx. Rev.: $1,265,162,000
Approx. Number Employees: 24,100
Year Founded: 1972
Business Description:
Casual Dining Restaurant Franchiser, Owner & Operator
S.I.C.: 5812; 5813
N.A.I.C.S.: 722110; 722410
Advertising Expenditures: $1,700,000
Media: 5-8-9-10-13-14-16-18-19-23-26
Distr.: Natl.; Reg.
Personnel:
Samuel E. Beall, III *(Chm, Pres & CEO)*
Margie Duffy *(CFO & Sr VP)*
Mark Young *(CMO & Sr VP)*
Nick Ibrahim *(CTO & Sr VP)*
Rob LeBoeuf *(Chief People Officer & Sr VP)*
John Brisco *(Pres-Dev-Intl)*
Scarlett May *(Gen Counsel, Sec & VP)*
Kimberly M. Grant *(Exec VP)*
John Doyle *(VP-IT Restaurant Sys)*
Belinda Kitts *(VP-HR)*
David Schmidt *(VP-Tax & Treasury)*
Jill Johnson *(Dir-Integrated Mktg Comm)*
Brands & Products:
RUBY TUESDAY
SIMPLY FRESH AMERICAN DINING
Advertising Agencies:
Ackermann PR
1111 Northshore Dr Ste N-400
Knoxville, TN 37919
Tel.: (865) 584-0550
Fax: (865) 588-3009
Toll Free: (866) 896-4069
Toll Free: (888) 414-7787

Buntin Out-of-Home Media
1001 Hawkins St
Nashville, TN 37203-4758
Tel.: (615) 244-5720
Fax: (615) 244-6511

TargetCast tcm
909 3rd Ave 31st Fl
New York, NY 10022
Tel.: (212) 500-6900
Fax: (212) 500-6880

RUTH'S HOSPITALITY GROUP, INC.
400 International Pkwy Ste 325
Heathrow, FL 32746
Tel.: (407) 333-7440
Fax: (407) 833-9625
Toll Free: (800) 544-0808
Web Site: www.ruthschris.com
Approx. Rev.: $357,625,000
Approx. Number Employees: 5,768
Year Founded: 1965
Business Description:
Restaurant Operating & Franchising Services
S.I.C.: 5812
N.A.I.C.S.: 722110
Advertising Expenditures: $11,600,000
Media: 6-7-8-13-14-15-18
Personnel:
Michael P. O'Donnell *(Chm, Pres & CEO)*
Arne Haak *(CFO)*
Samuel A. Tancredi *(Pres/COO-Mitchell's Fish Market)*

Key to Media (For complete agency information see *The Advertising Red Books-Agencies* edition):
1. Bus. Publs. 2. Cable T.V. 3. Catalogs & Directories. 4. Co-op Adv. 5. Consumer Mags. 6. D.M. to Bus. Estab.7. D.M. to Consumers 8. Daily Newsp. 9. Exhibits/Trade Shows 10. Foreign 11. Infomercial 12. Internet Adv.13. Multimedia 14. Network Radio 15. Network T.V. 16. Newsp. Distr. Mags. 17. Other 18. Outdoor (Posters, Transit) 19. Point of Purchase20. Premiums, Novelties 21. Product Samples 22. Special Events Mktg. 23. Spot Radio 24. Spot T.V. 25. Weekly Newsp. 26. Yellow Page Adv.

Kevin W. Toomy *(Pres/COO-Ruth's Chris Steak House)*
Cheryl Henry *(Chief Branding Officer & Sr VP)*
Robert M. Vincent *(Sr VP-Corp Strategy)*

Brands & Products:
RUTH'S CHRIS
RUTH'S CHRIS STEAK HOUSE

Advertising Agency:
Merkley + Partners
(Sub. of Omnicom Group, Inc.)
200 Varick St
New York, NY 10014-4810
Tel.: (212) 366-3500
Fax: (212) 805-7445
Agency of Record

RYAN'S RESTAURANT GROUP INC.

(Holding of CI Capital Partners LLC)
1020 Discovery Rd 100
Eagan, MN 55121
Mailing Address:
PO Box 100
Greer, SC 29652-0100
Tel.: (651) 994-8608
Fax: (651) 365-2356
E-mail: jgleitz@ryansinc.com
Web Site: www.ryansrg.com
Sales Range: $800-899.9 Million
Approx. Number Employees: 23,300
Year Founded: 1977
Business Description:
Operator of a Restaurant Chain
S.I.C.: 5812
N.A.I.C.S.: 722110
Media: 3-9-18-19-25
Personnel:
Mike Andrews *(Pres)*

Brands & Products:
MEGABAR
RYAN'S

SANDELLA'S FLATBREAD CAFE

9 Brookside Place
West Redding, CT 06896
Tel.: (203) 544-9984
Toll Free: (888) 544-9984
E-mail: info@sandellas.com
Web Site: www.sandellas.com
Year Founded: 1994
Business Description:
Flatbread Restaurant
N.A.I.C.S.: 722110
Advertising Expenditures: $200,000
Media: 8-13-25
Personnel:
Michael Stimola *(CEO)*

SAN'S PIZZERIA

4842 Ridgemoor Blvd
Palm Harbor, FL 34685
Tel.: (727) 216-6656
Fax: (727) 216-6658
Web Site: www.sanspizzeria.info
Business Description:
Pizzeria
S.I.C.: 5812
N.A.I.C.S.: 722110
Media: 13-16-28
Personnel:
Jackie Felder *(Co-Owner)*
Sanford Felder *(Co-Owner)*

SBARRO, INC.

(Holding of MidOcean Partners, LLP)
401 Broadhollow Rd
Melville, NY 11747-4721
Tel.: (631) 715-4100
Fax: (631) 715-4197
Toll Free: (800) 456-GUEST
E-mail: sbarroguestcomments@sbarro.com
Web Site: www.sbarro.com
Approx. Rev.: $339,285,000
Approx. Number Employees: 3,700
Year Founded: 1977
Business Description:
Cafeteria-Style Italian Restaurant Owner & Operator
S.I.C.: 5812
N.A.I.C.S.: 722211; 722212
Advertising Expenditures: $250,000
Media: 2-9-17-25-26
Distr.: Natl.
Personnel:
Dennis Malamatinas *(Chm)*
Nicholas McGrane *(Pres & CEO)*
Carolyn M. Spatafora *(CFO)*
Anthony J. Missano *(Pres-Sbarro Bus Dev)*
Stuart M. Steinberg *(Gen Counsel)*
Mike Dumelle *(Sr VP-Ops-USA)*

Brands & Products:
BOULDER CREEK
BURTON & DOYLE
CARMELA'S OF BROOKLYN
THE GLOBAL SYMBOL FOR GREAT ITALIAN FOOD
MAMA SBARRO'S
SBARRO
SBARRO THE ITALIAN EATERY

SCHLOTZSKY'S, LTD.

(Sub. of FOCUS Brands, Inc.)
Ste 1100 301 Congress Ave
Austin, TX 78701-2958
Tel.: (512) 236-3600
Fax: (512) 236-3601
Toll Free: (800) 846-BUNS
Web Site: www.schlotzskys.com
Sales Range: $200-249.9 Million
Year Founded: 1971
Business Description:
Restaurant Operator
S.I.C.: 5812
N.A.I.C.S.: 722211; 722110
Advertising Expenditures: $754,000
Media: 3-8-14-15-16-22-23-24-26
Personnel:
Kelly Roddy *(Pres)*
Greg Regian *(CMO-FOCUS Brands)*

Brands & Products:
BUN RUN
SCHLOTZSKY'S
SCHLOTZSKY'S DELI

THE SECOND CUP LTD.

(Sub. of Second Cup Income Fund)
6303 Airport Road
Mississauga, ON L4V 1R8, Canada
Tel.: (905) 362-1818
Toll Free: (877) 212-1818
E-mail: marketing@secondcup.com
Web Site: www.secondcup.com
E-Mail For Key Personnel:
Marketing Director: marketing@secondcup.com
Sales Range: $125-149.9 Million
Approx. Number Employees: 4,000
Year Founded: 1975
Business Description:
Specialty Coffee Retailer
S.I.C.: 5499
N.A.I.C.S.: 445299
Advertising Expenditures: $1,400,000
Media: 5-6-16-17
Personnel:
James Anas *(Chm)*
Stacey Mowbray *(Pres)*
Robert Masson *(CFO)*
Ian M. Baskerville *(VP-Legal Affairs)*
Ryan Brown *(VP-Mktg)*
Kimberly Clark *(VP-Mktg & Product Dev)*
Natasha Mackow *(Mgr-Promotions & Comm-Natl)*

Brands & Products:
CARAMEL CORRETTO
CARAMELO
CHILLATTE
COFFEE COLLEGE
COFFEE UNPLUGGED
CREME BRULEE RISTRETTO
FRRROZEN HOT CHOCOLATE
FRUIZZI
HOLIDAY BLEND
ICEPRESSO CHILLER
JUMPIN JUICE
LA MINITA
PARADISO
SAN AGUSTIN
SECOND CUP
SOHO
SOLID GROUNDS
WHAT'S BREWING
WHITE MOCCA

Advertising Agencies:
CP+B Canada
296 Richmond St W Ste 500
Toronto, ON M5V 1X2, Canada
Tel.: (416) 598-4944
Fax: (416) 593-4944

Due North Communications Inc.
35 The Esplanade 2nd Fl
Toronto, ON M5E 1Z4, Canada
Tel.: (416) 862-8181
Fax: (416) 862-9553
Agency of Record
Retail & Branding

SELECT RESTAURANTS, INC.

(Sub. of Select Management Holdings, Inc.)
2000 Auburn Dr Ste 410
Cleveland, OH 44122-4327
Tel.: (216) 464-6606
Fax: (216) 464-8565
Web Site: www.selectrestaurants.com
Approx. Number Employees: 13
Year Founded: 1992
Business Description:
Restaurant Services
S.I.C.: 5812; 5813
N.A.I.C.S.: 722110; 722410
Advertising Expenditures: $1,000,000
Media: 2-4-6-7-8-9-10-11-15-16-18-19-20-21-23-24-25-26
Distr.: Natl.

Brands & Products:
CHEESE CELLAR
J.B. WINBERIE
PARKERS BLUE ASH GRILL
PARKERS' LIGHTHOUSE
PIER W
ROXY CAFE
RUSTY SCUPPER
TOP OF THE HUB

Advertising Agency:
Haggman, Inc.
39 Dodge St PMB 331
Beverly, MA 01915
Tel.: (978) 525-3742
Fax: (978) 525-4867

SHAKEY'S USA, INC.

(Sub. of Jacmar Companies, Inc.)
2200 W Valley Blvd
Alhambra, CA 91803
Tel.: (626) 576-0616
Fax: (888) 444-6686
E-mail: info@shakeys.com
Web Site: www.shakeys.com
Approx. Number Employees: 19
Year Founded: 1954
Business Description:
Franchise Restaurant Chain
S.I.C.: 5812; 6794
N.A.I.C.S.: 722110; 533110
Advertising Expenditures: $6,500,000
Media: 3-19-23-24
Distr.: Intl.; Natl.
Budget Set: Feb.-Mar.
Personnel:
Joe Remsa *(Pres & CEO)*
Pam Cowin *(VP-HR)*
Linda Bryant *(Dir-Trng & Staffing)*
Cindy Staats *(Dir-Mktg)*

Brands & Products:
SHAKEY'S

Advertising Agency:
Big Imagination Group
3603 Hayden Ave
Culver City, CA 90232
Tel.: (310) 204-6100
Fax: (310) 204-6120

SHANE'S RIB SHACK

(Sub. of Petrus Brands, Inc.)
2136 Hwy 155 N
McDonough, GA 30252
Tel.: (770) 898-7878
Fax: (770) 898-0950
E-mail: info@shanesribsshack.com
Web Site: www.shanesribshack.com
Approx. Number Employees: 20
Year Founded: 2002
Business Description:
Fast-Food Franchiser
S.I.C.: 5812
N.A.I.C.S.: 722110; 722211
Personnel:
Shane Thompson *(Founder & Pres)*

Brands & Products:
SHANE'S SAUCE

Advertising Agency:
Trevelino/Keller Communications Group
949 W Marietta St NW Ste X106
Atlanta, GA 30318-5275
Tel.: (404) 214-0722
Fax: (404) 214-0729
— Heather Graham *(Acct Exec)*

SHONEY'S NORTH AMERICA CORP

(Sub. of Royal Hospitality Corp.)
1717 Elm Hill Pike
Nashville, TN 37210
Mailing Address:
PO Box 1260
Nashville, TN 37202-1260
Tel.: (615) 391-5395
Fax: (615) 231-2806

Key to Media (For complete agency information see *The Advertising Red Books-Agencies* edition):
1. Bus. Publs. 2. Cable T.V. 3. Catalogs & Directories. 4. Co-op Adv. 5. Consumer Mags. 6. D.M. to Bus. Estab.7. D.M. to Consumers 8. Daily Newsp. 9. Exhibits/Trade Shows 10. Foreign 11. Infomercial 12. Internet Adv.13. Multimedia 14. Network Radio 15. Network T.V. 16. Newsp. Distr. Mags. 17. Other 18. Outdoor (Posters, Transit) 19. Point of Purchase20. Premiums, Novelties 21. Product Samples 22. Special Events Mktg. 23. Spot Radio 24. Spot T.V. 25. Weekly Newsp. 26. Yellow Page Adv.

Shoney's North America Corp — (Continued)

Toll Free: (877) 474-6639
E-mail: info@shoneys.com
Web Site: www.shoneys.com
Sales Range: $650-699.9 Million
Approx. Number Employees: 70
Year Founded: 1947
Business Description:
Operator & Franchiser of Restaurant Chain
S.I.C.: 5812; 6794
N.A.I.C.S.: 722110; 533110
Import
Advertising Expenditures: $29,300,000
Media: 3-4-5-6-8-9-10-13-18-19-20-22-23-24-25-26
Distr.: Reg.
Budget Set: Sept. -Nov.
Personnel:
David Davoudpour *(Chm & CEO)*
Kamran Habeeb *(COO & Pres)*
Catherine Hite *(Gen Counsel & VP)*
Steve A. Sanders *(Sr VP-Franchise Ops)*
Debbie Campa *(VP-HR)*
Laurie Katapski *(VP-Mktg)*
Will Eudy *(Dir-R&D)*
Linda Kennedy *(Mgr-Field Mktg)*
Brands & Products:
CAPTAIN D'S
SHONEY'S
Advertising Agency:
Creative Communications Consultants, Inc.
1123 Zonolite Rd Ste 9
Atlanta, GA 30306
Tel.: (404) 898-0423
Fax: (404) 898-0424

SILVER DINER, INC.
11806 Rockville Pike
Rockville, MD 20852-2705
Tel.: (301) 770-0333
Fax: (301) 770-2832
E-mail: customerrelations@silverdiner.com
Web Site: www.silverdiner.com
Approx. Number Employees: 1,100
Year Founded: 1989
Business Description:
Operates Restaurants
S.I.C.: 5812
N.A.I.C.S.: 722110
Advertising Expenditures: $750,000
Media: 4-8-13-18-19
Personnel:
Mark Russell *(Dir-Dev)*
Brands & Products:
AN AUTHENTIC AMERICAN CLASSIC
METRO SILVER DINER
SILVER DINER

SMASHBURGER MASTER LLC
(d/b/a Smashburger)
1515 Arapahoe St, Tower 1, 10th Fl
Denver, CO 80202
Tel.: (303) 633-1500
E-mail: pr@smashburger.com
Web Site: www.smashburger.com/
Business Description:
Franchise Restaurant
S.I.C.: 5812
N.A.I.C.S.: 722110
Personnel:
Tom Ryan *(Founder & Chief Concept Officer)*
David Prokupek *(Chm & CEO)*
Greg Creighton *(Pres)*
Tim Mullany *(CFO)*
Craig Leonard *(Pres-Intl & Exec VP)*
Doug Branigan *(Sr VP-Franchising)*
Chris Chang *(Sr VP-Fin & Strategy)*
Jeremy Morgan *(Sr VP-Mktg & Consumer Insights)*
Max Sheets *(Sr VP-Real Estate)*
David Milliken *(VP-Mktg)*
Julie Reeves *(VP-Mktg)*
Doug Thielen *(VP-Comm)*
Chris Smith *(Reg Dir-Southern US)*
Jennifer Nash *(Dir-Mktg)*
Amy Weasler *(Dir-Franchise Sls)*
Advertising Agencies:
Cactus
(d/b/a Cactus Mktg Communications)
2128 15th St Ste 100
Denver, CO 80202
Tel.: (303) 455-7545
Fax: (303) 455-0408

S3
718 Main St
Boonton, NJ 07005
Tel.: (973) 257-5533
Fax: (973) 257-5543
Agency of Record

SMITH & SONS FOODS, INC.
2124 Riverside Dr
Macon, GA 31204-1747
Mailing Address:
PO Box 4688
Macon, GA 31213-0001
Tel.: (478) 745-4759
Fax: (478) 746-8233
E-mail: sscafeterias@aol.com
Web Site: www.sscafeterias.com
Sales Range: $25-49.9 Million
Approx. Number Employees: 950
Year Founded: 1936
Business Description:
Restaurants & Cafeterias
S.I.C.: 5812; 5141
N.A.I.C.S.: 722310; 424410
Advertising Expenditures: $500,000
Media: 3-8-9-10-17-18-19-20-23-24-25-26
Distr.: Natl.
Personnel:
James A. Smith, III *(Pres & CEO)*
Robert A. Smith *(Exec VP)*
Ralph M. Bennett *(Sr VP-Ops & Admin)*
Melissa C. Smith *(Dir-HR)*
Brands & Products:
S&S CAFETERIAS

THE SMITH & WOLLENSKY RESTAURANT GROUP, INC.
(Joint Venture of Patina Restaurant Group LLC & Bunker Hill Capital LP)
880 3rd Ave
New York, NY 10022-4730
Tel.: (212) 838-2061
Fax: (212) 758-6027
Web Site:
www.smithandwollensky.com
Year Founded: 1983
Business Description:
Management Services-Restaurants
S.I.C.: 5812
N.A.I.C.S.: 722110
Import Export
Advertising Expenditures: $1,860,000
Media: 5-6-8-9-22-23-24
Personnel:
Fortunato N. Valenti *(Pres & CEO)*
Kim Lapine *(VP-Mktg)*
Brands & Products:
A STEAKHOUSE TO END ALL ARGUMENTS
NATIONAL WINE WEEK
SMITH AND WOLLENSKY
Advertising Agencies:
Seiter & Miller Advertising, Inc.
460 Park Ave S
New York, NY 10016
Tel.: (212) 843-9900
Fax: (212) 843-9901

Walrus
18 E 17th St Fl 3
New York, NY 10003
Tel.: (212) 645-2646
Fax: (212) 645-2759
Make Smith & Wollensky Yours

SMOKEY BONES BARBEQUE & GRILL
(Holding of Sun Capital Partners, Inc.)
8529 S Pk Cir Ste 410
Orlando, FL 32819
Tel.: (407) 355-5800
Fax: (407) 363-1972
Web Site: www.smokeybones.com
Business Description:
Restaurant Operator
S.I.C.: 5812
N.A.I.C.S.: 722110
Media: 3-8-13-14-15-18-19-21-23-24-25
Advertising Agencies:
Buntin Out-of-Home Media
1001 Hawkins St
Nashville, TN 37203-4758
Tel.: (615) 244-5720
Fax: (615) 244-6511

PUSH
101 Ernestine St
Orlando, FL 32801-2317
Tel.: (407) 841-2299
Fax: (407) 841-0999
Restaurant Chain

SONIC CORPORATION
300 Johnny Bench Dr Ste 400
Oklahoma City, OK 73104
Tel.: (405) 225-5000
Fax: (405) 225-5975
Toll Free: (866) OK-SONIC
E-mail: soniccfo@sonicdrivein.com
Web Site: www.sonicdrivein.com
E-Mail For Key Personnel:
President: JHudson@sonicdrivein.com
Approx. Rev.: $550,926,000
Approx. Number Employees: 12,740
Year Founded: 1952
Business Description:
Licensing & Operation of Drive-In Franchised Restaurants
S.I.C.: 5812
N.A.I.C.S.: 722211
Advertising Expenditures: $22,537,000
Media: 4-5-9-16-22-26
Personnel:
J. Clifford Hudson *(Chm & CEO)*
W. Scott McLain *(Pres)*
Stephen C. Vaughan *(CFO & Exec VP)*
Craig Miller *(CIO & Sr VP)*
Danielle Vona *(CMO & VP)*
Omar Janjua *(Pres-Sonic Restaurants)*
Paige S. Bass *(Gen Counsel & VP)*
Robert J. Geresi *(Sr VP-Central Markets)*
Diane L. Prem *(Sr VP-West Markets)*
Andrew G. Ritger, Jr. *(Sr VP-Bus Plng & Pur)*
Nancy L. Robertson *(Sr VP-Comm)*
E.Edward Saroch *(Sr VP-East Markets)*
Alan Cantrell *(VP-SRI Field Fin)*
Keith O. Jossell *(VP-Market Strategies)*
Paul Macaluso *(VP-Mktg)*
Christi Woodworth *(Dir-External Comm)*
Brands & Products:
AMERICA'S DRIVE-IN
AMERICA'S FAVORITE DRIVE-IN
CAROLINA CLUB
CHED 'R' BITES
CHED 'R' PEPPERS
DRINK STOP
DRIVE-IN DEALS
DRIVE-IN FOR A CHANGE
DRIVE-IN TO SUMMER
FAVES AND CRAVES
FOUNTAIN FAVORITES
FROZEN FAVORITES
MONSTER CHOCOLATE
MY SONIC
OCEAN WATER
PREMI-YUM
ROUTE 44
ROUTE 44/BIG DRINK
SLUSH44.COM
SONIC
SONIC BLAST
SONIC CRUISERS
SONIC DRIVE-IN
SONIC-SIZE
SONIC SUNRISE
SONIC WAVE
SUNSHINE SMOOTHIE
SUPERSONIC
TOASTER
WACKY PACK
Advertising Agencies:
Euro RSCG Discovery
372 Danbury Rd Ste 100
Wilton, CT 06897
Tel.: (203) 563-3300
Fax: (203) 563-3435
Menus, Point of Sale, & Packaging

Goodby, Silverstein & Partners, Inc.
(Part of Omnicom Group, Inc.)
720 California St
San Francisco, CA 94108-2404
Tel.: (415) 392-0669
Fax: (415) 788-4303
Creative Agency of Record

Lopez Negrete Communications, Inc.
3336 Richmond Ave Ste 200
Houston, TX 77098
Tel.: (713) 877-8777
Fax: (713) 877-8796
Hispanic

Zenith Media Services
(Regional Headquarters for ZenithOptimedia, the Americas)

Key to Media (For complete agency information see *The Advertising Red Books-Agencies* edition):
1. Bus. Publs. 2. Cable T.V. 3. Catalogs & Directories. 4. Co-op Adv. 5. Consumer Mags. 6. D.M. to Bus. Estab.7. D.M. to Consumers 8. Daily Newsp. 9. Exhibits/Trade Shows 10. Foreign 11. Infomercial 12. Internet Adv.13. Multimedia 14. Network Radio 15. Network T.V. 16. Newsp. Distr. Mags. 17. Other 18. Outdoor (Posters, Transit) 19. Point of Purchase20. Premiums, Novelties 21. Product Samples 22. Special Events Mktg. 23. Spot Radio 24. Spot T.V. 25. Weekly Newsp. 26. Yellow Page Adv.

299 W Houston St 10th Fl
New York, NY 10014-4806
Tel.: (212) 859-5100
Fax: (212) 727-9495
Agency of Record

SONIC INDUSTRIES, INC.
(Div. of SONIC Corporation)
300 Johnny Bench Dr
Oklahoma City, OK 73104
Tel.: (405) 225-5000
Fax: (405) 225-5975
Web Site: www.sonicdrivein.com
Sales Range: $25-49.9 Million
Approx. Number Employees: 220
Year Founded: 1953
Business Description:
Franchised & Partnership, Drive-through Restaurants
S.I.C.: 5812
N.A.I.C.S.: 722211
Distr.: Natl.
Budget Set: Oct.
Personnel:
W. Scott McLain *(Pres)*
Stephen C. Vaughn *(CFO & Exec VP)*
Paige Bass *(Gen Counsel & VP)*
Drew Ritger *(Sr VP-Bus Plng & Pur)*
Advertising Agency:
Barkley Public Relations
1740 Main St
Kansas City, MO 64108
Tel.: (816) 842-1500

SONNY'S FRANCHISE COMPANY INC.
2605 Maitland Ave Ste C
Maitland, FL 32751
Tel.: (407) 660-8888
Fax: (407) 660-1305
E-mail: soates@sonnysbbq.com
Web Site: www.sonnysbbq.com
Approx. Sls.: $14,251,505
Approx. Number Employees: 18
Year Founded: 1968
Business Description:
Barbecue Restaurant
S.I.C.: 5812
N.A.I.C.S.: 722110
Media: 24
Personnel:
Jefferey Yarmuth *(Pres & COO)*
Brands & Products:
PLATE-HIDING PORTION
SONNY'S REAL PIT BAR-B-Q

SONNY'S REAL PIT BAR-B-QUE
1720 US Hwy 1 S
Saint Augustine, FL 32084-6016
Tel.: (904) 824-3220
Fax: (904) 825-0577
Web Site: www.sonnysbbq.com
Sales Range: $250-299.9 Million
Approx. Number Employees: 6,435
Year Founded: 1968
Business Description:
Family Restaurant Owner & Operator
S.I.C.: 5812
N.A.I.C.S.: 722110
Media: 8-13-24
Personnel:
Jeff Yarmuth *(Pres)*
Advertising Agencies:
Ad Partners Inc.
9800 4th St N Ste 200
Saint Petersburg, FL 33702
Tel.: (727) 289-8900
Fax: (727) 289-8999

GoConvergence
4545 36th St
Orlando, FL 32811
Tel.: (407) 235-3210
Fax: (407) 299-9907

SOUTH ST BURGER CO
(Sub. of New York Fries)
1220 Yonge St Ste 400
Toronto, ON Canada
Tel.: (416) 963-5005
Fax: (416) 963-4920
Web Site: www.southstburger.com
Approx. Number Employees: 25
Year Founded: 2005
Business Description:
Fast Food Restaurant
S.I.C.: 5812
N.A.I.C.S.: 722211
Media: 14-18-23
Personnel:
Alyssa Berenstein *(Mgr-Mktg)*

SPAGHETTI WAREHOUSE, INC.
(Sub. of Consolidated Restaurant Operations, Inc.)
12200 N Stemmons Fwy Ste 100
Dallas, TX 75234-5877
Tel.: (972) 241-5500
Fax: (972) 888-8198
E-mail: banquets@meatballs.com
Web Site: www.meatballs.com
Sales Range: $50-74.9 Million
Approx. Number Employees: 260
Year Founded: 1972
Business Description:
Family Style Italian Restaurants Operator & Franchiser
S.I.C.: 5812
N.A.I.C.S.: 722110
Advertising Expenditures: $1,500,000
Media: 4-6-8-9-18-23-24-25
Distr.: Direct to Consumer
Budget Set: Apr.
Personnel:
Gene E. Street *(Chm)*
John Harkey *(Pres & CEO)*
Bill Watson *(VP-Mktg)*

SPICY PICKLE FRANCHISING, INC.
90 Madison St Ste 700
Denver, CO 80206
Tel.: (303) 297-1902
Fax: (303) 297-1903
Web Site: www.spicypickle.com
Approx. Rev.: $4,463,661
Approx. Number Employees: 17
Business Description:
Restaurant Franchiser
S.I.C.: 7922; 5812
N.A.I.C.S.: 711110; 722110
Advertising Expenditures: $631,215
Personnel:
Kevin Morrison *(Owner)*
Presley Orelle Reed, Jr. *(Chm)*
Mark Laramie *(CEO)*
Clint Woodruff *(CFO)*
Jeffery Branton *(VP & Gen Mgr-Canadian Ops)*
Brendan Charles *(Head-Construction & Mgr-Real Estate/Facilities)*
Lisa Brown *(Dir-Trng)*
Chris Bue *(Dir-Ops)*

STAR BUFFET, INC.
1312 N Scottsdale Rd
Scottsdale, AZ 85257-3410
Tel.: (480) 425-0397
Fax: (801) 463-5595
E-mail: starbuffet@starbuffet.com
Web Site: www.starbuffet.com
Approx. Rev.: $77,996,000
Approx. Number Employees: 1,770
Year Founded: 1997
Business Description:
Owner & Operater of Restaurants & Eating Places
S.I.C.: 5812; 6519
N.A.I.C.S.: 722110; 531190
Import Export
Advertising Expenditures: $710,000
Media: 4-13-14-15-16-17-22
Personnel:
Robert E. Wheaton *(Pres & CEO)*
Brands & Products:
4B'S
BAR-H STEAKHOUSE
BUDDYFREDDY'S COUNTRY BUFFET
CASA BONITA
HOLIDAY HOUSE
JJ NORTH'S
PECOS DIAMOND STEAKHOUSE
STAR BUFFET
WHISTLE JUNCTION

STRANG CORPORATION
(d/b/a Dons Lighthouse)
8905 Lake Ave
Cleveland, OH 44102
Tel.: (216) 961-6767
Fax: (216) 961-1966
Web Site: www.strangcorp.com
Sales Range: $150-199.9 Million
Approx. Number Employees: 3,500
Year Founded: 1942
Business Description:
Hospitality Services
S.I.C.: 5812; 5813
N.A.I.C.S.: 722110; 722410
Personnel:
Donald W. Strang, Jr. *(Chm)*
Don Strang, III *(Pres)*
Peter Strang *(Exec VP)*
Advertising Agency:
Sampson/Carnegie, Co., Inc.
1419 E. 40th St
Cleveland, OH 44103
Tel.: (216) 881-2556
Fax: (216) 881-5252
Toll Free: (800) 277-5301

STRAW HAT COOPERATIVE CORPORATION
18 Crow Cyn Ct Ste 270
San Ramon, CA 94583-1669
Tel.: (925) 837-3400
Fax: (925) 820-1080
E-mail: info@strawhatpizza.com
Web Site: www.strawhatpizza.com
Sales Range: $10-24.9 Million
Approx. Number Employees: 7
Year Founded: 1987
Business Description:
Pizza Restaurants Cooperative
S.I.C.: 8741; 5812
N.A.I.C.S.: 561110; 722211
Advertising Expenditures: $5,510,000
Bus. Publs.: $10,000; Co-op Adv.: $150,000; D.M. to Bus. Estab.: $50,000; D.M. to Consumers: $800,000; Daily Newsp.: $200,000; Point of Purchase: $300,000; Premiums, Novelties: $100,000; Spot Radio: $400,000; Spot T.V.: $3,000,000; Weekly Newsp.: $300,000; Yellow Page Adv.: $200,000
Distr.: Direct to Consumer; Reg.
Personnel:
Jonathan C. Fornaci *(Pres)*
Brands & Products:
BIG BAMBINO
GENUINE CALIFORNIA PIZZA
GREEK MASTERPIZZA
HOT-HATS
MEAT-E-OR
MOJAVE HOT WINGS
Advertising Agency:
Next Marketing, Inc.
(House Agency)
18 Crow Canyon Ct., Ste. 150
San Ramon, CA 94583
Tel.: (925) 837-3400

STUART ANDERSON'S BLACK ANGUS & CATTLE COMPANY RESTAURANTS
(Sub. of American Restaurant Group, Inc.)
4410 El Camino Real Ste 201
Los Altos, CA 94022-1049
Tel.: (650) 949-6400
Fax: (650) 949-6425
Toll Free: (800) 382-3852
Web Site: www.stuartandersons.com
Approx. Sls.: $260,000,000
Approx. Number Employees: 6,000
Year Founded: 1964
Business Description:
Steak House Restaurants
S.I.C.: 5812
N.A.I.C.S.: 722110
Media: 3-5-8-9-13-18-19-20-22-25-26
Distr.: Reg.
Budget Set: Nov.
Personnel:
Meredith Taylor *(Pres & CEO)*
Brands & Products:
STUART ANDERSON'S
Advertising Agency:
ID Media-Los Angeles
8687 Melrose Ave 8th Fl
West Hollywood, CA 90069
Tel.: (310) 360-5700
Fax: (310) 360-5711

SUBWAY RESTAURANTS
(Div. of Doctor's Associates Inc.)
325 Bic Dr
Milford, CT 06461
Tel.: (203) 877-4281
Fax: (203) 783-7302
Web Site: www.subway.com
Approx. Number Employees: 900
Year Founded: 1965
Business Description:
Franchisor of Individually-Owned & Operated Deli-Style, Fast Food Restaurants
S.I.C.: 5812; 6519
N.A.I.C.S.: 722211; 531190
Media: 2-3-6-14-15-18-24-25
Personnel:
Fred DeLuca *(Founder & CEO)*

Key to Media (For complete agency information see *The Advertising Red Books-Agencies* edition):
1. Bus. Publs. 2. Cable T.V. 3. Catalogs & Directories. 4. Co-op Adv. 5. Consumer Mags. 6. D.M. to Bus. Estab.7. D.M. to Consumers
8. Daily Newsp. 9. Exhibits/Trade Shows 10. Foreign 11. Infomercial 12. Internet Adv.13. Multimedia 14. Network Radio
15. Network T.V. 16. Newsp. Distr. Mags. 17. Other 18. Outdoor (Posters, Transit) 19. Point of Purchase20. Premiums, Novelties
21. Product Samples 22. Special Events Mktg. 23. Spot Radio 24. Spot T.V. 25. Weekly Newsp. 26. Yellow Page Adv.

Subway Restaurants — (Continued)

Peter Buck *(Co-Founder)*
Bill Schettini *(CMO)*
Eddie Lindley *(Sr Brand Mgr-US Multicultural & Dir-Latin America)*
Shannon Bowers *(Brand Mgr-Subway Franchisee Adv Fund Trust)*
Dan Sokolik *(Mgr-Field Mktg)*
Carman Wenkoff *(Program Mgr)*

Brands & Products:
COLD CUT TRIO
FRESH VALUE MEALS
ITALIAN BMT
SEVEN UNDER SIX
SUBWAY
SUBWAY CLUB
SUBWAY FRESH FIT
SUBWAY MELT
SUBWAY SELECTS
VEGGIE DELITE

Advertising Agencies:
Catapult Marketing
55 Post Rd W
Westport, CT 06880
Tel.: (203) 682-4000
Fax: (203) 682-4097

GlobalHue
Ste 1600 4000 Town Ctr
Southfield, MI 48076
Tel.: (248) 223-8900
Fax: (248) 304-8877

Gosh! Advertising Pte. Ltd.
10 Anson Road #11-21 International Plaza
Singapore, 079903, Singapore
Tel.: (65) 6323 9359
Fax: (65) 6223 2787

Hughes
1141 S 7th St
Saint Louis, MO 63104
Tel.: (314) 571-6300
St. Louis, MO Area

kirshenbaum bond senecal + partners
Toronto
2 Bloor Street E 26th Fl
Toronto, ON M4W 3J4, Canada
Tel.: (416) 260-7000
Fax: (416) 260-7100

MediaCom
498 7th Ave
New York, NY 10018
Tel.: (212) 912-4200
Fax: (212) 508-4386

MMB
580 Harrison Ave
Boston, MA 02118
Tel.: (617) 670-9700
Fax: (617) 670-9711

PointRoll Inc.
951 E Hector St
Conshohocken, PA 19428
Tel.: (267) 558-1300
Fax: (267) 285-1141
Toll Free: (800) 203-6956

SCPF
1688 Meridian Ave Ste 200
Miami Beach, FL 33139
Tel.: (305) 674-3222
Fax: (305) 695-2777

Simmons Flint
33 S Third St Ste D
Grand Forks, ND 58201
Tel.: (701) 746-4573
Fax: (701) 746-8067

Source Communications
433 Hackensack Ave 8th Fl
Hackensack, NJ 07601-6319
Tel.: (201) 343-5222
Fax: (201) 343-5710

Upshot
350 N Orleans St 5th Fl
Chicago, IL 60654
Tel.: (312) 943-0900
Fax: (312) 943-9699
Marketing
Merchandising & Promotions Agency of Record
— Richard Scarle *(Sr VP)*
— Jerry Craven *(Sr VP)*

SWH CORPORATION

(Sub. of Mimi's Cafe, LLC)
(d/b/a Mimi's Cafe)
18872 Macarthur Blvd Ste 400
Irvine, CA 92612
Tel.: (714) 544-4826
Toll Free: (866) 566-4647
Web Site: www.mimiscafe.com
Sales Range: $200-249.9 Million
Approx. Number Employees: 7,695
Year Founded: 1973
Business Description:
Eating Place Services
S.I.C.: 5812
N.A.I.C.S.: 722110
Import Export
Media: 9-25
Personnel:
Tim Pulido *(COO)*

TACO BELL CORP.

(Sub. of YUM! Brands, Inc.)
1 Glen Bell Way
Irvine, CA 92618
Tel.: (949) 863-4500
Fax: (949) 863-4091
Toll Free: (800) TACOBEL
E-mail: webmaster@tacobell.com
Web Site: www.tacobell.com
Sales Range: $1-9.9 Million
Approx. Number Employees: 39,700
Year Founded: 1962
Business Description:
Franchiser of Fast Food Restaurants
S.I.C.: 5812; 6794
N.A.I.C.S.: 722211; 533110
Media: 9-10-14-15-18-19-20-22-23-24-31
Distr.: Intl.; Natl.
Personnel:
Greg Creed *(Pres & CEO)*
Rob Savage *(COO)*
Brian Niccol *(Chief Mktg & Innovation Officer)*
Bob Fulmer *(Exec Dir)*
Martin Hennessey *(Sr Brand Dir-Comm)*
Juliet Corsinita *(Dir-Media Svcs)*
Danielle Wolfson *(Sr Assoc Mgr-Interactive Mktg)*

Brands & Products:
FRUTISTA FREEZE

Advertising Agencies:
Draftfcb
17600 Gillette Ave
Irvine, CA 92614-5702
Tel.: (949) 851-3050
Fax: (949) 567-9465
Agency of Record
Frutista Freeze Drinks
Social Media CRM Program
— Adam Tompkins *(Dir-Creative)*

Draftfcb
101 E Erie St
Chicago, IL 60611-2812
Tel.: (312) 425-5000
Fax: (312) 425-5010
Social Media CRM Program

LevLane Advertising/PR/Interactive
100 Penn Sq E
Philadelphia, PA 19107
Tel.: (215) 825-9600
Fax: (215) 809-1900
Frutista Freeze

MEC, Global HQ, New York
825 7th Ave
New York, NY 10019-6014
Tel.: (212) 474-0000
Fax: (212) 474-0020
Fax: (212) 474-0003

R/GA
350 W 39th St
New York, NY 10018-1402
Tel.: (212) 946-4000
Fax: (212) 946-4010

Weber Shandwick
(Sub. of The Interpublic Group of Companies)
919 3rd Ave
New York, NY 10022
Tel.: (212) 445-8000
Fax: (212) 445-8001

TACO BUENO RESTAURANTS, L.P.

(Sub. of TB Corporation)
1605 LBJ Fwy Ste 800
Farmers Branch, TX 75234
Tel.: (972) 919-4800
Fax: (972) 919-4831
Toll Free: (866) 681-2312
Web Site: www.tacobueno.com
Sales Range: $125-149.9 Million
Approx. Number Employees: 3,000
Year Founded: 1967
Business Description:
Quick Service Mexican Restaurants
S.I.C.: 5812
N.A.I.C.S.: 722211
Advertising Expenditures: $400,000
Media: 8-9-16-18-19-20-23-24
Distr.: Direct to Consumer; Reg.
Budget Set: Nov.
Personnel:
Kim Hennig *(CMO)*
Jeff Platt *(Dir-Corp Real Estate & Design)*
Jeff Wohead *(Dir-Construction)*

Brands & Products:
MEXIDIPS & CHIPS
MUCHACO
TACO BUENO

TACO CABANA, INC.

(Sub. of Carrols Corporation)
8918 Tesoro Dr Ste 200
San Antonio, TX 78217-6219
Tel.: (210) 804-0990
Fax: (210) 804-1970
Web Site: www.tacocabana.com
Sales Range: $150-199.9 Million
Approx. Number Employees: 100
Year Founded: 1977
Business Description:
Corporate Offices for Restaurants
S.I.C.: 5812
N.A.I.C.S.: 722211
Advertising Expenditures: $4,300,000
Media: 3-5-7-8-13-17-18-19-21-22-23-24-25
Personnel:
Mike Biviano *(COO)*
Todd Coerver *(CMO)*
Shanna Garcia *(Gen Counsel)*
Mark Phillips *(Reg VP)*
Brian Maysent *(VP-Mktg)*

Brands & Products:
TACO CABANA

Advertising Agencies:
BradfordLawton, LLC
1020 Townsend Ave
San Antonio, TX 78209
Tel.: (210) 832-0555
Fax: (210) 732-8555
Account Planning
Branding
Creative Agency of Record
Digital Media
Local Store Marketing Development
Print, Broadcast & Digital Production

Calise & Sedei
501 Elm St, Ste 500
Dallas, TX 75202
Tel.: (469) 385-4790
Fax: (214) 760-7094

TACO DEL MAR FRANCHISING CORP.

(d/b/a Taco Del Mar)
400 Boren Ave North
Seattle, WA 98109
Tel.: (206) 624-7060
Fax: (206) 624-7065
Web Site: www.tacodelmar.com
Approx. Rev.: $5,000,000
Approx. Number Employees: 20
Year Founded: 1992
Business Description:
Eating Places
S.I.C.: 5812
N.A.I.C.S.: 722211
Personnel:
Larry Destro *(Pres & CEO)*

Advertising Agencies:
Wexley School for Girls
2218 5th Ave
Seattle, WA 98121
Tel.: (206) 438-8900
Agency of Record

Williams-Helde Marketing Communications
711 6th Av N
Seattle, WA 98109
Tel.: (206) 285-1940

Key to Media (For complete agency information see *The Advertising Red Books-Agencies* edition):
1. Bus. Publs. 2. Cable T.V. 3. Catalogs & Directories. 4. Co-op Adv. 5. Consumer Mags. 6. D.M. to Bus. Estab.7. D.M. to Consumers 8. Daily Newsp. 9. Exhibits/Trade Shows 10. Foreign 11. Infomercial 12. Internet Adv.13. Multimedia 14. Network Radio 15. Network T.V. 16. Newsp. Distr. Mags. 17. Other 18. Outdoor (Posters, Transit) 19. Point of Purchase20. Premiums, Novelties 21. Product Samples 22. Special Events Mktg. 23. Spot Radio 24. Spot T.V. 25. Weekly Newsp. 26. Yellow Page Adv.

TACO JOHN'S INTERNATIONAL, INC.

808 W 20th St
Cheyenne, WY 82001-3404
Tel.: (307) 635-0101
Fax: (307) 638-0603
Toll Free: (800) 854-0819
E-mail: email@tacojohns.com
Web Site: www.tacojohns.com
Approx. Number Employees: 60
Year Founded: 1969
Business Description:
Fast Food Franchised Restaurants
S.I.C.: 6794; 5812
N.A.I.C.S.: 533110; 722211
Media: 3-5-9-18-19-22-23-24-25
Distr.: Reg.
Budget Set: Oct.
Personnel:
Harold Holmes *(Founder)*
Barry D. Sims *(CEO)*
Jim Creel *(CFO & VP)*
Forest King *(VP-Trng & Workforce Dev)*
Brands & Products:
A WHOLE LOT OF MEXICAN
APPLE GRANDE
CHOCO TACO
CINI-SOPAPILLA BITES
CRUNCH TIME
THE FRESH TASTE OF WEST-MEX
MEXI ROLLS
NACHOS NAVIDAD
POTATO OLE'S
SNACKARITOS
SOFT SHELL SATURDAY
TACO BRAVO
TACO JOHN'S
TACO JOHN'S MEXPRESS
TACO TECH
TACO TUESDAY
WEST-MEX
Advertising Agencies:
Odney
1400 W Century Ave
Bismarck, ND 58503
Tel.: (701) 222-8721
Fax: (701) 222-8172
Toll Free: (888) 500-8721

Preston Kelly
222 First Ave NE
Minneapolis, MN 55413
Tel.: (612) 843-4000
Fax: (612) 843-3900

TASTEE FREEZ LLC

(Sub. of Galardi Group, Inc.)
4501 Jamboree Rd
Newport Beach, CA 92660
Tel.: (949) 752-9626
Web Site: www.tastee-freez.com
Approx. Number Employees: 11
Year Founded: 1950
Business Description:
Franchising of Quick Serve Restaurants
S.I.C.: 5812
N.A.I.C.S.: 722211
Media: 3-4-7-8-9-10-14-15-18-19-20-23-24-25-26
Distr.: Intl.; Natl.
Personnel:
Br... uish *(Owner)*
Brands & Products:
BIG T
BIG TEE BURGER
SEA-TEE
TASTEE CRISP
TASTEE FREEZ
Advertising Agency:
Adville/USA
44 S Mentor Ave
Pasadena, CA 91106-2902
Tel.: (626) 397-9911
Fax: (626) 397-9919
Toll Free: (800) 722-8145

TEXAS ROADHOUSE, INC.

6040 Dutchmans Ln
Louisville, KY 40205
Tel.: (502) 426-9984
Fax: (502) 426-3274
Toll Free: (800) 839-7623
E-mail: info@texasroadhouse.com
Web Site: www.texasroadhouse.com
Approx. Rev.: $942,331,000
Approx. Number Employees: 31,000
Year Founded: 1993
Business Description:
Steak Restaurant Chain Owner & Operator
S.I.C.: 5812; 7922
N.A.I.C.S.: 722110; 711110
Advertising Expenditures: $7,000,000
Media: 9-13-18-23-24-25
Personnel:
Wayne Kent Taylor *(Chm & CEO)*
Scott M. Colosi *(CFO)*
Steven L. Ortiz *(COO)*
Sheila C. Brown *(Gen Counsel & Sec)*
Brands & Products:
ANDY ARMADILLO
CACTUS BLOSSOM
CHICKEN CRITTERS
JAMAICAN COWBOY
LASSO YOUR LOVER
LEGENDARY FOOD, LEGENDARY SERVICE
ROADHOUSE GOLD
TEXAS ROADHOUSE

T.G.I. FRIDAY'S INC.

(Sub. of Carlson Restaurants Worldwide Inc.)
4201 Marsh Ln
Carrollton, TX 75007
Tel.: (972) 662-5400
Fax: (972) 662-5401
Web Site: www.fridays.com
Approx. Number Employees: 27,500
Year Founded: 1965
Business Description:
Restaurant Chain Owner, Operator & Licenses
S.I.C.: 5812; 5813
N.A.I.C.S.: 722110; 722410
Media: 3-6-8-9-13-14-15-18-19-20
Personnel:
Ian Saunders *(Pres & COO-Intl)*
Trey Hall *(CMO & Sr VP)*
Lee Sanders *(Pres-Franchising)*
Sherri Landry *(Sr Brand Mgr)*
Brands & Products:
FRIDAY'S
RIGHT PORTION, RIGHT PRICE
Advertising Agencies:
Digitas Inc.
33 Arch St
Boston, MA 02110
Tel.: (617) 867-1000
Fax: (617) 867-1111
Digital Agency

Horizon Media, Inc.
75 Varick St
New York, NY 10013
Tel.: (212) 220-5000
Toll Free: (800) 633-4201
Media Buying

pohMedia
1000 Sawgrass Pkwy Ste 110
Sunrise, FL 33323
Tel.: (954) 845-9454
Media Agency of Record

Publicis New York
4 Herald Sq 950 6th Ave
New York, NY 10001
Tel.: (212) 279-5550
Fax: (212) 279-5560
Creative Agency

The Richards Group, Inc.
8750 N Central Expy Ste 100
Dallas, TX 75231-6430
Tel.: (214) 891-5700
Fax: (214) 265-2933

THE THIRSTY MARLIN

1023 Florida Ave
Palm Harbor, FL 34683
Tel.: (727) 784-3469
E-mail: thirstymarlin@verizon.net
Web Site: www.thirstymarlin.com
Business Description:
Restaurant
S.I.C.: 5812
N.A.I.C.S.: 722110
Media: 13-16
Personnel:
Mike Flowers *(Owner)*
Brian St Arnold *(Owner)*

TIM HORTONS, INC.

874 Sinclair Rd
Oakville, ON L6K 2Y1, Canada
Tel.: (905) 845-6511
Fax: (905) 845-0265
E-mail: customer_service@timhortons.com
Web Site: www.timhortons.com
Approx. Rev.: $2,584,231,836
Approx. Number Employees: 186
Year Founded: 1964
Business Description:
Coffee & Fresh Baked Goods Food Chain
S.I.C.: 2096; 5499
N.A.I.C.S.: 311919; 445299
Advertising Expenditures: $5,400,000
Media: 5-14-15-18-22-23-24
Personnel:
Paul D. House *(Chm, Pres & Interim CEO)*
Cynthia J. Devine *(CFO)*
William A. Moir *(CMO & Chief Brand Officer)*
R. Scott Toop *(Gen Counsel & Exec VP)*
John M. Hemeon *(Exec VP-Supply Chain)*
Chriatian M. de Jahm *(Sr VP-Ops-Canada)*
Stephen A. Johnston *(Sr VP-Dev)*
Brigid V. Pelino *(Sr VP-HR)*
Ed Williams *(Mgr-US Construction-Natl)*
Brands & Products:
ROLL UP THE RIM TO WIN
TIM CARD
TIM HORTONS
TIMBITS
TIM'S OWN
Advertising Agencies:
henderson bas
479 Wellington Street West
Toronto, ON M5V 1E7, Canada
Tel.: (416) 977-6660
Fax: (416) 977-2226

JWT Canada
160 Bloor St E Ste 800
Toronto, ON M4W 3P7, Canada
Tel.: (416) 926-7300
Fax: (416) 967-2859

TRC HOLDINGS LLC

(Holding of Castle Harlan, Inc.)
6075 Poplar Ave Ste 800
Memphis, TN 38119
Tel.: (901) 766-6400
Web Site:
www.perkinsrestaurants.com
Sales Range: $75-99.9 Million
Approx. Number Employees: 9,800
Business Description:
Family Restaurant Operator
S.I.C.: 5812
N.A.I.C.S.: 722110
Advertising Expenditures: $21,130,000

TRUFOODS LLC

14 Penn Plaza Ste 1305
New York, NY 10122
Tel.: (212) 359-3600
Fax: (212) 359-3601
E-mail: info@trufoodscorp.com
Web Site: www.trufoods.com
Approx. Sls.: $75,000,000
Approx. Number Employees: 300
Year Founded: 1969
Business Description:
Operates & Licenses Specialty Restaurants
S.I.C.: 5812
N.A.I.C.S.: 722110
Advertising Expenditures: $600,000
Media: 3-5-8-9-19-20-24-25
Distr.: Natl.
Personnel:
Andy Unanue *(CEO)*
Robert J. Bagnell *(CFO)*
Michael Lerman *(COO & Exec VP)*
Tiffanie Morrison *(Mgr-Mktg)*
Brands & Products:
ARTHUR TREACHER'S

TUMBLEWEED, INC.

(Filed Ch 11 Bankruptcy #931525 on 03/27/09 in U.S. Bankruptcy Ct, Western Dist of KY, Louisville)
2301 River Rd Ste 200
Louisville, KY 40206
Tel.: (502) 893-0323
Fax: (502) 893-6676
E-mail: info@tumbleweedrestaurants.com
Web Site:
www.tumbleweedrestaurants.com
Sales Range: $75-99.9 Million
Approx. Number Employees: 1,800
Year Founded: 1975
Business Description:
Operator & Franchiser of Full Service Restaurants
S.I.C.: 5812; 5813
N.A.I.C.S.: 722110; 722410

Key to Media (For complete agency information see *The Advertising Red Books-Agencies* edition):
1. Bus. Publs. 2. Cable T.V. 3. Catalogs & Directories. 4. Co-op Adv. 5. Consumer Mags. 6. D.M. to Bus. Estab.7. D.M. to Consumers
8. Daily Newsp. 9. Exhibits/Trade Shows 10. Foreign 11. Infomercial 12. Internet Adv.13. Multimedia 14. Network Radio
15. Network T.V. 16. Newsp. Distr. Mags. 17. Other 18. Outdoor (Posters, Transit) 19. Point of Purchase20. Premiums, Novelties
21. Product Samples 22. Special Events Mktg. 23. Spot Radio 24. Spot T.V. 25. Weekly Newsp. 26. Yellow Page Adv.

Tumbleweed, Inc. — (Continued)

Export
Advertising Expenditures: $4,000,000
Media: 7-8-13-16-23-24
Personnel:
Glennon F. Mattingly *(CFO & VP)*
Brands & Products:
TEX MEX
TUMBLEWEED
TUMBLEWEED SOUTHWEST GRILL
TUMBLEWEED SOUTHWEST MESQUITE GRILL AND BAR

UFOOD RESTAURANT GROUP, INC.

(d/b/a UFood Grill)
255 Washington St Ste 100
Newton, MA 02458
Tel.: (617) 787-6000
Fax: (617) 787-6010
E-mail: info@ufoodgrill.com
Web Site: www.ufoodgrill.com
E-Mail For Key Personnel:
Marketing Director: marketing@ufoodgrill.com
Approx. Rev.: $4,942,939
Approx. Number Employees: 32
Year Founded: 2006
Business Description:
Restaurant Operator & Franchisor
S.I.C.: 5812
N.A.I.C.S.: 722110
Advertising Expenditures: $60,644
Media: 8-16-17
Personnel:
George A. Naddaff *(Chm & CEO)*
Charles A. Cocotas *(Pres & COO)*
Irma Norton *(CFO)*
Tom Mackey *(Sr VP-Ops)*
Brands & Products:
UFOOD

UGLY, INC.

(d/b/a Coyote Ugly Saloon)
153 1st Ave
New York, NY 10003-2946
Tel.: (212) 477-4431
Toll Free: (866) 520-UGLY
Web Site: www.coyoteuglysaloon.com
Approx. Sls.: $12,100,000
Business Description:
Saloon Owner
S.I.C.: 5813
N.A.I.C.S.: 722410
Media: 3-13-22
Personnel:
Liliana Lovell *(Founder-Owner)*
Jacqui Squatriglia *(Gen Mgr-Coyote Ugly New York)*
Brands & Products:
COYOTE UGLY

UNO RESTAURANT HOLDINGS CORPORATION

(Holding of Centre Partners Management LLC)
100 Charles Park Rd
West Roxbury, MA 02132
Tel.: (617) 323-9200
Fax: (617) 323-6906
E-mail: resumes@pizzeriauno.com
Web Site: www.unos.com
Sales Range: $400-449.9 Million
Approx. Number Employees: 6,500
Year Founded: 1943
Business Description:
Casual Theme Restaurant Operator
S.I.C.: 5812
N.A.I.C.S.: 722110
Advertising Expenditures: $4,500,000
Media: 5-7-8-9-18-19-25-26
Distr.: Natl.
Budget Set: July
Personnel:
Aaron D. Spencer *(Chm)*
Frank Guidara *(CEO)*
Louie Psallidas *(CFO & Sr VP-Fin)*
Roger Zingle *(COO)*
George W. Herz, II *(Gen Counsel & Sr VP)*
William J. Golden *(Exec VP-Ops)*
Richard K. Hendrie *(Sr VP-Mktg)*
Michael Dellemonico *(VP-Sls)*
Alan D. LaBatte *(VP-Info Sys)*
Kimberly Boynton *(Dir-Mktg)*
Alan M. Fox *(Sr Mgr-Production)*
Brands & Products:
NUMERO UNO
PIZZERIA UNO
SPINOCCOLI
UNO
UNO CHICAGO BAR & GRILL

THE VENUE CLUB

2675 Ulmerton Rd
Clearwater, FL 33762
Tel.: (727) 571-2222
Web Site: www.thevenueclub.com
Business Description:
Restaurant & Nightclub
S.I.C.: 5812
N.A.I.C.S.: 722110
Media: 9-13-22-23-24-25
Personnel:
Alan Shoopak *(Owner & Pres)*
Leah Weinbaum *(Mgr-Outside Sls & Mktg)*

VENUE OF SCOTTSDALE

7117 E 3rd Ave
Scottsdale, AZ 85251-3821
Tel.: (480) 945-5150
Fax: (480) 945-5208
E-mail: info@venueofscottsdale.com
Web Site: www.venueofscottsdale.com
Approx. Number Employees: 60
Year Founded: 1997
Business Description:
Live Music Venue, Night Club & Restaurant
S.I.C.: 7922
N.A.I.C.S.: 711110
Advertising Expenditures: $500,000
Media: 6-13-25
Personnel:
Victor Perrillo *(Pres)*

VILLAGE INN RESTAURANTS

(Joint Venture of Fidelity National Financial, Inc. & Newport Global Advisors, L.P.)
400 W 48th Ave
Denver, CO 80216-1806
Mailing Address:
PO Box 16601
Denver, CO 80216-0601
Tel.: (303) 296-2121
Fax: (303) 672-2677
Web Site: www.villageinnrestaurants.com
Sales Range: $125-149.9 Million
Approx. Number Employees: 18,000
Year Founded: 1958
Business Description:
Restaurants
S.I.C.: 5812
N.A.I.C.S.: 722110
Advertising Expenditures: $6,000,000
Media: 3-8-9-13-18-22-23-24-25
Distr.: Reg.
Personnel:
Jeffry L. Guido *(Pres)*
Brands & Products:
VILLAGE INN

WAFFLE HOUSE, INCORPORATED

5986 Financial Dr
Norcross, GA 30071-2949
Tel.: (770) 729-5700
Fax: (770) 729-5900
E-mail: resume@wafflehouse.com
Web Site: www.wafflehouse.com
Approx. Sls.: $91,000,000
Approx. Number Employees: 6,000
Year Founded: 1955
Business Description:
Short-Order Restaurants
S.I.C.: 5812; 6794
N.A.I.C.S.: 722110; 533110
Media: 5-13-18-20
Distr.: Direct to Consumer; Reg.
Personnel:
Joe W. Rogers, Jr. *(Chm)*
Jon Waller *(Gen Counsel)*
Pat Warner *(VP-Mktg)*
Brands & Products:
AMERICA'S PLACE TO WORK AMERICA'S PLACE TO EAT
WAFFLE HOUSE

WALL STREET DELI SYSTEMS, INC.

(Sub. of TruFoods LLC)
5 Dakota Drive Ste 302
Lake Success, NY 11042
Tel.: (516) 358-0600
Web Site: www.wallstreetdeli.com
Approx. Number Employees: 600
Year Founded: 1967
Business Description:
Operator of Quick Service, Delicatessen-Style Restaurant Chain
S.I.C.: 8741
N.A.I.C.S.: 561110
Advertising Expenditures: $350,000
Media: 9-17-18-19-23-26
Distr.: Direct to Consumer
Personnel:
Jeffrey Bernstein *(Pres & CEO)*
Brands & Products:
WALL STREET DELI

WENDY'S/ARBY'S GROUP, INC.

1155 Perimeter Center W
Atlanta, GA 30338
Tel.: (678) 514-4500
Toll Free: (888) 514-0924
Web Site: www.wendysarbys.com
Approx. Rev.: $3,416,414,000
Approx. Number Employees: 64,100
Year Founded: 1929
Business Description:
Holding Company; Fast Food Restaurant Chain Owner, Franchisor & Operator
S.I.C.: 6719; 5812; 6794
N.A.I.C.S.: 551112; 533110; 722211
Advertising Expenditures: $182,008,000
Media: 5-9-16-23-24
Distr.: Natl.
Personnel:
Nelson Peltz *(Chm)*
Peter W. May *(Vice Chm)*
Roland C. Smith *(Pres & CEO)*
Stephen E. Hare *(CFO & Sr VP)*
Andy Skehan *(COO)*
John D. Barker *(Chief Comm Officer & Sr VP)*
Sharron L. Barton *(Chief Admin Officer)*
Steven B. Graham *(Chief Acctg Officer & Sr VP)*
J. David Karam *(Pres-Wendys Intl)*
Nils H. Okeson *(Gen Counsel, Sec & Sr VP)*
Daniel T. Collins *(Treas & Sr VP)*
Bob Kraut *(Sr VP-Mktg & Adv)*
Darrell G. van Ligten *(Sr VP-Strategic Dev)*
Brands & Products:
ARBY'S
ARBY'S MARKET FRESH
FROSTY
GARDEN SENSATIONS
SIDEKICKERS
T.J. CINNAMONS
WENDY'S
WENDY'S ARBY'S GROUP
Advertising Agency:
The Kaplan Thaler Group
825 8th Ave 34th Fl
New York, NY 10019
Tel.: (212) 474-5000
Fax: (212) 474-5702

WENDY'S INTERNATIONAL, INC.

(Sub. of WENDY'S/ARBY'S GROUP, INC.)
4288 W Dublin Granville Rd
Dublin, OH 43017-1442
Mailing Address:
PO Box 256
Dublin, OH 43017-0256
Tel.: (614) 764-3100
Fax: (614) 766-3979
Web Site: www.wendys.com
Approx. Rev.: $2,450,000,000
Approx. Number Employees: 7,000
Year Founded: 1969
Business Description:
Fast Food Restaurants Operator, Developer & Franchisor
S.I.C.: 5812
N.A.I.C.S.: 722211
Advertising Expenditures: $134,100,000
Media: 3-6-13-15-18-19-22-23-24
Distr.: Intl.; Natl.
Personnel:
J. David Karam *(Pres)*
Stephen D. Farrar *(COO)*
David J. Near *(COO)*
Ken Calwell *(CMO & Chief Food Innovation Officer)*
Paul Kershisnik *(CMO-Interim)*
John D. Barker *(Chief Comm Officer & Sr VP)*
Nils H. Okeson *(Gen Counsel, Sec & Sr VP)*
Jeffrey M. Cava *(Exec VP-HR & Admin)*
Brendan P. Foley, Jr. *(Controller & Sr VP)*
Dana Klein *(Sr VP, Asst Sec & Assoc Gen Counsel)*

Key to Media (For complete agency information see *The Advertising Red Books-Agencies* edition):
1. Bus. Publs. 2. Cable T.V. 3. Catalogs & Directories. 4. Co-op Adv. 5. Consumer Mags. 6. D.M. to Bus. Estab.7. D.M. to Consumers 8. Daily Newsp. 9. Exhibits/Trade Shows 10. Foreign 11. Infomercial 12. Internet Adv.13. Multimedia 14. Network Radio 15. Network T.V. 16. Newsp. Distr. Mags. 17. Other 18. Outdoor (Posters, Transit) 19. Point of Purchase20. Premiums, Novelties 21. Product Samples 22. Special Events Mktg. 23. Spot Radio 24. Spot T.V. 25. Weekly Newsp. 26. Yellow Page Adv.

Edward L. Austin *(Sr VP)*
Bob Holtcamp *(Sr VP-Brand Mktg)*
Dennis L. Lynch *(Sr VP-Comm)*
John N. Peters *(Sr VP)*
Tom Spero *(Sr VP-Ops-North Region)*
Darrell G. van Ligten *(Sr VP-Strategic Dev)*
Ana Hernandez *(Dir-Multicultural Mktg)*
Bob Bertini *(Dir-Consumer Comm)*
Matt Dee *(Dir-Adv Production)*
Bob Stowe *(Dir-Mktg Svcs)*

Brands & Products:
FROSTY
TWISTED FROSTY
WENDY'S

Advertising Agencies:
The Bravo Group
Courvoisier Centre 601 Brickell Key Dr Ste 1100
Miami, FL 33131-4330
Tel.: (305) 503-8000
Fax: (305) 347-4331
(Hispanic Agency of Record)

Fitzgerald+CO
3060 Peachtree Rd NW
Atlanta, GA 30305
Tel.: (404) 504-6900
Fax: (404) 239-0548

The Kaplan Thaler Group
825 8th Ave 34th Fl
New York, NY 10019
Tel.: (212) 474-5000
Fax: (212) 474-5702

Ketchum
E Randolph Ste 3600
Chicago, IL 60601-5925
Tel.: (312) 228-6800
Fax: (312) 228-6868
(Public Relations)
— Jon Bellinger *(Acct Exec)*

The Vidal Partnership
228 E 45th St 11th Fl
New York, NY 10017-3303
Tel.: (646) 356-6600
Fax: (212) 661-7650
Hispanic Marketing

WESTERN SIZZLIN CORPORATION

(Sub. of Biglari Holdings Inc.)
PO Box 12157
Roanoke, VA 24023-2157
Tel.: (540) 345-3195
Fax: (540) 345-0831
Fax: (877) 329-6300
Toll Free: (800) 24-STEAK
Toll Free: (800) 247-8325
E-mail: ewilliams@western-sizzlin.com
Web Site: www.western-sizzlin.com
Approx. Rev.: $17,204,747
Approx. Number Employees: 271
Year Founded: 1962

Business Description:
Restaurant Operator & Franchisor
S.I.C.: 5812; 6794
N.A.I.C.S.: 722110; 533110
Advertising Expenditures: $169,000
Media: 8-18

Personnel:
Sardar Biglari *(Chm & CEO)*
Robyn B. Mabe *(CFO, COO & VP)*

Brands & Products:
BIG TEX
CHEYENNE
COLT 45
COOKIN' WHAT AMERICA LOVES BEST
DUDE
FLAMEKIST
GREAT AMERICAN STEAK & BUFFET
MARSHALL
RANGER
SIX SHOOTER
SIZZLIN
TRAILBLAZER
WESTERN
WESTERN SIZZLIN
WESTERN SIZZLIN COW
WESTERN SIZZLIN STEAK & MORE
WESTERN SIZZLIN STEAK HOUSE
WESTERN SIZZLIN WOOD GRILL

WHATABURGER, INC.

1 Whataburger Way
Corpus Christi, TX 78411-2930
Tel.: (361) 878-0650
Fax: (361) 878-0473
E-mail: tcoerver@wbhq.com
Web Site: www.whataburger.com
Sales Range: $500-549.9 Million
Approx. Number Employees: 12,000
Year Founded: 1950

Business Description:
Fast Food Restaurants Owner & Operator
S.I.C.: 5812; 6794
N.A.I.C.S.: 722211; 533110
Advertising Expenditures: $12,000,000
Media: 3-4-6-8-9-11-13-18-19-20-22-23-24
Distr.: Intl.
Budget Set: Sept.

Personnel:
Thomas Dobson *(Chm)*
Preston Atkinson *(Pres & COO)*
Michael McLellan *(Exec VP)*

Brands & Products:
ADDABOY
JUST LIKE YOU LIKE IT
JUSTABURGER
LEAN & MEAN
THICK & HEARTY BURGER
WHATABLENDER
WHATABLENDERS
WHATABURGER
WHATABURGER JR.
WHATACATCH
WHATACHICK'N
WHATAGUY
WHATAKIDS
WHATAMEAL
WHATAPALS
WHATASIZE IT!

Advertising Agencies:
Axxis Advertising LLC
1738 W Indian School Rd
Phoenix, AZ 85015
Tel.: (602) 200-0707

McGarrah Jessee
205 Brazos
Austin, TX 78701
Tel.: (512) 225-2000
Fax: (512) 225-2020

Southwest Media Group
2100 Ross Ave Ste 3200
Dallas, TX 75201
Tel.: (214) 561-5543
Fax: (214) 744-1086

SPM Communications
2030 Main St Ste 325
Dallas, TX 75201
Tel.: (214) 379-7000 (Main)
Tel.: (817) 329-3257 (24 Hour Media Line)
Fax: (214) 379-7007

WHITE CASTLE SYSTEM, INC.

555 W Goodale St
Columbus, OH 43215-1158
Tel.: (614) 228-5781
Fax: (614) 464-0596
Web Site: www.whitecastle.com
Sales Range: $550-599.9 Million
Approx. Number Employees: 11,815
Year Founded: 1921

Business Description:
Fast Food Hamburger & Frozen Grocery Hamburger & Cheeseburger Producer & Sales
S.I.C.: 5812; 5142
N.A.I.C.S.: 722211; 424420
Media: 3-5-8-13-14-15-18-19-20-23-24
Distr.: Reg.
Budget Set: Nov.

Personnel:
Russell J. Meyer *(CFO, Treas & VP)*
Nicholas W. Zuk *(Gen Counsel)*
Kim Kelly-Bartley *(VP-Mktg-Site Dev)*
Andrew F. Prakel *(Corp Controller & Asst Treas)*
Kelly Collins *(Supvr-Mktg)*

Brands & Products:
PSB COMPANY
WHITE CASTLE

Advertising Agencies:
Goodway Group
The Pavilion 261 Old York Rd Ste 930
Jenkintown, PA 19046
Tel.: (215) 887-5700
Fax: (215) 881-2239

Northlich
Sawyer Point Bldg 720 Pete Rose Way
Cincinnati, OH 45202
Tel.: (513) 421-8840
Fax: (513) 455-4749

Zimmerman Advertising
2200 W Commercial Blvd Ste 300
Fort Lauderdale, FL 33309-3064
Tel.: (954) 644-4000
Fax: (954) 731-2977
Toll Free: (800) 248-8522
Creative & Media Agency of Record

WINCHELL'S DONUT HOUSES OPERATING CO., LP

(Sub. of Yum Yum Donut Shops, Inc.)
3610 Venice Blvd 6th ave
Los Angeles, CA 90019
Tel.: (626) 964-1478
Web Site: www.winchells.com
Approx. Number Employees: 1,300

Business Description:
Doughnut Franchise Owner & Operator
S.I.C.: 5461; 6512
N.A.I.C.S.: 445291; 531120
Media: 19-20-23-24
Distr.: Intl.; Natl.
Budget Set: June

Brands & Products:
HOME OF THE WARM 'N FRESH DONUT

YUM! BRANDS, INC.

1441 Gardiner Ln
Louisville, KY 40213-1914
Tel.: (502) 874-8300
Tel.: (502) 874-7400 (Media Rels)
Fax: (502) 874-8790
Web Site: www.yum.com
Approx. Rev.: $11,343,000,000
Approx. Number Employees: 52,920
Year Founded: 1997

Business Description:
Restaurant Operator & Franchiser
S.I.C.: 5812; 6719; 6794
N.A.I.C.S.: 722211; 533110; 551112
Advertising Expenditures: $557,000,000
Media: 5-8-11-13-22

Personnel:
David C. Novak *(Chm, Pres & CEO)*
Samuel Su *(Vice Chm)*
Richard T. Carucci *(CFO)*
Emil J. Brolick *(COO)*
David Russell *(Chief Acctg Officer, VP & Controller)*
Micky Pant *(Pres-Global Branding)*
Christian L. Campbell *(Gen Counsel, Sec, Sr VP & Chief Franchise Policy Officer)*
Jonathan D. Blum *(Chief Pub Affairs Officer & Sr VP)*
Tim P. Jerzyk *(Sr VP-IR)*
Ted F. Knopf *(Sr VP-Fin)*
Amy Sherwood *(VP-PR & Consumer Affairs)*
Martin Hennessy *(Sr Dir-Brand Comm-Taco Bell)*
Debra Kassarjian *(Dir-Consumer Insights & Innovation)*
Javier Figueroa *(Mgr-Mktg-KFC)*

Brands & Products:
A & W
EAST DAWNING
KENTUCKY FRIED CHICKEN
LONG JOHN SILVERS
PASTA BRAVO
PIZZA HUT
TACO BELL
YUM

Advertising Agencies:
Draftfcb
101 E Erie St
Chicago, IL 60611
Tel.: (312) 425-5000
Fax: (312) 425-5010
Taco Bell

LevLane Advertising/PR/Interactive
100 Penn Sq E
Philadelphia, PA 19107
Tel.: (215) 825-9600
Fax: (215) 809-1900
KFC
Taco Bell
— Jason Rossano *(Acct Mgr)*

The Martin Agency
One Shockoe Plz
Richmond, VA 23219-4132
Tel.: (804) 698-8000
Fax: (804) 698-8001

Key to Media (For complete agency information see *The Advertising Red Books-Agencies* edition):
1. Bus. Publs. 2. Cable T.V. 3. Catalogs & Directories. 4. Co-op Adv. 5. Consumer Mags. 6. D.M. to Bus. Estab.7. D.M. to Consumers
8. Daily Newsp. 9. Exhibits/Trade Shows 10. Foreign 11. Infomercial 12. Internet Adv.13. Multimedia 14. Network Radio
15. Network T.V. 16. Newsp. Distr. Mags. 17. Other 18. Outdoor (Posters, Transit) 19. Point of Purchase20. Premiums, Novelties
21. Product Samples 22. Special Events Mktg. 23. Spot Radio 24. Spot T.V. 25. Weekly Newsp. 26. Yellow Page Adv.

YUM! Brands, Inc. — (Continued)

Pizza Hut

MEC Interaction
825 7th Ave
New York, NY 10019
Tel.: (212) 474-0000
Fax: (212) 474-0003

Northlich
Sawyer Point Bldg 720 Pete Rose Way
Cincinnati, OH 45202
Tel.: (513) 421-8840
Fax: (513) 455-4749
Kentucky Field Chicken
New Products

TracyLocke
1999 Bryan St Ste 2800
Dallas, TX 75201
Tel.: (214) 259-3500
Fax: (214) 259-3550

YUM! RESTAURANTS INTERNATIONAL (CANADA) LP

(Div. of Yum! Restaurants International)
101 Exchange Ave
Vaughan, ON L4K 5R6, Canada
Tel.: (416) 664-5200
Fax: (416) 739-7762
Web Site: www.priszm.com
Sales Range: $10-24.9 Million
Approx. Number Employees: 70
Year Founded: 1991
Business Description:
Restaurant
S.I.C.: 5812
N.A.I.C.S.: 722110
Personnel:
David Vivenes *(CMO)*
Sabir Sami *(Gen Mgr)*
Brands & Products:
YUM
Advertising Agency:
Grip Ltd.
179 John St 6th Fl
Toronto, ON M5T 1X4, Canada
Tel.: (416) 340-7111
Fax: (416) 340-7776
Kentucky Fried Chicken (KFC)
Pizza Hut
Taco Bell

ZAXBY'S FRANCHISING, INC.

1040 Founders Blvd
Athens, GA 30606
Tel.: (706) 353-8107
Fax: (706) 548-6002
Toll Free: (866) 892-9297
Web Site: www.zaxbys.com
Approx. Number Employees: 700
Year Founded: 1990
Business Description:
Restaurant Franchisor
S.I.C.: 5812
N.A.I.C.S.: 722211
Media: 5-15-18
Personnel:
Zach W. McLeroy *(Chm & CEO)*
Tony D. Townley *(CFO)*
Brands & Products:
A FRESH APPROACH TO CHICKEN
BIG ZAX SNAK
BUFFALO FINGERZ
KIDDIE CHEESE
KIDDIE FINGER
ONION PEEL
TONGUE TORCH
ZALADS
ZAPPETIZERS
ZAX SUACE
ZAXBY'S
Advertising Agency:
St. John & Partners
5220 Belfort Rd Ste 400
Jacksonville, FL 32256-6017
Tel.: (904) 281-2500
Fax: (904) 281-0030
— Amanda Harnish *(PR Acct Coord)*

ZIPPY'S, INC.

1765 S King St 2nd Fl
Honolulu, HI 96826-2134
Tel.: (808) 973-0880
Fax: (808) 973-0888
E-mail: customerservice@zippys.com
Web Site: www.zippys.com
Approx. Number Employees: 2,000
Year Founded: 1966
Business Description:
Eating Places
S.I.C.: 5812
N.A.I.C.S.: 722211
Import Export
Advertising Expenditures: $1,000,000
Media: 3-4-13-15-16-17-18-22-23-24-26
Personnel:
Jason Higa *(Pres)*
Douglas Shimabukuro *(CFO & Controller)*
Advertising Agency:
Hendrix Miyasaki Shin
1580 Makaloa St Ste 945
Honolulu, HI 96814
Tel.: (808) 944-8777
Fax: (808) 944-8788
(Creative)

Key to Media (For complete agency information see *The Advertising Red Books-Agencies* edition):
1. Bus. Publs. 2. Cable T.V. 3. Catalogs & Directories. 4. Co-op Adv. 5. Consumer Mags. 6. D.M. to Bus. Estab.7. D.M. to Consumers 8. Daily Newsp. 9. Exhibits/Trade Shows 10. Foreign 11. Infomercial 12. Internet Adv.13. Multimedia 14. Network Radio 15. Network T.V. 16. Newsp. Distr. Mags. 17. Other 18. Outdoor (Posters, Transit) 19. Point of Purchase20. Premiums, Novelties 21. Product Samples 22. Special Events Mktg. 23. Spot Radio 24. Spot T.V. 25. Weekly Newsp. 26. Yellow Page Adv.

Schools & Colleges

Academies — Camps — Colleges — Correspondence Schools — Dance Studios — Libraries

THE ACADEMY OF RADIO BROADCASTING, INC.
16052 Beach Blvd Ste 263
Huntington Beach, CA 92647-3819
Tel.: (714) 842-0100
Fax: (714) 842-1858
Toll Free: (714) 842-1643
Web Site: www.arbradio.com
Approx. Number Employees: 25
Year Founded: 1983
Business Description:
Vocational Training School for Radio & Television Broadcasting
S.I.C.: 8249
N.A.I.C.S.: 611519
Media: 9-17-23-25
Distr.: Reg.
Budget Set: Dec.
Personnel:
Lindy P. Thurell *(Co-Owner & Chm)*
Tom King *(Co-Owner)*
Thomas H. Gillenwater *(CEO)*
Dorine Dunn *(Chief Admin Officer)*

ACT INC.
500 A Ct Dr
Iowa City, IA 52243
Tel.: (319) 337-1024
Fax: (319) 337-1059
Web Site: www.act.org
E-Mail For Key Personnel:
Public Relations: mediarelations@act.org
Sales Range: $150-199.9 Million
Approx. Number Employees: 1,500
Year Founded: 1960
Business Description:
College Admissions Testing Program & Other Educational Services
S.I.C.: 8299
N.A.I.C.S.: 611710
Import Export
Media: 1-2-7-8-10-11-13-18-20
Personnel:
Richard L. Ferguson *(Chm & CEO)*
Thomas J. Goedken *(CFO & Sr VP)*
Arthur C. Peters *(VP-IT)*
Rose G. Rennekamp *(VP-Comm)*
Scott Gomer *(Dir-Media Rels)*
Brands & Products:
ACT
ACT ASSESSMENT
ACT CENTERS
ASSET
COMPASS
DISCOVER
EPAS
EXPLORE
PLAN
WORKKEYS

AMERICAN INSTITUTE FOR FOREIGN STUDY, INC.
9 W Broad St
Stamford, CT 06902-3734
Tel.: (203) 399-5000
Fax: (203) 399-5463
Toll Free: (800) 727-2437
E-mail: info@aifs.com
Web Site: www.aifs.com
Sales Range: $125-149.9 Million
Approx. Number Employees: 410
Year Founded: 1964
Business Description:
Organizes Cultural Exchange Programs Worldwide
S.I.C.: 8299; 8351
N.A.I.C.S.: 611710; 624410
Import Export
Personnel:
Cyril J.H. Taylor *(Chm)*
William Gertz *(Pres & CEO)*
Jack Burg *(CFO & Sr VP)*
Mike Dimauro *(Sr VP)*
Brands & Products:
AMERICAN INSTITUTE FOR FOREIGN STUDY
EDUCATIONAL TRAVEL
WE BRING THE WORLD TOGETHER
Advertising Agency:
Krutick Advertising
7 Hollow Ln
Poughkeepsie, NY 12603-5018
Tel.: (845) 462-4188
Fax: (845) 462-8586

AMERICAN PUBLIC EDUCATION, INC.
111 W Congress St
Charles Town, WV 25414
Tel.: (304) 724-3700
Fax: (304) 724-3780
Toll Free: (877) 468-6268
Web Site:
www.americanpubliceducation.com
Approx. Rev.: $198,174,000
Approx. Number Employees: 2,170
Year Founded: 1991
Business Description:
Online Post-Secondary Education for Military & Public Service Sectors
S.I.C.: 8221; 2741; 8299
N.A.I.C.S.: 611310; 516110; 611430; 611710
Advertising Expenditures: $22,046,000
Media: 2-7-8-10-13-18
Personnel:
J. Christopher Everett *(Chm)*
Timothy T. Weglicki *(Vice Chm)*
Wallace E. Boston, Jr. *(Pres & CEO)*
Harry T. Wilkins *(CFO & Exec VP)*
Carol S. Gilbert *(Exec VP-Mktg & Programs)*
Peter W. Gibbons *(Chief Admin Off & Sr VP)*

AMERICAN SCHOOL OF CORRESPONDENCE
2200 E 170th St
Lansing, IL 60438-1002
Tel.: (708) 418-2800
Toll Free: (800) 531-9268
Web Site:
www.americanschoolofcorr.com
Approx. Number Employees: 200
Year Founded: 1897
Business Description:
Educational Services
S.I.C.: 8249
N.A.I.C.S.: 611519
Export
Media: 6-9-10
Distr.: Natl.
Personnel:
Gary R. Masterton *(Pres)*
Roberta R. Allen *(Exec VP & Dir-Curriculum)*
Ann Holcomb *(Dir-Adv)*
Brands & Products:
AMERICAN SCHOOL
Advertising Agency:
DB Advertising Associates
2200 E 170th St
Lansing, IL 60438-1002
Tel.: (708) 418-2813

AMERICAN UNIVERSITY
4400 Massachusetts Ave NW
Washington, DC 20016-8001
Tel.: (202) 885-1000
Fax: (202) 885-3265
E-mail: afa@american.edu
Web Site: www.american.edu
E-Mail For Key Personnel:
Marketing Director: spencer@american.edu
Approx. Number Employees: 5,000
Year Founded: 1893
Business Description:
University
S.I.C.: 8221; 9411
N.A.I.C.S.: 611310; 923110
Advertising Expenditures: $350,000
Media: 1-2-3-4-7-8-9-10-16-18-20-23-25-26
Distr.: Natl.
Budget Set: Apr.
Personnel:
Bill Flitter *(CMO)*
Donald J. Myers *(VP-Fin & Treas)*
Jorge J. Abud *(Treas, Asst VP-Facilities Dev, Real EstateOffice & Fin)*
Douglas Kudravetz *(Assoc VP-Fin,Asst Treas-Office of Fin & Treas)*
Nana An *(Exec Dir-Budget & Payroll-Office of Fin & Treas)*
Teresa Flannery *(Exec Dir-Comm & Mktg)*
Beth Muha *(Exec Dir-HR)*
Kevin Grasty *(Sr Dir-Univ Publ)*
Maralee Csellar *(Dir-Media Rels-Acting)*
Greg Grauman *(Dir-Admissions)*
Jamie Hardin *(Mgr-Mktg)*
Brands & Products:
AMERICAN UNIVERSITY
AU EAGLES
KOHOD SCHOOL OF BUSINESS

APOLLO GROUP, INC.
4025 S Riverpoint Pkwy
Phoenix, AZ 85040
Tel.: (480) 966-5394
Fax: (480) 379-3503
Toll Free: (800) 990-2765
E-mail: ayla.dickey@apollogrp.edu
Web Site: www.apollogrp.edu
E-Mail For Key Personnel:
President: John.Sperling@apollogrp.edu
Approx. Rev.: $4,925,819,000
Approx. Number Employees: 55,703
Year Founded: 1973
Business Description:
Online Higher Education Program Services
S.I.C.: 8221; 8299

Key to Media (For complete agency information see *The Advertising Red Books-Agencies* edition):
1. Bus. Publs. 2. Cable T.V. 3. Catalogs & Directories. 4. Co-op Adv. 5. Consumer Mags. 6. D.M. to Bus. Estab.7. D.M. to Consumers 8. Daily Newsp. 9. Exhibits/Trade Shows 10. Foreign 11. Infomercial 12. Internet Adv.13. Multimedia 14. Network Radio 15. Network T.V. 16. Newsp. Distr. Mags. 17. Other 18. Outdoor (Posters, Transit) 19. Point of Purchase20. Premiums, Novelties 21. Product Samples 22. Special Events Mktg. 23. Spot Radio 24. Spot T.V. 25. Weekly Newsp. 26. Yellow Page Adv.

Apollo Group, Inc. — (Continued)

N.A.I.C.S.: 611310; 611710
Advertising Expenditures: $224,000,000
Media: 6-8-9-10-14-15-23-24-25
Personnel:
John G. Sperling *(Chm)*
Peter V. Sperling *(Vice Chm)*
Joseph L. D'Amico *(Pres & COO)*
Gregory W. Cappelli *(Co-CEO & Chm-Apollo Global, Inc.)*
Charles B. Edelstein *(Co-CEO)*
Brian L. Swartz *(CFO & Sr VP)*
Robert W. Wrubel *(CMO, Chief Product Officer & Exec VP)*
Frederick J. Newton *(Chief HR Officer & Sr VP)*
Gregory J. Iverson *(Chief Acctg Officer, VP & Controller)*
Timothy K. Daniels *(Pres-Apollo Global, Inc.)*
Sean B.W. Martin *(Gen Counsel, Sec & Sr VP)*
Terri C. Bishop *(Exec VP-External Affairs)*
Jorge Klor de Alva *(Sr VP)*
Advertising Agency:
Media Buying Services, Inc.
4545 E Shea Blvd Ste 162
Phoenix, AZ 85028-6008
Tel.: (602) 996-2232
Fax: (602) 996-5658
Toll Free: (888) 996-2232

ATI ENTERPRISES, INC.
(Holding of BC Partners, Inc.)
(d/b/a ATI Career Training Centers)
6627 Maple Ave
Dallas, TX 75235
Tel.: (817) 284-1141
Fax: (817) 284-0117
Web Site: www.aticareertraining.edu
Sales Range: $200-249.9 Million
Year Founded: 1965
Business Description:
Technical & Trade Career Training Schools
S.I.C.: 8249; 8244
N.A.I.C.S.: 611519; 611410
Personnel:
Arthur Benjamin *(Chm)*
Carli Strength *(Pres & CEO)*
Jon Vasconcellos *(CFO)*
Advertising Agency:
EdExperts
12977 N 40 Dr Ste 218
Saint Louis, MO 63141
Tel.: (636) 536-3656
Fax: (636) 536-9401

BERLITZ INTERNATIONAL, INC.
(Sub. of Benesse Corporation)
(d/b/a The Berlitz Language Centers)
400 Alexander Park
Princeton, NJ 08540-6306
Tel.: (609) 514-9650
Tel.: (609) 514-3400
Fax: (609) 514-9648
Toll Free: (800) 257-9449
Web Site: www.berlitz.com
E-Mail For Key Personnel:
Marketing Director: mpalm@berlitz.com
Approx. Sls.: $464,923,000
Approx. Number Employees: 140
Year Founded: 1878
Business Description:
Language Training
S.I.C.: 8299; 7389
N.A.I.C.S.: 611630; 541930
Media: 2-3-4-6-7-8-9-10-11-13-18-19-20-22-23-24-25-26
Distr.: Intl.; Natl.
Budget Set: Aug.
Personnel:
Yukako Uchinaga *(CEO & COO)*
Mark Harris *(Exec VP)*
Mike Kashani *(Dir & Sr VP-Emerging Markets)*
Brands & Products:
BERLITZ TOTAL IMMERSION
Advertising Agency:
Dentsu America, Inc.
32 Ave of the Americas 16th Fl
New York, NY 10013
Tel.: (212) 397-3333
Fax: (212) 397-3322

BRIARCLIFFE COLLEGE, INC.
(Sub. of Career Education Corporation)
1055 Stewart Ave
Bethpage, NY 11714-3596
Tel.: (516) 918-3600
Fax: (516) 918-3783
Web Site: www.bcbeth.com
Sales Range: $25-49.9 Million
Approx. Number Employees: 100
Business Description:
Vocational Education Services
S.I.C.: 8222; 8243
N.A.I.C.S.: 611210; 611420
Personnel:
George Santiago *(Pres)*
Advertising Agency:
Epoch 5 Public Relations
755 New York Ave
Huntington, NY 11743
Tel.: (631) 427-1713
Fax: (631) 427-1740
Curriculum & Community Outreach Programs

BRIDGEPOINT EDUCATION, INC.
13500 Evening Creek Dr N Ste 600
San Diego, CA 92128
Tel.: (858) 668-2586
Fax: (858) 408-2903
Web Site: www.bridgepointeducation.com/contactus/
E-Mail For Key Personnel:
Public Relations: shari.rodriguez@bridgepointeducation.com
Approx. Rev.: $713,233,000
Approx. Number Employees: 3,000
Year Founded: 2004
Business Description:
Postsecondary Education Services
S.I.C.: 8221; 8299; 9411
N.A.I.C.S.: 611310; 611710; 923110
Advertising Expenditures: $39,100,000
Media: 8-13
Personnel:
Patrick T. Hackett *(Chm)*
Andrew S. Clark *(CEO)*
Daniel J. Devine *(CFO & Exec VP)*
Thomas Ashbrook *(CIO & Sr VP)*
Ross L. Woodard *(CMO & Sr VP)*
Rodney T. Sheng *(Chief Admin Officer & Exec VP)*
Brandon Pope *(Chief Acctg Officer, VP & Controller)*
Diane Louise Thompson *(Gen Counsel, Sec & Sr VP)*
Jane McAuliffe *(Chief Academic Officer & Exec VP)*
Douglas C. Abts *(Sr VP-Strategy & Corp Dev)*
Charlene Dackerman *(Sr VP-HR)*
Linda Mignone *(VP-Mktg)*
Shari Rodriguez *(Assoc VP-PR)*

BROADVIEW UNIVERSITY
1902 W 7800 S
West Jordan, UT 84088
Toll Free: (877) 480-3335
Business Description:
University
S.I.C.: 8221
N.A.I.C.S.: 611310
Media: 1-8-9-13-18-23-24-25-26
Personnel:
Deeann Kerr *(Reg Dir)*

BRODY COMMUNICATIONS, LTD.
(d/b/a Brody Professional Development)
815 Greenwood Ave Ste 8
Jenkintown, PA 19046
Tel.: (215) 886-1688
Fax: (215) 886-1699
Toll Free: (800) 726-7936
E-mail: info@brodypro.com
Web Site: www.brodypro.com
Approx. Number Employees: 5
Year Founded: 1983
Business Description:
Business Communications Skills Company Offering Training, Executive Coaching, Presentations & Learning Tools
S.I.C.: 8249
N.A.I.C.S.: 611519
Media: 2-9-25
Personnel:
Marjorie Brody *(Founder & CEO)*
Miryam S. Roddy *(Mgr-Maximum Exposure)*

CAMBIUM LEARNING GROUP, INC.
17855 Dallas Pkwy Ste 400
Dallas, TX 75287
Tel.: (214) 932-9500
Toll Free: (888) 399-1995
E-mail: requests@cambiumlearning.com
Web Site: www.cambiumlearning.com
Approx. Sls.: $181,260,000
Approx. Number Employees: 564
Business Description:
Educational Products & Services
S.I.C.: 8299; 2731
N.A.I.C.S.: 611710; 511130
Advertising Expenditures: $1,300,000
Personnel:
Scott Joseph Troeller *(Chm)*
David F. Cappellucci *(Pres)*
Ronald D. Klausner *(CEO)*
Bradley C. Almond *(CFO & Sr VP)*
George A. Logue *(Pres-Sopris & Exec VP)*
John Campbell *(Pres-Cambium Learning Technologies & Sr VP)*
Todd W. Buchardt *(Gen Counsel, Sec & Sr VP)*
Carolyn W. Getridge *(Sr VP-HR & Urban Dev)*

CAPELLA EDUCATION COMPANY
225 S 6th St 9th Fl
Minneapolis, MN 55402
Tel.: (612) 339-8650
Fax: (612) 977-5060
Toll Free: (888) 227-3552
Toll Free: (888) CAPELLA
E-mail: investorrelations@capella.edu
Web Site: www.capella.edu
Approx. Rev.: $426,123,000
Approx. Number Employees: 2,968
Year Founded: 1991
Business Description:
Online Post-Secondary Education Services
S.I.C.: 7389; 8221; 9411
N.A.I.C.S.: 561421; 611310; 923110
Advertising Expenditures: $64,300,000
Personnel:
Kevin Gilligan *(Chm & CEO)*
Michael J. Offerman *(Vice Chm)*
Steven L. Polacek *(CFO & Sr VP)*
Gregory W. Thom *(VP-Govt Affairs, Gen Counsel & Sec)*
Kyle Carpenter *(Sr VP-Strategy & Bus Dev)*
Christopher Cassirer *(Sr VP)*
Sally B. Chial *(Sr VP-Capella Experience)*
Jen Klise *(VP-Mktg)*
Jason Van de Loo *(VP-Mktg & Portfolio Strategies)*
Jim Silburn *(Sr Dir-Brand & Differentiation)*
Heide Erickson *(Dir-IR)*
Michael Walsh *(Mgr-PR)*

CAREER EDUCATION CORPORATION
231 N Martingale Rd
Schaumburg, IL 60173
Tel.: (847) 781-3600
Fax: (847) 781-3610
Toll Free: (888) 781-3600
Web Site: www.careered.com
Approx. Rev.: $2,124,236,000
Approx. Number Employees: 8,675
Year Founded: 1994
Business Description:
Vocational Schools Operator
S.I.C.: 8299; 8244
N.A.I.C.S.: 611710; 611410; 611699
Advertising Expenditures: $302,800,000
Personnel:
Steven H. Lesnik *(Chm)*
Gary E. McCullough *(Pres & CEO)*
Michael J. Graham *(CFO & Exec VP)*
Robert DeYoung *(CMO & Sr VP-Corp Mktg)*
Thomas G. Budlong *(Chief Admin Officer & Sr VP)*
Colleen M. O'Sullivan *(Chief Acctg Officer & Sr VP)*
Jeffrey D. Ayers *(Gen Counsel, Sec & Sr VP)*
Jason T. Friesen *(Sr VP-Fin, Dir-IR & Treas)*
Robert M. McNamara, Jr. *(Sr VP-Divisional)*

Key to Media (For complete agency information see *The Advertising Red Books-Agencies* edition):
1. Bus. Publs. 2. Cable T.V. 3. Catalogs & Directories. 4. Co-op Adv. 5. Consumer Mags. 6. D.M. to Bus. Estab.7. D.M. to Consumers
8. Daily Newsp. 9. Exhibits/Trade Shows 10. Foreign 11. Infomercial 12. Internet Adv.13. Multimedia 14. Network Radio
15. Network T.V. 16. Newsp. Distr. Mags. 17. Other 18. Outdoor (Posters, Transit) 19. Point of Purchase20. Premiums, Novelties
21. Product Samples 22. Special Events Mktg. 23. Spot Radio 24. Spot T.V. 25. Weekly Newsp. 26. Yellow Page Adv.

Thomas A. McNamara *(Sr VP-Art & Design)*
Brian R. Williams *(Sr VP-Culinary Arts Strategic Bus Unit)*
Anjali Sant *(Dir-Mktg)*

Advertising Agency:
BCN Communications
900 N Franklin St Ste 800
Chicago, IL 60610
Tel.: (312) 787-2783
Fax: (312) 787-6097

CHARLES ATLAS, LTD.

PO Box D
New York, NY 10159-1049
Tel.: (201) 767-7704
Fax: (201) 767-7705
Toll Free: (888) 672-8527
E-mail: catlas@aol.com
Web Site: www.charlesatlas.com
E-Mail For Key Personnel:
President: jhogue9400@aol.com
Sales Range: $50-74.9 Million
Approx. Number Employees: 12
Year Founded: 1929
Business Description:
Instructor of Health & Fitness; Mail Order Sales
S.I.C.: 8249
N.A.I.C.S.: 611519
Export
Media: 1-3-5-6-7-8-9-10-11-13-15-16-17-20-22-24-25
Distr.: Natl.
Budget Set: Monthly
Personnel:
Jeffrey C. Hogue *(Pres & CEO)*
Cynthia Soroka *(Exec VP)*
J. Bean *(Mgr-Adv)*
Brands & Products:
ATLAS
CHARLES ATLAS
DYNAMIC-TENSION
MR. ATLAS
THE WORLDS MOST PERFECTLY DEVELOPED MAN.

CIBT EDUCATION GROUP INC.

777 West Broadway Suite 1200
Vancouver, BC V5Z 4J7, Canada
Tel.: (604) 871-9909
Fax: (604) 871-9919
E-mail: info@cibt.net
Web Site: www.cibtcorp.com
Approx. Rev.: $55,954,852
Approx. Number Employees: 129
Year Founded: 1986
Business Description:
Education, Training, Graphic Design & Advertising Services
S.I.C.: 9411; 7319; 7336; 8221; 8299
N.A.I.C.S.: 923110; 541430; 541890; 611310; 611430; 611710
Advertising Expenditures: $8,700,663
Personnel:
Toby Chu *(Vice Chm, Pres, CEO & Dir)*
Dennis Huang *(CFO & Exec VP)*
Tim Leong *(VP-Fin & Acctg)*

CIE DIRECT

1776 E 17th St
Cleveland, OH 44114-3636
Tel.: (216) 781-9400
Fax: (216) 781-0331
Toll Free: (800) 243-6446
E-mail: instruct@cie-wc.edu
Web Site: www.cie-wc.edu
Approx. Number Employees: 50
Year Founded: 1934
Business Description:
Independent Study Electronics Training
S.I.C.: 8249
N.A.I.C.S.: 611519
Import Export
Advertising Expenditures: $1,805,800
Cable T.V.: $60,000; Catalogs & Directories: $30,000; Consumer Mags.: $350,000; D.M. to Consumers: $800,000; Foreign: $5,000; Internet Adv.: $40,800; Point of Purchase: $500,000; Premiums, Novelties: $10,000; Weekly Newsp.: $10,000
Distr.: Direct to Consumer; Intl.; Natl.
Budget Set: Oct.
Personnel:
John D. Drinko *(Chm)*
John Randall Drinko *(Pres)*
Ted Sheroke *(Mgr-Adv-Mktg)*
Brands & Products:
CIE

CINCINNATI HILLS CHRISTIAN ACADEMY

11525 Snider Rd
Cincinnati, OH 45249
Tel.: (513) 247-0900
Fax: (513) 247-0950
Web Site: www.chca-oh.org
Business Description:
Pre-School Through Grade 12
S.I.C.: 8211
N.A.I.C.S.: 611110
Media: 6-8-13-18-22-23

CORINTHIAN COLLEGES INC.

6 Hutton Centre Dr Ste 400
Santa Ana, CA 92707-8762
Tel.: (714) 427-3000
Fax: (714) 427-5111
E-mail: employment@cci.edu
Web Site: www.cci.edu
Approx. Rev.: $1,763,797,000
Approx. Number Employees: 11,500
Year Founded: 1995
Business Description:
Operator of Career-Oriented Colleges
S.I.C.: 8221; 8299
N.A.I.C.S.: 611310; 611710
Advertising Expenditures: $150,000,000
Media: 1-4-8-11
Personnel:
Jack D. Massimino *(Chm & CEO)*
Paul R. St. Pierre *(Vice Chm)*
Robert C. Owen *(CFO)*
Carmella Cassetta *(CIO & Sr VP)*
Kenneth S. Ord *(Chief Admin Officer & Exec VP)*
David Poldoian *(Chief Compliance Officer & Exec VP)*
Richard B. Simpson *(Chief Academic Officer)*
Steve Quattrociocchi *(Pres-Online Learning)*
Stan A. Mortensen *(Gen Counsel & Exec VP)*
William B. Buchanan *(Exec VP-Mktg)*
Mark L. Pelesh *(Exec VP-Legislative & Regulatory Affairs)*
Beth A. Wilson *(Exec VP)*
Paul T. Dimeo *(Sr VP-Real Estate)*
Anna Marie Dunlap *(Sr VP-IR & Corp Comm)*
Jim Wade *(Chief Human Resource Officer & Sr VP)*
Laura Denniston *(Mgr-Mktg)*
Brands & Products:
CCI
WYOTECH
Advertising Agencies:
Inter/Media Advertising
15760 Ventura Blvd 1st Fl
Encino, CA 91436
Tel.: (818) 995-1455
Fax: (818) 995-7115
Toll Free: (800) TIMEBUY

PondelWilkinson Inc.
1880 Century Park E Ste 350
Los Angeles, CA 90067
Tel.: (310) 279-5980
Fax: (310) 279-5988

CORTINA LEARNING INTERNATIONAL, INC.

7 Hollyhock Rd
Wilton, CT 06897-4414
Tel.: (203) 762-2510
Fax: (203) 762-2514
Toll Free: (800) 245-2145
E-mail: info@cortina-languages.com
Web Site: www.cortina-languages.com
Approx. Sls.: $2,000,000
Approx. Number Employees: 10
Year Founded: 1882
Business Description:
Foreign Language, ESL Courses & Educational Services
S.I.C.: 8299; 8249
N.A.I.C.S.: 611710; 611519
Media: 2-4-6-7-10-14-25-26
Distr.: Intl.; Natl.
Personnel:
Robert E. Livesey *(Pres)*
Brands & Products:
CORTINA

CREDITSOUP, INC.

(d/b/a Commission Soup)
114 N Egan Ave
Madison, SD 57042
Tel.: (605) 256-9103
Fax: (605) 256-1522
E-mail: qualitycontrol@commissionsoup.com
Web Site: www.creditsoup.com
Approx. Rev.: $4,500,000
Approx. Number Employees: 13
Year Founded: 2000
Business Description:
Online Marketing Services
S.I.C.: 8742
N.A.I.C.S.: 541613
Media: 9-10-13-25
Personnel:
Darrin Namken *(Pres)*
Todd Knodel *(CEO)*
Brands & Products:
COMMITTED TO CUSTOMER SATISFICATION
CREDITSOUP

DALE CARNEGIE TRAINING

290 Motor Pkwy
Hauppauge, NY 11788
Tel.: (631) 415-9300
Fax: (631) 415-9358
Toll Free: (800) 231-5800
Web Site: www.dalecarnegie.com
Approx. Number Employees: 100
Year Founded: 1912
Business Description:
Business Courses & Seminars; Sales & Communication Training
S.I.C.: 8299
N.A.I.C.S.: 611699
Advertising Expenditures: $200,000
Media: 2-4-6-7-9-10-18
Distr.: Natl.
Budget Set: Aug. -Sept.
Personnel:
Donna Dale Carnegie *(Owner & Chm)*
Peter V. Handal *(CEO)*
David Fagiano *(COO & Sr VP)*
Michael A. Crom *(Chief Learning Officer)*
Brands & Products:
THE CARNEGIE COACH
DALE CARNEGIE
Advertising Agency:
DDB
226 Outram Road
169039
Singapore, Singapore
Tel.: (65) 6323 4811
Fax: (65) 6225 0030

DEVRY INC.

3005 Highland Pkwy
Downers Grove, IL 60515
Tel.: (630) 571-7700
Fax: (630) 571-0317
Toll Free: (866) DEVRY34
E-mail: inquiries@devry.com
Web Site: www.devry.com
Approx. Rev.: $2,182,371,000
Approx. Number Employees: 10,262
Year Founded: 1931
Business Description:
Undergraduate & Graduate Educational Programs
S.I.C.: 8221; 8299
N.A.I.C.S.: 611310; 611699; 611710
Advertising Expenditures: $179,400,000
Media: 2-6-8-9-13-23-24-25
Distr.: Natl.
Personnel:
Harold T. Shapiro *(Chm)*
Daniel M. Hamburger *(Pres & CEO)*
Richard M. Gunst *(CFO, Treas & Sr VP)*
Eric P. Dirst *(CIO & Sr VP)*
John Birmingham *(CMO)*
Sharon Thomas Parrott *(Chief Compliance Officer & Chief Regulatory Officer)*
William Hughson *(Pres-Healthcare Grp)*
Andrew Jeon *(Pres-DeVry Medical Intl)*
Robert Paul *(Pres-Carrington Colleges Grp)*
Steven P. Riehs *(Pres-K-12, Pro & Intl Education)*
Gregory S. Davis *(Gen Counsel, Sec & Sr VP)*
David J. Pauldine *(Exec VP)*
Donna M. Jennings *(Sr VP-HR)*
Adriano Allegrini *(VP-Strategy & Bus Dev)*
Fran Roberts *(VP-Strategic Alliances-Healthcare Grp)*
Joan Bates *(Sr Dir-IR & Media Rels)*
Brands & Products:
ADVANCED ACADEMICS

Key to Media (For complete agency information see *The Advertising Red Books-Agencies* edition):
1. Bus. Publs. 2. Cable T.V. 3. Catalogs & Directories. 4. Co-op Adv. 5. Consumer Mags. 6. D.M. to Bus. Estab.7. D.M. to Consumers 8. Daily Newsp. 9. Exhibits/Trade Shows 10. Foreign 11. Infomercial 12. Internet Adv.13. Multimedia 14. Network Radio 15. Network T.V. 16. Newsp. Distr. Mags. 17. Other 18. Outdoor (Posters, Transit) 19. Point of Purchase20. Premiums, Novelties 21. Product Samples 22. Special Events Mktg. 23. Spot Radio 24. Spot T.V. 25. Weekly Newsp. 26. Yellow Page Adv.

DeVry Inc. — (Continued)

AMERICAN UNIVERSITY OF THE CARIBBEAN
ATC INTERNATIONAL
BECKER CPA REVIEW
BECKER PROFESSIONAL EDUCATION
CARRINGTON COLLEGE
CARRINGTON COLLEGE CALIFORNIA
DERVY SHIELD DESIGN
DEVRY
DEVRY INSTITUTE OF TECHNOLOGY
DEVRY UNIVERSITY
EDUCARD
KELLER GRADUATE SCHOOL OF MANAGEMENT
ROSS UNIVERSITY
US EDUCATION CORPORATION
WE MAJOR IN CAREERS

Advertising Agencies:
Dresner Corporate Services
20 N Clark St Ste 3550
Chicago, IL 60602
Tel.: (312) 780-7211
Fax: (312) 726-7448
Toll Free: (800) 373-7637
Pub Rels

The Marketing Store
701 E 22nd St
Lombard, IL 60148
Tel.: (630) 693-1400
Fax: (630) 932-5200

DEVRY UNIVERSITY INC.
(Sub. of DeVry Inc.)
1 Tower Ln Ste 1000
Oakbrook Terrace, IL 60181
Tel.: (630) 571-7700
Fax: (630) 571-0317
Web Site: www.devry.edu
Sales Range: $150-199.9 Million
Approx. Number Employees: 700
Business Description:
Undergraduate & Graduate Educational Programs
S.I.C.: 8221
N.A.I.C.S.: 611310
Personnel:
David J. Pauldine *(Pres & Exec VP)*
John Birmingham *(CMO)*
Susan Friedberg *(Pres-Chicago)*
Jamal J. Scott *(Pres-Tinley Park Campus & Centers)*
Jerry R. Dill *(Reg VP)*
Rosetta Rolan *(Asst Dir-Career Svcs)*
Advertising Agencies:
Brunner
11 Stanwix St 5th Fl
Pittsburgh, PA 15222-1312
Tel.: (412) 995-9500
Fax: (412) 995-9501

Manning Selvage & Lee
222 Merchandise Mart Plz Ste 4-150
Chicago, IL 60654
Tel.: (312) 861-5200
Fax: (312) 861-5252

DUKE UNIVERSITY
Duke University
Durham, NC 27710
Tel.: (919) 684-8111
Fax: (919) 684-2597
E-mail: richard.brodhead@duke.edu
Web Site: www.duke.edu
Sales Range: $1-4.9 Billion
Approx. Number Employees: 35,000
Year Founded: 1924
Business Description:
College
S.I.C.: 8221
N.A.I.C.S.: 611310
Media: 4-10-13-22
Personnel:
Robert K. Steel *(Chm)*
Richard Brodhead *(Pres)*
Tracy Futhey *(CIO & VP-Info Tech)*
Tallman Trask, III *(Treas & Exec VP)*
John Burness *(Sr VP-Pub Affairs & Govt Rels)*
Advertising Agencies:
919 Marketing Company
102 Avent Ferry Rd
Holly Springs, NC 27540
Tel.: (919) 557-7890
Fax: (919) 557-0041

The Republik
211 Rigsbee Ave
Durham, NC 27701
Tel.: (919) 956-9400
Fax: (919) 956-9402

DUKE UNIVERSITY HEALTH SYSTEM
(Sub. of Duke University)
2301 Erwin Rd
Durham, NC 27710
Tel.: (919) 684-8111
Fax: (781) 280-4095
Toll Free: (888) ASK-DUKE
E-mail: info@dukehealth.org
Web Site: www.dukehealth.org
Sales Range: $1-4.9 Billion
Approx. Number Employees: 11,401
Business Description:
Hospital Network
S.I.C.: 8062
N.A.I.C.S.: 622110
Media: 2-6-9-10-11-13-17-18-22-23-24-25-26
Personnel:
Victor J. Dzau *(Pres & CEO)*
Jeffrey Ferranti *(Chief Medical Info Officer & VP-Clinical Informatics)*
William J. Fulkerson, Jr. *(Exec VP)*

ECOLLEGE.COM
(Sub. of Pearson Education)
4900 S Monaco St
Denver, CO 80237
Tel.: (303) 873-7400
Fax: (303) 873-7449
Web Site: www.ecollege.com
Approx. Rev.: $52,085,000
Approx. Number Employees: 270
Year Founded: 1996
Business Description:
Online Higher Education Programs & Support Services
S.I.C.: 8299
N.A.I.C.S.: 611710
Media: 10-13
Personnel:
Matt leavy *(CEO)*
John Dobbertin *(VP & Dir-Product & Infrastructure)*
John E. Vice, II *(VP-IT)*

EDUCATE, INC.
(Holding of Sterling Partners)
1001 Fleet St
Baltimore, MD 21022
Tel.: (410) 843-6200
Tel.: (410) 843-8000
Tel.: (410) 843-8794
Fax: (410) 843-8441
Web Site: www.educate-inc.com
Approx. Rev.: $354,668,000
Approx. Number Employees: 10,161
Business Description:
Supplemental Education Services
S.I.C.: 8299
N.A.I.C.S.: 611691; 611699; 611710
Advertising Expenditures: $35,584,000
Media: 8-9-15-24-25
Personnel:
R. Christopher Hoehn-Saric *(CEO)*
Kevin E. Shaffer *(CFO)*
C. Alan Schroeder *(Chief Legal Officer)*
Christopher J. Paucek *(Pres-Educate Products)*
Brands & Products:
CATAPULT LEARNING
ESYLVAN
IVY WEST
SCHULERHILFE
SYLVAN LEARNING CENTER
Advertising Agency:
Publicis Dallas
7300 Lonestar Dr
Plano, TX 75024
Tel.: (972) 628-7500
Fax: (972) 628-7864
Sylvan Learning Center

EDUCATION MANAGEMENT CORPORATION
(Holding of Providence Equity Partners LLC)
210 6th Ave
Pittsburgh, PA 15222-2598
Tel.: (412) 562-0900
Fax: (412) 562-0598
Toll Free: (800) 275-2440
Web Site: www.edumgt.com
Year Founded: 1962
Business Description:
Post-Secondary Education Services
S.I.C.: 8299; 7911; 8221
N.A.I.C.S.: 611710; 611310; 611610
Advertising Expenditures: $259,700,000
Media: 8-9-13-14-15-22-23-24-25
Personnel:
John R. McKernan, Jr. *(Chm)*
Edward H. West *(Pres & CFO)*
Todd S. Nelson *(CEO)*
Robert A. Carroll *(CIO & Sr VP)*
Craig D. Swenson *(Chief Academic Officer)*
John Kline *(Pres-Online Higher Education & Sr VP-Ops)*
J. Devitt Kramer *(Gen Counsel, Sec & Sr VP)*
Tony Digiovanni *(Sr VP-Mktg & Admissions)*
Danny Finuf *(Sr VP-Ops)*
Anthony J. Guida, Jr. *(Sr VP-External Affairs)*
John M. Mazzoni *(Sr VP-Ops)*
Stacey R. Sauchuk *(Sr VP-Academic Programs & Student Affairs)*
John T. South, III *(Sr VP)*
Roberta L. Troike *(Sr VP-HR)*
Jacquelyn P. Muller *(VP-Comm & PR)*
James R. Sober *(VP-Fin)*
Brands & Products:
AI THE ART INSTITUTES INTERNATIONAL
ARGOSY UNIVERSITY
THE ART INSTITUE ONLINE
THE ART INSTITUTE OF ATLANTA
THE ART INSTITUTE OF CALIFORNIA
THE ART INSTITUTE OF CHARLOTTE
THE ART INSTITUTE OF COLORADO
THE ART INSTITUTE OF DALLAS
THE ART INSTITUTE OF FORT LAUDERDALE
THE ART INSTITUTE OF HOUSTON
THE ART INSTITUTE OF LAS VEGAS
THE ART INSTITUTE OF NEW YORK CITY
THE ART INSTITUTE OF PHILADELPHIA
THE ART INSTITUTE OF PHOENIX
THE ART INSTITUTE OF PITTSBURGH
THE ART INSTITUTE OF PORTLAND
THE ART INSTITUTE OF SEATTLE
THE ART INSTITUTE OF TAMPA
THE ART INSTITUTE OF WASHINGTON
THE ART INSTITUTES INTERNATIONAL MINNESOTA
BROWN MACKIE COLLEGE
CALIFORNIA DESIGN COLLEGE
EDMC
THE ILLINOIS INSTITUTE OF ART
MIAMI INTERNATIONAL UNIVERSITY OF ART & DESIGN
THE NEW ENGLAND INSTITUTE OF ART
SOUTH UNIVERSITY
Advertising Agencies:
DoublePositive Marketing Group, Inc.
1501 S Clinton St Ste 1520
Baltimore, MD 21224
Tel.: (410) 332-0464
Fax: (410) 332-1059
Toll Free: (888) 376-7484
Online Marketing Agency of Record

Garrison Hughes
211 Fort Pitt Blvd
Pittsburgh, PA 15222
Tel.: (412) 338-0123

Rella:Cowan
300 W Morgan St Ste 1475
Durham, NC 27701
Tel.: (919) 956-5600
Fax: (919) 956-5605

EDUCATIONDYNAMICS
(Holding of Halyard Capital Management LLC)
5 Marine View Plaza Ste 212
Hoboken, NJ 07030
Tel.: (201) 377-3000
Business Description:
Higher Education Recruiting Agency
S.I.C.: 9411
N.A.I.C.S.: 923110
Personnel:
Steve Isaac *(Co-Founder)*
Tom Anderson *(CEO)*
Richard Stalzer *(COO)*
Venkat Gaddipati *(CIO)*

Key to Media (For complete agency information see *The Advertising Red Books-Agencies* edition):
1. Bus. Publs. 2. Cable T.V. 3. Catalogs & Directories. 4. Co-op Adv. 5. Consumer Mags. 6. D.M. to Bus. Estab.7. D.M. to Consumers 8. Daily Newsp. 9. Exhibits/Trade Shows 10. Foreign 11. Infomercial 12. Internet Adv.13. Multimedia 14. Network Radio 15. Network T.V. 16. Newsp. Distr. Mags. 17. Other 18. Outdoor (Posters, Transit) 19. Point of Purchase20. Premiums, Novelties 21. Product Samples 22. Special Events Mktg. 23. Spot Radio 24. Spot T.V. 25. Weekly Newsp. 26. Yellow Page Adv.

Advertising Agency:
The Communications Strategy Group, Inc.
42 Front St
Marblehead, MA 01945
Tel.: (781) 631-3117
Fax: (781) 631-3278

EDUTRADES INC.
(Sub. of TIGRENT INC.)
1612 E Cape Coral Pkwy Ste A
Cape Coral, FL 33904
Tel.: (239) 542-0643
Fax: (239) 540-6562
Web Site: www.edutrades.com
Sales Range: $300-349.9 Million
Business Description:
Educational Courses on Investment
S.I.C.: 9411; 6289
N.A.I.C.S.: 923110; 523999
Advertising Expenditures: $8,239,000
Media: 4-5-6-8-10-13-15-24-25

EMBRY-RIDDLE AERONAUTICAL UNIVERSITY
600 S Clyde Morris Blvd
Daytona Beach, FL 32114-3966
Tel.: (386) 226-6910
Fax: (386) 226-6158
E-mail: webmaster@erau.edu
Web Site: www.erau.edu
Approx. Number Employees: 1,300
Year Founded: 1926
Business Description:
Aeronautical University
S.I.C.: 8221
N.A.I.C.S.: 611310
Media: 2-4-6-8-10
Distr.: Intl.; Natl.
Budget Set: Feb.
Personnel:
John P. Johnson *(Pres & CEO)*
John R. Watret *(Chief Academic Officer & Exec VP)*
Irene McReynolds *(VP-HR)*
Matthew Brasmer *(Dir-Major & Planned Gifts)*
Rebecca Chapman *(Dir-Corp & Foundation Relations)*
Jeffrey Davis *(Dir-Dev)*
Advertising Agency:
Paskill Stapleton & Lord
1 Roberts Ave
Glenside, PA 19038-3497
Tel.: (215) 572-7938
Fax: (215) 572-7937

EVCI CAREER COLLEGES HOLDING CORP.
1 Van Der Donck St
Yonkers, NY 10704
Tel.: (914) 623-0700
Fax: (914) 964-8222
Toll Free: (888) 772-6553
Web Site: www.evcinc.com
Sales Range: $50-74.9 Million
Approx. Number Employees: 465
Year Founded: 1997
Business Description:
Holding Company; Educational Services
S.I.C.: 8299; 8742
N.A.I.C.S.: 611699; 541611; 611710
Advertising Expenditures: $5,105,000
Media: 8-9-10-18-22-25
Personnel:
Henry Hetherington *(CFO)*
Joseph D. Alperin *(Gen Counsel & VP-Corp Affairs)*

FLIGHTSAFETY INTERNATIONAL, INC.
(Holding of Berkshire Hathaway Inc.)
Marine Air Terminal Laguardia Airport
Flushing, NY 11371
Tel.: (718) 565-4100
Fax: (718) 565-4134
Telex: 667573UW
E-mail: webmaster@flightsafety.com
Web Site: www.flightsafety.com
Sales Range: $650-699.9 Million
Approx. Number Employees: 3,300
Year Founded: 1951
Business Description:
Aviation & Marine Training Consulting Services
S.I.C.: 8299; 3589
N.A.I.C.S.: 611699; 333319
Export
Advertising Expenditures: $2,000,000
Media: 2-7-8-10-11-13
Personnel:
A. L. Ueltschi *(Founder & Chm)*
Bruce N. Whitman *(Pres & CEO)*
Scott Fera *(VP-Mktg)*
Damon Cram *(Dir-Mktg-Simulation Products & Svcs)*
Scott Hunter *(Dir-Regional Airline Sls & Dir-Worldwide Sls)*
Mike King *(Dir-Bus Dev)*
Stephen Phillips *(Dir-Mktg Comm)*
Mark Malkosky *(Asst Dir-Maintenance Trng Bus Dev & Sls)*
Gary Porterfield *(Mgr-Learjet Learning Center)*
Advertising Agency:
Greteman Group
1425 E Douglas 2nd Fl
Wichita, KS 67211
Tel.: (316) 263-1004
Fax: (316) 263-1060

GOLDEN GATE UNIVERSITY
536 Mission St
San Francisco, CA 94105-2921
Tel.: (415) 442-7000
Tel.: (415) 442-7830 (Mktg)
Fax: (415) 442-7056
E-mail: ggu4you@ggu.edu
Web Site: www.ggu.edu
E-Mail For Key Personnel:
President: pfriedman@ggu.edu
Approx. Number Employees: 320
Year Founded: 1901
Business Description:
Graduate & Undergraduate University
S.I.C.: 8221
N.A.I.C.S.: 611310
Import Export
Advertising Expenditures: $2,400,000
Media: 1-2-4-7-8-9-10-11-18-20-22-23-25-26
Distr.: Intl.; Natl.
Budget Set: July
Personnel:
Dan Angel *(Pres)*
Robert D. Hite *(CFO & VP-Bus Affairs)*
Tasia Neeve *(Dir-Mktg & Comm)*
Nathaniel Henderson *(Dir-Exec MBA Program)*
Brands & Products:
CYBERCAMPUS
GOLDEN GATE UNIVERSITY
Advertising Agency:
Mortar Advertising
25 Maiden Ln 6th Fl
San Francisco, CA 94108
Tel.: (415) 772-9907
Fax: (415) 772-9952

GRAND CANYON EDUCATION, INC.
3300 W Camelback Rd
Phoenix, AZ 85017
Tel.: (602) 639-7500
Web Site: www.gcu.edu
Approx. Rev.: $385,825,000
Approx. Number Employees: 2,600
Year Founded: 2003
Business Description:
Online & Traditional Post-Secondary Education Services
S.I.C.: 8299; 8221
N.A.I.C.S.: 611699; 611310
Advertising Expenditures: $24,820,000
Media: 5-8-13-17-22
Personnel:
Brent D. Richardson *(Chm)*
Kathy Player *(Pres)*
Brian E. Mueller *(CEO & Dir)*
Daniel E. Bachus *(CFO)*
Christopher C. Richardson *(Gen Counsel)*
W. Stan Meyer *(Exec VP)*
Shawna Barnett *(Sr Mgr-Mktg)*

GURNICK ACADEMY OF MEDICAL ARTS
Bay View Plz 2121 S El Camino Real Bldg C-200
San Mateo, CA 94403
Tel.: (650) 685-6616
Fax: (650) 685-6640
E-mail: admissions@medacademy.org
Web Site: www.medacademy.org
Approx. Number Employees: 50
Business Description:
Medical Education; LVN, Ultrasound, MRI & Phlebotomy
S.I.C.: 9411
N.A.I.C.S.: 923110
Media: 13-24
Personnel:
Constantine Gourji *(CEO)*

HEALD CAPITAL LLC
601 Montgomery St 14th Fl
San Francisco, CA 94111
Tel.: (415) 808-1400
Fax: (415) 808-1598
E-mail: info@heald.edu
Web Site: www.heald.edu
Sales Range: $150-199.9 Million
Approx. Number Employees: 700
Year Founded: 1865
Business Description:
Business, Technical & Health Care Colleges
S.I.C.: 8244
N.A.I.C.S.: 611410
Media: 2-4-8-13-15
Distr.: Reg.
Budget Set: Mar. -May
Brands & Products:
GET IN. GET OUT. GET AHEAD.
HEALD COLLEGE
Advertising Agency:
Swirl Advertising
1620 Montgomery St Ste 140
San Francisco, CA 94111
Tel.: (415) 276-8300
Fax: (415) 276-8301

HEALING HANDS INSTITUTE FOR MASSAGE THERAPY, INC.
41 Bergenline Ave
Westwood, NJ 07675
Tel.: (201) 722-0099
Fax: (201) 722-0690
E-mail: info@hhi.edu
Web Site: www.hhi.edu
Year Founded: 1990
Business Description:
Professional Educational Programs & Facilities for Massage Therapy
S.I.C.: 7299
N.A.I.C.S.: 812990; 812199
Media: 2-4-8
Personnel:
Olga Kubicek *(Co-Founder)*
Eva R. Carey *(Dir-Admin)*
Alice Feuerstein *(Dir)*
Jackie Gilfillian *(Mgr-Adv)*

ITT EDUCATIONAL SERVICES, INC.
13000 N Meridian St
Carmel, IN 46032-1404
Tel.: (317) 706-9200
Fax: (317) 706-3040
Web Site: www.ittesi.com
Approx. Rev.: $1,596,529,000
Approx. Number Employees: 6,300
Year Founded: 1968
Business Description:
Business Schools & Technical Education
S.I.C.: 8299; 8221; 8222
N.A.I.C.S.: 611710; 611210; 611310
Media: 3-4-8-9-13-14-15-23-24-26
Distr.: Direct to Consumer; Natl.
Personnel:
Kevin M. Modany *(CEO)*
Daniel M. Fitzpatrick *(CFO & Exec VP)*
Martin Van Buren *(CIO & Exec VP)*
Glenn E. Tanner *(CMO & Exec VP)*
Jeffrey R. Cooper *(Chief Compliance Officer & Sr VP)*
Eugene W. Feichtner *(Exec VP & Pres-ITT Technical Institute)*
Christine G. Long *(Gen Counsel, Sec & Sr VP)*
Angela K. Knowlton *(Treas, Sr VP & Controller)*
Clark D. Elwood *(Chief Admin & Legal Officer & Exec VP)*
David E. Catalano *(Sr VP-Bus Dev)*
Nina F. Esbin *(Sr VP-HR)*
Barry S. Simich *(Sr VP-Ops)*
Phillip B. Frank *(VP, Dir-Real Estate & Asst Gen Counsel)*
Advertising Agencies:
JWT Action
111 Monument Cir Ste 2400
Indianapolis, IN 46204
Tel.: (317) 686-7800
Fax: (317) 686-7870

MGSCOMM - New York City
817 Broadway 2nd Fl
New York, NY 10003
Tel.: (212) 204-8340
Fax: (212) 979-9357

JAZZERCISE, INC.
2460 Impala Dr
Carlsbad, CA 92010
Tel.: (760) 476-1750
Fax: (760) 602-7180
Toll Free: (800) FIT-IS-IT
E-mail: info@jazzercise.com
Web Site: www.jazzercise.com
E-Mail For Key Personnel:
Marketing Director: marketing@jazzercise.com
Public Relations: pr@jazzercise.com
Sales Range: $10-24.9 Million
Approx. Number Employees: 150
Year Founded: 1969
Business Description:
Exercise Program Franchisor; Dancewear & Diet Program Retailer
S.I.C.: 6794; 5961
N.A.I.C.S.: 533110; 454113
Media: 2-5-8-11-13-17-19-21-23-24-25
Distr.: Natl.
Personnel:
Judi Missett *(Founder & CEO)*
Shanna Missett Nelson *(Pres)*
Sally Baldridge *(CFO & COO)*
Brad Jones *(VP-Tech)*
Brands & Products:
JAZZERCISE
JAZZERTOGS

THE JOHNS HOPKINS UNIVERSITY
3400 N Charles St
Baltimore, MD 21218
Tel.: (410) 516-8000
Fax: (410) 516-8035
Fax: (410) 516-7075
E-mail: info@jhu.edu
Web Site: www.jhu.edu
E-Mail For Key Personnel:
President: wrbrody@jhu.edu
Approx. Number Employees: 25,000
Year Founded: 1876
Business Description:
College University
S.I.C.: 8211
N.A.I.C.S.: 611110
Media: 2-8-10-13-23-24
Personnel:
C. Michael Armstrong *(Chm)*
Pamela P. Flaherty *(Chm)*
Raymond A. Mason *(Chm)*
Ernest A. Bates *(Vice Chm)*
George L. Bunting, Jr. *(Vice Chm)*
Richard S. Frary *(Vice Chm)*
Stephanie Reel *(CIO & Vice Provost for Information Tech)*
Edward D. Miller, Jr. *(CEO-Johns Hopkins Medicine & VP-Medicine)*
James T. McGill *(Sr VP-Fin & Admin)*
Charlene Moore Hayes *(VP-HR)*
Larry Kilduff *(Exec Dir-Facilities)*
Joan Levy *(Dir-Mktg)*
Benjamin S. Carson, Sr. *(Dir-Pediatric Neurosurgery)*
Jay S. Corey *(Dir-Video Strategy)*
Lauren Custer *(Dir-Digital Strategy)*
Mary Maushard *(Dir-Commun)*
Kathy Vitarelli *(Dir-Art)*
Kara A. Yeager *(Asst Dir-Mktg)*
Maggie Kennedy *(Assoc Dir)*
Andy Blumberg *(Mgr-Mktg Comm)*
Frederick Savage *(Deputy Gen Counsel)*

THE JUILLIARD SCHOOL
60 Lincoln Ctr Plz
New York, NY 10023-6500
Tel.: (212) 799-5000
Fax: (212) 724-0263
Telex: 3737011 JUILLIARDSCH
E-mail: communications@juilliard.edu
Web Site: www.juilliard.edu
Approx. Number Employees: 310
Year Founded: 1905
Business Description:
Music, Dance & Drama School
S.I.C.: 7911
N.A.I.C.S.: 611610
Advertising Expenditures: $560,000
Consumer Mags.: $150,000; D.M. to Consumers: $50,000; Daily Newsp.: $330,000; Outdoor (Posters, Transit): $10,000; Spot Radio: $20,000
Distr.: Natl.
Personnel:
Bruce Stanley Kovner *(Chm)*
Joseph W. Polisi *(Pres)*
Jon Rosenhein *(COO & VP)*
David Marcus *(Chief Investment Officer)*
Christine Todd *(VP-Fin & Controller)*
Janet Kessin *(Assoc VP-Comm)*
Christopher J. Mossey *(Assoc VP-Artistic & Strategic Initiatives)*
Tricia Ross *(Assoc VP-Exec Projects)*
Brian Zeger *(Artistic Dir-Vocal Arts)*
Carl Allen *(Dir-Jazz Studies)*
Tunde Giwa *(Dir-IT)*
Lawrence Rhodes *(Dir-Dance & Artistic)*
Nicholas Saunders *(Dir-Concert Ops)*
Nona Shengalaia *(Dir-Intl Adv)*
Robert Taibbi *(Dir-Recording)*
Sabrina Tanbara *(Dir-Student Affairs)*
Brands & Products:
JUILLIARD
Advertising Agency:
A.D. Lubow, LLC
1 Penn Plz Ste 5312
New York, NY 10119-5312
Tel.: (212) 564-3250
Fax: (212) 564-2866

JUNIOR ACHIEVEMENT INC.
JA Worldwide Head Quarters One Education Way
Colorado Springs, CO 80906
Tel.: (719) 540-8000
Fax: (719) 540-6299
E-mail: newmedia@ja.org
Web Site: www.ja.org
Approx. Number Employees: 50
Business Description:
School
S.I.C.: 8299
N.A.I.C.S.: 611699
Personnel:
Sean C. Rush *(Pres & CEO)*
Advertising Agencies:
The Buntin Group
1001 Hawkins St
Nashville, TN 37203-4758
Tel.: (615) 244-5720
Fax: (615) 244-6511

Porter Novelli
(Sub. of Omnicom Group, Inc.)
75 Varick St 6th Fl
New York, NY 10013
Tel.: (212) 601-8000
Fax: (212) 601-8101
Agency of Record
Digital Outreach
Media Relations
PR Strategy
Reputation Management

KAPLAN, INC.
(Sub. of The Washington Post Company)
888 7th Ave
New York, NY 10106
Tel.: (212) 492-5800
Fax: (212) 492-5933
E-mail: mrelations@kaplan.com
Web Site: www.kaplan.com
Sales Range: $1-4.9 Billion
Approx. Number Employees: 80
Year Founded: 1938
Business Description:
Educational & Career Services
S.I.C.: 8299
N.A.I.C.S.: 611710; 611699
Media: 6-8-9-18-20-22-23-24-26
Distr.: Direct to Consumer; Natl.
Budget Set: Jan.-Dec.
Personnel:
Andrew S. Rosen *(Chm & CEO)*
Robert Lane *(CFO & Sr VP)*
Anne K. Keehn *(Pres-Global Solutions-Americas)*
Jim Rosenthal *(CEO-Ventures)*
Melissa Mack *(Sr VP-Mktg)*
Laird Popkin *(VP-Engrg)*
Brands & Products:
SCORE!
Advertising Agencies:
Alliance Agency
200 5th Ave 4th Fl
New York, NY 10010
Tel.: (212) 546-1800
Fax: (212) 546-5549

Brainium Inc.
66 Hanover St Ste 101
Manchester, NH 03101
Tel.: (603) 624-2800

Ogilvy & Mather
(Sub. of WPP Group plc)
636 11th Ave
New York, NY 10036
Tel.: (212) 237-4000
Fax: (212) 237-5123

PlattForm Advertising
708 3rd Ave 12th Fl
New York, NY 10017
Tel.: (212) 684-4800
Fax: (212) 576-1129
Toll Free: (866) 671-4429

PlattForm Advertising
15500 W 113 Ste #200
Lenexa, KS 66219
Tel.: (913) 254-6000
Fax: (913) 538-5078

Shine Advertising
612 W Main St Ste 105
Madison, WI 53703
Tel.: (608) 442-7373
Fax: (608) 442-7374

KELLER GRADUATE SCHOOL OF MANAGEMENT
(Div. of DeVry University Inc.)
1 Tower Ln Ste 1000
Oakbrook Terrace, IL 60181-4624
Tel.: (630) 574-1960
Fax: (630) 574-1969
Toll Free: (888) KELLER8
E-mail: info@keller.edu
Web Site: www.keller.edu
E-Mail For Key Personnel:
Public Relations: jniffenegger@devry.com
Sales Range: $75-99.9 Million
Year Founded: 1973
Business Description:
Graduate School
S.I.C.: 8221
N.A.I.C.S.: 611310
Media: 2-3-4-6-7-8-9-10-13-23-25-26
Distr.: Natl.
Brands & Products:
KELLER
Advertising Agency:
Henry Gill Communications (d/b/a Henry Gill Advertising)
900 S Broadway Ste 300
Denver, CO 80209
Tel.: (303) 296-4100
Fax: (303) 296-3410

KINDERCARE LEARNING CENTERS, INC.
(Sub. of Knowledge Learning Corporation)
650 NE Holladay St Ste 1400
Portland, OR 97232
Mailing Address:
PO Box 6760
Portland, OR 97228-6760
Tel.: (503) 872-1300
Fax: (503) 872-1349
Toll Free: (800) 633-1488
E-mail: ccare@klcorp.cpm
Web Site: www.kindercare.com
Approx. Rev.: $855,933,000
Approx. Number Employees: 24,000
Year Founded: 1969
Business Description:
Early Childhood Education & Care
S.I.C.: 8351
N.A.I.C.S.: 624410
Brands & Products:
KIDS CHOICE
KINDERCARE
KINDERCARE AT WORK
MULBERRY
Advertising Agency:
Harland Clarke Corp.
10931 Laureate Dr
San Antonio, TX 78249
Tel.: (210) 697-8888
Toll Free: (800) 382-0818

KITCHEN ACADEMY
(Sub. of Career Education Corporation)
2800 W Higgins Rd
Hoffman Estates, IL 60169
Toll Free: (866) 548-2223
Web Site: www.kitchenacademy.com
Sales Range: $75-99.9 Million
Business Description:
Culinary Institute
S.I.C.: 8249
N.A.I.C.S.: 611519
Media: 13
Personnel:
Chris Becker *(Pres)*
Tom Ehrhardt *(Dir-Mktg & Adv)*

Key to Media (For complete agency information see *The Advertising Red Books-Agencies* edition):
1. Bus. Publs. 2. Cable T.V. 3. Catalogs & Directories. 4. Co-op Adv. 5. Consumer Mags. 6. D.M. to Bus. Estab.7. D.M. to Consumers 8. Daily Newsp. 9. Exhibits/Trade Shows 10. Foreign 11. Infomercial 12. Internet Adv.13. Multimedia 14. Network Radio 15. Network T.V. 16. Newsp. Distr. Mags. 17. Other 18. Outdoor (Posters, Transit) 19. Point of Purchase20. Premiums, Novelties 21. Product Samples 22. Special Events Mktg. 23. Spot Radio 24. Spot T.V. 25. Weekly Newsp. 26. Yellow Page Adv.

LA PETITE ACADEMY, INC.
(Joint Venture of Morgan Stanley & A.B.C. Learning Centres Limited)
130 S Jefferson St Ste 300
Chicago, IL 60661
Tel.: (312) 798-1200
Fax: (312) 382-1776
Toll Free: (800) LA-PETITE
E-mail: corporateservices@lpacorp.com
Web Site: www.lapetite.com
Sales Range: $400-449.9 Million
Approx. Number Employees: 13,000
Year Founded: 1968
Business Description:
Childcare & Preschool Facility Operator
S.I.C.: 8351; 6719
N.A.I.C.S.: 624410; 551112
Advertising Expenditures: $4,700,000
Media: 8-9-10-13-23-25-26
Distr.: Natl.
Personnel:
Bill Davis *(CEO)*
Robert Vanhees *(CFO)*
Marsh Whaling *(COO)*
Scott Smith *(Chief HR Officer)*
Katy Jellison *(Mktg & Head-Sls)*
Amy Popp *(Mgr-Mktg Comm)*
Brands & Products:
JOURNEY
LA PETITE ACADEMY
MONTESSORI UNLIMITED
Advertising Agency:
Cresta Group
1050 N State St
Chicago, IL 60610
Tel.: (312) 944-4700
Fax: (312) 944-1582

LAUREATE EDUCATION, INC.
(Holding of KKR & CO. L.P.)
650 S Exeter St
Baltimore, MD 21202
Tel.: (410) 843-6100
Fax: (410) 843-8065
Toll Free: (866) 4LAUREATE
Web Site: www.laureate-inc.com
Approx. Rev.: $1,145,761,024
Approx. Number Employees: 23,000
Year Founded: 1979
Business Description:
Higher Education Programs & Services at Campus Based & Online Universities
S.I.C.: 8221; 8299
N.A.I.C.S.: 611310; 611430; 611691; 611699; 611710
Advertising Expenditures: $50,170,000
Media: 2-3-4-5-6-8-9-10-11-13-15-18-19-20-21-25-26
Distr.: Natl.
Budget Set: Sept.
Personnel:
Douglas L. Becker *(Chm & CEO)*
Neal S. Cohen *(Pres & COO)*
Paula R. Singer *(Pres & CEO-Higher Education Grp)*
Eilif Serck-Hanssen *(CFO & Exec VP)*
Amit Rai *(Chief Acctg Officer & Sr VP)*
William C. Dennis, Jr. *(Pres-Latin America Operation)*
Robert W. Zentz *(Gen Counsel & Sr VP)*
Jill Cantor Nord *(Asst Gen Counsel)*
Daniel M. Nickel *(Exec VP-Corp Ops)*
Joseph D. Duffey *(Sr VP)*
Brands & Products:
LAUREATE EDUCATION
LAUREATE INTERNATIONAL UNIVERSITY

THE LEARNING ANNEX LLC
(Sub. of Learning Annex Holdings, LLC)
443 Park Ave S Ste 501
New York, NY 10016-7487
Tel.: (212) 371-0280
Fax: (212) 290-2430
E-mail: feedback@learningannex.com
Web Site: www.learningannex.com
Approx. Number Employees: 100
Year Founded: 1980
Business Description:
Specialty Learning Institution
S.I.C.: 8299
N.A.I.C.S.: 611699; 611710
Media: 10-13
Personnel:
William Zanker *(Founder & Pres)*

LEARNING CARE GROUP INC.
(Joint Venture of Morgan Stanley & A.B.C. Learning Centres Limited)
21333 Haggerty Rd Ste 300
Novi, MI 48375
Tel.: (248) 697-9000
Fax: (248) 697-9002
Toll Free: (866) 244-5384
E-mail: info@childtime.com
Web Site:
www.learningcaregroup.com
Sales Range: $600-649.9 Million
Approx. Number Employees: 23,000
Year Founded: 1970
Business Description:
Child Day Care Services
S.I.C.: 8351
N.A.I.C.S.: 624410
Advertising Expenditures: $2,200,000
Media: 8-26
Personnel:
Robert Vanhees *(CFO)*
Marsh Whaling *(COO)*
Scott W. Smith *(Chief HR Officer)*
Brands & Products:
CHILDTIME
TUTOR TIME

LEARNING TREE INTERNATIONAL, INC.
1805 Library St
Reston, VA 20190-5630
Tel.: (703) 709-9119
Tel.: (703) 925-7746 (IR)
Toll Free: (800) 843-8733
Web Site: www.learningtree.com
Approx. Rev.: $127,470,000
Approx. Number Employees: 468
Business Description:
Education & Training Services for Information Technology Professionals in Business & Government Organizations
S.I.C.: 8243; 8299
N.A.I.C.S.: 611420; 611430; 611699; 611710
Advertising Expenditures: $731,000
Media: 4-7
Personnel:
Eric R. Garen *(Chm)*
David C. Collins *(Vice Chm)*
Nicholas R. Schacht *(Pres & CEO)*
Charles R. Waldron *(CFO & Chief Acctg Officer)*
David Booker *(COO)*
Magnus Nylund *(CIO)*
Jennifer Urick *(VP-Product Dev)*

LEXICON MARKETING CORPORATION
(Holding of Golden Gate Capital)
640 S San Vicente Blvd
Los Angeles, CA 90048
Tel.: (323) 782-8282
Fax: (323) 782-7470
Toll Free: (800) 411-6666
E-mail: info@lexiconmarketing.com
Web Site: www.lexiconmarketing.com
Approx. Number Employees: 1,500
Year Founded: 1974
Business Description:
Retailer of English Language Learning Programs
S.I.C.: 8299
N.A.I.C.S.: 611630
Advertising Expenditures: $159,000,000
Media: 15
Personnel:
Valeria Rico *(Pres & CEO)*
Robert Ro *(CFO)*
Rosa N. Hernandez *(VP-Ops & HR)*
Judy Belleti *(Dir-Product Dev)*
Jorge Azpiazu Beristain *(Dir-Creative)*
Anrotsa Pinillos *(Dir-Credit & Collections)*
Yngriborg Richter-Tantalean *(Dir-Media)*
Marcia Tula *(Dir-Sls)*
Enrique Westup *(Dir-Fin Plng & Analysis)*
Brands & Products:
DISNEYS WORLD OF ENGLISH
HELLO AMERICA
INGLES SIN BARRERAS
LEXICOM
VIDEO TEACHER

LINCOLN EDUCATIONAL SERVICES CORPORATION
200 Executive Dr Ste 340
West Orange, NJ 07052
Tel.: (973) 736-9340
Fax: (973) 736-1750
E-mail: info@lincolntech.com
Web Site: www.lincolnedu.com
Approx. Rev.: $639,494,000
Approx. Number Employees: 1,173
Year Founded: 1946
Business Description:
Career Education & Training Services
S.I.C.: 8299; 8243; 8244; 8249
N.A.I.C.S.: 611699; 611410; 611420; 611430; 611519; 611710
Advertising Expenditures: $46,700,000
Media: 3-8-13-14-15-23-24
Personnel:
Shaun McAlmont *(Pres & CEO)*
Cesar Ribeiro *(CFO, Treas & Sr VP)*
Piper P. Jameson *(CMO & Sr VP)*
Scott M. Shaw *(Chief Admin Officer & Exec VP)*
Thomas F. Mchugh *(Chief Compliance Officer & Sr VP)*
Edward B. Abrams *(Pres-Lincoln Educational Grp)*
Deborah Ramentol *(Pres-Lincoln Tech Grp)*
Alexandra M. Luster *(Gen Counsel & VP)*
Stephen M. Buchenot *(Sr VP)*
Advertising Agency:
E&M Advertising
462 7th Ave 8th Fl
New York, NY 10018-7606
Tel.: (212) 981-5900
Fax: (212) 981-2121

LINCOLN TECHNICAL INSTITUTE
200 Executive Dr Ste 340
West Orange, NJ 07052
Tel.: (973) 736-9340
Fax: (973) 736-1750
Web Site: www.lincolnedu.com
Approx. Number Employees: 165
Year Founded: 1946
Business Description:
Vocational Schools & Junior College
S.I.C.: 8222; 5013
N.A.I.C.S.: 611210; 441310
Media: 4-8-10-12-13-18-19-20-22-23-24-25-26
Distr.: Natl.
Budget Set: Oct.

MILWAUKEE SCHOOL OF ENGINEERING
1025 N Broadway
Milwaukee, WI 53202-3109
Tel.: (414) 277-7300
Fax: (414) 277-7470
E-mail: explore@msoe.edu
Web Site: www.msoe.edu
Approx. Sls.: $51,262,199
Approx. Number Employees: 600
Year Founded: 1903
Business Description:
Academic Services in Electrical/ Mechanical Engineering, Nursing, Technical Communication & Construction Management
S.I.C.: 8221
N.A.I.C.S.: 611310
Media: 2-4-8-9-23-25-26
Distr.: Intl.; Natl.
Budget Set: Jan.
Personnel:
Herman Viets *(Pres)*
Armund Janto *(CFO & VP-Fin)*
Sandra Everts *(Dir-Mktg & Pub Affairs)*
Eaton Cutler-Hammer *(Mgr-Bus Devel & Mktg)*
Kent Peterson *(Webmaster)*
Brands & Products:
ATC
FLUID POWER INSTITUTE
MSOE
Advertising Agency:
Performance Communication Group
35 E Wacker Dr Ste 400
Chicago, IL 60601
Tel.: (312) 419-0735
Fax: (312) 419-9172
(Academic Programs)

MOODY BIBLE INSTITUTE
820 N La Salle Blvd
Chicago, IL 60610-3214
Tel.: (312) 329-4000
Fax: (312) 329-2099
Toll Free: (800) 356-6339
E-mail: pr@moody.edu

Key to Media (For complete agency information see *The Advertising Red Books-Agencies* edition):
1. Bus. Publs. 2. Cable T.V. 3. Catalogs & Directories. 4. Co-op Adv. 5. Consumer Mags. 6. D.M. to Bus. Estab.7. D.M. to Consumers
8. Daily Newsp. 9. Exhibits/Trade Shows 10. Foreign 11. Infomercial 12. Internet Adv.13. Multimedia 14. Network Radio
15. Network T.V. 16. Newsp. Distr. Mags. 17. Other 18. Outdoor (Posters, Transit) 19. Point of Purchase20. Premiums, Novelties
21. Product Samples 22. Special Events Mktg. 23. Spot Radio 24. Spot T.V. 25. Weekly Newsp. 26. Yellow Page Adv.

Moody Bible Institute — (Continued)

Web Site: www.moody.edu
Approx. Number Employees: 650
Year Founded: 1886
Business Description:
Bible Centered Education; Publishers of Books; Educational & Religious Broadcasting
S.I.C.: 8661; 8221
N.A.I.C.S.: 813110; 611310
Media: 4-6-7-8-9-10-11-14-19-20-23
Distr.: Intl.; Natl.
Budget Set: Annually
Personnel:
Paul Nyquist *(Pres)*
Ken Heulitt *(CFO)*
Lloyd Dodson *(VP-Corp Projects & HR)*
Eric Hufford *(Dir-Production)*
Brands & Products:
MOODY

NEW YORK INSTITUTE OF TECHNOLOGY

Northern Blvd PO Box 8000
Old Westbury, NY 11568
Tel.: (516) 686-7647
Tel.: (516) 686-7996
Tel.: (516) 686-1000
Fax: (516) 484-5693
Toll Free: (800) 345NYIT
E-mail: admissions@nyit.edu
Web Site: www.nyit.edu
Approx. Number Employees: 280
Year Founded: 1955
Business Description:
Professional Education Services
S.I.C.: 8221
N.A.I.C.S.: 611310
Advertising Expenditures: $1,900,000
Media: 2-4-6-8-9-11-13-14-18-23
Distr.: Direct to Consumer; Natl.
Personnel:
Edward Guiliano *(Pres & CEO)*
Leonard Aubrey *(CFO, Treas & VP-Fin Affairs)*
Catherine R. Flickinger *(Gen Counsel)*
Niyazi Bodur *(VP-IT & Infrastructure)*
Jacquelyn Nealon *(VP-Enrollment, Comm & Mktg)*
Daniel G. McGovern *(Comptroller)*
Susan Warner *(Dir-Publ)*
Kim Margan *(Coord-Media)*
Advertising Agencies:
Munn Rabot LLC
33 W 17th St Fl 3
New York, NY 10011-5511
Tel.: (212) 727-3900
Fax: (212) 604-9804
Toll Free: (888) 847-0290

Wheatley Adv.
PO Box 94
Greenvale, NY 11548
Tel.: (516) 621-8805

THE NEW YORK PUBLIC LIBRARY

5th Ave & 42nd St
New York, NY 10018
Tel.: (212) 930-0800
Tel.: (212) 592-7700 (Press)
Web Site: www.nypl.org
Sales Range: $300-349.9 Million
Approx. Number Employees: 3,124
Business Description:
Library Services
S.I.C.: 8231
N.A.I.C.S.: 519120
Media: 7-8-9-10-13-18-20-22-25
Personnel:
Paul LeClerc *(Pres & CEO)*
David G. Offensend *(COO)*
Robert Vanni *(Gen Counsel & VP)*
Catherine Carver Dunn *(Sr VP-External Affairs)*
James Pisaniello *(VP-Facilities Ops & Security)*
Priscilla Southon *(VP-HR)*
Sharon Hewitt Watkins *(VP-Fin)*
Bonnie Birman *(Associate Dir)*
Sara Abraham *(Dir-Retail Mktg Office)*
Marc Blaustein *(Dir-Art)*
Robert Fornabaio *(Dir-Client Support Svcs)*
Susan Halligan *(Dir-Mktg)*
Judith Johnson *(Dir-Software Dev & Support)*
Kathryn Laino *(Dir-Special Events)*
Herb Scher *(Dir-Pub Rel)*
Richard Stalzer *(Dir-Engineering, Infrastructure & Ops)*
Denise Szabo *(Dir-Dev Svcs)*
Ann Thornton *(Dir-Reference & Res Svcs)*
Gracelyn Pilgrim *(Office Mgr)*
Robert Kenselaar *(Mgr-Campaign Projects)*
Thomas Lisanti *(Mgr)*
Susan Rabbiner *(Mgr)*

NEW YORK SCHOOL OF INTERIOR DESIGN

170 E 70th St
New York, NY 10021-5110
Tel.: (212) 472-1500
Fax: (212) 472-3800
Toll Free: (800) 33NYSID
E-mail: admissions@nysid.edu
Web Site: www.nysid.edu
Approx. Number Employees: 34
Year Founded: 1916
Business Description:
College of Interior Design
S.I.C.: 8221
N.A.I.C.S.: 611310
Media: 4-6-8-9-16-25
Distr.: Intl.; Natl.
Budget Set: Apr.
Personnel:
Christopher Cyphers *(Pres)*

NOBEL LEARNING COMMUNITIES, INC.

1615 West Chester Pike Ste 200
West Chester, PA 19382-6233
Tel.: (484) 947-2000
Fax: (484) 947-2004
Toll Free: (888) 886-6235
E-mail: nobel@educating.com
Web Site: www.nobellearning.com
Approx. Rev.: $232,035,000
Approx. Number Employees: 4,700
Year Founded: 1998
Business Description:
For-Profit Private Education Services
S.I.C.: 8299; 8351
N.A.I.C.S.: 611699; 611710; 624410
Advertising Expenditures: $3,787,000
Media: 6-8-9-13-16-25-26
Distr.: Natl.
Budget Set: July -June
Personnel:
George H. Bernstein *(Pres & CEO)*
Thomas Frank *(CFO & Sr VP)*
Patricia B. Miller *(COO)*
Shari E. Anisman *(VP-Mktg)*
Scott B. Witmoyer *(VP-IT)*
Brands & Products:
CAMP ZONE
ICAMP
NOBEL LEARNING COMMUNITIES
THE PERFECT BALANCE OF LEARNING & PLAY
WATCH YOUR CHILD GROW,FLUORISH & EXCEL
Advertising Agency:
MGH, Inc.
100 Painters Mill Rd Ste 600
Owings Mills, MD 21117-7305
Tel.: (410) 902-5000
Fax: (410) 902-8712

NORTHEASTERN UNIVERSITY

360 Huntington Ave
Boston, MA 02115-5005
Tel.: (617) 373-2000
Fax: (617) 373-5121
Web Site: www.neu.edu
Approx. Number Employees: 4,480
Year Founded: 1898
Business Description:
Educational Institution
S.I.C.: 8221
N.A.I.C.S.: 611310
Advertising Expenditures: $3,000,000
Media: 2-4-8-9-10-18-25
Distr.: Reg.
Budget Set: Oct.
Personnel:
William E. Kneeland *(Treas, Sr VP-Admin, Fin & Controller)*
Tracey Dodenhoff *(Dir-Founding-Center for Res Innovation)*
Daniel J. McCarthy *(Professor-Strategic Mgmt)*

NORTHWESTERN UNIVERSITY

1800 Sherman Ave
Evanston, IL 60208-0001
Tel.: (847) 491-3741
Tel.: (847) 491-4892 (media)
Fax: (847) 491-2376
E-mail: media@northwestern.edu
Web Site: www.northwestern.edu
Sales Estimate: $300-399 Million
Approx. Number Employees: 4,700
Year Founded: 1851
Business Description:
University
S.I.C.: 8221
N.A.I.C.S.: 611310
Advertising Expenditures: $300,000
Media: 4-9-15-25
Distr.: Natl.
Budget Set: Aug.
Personnel:
William A. Osborn *(Chm)*
Donald S. Perkins *(Vice Chm)*
Anne Egger *(Dir-Publications)*
Charles Richard Loebbaka *(Dir-Media Rels)*
Mary Jane Twohey *(Dir-Media Rels)*
Philip Kotler *(Professor-Mktg)*

OFFSHORE SAILING SCHOOL, LTD., INC.

16731 McGregor Blvd
Fort Myers, FL 33908
Tel.: (239) 454-1700
Fax: (239) 454-1191
Fax: (239) 454-9201
E-mail: sail@offshoresailing.com
Web Site: www.offshoresailing.com
Business Description:
Sailing School
S.I.C.: 8299
N.A.I.C.S.: 611699
Media: 2-6-9-10-13-25
Personnel:
Steve Colgate *(Chm)*
Doris Colgate *(Pres & CEO)*

PENN FOSTER EDUCATION GROUP, INC.

(Sub. of The Princeton Review, Inc.)
925 Oak St
Scranton, PA 18515-0999
Tel.: (570) 342-7701
Fax: (570) 343-3620
Toll Free: (800) 275-4410
E-mail: info@pennfoster.edu
Web Site: www.pennfoster.edu
Approx. Rev.: $90,000,000
Approx. Number Employees: 750
Year Founded: 1890
Business Description:
Home Study Educational Services
S.I.C.: 8299; 8221; 8249
N.A.I.C.S.: 611699; 611310; 611519
Export
Advertising Expenditures: $20,000,000
Media: 2-3-6-7-8-11-13-16-20-24
Distr.: Intl.; Natl.
Budget Set: Jan. -Dec.
Personnel:
Frank F. Britt *(Interim Pres)*
Joe Piazza *(CFO)*
Connie C. Dempsey *(Chief Academic Officer)*
Kathryn Gorgol McIlwee *(VP-Mktg)*
Advertising Agency:
WOL Direct
925 Oak St
Scranton, PA 18515-0999
Tel.: (570) 342-7701
Fax: (570) 343-3620

PEOPLES EDUCATIONAL HOLDINGS INC.

299 Market St
Saddle Brook, NJ 07662
Tel.: (201) 712-0090
Fax: (201) 712-0045
Toll Free: (800) 822-1080
E-mail: customersupport@peoplesed.com
Web Site:
www.peoplespublishing.com
Approx. Rev.: $34,915,000
Approx. Number Employees: 91
Business Description:
Publishes Supplemental Educational Materials for Students in Grades K through 12
S.I.C.: 8299; 6719
N.A.I.C.S.: 611710; 551112; 611691
Advertising Expenditures: $10,500,000
Media: 4-7-9-10-13-21-22
Personnel:
Diane M. Miller *(Founder, Chief Creative Officer & Exec VP)*
James J. Peoples *(Chm)*
Brian T. Beckwith *(Pres & CEO)*
Matti A. Prima *(Sr VP-Bus Devel)*

PICCOLO EDUCATIONAL SYSTEMS, INC.
(d/b/a Piccolo International University)
15011 N 75th St
Scottsdale, AZ 85260
Tel.: (480) 398-7000
Fax: (480) 663-2942
E-mail: info@onlinepiu.com
Web Site: www.onlinepiu.com
Approx. Rev.: $48,335
Approx. Number Employees: 23
Business Description:
Online Postsecondary Education Services
S.I.C.: 8299; 2741
N.A.I.C.S.: 611710; 516110
Advertising Expenditures: $115,074
Media: 17
Personnel:
Laura Palmer Noone *(Pres & CEO)*
Gloria Zemla *(CFO, Treas & Sec)*
Jack Holloway, III *(COO)*
Eugene W. Hayes *(Dir-Intl Strategy)*

PRATT INSTITUTE
200 Willoughby Ave
Brooklyn, NY 11205
Tel.: (718) 636-3600
Fax: (718) 636-3670
Toll Free: (800) 331-0834
Web Site: www.pratt.edu
Sales Estimate: $100-119 Million
Approx. Number Employees: 900
Year Founded: 1887
Business Description:
Art & Design School
S.I.C.: 8221
N.A.I.C.S.: 611310
Import
Media: 1-2-4-6-8-9-10-11-13-25-26
Distr.: Reg.
Personnel:
James F. Fulton *(Chm)*
Thomas F. Schutte *(Pres)*
Edmund Rutkowski *(VP-Fin & Admin)*
Sylvia Acuesta *(Comptroller)*
Mara McGinnis *(Exec Dir-Comm)*
Sinclaire Alkire *(Dir-Mktg, Admissions)*
Brands & Products:
PRATT
Advertising Agency:
Brashe Advertising, Inc.
420 Jericho Tpke
Jericho, NY 11753-1344
Tel.: (516) 935-5544
Fax: (516) 931-1722

PRIMROSE HOLDINGS INC.
(Holding of AMERICAN CAPITAL, LTD.)
3660 Cedarcrest Rd
Acworth, GA 30101
Tel.: (770) 529-4100
Fax: (770) 529-1551
E-mail: info@primroseschools.com
Web Site: www.primroseschools.com
Sales Range: $10-24.9 Million
Approx. Number Employees: 34
Year Founded: 1988
Business Description:
Educational Pre-School Center Franchise Services
S.I.C.: 8211
N.A.I.C.S.: 611110
Media: 6
Personnel:
Jo Kirchner *(Pres & CEO)*
Bob Benowitz *(Exec VP-Ops)*
Keri Stoltz *(Dir-Mktg)*

PROFESSIONAL CAREER DEVELOPMENT INSTITUTE LLC
(Holding of DLJ Merchant Banking Partners)
430 Technology Pkwy
Norcross, GA 30092-3406
Tel.: (770) 729-8400
Fax: (770) 729-0961
Toll Free: (800) 417-2407
E-mail: info@pcdi.com
Web Site: www.ashwortacollege.com
Approx. Number Employees: 275
Year Founded: 1987
Business Description:
Long Distance Learning Services
S.I.C.: 8249
N.A.I.C.S.: 611519
Media: 3-4-11-13

RENAISSANCE LEARNING, INC.
2911 Peach St
Wisconsin Rapids, WI 54494-1905
Mailing Address:
PO Box 8036
Wisconsin Rapids, WI 54495-8036
Tel.: (715) 424-3636
Fax: (715) 424-4242
Toll Free: (800) 656-6740
E-mail: answers@renlearn.com
Web Site: www.renlearn.com
Approx. Sls.: $130,094,000
Approx. Number Employees: 893
Year Founded: 1986
Business Description:
Pre-K-12 School Assessment & Progress-Monitoring Technology
S.I.C.: 7372
N.A.I.C.S.: 334611; 511210
Advertising Expenditures: $2,900,000
Media: 10
Personnel:
Terrance D. Paul *(Founder & Chm)*
Judith Ames Paul *(Vice Chm)*
Steven A. Schmidt *(Pres & COO)*
Glenn R. James *(CEO)*
Mary T. Minch *(CFO)*
John Carrgall *(VP-HR)*
Brands & Products:
2KNOW
ACCELERATED GRAMMAR & SPELLING
ACCELERATED MATH
ACCELERATED READER
ACCELERATED VOCABULARY
ACCELERATED WRITER
ACCELSCAN
ACCELTEST
ADVANCED TECHNOLOGY FOR ESSENTIAL PRACTICE
ALPHAQUIZ
ALPHAWORD
AR BOOKFINDER
AR BOOKGUIDE
ASSESSMENTMASTER
ATOS
BETTER DATA. BETTER LEARNING
CLASSROOM RESPONSE SYSTEM
DANA
ENGLISH IN A FLASH
FLUENT READER
LANGUAGE ACQUISITION
MATH RENAISSANCE
MATHFACTS IN A FLASH
NEO 2
NEO TEXT2SPEECH
POWER LESSONS
READ NOW POWER UP!
READING INTERVENTION
RENAISSANCE CLASSROOM RESPONSE SYSTEM
RENAISSANCE LEARNING
RENAISSANCE PLACE
SCHOOL RENAISSANCE
STAR EARLY LITERACY
STAR MATH
STAR READING
SUCCESSFUL READER
TESTCHECK
WRITE ON!
WRITING RENAISSANCE

RUTGERS, THE STATE UNIVERSITY OF NEW JERSEY
Old Queens Bldg 83 Somerset St
New Brunswick, NJ 08901
Tel.: (732) 932-4636
Fax: (732) 932-8480
E-mail: info@rutgers.edu
Web Site: www.rutgers.edu
E-Mail For Key Personnel:
President: president@rutgers.edu
Sales Range: $10-24.9 Million
Approx. Number Employees: 10,000
Year Founded: 1766
Business Description:
State-Wide Public University of New Jersey
S.I.C.: 8221
N.A.I.C.S.: 611310
Media: 3-4-6-8-13-14-15-18-25
Personnel:
Richard L. McCormick *(Pres)*
Bruce C. Fehn *(Treas, Sr VP-Fin & Admin)*
Michael Karaban *(Sr VP-Mktg)*
Pamela A. Blake *(Asst VP-University Rels)*
Advertising Agencies:
BarkleyREI
2840 Liberty Ave Ste 100
Pittsburgh, PA 15222
Tel.: (412) 683-3700
Fax: (412) 683-1610

Finch Brands
325 Chestnut St Ste 1313
Philadelphia, PA 19106
Tel.: (215) 413-2686
Fax: (215) 413-2687
Rutgers-Camden

Lewis Advertising Agency
17 Academy St Ste 405
Newark, NJ 07102-2923
Tel.: (973) 642-4800
Fax: (973) 642-8948
Rutgers-Newark

Zullo Associates
1 Academy St
Princeton, NJ 08540
Tel.: (609) 683-1800
Fax: (609) 683-4773
Rutgers Athletic Dept.

SCHOOLWIRES
320 Rolling Ridge Dr Ste 201
State College, PA 16801
Tel.: (814) 689-1046
Fax: (814) 689-3962
E-mail: info@schoolwires.com
Web Site: www.schoolwires.com
Approx. Rev.: $6,844,230
Approx. Number Employees: 114
Year Founded: 2001
S.I.C.: 8299
N.A.I.C.S.: 611710
Personnel:
Edward S. Marflak *(Founder)*
Christiane Crawford *(Pres & CEO)*
Don Eisele *(CFO)*
Jason Coudriet *(VP-Product Dev)*
Melissa Kalinowski *(VP-Mktg)*
Peggi Munkittrick *(Sr Dir-Product Strategy)*
Rick Stiners *(Mgr-Network & IT Svcs)*
Advertising Agency:
Stein Rogan + Partners
432 Park Ave S
New York, NY 10016-8013
Tel.: (212) 213-1112
Fax: (212) 779-7305

SCIENTIFIC LEARNING CORPORATION
300 Frank H Ogawa Plz Ste 600
Oakland, CA 94612-2040
Tel.: (510) 444-3500
Fax: (510) 444-3580
Toll Free: (888) 665-9707
E-mail: info@scilearn.com
Web Site: www.scilearn.com
Approx. Rev.: $43,384,000
Approx. Number Employees: 212
Year Founded: 1996
Business Description:
Programs Developer & Services for Education
S.I.C.: 8299
N.A.I.C.S.: 611710
Advertising Expenditures: $172,000
Media: 7-10-13
Personnel:
William M. Jenkins *(Founder & Chief Scientific Officer)*
Robert C. Bowen *(Chm)*
Michael A. Moses *(Vice Chm)*
D. Andrew Myers *(Pres & CEO)*
Robert E. Feller *(CFO)*
Sherrelle Jiggitts Walker *(Chief Education Officer)*
Linda L. Carloni *(Gen Counsel, Sec & VP)*
David C. Myers *(Sr VP-Sls & Svcs)*
Jessica Lindl *(VP-Mktg)*
Martha Burns *(Dir-Clinical Specialist Market)*
Brands & Products:
AWAY WE GO
BRAINAPPS
BRAINCONNECTION
FAST FORWORD
FAST FORWORD BASICS
FAST FORWORD BOOKSHELF
FAST FORWORD LANGUAGE
FAST POWER LEARNING
LEARNING MAPS
READING ASSISTANT
READING EDGE
READING ROVER
SCIENTIFIC LEARNING

SHENANDOAH UNIVERSITY
1460 University Dr
Winchester, VA 22601
Tel.: (540) 665-4500
Fax: (540) 678-4331

Key to Media (For complete agency information see *The Advertising Red Books-Agencies* edition):
1. Bus. Publs. 2. Cable T.V. 3. Catalogs & Directories. 4. Co-op Adv. 5. Consumer Mags. 6. D.M. to Bus. Estab.7. D.M. to Consumers
8. Daily Newsp. 9. Exhibits/Trade Shows 10. Foreign 11. Infomercial 12. Internet Adv.13. Multimedia 14. Network Radio
15. Network T.V. 16. Newsp. Distr. Mags. 17. Other 18. Outdoor (Posters, Transit) 19. Point of Purchase20. Premiums, Novelties
21. Product Samples 22. Special Events Mktg. 23. Spot Radio 24. Spot T.V. 25. Weekly Newsp. 26. Yellow Page Adv.

Shenandoah University — (Continued)

Web Site: www.su.edu
Approx. Number Employees: 500
Business Description:
University
S.I.C.: 8221
N.A.I.C.S.: 611310
Media: 3-4-6-9-13-23-24-25
Personnel:
Tracy Fitzsimmons *(Pres)*
Cathy Loranger *(Assoc VP-Mktg & Comm)*

SIEBEL INSTITUTE OF TECHNOLOGY

(Sub. of Lallemand, Inc.)
1777 N Clybourn Ave Ste 2F
Chicago, IL 60614
Tel.: (312) 255-0705
Fax: (312) 255-1312
E-mail: info@siebelinstitute.com
Web Site: www.siebelinstitute.com
Approx. Sls.: $2,000,000
Approx. Number Employees: 7
Year Founded: 1872
Business Description:
Educational School & Laboratory Service for Brewing
S.I.C.: 8244
N.A.I.C.S.: 611410
Media: 2-10-13
Personnel:
Lyn Kruger *(Pres & COO)*

SPARTAN SCHOOL OF AERONAUTICS

8820 E Pine St
Tulsa, OK 74115-5802
Mailing Address:
PO Box 582833
Tulsa, OK 74158-2833
Tel.: (918) 836-6886
Fax: (918) 831-5287
Toll Free: (800) 331-1204
Telex: 49-7465
Web Site: www.spartan.edu
Approx. Number Employees: 300
Year Founded: 1928
Business Description:
Aviation Related Courses
S.I.C.: 8249
N.A.I.C.S.: 611519
Media: 6-8-10-13-25
Distr.: Natl.
Budget Set: Oct.
Personnel:
John Walker *(Chm)*
Damon Bowling *(VP-Mktg)*
Brands & Products:
SPARTAN

STRAYER EDUCATION INC.

1100 Wilson Blvd Ste 2500
Arlington, VA 22209
Mailing Address:
8360 Patuxent Range Rd
Jessup, MD 20794-9649
Tel.: (703) 247-2500
Fax: (703) 527-0112
Web Site: www.strayereducation.com
Approx. Rev.: $636,732,000
Approx. Number Employees: 2,099
Year Founded: 1892
Business Description:
Holding Company; Educational Services
S.I.C.: 8221; 8299; 9411
N.A.I.C.S.: 611310; 611710; 923110
Media: 8-9-13-23-24
Personnel:
Robert S. Silberman *(Chm & CEO)*
Karl McDonnell *(Pres & COO)*
Mark C. Brown *(CFO & Exec VP)*
Deborah A. Keller *(Sr VP-HR)*
Sonya G. Udler *(Sr VP-Corp Comm)*

TIGRENT INC.

1612 E Cape Coral Pkwy
Cape Coral, FL 33904
Tel.: (239) 542-0643
Fax: (239) 540-6562
Web Site: www.tigrent.com
Approx. Rev.: $102,635,000
Approx. Number Employees: 167
Year Founded: 1987
Business Description:
Educational & Training Services
S.I.C.: 9411; 8249
N.A.I.C.S.: 923110; 611519
Advertising Expenditures: $30,319,000
Personnel:
Murray A. Indick *(Chm)*
Steven C. Barre *(CEO)*
Charles F. Kuehne *(CFO)*
James E. May *(Chief Admin Officer & Gen Counsel)*
Brands & Products:
A UNIQUE CANADIAN OPPORTUNITY
BECAUSE WEALTH KNOWS NO BORDERS
CASH FLOW GENERATOR
CREATING THE NEXT GENERATION OF WEALTH
EDUTRADES
WEALTH CREATION THROUGH REAL ESTATE INVESTMENT
WEALTH INTELLIGENCE ACADEMY
WEALTH INTELLIGENCE NETWORK
WHITNEY
WHITNEY EDUCATION GROUP

TRINITY COLLEGE OF FLORIDA

2430 Welbilt Blvd
New Port Richey, FL 34655
Tel.: (727) 376-6911
Fax: (727) 376-0781
Web Site: www.trinitycollege.edu
Business Description:
College
S.I.C.: 8221
N.A.I.C.S.: 611310
Media: 8-13-23
Personnel:
Mark O'Farrell *(Pres)*
Kevin O'Farrell *(Asst VP-Comm & Mktg)*

UNIVERSAL TECHNICAL INSTITUTE, INC.

20410 N 19th Ave Ste 200
Phoenix, AZ 85027
Tel.: (623) 445-9500
Fax: (623) 445-9501
Toll Free: (800) 859-7249
E-mail: info@uticorp.com
Web Site: www.uti.edu
Approx. Rev.: $435,921,000
Approx. Number Employees: 2,470
Business Description:
Automotive Technician Training Services
S.I.C.: 8249
N.A.I.C.S.: 611519
Advertising Expenditures: $32,552,000
Personnel:
John C. White *(Chm)*
Eugene S. Putnam, Jr. *(Pres & CFO)*
Kimberly J. McWaters *(CEO)*
Chad A. Freed *(Gen Counsel, Sec & Sr VP-Bus Dev)*
Richard P. Crain *(Sr VP-Mktg & Strategy)*
Ken Cranston *(Sr VP-Admissions)*
Julian E. Gorman *(Sr VP)*
Thomas E. Riggs *(Sr VP-Campus Ops)*
Roger L. Speer *(Sr VP-Custom Trng Grp & Support Svcs)*
Terry Emig *(Dir-Motorsports & Event Mktg)*
Chelsea Evans *(Dir-Motorsports & Event Mktg)*
Jenny Swanson *(Dir-IR)*
Advertising Agency:
SSA Public Relations
8400 E Crescent Pkwy Ste 600
Greenwood Village, CO 80111
Tel.: (303) 707-1776
Fax: (303) 734-8831

UNIVERSITY OF ARKANSAS

1125 West Maple
Fayetteville, AR 72701
Tel.: (479) 575-2000
Tel.: (479) 575-5555 (Univ Rels)
Web Site: www.uark.edu
Approx. Rev.: $1,000,000,000
Approx. Number Employees: 14,000
Business Description:
College
S.I.C.: 8221
N.A.I.C.S.: 611310
Media: 4-9-10-13-18-22-23-24-25
Personnel:
Andy Albertson *(Dir-Comm)*
Melissa Lutz Blouin *(Dir-Science & Res Comm)*
Roy G. Cordell *(Dir-Visual & Creative Svcs)*
Dixie Terrell Kline *(Dir-Comm)*
Gail G. Piha *(Dir)*
Kim Randle *(Dir-Corp & Foundation Rls)*
Ken Vickers *(Dir-Microelectronics-Photonics Graduate Program)*
William K. Warnock *(Dir-Program Assessment)*
Yvonne Kochera Kirby *(Asst Dir-Res)*
Scott Lunsford *(Assoc Dir)*
Susan M. Rogers *(Assoc Dir-Internal Audit)*
Eric L. Pipkin *(Mgr-Design Svcs)*
Advertising Agency:
Mangan Holcomb Partners
2300 Cottondale Ln Ste 300
Little Rock, AR 72202
Tel.: (501) 376-0321
Fax: (501) 376-6127

UNIVERSITY OF ARKANSAS FOR MEDICAL SCIENCES

(Div. of University of Arkansas)
4301 W Markham
Little Rock, AR 72205-7199
Tel.: (501) 686-7000
Tel.: (501) 686-8990 (Commun & Mktg)
Fax: (501) 686-6020
Toll Free: (800) 248UAMS
Web Site: www.uams.edu
E-Mail For Key Personnel:
Marketing Director: irbytim@uams.edu
Approx. Number Employees: 9,200
Year Founded: 1879
Business Description:
Higher Education/Health Care
S.I.C.: 8011
N.A.I.C.S.: 621111
Import Export
Media: 4-9-11-13-18-23-24-25
Distr.: Direct to Consumer; Reg.
Budget Set: Apr.
Personnel:
Alan Sugg *(Pres)*
Tim Irby *(Dir-Mktg & Adv)*
Andrea Peel *(Dir-Comm)*
Jodiane Tritt *(Dir-Community Support)*
Karen D. Fleming *(Mgr-Special Projects)*
Jerri Jackson *(Mgr-Media Rels)*
Brands & Products:
ARKANSAS CANCER RESEARCH CENTER
JONES EYE INSTITUTE
REYNOLDS CENTER ON AGING
UAMS
WHER MEDICINE LIVES

UNIVERSITY OF MINNESOTA

100 Church St SE
Minneapolis, MN 55455
Tel.: (612) 624-6868
Fax: (612) 624-6369
E-mail: urelate@umn.edu
Web Site: www.umn.edu
Approx. Number Employees: 25
Personnel:
Ann Aronson *(Asst VP)*
Thomas C. Proehl *(Dir-Producing-Theatre Arts & Dance)*
Laura Johnson *(Associate Dir & Mgr-Mktg)*
Advertising Agencies:
Bayard Advertising Agency, Inc.
9801 Dupont Ave S Ste 300
Minneapolis, MN 55431
Tel.: (952) 881-4411
Fax: (952) 881-2266

Brandspring Solutions LLC
14500 Martin Dr Ste 1000
Eden Prairie, MN 55344-2075
Tel.: (952) 345-7260
Fax: (952) 345-7261
Landscape Arborteum

LaBreche
500 Washington Ave S Ste 2020
Minneapolis, MN 55415
Tel.: (612) 338-0901
Fax: (612) 338-0921

OLSON
1625 Hennepin Ave
Minneapolis, MN 55403
Tel.: (612) 215-9800
Fax: (612) 215-9801

Padilla Speer Beardsley
1101 W River Pkwy Ste 400
Minneapolis, MN 55415-1241
Tel.: (612) 455-1700
Fax: (612) 455-1060

SPM Marketing & Communications

Key to Media (For complete agency information see *The Advertising Red Books-Agencies* edition):
1. Bus. Publs. 2. Cable T.V. 3. Catalogs & Directories. 4. Co-op Adv. 5. Consumer Mags. 6. D.M. to Bus. Estab.7. D.M. to Consumers
8. Daily Newsp. 9. Exhibits/Trade Shows 10. Foreign 11. Infomercial 12. Internet Adv.13. Multimedia 14. Network Radio
15. Network T.V. 16. Newsp. Distr. Mags. 17. Other 18. Outdoor (Posters, Transit) 19. Point of Purchase20. Premiums, Novelties
21. Product Samples 22. Special Events Mktg. 23. Spot Radio 24. Spot T.V. 25. Weekly Newsp. 26. Yellow Page Adv.

15 W Harris Ave Ste 300
La Grange, IL 60525-2498
Tel.: (708) 246-7700
Fax: (708) 246-5184
Medical Center

UNIVERSITY OF PENNSYLVANIA

3451 Walnut St
Philadelphia, PA 19104
Tel.: (215) 898-5000
Fax: (215) 573-8090
E-mail: abgraham@pobox.upenn.edu
Web Site: www.upenn.edu
Approx. Number Employees: 20,000
Year Founded: 1740
Business Description:
Ivy League University
S.I.C.: 8221; 6513
N.A.I.C.S.: 611310; 531110
Advertising Expenditures: $5,000,000
Media: 2-4-7-8-10
Distr.: Natl.
Personnel:
Ralph W. Muller *(CEO-Health Sys)*
Wendy S. White *(Gen Counsel & Sr VP)*
Craig Carnaroli *(Exec VP)*
Robin Beck *(VP-Info Sys & Computing)*
Joann Mitchell *(VP-Intl Affairs)*
Aiasha Graham *(Dir-Publication Svcs & Comm)*
Laura Waldron *(Dir-Mktg)*
Sheryl L. Williams *(Dir-Pub Affairs)*
Advertising Agencies:
Ameredia, Inc.
101 Howard St Ste 380
San Francisco, CA 94105
Tel.: (415) 788-5100
Fax: (415) 449-3411

Publication Services
3819 Chestnut St Ste 140
Philadelphia, PA 19104-4011
Tel.: (215) 898-4838
Tel.: (215) 898-3627
Fax: (215) 573-2124
(Dr. Services, Medical Studies, University Program)

Tierney Communications
(A Div. of the Interpublic Group of Companies)
The Bellevue 200 S Broad St
Philadelphia, PA 19102-3803
Tel.: (215) 790-4100
Fax: (215) 790-4363

THE UNIVERSITY OF PHOENIX, INC.

(Sub. of Apollo Group, Inc.)
4025 S Riverpoint Pkwy
Phoenix, AZ 85040-1973
Tel.: (480) 966-5394
Fax: (480) 557-1899
Toll Free: (800) 776-4867
E-mail: info@phoenix.edu
Web Site: www.phoenix.edu
Sales Range: $400-449.9 Million
Approx. Number Employees: 3,000
Year Founded: 1976
Business Description:
Education
S.I.C.: 8221
N.A.I.C.S.: 611310
Personnel:
William J. Pepicello *(Pres)*
Dianne Pusch *(COO)*
Michael Sullivan *(Sr VP-Brand Mktg & Media)*
Bruce Williams *(VP-Mktg)*
Advertising Agencies:
Cramer-Krasselt Public Relations
225 N Michigan Ave
Chicago, IL 60601-7601
Tel.: (312) 616-9600

Harvest One Media
406 Main St Ste 501
Boonton, NJ 07005
Tel.: (973) 588-3335

Penna Powers Brian Haynes
1706 S Major St
Salt Lake City, UT 84115
Tel.: (801) 487-4800
Fax: (801) 487-0707
Toll Free: (800) 409-9346

Pereira & O'Dell
215 2nd St
San Francisco, CA 94105
Tel.: (415) 284-9916
Fax: (415) 284-9926
(Creative)

VALE NATIONAL TRAINING CENTER INC.

2424 E Randol Mill Rd
Arlington, TX 76011
Tel.: (817) 633-4800
Fax: (817) 633-2922
Toll Free: (800) 233-7095
E-mail: valenational@csbrand.com
Web Site: www.valenational.com
Approx. Number Employees: 16
Year Founded: 1949
Business Description:
Training of Appraisers for Auto & Property Physical Damage
S.I.C.: 8249
N.A.I.C.S.: 611519
Media: 4-6-7-8-10
Distr.: Natl.
Budget Set: May
Personnel:
Jon McCreath *(Pres)*
Brands & Products:
ADVANCED ESTIMATICS
AUTOMOTIVE ESTIMATICS
COMMERCIAL BUILDING BASICS
RESIDENTIAL BUILDING BASICS
STAR 2000
VALE TRAINING SOLUTIONS

WEST COAST UNIVERSITY

200 E Baker Ste 201
Costa Mesa, CA 92626
Tel.: (714) 415-6500
Fax: (714) 444-0641
E-mail: info@westcoastuniversity.com
Sales Range: $25-49.9 Million
Approx. Number Employees: 28
Business Description:
University
S.I.C.: 8221
N.A.I.C.S.: 611310
Media: 8-13
Personnel:
David Pyle *(Chm)*
Eric Chiusolo *(CFO)*

WESTLAWN INSTITUTE OF MARINE TECHNOLOGY

(Affil. of National Marine Manufacturers Association)
C/O Mystic Seaport 75 Greenmanville Ave
Mystic, CT 06355
Tel.: (860) 572-7900
Fax: (860) 572-7939
E-mail: westlawn@abycinc.org
Web Site: www.westlawn.edu
Approx. Number Employees: 5
Year Founded: 1930
Business Description:
Small-Craft Design School
S.I.C.: 8249
N.A.I.C.S.: 611519
Media: 6-16-17-25
Distr.: Intl.
Budget Set: Mar.
Personnel:
Skip Burdon *(Pres & CEO)*

Key to Media (For complete agency information see *The Advertising Red Books-Agencies* edition):
1. Bus. Publs. 2. Cable T.V. 3. Catalogs & Directories. 4. Co-op Adv. 5. Consumer Mags. 6. D.M. to Bus. Estab.7. D.M. to Consumers 8. Daily Newsp. 9. Exhibits/Trade Shows 10. Foreign 11. Infomercial 12. Internet Adv.13. Multimedia 14. Network Radio 15. Network T.V. 16. Newsp. Distr. Mags. 17. Other 18. Outdoor (Posters, Transit) 19. Point of Purchase20. Premiums, Novelties 21. Product Samples 22. Special Events Mktg. 23. Spot Radio 24. Spot T.V. 25. Weekly Newsp. 26. Yellow Page Adv.

Seeds, Plants & Fertilizers

Bulbs — Fertilizers — Florists — Flowers by Wire — Horticulturists — Insecticides — Lawn Care Services — Nursery Stock — Nurseries — Orchards — Perennials — Plants — Retail Garden Centers — Seeds — Spraying Compounds — Tree Surgeons

1-800-FLOWERS.COM, INC.
1 Old Country Rd Ste 500
Carle Place, NY 11514-1847
Tel.: (516) 237-6000
Tel.: (516) 237-6131 (Investor Rels)
Fax: (516) 237-6060
Toll Free: (800) FLOWERS
E-mail: invest@1800flowers.com
Web Site: www.1800flowers.com
Approx. Rev.: $689,787,000
Approx. Number Employees: 2,300
Year Founded: 1976
Business Description:
Flower & Gifts Mail-Order & Internet Retailer
S.I.C.: 5992; 5961; 5999
N.A.I.C.S.: 453110; 453998; 454111; 454113
Advertising Expenditures: $70,400,000
Media: 4-8-13-14-15-18
Distr.: Direct to Consumer; Intl.; Natl.
Budget Set: July
Personnel:
James F. McCann *(Chm & CEO)*
Christopher G. McCann *(Pres)*
William E. Shea *(CFO, Treas, Sr VP-Fin & Admin)*
Timothy J. Hopkins *(COO)*
Stephen J. Bozzo *(CIO & Sr VP)*
Mark Nance *(Pres-Bloomnet)*
David Taiclet *(Pres-Gourmet Food and Gift Baskets)*
Thomas G. Hartnett *(CFO-Consumer Floral Brand & Sr VP)*
Gerard M. Gallagher *(Gen Counsel, Sec & Sr VP-Bus Affairs)*
Vincent J. McVeigh *(Sr VP-BloomNet)*
Kevin Ranford *(VP-Online Marketing, Mobile & Social Media)*
Julie L. Kaufman *(Dir-Customer Svc)*
Brands & Products:

Maslansky, Luntz & Partners
1101 King St Ste 110
Alexandria, VA 22314
Tel.: (703) 358-0080
Fax: (703) 358-0089

MEC, Global HQ, New York
825 7th Ave
New York, NY 10019-6014
Tel.: (212) 474-0000
Fax: (212) 474-0020
Fax: (212) 474-0003

Moroch Partners
3625 N Hall St Ste 1100
Dallas, TX 75219-5122
Tel.: (214) 520-9700
Fax: (214) 252-1724

AGRILIANCE, LLC
(Joint Venture of Land O'Lakes, Inc. & CHS INC.)
5500 Cenex Dr
Inver Grove Heights, MN 55077-1733
Tel.: (651) 451-5000
Fax: (651) 451-5404
Toll Free: (800) 535-4635
Telex: 297-060
Approx. Number Employees: 2,504
Year Founded: 2000
Business Description:
Crop Protection Products & Services; Owned by CHS Inc. & Land O'Lakes, Inc.
S.I.C.: 5083; 2879
N.A.I.C.S.: 423820; 325320
Media: 2-11-13
Distr.: Reg.
Budget Set: July
Personnel:
Don Johnson *(Pres & CEO)*
John Schmitz *(CFO & Exec VP)*
Tracy Mack *(Dir-Logistics)*
Sally Sorlie *(Dir-Strategic Mktg & Supply)*
Brands & Products:
AGRILIANCE
AGRISOLUTIONS
ORIGEN
WISER
Advertising Agency:
Exponent
400 First Ave N Ste 600
Minneapolis, MN 55401-1954
Tel.: (612) 305-6000
Fax: (612) 305-6501

A.H. HOFFMAN, INC.
(Sub. of Good Earth, Inc.)
PO Box 290
Lancaster, NY 14086
Tel.: (716) 684-8111
Fax: (716) 684-3722
Web Site: www.goodearth.org/index.cfm
Approx. Number Employees: 50
Year Founded: 1900
Business Description:
Producer of Horticultural Specialty Products
S.I.C.: 5149
N.A.I.C.S.: 424490
Media: 2-4-5-6-7-8-9-10-18-19
Distr.: Reg.
Budget Set: Monthly
Personnel:
Guenter H. Burkhardt *(Pres)*
Monika Burkhardt *(VP-Mktg)*
Brands & Products:
HOFFMAN

ALBERT F. AMLING, LLC
(d/b/a Amling's Flowerland)
3011 Bransford Rd
Elmhurst, IL 60126
Tel.: (630) 850-5070
Fax: (630) 654-8051
Toll Free: (888) AMLINGS
Web Site: www.amlings.com
Approx. Number Employees: 300
Year Founded: 1889
Business Description:
Flowers, Garden Products & Gifts Retailer; Landscaping Servcies; Commercial Plant Rentals
S.I.C.: 5992; 5261
N.A.I.C.S.: 453110; 444220
Advertising Expenditures: $1,000,000
Media: 7-8-9-10-15-20-23-25-26
Distr.: Reg.
Budget Set: Jan.

ALL AMERICA-PHILLIP'S FLOWER SHOPS, INC.
524 N Cass Ave
Westmont, IL 60559-1503
Tel.: (630) 719-5200
Fax: (630) 719-2292
Toll Free: (800) 356-7257
E-mail: info@800florals.com
Web Site: www.800florals.com
Approx. Number Employees: 300
Year Founded: 1923
Business Description:
Online & Telephone Order Florists
S.I.C.: 5992; 5193
N.A.I.C.S.: 453110; 424930
Media: 4-6-13
Personnel:
Jim Phillip *(Chm)*
Baxter Phillip *(Exec VP)*
Nathan Pernia *(Dir-Mktg)*

AMERICAN VANGUARD CORPORATION
4695 MacArthur Ct Ste 1250
Newport Beach, CA 92660
Tel.: (949) 260-1200
Fax: (949) 260-1201
Toll Free: (888) 462-6822
Web Site: www.amvac-chemical.com
E-Mail For Key Personnel:
President: ericw@amvac-chemical.com
Approx. Sls.: $229,620,000
Approx. Number Employees: 350
Year Founded: 1969
Business Description:
Agricultural Chemicals Developer & Marketer
S.I.C.: 2752; 2879; 5191
N.A.I.C.S.: 323110; 325320; 424910
Export
Advertising Expenditures: $2,418,000
Media: 2-4-7-20-21
Distr.: Intl.; Natl.
Budget Set: Dec.
Personnel:
Herbert A. Kraft *(Co-Chm)*
Glenn A. Wintemute *(Co-Chm)*
Eric G. Wintemute *(Pres & CEO)*
David T. Johnson *(CFO & Sr VP)*
Glen D. Johnson *(Sr VP & Dir-Bus Dev)*
Doug Ashmore *(VP & Dir-Mfg)*
Ian S. Chart *(VP & Dir-Regulatory Affairs)*
Johann Venter *(VP & Dir-Tech)*
William A. Kuser *(Dir-IR & Corp Comm)*
Ann Manley *(Dir-Toxicology)*
Alfredo Palaez *(Dir-Intl Bus)*
Jon Wood *(Dir-Registrations)*
Ann Taylor *(Sr Mgr-Regulatory Affairs)*
Glen Anderson *(Mgr-Customer Svc)*
John A. Immaraju *(Mgr-Intl Product Dev)*
Bill O'Neal *(Mgr-Tech Product & Mgr-Product Dev-Northeast Reg)*
John E. Orr *(Mgr-Product Dev-Northern Region)*

Key to Media (For complete agency information see *The Advertising Red Books-Agencies* edition):
1. Bus. Publs. 2. Cable T.V. 3. Catalogs & Directories. 4. Co-op Adv. 5. Consumer Mags. 6. D.M. to Bus. Estab.7. D.M. to Consumers 8. Daily Newsp. 9. Exhibits/Trade Shows 10. Foreign 11. Infomercial 12. Internet Adv.13. Multimedia 14. Network Radio 15. Network T.V. 16. Newsp. Distr. Mags. 17. Other 18. Outdoor (Posters, Transit) 19. Point of Purchase20. Premiums, Novelties 21. Product Samples 22. Special Events Mktg. 23. Spot Radio 24. Spot T.V. 25. Weekly Newsp. 26. Yellow Page Adv.

Richard M. Porter *(Mgr-Product Dev-Midwest Region)*
Paul D. Vaculin *(Mgr-Product Dev-Southern Region)*
Brands & Products:
AMVAC
VAPAM
Advertising Agencies:
The Creative Gene
1113 Second Ave SE
Cedar Rapids, IA 52403-2405
Tel.: (319) 399-1234
Fax: (319) 247-1234
— Steve Fredericksen *(Pres & Dir-Creative)*

Fritzler Design
4500 Campus Ste 692
Newport Beach, CA 92660
Tel.: (949) 852-0827
Fax: (949) 852-8530
— Teresa Fritzler *(Pres)*

THE ANDERSONS INCORPORATED

480 W Dussel Dr
Maumee, OH 43537-1639
Mailing Address:
PO Box 119
Maumee, OH 43537-0119
Tel.: (419) 893-5050
Fax: (419) 891-6670
Toll Free: (800) 537-3370
E-mail: hostmaster@andersonsinc.com
Web Site: www.andersonsinc.com
Approx. Rev.: $3,393,791,000
Approx. Number Employees: 1,614
Year Founded: 1947
Business Description:
Grain Merchandising, Handling & Related Products; Retail Stores; Agricultural & Lawn Fertilizer Products; Corn Cob Milling
S.I.C.: 0119; 0711; 0723; 5153
N.A.I.C.S.: 111191; 111199; 115112; 115114; 424510
Import Export
Advertising Expenditures: $4,000,000
Media: 2-5-8-9-18-19-22-23-24-25
Distr.: Natl.
Personnel:
Michael J. Anderson *(Chm, Pres & CEO)*
Richard R. George *(CIO, VP & Controller)*
Daniel T. Anderson *(Pres-Retail Grp & VP-Corp Ops Svcs)*
Dennis J. Addis *(Pres-Plant Nutrient Grp)*
Harold M. Reed *(Pres-Grain & Ethanol Grp)*
Rasesh H. Shah *(Pres-Rail Group)*
Thomas L. Waggoner *(Pres-Turf & Specialty Grp)*
Naran U. Burchinow *(Gen Counsel, Corp Sec & VP)*
Nicholas C. Conrad *(Treas & VP-Fin)*
Arthur D. DePompei *(VP-HR)*
Tamara Sue Sparks *(VP-Corp Rels & Bus Analysis)*
Brands & Products:
THE ANDERSONS
BED-O' COBS
CLUMP-N-FLUSH
ENRICH-O COBS
FIELDFRESH
GOVERNOR
TEE TIME

ARIS HORTICULTURE, INC.

115 3rd St SE
Barberton, OH 44203-4208
Mailing Address:
PO Box 230
Barberton, OH 44203-0230
Tel.: (330) 745-2143
Fax: (330) 745-3098
Toll Free: (800) 232-9557
Web Site: arishort.com
Approx. Number Employees: 650
Year Founded: 1920
Business Description:
Ornamental Nursery Products
S.I.C.: 0181; 5261
N.A.I.C.S.: 111421; 444220
Import Export
Advertising Expenditures: $75,000
Media: 2-4-7-10-16-17-18-19-20-21-26
Personnel:
G. R. Yoder *(Chm)*
William G. Rasbach *(Pres & CEO)*
Scott Schaefer *(COO & VP-Fin)*
Chris Jacobs *(VP-Sls & Gen Mgr)*
Christine Kelleher *(Mgr-Mktg & Ops)*
Brands & Products:
BLOOMS OF BRESSINGHAM
FLEURETTES BY YODER
FLOWER FIELDS
GREEN LEAF PERENNIALS
KEEPSAKE
KEEPSAKE AZALEAS
PROPHETS
TRADEWINDS HIBISCUS
YODER

ARMSTRONG GARDEN CENTERS, INC.

2200 E Rte 66 Ste 200
Glendora, CA 91740
Tel.: (626) 914-1091
Fax: (626) 335-0257
Toll Free: (800) 55PLANT
E-mail: info@armstronggarden.com
Web Site: www.armstronggarden.com
E-Mail For Key Personnel:
President: mkunce@armstronggarden.com
Approx. Number Employees: 600
Year Founded: 1889
Business Description:
Retail Florist
S.I.C.: 5261; 0782
N.A.I.C.S.: 444220; 561730
Media: 4-6-9-19-23
Personnel:
Mike D. Kunce *(Co-Pres & CEO)*
Monte Enright *(Co-Pres & COO)*
David Weisman *(CFO & VP)*
Gary Jones *(VP-Mktg)*
Brands & Products:
ARMSTRONG GARDEN CENTERS
CALIFORNIA GARDENER
HOTBISCUS
PINK LEMONADE LEMON
WADDA TOMATO

ATLANTIC TREE NURSERY, INC.

(Sub. of Robert W. Baker Nursery Inc.)
1700 Mountain Rd
West Suffield, CT 06093
Tel.: (860) 668-7371
Fax: (860) 668-5802
Business Description:
Tree Whslr
S.I.C.: 0181
N.A.I.C.S.: 111421
Media: 4

BALL HORTICULTURAL COMPANY

622 Town Rd
West Chicago, IL 60185-2614
Tel.: (630) 231-3600
Fax: (630) 231-3592
E-mail: careers@ballhort.com
Web Site: www.ballhort.com
Approx. Number Employees: 500
Year Founded: 1905
Business Description:
Whslr of Supplies to the Flower Growing Industry; Super Seedlings, Flower Seeds, Plant Containers & Growing Supplies
S.I.C.: 0181; 5261
N.A.I.C.S.: 111422; 111421; 444220
Import Export
Personnel:
Anna C. Ball *(Pres & CEO)*
Bill Doeckel *(Gen Mgr)*
Diane Hund *(Dir-Mktg)*
Advertising Agency:
Bader Rutter & Associates, Inc.
13845 Bishops Dr
Brookfield, WI 53005
Tel.: (262) 784-7200
Fax: (262) 938-5595
Toll Free: (888) 742-2337
(Integrated Brand Communications)

BELLINGRATH GARDENS & HOME

12401 Bellingrath Gardens Rd
Theodore, AL 36582-8460
Tel.: (251) 973-2217
Fax: (251) 973-0540
Toll Free: (800) 247-8420
E-mail: bellingrath@bellingrath.org
Web Site: www.bellingrath.org
Approx. Sls.: $2,600,000
Approx. Number Employees: 50
Year Founded: 1932
Business Description:
Public Flower Garden
S.I.C.: 8422
N.A.I.C.S.: 712130
Media: 9-10-13-23-24
Distr.: Natl.
Budget Set: Sept.
Personnel:
William Barrick *(Exec Dir)*
Leslie Schraeder *(Dir-Mktg & PR)*

BONIDE PRODUCTS, INC.

6301 Sutliff Rd
Oriskany, NY 13424-4326
Tel.: (315) 736-8231
Fax: (315) 736-7582
E-mail: sales@bonideproducts.com
Web Site: www.bonideproducts.com
E-Mail For Key Personnel:
Sales Director: sales@bonideproducts.com
Approx. Sls.: $7,000,000
Approx. Number Employees: 150
Year Founded: 1926
Business Description:
Pesticides & Home Gardening Products
S.I.C.: 2899; 2879
N.A.I.C.S.: 325998; 325320
Export
Advertising Expenditures: $350,000
Media: 5-6-7-8-9-10-16-19-23-24
Distr.: Reg.
Budget Set: Nov.
Personnel:
James Wurz, Jr. *(Pres)*
J. J. Wurz *(Dir-Mktg-Sls)*
Brands & Products:
ALL SEASONS
BENOMYL
BONIDE
BONTONE
BUG BEATER
CAPTAIN
DELTA EIGHT
FLEA BEATER 210
FLOREL
FUNG-ONIL
GOPHERTOX
JET BEE
KLEENUP
MOLEMAX
MOSQUITO BEATER
ROT-STOP
SEA-GREEN
SHOTGUN
STUMP-OUT
TICKMASTER
WEED BEATER

CALLOWAY'S NURSERY, INC.

4200 Airport Fwy Ste 200
Fort Worth, TX 76117-6200
Tel.: (817) 222-1122
Fax: (817) 302-0031
E-mail: info@calloways.com
Web Site: www.calloways.com
Approx. Sls.: $47,346,000
Approx. Number Employees: 250
Year Founded: 1986
Business Description:
Specialty Retailer of Lawn & Garden Products
S.I.C.: 5261
N.A.I.C.S.: 444220
Advertising Expenditures: $1,782,000
Media: 8-23-24-25
Personnel:
James Estill *(Chm, Pres & CEO)*
Daniel Reynolds *(CFO & VP)*
Marce E. Ward *(VP-Mdsg)*
Robert Silva *(Gen Mgr)*
David Weger *(Dir-Recruitment & Trng)*

THE CHAS. C. HART SEED CO.

304 Main St
Wethersfield, CT 06109-1826
Tel.: (860) 529-2537
Fax: (860) 563-7221
E-mail: info@hartseed.com
Web Site: www.hartseed.com
Approx. Sls.: $5,000,000
Approx. Number Employees: 30
Year Founded: 1892
Business Description:
Producer & Distr of Packet Seeds, Bulk Vegetable & Flower Seeds, Lawn Seeds, Fertilizers & Other Landscape Products
S.I.C.: 5191; 5083
N.A.I.C.S.: 424910; 423820
Import Export
Advertising Expenditures: $200,000
Media: 2-4-7-8-9-10-13-19-20-21-23-26

The Chas. C. Hart Seed Co. — (Continued)

Distr.: Reg.
Personnel:
Charles H. Hart *(Chm, Pres & CEO)*
Robert Hart *(VP & Asst Treas)*
William Hart *(Sec & Mgr-Wholesale)*
Brands & Products:
HART'S
PLANT HART'S SEEDS

THE CIVIC GARDEN CENTER OF GREATER CINCINNATI
2715 Reading Rd
Cincinnati, OH 45206
Tel.: (513) 221-0981
Web Site: www.civicgardencenter.org
Business Description:
Horticultural Center
S.I.C.: 5261
N.A.I.C.S.: 444220
Media: 22
Personnel:
Karen Sills *(Pres)*
Sarah Merck *(Dir)*

THE CONARD-PYLE COMPANY
25 Lewis Rd
West Grove, PA 19390-9701
Tel.: (610) 869-2426
Fax: (610) 869-0651
Toll Free: (800) 458-6559
Web Site: www.starroses.com
Sales Range: $10-24.9 Million
Approx. Number Employees: 300
Year Founded: 1897
Business Description:
Roses & Nursery Stock Whslr
S.I.C.: 0181
N.A.I.C.S.: 111422
Advertising Expenditures: $300,000
Media: 2-4-5-6-7-8-10-13-19-20-26
Distr.: Reg.
Budget Set: Oct.
Personnel:
Steven Hutton *(Pres)*
Kyle McKean *(Mgr-Mktg)*
Brands & Products:
APRICOT DRIFT
BLUSHING KNOCK OUT
BONICA
CAREFREE DELIGHT
CAREFREE WONDER
CORAL DRIFT
DOUBLE KNOCK OUT
DRIFT
KNOCK OUT
MEIDILAND
PEACH DRIFT
PINK DOUBLE KNOCK OUT
PINK DRIFT
PINK KNOCK OUT
RAINBOW KNOCK OUT
RED DRIFT
ROMANTICA
STAR
SUNBLAZE
SUNNY KNOCK OUT
SWEET DRIFT
Advertising Agency:
Aloysius Butler & Clark
819 Washington St
Wilmington, DE 19801-1509
Tel.: (302) 655-1552
Fax: (302) 655-3105
Toll Free: (800) 848-1552
Creative

COOLEY'S GARDENS INC.
11553 Silverton Rd Ne
Silverton, OR 97381-9652
Tel.: (503) 873-5463
Fax: (503) 873-5812
Toll Free: (800) 225-5391
E-mail: office@cooleysgardens.com
Web Site: www.cooleysgardens.com
Sales Range: Less than $1 Million
Approx. Number Employees: 4
Year Founded: 1928
Business Description:
Iris Plants Whslr & Mail Order
S.I.C.: 0181; 5261
N.A.I.C.S.: 111421; 444220
Media: 4-6-8-9-13-17-20-23-26
Distr.: Direct to Consumer; Intl.; Natl.
Budget Set: Feb. -Apr.
Personnel:
Richard C. Ernst *(Pres)*
Brands & Products:
COOLEY'S GARDENS
FALL
SPRING

CORNELIUS NURSERIES
(Sub. of Calloway's Nursery, Inc.)
4200 Airport Frwy Ste 200
Fort Worth, TX 76117
Tel.: (713) 782-8640
Web Site:
www.corneliusnurseries.com
Business Description:
Specialty Retailer of Lawn & Garden Products
S.I.C.: 5261
N.A.I.C.S.: 444220
Media: 8-9-13-23
Personnel:
Jim Estill *(Pres)*

CROSMAN SEED CORPORATION
511 W Comml St
East Rochester, NY 14445
Tel.: (585) 586-1928
Fax: (585) 586-6093
Toll Free: (800) 446-7333
E-mail: crosman@crosmanseed.com
Web Site: www.crosmanseed.com
Sales Range: Less than $1 Million
Approx. Number Employees: 5
Year Founded: 1838
Business Description:
Wholesaler of Flower & Vegetable Packet Seeds, Lawn Seed Mixture, Grass Seed Mixture & Seed Packing Machines
S.I.C.: 5191; 5261
N.A.I.C.S.: 424910; 444220
Import Export
Media: 10-13
Distr.: Intl.; Natl.
Budget Set: Jan.
Personnel:
Craig H. Mapstone *(Dir-Ops)*
Justine A. Mapstone *(Dir-Ops)*
William R. Mapstone, Jr. *(Dir-Ops)*
William Mapstone, Sr. *(Dir-Ops)*
Brands & Products:
BLUE & RYE
CROSMAN SEED
CROSMAN'S SEED
OLD SCHOOL
SANDY SOIL
SHADY SPOT
TOWN & COUNTRY

THE DAVEY TREE EXPERT COMPANY
1500 N Mantua St
Kent, OH 44240
Tel.: (330) 673-9511
Fax: (330) 673-9843
E-mail: info@davey.com
Web Site: www.davey.com
Approx. Rev.: $562,120,000
Approx. Number Employees: 6,800
Year Founded: 1880
Business Description:
Horticultural Services
S.I.C.: 0781; 0782; 8744
N.A.I.C.S.: 541320; 561210; 561730
Advertising Expenditures: $700,000
Media: 2-3-4-6-8-9-10-13-20-23-24-25-26
Distr.: Natl.
Budget Set: Oct.
Personnel:
Karl J. Warnke *(Chm, Pres & CEO)*
David E. Adante *(Exec VP, CFO & Sec)*
Tom Countryman *(CIO)*
Marjorie L. Conner *(Corp Counsel)*
Patrick M. Covey *(Exec VP-Ops)*
Steven A. Marshall *(Exec VP-Ops)*
Howard D. Bowles *(Sr VP & Gen Mgr)*
Richard A. Ramsey *(VP & Gen Mgr-Canadian Ops)*
George M. Gaumer *(VP & Gen Mgr-Comml Landscape Svcs)*
Brent Repenning *(VP & Gen Mgr)*
Timothy E Jackson *(District Mgr)*
Jack McCabe *(Reg Mgr-Ops)*
John Bretsch *(District Mgr)*
Chuck Daum *(Mgr-Trainee)*
Sheryl Hatridge *(Mgr-Mktg & Sls Dev)*
Robert J. Laverne *(Mgr-Education & Trng)*
Greg Mazur *(Mgr-Production)*
Bal Rao *(Mgr-Devel)*
Karen Wise *(Mgr-Natural Resource Consulting)*
Brands & Products:
ARBOR GREEN
ARBOR GREEN PRO
DAVEY
DAVEY TREE
PROVEN SOLUTIONS FOR A GROWING WORLD

DELI, INC.
W 6585 Hwy 0
Millston, WI 54643
Mailing Address:
PO Box 437
Millston, WI 54643-0437
Tel.: (715) 284-2296
Fax: (715) 284-4403
Web Site: www.mosserlee.com
Approx. Number Employees: 25
Year Founded: 1932
Business Description:
Mfr. of Baled Sphagnum Moss; Seed Germinator; Spanish Moss; Green Sheet Moss; Plant Supports; Wreath Frames & Spray Bars; Plant Propagators; Bird Feeders & Bird Houses
S.I.C.: 5159; 5099
N.A.I.C.S.: 424590; 423990
Import Export
Advertising Expenditures: $200,000
Media: 2-4-6-7-10-13
Distr.: Natl.
Budget Set: Mar. -May
Personnel:
John LaCourse *(Pres)*
Brands & Products:
BIRDIE BISTRO
CARDINAL CREST
CHEEP CAFE
GREEN SHEET
MOSSER LEE
NO DAMPOFF
READY PAC
SPANISH MOSS
TOTEM POLES
WISCONSIN PRIDE

DELI UNIVERSAL, INC.
(Sub. of Universal Corporation)
(d/b/a Imperial Processing Corporation)
205 W Main St
Kenbridge, VA 23944
Tel.: (434) 676-8253
Fax: (434) 676-2460
Sales Range: $75-99.9 Million
Approx. Number Employees: 60
Year Founded: 1995
Business Description:
Cigar Processor
S.I.C.: 5149; 5191
N.A.I.C.S.: 424490; 424910
Media: 4
Personnel:
Tracy Estes *(Pres)*
Bagley Hawthorne *(Exec VP)*

DELTA & PINE LAND COMPANY
(Name Changed to Monsanto)

DENVER WHOLESALE FLORISTS COMPANY
4800 Dahlia St
Denver, CO 80216-3121
Tel.: (303) 399-0970
Fax: (303) 376-3123
Toll Free: (800) 776-2055
E-mail: dwfcorp@dwfwholesale.com
Web Site: www.dwfwholesale.com
Sales Range: $25-49.9 Million
Approx. Number Employees: 300
Year Founded: 1909
Business Description:
Whslr of Carnations, Roses, Cut Flowers & Florist Supplies
S.I.C.: 5193
N.A.I.C.S.: 424930
Import
Media: 2-4-10-13-16-20-25-26
Distr.: Intl.; Natl.
Budget Set: June
Personnel:
David A. Lisowski *(Pres)*
Debbie Barber *(VP-HR)*
David L. Gaul *(VP-Sls & Mktg)*
Brands & Products:
COLORADO CARNATIONS
PIXIE
REGAL
TRU-TINT

EARL MAY SEED & NURSERY L.C.
208 N Elm St
Shenandoah, IA 51603-1000
Tel.: (712) 246-1020
Fax: (712) 246-2210
E-mail: mail@earlmay.com
Web Site: www.earlmay.com
E-Mail For Key Personnel:

Key to Media (For complete agency information see *The Advertising Red Books-Agencies* edition):
1. Bus. Publs. 2. Cable T.V. 3. Catalogs & Directories. 4. Co-op Adv. 5. Consumer Mags. 6. D.M. to Bus. Estab.7. D.M. to Consumers
8. Daily Newsp. 9. Exhibits/Trade Shows 10. Foreign 11. Infomercial 12. Internet Adv.13. Multimedia 14. Network Radio
15. Network T.V. 16. Newsp. Distr. Mags. 17. Other 18. Outdoor (Posters, Transit) 19. Point of Purchase20. Premiums, Novelties
21. Product Samples 22. Special Events Mktg. 23. Spot Radio 24. Spot T.V. 25. Weekly Newsp. 26. Yellow Page Adv.

Marketing Director: GSherman@earlmay.com
Approx. Number Employees: 750
Year Founded: 1919
Business Description:
Garden Centers Operator; Seeds, Gifts, Pet Supplies, Wild Bird Products & Patio Furniture Sales
S.I.C.: 5261; 5999
N.A.I.C.S.: 444220; 453910
Import
Advertising Expenditures: $1,300,000
Media: 5-8-9-17-19-22-23-24-26
Distr.: Reg.
Budget Set: Aug. -July
Personnel:
Bill Shaw *(CEO)*
Angela Shaw *(Dir-Acctg)*
Gordon Sherman *(Dir-Mktg)*
Brands & Products:
EARL MAY SEED & NURSERY
Advertising Agency:
Walz Tetrick Advertising
6299 Nall Ave Ste 300
Mission, KS 66202-3547
Tel.: (913) 789-8778
Fax: (913) 789-8493

EXCEL INDUSTRIES, INC.

200 S Ridge Rd
Hesston, KS 67062
Tel.: (620) 327-4911
Fax: (620) 327-3123
Toll Free: (800) 395-4757
E-mail: amullet@excelii.com
Web Site: www.hustlerturfequipment.com
Sales Range: $25-49.9 Million
Approx. Number Employees: 220
Year Founded: 1964
Business Description:
Mfr of Commercial Turf & Grounds Equipment
S.I.C.: 3523; 3531
N.A.I.C.S.: 333111; 333120
Import Export
Media: 2-4-7-10-17
Distr.: Natl.
Budget Set: July
Personnel:
Paul Mullet *(Pres)*
Brad Unruh *(Product Mgr)*
Shelley Lujono *(Mgr-Adv)*
Brands & Products:
4000 SERIES
6400 HILLSIDER
ATZ
FAS TRAK
THE FASTEST OF THE FAST
FASTRAK
FLEX FORKS
H-BAR STEERING
HUSTLER
HUSTLER ATZ
HUSTLER BAR STEERING
HUSTLER MINI Z
HUSTLER Z
HYDRO WALKBEHIND
MINI Z
SMOOTHTRAK
SUPER MINI Z
SUPER WALKBEHIND
SUPER Z
SUPER Z DIESEL
TRIMSTAR

THE F.A. BARTLETT TREE EXPERT COMPANY

1290 E Main St
Stamford, CT 06902-3555
Tel.: (203) 323-1131
Fax: (203) 323-1129
Fax: (203) 323-0808
Toll Free: (877) 227-8538
E-mail: customerservicemgr@bartlett.com
Web Site: www.bartlett.com
Approx. Number Employees: 1,700
Year Founded: 1907
Business Description:
Provider of Tree & Shrub Maintenance Services
S.I.C.: 0782; 8748
N.A.I.C.S.: 561730; 541618
Advertising Expenditures: $500,000
Media: 2-6-8-10-13-16-26
Distr.: Natl.
Budget Set: Dec.
Personnel:
Robert A. Bartlett *(Chm & CEO)*
Gregory S. Daniels *(Pres & COO)*
Frederick M. Tobin *(Gen Counsel)*
John E. Signorini *(Treas & Exec VP)*
Ken Karp *(Mktg Dir)*
Brands & Products:
BARTLETT
BARTLETT BOOST
ROOT-RX
SOIL-RX

FERRY-MORSE SEED COMPANY

(Sub. of Jiffy Products of America, Inc.)
600 Stethen Beale Dr
Fulton, KY 42041
Tel.: (270) 472-3400
Fax: (270) 472-3402
E-mail: info@ferry-morse.com
Web Site: www.ferry-morse.com
Approx. Number Employees: 115
Year Founded: 1856
Business Description:
Marketing of Vegetable, Flower & Lawn Seeds for the Home Gardener
S.I.C.: 5191; 5261
N.A.I.C.S.: 424910; 444220
Import Export
Media: 19
Distr.: Natl.
Personnel:
Monika McCurdy *(Dir-Mktg)*
Brands & Products:
D.M. FERRY'S
JIFFY
LILLY MILLER
SEMILLA'S FERRY'S
SOURCE OF NATURE

FORREST KEELING NURSERY, INC.

88 Forest Keeling Ln
Elsberry, MO 63343
Mailing Address:
PO Box 135
Elsberry, MO 63343-0135
Tel.: (573) 898-5571
Fax: (573) 898-5803
Toll Free: (800) 356-2401
E-mail: info@fknursery.com
Web Site: www.fknursery.com
Approx. Number Employees: 65
Year Founded: 1949
Business Description:
Nursery Stock Retailer & Whslr
S.I.C.: 0181; 5193
N.A.I.C.S.: 111421; 424930
Import Export
Advertising Expenditures: $600,000
Media: 2-4-8-9-10-16-22-25
Distr.: Natl.
Budget Set: Jan.
Personnel:
Wayne Lovelace *(Pres & CEO)*
Brands & Products:
FORREST KEELING NURSERY
PLANTLAND U. S. A.
ROOT PRODUCTION METHOD
RPM TREES
SPECIALIZING IN NATIVE PLANTS

FTD GROUP, INC.

(Sub. of United Online, Inc.)
3113 Woodcreek Dr
Downers Grove, IL 60515
Tel.: (630) 719-7800
Fax: (630) 719-6170
Toll Free: (800) 788-9000
Web Site: www.ftd.com
E-Mail For Key Personnel:
Public Relations: lwitek@ftdi.com
Approx. Rev.: $614,895,000
Approx. Number Employees: 984
Year Founded: 1910
Business Description:
Holding Company; Flower Marketer
S.I.C.: 6719; 5193; 5992
N.A.I.C.S.: 551112; 424930; 453110
Advertising Expenditures: $63,900,000
Media: 3-4-6-7-8-9-10-13-14-15-22-24-26
Distr.: Natl.
Budget Set: Feb.
Personnel:
Mark R. Goldston *(Chm & CEO)*
Robert S. Apatoff *(Pres)*
Jon R. Burney *(Gen Counsel & Exec VP)*
Lisak Witek *(VP-Mktg & Sls)*
Brands & Products:
ANNIVERSARY BOUQUET
AUTUMN SPLENDOR BOUQUET
BASKET OF TREATS BOUQUET
BEAR ESSENTIALS BOUQUET
BECAUSE YOU'RE SPECIAL BOUQUET
BEST BOSS BOUQUET
BIG HUG BOUQUET
BIRTHDAY PARTY BOUQUET
BLOOMING COOKIES
BLOOMING MASTERPIECE BOUQUET
BOO-QUET
BUILD-A-BEAR WORKSHOP TEDDY BEARS
CANDY CANE CHRISTMAS BOUQUET
CHICKEN SOUP BOUQUET
THE DIANA PRINCESS OF WALES BOUQUET
DOLLARS & SCENTS
EASTER GARDEN BOUQUET
ESPECIALLY FOR DAD BOUQUET
THE FEELING NEVER ENDS
FOR MY SWEETHEART BOUQUET
FRIENDS'N SUCH BOUQUET
FTD
FTD MERCURY MAN
FTD YOUR DAY BOUQUET
GARDEN BASKET
GARDEN PUPPETS BOUQUET
HEARTS & KISSES BOUQUET
HOLIDAY CELEBRATIONS BOUQUET
I'M SWEET FOR YOU BOUQUET
LASTING ROMANCE BOUQUET
MERRY CAROLERS BOUQUET
MOTHER'S DAY WISHES BOUQUET
NABISCOGIFTS.COM
NEW LITTLE FRIEND BOUQUET
PICK-ME-UP
PUZZLE FUN BOUQUET
SAN FRANCISCO MUSIC BOX
SEASON OF JOY BOUQUET
SPRING BLOSSOMS BOUQUET
SPRING GARDEN BOUQUET
STAY IN TOUCH BOUQUET
SUNBURST BOUQUET
SWEET DREAMS BOUQUET
SWEET EXPRESSIONS BOUQUET
SWEET SURPRISE BOUQUET
SWEET TREATS BOUQUET
TEA FOR TWO BOUQUET
THANKS A BUNCH BOUQUET
THANKS TO YOU BOUQUET
THANKSGIVING HARVEST BOUQUET
TREASURED MEMORIES BOUQUET
TRUE FRIENDS BOUQUET
Advertising Agencies:
Doner
25900 Northwestern Hwy
Southfield, MI 48075
Tel.: (248) 354-9700
Fax: (248) 827-8440
(Bouquets; National & Trade Adv.)

GSP Marketing Services, Inc.
320 W Ohio St
Chicago, IL 60654
Tel.: (312) 944-3000
Fax: (312) 944-8587

GARDENMASTER

(Div. of PRO Group, Inc.)
6300 S Syracuse Way
Centennial, CO 80111-6725
Mailing Address:
PO Box 6585
Englewood, CO 80155
Tel.: (303) 792-3000
Fax: (303) 792-5589
Web Site: www.gardenmaster.com
Approx. Number Employees: 20
Business Description:
Indoor & Outdoor Plants, Flowers, Seeds, Gardening Tools, Supplies & Services
S.I.C.: 5261
N.A.I.C.S.: 444220
Media: 4-5-8-9-10-25
Brands & Products:
GARDENMASTER

GARDENS ALIVE!, INC.

5100 Schenley Pl
Lawrenceburg, IN 47025-2181
Tel.: (812) 537-8650
Fax: (513) 354-1484
E-mail: gardenhelp@gardensalive.com
Web Site: www.gardensalive.com
Approx. Number Employees: 150
Year Founded: 1987
Business Description:
Organic Gardening Products
S.I.C.: 5961

Key to Media (For complete agency information see *The Advertising Red Books-Agencies* edition):
1. Bus. Publs. 2. Cable T.V. 3. Catalogs & Directories. 4. Co-op Adv. 5. Consumer Mags. 6. D.M. to Bus. Estab.7. D.M. to Consumers
8. Daily Newsp. 9. Exhibits/Trade Shows 10. Foreign 11. Infomercial 12. Internet Adv.13. Multimedia 14. Network Radio
15. Network T.V. 16. Newsp. Distr. Mags. 17. Other 18. Outdoor (Posters, Transit) 19. Point of Purchase20. Premiums, Novelties
21. Product Samples 22. Special Events Mktg. 23. Spot Radio 24. Spot T.V. 25. Weekly Newsp. 26. Yellow Page Adv.

Gardens Alive!, Inc. — (Continued)

N.A.I.C.S.: 454113
Advertising Expenditures: $2,000,000
Media: 4-8-13-16-22
Personnel:
Niles Kinerk *(Founder & Pres)*
Rick Braden *(Gen Mgr)*
Brands & Products:
ACCUGROW
ALIVE
BEE-ALLURE
BEE-SCENT
BENALLURE
BIOBOOST
BIRD GRUB
BLOBOOST
BULBS ALIVE!
BULLS-EYE
COMPOST ALIVE!
CUPBOARD MOTH TRAP
DEER OFF
DRIED FRUIT TENDERS
EARTH ANSWER
ENVIRONMENTALLY RESPONSIBLE PRODUCTS THAT WORK!
ENZ-ROT
ESCAR-GO!
FALL LAWNS ALIVE!
FLEA SECURE
FLOWERS ALIVE
FRUIT TREES ALIVE!
GARDEN PLENTY
GARDEN SOLUTIONS
GARDENERS GOLD
GARDENS ALIVE!
GRANULATED WOW!
GREEN GUARD
GREEN STEP
GRUB-AWAY
GUARDIAN
HEALTHY GARDENS
HERBS ALIVE
HOME
HOUSEPLANTS ALIVE!
KNOCK-OUT GNATS
LAWN-GARD
MOLE-MED
MOLE-RELIEF
MOSS-ASIDE
MOTH-AWAY
N-LITE
NATURAL ANIMAL
NATURAL BEGINNINGS
NEEM-AWAY
NEMA-JECT
NORTHERN TURF
OIL-AWAY
ORIGINAL WOW!
PERFECT BALANCE
PERFECT START
PET PREFERRED
PETS ALIVE!
PLANTSKYDD
PYOLA
QUICK-CAL
QUICK-START
QUICK-TIES
REDI-MEAL
ROOT GUARDIAN
ROSES ALIVE!
ROT-STOP
SEA-RICH
SHIELD-ALL II
SHRUBS-ALIVE
SOAP-SHIELD
SOILGARD
SOUTHERN TURF ALIVE
SPRING LAWNS ALIVE!
STA-HOME
STING FREE
STRAWBERRIES ALIVE
SULFUR GUARD
SUPREME
SURE-CATCH
SURROUND
SWEET CORN ALIVE
TOMATOES ALIVE!
TUNICOVER
TUNLCOVER
TURBO-TOMATO
TURF ALIVE!
VEGETABLES ALIVE!
WEED-ASIDE
WOW!

GARST SEED COMPANY

(Sub. of Syngenta AG)
PO Box 300
Coon Rapids, IA 50058
Mailing Address:
PO Box 500
Slater, IA 50244
Tel.: (515) 685-5000
Fax: (712) 684-3222
Toll Free: (888) 464-2778
Web Site: www.garstseedco.com
E-Mail For Key Personnel:
Public Relations: lori.thomas@garstseedco.com
Approx. Number Employees: 625
Business Description:
Soybeans, Corn, Sorghum, Alfalfa, Sunflower & Canola Mfr
S.I.C.: 2075; 0115
N.A.I.C.S.: 311222; 111150
Media: 4-7-10-21
Distr.: Reg.
Budget Set: Apr.
Personnel:
David Witherspoon *(Pres)*
Gene Kassmeyer *(Product Mgr)*
Lori Thomas *(Mgr-Mktg)*
Advertising Agency:
Solutions Inc.
4725 Merle Hay Rd.
Des Moines, IA 50322
Tel.: (515) 247-0001

GILBERT H. WILD & SON, LLC

3044 State Hwy 37
Sarcoxie, MO 64862
Tel.: (417) 548-3514
Fax: (417) 548-6831
Fax: (888) 548-6831
Toll Free: (888) 449-4537
E-mail: wilds@socket.net
Web Site: www.gilberthwild.com
Approx. Number Employees: 70
Year Founded: 1885
Business Description:
Daylily, Iris & Peonies Plants Grower & Wholesaler
S.I.C.: 5961; 5193
N.A.I.C.S.: 454113; 424930
Import Export
Advertising Expenditures: $250,000
Media: 4-6-8-13
Distr.: Direct to Consumer; Natl.
Budget Set: Oct. -Nov.
Personnel:
Gregory P. Jones *(Pres)*
Brands & Products:
GILBERT H. WILD

GOOD EARTH, INC.

960 Broadway
Lancaster, NY 14086-0266
Tel.: (716) 684-8111
Fax: (716) 684-3722
Toll Free: (888) 323-2784
E-mail: goodearthsales@goodearth.org
Web Site: www.goodearth.org/index.cfm
E-Mail For Key Personnel:
Marketing Director: monika@goodearth.org
Approx. Number Employees: 150
Year Founded: 1958
Business Description:
Products for Lawns & Gardens; Horticultural Products Mfr
S.I.C.: 5191
N.A.I.C.S.: 424910
Export
Advertising Expenditures: $1,000,000
Media: 2-4-10-13-16-17-21
Personnel:
Monika Burkhardt *(VP-Mktg)*
Brands & Products:
A.H. HOFFMAN
COUNTRY COTTAGE
GOOD EARTH
PIONEER SOUTHERN

HARRIS MORAN SEED CO.

(Sub. of Groupe Limagrain Holding)
555 Codoni Ave
Modesto, CA 95357-0507
Mailing Address:
PO Box 4938
Modesto, CA 95357
Tel.: (209) 579-7333
Fax: (209) 527-5312
E-mail: info@harrismoran.com
Web Site: www.harrismoran.com
Approx. Number Employees: 260
Year Founded: 1856
Business Description:
Vegetable Seeds Producer
S.I.C.: 0181; 5191
N.A.I.C.S.: 111422; 424910
Import Export
Media: 1-2-4-5-6-7-8-9-10-11-16-19-20-21-25
Distr.: Intl.; Natl.
Budget Set: Aug.

H.G. HASTINGS CO.

3920 Peachtree Rd NE
Atlanta, GA 30319-3304
Tel.: (404) 869-7447
Fax: (404) 869-7449
E-mail: hghastings@mindspring.com
Web Site:
www.hastingsgardencenter.com
Approx. Sls.: $1,000,000
Approx. Number Employees: 25
Year Founded: 1889
Business Description:
Holding Company
S.I.C.: 0782; 5261
N.A.I.C.S.: 561730; 444220
Advertising Expenditures: $200,000
Media: 2-4-7-8-9-18-19-23-25-26
Distr.: Direct to Consumer; Reg.
Budget Set: Feb.
Personnel:
Kathy Bussey *(Pres)*

HINES NURSERIES, INC.

(Holding of Black Diamond Capital Management LLC)
12621 Jeffrey Rd
Irvine, CA 92620
Tel.: (949) 559-4444
Fax: (949) 786-0968
E-mail: info@hineshort.com
Web Site: www.hineshorticulture.com
Approx. Sls.: $232,570,000
Approx. Number Employees: 2,100
Year Founded: 1930
Business Description:
Horticultural Nurseries
S.I.C.: 5261; 5193
N.A.I.C.S.: 444220; 424930
Advertising Expenditures: $852,000
Media: 2-4-8-10-14-18-19-20-21
Personnel:
Joe Gray *(COO)*
Tom Batt *(Natl Account Dir, VP-Sls & Mktg)*

HYPONEX CORPORATION

(Sub. of Scotts Miracle-Gro Company)
14111 Scottslawn Rd
Marysville, OH 43041
Tel.: (937) 644-0011
Fax: (937) 644-7244
Sales Range: $1-4.9 Billion
Approx. Number Employees: 1,000
Business Description:
Natural Soils, Amendments & Mulches Mfr
S.I.C.: 1499; 2873
N.A.I.C.S.: 212399; 325311
Media: 6-8-10
Distr.: Natl.
Personnel:
James Hagedorn *(CEO)*

INTER-STATE NURSERIES, INC.

(Div. of Plantron, Inc.)
1800 Hamilton Rd
Bloomington, IL 61704
Tel.: (309) 663-6797
Fax: (309) 663-6691
E-mail: info@interstatenurseries.com
Web Site:
www.interstatenurseries.com
Approx. Number Employees: 45
Year Founded: 1954
Business Description:
Roses, Perennials, Flower Bulbs & Other General Nursery Stock
S.I.C.: 0181
N.A.I.C.S.: 111421
Advertising Expenditures: $45,000
Media: 2-4-6-8-9-13-16
Distr.: Direct to Consumer; Natl.
Budget Set: Various
Personnel:
Richard Owen *(Pres)*
Advertising Agency:
Adtron, Inc.
4415 E Cotton Center Blvd
Phoenix, AZ 85040
Tel.: (309) 662-1221
Fax: (602) 735-0349

JACKSON & PERKINS COMPANY

(Sub. of Evergreen SC, LLC)
2 Floral Ave
Hodges, SC 29653
Tel.: (800) 872-7673
Fax: (800) 242-0329

Key to Media (For complete agency information see *The Advertising Red Books-Agencies* edition):
1. Bus. Publs. 2. Cable T.V. 3. Catalogs & Directories. 4. Co-op Adv. 5. Consumer Mags. 6. D.M. to Bus. Estab.7. D.M. to Consumers
8. Daily Newsp. 9. Exhibits/Trade Shows 10. Foreign 11. Infomercial 12. Internet Adv.13. Multimedia 14. Network Radio
15. Network T.V. 16. Newsp. Distr. Mags. 17. Other 18. Outdoor (Posters, Transit) 19. Point of Purchase20. Premiums, Novelties
21. Product Samples 22. Special Events Mktg. 23. Spot Radio 24. Spot T.V. 25. Weekly Newsp. 26. Yellow Page Adv.

Toll Free: (800) 292-4769
Toll Free: (800) 872-7673
E-mail: service@jacksonandperkins.com
Web Site: www.jacksonandperkins.com
Sales Range: $75-99.9 Million
Approx. Number Employees: 3,000
Year Founded: 1872
Business Description:
Grower & Mail Order Retailer of Roses
S.I.C.: 5193
N.A.I.C.S.: 424930
Import
Media: 2-6-8-16-24
Distr.: Natl. Direct to Consumer
Budget Set: Apr.
Personnel:
Charles Fox, III *(Pres)*
Brands & Products:
GARDEN INSPIRED LIVING
GIFTLIST
JACKSON & PERKINS
NEW GENERATION ROSES

THE J.C. ROBINSON SEED COMPANY
100 JC Robinson Blvd
Waterloo, NE 68069
Mailing Address:
PO Box 307
Waterloo, NE 68069
Tel.: (402) 779-2531
Fax: (402) 779-3413
Toll Free: (800) 228-9906
Web Site: www.goldenharvestseeds.com/contactus.asp
Sales Range: $10-24.9 Million
Approx. Number Employees: 275
Year Founded: 1888
Business Description:
Wholesaler of Hybrid Seed, Corn, Sorghum, Soybeans & Alfalfa
S.I.C.: 5191; 0723
N.A.I.C.S.: 424910; 115114
Export
Media: 1-2-4-5-7-9-10-14-18-20-21-23-24-25-26
Distr.: Reg.
Budget Set: July -June
Personnel:
Edward T. Robinson, Jr. *(Chm & Pres)*
Brands & Products:
GOLDEN HARVEST

JIFFY PRODUCTS OF AMERICA, INC.
(Sub. of Jiffy Products International AS)
600 Industrial Pkwy
Norwalk, OH 44857
Tel.: (419) 660-1177
Fax: (419) 660-1188
Toll Free: (800) 323-1047
E-mail: jclair@jiffyproducts.com
Web Site: www.jiffyproducts.com
Approx. Number Employees: 35
Business Description:
Container-Based Plant Propagation Products
S.I.C.: 5261; 2499; 2531; 2874; 2879; 3082; 3084; 3089; 3589; 3999
N.A.I.C.S.: 444220; 321999; 325312; 325320; 326121; 326122; 326199; 333319; 337127; 339999
Advertising Expenditures: $200,000
Media: 2-4-7-10-17-19
Distr.: Natl.
Personnel:
Daniel Schrodt *(Pres)*
John Clair *(VP-Sls)*
Brands & Products:
JIFFY-7
JIFFY-MIX
JIFFY-POTS
JIFFY-STRIPS

J.R. SIMPLOT COMPANY, AGRI BUSINESS
(Group of J.R. Simplot Company)
999 Main St Ste 1300
Boise, ID 83702
Tel.: (208) 672-2700
Fax: (208) 389-7289
E-mail: info@simplot.com
Web Site: www.simplot.com
Approx. Number Employees: 300
Business Description:
Superphosphate Fertilizer & Phosphoric Acid (Wet Process), Ammonium Phosphates Agricultural Chemicals Formulation
S.I.C.: 2874
N.A.I.C.S.: 325312
Export
Media: 2-7-10-18-23
Distr.: Natl.
Budget Set: Apr.
Personnel:
Annette Elg *(CFO & Sr VP)*
Steve Gray *(Dir-Risk Mgmt)*
Brands & Products:
BEST BRAND
Advertising Agency:
Steele & Associates, Inc.
125 N Garfield
Pocatello, ID 83204
Tel.: (208) 233-7206
Fax: (208) 233-7384

J.W. JUNG SEED COMPANY
335 S High St
Randolph, WI 53957-0001
Tel.: (920) 326-3121
Fax: (920) 326-5769
E-mail: info@jungseed.com
Web Site: www.jungseed.com
Approx. Number Employees: 150
Year Founded: 1907
Business Description:
Retailer & Mail Order of Seeds, Plants, Shrubs & Bulbs
S.I.C.: 5261; 5961
N.A.I.C.S.: 444220; 454113
Import
Media: 3-4-6-8-9-13-23-24-25
Distr.: Direct to Consumer; Natl.
Budget Set: June -Aug.
Personnel:
Richard J. Zondag *(Pres & CEO)*
Brands & Products:
HORTICULTURAL PRODUCTS & SERVICES (HPS)
J. W. JUNG
MCCLURE & ZIMMERMAN
R.H. SHUMWAY
ROOTS & RHIZOMES
SEYMOUR SELECT SEEDS
TOTALLY TOMATO
VERMONT BEAN SEED COMPANY

KALO, INC.
13200 Metcalf Ave Ste 250
Overland Park, KS 66213
Tel.: (913) 491-9125
Fax: (913) 491-9146
Toll Free: (800) 255-5196
E-mail: sales@kalo.com
Web Site: www.kalo.com
E-Mail For Key Personnel:
President: cchampion@kalo.com
Sales Director: sales@kalo.com
Sales Range: $10-24.9 Million
Approx. Number Employees: 7
Year Founded: 1932
Business Description:
Mfr. & Sales of Agricultural Specialty Chemicals
S.I.C.: 2879
N.A.I.C.S.: 325320
Export
Advertising Expenditures: $40,000
Media: 2-4-7-10-13-20-21
Distr.: Natl.
Personnel:
Chuck Champion *(Pres)*
John E. Wise *(CEO)*
Doug John *(Dir-Sls & Mktg)*
Brands & Products:
ANTI-FOAM
BENCHMARK
BENCHMARK HT
BIO 90
BIO-FILM
BREAK-DOWN
CADENCE
COMPEX
COMPEX EXTRA
DRI
EMPIRIC
ENTRO
FIRST WATCH
FOAM-DYE
FOMARK
FRACTION
HYDRO-WET
K-KLEAN
KALO
MAINSTAY ELITE
ONE-AP
PRO-AP
REGULAID
RESTORE
SAV-OIL
SPARY PREP
SPECTRA
SPECTRA AMS
SPECTRA MAX TANK MIX
SPECTRA MAX TECH
SPRAY START
TANK CLEANER
TOURNAMENT-READY
TRONIC
WATER FX
WATERWORKS

KELLY NURSERIES
1708 Morrissey Dr
Bloomington, IL 61704-7107
Tel.: (309) 663-9551
Tel.: (309) 663-1800
Fax: (309) 663-6691
E-mail: customercare@kellynurseries.com
Web Site: www.kellynurseries.com
Approx. Number Employees: 50
Business Description:
Nursery Stock Retailer
S.I.C.: 0782
N.A.I.C.S.: 561730
Media: 2-4-8-9-14-20
Distr.: Direct to Consumer; Natl.
Personnel:
Richard Owen *(Pres)*

LAWN DOCTOR INC.
142 State Rte 34
Holmdel, NJ 07733
Tel.: (732) 946-0029
Fax: (732) 946-9089
Toll Free: (800) 631-5660
Web Site: www.lawndoctor.com
Approx. Number Employees: 70
Year Founded: 1967
Business Description:
Lawn Care Franchisor
S.I.C.: 6794; 7359
N.A.I.C.S.: 533110; 532299
Advertising Expenditures: $6,000,000
Media: 8-9-10-13-18-20-23-24-25-26
Distr.: Natl.
Budget Set: Nov.
Personnel:
Russell J. Frith *(CEO)*
Robert Magda *(Sr VP)*
Scott Frith *(VP-Mktg & Dev)*
Paul Mumm *(Dir-Mktg & Sls)*
Brands & Products:
CORE
GREEN THUMB
KEEPING LAWNS HEALTHY FOR LIFE.
LAWN DOCTOR
TURF TAMER
Advertising Agency:
Lado Agency, Inc.
142 State Rte 34
Holmdel, NJ 07733-2092
Tel.: (732) 946-0029
Fax: (732) 946-9089
(Lawn Doctor Care Services)

LEBANON SEABOARD CORPORATION
1600 E Cumberland St
Lebanon, PA 17042-8323
Tel.: (717) 273-1685
Fax: (717) 273-9466
Toll Free: (800) 233-0628
E-mail: customerservice@lebsea.com
Web Site: www.lebsea.com
Approx. Number Employees: 600
Year Founded: 1947
Business Description:
Supplier of Lawn & Garden Products, Wild Bird Food, Grass Seed & Professional Turf Products
S.I.C.: 2875; 5191
N.A.I.C.S.: 325314; 424910
Media: 2-4-5-6-7-8-9-10-18-19-22-23-24
Distr.: Natl.
Budget Set: Mar.
Personnel:
Katherine Bishop *(Chm, Pres & CEO)*
Rich Newmaster *(CFO)*
Dave Heegard *(Gen Mgr-Prof Products Div)*
Maryanne Bayoumy *(Mgr-Consumer Brand)*
Jim Kuhle *(Mgr-Ops)*
Harry Mathis *(Mgr-Supply Chain & Logistics)*
Ken Morrison *(Mgr-IT)*
Brands & Products:
COUNTRY CLUB
EXPO

Key to Media (For complete agency information see *The Advertising Red Books-Agencies* edition):
1. Bus. Publs. 2. Cable T.V. 3. Catalogs & Directories. 4. Co-op Adv. 5. Consumer Mags. 6. D.M. to Bus. Estab.7. D.M. to Consumers
8. Daily Newsp. 9. Exhibits/Trade Shows 10. Foreign 11. Infomercial 12. Internet Adv.13. Multimedia 14. Network Radio
15. Network T.V. 16. Newsp. Distr. Mags. 17. Other 18. Outdoor (Posters, Transit) 19. Point of Purchase20. Premiums, Novelties
21. Product Samples 22. Special Events Mktg. 23. Spot Radio 24. Spot T.V. 25. Weekly Newsp. 26. Yellow Page Adv.

Lebanon Seaboard Corporation — (Continued)

GREENSKEEPER
GREENVIEW
ISOTEK31
LEBANONTURF
LYRIC
LYRIC SUPREME
MESA
NX-PRO
PENNMULCH
PERK
PREEN
PREEN 'N GREEN
PREEN 'N GREEN FOR LAWNS
SONG AND BEAUTY

LESCO-JOHN DEERE LANDSCAPES

(Sub. of John Deere Landscapes)
1301 E 9th St Ste 1300
Cleveland, OH 44114-1849
Tel.: (216) 706-9250
Fax: (800) 820-4848
Fax: (216) 706-5240
Toll Free: (800) 321-5325
E-mail: customerservice@lesco.com
Web Site: www.lesco.com
Approx. Sls.: $550,605,000
Approx. Number Employees: 1,122
Year Founded: 1962
Business Description:
Turf & Pest Control Products Distr
S.I.C.: 2875; 2879; 5191
N.A.I.C.S.: 325314; 325320; 424910
Advertising Expenditures: $3,226,000
Media: 2-4-6-8-10-13-16
Personnel:
Dave Werning *(Pres)*
Michael A. Weisbarth *(CFO, Treas & VP)*
Kevin L. Wade *(CIO & VP)*
Gary A. Cook *(VP-Transition Zone)*
Dave Woznicki *(Mgr-Category)*
Brands & Products:
ELITE
LESCO
LESCO SERVICE CENTERS
LESCO STORES-ON-WHEELS
LESCOMELT II
NOVEX
POLY PLUS
VIPER ZTR
Z-TWO

LILYPONS WATER GARDENS INC.

6800 Lilypons Rd
Buckeystown, MD 21710
Tel.: (301) 874-5503
Fax: (301) 874-2959
Toll Free: (800) 999-5459
E-mail: info@lilypons.com
Web Site: www.lilypons.com
Sales Range: $10-24.9 Million
Approx. Number Employees: 20
Year Founded: 1917
Business Description:
Waterlilies & Goldfish Sales
S.I.C.: 5261
N.A.I.C.S.: 444220
Import Export
Media: 3-4-5-6-7-8-9-10-18-22-25-26
Distr.: Direct to Consumer; Natl.
Budget Set: Sept.
Personnel:
Margaret Thomas Koogle *(Pres)*
Richard M. Koogle *(Dir-Ops)*
Brands & Products:
FISHMATE
HARMSCO
LILYPONS KOI CUISINE
LILYPONS WATER GARDENS
LILYTABS
LITTLE GIANT

MCCLURE & ZIMMERMAN

(Sub. of J.W. Jung Seed Company)
335 S High St
Randolph, WI 53956
Tel.: (920) 326-3121
Fax: (800) 374-6120
Toll Free: (800) 883-6998
E-mail: info@mzbulb.com
Web Site: www.mzbulb.com
Year Founded: 1972
Business Description:
Fall Planted Bulb Specialty Catalog
S.I.C.: 5961
N.A.I.C.S.: 454113
Media: 4-6-8
Personnel:
Richard Zondag *(Pres)*

MCLAUGHLIN GORMLEY KING COMPANY

8810 10th Ave N
Minneapolis, MN 55427
Tel.: (763) 544-0341
Fax: (763) 544-6437
Toll Free: (800) 645-6466
E-mail: customerservice@mgk.com
Web Site: www.mgk.com
E-Mail For Key Personnel:
Sales Director: sales@mgk.com
Approx. Number Employees: 60
Year Founded: 1902
Business Description:
Pesticide Mfr
S.I.C.: 2879; 2899
N.A.I.C.S.: 325320; 325998
Import Export
Media: 2-4-7-8-10-13-17-20
Distr.: Intl.; Natl.
Personnel:
Steve Gullickson *(Pres)*
William D. Gullickson, Jr. *(CEO)*
Thomas S. Major *(CFO)*
Brands & Products:
AQUAPEL
CLEARMOL
D-TRANS
DRY PYROCIDE
ESBIOL
ETOC
EVERCIDE
EVERGREEN
MULTICIDE
NYLAR
PYGANIC
PYROCIDE

MOEWS SEED CO., INC.

Rte 89 S
Granville, IL 61326
Tel.: (815) 339-2201
Fax: (815) 339-2203
Toll Free: (800) 663-9795
E-mail: moews@moews.com
Web Site: www.moews.com
Sales Range: $1-9.9 Million
Approx. Number Employees: 50
Year Founded: 1927
Business Description:
Whslr of Hybrid Seed Corn & Field Seeds
S.I.C.: 0115; 5191
N.A.I.C.S.: 111150; 424910
Media: 2-9-10-20-21
Distr.: Reg.
Budget Set: Mar.
Personnel:
Jim Crowley *(Pres)*
Bettina M. Moews *(CEO)*
Brands & Products:
CLEARFIELD
HERCULEX
LIBERTY LINK
MOEWS
ROUNDUP READY
WAXY MAIZ

MONROVIA GROWERS

18331 E Foothill Blvd
Azusa, CA 91702-2638
Tel.: (626) 334-9321
Fax: (626) 334-3126
Toll Free: (800) 999-9321
Web Site: www.monrovia.com
Approx. Sls.: $140,000,000
Approx. Number Employees: 2,100
Year Founded: 1926
Business Description:
Ornamental Nursery Stock Grower & Whslr
S.I.C.: 0181; 5261
N.A.I.C.S.: 111421; 444220
Media: 2-4-6-8-10-19-22
Personnel:
Elin Dowd *(Pres)*
Miles Rosedale *(CEO)*
Pam Wasson *(VP-Mktg)*
Brands & Products:
ANGEL
ANGEL'S BLUSH
BALBOA SUNSET
BANANA SPLIT
BERRI-MAGIC
BERRIES JUBILEE
BLUE CREEPER
BLUE SKIES
BRIDAL BOUQUET
BRIDAL VEIL
BRIGHT 'N TIGHT
BUTTONS 'N BOWS
CALGARY CARPET
CAMARILLO FIESTA
CASABLANCA
CHARISMA
CHERRY BOMB
CHICA
CONFETTI
CRAFTSMEN COLLECTION
CRIMSON JEWEL
DIABOLO
DISTINCTIVELY BETTER
DON MARIO
DOUBLE SHOT
EMERALD CARPET
EMERALD FOUNTAIN
EMERALD ISLE
EMERALD KING
EMERALD SPREADER
EMERALD WAVE
ENCHANTRESS
FIREGLOW
FIRST LOVE
FIRST SNOW
FLAME
FROSTY
FULLMOON
GARDEN READY
GOLD COAST
GOLD RUSH
GOLDEN JACKPOT
GOLDEN NUGGET
GOLDEN PRINCE
GOLDEN SUNRISE
GOLDEN ZEBRA
GREEN ICE
GREEN TOWER
ICE ANGELS
ICEE BLUE
IMPERIAL PRINCESS
IMPERIAL QUEEN
INDIAN PRINCESS
ITSY BITSY
IVORY FEATHERS
LAVENDER SWIRL
LEMON SWIRL
LIMEMOUND
LITTLE OLLIE
LITTLE ONE
LITTLE RASCAL
MAGICAL
MAJESTIC BEAUTY
MAJESTIC ORCHID
MARREKESH
MIDGEE
MIDKNIGHT BLUE
MINT JULEP
MONROVIA
MONROVIA ORGANICS
MOONLIGHT PARFAIT
MOOR-DENSE
MOROCCO
MOSS GREEN COLOR
NEW & EXCEPTIONAL
OO-LA-LA
PETITE EMBERS
PETITE INDIGO
PETITE ORCHID
PETITE PINKIE
PETITE PLUM
PETITE RED IMP
PETITE SNOW
PINK-A-BOO
PINK ELF
PINK 'N PRETTY
PINK PARFAIT
PLANT SAVVY
PLUM CRAZY
PLUM PASSION
POP 1-2-3
POWDER PUFF
PRAIRIE PILLAR
PURPLE QUEEN
PURPLE RAIN
RAZZLEBERRI
RED DRAGON
RED ELF
RED 'N PRETTY
RED RHAPSODY
ROSEDALE'S BEAUTY
ROYAL CAPE
RUBY LACE
SEA OF GOLD
SHOGUN
SIENNA SUNRISE
SILVER PRINCESS
SILVER SPREADER
SILVER WHISPERS
SPARKLER
SPREADING SUNSHINE
SPRING RAPTURE
SPRINGTIME
STAR SHOWERS

Key to Media (For complete agency information see *The Advertising Red Books-Agencies* edition):
1. Bus. Publs. 2. Cable T.V. 3. Catalogs & Directories. 4. Co-op Adv. 5. Consumer Mags. 6. D.M. to Bus. Estab.7. D.M. to Consumers 8. Daily Newsp. 9. Exhibits/Trade Shows 10. Foreign 11. Infomercial 12. Internet Adv.13. Multimedia 14. Network Radio 15. Network T.V. 16. Newsp. Distr. Mags. 17. Other 18. Outdoor (Posters, Transit) 19. Point of Purchase20. Premiums, Novelties 21. Product Samples 22. Special Events Mktg. 23. Spot Radio 24. Spot T.V. 25. Weekly Newsp. 26. Yellow Page Adv.

STARBURST
STRAWBERRY LEMONADE
SUMMER SNOW
SUMMER SONG
SUN STRIPE
SUNBURST
SUNDAZE
SUNNY DAZE
SUNNY DELIGHT
SUNSATIA
SUNSATION
SUPER RED
SURPRISE BOUQUET
SWAN LAKE
TAHITIAN DAWN
TANGERINE
TANGIER
TANGO TWIRL
TEENIE GENIE
TEXAS DAWN
TIMELESS BEAUTY
TINY TOWER
TRIPAK
TROPICAL TREASURES
TURQUOISE SPREADER
URBAN PINE
WHITE CAPE
WHITE LIGHTNIN'
YUKON BELLE

Advertising Agency:
The Phelps Group
901 Wilshire Blvd
Santa Monica, CA 90401-1854
Tel.: (310) 752-4400
Fax: (310) 752-4444
(Monrovia)
— Judy Lynes *(Acct. Team Leader)*

MONSANTO

(Formerly Interstate Seed Company)
(Sub. of Monsanto Company)
304 Ctr St
West Fargo, ND 58078-3134
Mailing Address:
PO Box 338
West Fargo, ND 58078-0338
Tel.: (701) 282-7338
Fax: (701) 282-8218
Toll Free: (800) 437-4120
Sales Range: $50-74.9 Million
Approx. Number Employees: 20
Year Founded: 1917
Business Description:
Hybrid Seeds
S.I.C.: 5191
N.A.I.C.S.: 424910
Import Export
Advertising Expenditures: $200,000
Media: 2-4-6-10-13-18-20-25
Distr.: Reg.
Budget Set: May
Personnel:
Bob Sanders *(District Sls Mgr)*
Jim Johnson *(Mgr-Product Canola)*
Vic Nordstrom *(Mgr-Opers)*
Rod Erdmann *(Plant Supvr)*
Brands & Products:
4540NS
4575NS/CL
4704NS
470NS
FARMFLEX
HYLITE 225RR
HYLITE 292 CL
HYLITE 618 CL
HYOLA 357 RR MAGNUM
HYOLA 420
HYOLA 440
HYOLA 505 RR
HYOLA 514 RR
HYSUN
HYSUN525
IS639
SW PATRIOT RR
SW TITAN RRR

MONSANTO

(Formerly Delta & Pine Land Company)
(Sub. of Monsanto Company)
1 Cotton Row
Scott, MS 38772-0157
Tel.: (662) 742-4000
Fax: (662) 742-4196
Toll Free: (800) 321-8989
Web Site: www.monsanto.com
Approx. Sls.: $417,632,992
Approx. Number Employees: 533
Year Founded: 1911
Business Description:
Breeder & Producer of Branded Cotton, Hybrid Corn, Soybeans & Sorghum Seeds
S.I.C.: 0131; 0116; 0182; 5191
N.A.I.C.S.: 111920; 111110; 111419; 424910
Media: 1-2-4-5-6-8-9-10-11-14-15-18-19-20-21-23-24-25-26
Distr.: Natl.
Budget Set: Aug.
Personnel:
Kenneth M. Avery *(CFO, VP & Asst Sec)*
Donald Kimmel *(VP-Indus Rels)*
James Willeke *(VP-Sls & Mktg)*
Brands & Products:
BOLLGARD
D&PL
DELTA AND PINE LAND
DELTAPINE
ROUNDUP READY
ROUNDUP READY COTTON
SULFONYLUREA-TOLERANT SOYBEAN

MORGRO, INC.

145 W Central Ave
Salt Lake City, UT 84107-1418
Tel.: (801) 266-1132
Fax: (801) 266-1183
Web Site: www.morgro.com
E-Mail For Key Personnel:
President: del@morgro.com
Sales Director: russ@morgro.com
Sales Range: $10-24.9 Million
Approx. Number Employees: 12
Year Founded: 1980
Business Description:
Fertilizers, Wasp Traps, Garden Products & Log Fire Starters Mfr
S.I.C.: 2899; 2873
N.A.I.C.S.: 325998; 325311
Media: 2-5-7-9-10-19-21-23-24
Distr.: Reg.
Budget Set: Dec.
Personnel:
Delbert Davis *(Pres)*
Rick Jensen *(Mgr-Natl Sls)*
Brands & Products:
DEEP THAW
ICE FIGHTER PLUS
LIQUI-FIRE
MORGRO
SNO-PLOW

MOSQUITONIX FRANCHISE SYSTEMS, LTD.

12655 N Central Expwy Ste 425
Dallas, TX 75243
Tel.: (972) 934-3131
Fax: (972) 934-1055
Web Site: www.mosquitonix.com
Approx. Number Employees: 21
Year Founded: 2002
Business Description:
Pest Control & Pesticide Services
S.I.C.: 7342; 2879
N.A.I.C.S.: 561710; 325320
Media: 2-6-8-26
Personnel:
Dan O'Neal *(CEO)*
Brands & Products:
THE BUFFET IS OFFICIALLY CLOSED.
MAKE MOSQUITOES A THING OF THE PAST.
MOSQUITONIX
NO MORE MOSQUITOES. PERIOD.
PUT MOSQUITOES ON THE ENDANGERED SPECIES LIST.
STOP DONATING BLOOD.
Advertising Agency:
Firehouse, Inc.
14860 Landmark Blvd No 247
Dallas, TX 75254
Tel.: (972) 692-0911
Fax: (972) 692-0912

MUSSER FORESTS, INC.

Rte 119 N
Indiana, PA 15701
Mailing Address:
1880 Route 119 Hwy N
Indiana, PA 15701-7341
Tel.: (724) 465-5686
Fax: (724) 465-9893
Toll Free: (800) 643-8319
E-mail: info@musserforests.com
Web Site: www.musserforests.com
Sales Range: $1-9.9 Million
Approx. Number Employees: 180
Year Founded: 1928
Business Description:
Nursery Stock Whslr & Retail Mail Order
S.I.C.: 0181; 5261
N.A.I.C.S.: 111421; 444220
Advertising Expenditures: $500,000
Media: 2-3-4-6-8-10-13-24-26
Distr.: Reg.
Budget Set: June
Personnel:
Fred Musser *(Pres)*
Brands & Products:
MUSSER

NUFARM AMERICAS INC

(Sub. of Nufarm Australia Limited)
150 Harvester Dr Ste 200
Burr Ridge, IL 60527-0866
Tel.: (630) 455-2000
Fax: (630) 455-2001
Toll Free: (800) 345-3330
Web Site: www.usnufarm.com
Approx. Number Employees: 60
Year Founded: 1941
Business Description:
Agricultural & Turf & Vegetation Management Chemicals Mfr
S.I.C.: 2879; 2869
N.A.I.C.S.: 325320; 325199
Import Export
Media: 2-4-6-8-10-18-20-21-22
Distr.: Natl.
Personnel:
Gary Barber *(Exec VP-Fin & IS)*
Brands & Products:
2.4-D
COOL POWER
HORSEPOWER
MILLENNIUM ULTRA
PATRIOT
RAZOR
SPIDER
TRI-POWER
TRIAMINE
TRIPLET

OLDS SEED SOLUTIONS

(Sub. of Land O'Lakes, Inc.)
2901 Packers Ave
Madison, WI 53707
Mailing Address:
PO Box 7790
Madison, WI 53707-7790
Tel.: (608) 249-9291
Fax: (608) 249-0695
Toll Free: (800) 356-7333
Web Site: www.seedsolutions.com
Approx. Number Employees: 25
Year Founded: 1888
Business Description:
Mfr. of Seeds & Seed Corn
S.I.C.: 5261
N.A.I.C.S.: 444220
Import Export
Media: 5-6-9-10-19-23
Distr.: Reg.
Budget Set: June
Personnel:
Chris Wendorf *(Product Mgr-Turfgrass)*

ORKIN, INC.

(Sub. of Rollins, Inc.)
2170 Piedmont Rd NE
Atlanta, GA 30324-4135
Tel.: (404) 888-2000
Toll Free: (800) 800-ORKIN
Web Site: www.orkin.com
Sales Range: $900-999.9 Million
Approx. Number Employees: 7,500
Year Founded: 1964
Business Description:
Termite & Pest Control Services
S.I.C.: 7342; 0782
N.A.I.C.S.: 561710; 561730
Media: 2-4-7-8-10-11-13-14-18-20-23-24-26
Distr.: Reg.
Budget Set: Aug.
Personnel:
Gary W. Rollins *(Chm)*
Kevin Smith *(CMO)*
Greg Clendenin *(Pres-Southeast Div)*
John Wilson *(Pres-USA)*
Robert McFarland *(VP-Mktg)*
Bob Cipriano *(Asst VP-HR)*
Greg Baumann *(Dir-Tech Svcs)*
Allen Janusz *(Dir-E-Commerce)*
Brands & Products:
ORKIN
THE ORKIN MAN
Advertising Agencies:
The Richards Group, Inc.
8750 N Central Expy Ste 100
Dallas, TX 75231-6430
Tel.: (214) 891-5700
Fax: (214) 265-2933

Orkin, Inc. — (Continued)

TMP Worldwide/Advertising & Communications
47 Perimeter Ctr E Ste 350
Atlanta, GA 30346-2001
Tel.: (770) 280-4811
Fax: (770) 395-6868

THE PAGE SEED CO.
1A Green St
Greene, NY 13778-1108
Mailing Address:
PO Box 158
Greene, NY 13778-1108
Tel.: (607) 656-4107
Fax: (607) 656-8558
E-mail: pageseed@aol.com
Web Site: www.pageseed.com
Sales Range: $1-9.9 Million
Approx. Number Employees: 22
Year Founded: 1896
Business Description:
Garden, Flower & Lawn Seeds Whslr
S.I.C.: 5191
N.A.I.C.S.: 424910
Import Export
Media: 2-4-5-7-8-10-19-20-21
Distr.: Natl.
Personnel:
Lynda S. Granger *(Pres)*
Jefferey Serko *(VP-Sls)*
Linda LaRosa-Mosner *(Dir-Mktg)*
Brands & Products:
4 TO GROW
CREATE & GROW KITS
DOROTHY'S KIDS SERIES
GRANDPA'S GARDENS
GREENE VALLEY
IMPRESSION SERIES
NOSTALGIC MOMENTS
PAGE'S PACKET SEEDS
PAGE'S PREMIUM
PAGE'S PREMIUM COUNTER DISPLAY SERIES
RIPLEY'S "BELIEVE IT OR NOT!"
ROOTSWEET
SCENT SENSE
VALLEY GREEN
WEDDING ANNOUNCEMENT

PANAMERICAN SEED CO.
(Div. of Ball Horticultural Company)
622 Town Rd
West Chicago, IL 60185-2614
Tel.: (630) 231-1400
Fax: (630) 231-3605
Toll Free: (800) 231-4868
E-mail: webmaster@ballhort.com
Web Site: www.panamseed.com
Approx. Number Employees: 100
Year Founded: 1963
Business Description:
Retail Sales of Hybrid Flower Seeds
S.I.C.: 5261; 0181
N.A.I.C.S.: 111422; 111421; 444220
Media: 2-3-4-8-10-18
Distr.: Intl.; Natl.
Personnel:
Anna C. Ball *(CEO)*
Diane Hund *(Dir-Mktg)*
Ben Walraven *(Dir-Sls)*
Brands & Products:
RIDE THE WAVE
SORBET
SUPERSEED

PAX DIV
(Sub. of Martin Resource Management Corporation)
580 West 1300 South
Salt Lake City, UT 84115-5134
Tel.: (801) 973-2800
Fax: (801) 972-0904
Web Site: www.martinresources.com
Approx. Number Employees: 9
Year Founded: 1955
Business Description:
Lawn & Garden Fertilizer Mfr
S.I.C.: 2873; 2879
N.A.I.C.S.: 325311; 325320
Advertising Expenditures: $527,000
Media: 4-5-9-10-17-19-20-23-24-25
Distr.: Natl.
Personnel:
Richard Clark *(Gen Mgr)*
Brands & Products:
PAX
PAX SNOW & ICE MELTER

PCS NITROGEN
(Div. of PCS Sales)
1101 Skokie Blvd Ste 400
Northbrook, IL 60062
Tel.: (847) 849-4200
Fax: (847) 849-4695
Web Site: www.potashcorp.com
Approx. Number Employees: 200
Year Founded: 1989
Business Description:
Mfr. & Distributor of Nitrogen Chemicals & Fertilizers for Agricultural & Industrial Uses
S.I.C.: 2873; 2874
N.A.I.C.S.: 325311; 325312
Import Export
Media: 2-5-6-8-9-23
Distr.: Natl.
Budget Set: Aug. -Sept.
Personnel:
William J. Doyle *(Pres & CEO)*
Wayne R. Brownlee *(CFO & Exec VP)*
Garth W. Moore *(Pres-PCS Potash)*
Clark Bailey *(Sr VP-Projects & Tech Svcs)*
Robert A. Jaspar *(Sr VP-Info Tech)*
Brands & Products:
FLOWMASTER
POLY-N
S25
SURAN
URAN

PIONEER HI-BRED INTERNATIONAL, INC.
(Sub. of DuPont Agriculture & Nutrition)
7100 NW 62nd Ave
Johnston, IA 50131
Tel.: (515) 270-3200
Fax: (515) 270-3581
Toll Free: (800) 247-6803
Telex: 478-327
E-mail: web.editor@pioneer.com
Web Site: www.pioneer.com
Sales Range: $1-4.9 Billion
Approx. Number Employees: 5,025
Year Founded: 1926
Business Description:
Hybrid Seed Corn, Wheat, Alfalfa, Sunflower, Sorghum, Soybean, Microbial Genetic Inoculants, Hay & Livestock Mfr
S.I.C.: 5191
N.A.I.C.S.: 424910
Media: 3-4-5-6-8-9-14-15-18-20-23-24-25
Distr.: Natl.
Budget Set: Feb.
Personnel:
Paul E. Schickler *(Pres)*
Frank Ross *(CFO & VP)*
Susan Bunz *(VP-HR & Corp Svcs)*
Greg Friedman *(VP-Fin)*
Mike Gumina *(VP-Production, SHE & Risk Mgmt)*
Arun Baral *(Reg Dir-Asia Pacific)*
Daniel Glat *(Reg Dir-Canada & Latin America)*
Gyula Kovacs *(Reg Dir-Europe)*
Todd Frazier *(Bus Dir-Iowa & Missouri)*
Doyle Karr *(Dir-Comm)*
Jill Sandberg *(Dir-HR & Tech)*
Marv Wilson *(Dir-Ag Biotech Ops)*
Jennifer Goldston *(Sr Mgr-Pub Affairs-Global)*
Steve Betz *(Brand Mgr)*
Jerry Harrington *(Mgr-Sls, Mktg & PR)*
C. J. Osborn *(Mgr-Bus Dev Program)*
Brands & Products:
PIONEER
Advertising Agency:
McCormick Company
1201 NW Briarcliff Pkwy Ste 200
Kansas City, MO 64116-1774
Tel.: (816) 584-8444
Fax: (816) 584-8310
(Wheat, Sorghum, Forages, Alfalfa, Inoculants, Sunflowers)

PLANTABBS PRODUCTS COMPANY
(Div. of Tango Industries Ltd.)
8839 H Kelso Dr
Baltimore, MD 21221
Tel.: (410) 780-5495
Fax: (410) 780-5496
Toll Free: (800) 227-4340
E-mail: sales@plantabbsproducts.com
Web Site: www.plantabbsproducts.com
E-Mail For Key Personnel:
Sales Director: sales@plantabbsproducts.com
Approx. Sls.: $1,000,000
Approx. Number Employees: 8
Year Founded: 1921
Business Description:
Small Package Garden & Plant Chemicals, Animal Repellents
S.I.C.: 2874; 2873
N.A.I.C.S.: 325312; 325311
Import Export
Media: 2-6-9
Distr.: Intl.; Natl.
Budget Set: Sept.
Personnel:
Wayne Davis *(Pres)*
Brands & Products:
FLOWER-DRI
ORIGINAL SCOTTISH BARLEY BALES
PLANTABBS
PONDTABBS
PROLONG
SCENT OFF
STA-FRESH

PLANTATION PRODUCTS INC
202 S Washington St
Norton, MA 02766
Tel.: (508) 285-5800
Fax: (508) 285-7333
Web Site: www.plantationproducts.com
Sales Range: $25-49.9 Million
Approx. Number Employees: 400
Year Founded: 1990
Business Description:
Products for the Home Gardening
S.I.C.: 5191; 5261
N.A.I.C.S.: 424910; 444220
Import Export
Advertising Expenditures: $4,000,000
Media: 2-4-5-7-8-13-16-17-18
Personnel:
Joseph Raffaele *(Owner)*
Michael Pietrasiewicz *(Exec VP)*
Brands & Products:
FREDONIA
KIDSEED
KITCHEN CROP
NK
NK LAWN AND GARDEN
NOSTALGIA

PREMIER HORTICULTURE LTD.
(Sub. of Premier Tech Ltd.)
1 Premier Ave
Riviere-du-Loup, QC G5R 6C1, Canada
Tel.: (204) 422-8805
Fax: (418) 862-6685
Toll Free: (800) 667-5366
E-mail: services@premierhort.com
Web Site: www.premierhort.com
E-Mail For Key Personnel:
President: Christian.Dollo@premierhort.com
Sales Director: frank.zelko@premierhort.com
Approx. Number Employees: 15
Year Founded: 1923
Business Description:
Peat Moss, Sphagnum, Soilless Potting Media, Retail Soils & Soil Mixes, Composts & Potting Mixes Mfr
S.I.C.: 5191; 5194
N.A.I.C.S.: 424910; 424940
Export
Advertising Expenditures: $500,000
Media: 2-4-5-10-19-20-21
Distr.: Intl.; Natl.
Budget Set: Jan.
Personnel:
Ed Bloodnick *(Dir-Grower Svcs)*
Brands & Products:
BIOMAX
LITE WAY
PRO-MIX
PRO-MOSS

PREMIER TECH LTD.
1 Ave Premier
Riviere-du-Loup, QC G5R 6C1, Canada
Tel.: (418) 867-8883
Fax: (418) 862-6642
E-mail: info@premiertech.com
Web Site: www.premiertech.com
Approx. Sls.: $213,354,876
Approx. Number Employees: 1,500
Year Founded: 1987

Key to Media (For complete agency information see *The Advertising Red Books-Agencies* edition):
1. Bus. Publs. 2. Cable T.V. 3. Catalogs & Directories. 4. Co-op Adv. 5. Consumer Mags. 6. D.M. to Bus. Estab.7. D.M. to Consumers 8. Daily Newsp. 9. Exhibits/Trade Shows 10. Foreign 11. Infomercial 12. Internet Adv.13. Multimedia 14. Network Radio 15. Network T.V. 16. Newsp. Distr. Mags. 17. Other 18. Outdoor (Posters, Transit) 19. Point of Purchase20. Premiums, Novelties 21. Product Samples 22. Special Events Mktg. 23. Spot Radio 24. Spot T.V. 25. Weekly Newsp. 26. Yellow Page Adv.

Business Description:
Gardening Products & Sphagnum Peat Moss Producer & Distr
S.I.C.: 0139
N.A.I.C.S.: 111998
Export
Media: 9-10
Personnel:
Bernard Belanger *(Chm & CEO)*
Jean Belanger *(Pres & COO)*
Martin Noel *(CFO & Sr VP)*
Germain Ouellet *(Sec & Sr VP-HR)*
Jean-Pierre Berube *(VP-Tech & Infrastructure)*
Daniel Bourgeois *(VP-Product Dev & Mfg)*
Martin Pelletier *(Gen Mgr)*
Brands & Products:
PREMIER TECH
PRO MIX

PRT FOREST REGENERATION INCOME FUND
1006 Fort Street Unit 101
Victoria, BC V8V 3K4, Canada
Tel.: (250) 381-1404
Fax: (250) 381-0252
E-mail: investor_relations@prtgroup.com
Web Site: www.prtgroup.com
Approx. Rev.: $29,421,078
Approx. Number Employees: 382
Year Founded: 1997
Business Description:
Reforestation Products & Services
S.I.C.: 0139
N.A.I.C.S.: 111998
Media: 2-10-11-18-20-21
Personnel:
Colin A.C. Dobell *(Chm)*
Robert A. Miller *(Pres & CEO)*
Tony Pollard *(CFO & VP-Fin)*
Herb Markgraf *(VP-Mktg)*
Robert Maxwell *(VP-Production)*
Peter Richter *(Dir-HR & Reg Mgr-North)*
David Swain *(Dir-Crop Production)*
Tim Harradine *(Reg Mgr-South)*
Bret Hill *(Mgr-Info Sys)*

THE ROBERT BAKER COMPANIES
1700 Mtn Rd
West Suffield, CT 06093
Tel.: (860) 668-7371
Fax: (860) 668-5802
E-mail: inquiries@robertbaker.com
Web Site: www.robertbaker.com
Approx. Number Employees: 200
Business Description:
Holding Company
S.I.C.: 5193; 5261
N.A.I.C.S.: 424930; 444220
Media: 4-10

ROBERT W. BAKER NURSERY INC.
(Sub. of The Robert Baker Companies)
1700 Mountain Rd
West Suffield, CT 06093
Mailing Address:
PO Box 434
West Suffield, CT 06093
Tel.: (860) 668-7371
Fax: (860) 668-5802
E-mail: info@industrialbankkck.com
Web Site: www.robertbaker.com
Approx. Sls.: $45,300,000
Approx. Number Employees: 100
Year Founded: 1956
Business Description:
Flower & Plant Whslr
S.I.C.: 5193; 5261
N.A.I.C.S.: 424930; 444220
Media: 10
Personnel:
Robert W. Baker, Sr. *(Owner)*
Lew Paquin *(Customer Svc Mgr)*

SCOTTS MIRACLE-GRO COMPANY
14111 Scottslawn Rd
Marysville, OH 43041
Tel.: (937) 644-0011
Fax: (937) 644-7614
Toll Free: (800) 543-8873
Web Site: www.thescottsmiraclegrocompany.com
Approx. Sls.: $3,139,900,000
Approx. Number Employees: 6,750
Year Founded: 1868
Business Description:
Lawn Grass Seed, Chemical Fertilizers, Weed & Insect Controls, Mechanical Accessories & Spreaders Mfr
S.I.C.: 2873; 2874; 5191
N.A.I.C.S.: 325311; 325312; 424910
Export
Advertising Expenditures: $142,400,000
Media: 1-2-3-4-5-6-7-8-9-10-11-13-14-15-16-19-23-24-25-26
Distr.: Intl.; Natl.
Personnel:
James S. Hagedorn *(Chm & CEO)*
Michael P. Kelty *(Vice Chm)*
Barry W. Sanders *(Pres)*
Dave Evans *(CFO, Exec VP-Strategy & Bus Dev)*
Jim Lyski *(CMO & Exec VP)*
Brian Kura *(Pres-Midwest Reg)*
Claude Lopez *(Pres-Global Sls)*
Mike Lukemire *(Pres-Southeast Reg)*
Vincent C. Brockman *(Chief Ethics Officer, Gen Counsel, Sec & Exec VP)*
Denise Stump *(Exec VP-Global HR)*
Fred Bosch *(Sr VP-Global Prof)*
Randy Coleman *(Sr VP-Global Operating Fin)*
Andy Coogle *(Sr VP-Legal Compliance)*
Jeff Garascia *(Sr VP-Global R&D)*
Jim King *(Sr VP-IR & Corp Affairs)*
Dan Paradiso *(Sr VP)*
Richard Shank *(Chief Environ Officer, Sr VP-Regulatory & Govt Affairs)*
Pete Supron *(Sr VP-Bus Dev)*
Dave Swihart *(Sr VP-Global Supply Chain)*
Jan E. Valentic *(Sr VP-Sustainability)*
Keith Baeder *(VP-Mktg-Scotts LawnService)*
Mike Sutterer *(VP-Mktg)*
Ed Billmaier *(Sr Dir-Relationship & Interactive Mktg)*
Keri Butler *(Dir-Pub Affairs)*
Su Lok *(Dir-Corp & Community Partnerships)*
Joel Reimer *(Dir-Interactive Media)*
John Sass *(Dir-Grass Seed Mktg)*
Patrick Kaiser *(Asst Brand Mgr)*
John Price *(Brand Mgr-Lawns)*
Matt Taylor *(Asst Brand Mgr)*
Michela Baxter *(Mgr-Comm)*
Kip Edwardson *(Mgr-Interactive Mktg)*
Brands & Products:
ACCUGREEN
AGROBLEN
AGROCOTE
BASIC
BONUS
BONUS S
BUG-B-GON
CLASSIC
DELUXE
DIAL'N SPRAY
EARTHGRO
EASY
EASYGREEN
EDGEGUARD
EZ SEED
GRASS-B-GON
GRUBEX
HALTS
HANDYGREEN
HOME DEFENSE MAX
HYPONEX
IT'S GRO TIME
KB
KILLEX
LAWN PRO
LAWNSERVICE
LEVINGTON
LIQUAFEED
MAX
MINI
MIRACLE-GRO
MORNING SONG
NATURE SCAPES
NEXA-LOTTE
OH2
ORGANIC CHOICE
ORTHENE
ORTHO
OSMOCOTE
PATCHMASTER
PATHCLEAR
PETERS EXCEL
PETERS PROFESSIONAL
PURE PREMIUM
READY-SPRAY
ROSEPRIDE
ROUT
SCOTTKOTE
SCOTTS
SHAKE 'N FEED
SIERRABLEN PLUS
SMITH & HAWKEN
SONGBIRD SELECTION
SPEEDYGREEN
STANDARD
STARTER
SUBSTRAL
SUMMERIZER
SUN & SHADE MIX
SUPER BONUS
SUPERSOIL
TURF BUILDER
TURF BUILDER PLUS 2
TURF BUILDER PLUS HALTS
TURF BUILDER WITH WATER SMART
TURFSEED
WATER SMART.
WEED-B-GON
WEED-B-GON MAX
WEEDOL
WINTERIZER
Advertising Agencies:
MEC - NA HQ, New York
825 7th Ave
New York, NY 10019-5818
Tel.: (212) 474-0000
Fax: (212) 474-0003
Miracle-Gro

Young & Laramore
407 N Fulton St
Indianapolis, IN 46202
Tel.: (317) 264-8000
Fax: (317) 264-8002
Digital
Direct Mail
Out of Home
Print
Radio
Scotts Lawn Service (Agency of Record)

SEEDS OF CHANGE INC.
PO Box 15700
Santa Fe, NM 87592-5700
Tel.: (505) 438-8080
Fax: (505) 438-4591
Web Site: www.seedsofchange.com
Approx. Sls.: $12,600,000
Approx. Number Employees: 11
Year Founded: 1989
Business Description:
Seeds & Bulbs
S.I.C.: 5191; 5261
N.A.I.C.S.: 424910; 444220
Media: 6-13
Personnel:
Gemma Kew *(Brand Mgr)*
Brands & Products:
THE FIRST LINK IN A SAFE FOOD CHAIN
GARDENCYCLE
GOODNESS FROM THE GROUND UP
SEEDS OF CHANGE

THE SIEBENTHALER CO.
3001 Catalpa Dr
Dayton, OH 45405-1745
Tel.: (937) 274-1154
Fax: (937) 274-9448
E-mail: siebenthaler@erinet.com
Web Site: www.siebenthaler.com
Approx. Sls.: $3,400,000
Approx. Number Employees: 100
Year Founded: 1870
Business Description:
Landscape Nursery Services; Nursery Stock Retailer
S.I.C.: 0782; 5193
N.A.I.C.S.: 561730; 424930
Advertising Expenditures: $200,000
Media: 4-7-8-9-22-23-26
Distr.: Natl.
Budget Set: Nov.
Personnel:
Robert J. Siebenthaler *(Chm)*
Brands & Products:
MORAINE
SIEBENTHALAR'S

SIMPLOT PARTNERS INC.
(Sub. of J.R. Simplot Company)
999 Main St
Boise, ID 83702
Tel.: (208) 336-2110
Tel.: (208) 672-2822 (Mktg)
Fax: (208) 672-2889
E-mail: info@simplot.com

Key to Media (For complete agency information see *The Advertising Red Books-Agencies* edition):
1. Bus. Publs. 2. Cable T.V. 3. Catalogs & Directories. 4. Co-op Adv. 5. Consumer Mags. 6. D.M. to Bus. Estab.7. D.M. to Consumers
8. Daily Newsp. 9. Exhibits/Trade Shows 10. Foreign 11. Infomercial 12. Internet Adv.13. Multimedia 14. Network Radio
15. Network T.V. 16. Newsp. Distr. Mags. 17. Other 18. Outdoor (Posters, Transit) 19. Point of Purchase20. Premiums, Novelties
21. Product Samples 22. Special Events Mktg. 23. Spot Radio 24. Spot T.V. 25. Weekly Newsp. 26. Yellow Page Adv.

Simplot Partners Inc. — (Continued)
Web Site: www.simplotpartners.com
Approx. Number Employees: 70
Year Founded: 1979
Business Description:
Fertilizer, Turf Grass Seed & Chemical Products Distribution
S.I.C.: 2874
N.A.I.C.S.: 325312
Media: 2-4-5-19-20
Distr.: Natl.
Personnel:
Kristi Smith *(Mgr-Mktg)*
Brands & Products:
COLORPACK
GAME DAY
GROWTHPACK
LINKS
LO-DOWN BLUES
MATRIX
NUTRIPACK
PARTREE
PREMIERE
SHADY
SIMPLOT PARTNERS
SOLUPACK
SUNNY
SURFPACK
TECHPACK
TURF'S UP
WATERPACK

SMITHEREEN PEST MANAGEMENT SERVICES
7400 N Melvina Ave
Niles, IL 60714-3908
Tel.: (847) 675-0010
Fax: (847) 675-1326
E-mail: andy@smithereen.com
Web Site: www.smithereen.com
Approx. Number Employees: 75
Year Founded: 1888
Business Description:
Pest Control Service & Products
S.I.C.: 7342; 2879
N.A.I.C.S.: 561710; 325320
Export
Media: 2-7-8-13-18-26
Distr.: Direct to Consumer; Reg.
Budget Set: Oct.
Personnel:
Richard E. Jennings *(Pres)*
Brands & Products:
SMITHEREEN
YOUR PARTNER FOR A HEALTHY ENVIRONMENT

SPEEDLING INCORPORATED
4300 Old US Hwy 41 S
Sun City, FL 33586-7220
Mailing Address:
PO Box 7098
Sun City, FL 33586-7220
Tel.: (813) 645-3221
Fax: (813) 645-8123
Toll Free: (800) 426-4400
E-mail: speedling@aol.com
Web Site: www.speedling.com
Approx. Number Employees: 250
Year Founded: 1968
Business Description:
Mfr. of Expanded Polystyrene Products; Distr of Horticultural Products; Transplant Grower of Vegetables, Herbs & Tobacco; Ornamental Nurseries
S.I.C.: 0181; 0711
N.A.I.C.S.: 111422; 115112
Import Export
Advertising Expenditures: $500,000
Media: 4-10-19
Distr.: Natl.
Personnel:
Greg Daiz *(Pres)*
Joelle Doehring *(Office Mgr)*
Mark Dunlop *(Mktg Mgr)*
Brands & Products:
SPEEDLING
SPEEDLING FLATS

SPRING-GREEN LAWN CARE CORPORATION
11909 S Spaulding School Dr
Plainfield, IL 60585
Tel.: (815) 436-8777
Fax: (815) 436-9056
Toll Free: (800) 435-4051
Web Site: www.spring-green.com
Approx. Number Employees: 21
Year Founded: 1977
Business Description:
Lawn & Tree Care Services
S.I.C.: 0782
N.A.I.C.S.: 561730
Media: 4-6-8-9-10-20-25-26
Distr.: Reg.
Budget Set: Nov.
Personnel:
James Young *(Pres)*
Thomas W. Hofer *(CEO)*
Barry Matthews *(COO & VP)*
Brands & Products:
SPRING-GREEN

STARK BROTHERS NURSERIES & ORCHARDS CO.
20947 Hwy 54 W
Louisiana, MO 63353
Mailing Address:
PO Box 1800
Louisiana, MO 63353
Tel.: (573) 754-5111
Fax: (573) 754-8880
Toll Free: (800) 325-4180
E-mail: info@starkbros.com
Web Site: www.starkbros.com
Approx. Number Employees: 150
Year Founded: 1816
Business Description:
Whslr of Fruit Trees & Ornamental Plants
S.I.C.: 0181
N.A.I.C.S.: 111421
Advertising Expenditures: $250,000
Media: 2-4-5-7-8-9-10-13-16-19-20-25
Distr.: Direct to Consumer; Natl.
Budget Set: Varies
Personnel:
Lita Eatock *(Mgr-Mktg)*
Brands & Products:
BLUSHING GOLDEN
BRAESTAR
DOUBLE DELICIOUS
EARLIBLAZE
GRANDGALA
JON-A-RED
STARK
STARK BRO'S
STARK JUMBO
STARK KWIK KROP
STARK MOTHER LODE
STARKRIMSON
STARKSPUR
ULTRAMAC

SUN BULB COMPANY, INC.
1615 SW Hwy 17
Arcadia, FL 34266-7101
Tel.: (863) 494-4022
Fax: (863) 494-7568
E-mail: sunbulb@cyberstreet.com
Web Site: www.sunbulb.com
Approx. Number Employees: 45
Year Founded: 1956
Business Description:
Grower & Distributor of Flower Bulbs, Bromeliads, Orchids & Ferns
S.I.C.: 5191; 5193
N.A.I.C.S.: 424910; 424930
Import Export
Media: 2-4-7-8-10
Distr.: Intl.; Natl.
Budget Set: Jan.
Personnel:
Tom Hollingsworth *(Pres)*
Rodney Hollingsworth *(VP & Gen Mgr)*
Brands & Products:
BETTER GRO
ORCHID MOSS
ORCHID PLUS

SYNAGRO TECHNOLOGIES, INC.
(Sub. of Synatech Holdings, Inc.)
1800 Bering Dr Ste 1000
Houston, TX 77057-3169
Tel.: (713) 369-1700
Fax: (713) 369-1750
Toll Free: (800) 370-0035
E-mail: info@synagro.com
Web Site: www.synagro.com
Approx. Rev.: $345,806,016
Approx. Number Employees: 966
Year Founded: 1986
Business Description:
Waste Water Treatment & Residual Management Services
S.I.C.: 4953
N.A.I.C.S.: 562219; 562211; 562920
Media: 10
Personnel:
William Massa *(Pres & CEO)*
Tricia Papile *(CFO)*
Eric Zimmer *(Exec VP-Svcs Div)*
Douglas T. Barbe *(Gen Mgr-Facilities Div)*
Brands & Products:
GRANULITE
SOIL RICH
VITAL CYCLE
Advertising Agency:
Geto & deMilly Inc.
276 5th Ave Ste 806
New York, NY 10001
Tel.: (212) 686-4551
Fax: (212) 213-6850

SYNGENTA SEEDS, INC.
(Sub. of Syngenta AG)
11055 Wayzata Blvd
Minnetonka, MN 55305
Tel.: (612) 656-8600
Fax: (612) 656-8601
Toll Free: (800) 248-4767
Web Site: www.nk-us.com
Sales Range: $400-449.9 Million
Approx. Number Employees: 1,500
Year Founded: 1884
Business Description:
Breeding, Production, Conditioning & Marketing of Field Crop Seeds
S.I.C.: 5191; 0723
N.A.I.C.S.: 424910; 115114
Advertising Expenditures: $1,000,000
Media: 2-19-20
Distr.: Intl.; Natl.
Budget Set: Apr.
Personnel:
Bev Larson *(Mgr-Comm)*
Brands & Products:
COKER
HILLESHOG
NK
ROGERS
S&G
ZIMMERMAN
Advertising Agency:
Weber Shandwick-Minneapolis
8000 Norman Ctr Dr Ste 400
Minneapolis, MN 55437
Tel.: (952) 832-5000
Fax: (952) 831-8241

SYNGENTA SEEDS, INC.
(Sub. of Syngenta Seeds, Inc.)
4343 Commerce Ct
Lisle, IL 60532
Tel.: (630) 969-6300
Fax: (630) 969-6373
Toll Free: (800) 323-7253
Web Site: www.sg-flowers.com
Approx. Number Employees: 275
Year Founded: 1876
Business Description:
Seeds, Plants & Horticultural Products
S.I.C.: 5191
N.A.I.C.S.: 424910
Import Export
Advertising Expenditures: $500,000
Media: 2
Distr.: Natl.
Budget Set: July
Personnel:
Keith Cable *(Pres)*
Brands & Products:
S&G

TELEFLORA, LLC
(Sub. of Roll International Corporation)
11444 W Olympic Blvd
Los Angeles, CA 90064-1549
Tel.: (310) 231-9199
Fax: (310) 966-3658
Toll Free: (800) 321-2654
Web Site: www.teleflora.com
Approx. Number Employees: 700
Year Founded: 1934
Business Description:
Flowers by Wire Service; Floral Products
S.I.C.: 5992
N.A.I.C.S.: 453110
Media: 3-4-5-6-9-13-16-18-19-23-24-25-26
Distr.: Intl.; Natl.
Personnel:
Lariayn Payne *(VP-Mktg)*
Anda Pho *(Mgr-Mktg)*
Brands & Products:
TELEFLORA

TERRA INDUSTRIES-YAZOO
(Sub. of Terra Industries, Inc.)
4608 US Hwy 49 E
Yazoo City, MS 39194
Mailing Address:
PO Box 388
Yazoo City, MS 39194-0388

Key to Media (For complete agency information see *The Advertising Red Books-Agencies* edition):
1. Bus. Publs. 2. Cable T.V. 3. Catalogs & Directories. 4. Co-op Adv. 5. Consumer Mags. 6. D.M. to Bus. Estab.7. D.M. to Consumers 8. Daily Newsp. 9. Exhibits/Trade Shows 10. Foreign 11. Infomercial 12. Internet Adv.13. Multimedia 14. Network Radio 15. Network T.V. 16. Newsp. Distr. Mags. 17. Other 18. Outdoor (Posters, Transit) 19. Point of Purchase20. Premiums, Novelties 21. Product Samples 22. Special Events Mktg. 23. Spot Radio 24. Spot T.V. 25. Weekly Newsp. 26. Yellow Page Adv.

Tel.: (662) 746-4131
Fax: (662) 751-2913
Sales Range: $75-99.9 Million
Approx. Number Employees: 200
Year Founded: 1948
Business Description:
Chemical Fertilizers, Nitrogen Potash, & Phosphate Based Products Mfr
S.I.C.: 2873; 2874
N.A.I.C.S.: 325311; 325312
Import Export
Media: 2-9-10-20-22-23-24-25
Distr.: Natl.
Budget Set: Mar.
Personnel:
Steve Moore *(Mgr-Plant)*

TERRAL SEED, INC.
(Sub. of Pioneer Hi-Bred International, Inc.)
604 Blount St PO Box 826
Lake Providence, LA 71254-3322
Tel.: (318) 559-2840
Fax: (318) 559-2888
Toll Free: (800) 551-4152
E-mail: Info@terralseed.com
Web Site: www.terralseed.com
E-Mail For Key Personnel:
President: tterral@terralseed.com
Marketing Director: lmullen@terralseed.com
Public Relations: lmullen@terralseed.com
Approx. Number Employees: 60
Year Founded: 1950
Business Description:
Seeds, Soybeans, Rice, Wheat, Oats & Corn Distr
S.I.C.: 5191
N.A.I.C.S.: 424910
Export
Advertising Expenditures: $100,000
Media: 2-4-6-7-8-10-13-17-19
Distr.: Intl.; Natl.
Personnel:
Thomas F. Terral *(Pres & CEO)*
Larry J. Mullen *(Dir-Mktg & Sls)*
Cherie Pearson *(Dir-HR)*
Rick Davis *(Reg Mgr-Sls)*
Patsy King *(Office Mgr)*
Trey Cash *(Sls Mgr-District)*
David Doise *(Sls Mgr-District)*
Chad Ervin *(Sls Mgr-District)*
Peter Fox *(Sls Mgr)*
Danny Graham *(Sls Mgr-District)*
Bruce Jones *(Sls Mgr-District)*
Gregg Matheny *(Sls Mgr-District)*
Paul Sumner *(Sls Mgr-District)*
Goke Akinsola *(Mgr-Quality Control)*
Brands & Products:
LOTS OF WORK!!! PROVEN YIELD!!!
ROUNDUP READY
TERRAL SEED
YIELDGARD

TRUGREEN-CHEMLAWN
(Div. of The ServiceMaster Company)
860 Ridge Lake Blvd
Memphis, TN 38120-9421
Tel.: (901) 681-1800
Fax: (901) 597-1900
Fax: (808) 303-4051
Toll Free: (800) 878-4733
Toll Free: (800) TRUEGREEN
E-mail: webmaster@trugreenmail.com
Web Site: www.trugreen.com
Approx. Number Employees: 12,000
Year Founded: 1974
Business Description:
Lawn Care Services
S.I.C.: 0782; 7342
N.A.I.C.S.: 561730; 561710
Media: 9-14-15-17-26
Distr.: Natl.
Personnel:
Steve Donley *(Pres)*
Pat Spainhour *(CEO)*
Roy Cohen *(VP & Partner-HR Bus)*
Steve Martin *(CFO)*
Brad Cumings *(CMO-Interim)*
Brands & Products:
BAREFOOT
CHEMLAWN
TRUGREEN
Advertising Agencies:
archer malmo
65 Union Ave Ste 500
Memphis, TN 38103-5137
Tel.: (901) 523-2000
Fax: (901) 523-7654
Toll Free: (800) 535-8943

Javelin Marketing Group.
(Part of Omnicom Group Inc)
7850 N Belt Line Rd
Irving, TX 75063-6098
Tel.: (972) 443-7000
Fax: (972) 443-7194

Publicis USA
(Sub. of Publicis, S.A., Paris, France)
4 Herald Sq 950 6th Ave
New York, NY 10001
Tel.: (212) 279-5550
Fax: (212) 279-5560

TYGAR MANUFACTURING, INC.
425 Wilbanks Dr
Ball Ground, GA 30107
Tel.: (770) 345-6625
Fax: (770) 345-6625
Toll Free: (866) 999-9506
Web Site: www.tygarmfg.com
Sales Range: $10-24.9 Million
Approx. Number Employees: 10
Business Description:
Decorative Landscaping
S.I.C.: 0781
N.A.I.C.S.: 541320
Media: 6-10
Personnel:
Mark Crosswell *(Pres)*

W. ATLEE BURPEE & CO.
300 Pk Ave
Warminster, PA 18974-4808
Tel.: (215) 674-4900
Fax: (215) 674-4170
Fax: (800) 487-5530 (Orders)
Toll Free: (800) 888-1447 (Orders)
Toll Free: (800) 333-5808 (Customer Svc)
E-mail: custserv@burpee.com
Web Site: www.burpee.com
Approx. Number Employees: 240
Year Founded: 1876
Business Description:
Mail Order Seeds, Bulbs, Nursery Stock, & General Merchandise
S.I.C.: 0181; 5961
N.A.I.C.S.: 111422; 454113
Import Export
Advertising Expenditures: $250,000
Media: 4-7-8-9-10-13-16
Distr.: Natl.
Budget Set: Aug. -Oct.
Personnel:
George Ball, Jr. *(Chm & CEO)*
Chris Romas *(Pres)*
Hans Miller *(Sr VP-Bus Dev & CFO)*
Don Zeidler *(Dir-Direct Mktg)*
Brands & Products:
BURPEE
FORDHOOK

WALTHAM SERVICES, INC.
817 Moody St
Waltham, MA 02453
Tel.: (781) 893-1810
Fax: (781) 893-7921
Toll Free: (800) WSI-PEST
E-mail: contactus@walthamservices.com
Web Site: www.walthamservices.com
E-Mail For Key Personnel:
President: clarke@walthamservices.com
Sales Director: mikeb@walthamservices.com
Sales Range: $10-24.9 Million
Approx. Number Employees: 200
Year Founded: 1893
Business Description:
Termite & Pest Control Services
S.I.C.: 7342
N.A.I.C.S.: 561710
Advertising Expenditures: $450,000
Media: 3-4-8-20-24-25-26
Distr.: Direct to Consumer; Reg.
Budget Set: Nov.
Personnel:
Robert McGuire *(CFO)*
Clarke M. Keenan *(Pres-Waltham Svcs)*
Michael Botte *(Mgr-Sls & Mktg)*
Bob Knowlton *(Mgr-Svc)*
Brands & Products:
FLOWER CITY PEST ELIMINATOR
PIONEER WILDLIFE CONTROL

WAYNESBORO NURSERIES, INC.
2597 Lyndhurst Rd
Waynesboro, VA 22980
Tel.: (540) 946-3800
Fax: (540) 946-3814
Toll Free: (800) 868-8676
Web Site: www.waynesboronurseries.com
E-Mail For Key Personnel:
President: quillent@cfw.com
Approx. Sls.: $5,000,000
Approx. Number Employees: 60
Year Founded: 1932
Business Description:
Whslr of Nursery Stock, Garden Supplies & Landscape Services
S.I.C.: 0181; 5193
N.A.I.C.S.: 111421; 424930
Media: 2-4-7-10-13-26
Distr.: Direct to Consumer; Reg.
Personnel:
Ed Quillen *(Pres)*
Tim Quillen *(Treas, Sec & Mgr-Landscape)*
Kirk Quillen *(VP & Mgr-Wholesale-Sls)*
David Quillen *(VP-Production)*
Brands & Products:
WAYNESBORO

WHITE FLOWER FARM, INC.
30 Irene St
Torrington, CT 06790-6657
Tel.: (860) 496-9624
Fax: (860) 496-1418
Toll Free: (800) 503-9624
E-mail: custserv@whiteflowerfarm.com
Web Site: www.whiteflowerfarm.com
Sales Range: $25-49.9 Million
Approx. Number Employees: 150
Year Founded: 1950
Business Description:
Retailer & Catalog Sales of Perennials, Shrubs & Bulbs
S.I.C.: 5961; 5261
N.A.I.C.S.: 454113; 444220
Import
Media: 4-6-8-9-13
Distr.: Natl.
Budget Set: July
Personnel:
Elliot Worth *(Pres)*
Brands & Products:
WHITE FLOWER FARM

WHITMIRE MICRO-GEN RESEARCH LABORATORIES, INC.
(Sub. of Sorex Holdings Ltd.)
(d/b/a BASF Pest Control Solutions)
3568 Tree Ct Industrial Blvd
Saint Louis, MO 63122-6620
Tel.: (636) 225-5371
Tel.: (636) 825-9775
Fax: (636) 225-3739
Toll Free: (800) 777-8570
Web Site: www.pestcontrol.basf.us
E-Mail For Key Personnel:
President: andy.symons@wmmg.com
Approx. Number Employees: 100
Year Founded: 1934
Business Description:
Insecticides & Animal Pesticides Developer & Mfr
S.I.C.: 2879
N.A.I.C.S.: 325320
Media: 2-4-6-9-18-21-23
Distr.: Natl.
Budget Set: Nov.
Personnel:
Dan Carrothers *(Bus Mgr)*
Jim Derbyshire *(Mgr-Natl Sls)*
Jeff Vannoy *(Mgr-Sls-Eastern Reg)*
Brands & Products:
ADVANCE
CRACK & CREVICE
PRESCRIPTION TREATMENT
SYSTEM III

WILT-PRUF PRODUCTS, INC.
PO Box 469
Essex, CT 06426-0469
Tel.: (860) 767-7033
Fax: (860) 767-7265
Toll Free: (800) 972-0726
E-mail: wiltpruf@wiltpruf.com
Web Site: www.wiltpruf.com
Approx. Number Employees: 25
Year Founded: 1950
Business Description:
Mfr. & Sales of Anti-Transpirants
S.I.C.: 2879
N.A.I.C.S.: 325320
Export
Media: 2-4-5-6-7-9-10-18-19-21-23

Key to Media (For complete agency information see *The Advertising Red Books-Agencies* edition):
1. Bus. Publs. 2. Cable T.V. 3. Catalogs & Directories. 4. Co-op Adv. 5. Consumer Mags. 6. D.M. to Bus. Estab.7. D.M. to Consumers 8. Daily Newsp. 9. Exhibits/Trade Shows 10. Foreign 11. Infomercial 12. Internet Adv.13. Multimedia 14. Network Radio 15. Network T.V. 16. Newsp. Distr. Mags. 17. Other 18. Outdoor (Posters, Transit) 19. Point of Purchase20. Premiums, Novelties 21. Product Samples 22. Special Events Mktg. 23. Spot Radio 24. Spot T.V. 25. Weekly Newsp. 26. Yellow Page Adv.

Wilt-Pruf Products, Inc. — (Continued)

Distr.: Natl.
Budget Set: Jan.
Personnel:
Robert B. Nichols, Jr. *(Pres)*
Helene Nichols *(VP & Coord-Adv)*
Brands & Products:
PLANT PROTECTOR
WILT-PRUF

WINFIELD NURSERY, INC.

(Div. of Northern Nurseries, Inc.)
1320 Mountain Rd
West Suffield, CT 06093
Tel.: (860) 668-5225
Fax: (860) 668-5714
Business Description:
Landscaping; Wholesaler of Flowers & Other Plants
S.I.C.: 5193
N.A.I.C.S.: 424930
Media: 4

THE WOODSTREAM CORPORATION

(Holding of Code, Hennessy & Simmons, LLC)
69 N Locust St
Lititz, PA 17543-1714
Mailing Address:
PO Box 327
Lititz, PA 17543-0327
Tel.: (717) 626-2125
Fax: (717) 626-1912
Toll Free: (800) 800-1819
Web Site: www.woodstream.com
Approx. Number Employees: 200
Year Founded: 1903
Business Description:
Pest Control Equipment Mfr
S.I.C.: 3999; 3496
N.A.I.C.S.: 339999; 332618
Export
Media: 2-4-6-7-10-13-14-19-20-21-23
Distr.: Intl.; Natl.
Budget Set: Oct.
Personnel:
Harry Whaley *(Pres)*
Steve Lesher *(Exec VP-Customer Order Fullfillment)*
Andy Woolworth *(VP-Sls)*
Karolyn Warfel *(Mgr-Category Dev)*
Brands & Products:
BIONEEM
CONCERN
CONCERN NECESSARY ORGANICS
EASY SET
FAST-KILL
FLY MAGNET
GRASS PATCH
HAVAHART
MAGIC START
MULTI-KILL
NUBARK
OMRI LISTED
OUT O'SIGHT
PENTREX
PESTCHASER
POISON-FREE
RINGER
SAFER
SONIC PESTCHASER
TIN CAT
VICTOR
VICTOR BLACK BOX
WOODSTREAM

YARA N AMERICA, INC.

(Sub. of Yara International ASA)
100 N Tampa St Ste 3200
Tampa, FL 33602
Tel.: (813) 222-5700
Fax: (813) 875-5735
Toll Free: (800) 944-9376
E-mail: info@yara.com
Web Site: www.yara.us
Approx. Number Employees: 60
Year Founded: 1946
Business Description:
Mineral Fertilizer, Gas & Chemicals Mfr
S.I.C.: 5191; 5169
N.A.I.C.S.: 424910; 424690
Media: 1-2-5-10-19-21-25
Distr.: Natl.
Budget Set: Mar. -Sept.
Personnel:
Jerry Southwell *(Reg Mgr)*
Jim Haitz *(Mgr-Ammonia Sls & Shipping)*
Andy Hancock *(Mgr-Territory)*
Wes Johnson *(Mgr-Territory)*
Ron Naven *(Mgr-Territory)*
Greg Rambo *(Mgr-Sls)*
George Simpson *(Mgr-Territory)*
Brands & Products:
VIKING SHIP BRAND

Key to Media (For complete agency information see *The Advertising Red Books-Agencies* edition):
1. Bus. Publs. 2. Cable T.V. 3. Catalogs & Directories. 4. Co-op Adv. 5. Consumer Mags. 6. D.M. to Bus. Estab.7. D.M. to Consumers 8. Daily Newsp. 9. Exhibits/Trade Shows 10. Foreign 11. Infomercial 12. Internet Adv.13. Multimedia 14. Network Radio 15. Network T.V. 16. Newsp. Distr. Mags. 17. Other 18. Outdoor (Posters, Transit) 19. Point of Purchase20. Premiums, Novelties 21. Product Samples 22. Special Events Mktg. 23. Spot Radio 24. Spot T.V. 25. Weekly Newsp. 26. Yellow Page Adv.

Shoes

Boots — Foot Appliances — Leather — Rubber Heels — Rubber Footwear — Shoe Fittings — Slippers

ADIDAS NORTH AMERICA INC
(Sub. of adidas AG)
5055 N Greeley Ave
Portland, OR 97217
Tel.: (971) 234-2300
Fax: (971) 234-2450
Toll Free: (800) 423-4327
E-mail: customerservice@shopadidas.com
Web Site: www.adidas.com
Sales Range: $1-4.9 Billion
Approx. Number Employees: 1,200
Year Founded: 1993

Business Description:
Athletic Apparel & Footwear Mfr & Distr
S.I.C.: 3149; 3949
N.A.I.C.S.: 316219; 339920
Media: 2-3-4-6-8-15-16-17-18-22-24-31
Distr.: Natl.
Budget Set: Apr.

Personnel:
Patrik Nilsson *(Pres)*
Erich Stamminger *(CEO)*
Hermann Deininger *(CMO)*
Britt Jorgenson *(Dir-Brand Mktg-Sport Performance)*
Chris Murphy *(Dir-Digital Mktg)*

Advertising Agencies:
180 Los Angeles
1733 Ocean Ave 4th fl
Santa Monica, CA 90401
Tel.: (310) 382-1400
Fax: (310) 382-1401
The Bull

Carat
2450 Colorado Blvd Ste 300 E
Santa Monica, CA 90404
Tel.: (310) 255-1000
Fax: (310) 255-1021
Fax: (310) 255-1050

FUSE/ideas
255 Elm St Ste 201
Somerville, MA 02144
Tel.: (617) 776-5800
Fax: (617) 776-5821

SID LEE
75 Queen Street Ofc 1400
Montreal, QC H3C 2N6, Canada
Tel.: (514) 282-2200
Fax: (514) 282-0499
Adidas Originals

AEROGROUP INTERNATIONAL, INC.
(d/b/a Aerosoles)
201 Meadow Rd
Edison, NJ 08817-6002
Tel.: (732) 985-0495
Fax: (732) 985-3697
Toll Free: (800) 798-9478
E-mail: customerservice@aerosoles.com
Web Site: www.aerosoles.com
Approx. Number Employees: 125

Business Description:
Designer, Distributor & Retailer of Shoes & Foot Wear
S.I.C.: 5139; 5661
N.A.I.C.S.: 424340; 448210
Media: 2-4-5-6-8-10-17-18-19-22

Personnel:
Jules Schneider *(Pres)*
Richard Morris *(CFO)*
Melissa Smith *(Pres-Retail)*
Pat Taylor *(Pres-First Cost Div)*
Beth Sharp *(VP-HR)*

Brands & Products:
4 GIVE
A2
ADULATION
ADVENTURE
AEROLOGY
AEROSOLES
ALGEBRA
ARMY
AT LAST
ATHENS
BADMINTON
BARREL OF FUN
BEC TO BASICS
BECON N EGGS
BENCIL
BENEFIT
BETH
BLIND SIGHT
BLUE GENE
BOG HORN
BOG WILD
BUS STOP
CANYEN
CARD GAME
CAREFREE
CAROLINA
CHAPERONE
CHEER LEADER
CHEERY O
CHEERY TREE
CHRYSANTHEMOM
CINCH WORM
CINCHCERITY
CINCHRONIZE
CINCHSATIONAL
CINCINNATI
CLEAN SLATE
CRAWDAD
DAME GAME
DAME ROOM
DAME TIME
DEBUT
DECADE
DISC TAKER
DISCAL YEAR
DISCKETTE
DISCO DANCE
DUBBLEGUM
DUBLE TIME
DUBLE TROUBLE
EGG ROLE
ENDLESS
ENVY
FAX OF LIFE
FINAL EXAM
FIRE POWER
FLABBERGASTED
FLAGSTONE
FLEXATION
FOLKLORE
FROLIC
GADGET
GATHER ROUND
GIN RICKEY
GIN RUMMY
GINEVA
GRAM CENTRAL
HAP HAZARD
HEART N SOUL
HEDGE FUND
HEDGE MAPLE
INSPIRATION
KARMA
KATAPULT
LADDERY TICKET
LANCELOT
LASTICITY
LEGEND
LOR ME IN
LUV BIRD
MACROBAT
MATTER OF FACT
MEXIMUM
MOMENTS NOTICE
MOMENTUM
MOROCCO
MR SOFTEE
NU DAY
NUB SCOUT
OTHERWORLDLY
PATROLE CAR
PEDAL
PEP RALLY
PLAY DATE
PLAYFILL
PREP SCHOOL
PRETTY LAIDY
PRINTZTON
PROLIFIC
RASPBERRY
RATATOUILLE
REAL CHARMER
REDISCOVER
REKINDLE
REPUBLIC
RIDE LINE
RISOTTO
ROLETTE
ROTARY
ROWBOAT
SAVANNA
SAVVY
SBECKLE
SCREENPLAY
SLEEKEND
SMOOTHIE
SO SOFT
SOLE A
SOLSTICE
SORBET
SOTA WATER
SOUL MATE
SOUL SEARCH
SPRIG BREAK
SQUISH N CHIPS
SQUISHING TRIP
STAMINA
STEAMROLER
STRUT FEELING
SUGAR DAD
TEABERRY
TEX MEX
TOGATHER
TREAT YOURSELF
TRES CHIC
VENTRILOQUIST
WHAT'SWHAT

Key to Media (For complete agency information see *The Advertising Red Books-Agencies* edition):
1. Bus. Publs. 2. Cable T.V. 3. Catalogs & Directories. 4. Co-op Adv. 5. Consumer Mags. 6. D.M. to Bus. Estab.7. D.M. to Consumers 8. Daily Newsp. 9. Exhibits/Trade Shows 10. Foreign 11. Infomercial 12. Internet Adv.13. Multimedia 14. Network Radio 15. Network T.V. 16. Newsp. Distr. Mags. 17. Other 18. Outdoor (Posters, Transit) 19. Point of Purchase20. Premiums, Novelties 21. Product Samples 22. Special Events Mktg. 23. Spot Radio 24. Spot T.V. 25. Weekly Newsp. 26. Yellow Page Adv.

Aerogroup International, Inc. — (Continued)

WIP BALM
ZEN AGAIN
ZENACIOUS
ZENITH

Advertising Agency:
Gotham Incorporated
150 E 42nd St 12th Fl
New York, NY 10017
Tel.: (212) 414-7000
Fax: (212) 414-7095

THE ALDEN SHOE COMPANY

1 Taunton St
Middleboro, MA 02346-1426
Tel.: (508) 947-3926
Fax: (508) 947-7753
E-mail: general@aldenshoe.com
Web Site: www.aldenshoe.com
Approx. Number Employees: 150
Year Founded: 1884
Business Description:
Shoes Mfr
S.I.C.: 3143
N.A.I.C.S.: 316213
Export
Media: 4-5-8-13-18-19-23
Distr.: Intl.; Natl.
Budget Set: Feb.
Personnel:
Arthur S. Tarlow, Sr. *(Chm)*
Arthur S. Tarlow, Jr. *(Pres)*
Brands & Products:
ALDEN
ALDEN NEW ENGLAND
ALDEN PEDIC
CAPE COD COLLECTION
Advertising Agency:
Monteiro Design
Three Winslow St., Ste. 300
Plymouth, MA 02360
Tel.: (508) 747-6236
Fax: (508) 747-6236
Apparel

ALDO GROUP

2300 Emile-Belanger
Saint Laurent, QC Canada
Tel.: (514) 747-2536
Fax: (514) 747-7993
Toll Free: (888) 298-2536
Toll Free: (800) 326-2536
E-mail: comments@aldogoup.com
Web Site: www.aldoshoes.com
Approx. Number Employees: 100
Business Description:
Footwear Mfr & Distr
S.I.C.: 5139
N.A.I.C.S.: 424340
Media: 6-10-13
Personnel:
Aldo Bensadoun *(CEO)*
Brands & Products:
ALDO
BRAMPTON
COYAH
DEMASE
DEVOTO
GAIRO
MCKINZIE
MEDLING
MOJO
NOSEL
SHUSTER
SIRUS

ALLEN-EDMONDS SHOE CORP.

(Holding of Goldner Hawn Johnson & Morrison Inc.)
201 E Seven Hills Rd
Port Washington, WI 53074-2504
Mailing Address:
PO Box 998
Port Washington, WI 53074-0998
Tel.: (262) 235-6000
Fax: (262) 235-6265
Fax: (262) 268-7427
Web Site: www.allenedmonds.com
Approx. Number Employees: 700
Year Founded: 1922
Business Description:
Men's Shoe Mfr
S.I.C.: 3143; 5661
N.A.I.C.S.: 316213; 448210
Import Export
Media: 2-3-4-5-6-8-9-10-11-15-18-19-22-23-24-25-26
Distr.: Intl.; Natl.
Budget Set: Oct.
Personnel:
John J. Stollenwerk *(Chm)*
Jay Schauer *(CFO)*
Colin Hall *(CMO & Gen Mgr-Intl Bus)*
Timothy C. Cronin *(Sr VP-Sls)*
Warren Vail *(Mgr-Golf Shoe Line)*
Brands & Products:
ALLEN-EDMONDS
ANCONA
ASHTON
BENTON
BERGAMO
BERGLAND
BRADLEY
BRENTWOOD
BROADSTREET
BRUZZANO
BYRON
CAMERON
CANFIELD
CANNONDALE
CHESTER
CODY
CONCORD
CORTLAND
COTTON
DEERFIELD
FAIRFAX
FULTON
GARNER
GLASGOW
GLENFIELD
GRAYSON
HANCOCK
HARRISON
HILLCREST
HOLBROOK
HOLTON
HYANNIS
KEY LARGO
KINGALEY
KINGFIELD
KIRKWOOD
LAGRANGE
LAUDERDALE
LEEDS
LUGANO
MACNEIL
MAPLETON
MAXFIELD
MILANO
MILLBRIDGE
NASHUA
NEWPORT
NOTTINGHAM
ORLEAN
PARK AVENUE
RANDOLPH
RECRAFTING
RITZ
ROCKLAND
ROMA
SENECA
SHELTON
SIENA
SPENCER
STANFORD
ST.LUCIA
STOCKBRIDGE
STOWE
STUART
TIVOLI
TORINO
TROY
WALDEN
WATERBURY
WAVERLY
WESTPORT
WILBERT
WINGHAM
WOLCOTT
WOODSTOCK
Advertising Agency:
OLSON
1625 Hennepin Ave
Minneapolis, MN 55403
Tel.: (612) 215-9800
Fax: (612) 215-9801

AMERICAN SPORTING GOODS CORPORATION

(Sub. of Brown Shoe Company, Inc.)
101 Enterprise Ste 100
Aliso Viejo, CA 92656
Tel.: (949) 267-2800
Toll Free: (800) 848-8698
Web Site: www.avia.com
Approx. Number Employees: 325
Year Founded: 1971
Business Description:
Athletic Footwear Mfr & Marketer
S.I.C.: 5139
N.A.I.C.S.: 424340
Media: 4-5-6-10-18-19-23-24
Personnel:
Margaret Oung *(Chm)*
Timothy J. Joyce *(Sr VP & Gen Mgr)*
Brad Little *(VP & Brand Mgr-Avia & Nevados)*
Jorge Cabrera *(VP-Athletic Product Dev)*
Ed Goldman *(VP-Mktg)*
James Hoff *(VP-Sls)*
Brands & Products:
ARC
ART
AVI-BOLT
AVI-LITE
AVI-LITE GUIDE
AVI-RHYTHM
AVI-STOLTZ
AVIA
CANTILEVER
CONVEXUS
DURA-RYD
DURA-STRYK
FEATHERLITE
FOM

B.A. MASON

(Sub. of Mason Companies, Inc.)
1251 1st Ave
Chippewa Falls, WI 54729-1408
Tel.: (715) 723-1871
Fax: (800) 446-2329
Toll Free: (800) 422-1000
E-mail: sales@bamason.com
Web Site: www.bamason.com
E-Mail For Key Personnel:
Sales Director: sales@bamason.com
Approx. Number Employees: 25
Year Founded: 1984
Business Description:
Retailer & Mail Order of Men's & Women's Footwear
S.I.C.: 5961
N.A.I.C.S.: 454113
Import
Media: 4-8-13
Personnel:
William M. Scobie *(CEO)*

BALLY NORTH AMERICA, INC.

(Sub. of Bally Schuhfabriken AG)
689 5th Ave 4th Fl
New York, NY 10022
Tel.: (212) 446-3930
Fax: (212) 446-3901
Telex: 023 622533
E-mail: mprather@bally.ch
Approx. Rev.: $100,500,000
Approx. Number Employees: 137
Year Founded: 1851
Business Description:
Luxury Goods & Accessories Retailer
S.I.C.: 5999
N.A.I.C.S.: 453998
Import Export
Media: 4-5-6-10-11-16
Distr.: Natl.
Budget Set: Oct.
Personnel:
Marnie Prather *(Dir-PR & Mktg)*

BENNETT FOOTWEAR GROUP LLC

(Sub. of Brown Shoe Company, Inc.)
(d/b/a Bennett Brown Shoe)
693 Fifth Ave 11th Fl
New York, NY 10022
Tel.: (212) 223-0808
Fax: (617) 332-1968
Fax: (617) 965-6928
Sales Range: $75-99.9 Million
Approx. Number Employees: 50
Business Description:
Footwear Mfr
S.I.C.: 5139; 3149
N.A.I.C.S.: 424340; 316219
Advertising Expenditures: $300,000
Media: 3-5-6-7-9-23-25
Brands & Products:
ETIENNE AIGNER
FRANCO SARTO
NICKELS SOFT
VIA SPIGA

BIRKENSTOCK DISTRIBUTION USA INC.

8171 Redwood Blvd
Novato, CA 94945-1403
Mailing Address:
PO Box 6140
Novato, CA 94948
Tel.: (415) 892-4200
Fax: (415) 899-1324

Key to Media (For complete agency information see *The Advertising Red Books-Agencies* edition):
1. Bus. Publs. 2. Cable T.V. 3. Catalogs & Directories. 4. Co-op Adv. 5. Consumer Mags. 6. D.M. to Bus. Estab.7. D.M. to Consumers 8. Daily Newsp. 9. Exhibits/Trade Shows 10. Foreign 11. Infomercial 12. Internet Adv.13. Multimedia 14. Network Radio 15. Network T.V. 16. Newsp. Distr. Mags. 17. Other 18. Outdoor (Posters, Transit) 19. Point of Purchase20. Premiums, Novelties 21. Product Samples 22. Special Events Mktg. 23. Spot Radio 24. Spot T.V. 25. Weekly Newsp. 26. Yellow Page Adv.

Toll Free: (800) 487-9255
E-mail: info@birkenstockus.com
Web Site: www.birkenstockusa.com
Approx. Number Employees: 100
Year Founded: 1966
Business Description:
Comfort Footwear Distr
S.I.C.: 5139
N.A.I.C.S.: 424340
Media: 4-5-6-8-10
Distr.: Natl.
Budget Set: Sept.
Personnel:
Margot Fraser *(Founder)*
Jay McGregor *(VP-Sls & Mktg)*
Tiffany Dempton *(Mgr-Mktg)*

BROOKS SPORTS INC.

(Sub. of Russell Corporation)
19910 N Creek Pkwy Ste 200
Bothell, WA 98011-8223
Tel.: (425) 488-3131
Fax: (425) 483-8181
Toll Free: (800) 2-BROOKS
E-mail: homepage@brooksrunning.com
Web Site: www.brooksrunning.com
Sales Range: $50-74.9 Million
Approx. Number Employees: 140
Year Founded: 1914
Business Description:
Athletic Shoes, Apparel & Accessories Mfr
S.I.C.: 3021; 2389
N.A.I.C.S.: 316211; 315999
Media: 2-4-6-10-13-19-20-22
Personnel:
James W. Weber *(Pres & CEO)*
David Bohan *(COO)*
Dave Larson *(VP-Mktg)*
Rick Wilhelm *(VP-Sls-Specialty Retail Accts)*
Tamara Hills *(Mgr-Corp Comm)*
Brands & Products:
ADRENALINE GTS
AIREPLEX
BEAST
BROOKS
BROOKS EQUILIBRIUM
BROOKS SHELTER
DIAGONAL ROLLBAR
E-FUSION
HYDROFLOW
HYDROFLX
NIGHTLIFE
PODULAR TECHNOLOGY
POWERPRO
SILC
SUBSTANCE 257
TRANCE
VAPOR DRY
WATERBOY
Advertising Agencies:
North
1515 NW 19th Ave
Portland, OR 97209
Tel.: (503) 222-4117
Fax: (503) 222-4118

OMD San Francisco
555 Market St Ste 750
San Francisco, CA 94105
Tel.: (415) 229-8500
Fax: (415) 315-4250
Media Planning & Buying

BROWN SHOE COMPANY, INC.

8300 Maryland Ave
Saint Louis, MO 63105-3645
Mailing Address:
PO Box 29
Saint Louis, MO 63166-0029
Tel.: (314) 854-4000
Fax: (314) 854-4274
Toll Free: (800) 766-6465
E-mail: info@brownshoe.com
Web Site: www.brownshoe.com/index.asp
E-Mail For Key Personnel:
Public Relations: bfagan@brownshoe.com
Approx. Sls.: $2,504,091,000
Approx. Number Employees: 13,400
Year Founded: 1878
Business Description:
Shoe Importing, Wholesale & Retail
S.I.C.: 3149; 3021; 5139; 5661
N.A.I.C.S.: 316219; 316211; 424340; 448210
Import
Advertising Expenditures: $70,400,000
Media: 1-2-3-4-5-6-8-9-10-15-18-19-20-22-23-24-25-26
Distr.: Natl.
Personnel:
Ronald A. Fromm *(Chm & CEO)*
Diane M. Sullivan *(Pres & COO)*
Mark E. Hood *(CFO & Sr VP)*
Joseph Caro *(CIO & Sr VP)*
Richard M. Ausick *(Pres-Famous Footwear)*
Daniel R. Friedman *(Pres-Specialty Brands, Global Sourcing & Product Dev)*
Michael I. Oberlander *(Gen Counsel, Sec & Sr VP)*
Thomas Lucas *(Sr VP-Fin & Corp Dev & Treas)*
Clay Jenkins *(Sr VP-Wholesale)*
Daniel L. Karpel *(Sr VP-Fin)*
Douglas W. Koch *(Chief Talent Officer & Sr VP)*
Tim Meyer *(Sr VP-Fin-Retail Div)*
Donna Santoro *(Sr VP-Organizational Readiness)*
Jay Schmidt *(Sr VP-Image Brands)*
Willie A. Smith *(Sr VP-Mktg)*
Joan Durkin *(VP-Fin)*
Ken Golden *(Dir-IR)*
Maureen McCann *(Dir-Mktg & Strategic Dev)*
Todd Murray *(Dir-Mktg & Licensing)*
Liz Ott *(Dir-Mktg Famous Footwear)*
Brands & Products:
AIR STEP
BROWN SHOE
BUSTER BROWN
CHILL CHASERS BY BUSTER
CONNIE
CONNIE TOO
FANFARES
THE LEADER IN FOOTWEAR
LIFE STRIDE
NATURALSPORT
NATURE SOLE
NIGHT LIFE
RED GOOSE
T.R.E.A.T.S.
Advertising Agency:
Toth Brand Imaging
215 First St
Cambridge, MA 02142
Tel.: (617) 252-0787
Fax: (617) 252-0838
Naturalizer

BROWN SHOE CO. OF CANADA LTD.

(Holding of Brown Shoe Company, Inc.)
1857 Rogers Rd
Perth, ON K7H 3E8, Canada
Tel.: (613) 267-2000
Fax: (613) 267-7113
Toll Free: (800) 267-7962
E-mail: bbingley@brownshoe.com
Web Site: www.brownshoe.com
Sales Range: $25-49.9 Million
Approx. Number Employees: 35
Year Founded: 1893
Business Description:
Women's & Children's Shoes Whslr
S.I.C.: 3144
N.A.I.C.S.: 316214
Import
Media: 5-10-19
Distr.: Natl.
Budget Set: Jan.
Personnel:
Brian Bingley *(Mgr)*

CAPEZIO BALLET MAKERS INC.

1 Campus Rd
Totowa, NJ 07512
Tel.: (973) 595-9000
Tel.: (917) 472-3116 (Adv)
Fax: (973) 595-9120
Toll Free: (800) 533-1887
E-mail: info@capeziodance.com
Web Site: www.capeziodance.com
Sales Range: $75-99.9 Million
Approx. Number Employees: 500
Year Founded: 1887
Business Description:
Dance Shoes, Garments & Accessories Mfr
S.I.C.: 5661; 2331; 3149
N.A.I.C.S.: 448210; 315232; 316219
Import Export
Media: 2-4-7-10-19-22-26
Distr.: Natl.
Budget Set: Oct.
Personnel:
Michael Terlizzi *(Pres & CEO)*
Ben Pignataro *(VP-Sls)*
Brands & Products:
AERIAL
ATHENIAN
CABARET
CAN-CAN
CANVAS ROMEO
CAPEZIO
CAPRI
CHORUS
COBRA
COLETTE
CONTEMPORA
DAISY
DANCE SNEAKER
DANCE SPORT
DANSNEAKER
DEMI SOFT
ELLI
FOOTUNDEEZ
GIANNA
GLIDE
GLISS
GLISS PRO
GYM X
INFINITA
JAZZ ANKLE
JETE
JR. TYETTE
JULIET
LATINA
MANHATTAN
MARY JANE
NICOLINI
NIMBUS
NINA
PARIS
PAVLOWA
PEDINI
PEGGI
PHANTOM
PIROUETTE
PLI
QUADRAFLEX
RAVEN
RECITAL
ROMEO
SATIN SUZANA
SCORPION
SCULPTURE
SELVA
SOFIA
SOLESAVER
SPLIT-SOLE
STACCATO
SUZANA
T-STRAP
TAP JR. FOOTLIGHT
TEKNIK
TEKNO-LOW
TELE TONE
TENDU
TIPSEEZ
UNDERS & OVERS
VERVE
VIVIAN
Advertising Agency:
Giovatto Advertising & Consulting Inc.
95 Rte 17 S
Paramus, NJ 07652
Tel.: (201) 226-9700
Fax: (201) 226-9694

CHAMPS SPORTS

(Div. of Foot Locker, Inc.)
311 Manatee Ave W
Bradenton, FL 34205
Tel.: (941) 748-0577
Fax: (941) 741-7582
Toll Free: (800) 991-6813
E-mail: info@champssports.com
Web Site: www.champssports.com
Sales Range: $125-149.9 Million
Approx. Number Employees: 120
Business Description:
Athletic Footwear & Sporting Goods Retailer
S.I.C.: 5999; 5661; 5699; 5941
N.A.I.C.S.: 453998; 448190; 448210; 451110
Advertising Expenditures: $1,000,000
Media: 4-6-7-8-10-11-22-24
Distr.: Direct to Consumer; Reg.
Budget Set: Sept.
Personnel:
Ronald J. Halls *(Pres & CEO)*
Rob Broderson *(VP-Mktg)*
Advertising Agencies:
Brotman Winter Fried Communications
111 Park Pl
Falls Church, VA 22046
Tel.: (703) 534-4600

Key to Media (For complete agency information see *The Advertising Red Books-Agencies* edition):
1. Bus. Publs. 2. Cable T.V. 3. Catalogs & Directories. 4. Co-op Adv. 5. Consumer Mags. 6. D.M. to Bus. Estab.7. D.M. to Consumers 8. Daily Newsp. 9. Exhibits/Trade Shows 10. Foreign 11. Infomercial 12. Internet Adv.13. Multimedia 14. Network Radio 15. Network T.V. 16. Newsp. Distr. Mags. 17. Other 18. Outdoor (Posters, Transit) 19. Point of Purchase20. Premiums, Novelties 21. Product Samples 22. Special Events Mktg. 23. Spot Radio 24. Spot T.V. 25. Weekly Newsp. 26. Yellow Page Adv.

Champs Sports — (Continued)

Fax: (703) 536-2255

SapientNitro USA, Inc.
215 Park Ave S 2nd Fl
New York, NY 10003-1603
Tel.: (212) 206-1005
Fax: (212) 206-8510

CLARKS COMPANIES

(Sub. of Clarks Companies North America)
156 Oak St
Newton, MA 02464-1440
Tel.: (617) 964-1222
Fax: (617) 243-4300
E-mail: jobs@bostonianshoe.com
Web Site: www.bostonianshoe.com
E-Mail For Key Personnel:
Marketing Director: robertk@clarkshoe.com
Approx. Number Employees: 250
Year Founded: 1899
Business Description:
Mfr. & Retailer of Shoes & Blazers for Men
S.I.C.: 5139; 5661
N.A.I.C.S.: 424340; 448210
Import
Advertising Expenditures: $1,500,000
Media: 2-4-5-6-7-9-10-19-21-23-24-26
Distr.: Natl.
Budget Set: May
Personnel:
Jim Salzano *(Exec VP)*
Margaret Newville *(VP-Mktg)*
Robert Kiel *(Mgr-Sls)*
Brands & Products:
BOSTONIAN
BOSTONIAN BLUE
CLASSIC FIRST/FLEX
CROWN WINDSOR
FLORENTINE
METRO FLEX
STRADA

CLARKS COMPANIES NORTH AMERICA

(Sub. of C&J Clark Ltd.)
620 S Union St
Kennett Square, PA 19348-3534
Tel.: (610) 444-6550
Fax: (610) 444-3567
Web Site: www.clarksna.com
Approx. Number Employees: 40
Year Founded: 1977
Business Description:
Shoes Mfr & Whlslr
S.I.C.: 3143; 3144
N.A.I.C.S.: 316213; 316214
Personnel:
Margaret Newville *(VP-Mktg)*
Advertising Agency:
Greenough Communications
9 Harcourt St
Boston, MA 02116
Tel.: (617) 275-6500
Fax: (617) 275-6501

COBIAN CORP.

1739 Melrose Dr #101
San Marcos, CA 92078-2100
Tel.: (760) 734-1915
Fax: (760) 734-1917
Toll Free: (877) 726-2426
E-mail: info@cobianusa.com
Web Site: www.cobianusa.com
Approx. Number Employees: 25
Business Description:
Sandals Whslr
S.I.C.: 5139
N.A.I.C.S.: 424340
Media: 4-6-10-13
Personnel:
John Cobian *(Pres)*
Claudia De Soto *(CFO)*
Brands & Products:
AMP/OAM
ARV2
BAILEY
BELLE
BROOK
BUMP
CALI
CARA
CATALINA
CHRISTA
CIELO 2
COBI
COBIAN
CORDOVA
CUSH
DAISY
DOTTY
DRAINO
DRIFTER
DURBAN
EDEN
FIESTA
FIJI
FLIP
FLOATER
FLOP
FLORECITA
FOAM
GRIP
GTS
HERMOSA
HERRING/OAM
IVANA
JIU JITSU
JR .EXEC
KARLY
KIRRA
LADYBUG
LEXIE
LINDSEY
LION
LONE STAR
LUCIA
MARIPOSA
MIGUEL
MISSY
MMA
MONTEREY
NEON CUSH
NIAS
NICOYA
NUVE
ORV
PALA
PLAYA
RHONDA
ROXANNE
SAHARA
SALVADOR
SANDI
SAVANNAH
SELAH
SELENA
SEVILLA
SHARKY
SIENNA
SIESTA
SOLANA
SQUIRT
STITCHES
STRIDER
SUAVE
SUNSHINE
SWEEDEN
SWIRLY
TAVI
TWISTER
VALENCIA
VIDA CUSH
WATERKID
WATERMAN
XOXO
ZARA
ZEBRA

COLE-HAAN

(Div. of NIKE, Inc.)
1 Cole Haan Dr
Yarmouth, ME 04096-6706
Tel.: (207) 846-2500
Fax: (207) 846-6374
Toll Free: (800) 695-8945
Web Site: www.colehaan.com
Sales Range: $125-149.9 Million
Approx. Number Employees: 200
Year Founded: 1928
Business Description:
Footwear, Accessories & Outerwear Mfr
S.I.C.: 5139; 3144
N.A.I.C.S.: 424340; 316214
Import Export
Advertising Expenditures: $3,500,000
Media: 4-5-6-9-13-19
Distr.: Intl.; Natl.
Budget Set: Apr.
Personnel:
Dave McTague *(CEO)*
Lisa Kema *(CFO)*
Grant Hanson *(Gen Counsel)*
Doug Ritchie *(VP-Mktg)*
Brands & Products:
COLE-HAAN

COLLECTIVE BRANDS INC.

3231 SE 6th Ave
Topeka, KS 66607-2207
Tel.: (785) 233-5171
Web Site: www.collectivebrands.com
Approx. Sls.: $3,375,700,000
Approx. Number Employees: 29,000
Year Founded: 1956
Business Description:
Family Footwear; Self-Service Shoe Stores
S.I.C.: 5661
N.A.I.C.S.: 448210
Import Export
Advertising Expenditures: $159,200,000
Media: 3-4-8-9-13-15-18-19-23-24-25
Distr.: Natl.
Personnel:
Matthew E. Rubel *(Chm, Pres & CEO)*
Douglas G. Boessen *(CFO, Treas & Div Sr VP)*
Eric C. Gordon *(CIO & Div Sr VP)*
Vincent DeSantis *(CMO & Sr VP-Payless ShoeSource)*
Douglas J. Treff *(Chief Admin Officer & Exec VP)*
Frank Caruso *(Chief Admin Officer & Sr VP)*
Gregg S. Ribatt *(Pres/CEO-Collective Brands Performance + Lifestyle Group)*
Michael J. Massey *(General Counsel, Sec & Sr VP)*
Darrel J. Pavelka *(Exec VP-Supply Chain-Global)*
Patricia Williamson *(Mng Dir-Intl & Sr VP)*
Betty J. Click *(Sr VP-HR)*
Paul J. Fenaroli *(Sr VP-Corp Strategy Div)*
Michael Jeppesen *(Sr VP-Design, Global Sourcing & Product Dev)*
Michael F. McBreen *(Sr VP-Payless Product Dev)*
David W. Milton *(Sr VP-Global Logistics Div)*
James Grant *(Dir-IR)*
Cecilia Redmond *(Dir-Adv Svcs)*
Brands & Products:
COLLECTIVE BRANDS
COLLECTIVE LICENSING INTERNATIONAL
PAYLESS SHOESOURCE
THE STRIDE RITE CORPORATION
Advertising Agencies:
Martin/Williams Advertising Inc.
(A Member of Omnicom Group)
60 S 6th St Ste 2800
Minneapolis, MN 55402-4428
Tel.: (612) 340-0800
Fax: (612) 342-9700

Optimedia International U.S.
375 Hudson St 7th Fl
New York, NY 10014
Tel.: (212) 820-3200
Fax: (212) 820-3300
Stride Rite
Payless ShoeSource

CONSOLIDATED SHOE COMPANY INC.

22290 Timberlake Rd
Lynchburg, VA 24502-7305
Tel.: (434) 239-0391
Fax: (434) 582-5631
Web Site: www.musthaveshoes.com
Approx. Number Employees: 75
Year Founded: 1907
Business Description:
Mfr of Footwear
S.I.C.: 5139; 5661
N.A.I.C.S.: 424340; 448210
Import Export
Media: 4-8
Personnel:
William Carrington *(Owner, CEO & Mgr)*
Steve Winbigler *(CFO)*
Brands & Products:
NICOLE
TAKE IT EASY
Advertising Agency:
The Republik
211 Rigsbee Ave
Durham, NC 27701
Tel.: (919) 956-9400
Fax: (919) 956-9402

CROCS, INC.

6328 Monarch Park Pl
Longmont, CO 80503-7167
Tel.: (303) 848-7000
E-mail: customerservice@crocs.com
Web Site: www.crocs.com

Key to Media (For complete agency information see *The Advertising Red Books-Agencies* edition):
1. Bus. Publs. 2. Cable T.V. 3. Catalogs & Directories. 4. Co-op Adv. 5. Consumer Mags. 6. D.M. to Bus. Estab.7. D.M. to Consumers 8. Daily Newsp. 9. Exhibits/Trade Shows 10. Foreign 11. Infomercial 12. Internet Adv.13. Multimedia 14. Network Radio 15. Network T.V. 16. Newsp. Distr. Mags. 17. Other 18. Outdoor (Posters, Transit) 19. Point of Purchase20. Premiums, Novelties 21. Product Samples 22. Special Events Mktg. 23. Spot Radio 24. Spot T.V. 25. Weekly Newsp. 26. Yellow Page Adv.

Approx. Rev.: $789,695,000
Approx. Number Employees: 4,000
Business Description:
Footwear Designer, Mfr & Marketer
S.I.C.: 3021; 3149
N.A.I.C.S.: 316211; 316219
Advertising Expenditures:
$44,100,000
Media: 6-10-11-22
Personnel:
Richard L. Sharp *(Chm)*
John P. McCarvel *(Pres & CEO)*
Jeffrey J. Lasher *(CFO, Chief Acctg Officer & Controller)*
Andrew Davison *(CMO)*
Daniel P. Hart *(Chief Legal Officer, Chief Admin Officer & Exec VP)*
Becky Gebhardt *(Sr Dir-Creative)*
Mike Martin *(Dir-Brand Mktg-Americas)*
Allison Snyder *(Sr Product Line Sls Mgr-Americas)*
Brands & Products:
BITE
CROCS
CROCSRX
JIBBITZ
PREPAIR
SOLESUNITED
YOU BY CROCS
Advertising Agencies:
Cramer-Krasselt
225 N Michigan Ave
Chicago, IL 60601-7601
Tel.: (312) 616-9600
Fax: (312) 616-3839
Brand Strategy
Creative
Global Agency of Record
Interactive
Media Buying & Planning
Online
Public Relations

Linhart Public Relations
1514 Curtis St Ste 200
Denver, CO 80202
Tel.: (303) 620-9044
Fax: (303) 620-9043
— Elexis Lewis *(Acct Exec)*

Zimmerman Advertising
2200 W Commercial Blvd Ste 300
Fort Lauderdale, FL 33309-3064
Tel.: (954) 644-4000
Fax: (954) 731-2977
Toll Free: (800) 248-8522

DANSKO INC.
8 Federal Rd
West Grove, PA 19390
Tel.: (610) 869-8335
Fax: (817) 732-6756
Toll Free: (800) 326-7564
Web Site: www.dansko.com
Sales Range: $10-24.9 Million
Approx. Number Employees: 150
Year Founded: 1991
Business Description:
Footwear Distr
S.I.C.: 5139
N.A.I.C.S.: 424340
Media: 6
Personnel:
Amanda Cabot *(Co-CEO)*
Peter Kjellerup *(Co-CEO)*
Mimi Curry *(COO)*
Mark Diehl *(Sr VP-Sls)*
Embeth Pitman *(Dir-Mktg)*

DECKERS OUTDOOR CORPORATION
495A S Fairview Ave
Goleta, CA 93117
Tel.: (805) 967-7611
Fax: (805) 967-9722
E-mail: hr@deckers.com
Web Site: www.deckers.com
Approx. Sls.: $1,000,989,000
Approx. Number Employees: 1,500
Year Founded: 1972
Business Description:
Footwear Designer, Marketer & Distr
S.I.C.: 3021
N.A.I.C.S.: 316211
Advertising Expenditures:
$17,035,000
Media: 2-4-6
Distr.: Natl.
Budget Set: Sept.
Personnel:
Angel R. Martinez *(Chm, Pres & CEO)*
Rob van der Vis *(Mng Dir)*
Thomas A. George *(CFO)*
Zohar Ziv *(COO)*
Jake Brandman *(Pres-Sanuk)*
Stephen Murray *(Pres-Europe, Middle East & Africa)*
Constance X. Rishwain *(Pres-Simple & UGG Australia Div)*
Peter Worley *(Pres-Teva)*
Colin G. Clark *(Sr VP-Emerging Brands)*
Mark Fegley *(Sr VP-Supply Chain)*
Jessica Buttimer *(VP-Mktg)*
Stephanie E. S. Cucurullo *(VP-Legal)*
Ryan Erickson *(VP-Domestic Sls-Teva)*
Leslyn Nitta *(VP-Fin)*
Yul Vanek *(VP-IT)*
Joel Heath *(Dir-Mktg-Teva & Simple Brands)*
Mark Heintz *(Dir-Corp Responsibility & Sustainability)*
Karinda LaHens *(Mgr-Product Line)*
Julie Wellman *(Mgr-Natl Sls-Teva)*
Brands & Products:
DECKERS
DECKERS OUTDOOR CORPORATION
FIVE TEN
FLIP FLOPS
FLIPSOLE
GREEN TOE
PEDBED
SIMPLE
SIMPLE SHOES
TEVA
UGG
VIBRAM
Advertising Agency:
ICR
20 Custom House St Ste 930
Boston, MA 02110
Tel.: (617) 956-6725
Fax: (617) 956-6726

DEER STAGS INC.
1414 Ave of the Americas
New York, NY 10019-2514
Tel.: (212) 888-2424
Fax: (212) 980-5619
Toll Free: (888) 609-9008
E-mail: deerstags@deerstags.com
Web Site: www.deerstags.com
Approx. Number Employees: 35
Year Founded: 1929
Business Description:
Mfr., Retailer & Distr of Footwear
S.I.C.: 5139; 3144
N.A.I.C.S.: 424340; 316214
Advertising Expenditures: $300,000
Media: 2-4-6-7-8-9-10-19-23-24-25
Distr.: Intl.; Natl.
Budget Set: Monthly
Personnel:
Michael Muskat *(Pres)*
Brands & Products:
DEER STAGS
GLEN
SOMERSAULTS
ULTRON
Advertising Agency:
Direct Response Academy
140 Lotus Cir
Austin, TX 78737
Tel.: (512) 301-5900
Fax: (512) 301-7900

DEXTER SHOE COMPANY
(Sub. of H.H. Brown Shoe Company, Inc.)
100 Bricksyone Dr
Hanover, MA 01810
Tel.: (603) 880-8900
Fax: (207) 924-5802
Toll Free: (888) 833-9837
E-mail: dexterservice@hhbrown.com
Web Site: www.dextershoe.com
Sales Range: $500-549.9 Million
Approx. Number Employees: 3,000
Year Founded: 1957
Business Description:
Shoes Mfr
S.I.C.: 3149; 3143; 3144
N.A.I.C.S.: 316219; 316213; 316214
Export
Advertising Expenditures: $450,000
Media: 4-5-6-8-10-11-14-15-18-19-23-24-26
Distr.: Intl.; Natl.
Brands & Products:
ATLANTIC
CAPE
CHART
COMFORT SERIES
DAVENPORT
DEXTER
DRIVZ
ESQUIRE
ESSEX
FOCUS
HAMMOND
HUDSON
JACQUELINE
LADYBIRD
NAVIGATOR II
PLAYER SERIES
SOFTSHOE SERIES
SST
TIDE
TYLER
VANDERBILT
WEATHERLITE SERIES

DIADORA AMERICA, INC.
(Sub. of Diadora Invicta)
6102 S 225th St
Kent, WA 98032-1874
Tel.: (253) 520-8868
Fax: (253) 520-6333
Toll Free: (800) 423-9958
E-mail: customerservice@diadoraamerica.com
Web Site: www.diadoraamerica.com
E-Mail For Key Personnel:
Marketing Director: dgoodman@diadoraamerica.com
Approx. Number Employees: 550
Year Founded: 1988
Business Description:
Athletic Footwear & Apparel Distr & Mfr
S.I.C.: 5139; 5136
N.A.I.C.S.: 424340; 424320
Import Export
Media: 2-4-5-6-9-10-19
Distr.: Natl.
Budget Set: Oct.
Personnel:
William N. Nuttall *(Pres)*
Linda Walker *(COO)*
Mark Wachter *(Dir-Mktg & Footwear)*
Debra Goodman *(Mgr-Mktg)*
Brands & Products:
DIADORA
KAELIN
Advertising Agency:
Engstrom Public Relations
14722 102nd Ave NE
Bothell, WA 98011-7250
Tel.: (425) 487-0682
Fax: (425) 939-5286

DREW SHOE CORPORATION
(Sub. of Wexford Capital LLC)
252 Quarry Rd
Lancaster, OH 43130
Mailing Address:
252 Quarry Rd SE
Lancaster, OH 43130-8054
Tel.: (740) 653-4271
Fax: (740) 654-4979
E-mail: customerservice@drewshoe.com
Web Site: www.drewshoes.com
Approx. Number Employees: 55
Year Founded: 1875
Business Description:
Men's & Women's Orthopedic Shoes Mfr
S.I.C.: 3144; 3143; 5661
N.A.I.C.S.: 316214; 316213; 448210
Media: 2-4-5-6-7-8-9-10-14-18-20-21-23-25-26
Distr.: Natl.
Budget Set: Feb.
Brands & Products:
BAREFOOT FREEDOM
DREW
STANDING COMFORT

EASTLAND SHOE CORPORATION
4 Meetinghouse Rd
Freeport, ME 00004-0321
Tel.: (207) 865-6314
Fax: (207) 865-9261
Toll Free: (888) 988-1998
E-mail: info@eastlandshoe.com
Web Site: www.eastlandshoe.com
Approx. Number Employees: 50
Year Founded: 1955
Business Description:
Womens & Mens Casual Shoes Whslr
S.I.C.: 5139
N.A.I.C.S.: 424340
Media: 6

Key to Media (For complete agency information see *The Advertising Red Books-Agencies* edition):
1. Bus. Publs. 2. Cable T.V. 3. Catalogs & Directories. 4. Co-op Adv. 5. Consumer Mags. 6. D.M. to Bus. Estab.7. D.M. to Consumers
8. Daily Newsp. 9. Exhibits/Trade Shows 10. Foreign 11. Infomercial 12. Internet Adv.13. Multimedia 14. Network Radio
15. Network T.V. 16. Newsp. Distr. Mags. 17. Other 18. Outdoor (Posters, Transit) 19. Point of Purchase20. Premiums, Novelties
21. Product Samples 22. Special Events Mktg. 23. Spot Radio 24. Spot T.V. 25. Weekly Newsp. 26. Yellow Page Adv.

Eastland Shoe Corporation — (Continued)

Personnel:
James B. Klein *(Pres)*
David Merrill *(VP-Fin & Ops)*
Marc Gold *(Dir-Bus Dev)*

Brands & Products:
ACE
ALBUQUERQUE
ANGUILLA
ASHLAND
BADGER
BELLEVUE
BROOKLYN
BUCKSPORT
CALEDONIA
CAMBRIDGE
CAMEO
CAMERON
CARLETON
CARMELITA
CARMELLA
CELINA
CHANCELLOR
CHARLESTOWN
CLASSIC
CORRAL
COUNSELOR
COURTNEY
COVE
DAKOTA
DANVERS
ENTERPRISE
EXECUTIVE
FAIRVIEW
FINLAND
FOR FEET WITH A LIFE
FRANKLIN
FRISCO
GAMMA
GEMINI
GLORIA
GRENADA
HURRICANE
JAKE
LAILA
LOTUS
MEDFORD
MERIDEN
MERLIN
MONSOON
MUSTANG
NATALIE
NEWPORT
NORDIC
OPAL
OZARK
PACIFIC
PATIENCE
PEPPERDINE
PIKEVILLE
PLAINVIEW
PROVIDENCE
ROSALIE
SABATTUS
SABRINA
SANIBEL
SENECA
SEQUOIA
SEVILLE
SHERWOOD
SIERRA
SILVERADO
STANFORD
SUGARLOAF
SYRACUSE
TOUCAN
TOWSEND
TULANE
TYPHOON
VANESSA
VESPER
WINDSOR
WOODSIDE
YUKON

EL CHARRO LLC

2509 Wyoming St
El Paso, TX 79903
Tel.: (915) 534-7956
Fax: (915) 533-4735
Toll Free: (877) 980-1248
E-mail: sales@elcharro1.com
Web Site: www.elcharro1.com
E-Mail For Key Personnel:
Sales Director: sales@elcharro1.com
Approx. Sls.: $315,000
Approx. Number Employees: 10
Year Founded: 1959
Business Description:
Dance Shoes & Apparel Mfr
S.I.C.: 2389
N.A.I.C.S.: 315999
Media: 2-4-7-8-10
Distr.: Natl.
Budget Set: June
Personnel:
Salomon Bemaras *(Pres)*
Brands & Products:
EL CHARRO
KLING'S

ETIENNE AIGNER, INC.

(Sub. of The Hartstone Group Limited)
29 W 35th St
New York, NY 10001
Tel.: (212) 868-2770
Fax: (212) 239-7981
Toll Free: (800) 673-3001
Web Site: www.etienneaigner.com
Approx. Sls.: $141,700,000
Approx. Number Employees: 25
Year Founded: 1950
Business Description:
Leather Handbags, Shoes & Small Leather Goods Designer, Distr & Online Retailer
S.I.C.: 5199; 5961; 7389
N.A.I.C.S.: 424990; 454111; 541490
Import Export
Advertising Expenditures: $1,000,000
Media: 4-13-19
Personnel:
Terry McCormick *(VP-Sls)*
Brands & Products:
ETIENNE AIGNER

ETONIC WORLDWIDE LLC

2400 Computer Dr
Westborough, MA 01581
Tel.: (781) 419-3000
Fax: (508) 870-9989
Toll Free: (866) 8-ETONIC
Telex: 924488 ETONIC BROK
E-mail: customerservice@etonic.com
Web Site: www.etonic.com
Sales Range: $75-99.9 Million
Approx. Number Employees: 25
Year Founded: 1883
Business Description:
Whslr of Athletic Shoes
S.I.C.: 5091
N.A.I.C.S.: 423910
Import Export
Advertising Expenditures: $5,000,000
Media: 2-5-6-7-8-9-10-11-18-19-22-25-26
Distr.: Intl.; Natl.
Budget Set: Nov. -Dec.
Brands & Products:
AC FEEL
AC GRIP
AC TOUR
AT FEEL
DRI-LITES
ETONIC
EVER GRIP
G-SOK
KALEIDOSCOPE
LITES
STABILITE
STABILIZER PRO
ULTIMATE

FAMOUS FOOTWEAR

(Sub. of Brown Shoe Company, Inc.)
8300 Maryland Ave
Saint Louis, MO 63105
Tel.: (314) 854-4000
Fax: (314) 854-7749
E-mail: service@famousfootwear.com
Web Site: www.famousfootwear.com
Sales Range: $1-4.9 Billion
Approx. Number Employees: 10,000
Year Founded: 1960
Business Description:
Shoe Retailer
S.I.C.: 5661; 5139
N.A.I.C.S.: 448210; 424340
Media: 2-6-9-10-18-19-20-22-24-25-26
Distr.: Natl.
Personnel:
Joseph W. Wood *(Pres)*
Ron Fromm *(CEO)*
James M. Roe *(Sr VP-Real Estate)*
Willie Smith *(Sr VP-Mktg)*
Brands & Products:
FAMOUS

FILA USA, INC.

(Sub. of Fila Korea, Ltd.)
1 Fila Way
Sparks, MD 21152-3000
Tel.: (410) 773-3000
Fax: (410) 773-4989
Toll Free: (800) 787-3452
E-mail: info@fila.com
Web Site: www.fila.com
Approx. Number Employees: 2,301
Year Founded: 1923
Business Description:
Apparel & Athletic Footwear Distr & Mfr
S.I.C.: 5139; 3949
N.A.I.C.S.: 424340; 339920
Import Export
Media: 2-4-5-6-10-13-18-19
Distr.: Intl.; Natl.
Personnel:
Jon Epstein *(Pres)*
Lauren Mallon *(Mgr-Global Mktg)*
Brands & Products:
FILA
Advertising Agency:
Alexander & Tom
3500 Boston St Ste 225
Baltimore, MD 21224-5275
Tel.: (410) 327-7400
Fax: (410) 327-7403

FLORSHEIM, INC.

(Div. of Weyco Group, Inc.)
333 W Estabrook Blvd
Glendale, WI 53212
Tel.: (414) 908-1600
Fax: (414) 908-1601
E-mail: us.consumers@florsheim.com
Web Site: www.florsheim.com
Sales Range: $150-199.9 Million
Approx. Number Employees: 1,100
Year Founded: 1892
Business Description:
Men's Dress & Casual Footwear Mfr
S.I.C.: 5139
N.A.I.C.S.: 424340
Import Export
Media: 3-4-5-6-7-8-9-10-13-15-16-18-19-20-23-24
Distr.: Intl.
Personnel:
Peter Grossmen *(Pres)*
Tom Florsheim *(CEO)*
Jeff Douglass *(Mgr-Mktg)*
Brands & Products:
@EASE
FLORSHEIM
FLORSHEIM COMFORTECH
FLORSHEIM GOLF
FLORSHEIM IMPERIAL
FLORSHEIM SHOES
FLS FLORSHEIM
JOHN DEERE FOOTWEAR
MAGNEFORCE
Advertising Agency:
Laughlin/Constable, Inc.
207 E Michigan St
Milwaukee, WI 53202-4998
Tel.: (414) 272-2400
Fax: (414) 270-7140

FOOT LOCKER, INC.

112 W 34th St
New York, NY 10120-0101
Tel.: (212) 720-3700
Fax: (212) 720-4397
Web Site: www.footlocker-inc.com
Approx. Sls.: $5,049,000,000
Approx. Number Employees: 12,688
Year Founded: 1879
Business Description:
Athletic Footwear & Apparel Retailer
S.I.C.: 5661; 5941
N.A.I.C.S.: 448210; 451110
Import
Advertising Expenditures: $97,000,000
Media: 3-4-5-6-8-9-13-14-15-16-18-19-20-22-23-24-25
Distr.: Intl.; Natl.
Personnel:
Kenneth C. Hicks *(Chm, Pres & CEO)*
Robert W. McHugh *(CFO & Exec VP)*
Giovanna Cipriano *(Chief Acctg Officer & Sr VP)*
Ronald J. Halls *(Pres/CEO-Intl)*
Gary M. Bahler *(Gen Counsel & Sec)*
Jeffrey L. Berk *(Sr VP-Real Estate)*
Peter D. Brown *(Sr VP)*
Lauren B. Peters *(Sr VP-Strategic Plng)*
Laurie J. Petrucci *(Sr VP-HR)*
Patricia A. Peck *(VP-HR)*
Donnell Johnson *(Assoc Dir-Creative & Copywriter)*

Key to Media (For complete agency information see *The Advertising Red Books-Agencies* edition):
1. Bus. Publs. 2. Cable T.V. 3. Catalogs & Directories. 4. Co-op Adv. 5. Consumer Mags. 6. D.M. to Bus. Estab.7. D.M. to Consumers 8. Daily Newsp. 9. Exhibits/Trade Shows 10. Foreign 11. Infomercial 12. Internet Adv.13. Multimedia 14. Network Radio 15. Network T.V. 16. Newsp. Distr. Mags. 17. Other 18. Outdoor (Posters, Transit) 19. Point of Purchase20. Premiums, Novelties 21. Product Samples 22. Special Events Mktg. 23. Spot Radio 24. Spot T.V. 25. Weekly Newsp. 26. Yellow Page Adv.

Gary Rosen *(Assoc Dir-Creative & Copywriter)*
Jeff Neal *(Asst Mgr-Mktg)*
Brands & Products:
CHAMPS SPORTS
EASTBAY
FOOT LOCKER
FOOTACTION USA
FOOTLOCKER.COM
KIDS FOOT LOCKER
LADY FOOT LOCKER
Advertising Agency:
SapientNitro USA, Inc.
215 Park Ave S 2nd Fl
New York, NY 10003-1603
Tel.: (212) 206-1005
Fax: (212) 206-8510

FOOT PETALS, INC.
(Sub. of R.G. Barry Corporation)
6615 E Pacific Coast Hwy Ste 150
Long Beach, CA 90803
Tel.: (562) 795-1700
Fax: (562) 795-7700
Toll Free: (866) 847-8637
E-mail: info@footpetals.com
Web Site: www.footpetals.com
Sales Range: $1-9.9 Million
Approx. Number Employees: 15
Year Founded: 2001
Business Description:
Mfr of Cushions for Women's Shoes
S.I.C.: 3144
N.A.I.C.S.: 316214
Media: 4-10
Personnel:
Tina Aldatz-Norris *(Founder & Pres)*
Kristao Sicam *(Coord-Sls)*
Brands & Products:
FOOT PETALS
HAUTE HEELZ
HEAVENLY HEELZ
KILLER KUSHIONZ
SPALUX

FOOT-SO-PORT SHOE CORPORATION
405 E Forest St
Oconomowoc, WI 53066-3707
Tel.: (262) 567-4416
Fax: (262) 567-5323
E-mail: fsp@footsoport.com
Web Site: www.footsoport.com
Approx. Number Employees: 8
Year Founded: 1927
Business Description:
Men's & Women's Orthopedic Shoes Mfr & Wholesaler
S.I.C.: 3143; 3144; 5139
N.A.I.C.S.: 316213; 316214; 424340
Import Export
Advertising Expenditures: $25,000
Media: 2-4-8
Distr.: Natl.
Personnel:
Weston F. Miller *(Pres)*

FOOTACTION USA
(Div. of Foot Locker, Inc.)
112 W 34th St
New York, NY 10120
Tel.: (212) 720-3700
E-mail: support@footaction.com
Web Site: www.footaction.com
Sales Range: $300-349.9 Million
Approx. Number Employees: 7,700
Year Founded: 1976
Business Description:
Athletic Footwear Retailer
S.I.C.: 5661; 5941
N.A.I.C.S.: 448210; 451110
Media: 1-5-6-8-9-13-15-17-18-22-23
Personnel:
Richard Johnson *(Pres & CEO)*

FOOTSTAR, INC.
933 MacArthur Blvd
Mahwah, NJ 07430
Tel.: (201) 934-2000
Web Site: www.footstar.com
Sales Range: $1-9.9 Million
Approx. Number Employees: 5
Year Founded: 1996
Business Description:
Holding Company
S.I.C.: 6719
N.A.I.C.S.: 551112
Advertising Expenditures: $2,800,000
Personnel:
Jonathan M. Couchman *(Chm)*
William Lenich *(Exec VP)*
Dennis M. Lee *(Sr VP-HR)*
Brands & Products:
AIR THRUST
BUTTERFLIES
HYPERLITE
MAXTRAX
SMART STEP

THE FRYE COMPANY
(Sub. of Jimlar Corporation)
160 Great Neck Rd
Great Neck, NY 11021-3304
Tel.: (516) 829-1717
Fax: (516) 829-2970
Toll Free: (800) 826-3793
Web Site: www.fryeboots.com
Approx. Number Employees: 70
Year Founded: 1863
Business Description:
Shoes & Boots Whslr
S.I.C.: 5139
N.A.I.C.S.: 424340
Advertising Expenditures: $250,000
Media: 2-6-7-8-9-19-20
Distr.: Intl.; Natl.
Personnel:
Lawrence Tarica *(Pres)*
Frank Vignola *(CFO)*
Brands & Products:
FRYE

GENESCO INC.
1415 Murfreesboro Rd
Nashville, TN 37202
Mailing Address:
PO Box 731
Nashville, TN 37202-0731
Tel.: (615) 367-7000
Fax: (615) 367-8278
E-mail: investorrelations@genesco.com
Web Site: www.genesco.com
Approx. Sls.: $1,789,839,000
Approx. Number Employees: 15,200
Year Founded: 1924
Business Description:
Footwear & Men's Apparel Sales
S.I.C.: 5661; 5139
N.A.I.C.S.: 448210; 424340
Import Export
Advertising Expenditures: $35,100,000
Media: 1-2-3-4-5-6-7-8-9-10-11-13-16-17-19-20-21-22-23-25-26
Distr.: Natl.
Personnel:
Robert J. Dennis *(Chm, Pres & CEO)*
James S. Gulmi *(CFO, Treas & Sr VP-Fin)*
Paul D. Williams *(Chief Acctg Officer & VP)*
Jonathan D. Caplan *(Pres-Johnston, Murphy, CEO-Genesco Branded Grp & Sr VP)*
James C. Estepa *(Pres/CEO-Genesco Retail Grp & Sr VP)*
Kenneth J. Kocher *(Pres-Hat World & Sr VP)*
Roger G. Sisson *(Gen Counsel, Sec & Sr VP)*
John W. Clinard *(Sr VP-Admin & HR)*
Mimi Eckel Vaughn *(Sr VP-Strategy & Shared Svcs)*
Brands & Products:
GENESCO
HAT ZONE
HATWORLD
JARMAN
JOHNSTON & MURPHY
JOURNEYS
JOURNEYS KIDZ
LIDS
UNDERGROUND STATION
Advertising Agency:
Fitzgerald+CO
3060 Peachtree Rd NW
Atlanta, GA 30305
Tel.: (404) 504-6900
Fax: (404) 239-0548

GENFOOT INC.
1940 55th Ave
Lachine, QC H8T 3H3, Canada
Tel.: (514) 341-3950
Fax: (514) 341-1861
E-mail: info@kamik.com
Web Site: www.kamik.com
Sales Range: $100-124.9 Million
Approx. Number Employees: 150
Year Founded: 1898
Business Description:
Mfr. & Importer of Men's, Women's & Children's Footwear Including Rubber Boots, Winter Boots & Canvas Footwear
S.I.C.: 3143
N.A.I.C.S.: 316213
Import Export
Advertising Expenditures: $100,000
Media: 2-3-4-7-8-10-13-18-19-20-23-24
Distr.: Intl.; Natl.
Budget Set: July
Personnel:
Richard Cook *(Pres)*
Gordon Cook *(CEO)*
Norman Cook *(Exec VP)*
Stephen Cook *(Exec VP)*
Donald Flam *(VP-Intl Sls)*
Brands & Products:
DUFFS
KAMIK
SPYDER FOOTWEAR

G.H. BASS & CO.
(Sub. of Phillips Van Heusen Corporation)
200 Madison Ave
New York, NY 10016
Tel.: (212) 381-3900
Fax: (212) 381-3950
Toll Free: (800) 950BASS
Web Site: www.ghbass.com
Sales Range: $100-124.9 Million
Approx. Number Employees: 400
Year Founded: 1876
Business Description:
Footwear Manufacturer & Retailer
S.I.C.: 5661
N.A.I.C.S.: 448210
Import Export
Media: 1-2-4-5-6-9-10-18-19-20-21
Distr.: Natl.
Budget Set: Oct.
Personnel:
Michael Kelly *(Exec VP-Mktg)*
Todd Cook *(Dir-Mktg)*
Brands & Products:
BASS
COMPASS
SPORTOCASINS
SUNJUNS
WEEJUNS

HEELYS, INC.
3200 Belmeade Dr Ste 100
Carrollton, TX 75006
Tel.: (214) 390-1831
Fax: (214) 390-1661
Toll Free: (866) HEELING
Toll Free: (866) 433-5464
Web Site: www.heelys.com
Approx. Sls.: $30,436,000
Approx. Number Employees: 43
Year Founded: 2000
Business Description:
Sports Products Designer, Marketer & Distr
S.I.C.: 5091
N.A.I.C.S.: 423910
Advertising Expenditures: $4,000,000
Personnel:
Thomas C. Hansen *(CEO)*
Craig D. Storey *(CFO, COO & VP-Compliance)*
Ryan Wills *(Dir-Innovation)*
Brands & Products:
HEELYS
Advertising Agency:
Edelman
3131 Turtle Creek Blvd Ste 500
Dallas, TX 75219-5434
Tel.: (214) 520-3555
Fax: (214) 520-3458

H.H. BROWN SHOE COMPANY, INC.
(Sub. of BH Shoe Holdings, Inc.)
124 W Putnam Ave
Greenwich, CT 06830-5317
Tel.: (203) 661-2424
Fax: (203) 661-1818
Toll Free: (888) 4HHBROWN
Web Site: www.hhbrown.com
Sales Range: $400-449.9 Million
Approx. Number Employees: 1,300
Year Founded: 1883
Business Description:
Footwear Mfr
S.I.C.: 3143; 3144
N.A.I.C.S.: 316213; 316214
Import Export
Media: 2-4-5-7-8-10-11-23-24
Distr.: Natl.
Brands & Products:
ACME
BOLO
BORN
BROWNING FOOTWEAR

Key to Media (For complete agency information see *The Advertising Red Books-Agencies* edition):
1. Bus. Publs. 2. Cable T.V. 3. Catalogs & Directories. 4. Co-op Adv. 5. Consumer Mags. 6. D.M. to Bus. Estab.7. D.M. to Consumers
8. Daily Newsp. 9. Exhibits/Trade Shows 10. Foreign 11. Infomercial 12. Internet Adv.13. Multimedia 14. Network Radio
15. Network T.V. 16. Newsp. Distr. Mags. 17. Other 18. Outdoor (Posters, Transit) 19. Point of Purchase20. Premiums, Novelties
21. Product Samples 22. Special Events Mktg. 23. Spot Radio 24. Spot T.V. 25. Weekly Newsp. 26. Yellow Page Adv.

H.H. Brown Shoe Company, Inc. — (Continued)

BRUNSWICK
CAROLINA
CORCORAN
COVE
DEXTER
DOUBLE-H BOOTS
DRYZ
H.H. BROWN
HONDA FOOTWEAR
MATTERHORN
NURSE MATES
ORVIS
QUARK
SOFFT
SOFTSPOTS

Advertising Agency:
Katalina Group
2806 N Speer Blvd
Denver, CO 80211
Tel.: (303) 458-1035
Fax: (303) 458-1999

HI-TEC SPORTS USA, INC.

(Sub. of Hi-Tec Sports PLC)
4801 Stoddard Rd
Modesto, CA 95356-9318
Tel.: (209) 545-1111
Fax: (209) 545-2543
Toll Free: (800) 521-1698
E-mail: info@hi-tec.com
Web Site: www.hi-tec.com
Approx. Number Employees: 80
Year Founded: 1978
Business Description:
Mfr of Outdoor Rugged Footwear
S.I.C.: 5139; 3144
N.A.I.C.S.: 424340; 316214
Import Export
Media: 2-3-4-5-6-7-8-10-11-13-14-15-18-19-22-23-24
Distr.: Intl.
Budget Set: Nov.
Personnel:
Frank Van Wezel *(Chm)*
Paul Brooks *(Pres-Magnum Div)*
Brett Weitl *(Dir-Mktg)*
Simon Archer *(Mgr)*

HITCHCOCK SHOES, INC.

225 Beal St
Hingham, MA 02043-1543
Tel.: (781) 749-3260
Fax: (781) 749-3576
E-mail: hitchcock@wideshoes.com
Web Site: www.wideshoes.com
Approx. Number Employees: 22
Year Founded: 1951
Business Description:
Men's Footwear Mail Order & Marketer
S.I.C.: 5661
N.A.I.C.S.: 448210
Import
Advertising Expenditures: $300,000
Media: 2-4-6-8-9-13-16-25-26
Distr.: Natl.
Budget Set: May -Oct.
Personnel:
Evelyn F. Hitchcock *(Chm)*
Thomas R. Bright *(Pres)*
Brands & Products:
DUNHAM
HITCHCOCK
HITCHCOCK UPSIZED
SHOCK ABSORBER
WIDE SHOES FOR MEN

Advertising Agency:
Swanson Advertising
One Stiles Rd.
Salem, NH 03079
Tel.: (603) 893-8946
Fax: (603) 894-6452

JACK SCHWARTZ SHOES, INC.

(d/b/a Lugz)
155 Ave Of The Americas 9th Fl
New York, NY 10013
Tel.: (212) 691-4700
Fax: (212) 691-5350
E-mail: info@lugz.com
Web Site: www.lugz.com
E-Mail For Key Personnel:
President: jschwartz@jssi.com
Public Relations: lschwartz@jssi.com
Approx. Number Employees: 75
Year Founded: 1936
Business Description:
Casual Footwear & Clothing Distr
S.I.C.: 5139
N.A.I.C.S.: 424340
Import Export
Media: 3-6-10-15-19-23-24
Distr.: Intl.
Personnel:
Bernard Schwartz *(Chm)*
Jack Schwartz *(CEO)*
Ray Ricci *(COO)*
Larry W. Schwartz *(Exec VP)*
Joe Amoruso *(VP-Sls)*
Nicki Martin *(VP-Mktg)*
David Schwartz *(VP-Product Dev)*
Brands & Products:
ARC
BIZ
BRAZEN XL
CHILL SE
DIVA
DRIFTER
DRIFTER LO
FLIRT
LUGZ
OUTBACK
RADICAL
SCORCHER
SPHERE
STACKER
STRUTT
STRUTT LO
STRUTT LO SE
THROTTLE
VANTAGE
VANTAGE FLOSSIN'
Advertising Agency:
KathodeRay Media Inc.
20 Country Estates Rd PO Box 545
Greenville, NY 12083
Tel.: (518) 966-5600
Fax: (518) 966-5629

JIMLAR CORPORATION

160 Great Neck Rd
Great Neck, NY 11021
Tel.: (516) 829-1717
Fax: (516) 829-2970
Web Site: www.jimlar.com
Approx. Number Employees: 150
Year Founded: 1956
Business Description:
Importer & Whslr of Shoes
S.I.C.: 5139
N.A.I.C.S.: 424340
Import Export
Media: 4-5-6-8-10-17-19-20-21
Personnel:
James Tarica *(Chm & CEO)*
Lawrence Tarica *(Pres & COO)*
Frank Vignola *(CFO & VP)*
Vincent DeStefano *(Sr VP)*
Sarah Cohen *(Mgr-Mktg)*
Brands & Products:
AMERICAN EAGLE
FRYE
JIMLAR

JOHNSTON & MURPHY CO.

(Div. of Genesco Inc.)
1415 Murfreesboro Pike
Nashville, TN 37201
Tel.: (615) 367-8101
Fax: (615) 367-7139
Fax: (800) 654-2371
Toll Free: (800) 826-2690
Web Site: www.johnstonmurphy.com
Sales Range: $100-124.9 Million
Year Founded: 1850
Business Description:
Men's Shoes, Apparel & Accessories Mfr & Marketer
S.I.C.: 5661; 5139
N.A.I.C.S.: 448210; 424340
Import Export
Advertising Expenditures: $200,000
Media: 2-3-4-6
Distr.: Natl.
Budget Set: Dec.
Personnel:
Jonathan D. Caplan *(Pres)*
Jason Dasal *(VP-Mktg)*
Michael Humphrey *(Dir-Mktg)*
Brands & Products:
BEALS
BECKWORTH
BIRDIE
CARVER
CHADDOCK
CHESTER
DECKER
DOGWOOD
DRYZ
EAGLE
FARRIS
FROGHAIR
GRANT
GRIMES
HALLKIRK
HARTNEY
HECHE
HOGUE
J & M
PULLMAN
RADNOR
SCOVEL
SYLVAN
TRIBAL SPORT
TUCKER
WENDELL
ZIMMER
Advertising Agencies:
Dye, Van Mol & Lawrence
209 7th Ave N
Nashville, TN 37219-1802
Tel.: (615) 244-1818
Fax: (615) 780-3301

PGR Media, LLC.
34 Farnsworth St 2nd Fl
Boston, MA 02210
Tel.: (617) 502-8400
Fax: (617) 451-0451
Media Buying

Toth Brand Imaging
215 First St
Cambridge, MA 02142
Tel.: (617) 252-0787
Fax: (617) 252-0838
Shoes

JUMPING-JACKS SHOES DIV

(Div. of Munro & Company, Inc.)
3770 Malevrn Rd
Hot Springs National Park, AR 71901
Mailing Address:
PO Box 6048
Hot Springs National Park, AR 71902-6048
Tel.: (501) 262-6000
Fax: (501) 262-6165
Toll Free: (800) 654-7046
E-mail: jumpingjacks@munroshoe.com
Web Site: www.jumping-jacks.com/
Approx. Number Employees: 150
Year Founded: 1947
Business Description:
Children's Shoes Mfr
S.I.C.: 3149; 3144
N.A.I.C.S.: 316219; 316214
Import
Advertising Expenditures: $3,000,000
Media: 6-19-20-25
Distr.: Natl.
Personnel:
Molly Munro *(Dir-Mktg)*
Brands & Products:
JUMPING JACKS
PERFECTION

JUSTIN BRANDS, INC.

(Holding of Berkshire Hathaway Inc.)
610 W Daggett Ave
Fort Worth, TX 76104-1103
Mailing Address:
PO Box 548
Fort Worth, TX 76101-0548
Tel.: (817) 332-4385
Fax: (817) 348-2040
Toll Free: (800) 545-8707
E-mail: media@justinboots.com
Web Site: www.justinbrands.com
Sales Range: $300-349.9 Million
Approx. Number Employees: 950
Year Founded: 1879
Business Description:
Footwear Mfr
S.I.C.: 3143; 3144
N.A.I.C.S.: 316213; 316214
Import Export
Media: 2-3-4-5-6-10-13-18-19-20-23-24
Distr.: Natl.
Personnel:
Randy Watson *(Chm & CEO)*
Jamie Morgan *(Pres)*
Herbert A. Beckwith *(Sr VP-Intl Ops)*
Larry Nelson *(Sr VP-Mfg)*
Tom Hoefert *(VP-Fin)*
Lisa Lankes *(VP-Comm, Licensing & Social Media)*
Tom Feller *(Dir-Mktg & Special Events)*
Armando Romero *(Dir-Adv)*
Brands & Products:
CHIPPEWA
JUSTIN BOOTS
JUSTIN ORIGINAL WORKBOOT
NOCONA
TONY LAMA

Key to Media (For complete agency information see *The Advertising Red Books-Agencies* edition):
1. Bus. Publs. 2. Cable T.V. 3. Catalogs & Directories. 4. Co-op Adv. 5. Consumer Mags. 6. D.M. to Bus. Estab.7. D.M. to Consumers 8. Daily Newsp. 9. Exhibits/Trade Shows 10. Foreign 11. Infomercial 12. Internet Adv.13. Multimedia 14. Network Radio 15. Network T.V. 16. Newsp. Distr. Mags. 17. Other 18. Outdoor (Posters, Transit) 19. Point of Purchase20. Premiums, Novelties 21. Product Samples 22. Special Events Mktg. 23. Spot Radio 24. Spot T.V. 25. Weekly Newsp. 26. Yellow Page Adv.

Advertising Agency:
The Balcom Agency
1500 Ballinger
Fort Worth, TX 76201
Tel.: (817) 877-9933
Fax: (817) 877-5522

KENNETH COLE PRODUCTIONS, INC.

603 W 50th St
New York, NY 10019
Tel.: (212) 265-1500
Fax: (212) 830-7422
Toll Free: (800) KENCOLE
E-mail: members@kennethcole.com
Web Site: www.kennethcole.com
Approx. Rev.: $457,328,000
Approx. Number Employees: 700
Year Founded: 1982
Business Description:
Mfr & Designer Footwear & Accessories
S.I.C.: 5146; 3021; 3143; 3144
N.A.I.C.S.: 445220; 316211; 316213; 316214
Advertising Expenditures: $15,900,000
Media: 4-5-6-9-10-13-16-18-19
Distr.: Natl.
Budget Set: Oct.
Personnel:
Kenneth D. Cole *(Chm & Chief Creative Officer)*
Jill Granoff *(CEO)*
David P. Edelman *(CFO)*
Danesha Dixon Smith *(Chief HR Officer & Sr VP)*
Doug Jakubowski *(Chief Mdsg Officer)*
Michael Devirgilio *(Pres-Licensing & Intl)*
Harold Mitzona *(Pres-Consumer Direct)*
Chris Nakatani *(Pres-Wholesale)*
Michael F. Colosi *(Gen Counsel, Sec & VP)*
Robert Genovese *(VP-Mktg & Media)*
Heather Dumford *(Dir-Media Mktg)*
Advertising Agency:
Badger & Partners, Inc.
135 5th Ave 3rd Fl
New York, NY 10010
Tel.: (212) 533-3222
Fax: (212) 533-9380

L.A. GEAR, INC.

(Sub. of ACI International)
844 Moraga Dr
Los Angeles, CA 90049
Tel.: (310) 889-3499
Fax: (310) 889-3500
Toll Free: (800) 252-4327
E-mail: info@lagear.com
Web Site: www.lagear.com
Approx. Number Employees: 90
Year Founded: 1979
Business Description:
Athletic & Lifestyle Footwear, Apparel & Accessories Mfr
S.I.C.: 3149; 3143
N.A.I.C.S.: 316219; 316213
Media: 2-5-6-10-19-20-21-22-23
Distr.: Intl.; Natl.
Budget Set: Nov.
Personnel:
Steven Jackson *(Chm)*
David Mankowitz *(CFO)*
Sean Mitcheol *(Sr VP-Mktg)*
Sarah McAdams *(Office Mgr)*
Brands & Products:
CATAPULT
LA GEAR
LA LIGHTS

LACROSSE FOOTWEAR, INC.

17634 NE Airport Way
Portland, OR 97230-4999
Tel.: (503) 262-0110
Fax: (503) 262-0115
Toll Free: (800) 323-2668 (Customer Service)
E-mail: customerservice@lacrossefootwear.com
Web Site: www.lacrosse-outdoors.com
Approx. Sls.: $150,542,000
Approx. Number Employees: 516
Year Founded: 1897
Business Description:
Protective Footwear & Apparel Designer, Developer, Marketer & Mfr for the Sporting, Occupational & Recreational Markets
S.I.C.: 3021; 2329; 2339; 3143; 3144; 3149
N.A.I.C.S.: 316211; 315228; 315239; 316213; 316214; 316219
Advertising Expenditures: $2,900,000
Media: 4-13-15-19-22-25
Personnel:
Richard A. Rosenthal *(Chm)*
Joseph P. Schneider *(Pres & CEO)*
David P. Carlson *(CFO, Sec & Exec VP)*
C. Kirk Layton *(VP-Fin)*
Kirk S. Nichols *(VP-Sls & Mktg)*
Brands & Products:
ACADIA
ADIRONDACK
AIRTHOTIC
ALPHA
ALPHA SWAMPFOX
ALPHABURLY
BIG CHIEF
BRAWNY
BRUSH-TUFF
BURLY
CAMOHIDE
DANNER
DXTVENT
EXTREME ATS
FANG
FIRETECH
FOREMAN WELLINGTON
GAMEMASTER
GARRISON
GRANGE
HYPER-DRI
ICE KING
INSULATOR
LACROSSE
MARSH
OUTPOST
PACK-LITE
PACKER
PRONGHORN
PULL-ON PAC
QUAD COMFORT
RAINFAIR
RED BALL
RED BALL JETS
RIDGETOP
STRIKER
SUPER-TUFF
TERRA FORCE
TFX
TIMBERMASTER
TREKKER
UPLANDER
WORK FORCE

LUCCHESE, INC.

(Sub. of Arena Brands Inc.)
40 Walter Jones Blvd
El Paso, TX 79906
Tel.: (915) 778-3066
Fax: (915) 778-6796
Web Site: www.lucchese.com
Approx. Number Employees: 250
Year Founded: 1883
Business Description:
Western Boots Mfr
S.I.C.: 3143; 3144
N.A.I.C.S.: 316213; 316214
Import Export
Advertising Expenditures: $2,000,000
Media: 2-4-5-6-7-10-17-18-19-20-21-22-23
Distr.: Natl.
Brands & Products:
LUCCHESE 2000
LUCCHESE CLASSICS
LUCCHESE EXCLUSIVE

MASON COMPANIES, INC.

1251 1st Ave
Chippewa Falls, WI 54729-1408
Tel.: (715) 723-1871
Fax: (715) 720-4245
Toll Free: (800) 893-8508
Web Site: www.masoncompaniesinc.com
Approx. Number Employees: 400
Year Founded: 1904
Business Description:
Mail Order Catalog Men's & Women's Shoes
S.I.C.: 5961; 3144
N.A.I.C.S.: 454113; 316214
Import
Media: 2-4-5-6-8-10-16-18-19-20-21-23-25
Distr.: Natl.
Budget Set: Mar.-Sept.
Personnel:
Dan Hunt *(Pres & CEO)*
Brands & Products:
AXIDYNE
DRESSABOUT
ETONIC
EVERDURE
FOOTONIC ULTRA
G. WIZ
MASON
PROPET
QUICK GRIP
RESPONDER
STABILITY WEB
SUPPLE LEATHER STABILITY WALKER
TRANSAM DRX
WALKING STRIKE PATH

MAURICE J. MARKELL SHOE CO., INC.

PO Box 246
Yonkers, NY 10702-0246
Tel.: (914) 963-2258
Fax: (914) 963-9293
E-mail: info@markellshoe.com
Web Site: www.markellshoe.com
Sales Range: $25-49.9 Million
Approx. Number Employees: 10
Year Founded: 1914
Business Description:
Comfort & Orthopedic Shoes & Shoe Correction Products Mfr
S.I.C.: 3149; 3842
N.A.I.C.S.: 316219; 339113
Media: 2-4-8-10-13
Distr.: Natl.
Personnel:
Jonathan J. Markell *(Pres)*
Richard Markell *(Co-Pres)*
Brands & Products:
KEEPING PACE
TARSO MEDIUS
TARSO PRONATOR
TARSO SUPINATOR
TM 2000

MERCURY INTERNATIONAL TRADING CORP.

20 Alice Agnew Dr
North Attleboro, MA 02763
Tel.: (508) 699-9000
Fax: (508) 699-9088
Web Site: www.mercuryfootwear.com
Approx. Number Employees: 50
Business Description:
Mfr of Men's Casual Branded Shoes & Boots
S.I.C.: 5139
N.A.I.C.S.: 424340
Advertising Expenditures: $350,000
Media: 10
Distr.: Intl.; Natl.
Budget Set: Various
Personnel:
Irving Wiseman *(Chm)*
Howard Wiseman *(Pres & CEO)*

NEW BALANCE ATHLETIC SHOE, INC.

20 Guest St Ste 20
Boston, MA 02135-2040
Tel.: (617) 783-4000
Fax: (617) 787-9355
Toll Free: (800) 343-1395
E-mail: lyman@cshore.com
Web Site: www.newbalance.com
Sales Range: $1-4.9 Billion
Approx. Number Employees: 2,800
Year Founded: 1906
Business Description:
Athletic Footwear & Apparel Mfr
S.I.C.: 3149; 3949
N.A.I.C.S.: 316219; 339920
Import Export
Advertising Expenditures: $20,000,000
Media: 2-3-4-5-6-8-10-11-13-15-18-19-20-23-24
Distr.: Natl.
Budget Set: Sept.
Personnel:
James S. Davis *(Chm)*
Anne Davis *(Vice Chm & Exec VP-Admin)*
Robert DeMartini *(Pres & CEO)*
John Withee *(CFO & Exec VP)*
Alan Hed *(Exec VP-Intl)*
Joe Preston *(Exec VP-Product & Mktg-Global Footwear)*
Chris Quinn *(Exec VP-Sls & Retail-NA)*
Herb Spivak *(Exec VP-Comml Ops)*
John Wilson *(Exec VP-Mfg)*
Edward Haddad *(VP-Intellectual Property & Licensed Products)*
Bill Hayden *(VP-Fin)*
Stephanie Smith *(VP-Retail)*

Key to Media (For complete agency information see *The Advertising Red Books-Agencies* edition):
1. Bus. Publs. 2. Cable T.V. 3. Catalogs & Directories. 4. Co-op Adv. 5. Consumer Mags. 6. D.M. to Bus. Estab.7. D.M. to Consumers
8. Daily Newsp. 9. Exhibits/Trade Shows 10. Foreign 11. Infomercial 12. Internet Adv.13. Multimedia 14. Network Radio
15. Network T.V. 16. Newsp. Distr. Mags. 17. Other 18. Outdoor (Posters, Transit) 19. Point of Purchase20. Premiums, Novelties
21. Product Samples 22. Special Events Mktg. 23. Spot Radio 24. Spot T.V. 25. Weekly Newsp. 26. Yellow Page Adv.

New Balance Athletic Shoe, Inc. — (Continued)

Peter Zappala *(VP-Specialty Sls)*
Matt LeBretton *(Dir-Pub Affairs)*
Amy Vreeland *(Mgr-Corp Comm)*
Kevin Fitzpatrick *(Product Mgr)*
Bryan Gothie *(Product Mgr)*
Norma Delaney *(Mgr-Global Adv & Media)*

Brands & Products:
ARAVON
BRINE
DUNHAM
NB
NB ZIP
NBX
NEW BALANCE
PF FLYERS
WARRIOR

Advertising Agencies:
Almighty
300 Western Ave
Boston, MA 02134
Tel.: (617) 782-1511
Fax: (617) 782-1611
ZIP Shoes

Arnold Worldwide
101 Huntington Ave
Boston, MA 02199-7603
Tel.: (617) 587-8000
Fax: (617) 587-8004
Global Agency of Record
Strategic & Creative Duties

BBDO Worldwide Inc.
(Sub. of Omnicom Group, Inc.)
1285 Ave of the Americas
New York, NY 10019-6028
Tel.: (212) 459-5000
Fax: (212) 459-6645

CarryOn
5670 Wilshire Blvd
Los Angeles, CA 90036
Tel.: (323) 848-4300
Fax: (323) 848-4310
Toll Free: (888) 838-NEWS

Conover Tuttle Pace
77 N Washington St
Boston, MA 02114
Tel.: (617) 412-4000
Fax: (617) 412-4411

Dan Klores Communications
(d/b/a dkc)
386 Park Ave S 10th Fl
New York, NY 10016
Tel.: (212) 685-4300
Fax: (212) 685-9024

GolinHarris
18/F HuaiHai Plz
Shanghai, 200031, China
Tel.: (86) 21 2411 0088
Fax: (86) 21 2411 0066

Mother New York
595 11th Ave
New York, NY 10036
Tel.: (212) 254-2800
Fax: (212) 254-6121
(Lifestyle Products)

PHD New York
220 E 42nd St 7th Fl
New York, NY 10017-5806
Tel.: (212) 894-6600
Fax: (212) 894-4100
Media Buying

Warschawski
1501 Sulgrave Ave Ste 350
Baltimore, MD 21209
Tel.: (410) 367-2700
Fax: (410) 367-2400

NIKE, INC.

1 Bowerman Dr
Beaverton, OR 97005-6453
Tel.: (503) 671-6453
Fax: (503) 671-6300
Telex: 4742065
E-mail: corp.comm@nike.com
Web Site: www.nikebiz.com
E-Mail For Key Personnel:
Public Relations: corp.comm@nike.com

Approx. Rev.: $19,014,000,000
Approx. Number Employees: 34,400
Year Founded: 1964

Business Description:
Athletic Shoes, Apparel & Sporting Goods Mfr
S.I.C.: 3949; 2329; 2339; 3149; 5941
N.A.I.C.S.: 339920; 315228; 315239; 316219; 451110
Import Export
Advertising Expenditures: $2,448,000,000

Media: 1-3-4-5-6-10-11-13-18-19-20-22-28-31
Distr.: Intl.; Natl.
Budget Set: May

Personnel:
Philip H. Knight *(Chm)*
Mark G. Parker *(Pres & CEO)*
Donald W. Blair *(CFO & VP)*
Domingo Garcia *(Chief Tax Officer)*
Cindy Davis *(Pres-NIKE Golf & VP)*
Thomas E. Clarke *(Pres-New Bus Ventures)*
Charlie Denson *(Pres-NIKE Brand)*
Gary M. DeStefano *(Pres-Global Ops)*
Keith Houlemard *(Pres-Jordan Brand)*
Jeanne P. Jackson *(Pres-Direct to Consumer)*
Roger Wyett *(Pres-Affiliates)*
Hilary K. Krane *(Gen Counsel & VP)*
Kris Aman *(VP & Gen Mgr-Mens Athletic Trng)*
Ken Dice *(VP-Mktg-North America & Gen Mgr-USA Brand)*
Jim Godbout *(VP & Gen Mgr)*
Larry Harper *(VP & Gen Mgr-US Regs)*
Elliott Hill *(VP & Gen Mgr-North America)*
Hubertus Hoyt *(VP & Gen Mgr-Global Football)*
Heidi O'Neill *(VP & Gen Mgr-Global Womens Fitness)*
Brent Scrimshaw *(VP & Gen Mgr-Western Europe)*
Marc Van Pappelendam *(VP & Gen Mgr-UK & Ireland)*
Pat Zeedick *(VP & Gen Mgr-Category Kids)*
Oscar Cardona *(VP-HR, Global Infrastructure & Shared Svcs)*
David Clark *(VP-HR)*
David Heath *(VP-Sles & Cust Dev-Global)*
Ron B. Hill *(VP-Global Footwear Merchandising)*
Joe Monahan *(VP-Sls-North America)*
Joe Serino *(VP-Mdsg-North America)*
Chris Shimojima *(VP-E-Commerce)*
Eric Sprunk *(VP-Mdsg & Product)*
Hans Van Alebeek *(VP-Nike Global Ops & Tech)*
Mike Wilskey *(VP-Brand Mgmt, Subsidiaries & New Bus)*
Roland Wolfram *(VP-Sls-Global)*
Lorrie Vogel *(Gen Mgr-Considered)*
Kelley Hall *(Sr Dir-IR)*
Keith Crawford *(Dir-Brand Design-Jordan Brand)*
Nancy Monsarrat *(Brand Dir)*
Simon Nicholls *(Mktg Dir-Livestrong-Global)*
Lance Allega *(Dir-IR)*
Ricky Engelberg *(Dir-Digital Innovation-Global)*
Dave Genel *(Dir-Media)*
Michael Pai *(Dir-Golf Balls & Golf Bags)*
Adam Roth *(Dir-Adv)*
Andy Shih *(Dir-Mktg-Digital Commerce-US)*
John Springer *(Dir-Global Ops-Golf Div)*
Dean Stoyer *(Dir-Global Sports Comm)*
Debra Friedman *(Brand Mgr-Action Sports-Global)*
Erin Oranen *(Assoc Mgr)*
Kathy Strege *(Mgr-IR)*

Brands & Products:
10//2
AIR CLASSIC BW
AIR DIAMOND TURF
AIR JORDAN
AIR JORDAN XX3
AIR LEGEND
AIR MAX
AIR MAX 360
AIR MAX 90
AIR MAX 97
AIR MAX MVP
AIR MAX TURBULENCE
AIR MOGAN MID
AIR PEGASUS
AIR RIFT
AIR STAB
AIR STRUCTURE TRIAX
AIR TIEMPO RIVAL
AIR UNLIMITED
AIR VOS
AIR ZOOM
AIR ZOOM FLIGHT FIVE
AIR ZOOM MOIRE
AIR ZOOM SUPER BAD
AIR ZOOM SUPER SPEED
ATHLETIC
BAUER
BLAZER MID
CLIMA-FIT
CORTEZ
DIAMOND ELITE
DRI-FIT
DUNK HIGH
DUNK HIGH BE TRUE
DUNK LOW BE TRUE
DUNK LOW PREMIUM
HYPERDUNK
IF YOU HAVE A BODY, YOU ARE AN ATHLETE
JUMPMAN TEAM PRO
LARGE TEAM DUFFEL
LUNARTRAINER
LUNARTRAINER+ID
MERCURIAL TALARIA
MERCURIAL VAPOR
NIKE
NIKE 6.0
NIKE AIR
NIKE PRO
NIKEFREE
NIKEFREE DYNAMIC TRAINER
PATIENT
PRESTO
SERA
SHOX CLASSIC
SHOX EXPERIENCE
SHOX FIRST 2
SHOX MVP
SHOX NAVINA
SHOX NZ
SHOX SLAM
SHOX TURBO
SIDE I
SMALL TEAM DUFFEL
SPARQ TR
STORM-FIT
SWOOSH DESIGN
THERMA-FIT
TIEMPO
TOTAL90
TRIAX
TRIAX SWIFT DIGITAL
TROUPE MID
V CARBON MAX
VANDAL LOW
ZOOM BLUR
ZOOM KOBE IV
ZOOM SHARKLEY
ZOOM STRUCTURE TRIAX
ZOOM T-5
ZOOM TRAINER ESSENTIAL
ZOOM VICTORY+

Advertising Agencies:
72andSunny
6300 Arizona Cir
Los Angeles, CA 90045
Tel.: (310) 215-9009
Fax: (310) 215-9012
Nike Football

AKQA, Inc.
118 King St 6th Fl
San Francisco, CA 94107
Tel.: (415) 645-9400
Fax: (415) 645-9420
Sportswear
— Simon Jefferson *(Acct Dir)*

Arnold Worldwide
101 Huntington Ave
Boston, MA 02199-7603
Tel.: (617) 587-8000
Fax: (617) 587-8004
Fresh Air

Cornerstone
10715 Little Patuxent Pkwy Ste 120
Columbia, MD 21044
Tel.: (410) 727-2131
Fax: (443) 367-5911

Digitas Inc.
33 Arch St
Boston, MA 02110
Tel.: (617) 867-1000
Fax: (617) 867-1111

Hakuhodo Incorporated

Key to Media (For complete agency information see *The Advertising Red Books-Agencies* edition):
1. Bus. Publs. 2. Cable T.V. 3. Catalogs & Directories. 4. Co-op Adv. 5. Consumer Mags. 6. D.M. to Bus. Estab.7. D.M. to Consumers
8. Daily Newsp. 9. Exhibits/Trade Shows 10. Foreign 11. Infomercial 12. Internet Adv.13. Multimedia 14. Network Radio
15. Network T.V. 16. Newsp. Distr. Mags. 17. Other 18. Outdoor (Posters, Transit) 19. Point of Purchase20. Premiums, Novelties
21. Product Samples 22. Special Events Mktg. 23. Spot Radio 24. Spot T.V. 25. Weekly Newsp. 26. Yellow Page Adv.

Akasaka Biz Tower 5-3-1 Akasaka
Tokyo, 107-6322, Japan
Tel.: (81) 3 6441 6161
Fax: (81) 3 6441 6166
(Creative)

Indie
Hoogte Kadijk 143 F26
1018 BH
Amsterdam, Netherlands
Tel.: (31) 20 422 2999
Fax: (31) 20 422 2960

Mindshare
Yebisu Garden Place Tower 30F 4-20-3 Ebisu
Tokyo, 150-6030, Japan
Tel.: (81) 3 5791 2780
Fax: (81) 3 5791 2781

mktg, inc.
75 9th Ave 3rd Fl
New York, NY 10011
Tel.: (212) 660-3800
Fax: (212) 660-3878
Sports Apparel

OgilvyAction
35 Robinson Road #03 01 The Ogilvy Centre
Singapore, 068876, Singapore
Tel.: (65) 6213 7899
Fax: (65) 6293 7264

Opolis Design
The Gotham Bldg 2240 N Interstate Ave Ste 200
Portland, OR 97227
Tel.: (503) 287-7722
Fax: (503) 280-7788

Publicis (Malaysia) Sdn. Bhd.
M1 Mezanine Fl Wisme LYL
46100
Petaling Jaya, Selangor Malaysia
Tel.: (60) 3 7952 2222
Fax: (60) 3 7952 2220
(Nike Football)

R/GA
350 W 39th St
New York, NY 10018-1402
Tel.: (212) 946-4000
Fax: (212) 946-4010
Nike+ GPS

Villarrosas
Via Laietana 64 Principal
08003
Barcelona, Spain
Tel.: (34) 932 388 304
Fax: (34) 934 161 365

Wieden + Kennedy
Floor 5th No1035 ChangLe Road
Shanghai, 200031, China
Tel.: (86) 21 5158 3900
Fax: (86) 21 5158 3988

Wieden + Kennedy, Inc.
224 NW 13th Ave
Portland, OR 97209-2953
Tel.: (503) 937-7000
Fax: (503) 937-8000
(Hyperdunk Basketball Shoes, Nike Zoom LeBron VI)

The Black Mamba
— Spence Kramer *(Acct Dir)*

Wieden + Kennedy Japan
7-5-6 Roppongi
Tokyo, 106-0032, Japan
Tel.: (81) 3 5771 2900
Fax: (81) 3 5771 2711
Sportswear

Wieden + Kennedy-New York
150 Varick St Fl 7
New York, NY 10013-1218
Tel.: (917) 661-5200
Fax: (917) 661-5500
Jordan Brand

Wirestone
920 20th St
Sacramento, CA 95811
Tel.: (916) 446-6550
Fax: (916) 446-6551

NINE WEST GROUP, INC.

(Sub. of The Jones Group, Inc.)
Nine West Plz 1129 Westchester Ave
White Plains, NY 10604
Tel.: (914) 640-6400
Fax: (914) 640-3499
Toll Free: (800) 999-1877
E-mail: customer_relations@ninewest.com
Web Site: www.ninewest.com
Sales Range: $1-4.9 Billion
Approx. Number Employees: 15,000
Year Founded: 1977
Business Description:
Designer, Developer & Marketer of Women's Footwear & Accessories
S.I.C.: 5661
N.A.I.C.S.: 448210
Import
Advertising Expenditures: $300,000
Media: 4-8-10-13-18-19-22
Distr.: Natl.
Budget Set: Dec.
Personnel:
Patrick McLaughlin *(Pres)*
Richard Paterno *(Pres-Wholesale Better Footwear Brands)*
Sally Ross *(Exec VP-Mdsg-Nine West Direct)*
Michael Hines *(VP-Mktg & Dev)*
Sarah Conley *(Dir-Creative)*
Brands & Products:
BANDOLINO
EASY SPIRIT
NINE WEST

NUNN-BUSH SHOE COMPANY

(Div. of Weyco Group, Inc.)
333 W Estabrook Blvd
Glendale, WI 53212-1067
Mailing Address:
PO Box 1188
Milwaukee, WI 53201-2047
Tel.: (414) 908-1600
Fax: (414) 908-1601
E-mail: nbcustserv@nunnbush.com
Web Site: www.nunnbush.com
Sales Range: $450-499.9 Million
Year Founded: 1912
Business Description:
Men's Footwear Whslr & Mfr
S.I.C.: 5139; 3143
N.A.I.C.S.: 424340; 316213
Import Export
Advertising Expenditures: $1,000,000
Media: 2-3-4-5-6-7-8-9-10-11-13-16-18-19-20-21-22-23-24-25-26
Distr.: Natl.
Budget Set: May-Nov.
Personnel:
Thomas W. Florsheim *(Chm)*
Peter S. Grossman *(Pres)*
Thomas W. Florsheim, Jr. *(CEO)*
Brands & Products:
NUNN BUSH
NUNN BUSH NXXT
Advertising Agency:
BVK
250 W Coventry Ct #300
Milwaukee, WI 53217-3972
Tel.: (414) 228-1990
Fax: (414) 228-7561
Toll Free: (888) 347-3212

PHOENIX FOOTWEAR GROUP, INC.

5937 Darwin Ct Ste 109
Carlsbad, CA 92008
Tel.: (760) 602-9688
Fax: (800) 526-8151
Toll Free: (888) 218-7275
E-mail: nfo@phxg.com
Web Site: www.phoenixfootwear.com
Approx. Sls.: $17,262,000
Approx. Number Employees: 42
Year Founded: 1882
Business Description:
Men's & Women's Footwear & Apparel Designer, Developer, Mfr & Marketer
S.I.C.: 3021; 2389; 3143; 3144
N.A.I.C.S.: 316211; 315999; 316213; 316214
Advertising Expenditures: $127,000
Media: 2-4-5-6-7-8-10-19
Distr.: Natl.
Budget Set: Dec.
Personnel:
James R. Riedman *(Chm & CEO)*
Greg Slack *(CFO, Treas & Sec)*
Robert P. Orlando *(Pres-Royal Robbins Div)*
Robby L. Carter *(Exec VP-Sls)*
Brands & Products:
ALTAMA
AMANDA
AMY
ANDREA
ANNIE
ASH
ASHLEE
AUDREY
AUDREY WS
BARCELONA
BARI
BELLA
BETH
BETSY
BLAST TOO
BRANDIE
BRIDGET
BROADWATER
CHAMBERS
CHILL
CROSS TOWNE
DARCY
DEA
DELIGHT
DELILAH
DELORES
DIANA
DIEDRA
DINAH
DOREEN
DORIS
ELECTRIC CITY
EMANUELLE
EMMA
FISHING CAMP
FRANCIE
FROST
GALLATIN
GEORGIA
GIBSON FALLS
GLORIA
GOLD STRIKE
HS TRASK
JACKIE
JADE
JAMIE
JAZZY
JESS
JESSICA
JOYCE
LAGUNA
LANA
LIL' BUCKAROO
LISA
LIZ
LOREN
LUCIA
LUXE
MACKENZIE
MADELINE
MAGGIE
MANTECA
MARCELLA
MARGOT
MARIANGELA
MARTIE
MARY MARY
MAXINE
MCTAVISH FISHERMAN
MCTAVISH OXFORD
MCTAVISH SLIP-ON
MEGAN
MELISSA
MEREDITH
MODESTO
MOLLIE
MONTEGO
NADIA
NAOMI
NATALIE
NINA
NITA
NORA
PALOMA
PAOLA
PATIENCE
PISA
PORTLAND
REBECA
REITI
REVO
REYNA
RIMINI
RIVOLI
ROMA
SAN MATEO
SNOWFLAKES
SOFTWALK
STEP N UP
STROL
SUNDANCE
TROTTERS
VENUS
Advertising Agency:
Rossi Advertising
Mill Three 587 Main St.

Key to Media (For complete agency information see *The Advertising Red Books-Agencies* edition):
1. Bus. Publs. 2. Cable T.V. 3. Catalogs & Directories. 4. Co-op Adv. 5. Consumer Mags. 6. D.M. to Bus. Estab.7. D.M. to Consumers 8. Daily Newsp. 9. Exhibits/Trade Shows 10. Foreign 11. Infomercial 12. Internet Adv.13. Multimedia 14. Network Radio 15. Network T.V. 16. Newsp. Distr. Mags. 17. Other 18. Outdoor (Posters, Transit) 19. Point of Purchase20. Premiums, Novelties 21. Product Samples 22. Special Events Mktg. 23. Spot Radio 24. Spot T.V. 25. Weekly Newsp. 26. Yellow Page Adv.

Phoenix Footwear Group, Inc. — (Continued)

New York Mills, NY 13417
Tel.: (315) 768-0111
Fax: (315) 736-6674

PRINCIPLE PLASTICS, INC.

1136 W 135th St
Gardena, CA 90247-1919
Mailing Address:
PO Box 2408
Gardena, CA 90247-0408
Tel.: (310) 532-3411
Fax: (310) 532-0489
Toll Free: (877) 750-4437
E-mail: service@sloggers.com
Web Site: www.sloggers.com
Approx. Number Employees: 35
Year Founded: 1948
Business Description:
Gardening Apparel & Tool Mfr
S.I.C.: 3021; 3949
N.A.I.C.S.: 316211; 339920
Export
Media: 2-4-5-9-10-25
Distr.: Intl.; Natl.
Personnel:
David Hoyt *(Pres)*
Dennis Kursewicz *(VP-Sls)*
Brands & Products:
DRIZZLE BOOTS
GARDEN OUTFITTERS
SLOGGERS

PUMA NORTH AMERICA, INC.

(Sub. of Puma AG Rudolf Dassler Sport)
10 Lyberty Way
Westford, MA 01886
Tel.: (978) 698-1000
Fax: (978) 698-1174
Toll Free: (800) 782-7862
Telex: 978-698-1150
E-mail: customerservice@puma.com
Web Site: www.puma.com
Approx. Number Employees: 260
Year Founded: 1948
Business Description:
Casual & Athletic Shoes
S.I.C.: 5139; 5136
N.A.I.C.S.: 424340; 424320
Import Export
Advertising Expenditures: $2,000,000
Other: $2,000,000
Distr.: Natl.
Budget Set: Sept.
Personnel:
Jay Piccola *(Pres)*
Antonio Bertone *(CMO)*
Curtis Charles *(Sr VP-Sls & Mktg)*
John Trott *(VP-Retail Div)*
Theo Keetell *(Dir-Retail & Lifestyle Mktg-US)*
Ed Choi *(Mgr-Entertainment Mktg)*
Brands & Products:
FRENCH 77
Advertising Agencies:
Alexander & Tom
3500 Boston St Ste 225
Baltimore, MD 21224-5275
Tel.: (410) 327-7400
Fax: (410) 327-7403

Almighty
300 Western Ave
Boston, MA 02134
Tel.: (617) 782-1511
Fax: (617) 782-1611

BDS Marketing
10 Holland
Irvine, CA 92618
Tel.: (949) 472-6700
Fax: (949) 597-2220

droga5
400 Lafayette 5th Fl
New York, NY 10003
Tel.: (917) 237-8888
Fax: (917) 237-8889
(Global Marketing)
After Hours Athlete
HardChorus

Quaker City Mercantile
114-120 S 13th St
Philadelphia, PA 19107
Tel.: (215) 922-5220
Fax: (215) 922-5228
Shoes

Syrup
12 Vestry St 7th Fl
New York, NY 10013
Tel.: (212) 680-1477
Fax: (212) 680-1478

P.W. MINOR & SON, INC.

3 Treadeasy Ave
Batavia, NY 14020-3009
Tel.: (585) 343-1500
Fax: (585) 343-1514
E-mail: info@pwminor.com
Web Site: www.pwminor.com
Approx. Number Employees: 150
Year Founded: 1921
Business Description:
Women's & Men's Therapeutic Footwear Mfr
S.I.C.: 3143; 3144
N.A.I.C.S.: 316213; 316214
Export
Media: 2-4-5-6-7-9-10-14-19-21-23-26
Distr.: Intl.; Natl.
Budget Set: Jan.-July
Personnel:
Henry H. Minor, Jr. *(Chm & CEO)*
Wolcott Hinchey *(CFO)*
Maryl Bedenko *(VP-Fin)*
Donna Morrill *(VP-HR)*
Brands & Products:
ALGONQUIN
ALL AMERICAN
ARROW
ATLAS
BUD SPECIAL
CARESS
CASSIE
CHUKKA
CONTESSA
COUNTOUR
COZY
CURRANT
DANCER
DIPLOMAT
DUKE
DUTCHESS
ERIKA
EURO
FASHION
FINESSE
GRACE
HAMPTON
HAPPY GO LIGHTLY
HARMONY
HERCULES
HERCULES ST
HIKER
ITALIAN COLLECTION BY TREADEASY
KATIE
KEYSTONE
KRISTA
LACE TO TOE
LADY PILLOW BACK
LADYSPORT
LEISURE
LEISURE TIME
LEXINGTON
LS ORTHO
LS SENATOR
LS SUPER X
MELBOURNE
MISS CONTOUR
MONIKA
NATURAL
NEVADA
PACE
PATHFINDER
PILLOWBACKS
PLEASURE
PRESTO
PRIME MINISTER
PT SNAPPY
RANGER
RX SPECIAL
SABEL
SABEL OXFORD
SAMPSON
SANDY
SANTA FE
SCANDIA
SIR CONTOUR
SNAPPY
SPRINT
SQUARE DANCER
STRIDE
SUMMIT
SUPER DEPTH
SUPER X
SWING
THERMOLDS
TREADEASY
TRINKET
VANESSA
VELCRO
VELVET
VICTORIA
WEEKENDER
WILBUR COON
WINDSOR
XSENSIBLE
XTRA DEPTH

RED WING SHOE COMPANY, INC.

314 Main St
Red Wing, MN 55066-2300
Tel.: (651) 388-8211
Fax: (651) 385-0897
Toll Free: (800) 733-9464
E-mail: customer.service@redwingshoe.com
Web Site: www.redwingshoe.com
E-Mail For Key Personnel:
Public Relations: petenger@redwingshoe.com
Sales Range: $300-349.9 Million
Approx. Number Employees: 1,850
Year Founded: 1905
Business Description:
Footwear Mfr
S.I.C.: 3143; 3149
N.A.I.C.S.: 316213; 316219
Import Export
Advertising Expenditures: $7,500,000
Media: 1-2-3-4-5-6-7-8-9-13-15-18-19-23-26
Distr.: Intl.; Natl.
Budget Set: Dec.
Personnel:
David D. Murphy *(Pres)*
Rick Bawek *(CFO & Exec VP)*
Joe Copinka *(CIO)*
Dave Baker *(Gen Counsel & Exec VP)*
Carrie Glavir *(VP-HR)*
Peter D. Engel *(Dir-Mktg Comm)*
Brands & Products:
BUILT TO FIT. BUILT TO LAST.
CARHARTT
COMFORTFORCE
CRAFTSMAN
GRIP-TEC
HASSLE FREE
IRISH SETTER
IRISH SETTER SPORT BOOTS
MUSCLE SHOES
PECOS
R FACTORS
RED WING INTERNATIONAL
RED WING SHOES
SUPERSOLE
SUPERSOLE 2.0
TECH TOE
VASQUE
VASQUE OUTDOOR HIKING BOOTS
WORX
Advertising Agencies:
Campbell-Ewald
30400 Van Dyke Ave
Warren, MI 48093-2368
Tel.: (586) 574-3400
Fax: (586) 575-9925

Colle+McVoy
400 1st Ave N Ste 700
Minneapolis, MN 55401-1954
Tel.: (612) 305-6000
Fax: (612) 305-6500

Haworth Marketing & Media Company
TCF Tower 10th Fl 121 S 8th St
Minneapolis, MN 55402
Tel.: (612) 677-8900
Fax: (612) 677-8901
(Media Placement)

OLSON
1625 Hennepin Ave
Minneapolis, MN 55403
Tel.: (612) 215-9800
Fax: (612) 215-9801
(Vasque, Irish Setter, Holistic Planning & Media Planning)

REEBOK INTERNATIONAL LTD.

(Sub. of adidas AG)
1895 JW Foster Blvd
Canton, MA 02021-1099
Tel.: (781) 401-5000
Fax: (781) 401-7402
E-mail: corporate@reebok.com
Web Site: www.reebok.com
Approx. Sls.: $3,500,000,000
Approx. Number Employees: 9,102
Year Founded: 1979
Business Description:
Mfr, Distr & Marketer of Footwear & Athletic Apparel
S.I.C.: 3149; 3949

Key to Media (For complete agency information see *The Advertising Red Books-Agencies* edition):
1. Bus. Publs. 2. Cable T.V. 3. Catalogs & Directories. 4. Co-op Adv. 5. Consumer Mags. 6. D.M. to Bus. Estab.7. D.M. to Consumers
8. Daily Newsp. 9. Exhibits/Trade Shows 10. Foreign 11. Infomercial 12. Internet Adv.13. Multimedia 14. Network Radio
15. Network T.V. 16. Newsp. Distr. Mags. 17. Other 18. Outdoor (Posters, Transit) 19. Point of Purchase20. Premiums, Novelties
21. Product Samples 22. Special Events Mktg. 23. Spot Radio 24. Spot T.V. 25. Weekly Newsp. 26. Yellow Page Adv.

N.A.I.C.S.: 316219; 339920
Import Export
Advertising Expenditures: $137,062,000
Media: 1-3-4-5-6-8-9-10-11-14-15-16-18-19-22-23-24-25
Distr.: Intl.
Budget Set: Aug.
Personnel:
Uli Becker *(Pres)*
Sharon Bryan *(COO)*
Matt O'Toole *(CMO)*
Jim Gabel *(Pres-North America)*
John Lynch *(VP & Head-Mktg-US)*
Todd Krinsky *(VP-Sports & Entertainment Mktg)*
Bill Holmes *(Head-HR)*
Todd Klein *(Sr Dir-Mktg)*
Anastasia Bogdanova *(Dir-Art)*
Kristina Brandenburg *(Product Mgr)*
Brands & Products:
ABOVE THE RIM
ABOVE THE RIM HOOPWEAR
AGILITY RXT
ATHLITE
ATR
ATTACK LIFE
BIG THINKING IN LITTLE SIZES
BLACKTOP
BOKS
CITY JAM
CLASSIC CALI
DMX
DMX REFLEX
EX-O-FIT
FLOP-SOCKS
HEXALITE
HYDROMOVE
I3
INSTA-PUMP
IVERSON
J.W. FOSTER
OTC
PLAY DRY
PLAY WARM
PRESEASON
THE PUMP
P.U.M.P.
RBK
REEBOK
REEBOK CLASSIC
REEBOK STRENGTH CYCLE
SLIDE REEBOK
SPEEDWICK
STEP REEBOK
TT
VECTOR
VERSAFLEX
VY ELECTRIFY
WEEBOK
XBEAM
Advertising Agencies:
Berlin Cameron United
100 Ave of the Americas 2nd Fl
New York, NY 10013
Tel.: (212) 824-2000
Fax: (212) 268-8454

Cramer-Krasselt
246 E Chicago St
Milwaukee, WI 53202
Tel.: (414) 227-3500
Fax: (414) 276-8710
Reebok/CCM Hockey Equipment

DDB Group Germany
Neue Schoenhauser Strasse 3-5
10178
Berlin, Germany
Tel.: (49) 302 4084 0
Fax: (49) 302 4084 500
Reebok (Lead Creative Agency)
— Amir Kassaei *(Chief Creative Officer)*

DDB New York
437 Madison Ave
New York, NY 10022-7001
Tel.: (212) 415-2000
Fax: (212) 415-3506
Creative

Tribal DDB Worldwide
437 Madison Ave 8th Fl
New York, NY 10022
Tel.: (212) 515-8600
Fax: (212) 515-8660
Digital Agency of Record

R.G. BARRY CORPORATION

13405 Yarmouth Rd NW
Pickerington, OH 43147-8493
Mailing Address:
PO Box 129
Columbus, OH 43216-0129
Tel.: (614) 864-6400
Fax: (614) 866-9787
Toll Free: (800) 848-7560
E-mail: footwear@rgbarry.com
Web Site: www.rgbarry.com
Approx. Sls.: $123,787,000
Approx. Number Employees: 154
Year Founded: 1947
Business Description:
Mfr & Marketer of Accessory Footwear & Comfort Products
S.I.C.: 3142; 5139
N.A.I.C.S.: 316212; 424340
Import Export
Advertising Expenditures: $3,285,000
Media: 4-5-6-9-15-19-25
Distr.: Natl.
Budget Set: Various
Personnel:
Gordon Zacks *(Chm)*
Greg A. Tunney *(Pres & CEO)*
Jose G. Ibarra *(CFO, Sec & Sr VP-Fin)*
Steve McInerney *(Pres-Licensed Superga Canvas Fashion Footwear Bus)*
Greg A. Ackard *(Sr VP-Sls)*
Glenn D. Evans *(Sr VP-Global Ops)*
Yvonne E. Kalucis *(Sr VP-HR)*
Lee F. Smith *(Sr VP-Creative Svcs)*
Tom Stoughton *(Dir-IT)*
Roy Youst *(Dir-Investor & Corp Comm)*
Brands & Products:
ANGEL TREADS
DEARFOAMS
THE DEARFOAMS COMPANY
DF
R.G. BARRY CORPORATION
SNUG TREDS
SOFT NOTES
TERRASOLES
UTOPIA

RICHLEE SHOE COMPANY

(Sub. of Alto Enterprises, Inc.)
7311 Grove Rd Ste K
Frederick, MD 21704-3300
Mailing Address:
PO Box 3566
Frederick, MD 21705-3566
Tel.: (301) 663-5111
Fax: (301) 663-1066
Toll Free: (800) 343-3810
E-mail: richlee@elevatorshoes.com
Web Site: www.elevatorshoes.com
Approx. Number Employees: 13
Year Founded: 1939
Business Description:
Elevator Shoes Distr
S.I.C.: 5961; 5139
N.A.I.C.S.: 454113; 424340
Media: 4-6-8-9-24
Distr.: Natl.
Budget Set: Jan. -Aug.
Personnel:
Robert C. Martin *(Pres)*
Jim Martin *(VP-Mktg & Mgr-Adv)*
Brands & Products:
ELEVATORS

THE ROCKPORT COMPANY, LLC

(Sub. of Reebok International Ltd.)
1895 J W Foster Blvd
Canton, MA 02021
Tel.: (781) 401-5000
Fax: (781) 401-5230
Toll Free: (800) ROCKPORT
Toll Free: (800) 258-6666
E-mail: rockport@custhelp.com
Web Site: www.rockport.com
Sales Range: $350-399.9 Million
Approx. Number Employees: 400
Year Founded: 1971
Business Description:
Mfr, Distr & Marketer of Comfort Footwear
S.I.C.: 3143; 3144
N.A.I.C.S.: 316213; 316214
Import Export
Media: 3-6
Distr.: Natl.
Budget Set: Apr.
Personnel:
Michael Rupp *(Pres & CEO)*
Sharon Bryan *(COO)*
Tobias Reiss-Schmidt *(VP-Global Retail)*
Kimberley Correia Hunt *(Head-ECommerce)*
Emmanuelle Accad *(Dir-Global PR & Events)*
Brands & Products:
THE DIFFERENCES INSIDE
ROCKPORT
ROCKPORT KIDS
ROCKPORT RESERVE
ROCKPORT XCS
Advertising Agencies:
Carat
200 Clarendon St 23rd Fl
Boston, MA 02116
Tel.: (617) 449-4100
Fax: (617) 449-4200

Maloney & Fox
89 5th Ave 4th Fl
New York, NY 10003
Tel.: (212) 243-2000
Fax: (212) 243-5500

ROCKY BRANDS, INC.

39 E Canal St
Nelsonville, OH 45764
Tel.: (740) 753-1951
Fax: (740) 753-4024
Toll Free: (866) 762-5972
Web Site: www.rockyboots.com
Approx. Sls.: $252,792,263
Approx. Number Employees: 2,450
Year Founded: 1932
Business Description:
Men's & Women's Footwear & Apparel Designer, Mfr & Marketer
S.I.C.: 3149; 2329; 2339; 2389; 3143; 3144; 5139
N.A.I.C.S.: 316219; 315211; 315212; 315999; 316213; 316214; 424340
Advertising Expenditures: $5,247,000
Media: 6-10-13-18-24
Personnel:
Mike Brooks *(Chm & CEO)*
David Sharp *(Pres & COO)*
James E. McDonald *(CFO & Exec VP)*
Thomas R. Morrison *(Sr VP-Sls-West)*
Kevin Dotson *(Mgr-Retail)*
Brands & Products:
DURANGO
GEORGIA BOOT
LEHIGH
MICHELIN
ROCKY
ZUMFOOT

S.B. FOOT TANNING COMPANY

(Sub. of Red Wing Shoe Company, Inc.)
805 Bench St
Red Wing, MN 55066-9550
Tel.: (651) 388-4731
Fax: (651) 385-5322
E-mail: sales@sbfoot.com
Web Site: www.sbfoot.com
E-Mail For Key Personnel:
Sales Director: sales@sbfoot.com
Approx. Number Employees: 250
Year Founded: 1872
Business Description:
Leather, Tanning & Finishing for Shoes & Upholstery
S.I.C.: 3111
N.A.I.C.S.: 316110
Import Export
Media: 2-4-7-10-17
Distr.: Natl.
Budget Set: Nov.
Brands & Products:
LEATHER FOR LIFE

SCHWARTZ & BENJAMIN, INC.

20 W 57th St 4th Fl
New York, NY 10019
Tel.: (212) 541-9092
Fax: (212) 974-0609
Web Site: www.sbshoes.biz
Sales Range: $200-249.9 Million
Approx. Number Employees: 25
Year Founded: 1923
Business Description:
Shoes Importer, Distr, & Whslr
S.I.C.: 8742
N.A.I.C.S.: 541611
Import
Media: 5
Distr.: Natl.
Budget Set: Oct. -Nov.
Personnel:
Daniel L. Schwartz *(Owner & CEO)*
Arthur R. Schwartz *(Chm)*
Steve Shapiro *(Pres)*
Loran Wurdemann *(VP-Fin & Controller)*

Key to Media (For complete agency information see *The Advertising Red Books-Agencies* edition):
1. Bus. Publs. 2. Cable T.V. 3. Catalogs & Directories. 4. Co-op Adv. 5. Consumer Mags. 6. D.M. to Bus. Estab.7. D.M. to Consumers
8. Daily Newsp. 9. Exhibits/Trade Shows 10. Foreign 11. Infomercial 12. Internet Adv.13. Multimedia 14. Network Radio
15. Network T.V. 16. Newsp. Distr. Mags. 17. Other 18. Outdoor (Posters, Transit) 19. Point of Purchase20. Premiums, Novelties
21. Product Samples 22. Special Events Mktg. 23. Spot Radio 24. Spot T.V. 25. Weekly Newsp. 26. Yellow Page Adv.

Schwartz & Benjamin, Inc. — (Continued)

Brands & Products:
DANIBLACK

SHOE CARNIVAL, INC.

7500 E Columbia St
Evansville, IN 47715-9127
Tel.: (812) 867-6471
Fax: (812) 867-4570
E-mail: info@shoecarnival.com
Web Site: www.shoecarnival.com
Approx. Sls.: $739,189,000
Approx. Number Employees: 1,800
Year Founded: 1978
Business Description:
Footwear Retailer
S.I.C.: 5661
N.A.I.C.S.: 448210
Advertising Expenditures: $31,100,000
Media: 3-6-9-13-18-19-23-24-25
Personnel:
J. Wayne Weaver *(Chm)*
Mark L. Lemond *(Pres & CEO)*
W. Kerry Jackson *(CFO, Treas & Exec VP)*
Terry L. Clements *(CIO & Sr VP)*
Kathy A. Yearwood *(Chief Acctg Officer, Sr VP & Controller)*
David A. Kapp *(Sec, Sr VP-Plng & Allocation)*
Clifton E. Sifford *(Exec VP & Gen Mgr-Mdse)*
Timothy T. Baker *(Exec VP-Store Ops)*
Todd A. Beurman *(Sr VP-Mktg)*
Mitchell A. Chandler *(Sr VP & Div Mgr-Athletics & Children Mdse)*
Sean M. Georges *(Sr VP-HR)*
Steven D. Meyer *(Sr VP-Store Ops)*
Greg L. Brown *(VP & Mgr-North Div)*
Lisa A. Rosenbaum *(VP, Mgr-Divisional Mdse-Womens Non Athletics & Accessories)*
Samantha Payton *(Asst VP-Mktg)*
Tucker R. Robinson *(Asst VP-Buyer Mens Athletics)*
Thomas G Vernarsky *(Asst VP-Buyer Womens Sport & Casual)*
Pam Simpson *(Dir-Visual Mdsg)*
Pam Simpsons *(Dir-Visual Mdsg & Promos)*
Brands & Products:
THE CARNIVAL
CARNIVAL LITES
COLOR BLOCK DESIGN
DONNA LAWRENCE
INNOCENCE
OAK MEADOW
SHOE CARNIVAL
TRADE DRESS
VIA NOVA
VICTORIA SPENSER
Advertising Agency:
22squared
1170 Peachtree St NE 15th Fl
Atlanta, GA 30309-7649
Tel.: (404) 347-8700
Fax: (404) 347-8800
Fall 2008 Back-to-School Campaign

SIERRA TRADING POST INC.

5025 Campstool Rd
Cheyenne, WY 82007
Tel.: (307) 775-8050
Tel.: (307) 775-8369
Fax: (307) 775-8087
Toll Free: (800) 713-4543
Web Site: www.sierratradingpost.com
Sales Range: $100-124.9 Million
Approx. Number Employees: 800
Year Founded: 1986
Business Description:
Name Brand Clothes & Outdoor Gear Retailer
S.I.C.: 5961; 5651
N.A.I.C.S.: 454113; 448140
Media: 4-5-13
Personnel:
Keith Richardson *(Founder)*
Gary Imig *(Pres)*
Burt Adam *(Dir-Mktg-Online)*
TJ Croissant *(Dir-Mktg)*
Bria Kruseck *(Dir-Mktg-Print & Retail)*
Brands & Products:
SIERRA TRADING POST
YOUR IN-HOME OUTLET MALL

SKECHERS U.S.A., INC.

228 Manhattan Beach Blvd
Manhattan Beach, CA 90266-5347
Tel.: (310) 318-3100
Fax: (310) 318-5019
Toll Free: (800) 456-3627
E-mail: info@skechers.com
Web Site: www.skx.com
Approx. Sls.: $2,006,868,000
Approx. Number Employees: 2,517
Year Founded: 1992
Business Description:
Designs & Markets Branded Contemporary Casual, Active, Rugged & Lifestyle Footwear for Men, Women & Children
S.I.C.: 5139
N.A.I.C.S.: 424340
Advertising Expenditures: $98,300,000
Media: 1-4-5-6-10-11-13-15-18-19-22-23-24
Personnel:
Michael Greenberg *(Owner)*
Robert Greenberg *(Chm & CEO)*
David Weinberg *(CFO, COO & Exec VP)*
Philip G. Paccione *(Gen Counsel, Sec & Exec VP-Bus Affairs)*
Larry Clark *(Sr VP-Sourcing)*
Jason Greenberg *(Sr VP Mktg)*
Jeffrey Greenberg *(Sr VP-Active Electronic Media)*
Jennifer Weiderman *(VP & Gen Mgr-SKECHERS Fitness Grp)*
Mark Bravo *(VP-Fin)*
Jennifer Clay *(VP-Corp Comm)*
Brands & Products:

Flying Point Media
494 8th Ave 20th Fl
New York, NY 10001
Tel.: (212) 629-4960
Fax: (212) 629-4967

WMI Out-of-Home
Ste 201 1221 Post Rd E
Westport, CT 06880-5430
Tel.: (203) 256-4168
Fax: (203) 256-0883

SLJ RETAIL LLC

1580 Warsaw Rd # 206
Roswell, GA 30076-1532
Tel.: (770) 801-1200
Fax: (770) 801-0202
Toll Free: (800) 927-4402
E-mail: info@samandlibby.com
Approx. Number Employees: 500
Year Founded: 1926
Business Description:
Retail Shoes for Women
S.I.C.: 5947
N.A.I.C.S.: 453220
Import
Advertising Expenditures: $2,000,000
Media: 4-6-8-9-18
Distr.: Natl.
Budget Set: Feb.
Brands & Products:
BUTLER

SPORTO CORP.

65 Sprague St Ste 1
Boston, MA 02136-2062
Tel.: (617) 364-3001
Fax: (617) 364-3118
Toll Free: (888) 2SPORTO
E-mail: info@caravanproducts.com
Web Site: www.sporto.net
Approx. Number Employees: 26
Year Founded: 1926
Business Description:
Women's Winter Boots Mfr
S.I.C.: 2339
N.A.I.C.S.: 315212
Advertising Expenditures: $1,605,000
Bus. Publs.: $50,000; Catalogs & Directories: $100,000; Co-op Adv.: $400,000; Consumer Mags.: $300,000; D.M. to Bus. Estab.: $30,000; Exhibits/Trade Shows: $100,000; Outdoor (Posters, Transit): $50,000; Point of Purchase: $20,000; Premiums, Novelties: $200,000; Product Samples: $200,000; Special Events Mktg.: $50,000; Spot Radio: $5,000; Weekly Newsp.: $100,000
Distr.: Natl.
Personnel:
David Brilliant *(Pres & CEO)*
Noreen Brilliant *(VP-Operations & Mktg Dir)*
Karen Kennedy *(Dir-HR)*
Brands & Products:
ALICIA
ALISSA
ALLISON
AMBER
ANDREA
ANNA
ANNIE
APPLE
ASHTON
ASPEN
BEAUTY
BECCA
BELLA
BLAIR
BRADY
BRILLIANT
BRITNEY
BROOKE
BRYCE
BRYNN
CAILYN
CATE
CORY
DALIA
DARIA
DIVA
ERIN
EVANS
FUR-ME
FUR NOW
GARNET
GENA
GIANNA
GRACIE
GRETCHEN
HALLEY
HEATHER
HOPE
JAN
JANE
JOANNA
JULIA
JUPITER
KATRINA
KENDALL
LAURA
LEAH
LUCY
MADISON
MANDY
MARCIE
MARISKA
MEADOW
MIRANDA
NADIA
NELLIE
NORA
PARRIS
PAYTON
POLARTEC
PRESLEE
SASSY
SPLENDOR
SPORTO
STACEY
STARR
TAYLA
TENILLE
TIFANI
TOPAZ
TRACY
TRISTA
VALERIE
ZARA
ZETA

STANBEE COMPANY, INC.

70 Broad St
Carlstadt, NJ 07072-2006
Mailing Address:
PO Box 436
Carlstadt, NJ 07072-0436
Tel.: (201) 933-9666
Fax: (201) 933-7985
E-mail: info@stanbee.com
Web Site: www.stanbee.com
Approx. Number Employees: 20
Year Founded: 1947
Business Description:
Mfr. of Shoe Components
S.I.C.: 3149; 3089
N.A.I.C.S.: 316219; 326199
Import Export
Media: 2-6-7-13-17
Distr.: Natl.
Budget Set: Nov. -Dec.
Personnel:
Michael Berkson *(Pres)*
Bruce Goldberg *(Dir-Tech Svcs)*
Leo Provencher *(Mgr-Tech-Asia)*
Yasser Trisatriya *(Mgr-Sls-Stanbee Asia Limited)*
Brands & Products:
EDGE
SPORTOE
STANBEE
STANPLAS

Key to Media (For complete agency information see *The Advertising Red Books-Agencies* edition):
1. Bus. Publs. 2. Cable T.V. 3. Catalogs & Directories. 4. Co-op Adv. 5. Consumer Mags. 6. D.M. to Bus. Estab.7. D.M. to Consumers
8. Daily Newsp. 9. Exhibits/Trade Shows 10. Foreign 11. Infomercial 12. Internet Adv.13. Multimedia 14. Network Radio
15. Network T.V. 16. Newsp. Distr. Mags. 17. Other 18. Outdoor (Posters, Transit) 19. Point of Purchase20. Premiums, Novelties
21. Product Samples 22. Special Events Mktg. 23. Spot Radio 24. Spot T.V. 25. Weekly Newsp. 26. Yellow Page Adv.

VANTAGE

STEVEN MADDEN LTD
5216 Barnett Ave
Long Island City, NY 11104-1018
Tel.: (718) 446-1800
Fax: (718) 446-5599
Toll Free: (888) 275-3633
E-mail: info@smadden.com
Web Site: www.stevemadden.com
Approx. Sls.: $635,418,000
Approx. Number Employees: 780
Year Founded: 1993
Business Description:
Designer, Wholesaler & Retailer of Shoes
S.I.C.: 3144; 2389; 3021; 3143; 5699
N.A.I.C.S.: 316214; 315999; 316211; 316213; 448150
Advertising Expenditures: $4,713,000
Media: 4-5-6-13-18-19-22-23-24
Personnel:
Edward Rosenfeld *(Chm & CEO)*
Andrew Shames *(Pres)*
Arvind Dharia *(CFO & Sec)*
Awadhesh Sinha *(COO)*
Joseph Masella *(Pres-Sls-Adesso Madden)*
Amelia Newton Varela *(Exec VP-Wholesale & Retail)*
Brands & Products:
ACCEE
ADALINE
ADDISONN
ADORABL
ALICCE
ALISAH
AMMBER
ARLIZ
AVENSIS
AVINO
BACANO
BAMBOLA
BARBYY
BELAGIO
BELINI
BENITAA
BENZA
BERRIE
BEVAN
BHOTSTUDHB
BIANNA
BITTERR
BLOKEE
BLOYAL
BOLU
BONNNY
BOOGLE
BRANDDYY
BRANDE
BRAVVOO
BRIGGHT
BRUNELLA
BSAFARIHB
BUMMBLE
BWANDERHB
BWOVSTUDT
CAGED
CALYPPSO
CAMI
CAMORA
CAPRIE
CARLINN
CATELINA
CENTURIE
CHANCEE
CHARRGER
CHARRITY
CHERYL
CHIKAA
COASTER
COLONIAL
COMANCHI
COMPEET
CORALINE
CORKSCRU
CRAZZY
CREEDD
CYBUL
DECCK
DESYRE
DEVINNE
DOLLE
DOUBBLE
DR BUCK
DREEMM
DS-DENIM
DS-DITSY
DS-LACEY
DS-TUXEDO
EBYT
ELA
ELANNIE
EVELINA
EXTREEMM
EXYTE
EYELIT
FANTACY
FELLECIA
FENDORA
FIESSTAA
FINDD
FLORAH
FORTAY
FRINGYY
GARRCIA
GENEVIVA
GENIOUS
GESAR
GIMBAL
GLADIATORS
GLAMORUS
GLNLIVET
GRETCHAN
GUINNESS
H-JELLYB
HANAA
HAZZARD
HILARIE
HONOUR
INCENTIV
INRAGEE
INTYCE
JACKSONN
JAGGERR
JULIUS
JUNEAU
JUSTIFYY
JUSTINNA
KALISTAA
KANDRAA
KAPRISE
KAROLL
KASIDY
KASTRO
KAZLER
KENEDIE
KINKY
KOBRAA
LAINY
LASOO
LAYYLAA
LEBRA
LENNIN
LENORAH
LIBBIEE
LIENA
LONESTAR
LONGSMOCK
LULLABY
LUNNAR
MABBELL
MAJESTYY
MANDYY
MARILLA
MARK-IT
MARLENE
MARRVEL
MAXIMO
MAYANA
MERRIEE
MINNAH
MIRAKLE
MISSYY
MODESTYY
MONIKAA
MOTIF
MYKONOS
MYRAH
N-FLORAL
N-PEACE
N-TIDIED
NADIAH
NICOLETT
OAKWOODD
OTTOWA
PALACEE
PANDITA
PARADY
PASION
PAYTENN
PERAIDA
PERSIS
PHEDRA
PHEOBE
PICOLO
PIXELL
PLAYFIL
POINTTER
PRESCOTT
PRIMMMO
PYRENA
QUALITI
QUANTUMM
QUINNE
RACCER
RADIO
RAVIN
RAYAH
RETTRO
REVOLVOR
ROARR
ROCKII
ROMAAN
ROSSEY
RUFIO
RYTZ
S-FTIGHT
S-LEGIN
S563
S569
SALLLY
SALSERA
SAMBUKA
SAMUI
SANFRANN
SANTORNI
SASALITO
SCOTCHH
SEASYDE
SECCCO
SEERI
SENTER
SEQUINE
SERANADE
SERENITI
SERPANT
SERPICO
SHA
SHHIMER
SHOCKERR
SHOE BIZ
SHOOTERR
SHUTTLE
SIAM
SINNERR
SKORCH
SLADDE
SLASSSH
SLICCKK
SLINKY
SLIQUE
SMITTIN
SNIPP
SOHOE
SOYA
SPIIN
SPIRALL
SPRINKEL
STETSONN
STEVE MADDEN MENS
STEVEN BY STEVE MADDEN
STEVIES
STINNG
STOOPER
STUDS
SWAYYY
SWEATME
SWEEPT
SWEETIEZ
SWINDLEEV
SYBEL
SYMBILL
TAABOO
TACEE
TALENTT
TAMA
TANGITA
TANTLIZE
TAPPLE
TARNEYY
TAYLA
TEEPEA
TEMPESTT
TESSAA
TIAMORA
TOCARRA
TOWWER
TRACII
TRAMATIC
TRAXX
TRINITIE
TRIPLET
TRUFLE
TRUSST
TUXXEDO
VALARI
VENECIN
VHALEN
VICIOUUS
VIVACI
W-SNAKE
W-STUDS
W-WOVEN
WARLI
WEDGIEE
WENDE
WITNEY
WRAPPP

Key to Media (For complete agency information see *The Advertising Red Books-Agencies* edition):
1. Bus. Publs. 2. Cable T.V. 3. Catalogs & Directories. 4. Co-op Adv. 5. Consumer Mags. 6. D.M. to Bus. Estab.7. D.M. to Consumers
8. Daily Newsp. 9. Exhibits/Trade Shows 10. Foreign 11. Infomercial 12. Internet Adv.13. Multimedia 14. Network Radio
15. Network T.V. 16. Newsp. Distr. Mags. 17. Other 18. Outdoor (Posters, Transit) 19. Point of Purchase20. Premiums, Novelties
21. Product Samples 22. Special Events Mktg. 23. Spot Radio 24. Spot T.V. 25. Weekly Newsp. 26. Yellow Page Adv.

Steven Madden Ltd — (Continued)

WYSH
XCALIBUR
ZESTIE
ZIPUP
ZOEII

THE STRIDE RITE CORPORATION

(Sub. of Collective Brands Inc.)
191 Spring St
Lexington, MA 02421-8045
Mailing Address:
PO Box 9191
Lexington, MA 02420-9191
Tel.: (617) 824-6000
Fax: (617) 824-6549
E-mail: info@strideritecorp.com
Web Site: www.strideritecorp.com
Sales Range: $1-4.9 Billion
Approx. Number Employees: 3,100
Year Founded: 1919
Business Description:
Children's Shoes, Men's & Women's Casual Shoes, Work Shoes & Athletic Footwear
S.I.C.: 5661; 5139
N.A.I.C.S.: 448210; 424340
Import Export
Advertising Expenditures: $40,315,000
Media: 4-5-6-8-9-10-15-18-19-20-24-25
Distr.: Natl.
Budget Set: Oct.
Personnel:
Gregg S. Ribatt *(Pres & CEO)*
Melaine Walsh *(Dir-Creative Svcs)*
Brands & Products:
GRASSHOPPERS
KEDS
MUNCHKIN
PRO-KEDS
SPERRY TOP-SIDERS
STRIDE RITE
Advertising Agency:
Duffy & Shanley, Inc.
10 Charles St
Providence, RI 02904
Tel.: (401) 274-0001
Fax: (401) 274-3535

TEXON MATERIALS INC.

(Sub. of Texon International Group Ltd.)
1190 Huntington Rd
Russell, MA 01071
Tel.: (413) 862-3652
Fax: (413) 862-4543
Toll Free: (800) 800-3652
E-mail: enquiries@texon.com
Web Site: www.texon.com
Sales Range: $25-49.9 Million
Approx. Number Employees: 35
Year Founded: 1950
Business Description:
Elastomeric Fiber Materials Mfr Used in Footwear, Luggage, Leather Products, Hats & Caps
S.I.C.: 2824
N.A.I.C.S.: 325222
Import Export
Advertising Expenditures: $200,000
Media: 2-4-7-10
Distr.: Intl.; Natl.
Budget Set: Nov. -Dec.
Personnel:
Mark Reardon *(Gen Mgr)*

THE TIMBERLAND COMPANY

200 Domain Dr
Stratham, NH 03885-2575
Tel.: (603) 772-9500
Fax: (603) 773-1640
E-mail: info@timberland.com
Web Site: www.timberland.com
Approx. Rev.: $1,429,484,000
Approx. Number Employees: 5,600
Year Founded: 1973
Business Description:
Men's, Women's & Children's Footwear, Apparel & Sportswear
S.I.C.: 3143; 2389; 3144; 5651
N.A.I.C.S.: 316213; 315999; 316214; 448140
Import
Advertising Expenditures: $47,146,000
Media: 4-5-6-8-10-11-13-18-19-24-31
Distr.: Intl.; Natl.
Budget Set: Oct.
Personnel:
Sidney W. Swartz *(Chm)*
Jeffrey B. Swartz *(Pres & CEO)*
Carrie W. Teffner *(CFO)*
Suja Chandrasekaran *(CIO)*
Carden N. Welsh *(Chief Admin Officer & Sr VP)*
John J. Fitzgerald, Jr. *(Chief Acctg Officer, VP & Controller)*
Michael J. Harrison *(Chief Brand Officer)*
Danette Wineberg *(Gen Counsel, Sec & VP)*
Mark Bryden *(VP & Gen Mgr-North America)*
John Dolan *(VP-Sls)*
Jim O'Connor *(Dir-Mktg)*
Robin Giampa *(Dir-Corp Comm)*
Bob McCarthy *(Sr Mgr-Product)*
Brands & Products:
BALM PROOFER
BOOT SAUCE
EARTHKEEPERS
MADE TO WORK
MAKE IT BETTER
MOUNTAIN ATHLETICS
PRO
SMART COMFORT
TBL
TIMBERLAND
TIMBERLAND PRO
TITAN
WAXIMUM
WEATHERGEAR
Advertising Agencies:
Leagas Delaney Group Limited
1 Alfred Place
London, WC1E 7EB, United Kingdom
Tel.: (44) 207 758 1758
Fax: (44) 207 758 1760
Agency of Record
Earthkeepers
Escape Faster
Footwear & Apparel
Spring Tactical

Mullen
40 Broad St
Boston, MA 02109
Tel.: (617) 226-9000
Fax: (617) 226-9100
(Earthkeepers)

Porter Novelli
(Sub. of Omnicom Group, Inc.)
75 Varick St 6th Fl
New York, NY 10013
Tel.: (212) 601-8000
Fax: (212) 601-8101
Timberland PRO
— Alyson Campbell *(Acct Exec)*

Range Online Media
131 E Exchange Ave Ste 216
Fort Worth, TX 76164
Tel.: (817) 625-4157
Fax: (817) 625-4167

Titan
850 Third Ave
New York, NY 10022
Tel.: (212) 644-6200
Fax: (212) 644-2010

Vizeum UK Ltd.
90 Whitfield St
London, W1 T4EZ, United Kingdom
Tel.: (44) 2073799000
Fax: (44) 2075707415

Winsper Inc.
77 Summer St
Boston, MA 02110
Tel.: (617) 695-2900
Fax: (617) 696-2910

TINGLEY RUBBER CORPORATION

1 Cragwood Rd
South Plainfield, NJ 07080
Tel.: (908) 757-7474
Fax: (908) 757-9239
Toll Free: (800) 631-5498
E-mail: customerservice@tingleyrubber.com
Web Site: www.tingleyrubber.com
E-Mail For Key Personnel:
President: bmccollum@tingleyrubber.com
Marketing Director: jtowey@tingleyrubber.com
Public Relations: rsportiello@tingleyrubber.com
Approx. Number Employees: 35
Year Founded: 1896
Business Description:
Molded Rubber Footwear, Protective Clothing, Over the Sock Protective Footwear Mfr
S.I.C.: 3021; 3069
N.A.I.C.S.: 316211; 326299
Import Export
Distr.: Natl.
Personnel:
Bruce McCollum *(Chm)*
Paul Bolton *(Pres & COO)*
Jim Towey *(Mgr-Mktg)*
Brands & Products:
THE AMERICAN CLASSICS
COMFORT TUFF
DURA SCRIM
EAGLE
FLEXNET
THE IRON EAGLE
RAINTRACKS
SCRIM
STORM CHAMP
STORMFLEX
STORMTRACKS
TINGLEY
TINGLEY RUBBER
TUFF-ENUFF
TUFF-ENUFF PLUS
WEATHER FASHIONS
WEATHER TUFF
WEBDRI
WORKBRUTES
Advertising Agency:
PL Communications
417 Victor St
Scotch Plains, NJ 07076
Tel.: (908) 889-8884
Fax: (908) 889-8886
Toll Free: (800) 569-8882
— Paul Lavenhar *(Acct. Exec.)*

TT GROUP, INC.

(Sub. of TT Group Ltd.)
702 S Carnation Dr
Aurora, MO 65605
Tel.: (417) 678-2181
Fax: (417) 678-6901
Web Site: skyler.tt-group.com
Approx. Number Employees: 115
Business Description:
Misses & Junior Shoes Mfr & Distr
S.I.C.: 3144; 5139
N.A.I.C.S.: 316214; 424340
Import Export
Advertising Expenditures: $500,000
Media: 2-4-5-6-7-9-10-19-20-26
Distr.: Intl.; Natl.
Personnel:
James Perivolaris *(Pres & CEO)*
Tom Zens *(Sr VP-Sls)*
David McAllister *(Controller & Office Mgr)*
Mike Sheperd *(Plant Mgr)*
Brands & Products:
CLINIC
CLOUDLITES
FOOT THRILLS
SANDPIPERS
SPORTWALKS
TENDER TOOTSIES
TOE WARMERS
WANDERLUST

VANS, INC.

(Sub. of VF Corporation)
6550 Katella Ave
Cypress, CA 90630
Tel.: (714) 889-6100
E-mail: custserv@vans.com
Web Site: www.vans.com
Sales Range: $300-349.9 Million
Approx. Number Employees: 1,885
Year Founded: 1966
Business Description:
Footwear & Apparel Designer, Mfr & Whslr
S.I.C.: 5139; 2329; 5661; 5941
N.A.I.C.S.: 424340; 315228; 448210; 451110
Media: 1-2-3-4-5-6-8-10-13-15-18-22-31
Personnel:
Doug Palladini *(VP-Mktg)*
Amy Lee *(Mgr-Category Mktg, Classics, California Collection & Vault)*
Brands & Products:
AGENCY
AIRPORTS
ANAHEIM
AQUANET
AUDIE
AUTHENTIC

Key to Media (For complete agency information see *The Advertising Red Books-Agencies* edition):
1. Bus. Publs. 2. Cable T.V. 3. Catalogs & Directories. 4. Co-op Adv. 5. Consumer Mags. 6. D.M. to Bus. Estab.7. D.M. to Consumers
8. Daily Newsp. 9. Exhibits/Trade Shows 10. Foreign 11. Infomercial 12. Internet Adv.13. Multimedia 14. Network Radio
15. Network T.V. 16. Newsp. Distr. Mags. 17. Other 18. Outdoor (Posters, Transit) 19. Point of Purchase20. Premiums, Novelties
21. Product Samples 22. Special Events Mktg. 23. Spot Radio 24. Spot T.V. 25. Weekly Newsp. 26. Yellow Page Adv.

BADGES
BASHA
BATAVIA
BIGGIE
BIGMOUTH
BIKER SKULL
BLUE LETTER
BONE X TANK
BRISCO
BUCKY LASEK
BUENA
BUNGLE
BUTTERSKULLS
CAPITAL LETTERS
CHECKER
CHEK LO
CHESS QUEEN
CHEX
CHUKKA
CLASSIC
CONDOS
COUNTRY TIME
CRANDAL
DABNEY
DIM WITT
DOGHOUSE
DRAGON
DULCE
DUNBAR
EL PORTO
ELEPHANT BUBBALS
ELISE
ERA
ESCOBAR
ESTILO
FADED
FIASCO DIS
FLIP FLOP
FRESCA
GIA
GIBBO
GIRLY
GUAPA
HALF CAB
HARTON
HERMILT
HUDSON
ISIS
JESSEN
JETSIE STRIPE CAMI
KATINA
LAURS
LEANNA
LEISURE TIME
LUX
MANNAZ
MARIANNA
MARY
MOO SHOO
MOTTED
NESTER
NIMBLE
NOLEN
NOOGEN
OLD SKOOL
OLD SKULL
PINK ELEPHANTS
PLAT SIDESTRIPE
POGA
POSSE
PREPY
PRO TEC
QUINCY
RAE LYNN
RATA
RAY RAY
RIFFS
ROCA LOCA
ROSSMORE
SAMONE
SANFORD
SERENADE
SERPENTEE
SHAKEDOWN
SHELBY
SHOCKROCK
SHUNTZ
SKATE CHIC
SKATEBOARDERS
SKLUTTERBY
SKULL
SLEUTH
SLIM
STRUMMERTIME
SUGAR PIE
SUPER
SWIRL
TAKE 'EM
TAKEDOWN
TONY TRUJILLO
TOWNIE
TURBO CHARGED
TWITTER
VANSCURVES
VERMOUTH
WESLEY
WRANGLE

THE WALKING COMPANY, INC.

(Sub. of The Walking Company Holdings, Inc.)
2475 Townsgate Ste 200
Westlake Village, CA 91361
Tel.: (805) 496-3005
Fax: (805) 496-3240
Web Site: www.walkingco.com
Sales Range: $100-124.9 Million
Approx. Number Employees: 40
Year Founded: 1991
Business Description:
Shoes & Accessories Retailer
S.I.C.: 5661
N.A.I.C.S.: 448210
Import Export
Media: 3-4-8-9-13-18-19-20-22-23-24
Personnel:
Mike Grenley *(Sr VP)*
Brands & Products:
THE WALKING COMPANY COLLECTION

WEINBRENNER SHOE COMPANY, INC.

108 S Polk St
Merrill, WI 54452-2348
Tel.: (715) 536-5521
Fax: (715) 536-1172
Toll Free: (800) 826-0002
E-mail: wsc@weinbrennerusa.com
Web Site: www.weinbrennerusa.com
Approx. Number Employees: 350
Year Founded: 1892
Business Description:
Uniform, Work, Safety, Outdoor Boots & Shoes Mfr & Supplier
S.I.C.: 3143; 3144
N.A.I.C.S.: 316213; 316214
Import Export
Advertising Expenditures: $700,000
Media: 4-6-7-8-10-19-21
Distr.: Natl.
Budget Set: Nov.
Personnel:
Lance Nienow *(Pres & CEO)*
Pat Miner *(Sr VP-Sls & Mktg)*
Richard DiFalco *(VP-Sls)*
Dick Martens *(Mgr-Sls-Intl)*
Dave Hinke *(Coord-Adv)*
Brands & Products:
AEROMET
B.I.A.S
CARRIER PRO
FIRERANGE
GENERATION FLEX
MID HIGH DUAL AIR
N.E.O.S.
SYMPATEX
T.A.S.A.R
THOROGOOD
THROGRIP
ULTIMATE
VIBRAM
WEINBRENNER
WOOD N' STREAM
WORK ONE

WELLCO ENTERPRISES, INC.

(Holding of Golden Gate Capital)
150 Westwood Cir
Waynesville, NC 28786-1987
Mailing Address:
PO Box 188
Waynesville, NC 28786-0188
Tel.: (828) 456-3545
Fax: (828) 456-3547
Toll Free: (800) 840-3155
E-mail: info@wellco.com
Web Site: www.wellco.com
E-Mail For Key Personnel:
Sales Director: sales@wellco.com
Approx. Rev.: $44,022,000
Approx. Number Employees: 719
Year Founded: 1941
Business Description:
Mfr. of Footwear for U.S. Government
S.I.C.: 3143; 3021; 3559
N.A.I.C.S.: 316213; 316211; 333298
Import Export
Media: 2-6-9-10-13-26
Distr.: Natl.
Budget Set: Sept.
Personnel:
Lee Ferguson *(CEO)*
Tammy Francis *(Treas, Controller & Asst Sec)*
Neil Streeter *(VP-Sls & Mktg)*
Brands & Products:
SOLE ULTRA
SUPERFEET
SYNERGIZER GREEN
TUFFKUSHION
V-TRAX
WELLCO

WEYCO GROUP, INC.

333 W Estabrook Blvd
Glendale, WI 53212-1067
Mailing Address:
PO Box 1188
Milwaukee, WI 53201-1188
Tel.: (414) 908-1600
Fax: (414) 908-1601
E-mail: investor.relations@weycogroup.com
Web Site: www.weycogroup.com
Approx. Sls.: $229,231,000
Approx. Number Employees: 562
Year Founded: 1906
Business Description:
Shoe Mfr, Whslr & Retailer
S.I.C.: 5139; 3143
N.A.I.C.S.: 424340; 316213
Import Export
Advertising Expenditures: $7,900,000
Media: 2-4-5-6-8-10-13-19-23
Distr.: Natl.
Budget Set: Dec.
Personnel:
Thomas W. Florsheim, Jr. *(Chm & CEO)*
John W. Florsheim *(Pres, COO & Asst Sec)*
John F. Wittkowske *(CFO & Sr VP)*
Peter S. Grossman *(Pres-Nunn Bush Brand, Retail Div & Sr VP)*
Brian Flannery *(Pres-Stacy Adams Brand & VP)*
Kevin Schiff *(Pres-Florsheim Brand & VP)*
Judy Anderson *(Treas & VP-Fin)*
Matthew J. Engerman *(VP-Sls-Nunn Bush Brand)*
Beverly Goldberg *(VP-Sls-Florsheim Brand)*
Al Jackson *(VP-Customer Rels & Vendor Compliance)*
George Sotiros *(VP-IT)*
Allison Woss *(VP-Pur)*
Jeff Douglass *(Mgr-Mktg)*
Brands & Products:
BRASS BOOT
FLORSHEIM
NUNN-BUSH
NUNN BUSH NXXT
SAO
STACY ADAMS
Advertising Agencies:
BVK
250 W Coventry Ct #300
Milwaukee, WI 53217-3972
Tel.: (414) 228-1990
Fax: (414) 228-7561
Toll Free: (888) 347-3212

Cramer-Krasselt
246 E Chicago St
Milwaukee, WI 53202
Tel.: (414) 227-3500
Fax: (414) 276-8710
Branding
Digital
Florsheim
Media Agency of Record
Nunn Bush
Retail
Sales
Stacy Adams

Laughlin/Constable, Inc.
207 E Michigan St
Milwaukee, WI 53202-4998
Tel.: (414) 272-2400
Fax: (414) 270-7140
(Nunn Bush; Brass Boot (All Men's Shoes); Weyenberg; Stacy Adams)

WOLVERINE WORLD WIDE, INC.

9341 Courtland Dr
Rockford, MI 49351-0001
Tel.: (616) 866-5500
Fax: (616) 866-0257
E-mail: communications@wwwinc.com
Web Site:
www.wolverineworldwide.com
E-Mail For Key Personnel:
Public Relations: communications@wwwinc.com

Wolverine World Wide, Inc. — (Continued)

Approx. Rev.: $1,248,517,000
Approx. Number Employees: 4,139
Year Founded: 1883
Business Description:
Branded Casual, Active Lifestyle, Work, Outdoor Sport & Uniform Footwear & Slippers Designer, Mfr & Marketer
S.I.C.: 2329; 3143; 5661
N.A.I.C.S.: 315228; 316213; 448210
Import Export
Advertising Expenditures: $2,682,000
Media: 2-3-4-5-6-7-8-9-10-11-14-15-16-18-19-20-21-22-23-24-25
Distr.: Intl.; Natl.
Budget Set: Sept.
Personnel:
Blake W. Krueger *(Chm, Pres & CEO)*
Donald T. Grimes *(CFO, Treas & Sr VP)*
Christopher E. Hufnagel *(Pres-Retail)*
Mark Sandquist *(Pres-Global Apparel & Accessories)*
James D. Zwiers *(Pres-Outdoor Grp)*
Kenneth A. Grady *(Gen Counsel & Sec)*
Pamela L. Linton *(Sr VP-HR)*
Seth Cobb *(VP & Gen Mgr-Merrell-Outdoor Grp)*
Chip Coe *(VP & Gen Mgr-Chaco-Outdoor Grp)*
Todd Yates *(VP & Gen Mgr-Mktg & Apparel)*
Bill Dodge *(VP-Product Dev-Merrell, Patagonia Footwear, Chaco)*
Jodi Watson *(VP-ECommerce & Consumer Insights-Global)*
Christi Cowdin *(Dir-IR & Corp Comm)*
Brandan Hill *(Dir-Product Dev-Chaco-Outdoor Grp)*
Whitney Conner *(Mgr-Mktg-Chaco-Outdoor Grp)*
Tom Stolz *(Mgr-Natl Sls-Chaco-Outdoor Grp)*
Adam C. Vincent *(Mgr-US Supply Chain)*
Lauren Mack *(Specialist-Mktg-Wolverine Brand)*
Brands & Products:
BATES
BOUNCE
CHACO
COMFORT CURVE
CUSHE
DURASHOCKS
HIDDEN TRACKS
HUSH PUPPIES
HYTEST
ITECHNOLOGY
MERRELL
MULTISHOX
SEBAGO
TRACK 'N TRAIL
WOLVERINE
WOLVERINE BOOTS & SHOES - THEY DON'T QUIT
WOLVERINE WORLD WIDE
Advertising Agencies:
Cultivator Advertising & Design
2737 Larimer St Ste B
Denver, CO 80205
Tel.: (303) 444-4134
Fax: (800) 783-4152
Chaco

Hanson Dodge Inc.
220 E Buffalo St
Milwaukee, WI 53202
Tel.: (414) 347-1266
Fax: (414) 347-0493
Agency of Record

Lambert, Edwards & Associates, Inc.
171 Monroe NW Ste 400
Grand Rapids, MI 49503
Tel.: (616) 233-0500
Fax: (616) 233-0600

Key to Media (For complete agency information see *The Advertising Red Books-Agencies* edition):
1. Bus. Publs. 2. Cable T.V. 3. Catalogs & Directories. 4. Co-op Adv. 5. Consumer Mags. 6. D.M. to Bus. Estab.7. D.M. to Consumers 8. Daily Newsp. 9. Exhibits/Trade Shows 10. Foreign 11. Infomercial 12. Internet Adv.13. Multimedia 14. Network Radio 15. Network T.V. 16. Newsp. Distr. Mags. 17. Other 18. Outdoor (Posters, Transit) 19. Point of Purchase20. Premiums, Novelties 21. Product Samples 22. Special Events Mktg. 23. Spot Radio 24. Spot T.V. 25. Weekly Newsp. 26. Yellow Page Adv.

Sporting Goods

Active Sportswear — Air Rifles — Ammunition — Athletic Footwear — Billiard & Pool Tables — Bowling Centers — Camping Equipment — Exercise Equipment — Firearms — Fishing Tackle — Golf Supplies & Equipment — Skates — Skis — Tennis Supplies — Tents

180S, LLC
701 E Pratt St Ste 180
Baltimore, MD 21202
Tel.: (410) 534-6320
Fax: (410) 534-6321
E-mail: info@180s.com
Web Site: www.180s.com
Sales Range: $25-49.9 Million
Approx. Number Employees: 40
Year Founded: 1994
Business Description:
Mfr. of Athletic Performance Wear
S.I.C.: 7389
N.A.I.C.S.: 519190
Media: 4-10-17-18-22
Personnel:
Tom Lych *(Chief Legal Officer)*
Shelley Foland *(VP-Sls)*
George Campbell *(Dir-Design & Dev)*
Christina Isenhour *(Mgr-Production)*
Daniel Knisely *(Mgr-Sls-Natl Accts)*
Brands & Products:
180S
BASIC FLEECE 200
BO
CABLE KNIT
CATALYST
CHENILLE
CLASSIC
COLLEGIATE SPORT SHELL
DOVETAIL
DRI-RELEASE
ECO TEC
EXHALE
EXHALE HEATING SYSTEM
EXOLITE
EXOLITE ACOUSTIC
EXOLITE NITE TEC ACOUSTIC
EXOLITE PATROL
EXOLITE ULTRALITE
FASHION FLEECE
FESTO
FRESHGUARD
GORGONZ BASIC FLEECE
GORGONZ BROWN DUCK
GORGONZ HIGH-VIS REFLECTIVE
INTEGRAL
METRO SUEDE
MORTISE
MOTION FIT SYSTEM
NBA BASIC FLEECE
NFL SPORT SHELL
NITE TEC ACOUSTIC
PATROL
PIVOT GUARD SYSTEM
POWDER
POWDER MITT
POWER STRETCH
PRIMALOFT
PRO 150
PRO 350
PRO 360
PRO 750
PRO DEX 550
PUFFY QUILT
QUANTUM DRY
QUANTUM VENT
ROCKET
SOFT SHELL
SPRING
STORM
STORM XTG
TEC STRETCH
TEC TOUCH
THERMOLITE
ULTRALITE
ULTRALITE BEANIE
ULTRALITE CRG
UNISEX
VILLAGE KNIT
WIND PRO
WINTER PRO 250
WINTER PRO 475
WINTER PRO 475 HV
WINTER PRO 650X
WINTER PRO 850X
WINTER PRO 875
Advertising Agencies:
Alexander & Tom
3500 Boston St Ste 225
Baltimore, MD 21224-5275
Tel.: (410) 327-7400
Fax: (410) 327-7403

Dentsu America, Inc.
32 Ave of the Americas 16th Fl
New York, NY 10013
Tel.: (212) 397-3333
Fax: (212) 397-3322

Stiegler, Wells, Brunswick & Roth, Inc.
(d/b/a SWB&R)
3865 Adler Pl
Bethlehem, PA 18017-9000
Tel.: (610) 866-0611
Fax: (610) 866-8650

ACADEMY SPORTS & OUTDOORS, LTD.
1800 N Mason Rd
Katy, TX 77449-2826
Tel.: (281) 646-5200
Toll Free: (888) 922-2336
E-mail: academy@academy.com
Web Site: www.academy.com
Sales Range: $1-4.9 Billion
Approx. Number Employees: 13,000
Year Founded: 1938
Business Description:
Sporting Goods, Sports Apparel & Athletic Footwear Retailer
S.I.C.: 5941
N.A.I.C.S.: 451110
Media: 4-6-15-16-22
Distr.: Reg.
Personnel:
David Gochman *(Chm & CEO)*
Rodney Faldyn *(Pres)*
Robert Frennea *(Exec VP & Gen Mgr-Mdse-Apparel, Field & Stream)*
Beth Menuet *(Exec VP & Gen Mgr-Mdse)*
Carl Main *(VP-Mktg & Adv)*
Allen McConnell *(Dir-Store Svcs)*
Elise Hasbrook *(Sr Mgr-Comm)*

ACUSHNET COMPANY
(Sub. of Fila Korea, Ltd.)
333 Bridge St
Fairhaven, MA 02719-4905
Tel.: (508) 979-2000
Fax: (508) 979-3927
Web Site:
www.acushnetcompany.com
Approx. Rev.: $1,200,000,000
Approx. Number Employees: 5,000
Year Founded: 1932
Business Description:
Golfing Equipment & Accessories Mfr
S.I.C.: 2393; 2389; 3069; 3842; 3949
N.A.I.C.S.: 314911; 315299; 315999; 326299; 339113; 339920
Advertising Expenditures: $13,000,000
Media: 3-4-6-8-13-15-19-21-22
Distr.: Intl.; Natl.
Budget Set: June
Personnel:
Walter R. Uihlein *(Chm, Pres & CEO)*
William Burke *(CFO, Sr VP & Controller)*
Margaret G. Nicholson *(CIO & Sr VP)*
Gerald Bellis *(Pres-Titleist Golf Balls)*
James M. Connor *(Pres-Footjoy)*
Jeff Harmet *(Pres-Titleist Club)*
Joseph J. Nauman *(EVP-Corp & Legal)*
Dennis D. Doherty *(Sr VP-HR)*
John Worster *(Sr VP-Golf Club Ops)*
Chris McGinley *(VP-Mktg-Titleist Golf Clubs)*
Joseph Gomes *(Dir-Comm)*
Brands & Products:
ACUSHNET
ADVANCED PERFORMANCE LEATHER
AIRTRACK
AIRWEIGHT
THE ART OF PUTTING
AUSSIE SERIES
BI-FLOW
BIG SUR
BULLS EYE
CASUAL WALKERS
CLASSICS
CLASSICS DRY
CLASSICS DRY PREMIERE
CLASSICS TOUR
CLIMATE CONTROL PERFORMANCE
COMFORT SEAM
COMFORTAB
COMPOSITE TOP
CONTOUR SERIES
COOLJOYS
COTTONSOF
DISTANCE DOESN'T HAVE TO BE HARD
DRYJOYS
DRYJOYS PERFORMANCE COLLECTION
DRYJOYS PERFORMANCE FLEECE
DRYJOYS PERFORMANCE LIGHT
DT
DT SOLO
DUAL CLIMATE
DURAMAX
ECOMFORT
EXCEPTION
F3
FIBERSOF
FIRSTJOYS
FIT-BED
FITTING WORKS
FJ
FOOTJOY

Key to Media (For complete agency information see *The Advertising Red Books-Agencies* edition):
1. Bus. Publs. 2. Cable T.V. 3. Catalogs & Directories. 4. Co-op Adv. 5. Consumer Mags. 6. D.M. to Bus. Estab.7. D.M. to Consumers 8. Daily Newsp. 9. Exhibits/Trade Shows 10. Foreign 11. Infomercial 12. Internet Adv.13. Multimedia 14. Network Radio 15. Network T.V. 16. Newsp. Distr. Mags. 17. Other 18. Outdoor (Posters, Transit) 19. Point of Purchase20. Premiums, Novelties 21. Product Samples 22. Special Events Mktg. 23. Spot Radio 24. Spot T.V. 25. Weekly Newsp. 26. Yellow Page Adv.

Acushnet Company — (Continued)

FOOTJOY CAPE COD COLLECTION
FOOTJOY EUROPA COLLECTION
FUTURA
FUTURA PHANTOM
GELCOLLAR
GELFUSION
GELRIDE
GOLD DISTANCE
GOLD MAXIMUM VELOCITY
GOLF'S SYMBOL OF EXCELLENCE
GREENJOYS
HIT IT LONG, HIT IT STRAIGHT
HVC
HVC SOFT FEEL
INTELLIGEL
INTELLISHIELD EXTREME
INTERACTIVE COMFORT TECHNOLOGY
ISUSPENSION
IT'S A CINCH
JOYWALKERS
LAGUNA
MID SUR
MYJOYS
NEWPORT
NEWPORT BEACH
NEWPORT TWO
NO BALL GOES FARTHER
#1 BALL IN GOLF
NXT
OPTIFLEX
PERMA-FLEX
PERMA-SOFT
PERMA-TECH
PINNACLE
PINNACLE GOLD
PLAYERS
POWER CORE
POWERNET
P.R.O. (PLATFORM RESPONSIVE OUTSOLE)
PRO TITANIUM
PRO TRAJECTORY
PRO V1
PRO V1X
PRODRY
Q-MARK
RAINGRIP
RED X
SANTA FE
THE SCIENCE OF COMFORT
SCIFLEX
SCOTTY CAMERON
SOFJOY
SPIDER
SPIN MILLED
STA-DRY SYSTEM
STABILITY BRIDGE
STACOOLER
STACOOLER SPORT
STASOF
SUPER CUSHION
TITLEIST
TITLEIST DT
TITLEIST NXT
TITLEIST SO-LO
TITLEIST TITANIUM
TORQUE CONTROL
UNI-FLEX
UNI-TECH
VARI-FIT
VOKEY DESIGN
WATERLOC
WEATHERSOF
WINTERSOF
XDIMENSION
Y-FLEX

Advertising Agencies:
Arnold Worldwide
101 Huntington Ave
Boston, MA 02199-7603
Tel.: (617) 587-8000
Fax: (617) 587-8004
(Golf Balls, Clubs, Accessories, Shoes)

Ware Anthony Rust Ltd. (WAR)
CPC1
Cambridge, CB21 5XE, United Kingdom
Tel.: (44) 1223 884600
Fax: (44) 8456 800149

ADAMS GOLF, INC.

2801 E Plano Pkwy
Plano, TX 75074-7418
Tel.: (972) 673-9000
Fax: (972) 398-8818
Toll Free: (800) 709-6142
E-mail: info@adamsgolf.com
Web Site: www.adamsgolf.com
Approx. Sls.: $86,247,000
Approx. Number Employees: 129
Year Founded: 1987
Business Description:
Golf Clubs Mfr
S.I.C.: 3949
N.A.I.C.S.: 339920
Import Export
Advertising Expenditures: $4,022,000
Media: 6-17-18-19-24
Personnel:
Barney H. Adams *(Chm)*
Oliver G. Brewer, III *(Pres & CEO)*
Pamela J. High *(CFO)*
Jeff Wood *(Dir-Mktg)*
Ann Neff *(Mgr-HR)*
Brands & Products:
ADAMSGOLF
DIXX BLU
IDEA
INSIGHT TECH
INSIGHT XTD
OVATION
PUGLIELLI
REDLINE
SPEEDLINE
SPEEDLINE DRAW
SPEEDLINE TECH
TIGHT LIES
TOM WATSON
Advertising Agency:
The Richards Group, Inc.
8750 N Central Expy Ste 100
Dallas, TX 75231-6430
Tel.: (214) 891-5700
Fax: (214) 265-2933

ADRENALINA

20855 NE 16th Ave Ste C-16
Miami, FL 33179
Tel.: (954) 454-9978
Toll Free: (866) 770-4666
E-mail: info@adrenalinastore.com
Web Site: www.adrenalinastore.com
Sales Range: $1-9.9 Million
Approx. Number Employees: 50
Year Founded: 2006
Business Description:
Outdoor Adventure & Extreme Sports Equipment & Products Retailer; Magazine Publisher; Television Broadcasting Services
S.I.C.: 5941; 2721; 4833; 5961
N.A.I.C.S.: 451110; 454111; 454113; 511120; 515120
Advertising Expenditures: $127,306
Media: 3-6-13
Personnel:
Ilia Lekach *(Chm & CEO)*
Brands & Products:
ADRENALINA

ALDILA, INC.

14145 Danielson St Ste B
Poway, CA 92064
Tel.: (858) 513-1801
Fax: (858) 513-1870
E-mail: sales@aldila.com
Web Site: www.aldila.com
Approx. Sls.: $49,774,000
Approx. Number Employees: 1,186
Year Founded: 1972
Business Description:
Graphite Golf Shafts Designer, Mfr & Marketer
S.I.C.: 3949; 3624
N.A.I.C.S.: 339920; 335991
Advertising Expenditures: $899,000
Media: 2-3-6-22
Distr.: Intl.
Personnel:
Peter R. Mathewson *(Chm & CEO)*
Scott M. Bier *(CFO, Treas & VP)*
Robert J. Cierzan *(Sr VP-Composite Matls)*
John E. Oldenburg *(VP-Engrg & Product Dev)*
Michael J. Rossi *(VP-Sls & Mktg)*
Stewart Bahl *(Mgr-Mktg)*
Maryam Jacoub *(Mgr-HR & Safety)*
Brands & Products:
ALDILA
ARE YOU A PLAYER
DVS
EXCELERATOR
GAMER
MOI PROTO
NV
NV PROTOPYPE
NVS
PINK NV
S-CORE
TOUR
VALUE
VOODOO
VS
VS PROTO
Advertising Agency:
Golf Marketing Services, Inc.
2933 W SR 434 Ste 131
Longwood, FL 32779
Tel.: (407) 682-4853
Fax: (407) 682-4851

ALLIANCE SPORTS GROUP, L.P.

602 Fountain Pkwy
Grand Prairie, TX 75050-1407
Tel.: (972) 343-1000
Fax: (972) 343-1192
Toll Free: (800) 241-0276
E-mail: info@nebotoolf.com
Web Site: www.alliancesportsgroup.net
E-Mail For Key Personnel:
President: bob@bollingerfitness.com
Marketing Director: marketing@bollingerfitness.com
Approx. Number Employees: 100
Year Founded: 1974
Business Description:
Mfr. of Sporting Goods & Accessories
S.I.C.: 3845; 5091
N.A.I.C.S.: 334510; 423910
Import Export
Advertising Expenditures: $200,000
Media: 2-4-6-7-8-9-11-25
Distr.: Natl.
Personnel:
Bobby D. Bollinger *(Owner)*
Glenn D. Bollinger *(CEO)*
Brands & Products:
THE BAR
BODY PUMP
BOLLINGER
BRIGHTBELLS
FIELD & STREAM
LURE-EYES
MULTIGRIP
NEBO
QUARROW
ROCK FITNESS
SLIPLOCK
SMARTLOCK
SOFTONE
SOFTOUCH
SOLAR
SOLAR SUIT
STARLOCK
SUPER STEPPER BENCH SYSTEM
TAI AEROBICS
TRIAD
TRIAX
UPPERCUTS
WEATHERRITE OUTDOOR

ALVIMAR GENESIS

640 Three Mile Rd NW
Grand Rapids, MI 49544
Tel.: (616) 784-3803
Fax: (616) 784-5261
Toll Free: (800) 275-5986
E-mail: sales@alvimargenesis.com
Web Site: www.alvimargenesis.com
E-Mail For Key Personnel:
Sales Director: sales@alvimargenesis.com
Approx. Number Employees: 10
Year Founded: 1947
Business Description:
Mfr of P.O.P. Displays & Promotional Products
S.I.C.: 3944; 7319
N.A.I.C.S.: 339932; 541850
Import Export
Media: 4-10-13-19-20-21
Distr.: Natl.
Personnel:
James Randall *(Dir-Mktg)*

AMERICAN RECREATION PRODUCTS, INC.

(Sub. of Kellwood Company)
1224 Fern Rdg Pkwy 2nd Fl
Saint Louis, MO 63141-4404
Mailing Address:
PO Box 7048-A
Saint Louis, MO 63177
Tel.: (314) 576-8000
Fax: (314) 576-8009
Web Site: www.insta-bed.com/Contact.aspx
Approx. Number Employees: 60
Year Founded: 1887
Business Description:
Tents, Sleeping Bags, Backpacks, Outdoor Technical Clothing & Related Camping Accessories Mfr

Key to Media (For complete agency information see *The Advertising Red Books-Agencies* edition):
1. Bus. Publs. 2. Cable T.V. 3. Catalogs & Directories. 4. Co-op Adv. 5. Consumer Mags. 6. D.M. to Bus. Estab.7. D.M. to Consumers 8. Daily Newsp. 9. Exhibits/Trade Shows 10. Foreign 11. Infomercial 12. Internet Adv.13. Multimedia 14. Network Radio 15. Network T.V. 16. Newsp. Distr. Mags. 17. Other 18. Outdoor (Posters, Transit) 19. Point of Purchase20. Premiums, Novelties 21. Product Samples 22. Special Events Mktg. 23. Spot Radio 24. Spot T.V. 25. Weekly Newsp. 26. Yellow Page Adv.

S.I.C.: 3949
N.A.I.C.S.: 339920
Import Export
Advertising Expenditures: $400,000
Media: 1-2-4-5-6-8-9-11-16-18-19-20-21
Distr.: Intl.; Natl.
Personnel:
Dale Philippi *(Pres & CEO)*
Brands & Products:
THE CAMPING COMPANY
KELTY
SIERRA DESIGNS
SLUMBERJACK
WENZEL

AMERICAN STAR CORK CO., INC.

3353 62nd St
Woodside, NY 11377-2235
Tel.: (718) 335-3000
Fax: (718) 335-3037
Toll Free: (800) 338-3581
E-mail: info@acmepans.com
Web Site: www.acmepans.com
Approx. Sls.: $1,000,000
Approx. Number Employees: 30
Year Founded: 1902
Business Description:
Mfr. of Corks & Cork Products
S.I.C.: 5099
N.A.I.C.S.: 423990
Import Export
Media: 2-4-6-7-8-10
Distr.: Natl.
Personnel:
Thomas Petrosino *(Pres)*

AMF BOWLING WORLDWIDE, INC.

(Holding of Code, Hennessy & Simmons, LLC)
7313 Bell Creek Rd
Mechanicsville, VA 23111
Tel.: (804) 730-4000
Fax: (804) 559-6276
Toll Free: (800) 342-5263
Web Site: www.amf.com
Sales Range: $450-499.9 Million
Approx. Number Employees: 9,362
Year Founded: 1946
Business Description:
Bowling Equipment & Supplies Mfr; Bowling Lanes & Bowling Centers Operator
S.I.C.: 7933; 3949
N.A.I.C.S.: 713950; 339920
Advertising Expenditures: $12,447,000
Distr.: Intl.
Budget Set: Monthly
Personnel:
Frederick R. Hipp *(CEO)*
William A. McDonnell *(CFO & VP)*
Christopher F. Caesar *(Treas & Sr VP)*
Jay Buhl *(Sr VP-Sls)*
Anthony J. Ponsiglione *(Sr VP-HR)*
J. Simon Shearer *(Sr VP)*
Merrell Wreden *(VP-Mktg)*
Joan Phares *(Dir-Field Mktg)*
Brian Cook *(Mgr-Central Reg)*
Brands & Products:
ACCUSCORE XL
ADVANTAGE
AMF
AMFLITE II
CENTURY
FAIR LANES
GRAND PRIX
HPL ALLIANCE
HPL INTEGRA
SMART BALL
VISFLO

AMPAC ENTERPRISES, INC.

PO Box 1356
Shirley, MA 01464-1356
Tel.: (978) 425-6266
Fax: (978) 425-4068
Toll Free: (800) 777-3810
Web Site: www.all-starsports.com
Approx. Number Employees: 15
Year Founded: 1988
Business Description:
Mfr. of Baseball Equipment
S.I.C.: 3949; 5091
N.A.I.C.S.: 339920; 423910
Advertising Expenditures: $350,000
Media: 4-7-10-16-19-20
Distr.: Natl.
Personnel:
Stanley M. Jurga *(Pres, Gen Partner & COO)*
David J. Holden *(CEO)*
Jeff Johnson *(Dir-Mktg)*

ANC SPORTS ENTERPRISES, LLC

(Sub. of Celeritas Management, Inc.)
2 Manhattanville Rd Ste 402
Purchase, NY 10577
Tel.: (914) 696-2100
Fax: (914) 696-2101
E-mail: info@ancsports.com
Web Site: www.ancsports.com
Sales Range: $25-49.9 Million
Approx. Number Employees: 55
Year Founded: 1997
Business Description:
Multimedia Sports Marketing & Information Systems Developer
S.I.C.: 8742
N.A.I.C.S.: 541613; 519130
Media: 6
Personnel:
David Bialek *(Pres-ANC Sports Mktg)*
Daniel Fumai *(Exec VP-Fin)*
Chris Mascatello *(Exec VP-Tech Sls & Svcs)*
Siobhan Mason *(Sr VP-Admin)*
Colleen Duffy *(VP-Sls)*
Eric Gruner *(Mgr-Project & Opers Support)*
Brands & Products:
ANC
DLP
FASCIASOFT
SMARTVISION
VISIONSOFT

ANCHOR INDUSTRIES, INC.

1100 Burch Dr
Evansville, IN 47725-1702
Tel.: (812) 867-2421
Fax: (812) 867-0547
Toll Free: (800) 544-4445
E-mail: info@anchorinc.com
Web Site: www.anchorinc.com
Approx. Number Employees: 500
Year Founded: 1892
Business Description:
Mfr. of Canvas Awnings, Fabric & Vinyl-Laminated Tents, Trailer & Patio Awnings & Tarpaulins, Safety Pool Covers, Custom Canvas & Synthetic Fabric Industrial Covers, Private Label Bags
S.I.C.: 2394
N.A.I.C.S.: 314912
Export
Advertising Expenditures: $300,000
Media: 2-6-7-9-10-13-19-20
Distr.: Intl.
Personnel:
Pete Mogavero *(Chm & Pres)*
Brands & Products:
ANCHOR
ANCHOR CARRY-ALLS
ANCHORSPAN
CENTURY
ECLIPSE
FIESTA
FUNBRELLA
GERMINATOR
LLAZA
NAVI-TRAC
NAVI-TRAC LITE
NEW CENTURY
PARTY
SPANLATCH
SUPERWHITE

ANTHONY & SYLVAN POOLS CORPORATION

6690 Beta Dr Ste 300
Cleveland, OH 44143-2359
Tel.: (440) 720-3301
Fax: (440) 720-3303
Toll Free: (877) 307-7946
E-mail: customerservice@anthonysylvan.com
Web Site: www.anthonysylvan.com
Sales Range: $150-199.9 Million
Approx. Number Employees: 450
Year Founded: 1946
Business Description:
Designer & Retailer of Concrete Swimming Pools & Spas
S.I.C.: 1799; 5999
N.A.I.C.S.: 238990; 453998
Advertising Expenditures: $4,000,000
Media: 2-4-6-7-8-10-16-23-24-26
Distr.: Natl.
Personnel:
Stuart D. Neidus *(Chm & CEO)*
Martin A. Iles *(CFO)*
Ken F. Sloan *(VP-HR)*
Ron Dewitt *(Dir-IS Ops)*
Brands & Products:
ANTHONY & SYLVAN POOLS
I SWIM
IT'S WHERE AMERICA SWIMS
Advertising Agency:
Marketing Group
880 Louis Dr
Warminster, PA 18974
Tel.: (215) 259-1500
Fax: (215) 259-0290
(Swimming Pools)
— Randi Sherwood *(Acct. Exec.)*

APEX FITNESS, INC.

(Sub. of 24 Hour Fitness Worldwide Inc.)
100 Camino Ruiz
Camarillo, CA 93012
Tel.: (805) 449-1330
Fax: (805) 449-1370
Toll Free: (800) 656-2739
Web Site: www.apexfitness.com
Approx. Number Employees: 60
Business Description:
Health & Nutrition Products Research & Development & Various Other Services
S.I.C.: 5047; 2836; 8733
N.A.I.C.S.: 423450; 325414; 541710
Media: 6
Personnel:
Odd Haugen *(COO)*

AQUA LUNG AMERICA, INC.

(Sub. of Aqualung International)
2340 Cousteau Ct
Vista, CA 92081
Tel.: (760) 597-5000
Fax: (760) 597-4900
E-mail: support@aqualung.com
Web Site: www.aqualung.com
Approx. Number Employees: 400
Business Description:
Sport & Commercial Diving Life Support Products & Protective Breathing Systems Mfr
S.I.C.: 3949; 5091
N.A.I.C.S.: 339920; 423910
Advertising Expenditures: $1,500,000
Media: 2-4-6-7-8-10-18-19
Distr.: Intl.; Natl.
Budget Set: Mar.
Personnel:
Dave Stancil *(VP)*

ASHAWAY LINE & TWINE MFG. CO.

24 Laurel St
Ashaway, RI 02804-1515
Tel.: (401) 377-2221
Fax: (401) 377-9091
Toll Free: (800) 556-7260
E-mail: sales@ashawayusa.com
Web Site: www.ashawayusa.com
E-Mail For Key Personnel:
Sales Director: sales@ashawayusa.com
Approx. Number Employees: 74
Year Founded: 1824
Business Description:
Mfr. of Fishing Lines, Racket Strings, Industrial Cordage & Surgical Sutures
S.I.C.: 2298; 3949
N.A.I.C.S.: 314991; 339920
Import Export
Advertising Expenditures: $200,000
Media: 2-4-6-9-13
Distr.: Intl.; Natl.
Budget Set: May
Personnel:
Pamela A. Crandall *(Chm & Pres)*
Katherine Crandall *(Pres & Treas)*
Brands & Products:
ASHAWAY
ASHAWAY MONOGUT
COMPOSITE XL PRO
COMPOSITE XT PRO
CROSSFIRE
CROSSFIRE MONOGUT
DYNAMITE
FLEX 21
FLEX 21 MICRO
KILLFIRE
LIBERTY
MICROLEGEND
MICROPOWER
MONOFIRE
MONOFIRE XL
MONOGUT
MONOKILL

Ashaway Line & Twine Mfg. Co. — (Continued)

MULTI-PLY
POWERGUT 65 & 66
POWERKILL
POWERNICK
PRO-FECTED
RALLY
SUPERKILL
SUPERNICK XL
SUPERNICK XL MICRO
SUPERNICK XL PRO
SUPERNICK XL TITANIUM
VANTAGE

ASICS AMERICA CORPORATION

(Sub. of ASICS Corporation)
29 Parker Ste 100
Irvine, CA 92618
Tel.: (949) 453-8888
Fax: (949) 453-0292
Toll Free: (800) 333-8404
Web Site: www.asicsamerica.com
E-Mail For Key Personnel:
President: richb@asicstiger.com
Marketing Director: garys@asicstiger.com
Approx. Rev.: $150,000,000
Approx. Number Employees: 180
Year Founded: 1977
Business Description:
Sporting Apparel Mfr
S.I.C.: 5139; 5136
N.A.I.C.S.: 424340; 424320
Import
Advertising Expenditures: $8,000,000
Media: 1-2-4-5-6-10-18-19-20
Distr.: Natl.
Budget Set: Oct. -Apr.
Personnel:
Kevin G. Wulff *(Pres, CEO & COO)*
Patty Kelly *(Mgr-Product)*
Heather Moening *(Mgr-PR)*
Brands & Products:
ASICS
ASICS TIGER
TIGER
Advertising Agencies:
Outdoor Services
(Corporate Headquarters)
3025 Highland Pkwy Ste 700
Downers Grove, IL 60515
Tel.: (630) 729-7500
Fax: (630) 241-9185
(Media Buying)

The Pitch Agency
8825 National Blvd
Culver City, CA 90232
Tel.: (310) 838-7300
Onitsuka Tiger (Global Agency of Record)

VITRO
(An MDC Partners Company)
625 Broadway Fl 4
San Diego, CA 92101-5403
Tel.: (619) 234-0408
Fax: (619) 234-4015
(2008 ING New York City Marathon)

ATHLETE'S FOOT BRANDS, LLC

(Sub. of Global Franchise Management LLC)
(d/b/a TAF - The Athlete's Foot)
1346 Oakbrook Dr Ste 170
Norcross, GA 30093
Tel.: (770) 514-4500
Fax: (770) 514-4903
Toll Free: (800) 524-6444
E-mail: franchiseinfo@gfgmanagement.com
Web Site: www.theathletesfoot.com
Sales Range: $250-299.9 Million
Business Description:
Athletic Shoe & Apparel Retail Franchisor
S.I.C.: 6794; 5661
N.A.I.C.S.: 533110; 448210
Export
Advertising Expenditures: $5,000,000
Media: 1-3-5-6-9-11-13-16-19-22-23-24-26
Distr.: Intl.; Natl.
Personnel:
M. Christopher Dull *(Pres)*
Brands & Products:
THE ATHLETE'S FOOT
TAF
Advertising Agency:
TotalCom Marketing, Inc.
922 20th Ave
Tuscaloosa, AL 35401-2307
Tel.: (205) 345-7363
Fax: (205) 345-7373

AWR SPORTS LLC

(Sub. of Big Rock Sports Inc.)
Ste 211 1651 E Main St
El Cajon, CA 92021-5206
Tel.: (619) 593-0872
Fax: (619) 593-9514
Toll Free: (800) 456-4463
Web Site: www.awrsports.com
Business Description:
Sporting & Recreation Goods Retailer
S.I.C.: 5091
N.A.I.C.S.: 423910
Media: 10

BALANCED BODY, INC.

8220 Ferguson Ave
Sacramento, CA 95828
Tel.: (916) 388-2838
Fax: (916) 379-9277
Toll Free: (800) 745-2837
E-mail: info@pilates.com
Web Site: www.pilates.com
Sales Range: $50-74.9 Million
Approx. Number Employees: 100
Business Description:
Pilates Equipment
S.I.C.: 3949
N.A.I.C.S.: 339920
Media: 4-6-13
Personnel:
Ken Endelman *(Pres)*
Brands & Products:
ALLEGRO
BALANCE BODY
FIT FLEX
FLEX RING TONER
PILATES ARC
PILATES IQ
REVO FOOTBAR
STUDIO REFORMER
ULTRA FIT CIRCLE

BASS PRO SHOPS, INC.

2500 E Kearney St
Springfield, MO 65898-0001
Tel.: (417) 873-5000
Fax: (417) 873-4672
Web Site: www.basspro.com
Approx. Number Employees: 12,500
Year Founded: 1971
Business Description:
Mail Order Retail Sales of Fishing, Hunting & Camping Equipment & Supplies; Wholesale Distribution of Sporting Goods
S.I.C.: 3949
N.A.I.C.S.: 339920
Media: 4-8-10-13-22
Personnel:
John L. Morris *(Founder)*
James Hagale *(Pres & COO)*
Leslie Weber *(CIO)*
Stan Lippelman *(VP-Mktg)*
Martin MacDonald *(Dir-Conservation)*
Mike Roland *(Dir-HR)*
Larry L. Whiteley *(Mgr-Corp Comm)*
Brands & Products:
BASS PRO SHOPS
THE GREAT OUTDOORS...PASS IT ON
OUTDOOR WORLD
Advertising Agency:
Buntin Out-of-Home Media
1001 Hawkins St
Nashville, TN 37203-4758
Tel.: (615) 244-5720
Fax: (615) 244-6511

BEAR & SON CUTLERY, INC.

1111 Bear Blvd SW
Jacksonville, AL 36265
Tel.: (256) 435-2227
Fax: (256) 435-9348
Toll Free: (800) 844-3034
E-mail: info@bearandsoncutlery.com
Web Site: www.bearandsoncutlery.com
Approx. Sls.: $4,000,000
Approx. Number Employees: 80
Business Description:
Knives Mfr & Marketer
S.I.C.: 3421
N.A.I.C.S.: 332211
Media: 4-8-13
Personnel:
Kenneth Griffey *(Owner)*
Sandy Griffey *(Exec VP)*
Brands & Products:
AMARILLO BONE
ARMOR PIERCING BLACK BEAR
BLACK BUTTERFLY
BLACK DERLIN
EVERYONE RESPECTS A BEAR
GENUINE INDIA STAG BONE
SILVER VEIN BUTTERFLY

BELL SPORTS SPECIALTY RETAIL DIVISION

(Div. of Bell Sports, Inc.)
5550 Scotts Valley Dr
Scotts Valley, CA 95066-3438
Tel.: (831) 461-7500
Fax: (831) 457-4444
Web Site: www.bellsports.com
Approx. Number Employees: 110
Year Founded: 1989
Business Description:
Bicycle Helmets & Accessories Mfr
S.I.C.: 3949
N.A.I.C.S.: 339920
Import Export
Media: 1-2-3-4-6-7-8-10-13-18-19-22-24
Distr.: Intl.; Natl.
Budget Set: Sept.
Personnel:
Candi Whitsel *(VP-Mktg)*
Don Palermini *(Brand Mgr)*
Brands & Products:
BLACKBURN
COPILOT
GIRO
VISTALITE

BEN PEARSON ARCHERY, INC.

734 Indus Pk Dr
Brewton, AL 36426-8164
Tel.: (251) 867-8475
Fax: (251) 867-9005
E-mail: bowhunter@benpearson.com
Web Site: www.benpearson.com
Approx. Number Employees: 10
Year Founded: 1927
Business Description:
Archery & Hunting Equipment
S.I.C.: 3949
N.A.I.C.S.: 339920
Export
Advertising Expenditures: $280,000
Media: 2-4-6-7-10-11-13
Distr.: Natl.
Budget Set: Nov.
Personnel:
Jeremy Blackmon *(Pres)*
Brands & Products:
PEARSON

BENELLI USA CORPORATION

(Sub. of Beretta Holding S.p.A.)
17603 Indian Head Hwy Ste 200
Accokeek, MD 20607
Tel.: (301) 283-6981
Fax: (301) 283-6988
Toll Free: (800) 264-4962
E-mail: info@benelliusa.com
Web Site: www.benelliusa.com
Approx. Number Employees: 66
Year Founded: 1997
Business Description:
Mfr. & Supplier of Firearms & Accessories
S.I.C.: 5099
N.A.I.C.S.: 423990
Media: 2-4-7-8-10-13-18-19
Personnel:
Fred Humes *(CFO)*
Steve Otway *(VP & Gen Mgr)*
Stephen McKelvain *(VP-Mktg)*
Brands & Products:
BENELLI
FRANCHI
STOEGER
STOEGER BOOKS
UBERTI
Advertising Agency:
Gray Loon Marketing Group, Inc.
300 SE Riverside Dr Ste 200
Evansville, IN 47713
Tel.: (812) 422-9999
Fax: (812) 422-3342
Toll Free: (888) GRAYLOON

BERETTA U.S.A. CORP.

(Sub. of Fabbrica D'Armi Pietro Beretta S.p.A.)
17601 Beretta Dr
Accokeek, MD 20607-9515
Tel.: (301) 283-2191
Fax: (301) 283-0435
Toll Free: (800) 636-3420

Key to Media (For complete agency information see *The Advertising Red Books-Agencies* edition):
1. Bus. Publs. 2. Cable T.V. 3. Catalogs & Directories. 4. Co-op Adv. 5. Consumer Mags. 6. D.M. to Bus. Estab.7. D.M. to Consumers
8. Daily Newsp. 9. Exhibits/Trade Shows 10. Foreign 11. Infomercial 12. Internet Adv.13. Multimedia 14. Network Radio
15. Network T.V. 16. Newsp. Distr. Mags. 17. Other 18. Outdoor (Posters, Transit) 19. Point of Purchase20. Premiums, Novelties
21. Product Samples 22. Special Events Mktg. 23. Spot Radio 24. Spot T.V. 25. Weekly Newsp. 26. Yellow Page Adv.

Telex: 829729 BERETTA ACKK
E-mail: email@berettausa.com
Web Site: www.berettausa.com
Approx. Number Employees: 400
Year Founded: 1977
Business Description:
Mfr. of Firearms
S.I.C.: 3484
N.A.I.C.S.: 332994
Personnel:
Cavaliere Gussalli *(Pres)*
Gary Ramey *(VP-Sls & Mktg)*
Steven Biondi *(Dir-Fin)*
Brands & Products:
BERETTA
SAKO
TIKKA
Advertising Agency:
Hunter Outdoor Communications
5233 Timberland Hollow Pl
Glen Allen, VA 23060
Tel.: (804) 346-4309
Beretta
Sako
Tikka

BIANCHI U.S.A., INC.
21325A Cabot Blvd
Hayward, CA 94545-1650
Tel.: (510) 264-1001
E-mail: info@bianchiusa.com
Web Site: www.bianchiusa.com
Approx. Number Employees: 12
Business Description:
Bicycles, Clothing & Accessories
S.I.C.: 5091; 5941
N.A.I.C.S.: 423910; 451110
Advertising Expenditures: $1,500,000
Media: 2-5-6-9-10-23-24-25-26
Distr.: Intl.; Natl.
Budget Set: Jan.
Personnel:
Rodney Jewett *(Pres)*
Brands & Products:
CASTELLI
CELESTE CLUB
CROSS-TERRAIN

BIG 5 SPORTING GOODS CORPORATION
2525 E El Segundo Blvd
El Segundo, CA 90245-4632
Tel.: (310) 536-0611
Fax: (310) 297-7585
E-mail: jmills@icrinc.com
Web Site:
www.big5sportinggoods.com
Approx. Sls.: $896,813,000
Approx. Number Employees: 8,900
Year Founded: 1955
Business Description:
Sporting Goods Retailer
S.I.C.: 5941
N.A.I.C.S.: 451110
Import Export
Advertising Expenditures: $6,202,000
Media: 2-6-9-13-22
Personnel:
Steven G. Miller *(Chm, Pres & CEO)*
Barry D. Emerson *(CFO, Treas & Sr VP)*
Gary S. Meade *(Gen Counsel, Sec & Sr VP)*
Richard A. Johnson *(Exec VP)*
Jeffrey L. Fraley *(Sr VP-HR)*
Thomas J. Schlauch *(Sr VP-Buying)*
Rick Gridley *(Dir-Public Affairs)*
Brands & Products:
BIG 5
BIG 5 SPORTING GOODS
WE GET YOU READY TO PLAY

BIG C CORPORATION
600 Coolidge Rd
Lafayette, TN 37083-2306
Tel.: (615) 666-9102
Fax: (615) 666-9082
Approx. Number Employees: 40
Business Description:
General Trading Company
S.I.C.: 7389
N.A.I.C.S.: 561990
Media: 4-10-21
Distr.: Intl.; Natl.
Budget Set: July
Personnel:
Coy L. Groves *(Pres & Mgr)*

BILL BOATMAN & COMPANY, INC.
215 S Washington St
Greenfield, OH 45123-1466
Tel.: (937) 981-7788
Fax: (937) 981-0648
Toll Free: (800) 833-4518
Web Site: www.billboatmancoinc.com
Approx. Number Employees: 15
Year Founded: 1947
Business Description:
Dog Hunting Products Mail Order
S.I.C.: 5961
N.A.I.C.S.: 454113
Media: 4-8-18
Distr.: Natl.
Budget Set: Mar.
Personnel:
Carolyn Boatman *(Mgr-Adv)*

BILLIARD TOWNE
314 US Hwy 46
Denville, NJ 07834
Tel.: (973) 625-5400
Fax: (973) 625-5858
Toll Free: (800) 691-POOL
E-mail: info@billiardtowne.com
Web Site: www.billiardtowne.com
Approx. Sls.: $1,000,000
Approx. Number Employees: 5
Year Founded: 1978
Business Description:
Pool, Billiard Tables & Exclusive Distr of Olhausen Pool Tables
S.I.C.: 5941; 7699
N.A.I.C.S.: 451110; 811490
Media: 4-8-13-18-24

BLACK DIAMOND, INC.
(Formerly Clarus Corporation)
2084 E 3900 S
Salt Lake City, UT 84124
Tel.: (801) 278-5552
E-mail: info@blackdiamond-inc.com
Web Site: www.blackdiamond-inc.com
Approx. Sls.: $75,912,000
Approx. Number Employees: 475
Business Description:
Outdoor Recreation Products Mfr & Retailer
S.I.C.: 3949; 5941
N.A.I.C.S.: 339920; 451110
Advertising Expenditures: $979,000
Personnel:
Warren B. Kanders *(Chm)*
Robert R. Schiller *(Vice Chm)*
Peter R. Metcalf *(Pres & CEO)*
Robert Peay *(CFO, Treas & Sec)*
Brands & Products:
ASCENSION
ATC
AVALUNG
BIBLER
BLACK DIAMOND
CAMALOT
FLICKLOCK
GREGORY
HEXENTRIC
STOPPER
TIME IS LIFE

BLATT BOWLING & BILLIARD CORP.
809 Broadway
New York, NY 10003
Tel.: (212) 674-8855
Fax: (212) 598-4514
Toll Free: (800) 252-8855
E-mail: info@blattbilliards.com
Web Site: www.blattbilliards.com
Approx. Sls.: $6,500,000
Approx. Number Employees: 50
Year Founded: 1923
Business Description:
Billiard Equipment & Supplies
S.I.C.: 5941; 5091
N.A.I.C.S.: 451110; 423910
Media: 2-6
Personnel:
Ronald Blatt *(Pres)*
John Chermack *(CIO)*
Barry Dubow *(Dir-Mktg)*
Brands & Products:
ADIRONDACK
ADONIS
AMARINTH
AMBASSADOR
ARCA BELLA
ARISTOCRAT
ARTISAN
ASHBEE
ASTOR PLACE
ASTORIA
AVALON
AVANTI
BEAUTIFUL INVESTMENTS TO PLAY WITH
BELVEDERE
BENSINGER
BORDEAUX
BRADFORD
BRIARWOOD
BRILLIANT NOVELTY
BROADWAY
BROOKSTONE
BURLED YORK
CABARET
CAMDEN
CAMEO
CARLYLE
CENTURION
CHANEL
CLARIDGE
CONQUEROR
COSMOPOLITAN
CROMWELL
DOMINION
EQUESTRIAN
EXPOSITION
FIESTA
FRIAR BRIGGS
GARDEN
GIBSON
GOLD CROWN
GOTHIC
GRAMERCY PARK
GRAND DUKE
GREENBRIAR
GRIFFITH
HAWTHORN
HAYDEN
HUNTINGTON
JEWEL
KLING
LAGUNA
MADISON
MANSFIELD
MEDALIST
MILLENNIUM
MISSION
MONARCH
MONTE CARLO
MONTEBELLO
NARAGANSETT
NEW YORKER
OXFORD
PACE
PARK AVENUE
PENDENNIS
PFISTER
PRISM
RALIEGH
REGINA
ROYAL KNIGHT
SEASONS
SLOAN
SORRENTO
SPRINGER
STANFORD
ST.BERNARD
STERLING
SUTTON PLACE
TRAFALGER
UNION LEAGUE
VENTURA
VILLAGER
WALDORF
WALLINGTON
WILMINGTON
WINDSOR

BOTA OF BOULDER INC.
1670 S Cherryvale Rd
Boulder, CO 80303-9703
Mailing Address:
PO Box 3374
Boulder, CO 80307-3374
Tel.: (303) 494-8489
Fax: (303) 494-3263
Toll Free: (800) 530-8489
E-mail: bota@indra.com
Web Site: www.botaofboulder.com
Approx. Number Employees: 12
Year Founded: 1972
Business Description:
Water Bottles Mfr
S.I.C.: 2393
N.A.I.C.S.: 314911
Export
Media: 4-5-6-10-21-22
Distr.: Intl.; Natl.
Personnel:
Brady Robba *(Pres)*
Brands & Products:
BOTA
BOTTLESOCK
XX-REALTREE CORDURA

BRIDGESTONE GOLF, INC.
(Sub. of Bridgestone Sports Co., Ltd.)
14230 Lochridge Blvd Ste G
Covington, GA 30014-4953
Tel.: (770) 787-7400

Key to Media (For complete agency information see *The Advertising Red Books-Agencies* edition):
1. Bus. Publs. 2. Cable T.V. 3. Catalogs & Directories. 4. Co-op Adv. 5. Consumer Mags. 6. D.M. to Bus. Estab.7. D.M. to Consumers 8. Daily Newsp. 9. Exhibits/Trade Shows 10. Foreign 11. Infomercial 12. Internet Adv.13. Multimedia 14. Network Radio 15. Network T.V. 16. Newsp. Distr. Mags. 17. Other 18. Outdoor (Posters, Transit) 19. Point of Purchase20. Premiums, Novelties 21. Product Samples 22. Special Events Mktg. 23. Spot Radio 24. Spot T.V. 25. Weekly Newsp. 26. Yellow Page Adv.

Bridgestone Golf, Inc. — (Continued)

Fax: (770) 787-4915
Web Site: www.bridgestonegolf.com
Approx. Number Employees: 175
Business Description:
Golf Equipment Mfr & Sales
S.I.C.: 3949; 5941
N.A.I.C.S.: 339920; 451110
Advertising Expenditures: $6,000,000
Media: 3-4-9-13-16-24
Personnel:
Stan Murphy *(Sr Dir-Mktg)*
Brandon Sowell *(Dir-Mktg)*
Brands & Products:
BRIDGESTONE J33
BRIDGESTONE TOUR B330
LADDIE
MC LADY
PRECEPT
SPORTS LADY
Advertising Agencies:
Jeff Dezen Public Relations
13-A East Coffee Street
Greenville, SC 29601
Tel.: (864) 233-3776
Fax: (864) 370-3368
Public Relations Agency of Record

Nelson Creative
10290 Kinross Rd
Roswell, GA 30076
Tel.: (404) 606-3877
— Scott Nelson *(Dir-Creative)*

BRINE, INC.

(Sub. of New Balance Athletic Shoe, Inc.)
47 Sumner St
Milford, MA 01757-1656
Tel.: (508) 478-3250
Fax: (508) 478-2430
Toll Free: (800) 227-2722
Web Site: www.brine.com
Approx. Number Employees: 100
Year Founded: 1922
Business Description:
Sporting Goods Mfr & Distr
S.I.C.: 3949
N.A.I.C.S.: 339920
Media: 2-4-7
Distr.: Intl.; Natl.
Budget Set: Jan.
Personnel:
Judy Salzberg *(Asst VP-HR)*
Brands & Products:
AIR GUARD
ANSWER
ATTACK
BACKYARD WARS
BLUR
BRINE
CARBON
COLLEGIATE
CONCEPT
COUNTDOWN TO CHAOS
CYBER
DAYTONA
DEFT
DOT MATRIX
EDGE X
ELEMENT
ELITE
ENERGY
EVOLUTION
EXODUS
FADE
FIND YOUR GAME
FIRE
FIRE FLY
FLIGHT
FUSION
GHOST
GURU
HARPOON
HATTRICK
HIGH VISIBILITY
HUNTINGTON
HYPERSONIC
IGNITE
INSTINCT
LAGUNA
LOBO
MATRIX
MAXIMUS
MINI NITROUS
MONEY
MONTROSE
MOTIVE
NEPTUNE
NITROUS
PHANTOM
PHENOM
PRODIGY
PROPHECY
PULSE
PYTHON
QED
RADIUS
RHINOSKIN
RIPPER
ROCKET
ROYALE
SCANDIUM
SCEPTER
SHINGUARD
SHOOT-N-SCORE
SPARK
SPARTAN
SUPERCROSSE
SWEEPER
SWERVE
SWIZZLE
SYNERGY
TACTILE
TENACITY
TRIAD
TRIDENT
TRUTH
VANTAGE
VAPOR
VELOCITY
VENTILATOR
VORACITY
VORTEX
WALL
WEB-X
WHIRL
XCEL
XTREME
ZONE

BRODER BROS., CO.

(Holding of Bain Capital, LLC)
6 Neshaminy Interplex Dr 6th Fl
Trevose, PA 19053
Tel.: (215) 291-6140
Fax: (215) 291-6141
Toll Free: (800) 523-4585
Web Site: www.broderbros.com
Approx. Sls.: $926,074,000
Approx. Number Employees: 1,221
Year Founded: 1919
Business Description:
Imprintable Sportswear Whslr & Distr
S.I.C.: 5961; 5136; 5137
N.A.I.C.S.: 454111; 424320; 424330; 454113
Import
Advertising Expenditures: $700,000
Media: 4-7-10-13
Personnel:
Thomas Myers *(CEO)*
Martin J. Matthews *(CFO)*
Norman Hullinger *(COO & Exec VP)*
Henry E. Harrell *(Exec VP-Sls & Mktg)*
Christopher Blakeslee *(VP-Sls)*
Brands & Products:
CHESTNUT HILL
DESERT WASH
GREAT REPUBLIC
HARRITON
LUNA PIER
Advertising Agency:
Utopia Communications
145 Wyckoff Rd Ste 204
Eatontown, NJ 07724
Tel.: (732) 542-9100
Fax: (732) 542-9104
Apparel

BRUNSWICK BOWLING & BILLIARDS CORP.

(Sub. of Brunswick Indoor Recreation Group)
1 N Field Ct
Lake Forest, IL 60045-4811
Mailing Address:
PO Box 329
Muskegon, MI 49443-0329
Tel.: (847) 735-4700
Fax: (847) 735-4501
Fax: (231) 725-3457 (sales)
Toll Free: (800) 937-2695 (sales)
Web Site:
www.brunswickbowling.com
Sales Range: $350-399.9 Million
Approx. Number Employees: 5,475
Business Description:
Bowling Equipment Mfr
S.I.C.: 3949
N.A.I.C.S.: 339920
Media: 2-4-6-24-26
Distr.: Intl.; Natl.
Budget Set: Nov.-Dec.
Personnel:
Warren N. Hardie *(Pres)*
Keith L. Gibson *(Gen Counsel)*
Kristin Filz *(Mgr-Mktg Svcs)*
Brands & Products:
AIR HOCKEY
ANVILANE
BALL WALL
BRUNSWICK HOME & BILLIARD
BRUNSWICK PAVILION
BRUNSWICK ZONE
CENTENNIAL
CENTERMASTER
COSMIC BOWLING
DBA PRODUCTS
DOMINION
DYNAMO
FRAMEWORX
FUZE
GTO
INFERNO
IQ
KING
LANE SHIELD
LIGHTWORX
MONSTER
PRO LANE
THROBOT
TORNADO
VALLEY
VALLEY-DYNAMO
VECTOR
VIZ-A-BALL
ZONE

BRUNSWICK CORPORATION

1 N Field Ct
Lake Forest, IL 60045-4811
Tel.: (847) 735-4700
Fax: (847) 735-4765
E-mail: services@brunswick.com
Web Site: www.brunswick.com
Approx. Sls.: $3,403,300,000
Approx. Number Employees: 15,290
Year Founded: 1845
Business Description:
Boats, Marine Parts & Accessories, Engines & Recreational Products Marketer & Mfr
S.I.C.: 3732; 3519; 3949; 5088; 7933
N.A.I.C.S.: 336612; 333618; 339920; 423860; 713950
Advertising Expenditures: $34,800,000
Media: 2-6-9
Distr.: Intl.; Natl.
Personnel:
Dustan E. McCoy *(Chm & CEO)*
William J. Gress *(Pres & VP)*
Peter B. Hamilton *(CFO & Sr VP)*
B. Russell Lockridge *(Chief HR Officer & VP)*
Andrew E. Graves *(Pres-Brunswick Boat Grp & VP)*
Kevin S. Grodzki *(Pres-Mercury Sls, Mktg & Comml Ops & VP)*
Warren N. Hardie *(Pres-Brunswick Bowling & Billiards & VP)*
John C. Pfeifer *(Pres-Marine-EMEA & VP)*
Mark D. Schwabero *(Pres-Mercury Marine & VP)*
Jeffrey M. Kinsey *(Pres-Freshwater Boat Grp)*
Kristin Coleman *(Gen Counsel, Sec & VP)*
Daniel Kubera *(Dir-Media Rels)*
Brands & Products:
BAYLINER
BOSTON WHALER
BRUNSWICK
GENUINE INGENUITY
HAMMER STRENGTH
LIFE FITNESS
LUND
MARINER
MERCURY
PARABODY
SEA RAY

BUCK KNIVES, INC.

660 S Lochsa St
Post Falls, ID 83854-5200
Tel.: (208) 262-0500
Fax: (208) 262-0482
Toll Free: (800) 326-2825
Web Site: www.buckknives.com
Approx. Number Employees: 200
Year Founded: 1902
Business Description:
Mfr. of Outdoor Cutlery
S.I.C.: 3421; 3423
N.A.I.C.S.: 332211; 332212
Import Export
Advertising Expenditures: $1,520,000

Key to Media (For complete agency information see *The Advertising Red Books-Agencies* edition):
1. Bus. Publs. 2. Cable T.V. 3. Catalogs & Directories. 4. Co-op Adv. 5. Consumer Mags. 6. D.M. to Bus. Estab.7. D.M. to Consumers
8. Daily Newsp. 9. Exhibits/Trade Shows 10. Foreign 11. Infomercial 12. Internet Adv.13. Multimedia 14. Network Radio
15. Network T.V. 16. Newsp. Distr. Mags. 17. Other 18. Outdoor (Posters, Transit) 19. Point of Purchase20. Premiums, Novelties
21. Product Samples 22. Special Events Mktg. 23. Spot Radio 24. Spot T.V. 25. Weekly Newsp. 26. Yellow Page Adv.

Media: 5-6-13-15-19
Distr.: Intl.; Natl.
Budget Set: Aug.
Personnel:
Charles T. Buck *(CEO)*
Bob George *(Mgr-Sls & Mktg)*
Brands & Products:
THE 55
ACCESS
ADRENALINE SPX
AKONUA GUITAR
ALPHA CROSSLOCK
ALPHA DORADO
ALPHA HUNTER
BANTAM
BRAVO
BRAVO RESCUE
BUCK
BUCK CADET
BUCK KNIVES
BUCK/MAYO KAALA
BUCK/SIMONICH RAVEN LEGACY
BUCK ZIPPER
BUCKLITE
BUCKLITE MAX
CADET
COLLEAGUE
COMPANION
CROSSLOCK
DANIEL BOONE
DAVY CROCKETT
DIAMONDBACK GUIDE
DIAMONDBACK OUTFITTER
EDGE2X
ERGOHUNTER
ERGOHUNTER SMALL GAME
FAIR CHASE
FOLDING ALPHA HUNTER
FOLDING BUCKLITE MAX
FOLDING HUNTER
FOLDING KALINGA PRO
FOLDING KALINGA PRO EAGLE
FOLDING OMNI HUNTER
GAMUT
GEN-5
GENT
GHOST RIDER
IMPULSE
JUNO
KALINGA PRO
KNIGHT
LANCER
LARGE TRAPPER
LEATHER FOLDING HUNTER
LIGHTNING HTA
MANTIS
METRO
MINI ALPHA HUNTER
MINI BUCK
MINI TRAPPER
MUSKRAT
NANO BANTAM
NATIONAL PARKS
NOBLEMAN
ODYSSEY
OMNI HUNTER
PAPERSTONE
PATHFINDER
PILOT
PRINCE
PROTEGE
RANGER
REDPOINT
RUSH
SCHOLAR
SHORT NIGHTHAWK
SILVER CREEK
SIRUS
SKINNER
SMIDGEN
SOLO
SPECIAL
SQUIRE
STACKED BUFFALO
STACKED LEATHER
STOCKMAN
STOCKMAN ELK HOOF
T. ROOSEVELT
TEMPEST
TEXAS STAR
TOOTHPICK
TRANSPORT
TRIO
TWIN PEAKS
ULTI-MATE
UTILITY SHEARS
VANGUARD
VANTAGE
WOODSMAN
X-TRACT
X-TRACT ESSENTIAL
X-TRACT FIN
ZIPPER
Advertising Agency:
Venture
313 Laurel St
San Diego, CA 92101-1630
Tel.: (619) 234-7312
Fax: (619) 234-5159
(Knives, Multi-Function Tools)

BURNHAM BROTHERS, INC.

PO Box 427
Menard, TX 76859
Tel.: (325) 396-4572
Fax: (325) 396-4574
Toll Free: (800) 451-4572
E-mail: burnhamb@burnhambrothers.com
Web Site: www.burnhambrothers.com
Approx. Number Employees: 10
Year Founded: 1952
Business Description:
Animal Calls & Accessories Mfr
S.I.C.: 3949; 5941
N.A.I.C.S.: 339920; 451110
Export
Media: 4-6-10-13
Distr.: Direct to Consumer; Natl.
Budget Set: May
Personnel:
Gary Roberson *(Owner & Pres)*
Deb Roberson *(VP-Sls-Mktg)*
Brands & Products:
BURNHAM BROTHERS
CALLINGEST CALLS MADE
COMPUCALLER

BURTON SNOWBOARD COMPANY

80 Indus Pkwy
Burlington, VT 05401-5434
Tel.: (802) 862-4500
Fax: (802) 660-3250
Toll Free: (800) 881-3138
E-mail: info@burton.com
Web Site: www.burton.com
Approx. Sls.: $140,000,000
Approx. Number Employees: 650
Year Founded: 1977
Business Description:
Snowboard Related Items Seller & Mfr
S.I.C.: 3949
N.A.I.C.S.: 339920
Import Export
Media: 4-6-11-13
Personnel:
Jake Burton *(Chm)*
Mike Rees *(CFO)*
Scott Barton *(Gen Counsel)*
Brands & Products:
ANALOG
ANON
AUDEX
BURTON
GRAVIS
PARK AND PIPE
RADAR
R.E.D
RONIN
Advertising Agency:
Jager DiPaola Kemp
47 Maple St
Burlington, VT 05401-4784
Tel.: (802) 864-5884

CALLAWAY GOLF BALL OPERATIONS, INC.

(Sub. of Callaway Golf Company)
(Callaway Golf Ball Operations, Inc.)
425 Meadow St
Chicopee, MA 01013-2201
Tel.: (413) 536-1200
Fax: (413) 322-2216
Toll Free: (866) 834-65326
Web Site: www.topflite.com
Sales Range: $700-749.9 Million
Approx. Number Employees: 1,120
Year Founded: 1876
Business Description:
Sports Equipment Mfr
S.I.C.: 5941
N.A.I.C.S.: 451110
Advertising Expenditures: $15,000,000
Media: 3-4-5-6-8-9-10-13-15-18-19-21-22-24-25
Personnel:
Ron Tomasauckas *(Dir-HR)*
Brands & Products:
BEN HOGAN
STRATA BY TOP-FLITE
TOP-FLITE
Advertising Agencies:
COLANGELO
120 Tokeneke Rd
Darien, CT 06820
Tel.: (203) 662-6600
Fax: (203) 662-6601

KSL Media, Inc.
367 Park Ave S 4th Fl
New York, NY 10016
Tel.: (212) 352-5800
Fax: (212) 352-5935

Mason & Kichar Recruitment Advertising
260 Amity Rd
Woodbridge, CT 06525
Tel.: (203) 392-0252
Fax: (203) 392-0255

CALLAWAY GOLF COMPANY

2180 Rutherford Rd
Carlsbad, CA 92008-7328
Tel.: (760) 931-1771
Fax: (760) 930-5015
E-mail: intlcs@callawaygolf.com
Web Site: www.callawaygolf.com
Approx. Sls.: $967,656,000
Approx. Number Employees: 2,100
Year Founded: 1982
Business Description:
Golf Clubs & Related Equipment Mfr
S.I.C.: 3949
N.A.I.C.S.: 339920
Export
Advertising Expenditures: $47,366,000
Media: 1-3-6-8-10-13-15-22
Personnel:
Ronald S. Beard *(Chm)*
Anthony S. Thornley *(Interim Pres & Interim CEO)*
Bradley J. Holiday *(CFO & Sr Exec VP)*
Steven C. McCracken *(Chief Admin Officer, Sec & Sr Exec VP)*
Thomas Yang *(Pres-Intl & Sr VP)*
David A. Laverty *(Sr VP-Ops)*
Merle Marting *(VP-US Mktg)*
Michael Rolnick *(Dir-Integrated Mktg)*
Caroline Varhola *(Sr Mgr-Digital Mktg)*
Leda Buster *(Mgr-Interactive Mktg)*
Brands & Products:
A BETTER GAME BY DESIGN
BIG BERTHA
BIG BERTHA TITANIUM DRIVER
BIGBERTHA DIABLO
BIGGEST BIG BERTHA
CALLAWAY
CALLAWAY COLLECTION
CALLAWAY-CONNECT
CALLAWAY GOLF
CALLAWAY GOLF PERFORMANCE CENTER
CALLAWAY GOLF X SERIES
CALLAWAY PUTTERS
CALLAWAY YOUR WAY
CB1
CHEV
CID
CTU 30
DAWN PATROL
DAYTRIPPER
DEMONSTRABLY SUPERIOR & PLEASINGLY DIFFERENT
DEUCE
DFX
DIVINE NINE
DRYSPORT
DUAL FORCE
ELY WOULD
ERC
FIRMFEEL
FORGED
FT-3
FT-5
FT-I
FT TUNES
FTI-BRID
FUSION DRIVERS
GAME SERIES
GEMS
GES
GINTY
GREAT BIG BERTHA
HAWK EYE
HEAVENWOOD
HIT IT BELIEVE IT
HOW GOLF SHOULD FEEL
HX
HX HOT
HX HOT BITE
HX PEARL

Key to Media (For complete agency information see *The Advertising Red Books-Agencies* edition):
1. Bus. Publs. 2. Cable T.V. 3. Catalogs & Directories. 4. Co-op Adv. 5. Consumer Mags. 6. D.M. to Bus. Estab.7. D.M. to Consumers
8. Daily Newsp. 9. Exhibits/Trade Shows 10. Foreign 11. Infomercial 12. Internet Adv.13. Multimedia 14. Network Radio
15. Network T.V. 16. Newsp. Distr. Mags. 17. Other 18. Outdoor (Posters, Transit) 19. Point of Purchase20. Premiums, Novelties
21. Product Samples 22. Special Events Mktg. 23. Spot Radio 24. Spot T.V. 25. Weekly Newsp. 26. Yellow Page Adv.

Callaway Golf Company — (Continued)
HX TOUR
HYPER X
I-MIX
I-TRAX
ICT
LEGACY
MOBILE CADDIE
MOBILE TOUR
NETFITS
ODYSSEY
OPTIFIT
ORG 14
PENCIL
PUTTING CHALLENGE
RAINSPORT
RULE 35
S2H2
SENSERT
SHOPPING SPREE
SOFTFEEL
SQUAREWAY WOODS
STEELHEAD X-16
STRAPOLOGY
TECH SERIES
TOUR AUTHENTIC
TOUR I
TRADE IN TRADE UP
TRIHOT
TRU-BORE
TUBULAR LATTICE NETWORK
TUNITE
VFT
WAR BIRD
WARBIRD
WARMSPORT
WHITE HOT
WINDSPORT
WORLD'S FRIENDLIEST
X-12
X-14
X-16
X-18
X-18 PRO
X-20
X-20TOUR
X-FORGED
X-SOLE
X-SPANN
X-TOUR
XTRA TRACTION TECHNOLOGY
XTRA WIDTH TECHNOLOGY
YOU CAN'T ARGUE WITH PHYSICS
Advertising Agencies:
Factory Design Labs
158 Fillmore St
Denver, CO 80206
Tel.: (303) 573-9100
Fax: (303) 573-5975
Creative & Digital Agency of Record

Matthews/Evans/Albertazzi
1111 6th Ave Fl 6
San Diego, CA 92101
Tel.: (619) 238-8500
Fax: (619) 238-8505
Top-Flite
Ben Hogan

CAMERON BALLOONS U.S.

(Sub. of Cameron Balloons Ltd.)
7399 Newman Blvd
Dexter, MI 48130
Mailing Address:
PO Box 3672
Ann Arbor, MI 48106-3672
Tel.: (734) 426-5525
Fax: (734) 426-5026
E-mail: hotline@cameronballoons.com
Web Site: www.cameronballoons.com
E-Mail For Key Personnel:
Sales Director: baird@cameronballoons.com
Sales Range: $1-9.9 Million
Approx. Number Employees: 15
Year Founded: 1972
Business Description:
Hot-Air Balloon Mfr
S.I.C.: 3721; 3728
N.A.I.C.S.: 336411; 336413
Import Export
Advertising Expenditures: $100,000
Media: 2-4-7-10
Distr.: Direct to Consumer; Natl.
Personnel:
Dave Moody *(Mgr-Engrg)*
Brands & Products:
A-TYPE
CALIBER
CAMERON
CONCEPT
EASYVENT
MEDALIST
N-TYPE
O-TYPE
VIVA
Z-TYPE

CAMPING WORLD, INC.

(Sub. of FreedomRoads Holding Company, LLC)
650 3 Springs Rd
Bowling Green, KY 42104-7520
Mailing Address:
PO Box 90018
Bowling Green, KY 42102-9018
Tel.: (270) 781-2718
Fax: (270) 745-7192
Toll Free: (866) 694-1580
E-mail: info@campingworld.com
Web Site: www.campingworld.com
Approx. Number Employees: 450
Year Founded: 1966
Business Description:
Recreational Vehicle Accessories & Supplies Retailer
S.I.C.: 5561; 5961
N.A.I.C.S.: 441210; 454113
Import Export
Media: 2-3-4-5-6-7-8-10-13-15-17-18-19-20-22-23-24-25-26
Distr.: Natl.
Budget Set: Aug.
Personnel:
Marcus A. Lemonis *(Chm & CEO)*
Jim DeBruzzi *(CFO)*
Tamara Ward *(CMO)*
John A. Sirpilla *(Pres-Retail Stores)*
Zrinka Allen *(Exec VP-HR, Social Responsibility & Comm)*
Roger Anderson *(Reg VP-Atlantic)*
Paul Inman *(Reg VP-West)*
Bruce Wright *(Reg VP)*
David McKillip *(VP-Fin)*
Mike Siemens *(Exec Dir-Press Club)*
Rick Matar *(Dir-Natl Sls & Product Trng)*
Brad Woods *(Dir-Natl Sls & Product Trng)*

CARRON NET COMPANY, INC.

1623 17th St
Two Rivers, WI 54241-2916
Tel.: (920) 793-2217
Fax: (920) 793-2122
Toll Free: (888) BUY-NETS
E-mail: sales@carronnet.com
Web Site: www.carronnet.com
E-Mail For Key Personnel:
Sales Director: sales@carronnet.com
Sales Range: $25-49.9 Million
Approx. Number Employees: 40
Year Founded: 1934
Business Description:
Mfr. of Sports & Tennis Nets, Volleyball Nets & Made to Order Nets
S.I.C.: 3949; 2298
N.A.I.C.S.: 339920; 314991
Import Export
Media: 2-10-17-26
Distr.: Natl.
Budget Set: Jan.
Personnel:
Troy A Christiansen *(CFO & Exec VP)*
Brands & Products:
CARRONNET
HERCULES

CEDARBROOK SAUNA & STEAM

PO Box 535
Cashmere, WA 98815
Tel.: (509) 782-2447
Fax: (509) 782-3680
Toll Free: (800) 634-6334
E-mail: woodsauna@aol.com
Web Site: www.cedarbrooksauna.com
Sales Range: $10-24.9 Million
Approx. Number Employees: 20
Year Founded: 1974
Business Description:
Sauna Heaters, Rooms & Steam Generators Mfr
S.I.C.: 5999; 5211
N.A.I.C.S.: 453998; 444110
Import Export
Media: 26
Distr.: Direct to Consumer; Intl.; Natl.
Budget Set: Feb.
Personnel:
John Lysaker *(Founder)*

CITY SPORTS

(Sub. of Highland Capital Partners, LLC)
64 Industrial Way
Wilmington, MA 01887-3434
Tel.: (978) 253-5300
Web Site: www.citysports.com
Approx. Number Employees: 300
Year Founded: 1983
Business Description:
Sports Apparel & Accessories
S.I.C.: 5699; 5661
N.A.I.C.S.: 448190; 448210
Import Export
Media: 31
Personnel:
Michael R. Kennedy *(Co-Founder & CEO)*
Eric Martin *(Co-Founder)*
Jeff Connor *(Pres)*
Denise McDonald *(CFO)*
Sean Scales *(COO)*
Brands & Products:
CITY SPORT
Advertising Agency:
Sapient Corporation
17901 Old Cutler Rd Ste 400
Miami, FL 33157
Tel.: (305) 253-0100
Fax: (305) 253-0013

CLARUS CORPORATION

(Name Changed to Black Diamond, Inc.)

CLUB CAR, INC.

(Sub. of Ingersoll-Rand Company)
4125 Washington Rd
Evans, GA 30809-3067
Mailing Address:
PO Box 204658
Augusta, GA 30917-4658
Tel.: (706) 863-3000
Fax: (706) 863-5808
Toll Free: (800) 258-2227
Web Site: www.clubcar.com
Approx. Number Employees: 800
Year Founded: 1958
Business Description:
Mfr. of Electric & Gasoline Golf Cars & Light Utility Carryalls
S.I.C.: 3799; 3949
N.A.I.C.S.: 336999; 339920
Import Export
Media: 3-5-6-9-10-11-13-16-20-23-24-25
Distr.: Intl.
Personnel:
Philip J. Tralies *(Chm)*
Mike Packer *(VP & Mgr-Comml Bus)*
Mike Read *(Dir-Mktg Comm & Category Dir-Golf)*
Richard Fuhrmann *(Sls Mgr)*
Brands & Products:
ARMORFLEX
CARRYALL
IQ
PIONEER
POWERDRIVE
SYSTEM 48
TRANQUILITY

THE COLEMAN COMPANY, INC.

(Sub. of Jarden Outdoor Solutions)
3600 N Hydraulic St
Wichita, KS 67219-3812
Tel.: (316) 832-2700
Tel.: (316) 832-2653
Fax: (316) 832-3060
Toll Free: (800) 835-3278
E-mail: consumerservice@coleman.com
Web Site: www.coleman.com
Sales Range: $400-449.9 Million
Approx. Number Employees: 2,318
Year Founded: 1901
Business Description:
Sporting Goods & Equipment Mfr
S.I.C.: 3949; 5941; 5961
N.A.I.C.S.: 339920; 451110; 454111
Import Export
Media: 5-10-19-26
Distr.: Intl.; Natl.
Budget Set: Nov.
Personnel:
Robert F. Marcovitch *(Pres & CEO)*
Nicole Freund *(Dir-Market Res)*
Brands & Products:
COLEMAN
HOT WATER ON DEMAND
PROCAT
ROADTRIP

Key to Media (For complete agency information see *The Advertising Red Books-Agencies* edition):
1. Bus. Publs. 2. Cable T.V. 3. Catalogs & Directories. 4. Co-op Adv. 5. Consumer Mags. 6. D.M. to Bus. Estab.7. D.M. to Consumers
8. Daily Newsp. 9. Exhibits/Trade Shows 10. Foreign 11. Infomercial 12. Internet Adv.13. Multimedia 14. Network Radio
15. Network T.V. 16. Newsp. Distr. Mags. 17. Other 18. Outdoor (Posters, Transit) 19. Point of Purchase20. Premiums, Novelties
21. Product Samples 22. Special Events Mktg. 23. Spot Radio 24. Spot T.V. 25. Weekly Newsp. 26. Yellow Page Adv.

Advertising Agencies:
Celtic, Inc.
330 S Executive Dr Ste 206
Brookfield, WI 53005-4215
Tel.: (262) 789-7630
Fax: (262) 789-9454
Insenct Repelants

Doner
25900 Northwestern Hwy
Southfield, MI 48075
Tel.: (248) 354-9700
Fax: (248) 827-8440

COLUMBIA SPORTSWEAR COMPANY
14375 NW Science Park Dr
Portland, OR 97229-5418
Tel.: (503) 985-4000
Fax: (503) 985-5960
E-mail: dkiser@columbia.com
Web Site: www.columbia.com
Approx. Sls.: $1,483,524,000
Approx. Number Employees: 3,626
Year Founded: 1938
Business Description:
Active Outdoor Apparel Mfr
S.I.C.: 5136; 2241; 2329; 2339
N.A.I.C.S.: 424320; 313221; 315228; 315239
Advertising Expenditures: $77,978,000
Media: 3-5-6-9-11-13-15-18-19-24-25
Distr.: Intl.
Personnel:
Gertrude Boyle *(Chm)*
Timothy P. Boyle *(Pres & CEO)*
Bryan L. Timm *(COO & Exec VP)*
Peter J. Bragdon *(Gen Counsel, Sec, Sr VP-Legal & Corp Affairs)*
Michael W. McCormick *(Exec VP-Sls & Mktg-Global)*
Thomas B. Cusick *(Sr VP-Fin)*
Kerry W. Barnes *(VP-Retail)*
Daniel G. Hanson *(VP-Mktg)*
Susan G. Popp *(VP-HR)*
Adrienne Lefebre Moser *(Gen Mgr-Apparel Mdsg)*
Kathleen McNally *(Dir-Creative)*
Brianne Calandra *(Mgr-E-Commerce Tech)*
Brands & Products:
BUGABOO
BUGABOOT
COLUMBIA
CONVERT
GRT
OMNI-DRY
OMNI-GRIP
OMNI-SHADE
OMNI-TECH
OMNISHIELD
Q4 QUADENSITY
SOREL
TITANIUM
TITANIUM ALLOY
Advertising Agencies:
Butler, Shine, Stern & Partners
20 Liberty Ship Way
Sausalito, CA 94965-3312
Tel.: (415) 331-6049
Fax: (415) 331-3524

TsaiComms
112 NW Maywood Dr Ste B
Portland, OR 97210
Tel.: (971) 327-0628
Fax: (971) 327-0629

White Horse
3747 NE Sandy Blvd
Portland, OR 97232-1840
Tel.: (503) 471-4200
Fax: (503) 471-4299
Toll Free: (877) 471-4200

CONTINENTAL MARKETING
15381 E Proctor Ave
City of Industry, CA 91745
Tel.: (626) 582-8360
Fax: (626) 582-8889
Sales Range: Less than $1 Million
Approx. Number Employees: 20
Year Founded: 1986
Business Description:
Sports Bags, Fanny Packs, Lunch & Duffle Bags, Other Travel Related Accessories.
S.I.C.: 5063
N.A.I.C.S.: 423610
Media: 13-17
Distr.: Natl.
Personnel:
Dawn Du *(Gen Mgr)*

CONVERSE INC.
(Sub. of NIKE, Inc.)
1 High St
North Andover, MA 01845-2601
Tel.: (978) 983-3300
Fax: (978) 983-3502
Toll Free: (800) 547-2667
E-mail: pr@converse.com
Web Site: www.converse.com
Sales Range: $550-599.9 Million
Approx. Number Employees: 200
Year Founded: 1908
Business Description:
Mfr & Distr of Professional Sports & Leisure Footwear & Athletic Apparel
S.I.C.: 5139
N.A.I.C.S.: 424340
Advertising Expenditures: $20,000,000
Media: 3-4-6-8-10-15-18-19-20-22-23-24
Distr.: Intl.; Natl.
Budget Set: May
Personnel:
Michael Spillane *(CEO)*
Geoff Cottrill *(CMO)*
Willem Haitink *(VP & Gen Mgr-EMEA)*
Ian Stewart *(Reg Dir-Mktg-Asia Pacific)*
Brands & Products:
ALL STAR 2000
ALL STAR COLLECTION
CHUCK TAYLOR COLLECTION
CONVERSE
JACK PURCELL
ONE STAR
RE-ISSUE
REACT
WADE 3
Advertising Agencies:
Anomaly Communications LLC
536 Broadway 11th Fl
New York, NY 10012
Tel.: (917) 595-2200
Fax: (917) 595-2299
Wade 3

R/GA
350 W 39th St
New York, NY 10018-1402
Tel.: (212) 946-4000
Fax: (212) 946-4010
The Sampler

Wieden + Kennedy
Floor 5th No1035 ChangLe Road
Shanghai, 200031, China
Tel.: (86) 21 5158 3900
Fax: (86) 21 5158 3988

ZAAZ
414 Olive Way Ste 500
Seattle, WA 98101
Tel.: (206) 341-9885
Fax: (206) 749-9868
Web Site

CORTLAND LINE COMPANY
3736 Kellogg Rd
Cortland, NY 13045-8818
Tel.: (607) 756-2851
Fax: (607) 753-8835
Toll Free: (800) 847-6787
E-mail: info@cortlandline.com
Web Site: www.cortlandline.com
Approx. Number Employees: 60
Year Founded: 1915
Business Description:
Mfr & Distr of Sport Fishing Lines
S.I.C.: 2298
N.A.I.C.S.: 314991
Import Export
Media: 2-4-6-7-8-10-13-14-15-20-21-24
Distr.: Intl.; Natl.
Budget Set: June
Personnel:
Brian P. Ward *(Pres & CEO)*
Nate Dablock *(Mgr-Design)*
Brands & Products:
333HT
444
444 LAZERLINE
444 SL
BALDY
BERMUDA LITE
BERMUDA LITE MESH
CAM-O-FLAGE
CHECK OUTS
COBRA
CORTLAND
CORTLAND CHAMBRAY
CROWN II
CRUISE
DRY-UR-FLY
EXUMA
FAIR PLAY
FAIRPLAY
GRF-1000
HI-BULK
KERBOOM
KERPLUNK
LTD GRAPHITE
MICRO BRAID
MICRON
MIRACLE
MUSKY MASTER
PLION
POLARIZED CLIC
PRECISION
PRECISION I
RIMFLY
RODON
SPECTRON
TECH 60/40
TECH TWILL
TECH VENT
ULTRA-TECH

CRAZY CREEK PRODUCTS
1401 S Broadway PO Box 1050
Red Lodge, MT 59068-1050
Tel.: (406) 446-3446
Fax: (406) 446-1411
Toll Free: (800) 331-0304
E-mail: chairs@crazycreek.com
Web Site: www.crazycreek.com
Approx. Number Employees: 10
Year Founded: 1987
Business Description:
Mfr. of Portable Chairs
S.I.C.: 2531; 5021
N.A.I.C.S.: 337127; 423210
Import Export
Advertising Expenditures: $200,000
Media: 4-6-10-11-17-19-21-22
Brands & Products:
CRAZY CREEK
CRAZY LEGS
DON'T JUST DO SOMETHING...SIT THERE!
HEXALITE LONGBACK
HEXALITE POWERLOUNGER
LONGBACK
MULTISPORTS
POWERLOUNGER
Advertising Agency:
WG Communications
6430 Foxtrotter
Bozeman, MT 59715
Tel.: (406) 582-7347
Fax: (406) 582-7349

CREATIVE PLAYTHINGS LTD.
33 Loring Dr
Framingham, MA 01702
Tel.: (508) 620-0900
Fax: (508) 872-3120
Toll Free: (800) 24SWING
E-mail: info@creativeplaythings.com
Web Site: www.creativeplaythings.com
Approx. Number Employees: 175
Year Founded: 1951
Business Description:
Mfr. & Retailer of Playground Equipment
S.I.C.: 3949; 5091
N.A.I.C.S.: 339920; 423910
Media: 2-6-8-10
Personnel:
Donald Hoffman *(Pres & CEO)*
Brands & Products:
ALPINE
THE ALPINE
BIG RED
THE BOULDER
THE CHESAPEAKE
THE CONCORD
CREATIVE PLAYTHINGS
THE CRESCENT
THE DOVER
THE DURANGO
THE FAIRFAX
THE HAMPTON
THE LEXINGTON
NATURALINE
NATUREWOOD
NEWPORT
THE NEWPORT
SPECIAL PINE
STAND 'N SWING
THE WILLIAMSBURG

Key to Media (For complete agency information see *The Advertising Red Books-Agencies* edition):
1. Bus. Publs. 2. Cable T.V. 3. Catalogs & Directories. 4. Co-op Adv. 5. Consumer Mags. 6. D.M. to Bus. Estab.7. D.M. to Consumers 8. Daily Newsp. 9. Exhibits/Trade Shows 10. Foreign 11. Infomercial 12. Internet Adv.13. Multimedia 14. Network Radio 15. Network T.V. 16. Newsp. Distr. Mags. 17. Other 18. Outdoor (Posters, Transit) 19. Point of Purchase20. Premiums, Novelties 21. Product Samples 22. Special Events Mktg. 23. Spot Radio 24. Spot T.V. 25. Weekly Newsp. 26. Yellow Page Adv.

CREME LURE CO., INC.
PO Box 6162
Tyler, TX 75711-6162
Tel.: (903) 561-0522
Fax: (903) 561-0555
Toll Free: (800) 527-8652
E-mail: creme@gower.net
Web Site: www.cremelure.com
Approx. Number Employees: 50
Business Description:
Fishing Lures Mfr
S.I.C.: 3949
N.A.I.C.S.: 339920
Media: 2-4-6-10
Distr.: Natl.
Budget Set: Oct.
Personnel:
Wayne Kent *(Pres)*
Brands & Products:
ANGLE WORM
BABY TROUT
BIG PIG
BLACK ANT
BROWN CADDIS
BROWN MAYFLY NYMPH
BURKE BLACK ANT
BURKE BLACK FLOATING PANFISH SPIDER
BURKE CADDIS WORM
BURKE CATALPA WORM
BURKE GREEN GRASSHOPPER
BURKE LARGE GRUB
BURKE LARGE HELGRAMITE
BURKE MAYFLY NYMPH
BURKE MEDIUM BROWN FROG
BURKE MEDIUM GREEN FROG
BURKE SALMON FLY
BURKE SMALL BLACK CRICKET
BURKE SMALL GRAY CRICKET
BURKE SMALL GREEN GRASSHOPPER
BURKE SMALL HELGRAMITE
BURKE-SMALL WHITE GRUB
BURKE SMALL YELLOW GRASSHOPPER
BURKE STONEFLY NYMPH
BURKE YELLOW GRASSHOPPER
CADDIS WORM
CHANGE UP
CRAW WORM
CREME
DEVIL'S TONGUE
FISHFROG
JERK N' SHRIMP
KILLER DILLER
KING OF BAITS
LIPLESS CRANK
LIT'L CRITTER
LIT'L FISHIE
LIVIN' FROGS
MAD DAD
MAD DAD MINNOW
MAYFLY NYMPH
MEDIUM HELGRAMITE
MIDGET CRAWLER
POPPERS
PRERIGGED CURTAIL
RED ANT
SALMON FLY
SCALLY-WAG
SCOUNDREL
SHALLOW CRANK
SHRIMP TEASE
SILVER SIDE
SMALL HELGRAMITE
SMALL YELLOW GRASSHOPPER
SPOILER
SPOILER LIZARD
STONEFLY NYMPH
TOP WATER
TRU-LUR
TRU-LUR'S BABY BEE
TRU-LUR'S BROWN CADDIS FLY
TRU-LUR'S BROWN MAYFLY NYMPH
TRU-LUR'S CATALPA WORM
TRU-LUR'S DRAGON FLY NYMPH
TRU-LUR'S MAYFLY NYMPH
TRU-LUR'S SALMON FLY
TRU-LUR'S SMALL BROWN CRICKET
TRU-LUR'S SMALL BROWN FROG
TRU-LUR'S SMALL CATALPA WORM
TRU-LUR'S SMALL GREEN FROG
TRU-LUR'S STONE FLY NYMPH
TRU-LUR'S WOOLY WORM
WHACKY STICK
WHACKY WORM
WHITE GRUB
WOOLY WORM

CRL, INC.
(d/b/a Marble's Outdoors)
420 Industrial Pk
Gladstone, MI 49837-1130
Tel.: (906) 428-3710
Fax: (906) 428-3711
E-mail: info@marblescutlery.com
Web Site: www.marblesoutdoors.com
Approx. Number Employees: 20
Year Founded: 1893
Business Description:
Sporting Equipment Mfr
S.I.C.: 3949
N.A.I.C.S.: 339920
Export
Media: 2-4-6-8-10-16-19-22
Distr.: Intl.; Natl.
Personnel:
Craig R. Lauerman *(Pres)*
George Brinkley *(CEO)*
Brands & Products:
THE LEGACY LIVES ON MARBLE'S

DACOR CORPORATION
(Sub. of Mares America)
Shore Pointe 1 Selleck St
Norwalk, CT 06855
Tel.: (203) 852-7079
Fax: (203) 853-2892
Toll Free: (888) 800-0798
E-mail: mailservice@divedacor.com
Web Site: www.divedacor.com
Approx. Number Employees: 20
Year Founded: 1954
Business Description:
Scuba Equipment Mfr
S.I.C.: 3949
N.A.I.C.S.: 339920
Import Export
Media: 4-5-6-7-19
Distr.: Intl.; Natl.
Budget Set: Jan.
Personnel:
Karen Flood *(Mgr-Mktg)*
Brands & Products:
DACOR

DAISY MANUFACTURING COMPANY
(Holding of Charter Oak Capital Partners, L.P.)
(d/b/a Daisy Outdoor Products)
400 W Stribling Dr
Rogers, AR 72756-2411
Mailing Address:
PO Box 220
Rogers, AR 72757-0220
Tel.: (479) 636-1200
Fax: (479) 636-1601
Toll Free: (800) 643-3458
E-mail: info@daisy.com
Web Site: www.daisy.com
Sales Range: $50-74.9 Million
Approx. Number Employees: 170
Year Founded: 1886
Business Description:
Mfr. of B-B Guns, Pistols, Targets, CO-2 Gas Operated & Toy Play Guns
S.I.C.: 3484; 3482
N.A.I.C.S.: 332994; 332992
Import Export
Media: 2-4-6-7-10-15-19-20-22
Distr.: Intl.
Personnel:
Ray Hobbs *(Pres & CEO)*
Joe Murfin *(Dir-Mktg)*
Brands & Products:
AVANTI
COLT CO2
DAISY
MAX SPEED
POWERLINE
TAKE PRIDE. ITS A DAISY
Advertising Agency:
Brothers & Co.
4860 S Lewis Ave Ste 100
Tulsa, OK 74105-5171
Tel.: (918) 743-8822
Fax: (918) 742-9628

DAIWA CORPORATION
(Sub. of Globeride, Inc.)
12851 Midway Pl
Cerritos, CA 90703-2141
Mailing Address:
PO Box 6031
Artesia, CA 90702-6031
Tel.: (562) 802-9589
Fax: (562) 404-6212
E-mail: info@daiwa.com
Web Site: www.daiwa.com
Approx. Number Employees: 50
Year Founded: 1961
Business Description:
Fishing Rods & Reels Distr
S.I.C.: 5091; 3949
N.A.I.C.S.: 423910; 339920
Import Export
Advertising Expenditures: $1,000,000
Media: 2-4-6-7-10-18-19-20-21-24-25
Distr.: Natl.
Budget Set: May
Personnel:
Bill Liston *(VP-Adv & Promos)*
Terry Pederson *(VP-Sls)*
Sandy Tyler *(VP-Fin)*
Brands & Products:
ACCUDEPTH
ALGONQUIN
APOLLO
BEEFSTICK
BLACK GOLD
BLACK WIDOW
CAPRICE
CAPRICORN
COASTAL INSHORE
COMMITTED TO TOTAL QUALITY
CROSSFIRE
DAIWA
DAIWA SS-II
DENDOH
ELIMINATOR SERIES
EMBLEM
EMBLEM X-A
EMBLEM X-T
EMBLEM Z-A
EMCAST
FIREWOLF
GOLD SERIES
GOLDCAST
GRAND WAVE
GRAND WAVE Z
HEARTLAND
JUPITER S
JUPITER Z
KASTOR
LOCHMOR S
M ONE
MAGFORCE
MEGAFORCE I
MILLIONAIRE
MILLIONAIRE CV-X
MILLIONAIRE CV-Z
MILLIONAIRE S
MINI
MINICAST
MINISPIN
ONDINE
PROCASTER
PROCASTER ROJO
PROCASTER TOURNAMENT SERIES
PROCASTER Z
PROCYON
REGAL
REGAL BRI
REGAL PLUS BRI
REGAL XC
REGAL ZC
SALTIGA
SEALINE
SEALINE BR
SEALINE H
SEALINE LCA
SEALINE LEVER DRAG
SEALINE SGH
SEALINE SL-D
SEALINE SL-SH
SEALINE SL-T
SEALINE TOURNAMENT
SEALINE X-HC
SEALINE X-HV
SILVER CAST PLUS
SPINMATIC ST
SPINMATIC XT
SPINMATIC ZT
SPINSTAR XC
SPINSTAR ZC
SS TOURNAMENT
STEEZ
STRIKEFORCE
SWEEPFIRE
TEAM DAIWA-ADVANTAGE
TEAM DAIWA FUEGO
TEAM DAIWA LUNA
TEAM DAIWA SOL
TEAM DAIWA VIENTO
TEAM DAIWA X
TEAM DAIWA-Z CU
TEAM DAIWA ZILLION
TRIFORCE I
UNDERSPIN

DATREK PROFESSIONAL BAGS, INC.
835 Bill Jones Industrial Dr
Springfield, TN 37172

Key to Media (For complete agency information see *The Advertising Red Books-Agencies* edition):
1. Bus. Publs. 2. Cable T.V. 3. Catalogs & Directories. 4. Co-op Adv. 5. Consumer Mags. 6. D.M. to Bus. Estab.7. D.M. to Consumers
8. Daily Newsp. 9. Exhibits/Trade Shows 10. Foreign 11. Infomercial 12. Internet Adv.13. Multimedia 14. Network Radio
15. Network T.V. 16. Newsp. Distr. Mags. 17. Other 18. Outdoor (Posters, Transit) 19. Point of Purchase20. Premiums, Novelties
21. Product Samples 22. Special Events Mktg. 23. Spot Radio 24. Spot T.V. 25. Weekly Newsp. 26. Yellow Page Adv.

Tel.: (615) 384-1286
Fax: (615) 384-1290
Web Site: www.datrek.com
Approx. Number Employees: 100
Year Founded: 1981
Business Description:
Golf Bags, Head Covers, Tote Bags & Golf Accessories Mfr
S.I.C.: 3949
N.A.I.C.S.: 339920
Import Export
Media: 2-4
Distr.: Natl.
Personnel:
Karen Seabolt *(Mgr-Customer Svc)*
Mike Fox *(Engr-Devel)*
Brands & Products:
AIRWALK
ALEXIS
ALTIMA
BRIGHTON
CONEHEAD
COOLRIDER
DELUXE
HIGH DIVIDE
HIGH IMPACT
LITE RIDER
MILLER
MIRAGE
MIST
NAVIGATOR
PROLITE
QUIVER
RIVIERA
SCORE
SILHOUETTE
SOLITE
SPORT CROSS
SPORTSTER
STEALTH
STREAMER
SUNDANCER

DELTA/TRIMAX CORPORATION

20 S Main St Ste 17
Janesville, WI 53545-3959
Tel.: (608) 757-1477
Fax: (608) 754-1239
Toll Free: (800) 747-7077
E-mail: trimaxemail@aol.com
Web Site: www.mmpcompany.com/trimax/
Business Description:
Sporting Goods & Bicylces Direct Sales
S.I.C.: 5963; 5941
N.A.I.C.S.: 454390; 451110
Import Export
Media: 1-3-6-8-9-18-26
Distr.: Natl.

DESCENTE NORTH AMERICA, INC.

(Affil. of Descente Ltd.)
2550 Washington Blvd Ste 200
Ogden, UT 84401-3121
Tel.: (801) 317-0017
Fax: (801) 317-0020
Toll Free: (800) 999-0475
E-mail: info@descente.com
Web Site: www.descente.com
Approx. Number Employees: 12
Year Founded: 1991
Business Description:
Ski Apparel Mfr & Distr
S.I.C.: 5136
N.A.I.C.S.: 424320
Import
Advertising Expenditures: $150,000
Media: 2-6-7-8-10-17-19-22-26
Distr.: Natl.
Budget Set: Nov.
Personnel:
Kiyoshige Higeo *(Pres)*

DIAMOND BRAND CANVAS PRODUCTS CO., INC.

145 Cane Creek Industrial Pk Rd Ste 1
Fletcher, NC 28732
Tel.: (828) 684-9848
Fax: (828) 687-0965
Toll Free: (800) 258-9811
E-mail: dbo@diamondbrand.com
Web Site: www.diamondbrand.com
Approx. Number Employees: 100
Year Founded: 1881
Business Description:
Tents & Backpacks Whlsr
S.I.C.: 2394
N.A.I.C.S.: 314912
Import Export
Media: 2-4-5-6-7-8-10-13-14-15-18-23-24-26
Distr.: Natl.
Budget Set: Aug. -Sept.
Personnel:
William Gay *(Pres-Owner)*
Brands & Products:
DIAMOND

DICK'S SPORTING GOODS, INC.

345 Court St
Coraopolis, PA 15108
Tel.: (724) 273-3400
E-mail: investors@dcsg.com
Web Site: www.dickssportinggoods.com
Approx. Sls.: $4,871,492,000
Approx. Number Employees: 10,100
Year Founded: 1948
Business Description:
Sporting Goods Retailer
S.I.C.: 5941; 5091; 5699; 5961
N.A.I.C.S.: 451110; 423910; 448190; 454111; 454113
Advertising Expenditures: $185,200,000
Media: 3-8-9-13-14-15-18-23-24-26
Personnel:
Edward W. Stack *(Chm & CEO)*
William J. Colombo *(Vice Chm)*
Joseph H. Schmidt *(Pres & COO)*
Timothy E. Kullman *(CFO, Exec VP-Fin & Admin)*
Matthew J. Lynch *(CIO & Sr VP)*
Lauren R. Hobart *(CMO & Sr VP)*
Joseph R. Oliver *(Chief Acctg Officer, Sr VP & Controller)*
Peter J. Whitsett *(Pres-Golf Galaxy & Exec VP-Global Mdsg)*
David I. Mosse *(Gen Counsel, Sec & Sr VP-Legal)*
David G. Stanchak *(Sr VP-Real Estate)*
Kathy Sutter *(Sr VP-HR)*
Advertising Agencies:
Martino Flynn LLC
175 Sully's Trl Ste 100
Pittsford, NY 14534
Tel.: (585) 421-0100
Fax: (585) 421-0121

WMI Out-of-Home
Ste 201 1221 Post Rd E
Westport, CT 06880-5430
Tel.: (203) 256-4168
Fax: (203) 256-0883

DOREL INDUSTRIES, INC.

1255 Greene Ave Ste 300
Montreal, QC H3Z 2A4, Canada
Tel.: (514) 934-3034
Fax: (514) 934-9379
E-mail: info@dorel.com
Web Site: www.dorel.com
Approx. Rev.: $2,312,986,000
Approx. Number Employees: 4,600
Year Founded: 1962
Business Description:
Mfr of Consumer Products; Ready-to-Assemble Furniture, Juvenile Furniture & Home Furnishings
S.I.C.: 3999; 2511; 2519
N.A.I.C.S.: 339999; 337122; 337125
Import Export
Personnel:
Martin Schwartz *(Pres & CEO)*
Hani Basile *(Pres & COO-Juvenile Segment)*
Jeffrey Schwartz *(CFO, Sec & Exec VP)*
Andrew Coccari *(Global CMO-Recreation & Leisure)*
Norman Braunstein *(Grp Pres & CEO-Home Furnishings Segment)*
Alan Schwartz *(Exec VP-Ops)*
Jeffrey Segel *(Exec VP-Mktg & Sls)*
Frank Rana *(VP-Fin & Asst Sec)*
Edward Wyse *(VP-Global Procurement)*
Brands & Products:
AMERIWOOD
BABIDEAL
BABY RELAX
BEBE CONFORT
CANNONDALE
CARINA
CHARLESWOOD
COSCO
DOREL
DYNO
GT BICYCLE
INSTEP
MAXI-COSI
MONBEBE
MONGOOSE
MURRAY
PACIFIC
POWERLITE
QUINNY
ROADMASTER
SAFETY 1ST
SAFETY FIRST
SCHWINN
SUGOI
SYSTEMBUILD
Advertising Agencies:
360 Public Relations LLC
140 Clareedon St Ste 401
Boston, MA 02116
Tel.: (617) 585-5770
Fax: (617) 585-5789

Colle+McVoy
400 1st Ave N Ste 700
Minneapolis, MN 55401-1954
Tel.: (612) 305-6000
Fax: (612) 305-6500
Agency of Record
Creative Development
Global Strategic
Recreational Leisure Segment

DOVER SADDLERY, INC.

525 Great Rd PO Box 1100
Littleton, MA 01460
Tel.: (978) 952-8062
Toll Free: (800) 406-8204
E-mail: customerservice@doversaddlery.com
Web Site: www.doversaddlery.com
Approx. Rev.: $78,190,283
Approx. Number Employees: 186
Year Founded: 1975
Business Description:
Equestrian Products Retailer
S.I.C.: 5961; 5941
N.A.I.C.S.: 454113; 451110
Advertising Expenditures: $8,172,000
Personnel:
Stephen L. Day *(Chm, Pres, CEO & Treas)*
David R. Pearce *(CFO)*
Jonathan A.R. Grylls *(COO, Sec & VP)*
William G. Schmidt *(COO)*
Brands & Products:
CIRCUIT CLOSE CONTACT
CIRCUIT CLOSE CONTACT JR.
CIRCUIT ELITE
CIRCUIT PRO
DOVER SADDLERY
PROFESSIONAL HORSEMAN'S SUPPLY
RIDING SPORT

EASTERN MOUNTAIN SPORTS, INC.

1 Vose Farm Rd
Peterborough, NH 03458-2128
Tel.: (603) 924-9571
Fax: (603) 924-9138
Toll Free: (888) 463-6367
E-mail: customerservices@ems.com
Web Site: www.ems.com
Sales Range: $25-49.9 Million
Approx. Number Employees: 450
Business Description:
Outdoors Clothing & Equipment Whslr
S.I.C.: 5941; 5699
N.A.I.C.S.: 451110; 448190
Personnel:
Will Manzer *(CEO)*
Scott Barrett *(CMO)*
Advertising Agency:
CGPR
24 Prospect St
Marblehead, MA 01945
Tel.: (781) 639-4924
Fax: (781) 639-4328

EASTON SPORTS, INC.

7855 Haskell Ave Ste 200
Van Nuys, CA 91406-1907
Tel.: (818) 782-6445
Fax: (818) 782-9795
Toll Free: (800) 632-7866
Web Site: www.eastonsports.com
Approx. Number Employees: 1,500
Business Description:
Sports Equipment, Sport Bags & Accessories Mfr & Sales
S.I.C.: 5091
N.A.I.C.S.: 423910
Import Export
Media: 4-5-6-7-8-9-16-25
Personnel:
Jim Easton *(Chm)*
Chris Zimmerman *(Pres)*

Key to Media (For complete agency information see *The Advertising Red Books-Agencies* edition):
1. Bus. Publs. 2. Cable T.V. 3. Catalogs & Directories. 4. Co-op Adv. 5. Consumer Mags. 6. D.M. to Bus. Estab.7. D.M. to Consumers
8. Daily Newsp. 9. Exhibits/Trade Shows 10. Foreign 11. Infomercial 12. Internet Adv.13. Multimedia 14. Network Radio
15. Network T.V. 16. Newsp. Distr. Mags. 17. Other 18. Outdoor (Posters, Transit) 19. Point of Purchase20. Premiums, Novelties
21. Product Samples 22. Special Events Mktg. 23. Spot Radio 24. Spot T.V. 25. Weekly Newsp. 26. Yellow Page Adv.

Easton Sports, Inc. — (Continued)

Mark Tripp *(CFO & VP)*
Mike Zlaket *(Exec VP & Gen Mgr)*
Matt Arndt *(Sr VP-Baseball & Softball)*
John Graham *(Sr VP-Commerce)*
Duke Stump *(Sr VP-Culture, Creative & Brand Innovation)*
Jim Darby *(VP-Promo)*
Doug Appleton *(Gen Mgr-Lacrosse Div)*
Greg Barton *(Dir-Promotions)*
Trevor Anderson *(Product Mgr)*
Jon Konigsberg *(Sls Mgr)*

Brands & Products:
EASTON
INCREDIBALL

EASYTURF

(Sub. of FieldTurf, Inc.)
2418 Auto Pkwy
Escondido, CA 92029
Toll Free: (866) 327-9887
Web Site: www.easyturf.com
Business Description:
Installation & Distribution of Artificial Grass
S.I.C.: 3089; 0711
N.A.I.C.S.: 326199; 115112
Media: 10-22
Personnel:
David Hartman *(Pres)*

ECHO FARMS GOLF & COUNTRY CLUB, INC.

(Sub. of Matrix Golf & Hospitality)
4114 Echo Farms Blvd
Wilmington, NC 28412
Tel.: (910) 791-9318
Fax: (910) 799-9564
E-mail: echogolfgm@aol.com
Approx. Number Employees: 25
Business Description:
Land Subdividers & Developers
S.I.C.: 7997
N.A.I.C.S.: 713910
Media: 6-9-13-25-26
Personnel:
Jeff George *(Gen Mgr)*

ELITE SPORTSWEAR, L.P.

2136 N 13th St
Reading, PA 19604
Tel.: (610) 921-1469
Fax: (610) 921-0208
Toll Free: (800) 345-4087
E-mail: gkelite@gkelite.com
Web Site: www.gk-elitesportswear.com
Approx. Number Employees: 250
Year Founded: 1981
Business Description:
Mfr. of Gymnastics & Skating Apparel
S.I.C.: 2329; 2339
N.A.I.C.S.: 315228; 315239
Import Export
Advertising Expenditures: $400,000
Media: 2-4-6-7-10-11-13-21
Distr.: Natl.
Budget Set: Oct. -Nov.
Personnel:
Paul Honig *(COO)*
Alan Robezzoli *(Exec VP-Mktg)*
Connie Maloney *(Program Mgr)*

Brands & Products:
BACK TO SCHOOL
GK
NASTIA GOLD MEDAL
SHAWN JOHNSON
TOUSSE

ENDLESS POOLS, INC.

1601 Dutton Mill Rd
Aston, PA 19014
Tel.: (610) 497-8676
Fax: (610) 497-9328
Toll Free: (800) 732-8660
E-mail: swim@endlesspools.com
Web Site: www.endlesspools.com
Approx. Number Employees: 110
Year Founded: 1988
Business Description:
Swimming Pools Mfr & Distr
S.I.C.: 3949; 5999
N.A.I.C.S.: 339920; 453998
Media: 6
Personnel:
James Murdock *(Owner)*
Mark Langan *(Dir-Mktg)*

Brands & Products:
THE ENDLESS POOL

EPPINGER MANUFACTURING CO.

6340 Schaefer Rd
Dearborn, MI 48126-2285
Tel.: (313) 582-3205
Fax: (313) 582-0110
Toll Free: (888) 771-8277
E-mail: info@eppinger.net
Web Site: www.eppinger.net
Sales Range: $25-49.9 Million
Approx. Number Employees: 13
Year Founded: 1906
Business Description:
Fishing Lures Mfr
S.I.C.: 3949
N.A.I.C.S.: 339920
Export
Media: 1-2-4-5-10-16-18-20-21
Distr.: Intl.; Natl.
Budget Set: May
Personnel:
Karen Eppinger *(Pres)*
John Cleveland *(Mgr-Mktg)*

Brands & Products:
AMERICA'S FISHING LURES
DARDEVLE
EPPINGER
OSPREY

ESCALADE INC.

817 Maxwell Ave
Evansville, IN 47711
Mailing Address:
PO Box 889
Evansville, IN 47706-0889
Tel.: (812) 467-1200
Fax: (812) 467-1300
Toll Free: (800) 467-1200
E-mail: customerservice@escaladesports.com
Web Site: www.escaladeinc.com
Approx. Sls.: $120,656,000
Approx. Number Employees: 608
Year Founded: 1927
Business Description:
Recreational Items Mfr
S.I.C.: 3949
N.A.I.C.S.: 339920
Import Export
Media: 2-3-5-6-10-13-15-18-19-21-22-24
Distr.: Intl.; Natl.
Budget Set: Dec.

Personnel:
Robert E. Griffin *(Chm)*
Robert J. Keller *(Pres & CEO)*
Deborah Meinert *(CFO, Treas, Sec & VP)*
Larry Gajderowicz *(Mgr-Mktg)*
Doug Hunter *(Mgr-Natl Sls)*
Evan Lederman *(Mgr-Category)*
Jason Pickerill *(Mgr-Mktg-Archery)*

Brands & Products:
ACCUDART
BEAR
CHILDLIFE
ESCALADE
FRED BEAR
GOALIATH
GOALRILLA
HARVARD
INDIAN ARCHERY
JENNINGS
MASTER
MIZERAK
MOSCONI
MURREY
PING PONG
PREMIER
PSE
RHINO PLAY
SILVERBACK
THE STEP
STIGA
US WEIGHT
WINMAU
WOODPLAY

Advertising Agency:
Gray Loon Marketing Group, Inc.
300 SE Riverside Dr Ste 200
Evansville, IN 47713
Tel.: (812) 422-9999
Fax: (812) 422-3342
Toll Free: (888) GRAYLOON
(Harvard, Stiga, Ping Pong, Indian Archery, Xi, Table Tennis, Basketball, Pool, Game Tables & Archery)
— Tom Lewis *(Pres.)*

EVERLAST WORLDWIDE INC.

(Sub. of Sports Direct International plc)
183 Madison Ave Ste 1701
New York, NY 10016
Tel.: (212) 239-0990
Fax: (212) 239-4261
Toll Free: (800) 777-0313
Web Site: www.everlast.com
Approx. Rev.: $51,887,000
Approx. Number Employees: 140
Year Founded: 1992
Business Description:
Boxing Equipment Designer, Marketer, Retailer & Mfr
S.I.C.: 3949; 5091
N.A.I.C.S.: 339920; 423910
Advertising Expenditures: $2,400,000
Media: 5-6-10-13-16-22
Personnel:
Neil Morton *(CEO)*
Gary J. Dailey *(CFO & COO)*
Angelo V. Giusti *(Sr VP-Sls)*

Brands & Products:
EVERLAST

Advertising Agency:
Finch Brands
325 Chestnut St Ste 1313
Philadelphia, PA 19106
Tel.: (215) 413-2686
Fax: (215) 413-2687

EXERCYCLE CORPORATION

31 Hayward St
Franklin, MA 02038
Tel.: (508) 528-3100
Fax: (508) 528-8454
Toll Free: (800) 367-6712
E-mail: info@exercycle.com
Web Site: www.exercycle.com
E-Mail For Key Personnel:
President: david@exercycle.com
Approx. Number Employees: 25
Year Founded: 1932
Business Description:
Mfr & Retailer of Exercise & Health Equipment
S.I.C.: 3949
N.A.I.C.S.: 339920
Import Export
Advertising Expenditures: $200,000
Media: 1-2-3-4-6-8-9-12-13-14-15-18-20-22-23-24-25-26
Distr.: Natl.
Personnel:
Peter Blumenthal *(Owner)*
David E. St. Germain *(Pres)*
Peter Rowe *(Dir-HR)*

Brands & Products:
EXERCYCLE
THERACYCLE

FEDERAL PREMIUM AMMUNITION

(Sub. of Alliant Techsystems Inc.)
900 Bob Ehlen Dr
Anoka, MN 55303-1778
Tel.: (763) 323-2300
Fax: (763) 323-2506
Toll Free: (800) 322-2342
E-mail: prodserv@atk.com
Web Site: www.federalpremium.com
Sales Range: $200-249.9 Million
Approx. Number Employees: 925
Year Founded: 1916
Business Description:
Shotshell, Centerfire & Rimfire Cartridges, Ammunition Components & Clay Targets Mfr
S.I.C.: 3482; 3949
N.A.I.C.S.: 332992; 339920
Advertising Expenditures: $2,000,000
Media: 1-2-3-4-5-6-7-9-10-14-19-20
Distr.: Natl.
Budget Set: Jan.
Personnel:
Mark W. DeYoung *(CEO)*
Kyle Tengwall *(Dir-Mktg)*

Brands & Products:
FEDERAL
POWER-SHOK
PREMIUM
V-SHOK
WING-SHOK

FEEL GOLF CO., INC.

1354-T Dayton St Ste T
Salinas, CA 93901
Tel.: (831) 422-9300
Fax: (831) 422-9301
Toll Free: (877) 934-7387
E-mail: info@feelwedges.com
Web Site: www.feelwedges.com
Approx. Rev.: $391,594
Approx. Number Employees: 6
Year Founded: 2000
Business Description:
Golf Club Mfr & Sales
S.I.C.: 3949
N.A.I.C.S.: 339920

Key to Media (For complete agency information see *The Advertising Red Books-Agencies* edition):
1. Bus. Publs. 2. Cable T.V. 3. Catalogs & Directories. 4. Co-op Adv. 5. Consumer Mags. 6. D.M. to Bus. Estab.7. D.M. to Consumers 8. Daily Newsp. 9. Exhibits/Trade Shows 10. Foreign 11. Infomercial 12. Internet Adv.13. Multimedia 14. Network Radio 15. Network T.V. 16. Newsp. Distr. Mags. 17. Other 18. Outdoor (Posters, Transit) 19. Point of Purchase20. Premiums, Novelties 21. Product Samples 22. Special Events Mktg. 23. Spot Radio 24. Spot T.V. 25. Weekly Newsp. 26. Yellow Page Adv.

Advertising Expenditures: $266,197
Media: 3-6-12-13
Personnel:
Lee Miller *(CEO)*
David Otterbach *(COO)*
Brands & Products:
COMPETITOR
THE DART THROWER
DESIGNER WEDGES
DR. FEEL
FEEL
FEEL GOLF
FULL RELEASE
THE HEATER
PRO RELEASE
SENSATION

THE FINISH LINE, INC.
3308 N Mitthoeffer Rd
Indianapolis, IN 46235
Tel.: (317) 899-1022
Fax: (317) 899-0237
Toll Free: (888) 777-3949
Web Site: www.finishline.com
Approx. Sls.: $1,229,002,000
Approx. Number Employees: 3,200
Year Founded: 1976
Business Description:
Athletic Apparel & Accessories Retailer
S.I.C.: 3949; 5699
N.A.I.C.S.: 339920; 448190
Advertising Expenditures: $25,099,000
Media: 5-6-8-13-15-18-19
Personnel:
Glenn S. Lyon *(Chm)*
Steven J. Schneider *(Co-Pres & COO)*
Samuel M. Sato *(Co-Pres & Chief Mdsg Officer)*
Edward W. Wilhelm *(CFO)*
Terry Ledbetter *(CIO)*
Steven R. Schreibman *(CMO)*
Gary D. Cohen *(Chief Admin Officer)*
Beau J. Swenson *(Chief Acctg Officer & VP)*
Donald E. Courtney *(Pres-Ecommerce)*
Michael L. Marchetti *(Exec VP-Store Ops)*
George S. Sanders *(Exec VP-Real Estate & Store Dev)*
Robert A. Edwards *(Sr VP-Distr)*
Michael J. Smith *(Sr VP-Loss Prevention)*
Roger C. Underwood *(Sr VP-Info Sys)*
Sally McKelvey *(VP-Strategy)*
Brands & Products:
FINISH LINE
FINISH LINE BLUE LABEL
Advertising Agency:
Xylem CCI
1480 Humboldt St
Denver, CO 80218
Tel.: (303) 291-0246
Fax: (303) 291-0268

FIREARMS TRAINING SYSTEMS, INC.
(Name Changed to Meggitt Training Systems)

FITNESS RESOURCE, INC.
22714 Glenn Dr Ste 130
Sterling, VA 20164
Tel.: (703) 796-8810
Fax: (703) 707-9760
Toll Free: (866) 348-3000
E-mail: info@fitnessresource.com
Web Site: www.fitnessresource.com
E-Mail For Key Personnel:
President: dnees@fitnessresource.com
Sales Director: commercialsales@fitnessresource.com
Sales Range: $10-24.9 Million
Approx. Number Employees: 170
Year Founded: 1985
Business Description:
Fitness Equipment Retailer
S.I.C.: 5941
N.A.I.C.S.: 451110
Media: 3-13-14-15-17-23-24
Personnel:
David E. Nees *(Pres)*
Shawn Renfrow *(Sr VP)*

FOGDOG, INC.
(Sub. of GSI Commerce, Inc.)
935 1st Ave
King of Prussia, PA 19406
Fax: (610) 265-2866
Toll Free: (800) 624-2017
E-mail: sales@fogdog.com
Web Site: www.fogdog.com
Sales Range: $100-124.9 Million
Approx. Number Employees: 137
Year Founded: 1994
Business Description:
Sporting Goods Retailer
S.I.C.: 5961; 5091; 5941
N.A.I.C.S.: 454111; 423910; 451110
Advertising Expenditures: $450,000
Media: 13
Personnel:
Steven Davis *(Sr VP-Sls)*

THE FORZANI GROUP LTD.
824 41st Ave NE
Calgary, AB T2E 3R3, Canada
Tel.: (403) 717-1400
Fax: (403) 717-1491
E-mail: cjordan@forzani.com
Web Site: www.forzanigroup.com
Approx. Rev.: $1,475,983,892
Approx. Number Employees: 14,000
Year Founded: 1993
Business Description:
Retailer of Sporting Goods
S.I.C.: 5091
N.A.I.C.S.: 423910
Advertising Expenditures: $41,200,000
Media: 13-18
Personnel:
John M. Forzani *(Founder & Chm)*
Michael Medline *(Pres)*
Robert Sartor *(CEO)*
Gregory Craig *(CFO)*
Kristine Freudenthaler *(CIO, Chief Integration Officer & Sr VP-IT)*
Duncan Fulton *(CMO & Sr VP-Comm)*
Richard J. White *(Chief Mdsg Officer & Sr VP)*
John Hould *(Pres-Natl Sports, Sr VP & ECommerce)*
Doug Nathanson *(Legal Counsel)*
Jean-Stephane Tremblay *(Exec VP-Franchise)*
Richard Burnet *(Sr VP-Fin & Admin)*
Stephen Clements *(Sr VP-Ops-Natl Sports)*
Matthew Handford *(Sr VP-HR)*
Keith Lambert *(Sr VP-Supply Chain & Mdse Mgmt)*
Chad McKinnon *(Sr VP-Corp Store Ops)*
Ilona Meditskos *(VP & Gen Mgr-Athletes World)*
Mona Carriere *(VP-Pur & Mktg Franchise)*
Mark Hindman *(VP-Mktg)*
Kenneth MacDonald *(VP-Mdse Sys & Inventory Mgmt)*
Heidi Rolston *(VP-HR & Leadership Dev)*
Brands & Products:
ATHLETES WORLD
ATMOSPHERE
COAST MOUNTAIN SPORTS
ECONOSPORTS
FITNESS SOURCE
THE FORZANI GROUP
HOCKEY EXPERTS
INTERSPORT
NATIONAL SPORTS
NEVADA BOB'S GOLF
PEGASUS
RNR
S3
SPORT CHECK
SPORT MART
SPORTS EXPERTS
THE TECH SHOP

FRANKLIN SPORTS, INC.
17 Campanelli Parkway
Stoughton, MA 02072-0508
Mailing Address:
PO Box 508
Stoughton, MA 02072-0508
Tel.: (781) 344-1111
Fax: (781) 341-3646
Toll Free: (800) 225-8647
Web Site: www.franklinsports.com
Approx. Number Employees: 225
Year Founded: 1946
Business Description:
Athletic & Sporting Goods Whslr
S.I.C.: 3949
N.A.I.C.S.: 339920
Import Export
Advertising Expenditures: $2,000,000
Media: 4-6
Distr.: Natl.
Personnel:
Larry J. Franklin *(Pres)*
Michael Kirby *(VP-Info Sys)*
Joe Murphy *(VP-Sls)*
Charles Quinn *(VP-Mktg)*
Brands & Products:
2ND-SKINZ
ACD
AEGIS
AERO STRIKE
AGS
AIR TECH
ARMOR-TAN
ATV HUMMER
CARBON FIBRE
CHUX
CONTOUR FIT SYSTEM
COOL DRY
COOLMAX
DELUXE EUROPA
DIGITAL
EUROPA
FAN FACE
FLEX PRO
FOLDING INNERNET
FRANKLIN
FRANKLIN SPORTS
FREE KICK
GRIP-RITE
HOOPS TO GO
INNERNET
LEARN TO PLAY
MICRO-SHIELD
NEO-FIT
OFFICIAL NHL
PRO ACTION ROD
PRO COMMANDER
PRO FLEX
PRO HUMMER
PRO PVS 100 INNERNET
READY TO PLAY
ROLL-A-PUCK
RTP FIELD MASTER
SHAG-BAG
SHOK-SORB
SHOOT 'N SCORE
SHOT ZONE
SOCCER
SOFT SPORT
SOFT-STRIKE
SX PRO INNERNET
THT
TRI-CURVE
WHIRL BALL
ZERO GRAVITY SPORTS
Advertising Agency:
FORGE worldwide
142 Berkeley St
Boston, MA 02116
Tel.: (617) 262-4800

FREEDOM BOAT CLUB
27 Beach Rd Ste 101
Monmouth Beach, NJ 07750
Tel.: (732) 832-9458
Fax: (732) 899-3529
Toll Free: (888) 781-7363
E-mail: info@freedomboatclub.com
Web Site: freedomboatclub.com/locations/57-monmouth-beach-nj
Business Description:
Private Membership Boating Club
S.I.C.: 7997; 7941
N.A.I.C.S.: 713910; 711211
Media: 6-9-10-13-25
Personnel:
Genina Rehrer *(Owner)*

FREEDOM GROUP, INC.
(Holding of Cerberus Capital Management, L.P.)
870 Remington Dr
Madison, NC 27025-1776
Tel.: (336) 548-8700
Fax: (336) 548-7801
E-mail: Info@Remington.com
Web Site: www.freedom-group.com
Approx. Rev.: $722,500,000
Approx. Number Employees: 2,780
Business Description:
Firearms, Ammunition & Related Products Mfr & Distr
S.I.C.: 3484; 3482
N.A.I.C.S.: 332994; 332992
Advertising Expenditures: $17,000,000
Media: 4-5-6-24
Personnel:
John Blystone *(Chm)*
Walter McLallen *(Vice Chm)*
Stephen P. Jackson, Jr. *(CFO, Treas & Corp Sec)*
Fredric E. Roth, Jr. *(Chief Compliance Officer, Gen Counsel & Sec)*

Key to Media (For complete agency information see *The Advertising Red Books-Agencies* edition):
1. Bus. Publs. 2. Cable T.V. 3. Catalogs & Directories. 4. Co-op Adv. 5. Consumer Mags. 6. D.M. to Bus. Estab.7. D.M. to Consumers 8. Daily Newsp. 9. Exhibits/Trade Shows 10. Foreign 11. Infomercial 12. Internet Adv.13. Multimedia 14. Network Radio 15. Network T.V. 16. Newsp. Distr. Mags. 17. Other 18. Outdoor (Posters, Transit) 19. Point of Purchase20. Premiums, Novelties 21. Product Samples 22. Special Events Mktg. 23. Spot Radio 24. Spot T.V. 25. Weekly Newsp. 26. Yellow Page Adv.

FREEDOM GROUP, INC. — (Continued)

E. Scott Blackwell *(Chief Sls & Mktg Officer)*
Jay Bunting *(VP-Distr Sls)*

GANDER MOUNTAIN COMPANY

180 E 5th St Ste 1300
Saint Paul, MN 55101-1664
Tel.: (651) 325-4300
Fax: (651) 325-2003
Fax: (651) 325-2001 (Investor Rels)
Toll Free: (800) 282-5993
Toll Free: (888) 5GANDER
Web Site: www.gandermountain.com
Sales Range: $5-14.9 Billion
Approx. Number Employees: 2,325
Year Founded: 1960
Business Description:
Retailer of Hunting, Fishing, Boating & Camping Equipment
S.I.C.: 5941; 5961
N.A.I.C.S.: 451110; 454111; 454113
Advertising Expenditures: $37,243,000
Personnel:
David C. Pratt *(Chm & Interim CEO)*
Ronald A. Erickson *(Vice Chm)*
Robert J. Vold *(CFO, Treas & Sr VP)*
Michael Owens *(COO & Exec VP)*
Eric R. Jacobsen *(Gen Counsel, Sec & Exec VP)*
Steven Uline *(Exec VP-Mktg)*
Kerry D. Graskewicz *(Sr VP-Inventory Mgmt)*
Casey Ramm *(Sr VP-Mdsg)*

GEORGIA TENT & AWNING INC.

1356 English St NW
Atlanta, GA 30318
Tel.: (404) 523-7551
Fax: (404) 525-0606
Fax: (404) 525-0601
Toll Free: (800) 252-2391
E-mail: helen@georgiatent.com
Web Site: www.georgiatent.com
Approx. Number Employees: 75
Year Founded: 1930
Business Description:
Awnings & Canopies Mfr
S.I.C.: 2394
N.A.I.C.S.: 314912
Media: 26
Distr.: Direct to Consumer; Natl.
Personnel:
R. Kenneth Spooner *(Owner & Pres)*
Gary Mescher *(VP & Gen Mgr)*
Lisa How *(Controller)*

GERBER LEGENDARY BLADES

(Div. of Fiskars Brands, Inc.)
14200 SW 72nd Ave
Portland, OR 97224
Mailing Address:
14200 SW 72nd Ave
Portland, OR 97224-8010
Tel.: (503) 639-6161
Fax: (503) 403-1102
Toll Free: (800) 950-6161
E-mail: sales@gerberblades.com
Web Site: www.gerberblades.com
E-Mail For Key Personnel:
Marketing Director: jlandmark@gerberblades.com
Sales Director: sales@gerberblades.com
Approx. Number Employees: 150
Year Founded: 1939
Business Description:
Mfr. of Sportsmens Knives, Multi Function Tools & Outdoor Recreational Products
S.I.C.: 3421; 5941
N.A.I.C.S.: 332211; 451110
Import Export
Advertising Expenditures: $1,000,000
Media: 2-4-5-6-7-8-10-15-17-19-20-22
Distr.: Intl.; Natl.
Personnel:
Jason Landmark *(Pres)*
Brands & Products:
AIR RANGER
BACK PAXE
BONFIRE
CAMP AXE
DISK TOOL SHARPENING STONE
E-Z OUT
FEND FOR YOURSELF
FIELD & STREAM
FINE EDGE
FIRESTORM
FREEMAN
FREEMAN HUNTER
GAME PRO
GATOR
GATOR EXCHANGE-A-BLADE
GERBER EMERSON ALLIANCE
GERBER LEGENDARY BLADES
GREAT GOOFS
HANDY HINTS
HONING STEEL
INFINITY ULTRA
LST
MINI COVERT
MINI RIDGE
MULTI-PLIER
NAUTILUS
O-4 MINI
OUTSIDE
REACTOR
RECOIL
SAF-T-SHARP
SILVER KNIGHTS
SILVER TRIDENT
SOLSTICE
SONIC
SPECTRE
TOTAL ECLIPSE
TRACER
TRENDY
Advertising Agency:
Sasquatch - Advertising, Brand Strategy, Interactive, Design
5331 SW Macadam Ave Ste 348
Portland, OR 97239
Tel.: (503) 222-2346
Fax: (503) 222-2492

GILDAN ACTIVEWEAR INC.

600 de Maisonneuve Boulevard West
Montreal, QC H3A 3J2, Canada
Tel.: (514) 735-2023
Fax: (514) 735-6810
Toll Free: (866) 755-2023
E-mail: info@gildan.com
Web Site: gildan.com
Approx. Sls.: $1,311,463,000
Approx. Number Employees: 28,000
Business Description:
Imprintable Apparel & Activewear Mfr
S.I.C.: 2258; 2241; 2253; 2254; 2389
N.A.I.C.S.: 313249; 313221; 315191; 315192; 315299; 315999
Advertising Expenditures: $8,634,000
Media: 2-5-6-7-10-11
Personnel:
Robert M. Baylis *(Chm)*
Glenn J. Chamandy *(Pres & CEO)*
Laurence G. Sellyn *(CFO, Chief Admin Officer & Exec VP)*
Michael R. Hoffman *(Pres-Gildan Activewear SRL)*
Lindsay Matthews *(Sec & Dir-Legal Svcs)*
Cam Gentile *(Exec VP-Org Dev & Change Mgmt)*
Eric Lehman *(Exec VP-Supply Chain & IT & Operational Excellence)*
Benito Masi *(Exec VP-Mfg)*
Reynaud Serge *(Exec VP-HR)*
Georges Sam Yu Sum *(Exec VP-Ops)*
Edwin B. Tisch *(Exec VP-Mfg)*
David A. Esones *(VP-Security)*
Gilles Leger *(VP-Fin & Admin)*
Stephane Lemay *(VP-Pub & Legal Affairs)*
Rafael Antonio Lopez *(VP-HR)*
John A. Martin *(VP-Sls-North America)*
David Voizard *(VP-Fin Reporting)*
Gaetane Wagner *(VP-HR)*
Sophie Argiriou *(Dir-IR)*
Genevieve Gosselin *(Dir-Corp Comm)*
Brands & Products:
BETTER VALUE THROUGH BETTER DESIGN
GILDAN
HEAVY BLEND
ULTRA BLEND
ULTRA COTTON

GILL ATHLETICS, INC.

2808 Gemini Ct
Champaign, IL 61822
Mailing Address:
PO Box 1790
Champaign, IL 61824-1790
Tel.: (217) 367-8438
Fax: (217) 367-8440
Toll Free: (800) 637-3090
E-mail: websales@gillathletics.com
Web Site: www.gillathletics.com
Approx. Number Employees: 60
Year Founded: 1918
Business Description:
Athletic Track & Field Equipment, Volleyball, Soccer & Weights Distr
S.I.C.: 3949
N.A.I.C.S.: 339920
Import Export
Advertising Expenditures: $600,000
Media: 4-6-9-10-13-19
Distr.: Natl.
Budget Set: June
Personnel:
David Hodge *(Pres & CEO)*
Fred Dixon *(Dir-Sls & Mktg)*
Brands & Products:
GILL
GILL ATHLETICS
HOLLOWOOD STAR DISCUS
PACER

GLD PRODUCTS, INC.

S84 W 19093 Entp Dr
Muskego, WI 53150
Tel.: (262) 679-8730
Fax: (262) 679-8738
Toll Free: (800) 225-7593
E-mail: gld@gldmfg.com
Web Site: www.gldproducts.com
Approx. Number Employees: 60
Year Founded: 1980
Business Description:
Darts, Mugs, T-Shirts & Cases, Billiard Accessories & Cues, Games & Pool Tables Mfr
S.I.C.: 3944; 3949
N.A.I.C.S.: 339932; 339920
Advertising Expenditures: $250,000
Media: 2-4-7
Distr.: Intl.; Natl.
Budget Set: Jan.
Personnel:
Nick Voden *(Pres)*
Brands & Products:
AMERICAN SPIRIT
APOLLO 11
ARISTOCRAT
ASTRO
ATOMIC BEE
BALL BUSTER
BEE HIVE
BLACK ICE
BLACK MAGIC
BLACK MARIAH
BLACK WIDOW
BLITZ
BOBCAT
BRASS DELUXE
BULL BLASTER
CASEMASTER
CASINO ROYALE
CHEYENNE
COLD STEEL
COLETTE
CORAL
DEAD-ON
DIAMONDBACK
DIAMONDHEAD
DRAGON
DUO SURE GRIP
E-DART
ECLIPSE
ELITE
ELITE BRASS
EXCALIBUR
FALCON
FAT CAT
FIRE POWER
FLIPSTER
GLD
GORGON
GOTHIC
GRIM REAPER
HEAVY METAL
JACKAL
JAGUAR
JEWEL CUT
JUMP BREAK
KC'S
KILLER BEE
MAGNA TEC
MEGA GRIP
MILWAUKEE BRASS
MIRAGE
NIGHTMARES
NORTHERN LIGHTS
PEARL
PITBULL
PLATINUM
PORTER
PRESTIGE
PRO ELITE
PYTHONS
QUASAR

Key to Media (For complete agency information see *The Advertising Red Books-Agencies* edition):
1. Bus. Publs. 2. Cable T.V. 3. Catalogs & Directories. 4. Co-op Adv. 5. Consumer Mags. 6. D.M. to Bus. Estab.7. D.M. to Consumers 8. Daily Newsp. 9. Exhibits/Trade Shows 10. Foreign 11. Infomercial 12. Internet Adv.13. Multimedia 14. Network Radio 15. Network T.V. 16. Newsp. Distr. Mags. 17. Other 18. Outdoor (Posters, Transit) 19. Point of Purchase20. Premiums, Novelties 21. Product Samples 22. Special Events Mktg. 23. Spot Radio 24. Spot T.V. 25. Weekly Newsp. 26. Yellow Page Adv.

QUIVER
RANGER
RAZORBACK
REVOLUTION
ROUND-UP
SABER
SAVAGE
SENTINEL
SENTRY
SHOT KING
SIGNATURE SERIES
SILVER THUNDER
SOLAR BLAST
SPIDER LEG
SPINNING BEE
SPINSTER
STAR FIRE
STARBURST
STERLING
STRIKER
SUPER BEE
SURE GRIP
TRACER
TUNGSTEN BEE
VANITY
VIPER
WIND RUNNER
WIZARD
X-TREME
YUKON

GOLF GALAXY, INC.
(Sub. of Dick's Sporting Goods, Inc.)
345 Crt St
Coraopolis, PA 15108
Tel.: (724) 273-3400
Fax: (724) 695-2374
Toll Free: (877) 851-0584
Web Site: www.golfgalaxy.com
Approx. Sls.: $200,130,000
Approx. Number Employees: 100
Year Founded: 1995
Business Description:
Golf Equipment, Apparel & Accessories Retailer
S.I.C.: 5941; 5091; 5961
N.A.I.C.S.: 451110; 423910; 454111; 454113
Media: 3-8-9-13-14-15-19-25
Personnel:
Joseph H. Schmidt *(Co-Founder, Pres & COO)*
Brands & Products:
EVERYTHING FOR THE GAME

GOLF GIFTS & GALLERY
(d/b/a JEF World of Golf)
N 1675 Powers Lk Rd
Powers Lake, WI 53159
Mailing Address:
PO Box 166
Powers Lake, WI 53159
Tel.: (262) 279-9820
Fax: (262) 279-9830
Approx. Number Employees: 20
Year Founded: 1975
Business Description:
Golf Accessories & Gifts Mfr
S.I.C.: 5947
N.A.I.C.S.: 453220
Import Export
Media: 2-10-25
Distr.: Natl.
Personnel:
Dean Chudy *(Pres)*
Bob Hildebrandt *(Mgr-Sls)*
Brands & Products:
ULTIMATE CHOICE
WORLD OF GOLF

GOLFSMITH INTERNATIONAL HOLDINGS, INC.
(Sub. of First Atlantic Capital Ltd.)
11000 N Hwy 35
Austin, TX 78753-3195
Tel.: (512) 837-4810
Fax: (512) 837-1245
Toll Free: (800) 925-7709
Web Site: www.golfsmith.com
E-Mail For Key Personnel:
Sales Director: ken.brugh@golfsmith.com
Approx. Rev.: $351,851,394
Approx. Number Employees: 796
Year Founded: 1967
Business Description:
Golf Equipment & Related Accessories Retail & Mail Order
S.I.C.: 3949; 5941
N.A.I.C.S.: 339920; 451110
Advertising Expenditures: $9,700,000
Media: 4-6-8-9-10-13-18-19-22-23
Personnel:
Martin E. Hanaka *(Chm & CEO)*
Sue E. Gove *(CFO, COO & Exec VP)*
Matthew Corey *(Sr VP-Mktg & Brand)*
Gillian Felix *(Sr VP-HR & Guest Experience)*
Joseph J. Kester *(Sr VP-Store Ops)*
David Lowe *(VP-Product Dev & Intl Bus)*
Brands & Products:
CLUBVANTAGE
GEAR FOR GOLF
GIFTS FOR GOLF
GOLFSMITH
THE GOLFSMITH CREDIT CARD
HARVEY PENICK
KILLER BEE
LYNX
SNAKE EYES
ZEVO

HARRISON-HOGE INDUSTRIES, INC.
19 N Columbia St
Port Jefferson Station, NY 11777-2165
Tel.: (631) 473-7308
Fax: (631) 473-7398
Toll Free: (800) 852-0925
E-mail: staff@seaeagle.com
Web Site: www.seaeagle.com
Approx. Number Employees: 20
Year Founded: 1952
Business Description:
Fishing Lures & Inflatable Boats Importer & Mfr
S.I.C.: 5091; 5961
N.A.I.C.S.: 423910; 454113
Media: 2-6-9-13-25
Distr.: Natl.
Budget Set: Jan. -Dec.
Personnel:
John Hoge *(Partner)*
Brands & Products:
PANTHER MARTIN
SEA EAGLE

HEAD/PENN RACQUET SPORTS
(Sub. of Head N.V.)
306 S 45th Ave
Phoenix, AZ 85043-3913
Tel.: (602) 269-1492
Fax: (602) 484-0533
Toll Free: (800) 289-7366
E-mail: info@head.com
Web Site: www.pennracquet.com
Approx. Number Employees: 800
Year Founded: 1910
Business Description:
Tennis Balls, Racquetballs & Accessories Mfr & Marketer
S.I.C.: 3949
N.A.I.C.S.: 339920
Import Export
Media: 4-5-6-7-10-15-19-20-21-24
Distr.: Intl.; Natl.
Budget Set: Aug.
Personnel:
Kevin Kempin *(VP-Sls & Mktg)*
Brands & Products:
HEAD
PENN

HENRY BONA POOLS & SPAS
878 Rte 46
Kenvil, NJ 07847-2632
Tel.: (973) 584-1000
Fax: (973) 584-7665
E-mail: info@bonapools.com
Web Site: www.bonapools.com
Approx. Number Employees: 15
Year Founded: 1960
Business Description:
Pools & Spas Retailer
S.I.C.: 1799
N.A.I.C.S.: 238990
Media: 2-4-8-13-18-19-26
Personnel:
Hank Bona *(Owner)*
Nancy Bona *(Owner)*
Brands & Products:
BIOGUARD
HENRY BONA & SPAS
WHERE QUALITY SERVICE IS STILL AVAILABLE

HENRY MODELL & COMPANY, INC.
498 7th Ave 20th Fl
New York, NY 10018-6738
Tel.: (212) 822-1000
Fax: (212) 822-1025
E-mail: customersupport@modells.com
Web Site: www.modells.com
Sales Range: $500-549.9 Million
Approx. Number Employees: 200
Year Founded: 1889
Business Description:
Retailer of Men's, Women's & Children's Apparel, Footwear & Sporting Goods
S.I.C.: 5941; 5661
N.A.I.C.S.: 451110; 448210
Media: 8-13-22-23-24
Personnel:
Mitchell B. Modell *(CEO)*
Eric Spiel *(CFO)*
Hans Kantor *(CIO)*
Lawrence Brustein *(Exec VP-Fin)*
Joseph Conley *(Sr VP-Distr)*
Brands & Products:
GOTTA GO TO MO'S
MODELL'S

HIBBETT SPORTS, INC.
(d/b/a Hibbett Sporting Goods)
451 Industrial Ln
Birmingham, AL 35211-4464
Tel.: (205) 942-4292
Fax: (205) 912-7293
E-mail: webmaster@hibbett.com
Web Site: www.hibbett.com
Approx. Sls.: $664,954,000
Approx. Number Employees: 2,150
Business Description:
Sporting Good Stores Operator
S.I.C.: 5941; 1522; 5661
N.A.I.C.S.: 451110; 236220; 448210
Advertising Expenditures: $7,314,000
Media: 5-8-16-18
Personnel:
Michael J. Newsome *(Chm & CEO)*
Jeffry O. Rosenthal *(Pres & COO)*
Gary A. Smith *(CFO, Principal Acctg Officer & VP)*
Terry Mayfield *(CIO & VP)*
Rebecca Jones *(VP-Mdsg)*
Brands & Products:
HIBBETT SPORTS
TEAM MANAGER

HILLERICH & BRADSBY CO., INC.
800 W Main St
Louisville, KY 40202-2620
Tel.: (502) 585-5226
Fax: (502) 585-1179
Web Site: www.slugger.com
Sales Range: $100-124.9 Million
Approx. Number Employees: 600
Year Founded: 1884
Business Description:
Mfr. of Baseball & Softball Gloves & Bats, Golf Clubs, Hockey Sticks
S.I.C.: 3949
N.A.I.C.S.: 339920
Advertising Expenditures: $200,000
Media: 4-6-10-13-15-18-20-24
Distr.: Intl.; Natl.
Budget Set: Oct.
Personnel:
Marty Archer *(Pres-Louisville Slugger)*
Michael McGrath *(VP-Intl Mktg)*
James Sass *(Dir-Mktg)*
Vicki Boisseau *(Product Mgr)*
Brands & Products:
A. RODRIGUEZ SERIES
AH SERIES
AIR RESPONSE
ARMOR
BIONIC
D. JETER SERIES
DEUCE
FUNGO
GAMER
J. GIAMBI SERIES
LASER
LOUISVILLE SLUGGER
LP SERIES
LPP SERIES
LS SERIES
MLB SERIES
N. GARCIAPARRA SERIES
OMAHA XS
OPX SERIES
PLATINUM
POWERIZED
PRO SERIES
PRO SLUGGER
PRO STOCKLITE
RESPONSE
SILVER SLUGGER
TPS SERIES
TPX
Advertising Agencies:
imc2
12404 Park Central Ste 400

Key to Media (For complete agency information see *The Advertising Red Books-Agencies* edition):
1. Bus. Publs. 2. Cable T.V. 3. Catalogs & Directories. 4. Co-op Adv. 5. Consumer Mags. 6. D.M. to Bus. Estab.7. D.M. to Consumers 8. Daily Newsp. 9. Exhibits/Trade Shows 10. Foreign 11. Infomercial 12. Internet Adv.13. Multimedia 14. Network Radio 15. Network T.V. 16. Newsp. Distr. Mags. 17. Other 18. Outdoor (Posters, Transit) 19. Point of Purchase20. Premiums, Novelties 21. Product Samples 22. Special Events Mktg. 23. Spot Radio 24. Spot T.V. 25. Weekly Newsp. 26. Yellow Page Adv.

Hillerich & Bradsby Co., Inc. — (Continued)

Dallas, TX 75251
Tel.: (214) 224-1000
Fax: (214) 224-1100
Agency of Record
Bionic Gloves
Louisville Slugger

Power Creative
11701 Commonwealth Dr
Louisville, KY 40299-2358
Tel.: (502) 267-0772
Fax: (502) 267-1727

HORIZON FITNESS INC.

1620 Landmark Dr
Cottage Grove, WI 53527
Tel.: (608) 839-1250
Toll Free: (800) 244-4192
E-mail: comments@horizonfitness.com
Web Site: www.horizonfitness.com
Approx. Number Employees: 19
Business Description:
Distr of Fitness Equipment
S.I.C.: 5091
N.A.I.C.S.: 423910
Media: 6
Personnel:
Patty Parrot *(Mgr-Mktg)*
Brands & Products:
DESIGNED FOR LIFE
HORIZON

HORNADY MANUFACTURING COMPANY

3625 Old Potash Hwy
Grand Island, NE 68803
Tel.: (308) 382-1390
Fax: (308) 382-5761
Toll Free: (800) 338-3220
E-mail: webmaster@hornady.com
Web Site: www.hornady.com
E-Mail For Key Personnel:
President: shornady@aol.com
Approx. Number Employees: 175
Year Founded: 1949
Business Description:
Bullets Mfr; Premium Hunting & Match Ammunition
S.I.C.: 3482; 3559
N.A.I.C.S.: 332992; 333298
Export
Advertising Expenditures: $1,200,000
Media: 3-4-6-7-8-10-19-20
Personnel:
Steve Hornady *(Pres)*
Everett Deger *(Mgr-Mktg Comm)*
Brands & Products:
366
AMAX
CAM-LOCK
GO/NO GO
GREAT PLAINS
HEAVY MAGNUM
HORNADY
INTERLOCK
LIGHT MAGNUM
LOCK-N-LOAD
M2
NEW DIMENSION
ONE SHOT
TAP
VERSALITE
XTP

HQ SUSTAINABLE MARITIME INDUSTRIES, INC.

Melbourne Towers 1511 Third Ave
Ste 788
Seattle, WA 98101
Tel.: (206) 621-9888
Fax: (206) 621-0318
E-mail: sporns@hqfish.com
Web Site: www.hqfish.com
Approx. Sls.: $72,292,011
Approx. Number Employees: 620
Business Description:
Aquatic Fishing & Product Sales
S.I.C.: 0921; 0919; 5146
N.A.I.C.S.: 112511; 114119; 424460
Advertising Expenditures: $7,487,170
Media: 17
Personnel:
Norbert Sporns *(Co-Founder, Pres & CEO)*
Lillian Wang Li *(Chm & Sec)*
Harry Wang Hua *(COO)*
Jean-Pierre Dallaire *(Chief Acctg Officer)*
Trond Ringstad *(VP-Sls & Distr)*
Jian Bo He *(Mgr-Fin)*
Jie Liu *(Mgr-Plant)*
William Su *(Mgr-Compliance & Liaison-Intl Sls)*
Brands & Products:
TILOVEYA
Advertising Agency:
KCSA Strategic Communications
(Kanan, Corbin, Schupak & Aronow, Inc.)
880 3rd Ave 6th Fl
New York, NY 10022
Tel.: (212) 682-6300
Fax: (212) 697-0910

HUFFY CORPORATION

225 Byers Rd
Miamisburg, OH 45420-4031
Tel.: (937) 865-2800
Toll Free: (800) 872-2453
Web Site: www.huffy.com
Sales Range: $400-449.9 Million
Approx. Number Employees: 110
Year Founded: 1928
Business Description:
Bicycles, Basketball Equipment, Product Assembly Mfr & Merchandising & Inventory Services
S.I.C.: 3949; 3751
N.A.I.C.S.: 339920; 336991
Import Export
Advertising Expenditures: $2,000,000
Media: 2-4-5-7-10-19-20-24-26
Distr.: Intl.; Natl.
Budget Set: June
Personnel:
William A. Smith *(Pres & Gen Mgr)*
Steven D. Lipton *(CFO)*
Nancy Michaud *(Gen Counsel, Sec & Sr VP)*
Robert Diekman *(Sr VP-Opers & Logistics)*
Ray Thomson *(VP-Mktg)*
Brands & Products:
DUKES
GREEN MACHINE
HESPELER
HUFFY
HUFFY BIKES
HUFFY SPORTS
LAMAR
LTD
OXYGEN
RAGE
RAM
RAM GOLF
SIMS
TEARDROP GOLF
TOMMY ARMOUR
TOMMY ARMOUR GOLF
ULTRA WHEELS
ZEBRA

HUGGER MUGGER YOGA PRODUCTS LLC

1190 South Pioneer Rd
Salt Lake City, UT 84104
Tel.: (801) 268-9642
Fax: (801) 268-2629
Toll Free: (800) 473-4888
E-mail: comments@huggermugger.com
Web Site: www.huggermugger.com
Approx. Sls.: $10,000,000
Approx. Number Employees: 30
Business Description:
Mfr. of Yoga Products Including Clothing, Equipment & Related Accessories; DVDs, Videos, CDs
S.I.C.: 3949; 7999
N.A.I.C.S.: 339920; 611620
Media: 6-13
Personnel:
Tom Chamberlain *(Pres)*
Connie Tyler *(Dir-Sls & Mktg)*
Brands & Products:
AIREX
AROMA
BOLSTERS
BUFF
CHAKRA
CHARLOTTE
CW-X
EARTH ELEMENTS
HANOMAN
HUGGER MUGGER
INTENTION
IOLITE
JIVANA
MIND BODY SPIRIT
NETI
OM
PEACHSKIN
PRANAYAMA
SOLACE
SOLE FLIP FLOPS
TAPAS
TERRA
TINGSHA
TOLA
YOGADOT
YOGATARD
ZABUTONS
ZAFUS
ZEN

ICON HEALTH & FITNESS, INC.

1500 S 1000 W
Logan, UT 84321-8206
Tel.: (435) 750-5000
Fax: (435) 750-3917
E-mail: service@iconfitness.com
Web Site: www.iconfitness.com
Sales Range: $900-999.9 Million
Approx. Number Employees: 2,200
Year Founded: 1977
Business Description:
Home Fitness Equipment Mfr, Marketer & Distr
S.I.C.: 3949
N.A.I.C.S.: 339920
Advertising Expenditures: $12,442,000
Media: 3-4-5-8-11-12-13-26
Distr.: Natl.
Personnel:
David J. Watterson *(Chm & CEO)*
Matthew N. Allen *(Pres & Chief Mdsg Officer)*
S. Fred Beck *(CFO, Treas & VP)*
Evertt Smith *(Gen Counsel)*
Jace Jergensen *(Sr VP)*
David A. Brown *(Mgr-DBA, Applications & BI)*
Brands & Products:
ACCESS
AERO
AEROBICRIDER
AIR WALKER
AUTO INCLINE
CARDIO FIT PLUS
CARDIOGLIDE
CARDIOSHAPER
CHANGING LIVES WITH FITNESS INNOVATION
CUSHION DECK
DAYBREAK
EARN
EASY STRIDE
EPIC
EXERSCIENCE
FREEMOTION FITNESS
GOLD'S GYM
HEALTHRIDER
HOME PRO
ICON HEALTH & FITNESS
IFIT
IMAGE
MOTORVATION
NORDICTRACK
PRO-FORM
SOFT STRIDER
SOFTTRACK
SPACE SAVER
TAILWIND
UNIVERSAL TECHNICAL SERVICE
WEIDER
WESLO
ZONE TONER

IDG HOLDINGS INC.

202B 1012 Douglas St
Victoria, BC V8W 2C3, Canada
Tel.: (250) 384-0751
Fax: (250) 598-6624
Fax: (250) 384-0771
E-mail: info@idgholdings.com
Web Site: www.idgholdings.com
Approx. Rev.: $6,521
Year Founded: 1995
Business Description:
Holding Company; Outdoor Leisure Products Mfr; Protective Services
S.I.C.: 6719; 3949; 7382; 7993; 7999
N.A.I.C.S.: 551112; 339920; 561621; 713120; 713990
Advertising Expenditures: $46,524
Media: 10
Personnel:
Xen Stefanopoulos *(Pres & CEO)*
Glynn Jones *(CFO & Sec)*

IMPERIAL INTERNATIONAL

(Sub. of H. Betti Industries, Inc.)
303 Paterson Plank Rd E
Carlstadt, NJ 07072
Tel.: (201) 288-9199
Fax: (201) 288-8990

Key to Media (For complete agency information see *The Advertising Red Books-Agencies* edition):
1. Bus. Publs. 2. Cable T.V. 3. Catalogs & Directories. 4. Co-op Adv. 5. Consumer Mags. 6. D.M. to Bus. Estab.7. D.M. to Consumers
8. Daily Newsp. 9. Exhibits/Trade Shows 10. Foreign 11. Infomercial 12. Internet Adv.13. Multimedia 14. Network Radio
15. Network T.V. 16. Newsp. Distr. Mags. 17. Other 18. Outdoor (Posters, Transit) 19. Point of Purchase20. Premiums, Novelties
21. Product Samples 22. Special Events Mktg. 23. Spot Radio 24. Spot T.V. 25. Weekly Newsp. 26. Yellow Page Adv.

E-mail: inquiries@imperialusa.com
Web Site: www.imperialusa.com
Approx. Sls.: $10,000,000
Approx. Number Employees: 10
Year Founded: 1943
Business Description:
Billiard Equipment & Supplies Distr
S.I.C.: 5091
N.A.I.C.S.: 423910
Media: 4-13
Personnel:
Michael Dimotta *(Pres)*
Mike Cetinich *(Sls Mgr)*

INNOVATIVE DESIGNS, INC.

223 N Main St Ste 1
Pittsburgh, PA 15215
Tel.: (412) 799-0350
Fax: (412) 782-5303
E-mail: contact@idigear.com
Web Site: www.idigear.com
Approx. Rev.: $1,108,955
Approx. Number Employees: 2
Business Description:
Insulated Sporting Apparel Mfr
S.I.C.: 3949
N.A.I.C.S.: 339920
Media: 4-7-8-10-15-17-19
Personnel:
Joseph Riccelli *(CEO)*

IZZO GOLF, INC.

1635 Commons Pkwy
Macedon, NY 14502-9191
Tel.: (315) 986-0000
Fax: (800) 858-8337
Toll Free: (800) 284-1220
Web Site: www.izzo.com
E-Mail For Key Personnel:
Sales Director: sales@izzo.com
Approx. Number Employees: 50
Business Description:
Golf Products
S.I.C.: 3949
N.A.I.C.S.: 339920
Media: 4-8-22
Personnel:
Bruce Dan *(Pres)*
Brands & Products:
ATC PUSHCART
BACK CADDIE
BALANCE DISKS
BIG DADDY INSTA-NET
BIG MOUTH INSTANT RANGE NET
BLACK MAMBA
BREEZE
CHIP POCKET
CONTINUOUS RETURN MAT
CORE BALANCE BALL
EZ ROLLER
FLEX MAT
GEO
GIANT
GIANT JR.
HIGH ROLLER
HOLD-ALL
HOME ON THE RANGE
HORIZON
HORIZON JR.
IZZO EZ-2
IZZO GOLF
LINE A PUTT
MEDICINE BALL
MINI-MOUTH
MINI TOUR
PILOT
PURE PUTT PUTTING MIRROR
PUTTING MAT
PUTTING PEGZ
RESISTANCE CORDS
SCOUT
SENTRY TWO WHEEL TRAVEL COVER
SHOE CADDIE
SMOOTH SWING
SWAMI
SWAY STICK
SWEET SPOT
SWING & GRIP TRAINER
SWING MIRROR
SWING PLANE TRAINER
SWING STICK
TORNADO
TOUR BAG
TRANSIT
TRUNK LOCKER
Z-BRIDS
ZEPHYR
ZWOODS

JANDD MOUNTAINEERING, INC.

2365 Marconi Ct Ste F
San Diego, CA 92154-7265
Tel.: (760) 597-9021
Fax: (760) 597-9022
Web Site: www.jandd.com
E-Mail For Key Personnel:
Sales Director: sales@jandd.com
Approx. Number Employees: 100
Year Founded: 1983
Business Description:
Outdoor Bags & Accessories Mfr
S.I.C.: 2393
N.A.I.C.S.: 314911
Media: 13
Personnel:
Dave Sisson *(Pres)*
Brands & Products:
ANDREW
ESEK
GABRIEL
INIKI
JANDD MOUNTAINEERING
PANNIER
SHANA
TALMID

JANSPORT

(Sub. of VF Corporation)
N850 County Hwy CB
Appleton, WI 54914
Mailing Address:
PO Box 1817
Appleton, WI 54912-1817
Tel.: (920) 734-5708
Fax: (920) 735-1933
Web Site: www.jansport.com
Sales Range: $100-124.9 Million
Approx. Number Employees: 400
Year Founded: 1967
Business Description:
Marketer of Backpacks & Technical Packs & Luggage
S.I.C.: 3949; 3161
N.A.I.C.S.: 339920; 316991
Import Export
Media: 6
Personnel:
Courtney Blacker *(Brand Dir)*
Brands & Products:
AIRLIFT
BORNEO
BRAIN
CELESTIAL 3L
EAST PAK
ISIS 2L
JANSPORT, INC.
MESSENGER
METRO
OPTIMIZER
SHOCKSHIELD
SIERRA MADRE
STREET TECH
VENUS 2L
Advertising Agency:
Creature
1508 10th Ave
Seattle, WA 98122
Tel.: (206) 625-6994
Fax: (206) 625-6904

JERRY'S SPORTS CENTER, INC.

PO Box 121
Forest City, PA 18421-0121
Tel.: (570) 785-9400
Fax: (570) 785-9505
E-mail: info@jerryssportscenter.com
Web Site: www.jerryssportscenter.com
Sales Range: $150-199.9 Million
Approx. Number Employees: 375
Year Founded: 1950
Business Description:
Sports Equipment Whslr
S.I.C.: 5091
N.A.I.C.S.: 423910
Import
Advertising Expenditures: $900,000
Media: 4
Distr.: Intl.; Natl.
Budget Set: Monthly
Personnel:
Bernard Ziomek *(Chm)*
Andrew Kupchik *(Mgr-Outside Sls-Bus Dev & Mgr-Inside Sls)*
Brands & Products:
CENTURI

JOHNSON OUTDOORS INC.

555 Main St
Racine, WI 53403
Tel.: (262) 631-6600
Fax: (262) 631-6601
E-mail: corporate@johnsonoutdoors.com
Web Site: www.johnsonoutdoors.com
Approx. Sls.: $382,432,000
Approx. Number Employees: 1,255
Year Founded: 1985
Business Description:
Sporting Goods Mfr
S.I.C.: 3949; 3732
N.A.I.C.S.: 339920; 336612
Import Export
Advertising Expenditures: $20,107,000
Media: 6-17
Distr.: Intl.; Natl.
Budget Set: Sept.
Personnel:
Helen P. Johnson-Leipold *(Chm & CEO)*
Thomas F. Pyle, Jr. *(Vice Chm)*
David W. Johnson *(CFO & VP)*
John Moon *(CIO & VP)*
Alisa D. Swire *(Gen Counsel, Corp Sec & VP)*
Sara Vidian *(VP-HR)*
Brands & Products:
ALADIN
CAMP TRAILS
CANNON
CARLISLE
DIMENSION
ESCAPE
EUREKA!
EXTRASPORT
HUMMINBIRD
JOHNSON OUTDOORS
LEISURE LIFE
LENDEL
MINN KOTA
NECKY
OCEAN KAYAK
OLD TOWN
SCUBAPRO
SILVA
SNORKELPRO
UWATEC
Advertising Agency:
Hanson Dodge Inc.
220 E Buffalo St
Milwaukee, WI 53202
Tel.: (414) 347-1266
Fax: (414) 347-0493
Kayaking

K-SWISS, INC.

31248 Oak Crest Dr
Westlake Village, CA 91361
Tel.: (818) 706-5100
Fax: (818) 706-5390
Toll Free: (800) 938-8000
E-mail: kscs@k-swiss.com
Web Site: www.kswiss.com
E-Mail For Key Personnel:
Marketing Director: JWeiderman@k-swiss.com
Approx. Rev.: $216,987,000
Approx. Number Employees: 603
Year Founded: 1966
Business Description:
Athletic Footwear Designer, Developer & Marketer
S.I.C.: 3143; 3021
N.A.I.C.S.: 316213; 316211
Import Export
Advertising Expenditures: $43,955,000
Media: 3-6-8-11-15-18-19-20-22-31
Distr.: Intl.; Natl.
Personnel:
Steven B. Nichols *(Chm, Pres & CEO)*
George Powlick *(CFO, Chief Admin Officer, Sec & VP-Fin)*
Lee Green *(Gen Counsel)*
David Nichols *(Exec VP)*
Chris Kyle *(VP-Mktg)*
Ryan Babenzien *(Global Dir-Mktg)*
Michael Augustine *(Dir-Worldwide Apparel)*
Jennifer MacFarland *(Dir-Pub Rels)*
Brands & Products:
3/4 LENGTH SKINNY PANT
3/4 RUN CAPRI
7.0 SYSTEM
ACCOMPLISH
ACCOMPLISH CREW
ACCOMPLISH JACKET
ACCOMPLISH KNT SHORT
ACCOMPLISH PANT
ACCOMPLISH POLO
ACCOMPLISH RACR TANK
ACCOMPLISH SHORT
ACCOMPLISH SKIRT
ACCOMPLISH TANK
ADJUSTABLE TOP
AFTON

Key to Media (For complete agency information see *The Advertising Red Books-Agencies* edition):
1. Bus. Publs. 2. Cable T.V. 3. Catalogs & Directories. 4. Co-op Adv. 5. Consumer Mags. 6. D.M. to Bus. Estab.7. D.M. to Consumers
8. Daily Newsp. 9. Exhibits/Trade Shows 10. Foreign 11. Infomercial 12. Internet Adv.13. Multimedia 14. Network Radio
15. Network T.V. 16. Newsp. Distr. Mags. 17. Other 18. Outdoor (Posters, Transit) 19. Point of Purchase20. Premiums, Novelties
21. Product Samples 22. Special Events Mktg. 23. Spot Radio 24. Spot T.V. 25. Weekly Newsp. 26. Yellow Page Adv.

K-Swiss, Inc. — (Continued)

AOSTA
APPROACH
APPROACH MESH
ARIAKE
ARIAKE LITE MESH
ASCENDOR
BAYSHORE
BAYSHORE MESH
BERLO
BERLO L
BIO FEEDBACK
CAPSLEEVE POLO
CELANO
THE CLASSIC
THE CLASSIC LUXURY EDITION
CLASSIC ORIGINAL
THE CLASSIC REMASTERED
COLORBLOCK LS CREW
COLORBLOCKED CREW
COLYER
COMBO WARM UP JACKET
COMBO WARM UP PANT
COMBO WOVEN SHORT
COMMEND
COURT DELUXE
COURT DELUXE P
CRACEN
CUTOUT FITNESS TANK
DAHLOF
DEEP V TANK
DEFIER
DEFIER II
DEFIER MISOUL TECH
DEFIER RS
DURANT
DWAN
ELASTIC CLASSIC
ELLZEY CRIB
EMPIRE SEAM TOP
EVARO
FITNESS HOODIE
FORECOURT
GLACIATOR
GORZELL
GORZELL ULTRA
GOWBURY
GOWBURY CANVAS
GOWMET CANVAS
GOWMET LOW
GOWMET LOW VNZ
GRANCOURT
HERSHEY CLASSIC - SPECIAL EDITION
JANDO
JOSEL
K FORCE
K ONA S
K-SWISS
KAMPIDANO
KAYABU
KAYESTEE
KEAHOU
KEAHOU C
KNIT SHORT
KNIT SPORT SHORT
KONEJO
LAVATZA DELUXE
LAYERED RACERBACK TANK
LOCARNO
LOZAN
LUNDAHL NT
LUXE CLASSIC
LUXE PREMIUM CLASSIC
MARVID
MESH KNIT SHORT
MESH LONG SLEEVE
MESH RUN TOP
MOHR
MORLEY
MUSCLE TEE
NEWSTEAD
NIDO
NITEHAWK
ORICK
ORIGIN
OVERRULE
PIPED KNIT SHORT
PRATT
PREMIER '66 C
PRO C
RAMLI
REFLECTIVE CREW
REFLECTIVE JACKET
REFLECTIVE SLEEVELSS
REFLECTIVE TANK
RINZLER
RUN ONE MISOUL TECH
RUN SHORT
RUNNING JACKET
RUNNING PANT
SHOCK SPRING
SHORT SLEEVE CREW NECK
SI-18 BRISTEL
SI-18 PREMIERE
SIGNATURE DRESS
SLEEVELESS SPORT TOP
SPAGHETTI TOP
SPAGHETTI V-NECK TOP
SPEYER
SPINSHOT
ST329
ST330
ST359
ST363
STABILOR
STABILOR MESH
STRAPPY TANKINI
SUBLIMATED CREW
SUBLIMATED POLO
SURF & COURT CANVAS
SURF & COURT OG CNVS
SWISS MADE
TENNIS BALL TEE
THICK CLASSIC MID
TOPSTITCH POLO
TRAINING BOARDSHORT
TRAINING CAPRI
TRAINING CAPSLEEVE
TRAINING CREW
TRAINING JACKET
TRAINING PANT
TRUE WIND
ULTRA NATURAL RUN
ULTRA NTRL RUN II S
ULTRACEL CREW
ULTRACEL POLO
ULTRACEL TEE
ULTRASCENDOR
ULTRASCENDOR MID
VARADOS
VENICE VNZ
VERSTAD
VIBRANT 3
WALLIS
WARM UP JACKET
WORKOUT PANT
WRAP SEAM SKIRT
ZIP FRONT POLO
ZIP FRONT TANK

Advertising Agencies:
72andSunny
6300 Arizona Cir
Los Angeles, CA 90045
Tel.: (310) 215-9009
Fax: (310) 215-9012
— Thomas Martin *(Acct Exec)*

Concept Chaser Co., Inc.
222 N Sepulveda Blvd Ste 1518
El Segundo, CA 90245
Tel.: (310) 615-0700
Fax: (310) 615-0300

Toth Brand Imaging
215 First St
Cambridge, MA 02142
Tel.: (617) 252-0787
Fax: (617) 252-0838

K2 INC.

(Sub. of Jarden Outdoor Solutions)
5818 El Camino Real
Carlsbad, CA 92008
Tel.: (760) 494-1000
Fax: (760) 494-1099
Toll Free: (888) 5K2SPRT
Approx. Sls.: $1,394,656,000
Approx. Number Employees: 4,700
Year Founded: 1946
Business Description:
Skis, Snowboards, In-Line Skates, Water Safety & Sports Equipment, Fishing Tackle, Mountain Bicycles, Skateboards, Backpacks & Active Apparel & Other Sporting Goods Mfr, Designer & Marketer
S.I.C.: 3949; 3069
N.A.I.C.S.: 339920; 326299
Advertising Expenditures: $42,500,000
Media: 2-5-6-7-10-11-19-22-23-24
Distr.: Intl.; Natl.
Personnel:
J. Wayne Merck *(Pres & COO)*
Monte H. Baier *(Gen Counsel, Sec & VP)*
Brian R. Anderson *(Dir-Bus Dev)*
Mike Gutt *(Mgr-Mktg Intl-K2 Skis)*
Brands & Products:
ADIO
ADIO AND HAWK
AT THE TOP OF YOUR GAME
ATLAS
BRASS EAGLE
CHALLENGE PARK XTREME
DANA DESIGN
DANA DESIGNS
ENDOTECH
EX OFFICIO
EXOTECH
FOTOBALL
HAWK
JT
K2
K2 OUTDOOR
K2 ROFLEX
MADSHUS
MARKER
MARMOT
MIKEN
MORROW
OLIN
PFLUEGER
PLANET EARTH
RAWLINGS
RIDE
SHAKESPEARE
STEARNS
TUBBS
VOLKL
WORR GAMES
WORTH

KARSTEN MANUFACTURING CORPORATION

2201 W Desert Cove Ave
Phoenix, AZ 85029
Tel.: (602) 870-5000
Fax: (602) 687-4482
E-mail: advertising@karsten.com
Web Site: www.pinggolf.com
Approx. Number Employees: 800
Year Founded: 1959
Business Description:
Golf Equipment Mfr
S.I.C.: 3949; 3398
N.A.I.C.S.: 339920; 332811
Import Export
Media: 6-11-13-22
Personnel:
John Solheim *(Chm & CEO)*
Michael T. Trueblood *(CFO, Treas & VP)*
Rawleigh Grove *(Gen Counsel & VP)*
Pat Loftus *(VP-Mktg & Domestic Sls)*
Brands & Products:
ANSER
ECHO
G2L
ISO FORCE
JAS
K56
KARSTEN 2
MY DAY
O BLADE
PING

KNIGHT RIFLES, INC.

(Affil. of EBSCO Industries, Inc.)
715 B Summit Dr
Decatur, AL 35601
Tel.: (256) 260-8950
Fax: (256) 260-8951
E-mail: customer_service@knightrifles.com
Web Site: www.knightrifles.com
E-Mail For Key Personnel:
Sales Director: dcreger@knightrifles.com
Approx. Number Employees: 130
Business Description:
Muzzle Loading Firearms & Accessories Mfr
S.I.C.: 3484; 5941
N.A.I.C.S.: 332994; 451110
Media: 1-2-3-4-6-8-10-13-14-15-19-22-23-24
Distr.: Natl.
Personnel:
Tony Knight *(Founder)*
Dixon Brooks *(CEO)*
Brands & Products:
AMERICAN KNIGHT
DISC ELITE
DISC EXTREME
FULL PLASTIC JACKET
KNIGHT MASTER HUNTER DISC EXTREME
KNIGHT REVOLUTION
KNIGHT TK2000
ULTIMATE SLAM SERIES
WOLVERINE 209

KOMBI, LTD.

6 Thompson Dr
Essex Junction, VT 05452-3405
Tel.: (802) 879-3369
Fax: (802) 879-3246
Toll Free: (800) 243-6117

Key to Media (For complete agency information see *The Advertising Red Books-Agencies* edition):
1. Bus. Publs. 2. Cable T.V. 3. Catalogs & Directories. 4. Co-op Adv. 5. Consumer Mags. 6. D.M. to Bus. Estab.7. D.M. to Consumers 8. Daily Newsp. 9. Exhibits/Trade Shows 10. Foreign 11. Infomercial 12. Internet Adv.13. Multimedia 14. Network Radio 15. Network T.V. 16. Newsp. Distr. Mags. 17. Other 18. Outdoor (Posters, Transit) 19. Point of Purchase20. Premiums, Novelties 21. Product Samples 22. Special Events Mktg. 23. Spot Radio 24. Spot T.V. 25. Weekly Newsp. 26. Yellow Page Adv.

E-mail: customerservice@kombiltd.com
Web Site: www.kombisports.com
Approx. Number Employees: 20
Year Founded: 1969
Business Description:
Ski Gloves & Accessories; Thermal Underwear, Socks & Turtlenecks; Snowboard Gloves & Mitts Distr
S.I.C.: 5091
N.A.I.C.S.: 423910
Import Export
Media: 4-6
Distr.: Natl.
Budget Set: June
Personnel:
Phil Gellis *(CEO)*
Carol Small *(Gen Mgr)*
Brands & Products:
BACKCOUNTRY II
BAKKIE
BC HIKE
BFF
BRITNEY
BUMPS
CLONE
CYCLONE
EASY ON
EXTREME
EXTREME PARKER
FAUX FUR
FLEECE FLIP
FREEFORM
GRAFFITI II
KNUCKLE DOWN II
KOMBI
LALA
LONG TRAIL II
MADHATTER II
MALDEN POWER STRETCH
MIDWEY
MONTY
NOREASTER
PHOENIX
PILE CHOPPER
POLYPRO
RANCHER II
RIPPED GORE II
RIVERBEND
SHIFTY
STANLEY
STAR
STARFISH
STRETCH DOWN
STRETCH TECH
TEAZE
THERMOLITE BASE
TWIST
VALLEY II
WALKABOUT II
WINDBREAKER
WINDSTOPPER
ZEUS

L.A. T SPORTSWEAR, LLC
1200 Airport Dr
Ball Ground, GA 30107-4545
Tel.: (770) 479-1877
Fax: (770) 479-4078
Toll Free: (800) 414-5650
E-mail: info@latsportswear.com
Web Site: www.latsportswear.com
E-Mail For Key Personnel:
President: gina@latsportswear.com
Approx. Number Employees: 75
Year Founded: 1980
Business Description:
Imprintable Knitted Sportswear Mfr & Distr
S.I.C.: 5136; 5137
N.A.I.C.S.: 424320; 424330
Advertising Expenditures: $1,000,000
Media: 2-4-5-8-10
Personnel:
Gina Watson *(Pres & COO)*
Isador Mitzner *(CEO)*
Mickie Schneider *(CFO & Exec VP)*
Chuck Phares *(Exec VP-Sls)*
Mindy Anastos *(VP-Mktg & Production Plng)*
Brands & Products:
L.A. T SPORT
L.A. T SPORTSWEAR
L.A.L. SPORTSWEAR
LATE SPORT
LATE SPORTSWEAR
RABBIT SKINS
WOODBRIDGE

LBU, INC.
217 Brook Ave
Passaic, NJ 07055
Tel.: (973) 773-4800
Fax: (973) 773-6005
Toll Free: (800) 678-4LBU
E-mail: wlewis@lbuinc.com
Web Site: www.lbuinc.com
E-Mail For Key Personnel:
Sales Director: fking@lbuinc.com
Sales Range: $200-249.9 Million
Approx. Number Employees: 50
Year Founded: 1987
Business Description:
Mfr. of Sports Bags & Gear Bags
S.I.C.: 2393
N.A.I.C.S.: 314911
Export
Media: 2-4-5-7-10-20-21
Distr.: Natl.
Personnel:
Jeff Mayer *(CEO)*
Brands & Products:
THE FUTURE OF BAG TECHNOLOGY
GO GEAR
LBU, INC.
SOF-SACS
SUCCESS IS IN THE BAG

LESLIE'S POOLMART, INC.
(Holding of Leonard Green & Partners, L.P.)
3925 E Broadway Rd
Phoenix, AZ 85040
Tel.: (602) 366-3999
Fax: (602) 366-3934
Web Site: www.lesliespool.com
Approx. Sls.: $509,642,000
Approx. Number Employees: 2,280
Year Founded: 1963
Business Description:
Swimming Pools, Large Fish Tanks & Related Products Retailer
S.I.C.: 5999; 5941
N.A.I.C.S.: 453998; 451110
Advertising Expenditures: $8,500,000
Media: 4-8-13
Distr.: Natl.
Personnel:
Lawrence H. Hayward *(Chm & CEO)*
Michael L. Hatch *(Pres & COO)*
Steven L. Ortega *(CFO & Exec VP)*
Janet I. McDonald *(CIO & Sr VP)*
Rick D. Carlson *(Sr VP-Comml, Svc & Logistics)*
Brian P. Agnew *(Sr VP-Store Ops)*
Gail Griffin *(Dir-Mktg)*
Brands & Products:
LESLIE'S

LOMMA MINIATURE GOLF CO.
305 Cherry St
Scranton, PA 18505-1505
Tel.: (570) 346-5559
Fax: (570) 346-5580
E-mail: info@lommagolf.com
Web Site: www.lommagolf.com
Approx. Number Employees: 100
Year Founded: 1955
Business Description:
Indoor & Outdoor Miniature Golf Courses Mfr
S.I.C.: 1541
N.A.I.C.S.: 236210
Export
Media: 2-4-9-10-25-26
Distr.: Natl.
Personnel:
Ralph J. Lomma *(Founder & Pres)*
Joyce Lomma *(VP-Adv)*
Brands & Products:
19 HOLE PRO-AM
LOMMA
PRO-AM CHALLENGE
PRO-AM SPECIAL

LOOP-LOC LTD.
(Sub. of Interplex Industries Inc.)
390 Motor Pkwy
Hauppauge, NY 11788
Tel.: (631) 582-2626
Fax: (631) 582-2636
Toll Free: (800) LOC-LOOP
E-mail: info@looploc.com
Web Site: www.looploc.com
Business Description:
Safety Swimming Pool Covers, Removable Fencing & Vinyl Liners Mfr & Seller
S.I.C.: 3089; 3949
N.A.I.C.S.: 326199; 339920
Media: 2-5-6-10-13-16-18-19-22
Personnel:
LeeAnn Donaton-Pesta *(Pres)*
Brands & Products:
BABY-LOC
LOOP-LOC
Advertising Agency:
Walter F. Cameron Advertising Inc.
350 Motor Pkwy Ste 410
Hauppauge, NY 11788-5125
Tel.: (631) 232-3033
Fax: (631) 232-3111

LYMAN PRODUCTS CORPORATION
475 Smith St
Middletown, CT 06457
Tel.: (860) 632-2020
Fax: (860) 632-1699
Toll Free: (800) 225-9626
E-mail: lyman@cshore.com
Web Site: www.lymanproducts.com
Approx. Number Employees: 100
Year Founded: 1878
Business Description:
Hunting Accessories
S.I.C.: 3559; 3915
N.A.I.C.S.: 333298; 339913
Import Export
Advertising Expenditures: $500,000
Media: 1-4-6-10-20-25
Distr.: Intl.; Natl.
Budget Set: Dec.
Personnel:
J. Mace Thompson *(Pres)*
Rick Ranzinger *(VP-Sls & Mktg)*
Brands & Products:
A-ZOOM
ACCUTRIMMER
AUTO-FLO
BLACK POWDER GOLD
DEERSTALKER RIFLE
E-ZEE
E-ZEE FLO
GREAT PLAINS HUNTER
GREAT PLAINS RIFLE
LYMAN
ORANGE MAGIC
PACHMAYR
SILVER STAR
SUPER MOLY
T-MAG II
TACSTAR
TARGDOTS
TARGETMAN
TURBO
UNI-DOT
UNIVERSAL
UNIVERSAL TRIMMER

MACGREGOR GOLF COMPANY
(Sub. of Golfsmith International Holdings, Inc.)
1000 Pecan Grove Dr
Albany, GA 31701
Tel.: (229) 420-7000
Fax: (229) 420-7070
Toll Free: (800) 841-4358
E-mail: contact_us@macgregorgolf.com
Web Site: www.macgregorgolf.com
Approx. Number Employees: 100
Year Founded: 1897
Business Description:
Golf Equipment, Accessories & Outerwear Mfr, Marketer & Distr
S.I.C.: 3949; 5091
N.A.I.C.S.: 339920; 423910
Export
Media: 3-6
Distr.: Intl.; Natl.
Budget Set: Mar.
Personnel:
Michael J. Setola *(Pres & CEO)*
J. Richard Walker *(CFO)*
Brands & Products:
EYE-O-MATIC
V-FOIL 1025CM
V-FOIL 1025M
V-FOIL GO LONG
V-FOIL M445
V-FOIL MOI
Advertising Agency:
Nail Communications
63 Eddy St
Providence, RI 02903
Tel.: (401) 331-6245
Fax: (401) 331-2987

MAGID GLOVE SAFETY MANUFACTURING CO. LLC
(d/b/a Magid Glove Co)
2060 North Kolmar Ave
Chicago, IL 60639
Tel.: (773) 384-2070

Key to Media (For complete agency information see *The Advertising Red Books-Agencies* edition):
1. Bus. Publs. 2. Cable T.V. 3. Catalogs & Directories. 4. Co-op Adv. 5. Consumer Mags. 6. D.M. to Bus. Estab.7. D.M. to Consumers
8. Daily Newsp. 9. Exhibits/Trade Shows 10. Foreign 11. Infomercial 12. Internet Adv.13. Multimedia 14. Network Radio
15. Network T.V. 16. Newsp. Distr. Mags. 17. Other 18. Outdoor (Posters, Transit) 19. Point of Purchase20. Premiums, Novelties
21. Product Samples 22. Special Events Mktg. 23. Spot Radio 24. Spot T.V. 25. Weekly Newsp. 26. Yellow Page Adv.

Magid Glove Safety Manufacturing Co. LLC — (Continued)

Fax: (773) 384-6677
Web Site: www.magidglove.com
E-Mail For Key Personnel:
Sales Director: sales@magidglove.com
Approx. Number Employees: 400
Business Description:
Gloves, Leather: Work
S.I.C.: 3151
N.A.I.C.S.: 315992
Personnel:
Abe Cohen *(Co-Founder)*
Brands & Products:
ACCUTECH
AEROSITE
AIRSOFT
ALLEGRO
ALPHA
ALPHAWIPE
ANSWER
ANTI-ITCH CALAGEL
ANTI-ITCH CORTICOOL
AO SAFETY
ARKON
ASPEN
BACKBITER
BEATER
BESTVUE
BEX
BLACKJACK
BLAZE
BLUEWIPE
BONES
BOUTON
BRIGHT STAR
CABOFLEX
CANNONBALL
CHECKMATE
CHEMI-PRO
CHUMS
CLASSIC
CLEANTIPS
COBRA
CONFORM
CORRECT-TOUCH
CRUSADER
CUTLASS
CUTMASTER
DAVITS
DEFEND
DERMA THIN
DOUBLE TUFF
DOUBLE TUFFS
DRYBROW
DURA-TOUCH
DURAFLEX
DYAN-BRAKE
DYNA-HOIST
DYNA-LINE
DYNA-LOCK
DYNEVAC
E-ZFIT
EASY FLEX
ECONOLITE
ECONOWEAR
EDGE
ENGINEER
EUROLITE
EVER-FLEX
EXCALIBUR
EXPRESS
EYESALINE
FACE-FIT
FACE SAVER
FECTOGGLES
FECTOID
FLENTS
FLEX NIT
FOAM INSULATED
FOCUS
FUZZY DUCK
GLENEAGLE
GOGGLE GEAR
GOGGLES
GOJO
GOLDEN GRAB-IT
GRAB-IT
GRAPPLER
GREYT SHADOW
GUARD DOGS
HAND SENSE
HUSTLER
HYCRON
HYD-TUF
HYFLEX
HYLITE
HYNIT
HYPOCLEAN CRITICAL
INSULATED NEOPRENE
INSULATED NITTY GRITTY
INSULATED SUPER FLEX
IRON EAGLE
JACKSON
JAZZ
JOMAC
KLEENGUARD
KNITMASTER
KRISS-CROSS
KSR
LASER LITE
LASER SPOT
LASER-TRAK
LEGEND
LENSCLEAN
LEXA
LITE 'N KOOL
LITE N KOOL
MAGID
MAGNUM
MALIBU
MANYARD
MATRIX
MAX LITE
MAXIM
METALIST
MINILITE
MITYLITE
MOLDEX
MONKEY GRIP
MONOGOGGLE
MULTI-MAX
MULTIMASTER
N-DEX
NASSAU RAVE
NATURAL K
NEO HYDE
NEOPRENE
NEOX
NEXGEN
NEXT NITRO
NEXT NO-TOUCH
NEXT TRI-FLANGE
NITRASAFE
NITRI-SEAL
NITRILE
NOMEX
NORTH HAND
NU FANGLE
OBERON MAX PLUS
OPTEMA
PELTOR
PETROFLEX
PLUG DEPOT
POCKET-PAK
POD PLUGS
POLY PLUS
POLYSAFE
POWERMASTER
PREMIER
PRODIGY
PULLOVER
PURA-FIT
PUREBREDS
PURPLE NITRILE
PUSH-INS
QUIET
REDMONT
RETROSPEC
REVERSIBLE KEVLAR
ROADMASTER
ROC KEVLAR
ROCKETS
ROPOD
RUGGED SONTARA
SAFETYFLEX
SATIN PLUS
SCORPIO
SCRUBCARE
SEAMS-RITE
SENTRY
SERVUS
SHIELD
SKINNY DIP
SNORKEL
SOFTIES
SORBOTHANE
SOUTHERN
SPAEKPLUGS
SPARK GUARD
SPHERE
STANZOIL
STARLITE
STORM
STRAPPER
STRETCHSTOP
SUPER FLEX
SUPER MITYLITE
SUPER PELILITE
SUPER SABRELITE
SUPEREIGHT
TACOMA
TAHOE
TAPERFIT
TECHNICLOTH
TECHNISAT
TECNU
TERRYCLOTH KEVLAR
TERRYMASTER
TEXWIPE
TEXWRITE
THERMALWEAR
THERMO-GUARD
TIGERHOOD
TOMAHAWK
TOUR-GUARD
TRADESMAN
TYCHEM
TYVEK
UFO STARGAZE
ULTRAFIT
ULTRAFLEX
UVEX
V-GARD
VERSABRITE
VESTYPE
VISCOLAS
WAIST
WEBDRI
WERX
WERX-RITE
WET WEAR
WHIZARD
WILLSON
Advertising Agency:
Design North, Inc.
8007 Douglas Ave
Racine, WI 53402
Tel.: (262) 639-2080
Tel.: (262) 898-1090
Fax: (262) 639-5230
Toll Free: (800) 247-8494

THE MARLIN FIREARMS COMPANY, INC.

(Sub. of Remington Arms Company, Inc.)
100 Kenna Dr
North Haven, CT 06473-2516
Mailing Address:
PO Box 248
North Haven, CT 06473-0905
Tel.: (203) 239-5621
Fax: (203) 234-7991
E-mail: info@marlinfirearms.com
Web Site: www.marlinfirearms.com
Approx. Number Employees: 500
Year Founded: 1870
Business Description:
Sporting Rifle & Shotgun & Mfr
S.I.C.: 3484; 3489
N.A.I.C.S.: 332994; 332995
Export
Media: 2-3-4-5-6-7-10-13-23-24
Distr.: Intl.
Budget Set: Dec.
Personnel:
Frank Kenna, III *(Chm)*
Mike Jensen *(VP-Sls & Mktg)*
Brands & Products:
HARRINGTON & RICHARDSON
MARLIN
MARLIN GOLDEN
NEW ENGLAND FIREARMS

MCNETT CORPORATION

1411 Meador Ave
Bellingham, WA 98229
Tel.: (360) 392-2711
Fax: (360) 671-4521
E-mail: office@mcnett.com
Web Site: www.mcnett.com
E-Mail For Key Personnel:
Sales Director: sales@mcnett.com
Approx. Number Employees: 40
Business Description:
Marine & Sporting Rain Gear & Accessories Mfr
S.I.C.: 3949; 5091
N.A.I.C.S.: 339920; 423910
Media: 6-19-20
Personnel:
Duane V. McNett *(Pres)*
David Wiggs *(VP-Mktg)*
Brands & Products:
AQUAMIRA
AQUASEAL
AQUASURE
B.C. LIFE
BLAKELEY
BOAT BASIC
CAMO FORM
CAMO VAT
CLEAN TAPE
COTOL
COTOL 240

CUBIT
CV CRAVAT
CYPRESS
DELRIN
DRY MICRO
DURWARD ANKL WEIGHTS
EARPLANES
ESSENTIALS FOR ADVENTURE
FLEX FASHION
FLY TOP
FOLIO
FREELINE
FREESOLE
FRONTIER
GATHERNET
GOGGLE BRIGHT
GORE-TEX
GRUNTLINE
HYPALON
I PATCH
IRON MEND
LYCRA
MAX WAX
MCNETT
MEGATHANE
MELCO
MICRONET
MIRAZYME
MTB
NECK NACK
NECK NACK MD
NETLINE
OP DROPS
ORCAS
PRO TALC
PROTALC
QUICK FRESH
REVIVEX
SAMISH
SATURNA
SEA BAND
SEA BUFF
SEA DROPS
SEA GOLD
SEA ICE
SEA QUICK
SEAL CEMENT
SEAL SAVER
SEAM CLEANER
SEAM GRIP
SEAM SURE
SIL FIX
SIL NET
SILICONE PUMP
SILNET
SUPREMA
TENACIOUS
TENACIOUS TAPE
TENT SURE
THUNDER DOWN
THUNDER GUARD
THUNDER SHIELD
TRIPTONE
UV TECH
WET SUIT AND DRY SUIT
X-TREME
X-TREME WASH
ZIESTA
ZIP CARE
ZIP TECH

Advertising Agency:
Backbone Media LLC
65 N 4th St Ste 1
Carbondale, CO 81623
Tel.: (970) 963-4873
Fax: (303) 265-9854
Toll Free: (866) 963-4873

MEGGITT TRAINING SYSTEMS

(Formerly Firearms Training Systems, Inc.)
(Sub. of Meggitt Defense Systems, Inc.)
296 Brogdon Rd
Suwanee, GA 30024
Tel.: (678) 288-1090
Fax: (678) 288-1520
Toll Free: (800) 813-9046
E-mail: mgtts-militarysales@meggitt.com
Web Site: www.meggitttrainingsystems.com
Approx. Rev.: $78,570,000
Approx. Number Employees: 600
Year Founded: 1984
Business Description:
Firearm Simulation & Training Systems & Services Designer, Mfr & Marketer
S.I.C.: 3679; 3571; 3577; 7371; 7372; 7373
N.A.I.C.S.: 334419; 334111; 334119; 511210; 541511; 541512
Media: 10
Personnel:
Bob Dare *(VP-Sls)*
Steve Shiffman *(Dir-Customer Support)*
Advertising Agency:
communications 21
834 Inman Vlg Pky Ste 150
Atlanta, GA 30307
Tel.: (404) 814-1330
Fax: (404) 814-1332

MINI-GOLF, INC.

202 Bridge St
Jessup, PA 18434-1302
Tel.: (570) 489-8623
Fax: (570) 383-9970
Web Site: www.minigolfinc.com
E-Mail For Key Personnel:
Marketing Director: jrogari@epix.net
Sales Range: Less than $1 Million
Approx. Number Employees: 32
Year Founded: 1981
Business Description:
Portable, Pre-Fabricated Miniature Golf Course Mfr
S.I.C.: 3949
N.A.I.C.S.: 339920
Export
Media: 2-4-7-10
Distr.: Natl.
Personnel:
Joseph J. Rogari, Jr. *(VP-Mktg)*

MIRACLE RECREATION EQUIPMENT COMPANY

(Sub. of PlayPower, Inc.)
878 Hwy 60
Monett, MO 65708
Mailing Address:
PO Box 420
Monett, MO 65708-0420
Tel.: (417) 235-6917
Fax: (417) 235-3551
Toll Free: (800) 523-4202
E-mail: play@miracle-recreation.com
Web Site: www.miracle-recreation.com
Approx. Number Employees: 400
Year Founded: 1927
Business Description:
Mfr. of Playground Equipment, Water Slides, Picnic Tables, Grills, Outdoor Sports Equipment, Playground Safety Surfacing Indoor Soft-Play & Bleachers
S.I.C.: 3949; 2531
N.A.I.C.S.: 339920; 337127
Import Export
Media: 1-4-6-8-13
Distr.: Direct to Consumer; Intl.; Natl.
Budget Set: Oct.
Personnel:
Mike Sutton *(Dir-Sls)*
Alissa Jones *(Coord-Mktg)*
Brands & Products:
CENTER STAGE
CITY PARK SERIES
KIDS' CHOICE
TOTS' CHOICE

MIZUNO USA, INC.

(Sub. of Mizuno Corporation)
4925 Avalon Ridge Pkwy
Norcross, GA 30071-1571
Tel.: (770) 441-5553
Fax: (770) 448-3234
Toll Free: (800) 966-1234
Web Site: www.mizunousa.com
Approx. Number Employees: 250
Year Founded: 1982
Business Description:
Footwear, Equipment & Apparel Mfr for Baseball, Softball, Running, Track & Field, Volleyball, Court Sports, Soccer & Golf
S.I.C.: 5091; 3949
N.A.I.C.S.: 423910; 339920
Import Export
Advertising Expenditures: $2,500,000
Media: 6-7-8-9-10-19-23-24
Distr.: Natl.
Budget Set: May
Personnel:
Bob Puccini *(Pres)*
Dick Lyons *(VP & Gen Mgr)*
Rod Foley *(Dir-Mktg)*
Brands & Products:
GRAIN FLOW FORGING
MIZUNO
T-ZOID
WAVE
WAVE TECHNOLOGY
Advertising Agencies:
BooneOakley
1445 S Mint St
Charlotte, NC 28203
Tel.: (704) 333-9797
Fax: (704) 348-2834

Huey & Partners
812 - A Lambert Dr
Atlanta, GA 30324
Tel.: (404) 541-9990
Fax: (404) 541-9991
Golf Clubs

MODELL'S SPORTING GOODS INC.

(Sub. of Henry Modell & Company, Inc.)
498 7th Ave Fl 20
New York, NY 10018
Tel.: (212) 822-1000
Fax: (212) 822-1025
Toll Free: (800) ASK-MODELLS
Web Site: www.modells.com
Sales Range: $10-24.9 Million
Approx. Number Employees: 4,000
Business Description:
Sporting Goods
S.I.C.: 5941; 5661
N.A.I.C.S.: 451110; 448210
Personnel:
Mitchell Modell *(CEO)*
Jed Berger *(Sr VP-Mktg)*
Brands & Products:
MODELL'S
Advertising Agencies:
Berlin Cameron United
100 Ave of the Americas 2nd Fl
New York, NY 10013
Tel.: (212) 824-2000
Fax: (212) 268-8454

Horizon Media, Inc.
75 Varick St
New York, NY 10013
Tel.: (212) 220-5000
Toll Free: (800) 633-4201
Media Planning & Buying

MOUNTAIN HARDWEAR, INC.

(Sub. of Columbia Sportswear Company)
1414 Harbour Way S Ford Point Ste 1005
Richmond, CA 94804
Tel.: (510) 558-3000
Fax: (510) 559-6709
Toll Free: (800) 953-8375
E-mail: info@mountainhardwear.com
Web Site: www.mountainhardwear.com
Sales Range: $75-99.9 Million
Approx. Number Employees: 101
Year Founded: 1993
Business Description:
Outdoor Gear, Apparel & Accessories Mfr & Distr
S.I.C.: 5091; 2329; 2339
N.A.I.C.S.: 423910; 315228; 315239
Media: 5-6-10-11-13-18-22
Personnel:
Topher Gaylord *(Pres)*
Paige Boucher *(Co-Dir & Dir-PR)*
Brad Little *(Product Mgr-Outerwear)*
Brands & Products:
MONTRAIL
MOUNTAIN HARDWEAR
Advertising Agency:
Butler, Shine, Stern & Partners
20 Liberty Ship Way
Sausalito, CA 94965-3312
Tel.: (415) 331-6049
Fax: (415) 331-3524

NATURAL GOLF CORPORATION

2124 Stonington Ave
Hoffman Estates, IL 60169
Tel.: (847) 713-3994
Fax: (847) 795-0101
Toll Free: (888) 628-4653
E-mail: sales@naturalgolf.com
Web Site: www.naturalgolf.com
E-Mail For Key Personnel:
Sales Director: sales@naturalgolf.com
Sales Range: $1-9.9 Million
Approx. Number Employees: 23
Year Founded: 1990
Business Description:
Golf Equipment & Golf Instruction
S.I.C.: 3949; 7997
N.A.I.C.S.: 339920; 713910

Key to Media (For complete agency information see *The Advertising Red Books-Agencies* edition):
1. Bus. Publs. 2. Cable T.V. 3. Catalogs & Directories. 4. Co-op Adv. 5. Consumer Mags. 6. D.M. to Bus. Estab.7. D.M. to Consumers 8. Daily Newsp. 9. Exhibits/Trade Shows 10. Foreign 11. Infomercial 12. Internet Adv.13. Multimedia 14. Network Radio 15. Network T.V. 16. Newsp. Distr. Mags. 17. Other 18. Outdoor (Posters, Transit) 19. Point of Purchase20. Premiums, Novelties 21. Product Samples 22. Special Events Mktg. 23. Spot Radio 24. Spot T.V. 25. Weekly Newsp. 26. Yellow Page Adv.

Natural Golf Corporation — (Continued)

Advertising Expenditures: $4,168,830
Media: 6-8-12-13-14-15-23-24-25
Personnel:
Thomas Herskovits *(Chm)*
Richard A. Magid *(CFO)*
Brands & Products:
HAMMER
HOT PEPPER
THE MOE NORMAN WAY
NATURAL GOLF
NG SWING
SENSICORE
ST BERYLLIUM COPPER

NAUTILUS HUMAN PERFORMANCE SYSTEMS, INC.

(Sub. of Nautilus Inc.)
709 Powerhouse Rd
Independence, VA 24348-3782
Mailing Address:
PO Box 708
Independence, VA 24348-0708
Tel.: (276) 773-2881
Fax: (276) 773-3885
Toll Free: (800) NAUTILUS
E-mail: sales@nautilus.com
Web Site: www.nautilus.com
E-Mail For Key Personnel:
Sales Director: sales@nautilus.com
Approx. Rev.: $17,000,000
Approx. Number Employees: 185
Year Founded: 1970
Business Description:
Conditioning & Rehabilitation Equipment, Fitness Systems Mfr
S.I.C.: 3949
N.A.I.C.S.: 339920
Export
Media: 2-9-10-11-15-25
Distr.: Intl.; Natl.
Budget Set: Monthly
Personnel:
Cindy Rudy *(CFO)*
Ron Arp *(Sr VP-Corp Commun)*
Greg Webb *(VP-Mfg & Engrg)*
Brands & Products:
NAUTILUS

NAUTILUS INC.

16400 SE Nautilus Dr
Vancouver, WA 98683-5535
Tel.: (360) 694-7722
Fax: (360) 694-7755
E-mail: inforarp@nautilus.com
Web Site: www.nautilus.com
Approx. Sls.: $168,450,000
Approx. Number Employees: 330
Year Founded: 1986
Business Description:
Marketer of Consumer Health & Fitness Products
S.I.C.: 3949
N.A.I.C.S.: 339920
Advertising Expenditures: $40,600,000
Media: 1-2-3-4-6-8-10-12-13-24
Distr.: Natl.
Personnel:
Edward J. Bramson *(Chm & CEO)*
Mark A. Meussner *(Pres)*
Kenneth Fish *(CFO, Chief Admin Officer, VP & Gen Mgr-Comml Bus)*
James A. Heidenreich *(CMO & Sr VP-Global Mktg)*
Juergen Eckmann *(Pres-Nautilus Apparel Bus)*
Wayne M. Bolio *(Gen Counsel & Sr VP-Law)*
Bill McMahon *(Sr VP & Gen Mgr-Consumer Bus)*
Deborah Marsh *(Sr VP-HR)*
Patrick A. Warner *(Sr VP-Product Dev)*
Caroline J. Howe *(VP-Mktg)*
Aaron Brotherton *(Dir-Direct Response TV & Creative Dev)*
Amy Dorsett *(Mgr-Enterprise Web)*
Brands & Products:
BOWFLEX
NAUTILUS
SCHWINN
SCHWINN A.C.
SELECTTECH
STAIRMASTER
TREADCLIMBER
TRIMLINE

NEW ERA CAP COMPANY INC.

8061 Erie Rd
Derby, NY 14047
Tel.: (716) 549-0445
Fax: (716) 549-7247
Toll Free: (877) NEC5950
E-mail: yourvoice@neweracap.com
Web Site: www.neweracap.com
Sales Range: $600-649.9 Million
Approx. Number Employees: 1,500
Year Founded: 1920
Business Description:
Mfr & Distr of Sports-Licensed Headwear
S.I.C.: 2353; 3949
N.A.I.C.S.: 315991; 339920
Export
Advertising Expenditures: $1,000,000
Media: 4-6-7-10-20
Distr.: Natl.
Personnel:
Peter Augustine *(Pres)*
Chris Koch *(CEO)*
Raymond Barry *(CFO)*
Jim Grundtisch *(Sr VP-Global Sls)*
Bill Adams *(VP-Sls-US)*
Tony Swaffield *(Brand Dir- Protection)*
Kelli Coppola *(Global Dir-Brand Mktg)*
Clint Perez *(Dir-Mktg-North America)*
Peter Ciotta *(Sr Mgr-Brand Comm)*
Brands & Products:
59FIFTY
HARDWOOD CLASSICS
NEW ERA
NEW ERA FITS
ORIGINATORS OF THE TRUE FITTED
Advertising Agencies:
The Brooklyn Brothers
18 E 17th St 6th Fl
New York, NY 10003
Tel.: (212) 242-0200
Fax: (212) 242-0217
Agency of Record

Dan Klores Communications
(d/b/a dkc)
386 Park Ave S 10th Fl
New York, NY 10016
Tel.: (212) 685-4300
Fax: (212) 685-9024
Headwear

NICKLAUS GOLF EQUIPMENT COMPANY, L.C.

(Sub. of Nicklaus Companies, LLC)
3875 fiscal Ctr
West Palm Beach, FL 33404-3336
Tel.: (561) 881-7981
Fax: (561) 881-8214
Toll Free: (800) 322-1872
E-mail: contactus@nicklausgolf.com
Web Site: www.nicklausgolf.com
Approx. Number Employees: 25
Year Founded: 1992
Business Description:
Golf Clubs & Related Accessories Mfr, Whslr & Online Retailer
S.I.C.: 3949; 5091; 5961
N.A.I.C.S.: 339920; 423910; 454111
Import Export
Advertising Expenditures: $2,000,000
Media: 2-4-5-6-7-9-10-12-13-18-19-21-23-24
Distr.: Natl.
Budget Set: Sept. -Oct.
Personnel:
Jack William Nicklaus *(Founder & Chm)*
Robert P. Kelly *(CEO)*
Skip Seerer *(CFO)*
Tony Pando *(VP-Sls)*
Blake Snyder *(Mgr-Production)*
Brands & Products:
GOLDEN BEAR
JACK NICKLAUS
NICKLAUS

NIKE CANADA LTD.

(Sub. of NIKE, Inc.)
175 Commerce Valley Drive West Suite 500
Thornhill, ON L3T 7P6, Canada
Tel.: (905) 764-0400
Fax: (905) 764-1266
Web Site: www.nike.ca
Sales Range: $150-199.9 Million
Approx. Number Employees: 150
Business Description:
Sales & Marketing
S.I.C.: 5661
N.A.I.C.S.: 448210
Media: 31
Personnel:
Susan Angelidis *(Exec Asst & Office Mgr)*
Andrew Stewart *(Brand Comm Mgr)*
Advertising Agency:
Organic, Inc.
555 Market St 4th Fl
San Francisco, CA 94105
Tel.: (415) 581-5300
Fax: (415) 581-5400

THE NORTH FACE, INC.

(Sub. of VF Corporation)
2013 Farallon Dr
San Leandro, CA 94577-6601
Tel.: (510) 618-3500
Fax: (510) 618-3531
Toll Free: (800) 362-4963
Web Site: www.thenorthface.com
Sales Range: $200-249.9 Million
Approx. Number Employees: 400
Year Founded: 1966
Business Description:
High-Performance Climbing & Backpacking Equipment Mfr, Distr & Retailer
S.I.C.: 2389; 5941
N.A.I.C.S.: 315999; 451110
Media: 4-6-10
Personnel:
Steve Rendle *(Pres)*
Todd Spaletto *(Pres-Americas)*
Aaron Carpenter *(VP-Mktg)*
Dave Sweet *(VP-Retail)*
Brands & Products:
A5
ASCENTIALS
FLIGHT SERIES
THE NORTH FACE
TEKWARE
Advertising Agencies:
Factory Design Labs
158 Fillmore St
Denver, CO 80206
Tel.: (303) 573-9100
Fax: (303) 573-5975

hawkeye
2828 Routh St Ste 300
Dallas, TX 75201
Tel.: (214) 659-5615
Fax: (214) 747-1897

The Ruder Finn Group
301 E 57th St
New York, NY 10022-2900
Tel.: (212) 593-6400
Fax: (212) 593-6397

OAKLEY, INC.

(Sub. of Luxottica Group S.p.A.)
1 Icon
Foothill Ranch, CA 92610-3000
Tel.: (949) 951-0991
Fax: (949) 454-1071
Toll Free: (800) 403-7449
E-mail: info@oakley.com
Web Site: www.oakley.com
Sales Range: $750-799.9 Million
Approx. Number Employees: 3,400
Year Founded: 1975
Business Description:
Eyewear & Athletic Equipment Mfr, Designer & Distr
S.I.C.: 3851; 3842
N.A.I.C.S.: 339115; 339113
Export
Advertising Expenditures: $26,700,000
Media: 4-6-8-10-11-18-19-22-31
Personnel:
D. Scott Olivet *(Chm)*
Colin Baden *(Pres)*
Richard Shields *(CFO)*
Jon Krause *(Sr VP-Ops)*
Kent Lane *(Sr VP-Mfg)*
Donna Gordon *(VP-Fin)*
Pat McIlvain *(VP-Sports Mktg-Global)*
Cliff Neill *(VP-Sls)*
Jennifer Bradley *(Brand Dir)*
Daniella Gasaway *(Dir-Adv)*
Kenneth H. Lockwood *(Dir-Fin & Ops)*
Brianne DeWeese *(Mgr-PR)*
Brands & Products:
A WIRE
ABSORB
AGENDA
AIRWAVE
ALEX
AMBUSH
AMMO
ANA GUEVARA MAG
ANORAK
ARC
ARMOR

Key to Media (For complete agency information see *The Advertising Red Books-Agencies* edition):
1. Bus. Publs. 2. Cable T.V. 3. Catalogs & Directories. 4. Co-op Adv. 5. Consumer Mags. 6. D.M. to Bus. Estab.7. D.M. to Consumers
8. Daily Newsp. 9. Exhibits/Trade Shows 10. Foreign 11. Infomercial 12. Internet Adv.13. Multimedia 14. Network Radio
15. Network T.V. 16. Newsp. Distr. Mags. 17. Other 18. Outdoor (Posters, Transit) 19. Point of Purchase20. Premiums, Novelties
21. Product Samples 22. Special Events Mktg. 23. Spot Radio 24. Spot T.V. 25. Weekly Newsp. 26. Yellow Page Adv.

ASK
BACKLESS
BALLISTIC
BARNETT
BARRAGE
BARTACT
BENT
BIG TEE
BLADE
BLASTED
BOTTLECAP
BOW TYE
BOX SPRING 2.0
BOX SPRING 4.0
BOX TOP
BUCKSHOT
BULLDOZE
BULLET
BULLY
BURNER
BUTTON DOWN
CACTUS
CAGE
CAM
CAMO
CARTEL
CENTERFIRE
CHROME
CLASSIC
CODE RED
COHORT
COMMUTE
COMPRESSION
CONSCRIPT
CORROSION
COVERT
CRANK
CROSS HATCH
CROSSED
CROSSHAIR
CROWBAR
CRUSH
CRUSH 2.0
CRYPTIC
CULTURE
CUT-OFF
D1
D2
DAISY CUTTER
DANGEROUS
DARTBOARD
DEAL
DEMAND
DEPLOY
DETONATOR
DIFFUSION
DOPP KIT
DOT MATRIX
DOUBLE AGENT
DOUBLE BARREL
DUCATI JULIET
DUCATI MONSTER DOG
DUCATI ZERO
ELECTRODE
ELLIPSE
EPOXY
EXPERIMENT
FADE
FALCON
FIELD
FILTER
FILTERIZE
FINE KNIT
FIVES
FLINCH
FLORAL INK
FLORAL STRETCH
FLOW
FOCUS
FORGE
FORWARD
FRAME
FRENZY
FULL ASSAULT
GASCAN
GASKET
GMT
GOLF
GRAIN
GRAMPS
GRATE
GRAVITY
GRID IRON
HALF JACKET
HALF WIRE
HALFED
HALFTONE
HANDLE
HATCHET WIRE
HAYLON
HAZMAT
HEAT
HELIX
HOLLOW POINT
HUB
HYBRID
ICON
ICON BARS
ICON BEATER
ICON SMALL
IDENTITY
IGNITION
IMPOSTER
INVASION
JACKET ARRAY
JACQUARD
JOHNNY
JUAN PABLO
JUDGE
JULIET
JURY
KEVLAR
KNOCKOUT
LANCE ARMSTRONG
LASER
LATEX
LAZER
LEASH
LINEAR
LOGIC
LOUD
M FRAME
MACE
MAGNET
MARKER
MATRIX
MECHANIC
MEDUSA BOB
METALIZED
MINUTE
MONSTER
MONSTER DOGGLE
MX
MX O FRAME
NATIVE
NECK TYE
NETTING
NO TYE
O2
O6
O7
OFF LINE
ORBITAL
ORDER
ORE
OUTFIT
OUTLINE
OVER THE TOP
OVERDRIVE
OXIDATION
PARA TROOPER
PATROL
PEACE
PENNY
PERFORMANCE
PERMIT
PETITION
PLANET
PLUG
POISON
POLO
PRESS
PRESSURE
PROFORM
PROFORMER
PROPULSION
PUFFY
PUNK SKULL
QUEEN BEATER
QUEEN ZIP
RACING JACKET
RAGE
RANGE
RAZOR
REACTOR
REALIZE
REBOUND
RENNER AIR
REPEAT
REPORT
REPROGRAPH
REPUBLIC
RESPONSE
RETRO
REVOLVER
RIDDLE
RIM
ROMEO
ROTTEN
RUSTY WALLACE PRO
RX M
SADDLEBACK
SANDBAGER
SAW
SAW OFF
SCOPE
SCORE CARD
SCOTTY CANNON
SCRAMBLE
SECTION
SECTOR
SELF
SEQUENCE
SHOOTING ARRAY
SHOVEL
SHOW PONY
SIGNAL
SILENCE
SKATE CREW
SLAB
SLICE
SLIMLINE
SMOKE
SMOKE RING
SNOW
SNOW CROSS
SOFT TOP 2.0
SOFT TOP 4.0
SOLAR
SPIKE
SPILL
SPIN
SPINDLE
SPLATTER
SPLICE
SPLINE
SPLIT CRATER
SPLIT GRIP
SPLIT SMOKE
SPLIT TOP
SPRING
SPRINKLER
SPROCKET
SQUARE O
STAIRS
STATIC
STINGER
STRAIGHT JACKET
STREAM
STRETCH CROSS HATCH
STRETCH PLAID
STRETCH REPEAT
STROKE
SUBJECT
SULFUR
SUPERFICIAL
SWEEP ARRAY
TACTICAL
TANK BEATER
TEAM GRID
TEAM UP
TEASPOON
TECH
THERMAL BOB
THUMP
TIME BOMB
TITANIUM CHAIN
TITANIUM O3
TITANIUM WHY 3
TRACE
TRAP
TRAVEL
TRENCH
TRIO
TUXEDO
TYRANT
UNION
UNKNOWN
UNLEADED
VALVE
THE VAULT
VENTED ARRAY
VOID
WANT
WAR
WAR HAWK
WARTORN
WATER JACKET
WEBBED
WELLEN
WESTERN
WHISKER
WHY
WHY 8.0
WHY 8.1
WIRE SKULL
WIRE TAP
WIRETAP
WISDOM
WOVEN DAISY CUTTER
X METAL
YOURSELF
ZERO
ZERO L
ZIPPER

Advertising Agency:
Wirestone
920 20th St

Key to Media (For complete agency information see *The Advertising Red Books-Agencies* edition):
1. Bus. Publs. 2. Cable T.V. 3. Catalogs & Directories. 4. Co-op Adv. 5. Consumer Mags. 6. D.M. to Bus. Estab.7. D.M. to Consumers
8. Daily Newsp. 9. Exhibits/Trade Shows 10. Foreign 11. Infomercial 12. Internet Adv.13. Multimedia 14. Network Radio
15. Network T.V. 16. Newsp. Distr. Mags. 17. Other 18. Outdoor (Posters, Transit) 19. Point of Purchase20. Premiums, Novelties
21. Product Samples 22. Special Events Mktg. 23. Spot Radio 24. Spot T.V. 25. Weekly Newsp. 26. Yellow Page Adv.

Oakley, Inc. — (Continued)

Sacramento, CA 95811
Tel.: (916) 446-6550
Fax: (916) 446-6551

O.F. MOSSBERG & SONS, INC.

(Sub. of Mossberg Corporation)
7 Grasso Ave
North Haven, CT 06473-3237
Tel.: (203) 230-5300
Fax: (203) 230-5420
Web Site: www.mossberg.com
Approx. Number Employees: 285
Year Founded: 1919
Business Description:
Shotguns & Sporting Arms Mfr
S.I.C.: 3484
N.A.I.C.S.: 332994
Advertising Expenditures: $1,400,000
Media: 2-4-5-6-9-10-19-21-25
Distr.: Natl.
Budget Set: Dec.
Personnel:
Alan I. Mossberg *(Owner & Chm)*
Iver Mossberg *(CEO)*
Franz Jacque *(Mgr-IT)*
Brands & Products:
935 MAGNUM
ACCU-CHOKE
BOLT ACTION 695
MAVERICK
MOSSBERG
PUMP ACTION 500
PUMP ACTION 835
SLUGSTER
SPECIAL PURPOSE 500
SPECIAL PURPOSE 590
SSI-ONE

OHIO AWNING & MANUFACTURING CO.

2658 Scranton Rd
Cleveland, OH 44113-5144
Tel.: (216) 861-2400
Fax: (216) 687-0652
Toll Free: (800) 756-4471
Web Site: www.ohioawning.com
E-Mail For Key Personnel:
Sales Director: sales@ohioawning.com
Approx. Sls.: $2,300,000
Approx. Number Employees: 40
Year Founded: 1865
Business Description:
Mfr. of Awnings, Tarpaulins, Flags, Bags & Canvas Specialties, Industrial & Military Canvas Products, Truck Enclosures, Commercial, Residential Awnings & Canopies, Pool Covers; Provider of Tent Rentals
S.I.C.: 2394; 3993
N.A.I.C.S.: 314912; 339950
Media: 4-7-10-13-22-26
Distr.: Natl.
Personnel:
Andrew R. Morse *(Pres)*
Jeff Mitchell *(Gen Mgr)*

OLHAUSEN BILLIARD MFG, INC.

1124 Vaughn Pkwy
Portland, TN 37148
Tel.: (615) 323-8522
Fax: (615) 323-7585
E-mail: info@olhausenbilliards.com
Web Site: www.olhausenbilliards.com
Approx. Number Employees: 200
Business Description:
Billiard Tables Mfr & Distr
S.I.C.: 3949
N.A.I.C.S.: 339920
Media: 2-4-6-9-10-13-14-15-18-22-25
Personnel:
Donald Olhausen *(Chm & Pres)*

O'NEILL INC.

1071 41st Ave
Santa Cruz, CA 95062-4400
Tel.: (831) 475-7500
Fax: (831) 475-0544
E-mail: hrsc@oneill.com
Web Site: www.oneill.com
Approx. Number Employees: 231
Year Founded: 1952
Business Description:
Fabricated Rubber Products Mfr
S.I.C.: 3069; 5091
N.A.I.C.S.: 326299; 423910
Import Export
Media: 6-22
Personnel:
Pat O'Neill *(Pres & CEO)*
Michelle Molfino *(CFO)*
John Pope *(COO)*
Bert Aramburu *(Dir-Sls & Mktg)*
Kieran Horn *(Brand Mgr-Americas)*

ORANGE 21 INC.

2070 Las Palmas Dr
Carlsbad, CA 92009
Tel.: (760) 804-8420
Fax: (760) 804-8421
Toll Free: (800) 779-3937
Web Site: www.orangetwentyone.com
Approx. Sls.: $34,987,000
Approx. Number Employees: 89
Year Founded: 1992
Business Description:
Action Sports Products Designer, Developer & Marketer
S.I.C.: 3842; 3851; 3949; 5099
N.A.I.C.S.: 339113; 339115; 339920; 423990
Advertising Expenditures: $411,000
Media: 2-4-6-8-10-13-18-19-20-21-22
Personnel:
Seth W. Hamot *(Chm)*
Michael Marckx *(Pres)*
Carol A. Montgomery *(CEO & Sec)*
Michael D. Angel *(Interim CFO)*
Don Duster *(COO)*
Barry Buchholtz *(Pres-Italian Ops)*
Erik Darby *(VP-Sls)*
Brands & Products:
ORANGE.21

PARAMOUNT FITNESS CORP.

6450 E Bandini Blvd
Los Angeles, CA 90040-3118
Tel.: (323) 721-2121
Fax: (323) 724-2000
Toll Free: (800) 721-2121
E-mail: sales@paramountfitness.com
Web Site: www.paramountfitness.com
E-Mail For Key Personnel:
Sales Director: sales@paramountfitness.com
Approx. Number Employees: 145
Year Founded: 1975
Business Description:
Fitness Equipment Mfr
S.I.C.: 3949
N.A.I.C.S.: 339920
Import Export
Media: 2-10
Personnel:
Steve Rhodes *(Pres)*
Cherie Michele *(Mgr-Adv)*

PELICAN PRODUCTS, INC.

(Holding of Behrman Capital)
23215 Early Ave
Torrance, CA 90505
Tel.: (310) 326-4700
Fax: (310) 326-3311
Toll Free: (800) 473-5422
E-mail: sales@pelican.com
Web Site: www.pelican.com
E-Mail For Key Personnel:
Sales Director: sales@pelican.com
Approx. Number Employees: 450
Year Founded: 1976
Business Description:
Sports & Marine Accessories Mfr & Distr
S.I.C.: 3648; 3089
N.A.I.C.S.: 335129; 326199
Media: 1-2-5-6-13-16-19
Distr.: Intl.
Personnel:
Peter Pace *(Chm)*
Lyndon J. Faulkner *(Pres & CEO)*
John Padian *(COO)*
Joe Baltronis *(VP-Mktg-Worldwide)*
Kevin Deighton *(VP-Res & Product Dev)*
Mark Rolfes *(VP-Sls)*
Sharon Ward *(Dir-Pub & Media Rels)*
Brands & Products:
AQUA KINGLITE
BIG ED
HEADSUP LITE
KING PELICANLITE
LASERPRO
LITTLE ED
MICRO CASE
MINI FLASHER
MITYLITE
NEMO
PELICAN
PELICAN KINGLITE
POCKET SABRELITE
RECOIL
SABRELITE
STEALTHLITE
SUPER PELILITE
SUPER SABRELITE
TRACKER

PENN FISHING TACKLE MANUFACTURING COMPANY

3028 W Hunting Pk Ave
Philadelphia, PA 19132-1121
Tel.: (215) 229-9415
Fax: (215) 223-3017
Web Site: www.pennreels.com
Approx. Sls.: $50,000,000
Approx. Number Employees: 600
Year Founded: 1932
Business Description:
Mfr. of Fishing Reels
S.I.C.: 3949; 5091
N.A.I.C.S.: 339920; 423910
Media: 4-6-10
Distr.: Natl.
Personnel:
Brent Kane *(Dir-Pub Rels & Adv)*
Brands & Products:
INTERNATIONAL
PENN
PENNREEL
POWER GRAPH
SENATOR
SPINFISHER

PING INC.

(Sub. of Karsten Manufacturing Corporation)
2201 W Desert Cove Ave
Phoenix, AZ 85029-4912
Mailing Address:
PO Box 82000
Phoenix, AZ 85071-2000
Tel.: (602) 870-5000
Fax: (602) 687-4482
Web Site: www.pinggolf.com
Approx. Number Employees: 900
Year Founded: 1959
Business Description:
Mfr. of Golf Irons, Woods, Putters, Bags, Carry Bags & Wood Covers
S.I.C.: 5046
N.A.I.C.S.: 423440
Import Export
Media: 3-4-6-10-11-14-15-23-24
Distr.: Intl.; Natl.
Budget Set: Nov.
Personnel:
Allan Solheim *(Owner)*
John A. Solheim *(Chm & CEO)*
Michael T. Trueblood *(CFO & VP-Fin)*
Rawleigh Grove *(Gen Counsel & VP)*
Pat Loftus *(VP-Sls & Mktg)*
John K. Solheim *(VP-Engrg)*
Pete Samuels *(Dir-Adv)*
Brands & Products:
PING
Advertising Agency:
The Martin Agency
One Shockoe Plz
Richmond, VA 23219-4132
Tel.: (804) 698-8000
Fax: (804) 698-8001

PLASTIMAYD CORPORATION

14151 Fir St
Oregon City, OR 97045
Tel.: (503) 654-8502
Fax: (503) 654-7935
E-mail: plastimayd@aol.com
Web Site: www.plastimayd.com
Approx. Sls.: $30,000,000
Approx. Number Employees: 170
Business Description:
Swimming Pool Liners, Space-Arena Air Enclosure & Liners For Industrial Use
S.I.C.: 3081
N.A.I.C.S.: 326113
Media: 2-4-6-10-21
Distr.: Natl.
Budget Set: Various
Personnel:
Todd Mulvaney *(Pres)*
Brands & Products:
GARDALL
MONO-BOND
PLASTIMAYD
REDECORATE YOUR POOL
SPACE ARENA
SUN-PRUF
ULTRA-CLEAR
ULTRA-MAYD

PLAYWORLD SYSTEMS INCORPORATED

1000 Buffalo Rd
Lewisburg, PA 17837-9702
Tel.: (570) 522-9800
Fax: (570) 522-3030
E-mail: info@playworldsystems.com

Key to Media (For complete agency information see *The Advertising Red Books-Agencies* edition):
1. Bus. Publs. 2. Cable T.V. 3. Catalogs & Directories. 4. Co-op Adv. 5. Consumer Mags. 6. D.M. to Bus. Estab.7. D.M. to Consumers
8. Daily Newsp. 9. Exhibits/Trade Shows 10. Foreign 11. Infomercial 12. Internet Adv.13. Multimedia 14. Network Radio
15. Network T.V. 16. Newsp. Distr. Mags. 17. Other 18. Outdoor (Posters, Transit) 19. Point of Purchase20. Premiums, Novelties
21. Product Samples 22. Special Events Mktg. 23. Spot Radio 24. Spot T.V. 25. Weekly Newsp. 26. Yellow Page Adv.

Web Site: www.playworldsystems.com
Approx. Number Employees: 260
Year Founded: 1979
Business Description:
Sales of Commercial Playground Equipment
S.I.C.: 3949
N.A.I.C.S.: 339920
Import Export
Personnel:
Dale Miller *(Founder, Owner & CEO)*
Brands & Products:
BABBLE-ON
CHALLENGERS
CITYSCAPES
CLIMBING BOULDERS
EXPLORERS
FIRSTPLAY
GROUNDZERO
HUNA
LIFETRAIL
LILY PODS
LOLLITOP
MATRIX
PACHINKO PANEL
PLAYARMOUR
PLAYDESIGNS
PLAYMAKERS
PLAYWEB
PLAYWORLD
PLAYWORLD SYSTEMS
RECREATION FOR LIFE
ROCKBLOCKS
SKYTOWERS
TODDLERTOWN
WELLNESS STATIONS
WOODWARD
Advertising Agencies:
Carton Donofrio Partners, Inc.
100 N Charles St 15th Fl
Baltimore, MD 21201
Tel.: (410) 576-9000
Fax: (410) 528-8809

Rose Communications, Inc.
720 Monroe St Ste E314B
Hoboken, NJ 07030
Tel.: (201) 656-7178
Fax: (201) 221-8734
Media Relations
Social Media Strategy
Trade Show Support

POOL CORPORATION
109 Northpark Blvd
Covington, LA 70433-5005
Tel.: (985) 892-5521
Fax: (985) 892-1657
E-mail: investor.relations@scppool.com
Web Site: www.scppool.com
Approx. Sls.: $1,613,746,000
Approx. Number Employees: 3,200
Year Founded: 1980
Business Description:
Swimming Pool Supplies & Related Products Distr
S.I.C.: 5091
N.A.I.C.S.: 423910
Import Export
Advertising Expenditures: $4,990,000
Media: 13
Personnel:
Wilson B. Sexton *(Chm)*
Manuel Perez de la Mesa *(Pres & CEO)*
Mark W. Joslin *(CFO & VP)*
Melanie Housey *(Chief Acctg Officer & Controller)*
Craig K. Hubbard *(Officer-IR)*
Jennifer M. Neil *(Gen Counsel & Sec)*
A. David Cook *(Grp VP)*
Dominick Latino *(Dir-Mktg & Internet Strategies)*
Brands & Products:
COOL COVERS
E-Z CLOR
THE ELITE POOL
GARDEN
HELDOR
POOLCORP
PREMIUM POOLS
PRESTIGE
REGAL
REGATTA POOLS
SEABLUE
SIGNATURE POOLS
STERLING POOLS
ULTIMATE
WEATHERKING
WINDSOR

PRECOR, INC.
(Sub. of Amer Sports Corporation)
20031 142nd Ave NE
Woodinville, WA 98072-4002
Mailing Address:
PO Box 7202
Woodinville, WA 98072-4002
Tel.: (425) 486-9292
Fax: (425) 486-3856
Toll Free: (800) 786-8404
E-mail: customersupport@precor.com
Web Site: www.precor.com
E-Mail For Key Personnel:
Sales Director: commsls@precor.com
Approx. Number Employees: 400
Year Founded: 1986
Business Description:
Mfr of Exercise Equipment
S.I.C.: 3949
N.A.I.C.S.: 339920
Export
Media: 1-4-5-6-10-11-13-19-20-22-23-26
Distr.: Intl.; Natl.
Budget Set: Dec.
Personnel:
Paul Byrne *(Pres)*
Jim Birrell *(Chief Innovation Officer)*
Lynn Takaki *(VP-HR)*
Peggy Vo *(Sr Mgr-Mktg-Comml)*
Brands & Products:
EFX
PRECOR
Advertising Agency:
Hydrogen Advertising
1520 4th Ave Ste 600
Seattle, WA 98101
Tel.: (206) 389-9500
Fax: (206) 389-4849

PRINCE GOLF
1 Advantage Ct Ste G
Bordentown, NJ 08505
Tel.: (609) 291-5981
Fax: (609) 291-5986
Toll Free: (800) 99PRINCE
E-mail: info@princegolf.com
Web Site: www.princegolf.com
Approx. Number Employees: 5
Year Founded: 1988
Business Description:
Mfr. of Golf Clubs
S.I.C.: 3949
N.A.I.C.S.: 339920
Advertising Expenditures: $5,000,000
Media: 4-6-16-17-19
Distr.: Natl.
Personnel:
Chuck Stickelmaier *(Pres)*
Brands & Products:
FLATSTICK
PRINCE
THE SWEET SPOT COMPANY
THUNDERSTICK

PURE FISHING, INC.
(Sub. of The Coleman Company, Inc.)
1900 18th St
Spirit Lake, IA 51360-1041
Tel.: (712) 336-1520
Fax: (712) 336-5183
Toll Free: (877) 777-3850
E-mail: klridenour@purefishing.com
Web Site: www.purefishing.com
Sales Range: $250-299.9 Million
Approx. Number Employees: 1,400
Year Founded: 1937
Business Description:
Sporting & Athletic Goods Mfr
S.I.C.: 3949; 5941
N.A.I.C.S.: 339920; 451110
Import Export
Media: 1-2-3-4-5-6-7-8-10-13-19-21-23-24-26
Personnel:
Ron Kliegl *(Sr Dir-Mktg)*
Clay Norris *(Sr Mgr-Product)*
Brands & Products:
ABU GARCIA
ABU-MATIC
AMBASSADEUR
BERKLEY
CARDINAL
CHERRYWOOD
CROSS-LOK
FENWICK
FISH HAB
LIGHTNING ROD
MCMAHON
MITCHELL
NOT-A-KNOT
PURE FISHING
RED WOLF
SPIDER
SPIDERWIRE
STEELON
TRILENE
TRILENE BIG GAME
TRILENE XL
TRILENE XT
Advertising Agency:
Ahlquist & Co.
Drottningg 47
37436
Karlshamn, Sweden
Tel.: (46) 454 154 20
Fax: (46) 454 312 63

PURE FISHING, INC.
(Sub. of K2 Inc.)
7 Science Ct
Columbia, SC 29203
Tel.: (803) 754-7000
Fax: (803) 786-8902
Toll Free: (800) 334-9105
E-mail: shakespeare@purefishing.com
Web Site: www.shakespeare-fishing.com
E-Mail For Key Personnel:
President: scott@shakespeare-fishing.com
Sales Director: roxanne@shakespeare-fishing.com
Sales Range: $75-99.9 Million
Year Founded: 1897
Business Description:
Fishing Tackle & Antennas Mfr
S.I.C.: 3949; 3089
N.A.I.C.S.: 339920; 326199
Media: 2-3-6-7-10-13-15-19-23-24-26
Distr.: Intl.; Natl.
Budget Set: May
Personnel:
Chris VanDyke *(Sr VP-Supply Chain & Global Sourcing)*
Mike Rice *(Sr Product Mgr-PENN)*
Roxanne Coleman *(Mgr-Mktg)*
Brands & Products:
CAJUN LINE
SHAKESPEARE

QUBICAAMF
(Sub. of AMF Bowling Worldwide, Inc.)
8100 AMF Dr
Mechanicsville, VA 23111
Tel.: (804) 569-1000
Fax: (804) 559-8650
E-mail: info@qubicaamf.com
Web Site: www.qubicaamf.com
Approx. Number Employees: 15
Business Description:
Bowling Equipment & Supplies Mfr & Marketer
S.I.C.: 3949; 5941
N.A.I.C.S.: 339920; 451110
Media: 2-7-10-11-13-21
Personnel:
John Walker *(Pres & CEO)*
Stephanie Darby *(Mgr-Mktg Comm-Worldwide)*

RAPALA VMC CORPORATION
(Sub. of Rapala VMC Oyj)
10395 Yellow Cir Dr
Minnetonka, MN 55343-9101
Tel.: (952) 933-7060
Fax: (952) 933-0046
Approx. Number Employees: 60
Year Founded: 1959
Business Description:
Fishing Lures, Fillet Knives & Boards; Whetstones; Sporting & Recreation Goods Mfr
S.I.C.: 2051; 3949; 5091
N.A.I.C.S.: 311812; 339920; 423910
Import
Advertising Expenditures: $1,300,000
Media: 6-15-18-25
Distr.: Natl.
Brands & Products:
RAPALA

RAWLINGS SPORTING GOODS CO., INC.
(Sub. of K2 Inc.)
510 Maryville University Dr Ste 110
Saint Louis, MO 63141
Tel.: (314) 819-2800
Fax: (314) 819-2988
Fax: (636) 305-3310
Toll Free: (800) RAWLING
Web Site: www.rawlings.com

Key to Media (For complete agency information see *The Advertising Red Books-Agencies* edition):
1. Bus. Publs. 2. Cable T.V. 3. Catalogs & Directories. 4. Co-op Adv. 5. Consumer Mags. 6. D.M. to Bus. Estab.7. D.M. to Consumers
8. Daily Newsp. 9. Exhibits/Trade Shows 10. Foreign 11. Infomercial 12. Internet Adv.13. Multimedia 14. Network Radio
15. Network T.V. 16. Newsp. Distr. Mags. 17. Other 18. Outdoor (Posters, Transit) 19. Point of Purchase20. Premiums, Novelties
21. Product Samples 22. Special Events Mktg. 23. Spot Radio 24. Spot T.V. 25. Weekly Newsp. 26. Yellow Page Adv.

Rawlings Sporting Goods Co., Inc. — (Continued)

Approx. Rev.: $156,100,000
Approx. Number Employees: 1,500
Year Founded: 1886
Business Description:
Athletic Equipment, Apparel & Sporting Goods Mfr
S.I.C.: 3949; 2389
N.A.I.C.S.: 339920; 315299
Media: 5-6-9-15
Distr.: Intl.; Natl.
Budget Set: Aug.
Personnel:
Robert M. Parish *(Pres)*
Mark Malone *(Exec VP-Fin & Ops)*
Mark Barry *(Sr VP-Retail Sls)*
Mike Thompson *(Sr VP-Mktg)*
Rita Carel *(VP-HR)*
Jeff France *(Dir-Creative)*
Seth Elrod *(Brand Mgr)*
Lindsey Naber *(Brand Mgr)*
Brands & Products:
ADIRONDACK
FINEST IN THE FIELD
THE GOLD GLOVE AWARD
HEART OF THE HIDE
MARK OF A PRO
RAWLINGS
Advertising Agency:
Barkley
304 N Broadway
Saint Louis, MO 63102
Tel.: (314) 727-9500
Fax: (314) 727-0561
Toll Free: (800) 886-0561

RECREATIONAL EQUIPMENT, INC.

6750 S 228th St
Kent, WA 98032
Tel.: (253) 395-3780
Fax: (253) 395-5862
E-mail: contacts@rei.com
Web Site: www.rei.com
E-Mail For Key Personnel:
Sales Director: corporate-sales@rei.com
Sales Range: $900-999.9 Million
Approx. Number Employees: 8,000
Year Founded: 1938
Business Description:
Outdoor Gear Retailer & Mfr
S.I.C.: 5941; 5699
N.A.I.C.S.: 451110; 448190
Import Export
Advertising Expenditures: $800,000
Media: 5-6-8-11-13-14-16-23
Personnel:
Doug Walker *(Chm)*
Sally Jewell *(Pres & CEO)*
Catherine Walker *(Gen Counsel, Sec & Sr VP)*
Matthew L. Hyde *(Exec VP)*
Brian Unmacht *(Exec VP)*
Michelle Clements *(Sr VP-HR)*
Angela Owen *(Sr VP-Mdsg)*
Tim Spangler *(Sr VP-Retail)*
Tom Vogl *(Sr VP-Mktg)*
Bill Bauman *(VP-IT)*
Brad Brown *(VP-E-Commerce & Direct Sls)*
Sue Sallee *(VP-Acctg & Fin)*
Brands & Products:
REI
REI ADVENTURES
REI Coop
REI-OUTLET.COM
REI.COM
Advertising Agency:
BBDO Atlanta
3500 Lenox Rd NE Ste 1900
Atlanta, GA 30326-4232
Tel.: (404) 231-1700
Fax: (404) 841-1893

REEBOK-CCM HOCKEY, INC.

(Sub. of Reebok International Ltd.)
3400 Raymond Lasnier
Ville Saint Laurent, QC H4R 3L3, Canada
Tel.: (514) 461-8000
Fax: (514) 937-8276
Toll Free: (800) 636-5895
Web Site: www.ccmhockey.com
Sales Range: $200-249.9 Million
Approx. Number Employees: 1,376
Year Founded: 1899
Business Description:
Sporting Goods & Equipment Mfr
S.I.C.: 3949
N.A.I.C.S.: 339920
Import Export
Advertising Expenditures: $750,000
Media: 3-4-6-10-13-20-23
Distr.: Intl.; Natl.
Personnel:
Matt O'Toole *(Pres & CEO)*
Tony Pichirallo *(CFO & VP-Fin-Admin)*
Len Rhodes *(Sr VP & Gen Mgr)*
Marc Andre Charron *(Mgr-Mktg-Reebok)*
Brands & Products:
ADVANCED PROFORMANCE PROFILE STAINLESS
CCM
EXTERNO
F-I-T SYSTEM
H2O CONTROL
HEATON
INTEGRATED WEDGE
JOFA
KOHO
LACE BITE PROTECTOR
PANAMA PU2
POWERLINE
PRO TACKS
PROLITE
PROLITE 3
REFLEX-BAR
TITAN
VECTOR 100
VECTOR 110
X-RAY

REMINGTON ARMS COMPANY, INC.

(Sub. of FREEDOM GROUP, INC.)
870 Remington Dr
Madison, NC 27025-0700
Mailing Address:
PO Box 700
Madison, NC 27025-0700
Tel.: (336) 548-8700
Fax: (336) 548-7801
Toll Free: (800) 243-9700
E-mail: info@remington.com
Web Site: www.remington.com
Approx. Sls.: $591,100,000
Approx. Number Employees: 1,625
Year Founded: 1816
Business Description:
Sporting Firearms, Ammunition, Traps, Targets & Powder Metal Products Mfr
S.I.C.: 3484; 3482; 3489; 3949
N.A.I.C.S.: 332994; 332992; 332995; 339920
Import Export
Advertising Expenditures: $5,000,000
Media: 2-4-6-10-11-18-19-20-24
Distr.: Intl.; Natl.
Personnel:
Paul A. Miller *(Chm)*
Stephen P. Jackson, Jr. *(CFO, Treas & Sec)*
Jeffrey B. Constantin *(CIO)*
Igor Popov *(Chief Supply Chain Officer)*
E. Scott Blackwell *(Pres-Global Sls & Mktg)*
Theodore A. Torbeck *(CEO-Freedom Group Inc)*
John Trull *(VP-Product Mgt & Mktg)*
John Chisnall *(Dir-Mktg-Ammunition)*
Alfred Russo *(Dir-Mktg)*
Linda Powell *(Mgr-Media)*
Brands & Products:
BRITEBORE
BRUSHMASTER
CBEE22
COMPACT ALLOY
COPPER-LOKT
CORE-LOKT
CORE-LOKT ULTRA
DISINTEGRATOR
DUPLEX
EXPRESS
FIELDMASTER
FIREBALL
GRIT-EDGE
GUN CLUB
HEVI SHOT
IDEAL
INJECT ALLOY
KLEANBORE
LEAD-LOKT
M-27
MAGNATHIN
MARINE MAGNUM
NITRO 27
NITRO MAG
PEERLESS
POWER PISTON
PREMIER
RANGEMASTER
RATTLESNAKE
REM
REM-LITE
REM-TECH
REMCLOTH
REMINGTON
REMINGTON LAW INFORCEMENT
REMINGTON LEADLESS
REMINGTON SHOOTING SCHOOL
THE REMINGTON SPORTEMEN'S LIBRARY
SENDERO
SHUR SHOT
SLUGGER
SPEEDMASTER
STS
TARGETMASTER
THUNDERBOLT
ULTRA-MAG
VICTOR
VIPER
VORTEX
WINGMASTER
YELLOW JACKET
Advertising Agency:
Campbell-Ewald
30400 Van Dyke Ave
Warren, MI 48093-2368
Tel.: (586) 574-3400
Fax: (586) 575-9925
Agency of Record
Product Development
Social Media

REVOLUTION MFG.

1185 N 1200 W
Orem, UT 84057-2841
Mailing Address:
PO Box 1510
Orem, UT 84059-1510
Tel.: (801) 223-9500
Fax: (801) 223-9105
Fax: (801) 532-1991
Toll Free: (888) 542SNOW
E-mail: info@revolutionmfg.com
Web Site: www.rideharder.com/revolution_V2.html
Approx. Number Employees: 45
Year Founded: 1946
Business Description:
Snowboard & Ski Mfr
S.I.C.: 3949
N.A.I.C.S.: 339920
Advertising Expenditures: $200,000
Media: 2-6-8-9-11-25
Distr.: Natl.
Budget Set: Apr.
Personnel:
Brady Fox *(Gen Mgr)*
Brands & Products:
MILLER
MILLER SOFT

ROGER CLEVELAND GOLF COMPANY, INC.

(Sub. of SRI Sports Ltd.)
(d/b/a Cleveland Golf Company, Inc.)
5601 Skylab Rd
Huntington Beach, CA 92647
Mailing Address:
PO Box 6048
Cypress, CA 90630
Tel.: (714) 889-1300
Fax: (714) 889-5890
Toll Free: (800) 999-6263
E-mail: HumanResources@ClevelandGolf.com
Web Site: www.clevelandgolf.com
Approx. Number Employees: 350
Year Founded: 1979
Business Description:
Golfing Equipment & Apparel Mfr
S.I.C.: 3949
N.A.I.C.S.: 339920
Advertising Expenditures: $500,000
Consumer Mags.: $375,000; Other: $125,000
Personnel:
Greg Hopkins *(CEO)*
Bill Bird *(CFO)*
Stan Sopczyk *(COO)*
Stephen Gingrich *(VP-HR & Global Legal Enforcement)*
Randy Romberg *(VP-Mktg)*
Alessio Smith *(Dir-Online Mktg)*
Chris Beck *(Mgr-Brand & Srixon)*
Keith Patterson *(Mgr-Media & PR)*

Key to Media (For complete agency information see *The Advertising Red Books-Agencies* edition):
1. Bus. Publs. 2. Cable T.V. 3. Catalogs & Directories. 4. Co-op Adv. 5. Consumer Mags. 6. D.M. to Bus. Estab.7. D.M. to Consumers
8. Daily Newsp. 9. Exhibits/Trade Shows 10. Foreign 11. Infomercial 12. Internet Adv.13. Multimedia 14. Network Radio
15. Network T.V. 16. Newsp. Distr. Mags. 17. Other 18. Outdoor (Posters, Transit) 19. Point of Purchase20. Premiums, Novelties
21. Product Samples 22. Special Events Mktg. 23. Spot Radio 24. Spot T.V. 25. Weekly Newsp. 26. Yellow Page Adv.

Brands & Products:
HIBORE
NEVER COMPROMISE
STORMCORE

RON JON SURF SHOP OF FLORIDA INC.
3850 S Banana River Blvd
Cocoa Beach, FL 32931-3481
Tel.: (321) 799-8880
Fax: (321) 799-8882
Toll Free: (888) RJSURFS
E-mail: hr@ronjons.com
Web Site: www.ronjons.com
Approx. Sls.: $27,582,375
Approx. Number Employees: 500
Year Founded: 1961
Business Description:
Beach Apparel & Accessory Store
S.I.C.: 5699; 5941
N.A.I.C.S.: 448190; 451110
Import Export
Media: 3-4-6-8-9-10-18-20-22-23-24
Personnel:
Debbie Harvey *(Pres & CEO)*
Tom O'Keefe *(CFO & Exec VP)*
Brands & Products:
RON JON SURF SHOP
Advertising Agency:
GoConvergence
4545 36th St
Orlando, FL 32811
Tel.: (407) 235-3210
Fax: (407) 299-9907

SALOMON NORTH AMERICA, INC.
(Sub. of Amer Sports Corporation)
5055 N Greeley Ave
Portland, OR 97217-3524
Tel.: (971) 234-7001
Fax: (971) 234-7059
Toll Free: (877) 2-SALOMON
Web Site: www.amersports.com
Approx. Number Employees: 100
Business Description:
Ski & Golf Equipment Mfr
S.I.C.: 5091; 5139
N.A.I.C.S.: 423910; 424340
Media: 9-17
Personnel:
Jean-Marc Pambet *(Pres)*

SCHOOL-TECH, INC.
745 State Cir
Ann Arbor, MI 48106-1647
Tel.: (734) 761-5173
Fax: (734) 761-8711
Fax: (800) 654-4321
Toll Free: (800) 521-2832
E-mail: service@school-tech.com
Web Site: www.school-tech.com
Approx. Number Employees: 60
Year Founded: 1961
Business Description:
Mfr. & Importer of Institutional Athletic Equipment to Dealers
S.I.C.: 5091; 3949
N.A.I.C.S.: 423910; 339920
Import
Advertising Expenditures: $700,000
Media: 4-6-10-13-26
Distr.: Natl.
Personnel:
Don Canham *(CEO)*
Bill Mulka *(Gen Mgr-Sls-Olympia Pur)*
Brands & Products:
ADULT SUPER SPECS
AIR BLITZ
ARCADE BALL
AVENGER
BEAN BAG BALL
BRINE
CATCHBALL
CLASSIC
COBRA
COLORZ
COSOM
CRAZY LEGS
DOM SUPER-SAFE
DOUBLE SHOOTOUT
DURAHIDE
DURASKIN
FIT STRIP
FLOAT-R
FUN GRIPPER
GLASSCLOTH
GLASSFLEX
GYM-I-NEE
GYMNASTIK
HAND E BALM
HOLLYWOOD
HOPSACKERS
HOVA-BATOR
JUGGLEBEANBALLS
KWIK KIK
LO LO
LOOP FLAGZ
LOUISVILLE SLUGGER
MATT-KLEEN
MULTI-DOMES
NEXUS PIONEER
ODDBOUNDER
OHAUS
OLYMPIA
PHYSIOBALLS
PLAY SAFE & LEARN
POWERBACK
PRO SERIES
PROGRESSIVE
QUICK FEET
RACKET SPECS
RAINBOW BEGINNER
REAL PLAY
RHINO SKIN
ROUGHNECK
SAFE-T-HOLD
SCHOOL-TECH
SCHOOLMASTER SAFETY
SCHOOLMASTER SCIENCE
SLINGCHUTE
SOFT SPOKES
SPUD JUMPERS
SQUELLET
STICK-UMS
SUPER SPIKE
SUPLEX
TURBOPADDLE
ULTRA TONER
ULTRASOF
WOLVERINE SPORTS
XERCISE BANDS
XERTUBE
YOUTH SUPER SPECS

SHIELDS MANUFACTURING INC.
425 Fillmore Ave
Tonawanda, NY 14150-2512
Tel.: (716) 694-7100
Fax: (716) 694-8652
Toll Free: (800) 828-7669
E-mail: admin@shieldsports.com
Web Site: www.shieldsports.com
Approx. Number Employees: 30
Year Founded: 1945
Business Description:
Mouthguards & Hockey Equipment Mfr
S.I.C.: 3949
N.A.I.C.S.: 339920
Import Export
Media: 2-4-5-6-7-10-13-21
Distr.: Intl.; Natl.
Budget Set: Nov.
Personnel:
James Geraci *(Pres)*
David Berghash *(CEO)*
Brands & Products:
SHIELDS

SHIMANO AMERICAN CORPORATION
(Sub. of Shimano, Inc.)
1 Holland Dr
Irvine, CA 92618-2506
Tel.: (949) 951-5003
Fax: (949) 951-6212
Web Site: www.shimano.com
Approx. Number Employees: 150
Year Founded: 1965
Business Description:
Retailer of Bicycle Components & Fishing Tackle
S.I.C.: 5091
N.A.I.C.S.: 423910
Advertising Expenditures: $200,000
Media: 7-17
Personnel:
Dave Pfieffer *(Pres)*
Jim Lafrance *(CFO)*
David Lawrence *(Product Mgr)*

SIMMS FISHING PRODUCTS CORP.
101 Evergreen Dr
Bozeman, MT 59715-2400
Mailing Address:
PO Box 3645
Bozeman, MT 59772-3645
Tel.: (406) 585-3557
Fax: (406) 585-3562
E-mail: info@simmsfishing.com
Web Site: www.simmsfishing.com
Approx. Sls.: $11,000,000
Approx. Number Employees: 100
Year Founded: 1993
Business Description:
Fishing & Outdoor Supplies Mfr & Retailer
S.I.C.: 5091; 5136
N.A.I.C.S.: 423910; 424320
Media: 4
Distr.: Intl.; Natl.
Personnel:
K.C. Walsh *(Pres)*
Weston Fricke *(CFO)*
Diane Bristol *(Dir-Mktg & Mgmt)*
Andy Wunsch *(Dir-Sls)*
Brands & Products:
3XDRY
AQUASEAL
AQUASTEALTH
AQUIS
BACKSAVER
BLUEWATER
THE CHOICE OF PROFESSIONAL GUIDES WORLDWIDE
COOLMAX
DOBBY
DRY CREEK
EXSTREAM
FLATS SNEAKER
FREESTONE
G3 GUIDE
G4 PRO
G4Z
GRAVEL GUARDS
GUIDE
HEADWATERS
IN-VEST
POLARTEC
POWER DRY
POWER STRETCH
QUADRALAM
RIRI
RIVERSHED
RIVERTEK
ROGUE RIVER
SIMMS
SIMMS KEEN
SOLARMAX
SOUTH FORK
STORM
STREAMTREAD
SUNCLAVA
THERMAL PRO
THERMOLITE
VERTICAL MASTER
VIBRAM
WADERWICK
WINDSTOPPER
Advertising Agency:
Backbone Media LLC
65 N 4th St Ste 1
Carbondale, CO 81623
Tel.: (970) 963-4873
Fax: (303) 265-9854
Toll Free: (866) 963-4873
Pub Rels

SMITH & WESSON HOLDING CORPORATION
2100 Roosevelt Ave
Springfield, MA 01104
Tel.: (413) 781-8300
Fax: (413) 747-3317
Toll Free: (800) 331-0852
E-mail: qa@smith-wesson.com
Web Site: www.smith-wesson.com
Approx. Sls.: $392,300,000
Approx. Number Employees: 1,520
Year Founded: 1998
Business Description:
Small Arms, Law Enforcement Equipment & Sporting Goods Mfr
S.I.C.: 3484; 3482; 3489; 3949
N.A.I.C.S.: 332994; 332992; 332995; 339920
Advertising Expenditures: $15,443,000
Media: 2-3-4-8-10-13-16-18-20-22-23-24
Personnel:
Barry M. Monheit *(Chm)*
Michael F. Golden *(Vice Chm)*
P. James Debney *(Pres & CEO)*
Jeffrey D. Buchanan *(CFO, Treas & Exec VP)*
Ann B. Makkiya *(Corp Counsel, Sec & VP)*
Leland A. Nichols *(Sr VP-Sls, Mktg & Bus Dev)*
John R. Deneen *(VP-Fin-Firearm Div)*
Paul Pluff *(Dir-Mktg Svcs)*
Brands & Products:
CRIMSON TRACE
EMB
GRAB

Smith & Wesson Holding Corporation — (Continued)

HIVIZ
LADYSMITH
M & P
M&P45C
M&P9
MAGNUM
MODEL 10
MODEL 17 MASTERPIECE
MODEL 18 MASTERPIECE
MODEL 29 50TH ANNIVERSARY
MODEL 3 SCHOFIELD
MODEL 310 NIGHT GUARD
MODEL 317
MODEL 327 TRR8
MODEL 340PD
MODEL 357 NIGHT GUARD
MODEL 360PD
MODEL 3913TSW
MODEL 40 CENTENNIAL
MODEL 4003TSW
MODEL 4006TSW
MODEL 4013TSW
MODEL 42
MODEL 442
MODEL 442 SAF
MODEL 4513TSW
MODEL 4563TSW
MODEL 4566TSW
MODEL 460XVR
MODEL 58
MODEL 5903TSW
MODEL 5906TSW
MODEL 60
MODEL 60LS
MODEL 619
MODEL 620
MODEL 632 CARRY COMP PRO
MODEL 637
MODEL 638
MODEL 64
MODEL 640
MODEL 642
MODEL 642LS
MODEL 649
MODEL 67
MODEL 686 PLUS
MODEL 952 LONG SLIDE
MODEL CS45
MODEL CS9
MODEL SW1911
MODEL SW1911PD
ODDS
SAF-T-HAMMER
SAFETY, SECURITY, PROTECTION & SPORT
SMITH & WESSON
SW1911 .45ACP SUB COMPACT
SW1911 COMPACT ES
SW1911 PRO
TCA
VERSA VAULT
XMB

Advertising Agencies:
Berkshire Intermedia Group
PO Box 23
Simsbury, CT 06070-0014
Tel.: (860) 658-0012

Winstanley Partners
114 Main St
Lenox, MA 01240-2353
Tel.: (413) 637-9887
Fax: (413) 637-2045

SOLOFLEX, INC.
22590 NW Badertscher Rd
Hillsboro, OR 97124
Tel.: (503) 640-8891
Fax: (503) 640-1451
E-mail: customerservice@soloflex.com
Web Site: www.soloflex.com
Approx. Number Employees: 25
Business Description:
Mfr. of Weightlifting Machines
S.I.C.: 3949; 5961
N.A.I.C.S.: 339920; 454113
Media: 13
Personnel:
Jerry Wilson *(CEO)*
Brands & Products:
EXERCISE AND EAT RIGHT
THE ORIGINAL AND STILL THE BEST
SOLOFLEX

SPALDING
(Div. of Russell Corporation)
150 Brookdale Dr
Springfield, MA 01104
Tel.: (413) 735-1400
Fax: (413) 735-1571
Toll Free: (800) SPALDING
Telex: 955449
E-mail: consumerrelation@spalding.com
Web Site: www.spalding.com
Sales Range: $10-24.9 Million
Approx. Number Employees: 57
Year Founded: 1876
Business Description:
Basketballs, Footballs, Volleyballs, Soccer Balls & Other Inflatable Sports Related Products Mfr
S.I.C.: 3949
N.A.I.C.S.: 339920
Import Export
Media: 4-6-7-9-10-18-19-24-25
Distr.: Intl.; Natl.
Budget Set: Sept.
Personnel:
Dan Touhey *(VP-Mktg)*
Brands & Products:
DUDLEY
NEVERFLAT
Advertising Agency:
KSL Media, Inc.
367 Park Ave S 4th Fl
New York, NY 10016
Tel.: (212) 352-5800
Fax: (212) 352-5935
Media Buying

SPORT CHALET, INC.
1 Sports Chalet Dr
La Canada, CA 91011-3338
Tel.: (818) 949-5300
Fax: (818) 949-5301
E-mail: corporate@sportchalet.com
Web Site: www.sportchalet.com
Approx. Sls.: $362,483,000
Approx. Number Employees: 3,100
Year Founded: 1959
Business Description:
Full Service Sporting Goods Stores
S.I.C.: 5941; 5699
N.A.I.C.S.: 451110; 448190
Advertising Expenditures: $4,500,000
Media: 3-5-6-8-9-13-14-15-16-18-19-20-21-22-23-24-25-26
Distr.: Reg.
Budget Set: Feb.
Personnel:
Norbert Olberz *(Founder)*
Craig L. Levra *(Chm, Pres & CEO)*
Howard K. Kaminsky *(CFO, Sec & Exec VP-Fin)*
Ted Jackson *(CIO & VP-IT)*
Tom Tennyson *(Chief Mdsg Officer & Exec VP)*
Tim Anderson *(Exec VP-Retail Ops, Loss Prevention & Specialty Svcs)*
Dennis Trausch *(Exec VP-Growth & Dev)*
Brad Morton *(Sr VP-Sls)*
John Davidson *(Dir-Facilities & Construction)*
David Hacker *(Dir-Adv & Mktg)*
Brands & Products:
SPORT CHALET
Advertising Agency:
TM Advertising
1717 Main St Ste 2000
Dallas, TX 75201
Tel.: (972) 556-1100
Fax: (972) 830-2619
(Creative, Media Planning & Buying)

SPORT COURT INTERNATIONAL INC.
(Holding of The Riverside Company)
939 South 700 West
Salt Lake City, UT 84104
Tel.: (801) 972-0260
Fax: (801) 975-7752
Toll Free: (800) 421-8112
E-mail: info@sportcourt.com
Web Site: www.sportcourt.com
Approx. Rev.: $28,063,000
Approx. Number Employees: 120
Year Founded: 1974
Business Description:
Modular Athletic Flooring & Golf Surfaces
S.I.C.: 3081; 3949
N.A.I.C.S.: 326113; 339920
Media: 6-10
Personnel:
Ron Cerny *(Pres & CEO)*
Joel McCausland *(Dir-Sport Court Products)*
Advertising Agency:
Weber Shandwick-Chicago
676 N St Clair Ste 1000
Chicago, IL 60611
Tel.: (312) 988-2400
Fax: (312) 988-2363

SPORT OBERMEYER LTD.
115 ABC
Aspen, CO 81611
Tel.: (970) 925-5060
Fax: (970) 925-9203
E-mail: customerserv@obermeyer.com
Web Site: www.obermeyer.com
Approx. Number Employees: 40
Year Founded: 1947
Business Description:
Whslr of Ski Parkas, Sweaters, Suits & Accessories
S.I.C.: 5137; 5136
N.A.I.C.S.: 424330; 424320
Import
Advertising Expenditures: $500,000
Media: 5-6
Distr.: Natl.
Budget Set: June
Personnel:
Klaus Obermeyer *(Founder & CEO)*
Robert Yturri *(Sr VP-Product & Brand Mgmt)*
Biege Jones *(Dir-Internal Art & Mgr-Adv)*
Klaus Obermeyer, Jr. *(Dir-Creative)*
Brands & Products:
HYDROMESH
OBERMEYER
SKIWEAR FROM THE HEART OF MOUNTAINS
ULTRA GEAR
WINDBREAK

SPORT SUPPLY GROUP, INC.
(Sub. of Onex Corporation)
1901 Diplomat Dr
Dallas, TX 75234-8914
Tel.: (972) 484-9484
Fax: (972) 406-3467
E-mail: dallashr@sportsupplygroup.com
Web Site: www.sportsupplygroup.com
Approx. Sls.: $250,227,000
Approx. Number Employees: 760
Business Description:
Sporting Goods, Equipment, Team Uniforms, Physical Education, Recreational & Leisure Products Marketer & Distr
S.I.C.: 5091; 5961
N.A.I.C.S.: 423910; 454111; 454113
Advertising Expenditures: $7,200,000
Media: 5-7-8-13-20
Personnel:
Terrence M. Babilla *(Pres, COO & Gen Counsel)*
Adam Blumenfeld *(CEO)*
John Pitts *(CFO)*
Tevis Martin *(Exec VP)*
Brands & Products:
THE ATHLETIC CONNECTION
BRUTE FORCE
BSN
CHAMPION BARBELL
COLLEGIATE PACIFIC
FLAG-A-TAG
GAMECRAFT
GSC
PORT-A-PIT
PRO DOWN
SPORT SUPPLY GROUP

SPORTCRAFT, LTD.
313 Waterloo Vly Rd
Mount Olive, NJ 07828
Tel.: (973) 347-3800
Fax: (973) 347-5711
Toll Free: (800) 526-0244
E-mail: customerservice@sportcraft.com
Web Site: www.sportcraft.com
Approx. Sls.: $115,000,000
Approx. Number Employees: 125
Year Founded: 1926
Business Description:
Sports Equipment, Darts, Badminton, Table Tennis, Backyard Games & Table Games Marketer & Distr
S.I.C.: 3949; 5091
N.A.I.C.S.: 339920; 423910
Import Export
Media: 2-4-7-10-19-20-21-22
Distr.: Intl.; Natl.
Budget Set: Oct.
Personnel:
Brian Hart *(CFO & Exec VP)*

Key to Media (For complete agency information see *The Advertising Red Books-Agencies* edition):
1. Bus. Publs. 2. Cable T.V. 3. Catalogs & Directories. 4. Co-op Adv. 5. Consumer Mags. 6. D.M. to Bus. Estab.7. D.M. to Consumers 8. Daily Newsp. 9. Exhibits/Trade Shows 10. Foreign 11. Infomercial 12. Internet Adv.13. Multimedia 14. Network Radio 15. Network T.V. 16. Newsp. Distr. Mags. 17. Other 18. Outdoor (Posters, Transit) 19. Point of Purchase20. Premiums, Novelties 21. Product Samples 22. Special Events Mktg. 23. Spot Radio 24. Spot T.V. 25. Weekly Newsp. 26. Yellow Page Adv.

Brands & Products:
GAMELIFE
JENSPORT
KTSPORTS
LIVE TO PLAY. PLAY TO WIN
PHENOTECH
SPORTCRAFT
UNICORN

THE SPORTS AUTHORITY, INC.

(Holding of Leonard Green & Partners, L.P.)
1050 W Hampden Ave
Englewood, CO 80110
Tel.: (303) 200-5050
Fax: (303) 863-2240
E-mail: customersupport@thesportsauthority.com
Web Site: www.sportsauthority.com
Approx. Sls.: $2,509,330,000
Approx. Number Employees: 14,300
Year Founded: 1987
Business Description:
Sports Equipment, Fashion Activewear & Footwear Retailer
S.I.C.: 5941; 5699; 5999
N.A.I.C.S.: 451110; 448190; 453998
Advertising Expenditures: $113,000,000
Media: 3-5-6-8-9-13-18-19-22-23-24-26
Personnel:
David J. Campisi *(Chm, Pres & CEO)*
Darrell D. Webb *(Interim CEO)*
Thomas T. Hendrickson *(Chief Admin Officer, CFO, Treas & Exec VP)*
Greg A. Waters *(COO & Exec VP)*
Fred Argir *(CIO & Sr VP)*
Jeffrey Schumacher *(CMO, Chief Strategy Officer & Exec VP)*
Gwen Manto *(Exec VP)*
Simon MacGibbon *(Sr VP-Mktg)*
Lon Novatt *(Sr VP-Real Estate)*
Brands & Products:
GART SPORTS
OSHMAN'S SPORTING GOODS
SPORTMART
SPORTS AUTHORITY
Advertising Agencies:
deutschMedia
111 8th Ave 14th Fl
New York, NY 10011-5201
Tel.: (212) 981-7600
Fax: (212) 981-7525
(Media Buying/Planning; New Store Openings Public Relations)

JWT U.S.A., Inc.
(d/b/a JWT-Team Detroit)
550 Town Ctr Dr
Dearborn, MI 48126
Tel.: (313) 615-3100
Tel.: (313) 615-2000 (Team Detroit)
Fax: (313) 964-3191
Fax: (212) 615-4600
Agency of Record-Brand Experience & Consumer Communications

Mindshare Team Detroit
500 Town Ctr Dr 2nd Fl
Dearborn, MI 48126
Tel.: (313) 615-2900
Fax: (313) 964-3159
Agency of Record-Brand Experience & Consumer Communications

Newspaper Services of America, Inc.
3025 Highland Pkwy Ste 700
Downers Grove, IL 60515-5506
Tel.: (630) 729-7500
Fax: (630) 241-7223

Ogilvy Team Detroit
550 Town Center Dr
Dearborn, MI 48126
Tel.: (313) 615-3300
Fax: (313) 615-2000
Agency of Record-Brand Experience & Consumer Communications

TEAM/Y&R Detroit
550 Town Ctr Dr Ste 300
Dearborn, MI 48126-2750
Tel.: (313) 615-2000
Fax: (313) 583-8001
Toll Free: (800) 521-8038
Agency of Record-Brand Experience & Consumer Communications

Wunderman Team Detroit
Corp Crossing at Fairlane 550 Town Ctr Dr Ste 300
Dearborn, MI 48126
Tel.: (313) 615-3400
Fax: (313) 615-5054
Toll Free: (800) 521-8038
Agency of Record-Brand Experience & Consumer Communications

THE SPORTSMAN'S GUIDE, INC.

(Sub. of Redcats USA, Inc.)
411 Farwell Ave
South Saint Paul, MN 55075
Tel.: (651) 451-3030
Fax: (651) 450-6130
Toll Free: (800) 888-5222
Toll Free: (888) 844-0667
E-mail: custserv@sportsmansguide.com
Web Site: www.sportsmansguide.com
Approx. Number Employees: 754
Year Founded: 1976
Business Description:
Outdoor Gear, General Merchandise & Golf Equipment/Accessories Direct Marketer & Retailer
S.I.C.: 5961
N.A.I.C.S.: 454113
Import
Advertising Expenditures: $39,000,000
Media: 4-8-13-17-19
Distr.: Natl.
Personnel:
Dale D. Monson *(CIO & Sr VP-Ops & Distr)*
Tim Arland *(Sr VP-e-Commerce)*
Douglas E. Johnson *(Sr VP-Mktg)*
Matt Sullivan *(VP-Mktg)*
Brands & Products:
THE FUN TO BROWSE WEBSITE
THE FUN TO READ CATALOG
THE SPORTSMAN'S GUIDE
SPORTSMAN'S GUIDE

STEARNS INC.

(Sub. of Jarden Outdoor Solutions)
1100 Stearns Dr
Sauk Rapids, MN 56379
Mailing Address:
PO Box 1498
Saint Cloud, MN 56302
Tel.: (320) 252-1642
Fax: (320) 252-4425
Toll Free: (800) 328-3208
E-mail: stearns@stearnsnet.com
Web Site: www.stearnsinc.com
Sales Range: $75-99.9 Million
Approx. Number Employees: 400
Year Founded: 1941
Business Description:
Sporting Goods, Personal Flotation Devices & Drywear Mfr
S.I.C.: 3069; 3842
N.A.I.C.S.: 326299; 339113
Media: 6-8-10-13
Distr.: Intl.; Natl.
Budget Set: June
Personnel:
Paul Ebnet *(Pres)*
Michael Krmpotich *(CFO & VP-Fin)*
Brands & Products:
MAD DOG YEAR
STEARN OUTDOORS
STEARNS

STRATEGY PLUS INC.

14 Bear Swamp Rd
East Hampton, CT 06424
Mailing Address:
17 Ledgeland Dr
Mystic, CT 06355
Tel.: (860) 536-0645
Toll Free: (800) 952-9007
Web Site: www.strategyplus.com
Approx. Number Employees: 6
Business Description:
Paintball Games Planning
S.I.C.: 5941
N.A.I.C.S.: 451110
Media: 9-13-25
Personnel:
Jim Iulo *(Pres)*
Brands & Products:
A GREAT NEW GAME FOR THE GREAT OUTDOORS
STRATEGY PLUS

STUART SPORTS SPECIALTIES, INC.

34 Front St
Indian Orchard, MA 01151
Mailing Address:
PO Box 51013
Indian Orchard, MA 01151
Tel.: (413) 543-1524
Fax: (413) 543-3153
E-mail: goldfish@javanet.com
Web Site: www.alsgoldfish.com
Sales Range: Less than $1 Million
Approx. Number Employees: 5
Year Founded: 1954
Business Description:
Mfr. of Fishing Lures
S.I.C.: 3949
N.A.I.C.S.: 339920
Media: 2-4-6-10-13-20
Distr.: Natl.
Budget Set: Nov.
Personnel:
John Occhialini *(Pres)*

STURM, RUGER & COMPANY, INC.

1 Lacey Pl
Southport, CT 06890
Tel.: (203) 259-7843
Fax: (203) 256-3367
Web Site: www.ruger.com
Approx. Sls.: $255,206,000
Approx. Number Employees: 1,160
Year Founded: 1949
Business Description:
Pistols, Revolvers, Shotguns & Rifles Mfr & Sales; Golf Equipment
S.I.C.: 3484; 3482; 3489
N.A.I.C.S.: 332994; 332992; 332995
Export
Advertising Expenditures: $2,300,000
Media: 2-4-6-8-10-11-18-22
Distr.: Intl.; Natl.
Budget Set: Oct. -Nov.
Personnel:
C. Michael Jacobi *(Chm)*
John A. Cosentino, Jr. *(Vice Chm)*
Michael O. Fifer *(Pres & CEO)*
Thomas A. Dineen *(CFO, Treas & Principal Fin Officer)*
Kevin B. Reid, Sr. *(Gen Counsel & VP)*
Mark T. Lang *(Grp VP)*
Christopher J. Killoy *(VP-Sls & Mktg)*
Brands & Products:
10/22
22/45
22 CHARGER
22-OCT
77/22
77/44
77/50
ALL-WEATHER
ARM MAKERS FOR RESPONSIBLE CITIZENS
BEARCAT
BISLEY
BISLEY VAQUERO
BLACKHAWK
GOLD LABEL
GP100
HAWKEYE
LCP
LCR
M77
MARK
MARK II STANDARD
MARK II TARGET
MARK III
MINI-14
MINI THIRTY
NEW BEARCAT
NEW MODEL BLACKHAWK
NEW MODEL SUPER BLACKHAWK
NEW VACQERO
NO. 1
OLD ARMY
P-SERIES
RED LABEL
REDHAWK
RUGER
RUGER CARBINE RIFLE PC4
RUGER CARBINE RIFLE PC9
RUGER MARK III
RUGER MODEL 96
RUGER SR-556
SINGLE SIX
SP101
SR9
STURM, RUGER
SUPER BEARCAT
SUPER REDHAWK
TARGET GREY
VAQUERO
WOODSIDE

SUPERCOACH INTERNATIONAL, INC.

422 Ives Ter
Sunnyvale, CA 94087
Tel.: (408) 660-1173

Key to Media (For complete agency information see *The Advertising Red Books-Agencies* edition):
1. Bus. Publs. 2. Cable T.V. 3. Catalogs & Directories. 4. Co-op Adv. 5. Consumer Mags. 6. D.M. to Bus. Estab.7. D.M. to Consumers
8. Daily Newsp. 9. Exhibits/Trade Shows 10. Foreign 11. Infomercial 12. Internet Adv.13. Multimedia 14. Network Radio
15. Network T.V. 16. Newsp. Distr. Mags. 17. Other 18. Outdoor (Posters, Transit) 19. Point of Purchase20. Premiums, Novelties
21. Product Samples 22. Special Events Mktg. 23. Spot Radio 24. Spot T.V. 25. Weekly Newsp. 26. Yellow Page Adv.

SuperCoach International, Inc. — (Continued)

E-mail: info@tennismachine.com
Web Site: www.tennismachine.com
Approx. Number Employees: 4
Year Founded: 1995
Business Description:
Computer Controlled Tennis Machines Researcher, Developer & Marketer
S.I.C.: 3949
N.A.I.C.S.: 339920
Media: 6
Personnel:
Gabor Kardos *(Pres)*

TARPON TOTAL FITNESS

1888 Alt 19 S
Tarpon Springs, FL 34689
Tel.: (727) 938-8551
E-mail: joel@tarpontotalfitness.com
Web Site: www.tarpontotalfitness.com
Business Description:
Fitness Club
S.I.C.: 7991
N.A.I.C.S.: 713940
Media: 13-22
Personnel:
Celia Dubey *(Owner)*
Joel Dubey *(Owner)*
Richard Ilnicki *(Gen Mgr)*

TAYLORMADE-ADIDAS GOLF

(Sub. of Taylor Made Golf Co. Inc.)
5545 Fermi Ct
Carlsbad, CA 92008-7324
Tel.: (760) 918-6000
Fax: (760) 918-6014
E-mail: info@taylormadegolf.com
Web Site: www.taylormadegolf.com
Approx. Sls.: $1,200,000,000
Approx. Number Employees: 1,195
Year Founded: 1979
Business Description:
Golf Equipment Mfr
S.I.C.: 3949
N.A.I.C.S.: 339920
Personnel:
Mark King *(Pres & CEO)*
Klauf Flock *(CFO)*
David Abeles *(Sr VP & Gen Mgr)*
Blake McHenry *(Sr VP-Global HR)*
Pete Sanchez *(Sr VP-HR-Global)*
Joe Walsh *(Sr VP-HR-Global)*
Advertising Agency:
NYCA
1010 S Coast Hwy Ste 101
Encinitas, CA 92024
Tel.: (760) 436-7033
Fax: (760) 436-7047

TREK BICYCLE CORPORATION

801 W Madison St
Waterloo, WI 53594-1379
Tel.: (920) 478-2191
Fax: (920) 478-2774
E-mail: consumer_help@trekbikes.com
Web Site: www.trekbikes.com
Approx. Sls.: $550,000,000
Approx. Number Employees: 1,500
Year Founded: 1976
Business Description:
Bicycles Mfr
S.I.C.: 3751; 5091
N.A.I.C.S.: 336991; 423910
Media: 2-5-6-8-10-13-18-19-20-22
Personnel:
John Burke *(Pres)*
Joe Siefkes *(CFO)*
Krista Rettig *(Brand Mgr)*
Michael Browne *(Brand Mgr-Mountain Bike)*
Leslie Prevish *(Brand Mgr-Women)*
Scott Daubert *(Mgr)*
Brands & Products:
BONNIE
BONTRAGER
CALYPSO
CLYDE
CRUISELINER
CRUISER CLASSIC
DASH
DASH PRO
DELUXE DOODLEBUG
DISTRICT
DOODLEBUG
DRIFT
ELITE
EQUINOX
EQUINOX TTX
FUEL
FUEL EX
GARY FISHER
GOBUG
GROMMET
JACK
JET
KDR
KLEIN
LEMOND
LIME
LITTLEBUG
MADONE
MT. TRACK
MT. TRAIN
MYSTIC
NAVIGATOR
PILOT
POLICE BIKE
PORTLAND
PURE
REMEDY
SESSION
SOHO
SOLE RIDE 100
SPORT GOBUG
SUPER DOODLEBUG
SURFER GIRL
TANDEM
TEAM TIME TRAIL
TOP FUEL
TRACK
TRAILSTER WAGON
TREK
TRIKESTER
TTX
VALENCIA
WASABI
Advertising Agency:
Hanson Dodge Inc.
220 E Buffalo St
Milwaukee, WI 53202
Tel.: (414) 347-1266
Fax: (414) 347-0493
— Sally Siegel *(Acct Supvr)*

TRELLEBORG VIKING INC.

(Sub. of Trelleborg Protective Products AB)
170 W Rd Ste 1
Portsmouth, NH 03801-5663
Tel.: (603) 436-1236
Fax: (603) 436-1392
Toll Free: (800) 344-4458
E-mail: tvi.usa@trelleborg.com
Web Site: www.trelleborg.com
Approx. Number Employees: 7
Business Description:
Diving Equipment, Protective Clothing & Products Distr
S.I.C.: 5091; 5136
N.A.I.C.S.: 423910; 424320
Media: 2-7-8-10
Brands & Products:
TRELLECEM
VIKING

TRUE FITNESS TECHNOLOGY INC.

865 Hoff Rd
O Fallon, MO 63366-1900
Tel.: (636) 272-7100
Fax: (636) 272-7148
Toll Free: (800) 426-6570
E-mail: info@truefitness.com
Web Site: www.truefitness.com
Approx. Number Employees: 75
Year Founded: 1981
Business Description:
Commercial & Consumer Treadmills & Fitness Equipment Mfr
S.I.C.: 3949; 3842
N.A.I.C.S.: 339920; 339113
Media: 2-9-13-25
Distr.: Natl.
Personnel:
Frank Trulaske *(Founder & CEO)*
Brands & Products:
CORE DRIVE
CS
CSX
ES
HEART RATE CONTROL
PS
TRUE
TRUESTRETCH
Z

TRUE TEMPER SPORTS, INC.

(Filed Ch 11 Bankruptcy #913448 on 10/08/09 in U.S. Bankruptcy Ct, Dist of DE, Wilmington)
8275 Tournament Dr Ste 200
Memphis, TN 38125-8871
Tel.: (901) 746-2000
Fax: (901) 746-2160
Web Site: www.truetemper.com
Sales Range: $100-124.9 Million
Approx. Number Employees: 692
Business Description:
Golf Shafts & Bicycle Parts Mfr
S.I.C.: 3949
N.A.I.C.S.: 339920
Advertising Expenditures: $3,191,000
Media: 2-4-5-7-10-19-22-24
Personnel:
Scott C. Hennessy *(Pres & CEO)*
Jason A. Jenne *(CFO, Treas & VP)*
Adrian H. McCall *(Sr VP-Global Mktg & Product Dev)*
Stephen M. Brown *(VP-HR)*
Graeme Horwood *(VP-Engrg, R & D)*
Raeford P. Lucas *(VP-Global Sls & Mktg)*
Brands & Products:
BLACK GOLD
CUSTOM LITE
DYNALITE
DYNAMIC
GRIP TO TIP
PRECISION
RELEASE
RIFLE
SENSICORE
SHAFTFIT
SHAFTLAB
TRUE TEMPER
TT LITE XL

UNCLE JOSH BAIT COMPANY

525 Jefferson St
Fort Atkinson, WI 53538-1824
Tel.: (920) 563-2491
Fax: (920) 563-8622
Toll Free: (866) 244-2277
E-mail: sales@unclejosh.com
Web Site: www.unclejosh.com
E-Mail For Key Personnel:
Sales Director: sales@unclejosh.com
Approx. Number Employees: 20
Year Founded: 1922
Business Description:
Produces Fresh & Salt Water Pork Rind Baits; Scent Baits for Catfish, Carp & Trout; Salmon Eggs, Lures, Preserved Natural Baits, Camp Stoves & Soft Plastic Lures
S.I.C.: 2013
N.A.I.C.S.: 311613
Export
Media: 3-4-5-6-10-13-19-20-21-22-24
Distr.: Intl.; Natl.
Budget Set: May -June
Personnel:
Kurt Kellogg *(Pres)*
Brands & Products:
BAD BOY
BAD BOY JR.
BERGIE
BIG DADDY FROG
BUMP'N RUN
BURMEK
CRAWFROG
HANK PARKER'S PRO CUT FROG
INCREDIBLE
IT'S BACK
JUMBO FROG
KICKER FROG
LITTLE STINKER
MAXX PORK
MR. CATFISH
NATURA
PAK'R PORK
PHANTOM CRAW
PHANTOM FINESSE CRAW
PORK FROG
RIPPLE RIND
SALT BRINE SOLUTION REFILL
SIZMIC LURES
SPINNING FROG
TUBE N WORM
UNCLE JOSH

VARIFLEX INC.

(Sub. of Bravo Sports Corporation)
12801 Carmenita Rd
Santa Fe Springs, CA 90605
Tel.: (562) 484-5100
Fax: (562) 484-5183
Toll Free: (800) 327-0821
Web Site: www.bravosportscorp.com
Approx. Number Employees: 91
Year Founded: 1977
Business Description:
Inline Skates, Skateboards, Recreational Safety Helmets, Athletic Protective Equipment, Snowboards,

Key to Media (For complete agency information see *The Advertising Red Books-Agencies* edition):
1. Bus. Publs. 2. Cable T.V. 3. Catalogs & Directories. 4. Co-op Adv. 5. Consumer Mags. 6. D.M. to Bus. Estab.7. D.M. to Consumers 8. Daily Newsp. 9. Exhibits/Trade Shows 10. Foreign 11. Infomercial 12. Internet Adv.13. Multimedia 14. Network Radio 15. Network T.V. 16. Newsp. Distr. Mags. 17. Other 18. Outdoor (Posters, Transit) 19. Point of Purchase20. Premiums, Novelties 21. Product Samples 22. Special Events Mktg. 23. Spot Radio 24. Spot T.V. 25. Weekly Newsp. 26. Yellow Page Adv.

Portable Instant Canopies & Springless Trampolines Distr
S.I.C.: 5091
N.A.I.C.S.: 423910
Advertising Expenditures: $888,000
Media: 10
Personnel:
Joe Chichelo *(VP-Sls)*
Brands & Products:
AIRZONE
CYCLEFORCE
MOTOSHADE
MOTOSHED
QUIK SHADE
ROCKET POWER
STATIC
ULTRAFLEX
VARIFLEX
VFX

VARSITY BRANDS, INC.
(Joint Venture of Leonard Green & Partners, L.P. & Wingate Partners, L.P.)
6745 Lenox Ctr Ct Ste 300
Memphis, TN 38115
Tel.: (901) 387-4300
Fax: (901) 387-4337
Toll Free: (800) 792-4337
Web Site: www.varsity.com
Sales Range: $150-199.9 Million
Approx. Number Employees: 200
Year Founded: 1929
Business Description:
Cheerleading, Dance Apparel & Accessories Designer & Marketer; Cheerleading & Dance Camps Organizer
S.I.C.: 2339; 3949; 7032
N.A.I.C.S.: 315239; 339920; 721214
Media: 2-4-6-7-8-10-13-18-19-21-22
Distr.: Intl.; Natl.
Budget Set: Aug.
Personnel:
Jeffrey G. Webb *(CEO)*
John M. Nichols *(CFO)*
Nicole Lauchaire *(VP-Corp Mktg & Comm)*

VICTORINOX
(Div. of Swiss Army Brands, Inc.)
7 Victoria Dr
Monroe, CT 06468
Tel.: (203) 929-6391
Fax: (203) 929-3786
Web Site: www.swissarmy.com
Approx. Number Employees: 230
Business Description:
Marketing & Sales of Knives, Compasses & Sunglasses
S.I.C.: 5072
N.A.I.C.S.: 423710
Personnel:
Marc Gold *(Sr VP-Fin)*
Kristin DiCunzolo *(VP Mktg & Comm)*
Brands & Products:
SWISS ARMY
VICTORINOX
Advertising Agency:
WHITTMANHART
150 North Michigan Ave Ste 300
Chicago, IL 60601
Tel.: (312) 981-6000
Fax: (312) 981-6100
Interactive Advertising

VOLCOM, INC.
1740 Monrovia Ave
Costa Mesa, CA 92627
Tel.: (949) 646-2175
Fax: (949) 646-5247
Web Site: www.volcom.com
Approx. Rev.: $323,181,000
Approx. Number Employees: 543
Year Founded: 1991
Business Description:
Outdoor Gear & Apparel Designer, Marketer & Distr
S.I.C.: 2389; 2211; 2329; 3949; 5941
N.A.I.C.S.: 315999; 313210; 315228; 339920; 451110
Advertising Expenditures: $26,800,000
Media: 1-5-6-8-19-22
Personnel:
Richard R. Woolcott *(Chm)*
Jason W. Steris *(Pres & COO)*
Douglas P. Collier *(CFO, Treas & Sec)*
Tom D. Ruiz *(Exec VP-Sls)*
Ryan Immegarg *(Dir-Mktg)*
Advertising Agency:
PondelWilkinson Inc.
1880 Century Park E Ste 350
Los Angeles, CA 90067
Tel.: (310) 279-5980
Fax: (310) 279-5988

WEATHERBY, INC.
1605 Commerce Way
Paso Robles, CA 93446
Tel.: (805) 227-2600
Fax: (805) 237-0427
Toll Free: (800) 334-4423
Web Site: www.weatherby.com
Approx. Number Employees: 35
Year Founded: 1945
Business Description:
Mfr. of Rifles, Shotguns, Scopes & Ammunition
S.I.C.: 3484; 5091
N.A.I.C.S.: 332994; 423910
Import Export
Advertising Expenditures: $200,000
Media: 4-6-8
Distr.: Direct to Dealer; Intl.; Natl.
Budget Set: Dec.
Personnel:
Roy E. Weatherby, Jr. *(Pres)*
Bruce Dixon *(CFO & Exec VP)*
Brad Ruddell *(VP-Sls & Mktg)*
Brands & Products:
ACCUMARK
ATHENA
ATHENA IV
ATHENA SIDE BY SIDE
ATHENA V
FIBERMARK
LAZERMARK
MARK V
MARK V SYNTHETIC
MARK XXII
ORION
ORION I
ORION II
ORION III
SAS SPORTING CLAYS
SPORTER
STAINLESS
SUPER VARMINTMASTER
ULTRA LIGHTWEIGHT
VANGUARD
VANGUARD BACK COUNTRY
VANGUARD DELUXE
VANGUARD PREDATOR
VANGUARD SAGE COUNTRY
WEATHERBY
Advertising Agency:
Swanson Russell Associates
1222 P St
Lincoln, NE 68508-1425
Tel.: (402) 437-6400
Fax: (402) 437-6401
(Orion, Orion I, Orion II, Orion III, Athena V, Athena IV, Synthetic Mark V, Deluxe, Lazermark, Euromark, Sporter, Eurosport, Stainless)

WEST END DIVING & SALVAGE, INC.
12464 Natural Bridge Rd
Bridgeton, MO 63044
Tel.: (314) 731-5003
Tel.: (314) 209-7200
Fax: (314) 895-3160
Fax: (314) 291-1938
Toll Free: (888) 843-3483
E-mail: info@westenddiving.com
Web Site: www.westenddiving.com
Sales Range: $50-74.9 Million
Approx. Number Employees: 43
Year Founded: 1960
Business Description:
Scuba Equipment, Sales & Instruction; Resort Operator; Salvage Operations
S.I.C.: 5091
N.A.I.C.S.: 423910
Media: 1-5-6-8-9-18-20-22-26
Distr.: Direct to Consumer; Natl.
Budget Set: Mar.
Personnel:
Douglas Goergens *(Pres, CEO, CFO, CIO & Dir-Mktg)*
Catherine Goergens *(Treas, Exec VP & Dir-Promos)*
Brands & Products:
BONNETERRE MINES
MAYA PALMS
Advertising Agency:
West End Advertising
12464 Natural Bridge Rd
Bridgeton, MO 63044
Tel.: (314) 209-7200
Fax: (314) 291-1938
(Resorts, Restaurants, Retail Stores & Construction)

THE WIFFLE BALL INC.
275 Bridgeport Ave
Shelton, CT 06484
Tel.: (203) 924-4643
Fax: (203) 924-9433
Web Site: www.wiffle.com
Approx. Number Employees: 15
Year Founded: 1954
Business Description:
Plastic Balls & Bats Mfr & Distr
S.I.C.: 3949; 3082; 3084; 3089; 3751; 3944
N.A.I.C.S.: 339920; 326121; 326122; 326199; 336991; 339932
Media: 4
Personnel:
David J. Mullany *(Pres)*
Brands & Products:
WIFFLE

WILLIAMS GUN SIGHT COMPANY, INC.
7389 Lapeer Rd
Davison, MI 48423-2533
Tel.: (810) 653-2131
Fax: (810) 658-2140
Web Site: www.williamsgunsight.com
Approx. Number Employees: 51
Year Founded: 1926
Business Description:
Gun Sights & Accessories; Gun Cleaning Equipment, Scope Mounts
S.I.C.: 3827; 5941
N.A.I.C.S.: 333314; 451110
Media: 4-6-7-8-9-10-18-23-24
Distr.: Intl.; Natl.
Personnel:
Thomas Wright *(Pres)*
Dan Compeau *(COO)*
Brands & Products:
5D
FIRESIGHTS
FP
GUIDE
Q.C.
S-O-S
SHORTY
SIGHT-THRU
STREAMLINE
TWILIGHT
WGOS
WGRS
WHITE CENTER
WILLIAMS
WILLIAMS BEAD
WILLIAMS GUIDE LINE
WILLIAMS SWIVELS
Advertising Agency:
Canadian American Group
G 5115 Miller Rd.
Flint, MI 48507
Tel.: (810) 733-1400
(Firearm Accessories)

WILSON SPORTING GOODS CO.
(Sub. of Amer Sports Corporation)
8750 W Bryn Mawr Ave
Chicago, IL 60631
Tel.: (773) 714-6400
Fax: (773) 714-4565
Web Site: www.wilson.com
Approx. Number Employees: 300
Year Founded: 1914
Business Description:
Sporting & Athletic Goods
S.I.C.: 3949; 5091
N.A.I.C.S.: 339920; 423910
Import Export
Advertising Expenditures: $5,000,000
Media: 2-3-4-5-6-8-11-13-14-15-17-18-19-23-24
Distr.: Intl.; Natl.
Budget Set: Oct.
Personnel:
Chris Considine *(Pres-Team Sports)*
Steve Millea *(Pres-Golf & Racquet Sports)*
Tom Gruger *(VP-Mktg)*
Tim Clarke *(Gen Mgr-Wilson Golf)*
Molly Wallace *(Dir-Comm)*
Brands & Products:
F2 YOUTH
WILSON
Advertising Agency:
KemperLesnik
500 Skokie Blvd 4th Fl
Northbrook, IL 60062
Tel.: (847) 850-1818
Fax: (847) 559-0406
Wilson Golf

Key to Media (For complete agency information see *The Advertising Red Books-Agencies* edition):
1. Bus. Publs. 2. Cable T.V. 3. Catalogs & Directories. 4. Co-op Adv. 5. Consumer Mags. 6. D.M. to Bus. Estab.7. D.M. to Consumers
8. Daily Newsp. 9. Exhibits/Trade Shows 10. Foreign 11. Infomercial 12. Internet Adv.13. Multimedia 14. Network Radio
15. Network T.V. 16. Newsp. Distr. Mags. 17. Other 18. Outdoor (Posters, Transit) 19. Point of Purchase20. Premiums, Novelties
21. Product Samples 22. Special Events Mktg. 23. Spot Radio 24. Spot T.V. 25. Weekly Newsp. 26. Yellow Page Adv.

THE WORTH COMPANY
214 Sherman Ave
Stevens Point, WI 54481-5847
Tel.: (715) 344-6081
Fax: (715) 344-3021
Fax: (800) 374-3021
E-mail: sales@worthco.com
Web Site: www.worthco.com
E-Mail For Key Personnel:
Sales Director: sales@worthco.com
Approx. Number Employees: 80
Year Founded: 1942
Business Description:
Mfr. of Fishing Tackle & Leisure Time Products
S.I.C.: 3949
N.A.I.C.S.: 339920
Export
Media: 2-6-7-9-10
Distr.: Intl.; Natl.
Budget Set: Dec.
Personnel:
David Worth *(Pres & CEO)*
Robert K. Mayer *(VP-Fin)*
Denny Rosenthal *(Dir-Intl Sls & Customer Svc)*
Brands & Products:
ANCHORMATE
ANCHORMATE II
ANCHORMATE ST
MOORMATE
MOORMATE 19001
WORTH

WORTH INC.
(Sub. of K2 Inc.)
510 Maryville University Dr Ste 110
Saint Louis, MO 63141
Tel.: (314) 819-2800
Fax: (314) 819-2990
Toll Free: (800) 423-3714
E-mail: customerservice@worthsports.com
Web Site: www.worthsports.com
Sales Range: $50-74.9 Million
Approx. Number Employees: 190
Year Founded: 1912
Business Description:
Baseball & Sports Equipment Mfr
S.I.C.: 3949; 3111
N.A.I.C.S.: 339920; 316110
Media: 4-5-6-10-19
Distr.: Natl.
Personnel:
Kurt Hunzaker *(VP-Mktg)*
Tim Lord *(Sr Dir-Bus)*
Brands & Products:
3DX
BLUE DOT
EST
GREEN DOT
K-MASTER
RED DOT
RIF
SUPER DOT
SUPERCELL 2
THUMPER
U-TOTE
WORTH
WORTH COPPERHEAD
Advertising Agency:
Schawk Retail Marketing
1 N Dearborn Ste 700
Chicago, IL 60602
Tel.: (312) 666-9200
Fax: (312) 260-1970
Toll Free: (888) AMBROSI

WRIGHT & MCGILL CO.
4245 E 46th Ave
Denver, CO 80216
Tel.: (303) 321-1481
Fax: (303) 321-4750
E-mail: info@eagleclaw.com
Web Site: www.eagleclaw.com
E-Mail For Key Personnel:
President: jjilling@eagleclaw.com
Sales Director: mjackson@eagleclaw.com
Approx. Number Employees: 275
Year Founded: 1925
Business Description:
Fishhooks Mfr; Supplier of Rods, Reels, Terminal Tackle; Baits & Scents Mfr
S.I.C.: 3949
N.A.I.C.S.: 339920
Import Export
Media: 2-3-4-5-6-8-9-10-12-13-14-15-16-18-19-21-23-24-25-26
Distr.: Intl.; Natl.
Budget Set: July
Personnel:
Lee McGill *(Chm)*
John Jilling *(Pres)*
Don Schaible *(CFO)*
Tenny Mount *(Sr VP-Mktg)*
Joe Bartell *(VP-Engrg)*
Mike Jackson *(VP-Sls)*
Cory Steele *(Controller)*
Chris Russell *(Marketing Director)*
Matt Gray *(Product Mgr)*
Wandee Kirkland *(Product Mgr)*
Linda M. Martin *(Mgr-Adv)*
Brands & Products:
ARISTOCRAT
THE BEAST
BLACK EAGLE
BRAVE EAGLE
CATCLAW
DOMAIN
EAGLE CLAW
EAGLE CLAW BASS
EAGLE CLAW CATFISH
EAGLE CLAW PANFISH
EAGLE CLAW TROUT
EAGLE CLAW WALLEYE
FEATHERLIGHT
FRE-LINE
GOLD EAGLE
GRANGER
GRANGER XG
HP
LAZER LINE
LAZER SHARP
NITRO
PACK IT
SEA EAGLE
SEA GUARD
SUPER
SURF BEAST
TITAN
TRAILMASTER
TWO-WAY
WATER EAGLE
XG
Advertising Agency:
5 Stone Advertising
1738 Wynkoop St Ste 303
Denver, CO 80202
Tel.: (303) 298-1226
Fax: (303) 298-1140

YAKIMA BAIT CO.
1000 Bailey Ave
Granger, WA 98932
Tel.: (509) 854-1311
Fax: (509) 854-2263
E-mail: ybcinc@yakimabait.com
Web Site: www.yakimabait.com
Sales Range: $50-74.9 Million
Approx. Number Employees: 120
Year Founded: 1934
Business Description:
Mfr. of Fishing Tackle
S.I.C.: 3949; 5941
N.A.I.C.S.: 339920; 451110
Advertising Expenditures: $600,000
Media: 2-4-6-8-10-13-18
Distr.: Natl.
Personnel:
Mark Masterson *(Gen Mgr)*
Brands & Products:
BLUE STREAK
DROP DEAD FRED
FATFISH
FLASHGLO
FREAK
HAVANA JACKPOT
HAWG BOSS SUPER TOAD
HILDEBRANDT
LEE SISSION
LIL' CORKY
MAGNUM FATFISH
ORIGINAL ROOSTER TAIL
POE'S
POE'S HAND CRAFTED
PREMIUM BALSA
ROOSTER TAIL
ROOSTER TAIL LITE
ROOSTER TROLLS
SKINY-MINY
SONIC ROOSTER TAIL
SPIN-E-MINY
SPIN-N-GLO
SPINNING FLY
SPOON FLY
SUPER ROOSTER TAIL
VIBRIC ROOSTER TAIL
WALLEYE MAGIC
WEEDLESS CRANKBAIT
WOB-LURE
WOBBLE GLO
WOBBLE TROLL
Advertising Agency:
Smith, Phillips & Di Pietro
1440 N 16th Ave
Yakima, WA 98902
Tel.: (509) 248-1760
Fax: (509) 575-7895
(Fishing Lures)

YONEX CORPORATION
(Sub. of Yonex Co., Ltd.)
20140 S Western Ave
Torrance, CA 90501
Tel.: (800) 449-6639
Fax: (310) 793-3899
Toll Free: (800) 44-YONEX
E-mail: INFO@yonex.com
Web Site: www.yonex.com
Approx. Number Employees: 15
Year Founded: 1947
Business Description:
Tennis Racquets, Golf Clubs, Badminton Racquets & Accessories
S.I.C.: 5091
N.A.I.C.S.: 423910
Advertising Expenditures: $750,000
Media: 2-6-7-10-13
Distr.: Natl.
Budget Set: Jan.
Brands & Products:
CYBERSTAR POWERBRID

ZEBCO
(Sub. of W.C. Bradley Co.)
6101 E Apache St
Tulsa, OK 74115-3370
Mailing Address:
PO Box 270
Tulsa, OK 74101-0270
Tel.: (918) 836-5581
Fax: (918) 836-0154
Web Site: www.zebco.com
Approx. Number Employees: 100
Business Description:
Mfr. of Fishing Tackle & Electric Trolling Motors
S.I.C.: 5941
N.A.I.C.S.: 451110
Advertising Expenditures: $5,000,000
Media: 2-6-10-11-15-19-24
Distr.: Natl.
Budget Set: Nov.
Personnel:
W. Jeffrey Pontius *(Pres & COO)*
Jim Hillenbrand *(CFO)*
Bob Bagby *(VP-Mktg)*
Matt Fletcher *(VP-Sls)*
Charlie Noble *(Gen Mgr)*
Ray More *(Dir-Mktg Avid Brands)*
Brands & Products:
BROWNING
LEW'S
MARTIN
OMEGA
QUANTUM
VANSTAAL
ZEBCO

Key to Media (For complete agency information see *The Advertising Red Books-Agencies* edition):
1. Bus. Publs. 2. Cable T.V. 3. Catalogs & Directories. 4. Co-op Adv. 5. Consumer Mags. 6. D.M. to Bus. Estab.7. D.M. to Consumers 8. Daily Newsp. 9. Exhibits/Trade Shows 10. Foreign 11. Infomercial 12. Internet Adv.13. Multimedia 14. Network Radio 15. Network T.V. 16. Newsp. Distr. Mags. 17. Other 18. Outdoor (Posters, Transit) 19. Point of Purchase20. Premiums, Novelties 21. Product Samples 22. Special Events Mktg. 23. Spot Radio 24. Spot T.V. 25. Weekly Newsp. 26. Yellow Page Adv.

Sweets

Cakes — Candy — Chewing Gum — Cookies — Ice Cream — Nuts — Pies

AMERICAN LICORICE CO. INC.
2796 NW Clearwater Dr
Bend, OR 97701-7008
Tel.: (541) 617-0800
Fax: (541) 617-0224
Web Site: www.americanlicorice.com
Approx. Sls.: $100,000,000
Approx. Number Employees: 500
Business Description:
Licorice Candy Mfr
S.I.C.: 2099
N.A.I.C.S.: 311340
Personnel:
John Kretchmer *(CEO)*
Kate Dunning *(Dir-Mktg & Sls Fin)*
Jeff Gorden *(Dir-Acctg & Fin)*
Brands & Products:
AMERICAN LICORICE
EXTINGUISHER
RED VINES
SIP-N-CHEWS
SNAPS
SOUR PUNCH
SUPER ROPES
TWISTY PUNCH
Advertising Agency:
Dentsu America, Inc.
32 Ave of the Americas 16th Fl
New York, NY 10013
Tel.: (212) 397-3333
Fax: (212) 397-3322

ANDES CANDIES LP
(Sub. of Tootsie Roll Industries, Inc.)
1400 E Wisconsin St
Delavan, WI 53115-1470
Tel.: (262) 728-9121
Fax: (262) 728-6794
Telex: 910 278 2472
Sales Range: $75-99.9 Million
Approx. Number Employees: 150
Year Founded: 1921
Business Description:
Mfr. of Candy
S.I.C.: 2066; 5145
N.A.I.C.S.: 311320; 424450
Export
Media: 19
Brands & Products:
ANDES

ANNABELLE CANDY COMPANY, INC.
27211 Industrial Blvd
Hayward, CA 94545-3347
Mailing Address:
PO Box 3665
Hayward, CA 94540-3665
Tel.: (510) 783-2900
Fax: (510) 785-7675
Toll Free: (888) 451-2848
E-mail: info@annabelle-candy.com
Web Site: www.annabelle-candy.com
E-Mail For Key Personnel:
President: susan@annabelle-candy.com
Approx. Number Employees: 65
Year Founded: 1950
Business Description:
Mfr. of Candy
S.I.C.: 2064
N.A.I.C.S.: 311330
Export
Media: 3-6-8-12-19-20-21-23-24
Personnel:
Annabelle Block *(Chm)*
Susan Gampson Karl *(Pres & CEO)*
Jim McIntyre *(VP-Production)*
Brands & Products:
ABBA-ZABA
ABBA-ZABA CHERRY APPLE
ANNABELLE CANDY
BIG HUNK
LOOK
ROCKY ROAD
ROCKY ROAD DARK
ROCKY ROAD DARK CHOCOLATE
ROCKY ROAD MINT
ROCKYROAD
U-NO
U-NO BAR

BACHMAN COMPANY
1 Pk Plz
Wyomissing, PA 19610
Tel.: (610) 320-7800
Fax: (610) 320-7897
Toll Free: (800) 523-8253
Web Site:
www.thebachmancompany.com
Approx. Number Employees: 460
Year Founded: 1884
Business Description:
Mfr & Distr of Snack Foods
S.I.C.: 2096
N.A.I.C.S.: 311919
Export
Advertising Expenditures: $2,262,000
Bus. Publs.: $1,000; Co-op Adv.: $600,000; Daily Newsp.: $15,000; Exhibits/Trade Shows: $20,000; Network Radio: $650,000; Network T.V.: $800,000; Newsp. Distr. Mags.: $9,000; Point of Purchase: $100,000; Premiums, Novelties: $12,000; Product Samples: $15,000; Special Events Mktg.: $40,000
Distr.: Reg.
Budget Set: Sept.
Personnel:
Scott Capenter *(Pres)*
Joseph F. Welch *(CEO)*
Rory M. Emery *(CFO)*
Earl Englert *(CIO)*
Deanna Williams *(Treas & Mgr-HR)*
Brands & Products:
BACHMAN
CHIPITOS
DURANGOS
GOLDEN CRISP
GOLDEN RIDGES
GOLDEN WAVY
JAX
THE KIDZ
KIDZELS
NUTZELS
ROOS
THIN 'N RIGHT

BALDWIN RICHARDSON FOODS COMPANY
20201 S LaGrange Rd Ste 200
Frankfort, IL 60423
Tel.: (815) 464-9994
Fax: (815) 464-9995
Toll Free: (800) 762-6458
E-mail: foods@brfoods.com
Web Site: www.brfoods.com
Approx. Rev.: $69,000,000
Approx. Number Employees: 210
Year Founded: 1916
Business Description:
Liquid Ingredient Mfr
S.I.C.: 2024
N.A.I.C.S.: 311520
Advertising Expenditures: $300,000
Media: 6-21
Distr.: Reg.
Personnel:
Evelyn White *(CFO)*
Eric G. Johnson *(VP-Sls)*
Susan Ary *(Dir-Mktg)*
Brands & Products:
BALDWIN
BALDWIN RICHARDSON FOODS
MRS. RICHARDSON'S
NANCE'S

BANNER CANDY MFG. CORP.
700 Liberty Ave
Brooklyn, NY 11208-2115
Tel.: (718) 647-4747
Fax: (718) 647-7192
Sales Range: $1-9.9 Million
Approx. Number Employees: 40
Business Description:
Mfr. of Chocolate Coated Candies
S.I.C.: 2099; 2066
N.A.I.C.S.: 311340; 311320
Media: 9-14-18
Distr.: Natl.

BARREL O'FUN SNACK FOODS CO.
(Sub. of KLN Enterprises Inc.)
800 4th St NW
Perham, MN 56573-1226
Mailing Address:
PO Box 230
Perham, MN 56573-0230
Tel.: (218) 346-7000
Fax: (218) 346-7003
Toll Free: (800) 346-4910
E-mail: info@barrelofunsnacks.com
Web Site: www.barrelofunsnacks.com
Approx. Number Employees: 340
Year Founded: 1973
Business Description:
Mfr. of Potato Chips & Snacks
S.I.C.: 2096
N.A.I.C.S.: 311919
Export
Media: 4-8-9-10-13-16-18-19-21-23-24-25
Distr.: Reg.
Budget Set: June
Personnel:
Ken Nelson *(Pres & CEO)*
Wayne Caughey *(CFO)*
Kurt Nelson *(COO)*
Randy Johnson *(VP-Sls)*
Mike Bormann *(Gen Mgr)*
Nancy Belka *(Dir-HR)*
Brands & Products:
BARREL O'FUN
FUNITOS
VIC'S

BEER NUTS, INC.
103 N Robinson St
Bloomington, IL 61701-5424

Key to Media (For complete agency information see *The Advertising Red Books-Agencies* edition):
1. Bus. Publs. 2. Cable T.V. 3. Catalogs & Directories. 4. Co-op Adv. 5. Consumer Mags. 6. D.M. to Bus. Estab.7. D.M. to Consumers 8. Daily Newsp. 9. Exhibits/Trade Shows 10. Foreign 11. Infomercial 12. Internet Adv.13. Multimedia 14. Network Radio 15. Network T.V. 16. Newsp. Distr. Mags. 17. Other 18. Outdoor (Posters, Transit) 19. Point of Purchase20. Premiums, Novelties 21. Product Samples 22. Special Events Mktg. 23. Spot Radio 24. Spot T.V. 25. Weekly Newsp. 26. Yellow Page Adv.

Beer Nuts, Inc. — (Continued)

Mailing Address:
PO Box 1327
Bloomington, IL 61702-1327
Tel.: (309) 827-8580
Fax: (309) 827-0914
Toll Free: (800) 233-7688
Web Site: www.beernuts.com
Approx. Number Employees: 100
Year Founded: 1953
Business Description:
Mfr. & Distributor of Nut Products
S.I.C.: 2068
N.A.I.C.S.: 311911
Media: 2-4-7-8-9-10-13-14-18-19-20-21-23
Distr.: Natl.
Budget Set: Nov.-Dec.
Personnel:
James A. Shirk *(Pres)*
Jeff Combs *(CFO)*
Brands & Products:
BEER NUTS BRAND SNACKS
MIX-IT UP
NUTTIN' BUT THE BEST
UNLEASH THE NUT WITHIN.

BEN & JERRY'S HOMEMADE, INC.

(Sub. of Conopco, Inc.)
30 Community Dr
South Burlington, VT 05403-6828
Tel.: (802) 846-1500
Fax: (802) 846-1610
E-mail: info@benjerry.com
Web Site: www.benjerry.com
Sales Range: $250-299.9 Million
Approx. Number Employees: 115
Year Founded: 1978
Business Description:
Homemade Ice Cream & Frozen Yogurt Mfr & Retailer; Ice Cream Parlor Franchises Owner
S.I.C.: 2024; 5812
N.A.I.C.S.: 311520; 722211
Export
Media: 9-14-18-19-20-21-22-23-24-26-31
Distr.: Intl.
Personnel:
Ben R. Cohen *(Co-Founder)*
Jerry Greenfield *(Co-Founder)*
Jostein Solheim *(CEO & VP-Global Brand Dev-Ice Cream)*
Katie O'Brien *(Mgr-Internet Mktg)*
Sean Greenwood *(Mgr-PR)*
Jim Keyt *(Mgr-Interactive Design)*
Liz Brenna *(Media Coord)*
Brands & Products:
BEN & JERRY'S
BEN & JERRY'S LIGHT
BEN & JERRY'S LOWFAT FROZEN YOGURT
BEN & JERRY'S PEACE POPS
CHERRY GARCIA
CHUNKY MONKEY
Advertising Agency:
Amalgamated Advertising LLC
145 W 30th St 7th Fl
New York, NY 10001
Tel.: (646) 878-1700
Fax: (646) 878-1787

BENSON'S, INC.

(d/b/a Benson's Bakery)
134 Elder St
Bogart, GA 30622-1500
Tel.: (770) 725-5711
Fax: (770) 725-5888
Toll Free: (800) 888-6059
E-mail: info@bensonsbakery.com
Web Site: www.bensonsbakery.com
Sales Range: $25-49.9 Million
Approx. Number Employees: 250
Year Founded: 1918
Business Description:
Commercial Bakeries
S.I.C.: 2051; 7011
N.A.I.C.S.: 311812; 721110
Media: 7-10
Distr.: Natl.
Budget Set: June
Personnel:
Larry R. Benson *(Pres)*
Browning Adair *(VP-Mktg & Sls)*
Dan Hartley *(Asst Controller & Traffic Mgr)*
Brands & Products:
BENSON'S
BENSON'S OLD HOME

BESTSWEET INC.

(Sub. of Tamanda Holdings USA Inc.)
288 Mazeppa Rd
Mooresville, NC 28115
Tel.: (704) 664-4300
Fax: (704) 664-7493
Web Site: www.bestsweet.com
Approx. Rev.: $49,000,000
Approx. Number Employees: 250
Business Description:
Candy & Other Confectionery Products
S.I.C.: 2099
N.A.I.C.S.: 311340
Media: 6-19-21
Personnel:
Richard Zulman *(CEO)*
Victor Clark *(CFO)*
Steve Berkowitz *(Exec VP)*
Paul Hervey *(VP-Sls)*
Brands & Products:
BASKIN-ROBBINS CANDY
BESTHEALTH
GUMMEEZ

BIRDSONG CORPORATION

612 Madison Ave
Suffolk, VA 23434-4028
Mailing Address:
PO Box 1400
Suffolk, VA 23439-1400
Tel.: (757) 539-3456
Fax: (757) 539-7360
Sales Range: $450-499.9 Million
Approx. Number Employees: 570
Year Founded: 1911
Business Description:
Nuts & Nut By-Products
S.I.C.: 5159; 2068
N.A.I.C.S.: 424590; 311911
Import Export
Media: 2-17-21
Personnel:
George Y. Birdsong *(CEO)*

BLOMMER CHOCOLATE COMPANY

600 W Kinzie St
Chicago, IL 60654
Tel.: (312) 226-7700
Fax: (312) 226-4141
Toll Free: (800) 621-1606
E-mail: info@blommer.com
Web Site: www.blommer.com
Approx. Number Employees: 350
Year Founded: 1939
Business Description:
Chocolate Mfr
S.I.C.: 2066
N.A.I.C.S.: 311320
Import Export
Advertising Expenditures: $200,000
Media: 17
Distr.: Natl.
Personnel:
Henry Blommer, Jr. *(Chm & CEO)*
Peter Blommer *(Pres & COO)*
Jack Larsen *(CFO)*
Peter Drake *(VP-Sls & Mktg)*
Marlene Stauffer *(Dir)*
Brands & Products:
BLOMMER
SIGNATURE LINE

BLUE BELL CREAMERIES, L.P.

1101 S Blue Bell Rd
Brenham, TX 77833
Mailing Address:
PO Box 1807
Brenham, TX 77834
Tel.: (979) 836-7977
Fax: (979) 830-2198
Toll Free: (800) 327-8135
Web Site: www.bluebell.com
Approx. Number Employees: 2,400
Year Founded: 1907
Business Description:
Ice Cream & Frozen Desserts Mfr
S.I.C.: 2024
N.A.I.C.S.: 311520
Advertising Expenditures: $4,000,000
Media: 1-2-3-5-9-10-18-19-20-21-23-24-26
Distr.: Reg.
Budget Set: Oct.
Personnel:
Paul Kruse *(Pres & CEO)*
W. J. Rankin *(CFO)*
E. Kruse *(Gen Mgr)*
Carl Breed *(Dir-Mktg)*
Marty Kilgore *(Product Mgr)*
Jim Hayhurst *(Mgr-Adv)*
Brands & Products:
FROZEN YOGURT
SHERBET

BOYER CANDY COMPANY INC.

821 17th St
Altoona, PA 16601-2074
Tel.: (814) 944-9401
Fax: (814) 943-2354
E-mail: wfrank@boyercandies.com
Web Site: www.boyercandies.com
Approx. Number Employees: 64
Year Founded: 1936
Business Description:
Confectionery Products
S.I.C.: 2064
N.A.I.C.S.: 311330
Export
Media: 2-3-4-6-8-10-17-18-19-20-21-26
Distr.: Intl.
Budget Set: Oct.
Personnel:
Robert Faith *(CEO)*
Tina Baker *(VP-Sls)*
Jim Lidwell *(Plant Mgr)*
Brands & Products:
BOYER
MALLO CUP
MILK CHOCOLATE PEANUT BUTTER CUP
SMOOTHIE
SMOOTHIE PEANUT BUTTER CUP
TRIPLE TWIST

BROWN & HALEY

1940 E 11th St
Tacoma, WA 98421
Tel.: (253) 620-3000
Tel.: (252) 620-3085
Fax: (253) 272-6742
Toll Free: (800) 445-9020
E-mail: info@brown-haley.com
Web Site: www.brown-haley.com
E-Mail For Key Personnel:
President: clair@brown-haley.com
Approx. Number Employees: 275
Year Founded: 1912
Business Description:
Candy & Confectionery Products Mfr & Importer
S.I.C.: 2099; 5145
N.A.I.C.S.: 311340; 424450
Import Export
Catalogs & Directories: 2%; Co-op Adv.: 50%; D.M. to Bus. Estab.: 5%; D.M. to Consumers: 5%; Exhibits/Trade Shows: 10%; Foreign: 15%; Point of Purchase: 5%; Product Samples: 7%; Yellow Page Adv.: 1%
Distr.: Intl.; Natl.; Reg.
Budget Set: Feb. -Apr.
Personnel:
Pierson Clair *(Pres & CEO)*
Clarence Guimond *(CFO & Exec VP)*
Brands & Products:
ALMOND ROCA
BELGIAN CREMES
BROWN & HALEY
CARBS IN-LINE
MOUNTAIN
MOUNTAIN BAR
PREMIUM SELECTIONS
ROCA
ROCA BITS
SUGAR FREE ROCA
ZINGO
ZINGOS

BURLESON'S INC.

301 Peters St
Waxahachie, TX 75165-2855
Tel.: (972) 937-4810
Fax: (972) 937-8711
E-mail: sales@burleson-honey.com
Web Site: www.burlesons-honey.com
E-Mail For Key Personnel:
Sales Director: sales@burleson-honey.com
Approx. Number Employees: 30
Year Founded: 1907
Business Description:
Honey & Honey Related Products Mfr
S.I.C.: 2099
N.A.I.C.S.: 311999
Import Export
Advertising Expenditures: $2,000,000
Media: 6-9-10-13-18-19-20-23
Distr.: Reg.
Budget Set: Apr.
Personnel:
T. E. Burleson, Jr. *(Pres)*
Jim Phillips *(Dir-Mktg & Sls)*
Brands & Products:
BURLESON'S
DON AMUSAN

Key to Media (For complete agency information see *The Advertising Red Books-Agencies* edition):
1. Bus. Publs. 2. Cable T.V. 3. Catalogs & Directories. 4. Co-op Adv. 5. Consumer Mags. 6. D.M. to Bus. Estab.7. D.M. to Consumers 8. Daily Newsp. 9. Exhibits/Trade Shows 10. Foreign 11. Infomercial 12. Internet Adv.13. Multimedia 14. Network Radio 15. Network T.V. 16. Newsp. Distr. Mags. 17. Other 18. Outdoor (Posters, Transit) 19. Point of Purchase20. Premiums, Novelties 21. Product Samples 22. Special Events Mktg. 23. Spot Radio 24. Spot T.V. 25. Weekly Newsp. 26. Yellow Page Adv.

Advertising Agency:
Roger Christian & Company
8035 Broadway
San Antonio, TX 78209
Tel.: (210) 829-1953
Fax: (210) 829-1973

CE DE CANDY, INC.
1091 Lousons Rd
Union, NJ 07083
Tel.: (908) 964-0660
Fax: (908) 964-0911
E-mail: cede@smarties.com
Web Site: www.smarties.com
Approx. Number Employees: 115
Year Founded: 1949
Business Description:
Mfr. of Candies
S.I.C.: 2099
N.A.I.C.S.: 311340
Import Export
Media: 4-5-7-10-13-19-21
Distr.: Natl.
Personnel:
Edward Dee *(Chm)*
Jonathan Dee *(Pres)*
Eric Ostrow *(VP-Sls & Mktg)*
Brands & Products:
CANDY WATCHES
MEGA SMARTIES
SMARTIES
SMARTIES LOLLIES
SMARTIES NECKLACES
TROPICAL SMARTIES
X-TREME SOUR SMARTIES

CHARMS LLC
(Sub. of Tootsie Roll Industries, Inc.)
7401 S Cicero Ave
Chicago, IL 60629-5818
Tel.: (773) 838-3400
Fax: (773) 838-3564
Web Site: www.tootsie.com
Sales Range: $150-199.9 Million
Approx. Number Employees: 600
Business Description:
Hard Candies & Lollipops Mfr
S.I.C.: 5145
N.A.I.C.S.: 424450
Advertising Expenditures: $1,025,000
Daily Newsp.: $25,000; Spot T.V.: $1,000,000
Distr.: Natl.
Personnel:
Steve Greem *(Plant Mgr)*
Brands & Products:
CHARMS BLOW POPS
CHARMS SWEET & SOUR POPS

CIAO BELLA GELATO COMPANY
(Joint Venture of Encore Consumer Capital LLC & Sherbrooke Capital LLC)
25A Vreeland Rd Ste 104
Florham Park, NJ 07932
Tel.: (973) 373-1200
Fax: (973) 373-1224
E-mail: info@ciaobellagelato.com
Web Site: www.ciaobellagelato.com
Approx. Number Employees: 50
Year Founded: 1983
Business Description:
Ice Cream Mfr; Owned by Sherbrooke Capital LLC & Encore Consumer Capital LLC
S.I.C.: 5143; 5499
N.A.I.C.S.: 424430; 445299
Media: 10-15-22
Personnel:
Scott Sellers *(Chm)*
Tom Delaplane *(Vice Chm)*
Charlie Apt *(Pres & COO)*
Stan Fabian *(CEO)*

CLARK GUM COMPANY
(Sub. of Tzetzo Brothers, Inc.)
1100 Military Rd
Buffalo, NY 14217-2514
Mailing Address:
PO Box 40
Buffalo, NY 14217-0040
Tel.: (716) 877-0800
Approx. Number Employees: 50
Year Founded: 1912
Business Description:
Mfr. of Gum & Candy
S.I.C.: 5145
N.A.I.C.S.: 424450
Import Export
Advertising Expenditures: $250,000
Media: 4-6-10
Distr.: Intl.; Natl.
Brands & Products:
SPOUT
TEABERRY
TENDERMINT

COLLIN STREET BAKERY
401 W 7th Ave
Corsicana, TX 75110-6362
Tel.: (903) 872-8111
Tel.: (903) 654-6606
Fax: (903) 872-6879
Toll Free: (800) 292-7400
Toll Free: (800) 504-1896
E-mail: info@collinstreetbakery.com
Web Site: www.collinstreetbakery.com
Approx. Number Employees: 72
Year Founded: 1896
Business Description:
Deluxe Fruit Cakes & Gifts via Direct Mail
S.I.C.: 2051
N.A.I.C.S.: 311812
Import Export
Advertising Expenditures: $5,875,000
Consumer Mags.: $100,000; D.M. to Bus. Estab.: $750,000; D.M. to Consumers: $4,000,000; Daily Newsp.: $750,000; Foreign: $275,000
Distr.: Direct to Consumer; Intl.; Natl.
Budget Set: Jan.
Personnel:
Robert P. McNutt *(Pres)*
Scott Hollomon *(VP-Fin)*
Brands & Products:
COLLIN STREET BAKERY
DELUXE
HARVEST GROVE

CONOPCO
(Sub. of Conopco, Inc.)
(d/b/a Unilever Ice Cream)
920 Sylvan Ave 2nd Fl
Englewood Cliffs, NJ 07632
Mailing Address:
PO Box 19007
Green Bay, WI 54307-9007
Tel.: (920) 499-5151
Fax: (920) 497-6521
Toll Free: (800) 931-2826
Web Site: www.icecreamusa.com
Sales Range: $1-4.9 Billion
Approx. Number Employees: 3,500
Year Founded: 1938
Business Description:
Mfr of Ice Cream & Frozen Novelties
S.I.C.: 2024
N.A.I.C.S.: 311520
Advertising Expenditures: $23,000,000
Media: 1-2-3-4-6-7-8-9-10-11-15-18-19-20-21-23-24
Distr.: Natl.
Budget Set: Sept.
Personnel:
John LeBoutillier *(VP & Gen Mgr-Unilever Ice Cream)*
Pete Allcox *(VP-Fin)*
Jim Christensen *(VP-Sls)*
Joe Colligan *(VP-Sls)*
David Burrows *(Sr Brand Dir)*
Andrea Lokshin *(Brand Mgr)*
Advertising Agency:
Don Jagoda Associates, Inc.
100 Marcus Dr
Melville, NY 11747-4229
Tel.: (631) 454-1800
Fax: (631) 454-1834

CONSOLIDATED BISCUIT CO.
(Sub. of Hearthside Food Solutions, LLC)
312 Rader Rd
McComb, OH 45858-9751
Mailing Address:
PO Box 847
McComb, OH 45858
Tel.: (419) 293-2911
Fax: (419) 293-3366
Web Site:
www.consolidatedbiscuit.com
Approx. Number Employees: 900
Business Description:
Cookies & Crackers Mfr
S.I.C.: 2052
N.A.I.C.S.: 311821
Media: 7-17
Personnel:
James M. Appold *(Pres)*
Bill Varney *(VP-Fin)*
Brands & Products:
AMERICAN BRITTLE
FIRESIDE

COOKIE TREE BAKERIES
4122 South 500 West
Salt Lake City, UT 84123
Tel.: (801) 268-2253
Fax: (801) 265-2727
Toll Free: (800) 998-0111
E-mail: information@cookietree.com
Web Site: www.cookietree.com
E-Mail For Key Personnel:
Sales Director: mike@cookietree.com
Approx. Number Employees: 150
Year Founded: 1981
Business Description:
Mfr. of Gourmet Cookies
S.I.C.: 2052; 2045
N.A.I.C.S.: 311821; 311822
Export
Advertising Expenditures: $200,000
Media: 4-7-10-19-21
Distr.: Intl.; Natl.
Budget Set: Sept.
Personnel:
Greg F. Schenk *(Owner)*
Harold Rosemann *(CFO & COO)*
Mike Daugherty *(VP-Sls)*
Cheryl Curtis *(Asst VP-Sls-Mktg)*
Brands & Products:
BAKE-AND-SERVE
COOKIE TREE
MEGA BITE
THAW-AND-SERVE
Advertising Agency:
Cookie Tree Bakeries
(House Agency)
4122 S 500 W
Salt Lake City, UT 84123
Tel.: (801) 268-2253
Fax: (801) 265-2727
(Gourmet Frozen Cookies & Frozen Dough)

DAN'S CHOCOLATES
45 Overland Park
Burlington, VT 05402-0668
Mailing Address:
PO Box 668
Burlington, VT 54020-0668
Tel.: (802) 862-0333
Toll Free: (800) -800-DANS
E-mail: wecare@dans.com
Web Site: www.danschocolates.com
Approx. Number Employees: 10
Year Founded: 1995
Business Description:
Online Chocolate Retailer
S.I.C.: 5441
N.A.I.C.S.: 445292
Advertising Expenditures: $1,200,000
Media: 7-8-13
Brands & Products:
DAN'S CHOCOLATES

DIAMOND FOODS, INC.
600 Montgomery St 17th Fl
San Francisco, CA 94111
Tel.: (415) 912-3180
Web Site: www.diamondfoods.com
Approx. Sls.: $965,922,000
Approx. Number Employees: 1,797
Year Founded: 1912
Business Description:
Assorted Snack Foods, Nuts & Fruits Producer & Retailer
S.I.C.: 2032; 0723; 2068; 2096
N.A.I.C.S.: 311422; 115114; 311911; 311919
Advertising Expenditures: $33,000,000
Media: 3-5-6-13-15-19
Personnel:
Michael J. Mendes *(Chm, Pres & CEO)*
Steven M. Neil *(CFO, Chief Admin Officer & Exec VP)*
Andrew Burke *(CMO & Exec VP)*
Lloyd J. Johnson *(Chief Sls Officer & Exec VP)*
Stephen Kim *(Gen Counsel & Sr VP-HR)*
Linda B. Segre *(Sr VP-Corp Strategy)*
Stephen Sibert *(VP-Corp Affairs)*
Andy Allcock *(Brand Mgr-Pop Secret)*
Brands & Products:
DIAMOND FOODS
DIAMOND OF CALIFORNIA
EMERALD
HARMONY
KETTLE
POP SECRET
Advertising Agencies:
Access Communications, LLC
101 Howard St 2nd Fl
San Francisco, CA 94105
Tel.: (415) 904-7070

Key to Media (For complete agency information see *The Advertising Red Books-Agencies* edition):
1. Bus. Publs. 2. Cable T.V. 3. Catalogs & Directories. 4. Co-op Adv. 5. Consumer Mags. 6. D.M. to Bus. Estab.7. D.M. to Consumers 8. Daily Newsp. 9. Exhibits/Trade Shows 10. Foreign 11. Infomercial 12. Internet Adv.13. Multimedia 14. Network Radio 15. Network T.V. 16. Newsp. Distr. Mags. 17. Other 18. Outdoor (Posters, Transit) 19. Point of Purchase20. Premiums, Novelties 21. Product Samples 22. Special Events Mktg. 23. Spot Radio 24. Spot T.V. 25. Weekly Newsp. 26. Yellow Page Adv.

Diamond Foods, Inc. — (Continued)

Fax: (415) 904-7055

Deutsch LA
5454 Beethoven St
Los Angeles, CA 90066-7017
Tel.: (310) 862-3000
Fax: (310) 862-3100
Agency of Record

DRAKE BAKERIES, INC.
(Sub. of Interstate Brands Corporation)
75 Demarest Dr
Wayne, NJ 07470-6701
Tel.: (973) 696-5010
Fax: (973) 696-2485
Web Site: www.hostessbrands.com
Approx. Number Employees: 250
Year Founded: 1888
Business Description:
Snack Cakes Mfr
S.I.C.: 2051
N.A.I.C.S.: 311812
Advertising Expenditures: $4,850,000
Media: 1-5-9-10-18-19-20-21-23-24
Distr.: Natl.
Budget Set: Oct.
Brands & Products:
DEVIL DOGS
FUNNY BONES
RING DINGS
YANKEE DOODLES
YODELS

DREYER'S GRAND ICE CREAM HOLDINGS, INC.
(Sub. of Nestle USA, Inc.)
5929 College Ave
Oakland, CA 94618
Tel.: (510) 652-8187
Fax: (510) 450-4592
Web Site: www.dreyersinc.com
Approx. Number Employees: 5,979
Year Founded: 1928
Business Description:
Ice Cream & Frozen Dairy Dessert Products
S.I.C.: 2024; 5143
N.A.I.C.S.: 311520; 424430
Media: 2-3-4-6-7-8-9-10-13-18-19-20-21-22-23-26
Distr.: Reg.
Personnel:
Mike Mitchell *(Pres & CEO)*
Tony Sarsam *(Exec VP-Ops)*
Kim Goeller-Johnson *(Sr Mgr-Media Rels)*
Doug Cornille *(Sr Brand Mgr)*
Kerry Hopkins *(Brand Mgr)*
Diane McIntyre *(Mgr-PR)*
Brands & Products:
DIBS
DREYER'S
EDY'S
SLOW CHURNED
Advertising Agencies:
Alcone Marketing Group
(Division of Omnicom Group, Inc.)
4 Studebaker
Irvine, CA 92618-2012
Tel.: (949) 770-4400
Fax: (949) 770-2957

Goodby, Silverstein & Partners, Inc.
(Part of Omnicom Group, Inc.)
720 California St
San Francisco, CA 94108-2404
Tel.: (415) 392-0669
Fax: (415) 788-4303

Smith Brothers Agency, LP
116 Federal St
Pittsburgh, PA 15212
Tel.: (412) 391-0555
Fax: (412) 391-3562
Digital Agency of Record
Eskimo Pie
Nestle Drumstick
Nestle Push-up
The Skinny Cow
www.drumstick.com
www.skinnycow.com

ELI'S CHEESECAKE COMPANY
6701 W Forest Preserve Dr
Chicago, IL 60634
Tel.: (773) 736-3417
Fax: (773) 736-1169
Toll Free: (800) 999-8300
E-mail: sales@elicheesecake.com
Web Site: www.elicheesecake.com
E-Mail For Key Personnel:
President: marc_schulman@elicheesecake.com
Sales Director: sales@elicheesecake.com
Sales Range: $200-249.9 Million
Approx. Number Employees: 256
Year Founded: 1980
Business Description:
Cheesecakes & Desserts Mfr
S.I.C.: 2053; 5812
N.A.I.C.S.: 311813; 722110
Export
Media: 2-3-4-5-6-7-8-9-10-13-17-18-19-20-21-22-23-25-26
Distr.: Natl.
Personnel:
Marc S. Schulman *(Pres)*
Pete Filippelli *(Sr VP-Sls & Mktg)*
Debbie Littmann Marchok *(VP-Mktg)*
Brands & Products:
ELIS APPLE CRANBERRY TART
ELIS GLAMOUR CAKES
ELIS NO SUGAR ADDED ORIGINAL CHEESECAKE
ELIS ORIGINAL PLAIN CHEESECAKE
ELIS PECAN PIE
GRAND MARNIER MOUSSE CAKE

ETHEL M. CHOCOLATES, INC.
(Sub. of Mars North America)
1 Sunset Way
Henderson, NV 89014-2309
Tel.: (702) 458-8864
Fax: (702) 451-8379
Toll Free: (800) 471-0352
Web Site: www.ethelschocolate.com
Sales Range: $10-24.9 Million
Approx. Number Employees: 300
Year Founded: 1981
Business Description:
Chocolate Mfr & Whlsr
S.I.C.: 2066; 5441
N.A.I.C.S.: 311320; 445292
Media: 4-8-9-10-13-19-20-21-22-23
Brands & Products:
ETHEL M

F.B. WASHBURN CANDY CORP.
137 Perkins Ave
Brockton, MA 02302-3850
Tel.: (508) 588-0820
Fax: (508) 588-2205
E-mail: info@fbwashburncandy.com
Web Site: www.fbwashburncandy.com
Sales Range: $10-24.9 Million
Approx. Number Employees: 35
Year Founded: 1856
Business Description:
Hard Candies Mfr
S.I.C.: 2099
N.A.I.C.S.: 311340
Export
Media: 5-10-25
Distr.: Natl.
Budget Set: Jan.
Personnel:
James R. Gilson *(Pres)*
Douglas B. Gilson *(VP)*
Brands & Products:
F.B. WASHBURN CANDY CORPORATION
SEVIGNY'S
WALEECO

FERRARA PAN CANDY CO.
7301 W Harrison St
Forest Park, IL 60130-2016
Tel.: (708) 366-0500
Fax: (708) 366-5921
Toll Free: (800) 323-1768
E-mail: customer.service@ferrarapan.com
Web Site: www.ferrarapan.com
Approx. Number Employees: 12
Year Founded: 1908
Business Description:
Candy Mfr
S.I.C.: 2099
N.A.I.C.S.: 311340
Advertising Expenditures: $500,000
Media: 9-19-20-25
Distr.: Natl.
Personnel:
Salvatore Ferrara, II *(Pres & COO)*
James Buffardi *(CFO)*
Brands & Products:
ASSORTMENT
ATOMIC FIREBALLS
BLACK FOREST GUMMIES
BOSTON BAKED BEANS
CINNAMON IMPERIALS
FERRARA PAN
JAWBUSTERS
LEMONHEADS
NARBLES
REDHOTS

FERRERO U.S.A., INC.
(Sub. of Ferrero S.p.A.)
600 Cottontail Ln
Somerset, NJ 08873
Tel.: (732) 764-9300
Fax: (732) 764-2700
Toll Free: (800) FERRERO
E-mail: info@ferrerousa.com
Web Site: www.ferrerousa.com
E-Mail For Key Personnel:
Sales Director: JKennington@ferrerousa.com
Approx. Number Employees: 250
Year Founded: 1969
Business Description:
Candy & Confectionery Products Mfr
S.I.C.: 5145; 2099
N.A.I.C.S.: 424450; 311340
Import Export
Advertising Expenditures: $25,000,000
Media: 1-3-5-9-10-15-21-23-24
Distr.: Natl.
Budget Set: Monthly
Personnel:
Michael Skalski *(Brand Mgr-Pralines)*
Advertising Agency:
Merkley + Partners
(Sub. of Omnicom Group, Inc.)
200 Varick St
New York, NY 10014-4810
Tel.: (212) 366-3500
Fax: (212) 805-7445

FIELDBROOK FOODS INC.
1 Ice Cream Dr
Dunkirk, NY 14048-6318
Mailing Address:
PO Box 1318
Dunkirk, NY 14048-6318
Tel.: (716) 366-5400
Fax: (716) 366-5483
Toll Free: (800) 333-0805
Web Site: www.fieldbrookfoods.com
Approx. Number Employees: 350
Year Founded: 1996
Business Description:
Ice Cream Products Mfr
S.I.C.: 2024
N.A.I.C.S.: 311520
Media: 6-9-10-14-15-19-21-23-24-25
Distr.: Reg.
Budget Set: Dec.
Personnel:
Kenneth A Johnson *(Pres & CEO)*
Kevin Grismore *(Mgr-Ops)*
Brands & Products:
THE COMPLETE TREAT COMPANY FOODS
FIELDBROOK
PRIVATE LABEL

THE FOREIGN CANDY COMPANY, INC.
1 Foreign Candy Dr
Hull, IA 51239-7499
Tel.: (712) 439-1496
Fax: (712) 439-1434
Fax: (800) 832-8541
Toll Free: (877) 937-8322
E-mail: consumeraffairs@foreigncandy.com
Web Site: www.foreign-candy.com
Sales Range: $25-49.9 Million
Approx. Number Employees: 35
Year Founded: 1978
Business Description:
Retailer of Imported Candy
S.I.C.: 5145
N.A.I.C.S.: 424450
Import Export
Media: 4-10-13-16
Distr.: Natl.
Personnel:
Peter W. De Yager *(Pres)*
Perry Borchard *(VP-Fin & Admin)*
Brands & Products:
COFFEE SHOP COFFEE CANDY
RIP ROLLS
SUPRISE BAG
YARDSTICK BUBBLE GUM

FOSTERS FREEZE, INC.
8360 Red Oak Ave Ste 202
Rancho Cucamonga, CA 91730-3880
Tel.: (909) 944-0815
Fax: (909) 944-0895
Web Site: www.fostersfreeze.com
Approx. Number Employees: 5
Year Founded: 1946

Key to Media (For complete agency information see *The Advertising Red Books-Agencies* edition):
1. Bus. Publs. 2. Cable T.V. 3. Catalogs & Directories. 4. Co-op Adv. 5. Consumer Mags. 6. D.M. to Bus. Estab.7. D.M. to Consumers 8. Daily Newsp. 9. Exhibits/Trade Shows 10. Foreign 11. Infomercial 12. Internet Adv.13. Multimedia 14. Network Radio 15. Network T.V. 16. Newsp. Distr. Mags. 17. Other 18. Outdoor (Posters, Transit) 19. Point of Purchase20. Premiums, Novelties 21. Product Samples 22. Special Events Mktg. 23. Spot Radio 24. Spot T.V. 25. Weekly Newsp. 26. Yellow Page Adv.

Business Description:
Owner & Franchiser of Restaurants & Ice Cream Parlors
S.I.C.: 6794
N.A.I.C.S.: 533110
Media: 3-9-17-18-19-23-24-25-26
Distr.: Reg.
Budget Set: Dec.-Jan.
Brands & Products:
FOSTERS FREEZE

FRIENDLY ICE CREAM CORPORATION
(Holding of Sun Capital Partners, Inc.)
1855 Boston Rd
Wilbraham, MA 01095-1002
Tel.: (413) 543-2400
Tel.: (413) 731-4000
Fax: (413) 731-4472
Toll Free: (800) 966-9970
Web Site: www.friendlys.com
Approx. Rev.: $531,455,008
Approx. Number Employees: 12,800
Year Founded: 1935
Business Description:
Restaurant Chain Management & Ice Cream Mfr
S.I.C.: 5812; 2024
N.A.I.C.S.: 722110; 311520
Advertising Expenditures: $20,734,000
Media: 6-8-9-13-19-22-23-24
Distr.: Reg.
Personnel:
Harsha V. Agadi *(Chm & CEO)*
Steve Sanchioni *(CFO)*
Andrea M. McKenna *(CMO & Exec VP)*
James M. Parrish *(Exec VP-Ops)*
Florence A. Tassinari *(VP & Controller)*
Cheryl Hutchinson *(VP-HR)*
Maura Tobias *(Dir-Consumer Engagement)*
Brands & Products:
BEYOND CHOCOLATE
BIG BEEFS
CAPPUCCINO DREAM
FISHAMAJIG
FRIBBLE
FRIENDLY
FRIENDLY'S
HAPPY ENDING
SUPERMELTS
Advertising Agencies:
Cone
(A Member of Omnicom Group)
855 Boylston St
Boston, MA 02116
Tel.: (617) 227-2111
Fax: (617) 523-3955

Goodway Group
The Pavilion 261 Old York Rd Ste 930
Jenkintown, PA 19046
Tel.: (215) 887-5700
Fax: (215) 881-2239

Laughlin/Constable, Inc.
360 N Michigan Ave 12th Fl
Chicago, IL 60601
Tel.: (414) 272-2400
Fax: (312) 422-5901

One to One Interactive, LLC
(d/b/a OTOi)
465 Medford St Ste 300
Charlestown, MA 02129
Tel.: (617) 425-7300
Fax: (617) 242-0632

The VIA Group LLC
34 Danforth St Ste 309
Portland, ME 04101
Tel.: (207) 221-3000
Fax: (207) 761-9422
Agency of Record

FRITO-LAY, INC.
(Sub. of PepsiCo Americas Foods)
7701 Legacy Dr
Plano, TX 75024-4002
Tel.: (972) 334-7000
Fax: (972) 334-2019
Toll Free: (800) 352-4477
Web Site: www.fritolay.com
Sales Range: $5-14.9 Billion
Approx. Number Employees: 30,000
Year Founded: 1961
Business Description:
Snack Foods Mfr
S.I.C.: 2096; 2052
N.A.I.C.S.: 311919; 311821
Advertising Expenditures: $120,000,000
Media: 2-3-5-6-9-10-14-15-18-19-20-21-23-24-25
Distr.: Intl.; Natl.
Personnel:
Albert P. Carey *(Pres & CEO)*
Jaime Montemayor *(CIO & Sr VP-North America)*
Anindita Mukherjee *(CMO-Frito-Lay North America & Sr VP)*
Daniel Naor *(Sr VP-Bus Innovation)*
Rich Beck *(Sr VP-Ops)*
Rocco Papalia *(Sr VP-Res & Devel)*
Jim Rich *(Sr VP-Ops)*
Michele Thatcher *(Sr VP-HR)*
Rudy Wilson *(VP-Mktg-Doritos, Cheetos, SunChips, Fritos)*
Janelle Anderson Hottinger *(Dir-Tostitos, Santitas & Dips)*
Scott Davies *(Dir-Brand Innovation)*
Donna M. Romeo *(Dir-Strategic Insights, Human Understanding)*
Ryan Boyle *(Sr Mgr-Mktg)*
Alexa Williams *(Sr Mgr-Res)*
Melissa Jarratt *(Brand Mgr-Cheetos)*
Christine Galofre Allen *(Brand Mgr)*
Linda Bethea *(Brand Mgr)*
Brian Graybill *(Product Mgr)*
Brands & Products:
3D'S
BAKED DORITOS
BAKED RUFFLES
BAKED TOSTITOS
BAKEN-ETS
BETCHA CAN'T EAT JUST ONE!
BOCABITS
CHEETOS
CHEETOS SHOTS
CHESTER'S
CHURRUMAIS
CRACKER JACK
CRUJITOS
DELICIOUSLY TWISTED. DELICIOUSLY CHEESY.
DORITOS
DORITOS A LA TURCA
DORITOS COLLISIONS
DORITOS DIPPAS
DORITOS ROLLITOS
FANDANGOS
FLAT EARTH
FOOD FOR THE FUN OF IT
FRITOS
FUNYUNS
GO SNACKS
GRANDMA'S
HAMKA'S
HICKORY STICKS
KURKURE
LAY'S
LAY'S FRIES
LAY'S KETTLE COOKED
LAY'S MEDITERANNEAS
LAY'S STAX
MAUI STYLE
MEET YOU AT THE TOSTITOS
MINI BITES
MISS VICKIE'S
MUNCHOS
NATURAL LAYS
NATURAL RUFFLES
NATURAL TOSTITOS
NIKNAKS
NOTHING SATISFIES LIKE FRITOS
NUT HARVEST
OBERTO
QUAVERS
QUAVERS SNACKS
RED ROCK DELI
ROLD GOLD
RUFFLES
RUFFLES FLAVOR RUSH
RUSTLER'S
SABRITAS
SABRITONES
SALSA RIO
SANTITAS
SMARTFOOD
SMITHS
SMITHS SENSATIONS
SONRIC'S
SUN CHIPS
TOSTITOS
TRUE NORTH
WAVY-LAY'S
WOTSITS
Advertising Agencies:
BBDO New York
1285 Ave of the Americas 7th Fl
New York, NY 10019-6028
Tel.: (212) 459-5000
(Sunchips Multigrain Snacks, Ruffles, Baked Lay's Potato Chips, Doritos, Tostitos)

Brand Agent
2828 Routh St Ste 825
Dallas, TX 75201
Tel.: (214) 979-2040
Fax: (214) 979-2100

Goodby, Silverstein & Partners, Inc.
(Part of Omnicom Group, Inc.)
720 California St
San Francisco, CA 94108-2404
Tel.: (415) 392-0669
Fax: (415) 788-4303
Cheetos
Dips
Doritos
Doritos Collisions
Doritos Late Night Rihana
Tostitos

OMD-USA
195 Broadway
New York, NY 10007
Tel.: (212) 590-7100
Media Buying
Doritos

THE FROZFRUIT COMPANY
1193 McDonald Ave
Brooklyn, NY 11230-3320
Tel.: (718) 758-3060
Fax: (718) 758-3065
Toll Free: (888) 700-4700
E-mail: comments@frozfruit.com
Web Site: www.frozfruit.com
Approx. Number Employees: 75
Year Founded: 1979
Business Description:
Mfr. & Sale of Frozen Desserts
S.I.C.: 2024
N.A.I.C.S.: 311520
Import Export
Advertising Expenditures: $200,000
Media: 5-6-10-19-20-21-22
Distr.: Intl.; Natl.; Reg.
Budget Set: Oct. -Nov.
Brands & Products:
CHILL
COOL COTTON CANDY
FROZFRUIT
GIVE PEACH A CHANCE
SMOOTHIE.YUM
STRAWBERRY BANANA YUMTONIC
THAT KIND OF GOOD

GHIRARDELLI CHOCOLATE COMPANY
(Sub. of Lindt & Sprungli (International) AG)
1111 139th Ave
San Leandro, CA 94578-2631
Tel.: (510) 483-6970
Fax: (510) 297-2649
Web Site: www.ghirardelli.com
Approx. Number Employees: 550
Year Founded: 1852
Business Description:
Chocolate Mfr
S.I.C.: 2066; 5441
N.A.I.C.S.: 311320; 445292
Import Export
Media: 3-4-10-11-15-19-20-21
Distr.: Natl.
Personnel:
Jackie DiLaura *(Sr Brand Mgr)*
Brands & Products:
A TIMELESS PLEASURE
AMERICA'S PREMIUM CHOCOLATE
GHIRARDELLI
GHIRARDELLI CHOCOLATE
GHIRARDELLI CHOCOLATE BAR COLLECTION
GHIRARDELLI CHOCOLATE SQUARES
GHIRARDELLI PREMIUM BAKING CHOCOLATE
GHIRARDELLI SODA FOUNTAIN AND CHOCOLATE SHOPS
PREMIUM CHOCOLATE MASTERPIECES COLLECTION
Advertising Agency:
Campbell-Ewald Los Angeles
8687 Melrose Ave Ste G510
West Hollywood, CA 90069
Tel.: (310) 358-4800

GODIVA CHOCOLATIER, INC.
(Sub. of Ulker Biskuvi Sanayi A.S.)
355 Lexington Ave
New York, NY 10017-6603
Tel.: (212) 984-5900
Fax: (212) 984-5901

Key to Media (For complete agency information see *The Advertising Red Books-Agencies* edition):
1. Bus. Publs. 2. Cable T.V. 3. Catalogs & Directories. 4. Co-op Adv. 5. Consumer Mags. 6. D.M. to Bus. Estab.7. D.M. to Consumers 8. Daily Newsp. 9. Exhibits/Trade Shows 10. Foreign 11. Infomercial 12. Internet Adv.13. Multimedia 14. Network Radio 15. Network T.V. 16. Newsp. Distr. Mags. 17. Other 18. Outdoor (Posters, Transit) 19. Point of Purchase20. Premiums, Novelties 21. Product Samples 22. Special Events Mktg. 23. Spot Radio 24. Spot T.V. 25. Weekly Newsp. 26. Yellow Page Adv.

Godiva Chocolatier, Inc. — (Continued)

Toll Free: (800) 9GODIVA
Telex: 645173 GODIVA NYK
E-mail: letters@godiva.com
Web Site: www.godiva.com
Sales Range: $500-549.9 Million
Approx. Number Employees: 100
Year Founded: 1926
Business Description:
Chocolate Mfr
S.I.C.: 2066
N.A.I.C.S.: 311320
Media: 2-4-6-9-13-18-19-25
Distr.: Natl.
Budget Set: June
Personnel:
James A. Goldman *(Pres & CEO)*
David S. Marberger *(CFO)*
Rich Keller *(VP-Mktg Innovation)*
Joseph W. Carboy *(Dir-Ops)*
Chad Ramsey *(Dir-Strategic Analysis)*
Brands & Products:
CORNE DE LA TOISON D'OR
GODIVA
GODIVA CHOCOISTE
Advertising Agencies:
Alison Brod Public Relations
373 Park Ave S 4th Fl
New York, NY 10016
Tel.: (212) 230-1800
Fax: (212) 230-1161
— Alana Radmin *(Acct Exec)*
— Ali Vilensky *(Acct Exec)*

Brierley & Partners
8401 N Central Expy Ste 1000 LB-37
Dallas, TX 75225-4403
Tel.: (214) 760-8700
Fax: (214) 743-5511

Empower MediaMarketing
(MEDIA THAT WORKS)
1111 Saint Gregory St
Cincinnati, OH 45202
Tel.: (513) 871-9454
Fax: (513) 871-1804
(Media Buying & Planning)

GOLDEN ENTERPRISES INC.

1 Golden Flake Dr
Birmingham, AL 35201
Tel.: (205) 323-6161
Fax: (205) 458-7335
Toll Free: (800) 239-2447
Web Site: www.goldenflake.com
Approx. Sls.: $131,047,850
Approx. Number Employees: 767
Year Founded: 1946
Business Description:
Holding Company; Confectionery Products, Potato Chips & Popcorn & Peanut Butter & Salted Peanuts Mfr & Distr
S.I.C.: 2096; 2037; 2099
N.A.I.C.S.: 311919; 311411; 311999
Advertising Expenditures: $6,587,476
Media: 2-4-9-18-19-21-23-24-25
Personnel:
Mark W. McCutcheon *(Chm, Pres & CEO)*
Patty Townsend *(CFO, Sec & VP)*

GOLDEN FLAKE SNACK FOODS, INC.

(Sub. of Golden Enterprises Inc.)
1 Golden Flake Dr
Birmingham, AL 35205
Mailing Address:
PO Box 2447
Birmingham, AL 35201-2447
Tel.: (205) 323-6161
Fax: (205) 458-7335
E-mail: goldenflake@goldenflake.com
Web Site: www.goldenflake.com
Sales Range: $550-599.9 Million
Approx. Number Employees: 1,200
Year Founded: 1923
Business Description:
Snack Foods Mfr & Distr
S.I.C.: 2096
N.A.I.C.S.: 311919
Export
Media: 9-10-17-18-19-20-23
Distr.: Reg.
Budget Set: May
Personnel:
Mark W. McCutcheon *(Pres & Treas)*
Paul R. Bates *(Exec VP)*
David Jones *(Exec VP-Opers & HR & Quality Control)*
Julie Strauss *(Dir-Mktg)*
Brands & Products:
BAKED FLAKE
GOLDEN FLAKE
MAIZETOS
TOSTADOS

GOLDEN PEANUT COMPANY, L.L.C.

(Joint Venture of Archer-Daniels-Midland Company & Alimenta S.A.)
100 N Point Ctr E Ste 400
Alpharetta, GA 30022-8262
Tel.: (770) 752-8160
Fax: (770) 752-8306
Web Site: www.goldenpeanut.com
Sales Range: $600-649.9 Million
Approx. Number Employees: 55
Year Founded: 1986
Business Description:
Raw & Processed Peanuts Mfr; Owned 50% by Archer Daniels Midland Co. & 50% by Alimenta S.A.
S.I.C.: 0139
N.A.I.C.S.: 111992
Media: 2-6-10
Distr.: Natl.
Budget Set: Feb.
Personnel:
James Dorsett *(Pres & CEO)*
Bruce Kotz *(VP-Specialty Products)*
Alex Izmirlian *(VP-Intl Sls)*
Robert Parker *(VP-Procurement)*

GRAETER'S, INC.

2145 Reading Rd
Cincinnati, OH 45202-1417
Tel.: (513) 721-3323
Fax: (513) 721-3385
Web Site: www.graeters.com
Approx. Number Employees: 350
Year Founded: 1870
Business Description:
Mfr. of Packaged Ice Cream, Molded, On Sticks; Bread, Cake & Related Products
S.I.C.: 2024; 2051
N.A.I.C.S.: 311520; 311812
Advertising Expenditures: $100,000
Media: 2-4-7
Distr.: Reg.
Personnel:
Bob Graeter *(Owner & VP)*
Richard Graeter *(Pres & CEO)*
Brands & Products:
GRAETER'S
Advertising Agency:
Sunrise Advertising
700 Walnut St Ste 500
Cincinnati, OH 45202
Tel.: (513) 333-4100
Fax: (513) 333-4101

GREEN & BLACK'S USA, INC.

(Sub. of Green & Black's Limited)
389 Interpace Pkwy
Parsippany, NJ 07054-1198
Tel.: (973) 909-3900
Fax: (973) 673-7171
Web Site: www.greenandblacks.com
Business Description:
Chocolate Mfr & Distr
S.I.C.: 2066; 5145
N.A.I.C.S.: 311320; 424450
Media: 6-10

GUITTARD CHOCOLATE COMPANY

10 Guittard Rd
Burlingame, CA 94010-2203
Tel.: (650) 697-4427
Fax: (650) 692-2761
Toll Free: (800) 468-2462
E-mail: customer_service@guittard.com
Web Site: www.guittard.com
Approx. Number Employees: 200
Year Founded: 1868
Business Description:
Mfr. of Chocolate Products
S.I.C.: 2066; 2099
N.A.I.C.S.: 311320; 311340
Media: 2-6-10-21
Distr.: Natl.
Budget Set: Sept. -Oct.
Personnel:
Gary Guittard *(Pres & CEO)*
Mark Spini *(Dir-Industrial Sls)*
Mel Cohen *(Mgr-Sls & Mktg)*
Brands & Products:
AMBANJA
CHUCURI
DECORATIFS
GUITTARD
NOCTURNE
OLD DUTCH COCOA
ORINOCO
PASTEL COATINGS
QUETZALCOATL
QUEVEDO
SUR DEL LAGO
TSARATANA
Advertising Agency:
Hawk Media, Inc.
PO Box 623
Diablo, CA 94528
Tel.: (415) 860-2500
Fax: (925) 855-1843
(Media Placement)

HAMMONS PRODUCTS COMPANY

105 Hammons Dr
Stockton, MO 65785
Tel.: (417) 276-5181
Fax: (417) 276-5187
Toll Free: (888) 4BWNUTS
E-mail: hagerty100@aol.com
Web Site: www.black-walnuts.com
Sales Range: $1-9.9 Million
Approx. Number Employees: 55
Year Founded: 1946
Business Description:
Processor & Supplier of Nuts & Nut Products
S.I.C.: 2068; 5812
N.A.I.C.S.: 311911; 722110
Export
Media: 2-4-6-7-8-9-10-19-21-23-25-26
Distr.: Natl.
Personnel:
R. Dwain Hammons *(Chm)*
Brian K. Hammons *(Pres)*
Dave Steinmuller *(VP-Sls)*
Brands & Products:
HAMMONS
INSHELL
TRUE GRIT
Advertising Agency:
Wannenmacher Advertising Co.
211 E. Walnut St.
Springfield, MO 65806
Tel.: (417) 869-4848
Fax: (417) 869-6201
(Procurement/Buying Season)

HERSHEY CANADA, INC.

(Sub. of The Hershey Co.)
5750 Explore Dr Ste 400
Mississauga, ON L4W 0B1, Canada
Tel.: (905) 602-9200
Fax: (905) 602-8766
E-mail: cdnheadoffice@hersheys.com
Web Site: www.hersheys.com
Sales Range: $50-74.9 Million
Approx. Number Employees: 150
Business Description:
Mfr. of Chocolate, Cocoa & Confectionery Products
S.I.C.: 2064
N.A.I.C.S.: 311330
Import Export
Media: 6-15-18-19-23
Distr.: Natl.
Budget Set: July -Sept.
Personnel:
Lynn Beumgartnar *(VP-Mktg)*
Advertising Agency:
Sparkplug Marketing & Communications Inc.
57 Lascelles Blvd
M5P 2C9
Toronto, ON Canada
Tel.: (416) 488-8867
Fax: (416) 485-3481

THE HERSHEY CO.

100 Crystal A Dr
Hershey, PA 17033-9529
Tel.: (717) 534-4200
Fax: (717) 534-6760
Toll Free: (800) 539-0261
Telex: 6711079
E-mail: info@hersheys.com
Web Site: www.hersheys.com
E-Mail For Key Personnel:
Public Relations: pr@hersheys.com
Approx. Sls.: $5,671,009,000
Approx. Number Employees: 11,300
Year Founded: 1893
Business Description:
Cocoa, Chocolate & Confectionery Products Mfr
S.I.C.: 2066; 2099; 5145; 5441
N.A.I.C.S.: 311320; 311340; 424450; 445292
Export
Advertising Expenditures: $391,100,000

Key to Media (For complete agency information see *The Advertising Red Books-Agencies* edition):
1. Bus. Publs. 2. Cable T.V. 3. Catalogs & Directories. 4. Co-op Adv. 5. Consumer Mags. 6. D.M. to Bus. Estab.7. D.M. to Consumers
8. Daily Newsp. 9. Exhibits/Trade Shows 10. Foreign 11. Infomercial 12. Internet Adv.13. Multimedia 14. Network Radio
15. Network T.V. 16. Newsp. Distr. Mags. 17. Other 18. Outdoor (Posters, Transit) 19. Point of Purchase20. Premiums, Novelties
21. Product Samples 22. Special Events Mktg. 23. Spot Radio 24. Spot T.V. 25. Weekly Newsp. 26. Yellow Page Adv.

Media: 3-6-9-11-13-15-16-19-21-24-25

Personnel:
James Edwin Nevels *(Chm)*
David J. West *(Pres & CEO)*
Humberto P. Alfonso *(CFO & Sr VP)*
John P. Bilbrey *(COO & Exec VP)*
George F. Davis *(CIO & Sr VP)*
Michele G. Buck *(CMO & Sr VP)*
Charlene H. Binder *(Sr VP & Chief People Officer)*
David W. Tacka *(Chief Acctg Officer & VP)*
E. Daniel Vucovich *(VP & Chief Customer Officer-Global)*
Thaddeus J. Jastrzebski *(Pres-Hershey Intl & Sr VP)*
Burton H. Snyder *(Gen Counsel, Sec & Sr VP)*
James G. Nolan *(Asst Treas)*
John R. Steller, III *(Asst Treas)*
C. Daniel Azzara *(Sr VP-Global R&D)*
Javier H. Idrovo *(Sr VP-Strategy & Bus Dev)*
Terence L. O'Day *(Sr VP-Ops-Global)*
Andrew W. Jacobs *(VP & Gen Mgr-US Customers)*
Susan M. Angele *(VP & Deputy Gen Counsel)*
Milton P. Brice *(VP-Fin)*
Timothy P. Dunigan *(VP-Sls-Hershey Intl)*
Bryon L. Klemens *(VP-Fin & Plng-Hershey North America)*
Eric Lent *(VP-Global Mktg Excellence & Strategy)*
Kathryn M. McGrath *(VP-Comp & Benefits)*
David G. Onorato *(VP-Global Convenience Stores & Specialty Retail)*
Kirk Saville *(VP-Corp Comm)*
Joseph A. Cottonaro *(Sr Dir-Taxes)*
Robin Alex *(Dir-Consumer Insights-Global)*
David Forney *(Dir-Global Consumer Comm)*
Ed Martin *(Dir-Consumer Insights & New Methods-Intl)*
Jim St John *(Dir-Product Dev & Tech Center Ops)*
Jeff Stern *(Dir-Brand Strategy-Global)*
David A. Stuart *(Dir-Natural Product Sciences)*
Gerald R. Urich *(Dir-External Reporting & Compliance)*
David Witt *(Dir-Brand PR & Consumer Engagement-Global)*
Dan Klinger *(Sr Mgr-Global Info Security)*
Michelle Bentley *(Mgr-Natl Accounts-Food Svc)*
Anna Lingeris *(Mgr-PR & Brand Comm)*
John San Miguel *(Mgr-Travel Retail Mktg-Global)*
Vincent R. Clempson *(Asst Sec)*
Steven J. Holsinger *(Asst Sec)*
Bonnie S. Martin *(Asst Sec)*

Brands & Products:
100 CALORIE BARS
5TH AVENUE
BAR NONE
BLISS
BREATHSAVERS
BUBBLE YUM
CACAO RESERVE BY HERSHEY'S
CADBURY
CADBURY'S CARAMELLO
CADBURY'S CREME EGGS
CADBURY'S DAIRY MILK
CADBURY'S FRUIT & NUT
CADBURY'S KRISP
CADBURY'S MINI EGGS
CADBURY'S ROAST ALMOND
CARAMELLO
CARB ALTERNATIVES
CAREFREE
CHERRY BLOSSOM
CHIPITS
CHOCOLATE WORLD
COOKIES 'N' CREME
CREME EGG
DAIRY MILK
EAT-MORE
FAST BREAK
FRUIT & NUT
GIANT KISS
GLOSETTE
GOLDEN ALMOND
GOLDEN ALMOND NUGGETS
GOLDEN ALMOND SOLITAIRES
GOOD & PLENTY
HEATH
HEATH BITS 'O BRICKLE
HERSHEY'S
HERSHEY'S BITES
HERSHEY'S BLISS
HERSHEY'S CHOCOLATE MILK
HERSHEY'S CHOCOLATE SHOPPE
HERSHEY'S CLASSIC CARAMELS
HERSHEY'S COOKIES
HERSHEY'S COOKIES 'N' CREME
HERSHEY'S COOKIES 'N' CREME NUGGETS
HERSHEY'S EXTRA DARK
HERSHEY'S GOODNIGHT HUGS
HERSHEY'S GOODNIGHT KISSES
HERSHEY'S HOT COCOA
HERSHEY'S HUGS
HERSHEY'S KISSES
HERSHEY'S KISSES WITH ALMONDS
HERSHEY'S MINIATURES
HERSHEY'S NUGGETS
HERSHEY'S POT OF GOLD
HERSHEY'S S'MORES
HERSHEY'S SUGAR FREE
HERSHEY'S SYMPHONY
HERSHEY'S SYRUP
HERSHEY'S TAKE 5
HERSHEY'S TOP SCOTCH
HERSHEY'S.COM
ICE BREAKERS
IO-IO
JOLLY RANCHER
JOLLY RANCHER JOLLY BEANS
JOLLY RANCHER JOLLY JELLIES
KOOLERZ
KRACKEL
MAUNA LOA
MILK DUDS
MINI EGGS
MINI KISSES
MINICHIPS
MR. GOODBAR
NIBS
NUTRAGEOUS
OH HENRY!
PAYDAY
PETER PAUL ALMOND JOY
REESE'S
REESE'S CRUNCHY PEANUT BUTTER CUPS
REESE'S FAST BREAK
REESE'S MINIATURES
REESE'S NUTRAGEOUS
REESE'S PEANUT BUTTER CHIPS
REESE'S PEANUT BUTTER CUPS
REESE'S PIECES
REESESTICKS
ROAST ALMOND
ROLO
ROYAL DARK
SKOR
SMARTZONE
SNACKBARZ
SNACKSTERS
SPECIAL CRISP
SPECIAL DARK
THE SWEETEST SITE ON THE WEB
SWOOPS
SYMPHONY
TAKE 5
TASTETATIONS
TWIZZLERS
TWIZZLERS PULL-N-PEEL
VISCONTI
WHATCHAMACALLIT
WHOPPERS
YORK
YOUNG & SMYLIE
ZAGNUT
ZERO

Advertising Agencies:

Arnold
530 E Swedesford Rd Ste 101
Wayne, PA 19087
Tel.: (610) 254-0500
Fax: (610) 254-0501

Euro RSCG Shanghai
11/F, Novel Building
Shanghai, China
Tel.: (86) 21 6467 5868
Fax: (86) 21 6467 6526
Hershey Kisses

The Geppetto Group
95 Morton St 8th Fl
New York, NY 10014-3336
Tel.: (212) 462-8140
Fax: (212) 462-8197

OMD-USA
195 Broadway
New York, NY 10007
Tel.: (212) 590-7100
Hershey Bar
Kisses
Take 5
Media Buying & Planning

Pavone
1006 Market St
Harrisburg, PA 17101-2811
Tel.: (717) 234-8886
Fax: (717) 234-8940

READY366
33 E 17th St Union Sq
New York, NY 10003
Tel.: (212) 488-5366
Fax: (212) 228-2474

TracyLocke
1999 Bryan St Ste 2800
Dallas, TX 75201
Tel.: (214) 259-3500
Fax: (214) 259-3550

HOSTESS BRANDS

12 E Armour Blvd
Kansas City, MO 64111
Tel.: (816) 502-4000
Fax: (816) 502-4155
Web Site:
www.interstatebakeriescorp.com
Sales Range: $1-4.9 Billion
Approx. Number Employees: 20,000
Year Founded: 1987

Business Description:
Holding Company; Baked Goods Mfr, Distr & Specialty Outlet Retailer
S.I.C.: 6719; 2051; 5149; 5461
N.A.I.C.S.: 551112; 311812; 424490; 445291
Media: 2-3-6-9-10-16-18-19-21-22-23-24-25
Distr.: Natl.

Personnel:
John T. Cahill *(Chm)*
Brian J. Driscoll *(CEO)*
J. Randall Vance *(CFO, Treas & Sr VP)*
John O. Stewart *(CFO & Exec VP)*
Mike Touhey *(VP-Mktg)*
Russ Schleiden *(Dir-Mktg-Snacks)*

Brands & Products:
BAKER'S INN
BEEFSTEAK
BREAD DU JOUR
BUTTERNUT
DI CARLO
DING DONGS
DOLLY MADISON
DRAKE'S
EDDY'S
HOHOS
HOME PRIDE
IBC
J.J. NISSEN
MERITA
MILLBROOK
SUZY-QS
SWEETHEART
TWINKIES
WONDER
WONDER SMARTWHITE
ZINGERS

Advertising Agencies:

Bernstein-Rein Advertising, Inc.
4600 Madison Ave Ste 1500
Kansas City, MO 64112-3016
Tel.: (816) 756-0640
Fax: (816) 399-6000
Toll Free: (800) 571-6246
Butternut
Digital
Dolly Madison
Drake
Home Pride
Hostess
Media Buying & Planning
Media Buying Agency of Record
Wonder

Campbell Mithun, Inc.
Campbell Mithun Tower 222 S 9th St
Minneapolis, MN 55402-3389
Tel.: (612) 347-1000
Fax: (612) 347-1515
(Dolly Madison Cakes, Butternut Bread, Merita Bread, Webers Bread)

Key to Media (For complete agency information see *The Advertising Red Books-Agencies* edition):
1. Bus. Publs. 2. Cable T.V. 3. Catalogs & Directories. 4. Co-op Adv. 5. Consumer Mags. 6. D.M. to Bus. Estab.7. D.M. to Consumers 8. Daily Newsp. 9. Exhibits/Trade Shows 10. Foreign 11. Infomercial 12. Internet Adv.13. Multimedia 14. Network Radio 15. Network T.V. 16. Newsp. Distr. Mags. 17. Other 18. Outdoor (Posters, Transit) 19. Point of Purchase20. Premiums, Novelties 21. Product Samples 22. Special Events Mktg. 23. Spot Radio 24. Spot T.V. 25. Weekly Newsp. 26. Yellow Page Adv.

JELLY BELLY CANDY COMPANY
1 Jelly Belly Ln
Fairfield, CA 94533
Tel.: (707) 428-2800
Fax: (707) 423-4436
Toll Free: (800) JB-BEANS
Web Site: www.jellybelly.com
E-Mail For Key Personnel:
Marketing Director: marketing@jellybelly.com
Approx. Number Employees: 455
Year Founded: 1869
Business Description:
Mfr & Marketer Jelly Beans & Other Candies
S.I.C.: 2099
N.A.I.C.S.: 311340
Advertising Expenditures: $250,000
Media: 2-4-6-10-13-16-18-19-20-21-22-26
Personnel:
Herman G. Rowland, Sr. *(Chm)*
Bill Kelley *(Vice Chm)*
Robert Simpson *(Pres & COO)*
Andrew Joffer *(VP-Sls)*
John Pola *(VP-Sls)*
Jason Marrone *(Mgr-E-Commerce Mktg)*
Stephanie Scott *(Mgr-Events Mktg)*
Brands & Products:
BEAN POD
BEANBOOZLED
CHOCOLATE DUTCH MINTS
JB GUM
JBZ
JELLY BEANS
JELLY BELLY
SPORT BEANS
WIGGLE WORMS

JOHN PATON, INC.
73 E State St
Doylestown, PA 18901-4359
Tel.: (215) 348-7050
Fax: (215) 348-8147
E-mail: joan@goldenblossomhoney.com
Web Site:
www.goldenblossomhoney.com
Sales Range: Less than $1 Million
Approx. Number Employees: 7
Year Founded: 1921
Business Description:
Honey Mfr & Distr
S.I.C.: 5149
N.A.I.C.S.: 424490
Advertising Expenditures: $300,000
Media: 9-13-14-15-23-24-25
Distr.: Reg.
Budget Set: Nov.
Personnel:
Joan Lucas *(Dir-Sls)*
Brands & Products:
GENIUINE NATURAL PURE HONEY
GOLDEN BLOSSOM
Advertising Agency:
Furman Roth Advertising
801 2nd Ave 14th Fl
New York, NY 10017-4706
Tel.: (212) 687-2300
Fax: (212) 687-0858

JOYVA CORPORATION
53 Varick Ave
Brooklyn, NY 11237
Tel.: (718) 497-0170
Fax: (718) 366-8504
E-mail: joyva53@jaoyva.com
Web Site: www.joyva.com
Approx. Number Employees: 75
Year Founded: 1910
Business Description:
Mfr. of Halvah, Candies & Sesame Products
S.I.C.: 2099
N.A.I.C.S.: 311340; 311999
Import Export
Media: 5-10-16-19-23
Distr.: Intl.; Natl.
Budget Set: July -Aug.
Personnel:
Milton Radutzky *(Pres)*
Brands & Products:
JOYVA

JUDSON-ATKINSON CANDIES, INC.
4266 Dividend
San Antonio, TX 78219
Tel.: (210) 359-8380
Fax: (210) 359-8392
Toll Free: (800) 962-3984
E-mail: info@judsonatkinsoncandies.com
Web Site:
www.judsonatkinsoncandies.com
Approx. Number Employees: 120
Year Founded: 1899
Business Description:
Candy Mfr
S.I.C.: 2099
N.A.I.C.S.: 311340
Import Export
Media: 2-4-7-10-17
Distr.: Natl.
Budget Set: Dec.
Personnel:
Basil Atkinson *(Owner, Chm, Pres & CEO)*
Amy Voltz *(Exec VP)*
Doyle Huntsman *(VP-Sls & Mktg)*
Ken Deecken *(Reg Mgr-Eastern Sls)*
Brands & Products:
BIG TEX
HOT-N-SPICY BIG TEX
JUDSON-ATKISON
SWEET PERFECTION

JUST BORN, INC.
1300 Stefko Blvd
Bethlehem, PA 18017-6620
Tel.: (610) 867-7568
Fax: (610) 867-7870
Toll Free: (800) 445-5787
Web Site: www.justborn.com
E-Mail For Key Personnel:
Marketing Director: MPetronio@justborn.com
Sales Director: jleipold@justborn.com
Approx. Number Employees: 525
Year Founded: 1923
Business Description:
Candy Mfr
S.I.C.: 2099; 2064
N.A.I.C.S.: 311340; 311330
Export
Media: 1-2-3-4-6-7-10-11-13-15-19-20-21-22
Distr.: Intl.; Natl.
Budget Set: July
Personnel:
David L. Yale *(Pres & COO)*
Ross J. Born *(Co-CEO)*
David Shaffer *(Co-CEO)*
Matt Petronio *(COO & Exec VP)*
John Kerr *(Dir-Mktg Svcs)*
Brian Bachrach *(Brand Mgr-Peanut Chews & Hot Tamales)*
Mark Hoffman *(Brand Mgr-Peeps)*
Donald Houston *(Sr Brand Mgr-Mike & Ike)*
Brands & Products:
A GREAT CANDY ISN'T MADE . . . IT'S JUST BORN
CHEW-ETS
HOT TAMALES
JUSTBORN
MARSHMALLOW PEEPS
MIKE AND IKE
PEANUT CHEWS
PEEPS
SPOOKY FRIENDS
TEENEE BEENEE
ZOURS
Advertising Agency:
Mediaworx
4 Research Dr, Ste 402
Shelton, CT 06484
Tel.: (203) 402-7242

KANAN ENTERPRISES, INC.
(d/b/a King Nut)
31900 Solon Rd
Solon, OH 44139
Tel.: (440) 248-8484
Fax: (440) 248-0153
E-mail: info@kingnut.com
Web Site: www.kingnut.com
E-Mail For Key Personnel:
Marketing Director: mrkanan@kingnut.com
Approx. Number Employees: 125
Business Description:
Processor, Retailer & Distr Nuts & Other Snacks
S.I.C.: 2068; 2034
N.A.I.C.S.: 311911; 311423
Personnel:
Michael Kanan *(Chm)*
Martin Kanan *(Pres & CEO)*
Matthew Kanan *(Exec VP-Sls & Mktg)*
Lynn Gordon *(Mgr-Natl Sls)*
Brian Keegan *(Mgr-West)*
Eric Riester *(Mgr-East)*
John Tutolo *(Mgr-Natl Sls)*
Brands & Products:
KING NUT
PETERSON'S
Advertising Agency:
Harvey Alpert & Co. Inc.
2014 S Sepulveda Blvd Ste 200
Los Angeles, CA 90025
Tel.: (310) 689-6000
Fax: (310) 689-6010

LIBERTY ORCHARDS CO., INC.
117 Mission St
Cashmere, WA 98815
Mailing Address:
PO Box C
Cashmere, WA 98815
Tel.: (509) 782-2191
Fax: (509) 782-1487
Toll Free: (800) 888-5696
E-mail: service@libertyorchards.com
Web Site: www.libertyorchards.com
Approx. Number Employees: 50
Year Founded: 1920
Business Description:
Candy & Confection Mfr & Retailer
S.I.C.: 2099; 5961
N.A.I.C.S.: 311340; 454113
Export
Media: 8-18-21-26
Distr.: Natl.
Budget Set: Jan.
Personnel:
Gregory A. Taylor *(Pres & CEO)*
Brad Thomas *(CFO & COO)*
J. Michael Rainey *(Sr VP-Sls)*
Brands & Products:
APLETS
BERRY DELIGHTS
CHOCOLATE DREAMLETS
COTLETS
CRANBERRY-APLETS
FRUIT CHOCOLATES
FRUIT DELIGHTS
GRAPELETS
HAWAIIAN FRUIT DELIGHTS
LIBERTY ORCHARDS
NUT-FREE APPLE & APRICOT SMOOTHEES
NUT-FREE FRUIT PARFAITS
NUT FREE MINT-SMOOTHEES
NUT-FREE SMOOTHEES
OLD-FASHIONED LOCOUM
SUGAR-FREE DELIGHTS

LINDT & SPRUNGLI (USA) INC.
(Sub. of Lindt & Sprungli (International) AG)
1 Fine Chocolate Pl
Stratham, NH 03885
Tel.: (603) 778-8100
Fax: (603) 778-6210
Toll Free: (877) 695-4638
E-mail: info@lindt.com
Web Site: www.lindtusa.com
Approx. Number Employees: 250
Year Founded: 1925
Business Description:
Chocolate Products Mfr & Distr
S.I.C.: 2066; 5149
N.A.I.C.S.: 311320; 424490
Personnel:
Thomas Linemayr *(Pres & CEO)*
Danielle LaChance *(Dir-Mktg)*
Brands & Products:
LINDT
Advertising Agency:
Gotham Incorporated
150 E 42nd St 12th Fl
New York, NY 10017
Tel.: (212) 414-7000
Fax: (212) 414-7095

LUCKS FOOD DECORATING COMPANY
3003 S Pine St
Tacoma, WA 98409-4713
Tel.: (253) 383-4815
Fax: (253) 383-0071
Toll Free: (800) 426-9778
E-mail: info@lucks.com
Web Site: www.lucks.com
Approx. Number Employees: 225
Year Founded: 1903
Business Description:
Pastry Decoration Mfr
S.I.C.: 5149; 5046
N.A.I.C.S.: 424490; 423440
Import Export
Advertising Expenditures: $500,000
Media: 4-13-16-26
Personnel:
William G. Lucks *(Owner)*

Key to Media (For complete agency information see *The Advertising Red Books-Agencies* edition):
1. Bus. Publs. 2. Cable T.V. 3. Catalogs & Directories. 4. Co-op Adv. 5. Consumer Mags. 6. D.M. to Bus. Estab.7. D.M. to Consumers
8. Daily Newsp. 9. Exhibits/Trade Shows 10. Foreign 11. Infomercial 12. Internet Adv.13. Multimedia 14. Network Radio
15. Network T.V. 16. Newsp. Distr. Mags. 17. Other 18. Outdoor (Posters, Transit) 19. Point of Purchase20. Premiums, Novelties
21. Product Samples 22. Special Events Mktg. 23. Spot Radio 24. Spot T.V. 25. Weekly Newsp. 26. Yellow Page Adv.

Brands & Products:
DEC-ONS
DESIGNER PRINTS
EDIBLE IMAGE
LUCKS
PRINT-ONS

MAFCO WORLDWIDE CORPORATION

(Sub. of M & F Worldwide Corp.)
3rd St & Jefferson Ave
Camden, NJ 08104
Tel.: (856) 964-8840
Fax: (856) 964-6029
E-mail: jswanson@mafcolicorice.com
Web Site: www.mafcolicorice.com
Approx. Sls.: $24,200,000
Approx. Number Employees: 275
Year Founded: 1850
Business Description:
Licorice Products & Flavor Additive Mfr
S.I.C.: 2099
N.A.I.C.S.: 311340
Media: 2
Distr.: Intl.; Natl.
Budget Set: Dec.
Personnel:
Stephen G. Taub *(Pres & CEO)*
Jeffrey S. Robinson *(CFO & SVP)*
Brands & Products:
MAGNASWEET

MARS, INCORPORATED

6885 Elm St
McLean, VA 22101
Tel.: (703) 821-4900
Fax: (703) 448-9678
Web Site: www.mars.com
Sales Range: $15-24.9 Billion
Approx. Number Employees: 48,000
Year Founded: 1911
Business Description:
Candy & Other Food Products Mfr & Whslr
S.I.C.: 2064; 2048; 2099; 3556; 5145
N.A.I.C.S.: 311330; 311119; 311340; 333294; 424450
Export
Advertising Expenditures: $253,900,000
Cable T.V.: $16,590,000; Consumer Mags.: $12,315,000; Daily Newsp.: $997,000; Network Radio: $1,704,000; Network T.V.: $64,605,000; Other: $125,700,000; Outdoor (Posters, Transit): $239,000; Spot Radio: $1,373,000; Spot T.V.: $30,377,000
Distr.: Intl.; Natl.
Personnel:
John Franklyn Mars *(Chm)*
Paul S. Michaels *(Pres & CEO)*
Olivier Goudet *(CFO & Exec VP)*
Bruce McColl *(Global CMO)*
Harold Schmitz *(Chief Science Officer)*
Alberto Mora *(Gen Counsel, Sec & VP)*
Timothy LeBel *(VP-Sls-In Store Solutions, Grocery & Value Channels)*
Aileen Richards *(VP-Personnel & Org)*
Anibal Martini *(Dir-Global Mktg-M & M's)*
Paul Aitkin *(Brand Mgr-Dolmio)*
Crystal Caughill *(Brand Mgr)*
Charlotte Moffat *(Brand Mgr)*
Gavin White *(Brand Mgr)*
Brian Crowley *(Mgr-ECommerce & CRM)*
Cristina Smejkal *(Mgr-Media)*
Brands & Products:
3 MUSKETEERS
AMICELLI
AQUARIAN
BISC & BOUNTY
CANIGOU
CASTELLARI
CATSAN
CELEBRATIONS
CESAR
CHAPPI
CHOOZERS
COCOAVIA
COMBOS
COOKIES & CRAZY HAIR
DOLMIO
DOVE
DOVEBARS
EBLY
ETHEL-M
EXELPET
FANFARE
FLAVIA
FLING
FLYTE
FROLIC
GALAXY
GOLDEN COB
GOOD-O
GOODLIFE
GUMMIBURSTS
KAL KAN
KAN TONG
KIT E KAT
KLIX
KUDOS
LINGUANOTTO
LOYAL
LUCKY
M&M'S
MALTESERS
MARS
MASTERFOOD SERVICES
MASTERFOODS
MILKYWAY
MONDO
MY DOG
PEDIGREE
PEDIGREE DENTABONE
PEDIGREE MEATY BITES
PEDIGREE OPTIMUM
PEDIGREE PAL
RARIS
REVELS
RONRON
SEEDS OF CHANGE
SHEBA
SNICKERS
SNICKERS CHARGED
SUZI-WAN
TRACKER
TRILL
TUNES
TWIX
TWIX JAVA
UNCLE BEN'S
WALTHAM
WHISKAS
WINERGY
Advertising Agencies:
Abbott Mead Vickers BBDO
151 Marylebone Rd
London, NW1 5QE, United Kingdom
Tel.: (44) 20 7616 3500
Fax: (44) 207 616 3600

BBDO New York
1285 Ave of the Americas 7th Fl
New York, NY 10019-6028
Tel.: (212) 459-5000
Cesar
Extra
M&M's
Mars/Milky Way
Sheba
Snickers

BBDO Worldwide Inc.
(Sub. of Omnicom Group, Inc.)
1285 Ave of the Americas
New York, NY 10019-6028
Tel.: (212) 459-5000
Fax: (212) 459-6645
Snickers
Uncle Ben's

Big Spaceship
45 Main St Ste 716
Brooklyn, NY 11201
Tel.: (718) 222-0281
Fax: (718) 971-1062
Skittles Website

Charlex
2 W 45th St
New York, NY 10036
Tel.: (212) 719-4600
Fax: (212) 840-2747

Digitas Inc.
33 Arch St
Boston, MA 02110
Tel.: (617) 867-1000
Fax: (617) 867-1111
GummiBursts

Gotham Direct
353 Lexington Ave 14th Fl
New York, NY 10016
Tel.: (212) 279-1474
Fax: (212) 279-1475
M&M's

ID Media
(Part of the Interpublic Group of Companies)
100 W 33rd St
New York, NY 10001
Tel.: (212) 907-7011
Fax: (212) 907-7290

imc2
12404 Park Central Ste 400
Dallas, TX 75251
Tel.: (214) 224-1000
Fax: (214) 224-1100

Mediacom Interaction
198 7th Ave
New York, NY 10018
Tel.: (212) 912-5200
Fax: (212) 912-5485

Net#work BBDO
East Block
Dunkeld Office Park
Hyde Park
Gauteng, 2196, South Africa
Tel.: (27) 11 912 0000
Fax: (27) 11 447 4529
Snickers

SapientNitro USA, Inc.
215 Park Ave S 2nd Fl
New York, NY 10003-1603
Tel.: (212) 206-1005
Fax: (212) 206-8510
Dove Chocolate

TBWA Chiat Day Los Angeles
5353 Grosvenor Blvd
Los Angeles, CA 90066
Tel.: (310) 305-5000
Fax: (310) 305-6000
(Pedigree, Pet Adoption)
Twix

TBWA/Worldwide
(Sub. of Omnicom Group, Inc.)
488 Madison Ave 5th Fl
New York, NY 10022-5702
Tel.: (212) 804-1300
Fax: (212) 804-1333
Balisto Chocolate (Pan-European Creative Duties)
Pedigree
Skittles
Starburst
Twix
Whiskas

Weber Shandwick
(Sub. of The Interpublic Group of Companies)
919 3rd Ave
New York, NY 10022
Tel.: (212) 445-8000
Fax: (212) 445-8001
M&M's
Snicker
— Betsy Shea *(Acct Exec)*

Weber Shandwick-Chicago
676 N St Clair Ste 1000
Chicago, IL 60611
Tel.: (312) 988-2400
Fax: (312) 988-2363
(Pedigree, Pet Adoption)

MARS NORTH AMERICA

(Div. of Mars, Incorporated)
800 High St
Hackettstown, NJ 07840-1552
Tel.: (908) 852-1000
Fax: (908) 813-8126
Fax: (908) 850-2624
Toll Free: (800) 551-0702
Web Site: www.mars.com
Approx. Number Employees: 150
Year Founded: 1911
Business Description:
Food, Snack & Petcare Products Mfr
S.I.C.: 2066; 2047
N.A.I.C.S.: 311320; 311111
Import Export
Media: 2-3-6-9-10-11-13-14-15-16-18-19-20-21-22-23-24-25
Personnel:
Olivier Goudet *(CFO & Exec VP)*
Bob Gamgort *(Pres-North America)*
Alberto Mora *(Sec, VP & Gen Counsel)*
Jim Cass *(VP & Gen Mgr-MARS Direct)*
Margaret Asselin-Woods *(VP-Sls-Dove Chocolate Discoveries)*
Aileen Richards *(VP-Personnel & Org)*
Richard Ware *(VP-Supply, Res, Dev & Procurement)*

Key to Media (For complete agency information see *The Advertising Red Books-Agencies* edition):
1. Bus. Publs. 2. Cable T.V. 3. Catalogs & Directories. 4. Co-op Adv. 5. Consumer Mags. 6. D.M. to Bus. Estab.7. D.M. to Consumers 8. Daily Newsp. 9. Exhibits/Trade Shows 10. Foreign 11. Infomercial 12. Internet Adv.13. Multimedia 14. Network Radio 15. Network T.V. 16. Newsp. Distr. Mags. 17. Other 18. Outdoor (Posters, Transit) 19. Point of Purchase20. Premiums, Novelties 21. Product Samples 22. Special Events Mktg. 23. Spot Radio 24. Spot T.V. 25. Weekly Newsp. 26. Yellow Page Adv.

Mars North America — (Continued)

Anibal Martini *(Dir-Global Mktg-M & M's)*
Ryan Bowling *(Dir-External Comm)*

Advertising Agencies:
BBDO New York
1285 Ave of the Americas 7th Fl
New York, NY 10019-6028
Tel.: (212) 459-5000
Dark Chocolate M&Ms

BBDO West
555 Market St 17th Fl
San Francisco, CA 94105
Tel.: (415) 808-6200
Fax: (415) 808-6221
Cesar

Capita Technologies, Inc.
17600 Gillette Ave
Irvine, CA 92614
Tel.: (949) 260-3000
Fax: (949) 851-9875

imc2
12404 Park Central Ste 400
Dallas, TX 75251
Tel.: (214) 224-1000
Fax: (214) 224-1100
MARS Direct

TBWA Chiat Day New York
488 Madison Ave
New York, NY 10022
Tel.: (212) 804-1000
Fax: (212) 804-1200
Skittles
GummiBursts

MARTIN'S FAMOUS PASTRY SHOPPES

1000 Potato Roll Ln
Chambersburg, PA 17201
Tel.: (717) 263-9580
Fax: (717) 263-6687
Web Site: www.potatoroll.com
Approx. Number Employees: 500
Business Description:
Snack Foods, Pastries & Cookies Mfr
S.I.C.: 2051; 2052
N.A.I.C.S.: 311812; 311821
Media: 6-10-18-19-21-22-23-25
Personnel:
James Martin *(Pres)*
Dennis Wenrick *(VP-Sls & Mktg)*

MCKEE FOODS CORPORATION

10260 McKee Rd
Collegedale, TN 37315
Mailing Address:
PO Box 750
Collegedale, TN 37315-0750
Tel.: (423) 238-7111
Fax: (423) 238-7170
E-mail: comment@mckeefoods.com
Web Site: www.mckeefoods.com
Approx. Sls.: $1,100,000,000
Approx. Number Employees: 6,570
Year Founded: 1934
Business Description:
Cake & Cookie Baker
S.I.C.: 2051; 2052
N.A.I.C.S.: 311812; 311821
Export
Media: 3-6-15-23-24
Distr.: Natl.
Budget Set: June
Personnel:
Ellsworth McKee *(Chm & Chief Admin Officer)*
Mike McKee *(Pres & CEO)*
Barry Patterson *(CFO)*
Eva Lynne Disbro *(VP-HR)*
Barry Anthony *(Dir-Mktg)*
Jeff Badger *(Brand Mgr-Sunbelt)*
Don Burton *(Sr Product Mgr)*
Chip Stenberg *(Mgr-Product-Little Debbie)*
Brands & Products:
FIELDSTONE
LITTLE DEBBIE
MCKEE
SUNBELT
UNWRAP A SMILE
Advertising Agencies:
Alliance Promotions, Inc.
8014 Cumming Hwy Ste 403-348
Canton, GA 30115
Tel.: (770) 479-0036
Fax: (770) 479-0047

Luckie & Company
600 Luckie Dr Ste 150
Birmingham, AL 35223-2429
Tel.: (205) 879-2121
Fax: (205) 877-9855
(Little Debbie & Sunbelt Snack & Cereals)

Robert N. Pyle & Associates
1223 Potomac St NW
Washington, DC 20007
Tel.: (202) 333-8190
Fax: (202) 337-3809

MIKE-SELL'S POTATO CHIP COMPANY

333 Leo St
Dayton, OH 45404-1007
Tel.: (937) 228-9400
Fax: (937) 461-5707
E-mail: info@mike-sells.com
Web Site: www.mike-sells.com
Approx. Number Employees: 270
Year Founded: 1910
Business Description:
Snack Food Mfr
S.I.C.: 2096; 5145
N.A.I.C.S.: 311919; 424450
Import Export
Advertising Expenditures: $100,000
Media: 2-4-16-26
Personnel:
David Ray *(Pres & CEO)*
Larry Pounds *(CFO)*
Brands & Products:
GROOVY
MIKE-SELL'S
THEY ARE DELICIOUS
Advertising Agencies:
Holland Advertising:Interactive
700 Walnut St Ste 205
Cincinnati, OH 45202-2011
Tel.: (513) 744-3000
Fax: (513) 721-1269

Willis Case Harwood Marketing Communications Inc.
(d/b/a WCH Marketing Communications)
3411 Office Park Dr
Dayton, OH 45439-2285
Tel.: (937) 299-7394
Fax: (937) 299-9290
Toll Free: (888) 299-7394

MILLER'S HONEY COMPANY

125 E Laurel St
Colton, CA 92324-2462
Tel.: (909) 825-1722
Fax: (909) 825-5932
E-mail: bee@millershoney.com
Web Site: www.millershoney.com
Sales Range: $10-24.9 Million
Approx. Number Employees: 25
Year Founded: 1894
Business Description:
Mfr of Honey Products
S.I.C.: 2099
N.A.I.C.S.: 311999
Import Export
Media: 21
Distr.: Reg.
Personnel:
Merrill Paxman *(VP-Sls & Mktg)*
Brands & Products:
ALFALFA BLOSSOM
AVOCADO BLOSSOM
BUCKWHEAT BLOSSOM
CLOVER BLOSSOM
EUCALYPTUS BLOSSOM
GOLDEN MEADOW
HAWAIIAN BLOSSOM
MILLER'S HONEY
ORANGE BLOSSOM
RITA MILLER'S
SAGE BLOSSOM
SUPERIOR HONEY
TUPELO BLOSSOM
WILD HONEY
WILDFLOWER BLOSSOM

MRS. BAIRD'S BAKERIES, INC.

(Sub. of Bimbo Bakeries USA Inc.)
7301 S Fwy
Fort Worth, TX 76134-4004
Mailing Address:
PO Box 937
Fort Worth, TX 76101-0937
Tel.: (817) 293-6230
Fax: (817) 615-3090
Toll Free: (877) 224-7374
Toll Free: (800) 366-7921
Web Site: www.mrsbairds.com
Approx. Rev.: $415,000,000
Approx. Number Employees: 900
Business Description:
Bread, Cakes & Sweets Mfr
S.I.C.: 2051
N.A.I.C.S.: 311812
Media: 8-18-19-20-21-22-23
Distr.: Reg.
Budget Set: Sept.
Personnel:
Gary Prince *(Pres)*
Arturo Chavez *(VP-Mktg)*
Brands & Products:
MRS. BAIRD'S
Advertising Agency:
Moroch Partners
3625 N Hall St Ste 1100
Dallas, TX 75219-5122
Tel.: (214) 520-9700
Fax: (214) 252-1724
Bakery Products
— Ashley Movold *(Asst Acct Exec)*

MRS. FIELDS GIFTS, INC.

(Sub. of Mrs. Fields Famous Brands, LLC)
1717 S 4800 W
Salt Lake City, UT 84104
Tel.: (801) 412-8803
Fax: (801) 412-8899
Toll Free: (800) 266-5437
Web Site: www.mrsfields.com
Approx. Number Employees: 200
Year Founded: 1996
Business Description:
Gourmet Cookie & Confection Online Retailer
S.I.C.: 5961; 2052
N.A.I.C.S.: 454111; 311821
Import Export
Media: 4-7-8-13

MRS. FIELDS' ORIGINAL COOKIES, INC.

(Holding of Capricorn Holdings, Inc.)
2855 E Cottonwood Pkwy Ste 400
Salt Lake City, UT 84121-7050
Tel.: (801) 736-5600
Fax: (801) 736-5970
Toll Free: (800) 266-5437
E-mail: resumes@mrsfields.com
Web Site: www.mrsfields.com
Sales Range: $100-124.9 Million
Approx. Number Employees: 300
Year Founded: 1977
Business Description:
Holding Company; Cookie, Confectionery & Frozen Yogurt Products Mfr, Retailer & Quick-Service Restaurant Owner & Franchisor
S.I.C.: 6719; 2052; 2096; 5461; 6794
N.A.I.C.S.: 551112; 311821; 311919; 445291; 533110
Advertising Expenditures: $5,000,000
Media: 5-7-8-9-10-14-15-16-19-21-25
Distr.: Intl.; Natl.
Personnel:
Timothy Casey *(Pres & CEO)*
Michael R. Ward *(Chief Legal Officer & Sec)*
Rob Streett *(Sr VP-Franchise Dev/ Strategic Partnerships)*
Brands & Products:
MRS. FIELDS
TCBY
Advertising Agency:
StruckAxiom
159 W Broadway Ste 200
Salt Lake City, UT 84101
Tel.: (801) 531-0122
Fax: (801) 531-0123

NEW ENGLAND CONFECTIONERY COMPANY INC.

(Holding of AMERICAN CAPITAL, LTD.)
(d/b/a NECCO)
135 American Legion Hwy
Revere, MA 02151
Tel.: (781) 485-4500
Fax: (781) 485-4509
Toll Free: (800) 225-1470
E-mail: wafer2wafer@necco.com
Web Site: www.necco.com
Sales Range: $250-299.9 Million
Approx. Number Employees: 550
Year Founded: 1847
Business Description:
Candy Mfr
S.I.C.: 2099; 2066
N.A.I.C.S.: 311340; 311320

Key to Media (For complete agency information see *The Advertising Red Books-Agencies* edition):
1. Bus. Publs. 2. Cable T.V. 3. Catalogs & Directories. 4. Co-op Adv. 5. Consumer Mags. 6. D.M. to Bus. Estab.7. D.M. to Consumers
8. Daily Newsp. 9. Exhibits/Trade Shows 10. Foreign 11. Infomercial 12. Internet Adv.13. Multimedia 14. Network Radio
15. Network T.V. 16. Newsp. Distr. Mags. 17. Other 18. Outdoor (Posters, Transit) 19. Point of Purchase20. Premiums, Novelties
21. Product Samples 22. Special Events Mktg. 23. Spot Radio 24. Spot T.V. 25. Weekly Newsp. 26. Yellow Page Adv.

Export
Advertising Expenditures: $430,000
Bus. Publs.: $25,000; Co-op Adv.: $50,000; Consumer Mags.: $90,000; Daily Newsp.: $50,000; Exhibits/Trade Shows: $50,000; Other: $20,000; Point of Purchase: $20,000; Product Samples: $50,000; Special Events Mktg.: $50,000; Spot Radio: $25,000
Distr.: Natl.
Budget Set: Nov.
Personnel:
Hans Becher *(VP-Sls)*
Brands & Products:
BANANA SPLIT PEG BAG
CLARK BAR
CLARK JUNIOR TUB
CYBERSPEAK
DOUBLE DIPPED PEANUTS
HAVILAND
MARY JANE
NECCO CANDY BUTTONS
NECCO CHOCOLATE WAFERS
SKY BAR
SLAP STIX
SWEETHEARTS
ULTRA MINTS

THE NUTRASWEET COMPANY
(Holding of J.W. Childs Associates, L.P.)
222 Merchandise Mart Plz Ste 936
Chicago, IL 60654-1001
Tel.: (312) 873-5000
Fax: (312) 873-5050
Toll Free: (800) 323-5316
Web Site: www.nutrasweet.com
Approx. Number Employees: 500
Business Description:
Low Calorie Sweetener Mfr
S.I.C.: 2869; 5169
N.A.I.C.S.: 325199; 424690
Personnel:
William DeFer *(Pres)*
Craig R. Petray *(CEO)*
Brands & Products:
NUTRASWEET
Advertising Agency:
DesignKitchen
1140 W Fulton Market
Chicago, IL 60607-1219
Tel.: (312) 455-0388
Fax: (312) 455-0285

PERFETTI VAN MELLE USA, INC.
(Sub. of Perfetti Van Melle International Trust B.V.)
3645 Turfway Rd
Erlanger, KY 41018
Mailing Address:
PO Box 18190
Erlanger, KY 41018-0190
Tel.: (859) 283-1234
Fax: (859) 283-1316
E-mail: customer.relations@uspvmgrp.com
Web Site: www.Perfetti.com
Approx. Number Employees: 200
Year Founded: 1972
Business Description:
Mfr. of Confectionery Products
S.I.C.: 5145; 2099
N.A.I.C.S.: 424450; 311340
Import Export
Advertising Expenditures: $750,000
Media: 6-9-10-11-13-15-16-19-21-24
Distr.: Natl.
Personnel:
Ronald Korenhof *(Pres)*
Irene Pritchett *(Brand Mgr-Airheads)*
Ken Brock *(Mgr-Trade Mktg & Analytics-North America)*
Advertising Agency:
The Martin Agency
One Shockoe Plz
Richmond, VA 23219-4132
Tel.: (804) 698-8000
Fax: (804) 698-8001
Mentos
Microsite

PERRY'S ICE CREAM CO., INC.
1 Ice Cream Plz
Akron, NY 14001-1036
Tel.: (716) 542-5492
Fax: (716) 542-2544
Toll Free: (800) 873-7797
Web Site: www.perrysicecream.com
Approx. Sls.: $42,000,000
Approx. Number Employees: 300
Year Founded: 1918
Business Description:
Mfr. of Ice Cream
S.I.C.: 2024; 5812
N.A.I.C.S.: 311520; 722110
Import
Advertising Expenditures: $694,000
Bus. Publs.: $3,000; Co-op Adv.: $50,000; Consumer Mags.: $5,000; D.M. to Bus. Estab.: $2,000; Daily Newsp.: $70,000; Exhibits/Trade Shows: $10,000; Other: $10,000; Outdoor (Posters, Transit): $24,000; Point of Purchase: $25,000; Premiums, Novelties: $25,000; Product Samples: $200,000; Special Events Mktg.: $20,000; Spot Radio: $50,000; Spot T.V.: $200,000
Distr.: Reg.
Budget Set: Jan.
Personnel:
Robert Denning *(Pres & CEO)*
David Hodgson *(CIO)*
Timothy Cooley *(VP-Sls & Mktg)*
Nichole Buryta *(Asst Product Mgr)*
Brands & Products:
ANDES
CARB DELITE
FOOL'S GOLD
IT'S THE ICE CREAM-IEST
PANDA PAWS
PERRY'S ICE CREAM
PINT SIZE TEMPTATIONS
SWEDISH GLACE

PEZ CANDY, INC.
35 Prindle Hill Rd
Orange, CT 06477-3616
Tel.: (203) 795-0531
Fax: (203) 799-1679
E-mail: info@pez.com
Web Site: www.pez.com
Approx. Number Employees: 150
Year Founded: 1952
Business Description:
Mfr. of Candy, Dispensers & Wafers
S.I.C.: 5145
N.A.I.C.S.: 424450
Import Export
Media: 2-4-5-8-10-13-19-21
Distr.: Intl.; Natl.
Personnel:
Joseph V Vittoria *(CEO)*
Mark Morrissey *(COO)*
William Damberg *(Reg Mgr-Sls)*
Brands & Products:
PEZ

PIERRE'S FRENCH ICE CREAM COMPANY
6200 Euclid Ave
Cleveland, OH 44103
Tel.: (216) 432-1144
Fax: (216) 432-0001
E-mail: icecream@pierres.com
Web Site: www.pierres.com
Approx. Number Employees: 150
Year Founded: 1932
Business Description:
Ice Cream Mfr & Sales
S.I.C.: 2024; 5812
N.A.I.C.S.: 311520; 722110
Media: 1-2-4-5-6-7-8-9-10-13-16-17-18-19-20-21-22-23-25-26
Brands & Products:
BANANA BUDDIES
CARB SUCCESS
FROSTED SMOOTHIES
GUITAR MANIA
IS IT IN YOUR FREEZER?
KITCHEN SINK
PIERRE'S
PIERRE'S FRENCH ICE CREAM
PIERRE'S FROSTED SMOOTHIES
PIERRE'S SLENDER
SLENDER
SLIDE-UPS
SPIRIT OF AMERICA
THUNDER
TURTLICIOUS

THE POPCORN FACTORY
(Sub. of 1-800-Flowers.com, Inc.)
13970 W Laurel Dr
Lake Forest, IL 60045-4533
Tel.: (847) 362-0028
Fax: (847) 362-9680
Toll Free: (800) 323-2676
E-mail: sales@thepopcornfactory.com
Web Site:
www.thepopcornfactory.com
E-Mail For Key Personnel:
Sales Director: sales@thepopcornfactory.com
Sales Range: $50-74.9 Million
Approx. Number Employees: 70
Year Founded: 1979
Business Description:
Mfr. & Retailer of Large Gift Canisters of Popcorn
S.I.C.: 2096; 5961
N.A.I.C.S.: 311919; 454113
Import Export
Media: 4-7-8-13-17
Distr.: Bus.-to-Bus; Direct to Consumer
Budget Set: Oct.
Personnel:
James F. McCann *(Chm & CEO)*
Guy G. Minetti *(Vice Chm)*
Christopher McCann *(Pres)*
Alan Petrik *(COO)*
Trish Popiolek *(Mgr-Circulation)*
Brands & Products:
E-MMEDIATE GIFTS
GREETING CANS
KETTLECORN
OCASSIONS
THE POPCORN FACTORY
PUMPKINS ON PARADE
SNACK OF THE MONTH
SNACK TO SCHOOL

PROMOTION IN MOTION, INC.
3 Reuten Dr
Closter, NJ 07624-0558
Tel.: (201) 784-5800
Fax: (201) 784-1010
Toll Free: (800) 369-7391
E-mail: mail@promotioninmotion.com
Web Site:
www.promotioninmotion.com
Approx. Number Employees: 35
Year Founded: 1953
Business Description:
Food & Confectionery Products, Fruit Snacks, Juices & Bottled Water Mfr, Marketer, Exporter & Distr
S.I.C.: 2099; 5441
N.A.I.C.S.: 311340; 445292
Import Export
Media: 2-4-6-9-10-11-18-20-21-23-24
Distr.: Intl.; Natl.
Personnel:
Michael Rosenberg *(Founder & CEO)*
Kurt Rosenberg *(Chm)*
Basant Dwivedi *(COO)*
James Finelli *(VP-Sls)*
Jeff Scutillo *(Sr Dir-Mktg)*
Josh Sharipo *(Dir-Mktg)*
Thomas Walsh *(Dir-Art)*
Brands & Products:
BUDDY BEARS
BUDDY BEARS GUMMY BEARS
CHOCOLAT SUISSE CHOCOLATE BARS
CREAMSICLE
CREAMSICLE CANDY TWISTS
FAMOUS SQWISH CANDY FISH
FARMERS CHOICE BRAND FOOD PRODUCTS
FISHER
FISHER MILK CHOCOLATE PEANUTS
FRUIT PARADE
FRUIT PARADE FRUIT ROLLS & FRUIT SNACKS
FUDGSICLE CANDY TWISTS
MIGHTY MALTS CHOCOLATE MALTED MILK BALLS
MONSTER MALTS
NUCLEAR SQWORMS GUMMI WORMS
PROMOTION IN MOTION
REFRESHMINTS
SOUR JACKS
SOUR JACKS SOUR CANDY
SPEED STRIPS
SQWISH
SUISSE
SUN MAID MILK CHOCOLATE RAISINS
TOGGI
TOGGI CHOCOLATE COVERED WAFERS
TUXEDOS
WE MAKE THE BRANDS YOU LOVE
WELCH'S FRUIT SNACKS

PURECIRCLE USA INC.
915 Harger Rd Ste 250
Oak Brook, IL 60523
Tel.: (630) 361-0374
E-mail: info@purecircleusa.com
Web Site: www.purecircle.com
Business Description:
Producer of Natural High Intensity Sweetener

Key to Media (For complete agency information see *The Advertising Red Books-Agencies* edition):
1. Bus. Publs. 2. Cable T.V. 3. Catalogs & Directories. 4. Co-op Adv. 5. Consumer Mags. 6. D.M. to Bus. Estab.7. D.M. to Consumers 8. Daily Newsp. 9. Exhibits/Trade Shows 10. Foreign 11. Infomercial 12. Internet Adv.13. Multimedia 14. Network Radio 15. Network T.V. 16. Newsp. Distr. Mags. 17. Other 18. Outdoor (Posters, Transit) 19. Point of Purchase20. Premiums, Novelties 21. Product Samples 22. Special Events Mktg. 23. Spot Radio 24. Spot T.V. 25. Weekly Newsp. 26. Yellow Page Adv.

PureCircle USA Inc. — (Continued)
S.I.C.: 2087
N.A.I.C.S.: 311930
Personnel:
Jason Hecker *(Dir-Mktg & PureCircle USA)*
Advertising Agencies:
Euro RSCG Worldwide
36 E Grand Ave
Chicago, IL 60611-3506
Tel.: (312) 337-4400
Fax: (312) 337-5930
Fax: (312) 337-2316
Integrated Agency of Record

Ketchum
1050 Battery St
San Francisco, CA 94111-1209
Tel.: (415) 984-6100
Fax: (415) 984-6102
Public Relations Agency of Record

PURITY FACTORIES LIMITED
96 Blackmarsh Rd
Saint John's, NL A1C 5M9, Canada
Tel.: (709) 579-2035
Fax: (709) 738-2426
Toll Free: (800) 563-3411
E-mail: info@purity.nf.ca
Web Site: www.purity.nf.ca
Approx. Number Employees: 70
Year Founded: 1924
Business Description:
Biscuits, Confectionery, Jams & Fruit Syrups Mfr
S.I.C.: 2052
N.A.I.C.S.: 311821
Advertising Expenditures: $1,000,000
Media: 2-4-5-6-10-14-15-19-20-21-23-24-26
Distr.: Natl.
Budget Set: Oct. -Nov.
Brands & Products:
PURITY
Advertising Agency:
Waterwerks Communications
96 LeMarchant Rd
Saint John's, NL A1C 2H2, Canada
Tel.: (709) 738-5090
Fax: (709) 738-6209
Toll Free: (877) 998-5090

R.L. ALBERT & SON, INC.
2001 W Main St Ste 155
Stanford, CT 06902
Tel.: (203) 622-8655
Fax: (203) 622-7454
E-mail: mainmail@albertscandy.com
Web Site: www.albertscandy.com
Approx. Number Employees: 23
Year Founded: 1915
Business Description:
Importer & Distr. of Confections
S.I.C.: 5145
N.A.I.C.S.: 424450
Import
Media: 5-6-10-11-13
Distr.: Intl.; Natl.
Budget Set: Nov. -Dec.
Brands & Products:
ALBERT'S
JUNGLE JOLLIES

R.M. PALMER COMPANY
77 S 2nd Ave
Reading, PA 19611-1223
Tel.: (610) 372-8971
Fax: (610) 378-5208
E-mail: rmpmail@rmpalmer.com
Web Site: www.rmpalmer.com
E-Mail For Key Personnel:
Sales Director: sales@rmpalmer.com
Approx. Number Employees: 800
Year Founded: 1948
Business Description:
Chocolate & Confectionery Mfr
S.I.C.: 2066; 2064
N.A.I.C.S.: 311320; 311330
Media: 2-4-8-10-21
Distr.: Intl.; Natl.
Budget Set: Apr. -May
Personnel:
Richard M. Palmer *(Pres)*
Dave Abramson *(VP-Sls & Mktg)*
Brands & Products:
AMERICA'S FAVOURITE HOLIDAY CANDY
BUNNY CRISP
EGGBERT
GHOSTLY GOODIES
GHOSTLY TREATS
PALMER
PLUMPKINS
RASPBERRY HEARTS
SUPER SPORTS
TRICKY TREATS
Advertising Agencies:
Harris, Baio & McCullough Inc.
520 S Frnt St
Philadelphia, PA 19147-1723
Tel.: (215) 440-9800
Fax: (215) 440-9812

Volume Public Relations
7000 S Yosemite St Ste 201
Centennial, CO 80112
Tel.: (720) 529-4850

RUSSELL STOVER CANDIES, INC.
4900 Oak St
Kansas City, MO 64112-2702
Tel.: (816) 842-9240
Fax: (816) 561-4350
Toll Free: (800) 777-4028
E-mail: info@russellstover.com
Web Site: www.russellstover.com
E-Mail For Key Personnel:
President: scott.ward@rstover.com
Sales Range: $400-449.9 Million
Approx. Number Employees: 200
Year Founded: 1923
Business Description:
Candy Mfr
S.I.C.: 2064; 5441
N.A.I.C.S.: 311330; 445292
Import Export
Media: 3-4-6-7-8-9-13-15-18-19-20-21-22-23-24-25-26
Distr.: Direct to Consumer; Intl.; Natl.
Personnel:
Thomas S. Ward *(Co-Owner-Kansas City)*
Scott H. Ward *(Co-Pres)*
Paul Bellington *(Treas & Sr VP-Fin)*
Robin Weber *(Sr VP)*
Darrin Buehler *(VP-Pur)*
Angela Ellsworth *(VP-Retail & Adv)*
John O'Hara *(VP-Adv & PR)*
Brands & Products:
ADELAIDES
AMERICAN CLASSICS
BUILD-A-BOX
INTERNATIONALE
MINT DREAM
ORIGIN SELECT
PANGBURNS
PANGBURNS MILLIONAIRES
RUSSELL STOVER
RUSSELL STOVER CANDIES
RUSSELL STOVER COOKIE DOUGH
SOHO
WEIGHTWATCHERS
WHITMAN'S
WHITMAN'S SAMPLER
Advertising Agency:
INK, Inc.
511 Delaware St Ste 200
Kansas City, MO 64105
Tel.: (816) 753-6222
Fax: (816) 753-8188
Toll Free: (866) 753-6222

SARA LEE BAKERY GROUP
(Div. of Sara Lee Corporation)
3500 Lacey Rd
Downers Grove, IL 60515
Tel.: (630) 513-7000
Fax: (630) 598-6081
Toll Free: (800) 449-4284
Web Site: www.saralee.com
Approx. Sls.: $1,100,000,000
Approx. Number Employees: 5,172
Business Description:
Frozen Bakery Products Mfr
S.I.C.: 2051
N.A.I.C.S.: 311812
Media: 2-5-6-10-15-16-19-20-24
Distr.: Natl.
Budget Set: July
Personnel:
Peter Reiner *(VP-Mktg)*
Brands & Products:
SARA LEE BAGELS
SARA LEE CAKE BITES
SARA LEE CALZONE CREATIONS
SARA LEE CHEESECAKE
SARA LEE CHEESECAKE BITES
SARA LEE CINNAMON ROLLS
SARA LEE COFFEE CAKES
SARA LEE CROISSANTS
SARA LEE INDIVIDUAL PASTRIES
SARA LEE LAYER CAKES
SARA LEE MUFFINS
SARA LEE PIES

SCHWAN'S BAKERY INC
(Div. of The Schwan Food Company)
2900 Rolling Pin Ln Ste A
Suwanee, GA 30024
Tel.: (678) 482-3339
Fax: (770) 932-6513
Web Site: www.schwans.com
Sales Range: $150-199.9 Million
Approx. Number Employees: 500
Year Founded: 1950
Business Description:
Dessert Mfr & Distr
S.I.C.: 2053
N.A.I.C.S.: 311813
Advertising Expenditures: $400,000
Media: 2-4-6-9-16-19-21
Distr.: Reg.
Budget Set: Oct.
Personnel:
Greg Flack *(Pres & CEO)*
Brands & Products:
EDWARDS
HEIDI'S GOURMET DESSERTS
Advertising Agencies:
Bolin Marketing & Advertising
2523 Wayzata Blvd Ste 300
Minneapolis, MN 55405
Tel.: (612) 374-1200
Fax: (612) 377-4226
Edwards Desserts
Integrated Social Media Contest

GolinHarris
(Part of the Interpublic Group of Companies)
111 E Wacker Dr 11th Fl
Chicago, IL 60601-4306
Tel.: (312) 729-4000
Fax: (312) 729-4010
Edwards Desserts
Integrated Social Media Contest

SHERWOOD BRANDS INC.
1803 Research Blvd Ste 201
Rockville, MD 20850-6106
Tel.: (301) 309-6161
Fax: (301) 309-6162
E-mail: sales@sherwoodbrands.com
Web Site: www.sherwoodbrands.com
E-Mail For Key Personnel:
Sales Director: sales@sherwoodbrands.com
Sales Range: $25-49.9 Million
Approx. Number Employees: 50
Year Founded: 1985
Business Description:
Confectionery Products & Gift Items Marketer
S.I.C.: 2099; 2052; 2064
N.A.I.C.S.: 311340; 311330; 311821
Import Export
Advertising Expenditures: $1,418,000
Media: 2-4-5-6-10-19-20-21-22-23
Distr.: Intl.
Budget Set: May -June
Personnel:
Uziel Frydman *(CEO)*
Brands & Products:
SOUP DU JOUR

SNYDER'S OF HANOVER, INC.
(Sub. of Snyder's-Lance, Inc.)
1250 York St
Hanover, PA 17331
Tel.: (717) 632-4477
Fax: (717) 632-7207
Toll Free: (800) 233-7125
Web Site:
www.snydersofhanover.com
Sales Range: $650-699.9 Million
Approx. Number Employees: 2,250
Year Founded: 1909
Business Description:
Snack Foods Mfr & Distr
S.I.C.: 2096
N.A.I.C.S.: 311919
Export
Advertising Expenditures: $550,000
Media: 6-9-14-17-18-19-21-23-25
Distr.: Natl.
Budget Set: Nov.
Personnel:
Michael A. Warehime *(Chm)*
Carl Lee *(Pres & CEO)*
Charles E. Good *(CFO)*
John Bartman *(VP-HR)*
Claude O'Connor *(VP-Mktg)*
Brands & Products:
AMERICA'S PRETZEL BAKERY SINCE 1909
CARB-FIX

Key to Media (For complete agency information see *The Advertising Red Books-Agencies* edition):
1. Bus. Publs. 2. Cable T.V. 3. Catalogs & Directories. 4. Co-op Adv. 5. Consumer Mags. 6. D.M. to Bus. Estab.7. D.M. to Consumers
8. Daily Newsp. 9. Exhibits/Trade Shows 10. Foreign 11. Infomercial 12. Internet Adv.13. Multimedia 14. Network Radio
15. Network T.V. 16. Newsp. Distr. Mags. 17. Other 18. Outdoor (Posters, Transit) 19. Point of Purchase20. Premiums, Novelties
21. Product Samples 22. Special Events Mktg. 23. Spot Radio 24. Spot T.V. 25. Weekly Newsp. 26. Yellow Page Adv.

CHEDDAIRS
CHEESE TWISTS
EATSMART
HOMESTYLE
HONEY WHEAT STICKS
JALAPENO
KOSHER DILL
MULTIGRAIN
NIBBLERS
OAT BRAN STICKS
OLDE TYME
OLDE TYME STICKS
RIPPLE
SNAPS
SNYDER'S
SNYDER'S OF HANOVER
VEGGIE CRISPS

Advertising Agency:
Azzam Jordan
305 Washington Ave Ste 305
Baltimore, MD 21204
Tel.: (410) 825-1800
Fax: (410) 825-3997

SOKOL & COMPANY

5315 Dansher Rd
Countryside, IL 60525-3101
Tel.: (708) 482-8250
Fax: (708) 482-9750
Toll Free: (800) EATSOLO
E-mail: info@solofoods.com
Web Site: www.solofoods.com
Approx. Number Employees: 50
Year Founded: 1895
Business Description:
Cake, Pastry & Dessert Fillings, Fruit Glazes, Ice Cream Toppings, Crunches & Almond Paste
S.I.C.: 2099; 2033
N.A.I.C.S.: 311999; 311421
Media: 2-4-5-6-8-9-10-16-19-20-21
Distr.: Natl.
Budget Set: Oct.
Personnel:
John S. Novak, Jr. *(Pres)*
Ralph Pirritano *(COO & Exec VP)*
Pat Rochan *(Controller)*
Eva Karnezis *(Mgr-Mktg)*
Brands & Products:
BAKER
BOHEMIAN KITCHEN
CHUN'S
GREAT TASTES FROM THE INSIDE OUT!
SIMON FISCHER
SOLO

SOPHIE MAE CANDY COMPANY

(Sub. of Family Brands, LLC)
317 N Ave
Atlanta, GA 30308
Tel.: (404) 874-0868
Fax: (404) 875-1910
Web Site: www.smcandy.com
Sales Range: $1-9.9 Million
Approx. Number Employees: 50
Year Founded: 1884
Business Description:
Candy Mfr
S.I.C.: 2096
N.A.I.C.S.: 311919
Media: 4-16
Brands & Products:
B.B. BATS
KITS
SLO POKE
SOPHIE MAE

SORBEE INTERNATIONAL, LLC

9990 Global Rd
Philadelphia, PA 19115
Tel.: (215) 677-5200
Fax: (215) 677-7736
Toll Free: (800) 654-3997
Web Site: www.sorbee.com
Approx. Number Employees: 100
Year Founded: 1981
Business Description:
Sugar-Free Candy, Cookies & Condiments Mfr; Owned by Werther Partners, LLC
S.I.C.: 2087; 2052; 2064; 2099
N.A.I.C.S.: 311999; 311330; 311340; 311821; 311930
Import Export
Advertising Expenditures: $200,000
Media: 2-10
Distr.: Natl.
Personnel:
Elliot Stone *(Founder & Pres)*
Daniel Werther *(Principal)*
Barry H. Sokol *(Exec VP)*
Brands & Products:
DREAM BARS
DREAM CANDY
FRUGELI
SORBEE
STARLITE MINTS
WOW BARS

SPANGLER CANDY COMPANY

400 N Portland St
Bryan, OH 43506-1200
Mailing Address:
PO Box 71
Bryan, OH 43506-0071
Tel.: (419) 636-4221
Fax: (419) 636-3695
E-mail: spangler@bright.net
Web Site: www.spanglercandy.com
Approx. Number Employees: 500
Year Founded: 1906
Business Description:
Mfr. of Candy
S.I.C.: 2099; 2066
N.A.I.C.S.: 311340; 311320
Import Export
Advertising Expenditures: $1,000,000
Media: 2-3-6-7-8-9-13-19-20-21-22-24-25
Distr.: Natl.
Budget Set: July
Personnel:
Dean L. Spangler *(Chm & CEO)*
William Martin *(CFO)*
Jim Knight *(VP-Mktg)*
Evan S. Brock *(Brand Mgr)*
Stacy Shoup *(Mgr-Mktg)*
Brands & Products:
ATOMIC FIREBALL LOLLIPOPS
CANE CLASSICS
CRAZY DIPS
CREMOSA
DUM DUM
DUM DUM CHEWY POPS
DUM DUM GUM POPS
DUM-DUMS
JELLY BASLER BELLY
MARSHMALLOW CIRCUS PEANUTS
PICTURE POPS
RUSH ROX
SAF-T-POP
SAF-T-POPS
SAVE WRAPS FOR STUFF
SMINT
SPANGLER
SPANGLER CANDY CANES
SPANGLER CHOCOLATES
SPANGLER GOLD LEAF
WHISTLE POPS

Advertising Agency:
The Geppetto Group
95 Morton St 8th Fl
New York, NY 10014-3336
Tel.: (212) 462-8140
Fax: (212) 462-8197

STANDARD FUNCTIONAL FOODS GROUP(SFFG)

715 Massman Dr
Nashville, TN 37210-3723
Tel.: (615) 889-6360
Fax: (615) 889-7775
Toll Free: (800) 226-4340
E-mail: sales@standardcandy.com
Web Site: www.sffgi.com
E-Mail For Key Personnel:
Sales Director: sales@standardcandy.com
Approx. Number Employees: 500
Year Founded: 1901
Business Description:
Mfr. of Candy
S.I.C.: 2064
N.A.I.C.S.: 311330
Export
Advertising Expenditures: $240,000
Catalogs & Directories: $30,000; Co-op Adv.: $25,000; Exhibits/Trade Shows: $50,000; Network Radio: $85,000; Other: $30,000; Product Samples: $20,000
Distr.: Natl.
Budget Set: Apr.
Personnel:
Tom Drummond *(Pres & COO)*
James W. Spradley, Jr. *(CEO)*
Neil Spradley *(VP-Ops)*
Joanne Barthel *(Dir-Mktg)*
Brands & Products:
CUMBERLAND RIDGE
GOO GOO CLUSTER

STORCK USA, L.P.

(Sub. of Storck GmbH & Co.)
325 N LaSalle Ste 400
Chicago, IL 60654
Tel.: (312) 467-5700
Fax: (312) 467-9722
Toll Free: (800) 621-7772
E-mail: info@us.storck.com
Web Site: www.storck.com
Approx. Number Employees: 50
Year Founded: 1977
Business Description:
Mfr & Distr of Candy Products
S.I.C.: 5145
N.A.I.C.S.: 424450
Import
Advertising Expenditures: $600,000
Media: 2-4-5-6-8-9-10-15-19-20-21-23-24-25-26
Distr.: Natl.
Budget Set: July
Personnel:
Ralph Hilpuesch *(CEO)*
Andrew Ruttgers *(CFO)*
Scott Ellis *(VP-Mktg)*

SWEET CANDY COMPANY

3780 W Directors Row 1100 S
Salt Lake City, UT 84104-5502
Tel.: (801) 886-1444
Fax: (801) 886-1404
Toll Free: (800) 669-8669
E-mail: mail@sweetcandy.com
Web Site: www.sweetcandy.com
E-Mail For Key Personnel:
President: R.S@sweetcandy.com
Sales Director: brucet@sweetcandy.com
Approx. Number Employees: 150
Year Founded: 1892
Business Description:
Mfr. of Candy
S.I.C.: 2099
N.A.I.C.S.: 311340
Import Export
Media: 2-4-7-10-11-20-21
Distr.: Intl.; Natl.
Personnel:
Richard Kay *(Pres & COO)*
Curtis Fulton *(Dir)*
Bruce Thompson *(Mgr-Natl Sls)*
Brands & Products:
BEAR NECESSITIES
CHERRY STICKS
COUGAR TAFFY
DULCE DE LECHE
MINT STICKS
ORANGE STICKS
PEPPERMINT STICKS
PUMPKIN FACE
RASPBERRY STICKS
SALT WATER TAFFY
SWEET
SWEET'S CINNAMON BEARS
SWEET'S ORANGE STICKS
SWEET'S SALTWATER TAFFY
TART 'N TANGY TOTALLY
TOTALLY TAFFY
UTE TAFFY
YUMMY BEARS

TASTY BAKING COMPANY

Navy Yard Corporate Ctr 3 Crescent Dr Ste 200
Philadelphia, PA 19112
Tel.: (215) 221-8500
Fax: (215) 223-3288
Toll Free: (800) 24TASTY
E-mail: chad.ramsey@tastykake.com
Web Site: www.tastykake.com
Approx. Sls.: $288,590,000
Approx. Number Employees: 625
Year Founded: 1914
Business Description:
Cakes, Pies, Cookies & Donuts Mfr & Sales
S.I.C.: 2051; 2052
N.A.I.C.S.: 311812; 311821
Advertising Expenditures: $3,320,000
Media: 2-5-9-10-17-18-19-20-21-22-23-24-25
Distr.: Reg.
Budget Set: Sept.
Personnel:
James E. Ksansnak *(Chm)*
Charles P. Pizzi *(Pres & CEO)*
Paul D. Ridder *(CFO & Sr VP)*
Laurence Weilheimer *(Gen Counsel, Sec & Sr VP)*
Autumn R. Bayles *(Sr VP-Strategic Ops)*
Robert V. Brown *(Sr VP-Sls)*

Key to Media (For complete agency information see *The Advertising Red Books-Agencies* edition):
1. Bus. Publs. 2. Cable T.V. 3. Catalogs & Directories. 4. Co-op Adv. 5. Consumer Mags. 6. D.M. to Bus. Estab.7. D.M. to Consumers 8. Daily Newsp. 9. Exhibits/Trade Shows 10. Foreign 11. Infomercial 12. Internet Adv.13. Multimedia 14. Network Radio 15. Network T.V. 16. Newsp. Distr. Mags. 17. Other 18. Outdoor (Posters, Transit) 19. Point of Purchase20. Premiums, Novelties 21. Product Samples 22. Special Events Mktg. 23. Spot Radio 24. Spot T.V. 25. Weekly Newsp. 26. Yellow Page Adv.

TASTY BAKING COMPANY — (Continued)

Edwin E. Pixler *(VP & Gen Mgr-Oxford)*
Brendan O'Malley *(VP-Sls)*
Jonathan L. Silvon *(VP-Mktg)*
David A. Vidovich *(VP-HR & Labor Rels)*

Brands & Products:
AUNT SWEETIES
DUTCH MILL
JUNIORS
KANDY KAKES
KREAMIES
KRIMPETS
SENSABLES
SNAK N' FRESH
TASTYKAKE

TOFUTTI BRANDS INC.

50 Jackson Dr
Cranford, NJ 07016-3504
Tel.: (908) 272-2400
Fax: (908) 272-9492
E-mail: info@tofutti.com
Web Site: www.tofutti.com
Approx. Sls.: $17,713,000
Approx. Number Employees: 8
Year Founded: 1987
Business Description:
Mfr & Sales of Soy-Based Frozen Dessert & Food
S.I.C.: 2038; 2024
N.A.I.C.S.: 311412; 311520
Advertising Expenditures: $295,000
Media: 5-6-10-17-19-21-22-23-24-25
Distr.: Intl.; Natl.
Personnel:
David Mintz *(Chm & CEO)*

Brands & Products:
BETTER PECAN
BETTER THAN CREAM CHEESE
BETTER THAN SOUR CREAM
BLUEBERRY CHEESE
CHOCOLATE FUDGE TREATS
COFFEE BREAK TREATS
EGG WATCHERS
HOORAY HOORAY BARS
KEY LIME
LIVING HEALTHY DAIRY FREE & LOVING IT
MARRY ME BARS
MINT BY MINTZ
MINTZ'S BLINTZES
MONKEY BARS
SOUR SUPREME
SOY-CHEESE SLICES
TOFIGGY
TOFUTTI
TOFUTTI CUTIES
TOFUTTI KIDS
TOFUTTI PIZZA PIZZAZ
TOFUTTI SOY-CHEESE SLICES
TOTALLY FUDGE
VANILLA ALMOND BARK
WAVE CUTIES
WILD BERRY

Advertising Agency:
Rubenstein Public Relations
1345 Ave of the Americas
New York, NY 10105
Tel.: (212) 843-8000
Fax: (212) 843-9200
Brand Awareness

TOOTSIE ROLL INDUSTRIES, INC.

7401 S Cicero Ave
Chicago, IL 60629-5818
Tel.: (773) 838-3400
Web Site: www.tootsie.com
Approx. Rev.: $521,448,000
Approx. Number Employees: 2,200
Year Founded: 1896
Business Description:
Candy Mfr
S.I.C.: 2064; 2034; 2061; 2098
N.A.I.C.S.: 311330; 311311; 311423; 311823
Import Export
Advertising Expenditures: $19,350,000
Media: 2-6-7-8-9-14-15-19-23-24
Distr.: Intl.; Natl.
Budget Set: Oct.
Personnel:
Melvin J. Gordon *(Chm & CEO)*
Ellen R. Gordon *(Pres & COO)*
G. Howard Ember *(CFO & VP-Fin)*
Thomas E. Corr *(VP-Mktg & Sls)*
John Grodoski *(Dir-HR)*

Brands & Products:
ANDES
BLOW POPS
BUBBLE BLOX
CARAMEL APPLE POPS
CELLA'S
CHARLESTON CHEW
CHARMS
CHILD'S PLAY
CRY BABY
DOTS & CROWS
DUBBLE BUBBLE
FLUFFY STUFF
FROOTIES
FRUIT ROLLS
JUNIOR KMINTS
JUNIOR MINTS
MASON CROWS
MASON DOTS
NIK-L-NIP
RAZZLES
SUGAR BABIES
SUGAR DADDY
TOOTSIE POPS
TOOTSIE ROLL
TROPICAL STORMZ POPS
WACK-O-WAX
WHERE CANDY FAVORITES COME FROM
ZIP-A-DEE MINI POP

VOORTMAN COOKIES LIMITED

4455 N Service Rd
Burlington, ON L7L 4X7, Canada
Tel.: (905) 335-9500
Fax: (905) 332-5499
E-mail: info@voortman.com
Web Site: www.voortman.com
Approx. Number Employees: 450
Year Founded: 1951
Business Description:
Cookies Mfr & Retailer
S.I.C.: 2052
N.A.I.C.S.: 311821
Media: 11-16
Personnel:
Harry Voortman *(Co-Founder)*
Garry Postma *(Pres)*
Adrian Voortman *(VP-Sls)*
Orlando Decarlo *(Plant Mgr)*
Ronald Baayen *(Mgr-IT)*

Brands & Products:
VOORTMAN COOKIES

WEAVER POPCORN COMPANY, INC.

9850 W Point Dr Ste 100
Indianapolis, IN 46250
Tel.: (765) 934-2101
Fax: (765) 934-4052
Toll Free: (800) 227-6159
E-mail: consumercare@popweaver.com
Web Site: www.popweaver.com
Sales Range: $100-124.9 Million
Approx. Number Employees: 250
Year Founded: 1928
Business Description:
Popcorn Producer & Processor
S.I.C.: 5145
N.A.I.C.S.: 424450
Export
Media: 5-6-7-10-20-21-23-24
Distr.: Intl.
Personnel:
Michael E. Weaver *(Pres & CEO)*

Brands & Products:
NAKSPAKS
POP WEAVER
WEAVER
WEAVER GOLD

WHITMAN'S CANDIES, INC.

(Sub. of Russell Stover Candies, Inc.)
4900 Oak St
Kansas City, MO 64112-2702
Tel.: (816) 842-9240
Fax: (816) 561-4350
E-mail: info@russelstovers.com
Web Site: www.russelstovers.com
E-Mail For Key Personnel:
President: scott.ward@rstover.com
Year Founded: 1842
Business Description:
Wholesaler of Candy
S.I.C.: 5145; 8742
N.A.I.C.S.: 424450; 541611
Import Export
Media: 6-17-19-20-21-22
Distr.: Natl.
Budget Set: Jan.
Personnel:
Thomas S. Ward *(Pres)*
Angela Ellsworth *(VP-Retail & Adv)*
Mark R. Frame *(VP-Sls)*
John O'Hara *(VP-Mktg)*
Kevin Dirks *(Dir-Risk Mngmt & Safety)*

WILBUR CHOCOLATE CO., INC.

(Sub. of Cargill, Inc.)
20 N Broad St
Lititz, PA 17543-1005
Tel.: (717) 626-1131
Fax: (717) 625-2349
Toll Free: (800) 233-0139
Toll Free: (888) 294-5287
Web Site: www.wilburchocolate.com
Approx. Number Employees: 350
Year Founded: 1884
Business Description:
Chocolate, Chocolate Coatings, Bulk Cocoas, Chocolate Chips & Drops, Ice Cream Mixes, Confectionery Coatings Mfr
S.I.C.: 2066
N.A.I.C.S.: 311320
Import Export
Advertising Expenditures: $500,000
Media: 2-4-6-10-13
Distr.: Natl.
Budget Set: Jan.

WM. WRIGLEY JR. COMPANY

(Sub. of Mars, Incorporated)
410 N Michigan Ave Wrigley Bldg
Chicago, IL 60611
Mailing Address:
PO Box 3900
Peoria, IL 61614
Tel.: (312) 644-2121
Fax: (312) 644-0015
Toll Free: (800) WRIGLEY
E-mail: Chris.Perille@wrigley.com
Web Site: www.wrigley.com
E-Mail For Key Personnel:
Public Relations: cperille@wrigley.com
Sales Range: $1-4.9 Billion
Approx. Number Employees: 16,400
Year Founded: 1891
Business Description:
Chewing Gum Mfr
S.I.C.: 5499; 2034; 2098
N.A.I.C.S.: 445299; 311423; 311823
Advertising Expenditures: $479,251,000
Media: 9-13-15-18-19-20-21-22-25
Distr.: Intl.; Natl.
Personnel:
Dushan Petrovich *(Pres)*
Reuben Gamoran *(CFO & VP)*
Martin Schlatter *(CMO)*
Albert Manzone *(Pres-Europe)*
Patrick D. Mitchell *(Chief Procurement Officer & Sr VP-Supply Chain)*
Robert Peterson *(Chief Innovation Officer & Sr VP)*
Paul Chibe *(VP & Gen Mgr-Gums & Mints-US)*
Steve Brunner *(VP-Procurement-WW)*

Brands & Products:
5
AIRWAVES
ALPINE
ALTOIDS
BENEFITS OF CHEWING
BIG LEAGUE CHEW
BIG RED
BOOMER
BUBBLE JUG
BUBBLE TAPE
COBALT
CREME SAVERS
DOUBLEMINT
ECLIPSE
ELIXIR
EXCEL
EXTRA
FLARE
FREEDENT
HUBBA BUBBA
JUICY FRUIT
KENMAN
LIFE SAVERS
LOCKETS
LUCAS
LUSH
ORBIT
PK
RAIN
RONDO
SKWINKLES
SOLANO
SOLSTICE
SQUEEZE POP

Key to Media (For complete agency information see *The Advertising Red Books-Agencies* edition):
1. Bus. Publs. 2. Cable T.V. 3. Catalogs & Directories. 4. Co-op Adv. 5. Consumer Mags. 6. D.M. to Bus. Estab.7. D.M. to Consumers 8. Daily Newsp. 9. Exhibits/Trade Shows 10. Foreign 11. Infomercial 12. Internet Adv.13. Multimedia 14. Network Radio 15. Network T.V. 16. Newsp. Distr. Mags. 17. Other 18. Outdoor (Posters, Transit) 19. Point of Purchase20. Premiums, Novelties 21. Product Samples 22. Special Events Mktg. 23. Spot Radio 24. Spot T.V. 25. Weekly Newsp. 26. Yellow Page Adv.

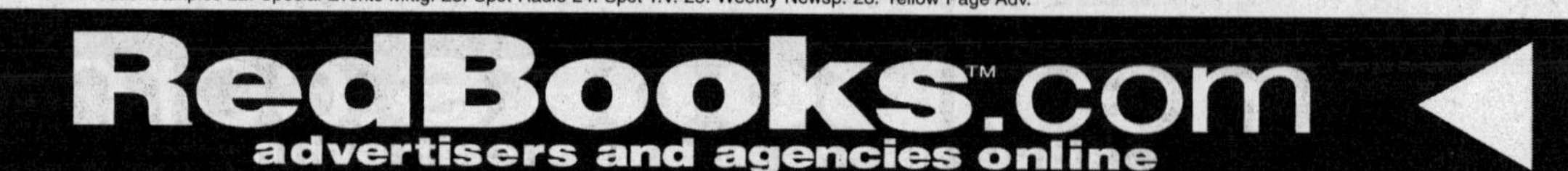

STARBURST
SUGUS
TUENS
WINTERFRESH
WRIGLEY
WRIGLEY'S SPEARMINT
ZING

Advertising Agencies:
Abbott Mead Vickers BBDO
151 Marylebone Rd
London, NW1 5QE, United Kingdom
Tel.: (44) 20 7616 3500
Fax: (44) 207 616 3600
5 Gum

Big Spaceship
45 Main St Ste 716
Brooklyn, NY 11201
Tel.: (718) 222-0281
Fax: (718) 971-1062

The Bravo Group HQ
285 Madison Ave 12th Fl
New York, NY 10017
Tel.: (212) 780-5800
Hispanic
Eclipse

CLM BBDO
93 Rue Nationale
Boulogne-Billancourt, 92513, France
Tel.: (33) 1 4123 4123
Fax: (33) 1 4123 4240
Freedent Tabs White

DDB Chicago
200 E Randolph St
Chicago, IL 60601
Tel.: (312) 552-6000
Fax: (312) 552-2370
Extra
Big Red

DDB South Africa
Silverpoint Office Park Bldg 1 22 Ealing Crescent
Johannesburg, South Africa
Tel.: (27) 11 267 2800
Fax: (27) 86 632 6270
Airwaves
Orbit
Eclipse

DDB Sydney Pty. Ltd.
46-52 Mountain Street Level 3
Ultimo, NSW 2007, Australia
Tel.: (61) 2 8260 2222
Fax: (61) 2 8260 2444
Eclipse

DDB Worldwide Communications Group Inc.
(Sub. of Omnicom Group, Inc.)
(Corporate Headquarters)
437 Madison Ave 5nd Fl
New York, NY 10022-7001
Tel.: (212) 415-2000
Fax: (212) 415-3414
Airwaves
Boomer
Hubba Bubba
Juicy Fruit
Solano
Sugus
LifeSavers

Dig Communications
549 W Randolph Ste 201
Chicago, IL 60661
Tel.: (312) 577-1750
Fax: (312) 577-1760

Energy BBDO
410 N Michigan Ave
Chicago, IL 60611-4213
Tel.: (312) 337-7860
Fax: (312) 337-6871
(Radio, TV, Print & Trade Papers, 5 Gum, Extra Sugarfree Bubble Gum, Extra Sugarfree Gum, Wrigley's Spearmint, Doublemint, Juicy Fruit, Freedent, Hubba Bubba, Winterfresh, Orbit & Big Red Brands)
Creative Agency of Record - Orbit Gum
— Tonise Paul *(Pres.)*

Interbrand
4000 Smith Rd
Cincinnati, OH 45209
Tel.: (513) 421-2210
Fax: (513) 421-2386
Orbit Gum

MediaCom
498 7th Ave
New York, NY 10018
Tel.: (212) 912-4200
Fax: (212) 508-4386

Mindshare
350 W Mart Center Dr Ste 1270
Chicago, IL 60654-1270
Tel.: (312) 242-1100
Fax: (312) 242-1350
5 Gum

RAPP
437 Madison Ave 3rd Fl
New York, NY 10022
Tel.: (212) 817-6800
Fax: (212) 590-8400
5 Gum

Ryan Partnership
(dba D.L. Ryan Companies, Ltd.)
50 Danbury Rd
Wilton, CT 06897-4448
Tel.: (203) 210-3000
Fax: (203) 210-7926
Altoids
Eclipse
Extra
Orbit

Starcom USA
35 W Wacker Dr
Chicago, IL 60601
Tel.: (312) 220-3535
Fax: (312) 220-6530
Mars
Media Buying
Wrigley

WORLD'S FINEST CHOCOLATE, INC.

4801 S Lawndale Ave
Chicago, IL 60632-3065
Tel.: (773) 847-4600
Fax: (773) 847-7804
Fax: (877) 256-2685
Toll Free: (800) 366-2462, ext. 5635
Toll Free: (888) 821-8452
E-mail: contactus@wfchocolate.com
Web Site: www.wfchocolate.com
Approx. Number Employees: 700
Year Founded: 1938
Business Description:
Mfr. of Chocolate & Cocoa Products
S.I.C.: 2066; 5947
N.A.I.C.S.: 311320; 453220
Import Export
Advertising Expenditures: $45,000
Media: 2-4-5-7-8-10-13-21
Distr.: Direct to Consumer; Natl.
Budget Set: Jan.
Personnel:
Edmond F. Opler, III *(Chm & CEO)*
Michael Broz *(CFO)*
Mary Holland *(VP-HR)*
Tyler Jeffery *(VP-Sls & Mktg)*
Brands & Products:
CARAMELS WHIRLS
CONTINENTAL
FUND RAISIN'S
IMPERIAL
MAJESTIQUE
MINT MELTAWAYS
RAVIN' RAISINS
WORLD'S FINEST

YOUNG PECAN, INC.

(Sub. of King Ranch, Inc.)
1200 Pecan St
Florence, SC 29501-2827
Mailing Address:
PO Box 5779
Florence, SC 29502-5779
Tel.: (843) 664-2330
Fax: (843) 664-2344
Toll Free: (800) 829-6864
E-mail: sales@youngpecan.com
Web Site: www.youngpecan.com
E-Mail For Key Personnel:
Sales Director: sales@youngpecan.com
Sales Range: $75-99.9 Million
Approx. Number Employees: 183
Business Description:
Pecan Farming & Distr
S.I.C.: 0173; 5159
N.A.I.C.S.: 111335; 424590
Import Export
Media: 2-4-13-21-23-24
Personnel:
James W. Swink *(Pres & CEO)*
Helen M. Watts *(Exec VP)*
Brands & Products:
YOUNG'S GOLD SWEET

ZAPP'S POTATO CHIPS, INC.

307 E Airline Hwy
Gramercy, LA 70052
Tel.: (225) 869-9777
Fax: (225) 869-9779
Toll Free: (800) HOTCHIP
Web Site: www.zapps.com
Approx. Number Employees: 100
Year Founded: 1985
Business Description:
Mfr. of Potato Chips
S.I.C.: 2096
N.A.I.C.S.: 311919
Advertising Expenditures: $100,000
Media: 6-17-21
Distr.: Reg.
Personnel:
Rod Olson *(Pres)*
Brands & Products:
BEE-LICIOUS
BORN TO FRY
CAJUN CRAWTATOR
CAJUN DILL
HOTTER 'N HOT JALAPENO
MESQUITE BBQ
NEW ORLEANS MARDI-GRAS
ZAPP'S

Key to Media (For complete agency information see *The Advertising Red Books-Agencies* edition):
1. Bus. Publs. 2. Cable T.V. 3. Catalogs & Directories. 4. Co-op Adv. 5. Consumer Mags. 6. D.M. to Bus. Estab.7. D.M. to Consumers 8. Daily Newsp. 9. Exhibits/Trade Shows 10. Foreign 11. Infomercial 12. Internet Adv.13. Multimedia 14. Network Radio 15. Network T.V. 16. Newsp. Distr. Mags. 17. Other 18. Outdoor (Posters, Transit) 19. Point of Purchase20. Premiums, Novelties 21. Product Samples 22. Special Events Mktg. 23. Spot Radio 24. Spot T.V. 25. Weekly Newsp. 26. Yellow Page Adv.

Tires, Tubes, Rubber Molded Products & Plastics

Automobile Tires & Tubes — Bicycle Tires — Plastics — Rubber

ABNOTE NORTH AMERICA
(Div. of American Banknote Corporation)
225 Rivermoor St
Boston, MA 02132-4905
Tel.: (617) 325-9600
Fax: (617) 327-1235
Toll Free: (800) 776-7333
E-mail: abco@abco.com
Web Site: www.arthurblank.com
Approx. Number Employees: 190
Year Founded: 1934
Business Description:
Specialty Printing & Integrated Card Solutions
S.I.C.: 3081; 2752
N.A.I.C.S.: 326113; 323110
Advertising Expenditures: $500,000
Media: 2-7-10
Distr.: Intl.; Natl.
Budget Set: Oct.
Personnel:
Keith E. Goldstein *(CEO-US Ops)*
Jake Jacobs *(Exec VP-Sls & Mktg)*
Joe Caffarella *(Sr VP-Govt Contracts)*
Cheryl Bacon *(Mgr-Customer Svc)*
Jeffery White *(Mgr-Pre-Press)*
Brands & Products:
ACTIVE LABEL
ARTHUR BLANK
COMBO CARD
RAC
SCANGUARD

ACHILLES USA, INC.
(Sub. of Achilles Corporation)
1407 80th St SW
Everett, WA 98203-6220
Tel.: (425) 353-7000
Fax: (425) 348-6683
Web Site: www.achillesusa.com
Approx. Number Employees: 175
Business Description:
Plastics Products Mfr
S.I.C.: 3081; 3089
N.A.I.C.S.: 326113; 326199
Media: 2-10
Personnel:
Scott Bollinger *(VP-Sls)*

ADVANCED DRAINAGE SYSTEMS, INC.
4640 Truman Rd
Hilliard, OH 43026-2438
Tel.: (614) 658-0050
Fax: (614) 457-2512
Toll Free: (800) 821-6710
E-mail: info@ads-pipe.com
Web Site: www.ads-pipe.com
Approx. Number Employees: 1,800
Year Founded: 1966
Business Description:
Polyethylene Drainage Products Mfr
S.I.C.: 3084; 3083
N.A.I.C.S.: 326122; 326130
Import Export
Media: 2-7-10-13
Personnel:
Joseph Chlapaty *(Chm, Pres & CEO)*
Mark B. Sturgeon *(CFO & Exec VP)*
Brands & Products:
ADS
ADS 3000
ADS 6000
ADVANCED DRAINAGE SYSTEMS
ADVANEDGE
BRAVAL
DURASLOT
GEOTEX
ISOLATOR
LANDLOK
MEGA GREEN
MYCELX
NYLOPLAST
SANITITE
STORM-PURE
STORMTECH

AEP INDUSTRIES INC.
125 Phillips Ave
South Hackensack, NJ 07606-1456
Tel.: (201) 641-6600
Fax: (201) 807-2567
E-mail: info@aepinc.com
Web Site: www.aepinc.com
Approx. Sls.: $800,570,000
Approx. Number Employees: 2,000
Year Founded: 1970
Business Description:
Polyethylene Film Products Mfr
S.I.C.: 2671; 3081
N.A.I.C.S.: 322221; 326113
Export
Media: 2-7-8-10-19-25-26
Personnel:
J. Brendan Barba *(Chm, Pres & CEO)*
Paul M. Feeney *(CFO & Exec VP-Fin)*
David J. Cron *(Exec VP-Mfg)*
Robert E. Cron *(Exec VP-Natl Accts)*
John J. Powers *(Exec VP-Sls & Mktg)*
Paul C. Vegliante *(Exec VP-Ops)*
Joe Webb *(Mgr-Resinite Products)*
Brands & Products:
ACRYPTER
AEP
AEPLEX
AEPRO
AF-50
ALPHACENE
ARMALOC
ARMASEAL
ARMASTUFF
ARMATHENE
ARMATUFF
ARMATUFF TWIN
ATTACHE
BEADSEAL
BORDEX
CITIBAG
CLEARSEAL
CLING
CLINGCLASSIC
CLINGMASTER
DIOPEEL
EURO M
F-O-F
FAB WRAP
FABGUARD
FELXIPAC
FIAP S.P.A. DEVICE
FILM ON FILM
FIRST WRAP
FLEXIPAC
FLXTITE
GREEN GUARD
HI LO
KEY-LOC
LIQUIPAC
LIQUITAINER
LOADMASTER
MAPAC
MINIWRAP
ONE SOURCE. THE SOLUTION.
ONE WORLD. ONE SOURCE.
OSC
PALLETFAST
PEEL & SEAL
PERFOCUT
PERFORMANCE PLUS
PERFOROLL
POUCHPAC
PRO-EX
THE PROFESSIONALS' CHOICE.
PROFORMANCE FILMS
PROPEX
RESINEX
RESINITE
RESINITE HI LO
RMF-61HY
SEAL WRAP
SHRINK MATE
SLC
SUNFILM
TERMOVIR
TRIDENT
TRUSEAL
UNITER
UNIVEDER
VERSA WRAP II
VINOPHANE
VISQUEEN
WRAP/UP
ZIPSAFE

AIRBOSS OF AMERICA CORP.
16441 Yonge St
Newmarket, ON L3X 2G8, Canada
Tel.: (905) 751-1188
Fax: (905) 751-1101
E-mail: info@airbossofamerica.com
Web Site: www.airbossofamerica.com
E-Mail For Key Personnel:
President: rlh@airbossofamerica.com
Approx. Sls.: $205,445,484
Approx. Number Employees: 764
Business Description:
Rubber Based Products Developer & Mfr
S.I.C.: 3052
N.A.I.C.S.: 326220
Media: 2-10
Personnel:
P. Grenville Schoch *(Chm)*
Robert L. Hagerman *(Pres & CEO)*
Stephen Richards *(CFO & VP-Fin)*
Robert Dodd *(Exec VP)*
John Tomins *(VP-Sls & Mktg)*
Marcel Courtemanche *(Mgr-Sls)*

AJAX CUSTOM MANUFACTURING
(Formerly Ajax-United Patterns & Molds, Inc.)
34585 7th St
Union City, CA 94587-3673
Tel.: (510) 476-8000
Fax: (510) 476-8001

Key to Media (For complete agency information see *The Advertising Red Books-Agencies* edition):
1. Bus. Publs. 2. Cable T.V. 3. Catalogs & Directories. 4. Co-op Adv. 5. Consumer Mags. 6. D.M. to Bus. Estab.7. D.M. to Consumers
8. Daily Newsp. 9. Exhibits/Trade Shows 10. Foreign 11. Infomercial 12. Internet Adv.13. Multimedia 14. Network Radio
15. Network T.V. 16. Newsp. Distr. Mags. 17. Other 18. Outdoor (Posters, Transit) 19. Point of Purchase20. Premiums, Novelties
21. Product Samples 22. Special Events Mktg. 23. Spot Radio 24. Spot T.V. 25. Weekly Newsp. 26. Yellow Page Adv.

E-mail: info@ajaxmfg.com
Web Site: www.ajaxmfg.com
Approx. Sls.: $23,000,000
Approx. Number Employees: 200
Year Founded: 1945
Business Description:
Plastic Products Mfr
S.I.C.: 3089; 3599
N.A.I.C.S.: 326199; 332710
Media: 10

ALESSCO INC.
2525 N Elston Ave
Chicago, IL 60647
Tel.: (773) 235-6287
Fax: (773) 348-9943
Toll Free: (800) ALESSCO
E-mail: info@alessco.com
Web Site: www.alessco.com
Approx. Number Employees: 15
Business Description:
Rubber Floor Coverings Mfr
S.I.C.: 3996
N.A.I.C.S.: 326192
Media: 10
Personnel:
Jeffrey A. D'Alessio *(Owner)*
Brands & Products:
ALESSCO

ALLFLEX USA, INC.
2805 E 14th St DFW Airport
Irving, TX 75261
Tel.: (972) 456-3686
Fax: (972) 456-3882
Web Site: www.allflexusa.com
Approx. Sls.: $11,900,000
Approx. Number Employees: 65
Business Description:
Plastic Identification Tag & Product Mfr
S.I.C.: 3089
N.A.I.C.S.: 326199
Media: 4-10
Personnel:
Brian Bolton *(Pres & CEO)*
Glenn Fischer *(Sr VP-Mktg)*
Jon Becerril *(Mgr-Natl Accts)*
Donna James *(Mgr-Comml Svcs)*
Robert May *(Mgr-Laser Technical)*
Brands & Products:
ALLFLEX
RETRACT-O-MATIC
TAMPERPROOF

ALLIED RUBBER & RIGGING SUPPLY
(Sub. of Industrial Sales Company Inc.)
101 Hindman Ln
Butler, PA 16001
Tel.: (724) 482-2965
Fax: (724) 482-4891
Toll Free: (800) 242-1670
Web Site: www.alliedrubber.com
Year Founded: 1993
Business Description:
Hose, Fittings, Gaskets, Rubber Tubing & Conveyor Belting Retailer
S.I.C.: 5085; 5084
N.A.I.C.S.: 423840; 423830
Import Export
Media: 26
Personnel:
David Markl *(VP & Gen Mgr)*

ALLIED TIRES & SERVICE
(Sub. of The Goodyear Tire & Rubber Company)
4400 S Semoran Blvd
Orlando, FL 32807
Tel.: (813) 754-5828
Fax: (407) 481-1609
Web Site: www.alliedtires.com
Sales Range: $150-199.9 Million
Approx. Number Employees: 420
Year Founded: 1989
Business Description:
Provider of Auto Tires, Truck & Auto Batteries & Auto Accessories
S.I.C.: 5014
N.A.I.C.S.: 441320
Advertising Expenditures: $2,500,000
Media: 8-9-13-17-18-19-20-23-24-26
Distr.: Natl.

AMERICAN BILTRITE INC.
57 River St Ste 302
Wellesley Hills, MA 02481-2097
Tel.: (781) 237-6655
Fax: (781) 237-6880
E-mail: info@ambilt.com
Web Site:
www.americanbiltriteinc.com
Approx. Sls.: $201,628,000
Approx. Number Employees: 625
Year Founded: 1908
Business Description:
Vinyl & Rubber Floor Tile, Hard Wood Floors, Rubber & Vinyl Tape, Protective Film Tape, Paper Tape & Other Pressure Sensitive Tape Mfr & Distr
S.I.C.: 3842; 2672; 3069; 3082; 3084; 3253
N.A.I.C.S.: 339113; 322222; 326121; 326122; 326299; 327122
Import Export
Advertising Expenditures: $1,200,000
Media: 2-4-5-6-9-10-20-21-23-26
Distr.: Natl.
Budget Set: Jan.
Personnel:
Roger S. Marcus *(Chm & CEO)*
Richard G. Marcus *(Pres & COO)*
Howard N. Feist, III *(CFO & VP-Fin)*
Henry W. Winkleman *(VP, Gen Counsel & Sec)*
William M. Marcus *(Treas & Exec VP)*
Rock Leblanc *(VP & Gen Mgr)*
Michelle Mirks *(VP & Gen Mgr-Tape Prods)*
Jean A. Richard *(VP & Gen Mgr)*
Adele Muller *(Asst Treas)*
Brands & Products:
AB
AMTICO
AUTOWRAP
BILTRITE
BULL DOG
CAT'S PAW
COLORSPLUS
CONGOLEUM
DURASTEP
DURAVINYL
ESTRIE
METROPOLITAN
PANAMA JACK
PROTECRITE
SPLICE KING
TRANSFERITE
VENDOME

AMERITYRE CORPORATION
1501 Industrial Rd
Boulder City, NV 89005
Tel.: (702) 294-2689
Fax: (702) 293-1930
Toll Free: (800) 808-1268
E-mail: information@amerityre.com
Web Site: www.amerityre.com
Approx. Rev.: $3,698,829
Approx. Number Employees: 10
Year Founded: 1995
Business Description:
Polyurethane Tire Mfr
S.I.C.: 3011
N.A.I.C.S.: 326211
Advertising Expenditures: $26,394
Media: 17
Personnel:
Louis M. Haynie *(Chm)*
Michael Kapral *(Pres & CEO)*
Brands & Products:
AMERIFILL
AMERITYRE
ARCUS
ATMOSPHERIC
ELASTOTHANE
FLATFREE
TIRE TECHNOLOGY FOR THE 21ST CENTURY

ANVIL INTERNATIONAL, INC.
(Sub. of Mueller Water Products, Inc.)
110 Corporate Dr Ste 10
Portsmouth, NH 03801
Mailing Address:
PO Box 3180
Portsmouth, NH 03802-3180
Tel.: (603) 422-8000
Fax: (603) 422-8033
E-mail: webmaster@anvilintl.com
Web Site: www.anvilintl.com
Sales Range: $50-74.9 Million
Approx. Number Employees: 35
Business Description:
Pipe Fittings & Pipe Hangers Mfr
S.I.C.: 3498; 3321
N.A.I.C.S.: 332996; 331511
Export
Media: 10
Personnel:
Thomas E. Fish *(Pres)*

AVON RUBBER & PLASTICS INC.
(Sub. of Avon Rubber plc)
805 W 13th St
Cadillac, MI 49601-9281
Tel.: (231) 775-6571
Fax: (231) 775-7304
E-mail: enquiries@avon-rubber.com
Web Site: www.avon-rubber.com
Approx. Number Employees: 500
Year Founded: 1959
Business Description:
Rubber Products Mfr
S.I.C.: 3089; 3061
N.A.I.C.S.: 326199; 326291
Export
Media: 1-2-4-7-10
Distr.: Intl.; Natl.

BANDAG INCORPORATED
(Sub. of Bridgestone Corporation)
2905 N Hwy 61
Muscatine, IA 52761
Tel.: (563) 262-1400
Toll Free: (800) 822-6324
E-mail: webmaster@bandag.com
Web Site: www.bandag.com
Approx. Rev.: $984,110,000
Approx. Number Employees: 3,362
Business Description:
Tire Treads Mfr
S.I.C.: 7534; 3011; 3559
N.A.I.C.S.: 326212; 326211; 333220
Advertising Expenditures: $6,596,000
Media: 4-10-13
Personnel:
Kurk Danielson *(Pres)*
Troy Geuther *(Treas & VP-Fin)*
Brands & Products:
BANDAG
BRAWNY
METROMAX
MICRO-SIPE
MILEDGES
NO DETOURS
OMNI BUS
R4200
RTP AND RTP
ULTRA ALL-POSITION
WH RIB
Advertising Agency:
Periscope
921 Washington Ave S
Minneapolis, MN 55415
Tel.: (612) 399-0500
Fax: (612) 399-0600
Toll Free: (800) 339-2103

BEEMAK PLASTICS, INC.
(Sub. of Jordan Industries, Inc.)
13921 Bettencourt St
Cerritos, CA 90703
Tel.: (310) 886-5880
Fax: (310) 764-0330
Toll Free: (800) 421-4393
E-mail: info@beemak.com
Web Site: www.beemak.com
Approx. Number Employees: 74
Year Founded: 1951
Business Description:
Plastic Literature & Card Holders; Point of Purchase Displays Mfr
S.I.C.: 3089; 3993
N.A.I.C.S.: 326199; 339950
Export
Media: 2-4-10
Distr.: Intl.; Natl.
Budget Set: Annually
Personnel:
Robert Gray *(Pres)*
Brands & Products:
BEEMAK

BEL-ART PRODUCTS, INC.
6 Industrial Rd
Pequannock, NJ 07440-1920
Tel.: (973) 694-0500
Fax: (973) 694-7199
E-mail: info@belart.com
Web Site: www.belart.com
E-Mail For Key Personnel:
Marketing Director: slevine@belart.com
Approx. Number Employees: 310
Year Founded: 1946
Business Description:
Molded & Fabricated Plastics Mfr for Science & Industry
S.I.C.: 3089; 2752
N.A.I.C.S.: 326199; 323110
Import Export
Advertising Expenditures: $150,000
Media: 2-4-10-21
Distr.: Intl.; Natl.
Budget Set: Jan.
Personnel:
Kurt Landsberger *(Founder)*

Key to Media (For complete agency information see *The Advertising Red Books-Agencies* edition):
1. Bus. Publs. 2. Cable T.V. 3. Catalogs & Directories. 4. Co-op Adv. 5. Consumer Mags. 6. D.M. to Bus. Estab.7. D.M. to Consumers
8. Daily Newsp. 9. Exhibits/Trade Shows 10. Foreign 11. Infomercial 12. Internet Adv.13. Multimedia 14. Network Radio
15. Network T.V. 16. Newsp. Distr. Mags. 17. Other 18. Outdoor (Posters, Transit) 19. Point of Purchase20. Premiums, Novelties
21. Product Samples 22. Special Events Mktg. 23. Spot Radio 24. Spot T.V. 25. Weekly Newsp. 26. Yellow Page Adv.

Bel-Art Products, Inc. — (Continued)

David Landsberger *(Pres)*
Richard johnson *(CFO)*
Brands & Products:
CLAVIES
PIPETTE PUMP III
POXYGRID
PRECISIONWARE
SCIENCEWARE
SECADOR
SPINBAR
STERILEWARE

BENDIX CVS CANADA INC.
(Sub. of Bendix Commercial Vehicle Systems LLC)
(d/b/a SmarTire Systems)
13151 Vanier Place Suite 150
Richmond, BC V6V 2J1, Canada
Tel.: (604) 276-9884
Fax: (604) 276-2350
Toll Free: (888) 982-3001
Web Site: www.smartire.com
Sales Range: $1-9.9 Million
Approx. Number Employees: 24
Business Description:
Tire Pressure/Temperature Monitoring Products Developer & Marketer
S.I.C.: 3823; 3011
N.A.I.C.S.: 334513; 326211
Advertising Expenditures: $1,642,384
Media: 4-6-7-8-10-19
Brands & Products:
ACTIVE TIRE PRESSURE MONITORING SYSTEMS
SMARTIRE
SMARTWAVE

THE BILTRITE CORPORATION
51 Sawyer Rd
Waltham, MA 02454
Tel.: (781) 647-1700
Fax: (781) 647-0919
E-mail: info@biltrite.com
Web Site: www.biltrite.com
Approx. Number Employees: 525
Year Founded: 1908
Business Description:
Mfr. of Rubber Materials
S.I.C.: 3021; 3069
N.A.I.C.S.: 316211; 326299
Export
Media: 4-7-10
Distr.: Natl.
Personnel:
Stanley J. Bernstein *(Chm)*
Stephen A. Fine *(Pres)*
David Amidon *(Gen Counsel & VP-Legal)*
Brands & Products:
BILTRITE
CLEAN TRAC
EASY-SWEEP
ELDORADO
ENDURA
FINGER TRAC
GOLF SPIKE
KLEAR-TRAC
KLEEN-RITE
NU-TRED
SAFETY EDGE
STIPPLE
TREDAIR
TUFF-TRAC

BRIDGESTONE AMERICAS HOLDING, INC.
(Sub. of Bridgestone Corporation)
535 Marriott Dr
Nashville, TN 37214-3672
Tel.: (615) 937-1000
Fax: (615) 937-3621
Web Site: www.bridgestone-firestone.com
Approx. Number Employees: 900
Year Founded: 1900
Business Description:
Holding Company
S.I.C.: 3011; 3493
N.A.I.C.S.: 326211; 332611
Import Export
Advertising Expenditures: $34,000,000
Media: 2-4-5-6-7-9-11-14-15-18-23-24-25-26
Distr.: Intl.; Natl.
Budget Set: Sept.
Personnel:
Asahiko Nishiyama *(Chm)*
Gary Garfield *(Pres & CEO)*
Eduardo Minardi *(COO)*
Stephen Brooks *(CIO)*
Christine Karbowiak *(Exec VP)*
Patti James *(VP-HR)*
Don Darden *(Exec Dir-Comm)*
Michael Fluck *(Dir-Brand & Retail Mktg)*
Brands & Products:
BRIDGESTONE
BRIDGESTONE OR NOTHING
DAYTON
Advertising Agencies:
Laughlin/Constable, Inc.
360 N Michigan Ave 12th Fl
Chicago, IL 60601
Tel.: (414) 272-2400
Fax: (312) 422-5901

The Richards Group, Inc.
8750 N Central Expy Ste 100
Dallas, TX 75231-6430
Tel.: (214) 891-5700
Fax: (214) 265-2933

BRYCE CORPORATION
4505 Old Lamar Ave
Memphis, TN 38118
Mailing Address:
PO Box 18338
Memphis, TN 38181-0338
Tel.: (901) 369-4400
Toll Free: (800) 238-7277
E-mail: webinfo@brycecorp.com
Web Site: www.brycecorp.com
Approx. Number Employees: 1,000
Year Founded: 1969
Business Description:
Convert Coated or Laminated Plastic Film for Packaging
S.I.C.: 2671; 3499
N.A.I.C.S.: 326112; 332999
Import Export
Media: 7-10-21
Personnel:
Thomas J. Bryce *(Chm & CEO)*
Tad Feeney *(CFO)*
Raymond Marus *(CFO)*

CAPSONIC GROUP LLC
460 2nd St
Elgin, IL 60123-7008
Tel.: (847) 888-7300
Fax: (847) 888-7261
E-mail: capsale@capsonicgroup.com
Web Site: www.capsonic.com
Sales Range: $25-49.9 Million
Approx. Number Employees: 210
Year Founded: 1968
Business Description:
Plastic Composite Components & High Volume Custom Composite & Insert Molding Mfr
S.I.C.: 3089; 3714
N.A.I.C.S.: 326199; 336399
Export
Media: 2-4-6-10-17-20
Distr.: Natl.
Budget Set: Dec.
Personnel:
Dale White *(Pres)*
Paul Gingrich *(Mgr-Bus Unit)*
Brands & Products:
CAPASONIC

CARLISLE TIRE & WHEEL COMPANY
(Sub. of Carlisle Transportation Products Group)
23 Windham Blvd
Aiken, SC 29805-9320
Tel.: (803) 643-2900
Fax: (803) 643-2919
Telex: 842330
E-mail: infotire@carlisletire.com
Web Site: www.carlisletire.com
Sales Range: $450-499.9 Million
Approx. Number Employees: 1,000
Year Founded: 1917
Business Description:
Small Pneumatic Tubes & Tires
S.I.C.: 3011; 3711; 3714
N.A.I.C.S.: 326211; 336211; 336312; 336322; 336340; 336350; 336399
Import
Media: 2-4-5-7-10-13-18
Distr.: Natl.
Budget Set: Nov.
Personnel:
Fred Sutter *(Pres)*
Brands & Products:
ALL TRAIL
CARLISLE
FAIRWAY
FARM SPECIALIST
GROUND FORCE GSE
GUARD DOG
LINKS
STRYKER
SURE TRAIL
SURE TRAIL LT
TOUR MAX
TRAC CHIEF
TRAIL HAWK
TRAIL PRO
TRAIL WOLF
TRAKS MAX
TURF BUSTER
TURF MASTER
TURF MATE
TURF PRO
USA LOADER
USA TRAIL
WORK MATE

CENTRAL PLASTICS & RUBBER CO., INC.
3320 W Vernon Ave
Phoenix, AZ 85009
Tel.: (602) 268-6368
Fax: (602) 268-0063
E-mail: contact@centralplastic.com
Web Site: www.centralplastic.com
E-Mail For Key Personnel:
Sales Director: sales@centralplastic.com
Sales Range: $10-24.9 Million
Approx. Number Employees: 12
Year Founded: 1960
Business Description:
Plastic Fabrications
S.I.C.: 3089; 3053
N.A.I.C.S.: 326199; 339991
Advertising Expenditures: $70,000
Media: 1-2-4-5-7-10-11-20-21
Distr.: Intl.; Natl.
Budget Set: Monthly
Personnel:
Robert Weiss *(Pres)*
Brands & Products:
CENTRAL
FOODFXTRS
HOTDOG
JOCK
PAPERFXTRS
WELL GUARD

CEREPLAST, INC.
300 Continental Blvd Ste 100
El Segundo, CA 90245
Tel.: (310) 676-5000
Fax: (310) 615-9800
E-mail: info@cereplast.com
Web Site: www.cereplast.com
Approx. Sls.: $6,416,000
Approx. Number Employees: 53
Business Description:
Bio-Based Resins & Plastics Mfr & Marketer
S.I.C.: 2821; 3089; 5162
N.A.I.C.S.: 325211; 326199; 424610
Advertising Expenditures: $371,237
Personnel:
Frederic Scheer *(Chm & CEO)*
Heather E. Sheehan *(CFO & Sr VP)*
Margaret McMurray *(Chief Admin Officer & VP)*
Mark Barton *(Sr VP-Mfg)*
Robert C. Findlen *(Sr VP-Global Sls & Mktg)*
William Kelly *(Sr VP-Tech)*
David J. Homyak *(Reg Dir-Sls & Mktg-West Coast)*
Bob Williams *(Reg Dir-Sls & Mktg-East Coast)*
Brands & Products:
CEREPLAST COMPOSTABLES
CEREPLAST HYBRID

COKER TIRE COMPANY
1317 Chestnut St
Chattanooga, TN 37402-4418
Tel.: (423) 265-6368
Fax: (423) 756-5607
E-mail: info@coker.com
Web Site: www.coker.com
Sales Range: $25-49.9 Million
Approx. Number Employees: 50
Year Founded: 1958
Business Description:
Supplier of Vintage & Antique Tires
S.I.C.: 5014
N.A.I.C.S.: 423130; 441320
Media: 2-3-4-6-7-8-10-13-20-22
Personnel:
Joseph Coker *(Pres)*
Kevin Loveday *(VP-Fin)*
David Leach *(Dir-Mktg)*

Key to Media (For complete agency information see *The Advertising Red Books-Agencies* edition):
1. Bus. Publs. 2. Cable T.V. 3. Catalogs & Directories. 4. Co-op Adv. 5. Consumer Mags. 6. D.M. to Bus. Estab.7. D.M. to Consumers 8. Daily Newsp. 9. Exhibits/Trade Shows 10. Foreign 11. Infomercial 12. Internet Adv.13. Multimedia 14. Network Radio 15. Network T.V. 16. Newsp. Distr. Mags. 17. Other 18. Outdoor (Posters, Transit) 19. Point of Purchase20. Premiums, Novelties 21. Product Samples 22. Special Events Mktg. 23. Spot Radio 24. Spot T.V. 25. Weekly Newsp. 26. Yellow Page Adv.

Brands & Products:
COKER CLASSIC
COKER TIRE
IT'S ALL ABOUT THE TIRE

CONSTAR INTERNATIONAL INC.
1 Crown Way
Philadelphia, PA 19154
Tel.: (215) 552-3700
Fax: (215) 552-3707
E-mail: constar@constar.net
Web Site: www.constar.net
Approx. Sls.: $638,368,000
Approx. Number Employees: 1,238
Business Description:
Plastic Container Mfr
S.I.C.: 3085; 3089
N.A.I.C.S.: 326160; 326199
Media: 10
Personnel:
L. White Matthews, III *(Chm)*
Grant H. Beard *(Pres & CEO)*
J. Mark Borseth *(CFO & Exec VP)*
Scott D. Stanton *(Chief Acctg Officer, VP & Controller)*
David J. Waksman *(Gen Counsel, Sec & Sr VP-HR)*
Joseph Bione *(Acting Exec VP-Ops)*
George Caplea *(Exec VP)*
James C.T. Bolton *(Sr VP-Strategy & Admin)*
Donald P. Deubel *(Sr VP-Corp Technologies)*
Daniel Ingram *(Sr VP-Corp Technologies)*
Timothy Kaiser *(Sr VP-Supply Chain)*
Matt Dauzvardis *(VP-Corp Tech-R&D Center-Alsip)*
Suzanne Cohen *(Sr Mgr-Mktg Svcs)*
Mark Cooper *(Mgr-Sls-Southeast Reg)*
Mark Hubbuch *(Mgr-Sls-Midwest Reg)*
Brands & Products:
CONSTAR
CONSTRUCT
CONVERT IT
DIAMONDCLEAR
I-DESIGN
MONOXBAR
OXBAR
STARSHIELD
VCT
X-4

CONTINENTAL AMERICAN CORP.
(d/b/a Pioneer Balloon Company)
5000 E 29th St N
Wichita, KS 67220-2111
Tel.: (316) 685-2266
Fax: (316) 685-2409
E-mail: contactus@qualatex.com
Web Site: www.qualatex.com
Approx. Number Employees: 1,000
Year Founded: 1974
Business Description:
Mfr. & Printer of Latex & Metallic Balloons
S.I.C.: 3069; 2759
N.A.I.C.S.: 326299; 323113
Import Export
Media: 2-10
Personnel:
Ted A. Vlamis *(Pres)*
Daniel Flynn *(COO)*
Betty Vlamis *(Exec VP)*
H. Wayne Roberts *(VP-Adv Premium Markets)*
Brands & Products:
AIRWEAR
ANGLE SHEER
BALLOON MAGIC
BALLOON TWINKLERS
BANNER
BUBBLE BALLOON
CBA
CLIP 'N STICK
CONNECT-A-DOT
CRYSTAL
DESIGN-A-ROUND
DIMENSIONAIR
FLOAT NOTE
FUNFONE FUNSATIONAL
GEO
GEO BLOSSOM
GEO DONUT
GLITTERPRINT
GLOPRINT
IMPRESS II
IMPRESS V
INCREDIBOW
JUST WRITE
MESSSAGE-A-ROUND
MICROCLEAR
MICROFOIL
MILORI
NANOFILM
OPAL EDGE
PARTYMATE
QBN
QUALATEX B-BOPS
QUALATEX BALLOON NETWORK
QUALATEX BALLOONRIBBON
QUALATEX MAGICPIPE
QUALATEX MASTERBOW
QUALATEX PROSIZER
QUALATEX SPARKLE
QUALATEX SPINNER
QUALATEX SUPRAFOIL
QUICKIE CLIPPER
QUICKIE CLIPS
QUIKCLIP
QUIKFRAME
SDS
SIGNATURE SERIES
SPORTSBALL
SUPERAGATE
SUPERSCRIPT
THOUGHT BUBBLE
TOPPRINT

CONTINENTAL GENERAL TIRE INC.
(Sub. of Continental Aktiengesellschaft)
6110 Cantay Rd
Mississauga, ON L5R 3W5, Canada
Tel.: (905) 856-4363
Fax: (905) 856-4363
E-mail: info@continentaltire.com
Web Site: www.continentaltire.com
Sales Range: $200-249.9 Million
Approx. Number Employees: 25
Business Description:
Mfr. & Distributor of Tires
S.I.C.: 3011
N.A.I.C.S.: 326211
Media: 2-4-5-6-10-14-15-18-19-20-21-22-23-24
Personnel:
Oliver Winschiers *(Gen Mgr)*
Bruce Foss *(Product Mgr)*
Brands & Products:
CONTINENTAL GENERAL

CONTINENTAL INDUSTRIES INC.
(Sub. of Handy & Harman Ltd.)
4102 S 74th East Ave
Tulsa, OK 74145-4700
Mailing Address:
PO Box 994
Tulsa, OK 74101-0994
Tel.: (918) 627-5210
Fax: (918) 622-1275
Fax: (800) 788-1668
Toll Free: (800) 788-1668
Web Site: www.conind.com
Business Description:
Gas & Water Distribution Systems
S.I.C.: 3084; 3494
N.A.I.C.S.: 326122; 332919
Media: 10

CONTINENTAL TIRE NORTH AMERICA, INC.
(Sub. of Continental Aktiengesellschaft)
1830 MacMillan Park Dr
Fort Mill, SC 29707
Tel.: (704) 588-5895
Fax: (704) 583-8540
Toll Free: (800) 847-3349
Telex: 986426
E-mail: kathryn.blackwell@continental-corporation.com
Web Site: www.continentaltire.com
Sales Range: $1-4.9 Billion
Approx. Number Employees: 230
Year Founded: 1915
Business Description:
Passenger Vehicle Tire Mfr
S.I.C.: 3011
N.A.I.C.S.: 326211
Import Export
Media: 2-4-5-6-8-9-13-19-20-22-23-24-25-26
Distr.: Intl.; Natl.
Budget Set: Aug.
Personnel:
Matthias Schoenberg *(CEO)*
Paul Williams *(Exec VP-Truck-The Americas)*
Kathryn Blackwell *(VP-Mktg & Pub Rel)*
David Whitmore *(Mgr-Sls-Original Equipment)*

COOPER-STANDARD AUTOMOTIVE INC.
(Sub. of Cooper-Standard Holdings Inc.)
39550 Orchard Hill Pl Dr
Novi, MI 48375
Tel.: (248) 596-5900
Fax: (248) 596-6535
E-mail: automotiveinfo@cooperstandard.com
Web Site: www.cooperstandard.com
Sales Range: $1-4.9 Billion
Approx. Number Employees: 16,266
Year Founded: 1927
Business Description:
Rubber & Plastic Automotive Parts
S.I.C.: 3061; 3069
N.A.I.C.S.: 326291; 326299
Import Export
Advertising Expenditures: $300,000
Media: 2-4-10-17-20
Distr.: Natl.
Budget Set: May
Personnel:
James S. McElya *(CEO)*
Allen J. Campbell *(CFO & VP)*
Bill Pumphrey *(Pres-Ops-North America)*
Timothy W. Hefferon *(Gen Counsel, Sec & VP)*
Brian O'Loughlin *(VP-IT)*
Sharon S. Wenzl *(VP-Corp Comm)*
Brands & Products:
ARCTUBE
ENVISYS
STANPRO
Advertising Agency:
Bianchi Public Relations Inc.
888 W Big Beaver Rd Ste 777
Troy, MI 48084
Tel.: (248) 269-1122
Fax: (248) 269-8202

COOPER TIRE & RUBBER COMPANY
701 Lima Ave
Findlay, OH 45840-2315
Mailing Address:
PO Box 550
Findlay, OH 45839-0550
Tel.: (419) 423-1321
Fax: (419) 424-4212
Toll Free: (800) 854-6288
E-mail: cooperinfo@coopertire.com
Web Site: www.coopertire.com
Approx. Sls.: $3,360,984,000
Approx. Number Employees: 12,898
Year Founded: 1914
Business Description:
Replacement Tires Mfr
S.I.C.: 3011; 3069
N.A.I.C.S.: 326211; 326299
Import Export
Advertising Expenditures: $48,432,000
Media: 2-3-5-6-7-9-10-18-19-20-23-26
Distr.: Natl.
Budget Set: Oct.
Personnel:
Roy V. Armes *(Chm, Pres & CEO)*
Bradley E. Hughes *(CFO & VP)*
Carl Montalbine *(CIO & VP-Global Quality-OPEX)*
Brenda Harmon *(Chief HR Officer & VP)*
Harold C. Miller *(Pres-Intl Tire Div)*
Christopher E. Ostrander *(Pres-Tire Ops-North America)*
Stephen Zamansky *(Gen Counsel, Sec & VP)*
Charles F. Nagy *(Asst Treas)*
Phillip D. Caris *(VP-Sls & Mktg)*
Phil F. Kortokrax *(VP-Dealer Channel Sls)*
Linda L. Rennels *(VP-Pur)*
Charles G. Yurkovich, Jr. *(VP-Tech)*
Dwayne E. Beach *(Dir-Product Mgmt)*
Donald S. Bruce *(Dir-Corp Engrg)*
David Craig *(Dir-Intl Sls & Dir-Intl Sls & Mktg-Cooper Tire & Rubber Co)*
Craig Durliat *(Dir-Credit-Tire Div-North America)*
Cathy Hissong *(Dir-Corp Commun)*
Robert W. Huber *(Dir-External Reporting)*

Key to Media (For complete agency information see *The Advertising Red Books-Agencies* edition):
1. Bus. Publs. 2. Cable T.V. 3. Catalogs & Directories. 4. Co-op Adv. 5. Consumer Mags. 6. D.M. to Bus. Estab.7. D.M. to Consumers
8. Daily Newsp. 9. Exhibits/Trade Shows 10. Foreign 11. Infomercial 12. Internet Adv.13. Multimedia 14. Network Radio
15. Network T.V. 16. Newsp. Distr. Mags. 17. Other 18. Outdoor (Posters, Transit) 19. Point of Purchase20. Premiums, Novelties
21. Product Samples 22. Special Events Mktg. 23. Spot Radio 24. Spot T.V. 25. Weekly Newsp. 26. Yellow Page Adv.

Cooper Tire & Rubber Company — (Continued)

Jon Huffman *(Dir-Pricing & Program Mgmt)*
John Kairys *(Dir-Natl Retailer Sls)*
Steve Sawyer *(Dir-Brand & Product Mgmt)*
Curtis Schneekloth *(Dir-IR)*
Adam Zickert *(Dir-Channel Dev)*
Rodney A. Kreinbrink *(Sr Mgr-Special Projects)*
Daren Cable *(Mgr-Tall Timbers Mold Ops Plant)*
Elicia M. Davis *(Mgr-Talent)*
Jeffrey L. Forsyth *(Mgr-Quality Assurance)*
William G. Hoban *(Mgr-Sls)*
Robert F. Murphy *(Mgr-Bus Dev)*
Curtis D. Selhorst *(Mgr-Tire Testing)*
Jack J. McCracken *(Asst Sec)*

Brands & Products:
ARMOR TEK 3
AVON TYRES
CHALLENGER
COOPER
COOPER LIFELINER CLASSIC
COOPER TIRES ULTIMATE BOWL TOUR
COURSER
DEAN
MASTERCRAFT
ROADMASTER
STARFIRE
STINGER

Advertising Agency:
Fahlgren Mortine
4030 Easton Station Ste 300
Columbus, OH 43219
Tel.: (614) 383-1500
Fax: (614) 383-1501
(Cooper Tires)

CORE MOLDING TECHNOLOGIES, INC.

800 Manor Park Dr
Columbus, OH 43228
Mailing Address:
PO Box 28183
Columbus, OH 43228
Tel.: (614) 870-5000
Fax: (614) 870-5051
E-mail: info@coremt.com
Web Site: www.coremt.com/
Approx. Sls.: $100,257,644
Approx. Number Employees: 1,014
Year Founded: 1996
Business Description:
Mfr. of Plastic & Fiberglass Molded Products
S.I.C.: 3842; 3082; 3089; 3714
N.A.I.C.S.: 339113; 326121; 326199; 336399
Media: 17
Personnel:
Malcolm M. Prine *(Chm)*
Kevin L. Barnett *(Pres & CEO)*
Herman F. Dick, Jr. *(CFO, Treas, Sec & VP)*
Stephen J. Klestinec *(COO & VP)*
Terrence J. O'Donovan *(VP-Mktg & Sls)*

CPG INTERNATIONAL, INC.

888 N Keyser Ave
Scranton, PA 18504
Mailing Address:
801 E Corey St
Scranton, PA 18505
Tel.: (570) 558-8000
Fax: (570) 346-4122
Toll Free: (800) 235-8320
E-mail: info@cpgint.com
Web Site: www.cpgint.com
Approx. Sls.: $327,535,000
Approx. Number Employees: 692
Business Description:
Building Products Whslr
S.I.C.: 3089; 5211
N.A.I.C.S.: 326199; 444190
Advertising Expenditures: $9,211,000
Personnel:
Brian R. Hoesterey *(Chm)*
Eric K. Jungbluth *(CEO)*
Scott Harrison *(CFO, Exec VP & Treas)*
Donald Wharton *(Pres-Scranton Products & Vycom)*
Ken Buck *(Sr VP-HR)*
Jason Grommon *(Sr VP-Ops)*
Brands & Products:
AZEK
SCRANTON PRODUCTS
VYCOM

CRANE PLASTICS HOLDING COMPANY

2141 Fairwood Ave
Columbus, OH 43207
Tel.: (614) 542-1100
Fax: (614) 445-4650
E-mail: crane@craneplastics.com
Web Site: www.crane-plastics.com
Approx. Sls.: $135,000,000
Approx. Number Employees: 750
Year Founded: 1947
Business Description:
Mfr. of Vinyl House Siding; Custom Extruded Thermoplastics
S.I.C.: 3089
N.A.I.C.S.: 326199
Advertising Expenditures: $840,000
Media: 2-4-7-10-17
Distr.: Natl.
Budget Set: Oct.
Personnel:
Mike Crane *(Pres & CEO)*
Randy Fortener *(CFO & VP)*
John Previte *(Mgr-Mktg)*
Brands & Products:
ARMORWARE
C-LOC
CRANE PLASTICS
GEOGUARD
MAXIMUM
SHOREGUARD
TIMBERGUARD
TIMBERTECH
ULTRA COMPOSITE

CRESLINE PLASTIC PIPE CO., INC.

600 Cross Pointe Blvd
Evansville, IN 47715
Tel.: (812) 428-9300
Fax: (812) 428-9353
Web Site: www.cresline.com
Approx. Number Employees: 150
Year Founded: 1949
Business Description:
Mfr. of Plastic Pipe & Fittings
S.I.C.: 3084
N.A.I.C.S.: 326122
Import Export
Advertising Expenditures: $250,000
Media: 4-21
Distr.: Natl.
Budget Set: Nov.
Personnel:
Richard Schroeder *(Pres)*
Brands & Products:
CE BLUE
CRESLINE
SPARTAN

CREST FOAM INDUSTRIES, INC.

(Sub. of British Vita Group Sarl)
100 Carol Pl
Moonachie, NJ 07074
Tel.: (201) 807-0809
Fax: (201) 807-1113
E-mail: info@crestfoam.com
Web Site: www.crestfoam.com
Sales Range: $25-49.9 Million
Approx. Number Employees: 85
Business Description:
Polyurethane Foam & Foam Products Mfr
S.I.C.: 3086
N.A.I.C.S.: 326150
Media: 2
Personnel:
Raj Mehta *(Pres & CEO)*
Philip B. Laut *(VP-Sls & Mktg)*
Brands & Products:
EZ-DRI FOAM
FELTCREST FOAM
FILTERCREST FOAM
SAFECREST

CSL PLASTICS INC.

9136 196A St
Langley, BC Canada
Tel.: (604) 888-2008
Fax: (604) 888-3688
E-mail: info@cslplastics.com
Web Site: www.cslplastics.com
E-Mail For Key Personnel:
President: lnovak@cslplastics.com
Approx. Number Employees: 50
Year Founded: 1981
Business Description:
Designer, Developer & Producer of Custom Plastic Products
S.I.C.: 3089; 3082; 3084
N.A.I.C.S.: 326199; 326121; 326122
Media: 10-13
Personnel:
Larrie A. Novak *(Pres)*

CTI INDUSTRIES CORPORATION

22160 N Pepper Rd
Barrington, IL 60010
Tel.: (847) 382-1000
Fax: (847) 382-1219
Fax: (800) 333-1831
Toll Free: (800) 284-5605
Web Site: www.ctiindustries.com
Approx. Sls.: $47,747,611
Approx. Number Employees: 112
Year Founded: 1976
Business Description:
Mylar & Latex Balloons Mfr
S.I.C.: 2822; 3069
N.A.I.C.S.: 325212; 326299
Advertising Expenditures: $203,000
Media: 4-10
Personnel:
John H. Schwan *(Chm & Exec VP)*
Howard W. Schwan *(Pres)*
Stephen M. Merrick *(CFO)*
Timothy Patterson *(VP-Fin)*
Brands & Products:
BALLOON JAMZ
CTI
MINILOONS
MINISHAPES
SHAPE-A-LOONS
SUPERLOONS
ULTRALOONS
XARD-B-LOONS

CUSTOM PAK, INC.

86 16th Ave N
Clinton, IA 52732
Tel.: (563) 242-1801
Fax: (563) 244-5362
E-mail: sales@custom-pak.com
Web Site: www.custom-pak.com
E-Mail For Key Personnel:
Sales Director: sales@custom-pak.com
Approx. Number Employees: 600
Year Founded: 1974
Business Description:
Blow Molded Finished Plastic Products Mfr
S.I.C.: 3089
N.A.I.C.S.: 326199
Media: 2-10
Personnel:
Richard Olsen *(CEO)*
Louise Laurent *(VP-Fin)*

DELSTAR TECHNOLOGIES, INC.

(Holding of AMERICAN CAPITAL, LTD.)
601 Industrial Dr
Middletown, DE 19709
Tel.: (302) 378-8888
Fax: (302) 378-4482
Toll Free: (800) 521-6713
E-mail: info@delstarinc.com
Web Site: www.delstarinc.com
Sales Range: $100-124.9 Million
Approx. Number Employees: 300
Year Founded: 1946
Business Description:
Mfr of Thermoplastic Nonwoven Products
S.I.C.: 3089
N.A.I.C.S.: 326199
Export
Advertising Expenditures: $250,000
Media: 2-4-7-10-13-21
Distr.: Intl.; Natl.
Budget Set: Nov.
Personnel:
Mark Abrahams *(Pres & CEO)*
Marjorie Wilcox *(Mgr-Comm)*
Brands & Products:
CORETEC
DELNET
DELPORE
NALTEX
STRATEX

DIMCO-GRAY COMPANY

900 Dimco Way
Centerville, OH 45458-2710
Tel.: (937) 433-7600
Fax: (937) 433-0520
Toll Free: (800) 876-8353
E-mail: sales@dimco-gray.com
Web Site: www.dimcogray.com
E-Mail For Key Personnel:
President: MSieron@dimco-gray.com
Sales Director: sales@dimco-gray.com

Key to Media (For complete agency information see *The Advertising Red Books-Agencies* edition):
1. Bus. Publs. 2. Cable T.V. 3. Catalogs & Directories. 4. Co-op Adv. 5. Consumer Mags. 6. D.M. to Bus. Estab.7. D.M. to Consumers 8. Daily Newsp. 9. Exhibits/Trade Shows 10. Foreign 11. Infomercial 12. Internet Adv.13. Multimedia 14. Network Radio 15. Network T.V. 16. Newsp. Distr. Mags. 17. Other 18. Outdoor (Posters, Transit) 19. Point of Purchase20. Premiums, Novelties 21. Product Samples 22. Special Events Mktg. 23. Spot Radio 24. Spot T.V. 25. Weekly Newsp. 26. Yellow Page Adv.

Sales Range: $10-24.9 Million
Approx. Number Employees: 55
Year Founded: 1924
Business Description:
Mfr. & Sales of Electric Timing Devices, Molded Plastic Knobs, Handles & Snap Slide Fasteners
S.I.C.: 3089; 3873
N.A.I.C.S.: 326199; 334518
Export
Media: 2-4-7-10-21-26
Distr.: Natl.
Budget Set: Nov.
Personnel:
Mike Sieron *(Pres & CEO)*
Brands & Products:
COLOR-ME
DGC-PLASTIC MOULDING
DIMCOGRAY
DIMCOGRIP
SOLUTIONS AT HAND

DOW ROOFING SYSTEMS LLC
(Sub. of Dow Building Solutions)
9 Sullivan Rd
Holyoke, MA 01040-2800
Tel.: (413) 533-8100
Fax: (413) 552-1199
Toll Free: (800) 621ROOF
Web Site:
www.dowroofingsystems.com
Sales Range: $75-99.9 Million
Approx. Number Employees: 26
Year Founded: 1863
Business Description:
Roofing Membrane Mfr & Marketer
S.I.C.: 3069
N.A.I.C.S.: 326299
Export
Media: 2-4-5-7-10-11-13
Distr.: Intl.; Natl.
Brands & Products:
STEVENS GEOMEMBRANES
STEVENS ROOFING SYSTEMS
STEVENS URETHANE

DYNARIC, INC.
5740 Bayside Rd
Virginia Beach, VA 23455
Tel.: (757) 460-3794
Fax: (757) 363-8016
Toll Free: (800) 526-0827
Web Site: www.dynaric.com
E-Mail For Key Personnel:
President: mikem@dynaric.com
Sales Director: joem@dynaric.com
Approx. Number Employees: 225
Year Founded: 1973
Business Description:
Plastic Strapping Systems Mfr
S.I.C.: 3089
N.A.I.C.S.: 326199
Media: 10-17
Personnel:
Joseph Martinez *(Pres)*
Michael Moses *(VP-Sls)*
Brian Clancy *(Mgr-Acctg)*
Brands & Products:
DYNARIC
ULTRABAND

ELKAY PLASTICS COMPANY, INC.
6000 Sheila St
Commerce, CA 90040
Tel.: (323) 722-7073
Fax: (323) 869-3911
Toll Free: (888) 352-9710
E-mail: info@elkayplastics.com
Web Site: www.elkayplastics.com
E-Mail For Key Personnel:
President: lchertkow@elkayplastics.com
Approx. Number Employees: 150
Year Founded: 1968
Business Description:
Plastic Products Mfr
S.I.C.: 2671; 5113
N.A.I.C.S.: 326112; 424130
Import Export
Media: 2-4-10
Personnel:
Louis Chertkow *(Pres & CEO)*
Stewart Horwitz *(CFO)*
Bill Lindenmoore *(Dir-Mktg)*
Brands & Products:
HEADER PAK
KWIK-FILL
LAB-LOC
PLASTRONIC
PULL-TITE
SEAL-N-RIP
SNAP-EZE
SNAP-EZE T-SHIRT BAGS
STRATOGREY
TUF-R

ENTEGRIS, INC.
129 Concord Road
Billerica, MA 01821
Tel.: (978) 436-6500
Fax: (978) 436-6735
Toll Free: (800) 394-4083
E-mail: irelations@entegris.com
Web Site: www.entegris.com
E-Mail For Key Personnel:
Public Relations: scott_moroney@entegris.com
Approx. Sls.: $688,416,000
Approx. Number Employees: 2,600
Year Founded: 1966
Business Description:
Semiconductor & Disk Drive Materials Transport & Protection Services
S.I.C.: 3674; 3082
N.A.I.C.S.: 334413; 326121
Import Export
Media: 2-10-17
Personnel:
Roger D. McDaniel *(Chm)*
Gideon Argov *(Pres & CEO)*
Gregory B. Graves *(CFO, Treas & Exec VP)*
Bertrand Loy *(COO & Exec VP)*
Peter W. Walcott *(Gen Counsel, Sec & Sr VP)*
John J. Murphy *(Sr VP-HR)*
Todd Edlund *(VP & Gen Mgr-CCS Div)*
William Shaner *(VP & Gen Mgr-Microenvironments)*
Lynn L. Blake *(VP-Fin)*
Gregory Morris *(VP-Global Field Ops)*
Scott Moroney *(Mgr-Comm-Global)*
Brands & Products:
AERONEX
CHACOLLET
CHEMLOCK
CONNECTOLOGY
CRYSTALPAK
CYNERGY
DEVICECARE
DYMENSION
ENABLING YIELD
ENCOMPASS
ENTEGRIS
ENTEGRIS RINGS DESIGN
ESPY
F10 EVO
FLUOROGARD
FLUOROLINE
FLUOROPURE
GALTEK
GATEKEEPER
HOT ZONE
I-CU
IMPACT
INERTRA
INTEGRA
INTELLIGEN
INTERCEPT
OPTICS GAS PURIFIER
OPTIMIZER
PHASOR II
PHASOR X
PLANARCAP
PLANARCORE
PLANARGARD
PROCESSGARD
PROTEGO
PUREBOND
PUREPOLYMER
QUICKCHANGE
RGEN
RINSEGARD
ROBOX
SOLARIS
STAT-PRO
STREAM
TERA
TORRENTO
ULTRAPAK
WAFERCARE
WAFERGARD
WAFERPURE
XCDA
ZIRAMIC
Advertising Agency:
Padilla Speer Beardsley
1101 W River Pkwy Ste 400
Minneapolis, MN 55415-1241
Tel.: (612) 455-1700
Fax: (612) 455-1060

ENTERMARKET CORPORATION
8 Madison Ave
Valhalla, NY 10595
Tel.: (914) 437-7270
Fax: (914) 437-7269
E-mail: sales@entermarket.com
Web Site: www.entermarket.com
E-Mail For Key Personnel:
Sales Director: jeff@entermarket.com
Approx. Number Employees: 60
Year Founded: 1936
Business Description:
Plastic In-Store Merchandising Mfr
S.I.C.: 3089
N.A.I.C.S.: 326199
Media: 2-21
Distr.: Natl.
Budget Set: July
Brands & Products:
DANGLERS
ENTERMARKET
WE'RE GOING GREEN

FABREEKA INTERNATIONAL, INC.
1023 Tpke St
Stoughton, MA 02072-1156
Mailing Address:
PO Box 210
Stoughton, MA 02072-0210
Tel.: (781) 341-3655
Fax: (781) 341-3983
Toll Free: (800) 322-7352
E-mail: info@fabreeka.com
Web Site: www.fabreeka.com
Approx. Number Employees: 100
Year Founded: 1918
Business Description:
Mfr. & Retailer of Anti-Shock & Vibration Pads; Rubber Composition Belting & Engineered Vibration Isolation Systems
S.I.C.: 3069; 5085
N.A.I.C.S.: 326299; 423840
Import Export
Media: 1-2-4-5-7-10-11-13-17
Distr.: Intl.; Natl.
Budget Set: Dec.
Personnel:
Daniel R. Rork *(COO & VP)*
Pam Goulart *(Mgr-Mktg Svcs)*
Brands & Products:
DIMFAB
FABCEL
FABCEL LEV-L MOUNT
FABCO
FABLENE
FABLON
FABREEKA
FABREEKA INTERNATIONAL
FABSORB
FABSYN
INFAB
ISO TAB-L
LEV-L
PRECISION-AIR
PRECISION AIRE
PRECISION-AIRE

FIRESTONE INDUSTRIAL PRODUCTS DIVISION
(Div. of BFS Diversified Products, LLC)
250 W 96th St
Indiana, IN 46260
Tel.: (317) 818-8600
Fax: (317) 818-8645
Web Site:
www.firestoneindustrial.com
Approx. Number Employees: 100
Year Founded: 1934
Business Description:
Vehicular Suspension Systems & Industrial Air Springs Mfr
S.I.C.: 3493
N.A.I.C.S.: 332611
Advertising Expenditures: $200,000
Media: 2-4-10-11
Distr.: Intl.; Natl.
Budget Set: Dec.
Personnel:
John Geary *(Dir-Tech)*
Michael Sigillito *(Dir-Sls & Mktg)*
Bill Smith *(Dir-Mfg)*
Mark Hilburger *(Mgr-Div Mktg)*
Emily Poladian *(Mgr-North American Distributor Sls)*
Brands & Products:
AIRMOUNT
AIRRIDE
AIRSTROKE
COIL-RITE
INTELLIRIDE
MARSHMELLOW
RIDE-RITE

Key to Media (For complete agency information see *The Advertising Red Books-Agencies* edition):
1. Bus. Publs. 2. Cable T.V. 3. Catalogs & Directories. 4. Co-op Adv. 5. Consumer Mags. 6. D.M. to Bus. Estab.7. D.M. to Consumers 8. Daily Newsp. 9. Exhibits/Trade Shows 10. Foreign 11. Infomercial 12. Internet Adv.13. Multimedia 14. Network Radio 15. Network T.V. 16. Newsp. Distr. Mags. 17. Other 18. Outdoor (Posters, Transit) 19. Point of Purchase20. Premiums, Novelties 21. Product Samples 22. Special Events Mktg. 23. Spot Radio 24. Spot T.V. 25. Weekly Newsp. 26. Yellow Page Adv.

Firestone Industrial Products Division — (Continued)

SPORT-RITE

FORMFACTOR, INC.
7005 S Front St
Livermore, CA 94551
Tel.: (925) 290-4000
Fax: (925) 290-4010
E-mail: info@formfactor.com
Web Site: www.formfactor.com
Approx. Rev.: $188,565,000
Approx. Number Employees: 729
Business Description:
Semiconductor Wafer Probe Cards Mfr & Retailer
S.I.C.: 3674
N.A.I.C.S.: 334413
Advertising Expenditures: $190,000
Media: 2-7-10
Personnel:
George Carl Everett, Jr. *(Chm)*
Thomas St. Dennis *(CEO)*
Michael M. Ludwig *(CFO & Sr VP)*
Benjamin N. Eldridge *(CTO & Sr VP-R & D)*
Stuart L. Merkadeau *(Gen Counsel, Sec & Sr VP)*
Henry I. Feir *(Sr VP-HR)*
Richard M. Freeman *(Sr VP-Mfg)*
Roger Hitchcock *(Sr VP-Customer Grp-Worldwide)*
Brands & Products:
BLADERUNNER 175
DRAM
FORMFACTOR
HARMONY
INNOVATION PUT TO THE TEST
MICROFORCE
MICROSPRING
ONETOUCH
TRE
TRUESCALE
UPSTREAM

FREUDENBERG-NOK
(Joint Venture of Freudenberg & Co. Kommanditgesellschaft & NOK Corporation)
47690 E Anchor Ct
Plymouth, MI 48170-2400
Tel.: (734) 451-0020
Fax: (734) 451-2547
Toll Free: (800) 533-5656
Web Site: www.freudenberg-nok.com
Sales Range: $1-4.9 Billion
Approx. Number Employees: 6,000
Year Founded: 1989
Business Description:
Elastomeric Seals, Custom Molded Products & Vibration Control Technologies Mfr; Owned 75% by Freudenberg & Co. Kommanditgesellschaft & 25% by NOK Corporation
S.I.C.: 3053; 3714
N.A.I.C.S.: 339991; 336340; 336399
Export
Advertising Expenditures: $980,000
Media: 1-2-4-7-10-18-20-23
Distr.: Intl.; Natl.
Budget Set: Sept.-Oct.
Personnel:
Richard E. Allen *(Grp CEO)*
Pierre Y. Abboud *(Pres-Vibracoustic-North America)*
Robert G. Evans *(Gen Counsel & VP)*
Ralf Krieger *(Sr VP-Fin & Admin)*
Theodore G. Duclos *(VP & Gen Mgr-Fluid Power Div-Global)*
Sarah A. O'Hare *(VP-HR & Comm)*
Brands & Products:
DISOGRIN
GROWTTH
TRANSTEC
Advertising Agency:
Knudsen, Gardner & Howe, Inc.
2103 Saint Clair Ave NE
Cleveland, OH 44114-4018
Tel.: (216) 781-5000
Fax: (216) 781-5004

FYPON, LTD.
960 W Barre Rd
Archbold, OH 43502
Tel.: (419) 445-0116
Fax: (419) 445-4440
Toll Free: (800) 955-5748
Web Site: www.fypon.com
Approx. Number Employees: 340
Year Founded: 1997
Business Description:
Mfr. of Plastics Products
S.I.C.: 5031
N.A.I.C.S.: 423310
Import Export
Personnel:
Tim Grieser *(Dir-Ops)*
Tina Mealer *(Mgr-Mktg)*
Brands & Products:
FYPON
MOULDED MILLWORK
PVC TRIM
QUICKRAIL
QUICKWRAP
Advertising Agency:
Hitchcock Fleming & Associates, Inc.
500 Wolf Ledges Pkwy
Akron, OH 44311-1022
Tel.: (330) 376-2111
Fax: (330) 376-2220
Toll Free: (888) 376-7601

G&D TECHNOLOGIES, LLC
(d/b/a Performance Coatings International)
10 Henderson Dr
West Caldwell, NJ 07006
Mailing Address:
PO Box 1265
West Caldwell, NJ 07007-1265
Tel.: (973) 227-5401
Fax: (973) 227-5402
E-mail: info@panelgraphic.com
Web Site: www.panelgraphic.com
Approx. Sls.: $2,000,000
Approx. Number Employees: 20
Year Founded: 1955
Business Description:
Plastic Parts Mfr Including Machining, Screen Printing & Proprietary Coating
S.I.C.: 3089
N.A.I.C.S.: 326199
Export
Media: 2-4-7-10-13-17-21-26
Distr.: Natl.
Personnel:
George E. Drazinakis *(Pres)*
Ken McAdams *(Mgr-Sls & Customer Svc)*
Brands & Products:
CHROMAFILTER
LENSGUARD
SOLARIS
THERMAL
TOPPRO
TOPPRO WOW
VUEGUARD

GLASTIC CORPORATION
(Sub. of Rochling Engineering Plastics KG)
4321 Glenridge Rd
Cleveland, OH 44121-2805
Tel.: (216) 486-0100
Fax: (216) 486-1091
E-mail: sales@glastic.com
Web Site: www.glastic.com
E-Mail For Key Personnel:
Sales Director: sales@glastic.com
Sales Range: $25-49.9 Million
Approx. Number Employees: 160
Year Founded: 1947
Business Description:
Mfr. & Sale of Glass Fiber-Reinforced Plastic Materials
S.I.C.: 3089; 2821
N.A.I.C.S.: 326199; 325211
Import Export
Advertising Expenditures: $230,000
Media: 2-4-7-10-21
Distr.: Intl.
Budget Set: Nov.
Personnel:
Darren Keegan *(Gen Mgr-North American Composites)*
James Azzarello *(Mgr-Sls)*
William Couch *(Mgr-Sys & Procedures)*
Robyn Kral *(Mgr-HR)*
Kerry Mullally *(Mgr-Key Acct)*
Mark Stofan *(Mgr-Laminate Mfg)*
Sean Mott *(Coord-Sls Svc)*
Brands & Products:
DI-ELYTE
GLASROD
GLASTHERM
GLASTIC
Advertising Agency:
Media II, Inc.
2778 SOM Center Rd Ste 200
Willoughby, OH 44094
Tel.: (440) 943-3600
Fax: (440) 943-3660
— Roy W. Harry *(Chm. Bd. & Pres.)*

GLOBE COMPOSITE SOLUTIONS, LTD.
254 Beech St
Rockland, MA 02370-2749
Tel.: (781) 871-3700
Fax: (781) 871-6631
E-mail: info@globecomposite.com
Web Site: www.globecomposite.com
Approx. Number Employees: 50
Year Founded: 1890
Business Description:
Mfr of Industrial Rubber, Marine & Vibration Control Products
S.I.C.: 3089
N.A.I.C.S.: 326199
Export
Media: 2-4-7-10-13-26
Distr.: Intl.; Natl.
Budget Set: Jan.
Personnel:
Carl W. Forsythe *(Pres & CEO)*
William McCourt *(CFO & COO)*
Brian Evans *(VP-Product Dev)*
Brands & Products:
BRANDONITE
DRIVESAVER
ENDURO-STS
EVER-STAY
FUTURE SOLUTIONS: TODAY
GLOBE
GLOBE COMPOSITE SOLUTIONS
RCS-6689
RUN-DRY
SHAFTKEEPER
TUFF-TOTE

GOODYEAR CANADA INC.
(Sub. of The Goodyear Tire & Rubber Company)
450 Kipling Ave
Toronto, ON M8Z 5E1, Canada
Tel.: (416) 201-4300
Fax: (416) 201-4242
Web Site: www.goodyear.ca
Sales Range: $125-149.9 Million
Approx. Number Employees: 4,000
Year Founded: 1910
Business Description:
Tires & Rubber Products Distr
S.I.C.: 3011
N.A.I.C.S.: 326211
Personnel:
Gus Liotta *(Dir-Consumer Tires Canada)*
Julie Thomson *(Mgr-Svcs)*
Advertising Agency:
Due North Communications Inc.
35 The Esplanade 2nd Fl
Toronto, ON M5E 1Z4, Canada
Tel.: (416) 862-8181
Fax: (416) 862-9553

THE GOODYEAR TIRE & RUBBER COMPANY
1144 E Market St
Akron, OH 44316-0001
Tel.: (330) 796-2121
Fax: (330) 796-2222
E-mail: goodyear.investor.relations@goodyear.com
Web Site: www.goodyear.com
E-Mail For Key Personnel:
Public Relations: kprice@goodyear.com
Approx. Sls.: $18,832,000,000
Approx. Number Employees: 72,000
Year Founded: 1898
Business Description:
Tires & Tubes Mfr for Industrial, Auto, Truck, Earthmover, Aviation; Industrial & Engineered Products; Shoe & Graphic Products; Plastics & Films; Chemicals & Adhesives
S.I.C.: 3011; 7538
N.A.I.C.S.: 326211; 811111
Import Export
Advertising Expenditures: $396,000,000
Media: 1-2-3-5-6-8-9-10-13-14-15-20-23-24-26
Distr.: Intl.; Natl.
Budget Set: Aug.
Personnel:
Richard J. Kramer *(Chm, Pres & CEO)*
Darren R. Wells *(CFO & Exec VP)*
R. Scott Rogers *(CMO-Consumer-North American)*

Key to Media (For complete agency information see *The Advertising Red Books-Agencies* edition):
1. Bus. Publs. 2. Cable T.V. 3. Catalogs & Directories. 4. Co-op Adv. 5. Consumer Mags. 6. D.M. to Bus. Estab.7. D.M. to Consumers
8. Daily Newsp. 9. Exhibits/Trade Shows 10. Foreign 11. Infomercial 12. Internet Adv.13. Multimedia 14. Network Radio
15. Network T.V. 16. Newsp. Distr. Mags. 17. Other 18. Outdoor (Posters, Transit) 19. Point of Purchase20. Premiums, Novelties
21. Product Samples 22. Special Events Mktg. 23. Spot Radio 24. Spot T.V. 25. Weekly Newsp. 26. Yellow Page Adv.

Jean-Claude Kihn *(CTO & Sr VP)*
Pierre E. Cohade *(Pres-Asia Pacific Reg)*
Jaime Cohen-Szulc *(Pres-Latin American Reg)*
Arthur De Bok *(Pres-Europe, Middle East & Africa)*
Stephen McClellan *(Pres-Consumer Tires-North American Tire)*
Jon Rich *(Pres-North American Tire Bus)*
Michel Rzonzef *(Pres-Eastern Europe, Middle East & Africa Countries)*
David L. Bialosky *(Gen Counsel, Sec & Sr VP)*
Chris Clark *(Sr VP-Global Sourcing)*
John D. Fish *(Sr VP-Ops-Global)*
Joseph B. Ruocco *(Sr VP-HR)*
Chuck Mick *(VP & Gen Mgr-Holdings & Integration-North America)*
Pierre Jambon *(Gen Mgr-Global Aviation)*
Bob Toth *(Gen Mgr-Goodyear Brand HP)*
John Cavanaugh *(Dir-Race Tire Ops)*
Paul Gerrard *(Dir-First Procurement)*
Keith J. Price *(Dir-Natl Media Rels & Bus Comm)*
Patrick Stobb *(Dir-IR)*
Justin Fantozzi *(Mktg Mgr-Goodyear Motorsports)*
Janice Consolacion *(Mktg Mgr-Dunlop)*
Bertram Bell *(Asst Gen Counsel & Asst Sec)*
Anthony E. Miller *(Assoc Gen Counsel & Asst Sec)*

Brands & Products:
ALL-AMERICAN
AQUATRED
ARRIVA
ASSURANCE
ASSURANCE COMFORTRED
ASSURANCE TRIPLETRED
BREWLINE
BUDENE
CENTENNIAL
CHEMIGUM
CLUB
CONCORDE
CONQUEST
CONTENDER
CROWN NEOLITE
DEBICA
DESERT FOX
DIVERSIFLEX
DOUBLE EAGLE
DRAG
DUNLOP
DURASEAL
DYRA TORQUE
EAGLE
EAGLE #1
EAGLE PD
FLEXDOCK
FLEXPULSE
FLIGHT CUSTOM II
FLIGHT EAGLE
FLIGHT LEADER
FLIGHT RADIAL
FLIGHT SPECIAL II
FORTERA
FULDA
G-METRIC
GALAXY
GATORBACK
GEMINI
GEMINI AUTOMOTIVE CARE
GOODYEAR
GOODYEAR AUTO SERVICE CENTERS
GOODYEAR BLIMP LOGO
GOODYEAR CERTIFIED AUTO SERVICE
GORILLA
HALLMARK
HI MILER
HI-Q
HIGHWAY HERO
HORIZON
HP MINER
INDY 500
INTEGRITY
INVICTA
JUSTTIRES
KELLY
LEE
MARATHON
MATCHMAKER
MAXXIM
MONARCH
MYRIADE
NASCAR
NATSYN
NEOLITE
ORTAC
PLIOCORD
PLIOFLEX
PLIOLITE
PLIOTEC LS
PLIOTONE
PLIOVIC
PLIOWAY
PLYLON
PNEUMANT
POLYSTAY
PREMIER
PREMIO
PRIMELINE
REGIONAL
REMINGTON
REPETE
REPUBLIC
SAVA
SENSOR GUARD
SERTASERVIS
SOF SPUN
SOLO LLANTAS
SOLOFLEX
SPIRAFLEX
STAR
SUPER-CUSHION
SURELINE
TERRA-TIRE
TIEMPO
TORQUE TEAM
TYRE PRO
UNICIRCLE
UNISTEEL
VENTURA
VIPER
WINELINE
WING-FIL
WINGCURE
WINGED FOOT DESIGN
WINGFOOT
WINGSTAY
WINGSTOP
WINGTACK
WRANGLER
YUKON

Advertising Agencies:
Digitas Inc.
33 Arch St
Boston, MA 02110
Tel.: (617) 867-1000
Fax: (617) 867-1111
Consumer Web Development
CRM Activities
Digital Media Planning & Buying
Interactive Agency of Record
Mobile Marketing
Search Advertising
Social Media Marketing

GSD&M
828 W 6th St
Austin, TX 78703-5420
Tel.: (512) 242-4736
Fax: (512) 242-4700
Brand Agency of Record

Hitchcock Fleming & Associates, Inc.
500 Wolf Ledges Pkwy
Akron, OH 44311-1022
Tel.: (330) 376-2111
Fax: (330) 376-2220
Toll Free: (888) 376-7601
(Mailers, Direct Marketing & Direct Mail)
— Christina Cyrus *(Acct Mgr)*
— Ted Paynter *(Acct Supvr)*

Innis Maggiore
4715 Whipple Ave NW
Canton, OH 44718-2651
Tel.: (330) 492-5500
Fax: (330) 492-5568
Toll Free: (800) 460-4111

McCann Worldgroup Thailand
555 Narathiwas Rd
Bangkok, 10120, Thailand
Tel.: (66) 2 343 6000
Fax: (66) 2 343 6001

MPG
(Div. of HAVAS)
195 Broadway 12th Fl
New York, NY 10007
Tel.: (646) 587-5000
Fax: (646) 587-5005

GREENMAN TECHNOLOGIES, INC.

205 S Garfield
Carlisle, IA 50047
Tel.: (781) 224-2411
Fax: (781) 224-4114
Toll Free: (800) 957-9575
Toll Free: (800) 526-0860
E-mail: info@tirerecyclersgmt.com
Web Site: www.greenman.biz
Approx. Sls.: $2,574,514
Approx. Number Employees: 35
Year Founded: 1992
Business Description:
Tire Recycling; Collecting, Shredding & Marketing Scrap Tires
S.I.C.: 3084; 3082; 4953
N.A.I.C.S.: 326122; 326121; 562920
Advertising Expenditures: $177,322
Media: 17
Personnel:
Maurice E. Needham *(Chm)*
Lyle E. Jensen *(CEO)*
Charles E. Coppa *(CFO, Treas & Sec)*

THE HERCULES TIRE & RUBBER COMPANY

16380 E US Rte 224 Ste 200
Findlay, OH 45840
Tel.: (419) 425-6400
Fax: (419) 425-6402
E-mail: info@herculestire.com
Web Site: www.herculestire.com
Sales Range: $400-449.9 Million
Approx. Number Employees: 35
Year Founded: 1952
Business Description:
Distr of Tires & Automotive Products
S.I.C.: 5014; 3011
N.A.I.C.S.: 423130; 326211
Import Export
Media: 2-4-10-11-19-21
Distr.: Intl.; Natl.
Budget Set: Oct.
Personnel:
Bill Trimarco *(Pres & CEO)*
Vic Siewert *(Sr VP-Admin & Plng)*
Brands & Products:
GIANT
HERCULES
MERIT
PARNELLI JONES DIRT GRIPZ
SIGNET
TIRECO

HEXCEL CORPORATION

2 Stamford Plz 16th Fl 281 Tresser Blvd
Stamford, CT 06901-3238
Tel.: (203) 969-0666
Fax: (203) 358-3977
E-mail: info@hexcel.com
Web Site: www.hexcel.com
Approx. Sls.: $1,173,600,000
Approx. Number Employees: 4,043
Year Founded: 1946
Business Description:
Advanced Structural Materials Developer, Mfr & Retailer
S.I.C.: 2821; 3089; 3728
N.A.I.C.S.: 325211; 326199; 336413
Import Export
Media: 2-7-10
Distr.: Natl.
Budget Set: Oct.
Personnel:
David E. Berges *(Chm & CEO)*
Nick L. Stanage *(Pres)*
Wayne C. Pensky *(CFO & Sr VP)*
Kimberly A. Hendricks *(Chief Acctg Officer, VP & Controller)*
Ira J. Krakower *(Gen Counsel, Sec & Sr VP)*
Andrea Domenichini *(Sr VP & Gen Mgr-Wind Energy)*
Robert G. Hennemuth *(Sr VP-HR)*
Michael Bacal *(Mgr-Comm & IR)*
Brands & Products:
BECOME A PART OF THE STRENGTH WITHIN
FIBRELAM
HEXCEL
HEXCOAT
HEXFIT
HEXFLOW
HEXFORCE
HEXLITE
HEXMC
HEXPLY
HEXTOOL
HEXTOW
HEXWEB
KEVLAR
MAGNAMITE
MODIPUR
POLYSPEED

Key to Media (For complete agency information see *The Advertising Red Books-Agencies* edition):
1. Bus. Publs. 2. Cable T.V. 3. Catalogs & Directories. 4. Co-op Adv. 5. Consumer Mags. 6. D.M. to Bus. Estab.7. D.M. to Consumers
8. Daily Newsp. 9. Exhibits/Trade Shows 10. Foreign 11. Infomercial 12. Internet Adv.13. Multimedia 14. Network Radio
15. Network T.V. 16. Newsp. Distr. Mags. 17. Other 18. Outdoor (Posters, Transit) 19. Point of Purchase20. Premiums, Novelties
21. Product Samples 22. Special Events Mktg. 23. Spot Radio 24. Spot T.V. 25. Weekly Newsp. 26. Yellow Page Adv.

Hexcel Corporation — (Continued)

REDUX
SPECTRA
TOWFLEX
TWARON

Advertising Agency:
Shennum Green, Inc.
6160 Stoneridge Mall Rd Ste 290
Pleasanton, CA 94588
Tel.: (925) 460-8301
Fax: (925) 460-8307

HICKORY SPRINGS MANUFACTURING COMPANY

235 2nd Ave NW
Hickory, NC 28601-4950
Tel.: (828) 328-2201
Fax: (828) 328-5501
Toll Free: (800) 438-5341
E-mail: info@hickorysprings.com
Web Site: www.hickorysprings.com
Approx. Number Employees: 1,000
Year Founded: 1944
Business Description:
Mfr. & Supplier of Components for the Furniture & Bedding Industries
S.I.C.: 3069; 3495
N.A.I.C.S.: 326299; 332612
Media: 2-10
Personnel:
J. Don Coleman *(Pres)*
Steve Ellis *(CFO & Dir)*
Brands & Products:
BEDSECURE
CLASSICREST
CODE RED
CODE RED II
CONTRACTSLEEPER
CROSS BAR
ELDORADO
ENDUROFLEX
ENDUROFOAM
ENDUROLOFT
ENDUROPAD
ENDUROPLUSH
FABRI FAST
FABRI FAST II
HALO
HICKORY SPRINGS MANUFACTURING COMPANY
INNERACT
INNOVATOR
OVERNIGHTER
POWERSTACK
POWERSTEP
RESTWELL
ROCK N LOCK
SUPERCENTER
TRADITION, INNOVATION, PERFORMANCE.
VINESS

HILEX POLY CO., LLC

(Sub. of HPC Industries, LLC)
101 E Carolina Ave
Hartsville, SC 29550
Tel.: (843) 857-4800
Fax: (843) 857-4811
Toll Free: (800) 432-1050
Web Site: www.hilexpoly.com
Approx. Number Employees: 1,000
Business Description:
Plastic Bag & Film Mfr
S.I.C.: 2673; 2671
N.A.I.C.S.: 326111; 322221; 326112
Media: 10
Brands & Products:
HILEX
QUIKMATE EZ
QUIKSERVE
QUIKSTAR
QUIKTAB
ROLLMATE

HONEYWELL SALISBURY ELECTRICAL SAFETY

(Div. of Honeywell Safety Products)
7520 N Long Ave
Skokie, IL 60077
Tel.: (847) 679-6700
Fax: (847) 679-2401
Fax: (866) 824-4922
Toll Free: (877) 406-4501
Web Site: www.whsalisbury.com
Sales Range: $75-99.9 Million
Approx. Number Employees: 220
Year Founded: 1855
Business Description:
Electrical Safety Products Mfr
S.I.C.: 3069; 3061
N.A.I.C.S.: 326299; 326291
Export
Media: 2-4-8-10-21
Distr.: Intl.; Natl.
Budget Set: Aug. -Sept.

HYGRADE METAL MOULDING MANUFACTURING CORP.

(Sub. of Hygrade Acquisition Metal Molding)
1990 Highland Ave
Bethlehem, PA 18020-9083
Tel.: (610) 866-2441
Fax: (610) 866-3761
Toll Free: (800) 645-9475
E-mail: sales@hygrademetal.com
Web Site: www.hygrademetal.com
E-Mail For Key Personnel:
Sales Director: sales@hygrademetal.com
Sales Range: $10-24.9 Million
Approx. Number Employees: 50
Year Founded: 1939
Business Description:
Roll Formed Metal Shapes, Spacer Tubing Mfr for Insulated Glass
S.I.C.: 3354; 3356
N.A.I.C.S.: 331316; 331491
Export
Media: 2-4-7-10
Distr.: Natl.
Personnel:
Vincent A. Pagano *(Chm)*
Douglas Sherman *(Vice Chm)*
Mike Erb *(Mgr-Materials & Buyer)*
Doreen Murphy *(Mgr-Customer Svc)*

ICO INC.

(Sub. of A. Schulman, Inc.)
1811 Bering Dr Ste 200
Houston, TX 77057-3186
Tel.: (713) 351-4100
Fax: (713) 335-2201
E-mail: webmaster@icoinc.com
Web Site: www.icopolymers.com
Approx. Rev.: $299,965,000
Approx. Number Employees: 805
Year Founded: 1978
Business Description:
Custom Polymer Powders & Plastic Film Concentrates Mfr
S.I.C.: 3082; 1389; 3086
N.A.I.C.S.: 326121; 213112; 326150
Import Export
Media: 4-10-11
Personnel:
Gregory T. Barmore *(Chm)*
Charlotte Fischer Ewart *(Gen Counsel & Sec)*
Charlie Busceme *(Sr VP-Sls & Mktg)*
Greg Agnew *(Dir-Continuous Improvement-Americas)*
Brands & Products:
COTENE
ICO
ICOFLO
ICORENE
ICOTEX
THE INNOVATIVE COMPANY
POWDER THE WAY YOU WANT IT
WEDCO

INDUSTRIAL SERVICES OF AMERICA, INC.

7100 Grade Ln
Louisville, KY 40213-3424
Mailing Address:
PO Box 32428
Louisville, KY 40232-2428
Tel.: (502) 368-1661
Tel.: (502) 366-3452
Fax: (502) 368-1440
Toll Free: (888) 494-4472
Toll Free: (888) 4944-ISA
E-mail: chulsman@isa-inc.com
Web Site: www.isa-inc.com
E-Mail For Key Personnel:
Sales Director: bmoore@isa-inc.com
Approx. Rev.: $343,005,315
Approx. Number Employees: 185
Year Founded: 1953
Business Description:
Recycling, Scrap, Waste Management & Recycling Services
S.I.C.: 8742; 4953; 5093
N.A.I.C.S.: 541614; 423930; 541611; 562920
Advertising Expenditures: $218,859
Media: 1-2-7-10-22-26
Distr.: Natl.
Budget Set: Mar.
Personnel:
Harry Kletter *(Chm & CEO)*
Brian Donaghy *(Pres & COO)*
Alan L. Schroering *(CFO)*
Daniel C. Gascoyne *(Exec VP-Ferrous & Non Ferrous Recycling Ops-Kentucky & Indiana)*
Charles Hulsman *(Dir)*

INTERNATIONAL BIO RECOVERY CORPORATION

52 Riverside Dr
North Vancouver, BC V7H 1T4, Canada
Tel.: (604) 924-1023
Fax: (604) 924-1043
E-mail: info@ibrcorp.com
Web Site: www.ibrcorp.com
Approx. Rev.: $10,312
Approx. Number Employees: 15
Year Founded: 1993
Business Description:
Waste Conversion Services
S.I.C.: 9511; 1479
N.A.I.C.S.: 924110; 212393
Media: 17
Personnel:
Henry J. Bow *(Pres & CEO)*
Robert Nowell *(CFO)*

INTERTAPE POLYMER GROUP INC.

9999 Cavendish Blvd Ste 200
Ville Saint Laurent, QC H4M 2X5, Canada
Tel.: (514) 731-7591
E-mail: info@itape.com
Web Site: www.intertapepolymer.com
Approx. Sls.: $720,516,000
Approx. Number Employees: 2,024
Year Founded: 1981
Business Description:
Specialized Polyolefin Plastic & Paper Packaging Products Developer & Mfr
S.I.C.: 2671
N.A.I.C.S.: 322221; 326112
Media: 2-10
Personnel:
Eric E. Baker *(Chm)*
Gregory A. C. Yull *(Pres & CEO)*
Bernard J. Pitz *(CFO)*
Melbourne F. Yull *(Exec Dir)*

JANESVILLE ACOUSTICS

(Div. of Jason Incorporated)
25330 Telegraph Rd Raleigh Officentre Ste 150
Southfield, MI 48033
Tel.: (248) 948-1811
Fax: (248) 948-1822
Web Site:
www.janesvilleacoustics.com
Approx. Number Employees: 100
Year Founded: 1981
Business Description:
Acoustical & Thermal Fiber Insulation Mfr for the Automotive Industry
S.I.C.: 3086; 3714
N.A.I.C.S.: 326150; 336399
Media: 10-21
Distr.: Natl.
Budget Set: July
Personnel:
Barry Wyerman *(Mgr-Res & Dev)*
Brands & Products:
JANESVILLE

JARDEN CORPORATION

555 Theodore Fremd Ave Ste B-302
Rye, NY 10580
Tel.: (914) 967-9400
Fax: (914) 967-9405
Web Site: www.jarden.com
Approx. Sls.: $6,022,700,000
Approx. Number Employees: 24,000
Year Founded: 1997
Business Description:
Household Consumer Products
S.I.C.: 3631; 3634; 3639; 3991
N.A.I.C.S.: 335221; 335211; 335228; 339994
Import Export
Advertising Expenditures: $68,400,000
Media: 2-6-7-10-12
Personnel:
Martin E. Franklin *(Chm)*
Ian G. H. Ashken *(Vice Chm & CFO)*
James E. Lillie *(CEO)*
Richard T. Sansone *(Chief Acctg Officer & Sr VP)*
John E. Capps *(Gen Counsel, Sec & Exec VP)*
Patricia J. Gaglione *(Sr VP-Bus Ops & Supply Chain)*
Patricia A. Mount *(Chief Transition Officer & Sr VP)*

Key to Media (For complete agency information see *The Advertising Red Books-Agencies* edition):
1. Bus. Publs. 2. Cable T.V. 3. Catalogs & Directories. 4. Co-op Adv. 5. Consumer Mags. 6. D.M. to Bus. Estab.7. D.M. to Consumers 8. Daily Newsp. 9. Exhibits/Trade Shows 10. Foreign 11. Infomercial 12. Internet Adv.13. Multimedia 14. Network Radio 15. Network T.V. 16. Newsp. Distr. Mags. 17. Other 18. Outdoor (Posters, Transit) 19. Point of Purchase20. Premiums, Novelties 21. Product Samples 22. Special Events Mktg. 23. Spot Radio 24. Spot T.V. 25. Weekly Newsp. 26. Yellow Page Adv.

J. David Tolbert *(Sr VP-HR & Corp Risk)*
Paul Warburg *(VP-Fin)*
Brands & Products:
BALL
THE BRANDS OF EVERYDAY LIFE
DIAMOND
DOME
FRUIT JELL
JARDEN CORPORATION
KERR
LOEW-CORNELL
PINE MOUNTAIN
WHITE RIVER FARMS
YORKER

JAY PLASTICS, INC.
5200 City Line Rd
Hampton, VA 23661-1206
Tel.: (757) 247-5200
Fax: (757) 247-5271
E-mail: jplastics@aol.com
Web Site: www.jayplastics.com
Approx. Number Employees: 100
Year Founded: 1948
Business Description:
Advertising Specialties Including Wallet Inserts & Photo Album Pages
S.I.C.: 3089
N.A.I.C.S.: 326199
Export
Media: 2-4-10-26
Distr.: Natl.
Personnel:
Steven J. Zelig *(Owner & Pres)*
Brands & Products:
JP FAMILY

KAUFFMAN TIRE INC.
2832 Anivelle Block Rd
Ellenwood, GA 30294-6009
Tel.: (404) 762-4944
Fax: (770) 767-5332
E-mail: careers@kauffmantire.com
Web Site: www.kauffmantire.com
Approx. Number Employees: 300
Year Founded: 1936
Business Description:
Supplier of Tires
S.I.C.: 5014
N.A.I.C.S.: 423130; 441320
Import Export
Media: 4-13-16
Personnel:
John Kauffman *(CEO)*
Advertising Agency:
Wolfbone Marketing
3455 Peachtree Rd NE Ste 600
Atlanta, GA 30326
Tel.: (404) 995-4620
Fax: (404) 995-4625

KITCHEN-QUIP, INC.
405 E Marion St
Waterloo, IN 46793
Tel.: (260) 837-8311
Fax: (260) 837-7919
E-mail: info@kqcasting.com
Web Site: www.kqcasting.com
E-Mail For Key Personnel:
President: steve.sparling@kqcasting.com
Sales Range: $10-24.9 Million
Approx. Number Employees: 20
Year Founded: 1946
Business Description:
Aluminum & Zinc Die-Casting Services
S.I.C.: 3363; 3369
N.A.I.C.S.: 331521; 331528
Media: 7
Distr.: Direct to Consumer; Intl.; Natl.
Budget Set: June
Personnel:
Steve Sparling *(Pres)*
Judy Maysa *(Mgr-HR)*

KLOCKNER PENTAPLAST OF AMERICA, INC.
(Sub. of Klockner Pentaplast GmbH & Co. KG)
3585 Klockner Rd
Gordonsville, VA 22942-0500
Mailing Address:
PO Box 500
Gordonsville, VA 22942
Tel.: (540) 832-3600
Fax: (540) 832-5656
Telex: 822432
E-mail: info@kpfilms.com
Web Site: www.kpfilms.com
E-Mail For Key Personnel:
Public Relations: nryan@kpafilms.com
Sales Range: $150-199.9 Million
Approx. Number Employees: 700
Year Founded: 1977
Business Description:
Plastic Film & Sheet Mfr
S.I.C.: 3081
N.A.I.C.S.: 326113
Import Export
Advertising Expenditures: $1,000,000
Media: 2-7-9-10-13-25
Distr.: Intl.; Natl.
Budget Set: May
Personnel:
Michael F. Tubridy *(Pres & COO)*
Thomas J. Goeke *(CEO)*
Nancy E. Ryan *(Dir-Corp Comm)*
Advertising Agency:
Payne, Ross & Associates Advertising, Inc.
206 E Jefferson St
Charlottesville, VA 22902-5105
Tel.: (434) 977-7607
Fax: (434) 977-7610
— Lisa Ross *(V.P.)*

LEIDEL CORPORATION
500 Smith St
Farmingdale, NY 11735
Tel.: (631) 694-7797
Fax: (631) 694-7876
E-mail: leidelcorp@aol.com
Web Site: www.leidelcorp.com
Approx. Number Employees: 27
Year Founded: 1902
Business Description:
Closure Molds & Components Mfr
S.I.C.: 3089
N.A.I.C.S.: 326199
Export
Media: 2-4-7-10
Distr.: Natl.

LUDLOW COMPOSITES CORPORATION
2100 Commerce Dr
Fremont, OH 43420
Tel.: (419) 332-5531
Fax: (419) 332-7776
Toll Free: (800) 628-5463
E-mail: industrialsales@ludlow-comp.com
Web Site: www.ludlow-comp.com
Approx. Number Employees: 190
Year Founded: 1943
Business Description:
Mfr. of Carpet-Topped Vinyl-Backed Floor Mats, Latex, Sponge Vinyl Anti-Fatigue Products, Latex Foam Rubber & PVC Foams for OEM Applications
S.I.C.: 3069; 3081
N.A.I.C.S.: 326299; 326113
Import Export
Media: 2-4-10-13-21
Distr.: Intl.; Natl.
Budget Set: June
Brands & Products:
AIRTUFF
CROWN MATS & MATTING
FIRM AIRTUFF
FIRM FOAMCOTE
FOAMCOTE
FOAMPUFF
REACTION
ZEDLAN

LYONDELLBASELL ADVANCED POLYOLEFINS USA, INC.
(Sub. of LyondellBasell Industries)
100 S Mitchell Rd
Mansfield, TX 76063
Tel.: (817) 792-1400
Fax: (817) 792-2850
Web Site: www.apo.lyondellbasell.com
Approx. Number Employees: 300
Business Description:
Custom-Engineered Polyolefin Materials
S.I.C.: 2821
N.A.I.C.S.: 325211
Media: 2-4-10-22
Personnel:
Robert Gerlach *(VP-Sls & Mktg)*
Brands & Products:
DEXLEX
DEXPRO
INDURE
NEXPRENE
RESPOND
SEQUEL

MAAX INC.-MINNEAPOLIS
(Branch of MAAX Bath Inc.)
9224 73rd Ave N
Minneapolis, MN 55428
Tel.: (763) 424-3335
Fax: (763) 424-9808
Toll Free: (800) 328-2531
E-mail: minneapoliscustomercare@maax.com
Web Site: www.maax.com
Approx. Number Employees: 120
Year Founded: 1978
Business Description:
Sauna & Acrylic Spa Mfr
S.I.C.: 3088
N.A.I.C.S.: 326191
Media: 5-8-10
Personnel:
Adria Ensrud *(Project Mgr-Mktg)*
Brands & Products:
ADAGIO
ANDORRA
APOGE
MAAX PEARL

MAPA PROFESSIONAL
(Sub. of Mapa Spontex S.A.)
100 Spontex Dr
Columbia, TN 38401
Tel.: (931) 388-5632
Fax: (800) 537-3299
Toll Free: (800) 537-2897
E-mail: sales@mapaglove.com
Web Site: www.mapa-professional.com
E-Mail For Key Personnel:
Sales Director: sales@mapaglove.com
Approx. Sls.: $30,000,000
Approx. Number Employees: 12
Year Founded: 1918
Business Description:
Industrial & Consumer Latex Gloves Marketer
S.I.C.: 3069; 2842
N.A.I.C.S.: 326299; 325612
Export
Media: 6-10-22
Distr.: Natl.
Budget Set: Oct.
Personnel:
Carmen Castro *(Mgr-Mktg)*
Tom Jordan *(Mgr-Info Sys)*
Brands & Products:
STANZOIL

MARSH BELLOFRAM CORPORATION
(Sub. of Desco Corporation)
State Rte 2 PO Box 305
Newell, WV 26050
Tel.: (304) 387-1200
Fax: (304) 387-4417
Toll Free: (800) 727-5646
E-mail: info@marshbellofram.com
Web Site: www.marshbellofram.com
Approx. Number Employees: 300
Year Founded: 1865
Business Description:
Component, Instrumentation & Control Mfr
S.I.C.: 3612; 3829
N.A.I.C.S.: 335311; 334519
Export
Media: 2-4-10-13
Distr.: Intl.; Natl.
Budget Set: Nov.
Personnel:
Dwight Nafziger *(VP-Sls & Mktg)*
Brands & Products:
SUPER CYLINDERS

MARYLAND PLASTICS, INC.
(Sub. of Lab Products, Inc.)
251 E Central Ave
Federalsburg, MD 21632
Tel.: (410) 754-5566
Fax: (410) 754-8882
Toll Free: (800) 544-5582
E-mail: sales@marylandplastics.com
Web Site: www.marylandplastics.com
E-Mail For Key Personnel:
Sales Director: sales@marylandplastics.com
Approx. Number Employees: 95
Business Description:
Plastic Cutlery, Plastic Laboratory Equipment & Custom Molded Products Mfr
S.I.C.: 3089; 3069
N.A.I.C.S.: 326199; 326299
Advertising Expenditures: $300,000
Media: 2-4-6-7-8-10
Distr.: Natl.
Budget Set: May

Key to Media (For complete agency information see *The Advertising Red Books-Agencies* edition):
1. Bus. Publs. 2. Cable T.V. 3. Catalogs & Directories. 4. Co-op Adv. 5. Consumer Mags. 6. D.M. to Bus. Estab.7. D.M. to Consumers 8. Daily Newsp. 9. Exhibits/Trade Shows 10. Foreign 11. Infomercial 12. Internet Adv.13. Multimedia 14. Network Radio 15. Network T.V. 16. Newsp. Distr. Mags. 17. Other 18. Outdoor (Posters, Transit) 19. Point of Purchase20. Premiums, Novelties 21. Product Samples 22. Special Events Mktg. 23. Spot Radio 24. Spot T.V. 25. Weekly Newsp. 26. Yellow Page Adv.

Maryland Plastics, Inc. — (Continued)

Brands & Products:
JUBILEE
KINGSMEN
THE NEWBURY COLLECTION
PREMIERWARE
SOVEREIGN

MASON INDUSTRIES

350 Rabro Dr
Hauppauge, NY 11788
Mailing Address:
PO Box 410
Smithtown, NY 11787
Tel.: (631) 348-0282
Fax: (631) 348-0279
E-mail: info@mason-ind.com
Web Site: www.mason-ind.com
Approx. Number Employees: 200
Year Founded: 1958
Business Description:
Noise & Vibration Control Products & Rubber Products Mfr
S.I.C.: 3625; 3069
N.A.I.C.S.: 335314; 326299
Media: 2-4-10-18-21
Personnel:
Norman J. Mason *(Pres)*
Brands & Products:
MASON INDUSTRIES
MASONFLEX
SAFEFLEX
SUPERFLEX

THE MERCER RUBBER COMPANY

(Sub. of Mason Industries)
350 Rabro Dr
Hauppauge, NY 11788-4257
Mailing Address:
PO Box 410
Smithtown, NY 11787-0410
Tel.: (631) 348-0282
Fax: (631) 348-0279
E-mail: info@mercer-rubber.com
Web Site: www.mercer-rubber.com
Sales Range: $1-9.9 Million
Approx. Number Employees: 100
Year Founded: 1866
Business Description:
Mfr. of Mechanical Rubber Products
S.I.C.: 3069; 3052
N.A.I.C.S.: 326299; 326220
Import Export
Media: 2-7-10-20-22
Distr.: Intl.; Natl.
Budget Set: Jan.
Personnel:
Norman J. Mason *(Pres)*
Brands & Products:
ABRASION BUSTER
INVINCIBLE
VIBRA FLEX PIPE

MHI INJECTION MOLDING MACHINERY, INC.

(Div. of Mitsubishi Heavy Industries America, Inc. (MHIA))
520 Thomas Dr
Bensenville, IL 60106
Tel.: (630) 693-4880
Fax: (630) 693-0915
Web Site: www.mhiinj.com
Approx. Number Employees: 35
Year Founded: 1989
Business Description:
Plastic Injection Molding Machine Retailer
S.I.C.: 5084
N.A.I.C.S.: 423830
Personnel:
Nobou Maki *(Pres-Japan)*
Akira Someya *(Gen Mgr)*
Tom Geddes *(Mgr-Natl Sls)*
Advertising Agency:
Goda Advertising
1603 Colonial Pkwy
Inverness, IL 60067
Tel.: (847) 776-9900
Fax: (847) 776-9901

MICHELIN AMERICAS SMALL TIRES (MAST)

(Sub. of Michelin North America, Inc.)
1 Parkway S
Greenville, SC 29615-5022
Mailing Address:
PO Box 19001
Greenville, SC 29602-9001
Tel.: (864) 458-5000
Toll Free: (800) 847-3435
Web Site: www.michelinman.com
Approx. Number Employees: 13,000
Business Description:
Tires Mfr
S.I.C.: 3011; 5014
N.A.I.C.S.: 326211; 423130
Import Export
Distr.: Natl.
Personnel:
James M. Micali *(Chm & Pres)*
Scott Clark *(COO)*
Pascal Couasnon *(VP-Mktg)*
Sheryl Henderson *(Dir-Adv)*
Advertising Agency:
TBWA Chiat Day New York
488 Madison Ave
New York, NY 10022
Tel.: (212) 804-1000
Fax: (212) 804-1200

MICHELIN NORTH AMERICA (CANADA) INC.

(Sub. of Compagnie Generale des Etablissements Michelin SCA)
3020 Jacques Bureau Ave
Laval, QC H7P 6G2, Canada
Tel.: (450) 978-4700
Fax: (450) 978-7600
Web Site: www.michelin.ca
Approx. Number Employees: 150
Business Description:
Commercial Tire Distr
S.I.C.: 5014
N.A.I.C.S.: 441320
Export
Advertising Expenditures: $200,000
Media: 5-6-9-10-15-18-19-20-22-23-24-25-26
Distr.: Natl.
Personnel:
Jean Moreau *(VP-Personnel)*
Nadine Lussier *(Mgr-Uniroyal PR)*
Brands & Products:
A BETTER WAY FORWARD
BFGOODRICH PASSENGER & LIGHT TRUCK TIRES

MICHELIN NORTH AMERICA, INC.

(Sub. of Compagnie Generale des Etablissements Michelin SCA)
1 Pkwy S
Greenville, SC 29615
Tel.: (864) 458-5000
Fax: (864) 458-6764
Toll Free: (800) 847-3435
Web Site: www.michelin-us.com
Approx. Number Employees: 22,300
Year Founded: 1950
Business Description:
Designs, Manufactures & Sells Tires for Every Type of Vehicle, Including Airplanes, Automobiles, Bicycles, Earthmovers, Farm Equipment, Heavy-Duty Trucks, Motorcycles & the Space Shuttle; Publishes Travel Guides, Hotel & Restaurant Guides, Maps & Road Atlases
S.I.C.: 3011; 2741; 5014
N.A.I.C.S.: 326211; 423130; 511199
Import Export
Advertising Expenditures: $100,000,000
Media: 1-2-3-4-5-6-7-8-9-10-11-14-15-18-19-20-22-23-24-25-26
Distr.: Intl.; Natl.
Personnel:
Richard Wilkerson *(Chm & Pres)*
James Fish *(Dir-Mktg)*
Kaz Holley *(Dir-BFGoodrich, Uniroyal, Private & Assoc Brands)*
Ame Sanders *(Dir-EBus)*
Don Baldwin *(Product Mgr-Mktg)*
Brands & Products:
BFGOODRICH
CAVALIER
FISK
MEDALIST
MICHELIN
REGUL
RIKEN
UNIROYAL
WARRIOR
Advertising Agencies:
Ketchum Directory Advertising/Kansas City
7015 College Blvd Ste 700
Overland Park, KS 66211-1524
Tel.: (913) 344-1900
Fax: (913) 344-1960
Toll Free: (800) 922-6977

The Martin Agency
One Shockoe Plz
Richmond, VA 23219-4132
Tel.: (804) 698-8000
Fax: (804) 698-8001
BF Goodrich Brand

MediaCom
498 7th Ave
New York, NY 10018
Tel.: (212) 912-4200
Fax: (212) 508-4386
BF Goodrich
TCI Tire Centers
Uniroyal
Michelin Maps & Guides

Trone Inc.
4035 Piedmont Pkwy
High Point, NC 27265-9402
Tel.: (336) 886-1622
Fax: (336) 886-2174
(Uniroyal Brand)
— Helga Moya *(Asst Acct Exec)*

MILLER PRODUCTS COMPANY, INC.

2511 S TriCenter Blvd
Durham, NC 27713
Tel.: (919) 313-2100
Fax: (919) 313-2101
Toll Free: (800) 782-7437
E-mail: sales@millerproducts.com
Web Site: www.millerproducts.com
E-Mail For Key Personnel:
Sales Director: sales@millerproducts.com
Approx. Sls.: $10,000,000
Approx. Number Employees: 23
Year Founded: 1930
Business Description:
Mfr of Rubber & Synthetic Rubber Products & Plastic Molded Products
S.I.C.: 3069; 3061
N.A.I.C.S.: 326299; 326291
Media: 2-8-17-21-26
Distr.: Direct to Consumer; Natl.
Budget Set: Jan.-July
Personnel:
Stuart A. Miller *(Chm)*
Brands & Products:
TUFF 'N RUFF

MINOR RUBBER CO., INC.

49 Ackerman St
Bloomfield, NJ 07003
Tel.: (973) 338-6800
Fax: (973) 893-1399
Toll Free: (800) 433-6886
E-mail: sales@minorrubber.com
Web Site: www.minorrubber.com
E-Mail For Key Personnel:
Sales Director: sales@minorrubber.com
Approx. Number Employees: 120
Year Founded: 1914
Business Description:
Mfr. of Molded, Dipped, Extruded, Industrial Rubber & Synthetic Rubber Components & Assemblies
S.I.C.: 3061; 3052
N.A.I.C.S.: 326291; 326220
Export
Media: 2-4-7-10-11-13-21
Distr.: Natl.
Budget Set: Nov.
Personnel:
R.W. Krumscheid, Jr. *(Pres)*
Brands & Products:
AMTEX
MATCHLESS
MINOR
MIRCO
MR
QUALATEX
THERMOFLEX
VICHEM

MOELLER PRODUCTS COMPANY, INC.

1281 Pickett St PO Box 1736
Greenville, MS 38703-2454
Tel.: (662) 335-2325
Fax: (662) 332-9056
E-mail: sales@moellerproducts.com
Web Site: www.moellerproducts.com
E-Mail For Key Personnel:
Sales Director: sales@moellerproducts.com
Approx. Number Employees: 70
Year Founded: 1940

Key to Media (For complete agency information see *The Advertising Red Books-Agencies* edition):
1. Bus. Publs. 2. Cable T.V. 3. Catalogs & Directories. 4. Co-op Adv. 5. Consumer Mags. 6. D.M. to Bus. Estab.7. D.M. to Consumers
8. Daily Newsp. 9. Exhibits/Trade Shows 10. Foreign 11. Infomercial 12. Internet Adv.13. Multimedia 14. Network Radio
15. Network T.V. 16. Newsp. Distr. Mags. 17. Other 18. Outdoor (Posters, Transit) 19. Point of Purchase20. Premiums, Novelties
21. Product Samples 22. Special Events Mktg. 23. Spot Radio 24. Spot T.V. 25. Weekly Newsp. 26. Yellow Page Adv.

Business Description:
Mfr. of Oil Level Gauge Dipstick Assemblies, Oil Filler Caps & Custom Injection Molded Thermoplastic Products
S.I.C.: 3714
N.A.I.C.S.: 336399
Export
Media: 2-4-10-13
Distr.: Intl.; Natl.
Brands & Products:
EASY GRIP
LOCK-N-SEAL
MOELLER

MOLDED FIBER GLASS COMPANIES
2925 MFG Pl PO Box 675
Ashtabula, OH 44005-0675
Tel.: (440) 997-5851
Fax: (440) 994-5162
E-mail: info@moldedfiberglass.com
Web Site: www.moldedfiberglass.com
Approx. Number Employees: 2,000
Year Founded: 1948
Business Description:
Custom Fiber Glass Products Mfr
S.I.C.: 3089; 3083
N.A.I.C.S.: 326199; 326130
Export
Advertising Expenditures: $200,000
Media: 2-4-6-21
Distr.: Intl.; Natl.
Budget Set: Oct.
Personnel:
Richard S. Morrison *(CEO)*
Greg Tilton *(COO & Exec VP)*
Glen Warner *(Corp VP-Mktg)*
David Boden *(Dir-Quality)*
Dan Plona *(Dir-Pur)*
Brands & Products:
BOKAY
FIBRILLA
ICOM
MFG
PLYGLASS
PRIME
TOTELINE
WIDEWALL
WONDER

MOTAN, INC.
320 N Acorn St
Plainwell, MI 49080
Mailing Address:
PO Box 248
Plainwell, MI 49080
Tel.: (269) 685-1050
Fax: (269) 685-1059
Toll Free: (800) 991-9921
E-mail: motanusa@motan-inc.com
Web Site: www.motan.com
Sales Range: $10-24.9 Million
Approx. Number Employees: 15
Year Founded: 1980
Business Description:
Plastic Pellet Material Handling & Drying Equipment
S.I.C.: 3535; 3537
N.A.I.C.S.: 333922; 333924
Import Export
Advertising Expenditures: $400,000
Media: 1-2-6-7-8-10-13
Distr.: Natl.
Personnel:
Mark McKibbin *(Pres)*
Brands & Products:
DUOMIX
ETA-PROCESS
FLEXSIDE
GRAVICOLOR 100
GRAVICOLOR 1000
GRAVICOLOR 30
GRAVICOLOR 300
LINKNET
LUXOR
LUXORBIN
LUXORNET
MB-COLOR
METRO ML
METROLINK
METROLUX
METROMIX
METRONET
MINICOLOR
MOTAN
POWER TO CHANGE
SUPPORTNET

MULTI-PLASTICS, INC.
7770 N Central Dr
Lewis Center, OH 43035-9404
Tel.: (740) 548-4894
Fax: (740) 548-5177
Toll Free: (800) 848-6982
E-mail: multi@multi-plastics.com
Web Site: www.multi-plastics.com
Approx. Number Employees: 140
Year Founded: 1979
Business Description:
Thin-Gauged Plastic Film Distr
S.I.C.: 5162
N.A.I.C.S.: 424610
Import Export
Media: 2-7-10-21
Personnel:
John Parsio *(Pres)*
Mike Hickey *(CFO)*
Wesley Hall *(VP-Sls & Mktg)*
Cheryl Caudill *(Mgr-Corp Comm)*
Brands & Products:
CARTON WINDOW FILM
ENVELOPE WINDOW FILM
LAMINATING & CONVERTING FILMS
ROWTEC
SOLTUF
SPECTRALITE
WIDE WEB LAMINATING

MYERS INDUSTRIES, INC.
1293 S Main St
Akron, OH 44301-1302
Tel.: (330) 253-5592
Fax: (330) 761-6156
E-mail: webmaster@po.myersind.com
Web Site: www.myersind.com
Approx. Sls.: $737,618,000
Approx. Number Employees: 3,332
Year Founded: 1933
Business Description:
Molded Plastic, Rubber & Formed Metal Products Distr & Mfr
S.I.C.: 3082; 3061; 3086; 5013; 5014
N.A.I.C.S.: 326121; 326150; 326291; 423120; 423130
Import Export
Advertising Expenditures: $1,940,000
Media: 2-4-7-10-13-19
Distr.: Natl.
Budget Set: Oct.
Personnel:
John C. Orr *(Pres & CEO)*
Donald A. Merril *(CFO, Corp Sec & Sr VP)*
David B. Knowles *(COO & Exec VP)*
Joel Grant *(VP & Gen Mgr-Matl Handling Segment)*
Chris Koscho *(VP & Gen Mgr-Lawn & Garden Segment)*
Todd Smith *(VP & Gen Mgr-Distr Segment)*
Ray Cunningham *(VP-HR, Org Dev & Trng)*
John McFadden *(Dir-Fin & MIS)*
Jim Rastetter *(Dir-Sls & Mktg)*
Melissa Johnson *(Mgr-Tax)*
Brands & Products:
AKRO-MILS
AKROBINS
ALLIBERT BUCKHORN
AMERI-KART
ATM
BUCKHORN
BUCKHORN RUBBER
DILLEN
LEADERSHIP BRANDS HELPING CUSTOMERS GROW!
LISTO
MYERS INDUSTRIES, INC.
MYERS TIRE SUPPLY
NSBEES
PATCH RUBBER
PRO CAL
RAACO

NATIONAL MOLDING CORPORATION
5 Dubon Ct
Farmingdale, NY 11735-1007
Tel.: (631) 293-8696
Fax: (631) 293-0988
Toll Free: (800) 544-7162
E-mail: sales@natmo.com
Web Site: www.nationalmolding.com
E-Mail For Key Personnel:
Sales Director: sales@natmo.com
Approx. Number Employees: 80
Year Founded: 1965
Business Description:
Molded Plastic Products & Assemblies Mfr
S.I.C.: 3089
N.A.I.C.S.: 326199
Media: 2-4-10-13
Personnel:
Joseph Anscher *(Pres)*
Brands & Products:
DURAFLEX
HETERO CAVITY
NATIONAL MOLDING

NUSIL TECHNOLOGY LLC
(Holding of Quad-C Management, Inc.)
1050 Cindy Ln
Carpinteria, CA 93013
Tel.: (805) 684-8780
Fax: (805) 684-2365
E-mail: info@nusil.com
Web Site: www.nusil.com
Sales Range: $25-49.9 Million
Approx. Number Employees: 370
Business Description:
Formulator of Silicone Compounds for Aerospace, Healthcare & Electronics
S.I.C.: 3069; 2891
N.A.I.C.S.: 326299; 325520
Import Export
Advertising Expenditures: $400,000
Media: 2-10-13-22
Personnel:
Richard A. Compton *(Co-Founder & CEO)*
Scott Mraz *(Pres)*
Brian Nash *(VP-Mktg & Sls)*
Jim Yabsley *(VP-Engrg)*
Stephanie Supina *(Dir-Mktg)*
Advertising Agency:
The Phelps Group
901 Wilshire Blvd
Santa Monica, CA 90401-1854
Tel.: (310) 752-4400
Fax: (310) 752-4444

OLIVER RUBBER COMPANY
(Sub. of Michelin North America, Inc.)
408 Telephone Ave
Asheboro, NC 27205
Tel.: (336) 629-1436
Fax: (336) 629-1430
E-mail: service@oliverrubber.com
Web Site: www.oliverrubber.com
Approx. Number Employees: 285
Year Founded: 1912
Business Description:
Retread Rubber, Bonding Gum & Equipment Mfr
S.I.C.: 3061
N.A.I.C.S.: 326291
Import Export
Media: 2-4-7-10
Distr.: Intl.; Natl.
Budget Set: Sept.
Personnel:
Phil Boarts *(Dir-Mktg)*
Brands & Products:
MEGA MILE
OLIVER
TUFF CURE

PARKER HANNIFIN - WEBSTER PLASTICS INC
(Holding of The Jordan Company, L.P.)
83 Estates Dr W
Fairport, NY 14450
Tel.: (781) 935-4850
Fax: (585) 425-7238
Web Site: www.websterplastics.com
Approx. Number Employees: 150
Year Founded: 1946
Business Description:
Custom Plastic Injection Molder
S.I.C.: 3089
N.A.I.C.S.: 326199
Media: 2-10-13

PAWLING CORPORATION-ARCHITECTURAL PRODUCTS DIVISION
(Div. of Pawling Corporation)
32 Nelson Hill Rd
Wassaic, NY 12592-2121
Mailing Address:
PO Box 200
Wassaic, NY 12592
Tel.: (845) 373-9300
Fax: (845) 373-7827
Toll Free: (800) 431-3456
E-mail: info@pawling.com
Web Site: www.pawling.com
E-Mail For Key Personnel:
Sales Director: sales@pawling.com
Approx. Number Employees: 310
Business Description:
Rubber & Plastic Extrusions Mfr
S.I.C.: 3061; 3446

Key to Media (For complete agency information see *The Advertising Red Books-Agencies* edition):
1. Bus. Publs. 2. Cable T.V. 3. Catalogs & Directories. 4. Co-op Adv. 5. Consumer Mags. 6. D.M. to Bus. Estab.7. D.M. to Consumers
8. Daily Newsp. 9. Exhibits/Trade Shows 10. Foreign 11. Infomercial 12. Internet Adv.13. Multimedia 14. Network Radio
15. Network T.V. 16. Newsp. Distr. Mags. 17. Other 18. Outdoor (Posters, Transit) 19. Point of Purchase20. Premiums, Novelties
21. Product Samples 22. Special Events Mktg. 23. Spot Radio 24. Spot T.V. 25. Weekly Newsp. 26. Yellow Page Adv.

Pawling Corporation-Architectural Products Division — (Continued)

N.A.I.C.S.: 326291; 332323
Media: 2-4-7-10-21
Distr.: Reg.
Budget Set: June

PEERLESS CHAIN COMPANY
1416 E Sanborn St
Winona, MN 55987
Tel.: (507) 457-9100
Fax: (507) 457-9187
Toll Free: (800) 533-8056
E-mail: custserv@peerlesschain.com
Web Site: www.peerlesschain.com
E-Mail For Key Personnel:
Sales Director: sales@peerlesschain.com
Approx. Number Employees: 300
Year Founded: 1917
Business Description:
Tire Chains Mfr
S.I.C.: 3496; 3462
N.A.I.C.S.: 332618; 332111
Import Export
Media: 4-6-13-17-25
Personnel:
Tom Wynn *(Pres)*
Phil Heimbecker *(Dir-HR)*

PERMALITH PLASTICS LLC
6901 N Crescent Blvd
Pennsauken, NJ 08110
Tel.: (856) 488-8000
Fax: (856) 488-2455
E-mail: info@permalith.com
Web Site: www.permalith.com
Approx. Number Employees: 50
Year Founded: 1957
Business Description:
Mfr. of Printed & Laminated Plastics, Point of Purchase Displays, Sales Aids, Plastic Slide Rules & Rotary Calculators, Membership Cards, Plastic Signs, Back-Lit Signs, Hospital Charts & Decals
S.I.C.: 3089; 3993
N.A.I.C.S.: 326199; 339950
Media: 4-10-21
Distr.: Natl.
Budget Set: July
Personnel:
Bill Callanan *(Owner)*
Nancy Manion *(Office Mgr)*
Brands & Products:
PERMALITH PLASTICS

PHILLIPS PLASTICS CORPORATION
7 Long Lk Rd
Phillips, WI 54555-1528
Tel.: (715) 339-3005
Fax: (715) 339-3092
Fax: (715) 381-3291
Toll Free: (877) 508-0252
E-mail: info@phillipsplastics.com
Web Site: www.phillipsplastics.com
Approx. Number Employees: 350
Year Founded: 1964
Business Description:
Mfr of Decorative Custom Injection Molded Plastic Products & Metals
S.I.C.: 3089; 3544
N.A.I.C.S.: 326199; 333514
Export
Media: 2-4-7-9-10-13-22-25-26
Distr.: Natl.
Budget Set: Nov.
Personnel:
Robert Cervenka *(Founder & Chm)*
Larry D. Smith *(Vice Chm)*
Brad Wucherpfennig *(COO)*
Leslie Lagerstrom *(VP-Mktg)*
Brands & Products:
ANSYS
CADKEY
CATIA
INTEGREL
MOLDFLOW
ORIGEN
PHILLIPS PLASTICS CORPORATION
PRO/ENGINEER
SOLID WORKS
UNIGRAPHICS

PILGRIM PLASTIC PRODUCTS COMPANY
1200 W Chestnut St
Brockton, MA 02301-5574
Tel.: (508) 436-6300
Fax: (508) 580-3542
E-mail: pilgrimsales@pilgrimplastics.com
Web Site: www.pilgrimplastics.com
Sales Range: $100-124.9 Million
Approx. Number Employees: 40
Year Founded: 1913
Business Description:
Mfr & Sales of Plastic Printing Credit Cards, Calendar Cards, Rulers, Plastic Point of Purchase, Plastic Cards on Continous Paper Carriers, Plastic Wall Calendars, Plastic Luggage Tags, Hotel Signs & Stress Testing Cards, Breast Self Exam Charts Membership Cards
S.I.C.: 3083; 3993
N.A.I.C.S.: 326130; 339950
Import Export
Advertising Expenditures: $300,000
Media: 2-4-7-10-13-20-21
Distr.: Intl.; Natl.
Budget Set: Jan.
Personnel:
Mark Abrams *(Pres)*
Brands & Products:
BREAST SELF EXAM SHOWER CARD
OPEN-CLOSE DOOR SIGN
PILGRIM
PROMOTIONS IN PLASTIC
ROLL-A-CARD
STRESS TESTING CARD

PIRELLI TIRE NORTH AMERICA
(Holding of Pirelli & C. S.p.A.)
100 Pirelli Dr
Rome, GA 30161
Tel.: (706) 368-5800
Fax: (706) 368-5832
Toll Free: (800) PIRELLI
Telex: 7104652389 NHVN UR
E-mail: info@pirelli.com
Web Site: www.us.pirelli.com
Sales Range: $750-799.9 Million
Approx. Number Employees: 275
Year Founded: 1912
Business Description:
Mfr. of Tires, Tubes, Synthetic Rubber & Specialty Polymers
S.I.C.: 3011; 2296
N.A.I.C.S.: 326211; 314992
Advertising Expenditures: $5,000,000
Media: 1-2-3-6-8-9-10-11-14-15-17-18-19-20-23-24-26
Distr.: Intl.; Natl.
Budget Set: Nov.
Personnel:
Rafael Navarro, III *(VP-Comm & Media Rels)*
Advertising Agency:
Rosetta
100 American Metro Blvd
Hamilton, NJ 08619
Tel.: (609) 689-6100
Fax: (609) 631-0184
Toll Free: (800) 374-6008

PLANO MOLDING COMPANY
(Holding of Tinicum Incorporated)
431 E S St
Plano, IL 60545-1676
Tel.: (630) 552-3111
Fax: (630) 552-8989
Toll Free: (800) 226-9868
E-mail: customercare@planomolding.com
Web Site: www.planomolding.com
Sales Range: $100-124.9 Million
Approx. Number Employees: 700
Year Founded: 1932
Business Description:
Mfr of Plastic Tackle Boxes, Utility Boxes, Tool Boxes, Paramedic Boxes, Cosmetic & Home Organizers
S.I.C.: 3089
N.A.I.C.S.: 326199
Media: 2-3-4-5-6-8-10-15-19
Distr.: Natl.
Budget Set: June
Personnel:
Peter H. Henning *(Chm & CEO)*
Tom Hurt *(Sr VP)*
Randy Lemcke *(Sr VP-Sls)*
Lisa Hjorth *(VP-HR)*
Sean Wheatley *(Mgr-Mktg)*
Brands & Products:
AIRGLIDE
BOW-MAX
FIELD BOXES
GUNSLINGER GRAB-N-GO
HARDBOTTOM
HUNTERLOGIC
INHIBITOR
PLANO
PLANO OUTDOOR SYSTEMS
PRO-MAX
PROTECTOR SERIES
Advertising Agency:
5 Stone Advertising
1738 Wynkoop St Ste 303
Denver, CO 80202
Tel.: (303) 298-1226
Fax: (303) 298-1140

PLASKOLITE, INC.
1770 Joyce Ave
Columbus, OH 43219-1026
Tel.: (614) 294-3281
Fax: (614) 297-7295
Toll Free: (800) 848-9124
E-mail: plaskolite@plaskolite.com
Web Site: www.plaskolite.com
Approx. Number Employees: 200
Year Founded: 1950
Business Description:
Acrylic Sheets Mfr
S.I.C.: 3083; 3089
N.A.I.C.S.: 326130; 326199
Export
Advertising Expenditures: $220,000
Media: 2-6-19
Distr.: Natl.
Budget Set: Mar.-Apr.
Personnel:
James Dunn *(Pres)*
Richard Larkin *(CFO)*
David Chan *(VP-Tech)*
Brands & Products:
DURALENS
DURAPLEX
FABBACK
INNOVATIVE ACRYLIC SOLUTIONS
KSH
MUSTANG
OPTIX
PLASKOLITE

PLASTI-FAB LTD.
(Sub. of PFB Corp.)
Ste 100 2886 Sunridge Way NE
Calgary, AB T1Y 7H9, Canada
Tel.: (403) 248-9306
Fax: (403) 248-9325
Toll Free: (888) 446-5377
E-mail: mailbox@plastifab.com
Web Site: www.plastifab.com
Approx. Number Employees: 35
Business Description:
Plastics Mfr
S.I.C.: 3089
N.A.I.C.S.: 326199
Media: 10-17
Personnel:
Bruce M. Carruthers *(Pres & COO)*
Peter Jelinek *(Sls Mgr-British Columbia)*
Richard Baumgartner *(Mgr-Sls-Ontario & Quebec)*
Greg Doren *(Mgr-Advantage ICF Sys)*
Jack Hoogstraten *(Mgr-Plasti-Fab Products)*
Jim Whalen *(Mgr-Tech Mktg)*

PLASTIC SUPPLIERS, INC.
2887 Johnstown Rd
Columbus, OH 43219-1719
Mailing Address:
PO Box 360478
Columbus, OH 43236-0478
Tel.: (614) 471-9100
Fax: (614) 471-9033
Toll Free: (800) 722-5577
E-mail: psinfo@plasticsuppliers.com
Web Site: www.plasticsuppliers.com
Approx. Sls.: $131,760,732
Approx. Number Employees: 370
Year Founded: 1949
Business Description:
Plastic Films Mfr & Distr
S.I.C.: 3081
N.A.I.C.S.: 326113
Import Export
Advertising Expenditures: $66,000
Bus. Publs.: $36,000; Exhibits/Trade Shows: $30,000
Distr.: Intl.
Budget Set: Oct.
Personnel:
Theodore Riegert *(Pres & CEO)*
Phil Ludwig *(VP-Polyflex Sls)*
Scott Cordial *(Mgr-Mktg)*
Tom Rittman *(Mgr-Technical Svc)*
Brands & Products:
CARD MASK
EARTHFIRST
FREEZEFLEX
GLASSINE
LABELFLEX

Key to Media (For complete agency information see *The Advertising Red Books-Agencies* edition):
1. Bus. Publs. 2. Cable T.V. 3. Catalogs & Directories. 4. Co-op Adv. 5. Consumer Mags. 6. D.M. to Bus. Estab.7. D.M. to Consumers 8. Daily Newsp. 9. Exhibits/Trade Shows 10. Foreign 11. Infomercial 12. Internet Adv.13. Multimedia 14. Network Radio 15. Network T.V. 16. Newsp. Distr. Mags. 17. Other 18. Outdoor (Posters, Transit) 19. Point of Purchase20. Premiums, Novelties 21. Product Samples 22. Special Events Mktg. 23. Spot Radio 24. Spot T.V. 25. Weekly Newsp. 26. Yellow Page Adv.

MASK-OR
MATTEFLEX
OMV
POLYFLEX
TIP-ON
TMOPS

SHEFFIELD PLASTICS INC.
(Sub. of Bayer MaterialScience AG)
119 Salisbury Rd
Sheffield, MA 01257
Tel.: (413) 229-8711
Fax: (413) 229-8717
Toll Free: (800) 628-5084
E-mail: info@sheffieldplastics.com
Web Site: www.sheffieldplastics.com
Approx. Number Employees: 160
Year Founded: 1949
Business Description:
Plastic Products Mfr
S.I.C.: 3081; 3089
N.A.I.C.S.: 326113; 326199
Import Export
Advertising Expenditures: $500,000
Media: 2-4-7-10-20-21
Distr.: Intl.; Natl.
Budget Set: Nov.
Personnel:
Dennis Duff *(Pres)*
Kurt Glaser *(VP-Mktg & Sls)*
Cindy Kahlstrom *(Mgr-Media)*
Brands & Products:
HYZOD
MAKROLON AR
MAKROLON FD
MAKROLON FI
MAKROLON GP
MAKROLON GP PRISMATIC P12
MAKROLON HYGARD
MAKROLON MG
MAKROLON OP
MAKROLON SL
MAKROLON SL SIGN MATTE
MAKROLON TG
VIVAK

PMP COMPOSITES
572 Whitehead Rd Ste 101
Trenton, NJ 08619-4804
Tel.: (609) 587-1188
Fax: (609) 587-3463
Approx. Number Employees: 30
Year Founded: 1975
Business Description:
Fiber Reinforced Composite Products Mfr & Molder
S.I.C.: 3089
N.A.I.C.S.: 326199
Media: 2-7-9
Distr.: Natl.
Budget Set: Oct.
Personnel:
Peter Andrew Horvath *(Chm)*
Judy Hovrath *(Office Mgr)*
Brands & Products:
PMP COMPOSITES

POLYCEL STRUCTURAL FOAM, INC.
(Sub. of Polycel Holdings Inc.)
68 County Line Rd
Somerville, NJ 08876-3467
Tel.: (908) 722-5254
Fax: (908) 722-7457
E-mail: info@polycel.com
Web Site: www.polycel.com
Approx. Number Employees: 175
Year Founded: 1967
Business Description:
Injection Molder of Structural Foam
S.I.C.: 3089
N.A.I.C.S.: 326199
Export
Media: 7-10
Personnel:
Otto J. del Prado *(Pres)*

PREMIX INC.
Rte 20 and Harmon Rd
North Kingsville, OH 44068-0281
Tel.: (440) 224-2181
Fax: (440) 224-2766
E-mail: premix@premix.com
Web Site: www.premix.com
Approx. Sls.: $40,000,000
Approx. Number Employees: 350
Year Founded: 1959
Business Description:
Mfr of Plastic Products
S.I.C.: 3089; 2821
N.A.I.C.S.: 326199; 325211
Import Export
Media: 2-7-10
Personnel:
Tom Meola *(Pres & COO)*
William Kennedy *(CEO)*
Brands & Products:
LYTEX
OVENAL
PERMI-GLAS
PREMI-JECT
PREMIX
QC
SHAPING THE WORLD OF COMPOSITES

PROFESSIONAL PLASTICS, INC.
1810 E Valencia Dr
Fullerton, CA 92831-4847
Tel.: (714) 446-6500
Fax: (714) 447-0114
Toll Free: (800) 878-0755
Toll Free: (800) 966PROS
E-mail: sales@proplas.com
Web Site:
www.professionalplastics.com
E-Mail For Key Personnel:
President: lkietzke@proplas.com
Sales Director: sales@proplas.com
Approx. Number Employees: 200
Year Founded: 1984
Business Description:
Supplier of Plastics Materials
S.I.C.: 5162
N.A.I.C.S.: 424610
Import Export
Media: 2-10
Personnel:
Lawrence Kietzke *(Pres)*
David Kietzke *(CFO)*
Michael Kietzke *(Exec VP)*
Chris Kietzke *(VP-Mktg & Mgr-Export)*
Candy Nyberg *(Mgr-HR)*

PTA CORPORATION
148 Christian St
Oxford, CT 06478
Tel.: (203) 888-0585
Fax: (203) 888-1757
E-mail: data@ptacorp.com
Web Site: www.ptacorp.com
Approx. Number Employees: 75
Year Founded: 1953
Business Description:
Industrial Molds & Plastic Products Mfr
S.I.C.: 3089; 7389
N.A.I.C.S.: 326199; 541420
Advertising Expenditures: $700,000
Media: 2-4-7-10
Distr.: Natl.
Personnel:
Raynor M. Seeley *(Pres & CEO)*
Richard Dorans *(VP-Opers)*
Jim Meyer *(Dir-Application Dev)*
Ramona Streetman *(Mgr-Customer Svc)*

PVC CONTAINER CORPORATION
(Sub. of Pretium Packaging, L.L.C.)
(d/b/a Pretium Packaging)
2 Industrial Way W Ste 7
Eatontown, NJ 07724-2266
Mailing Address:
PO Box 597
Eatontown, NJ 07724-0597
Tel.: (732) 542-0060
Fax: (732) 542-7706
Sales Range: $75-99.9 Million
Approx. Number Employees: 36
Year Founded: 1968
Business Description:
Plastic Container Mfr
S.I.C.: 3085
N.A.I.C.S.: 326160
Media: 4-7-8-10-20-26
Personnel:
Ken Stufko *(VP-Sls)*
Brands & Products:
AIROPAK
MARPAC
NOVABLEND
NOVALOY
NOVAPAK
NOVATEC

QUADION CORPORATION
1100 Xenium Ln N
Minneapolis, MN 55441-4405
Tel.: (952) 927-1400
Fax: (952) 927-1470
Telex: 882211
Web Site: www.quadion.com
Approx. Number Employees: 1,500
Year Founded: 1945
Business Description:
Custom Molded Rubber & Plastic Components Mfr
S.I.C.: 3069
N.A.I.C.S.: 326299
Import Export
Media: 2-10
Personnel:
Robert W. Carlson, Jr. *(Chm)*
James R. Lande *(CEO)*
Michael Iblings *(VP-Sls & Mktg)*
Mike Kosiak *(Mgr-Natl Sls)*
Bill Pederson *(Mgr-Mktg Commun)*
Brands & Products:
MINNESOTA RUBBER
QUADION

RAVEN INDUSTRIES, INC.
205 E 6th St
Sioux Falls, SD 57104-5931
Mailing Address:
PO Box 5107
Sioux Falls, SD 57117-5107
Tel.: (605) 336-2750
Fax: (605) 335-0268
E-mail: raveninfo@ravenind.com
Web Site: www.ravenind.com
Approx. Sls.: $314,708,000
Approx. Number Employees: 1,112
Year Founded: 1956
Business Description:
Extruded Plastic Sheeting Mfr
S.I.C.: 3089; 3081
N.A.I.C.S.: 326199; 326113
Export
Advertising Expenditures: $350,000
Media: 2-4-6-7-10-19-21-26
Distr.: Natl.
Budget Set: Dec.
Personnel:
Thomas S. Everist *(Chm)*
Daniel A. Rykhus *(Pres & CEO)*
Thomas Iacarella *(CFO & VP)*
David R. Bair *(Gen Mgr-Electronic Sys Div & Div VP)*
James D. Groninger *(Gen Mgr-Engineered Films Div & Div VP)*
Brands & Products:
AFRC
CANVEX
CONKURE
DURA-SKRIM
FORTRESS
RALLY
RAVEN INDUSTRIES
THE RIGHT BALANCE OF BREATHABILITY.
RUFCO
VAPORBLOCK
Advertising Agencies:
Lawrence & Schiller, Inc.
3932 S Willow Ave
Sioux Falls, SD 57105-6234
Tel.: (605) 338-8000
Fax: (605) 338-8892
Toll Free: (888) 836-6224

Main Ideas
26485 482nd Ave
Brandon, SD 57005
Tel.: (605) 582-7800
Fax: (605) 582-8922
(Films)
— Lisa Peterson *(Acct. Exec.)*

Paulsen Marketing Communications, Inc.
(d/b/a Paulsen AgriBranding)
3510 S 1st Ave Cir
Sioux Falls, SD 57105-5807
Tel.: (605) 336-1745
Fax: (605) 336-2305

RB RUBBER PRODUCTS INC.
(Sub. of Dash Multi-Corp, Inc.)
904 NE 10th Ave
McMinnville, OR 97128
Tel.: (503) 472-4691
Fax: (503) 434-4455
Toll Free: (800) 525-5530
Web Site: www.rbrubber.com
Approx. Number Employees: 100
Business Description:
Mfr. of Rubber Products from Recycled Tires
S.I.C.: 3069
N.A.I.C.S.: 326299
Media: 17
Personnel:
Donald Overturf *(CFO)*

Key to Media (For complete agency information see *The Advertising Red Books-Agencies* edition):
1. Bus. Publs. 2. Cable T.V. 3. Catalogs & Directories. 4. Co-op Adv. 5. Consumer Mags. 6. D.M. to Bus. Estab.7. D.M. to Consumers
8. Daily Newsp. 9. Exhibits/Trade Shows 10. Foreign 11. Infomercial 12. Internet Adv.13. Multimedia 14. Network Radio
15. Network T.V. 16. Newsp. Distr. Mags. 17. Other 18. Outdoor (Posters, Transit) 19. Point of Purchase20. Premiums, Novelties
21. Product Samples 22. Special Events Mktg. 23. Spot Radio 24. Spot T.V. 25. Weekly Newsp. 26. Yellow Page Adv.

RB Rubber Products Inc. — (Continued)

Gregory J. Divis *(Sr VP & Dir)*
Larry Lane *(VP-Sls & Mktg)*
Willie Pelzer *(VP-Production)*

R.C.A. RUBBER COMPANY

1833 E Market St
Akron, OH 44305-4214
Tel.: (330) 784-1291
Fax: (330) 784-2899
Toll Free: (800) 321-2340
E-mail: info@rcarubber.com
Web Site: www.rcarubber.com
Sales Range: $50-74.9 Million
Approx. Number Employees: 125
Year Founded: 1931
Business Description:
Rubber Stair Treads & Flooring Mfr
S.I.C.: 3069; 3061
N.A.I.C.S.: 326299; 326291
Export
Media: 2-4-7-14
Distr.: Intl.; Natl.
Brands & Products:
APEX STEP
FLEXI-FLOR
GLO-STRIP
GRANITE
LO-PRO
REDONDO
TALON TREAD
TARGET
TRANSIFLOR
TRANSITE-FLOR

REESE ENTERPRISES, INC.

16350 Asher Ave PO Box 459
Rosemount, MN 55068
Tel.: (651) 423-1174
Fax: (651) 423-2662
Toll Free: (800) 824-3348
Toll Free: (800) 334-8823 (Fax)
E-mail: info@reeseusa.com
Web Site: www.reeseusa.com
Approx. Number Employees: 150
Year Founded: 1917
Business Description:
Weather Strips, Plastic Extrusions, Footmats & Gratings Mfr
S.I.C.: 3089; 3069
N.A.I.C.S.: 326199; 326299
Media: 2-4-10
Personnel:
Chester W. Ellingson, III *(Pres)*
Robert T. Ellingson *(CEO)*
Mike Glaus *(CFO)*
Terry Deering *(Dir Mktg Sls)*
Brands & Products:
ASTRO PLASTICS
PERFEC GRATE
PERFEC MAT
PERFEC ROLL-UP
PERFEC VIEW
REESE
REESE PERFEC

REINALT-THOMAS CORP.

(d/b/a Discount Tire Co.)
20225 N Scottsdale Rd
Scottsdale, AZ 85255
Tel.: (480) 606-6000
Fax: (480) 951-0206
E-mail: sales@discounttire.com
Web Site: www.discounttire.com
E-Mail For Key Personnel:
Sales Director: sales@discounttire.com
Approx. Number Employees: 11,000
Year Founded: 1960
Business Description:
Tire Sales
S.I.C.: 5014
N.A.I.C.S.: 441320
Import
Media: 8-13
Personnel:
Bruce T. Halle *(Chm)*
Gary Van Brunt *(Vice Chm)*
Tom Englert *(CEO)*
Christian Roe *(CFO)*
Dean Butler *(Sr VP-Pur)*
Timothy J. Schafer *(Sr VP-Fin & Taxation)*
Jess Stine *(Sr VP-Adv)*
Brands & Products:
AMERICA'S TIRE
DISCOUNT TIRE
DISCOUNT TIRE DIRECT

REMA TIP TOP/NORTH AMERICA, INC.

(Sub. of Stahlgruber Otto Gruber GmbH & Co. KG)
119 Rockland Ave
Northvale, NJ 07647
Mailing Address:
PO Box 76
Northvale, NJ 07647-0076
Tel.: (201) 768-8100
Fax: (201) 768-0946
Toll Free: (800) 334-7362
Toll Free: (800) 225-7362
Web Site: www.rema.com
Year Founded: 1935
Business Description:
Tire Repair Product Distr
S.I.C.: 5014; 5085
N.A.I.C.S.: 423130; 423840
Advertising Expenditures: $500,000
Media: 7-19
Personnel:
Olafur Gunnarsson *(Pres)*
Jeffrey Xu *(CFO)*
Brands & Products:
REMA TIP TOP

REXAM CLOSURES & CONTAINERS

(Sub. of Rexam PLC)
3245 Kansas Rd
Evansville, IN 47725-9757
Tel.: (812) 867-6671
Fax: (812) 867-6861
Web Site: www.closures.com
Approx. Number Employees: 350
Year Founded: 1953
Business Description:
Child Resistant & Screw Closures Mfr
S.I.C.: 3089
N.A.I.C.S.: 326199
Advertising Expenditures: $500,000
Media: 9-10-16-26
Distr.: Natl.
Budget Set: Oct.
Personnel:
Becky Biever *(Mgr-Mktg Comm)*

ROCHEUX INTERNATIONAL INC.

220 Centennial Ave
Passaic, NJ 08854
Tel.: (732) 885-3898
Fax: (732) 885-3868
E-mail: administrator@rocheux.com
Web Site: www.rocheux.com
Approx. Number Employees: 100
Year Founded: 1996
Business Description:
Plastics, Materials & Basic Shapes
S.I.C.: 5162
N.A.I.C.S.: 424610
Import Export
Media: 10
Personnel:
Vanessa Wong *(CEO)*
Brands & Products:
ROCHEUX
SYNTHETEK

ROTONICS MANUFACTURING INC.

(Sub. of Spell Capital Partners LLC)
17022 S Figueroa St
Gardena, CA 90248-3019
Tel.: (310) 327-5401
Fax: (310) 323-9567
E-mail: corporate@rotonics.com
Web Site: www.rotocast.com
Approx. Sls.: $48,051,200
Approx. Number Employees: 429
Year Founded: 1973
Business Description:
Mfr of Plastic Products Utilizing Rotational Molding Process for Industrial, Agricultural, Refuse & Recreational Applications, Commercial, Retail, Healthcare, Marine, Medical Waste, Pharmaceutical, P.O.P. Display, Lawn & Garden, Linen & Laundry & Architectural Planters & Light Poles
S.I.C.: 3082; 3089
N.A.I.C.S.: 326121; 326199
Export
Media: 2-4-6-8-10-21-26
Distr.: Natl.
Budget Set: June
Personnel:
Tim Czmiel *(CEO)*
Brands & Products:
BULKITANKS
CLASSIC LIGHTING
DURA FLOAT
FENDER TAINER
GUIDO
HYDRA
NUTRON
RMI
RMI-B
RMI-C
RMI-D
RMI-F
RMI-G
RMI-I
RMI-NEVADA
RMI-T
ROTOCAST OF TENNESSEE
ROYAL
SEGRI-MED
SOLUTION
TERRACAST
TOOL TAINER

RYAN HERCO PRODUCTS CORPORATION

(Sub. of Morgenthaler Private Equity)
3010 N San Fernando Blvd
Burbank, CA 91503
Mailing Address:
PO Box 588
Burbank, CA 91503-0588
Tel.: (818) 841-1141
Fax: (818) 973-2600
Toll Free: (800) 848-1141
E-mail: info@ryanherco.com
Web Site: www.ryanherco.com
E-Mail For Key Personnel:
President: fgibbs@ryanherco.com
Sales Range: $100-124.9 Million
Approx. Number Employees: 80
Year Founded: 1948
Business Description:
Distr of Plastic Fluid-Handling Systems
S.I.C.: 5162; 5074
N.A.I.C.S.: 424610; 423720
Import Export
Advertising Expenditures: $250,000
Bus. Publs.: $200,000; D.M. to Consumers: $50,000
Distr.: Natl.
Personnel:
David Patterson *(CEO)*
Brian Bowman *(CFO)*
Randy Beckwith *(VP-Sls & Mktg)*

SAFE-HIT CORPORATION

(Div. of Energy Absorption Systems, Inc.)
35 E Wacker Dr 11 FL
Chicago, IL 60601
Tel.: (312) 467-6750
Fax: (800) 770-6755
Toll Free: (888) 323-6374
E-mail: info@safehit.com
Web Site: www.safehit.com
Sales Range: $10-24.9 Million
Approx. Number Employees: 16
Year Founded: 1979
Business Description:
Co-Extruded, Two-Part Flexible Delineator & Guidance Systems Designer & Mfr
S.I.C.: 3089
N.A.I.C.S.: 326199
Media: 2-4-7-10
Personnel:
James Crowley *(Pres, CEO & VP-Mktg)*
Kent Kekeis *(Mgr-Mktg)*
Brands & Products:
SAFE-HIT

SAINT-GOBAIN PERFORMANCE PLASTICS CORP.

(Sub. of Norton Company)
150 Dey Rd
Wayne, NJ 07470-4670
Tel.: (973) 696-4700
Fax: (973) 696-4056
E-mail: info@saint-gobain.com
Web Site: www.plastics.saint-gobain.com
Sales Range: $800-899.9 Million
Approx. Number Employees: 150
Year Founded: 1950
Business Description:
Mfr. of Engineered Plastic Products & Materials; High Performance Polymer Products
S.I.C.: 3089; 3053
N.A.I.C.S.: 326199; 339991
Import Export
Advertising Expenditures: $1,250,000
Multimedia: $100,000; Bus. Publs.: $450,000; Catalogs & Directories: $200,000; D.M. to Bus. Estab.: $100,000; Exhibits/Trade Shows: $150,000; Other: $200,000; Premiums, Novelties: $50,000
Distr.: Intl.; Natl.

Key to Media (For complete agency information see *The Advertising Red Books-Agencies* edition):
1. Bus. Publs. 2. Cable T.V. 3. Catalogs & Directories. 4. Co-op Adv. 5. Consumer Mags. 6. D.M. to Bus. Estab.7. D.M. to Consumers 8. Daily Newsp. 9. Exhibits/Trade Shows 10. Foreign 11. Infomercial 12. Internet Adv.13. Multimedia 14. Network Radio 15. Network T.V. 16. Newsp. Distr. Mags. 17. Other 18. Outdoor (Posters, Transit) 19. Point of Purchase20. Premiums, Novelties 21. Product Samples 22. Special Events Mktg. 23. Spot Radio 24. Spot T.V. 25. Weekly Newsp. 26. Yellow Page Adv.

Budget Set: Sept.
Brands & Products:
CHEMFLOUR
CHEMGRIP
CHEMWARE
CHR
EXAC
FLUOROGLIDE
FLURAN
FURON
HALO CELL
KEMID
KORTON
KORVEX
LOG HOME FOAM
NOREX
NORGLIDE
NORMOUNT
NORPRENE
NORSEAL
NORTON
NORWELL
PHARMED
PLYTRAX
PUREFIT
RULON
SANITECH
SIL-MED
S.I.R. GASKET
SYNFLEX
T-BOND II
THERM-A-LECTRIC
THERMALBOND
THERMOFLON
TITE-R-BOND
TRANSFLOW
TYGON
TYGOTHANE
ZITEX

SEALING DEVICES INC.
4400 Walden Ave
Lancaster, NY 14086-9716
Tel.: (716) 684-7600
Fax: (716) 684-0644
Fax: (716) 684-0760
Toll Free: (800) 727-3257
Telex: 716-684-0760
E-mail: seals@sealingdevices.com
Web Site: www.sealingdevices.com
Approx. Number Employees: 150
Year Founded: 1964
Business Description:
Mfr. & Distributor of Industrial Gaskets, Seals & Sealing Materials
S.I.C.: 3053; 5085
N.A.I.C.S.: 339991; 423840
Export
Media: 2-10
Personnel:
Terry S. Galanis, Jr. *(Owner)*
Terry S. Galanis, Sr. *(Owner)*
Vincent Andolina *(VP-Sls & Ops)*
Tim Smith *(Dir-Quality)*
Doug Eberhardt *(Mgr-Mktg)*
Scott Walrath *(Mgr-Sourcing)*
Brands & Products:
ARLON
CANNULAIDE
CHESTERTON
COLOPLAST
CONVEEN
D-STAT
ENVOMAXISEAL
HERMETIC ADVANTAGE
INCHEMREZ
KALSI SEALS
MARSH BIO PRODUCTS
MULTICENTRIC
PARTNERS WITH TOMORROW
PARTSDRAWER
PERISTEEN
POLY-CLIP
POLYSEALER
RELEEN
ROTOLOC
SEALING DEVICES
SECURELIFE +
SHAWCOR
SMARTSEALER
SUPER SEALS, EXCEPTIONAL SERVICE
ZEVA
ZURON

SIGNCASTER CORPORATION
(d/b/a Johnson Plastics)
9240 Grand Ave S
Bloomington, MN 55420
Tel.: (952) 888-9507
Fax: (952) 888-4997
Toll Free: (800) 869-7800
E-mail: service@johnsonplastics.com
Web Site: www.johnsonplastics.com
Sales Range: $10-24.9 Million
Approx. Number Employees: 80
Year Founded: 1970
Business Description:
Plastic Engraving Materials, Sign Supplies & Products for Personalization Distr
S.I.C.: 3479; 3993; 5162
N.A.I.C.S.: 332812; 339950; 424610
Media: 10-13
Personnel:
Thomas Johnson *(Founder & Pres)*
Margaret Johnson *(Founder & VP)*
Brands & Products:
JOHNSON PLASTICS

SPARTECH POLYCOM
(Div. of Spartech Corporation)
113 Passaic Ave
Kearny, NJ 07032
Tel.: (201) 998-8002
Fax: (201) 998-1533
Toll Free: (800) 631-8002
Web Site: www.spartech.com
Sales Range: $25-49.9 Million
Approx. Number Employees: 50
Business Description:
Custom Compounding of Purchased Resins
S.I.C.: 3083; 3089
N.A.I.C.S.: 326130; 326199
Media: 2-4-7-10-17
Distr.: Natl.
Personnel:
Randy Martin *(CEO, CFO & Exec VP-Corp Dev)*
Michael Marcely *(Sr VP-Plng & Controller)*
Nate Sofer *(Bus Mgr)*

SPENCER INDUSTRIES, INC.
(Sub. of Applied Industrial Technologies, Inc.)
(d/b/a Spencer Fluid Power)
19308 68th Ave S
Kent, WA 98032
Tel.: (253) 796-1100
Fax: (253) 796-1101
Web Site:
www.spencerfluidpower.com
Sales Range: $25-49.9 Million
Approx. Number Employees: 39
Business Description:
Hydraulic Components & Systems Whslr & Distr
S.I.C.: 5084; 5072
N.A.I.C.S.: 423830; 423710
Media: 2-4-7-10
Personnel:
John Anderson *(Gen Mgr)*

THE STEP2 COMPANY LLC
(Sub. of Liberty Partners, L.P.)
10010 Aurora-Hudson Rd
Streetsboro, OH 44241
Tel.: (330) 656-0440
Fax: (330) 655-9685
Toll Free: (800) 347-8372
E-mail: step2-company@step2.net
Web Site: www.step2company.com
Sales Range: $100-124.9 Million
Approx. Number Employees: 900
Year Founded: 1991
Business Description:
Home & Garden & Children's Products Mfr
S.I.C.: 3089; 3524; 3944
N.A.I.C.S.: 326199; 333112; 339932
Media: 4-6
Personnel:
Jack Vresics *(Pres & CEO)*
Dotti Foltz *(VP-Mktg Comm)*
Jean Ruper *(VP-Mktg)*
Brands & Products:
HAPPY TOTE
LIFESCAPES
LIFESTYLE
MAILMASTER
NATURALLY PLAYFUL
STEP2
SUNNYTIME
WICKERWEAVE
Advertising Agencies:
Marcus Thomas LLC
24865 Emery Rd
Cleveland, OH 44128
Tel.: (216) 292-4700
Fax: (216) 378-0396
Toll Free: (888) 482-4455

Optiem, LLC
1370 W 6th St Fl 3
Cleveland, OH 44113
Tel.: (216) 574-8700
Fax: (216) 574-6131

STULL TECHNOLOGIES INC.
17 Veronica Ave
Somerset, NJ 08873-3448
Tel.: (732) 873-5000
Fax: (732) 873-1295
Web Site: www.stulltech.com
Approx. Number Employees: 100
Year Founded: 1947
Business Description:
Mfr., Designer & Developer of Injection-Molded Closures & Other Packaging Solutions
S.I.C.: 3089
N.A.I.C.S.: 326199
Import Export
Media: 2-7-10
Personnel:
Mark Russo *(Pres)*
Gene Stull *(CEO)*
Jason Stull *(Mgr-Mktg Svcs)*
Brands & Products:
THE INNOVATIVE DIFFERENCE
STULLCONTROL
STULLGUARD
STULLSURE

TBC CORPORATION
(Sub. of Sumitomo Corporation of America)
4300 TBC Way
Palm Beach Gardens, FL 33410
Tel.: (561) 227-0955
Fax: (561) 775-4993
Web Site: www.tbccorp.com
Approx. Number Employees: 9,400
Year Founded: 1956
Business Description:
Wholesale Distr of Automotive Replacement Tires; Operator of Automotive Service Centers & Franchisor of Tire Retail Centers
S.I.C.: 5014; 7539
N.A.I.C.S.: 423130; 441320; 811198
Media: 2-22
Personnel:
Lawrence C. Day *(Chm, Pres & CEO)*
Tim Miller *(CFO, Treas & Exec VP)*
Erik R. Olsen *(Pres/CEO-TBC Wholesale Grp)*
Orland M. Wolford *(Pres/CEO-TBC Retail Grp)*
J. Glenn Gravatt *(Pres-TBC Pur & Distr)*
Linda Petruska *(Mgr-Corp HR)*
Brands & Products:
BIG O
CORDOVAN
FULDA
HARVEST KING
MERCHANT'S TIRE & AUTO CENTERS
MULTI-MILE
NATIONAL TIRE & BATTERY
NAVITRAC
POWER KING
SIGMA
TIRE KINGDOM
TURBO-TECH
VANDERBILT
Advertising Agency:
Viva Partnership
8101 Briscayne Blvd Ste 303
Miami, FL 33138
Tel.: (305) 576-6007
Fax: (305) 590-5863

TCI TIRE CENTERS, LLC
(Sub. of Michelin North America, Inc.)
310 Inglesby Pkwy
Duncan, SC 29334
Mailing Address:
PO Box 218
Duncan, SC 29334-0218
Tel.: (864) 329-2700
Fax: (864) 329-2929
Toll Free: (800) 603-2430
E-mail: humanresources@tirecenters.com
Web Site: www.tirecenters.com
Sales Range: $600-649.9 Million
Approx. Number Employees: 2,400
Business Description:
Automotive Tires Whslr
S.I.C.: 5014
N.A.I.C.S.: 423130
Media: 17-22

TEGRANT CORPORATION
(Holding of Metalmark Capital LLC)
1401 Pleasant St
Dekalb, IL 60115
Mailing Address:

Key to Media (For complete agency information see *The Advertising Red Books-Agencies* edition):
1. Bus. Publs. 2. Cable T.V. 3. Catalogs & Directories. 4. Co-op Adv. 5. Consumer Mags. 6. D.M. to Bus. Estab.7. D.M. to Consumers 8. Daily Newsp. 9. Exhibits/Trade Shows 10. Foreign 11. Infomercial 12. Internet Adv.13. Multimedia 14. Network Radio 15. Network T.V. 16. Newsp. Distr. Mags. 17. Other 18. Outdoor (Posters, Transit) 19. Point of Purchase20. Premiums, Novelties 21. Product Samples 22. Special Events Mktg. 23. Spot Radio 24. Spot T.V. 25. Weekly Newsp. 26. Yellow Page Adv.

Tegrant Corporation — (Continued)

PO Box 448
New Brighton, PA 15066-0448
Tel.: (815) 756-8451
Fax: (815) 756-1623
Toll Free: (800) 756-7639
Telex: 820314
E-mail: info@tegrant.com
Web Site: www.tegrant.com
Sales Range: $75-99.9 Million
Approx. Number Employees: 330
Year Founded: 1962
Business Description:
Temperature Control Product, Concrete Forming Mold & Packaging Materials Developer & Mfr
S.I.C.: 3086; 2671; 2679
N.A.I.C.S.: 326150; 322221; 322299
Export
Media: 1-2-4-7-10-11-13-20-21-22-26
Distr.: Intl.
Personnel:
Ron Leach *(Pres & CEO)*
Gregory T. Sipla *(Exec VP)*
Marianne Abreu *(Mgr-Corp & Mktg Comm)*

TEKNOR APEX COMPANY

505 Central Ave
Pawtucket, RI 02861-1945
Tel.: (401) 725-8000
Fax: (401) 725-8095
E-mail: info@teknorcolor.com
Web Site: www.teknorapex.com
Approx. Number Employees: 2,400
Year Founded: 1924
Business Description:
Mfr. of PVC & TPE Compounds, Chemicals, Rubber, Color Concentrates for Plastics, Garden Hoses, Anti-Fatigue Mats & Cutting Boards; Custom Processing Systems
S.I.C.: 3087; 3069
N.A.I.C.S.: 325991; 326299
Export
Media: 2-10
Personnel:
Victor J. Baxt *(Chm)*
Jonathan D. Fain *(Pres & CEO)*
James E. Morrison *(CFO)*
Gregory Anderson *(Mgr-Plant Technical)*
Sandy Hopkins *(Mgr-Corp Mktg & Comm)*
Brands & Products:
APEX
AQUA EDGE
AQUADRAIN
ATLANTIC OLEFIN
BOAT AND CAMPER
BRISTOL RIDGE
CHALLENGER
CHALLENGER LITE
CHEMLON
COMPETITOR
CORRUGATED RUNNER
DURLEX
ELEXAR
ERGO GRIP
FIREGUARD
FIREGUARD LSZH
FLEXALLOY
FOOTSAVER
FORMAX
GARDEN MATE
GRIP TRUE
HANDY HOLDER
HERCULES
INSTEX
MAGIC COLOR
MBOSS
MICROSHIELD
MONPRENE
MULTI-MAT
NEVERKINK
OPTIMAT
PATRIOT POLYESTER
PLASTI-TILE
PLASTI-TUFF
POWER COIL
RAINBOX PAK
RED RIVER
REEL HOSE
REFLEX MESH
RIDGE SCRAPER
SAN-EZE
SANI-TUFF
STAY-PUT-STAKES
STEP LIGHT
STOW-A-WAY
SUPER CONCENTRATE
SUPERFLOW
SUPERFOAM
TEK-CONNECT
TEK-SPHERES
TEK-TOUGH
TEKBOND
TEKRON
TEKTUFF
TELCAR
THUMB THING
TRACTION MAT
ULTRA FLEXIBLE
ULTRA MAT
UNIPRENE
VARIOCROM
VIDUX

TEXTILE RUBBER & CHEMICAL COMPANY

1300 Tiarco Dr
Dalton, GA 30721-1907
Tel.: (706) 277-1300
Fax: (706) 277-3738
Toll Free: (800) 727-8453
E-mail: info@trcc.com
Web Site: www.trcc.com
Approx. Number Employees: 400
Year Founded: 1953
Business Description:
Chemical & Machinery Mfr
S.I.C.: 2891; 2851; 2899; 3069
N.A.I.C.S.: 325520; 325510; 325998; 326299
Media: 2-10
Personnel:
F. Harvey Howalt *(Chm)*
Chip Howalt *(Pres)*
Chris Horton *(CFO)*
Mark N. Cline *(VP & Gen Mgr)*
Eric Gibson *(VP & Gen Mgr)*
Van Doesburg *(Dir-R&D Lab)*
Terry Wilson *(Dir-Sls & Mktg)*
Ted Jones *(Mgr-Sls)*
Doug Keener *(Mgr-Corp Credit)*
Steve Pieniaszek *(Mgr-HR)*
Danny Welch *(Mgr-Environ & Safety)*
Brands & Products:
GREAT STRIDES
KANGATAPE
KANGATOOLS
TEXTILE RUBBER & CHEMICAL CO. INC.

THE TIRE RACK INC.

7101 Vorden Pkwy
South Bend, IN 46628
Tel.: (574) 287-2345
Fax: (574) 236-7707
Toll Free: (888) 981-3953
E-mail: sales@tirerack.com
Web Site: www.tirerack.com
E-Mail For Key Personnel:
Sales Director: sales@tirerack.com
Approx. Number Employees: 400
Year Founded: 1979
Business Description:
High-Performance Wheels & Tires Online Distr
S.I.C.: 5963; 5014
N.A.I.C.S.: 454390; 423130
Advertising Expenditures: $200,000
Media: 6-7-8-13
Personnel:
Pete Veldman *(Pres)*
Matt Edmans *(Dir-Mktg)*
Brands & Products:
TIRE RACK

TOTER INCORPORATED

(Sub. of Wastequip, Inc.)
841 Meacham Rd
Statesville, NC 28677-2983
Mailing Address:
PO Box 5338
Statesville, NC 28687-5338
Tel.: (704) 872-8171
Fax: (704) 878-0734
Toll Free: (800) 772-0071
Toll Free: (800) 424-0422
E-mail: toter@toter.com
Web Site: www.toter.com
Approx. Rev.: $85,000,000
Approx. Number Employees: 175
Year Founded: 1962
Business Description:
Mfr. of Plastic Industrial Containers; Plastic Municipal Trash Systems
S.I.C.: 3089; 3536
N.A.I.C.S.: 326199; 333923
Export
Advertising Expenditures: $900,000
Media: 2-4-7-10-13-17-19-20-21-22
Distr.: Natl.
Budget Set: Nov.
Personnel:
Jeff Gilliam *(Pres)*
Brands & Products:
ADVANCED ROTATIONAL MOLDING
ATLAS
ECONOLIFT
EVR
HIGHLIFT
READY TO ROLL
RUGGED RIM
SLIMLINE
SMARTWAY
TOTER
TRIMLIFT

TOYO TIRE (U.S.A.) CORPORATION

(Sub. of Toyo Tire & Rubber Co., Ltd.)
6261 Katella Ave Ste 2B
Cypress, CA 90630-5245
Tel.: (714) 236-2080
Fax: (714) 229-6199
E-mail: info@toyo.com
Web Site: www.toyo.com
Approx. Number Employees: 50
Year Founded: 1966
Business Description:
Tires Distributer & Mfr
S.I.C.: 5014
N.A.I.C.S.: 423130
Personnel:
Shozo Kibata *(Chm)*
Yasushi Takagi *(Pres & CEO)*
Marty Furman *(COO)*
Amy Coleman *(Sr Dir-Mktg)*
Advertising Agency:
The Market Connection
1820 E Garry Ave Ste 118
Santa Ana, CA 92705
Tel.: (949) 851-6313
Fax: (949) 833-0253

TREDEGAR CORPORATION

1100 Boulders Pkwy
Richmond, VA 23225-4035
Tel.: (804) 330-1000
Fax: (804) 330-1177
Toll Free: (800) 411-7441
E-mail: invest@tredegar.com
Web Site: www.tredegar.com
Approx. Rev.: $739,535,000
Approx. Number Employees: 2,000
Year Founded: 1988
Business Description:
Plastic Films & Aluminum Extrusions Mfr
S.I.C.: 3089; 2671; 3354; 3442
N.A.I.C.S.: 326199; 322221; 331316; 332321
Export
Media: 2-4-7-9-10-20-25
Distr.: Natl.
Personnel:
R. Gregory Williams *(Chm)*
William M. Gottwald *(Vice Chm)*
Norman A. Scher *(Vice Chm)*
Duncan A. Crowdis *(Pres)*
Kevin A. O'Leary *(CFO, Treas & VP)*
A. Brent King *(Gen Counsel, Sec & VP)*
Brands & Products:
AQUIDRY
COMFORTAIRE
COMFORTCLEAN
COMFORTQUIT
EXTREL
FABRIFLEX
FORCE FIELD
FORCEFIELD
FRESH PEEL
STRETCH TAB

TRIENDA, LLC

N7660 Industrial Rd
Portage, WI 53901-9451
Tel.: (608) 742-5303
Fax: (608) 742-9164
Toll Free: (800) 356-8150
E-mail: mholmes@trienda.com
Web Site: www.trienda.com
Approx. Number Employees: 460
Year Founded: 1975
Business Description:
Pallets & Custom Material Handling Trays; Plastics Mfr
S.I.C.: 3081; 3089
N.A.I.C.S.: 326113; 326199
Export
Advertising Expenditures: $500,000
Media: 2-4-5-6-7-8-10-19-20
Distr.: Intl.
Budget Set: Oct.
Personnel:
Curtis J. Zamec *(Chm)*
Mark Holmes *(Sls Mgr)*

Key to Media (For complete agency information see *The Advertising Red Books-Agencies* edition):
1. Bus. Publs. 2. Cable T.V. 3. Catalogs & Directories. 4. Co-op Adv. 5. Consumer Mags. 6. D.M. to Bus. Estab.7. D.M. to Consumers 8. Daily Newsp. 9. Exhibits/Trade Shows 10. Foreign 11. Infomercial 12. Internet Adv.13. Multimedia 14. Network Radio 15. Network T.V. 16. Newsp. Distr. Mags. 17. Other 18. Outdoor (Posters, Transit) 19. Point of Purchase20. Premiums, Novelties 21. Product Samples 22. Special Events Mktg. 23. Spot Radio 24. Spot T.V. 25. Weekly Newsp. 26. Yellow Page Adv.

Brands & Products:
BIG PAK
EVER-LOK
TRIENDA
WHEEL PAK
YARN PAK

TYCO INTERNATIONAL (US) INC.
(Div. of Tyco International Ltd.)
9 Roszel Rd
Princeton, NJ 08540
Tel.: (609) 720-4200
Fax: (609) 720-4208
Web Site: www.tyco.com
Approx. Number Employees: 600
Business Description:
Holding Company; Plastics, Adhesives, Engineered Products, Healthcare Products, Fire & Security Products
S.I.C.: 6719; 2891; 3089; 3679; 3841; 3845; 7382; 8711; 9224
N.A.I.C.S.: 551112; 325520; 326199; 334418; 334510; 339112; 541330; 561621; 922160
Advertising Expenditures: $133,000,000
Personnel:
Edward D. Breen *(Chm & CEO)*
Anita Graham *(VP-HR-Tyco Security Solutions)*

UFE INCORPORATED
105 Prospect Way
Osceola, WI 54020
Tel.: (715) 294-1500
Fax: (715) 294-1501
E-mail: ask@ufeinc.com
Web Site: www.ufeinc.com
Approx. Number Employees: 450
Year Founded: 1953
Business Description:
Contract Mfr for Plastic Injection Molded Parts & Tooling for Injection Molding; Contract Assembly Services
S.I.C.: 3089; 8711
N.A.I.C.S.: 326199; 541330
Export
Advertising Expenditures: $300,000
Media: 2-4-7-10-13
Personnel:
Orville D. Johnson *(Chm)*
Cathy Zickfeld *(CFO)*
Brands & Products:
UFE
Advertising Agency:
Next Communications
10249 Yellow Circle Dr
Minnetonka, MN 55343
Tel.: (952) 934-8220
Fax: (952) 934-2375

UFP TECHNOLOGIES, INC.
172 E Main St
Georgetown, MA 01833-2107
Tel.: (978) 352-2200
Fax: (978) 352-7169
Toll Free: (800) 372-3172
E-mail: info@ufpt.com
Web Site: www.ufpt.com
Approx. Sls.: $120,766,450
Approx. Number Employees: 609
Year Founded: 1963
Business Description:
Foam & Plastic Packaging & Products Mfr
S.I.C.: 3086
N.A.I.C.S.: 326150; 326140
Import Export
Media: 10
Personnel:
R. Jeffrey Bailly *(Chm, Pres & CEO)*
Ronald J. Lataille *(CFO, Treas & VP)*
Mitchell C. Rock *(VP-Sls & Mktg)*
Daniel J. Shaw, Jr. *(VP-Engrg)*
Donald C. Reilly *(Gen Mgr)*
Advertising Agency:
Stackpole & Partners Advertising
222 Merrimac St
Newburyport, MA 01950
Tel.: (978) 463-6600
Fax: (978) 463-6610

VAIL RUBBER WORKS, INC.
521 Langley Ave
Saint Joseph, MI 49085-1725
Tel.: (269) 983-1595
Fax: (269) 983-0155
E-mail: sales@vailrubber.com
Web Site: www.vailrubber.com
E-Mail For Key Personnel:
Sales Director: sales@vailrubber.com
Approx. Number Employees: 105
Year Founded: 1904
Business Description:
Rubber & Polyurethane Covered Rolls; Non-Woven Fiber Rolls; Molded Goods; Pulley Laggings for Industry; Roll Covers; New & Used; Millwright Services
S.I.C.: 3069
N.A.I.C.S.: 326299
Export
Media: 2-4-7-10
Distr.: Intl.; Natl.
Budget Set: Aug.
Personnel:
J. William Hanley *(Pres)*
Peter A. Fellows *(VP-Tech Svcs & Gen Mgr)*
Michael J. Hanley *(VP, Sls)*
Richard N. Mackie *(VP-Fin)*
Brands & Products:
BLACK ROCK
BLUE COAT
BLUE COAT II
BLUE COAT III
BLUE COAT X
COUCH COAT III
DRILL PRESS
DRILL PRESS II
DRILL PRESS X
EBONITE
EMERALD STONE
EMERALD STONE II
EMERALD STONE X
INSUL 250
LONG LEASE
LONG LEASE III
MANDREL SLEEVES & SEGMENTS
MASROLL
MAX COAT II
MAXSIZE
NI-CHEM II
NICHEM
ORANGE SQUEEZE
PL SERIES
POLY-CAST PLUS
POLY CC
POLY DRY
POLY MATE
POLYCAST
POLYCAST PLUS
REEL ROCK
S-SERIES
SLIK LEASE II
SLIK LEASE III
TEMP ROCK
TOP LEASE
TOP LEASE II
TOP LEASE X
TOP TEX
THE TOUGH ONES COME TO US
ULTRAMATE X
V-DRIVE
V-DRIVE II
V-PRESS
V-PRESS G
V-PRESS G II
V-PRESS G X
V-PRESS II
V-PRESS X
V-SIZE
V-SIZE II
V-SIZE III
VAIL PRESS
VAIL RUBBER WORKS, INC.
VAIL-THERM
Z-SERIES
Z-SERIES CV

VALERON STRENGTH FILMS
(Sub. of Illinois Tool Works Inc.)
9505 Bamboo Rd
Houston, TX 77041-7705
Mailing Address:
PO Box 40159
Houston, TX 77240-0159
Tel.: (713) 996-4200
Fax: (713) 690-2746
Toll Free: (800) 825-3766
E-mail: info@valeron.com
Web Site: www.valeron.com
Sales Range: $25-49.9 Million
Approx. Number Employees: 100
Year Founded: 2000
Business Description:
Polyethylene Film Mfr
S.I.C.: 3081
N.A.I.C.S.: 326113
Media: 10
Personnel:
Clint Beutelschies *(VP-Sls & Mktg)*
Brands & Products:
STRENGTHPACK
V-MAX
VALERON
Advertising Agency:
Advent Marketing Communications
8708 W Little York Ste 100
Houston, TX 77040
Tel.: (713) 462-8347
Fax: (713) 462-8337
Pub Rels
— Laura Ehrlich *(Acct Exec)*

VALLEY CASTING, INC.
9462 Deerwood Ln N
Maple Grove, MN 55369
Tel.: (763) 425-1411
Fax: (800) 739-9102
Toll Free: (800) 695-8260
E-mail: info@valleycasting.com
Web Site: www.valleycasting.com
Approx. Sls.: $2,500,000
Approx. Number Employees: 25
Year Founded: 1931
Business Description:
Coin Banks, Slush Castings, Vinyl Reproductions, Replicas & Lapel Pins
S.I.C.: 3944; 3911
N.A.I.C.S.: 339932; 339911
Media: 2-4-10-21
Distr.: Intl.; Natl.
Brands & Products:
VALLEY CASTING

VANGUARD PIPING SYSTEMS, INC.
(Sub. of Viega North America)
901 N Vanguard St
McPherson, KS 67460-3118
Tel.: (620) 241-6369
Fax: (620) 241-2123
Fax: (800) 775-4068
Toll Free: (800) 775-5039
E-mail: service@vanguardpipe.com
Web Site: www.vanguardpipe.com
Approx. Number Employees: 220
Year Founded: 1977
Business Description:
Mfr of Plastic Pipes & Fittings
S.I.C.: 3084; 3432
N.A.I.C.S.: 326122; 332913
Import Export
Advertising Expenditures: $250,000
Media: 4-7-10-13-26
Personnel:
Dan Schmierer *(Pres & CEO)*
Nathan Spearman *(CFO)*
William Seiler *(Chief Legal Officer-Viega)*
Brands & Products:
COMPAX-L
CRIMPSERT
MANABLOC
VANEX
VANGUARD

VERNAY LABORATORIES, INC.
120 E S College St
Yellow Springs, OH 45387
Tel.: (937) 767-7261
Fax: (937) 767-7913
Toll Free: (866) VERNAY-1
E-mail: sales@vernay.com
Web Site: www.vernay.com
E-Mail For Key Personnel:
President: tomallen@vernay.com
Sales Director: sales@vernay.com
Public Relations: carldiem@vernay.com
Sales Range: $25-49.9 Million
Approx. Number Employees: 400
Year Founded: 1945
Business Description:
Mfr. of Precision Molded Rubber Parts
S.I.C.: 3061
N.A.I.C.S.: 326291
Import Export
Media: 2-10
Personnel:
Carl Diem *(Sr VP-Global Bus Dev)*
Rick Gudorf *(MIS Dir)*
Brands & Products:
DUCKBILL
POPPET
UMBRELLA
V-BALL
V-TIP
VERNAFLO
VERNAY

VOORHEES RUBBER MFG. COMPANY, INC.
6846 Basket Switch Rd
Newark, MD 21841-2214
Mailing Address:

Key to Media (For complete agency information see *The Advertising Red Books-Agencies* edition):
1. Bus. Publs. 2. Cable T.V. 3. Catalogs & Directories. 4. Co-op Adv. 5. Consumer Mags. 6. D.M. to Bus. Estab.7. D.M. to Consumers 8. Daily Newsp. 9. Exhibits/Trade Shows 10. Foreign 11. Infomercial 12. Internet Adv.13. Multimedia 14. Network Radio 15. Network T.V. 16. Newsp. Distr. Mags. 17. Other 18. Outdoor (Posters, Transit) 19. Point of Purchase20. Premiums, Novelties 21. Product Samples 22. Special Events Mktg. 23. Spot Radio 24. Spot T.V. 25. Weekly Newsp. 26. Yellow Page Adv.

Voorhees Rubber Mfg. Company, Inc. — (Continued)

PO Box 27
Newark, MD 21841-0027
Tel.: (410) 632-1582
Fax: (410) 632-1522
E-mail: info@voorheesrubber.com
Web Site: www.voorheesrubber.com
Approx. Number Employees: 4
Year Founded: 1898
Business Description:
Rubber Candy Molds Mfr
S.I.C.: 3069
N.A.I.C.S.: 326299
Export
Media: 2-6
Distr.: Natl.
Budget Set: Apr.-May
Personnel:
Richard B. Jackson *(Pres)*
Brands & Products:
VOORHEES

VYSTAR CORPORATION
3235 Satellite Blvd Bldg 400 Ste 290
Duluth, GA 30096
Tel.: (770) 965-0383
Fax: (770) 965-0162
E-mail: wdoyle@vytex.com
Web Site: www.vytex.com
Approx. Rev.: $861,982
Approx. Number Employees: 5
Year Founded: 2000
Business Description:
Natural Rubber Latex Mfr
S.I.C.: 3069
N.A.I.C.S.: 326299
Personnel:
William R. Doyle *(Chm, Pres & CEO)*
Jack W. Callicutt *(CFO)*
Dawn E. Ely *(Gen Counsel)*
Joanne Kearney *(VP-Mktg)*
Brands & Products:
CREATED BY NATURE.
RECREATED BY SCIENCE.
VYSTAR
VYTEX
Advertising Agency:
Cookerly Public Relations
3500 Lenox Rd 1 Alliance Ctr Ste 510
Atlanta, GA 30326
Tel.: (404) 816-2037
Fax: (404) 816-3037
(Vytex Natural Rubber Latex)

WATERBURY COMPANIES, INC.
64 Ave of Industry
Waterbury, CT 06705
Tel.: (203) 597-1812
Fax: (203) 756-2285
Toll Free: (800) 845-3495
E-mail: info@watco.com
Web Site: www.watco.com
E-Mail For Key Personnel:
Marketing Director: phebert@watco.com
Approx. Number Employees: 120
Year Founded: 1812
Business Description:
Custom Molded Plastic Products Mfr
S.I.C.: 2813
N.A.I.C.S.: 325120
Media: 2-10
Personnel:
Carl Contalini *(Pres)*
Paul Hebert *(Mgr-Natl Retail Sls)*
Brands & Products:
COUNTRY VET
WATERBURY COMPANIES

WATERVILLE TG INC.
(Sub. of Toyoda Gosei Co., Ltd.)
10 Depot St
Waterville, QC J0B 3H0, Canada
Tel.: (819) 837-2421
Fax: (819) 837-3178
E-mail: webmaster@wtg.ca
Web Site: www.wtg.ca
Approx. Number Employees: 1,800
Year Founded: 1986
Business Description:
Sealing Systems Mfr for Automotive OEMs
S.I.C.: 3053
N.A.I.C.S.: 339991
Export
Media: 4-7-9-25
Distr.: Intl.
Budget Set: June
Personnel:
Maede Kezuake *(Pres)*

WELLMAN, INC.
3303 Port & Harbor Dr Port Bienville Industrial Park
Bay Saint Louis, MS 39520
Tel.: (228) 533-4480
Fax: (228) 533-4548
E-mail: home@wellmaninc.com
Web Site: www.wellmaninc.com
Sales Range: $1-4.9 Billion
Approx. Number Employees: 1,025
Year Founded: 1927
Business Description:
Fibers, Plastic Packaging & Engineering Resins Mfr
S.I.C.: 2824; 2671; 2821
N.A.I.C.S.: 325222; 322221; 325211
Advertising Expenditures: $300,000
Media: 2-10
Personnel:
Mark Ruday *(Pres & CEO)*
Brands & Products:
BACTISHIELD
COMFORTREL
ECOCLEAR
ECOLON
ECOSPUN
FORTREL
PERMACLEAR
SENSURA
ULTURA
WELLAMID
WELLPET

WENTWORTH TECHNOLOGIES CO. LTD.
5330 Mainway Dr
Burlington, ON Canada
Tel.: (905) 332-1096
Fax: (905) 332-7802
E-mail: wtbvc@wtbvc.com
Web Site: www.wtbvc.com
Approx. Number Employees: 6
Business Description:
Injection Molding & Plastics Mfr
S.I.C.: 3544; 3089
N.A.I.C.S.: 333511; 326199
Media: 10-11
Personnel:
Walter T. Kuskowski *(Pres & CEO)*
Bruce H. McNichol *(COO & Exec VP)*
Jeffrey D. Barclay *(VP-Fin)*
Brands & Products:
FAST TO MARKET
WENTWORTH TECH

WESTLAKE PLASTICS COMPANY
490 Lenni Rd
Lenni, PA 19052
Tel.: (610) 459-1000
Fax: (610) 459-1084
Toll Free: (800) 999-1700
E-mail: westlakeplastics@westlakeplastics.com
Web Site: www.westlakeplastics.com
Approx. Number Employees: 230
Year Founded: 1952
Business Description:
Mfr. of Plastic Products
S.I.C.: 3082; 3081
N.A.I.C.S.: 326121; 326113
Media: 2-4-5-7-10-13-21-22
Brands & Products:
ABSYLUX
ARDEL
CRYSTAT
DIELUX
HALAR
KYNAR
LENNITE
NORYLUX
POMALUX
PROPYLUX
RADEL
TEMPALUX
UDEL
ULTEM
ZELUX

WEVAC PLASTICS
2401 S 17th St
Elkhart, IN 46517-1415
Tel.: (574) 294-2585
Fax: (574) 294-2723
Web Site: www.wevacplastics.com
Approx. Number Employees: 45
Year Founded: 1965
Business Description:
Plastic Vacuum/Pressure Formings Mfr
S.I.C.: 3089
N.A.I.C.S.: 326199
Media: 10
Personnel:
Jeff Davis *(Gen Mgr)*

WHIRLEY INDUSTRIES, INC.
618 4th Ave
Warren, PA 16365-0988
Tel.: (814) 723-7600
Fax: (814) 723-3245
Toll Free: (800) 825-5575
E-mail: info@whirley.com
Web Site:
www.whirleydrinkworks.com
Approx. Number Employees: 410
Year Founded: 1960
Business Description:
Mfr. of Plastic Mugs
S.I.C.: 3089; 3085
N.A.I.C.S.: 326199; 326160
Media: 7-10
Personnel:
Robert D. Sokolski *(CEO)*
Gregory Gross *(CFO, COO & Exec VP)*
Lincoln Sokolski *(Pres-Whirley-DrinkWorks)*
Brands & Products:
BARWORKS
CHILLWORKS
JAVAWORKS
KIDWORKS
WHIRLEY DRINK WORKS

WINGFOOT COMMERCIAL TIRE SYSTEMS, LLC
(Sub. of The Goodyear Tire & Rubber Company)
1000 S 21st St
Fort Smith, AR 72901-4008
Mailing Address:
PO Box 48
Fort Smith, AR 72902-0048
Tel.: (479) 788-6400
Fax: (479) 788-6278
Toll Free: (800) 643-7330
Web Site: www.wingfootct.com
Sales Range: $700-749.9 Million
Approx. Number Employees: 4,000
Year Founded: 1958
Business Description:
Tire Distr & Retreader
S.I.C.: 7534; 5014
N.A.I.C.S.: 326212; 441320
Import Export
Media: 2-7-10
Distr.: Intl.; Natl.
Personnel:
Brent Copeland *(Pres & COO)*

WINZELER GEAR
7355 W Wilson Ave
Harwood Heights, IL 60706-4707
Tel.: (708) 867-7971
Fax: (708) 867-7974
Web Site: www.winzelergear.com
E-Mail For Key Personnel:
President: jwinzeler@winzelergear.com
Approx. Number Employees: 35
Year Founded: 1940
Business Description:
Mfr. of Molded Polymer Gears
S.I.C.: 3089
N.A.I.C.S.: 326199
Import Export
Advertising Expenditures: $200,000
Media: 2-7-13
Distr.: Intl.
Personnel:
John H. Winzeler, Jr. *(Owner)*

YOKOHAMA TIRE CORPORATION
(Holding of The Yokohama Rubber Co., Ltd.)
601 S Acacia Ave
Fullerton, CA 92831-5106
Mailing Address:
PO Box 4550
Fullerton, CA 92834-4550
Tel.: (714) 870-3800
Fax: (714) 870-3838
Toll Free: (800) 423-4544
Web Site: www.yokohamatire.com
Approx. Number Employees: 150
Year Founded: 1969
Business Description:
Tire Mfr & Whslr
S.I.C.: 5014; 3011
N.A.I.C.S.: 423130; 326211

Key to Media (For complete agency information see *The Advertising Red Books-Agencies* edition):
1. Bus. Publs. 2. Cable T.V. 3. Catalogs & Directories. 4. Co-op Adv. 5. Consumer Mags. 6. D.M. to Bus. Estab.7. D.M. to Consumers 8. Daily Newsp. 9. Exhibits/Trade Shows 10. Foreign 11. Infomercial 12. Internet Adv.13. Multimedia 14. Network Radio 15. Network T.V. 16. Newsp. Distr. Mags. 17. Other 18. Outdoor (Posters, Transit) 19. Point of Purchase20. Premiums, Novelties 21. Product Samples 22. Special Events Mktg. 23. Spot Radio 24. Spot T.V. 25. Weekly Newsp. 26. Yellow Page Adv.

Import Export
Media: 2-3-4-5-6-19-20-23-26
Distr.: Natl.
Personnel:
Takao Oishi *(Pres & CEO)*
Jim MacMaster *(COO & Exec VP)*
Dan King *(Sr VP-Sls & Mktg)*
Iwao Shimomura *(Sr Dir-Corp Quality Assurance)*
Jim Mayfield *(Dir-ADVAN)*
Mark Chung *(Dir-Corp Strategy & Product Plng & Strategic Mktg)*
Fred Koplin *(Dir-Mktg)*
Lynn Sweeney *(Mgr-Mktg Commun)*
Brands & Products:
MOHAWK BRAND
PRIVATE LABEL
PRODIGY BRAND
YOKOHAMA TIRES-PASSENGER AND COMMERCIAL
Advertising Agency:
The Arras Group
Terminal Tower Ste 444 50 Public Sq
Cleveland, OH 44113
Tel.: (216) 621-1601
Fax: (216) 377-1919

ZCL COMPOSITES INC.

6907 36th Street
Edmonton, AB T6B 2Z6, Canada
Tel.: (780) 466-6648
Fax: (780) 466-6126
Toll Free: (800) 661-8265
E-mail: webmaster@zcl.com
Web Site: www.zcl.com
E-Mail For Key Personnel:
President: ven.cote@zcl.com
Approx. Rev.: $107,161,545
Approx. Number Employees: 500
Year Founded: 1987
Business Description:
Fiberglass Reinforced Plastic & Steel Underground Storage Tanks Designer, Mfr & Supplier
S.I.C.: 3089; 3462
N.A.I.C.S.: 326199; 332111
Media: 2-7-10
Personnel:
James S. Edwards *(Chm)*
Roderick Graham *(Pres & CEO)*
Kathy Demuth *(CFO)*
Ronald M. Bachmeier *(COO)*
Ron Fink *(Exec VP)*
Kent Halliday *(VP-Sls & Mktg)*
Robin MacGregor *(Dir-Mktg-Heating Oil Tanks)*
Richard Scragg *(Engr-Natl Standards & Mgr-Engring)*
Claude Duval *(Mgr-Natl Sls/Mktg)*
Richard Whitford *(Mgr-Natl Customer Svc)*
Brands & Products:
GREENTANK
LIFELINER SYSTEM
PHOENIX LINING SYSTEM
PINNACLE
PREZERVER
PREZERVER+PLUS+
PROTEKTOR
THE SAFER TANK
ZCL

ZERO MANUFACTURING, INC.

(Sub. of Zero Corporation)
500 West 200 North
North Salt Lake, UT 84054
Tel.: (801) 298-5900
Fax: (801) 292-9450
Toll Free: (800) 500-9376
E-mail: sales@zerocases.com
Web Site: www.zerocases.com
E-Mail For Key Personnel:
Sales Director: sales@zerocases.com
Sales Range: $25-49.9 Million
Approx. Number Employees: 283
Business Description:
Designer & Mfr of Standard & Custom Deep Drawn Products, Cases & Enclosures
S.I.C.: 3354; 3089; 3161
N.A.I.C.S.: 331316; 316991; 326199
Media: 10-17-21
Personnel:
Daniel Leininger *(Pres)*
Brands & Products:
CENTURION
VAL-AN
ZERO

THE ZIPPERTUBING COMPANY

13000 S Broadway
Los Angeles, CA 90061-1120
Tel.: (310) 527-0488
Fax: (310) 767-1714
Toll Free: (800) 321-8178
E-mail: info@zippertubing.com
Web Site: www.zippertubing.com
Approx. Number Employees: 35
Year Founded: 1957
Business Description:
Mfr. of Jacketing & Shielding Materials
S.I.C.: 3089; 3082
N.A.I.C.S.: 326199; 326121
Export
Advertising Expenditures: $215,000
Media: 2-4-10-21
Distr.: Reg.
Budget Set: Jan.
Personnel:
Terry Plummer *(Pres)*
Mike Bolen *(Dir-Sls & Mktg)*
Kira Carlston *(Mgr-Pur, HR & Mktg)*
Brands & Products:
HOT SPOTZ
HYPALON
SHIELDED ZT-TAPE
SNAP-GRIP
TEDLAR
Z-CLOTH
Z-FLEX
Z-SHIELD
Z-WRAP
ZIP-MESH
ZIPPER-MESH
ZIPPERTUBING
THE ZIPPERTUBING
ZT
ZT-TAPE

Key to Media (For complete agency information see *The Advertising Red Books-Agencies* edition):
1. Bus. Publs. 2. Cable T.V. 3. Catalogs & Directories. 4. Co-op Adv. 5. Consumer Mags. 6. D.M. to Bus. Estab.7. D.M. to Consumers 8. Daily Newsp. 9. Exhibits/Trade Shows 10. Foreign 11. Infomercial 12. Internet Adv.13. Multimedia 14. Network Radio 15. Network T.V. 16. Newsp. Distr. Mags. 17. Other 18. Outdoor (Posters, Transit) 19. Point of Purchase20. Premiums, Novelties 21. Product Samples 22. Special Events Mktg. 23. Spot Radio 24. Spot T.V. 25. Weekly Newsp. 26. Yellow Page Adv.

Tobacco Products & Supplies

Cigarettes — Cigars — Lighters — Pipes — Tobacco

ALLIANCE ONE INTERNATIONAL, INC.
8001 Aerial Center Pkwy PO Box 2009
Morrisville, NC 27560-2009
Tel.: (919) 379-4300
Fax: (919) 379-4346
Web Site: www.aointl.com
Approx. Rev.: $2,094,062,000
Approx. Number Employees: 3,300
Year Founded: 2005
Business Description:
Leaf Tobacco Purchaser, Processor & Distr Services
S.I.C.: 5194; 0119; 5159
N.A.I.C.S.: 424940; 111199; 424590
Import Export
Media: 2-7-10-21
Distr.: Intl.; Natl.
Budget Set: Dec.
Personnel:
Mark W. Kehaya *(Chm & Interim CEO)*
J. Pieter Sikkel *(Pres)*
Robert A. Sheets *(CFO, Chief Admin Officer & Exec VP)*
William L. O'Quinn, Jr. *(Chief Legal Officer, Sec & Sr VP)*
J. Henry Denny *(Exec VP-Global Ops)*

ALTADIS USA, INC.
(Sub. of Altadis, S.A.)
5900 N Andrews Ave Ste 1100
Fort Lauderdale, FL 33309-2300
Tel.: (954) 772-9000
Fax: (954) 938-7811
E-mail: info@altadisusa.com
Web Site: www.altadisusa.com
E-Mail For Key Personnel:
Marketing Director: jverruso@concigar.com
Sales Range: $500-549.9 Million
Approx. Number Employees: 92
Business Description:
Mfr. of Cigars, Pipe Tobaccos, Cigarette Rolling Tobaccos & Smoking Accessories
S.I.C.: 2141; 0132; 2111
N.A.I.C.S.: 312229; 111910; 312210; 312221
Import Export
Media: 6-8-10-11-13-18-19-22
Distr.: Intl.; Natl.
Personnel:
James Colucci *(Exec VP-Sls & Mktg)*
Denis McQuillen *(Sr VP-Opers)*
Janelle Rosenfeld *(VP-Mktg Premium Cigars & Corp Comm)*
Jan Verruso *(VP-Sls & Admin)*
Brands & Products:
AYC GRENADIERS
BACKWOODS
BEN FRANKLIN
BETWEEN THE ACTS
BIG BUTT
CHINA BLACK
DON CAMILO
DON DIEGO
DON MATEO
DON MELO CENTENARIO
DON MIGUEL
DUTCH MASTERS
DUTCH TREATS
EDWARD G. ROBINSON
EL CID BRAZILIAN
EL DORADO GOLD RESERVE
EL PRODUCTO
ERIK
FLAMENCO
FLOR DE COPAN
GEORGE BURNS VINTAGE
GISPERT
HARVESTERS
HEINE'S BLEND
HENRY CLAY
HONDURAN BUNDLES
LA CORONA
LAS CABRILLAS
MASTERS COLLECTION
MIAMI SUITES
MIXTURE NO. 79
MONTECRUZ
MURIEL
OMEGA
ONLY RESERVE
OUT WEST
PHILLIES
PLAYBOY BY DON DIEGO
PLAYERS CLUB BY DON DIEGO
PRIMO DEL REY
ROI-TAN
ROYAL JAMAICA
RUSTLERS
SAINT LUIS REY
SANTA DAMIANA
SUPER VALUE
SUPRE SWEETS
TAMPA NUGGET
TAMPA SWEET
TE AMO

ALTRIA GROUP, INC.
6601 W Broad St
Richmond, VA 23230
Tel.: (804) 274-2200
Web Site: www.altria.com
Approx. Rev.: $24,363,000,000
Approx. Number Employees: 10,000
Year Founded: 1887
Business Description:
Holding Company; Cigarettes & Other Tobacco Products Mfr & Distr
S.I.C.: 6719; 2111; 5194
N.A.I.C.S.: 551112; 312221; 424940
Import Export
Advertising Expenditures: $5,000,000
Media: 3-6-9-10-15-16-18-21-24
Distr.: Intl.; Natl.
Personnel:
Michael E. Szymanczyk *(Chm & CEO)*
Martin J. Barrington *(Vice Chm)*
David R. Beran *(Vice Chm)*
Howard A. Willard, III *(CFO & Exec VP)*
John R. Nelson *(CTO & Exec VP)*
Denise F. Keane *(Gen Counsel & Exec VP)*
Craig A. Johnson *(Exec VP)*
Leyla Namiranian *(Dir-Mktg & Consumer Res)*
David Sylvia *(Dir-Strategy & Bus Dev)*

AMERICAN SNUFF COMPANY
(Formerly Conwood Company LLC)
(Sub. of Reynolds American Inc.)
813 Ridge Lake Blvd
Memphis, TN 38120-9470
Mailing Address:
PO Box 217
Memphis, TN 38101-0217
Tel.: (901) 761-2050
Fax: (800) 727-0949
Toll Free: (800) 238-5990
Web Site: www.americansnuffco.com/
Sales Range: $450-499.9 Million
Approx. Number Employees: 900
Year Founded: 1782
Business Description:
Mfr of Smokeless Tobacco Products
S.I.C.: 2141
N.A.I.C.S.: 312229; 312210
Media: 2-5-6-7-9-10-16-18-19-20-21
Distr.: Natl.
Budget Set: Oct.
Personnel:
Michael D. Flaherty *(CFO & VP)*
Kevan Ostrander *(CIO & VP)*
J.S. Wilson, III *(Gen Counsel & Sec)*
James W. Cothren *(VP-Mktg)*
Carol Novosad *(VP-HR)*
Terry W. Williams *(Mgr-Natl Sls)*
Brands & Products:
B.G.
BIG TWIST
BLACK MARIA
BLOODHOUND
BLOODHOUND THICK
BULL OF THE WOODS
CANNON BALL
CLOVER BLOOM
COTTON BOLL
COUGAR
CUMBERLAND
DENTAL
GARRETT
GARRETT SWEET
GRIZZLEY
HAWKEN
HAWKEN WINTERGREEN
H.B. SCOTT'S
HONEST
KENTUCKY
KENTUCKY KING
KODIAK
KODIAK ICE
KODIAK STRAIGHT
LEVI EXTRA
LEVI GARRETT
LIEBERMAN'S
LONG CUT COUGAR
MAMMOTH
MAMMOTH CAVE
MOORE'S
MOORE'S RED LEAF
MORGAN'S
OLD TAYLOR
PEACH
PEACH SWEET
PEACHEY
R. T. JUNIOR
RAINBOW SWEET
ROUGH
ROUGH COUNTRY
R.T. JUNIOR
R.T. JUNIOR (PRESSED)
SAMSON'S
SAMSON'S BIG 4
SUN CURED
TAYLOR'S PRIDE
TUBE ROSE

Key to Media (For complete agency information see *The Advertising Red Books-Agencies* edition):
1. Bus. Publs. 2. Cable T.V. 3. Catalogs & Directories. 4. Co-op Adv. 5. Consumer Mags. 6. D.M. to Bus. Estab.7. D.M. to Consumers 8. Daily Newsp. 9. Exhibits/Trade Shows 10. Foreign 11. Infomercial 12. Internet Adv.13. Multimedia 14. Network Radio 15. Network T.V. 16. Newsp. Distr. Mags. 17. Other 18. Outdoor (Posters, Transit) 19. Point of Purchase20. Premiums, Novelties 21. Product Samples 22. Special Events Mktg. 23. Spot Radio 24. Spot T.V. 25. Weekly Newsp. 26. Yellow Page Adv.

UNION WORKMAN
WARREN
WARREN COUNTY
W.E. GARRETT
WINTERGREEN XTREME
XTREME

Advertising Agency:
archer malmo
65 Union Ave Ste 500
Memphis, TN 38103-5137
Tel.: (901) 523-2000
Fax: (901) 523-7654
Toll Free: (800) 535-8943
(Smokeless Tobacco)

AVANTI CIGAR CORPORATION

1015 N Main Ave
Scranton, PA 18508-2127
Mailing Address:
PO Box 78
Scranton, PA 18504-0078
Tel.: (570) 344-8566
Fax: (570) 344-0402
E-mail: avanti@epix.net
Web Site: www.avanticigar.com
Sales Range: $25-49.9 Million
Approx. Number Employees: 50
Year Founded: 1913
Business Description:
Mfr. of Cigars
S.I.C.: 2141
N.A.I.C.S.: 312229
Export
Advertising Expenditures: $200,000
Media: 2-10-18-19-21-23
Distr.: Natl.
Personnel:
Dominic Keating *(Pres)*
Anthony F. Suraci *(CEO)*
Anthony D. Suraci, Jr. *(Exec VP-Sls)*
Brands & Products:
AVANTI
DE NOBILI
PARODI
PETRI
RAMROD
TOSCANO

BLU

500 Archdale Dr
Charlotte, NC 28217
Toll Free: (888) 207-4588
Web Site: www.blucigs.com
Business Description:
Smoke Anywhere Cigarettes Mfr
S.I.C.: 2111
N.A.I.C.S.: 312221
Media: 13
Personnel:
Jason Healey *(Pres)*

THE COLIBRI GROUP, INC.

(Joint Venture of CITIC Group, Main Street Resources & Founders Equity, Inc.)
25 Fairmount Ave
East Providence, RI 02914
Tel.: (401) 943-2100
Fax: (401) 943-1027
Web Site: www.colibri.com
Sales Range: $100-124.9 Million
Approx. Number Employees: 500
Year Founded: 1969
Business Description:
Mfr & Distr of Jewelry, Lighters, Accessories & Clocks; Owned by Founders Equity Inc., Main Street Resources & CITIC Group
S.I.C.: 5094
N.A.I.C.S.: 423940
Import Export
Media: 2-4-6-7-8-9-10-13-15-19-20-24-25
Distr.: Natl.
Budget Set: Nov.
Personnel:
Jim Fleet *(CEO)*
Brands & Products:
COLIBRI
DARING DIAMONDS
DOLAN & BULLOCK
KREMENTZ
LINDEN
SETH THOMAS

FINCK CIGAR CO.

414 Vera Cruz
San Antonio, TX 78207-5642
Mailing Address:
PO Box 831007
San Antonio, TX 78283-1007
Tel.: (210) 226-4191
Fax: (210) 226-2825
Toll Free: (800) 221-0638
E-mail: custser@finckcigarcompany.com
Web Site:
www.finckcigarcompany.com
Approx. Number Employees: 100
Year Founded: 1893
Business Description:
Pipe, Tobacco & Cigar Retailer & Mfr
S.I.C.: 2141; 5961
N.A.I.C.S.: 312229; 454113
Import Export
Advertising Expenditures: $243,000
Consumer Mags.: $10,000; D.M. to Consumers: $200,000; Daily Newsp.: $10,000; Premiums, Novelties: $10,000; Product Samples: $10,000; Yellow Page Adv.: $3,000
Distr.: Direct to Consumer
Personnel:
Bill Finck, Sr. *(Pres)*
Bill Finck, Jr. *(VP-Adv)*
Brands & Products:
ARTURO FUENTE PREMIUM
ASHTON CLASSIC
BLUE RIBBON SAMPLER
BREAD AND BUTTER COMBO
CHARLES THE GREAT
FINCK BRANDS SAMPLER
FINCK CIGAR
FINCK'S 1893
FINCK'S COMMERCE
FINCK'S RESAGOS SABOR NUEVO
HAVANA BLEND
LAMB'S CLUB
PADRON
ROMEO Y JULIETA RESERVA REAL
TEXAS SWEETS
TORO PREMIUM CIGAR TASTER
TRAVIS CLUB
Advertising Agency:
Tobacco Advertising Assocs.
(House Agency)
PO Box 831007
San Antonio, TX 78283
Tel.: (210) 226-4191
(Cigars, Pipes, Pipe Tobacco, Chewing Tobacco, Cigarette Tobacco, Gifts and Accessories)

IMPERIAL TOBACCO CANADA LIMITED

(Sub. of British American Tobacco plc)
3711 Saint-Antoine Street
Montreal, QC H4C 3P6, Canada
Mailing Address:
P.O. Box 6500
Montreal, QC H3C 3L6, Canada
Tel.: (514) 932-6161
Fax: (514) 939-0432
Telex: 55-60673
Web Site:
www.imperialtobaccocanada.com
Approx. Number Employees: 400
Year Founded: 1912
Business Description:
Cigarettes, Tobacco & Tobacco Products Mfr & Distr
S.I.C.: 2141; 5194
N.A.I.C.S.: 312229; 424940
Export
Personnel:
Benjamin Kemball *(Pres & CEO)*
Catherine Doyle *(Mgr-Corp Comm)*
Advertising Agency:
OgilvyAction
636 W 11th Ave
New York, NY 10036
Tel.: (212) 297-8000
Fax: (212) 297-8006

IWAN RIES & CO.

19 S Wabash Ave 2nd Fl
Chicago, IL 60603-3017
Tel.: (312) 372-1306
Fax: (312) 372-1416
Toll Free: (800) 621-1457
E-mail: iwanries@att.net
Web Site: www.iwanries.com
Approx. Number Employees: 12
Year Founded: 1857
Business Description:
Pipe Tobacco, Tobacco Pouches & Cigars Whslr
S.I.C.: 5961; 5993
N.A.I.C.S.: 454113; 453991
Media: 4-8-9-10-13-19-21-23-26
Distr.: Natl.
Budget Set: Jan. -July
Personnel:
Charles S. Levi *(Owner)*
Brands & Products:
HOFFMAN HOUSE
IWAN RIES
THREE STAR
THREE STAR CORDIAL BUTTERED RUM
THREE STAR CORDIAL VANILLA

LORILLARD, INC.

714 Green Valley Rd
Greensboro, NC 27408-7018
Tel.: (336) 335-7718
Fax: (336) 335-7707
E-mail: externalaffairs@lorillard.com
Web Site: www.lorillard.com
Approx. Rev.: $5,932,000,000
Approx. Number Employees: 2,700
Year Founded: 1760
Business Description:
Holding Company; Cigarette Mfr
S.I.C.: 6719; 2111
N.A.I.C.S.: 551112; 312221
Advertising Expenditures: $35,000,000
Media: 2-6-7-8-9-10-11-16-19-21-25
Distr.: Natl.
Budget Set: Various
Personnel:
Murray S. Kessler *(Chm, CEO & Pres)*
David H. Taylor *(CFO & Exec VP-Fin & Plng)*
Neil L. Wilcox *(Chief Compliance Officer & Sr VP-Product Related Regulations)*
Anthony B. Petitt *(Chief Acctg Officer, VP & Controller)*
Ronald S. Milstein *(Sec, Sr VP-Legal, External Affairs & Gen Counsel)*
Charles E. Hennighausen *(Exec VP-Production Ops)*
Randy B. Spell *(Exec VP-Mktg & Sls)*
Brands & Products:
KENT
LORILLARD
MAVERICK
MAX
NEWPORT
OLD GOLD
SATIN
TRUE
Advertising Agencies:
Avrett Free Ginsberg
1 Dag Hammarskjold Plz 885 2nd Ave
New York, NY 10017-2205
Tel.: (212) 832-3800
Fax: (212) 418-7331

Centra360
1400 Old Country Rd Ste 420
Westbury, NY 11590-5119
Tel.: (516) 997-3147
Fax: (516) 334-7798

PHILIP MORRIS INTERNATIONAL INC.

120 Park Ave
New York, NY 10017-5579
Tel.: (917) 663-8000
Web Site:
www.philipmorrisinternational.com
Approx. Rev.: $67,713,000,000
Approx. Number Employees: 78,300
Business Description:
Producer, Marketer & Distr of Cigarettes
S.I.C.: 2111
N.A.I.C.S.: 312221
Advertising Expenditures: $387,000,000
Personnel:
Louis C. Camilleri *(Chm & CEO)*
Charles R. Wall *(Vice Chm)*
Hermann Waldemer *(CFO)*
Andre Calantzopoulos *(COO)*
Kevin Click *(CIO & Sr VP)*
Jacek Olczak *(Pres-European Union Reg)*
Matteo Pellegrini *(Pres-Asia)*
Miroslaw Zielinski *(Pres-EEMA Reg & PMI Duty Free)*
David M. Bernick *(Gen Counsel & Sr VP)*
Marco Kuepfer *(Treas & VP-Fin)*
Doug Dean *(Sr VP-R & D)*
Even Hurwitz *(Sr VP-Corp Affairs)*
Daniele Regorda *(Sr VP-HR)*
Nick Rolli *(VP-IR & Fin Comm)*
Andrea Gontkovicova *(Dir-Pub Rels)*

PHILIP MORRIS USA INC.

(Sub. of Altria Group, Inc.)
6601 W Broad St
Richmond, VA 23230

Key to Media (For complete agency information see *The Advertising Red Books-Agencies* edition):
1. Bus. Publs. 2. Cable T.V. 3. Catalogs & Directories. 4. Co-op Adv. 5. Consumer Mags. 6. D.M. to Bus. Estab.7. D.M. to Consumers 8. Daily Newsp. 9. Exhibits/Trade Shows 10. Foreign 11. Infomercial 12. Internet Adv.13. Multimedia 14. Network Radio 15. Network T.V. 16. Newsp. Distr. Mags. 17. Other 18. Outdoor (Posters, Transit) 19. Point of Purchase20. Premiums, Novelties 21. Product Samples 22. Special Events Mktg. 23. Spot Radio 24. Spot T.V. 25. Weekly Newsp. 26. Yellow Page Adv.

Philip Morris USA Inc. — (Continued)

Mailing Address:
615 Maury St
Richmond, VA 23224
Tel.: (804) 274-2000
Web Site: www.philipmorrisusa.com
Sales Range: $1-4.9 Billion
Approx. Number Employees: 6,000
Business Description:
Mfr. of Cigarettes
S.I.C.: 2111; 2082
N.A.I.C.S.: 312221; 312120
Advertising Expenditures: $200,000
Media: 2-6-8-9-10-17-18-19-20-22
Distr.: Natl.
Personnel:
Craig A. Johnson *(Pres)*
Peter P. Paoli *(Sr VP-Sls)*
Gary R. Ruth *(Sr VP-Mfg Ops)*
Brands & Products:
ALL WOMAN
ALPINE
ALWAYS A LADY
BASIC
BENSON & HEDGES
BENSON & HEDGES 100'S
BENSON & HEDGES BLUES
BENSON & HEDGES SIGNATURE COLLECTION
BLEND # 27
BRISTOL
BUCKS
CAMBRIDGE
CHESTERFIELD
COLLECTOR'S CHOICE
COMMANDER
COPPER LABEL
CRAZY MOUNTAIN RANCH
ENGLISH OVALS
FILTER SELECT
FREEPORT
GENERALS
L&M
LARK
MARK TEN
MARLBORO
MARLBORO FILTER CIGARETTES LONG
MARLBORO MENTHOL
MARLBORO MENTHOL NO. 2
MARLBORO SMOOTH
MARLBORO UNLIMITED
MERIT
NEW TOWN HALL
QUITASSIST
SARATOGA
SUPERSLIMS
VIRGINIA SLIMS
Advertising Agencies:
D.L. Blair Inc.
1051 Franklin Ave
Garden City, NY 11530
Tel.: (516) 746-3700
Fax: (516) 746-3889

Guthrie/Mayes
710 W Main St
Louisville, KY 40202-2676
Tel.: (502) 584-0371
Fax: (502) 584-0207

Leo Burnett Worldwide, Inc.
35 W Wacker Dr
Chicago, IL 60601-1723
Tel.: (312) 220-5959
Fax: (312) 220-3299

Y&R
285 Madison Ave
New York, NY 10017-6401
Tel.: (212) 210-3000
Fax: (212) 490-9073
Fax: (212) 370-3796
Fax: (212) 210-5169
(Dave's, Parliament)

REPUBLIC AIRWAYS HOLDINGS INC.
8909 Perdu Rd Ste 300
Indianapolis, IN 46268
Tel.: (317) 484-6000
Fax: (317) 484-6040
E-mail: marketing@rjet.com
Web Site: www.republicairways.com
Approx. Rev.: $2,653,651,000
Approx. Number Employees: 9,850
Year Founded: 1996
Business Description:
Holding Company
S.I.C.: 6719
N.A.I.C.S.: 551112
Advertising Expenditures: $14,200,000
Personnel:
Bryan K. Bedford *(Chm, Pres & CEO)*
Timothy P. Dooley *(CFO & Sr VP-Fin)*
Wayne C. Heller *(COO & Exec VP)*
Lars-Eric Arnell *(Sr VP-Corp Dev)*
Ian Arthur *(VP-Mktg)*
Jerry Balsano *(VP-Customer Svc)*
Jan Fogelberg *(VP-Customer Experience & Tech)*
Daniel Shurz *(VP-Plng & Strategy-Branded Airline Ops)*
Kathy Wooldridge *(VP-HR)*
Aaron Workman *(VP-IT)*

REPUBLIC TOBACCO LP
2301 Ravine Way
Glenview, IL 60025
Tel.: (847) 832-9700
Fax: (847) 832-9710
Toll Free: (800) 288-8888
E-Mail For Key Personnel:
Sales Director: sales@macintyreauto.com
Approx. Sls.: $25,516,000
Approx. Number Employees: 50
Business Description:
Smoking Tobacco
S.I.C.: 5194
N.A.I.C.S.: 424940
Media: 4-21
Personnel:
Donald R. Levin *(Chm, Pres & CEO)*
Ellis Levin *(Pres)*

REYNOLDS AMERICAN INC.
401 N Main St
Winston Salem, NC 27102-2866
Mailing Address:
PO Box 2990
Winston Salem, NC 27102-2990
Tel.: (336) 741-7693 (Pub Rels)
Tel.: (336) 741-2000
Fax: (336) 741-5511
Fax: (336) 741-0881 (Pub Rels)
E-mail: shareholderservices@reynoldsamerican.com
Web Site:
www.reynoldsamerican.com
Approx. Sls.: $8,551,000,000
Approx. Number Employees: 5,700
Business Description:
Cigarettes & Other Tobacco Products Mfr
S.I.C.: 2111; 2141
N.A.I.C.S.: 312221; 312229
Advertising Expenditures: $99,000,000
Media: 6-8-19
Personnel:
Thomas R. Adams *(CFO, CIO & Exec VP)*
Lisa J. Caldwell *(Chief HR Officer & Exec VP)*
Tommy J. Payne *(Pres-Niconovum USA)*
Martin L. Holton, III *(Gen Counsel, Exec VP & Asst Sec)*
Daniel A. Fawley *(Treas & Sr VP)*
Jeffery S. Gentry *(Grp Exec VP)*
McDara P. Folan III *(Sr VP & Deputy Gen Counsel)*
E. Kenan Whitehurst *(Sr VP-Strategy & Bus Dev)*
Susan B. Wilson *(Sr VP-Risk & Compliance Svcs-Reynolds American)*
Brands & Products:
CAMEL
CAMEL NO 9
LUCKY STRIKE
NOW
REYNOLDS AMERICAN
VICEROY

R.J. REYNOLDS TOBACCO CO.
(Sub. of Reynolds American Inc.)
401 N Main St
Winston Salem, NC 27102-2866
Mailing Address:
PO Box 2959
Winston Salem, NC 27102-2959
Tel.: (336) 741-5000
Fax: (336) 741-4238
Web Site: www.rjrt.com
Approx. Number Employees: 7,000
Year Founded: 1875
Business Description:
Cigarettes & Other Tobacco Products Mfr
S.I.C.: 2111; 2141
N.A.I.C.S.: 312221; 312229
Import Export
Media: 6-8-9-19-21-22-25
Distr.: Natl.
Personnel:
Andrew D. Gilchrist *(Pres & Chief Comml Officer)*
Mark Peters *(CFO)*
Lisa J. Caldwell *(Chief HR Officer & Exec VP)*
Morris L. Moore *(VP & Asst Treasurer)*
J. Brice O'Brien *(Exec VP-Consumer Mktg)*
Ken Whitehurst *(Sr VP-Strategy & Bus Dev)*
Advertising Agencies:
Mullen
101 N Cherry St Ste 600
Winston Salem, NC 27101-4035
Tel.: (336) 765-3630
Fax: (336) 774-9550
(Media Planning & Buying)

OgilvyAction
636 W 11th Ave
New York, NY 10036
Tel.: (212) 297-8000
Fax: (212) 297-8006

ROTHMANS BENSON & HEDGES INC.
(Joint Venture of Altria Group, Inc. & Philip Morris International Inc.)
1500 Don Mills Rd
North York, ON M3B 3L1, Canada
Tel.: (416) 449-5525
Fax: (416) 449-9601
Sales Range: $400-449.9 Million
Approx. Number Employees: 150
Business Description:
Tobacco Product Mfr & Distr; Owned 60% by Rothmans Inc. & 40% by Altria Group Inc.
S.I.C.: 2111
N.A.I.C.S.: 312221
Media: 5-9-16-19-22-25
Distr.: Natl.
Budget Set: Feb.-Mar.
Personnel:
Michael E. Frater *(CFO)*
John R. Barnett *(Pres-Canada)*
Robert J. Carew *(Exec VP-Regulatory & Legal Affairs)*
Brands & Products:
BELVEDERE
BENSON & HEDGES
CRAVEN A
MARK TEN
NUMBER 7
ROTHMANS
VISCOUNT

SCHWEITZER-MAUDUIT INTERNATIONAL, INC.
100 North Point Ctr E Ste 600
Alpharetta, GA 30022-8263
Tel.: (770) 569-4200
Fax: (770) 569-4209
Toll Free: (800) 514-0186
E-mail: investors@swm-us.com
Web Site: www.schweitzer-mauduit.com
Approx. Sls.: $740,200,000
Approx. Number Employees: 2,800
Year Founded: 1994
Business Description:
Cigarette Paper & Fine Paper Mfr
S.I.C.: 2621; 3955
N.A.I.C.S.: 322122; 322121; 339944
Export
Media: 16-17
Personnel:
Frederic P. Villoutreix *(Chm & CEO)*
Otto R. Herbst *(COO & Exec VP)*
Wilfred A. Martinez *(VP-LIP Ops & Pres-Americas)*
John W. Rumely Jr. *(Gen Counsel & Sec)*
Michel Fievez *(Exec VP)*
Peter J. Thompson *(Exec VP-Fin & Strategic)*

S.M. FRANK & CO., INC.
1000 N Division St
Peekskill, NY 10566-1830
Tel.: (914) 739-3100
Fax: (914) 739-3105
Toll Free: (800) 431-2752
E-mail: smfrankco@aol.com
Web Site: www.smfrankcoinc.com
Sales Range: $10-24.9 Million
Approx. Number Employees: 12
Year Founded: 1922
Business Description:
Smoking Pipe Importer & Mfr

Key to Media (For complete agency information see *The Advertising Red Books-Agencies* edition):
1. Bus. Publs. 2. Cable T.V. 3. Catalogs & Directories. 4. Co-op Adv. 5. Consumer Mags. 6. D.M. to Bus. Estab.7. D.M. to Consumers
8. Daily Newsp. 9. Exhibits/Trade Shows 10. Foreign 11. Infomercial 12. Internet Adv.13. Multimedia 14. Network Radio
15. Network T.V. 16. Newsp. Distr. Mags. 17. Other 18. Outdoor (Posters, Transit) 19. Point of Purchase20. Premiums, Novelties
21. Product Samples 22. Special Events Mktg. 23. Spot Radio 24. Spot T.V. 25. Weekly Newsp. 26. Yellow Page Adv.

S.I.C.: 3999; 2141
N.A.I.C.S.: 339999; 312229
Import Export
Media: 2-5-6-9-10-19-20-24-25
Distr.: Intl.; Natl.
Budget Set: Feb.-Dec.
Personnel:
William F. Fuerbach, Jr. *(Pres & Treas)*
William F. Fuerbach, III *(VP-Mktg)*
Brands & Products:
KAYWOODIE
MEDICO
YELLO-BOLE

STAR SCIENTIFIC, INC.
4470 Cox Rd Ste 110
Glen Allen, VA 23060
Tel.: (804) 527-1970
Toll Free: (800) 867-6653
E-mail: smachir@starscientific.com
Web Site: www.starscientific.com
Approx. Sls.: $848,000
Approx. Number Employees: 31
Year Founded: 1998
Business Description:
Tobacco Product Mfr
S.I.C.: 2111; 2141
N.A.I.C.S.: 312221; 312229
Advertising Expenditures: $556,000
Media: 5
Personnel:
Paul L. Perito *(Chm, Pres & COO)*
Jonnie R. Williams *(CEO)*
Park A. Dodd, III *(CFO, Treas & Asst Sec)*
Robert E. Pokusa *(Gen Counsel)*
David M. Dean *(VP-Sls & Mktg)*
Sara Troy Machir *(VP-Comm & IR)*
Brands & Products:
A NEW STANDARD OF RESPONSIBILITY
ADVANCE
ARIVA
CIGALETT
CIGRX
GSSMOKE
MAINSTREET
SPORT
STAR SCIENTIFIC, INC.
STARCURED
STONEWALL
STONEWALL HARD SNUFF

SWISHER INTERNATIONAL, INC.
(Sub. of Hay Island Holding Corporation)
20 Thorndal Cir
Darien, CT 06820-5421
Tel.: (203) 656-8000
Fax: (203) 656-3151
Web Site: www.swisher.com
Year Founded: 1861
Business Description:
Cigars & Smokeless Tobacco Mfr
S.I.C.: 2141
N.A.I.C.S.: 312229
Import Export
Media: 6-10-20
Distr.: Natl.
Budget Set: Oct.
Personnel:
Karl H. Ziegler *(Owner)*
Tom Ryan *(Pres)*
Robert A. Britton *(CFO & Exec VP)*
William Ziegler, III *(COO)*
Cynthia Z. Brighton *(Treas & VP-Fin Svcs)*
Barry Drugg *(Sr VP-Admin)*
Jackie Ziegler *(Sr VP-Mktg)*
Brands & Products:
APPLE JACK
BLACKSTONE
BUTTERCUP
CHATTANOOGA CHEW
COUNTRY BLEND
EL TRELLIS
GOLD RIVER
HALLMARK
KAYAK
KING EDWARD
LA INTIMIDAD
LANCASTER
MACBETH
MAIL POUCH
NAVY SWEET
OPTIMO
PENNS
RAILROAD MILLS
REDWOOD
SABROSO
SANTA FE
SIGLO 21
SILVERCREEK
SUPERIOR
SWISHER SWEETS
TOPS MILD
TOPS SWEET

SYNERGY BRANDS, INC.
310 Michael Dr
Syosset, NY 11791-3409
Tel.: (516) 714-8200
Fax: (516) 714-8030
E-mail: contactus@synergybrands.com
Web Site: www.synergybrands.com
Approx. Sls.: $108,959,535
Approx. Number Employees: 40
Year Founded: 1988
Business Description:
Holding Company
S.I.C.: 5141
N.A.I.C.S.: 424410
Advertising Expenditures: $130,965
Media: 13-22
Personnel:
Mair Faibish *(Chm & CEO)*
Mitchell Gerstein *(CFO, Treas, Sec & VP)*
Randall J. Perry *(Gen Counsel)*

VECTOR GROUP LTD.
100 SE 2nd St 32nd Fl
Miami, FL 33131
Tel.: (305) 579-8000
Fax: (305) 579-8001
Web Site: www.vectorgroupltd.com
Approx. Rev.: $1,063,289,000
Approx. Number Employees: 512
Year Founded: 1980
Business Description:
Holding Company; Tobacco Interests
S.I.C.: 2111
N.A.I.C.S.: 312221
Advertising Expenditures: $3,159,000
Media: 2-4-6-8-10-13-18-19-21
Distr.: Natl.
Personnel:
Bennett LeBow *(Chm)*
Howard M. Lorber *(Pres & CEO)*
Richard J. Lampen *(Exec VP)*
Brands & Products:
EVE
JADE
PYRAMID
QUEST

ZIPPO CANADA SALES, LLC
(Div. of Hyde's Distribution)
6868 Kinsman Ct
Niagara Falls, ON L2E 6S4, Canada
Tel.: (905) 358-3674
Fax: (905) 358-9419
Toll Free: (888) 445-9097
Web Site: www.zippo.ca
Approx. Number Employees: 12
Year Founded: 1949
Business Description:
Mfr of Cigarette Lighters & Writing Instruments
S.I.C.: 3999
N.A.I.C.S.: 339999
Export
Media: 6-7-9-19-21-26
Distr.: Natl.
Personnel:
Don Grigor *(Gen Mgr & Mgr-Adv)*

ZIPPO MANUFACTURING COMPANY, INC.
33 Barbour St
Bradford, PA 16701-1973
Tel.: (814) 368-2700
Fax: (814) 362-7327
Web Site: www.zippo.com
Approx. Number Employees: 520
Year Founded: 1932
Business Description:
Cigarette Lighters, Knives, Magnifiers, Letter Openers, Pill Boxes & Writing Instruments Mfr
S.I.C.: 3499; 2111
N.A.I.C.S.: 332999; 312221
Export
Media: 2-4-6-7-10-13-18-20-23
Distr.: Natl.
Budget Set: Nov.
Personnel:
Gregory W. Booth *(Pres & CEO)*
Richard Roupe *(CFO)*
Peggy Errera *(Mgr-Mktg Comm)*
Brands & Products:
ZIPPO
Advertising Agency:
Brunner
11 Stanwix St 5th Fl
Pittsburgh, PA 15222-1312
Tel.: (412) 995-9500
Fax: (412) 995-9501
Lighters
— Mary Kay Modaffari *(Dir-Acct Mngmt)*

Key to Media (For complete agency information see *The Advertising Red Books-Agencies* edition):
1. Bus. Publs. 2. Cable T.V. 3. Catalogs & Directories. 4. Co-op Adv. 5. Consumer Mags. 6. D.M. to Bus. Estab.7. D.M. to Consumers 8. Daily Newsp. 9. Exhibits/Trade Shows 10. Foreign 11. Infomercial 12. Internet Adv.13. Multimedia 14. Network Radio 15. Network T.V. 16. Newsp. Distr. Mags. 17. Other 18. Outdoor (Posters, Transit) 19. Point of Purchase20. Premiums, Novelties 21. Product Samples 22. Special Events Mktg. 23. Spot Radio 24. Spot T.V. 25. Weekly Newsp. 26. Yellow Page Adv.

Travel & Transportation

Airlines — Automobile Dealerships — Bus Lines — Car Rentals — Express Forwarders — Moving & Storage Companies — Port Authorities — Railroads — Steamship Lines — Tours — Travel Agencies — Truck Lines

A&K RAILROAD MATERIALS INC.
1505 S Redwood Rd
Salt Lake City, UT 84104
Mailing Address:
PO Box 30076
Salt Lake City, UT 84130
Tel.: (801) 974-5484
Fax: (801) 972-2041
Toll Free: (800) 453-8812
E-mail: info@akrailroad.com
Web Site: www.akrailroad.com
Approx. Number Employees: 550
Year Founded: 1959
Business Description:
Railroad Equipment Mfr & Sales
S.I.C.: 5088
N.A.I.C.S.: 423860
Import Export
Media: 2-4-7-10-18-26
Personnel:
Morris H. Kulmer *(Vice Chm)*
Michael Van Wagenen *(Gen Counsel & VP)*
Dan Britten *(VP & Gen Mgr-Fastener Div)*
Allen Vickers *(Mgr-Credit)*

ABERCROMBIE & KENT USA, LLC
(Sub. of Intrawest ULC)
1411 Opus Pl Exec Towers W II Ste 300
Downers Grove, IL 60515-1182
Tel.: (630) 725-3400
Fax: (630) 725-3401
Toll Free: (800) 554-7016
E-mail: aweyman@abercrombiekent.com
Web Site: www.abercrombiekent.com
Sales Range: $25-49.9 Million
Approx. Number Employees: 140
Year Founded: 1962
Business Description:
Tour & Travel Services
S.I.C.: 4724
N.A.I.C.S.: 561510
Media: 2-4-6-7-10
Personnel:
Geoffrey J.W. Kent *(Chm, Pres & CEO)*
Jorie Butler Kent *(Vice Chm)*
Steve Filipiak *(Dir-Internet Mktg & Ops)*
Brands & Products:
MARCO POLO CLUB
Advertising Agency:
ISM
745 Boylston St 7th Fl
Boston, MA 02116
Tel.: (617) 353-1822
Fax: (617) 266-1890

ABF FREIGHT SYSTEM, INC.
(Sub. of Arkansas Best Corporation)
3801 Old Greenwood Rd
Fort Smith, AR 72903-5937
Mailing Address:
PO Box 10048
Fort Smith, AR 72917-0048
Tel.: (479) 785-8803
Fax: (800) 599-2810
Fax: (479) 785-8992
Toll Free: (800) 610-5544
E-mail: abf@abf.com
Web Site: www.abfs.com
Sales Range: $1-4.9 Billion
Approx. Number Employees: 12,000
Year Founded: 1923
Business Description:
Freight Services
S.I.C.: 4213
N.A.I.C.S.: 484121
Advertising Expenditures: $670,000
Multimedia: $25,000; Bus. Publs.: $165,000; Catalogs & Directories: $30,000; D.M. to Bus. Estab.: $250,000; Other: $200,000
Distr.: Direct to Consumer; Intl.; Natl.
Budget Set: Oct.
Personnel:
Wesley B. Kemp *(Pres & CEO)*
Roy M. Slagle *(Sr VP-Sls & Mktg)*
James Keenan *(VP-Sls)*
Kirk R. May *(VP-Corp Sls)*
Frank Ward *(Comptroller)*
Russ Aikman *(Dir-Mktg & Pub Rel)*
Brands & Products:
ABF
Advertising Agency:
Stone Ward
225 E Markham St Ste 450
Little Rock, AR 72201-1629
Tel.: (501) 375-3003
Fax: (501) 375-8314

ACADEMIC TRAVEL ABROAD, INC.
1920 N St NW Ste 200
Washington, DC 20036
Tel.: (202) 785-9000
Fax: (202) 342-0317
Toll Free: (800) 556-7896
E-mail: info@academic-travel.com
Web Site: www.academic-travel.com
Approx. Sls.: $14,000,000
Approx. Number Employees: 50
Business Description:
Travel & Touring Services
S.I.C.: 4725
N.A.I.C.S.: 561520
Media: 6-8-13
Personnel:
David Parry *(Chm)*
Chase Poffenberger *(Exec VP)*
Sarah Saleh *(VP-Fin & Admin)*
Janet Varn *(Sr Mgr-Program)*
Emma Impavido *(Sr Mgr-Program)*
Marie-Rose Lohier *(Sr Mgr-Program)*
Chris Roper *(Sr Mgr-Programs-Asia)*

ACE AVIATION HOLDINGS INC.
5100 de Maisonneuve Blvd West
Air Canada Center
Montreal, QC H4A 3T2, Canada
Tel.: (514) 422-5000
Fax: (514) 422-5789
E-mail: des.beaumont@aceaviation.com
Web Site: www.aceaviation.com
Approx. Number Employees: 22,994
Year Founded: 1937
Business Description:
International Passenger & Cargo Air Carrier
S.I.C.: 4512
N.A.I.C.S.: 481111
Import Export
Advertising Expenditures: $12,000,000
Media: 2-6-9-17
Distr.: Intl.
Budget Set: Dec.
Personnel:
Robert A. Milton *(Chm & CEO)*
Brian Dunne *(Pres & CFO)*
Duncan Dee *(Chief Admin Officer & Sr VP-Corp Affairs)*
Sydney John Isaacs *(Chief Legal Officer & Sr VP-Corp Dev)*
Greg Cote *(Sr VP-Corp Fin & Strategy)*
Brands & Products:
ACE AVIATION
AIRVELOP
COURIAIR
ENROUTE

ACP MARKETING, INC.
785 Plymouth Ave Ste 305
Montreal, QC H4P 1B3, Canada
Tel.: (514) 733-5247
Fax: (514) 733-5541
E-mail: info@acpmarketing.net
Web Site: www.acpmarketing.net
Approx. Number Employees: 35
Year Founded: 1994
Business Description:
Rail Ticket & Rail Pass Marketer, Retailer & Distr
S.I.C.: 4789
N.A.I.C.S.: 488999
Media: 7-13-17
Personnel:
Alex Popescu *(Founder & Pres)*
Andrew Hannan *(Dir-Mktg)*
Brands & Products:
ACP MARKETING
ACP RAIL INTERNATIONAL

AER LINGUS
(Sub. of Aer Lingus Group PLC)
538 Broadhollow Rd
Melville, NY 11747-3676
Tel.: (631) 577-5700
Fax: (631) 752-2044
Toll Free: (800) IRISH-AIR
E-mail: goldcircleusa@aerlingus.com
Web Site: www.aerlingus.ie
Approx. Sls.: $90,000,000
Approx. Number Employees: 300
Year Founded: 1936
Business Description:
Air Transportation Services
S.I.C.: 4512
N.A.I.C.S.: 481111
Advertising Expenditures: $2,000,000
Media: 2-6-8-9-11-20-22-23-25
Distr.: Natl.
Budget Set: Nov.
Brands & Products:
AERLINGUS.COM
LOW FARES, WAY BETTER

Key to Media (For complete agency information see *The Advertising Red Books-Agencies* edition):
1. Bus. Publs. 2. Cable T.V. 3. Catalogs & Directories. 4. Co-op Adv. 5. Consumer Mags. 6. D.M. to Bus. Estab.7. D.M. to Consumers
8. Daily Newsp. 9. Exhibits/Trade Shows 10. Foreign 11. Infomercial 12. Internet Adv.13. Multimedia 14. Network Radio
15. Network T.V. 16. Newsp. Distr. Mags. 17. Other 18. Outdoor (Posters, Transit) 19. Point of Purchase20. Premiums, Novelties
21. Product Samples 22. Special Events Mktg. 23. Spot Radio 24. Spot T.V. 25. Weekly Newsp. 26. Yellow Page Adv.

AEROLINEAS ARGENTINAS
(Branch of Aerolineas Argentinas)
1000 NW 57 Ct Ste 120
Miami, FL 33126
Tel.: (305) 261-0100
Fax: (305) 648-4102
Toll Free: (800) 333-0276
E-mail: reserve@aeroargentinas.com
Web Site: www.aerolineas.com
Approx. Number Employees: 35
Year Founded: 1950
Business Description:
Airline Services
S.I.C.: 4512
N.A.I.C.S.: 481111
Media: 2-3-5-6-9-10-18-23
Distr.: Intl.; Natl.
Personnel:
Marcelo Bottini *(Gen Mgr-USA)*

AIR CANADA
(Sub. of ACE Aviation Holdings Inc.)
1601 Airport Rd NE Ste 708
Calgary, AB T2E 6Z8, Canada
Fax: (866) 584-0380
Toll Free: (888) 247-2262
Web Site: www.aircanada.com
Approx. Number Employees: 14,399
Year Founded: 1956
Business Description:
Commercial Airlines
S.I.C.: 4512
N.A.I.C.S.: 481111
Personnel:
Calin Rovinescu *(Pres & CEO)*
Duncan Dee *(COO & Exec VP)*
Priscille LeBlanc *(VP-Corp Comm)*
Claude Morin *(VP-Sls)*
Brands & Products:
CANADIAN INTER@CTIVE
CANADIAN PLUS
CANADIAN SHUTTLE
EMPRESS CLUB
Advertising Agencies:
Bluestreak
343 Arsenal St
Watertown, MA 02472
Tel.: (617) 218-0700
Fax: (617) 218-6502

PointRoll Inc.
951 E Hector St
Conshohocken, PA 19428
Tel.: (267) 558-1300
Fax: (267) 285-1141
Toll Free: (800) 203-6956

AIR CHARTERS, INC.
333 Industrial Ave Ste 3
Teterboro, NJ 07608
Tel.: (201) 288-9000
Fax: (201) 288-2749
Web Site: www.airchartersteb.com
Approx. Rev.: $2,600,000
Approx. Number Employees: 30
Year Founded: 1996
Business Description:
Scheduled Air Transportation
Equipment Rental/Leasing
S.I.C.: 4512
N.A.I.C.S.: 481111
Personnel:
Susan Bopp *(Owner)*
Advertising Agencies:
Bernstein-Rein Advertising, Inc.
4600 Madison Ave Ste 1500
Kansas City, MO 64112-3016
Tel.: (816) 756-0640
Fax: (816) 399-6000
Toll Free: (800) 571-6246

Graham & Company Advertising, Inc.
510 Broadhollow Rd Ste 301
Melville, NY 11747
Tel.: (631) 939-6492

AIR FRANCE, USA
(Branch of Air France-KLM Group)
125 W 55th St 2nd Fl
New York, NY 10019
Tel.: (212) 830-4000
Fax: (212) 830-4244
Web Site: www.airfrance.com
Approx. Number Employees: 850
Year Founded: 1943
Business Description:
International Air Transportation (Passenger & Cargo)
S.I.C.: 4512
N.A.I.C.S.: 481111
Import Export
Advertising Expenditures: $10,000,000
Bus. Publs.: $2,000,000; Consumer Mags.: $5,000,000; D.M. to Consumers: $500,000; Daily Newsp.: $2,000,000; Exhibits/Trade Shows: $500,000
Distr.: Intl.; Natl.
Budget Set: July
Personnel:
Jean-Cyril Spinetta *(Chm & CEO)*
Christian Herzog *(Sr VP-Mktg)*
Marie-Joseph Male *(VP & Gen Mgr)*
Kristen Loughman *(Mgr-Media Rels)*
Advertising Agency:
The Ruder Finn Group
301 E 57th St
New York, NY 10022-2900
Tel.: (212) 593-6400
Fax: (212) 593-6397

AIR INDIA
(Branch of Air India Limited)
570 Lexington Ave 15th Fl
New York, NY 10022
Tel.: (212) 407-1300
Fax: (212) 838-9533
Toll Free: (800) 223-7776
Telex: 12352
Web Site: www.airindia.com
Approx. Number Employees: 100
Year Founded: 1960
Business Description:
International Airline Svcs
S.I.C.: 4729; 4724
N.A.I.C.S.: 561599; 561510
Consumer Mags.: 1%; Weekly Newsp.: 99%
Distr.: Intl.; Natl.
Budget Set: Nov.
Personnel:
Arvind Jadhav *(Chm & Mng Dir)*
Urmila Subbarao *(Chief Vigilence Officer)*
K. M. Unni *(Head-Airframes)*
L. P. Nakhwa *(Exec Dir-Medical)*
V. Srikrishnan *(Exec Dir-Headquarters & Personnel)*
S. Venkat *(Exec Dir-Fin & Company Sec)*
S. Chandrasekhar *(Dir-Fin)*
Anup Srivastava *(Dir-HR)*
Brands & Products:
AIR-INDIA

AIR JAMAICA LTD.
(Branch of Air Jamaica)
8300 NW 33rd St Ste 440
Miami, FL 33122-1940
Tel.: (305) 670-3222
Fax: (305) 669-6632
Fax: (305) 669-6631
Web Site: www.airjamaica.com
Approx. Number Employees: 1,500
Year Founded: 1995
Business Description:
Provider of Commercial Air Line Services
S.I.C.: 4512
N.A.I.C.S.: 481112
Media: 2-4-6-7-8-9-10-11-13-16-18-19-20-23-24-25-26-31
Distr.: Intl.; Natl.
Budget Set: Nov.
Personnel:
Joy Schaaffe *(Dir-Mktg & Comm)*
Brands & Products:
AIR JAMAICA
AIR JAMAICA CARGO
AIR JAMAICA EXPRESS
AIR JAMAICA VACATIONS

AIR NEW ZEALAND LTD. (U.S.A.)
(Branch of Air New Zealand Limited)
1960 E Grand Ave
El Segundo, CA 90245-5000
Tel.: (310) 648-7000
Fax: (310) 648-7017
Toll Free: (800) 262-1234
Web Site: www.airnz.com
Approx. Number Employees: 80
Year Founded: 1941
Business Description:
Operator of Commercial & Cargo Air Lines
S.I.C.: 4724; 4512
N.A.I.C.S.: 561510; 481111
Advertising Expenditures: $6,000,000
Media: 4-6-8-10-11-13-18-20
Distr.: Intl.; Natl.
Budget Set: July
Personnel:
Catherine Gregory *(Mgr-Mktg)*
Advertising Agencies:
BBDO West
555 Market St 17th Fl
San Francisco, CA 94105
Tel.: (415) 808-6200
Fax: (415) 808-6221

CRT/tanaka
8733 Sunset Blvd Ste 205
Los Angeles, CA 90069
Tel.: (310) 659-5380
Fax: (310) 659-5257

AIRBUS NORTH AMERICA HOLDINGS, INC.
(Holding of Airbus S.A.S.)
198 Van Buren St
Herndon, VA 20170
Tel.: (703) 834-3400
Fax: (703) 834-3341
Web Site: www.airbusnorthamerica.com
Approx. Number Employees: 100
Business Description:
Airplane Distr
S.I.C.: 3721
N.A.I.C.S.: 336411
Import Export
Advertising Expenditures: $2,500,000
Media: 2-7-9-10
Distr.: Natl.
Budget Set: Oct.
Personnel:
T. Allan McArtor *(Chm)*
Barry Eccleston *(Pres & CEO)*
Mary Prettyman *(VP-Mktg, North America)*
Advertising Agency:
Cresta Group
1050 N State St
Chicago, IL 60610
Tel.: (312) 944-4700
Fax: (312) 944-1582

AIRTRAN HOLDINGS, INC.
(Sub. of Southwest Airlines Co.)
9955 AirTran Blvd
Orlando, FL 32827-5330
Tel.: (678) 254-7999
Toll Free: (800) 247-8726
E-mail: info@airtranweb.com
Web Site: www.airtran.com
Approx. Rev.: $2,619,172,000
Approx. Number Employees: 7,992
Year Founded: 1993
Business Description:
Airline Holding Company
S.I.C.: 4512
N.A.I.C.S.: 481111
Advertising Expenditures: $31,100,000
Media: 13
Personnel:
Robert E. Jordan *(Pres)*
Arne Haak *(CFO, Treas & Sr VP)*
Rocky Wiggins *(CIO & Sr VP)*
Mark W. Osterberg *(Chief Acctg Officer & VP)*
Steven A. Rossum *(Gen Counsel, Sec & Exec VP)*
Klaus Goersch *(Exec VP-Ops & Customer Svc)*
Loral Blinde *(Sr VP-HR & Admin)*
Kevin P. Healy *(Sr VP-Plng & Mktg)*
Jack Smith *(Sr VP-Customer Svc)*
Tad Hutcheson *(VP-Sls & Mktg)*
Kirk Thornburg *(VP-Maintenance & Engrg)*
Jean-Pierre Dagon *(Dir-Corp Safety)*
Judy Graham-Weaver *(Mgr-Pub Rels)*
Brands & Products:
A PLUS REWARDS
AIRTRAN
AIRTRAN AIRWAYS
AIRTRAN AIRWAYS VACATIONS
EVENTSAVERS
GO. THERE'S NOTHING STOPPING YOU.
NET ESCAPES
Advertising Agency:
Cramer-Krasselt
225 N Michigan Ave
Chicago, IL 60601-7601
Tel.: (312) 616-9600
Fax: (312) 616-3839

ALAMO RENT-A-CAR, LLC
(Sub. of Enterprise Holdings, Inc.)
6929 N Lakewood Ave Ste 100
Tulsa, OK 74117
Tel.: (918) 401-6000
Fax: (954) 320-4077
Toll Free: (800) GOALAMO
Web Site: www.alamo.com
Approx. Number Employees: 70
Year Founded: 1974

Key to Media (For complete agency information see *The Advertising Red Books-Agencies* edition):
1. Bus. Publs. 2. Cable T.V. 3. Catalogs & Directories. 4. Co-op Adv. 5. Consumer Mags. 6. D.M. to Bus. Estab.7. D.M. to Consumers
8. Daily Newsp. 9. Exhibits/Trade Shows 10. Foreign 11. Infomercial 12. Internet Adv.13. Multimedia 14. Network Radio
15. Network T.V. 16. Newsp. Distr. Mags. 17. Other 18. Outdoor (Posters, Transit) 19. Point of Purchase20. Premiums, Novelties
21. Product Samples 22. Special Events Mktg. 23. Spot Radio 24. Spot T.V. 25. Weekly Newsp. 26. Yellow Page Adv.

Alamo Rent-A-Car, LLC — (Continued)

Business Description:
Passengere Car Rental
S.I.C.: 7514
N.A.I.C.S.: 532111
Media: 1-2-3-5-6-7-8-9-10-11-13-15-18-19-24-26
Distr.: Natl.
Personnel:
Greg Stubblefield *(Pres-National Car Rental)*
Susan Madigan *(Dir-Retail MKtg)*
Brands & Products:
ALAMO

ALASKA AIR GROUP, INC.
19300 International Blvd
Seattle, WA 98188-5304
Mailing Address:
PO Box 68900
Seattle, WA 98168-0900
Tel.: (206) 392-5885
Fax: (206) 433-3379
Toll Free: (800) 252-7522
Web Site: www.alaskaair.com
Approx. Rev.: $3,832,300,000
Approx. Number Employees: 12,039
Year Founded: 1985
Business Description:
Regional Airline Holding Company
S.I.C.: 4512; 6719
N.A.I.C.S.: 481111; 551112
Advertising Expenditures: $16,000,000
Media: 5-6-7-8-9-10-11-13-22-23-24-25-26
Distr.: Direct to Consumer; Reg.
Budget Set: Oct.
Personnel:
William S. Ayer *(Chm, Pres & CEO)*
Brandon S. Pedersen *(CFO)*
Tom O'Grady *(Chief Compliance Officer & Deputy Gen Counsel)*
Benito Minicucci *(Exec VP-Ops & COO-Alaska Airlines Inc)*
Keith Loveless *(Gen Counsel)*
Jay Schaefer *(Treas & VP-Fin)*
Thomas M. Gerharter *(Sr VP-Ops-Horizon Air Industries, Inc)*
Dean Duvall *(Mng Dir-Procurement)*
Ann Ardizzone *(VP-Strategic Sourcing & Supply Chain Mgmt)*
Kelley Dobbs *(VP-HR)*
Kris Kutchera *(VP-IT & Strategy Mgmt)*
Joseph A. Sprague *(VP-Mktg)*
Molly Brown *(Mgr-Adv & Promos)*
Darbie Kirk *(Mgr-Mktg-Cargo)*
Susan Peterson *(Coord-Adv & Promo)*
Advertising Agency:
Wong, Doody, Crandall, Wiener
1011 Western Ave Ste 900
Seattle, WA 98104
Tel.: (206) 624-5325
Fax: (206) 624-2369

ALASKA AIRLINES, INC.
(Sub. of Alaska Air Group, Inc.)
19300 Pacific Hwy S
Seattle, WA 98188-5304
Mailing Address:
PO Box 68900
Seattle, WA 98168-0900
Tel.: (206) 392-5040
Web Site: www.alaskaair.com
Approx. Rev.: $3,006,000,000
Year Founded: 1932
Business Description:
Air Transportation, Tours & Cargo
S.I.C.: 4512
N.A.I.C.S.: 481111
Advertising Expenditures: $12,600,000
Distr.: Intl.; Natl.
Budget Set: Nov.
Personnel:
William S. Ayer *(Chm & CEO)*
Bradley D. Tilden *(Pres)*
Brandon S. Pedersen *(CFO & VP-Fin)*
Ben Minicucci *(COO & Exec VP-Ops)*
Keith Loveless *(Gen Counsel, Sec & VP-Legal/Corp Affairs)*
William L. Mackay *(Sr VP-Alaska)*
Arnie Stapnes *(Mng Dir-IT Customer Svcs & Infrastructure)*
Jeff Butler *(VP-Customer Svc)*
Kelley Dobbs *(VP-HR & Labor Rels)*
Frederick L. Mohr *(VP-Maintenance & Engrg)*
Joe Sprague *(VP-Mktg)*
Tim Thompson *(Mgr-Pub Affairs-Alaska)*
Brands & Products:
ALASKA
Advertising Agencies:
Acento Advertising, Inc.
2254 S Sepulveda Blvd
Los Angeles, CA 90064
Tel.: (310) 943-8300
Fax: (310) 943-8310

Gogerty Marriott
2900 Century Sq 1501 4th Ave Ste 2900
Seattle, WA 98101
Tel.: (206) 292-3000

Razorfish
821 2nd Ave Ste 1800
Seattle, WA 98104-2343
Tel.: (206) 816-8800
Fax: (206) 816-8808

Razorfish Philadelphia
417 N 8th St Fl 2
Philadelphia, PA 19123-3916
Tel.: (267) 295-7100
Fax: (267) 295-7101

Razorfish UK
23 Howland St
London, W1A 1AQ, United Kingdom
Tel.: (44) 207 907 4545
Fax: (44) 207 907 4546

Wong, Doody, Crandall, Wiener
1011 Western Ave Ste 900
Seattle, WA 98104
Tel.: (206) 624-5325
Fax: (206) 624-2369

Wong, Doody, Crandall, Wiener
8500 Steller Dr Ste 5
Culver City, CA 90232-2427
Tel.: (310) 280-7800
Fax: (310) 280-7780

ALBA WHEELS UP INTERNATIONAL, INC.
150 30 132nd Ave
Jamaica, NY 11434
Tel.: (718) 276-3000
Fax: (718) 712-1222
E-mail: jfk@alba-wheelsup.com
Web Site: www.albawheelsup.com
Sales Range: $25-49.9 Million
Approx. Number Employees: 100
Year Founded: 1949
Business Description:
Custom House Broker & International Freight Forwarder
S.I.C.: 4731
N.A.I.C.S.: 488510
Media: 2-4-10
Personnel:
Damien Stile *(Owner)*
Salvatore J. Stile *(Pres)*

ALGOMA CENTRAL CORPORATION
63 Church St Ste 600
PO Box 7000
Saint Catharines, ON L2R 3C4, Canada
Tel.: (905) 687-7888
Fax: (905) 687-7840
Web Site: www.algonet.com
Approx. Rev.: $546,467,540
Approx. Number Employees: 1,500
Year Founded: 1899
Business Description:
Marine Transport Company
S.I.C.: 4499
N.A.I.C.S.: 488390
Media: 2-10
Personnel:
Duncan N.R. Jackman *(Chm)*
Greg D. Wight *(Pres & CEO)*
Peter D. Winkley *(CFO & VP-Fin)*
Wayne A. Smith *(Sr VP-Comml)*
Al J. Vanagas *(Sr VP-Techl)*
David G. Allen *(VP-Fin)*
Karen A. Watt *(VP-HR)*

ALLIED VAN LINES, INC.
(Sub. of SIRVA, Inc.)
700 Oakmont Ln
Westmont, IL 60559
Tel.: (630) 570-3686
Web Site: www.alliedvan.com
Approx. Number Employees: 1,000
Business Description:
Moving Services
S.I.C.: 4214
N.A.I.C.S.: 484210
Advertising Expenditures: $2,500,000
Media: 2-4-5-7-8-10-13-23-24-26
Advertising Agency:
Deforest Creative Group
300 W Lake St
Elmhurst, IL 60126
Tel.: (630) 834-7200
Fax: (630) 279-8410

ALLSTATES WORLDCARGO, INC.
1 Telican Dr
Bayville, NJ 08721
Tel.: (732) 831-6868
Fax: (732) 831-6869
Fax: (609) 693-6667
Fax: (609) 693-5550
Web Site: www.allstates-worldcargo.com
Sales Range: $50-74.9 Million
Approx. Number Employees: 85
Year Founded: 1961
Business Description:
Freight Forwarding
S.I.C.: 4731
N.A.I.C.S.: 488510
Advertising Expenditures: $29,930
Media: 2-7
Personnel:
Joseph M. Guido *(Chm)*
Sam Digiralomo *(Pres & CEO)*
Craig D. Stratton *(CFO)*
Barton C. Theile *(COO & Exec VP)*

AMBASSADORS GROUP, INC.
2001 S Flint Rd
Spokane, WA 99224
Tel.: (509) 568-7000
Tel.: (509) 568-7800
Fax: (509) 534-5245
Web Site: www.ambassadorsgroup.com
Approx. Rev.: $76,146,000
Approx. Number Employees: 212
Year Founded: 1967
Business Description:
Educational Travel Program Services
S.I.C.: 9411; 4729; 8299
N.A.I.C.S.: 923110; 561599; 611710
Media: 4-8-10-11-13-18
Personnel:
Jeffrey D. Thomas *(Pres & CEO)*
Anthony F. Dombrowik *(CFO, Treas, Sec & Sr VP)*
Margaret M. Thomas *(COO & Exec VP-Ambassador Programs, Inc)*
Meredith Banka *(VP-Mktg)*
Julie Strugar *(Dir-IR)*

AMERCO
1325 Airmotive Way Ste 100
Reno, NV 89502
Tel.: (775) 688-6300
Fax: (775) 688-6338
E-mail: investorrelations@amerco.com
Web Site: www.amerco.com
Approx. Rev.: $2,241,275,000
Approx. Number Employees: 7,470
Year Founded: 1969
Business Description:
Holding Company; Owner of Moving & Storage, Real Estate, Property & Casualty Insurance & Life Insurance Companies
S.I.C.: 7519; 6311; 6331; 6719
N.A.I.C.S.: 532120; 524113; 524126; 551112
Advertising Expenditures: $14,900,000
Media: 4-10-13-18-26
Personnel:
Edward J. Shoen *(Chm & Pres)*
Laurence J. De Respino *(Gen Counsel)*
Jennifer Flachman *(Dir-IR)*
Rocky D. Wardrip *(Asst Treas)*
Brands & Products:
AMERCO
EMOVE
U-HAUL

AMERICAN AIRLINES, INC.
(Sub. of AMR Corporation)
4333 Amon Carter Blvd
Fort Worth, TX 76155-2604
Tel.: (817) 963-1234
Fax: (817) 963-6015
Web Site: www.aa.com
Approx. Rev.: $22,150,000,000
Approx. Number Employees: 65,525
Year Founded: 1934
Business Description:
Air Transportation

Key to Media (For complete agency information see *The Advertising Red Books-Agencies* edition):
1. Bus. Publs. 2. Cable T.V. 3. Catalogs & Directories. 4. Co-op Adv. 5. Consumer Mags. 6. D.M. to Bus. Estab.7. D.M. to Consumers 8. Daily Newsp. 9. Exhibits/Trade Shows 10. Foreign 11. Infomercial 12. Internet Adv.13. Multimedia 14. Network Radio 15. Network T.V. 16. Newsp. Distr. Mags. 17. Other 18. Outdoor (Posters, Transit) 19. Point of Purchase20. Premiums, Novelties 21. Product Samples 22. Special Events Mktg. 23. Spot Radio 24. Spot T.V. 25. Weekly Newsp. 26. Yellow Page Adv.

S.I.C.: 4729; 4512; 4581; 4789
N.A.I.C.S.: 488119; 481111; 488190; 488999; 561599
Personnel:
Gerard J. Arpey *(Chm & CEO)*
Thomas W. Horton *(Pres)*
Isabella D. Goren *(CFO & Sr VP)*
Monte E. Ford *(CIO-American Airlines & AMR & Sr VP)*
Virasb Vahidi *(Sr VP-Mktg & Plng, Chief Comml Officer)*
David R. Brooks *(Pres-American Airlines Cargo)*
Maya Leibman *(Pres-Aadvantage)*
Robert B. Reding *(Exec VP-Ops)*
Jeffrey J. Brundage *(Sr VP-HR)*
Thomas R. Del Valle *(Sr VP-Airport Svcs)*
Peter J. Dolara *(Sr VP-Mexico, Caribbean & Latin America)*
Craig S. Kreeger *(Sr VP-Customer Experience)*
Jim Ream *(Sr VP-Maintenance & Engrg)*
William K. Ris, Jr. *(Sr VP-Govt Affairs)*
Rick Wibins *(Mng Dir-Brand Dev & Adv)*
Peter A. Stanham *(Mng Dir-Fin-Mexico/Caribbean/Latin America Div)*
David L. Campbell *(VP-Safety, Security & Environmental)*
Robert J. Friedman *(VP-Mktg)*
Roger Frizzell *(VP-Corp Comm)*
William T. Greene *(VP-Maintenance & Engrg Fin)*
John R. MacLean *(VP-Pur & Transportation)*
Johna Johnson *(Dir-Sls-New York)*
Jennifer Pemberton *(Mgr-Cargo Adv & Media Rels)*
Neeraj Raj *(Mgr-Bus Sls-India)*
Brands & Products:
AADVANTAGE
AMERICAN AIRLINES
NET SAAVER
Advertising Agencies:
Levenson & Brinker Public Relations
717 Harwood 20th Fl
Dallas, TX 75201
Tel.: (214) 932-6057
Tel.: (214) 932-6076
Fax: (214) 880-0628

Mass Transmit
453 W17th St
New York, NY 10011
Tel.: (704) 706-2670
Fax: (704) 447-7262

McCann Erickson (Peru) Publicidad S.A.
Calle Tripoli 102 Miraflores Apartado 180668
L18-0368
Lima, 18, Peru
Tel.: (51) 1 610 8100
Fax: (51) 1 447 8110

McCann Erickson S.A. de Publicidad
Ave Andres Bello 2711, 7th Fl
Santiago, Chile
Tel.: (56) 2337 6777
Fax: (56) 2337 6800

PointRoll Inc.
951 E Hector St
Conshohocken, PA 19428
Tel.: (267) 558-1300
Fax: (267) 285-1141
Toll Free: (800) 203-6956

Research Development & Promotions (d/b/a RDP)
360 Menores Ave
Coral Gables, FL 33134
Tel.: (305) 445-4997
Fax: (305) 445-4221

Spafax
The Pumphouse 13-16 Jacob's Well Mews
London, W1U 3DY, United Kingdom
Tel.: (44) 20 7906 2001
Fax: (44) 20 7906 2003

TM Advertising
1717 Main St Ste 2000
Dallas, TX 75201
Tel.: (972) 556-1100
Fax: (972) 830-2619
Agency of Record
Putting Them First Television Spot
Thank You Television Spot

Universal McCann
100 33rd St 8th Fl
New York, NY 10001
Tel.: (212) 883-4700

Weber Shandwick-Dallas
1717 9th St Ste 1600
Dallas, TX 75201
Tel.: (469) 375-0200
Fax: (972) 868-7671
— Liza Marino *(Sr Acct Exec)*

Witeck-Combs Communications
2120 L St NW Ste 850
Washington, DC 20037
Tel.: (202) 887-0500
Fax: (202) 887-5633

Zubi Advertising Services, Inc.
355 Alhambra Cir 10th Fl
Coral Gables, FL 33134-5006
Tel.: (305) 448-9824
Fax: (305) 460-6393
(Spanish-Language Advertising)

AMERICAN ANTIQUITIES, INC.
(Name Changed to Pet Airways, Inc.)

AMERICAN CANADIAN CARIBBEAN LINE, INC.
461 Water St
Warren, RI 02885
Tel.: (401) 247-0955
Fax: (401) 247-2350
Toll Free: (800) 556-7450
E-mail: info@accl-smallships.com
Web Site: www.accl-smallships.com
Approx. Sls.: $9,000,000
Approx. Number Employees: 65
Year Founded: 1966
Business Description:
Provider of Small Ship Cruises
S.I.C.: 7999
N.A.I.C.S.: 487210
Media: 4-6-7-9
Personnel:
Nancy Blount *(Pres)*
Brands & Products:
ACCL
THE SMALL SHIP CRUISE LINE
Advertising Agency:
ISM
745 Boylston St 7th Fl
Boston, MA 02116
Tel.: (617) 353-1822
Fax: (617) 266-1890
Brand Strategy
Consumer & Travel Agent Research
Creative Development
Graphic Identigy

AMERICAN RED BALL TRANSIT CO. INC.
1335 Sadlier Cir E
Indianapolis, IN 46239-1051
Tel.: (317) 353-8331
Fax: (317) 351-0652
Toll Free: (800) 733-8077
Web Site: www.redball.com
Approx. Number Employees: 50
Year Founded: 1919
Business Description:
Moving Services
S.I.C.: 4214; 4731
N.A.I.C.S.: 484210; 488510
Export
Media: 2-4-5-6-7-8-9-13-14-15-20-22-23-24-25-26
Distr.: Natl.
Personnel:
Katrina Blackwell *(Owner)*
Brad Beal *(Chm & Sec)*
David Combs *(CFO)*
Brands & Products:
AMERICAN RED BALL
WORLD WIDE MOVERS

ANDREW HARPER, INC.
1703 W 5th St Ste 800
Austin, TX 78703
Mailing Address:
PO Box 684368
Austin, TX 78768-4368
Tel.: (512) 904-7320
Fax: (512) 904-7350
Fax: (888) 701-6177
Toll Free: (800) 235-9622
E-mail: membership@andrewharper.com
Web Site: www.andrewharper.com
Approx. Number Employees: 20
Business Description:
High End Travel Agency, Publishing & Services Firm
S.I.C.: 4724
N.A.I.C.S.: 561510
Media: 2-16-17
Personnel:
John Cullen *(Pres)*
Sean McKenna *(Dir-Mktg & Brand Strategy)*

THE ANDREWS MOVING & STORAGE COMPANY INC.
10235 Philipp Pkwy
Streetsboro, OH 44241
Tel.: (330) 656-8700
Tel.: (614) 777-1515
Fax: (330) 656-8712
Fax: (614) 777-1528
Toll Free: (800) 321-8680
E-mail: info@andrewsmoving.com
Web Site: www.andrewsmoving.com
Sales Range: $25-49.9 Million
Approx. Number Employees: 50
Year Founded: 1908
Business Description:
Trucking Services
S.I.C.: 4214
N.A.I.C.S.: 484210
Import Export
Media: 7-8-10-20-26
Brands & Products:
ANDREWS RECORDS MANAGEMENT

APPLE VACATIONS INC.
7 Campus Blvd
Newtown Square, PA 19073
Tel.: (610) 359-6500
Fax: (610) 359-6519
Toll Free: (800) 727-3550
E-mail: eherncane@applevacations.com
Web Site: www.applevacations.com
Approx. Number Employees: 300
Year Founded: 1969
Business Description:
Retailer of Package Tours & Travel Plans
S.I.C.: 4725; 4724
N.A.I.C.S.: 561520; 561510
Media: 5-6-9-18-19-23-24-25
Distr.: Natl.; Reg.
Budget Set: Nov.
Personnel:
J. J. Mullen *(Pres)*
Julia Davidson *(CFO)*
Eileen Herncane *(Dir-Mktg)*
Brands & Products:
APPLE VACATIONS
AV-OK
SERVICE BEYOND THE CLICK
Advertising Agency:
Janine
(House Agency)
101 Northwest Point Blvd.
Elk Grove Village, IL 60007
Tel.: (847) 640-1150

ARKANSAS BEST CORPORATION
3801 Old Greenwood Rd
Fort Smith, AR 72903-5937
Mailing Address:
PO Box 10048
Fort Smith, AR 72917-0048
Tel.: (479) 785-6000
Fax: (479) 785-6004
Telex: 9107237686
E-mail: info@arkbest.com
Web Site: www.arkbest.com
Approx. Rev.: $1,657,864,000
Approx. Number Employees: 10,750
Year Founded: 1923
Business Description:
Diversified Holding Company Engaged in Motor Freight Transportation, Computer Services & Truck Tire Retreading
S.I.C.: 4214; 4213; 4731
N.A.I.C.S.: 484210; 484121; 484122; 488510
Export
Media: 26
Personnel:
Robert A. Young, III *(Chm)*
Judy R. McReynolds *(Pres & CEO)*
Michael E. Newcity *(CFO)*
Michael R. Johns *(Gen Counsel, Sec & VP)*
J. Lavon Morton *(Sr VP-Tax & Chief Audit Exec)*
Erin K. Gattis *(VP-HR)*

Key to Media (For complete agency information see *The Advertising Red Books-Agencies* edition):
1. Bus. Publs. 2. Cable T.V. 3. Catalogs & Directories. 4. Co-op Adv. 5. Consumer Mags. 6. D.M. to Bus. Estab.7. D.M. to Consumers
8. Daily Newsp. 9. Exhibits/Trade Shows 10. Foreign 11. Infomercial 12. Internet Adv.13. Multimedia 14. Network Radio
15. Network T.V. 16. Newsp. Distr. Mags. 17. Other 18. Outdoor (Posters, Transit) 19. Point of Purchase20. Premiums, Novelties
21. Product Samples 22. Special Events Mktg. 23. Spot Radio 24. Spot T.V. 25. Weekly Newsp. 26. Yellow Page Adv.

Arkansas Best Corporation — (Continued)
R. David Humphrey *(VP-IR & Corp Comm)*
Jennifer J. Boyd *(Mgr-Mktg & PR)*
Advertising Agency:
Stone Ward
225 E Markham St Ste 450
Little Rock, AR 72201-1629
Tel.: (501) 375-3003
Fax: (501) 375-8314

ARUBA TOURISM AUTHORITY
100 Plz Dr 1st Fl
Secaucus, NJ 07094
Tel.: (201) 330-0800
Fax: (201) 558-4767
Toll Free: (800) TOARUBA
E-mail: ata.newjersey@aruba.com
Web Site: www.aruba.com
Approx. Number Employees: 15
Year Founded: 1970
Business Description:
Promoter of Tourism to Aruba
S.I.C.: 9721; 7389
N.A.I.C.S.: 928120; 561591
Advertising Expenditures: $5,000,000
Media: 2-4-6-13-23-24-31
Distr.: Intl.; Natl.
Budget Set: Oct. -Dec.
Personnel:
Theresita Chai *(Dir-Mktg)*
Advertising Agency:
M. Silver Associates Inc. - Public Relations
747 3rd Ave Fl 23
New York, NY 10017-2803
Tel.: (212) 754-6500
Fax: (212) 754-6711

ASIANA AIRLINES
(Sub. of Asiana Airlines, Inc.)
3530 Wilshire Blvd Ste 1700
Los Angeles, CA 90010-2341
Tel.: (213) 365-4500
Fax: (213) 380-1710
Toll Free: (800) 227-4262
E-mail: info@flyasiana.com
Web Site: www.flyasiana.com
Business Description:
Air Transportation
S.I.C.: 8741
N.A.I.C.S.: 561110
Import Export
Media: 2-6-9
Distr.: Natl.

ASSOCIATED GLOBAL SYSTEMS, INC.
3333 New Hyde Pk Rd
New Hyde Park, NY 11042-1205
Tel.: (516) 627-8910
Fax: (516) 627-6051
Toll Free: (800) 645-8300
Web Site: www.agsystems.com
E-Mail For Key Personnel:
President: norman.freeman@agsystems.com
Approx. Number Employees: 450
Year Founded: 1958
Business Description:
Freight Transportation, Logistics, Warehousing & Supply Chain Management
S.I.C.: 4731
N.A.I.C.S.: 488510
Import Export
Media: 2-4-7-17-26
Personnel:
Norman Freeman *(Pres)*
Jim Tucci *(Exec VP)*
Michael J. Occhicone *(Sr VP-Fin)*
Anthony Vella *(Dir-Natl Call Center)*
Brands & Products:
800SAMEDAY.COM
AGS
THE AGS INBOUND PROCUREMENT PROGRAM
ASSOCIATED OVERNIGHT
ASSOCIATED SAME DAY
C-ASPIN

ASTAR AIR CARGO INC
1200 Brickell Ave 16th F
Miami, FL 33131
Tel.: (305) 982-0501
Fax: (305) 416-9564
Web Site: www.astaraircargo.com
E-Mail For Key Personnel:
Public Relations: media.relations@astaraircargo.us
Sales Range: $300-349.9 Million
Approx. Number Employees: 500
Business Description:
Air Courier Services
S.I.C.: 4513; 4731
N.A.I.C.S.: 492110; 488510
Personnel:
John H. Dasburg *(Chm & CEO)*
Gary L. Hammes *(COO & Sr VP)*
Brands & Products:
ASTAR AIR CARGO
Advertising Agency:
VML, Inc.
250 Richards Rd
Kansas City, MO 64116-4279
Tel.: (816) 283-0700
Fax: (816) 283-0954
Toll Free: (800) 990-2468
— Amanda Kelly *(Acct Exec)*

@ROAD, INC.
(Sub. of Trimble Mobile Solutions, Inc.)
47071 Bayside Pkwy
Fremont, CA 94538
Tel.: (510) 668-1638
Fax: (510) 353-6021
Toll Free: (877) 2ATROAD
Web Site: www.trimble.com/mrm
Sales Range: $75-99.9 Million
Approx. Number Employees: 200
Year Founded: 1996
Business Description:
Mobile Resource Management Services
S.I.C.: 8742; 4812; 4899; 7379; 7389
N.A.I.C.S.: 541614; 517212; 517410; 541490; 541519
Advertising Expenditures: $1,100,000
Media: 5-7-10
Personnel:
Scott Harmon *(Sr VP-Strategy & Bus Dev)*
Prakash Iyer *(Sr VP-Products)*

ATLANTIC MARINE HOLDING COMPANY
(Holding of J.F. Lehman & Company)
8500 Heckscher Dr
Jacksonville, FL 32226-2434
Tel.: (904) 251-1790
Tel.: (904) 251-1545
Fax: (904) 251-3500
E-mail: jaxsales@atlanticmarine.com
Web Site: www.atlanticmarine.com
Sales Range: $300-349.9 Million
Approx. Number Employees: 1,000
Year Founded: 1964
Business Description:
Maintenance, Repair, Overhaul & Conversion Services for Commercial & Military Vessels
S.I.C.: 3731; 1389
N.A.I.C.S.: 336611; 213112
Import Export
Media: 2-4-10-20-26
Personnel:
Ed Fleming *(CEO)*
Craig Honour *(CIO)*
Bill Quinn *(VP-Fin)*
Kevin E. Wilson *(Mgr-Sls & Mktg)*

ATLANTIC SOUTHEAST AIRLINES INC.
(Sub. of Skywest Inc.)
A-Tech Center 990 Toffie Terrace
Atlanta, GA 30354-1356
Tel.: (404) 856-1000
Fax: (404) 856-1203
Web Site: www.flyasa.com
Sales Range: $1-4.9 Billion
Year Founded: 1979
Business Description:
Regional Air Carrier
S.I.C.: 4512
N.A.I.C.S.: 481111
Media: 1-5-7-8-9-18-19-20-23-24-26
Distr.: Direct to Consumer; Reg.
Personnel:
Bradford R. Holt *(Pres & COO)*
Brad Sheehan *(Dir-Safety)*

ATLAS VAN LINES, INC.
(Sub. of Atlas World Group, Inc.)
1212 Saint George Rd
Evansville, IN 47711-2364
Tel.: (812) 424-2222
Fax: (812) 421-7125
Toll Free: (800) 252-8885
E-mail: info@atlasvanlines.com
Web Site: www.atlasvanlines.com
Year Founded: 1948
Business Description:
Domestic & International Transportation of Household Goods & Sensitive Shipments
S.I.C.: 4214; 4731
N.A.I.C.S.: 484210; 488510
Import Export
Media: 2-10-13-18-26
Distr.: Intl.; Natl.
Budget Set: Oct.
Personnel:
Richard J Olson *(CFO & Sr VP)*
Dennie D. Lynn *(Sr VP-Transportation Svcs)*
Mark Spiehler *(Sr VP-Acct, Agent & Claims Svcs)*
Jeff Schimmel *(Sr Dir-Ops-Relocation Svcs Grp & Specialized Trans)*
Brenda McCandless *(Sr Dir-Claims Svcs)*
Kathy Godsey *(Mgr-Travel)*
Brands & Products:
ATLAS VAN LINES
Advertising Agency:
Daniel, Burton, Dean Advertising & Design, Inc.
225 Court St
Evansville, IN 47708
Tel.: (812) 426-0551
Fax: (812) 422-5386
Toll Free: (800) 687-4599

AUTO DRIVEAWAY CO.
11 E Adams Ste 1402
Chicago, IL 60603
Tel.: (312) 341-1900
Fax: (312) 341-9100
Toll Free: (800) 346-2277
Web Site: www.autodriveaway.com
Sales Range: $10-24.9 Million
Approx. Number Employees: 100
Year Founded: 1952
Business Description:
Delivery Services for Automobiles, Trucks & Other Vehicles
S.I.C.: 7389; 7549
N.A.I.C.S.: 561990; 488410
Export
Advertising Expenditures: $100,000
Media: 2-7-10-20-26
Distr.: Natl.
Budget Set: June
Personnel:
Rodney Ruth *(Pres & CEO)*
Scott Okun *(Dir-Sls & Mktg-Natl)*
Brands & Products:
AUTO DRIVEAWAY

AUTO EUROPE, LLC
39 Commercial St
Portland, ME 04101
Tel.: (207) 842-2000
Fax: (207) 842-2222
Toll Free: (888) 223-5555
E-mail: cfo@autoeurope.com
Web Site: www.autoeurope.com
E-Mail For Key Personnel:
President: president@autoeurope.com
Sales Director: sales@autoeurope.com
Sales Range: $1-4.9 Billion
Approx. Number Employees: 400
Year Founded: 1954
Business Description:
Automobile Rental Services
S.I.C.: 4729; 7514
N.A.I.C.S.: 561599; 532111
Media: 5-7-8-10-13-25-26
Personnel:
Imad Khalidi *(CEO)*
Steve Grant *(VP-IT)*

AUTOMOTIVE RESOURCES INTERNATIONAL (ARI)
(Sub. of Holman Automotive Group, Inc.)
4001 Leabenhall Rd
Mount Laurel, NJ 08054-1539
Tel.: (856) 778-1500
Fax: (856) 231-9106
E-mail: communications@arifleet.com
Web Site: www.arifleet.com
Sales Range: $100-124.9 Million
Approx. Number Employees: 1,200
Year Founded: 1948
Business Description:
Fleet Leasing & Management Services
S.I.C.: 7519; 7515
N.A.I.C.S.: 532120; 532112
Advertising Expenditures: $265,000
Multimedia: $50,000; Bus. Publs.: $100,000; Catalogs & Directories: $5,000; D.M. to Bus. Estab.: $50,000; Exhibits/Trade Shows: $30,000; Premiums, Novelties: $25,000; Yellow Page Adv.: $5,000
Distr.: Intl.
Budget Set: Jan.

Key to Media (For complete agency information see *The Advertising Red Books-Agencies* edition):
1. Bus. Publs. 2. Cable T.V. 3. Catalogs & Directories. 4. Co-op Adv. 5. Consumer Mags. 6. D.M. to Bus. Estab.7. D.M. to Consumers 8. Daily Newsp. 9. Exhibits/Trade Shows 10. Foreign 11. Infomercial 12. Internet Adv.13. Multimedia 14. Network Radio 15. Network T.V. 16. Newsp. Distr. Mags. 17. Other 18. Outdoor (Posters, Transit) 19. Point of Purchase20. Premiums, Novelties 21. Product Samples 22. Special Events Mktg. 23. Spot Radio 24. Spot T.V. 25. Weekly Newsp. 26. Yellow Page Adv.

Personnel:
Carl A. Ortell *(Exec VP-Fin)*
Brian Bates *(Sr VP-Fin)*
Gene Welsh *(Sr VP-Sls & Mktg)*

AVIS BUDGET GROUP, INC.

6 Sylvan Way
Parsippany, NJ 07054
Tel.: (973) 496-3500
Fax: (973) 496-7999
E-mail: investorrelations@avisbudget.com
Web Site: www.avisbudgetgroup.com
Approx. Rev.: $5,185,000,000
Approx. Number Employees: 14,000
Business Description:
Car & Truck Rental Services
S.I.C.: 9311; 6794; 7514; 7519
N.A.I.C.S.: 921130; 532111; 532120; 533110
Advertising Expenditures: $106,000,000
Media: 3-7-8-13-16-18-24-25-26
Personnel:
Ronald L. Nelson *(Chm & CEO)*
F. Robert Salerno *(Vice Chm)*
David B. Wyshner *(CFO & Sr Exec VP)*
Gerard Insall *(CIO & Sr VP)*
Mark J. Servodidio *(Chief Admin Officer & Exec VP)*
Izilda P. Martins *(Acting Chief Acctg Officer & VP)*
Larry D. De Shon *(Pres-EMEA)*
Thomas M. Gartland *(Pres-North America)*
Patric T. Siniscalchi *(Pres-Latin America & Asia Pacific)*
Michael K. Tucker *(Gen Counsel & Exec VP)*
Scott Salerno Deaver *(Exec VP-Strategy)*
Becky Alseth *(Sr VP-Mktg)*
Kaye Ceille *(Sr VP-Intl Sls & Mktg)*
Edward Gitlitz *(Sr VP-Fleet Svcs)*
Robert Lambert *(Sr VP-Global Acct Sls)*
Stephen J. Tyburski *(Sr Dir-Strategic Alliances)*
Elysa Strug *(Dir-Interactive Mktg)*
Brands & Products:
AVIS
AVIS BUDGET GROUP
BUDGET
BUDGET RENT A CAR
BUDGET TRUCK RENTAL
Advertising Agencies:
LM&O Advertising
2000 N 14th St 8th Fl
Arlington, VA 22201-2573
Tel.: (703) 875-2193
Fax: (703) 875-2199
Avis Canada
Avis Europe
Avis Rent a Car
Budget Japan
Budget Rent a Car

McCann Erickson/New York
622 3rd Ave
New York, NY 10017
Tel.: (646) 865-2000
Fax: (646) 487-9610

AWAY.COM, INC.

(Sub. of Orbitz Worldwide, Inc.)
702 H St Ste 200
Washington, DC 20001-4549
Tel.: (202) 654-8000
Fax: (202) 654-8081
Web Site: www.away.com
Sales Range: $10-24.9 Million
Approx. Number Employees: 45
Business Description:
Online Travel Services
S.I.C.: 4724
N.A.I.C.S.: 561510
Media: 13
Personnel:
Sean Green *(Pres)*
Scott Parmelee *(Publr & VP)*
Eileen Rhine *(Mgr-Production)*
Brands & Products:
AWAY.COM
GORP.COM
OUTSIDEONLINE.COM

BAHAMAS TOURISM CENTER

(Sub. of The Bahamas Ministry of Tourism)
1200 S Pine Is Rd Ste 750
Plantation, FL 33324
Tel.: (954) 236-9292
Fax: (954) 236-9282
Toll Free: (800) BAHAMAS
Toll Free: (888) 627-7281
E-mail: bmotfl@bahamas.com
Web Site: www.bahamas.com
Approx. Number Employees: 60
Year Founded: 1979
Business Description:
Bahamas Tourism Promoter
S.I.C.: 4729; 4725
N.A.I.C.S.: 561599; 561520
Advertising Expenditures: $15,000,000
Media: 2-3-5-6-9-10-18-19-20-23-24-31
Distr.: Intl.; Natl.
Budget Set: July
Personnel:
Tom Crockett *(CMO)*
Anita Patty *(Gen Mgr-Comm)*

BALTIMORE WASHINGTON THURGOOD MARSHALL INTERNATIONAL AIRPORT

(d/b/a BWI Airport/Maryland Aviation Administration)
Third Fl Terminal Bldg PO Box 8766
Baltimore, MD 21240-0766
Tel.: (410) 859-7111
Tel.: (410) 859-7027 (Comm)
Web Site: www.bwiairport.com
Approx. Number Employees: 500
Business Description:
Airport Operations
S.I.C.: 4581
N.A.I.C.S.: 488119
Personnel:
Paul J. Wiedefeld *(Exec Dir)*
Jonathan O. Dean *(Mgr-Comm)*
Advertising Agency:
Azzam Jordan
305 Washington Ave Ste 305
Baltimore, MD 21204
Tel.: (410) 825-1800
Fax: (410) 825-3997

BARBADOS TOURISM AUTHORITY

820 2nd Ave 5th Fl
New York, NY 10017-4709
Tel.: (212) 986-6516
Fax: (212) 573-9850
Toll Free: (800) 221-9831
E-mail: btany@barbados.org
Web Site: www.visitbarbados.org
Sales Range: $100-124.9 Million
Approx. Number Employees: 100
Year Founded: 1967
Business Description:
Barbados Travel Promoter
S.I.C.: 4724; 4725
N.A.I.C.S.: 561510; 561520
Advertising Expenditures: $2,000,000
Media: 1-6-9-19-22-23-25-31
Distr.: Intl.; Natl.
Personnel:
Ralph Taylor *(Chm)*
David Rice *(Pres & CEO)*
Chris Trew *(Mng Dir)*
Campbell Rudder *(VP-Mktg)*
Wayne Noseworthy *(Product Dir)*
Michele Rauzon *(Natl Sls Dir)*
Jill Wykes *(Dir-Sls)*
Carlton Cumberbatch *(Office Mgr)*
Vickie Ioannou-Theophilou *(Natl Sls Mgr)*
Advertising Agency:
SOJE/Lonsdale Communications Inc./Y&R
Hastings House Balmoral Gap
Christchurch, BB1 4034, Barbados
Tel.: (246) 430 2650
Fax: (246) 429 3077

BDP INTERNATIONAL INC.

510 Walnut St Fl 2A
Philadelphia, PA 19106-3621
Tel.: (215) 629-8900
Fax: (215) 629-8995
Web Site: www.bdpinternational.com
E-Mail For Key Personnel:
President: rbolte@bdpnet.com
Sales Range: $75-99.9 Million
Approx. Number Employees: 900
Year Founded: 1972
Business Description:
Freight Transportation Arrangement Services
S.I.C.: 4731
N.A.I.C.S.: 488510
Import Export
Personnel:
Richard Bolte, Jr. *(Pres & CEO)*
Yone Dewberry *(Mng Dir)*
Frank P. Osusky *(CFO)*
John Bolte *(COO)*
Arnie F. Bornstein *(Exec Dir-Mktg & Corp Comm)*
Adrianne Graddy *(Dir-Compliance Solutions)*
Rose Pace *(Dir-Pur & Facilities)*
Bill Skroskis *(Dir-Sls)*
Brands & Products:
BDP
BDP XPEDION
CENTRX
CENTRX A BDP KNOWLEDGE VENTURE
Advertising Agency:
Stiegler, Wells, Brunswick & Roth, Inc.
(d/b/a SWB&R)
3865 Adler Pl
Bethlehem, PA 18017-9000
Tel.: (610) 866-0611
Fax: (610) 866-8650

BLUE STAR JETS, INC.

805 3rd Ave Fl 16
New York, NY 10022
Tel.: (212) 446-9037
Fax: (212) 446-9061
Toll Free: (866) JET-TIME
E-mail: info@bluestarjets.com
Web Site: www.bluestarjets.com
Sales Range: $200-249.9 Million
Approx. Number Employees: 25
Business Description:
Private Jet Services
S.I.C.: 7389
N.A.I.C.S.: 541990
Media: 6
Personnel:
Todd Rome *(Pres)*
Richard Sitomer *(CEO)*
Ryan Auer *(Mgr-Mktg)*
Brands & Products:
ANY JET. ANY TIME. ANY PLACE.
BLUESTARJETS

BOB TRAILERS, INC.

5475 Gage St
Boise, ID 83706-1547
Tel.: (208) 375-5171
Fax: (208) 375-5172
Toll Free: (800) 893-2447
Web Site: www.bobgear.com
Business Description:
Bicycle Cargo Trailers & Jogging Strollers
S.I.C.: 3792
N.A.I.C.S.: 336214
Media: 6-7
Personnel:
Roger Malinowski *(Pres)*
Advertising Agency:
Noot Group
960 Broadway Ste 530
Boise, ID 83706
Tel.: (208) 424-1100

BRINK'S U.S.

(Div. of Brink's, Incorporated)
555 Dividend Dr
Coppell, TX 75019
Tel.: (469) 549-6000
Fax: (469) 549-6800
Toll Free: (800) 962-3515
E-mail: brinksus@brinksinc.com
Web Site: www.us.brinksinc.com
Sales Range: $1-4.9 Billion
Approx. Number Employees: 500
Business Description:
Security Guard & Armored Car Services
S.I.C.: 7381
N.A.I.C.S.: 561612; 561613
Advertising Expenditures: $100,000
Bus. Publs.: $100,000
Distr.: Natl.
Budget Set: Oct.-Nov.
Brands & Products:
COMPUSAFE

BRITISH AIRWAYS

(Sub. of British Airways PLC)
7520 Astoria Blvd Ste 200
East Elmhurst, NY 11370-1131
Tel.: (347) 418-4000
Fax: (718) 425-5039
Toll Free: (800) AIRWAYS
Web Site: www.baworldcargo.com
Approx. Number Employees: 1,800
Year Founded: 1983
Business Description:
Airline Services
S.I.C.: 4512
N.A.I.C.S.: 481111
Export

Key to Media (For complete agency information see *The Advertising Red Books-Agencies* edition):
1. Bus. Publs. 2. Cable T.V. 3. Catalogs & Directories. 4. Co-op Adv. 5. Consumer Mags. 6. D.M. to Bus. Estab.7. D.M. to Consumers 8. Daily Newsp. 9. Exhibits/Trade Shows 10. Foreign 11. Infomercial 12. Internet Adv.13. Multimedia 14. Network Radio 15. Network T.V. 16. Newsp. Distr. Mags. 17. Other 18. Outdoor (Posters, Transit) 19. Point of Purchase20. Premiums, Novelties 21. Product Samples 22. Special Events Mktg. 23. Spot Radio 24. Spot T.V. 25. Weekly Newsp. 26. Yellow Page Adv.

British Airways — (Continued)

Media: 1-2-3-6-7-8-9-10-11-13-14-15-18-19-20-26
Distr.: Direct to Customer; Intl.; Natl.
Budget Set: Mar.
Personnel:
Michael Chowdry *(Chm, Pres & CEO)*
Simon Talling-Smith *(Exec VP)*
Joe Laughlin *(VP-Sls-OpenSkies Div-North America)*
Peter Schinasi *(Dir-Relationship Mktg)*
Advertising Agencies:
Agnes Huff Communications Group, LLC.
Howard Hughes Ctr 6601 Ctr Dr W Ste 100
Los Angeles, CA 90045
Tel.: (310) 641-2525
Fax: (310) 641-2544

Porter Novelli
(Sub. of Omnicom Group, Inc.)
75 Varick St 6th Fl
New York, NY 10013
Tel.: (212) 601-8000
Fax: (212) 601-8101

BRITISH COLUMBIA FERRY SERVICES INC

1112 Fort Street
Victoria, BC V8V 4V2, Canada
Tel.: (250) 381-1401
Tel.: (250) 978-1267 (Media Rels)
Fax: (250) 978-1119
Toll Free: (888) 223-3779
Web Site: www.bcferries.com
Approx. Rev.: $746,086,980
Approx. Number Employees: 4,500
Business Description:
Ferry Services
S.I.C.: 4482; 4449
N.A.I.C.S.: 483212; 483211
Personnel:
Donald P. Hayes *(Chm)*
David L. Hahn *(Pres & CEO)*
Rob Clark *(CFO & Exec VP)*
Mike Corrigan *(COO & Exec VP)*
William R. Cottick *(Gen Counsel & Exec VP-Corp Affairs)*
Glen N. Schwartz *(Exec VP-HR & Corp Dev)*
Trafford Taylor *(Exec VP-New Vessel Construction & Industry Affairs)*
Advertising Agency:
Copeland Communications Ltd.
536 Broughton St 3rd Fl
Victoria, BC V8W 1C6, Canada
Tel.: (250) 381-4494
Fax: (250) 381-7714

BUDD VAN LINES INC.

(d/b/a Budd Van Lines)
24 Schoolhouse Rd
Somerset, NJ 08873
Tel.: (732) 627-0600
Fax: (732) 627-0018
E-mail: arodriguez@buddvanlines.com
Web Site: www.buddvanlines.com
Sales Range: $25-49.9 Million
Approx. Number Employees: 150
Business Description:
Household Goods Transport
S.I.C.: 4214
N.A.I.C.S.: 484210
Personnel:
David W. Budd, Sr. *(CEO)*
William Soltesz *(CFO & VP)*
Advertising Agency:
Kalmar Responsive Ad/Marketing Corp.
1 Blue Hill Plz PO Box 1501
Pearl River, NY 10965
Tel.: (845) 201-8035
Fax: (845) 201-8036

BUDGET RENT A CAR SYSTEM, INC.

(Sub. of Avis Budget Group, Inc.)
6 Sylvan Way
Parsippany, NJ 07054
Tel.: (800) 621-2844
Fax: (973) 496-7999
Toll Free: (800) GO-BUDGET
Web Site: www.budget.com
Sales Range: $1-4.9 Billion
Approx. Number Employees: 7,000
Year Founded: 1958
Business Description:
Car & Truck Rental Services
S.I.C.: 7514; 7519
N.A.I.C.S.: 532111; 532120
Media: 2-3-6-7-8-13-15-18-24-26
Personnel:
Ronald L. Nelson *(Chm & CEO)*
David B. Wyshner *(CFO)*
Mark J. Servodidio *(Chief Admin Officer & Exec VP)*
Scott Deaver *(Exec VP-Strategy)*
Patric Siniscalchi *(Exec VP-Intl Ops)*
Becky Alseth *(Sr VP-Mktg)*
Robert Bouta *(Sr VP-Properties)*
Robert Lambert *(Sr VP-Corp Sls)*

BUFFALO NIAGARA CONVENTION & VISITORS BUREAU, INC.

617 Main St Ste 200
Buffalo, NY 14203-1400
Tel.: (716) 852-0511
Fax: (716) 852-0131
Toll Free: (800) BUFFALO
Toll Free: (888) 228-3369
E-mail: info@buffalocvb.org
Web Site: www.buffaloniagara.com
Approx. Number Employees: 25
Business Description:
Travel & Tourism Promoter
S.I.C.: 4724; 8611; 9199
N.A.I.C.S.: 561510; 813910; 921190
Advertising Expenditures: $500,000
Media: 4-13-20-22
Personnel:
David Marzo *(CFO)*
Michael Even *(VP-Sls)*
Edward J. Healy *(VP-Mktg)*
Linda D'Agostino *(Dir-Sls & Govt Rels)*
Charles Giglia *(Dir-Sports Sls)*
Leah Mueller *(Dir-Tourism Sls)*
Judy Smith *(Dir-Admin)*
Matthew Steinberg *(Dir-Creative Svcs)*
Kathy Benzel *(Mgr-IT & Online Content)*
Michele Butlak *(Mgr-Acctg & Benefits)*
Karen Cox *(Mgr-Convention Sls & Svcs)*
Denise Drews *(Mgr-Visitor Center)*
Dionne Williamson *(Mgr-Multicultural Sls)*
Advertising Agency:
Travers Collins & Company
726 Exchange St Ste 500
Buffalo, NY 14210-1495
Tel.: (716) 842-2222
Fax: (716) 842-6424

BULLDOG MOVERS, INC.

2282 Defoor Sales Rd
Atlanta, GA 30318
Tel.: (770) 333-8100
Fax: (678) 623-9977
E-mail: info@bulldogmovers.net
Web Site: www.bulldogmovers.net
Sales Range: $25-49.9 Million
Approx. Number Employees: 27
Year Founded: 1999
Business Description:
Local Trucking with Storage
S.I.C.: 4214
N.A.I.C.S.: 484210
Import Export
Media: 2-4-8-10-22
Personnel:
Erik Christensen *(Pres)*

BURLINGTON NORTHERN SANTA FE, LLC

(Holding of Berkshire Hathaway Inc.)
2650 Lou Menk Dr
Fort Worth, TX 76131-2830
Tel.: (817) 352-1000
Fax: (817) 352-7171
Toll Free: (800) 289-2673
E-mail: inquires@bnsf.com
Web Site: www.bnsf.com
Approx. Rev.: $15,059,000,000
Approx. Number Employees: 38,000
Year Founded: 1995
Business Description:
Holding Company; Coal, Grain, Intermodal Containers, Trailers & Various Industrial, Consumer, Automotive & Forest Products Rail Transportation Services
S.I.C.: 4011; 4013; 6719
N.A.I.C.S.: 482111; 488210; 551112
Distr.: Intl.; Natl.
Personnel:
Matthew K. Rose *(Chm & CEO)*
Thomas N. Hund *(CFO & Exec VP)*
Carl R. Ice *(COO & Exec VP)*
Jo-anne M. Olsovsky *(CIO & VP-Tech Svcs)*
John P. Lanigan, Jr. *(CMO & Exec VP)*
Steve Forsberg *(Gen Dir-Pub Affairs-CO, IA, IL, KS, KY, MN, MO, NE, WI)*
John Risolvato *(Gen Dir-Mktg-Sugar, Sweeteners, Oils & Feeds)*
Barbara Haerlting *(Gen Dir-Fertilizers & Oil Seeds)*
Brant Ring *(Gen Dir-Ops-Agricultural)*
Al Vergin *(Gen Dir-Agricultural Products-Wheat & Flour Mktg)*
James H. Gallegos *(VP & Corp Gen Counsel)*
Charles W. Shewmake *(Gen Counsel & VP)*
Richard E. Weicher *(Gen Counsel-Regulatory & VP)*
C. Alec Vincent *(Treas & Asst VP-Fin)*
Roger Nober *(Sec & Exec VP-Law)*
Gregory C. Fox *(Exec VP-Ops)*
Stevan B. Bobb *(Grp VP-Coal Bus Unit)*
Stephen G. Branscum *(Grp VP-Consumer Products)*
David L. Garin *(Grp VP-Indus Products)*
Kevin Kaufman *(Grp VP-Agricultural Products)*
Robert W. Lease *(Reg VP-Ops)*
Sanford C. Sexhus *(Reg VP-Ops)*
Jeffrey B. Wright *(Reg VP-Ops)*
Paul B. Anderson *(VP-Mktg Support)*
Frederick G. Draper *(VP-Bus Unit Ops & Support)*
George T. Duggan *(VP-Domestic Intermodal Mktg)*
Kathryn M. Farmer *(VP-Indus Products Sls)*
David L. Freeman *(VP-Engrg)*
Linda Longo-Kazanova *(VP-HR & Medical)*
Fred Malesa *(VP-Intl Intermodal Mktg)*
Chris A. Roberts *(VP-Mechanical & Value Engrg)*
Mark A. Schulze *(VP-Safety, Trng & Ops Support)*
Sami M. Shalah *(VP-Coal Mktg)*
Denis Smith *(VP-Indus Products Mktg)*
Dean H. Wise *(VP-Network Strategy)*
Zak A. Andersen *(Asst VP-Govt Affairs)*
Andrew K. Johnsen *(Asst VP-Govt Affairs)*
John Miller *(Asst VP-Agricultural Products Mktg)*
Joseph Faust *(Reg Dir-Pub Affairs-AL, AR, LA MS, NM, OK, TN, TX)*
Lena Kent *(Reg Dir-Pub Affairs-AZ, CA, NV, UT)*
Gus Melonas *(Reg Dir-Pub Affairs-ID, MT, ND, OR, SD, WA, WY, Canada)*
Patricia Collins *(Dir-Feedgrains)*
Stephen Griego *(Dir-Northern Corridor)*
Greg Guthrie *(Dir-Customer Svc-Agricultural Products)*
Suann Lundsberg *(Dir-Media Relations)*
Larry Rankin *(Dir-Fertilizers)*
Mark Summers *(Dir-Wheat)*
Victor Valdes *(Dir-Mexico Bus Unit)*
Todd Whitmore *(Dir-Mktg-Bulk Foods)*
Mike Bornus *(Sr Mgr-Homeland Security)*
Phil Johnson *(Sr Mgr-Homeland Security)*
Miles Beard *(Mgr-Fertilizer)*
Dennis Bell *(Mgr-Wheat)*
Roger Halper *(Mgr-Corn Sweeteners)*
Sean Hower *(Mgr-Barley, Malt, Oats & Wheat Flour)*
Don Karls *(Mgr-Market Support-MT)*
Mignon Lambley *(Mgr-Market Support-Southwest Reg)*
Jock Luckett *(Mgr-Equipment Utilization & Supply Chain)*
Bryan Madden *(Mgr-Homeland Security)*
Roger Nash *(Mgr-Comml Dev-Fertilizer)*
Jim Rogers *(Mgr-Media Relations-Intermodal Transportation Issues)*
Ted Rowland *(Mgr-Bus Dev-Agricultural Products)*
Brands & Products:
BNSF
Advertising Agency:
Sullivan Perkins
2811 McKinney Ave Ste 320
Dallas, TX 75204-8566
Tel.: (214) 922-9080
Fax: (214) 922-0044

Key to Media (For complete agency information see *The Advertising Red Books-Agencies* edition):
1. Bus. Publs. 2. Cable T.V. 3. Catalogs & Directories. 4. Co-op Adv. 5. Consumer Mags. 6. D.M. to Bus. Estab.7. D.M. to Consumers 8. Daily Newsp. 9. Exhibits/Trade Shows 10. Foreign 11. Infomercial 12. Internet Adv.13. Multimedia 14. Network Radio 15. Network T.V. 16. Newsp. Distr. Mags. 17. Other 18. Outdoor (Posters, Transit) 19. Point of Purchase20. Premiums, Novelties 21. Product Samples 22. Special Events Mktg. 23. Spot Radio 24. Spot T.V. 25. Weekly Newsp. 26. Yellow Page Adv.

CANADIAN NATIONAL RAILWAY COMPANY
935 de La Gauchetiere Street West
Montreal, QC H3B 2M9, Canada
Tel.: (514) 399-5966
Tel.: (514) 399-5430
Tel.: (514) 399-7091
Fax: (514) 399-5537
Fax: (514) 399-5985
Toll Free: (888) 888-5909
Telex: 55 61497
E-mail: contact@cn.ca
Web Site: www.cn.ca
Approx. Rev.: $8,453,149,540
Approx. Number Employees: 21,501
Year Founded: 1919
Business Description:
Freight & Railway Transportation Services
S.I.C.: 4011; 4731
N.A.I.C.S.: 482111; 488510
Import Export
Media: 1-2-7-9-11-20-22
Distr.: Intl.
Budget Set: Sept.
Personnel:
David G. A. McLean *(Chm)*
Claude Mongeau *(Pres & CEO)*
Anita Ernesaks *(VP & Global Mng Dir-CN WorldWide)*
Luc Jobin *(CFO & Exec VP)*
Keith E. Creel *(COO & Exec VP)*
James Bright *(CIO & VP-IT)*
Jean-Jacques Ruest *(CMO & Exec VP)*
Sean Finn *(Chief Legal Officer & Exec VP-Corp Svcs)*
Timothy J. Koerner *(Chief Security Officer & VP)*
Paul C. Miller *(Chief Safety & Sustainability Officer)*
Russell J. Hiscock *(Pres/CEO-Investments Div)*
Mike Cory *(Sr VP-Western Reg)*
Sameh Fahmy *(Sr VP-Engrg, Mechanical & Suppy Mgmt)*
Jeff Liepelt *(Sr VP-Eastern Reg)*
Gordon T. Trafton *(Sr VP-Strategic Acq & Integration)*
James Vena *(Sr VP-Southern Reg)*
Serge Pharand *(VP & Comptroller)*
David W. Ferryman *(VP-Sys Engrg)*
Francois C. Hebert *(VP-Network Strategies)*
Ghislain Houle *(VP-Fin Plng)*
Doug MacDonald *(VP-Corp Mktg)*
Kimberly A. Madigan *(VP-HR)*
Mark Hallman *(Dir-Comm & Public Affairs)*
Louie Smith *(Mgr-Bus Dev & Real Estate)*
Brands & Products:
AQUATRAIN
CN
NORTH AMERICA'S RAILROAD
PIPELINEONRAIL
SMARTYARD
SPEED GATE
VELOCITY POWERED BY CN

CARAVAN TOURS, INC.
401 N Michigan Ave
Chicago, IL 60611-4255
Tel.: (312) 321-9800
Fax: (312) 321-9845
Toll Free: (800) CARAVAN
E-mail: info@caravan.com
Web Site: www.caravan.com
Approx. Number Employees: 50
Year Founded: 1952
Business Description:
Tour Operator
S.I.C.: 4725; 4724
N.A.I.C.S.: 561520; 561510
Advertising Expenditures: $300,000
Media: 2-4-6-9-13
Distr.: Natl.
Budget Set: Sept.
Personnel:
T. Dennis Duffy *(Pres)*
Brendan Duffy *(Dir-Mktg & Sls)*
Brands & Products:
CARAVAN

CAREY INTERNATIONAL, INC.
(Joint Venture of Ford Motor Company, Avis Budget Group, Inc. & Chartwell Investments, LLP)
4530 Wisconsin Ave NW
Washington, DC 20016
Tel.: (202) 895-1200
Fax: (202) 895-1281
Toll Free: (800) 336-1355
Toll Free: (800) 336-4646
Web Site: www.carey.com
Approx. Rev.: $250,000,000
Approx. Number Employees: 1,533
Year Founded: 1921
Business Description:
Worldwide Chauffeur Services; Owned by Chartwell Investments, LLP, Ford Motor Company & Avis Budget Group, Inc.
S.I.C.: 4119
N.A.I.C.S.: 485320
Export
Advertising Expenditures: $19,000,000
Media: 3-13-15-26
Personnel:
Gary L. Kessler *(Pres & CEO)*
Mitchell J. Lahr *(CFO & Exec VP)*
Rae D. Fawcett *(Sr VP-Organizational Dev & Human Capital)*
Sally A. Snead *(Sr VP-Ops)*
Philip J. Gilpin *(Reg VP-Opers)*
Brands & Products:
CAREY
DRIVING SUCCESS

CARLSON WAGONLIT TRAVEL
(Joint Venture of Carlson Companies Inc.)
701 Carlson Pkwy
Minnetonka, MN 55305
Tel.: (763) 212-2197
Fax: (763) 212-2409
E-mail: cwtwebmaster@carlsonwagonlit.com
Web Site: www.carlsonwagonlit.com
Approx. Sls.: $25,500,000,000
Approx. Number Employees: 22,000
Year Founded: 1888
Business Description:
Global Corporate Travel Services; Owned 55% by Carlson Companies, Inc. & 45% by JPMorgan Chase & Co.
S.I.C.: 4729; 4724; 7011; 8742
N.A.I.C.S.: 561599; 541611; 561510; 721199
Media: 3-5-6-8-9-18-23-24-26
Distr.: Natl.
Budget Set: Sept.
Personnel:
Douglas Anderson *(Pres & CEO)*
Pierre Milet *(Grp CFO & Exec VP)*
Jack O'Neill *(Pres-CWT North America)*
Marc Karako *(Exec VP)*
Berthold Trenkel *(Exec VP-Traveler & Transaction Svcs)*
Philippe Vinay *(Exec VP-HR)*
Leslie Conzelman *(Sr VP-Multi-Natl Clients)*
Sam DeFranco *(Sr VP-U S Natl Clients)*
David Moran *(Sr VP-Global Program Svcs-North America)*
Ron Wagner *(Sr VP-Acct Mgmt-US West)*
Barb Barnard *(VP-Corp Sls & Mktg)*
Bindu Bhatia *(VP-Global Sls-North America)*
Nick DeNicola *(VP-HR)*
Brands & Products:
CARLSON WAGONLIT TRAVEL

CARNIVAL CORPORATION
Carnival Pl 3655 NW 87th Ave PO Box 1347
Miami, FL 33178
Tel.: (305) 599-2600
Fax: (305) 406-4700
Toll Free: (800) CARNIVAL
E-mail: media@carnival.com
Web Site: www.carnivalcorp.com
E-Mail For Key Personnel:
Public Relations: pr@carnival.com
Approx. Rev.: $14,469,000,000
Approx. Number Employees: 10,200
Year Founded: 1993
Business Description:
Holding Company; Cruise Line Owner & Operator
S.I.C.: 6719; 4481; 4499; 7999
N.A.I.C.S.: 551112; 483112; 487210; 488390
Advertising Expenditures: $455,000,000
Media: 5-6-8-9-13-16-20-22-23-24-25
Personnel:
Micky M. Arison *(Chm & CEO)*
Howard S. Frank *(Vice Chm & COO)*
David Bernstein *(CFO & Sr VP)*
Larry Freedman *(Chief Acctg Officer, VP & Controller)*
Alan B. Buckelew *(Pres/CEO-Princess Cruises)*
Gerald R. Cahill *(Pres/CEO-Carnival Cruises)*
Michael Thamm *(Pres-Aida Cruises)*
Arnaldo Perez *(Gen Counsel, Sec & Sr VP)*
Richard D. Ames *(Sr VP-Shared Svcs)*
Robert Montgomery *(Sr VP-Global HR)*
Tim Gallagher *(VP-Pub Rel)*
Bill Harber *(Sr Dir-Mktg)*
John Heald *(Sr Dir-Cruises)*
Jennifer de la Cruz *(Dir-Pub Rel)*
Brands & Products:
AIDA
CARNIVAL
CARNIVAL CRUISE LINES
COSTA CRUISES
CUNARD LINE
HOLLAND AMERICA
IBERO CRUISES
OCEAN VILLAGE
P&O CRUISES
P&O CRUISES AUSTRALIA
PRINCESS CRUISE LINE
THE YACHTS OF SEABOURN
Advertising Agencies:
DDB Miami
770 S Dixie Hwy
Coral Gables, FL 33146
Tel.: (305) 529-4300
Fax: (305) 662-3166

The Glenn Group
50 Washington St
Reno, NV 89503-5603
Tel.: (775) 686-7777
Fax: (775) 686-7750

CARNIVAL CRUISE LINES
(Sub. of Carnival plc)
Carnival Pl 3655 NW 87th Ave
Miami, FL 33178-2428
Tel.: (305) 599-2600
Fax: (305) 406-8630
Toll Free: (800) CARNIVAL
Web Site: www.carnival.com
E-Mail For Key Personnel:
Marketing Director: carnholt@carnival.com
Sales Range: $1-4.9 Billion
Approx. Number Employees: 20,000
Year Founded: 1972
Business Description:
Cruise Line Services
S.I.C.: 4481; 4725
N.A.I.C.S.: 483112; 561520
Media: 3-4-5-6-7-8-9-10-11-13-15-16-18-19-22-23-24-25
Personnel:
Gerald R. Cahill *(Chief Fin & Acctg Officer)*
Dwayne Warner *(CIO)*
Ruben Rodriguez *(Exec VP-Ship Ops)*
Gus Antorcha *(Sr VP-Guest Commerce)*
Jim Berra *(Sr VP-Mktg)*
Roberta Jacoby *(Sr VP-Hotel Ops)*
Mark Tamis *(Sr VP-Guest Ops)*
Lynn C. Torrent *(Sr VP-Sls & Guest Svcs)*
Brenda Yester *(Sr VP-Revenue Mgmt)*
Christine Arnholt *(VP-Onboard Mktg)*
John Meszaros *(VP-Supply Chain Mgmt)*
Joni L. Rein *(VP-Worldwide Sls)*
Lania Rittenhouse *(VP-Product Dev)*
Karla Jimenez *(Supvr-Adv & Collateral)*
Brands & Products:
CAMP CARNIVAL
CARNIVAL
THE FUN SHIPS
TODAY'S CARNIVAL
TOTAL CHOICE DINING
VACATION GUARANTEE
Advertising Agency:
Arnold Worldwide
101 Huntington Ave
Boston, MA 02199-7603
Tel.: (617) 587-8000
Fax: (617) 587-8004
Carnival Cruise Lines
— Roger Baldacci *(Exec VP & Dir-Creative)*

CELADON GROUP, INC.
9503 E 33rd St
Indianapolis, IN 46235-4207
Tel.: (317) 972-7000
Fax: (317) 890-8099
Toll Free: (800) CELADON
E-mail: media@celadontrucking.com

Key to Media (For complete agency information see *The Advertising Red Books-Agencies* edition):
1. Bus. Publs. 2. Cable T.V. 3. Catalogs & Directories. 4. Co-op Adv. 5. Consumer Mags. 6. D.M. to Bus. Estab.7. D.M. to Consumers
8. Daily Newsp. 9. Exhibits/Trade Shows 10. Foreign 11. Infomercial 12. Internet Adv.13. Multimedia 14. Network Radio
15. Network T.V. 16. Newsp. Distr. Mags. 17. Other 18. Outdoor (Posters, Transit) 19. Point of Purchase20. Premiums, Novelties
21. Product Samples 22. Special Events Mktg. 23. Spot Radio 24. Spot T.V. 25. Weekly Newsp. 26. Yellow Page Adv.

Celadon Group, Inc. — (Continued)

Web Site: www.celadontrucking.com
Approx. Rev.: $556,694,000
Approx. Number Employees: 3,478
Year Founded: 1985
Business Description:
Long-Haul, Flatbed & Full-Truckload Services
S.I.C.: 4213; 4212
N.A.I.C.S.: 484121; 484110
Advertising Expenditures: $1,200,000
Media: 2
Personnel:
Stephen Russell *(Founder, Chm & CEO)*
Paul A. Will *(Vice Chm, Pres & COO)*
William E. Meek *(CFO, Treas & VP)*
Bart Middleton *(Chief Acctg Officer & VP)*
Jonathan Russell *(Pres-Celadon Logistics)*
Sara Glore *(VP-HR-Celadon Trucking Svcs)*

CENTRAL FLORIDA REGIONAL TRANSPORT AUTHORITY

(d/b/a LYNX)
455 N Garland Ave
Orlando, FL 32801
Tel.: (407) 841-2279
Web Site: www.golynx.com
Approx. Number Employees: 940
Year Founded: 1972
Business Description:
Bus Line Operations
S.I.C.: 4111
N.A.I.C.S.: 485113
Media: 6
Personnel:
Carlton Henley *(Chm)*
Brandon Arrington *(Vice Chm)*
Linda Watson *(CEO)*
Matt Friedman *(Mgr-Media Rels)*
Blanche Sherman *(Mgr-Fin)*

CHEAPTICKETS, INC.

(Sub. of Orbitz Worldwide, Inc.)
500 W Madison St Ste 1000
Chicago, IL 60661
Tel.: (312) 260-8100
Tel.: (312) 260-8304 (Pub Rels)
Fax: (312) 260-8101
Web Site: www.cheaptickets.com
E-Mail For Key Personnel:
Marketing Director: marketing@cheaptickets.com
Public Relations: marita.hudson@cheaptickets.com
Sales Range: $800-899.9 Million
Approx. Number Employees: 1,050
Year Founded: 1986
Business Description:
Discount Travel Agent & Airline Ticket Whslr
S.I.C.: 4729; 4724
N.A.I.C.S.: 561599; 561510
Media: 3-5-6-8-13-14-15-18
Personnel:
Randy Wagner *(CMO)*
Tom Russell *(VP-Brand Mktg)*
Brands & Products:
CHEAPTICKETS.COM

CHINA AIRLINES LTD.

(Branch of China Airlines Ltd.)
200 Continental Blvd
El Segundo, CA 90245
Tel.: (310) 322-2888
Fax: (310) 322-3888
Toll Free: (800) 227-5118
Web Site: www.china-airlines.com/en/about/about-3-3.htm
Approx. Number Employees: 75
Year Founded: 1959
Business Description:
Airline Service
S.I.C.: 4512
N.A.I.C.S.: 481112
Advertising Expenditures: $1,166,000
Media: 2-3-6-7-8-9-11-16-18-23-24-25-26
Distr.: Intl.; Natl.
Budget Set: Nov.

CIRCOR AEROSPACE

(Formerly STL Enterprises, Inc.)
(Sub. of CIRCOR Aerospace, Inc.)
15148 Bledsoe St
Sylmar, CA 91342-2709
Tel.: (818) 362-5665
Fax: (818) 367-8936
Web Site: www.circoraerospace.com
Approx. Number Employees: 250
Year Founded: 1973
Business Description:
Precision Machining Mfr.
S.I.C.: 3542; 3728
N.A.I.C.S.: 333513; 336413
Import Export
Media: 2-4-7-10

CITATIONAIR

(Sub. of Cessna Aircraft Company)
Greenwich American Ctr 5 American Ln
Greenwich, CT 06831
Tel.: (203) 542-3000
Fax: (203) 861-2707
Toll Free: (800) 340-7767
E-mail: info@citationair.com
Web Site: www.citationshares.com
Sales Range: $250-299.9 Million
Approx. Number Employees: 360
Year Founded: 2000
Business Description:
Private Jet Airplane Fractional Ownership Sales & Fleet Management Services
S.I.C.: 5088; 4522; 4581
N.A.I.C.S.: 423860; 481211; 481219; 488190
Media: 2-6
Personnel:
Steven F. O'Neill *(CEO)*
J. Matthew Singleton *(CFO)*
William J. Schultz *(COO & Exec VP)*
William Hall *(CIO)*
Phil Marraccini *(Chief Compliance Officer, Gen Counsel & Sr VP)*
William B. Harford *(Chief Revenue Officer & Sr VP)*
Karena E. Kefalas *(Sr VP-HR)*
Jean Kelly *(Sr VP-Product Delivery)*
John P. O'Neill *(Sr VP-Operational Plng)*
Sean C. Toth *(Sr VP-Fleet Mgmt)*
John D. Witzig *(Sr VP-Flight Ops)*
Brands & Products:
CITATIONAIR
Advertising Agency:
Hornall Anderson
Ste 1300 710 2nd Ave
Seattle, WA 98104-1712
Tel.: (206) 467-5800
Fax: (206) 467-6411

CLASSIC VACATIONS, LLC

(Sub. of Expedia, Inc.)
5893 Rue Ferrari
San Jose, CA 95138
Tel.: (408) 287-4550
Fax: (800) 331-3949
Toll Free: (800) 635-1333
E-mail: info@classicvacations.com
Web Site: www.classicvacations.com
Sales Range: $125-149.9 Million
Approx. Number Employees: 200
Year Founded: 1972
Business Description:
Travel Services
S.I.C.: 4725; 4724
N.A.I.C.S.: 561520; 561510
Media: 2-4-5-6-7-8-9-10-13-16-18-19-20-25
Distr.: Natl.
Personnel:
Greg Bernd *(Co-Pres)*
David Hu *(Co-Pres)*
Federico Moreno-Nickerson *(Dir-Product Dev Caribbean & Mexico)*

CLUB MED SALES, INC.

(Sub. of Club Mediterranee S.A.)
65005 Blue Lagoon Dr Ste 225
Miami, FL 33126
Tel.: (305) 925-9000
Fax: (305) 925-9052
Toll Free: (800) CLUB-MED
E-mail: reception.desk@clubmed.com
Web Site: www.clubmed.com
Approx. Number Employees: 100
Year Founded: 1950
Business Description:
Tour Operator Services
S.I.C.: 4724; 4725
N.A.I.C.S.: 561510; 561520
Advertising Expenditures: $10,000,000
Media: 1-2-4-6-8-9-10-11-13-23-24-31
Distr.: Intl.; Natl.
Budget Set: Sept.
Personnel:
Howard Tanenbaum *(VP-Sls)*
Dinah Marzullo *(Dir-Mktg)*

COMM GROUP, INC.

2003 S Easton Rd Ste 100
Doylestown, PA 18901
Tel.: (215) 348-8775
E-mail: info@commgroupinc.com
Web Site: www.commgroupinc.com
Approx. Number Employees: 100
Business Description:
Travel Services
S.I.C.: 4729
N.A.I.C.S.: 561599
Media: 6-13
Personnel:
Jim Hobbs *(Co-Founder & Pres)*
Marta Hobbs *(Founder & Exec VP)*
Alberto Cortes *(CEO)*
Sue Jacobs *(Dir-Mexico & Central America)*
Brands & Products:
BOOKARUBANOW.COM
BOOKBERMUDANOW.COM
BOOKMARTINIQUE.COM
BOOKPUERTORICO.COM
CARIBBEANHOTDEALS.COM
CARIBBEANIDO.COM
CHEAPCARRIBEAN.COM
CHEAPFINDER.NET
CHEAPUSAGETAWAY.COM
DAILYDYNAMITEDEAL.COM
DOORLANDO.COM
PUNTACANAHOLIDAYS.COM
TRAVELHUNTERS.COM

CON-WAY INC.

2211 Old Earhart Rd Ste 100
Ann Arbor, MI 48105
Tel.: (734) 994-6600
Telex: 910-373-2105
E-mail: info@con-way.com
Web Site: www.con-way.com
Approx. Rev.: $4,952,000,000
Approx. Number Employees: 27,900
Year Founded: 1929
Business Description:
Trucking & Logistic Services; Global Supply-Chain Management Services
S.I.C.: 4213; 4512; 7389
N.A.I.C.S.: 484121; 481112; 484230; 561499
Advertising Expenditures: $700,000
Media: 2-13
Distr.: Natl.
Personnel:
W. Keith Kennedy, Jr. *(Chm)*
Douglas W. Stotlar *(Pres & CEO)*
Stephen Bruffett *(CFO & Exec VP)*
Jacquelyn A. Barretta *(CIO)*
Thomas Nightingale *(CMO & VP-Comm)*
Nancy Heafey *(Chief Compliance Officer, VP & Deputy Gen Counsel)*
Herbert J. Schmidt, Jr. *(Pres-Truckload & Exec VP)*
Stephen K. Krull *(Sec, Gen Counsel & Exec VP)*
Robert L. Bianco *(Exec VP)*
Kevin S. Coel *(Sr VP & Corp Controller)*
Leslie P. Lundberg *(Sr VP-HR)*
Gary S. Cullen *(Deputy Gen Counsel & VP)*
Julia P. Jannausch *(VP-Culture & Trng)*
Mitchell E. Plaat *(VP-Procurement)*
Brands & Products:
CONWAY
MENLO WORLDWIDE
Advertising Agency:
Rodgers Townsend, LLC
1000 Clark Ave 5th Fl
Saint Louis, MO 63102
Tel.: (314) 436-9960
Fax: (314) 436-9961

CONSOLIDATED RAIL CORPORATION

(Joint Venture of CSX Corporation & Norfolk Southern Corporation)
(d/b/a Conrail)
1717 Arch St
Philadelphia, PA 19103
Tel.: (215) 209-2000
Fax: (215) 209-4819
Toll Free: (800) 272-0911
E-mail: info1@conrail.com
Web Site: www.conrail.com
Sales Range: $1-4.9 Billion
Approx. Number Employees: 22,000
Year Founded: 1976
Business Description:
Railway Systems & Service; Joint Venture of Norfolk Southern Corporation (50%) & CSX Corporation (50%)
S.I.C.: 4011
N.A.I.C.S.: 482111
Media: 1-2-5-7-9-10-20-22-23-25-26

Key to Media (For complete agency information see *The Advertising Red Books-Agencies* edition):
1. Bus. Publs. 2. Cable T.V. 3. Catalogs & Directories. 4. Co-op Adv. 5. Consumer Mags. 6. D.M. to Bus. Estab.7. D.M. to Consumers 8. Daily Newsp. 9. Exhibits/Trade Shows 10. Foreign 11. Infomercial 12. Internet Adv.13. Multimedia 14. Network Radio 15. Network T.V. 16. Newsp. Distr. Mags. 17. Other 18. Outdoor (Posters, Transit) 19. Point of Purchase20. Premiums, Novelties 21. Product Samples 22. Special Events Mktg. 23. Spot Radio 24. Spot T.V. 25. Weekly Newsp. 26. Yellow Page Adv.

Distr.: Natl.
Budget Set: Oct.
Brands & Products:
AUTONET
FLEXI FLO
STEELNET

CONTINENTAL AIRLINES INC.
(Sub. of United Continental Holdings, Inc.)
1600 Smith St 32nd Fl
Houston, TX 77002-7362
Mailing Address:
PO Box 4607
Houston, TX 77210-4607
Tel.: (713) 324-5000
Tel.: (713) 324-5080 (Corp Comm)
Fax: (713) 324-2637
Web Site: www.continental.com
Sales Range: $5-14.9 Billion
Approx. Number Employees: 39,640
Year Founded: 1934
Business Description:
Scheduled Air Transportation
S.I.C.: 4512; 4522
N.A.I.C.S.: 481111; 481211
Advertising Expenditures: $102,000,000
Media: 4-6-8-9-11-18-23-24
Distr.: Intl.; Natl.
Personnel:
Jeffery A. Smisek *(Chm, Pres & CEO)*
Kevin McKenna *(Mng Dir-Brand Mktg)*
Zane C. Rowe *(CFO & Exec VP)*
Peter D. McDonald *(COO & Exec VP)*
R. Keith Halbert *(CIO & Exec VP)*
James E. Compton *(Chief Revenue Officer & Exec VP)*
Brett J. Hart *(Gen Counsel, Sr VP & Sec)*
Gerald Laderman *(Treas & Sr VP-Fin)*
Michael P. Bonds *(Exec VP-HR & Labor Rels)*
Jeffrey T. Foland *(Exec VP)*
Irene E. Foxhall *(Exec VP-Comm & Govt Affairs)*
Rebecca G. Cox *(Sr VP-Govt Affairs)*
Mark Erwin *(Sr VP-Corp Dev & Alliances)*
David L. Hilfman *(Sr VP-Sls)*
Bill Meehan *(Sr VP-Airport Svcs)*
Katrina Manning *(VP-Corp Pur & Matl Svcs)*
Diedra Fontaine *(Dir-Diversity & Sls Dev)*
Julio Banfi *(Country Mgr-Argentina)*
Brands & Products:
BUSINESS FIRST
CONTINENTAL AIRLINES
CONTINENTAL AIRLINES PRESIDENTIAL PLUS
SHOPONEPASS
WORLD MASTER CARD

COOK MOVING SYSTEMS, INC.
1845 Dale Rd
Buffalo, NY 14225-4909
Tel.: (716) 897-0700
Fax: (716) 893-0500
Toll Free: (800) 828-7144
E-mail: buffalo@cookmoving.com
Web Site: www.cookmoving.com
Approx. Number Employees: 250
Year Founded: 1912
Business Description:
Moving & Storage of Household Goods, Electronics, Art & Special Products
S.I.C.: 4214; 4225
N.A.I.C.S.: 484210; 493110
Media: 26
Personnel:
Gregory Fierle *(Pres & CEO)*
Debra R. Fierle *(Mgr-HR)*

COSTA CRUISE LINES N.V.
(Sub. of Costa Crociere S.p.A.)
St 200 S Park Rd
Hollywood, FL 33021-8592
Tel.: (954) 266-5600
Fax: (954) 266-2100
Toll Free: (800) 462-6782
E-mail: info@costa.it.com
Web Site: www.costacruises.com
Sales Range: $25-49.9 Million
Approx. Number Employees: 120
Year Founded: 1948
Business Description:
Cruise Line Operator
S.I.C.: 4481
N.A.I.C.S.: 483112
Media: 1-2-4-5-6-8-9-10-13-17-20-22-23-25
Distr.: Natl.
Budget Set: Sept.
Personnel:
Maurice Zarmati *(Pres & CEO-North America)*
George Delpino *(CFO & VP-Fin)*
Ruben Perez *(Sr VP-Guest Svc)*
Scott Knutson *(VP-Sls)*
Wendi Mannix *(Sr Dir)*
Dario Rustico *(Dir-Sls & Mktg-Pacific Asia Ops)*
Brands & Products:
RESORT CRUISING
Advertising Agency:
Costa Advertising (House Agency)
200 S. Park Rd.
Hollywood, FL 33021
Tel.: (954) 266-5600
Fax: (954) 266-2100
(Caribbean Cruises, European Cruises)

CR ENGLAND, INC.
4701 W 2100 S
Salt Lake City, UT 84120-1223
Tel.: (801) 972-2712
Fax: (801) 977-5765
Toll Free: (800) 356-5046
E-mail: kayoaj@crengland.com
Web Site: www.crengland.com
Sales Range: $550-599.9 Million
Approx. Number Employees: 4,500
Year Founded: 1920
Business Description:
Refrigerated Cargo Transport
S.I.C.: 4213
N.A.I.C.S.: 484230
Import Export
Media: 13-25
Personnel:
Daniel E. England *(Chm & Pres)*
Dean England *(CEO)*
Keith Wallace *(CFO & Sr VP)*
Wayne Cederholm *(COO)*
Josh England *(Pres-England Logistics)*
Sean H. Snow *(Pres-England Logistics)*
Nelson Hayes *(Corp Counsel)*
Corey England *(Exec VP-Ops Support)*
Todd England *(Exec VP-Maintenance)*
David A. Kramer *(Exec VP-Corp Sls)*
Dirk Anderson *(Corp VP-Tech)*
Alan Bendesky *(Gen Mgr)*
Jim Burke *(Dir-Intermodal)*
David Conroy *(Dir-Intermodal Sls)*
Jeff Madison *(Dir-IT)*
Jeff VanWagoner *(Dir-Agent Ops)*
Joel Ashby *(Mgr-Mexico Bus Dev)*
Chad Rankin *(Distr Mgr)*

CROWLEY MARITIME CORPORATION
155 Grand Ave
Oakland, CA 94612-3758
Tel.: (510) 251-7500
Fax: (510) 251-7788
Toll Free: (800) CROWLEY
E-mail: webservices@crowley.com
Web Site: www.crowley.com
E-Mail For Key Personnel:
Public Relations: miller@crowley.com
Sales Range: $1-4.9 Billion
Approx. Number Employees: 4,074
Year Founded: 1892
Business Description:
Worldwide Logistics, Marine Transportation, Chemical Transportation & Energy Support Services
S.I.C.: 4412; 4432
N.A.I.C.S.: 483111; 483113
Media: 2-10
Personnel:
William A. Pennella *(Vice Chm & Exec VP)*
Thomas B. Crowley, Jr. *(Pres, CEO, COO & COB)*
John Ara *(Gen Dir)*
Arthur F. Mead, III *(Gen Counsel, VP & Asst Corp Sec)*
Daniel L. Warner *(Treas & Sr VP)*
John C. Calvin *(Sr VP & Controller)*
Steve Collar *(Sr VP & Gen Mgr-Logistics)*
John Douglass *(Sr VP & Gen Mgr-Puerto Rico & Caribbean Liner Svcs)*
John Hourihan *(Sr VP & Gen Mgr-Latin America Svcs)*
Rocky Smith *(Sr VP & Gen Mgr-Petroleum Distr & Marine Svcs)*
Susan L. Rodgers *(Sr VP-Admin)*
Richard L. Swinton *(VP-Tax & Audit)*
Mike Rampolla *(Gen Mgr-Contract Svcs-Atlantic/Gulf Bus Unit)*
Mark Miller *(Dir-Corp Comm)*
Margaret Reasoner *(Dir)*
Advertising Agency:
Nerland Agency Worldwide Partners
808 E St
Anchorage, AK 99501-3532
Tel.: (907) 274-9553
Tel.: (907) 274-9549 (Marketing)
Fax: (907) 274-9990

CRUISESONLY INC.
(Sub. of World Travel Holdings)
1011 E Colonial Dr
Orlando, FL 32803-4607
Tel.: (407) 898-5353
Fax: (407) 895-0244
Toll Free: (800) 278-4737
Web Site: www.cruisesonly.com
Approx. Number Employees: 200
Business Description:
Cruise Travel Agency
S.I.C.: 4724; 4729
N.A.I.C.S.: 561510; 561599
Media: 2-6-8-9-13-14-15-23-25-26
Distr.: Direct to Consumer; Natl.; Reg.
Budget Set: July -Oct.
Personnel:
Jeff Sherota *(Sr VP)*

CRYSTAL CRUISES, INC.
(Sub. of Nippon Yusen Kabushiki Kaisha)
2049 Century Park E Ste 1400
Los Angeles, CA 90067
Tel.: (310) 785-9300
Fax: (310) 785-0011
Toll Free: (800) 446-6620
E-mail: publicrelations@crystalcruises.com
Web Site: www.crystalcruises.com
Approx. Number Employees: 200
Year Founded: 1988
Business Description:
Cruise Operator
S.I.C.: 4481; 4724
N.A.I.C.S.: 483112; 561510
Advertising Expenditures: $3,500,000
Media: 2-5-6-7-8-9-10-11-13-18-19-22
Distr.: Intl.
Budget Set: Oct.
Personnel:
Greg L. Michel *(Pres)*
Jack Anderson *(Sr VP-Mktg & Sls)*
Bob Koven *(VP-Pur)*
Nitsa Lewis *(VP-Mktg)*
Erica Upshur *(Mgr-Adv & Partnership Mktg)*
Brands & Products:
CRYSTAL CRUISES
CRYSTAL HARMONY
CRYSTAL SERENITY
CRYSTAL SYMPHONY
Advertising Agency:
Round2 Communications, LLC
10866 Wilshire Blvd Ste 900
Los Angeles, CA 90024
Tel.: (310) 481-8040
Fax: (310) 571-1827

CSX CORPORATION
500 Water St 15th Fl
Jacksonville, FL 32202
Tel.: (904) 359-3200
Tel.: (904) 359-3100
Fax: (904) 359-3472
Toll Free: (800) 327-5405
E-mail: tellcsx@csx.com
Web Site: www.csx.com
Approx. Rev.: $10,636,000,000
Approx. Number Employees: 29,916
Year Founded: 1980
Business Description:
Holding Company; Transportation Operations
S.I.C.: 4011; 4013; 4412; 4491; 4499; 4731
N.A.I.C.S.: 482111; 482112; 483111; 488310; 488320; 488510
Advertising Expenditures: $3,000,000
Media: 1-2-8-9-10-18-20
Distr.: Natl.
Budget Set: Jan.
Personnel:
Michael Jon Ward *(Chm, Pres & CEO)*
Oscar Munoz *(CFO & Exec VP)*

Key to Media (For complete agency information see *The Advertising Red Books-Agencies* edition):
1. Bus. Publs. 2. Cable T.V. 3. Catalogs & Directories. 4. Co-op Adv. 5. Consumer Mags. 6. D.M. to Bus. Estab.7. D.M. to Consumers 8. Daily Newsp. 9. Exhibits/Trade Shows 10. Foreign 11. Infomercial 12. Internet Adv.13. Multimedia 14. Network Radio 15. Network T.V. 16. Newsp. Distr. Mags. 17. Other 18. Outdoor (Posters, Transit) 19. Point of Purchase20. Premiums, Novelties 21. Product Samples 22. Special Events Mktg. 23. Spot Radio 24. Spot T.V. 25. Weekly Newsp. 26. Yellow Page Adv.

CSX Corporation — (Continued)

Lisa A. Mancini *(Chief Admin Officer & Sr VP)*
Clarence Gooden *(Chief Comml Officer, Exec VP-Sls & Mktg)*
Ellen M. Fitzsimmons *(Gen Counsel, Sec & Sr VP-Law/Pub Affairs)*
David Bowling *(Gen Counsel-Tax & Insurance)*
Nathan D. Goldman *(Gen Counsel-Corp & Transportation Law)*
Alison Brown *(VP-HR)*
Louis E. Renjel *(VP-Strategic Infrastructure)*
Shantel Johnson *(Dir-Sls)*
Jim VanCleave *(Dir-Mktg)*
Janet Hicks *(Mgr-Market & Nonferrous Products)*

CSX TRANSPORTATION, INC.

(Sub. of CSX Corporation)
500 Water St
Jacksonville, FL 32202-4423
Tel.: (904) 359-3200
Fax: (904) 245-2686
E-mail: tellcsx@csx.com
Approx. Number Employees: 32,074
Year Founded: 1985
Business Description:
Railroad Transportation & Distribution Services
S.I.C.: 4011
N.A.I.C.S.: 482111
Media: 2-4-7-9-10-18-19-20-23-25
Distr.: Reg.
Budget Set: Jan.
Personnel:
Michael Jon Ward *(Chm, Pres & CEO)*
David A. Brown *(COO & Exec VP)*
Clarence Gooden *(Chief Comml Officer, Exec VP-Sls & Mktg)*
Lisa Mancini *(Sr VP-HR)*
Susan Arko *(Asst VP-Customer Svc Ops)*
Clark Robertson *(Asst VP-Reg Dev)*

CUBIC TRANSPORTATION SYSTEMS, INC.

(Sub. of Cubic Corporation)
5650 Kearny Mesa Rd
San Diego, CA 92111-5587
Mailing Address:
PO Box 85587
San Diego, CA 92186-5587
Tel.: (858) 268-3100
Fax: (858) 292-9987
Web Site: www.cts.cubic.com
Approx. Number Employees: 1,500
Year Founded: 1951
Business Description:
Fare Collection Systems For Mass Transportation
S.I.C.: 3829; 7373
N.A.I.C.S.: 334519; 541512
Media: 10-11
Personnel:
Stephen O. Shewmaker *(Pres)*
Jim Edwards *(Gen Counsel, Sec & Sr VP)*
David Lapczynski *(Sr VP-New Products & Svcs)*
Richard Wunderle *(Sr VP-Bus Ops)*
Min Wei *(VP-Fin Ops)*

CUMMINGS MOVING SYSTEMS L.L.C.

(Sub. of Cummings Transfer Co.)
740 29th Ave SW
Albany, OR 97321
Mailing Address:
PO Box 3130
Albany, OR 97321
Tel.: (541) 928-3385
Fax: (541) 926-5322
Toll Free: (800) 344-0852
Web Site: www.ctcmovers.com
Approx. Rev.: $8,000,000
Approx. Number Employees: 25
Year Founded: 1901
Business Description:
Movers of Household Goods
S.I.C.: 4783; 4212
N.A.I.C.S.: 488991; 484110
Media: 4-8-10-18-23-26

CUNARD LINE LTD.

(Sub. of Carnival plc)
24303 Town Ctr Dr Ste 200
Valencia, CA 91355
Tel.: (661) 753-1000
Fax: (661) 281-4773
Toll Free: (800) 7CUNARD
Web Site: www.cunard.com
Approx. Sls.: $422,000,000
Approx. Number Employees: 400
Year Founded: 1840
Business Description:
Cruise Line Operator
S.I.C.: 4481
N.A.I.C.S.: 483112
Media: 2-6-8-9-10-18-19-22
Distr.: Natl.
Personnel:
Carol Marlow *(Mng Dir)*
Brands & Products:
CUNARD LINE
Advertising Agency:
Dailey & Associates
(Sub. of The Interpublic Group of Cos., Inc.)
8687 Melrose Ave Ste G300
West Hollywood, CA 90069-5701
Tel.: (310) 360-3100
Fax: (310) 360-0810

DART TRANSIT COMPANY

800 Lone Oak Rd
Eagan, MN 55121-2212
Tel.: (651) 688-2000
Fax: (651) 683-1650
Toll Free: (800) 366-9000
E-mail: webmaster@dart.net
Web Site: www.dart.net
Approx. Number Employees: 400
Year Founded: 1934
Business Description:
Transportation Services
S.I.C.: 4213
N.A.I.C.S.: 484121
Media: 2-9-10-13-14-18-25-26
Personnel:
Donald G. Oren *(Chm)*
David O. Oren *(Pres)*
Scott Buchanan *(CFO)*
Joyce Jordan *(Exec VP-Sls & Mktg-Dart Transit Company)*
Alan D. Swenson *(Exec VP)*
John Basill *(VP-HR)*
Steve Gundale *(Mgr-Corp Comm)*
Brands & Products:
ADVANTAGE
ADVANTAGE DIGEST
DART
FLEETLINE INC

DELAWARE RIVER PORT AUTHORITY OF PENNSYLVANIA & NEW JERSEY

1 Port Ctr 2 Riverside Dr
Camden, NJ 08101-1003
Mailing Address:
PO Box 1949
Camden, NJ 08101-1949
Tel.: (856) 968-2000
Fax: (856) 968-2242
Toll Free: (877) 567-3772
E-mail: info@listsdrpa.org
Web Site: www.drpa.org
Approx. Number Employees: 900
Year Founded: 1919
Business Description:
Regional Waterway Transportation Agency
S.I.C.: 9621
N.A.I.C.S.: 926120
Personnel:
Jeffrey L. Nash *(Vice Chm)*
John J. Matheussen *(CEO-DRPA & Pres-PATCO)*
Brands & Products:
DELAWARE RIVER PORT AUTHORITY
WE KEEP THE REGION MOVING!
Advertising Agency:
Titan
850 Third Ave
New York, NY 10022
Tel.: (212) 644-6200
Fax: (212) 644-2010
(Out-of-Home)

DELTA AIR LINES, INC.

1030 Delta Blvd
Atlanta, GA 30354-1989
Mailing Address:
PO Box 20706
Atlanta, GA 30320-6001
Tel.: (404) 715-2600
Fax: (404) 715-5042
Web Site: www.delta.com
Approx. Rev.: $31,755,000,000
Approx. Number Employees: 80,000
Year Founded: 1924
Business Description:
Air Transportation & Air Cargo
S.I.C.: 4512
N.A.I.C.S.: 481111
Advertising Expenditures: $169,000,000
Media: 3-6-9-15-16-17-18-23-24
Distr.: Direct to Consumer; Natl.
Personnel:
Edward H. Bastian *(Pres)*
Richard H. Anderson *(CEO)*
Hank Halter *(CFO & Sr VP)*
Stephen E. Gorman *(COO & Exec VP)*
Theresa Wise *(CIO & Sr VP)*
John E. Walker *(Sr VP-Corp Comm)*
Neel Shah *(Sr VP)*
Tony Charaf *(Pres-Technical Ops)*
Richard B. Hirst *(Gen Counsel & Sr VP)*
Michael H. Campbell *(Exec VP-HR & Labor Rels)*
Glen W. Hauenstein *(Exec VP)*
John Laughter *(Sr VP-Maintenance Ops)*
Tim Mapes *(Sr VP-Mktg)*
Andrea Fischer Newman *(Sr VP-Govt Affairs)*
Holden Shannon *(Sr VP-Corp Strategy & Real Estate)*
Neil Stronach *(Sr VP-Ops)*
Gil West *(Sr VP-Airport Customer Svcs)*
Wayne Aaron *(VP-Mktg Programs & Distr Strategy)*
Jeff Arinder *(VP-Corp Strategy & Bus Dev)*
Sandy Gordon *(VP-Ops & Trng-In-Flight Svcs)*
Jacob Morris *(Product Mgr-Customer Experience)*
Chris Babb *(Mgr-Customer Experience, Plng & Dev)*
Brands & Products:
BUSINESSELITE
DELTA CONNECTION
DELTA SHUTTLE
DELTA SKY CLUB
MEDALLION
SKY TEAM
SKYBONUS
SKYMILES
Advertising Agencies:
Digitas Inc.
33 Arch St
Boston, MA 02110
Tel.: (617) 867-1000
Fax: (617) 867-1111

GolinHarris
18/F HuaiHai Plz
Shanghai, 200031, China
Tel.: (86) 21 2411 0088
Fax: (86) 21 2411 0066

The Media Kitchen
160 Varick St
New York, NY 10013
Tel.: (212) 633-0080
Fax: (212) 633-0080

RL Public Relations + Marketing
27 W 24th St Ste 901
New York, NY 10010
Tel.: (212) 206-8668
Fax: (212) 206-8778
Community Outreach
Hispanic Agency of Record
Hispanic Media
Latin America & Caribbean Flights

SS&K
88 Pine St 30th Fl
New York, NY 10005
Tel.: (212) 274-9500
Fax: (212) 274-9598
Toll Free: (800) 274-7765
Song

Wieden + Kennedy, Inc.
224 NW 13th Ave
Portland, OR 97209-2953
Tel.: (503) 937-7000
Fax: (503) 937-8000

Wieden + Kennedy-New York
150 Varick St Fl 7
New York, NY 10013-1218
Tel.: (917) 661-5200
Fax: (917) 661-5500

DEMATIC CORP.

(Sub. of Dematic Holding S.a.r.l.)
(d/b/a Dematic North America)
507 Plymouth NE

Key to Media (For complete agency information see *The Advertising Red Books-Agencies* edition):
1. Bus. Publs. 2. Cable T.V. 3. Catalogs & Directories. 4. Co-op Adv. 5. Consumer Mags. 6. D.M. to Bus. Estab.7. D.M. to Consumers
8. Daily Newsp. 9. Exhibits/Trade Shows 10. Foreign 11. Infomercial 12. Internet Adv.13. Multimedia 14. Network Radio
15. Network T.V. 16. Newsp. Distr. Mags. 17. Other 18. Outdoor (Posters, Transit) 19. Point of Purchase20. Premiums, Novelties
21. Product Samples 22. Special Events Mktg. 23. Spot Radio 24. Spot T.V. 25. Weekly Newsp. 26. Yellow Page Adv.

Grand Rapids, MI 49505
Tel.: (616) 913-7700
Fax: (616) 913-6200
Web Site: www.dematic.com
Approx. Number Employees: 1,000
Business Description:
Materials Handling Equipment & Logistics Systems Mfr & Distr
S.I.C.: 3535; 5084
N.A.I.C.S.: 333922; 423830
Personnel:
John K. Baysore *(Pres & CEO)*
Daniel Killeen *(CFO & Sr VP)*
Ken Ruehrean *(Product Mgr)*
Advertising Agency:
Chletcos/Gallagher Inc.
63 Greene St Ste 602
New York, NY 10012
Tel.: (212) 334-2455
Fax: (212) 334-2463

DENNIS TRUCKING CO. INC.

6951 Norwich Dr
Philadelphia, PA 19153-3405
Tel.: (215) 492-8200
Fax: (215) 492-9148
Approx. Sls.: $6,000,000
Approx. Number Employees: 60
Year Founded: 1953
Business Description:
Operator of Long Distance Hauling Trucks
S.I.C.: 4213
N.A.I.C.S.: 484121
Media: 7-17-26
Distr.: Natl.
Budget Set: Oct.
Brands & Products:
DENNIS TRUCKING

DHL HOLDINGS (USA), INC.

(Sub. of DHL International S.A./N.V.)
1200 S Pine Island Rd Ste 600
Plantation, FL 33324
Tel.: (954) 888-7000
Fax: (954) 888-7330
Toll Free: (800) 225-5345
Telex: 261208
E-mail: general@wkrn.com
Web Site: www.dhl-usa.com
E-Mail For Key Personnel:
Public Relations: pr@us.dhl.com
Approx. Number Employees: 20,000
Year Founded: 1969
Business Description:
Express Delivery & Logistics Services
S.I.C.: 4513; 4215
N.A.I.C.S.: 492110; 492210
Export
Media: 1-2-4-5-7-8-10-11-13-15-19-20-23-26
Distr.: Natl.
Budget Set: Nov.
Personnel:
Ken Alan *(Pres)*
John Mullen *(CEO)*
Mary E. Wood *(CFO & Exec VP)*
Stephen Fenwick *(CEO-Americas Reg)*
Karen Jones *(VP-Adv)*
Lori Folts *(Head-Mktg Comm)*
Brands & Products:
DHL
DHL CONNECT
INTERNATIONAL DOCUMENT SERVICE
SAME DAY SERVICE
THERMOEXPRESS
USA OVERNIGHT
VISA-PAC
WEB SHIPPING
WORLDFREIGHT
WORLDMAIL
WORLDWIDE EXPRESS
WORLDWIDE PRIORITY EXPRESS
Advertising Agency:
SCPF
1688 Meridian Ave Ste 200
Miami Beach, FL 33139
Tel.: (305) 674-3222
Fax: (305) 695-2777

DISCOVERY CRUISE LINES

1775 NW 70th Ave
Miami, FL 33126
Tel.: (305) 597-0336
Fax: (305) 718-9623
Toll Free: (800) 93SHIPS
E-mail: administrative@discoverycruise.com
Web Site:
www.discoverycruiseline.com
E-Mail For Key Personnel:
Sales Director: sales@discoverycruise.com
Approx. Number Employees: 75
Year Founded: 1987
Business Description:
Tour Operators
S.I.C.: 4724
N.A.I.C.S.: 561510
Media: 6-8-9-14-15-16-17-23-24-25-26
Distr.: Direct to Consumer; Intl.; Natl.
Budget Set: Jan.
Personnel:
Hanns J. Hahn *(Gen Mgr)*
Brands & Products:
AMERICA'S FAVORITE ONE DAY CRUISE
DISCOVERY CRUISE LINE
DISCOVERY VACATIONS
Advertising Agency:
Backus Turner International
3108 N Federal Hwy
Lighthouse Point, FL 33064
Tel.: (305) 573-9996
Tel.: (954) 727-9977
Fax: (954) 727-9966

DOLLAR RENT A CAR SYSTEMS, INC.

(Sub. of Dollar Thrifty Automotive Group, Inc.)
5330 E 31st St
Tulsa, OK 74135-5076
Tel.: (918) 669-3000
Fax: (918) 668-8563
E-mail: cservice@dollar.com
Web Site: www.dollar.com
Approx. Sls.: $823,900,000
Approx. Number Employees: 700
Year Founded: 1965
Business Description:
Daily Auto Rentals Franchise
S.I.C.: 7514; 4724
N.A.I.C.S.: 532111; 561510
Media: 5-7-17-18-19-22-26
Distr.: Natl.
Budget Set: Nov. -Dec.
Personnel:
Scott Thompson *(Pres & CEO)*
Advertising Agency:
FKQ Advertising + Marketing
15351 Roosevelt Blvd
Clearwater, FL 33760-3534
Tel.: (727) 539-8800
Fax: (866) 707-6648

DOWN UNDER ANSWERS, LLC

400 108th Ave NE Ste 700
Bellevue, WA 98004
Tel.: (425) 460-0895
Fax: (425) 460-0890
Toll Free: (800) 788-6685
E-mail: info@duatravel.com
Web Site: www.duatravel.com
Sales Range: $1-9.9 Million
Approx. Number Employees: 22
Business Description:
Travel Agency
S.I.C.: 4724
N.A.I.C.S.: 561510
Media: 6
Personnel:
Kirk Demeter *(Pres)*
Larry Covell *(Mgr-Sls)*
Sue-Anne Hime *(Mgr-Accts)*
Anita Lan *(Mgr-Air)*

DYNAMEX, INC.

(Sub. of TransForce Inc.)
5429 LBJ Fwy Ste 1000
Dallas, TX 75240
Tel.: (214) 560-9000
Fax: (214) 561-7499
Fax: (214) 560-9349
E-mail: dynamex.us@dynamex.com
Web Site: www.dynamex.com
Approx. Sls.: $406,448,000
Approx. Number Employees: 1,500
Year Founded: 1992
Business Description:
Same-Day Delivery & Logistics Services
S.I.C.: 4513
N.A.I.C.S.: 492110
Import Export
Media: 2-10-18-20
Personnel:
James L. Welch *(Pres & CEO)*
Ray E. Schmitz *(CFO, Exec VP & Asst Sec)*
Maynard F. Skarka *(COO)*
Andrew B. Argento *(VP-Field Svcs-North American)*
Brands & Products:
DXNOW
DYNAMEX
DYNAMEX DELIVERS NOW
EXPEDITE

EGYPTIAN TOURIST AUTHORITY

630 5th Ave Ste 2305
New York, NY 10111
Tel.: (212) 332-2570
Fax: (212) 956-6439
Toll Free: (877) 77EGYPT
E-mail: info.us@egypt.travel
Web Site: www.egypt.travel
Approx. Number Employees: 4
Media: 1-10-13-16
Advertising Agency:
Alexander & Richardson
161 Washington Valley Rd Ste 205
Warren, NJ 07059-7121
Tel.: (732) 302-1223
Fax: (732) 356-9574

EL AL ISRAEL AIRLINES, LTD.

(Sub. of El Al Airlines Ltd.)
15 E 26th St 6th Fl
New York, NY 10010
Tel.: (212) 852-0600
Tel.: (212) 852-0627
Fax: (212) 852-0641
Toll Free: (800) 223-6700
Web Site: www.elal.com
Approx. Number Employees: 160
Year Founded: 1948
Business Description:
International Airline Services
S.I.C.: 4512; 4581
N.A.I.C.S.: 481111; 481112; 488119
Advertising Expenditures: $800,000
Media: 2-5-6-9-13-17-18-23-25
Distr.: Direct to Consumer; Intl.; Natl.
Personnel:
Eliezer Shkedi *(CEO)*
Offer Gat *(VP-Sls)*
Brands & Products:
EL AL ISRAEL AIRLINES
MILK & HONEY VACATIONS

EMKAY, INC.

805 W Thorndale Ave
Itasca, IL 60143-1338
Tel.: (630) 250-7400
Fax: (630) 250-7422
Toll Free: (800) 621-2001
E-mail: webmaster@emkay.com
Web Site: www.emkay.com
Sales Range: $10-24.9 Million
Approx. Number Employees: 120
Year Founded: 1946
Business Description:
Full-Service Fleet Leasing & Management
S.I.C.: 6141
N.A.I.C.S.: 522220
Media: 2-26
Distr.: Natl.
Budget Set: Oct.
Personnel:
Chris Tepas *(CMO)*
Jack Rennels *(Sr VP-Mktg)*
James Tangney *(VP-Pur)*
Andy Vella *(VP-Fin)*
Brands & Products:
EMKAY

ENTERPRISE HOLDINGS, INC.

600 Corporate Park Dr
Saint Louis, MO 63105-4204
Tel.: (314) 512-1000
Fax: (314) 512-4706
Toll Free: (877) 858-3884
E-mail: oneway@enterprise.com
Web Site:
www.enterpriseholdings.com
E-Mail For Key Personnel:
Public Relations: Laura.Bryant@erac.com
Sales Range: $5-14.9 Billion
Approx. Number Employees: 68,000
Year Founded: 1957
Business Description:
Holding Company: Automobile Leasing & Rental & Retail Used Automobiles
S.I.C.: 6719; 5521; 7515
N.A.I.C.S.: 551112; 441120; 532112
Media: 2-3-6-7-9-14-15-17-18-19-20-25-26
Distr.: Direct to Consumer; Natl.
Personnel:
Andrew C. Taylor *(Chm & CEO)*
Donald L. Ross *(Vice Chm)*
Pamela M. Nicholson *(Pres & COO)*
William W. Snyder *(CFO & Exec VP)*
Craig Kennedy *(CIO & Sr VP)*

Key to Media (For complete agency information see *The Advertising Red Books-Agencies* edition):
1. Bus. Publs. 2. Cable T.V. 3. Catalogs & Directories. 4. Co-op Adv. 5. Consumer Mags. 6. D.M. to Bus. Estab.7. D.M. to Consumers
8. Daily Newsp. 9. Exhibits/Trade Shows 10. Foreign 11. Infomercial 12. Internet Adv.13. Multimedia 14. Network Radio
15. Network T.V. 16. Newsp. Distr. Mags. 17. Other 18. Outdoor (Posters, Transit) 19. Point of Purchase20. Premiums, Novelties
21. Product Samples 22. Special Events Mktg. 23. Spot Radio 24. Spot T.V. 25. Weekly Newsp. 26. Yellow Page Adv.

Enterprise Holdings, Inc. — (Continued)

Greg Stubblefield *(Chief Strategy Officer & Exec VP)*
Lee Kaplan *(Chief Admin Officer & Sr VP)*
Jo Ann Taylor Kindle *(Pres-Enterprise Holdings Foundation)*
Matthew G. Darrah *(Exec VP-North American Ops)*
Edward Adams *(Sr VP-HR)*
Steve Bloom *(Sr VP-Enterprise Fleet Mgmt & Car Sls)*
Jim Burrell *(Sr VP-European Ops-Enterprise Rent-A-Car)*
Jim Runnels *(Sr VP-Rentals)*
Boyd Sumner *(Reg VP-San Fernando Valley)*
Holly Nicole Campbell *(VP-Creative, Media & Sponsorships)*
Christy Conrad *(VP-Comm)*
Patrick Farrell *(VP-Mktg & Comm)*
John Howell *(Asst VP)*
Lee Broughton *(Dir-Sustainability)*
Barry Dvoracek *(Dir-Social Media)*
Carol Perry *(Dir-Insights & Intelligence)*
Richard Sayre *(Dir-Renewable Fuels)*
Donna Stamp *(Dir-Procurement)*
Andriana Thro *(Mgr-Social Media)*
Angela Umali *(Mgr-Media)*

Brands & Products:
ARMS
BORROW SMART.BUY SMART
ENTERPRISE
ENTERPRISE RENT-A-CAR
HAGGLE-FREE BUYING.WORRY FREE OWNERSHIP
WE'LL PICK YOU UP

Advertising Agencies:
The Arnold Agency
117 Summers St
Charleston, WV 25301
Tel.: (304) 342-1200
Fax: (304) 342-1285

Avrett Free Ginsberg
1 Dag Hammarskjold Plz 885 2nd Ave
New York, NY 10017-2205
Tel.: (212) 832-3800
Fax: (212) 418-7331

G&G Advertising
2804 3rd Ave N
Billings, MT 59101
Tel.: (406) 294-8113
Fax: (406) 294-8120
Toll Free: (800) 390-2892

EXECUTIVE CAR LEASING CO.

7807 Santa Monica Blvd
Los Angeles, CA 90046-5302
Tel.: (323) 654-5000
Fax: (323) 848-9015
Toll Free: (800) 800-3932
E-mail: sales@executivecarleasing.com
Web Site: www.executivecarleasing.com
E-Mail For Key Personnel:
Sales Director: sales@executivecarleasing.com
Approx. Number Employees: 150
Year Founded: 1955
Business Description:
Passenger Car Leasing Services
S.I.C.: 7515; 7519
N.A.I.C.S.: 532112; 532120
Media: 2-7-17-20-26
Distr.: Direct to Consumer; Natl.
Personnel:
Sam Goldman *(Pres & CEO)*
David Goldman *(CFO)*
Richard Schrieken *(VP-HR & Controller)*
Jim Keller *(VP-DP)*

EXPLORICA, INC.

145 Tremont St 6 Fl
Boston, MA 02111-1208
Tel.: (617) 210-6100
Fax: (888) 310-7088
Toll Free: (888) 310-7120
E-mail: info@explorica.com
Web Site: www.explorica.com
Approx. Number Employees: 40
Year Founded: 2000
Business Description:
Educational Travel Products & Services
S.I.C.: 4725
N.A.I.C.S.: 561520
Export
Media: 8-10-11-13
Personnel:
Olle A. Olsson *(Founder & Pres)*
Peter Nilsson *(CEO)*
Brands & Products:
EXPLORICA
TRAVEL, LEARN.

EXPRESSJET AIRLINES, INC.

(Sub. of Atlantic Southeast Airlines Inc.)
A-Tech Center 990 Toffie Terrace
Atlanta, GA 30354-1356
Tel.: (404) 856-1000
Sales Range: $1-4.9 Billion
Year Founded: 2002
Business Description:
Regional & Chartered Air Transportation Services
S.I.C.: 4512; 4522
N.A.I.C.S.: 481111; 481211
Advertising Agency:
Dentsu America, Inc.
32 Ave of the Americas 16th Fl
New York, NY 10013
Tel.: (212) 397-3333
Fax: (212) 397-3322

FEDERAL EXPRESS CORPORATION

(Sub. of FedEx Corporation)
(d/b/a FedEx Express)
3610 Hacks Cross Rd
Memphis, TN 38125
Tel.: (901) 369-3600
Fax: (901) 395-2000
Web Site: www.fedex.com
Approx. Rev.: $21,243,000,000
Approx. Number Employees: 93,000
Year Founded: 1973
Business Description:
Express Mail Shipping Services
S.I.C.: 7389
N.A.I.C.S.: 561431
Advertising Expenditures: $92,000,000
Personnel:
David J. Bronczek *(Pres & CEO)*
Cathy D. Ross *(CFO & Sr VP)*
William J. Logue *(COO-US & Exec VP)*

FEDEX CORPORATION

942 S Shady Grove Rd
Memphis, TN 38120
Tel.: (901) 818-7500
Fax: (901) 395-2000
Toll Free: (800) GOFEDEX
E-mail: ir@fedex.com
Web Site: www.fedex.com
Approx. Rev.: $34,734,000,000
Approx. Number Employees: 245,109
Year Founded: 1997
Business Description:
Holding Company; Shipping, E-commerce & Business Services
S.I.C.: 6719; 4212; 4213; 4512; 4731
N.A.I.C.S.: 551112; 481112; 484110; 484121; 484122; 488510
Import Export
Advertising Expenditures: $375,000,000
Media: 2-3-6-7-8-9-13-14-15-20-22-23-24-25-26
Distr.: Intl.; Natl.
Budget Set: May
Personnel:
Frederick W. Smith *(Chm, Pres & CEO)*
Alan B. Graf, Jr. *(CFO & Exec VP)*
Robert B. Carter *(CIO & Exec VP-Info Svcs)*
John L. Merino *(Chief Acctg Officer)*
Christine P. Richards *(Gen Counsel, Sec & Exec VP)*
T. Michael Glenn *(Exec VP-Market Dev & Corp Comm)*
William G. Margaritis *(Sr VP-Comm & IR-Global)*
Judith H. Edge *(Corp VP-HR)*
Steve Pacheco *(Dir-Adv)*
Brands & Products:
CARIBBEAN TRANSPORTATION SERVICES
EXPRESS SAVER
EXTREME SERVICE
FEDEX
FEDEX 1DAY
FEDEX 2DAY
FEDEX 3DAY
FEDEX ASIAONE
FEDEX ASSOCIATION ADVANTAGE
FEDEX AUTHORIZED SHIPCENTER
FEDEX BUSINESS BONUS
FEDEX CHAMPIONSHIP SERIES
FEDEX CHARTERS
FEDEX COLLECT ON DELIVERY
FEDEX COLLECTION
FEDEX COMMERCE SERVER
FEDEX COSMOS
FEDEX CUSTOM CRITICAL
FEDEX CUSTOMER RESOURCE CENTER
FEDEX DIRECTLINK
FEDEX E-LABEL
FEDEX EDI INVOICE
FEDEX EXPRESS
FEDEX EXPRESS CLEAR
FEDEX FREIGHT
FEDEX GROUND
FEDEX HOME DELIVERY
FEDEX INSIGHT
FEDEX INTERNATIONAL PRIORITY DIRECT DISTRIBUTION
FEDEX SERVICES
FEDEX SERVICES GUIDE
FEDEX SUPPLY CHAIN SERVICES
FEDEX TRADE NETWORKS
IPFS
IXF
MAGIC WINDOW
NEXT DAY NEIGHBOR ISLAND SERVICE
PARTSBANK
POWERPICKUP
PRIORITY OVERNIGHT
SHIPPING SAVVY
SPOTCOM
STANDARD OVERNIGHT
SUPERTRACKER
TEMP-ASSURE AIR
TEMP-ASSURE VALIDATED AIR

Advertising Agencies:
Ad Club
1304 W Roseburg Ave
Modesto, CA 95350-4855
Tel.: (209) 529-9067
Fax: (209) 529-5265
Toll Free: (800) 333-1228

AdAsia Communications, Inc.
85 Fifth Ave 7th Fl
New York, NY 10003
Tel.: (212) 871-6886
Fax: (212) 871-6883

BBDO New York
1285 Ave of the Americas 7th Fl
New York, NY 10019-6028
Tel.: (212) 459-5000
AAAAAA Auto Repair
Exchange Student
FedEx Kinkos
Names
Retirement

Drake Advertising, Inc.
4141 Brownsville Rd Ste 1
Pittsburgh, PA 15227
Tel.: (412) 882-4700
Fax: (412) 882-4702
Toll Free: (877) 583-7253

Good Advertising, Inc.
5100 Poplar Ave Ste 1700
Memphis, TN 38137
Tel.: (901) 761-0741
Fax: (901) 682-2568
Toll Free: (800) 325-9857

GyroHSR
60 Madison Ave Ste 1101
New York, NY 10010
Tel.: (212) 915-2490
Fax: (212) 915-2491
pan-European

OMD-USA
195 Broadway
New York, NY 10007
Tel.: (212) 590-7100

FEDEX SMARTPOST, INC.

(Sub. of FedEx Ground Package System, Inc.)
16555 W Rogers Dr
New Berlin, WI 53151
Tel.: (262) 796-6800
Fax: (262) 796-6852
Toll Free: (888) 505-3400
Web Site: www.fedex.com/us/smartpost
Sales Range: $200-249.9 Million
Approx. Number Employees: 450
Year Founded: 1998
Business Description:
Parcel Delivery Expediting Services

Key to Media (For complete agency information see *The Advertising Red Books-Agencies* edition):
1. Bus. Publs. 2. Cable T.V. 3. Catalogs & Directories. 4. Co-op Adv. 5. Consumer Mags. 6. D.M. to Bus. Estab.7. D.M. to Consumers 8. Daily Newsp. 9. Exhibits/Trade Shows 10. Foreign 11. Infomercial 12. Internet Adv.13. Multimedia 14. Network Radio 15. Network T.V. 16. Newsp. Distr. Mags. 17. Other 18. Outdoor (Posters, Transit) 19. Point of Purchase20. Premiums, Novelties 21. Product Samples 22. Special Events Mktg. 23. Spot Radio 24. Spot T.V. 25. Weekly Newsp. 26. Yellow Page Adv.

S.I.C.: 4513; 4215
N.A.I.C.S.: 492110; 492210
Media: 10
Personnel:
Ward B. Strang *(Pres & CEO)*

FINNAIR OYJ-NEW YORK
(Sub. of Finnair Oyj)
228 E 45th St Fl 8
New York, NY 10017-3303
Tel.: (212) 499-9000
Fax: (212) 499-9040
Toll Free: (800) 950-5000
Telex: 12-7045
E-mail: webmaster@us.finnair.com
Web Site: www.finnair.com
Approx. Number Employees: 16
Year Founded: 1965
Business Description:
International Airline Services
S.I.C.: 4512
N.A.I.C.S.: 481111
Advertising Expenditures: $550,000
Media: 1-2-3-6-7-8-9-10-20-23-25
Distr.: Natl.
Budget Set: Nov. -Dec.
Personnel:
Anthony Larusso *(Dir-Cargo-Americas)*
Antti Nieminen *(Dir-Mktg Innovations)*
Markku Remes *(Product Mgr)*
Anssi Partanen *(Mgr-Mktg)*

FLAT RATE MOVING NEW YORK
466 Broome St 5th FL
New York, NY 10013
Tel.: (718) 475-5787
Fax: (212) 269-2769
E-mail: hr@flatrate.com
Web Site: www.flatrate.com
Sales Range: $10-24.9 Million
Approx. Number Employees: 130
Business Description:
Trucking Services
S.I.C.: 4212
N.A.I.C.S.: 484110
Personnel:
Sharone Ben-Harosh *(Founder)*
Israel Carmel *(CFO)*
Zvi Klepar *(Gen Mgr)*
Advertising Agency:
Earthquake Media, LLC
15 E 26th St Ste 802
New York, NY 10010-1505
Tel.: (212) 204-9200
Fax: (212) 967-1210

FLEXI-VAN LEASING, INC.
251 Monroe Ave
Kenilworth, NJ 07033-1106
Tel.: (908) 276-8000
Fax: (908) 276-7666
E-mail: sales@flexi-van.com
Web Site: www.flexi-van.com
E-Mail For Key Personnel:
Sales Director: sales@flexi-van.com
Approx. Number Employees: 210
Year Founded: 1955
Business Description:
Supplier of Intermodal Equipment; Utility Trailer & Chassis Rental
S.I.C.: 7359; 1521
N.A.I.C.S.: 532490; 236115
Export
Media: 2-7-10
Distr.: Intl.; Natl.

Personnel:
David H. Murdock *(Chm & CEO)*
George Elkas *(Pres & COO)*
Jeffrey M. Heck *(CFO & VP)*
Bernard Vaughan *(Gen Counsel & Sr VP)*
Philip Connors *(Exec VP)*

FLORIDA EAST COAST INDUSTRIES, INC.
(Holding of Fortress Investment Group LLC)
(d/b/a Flagler Group)
7411 Fullerton St Ste 300
Jacksonville, FL 32256
Tel.: (904) 538-6161
Fax: (904) 996-2829
Toll Free: (800) 342-1131
E-mail: fecicontact@feci.com
Web Site: www.feci.com
Approx. Rev.: $458,202,000
Approx. Number Employees: 1,053
Year Founded: 1983
Business Description:
Holding Company; Railroad Freight Transportation & Real Estate Development
S.I.C.: 6719; 1522; 4011; 6519; 6531; 6552
N.A.I.C.S.: 551112; 236220; 237210; 482111; 531190; 531390
Media: 10-18
Personnel:
John Giles *(Pres & CEO)*
Daniel H. Popky *(CFO & Exec VP)*
Jorge B. San Miguel *(Chief Investment Officer & Exec VP)*
Edward Manno Shumsky *(Chief HR Officer & Exec VP)*
John D. McPherson *(Exec VP-FECI)*

FORETRAVEL INC.
1221 NW Stallings Dr
Nacogdoches, TX 75964
Tel.: (936) 564-8367
Fax: (936) 564-0391
E-mail: info@foretravel.com
Web Site: www.foretravel.com
Approx. Sls.: $90,000,000
Approx. Number Employees: 130
Year Founded: 1976
Business Description:
Motor Homes Mfr
S.I.C.: 3716
N.A.I.C.S.: 336213
Media: 2-8-10-18-19
Personnel:
Greg Amys *(Pres)*
David King *(Dir-HR)*
Brands & Products:
FORETRAVEL
PHENIX
TRAVELRIDE

FREIGHTGURU
14825 Ballantyne Ste 240-9
Charlotte, NC 28277
Fax: (704) 369-5238
Toll Free: (877) 937-3734
Web Site: www.freightguru.com
Business Description:
Freight Brokerage
S.I.C.: 4731
N.A.I.C.S.: 488510
Media: 13
Personnel:
Kam Pardasani *(Pres)*

FRONTIER AIRLINES, INC.
(Sub. of Republic Airways Holdings Inc.)
7001 Tower Rd
Denver, CO 80249-7312
Tel.: (720) 374-4200
Fax: (720) 374-4375
Toll Free: (800) 265-5505
E-mail: info@flyfrontier.com
Web Site: www.frontierairlines.com
E-Mail For Key Personnel:
Sales Director: tallee@flyfrontier.com
Approx. Rev.: $1,289,382,000
Approx. Number Employees: 4,253
Year Founded: 1994
Business Description:
Scheduled Air Service
S.I.C.: 4512
N.A.I.C.S.: 481111
Import Export
Advertising Expenditures: $4,500,000
Media: 2-3-5-6-8-9-10-11-13-14-15-18-19-23-24-25-26
Distr.: Reg.
Budget Set: Oct.
Personnel:
Sean E. Menke *(Pres & CEO)*
Edward Christie, III *(CFO & Sr VP)*
Ted Christie *(CFO & Sr VP)*
Christopher L. Collins *(COO & Exec VP)*
Ann E. Block *(Sr VP-People)*
Ronald L. McClellan *(VP-Maintenance & Engrg)*
Diane Willmann *(Dir-Adv)*
Julie James *(Sr Mgr-Media)*
Advertising Agencies:
G&G Outfitters Inc.
4901 Forbes Blvd
Lanham, MD 20706
Tel.: (301) 731-2099
Fax: (301) 731-5199

Henry Gill Communications
(d/b/a Henry Gill Advertising)
900 S Broadway Ste 300
Denver, CO 80209
Tel.: (303) 296-4100
Fax: (303) 296-3410

Possible Worldwide
302 W Third St Ste 900
Cincinnati, OH 45202
Tel.: (513) 381-1380
Fax: (513) 381-0248

FRONTIER LOGISTICS, LP
101 E Barbours Cut Blvd
Morgan's Point, TX 77571
Tel.: (281) 307-2000
Fax: (281) 307-2099
Toll Free: (800) 610-6808
E-mail: webinquiry@frontierlogistics.com
Web Site: www.frontierlogistics.com
E-Mail For Key Personnel:
President: gwiseman@ar1.net
Approx. Number Employees: 100
Year Founded: 1997
Business Description:
Supply Chain Management Services
S.I.C.: 4213
N.A.I.C.S.: 484121
Media: 13

Personnel:
Glenn Wiseman *(Pres)*
George Cook *(CFO)*

FUGAZY INTERNATIONAL CORPORATION
1270 Ave Of The Americas
New York, NY 10020
Tel.: (212) 661-4155
Fax: (212) 661-7630
E-mail: info@fugazy.com
Web Site: www.fugazy.com
E-Mail For Key Personnel:
President: rfugazy@fugazyintl.com
Sales Range: $10-24.9 Million
Approx. Number Employees: 5
Year Founded: 1870
Business Description:
Travel & Tourism Services
S.I.C.: 4119; 4142
N.A.I.C.S.: 485320; 485510
Advertising Expenditures: $1,000,000
Media: 2-7-8-9-25
Distr.: Natl.
Budget Set: Apr.
Personnel:
Roy D. Fugazy *(Pres)*

G&A GOLDEN PACIFIC
13260 Temple Ave
City of Industry, CA 91746
Tel.: (626) 961-3903
Fax: (626) 961-6526
Toll Free: (888) 388-8842
E-mail: info@golden-pacific.com
Web Site: www.golden-pacific.com
Approx. Sls.: $20,000,000
Approx. Number Employees: 40
Year Founded: 1991
Business Description:
Luggage Mfr
S.I.C.: 3161
N.A.I.C.S.: 316991
Advertising Expenditures: $200,000
Media: 4-6-10-21
Distr.: Natl.
Personnel:
Roger Young *(Pres)*
Brands & Products:
GOLDEN-PACIFIC

GALILEO INTERNATIONAL, LLC
(Sub. of Travelport Limited)
7 Sylvan Way
Parsippany, NJ 07054
Tel.: (973) 496-6000
Fax: (973) 496-0612
Web Site: www.galileo.com
Sales Range: $550-599.9 Million
Approx. Number Employees: 2,000
Business Description:
Electronic Global Travel Distribution Services
S.I.C.: 7373; 4729
N.A.I.C.S.: 541512; 561599
Media: 2-4-7-10
Personnel:
Gordon A. Wilson *(Pres, CEO-Travelport GDS & Deputy CEO-Travelport)*
Rogier Boer *(Mktg Mgr)*

GENERAL TOURS WORLD TRAVELER, INC.
53 Summer St
Keene, NH 03431-3318
Tel.: (603) 357-5033

Key to Media (For complete agency information see *The Advertising Red Books-Agencies* edition):
1. Bus. Publs. 2. Cable T.V. 3. Catalogs & Directories. 4. Co-op Adv. 5. Consumer Mags. 6. D.M. to Bus. Estab.7. D.M. to Consumers
8. Daily Newsp. 9. Exhibits/Trade Shows 10. Foreign 11. Infomercial 12. Internet Adv.13. Multimedia 14. Network Radio
15. Network T.V. 16. Newsp. Distr. Mags. 17. Other 18. Outdoor (Posters, Transit) 19. Point of Purchase20. Premiums, Novelties
21. Product Samples 22. Special Events Mktg. 23. Spot Radio 24. Spot T.V. 25. Weekly Newsp. 26. Yellow Page Adv.

General Tours World Traveler, Inc. — (Continued)

Fax: (603) 357-4548
Toll Free: (800) 221-2216
E-mail: info@generaltours.com
Web Site: www.generaltours.com
E-Mail For Key Personnel:
President: rdrumm@generaltours.com
Approx. Number Employees: 47
Year Founded: 1947
Business Description:
Tour Operator
S.I.C.: 4725; 4724
N.A.I.C.S.: 561520; 561510
Advertising Expenditures: $500,000
Bus. Publs.: $60,000; Catalogs & Directories: $20,000; Co-op Adv.: $60,000; D.M. to Consumers: $30,000; Daily Newsp.: $100,000; Exhibits/ Trade Shows: $5,000; Other: $200,000; Premiums, Novelties: $3,000; Special Events Mktg.: $2,000; Spot Radio: $20,000
Distr.: Direct; Natl.
Budget Set: Aug.
Personnel:
Alex Harris *(Chm)*
Robert Drumm *(Pres)*
Raafat Shoukry *(Mgr)*
Brands & Products:
GENERAL TOURS

GLEN OAKS INDUSTRIES, INC.
3000 West Commerce St
Dallas, TX 75247-5525
Tel.: (214) 631-1340
Fax: (214) 688-0354
Approx. Number Employees: 14
Year Founded: 1917
Business Description:
Logistics Services
S.I.C.: 2325; 5136
N.A.I.C.S.: 315224; 424320
Advertising Expenditures: $300,000
Media: 2-5-9-23-24
Distr.: Natl.
Budget Set: Oct. -Nov.

GLOBAL AERO LOGISTICS, INC.
(Holding of MatlinPatterson Global Advisers LLC)
7337 W Washington St
Indianapolis, IN 46231-1328
Mailing Address:
PO Box 51609
Indianapolis, IN 46251-0609
Tel.: (770) 632-8000
Fax: (317) 282-7091
E-mail: info@globalaerologistics.com
Web Site:
www.globalaerologistics.com
Sales Range: $1-4.9 Billion
Approx. Number Employees: 2,483
Year Founded: 1984
Business Description:
Holding Company
S.I.C.: 4512; 4522; 6719
N.A.I.C.S.: 481111; 481219; 551112
Advertising Expenditures: $33,500,000
Media: 2-3-5-6-7-8-9-10-11-18-19-20-22-23-24-25-26
Distr.: Direct to Consumer; Natl.
Personnel:
Robert Binns *(Chm & CEO)*
Charles McDonald *(Pres)*
William A. Garrett *(CFO)*
Jeff Sanborn *(CMO)*
Richard W. Meyer, Jr. *(Sr VP-HR & Plng)*

GRAMMER INDUSTRIES INC.
18375 E 345 S
Grammer, IN 47236
Tel.: (812) 579-5655
Fax: (812) 579-5643
Web Site:
www.grammerindustries.com
Sales Range: $10-24.9 Million
Approx. Number Employees: 30
Business Description:
Provider of Trucking Services
S.I.C.: 4213
N.A.I.C.S.: 484121
Personnel:
Charles L. Whittington *(Pres)*
Advertising Agency:
AutoCom Associates
74 W Long Lk Rd Ste 103
Bloomfield Hills, MI 48304-2770
Tel.: (248) 647-8621
Fax: (248) 642-2110

GREAT LAKES AVIATION, LTD.
1022 Airport Pkwy
Cheyenne, WY 82001-1551
Tel.: (307) 432-7000
Fax: (307) 432-7001
E-mail: custrel@flygreatlakes.com
Web Site: www.flygreatlakes.com
Approx. Rev.: $125,400,330
Approx. Number Employees: 759
Year Founded: 1977
Business Description:
Regional Airline Services
S.I.C.: 4512
N.A.I.C.S.: 481111
Export
Advertising Expenditures: $912,000
Media: 5-7-8-13-20
Personnel:
Douglas G. Voss *(Chm & Pres)*
Charles R. Howell, IV *(CEO)*
Michael O. Matthews *(CFO & VP)*
Kurt Franklin *(Dir-Maintenance)*

GREATER CLEVELAND REGIONAL TRANSIT AUTHORITY
1240 W 6th St
Cleveland, OH 44113-1302
Tel.: (216) 566-5285
Fax: (216) 781-4043
Web Site: www.riderta.com
Approx. Sls.: $44,974,540
Approx. Number Employees: 2,700
Year Founded: 1975
Business Description:
Provider of Transportation Services
S.I.C.: 4111
N.A.I.C.S.: 485119
Personnel:
George F. Dixon, III *(Pres)*
Joseph A. Calabrese *(CEO, Treas, Sec & Gen Mgr)*
Sheryl King Benford *(Gen Counsel & Deputy Gen Mgr-Legal Affairs)*
Michael York *(Deputy Gen Mgr-Ops)*
Bruce Hampton *(Deputy Gen Mgr-HR)*
Doug Seger *(Dir-Fleet Mgmt)*
Steven Sims *(Dir-Bus Dev)*
Advertising Agency:
Brokaw Inc.
425 W Lakeside Ave
Cleveland, OH 44113-1029
Tel.: (216) 241-8003
Fax: (216) 241-8033

GREYHOUND CANADA TRANSPORTATION CORP.
(Sub. of Greyhound Lines, Inc.)
877 Greyhound Way SW
Calgary, AB T3C 3V8, Canada
Tel.: (403) 260-0877
Fax: (403) 260-0742
E-mail: info@greyhound.ca
Web Site: www.greyhound.ca
Approx. Number Employees: 2,500
Year Founded: 1929
Business Description:
Commercial Passenger Carrier & Charter Transportation
S.I.C.: 4131
N.A.I.C.S.: 485210
Media: 6-7-8-9-15-17-18-19-22-26
Distr.: Natl.
Budget Set: Nov. -Dec.
Personnel:
Stuart Kendrick *(Sr VP)*

GREYHOUND LINES, INC.
(Sub. of FirstGroup America Inc.)
350 N St Paul
Dallas, TX 75201
Mailing Address:
PO Box 660362
Dallas, TX 75266-0362
Tel.: (214) 849-8000
Tel.: (214) 849-8966 (Customer Service)
Toll Free: (800) 454-2487
Web Site: www.greyhound.com
Approx. Rev.: $1,200,000,000
Approx. Number Employees: 8,400
Year Founded: 1914
Business Description:
Bus Charters & Tours, Package Express, Regular Route Passenger Service, Travel Services & Sightseeing
S.I.C.: 4111
N.A.I.C.S.: 485119
Advertising Expenditures: $10,000,000
Media: 8-13-14-15-18-19-25
Personnel:
Dave Leach *(Pres & CEO)*
Chris Boult *(Sr VP-IT)*
Ted F. Burk *(Sr VP-Corp Dev)*
Rhonda Piar MacAndrew *(Sr VP-HR)*
Kim Plaskett *(Dir-Mktg)*
Brands & Products:
CAMPUSLINK
FLIGHTLINK
FRIENDLY E-SAVERS
GPX
GREYHOUND
GREYHOUND PACKAGEXPRESS
GREYHOUND TRAVEL SERVICES
LUCKY STREAK
QUICKLINK
Advertising Agencies:
Butler, Shine, Stern & Partners
20 Liberty Ship Way
Sausalito, CA 94965-3312
Tel.: (415) 331-6049
Fax: (415) 331-3524

Edelman
525 Market St Ste 1400
San Francisco, CA 94105
Tel.: (415) 222-9944
Fax: (415) 222-9924

Slingshot, LLC
208 N Market St Ste 500
Dallas, TX 75202
Tel.: (214) 634-4411
Fax: (214) 634-5511

GROENDYKE TRANSPORT, INC.
2510 Rock Is Blvd
Enid, OK 73701
Tel.: (580) 234-4663
Fax: (580) 234-1216
E-mail: webmaster@groendyke.com
Web Site: www.groendyke.com
Approx. Number Employees: 1,300
Year Founded: 1932
Business Description:
Tank & Truck Carrier Services
S.I.C.: 4213
N.A.I.C.S.: 484121
Media: 2-7
Personnel:
John D. Groendyke *(Chm & CEO)*
Greg Hodgen *(Pres & COO)*
Gene Brown *(Exec VP)*
David James *(Sr VP-Ops)*
Rob Fries *(VP-HR & Employment Law)*
Thomas T. Thompson *(Dir-Sls)*
Scott Bradbury *(Mgr-Sls)*
Brands & Products:
GT

GROUP VOYAGERS, INC.
(d/b/a Globus & Cosmos)
5301 S Federal Cir
Littleton, CO 80123-2980
Tel.: (303) 797-2800
Fax: (303) 798-5441
Toll Free: (800) 851-0728
E-mail: marketing@globusandcosmos.com
Web Site:
www.globusandcosmos.com
Sales Range: $25-49.9 Million
Approx. Number Employees: 350
Year Founded: 1940
Business Description:
International Travel Tours
S.I.C.: 4725; 4724
N.A.I.C.S.: 561520; 561510
Advertising Expenditures: $950,000
Media: 4-8-10
Distr.: Direct to Consumer; Natl.; Reg.
Budget Set: Sept.
Personnel:
Steve Born *(VP-Mktg)*
Brands & Products:
AVALON
COSMOS
GLOBUS
MONOGRAMS
Advertising Agency:
Cactus
(d/b/a Cactus Mktg Communications)
2128 15th St Ste 100
Denver, CO 80202
Tel.: (303) 455-7545
Fax: (303) 455-0408
Advertising
Agency of Record
Branding
Design

Key to Media (For complete agency information see *The Advertising Red Books-Agencies* edition):
1. Bus. Publs. 2. Cable T.V. 3. Catalogs & Directories. 4. Co-op Adv. 5. Consumer Mags. 6. D.M. to Bus. Estab.7. D.M. to Consumers 8. Daily Newsp. 9. Exhibits/Trade Shows 10. Foreign 11. Infomercial 12. Internet Adv.13. Multimedia 14. Network Radio 15. Network T.V. 16. Newsp. Distr. Mags. 17. Other 18. Outdoor (Posters, Transit) 19. Point of Purchase20. Premiums, Novelties 21. Product Samples 22. Special Events Mktg. 23. Spot Radio 24. Spot T.V. 25. Weekly Newsp. 26. Yellow Page Adv.

Digital
Media
Print
Production

GULFSTREAM INTERNATIONAL GROUP INC.
(Filed Ch 11 Bankruptcy #1044131 on 11/4/10 in U.S. Bankruptcy Ct, Southern Dist of FL, Ft. Lauderdale)
3201 Griffin Rd 4th Fl
Fort Lauderdale, FL 33312
Tel.: (954) 985-1500
Fax: (954) 985-5245
E-mail: info@gulfstreamair.com
Web Site: www.gulfstreamair.com
Approx. Rev.: $87,304,000
Approx. Number Employees: 604
Year Founded: 1988
Business Description:
Airline Operations
S.I.C.: 4512
N.A.I.C.S.: 481111
Media: 5-22
Personnel:
David F. Hackett *(Pres, CEO & Interim CFO)*

HAWAIIAN AIRLINES, INC.
(Sub. of Hawaiian Holdings, Inc.)
3375 Koapaka St Ste G-350
Honolulu, HI 96819
Mailing Address:
PO Box 3008
Honolulu, HI 96820
Tel.: (808) 835-3700
Fax: (808) 835-3690
Web Site: www.hawaiianair.com
Approx. Number Employees: 3,800
Year Founded: 1929
Business Description:
Commercial Passenger Airline
S.I.C.: 4512
N.A.I.C.S.: 481111
Personnel:
Mark B. Dunkerley *(Pres & CEO)*
Scott E. Topping *(CFO, Treas & Exec VP)*
David J. Osborne *(CIO & Exec VP)*
Peter R. Ingram *(Chief Comml Officer & Exec VP)*
Ann Botticelli *(Sr VP-Corp Comm & Pub Affairs)*
Barbara D. Falvey *(Sr VP-HR)*
Charles R. Nardello *(Sr VP-Ops)*
Glenn G. Taniguchi *(Sr VP-Mktg & Sls)*
Monisa Cline *(VP-Sls & Alliances)*
Dennis Manibusan *(VP-Maintenance & Engrg)*
Avi Mannis *(VP-Mktg)*
Blaine J. Miyasato *(VP-Product Dev)*
Lorrin Sardinha *(VP-Maintenance & Engrg)*
Susan Donofrio *(Sr Dir-HR)*
Beryl Fajardo *(Dir-Leadership Dev & Training)*
Kevin B. Yim *(Dir-Adv & Promos)*
Advertising Agencies:
McNeil Wilson Communications, Inc.
1003 Bishop St 9th Fl
Honolulu, HI 96813
Tel.: (808) 531-0244
Fax: (808) 531-0089
— Patrick Dugan *(Acct Exec)*

Sapient Corporation
17901 Old Cutler Rd Ste 400
Miami, FL 33157
Tel.: (305) 253-0100
Fax: (305) 253-0013

HAWAIIAN HOLDINGS, INC.
(Sub. of Airline Investors Partnership L.P.)
3375 Koapaka St Ste G-350
Honolulu, HI 96819
Mailing Address:
PO Box 30008
Honolulu, HI 96820-0008
Tel.: (808) 835-3700
Fax: (808) 835-3690
Web Site: www.hawaiianair.com
Approx. Rev.: $1,310,093,000
Approx. Number Employees: 4,023
Year Founded: 1929
Business Description:
Holding Company; Air Transportation
S.I.C.: 4512; 6719
N.A.I.C.S.: 481111; 481112; 551112
Advertising Expenditures: $11,000,000
Media: 2-3-5-6-7-8-9-13-18-20-23-24-26
Distr.: West Coast, Hawaii, Tahiti & Samoa
Personnel:
Lawrence S. Hershfield *(Chm)*
Mark B. Dunkerley *(Pres & CEO)*
Scott E. Topping *(CFO, Treas & Exec VP)*
David J. Osborne *(CIO & Exec VP)*
Hoyt H. Zia *(Gen Counsel, Sec & Sr VP)*
Barbara D. Falvey *(Sr VP-HR)*
Charles R. Nardello *(Sr VP-Ops)*
Glenn G. Taniguchi *(Sr VP-Sls & Mktg)*
Brands & Products:
HAWAIIAN AIRLINES
HAWAIIAN MILES
Advertising Agency:
McNeil Wilson Communications, Inc.
1003 Bishop St 9th Fl
Honolulu, HI 96813
Tel.: (808) 531-0244
Fax: (808) 531-0089

HEARTLAND EXPRESS, INC.
901 N Kansas Ave
North Liberty, IA 52317
Tel.: (319) 626-3600
Fax: (319) 626-3355
Toll Free: (800) 654-0025
E-mail: finance@heartlandexpress.com
Web Site: www.heartlandexpress.com
Approx. Rev.: $499,516,000
Approx. Number Employees: 2,990
Year Founded: 1978
Business Description:
Holding Company; Short-to-Medium Haul Freight Carriers
S.I.C.: 4212; 4213; 7389
N.A.I.C.S.: 484110; 484121; 561499
Advertising Expenditures: $700,000
Media: 2-9-10
Distr.: Natl.
Personnel:
Michael J. Gerdin *(Chm & CEO)*
John P. Cosaert *(CFO)*
Richard Meehan *(Exec VP-Mktg & Ops)*
Advertising Agency:
Midwest Media Services
PO Box 4512
North Liberty, IA 52317
Tel.: (319) 626-3364
Fax: (319) 626-3643

THE HERTZ CORPORATION
(Joint Venture of Bank of America Corporation, Carlyle Holding Corporation & Clayton, Dubilier & Rice, LLC)
225 Brae Blvd
Park Ridge, NJ 07656-1870
Tel.: (201) 307-2000
Fax: (201) 307-2644
Toll Free: (800) 654-3131
Web Site: www.hertz.com
Approx. Rev.: $7,562,534,000
Approx. Number Employees: 22,900
Year Founded: 1918
Business Description:
Automobiles, Trucks & Equipment Renting & Leasing
S.I.C.: 7359; 7514; 7515
N.A.I.C.S.: 532490; 532111; 532112
Advertising Expenditures: $116,300,000
Media: 1-2-3-6-7-8-9-10-11-13-15-18-19-20-23-24-25-26
Distr.: Natl.
Personnel:
Mark P. Frissora *(Chm & CEO)*
Elyse Douglas *(CFO & Exec VP)*
Joseph F. Eckroth *(CIO & Sr VP)*
Michael Senackerib *(Sr VP & CMO)*
LeighAnne G. Baker *(Chief HR Officer & Sr VP)*
Michel Taride *(Pres-Hertz Europe & Exec VP)*
Joseph R. Nothwang *(Pres-Rentala & Leasing Americas & Pacific)*
Harold E. Rolfe *(Gen Counsel, Sec & Sr VP)*
John A. Thomas *(Exec VP-Global Supply Chain Mgmt)*
Jatindar Kapur *(Controller & Sr VP-Fin)*
Robert J. Stuart *(Sr VP-Global Sls)*
Lisa Diliberto *(Sr Dir-Global Brand Mktg)*
Advertising Agencies:
BBDO New York
1285 Ave of the Americas 7th Fl
New York, NY 10019-6028
Tel.: (212) 459-5000

Brierley & Partners
8401 N Central Expy Ste 1000 LB-37
Dallas, TX 75225-4403
Tel.: (214) 760-8700
Fax: (214) 743-5511

DDB New York
437 Madison Ave
New York, NY 10022-7001
Tel.: (212) 415-2000
Fax: (212) 415-3506

G2 USA
200 5th Ave
New York, NY 10010
Tel.: (212) 537-3700
Fax: (212) 537-3737
Digital

Initiative
42 St John Square
London, EC1M 4EA, United Kingdom
Tel.: (44) 20 7663 7000
Fax: (44) 20 7663 7001

MMG Worldwide
4601 Madison Ave
Kansas City, MO 64112
Tel.: (816) 472-5988
Fax: (816) 471-5395

OMD-USA
195 Broadway
New York, NY 10007
Tel.: (212) 590-7100

HERTZ RENTAL CARS
(Sub. of Overland West Inc.)
Billings Logan Airport 1901 Terminal Cir
Billings, MT 59105
Tel.: (406) 248-9151
Fax: (406) 248-8323
E-mail: info@hertz.com
Web Site: www.hertz.com
Approx. Number Employees: 12
Year Founded: 1981
Business Description:
Passenger Car Rental
S.I.C.: 7514
N.A.I.C.S.: 532111
Import Export
Personnel:
Dan Petersen *(Owner)*
Advertising Agencies:
Atmosphere Proximity
1285 Ave of the Americas 5th Fl
New York, NY 10019
Tel.: (212) 827-2500
Fax: (212) 827-2525
Agency of Record
Mobile Ads
Online Display Ads
Print Ads
Rent2Buy - Creative Assignment
Social Networking
Web Search Ads

OMD-USA
195 Broadway
New York, NY 10007
Tel.: (212) 590-7100
Rent2Buy Campaign-Media Duties

Resolution Media
314 W Superior 2nd Fl
Chicago, IL 60610
Tel.: (312) 980-1600
Fax: (312) 980-1699
Rent2Buy - Media Duties

HIGHLANDS COUNTY TOURIST DEVELOPMENT COUNCIL
501 S Commerce Ave
Sebring, FL 33870
Tel.: (863) 402-6909
Web Site: www.highlandscvb.com
Business Description:
Florida Travel & Tourism Promoter
S.I.C.: 7389
N.A.I.C.S.: 561591
Advertising Agency:
Clark/Nikdel/Powell
62 4th St NW
Winter Haven, FL 33881
Tel.: (863) 299-9980
Fax: (863) 297-9061

HOLLAND AMERICA LINE INC.
(Sub. of Carnival plc)
300 Elliott Ave W
Seattle, WA 98119-4198
Tel.: (206) 281-3535

Key to Media (For complete agency information see *The Advertising Red Books-Agencies* edition):
1. Bus. Publs. 2. Cable T.V. 3. Catalogs & Directories. 4. Co-op Adv. 5. Consumer Mags. 6. D.M. to Bus. Estab.7. D.M. to Consumers
8. Daily Newsp. 9. Exhibits/Trade Shows 10. Foreign 11. Infomercial 12. Internet Adv.13. Multimedia 14. Network Radio
15. Network T.V. 16. Newsp. Distr. Mags. 17. Other 18. Outdoor (Posters, Transit) 19. Point of Purchase20. Premiums, Novelties
21. Product Samples 22. Special Events Mktg. 23. Spot Radio 24. Spot T.V. 25. Weekly Newsp. 26. Yellow Page Adv.

Holland America Line Inc. — (Continued)

Fax: (206) 281-7110
E-mail: info@hollandamerica.com
Web Site: www.hollandamerica.com
Sales Range: $800-899.9 Million
Approx. Number Employees: 1,155
Business Description:
Operator of Cruise Line
S.I.C.: 4725; 4724
N.A.I.C.S.: 561520; 561510
Advertising Expenditures: $21,000,000
Media: 2-6-9-17
Distr.: Natl.
Personnel:
Stein Kruse *(Pres & CEO)*
Larry D. Calkins *(CFO & Sr VP-Fin-IT)*
Richard D. Meadows *(Exec VP-Mktg & Sls & Guest Programs)*
Dan Grausz *(Sr VP-Fleet Ops)*
Paul T. Allen *(VP-Sls)*
Sally Andrews *(VP-Pub Rels)*
Judy Palmer *(VP-Mktg Communications)*
Joseph Slattery *(VP-Intl Sls & Mktg & Plng)*
Brendan J. Vierra *(VP-HR)*
Charles Dunwoody *(Sr Dir-Acct Sls-Natl)*
Brands & Products:
HOLLAND AMERICA LINE
SIGNATURE OF EXCELLENCE
TRADITION OF EXCELLENCE
Advertising Agency:
Hornall Anderson
Ste 1300 710 2nd Ave
Seattle, WA 98104-1712
Tel.: (206) 467-5800
Fax: (206) 467-6411

HOMEAWAY, INC.

1011 W Fifth St Ste 300
Austin, TX 78703
Tel.: (512) 684-1100
Web Site: www.homeaway.com
Approx. Rev.: $167,884,000
Approx. Number Employees: 781
Year Founded: 2005
Business Description:
Online Vacation Rental Sites Operator
S.I.C.: 4729; 2741
N.A.I.C.S.: 561599; 516110
Advertising Expenditures: $35,071,000
Personnel:
Brian Sharples *(Co-Founder & CEO)*
Lynn Atchison *(CFO & Sec)*
Brent Bellm *(COO)*
Carl G. Shepherd *(Chief Strategy Officer & Chief Dev Officer)*
Tom Hale *(Chief Product Officer)*
Eileen Buesing *(Sr Dir-PR)*
Matt Cohen *(Sr Dir-Brand Mktg-Global)*
Advertising Agencies:
Publicis West
424 2nd Ave W
Seattle, WA 98119-4013
Tel.: (206) 285-2222
Fax: (206) 273-4219

Vendor Inc
801 W 17th St
Austin, TX 78701
Tel.: (512) 474-8363

HONG KONG TOURISM BOARD - NEW YORK

(Branch of Hong Kong Tourism Board)
115 E 54th St 2nd Fl
New York, NY 10022-4512
Tel.: (212) 421-3382
Fax: (212) 421-8428
E-mail: nycwwo@hktb.com
Web Site: www.discoverhongkong.com/usa
Approx. Number Employees: 5
Business Description:
Tourism Marketing & Promotion Services
S.I.C.: 9611
N.A.I.C.S.: 926110
Personnel:
Lillibeth Bishop *(Dir-Promos)*
Linda Ho *(Asst Mgr-Mktg)*
Advertising Agency:
KCSA Strategic Communications
(Kanan, Corbin, Schupak & Aronow, Inc.)
880 3rd Ave 6th Fl
New York, NY 10022
Tel.: (212) 682-6300
Fax: (212) 697-0910

HORIZON AIR INDUSTRIES

(Sub. of Alaska Air Group, Inc.)
19521 International Blvd
Seattle, WA 98188-5402
Tel.: (206) 241-6757
Fax: (206) 248-6361
Toll Free: (800) 547-9308
Web Site: www.alaskaair.com
Approx. Sls.: $300,000,000
Approx. Number Employees: 120
Year Founded: 1981
Business Description:
Airline
S.I.C.: 4512; 4522
N.A.I.C.S.: 481111; 481219
Media: 5-6-7-8-9-10-11-13-23-25-26
Distr.: Natl.
Personnel:
Glenn S. Johnson *(Pres)*
Tom Gerharter *(Sr VP-Ops)*
Yvonne Daverin *(VP-Maintenance & Engrg)*
Mark Eliasen *(VP-Fin)*
Dan Russo *(VP-Mktg & Comm)*
Joe Samudovsky *(Dir-Cargo Sls)*
Brands & Products:
HORIZON AIR

HOTWIRE, INC.

(Sub. of Expedia, Inc.)
333 Market St Ste 100
San Francisco, CA 94105-2146
Tel.: (415) 343-8400
Fax: (415) 343-8401
Toll Free: (877) HOTWIRE
E-mail: bizdev@hotwire.com
Web Site: www.hotwire.com
Sales Range: $25-49.9 Million
Approx. Number Employees: 35
Year Founded: 2000
Business Description:
Discount Travel & Airfare Products & Services Online
S.I.C.: 4724; 2741
N.A.I.C.S.: 561510; 516110
Media: 5-13-14-15
Personnel:
Clem Bason *(Pres)*
Ravi Chandrasekaran *(VP-Product Dev)*
Cheryl Law *(VP-Mktg)*
Joe Selsavage *(VP-Fin)*
Jaideep Vijan *(VP-Engrg)*
Advertising Agencies:
Atomic Public Relations
735 Market St 4th Fl
San Francisco, CA 94103
Tel.: (415) 402-0230
Fax: (415) 402-0237
— Rachel Rogers *(Acct Exec)*

DonatWald+Haque
1316 Third St Ste 301
Santa Monica, CA 90401
Tel.: (310) 394-1717
Fax: (310) 394-1716

Gotham Direct
353 Lexington Ave 14th Fl
New York, NY 10016
Tel.: (212) 279-1474
Fax: (212) 279-1475

T3 (The Think Tank)
1806 Rio Grande
Austin, TX 78701
Tel.: (512) 499-8811
Fax: (512) 499-8552
CarRentals.com
Creative Agency of Record
Travel Ticker

IBERIA AIR LINES OF SPAIN

(Branch of Iberia Lineas Aereas de Espana, S.A.)
5835 Blue Lagoon Dr Ste 200
Miami, FL 33126-2062
Tel.: (305) 267-7747
Fax: (305) 262-1685
Toll Free: (800) 772-4642
Approx. Number Employees: 150
Year Founded: 1927
Business Description:
Provider of International Air Service
S.I.C.: 4522
N.A.I.C.S.: 481211
Advertising Expenditures: $10,000,000
Media: 2-5-6-8-9-10-16-19-23-24-25-26
Distr.: Direct to Consumer; Intl.; Natl.
Budget Set: Sept.
Personnel:
Cesar Alcazar *(Mgr)*

ICELANDAIR NORTH AMERICA

(Sub. of Flugleidir HF)
5950 Symphony Woods Rd Ste 410
Columbia, MD 21044
Tel.: (800) 779-2899
Fax: (410) 715-3547
Toll Free: (800) 223-5500
Telex: 4970657
Web Site: www.icelandair.com
Approx. Number Employees: 1,800
Year Founded: 1937
Business Description:
International Air Carrier
S.I.C.: 4512
N.A.I.C.S.: 481111
Advertising Expenditures: $1,500,000
Media: 2-6-7-8-9-10-13-16-18-20-22-23-25
Distr.: Natl.
Budget Set: Nov.

IGOUGO, INC.

(Unit of Travelocity.com LP)
325 Hudson St 10th Flr
New York, NY 10013
Tel.: (212) 372-5117
Fax: (682) 606-7117
E-mail: info@igougo.com
Web Site: www.igougo.com
Approx. Number Employees: 35
Business Description:
On-Line Travel Destination Information
S.I.C.: 2741
N.A.I.C.S.: 516110
Media: 13
Personnel:
Aditi Gokhale *(Gen Mgr)*

INTERNATIONAL ROAD DYNAMICS INC.

(d/b/a IRD)
702 43rd Street East
Saskatoon, SK S7K 3T9, Canada
Tel.: (306) 653-6600
Fax: (306) 242-5599
E-mail: info@irdinc.com
Web Site: www.irdinc.com
Approx. Sls.: $45,312,375
Approx. Number Employees: 50
Year Founded: 1980
Business Description:
Traffic Management, Monitoring & Enforcement Systems Developer & Mfr
S.I.C.: 3589; 3559; 7373; 7389
N.A.I.C.S.: 333319; 333298; 488490; 541512
Advertising Expenditures: $73,584
Media: 2-7-10
Personnel:
Arthur Bergan *(Chm)*
Terry Bergan *(Pres & CEO)*
Mel Karakochuk *(CFO & VP-Fin)*
Randy Hanson *(COO & Exec VP)*
Rod Klashinsky *(VP-Sls & Special Projects)*
Brands & Products:
DYNAX
INSTALERT
INSTALERT RAPID MESSENGER
IRD
ITOLL
ROADRAMP
SONOBLASTER!
SPEEDSENTRY
TRAFFIC ACE
TRAFFIC TALLY PEGASUS
UNICORN LIMITED

INTERNATIONAL SHIPHOLDING CORPORATION

11 N Water St Ste 18290
Mobile, AL 36602
Mailing Address:
PO Box 2004
Mobile, AL 36652
Tel.: (251) 243-9100
Toll Free: (888) 354-5274
Telex: 0587435
E-mail: fli-sales@intship.com
Web Site: www.intship.com
Approx. Rev.: $290,049,000
Approx. Number Employees: 501
Year Founded: 1978
Business Description:
Worldwide Waterborne Freight Transportation
S.I.C.: 4412; 4432
N.A.I.C.S.: 483111; 483113
Media: 2
Personnel:
Niels M. Johnsen *(Chm & CEO)*

Key to Media (For complete agency information see *The Advertising Red Books-Agencies* edition):
1. Bus. Publs. 2. Cable T.V. 3. Catalogs & Directories. 4. Co-op Adv. 5. Consumer Mags. 6. D.M. to Bus. Estab.7. D.M. to Consumers 8. Daily Newsp. 9. Exhibits/Trade Shows 10. Foreign 11. Infomercial 12. Internet Adv.13. Multimedia 14. Network Radio 15. Network T.V. 16. Newsp. Distr. Mags. 17. Other 18. Outdoor (Posters, Transit) 19. Point of Purchase20. Premiums, Novelties 21. Product Samples 22. Special Events Mktg. 23. Spot Radio 24. Spot T.V. 25. Weekly Newsp. 26. Yellow Page Adv.

Erik L. Johnsen *(Pres)*
Manuel G. Estrada *(CFO)*
Peter M. Johnston *(Dir-Ops)*
Timothy A. Delong *(Mgr-Fin Acctg & SEC Reporting)*

INTERSTATE WORLDWIDE RELOCATION, INC.
5801 Rolling Rd
Springfield, VA 22152-1064
Tel.: (703) 569-2121
Fax: (703) 569-3006
Toll Free: (800) 745MOVE
E-mail: interstate@invan.com
Web Site: www.interstateworldwide.com
Approx. Number Employees: 300
Year Founded: 1943
Business Description:
Local, Interstate, Long Distance & International Household Goods Carrier; Storage Facilities; Full Relocation Services & Logistics
S.I.C.: 4731; 8742
N.A.I.C.S.: 488510; 541614
Import Export
Media: 2-4-5-7-9-10-13-16-17-18-20-22-23-25-26
Distr.: Direct to Customer; Intl.; Natl.; Reg.
Budget Set: Dec.
Personnel:
Arthur E. Morrissette *(Chm)*
Don J. Morrisette *(Pres)*
Mike Larkin *(CFO & Exec VP)*
Kenneth Morrisette *(Pres-Interstate Svc Grp)*
Arthur E. Morrissette, IV *(Pres-Interstate Relocation Svcs & Interstate-Intl)*
John D. Morrissette *(Pres-Interstate Van Lines)*
Ron Gallier *(VP-HR & Quality Control)*
Sharon Cornell *(Mgr-Revenue Acctg)*
Daryl Flosi *(Mgr-Customer Svc)*
Dave France *(Mgr-Acctg)*
Albert Greene *(Mgr-MIS)*
Brands & Products:
AMERICA'S FAVORITE MOVER
MOVING LIFE'S MEMORIES
ULTRAPAK

INTERVAL LEISURE GROUP, INC.
6262 Sunset Dr
Miami, FL 33143-4843
Tel.: (305) 666-1861
Fax: (305) 667-5948
Toll Free: (800) 622-1861
Web Site: www.iilg.com
Approx. Rev.: $409,440,000
Approx. Number Employees: 2,900
Year Founded: 1976
Business Description:
Vacation Exchange Network & Travel & Leisure Services
S.I.C.: 4729
N.A.I.C.S.: 561599
Advertising Expenditures: $15,500,000
Media: 4-7-8-10-11
Personnel:
Craig M. Nash *(Chm, Pres & CEO)*
William L. Harvey *(CFO & Exec VP)*
Jeanette E. Marbert *(COO)*
Marie A. Lee *(CIO)*
John Galea *(Chief Acctg Officer)*
Victoria J. Kincke *(Gen Counsel)*
David C. Gilbert *(Exec VP-Resort Sls & Mktg-Americas)*
Advertising Agency:
Kahn Travel Communications
77 N Centre Ave Ste 215
Rockville Centre, NY 11570
Tel.: (516) 594-4100
Fax: (516) 594-4104

INTRAV, INC.
(Sub. of Kuoni Travel Holding Ltd.)
11969 Westline Industrial Dr
Saint Louis, MO 63146
Tel.: (314) 655-6700
Fax: (314) 655-6670
Toll Free: (800) 456-8100
E-mail: info@intrav.com
Web Site: www.intrav.com
Approx. Number Employees: 100
Year Founded: 1959
Business Description:
Offers Upscale, Exotic Land & Sea Vacations
S.I.C.: 4724
N.A.I.C.S.: 561510
Export
Media: 4-8-10-11-13
Brands & Products:
INTRAV

ISRAM WHOLESALE TOURS & TRAVEL LTD.
(d/b/a Isram World of Travel (ISRAMWORLD))
233 Pk Ave S
New York, NY 10003
Tel.: (212) 661-1193
Fax: (212) 370-1477
Toll Free: (800) 223-7460
Telex: 423241
E-mail: info@isram.com
Web Site: www.isram.com
Approx. Number Employees: 200
Year Founded: 1967
Business Description:
Tour Operator
S.I.C.: 4725
N.A.I.C.S.: 561520
Media: 2-4-7-8-9-11-13-25
Distr.: Natl.
Personnel:
Ady Gelber *(Owner & CEO)*
Ilana Apelboim *(COO & Sr VP)*
Eileen Lowe Hart *(Sr VP-Mktg & Product Dev)*
Betty Van Dyke *(Sr VP-R&D)*
Lisa Buhasira *(VP-Sls, Bus Dev & Indus Rels)*
Brands & Products:
ESCAPADE VACATIONS
HOLY LANDS SUN TOURS
JEWISH HERITAGE TOURS
LATOUR
ORIENT FLEXI-PAX TOURS

JAPAN AIRLINES COMPANY, LTD.
(Sub. of Japan Airlines International Co., Ltd.)
461 5th Ave
New York, NY 10017
Tel.: (212) 310-1337
Fax: (212) 310-1376
Toll Free: (800) 525-3663
Telex: 8384400
Web Site: www.jal.com
Approx. Number Employees: 900
Year Founded: 1953
Business Description:
Scheduled Passenger & Cargo International Airline
S.I.C.: 4581
N.A.I.C.S.: 488119
Import Export
Advertising Expenditures: $4,500,000
Media: 2-3-4-6-7-9-10-11-18-19-20-23-24-25-26
Distr.: Intl.; Natl.
Budget Set: Dec.
Brands & Products:
JAPAN AIRLINES

JETBLUE AIRWAYS CORPORATION
118-29 Queens Blvd
Forest Hills, NY 11375
Tel.: (718) 286-7900
Fax: (718) 709-3621
Toll Free: (800) 538-2583
E-mail: ir@jetblue.com
Web Site: www.jetblue.com
Approx. Rev.: $3,779,000,000
Approx. Number Employees: 9,626
Year Founded: 1999
Business Description:
Airline Operations
S.I.C.: 4512; 4581
N.A.I.C.S.: 481111; 488190
Export
Advertising Expenditures: $53,000,000
Media: 6-9-13-14-18-22-23-24-25-26
Personnel:
Joel C. Peterson *(Chm)*
Frank V. Sica *(Vice Chm)*
David Barger *(Pres & CEO)*
Edward Barnes *(CFO & Sr VP)*
Robert Maruster *(COO & Exec VP)*
Joseph Eng *(CIO & Exec VP)*
Joanna Geraghty *(Chief People Officer)*
Robin Hayes *(Chief Comml Officer & Exec VP)*
James Hnat *(Gen Counsel & Exec VP-Corp Affairs)*
Robert Land *(Sr VP-Govt Affairs & Assoc Gen Counsel)*
Martin St. George *(Sr VP-Mktg & Comml)*
Jenny Dervin *(VP-Corp Comm)*
Fiona Morrisson *(Dir-Brand & Adv)*
David Conty *(Dir-Loyalty & Partnerships)*
Jeffrey Goodell *(Dir-Govt Affairs)*
Brandon Nelson *(Dir-Contracts Counsel)*
Alison Croyle *(Mgr-Corp Comm)*
Leann Guinn *(Coord-Mktg Programs)*
Brands & Products:
COMPANYBLUE
FLIGHTGRATITUDE
JETBLUE
JETBLUE AIRWAYS
JETBLUE FEATURES
SHOPBLUE
SHUT-EYE SERVICE
TRUEBLUE
WE LIKE YOU TOO
Advertising Agencies:
Carson Marketing, Inc.
1740 E Garry Ave Ste 231
Santa Ana, CA 92705-5844
Tel.: (949) 477-9400
Fax: (949) 477-2425
"TruBlu" Customer Loyalty Program
Airport Spots
E-Mail Marketing
In Flight
Online
Out of Home Advertising

Centra360
1400 Old Country Rd Ste 420
Westbury, NY 11590-5119
Tel.: (516) 997-3147
Fax: (516) 334-7798

Mullen
40 Broad St
Boston, MA 02109
Tel.: (617) 226-9000
Fax: (617) 226-9100
Creative & Media Agency of Record
Digital
Non-Traditional Advertising
Outdoor
Print
Radio
Social
Television

The MWW Group
1 Meadowlands Plz 6th Fl
East Rutherford, NJ 07073
Tel.: (201) 507-9500
Fax: (201) 507-0092
Issues Management Counseling

Rokkan
176 Grand St 2nd Fl
New York, NY 10012-4003
Tel.: (212) 835-9300
Fax: (212) 251-9393
Digital

JOHNSON STORAGE & MOVING COMPANY
221 Broadway
Denver, CO 80203-3918
Tel.: (303) 778-6683
Fax: (303) 698-0512
Toll Free: (800) 289-6683
E-mail: questions@johnson-united.com
Web Site: www.johnsonstorage.com
Approx. Number Employees: 400
Year Founded: 1900
Business Description:
Moving & Storage Company
S.I.C.: 4214
N.A.I.C.S.: 484210
Import Export
Media: 5-8-23
Personnel:
Mark K. Johnson *(Owner)*

JTB USA
(Branch of JTB Corp.)
810 7th Ave 34th Fl
New York, NY 10019
Tel.: (212) 698-4900
Fax: (212) 586-9686
Toll Free: (800) 235-3523
E-mail: mth@jtbusa.com
Web Site: www.jtbusa.com
Approx. Number Employees: 1,400
Year Founded: 1964
Business Description:
Package, Convention, Group & Individual Tours

Key to Media (For complete agency information see *The Advertising Red Books-Agencies* edition):
1. Bus. Publs. 2. Cable T.V. 3. Catalogs & Directories. 4. Co-op Adv. 5. Consumer Mags. 6. D.M. to Bus. Estab.7. D.M. to Consumers
8. Daily Newsp. 9. Exhibits/Trade Shows 10. Foreign 11. Infomercial 12. Internet Adv.13. Multimedia 14. Network Radio
15. Network T.V. 16. Newsp. Distr. Mags. 17. Other 18. Outdoor (Posters, Transit) 19. Point of Purchase20. Premiums, Novelties
21. Product Samples 22. Special Events Mktg. 23. Spot Radio 24. Spot T.V. 25. Weekly Newsp. 26. Yellow Page Adv.

JTB USA — (Continued)

S.I.C.: 4724
N.A.I.C.S.: 561510
Media: 7-8-9-11-13-25
Personnel:
Masaya Yoshimoto *(Branch Mgr)*
Brands & Products:
YOUR GLOBAL LIFESTYLE PARTNER

THE KANSAS CITY SOUTHERN RAILWAY COMPANY

(Sub. of Kansas City Southern)
427 W 12th St
Kansas City, MO 64105
Mailing Address:
PO Box 219335
Kansas City, MO 64121-9335
Tel.: (816) 983-1303
Fax: (816) 983-1418
Toll Free: (800) 282-8700
Web Site: www.kcsr.com
Sales Range: $550-599.9 Million
Approx. Number Employees: 2,700
Year Founded: 1887
Business Description:
Railroad
S.I.C.: 4011; 4213
N.A.I.C.S.: 482111; 484121
Media: 2-4
Distr.: Direct to Consumer; Reg.
Budget Set: Feb.
Personnel:
Michael R. Haverty *(Chm)*
David L. Starling *(Pres & CEO)*
Rodney E. Slater *(Partner)*
Michael W. Upchurch *(CFO & Exec VP)*
David R. Ebbrecht *(Sr VP-Ops)*
John S. Jacobsen *(Sr VP & Chief Engr Officer)*
Brands & Products:
KANSAS CITY SOUTHERN
NAFTA RAILWAY
PANAMA CANAL RAILWAY COMPANY
TEXAS MEXICAN RAILWAYS
TFM

THE KENAN ADVANTAGE GROUP, INC.

(Holding of Littlejohn & Co. LLC)
4366 MT Pleasent St
Canton, OH 44720
Tel.: (330) 491-0474
Fax: (330) 491-1471
Toll Free: (800) 969-5419
Web Site: www.thekag.com
Approx. Rev.: $570,000,000
Approx. Number Employees: 3,545
Year Founded: 2005
Business Description:
Fuel Transporter
S.I.C.: 1389; 4212
N.A.I.C.S.: 213112; 484110
Advertising Expenditures: $617,000
Personnel:
Bruce Blaise *(Pres)*
Dennis A. Nash *(CEO)*
Carl Young *(CFO)*
Douglas Allen *(COO, VP & Gen Mgr)*
William Downey *(Exec VP-Corp Affairs)*
Robert Schurer *(Exec VP-Specialty Products Grp)*
Kevin Spencer *(Exec VP-Logistics Grp)*
Stan Tedder *(VP-Sls & Mktg)*
Tom Baughman, Jr. *(Dir-Info Tech)*
Nichole Destefano *(Mgr-Sls & Mktg)*
Vickie Edwards *(Mgr-Compliance)*

KILLINGTON LIMITED

(Sub. of Powdr Corp)
4763 Killington Rd
Killington, VT 05751
Tel.: (802) 422-3333
E-mail: info@killington.com
Web Site: www.killington.com
E-Mail For Key Personnel:
Public Relations: snownews@vermontel.com
Approx. Number Employees: 1,000
Year Founded: 1958
Business Description:
Resort & Ski Area Operator
S.I.C.: 7999; 7011
N.A.I.C.S.: 487990; 721199
Media: 1-8-10-18-19-20-22-23-24
Distr.: Intl.; Natl.; Reg.
Personnel:
Tracy Taylor *(Dir-Resort Svcs)*

KLLM TRANSPORT SERVICES, INC.

134 Riverview Dr
Richland, MS 39218
Tel.: (601) 939-2545
Fax: (601) 936-5496
Toll Free: (800) 925-1000
E-mail: info@kllm.com
Web Site: www.kllm.com
Sales Range: $25-49.9 Million
Approx. Number Employees: 2,100
Year Founded: 1963
Business Description:
Truckload Transportation & Dedicated Logistics Services to North America
S.I.C.: 4213
N.A.I.C.S.: 484121
Advertising Expenditures: $340,000
Media: 2-9-20-23
Distr.: Direct to Consumer; Natl.
Personnel:
James M. Richards *(Pres & CEO)*
Kevin Adams *(CFO)*
Steve Szado *(VP-HR)*
Brands & Products:
COMMITTED TO DRIVERS. COMMITTED TO YOU.
KLLM
SAFETY THE ONLY CHOICE
VERNON SAWYER
Advertising Agency:
Godwin Advertising Agency, Inc.
(d/b/a GodwinGroup)
1 Jackson Pl 188 E Capitol St Ste 800
Jackson, MS 39201
Tel.: (601) 354-5711
Fax: (601) 960-5869

KLM ROYAL DUTCH AIRLINES

(Div. of KLM Royal Dutch Airlines)
565 Taxter Rd 3rd Fl
Elmsford, NY 10523
Tel.: (914) 784-2000
Web Site: www.klm.com
Approx. Number Employees: 60
Business Description:
International Airline Services
S.I.C.: 4512
N.A.I.C.S.: 481111
Media: 2-5-6-7-8-9-10-18-23-26
Distr.: Intl.; Natl.
Budget Set: Oct.
Personnel:
L.M. Van Wijk *(Pres & CEO)*
Winni Notenboom *(Mgr-Affiliate Mktg)*
Advertising Agencies:
Campbell-Ewald
Building 6 Office 210
PO Box 502146
Dubai, Media City United Arab Emirates
Tel.: (971) 4 391 0377
Fax: (971) 4 390 4854

Northwest Media Relations
5101 NW Dr Dept A1186
Saint Paul, MN 55111
Tel.: (612) 726-2331
Fax: (612) 726-3942

KUWAIT AIRWAYS CORP.

(Sub. of Kuwait Airways Corp.)
Parker Plz 400 Kelby St
Fort Lee, NJ 07024
Tel.: (201) 582-9222
Tel.: (201) 582-9223
Fax: (201) 947-8113
Toll Free: (800) 4KUWAIT
E-mail: nyc@kuwaitairways.com
Web Site: www.kuwait-airways.com
Sales Range: $500-549.9 Million
Approx. Number Employees: 5,000
Year Founded: 1967
Business Description:
Airline Services
S.I.C.: 4512
N.A.I.C.S.: 481111
Media: 2-4-7-9
Distr.: Natl.
Personnel:
Mohammad Al-Awadi *(Dir-Flight Svcs Dept)*
Ali Al-Hamdan *(Dir-Internal Audit Dept)*
Mona Al-Hazaa *(Dir-Legal)*
Mohammad Al-Shatti *(Dir-Pur & Housing Dept)*
Essam Al-Shaye *(Dir-HR)*
Adel Boresly *(Dir-PR & Info Dept)*

LANDSTAR SYSTEM, INC.

13410 Sutton Park Dr S
Jacksonville, FL 32224-5270
Tel.: (904) 398-9400
Fax: (904) 390-1437
E-mail: corpcomm@landstar.com
Web Site: www.landstar.com
E-Mail For Key Personnel:
President: hgerkens@landstar.com
Approx. Rev.: $2,400,170,000
Approx. Number Employees: 1,353
Year Founded: 1991
Business Description:
Transportation & Logistics Services
S.I.C.: 4213
N.A.I.C.S.: 484121
Media: 2-7-10-13-23
Budget Set: Oct. -Nov.
Personnel:
Henry H. Gerkens *(Chm, Pres & CEO)*
James B. Gattoni *(CFO & VP)*
Patrick O'Malley *(COO)*
Larry S. Thomas *(CIO & VP)*
Jeffrey Pundt *(Pres-Carrier Grp)*
Michael Kneller *(Gen Counsel, Sec & VP)*
Joe Beacom *(Chief Compliance, Security & Safety Officer & VP)*
Patty McMenamin *(VP-Corp Comm)*
Ginger Whitcher *(Dir-Corp Comm)*
Brands & Products:
BCO
LANDSTAR
LANDSTAR GEMINI
LANDSTAR INWAY
LANDSTAR LIGON
LANDSTAR RANGER
LANDSTAR SYSTEM INC.
LANDSTARBROKER.COM
LANDSTAR.COM
LANDSTARCOMPANYSTORE.COM
LANDSTARONLINE.COM
LCAPP
LCAPP.COM
LEADS
POWER BUYING. BUYING POWER.
THE ROAD TO SUCCESS
SOLUTIONS IN MOTION

LIBERTY TRAVEL, INC.

(Sub. of Flight Centre Ltd.)
69 Spring St
Ramsey, NJ 07446
Tel.: (201) 934-3500
Fax: (201) 934-3651
Web Site: www.libertytravel.com
Approx. Number Employees: 2,500
Year Founded: 1951
Business Description:
Travel & Tourism Services
S.I.C.: 4724; 4729
N.A.I.C.S.: 561510; 561599
Media: 2-3-4-5-6-7-8-9-10-13-19-20-23-25-26
Distr.: Reg.
Advertising Agency:
Resort Advertising Service
(House Agency)
69 Spring St.
Ramsey, NJ 07446
Tel.: (201) 934-3500

LONG ISLAND RAIL ROAD

(Sub. of Metropolitan Transportation Authority)
Jamaica Sta
Jamaica, NY 11435
Tel.: (718) 558-7400
Fax: (718) 558-7633
Web Site: mta.info/lirr
Sales Range: $350-399.9 Million
Approx. Number Employees: 6,381
Year Founded: 1834
Business Description:
Local Railroad Operator
S.I.C.: 4111
N.A.I.C.S.: 485119
Media: 9-17-18-23-25
Distr.: Direct to Consumer; Reg.
Personnel:
Helena Williams *(Pres)*
Mary Mahon *(Gen Counsel, Sec & VP)*
Albert C. Cosenza *(Exec VP)*
Michael J. Reilly *(Asst Controller)*
Theresa Conetta *(Gen Mgr)*
Katherine N. Lapp *(Exec Dir)*
Yannis Takos *(Dir-Mktg Res)*
Brands & Products:
THE LONG ISLAND RAIL ROAD
MTA LONG ISLAND RAIL ROAD
Advertising Agency:
Korey Kay & Partners
130 5th Ave
New York, NY 10011-4306
Tel.: (212) 620-4300
Fax: (212) 620-7055
Fax: (212) 620-7149

Key to Media (For complete agency information see *The Advertising Red Books-Agencies* edition):
1. Bus. Publs. 2. Cable T.V. 3. Catalogs & Directories. 4. Co-op Adv. 5. Consumer Mags. 6. D.M. to Bus. Estab.7. D.M. to Consumers
8. Daily Newsp. 9. Exhibits/Trade Shows 10. Foreign 11. Infomercial 12. Internet Adv.13. Multimedia 14. Network Radio
15. Network T.V. 16. Newsp. Distr. Mags. 17. Other 18. Outdoor (Posters, Transit) 19. Point of Purchase20. Premiums, Novelties
21. Product Samples 22. Special Events Mktg. 23. Spot Radio 24. Spot T.V. 25. Weekly Newsp. 26. Yellow Page Adv.

(Transportation)

LOS ANGELES COUNTY METROPOLITAN TRANSPORTATION AUTHORITY
(d/b/a MTA)
1 Gateway Plz
Los Angeles, CA 90012
Tel.: (213) 922-6000
Fax: (213) 922-7447
Toll Free: (800) COMMUTE
E-mail: raimondm@metro.net
Web Site: www.metro.net
Sales Range: $1-4.9 Billion
Approx. Number Employees: 9,000
Business Description:
Bus & Rail Transit System Operator
S.I.C.: 4111
N.A.I.C.S.: 485113
Media: 1-4-9-13-18-25
Personnel:
Don Knabe *(Chm)*
Arthur T. Leahy *(CEO)*
Terry Matsumoto *(CFO)*
Lonnie Mitchell *(Chief Admin Officer & Interim COO)*
Greg K. Kildare *(Exec Officer-Risk Mngmt)*
Karen Gorman *(Ethics Officer)*
Charles Safer *(Gen Counsel)*
Mike Cannell *(Gen Mgr-Rail Ops)*
Doug Failing *(Exec Dir-Highway Programs)*
Marc Littman *(Dir-Pub Rels)*

LOT POLISH AIRLINES SA
(Branch of LOT Polish Airlines S.A.)
500 5th Ave Ste 408
New York, NY 10110
Tel.: (212) 852-0244
Fax: (212) 852-0293
Toll Free: (800) 223-0593
Web Site: www.lot.com
Year Founded: 1929
Business Description:
Airline Services
S.I.C.: 4512
N.A.I.C.S.: 481111
Media: 2-6-9-10
Distr.: Direct to Consumer; Intl.; Natl.
Brands & Products:
LOT
Advertising Agency:
Global Advertising Strategies
55 Broad St 19th Fl
New York, NY 10004
Tel.: (212) 964-0030
Fax: (212) 964-0040

MACQUARIE AMERICAS PARKING CORPORATION
(Sub. of MACQUARIE INFRASTRUCTURE COMPANY LLC)
125 W 55th St
New York, NY 10019
Tel.: (212) 231-1000
Fax: (212) 231-2030
Approx. Number Employees: 50
Year Founded: 2002
Business Description:
Off-Site Airport Parking Operations
S.I.C.: 7521
N.A.I.C.S.: 812930
Advertising Expenditures: $1,265,643

MAERSK INC.
(Sub. of A.P. Moller-Maersk A/S)
2 Giralda Farms Madison Ave
Madison, NJ 07940
Mailing Address:
PO Box 880
Madison, NJ 07940-0880
Tel.: (973) 514-5000
Fax: (973) 514-5410
Toll Free: (800) 321-8807
E-mail: grf@maersk.com
Web Site: www.maersk.com
Approx. Number Employees: 750
Year Founded: 1943
Business Description:
Sea & Land Transporter Containerized Cargo
S.I.C.: 4731; 4491
N.A.I.C.S.: 488510; 488320
Media: 2-4-7-10-11-13-20
Distr.: Intl.; Natl.
Personnel:
J. Russell Bruner *(Chm-Maersk Line)*
John P. Clancey *(Chm)*
John Boudreau *(Pres)*
Morten K. Nicolaisen *(CFO)*
Bob Copaldo *(CIO & VP-Bus Process & Quality)*
Gene Pentimonti *(Sr VP-Govt Affairs)*
William Woodhour *(Sr VP)*

MARITZ INC.
1375 N Hwy Dr
Fenton, MO 63099
Tel.: (636) 827-4000
Fax: (636) 827-3312
Toll Free: (877) 4MARITZ
E-mail: webmaster@maritz.com
Web Site: www.maritz.com
E-Mail For Key Personnel:
Public Relations: beth.rusert@maritz.com
Approx. Rev.: $1,270,000,000
Approx. Number Employees: 3,665
Year Founded: 1894
Business Description:
Consulting Services
S.I.C.: 7389; 4724; 4729; 8732; 8742; 8748
N.A.I.C.S.: 519190; 541613; 541690; 541910; 561510; 561599
Import
Media: 2-4-7
Distr.: Intl.; Natl.
Budget Set: Jan.
Personnel:
W. Stephen Maritz *(Chm & CEO)*
Gil Hoffman *(CIO)*
Con McGrath *(VP-HR)*
Beth Rusert *(VP-Comm & Pub Affairs)*
Jennifer Larsen *(Dir-PR)*
Liz Drazen *(Sr Mgr-Comm)*
Brands & Products:
BRANDXCELLENCE
DELVE
ENVOY
IMPACT
MARITZ
ONE
THE SCIENCE AND ART OF PEOPLE AND POTENTIAL
WACAM
Advertising Agencies:
Attack Marketing, LLC
367 Nineth St Ste B
San Francisco, CA 94103
Tel.: (415) 433-1499
Fax: (415) 276-5759

Oneupweb
13561 S W Bayshore Dr Ste 3000
Traverse City, MI 49684
Tel.: (231) 922-9977
Fax: (231) 922-9966
Toll Free: (877) 568-7477

Rodgers Townsend, LLC
1000 Clark Ave 5th Fl
Saint Louis, MO 63102
Tel.: (314) 436-9960
Fax: (314) 436-9961

Standing Partnership
540 Maryville Ctr Dr Ste 100
Saint Louis, MO 63141
Tel.: (314) 469-3500
Fax: (314) 469-3512

MARK TRAVEL CORPORATION
8969 N Port Washington Rd
Milwaukee, WI 53217-1634
Tel.: (414) 228-7472
Fax: (414) 351-5256
Web Site: www.marktravel.com
Sales Range: $125-149.9 Million
Approx. Number Employees: 1,500
Year Founded: 1974
Business Description:
Vacation & Travel Planning Services
S.I.C.: 4724
N.A.I.C.S.: 561510
Import Export
Media: 8-13
Personnel:
William E. La Macchia *(COO)*
Brands & Products:
MARK TRAVEL
Advertising Agency:
BVK
250 W Coventry Ct #300
Milwaukee, WI 53217-3972
Tel.: (414) 228-1990
Fax: (414) 228-7561
Toll Free: (888) 347-3212

MARQUIS JET PARTNERS INC.
(Sub. of NetJets Inc.)
230 Park Ave Ste 840
New York, NY 10169
Tel.: (212) 499-3790
Fax: (212) 499-3710
Toll Free: (866) 538-0707
E-mail: corporate@marquisjet.com
Web Site: www.marquisjet.com
Approx. Number Employees: 70
Business Description:
Private Jet Leasing Services
S.I.C.: 4522
N.A.I.C.S.: 481219
Media: 6
Personnel:
Kenny Dichter *(Founder, Chm & CEO)*
Henry Schachar *(Vice Chm)*
Ken Austin *(Pres)*
Carl Thorsberg *(CFO)*
Randy Brandoff *(CMO)*
David Lawrence *(Exec VP-Fin & Admin)*
Ken Hogan *(VP-Adv)*
Brands & Products:
FLEET BY NETJETS
MARQUIS JET CARD
MARQUISJET

MATSON NAVIGATION COMPANY, INC.
(Sub. of Alexander & Baldwin, Inc.)
555 12th St 7th Fl
Oakland, CA 94607
Tel.: (510) 628-4000
Fax: (510) 628-7359
E-mail: general_info@matson.com
Web Site: www.matson.com
E-Mail For Key Personnel:
Marketing Director: mmiller@matson.com
Sales Range: $1-4.9 Billion
Approx. Number Employees: 898
Year Founded: 1882
Business Description:
Freight Transportation & Marine Cargo Handling Services
S.I.C.: 4412; 4491
N.A.I.C.S.: 483111; 488320
Media: 2-4-7-9-25-26
Distr.: Natl.
Budget Set: Aug.
Personnel:
Kevin C. O'Rourke *(Gen Counsel & Sr VP)*
Ronald J. Forest *(Sr VP-Ops)*
David L. Hoppes *(Sr VP-Ocean Svcs)*
Yolanda V. Gonzalez *(VP-HR)*
Jeff Hull *(Dir-Pub Rels)*
Mark D. Miller *(Mgr-Mktg)*
Advertising Agency:
MVNP
999 Bishop St 21th Fl
Honolulu, HI 96813-4429
Tel.: (808) 536-0881
Fax: (808) 529-6208

MAUPINTOUR HOLDINGS, LLC
2400 N Commerce Pkwy Ste 105
Weston, FL 33326
Tel.: (702) 260-3600
Fax: (702) 260-3787
Toll Free: (800) 255-4266
Telex: 426237
E-mail: info@maupintour.com
Web Site: www.maupintour.com
E-Mail For Key Personnel:
Public Relations: SBailey@maupintour.com
Approx. Number Employees: 70
Year Founded: 1951
Business Description:
Tour Operators
S.I.C.: 4725; 4724
N.A.I.C.S.: 561520; 561510
Advertising Expenditures: $3,260,000
Media: 1-2-4-5-6-7-8-9-13-18
Distr.: Intl.; Natl.
Budget Set: Aug.
Brands & Products:
MAUPIN ADVENTURES
MAUPIN FLEX
MAUPIN TOUR
MAUPIN WATERWAYS

MAVERICK TRANSPORTATION, INC.
13301 Valentine Rd
North Little Rock, AR 72117
Tel.: (501) 945-6130
Fax: (501) 955-1500
Toll Free: (800) 289-6600
Web Site: www.maverickusa.com
Approx. Number Employees: 1,000
Year Founded: 1980

Key to Media (For complete agency information see *The Advertising Red Books-Agencies* edition):
1. Bus. Publs. 2. Cable T.V. 3. Catalogs & Directories. 4. Co-op Adv. 5. Consumer Mags. 6. D.M. to Bus. Estab.7. D.M. to Consumers 8. Daily Newsp. 9. Exhibits/Trade Shows 10. Foreign 11. Infomercial 12. Internet Adv.13. Multimedia 14. Network Radio 15. Network T.V. 16. Newsp. Distr. Mags. 17. Other 18. Outdoor (Posters, Transit) 19. Point of Purchase20. Premiums, Novelties 21. Product Samples 22. Special Events Mktg. 23. Spot Radio 24. Spot T.V. 25. Weekly Newsp. 26. Yellow Page Adv.

Maverick Transportation, Inc. — (Continued)

Business Description:
Long Distance, Local Logistics & Transportation Services
S.I.C.: 4213; 4212
N.A.I.C.S.: 484230; 484110
Media: 2-7-8-9-10-13-18-25
Personnel:
Steven R. Williams *(Chm & CEO)*
Stephen Selig *(Pres & COO)*
John A. Culp *(CFO & Exec VP)*
Debbie Mitchell *(VP-Fin)*

MAY TRUCKING COMPANY INC.

4185 Brooklake Rd
Salem, OR 97303
Mailing Address:
PO Box 9039
Salem, OR 97305
Tel.: (503) 393-7030
Fax: (503) 390-3594
Toll Free: (800) 547-9169
Web Site: www.maytrucking.com
Approx. Number Employees: 1,000
Year Founded: 1945
Business Description:
Trucking Services
S.I.C.: 4213; 4212
N.A.I.C.S.: 484121; 484110
Import Export
Media: 2-9-18-25
Personnel:
David M. Daniels *(Pres)*
C. Marvin May *(CEO)*
Dave Temple *(CFO)*

MEDITERRANEAN SHIPPING COMPANY USA INC.

(Sub. of Mediterranean Shipping Company, S.A.)
420 5th Ave 8th Fl
New York, NY 10018-0222
Tel.: (212) 764-4800
Fax: (212) 764-8593
E-mail: info@msc.us
Web Site: www.msc.us
Sales Range: $25-49.9 Million
Approx. Number Employees: 460
Year Founded: 1971
Business Description:
Freight Transportation Arrangement Services
S.I.C.: 4731
N.A.I.C.S.: 488510
Personnel:
Nicola Arena *(Chm & CEO)*
Claudio Bovvo *(Pres)*
Allen Clifford *(Exec VP)*
Robert A. Magna *(VP-Sls-West Coast)*
Advertising Agency:
JI Advertising
Danbury, CT 06810
Tel.: (203) 744-4239

MENLO WORLDWIDE, LLC

(Sub. of Con-way Inc.)
(d/b/a Menlo Worldwide Logistics)
2855 Campus Dr Ste 300
San Mateo, CA 94403-2512
Tel.: (630) 449-1084
Fax: (650) 596-4150
E-mail: info@menloworldwide.com
Web Site: www.menloworldwide.com
Approx. Number Employees: 4,800
Year Founded: 1990
Business Description:
Transportation, Warehouse & Supply Chain Management Services
S.I.C.: 4731
N.A.I.C.S.: 488510
Media: 2
Personnel:
Robert L. Bianco *(Pres)*
Robert W. Bassett *(Dir-Bus Dev-Global)*

MESA AIR GROUP, INC.

410 N 44th St Ste 700
Phoenix, AZ 85008-7608
Tel.: (602) 685-4000
Fax: (602) 685-4350
E-mail: webmaster@mesa-air.com
Web Site: www.mesa-air.com
E-Mail For Key Personnel:
Public Relations: pr@mesa-air.com
Approx. Number Employees: 4,113
Year Founded: 1982
Business Description:
Holding Company & Regional Airline
S.I.C.: 4512; 4522; 6719
N.A.I.C.S.: 481111; 481219; 551112
Media: 13-25
Personnel:
Jonathan G. Ornstein *(Chm & CEO)*
Michael J. Lotz *(Pres & CFO)*
Paul J. Foley *(COO & Exec VP)*
Robert Hornberg *(CIO & VP)*
Christopher Pappaioanou *(Gen Counsel, VP & Sec)*
Gary Appling *(Sr VP-Tech Svcs & Engrg)*
David Butler *(Sr VP-HR & Admin)*
F. Carter Leake *(Sr VP-Plng)*
Charles Kettler *(VP-Pur & Tech Svcs)*
Keith Kranzow *(VP-Fin & Plng)*
Allan Lowery *(VP-Trng)*
Zakaullah Khogyani *(Sr Dir-Ops)*
Bud Tyler *(Dir-Contract Revenue Mgmt)*
Todd Bourg *(Dir-Plng)*
Michael Wuerger *(Dir-Safety & Regulatory Compliance)*
Advertising Agency:
Bayard Advertising Agency, Inc.
8777 E Via de Ventura
Scottsdale, AZ 85258
Tel.: (480) 922-8808
Fax: (480) 922-8834
— Linda Kooltonow *(Acct Exec)*

METRO

707 N 1st St Stop 1
Saint Louis, MO 63102
Tel.: (314) 982-1400
Fax: (314) 982-1522
Web Site: www.metrostlouis.org
Sales Range: $25-49.9 Million
Approx. Number Employees: 200
Business Description:
Commuter Bus Operation
S.I.C.: 4111; 4581
N.A.I.C.S.: 485113; 488119
Personnel:
Dianne H. Williams *(Dir-Comm)*
Advertising Agency:
Schupp Company, Inc.
401 Pine St
Saint Louis, MO 63102-2731
Tel.: (314) 421-5200
Fax: (314) 421-5554

METROPOLITAN ATLANTA RAPID TRANSIT AUTHORITY

(d/b/a MARTA)
2424 Piedmont Rd NE
Atlanta, GA 30324-3311
Tel.: (404) 848-5000
E-mail: custserv@itsmarta.com
Web Site: www.itsmarta.com
Sales Range: $100-124.9 Million
Approx. Number Employees: 4,800
Year Founded: 1971
Business Description:
Provider of Transit Services
S.I.C.: 4111
N.A.I.C.S.: 485113
Import Export
Personnel:
Beverly A. Scott *(CEO & Gen Mgr)*
Advertising Agency:
BGT Partners
2627 NE 203rd St Ste 202
Miami, FL 33180
Tel.: (305) 438-1800
Fax: (305) 438-1560

METROPOLITAN TRANSPORTATION AUTHORITY

347 Madison Ave
New York, NY 10017-3706
Tel.: (212) 878-7000
Fax: (212) 878-0166
Toll Free: (800) 638-7646
Web Site: www.mta.nyc.ny.us
Sales Range: $5-14.9 Billion
Approx. Number Employees: 63,511
Year Founded: 1965
Business Description:
Integrated Transportation Network
S.I.C.: 4111
N.A.I.C.S.: 485119
Import
Advertising Expenditures: $5,000,000
Media: 3-6-8-9-18-23-24-25
Distr.: Direct to Consumer; Reg.
Budget Set: Jan.
Personnel:
Andrew M. Saul *(Vice Chm)*
Susan Kupferman *(Pres)*
Robert E. Foran *(CFO)*
Richard L. Osborne *(Chief-Creative Svcs)*
James B. Henly *(Gen Counsel & Deputy Exec Dir)*
Christopher P. Boylan *(Exec Dir)*
Linda G. Kleinbaum *(Exec Dir-Admin)*
William A. Morange *(Deputy Exec Dir-Security)*
Richard Coniglione *(Dir-Editorial Svcs)*
Ben Fernandez *(Dir-Labor Rels)*
Alicia Martinez *(Dir-Mktg & Corp Comm)*
Patrick J. McCoy *(Dir-Fin)*
Hilary D. Ring *(Dir-Govt Affairs)*
Ernest Tollerson *(Dir-Environmental Sustainability & Compliance)*
William Wheeler *(Dir-Special Project Dev & Plng)*
Brands & Products:
E-ZPASS
GOING YOUR WAY
IF YOU SEE SOMETHING, SAY SOMETHING
METROCARD
MTA BRIDGES & TUNNELS
MTA LONG ISLAND BUS
MTA LONG ISLAND RAILROAD
MTA METRO-NORTH RAILROAD
MTA NEW YORK CITY TRANSIT
Advertising Agencies:
Korey Kay & Partners
130 5th Ave
New York, NY 10011-4306
Tel.: (212) 620-4300
Fax: (212) 620-7055
Fax: (212) 620-7149
(Creative)

Miller Advertising Agency Inc.
71 5th Ave 5th Fl
New York, NY 10003-3004
Tel.: (212) 929-2200
Fax: (212) 727-4734
Toll Free: (800) 229-6574
(Classifieds)

MIAMI INTERNATIONAL AIRPORT

PO Box 592075
Miami, FL 33159
Tel.: (305) 876-7000
E-mail: marketing@miami-airport.com
Web Site: www.miami-airport.com
Sales Range: $450-499.9 Million
Approx. Number Employees: 1,600
Business Description:
Airport Transportation Services
S.I.C.: 4581
N.A.I.C.S.: 488119
Media: 2-6-10-22
Personnel:
Anne Syrcle Lee *(CFO)*
Narinder Jolly *(Asst Dir-CIP)*
Jose Abreu *(Dir-Aviation)*
Miguel Southwell *(Dir)*
Lauren Stover *(Asst Dir)*

MILAN EXPRESS CO., INC.

1091 Kefauver Dr
Milan, TN 38358-3412
Tel.: (731) 686-7428
Fax: (731) 686-9858
Toll Free: (800) 231-7303
Web Site: www.milanexpress.com
E-Mail For Key Personnel:
President: tross@milanexpress.com
Marketing Director: manderson@milanexpress.com
Approx. Rev.: $168,000,000
Approx. Number Employees: 1,850
Year Founded: 1969
Business Description:
Local & Interstate Trucking
S.I.C.: 4212; 4213
N.A.I.C.S.: 484110; 484121
Import Export
Media: 2-4
Personnel:
Tommy Wayne Ross *(Founder)*
John Ross *(Owner)*
Mike Stone *(Pres)*
Bruce Kalem *(CFO & VP)*
Mitch Anderson *(VP-Sls & Mktg)*
Spencer Avis *(Dir-Corp Accts)*
Brad Morris *(Dir-Corporate Bus)*
Carl McDole *(Mgr-Claims)*

MN AIRLINES LLC

(d/b/a Sun Country Airlines)
1300 Mendota Hts Rd
Mendota Heights, MN 55120
Tel.: (651) 681-3900
Fax: (651) 681-3970
Web Site: www.suncountry.com

Key to Media (For complete agency information see *The Advertising Red Books-Agencies* edition):
1. Bus. Publs. 2. Cable T.V. 3. Catalogs & Directories. 4. Co-op Adv. 5. Consumer Mags. 6. D.M. to Bus. Estab.7. D.M. to Consumers 8. Daily Newsp. 9. Exhibits/Trade Shows 10. Foreign 11. Infomercial 12. Internet Adv.13. Multimedia 14. Network Radio 15. Network T.V. 16. Newsp. Distr. Mags. 17. Other 18. Outdoor (Posters, Transit) 19. Point of Purchase20. Premiums, Novelties 21. Product Samples 22. Special Events Mktg. 23. Spot Radio 24. Spot T.V. 25. Weekly Newsp. 26. Yellow Page Adv.

Sales Range: $10-24.9 Million
Approx. Number Employees: 1,000
Business Description:
Regional Airline Service
S.I.C.: 4512
N.A.I.C.S.: 481112
Media: 4-9-18-25
Personnel:
Stan Gadek *(Chm, Pres & CEO)*
Roger Harris *(COO)*

THE MOTORLEASE CORPORATION

1506 New Britain Ave
Farmington, CT 06032-3126
Tel.: (860) 677-9711
Fax: (860) 674-8677
Toll Free: (800) 243-0182
E-mail: info@motorleasecorp.com
Web Site: www.motorleasecorp.com
Sales Range: $10-24.9 Million
Approx. Number Employees: 30
Year Founded: 1946
Business Description:
Passenger Automobile Leasing
S.I.C.: 7515
N.A.I.C.S.: 532112
Advertising Expenditures: $300,000
Media: 7-8-20-23-24
Distr.: Direct to Consumer; Reg.
Personnel:
Jack Leary *(Pres)*
Beth Kandrysawtz *(CFO)*

NATIONAL CAR RENTAL

(Sub. of Enterprise Holdings, Inc.)
6929 N Lakewood Ave Ste 100
Tulsa, OK 74117-1808
Tel.: (918) 401-6000
Toll Free: (866) 244-3800
Web Site: www.nationalcar.com
Approx. Number Employees: 200
Year Founded: 1947
Business Description:
Rent-A-Car Services
S.I.C.: 7514
N.A.I.C.S.: 532111
Media: 2-3-5-6-8-9-10-11-13-18-24-26
Distr.: Direct to Consumer; Natl.
Personnel:
Greg Stubblefield *(Pres)*
Layla Bryan *(Mgr- Leisure Bus Dev)*
Brands & Products:
NATIONAL CAR RENTAL
NATIONAL/INTERRENT
NATIONAL TILDEN/INTERRENT

NATIONAL RAILROAD PASSENGER CORPORATION

(d/b/a Amtrak)
60 Massachusetts Ave NE
Washington, DC 20002-4285
Tel.: (202) 906-3000
Fax: (202) 906-4804
Toll Free: (800) USA-RAIL
Telex: 892418
E-mail: mediarelations@amtrak.com
Web Site: www.amtrak.com
Approx. Rev.: $2,513,384,000
Approx. Number Employees: 24,600
Year Founded: 1971
Business Description:
Amtrak National Inter-City Rail Passenger System
S.I.C.: 4011; 9621
N.A.I.C.S.: 482111; 926120
Advertising Expenditures: $30,890,000
Media: 2-3-5-6-7-8-9-10-11-13-14-15-16-18-19-20-22-23-24-25-26
Distr.: Natl.
Budget Set: Sept.
Personnel:
Thomas C. Carper *(Chm)*
Donna McLean *(Vice Chm)*
Joseph H. Boardman *(Pres & CEO)*
D. J. Stadtler *(CFO)*
William L. Crosbie *(COO)*
H. Edgar Trainor *(CIO)*
Eleanor D. Acheson *(Gen Counsel, Sec & VP)*
Emmett H. Fremaux *(VP-Mktg & Product Mgmt)*
Lorraine A. Green *(VP-HR & Diversity Initiatives)*
Joseph H. McHugh *(VP-Gov Affairs & Corp Comm)*
William Rooney *(VP-Security Strategy & Special Ops)*
Anne Witt *(VP-Strategic Partnerships & Bus Dev)*
Margaret Sherry *(Sr Dir-Employee & Customer Comm)*
Michael Blakey *(Sr Dir-Loyalty Mktg)*
Jeff Mann *(Sr Dir-Policy & Dev)*
Gail Reisman *(Sr Dir-Natl Adv & Mktg Programs)*
Dick Salmon *(Sr Dir-Scheduling)*
Brands & Products:
AMTRAK
Advertising Agencies:
Arnold Worldwide
101 Huntington Ave
Boston, MA 02199-7603
Tel.: (617) 587-8000
Fax: (617) 587-8004

IMAGES USA
1320 Ellsworth Industrial Blvd
Atlanta, GA 30318
Tel.: (404) 892-2931
Fax: (404) 892-8651

Source Communications
433 Hackensack Ave 8th Fl
Hackensack, NJ 07601-6319
Tel.: (201) 343-5222
Fax: (201) 343-5710
(Sports Marketing)

NATIONAL TRUCK LEASING SYSTEM

(Sub. of AmeriQuest Transportation and Logistics Resources Corp.)
(d/b/a NationaLease)
1 S 450 Summit Ave Ste 300
Oakbrook Terrace, IL 60181
Tel.: (630) 953-8878
Fax: (630) 953-0040
Web Site: www.nationalease.com
Sales Range: $200-249.9 Million
Approx. Number Employees: 30
Year Founded: 1944
Business Description:
Full Service Truck, Tractor & Trailer Leasing Services
S.I.C.: 7519
N.A.I.C.S.: 532120
Media: 10-18-20
Personnel:
Gene Scoggins *(Pres)*
Kate Barnes *(Dir-Meetings)*

NATIONAL VAN LINES, INC.

2800 W Roosevelt Rd
Broadview, IL 60155-3756
Tel.: (708) 450-2900
Fax: (708) 450-9320
Toll Free: (800) 323-1962
E-mail: nvl@nationalvanlines.com
Web Site: www.nationalvanlines.com
Approx. Number Employees: 100
Year Founded: 1934
Business Description:
Household Goods Moving Services
S.I.C.: 4214; 4731
N.A.I.C.S.: 484210; 488510
Advertising Expenditures: $1,400,000
Media: 2-4-5-6-7-10-18-20-25-26
Distr.: Natl.
Budget Set: Oct.
Personnel:
Maureen Beal *(CEO)*
Ronald McKee *(Sr VP)*
Bob Buti *(VP-Fin)*
Georgia Colter *(VP-Mktg & Trng)*
Brands & Products:
MOVING YOUR MEMORIES
NATIONAL VAN LINES
Advertising Agency:
Scott Communications, Inc.
4749 Lincoln Mall Dr Ste 415
Matteson, IL 60443
Tel.: (708) 957-7274
Fax: (708) 481-7559
— Stewart M. Scott *(Pres.)*

NCL CORPORATION LTD.

(Joint Venture of Apollo Advisors, L.P., Genting Hong Kong Limited & TPG Capital, L.P.)
7665 Corporate Center Dr
Miami, FL 33126
Tel.: (305) 436-4000
Fax: (305) 436-4111
E-mail: publicrelations@ncl.com
Web Site: www.ncl.com
Approx. Rev.: $2,012,128,000
Approx. Number Employees: 13,769
Business Description:
Passenger Cruise Operator; Owned by Genting Hong Kong Limited (50%), Apollo Advisors L.P. (37.5%) & TPG Capital (12.5%)
S.I.C.: 4481
N.A.I.C.S.: 483112
Advertising Expenditures: $87,400,000
Personnel:
Kok Thay Lim *(Chm)*
Kevin M. Sheehan *(Pres & CEO)*
Wendy A. Beck *(CFO & VP)*
Vincent Cirel *(CIO & Sr VP)*
Daniel S. Farkas *(Gen Counsel, Sec & Sr VP)*
Howard L. Flanders *(Treas & Sr VP-Fin)*
Andrew Stuart *(Exec VP-Global Sls & Passenger Svcs)*
Bob Becker *(Sr VP-Consumer Res)*
Maria Miller *(Sr VP-Mktg)*
AnneMarie Mathews *(VP-PR)*

NETJETS INC.

(Holding of Berkshire Hathaway Inc.)
4111 Bridgeway Ave
Columbus, OH 43219
Tel.: (614) 239-5500
Toll Free: (877) 356-5823
E-mail: headquarters@netjets.com
Web Site: www.netjets.com
Sales Range: $500-549.9 Million
Approx. Number Employees: 1,000
Year Founded: 1964
Business Description:
Business Jet Charters, Management, Maintenance, Pilot Training, Avionics Service & Installation, Aircraft Brokerage, Sales & Leasing
S.I.C.: 4522; 5088
N.A.I.C.S.: 481219; 423860
Advertising Expenditures: $300,000
Media: 2-6-7-8-26
Distr.: Natl.
Budget Set: Jan.
Personnel:
David Sokol *(Chm & CEO)*
Bill Noe *(Co-Pres-North America)*
Jordan Hansell *(Pres)*
Randy Brandoff *(CMO & Sr VP)*
Lauren Fryefield *(Sr VP-Mktg)*
Adam Johnson *(Sr VP)*
Adam Berman *(VP-Media)*
Brands & Products:
INTELIJET
LEAVE NOTHING TO CHANCE
MAKE EVERY MOMENT COUNT
NETJETS
Advertising Agencies:
AKQA, Inc.
1 Saint John's Ln
London, EC1M 4BL, United Kingdom
Tel.: (44) 207 780 4786
Fax: (44) 207 780 4787
(Pan-European Digital Media)

kirshenbaum bond senecal + partners
160 Varick St 4th Fl
New York, NY 10013
Tel.: (212) 633-0080
Fax: (212) 463-8643

NFI INDUSTRIES INC.

71 W Park Ave
Vineland, NJ 08360-3508
Tel.: (856) 691-7000
Fax: (856) 794-4591
E-mail: info@natlfreight.com
Web Site: www.nfiindustries.com
Approx. Number Employees: 2,271
Year Founded: 1932
Business Description:
Transportation Logistics & Warehousing
S.I.C.: 4213; 4212; 4225
N.A.I.C.S.: 484121; 484110; 493110
Import Export
Media: 2-4
Personnel:
Sidney R. Brown *(Chm & CEO)*
Jeffrey S. Brown *(Vice Chm & Pres)*
Irwin J. Brown *(Vice Chm)*
Bernard A. Brown *(Pres)*
Frank Rashilla *(CFO)*
Brands & Products:
HOW BUSINESS IS ONE
NFI
Advertising Agency:
Suasion Communications Group
1742 Mays Landing Somers Point Rd
PO Box 388
Egg Harbor Township, NJ 08234
Tel.: (609) 653-0400
Fax: (609) 653-6483
Toll Free: (800) 222-0461

NIAGARA FRONTIER TRANSPORTATION AUTHORITY

181 Ellicott St
Buffalo, NY 14203

Key to Media (For complete agency information see *The Advertising Red Books-Agencies* edition):
1. Bus. Publs. 2. Cable T.V. 3. Catalogs & Directories. 4. Co-op Adv. 5. Consumer Mags. 6. D.M. to Bus. Estab.7. D.M. to Consumers
8. Daily Newsp. 9. Exhibits/Trade Shows 10. Foreign 11. Infomercial 12. Internet Adv.13. Multimedia 14. Network Radio
15. Network T.V. 16. Newsp. Distr. Mags. 17. Other 18. Outdoor (Posters, Transit) 19. Point of Purchase20. Premiums, Novelties
21. Product Samples 22. Special Events Mktg. 23. Spot Radio 24. Spot T.V. 25. Weekly Newsp. 26. Yellow Page Adv.

Niagara Frontier Transportation Authority — (Continued)

Tel.: (716) 855-7300
Fax: (716) 855-6682
E-mail: info@nfta.com
Web Site: www.nfta.com
Approx. Number Employees: 1,300
Year Founded: 1967
Business Description:
Transportation Administration Services
S.I.C.: 9621
N.A.I.C.S.: 926120
Media: 9-13-18-23-25
Personnel:
Henry M. Sloma *(Chm)*
Deborah Leous *(CFO)*
David M. Gregory *(Gen Counsel)*
Lawrence Meckler *(Exec Dir)*
Kim Minkel *(Exec Dir)*
James A. Bryant *(Dir-EAP)*
Patrick Dalton *(Dir-Internal Auditing)*
Douglas Hartmayer *(Dir-Pub Affairs)*
Linda Saey *(Dir-EEO/Diversity Dev)*
William Vanecek *(Dir-Aviation)*

NJ TRANSIT CORPORATION

1 Penn Plz E
Newark, NJ 07105-2245
Tel.: (973) 491-7000
Fax: (973) 491-7314
Toll Free: (800) 772-2222
E-mail: njt_customer_svc@njtransit.com
Web Site: www.njtransit.com
Approx. Rev.: $838,715,000
Approx. Number Employees: 11,000
Year Founded: 1979
Business Description:
Operator of Public Transportation Services
S.I.C.: 9621; 4111; 4789
N.A.I.C.S.: 926120; 485112; 485113; 488999
Advertising Expenditures: $1,700,000
Media: 1-2-3-4-5-6-7-8-9-10-13-16-18-19-20-22-23-24-25-26
Distr.: Reg. Direct to Consumer
Budget Set: July
Personnel:
James S. Simpson *(Chm)*
Myron P. Shevell *(Vice Chm)*
James Weinstein *(Exec Dir)*
Kim Vaccari *(CFO & Treas)*
James J. Gigantino *(VP & Gen Mgr-Bus Ops)*
Kevin O'Connor *(Acting VP & Gen Mgr-Rail Ops)*
Penny Bassett-Hackett *(Acting Asst Exec Dir-Comm & Customer Svc)*
Steve Santoro *(Asst Exec Dir-Capital Plng & Programs)*
Alma R. Scott-Buczak *(Asst Exec Dir-HR)*

NORFOLK SOUTHERN CORPORATION

3 Commercial Pl
Norfolk, VA 23510-2191
Tel.: (757) 629-2600
Tel.: (757) 629-2680
Fax: (757) 664-5069
E-mail: webmaster@nscorp.com
Web Site: www.nscorp.com
Approx. Rev.: $9,516,000,000
Approx. Number Employees: 28,559
Year Founded: 1980
Business Description:
Transportation Holding Company; Railroad System Lines
S.I.C.: 4011
N.A.I.C.S.: 482111
Export
Advertising Expenditures: $4,000,000
Media: 1-2-7-9-13-18-20
Distr.: Direct to Consumer; Natl.
Budget Set: Oct. -Nov.
Personnel:
Charles W. Moorman, IV *(Chm, Pres & CEO)*
James A. Squires *(CFO & Exec VP-Fin)*
Mark D. Manion *(COO & Exec VP)*
Deborah H. Butler *(CIO & Exec VP-Plng)*
Donald W. Seale *(CMO & Exec VP)*
James A. Hixon *(Exec VP-Law & Corp Rnts)*
John P. Rathbone *(Exec VP-Admin)*
Ronald Listwak *(Grp VP-Comml)*
Alan Shaw *(Grp VP-Chemicals)*
James E. Carter, Jr. *(VP-Internal Audit)*
Cindy C. Earhart *(VP-HR)*
Fredric M. Ehlers *(VP-Customer Svcs)*
Thomas G. Werner *(VP-IT)*
Gary W. Woods *(VP-Engrg)*
Jeffrey M. Heller *(Asst VP-Mktg, Intl & Sls)*
Thomas Bayrer *(Dir-Resource Plng & Forecasting)*
Ed Elkins *(Dir-Mktg Sls & Domestic)*
Douglas Evans *(Dir-Utility Coal Mktg-North)*
Leanne D. Marilley *(Dir-IR)*
Tom Reese *(Dir-Sls)*
Christine Traubel *(Dir-Intermodal Plng & Pricing)*
Rob Zehringer *(Dir-Domestic Metallurgical Coal Mktg)*
Marie Coleman *(Office Mgr)*
Cheryl Manning *(Product Mgr-Plastics)*
Robert Poole *(Product Mgr-Industrial Intermediates)*
Charles Baldwin *(Mgr-Coal Resources)*
Randy Bayles *(Mgr-Natl Accts Market)*
Hugh Dodd *(Mgr-Market-Intl)*
Augie Eckhardt *(Mgr-Market-Intl)*
Bob Feit *(Mgr-Performance UPS)*
Charles Fike *(Mgr-Utility Coal Mktg-North)*
James Forrester *(Mgr-Equipment-Bus Dev)*
Joseph Frye *(Mgr-Coal Mktg-Industrial Coal)*
Mark Griffin *(Mgr-Utility Coal Mktg-South)*
Roger Hollandsworth *(Mgr-Domestic Coal)*
Dave Hrusovsky *(Mgr-Coal Grp)*
Thomas Johnson *(Mgr-Transportation Plng-Train Dispatcher)*
Kenneth Joyner *(Mgr-Coal Mktg)*
Joe Keeley *(Mgr-Customer Contracts)*
Russ Kirchoff *(Mgr-IMCs)*
Kimberly Kitchen *(Mgr-Metallurgical Coal Mktg)*
Art Lewis *(Mgr-IMCs)*
Randy L. McFarland *(Mgr-Utility Coal Mktg-South)*
Anne McMahon *(Mgr-IMCs)*
Dave Middleton *(Mgr-Performance LTL)*
Jerome Nassar *(Mgr-Resource Dev)*
David Riggs *(Mgr-Domestic Coal North)*
James Skeens *(Mgr-Market & Coal Resources)*
Stephen Stutsman *(Mgr-Coal Mktg-South)*
Booker Thomas *(Mgr-Coal Transportation)*
Shawn Tureman *(Mgr-Yield)*
Brands & Products:
ACCESSNS
ENVIROSTONE
MODALGISTICS
MODALVIEW
NORFOLK SOUTHERN
OUR WORLD, OUR CHOICE
T-CUBED
THE THOROUGHBRED
TOP GON
TRIPLE CROWN SERVICE
Advertising Agencies:
archer malmo
65 Union Ave Ste 500
Memphis, TN 38103-5137
Tel.: (901) 523-2000
Fax: (901) 523-7654
Toll Free: (800) 535-8943

JWT U.S.A., Inc.
10 B Glenlake Pkwy NE N Twr 4th Fl
Atlanta, GA 30328
Tel.: (404) 365-7300
Fax: (404) 365-7333
(Transportation Services)
— Samantha Bryan *(Acct Exec)*

NORTH AMERICAN VAN LINES

(Sub. of SIRVA, Inc.)
5001 US Hwy 30 W
Fort Wayne, IN 46818-9701
Mailing Address:
PO Box 988
Fort Wayne, IN 46801-0988
Tel.: (260) 429-2511
Fax: (260) 429-1802
Toll Free: (800) 348-2111
E-mail: joewiktorowicz@sirva.com
Web Site: www.navl.com
Sales Range: $1-4.9 Billion
Approx. Number Employees: 500
Year Founded: 1933
Business Description:
Transportation Moving Services
S.I.C.: 4213; 4731
N.A.I.C.S.: 484121; 488510
Import Export
Advertising Expenditures: $1,500,000
Media: 2-4-5-7-8-10-13-23-24-26
Distr.: Natl.
Budget Set: Oct.
Personnel:
Doug Gathany *(Treas & Sr VP)*
Denny Thomson *(VP-Fin)*

NORTHWEST AIRLINES CORPORATION

(Sub. of Delta Air Lines, Inc.)
2700 Lone Oak Pkwy
Eagan, MN 55121
Mailing Address:
5101 Northwest Dr
Saint Paul, MN 55111-3034
Tel.: (612) 726-2111
Fax: (612) 727-7123
Telex: HDQBYNW
Web Site: www.nwa.com
Sales Range: $1-4.9 Billion
Year Founded: 1926
Business Description:
Air Transportation & Travel Arrangement Services
S.I.C.: 4512; 4729
N.A.I.C.S.: 481111; 561599
Advertising Expenditures: $70,000,000
Media: 1-2-3-5-6-8-9-10-11-13-14-15-18-19-20-22-23-24-25-26
Distr.: Direct to Consumer; Intl.; Natl.
Budget Set: Oct.
Personnel:
Hank Halter *(CFO & Sr VP)*
Stephen E. Gorman *(COO & Exec VP)*
Michael H. Campell *(Exec VP-HR & Labour Rels)*
Glen W. Hauenstein *(Exec VP-Network Plng & Revenue Mgmt)*
Holden Shannon *(Sr VP-Corp Strategy & Real Estate)*
Brands & Products:
NORTHWEST AIRLINES
NWA
Advertising Agencies:
Carlson Marketing
1405 Xenium Ln N
Plymouth, MN 55441
Tel.: (763) 445-3000

Draftfcb
101 E Erie St
Chicago, IL 60611
Tel.: (312) 425-5000
Fax: (312) 425-5010

Edelman
701 Central Plaza 18 Harbour Rd
Hong Kong, China (Hong Kong)
Tel.: (852) 2804 1338
Fax: (852) 2804 1303

Initiative Worldwide
(Part of The Interpublic Group of Companies, Inc.)
1 Dag Hammerskjold Plz 5th Fl
New York, NY 10017
Tel.: (212) 605-7000
Fax: (212) 605-7200

interTrend Communications, Inc.
555 E Ocean Blvd
Long Beach, CA 90802-5003
Tel.: (562) 733-1888
Fax: (562) 733-1889

NORWEGIAN CRUISE LINE

(Joint Venture of Apollo Advisors, L.P., Genting Hong Kong Limited & TPG Capital, L.P.)
7665 NW 19th St
Miami, FL 33126-1201
Tel.: (305) 436-4000
Fax: (305) 436-4111
Toll Free: (800) 327-7030
E-mail: webmaster@ncl.com
Web Site: www.ncl.com
E-Mail For Key Personnel:
Marketing Director: gcallahan@ncl.com
Approx. Number Employees: 6,700
Year Founded: 1966
Business Description:
Travel Cruise Services
S.I.C.: 4481; 4724
N.A.I.C.S.: 483112; 561510

Key to Media (For complete agency information see *The Advertising Red Books-Agencies* edition):
1. Bus. Publs. 2. Cable T.V. 3. Catalogs & Directories. 4. Co-op Adv. 5. Consumer Mags. 6. D.M. to Bus. Estab.7. D.M. to Consumers 8. Daily Newsp. 9. Exhibits/Trade Shows 10. Foreign 11. Infomercial 12. Internet Adv.13. Multimedia 14. Network Radio 15. Network T.V. 16. Newsp. Distr. Mags. 17. Other 18. Outdoor (Posters, Transit) 19. Point of Purchase20. Premiums, Novelties 21. Product Samples 22. Special Events Mktg. 23. Spot Radio 24. Spot T.V. 25. Weekly Newsp. 26. Yellow Page Adv.

Advertising Expenditures: $18,000,000
Media: 1-2-3-4-5-6-7-8-9-10-11-13-18-19-20-23-24-25
Distr.: Intl.; Natl.
Budget Set: Sept.
Personnel:
Colin Veitch *(Pres & CEO)*
Andrew Stuart *(Exec VP-Global Sls & Passenger Svcs)*
Amy Hiles-Maynard *(VP-Mktg)*
Camille Olivere *(VP-Sls)*
Stephen Park *(Gen Mgr-UK)*
Claudia Johnson *(Dir-Brand & Adv)*
Meg Lee *(Dir-Direct Mktg)*
Bettina Osterwind *(Dir-Strategic Alliances & Product Integration)*
Brands & Products:
NORWEGIAN CROWN
NORWEGIAN CRUISE LINE
NORWEGIAN DAWN
NORWEGIAN DREAM
NORWEGIAN DYNASTY
NORWEGIAN MAJESTY
NORWEGIAN SEA
NORWEGIAN SKY
NORWEGIAN STAR
NORWEGIAN WIND
ORIENT LINES LTD
Advertising Agencies:
GSD&M
828 W 6th St
Austin, TX 78703-5420
Tel.: (512) 242-4736
Fax: (512) 242-4700
Freestyle Cruising

Kaiser Marketing, Inc.
11400 W Olympic Blvd Ste 600
Los Angeles, CA 90064
Tel.: (310) 479-8999
Fax: (310) 479-0414

The Martin Agency
One Shockoe Plz
Richmond, VA 23219-4132
Tel.: (804) 698-8000
Fax: (804) 698-8001
Agency of Record
Digital
Marketing
Social Media
TV

ODYSSEY MARINE EXPLORATION, INC.

5215 W Laurel St Ste 210
Tampa, FL 33607
Tel.: (813) 876-1776
Fax: (813) 876-1777
Web Site: www.shipwreck.net
Approx. Rev.: $21,000,695
Approx. Number Employees: 42
Year Founded: 1994
Business Description:
Deep-Water Shipwrecks Exploration & Recovery Services Throughout the World; Traveling Exhibits & Attractions Operator
S.I.C.: 4481; 4499; 7999
N.A.I.C.S.: 483112; 488390; 713990
Advertising Expenditures: $163,537
Media: 10-23-24
Personnel:
Mark D. Gordon *(Pres & COO)*
Gregory P. Stemm *(CEO)*
Michael J. Holmes *(CFO)*
Jay A. Nudi *(Chief Acctg Officer & Controller)*

OLD DOMINION FREIGHT LINE, INC.

500 Old Dominion Way
Thomasville, NC 27360-8923
Tel.: (336) 889-5000
Fax: (336) 822-5229
Toll Free: (800) 432-6335
E-mail: customer.service@odfl.com
Web Site: www.odfl.com
E-Mail For Key Personnel:
President: david.congdon@odfl.com
Approx. Rev.: $1,480,998,000
Approx. Number Employees: 11,179
Year Founded: 1934
Business Description:
Freight & Trucking Services
S.I.C.: 4213; 4731
N.A.I.C.S.: 484121; 488510
Advertising Expenditures: $4,100,000
Media: 10-13
Personnel:
Earl E. Congdon *(Chm)*
John R. Congdon *(Vice Chm & Sr VP)*
David S. Congdon *(Pres & CEO)*
J. Wes Frye *(CFO & Sr VP-Fin)*
Greg C. Gantt *(COO & Exec VP)*
Joel B. McCarty, Jr. *(Gen Counsel, Sec & Sr VP)*
Rick Keeler *(Sr VP-Pricing & Strategic Dev)*
Walt Metz *(VP & Asst Gen Counsel-Legal Dept)*
Chip Overbey *(VP-Natl Accts-Mktg)*
Todd Dayley *(Sls Dir)*
Advertising Agency:
Fitzgerald+CO
3060 Peachtree Rd NW
Atlanta, GA 30305
Tel.: (404) 504-6900
Fax: (404) 239-0548

OLYMPIC AIRWAYS

(Sub. of Olympic Airways, S.A.)
7000 Austin St
Forest Hills, NY 11375
Tel.: (718) 269-2200
Fax: (718) 269-2215
Telex: NYCVDOA
E-mail: oausa@olympic-airways.org
Web Site: www.olympic-airways.org
Approx. Number Employees: 49
Year Founded: 1957
Business Description:
Airlines
S.I.C.: 4729
N.A.I.C.S.: 561599
Advertising Expenditures: $500,000
Media: 1-2-4-5-6-7-9-10-11-14-15-23-25-26
Distr.: Natl.
Brands & Products:
OA

ORBITZ WORLDWIDE, INC.

(Sub. of Travelport Limited)
500 W Madison Ave Ste 1000
Chicago, IL 60661
Tel.: (312) 894-5000
Tel.: (312) 416-0018 (Customer Svc)
Fax: (312) 894-5001
Toll Free: (888) 656-4546 (Customer Svc)
Web Site: www.orbitz.com
E-Mail For Key Personnel:
Marketing Director: marketing@orbitz.com
Approx. Rev.: $757,487,000
Approx. Number Employees: 1,400
Year Founded: 2000
Business Description:
Online Travel Services
S.I.C.: 6099; 2741; 4724; 4729; 7011
N.A.I.C.S.: 522390; 516110; 561510; 561599; 721199
Advertising Expenditures: $277,000,000
Media: 6-13-23-24
Personnel:
Jeffrey J. Clarke *(Chm)*
Ronnie Gurion *(Pres)*
Barney Harford *(CEO)*
Russell Hammer *(CFO)*
Chris Orton *(CMO & SVP-Mktg)*
Thomas L. Kram *(Chief Acctg Officer)*
Mike Nelson *(Pres-Partner Svcs)*
Brian Hoyt *(VP-Comm & Govt Affairs)*
Jeanenne Tornatore *(Dir-Consumer Pub Rel)*
Brands & Products:
AOYOU.COM
THE AWAY NETWORK
EBOOKERS
HOTELCLUB
NEEDAHOTEL.COM
OCTOPUSTRAVEL.COM
ORBITZ.COM
RATESTOGO.COM
TRAVELBAG
Advertising Agencies:
BBDO Worldwide Inc.
(Sub. of Omnicom Group, Inc.)
1285 Ave of the Americas
New York, NY 10019-6028
Tel.: (212) 459-5000
Fax: (212) 459-6645

Optimedia International U.S.
375 Hudson St 7th Fl
New York, NY 10014
Tel.: (212) 820-3200
Fax: (212) 820-3300

OSHKOSH SPECIALTY VEHICLES

(Sub. of Oshkosh Corporation)
2150 E Dolton Rd
Calumet City, IL 60409
Tel.: (708) 596-5066
Fax: (708) 596-2480
Web Site: www.oshkoshsv.com
Sales Range: $250-299.9 Million
Business Description:
Specialty Truck, Trailer & Van Mfr & Retailer
S.I.C.: 3711; 3714
N.A.I.C.S.: 336120; 336399
Import Export
Media: 7-10
Personnel:
Tom Biwan *(Sr VP-Sls & Mktg)*
Mike Bamrick *(Mgr-Natl Sls)*
Brands & Products:
AK SPECIALTY VEHICLES
AKSV

OUTER BANKS VISITORS BUREAU

One Visitors Center Cir
Manteo, NC 27954
Tel.: (252) 473-2138
Fax: (252) 473-5777
Toll Free: (877) 629-4386
E-mail: info@outerbanks.org
Web Site: www.outerbanks.org
Business Description:
Public Authority for Tourism
S.I.C.: 4725
N.A.I.C.S.: 561520
Advertising Expenditures: $900,000
Media: 6-13
Personnel:
Diane Bognich *(Mgr-Finance)*

PACE

(Div. of Regional Transportation Authority)
550 W Algonquin Rd
Arlington Heights, IL 60005-4412
Tel.: (847) 364-7223
Fax: (847) 228-4206
E-mail: passenger.services@pacebus.com
Web Site: www.pacebus.com
Approx. Number Employees: 1,500
Year Founded: 1983
Business Description:
Suburban Bus Services
S.I.C.: 4111
N.A.I.C.S.: 485113
Advertising Expenditures: $865,000
Media: 1-2-9-14-15-25
Distr.: Reg.
Personnel:
Kyle R. Hastings *(Pres-Village of Orland Hills)*
Alan P. Nowaczyk *(Pres-Village of Willow Springs)*
Terry R. Wells *(Pres-Village of Phoenix)*
Thomas J. Ross *(Exec Dir)*
Terrance Brannon *(Deputy Dir-Internal Svcs)*
Maggie Daly *(Mgr-Mktg)*
Susan Jung Lundy *(Mgr-Pur)*
Brands & Products:
PACE
Advertising Agency:
Noble
33 W Monroe St Ste 300
Chicago, IL 60603
Tel.: (312) 670-2900
Fax: (312) 670-7420
Toll Free: (800) 986-6253

PACER INTERNATIONAL, INC.

6805 Perimeter Dr
Dublin, OH 43016
Tel.: (614) 923-1400
Toll Free: (888) 722-7404
E-mail: info@pacer.com
Web Site: www.pacer.com
Approx. Rev.: $1,502,800,000
Approx. Number Employees: 1,060
Business Description:
Logistics & Intermodal Freight Transportation Services
S.I.C.: 4731; 4213; 7389; 8742
N.A.I.C.S.: 488510; 484121; 488490; 541614
Personnel:
Daniel W. Avramovich *(Chm, Pres & CEO)*
John J. Hafferty *(CFO & Exec VP)*
James E. Ward *(CIO & Exec VP)*
Michael F. Killea *(Chief Legal Officer, Gen Counsel & Exec VP-Intl Logistics)*
Michael A. Burns *(Chief Comml Officer & Exec VP)*

Key to Media (For complete agency information see *The Advertising Red Books-Agencies* edition):
1. Bus. Publs. 2. Cable T.V. 3. Catalogs & Directories. 4. Co-op Adv. 5. Consumer Mags. 6. D.M. to Bus. Estab.7. D.M. to Consumers
8. Daily Newsp. 9. Exhibits/Trade Shows 10. Foreign 11. Infomercial 12. Internet Adv.13. Multimedia 14. Network Radio
15. Network T.V. 16. Newsp. Distr. Mags. 17. Other 18. Outdoor (Posters, Transit) 19. Point of Purchase20. Premiums, Novelties
21. Product Samples 22. Special Events Mktg. 23. Spot Radio 24. Spot T.V. 25. Weekly Newsp. 26. Yellow Page Adv.

Pacer International, Inc. — (Continued)

Michael D. Gordon *(Chief Acctg Officer, VP & Controller)*
Lisa O. Taylor *(Sec, VP & Asst Gen Counsel)*
Mike Clark *(Exec VP-Capacity Plng)*
Val T. Noel *(Exec VP-Field Ops)*
F. Franklin Sutherland *(Exec VP-Network Svcs)*
Robert D. Williams *(VP-HR)*

Advertising Agency:
James Street Associates, Ltd.
2412 James St
Blue Island, IL 60406
Tel.: (708) 371-0110
Fax: (708) 371-1979

PACIFIC MARINE & SUPPLY CO. LTD. INC.

841 Bishop St Ste 1110
Honolulu, HI 96813-3908
Mailing Address:
PO Box 29816
Honolulu, HI 96820-2216
Tel.: (808) 531-7001, ext. 18
Fax: (808) 523-7668
Toll Free: (866) 531-7004
E-mail: schmicker@NavatekLtd.com
Web Site: www.navatekltd.com
Approx. Number Employees: 500
Year Founded: 1950
Business Description:
Deep Sea Passenger Transportation
S.I.C.: 4481; 4953
N.A.I.C.S.: 483112; 562211
Import Export
Media: 7-10
Personnel:
Steven Loui *(Pres & CTO)*
Michael Schmicker *(VP-Mktg & Corp Comm)*

PAKISTAN INTERNATIONAL AIRLINES CORPORATION

(Sub. of Pakistan International Airlines Corporation)
505 8th Ave 6th Fl
New York, NY 10018
Tel.: (212) 760-8484
Tel.: (212) 760-8455
Fax: (212) 971-5434
Toll Free: (800) 221-2552
E-mail: info@piac.com
Web Site: www.piac.com.pk
Approx. Number Employees: 25
Year Founded: 1952
Business Description:
International Airline
S.I.C.: 4512
N.A.I.C.S.: 481111
Media: 10-18
Personnel:
Tariq Yaseen *(Gen Mgr)*
Brands & Products:
PIA

P.A.M. TRANSPORTATION SERVICES, INC.

297 Henri Detonti Blvd
Tontitown, AR 72770
Mailing Address:
PO Box 188
Tontitown, AR 72770
Tel.: (479) 361-9111
Fax: (479) 361-5335
Toll Free: (800) 879-7261
E-mail: webteam@pamt.com
Web Site: www.pamt.com
Approx. Rev.: $331,994,000
Approx. Number Employees: 2,658
Year Founded: 1986
Business Description:
Transportation Services; Holding Company
S.I.C.: 4213
N.A.I.C.S.: 484230; 484121
Advertising Expenditures: $239,000
Media: 17
Personnel:
Matthew T. Moroun *(Chm)*
Daniel H. Cushman *(Pres & CEO)*
Lance K. Stewart *(CFO, Treas, Sec & VP-Fin)*
Larry J. Goddard *(Exec VP)*

PAUL ARPIN VAN LINES, INC.

99 James P Murphy Hwy
West Warwick, RI 02893
Mailing Address:
PO Box 1302
East Greenwich, RI 02818-0998
Tel.: (401) 828-8111
Fax: (401) 822-7856
Toll Free: (800) 343-3500
E-mail: info@arpin.com
Web Site: www.arpin.com
Sales Range: $100-124.9 Million
Approx. Number Employees: 325
Year Founded: 1900
Business Description:
Local & Long Distance Trucking & Relocation Services
S.I.C.: 4213; 4212
N.A.I.C.S.: 484121; 484110
Advertising Expenditures: $1,135,000
Bus. Publs.: $25,000; Exhibits/Trade Shows: $70,000; Internet Adv.: $35,000; Other: $40,000; Premiums, Novelties: $10,000; Special Events Mktg.: $55,000; Yellow Page Adv.: $900,000
Distr.: Intl.
Budget Set: Oct.
Personnel:
David Arpin *(Pres & CEO)*
Ed Braks *(CFO)*
Conrad Swanson *(Sr VP-Agency Dev)*
Keith Gilbert *(Gen Mgr)*
Brands & Products:
CREATING CUSTOMERS FOR LIFE

PET AIRWAYS, INC.

(Formerly American Antiquities, Inc.)
777 E Atlantic Ave #C2-264
Delray Beach, FL 33483
Tel.: (408) 274-6000
Toll Free: (888) PETAIRWAYS
E-mail: info@petairways.com
Web Site: www.petairways.com
Approx. Rev.: $1,348,491
Approx. Number Employees: 13
Year Founded: 2005
Business Description:
Pet Airline
S.I.C.: 4512
N.A.I.C.S.: 481112
Advertising Expenditures: $84,403
Media: 17
Personnel:
Dan Wiesel *(Chm & CEO)*
Andrew Warner *(CFO)*
Alysa Binder *(Exec VP-Bus Dev)*

PETER DEILMANN EUROPAMERICA INC.

1800 Diagonal Rd Ste 170
Alexandria, VA 22314
Tel.: (703) 549-1741
Fax: (703) 549-7924
Toll Free: (800) 348-8287
E-mail: pdcmail@deilmann-cruises.com
Web Site: www.deilmann-cruises.com
Approx. Sls.: $14,000,000
Approx. Number Employees: 500
Business Description:
Cruise Line
S.I.C.: 4481
N.A.I.C.S.: 483112
Media: 6
Personnel:
Ronald Santangelo *(Pres)*

PETER PAN BUS LINES, INC.

1776 Main St
Springfield, MA 01102-1776
Tel.: (413) 781-2900
Fax: (413) 746-8671
Toll Free: (800) 343-9999
E-mail: webmaster@peterpanbus.com
Web Site: www.peterpanbus.com
E-Mail For Key Personnel:
President: president@peterpan.com
Sales Range: $100-124.9 Million
Approx. Number Employees: 1,500
Year Founded: 1933
Business Description:
Interstate Bus Line & Charter Bus Services
S.I.C.: 4131; 4142
N.A.I.C.S.: 485210; 485510
Advertising Expenditures: $552,000
Bus. Publs.: $20,000; Co-op Adv.: $25,000; Consumer Mags.: $38,000; D.M. to Consumers: $32,000; Exhibits/Trade Shows: $10,000; Premiums, Novelties: $15,000; Spot Radio: $250,000; Weekly Newsp.: $87,000; Yellow Page Adv.: $75,000
Distr.: Reg.
Budget Set: Jan.
Personnel:
Peter A. Picknelly *(Pres & CEO)*
Brian Stefano *(CFO, COO & Exec VP)*
Robert Schwarz *(Exec VP-PR)*
Thomas Picknally *(Sr VP-Maintenance)*
Chris Crean *(VP-Safety & Security)*
Bob Montana *(Gen Mgr-Maintenance)*
Bill Sinico *(Gen Mgr-Coachbuilders)*
Kathy Girard *(Dir-Sls & Revenue)*
Carl Lajeunesse *(Dir-Charter Sls)*
Kevin Mulcahy *(Dir-Ops)*
John Shecrallah *(Dir-Ops)*
Advertising Agency:
Duffy & Shanley, Inc.
10 Charles St
Providence, RI 02904
Tel.: (401) 274-0001
Fax: (401) 274-3535

PILOT FREIGHT SERVICES

314 N Middletown Rd
Lima, PA 19037
Tel.: (610) 891-8100
Fax: (610) 565-4267
Web Site: www.pilotdelivers.com
Approx. Number Employees: 170
Business Description:
Holding Company; Freight Forwarding
S.I.C.: 4731; 4581
N.A.I.C.S.: 488510; 488119
Media: 17
Personnel:
Richard G. Phillips *(Chm)*
Lou Cortese *(Pres)*
Richard G. Phillips, Jr. *(CEO)*
Stephanie Phillips *(CMO)*
Abe Achackzad *(Exec VP-Ops & Transportation)*
Gordon Branov *(Exec VP-Bus Dev)*
John Hill *(Exec VP-Sls)*
Frank Perri *(Exec VP-Franchise Dev)*
Michael Miller *(VP-IT)*
Larry Wenrich *(VP-Govt Sls)*
Steve Bullard *(Sr Dir-Logistics)*
Dale Page *(Sr Dir-Automotive Svcs)*
Peter Placido *(Dir-Mktg)*
Brands & Products:
PILOT
Advertising Agency:
Lefton Company
100 Independence Mall W
Philadelphia, PA 19106-2399
Tel.: (215) 923-9600
Fax: (215) 351-4298

PINELLAS SUNCOAST TRANSIT AUTHORITY

(d/b/a PSTA)
3201 Scherer Dr N
Saint Petersburg, FL 33716-1004
Tel.: (727) 540-1800
Fax: (727) 535-5580
Web Site: www.psta.net
Approx. Number Employees: 600
Business Description:
Transportation Services
S.I.C.: 4119; 4131; 7389
N.A.I.C.S.: 485999; 485210; 488490
Media: 3-9-24
Personnel:
R.B. Johnson *(Chm)*
Deborah Kynes *(Vice Chm)*
Janet A. Recca *(Dir-Mktg)*

PLAN ASIA, INC

(Sub. of Singapore Airlines Ltd.)
(d/b/a AsiaLuxe Holidays)
360 N Sepulveda Blvd Ste 3008
El Segundo, CA 90245
Tel.: (310) 563-6970
Fax: (310) 563-6978
Toll Free: (800) 742-3133
Web Site: www.asialuxeholidays.com
Business Description:
Asian Destinations Tour Operator
S.I.C.: 4725
N.A.I.C.S.: 561520
Media: 13-17
Personnel:
Helen Clausen *(Gen Mgr)*

PLANES MOVING & STORAGE, INC.

9823 Cincinnati Dayton Rd
West Chester, OH 45069-3825
Tel.: (513) 759-6000
Fax: (513) 759-3699
Toll Free: (800) 543-4977
E-mail: info@planescompanies.com
Web Site: www.planescompanies.com
Approx. Number Employees: 197
Year Founded: 1921
Business Description:
Interstate & Local Trucking

Key to Media (For complete agency information see *The Advertising Red Books-Agencies* edition):
1. Bus. Publs. 2. Cable T.V. 3. Catalogs & Directories. 4. Co-op Adv. 5. Consumer Mags. 6. D.M. to Bus. Estab.7. D.M. to Consumers
8. Daily Newsp. 9. Exhibits/Trade Shows 10. Foreign 11. Infomercial 12. Internet Adv.13. Multimedia 14. Network Radio
15. Network T.V. 16. Newsp. Distr. Mags. 17. Other 18. Outdoor (Posters, Transit) 19. Point of Purchase20. Premiums, Novelties
21. Product Samples 22. Special Events Mktg. 23. Spot Radio 24. Spot T.V. 25. Weekly Newsp. 26. Yellow Page Adv.

S.I.C.: 4213; 4212
N.A.I.C.S.: 484121; 484110
Import Export
Advertising Expenditures: $300,000
Media: 8-9-20-23-25-26
Personnel:
John Planes *(CEO)*
James H. Baughman *(Dir-Sls & Mktg)*

PLEASANT HOLIDAYS LLC
2404 Townsgate Rd
Westlake Village, CA 91361-2505
Tel.: (818) 991-3390
Fax: (805) 744-6268
Toll Free: (800) 742-9244
Web Site: www.pleasantholidays.com
Approx. Number Employees: 650
Year Founded: 1959
Business Description:
Wholesale Tour Operator
S.I.C.: 4725; 4724
N.A.I.C.S.: 561520; 561510
Advertising Expenditures: $1,000,000
Media: 2-4-8-9-10-13-23-24
Distr.: Intl.; Natl.
Budget Set: Dec.
Personnel:
Tim Irwin *(Pres & CEO)*
Ron Krueger *(CFO & COO)*
Jerry Healy *(VP-Sls)*
Kevin Burnett *(Dir-Creative)*
Brands & Products:
POSH HAWAII

PORT AUTHORITY OF NEW YORK & NEW JERSEY
225 Pk Ave S 15th Fl
New York, NY 10003
Tel.: (212) 435-7000
Tel.: (212) 435-7777 (Media Rels)
Fax: (212) 435-4032
Web Site: www.panynj.gov
Approx. Number Employees: 7,000
Year Founded: 1921
Business Description:
Transportation, Port & Commerce Facilities & Services
S.I.C.: 4119; 4499; 7389
N.A.I.C.S.: 485999; 488310; 488490
Advertising Expenditures: $4,000,000
Media: 1-2-4-7-8-9-10-11-16-17-18-22-23-25-26
Distr.: Reg.
Personnel:
Anthony R. Coscia *(Chm)*
Ernesto L. Butcher *(COO)*
Louis J. LaCapra *(Chief Admin Officer)*
Michael B. Francois *(Chief-Real Estate & Dev)*
Darrell Buchbinder *(Gen Counsel)*
Wilfred Chabrier *(Gen Mgr)*
Rae Hoffmann *(Gen Mgr, Mktg Comm)*
John D. Brill *(Dir-Audit)*
Susan Daer *(Dir-Aviation)*
Francis A. DiMola *(Dir)*
Brian Lacey *(Dir-Emergency Mgmt)*
Francis J. Lombardi *(Deputy Dir-Port Commerce)*
Michael Nestor *(Dir-Investigation)*
Steven P. Plate *(Dir-Priority Capital Programs)*
Alan I. Rhome *(Dir-Opers Svcs)*
Christopher Zeppie *(Dir-Environ Policy, Programs & Compliance)*
Brands & Products:
PORT AUTHORITY OF NEW YORK & NEW JERSEY

PORT OF GALVESTON
123 25th St 8th Fl
Galveston, TX 77550-1494
Mailing Address:
PO Box 328
Galveston, TX 77553-0328
Tel.: (409) 765-9321
Fax: (409) 766-6171
E-mail: portgalv@portofgalveston.com
Web Site: www.portofgalveston.com
Sales Range: $10-24.9 Million
Approx. Number Employees: 100
Year Founded: 1825
Business Description:
Marine Cargo Handling
S.I.C.: 9621; 4491
N.A.I.C.S.: 926120; 488320
Advertising Expenditures: $550,000
Media: 2-9-10-20-22
Distr.: Reg.
Budget Set: Dec.
Personnel:
Gerald Sullivan *(Chm)*
John Eckel *(Vice Chm-Bd Trustee)*
John G. Peterlin, III *(Sr Dir-Mktg & Admin)*
R. Wayne Byrd *(Dir-Fin)*
Steven M. Cernak *(Dir-Port)*
John Eckel *(Trustees:)*
Bernard A. Curran *(Dir-Admin)*
Diane P. Falcioni *(Dir-Legislative Affairs)*
Michael J. Mierzwa *(Dir-Deputy Port)*
Judy K. Esponge *(Sr Mgr-Admin)*
Cristina Galego *(Mgr-PR)*
H. L. Smith *(Mgr-Cruise Terminal)*

PORT OF HOUSTON AUTHORITY
111 E Loop N
Houston, TX 77029-4326
Tel.: (713) 670-2400
Fax: (713) 670-2429
Toll Free: (800) 688DOCK
E-mail: questions@poha.com
Web Site: www.portofhouston.com
Sales Range: $100-124.9 Million
Approx. Number Employees: 500
Year Founded: 1914
Business Description:
Operator of a World Trade Port
S.I.C.: 9621
N.A.I.C.S.: 926120
Advertising Expenditures: $1,500,000
Media: 2-4-6-13-16-22-23-24
Distr.: Intl.; Natl.
Budget Set: Sept.
Personnel:
James T. Edmonds *(Chm)*
Alec G. Dreyer *(CEO)*
Erik Eriksson *(Gen Counsel & Sr VP)*
James B. Jackson *(Sr VP)*
Jimmy Jamison *(Sr VP)*
Lisa Ashley *(Dir-Corp Comm)*
Spencer Chambers *(Dir-Govt Rels)*
Rainer Lilienthal *(Dir-Bus Dev)*
Aston Hinds *(Sr Mgr-Environmental Affairs)*
Angus Hanes *(Asst Mgr)*
Ricardo J. Arias *(Mgr-Trade Devel)*
Carolyn Ashley *(Mgr-E-training)*
Brenda McDonald *(Mgr-Real Estate)*
Robert Morgan *(Mgr-Maritime Academy)*
Brian T. Reeves *(Mgr-Market Devel)*
Curtis Rose *(Mgr-Pur)*
Margot Campbell *(Asst Gen Counsel & Records Mgmt Officer)*
Linda Henry *(Asst Gen Counsel)*
Advertising Agency:
MusiGraphics Advertising
10110 Sands Trail Ct
Houston, TX 77064
Tel.: (281) 970-8800
Toll Free: (866) 970-8844

PORT OF MIAMI TERMINAL OPERATING COMPANY, LC
1007 N America Way Ste 400
Miami, FL 33132
Tel.: (305) 416-7600
Fax: (305) 374-6724
Web Site: www.pomtoc.com
Sales Range: $10-24.9 Million
Approx. Number Employees: 20
Business Description:
Marine Cargo Handling
S.I.C.: 4491
N.A.I.C.S.: 488320
Media: 6
Personnel:
Charles O'Malley *(CFO)*
John Ballestero *(COO)*
George Arocha *(Mgr-Opers)*
Kerry Bosse *(Mgr-MIS)*
Carlos Garcia *(Mgr-Billing)*
Don Haggerty *(Mgr-Ops)*
Robert Stark *(Mgr-Terminal Operating Sys)*
Hilda Torres *(Mgr-Customer Svc)*
Howard Weintraub *(Mgr-Safety & Security)*

PORT OF OAKLAND
530 Water St
Oakland, CA 94607-3746
Tel.: (510) 627-1100
Fax: (510) 839-1766
Web Site: www.portofoakland.com
Approx. Rev.: $267,461,000
Approx. Number Employees: 600
Year Founded: 1927
Business Description:
Operator of Airport, Marine Terminals, Restaurants, Shopping Complexes, Office & Marina Complex & Business Park
S.I.C.: 9621
N.A.I.C.S.: 926120
Advertising Expenditures: $201,000
Bus. Publs.: $100,000; Daily Newsp.: $20,000; Exhibits/Trade Shows: $6,000; Foreign: $50,000; Outdoor (Posters, Transit): $25,000
Distr.: Intl.; Natl.
Budget Set: July

PORT OF PORTLAND
7200 NE Airport Way
Portland, OR 97218-4049
Tel.: (503) 944-7000
Fax: (503) 548-5939
Toll Free: (800) 547-8411
Telex: 4742039
E-mail: contactus@portofportland.com
Web Site: www.portofportland.com
Sales Range: $200-249.9 Million
Approx. Number Employees: 787
Year Founded: 1891
Business Description:
Marine Cargo; Industrial Parks; Aviation & Distr; Industrial & Commercial Property Development
S.I.C.: 9621
N.A.I.C.S.: 926120
Import Export
Advertising Expenditures: $750,000
Media: 1-2-7-9-10-11-13-20-23-24-25-26
Distr.: Intl.; Natl.
Budget Set: Jan. -Feb.
Personnel:
Judith Ann Johansen *(Pres)*
Carla Kelley *(Gen Counsel)*
Joe Mollusky *(Gen Mgr)*
David Zielke *(Gen Mgr-Air Svc Devel)*
Bill Wyatt *(Exec Dir)*
Sam Ruda *(Dir-Marine)*
Steve Schreiber *(Dir-Aviation)*
Gail Woodworth *(Dir-HR)*
Brands & Products:
PDX
POSSIBILITY. IN EVERY DIRECTION.

PRESTIGE TRAVEL, INC.
9895 Montgomery Rd
Cincinnati, OH 45242-6424
Tel.: (513) 793-6586
Fax: (513) 793-2819
Toll Free: (800) 783-9859
E-mail: traveller@prestige-travel.com
Web Site: www.prestige-travel.com
Sales Range: $25-49.9 Million
Approx. Number Employees: 20
Business Description:
Travel Management
S.I.C.: 4724
N.A.I.C.S.: 561510
Media: 13
Personnel:
Pete Hershberger *(Pres)*

PRINCESS CRUISES
(Sub. of Carnival plc)
24844 Rockefeller Ave
Santa Clarita, CA 91355
Tel.: (661) 753-0000
Fax: (661) 284-4585
Telex: 188472
Web Site: www.princess.com
Sales Range: $350-399.9 Million
Approx. Number Employees: 1,500
Business Description:
Cruise Operator
S.I.C.: 4481
N.A.I.C.S.: 483112
Media: 2-6-8-9-14-18-24-25
Distr.: Natl.
Budget Set: Aug.
Personnel:
Alan B. Buckelew *(Pres)*
Dean Brown *(Exec VP)*
Todd Putman *(VP-Mktg)*
Brands & Products:
PRINCESS
Advertising Agency:
Ignited
2221 Park Pl
El Segundo, CA 90245
Tel.: (310) 773-3100
Fax: (310) 773-3101
Creative & Media

PRINCESS TOURS
(Div. of Princess Cruises)
800 5th Ave Ste 2600
Seattle, WA 98104
Tel.: (206) 336-6000
Fax: (206) 336-6100
Toll Free: (800) 426-0500
E-mail: aklodges@princesstours.com

Key to Media (For complete agency information see *The Advertising Red Books-Agencies* edition):
1. Bus. Publs. 2. Cable T.V. 3. Catalogs & Directories. 4. Co-op Adv. 5. Consumer Mags. 6. D.M. to Bus. Estab.7. D.M. to Consumers
8. Daily Newsp. 9. Exhibits/Trade Shows 10. Foreign 11. Infomercial 12. Internet Adv.13. Multimedia 14. Network Radio
15. Network T.V. 16. Newsp. Distr. Mags. 17. Other 18. Outdoor (Posters, Transit) 19. Point of Purchase20. Premiums, Novelties
21. Product Samples 22. Special Events Mktg. 23. Spot Radio 24. Spot T.V. 25. Weekly Newsp. 26. Yellow Page Adv.

Princess Tours — (Continued)

Web Site: www.princesslodges.com
E-Mail For Key Personnel:
Marketing Director: ptmarketing@princesstours.com
Sales Director: ptsales@princesstours.com
Sales Range: $1-9.9 Million
Approx. Number Employees: 200
Year Founded: 1972
Business Description:
Cruise & Tour Operator
S.I.C.: 7999
N.A.I.C.S.: 487110
Media: 1-2-4-5-6-8-9-13-19-23-25-26
Distr.: Intl.; Natl.
Budget Set: June
Personnel:
Dean Brown *(Exec VP)*
Allyson McBride *(Mgr-Mktg)*
Brands & Products:
DENALI PRINCESS LODGE
FAIRBANKS PRINCESS LODGE
KENAI PRINCESS LODGE
MIDNIGHT SUN EXPRESS ULTRA DOME
MT. MCKINLEY PRINCESS LODGE
PRINCESS TOURS

PROPHESY TRANSPORTATION SOLUTIONS, INC.

204C W Newberry Rd
Bloomfield, CT 06002-1308
Tel.: (860) 243-0533
Fax: (860) 243-2619
Toll Free: (800) 776-6706
E-mail: sales@mile.com
Web Site: www.mile.com
E-Mail For Key Personnel:
President: eforman@mile.com
Sales Director: sales@mile.com
Approx. Number Employees: 30
Year Founded: 1984
Business Description:
Supplier of Dispatch & Accounting Software, Mileage & Routing; Fuel Tax; Driver Log Audit, Fleet Maintenance & Logistics Software to the Transportation Industry
S.I.C.: 7371
N.A.I.C.S.: 541511
Export
Media: 2-4-7-10-13-26
Distr.: Intl.
Budget Set: Dec.
Brands & Products:
DISPATCH AND ACCOUNTING
DRIVERTRAX
FLEETTRAX PREMIER
FUELLOGIC
LOGPLUS
MILEAGE AND ROUTING
PROPHESY SHIPPERMAIL
PROPHESY SHIPPERPLUS
PROPHESY SHIPPERTPL
PROPHESYONE
QUICKBOOKS
SHIPPERPLUS LOADBUILDER
STREETROUTER
TAXTALLY

QANTAS AIRWAYS - USA

(Branch of Qantas Airways Limited)
6080 Ctr Dr Ste 400
Los Angeles, CA 90045
Tel.: (310) 726-1400
Fax: (310) 726-1401
Toll Free: (800) 227-4500
Web Site: www.qantas.com.au
Sales Range: $300-349.9 Million
Approx. Number Employees: 45
Year Founded: 1972
Business Description:
Operator of Airlines
S.I.C.: 8743; 4512
N.A.I.C.S.: 541820; 481111
Advertising Expenditures: $1,000,000
Daily Newsp.: $750,000; Other: $250,000
Distr.: Intl.; Natl.
Personnel:
Rohan Garnett *(Sr VP-Sls-The Americas)*
Dina Louie *(Dir-Online Sls & Mktg)*
Melissa Rose *(Dir-Mktg)*
Brands & Products:
QANTAS

RAIL EUROPE INC.

(Sub. of Societe Nationale des Chemins de Fer Francais)
44 S Broadway Fl 11
White Plains, NY 10601-4411
Tel.: (914) 682-2999
Fax: (914) 682-2821
Toll Free: (888) 382-7245
Web Site: www.raileurope.com
Approx. Sls.: $300,000,000
Approx. Number Employees: 120
Year Founded: 1991
Business Description:
Distr of Travel Products Including Train Passes & Transatlantic Air, Hotel & Car Rental in Europe
S.I.C.: 4724
N.A.I.C.S.: 561510
Advertising Expenditures: $1,580,000
Multimedia: $10,000; Bus. Publs.: $250,000; Catalogs & Directories: $10,000; Co-op Adv.: $50,000; Consumer Mags.: $600,000; D.M. to Consumers: $50,000; Exhibits/Trade Shows: $40,000; Internet Adv.: $50,000; Other: $200,000; Premiums, Novelties: $20,000; Weekly Newsp.: $300,000
Distr.: Natl.
Budget Set: Oct.
Personnel:
Peter Rahaman *(VP-Sls-North America)*
Beth De Marte *(Dir-Mktg)*
Simone Ruf *(Dir-Products)*
Advertising Agency:
Lou Hammond & Associates, Inc.
39 E 51st St
New York, NY 10022-5916
Tel.: (212) 308-8880
Fax: (212) 891-0200

RAILSERVE INC.

(Sub. of Marmon Transportation Services & Engineered Products)
1691 Phoenix Blvd Ste 250
Atlanta, GA 30349-5565
Tel.: (770) 996-6838
E-mail: marketing@railserveinc.com
Web Site: www.railserveinc.com
Sales Range: $250-299.9 Million
Approx. Number Employees: 750
Year Founded: 1994
Business Description:
Switching & Terminal Services
S.I.C.: 4013
N.A.I.C.S.: 488210
Media: 4
Personnel:
Bobby R. Ross *(Co-Pres & Sr VP)*
Timothy J. Benjamin *(Co-Pres & VP)*
Tim Pullen *(VP-HR)*
John P. Roberts *(Asst VP-Ops)*
Timothy K. Lawler *(Dir-Mktg)*
Mark T. Bradshaw *(Dir-Mktg)*
Stephanie A. Renner *(Dir-Mktg)*

RCI, LLC

(Div. of Wyndham Worldwide Corporation)
9998 North Michigan Rd
Carmel, IN 46032
Tel.: (317) 805-9000
Fax: (317) 805-9335
Web Site: www.rci.com
Sales Range: $150-199.9 Million
Approx. Number Employees: 4,200
Year Founded: 1974
Business Description:
Leisure, Travel & Exchange Service for Owners of Time Share Units
S.I.C.: 7032
N.A.I.C.S.: 721214
Advertising Expenditures: $5,000,000
D.M. to Consumers: $5,000,000
Distr.: Direct to Consumer; Reg.
Personnel:
Geoff Ballotti *(Pres & CEO)*
Jeff Talotti *(CFO & Exec VP)*
Suzanne Wetherington *(Exec VP & Chief Innovation Officer)*
Julie Tenney *(VP-Corp Comm)*

REGIONAL TRANSPORTATION AUTHORITY

(d/b/a RTA)
175 W Jackson St Ste 1550
Chicago, IL 60602-4501
Tel.: (312) 913-3200
Fax: (312) 913-3216
E-mail: communications@rtachicago.org
Web Site: www.rtachicago.com
Sales Range: $1-4.9 Billion
Approx. Number Employees: 1,630
Year Founded: 1974
Business Description:
Transportation
S.I.C.: 9621
N.A.I.C.S.: 926120
Advertising Expenditures: $535,000
Media: 15-23
Distr.: Reg.
Budget Set: Nov.
Personnel:
Jim Reilly *(Chm)*
Joseph Costello *(Exec Dir)*
Patrick V. Riley *(Dir-Conferences)*
Brands & Products:
RTA
RTA TRAVEL INFORMATION
TRANSIT CHECK

RENT-A-WRECK OF AMERICA, INC.

(Sub. of JJF Management Services, Inc.)
105 Main St
Laurel, MD 20707
Tel.: (240) 581-1350
Toll Free: (800) 944-7501
E-mail: jmanelli@rentawreck.com
Web Site: www.rent-a-wreck.com
E-Mail For Key Personnel:
Marketing Director: jmanelli@rent-a-wreck.com
Sales Range: $1-9.9 Million
Approx. Number Employees: 14
Year Founded: 1968
Business Description:
Franchiser for Rental & Leasing of New & Used Cars, Trucks & Vans
S.I.C.: 7519; 7514
N.A.I.C.S.: 532120; 532111
Media: 5-13-18
Distr.: Natl.
Budget Set: Apr.
Personnel:
William Cash *(Pres)*
Jason Manelli *(Dir-Comm)*
Dale Tripp *(Mgr-Franchise Dev)*
Brands & Products:
DON'T LET THE NAME FOOL YOU!
RENT-A-WRECK

RESIDENSEA

(d/b/a World Residensea, The)
5200 Blue Lagoon Dr Ste 7
Miami, FL 33126
Tel.: (305) 269-5151
Web Site: www.residensea.com
Approx. Rev.: $1,000,000
Approx. Number Employees: 26
Year Founded: 2001
Business Description:
Hotel/Motel Operation Drinking Place Eating Place
S.I.C.: 7011
N.A.I.C.S.: 721110
Advertising Agency:
Mascola Advertising
434 Forbes Ave
New Haven, CT 06512-1932
Tel.: (203) 469-6900
Fax: (203) 467-8558
Agency of Record

ROYAL CARIBBEAN CRUISES LTD

1050 Caribbean Way
Miami, FL 33132-2096
Tel.: (305) 539-6000
Fax: (305) 374-7354
Toll Free: (800) 398-9819 (Cust Svc)
E-mail: investorrelations@rccl.com
Web Site: www.royalcaribbean.com
Approx. Rev.: $6,752,504,000
Approx. Number Employees: 5,200
Year Founded: 1969
Business Description:
Caribbean Cruise Operator
S.I.C.: 4481; 4482; 4729
N.A.I.C.S.: 483112; 483114; 561599
Advertising Expenditures: $152,200,000
Media: 2-5-6-8-9-13-15-19-31
Distr.: Intl.; Natl.
Budget Set: Jan.
Personnel:
Richard D. Fain *(Chm & CEO)*
Adam M. Goldstein *(Pres & CEO-Royal Caribbean Intl)*
Daniel J. Hanrahan *(Pres & CEO-Celebrity Cruises & Azamara Cruises)*
Larry Pimentel *(Pres & CEO-Azamara Cruises)*
Brian J. Rice *(CFO & Exec VP)*
William Marin *(CIO)*
Maria Del Busto *(Global Chief HR Officer)*
Craig S. Milan *(Pres-Royal Celebrity Tours)*

Key to Media (For complete agency information see *The Advertising Red Books-Agencies* edition):
1. Bus. Publs. 2. Cable T.V. 3. Catalogs & Directories. 4. Co-op Adv. 5. Consumer Mags. 6. D.M. to Bus. Estab.7. D.M. to Consumers 8. Daily Newsp. 9. Exhibits/Trade Shows 10. Foreign 11. Infomercial 12. Internet Adv.13. Multimedia 14. Network Radio 15. Network T.V. 16. Newsp. Distr. Mags. 17. Other 18. Outdoor (Posters, Transit) 19. Point of Purchase20. Premiums, Novelties 21. Product Samples 22. Special Events Mktg. 23. Spot Radio 24. Spot T.V. 25. Weekly Newsp. 26. Yellow Page Adv.

Bradley Stein *(Gen Counsel, Sec & VP)*
Michael Bayley *(Exec VP-Intl Royal Caribbean Cruises Ltd)*
Harri U. Kulovaara *(Exec VP-Maritime)*
Lisa Bauer *(Sr VP-Hotel Ops-Royal Caribbean Intl)*
Vicki Freed *(Sr VP-Sls)*
Betsy O'Rourke *(Sr VP-Mktg)*
William Wright *(Sr VP-Marine Ops-Royal Caribbean Intl)*
Ken Muskat *(VP-Sls)*
Magnus Wrahme *(Assoc VP-Intl Market Dev)*
Jonathan M. Jaffe *(Dir & Assoc Counsel)*
Juan Silva *(Dir-E-Distr, Strategy & Dev)*
Angela Stephen *(Dir-Accts-Natl)*
Rebecca A. Barba *(Mgr-Global Mktg, Mktg Strategy, Multicultural Mktg & Comm)*
Suparna Chhibber *(Mgr-Relationship Mktg-Intl)*
Lyan Sierra-Caro *(Sr Acct Exec)*

Brands & Products:
ADVENTURE OCEAN
ADVENTURE OF THE SEAS
BRILLIANCE OF THE SEAS
CDF CROISIERES DE FRANCE
CELEBRITY CRUISES
CLUB ROYALE
COCOCAY
EMPRESS OF THE SEAS
ENCHANTMENT OF THE SEAS
EXPLORER OF THE SEAS
FREEDOM OF THE SEAS
GALAXY
GET OUT THERE
GOLD ANCHOR SERVICE
GRANDEUR OF THE SEAS
JEWEL OF THE SEAS
LABADEE
LEGEND OF THE SEAS
LIBERTY OF THE SEAS
MAJESTY OF THE SEAS
MARINER OF THE SEAS
MERCURY
MILLENNIUM
MONARCH OF THE SEAS
NAVIGATOR OF THE SEAS
RADIANCE OF THE SEAS
RHAPSODY OF THE SEAS
ROYAL CARIBBEAN
ROYAL CARIBBEAN INTERNATIONAL
SAVE THE WAVES
SAVOR
SERENADE OF THE SEAS
SHIPSHAPE
SOVEREIGN OF THE SEAS
SPLENDOUR OF THE SEAS
SUMMIT
VIKING CROWN LOUNGE
VISION OF THE SEAS
VOYAGER OF THE SEAS
THE WILDERNESS EXPRESS
XPEDITION
ZENITH

Advertising Agencies:
Element 79
(Part of the Omincom Group)
200 E Randolph St 33rd Fl
Chicago, IL 60601
Tel.: (312) 233-8100
Fax: (312) 233-8298
Celebrity Cruises

J. Walter Thompson Company
(d/b/a JWT)
466 Lexington Ave
New York, NY 10017-3140
Tel.: (212) 210-7000
Fax: (212) 210-7299

Mindshare
498 7th Ave
New York, NY 10018
Tel.: (212) 297-7000
Fax: (212) 297-7001

Spike/DDB
55 Washington St Ste 650
Brooklyn, NY 11201
Tel.: (718) 596-5400
Fax: (212) 415-3101

ROYAL COACHMAN WORLDWIDE

88 Ford Rd Unit 26
Denville, NJ 07834
Tel.: (973) 400-3200
Fax: (973) 675-4365
Toll Free: (800) 4RC-RIDE
E-mail: reservations@royalcoachman.com
Web Site: www.royalcoachman.com
Year Founded: 1969
Business Description:
Chauffeured Ground Transportation
S.I.C.: 4119
N.A.I.C.S.: 485320
Media: 17
Personnel:
John Epstein *(Pres)*
Amy Birnbaum *(CEO)*
Advertising Agency:
Andover Communications, Inc.
1 Bridge Plz N Ste 325
Fort Lee, NJ 07024-7586
Tel.: (201) 947-4133
Fax: (201) 947-5580
Toll Free: (800) 866-5580

RYDER SYSTEM, INC.

11690 NW 105 St
Miami, FL 33178
Tel.: (305) 500-3726
Fax: (305) 500-3203
E-mail: info@ryder.com
Web Site: www.ryder.com
Approx. Rev.: $5,136,435,000
Approx. Number Employees: 25,900
Year Founded: 1933
Business Description:
Commercial Truck Leasing & Rental & Logistics Services
S.I.C.: 7519; 4731; 8742
N.A.I.C.S.: 532120; 488510; 541614
Export
Media: 2-7-10-13-19-22-26
Distr.: Intl.; Natl.
Personnel:
Gregory T. Swienton *(Chm & CEO)*
Art A. Garcia *(CFO & Exec VP)*
Keyvan Bohlooli *(CIO & Sr VP)*
Robert D. Fatovic *(Chief Legal Officer, Exec VP & Corp Sec)*
Gregory F. Greene *(Chief Admin Officer & Exec VP)*
Cristina A. Gallo-Aquino *(Chief Acctg Officer, VP & Controller)*
Robert E. Sanchez *(Pres-Global Fleet Mgmt Solutions)*
John H. Williford *(Pres-Global Supply Chain Solution)*
Rosario Rizzo *(Sr VP & Gen Mgr)*
Stephen F. Dean *(Sr VP-Sls, Mktg & Supply Chain Solutions)*
John J. Gleason *(Sr VP-Sls & Mktg-Fleet Mgmt Solutions)*
Todd Carter *(VP & Gen Mgr-Global Transportation Mgmt)*
David Bruce *(VP-Corp Comm)*
Sheryl Pattek *(VP-Mktg)*
Lisa Hagen *(Dir-Corp Comm)*
Brands & Products:
RYDER
RYDER FLEETCARE
RYDERFLOW
RYDERSHIP
RYDERTRAC
RYDESMART
Advertising Agency:
The Weinbach Group, Inc.
7301 SW 57th Ct Ste 550
South Miami, FL 33143-5334
Tel.: (305) 668-0070
Fax: (305) 668-3029

SABRE HOLDINGS CORPORATION

(Holding of Silver Lake Partners, L.P.)
3150 Sabre Dr
Southlake, TX 76092-2103
Tel.: (682) 605-1000
Fax: (682) 605-8267
E-mail: hotel.eservices@sabre.com
Web Site: www.sabre-holdings.com
Approx. Rev.: $2,823,797,000
Approx. Number Employees: 9,000
Year Founded: 1996
Business Description:
Holding Company; Airline Computer Services & Travel Services
S.I.C.: 4729; 2741; 6719; 7374
N.A.I.C.S.: 561599; 516110; 518210; 551112
Advertising Expenditures: $216,000,000
Media: 2-4-7-9-10-14-17
Personnel:
Michael Sam Gilliland *(Chm & CEO)*
Mark K. Miller *(CFO & Exec VP)*
Barry Vandevier *(CIO)*
Brad Wilson *(Chief Mktg Officer-Travelocity North America)*
Thomas Klein *(Pres-Sabre Holdings)*
Sterling L. Miller *(Gen Counsel, Corp Sec & Exec VP)*
Jeffery M. Jackson *(Exec VP-Corp Bus Dev)*
Paul Rostron *(Exec VP-HR)*
Dan Toporek *(VP-Pub Rels)*
Brands & Products:
GETTHERE
SABRE
SABRE AIRLINE SOLUTIONS
SABRE HOLDINGS
SABRE TRAVEL NETWORK
TRAVELOCITY

SAIA, INC.

11465 Johns Creek Pkwy Ste 400
Johns Creek, GA 30097
Tel.: (770) 232-5067
Toll Free: (800) 765-7242
E-mail: investors@saia.com
Web Site: www.saia.com
Approx. Rev.: $902,660,000
Approx. Number Employees: 7,500
Business Description:
Truck Transportation
S.I.C.: 4213
N.A.I.C.S.: 484121; 484122
Advertising Expenditures: $300,000
Personnel:
Herbert A. Trucksess, III *(Chm)*
Richard D. O'Dell *(Pres & CEO)*
James A. Darby *(CFO & VP-Fin)*
Mark H. Robinson *(CIO & VP)*
Sally Buchholz *(VP-Mktg & Customer Svc)*
Mark A. Hamblin *(VP-Sls-West)*
Raymond R. Ramu *(VP-Sls-East)*
Marty R. Ready *(VP-HR)*
Brands & Products:
SAIA
SAIA CUSTOMER SERVICE INDICATORS
SAIA GUARANTEED SELECT
SAIA XTREME GUARANTEE

SAINT PAUL PORT AUTHORITY

1900 Landmark Towers 345 St Peter St
Saint Paul, MN 55102
Tel.: (651) 224-5686
Fax: (651) 223-5198
Toll Free: (800) 328-8417
E-mail: info@sppa.com
Web Site: www.sppa.com
Sales Range: $10-24.9 Million
Approx. Number Employees: 21
Year Founded: 1932
Business Description:
Provider of Citywide Industrial Development
S.I.C.: 9621
N.A.I.C.S.: 926120
Advertising Expenditures: $200,000
Media: 1-2-5-6-7-9-10-25
Distr.: Reg.
Personnel:
Joan A. Grzywinski *(Chm)*
Louis F. Jambois *(Pres)*
Laurie J. Hansen *(CFO)*
Lorrie J. Louder *(Dir-Bus InterGovermental Affairs)*
William M. Morin *(Dir-Real Estate)*
Laurie A. Siever *(Dir-HR)*

SAN LUIS OBISPO COUNTY VISITORS & CONFERENCE BUREAU

811 El Capitan Way
San Luis Obispo, CA 93401
Tel.: (805) 541-8000
Fax: (805) 543-9498
E-mail: info@sanluisobispocounty.com
Web Site: www.sanluisobispocounty.com
Sales Range: Less than $1 Million
Approx. Number Employees: 4
Business Description:
Tourism Promoter
S.I.C.: 4729
N.A.I.C.S.: 561599
Advertising Agency:
McMurry
1010 E Missouri Ave
Phoenix, AZ 85014
Tel.: (602) 395-5850
Fax: (602) 248-2925
Toll Free: (888) MCMURRY
Toll Free: (888) 626-8779

SEACOR HOLDINGS INC.

2200 Eller Dr
Fort Lauderdale, FL 33316

Key to Media (For complete agency information see *The Advertising Red Books-Agencies* edition):
1. Bus. Publs. 2. Cable T.V. 3. Catalogs & Directories. 4. Co-op Adv. 5. Consumer Mags. 6. D.M. to Bus. Estab.7. D.M. to Consumers 8. Daily Newsp. 9. Exhibits/Trade Shows 10. Foreign 11. Infomercial 12. Internet Adv.13. Multimedia 14. Network Radio 15. Network T.V. 16. Newsp. Distr. Mags. 17. Other 18. Outdoor (Posters, Transit) 19. Point of Purchase20. Premiums, Novelties 21. Product Samples 22. Special Events Mktg. 23. Spot Radio 24. Spot T.V. 25. Weekly Newsp. 26. Yellow Page Adv.

SEACOR Holdings Inc. — (Continued)

Tel.: (954) 254-2200
Fax: (954) 763-1501
E-mail: info.ftl@ckor.com
Web Site: www.seacorsmit.com
Approx. Rev.: $2,649,368,000
Approx. Number Employees: 5,311
Year Founded: 1989
Business Description:
Marine Services for Offshore Oil Operations
S.I.C.: 4412; 4432
N.A.I.C.S.: 483111; 483113
Media: 2
Personnel:
Richard Ryan *(CFO & Sr VP)*
Matthew Cenac *(Chief Acctg Officer & VP)*
Paul Robinson *(Gen Counsel, Sec & Sr VP)*
Dick Fagerstal *(Treas & Sr VP-Corp Dev)*
Randall Blank *(Sr VP)*
James Cowderoy *(Sr VP)*
John Gellert *(Sr VP)*
Alice Gran *(Sr VP-Legal Affairs & Risk Mgmt)*

SEAESCAPE ENTERTAINMENT, INC.
(d/b/a SeaEscape Cruises)
3049 N Federal Hwy Bldg 7
Fort Lauderdale, FL 33306-1431
Tel.: (954) 453-2200
Fax: (954) 453-6555
Toll Free: (877) -SEA-ESCAPE
E-mail: corpinfo@seaescape.com
Web Site: www.seaescape.com
E-Mail For Key Personnel:
Sales Director: sales@seaescape.com
Approx. Number Employees: 90
Year Founded: 1996
Business Description:
Cruise Related Services
S.I.C.: 4481
N.A.I.C.S.: 483112
Advertising Expenditures: $700,000
Media: 3-8-16-18-23-25
Distr.: Natl.
Personnel:
Richard Barrow *(Dir-Revenue Mngmt)*
Nicholas P. Sims *(Mgr-SeaEscape Casino)*
Brands & Products:
LAS VEGAS WITH AN OCEANVIEW
SEAESCAPE
TO A SHIP FULL OF FUN!
Advertising Agency:
5W Public Relations
888 7th Ave 12th Fl
New York, NY 10106
Tel.: (212) 999-5585
Fax: (646) 328-1711

SECURITY VAN LINES
(Affil. of Johnson Storage & Moving Company)
100 W Airline Dr
Kenner, LA 70062
Tel.: (504) 466-4449
Fax: (504) 464-1818
Toll Free: (800) 794-5961
Web Site: www.securityvanlines.net
Approx. Number Employees: 150
Year Founded: 1937
Business Description:
Household Goods Transport; Local Furniture Moving & Storage
S.I.C.: 4214
N.A.I.C.S.: 484210
Media: 7-8-13-17
Distr.: Reg.
Personnel:
Tina Heaney *(Mgr)*

SEGWAY INC.
14 Technology Dr
Bedford, NH 03110
Tel.: (603) 222-6000
Fax: (603) 222-6001
Toll Free: (866) 858-2455
Toll Free: (866) 4SEGWAY
Web Site: www.segway.com
Sales Range: $10-24.9 Million
Approx. Number Employees: 100
Year Founded: 1999
Business Description:
Transportation Products Developer & Mfr
S.I.C.: 3751
N.A.I.C.S.: 336991
Media: 4-6-13-20
Personnel:
Wayne Mitchell *(Pres & CEO)*
Brands & Products:
GET MOVING
I2 CARGO
I2 COMMUTER
SEGWAY
X2 ADVENTURE
X2 GOLF
X2 TURF
Advertising Agency:
Humongo
155 Main St 4th Fl
Danbury, CT 06810
Tel.: (203) 730-6300
Fax: (203) 730-6303
Segway Social - Social Networking Site

SILVER SHIPS, INC.
9243 Bellingrath Rd
Theodore, AL 36582-2710
Tel.: (251) 973-0000
Fax: (251) 973-2711
E-mail: slvr_shp@silverships.com
Web Site: www.silverships.com
Approx. Number Employees: 40
Year Founded: 1985
Business Description:
Custom Aluminum Ships
S.I.C.: 3732
N.A.I.C.S.: 336612
Media: 10
Personnel:
Mike McCarty *(Pres)*
Jason Powers *(Gen Mgr)*
Brands & Products:
AMBAR MARINE
SILVER SHIPS

SINGAPORE AIRLINES
(Sub. of Singapore Airlines Ltd.)
222 N Sepulveda Blvd Ste 1600
El Segundo, CA 90245
Tel.: (310) 647-1922
Fax: (310) 645-7030
Toll Free: (800) 742-3333
Toll Free: (800) 742-8474
Web Site: www.singaporeair.com
Approx. Number Employees: 13,720
Year Founded: 1947
Business Description:
Air Transportation
S.I.C.: 4512
N.A.I.C.S.: 481112
Advertising Expenditures: $7,524,000
Bus. Publs.: $1,128,600; Catalogs & Directories: $376,200; Consumer Mags.: $1,504,800; Exhibits/Trade Shows: $1,504,800; Other: $376,200; Point of Purchase: $1,504,800; Premiums, Novelties: $1,128,600
Distr.: Intl.; Natl.
Budget Set: Sept.
Personnel:
Koh Boon Hwee *(Chm)*
Chew Choon Seng *(CEO)*
Chew Leng Seng *(Exec VP-Tech)*
Brands & Products:
SINGAPORE AIRLINES

SIRVA, INC.
700 Oakmont Ln
Westmont, IL 60559
Tel.: (630) 570-3047
Fax: (630) 570-3606
Toll Free: (800) 234-2788
E-mail: SIRVAMedia@sirva.com
Web Site: www.sirva.com
Sales Range: $1-4.9 Billion
Approx. Number Employees: 3,800
Business Description:
Corporate & Consumer Relocation Services
S.I.C.: 4213; 7011
N.A.I.C.S.: 484230; 721199
Advertising Expenditures: $10,800,000
Personnel:
Wes Lucas *(Pres & CEO)*
J. Gordon Smith *(CFO)*
Daniel P. Mullin *(Chief Acctg Officer)*
Deborah L. Balli *(Pres-Global Relocation Svcs)*
Jacob George *(Pres-Asia & Middle East Markets)*
Michael T. Wolfe *(Pres-Moving Svcs-North America)*
Douglas V. Gathany *(Treas & Sr VP-IR)*
Brands & Products:
ALLIED
ALLIED PICKFORDS
ALLIED SPECIAL PRODUCTS
DJK RESIDENTIAL
GLOBAL
IMOVE
NORTH AMERICAN
NORTH AMERICAN INTERNATIONAL
RELOCATION REDEFINED
SIRVA
SIRVA MORTGAGE
SIRVA RELOCATION
SIRVA SETTLEMENT

SKYWEST INC.
444 S River Rd
Saint George, UT 84790-2085
Tel.: (435) 634-3000
Fax: (435) 634-3105
E-mail: info@skywest.com
Web Site: www.skywest.com
Approx. Rev.: $2,765,145,000
Approx. Number Employees: 18,378
Year Founded: 1972
Business Description:
Airline Holding Company
S.I.C.: 4729; 4512
N.A.I.C.S.: 561599; 481111
Advertising Expenditures: $400,000
Media: 5-9-10-13-18-22-23-25
Distr.: Intl.; Natl.; Reg.
Budget Set: Oct.
Personnel:
Jerry C. Atkin *(Chm & CEO)*
Russell A. Childs *(Pres & COO)*
Bradford R. Rich *(CFO & Exec VP)*
Michael J. Kraupp *(Treas & VP-Fin)*
James K. Boyd *(VP-Customer Svc)*
James B. Jensen *(VP-IT)*
Marissa Snow *(Mgr-Corp Comm)*
Brands & Products:
SKYWEST
SKYWEST AIRLINES
Advertising Agency:
KemperLesnik
500 Skokie Blvd 4th Fl
Northbrook, IL 60062
Tel.: (847) 850-1818
Fax: (847) 559-0406

SOUTHEASTERN PENNSYLVANIA TRANSPORTATION AUTHORITY
(d/b/a SEPTA)
1234 Market St
Philadelphia, PA 19107-3721
Tel.: (215) 580-4000
Fax: (215) 580-7534
Web Site: www.septa.org
Sales Range: $400-449.9 Million
Approx. Number Employees: 12,000
Year Founded: 1963
Business Description:
Passenger Transportation Services
S.I.C.: 4111
N.A.I.C.S.: 485119
Advertising Expenditures: $1,600,000
Multimedia: $20,000; Cable T.V.: $30,000; Co-op Adv.: $60,000; D.M. to Consumers: $80,000; Daily Newsp.: $200,000; Exhibits/Trade Shows: $10,000; Outdoor (Posters, Transit): $150,000; Point of Purchase: $10,000; Premiums, Novelties: $10,000; Special Events Mktg.: $43,000; Spot Radio: $762,000; Spot T.V.: $50,000; Weekly Newsp.: $150,000; Yellow Page Adv.: $25,000
Distr.: Direct to Consumer; Reg.
Budget Set: Feb. -Mar.
Personnel:
Pasquale T. Deon, Sr. *(Chm)*
James C. Schwartzman *(Vice Chm)*
Joseph Casey *(Gen Mgr)*
Richard DiLullo *(Dir-Mktg & Promo)*
John Kerrigan *(Mgr)*
Brands & Products:
SEPTA
Advertising Agency:
Titan Worldwide
10601 Decatur Rd Ste 300
Philadelphia, PA 19154
Tel.: (215) 281-1980
Fax: (215) 281-1990

SOUTHWEST AIRLINES CO.
2702 Love Field Dr
Dallas, TX 75235-1908
Mailing Address:
PO Box 36611
Dallas, TX 75235-1611
Tel.: (214) 792-4000
Fax: (214) 792-5015

Key to Media (For complete agency information see *The Advertising Red Books-Agencies* edition):
1. Bus. Publs. 2. Cable T.V. 3. Catalogs & Directories. 4. Co-op Adv. 5. Consumer Mags. 6. D.M. to Bus. Estab.7. D.M. to Consumers
8. Daily Newsp. 9. Exhibits/Trade Shows 10. Foreign 11. Infomercial 12. Internet Adv.13. Multimedia 14. Network Radio
15. Network T.V. 16. Newsp. Distr. Mags. 17. Other 18. Outdoor (Posters, Transit) 19. Point of Purchase20. Premiums, Novelties
21. Product Samples 22. Special Events Mktg. 23. Spot Radio 24. Spot T.V. 25. Weekly Newsp. 26. Yellow Page Adv.

Toll Free: (800) 435-9792
Telex: 988124
Web Site: www.southwest.com
Approx. Rev.: $12,104,000,000
Approx. Number Employees: 34,901
Year Founded: 1971
Business Description:
Airline
S.I.C.: 4512
N.A.I.C.S.: 481111
Advertising Expenditures: $202,000,000
Media: 2-3-6-8-9-13-14-15-18-20-23-24-25-26
Distr.: Reg.
Budget Set: Jan.
Personnel:
Gary C. Kelly *(Chm, Pres & CEO)*
Laura H. Wright *(CFO & Sr VP-Fin)*
Michael G. Van De Ven *(COO & Exec VP)*
Jan Marshall *(CIO & VP-Tech)*
Davis S. Ridley *(CMO & Sr VP)*
Jeff Lamb *(Chief People Officer & Sr VP-Admin)*
Madeleine Johnson *(VP & Gen Counsel)*
Ron Ricks *(Exec VP-Corp Svcs & Corp Sec)*
Donna D. Conover *(Exec VP-Customer Ops)*
Ginger C. Hardage *(Sr VP-Corp Comm)*
Daryl Krause *(Sr VP-Procurement)*
Teresa Laraba *(Sr VP-Customer Svcs)*
Tammy Romo *(Sr VP-Plng)*
Greg D. Wells *(Sr VP-Ops)*
Scott Halfmann *(VP-Safety & Security)*
Brian Hirshman *(VP-Maintenance & Engrg)*
Laurie Hulin *(VP-Tech, Enterprise Mgmt Applications & Testing Svcs Portfolio)*
Kevin M. Krone *(VP-Mktg & Sls & Distr)*
Linda B. Rutherford *(VP-Comm & Strategic Outreach)*
Kathleen Wayton *(VP-Strategy & Change Leadership)*
Anne Murray *(Sr Dir-Mktg Comm)*
Laura Adams *(Dir-Baggage Svcs)*
Gregory N. Crum *(Dir-Ops)*
Dana Williams *(Dir-Brand Integration)*
Katie Love *(Mgr-Digital)*
Ashley Pettit *(Analyst-Comm)*
Brands & Products:
BE MORE PRODUCTIVE
CLICK 'N SAVE
RAPID REWARDS
SOUTHWEST
SOUTHWEST.COM
SWA
Advertising Agencies:
C & T Yellow Page Advertising Agency
520 E Central Pkwy Ste 209
Plano, TX 75074
Tel.: (972) 423-4122

Camelot Communications, Inc.
8140 Walnut Hill Ln Ste 700
Dallas, TX 75231
Tel.: (214) 373-6999
Fax: (214) 373-6854
(Media)

DAE Advertising, Inc.
71 Stevenson St Ste 750
San Francisco, CA 94105
Tel.: (415) 341-1280
Fax: (415) 296-8378
Asian Advertising

Dieste
1999 Bryan St Ste 2700
Dallas, TX 75201
Tel.: (214) 259-8000
Fax: (214) 259-8040
(Hispanic Marketing)

G2 USA
200 5th Ave
New York, NY 10010
Tel.: (212) 537-3700
Fax: (212) 537-3737

GSD&M
828 W 6th St
Austin, TX 78703-5420
Tel.: (512) 242-4736
Fax: (512) 242-4700
(Print & Broadcast Creative for Airline)
Business Select

Proxy Partners LLC
1099 18th St Ste 500
Denver, CO 80202
Tel.: (303) 293-3020
Fax: (303) 296-3410

Targetbase
7850 N Belt Line Rd
Irving, TX 75063-6098
Tel.: (972) 506-3400
Fax: (972) 506-3505
Toll Free: (866) 506-7850

SOVEREIGN CRUISES LLC

118 Woodland Ct
Safety Harbor, FL 34695
Tel.: (727) 669-8820
Fax: (877) 768-2784
Toll Free: (877) SOV-CRUISE
E-mail: cruise@sovereigncruises.org
Web Site: www.sovereigncruises.org
Business Description:
Cruise Line Operator
S.I.C.: 7011
N.A.I.C.S.: 721199
Media: 13
Personnel:
Michael O'Fallon *(Pres & CEO)*

SPIRIT CRUISES LLC

(Sub. of Entertainment Cruises, Inc.)
5700 Lake Wright Dr Ste 203
Norfolk, VA 23502-1859
Tel.: (757) 627-2900
Fax: (757) 640-9315
Web Site: www.spiritcruises.com
Approx. Number Employees: 35
Year Founded: 1983
Business Description:
Harbor Cruise Reservation Services
S.I.C.: 7999
N.A.I.C.S.: 487210
Advertising Expenditures: $4,100,000
Cable T.V.: $50,000; Catalogs & Directories: $100,000; Consumer Mags.: $200,000; D.M. to Bus. Estab.: $1,000,000; Daily Newsp.: $1,000,000; Other: $300,000; Outdoor (Posters, Transit): $100,000; Point of Purchase: $100,000; Spot Radio: $1,000,000; Spot T.V.: $50,000; Yellow Page Adv.: $200,000
Media: 31
Distr.: Direct to Consumer; Natl.
Budget Set: Aug.
Brands & Products:
BATEAUX NEW YORK
POTOMAC SPIRIT
SPIRIT OF BOSTON
SPIRIT OF CHICAGO
SPIRIT OF NEW JERSEY
SPIRIT OF NEW YORK
SPIRIT OF NORFOLK
SPIRIT OF PHILADELPHIA
SPIRIT OF PUGET SOUND
SPIRIT OF WASHINGTON

STEVENS GROUP, INC.

527 Morley Dr
Saginaw, MI 48601
Tel.: (989) 755-3000
Fax: (989) 755-0570
E-mail: stevens@stevensworldwide.com
Web Site: www.stevensworldwide.com
Approx. Number Employees: 290
Year Founded: 1905
Business Description:
Trucking Services
S.I.C.: 4214; 4731
N.A.I.C.S.: 484210; 488510
Advertising Expenditures: $250,000
Media: 2-5-7-8-9-10-13-16-18-19-20-22-25-26
Personnel:
Morrison Stevens *(Pres)*
Lindsay Stevens *(VP-Fin)*
Brands & Products:
STEVENS WORLDWIDE VAN LINES

THE SUDDATH COMPANIES INC.

815 S Main St
Jacksonville, FL 32207-9050
Tel.: (904) 390-7100
Fax: (904) 390-7135
Toll Free: (800) 395-7100
E-mail: suddath@suddath.com
Web Site: www.suddath.com
Approx. Number Employees: 1,200
Year Founded: 1919
Business Description:
Moving & Relocation Services
S.I.C.: 4214; 4731
N.A.I.C.S.: 484210; 488510
Import Export
Media: 2-7-8-9-10-13-23-25
Personnel:
Stephen M. Suddath *(Chm)*
James G. Barnett *(CFO & Treas)*
Barry S. Vaughn *(COO)*
Brad Estrin *(Exec VP)*
Elizabeth Spradley *(Sr VP-HR)*
Kelly Evans *(Dir-Social Media & Internet Mktg)*
Matt Lamb *(Mgr-Intl, SDHR & Special Govt Svcs)*
Brands & Products:
SUDDATH
WE TAKE CARE OF IT

TAMPA PORT AUTHORITY INC.

1101 Channelside Dr
Tampa, FL 33602
Tel.: (813) 905-7678
Fax: (813) 905-5109
Toll Free: (800) 741-2297
E-mail: info@tampaport.com
Web Site: www.tampaport.com
Sales Range: $75-99.9 Million
Approx. Number Employees: 100
Business Description:
Port Authority
S.I.C.: 9621
N.A.I.C.S.: 926120
Media: 2-6-9
Personnel:
Richard Wainio *(CEO & Port Dir)*
Mike Macaluso *(CFO)*
Ken Washington *(CIO)*
Charles Klug *(Deputy Dir-Admin & Gen Counsel)*
Wade Elliott *(Sr Dir-Mktg)*
Ram Kancharla *(Sr Dir-Plng & Economic)*
Charles Dowless *(Dir-Facilities Mngmt)*
Wade Elliot *(Dir-Project Mktg)*
Andy Fobes *(Dir-PR)*
Greg Lovelace *(Dir-Cargo & Cruise Mktg)*
Jim Pyburn *(Dir-Trade Devel)*
Vickie Russo-Gonzalez *(Dir-HR)*

TAP PORTUGAL

(Branch of TAP Portugal S.A.)
263 Lafayette St 3rd Flr
Newark, NJ 07105
Tel.: (973) 854-6800
Fax: (973) 854-6829
Toll Free: (800) 221-7370
Telex: 49576441
E-mail: tapusa@tap.pt
Web Site: www.flytap.com
E-Mail For Key Personnel:
Sales Director: sales-ewr@tapainportugal.com
Public Relations: pr@tap-airportugal.com
Approx. Sls.: $50,000,000
Approx. Number Employees: 47
Year Founded: 1966
Business Description:
Air Transportation Services
S.I.C.: 4512; 4581
N.A.I.C.S.: 481111; 488119
Advertising Expenditures: $200,000
Media: 2-3-5-6-9-11-26
Distr.: Intl.; Natl.
Personnel:
Jose M. Coelho *(Gen Mgr-North America)*

THAI AIRWAYS INTERNATIONAL LTD.

(Sub. of Thai Airways International Public Company Limited)
222 N Sepulveda Blvd Ste 1950
El Segundo, CA 90245
Tel.: (310) 640-0097
Fax: (310) 322-8728
Toll Free: (800) 426-5204
E-mail: thailaxsd@earthlink.net
Web Site: www.thaiair.com
Approx. Number Employees: 60
Business Description:
Airline Passenger & Freight Services
S.I.C.: 4729; 4512
N.A.I.C.S.: 561599; 481111
Media: 6-7-8-10-11-13-18-25
Distr.: Direct to Consumer; Intl.; Natl.
Personnel:
Sue Marr *(Mgr-Mktg & Comm-Australia)*
Advertising Agency:
Saeshe Advertising
1055 W Seventh St Ste 2150

Key to Media (For complete agency information see *The Advertising Red Books-Agencies* edition):
1. Bus. Publs. 2. Cable T.V. 3. Catalogs & Directories. 4. Co-op Adv. 5. Consumer Mags. 6. D.M. to Bus. Estab. 7. D.M. to Consumers 8. Daily Newsp. 9. Exhibits/Trade Shows 10. Foreign 11. Infomercial 12. Internet Adv. 13. Multimedia 14. Network Radio 15. Network T.V. 16. Newsp. Distr. Mags. 17. Other 18. Outdoor (Posters, Transit) 19. Point of Purchase 20. Premiums, Novelties 21. Product Samples 22. Special Events Mktg. 23. Spot Radio 24. Spot T.V. 25. Weekly Newsp. 26. Yellow Page Adv.

Thai Airways International Ltd. — (Continued)

Los Angeles, CA 90017-2577
Tel.: (213) 683-2100
Fax: (213) 683-2103
(Korean Market)

THRIFTY, INC.

(Sub. of Dollar Thrifty Automotive Group, Inc.)
5330 E 31st St
Tulsa, OK 74135
Mailing Address:
PO Box 35250
Tulsa, OK 74153-0250
Tel.: (918) 665-3930
Fax: (918) 669-2934
Toll Free: (800) THRIFTY
Telex: 709 709
Web Site: www.thrifty.com
E-Mail For Key Personnel:
Sales Director: bob.thunell@thrifty.com
Sales Range: $350-399.9 Million
Year Founded: 1958
Business Description:
Automobile Rentals, Leasing & Parking
S.I.C.: 7514; 7515
N.A.I.C.S.: 532111; 532112
Media: 2-3-6-8-9-13-14-15-18-24-26
Distr.: Intl.; Natl.
Budget Set: Sept.
Personnel:
Scott Thompson *(Pres)*

TIETEK

(Formerly North American Technologies Group, Inc.)
13747 Montfort Dr Ste 205
Dallas, TX 75240
Tel.: (972) 996-5750
E-mail: sales@natk.com
Web Site: www.tietek.com
Approx. Number Employees: 131
Year Founded: 1986
Business Description:
Recycled Rubber Products Mfr
S.I.C.: 3069
N.A.I.C.S.: 326299
Media: 2
Personnel:
D. Patrick Long *(Chm & CEO)*
Joe B. Dorman *(Gen Counsel-IR)*
Dennis Guth *(VP-Mktg & Bus Dev)*
Brands & Products:
NAMC
TIETEK

TNT VACATIONS

(Sub. of Trans National Group Services)
2 Charlesgate W
Boston, MA 02215
Tel.: (617) 262-9200
Fax: (617) 638-3445
Toll Free: (800) 262-0123
Web Site: www.tntvacations.com
Sales Range: $10-24.9 Million
Approx. Number Employees: 200
Year Founded: 1974
Business Description:
Travel Agency
S.I.C.: 4725
N.A.I.C.S.: 561520
Advertising Expenditures: $200,000
Bus. Publs.: $10,000; Catalogs & Directories: $10,000; Consumer Mags.: $110,000; D.M. to Bus. Estab.: $6,000; Daily Newsp.: $20,000; Exhibits/Trade Shows: $4,000; Other: $20,000; Premiums, Novelties: $20,000
Distr.: Natl.
Budget Set: Sept.
Personnel:
Thomas Lew *(CIO)*
Darcy Vangel *(Asst VP-HR)*
Linda Maduro *(Mgr-Destination)*
Brands & Products:
TRANS NATIONAL GROUP SERVICES

TOWNE HOLDINGS INC.

24805 US Hwy 20 W
South Bend, IN 46628-5911
Tel.: (574) 233-3183
Fax: (574) 234-0702
Toll Free: (800) 755-3183
E-mail: webmaster@towneair.com
Web Site: www.towneair.com
Approx. Number Employees: 1,201
Year Founded: 1994
Business Description:
Freight Transportation Services
S.I.C.: 4213
N.A.I.C.S.: 484121
Import Export
Media: 2-8-10
Personnel:
Tom Downey *(Pres & CEO)*
Jerry Scott *(VP-HR)*

TRANSAT A.T., INC.

Place du Parc 300 Leo-Pariseau St Ste 600
Montreal, QC H2X 4C2, Canada
Tel.: (514) 987-1660
Fax: (514) 987-8035
E-mail: info@transat.com
Web Site: www.transat.com
Approx. Rev.: $3,564,725,865
Approx. Number Employees: 5,819
Year Founded: 1987
Business Description:
Travel Industry; Retail Sales through Travel Agencies, Organizes & Distributes Vacation Packages through Tour Operators, Air Transportation, Hotel Management
S.I.C.: 4725
N.A.I.C.S.: 561520
Export
Media: 2-4-5-6-7-8-10-11
Personnel:
Jean-Marc Eustache *(Co-Founder, Chm, Pres & CEO)*
Denis Petrin *(CFO & VP-Fin & Admin)*
Nelson Gentiletti *(COO)*
Michel Bellefeuille *(CIO & VP)*
Jean-Luk Pellerin *(Chief Talent Officer & VP-HR)*
Michel Lemay *(Chief Brand Officer)*
Yves Lalumiere *(Pres-Transat Distr Canada)*
Lina De Cesare *(Exec VP-Tour Ops)*
Denis Codere *(VP-Sls, Commercialization & Dev-Europe & Cruises)*
Denise Heffron *(VP-Natl Sls & Comml)*

TRANSCARE NEW YORK INC.

1 Metrotech Ctr Ste 2000 20th Fl
Brooklyn, NY 11201
Tel.: (718) 763-8888
Fax: (718) 251-8916
Web Site: www.transcare.com
Approx. Sls.: $52,200,000
Approx. Number Employees: 2,400
Business Description:
Ambulance Services
S.I.C.: 4119
N.A.I.C.S.: 621910
Media: 6
Personnel:
Patrick Seiler *(CFO)*
James O'Connor *(Sr VP)*

TRANSPLACE INC.

(Holding of CI Capital Partners LLC)
3010 Gaylord Pkwy Ste 200
Frisco, TX 75034
Tel.: (972) 731-4500
Fax: (972) 731-4501
E-mail: tom.sanderson@transplace.com
Web Site: www.transplace.com
Sales Range: $50-74.9 Million
Approx. Number Employees: 500
Business Description:
Freight Transportation Arrangement Services
S.I.C.: 4731
N.A.I.C.S.: 488510
Personnel:
George Abernathy *(Pres)*
Thomas K. Sanderson *(CEO)*
Steve Crowther *(CFO & Exec VP)*
Kyle Alexander *(Gen Mgr-Strategic Dev)*
Tony Labriola *(Mgr-Carrier)*
Joe McCrabb *(Mgr-Carrier-East Coast)*
Brands & Products:
THE 3PL & TECHNOLOGY COMPANY
DENSE NETWORK EFFICIENCY
TRANSPLACE
Advertising Agency:
Finn Partners
211 E Ontario St Ste 1600
Chicago, IL 60611-3297
Tel.: (312) 644-8600
Fax: (312) 932-0367

TRAVEL-BY-NET, INC.

(Sub. of Cappy Devlin International)
195 N Bedford Rd
Mount Kisco, NY 10549-1140
Tel.: (914) 241-0383
Fax: (914) 241-0264
Toll Free: (800) 227-7975
E-mail: cappy@travel-by-net.com
Web Site: www.travel-by-net.com
Year Founded: 1973
Business Description:
Online Travel Agency
S.I.C.: 4729
N.A.I.C.S.: 561599
Media: 2-6-7-9-17-26
Distr.: Natl.
Budget Set: Oct.
Personnel:
Catherine F. Devlin *(Pres)*
Brands & Products:
CAPPY'S
THE WORLD IS OPEN TO YOU. EXPERIENCE IT!

TRAVEL GUARD GROUP, INC.

(Sub. of American International Group, Inc.)
3300 Business Pk Dr
Stevens Point, WI 54481
Tel.: (715) 345-0505
Fax: (715) 345-2915
Toll Free: (800) 826-4919
E-mail: inquire@travelguard.com
Web Site: www.travelguard.com
E-Mail For Key Personnel:
Public Relations: dmcginn@noelgroup.com
Sales Range: $10-24.9 Million
Approx. Number Employees: 312
Year Founded: 1985
Business Description:
Retail Travel Insurance
S.I.C.: 6411
N.A.I.C.S.: 524210; 524298
Advertising Expenditures: $531,000
Media: 1-2-5-6-7-8-9-10-13-19-20-23
Distr.: Natl.
Budget Set: Nov.
Personnel:
Jim Koziol *(CFO)*
Dean Sivley *(CEO-Travel Guard)*
Tom Zavadsky *(Exec VP-Sls & Underwriting)*
Dan McGinnity *(VP-Commun)*
Brands & Products:
BAGTRAK
COLLISION DAMAGE WAIVER
CRUISE, TOUR & TRAVEL
FLIGHT GUARD
INSURE AMERICA
MAKE A MARK
PROTECTASSIST
SENSE OF SECURITY
STUDENTGUARD
SUPER SAVER
TRAVEL GUARD
TRAVEL RITE ANNUAL PROTECTION

TRAVEL HOLDINGS, INC.

220 E Central Pkwy Ste 4010
Altamonte Springs, FL 32701
Tel.: (407) 215-7465
Fax: (407) 215-1372
E-mail: opportunity@travelholdings.com
Web Site: www.travelholdings.com
Approx. Number Employees: 114
Year Founded: 2004
Business Description:
Travel & Tour Services
S.I.C.: 4729
N.A.I.C.S.: 561599
Personnel:
Uri Argov *(Pres, CEO & Member-Board-Dirs)*
Robert F. Stockwell *(CFO)*
Paul Kitching *(Sr VP-Global Product Dev-Tourico Holidays)*
Lauren Volcheff *(Dir-Mktg)*
Brands & Products:
TRAVEL HOLDINGS
Advertising Agency:
Ypartnership
423 S Keller Rd Ste 100
Orlando, FL 32810-6121
Tel.: (407) 875-1111
Fax: (407) 875-1115
LastMinuteTravel.com

TRAVEL IMPRESSIONS, LTD.

(Sub. of American Express Travel Related Services Company, Inc.)
465 Smith St Ste A
Farmingdale, NY 11735-1106
Tel.: (631) 845-8000
Fax: (631) 420-5205
Toll Free: (800) 284-0022

Key to Media (For complete agency information see *The Advertising Red Books-Agencies* edition):
1. Bus. Publs. 2. Cable T.V. 3. Catalogs & Directories. 4. Co-op Adv. 5. Consumer Mags. 6. D.M. to Bus. Estab.7. D.M. to Consumers 8. Daily Newsp. 9. Exhibits/Trade Shows 10. Foreign 11. Infomercial 12. Internet Adv.13. Multimedia 14. Network Radio 15. Network T.V. 16. Newsp. Distr. Mags. 17. Other 18. Outdoor (Posters, Transit) 19. Point of Purchase20. Premiums, Novelties 21. Product Samples 22. Special Events Mktg. 23. Spot Radio 24. Spot T.V. 25. Weekly Newsp. 26. Yellow Page Adv.

Telex: 234368
E-mail: info@travimp.com
Web Site: www.travimp.com
Sales Range: $75-99.9 Million
Approx. Number Employees: 500
Year Founded: 1974
Business Description:
Travel Services
S.I.C.: 4725
N.A.I.C.S.: 561520
Advertising Expenditures: $1,000,000
Media: 4-7-8-9-10-13-16-23-25-26
Distr.: Intl.; Natl.
Budget Set: Quarterly
Personnel:
Stacy Rybeck *(CFO)*

TRAVELCENTERS OF AMERICA, LLC

24601 Center Ridge Rd Ste 200
Westlake, OH 44145
Tel.: (440) 808-9100
Toll Free: (888) 982-5528
E-mail: info@travelcenters.com
Web Site: www.tatravelcenters.com
Approx. Rev.: $5,962,481,000
Approx. Number Employees: 15,170
Year Founded: 1993
Business Description:
Full-Service Travel Centers
S.I.C.: 4724; 7011
N.A.I.C.S.: 561510; 721199
Advertising Expenditures:
$17,095,000
Media: 2-6-23-24
Personnel:
Thomas M. O'Brien *(Pres, CEO & Mng Dir)*
Barry Michael Portnoy *(Mng Dir)*
Andrew J. Rebholz *(CFO & Exec VP)*
Mark R. Young *(Gen Counsel & Exec VP)*
Ara A. Bagdasarian *(Exec VP)*
Michael J. Lombardi *(Exec VP-Sls)*
Barry A. Richards *(Exec VP)*
Randy A. Graham *(Sr VP-Retail Mktg & Other Income)*
John Ponczoch *(Sr VP-Food Mktg & Ops)*
Peter P. Ward *(Sr VP-Construction, Maintenance & Environmental)*
William J. Sheehan *(Dir-Internal Audit & Compliance)*
Advertising Agencies:
The Idea Mill
6101 Penn Ave Ste 400
Pittsburgh, PA 15206
Tel.: (412) 924-0027
Fax: (412) 924-0034

Jaeger, Inc.
8981 Timberedge Dr
North Ridgeville, OH 44039
Tel.: (440) 243-8700
Toll Free: (800) 237-7585

TRAVELPORT LIMITED

(Holding of The Blackstone Group L.P.)
405 Lexington Ave 57 Fl
New York, NY 10174
Tel.: (212) 915-9150
Fax: (212) 939-1096
E-mail: info@travelport.com
Web Site: www.travelport.com
E-Mail For Key Personnel:
Public Relations: elizabeth.harraway@travelport.com
Approx. Rev.: $2,290,000,000
Approx. Number Employees: 5,475
Business Description:
Online Travel Tools & Services
S.I.C.: 4729; 4724
N.A.I.C.S.: 561599; 561510
Advertising Expenditures:
$23,000,000
Media: 1-3-6-13-15-24
Personnel:
Jeffrey J. Clarke *(Chm)*
Derek Sharp *(Pres & Mng Dir-Americas)*
Gordon A. Wilson *(CEO)*
Philip Emery *(CFO & Exec VP)*
Eric J. Bock *(Chief Admin Officer, Gen Counsel & Exec VP)*
Simon Gray *(Chief Acctg Officer & Sr VP)*
Lee K. Golding *(Chief HR Officer & Exec VP)*
Ken Esterow *(Pres/CEO-GTA Bus)*
Raffaele Sadun *(Sr VP-Enterprise Plng & Strategy)*
Scott Hyden *(VP-Sls)*
Brands & Products:
AIRES
GALILEO
GULLIVERS TRAVEL ASSOCIATES
NEAT
ORBITZ
ORBITZ FOR BUSINESS
SHEPHERD BUSINESS INTELLIGENCE
THOR
TRAVEL BOUND
TRAVELPORT CORPORATE MATRIX
TRAVELPORT FOR BUSINESS
TRUST INTERNATIONAL
WIZCOM

TRAVELZOO INC

590 Madison Ave 37th Fl
New York, NY 10022
Tel.: (212) 521-4200
Fax: (212) 521-4230
Web Site: www.travelzoo.com
Approx. Rev.: $112,784,000
Approx. Number Employees: 255
Year Founded: 1998
Business Description:
Online Sales & Marketing Services for the Travel Industry
S.I.C.: 4724; 2741; 4729
N.A.I.C.S.: 561510; 516110; 561599
Advertising Expenditures:
$31,600,000
Media: 11-13
Personnel:
Holger Bartel *(Chm)*
Christopher Loughlin *(CEO)*
Wayne Lee *(CFO)*
Shirley Tafoya *(Pres-North America)*
Jason Yap *(CEO-Asia Pacific)*
Steve Savad *(Sr VP-Bus Dev-Local Deals-North America)*
Craig Calder *(VP-Mktg)*
Mike Stitt *(Gen Mgr-Local Deals-North America)*
Brands & Products:
TEST BOOKING CENTER
TOP 20
TRAVELZOO

TRI-STATE MOTOR TRANSIT CO.

8141 E 7th St
Joplin, MO 64801
Mailing Address:
PO Box 113
Joplin, MO 64802
Tel.: (417) 624-3131
Toll Free: (800) 234-TSMT
Web Site: www.tsmtco.com
Year Founded: 1929
Business Description:
Trucking & Storage Facilities
S.I.C.: 4213; 4731
N.A.I.C.S.: 484121; 488510
Media: 2-17
Personnel:
Glen Garrett *(Chm & Pres)*
David Bennett *(Exec VP)*
Jim Wingfield *(Exec VP-Risk Mgmt)*
Brands & Products:
TSMT

TRIMAC CORPORATION

(d/b/a Trimac Transportation L.P.)
800 5th Ave SW Ste 1700
Calgary, AB T2P 5A3, Canada
Tel.: (403) 298-5100
Fax: (403) 298-5258
E-mail: info@trimac.com
Web Site: www.trimac.com
Sales Range: $550-599.9 Million
Approx. Number Employees: 6,000
Year Founded: 1945
Business Description:
Trucking Company
S.I.C.: 4212
N.A.I.C.S.: 484110
Export
Media: 2-7-11
Personnel:
Jeffery J. McCaig *(Chm & CEO)*
Edward V. Malysa *(Pres & COO)*
Barry W. Davy *(Sr VP)*
Robert J. Kennedy *(Sr VP-Corp Svcs)*
Jim D'Alessio *(VP-Mktg)*
Jean Kipp *(VP-Mktg & Bus Dev-Western Div)*
Jennifer Grant *(Mgr-Sealed Support)*
Brands & Products:
TRIMAC

TRIPADVISOR LLC

(Sub. of Expedia, Inc.)
141 Needham Street
Needham, MA 02464
Tel.: (781) 444-1113
Fax: (781) 444-1146
E-mail: uspr@tripadvisor.com
Web Site: www.tripadvisor.com
E-Mail For Key Personnel:
Sales Director: sales@tripadvisor.com
Public Relations: brooke@tripadvisor.com
Sales Range: $25-49.9 Million
Year Founded: 2000
Business Description:
Online Travel Information & Advice Services
S.I.C.: 7011
N.A.I.C.S.: 519130; 721199
Personnel:
Stephen Kaufer *(Founder & CEO)*
Julie M. B. Bradley *(CFO)*
Barbara Messing *(CMO)*
Christine Petersen *(Pres-TripAdvisor for Bus)*
David Morris *(Corp Counsel)*
Robin Ingle *(Sr VP-Adv Sls)*
Eric Rosenzweig *(Sr VP-Strategic Dev & Sls)*
Julio Bruno *(Global VP-Sls-TripAdvisor for Bus)*
Andy Gelfond *(VP-Engrg)*
Tyler Young *(VP-Fin & Admin)*
Bryan Saltzburg *(Gen Mgr-New Initiatives)*
Bernard Bernstein *(Sr Dir-Engrg)*
Chris Christensen *(Dir-Engrg)*
John Dila *(Dir-Customer Care)*
Eric Lombardo *(Dir-HR)*
Karen Plumb *(Dir-Comml-EMEA-Bus Listings)*
Sarah Welch *(Mgr-Sls)*
Brands & Products:
TRIPADVISOR
TRIPADVISOR.COM
Advertising Agency:
Connelly Partners
46 Waltham St Fl 4
Boston, MA 02118
Tel.: (617) 956-5050
Fax: (617) 956-5054

TRX INC.

2970 Clairmont Rd Ste 300
Atlanta, GA 30329
Tel.: (404) 929-6100
Fax: (404) 929-6146
E-mail: trxmarketing@trx.com
Web Site: www.trx.com
Approx. Rev.: $56,731,000
Approx. Number Employees: 767
Business Description:
Travel Technology & Data Services
S.I.C.: 7374; 7371; 7373; 7389
N.A.I.C.S.: 518210; 541511; 541512; 561499
Media: 7-10-13-17
Personnel:
Norwood H. Davis, III *(Co-Founder & Chm)*
H. Shane Hammond *(Pres & CEO)*
David D. Cathcart *(CFO)*
Gail Gunnells *(Gen Counsel)*
Kevin G. Austin *(Exec VP)*
Aaron Aycock *(VP-IT & Product Dev)*
David Jackson *(VP-Product Dev)*
Brands & Products:
CORREX
FINDING NEW WAYS
RESX
TRAVELTRAX
TRX
TRX-PROFESSIONAL SERVICES
TRX-TRAVEL ANALYTICS

U-HAUL INTERNATIONAL, INC.

(Sub. of AMERCO)
2727 N Central Ave
Phoenix, AZ 85004-1155
Mailing Address:
PO Box 21502
Phoenix, AZ 85004
Tel.: (602) 263-6011
Tel.: (602) 263-6194
Tel.: (602) 263-6645
Fax: (800) 789-3638
Toll Free: (800) 528-0463
E-mail: publicrelations@uhaul.com
Web Site: www.uhaul.com
Approx. Rev.: $2,085,600,000
Year Founded: 1945
Business Description:
Rental Trucks, Trailers, Self-Storage Units, Permanent Hitches, Moving Aids & General Equipment Rentals
S.I.C.: 7519; 7299
N.A.I.C.S.: 532120; 532220

Key to Media (For complete agency information see *The Advertising Red Books-Agencies* edition):
1. Bus. Publs. 2. Cable T.V. 3. Catalogs & Directories. 4. Co-op Adv. 5. Consumer Mags. 6. D.M. to Bus. Estab.7. D.M. to Consumers
8. Daily Newsp. 9. Exhibits/Trade Shows 10. Foreign 11. Infomercial 12. Internet Adv.13. Multimedia 14. Network Radio
15. Network T.V. 16. Newsp. Distr. Mags. 17. Other 18. Outdoor (Posters, Transit) 19. Point of Purchase20. Premiums, Novelties
21. Product Samples 22. Special Events Mktg. 23. Spot Radio 24. Spot T.V. 25. Weekly Newsp. 26. Yellow Page Adv.

U-Haul International, Inc. — (Continued)

Advertising Expenditures:
$24,300,000
Media: 2-5-9-10-13-19-26
Distr.: Natl.
Budget Set: Nov.
Personnel:
Edward J. Shoen *(Chm & CEO)*
John Taylor *(Pres-Phoenix Ops)*
Ronald C. Frank *(Exec VP-Field Opers)*
Renee Royer *(Exec VP-Risk Mgmt)*
Joanne Fried *(Dir-Media & Pub Rel)*

Brands & Products:
1-800-GO-UHAUL
E-MOVE
HITCH WORLD
U-HAUL
UHAUL.COM

Advertising Agency:
NMA Entertainment & Marketing
11059 Sherman Way
Sun Valley, CA 91352
Tel.: (818) 982-3505
Fax: (818) 503-1936

ULTIMATE JETCHARTERS, INC.

6060 W Airport Dr
Canton, OH 44720
Tel.: (330) 497-3344
Fax: (330) 497-3644
Toll Free: (800) 437-3931
Web Site:
www.ultimatejetcharters.com
Approx. Rev.: $1,300,000
Approx. Number Employees: 37
Year Founded: 2003
Business Description:
Private Charter with 30 Seat Jets
S.I.C.: 4581
N.A.I.C.S.: 488119
Media: 2-8-13-23-24-29
Personnel:
John Gordon *(Founder)*
Eddie Moneypenny *(Dir-Sls & Mktg)*

UNIGROUP, INC.

1 Premier Dr
Fenton, MO 63026
Tel.: (636) 305-5000
Fax: (636) 326-1106
E-mail: webmaster@unigroupinc.com
Web Site: www.unigroupinc.com
Sales Range: $1-4.9 Billion
Approx. Number Employees: 1,350
Year Founded: 1987
Business Description:
Transportation & Freight Services
S.I.C.: 4214
N.A.I.C.S.: 484210
Media: 7-10-13-18
Personnel:
H. Daniel McCollister *(Chm)*
Richard McClure *(Pres & COO)*
James Powers *(CFO)*
Jan R. Alonzo *(Gen Counsel, Sr VP & Compliance Officer)*
Jason Mills *(Dir-Strategic Mktg & Brand Mngmt)*
Brands & Products:
MAYFLOWER TRANSIT
UNIGROUP
UNITED VAN LINES

Advertising Agency:
TargetCast tcm
909 3rd Ave 31st Fl
New York, NY 10022
Tel.: (212) 500-6900
Fax: (212) 500-6880

UNION PACIFIC CORPORATION

1400 Douglas St
Omaha, NE 68179
Tel.: (402) 544-5000
Toll Free: (888) 870-8777
Web Site: www.up.com
Approx. Rev.: $16,965,000,000
Approx. Number Employees: 42,884
Year Founded: 1862
Business Description:
Holding Company; Railway Transportation
S.I.C.: 4011
N.A.I.C.S.: 482111
Advertising Expenditures: $200,000
Bus. Publs.: $101,000; Other: $99,000
Distr.: Natl.
Budget Set: Dec.
Personnel:
James R. Young *(Chm & CEO)*
Robert M. Knight Jr. *(CFO & Exec VP-Fin)*
Lynden L. Tennison *(CIO & Sr VP)*
J. Michael Hemmer *(Gen Counsel & Sr VP-Law)*
Barbara W. Schaefer *(Sec & Sr VP-HR)*
Lance M. Fritz *(Exec VP-Ops)*
John J. Koraleski *(Exec VP-Mktg & Sls)*
Charles R. Eisele *(Sr VP-Strategic Plng & Admin)*
Richard Turner *(Sr VP-Corp Rels)*
Robert W. Turner *(Sr VP-Corp Rels)*
Eric L. Butler *(VP & Gen Mgr-Indus Industrial Products)*
Julie Krehbiel *(VP & Gen Mgr)*
Linda Brandl *(VP-Natl Customer Svc Center)*
Robert M. Grimaila *(VP-Safety & Security & Environ)*
Joseph E. O'Connor, Jr. *(VP-Pur)*
Bryan Clark *(Asst VP-Federal Tax)*
Daniel Shudak *(Asst VP-Ops-Southern Region)*
Mark Davis *(Dir-Corp Rels & Media)*
Dick Hartman *(Dir-Pub Affairs-Wyoming & Colorado)*
Ben Jones *(Dir-Pub Rel-Missouri & Kansas)*
Brenda Mainwaring *(Dir-Pub Affairs-Nebraska & Iowa)*
Tom Zapler *(Dir-Pub Affairs)*
Brands & Products:
BUILDING AMERICA
UNION PACIFIC

UNION PACIFIC RAILROAD COMPANY

(Sub. of Union Pacific Corporation)
1400 Douglas St
Omaha, NE 68179-0001
Tel.: (402) 544-5000
Fax: (800) 633-2560
Toll Free: (888) 870-8777
Web Site: www.up.com
Approx. Rev.: $15,546,000,000
Approx. Number Employees: 50,379
Year Founded: 1862
Business Description:
Rail Carrier
S.I.C.: 4011
N.A.I.C.S.: 482111
Media: 2-4-6-9-10-18-20-23-25
Distr.: Direct to Consumer; Natl.
Budget Set: Nov. -Dec.
Personnel:
James R. Young *(Chm, Pres & CEO)*
Dennis J. Duffy *(Vice Chm-Ops)*
Lance M. Fritz *(Exec VP-Ops)*
John J. Koraleski *(Exec VP-Mktg & Sls)*
Mark Davis *(Asst VP)*
Shane Keller *(Asst VP-Network Integration & Scheduling)*
Donna Kush *(Asst VP-Corp Comm)*
Tom Lange *(Dir-Corp Comm)*

Advertising Agency:
Bailey Lauerman
1299 Farnam St Ste 930
Omaha, NE 68102-1157
Tel.: (402) 514-9400
Fax: (402) 514-9401

UNITED AIR LINES, INC.

(Sub. of United Continental Holdings, Inc.)
77 Wacker Dr
Chicago, IL 60601
Mailing Address:
PO Box 66100
Chicago, IL 60666-0100
Tel.: (312) 997-8000
Web Site: www.united.com
Approx. Rev.: $19,682,000,000
Year Founded: 1968
Business Description:
Air Transportation of Passengers & Mail, Express & Freight
S.I.C.: 4512; 4581
N.A.I.C.S.: 481112; 481111; 488119; 488190
Advertising Expenditures:
$90,000,000
Media: 3-6-8-9-10-11-13-14-15-16-17-18-19-22-23-24-25-26
Distr.: Direct to Consumer; Natl.
Personnel:
Peter D. McDonald *(Exec VP & Chief Ops Officer)*
Gerald F. Kelly *(CIO & Sr VP-Strategic Sourcing)*
Antonio B. Cervone *(Sr VP-Corp Comm & Chief Comm Officer)*
Paul R. Lovejoy *(Gen Counsel, Sec & Sr VP)*
Douglas McKeen *(Sr VP-Labor Rels)*
Rosemary Moore *(Sr VP-Corp & Govt Affairs)*
Rohit Philip *(Sr VP-Corp Strategy & Bus Dev)*
M. Lynn Hughitt *(VP-HR-Airlines Ops)*
John R. Gebo *(Mgr-Bus & Cash Plng)*
Aaron Stash *(Mgr-Mktg, Comm, & Strategy)*
Robin Urbanski *(Mgr-Media Rels)*
Mark R. Anderson *(Supvr-Station)*
Christine S. Grawemeyer *(Asst Sec)*

Advertising Agency:
Studiocom
191 Peachtree St NE Ste 4025
Atlanta, GA 30303
Tel.: (404) 541-9555
Web-Based Tutorial for Travelers

UNITED CONTINENTAL HOLDINGS, INC.

77 W Wacker Dr
Chicago, IL 60601
Mailing Address:
PO Box 66100
Chicago, IL 60666-0100
Tel.: (312) 997-8000
Tel.: (312) 997-8610 (IR)
Telex: RCA 275362 WU 287419
E-mail: investorrelations@united.com
Web Site:
www.unitedcontinentalholdings.com
Approx. Rev.: $23,229,000,000
Approx. Number Employees: 86,000
Year Founded: 1968
Business Description:
Holding Company; Passenger & Freight Air Transportation Services
S.I.C.: 6719; 4512; 4731
N.A.I.C.S.: 551112; 481111; 481112; 488510
Advertising Expenditures:
$202,000,000
Personnel:
Jeffery A. Smisek *(Pres & CEO)*
Zane C. Rowe *(CFO & Exec VP)*
Peter D. McDonald *(COO & Exec VP)*
Keith Halbert *(CIO & Exec VP)*
Chris T. Kenny *(Chief Acctg Officer, Controller & VP)*
James E. Compton *(Chief Revenue Officer & Exec VP)*
Brett J. Hart *(Gen Counsel, Sec & Sr VP)*
Gerry Laderman *(Treas & Sr VP-Fin)*
Michael P. Bonds *(Exec VP-HR & Labor Rels)*
Nene Foxhall *(Exec VP-Comm & Govt Affairs)*
Frederick C. Abbott *(Sr VP-Flight Ops)*
Mark Bergsrud *(Sr VP-Mktg)*
Scott Dolan *(Sr VP-Airport Ops)*
Greg Hart *(Sr VP-Network)*
Dave Hilfman *(Sr VP-Sls)*
James E. Keenan *(Sr VP-Tech Ops)*
Leon Kinloch *(Sr VP-Pricing & Revenue Mgmt)*
Joe C. Kolshak *(Sr VP-Ops)*
Alexandria P. Marren *(Sr VP-Sys Ops Control & United Express)*
Rohit Philip *(Sr VP-Corp Strategy & Bus Dev)*
John Rainey *(Sr VP-Fin Plng & Analysis)*
Mark F. Schwab *(Sr VP-Alliances)*
Michael Quiello *(VP-Safety & Security, Quality & Environment)*
Dana Sacks *(VP-HR Partners & Talent Acq)*
Sarah Rae Murphy *(Mgr-IR)*
Brands & Products:
ARRIVALS SUITES
BULLSEYE
BUSINESSONE
CHARIOT
CHICAGO'S HOMETOWN AIRLINE
EASY REBOOK
EASY SCHEDULE
MILEAGE PLUS
RED CARPET CLUB
THREE PERFECT DAYS
UNITED
UNITED AIRLINES
UNITED EASYACCESS
UNITED EASYCHECK-IN
UNITED EASYINFO

Key to Media (For complete agency information see *The Advertising Red Books-Agencies* edition):
1. Bus. Publs. 2. Cable T.V. 3. Catalogs & Directories. 4. Co-op Adv. 5. Consumer Mags. 6. D.M. to Bus. Estab.7. D.M. to Consumers 8. Daily Newsp. 9. Exhibits/Trade Shows 10. Foreign 11. Infomercial 12. Internet Adv.13. Multimedia 14. Network Radio 15. Network T.V. 16. Newsp. Distr. Mags. 17. Other 18. Outdoor (Posters, Transit) 19. Point of Purchase20. Premiums, Novelties 21. Product Samples 22. Special Events Mktg. 23. Spot Radio 24. Spot T.V. 25. Weekly Newsp. 26. Yellow Page Adv.

UNITED EASYUPDATE
UNITED ECONOMY
UNITED ECONOMY PLUS
UNITED FIRST
UNITED FIRST SUITE

Advertising Agencies:
Horizon Media, Inc.
75 Varick St
New York, NY 10013
Tel.: (212) 220-5000
Toll Free: (800) 633-4201
Creative
Digital
Media

McGarry Bowen, LLC
601 W 26th St Ste 1150
New York, NY 10001
Tel.: (212) 598-2900
Fax: (212) 598-2996
Creative
Digital
Media

Studiocom
191 Peachtree St NE Ste 4025
Atlanta, GA 30303
Tel.: (404) 541-9555

UNITED PARCEL SERVICE, INC.

(dba UPS)
55 Glenlake Pkwy NE
Atlanta, GA 30328
Tel.: (404) 828-7123
Fax: (404) 828-6562
Toll Free: (800) PICK-UPS
Web Site: www.ups.com
E-Mail For Key Personnel:
Public Relations: pr@ups.com
Approx. Rev.: $49,545,000,000
Approx. Number Employees: 400,600
Year Founded: 1907
Business Description:
Parcel Deliveries, Surface & Air; UPS International Air, UPS Next Day Air, Second Day Air, Expedited Air & Ground Package Delivery, Financial Services & Logistics
S.I.C.: 4213; 4215; 4513
N.A.I.C.S.: 484121; 484122; 492110; 492210
Media: 2-3-6-7-9-10-11-13-15-18-22-23-24-25-26
Distr.: Intl.; Natl.
Personnel:
D. Scott Davis *(Chm & CEO)*
Kurt P. Kuehn *(CFO)*
David P. Abney *(COO)*
David A. Barnes *(CIO & Sr VP)*
Scott Wicker *(Chief Sustainability Officer)*
Alan Gershenhorn *(Chief Sls & Mktg Officer)*
Gerald R. Mattes *(Pres-Pacific Region)*
Rocky Romanella *(Pres-Southeast Region)*
Carolyn J. Walsh *(Pres-Western Region)*
George W. Brooks, Jr. *(Pres-Central Reg)*
Daniel J. Brutto *(Pres-UPS Intl)*
Wolfgang Flick *(Pres-Europe)*
Stephen D. Flowers *(Pres-Global Freight Forwarding)*
Myron Gray *(Pres-US Ops)*
Lisa Hamilton *(Pres-UPS Foundation)*
Robert L. Lekites *(Pres-UPS Airlines)*
Romaine Seguin *(Pres-Americas Reg)*
Derek S. Woodward *(Pres-Asia Pacific Region)*
Allen E. Hill *(Gen Counsel & Corp Sec & Sr VP-Legal & Pub Affairs)*
Teri Plummer McClure *(Gen Counsel, Corp Sec, Sr VP-Legal, Compliance & Pub Affairs)*
John J. McDevitt *(Sr VP-Strategic Integration)*
Christine M. Owens *(Sr VP-Comm & Brand Mgmt)*
Robert E. Stoffel *(Sr VP-Supply Chain Grp)*
Jordan Colletta *(VP-Customer Tech Mktg)*
Rich Peretz *(VP-Fin)*
Mike Horman *(Dir-Sls)*
Doug Gibeaut *(Dir-Global Relationship Mktg)*
Rhonda Knight *(Dir-Digital Mktg)*
Mark Davis *(Product Mgr-Healthcare Logistics)*
Rhonda Clark *(Mgr-Plant Engrg-UPS Air Grp)*
Denise Foster *(Mgr-Defined Contribution Plans)*
Anita Kew *(Mgr-Comm)*
Greg Maurer *(Mgr-Pub Affairs)*
Cindy Miller *(Mgr-Country)*
Justine Peddle *(Mgr-Retirement & Fin Portfolio)*

Brands & Products:
1-800-PICK-UPS
3 DAY SELECT
A GREAT PLACE TO BE
BIG BROWN TRUCK
BIG OR SMALL WE SHIP IT ALL
BLUE LABEL AIR
C.O.D. SECURE
C.O.D. SELECT
COLOR BROWN
E-PACKAGE
EARLY A.M.
EASY ROUTE
FLEET LOADER
FLEX
GROUNDSAVER
GROUNDTRAC
IMPOWER
K-VAN
MAIL BOXES ETC
MAXISHIP
MAXITRAC
MOBILECAST
MOVING AT THE SPEED OF BUSINESS
NOTICE SYMBOL
ON CALL AIR PICKUP
PRECEDUS
QUANTUM VIEW
RED ARROW
RED ARROW MESSENGER
ROADNET
ROADNET 5000
ROADNET ANYWHERE
ROUTENET
SONICAIR
TELESHIP
TERRITORY PLANNER
UNITED PARCEL SERVICE
UPS
UPS 10 KG BOX
UPS 25 KG BOX
UPS 2ND DAY AIR
UPS 2ND DAY AIR A.M.
UPS AIR CARGO SERVICE
UPS AIR FREIGHT DIRECT
UPS AUTOGISTICS
UPS BRAND EXCHANGE
UPS CAMPUSSHIP
UPS CAPITAL
UPS CAPITAL BUSINESS CREDIT
UPS DELIVER MORE
UPS DELIVERY INTERCEPT
UPS DELIVERY LINK
UPS EARLY A.M.
UPS EXCHANGE COLLECT
UPS EXPEDITE
UPS EXPRESS
UPS EXPRESS CRITICAL
UPS FREIGHT OVER THE ROAD
UPS GROUNDSAVER
UPS HUNDREDWEIGHT SERVICE
UPS INNOPLEX
UPS INTELLIVERSE
UPS INTERNET TOOLS
UPS MAIL INNOVATIONS
UPS MAIL LOGIC
UPS NEXT DAY AIR SAVER
UPS ONLINE
UPS ONLINE COURIER
UPS PREFERRED
UPS SAVER
UPS SIGNATURE TRACKING
THE UPS STORE
UPS TOTALTRACK
UPS TRACKPAD
UPS TRADE ABILITY
UPS TRADE DIRECT
UPS TRADE SENSE
UPS VOICE NOTIFICATION
UPS WORLDWIDE EXPRESS
UPS WORLDWIDE LOGISTICS
UPS.COM
UPSERS
UPSNET
WE RUN THE TIGHTEST SHIP IN THE SHIPPING BUSINESS
WORLDPORT
WORLDSHIP

Advertising Agencies:
Maxus Global
498 Seventh Ave
New York, NY 10018
Tel.: (212) 297-8300
Media Planning & Buying

Ogilvy & Mather
(Sub. of WPP Group plc)
636 11th Ave
New York, NY 10036
Tel.: (212) 237-4000
Fax: (212) 237-5123
Creative

UNITED STATIONERS INC.

1 N Parkway Blvd Ste 100
Deerfield, IL 60015
Tel.: (847) 627-7000
Fax: (847) 627-7001
Toll Free: (800) 424-4003
E-mail: info@ussco.com
Web Site: www.unitedstationers.com
E-Mail For Key Personnel:
Public Relations: JHoward@ussco.com
Approx. Sls.: $4,832,237,000
Approx. Number Employees: 5,950
Year Founded: 1921
Business Description:
Business Products Distr
S.I.C.: 5112
N.A.I.C.S.: 424120
Import
Media: 2-4-7-10
Distr.: Reg.
Personnel:
Frederick B. Hegi, Jr. *(Chm)*
Paul Cody Phipps *(Pres & COO)*
Fareed A. Khan *(CFO & Sr VP)*
S.David Bent *(CIO & Sr VP)*
Kenneth M. Nickel *(Chief Acctg Officer, VP & Controller)*
Timothy P. Connolly *(Pres-Ops & Logistics Svcs)*
James K. Fahey *(Pres-Furniture Div)*
Stephen A. Schultz *(Pres-LagasseSweet & ORS Nasco)*
Eric A. Blanchard *(Gen Counsel, Sec & Sr VP)*
Ronald C. Berg *(Sr VP-Supply Chain)*
Patrick T. Collins *(Sr VP-Sls)*
Jeffrey G. Howard *(Sr VP-Natl Accts & Channel Mgmt)*
Joseph R. Templet *(Sr VP-Trade Dev)*
Brands & Products:
UNITED STATIONERS
Advertising Agencies:
LKH&S
54 W Hubbard Ste 100
Chicago, IL 60610
Tel.: (312) 595-0200
Fax: (312) 595-0300

NM Marketing Communications, Inc.
706 Waukegan Rd
Glenview, IL 60025
Tel.: (847) 657-6011
Fax: (847) 657-8425

UNITED VACATIONS, INC.

(Sub. of United Air Lines, Inc.)
1200 E Algonquin Rd
Arlington Heights, IL 60005-4712
Tel.: (847) 700-4000
Web Site: www.unitedvacations.com
Sales Range: $100-124.9 Million
Year Founded: 1984
Business Description:
Tour Packages
S.I.C.: 4724
N.A.I.C.S.: 561510
Media: 11-13-17
Personnel:
David A. Coltman *(Chm & Pres)*
Advertising Agency:
BVK-Chicago
999 Oakmont Plz Dr Ste 300
Westmont, IL 60559-1368
Tel.: (630) 789-3222
Fax: (630) 789-3223
Toll Free: (800) 574-0039

UNITED VAN LINES, LLC

(Sub. of UniGroup, Inc.)
1 United Dr
Fenton, MO 63026-2535
Tel.: (636) 326-3100
Tel.: (636) 343-3900
Fax: (636) 349-8747
Toll Free: (800) 948-4885
E-mail: webmaster@unitedvanlines.com
Web Site: www.unitedvanlines.com
Approx. Number Employees: 1,200
Year Founded: 1947
Business Description:
Transportation of Household Goods & Other Specialized Commodities
S.I.C.: 4213

United Van Lines, LLC — (Continued)

N.A.I.C.S.: 484121
Advertising Expenditures: $800,000
Media: 2-3-5-6-7-10-14-15-18-20-23-24-25-26
Distr.: Natl.
Budget Set: Oct.
Personnel:
H. Daniel McCollister *(Chm & CEO-Unigroup)*
Pat Larch *(Pres & COO-United Van Lines)*
Rich McClure *(Pres-Unigroup & CEO-United Van Lines)*
Casey Ellis *(Exec VP-Sls-Mktg)*
Keith Dailey *(Dir-Adv & Promos)*

Brands & Products:
THE QUALITY SHOWS IN EVERY MOVE WE MAKE
UNITED

Advertising Agencies:
Adams & Knight Advertising/Public Relations
80 Avon Meadow Ln
Avon, CT 06001
Tel.: (860) 676-2300
Fax: (860) 676-1940

Barkley
304 N Broadway
Saint Louis, MO 63102
Tel.: (314) 727-9500
Fax: (314) 727-0561
Toll Free: (800) 886-0561

Grey New York
777 3rd Ave
New York, NY 10017-1401
Tel.: (212) 546-2000
Fax: (212) 546-1495
"There's Moving, and there's moving United" Campaign

Lippincott
499 Park Ave
New York, NY 10022-1240
Tel.: (212) 521-0000
Fax: (212) 308-8952
Logo

UPS GROUND FREIGHT, INC.
(Sub. of United Parcel Service of America, Inc.)
(d/b/a UPS Freight)
1000 Semmes Ave
Richmond, VA 23224
Tel.: (804) 231-8000
Fax: (804) 231-8752
Web Site: www.ltl.upsfreight.com
E-Mail For Key Personnel:
Public Relations: irosenfeld@overnite.com
Sales Range: $1-4.9 Billion
Approx. Number Employees: 1,100
Year Founded: 1935
Business Description:
Less-Than-Truckload & Long-Distance Freight Transportation Services
S.I.C.: 4213
N.A.I.C.S.: 484122; 484121
Media: 2-25
Personnel:
Jack A. Holmes *(Pres)*
John W. Fain *(Sr VP)*
Tom Murphy *(Mgr-Mktg)*

UPS SUPPLY CHAIN SOLUTIONS, INC.
(Sub. of United Parcel Service of America, Inc.)
12380 Morris Rd
Alpharetta, GA 30005
Tel.: (678) 746-4365
Tel.: (678) 746-4100
Fax: (678) 746-6615
Toll Free: (800) 742-5727
Web Site: www.ups-scs.com
Sales Range: $1-4.9 Billion
Approx. Number Employees: 20,000
Business Description:
Transportation, Freight, Logistics, International Trade Management & Distribution Services
S.I.C.: 4432; 4513
N.A.I.C.S.: 483113; 492110
Media: 2-13
Personnel:
Alan Gershenhorn *(Chief Sls Officer & CMO)*
John Haack *(Pres-Global Enterprise Sls)*

Advertising Agency:
The Martin Agency
One Shockoe Plz
Richmond, VA 23219-4132
Tel.: (804) 698-8000
Fax: (804) 698-8001

US 1 INDUSTRIES, INC.
336 W US Hwy 30 Ste 201
Valparaiso, IN 46385-5345
Tel.: (219) 476-1300
Tel.: (219) 977-5225
Fax: (219) 476-1376
Fax: (219) 476-1685
Toll Free: (800) 377-3714
E-mail: info@us1industries.biz
Web Site: us1industries.com/
Approx. Rev.: $210,751,131
Approx. Number Employees: 90
Year Founded: 1946
Business Description:
Trucking, Logistics & Management Services
S.I.C.: 4213; 4731
N.A.I.C.S.: 484230; 484121; 488510
Media: 2-9-13-25
Personnel:
Michael E. Kibler *(Pres & CEO)*
Harold E. Antonson *(CFO)*
David Antonson *(VP-Sls & Mktg)*

US AIRWAYS GROUP, INC.
111 W Rio Salado Pkwy
Tempe, AZ 85281
Tel.: (480) 693-0800
Fax: (480) 693-5546
Web Site: www.usairways.com
Approx. Rev.: $11,908,000,000
Approx. Number Employees: 30,900
Year Founded: 1939
Business Description:
Holding Company; Scheduled Passenger & Freight Air Transportation Services
S.I.C.: 6719; 4512; 4581
N.A.I.C.S.: 551112; 481111; 481112; 488190
Advertising Expenditures: $10,000,000
Media: 1-2-3-4-5-6-7-8-9-11-13-14-15-16-18-19-20-22-23-24-25-26
Distr.: Direct to Consumer; Intl.; Natl.
Budget Set: Oct.
Personnel:
William Douglas Parker *(Chm & CEO)*
Bruce R. Lakefield *(Vice Chm)*
J. Scott Kirby *(Pres)*
Derek J. Kerr *(CFO & Exec VP)*
Robert Isom *(COO & Exec VP)*
Brad Jensen *(CIO & Sr VP)*
Dion J. Flannery *(Pres-US Airways Express & VP)*
Elise R. Eberwein *(Exec VP-People, Comm & Pub Affairs)*
Stephen L. Johnson *(Exec VP-Corp & Govt Affairs)*
Suzanne Boda *(Sr VP-Airport Customer Svc-Intl & Cargo)*
Edward W. Bular *(Sr VP-Flight Ops & InFlight)*
Kerry Hester *(Sr VP-Ops Plng & Support)*
C. A. Howlett *(Sr VP-Pub Affairs)*
Andrew P. Nocella *(Sr VP-Mktg & Plng)*
David G. Seymour *(Sr VP-Tech Ops)*
Paul Galleberg *(VP-Legal Affairs)*
Paul Jones *(VP-Legal Affairs)*
Howard Kass *(VP-Legal & Govt Affairs)*
Paul M. Lambert *(VP-Legal)*
John McDonald *(VP-Corp Comm)*
Daniel P. Pon *(VP-HR)*

Brands & Products:
FLY WITH US
U.S AIRWAYS
US AIRWAYS CLUB
US AIRWAYS EXPRESS
US AIRWAYS SHUTTLE

US AIRWAYS, INC.
(Sub. of US Airways Group, Inc.)
111 W Rio Salado Pkwy
Tempe, AZ 85281
Tel.: (480) 693-0800
Web Site: www.usairways.com
Year Founded: 1939
Business Description:
Scheduled Passenger & Freight Air Transportation Services
S.I.C.: 4512; 4581
N.A.I.C.S.: 481111; 481112; 488190
Advertising Expenditures: $11,000,000
Media: 1-2-3-4-5-6-7-8-9-10-11-13-14-15-16-17-18-19-22-23-24-25-26-31
Distr.: Direct to Consumer; Intl.; Natl.
Budget Set: Varies
Personnel:
William Douglas Parker *(Chm & CEO)*
Derek J. Kerr *(CFO & Exec VP)*
Stephen L. Johnson *(Exec VP-Corp & Govt Affairs)*

Advertising Agencies:
MichaelsWilder
7773 W Golden Ln
Peoria, AZ 85345-7977
Tel.: (623) 334-0100
Fax: (623) 334-0200
Toll Free: (800) 423-6468

Moses Anshell, Inc.
20 W Jackson St
Phoenix, AZ 85003
Tel.: (602) 254-7312
Fax: (602) 324-1222

SiboneyUSA/New York
729 7th Ave 9th Fl
New York, NY 10019
Tel.: (212) 337-8956
Fax: (212) 337-8901

Universal McCann Worldwide
42-47 Saint Johns Square
London, EC1M 4EA, United Kingdom
Tel.: (44) 20 7 833 5858
Fax: (44) 20 7 073 7413

U.S. XPRESS ENTERPRISES, INC.
4080 Jenkins Rd
Chattanooga, TN 37421-1174
Tel.: (423) 510-3000
Fax: (423) 510-4081
Toll Free: (800) 251-6291
E-mail: rbrown@usxpress.com
Web Site: www.usxpress.com
Sales Range: $700-749.9 Million
Approx. Number Employees: 10,885
Year Founded: 1986
Business Description:
Transportation Service & Technology
S.I.C.: 4213; 4731
N.A.I.C.S.: 484121; 488510
Media: 10
Personnel:
Patrick E. Quinn *(Co-Chm & Co-Pres)*
Max L. Fuller *(Co-Chm & CEO)*
John White *(Co-Pres)*
Ray M. Harlin *(CFO & Exec VP-Fin)*
Jeffrey Wardeberg *(COO)*

Advertising Agency:
The Johnson Group
436 Market St
Chattanooga, TN 37402-1203
Tel.: (423) 756-2608
Fax: (423) 267-0475

USA TRUCK, INC.
3200 Industrial Park Rd
Van Buren, AR 72956-6110
Tel.: (479) 471-2500
Fax: (479) 471-2526
Toll Free: (800) USA-TRUC
E-mail: webmaster@usa-truck.com
Web Site: www.usa-truck.com
Approx. Rev.: $460,161,000
Approx. Number Employees: 3,000
Year Founded: 1986
Business Description:
Freight Transportation Services
S.I.C.: 4213
N.A.I.C.S.: 484121
Advertising Expenditures: $3,327,000
Personnel:
Terry A. Elliott *(Chm)*
Clifton R. Beckham *(Pres & CEO)*
Darron R. Ming *(CFO & VP-Fin)*
David B. Hartline *(COO-Trucking & Exec VP)*
J. Rodney Mills *(Gen Counsel & VP-Admin)*
Craig S. Shelly *(VP-Corp Strategy)*
B. Chad Van Kooten *(VP-Sls)*

Brands & Products:
USA LOGISTICS
USA TRUCK

Advertising Agency:
Hightower Agency
970 Ebenezer Blvd
Madison, MS 39110
Tel.: (601) 853-1822
Fax: (601) 853-1069

VALEF YACHTS, LTD.
7254 Fir Rd
Ambler, PA 19002
Tel.: (215) 641-1624
Fax: (215) 641-1746

Key to Media (For complete agency information see *The Advertising Red Books-Agencies* edition):
1. Bus. Publs. 2. Cable T.V. 3. Catalogs & Directories. 4. Co-op Adv. 5. Consumer Mags. 6. D.M. to Bus. Estab.7. D.M. to Consumers 8. Daily Newsp. 9. Exhibits/Trade Shows 10. Foreign 11. Infomercial 12. Internet Adv.13. Multimedia 14. Network Radio 15. Network T.V. 16. Newsp. Distr. Mags. 17. Other 18. Outdoor (Posters, Transit) 19. Point of Purchase20. Premiums, Novelties 21. Product Samples 22. Special Events Mktg. 23. Spot Radio 24. Spot T.V. 25. Weekly Newsp. 26. Yellow Page Adv.

Toll Free: (800) 223-3845
E-mail: info@valefyachts.com
Web Site: www.valefyachts.com
Approx. Sls.: $6,500,000
Approx. Number Employees: 11
Year Founded: 1969
Business Description:
Yacht Charter Services
S.I.C.: 7999
N.A.I.C.S.: 487210
Media: 2-4-6-10-22
Personnel:
Vassilios J. Lefakinis *(Chm)*

VELOCITY EXPRESS
(Sub. of Velocity Express Corporation)
25 Central Ave
Teterboro, NJ 07608
Tel.: (201) 487-7740
Fax: (201) 994-1924
E-mail: corporate@cdl.net
Web Site: www.cdl.net
Sales Range: $200-249.9 Million
Approx. Number Employees: 1,500
Business Description:
Customized, Time-Critical Air & Ground Delivery Systems
S.I.C.: 4213; 4215; 4731
N.A.I.C.S.: 484121; 488510; 492210
Media: 7

VIA METROPOLITAN TRANSIT
800 W Myrtle St
San Antonio, TX 78212
Tel.: (210) 362-2000
Tel.: (210) 362-2370 (Pub Affairs)
Fax: (210) 362-2570
Web Site: www.viainfo.net
Sales Range: $10-24.9 Million
Approx. Number Employees: 2,000
Year Founded: 1978
Business Description:
Provider of Transit Operations
S.I.C.: 4111
N.A.I.C.S.: 485113
Personnel:
Keith T Parker *(Pres & CEO)*
Steve Lange *(CFO & VP-Fiscal Mgmt)*
Priscilla Ingle *(VP-Pub Affairs)*
Terry Dudley *(Mgr-Procurement)*
Michael Ledesma *(Mgr-Bus Svc Transportation)*
Advertising Agency:
Creative Civilization An Aguilar/Girard Agency
106 Auditorium Cir 2nd Fl
San Antonio, TX 78205-1310
Tel.: (210) 227-1999
Fax: (210) 227-5999

VIA RAIL CANADA INC.
Sta A 3 Pl Ville Marie
Montreal, QC H3B 2C9, Canada
Tel.: (514) 871-6000
Web Site: www.viarail.ca
Approx. Number Employees: 3,027
Year Founded: 1978
Business Description:
Passenger Rail Services
S.I.C.: 4119
N.A.I.C.S.: 485999
Personnel:
Paul Smith *(Chm)*
Marc Laliberte *(Pres & CEO)*
Robert St-Jean *(CFO & Chief Admin Officer)*
John Marginson *(COO)*
Denis Pinsonneault *(Chief Customer Experience Officer)*
Advertising Agency:
NATIONAL Public Relations
2001 McGill College Ave Ste 800
Montreal, QC H3A 1G1, Canada
Tel.: (514) 843-7171
Fax: (514) 843-6976

VIRGIN AMERICA
(Joint Venture of Virgin Group Ltd., Black Canyon Capital LLC & Cyrus Capital Partners, LP)
555 Airport Blvd
Burlingame, CA 94010
Tel.: (650) 343-1827
Web Site: www.virginamerica.com
Approx. Number Employees: 550
Year Founded: 2007
Business Description:
Airline Operator; Owned 75% by VAI Partners LLC & 25% by Virgin Group Ltd
S.I.C.: 4512
N.A.I.C.S.: 481111
Personnel:
Donald J. Carty *(Chm)*
C. David Cush *(Pres & CEO)*
Peter D. Hunt *(CFO & Sr VP)*
Dean Cookson *(CIO & VP)*
John Varley *(Gen Counsel & Sr VP)*
Anthony Mosse *(VP-Fin & Treas)*
Mark Bianchi *(Sr VP-Technical Ops)*
Diana Walke *(VP-Plng & Sls)*
Bowen Payson *(Mgr-Online & Digital Mktg)*
Advertising Agencies:
Eleven Inc.
445 Bush St 8th Fl
San Francisco, CA 94108
Tel.: (415) 707-1111
Fax: (415) 707-1100

Ogilvy Public Relations Worldwide
1111 19th St NW 10th Fl
Washington, DC 20036
Tel.: (202) 729-4000
Fax: (202) 729-4001

Rokkan
176 Grand St 2nd Fl
New York, NY 10012-4003
Tel.: (212) 835-9300
Fax: (212) 251-9393
Agency of Record

VIRGINIA PORT AUTHORITY
600 World Trade Ctr
Norfolk, VA 23510
Tel.: (757) 683-8000
Fax: (757) 683-8500
Toll Free: (800) 446-8098
E-mail: roliver@portofvirginia.com
Web Site: www.vaport.com
Sales Range: $200-249.9 Million
Approx. Number Employees: 135
Year Founded: 1952
Business Description:
Port Services for International Transportation & Maritime Commerce in Virginia that Operates & Markets Marine Terminal Facilities
S.I.C.: 9621; 4491
N.A.I.C.S.: 926120; 488320
Import Export
Media: 2-7-8-11-13
Personnel:
John G. Milliken *(Chm)*
Rodney W. Oliver *(CFO & Deputy Exec Dir)*
Jeff Florin *(COO & Deputy Exec Dir-Ops)*
Russell J. Held *(Exec Dir-Dev)*
Jeff Keever *(Exec Dir-External Affairs)*
Russell Young *(Dir-Economic Dev)*
Advertising Agency:
Barber Martin Agency
7400 Beaufont Springs Dr Ste 201
Richmond, VA 23225-5519
Tel.: (804) 320-3232
Fax: (804) 320-1729

VIRTUOSO LTD.
505 Main St Ste 500
Fort Worth, TX 76102-3941
Tel.: (817) 870-0300
Fax: (817) 870-1050
Toll Free: (800) 401-4274
E-mail: information@virtuoso.com
Web Site: www.virtuoso.com
E-Mail For Key Personnel:
Public Relations: kwaldon@virtuoso.com
Approx. Number Employees: 150
Year Founded: 2000
Business Description:
Marketing Consortium for Travel Agencies
S.I.C.: 4724
N.A.I.C.S.: 561510
Advertising Expenditures: $650,000
Media: 6-7-9-10-18-20-25
Distr.: Direct to Consumer; Natl.
Budget Set: Oct.
Personnel:
Jesse Upchurch *(Chm)*
Kristi Jones *(Pres & Principal)*
Matthew D. Upchurch *(CEO)*
Advertising Agency:
The Brandman Agency
261 5th Ave Fl 22
New York, NY 10016
Tel.: (212) 683-2442
Fax: (212) 683-2022
(Public Relations, Travel Mart Conference)

VITRAN CORPORATION, INC.
185 The West Mall Ste 701
Toronto, ON M9C 5L5, Canada
Tel.: (416) 596-7664
Fax: (416) 596-8039
E-mail: information@vitran.com
Web Site: www.vitran.com
Approx. Rev.: $672,556,000
Approx. Number Employees: 4,895
Year Founded: 1983
Business Description:
Transportation Services
S.I.C.: 4512; 4731
N.A.I.C.S.: 481112; 488510
Advertising Expenditures: $324,000
Personnel:
Richard D. McGraw *(Chm)*
Richard E. Gaetz *(Pres & CEO)*
Fayaz D. Suleman *(CFO & VP-Fin)*
Steve Cook *(Pres-US Truckload Ops)*
Mark Kosovec *(Pres-Vitran Express Inc)*
Tony Trichilo *(Pres-Vitran Express Canada Inc)*

WAGNER INDUSTRIES, INC.
1201 E 12th Ave
Kansas City, MO 64116
Tel.: (816) 421-3520
Fax: (816) 421-2568
Toll Free: (800) 817-1264
E-mail: info@wagnerindustries.com
Web Site: www.wagnerindustries.com
Approx. Number Employees: 200
Year Founded: 1946
Business Description:
Public Warehousing & Distr
S.I.C.: 4212
N.A.I.C.S.: 484110
Media: 2-7-10-26
Personnel:
John Wagner, Jr. *(Pres)*
Kevin Service *(CFO)*
Mike Moon *(VP-HR)*

WASHINGTON METROPOLITAN AREA TRANSIT AUTHORITY
600 5th St NW
Washington, DC 20001-2610
Tel.: (202) 637-7000
Fax: (202) 962-1180
Web Site: www.wmata.com
Sales Range: $450-499.9 Million
Approx. Number Employees: 10,000
Year Founded: 1976
Business Description:
Mass Transit Service
S.I.C.: 4111
N.A.I.C.S.: 485119
Advertising Expenditures: $1,600,000
Personnel:
Leona Agouridis *(Asst Gen Mgr-Comm)*
Jack Requa *(Asst Gen Mgr-Bus Svcs)*
Michael Bride *(Mgr-MetroArts)*
Brands & Products:
METRO
METROACCESS
METROBUS
METRORAIL
SMARTRIP
Advertising Agency:
LM&O Advertising
2000 N 14th St 8th Fl
Arlington, VA 22201-2573
Tel.: (703) 875-2193
Fax: (703) 875-2199

WEST MICHIGAN TOURIST ASSOCIATION
741 Kenmoor Ave Ste E
Grand Rapids, MI 49546
Tel.: (616) 245-2217
Fax: (616) 954-3924
Toll Free: (800) 442-2084
E-mail: travel@wmta.org
Web Site: www.wmta.org
Sales Range: Less than $1 Million
Approx. Number Employees: 6
Year Founded: 1917
Business Description:
Tourism Promoter
S.I.C.: 8611
N.A.I.C.S.: 813910
Daily Newsp.: 20%; Exhibits/Trade Shows: 70%; Internet Adv.: 9%; Yellow Page Adv.: 1%
Distr.: Reg.
Personnel:
Rick Hert *(Exec Dir)*
Cheri Spencer *(Office Mgr)*
Brands & Products:
TRAVEL TIPS
WEST MICHIGAN CAREFREE TRAVEL
WEST MICHIGAN TOURIST ASSOCIATION

Key to Media (For complete agency information see *The Advertising Red Books-Agencies* edition):
1. Bus. Publs. 2. Cable T.V. 3. Catalogs & Directories. 4. Co-op Adv. 5. Consumer Mags. 6. D.M. to Bus. Estab.7. D.M. to Consumers 8. Daily Newsp. 9. Exhibits/Trade Shows 10. Foreign 11. Infomercial 12. Internet Adv.13. Multimedia 14. Network Radio 15. Network T.V. 16. Newsp. Distr. Mags. 17. Other 18. Outdoor (Posters, Transit) 19. Point of Purchase20. Premiums, Novelties 21. Product Samples 22. Special Events Mktg. 23. Spot Radio 24. Spot T.V. 25. Weekly Newsp. 26. Yellow Page Adv.

West Michigan Tourist Association — (Continued)

WMTA

WESTJET AIRLINES LTD.
22 Arial Pl NE
Calgary, AB T2E 1J2, Canada
Tel.: (403) 444-2600
Fax: (403) 444-2301
E-mail: conventions@westjet.com
Web Site: www.westjet.com
Approx. Rev.: $2,658,367,292
Approx. Number Employees: 6,877
Year Founded: 1996
Business Description:
Air Transportation Services
S.I.C.: 4512
N.A.I.C.S.: 481111
Personnel:
Clive J. Beddoe *(Chm)*
Gregg Saretsky *(Pres & CEO)*
Vito Culmone *(CFO & Exec VP-Fin)*
Bob Cummings *(Exec VP-Sls & Mktg)*
Hugh Dunleavy *(Exec VP-Strategy & Plng)*
Ferio Pugliese *(Exec VP-People & Culture)*
Brands & Products:
BECAUSE OWNERS CARE
WESTJET
Advertising Agency:
Hill & Knowlton (Canada) Limited
55 Metcalfe St Ste 1100
Ottawa, ON K1P 6L5, Canada
Tel.: (613) 238-4371
Fax: (613) 238-8642

WHEATON VAN LINES, INC.
(d/b/a Wheaton World Wide Moving)
8010 Castleton Rd
Indianapolis, IN 46250-2005
Tel.: (317) 849-7900
Fax: (317) 849-3718
Toll Free: (800) 992-5202
E-mail: wheatoncustomercare@wvlcorp.com
Web Site:
www.wheatonworldwide.com
Sales Range: $100-124.9 Million
Approx. Number Employees: 200
Year Founded: 1945
Business Description:
Transportation Services
S.I.C.: 4214; 4731
N.A.I.C.S.: 484210; 488510
Advertising Expenditures: $500,000
Media: 2-3-6-9-10-18-20-26
Distr.: Natl.
Budget Set: Oct.
Personnel:
Stephen F. Burns *(Chm)*
Mark Kirschner *(CEO)*
David Witzerman *(Pres-Wheaton World Wide Moving)*
Brands & Products:
WHEATON WORLDWIDE MOVING

WHEELS INC.
(Sub. of Frank Consolidated Enterprises)
666 Garland Pl
Des Plaines, IL 60016-4725
Tel.: (847) 699-7000
Fax: (847) 699-6494
E-mail: info@wheels.com
Web Site: www.wheels.com
Year Founded: 1939
Business Description:
Automobiles & Trucks Leasing Services
S.I.C.: 7515; 7519
N.A.I.C.S.: 532112; 532120
Media: 1-2-8-10-13-20-22
Distr.: Bus.-to-Bus
Budget Set: Aug.
Personnel:
James Frank *(Pres & CEO)*
Mary Ann O'Dwyer *(CFO & Sr VP-Fin & Ops)*
Steven Loos *(CIO & VP-IT)*
Daniel Z. Frank *(Pres-Wheels Svcs)*
Scott Pattullo *(Sr VP-Sls & Mktg)*
Shlomo Crandus *(VP-Fin)*
Prentiss Harvey *(VP-Sls)*
Joan Richards *(VP-HR)*
John Round *(Asst VP-Sls)*

WORLD TRAVEL HOLDINGS
(Branch of World Travel Holdings, Inc.)
100 Sylvan Rd Ste 600
Woburn, MA 01801-1852
Tel.: (617) 424-7990
Fax: (617) 424-1943
Web Site:
www.worldtravelholdings.com
Approx. Number Employees: 900
Year Founded: 1986
Business Description:
Cruise & Travel Agencies
S.I.C.: 4724; 4729
N.A.I.C.S.: 561510; 561599
Media: 2-7-8-10-13-16
Personnel:
Don Graff *(CFO)*
Jamie Cash *(Sr VP-Tech)*
David Crooks *(Sr VP-Product & Ops)*
Vivian Ewart *(Sr VP)*
Kathleen Federico *(Sr VP-Sls & HR)*
Simon Goodall *(Sr VP-Private Label Programs)*
Jeff Sherota *(Sr VP-House Brand Mktg)*
Jeff Smith *(Sr VP-Customer Care)*
Brands & Products:
VACATION OUTLET

YMT VACATIONS
(Formerly Your Man Tours, Inc.)
100 N Sepulveda Blvd Ste 1700
El Segundo, CA 90245
Tel.: (310) 649-3820
Fax: (310) 649-2118
Toll Free: (800) 922-9000
E-mail: ymt@earthlink.net
Web Site: www.ymtvacations.com
Sales Range: $10-24.9 Million
Approx. Number Employees: 100
Year Founded: 1967
Business Description:
Travel Agency
S.I.C.: 4724; 4725
N.A.I.C.S.: 561510; 561520
Advertising Expenditures: $4,110,000
Distr.: Direct to Consumer
Budget Set: Various
Personnel:
Jerre Fuqua *(Pres)*
Charles Suppnick *(VP-Detroit)*
Oliver Milton *(Gen Mgr-Mktg)*
Advertising Agency:
YMT Vacations
100 N Sepulveda Blvd Ste 1700
El Segundo, CA 90245
Tel.: (310) 649-3820
Fax: (310) 649-2118
Toll Free: (800) 922-9000
(Package Sightseeing Tours)

YOUR MAN TOURS, INC.
(Name Changed to YMT Vacations)

YRC WORLDWIDE INC.
10990 Roe Ave
Overland Park, KS 66211-1213
Mailing Address:
PO Box 7563
Overland Park, KS 66207-0563
Tel.: (913) 696-6100
Fax: (913) 696-6116
Toll Free: (800) 846-4300
Web Site: www.yrcw.com
Approx. Rev.: $4,334,640,000
Approx. Number Employees: 32,000
Year Founded: 1983
Business Description:
Holding Company; Transportation Services
S.I.C.: 4731; 4212; 4213; 4214; 6719; 7361; 8742
N.A.I.C.S.: 488510; 484110; 484121; 484122; 484220; 541611; 541612; 541613; 541614; 551112
Media: 1-2-7-10-20-26
Distr.: Intl.; Natl.; Reg.
Budget Set: Oct.-Nov.
Personnel:
William D. Zollars *(Chm)*
Michael J. Smid *(Pres & COO)*
James L. Welch *(CEO)*
William L. Trubeck *(Interim CFO & Interim Exec VP)*
Gregory A. Reid *(CMO & Exec VP-Enterprise Solutions Grp)*
James G. Kissinger *(Chief Admin Officer & Exec VP)*
Paul F. Liljegren *(Chief Acctg Officer, VP-IR & Corp Controller)*
J. Mike Kelley *(Chief Sustainability Officer & VP-External Affairs)*
Michael J. Naatz *(Chief Customer Officer & Pres-Customer Care Div)*
Thomas A. Gerke *(Gen Counsel, Sec & Exec VP)*
Christopher C. Wren *(Treas & Sr VP)*
Phil J. Gaines *(Sr VP-Fin)*
Brands & Products:
DEFINITE DELIVERY
EXACT EXPRESS
STANDARD GROUND
YELLOW ROADWAY
YELLOW TRANSPORTATION
YRC WORLDWIDE
Advertising Agency:
The David James Agency
223 E Thousand Oaks Blvd Ste 417
Thousand Oaks, CA 91360
Tel.: (805) 494-9508
Fax: (805) 494-8610

ZIM-AMERICAN ISRAELI SHIPPING CO.
(Sub. of Zim Integrated Shipping Services, Ltd.)
5801 Lk Wright Dr
Norfolk, VA 23502-1862
Tel.: (757) 228-1300
Fax: (757) 228-1420
Telex: ITT 427152
E-mail: info@zim.com
Web Site: www.zim.com
Approx. Sls.: $300,000,000
Approx. Number Employees: 400
Business Description:
Container Shipping for Worldwide Importing & Exporting
S.I.C.: 4731; 3499
N.A.I.C.S.: 488510; 332439
Import Export
Advertising Expenditures: $950,000
Media: 2-7-8-11-20
Distr.: Intl.; Natl.
Budget Set: Oct.
Personnel:
Gordon Kay *(Pres-America)*
T. Keen *(VP-Sls)*

ZIPCAR, INC.
(Holding of Revolution, LLC)
25 First St 4th Fl
Cambridge, MA 02141
Tel.: (617) 995-4231
Fax: (617) 995-4300
Toll Free: (866) 4ZIPCAR
E-mail: info@zipcar.com
Web Site: www.zipcar.com
Approx. Rev.: $186,101,000
Approx. Number Employees: 474
Year Founded: 1999
Business Description:
Car Sharing Services
S.I.C.: 7514
N.A.I.C.S.: 532111
Advertising Expenditures: $3,177,000
Personnel:
Scott W. Griffith *(Chm & CEO)*
Mark D. Norman *(Pres & COO)*
Edward G. Goldfinger *(CFO)*
Robert J. Weisberg *(CMO)*
Jon Zietler *(Exec VP-Corp Dev)*
Sean Quimby *(VP-HR)*
Doug Williams *(VP-Engrg)*
Greg Winter *(VP-Comm)*
Brands & Products:
ZIPCAR
Advertising Agencies:
Ansira
15851 Dallas Pkwy Ste 725
Addison, TX 75001
Tel.: (972) 663-1100
Fax: (972) 663-1300

Deutsch, Inc.
(A Lowe & Partners Company)
111 8th Ave 14th Fl
New York, NY 10011-5201
Tel.: (212) 981-7600
Fax: (212) 981-7525

Key to Media (For complete agency information see *The Advertising Red Books-Agencies* edition):
1. Bus. Publs. 2. Cable T.V. 3. Catalogs & Directories. 4. Co-op Adv. 5. Consumer Mags. 6. D.M. to Bus. Estab.7. D.M. to Consumers 8. Daily Newsp. 9. Exhibits/Trade Shows 10. Foreign 11. Infomercial 12. Internet Adv.13. Multimedia 14. Network Radio 15. Network T.V. 16. Newsp. Distr. Mags. 17. Other 18. Outdoor (Posters, Transit) 19. Point of Purchase20. Premiums, Novelties 21. Product Samples 22. Special Events Mktg. 23. Spot Radio 24. Spot T.V. 25. Weekly Newsp. 26. Yellow Page Adv.

Wines & Liquors

Champagne — Cordials — Gin — Liqueurs — Rum — Vermouth — Vodka — Whiskey — Wines

A. SMITH BOWMAN DISTILLERY
(Sub. of Sazerac Company, Inc.)
1 Bowman Dr Ste 100
Fredericksburg, VA 22408-7318
Tel.: (540) 373-4555
Fax: (540) 371-2236
E-mail: bowmansales@sazerac.com
Web Site: www.asmithbowman.com
Approx. Number Employees: 5
Year Founded: 1935
Business Description:
Mfr. of Distilled Liquors
S.I.C.: 2085
N.A.I.C.S.: 312140
Import Export
Media: 4-6-9-10-13-16-19-22
Distr.: Reg.
Budget Set: Jan.
Personnel:
Mark Brown *(Pres & CEO)*
Joseph Dangler *(VP-Production)*
Brands & Products:
BOWMAN'S
VIRGINIA GENTLEMAN

THE ABSOLUT SPIRITS COMPANY INC.
(Sub. of The Absolut Company)
401 Park Ave S
New York, NY 10019
Tel.: (212) 641-8700
Fax: (212) 641-8703
Web Site: www.absolut.com
Approx. Number Employees: 30
Business Description:
Spirits Distr
S.I.C.: 5182
N.A.I.C.S.: 424820
Personnel:
Tim Murphy *(VP-Mktg)*
Ian Crystal *(Brand Dir-ABSOLUT Vodka)*
Jeffrey Moran *(Dir-Comm)*
Kate Pomeroy *(Dir-Consumer Insights & Plng)*
Advertising Agencies:
Access Communications, LLC
101 Howard St 2nd Fl
San Francisco, CA 94105
Tel.: (415) 904-7070
Fax: (415) 904-7055

Ketchum
(Part of Omnicom)
1285 Ave of the Americas
New York, NY 10019
Tel.: (646) 935-3900
Fax: (646) 935-4482
PR Agency of Record

TBWA Chiat Day New York
488 Madison Ave
New York, NY 10022
Tel.: (212) 804-1000
Fax: (212) 804-1200

TBWA/Worldwide
(Sub. of Omnicom Group, Inc.)
488 Madison Ave 5th Fl
New York, NY 10022-5702
Tel.: (212) 804-1300
Fax: (212) 804-1333
Creative

ADAMBA IMPORTS INTERNATIONAL
585 Meserole St
Brooklyn, NY 11237
Tel.: (718) 628-9700
Fax: (718) 628-0920
E-mail: info@adamba.com
Web Site: www.adamba.com
Approx. Number Employees: 11
Year Founded: 1978
Business Description:
Liqueur Importer
S.I.C.: 5182
N.A.I.C.S.: 424820
Import
Advertising Expenditures: $500,000
Media: 4-10-18-19-21
Distr.: Natl.
Personnel:
Adam M. Bak *(Pres)*

ADMIRAL WINE & LIQUOR CO.
74 Sand Pk Rd
Cedar Grove, NJ 07009
Tel.: (973) 857-2100
Fax: (973) 857-2277
Toll Free: (800) 582-9463
Web Site: www.admiralwine.com
Approx. Number Employees: 65
Year Founded: 1961
Business Description:
Wine Buying & Selling
S.I.C.: 5182
N.A.I.C.S.: 424820
Import Export
Advertising Expenditures: $200,000
Media: 4-8-10-17-19
Distr.: Intl.; Natl.
Personnel:
Michael Zieger *(Owner & Pres)*
Lu Abb *(Mgr-Sls)*

ANDREW PELLER LIMITED
697 S Service Rd
Grimsby, ON L3M 4E8, Canada
Tel.: (905) 643-4131
Fax: (905) 643-4944
E-mail: info@andrewpeller.com
Web Site: www.andrewpeller.com
Approx. Sls.: $257,540,621
Approx. Number Employees: 850
Year Founded: 1961
Business Description:
Winery Owner & Wine Retailer
S.I.C.: 2084; 5182
N.A.I.C.S.: 312130; 424820
Import Export
Advertising Expenditures: $3,000,000
Media: 15-19-24
Distr.: Intl.; Natl.
Budget Set: Sept. -Oct.
Personnel:
Joseph A. Peller *(Chm)*
John F. Petch *(Vice Chm)*
John E. Peller *(Pres & CEO)*
Peter B. Patchet *(CFO & Exec VP-HR)*
Anthony M. Bristow *(COO)*
Robert P. Van Wely *(Pres-Global Vintners Inc.)*
Shari A. Niles *(Exec VP-Mktg)*
Brendan P. Wall *(Exec VP-Ops)*
J. Christopher Zarafonitis *(Exec VP-Sls)*
James H. Cole *(VP-Retail Div)*
Hanna Latkowski *(Brand Mgr)*
Brands & Products:
ANDRES
ANDREW PELLER
DOMAINE D'OR
HILLEBRAND ESTATES
HOCHTALER
PELLER ESTATES
SIMILKAMEEN
TRIUS

B-21 FINE WINE & SPIRITS INC.
43380 Hwy 19 N
Tarpon Springs, FL 34689-0849
Mailing Address:
PO Box 849
Tarpon Springs, FL 34688
Tel.: (727) 937-5049
Fax: (866) 499-6700
Toll Free: (888) B21-WINE
E-mail: info@b-21.com
Web Site: www.b-21.com
Approx. Number Employees: 25
Year Founded: 1966
Business Description:
Wine & Spirits Retailer
S.I.C.: 5921
N.A.I.C.S.: 445310
Media: 4-6-13-25
Personnel:
Bob Sprentall *(Pres-B-21 Liquors)*
Steve Rayman *(Mgr-Mktg)*

BACARDI GLOBAL BRANDS INC.
(Sub. of Bacardi Limited)
866 Ponce De Leon Blvd Fl 2
Coral Gables, FL 33134-3039
Tel.: (305) 446-9050
Fax: (305) 446-2137
Web Site: www.bacardi.com
Approx. Number Employees: 20
Business Description:
Distilled & Blended Liquors
S.I.C.: 5182
N.A.I.C.S.: 424820
Personnel:
Giles Woodyer *(VP-Brand Mng Dir)*
Chauncey Hamlett *(Brand Mgr-Grey Goose)*
Pepin R. Argamasilla *(Global Mgr)*
Advertising Agencies:
David & Goliath
909 N Sepulveda Blvd Ste 700
El Segundo, CA 90245
Tel.: (310) 445-5200
Fax: (310) 445-5201
Martini Asti Sparkling Wine

Johannes Leonardo
41 East 11th St 6th Fl
New York, NY 10003
Tel.: (212) 462-8111
Fax: (212) 645-0861

BACARDI USA, INC.
(Sub. of Bacardi Limited)
2701 Le Jeu Rd
Coral Gables, FL 33134-5014

Key to Media (For complete agency information see *The Advertising Red Books-Agencies* edition):
1. Bus. Publs. 2. Cable T.V. 3. Catalogs & Directories. 4. Co-op Adv. 5. Consumer Mags. 6. D.M. to Bus. Estab.7. D.M. to Consumers
8. Daily Newsp. 9. Exhibits/Trade Shows 10. Foreign 11. Infomercial 12. Internet Adv.13. Multimedia 14. Network Radio
15. Network T.V. 16. Newsp. Distr. Mags. 17. Other 18. Outdoor (Posters, Transit) 19. Point of Purchase20. Premiums, Novelties
21. Product Samples 22. Special Events Mktg. 23. Spot Radio 24. Spot T.V. 25. Weekly Newsp. 26. Yellow Page Adv.

Bacardi USA, Inc. — (Continued)

Tel.: (305) 573-8511
Fax: (305) 573-7507
Telex: 305-573-1235
E-mail: info@bacardi.com
Web Site: www.bacardi.com
Sales Range: $1-4.9 Billion
Approx. Number Employees: 400
Year Founded: 1944
Business Description:
Wholesale Spirits & Liquor
S.I.C.: 5182
N.A.I.C.S.: 424820
Import
Media: 2-5-6-7-9-10-13-15-18-19-20-21-22-23-24-25
Distr.: Natl.
Budget Set: Oct.
Personnel:
Michael Misiorski *(CFO & Sr VP)*
Robert Furniss-Roe *(Pres-North America)*
Monsell Darville *(VP & Dir-Mktg)*
Stacie Thomas *(VP-HR)*
Nick Boyce *(Brand Dir)*
Joe Metevier *(Brand Dir-Grey Goose Vodka)*
Joe Gerbino *(Sr Mgr-Corp Comm & PR)*
Brian Shaifer *(Mgr-Mktg)*
Advertising Agencies:
Imagery Creative
1430 Southdixie Hwy Ste 307
Coral Gables, FL 33146
Tel.: (305) 667-4468
Fax: (786) 953-7168

KSL Media, Inc.
367 Park Ave S 4th Fl
New York, NY 10016
Tel.: (212) 352-5800
Fax: (212) 352-5935
42 Below
Bacardi Rum
Bombay Sapphire Gin
Dewars
Grey Goose Vodka
Martini and Rossi
Media Planning & Buying

Maloney & Fox
89 5th Ave 4th Fl
New York, NY 10003
Tel.: (212) 243-2000
Fax: (212) 243-5500

Research Development & Promotions (d/b/a RDP)
360 Menores Ave
Coral Gables, FL 33134
Tel.: (305) 445-4997
Fax: (305) 445-4221

BANFI VINTNERS

(Unit of Banfi Product Corp.)
1111 Cedar Swamp Rd
Glen Head, NY 11545-2109
Tel.: (516) 626-9200
Fax: (516) 626-2611
Toll Free: (800) 645-6511
E-mail: info@banfivintners.com
Web Site: www.banfivintners.com
Approx. Number Employees: 150
Year Founded: 1919
Business Description:
Importers of Classic Wines of Italy, Australia & Chile
S.I.C.: 5182
N.A.I.C.S.: 424820
Import Export
Advertising Expenditures: $20,000,000
Media: 3-6-9-14-15-16-17-18-19-20-22-23-24
Distr.: Intl.; Natl.
Personnel:
Harry F. Mariani *(Pres)*
James W. Mariani *(Co-CEO)*
Cristina N. Mariani-May *(Co-CEO)*
Marc Goodrich *(COO & Exec VP)*
Lars Leicht *(VP & Dir-Comm)*
Neill Trimble *(VP-Adv)*
Brands & Products:
BORGOGNO
CASTELLO BANFI
CECCHI
CONCHA Y TORO
OLD BROOKVILLE
PLACIDO
PRINCIPESSA GAVI
RIUNITE
SARTORI
STONEHAVEN VINEYARDS
TRIVENTO
VIGNE REGALI
VILLA CERNA
WALNUT CREST
WISDOM & WARTER
Advertising Agencies:
DeVito Fitterman Advertising
151 W 19th St 4th Fl
New York, NY 10011-5511
Tel.: (212) 924-7430
Fax: (212) 924-7946
(Riunite, Concha y Toro, Walnut Crest & Stonehaven Brands)

Villadco Inc.
1111 Cedar Swamp Rd
Glen Head, NY 11545-2109
Tel.: (516) 626-9200
Fax: (516) 626-6282

Vinum Inc.
1111 Cedar Swamp Rd
Glen Head, NY 11545-2109
Tel.: (516) 626-9200
Fax: (516) 626-9218

BEAM GLOBAL SPIRITS & WINE, INC.

(Sub. of Fortune Brands, Inc.)
510 Lake Cook Rd Ste 200
Deerfield, IL 60015
Tel.: (847) 948-8888
Fax: (847) 948-0395
Web Site: www.beamglobal.com
Sales Range: $1-4.9 Billion
Approx. Number Employees: 1,253
Business Description:
Holding Company; Alcoholic Beverages Mfr & Distr
S.I.C.: 6719; 2085; 5182
N.A.I.C.S.: 551112; 312140; 424820
Import Export
Media: 2-3-4-5-6-8-9-10-18-19-20-21-22-25
Distr.: Natl.
Budget Set: Nov.
Personnel:
Matthew J. Shattock *(Pres & CEO)*
Robert Probst *(CFO & Sr VP)*
Bill Newlands *(Pres-North America)*
Kevin George *(Global CMO & Sr VP)*
Mindy Mackenzie *(Sr VP-HR)*
Paula Erickson *(VP-Global Comm & Brand Pub Rels)*
Dana Sacks *(VP-HR)*
Jay Mathew *(Gen Mgr)*
Drew Munro *(Gen Mgr-Bourbons Bus Unit-USA)*
Kelly Doss *(Sr Dir)*
Amy Weisenbach *(Sr Dir)*
David Turo *(Brand Dir-Cruzan Rum)*
Bryan Dixon *(Dir-Art)*
Kevin Smith *(Dir-Bourbon Distillery Ops)*
Antonio Portillo *(Brand Mgr-Tequila 100 Anos)*
Mara Malamed *(Brand Mgr-Smallbatch)*
Dan Cohen *(Mgr-PR-North America)*
Advertising Agencies:
The Champions Ltd.
23 James Boucher blv
1164
Sofia, Bulgaria
Tel.: (359) 2 969 4340
Fax: (359) 2 969 4364

Qorvis Communications
1201 Connecticut Ave NW Ste 500
Washington, DC 20036
Tel.: (202) 496-1000
Fax: (202) 496-1300
— Nicole Chardavoyne *(Acct Exec)*

SHIFT Communications LLC
20 Guest St Ste 200
Brighton, MA 02135
Tel.: (617) 779-1800
Fax: (617) 779-1899

Starcom USA
35 W Wacker Dr
Chicago, IL 60601
Tel.: (312) 220-3535
Fax: (312) 220-6530

StrawberryFrog
60 Madison Ave Ph
New York, NY 10010
Tel.: (212) 366-0500
Jim Beam (Creative Duties)
Jim Beam Black
Red Stag
— Jason Koxvold *(Dir-Creative)*

BIANCHI VINEYARDS

(Div. of Modern Development Company)
3333 W Coast Hwy Ste 400
Newport Beach, CA 92663
Tel.: (949) 646-9100
Fax: (949) 646-1600
E-mail: sales@bianchiwine.com
Web Site: www.bianchiwine.com
Sales Range: $1-9.9 Million
Approx. Number Employees: 50
Year Founded: 1974
Business Description:
Wine Producer, Bottler & Supplier
S.I.C.: 2084; 0172
N.A.I.C.S.: 312130; 111332
Import Export
Media: 2-8-10-19-20-21
Distr.: Natl.
Budget Set: Monthly

BILTMORE ESTATE WINE COMPANY

1 N Pack Sq
Asheville, NC 28801
Tel.: (828) 255-1776
Fax: (828) 255-6392
E-mail: happenings@biltmore.com
Web Site: www.biltmore.com
Sales Range: $10-24.9 Million
Approx. Number Employees: 1,800
Year Founded: 1985
Business Description:
Mfr. of Wines
S.I.C.: 2084
N.A.I.C.S.: 312130
Personnel:
William A.V. Cecil, Jr. *(Pres & CEO)*
Steve Watson *(CFO & Sr VP-Fin & IT)*
Debbie Robinson *(Coord-Mktg)*
Brands & Products:
BLANCS-BRUT
CABERNET FRANC
CARDINAL'S CREST
CHAMPENOISE-BRUT
CHAMPENOISE-SEC
CHARDONNAY SUR LIES
DE NOIR
NOIR BRUT
SPARKLING-SEC
SYRAH
VIOGNIER
Advertising Agency:
The Richards Group, Inc.
8750 N Central Expy Ste 100
Dallas, TX 75231-6430
Tel.: (214) 891-5700
Fax: (214) 265-2933

BOISSET AMERICA

(Sub. of Boisset la Famille des Grands Vins)
2320 Marinship Way Ste 140
Sausalito, CA 94965
Tel.: (415) 289-4500
Fax: (415) 339-0236
Toll Free: (800) 878-1123
E-mail: info@boissetamerica.com
Web Site: www.boissetamerica.com
Approx. Number Employees: 40
Year Founded: 1980
Business Description:
Wine & Spirits Importer & Supplier
S.I.C.: 5182
N.A.I.C.S.: 424820
Import Export
Advertising Expenditures: $1,800,000
Media: 2-4-7-18
Distr.: Natl.
Budget Set: Apr.
Personnel:
Patrick Egan *(Mgr-Mktg)*
Lisa Heisinger *(Mgr)*
Brands & Products:
ASHBOURNE
BASILICA
BATASIOLO
BERGSIG
CASTELLARIN
CHASKA
CHATEAU CLARKE
CHATEAU HAUT CORMEY
CHATEAU LIVERSAN
COLI
COLI CHIANTI
CORTEL
DUC DE VALMER
EL CRUCERO

Key to Media (For complete agency information see *The Advertising Red Books-Agencies* edition):
1. Bus. Publs. 2. Cable T.V. 3. Catalogs & Directories. 4. Co-op Adv. 5. Consumer Mags. 6. D.M. to Bus. Estab.7. D.M. to Consumers 8. Daily Newsp. 9. Exhibits/Trade Shows 10. Foreign 11. Infomercial 12. Internet Adv.13. Multimedia 14. Network Radio 15. Network T.V. 16. Newsp. Distr. Mags. 17. Other 18. Outdoor (Posters, Transit) 19. Point of Purchase20. Premiums, Novelties 21. Product Samples 22. Special Events Mktg. 23. Spot Radio 24. Spot T.V. 25. Weekly Newsp. 26. Yellow Page Adv.

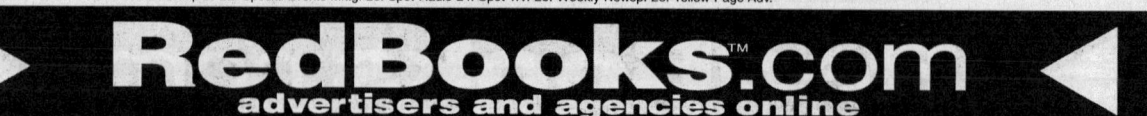

FINDLATERS
G.M. TIDDY'S
GOSLING'S BLACK SEAL
GRANDIN
INCA PISCO
JEAN DANFLOU
JEAN DORSENE
KRIZIA
LA PRISONNIER
LIQUORE
MARIE BRIZARD
MARQUES DEL PUERTO
MELONE
MOHAWK
MOMMESSIN
NEWPORT
NORMANDIN
OLD ST. CROIX
PALANDRI
PINAR DEL RIO XO
PRINCE DE CONDE
PUERTO NUEVO
RAINBOW SPIRITS
ROSITA
TOMINTOUL
VEUVE DU VERNAY
VILLA ABA

BRANDY PEAK DISTILLERY
18526 Tetley Rd
Brookings, OR 97415
Tel.: (541) 469-0194
Fax: (541) 469-0194
Web Site: www.brandypeak.com
Business Description:
Distillery
S.I.C.: 2085; 5182
N.A.I.C.S.: 312140; 424820
Advertising Expenditures: $25,000
Media: 4-13-21-22
Personnel:
David Nowlin *(Pres)*
Brands & Products:
BRANDY PEAK
GEWURZTRAMINER
MARC

BROWN-FORMAN BEVERAGES
(Div. of Brown-Forman Corporation)
850 Dixie Hwy
Louisville, KY 40210-1038
Mailing Address:
PO Box 1080
Louisville, KY 40201-1080
Tel.: (502) 585-1100
Fax: (502) 774-6633
Web Site: www.brown-forman.com
Sales Range: $750-799.9 Million
Approx. Number Employees: 3,000
Year Founded: 1870
Business Description:
Distilled Spirits & Wines
S.I.C.: 2085; 2084
N.A.I.C.S.: 312140; 312130
Import Export
Media: 2-6-9-10-14-15-18-19-20-23-24
Distr.: Natl.
Budget Set: Dec. -Apr.
Personnel:
Julie Lynn York *(Partner-Mktg, Head-Strategic & Promo)*
Laura Webb *(Brand Dir-Chambord)*
Advertising Agencies:
Arnold Worldwide
101 Huntington Ave
Boston, MA 02199-7603
Tel.: (617) 587-8000
Fax: (617) 587-8004
(Southern Comfort)

Brown-Forman Media Services/B-F Advertising
3310 W End Ave Ste 600
Nashville, TN 37203-1058
Tel.: (615) 279-4169
Fax: (615) 279-7225
(Media Placement)

Dye, Van Mol & Lawrence
209 7th Ave N
Nashville, TN 37219-1802
Tel.: (615) 244-1818
Fax: (615) 780-3301

Northlich Public Relations
720 E Pete Rose Way Ste 120
Cincinnati, OH 45202-3579
Tel.: (513) 421-8840
Fax: (513) 287-1858

PriceWeber Marketing Communications, Inc.
10701 Shelbyville Rd
Louisville, KY 40243
Tel.: (502) 499-9220
Fax: (502) 491-5593
(Korbel Champagne, Bolla Wine, & Early Times Kentucky Whiskey)

Universal McCann
100 33rd St 8th Fl
New York, NY 10001
Tel.: (212) 883-4700

BROWN-FORMAN CORPORATION
850 Dixie Hwy
Louisville, KY 40210-1038
Mailing Address:
PO Box 1080
Louisville, KY 40201-1080
Tel.: (502) 585-1100
Fax: (502) 774-7876
E-mail: Investor_Relations@b-f.com
Web Site: www.brown-forman.com
Approx. Sls.: $3,404,000,000
Approx. Number Employees: 3,700
Year Founded: 1870
Business Description:
Holding Company; Alcoholic Beverages
S.I.C.: 6719; 2084; 2085; 5182
N.A.I.C.S.: 551112; 312130; 312140; 424820
Import Export
Advertising Expenditures: $366,000,000
Media: 8-13
Distr.: Intl.; Natl.
Personnel:
Paul C. Varga *(Co-Chm & CEO)*
George Garvin Brown, IV *(Co-Chm & VP)*
James S. Welch, Jr. *(Vice Chm)*
Donald Berg *(CFO & Exec VP)*
Mark I. McCallum *(COO & Exec VP)*
T. J. Graven *(CIO & VP)*
John Kristin Sirchio *(CMO & Exec VP)*
Jill Jones *(Chief Production Officer & Sr VP)*
Ralph de Chabert *(Chief Diversity Officer)*
Michael J. Keyes *(Pres-North America)*
Matthew E. Hamel *(Gen Counsel, Sec & Exec VP)*
Jane C. Morreau *(Sr VP & Dir-Fin, Acctg & Tech)*
Phil Lichtenfels *(Sr VP)*
James A. O'Malley *(Sr VP-Global Corp Affairs)*
Lisa Steiner *(Sr VP-Global HR)*
Philip J. Lynch *(VP & Dir-Corp Comm)*
Ben Marmor *(Asst VP & Dir-IR)*
Lena DerOhannessian *(Dir-Mktg-Southern Comfort-US)*
Jason Kempf *(Assoc Dir-Global Mktg)*
Laura Petry *(Brand Mgr)*
Brands & Products:
ANTIGUO
ARDBEG
BEL ARBOR
BOLLA
BONTERRA VINEYARDS
BROWN-FOREMAN
CANADIAN MIST
CASA HERRADURA
CHAMBORD
CHAMBORD VODKA
DON EDUARDO
EARLY TIMES BOURBON
EARLY TIMES KENTUCKY WHISKY
EL JIMADOR
ELEVEN TONGUES
FETZER
FINLANDIA
FINLANDIA VODKA
FIVE RIVERS
FONTANA CANDIDA
GALA ROUGE
GENTLEMAN JACK
GLENMORANGIE
HARTMANN
HERRADURA
JACK DANIEL'S
JACK DANIEL'S COUNTRY COCKTAILS
JACK DANIEL'S SINGLE BARREL TENNESSEE WHISKEY
JACK DANIEL'S TENNESSEE WHISKEY
JACK DANIEL?S READY-TO-DRINKS
JACK DANIEL?S TENNESSEE HONEY
JEKEL
JEKEL VINEYARDS
KORBEL
LITTLE BLACK DRESS
MARIAH
MICHEL PICARD
NEW MIX READY TO DRINKS
NOILLY PRAT
OLD FORESTER
PEPE LOPEZ
SANCTUARY
SONOMA-CUTRER
SOUTHERN COMFORT
SOUTHERN COMFORT LIME
SOUTHERN COMFORT READY-TO-DRINKS
SOUTHERN COMFORT READY-TO-POURS
STELLAR
TUACA
VIRGIN VINES
WAKEFIELD
WOODFORD RESERVE
Advertising Agencies:
Arnold Worldwide
101 Huntington Ave
Boston, MA 02199-7603
Tel.: (617) 587-8000
Fax: (617) 587-8004
(Southern Comfort)

Boxing Clever
3116 Locust St
Saint Louis, MO 63103
Tel.: (314) 446-1861
Finlandia Vodka

Brown-Forman Media Services/B-F Advertising
3310 W End Ave Ste 600
Nashville, TN 37203-1058
Tel.: (615) 279-4169
Fax: (615) 279-7225
(Corporate Advertising)

Draftfcb
101 E Erie St
Chicago, IL 60611
Tel.: (312) 425-5000
Fax: (312) 425-5010

Heckart Studios
9320 Wilshire Blvd
Beverly Hills, CA 90212
Tel.: (310) 247-0079
Fax: (310) 247-4563

KYK Advertising Marketing Promotions
2600 Constant Comment Pl
Louisville, KY 40299
Tel.: (502) 636-0288
Fax: (502) 636-0635
Toll Free: (800) 531-6999

PriceWeber Marketing Communications, Inc.
10701 Shelbyville Rd
Louisville, KY 40243
Tel.: (502) 499-9220
Fax: (502) 491-5593
(Canadian Mist, Early Times, Old Forrester, Usher's Scotch, Finlandia & Bolla)

Red Moon Marketing
4100 Coca-Cola Plz Ste 215
Charlotte, NC 28211
Tel.: (704) 366-1147
Fax: (704) 366-2283

TracyLocke
1999 Bryan St Ste 2800
Dallas, TX 75201
Tel.: (214) 259-3500
Fax: (214) 259-3550
Southern Comfort

BUENA VISTA CARNEROS WINERY INC.
(Sub. of Eight Estates Fine Wines LLC)
27000 Ramal Rd
Sonoma, CA 95476-9791
Mailing Address:
PO Box 182
Sonoma, CA 95476-0182
Tel.: (707) 252-7117
Fax: (707) 252-0392
Toll Free: (800) 678-8504
Web Site: www.buenavistawinery.com
Approx. Number Employees: 102
Year Founded: 1857
Business Description:
Wine Producer
S.I.C.: 2084; 5182

Key to Media (For complete agency information see *The Advertising Red Books-Agencies* edition):
1. Bus. Publs. 2. Cable T.V. 3. Catalogs & Directories. 4. Co-op Adv. 5. Consumer Mags. 6. D.M. to Bus. Estab.7. D.M. to Consumers
8. Daily Newsp. 9. Exhibits/Trade Shows 10. Foreign 11. Infomercial 12. Internet Adv.13. Multimedia 14. Network Radio
15. Network T.V. 16. Newsp. Distr. Mags. 17. Other 18. Outdoor (Posters, Transit) 19. Point of Purchase20. Premiums, Novelties
21. Product Samples 22. Special Events Mktg. 23. Spot Radio 24. Spot T.V. 25. Weekly Newsp. 26. Yellow Page Adv.

Buena Vista Carneros Winery Inc. — (Continued)

N.A.I.C.S.: 312130; 424820
Import Export
Media: 2-4-6-10-18-19-21-22
Distr.: Intl.; Natl.

CALLAWAY VINEYARD & WINERY
(Sub. of Callaway Temecula Limited Partnership)
32720 Rancho California Rd
Temecula, CA 92591
Tel.: (951) 676-4001
Fax: (951) 676-5209
Toll Free: (800) 472-2377
E-mail: info@callawaywinery.com
Web Site: www.callawaywinery.com
Approx. Number Employees: 75
Year Founded: 1969
Business Description:
Vineyard & Winery
S.I.C.: 0172; 2084
N.A.I.C.S.: 111332; 312130
Media: 4-10-18-21
Distr.: Intl.; Natl.
Personnel:
Peter Chang *(Gen Mgr)*
Brands & Products:
CALLAWAY COASTAL

CAMERON HUGHES WINE
444 De Haro St Ste 101
San Francisco, CA 94107-2349
Tel.: (415) 495-1350
E-mail: info@chwine.com
Web Site: www.chwine.com
Business Description:
Winery
S.I.C.: 2084
N.A.I.C.S.: 312130
Media: 22
Personnel:
Cameron Hughes *(Founder & CEO)*
Jessica Kogan *(Founder & CMO)*
Jay Conway *(Partner & EVP-Sls)*
Doug Rogers *(COO)*

CENTERRA WINE COMPANY
(Div. of Constellation Wines US)
116 Buffalo St
Canandaigua, NY 14424-1059
Tel.: (585) 396-7600
Fax: (585) 396-7833
Toll Free: (888) 659-7900
Web Site: www.cwine.com
Sales Range: $800-899.9 Million
Approx. Number Employees: 2,100
Year Founded: 1945
Business Description:
Sparkling Wines & Related Beverages
Mfr, Markets & Sales
S.I.C.: 2084
N.A.I.C.S.: 312130
Export
Advertising Expenditures: $3,000,000
Media: 2-6-15-19
Distr.: Intl.; Natl.
Personnel:
Oren Lewin *(Sr VP-Mktg)*
Angie Blackwell *(VP-Corp Commun)*
Mark Gabrielli *(VP-Winemaking & Production)*
Brands & Products:
CALIFORNIA CELLARS OF CHASE-LIMOGERE
CISCO
COOK'S AMERICAN CHAMPAGNE
COOK'S CAPTAIN'S RESERVE
COVEY RUN
CRIBARI
DUNNEWOOD VINEYARDS & WINERY
INGLENOOK
JACQUE BONET
K CIDER
LA TERRE
LE DOMAINE CHAMPAGNE
PAUL THOMAS
TAYLOR
VSOP
WILD IRISH ROSE

CHATEAU ST. JEAN WINERY
(Sub. of Treasury Wine Estates)
8555 Sonoma Hwy
Kenwood, CA 95452-0293
Mailing Address:
PO Box 293
Kenwood, CA 95452
Tel.: (707) 833-4134
Fax: (707) 833-4200
Toll Free: (877) 4ST-JEAN
E-mail: csjstore@chateaustjean.com
Web Site: www.chateaustjean.com
Approx. Number Employees: 70
Year Founded: 1973
Business Description:
Produces & Markets California Wines
S.I.C.: 2084; 0172
N.A.I.C.S.: 312130; 111332
Advertising Expenditures: $1,500,000
Media: 19-21
Distr.: Intl.; Natl.
Personnel:
Carrie Reed *(Dir-Brand)*
Brands & Products:
CHATEAU ST. JEAN

CONSTELLATION BRANDS, INC.
207 High Point Dr Bldg 100
Victor, NY 14564
Tel.: (585) 678-7100
Fax: (585) 678-7103
E-mail: bob.czudak@cbrands.com
Web Site: www.cbrands.com
Approx. Sls.: $4,096,700,000
Approx. Number Employees: 4,300
Year Founded: 1945
Business Description:
Wine, Spirits & Imported Beer Marketing & Distr
S.I.C.: 2084; 8742
N.A.I.C.S.: 312130; 541614
Import Export
Advertising Expenditures: $128,600,000
Media: 2-17-19-20-22
Distr.: Natl.
Personnel:
Richard Sands *(Chm)*
Robert S. Sands *(Pres & CEO)*
Robert P. Ryder *(CFO & Exec VP)*
Harish Ramani *(CIO)*
W. Keith Wilson *(Chief HR Officer, Chief Admin Officer & Exec VP)*
Martin Birkel *(Pres-Sls)*
Jay Wright *(Pres-Constellation Wines North America)*
Thomas J. Mullin *(Gen Counsel & Exec VP)*
F. Paul Hetterich *(Exec VP-Bus Dev & Strategy)*
James P. Finkle *(Sr VP-External Affairs)*
Cheryl Gossin *(VP Corp Commun)*
Angie Blackwell *(Dir-Corp Comm)*
Bob Czudak *(Dir-IR)*
Genevieve Janssens *(Dir-Winemaking)*
Eric Thomas *(Mgr-Corp Comm)*
Mikaela Sullivan *(Asst Mgr-Mktg)*
Brands & Products:
ALMADEN
BALBLAIR
CONSTELLATION
DUNNEWOOD
FOUR EMUS
KELLYS REVENGE
SCHENLEY RESERVE
Advertising Agencies:
AGENCYSACKS
345 7th Ave 7th Fl
New York, NY 10001-5006
Tel.: (212) 826-4004
Fax: (212) 593-7824

Butler, Shine, Stern & Partners
20 Liberty Ship Way
Sausalito, CA 94965-3312
Tel.: (415) 331-6049
Fax: (415) 331-3524
Blackstone Wine
Communications Strategy

Butler/Till Media Services, Inc.
2349 Monroe Ave
Rochester, NY 14618
Tel.: (585) 473-3740
Fax: (585) 473-3862

Mason Selkowitz Marketing, Inc
400 Whitney Rd
Penfield, NY 14526
Tel.: (585) 249-1100
Fax: (585) 249-1060

Partners+Napier
192 Mill St Ste 600
Rochester, NY 14614-1022
Tel.: (585) 454-1010
Fax: (585) 454-1575
Toll Free: (800) 274-4954

CONSTELLATION WINES US
(Div. of Constellation Brands, Inc.)
235 N Bloomfield Rd
Canandaigua, NY 14424
Tel.: (585) 396-7600
Fax: (585) 396-7833
Web Site: www.cwine.com
Sales Range: $100-124.9 Million
Approx. Number Employees: 250
Business Description:
Wine Mfr
S.I.C.: 2084
N.A.I.C.S.: 312130
Personnel:
Jay Wright *(Pres)*
Tim Richenberg *(Sr VP-Sls)*
Jon Guggino *(VP-Mktg)*
Advertising Agency:
Partners & Napier
192 Mill St Ste 600
Rochester, NY 14614
Tel.: (585) 454-1010
Fax: (585) 454-1575
Toll Free: (800) 274-4954

CORBY DISTILLERIES LTD.
(Sub. of Pernod Ricard S.A.)
225 Kings Street West Suite 1100
Toronto, ON M5B 3M2, Canada
Tel.: (416) 369-1859
Fax: (416) 369-9809
Fax: (416) 369-9537
Web Site: www.corby.ca
Approx. Sls.: $143,910,979
Approx. Number Employees: 212
Year Founded: 1859
Business Description:
Mfr. & Marketer of Spirits
S.I.C.: 2085
N.A.I.C.S.: 312140
Media: 6-15
Personnel:
George McCarthy *(Chm)*
Patrick O'Driscoll *(Pres & CEO)*
Thierry Pourchet *(CFO & VP-Fin)*
Mark Valencia *(VP, Gen Counsel, Sec & Chief Privacy Officer)*
Jeff Agdern *(VP-Mktg)*
Andrew Alexander *(VP-Sls)*
Paul Holub *(VP-HR)*
Jim Stanski *(VP-Production)*
Brands & Products:
LAMB'S NAVY
LAMB'S PALM BREEZE
LAMB'S WHITE
WISER'S
WISER'S DE LUXE
WISER'S SPECIAL BLEND
WISER'S VERY OLD

DELICATO VINEYARDS
455 Devlin Rd Ste 201
Napa, CA 94558
Tel.: (707) 265-1700
Fax: (707) 265-7837
Toll Free: (877) 824-3600
E-mail: info@delicato.com
Web Site: www.delicato.com
Approx. Number Employees: 330
Year Founded: 1924
Business Description:
Winery & Vineyards
S.I.C.: 0172
N.A.I.C.S.: 111332
Import Export
Advertising Expenditures: $660,000
Catalogs & Directories: $10,000; Consumer Mags.: $175,000; Daily Newsp.: $20,000; Outdoor (Posters, Transit): $50,000; Point of Purchase: $300,000; Premiums, Novelties: $10,000; Product Samples: $10,000; Special Events Mktg.: $40,000; Spot Radio: $40,000; Yellow Page Adv.: $5,000
Distr.: Intl.; Natl.
Budget Set: Nov.
Personnel:
Vincent Indelicato *(Chm)*
Don Allen *(CFO)*
Rita Graham *(CIO)*
Jay Indelicato *(Sr VP-Opers)*
Mike Jackson *(Sr VP-Sls-Natl)*
Lillian Bynum *(VP-HR)*
David DeBoer *(VP-Intl Sls)*
Brands & Products:
DELICATO
DELICATO FAMILY VINEYARDS
DELICATO SHIRAZ

DIAGEO CANADA, INC.
(Sub. of Diageo plc)
401 The W Mall Ste 800

Key to Media (For complete agency information see *The Advertising Red Books-Agencies* edition):
1. Bus. Publs. 2. Cable T.V. 3. Catalogs & Directories. 4. Co-op Adv. 5. Consumer Mags. 6. D.M. to Bus. Estab.7. D.M. to Consumers 8. Daily Newsp. 9. Exhibits/Trade Shows 10. Foreign 11. Infomercial 12. Internet Adv.13. Multimedia 14. Network Radio 15. Network T.V. 16. Newsp. Distr. Mags. 17. Other 18. Outdoor (Posters, Transit) 19. Point of Purchase20. Premiums, Novelties 21. Product Samples 22. Special Events Mktg. 23. Spot Radio 24. Spot T.V. 25. Weekly Newsp. 26. Yellow Page Adv.

Toronto, ON M9C 5P8, Canada
Tel.: (416) 626-2000
Fax: (416) 626-2688
E-mail: info@diageo.com
Web Site: www.diageo.com
Sales Range: $150-199.9 Million
Approx. Number Employees: 1,400
Year Founded: 1928
Business Description:
Distilled Spirits & Wines, Fruit Juices & Juice Beverages Mfr & Marketer
S.I.C.: 2084
N.A.I.C.S.: 312130
Export
Media: 2-6-8-9-11-13-18-25
Distr.: Intl.
Budget Set: Jan. -June
Personnel:
Debra J. Kelly-Ennis *(Pres & CEO)*
Dominic Dellapena *(VP-Fin)*
David Allard *(Dir-Mktg)*
Brands & Products:
7 CROWN
B&G
BOODLES BRITISH GIN
BURNETTS
CROWN ROYAL
CROWN ROYAL RESERVE
FOUR ROSES
THE GLENLIVET
GODIVA LIQUEUR
GROLSCH PREMIUM DUTCH
MACIEIRA
MUMM VSOP COGNAC
MYER'S GOLDEN RICH
MYER'S ORIGINAL DARK
MYER'S PLATINUM WHITE
PASSPORT
QUEEN ANNE
RON LLAVE
ROYAL PAISLEY
ROYAL SALUTE
SABRA
SOMETHING SPECIAL
STERLING VINEYARDS
VO
Advertising Agencies:
Grey Canada
1881 Yonge St Ste 800
Toronto, ON M4S 3C4, Canada
Tel.: (416) 486-0700
Fax: (416) 486-8907

Smith Roberts & Co.
55 Mill St Bldg #36 Ste 200
Toronto, ON M5A 3C4, Canada
Tel.: (416) 364-0797
Fax: (416) 364-8410

Strategic Objectives
184 Front Street E 4th Floor
Toronto, ON M5A 4N3, Canada
Tel.: (416) 366-7735
Fax: (416) 366-2295

DIAGEO NORTH AMERICA, INC.

(Sub. of Diageo plc)
801 Main Ave
Norwalk, CT 06851
Tel.: (203) 229-2100
Fax: (203) 229-8901
Web Site: www.diageo.com
Sales Range: $1-4.9 Billion
Approx. Number Employees: 1,000
Year Founded: 1875
Business Description:
Spirits & Wines Producer, Importer & Marketer
S.I.C.: 5182; 2085
N.A.I.C.S.: 424820; 312140
Import Export
Media: 6-9-18-19-20-22
Distr.: Intl.; Natl.
Personnel:
Peter McDonough *(Pres & Chief Mktg & Innovation Officer)*
Jon Potter *(CMO-North America)*
Ivan M. Menezes *(Pres-North America & Chm-Asia Pacific, Diageo plc)*
Pete Carr *(Pres-Sls-USA)*
Maggie Lapcewich *(Pres-Global Tequilas)*
Sheila Stanziale *(Pres-Diageo-Guinness USA)*
Guy L. Smith *(Exec VP)*
Mark Hubler *(Sr VP & Gen Mgr)*
Steve Wallet *(VP-Channel Mktg)*
Patrick Hughes *(Brand Dir-Guinness USA)*
Brian Radics *(Brand Dir-Jose Cuervo)*
David Tapscott *(Brand Dir-Smirnoff Vodka)*
Manny Gonzalez *(Sr Mgr-Brand & Scotch)*
Ingrid Bekkers *(Mgr-Guinness Brand)*
Brands & Products:
BEAULIEU VINEYARD WINES
BLOSSOM HILL
THE CLUB COCKTAILS
COCKTAILS FOR TWO
GLEN ELLEN WINES
HEUBLEIN COCKTAILS
JOSE CUERVO PLATINO
LANCERS WINES
MOUTON-CADET WINES
POPOV VODKA
RELSKA VODKA
SMIRNOFF
SMIRNOFF BLACK
SMIRNOFF CITRUS TWIST
T.G.I. FRIDAY'S FROZEN COCKTAILS
YUKON JACK CANADIAN LIQUEUR
Advertising Agencies:
AKQA, Inc.
118 King St 6th Fl
San Francisco, CA 94107
Tel.: (415) 645-9400
Fax: (415) 645-9420

Anomaly Communications LLC
536 Broadway 11th Fl
New York, NY 10012
Tel.: (917) 595-2200
Fax: (917) 595-2299
Captain Morgan

Arc Worldwide
(Sub. of Publicis Groupe S.A.)
35 W Wacker Dr 15th Fl
Chicago, IL 60601
Tel.: (312) 220-3200
Fax: (312) 220-1995

BBDO New York
1285 Ave of the Americas 7th Fl
New York, NY 10019-6028
Tel.: (212) 459-5000
Bold
Guinness Draft
Harp Lager
Red Stripe
Smithwicks

Carat
150 E 42nd St
New York, NY 10017
Tel.: (212) 689-6800
Fax: (212) 689-6005
Smirnoff, Johnnie Walker, Baileys, J&B and Guinness.

MediaCom
498 7th Ave
New York, NY 10018
Tel.: (212) 912-4200
Fax: (212) 508-4386

MRM Worldwide
622 3rd Ave
New York, NY 10017-6707
Tel.: (646) 865-6230
Fax: (646) 865-6264
Bulleit, Captain Morgan, Crown Royal, Jose Cuervo, Smirnoff, Zacapa

The Vidal Partnership
228 E 45th St 11th Fl
New York, NY 10017-3303
Tel.: (646) 356-6600
Fax: (212) 661-7650

DISTILLERIE STOCK USA LTD.

(Sub. of Stock Spirits Group Limited)
58-58 Laurel Hill Blvd
Woodside, NY 11377
Tel.: (718) 651-9800
Fax: (718) 651-7806
Toll Free: (800) 323-1884
E-mail: info@stockusaltd.com
Web Site: www.grangala.com
Sales Range: $1-9.9 Million
Approx. Number Employees: 35
Year Founded: 1884
Business Description:
Mfr. & Importer of Liqueurs & Wines
S.I.C.: 5182
N.A.I.C.S.: 424820
Import
Advertising Expenditures: $500,000
Media: 6-7-8-9-13-19-20-23-25
Distr.: Natl.
Personnel:
David J. Morel *(Pres)*
Brands & Products:
AMARETTO DEL L'ORSO
BORA SAMBUCA
CHERRISTOCK
GRANGALA
GRAPPA JULIA
KEGLEVICH LIQUEUR & VODKA
MOREL
ROIAND LIQUORE
ROYAL STOCK
STOCK
STOCK 84
STOCK ASTI SPUMANTE
STOCK SWEET, DRY, BIANCO

DOMAINE CHANDON, INC.

(Sub. of Moet-Hennessy SNC)
One California Dr
Yountville, CA 94599
Tel.: (707) 944-8844
Fax: (707) 944-1123
Web Site: www.chandon.com
Approx. Number Employees: 100
Business Description:
Mfr. of Wines & Champagnes
S.I.C.: 5812; 2084
N.A.I.C.S.: 722110; 312130
Personnel:
Malcolm Dunbar *(Pres & CEO)*
Michael Stedman *(Dir-Bus Dev)*
Brands & Products:
DOMAIN CHANDON
ETOILE
ETOILE ROSE
Advertising Agencies:
Dentsu America, Inc.
32 Ave of the Americas 16th Fl
New York, NY 10013
Tel.: (212) 397-3333
Fax: (212) 397-3322

MediaCom Los Angeles
3500 W Olive Ave Ste 800
Burbank, CA 91505
Tel.: (818) 525-3000
Fax: (818) 525-3050

THE DONUM ESTATE, INC

(Sub. of A. Racke GmbH)
PO Box 154
Sonoma, CA 95476-0154
Tel.: (707) 939-2290
Fax: (707) 939-0651
Toll Free: (800) 678-8504
E-mail: info@thedonumestate.com
Web Site: www.thedonumestate.com
Approx. Number Employees: 14
Year Founded: 1930
Business Description:
Premium Wines Producer
S.I.C.: 2084
N.A.I.C.S.: 312130
Import Export
Media: 10
Distr.: Natl.
Personnel:
Anne Moller-Racke *(Pres)*
Brands & Products:
PIONERO
ROBERT STEMMLER
VIALA

DREYFUS ASHBY INC.

630 3rd Ave 15th Fl
New York, NY 10017
Tel.: (212) 818-0770
Fax: (212) 953-2366
E-mail: info@dreyfusashby.com
Web Site: www.dreyfusashby.com
Approx. Number Employees: 35
Year Founded: 1957
Business Description:
Wines & Spirits Importer
S.I.C.: 5182
N.A.I.C.S.: 424820
Import
Advertising Expenditures: $100,000
Media: 4-6-10-19-20
Distr.: Natl.
Personnel:
Christopher Ryan *(Pres & CEO)*
Brands & Products:
A. MELLOT
BOLLINGER
CHATEAU LOUDENNE
DREYFUS ASHBY
DROUHIN
GILBEY DE LOUDENNE
GILLIARD
HAKUTSURU
LA COUR PAVILLON
MASSENEZ
MOUEIX

Key to Media (For complete agency information see *The Advertising Red Books-Agencies* edition):
1. Bus. Publs. 2. Cable T.V. 3. Catalogs & Directories. 4. Co-op Adv. 5. Consumer Mags. 6. D.M. to Bus. Estab.7. D.M. to Consumers 8. Daily Newsp. 9. Exhibits/Trade Shows 10. Foreign 11. Infomercial 12. Internet Adv.13. Multimedia 14. Network Radio 15. Network T.V. 16. Newsp. Distr. Mags. 17. Other 18. Outdoor (Posters, Transit) 19. Point of Purchase20. Premiums, Novelties 21. Product Samples 22. Special Events Mktg. 23. Spot Radio 24. Spot T.V. 25. Weekly Newsp. 26. Yellow Page Adv.

Dreyfus Ashby Inc. — (Continued)

NAPA VALLEY
NEDERBURG
SAUTEJEAU
ZONNEBLOEM

E&J GALLO WINERY
600 Yosemite Blvd
Modesto, CA 95354-2760
Mailing Address:
PO Box 1130
Modesto, CA 95353-1130
Tel.: (209) 341-3111
Fax: (209) 341-8861
Toll Free: (877) 687-9463
E-mail: webmaster@ejgallo.com
Web Site: www.gallo.com
Approx. Number Employees: 5,000
Year Founded: 1933
Business Description:
Wine & Wine Products Producer & Distr
S.I.C.: 2084; 3221
N.A.I.C.S.: 312130; 327213
Import Export
Media: 2-4-9-13-17-18-21-23-24
Distr.: Intl.; Natl.
Budget Set: June
Personnel:
George Marsden *(VP & Gen Mgr-Europe)*
Stephanie Gallo *(Dir-Mktg)*
Brands & Products:
ALCOTT RIDGE
ANAPAMU
ANDRE
BALLATORE
BARTLES & JAYMES
BELLA SERA
BLACK SWAN
BOONE'S FARM
BRIDLEWOOD
CARLO ROSSI
CASK & CREAM
DANCING BULL
E&J BRANDY
E. & J. GALLO WINERY
ECCO DOMANI
FREI BROTHERS
GALLO OF SONOMA
GOSSAMER BAY
HORNSBY'S
INDIGO HILLS
LIVINGSTON CELLARS
LOUIS M. MARTINI
MACMURRAY RANCH
MARCELINA
MASO CANALI
MIRASSOU
PETER VELLA
RANCHO ZABACO
RED BICYCLETTE
RED ROCK WINERY
REDWOOD CREEK
SEBEKA
SHEFFIELD CELLARS
THUNDERBIRD
TOTT'S
TURNING LEAF
WHITEHAVEN
WILD VINES
Advertising Agencies:
BBDO West
555 Market St 17th Fl
San Francisco, CA 94105
Tel.: (415) 808-6200
Fax: (415) 808-6221

Centra360
1400 Old Country Rd Ste 420
Westbury, NY 11590-5119
Tel.: (516) 997-3147
Fax: (516) 334-7798

DeVries Public Relations
30 E 60th St 14th Fl
New York, NY 10022
Tel.: (212) 891-0400
Fax: (212) 644-0291

F. KORBEL BROS. INC.
13250 River Rd
Guerneville, CA 95446-9593
Tel.: (707) 824-7000
Fax: (707) 869-2981
Toll Free: (800) 656-7235
E-mail: info@korbel.com
Web Site: www.korbel.com
E-Mail For Key Personnel:
Public Relations: mhealy@Korbel.com
Approx. Number Employees: 537
Year Founded: 1882
Business Description:
Champagne Mfr; Winery
S.I.C.: 0172; 2084
N.A.I.C.S.: 111332; 312130
Export
Advertising Expenditures: $5,000,000
Media: 6-10-13-15-18-19-20
Distr.: Direct to Consumer; Intl.; Natl.; Reg.
Personnel:
Gary B. Heck *(Chm, Pres & CEO)*
Dan Baker *(Exec VP)*
Harold Duncan *(Sr VP-Ops)*
Matt Healey *(VP-Fin)*
Margie Healy *(Dir-PR)*
Melvin J. Sanchietti *(Vineyard Mgr)*
Brands & Products:
KORBEL
KORBEL BLANC DE NOIRS
KORBEL BRUT
KORBEL BRUT ROSE
KORBEL CHARDONNAY
KORBEL EXTRA DRY
KORBEL MOSCATO FRIZZANTE
KORBEL SEC
KORBEL.COM
TURNING MOMENTS INTO MEMORIES SINCE 1882
Advertising Agency:
Heckart Studios
9320 Wilshire Blvd
Beverly Hills, CA 90212
Tel.: (310) 247-0079
Fax: (310) 247-4563

FETZER VINEYARDS
(Sub. of Vina Concha y Toro S.A.)
12901 Old River Rd
Hopland, CA 95449
Mailing Address:
PO Box 611
Hopland, CA 95449-0611
Tel.: (707) 744-7600
Fax: (707) 744-7605
Toll Free: (800) 846-8637
Web Site: www.fetzer.com
Sales Range: $125-149.9 Million
Approx. Number Employees: 300
Year Founded: 1968
Business Description:
Wine Producer
S.I.C.: 2084
N.A.I.C.S.: 312130
Media: 6
Personnel:
Barry Marek *(MD-Sales, Customer Mktg & Strategic Planning)*
Dennis Martin *(VP & Dir-Winemaking)*
Brands & Products:
VALLEY OAKS
Advertising Agency:
Red Moon Marketing
4100 Coca-Cola Plz Ste 215
Charlotte, NC 28211
Tel.: (704) 366-1147
Fax: (704) 366-2283

FLANIGAN'S ENTERPRISES, INC.
5059 NE 18th Ave
Fort Lauderdale, FL 33334-5724
Tel.: (954) 377-1961
Fax: (954) 351-1245
Web Site: www.flanigans.net
Approx. Rev.: $69,993,000
Approx. Number Employees: 750
Year Founded: 1959
Business Description:
Restaurant Owner & Operator
S.I.C.: 5812; 5921
N.A.I.C.S.: 722110; 445310
Advertising Expenditures: $465,000
Media: 3-8-13-18-24-26
Personnel:
Jeffrey D. Kastner *(CFO, Gen Counsel & Sec)*
August Bucci *(COO & Exec VP)*
James G. Flanigan, II *(Compliance Officer)*
Dwight Rowe *(Dir-MIS)*
Brands & Products:
BIG DADDY'S
FLANIGAN'S
SEAFOOD BAR & GRILL
Advertising Agency:
Lipof Advertising
830 Peters Rd Ste D100
Plantation, FL 33324
Tel.: (954) 472-9999
Fax: (954) 472-1222

FOSTER'S WINE ESTATES
(Name Changed to Treasury Wine Estates)

FREDERICK WILDMAN & SONS LTD.
(Holding of Gruppo Italiano Vini S.p.A.)
307 E 53rd St
New York, NY 10022-4985
Tel.: (212) 355-0700
Fax: (212) 355-4719
Toll Free: (800) RED-WINE
E-mail: info@frederickwildman.com
Web Site: www.frederickwildman.com
Approx. Number Employees: 75
Year Founded: 1967
Business Description:
French & Italian Wines Importer
S.I.C.: 5182
N.A.I.C.S.: 424820
Import
Advertising Expenditures: $1,000,000
Media: 4-8-9-10-19
Distr.: Natl.
Budget Set: Aug.
Personnel:
Richard Cacciato *(Pres & CEO)*
Rocco Lombardo *(COO & Sr VP)*
John Celler *(VP-Supplier Relations & Coord-Pricing)*
Tim Master *(Dir-Specialty Spirits & Trade Education)*
Christine Khawam *(Brand Mgr)*
Caterina Hausmann *(Brand Mgr)*
Advertising Agency:
Lisa Lori Communications
121 E 1st St Ste 2
New York, NY 10009
Tel.: (212) 925-2300
Fax: (212) 925-5624

FREIXENET U.S.A.
(Sub. of Freixenet S.A.)
23555 Hwy 121
Sonoma, CA 95476-9285
Mailing Address:
PO Box 1949
Sonoma, CA 95476-1949
Tel.: (707) 996-4981
Fax: (707) 996-0720
E-mail: info@freixenetusa.com
Web Site: www.freixenetusa.com
Approx. Number Employees: 100
Year Founded: 1979
Business Description:
Wines, Sparkling Wines & Champagnes
S.I.C.: 5182
N.A.I.C.S.: 424820
Import
Advertising Expenditures: $6,000,000
Media: 5-6-10-19-23
Distr.: Natl.
Personnel:
David Brown *(VP & Dir-Mktg)*
Advertising Agency:
Cuvee Advertising
23555 Carneros Hwy 121
Sonoma, CA 95476-9285
Tel.: (707) 996-4981
Fax: (707) 996-0720

GARY'S WINE & MARKETPLACE
121 Main St
Madison, NJ 07940-2115
Tel.: (973) 822-0200
Fax: (973) 822-3556
E-mail: info@garyswine.com
Web Site: www.garyswine.com
Approx. Number Employees: 200
Year Founded: 1995
Business Description:
Wine Retailer
S.I.C.: 5921
N.A.I.C.S.: 445310
Advertising Expenditures: $500,000
Media: 13-26
Personnel:
Gary Fisch *(Owner)*

GEYSER PEAK WINERY
(Sub. of Eight Estates Fine Wines LLC)
PO Box 25 22281 Chianti Road
Geyserville, CA 95441
Mailing Address:
PO Box 25
Geyserville, CA 95441-0025
Tel.: (707) 857-2500
Fax: (707) 857-9401
Toll Free: (800) 255-WINE
E-mail: wineclub@geyserpeakwinery.com
Web Site:
www.geyserpeakwinery.com

Key to Media (For complete agency information see *The Advertising Red Books-Agencies* edition):
1. Bus. Publs. 2. Cable T.V. 3. Catalogs & Directories. 4. Co-op Adv. 5. Consumer Mags. 6. D.M. to Bus. Estab.7. D.M. to Consumers
8. Daily Newsp. 9. Exhibits/Trade Shows 10. Foreign 11. Infomercial 12. Internet Adv.13. Multimedia 14. Network Radio
15. Network T.V. 16. Newsp. Distr. Mags. 17. Other 18. Outdoor (Posters, Transit) 19. Point of Purchase20. Premiums, Novelties
21. Product Samples 22. Special Events Mktg. 23. Spot Radio 24. Spot T.V. 25. Weekly Newsp. 26. Yellow Page Adv.

Approx. Number Employees: 80
Year Founded: 1880
Business Description:
Wine Producer & Distr
S.I.C.: 2084
N.A.I.C.S.: 312130
Import Export
Media: 2-6-7-8-9-10-18-19-21-22-23-25
Distr.: Intl.; Natl.
Brands & Products:
ALTIMIRA
CANYON ROAD
FOX RIDGE
GEYSER PEAK
GEYSER PEAK WINERY
HOFFMAN GROVE
RESERVE ALEXANDRE
SEQUOIA

GIBSON WINE COMPANY
1720 Academy Ave
Sanger, CA 93657-3704
Tel.: (559) 875-2505
Fax: (559) 875-4761
Approx. Number Employees: 9
Year Founded: 1939
Business Description:
Mfr. & Distribution of Wines & Alcoholic Beverages
S.I.C.: 2084
N.A.I.C.S.: 312130
Export
Advertising Expenditures: $550,000
Media: 10-11-19-21
Distr.: Intl.; Natl.
Personnel:
Kim Spruance *(Gen Mgr)*
Brands & Products:
GIBSON VINEYARDS
KITCHENS BEST
SILVERSTONE CELLARS

GIUMARRA VINEYARDS CORPORATION
(d/b/a Giumarra Companies)
PO Box 1969
Bakersfield, CA 93303-1969
Tel.: (661) 395-7100
Fax: (661) 395-7195
E-mail: info@giumarra.com
Web Site: www.giumarra.com
Approx. Number Employees: 1,500
Year Founded: 1974
Business Description:
Grower, Distr & Marketer of Wines
S.I.C.: 0172; 2084
N.A.I.C.S.: 111332; 312130
Export
Media: 4-6-8-9-10-13-19-23-24
Distr.: Direct; Intl.; Natl.
Budget Set: June
Personnel:
Sal Giumarra *(Pres & CEO)*
William Butler *(CFO)*
Hillary Brick *(Mgr-Mktg)*
Brands & Products:
AGRICOM
ARRA
BEAR CREEK
CHILEAN KING
DESERT SWEET
GIUMARRA ORGANICS
GRAPE KING
KING KIWI
LAS DELICIAS
LTD CLASSIC
MAS FINO
NATURE'S PARTNER
RIO VISTA
ROYAL
SHICK
SUMMER FRUIT
SUN KING
TORO
VBM
VIEWMONT
WAITAKI

GLOBAL WINE COMPANY
10 Liberty Ship Way Ste 300
Sausalito, CA 94965
Tel.: (415) 339-3050
Fax: (415) 339-9106
Web Site: www.globalwineco.com
Business Description:
Wine Club
S.I.C.: 2084
N.A.I.C.S.: 312130
Media: 22
Personnel:
Simon Littler *(Founder & CEO)*
Donald Munro *(Founder & VP-Editorial)*
John Davis *(VP-IT)*

GRAND TRAVERSE DISTILLERY
781 Industrial Cir Ste 5
Traverse City, MI 49686
Tel.: (231) 947-8635
Web Site:
www.grandtraversedistillery.com
Business Description:
Vodka Micro-Distillery
S.I.C.: 5182
N.A.I.C.S.: 424820
Media: 9-14-23-25
Personnel:
Kent Rabish *(Pres)*
Brands & Products:
TRUE NORTH VODKA

HAAS BROTHERS, LTD.
795 Folsom St 1st Fl Ste 1125
San Francisco, CA 94107
Mailing Address:
PO Box 77745
San Francisco, CA 94124
Tel.: (415) 282-8585
Web Site: www.haas-brothers.com
Approx. Sls.: $5,500,000
Approx. Number Employees: 4
Year Founded: 1851
Business Description:
Wholesaler of Imported & Domestic Distilled Spirits
S.I.C.: 5182
N.A.I.C.S.: 424820
Import
Advertising Expenditures: $400,000
Media: 2-6-8-9-10-13-18-23
Distr.: Reg.
Budget Set: Sept. -Oct.
Personnel:
Jane T. Burrows *(Chm Pres)*
Cho Chin *(Treas & Sec)*
Brands & Products:
CABRITO
CENTINELA
DON AMADO
HAAS BROTHERS
ROYAL GATE
WHITE CHRISTMAS
Advertising Agency:
GenerH
2281 W 205th St Ste 104
Torrance, CA 90501
Tel.: (888) 312-3443
Fax: (310) 212-0052
Toll Free: (888) 312-3443

HEAVEN HILL DISTILLERIES, INC.
1064 Loretto Rd
Bardstown, KY 40004-2229
Tel.: (502) 348-3921
Fax: (502) 348-0162
Web Site: www.heaven-hill.com
E-Mail For Key Personnel:
Sales Director: sales@heaven-hill.com
Approx. Number Employees: 350
Year Founded: 1934
Business Description:
Mfr. & Distr. of Distilled Spirits
S.I.C.: 5182; 2085
N.A.I.C.S.: 424820; 312140
Import Export
Advertising Expenditures: $200,000
Media: 2-6-8-11-13
Distr.: Natl.
Budget Set: July
Personnel:
Jonathan Newman *(Chm)*
Max L. Shapira *(Pres)*
Harry J. Shapira *(Exec VP)*
Mark Pulliam *(VP-Fin)*
Larry Kass *(Dir-Corp Comm)*
Kate Latts *(Dir-Mktg)*
Susan Wahl *(Brand Mgr)*
Josh Hafer *(Mgr-Corp Comm)*
Reid Massie *(Mgr-Mktg)*
Brands & Products:
ANSAC
CHRISTIAN BROTHERS AMBER CREAM
CONTINUING THE TRADITION OF INDEPENDENCE
COPA DE ORO
CORONET VSQ
EL CONQUISTADOR
EVAN WILLIAMS
GLEN SALEN
HARLEQUIN
HEAVEN HILL
HENRY MCKENNA
LAZZARONI
OLD FITZGERALD
RON LLAVE
TWO FINGERS
Advertising Agencies:
Inventiva
522 E Borgfeld Dr
San Antonio, TX 78260-1622
Tel.: (830) 438-7599
Fax: (830) 438-7566
(Spanish-Lanuage Marketing for Christian Brothers)

Keller Crescent Advertising
1100 E Louisiana St
Evansville, IN 47711
Tel.: (812) 464-2461
Toll Free: (800) 457-3837
(All Brands)
— Drew Wesley *(Acct. Exec.)*

HOOD RIVER DISTILLERS INC.
660 Riverside Dr
Hood River, OR 97031-1177
Tel.: (541) 386-1588
Fax: (541) 386-2520
E-mail: hrdspirits@gorge.net
Web Site: www.hrdspirits.com
Approx. Number Employees: 40
Year Founded: 1949
Business Description:
Mfr. of Distilled & Blended Liquors
S.I.C.: 2085
N.A.I.C.S.: 312140
Import Export
Media: 10-17-22
Personnel:
Ronald Dodge *(Pres & CEO)*
Linda Weber *(VP & Gen Mgr)*
Erik Svenson *(VP-Sls-Intl)*
Vincent E. Melita *(Mgr-Sls-Eastern Reg)*
Brands & Products:
BROKERS GIN
DISTILLED SPIRITS
FOUR SEASONS
HRD
IDAHO GOLD
IDAHO SILVER
KNICKERS IRISH CREAM WHISKY
LEWIS & CLARK
MARIMBA RUM
MONARCH
MONTANA GOLD
MONTANA SILVER
PENDLETON 10 YEAR CANADIAN WHISKY
SPUDKA VODKA
WHITE FANG SCHNAPPS
YAZI GINGER VODKA
Advertising Agencies:
French/West/Vaughan, Inc.
112 E Hargett St
Raleigh, NC 27601
Tel.: (919) 832-6300
Fax: (919) 832-6360
Broker's Gin
Creative Campaigns
Pendleton Whisky
ULLR Nordic Libation
Yazi Ginger Vodka

Leopold Ketel & Partners
112 SW 1st Ave
Portland, OR 97204
Tel.: (503) 295-1918
Fax: (503) 295-3601

INFINITE SPIRITS, INC.
3212 Jefferson St Ste 424
Napa, CA 94558
Toll Free: (800) 842-2954
Web Site: www.shakersvodka.com
Approx. Rev.: $5,700,000
Approx. Number Employees: 13
Year Founded: 2003
Business Description:
Vodka Producer
S.I.C.: 2085
N.A.I.C.S.: 312140
Media: 2-8-9-14-23-25
Personnel:
Mark Bozzini *(CEO)*

INTERNATIONAL WINE ACCESSORIES, INC.
(Sub. of Foster's Group Limited)
10246 Miller Rd
Dallas, TX 75238-1206
Tel.: (214) 349-6097
Fax: (214) 349-8712
Toll Free: (800) 527-4072
E-mail: generalinfo@iwawine.com

Key to Media (For complete agency information see *The Advertising Red Books-Agencies* edition):
1. Bus. Publs. 2. Cable T.V. 3. Catalogs & Directories. 4. Co-op Adv. 5. Consumer Mags. 6. D.M. to Bus. Estab.7. D.M. to Consumers 8. Daily Newsp. 9. Exhibits/Trade Shows 10. Foreign 11. Infomercial 12. Internet Adv.13. Multimedia 14. Network Radio 15. Network T.V. 16. Newsp. Distr. Mags. 17. Other 18. Outdoor (Posters, Transit) 19. Point of Purchase20. Premiums, Novelties 21. Product Samples 22. Special Events Mktg. 23. Spot Radio 24. Spot T.V. 25. Weekly Newsp. 26. Yellow Page Adv.

International Wine Accessories, Inc. — (Continued)

Web Site: www.iwawine.com
Sales Range: $10-24.9 Million
Approx. Number Employees: 32
Year Founded: 1983
Business Description:
Retail & Mail Order Wine Accessories
S.I.C.: 5961; 5023
N.A.I.C.S.: 454113; 423220
Import Export
Advertising Expenditures: $3,000,000
Media: 2-4-6-7-8-10-13-26
Distr.: Direct to Consumer; Intl.; Natl.

Brands & Products:
IWA
SCREWPULL

JACK DANIEL'S DISTILLERY
(Sub. of Jack Daniel's Properties, Inc.)
Hwy 55
Lynchburg, TN 37352
Tel.: (931) 759-4221
Fax: (931) 759-6118
Web Site: www.jackdaniels.com
Sales Range: $150-199.9 Million
Approx. Number Employees: 350
Business Description:
Whiskey Distiller & Marketer
S.I.C.: 2085
N.A.I.C.S.: 312140
Media: 3-6-9-18-20-24-25
Personnel:
Mike Keyes *(Pres-North Amer Region)*
Tommy Beams *(Sr VP & Gen Mgr)*
Jennifer Powell *(Sr Brand Mgr)*
Marjorie Dufek *(Mgr-Mktg Interative)*

Advertising Agencies:
Dye, Van Mol & Lawrence
209 7th Ave N
Nashville, TN 37219-1802
Tel.: (615) 244-1818
Fax: (615) 780-3301

Slingshot, LLC
208 N Market St Ste 500
Dallas, TX 75202
Tel.: (214) 634-4411
Fax: (214) 634-5511

JACK POUST & COMPANY, INC.
250 W 57th St Ste 1505
New York, NY 10107
Tel.: (212) 582-3330
Fax: (212) 582-3332
E-mail: jackpoust@aol.com
Web Site: www.jackpoust.com
Sales Range: Less than $1 Million
Approx. Number Employees: 5
Year Founded: 1945
Business Description:
Wines Importer
S.I.C.: 5182
N.A.I.C.S.: 424820
Import
Media: 2
Distr.: Natl.
Budget Set: Sept. -Nov.
Personnel:
Jay Poust *(Pres)*
Brands & Products:
ENRICO
HARTLEY & GIBSON
JACK POUST & COMPANY
MELILLO
SAINT HILAIRE
THAI BLOSSOM

JIM BEAM BRANDS CO.
(Sub. of Beam Global Spirits & Wine, Inc.)
510 Lake Cook Rd
Deerfield, IL 60015
Tel.: (847) 948-8888
Fax: (847) 948-0395
Web Site: www.jimbeam.com
Sales Range: $1-9.9 Million
Approx. Number Employees: 250
Business Description:
Distilled Spirits Mfr, Marketer & Importer
S.I.C.: 2085; 5182
N.A.I.C.S.: 312140; 424820
Import
Media: 1-4-6-8-9-11-13-18-19-20-23-24-30
Personnel:
Matthew Shattock *(Pres & CEO)*
Mike Ginal *(Brand Mgr-Canadian Club)*
Brands & Products:
AFTER SHOCK
AVALANCHE
BAKER'S
BARANOF
BARON VON SCHEUTERS
BASIL HAYDEN'S
BEAM & COLA
BEAMERO
BEAM'S EIGHT STAR
BELLOWS
BLOCK COLLECTION
BLUEBERRY MUFFIN
BOOKER'S
CALVERT
CALVERT EXTRA
CANADIAN CLUB
CARMA
CASTELLANA
CENTENARIO
CHINACO
CLEAR SPRING
CLOS DU BOIS
COCKBURN'S
COURVOISIER
THE DALMORE
DARK EYES
DEKUYPER
DISTILLERS' MASTERPIECE
DOUBLE CASKED
DRINK SMART
EL TESORO DE DON FELIPE
FUNDADOR
GARY FARRELL
GENUINE BEAM
GILBEY'S
HARVEYS
HAYWOOD ESTATE
J. GARCIA
JACOBI
JAKES FAULT
JIM BEAM
JIM BEAM & COLA
JIM BEAM BLACK
JIM BEAM BLACK & COLA
JIM BEAM CHOICE & DRY
JIM BEAM KENTUCKY ROADHOUSE
JIM BEAM RYE
KAMCHATKA
KAMORA
KESSLER
KNOB CREEK
KUEMMERLING
LAPHROAIG
LARIOS
LEROUX
LIGHTWEIGHT TRAVELER
LORD CALVERT
MAKER'S MARK
MOUNT VERNON
OCHO DIAS
OLD CROW
OLD GRAND DAD
OLD OVERHOLT
RONRICO
SAUZA
SOURZ
STARBUCKS
TANGLE RIDGE
TEACHERS
TEMPO
THREE MONKEYS
TRAVE
VOX
WALKING TREE
WHISKY DYC
WILD HORSE
WILLIAM HILL
WINDSOR
WOLFSCHMIDT
XY ZIN

Advertising Agencies:
GMR Marketing
225 N Michigan Ave Ste 2000
Chicago, IL 60601
Tel.: (312) 324-8950
Fax: (312) 324-8960

SHIFT Communications LLC
20 Guest St Ste 200
Brighton, MA 02135
Tel.: (617) 779-1800
Fax: (617) 779-1899

The Virtual Publishing House
30 Grays Inn Rd.
London, W1X 8MR, United Kingdom
Tel.: (44) 20 7405 6066
Fax: (44) 20 7405 5699

JOHNSON BROTHERS LIQUOR COMPANY
1999 Shepard Rd
Saint Paul, MN 55116
Tel.: (651) 649-5800
Fax: (651) 649-5894
E-mail: admin@johnsonbrothers.com
Web Site: www.johnsonbrothers.com
Sales Range: $550-599.9 Million
Approx. Number Employees: 1,600
Year Founded: 1953
Business Description:
Wine & Spirits Distr
S.I.C.: 5182; 5149
N.A.I.C.S.: 424820; 424490
Media: 2-5-10
Personnel:
Lynn Johnson *(CEO)*
Scott Belsaas *(CFO)*

KENDALL-JACKSON WINE ESTATES, LTD.
421 Aviation Blvd
Santa Rosa, CA 95403
Tel.: (707) 544-4000
Fax: (707) 569-0105
Toll Free: (800) 769-3649
E-mail: deborah.hunt@kjmail.com
Web Site: www.kj.com
Sales Range: $400-449.9 Million
Approx. Number Employees: 1,200
Year Founded: 1982
Business Description:
Winemaker
S.I.C.: 2084
N.A.I.C.S.: 312130
Import Export
Advertising Expenditures: $600,000
Media: 2-7-8-10-13-16-22
Personnel:
Barbara Banke *(Chm)*
Rick Tigner *(CEO)*
Stephen Croncota *(CMO)*
Brands & Products:
CAMELOT
COLLAGE
GRAND RESERVE
GREAT ESTATES
HIGHLAND ESTATE
KENDALL-JACKSON
SANGIOWESE
STATURE
VINTNER'S RESERVE
VIOGNIER
Advertising Agencies:
Digital Brewing Company
720 Market St 3rd Fl
San Francisco, CA 94102
Tel.: (415) 398-1333
Fax: (415) 398-2266

Open Minds
(An RPA Co.)
2525 Colorado Ave
Santa Monica, CA 90401
Tel.: (949) 255-4300
Fax: (949) 255-4400

KING ESTATE OREGON WINES
80854 Territorial Hwy
Eugene, OR 97405
Tel.: (541) 942-9874
Fax: (541) 942-9867
E-mail: info@kingestate.com
Web Site: www.kingestate.com
Sales Range: $75-99.9 Million
Approx. Number Employees: 100
Business Description:
Winery
S.I.C.: 2084
N.A.I.C.S.: 312130
Media: 15
Personnel:
Edward King, III *(Founder & CEO)*
Steve Thomson *(Exec VP)*

KOBRAND CORPORATION
1 Manhattanville Rd Fl 4
Purchase, NY 10577-2126
Tel.: (212) 490-9300
Fax: (914) 253-7904
Web Site: www.kobrand.com
Approx. Number Employees: 200
Year Founded: 1944
Business Description:
Wine & Distilled Beverage Mfr, Importer & Retailer
S.I.C.: 5182; 5812
N.A.I.C.S.: 424820; 722110
Import
Advertising Expenditures: $5,000,000
Media: 2-6-7-9-10-16-18-19-20-23-24-25
Distr.: Natl.
Personnel:
Robert De Roose *(Pres & CEO)*
Cathleen Burke *(Sr VP & Dir-Mktg)*
Tom Congdon *(VP & Dir-Spirits)*
Cheryl Talley *(Brand Mgr)*

Key to Media (For complete agency information see *The Advertising Red Books-Agencies* edition):
1. Bus. Publs. 2. Cable T.V. 3. Catalogs & Directories. 4. Co-op Adv. 5. Consumer Mags. 6. D.M. to Bus. Estab.7. D.M. to Consumers 8. Daily Newsp. 9. Exhibits/Trade Shows 10. Foreign 11. Infomercial 12. Internet Adv.13. Multimedia 14. Network Radio 15. Network T.V. 16. Newsp. Distr. Mags. 17. Other 18. Outdoor (Posters, Transit) 19. Point of Purchase20. Premiums, Novelties 21. Product Samples 22. Special Events Mktg. 23. Spot Radio 24. Spot T.V. 25. Weekly Newsp. 26. Yellow Page Adv.

Brands & Products:
ALIZE
ALIZE VS
ALIZE VSOP
KOBRAND
SEQUOIA GROVE
ST. FRANCIS
Advertising Agencies:
AGENCYSACKS
345 7th Ave 7th Fl
New York, NY 10001-5006
Tel.: (212) 826-4004
Fax: (212) 593-7824

DeVito/Verdi
100 5th Ave 16th Fl
New York, NY 10011
Tel.: (212) 431-4694
Fax: (212) 431-4940
(Kobrand Spirits, Appleton Rum)

Venue Public Relations
14 Desbrosses St
New York, NY 10013
Tel.: (212) 758-5322
Fax: (646) 365-0623

Wilson Media
928 Broadway, Ste. 200
New York, NY 10010
Tel.: (212) 533-5970

LAIRD & COMPANY, INC.
1 Laird Rd
Scobeyville, NJ 07724-9724
Tel.: (732) 542-0312
Fax: (732) 542-2244
E-mail: ajlaird@msn.com
Web Site: www.lairdandcompany.com
E-Mail For Key Personnel:
Sales Director: sales@lairdandcompany.com
Sales Range: $10-24.9 Million
Approx. Number Employees: 50
Year Founded: 1780
Business Description:
Liquor & Wine Importer & Mfr
S.I.C.: 5182; 2084
N.A.I.C.S.: 424820; 312130
Import Export
Advertising Expenditures: $2,500,000
Media: 4-7-10-13
Distr.: Intl.; Natl.; Reg.
Personnel:
Larrie W. Laird *(Pres)*
Thomas Alberico *(Sr VP-Sls & Mktg)*
Janice Custer *(VP-Production)*
Brands & Products:
AMADEO CHIANTI
ANTONELLI
ARTIC
BANKERS CLUB
BARRISTERS SCOTCH
BISO
CA RUGATE
CANADIAN GOLD
CAPTAIN APPLEJACK
COUNTRY CLUB BOURBON
DUNHEATH SCOTCH
FIVE O'CLOCK
FIVE STAR AMERICAN
FONTEVECCHIA
FOUR QUEENS BLEND
FRANCOIS LABET
GAROFOLI
KASSER
KASSERS '51' BLEND
LABET
LAIRD & COMPANY
LAIRD'S
LAIRD'S APPLEJACK
LAIRD'S BOTTLED IN BOND APPLE BRANDY
LAIRD'S RARE OLD BRANDY
LITTLE RHINE BEAR LIEBFRAUMILCH
MAREGA
MAZZETTI GRAPPA
MELONI CANNONAU
MOLETTO
MONOGRAM BLEND
PIETRAFITTA
PREMIUM CANADIAN
PRESS CLUB BLEND
PRIVATE STOCK
ROCCHE CASTAGMAGNA
SAN ROCCO
SANTA SOFIA
SCOTS LION
SENATORS CLUB
SEVEN STAR
SPEAKER'S
STIVAL
STRAIGHT APPLE B-I-B
STULSKI
VALDIVIESO
VICCHIOMAGGIO
VILLA MASSA
WILLIAM PENN
ZAPATA WHITE & GOLD

MAGNET ENTERPRISES, INC.
2211 N Elston Ave
Chicago, IL 60614
Tel.: (773) 235-9463
Toll Free: (800) 615-7304
Web Site: www.wineinsiders.com
Approx. Number Employees: 35
Year Founded: 1982
Business Description:
Wine Clubs
S.I.C.: 2084
N.A.I.C.S.: 312130
Import
Media: 4-8-10-11-13
Personnel:
John D. Davis *(Founder)*
Brands & Products:
A TASTE OF CALIFORNIA
WINE INSIDERS

MAKER'S MARK DISTILLERY, INC.
(Sub. of Allied Domecq North America Corp.)
3350 Burks Springs Rd
Loretto, KY 40037
Tel.: (270) 865-2881
Fax: (270) 865-2196
Web Site: www.makersmark.com
Sales Range: $25-49.9 Million
Approx. Number Employees: 70
Year Founded: 1953
Business Description:
Whisky Distillery
S.I.C.: 2085
N.A.I.C.S.: 312140
Export
Advertising Expenditures: $1,000,000
Media: 2-6-7-8-9-18-19-20
Distr.: Intl.; Natl.
Budget Set: Oct.
Personnel:
Bill Samuels *(Pres)*
Rob Samuels *(COO)*
Kelly Doss *(VP-Mktg-Global)*
Donna Lucey *(VP-HR)*
Advertising Agencies:
Doe-Anderson
620 W Main St
Louisville, KY 40202-2933
Tel.: (502) 589-1700
Fax: (502) 587-8349
Maker's Mark Bourbon

Evins Communications, Ltd.
635 Madison Ave
New York, NY 10022-1009
Tel.: (212) 688-8200
Fax: (212) 935-6730

MARNIER-LAPOSTOLLE INC.
(Sub. of Societe des Produits Marnier-Lapostolle S.A.)
717 5th Ave
New York, NY 10022
Tel.: (212) 207-4350
Fax: (212) 207-4351
E-mail: info@grand-marnier.com
Web Site: www.grand-marnier.com
Approx. Number Employees: 5
Business Description:
Liquor & Wine Importer
S.I.C.: 2082; 5182
N.A.I.C.S.: 312120; 424820
Media: 6
Personnel:
Scott Green *(VP-Mktg & Sls)*
Brands & Products:
NAVAN

MCCORMICK DISTILLING CO., INC.
1 McCormick Ln
Weston, MO 64098-9558
Tel.: (816) 640-2276
Fax: (816) 640-3082
Web Site:
www.mccormickdistilling.com
Approx. Number Employees: 185
Year Founded: 1856
Business Description:
Mfr & Importer Distilled Spirits
S.I.C.: 2085
N.A.I.C.S.: 312140
Media: 2-18
Distr.: Reg.
Budget Set: Mar.
Personnel:
Ed Pechar *(Owner & Chm)*
Mick Harris *(Vice Chm & Mgr-Natl Sls)*
Jim Zargo *(Pres)*
Chris Fernandez *(CFO)*
Vic Morrison *(VP-Mktg)*
Brands & Products:
360 VODKA
B.J. HOLLADAY
CANADIAN WOODS
EL CHARRO
HUSSONG'S
KEKE BEACH
LOT #40
MCCORMICK'S IRISH CREAM
MONTEGO BAY
PIKE CREEK
POLAR ICE
RON RIO
Advertising Agencies:
Goodman Media International, Inc.
750 7th Ave 28th Fl
New York, NY 10016
Tel.: (212) 576-2700
Fax: (212) 576-2701
360 Vodka

Sagon-Phior
The Sawtelle Ctr 2107 Sawtelle Blvd
West Los Angeles, CA 90025
Tel.: (310) 575-4441
Fax: (310) 575-4995
360 Vodka

MEIER'S WINE CELLARS, INC.
(Sub. of Paramount Distillers, Inc.)
6955 Plainfield Rd
Cincinnati, OH 45236-3733
Tel.: (513) 891-2900
Fax: (513) 891-6370
E-mail: info@meierswinecellars.com
Web Site:
www.meierswinecellars.com
Approx. Number Employees: 30
Year Founded: 1976
Business Description:
Wines, Champagnes & Vermouth Producer
S.I.C.: 2033; 2084
N.A.I.C.S.: 311421; 312130
Media: 2-6-10-20-23
Distr.: Intl.; Natl.
Personnel:
John Pallo *(VP-Sls)*
Brands & Products:
JC MEIER JUICE
MEIER'S WINE
Advertising Agency:
Marcus Thomas LLC
24865 Emery Rd
Cleveland, OH 44128
Tel.: (216) 292-4700
Fax: (216) 378-0396
Toll Free: (888) 482-4455

MILLENNIUM IMPORT LLC
(Sub. of Moet-Hennessy SNC)
25 Main St SE
Minneapolis, MN 55414
Tel.: (612) 331-6230
Fax: (612) 623-1644
Toll Free: (800) 462-5390
Web Site: www.belvederevodka.com
Approx. Number Employees: 20
Business Description:
Vodka Importer
S.I.C.: 5182
N.A.I.C.S.: 424820
Media: 6-13
Personnel:
Charles Gibb *(Pres)*
Brands & Products:
BELVEDERE

MOET HENNESSY
(Sub. of Veuve Clicquot Ponsardin S.A.)
85 10th Ave Fl 2
New York, NY 10011
Tel.: (212) 888-7575
Fax: (212) 251-8388
Telex: 494-8192
E-mail: info@mhusa.com
Web Site: www.mhusa.com
Approx. Number Employees: 275
Business Description:
Wine Importer
S.I.C.: 5182
N.A.I.C.S.: 424820
Media: 2-4-6-7-9-16-18-20-23-30
Distr.: Intl.; Natl.

Key to Media (For complete agency information see *The Advertising Red Books-Agencies* edition):
1. Bus. Publs. 2. Cable T.V. 3. Catalogs & Directories. 4. Co-op Adv. 5. Consumer Mags. 6. D.M. to Bus. Estab.7. D.M. to Consumers 8. Daily Newsp. 9. Exhibits/Trade Shows 10. Foreign 11. Infomercial 12. Internet Adv.13. Multimedia 14. Network Radio 15. Network T.V. 16. Newsp. Distr. Mags. 17. Other 18. Outdoor (Posters, Transit) 19. Point of Purchase20. Premiums, Novelties 21. Product Samples 22. Special Events Mktg. 23. Spot Radio 24. Spot T.V. 25. Weekly Newsp. 26. Yellow Page Adv.

Moet Hennessy — (Continued)

Personnel:
Geraud Leclercq *(Brand Dir-Veuve Clicquot)*
Sapna Santos *(Brand Dir-Hennessy)*
Advertising Agencies:
Berlin Cameron United
100 Ave of the Americas 2nd Fl
New York, NY 10013
Tel.: (212) 824-2000
Fax: (212) 268-8454
Hennessy

mktg, inc.
75 9th Ave 3rd Fl
New York, NY 10011
Tel.: (212) 660-3800
Fax: (212) 660-3878

Mother New York
595 11th Ave
New York, NY 10036
Tel.: (212) 254-2800
Fax: (212) 254-6121
10 Cane Rum

MONSIEUR HENRI WINE COMPANY

(Sub. of Sazerac Company, Inc.)
6125 King Rd Ste 202
Loomis, CA 95650-8809
Tel.: (916) 652-3791
Fax: (916) 630-3110
E-mail: inquiry@monsieurhenri.com
Web Site: www.monsieurhenri.com
Approx. Number Employees: 15
Year Founded: 1934
Business Description:
Importers of Imported Wines
S.I.C.: 5182
N.A.I.C.S.: 424820
Import
Media: 6-15-23-25
Distr.: Natl.
Budget Set: Oct.
Advertising Agency:
Spar, Incorporated
501 Coolidge St PO Box 52831
New Orleans, LA 70121
Tel.: (504) 849-6410
Fax: (504) 849-6555
(Wines)

MONTEBELLO BRANDS INC.

1919 Willow Spring Rd
Baltimore, MD 21222-2939
Tel.: (410) 282-8800
Fax: (410) 282-8809
Sales Range: $10-24.9 Million
Approx. Number Employees: 20
Year Founded: 1933
Business Description:
Mfr. of Spirits
S.I.C.: 2085
N.A.I.C.S.: 312140
Import Export
Advertising Expenditures: $300,000
Media: 6-9-10-18-19-24
Distr.: Natl.
Budget Set: Apr.
Personnel:
Leo Conte *(Pres & CEO)*
Nancy Hogan *(Office Mgr)*
Brands & Products:
BRITANNIA ALCOHOLIC BEVERAGES
EL CONDOR
HEATHER-GLO
KAMAKAZI
KINGS CROWN
McCALLS
McCALLS CANADIAN
MONTEBELLO BLOODY MARIA
MONTEBELLO ORIGINAL KIR
MONTEBELLO ORIGINAL LONG ISLAND ICED TEA
OLD MCCALL
ORANGE DRIVER
VLADIMIR

M.S. WALKER, INC.

20 3rd Ave
Somerville, MA 02143-4450
Tel.: (617) 776-6700
Fax: (617) 776-5808
Toll Free: (800) 962-3522 (MA)
E-mail: info@mswalker.com
Web Site: www.mswalker.com
Approx. Number Employees: 275
Year Founded: 1931
Business Description:
Marketer & Distr Wines, Spirits & Cigars; Spirits Mfr
S.I.C.: 2085; 5182
N.A.I.C.S.: 312140; 424820
Import Export
Advertising Expenditures: $500,000
Media: 1-2-6-9-10-18-19-20-21-22-25
Distr.: Natl.
Personnel:
Richard Sandler *(CFO)*
John Garland *(VP)*
Maurice S. Walker *(Mgr-Sls)*
Brands & Products:
M.S. WALKER

NATIONAL WINE & SPIRITS, INC.

700 W Morris St
Indianapolis, IN 46206
Tel.: (317) 636-6092
Fax: (317) 685-8810
E-mail: contact@nwscorp.com
Web Site: www.nwscorp.com
Sales Range: $700-749.9 Million
Approx. Number Employees: 1,725
Business Description:
Beverages, Liquors, Wines & Spirits Whslr
S.I.C.: 5181; 5182; 5499
N.A.I.C.S.: 424810; 424820; 445299
Advertising Expenditures: $10,729,000
Media: 2-4-10-19-20-21-22
Personnel:
James E. Lacrosse *(Chm, Pres, CEO & CFO)*
John J. Baker *(COO, Sec & Exec VP)*
Gregory J. Mauloff *(Exec VP-Sls-Mktg)*
Catherine M. Lacrosse *(Dir, Sr VP-Corp Dev & Fine Wine)*
Dwight Deming *(Corp VP-Info Sys)*

NEW ENGLAND BREWING COMPANY

7 Seldon St
Woodbridge, CT 06525
Tel.: (203) 387-2222
E-mail: rob@newenglandbrewing.com
Web Site:
www.newenglandbrewing.com
Approx. Number Employees: 1
Business Description:
Brewery
S.I.C.: 2082
N.A.I.C.S.: 312120
Media: 13-22
Personnel:
Rob Leonard *(Owner)*
Brands & Products:
ATLANTIC AMBER
DRINK IT. ITS GOOD
ELM CITY LAGER
NEW ENGLAND
SEA HAG IPA
Advertising Agency:
HeavyBag Media
1514 17th St Ste 207
Santa Monica, CA 90404
Tel.: (310) 472-9803
Fax: (203) 624-0779

NEWTON VINEYARDS

(Sub. of Domaine Chandon, Inc.)
1 California Dr
Yountville, CA 94599-1426
Tel.: (707) 963-9000
Fax: (707) 963-7450
E-mail: winery@newtonvineyard.com
Web Site: www.newtonvineyard.com
Approx. Number Employees: 70
Year Founded: 1977
Business Description:
Mfr. of Wines
S.I.C.: 2084; 0172
N.A.I.C.S.: 312130; 111332
Personnel:
Peter Newton *(Co-Founder)*
Su Hua Newton *(Owner)*
Michael Stedman *(Dir-Bus Dev-Estates & Wine)*
Advertising Agency:
Dentsu America, Inc.
32 Ave of the Americas 16th Fl
New York, NY 10013
Tel.: (212) 397-3333
Fax: (212) 397-3322

NOLET SPIRITS USA INC.

(Sub. of Nolet Distillery)
30 Journey
Aliso Viejo, CA 92656
Tel.: (949) 448-5700
Fax: (949) 448-5733
Web Site: www.noletspirits.com
Approx. Sls.: $9,600,000
Approx. Number Employees: 36
Business Description:
Spirits Distiller & Distributor
S.I.C.: 2084; 5182
N.A.I.C.S.: 312130; 424820
Personnel:
Carolus Nolet, Sr. *(Owner)*
William Eldien *(Pres & CEO)*
Eduardo Jordan *(CFO & Sr VP-Ops)*
Carl Nolet, Jr. *(Exec VP)*
Laurel Chowdhury *(Sr Mgr-Mktg)*
Amy Dalzell *(Exec-HR)*
Brands & Products:
KETEL ONE CITROEN
KETEL ONE VODKA
Advertising Agencies:
HEILBrice
9840 Irvine Center Dr
Irvine, CA 92618
Tel.: (949) 336-8800
Fax: (949) 336-8819

M&C Saatchi plc
36 Golden Sq
London, W1F 9EE, United Kingdom
Tel.: (44) 20 7543 4500
Fax: (44) 20 7543 4501

Renegade, LLC
75 9th Ave 8th Fl
New York, NY 10011
Tel.: (646) 486-7700
Fax: (646) 486-7800

Weber Shandwick-Los Angeles
8687 Melrose Ave 7th Fl
Los Angeles, CA 90069
Tel.: (310) 854-8200
Fax: (310) 854-8201
Ketel One Vodka

OPICI WINE GROUP INC.

25 De Boer Dr
Glen Rock, NJ 07452-3301
Tel.: (201) 689-1200
Fax: (201) 689-1550
E-mail: dinao@opici.com
Web Site: www.opici.com
Approx. Rev.: $150,000,000
Approx. Number Employees: 166
Year Founded: 1899
Business Description:
Wine & Distilled Beverages Producer
S.I.C.: 5182
N.A.I.C.S.: 424820
Import Export
Advertising Expenditures: $1,000,000
Media: 4-13-14-15-16
Personnel:
Dina Opici *(Pres)*
Linda Opici *(CEO)*
Brands & Products:
THE OPICI WINE GROUP

PARAMOUNT DISTILLERS, INC.

3116 Berea Rd
Cleveland, OH 44111-1501
Tel.: (216) 671-6300
Fax: (216) 671-2299
E-mail: info@paramountdistillers.com
Web Site:
www.paramountdistillers.com
Approx. Number Employees: 60
Year Founded: 1934
Business Description:
Mfr. of Vodka, Cordials, Flavored Brandies, Bourbon, Canadian Scotch Whiskies, French Brandy, Champagne, Still Wines & Grape Juice
S.I.C.: 2085; 2084
N.A.I.C.S.: 312140; 312130
Advertising Expenditures: $500,000
Media: 2-5-6-9-10-18-19-20-21-22-23-25
Distr.: Natl.
Personnel:
Robert Manchick *(Chm)*
Lynn Lubin *(Dir-Mktg)*
Brands & Products:
BLACK DUCK
CANADIAN BAY
COLONIAL CLUB
KARIMBA
LA PRIMA
LADY BLIGH
LASALLE
PARAMOUNT
PARAMOUNT DISTILLERS

Key to Media (For complete agency information see *The Advertising Red Books-Agencies* edition):
1. Bus. Publs. 2. Cable T.V. 3. Catalogs & Directories. 4. Co-op Adv. 5. Consumer Mags. 6. D.M. to Bus. Estab.7. D.M. to Consumers 8. Daily Newsp. 9. Exhibits/Trade Shows 10. Foreign 11. Infomercial 12. Internet Adv.13. Multimedia 14. Network Radio 15. Network T.V. 16. Newsp. Distr. Mags. 17. Other 18. Outdoor (Posters, Transit) 19. Point of Purchase20. Premiums, Novelties 21. Product Samples 22. Special Events Mktg. 23. Spot Radio 24. Spot T.V. 25. Weekly Newsp. 26. Yellow Page Adv.

PARTIDA TEQUILA, LLC
150 California St Ste 500
San Francisco, CA 94111
Tel.: (415) 434-3100
Fax: (415) 434-3103
Web Site: www.partidatequila.com
Approx. Number Employees: 20
Business Description:
Tequila Importer & Distr
S.I.C.: 5182
N.A.I.C.S.: 424820
Personnel:
J. Gary Shansby *(Founder, Chm & CEO)*
Kevin Moodie *(COO & Exec VP)*
Brands & Products:
PARTIDA ANEJO TEQUILA
PARTIDA BLANCO TEQUILA
PARTIDA ELEGANTE TEQUILA
PARTIDA REPOSADO TEQUILA
Advertising Agency:
Colangelo & Partners Public Relations
26 W 23rd St 6th Fl
New York, NY 10010
Tel.: (646) 624-2885
Fax: (646) 624-2893

THE PATRON SPIRITS COMPANY
6670 S Vly View
Las Vegas, NV 89118-4516
Tel.: (702) 262-9446
Fax: (702) 262-9450
E-mail: info@patronspirits.com
Web Site: www.patronspirits.com
Approx. Number Employees: 30
Year Founded: 1989
Business Description:
Alcoholic Beverages Mfr
S.I.C.: 2085; 5182
N.A.I.C.S.: 312140; 424820
Advertising Expenditures: $20,000,000
Media: 3-13-15-16-18-22-24
Personnel:
John Paul DeJoria *(Founder)*
Edward J. Brown *(Pres & CEO)*
Dave Lowren *(CFO)*
John McDonnell *(COO)*
Matt Carroll *(CMO)*
Greg Cohen *(Dir-Corp Comm)*
Chris Spake *(Mgr-Global Brand)*
Brands & Products:
GRAN PATRON BURDEOS
GRAN PATRON PLATINUM
PATRON
PATRON ANEJO
PATRON REPOSADO
PATRON SILVER
Advertising Agencies:
Amalgamated Advertising LLC
145 W 30th St 7th Fl
New York, NY 10001
Tel.: (646) 878-1700
Fax: (646) 878-1787
Ultimat Vodka (Agency of Record)

The Richards Group, Inc.
8750 N Central Expy Ste 100
Dallas, TX 75231-6430
Tel.: (214) 891-5700
Fax: (214) 265-2933

PERNOD RICARD USA, INC.
(Sub. of Pernod Ricard S.A.)
100 Manhattanville Rd
Purchase, NY 10577
Tel.: (914) 848-4800
Fax: (914) 848-4777
Toll Free: (800) 4TURKEY
Web Site: www.pernod-ricard-usa.com
Approx. Number Employees: 300
Year Founded: 1855
Business Description:
Mfr. of Spirits
S.I.C.: 2085
N.A.I.C.S.: 312140
Import Export
Advertising Expenditures: $8,600,000
Media: 1-2-5-6-9-11-18-19-20-25
Distr.: Intl.; Natl.
Budget Set: Oct.
Personnel:
Paul Duffy *(Pres & CEO)*
Thomas R. Lálla, Jr. *(Gen Counsel & SVP)*
Matt Aeppli *(Sr VP-Spirits Mktg)*
Emmanuel Cargill *(Sr VP-HR & Corp Svcs)*
Marty Crane *(Sr VP-Spirits Sls)*
Lori Gage *(Sr VP-HR)*
Charles Smith *(Sr VP-Trade Rels)*
Peter Szemenyei *(Sr VP-Comml Plng & Analysis)*
John Trainer *(VP & Gen Mgr-Control States)*
Paul Campbell *(VP-Mktg)*
Jeanne Eliades *(VP-Mktg)*
Tim Murphy *(VP-Mktg-Absolut Vodka, Beefeater Gin, Plymouth Gin, Fris Vodka)*
Jonas Tahlin *(VP-Mktg-Vodkas)*
Christopher Willis *(VP-Mktg Svcs)*
Shawn Higgins *(Gen Mgr-West Div)*
Howard Jeffery *(Gen Mgr-Continental Div)*
Lauren Simkin *(Gen Mgr-PR USA Wines & Champagnes)*
Wayne Hartunian *(Dir-Brand)*
Craig Johnson *(Dir-Brand-Chivas/ Stolichnaya)*
Melissa Frank *(Brand Dir-Kahlua-Global)*
Suzy Kilgore *(Brand Dir)*
Andy Nash *(Brand Dir-Kahlua)*
James Slack *(Brand Dir-Chivas Regal)*
Terry Boyer *(Dir-Natl Accounts)*
Duncan Maurer *(Dir-Media & Production)*
AnnaMarie Battiloro *(Sr Brand Mgr-Malibu Rum)*
Lauren Rinkey *(Mgr-National Event Mktg)*
Brands & Products:
BEEFEATER
BRANCOTT ESTATE
CHIVAS REGAL
CHOOSE AUTHENTICITY
THE GLENLIVET
JACOB'S CREEK
JAMESON
MALIBU
NAPA
PERNOD
STOLICHNAYA
Advertising Agencies:
Alcone Marketing Group
(Division of Omnicom Group, Inc.)
4 Studebaker
Irvine, CA 92618-2012
Tel.: (949) 770-4400
Fax: (949) 770-2957

Berlin Cameron United
100 Ave of the Americas 2nd Fl
New York, NY 10013
Tel.: (212) 824-2000
Fax: (212) 268-8454
Global Creative Agency

Carat
150 E 42nd St
New York, NY 10017
Tel.: (212) 689-6800
Fax: (212) 689-6005
Chivas
Jameson
The Glenlivet
Wild Turkey
Stolichnaya
Malibu
Kahlua
Beefeater Gin
Segram's Gin
Jacob's Creek Wines
Perrier Jouet

FD Americas Public Affairs
1101 K St NW 9th Fl
Washington, DC 20005
Tel.: (202) 346-8800
Fax: (202) 346-8804

Marketing Drive
800 Connecticut Ave 3rd Fl E
Norwalk, CT 06854
Tel.: (203) 857-6100
Fax: (203) 857-6171
Jacob's Creek
Wyndham Estate
Perrier-Jouet

Rokkan
176 Grand St 2nd Fl
New York, NY 10012-4003
Tel.: (212) 835-9300
Fax: (212) 251-9393
Digital communications
Stolichnaya Vodka (Digital Agency of Record)
Strategy

TBWA/Chiat/Day
(Regional Headquarters)
488 Madison Ave
New York, NY 10022
Tel.: (212) 804-1000
Fax: (212) 804-1200
Kahlua (Global Communications Agency)

PHOENIX VINTNERS, LLC
(d/b/a The Traveling Vineyard)
755 Baywood Dr 2nd Fl
Petaluma, CA 94954
Toll Free: (877) 340-9869
Web Site: www.travelingvineyard.com

Sales Range: $1-9.9 Million
Approx. Number Employees: 45
Year Founded: 1986
Business Description:
Wines & Wine-Related Merchandise Direct Marketer & Retailer
S.I.C.: 5961; 5921
N.A.I.C.S.: 454113; 445310
Advertising Expenditures: $5,400,058
Media: 4-8-13-16-23
Personnel:
Rick Libby *(Pres & Founder)*
Brands & Products:
ALAZAR WINERY
AMSBURY WINERY
BESTWINEBUYS.COM
BRAVA TERRA
BRYAN WOODS WINERY
DEVINA ESTATES
DOMAINE PAUL
EXPEDITIONS
GEERLINGS & WADE
GEERLINGS & WADE PERSONAL WINE SERVICE
GLASS RIDGE
HAMILTON ESTATES
INTERNATIONAL BEER & ALE SOCIETY
J. KRANT CELLARS
JACK CANYON CELLARS
LAPIS LAZULI WINERY & VINEYARDS
MARIEL WINERY
MIRA LUNA
MISCHLER ESTATES
REDBRICK CELLARS
SAN VALENCIA WINERY
ST. CAROLYNE WINERY
VINTAGE IMPRESSION PLUS
VINTAGE REWARDS
WINEBINS.COM
WINEBINS.COM WINE REDEFINED
WINEFIRST.COM

R&R MARKETING, LLC
(Affil. of The Charmer Sunbelt Group)
10 Patton Dr
West Caldwell, NJ 07006
Tel.: (973) 228-5100
Fax: (973) 226-2811
Toll Free: (800) 222-1260
E-mail: csrv@rrmarketing.com
Web Site: www.rrmarketing.com
Approx. Number Employees: 240
Year Founded: 1988
Business Description:
Wine & Spirits Distr
S.I.C.: 5182
N.A.I.C.S.: 424820
Personnel:
Howard Jacobs *(Chm)*
Jon Maslin *(Pres & CEO)*
Dennis M. Portsmore *(CFO & VP)*
Advertising Agency:
Raritan Advertising Agency
10 Patton Dr
West Caldwell, NJ 07006-6405
Tel.: (973) 228-5100
Fax: (973) 403-8679

REMY COINTREAU USA INC.
(Holding of Remy Cointreau S.A.)
1290 Avenue of the Americas 10th Fl
New York, NY 10104
Tel.: (212) 399-4200
Fax: (212) 399-6909
Toll Free: (800) 858-9898
Web Site: www.remy.com
Approx. Number Employees: 150
Year Founded: 1981
Business Description:
Importer & Distributor of Wines & Distilled Alcoholic Beverages
S.I.C.: 5182
N.A.I.C.S.: 424820
Import
Media: 2-3-4-5-6-7-9-10-11-13-14-18-19-20-22-23-24-25-30
Personnel:
Tom Jensen *(Pres & CEO)*

Key to Media (For complete agency information see *The Advertising Red Books-Agencies* edition):
1. Bus. Publs. 2. Cable T.V. 3. Catalogs & Directories. 4. Co-op Adv. 5. Consumer Mags. 6. D.M. to Bus. Estab.7. D.M. to Consumers
8. Daily Newsp. 9. Exhibits/Trade Shows 10. Foreign 11. Infomercial 12. Internet Adv.13. Multimedia 14. Network Radio
15. Network T.V. 16. Newsp. Distr. Mags. 17. Other 18. Outdoor (Posters, Transit) 19. Point of Purchase20. Premiums, Novelties
21. Product Samples 22. Special Events Mktg. 23. Spot Radio 24. Spot T.V. 25. Weekly Newsp. 26. Yellow Page Adv.

Remy Cointreau USA Inc. — (Continued)

Dennis Floam *(CFO)*
Philippe Roederer *(Sr VP-Mktg)*
Charles Ho *(VP-Mktg-Remy Martin)*
Nicolas Heriard Dubreuil *(Dir-Digital Mktg & Social Media)*
Todd Schuessler *(Dir-Mktg & Natl Accounts)*

Brands & Products:
ANTINORI
BAREBOAT
BIONDI SANTI
DAMRAQ
GALLIANO LIQUEUR
GONZALEZ-BYASS
HARAS DE PIRQUE
HIGHLAND PARK
LA ROCHE
MASI
PASSOA LIQUEUR
PIPER SONOMA
REMY MARTIN 1738
REMY MARTIN EXTRA
REMY MARTIN GRAND CRU
REMY MARTIN LOUIS XIII
REMY MARTIN VSOP
REMY MARTIN XO
REMY RED
RENE JUNOT
TIO PEPE
VIETTE

Advertising Agencies:
Dan Klores Communications (d/b/a dkc)
386 Park Ave S 10th Fl
New York, NY 10016
Tel.: (212) 685-4300
Fax: (212) 685-9024
Liqueur

Euro RSCG Worldwide HQ
350 Hudson St
New York, NY 10014-4504
Tel.: (212) 886-2000
Fax: (212) 886-2016

John Ayling & Associates Limited
27 Soho Square
London, W1D 3QR, United Kingdom
Tel.: (44) 207 439 6070
Fax: (44) 207 437 8473

La Comunidad
6400 Biscayne Blvd
Miami, FL 33138
Tel.: (305) 993-5700
Tel.: (305) 865-9600
Fax: (305) 865-9609
(Remy Martin)

Nurun Inc.
18 E 16th St 7th Fl
New York, NY 10003
Tel.: (212) 524-8100
Fax: (212) 524-8101

Power Ads Corp.
San Alsonso 278 Ext College Pk
San Juan, PR 00951
Tel.: (787) 528-1303
Fax: (787) 727-5004

The Vidal Partnership
228 E 45th St 11th Fl
New York, NY 10017-3303
Tel.: (646) 356-6600
Fax: (212) 661-7650
Agency of Record
Brand Advertising
Digital
Remy Martin Cognac
Strategy

REX HILL VINEYARDS

30835 N Hwy 99 W
Newberg, OR 97132
Tel.: (503) 538-0666
Fax: (503) 538-1409
Toll Free: (800) 739-4455
E-mail: info@rexhill.com
Web Site: www.rexhill.com
Approx. Number Employees: 50
Year Founded: 1982
Business Description:
Winery
S.I.C.: 2084; 5182
N.A.I.C.S.: 312130; 424820
Media: 8-13-20-21-22
Personnel:
Bill Hatcher *(CEO)*
Brands & Products:
REX HILL

ROBERT MONDAVI WINERY

(Div. of Constellation Wines US)
7801 Saint Helena Hwy
Oakville, CA 94562
Mailing Address:
PO Box 106
Oakville, CA 94562-0106
Tel.: (707) 226-1395
Fax: (707) 251-4110
Toll Free: (888) RMONDAVI
Toll Free: (888) 766-6328
E-mail: info@robertmondaviwinery.com
Web Site:
www.robertmondaviwinery.com
Sales Range: $450-499.9 Million
Approx. Number Employees: 1,000
Year Founded: 1966
Business Description:
Premium Table Wine Producer
S.I.C.: 2084
N.A.I.C.S.: 312130
Import Export
Advertising Expenditures: $3,000,000
Media: 4-6-13-17-23
Budget Set: July
Personnel:
Kevin Conner *(VP-Mktg)*
Brands & Products:
ARROWOOD
BYRON
CALITTERA & ARBOLEDA
DANZANTE
FUME BLANC
IO
KIRRALAA
LA FAMIGLIA DI ROBERT MONDAVI
LUCE & LUCENTE
MARCHESI DE' FRESCOBALDI
MOSCATO D'ORO
OPUS ONE
ROBERT MONDAVI PRIVATE SELECTION
ROBERT MONDAVI WINERY
SENA
VINA ERRAZURIZ
WOODBRIDGE
Advertising Agency:
Spin Recruitment Advertising
712 Bancroft Rd Ste 521
Walnut Creek, CA 94598
Tel.: (925) 944-6060
Fax: (925) 944-6063

ROBERT STEMMLER WINERY

(Sub. of A. Racke GmbH)
PO Box 154 24520 Ramal Rd
Sonoma, CA 95476-9790
Tel.: (707) 939-2293
Fax: (707) 939-0651
Toll Free: (800) 679-7355
E-mail: tastingroom@robertstemmlerwinery.com
Web Site:
www.robertstemmlerwinery.com
Approx. Number Employees: 350
Year Founded: 1976
Business Description:
Wines & Spirits Mfr
S.I.C.: 2084
N.A.I.C.S.: 312130
Export
Advertising Expenditures: $2,000,000
Media: 4-13-17
Brands & Products:
ROBERT STEMMLER

RUBICON ESTATE WINERY

1991 St Helena Hwy
Rutherford, CA 94573
Mailing Address:
PO Box 208
Rutherford, CA 94573
Tel.: (707) 963-9099
Tel.: (707) 968-1100
Fax: (707) 963-9084
Toll Free: (800) 782-4266
Web Site: www.rubiconestate.com
Approx. Number Employees: 150
Business Description:
Winery
S.I.C.: 2084
N.A.I.C.S.: 312130
Media: 6-10
Personnel:
Jay Shoemaker *(CEO)*
Gordon Wany *(CFO)*
Advertising Agency:
Talbert Communications
80 5th Ave Ste 805
New York, NY 10028
Tel.: (212) 675-5525
Public Relations

RUMS OF PUERTO RICO

(Div. of Puerto Rico Industrial Development Company - New York)
135 W 53 St 22nd FL
New York, NY 10020-1599
Tel.: (212) 245-1200
Fax: (212) 333-0374
Web Site: www.rumspuertorico.com
Sales Range: $250-299.9 Million
Approx. Number Employees: 5
Year Founded: 1948
Business Description:
Promoter & Distr of Rums
S.I.C.: 5182
N.A.I.C.S.: 424820
Import Export
Advertising Expenditures: $10,000,000
Media: 1-2-4-6-8-10-11-13-18-19-20-22
Distr.: Natl.
Personnel:
Fernando Martinez *(Dir)*

SAPPORO U.S.A., INC.

(Holding of Sapporo Holdings Limited)
1821250 Hawthorne Blvd
Torrance, CA 90503
Tel.: (310) 792-7458
Fax: (310) 792-7459
E-mail: mktg@sapporo.com
Web Site: www.sapporobeer.com
Approx. Number Employees: 5
Year Founded: 1984
Business Description:
Import & Marketing of Beer in the U.S. & Producer of Wine
S.I.C.: 5181
N.A.I.C.S.: 424810
Import
Advertising Expenditures: $1,000,000
Media: 2-5-10-16-19-20-21-23-24-26
Personnel:
Sage Ubukata *(Pres)*
Brands & Products:
YEBISU STOUT
Advertising Agency:
Moosylvania Marketing
7303 Marietta
Saint Louis, MO 63143
Tel.: (314) 533-5800
Fax: (314) 533-8056

SAZERAC COMPANY, INC.

803 Jefferson Hwy
New Orleans, LA 70121-2522
Mailing Address:
PO Box 52821
New Orleans, LA 70152-2821
Tel.: (504) 831-9450
Fax: (504) 831-2383
E-mail: info@sazerac.com
Web Site: www.sazerac.com
Approx. Number Employees: 300
Year Founded: 1850
Business Description:
Wine & Spirits Importer, Exporter & Mfr
S.I.C.: 2085; 5182
N.A.I.C.S.: 312140; 424820
Import Export
Advertising Expenditures: $200,000
Media: 18-19
Distr.: Natl.
Personnel:
Kevin Richards *(Brand Mgr-Whiskeys & Specialty Brands)*
Tracey Clapp *(Brand Mgr-Wave Vodka)*
Brands & Products:
AMARETTO DI PADRINO
BLACK TOWER
CARSTAIRS' WHITE SEAL AMERICAN
CHATEAU ALTER EGO
CROWN RUSSE
DENAKA IMPORTED VODKA
DOBRA
DR. MCGILLICUDDY'S
EAGLE RARE
FIREBALL
FRENCH KISS
GLENTROMIE HIGHLAND MALT SCOTCH
HERBSAINT LIQUEUR D'ANIS
HERRADURA
JAMES FOXE
JOHN HANDY
KENTUCKY DALE
LEGACY

Key to Media (For complete agency information see *The Advertising Red Books-Agencies* edition):
1. Bus. Publs. 2. Cable T.V. 3. Catalogs & Directories. 4. Co-op Adv. 5. Consumer Mags. 6. D.M. to Bus. Estab.7. D.M. to Consumers 8. Daily Newsp. 9. Exhibits/Trade Shows 10. Foreign 11. Infomercial 12. Internet Adv.13. Multimedia 14. Network Radio 15. Network T.V. 16. Newsp. Distr. Mags. 17. Other 18. Outdoor (Posters, Transit) 19. Point of Purchase20. Premiums, Novelties 21. Product Samples 22. Special Events Mktg. 23. Spot Radio 24. Spot T.V. 25. Weekly Newsp. 26. Yellow Page Adv.

MILES
MIMS
MONSIEUR HENRI
NIKOLAI
OLD CHARTER
OLE TEQUILA
PEYCHAUD'S
PIRASSUNUNGA 51 CACHACA
PRALINE
PREMIAT
RAIN
SAZERAC
SIR MALCOLM
SPEYSIDE 21-YEAR-OLD
TAAKA
TIJUANA
TORADA
WL WELLER

Advertising Agency:
Spar, Incorporated
501 Coolidge St PO Box 52831
New Orleans, LA 70121
Tel.: (504) 849-6410
Fax: (504) 849-6555

SCHEID VINEYARDS INC.
305 Hilltown Rd
Salinas, CA 93908-8902
Tel.: (831) 455-9990
Fax: (831) 455-9998
E-mail: info@scheidvineyards.com
Web Site: www.scheidvineyards.com
E-Mail For Key Personnel:
President: scott@scheidvineyards.com
Sales Range: $10-24.9 Million
Approx. Number Employees: 100
Year Founded: 1972
Business Description:
Wine Producer
S.I.C.: 0172; 2084
N.A.I.C.S.: 111332; 312130
Media: 2-4-10-16-22-26
Personnel:
Alfred G. Scheid *(Chm)*
Scott D. Scheid *(Pres & CEO)*
Michael S. Thomsen *(CFO)*
Kurt J. Gollnick *(COO & Sr VP)*
Heidi M. Scheid *(Sr VP)*

SCOTTISH & NEWCASTLE IMPORTERS CO., INC.
(Sub. of Scottish Newcastle UK Limited)
4040 Civic Center Dr Ste 401
San Rafael, CA 94903-4191
Tel.: (415) 479-5700
Fax: (415) 479-5800
Web Site: www.newcastlebrown.com
Approx. Number Employees: 14
Year Founded: 1962
Business Description:
Beer Importer & Distr
S.I.C.: 5181
N.A.I.C.S.: 424810
Media: 2-4-6-9-18-19-22-23-25
Distr.: Reg.
Budget Set: Feb.
Personnel:
Steve Greig *(Dir-Consumer Mktg)*
Advertising Agency:
VITRO
(An MDC Partners Company)
625 Broadway Fl 4
San Diego, CA 92101-5403
Tel.: (619) 234-0408
Fax: (619) 234-4015
Newcastle Brown Ale
— Andrea Bullock *(Acct Exec)*

SHAW ROSS INTERNATIONAL IMPORTERS
2400 SW 145th Ave Ste 201
Miramar, FL 33027
Tel.: (954) 430-5020
Fax: (954) 430-5030
Toll Free: (800) 255-1350
E-mail: info@shaw-ross.com
Web Site: www.shaw-ross.com
Approx. Number Employees: 43
Year Founded: 1970
Business Description:
Importers of Wines & Spirits
S.I.C.: 5182
N.A.I.C.S.: 424820
Import
Advertising Expenditures: $250,000
Media: 2-6-9-10-16-19-23-24-25
Distr.: Natl.
Budget Set: Jan.
Personnel:
Harvey R. Chaplin *(Chm & CEO)*
Wayne E. Chaplin *(Pres & COO)*
Bruce Hunter *(Mng Dir)*
Rod Simmons *(Brand Mgr-Brugal Rums)*
Brands & Products:
35 SOUTH
AGUARDIENTE CRISTAL
CABO DE HORNOS
CARDENAL MENDOZA
CASTILLO DE MOLINA
CELLA
COLLE NERO CHIANTI
DUCAROSSO CHIANTI RESERVA
GAETANO
GATO
GILIA PINOT GRIGIO
GLENGOYNE SINGLE MALT SCOTCH
IL BRUNONE
JACK & BERNIE'S BLOODY MARY MIX
LA CHIARA GAVI DI GAVI
LOMBARDO
LONG NECK
MANGIAVINO
MARQUES DE RISCAL
PEOPLE BUILDING BRANDS
PISCO CAPEL
PUSSER'S ORIGINAL NAVY RUM
REAL SANGRIA
ROCAR
ROMATE
RON VIEJO DE CALDAS
SACCHETTO PINOT GRIGIO
SHAW-ROSS INTERNATIONAL IMPORTERS
STREGA
WAN FU

SIDNEY FRANK IMPORTING CO., INC.
20 Cedar St
New Rochelle, NY 10801
Tel.: (914) 633-5630
Fax: (914) 633-5637
Web Site: www.sidneyfrank.com/lpa
E-Mail For Key Personnel:
Sales Director: sales@sidneyfrankco.com
Sales Range: $250-299.9 Million
Approx. Number Employees: 75
Year Founded: 1972
Business Description:
Wine & Distilled Beverages
S.I.C.: 5182
N.A.I.C.S.: 424820
Advertising Expenditures: $30,000,000
Media: 2-3-4-6-9-13-14-18-19-20-23-25
Personnel:
Lee R. Einsidler *(CEO)*
Stuart W. Moselman *(CFO)*
William L. Henderson *(Sr VP-Mktg & Adv)*
James Verrier *(VP-Mktg & Adv)*
Kate Laufer *(Dir-PR)*
Brands & Products:
BARENJAGER LIQUEUR
GEKKEIKAN PLUM WINES & SAKE
HENRI SAVARD BLANC DE BLANCS
HUDSON'S BAY SCOTCH
JACQUES CARDIN NAPOLEON VSOP BRANDY
JACQUES CARDIN XO BRANDY
JAGERMEISTER
REYNAC PINEAU DES CHARENTES
ST. VIVANT ARMAGNAC
TEQUILA CORAZON
TOMMY BAHAMA
Advertising Agencies:
DeVito/Verdi
100 5th Ave 16th Fl
New York, NY 10011
Tel.: (212) 431-4694
Fax: (212) 431-4940
Television

TargetCast tcm
909 3rd Ave 31st Fl
New York, NY 10022
Tel.: (212) 500-6900
Fax: (212) 500-6880
Jagermeister
Tommy Bahama
Jacques Cardin Cognac

SIMI WINERY
(Unit of Icon Estates)
16275 Healdsburg Ave
Healdsburg, CA 95448-9075
Mailing Address:
PO Box 698
Healdsburg, CA 95448-0698
Tel.: (707) 433-6981
Fax: (707) 433-6253
Toll Free: (800) 746-4880
E-mail: jobs@simiwinery.com
Web Site: www.simiwinery.com
Sales Range: $50-74.9 Million
Approx. Number Employees: 75
Year Founded: 1876
Business Description:
Producers of Wines
S.I.C.: 2084; 0172
N.A.I.C.S.: 312130; 111332
Export
Media: 4-13-20-21

SKYY SPIRITS LLC
(Sub. of Davide Campari-Milano S.p.A.)
1 Beach St Ste 300
San Francisco, CA 94133
Tel.: (415) 315-8000
Fax: (415) 315-8001
E-mail: comments@skyyspirits.com
Web Site: www.skyyspirits.com
Approx. Number Employees: 200
Year Founded: 1992
Business Description:
Alcoholic Beverages Mfr
S.I.C.: 5182; 2085
N.A.I.C.S.: 424820; 312140
Import Export
Advertising Expenditures: $500,000
Media: 2-3-6-8-9-10-13-14-15-18-20-21-22-23-24-25
Distr.: Intl.
Personnel:
Gerard Ruvo *(Chm & CEO)*
Andrea Conzonato *(COO & CMO)*
Dave Karraker *(Dir-PR & Events)*
Kirsten Van Sickle *(Brand Mgr-Skyy Infusions)*
Jason Daniel *(Brand Mgr-Skyy Vodka)*
Lynn Lackey *(Brand Mgr-Campari)*
Brands & Products:
GLEN GOYNE
GLEN ROTHES
OUZO 12
PALLINI LEMONCELLO
SKYY
SKYY CITRUS
SKYY INFUSIONS
Advertising Agencies:
Alison Brod Public Relations
373 Park Ave S 4th Fl
New York, NY 10016
Tel.: (212) 230-1800
Fax: (212) 230-1161
Agency of Record
Event Support
Midori Melon
Online Awareness
Public Relations
Skyy Vodka
X-Rated Fusion

Benson Marketing Group LLC
2700 Napa Vly Corporate Dr Ste H
Napa, CA 94558
Tel.: (707) 254-9292
Fax: (707) 254-0433

Fathom Communications
(Part of Omnicom Group of Companies)
437 Madison Ave
New York, NY 10022
Tel.: (212) 817-6600
Fax: (212) 415-3514
Midori Melon Liqueur

Lambesis, Inc.
2800 Roosevelt St
Carlsbad, CA 92008-1670
Tel.: (760) 547-2333
Fax: (760) 547-2331
(Vodka)

STE. MICHELLE WINE ESTATES LTD.
(Sub. of International Wine & Spirits Ltd.)
(d/b/a Chateau Ste. Michelle)
14111 NE 145th St
Woodinville, WA 98072
Tel.: (425) 488-1133
Fax: (425) 415-3657
E-mail: info@ste-michelle.com
Web Site: www.ste-michelle.com
Sales Range: $200-249.9 Million
Approx. Number Employees: 700
Year Founded: 1974
Business Description:
Wineries

Key to Media (For complete agency information see *The Advertising Red Books-Agencies* edition):
1. Bus. Publs. 2. Cable T.V. 3. Catalogs & Directories. 4. Co-op Adv. 5. Consumer Mags. 6. D.M. to Bus. Estab.7. D.M. to Consumers
8. Daily Newsp. 9. Exhibits/Trade Shows 10. Foreign 11. Infomercial 12. Internet Adv.13. Multimedia 14. Network Radio
15. Network T.V. 16. Newsp. Distr. Mags. 17. Other 18. Outdoor (Posters, Transit) 19. Point of Purchase20. Premiums, Novelties
21. Product Samples 22. Special Events Mktg. 23. Spot Radio 24. Spot T.V. 25. Weekly Newsp. 26. Yellow Page Adv.

Ste. Michelle Wine Estates Ltd. — (Continued)

S.I.C.: 2084
N.A.I.C.S.: 312130
Import Export
Media: 1-2-3-4-6-8-9-10-18-19-21-22-23-24-25
Personnel:
Theodore P. Baseler *(Pres & CEO)*
Sheila Newlands *(CFO & VP)*
Glenn Yaffa *(Exec VP-Sls)*
Rachael Ellas *(Reg VP-NW)*
Brett Scalan *(VP & Grp Dir-Brands)*
Frank Genovese *(VP & Mgr-Natl Sls)*
Sean Dimmick *(VP-Retail Chain Sls)*
Tom Patinella *(VP-Sls-Midwest Div)*
Brands & Products:
CHATEAU STE. MICHELLE
Advertising Agency:
DDB Seattle
1000 2nd Ave Ste 1000
Seattle, WA 98104
Tel.: (206) 442-9900
Fax: (206) 223-6309
(Columbia Crest, Chateau Ste. Michelle, Domaine Ste. Michelle & Colour Volant)

STONE BRIDGE CELLARS INC.
200 Taplin Rd
Saint Helena, CA 94574-9601
Tel.: (707) 963-2745
Fax: (707) 963-4831
E-mail: info@jpvwines.com
Web Site: www.jpvwines.com
Approx. Rev.: $19,200,000
Approx. Number Employees: 250
Year Founded: 1981
Business Description:
Wines, Brandy & Brandy Spirits
S.I.C.: 2084
N.A.I.C.S.: 312130
Import Export
Advertising Expenditures: $500,000
Media: 4-14-15-16-22-26
Personnel:
William Phelps *(Chm)*
Robert Boyd *(CFO & VP)*
Damian Parker *(VP & Dir-Winemaking)*

THE TERLATO WINE GROUP
2401 Waukegan Rd
Bannockburn, IL 60044
Tel.: (847) 604-8900
Fax: (847) 236-0848
Toll Free: (800) 950-7676
E-mail: info@terlatowinegroup.com
Web Site: www.terlatowinegroup.com
Approx. Number Employees: 600
Year Founded: 1946
Business Description:
Importing, Marketing & Distribution of Wine
S.I.C.: 5182
N.A.I.C.S.: 424820
Advertising Expenditures: $3,000,000
Media: 1-6-7-8-9-10-11-19-20-21-23-24
Distr.: Natl.
Personnel:
Anthony J. Terlato *(Chm)*
William A. Terlato *(Pres & CEO)*
Laura Dillon *(Mgr-Mktg)*
Brands & Products:
TERLATO

TREASURY WINE ESTATES
(Formerly Foster's Wine Estates)
(Div. of Treasury Wine Estates Ltd.)
600 Airpark Rd
Napa, CA 94558-7516
Tel.: (707) 259-4500
Fax: (707) 259-4542
E-mail: info@beringer.com
Web Site: www.beringer.com
Approx. Number Employees: 600
Year Founded: 1876
Business Description:
California Wines Producer & Marketer
S.I.C.: 2084; 0172
N.A.I.C.S.: 312130; 111332
Advertising Expenditures: $8,000,000
Media: 1-18-20-21-22
Personnel:
Stephen Brauer *(Mng Dir)*
Francesca Schuler *(CMO)*
Mike Holden *(Sr VP-Sls)*
Joe Fraser *(Dir-Pkg Ops)*
Myron Nightingale *(Mgr)*
Advertising Agency:
Alcone Marketing Group
(Division of Omnicom Group, Inc.)
4 Studebaker
Irvine, CA 92618-2012
Tel.: (949) 770-4400
Fax: (949) 770-2957

TRINCHERO FAMILY ESTATES
100 Main St
Saint Helena, CA 94574-2166
Mailing Address:
PO Box 248
Saint Helena, CA 94574-2166
Tel.: (707) 963-3104
Fax: (707) 963-2381
E-mail: info@tfewines.com
Web Site: www.tfewines.com
Approx. Number Employees: 500
Year Founded: 1890
Business Description:
Winery
S.I.C.: 2084; 0172
N.A.I.C.S.: 312130; 111332
Export
Advertising Expenditures: $5,000,000
Media: 3-6-13-18-19-20-21-23
Distr.: Natl.; Reg.
Budget Set: June
Personnel:
Louis Trinchero *(Chm)*
Roger J. Trinchero *(Pres)*
Mark Smithers *(CFO & Sr VP-Fin)*
Anthony R. Torres *(Principal & Sr VP-Admin)*
Brands & Products:
ANGOVE'S
BANDIT
FOLIE A DEUX
FRE
LITTLE BOOMEY
MENAGE A TROIS
MONTEVINA
REYNOLDS
REYNOLDS VINEYARDS
SUTTER HOME
SYCAMORE LANE
TERRADORO
THREE THIEVES
TRINCHERO
TRINITY OAKS
WILD BUNCH

Advertising Agency:
Dentsu America
2001 Wilshire Blvd 6th Fl
Santa Monica, CA 90403-5641
Tel.: (310) 586-5600
Fax: (310) 586-5894

UNITED DISTRIBUTORS, INC.
(Sub. of Unistan Inc.)
5500 United Dr
Smyrna, GA 30082-4755
Tel.: (678) 305-2000
Fax: (678) 305-2050
E-mail: info@unitedistinc.com
Web Site: www.unitedistinc.com
Approx. Number Employees: 750
Year Founded: 1941
Business Description:
Wine, Beer, Liquor & Non-Alcoholic Beverages Distr
S.I.C.: 5182; 5181
N.A.I.C.S.: 424820; 424810
Advertising Expenditures: $1,000,000
Media: 2-7-9-10-19-23-24-25
Distr.: Natl.
Budget Set: Oct.
Personnel:
Jennings M. Hertz, Jr. *(Chm)*
Douglas J. Hertz *(Pres)*
Mark Popowski *(VP-Fin)*
Chris Brown *(Dir-Mktg)*

VEEV ACAI SPIRITS
5979 W 3rd St Ste 204
Los Angeles, CA 90036
Tel.: (323) 937-0345
Fax: (310) 362-8489
Web Site: www.veevlife.com
Business Description:
Acai Spirits Mfr
S.I.C.: 5182
N.A.I.C.S.: 424820
Media: 8-13-18-21
Personnel:
Courtney Reum *(Founder & CEO)*
Carter Reum *(Owner)*
Stephanie Phan *(Mgr-Bus Dev)*

VINCOR CANADA
(Sub. of Constellation Brands, Inc.)
441 Courtneypark Dr E
Mississauga, ON L5T 2V3, Canada
Tel.: (905) 564-6900
Fax: (905) 564-6909
Toll Free: (800) 265-9463
Web Site:
www.vincorinternational.com
Sales Range: $500-549.9 Million
Approx. Number Employees: 2,009
Year Founded: 1993
Business Description:
Producer of Wine & Wine Coolers
S.I.C.: 2084
N.A.I.C.S.: 312130
Media: 4-6-10-18-19-22-23-24
Personnel:
Eric Morham *(Pres & CEO)*
Don Dychuck *(CFO)*
Bruce D. Walker *(Exec VP-Govt Rel)*
Ian Burge *(Sr VP & Gen Mgr-RJ Spagnols)*
Ron Pasternak *(Sr VP & Gen Mgr-Wine Rack)*
Rob Scapin *(Sr VP-Tech Svcs & Chief Wine Maker)*
Martin van der Merwe *(Sr VP-Ops)*
Brands & Products:
AMBERLEY ESTATE
GOUNDREY
HAWTHORNE MOUNTAIN
HOGUE
INNISKILLIN
JACKSON-TRIGGS
KIM CRAWFORD
SUMAC RIDGE
TOASTED HEAD
Advertising Agency:
Blammo Worldwide
154 Pearl Street
Toronto, ON M5H 1L3, Canada
Tel.: (416) 979-7999
Fax: (416) 979-9750

WARNER VINEYARDS
706 S Kalamazoo St
Paw Paw, MI 49079-1558
Tel.: (269) 657-3165
Fax: (269) 657-4154
Toll Free: (800) 756-5357
E-mail: info@warnervineyards.com
Web Site: www.warnerwines.com
E-Mail For Key Personnel:
Sales Director: sales@warnervineyards.com
Sales Range: Less than $1 Million
Approx. Number Employees: 10
Year Founded: 1938
Business Description:
Wines, Champagnes & Non-Alcoholic Sparkling Juices Mfr
S.I.C.: 2084; 2086
N.A.I.C.S.: 312130; 312111
Advertising Expenditures: $40,000
Media: 2-4-7-9-10-16-19-23-24-25
Budget Set: July
Personnel:
Patrick K. Warner *(Pres)*
Brands & Products:
TASTE THE ART
WARNER

WEIBEL, INC.
1 Winemaster Way
Lodi, CA 95240-0860
Tel.: (209) 365-9463
Fax: (209) 365-9469
Toll Free: (800) 932-9463
E-mail: weibelwines@sbcglobal.net
Web Site: www.weibel.com
Approx. Number Employees: 30
Year Founded: 1945
Business Description:
Producer of Wine & Champagne
S.I.C.: 2084
N.A.I.C.S.: 312130
Import Export
Advertising Expenditures: $250,000
Media: 9-13-19-20-21-22-23-25
Distr.: Natl.
Budget Set: Dec.
Personnel:
Fred E. Weibel, Jr. *(Pres & CEO)*
Douglas Richards *(VP-Sls)*
Brands & Products:
CHATEAU DE FLEUR
KNIGHTSDALE PINOT NOIR
PRIVATE LABEL
ROAD I
STANFORD
TRUSCOTT
WEIBEL
WEIBEL FAMILY VINEYARDS & WINERY

WENTE VINEYARDS
5565 Tesla Rd
Livermore, CA 94550-9149

Key to Media (For complete agency information see *The Advertising Red Books-Agencies* edition):
1. Bus. Publs. 2. Cable T.V. 3. Catalogs & Directories. 4. Co-op Adv. 5. Consumer Mags. 6. D.M. to Bus. Estab.7. D.M. to Consumers
8. Daily Newsp. 9. Exhibits/Trade Shows 10. Foreign 11. Infomercial 12. Internet Adv.13. Multimedia 14. Network Radio
15. Network T.V. 16. Newsp. Distr. Mags. 17. Other 18. Outdoor (Posters, Transit) 19. Point of Purchase20. Premiums, Novelties
21. Product Samples 22. Special Events Mktg. 23. Spot Radio 24. Spot T.V. 25. Weekly Newsp. 26. Yellow Page Adv.

Tel.: (925) 456-2300
Fax: (925) 456-2301
Web Site: www.wentevineyards.com
E-Mail For Key Personnel:
Marketing Director: christinew@wentevineyards.com
Sales Range: $25-49.9 Million
Approx. Number Employees: 150
Year Founded: 1883
Business Description:
Mfr. of Wines, Brandy & Spirits
S.I.C.: 2084; 8748
N.A.I.C.S.: 312130; 541618
Advertising Expenditures: $200,000
Media: 5-6-19
Distr.: Intl.; Natl.
Personnel:
Eric Wente *(Chm)*
Philip Wente *(Vice Chm)*
Carolyn Wente *(Pres)*
Amy Hoopes *(CMO & Exec VP-Global Sales)*
Christine Wente *(Sr VP-Hospitality)*
Larry Di Pietro *(VP-Natl Sls)*
Brands & Products:
MURRIETA'S WELL WINERY
TAMAS ESTATES WINERY
WENTE VINEYARDS

WHITE ROCK DISTILLERIES INC.

21 Saratoga St PO Box 1829
Lewiston, ME 04241
Tel.: (207) 783-1433
Fax: (207) 783-8409
E-mail: wrdsales@whiterockdistilleries.com
Web Site:
www.whiterockdistilleries.com
Approx. Number Employees: 200
Year Founded: 1928
Business Description:
Holding Company; Beverage Mfr & Whslr
S.I.C.: 2085
N.A.I.C.S.: 312140
Import Export
Advertising Expenditures: $3,500,000
Media: 2-6-7-9-10-19-20-21-22-25
Distr.: Natl.
Brands & Products:
BAJA
CANADIAN HUNTER
DESTINEE LINE
FIRE WATER SCHNAPPS
GOLD CROWN
GOLD RUSH
ICE 101
JENKINS
MAUI
SAN FRANCISCO COOKIES 'N CREAM
THREE OLIVES VODKAS
TORTILLA TEQUILA
ZHENKA

WILLAMETTE VALLEY VINEYARDS, INC.

8800 Enchanted Way SE
Turner, OR 97392-9580
Tel.: (503) 588-9463
Fax: (503) 588-8894
Toll Free: (800) 344-9463
E-mail: info@wvv.com
Web Site: www.wvv.com
E-Mail For Key Personnel:
President: JimBernau@wvv.com
Approx. Rev.: $17,370,803
Approx. Number Employees: 75
Year Founded: 1983
Business Description:
Wine Producer & Seller
S.I.C.: 2084; 5182
N.A.I.C.S.: 312130; 424820
Advertising Expenditures: $23,000
Media: 4-16-26
Personnel:
James W. Bernau *(Pres)*
R. Steven Caldwell *(CFO)*
Brands & Products:
BACCHUS
GRIFFIN CREEK
GRIFFIN CREEK LABELS
TUALATIN ESTATE
WHOLE CLUSTER
WILLAMETTE VALLEY VINEYARDS

WILLIAM GRANT & SONS, INC.

(Sub. of William Grant & Sons Ltd.)
130 Fieldcrest Ave
Edison, NJ 08837
Tel.: (732) 225-9000
Fax: (732) 225-0950
Web Site: www.grantusa.com
Approx. Number Employees: 140
Year Founded: 1964
Business Description:
Importer/Distributor of Fine Wines & Spirits
S.I.C.: 5182; 2085
N.A.I.C.S.: 424820; 312140
Import
Media: 6-8-18-23
Distr.: Intl.; Natl.
Personnel:
Simon Dennis Hunt *(Pres & Gen Mgr-North America & Mexico)*
Ronald Wall *(CFO-North America)*
Theodore C. Roman *(Sr VP-Sls)*
Phil West *(Sr VP-Mktg)*
Jenny Logan *(Sr Brand Mgr-Reyka Vodka)*
Brands & Products:
ARMADALE
BALVENIE
BERENTZEN APPEL
CASTELLO DI VOLPAIA
CLAN MACGREGOR
COLOMBO
HENDRICK'S
JOSEF BRIGL
LA POMMERAIE CALVADOS
LICOR 43
MARQUES DE MURRIETA
SAILOR JERRY
SCARLATTA
TAFT STREET

THE WINE GROUP, INC.

240 Stockton St Ste 800
San Francisco, CA 94108-5325
Tel.: (415) 986-8700
Fax: (415) 986-4305
Sales Range: $300-349.9 Million
Approx. Number Employees: 100
Business Description:
Wine Distr
S.I.C.: 5182
N.A.I.C.S.: 424820
Export
Advertising Expenditures: $1,000,000
Media: 14-15-23
Distr.: Natl.
Personnel:
David Kent *(CEO)*
Brands & Products:
CORBETT CANYON VINEYARDS
FOXHORN VINEYARDS
FRANZIA WINETAPS
GLEN ELLEN
LEJON
MD 20/20
MOGEN DAVID
TRIBUNO
Advertising Agency:
B.A.R.C. Communications, Inc.
170 Columbus Ave 5th Fl
San Francisco, CA 94133-5128
Tel.: (415) 772-1989
Fax: (415) 772-8964

WINE.COM, INC.

114 Sansome St Ste 210
San Francisco, CA 94104
Tel.: (415) 291-9500
Fax: (415) 291-9599
Toll Free: (877) 289-6886
E-mail: support@wine.com
Web Site: www.wine.com
Approx. Number Employees: 60
Year Founded: 1999
Business Description:
Online Wine Retailer
S.I.C.: 5921
N.A.I.C.S.: 445310
Media: 4-8-13-20-21-22
Personnel:
Michael J. Osborn *(Founder & VP-Mdsg)*
Rich Bergsund *(CEO)*
Advertising Agency:
LaunchSquad
116 New Montgomery St Ste 620
San Francisco, CA 94105
Tel.: (415) 625-8555
Fax: (415) 625-8559
Public Relations

Key to Media (For complete agency information see *The Advertising Red Books-Agencies* edition):
1. Bus. Publs. 2. Cable T.V. 3. Catalogs & Directories. 4. Co-op Adv. 5. Consumer Mags. 6. D.M. to Bus. Estab.7. D.M. to Consumers 8. Daily Newsp. 9. Exhibits/Trade Shows 10. Foreign 11. Infomercial 12. Internet Adv.13. Multimedia 14. Network Radio 15. Network T.V. 16. Newsp. Distr. Mags. 17. Other 18. Outdoor (Posters, Transit) 19. Point of Purchase20. Premiums, Novelties 21. Product Samples 22. Special Events Mktg. 23. Spot Radio 24. Spot T.V. 25. Weekly Newsp. 26. Yellow Page Adv.